THE OFFICIAL

Music Master

SINGLES CATALOGUE

AS SEEN ON TV

PICTURE DISCS
CD SINGLES
7" AND 12" SINGLES
CASSETTE SINGLES

3rd edition

FULLY REVISED AND UPDATED

OVER 69,000 ENTRIES

MUSIC MASTER SINGLES CATALOGUE

First published 1976, then as 'British Pop Singles '75 - '84 in 1984; this, the 3rd edition, was published in 1990. Published by John Humphries (Publishing) Ltd, Music House, 1 De Cham Avenue, Hastings, Sussex, England.

ISBN 0 904520 43 9.

General editor John Humphries.

Booktrade enquiries: Harrap Publishing Group Ltd. Chelsea House, 26 Market Square, Bromley, Kent England. BR1 1NA. Tel: 01-313 3484. Fax: 01-313 0702.

Record trade and private enquiries. John Humphries (Publishing) Ltd, Music House, 1, De Cham Avenue, Hastings, Sussex, England. TN37 6HE. Telephone 0424-715181. Telex 957485 (ROBINC G). Fax 0424 422805.

Front cover record sleeves. Top row: Beautiful South "Song for whoever" (released on Go! Discs), Bob Marley & The Wailers "Waiting in vain" (Island), The Beatles "Twist and shout" (Parlophone).**Centre row:** Bad Dream Fancy Dress "The Supremes" (El), The Dead Kennedys "Holiday in Cambodia" (Cherry Red), Alien Sex Fiend "Hurricane fighter plane" (Plague Records).**Bottom row**: Bananarama "Shy boy" (London), Kylie Minogue & Jason Donovan "Especially for you" (PWL), Beatmasters "Hey DJ" (Rhythm King).

Spine record sleeves Top. Jefferson Airplane "White rabbit" (RCA), **Centre:** Divine "I'm so beautiful" (Proto), **Bottom:** Plasmatics "Monkey suit" (Stiff).

Back cover record sleeves. Top row: Jive Bunny "Swing the mood" (Music Factory), Prefab Sprout "Faron Young" (Kitchenware), Sinitta "Right back where we started from" (Fanfare).**Bottom row:** Transvision Vamp "Landslide of love" (MCA), Culture Club "White boy" (Virgin), Prince "Paisley Park" (Warner Brothers).

Printed and bound in Great Britain.

SINGLES CATALOGUE

Contents

Introduction

The Music Master database is the world's largest published database of information about recorded music available in Britain. Collected here are all the singles on our database at the time of going to press: all 7",12", CD singles, cassingles, and all picture disc singles. There is a staggering total of some 70,000 entries in this book. All singles that were currently available at the time of going to press are included plus thousands of 'deleted' singles. As much information as possible is given for each single: artists, recording names, tracks, labels, companies, release dates, deletion dates, catalogue numbers and formats. The text is generously supplied with hundreds of biographies and illustrations. For record collectors, record dealers, DJ's and music lovers everywhere, this book is for you.

How to use the Singles Catalogue

This is simplicity itself. All the entries are arranged alphabetically by artist or group. The pages of each letter are numbered referring to that letter; for instance, A1-A39, B1-B92, and so on.Once you have located the artist you will notice that the recording s are listed in alphabetical order by title. For example, if you look up 'Abba' you will see their singles arranged in an alphabetical list:

ANGEL EYES
CHIQUITITA
DANCING QUEEN
DAY BEFORE YOU CAME
DOES YOUR MOTHER KNOW
FERNANDO
GIMME GIMME GIMME (A MAN AFTER MIDNIGHT)

And if you then look at one of these entries, you will then see a list of the tracks on the single, followed by format, release date, label, record company, deletion date and catalogue number. There may also be additional information such as notes pertaining to that particular recording. For example, if you look at the entry for 'Angel eyes' you will see:

ANGEL EYES
Tracks: / Angel eyes / Voulez vous.
7" Single: Released Aug '79, on Epic, by CBS Records. Deleted '82. Catalogue no: **EPC 7499**
7" Single: Released Feb '89, on Old Gold, by Old Gold Records. Catalogue no: **OG 9856**

What this means of course, is that the songs on the single 'Angel eyes' are 'Angel eyes' and 'Voulez vous'; that it was released on a 7" single in 1979 on the Epic label by CBS Records, but was deleted by CBS from their catalogue in 1982. However, it was released again in 1989 by Old Gold Records. The absence of a deletion date for the Old Gold record means only that we have not been notified of a deletion date. Some record companies are a little lax when it comes to announcing deletions and there are many records in this book without deletion dates that have almost certainly been deleted by their respective record companies.You cannot assume therefore that records without deletion dates are still available. It is hoped that this present addition to the 'Music Master' range of record catalogues will prove to be as popular with our trade and private customers as our other publications. We are always very pleased to hear from our readers telling us what they like - and don't like - about our catalogues and pointing out our errors of omission and commission.

John Humphries, Hastings 1990.

A

The following information was taken from the Music Master database on 20th October, 1989.

A2L

TRIP MAN
Tracks: / Trip man (tracer & inst. mix) / Come on (acid love & Mellow love inst mix) / Play me some beautiful dance music / People on earth.
12" Single: Released Dec '88, on 1st Bass, Catalogue no: **RUFF 2**

A, Avril

MAN IN MY LIFE
Tracks: / Man in my life.
12" Single: Released Jul '88, on No Logo, by No Logo Records. Catalogue no: **001A-T**

PARIS IS FOR LOVERS
Tracks: / Paris is for lovers / Little lady dynamite.
7" Single: Released Jun '82, on Out Of Town, Catalogue no: **HOOT 9**

A Black Man

I BELIEVE
Tracks: / I believe.
12" Single: Released Oct '87, on House (USA), Catalogue no: **HU 35**

A Bones

TEMPO TANTRUM EP
Tracks: / Tempo tantrum.
10" single: Released May '86, on Exile, Catalogue no: **EX 10EP 03**

A Certain Ratio

Biographical details: A Certain Ratio, a British punk-influenced funk band, consist of Andy Connell, Donald Johnstone, Jeremy Kerr and Martin Moscrop.
The group's first release was a 1979 cassette entitled *The Graveyard And The Ballroom*. One side was recorded at the Graveyard Studios, the other side was a live recording of their support gig to the Talking Heads at London's Electric Ballroom. The following year saw them issue a 12-inch EP *Blown Away* plus their first single *Shack Up*. Their debut album, curiously called *To Each...*, hit the shops in '81. Having won support from BBC Radio One's influential DJ John Peel and having established their name in the UK's independent charts, they hit the national charts for the first time with 1982's *Sextet*, peaking at No. 53 on the album listings.
A Certain Ratio's early line-up included Johnstone, Kerr and Moscrop, plus Peter Terel and Simon Topping. By the time of 1984's *Life's A Scream* single, the latter two members had departed, to be replaced solely by Andy Connell. The group come from Manchester and are signed to that city's Factory label, famous for Joy Division/New Order. (Bob MacDonald).

BACKS TO THE WALL
Tracks: / Backs to the wall / Be what you wanna be.
7" Single: Released Aug '89, on A&M, by A&M Records. Catalogue no: **ACR 517**
12" Single: Released Aug '89, on A&M, by A&M Records. Catalogue no: **ACRY 517**
CD 5": Released Aug '89, on A&M, by A&M Records. Catalogue no: **ACRD 517**

BIG E, THE
Tracks: / Beg E, The / Love is the way / Day 2 (On 12" only.).
12" Single: Released 12 Jun '89, on A&M, by A&M Records. Catalogue no: **ACRY 514**
CD 5": Released 12 Jun '89, on A&M, by A&M Records. Catalogue no: **ACRCD 514**
7" Single: Released 12 Jun '89, on A&M, by A&M Records. Catalogue no: **ACR 514**

BRAZILIA
Tracks: / Brazilia.
12" Single: Released Feb '85, on Factory Benelux, by Rough Trade Records. Catalogue no: **FBN 32**

FLIGHT, A
Tracks: / Flight.
7" Single: Released Nov '80, on Factory (1), by Factory Records. Catalogue no: **FAC 22**

GREETINGS FOUR
12" Single: Released 1 Jun '87, on Materiali Sonori, Catalogue no: **MASO 70004**

GREETINGS TOO
Tracks: / Greetings too.
7" Single: Released 20 Jun '87, on Materiali Sonori, Catalogue no: **MASO 70002**

GUESS WHO
Tracks: / Guess who.
12" Single: Released Jul '82, on Factory Benelux, by Rough Trade Records. Catalogue no: **FBN 17**

I NEED SOMEONE TONIGHT
Tracks: / I need someone tonight.
12" Single: Released Jul '83, on Factory (1), by Factory Records. Catalogue no: **FAC 7212**
7" Single: Released Jul '83, on Factory (1), by Factory Records. Catalogue no: **FAC 72**

KNIFE SLITS WATER EP
Tracks: / Knife slits water.
12" Single: Released Oct '82, on Factory (1), by Factory Records. Catalogue no: **12 FAC 62**
7" Single: Released Oct '82, on Factory (1), by Factory Records. Catalogue no: **FAC 62**

MICKEY WAY
Tracks: / Mickey way.
12" Single: Released Sep '86, on Factory (1), by Factory Records. Catalogue no: **FAC 168**

THERE'S ONLY THIS
Tracks: / There's only this / Life's a scream.
12" Single: Released Sep '84, on Factory (1), by Factory Records. Catalogue no: **FAC 112**

WATERLINE
Tracks: / Waterline / Funaezka.
7" Single: Released Dec '81, on Factory (1), by Factory Records. Catalogue no: **FAC 52**

WILD PARTY
Tracks: / Wild party.
12" Single: Released Jun '85, on Factory (1), by Factory Records. Catalogue no: **FAC 128T**
7" Single: Released Jun '85, on Factory (1), by Factory Records. Catalogue no: **FAC 128**

YOUR BLUE EYES
Tracks: / Your blue eyes / Thin grey line / Coldest days (Available on 12" only.).
7" Single: Released Oct '89, on A&M, by A&M Records. Catalogue no: **ACR 534**
12" Single: Released Oct '89, on A&M, by A&M Records. Catalogue no: **ACRY 534**

A House

CALL ME BLUE
Tracks: / Call me blue / Freak out / Michael (12" only) / Plane or pearl (12" only).
7" Single: Released Mar '89, on Blanco Y Negro, by Blanco Y Negro Records. Catalogue no: **NEG 35**
12" Single: Released Mar '89, on Blanco Y Negro, by Blanco Y Negro Records. Catalogue no: **NEG 35T**

HEART HAPPY
Tracks: / Heart happy / Pretty something / Oh God I hurt inside (on 12" only.).
7" Single: Released Nov '87, on Blanco Y Negro, by Blanco Y Negro Records. Deleted Jul '88. Catalogue no: **NEG 28**
12" Single: Released Nov '87, on Blanco Y Negro, by Blanco Y Negro Records. Deleted Jul '88. Catalogue no: **NEG 28T**

I'LL ALWAYS BE GRATEFUL
Tracks: / I'll always be grateful.
7" Single: Released Oct '88, on Blanco Y Negro, by Blanco Y Negro Records. Catalogue no: **NEG 38**
12" Single: Released Oct '88, on Blanco Y Negro, by Blanco Y Negro Records. Catalogue no: **NEGT 38**

KICK ME AGAIN JESUS
Tracks: / Kick me again Jesus.
7" Single: Released '87, on Rip, Catalogue no: **ARIP 1**
12" Single: Released '87, on Rip, Catalogue no: **ARIPT 1**

KICK ME AGAIN JESUS (REISSUE)
Tracks: / Kick me again Jesus / Snowball down.
12" Single: Released 24 Aug '87, on Rip, Catalogue no: **ARIPT 003**

SNOWBALL DOWN
Tracks: / Snowball down / Y.O.U..
7" Single: Released 6 Jun '87, on Rip, Catalogue no: **ARIP 2**

A II Z

I'M THE ONE WHO LOVE YOU
Tracks: / I'm the one who love you / Ringside seat.
7" Single: Released Oct '81, on Polydor by Polydor Ltd. Deleted Oct '84. Catalogue no: **POSP 314**

NO SUN AFTER MIDNIGHT
Tracks: / No sun after midnight / Treason / Valhalla force (12" only).
12" Single: Released Oct '81, on Polydor, by Polydor Ltd. Deleted '85. Catalogue no: **POSPX 243**
7" Single: Released Oct '81, on Polydor, by Polydor Ltd. Deleted '85. Catalogue no: **POSP 243**

A La Carte

HAVE YOU FORGOTTEN (VOLGA SONG)
Tracks: / Have you forgotten (volga song).
7" Single: Released Oct '82, on PRT, by Castle Communications Records. Deleted '88. Catalogue no: **7P 249**

A Popular History...

DANCING WITH IDEAS
7" Single: Released Oct '82, on Melodia, Deleted '83. Catalogue no: **M 4**

LADDERJACK
12" Single: Released Dec '84, on Wax Trax, by Wax Trax Records. Deleted '88. Catalogue no: **WAX 005**

A Split Second

ANOTHER VIOLENT BREED (LIVE)
Tracks: / Another violent breed (live).
CD 5": Released Jul '89, on Antler, by Antler Records (Belgium). Catalogue no: **ANT 106CD**
12" Single: Released Jul '89, on Antler, by Antler Records (Belgium). Catalogue no: **ANT 106**

SCANDINAVIAN BELLYDANCE
Tracks: / Scandinavian bellydance.
12" Single: Released Apr '88, on Antler, by Antler Records (Belgium). Catalogue no: **ANT 076**

Aaron, Lee

BARELY HOLDING ON
Tracks: / Barely holding on.
12" Single: Released Aug '85, on Attic Records, by Road Runner Records. Deleted '88. Catalogue no: **RRP 65488**
7" Single: Released Jul '85, on Attic Records, by Road Runner Records. Catalogue no: **RR 5488**
12" Single: Released Jul '85, on Attic Records, by Road Runner Records. Catalogue no: **RR 125488**

METAL QUEEN
12" Single: Released Sep '84, on Music For Nations, by Music For Nations Records. Catalogue no: **RR 12 5507**

ONLY HUMAN
Tracks: / Only human / Empty heart / Call of the wild (This extra track on 12" version only.).
12" Single: Released '87, on 10 Records, by Virgin Records. Deleted May '88. Catalogue no: **TENT 155**
7" Single: Released '87, on 10 Records, by Virgin Records. Deleted May '88. Catalogue no: **TEN 155**

ROCK ME ALL OVER
Tracks: / Rock me all over.
12" Single: Released Jun '85, on Noir, by Noir Records. Catalogue no: **RR 12 5495**

Aaron, Paul

STREETS OF HEAVEN
Tracks: / Streets of heaven.
7" Single: Released Jan '87, on Musik, Catalogue no: **MUK 3**

Abacush

STAND FIRM
Tracks: / Stand firm / Africa.
12" Single: Released May '86, on Abacush, Catalogue no: **AB 007**

SUNSHINE ISLAND
Tracks: / Sunshine Island / Sunshine Island (version).
12" Single: Released Jun '86, on Abacush, Catalogue no: **AB 003**
7" Single: Released Jun '86, on Abacush, Catalogue no: **7 AB 003**

Abba - I Have A Dream (Released on Epic)

Abba - Supertrouper (Released on Epic)

TRAIN IS COMING, THE
12" Single: Released Jun '84, on Abacush, Catalogue no: **AB 002**

Abba

Biographical details:
Most members were in other successful groups before ABBA. The band became big in Sweden, then made themselves known to the rest of the world via the winning of 1974's Eurovision Song Contest with 'Waterloo'. They quickly attained superstar status, accompanied by the usual 'bigger than the Beatles' comparisons.
Their hugeness increased throughout the 70's, with the aid of hits such as *Fernando*('76), *Money, money, money* ('76), *Take a Chance on Me*('78), and *The Winner Takes It All*('80). In all they clocked up 9 No. 1's in the U.K.
The two couples, Benny and Anni-Frid, Bjorn and Agnetha, survived divorce, but the early 80's saw the group's popularity begin the wane, and as the members embarked on various solo projects (most notably Ulvaeus and Anderson's 'Chess'), ABBA faded away.
(Robert Cohen, 1988).

Abba were formed in their native Sweden in 1971 when Bjorn and Benny, already popular at home as a duo were invited by the Swedish Broadcasting Company to submit an entry for the local heats of the Eurovision Song Contest. For this purpose the pair enlisted their singing girlfriends as permanent members of a new quartet, the name being derived from the initial letter of each member's Christian name.
Their opening salvo *Ring Ring* failed to be selected as Sweden's Song For Europe, but nevertheless topped charts all over Scandinavia as well as four other countries.
With all four having had several years' music business experience, Abba's records were, from the outset, brilliantly conceived and superbly executed. In 1974, *Waterloo* stormed through Eurovision, held that year in Brighton, and went to No.1 in the UK and even No.6 in the US.
Having tasted their first British success, however, the quartet failed to overcome the One Hit Wonder stigma automatically attached to Eurovision winners, and languished in the lower reaches of the Top 50 for the next eighteen months. Towards the end of '75, *SOS* restored them to the Top 10 and the group quickly consolidated with *Mamma Mia*, their second No.1, in early '76.
1976 was Abba's peak year in the UK, scoring three chart-topping singles plus two blockbusting albums, the cleverly timed *Greatest Hits* collection and *Arrival*. Phenomenal success continued until the end of 1980, by which time the group had chalked up a total of nine No.1 singles, more than any other act save the Beatles, Elvis and Cliff.
In addition to *Waterloo* and *Mamma Mia*, these comprised *Fernando*, *Dancing Queen*, *Knowing Me Knowing You*, *Name of the Game*, *Take a Chance on Me*, *The Winner Takes It All* and *Super Trouper*. No.1 albums included *Greatest Hits*, *Arrival*, *The Album* (companion the *The Movie*), *Voulez-Vous*, *Greatest Hits Volume 2* and *Super Trouper*.
Abba did tour, and also made one critically slammed film, but their great strength was always the recording studio. Their world sales figures through the Seventies established them as the biggest showbusiness phenomenon since the Beatles.
The one territory which the group failed to conquer was America. *Dancing Queen* was their only US No.1 single and, although many other records have received respectable Billboard chart positions, Abba were never able to achieve the domination that they managed in the rest of the world.
In 1981, *Lay All Your Love On Me* became the first single to crack the British Top 10 on 12" sales alone, peaking at No.7. This apparent triumph disguised the fact that it was also the act's lowest chart placing for six years, and heralded the start of their demise. *The Visitors*, an album released at the end of that year, went triple platinum on advance orders, but the underlying trend was downward. Its first single *One Of Us* was the last Abba 45 to make the Top 20, and the group were gradually disintegrating in both personal and musical terms.
A comprehensive third compilation *The Singles - The First Ten Years* became their eighth consecutive No.1 LP, but whatever happened to the next ten years? Although no official split was announced, the two women both began solo recording careers. The two songwriters, Bjorn and Benny, commenced work with Tim Rice on the stage/album project *Chess*.
The wheel had turned full circle. Three separate careers were being pursued, the same state of affairs that had been in force until 1973.
In the intervening decade, Abba had provided the world of pop music with some of the classiest, catchiest and most commercial material it had ever heard.
(Bob MacDonald 1986).

Abba - One of Us (Released on Epic)

ANGEL EYES
Tracks: / Angel eyes / Voulez vous.
7" Single: Released Aug '79, on Epic, by CBS Records. Deleted '82. Catalogue no: **EPC 7499**
7" Single: Released Feb '89, on Old Gold, by Old Gold Records. Catalogue no: **OG 9856**

CHIQUITITA
Tracks: / Chiquitita.
7" Single: Released May '82, on Epic, by CBS Records. Deleted '88. Catalogue no: **EPC 7030**

DANCING QUEEN
Tracks: / Dancing queen / Fernando.
7" Single: Released 21 Nov '87, on Old Gold, by Old Gold Records. Catalogue no: **OG 9726**

DANCING QUEEN (ORIGINAL)
Tracks: / Dancing queen.
7" Single: Released Aug '76, on Epic, by CBS Records. Deleted '79. Catalogue no: **EPC 4499**

DAY BEFORE YOU CAME
Tracks: / Day before you came, The / Cassandra.
7" Single: Released Oct '82, on Epic, by CBS Records. Deleted '88. Catalogue no: **EPC A 2847**

DOES YOUR MOTHER KNOW
Tracks: / Does your mother know.
7" Single: Released May '82, on Epic, by CBS Records. Deleted '88. Catalogue no: **EPC 7316**

FERNANDO
Tracks: / Fernando.
7" Single: Released May '82, on Epic, by CBS Records. Deleted '88. Catalogue no: **CBS 5962**
7" Single: Released Mar '76, on Epic, by CBS Records. Deleted '79. Catalogue no: **EPC 4036**

GIMME GIMME GIMME (A MAN AFTER MIDNIGHT)
Tracks: / Gimme gimme gimme.
7" Single: Released Oct '79, on Epic, by CBS Records. Deleted '82. Catalogue no: **EPC 7914**

GIMME GIMME GIMME (OLD GOLD)
Tracks: / Gimme gimme gimme / Does your mother know.
7" Single: Released 27 Feb '89, on Old Gold, by Old Gold Records. Catalogue no: **OG 9860**

GREATEST ORIGINAL HITS
7" EP: Released Mar '83, on Epic, by CBS Records. Deleted '88. Catalogue no: **EPC A 2618**

HEAD OVER HEELS
Tracks: / Head over heels / Visitors.
7" Single: Released Feb '82, on Epic, by CBS Records. Deleted '85. Catalogue no: **EPC A 2037**

I DO I DO I DO I DO
Tracks: / I do, I do, I do.
7" Single: Released Jul '75, on Epic, by CBS Records. Deleted '78. Catalogue no: **EPC 3229**

I HAVE A DREAM
Tracks: / I have a dream / Take a chance on me.
7" Single: Released Dec '79, on Epic, by CBS Records. Deleted '82. Catalogue no: **EPC 8088**

KNOWING ME KNOWING YOU
7" Single: Released May '82, on Epic, by CBS Records. Deleted '88. Catalogue no: **EPC 4955**

KNOWING ME KNOWING YOU (OLD GOLD)
Tracks: / Knowing me knowing you / Winner takes it all, The.
7" Single: Released 27 Feb '89, on Old Gold, by Old Gold Records. Catalogue no: **OG 9858**

LAY ALL YOUR LOVE ON ME
Tracks: / Lay all your love on me / On and on and on.
12" Single: Released Jul '81, on Epic, by CBS Records. Deleted '84. Catalogue no: **EPC A 131456**
CD 5": Released '88, on Polydor (Germany), by Polydor Ltd. Catalogue no: **871 115-2**

MAMA MIA
Tracks: / Mama mia.
7" Single: Released May '82, on Epic, by CBS Records. Deleted '88. Catalogue no: **Unknown**

MAMMA MIA
Tracks: / Mamma mia.
7" Single: Released Dec '75, on Epic, by CBS Records. Deleted '78. Catalogue no: **EPC 3790**

MONEY MONEY MONEY
Tracks: / Money money money.
7" Single: Released Nov '76, on Epic, by CBS Records. Deleted '88. Catalogue no: **EPC 4713**

NAME OF THE GAME
Tracks: / Name of the game.
7" Single: Released May '82, on Epic, by CBS Records. Catalogue no: **EPC 5750**

ONE OF US
Tracks: / One of us / Should i laugh or cry.
7" Single: Released Dec '81, on Epic, by CBS Records. Catalogue no: **EPC A 1740**

RING RING (SINGLE)
Tracks: / Ring ring.
7" Single: Released 13 Jul '74, on Epic, by CBS Records. Catalogue no: **EPC 2452**

S.O.S.
Tracks: / S.O.S..
7" Single: Released Sep '75, on Epic, by CBS Records. Deleted '78. Catalogue no: **EPC 3576**

SUMMER NIGHT CITY
Tracks: / Summer night city.
7" Single: Released May '82, on Epic, by CBS Records. Deleted '88. Catalogue no: **EPC 6595**

SUPER TROUPER (SINGLE)
Tracks: / Super trouper / Piper, The / Winner takes all / One of us / Lay all your love on me.
Cassingle: Released Sep '82, on Epic, by CBS Records. Deleted '85. Catalogue no: **EPCA 40-2618**
7" Single: Released Nov '80, on Epic, by CBS Records. Deleted '83. Catalogue no: **EPC 9089**

TAKE A CHANCE ON ME
Tracks: / Take a chance on me / Chiquitita.
7" Single: Released May '82, on Epic, by CBS Records. Deleted '88. Catalogue no: **CBS 8088**
7" Single: Released 21 Nov '87, on Old Gold, by Old Gold Records. Catalogue no: **OG 9727**
7" Single: Released Feb '78, on Epic, by CBS Records. Deleted '81. Catalogue no: **EPC 5950**

THANK YOU FOR THE MUSIC
Tracks: / Thank you for the music / Our last summer.
7" Single: Released Nov '83, on CBS, by CBS Records. Deleted '86. Catalogue no:

ABC - ALL OF MY HEART (Released on Neutron)

CBS A 3894

UNDER ATTACK
Tracks: / Under attack / You owe me one.
7" Single: Released Dec '82, on Epic, by CBS Records. Deleted '85. Catalogue no: **EPC A 2971**

WATERLOO (SINGLE)
Tracks: / Waterloo / Mama mia.
7" Single: Released 20 Apr '74, on Epic, by CBS Records. Catalogue no: **EPC 2240**
7" Single: Released '86, on Epic, by CBS Records. Catalogue no: **650252 7**
7" Single: Released Jan '88, on Old Gold, by Old Gold Records. Catalogue no: **OG 9741**

WINNER TAKES IT ALL
Tracks: / Winner takes it all, The.
7" Single: Released May '82, on Epic, by CBS Records. Deleted '88. Catalogue no: **EPC 8835**

Abbott, Gregory

I GOT THE FEELING
Tracks: / Rhyme and reason / I got the feelin'.
7" Single: Released Feb '87, on CBS, by CBS Records. Deleted Aug '87. Catalogue no: **ABB 2**
12" Single: Released Feb '87, on CBS, by CBS Records. Deleted Aug '87. Catalogue no: **ABBT 2**

SHAKE YOU DOWN (SINGLE)
Tracks: / Shake you down / Shake you down (ext. version) (On 12" only) / Wait until tomorrow.
7" Single: Released Sep '86, on CBS, by CBS Records. Deleted Aug '87. Catalogue no: **A 7326**
12" Single: Released Sep '86, on CBS, by CBS Records. Deleted '87. Catalogue no: **TA 7326**

YOU'RE MY ANGEL
Tracks: / You're my angel.
7" Single: Released May '87, on CBS, by CBS Records. Deleted Nov '87. Catalogue no: **ABB 3**
12" Single: Released May '87, on CBS, by CBS Records. Deleted Nov '87. Catalogue no: **ABBT 3**

Abbott & Johnson

HOMETOWN GIRL
Tracks: / Home town girl / Faithless.
7" Single: Released Jan '89, on Cold Harbour, by Cold Harbour Records. Catalogue no: **COLD 7**

Abbott, Russ

Biographical details: ITV's Saturday night musical satirist scored a minor hit single n 1982 with "A Day In The Life Of Vince Prince". In 1983 he found himself in commercial breaks as well as programmes, to promote Ronco's compilation. (Bob MacDonald 1986)

British TV comedy star, former member of the Barron Knights. Like most comedians, he has singing ambitions, and first tried his hand in 1982 with *A Day in the Life of Vince 'Prince'. Finally made it big in 1985 with Atmosphere.* (Robert Cohen October 1987).

ALL NIGHT HOLIDAY
Tracks: / All night holiday.
12" Single: Released Jun '85, on Spirit (1), by Spirit Records. Deleted '88. Catalogue no: **FIRET 6**
7" Single: Released Jun '87, on Spirit (1), by Spirit Records. Catalogue no: **FIRE 6**

ATMOSPHERE
Tracks: / Atmosphere / Thoughts of a child.
12" Single: Released Dec '86, on Spirit (2), Catalogue no: **FIRET 4**
7" Single: Released Dec '86, on Spirit (2), Catalogue no: **FIRE 4**

DAY IN THE LIFE OF VINCE PRINCE, A
Tracks: / Day in the life of Vince Prince, A / I love 'em.
7" Single: Released Feb '82, on EMI, by EMI Records. Deleted '85. Catalogue no: **EMI 5249**

LET'S GO TO THE DISCO
Tracks: / Let's go to the disco / Atmosphere.
7" Single: Released Dec '85, on Spirit (1), by Spirit Records. Catalogue no: **FIRE 9**
12" Single: Released Nov '85, on Spirit (1), by Spirit Records. Deleted '88. Catalogue no: **FIRET 9**

SPACE INVADERS MEET THE PURPLE PEOPLE EATER
Tracks: / Space invaders meet the purple people eater / Country cooperman.
7" Single: Released Aug '80, on EMI, by EMI Records. Deleted '83. Catalogue no: **EMI 5098**

Abbreviated Calling

D.W.I.
Tracks: / D.W.I..
12" Single: Released Apr '85, on Homestead, Deleted '88. Catalogue no: **FOY 010**

ABC

Biographical details: ABC were formed at the end of 1980 by singer Martin Fry. The orignal line-up included fifth member, bassist Mark Lickley, who came to be regarded as a guest musician rather than a permanent fixture. The group enjoyed rapid success, their first single climbing to No.19 in the autumn of '81 (*Tears Are Not Enough*). Fry then hired ex-Buggles/Yes member Trevor Horn, who had recently scored a Top 20 single with his lush, multi-textured production of Dollar's *Hand Held In Black And White*. The combination was a winner. The Sheffield-based band wrote strong, commercial love songs, Fry sung them powerfully, and Horn's majestic, orchestrated production gave them a sleek commercial appeal. In addition the group's hi-gloss, dapper image made them magazine pin-up favourites. The result was three consecutive Top 10 singles, all included on the band's debut LP *The Lexicon Of Love*, which entered the album chart at No.1 in July '82 and stayed there for four weeks. ABC also achieved Top 30 single and album success in the States. However the follow-up album *Beauty Stab*, released in November '83, was a major disappointment. The LP could only manage a meagre chart run, with its first single *That Was Then But This Is Now* quickly dropping down after peaking at No.18. The second 45, appropriately titled *SOS*, reached only No.39. The absence of Trevor Horn was the clear reason. Also on his way out was drummer David Palmer, leaving ABC as a three-piece. The depleted outfit returned in October 1984 with a more optimistically titled single *Millionaire*. (Bob MacDonald 1986).

ABC made the British Top Twenty in late 1981 with *Tears Are Not Enough*, but shot to big success in mid-'82 with three Top-Tenners: *Poison Arrow*, *Look of Love*, and the torch-song, *All of my Heart*. All the singles appeared on their first album, *Lexicon of Love*, which was produced by Trevor Horn, and went gold. *Beauty Stab* was considerably less successful, and ABC went through numerous line-up changes in the mid-80s, virtually disappearing, but for an American hit, *Be Near Me* (from *How to be a Millionaire*. In 1987, they re-emerged with *WHen Smokey Sings*, a major hit on both sides of the Atlantic: this appeared on the album *Alphabet City*. (Robert Cohen October 1987).

The UK pop/rock band was formed in 1981. The original lineup had vocalist Martin Fry, born in 1958 in Manchester; guitarist Mark White, born in 1961 in Sheffield; and saxist Stephen Singleton, born in 1959 in Sheffield. Fry started a fanzine called *Modern Drugs* and interviewed the other two, who were both in local band Vice Versa; they asked him to join whereupon the name was changed, more poppish style adopted and Mark Lickley (bass) and David Robinson (drums) were recruited. Drummer David Palmer (born in 1961 in Chesterfield) joined for debut album, *The Lexicon of Love* which was No.1 in the UK. By 1984 songwriters Fry and White were the only remaining original members; Fry developed Hodgkin's Disease, a form of cancer, and recovered; *Alphabet City* in 1987 was praised as good pop. (Donald Clarke 21 July 1988)

ALL OF MY HEART(see panel above)
Tracks: / All of my heart / Overture.
7" EP: Released Aug '82, on Neutron, by Neutron Records. Deleted '87. Catalogue no: **NTE 110**
7" Single: Released Sep '82, on Neutron, by Neutron Records. Deleted '85. Catalogue no: **NT 104**

BE NEAR ME
Tracks: / Be near me / A to Z / What's your destination (on 12" only).
7" Single: Released Apr '85, on Neutron, by Neutron Records. Deleted '88. Catalogue no: **NT 108**

HOW TO BE A MILLIONAIRE
Tracks: / How to be a millionaire.
7" Single: Released Nov '84, on Neutron, by Neutron Records. Deleted '87. Catalogue no: **NT 107**

KING WITHOUT A CROWN
Tracks: / King without a crown / Look of love, The (live) / Monarchy mix (Available on 12" version only.) / Look of love, The / Poison arrow.
Cassingle: Released Nov '87, on Neutron, by Neutron Records. Deleted Feb '89. Catalogue no: **NTMC 113**
7" Single: Released Nov '87, on Neutron, by Neutron Records. Deleted Oct '88. Catalogue no: **NT 113**
CD 5": Released Nov '87, on Neutron, by Neutron Records. Deleted Oct '88. Catalogue no: **NTCD 113**
12" Single: Released Nov '87, on Neutron, by Neutron Records. Deleted Oct '88. Catalogue no: **NTX 113**
12" Single: Released Dec '87, on Neutron, by Neutron Records. Deleted Oct '88. Catalogue no: **NTXR 113**

LOOK OF LOVE, THE
Tracks: / Look of love, The / Look of love, The (part 2).
7" Single: Released Oct '84, on Neutron, by Neutron Records. Deleted '88. Catalogue no: **NT 103**
12" Single: Released '88, on Mercury (Germany), Catalogue no: **6400 604**
12" Single: Released Oct '84, on Neutron, by Neutron Records. Deleted '88. Catalogue no: **NTX 103**

NIGHT YOU MURDERED LOVE
Tracks: / Night you murdered love, The.
12" Single: Released Aug '87, on Neutron, by Neutron Records. Deleted '88. Catalogue no: **NTX 112**
7" Single: Released Aug '87, on Neutron, by Neutron Records. Deleted '88. Catalogue no: **NT 112**

OCEAN BLUE
Tracks: / Ocean blue / Tower of London / Be near me (On 12" only).
7" Single: Released Dec '85, on Neutron, by Neutron Records. Deleted '87. Catalogue no: **NT 110**
12" Single: Released Dec '85, on Neutron, by Neutron Records. Deleted '87. Catalogue no: **NTX 110**

ONE BETTER WORLD (see panel below)
Tracks: / One better world / One better world (version).
7" Single: Released May '89, on Phonogram, by Phonogram Ltd. Deleted Oct '89. Catalogue no: **NT 114**
12" Single: Released May '89, on Phonogram, by Phonogram Ltd. Deleted Oct '89. Catalogue no: **NTX 114**
CD 5": Released May '89, on Phonogram, by Phonogram Ltd. Deleted Oct '89. Catalogue no: **NTCD 114**
12" Single: Released May '89, on Phonogram, by Phonogram Ltd. Deleted Oct '89. Catalogue no: **NTXR 114**

POISON ARROW
Tracks: / Poison arrow / Man trap.
7" Single: Released Feb '82, on Neutron, by Neutron Records. Deleted '85. Catalogue no: **NT 102**
12" Single: Released Feb '82, on Neutron, by Neutron Records. Deleted '85. Catalogue no: **NTX 102**

REAL THING, THE
Tracks: / Real thing, The / Greatest love of all, The / CD North (Avaliable on CD single only.) / Look of love, The (part 5) (Available on CD and cassette single only) / MC North (Avaliable on cassette single only.) / When smokey sings / Be near me.
Cassingle: Released Sep '89, on Neutron, by Neutron Records. Catalogue no: **NTMC 115**
CD 5": Released Sep '89, on Neutron, by Neutron Records. Catalogue no: **NTCD 115**
12" Single: Released Sep '89, on Neutron, by Neutron Records. Catalogue no: **NTX 115**
12" Pic: Released Sep '89, on Neutron, by

ABC - ONE BETTER WORLD (Released on Phonogram)

ABC - TEARS ARE NOT ENOUGH (Released on Neutron)

Neutron Records. Catalogue no: **NTXR 115**
7" Single: Released Sep '89, on Neutron, by Neutron Records. Catalogue no: **NT 115**

SOS
Tracks: / S.O.S..
7" Single: Released Jan '84, on Neutron, by Neutron Records. Deleted '87. Catalogue no: **NT 106**

TEARS ARE NOT ENOUGH (see panel above)
Tracks: / Tears are not enough / Alphabet soup.
12" Single: Released Oct '81, on Neutron, by Neutron Records. Deleted '84. Catalogue no: **NTX 101**
7" Single: Released Oct '81, on Neutron, by Neutron Records. Deleted '84. Catalogue no: **NT 101**

THAT WAS THEN BUT THIS IS NOW
Tracks: / That was then but this is now.
7" Single: Released Nov '83, on Neutron, by Neutron Records. Deleted '86. Catalogue no: **NT 105**

VANITY KILLS
Tracks: / Vanity kills / Judy's jewels / Be near me (on 12" only).
7" Single: Released Jun '85, on Neutron, by Neutron Records. Deleted '88. Catalogue no: **NT 109**
12" Single: Released Jun '85, on Neutron, by Neutron Records. Catalogue no: **NTX 109**

WHEN SMOKEY SINGS (see panel below)
Tracks: / When Smokey sings / Chicago pt.1.
CD 5": Released 23 May '87, on Neutron, by Neutron Records. Deleted Feb '89. Catalogue no: **NTCD 111**
7" Single: Released 23 May '87, on Neutron, by Neutron Records. Deleted '88. Catalogue no: **NT 111**
12" Single: Released 23 May '87, on Neutron, by Neutron Records. Deleted Feb '89. Catalogue no: **NTX 111**

Abdul

MAKING A MILLION IN MY CORNER SHOP
Tracks: / Making a million in my corner shop / Pasa.
12" Single: Released Jun '88, on B.C., Catalogue no: **BBA 01 T**
7" Single: Released Jul '88, on B.C., Catalogue no: **BBA 01**

Abdul, Paula

COLD HEARTED SNAKE
Tracks: / Cold hearted snake.
7" Single: Released Sep '89, on Siren, by Virgin Records. Catalogue no: **SRN 117**
12" Single: Released Sep '89, on Siren, by Virgin Records. Catalogue no: **SRN 117CD**

FOREVER YOUR GIRL (SINGLE)
Tracks: / Forever your girl / Next to you / Straight up (12" version) (Only on 12" single.).
CD 5": Released 15 May '89, on Siren, by Virgin Records. Catalogue no: **SRNCD 112**
Cassingle: Released 15 May '89, on Siren, by Virgin Records. Catalogue no: **SRNC 112**
7" Single: Released 15 May '89, on Siren, by Virgin Records. Catalogue no: **SRN 112**
12" Single: Released 15 May '89, on Siren, by Virgin Records. Catalogue no: **SRNX 112**
12" Single: Released 15 May '89, on Siren, by Virgin Records. Catalogue no: **SRNT 112**

(IT'S JUST) THE WAY THAT YOU LOVE ME
Tracks: / (It's just) the way that you love me (7" only) / (It's just) the way that you love me (dub) / (It's just) the way that you love me (12" remix) (12" only) / (It's just) the way that you love me (housafire mix) (12" only).
12" Single: Released 14 Nov '88, on Siren, by Virgin Records. Catalogue no: **SRNT 101**
7" Single: Released 14 Nov '88, on Siren, by Virgin Records. Catalogue no: **SRN 101**

KNOCKED OUT
Tracks: / Knocked out (Not on 12") / Knocked out (instrumental) (On 7" only) / Knocked out (round 1-extended mix) (ON CD & 12" only) / Knocked out (round 2-instrumental) (On CD & 12" only) / Knocked out (TKO dub) (On CD & 12" only).
Special: Released '88, on Siren, by Virgin Records. Catalogue no: **SRNP 92**
12" Single: Released 5 Sep '88, on Siren, by Virgin Records. Catalogue no: **SRNT 92**
7" Single: Released Aug '88, on Virgin (USA), by Virgin Records. Catalogue no: **DMD 1171**
7" Single: Released '88, on Siren, by Virgin Records. Catalogue no: **SRNS 92**
Cassingle: Released '88, on Siren, by Virgin Records. Catalogue no: **SRNC 92**
CD 5": Released '88, on Siren, by Virgin Records. Catalogue no: **SRNCD 92**
7" Single: Released '88, on Siren, by Virgin Records. Catalogue no: **SRNX 92**
7" Single: Released 5 Sep '88, on Siren, by Virgin Records. Catalogue no: **SRN 92**

STRAIGHT UP
Tracks: / Straight up / Cold heart / Straight up (power mix) / Straight up (Kevin Saunderson house mix) / Straight up (Marley Marl mix) / Straight up (house mix).
7" Single: Released Feb '89, on Siren, by Virgin Records. Catalogue no: **SRNN 111**
12" Single: Released Feb '89, on Siren, by Virgin Records. Catalogue no: **SRNX 111**
12" Single: Released Feb '89, on Siren, by Virgin Records. Catalogue no: **SRNT 111**
CD 3": Released Feb '89, on Siren, by Virgin Records. Catalogue no: **SRNCD 111**
7" Single: Released Feb '89, on Siren, by Virgin Records. Catalogue no: **SRN 111**

Abecedarians

SMILING MONARCHS
Tracks: / Smiling monarchs / Benway's carnival.
12" Single: Released May '85, on Factory (1), by Factory Records. Catalogue no: **FAC 117**

Aberdeen Football Club

EUROPEAN LIGHTS
Tracks: / European lights / Northern lights of old Aberdeen.
7" Single: Released Mar '83, on AFC (Aberdeen FC), by AFC Records. Deleted '88. Catalogue no: **AFC 1**

PHONE HOME
Tracks: / Phone home.
7" Single: on Satril, by Satril Records. Catalogue no: **SAT 501**

Abie

MONA LISA'S LOST HER SMILE
Tracks: / Mona Lisa's lost her smile.
7" Single: Released May '85, on Klub, by Klub Records. Deleted '88. Catalogue no: **KLUB 49**

Abi-Ola

YOURS UNTIL TOMORROW
Tracks: / Yours until tomorrow / Play me all night.
12" Single: Released Apr '86, on MGR, Catalogue no: **MGR 2**

Aborted

NO RULES
Tracks: / No rules.
7" Single: Released Nov '83, on Chaos, by Backs Recording Co.. Catalogue no: **CHS 2**

Abrams, Colonel

HOW SOON WE FORGET
Tracks: / How soon we forget / How soon we forget (dub).
7" Single: Released Jul '87, on MCA, by MCA Records. Catalogue no: **MCA 1179**
12" Single: Released Jul '87, on MCA, by MCA Records. Catalogue no: **MCAX 1179**

I'M NOT GONNA LET YOU (GET THE BEST OF ME)
Tracks: / I'm not gonna let you / I'm not gonna let you (percapella mix) / I'm not gonna let you (ext) (On ext. 12" only) / I'm not gonna let you (ext dub) (On ext. 12" only).
7" Single: Released Mar '86, on MCA, by MCA Records. Deleted '88. Catalogue no: **MCA 1031**
12" Single: Released Mar '86, on MCA, by MCA Records. Deleted '88. Catalogue no: **MCAX 1031**
12" Single: Released Mar '86, on MCA, by MCA Records. Deleted '88. Catalogue no: **MCAT 1031**

TRUTH, THE
Tracks: / Truth, The.
7" Single: Released Dec '85, on MCA, by MCA Records. Deleted '88. Catalogue no: **MCA 1022**

Abrasive Wheels

ARMY SONG (EP)
7" Single: Released Mar '82, on Riot City, by Riot City Records. Deleted '88. Catalogue no: **RIOT 9**

BANNER OF HOPE
Tracks: / Banner of hope / Law of the jungle.
7" Single: Released Nov '83, on Clay, by Clay Records. Deleted '88. Catalogue no: **CLAY 28**

BURN THE SCHOOLS
Tracks: / Burn the schools.
7" Single: Released Oct '82, on Riot City, by Riot City Records. Deleted '88. Catalogue no: **RIOT 16**

JAILHOUSE ROCK
Tracks: / Jailhouse rock.
7" Single: Released May '83, on Clay, by Clay Records. Deleted '88. Catalogue no: **CLAY 24**

PRISONER, THE
Tracks: / Prisoner, The.
12" Single: Released May '84, on Clay, by Clay Records. Deleted '88. Catalogue no: **12 CLAY 33**
7" Single: Released May '84, on Clay, by Clay Records. Deleted '88. Catalogue no: **CLAY 33**

VICIOUS CIRCLE (EP)
12" Single: Released Feb '82, on Riot City, by Riot City Records. Deleted '88. Catalogue no: **RIOT 4**

ABs

ABS, THE
Tracks: / Abs, The / Turbo sphynct.
12" Single: Released Jan '88, on Vinyl Solution, by Vinyl Solution Records. Catalogue no: **VS 7**

GREASE YOUR RALPH
Tracks: / Grease your Ralph.
7" Single: Released Aug '87, on Winking Ring, Catalogue no: **TURD 001**

Absolute Albert

NOISES
Tracks: / Noises / In flight.
7" Single: Released Apr '82, on Completely Different, by Neat Records. Deleted '88. Catalogue no: **MAD 1**

Absolute Beginners

DREAM IN A HAZE
Tracks: / Dream in a haze.
7" Single: Released Sep '84, on Roundabout, Deleted '88. Catalogue no: **RBA BS 1**

Absolute (group)

CAN'T YOU SEE
Tracks: / Can't you see / Love in my heart.
7" Single: Released May '87, on Absolute, by Absolute Records. Catalogue no: **7 REST 8**

TV GLARE
Tracks: / T.V. glare.
7" Single: Released Apr '85, on Reset, Catalogue no: **7 REST 5**

ABT 409

ABT 409
Tracks: / ABT 409.
12" Single: Released 13 Jul '87, on Helvette Underground, Catalogue no: **HEND 86005**

Abu, Sammy

RISE UP
Tracks: / Rise up / Dance dance dance.
7" Single: Released Oct '80, on WEA, by WEA Records. Deleted Oct '83. Catalogue no: **K 18366**

Abyssinians

TENAYISTILLIN
Tracks: / Tenayistillin / Mandela / Tenayistillin.
12" Single: Released Jul '88, on Clinch, Catalogue no: **CR 2688**

Academy

KEEP ON PUSHING
Tracks: / Keep on pushing / Turn it up.
7" Single: Released Apr '86, on RCA, by BMG Records (UK). Catalogue no: **PB 40647**

ON THE BEACH
Tracks: / On the beach / Keep quiet.
12" Single: Released Mar '84, on RCA, by BMG Records (UK). Catalogue no: **ACADT 1**

ABC - WHEN SMOKEY SINGS (Released on Neutron)

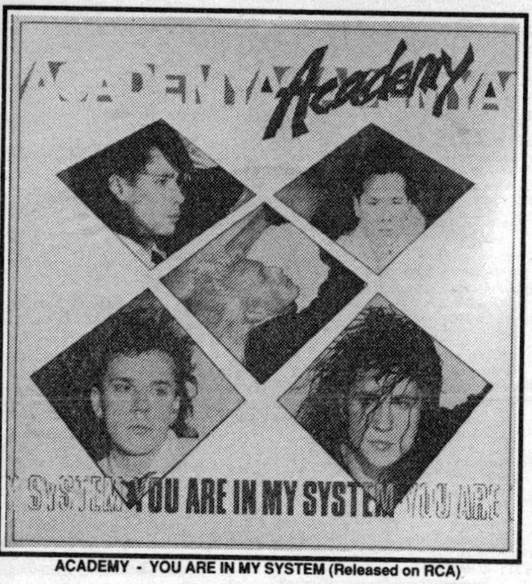

ACADEMY - YOU ARE IN MY SYSTEM (Released on RCA)

7" Single: on RCA, by BMG Records (UK). Catalogue no: **ACAD 1**

STAND UP
Tracks: / Stand up.
7" Single: Released Jul '85, on RCA, by BMG Records (UK). Catalogue no: **PB 40293**
12" Single: Released Aug '85, on RCA, by BMG Records (UK). Catalogue no: **PT 40294**

TONIGHT (THE WORLD KEEPS SWINGING)
Tracks: / Tonight (the world keeps swinging) / Paint me blue.
7" Single: Released May '85, on RCA, by BMG Records (UK). Catalogue no: **PB 40137**
12" Single: Released May '85, on RCA, by BMG Records (UK). Catalogue no: **PT 40138**

YOU'RE IN MY SYSTEM (see panel above)
Tracks: / You're in my system / You're in my system (extra inch remix) (On 12" only) / Heaven waits / System (Bernard remix) (On 12" only).
7" Single: Released Jan '86, on RCA, by BMG Records (UK). Catalogue no: **PB 40537**
12" Single: Released Jan '86, on RCA, by BMG Records (UK). Catalogue no: **PT 40538**

Academy Of Unrest

SHEOL HEX
Tracks: / Sheol hex.
7" Single: Released Jun '85, on Dead Fly, by Dead Fly Records. Deleted '88. Catalogue no: **ACAD 001**

Academy One

FOREVER AND EVER
Tracks: / Forever and ever / Heaven.
7" Single: Released Apr '82, on Armageddon, by Armageddon Records. Deleted '88. Catalogue no: **AS 021**

Accelerators

REASON FOR TREASON (EP)
12" Single: Released Feb '80, on Spiv, by Spiv Records. Deleted '88. Catalogue no: **ACCEL EP**

Accent

LOSER, THE
Tracks: / Loser, The.
7" Single: Released Apr '89, on UNKNOWN, Catalogue no: **ACC 001**

WE ARE LOST
Tracks: / We are lost.
7" Single: Released Dec '84, on Motion, Catalogue no: **MOTION 111**

Accept

Biographical details: German five-piece heavy rock group formed 1977. First signed to the German Metronome label. In 1978 released first album 'Accept'. Second album 'Breaker' appeared 79/80. First appeared in UK as back-up group to Judas Priest, in '81. Third album was 'Restless & Wild'. They made a UK tour in 82/83. Fourth album 'Balls To The Walls' was released in Jan '84 by Epic..

RESTLESS AND WILD (SINGLE)
Tracks: / Restless and wild / Fast as a shark.
12" Single: Released Feb '84, on Heavy Metal, by FM-Revolver Records. Catalogue no: **12 HIGH 3**

Accursed

GOING DOWN
Tracks: / Going down.
7" Single: Released Mar '84, on Wreck 'Em, Deleted '88. Catalogue no: **ACC 3**

AC/DC

Biographical details: AC/DC were formed in Australia by the Young brothers in 1974. After building a following in their home country, they toured Britain in 1976 and released two albums, *Dirty Deeds Done Dirt Cheap* and *High Voltage*. They arrived in the UK at the worst possible time for a heavy metal band-right at the start of the punk era. Atlantic Records overcame this disadvantage by opportunistically presenting them as a punk band with a schoolboy image. This pretence could not be kept up for long, though, and AC/DC were soon given deserved credit for being one of the few HM act to break through during the Punk/New Wave period. *Let There Be Rock* was their first UK chart album, reaching the Top 20 in 1977, the same year that original basssist Mark Evans was replaced by Cliff Williams. The group's sixth album *Highway To Hell*, issued in 1979 was one of the forerunners of a major heavy metal resurgence in the charts. But just as the band were entering the top league tragedy struck. Vital vocalist Bon Scott, whose supersonic singing was one of AC/DC's main trademarks, died from alcohol abuse in early 1980. The remaining members quickly overcame this bombshell by finding an equally energetic replacement in British singer Brian Johnson, formerly of early Seventies singles band Geordie. Public acceptance of the new recruit was immediate. *Back In Black* (title being a tasteful tribute to Scott) entered the album chart at No.1 and yielded the band's first Top 20 single, *Rock 'n' Roll Ain't Noise Pollution*. *Rock 'n' Roll Damnation* had been their first hit single in 1978, peaking at No.24, but most of their 45's had tended to be only minor hits. AC/DC's biggest single came in 1982 when *Let's Get It Up* reached No.13, and both albums and singles have continued to sell well. In August 1984 they reiterated their status as one of the world's leading heavy bands by headlining the *Monsters Of Rock* festival at Castle Donnington. Their biggest Stateside triumph csme at the end of '81, when *For Those About To Rock* topped the Billboard album chart. (Bob McDonald)

This rock band was formed in Australia in 1974; its original vocalist was 'Bon' Scott (born in 1946 in Scotland; died in 1980 in London of too much drink); guitarists Angus and Malcolm Young from Glasgow had emigrated in the 1960s with their older brother George, who was in the Easybeats; they recruited drummer Phil Rudd and bassist Mark Evans, both from Melbourne. Their first international album in 1976 was a compilation from Aussie hit albums; Cliff Williams from Romford replaced Evans; Scott was replaced by Brian Johnson (born in 1947 in North Shields), and they're still at it in 1988. (Donald Clarke 21 July 1988).

Built up a huge popularity in Australia, then toured Britain in mid/late 70s and gained moderate chart success: *Touch Too Much, Whole Lotta Rosie* etc. Bon Scott's death came at the verge of the band's greatest success, but they replaced him with Brian Johnson and continued, without any loss in popularity, to produce albums such as *Back in Black* and *For Those About to Rock*. (Robert Cohen October 1987)

DANGER
Tracks: / Danger.
7" Single: Released Jul '85, on Atlantic, by WEA Records. Deleted '88. Catalogue no: **A 9532**

DIRTY DEEDS DONE DIRT CHEAP (SINGLE)
Tracks: / Dirty deeds done dirt cheap.
7" Single: Released Jun '80, on Atlantic, by WEA Records. Deleted '83. Catalogue no: **HM 2**

FOR THOSE ABOUT TO ROCK (WE SALUTE YOU) (SINGLE)
Tracks: / For those about to rock (we salute you) / Let there be rock.
7" Single: Released Jul '82, on Atlantic, by WEA Records. Deleted '85. Catalogue no: **K 11721**

GUNS FOR HIRE
Tracks: / Guns for hire.
7" Single: Released Oct '83, on Atlantic, by WEA Records. Deleted '86. Catalogue no: **A 9774**

HEAT SEEKER
Tracks: / Heat seeker / Go zone / Snake high*.
Note: * extra track on 12"
12" Single: Released Dec '87, on Atlantic, by WEA Records. Catalogue no: **A 9136 T**
7" Single: Released Dec '87, on Atlantic, by WEA Records. Catalogue no: **A 9136**

HIGH VOLTAGE
Tracks: / High voltage.
7" Single: Released Jun '80, on Atlantic, by WEA Records. Deleted '88. Catalogue no: **HM 1**

HIGHWAY TO HELL (SINGLE)
Tracks: / Highway to Hell / If you want blood you've got it.
7" Single: Released Jul '87, on Atlantic, by WEA Records. Deleted '88. Catalogue no: **K 11321**

IT'S A LONG WAY TO THE TOP IF YOU WANNA ...
Tracks: / It's a long way to the top if you wanna....
7" Single: Released '87, on Atlantic, by WEA Records. Deleted '88. Catalogue no: **HM 3**

LET'S GET IT UP
Tracks: / Let's get it up / Back in black.
7" Single: Released Feb '82, on Atlantic, by WEA Records. Deleted '85. Catalogue no: **K 11706**

NERVOUS SHAKEDOWN
Tracks: / Nervous shakedown.
7" Single: Released Jul '84, on Atlantic, by WEA Records. Deleted Jun '87. Catalogue no: **A 9651**
12" Single: Released Jul '84, on Atlantic, by WEA Records. Deleted Jun '87. Catalogue no: **A 9651 T**

ROCK'N'ROLL AIN'T NOISE POLLUTION
Tracks: / Rock 'n' roll ain't noise pollution / Hell's bells.
7" Single: Released Nov '80, on Atlantic, by WEA Records. Deleted '83. Catalogue no: **K 11630**

ROCK'N'ROLL DAMNATION
Tracks: / Rock 'n' roll damnation.
7" Single: Released Jun '78, on Atlantic, by WEA Records. Deleted '81. Catalogue no: **K 11142**

SHAKE YOUR FOUNDATIONS
Tracks: / Shake your foundations / Stand up / Jailbreak (On 12" only.).
12" Single: Released May '88, on Atlantic (Germany), by WEA Records. Catalogue no: **786837 0**
7" Single: Released Jan '86, on Atlantic, by WEA Records. Deleted Jun '87. Catalogue no: **A 9474**
CD 5": on Atlantic by WEA Records. Deleted Jun '87. Catalogue no: **A 9474 CD**
12" Single: Released Jan '86, on Atlantic, by WEA Records. Deleted Jan '88. Catalogue no: **A 9474 T**

THAT'S THE WAY I WANNA ROCK 'N' ROLL EP
Tracks: / That's the way I wanna rock'n'roll / Whole lotta Rosie.
CD 3": Released Aug '88, on Atlantic (Germany), by WEA Records. Catalogue no: **786586 2**
7" Single: Released Mar '88, on Atlantic, by WEA Records. Catalogue no: **A 9098**
12" Single: Released Mar '88, on Atlantic, by WEA Records. Catalogue no: **A 9098 T**
CD 5": Released Mar '88, on Atlantic, by WEA Records. Catalogue no: **A 9098 CD**

TOUCH TOO MUCH
Tracks: / Touch too much / Live wire / Shot down in flames.
7" Single: Released Jan '80, on Atlantic, by WEA Records. Deleted '88. Catalogue no: **K 11435**

WHO MADE WHO (SINGLE)
Tracks: / Who made who / Guns for hire (live).
CD 5": Released May '85, on Atlantic, by WEA Records. Deleted Jun '87. Catalogue no: **A 9425 CD**
7" Single: Released May '85, on Atlantic, by WEA Records. Deleted Jun '87. Catalogue no: **A 9425**
12" Single: Released May '85, on Atlantic, by WEA Records. Deleted Jan '88. Catalogue no: **A 9425 T**

WHOLE LOTTA ROSIE
Tracks: / Whole lotta Rosie / Hell ain't a bad place....
7" Single: Released Jun '80, on Atlantic, by WEA Records. Catalogue no: **HM 4**

YOU SHOOK ME ALL NIGHT LONG
Tracks: / You shook me all night long / She's got balls (version) / You shook me (live) / She's got balls (live).
7" Single: Released Sep '86, on Atlantic, by WEA Records. Deleted Jun '87. Catalogue no: **A 9377**
12" Single: Released Sep '86, on Atlantic, by WEA Records. Deleted Jan '88. Catalogue no: **A 9377 T**
12" Single: Released May '88, on Atlantic (Germany), by WEA Records. Catalogue no: **786 792 0**
7" Pic: Released Sep '86, on Atlantic, by WEA Records. Deleted Jun '87. Catalogue no: **A 9377 P**
7" Single: Released Sep '80, on Atlantic, by WEA Records. Deleted '83. Catalogue no: **K 11600**

Ace

Biographical details: Ace were formed as a pub band in 1972 by Comer, Harris and King. Vocalist Carrick joined in '73 and Byrne in '74. *How Long*, a pre-Hall & Oates style soft rock/soul single, reached No.3 in the US in '75. However the group failed to live up to its early promise and quickly faded. Paul Carrack later enjoyed record success with Squeeze, toured with Nick Lowe and then pursued a solo career. (Bob MacDonald, 1988).

HOW LONG (OLD GOLD)
7" Single: Released 21 Nov '87, on Old Gold, by Old Gold Records. Catalogue no: **OG 9731**

HOW LONG (ORIGINAL)
Tracks: / How long.
7" Single: Released Nov '74, on Anchor (1), by Anchor Records. Deleted '77. Catalogue no: **ANC 1002**

Ace, Richard

STAYIN' ALIVE
Tracks: / Stayin' alive.
7" Single: Released Dec '78, on Blue Inc, Deleted '81. Catalogue no: **INC 2**

Aces

GOT TO GET SOME MONEY
Tracks: / Got to get some money.
12" Single: Released Aug '84, on Clair, Deleted '88. Catalogue no: **CM 12**

ONE WAY STREET
Tracks: / One way street / Why it should be.
7" Single: Released Oct '82, on ETC, Deleted '88. Catalogue no: **ETC 01**

Aces And Eights

HARD LUCK STORIES
Tracks: / Hard luck stories / Love is duel.
7" Single: Released Nov '87, on Other, by Waterfall Records. Deleted '88. Catalogue no: **OTH 8**

Acid

HELL ON WHEELS
Tracks: / Hell on wheels / Hooked on metal.
7" Single: Released Jul '82, on Roadrunner (Germany), Deleted '88. Catalogue no: **841 691**

Acid Angels

SPEED SPEED ECSTACY
Tracks: / Speed speed ecstasy.
12" Single: Released Sep '88, on Product Inc., Catalogue no: **FUEL 001 T**
7" Single: Released Sep '88, on Product Inc., Catalogue no: **FUEL 001**

Acid Boyz

WE DON'T EXIST
Tracks: / We don't exist.
12" Single: Released Sep '88, on Premiere, by Premiere Records. Catalogue no: **ERET 504**

Acid In The...

ACID IN THE HOUSE MIX, VOLUME

1
CD 5": Released Feb '89, on ZYX (Germany), Catalogue no: **ZYX 60668**
12" Single: Released Feb '89, on ZYX (Germany), Catalogue no: **ZYX 606612**

Acid Reign

HUMANOIA
Tracks: / Humanoia.
10" single: Released Jun '89, on Music For Nations, by Music For Nations Records. Catalogue no: **10FLAG 106**

Ackee

RUGAMUFFIN BOOGIE ROCK
Tracks: / Rugamuffin boogie rock.
12" Single: Released Oct '87, on Root, Catalogue no: **1 RO 004**

Acker, Luc Van

ZANNA (with Anna Domino)
Tracks: / Zanna.
12" Single: Released '87, on Wax Trax, by Wax Trax Records. Catalogue no: **WAXUK 023**

Ackerman, Tracy

CHRISTMAS SONG, THE
Tracks: / Christmas song, The.
7" Single: Released Dec '87, on Debut, by Skratch Records. Catalogue no: **DEBT 3038**

DON'T WANT IT
Tracks: / Don't want it (don't need it) / With regrets.
12" Single: Released Mar '86, on Polydor, by Polydor Ltd. Deleted '88. Catalogue no: **POSPX 781**
7" Single: Released Mar '86, on Polydor, by Polydor Ltd. Deleted '88. Catalogue no: **POSP 781**

I JUST DON'T KNOW WHAT TO DO WITH MYSELF
Tracks: / I just don't know what to do with myself / You blow hot and cold.
12" Single: Released Sep '89, on Passion, by Skratch Records. Catalogue no: **PASH 1292**

LOVE HANGOVER
Tracks: / Love hangover / Head over heels.
12" Single: Released Nov '86, on Debut, by Skratch Records. Catalogue no: **DEBTX 3012**
7" Single: Released Nov '86, on Debut, by Skratch Records. Catalogue no: **DEBT 3012**

SLAVE (FOR YOUR DESIRE)
Tracks: / Slave (for your desire) / Slave (for your desire)(instrumental mix).
12" Single: Released 7 Mar '88, on Passion, by Skratch Records. Catalogue no: **PASH 81(12)**

TAKE MY BODY
Tracks: / Take my body.
12" Single: Released '87, on Skratch, by Skratch Records. Catalogue no: **PASH 79(12)**

Acklin, Barbara

AM I THE SAME GIRL
Tracks: / Am I the same girl / Love makes a woman.
7" Single: Released 20 Jun '87, on Debut, by Skratch Records. Catalogue no: **DEBT 3024**
12" Single: Released May '87, on Debut, by Skratch Records. Catalogue no: **DEBTX 3024**

Acoustic Alchemy

CASINO
Tracks: / Casino / Sarah Victoria / Drake's drum.
7" Single: Released Sep '83, on Moonstone, by Ampersand Music. Deleted '88. Catalogue no: **MONS 1934**
7" Single: Released 22 Aug '88, on MCA, by MCA Records. Catalogue no: **MCA 1277**

Across The Border

CAN'T GET THROUGH
Tracks: / Can't get through.
7" Single: Released Sep '85, on President, by President Records. Deleted '88. Catalogue no: **PT 536**

Act

ABSOLUTELY IMMUNE
Tracks: / Absolutely immune / Blood rush / White rabbit.
Note: * Extra track on 12" version
12" Single: Released Sep '87, on ZTT, by ZTT Records. Catalogue no: **TIMM 1**
7" Single: Released Sep '87, on ZTT, by ZTT Records. Catalogue no: **IMM 1**

ABSOLUTELY IMMUNE II
Tracks: / State of logic (Extra track available on pic bag single.) / Absolutely immune II / Bloodrush.
7" Single: Released Oct '87, on ZTT, by ZTT Records. Catalogue no: **VIMM 1**

CHANCE
Tracks: / Chance / Winner 88.
12" Single: Released Jul '88, on WEA, by WEA Records. Catalogue no: **BETT 1**
7" Single: Released Jul '88, on WEA, by WEA Records. Catalogue no: **BET 1**

I CAN'T ESCAPE FROM YOU
Tracks: / I can't escape from you / Dear life / I can't escape from you (love & hate) / Heaven knows I'm miserable now (Available on 12" and CD only) / I can't escape from you (theme).
7" Single: Released Feb '88, on ZTT, by ZTT Records. Catalogue no: **IMM 2**
CD 5": Released Feb '88, on ZTT, by ZTT Records. Catalogue no: **CDIMM 2**
12" Single: Released Feb '88, on ZTT, by ZTT Records. Catalogue no: **TIMM 2**

SNOBBERY AND DECAY
Tracks: / Snobbery and Decay / Poison / I'd be surprisingly good for you.
12" Single: Released 30 May '87, on ZTT, by ZTT Records. Catalogue no: **12 XACT 28**
CD 5": Released May '87, on ZTT, by ZTT Records. Deleted Jun '88. Catalogue no: **CID 28**
12" Single: Released Apr '87, on ZTT, by ZTT Records. Deleted Jun '88. Catalogue no: **12 ZTS 28**
12" Single: Released Apr '87, on ZTT, by ZTT Records. Catalogue no: **12 XCT 28**
7" Single: Released Apr '87, on ZTT, by ZTT Records. Deleted Jun '88. Catalogue no: **ZTAS 28**
Cassingle: Released May '87, on ZTT, by ZTT Records. Deleted Jun '88. Catalogue no: **CTIS 28**

TOO LATE AT 20
Tracks: / Too late at 20.
7" Single: Released Sep '81, on Hannibal, by Hannibal Records. Deleted '88. Catalogue no: **HNS 701**

WHO LET THE FLOWERS FALL?
Tracks: / Who let the flowers fall.
7" Single: Released Oct '81, on Act, Deleted '88. Catalogue no: **ACT 001**

Act Fuseli

BEG BEG RICHER
Tracks: / Beg beg richer.
12" Single: Released Dec '85, on Trinity Disques, Deleted '88. Catalogue no: **GFK 1T**
7" Single: Released Dec '85, on Trinity Disques, Deleted '88. Catalogue no: **GFK 1**

SOLANGE
Tracks: / Solange / White silence / Benjamin boy (On 12" only) / Solange pavana (On 12" only).
7" Single: Released Jun '86, on WEA, by WEA Records. Catalogue no: **YZ 74**
12" Single: Released Jun '86, on WEA, by WEA Records. Deleted '88. Catalogue no: **YZ 74T**

Act One

TOM THE PEEPER
Tracks: / Tom the peeper.
7" Single: Released May '74, on Mercury, by Phonogram Ltd. Deleted '77. Catalogue no: **6008 005**

Actifed

CRUCIFIXION
Tracks: / Crucifixion.
12" Single: Released Jun '84, on Jungle, by Jungle Records. Deleted '88. Catalogue no: **JUNG 11**

DAWN OF A LEGION
Tracks: / Dawn of a legion.
12" Single: Released Aug '83, on Jungle, by Jungle Records. Catalogue no: **JUNG 7**

Action

HEY SHA-LO-NEY
Tracks: / Hey sha-lo-ney / Come on, come with me.
7" Single: Released May '84, on Edsel, by Demon Records. Catalogue no: **E 5008**

I'LL KEEP HOLDING ON
Tracks: / I'll keep holding on.
7" Single: Released Jul '81, on Edsel, by Demon Records. Deleted '88. Catalogue no: **E 5001**

SHADOWS AND REFLECTIONS
Tracks: / Shadows and reflections.
7" Single: Released Jun '82, on Edsel, by Demon Records. Deleted '88. Catalogue no: **E 5003**

SINCE I LOST MY BABY
Tracks: / Since I lost my baby.
7" Single: Released Sep '81, on Edsel, by Demon Records. Deleted '88. Catalogue no: **E 5002**

Action Pact

COCKTAIL CREDIBILITY
Tracks: / Cocktail credibility.
7" Single: Released Oct '84, on Fall Out, Catalogue no: **FALL 029**

LONDON BOUNCERS
Tracks: / London bouncers.
7" Single: Released Jul '83, on Fall Out, Catalogue no: **FALL 016**
12" Single: Released Jul '83, on Fall Out, Catalogue no: **FALL 12016**

PEOPLE
Tracks: / People / Times must change.
7" Single: Released Mar '83, on Fall Out, Catalogue no: **FALL 010**

QUESTION OF CHOICE
Tracks: / Question of choice / Hook, line and sinker / Suss of the Swiss.
7" Single: Released Nov '83, on Fall Out, Catalogue no: **FALL 019**

SUICIDE BAG
Tracks: / Suicide bag.
7" Single: Released Aug '82, on Fall Out, Catalogue no: **FALL 003**

YET ANOTHER DOLE QUEUE SONG
Tracks: / Yet another dole queue song.
7" Single: Released Aug '84, on Fall Out, Catalogue no: **FALL 026**
12" Single: Released Aug '84, on Fall Out, Catalogue no: **FALL 12026**

Action Transfers

IF I LOSE IT
Tracks: / If I lose it.
7" Single: Released Oct '84, on Rewind, Deleted '88. Catalogue no: **REW 20**

LIGHT OH BABY, THE
Tracks: / Light oh baby, The / Right to remain silent.
12" Single: Released Aug '84, on Rewind, Catalogue no: **12 REW 17**
7" Single: Released Apr '84, on Rewind, Catalogue no: **REW 17**

Active Force

GIMME YOUR LOVE
Tracks: / Gimme your love / My sunshine.
12" Single: Released Aug '86, on A&M, by A&M Records. Deleted '87. Catalogue no: **AMY 345**
7" Single: Released Aug '86, on A&M, by A&M Records. Deleted '87. Catalogue no: **AM 345**

Active Minds

MURDER IN THE LABORATORY
Tracks: / Murder in the laboratory.
7" Single: Released Jul '87, on Loony Tunes, by Loony Tunes Records. Catalogue no: **TUNE 004**

WELCOME TO THE SLAUGHTERHOUSE
Tracks: / Welcome to the slaughterhouse.
7" Single: Released Jun '88, on Loony Tunes, by Loony Tunes Records. Catalogue no: **TUNE 011**

Actives

RIOT (EP)
Tracks: / Riot.
7" Single: Released Jun '83, on Quiet, by Quiet Records. Catalogue no: **QS 001**

WAIT AND SEE
Tracks: / Wait and see.
12" Single: Released Jun '84, on Quiet, by Quiet Records. Catalogue no: **QST 004**

Actors & Famous People

IT DON'T MATTER (EP)
12" Single: Released Sep '84, on Actor, Catalogue no: **ACT 1**

Acuff, Roy

Biographical details: ACUFF, Roy was born in 1903 in Maynardsville, Tennessee; the singer, fiddler and bandleader remains the grand old man of country music. He first performed on the radio in 1933 and began recording in 1936 for one of the ancestors of today's CBS label, with the legendary producer Art Satherley. His biggest hits included *Great Speckled Bird*, the hymn based on Jeremiah 12:9 used the traditional melody known as *I'm Thinking Tonight Of My Blue Eyes* (recorded by the Carter family) and was sung in Southern churches. *Wabash Cannon Ball* was also sung by the Carters; Roy's version sold a million and is one of the most famous country records ever made. His band, the Smoky Mountain Boys, was one of the first to include a dobro or Hawaiian guitar. He formed Acuff-Rose in Nashville in 1942 with Fred Rose, which published all of Hank Williams' songs. A postwar poll of the USA Armed Forces Network saw Acuff beat Frank Sinatra as the soldiers' favourite vocalist. (Donald Clarke 21 July 1988.)

FIREBALL MAIL
Tracks: / Fireball mail / Stage.
7" Single: Released Jun '83, on Everest(Premier), by Everest Records. Deleted '88. Catalogue no: **EVB 1002**

AD 1984

1984
Tracks: / 1984 / Mushroom music.
7" Single: Released Dec '83, on Grand Prix, Deleted '88. Catalogue no: **GP 014**

AD 2000

HANG ON SNOOPY
Tracks: / Hang on Snoopy / Doggy dub.
7" Single: Released Jul '83, on Excaliber, by Red Bus Records. Deleted '88. Catalogue no: **EXC 533**
12" Single: Released Jul '83, on Excaliber, by Red Bus Records. Deleted '88. Catalogue no: **EXCL 533**

PAPA WAS A ROLLIN' STONE
Tracks: / Papa was a rollin' stone.
12" Single: Released Mar '83, on Excaliber, by Red Bus Records. Deleted '88. Catalogue no: **EXCL 529**
7" Single: Released Mar '83, on Excaliber, by Red Bus Records. Deleted '88. Catalogue no: **EXC 529**

RHYTHM & CHIPS
Tracks: / Rhythm and chips / Don't play the disco.
7" Single: Released Apr '82, on Ash, by Ash Records. Deleted '88. Catalogue no: **ASH 007**

Ad Infinitum

TELSTAR
Tracks: / Telstar.
7" Single: Released Mar '84, on Factory (1), by Factory Records. Catalogue no: **FAC 96**

Ad Libs

Biographical details: A pop vocal group from New Jersey. They were hitmakers for the short-lived but influential label Blue Cat, formed by Lieber & Stoller with George Goldner. Lineup had Mary Ann Thomas and Hughie Harris alternating lead vocals, with Danny Austin and David Watt. Their biggest hit was *The Boy from New York City*, USA top 10 in 1965. Donald Clarke 21 July 1988..

NEW YORK IN THE DARK
Tracks: / New York in the dark / Boy from New York City.
7" Single: Released May '79, on Inferno (1), by Inferno Records. Deleted '88. Catalogue no: **HEAT 1**

Ad Nauseum

BRAINSTORM
Tracks: / Brainstorm.
7" EP: Released Jan '83, on Flicknife, by Flicknife Records. Catalogue no: **FLS 212**

Adams Affair

JUST A GROOVE
Tracks: / Just a groove / We've got to make it.
7" Single: Released Nov '80, on Excaliber by Red Bus Records. Deleted Nov '83 Catalogue no: **EXC 502**

Adams, Andy

NOBODY HAS BROKEN HEART LIKE ME
Tracks: / Nobody has a broken heart like me / Don't you ever read your mail.
7" Single: Released Aug '80, on DJM Deleted Aug '83. Catalogue no: **DJS 1095**

Adams Apples

DON'T TAKE IT OUT ON THIS WORLD
Tracks: / Don't want to lose you / I don want to lose you.
7" Single: Released Apr '85, on Kent, b Ace Records. Deleted '88. Catalogue n **TOWN 101**

Adams, Arthur

YOU GOT THE FLOOR
Tracks: / You got the floor / Stay with m tonight.
7" Single: Released Oct '81, on RCA, b BMG Records (UK). Deleted '84. Cat logue no: **RCA 146**
12" Single: Released Oct '81, on RCA, b BMG Records (UK). Deleted '84. Cat logue no: **RCAT 146**

Adams, Bryan

Biographical details:
Bryan Adams was born in Kingston, Ont rio, Canada in November 1959. He bega his career by writing songs for the likes Bachman Turner Overdrive and Kiss.
He was signed to A&M Records as an a ist in his own right in 1979. Much giggi and supporting finally led to a string of T

20 hits in America, though he didn't come to prominence in the U.K. until the release of Run To Him in 1985 and his appearance in the Live Aid Show. Since then, he has toured with Tina Turner as well as recording a single It's Only Love, with her. In 1987 he released the album *Into The Fire*. (Robert Cohen October 1987).

Bryan Adams was born in 1959 in Vancouver. The singer, guitarist and songwriter placed hits with Ian Lloyd in Canada, Prism in USA; then formed his own five-piece band, and had USA top 20 hits with *Cuts Like a Knife* and *Straight From the Heart*, his act with 'outlaw' overtones somewhat like Bruce Springsteen was popular on the MTV video channel. He wrote *Tears Are Not Enough* for the Canadian Band Aid disc; he toured with Tina Turner in 1985; when the album *Reckless* had sold seven million copies he was not too big to play London's Marquee club on 48 hours notice in mid 1987 with co-star second guitar Keith Scott. (Donald Clarke 21 July 1988).

CHRISTMAS TIME
Tracks: / Christmas time / Reggae Christmas.
7" Single: Released Dec '85, on A&M, by A&M Records. Deleted Mar '88. Catalogue no: **AM 297**
12" Single: Released Dec '85, on A&M, by A&M Records. Deleted '88. Catalogue no: **AMY 297**

DIANA
Tracks: / Diana.
12" Single: Released May '88, on A&M (Canada), by A&M Records. Catalogue no: **P 23030**

HEARTS ON FIRE
Tracks: / Hearts on fire / Run to you / Native son (on 12" only.).
12" Single: Released 23 May '87, on A&M, by A&M Records. Deleted 1 Aug '88. Catalogue no: **ADAM 312**
Cassingle: Released 23 May '87, on A&M, by A&M Records. Deleted 1 Aug '88. Catalogue no: **ADAMC 312**
7" Single: Released 23 May '87, on A&M, by A&M Records. Deleted 1 Aug '88. Catalogue no: **ADAM 3**

HEAT OF THE NIGHT
Tracks: / Heat of the night / Another day.
7" Single: Released Mar '87, on A&M, by A&M Records. Deleted 1 Aug '88. Catalogue no: **ADAM 2**
12" Single: Released Mar '87, on A&M, by A&M Records. Deleted 1 Aug '88. Catalogue no: **ADAM 12**

HEAVEN
Tracks: / Heaven.
7" Single: Released May '85, on A&M, by A&M Records. Deleted '88. Catalogue no: **AM 256**

HIDIN' FROM LOVE
Tracks: / Hidin' from love / Wait and see.
7" Single: Released Apr '80, on A&M, by A&M Records. Deleted Apr '83. Catalogue no: **AMS 7520**

IT'S ONLY LOVE
Tracks: / It's only love.
7" Single: Released Oct '85, on A&M, by A&M Records. Deleted '87. Catalogue no: **AM 285**
12" Single: Released Oct '85, on A&M, by A&M Records. Deleted '87. Catalogue no: **AMY 285**

LONELY NIGHTS
Tracks: / Lonely nighs / Don't look now.
7" Single: Released Nov '81, on A&M, by A&M Records. Deleted Nov '84. Catalogue no: **AMS 8183**

ONE GOOD REASON
Tracks: / One good reason.
7" Single: Released Jan '84, on A&M, by A&M Records. Deleted '88. Catalogue no: **AM 170**

RUN TO YOU
Tracks: / Run to you / I'm ready / Cuts like a knife.
7" Single: Released Dec '84, on A&M, by A&M Records. Deleted '87. Catalogue no: **AM 224**
12" Single: Released Dec '84, on A&M, by A&M Records. Deleted '87. Catalogue no: **AMY 224**

SOMEBODY
Tracks: / Somebody / Long gone.
7" Single: Released Mar '85, on A&M, by A&M Records. Deleted '88. Catalogue no: **AM 236**
7" Pic: Released Mar '85, on A&M, by A&M Records. Deleted '88. Catalogue no: **AMP**

STRAIGHT FROM THE HEART
Tracks: / Straight from the heart / Fits you good / Straight from the heart (live) (On 12" only) / Run too close (In doublepack only) / Somebody (In doublepack only).
7" Single: Released Jun '86, on A&M, by A&M Records. Deleted '87. Catalogue no: **AM 322**
7" Single: Released Jun '86, on A&M, by A&M Records. Deleted '87. Catalogue no: **AM 322**
7" Set: Released Jun '86, on A&M, by A&M Records. Deleted '87. Catalogue no: **AMS 322**

SUMMER OF '69
Tracks: / Summer of '69.
12" Single: Released Jul '85, on A&M, by A&M Records. Deleted '87. Catalogue no: **AMY 267**
7" Single: Released Jul '85, on A&M, by A&M Records. Deleted '87. Catalogue no: **AM 267**

THIS TIME
Tracks: / This time / I'm ready / Lonely nights (On 12" only).
7" Single: Released Feb '86, on A&M, by A&M Records. Deleted '87. Catalogue no: **AM 295**
12" Single: Released Feb '86, on A&M, by A&M Records. Deleted '87. Catalogue no: **AMY 295**

VICTIM OF LOVE
Tracks: / Victim of love / Heat of the night (live).
Note: Available on 7" in limited edition box set including full colour postcards and sew-on patch, and on 12" backed with exclusive live versions of "Heat Of The Night' and 'Victim Of Love'. The 7" also carries a live version of 'Heat Of The Night'.
12" Single: Released Oct '87, on A&M, by A&M Records. Deleted Mar '88. Catalogue no: **AMY 407**
Cassingle: Released Oct '87, on A&M, by A&M Records. Deleted Feb '89. Catalogue no: **AMF 407**
7" Single: Released Oct '87, on A&M, by A&M Records. Catalogue no: **AM 407**

Adams, Cliff

Biographical details: Over the past 25 years Cliff Adams and his Singers have scored four charted albums, all based on Rakio 2's long running Sunday series *Sing Something Simple*. The British-born Adams also had a minor instrumental hit single in 1960 with his orchestra's *Lonely Man Theme*. (Bob MacDonald, 1988).

LONELY MAN
Tracks: / Lonely man.
7" Single: Released Apr '60, on Pye International, Deleted '63. Catalogue no: **7N 25056**

Adams, Danny

I WILL NEVER LET YOU GO OUT OF MY LIFE
Tracks: / I will never let you go out of my life / Dreadlocks afair.
12" Single: Released Feb '83, on Tree Roots, Deleted '88. Catalogue no: **VG 0001**

Adams Family

WARTOWN
Tracks: / Wartown.
12" Single: Released May '84, on Adams Family, by Revolver Records. Catalogue no: **AD 1**

Adams, Gayle

BABY I NEED YOUR LOVING
Tracks: / Baby I need your loving / Don't jump to conclusions.
7" Single: Released Apr '82, on Epic, by CBS Records. Deleted Apr '85. Catalogue no: **EPC A2167**
12" Single: Released Apr '82, on Epic, by CBS Records. Deleted Apr '85. Catalogue no: **EPC A13 2167**

I'M WARNING YOU
Tracks: / I'm warning you.
12" Single: Released Oct '84, on 4th & Broadway, by Island Records. Deleted '87. Catalogue no: **12 BRW 16**
7" Single: Released Oct '84, on 4th & Broadway, by Island Records. Catalogue no: **BRW 16**

LOVE FEVER
Tracks: / Love fever / I don't want to hear it.
7" Single: Released Dec '81, on Epic, by CBS Records. Deleted Dec '81. Catalogue no: **A1881**

STRETCHIN' OUT
Tracks: / Stretchin' out.
7" Single: Released Jul '80, on Epic, by CBS Records. Deleted '83. Catalogue no: **EPC 8791**

YOUR LOVE IS A LIFE SAVER
Tracks: / Your love is a life saver / For the love of my man.
7" Single: Released Sep '80, on Epic, by CBS Records. Deleted '83. Catalogue no: **EPC 8987**

Adams, Glen Affair

JUST A GROOVE
Tracks: / Just a groove / We've got to make it.
12" Single: Released Nov '80, on Excaliber, by Red Bus Records. Deleted '88. Catalogue no: **EXCL 502**
7" Single: Released Nov '80, on Excaliber, by Red Bus Records. Deleted '88. Catalogue no: **EXC 502**

SATURDAY NIGHT
Tracks: / Saturday night.
12" Single: Released Nov '84, on Nunk, Deleted '88. Catalogue no: **NUNK 1008**

Adams, John

STRIP THIS HEART
Tracks: / Strip this heart / Precious one.
Note: Available on 7" and 4-track 12" remixed by D.J. mixer Bruce Forest.
12" Single: Released Jul '87, on A&M, by A&M Records. Deleted Mar '88. Catalogue no: **AMY 398**
7" Single: Released Jul '87, on A&M, by A&M Records. Deleted Mar '88. Catalogue no: **AM 398**

THROUGH THE EYES OF LOVE
Tracks: / Through the eyes of love.
12" Single: Released Sep '85, on Parlophone, by EMI Records. Deleted '88. Catalogue no: **12R 6108**
7" Single: Released Sep '85, on Parlophone, by EMI Records. Deleted '88. Catalogue no: **R 6108**

Adams, Johnny

Biographical details: Johnny Adams is a superior singer with a wide range of stylistic influence. "The Tan Nightingale" was born in New Orleans in 1932. He sang in gospel groups and switched to R&B in 1959. He had hits on Ric and on Shelby Singleton's SSS International label; in the early '70s he had less luck on Atlantic, then on several smaller labels. His earlier hits are now available on Charly and recently he's begun a new career on the excellent Rounder label: *From the Heart* includes songs by Tony Joe White, Sam Cooke, Doc Pomus and Percy Mayfield. Donald Clarke 21 July 1988.

WHEN I NEED YOU
Tracks: / When I need you / Cry cry darlin'.
7" Single: Released Oct '83, on Hep Me, Deleted '88. Catalogue no: **HEPME 45-180**

Adamson, Barry

MAN WITH THE GOLDEN ARM
Tracks: / Man with the golden arm / Bombasto / Fifteen rounds / Suck on the honey of love.
12" Single: Released '88, on Mute, by Mute Records. Catalogue no: **12 MUTE 77**
7" Single: Released '88, on Mute, by Mute Records. Catalogue no: **MUTE 77**

TAMING OF THE SHREWD
Tracks: / Taming of the shrewd.
12" Single: Released Sep '89, on Mute, by Mute Records. Catalogue no: **12 MUTE 097**
CD 3": Released Oct '89, on Mute, by Mute Records. Catalogue no: **MUTE 097**

Addrisi Brothers

GHOST DANCER
Tracks: / Ghost dancer.
7" Single: Released Oct '79, on Scotti Bros (USA), Deleted '82. Catalogue no: **K 11361**

Ade, Sunny

MA JAIYE OUI
Tracks: / Ma jaiye oui / Message.
12" Single: Released Jun '82, on Island, by Island Records. Deleted Jun '85. Catalogue no: **IPR 2054**

Adebambo, Jean

I LIKE IT
Tracks: / I like it.
12" Single: Released Jun '84, on Ade J., Deleted '88. Catalogue no: **AJ 105**

NEVER GONNA GIVE YOU UP
Tracks: / Never gonna give you up.
12" Single: Released 10 Oct '87, on Pioneer International, Catalogue no: **PR 48**

PAIN
Tracks: / Pain / Aches and pains.
12" Single: Released Mar '86, on Now Generation, Catalogue no: **NG 005**

PIPEDRUMS
Tracks: / Pipedrums / Pipedrums (dub).
12" Single: Released Jul '82, on Ade J., Catalogue no: **AJ 102**

RE-UNITED
Tracks: / Re-united / United dub.
12" Single: Released Jul '83, on Ital, by Ital Records. Deleted '88. Catalogue no: **ITD 0018**

SAY THAT YOU LOVE ME
Tracks: / Say that you love me.
12" Single: Released Aug '81, on Ade J., Catalogue no: **AJ 101**

TELL ME
Tracks: / Tell me / Tell me (version).
12" Single: Released Sep '83, on Ade J., Catalogue no: **AJ 104**

WAKE UP
Tracks: / Wake up / Hardships of life.
12" Single: Released Sep '82, on Ade J., Catalogue no: **AJ 103**

YOU ARE THE ONE
Tracks: / You are the one / You are the one (version).
12" Single: Released Mar '84, on Ital, by Ital Records. Catalogue no: **ITD 2007**

Adekile, Toyin

SMILE
Tracks: / Smile / It's not love.
12" Single: Released Mar '85, on Sir George, Catalogue no: **SG 021T**

Adeva

I THANK YOU
Tracks: / I thank you.
12" Single: Released Oct '89, on Cool Tempo, by Chrysalis Records. Catalogue no: **COOLX 192**

RESPECT
Tracks: / Respect.
12" Single: Released Dec '88, on Cool Tempo, by Chrysalis Records. Catalogue no: **COOLX 179**
7" Single: Released Dec '88, on Cool Tempo, by Chrysalis Records. Catalogue no: **COOL 179**
12" Single: Released Dec '88, on Cool Tempo, by Chrysalis Records. Catalogue no: **4 V 943329**

WARNING! (see panel below)
Tracks: / Warning / Respect.
7" Single: Released Jul '89, on Cool Tempo, by Chrysalis Records. Catalogue no: **COOL 185**
CD 5": Released Jul '89, on Cool Tempo, by

ADEVA - WARNING (Released on Cool Tempo)

Chrysalis Records. Catalogue no: **COOLCD 185**
Cassingle: Released Jul '89, on Cool Tempo, by Chrysalis Records. Catalogue no: **COOLMC 185**
12" Single: Released Jul '89, on Cool Tempo, by Chrysalis Records. Catalogue no: **COOL X 185**

Adicts

Biographical details: This pleasant bunch of lads, who fail to even spell their own name correctly, secured their only piece of chart immortality in late '82. Their *Sound Of Music* album spent one week on the LP charts, just 380 less than the Julie Andrews version. (BOB MACDONALD, 1988).

BAD BOY
Tracks: / Bad boy / Shake, rattle, bang your head.
7" Single: Released Jun '83, on Razor, by Razor Records. Catalogue no: **RZS 104**
7" Pic: Released Jun '83, on Razor, by Razor Records. Catalogue no: **RZLP 104**

BAR ROOM BOP - CHAMPS ELYSEES
Tracks: / Bar room bop - Champs Elysees / Sound of music / Who spilt my beer / Cowboys.
12" Single: Released Nov '85, on Fall Out, Catalogue no: **FALL 12038**

CHINESE TAKEAWAY
Tracks: / Chinese takeaway / You'll never walk alone / Too young.
7" Single: Released Nov '82, on Razor, by Razor Records. Catalogue no: **RZS 101**

LUNCH WITH THE ADICTS
Tracks: / Lunch with the adicts.
7" Single: Released Jun '81, on Dining Out, by Dining Out Records. Catalogue no: **TUX 1**

VIVA LA REVOLUTION
Tracks: / Viva la revolution / Steamroller.
7" Single: Released Jul '82, on Fall Out, Deleted '88. Catalogue no: **FALL 002**

Adioa

BUMA DUN YENE
Tracks: / Buma dun yene / Toubab bile.
12" Single: Released Aug '89, on Mango, by Island Records. Catalogue no: **12 MNG 714**

Adkins, Hasil

SHE SAID (SINGLE)
Tracks: / She said.
7" Single: Released Jan '85, on Bison Bop, by Bear Family Records (Germany). Catalogue no: **45 126**

Administrators

EMERGENCY
Tracks: / Emergency.
12" Single: Released Oct '89, on Groove & A Quarter, Catalogue no: **CRD 007**

SHE'S MY LADY
Tracks: / She's my lady / Groove & 7.
7" Single: Released Jul '87, on C.R.D., by C.R.D. Records. Catalogue no: **CRD 003**

THIS IS REGGAE MUSIC
Tracks: / This is reggae music / Unfinished symphony.
12" Single: Released Sep '86, on Groove & A Quarter, Catalogue no: **CRD 001**

Admiral

GENERAL GOVENOR
Tracks: / General govenor.
12" Single: Released Jul '85, on Jah Tubbys, Catalogue no: **JT 010**

Admiral Bailey

CATER FOR WOMAN
Tracks: / Cater for woman.
12" Single: Released May '88, on Live & Love, Catalogue no: **LLD 73**

DELLA MOVE
Tracks: / Della move.
12" Single: Released Sep '88, on Live & Love, Catalogue no: **LLD 90**

DON'T HAVE ME UP
Tracks: / Don't have me up.
7" Single: Released Jan '89, on Jammy's, Catalogue no: **Unknown**

LAUGH AFTER THEM
Tracks: / Laugh after them.
12" Single: Released Jul '88, on Jammy's, Catalogue no: **VPRD 320**

LAUGH AFTER THEM (2)
Tracks: / Laugh after them.
12" Single: Released Sep '88, on Live & Love, Catalogue no: **LLD 91**

MI A GOD PICKNEY
Tracks: / Mi a God Pickney.
12" Single: Released Sep '88, on You're Right, Catalogue no: **YR 009**

NO WAY BETTER THAN YARD
Tracks: / No way, no better than / No way, no better than(dub).
12" Single: Released 14 Aug '88, on Live & Love, Catalogue no: **LLD 81**

WINEY WINEY
Tracks: / Winey winey.
12" Single: Released Dec '88, on Live & Love, Catalogue no: **LLD 102**

Admiral Tibet

LEAVE PEOPLE BUSINESS ALONE
Tracks: / Leave people business alone / Gone man lyric.
12" Single: Released May '86, on Technique, Catalogue no: **WRT 03**

SUFFERER
Tracks: / Sufferer.
12" Single: Released Jun '88, on Guiding Star, Catalogue no: **GS 003**

TERRORIST
Tracks: / Terrorist / Terrorist (version).
12" Single: Released Jun '87, on Technics, Catalogue no: **WRT 16**

TOO MUCH JEALOUSY
Tracks: / Too much jealousy.
12" Single: Released Jun '88, on Jammy's, Catalogue no: **VPRD 310**

WORDS FROM MY MOUTH
Tracks: / Words from my mouth.
12" Single: Released Nov '88, on Jammy's, Catalogue no: **VPRD 360**

YOU KEEP ON TELLING ME
Tracks: / You keep on telling me.
12" Single: Released Sep '88, on Jammy's, Catalogue no: **VPRD 337**

Admiros

COME INTO MY LIFE RAP
Tracks: / Come into my life rap.
12" Single: Released Mar '89, on Music Man, Catalogue no: **MMPT 12002**

Admit You're Shit

EXPECT NO MERCY
Tracks: / Expect no mercy.
7" Single: Released Sep '85, on Mortarhate, by Mortarhate Records. Catalogue no: **MORT 17**

Adonis

ACID POKE
Tracks: / Acid poke / Acid poke (inst).
12" Single: Released Dec '88, on Desire, by Desire Records. Catalogue no: **WANTX 8**

HOUSE
Tracks: / House / House (version).
7" Single: Released Jul '88, on Anxious, by Anxious Records. Catalogue no: **BLMK 2**

NO WAY BACK
Tracks: / No way back / No way (do it properly).
12" Single: Released 30 May '87, on London Records, by London Records. Deleted Feb '89. Catalogue no: **LONX 136**
7" Single: Released 30 May '87, on London Records, by London Records. Deleted Sep '87. Catalogue no: **LON 136**

Adonte

DREAMS
Tracks: / Dreams / Dreams (african house mix).
12" Single: Released Sep '89, on G.T.I. Records, by G.T.I. Music. Catalogue no: **GTI 007 T**

Adrenalin

FRIENDS AND LOVERS
Tracks: / Friends and lovers / Too hot.
7" Single: Released Feb '89, on LHM, Catalogue no: **LH 1**

Adrenalin M.O.D.

BOUNCY HOUSE
Tracks: / Bouncy house / Bouncy house (underground mix) / Bouncy house (metropolitan mix) / Bouncy house (inst).
12" Single: Released Mar '88, on MCA Dance, by MCA Records. Catalogue no: **RAGAT 1**
7" Single: Released Mar '88, on MCA Dance, by MCA Records. Catalogue no: **RAGA 1**

O.O.O.
Tracks: / O.o.o / Ecstasy (Wherever you may be) / Track this / Come on let's jam.
12" Single: Released Sep '88, on MCA, by MCA Records. Catalogue no: **RAGAX 2**
7" Single: Released Sep '88, on MCA, by MCA Records. Catalogue no: **RAGA 2**
12" Single: Released Sep '88, on MCA, by MCA Records. Catalogue no: **RAGAT 2**

Adrenalin O.D.

IMAGINARY MIDGET WESTERN, THEME FROM
Tracks: / Theme from an imaginary midget western / Detroit rock city / Coffin cruiser.
10" single: Released Oct '88, on Rough Justice, by Music For Nations Records. Catalogue no: **10 KORE 105**

Adrissi Brothers

AS LONG AS THE MUSIC
Tracks: / As long as the music / Lady broke my heart.
7" Single: Released Jan '81, on Scotti Bros (USA), Deleted Jan '84. Catalogue no: **K 11632**

Adu

BURKINA FASO
Tracks: / Burkina faso.
7" Single: Released 21 Nov '87, on Copasetic, by Copasetic Records. Catalogue no: **COP 002**

ECHOES FROM TELETANIA
Tracks: / Echoes from teletania.
7" Single: Released Sep '83, on Arro Musik, Catalogue no: **ARM 001**

WORKING FOR THE GOVERNMENT
Tracks: / Working for the government.
7" Single: Released Aug '85, on Modtone, Catalogue no: **ADU 2**
12" Single: Released Aug '85, on Modtone, Catalogue no: **ADU 212**

Adult Net

EDIE
Tracks: / Edie / Get around / Phantom power (On 12" only).
7" Single: Released Dec '85, on Beggars Banquet, by Beggars Banquet Records. Deleted Jun '87. Catalogue no: **BEG 148**
12" Single: Released Dec '85, on Beggars Banquet, by Beggars Banquet Records. Deleted Jun '88. Catalogue no: **BEG 148T**

INCENSE AND PEPPERMINTS
Tracks: / Incense and peppermints.
12" Single: Released Apr '85, on Beggars Banquet, by Beggars Banquet Records. Deleted Jun '88. Catalogue no: **BEG 137T**
7" Single: Released Apr '85, on Beggars Banquet, by Beggars Banquet Records. Deleted Jun '87. Catalogue no: **BEG 137**

STARS SAY GO (WHITE NIGHTS)
Tracks: / Stars say go / Walking in the sand.
12" Single: Released Jun '86, on Beggars Banquet, by Beggars Banquet Records. Deleted Jul '88. Catalogue no: **BEG 164T**
7" Single: Released Jun '86, on Beggars Banquet, by Beggars Banquet Records. Deleted Jan '88. Catalogue no: **BEG 164**

TAKE ME
Tracks: / Take me / Sea of rain / Incense and peppermints / Going nowhere.
Special: Released Mar '89, on Fontana, by Phonogram Ltd. Deleted Oct '89. Catalogue no: **BRX 110**
CD 5": Released 6 Mar '89, on Fontana, by Phonogram Ltd. Catalogue no: **BRXCD 1**
12" Single: Released 6 Mar '89, on Fontana, by Phonogram Ltd. Deleted 31 Jul '89. Catalogue no: **BRX 112**
7" Single: Released 6 Mar '89, on Fontana, by Phonogram Ltd. Deleted 31 Jul '89. Catalogue no: **BRX 1**

WAKING UP IN THE SUN
Tracks: / Waking up in the sun / Walking in the sand / August (On re-issue only).
12" Single: Released Sep '86, on Beggars Banquet, by Beggars Banquet Records. Deleted Jun '88. Catalogue no: **BEG 171T**
12" Single: Released 31 Jul '89, on Fontana, by Phonogram Ltd. Deleted Oct '89. Catalogue no: **BRX 312**
7" Pic: Released Jul '89, on Fontana, by Phonogram Ltd. Deleted Oct '89. Catalogue no: **BRXP 3**
7" Single: Released 31 Jul '89, on Fontana, by Phonogram Ltd. Deleted Oct '89. Catalogue no: **BRX 3**
CD 5": Released 31 Jul '89, on Fontana, by Phonogram Ltd. Deleted Oct '89. Catalogue no: **BRXCD 3**
7" Single: Released Sep '86, on Beggars Banquet, by Beggars Banquet Records. Deleted Jun '88. Catalogue no: **BEG 171**

WHERE WERE YOU
Tracks: / Where were you / Over the river.
12" Single: Released May '89, on Fontana, by Phonogram Ltd. Deleted Feb '89. Catalogue no: **BRX 212**
7" Single: Released May '89, on Fontana, by Phonogram Ltd. Deleted Feb '89. Catalogue no: **BRX 2**
CD 5": Released May '89, on Fontana, by Phonogram Ltd. Deleted Feb '89. Catalogue no: **BRXCD 2**

Adults

WHERE DID OUR LOVE GO
Tracks: / Where did our love go / Can't take it.
12" Single: Released Oct '84, on Loose, by Loose Records. Catalogue no: **LSE 12T**
7" Single: Released Oct '84, on Loose, by Loose Records. Catalogue no: **LSE 12**

Advance

TAKE IT TO THE TOP
12" Single: Released Oct '87, on Cham pion, by Champion Records. Catalogue no **CHAMP 1245**
7" Single: Released Oct '87, on Champion by Champion Records. Deleted Jul '89 Catalogue no: **CHAMP 45**

Adventures

ANOTHER SILENT DAY
Tracks: / Another silent day.
12" Single: Released Jul '84, on Chrysalis by Chrysalis Records. Catalogue no: **CHS 12-2000**
7" Single: Released Jul '84, on Chrysalis, b Chrysalis Records. Catalogue no: **CHS 2000**

BROKEN LAND
Tracks: / Broken land / Don't stand on me
7" Single: Released Mar '88, on Elektra, b Elektra Records (UK). Catalogue no: **EK 69**
12" Single: Released Mar '88, on Elektra by Elektra Records (UK). Catalogue n **EKR 69T**

DROWNING IN THE SEA OF LOVE
Tracks: / Drowning in the sea of love / Sta away / Curragh of Kildare, The (Only o 12".).
CD 5": Released Jun '88, on Elektra, b Elektra Records (UK). Catalogue no: **EK 76CD**
7" Single: Released Jul '88, on WEA, b WEA Records. Catalogue no: **EKR 76**
12" Single: Released Jul '88, on WEA, b WEA Records. Catalogue no: **EKR 76T**

FEEL THE RAINDROPS
Tracks: / Feel the raindrops.
7" Single: Released Jul '85, on Chrysalis, Chrysalis Records. Deleted '88. Catalogu no: **AD 1**

ONE STEP FROM HEAVEN
Tracks: / One step from heaven / Trip to th bountiful (when the rain comes down) / I

ADVENTURES - SEND MY HEART (Released on Chysalis)

stant karma (Only on CD single.).
7" Single: Released Oct '88, on Elektra, by Elektra Records (UK). Catalogue no: **EKR 80**
CD 5": Released Oct '88, on Elektra, by Elektra Records (UK). Catalogue no: **EKR 80CD**
12" Single: Released Oct '88, on Elektra, by Elektra Records (UK). Catalogue no: **EKR 80T**

SEND MY HEART (see panel on previos page)
Tracks: / Send my heart / These children.
7" Single: Released Oct '84, on Chrysalis, by Chrysalis Records. Deleted '87. Catalogue no: **CHS 2001**
12" Single: Released Oct '84, on Chrysalis, by Chrysalis Records. Deleted '87. Catalogue no: **CHS 122001**

Adverse, Anthony

CENTRE OF YOUR WORLD
Tracks: / Centre of your world.
12" Single: Released Sep '89, on Profile (USA), by Profile Records (USA). Catalogue no: **PROFT 263**
7" Single: Released Sep '89, on Profile (USA), by Profile Records (USA). Catalogue no: **PROF 263**

IMPERIAL VIOLETS
Tracks: / Imperial violets / Fountain, The.
7" Single: Released Oct '87, on El, by Cherry Red Records. Catalogue no: **GPO 29**

OUR FAIRY TALE
Tracks: / Our fairy tale / Eine symphonie des grauens.
7" Single: Released Jul '86, on El, by Cherry Red Records. Catalogue no: **GPO 13**

RULING CLASS
Tracks: / Ruling class, The / Trouble (On 12" only) / Straits of Malacca (On 12" only) / How to get on in society (On 12" only).
7" Single: Released Jun '86, on El, by Cherry Red Records. Catalogue no: **GPO 7**
12" Single: Released Jun '86, on El, by Cherry Red Records. Catalogue no: **GPO 7 T**

Adverts

Biographical details: In 1977 the Adverts hit the Top 20 with one of the most acclaimed singles of the punk era, "Gary Gilmore's Eyes". Early promise was not fulfilled, however, and the band could only manage one lesser hit *No Time To Be 21* and a one-week chart album *Crossing The Red Sea With The Adverts*.
Gaye Advert and TV Smith have continued to attract spasmodic attention from the music press in their subsequent ventures. All members of the Adverts were British. (Bob MacDonald, 1988)

A punk group formed in 1977. Original lineup: Tim 'T.V.' Smith, vocals, guitar; Gaye Advert, bass; Howard Pickup, guitar; Laurie Driver, drums. Smith moved from Cornwall to London inspired by the punk movement and formed the group with Advert. First single for Stiff was *One Chord Wonders*; they switched to Anchor and had their biggest hit *Gary Gilmore's Eyes* (UK top 20) in 1977. First LP *Crossing the Red Sea* briefly made UK top 40 '78; Driver left, replaced by John Towe (ex Generation X), himself replaced by Rod Latter. Tim Cross (keyboards) joined for a final LP in 1979; they broke up. Smith did solo work and formed short-lived T.V. Smith's Explorers. (Donald Clarke 21 July 1988)
.

GARY GILMORE'S EYES
Tracks: / Gary Gilmore's eyes / New day dawning.
7" Single: Released Jun '83, on Bright, by Bright Records. Catalogue no: **BULB 1**
7" Single: Released Aug '77, on Anchor (1), by Anchor Records. Deleted '80. Catalogue no: **ANC 1043**

NO TIME TO BE 21
Tracks: / No time to be 21.
7" Single: Released Feb '78, on Bright, by Bright Records. Deleted '81. Catalogue no: **BRI**

PEEL SESSIONS:ADVERTS
Tracks: / Quickstep / Gary Gilmore's eyes / One chord wonders / New boys / Bored teenagers.
12" Single: Released Sep '87, on Strange Fruit, by Strange Fruit Records. Catalogue no: **SFPS 034**

Aerial FX

INSTANT FEELINGS
Tracks: / Instant feelings / 5.15.
7" Single: Released Oct '82, on Kamera, Deleted '88. Catalogue no: **ERA 012**

SO HARD
Tracks: / So hard / It's about time.
7" Single: Released Feb '81, on Square, Catalogue no: **SQS 3**

Aero

CALIFORNIA GOLD
Tracks: / California gold / Summer girls.
7" Single: Released Jun '80, on Polo, by Polo Records. Deleted '88. Catalogue no: **POLO 5**
12" Single: Released Jun '80, on Polo, by Polo Records. Deleted '88. Catalogue no: **POLO 12-5**

Aerosmith

Biographical details: After much gigging around New England, Aerosmith were signed to C.B.S. and released their first, eponymous album in 1973. Another two years of dedicated touring finally brought them major success in 1975 despite constant accusations of being a Rolling Stones rip-off when their *Toys In The Attic* album went platinum. There were several line-up changes at the end of the seventies, but the original one re-formed for 1985 *Done With Mirrors*. Their most recent success has been *Permanent Vacation*. (Robert Cohen October 1987).

A USA rock group formed in New Hampshire in 1970. Original lineup was vocalist Steven Tyler, guitarists Joe Perry and Brad Whitford, Bassist Tom Hamilton, drummer Joey Kramer. They were spotted at Max's Kansas City and signed to CBS in 1972. Accused at first of being Rolling Stones imitators, their third album *Toys in the Attic* was a huge success in 1975. After *Night in the Ruts* in 1979 Perry left to form the Joe Perry Project, replaced Whitford in 1981. After *Rock in a Hard Place* in 1982 they switched to Geffen for *Done With Mirrors* '85, and *Permanent Vacation* '87. (Donald Clarke 21 July 1988).
.

ANGEL
Tracks: / Angel / Girl keeps comin' apart.
7" Single: Released Apr '88, on Geffen, by Geffen Records (USA). Catalogue no: **GEF 34**
CD 5": Released Apr '88, on Geffen, by Geffen Records (USA). Catalogue no: **GEF 34 CD**
12" Pic: Released Apr '88, on Geffen, by Geffen Records (USA). Catalogue no: **GEF 34 TP**
12" Single: Released Apr '88, on Geffen, by Geffen Records (USA). Catalogue no: **GEF 34T**

DUDE (LOOKS LIKE A LADY)
Tracks: / Dude (looks like a lady) / Simoriah / Once is enough (Available on 12" only.).
7" Single: Released Oct '87, on Geffen, by Geffen Records (USA). Catalogue no: **GEF 29**
7" Pic: Released Oct '87, on Geffen, by Geffen Records (USA). Deleted Jul '88. Catalogue no: **GEF 29TP**
12" Single: Released Oct '87, on Geffen, by Geffen Records (USA). Catalogue no: **GEF 29T**

LOVE IN AN ELEVATOR
Tracks: / Love in an elevator / Young lust / Ain't enough (Available on CD single only).
12" Single: Released Aug '89, on Geffen, by Geffen Records (USA). Catalogue no: **GEF 63T**
7" Pic: Released Sep '89, on Geffen, by Geffen Records (USA). Catalogue no: **GEF 63TP**
Special: Released Sep '89, on Geffen, by Geffen Records (USA). Catalogue no: **GEF 63X**
7" Single: Released Aug '89, on Geffen, by Geffen Records (USA). Catalogue no: **GEF 63**
Cassingle: Released Sep '89, on Geffen, by Geffen Records (USA). Catalogue no: **GEF 63C**
CD 3": Released Aug '89, on Geffen, by Geffen Records (USA). Catalogue no: **GEF 63CD**

RAG DOLL
Tracks: / Rag doll (version 1) / Rag doll (version 2) / Rag doll (version 3) / St. John.
12" Single: Released Jul '88, on Geffen (USA), by Geffen Records (USA). Catalogue no: **020919**

REMEMBER (WALKING IN THE SAND)
Tracks: / Remember (walking in the sand) / Bone to bone.
7" Single: Released Feb '80, on CBS, by CBS Records. Deleted Feb '85. Catalogue no: **CBS 8220**

WALK THIS WAY (IMPORT)
Tracks: / Walk this way / Dream on.
CD 3": Released Aug '88, on Columbia (USA), by CBS Records (USA). Catalogue no: **38K07952**

Affair

IF WE'RE NOT IN LOVE
Tracks: / If we're not in love / You are, you are.
7" Single: Released May '84, on Bronze, by Bronze Records. Catalogue no: **BRO 181**

PLEASE DON'T BREAK MY HEART
12" Single: Released Jun '85, on 10 Records, by Virgin Records. Deleted '87. Catalogue no: **TEN 53-12**
7" Single: Released Jun '85, on 10 Records, by Virgin Records. Deleted '87. Catalogue no: **TEN 53**

Affairs Of The Heart

WATERLOO SUNSET
Tracks: / Waterloo sunset.
7" Single: Released Jun '84, on Riot City, by Riot City Records. Catalogue no: **PULSE 100**
12" Single: Released Jun '84, on Riot City, by Riot City Records. Catalogue no: **PULSE 100T**
12" Single: Released Jun '88, on Antler, by Antler Records (Belgium). Catalogue no: **ANT 019**

Afraid Of Mice

I'M ON FIRE
Tracks: / I'm on fire / Down in the dark.
7" Single: Released Jun '81, on Charisma, by Virgin Records. Deleted Jun '84. Catalogue no: **CB 3838**

INTERCONTINENTAL
Tracks: / Intercontinental / What shall we do.
7" Single: Released Aug '81, on Charisma, by Virgin Records. Deleted Aug '84. Catalogue no: **CB 389**

TRANSPARENTS
Tracks: / Transparents / That's not true.
7" Single: Released Apr '82, on Charisma, by Virgin Records. Deleted Apr '85. Catalogue no: **CB 397**

African Blood

ANGEL, THE
Tracks: / Angel, The.
12" Single: Released Sep '85, on Three Kings, Catalogue no: **TK 033**

African Connexion

C'EST LA DASE
Tracks: / C'est la dase / Moziki / City limits / Midnight pressure.
12" Single: Released Feb '84, on Oval, by Oval Records. Catalogue no: **OVALT 28-12**

DANCING ON THE SIDEWALK
Tracks: / Dancing on the sidewalk.
12" Single: Released Dec '84, on Oval, by Oval Records. Catalogue no: **OVALT 32-12**

TELL MANDELA (THINGS ARE GOING TO CHANGE)
Tracks: / Tell Mandela (things are going to change).
7" Single: Released Aug '86, on Tout Ensemble, Catalogue no: **LUTE 5**
12" Single: Released Aug '86, on Tout Ensemble, Catalogue no: **12LUTE 5**

African Pearl

BANDWAGON
Tracks: / Bandwagon / East meets west.
12" Single: Released Apr '84, on Ariwa Sounds, by Ariwa Sounds. Catalogue no: **ARI 30**

African Pioneers

CRAZY ZULU (LONDON MIX)
Tracks: / Crazy Zulu (London mix).
12" Single: Released Aug '84, on 10 Records, by Virgin Records. Deleted '86. Catalogue no: **TEN 26-12**
7" Single: Released Aug '84, on 10 Records, by Virgin Records. Deleted '86. Catalogue no: **TEN 26**

African Queen

ENGLISH GIRL
Tracks: / English girl / Audrey.
12" Single: Released Oct '82, on Jah Shaka, Catalogue no: **SHAKA 826**

African Star

TOO RUDE Marshall, Larry
Tracks: / Too rude / Let the music play.
12" Single: Released Nov '83, on Mobiliser, by Jetstar Records. Catalogue no: **MM 72**

After Dark(group)

DEATHBRINGER
7" Pic: Released Oct '83, on Lazer, Catalogue no: **PROMO 1**

EVIL WOMAN
Tracks: / Evil woman.
7" Single: Released Dec '81, on After Dark, Deleted Dec '84. Catalogue no: **AD 001**

After The Fire

Biographical details: This British band released their first album *Signs Of Change* (also referred to as simply *After The Fire*) in April 1978. Two small hit singles and a minor chart album *Laser Love* followed in '79. Drummer Ivor Twidell was then replaced by Pete King. The group failed to capitalise on their initial success and their fortunes did not improve until 1983, when they covered Falco's German hit *Der Kommissar* and took it to the US Top 5. Once again however, they could not follow it up. (Bob MacDonald, 1988).

A UK pop group formed in 1977. Keyboardist Peter Banks formed the band on a sometime basis in 1972; Andy Piercy joined on guitar in 1974, Ivor Twidell on drums in 1977. They released their first album on their own label, after which the bass player left, Piercey moved to bass and John Russell joined on guitar. Their Christian belief was thought commercially unviable, but after signing with CBS *One Rule for You* made the UK top 40 in 1979. Twidell left in 1980, replaced by Pete King; third LP *Batteries Not Included* in 1982 was dismissed as 'easy listening'; the unexpected success in the USA of the 1983 single *Der Kommissar* (title cut of 1982 album) came too late to stop the others leaving Piercey as sole original member. (Donald Clarke 21 July 1988).
.

DER KOMMISSAR (SINGLE)
Tracks: / Der Kommissar / Nobody else but you.
12" Single: Released Jun '82, on CBS, by CBS Records. Deleted Jun '85. Catalogue no: **A13 2399**
12" Single: Released Apr '83, on CBS, by CBS Records. Deleted '86. Catalogue no: **A13 2399**
7" Single: Released Apr '83, on CBS, by CBS Records. Deleted '86. Catalogue no: **A 2399**

EIGHT BALL IN THE TOP POCKET
Tracks: / Eight ball in the top pocket.
7" Single: Released Oct '83, on CBS, by CBS Records. Catalogue no: **A 3883**

FROZEN RIVERS
Tracks: / Frozen rivers / Starflight.
7" Single: Released Sep '81, on Epic, by CBS Records. Deleted Sep '84. Catalogue no: **EPC A 1613**
12" Single: Released Sep '81, on Epic, by CBS Records. Deleted Sep '84. Catalogue no: **EPC A 13 1613**

LASER LOVE (SINGLE)
Tracks: / Laser love.
7" Single: Released Sep '79, on CBS, by CBS Records. Deleted '82. Catalogue no: **CBS 7769**

LOVE WILL ALWAYS MAKE YOU CRY
Tracks: / Love will always make you cry / Every mother's son.
7" Single: Released Apr '80, on Epic, by CBS Records. Deleted Apr '83. Catalogue no: **EPC 8394**
7" Single: Released Apr '80, on Epic, by CBS Records. Deleted Apr '83. Catalogue no: **EPC 8942**

ONE RULE FOR YOU
Tracks: / One rule for you.
7" Single: Released Jun '79, on CBS, by CBS Records. Deleted '82. Catalogue no: **CBS 7025**

RICH BOYS
Tracks: / Rich boys / One rule for you.
7" Single: Released Feb '82, on CBS, by CBS Records. Deleted Feb '87. Catalogue no: **A 1951**
12" Single: Released Feb '82, on CBS, by CBS Records. Deleted May '85. Catalogue no: **A13 1951**

WILD WEST SHOW
Tracks: / Wild West show / Every mother's son.
7" Single: Released Oct '80, on Epic, by CBS Records. Deleted Oct '83. Catalogue no: **EPC 9095**

After This

FIELDS
Tracks: / Fields.
12" Single: Released Feb '86, on Himalaya, Catalogue no: **12 OPA 012**
7" Single: Released Feb '86, on Himalaya, Catalogue no: **OPA 012**

After Tonite

THIN LINE
Tracks: / Thin line / Got to find a way.
7" Single: Released 25 Apr '88, on BGP, by Ace Records. Catalogue no: **BGPS 003**
12" Single: Released 25 Apr '88, on BGP, by Ace Records. Catalogue no: **BGPT 003**

TIME FOR A CHANGE
Tracks: / Time for a change.
12" Single: Released Nov '86, on IDK, by IDK Records. Catalogue no: **IDK T002**

Afternoon Delights

GENERAL HOSPI-TALE
Tracks: / General hospi-tale.

7" Single: Released Oct '81, on MCA, by MCA Records. Deleted '84. Catalogue no: **MCA 745**
12" Single: Released Oct '81, on MCA, by MCA Records. Deleted '84. Catalogue no: **MCAT 745**

Agaric

I'M GONNA BEAT DIS
Tracks: / I'm gonna beat dis.
12" Single: Released '89, on Kaos, Catalogue no: **KAOS 016**
CD 5": Released '89, on Kaos, Catalogue no: **KAOS 016CD**

Agawa, Yasuko

L.A. NIGHTS
Tracks: / L.A. nights.
12" Single: Released Jun '89, on Blue Bird (1), by Blue Sun Records (USA). Catalogue no: **BRT 26**

Age Of Chance

BIBLE OF THE BEAT
Tracks: / Bible of the beat.
7" Single: Released Jan '86, on Riot Bible, Catalogue no: **RIOT 2**

DON'T GET MAD GET EVEN
Tracks: / Don't get mad get even (7" only) / Gettin' mad (instrumental) / Don't get mad get even (the all nite crank-power mix) (12" only) / Gettin' even (bonus beats) (12" only).
CD 5": Released Jul '88, on Virgin, by Virgin Records. Deleted '88. Catalogue no: **CDEP 7**
12" Single: Released Sep '87, on EMI, by EMI Records. Catalogue no: **VS 989-12**
7" Single: Released Sep '87, on EMI, by EMI Records. Deleted May '88. Catalogue no: **VS 989**

KISS
Tracks: / Kiss.
7" Single: Released Nov '86, on Fon, by FON Records. Catalogue no: **AGE 5**
12" Single: Released Nov '86, on Fon, by FON Records. Catalogue no: **AGET 5**

MOTOR CITY
Tracks: / Motor city.
7" Single: Released Apr '85, on Riot Bible, Catalogue no: **RIOT 1**

NEW YORK'S REVENGE
Tracks: / New York's revenge / Beats of New York, The / Gettin' mad / N.Y.C. versus A.O.C..
12" Single: Released '88, on Virgin, by Virgin Records. Catalogue no: **VS 989-13**

TAKE IT
Tracks: / Take it / Taking top dollars (bonus beats) / Take it (unlimited credit mix) (12" only).
7" Single: Released Jan '88, on Virgin, by Virgin Records. Catalogue no: **VS 1035**
12" Single: Released Jan '88, on Virgin, by Virgin Records. Catalogue no: **VST 1035**

TWILIGHT WORLD OF SONIC DISCO, THE
Tracks: / Twilight world of sonic disco, The.
7" Single: Released May '86, on Riot Bible, Catalogue no: **BIBLE 1**

WHO'S AFRAID OF THE BIG BAD NOISE
Tracks: / Who's afraid of the big bad noise / Big bad rap.
12" Single: Released May '87, on Virgin, by Virgin Records. Deleted May '88. Catalogue no: **VS 962-12**
7" Single: Released May '87, on Virgin, by Virgin Records. Deleted May '88. Catalogue no: **VS 962**

Agency Music

PAINTER PAINS
Tracks: / Painter pains.
7" Single: Released Jun '82, on Out Of Town, Catalogue no: **HOOT 3**

Agent Steel

MAD LOCUST RISING
Tracks: / Swarm is on us / Mad locust rising / Ripper / Let it be done / Day at Guyana The.
12" Single: Released Aug '86, on Music For Nations, by Music For Nations Records. Catalogue no: **12 KUT 124**

Agony Bag

RABIES IS A KILLER
Tracks: / Rabies is a killer / Never never land.
7" Single: Released Apr '80, on Monza, Deleted '83. Catalogue no: **MONZA 002**

Agony Column

GOODBYE
Tracks: / Goodbye.
7" Single: Released Jan '88, on Basement, Catalogue no: **BAS 001**

LOVE IN THE HEAD
Tracks: / Love in the head / Free of love.
7" Single: Released Jun '80, on Black Door, Deleted Jun '84. Catalogue no: **DOOR 8**

LOVE IS A BLANKET EXPRESSION
Tracks: / Love is a blanket expression.
7" Single: Released Jul '82, on Lightbeat, Catalogue no: **LIGHT 003**

Agra

GANDHI'S PRAYER
Tracks: / Gandhi's prayer.
7" Single: Released Nov '83, on Sticky, Catalogue no: **STICK 103**

A-Grumh

BLOODY SIDE
Tracks: / Bloody side.
CD 5": Released '88, on Play It Again Sam(Belgium), by Play It Again Sam (Belgium). Catalogue no: **CDBIAS 85**
12" Single: Released '88, on Play It Again Sam(Belgium), by Play It Again Sam (Belgium). Catalogue no: **BIAS 85**

TOO MANY COCKS SPOIL THE BREATH
Tracks: / Too many cocks spoil the breath.
12" Single: Released Sep '87, on Play It Again Sam(Belgium), by Play It Again Sam (Belgium). Catalogue no: **BIAS 057**

UNDERGROUND
Tracks: / Underground.
12" Single: Released Aug '86, on Play It Again Sam(Belgium), by Play It Again Sam (Belgium). Deleted '88. Catalogue no: **BIAS 033**

A-ha

Biographical details: The band's initial success, with *Take On Me* in 1985 was helped in no small way by the stunning mix of live-action and animation in the accompanying video, They have built on this success with *the Sun Always Shines On T.V.*, *Hunting High And Low* (also the name of their first album), *Cry Wolf* and the theme to the most recent James Bond movie *The Living Daylights* (1987). (Robert Cohen 1987).

BLOOD THAT MOVES THE BODY, THE
Tracks: / Blood that moves the body, The / There's never a forever thing / Living daylights, The (on CDS version only.).
CD 5": Released May '88, on Warner Bros., by WEA Records. Catalogue no: **W 7840CD**
12" Single: Released May '88, on Warner Bros., by WEA Records. Catalogue no: **W 7840T**
7" Single: Released May '88, on Warner Bros., by WEA Records. Catalogue no: **W 7840**

CRY WOLF
Tracks: / Cry wolf.
7" Single: Released '87, on Warner Bros., by WEA Records. Deleted Jan '88. Catalogue no: **W 8500**
12" Single: Released '87, on Warner Bros., by WEA Records. Deleted Jul '88. Catalogue no: **W 8500 T**

HUNTING HIGH AND LOW (SINGLE)
Tracks: / Hunting high and low / Hunting high and low (remix) (On 12" only) / Blue sky (demon version).
7" Single: Released May '86, on Warner Bros., by WEA Records. Deleted Jan '88. Catalogue no: **W 6663**
12" Pic: Released May '86, on Warner Bros., by WEA Records. Deleted Jun '87. Catalogue no: **W 6663 TP**
12" Single: Released May '86, on Warner Bros., by WEA Records. Catalogue no: **W 6663 T**

I'VE BEEN LOSING YOU
Tracks: / I've been losing you / This alone is love.
7" Single: Released Sep '86, on Warner Bros., by WEA Records. Deleted Jan '88. Catalogue no: **W 8594**
12" Single: Released Sep '86, on Warner Bros., by WEA Records. Deleted Jan '88. Catalogue no: **W 8594 T**
12" Pic: Released Sep '86, on Warner Bros., by WEA Records. Deleted Jun '87. Catalogue no: **W 8594 TP**

LIVING DAYLIGHTS, THE
Tracks: / Living daylights, The / Living daylights, The (instrumental).
12" Single: Released 20 Jun '87, on Warner Bros., by WEA Records. Catalogue no: **W 8305 T**
7" Single: Released 20 Jun '87, on Warner Bros., by WEA Records. Catalogue no: **W 8305**
12" Pic: Released Jun '87, on Warner Bros., by WEA Records. Deleted Jul '88. Catalogue no: **W 8305TP**

MANHATTAN SKYLINE
Tracks: / We're looking for the whales (live version) / Manhattan skyline.
12" Single: Released Feb '87, on Warner Bros., by WEA Records. Deleted Jul '88. Catalogue no: **W 8405T**
7" Single: Released Feb '87, on Warner Bros., by WEA Records. Deleted Jan '88. Catalogue no: **W 8405**

SCOUNDREL CLUB EP (IMPORT)
Tracks: / Cry wolf(extended version) / Manhattan skyline (extended mix) / Hunting high and low (extended) / Looking for the whales (live).
Note: Japan-only 4-track EP with high quality packaging & lyrics.
12" Single: Released Oct '88, on Warner Bros.(Japan), by WEA Records. Catalogue no: **P 6259**

STAY ON THESE ROADS (SINGLE)
Tracks: / Stay on these roads / Soft rains of April / Cry wolf (Only on CD) / Take on me (Only on CD).
CD 5": Released Mar '88, on Warner Bros., by WEA Records. Catalogue no: **W 7936 CD**
12" Single: Released Mar '88, on Warner Bros., by WEA Records. Catalogue no: **W 7936 T**
CD 3": Released Sep '88, on Warner Bros.(Japan), by WEA Records. Catalogue no: **10 SW 44**
7" Single: Released Mar '88, on Warner Bros., by WEA Records. Catalogue no: **W 7936**

SUN ALWAYS SHINES ON TV
Tracks: / Sun always shines on TV, The / Driftwood.
7" Single: Released Dec '85, on Warner Bros., by WEA Records. Deleted Jan '88. Catalogue no: **W 8846**
12" Single: Released Dec '85, on Warner Bros., by WEA Records. Catalogue no: **W 8846T**

TAKE ON ME
Tracks: / Take on me / Love is the reason.
7" Single: Released Sep '85, on Warner Bros., by WEA Records. Catalogue no: **W 9006**
12" Single: Released Sep '85, on Warner Bros., by WEA Records. Catalogue no: **W 9006T**

TOUCHY
Tracks: / Touchy / Hurry home.
7" Single: Released 22 Aug '88, on Warner Bros.(Germany), by WEA Records. Catalogue no: **W 7749**
CD 5": Released Aug '88, on Warner Bros., by WEA Records. Catalogue no: **W 7749 CD**
12" Single: Released Aug '88, on Warner Bros., by WEA Records. Catalogue no: **W 7749 T**

TRAIN OF THOUGHT
Tracks: / Train of thought / And you tell me.
7" Pic: Released Mar '86, on Warner Bros., by WEA Records. Deleted Jun '87. Catalogue no: **W 8736 P**
7" Single: Released Mar '86, on Warner Bros., by WEA Records. Deleted Jan '88. Catalogue no: **W 8736**
12" Single: Released Mar '86, on Warner Bros., by WEA Records. Deleted Jul '88. Catalogue no: **W 8736 T**

TWELVE INCH CLUB
Tracks: / Train of thought (S.Thompson mix) / Sun always shines on TV, The (S.Thompson mix) / And you tell me (demo) / Train of thought (dub).
12" Single: Released Jul '88, on Reprise (Japan), by WEA Records. Catalogue no: **P6238**

YOU ARE THE ONE
Tracks: / You are the one / Out of blue comes green.
12" Single: Released Nov '88, on Warner Bros., by WEA Records. Catalogue no: **W 7636 T**
CD 5": Released Nov '88, on Warner Bros., by WEA Records. Catalogue no: **W 7636 CD**
7" Single: Released Nov '88, on Warner Bros., by WEA Records. Catalogue no: **W 7636**

Ahab

PARTY GIRL
Tracks: / Party girl.
7" Single: Released Sep '82, on Chicken Jazz, Catalogue no: **JAZZ 5**

A-Heads

DYING MAN
Tracks: / Dying man / Hell cell / Changing places never works.
7" Single: Released Mar '83, on T.W., by T.W. Records. Catalogue no: **HIT 107**

Aihe, David

GET YOUR DANCING SHOES ON
Tracks: / Get your dancing shoes on.
12" Single: Released Feb '89, on Royalle, Catalogue no: **RRYT 3**

Aimless Device

MUD IN YOUR EYE
Tracks: / Mud in your eyes.
12" Single: Released Jul '89, on Anything But, Catalogue no: **ABR 23**

WORLD OF COATS
Tracks: / World of coats.
12" Single: Released Nov '86, on Anything But, Catalogue no: **ABR 014**

Air

Biographical details: Black Music trio formed in Chicago in 1971: Henry Threadgill, saxophones, flutes, hubkaphone (a homemade percussion array), Fred Hopkins on bass and Steve McCall on percussion; all alumni of AACM (see Richard ABRAMS). They have made many fine albums on several labels; McCall was replaced by Pheeroan akLaff to make New Air; both Hopkins and akLaff now play in Threadgill's highly acclaimed Sextett. (Donald Clarke 21 July 1988).

MY IMAGINATION
Tracks: / My imagination / Every minute of the day.
7" Single: Released Oct '81, on Towerbell, Deleted Oct '84. Catalogue no: **TOW 14**

Air Supply

Biographical details: This Australian group broke in America in 1980 and came to epitomise the term Adult Contemporary, the US equivalent of MoR. Combining mass-appeal melodies and standard love lyrics with a sweeping lush production, their music has been bland and predictable, but always catchy.
They are the only act in American chart history to open their chart career with seven consecutive Top 5 singles. Five members were present throughout this hot streak, but three others (Criston Barker, Tommy Emmmanuel and Sam McNally) left during its course to be replaced by only two new recruits (Rex Goh and David Green). The fourth of the seven singles , *The One That You Love*, was a No. 11 hit in 1980.
After a brief lull in their American fortunes, Air Supply returned to the US Top 5 in the autumn of '83 with *Making Love Out Of Nothing At All*, an epic production by Meat Loaf mentor Jim Steinman. (Bob MacDonald).

Russell and Hitchcock met in a production of *Jesus Christ Superstar* in Australia and formed Air Supply. After an Australian No.2 with *Love and Other Bruises*, they went on to conquer America with seven Top Ten records, including the British hits *All Out of Love* ('80), *Even the Nights Are Better* ('82) and *Making Love Out of Nothing At All* ('83). In 1985 they reached No.19 in the American charts, with *Just As I Am*. (Robert Cohen October 1987)

ALL OUT OF LOVE (OLD GOLD)
Tracks: / All out of love / Even the nights are better.
7" Single: Released Jul '84, on Old Gold, by Old Gold Records. Catalogue no: **OG 9453**

ALL OUT OF LOVE (ORIGINAL)
Tracks: / All out of love / Habits die hard.
7" Single: Released Sep '80, on Arista, by BMG Records (UK). Deleted '83. Catalogue no: **ARIST 362**

EVEN THE NIGHTS ARE BETTER
Tracks: / Even the nights are better.
7" Single: Released Oct '82, on Arista, by BMG Records (UK). Deleted '85. Catalogue no: **ARIST 474**

EVERY WOMAN IN THE WORLD
Tracks: / Every woman in the world / Having you near me.
7" Single: Released Dec '80, on Arista, by BMG Records (UK). Deleted Dec '85. Catalogue no: **ARIST 383**

HERE I AM
Tracks: / Here I am / Don't turn me away.
7" Single: Released Nov '81, on Arista, by BMG Records (UK). Deleted Nov '84. Catalogue no: **ARIST 435**

JUST AS I AM
Tracks: / Just as I am / Crazy love / All out of love / Lost in love / Even the nights are better.
12" Single: Released Jul '85, on Arista, by BMG Records (UK). Catalogue no: **ARIST 12623**
7" Single: Released Jul '85, on Arista, by BMG Records (UK). Catalogue no: **ARIST 623**

LONELY IS THE NIGHT (SINGLE)
Tracks: / Lonely is the night / I'd die for you.
12" Single: Released Sep '86, on Arista, by BMG Records (UK). Catalogue no: **ARIST 12677**
7" Single: Released Sep '86, on Arista, by BMG Records (UK). Catalogue no: **ARIST 677**

LOST IN LOVE (SINGLE)
Tracks: / Lost in love / I don't want to lose you.
7" Single: Released Feb '81, on Arista, by BMG Records (UK). Deleted '84. Catalogue no: **ARIST 329**

MAKING LOVE OUT OF NOTHING AT ALL
Tracks: / Making love out of nothing at all.
12" Single: Released '83, on Arista, by BMG Records (UK). Deleted '86. Catalogue no: **ARIST 12541**
7" Single: Released '83, on Arista, by BMG Records (UK). Deleted '86. Catalogue no: **ARIST 541**

ONE THAT YOU LOVE
Tracks: / One that you love / I want to give it all.
7" Single: Released May '81, on Arista, by BMG Records (UK). Deleted May '86. Catalogue no: **ARIST 412**

SWEET DREAMS
Tracks: / Sweet dreams / Don't turn me away.
7" Single: Released '82, on Arista, by BMG Records (UK). Deleted '87. Catalogue no: **ARIST 458**

Aire, Jane

I CLOSE MY EYES AND COUNT TO TEN
Tracks: / I close my eyes and count to ten.
7" Single: Released May '82, on Stiff, by Stiff Records. Catalogue no: **BUY 147**

YANKEE WHEELS (See adjacent panel)
Tracks: / Yankee wheels / Nasty nice.
7" Single: Released '78, on Stiff, by Stiff Records. Catalogue no: **BUY 26**

Airkraft

MOVE IN RHYTHM
Tracks: / Move in rhythm / Pumping iron.
7" Single: Released Jan '81, on Square, Deleted Jan '84. Catalogue no: **SQS 3**

Airplane Crashes

WHITE RABBIT
Tracks: / White rabbit.
12" Single: Released May '89, on Subway, by Subway Records. Catalogue no: **SUB 68**

Airplay

DEJA VU
Tracks: / Deja vu / Miss you baby / Last time.
7" Single: Released Jun '82, on Out Of Town, Catalogue no: **HOOT 4**

Airport & Dean

BILLY LIAR
Tracks: / Billy Liar / Other side of me.
7" Single: Released Nov '81, on Polydor, by Polydor Ltd. Deleted '84. Catalogue no: **POSP 367**

LOST IN SPACE
Tracks: / Lost in space / Window in the sky.
7" Single: Released Sep '81, on Polydor, by Polydor Ltd. Deleted '84. Catalogue no: **POSP 312**

Airrace

I DON'T CARE
Tracks: / I don't care.
7" Single: Released Dec '84, on Atco, by Atlantic Recording Corp.(USA). Catalogue no: **B 9702**

Airspace

SOME GIRLS
Tracks: / Some girls / I'm not made of plastic.
7" Single: Released Jan '81, on Diversion, by Dingle's Records. Deleted Jan '84. Catalogue no: **DIV 112**

Airstrip 1

LONGER TO LIVE
Tracks: / Longer to live / English guns / Crime.
12" Single: Released Jun '82, on Oval, by Oval Records. Catalogue no: **OVEP 19/84**

SATELLITE
Tracks: / Satellite / All fall down.
7" Single: Released Nov '82, on Polydor, by Polydor Ltd. Deleted Nov '85. Catalogue no: **AIR 2**
12" Single: Released Nov '82, on Polydor, by Polydor Ltd. Deleted Nov '85. Catalogue no: **AIRX 2**

Airwave Orchestra

FOURSCORE (CHANNEL 4 THEME)
Tracks: / Fourscore / Fourscore II.
7" Single: Released Nov '82, on Polydor, by Polydor Ltd. Deleted Nov '85. Catalogue no: **CHANN 401**

Aisha

I KNOW A PLACE
Tracks: / I know a place.
12" Single: Released Sep '89, on Ariwa Sounds, by Ariwa Sounds. Catalogue no: **ARI 93**

Jane Aire - Yankee Wheels (Released on Epic)

PROPHECY
Tracks: / Prophecy.
12" Single: Released May '87, on Ariwa Sounds, by Ariwa Sounds. Catalogue no: **ARI 60**

THAT'S HOW HEARTACHES ARE MADE
Tracks: / That's how heartaches are made / Prophecy.
12" Single: Released Aug '86, on Ariwa Sounds, by Ariwa Sounds. Catalogue no: **ARI 52**

Aitch Brothers

WON'T CHANGE MY MIND
Tracks: / Won't change my mind.
7" Single: Released Nov '85, on Ashland, Catalogue no: **ALD 1**

Aitken, Laurel

Biographical details: This Jamaican reggae singer charted briefly, with backing group the Unitone, in 1980 with *Rudi Got Married*. This was due to the fact that it was embraced by the then prevalent 2 Tone/ska community, a sort of answer to the Specials' *A Message To You Rudy*. (Bob MacDonald, 1988).

Laurel Aitken was born in Cuba, emigrated to Jamaica, then to the UK in the early '60s. He made the first Jamaican record issued in the UK, *Boogie In My Bones / Little Sheila* in 1958, and the first release on the Bluebeat label, *Boogey Rock* in 1960. His earliest work was in two styles: jump R&B and revivalist tunes; then singing ska and later reggae he made hundreds of sides on many subjects; he concentrated on singles, but teamed with female singer Girly for *Scandal In Brixton Market*. In the 2-Tone era he enjoyed a revival; he still performs now and then with his band The Full Circle. (Donald Clarke 21 July 1988).

COME DOWN TO THE PARTY
Tracks: / Come down to the party / Let me love you little darling.
12" Single: Released May '86, on Fantasy (1), by BMG Records (UK). Catalogue no: **F 0006**

EVERYBODY SKA
Tracks: / Everybody ska.
7" Single: Released Jun '89, on Unicorn Records, by Unicorn Records. Catalogue no: **PHZA 40**
12" Single: Released Jun '89, on Unicorn Records, by Unicorn Records. Catalogue no: **12PHZA 40**

FIRE IN YOUR WIRE
Tracks: / Fire in your wire.
12" Single: Released Sep '84, on Black Fantasy, Catalogue no: **BF 006**

Jewel Akins - Birds and the Bees (Released on London-American)

HOOCHIE COOCHIE MAN
Tracks: / Hoocie coochie man / Sexy boogie.
12" Single: Released Sep '80, on Plastic, Deleted Sep '83. Catalogue no: **PFUL 2005**

MAD ABOUT YOU
Tracks: / Mad about you.
7" Single: Released Apr '89, on Gaz's, Catalogue no: **GAZ 002**

MY CONFESSION (TO THE ONE I LOVE)
Tracks: / My confession / Million years, A.
12" Single: Released Dec '85, on BB, Catalogue no: **BBD 174**

NO MORE SORROWS (2 PARTS)
Tracks: / No more sorrows.
12" Single: Released Oct '82, on Salamo, Catalogue no: **S 002**

RUDI GOT MARRIED
Tracks: / Rudi got married.
7" Single: Released May '80, on I-Spy, Deleted '83. Catalogue no: **SEE 6**

RUDY GOT MARRIED
Tracks: / Rudy got married / Honey come back to me.
7" Single: Released Mar '80, on I-Spy, Deleted Mar '83. Catalogue no: **SEE 006**

SAHARA
Tracks: / Sahara.
7" Single: Released Jan '87, on Gaz's, Catalogue no: **GAZ 003**

SHE WAS MY GIRL
Tracks: / She was my girl.
12" Single: Released Jul '89, on Unicorn Records, by Unicorn Records. Catalogue no: **12 PHZ 53**
7" Single: Released Oct '89, on Unicorn Records, by Unicorn Records. Catalogue no: **PHZ 53**

Aitken, Marcia

STILL IN LOVE WITH YOU BOY
Tracks: / Still in love with you boy.
7" Single: Released '87, on UNKNOWN, Deleted Jun '89. Catalogue no: **LIGS 102**

Aitkin, Laurel

BIG FAT MAN
Tracks: / Big fat man / It's too late.
7" Single: Released Jul '80, on Arista, by BMG Records (UK). Deleted '83. Catalogue no: **SEE 7**

Ajamu

MISSING MY WOMAN
Tracks: / Missing my woman.
12" Single: Released 31 Jul '89, on J.O.B., by Charly Records. Catalogue no: **JOB 001**

AK Band

8 3 12
Tracks: / 8 3 12 / Walnut moleteazerz.
7" Single: Released May '81, on RCA, by BMG Records (UK). Deleted May '84. Catalogue no: **RCA 83**

OVER YOU
Tracks: / Over you / Dead slumber.
7" Single: Released Aug '81, on RCA, by BMG Records (UK). Deleted '84. Catalogue no: **RCA 107**

PINK SLIPPERS
Tracks: / Pink slippers / Skegaway.
7" Single: Released Oct '82, on Battle Of The Bands, Deleted Oct '85. Catalogue no: **BOB 1**

Akabu

WATCH YOURSELF
Tracks: / Watch yourself.
12" Single: Released Jun '84, on Body Rock, Catalogue no: **BR 5003**

Akaoldren, Viv

EYESUCK
Tracks: / Eyesuck.
7" Single: Released '88, on Akashic (USA), by Akashic Records (USA). Catalogue no: **VIVAK 002**
Special: Released '88, on Akashic (USA), by Akashic Records (USA). Catalogue no: **VIVAK 002X**

WITNESS
Tracks: / Witness.
12" Single: Released '88, on Resonance, Catalogue no: **R 33 8818**

Akasa

ONE NIGHT IN MY LIFE
Tracks: / One night in my life / Shadows.
12" Single: Released 24 Jul '89, on WEA, by WEA Records. Catalogue no: **YZ 405T**
7" Single: Released 24 Jul '89, on WEA, by WEA Records. Catalogue no: **YZ 405**
CD 5": Released 24 Jul '89, on WEA, by WEA Records. Catalogue no: **YZ 405CD**

Akela & The Cubs

MODERN GIRL
Tracks: / Modern girl.
7" Single: Released Jul '83, on Hot Shot, Catalogue no: **HS 001**

Akens, Jewel

BIRDS AND THE BEES (See panel on previous page)
Tracks: / Birds and the bees, The / Fenderman.
7" Single: Released Mar '65, on London-American, Deleted '68. Catalogue no: **HLN 9954**

Akimbo

SO LONG TROUBLE
Tracks: / So long trouble / Machine, The.
7" Single: Released Jan '86, on Foreward Sounds, by Foreward Sounds Records. Catalogue no: **FORWARD 7003**

Akin, Chuck

CHUCK AKIN & CHARLES WATTS
7" Single: Released '88, on JSP, by JSP Records. Catalogue no: **JSP 4505**

Akkerman, Jan

Biographical details:
Jan Akkerman plays electric and acoustic guitar, also lute. He was born in 1946 in Amsterdam. He played in bands including Brainbox, then jazz/rock band Focus (with Thijs Van Leer on organ, flute, occasional vocals; Martin Dresden on bass, various drummers, other occasional personnel incl. Philip Catherine on guitar in 1976; there was an album with P.J. Proby and Catherine in 1978).
Akkerman formed Eli with Kaz Lux (vocals) and drummer Pierre Van der Linden, both ex-Brainbox (Van der Linden also played on a couple of Focus LPs). Akkerman has made several albums of his own and rejoined Focus in 1985 for an album on Vertigo.
(Donald Clarke 1988)..

SHE'S SO DIVINE
Tracks: / She's so divine / Spy dancer.
7" Single: Released Jan '80, on Atlantic, by WEA Records. Deleted Jan '85. Catalogue no: **K11374**

Akrylykz

J.D.
Tracks: / J.D. / Ska'd for life.
7" Single: Released Jun '80, on Polydor, by Polydor Ltd. Deleted '83. Catalogue no: **2059253**

SMART BOY
Tracks: / Smart boy / Spyder man.
7" Single: Released Mar '80, on Polydor, by Polydor Ltd. Deleted Mar '83. Catalogue no: **POSP 128**

SPIDERMAN
Tracks: / Spiderman.
7" Single: Released 26 Jun '85, on Red Rhino, by Red Rhino Records. Deleted '88. Catalogue no: **RED 002**

Akwaba

MAN IN ME, THE
Tracks: / Man in me, The.
12" Single: Released Oct '89, on Axe, Catalogue no: **AXE 12005**

NEGRO MAN
Tracks: / Negro man.
7" Single: Released Apr '89, on Axe, Catalogue no: **AXE 1204**

Al Di Meola

ROLLER JUBILEE
Tracks: / Roller jubilee / Splendido sundance.
7" Single: Released Aug '80, on CBS, by CBS Records. Deleted '83. Catalogue no: **CBS 8803**
12" Single: Released Aug '80, on CBS, by CBS Records. Deleted '83. Catalogue no: **CBS 13 8803**

Alabama

Biographical details:
Slick, successful USA country-rock group formed in 1969 as Wild Country. Guitarists Jeffrey Alan Cook and Randy Yeull Owen are cousins born in 1949; they began playing with bassist Teddy Wayne Gentry while still in school; all three sing; another cousin, Jackie Owen, was their first drummer.
They backed visiting stars and played dances, turned to full-time music in 1973, changed their name in 1977, signed with RCA in 1980; soon crossed over to pop chart.
(Donald Clarke 21 July 1988).

CLOSER YOU GET (SINGLE)
Tracks: / Closer you get / Dixieland delight.
7" Single: Released Jun '83, on RCA, by BMG Records (UK). Catalogue no: **RCA 337**

FANTASY
Tracks: / Fantasy / Can't forget about you.
7" Single: Released May '84, on RCA, by BMG Records (UK). Catalogue no: **RCA 421**

FEELS SO RIGHT (SINGLE)
Tracks: / Feels so right / See the embers feel the flame.
7" Single: Released Feb '84, on RCA, by BMG Records (UK). Catalogue no: **RCA 382**
7" Single: Released Feb '84, on RCA, by BMG Records (UK). Catalogue no: **RCAV 382**

TAKE ME DOWN
Tracks: / Take me down / Love in the first degree.
7" Single: Released Jul '82, on RCA, by BMG Records (UK). Catalogue no: **RCA 251**

TENNESSEE RIVER
Tracks: / Tennessee river / Can't forget about you.
7" Single: Released Oct '80, on RCA, by BMG Records (UK). Deleted '83. Catalogue no: **PB 2018**

THERE'S NO WAY
Tracks: / There's no way.
7" Single: Released Apr '85, on RCA, by BMG Records (UK). Catalogue no: **PB 49991**

Alan & Blewitt

CHIP SHOP WRAPPING
Tracks: / Chip shop wrapping / Chip shop.
7" Single: Released Jan '82, on Pye, Deleted Jan '85. Catalogue no: **7 P 175**

Alarm

Biographical details:
Despite the success of their first two singles, *68 Guns* and *Where were you hiding when the storm broke?* The Alarm found it difficult to escape from constant critical references to The Clash. After *Declaration* (which reached number six in the British album charts of early 1984), they seemed to try and counter these comparisons by getting increasingly 'heavy' as with the 1986's ironically-titles *Spirit of 76*.
1987, however, brought a considerable mellowing with *Rain in the Summertime*.
(Robert Cohen October 1987).

This Welsh band first caused a stir in the spring of '83 with *The Stand*, a single derivative of 1979-style post punk/Mod revival rock. Its follow-up *68 Guns* gave them their first chart success, reaching the Top 20. Their debut LP *Declaration* was released in early '84 and met with considerable success. Their brand of music is unoriginal but energetic.
(Bob MacDonald 1986).

A UK rock band formed in 1981 in South Wales. All four born in 1958-59 had been 17-year-olds in a band called 17. Guitarists Mike Peters and Dave Sharp, bassist Eddie MacDonald, drummer Nigel Twist. Peters is the vocalist. Signed by Miles Copeland to his IRS label, their pompous 'revolutionary' rock appealed to audiences too young to have heard of the Byrds.
(Donald Clarke 21 July 1988).

68 GUNS
Tracks: / 68 guns (part 1) / 68 guns (part 2) / Thoughts of a young man (on 12" only).
7" Single: Released Sep '83, on I.R.S, Deleted Mar '88. Catalogue no: **PFP 1023**

ABSOLUTE REALITY
Tracks: / Absolute reality / Blaze of glory.
7" Single: Released Feb '85, on Priority, by Priority Records. Catalogue no: **ALARM 1**
12" Single: Released Feb '85, on Priority, by Priority Records. Deleted Nov '87. Catalogue no: **ALARM 12**

BLACK SUN
Tracks: / Black sun / How the mighty fall.
7" Single: Released Sep '89, on I.R.S, Catalogue no: **EIRSF 128**

CHANT HAS JUST BEGUN
Tracks: / Chant has just begun / Bells of Rhymney / Stand, The (12" only.).
12" Single: Released Oct '84, on I.R.S, Deleted Mar '88. Catalogue no: **IRSX 114**
7" Single: Released Oct '84, on I.R.S, Deleted '87. Catalogue no: **IRS 114**

COMPACT HITS: THE ALARM
Tracks: / Sixty eight guns / Blaze of glory / Shout to the devil / Where were you hiding when the storm broke?.

CD 5": Released Apr '88, on A&M, by A&M Records. Deleted Apr '88. Catalogue no: **AMCD 906**

DECEIVER, THE
Tracks: / Deceiver / Reason 41 / Second generation (12" only.).
7" Single: Released Mar '84, on I.R.S, Deleted '87. Catalogue no: **IRS 103**
12" Single: Released Mar '84, on I.R.S, Deleted Mar '88. Catalogue no: **IRSX 103**

KNIFE EDGE
Tracks: / Knife edge / Caroline Isenberg / Howling wind (On 12" only) / Promise, The (On 12" only).

12" Single: Released Apr '86, on I.R.S, Catalogue no: **IRMT112**
7" Single: Released Apr '86, on I.R.S, Catalogue no: **IRM 112**

MARCHING ON
Tracks: / Marching on / Across the border / Lie of the land.
7" Single: Released Oct '82, on Illegal, by Faulty Products Records. Deleted '85. Catalogue no: **ILS 0032**

PRESENCE OF LOVE (LAUGHARNE)
Tracks: / Presence of love / Knife edge (live) (12"s only.) / Strength (On IRMT 155 only.) / This train is bound for glory (live) (On IRMX 155 only.) / Dawn chorus (live) (On IRMX 155 only.).

12" Single: Released Feb '88, on MCA, by MCA Records. Catalogue no: **IRMT 155**
CD 5": Released Feb '88, on I.R.S, Catalogue no: **DIRM 155**
7" Single: Released Feb '88, on MCA, by MCA Records. Deleted 1 Jul '89. Catalogue no: **IRM 155**
12" Single: Released Feb '88, on MCA, by MCA Records. Catalogue no: **IRMX 155**

RAIN IN THE SUMMERTIME
Tracks: / Rain in the summertime / Rose beyond the wall / Bells of Rhymney (live) (On 12" only) / Time to believe (On 12" only.) / Rain in the summertime (through the haze mix) (On IRMX 144).

12" Single: Released Sep '87, on MCA, by MCA Records. Catalogue no: **IRMT 144**
12" Single: Released Oct '87, on MCA, by MCA Records. Catalogue no: **IRMX 144**
7" Single: Released Sep '87, on MCA, by MCA Records. Deleted 1 Jul '89. Catalogue no: **IRM 144**

RESCUE ME
Tracks: / Rescue me / My land your land / Elder's & folklore (On 12" only) / Pastures of plenty (On 12" only).
Note: IRMBV 150 is a special edition blue vinyl.
7" Single: Released Nov '87, on I.R.S, Catalogue no: **IRM 150**
7" Single: Released Dec '87, on I.R.S, Catalogue no: **IRMBV 150**
12" Single: Released Nov '87, on I.R.S, Catalogue no: **IRMT 150**

SOLD ME DOWN THE RIVER
Tracks: / Sold me down the river / Gwethoch fi I lawr yr afon (Welsh version of A side.) / Corridors of power (Not on 7".) / Firing line (10" only.).

10" single: Released Aug '89, on I.R.S, Catalogue no: **EIRSIO 123**
CD 5": Released Aug '89, on I.R.S, Catalogue no: **EIRSCD 123**
Special: Released Aug '89, on I.R.S, Catalogue no: **EIRSP 123**
12" Single: Released Aug '89, on I.R.S, Catalogue no: **EIRST 123**
7" Single: Released Aug '89, on I.R.S, Catalogue no: **EIRS 123**

SPIRIT OF '76
Tracks: / Spirit of '76 / Where were you hiding when the storm broke? / Deeside (On 12" only) / Knocking on heaven's door (In double pack only) / Sixty eight guns (In double pack only).

7" Set: Released Jan '86, on I.R.S, Catalogue no: **IRMTD 109**
7" Single: Released Jan '86, on I.R.S, Catalogue no: **IRM 109**
12" Single: Released Jan '86, on I.R.S, Catalogue no: **IRMT 109**

STRENGTH (SINGLE)
Tracks: / Strength / Majority.
7" Single: Released Sep '85, on I.R.S, Catalogue no: **IRM 104**
12" Single: Released Sep '85, on I.R.S, Catalogue no: **IRT 104**

WHERE WERE YOU HIDING WHEN THE STORM BROKE
Tracks: / Where were you hiding when the storm broke / Pavillion steps / What kind of hell.

12" Single: Released Jan '84, on I.R.S, Deleted Feb '89. Catalogue no: **IRSX 101**
7" Single: Released Jan '84, on I.R.S, Deleted '87. Catalogue no: **IRS 101**

Alaska

BAILANDO
Tracks: / Bailando (Balearic matey mix) / Bailando (acido espanol mix).
7" Single: Released Aug '88, on Syncopate, by EMI Records. Deleted Jun '89. Catalogue no: **SY 17**
12" Single: Released Aug '88, on Syncopate, by EMI Records. Deleted Jun '89. Catalogue no: **12 SY 17**

BAILANDO RED RUM
Tracks: / Bailando red rum / La tribu de las Chochoni.
12" Single: Released Oct '82, on Kingdom, by Kingdom Records. Deleted '84. Catalogue no: **KV 8025 12**
7" Single: Released Oct '82, on Kingdom, by Kingdom Records. Deleted '84. Catalogue no: **KV 8025**

HEADLINES
Tracks: / Headlines / Sorcerer, The.
7" Single: Released Sep '88, on Music For Nations, by Music For Nations Records. Catalogue no: **KUT 130**

MISS YOU TONIGHT
Tracks: / Miss you tonight.

12" Single: Released May '85, on Music For Nations, by Music For Nations Records. Catalogue no: **12 KUT 116**
7" Single: Released May '85, on Music For Nations, by Music For Nations Records. Catalogue no: **KUT 116**

SUSIE BLUE
Tracks: / Susie blue.

12" Single: Released Apr '84, on Music For Nations, by Music For Nations Records. Catalogue no: **12 KUT 108**
7" Single: Released Apr '84, on Music For Nations, by Music For Nations Records. Catalogue no: **KUT 108**

Albania (group)

ALBANIA
Tracks: / Albania / Take it away.
7" Single: Released Sep '80, on Chiswick Records, Deleted '83. Catalogue no: **CHIS 136**

COULD THIS BE LOVE
Tracks: / Could this be love / Little baby.
7" Single: Released Sep '82, on Stiff, by Stiff Records. Catalogue no: **BUY 156**
12" Single: Released Sep '82, on Stiff, by Stiff Records. Catalogue no: **BUYIT 156**

GO GO GO
Tracks: / Go go go / Today & tomorrow.
7" Single: Released Jun '81, on Chiswick Records, Deleted Jun '84. Catalogue no: **CHIS 150**

KAYTIE KING
Tracks: / Kaytie King / Word is out.
7" Single: Released Jan '81, on Chiswick Records, Deleted Jan '84. Catalogue no: **CHIS 141**

MEN IN A MILLION
Tracks: / Men in a million / So o.k. / French farewell.
12" Single: Released Mar '81, on Chiswick Records, Deleted Mar '84. Catalogue no: **12CHIS 143**

Albert, Dale

I HAVE BEEN HURT BY LOVE
Tracks: / I have been hurt by love / Love song serenade.
12" Single: Released Jul '82, on Mass Media, Deleted '85. Catalogue no: **MMM 12-1010**

I'VE BEEN HURT BY LOVE
Tracks: / I've been hurt by love.
12" Single: Released Jul '82, on Mass Media, Catalogue no: **MMM 12 1010**

Albert, Ken

GUNSHOT
Tracks: / Gunshot.
12" Single: Released Mar '89, on Digital English, Catalogue no: **DE 012**

Albert, Morris

FEELINGS
Tracks: / Feelings.
7" Single: Released Sep '75, on Decca, by Decca Records. Deleted '78. Catalogue no: **F 13591**

FEELINGS (OLD GOLD) natural high (bloodstone)
Tracks: / Feelings.
7" Single: Released Oct '83, on Old Gold, by Old Gold Records. Catalogue no: **OG 9360**

Alberto

CRUISING WITH SANTA
Tracks: / Cruising with Santa.
7" Single: Released Dec '82, on New Hormones, Catalogue no: **ORG 30**

HEADS DOWN NO NONSENSE MINDLESS BOOGIE
Tracks: / Heads down no nonsense mindless boogie.
7" Single: Released Sep '78, on Logo, by Logo Records. Deleted '81. Catalogue no: **GO 323**

Alcapone, Dennis

GREATEST LOVER
Tracks: / Greatest lover.
12" Single: Released Nov '86, on Stop'n'Rock, Catalogue no: **SNRIT 001**

THREE WISE MEN
Tracks: / Three wise men / Wise men dub.
12" Single: Released Nov '82, on Empire (reggae), Catalogue no: **EMPDC 317**

WORLD CUP FOOTBALL
Tracks: / World cup football / Football dub.
12" Single: Released Jul '82, on Empire Records, Catalogue no: **EMPBC 316**
7" Single: Released Jul '82, on Empire Records, Catalogue no: **DMP 316**

Alcatrazz

ISLAND IN THE SUN
Tracks: / Island in the sun.
7" Single: Released Aug '84, on Rocshire, by BMG Records (UK). Catalogue no: **RCA 434**
12" Single: Released Aug '84, on Rocshire, by BMG Records (UK). Catalogue no: **RCAT 434**

ROCKIN' HIGH
Tracks: / Rockin' high / Run wild.
7" Single: Released Jan '81, on RCA, by BMG Records (UK). Deleted Jan '84. Catalogue no: **RCA 29**

YOU AND THE NIGHT
Tracks: / You and the night / Run wild.
7" Single: Released May '81, on RCA, by BMG Records (UK). Deleted May '84. Catalogue no: **RCA 81**

Alcool d'Apres

BEGINNING (EP)
Tracks: / On Broadway / One little girl / Wasting your time / Night fright.
12" Single: Released Feb '87, on JJ, by JJ Records. Catalogue no: **JJ ALC 1001**

Aldrich, Renee

JUST BEGUN TO LOVE YOU
Tracks: / Just begun to love you.
12" Single: Released Sep '87, on Jam Packed (USA), Catalogue no: **JP 12010**

Ale, Charlie

ZIPPIN' UP THE HOUSE
Tracks: / Zippin' up the house.
12" Single: Released Oct '88, on Priority, by Priority Records. Deleted Aug '89. Catalogue no: **PX 23**
7" Single: Released Oct '88, on Priority, by Priority Records. Deleted Aug '89. Catalogue no: **P 23**

Aleem

FINE YOUNG TENDER
Tracks: / Fine young tender / Two faces.
12" Single: Released Jun '86, on Atlantic, by WEA Records. Deleted Jun '87. Catalogue no: **A 9401 T**
7" Single: Released Jul '86, on Atlantic, by WEA Records. Catalogue no: **A 9401**

GET LOOSE
Tracks: / Get loose.
12" Single: Released Dec '85, on Streetwave, Catalogue no: **MKHAN 61**

Alessi

Biographical details: Brothers Billy and Bobby Alessi reached the British Top 10 in 1977 with their summery pop single *'Oh Lori'*, but could not match that success in their native USA. A series of albums in the late Seventies failed to make an impact in either country. (Bob MacDonald, 1988).

JAGGED EDGE
Tracks: / Jagged edge / Rise up.
7" Single: Released Aug '82, on Qwest (USA), by Qwest Records (USA). Deleted Aug '85. Catalogue no: **K 17979**

OH LORI
Tracks: / Oh Lori.
7" Single: Released Jun '77, on A&M, by A&M Records. Deleted '80. Catalogue no: **AMS 7289**

PUT AWAY YOUR LOVE
Tracks: / Put away your love / Long time friends.

7" Single: Released May '82, on Warner Bros., by WEA Records. Deleted May '85. Catalogue no: **K 17949**

Alex

RELIABLE
Tracks: / Reliable / Sugar me.
12" Single: Released Mar '82, on Roots Radics, Catalogue no: **SSO1**

Alexa

WE DON'T REMEMBER WHY
Tracks: / We don't remember why / Heart to heart.
7" Single: Released Feb '89, on Savage, by Savage Records. Catalogue no: **7 VAG 903**
CD 3": Released Feb '89, on Savage, by Savage Records. Catalogue no: **3 VAG 903**
CD 5": Released Feb '89, on Savage, by Savage Records. Catalogue no: **CDVAG 903**

Alexander Brothers

FAREWELL MY LOVE
Tracks: / Farewell my love.
7" Single: Released Nov '86, on Lismor, by Lismor Records. Deleted '88. Catalogue no: **LISP 2009**

GENTLE ANNIE
Tracks: / Gentle Annie.
7" Single: Released Nov '86, on Lismor, by Lismor Records. Deleted '88. Catalogue no: **LISP 2010**

WAY OLD FRIENDS DO
Tracks: / Way old friends do, The / Bilitis.
7" Single: Released Nov '81, on Lismor, by Lismor Records. Deleted '88. Catalogue no: **LISP 2005**
7" Single: Released Dec '82, on Mervyn Conn Presents, Catalogue no: **MRE 002**

Alexander, David

COME HOME RHONDA BOY
Tracks: / Come home rhonda boy / Green green grass of home.
7" Single: Released Mar '80, on Columbia, by EMI Records. Deleted '83. Catalogue no: **DB 9078**

Alexander, Goldie

KNOCKING DOWN YOUR LOVE (2 PARTS)
Tracks: / Knock down your love.
12" Single: Released Mar '83, on Proto, by Proto Records. Catalogue no: **ENAT 104**

Alexander, Gorden

SAVE YOUR KISSES FOR ME
Tracks: / Save your kisses for me.
7" Single: Released '81, on Starward, Catalogue no: **STU 1**

Alexander, Leszcek

IF I HAD YOU
Tracks: / If I had you / Soul music.
7" Single: Released Jun '80, on Charisma, by Virgin Records. Deleted Jun '83. Catalogue no: **CB 366**

Alexander, Mel

MY BABY DRIVES A FORD CORTINA
Tracks: / My baby drives a Ford Cortina.
7" Single: Released '85, on Big Boy, by Big Boy Records. Catalogue no: **PIER 73**

Alexander, Simon

MAD ABOUT YOU
Tracks: / Mad about you / Which door to paradise?.
7" Single: Released Aug '80, on Bronze, by Bronze Records. Deleted '83. Catalogue no: **BRO 102**

STAY
Tracks: / Stay / Where do i stand.
7" Single: Released Jan '80, on Bronze, by Bronze Records. Deleted Jan '85. Catalogue no: **BRO 87**

Alexander, Yasim

KEEP ON MOVING
Tracks: / Keep on moving.
12" Single: Released 10 Jul '89, on Eye to Eye, Catalogue no: **CSNC 001**

Alexandre

MY LANCASHIRE
Tracks: / My Lancashire / It's Xmas.
7" Single: Released Feb '86, on Rockin' Ronnie, Catalogue no: **RRR 3**

Alexei's Midnight

POP UP TOASTERS
Tracks: / Pop up toasters / Page 3 girls / I'm evil.
7" Single: Released Oct '81, on Island, by Island Records. Deleted Oct '84. Catalogue no: **WIP 6725**

Alf

ALF ON FAULTY FIVE
Tracks: / Alf on faulty five.
7" Single: Released '81, on Singing Dog, by Safari Records. Catalogue no: **PUP 2**

STUCK ON EARTH
Tracks: / Stuck on earth / Cruisin' on Melmac Interstate.
12" Single: Released 5 Mar '88, on RCA, by BMG Records (UK). Deleted May '89. Catalogue no: **PT 41804**
7" Single: Released 5 Mar '88, on RCA, by BMG Records (UK). Deleted May '89. Catalogue no: **PB 41663**

Alf & Tel

CARIBBEAN BLUES
Tracks: / Sally / Caribbean blues.
7" Single: Released Aug '87, on Sahara, Catalogue no: **ALF 1**

Alfi & Harry

TROUBLE WITH HARRY, THE
Tracks: / Trouble with Harry, The.
7" Single: Released Mar '56, on London-American, Deleted '59. Catalogue no: **HLU 8242**

Alfie

STAR
Tracks: / Star.
7" Single: Released '85, on Motown, by BMG Records (UK). Catalogue no: **TMG 1390**
12" Single: Released '85, on Motown, by BMG Records (UK). Catalogue no: **TMGT 1390**

Alibi

BROKEN GLASS
Tracks: / Broken glass / Brother orchid.
7" Single: Released Jun '82, on Kaleidoscope Sound, by Kaleidoscope Sound Records. Deleted Jun '85. Catalogue no: **KRLA 2307**

FRIENDS (SINGLE)
Tracks: / Friends / Hands off.
7" Single: Released Jul '80, on Magnet, by WEA Records. Deleted '83. Catalogue no: **MAG 173**

Alice

WALKING SHOES
Tracks: / Walking shoes.
7" Single: Released Jun '89, on Theobald Dickson Productions, Catalogue no: **TDP 004**

Alien (group)

VIDEO GAME
Tracks: / Video game / You gotta spend.
7" Single: Released Nov '81, on Solid Gold (1), by Creole Records. Deleted Nov '84. Catalogue no: **SGR 109**

Alien Sex Fiend

BUN HO
Tracks: / Bun ho / Silver machine / Satisfaction.
12" Single: Released Nov '88, on Anagram, by Cherry Red Records. Catalogue no: **12 ANA 45**

DEAD AND BURIED
Tracks: / Dead and buried.
12" Single: Released '84, on Anagram, by Cherry Red Records. Catalogue no: **12 ANA 23**
7" Single: Released '84, on Anagram, by Cherry Red Records. Catalogue no: **PANA 23**
7" Pic: Released '84, on Anagram, by Cherry Red Records. Catalogue no: **E ANA 23**

E.S.T (TRIP TO THE MOON)
7" Single: Released '84, on Anagram, by Cherry Red Records. Deleted '88. Catalogue no: **ANA 25**

HAUNTED HOUSE
Tracks: / Haunted house / Haunted house (dub).
12" Single: Released Apr '89, on Anagram, by Cherry Red Records. Catalogue no: **12 ANA 46**
7" Single: Released Apr '89, on Anagram, by Cherry Red Records. Catalogue no: **ANA 46**
CD 5": Released Apr '89, on Anagram, by Cherry Red Records. Catalogue no: **CD ANA 46**

HERE CUM GERMS
Tracks: / Here cum germs.
12" Single: Released Aug '87, on Cherry Red, by Cherry Red Records. Catalogue no: **12 ANA 38**
7" Single: Released Aug '87, on Cherry Red, by Cherry Red Records. Catalogue no: **ANA 38**

HURRICANE FIGHTER PLANE
Tracks: / It lives again / Hurricane fighter plane.
7" Single: Released Feb '87, on Anagram, by Cherry Red Records. Catalogue no: **ANA 33**
12" Single: Released Feb '87, on Anagram, by Cherry Red Records. Catalogue no: **12 ANA 33**

I WALK THE LINE
Tracks: / I walk the line / School's out / Here she comes (On 12" only) / Can't stop smoking (On 12" only).
12" Single: Released Apr '86, on Flicknife, by Flicknife Records. Catalogue no: **FLEP 106**
7" Single: Released Apr '86, on Flicknife, by Flicknife Records. Catalogue no: **SFLEP 106**

IGNORE THE MACHINE
Tracks: / Ignore the machine / Girl at the end of my gun.
CD 5": Released 13 Sep '88, on Anagram, by Cherry Red Records. Catalogue no: **CD ANA 11**
12" Single: Released '85, on Anagram, by Cherry Red Records. Catalogue no: **12 ANA 11**
7" Pic: Released '85, on Anagram, by Cherry Red Records. Catalogue no: **PANA 11**
12" Single: Released '85, on Anagram, by Cherry Red Records. Catalogue no: **SANA 11**

I'M DOING TIME IN A MAXIMUM SECURITY TWILIGHT
Tracks: / I'm doing time in a maximum security twilight.
12" Single: Released '85, on Anagram, by Cherry Red Records. Catalogue no: **12 ANA 30**

IMPOSSIBLE MISSION, THE
Tracks: / Impossible mission / My brain is in the cupboard above the kitchen sink / Impossible mission 2 (Track on 12" version only.).
12" Single: Released 13 Jun '87, on Anagram, by Cherry Red Records. Catalogue no: **12 ANA 34**
7" Single: Released 13 Jun '87, on Anagram, by Cherry Red Records. Catalogue no: **ANA 34**

LIPS CAN'T GO
Tracks: / Lips can't go / Drive my rocket.
7" Single: Released '83, on Anagram, by Cherry Red Records. Deleted '88. Catalogue no: **ANA 15**
12" Single: Released '83, on Anagram, by Cherry Red Records. Catalogue no: **12 ANA 15**

R.I.P.
Tracks: / R.I.P. / New christian music.
7" Single: Released '84, on Anagram, by Cherry Red Records. Deleted '88. Catalogue no: **ANA 18**
10" single: Released '84, on Anagram, by Cherry Red Records. Deleted '88. Catalogue no: **10 ANA 18**
12" Single: Released '84, on Anagram, by Cherry Red Records. Catalogue no: **12 ANA 18**

SMELLS LIKE SHIT
Tracks: / Smells like shit / Biggin' me.
7" Single: Released Oct '86, on Anagram, by Cherry Red Records. Catalogue no: **ANA 32**
12" Single: Released Oct '86, on Anagram, by Cherry Red Records. Catalogue no: **12 ANA 32**

STUFF THE TURKEY
Tracks: / Stuff the turkey / They call me crazee.
7" Single: Released Dec '87, on Anagram, by Cherry Red Records. Catalogue no: **ANA 40**

Aliki

DANCING THROUGH THE NIGHT
7" Single: Released '84, on Ecstasy, by Creole Records. Catalogue no: **XTC 8**
12" Single: Released '84, on Ecstasy, by Creole Records. Catalogue no: **XTCT 8**

DON'T WANT TO KNOW ABOUT THE WORLD TODAY
Tracks: / Don't want to know about the world today / Walk away.
7" Single: Released '82, on President, by President Records. Catalogue no: **PT 505**

Alim, Kamal Abdul

KAMAL & THE BROTHERS DANCE
Tracks: / Kamal & the brothers dance.
7" Single: Released May '89, on Stash (USA), Catalogue no: **ST 279**

Alisha

ALL NIGHT PASSION
Tracks: / All night passion / Short radio.
7" Single: Released Mar '84, on 4th & Broadway, by Island Records. Catalogue no: **BRW 3**

BABY TALK
Tracks: / Baby talk / Baby talk (dub vocals).
12" Single: Released Jan '86, on Total Control, by Total Control Records. Catalogue no: **12 TOCO 6**
7" Single: Released Jan '86, on Total Control, by Total Control Records. Catalogue no: **TOCO 6**

Alison's Secret

FRANKIE'S ROOM
Tracks: / Frankie's room.
7" Single: Released Feb '85, on Surprise, Catalogue no: **SKT 1**

Alkatrazz

THINK IT OVER
Tracks: / Think it over / Halfway there.
7" Single: Released Feb '82, on RCA, by BMG Records (UK). Deleted May '85. Catalogue no: **RCA 183**

All About Eve

Biographical details: English gothic style group formed in 1985, consisting of members Julianne Reagan (vocals), Tim Bricheno, Andy Cousin and Mark Price. Their first single D For Desire appeared on their own independent label Eden, but it wasn't until the release of their album All About Eve in 1988 that they achieved any real commercial success. The album contained four hit singles, including a UK No.7 hit Martha's Harbour. (P.Williams 7/88)t.

D FOR DESIRE
Tracks: / D for desire.
7" Single: Released Jun '85, on Eden, Deleted '88. Catalogue no: **EDEN 1**

EVERY ANGEL
Tracks: / Every angel / Wild flowers / Every angel (extended) (track on 12" version only.) / Candy tree (Track on 12" version only.) / More than this hour (+Track on CD single only.).
Note: * Extra track on 12". + Extra track on CD single.
CD 5": Released 28 Mar '88, on Mercury, by Phonogram Ltd. Catalogue no: **EVNCD 7**
7" Single: Released Apr '88, on Mercury, by Phonogram Ltd. Catalogue no: **EVENG 7**
7" Single: Released 28 Mar '88, on Mercury, by Phonogram Ltd. Catalogue no: **EVEN 7**
12" Single: Released 28 Mar '88, on Mercury, by Phonogram Ltd. Catalogue no: **EVENX 7**
10" single: Released Apr '88, on Mercury, by Phonogram Ltd. Catalogue no: **EVEN 710**

FLOWERS IN OUR HAIR
Tracks: / Flowers in our hair / Paradise / Devil woman.
12" Single: Released Jul '87, on Eden, Catalogue no: **EVENX 4**
7" Single: Released Jul '87, on Eden, Catalogue no: **EVEN 4**

IN THE CLOUDS
Tracks: / In the clouds / She moved through the fair.
Note: Produced by Paul Samwell-Smith (ex Yardbirds). * extra track on 12" version.
12" Single: Released Apr '86, on Eden, Deleted '88. Catalogue no: **EDEN 002**
7" Single: Released Oct '87, on Mercury, by Phonogram Ltd. Catalogue no: **EVEN 5**
12" Single: Released Oct '87, on Mercury, by Phonogram Ltd. Catalogue no: **EVENX 5**

MARTHA'S HARBOUR
Tracks: / Martha's harbour / Another door (Previously unavailable track) / Never promise (anyone forever)(live) (Previously unavailable track) / Wild flowers (CD single only.) / She moved through the fair (CD single only.).
Cassingle: Released 23 Jul '88, on Mercury, by Phonogram Ltd. Catalogue no: **EVEN M8**
CD 5": Released 18 Jul '88, on Mercury, by Phonogram Ltd. Catalogue no: **EVENCD 8**
12" Single: Released 18 Jul '88, on Mercury, by Phonogram Ltd. Deleted 31 May '89. Catalogue no: **EVENX 8**
12" Single: Released 18 Jul '88, on Mercury, by Phonogram Ltd. Deleted 31 May '89. Catalogue no: **EVNXB**
7" Single: Released 18 Jul '88, on Mercury, by Phonogram Ltd. Deleted 31 May '89. Catalogue no: **EVEN 8**

OUR SUMMER
Tracks: / Our summer / Lady Moonlight / Shelter from the rain*.
Note: * = Extra track on 12" only.
7" Single: Released Apr '87, on Eden, Catalogue no: **EVEN 3**
12" Single: Released Apr '87, on Eden, Catalogue no: **EVENX 3**

ROAD TO YOUR SOUL
Tracks: / Road to your soul / Pieces of our heart.
12" Single: Released Sep '89, on Mercury, by Phonogram Ltd. Catalogue no: **EVENX 10**
7" Single: Released Sep '89, on Mercury, by Phonogram Ltd. Catalogue no: **EVEN 10**
CD 5": Released Sep '89, on Mercury, by Phonogram Ltd. Catalogue no: **EVNCD 10**
12" Single: Released Sep '89, on Mercury, by Phonogram Ltd. Catalogue no: **EVNXP 10**
Cassingle: Released Sep '89, on Mercury, by Phonogram Ltd. Catalogue no: **EVNMC 10**

WHAT KIND OF FOOL
Tracks: / What kind of fool / Gold and silver / What kind of fool (12" and CD only) / Garden of Jane Delawney, The (12" and CD only).
12" Single: Released 31 Oct '88, on Mercury, by Phonogram Ltd. Deleted 31 May '89. Catalogue no: **EVENX 9**
12" Single: Released Oct '88, on Mercury, by Phonogram Ltd. Deleted 31 May '89. Catalogue no: **EVNXB 9**
CD 5": Released 31 Oct '88, on Mercury, by Phonogram Ltd. Catalogue no: **EVNCD 9**
10" single: Released Nov '88, on Mercury, by Phonogram Ltd. Deleted 31 May '89. Catalogue no: **EVEN 910**
7" Single: Released 31 Oct '88, on Mercury, by Phonogram Ltd. Deleted 31 May '89. Catalogue no: **EVEN 9**

WILD HEARTED WOMAN
Tracks: / Wild hearted woman / Apple tree man / Like Emily (Available on 12" only).
Note: * extra track on 12" version.
12" Single: Released Jan '88, on Mercury, by Phonogram Ltd. Catalogue no: **EVENX 6**
7" Single: Released Jan '88, on Mercury, by Phonogram Ltd. Catalogue no: **EVEN 6**
Cassingle: Released Jan '88, on Mercury, by Phonogram Ltd. Catalogue no: **EVEN M6**

All Fall Down

ARECIBO
Tracks: / Arecibo.
7" Single: Released Jul '83, on Confidential, by Confidential Records. Catalogue no: **KIS 01**

All Night Band

JOKER, THE (THE WIGAN JOKER)
Tracks: / Joker, (The Wigan Joker), The.
7" Single: Released Feb '79, on Casino Classics, by RK Records. Catalogue no: **CC 6**

All Stars...

ALL STAR'S VOL 1
12" Single: Released Jul '88, on Black Scorpio, Catalogue no: **BSLP 8803**

All Systems Go

POP MUZIK
7" Single: Released Jun '88, on Unique, by Unique Records. Catalogue no: **NIQ 03**
7" Single: Released Aug '88, on Unique, by Unique Records. Catalogue no: **NIQX 3**
12" Single: Released Jun '88, on Unique, by Unique Records. Catalogue no: **12NIQ 03**

POP MUZIK(REMIX)
Tracks: / Pop muzik (remix).
12" Single: Released Jul '88, on Unique, by Unique Records. Catalogue no: **12NIQX 3**

All That Jazz

EVEN THE TREES
Tracks: / Even the trees / Me and lillieth (part 1) / Sunday (12" only).
12" Single: Released Feb '88, on Virgin, by Virgin Records. Catalogue no: **VST 1030**
7" Single: Released Feb '88, on Virgin, by Virgin Records. Catalogue no: **VS 1030**

All the Rage

CONCRETE CITY
Tracks: / Concrete city.
7" Single: on Rage, Catalogue no: **RR 001**

Allan, Charlie

AULD FOLKS ON THE WA', THE
Tracks: / Auld folks on the wa', The / To be a farmers boy.
7" Single: Released Jan '88, on Ardo, by Ardo Records. Catalogue no: **ARDO 108**

Allan, Johnnie

PROMISED LAND
Tracks: / Promised land / Sweet dreams.
7" Single: Released Mar '82, on Oval, by Oval Records. Catalogue no: **CAJUN 1**

Allan, Richard

AS TIME GOES BY
Tracks: / As time goes by.
7" Single: Released Mar '60, on Parlophone, by EMI Records. Deleted '63. Catalogue no: **R 4634**

Allan, Steve

TOGETHER WE ARE BEAUTIFUL
Tracks: / Together we are beautiful / All mine.
7" Single: Released Jan '79, on Creole, by Creole Records. Catalogue no: **CR 164**

Allen, Alan

FRENCH GIRLS
Tracks: / French girls / City.
12" Single: Released Feb '83, on Cynic, Catalogue no: **BL 001**

Allen & Blewitt

(I'M GONNA WATCH) CROSSROADS
Tracks: / (I'm gonna watch) crossroads / And the birds were dying.
7" Single: Released May '81, on EMI, by EMI Records. Deleted May '84. Catalogue no: **EMI 5192**

Allen, Christie

GOOSEBUMPS
Tracks: / Goosebumps / Count me out.
7" Single: Released Jun '80, on WEA, by WEA Records. Deleted '83. Catalogue no: **K79138**

HE'S MY NUMBER ONE
Tracks: / He's my number one / Ships that pass in the night.
7" Single: Released Nov '80, on WEA, by WEA Records. Deleted '83. Catalogue no: **K 79184**

Allen, Clinton

LOAF INA DE DANCE
Tracks: / Loaf ina de dance.
12" Single: Released Oct '84, on Gorgon, Catalogue no: **Unknown**

Allen, Daevid

ALIEN IN NEW YORK
Tracks: / Alien in New York.
12" Single: Released May '83, on Celluloid (USA), by Celluloid Records (USA). Deleted '88. Catalogue no: **CYZ 101**

JUNGLE WINDOW
Tracks: / Jungle window.
7" Single: Released Jan '82, on Charly, by Charly Records. Deleted '88. Catalogue no: **CYX 203**

Allen, Dennis

LIMERICK YOU'RE A LADY
Tracks: / Limerick you're a lady.
7" Single: Released Oct '79, on Release (Ireland), Catalogue no: **RL 973**

Allen, Donna

CAN WE TALK
Tracks: / Can we talk / Can we talk (version).
7" Single: Released Aug '89, on BCM Records, Catalogue no: **BCM 277**
12" Single: Released Aug '89, on BCM Records, Catalogue no: **BCM 277 X**
CD 5": Released Aug '89, on BCM Records, Catalogue no: **BCM 277 CD**

JOY AND PAIN
Tracks: / Joy and pain.
CD 5": Released May '89, on BCM Records, Catalogue no: **BCM 257 CD**
12" Single: Released May '89, on BCM Records, Catalogue no: **BCM 257 X**
7" Single: Released Mar '89, on Oceana, Catalogue no: **096 575**
7" Single: Released May '89, on BCM Records, Catalogue no: **BCM 257**

SATISFIED
Tracks: / Satisfied / Another affair.
12" Single: Released Jun '87, on Portrait, by CBS Records. Deleted Nov '87. Catalogue no: **UXX T1**
7" Single: Released Jun '87, on Portrait, by CBS Records. Deleted Nov '87. Catalogue no: **XXX 1**
7" Single: Released Jun '87, on Epic, by CBS Records. Catalogue no: **650751 7**

SATISFIED (BLUE MIX)
Tracks: / Satisfied (blue mix) / Satisfied (acappella version) / Another affair / Serious.
7" Single: Released Jul '87, on Portrait, by CBS Records. Catalogue no: **XXXQT 1**

SERIOUS
12" Single: Released Mar '87, on Portrait, by CBS Records. Deleted Nov '87. Catalogue no: **650744 6**
7" Single: Released Mar '87, on Portrait, by CBS Records. Deleted Nov '87. Catalogue no: **650744 7**

SWEET SOMEBODY
Tracks: / Sweet somebody / Bit by bit / Sweet somebody (version).
12" Single: Released 19 Sep '87, on Portrait, by CBS Records. Catalogue no: **XXT 2**
7" Single: Released Oct '87, on Portrait, by CBS Records. Deleted Jun '88. Catalogue no: **XXX 2**
12" Single: Released Sep '87, on 21 (USA), by 21 Records (USA). Deleted Oct '87. Catalogue no: **096745**
7" Single: Released 19 Sep '87, on Portrait, by CBS Records. Catalogue no: **XX2**

Allen, Gary D

I JUST GLIDE
Tracks: / I just glide / I just glide (version).
Note: Featuring Lisa Lee.u
7" Single: Released Jul '89, on Tek, by Tek Records. Catalogue no: **TEKK 027**
12" Single: Released Jul '89, on Tek, by Tek Records. Catalogue no: **TEKK 02**

Allen, Jack

SARAH JANE
Tracks: / Sarah Jane / Highreel.
7" Single: Released Jan '88, on Crest, Deleted Jan '89. Catalogue no: **CRE 002**

Allen, Lee

Biographical details: ALLEN, Lee was born in 1926 in Pittsburgh, Kansas, but went to school in New Orleans, where he took up the tenor sax. Kids danced to his rocking horn for a generation; he joined Dave Bartholomew's band and originated classic solos on records by Little Richard, Fats Domino, Amos Milburn, Lloyd Price, Etta James and many others:kids danced to his rocking sax all through the '50s. His album *Walkin' With Mr Lee* in 1958 went gold, its title track making the pop chart. He worked in an aircraft factory in the late '60s but returned to music; he sessioned with the Blasters in the'80s. Donald Clarke 21 July 1988.

ZABO
Tracks: / Zabo / Walkin' with Mr. Lee.
7" Single: Released Oct '81, on Nola, Deleted Oct '84. Catalogue no: **JBS 4**

Allen, R. Justice

CRACKIN' UP
Tracks: / Crackin' up / Crackin' up (dub version).
7" Single: Released Oct '86, on Lisson, by PWL Records. Catalogue no: **DOLE 5**
12" Single: Released Oct '86, on Lisson, by PWL Records. Catalogue no: **DOLEQ 5**

Allen, Rodney

CIRCLE LINE
Tracks: / Circle line.
12" Single: Released 23 Jul '88, on Subway, by Subway Records. Catalogue no: **SUBWAY 18T**

Allen, Steve

LOVE IS IN THE AIR
Tracks: / Love is in the air.
12" Single: Released May '87, on WEA, by WEA Records. Deleted Jul '88. Catalogue no: **YZ 126T**
7" Single: Released May '87, on WEA, by WEA Records. Deleted Jan '88. Catalogue no: **YZ 126**

Allen, Terry

SMOKIN THE DUMMY (SINGLE)
Tracks: / Smokin' the dummy.
7" Single: Released Jun '88, on Fate, Catalogue no: **FATE 2**

WHATEVER HAPPENED TO JESUS
Tracks: / Whatever happened to Jesus? / Cajun roll.
7" Single: Released Jun '89, on Fate, Catalogue no: **FRSS 1001**

Allen, Verden

ABOUT TOMORROW
Tracks: / About tomorrow.
7" Single: Released Feb '85, on Spirit (1), by Spirit Records. Catalogue no: **VA 2**

COME ON BACK
Tracks: / Come on back / Sweet sweet girl.
7" Single: Released Mar '84, on Spirit (1), by Spirit Records. Catalogue no: **VA 3**

Allen, Vince

PLAYGROUND LOVE
Tracks: / Playground love / Have you ever had a dream.
7" Single: Released Jul '89, on Infinitive, Catalogue no: **SVA 1**

Allen, Woody

AIRPORT 89
Tracks: / Airport 89.
12" Single: Released Sep '89, on BCM Records, Catalogue no: **BCM 12326**

Allendale

FROST IS ALL OVER, THE
Tracks: / Frost is all over, The.
7" Single: Released '88, on I&B, by I & B Records. Catalogue no: **CRE 001**

GOLDEN VOICE OF MICHAEL O'HEHIR, THE
Tracks: / Golden voice of Michael O'Hehir, The.
7" Single: Released '88, on I&B, by I & B Records. Catalogue no: **CRE 003**

Allers, Carmine

TO BE YOUR LOVER
Tracks: / To be your lover / To be your lover (version).
12" Single: Released Jun '88, on Citybeat, by Beggars Banquet Records. Catalogue no: **CBE 1227**
7" Single: Released Jun '88, on Citybeat, by Beggars Banquet Records. Catalogue no: **CBE 727**

Alley Orchestra

PETER GUNN
Tracks: / Peter Gunn / Yep.
7" Single: Released May '81, on Cheapskate, Deleted May '84. Catalogue no: **CHEAP 23**

Alley, Patrick

JUST ANOTHER NIGHT
Tracks: / Just another night / You're all I need.
12" Single: Released Jul '82, on Tabs, Catalogue no: **TRD 14382**

Alleyne, Sonia

FOR THE LOVE OF YOU
Tracks: / For the love of you.
12" Single: Released Oct '89, on Exodus, Catalogue no: **EXO 15**

Allez Allez

ALLEZ ALLEZ
Tracks: / Allez allez / African queen.
7" Single: Released Jun '82, on Kamera, Deleted '88. Catalogue no: **ERA 010**

FLESH AND BLOOD
Tracks: / Flesh and blood / Time you cost me.
12" Single: Released Jan '83, on Virgin, by Virgin Records. Deleted '89. Catalogue no: **VS 565-12**
7" Single: Released Jan '83, on Virgin, by Virgin Records. Deleted '89. Catalogue no: **VS 565**

VALLEY OF THE KINGS
Tracks: / Valley of the kings / Wrap your legs around your head.
12" Single: Released Nov '82, on Virgin, by Virgin Records. Deleted Nov '85. Catalogue no: **VS 556-12**
7" Single: Released Nov '82, on Virgin, by Virgin Records. Deleted Nov '85. Catalogue no: **VS 556**

Allington, Valerie

STOP
Tracks: / Stop.
7" Single: Released Apr '83, on Carrere, Catalogue no: **CAR 269**
12" Single: Released Apr '83, on Carrere, Catalogue no: **CART 269**

Allison, George

AFRAID OF LOVE
Tracks: / Afraid of love / Little girl.
12" Single: Released Dec '82, on Redman International, Catalogue no: **GBM 1160**

NO ONE ELSE
Tracks: / No one else.
12" Single: Released Oct '82, on Gibbous, Catalogue no: **G101**

YOU WILL NEVER KNOW
Tracks: / You will never know.
12" Single: Released Sep '83, on Buzzin, Catalogue no: **BUZZ 001**

Allisons

Biographical details: John Alford and Bob Day became honorary Allison 'brothers' in 1961, when they represented the United Kingdom in the Eurovision Song Contest. Their self-penned entry *Are You Sure* came second both in the contest and in the charts. Two smaller hits followed, then the Allisons drifted into obscurity. (Bob McDonald).

ARE YOU SURE
Tracks: / Are you sure / Hey Paula.
7" Single: Released Oct '82, on Phonogram, by Phonogram Ltd. Deleted Oct '85. Catalogue no: **CUT 101**
7" Single: Released Jul '82, on Old Gold, by Old Gold Records. Catalogue no: **OG 9247**

ARE YOU SURE (ORIGINAL)
Tracks: / Are you sure.
7" Single: Released Feb '61, on Fontana, by Phonogram Ltd. Deleted '64. Catalogue no: **H 294**

LESSONS IN LOVE
Tracks: / Lessons in love.
7" Single: Released Feb '62, on Fontana, by Phonogram Ltd. Deleted '65. Catalogue no: **H 362**

WORDS
Tracks: / Words.
7" Single: Released May '61, on Fontana, by Phonogram Ltd. Deleted '64. Catalogue no: **H 304**

Allman Brothers

JESSICA
Tracks: / Jessica.
12" Single: Released '82, on Polydor, by Polydor Ltd. Catalogue no: **POSPX 607**
12" Single: Released Feb '88, on Old Gold, by Old Gold Records. Catalogue no: **OG 4046**
7" Single: Released Jul '84, on Old Gold, by Old Gold Records. Catalogue no: **OG 9437**

STRAIGHT FROM THE HEART
Tracks: / Straight from the heart / Leaving.
7" Single: Released Oct '81, on Arista, by BMG Records (UK). Deleted Oct '84. Catalogue no: **ARIST 432**

Allman, Ingrid

STOP WASTING YOUR TIME
Tracks: / Stop wasting your time / Sister Slow.
7" Single: Released May '81, on Polydor, by Polydor Ltd. Deleted May '84. Catalogue no: **POSP 277**
12" Single: Released May '81, on Polydor, by Polydor Ltd. Deleted May '84. Catalogue no: **POSPX 277**

Allnighters

LOVE AND AFFECTION
Tracks: / Love and affection.
7" Single: Released Jul '84, on A.1, by A.1 Records. Deleted '88. Catalogue no: **A1 288**
12" Single: Released Jul '84, on A.1, by A.1 Records. Deleted '88. Catalogue no: **12 A1 288**

TAKING A CHANCE ON LOVE
Tracks: / Taking a chance on love / Gloria.
7" Single: Released Apr '81, on Flamingo, by Airwave Records (USA). Deleted Apr '84. Catalogue no: **FM 15**

Allyson

HOW FAR TO GO TO LOVE
Tracks: / How far to go to love.
7" Single: Released Apr '88, on Acorn (1), Catalogue no: **ACOR 1**

Almond, Marc

Biographical details: Almond first came to prominence as half of Soft Cell, but during his time with the duo he also performed as Marc & The Mambas. Following Soft Cell's split, Almond embarked on a solo career, achieving a few minor hits like Stories Of Johnny and Tears Run Rings. In 1989 he teamed up with Gene Pitney to cover Something's Gotten Hold Of My Heart and returned to the No.1 spot for the first time since the 1981 best seller Tainted Love. (P.Williams 7/88)s.

BITTER SWEET
Tracks: / Bitter sweet / King of the fools / Tears run rings (Justin Strauss remix) (Not on 7".) / Bittersweet (12" version) (Not on 7".) / Bitter sweet (Big beat mix) (12" remix only.).
Note: Produced by Marc Almond and La Magia.
Special: Released Oct '88, on Parlophone, by EMI Records. Deleted Aug '89. Catalogue no: **12RS 6194**
12" Single: Released Oct '88, on Parlophone, by EMI Records. Deleted Aug '89. Catalogue no: **12R 6194**
12" Single: Released Oct '88, on Parlophone, by EMI Records. Deleted Aug '89. Catalogue no: **12RX 6194**
7" Single: Released Oct '88, on Parlophone, by EMI Records. Deleted Aug '89. Catalogue no: **R 6194**
CD 5": Released Oct '88, on Parlophone, by EMI Records. Deleted Aug '89. Catalogue no: **CDR 6194**
7" Single: Released Oct '88, on Parlophone, by EMI Records. Deleted Jun '89. Catalogue no: **RC 6194**
7" Single: Released Oct '88, on Parlophone, by EMI Records. Deleted Aug '89. Catalogue no: **RG 6194**
12" Single: Released Oct '88, on Parlophone, by EMI Records. Deleted Aug '89. Catalogue no: **12RG 6194**

BOY WHO CAME BACK
Tracks: / Boy who came back, The / Joey Demento.
10" single: Released Jun '84, on Some Bizzare, by Some Bizzare Records. Catalogue no: **BZS 2310**
7" Single: Released Jun '84, on Some Bizzare, by Some Bizzare Records. Deleted '87. Catalogue no: **BZS 23**

HOUSE IS HAUNTED, THE
Tracks: / House is haunted, The (On 7" only) / Broken bracelets / Cara a cara / Unchain my heart (part 1 of medley) / Burning boats (On 12" only) / Black heart (part 2 of medley) / Take my heart (part 3 of medley) / House is haunted, The (ectoplasmix) (On 12" only).
7" Set: Released Dec '85, on Some Bizzare, by Some Bizzare Records. Catalogue no: **GLOWD 1**
12" Single: Released Dec '85, on Some Bizzare, by Some Bizzare Records. Catalogue no: **GLOW 112**
7" Single: Released Jan '86, on Some Bizzare, by Some Bizzare Records. Deleted '89. Catalogue no: **GLOW 1**

IN YOUR BED Book & 7" single
Note: 150 page 7" sized book with many rare photos/drawings and full English & Italian lyrics to nearly 100 songs & full discography. Comes with 1-sided unreleased single 'In your bed', which is also in picture cover.
Special: Released Nov '87, on Stampa Alternative (Italy), Catalogue no: **SCONC 003**

LOVE LETTER
Tracks: / Love letters.
12" Single: Released Oct '85, on Some Bizzare, by Some Bizzare Records. Deleted May '88. Catalogue no: **BONK 212**
7" Single: Released Oct '85, on Some Bizzare, by Some Bizzare Records. Deleted '89. Catalogue no: **BONK 2**

LOVER SPURNED, A
Tracks: / Lover spurned, A / Kept boy / Lover spurned, A (12") / Lover spurned, A (radio version) (12" only.).
Cassingle: Released Oct '89, on Parlophone, by EMI Records. Catalogue no: **TCR 6229**
12" Single: Released Oct '89, on Parlophone, by EMI Records. Catalogue no: **203 527 6**
Cassingle: Released Oct '89, on Parlophone, by EMI Records. Catalogue no: **203 527 4**
CD 5": Released Oct '89, on Parlophone, by EMI Records. Catalogue no: **203 527 2**
12" Single: Released Oct '89, on Parlophone, by EMI Records. Catalogue no: **12R 6229**
7" Single: Released Oct '89, on Parlophone, by EMI Records. Catalogue no: **R 6229**
CD 5": Released Oct '89, on Parlophone, by EMI Records. Catalogue no: **CDR 6229**
7" Single: Released Oct '89, on Parlophone, by EMI Records. Catalogue no: **203 527 7**

MELANCHOLY ROSE
Tracks: / Melancholy rose / Gyp the blood / Pirate Jenny / Surabaya Johnny.
7" Set: on Virgin, by Virgin Records. Catalogue no: **GLOWD 4**

MOTHER FIST (12" SINGLE)
Tracks: / Mother fist / Two sailors on a beach / Hustler, The.
12" Single: Released Mar '87, on Some Bizzare, by Some Bizzare Records. Catalogue no: **GLOW 512**

ONLY THE MOMENT
Tracks: / Only the moment (Not on 12".) / Only the moment (ext.) (12" only.) / She took my soul in Istanbul (CD single only.) / She took my soul in Istanbul (12" version) (12" only.) / Real evil (Not on 12".).
7" Single: Released Mar '89, on Parlophone, by EMI Records. Deleted Aug '89. Catalogue no: **RC 6210**
CD 5": Released Mar '89, on Parlophone, by EMI Records. Deleted Aug '89. Catalogue no: **CDR 6210**
12" Single: Released Mar '89, on Parlophone, by EMI Records. Deleted Aug '89. Catalogue no: **12RS 6210**
12" Single: Released Mar '89, on Parlophone, by EMI Records. Deleted Aug '89. Catalogue no: **12R 6210**
7" Single: Released Mar '89, on Parlophone, by EMI Records. Deleted Aug '89. Catalogue no: **R 6210**

RUBY RED
Tracks: / Ruby red / I'm sick of your tasting of somebody else / Anarcoma (On 12" only) / Broken hearted and beautiful (On 12" only) / Jackal jackal (On 12" only).
12" Single: Released Oct '86, on Some Bizzare, by Some Bizzare Records. Deleted May '88. Catalogue no: **GLOW 312**
7" Single: Released Oct '86, on Some Bizzare, by Some Bizzare Records. Deleted May '88. Catalogue no: **GLOW 3**

SOMETHING'S GOTTEN HOLD OF MY HEART
Tracks: / Something's gotten hold of my heart / Frost comes tomorrow, The (12" & CD single only.) / Something's gotten hold of my heart.
Note: Produced by Bob Kraushaar. Arranged by Marc & La Magia. Special guest star Gene Pitney.
7" Single: Released Jan '89, on Parlophone, by EMI Records. Deleted Oct '89. Catalogue no: **RX 6201**
Special: Released Jan '89, on Parlophone, by EMI Records. Deleted Oct '89. Catalogue no: **12RS 6201**
12" Single: Released Jan '89, on Parlophone, by EMI Records. Deleted Oct '89. Catalogue no: **12R 6201**
CD 5": Released Jan '89, on Parlophone, by EMI Records. Deleted Oct '89. Catalogue no: **CDR 6201**
7" Single: Released Jan '89, on Parlophone, by EMI Records. Catalogue no: **R 6201**

STORIES OF JOHNNY (SINGLE)
Tracks: / Stories of johnny / Blond boy / Take my heart.
12" Single: Released Aug '85, on Some Bizzare, by Some Bizzare Records. Catalogue no: **BONK 112**
7" Single: Released Aug '85, on Some Bizzare, by Some Bizzare Records. Deleted '89. Catalogue no: **BONK 1**

TEARS RUN RINGS
Tracks: / Tears run rings / Everything I wanted love to be / Tears run rings (Justin Strauss mix) (12RX only.) / Tears run rings (La Magia dance mix) (12RX only.).
12" Single: Released Aug '88, on Parlophone, by EMI Records. Deleted Jun '89. Catalogue no: **12RS 6186**
12" Single: Released '88, on EMI (Germany), by EMI Records. Catalogue no: **2031086**
7" Single: Released Aug '88, on Parlophone, by EMI Records. Deleted Aug '89. Catalogue no: **R 6186**
7" Single: Released Aug '88, on Parlophone, by EMI Records. Deleted Jun '89. Catalogue no: **RX 6186**
12" Single: Released Aug '88, on Parlophone, by EMI Records. Deleted Jun '89. Catalogue no: **12RX 6186**
CD 5": Released Aug '88, on Parlophone, by EMI Records. Deleted Jun '89. Catalogue no: **CDR 6186**
12" Single: Released Aug '88, on Parlophone, by EMI Records. Deleted Aug '89. Catalogue no: **12R 6186**

TEARS RUN RINGS (IMPORT)
Tracks: / Tears run rings (just rite mix) / Tears run rings (just rite edit) / Tears run rings (acid tears dub) / Everything I wanted to love to be.
12" Single: Released Dec '88, on Capitol (USA), by Capitol (USA) Records. Catalogue no: **V 15418**

WOMAN'S STORY, A
Tracks: / Woman's story, A / For one moment / Heel, The / Salty dog / Plague, The / Little white cloud that cried, The / Just good friends.
12" Single: Released May '86, on Some Bizzare, by Some Bizzare Records. Catalogue no: **GLOW 212**
Cassingle: Released May '86, on Some Bizzare, by Some Bizzare Records. Catalogue no: **TGLOW 212**
7" Single: Released May '86, on Some Bizzare, by Some Bizzare Records. Deleted May '88. Catalogue no: **GLOW 2**

YOU HAVE
Tracks: / You have.
7" Single: Released Sep '84, on Some Bizzare, by Some Bizzare Records. Deleted '87. Catalogue no: **BZS 24**

Almost Brothers

ALMOST BROTHERS
Tracks: / Almost brothers.
7" EP: Released Oct '82, on Rat Race, by Rat Race Records. Catalogue no: **RAT 9**

BUM'S RUSH
Tracks: / Bum's rush.
7" Single: Released Jan '82, on Rat Race, by Rat Race Records. Catalogue no: **RAT 8**

Alone Again

DREAM COME TRUE
Tracks: / Dream come true / Smarter than the average bear / Drum the bear (on 12" only).
7" Single: Released Mar '85, on Polydor, by Polydor Ltd. Catalogue no: **ALG 2**

DRUM THE BEAT
Tracks: / Drum the beat.
7" Single: Released Dec '84, on All One, Catalogue no: **ALG 1**

Alpert, Herb

Biographical details: Herb Alpert is a rare example of a man successful as both recording artist and record executive. Even if his own discs had never sold he would still have been remembered - first as co-founder of the highly successful A & M label (with Jerry Moss, hence the name), second as the man who discovered the Carpenters. But his own discs did sell. *The Lonely Bull*, his label's third single, was released in 1962, reaching No 2 in his native USA and No 22 in Britain. Alpert played trumpet on this instrumental single, backed by his group, Tijuana Brass. This pattern was to be repeated on most subsequent recordings. After a two-year lull Herb Alpert & The Tijuana Brass hit the Top Ten on both sides of the Atlantic but with different tunes: *Taste Of Honey* reached No 7 in the US, *Spanish Flea* No 3 in the UK. During '66 and '67 the singles sold reasonably well but the ensemble's real strength came in the older middle-of-the-road album market. This was particularly true in the States, where the mid-60's saw Alpert performing exceptionally well on the album charts, riding the higher echelons of the list with several simultaneous successes. In 1968 the man surprised his public by singing. *This Guy's In Love With You*, an ultra-smoochy MoR ballad, gave him his first US No 1 and reached No 3 in Britain. A commercial gamble had paid off handsomely in the short term but, in the long term, may have been the cause of the ensuing decline in his recording fortunes: he had confused a previously loyal following. Deciding to spend the 70's concentrating on behind-the-scenes work with A & M, Alpert returned to the top of the American charts at the end of that decade with *Rise*, back in his old instrumental mould. Thereafter he aimed his music at the jazz-funk market where his records were critically acclaimed. (Bob MacDonald, 1984.)
The trumpeter, composer, arranger, producer and label boss was born in 1937 in Los Angeles and is one of the most popular and likeable entertainers in show business: working for him according to singer, pianist and songwriter Dave Frishberg, was first class all the way. With Lou Adler he managed the legendary surfers Jan & Dean; they also produced the novelty hit *Alley oop* in 1960 by Dante and the Evergreens (later Alpert allegedly said that the group was himself and Adler). He had played trumpet in the US Army; over dubbing experiments with a song called *Twinkle star* led to a quasi Mexican sound with bullfight/crowd noises dubbed in: the single was produced for $200, retitled *The lonely bull* in 1962 and led to a long series of hit albums and singles. He formed A&M records with Jerry Moss, and later abandoned the 'Ameriachi' style for straight MOR. His vocal on *This guy's in love with you* re-entered the UK chart three times. (Donald Clarke, July 1988).

CASINO ROYALE
Tracks: / Casino royale.
7" Single: Released Apr '67, on A&M, by A&M Records. Deleted '70. Catalogue no: **AMS 700**

COMPACT HITS: HERB ALPERT
Tracks: / Keep your eye on me / Diamonds / Rise / Rotation.
CD 5": Released Apr '88, on A&M, by A&M Records. Deleted Apr '88. Catalogue no: **AMCD 910**

DIAMONDS
Tracks: / Diamonds / Rocket to the moon.
Cassingle: Released May '87, on Breakout, by A&M Records. Catalogue no: **USATC**
7" Single: Released May '87, on Breakout, by A&M Records. Catalogue no: **USA 605**
12" Single: Released May '87, on Breakout, by A&M Records. Catalogue no: **USAT 605**

DIAMONDS (COOL SUMMER MIX)
Tracks: / Diamonds (cool summer mix) / Diamonds (12" dance mix) / Rocket to the moon.
12" Single: Released 6 Jun '87, on Breakout, by A&M Records. Deleted Mar '88. Catalogue no: **USAF 605**

I NEED YOU
Tracks: / I need you / Lady in my life, The.
7" Single: Released 5 Sep '88, on A&M, by A&M Records. Deleted Feb '89. Catalogue no: **AM 464**
12" Single: Released 5 Sep '88, on A&M, by A&M Records. Deleted Feb '89. Catalogue no: **AMY 464**

JERUSALEM
Tracks: / Jerusalem.
7" Single: Released Dec '70, on A&M, by A&M Records. Deleted '73. Catalogue no: **AMS 810**

KEEP YOUR EYE ON ME (SINGLE)
Tracks: / Keep your eye on me / Our song.
7" Single: Released Mar '87, on A&M, by A&M Records. Catalogue no: **AM 387**
12" Single: Released Mar '87, on A&M, by A&M Records. Deleted 1 Aug '88. Catalogue no: **AMY 387**

LONELY BULL, THE
Tracks: / Lonely bull, The.
7" Single: Released Jan '63, on Stateside, by EMI Records. Deleted '66. Catalogue no: **SS 138**

MAKING LOVE IN THE RAIN
Tracks: / Making love in the rain.
7" Single: Released Aug '87, on Breakout, by A&M Records. Catalogue no: **USA 608**
12" Single: Released Aug '87, on Breakout, by A&M Records. Catalogue no: **USAT 608**

RED HOT
Tracks: / Red hot / Interlude.
7" Single: Released Sep '80, on A&M, by A&M Records. Deleted '83. Catalogue no: **AMS 7557**

RISE (SINGLE)
Tracks: / Rise.
7" Single: Released Sep '85, on Old Gold, by Old Gold Records. Catalogue no: **OG 9540**
7" Single: Released Oct '79, on A&M, by A&M Records. Deleted '82. Catalogue no: **AMS 7465**

ROTATION
Tracks: / Rotation / Behind the rain.
7" Single: Released 19 Jan '80, on A&M, by A&M Records. Catalogue no: **AMS 7500**

ROUTE 101
Tracks: / Route 101 / Angel.
7" Single: Released Aug '82, on A&M, by A&M Records. Deleted Aug '85. Catalogue no: **AMS 8248**

SPANISH FLEA
Tracks: / Spanish flea.
7" Single: Released Dec '65, on Pye International, Deleted '68. Catalogue no: **7N 25335**

STREET LIFE
Tracks: / Street life / 1980.
7" Single: Released Mar '80, on A&M, by A&M Records. Deleted Mar '83. Catalogue no: **AMS 7511**
12" Single: Released Mar '80, on A&M, by A&M Records. Deleted Mar '83. Catalogue no: **AMSP 7511**

THIS GUY'S IN LOVE WITH YOU
Tracks: / This guy's in love with you.
7" Single: Released Jul '68, on A&M, by A&M Records. Deleted '71. Catalogue no: **AMS 727**

TIJUANA TAXI
Tracks: / Tijuana taxi.
7" Single: Released Mar '66, on Pye International, Deleted '69. Catalogue no: **7N 25352**

WITHOUT HER
Tracks: / Without her.
7" Single: Released Jun '69, on A&M, by A&M Records. Deleted '72. Catalogue no: **AMS 755**

Alpha

HAVE SOME FUN
Tracks: / Have some fun / Musical career.
7" Single: Released Nov '80, on Greensleeves, by Greensleeves Records. Deleted Nov '83. Catalogue no: **NICE 110**

Alpha Blondy

RASTA POUE
Tracks: / Rasta poue.
12" Single: Released Mar '85, on Syllart, by Earthworks Records. Deleted '88. Catalogue no: **SYLL 8312**

WE KEEP ON ROCKING
Tracks: / We keep on rocking.
12" Single: Released Mar '82, on Ambassador, Catalogue no: **SEXY 4**

Alphaville

BIG IN JAPAN
Tracks: / Big in Japan / Seeds.
7" Single: Released May '84, on WEA (International), by WEA Records. Deleted Jun '87. Catalogue no: **X 9505**
12" Single: Released May '84, on WEA (International), by WEA Records. Deleted Jan '88. Catalogue no: **X 9505T**

DANCE WITH ME
Tracks: / Dance with me.
7" Single: Released Apr '86, on WEA, by WEA Records. Deleted Jun '87. Catalogue no: **X 8747**
12" Single: Released Apr '86, on WEA, by WEA Records. Deleted Jun '87. Catalogue no: **X 8747T**

FOREVER YOUNG (SINGLE)
Tracks: / Forever young.
12" Single: Released Oct '84, on WEA, by WEA Records. Deleted Jun '87. Catalogue no: **X 9264T**
7" Single: Released Oct '84, on WEA, by WEA Records. Catalogue no: **X 9264**

NEXT GENERATION
Tracks: / Next generation.
12" Single: Released Nov '86, on WEA, by WEA Records. Catalogue no: **X 8643T**
7" Single: Released Nov '86, on WEA, by WEA Records. Catalogue no: **X 8643**

UNIVERSAL DADDY
Tracks: / Universal daddy / Next generation.
7" Single: Released Nov '86, on WEA, by WEA Records. Deleted Jun '87. Catalogue no: **X 8643**
12" Single: Released Nov '86, on WEA, by WEA Records. Deleted Jun '87. Catalogue no: **X 8643T**

Alphonso, Roland

Biographical details: ALPHONSO, Roland is a Jamaican tenor saxophonist and was founder member of the Skatalites, a ska instrumental outfit, with whom he was featured soloist on scores of records in the '60s, mostly at Studio One. He has released several collections and albums, the *Roll On* session being done recently for the NYC reggae specialist label Wackies. Donald Clarke 21 July 1988e.

AL CAPONE
Tracks: / Al Capone.
7" Single: on Trojan, by Trojan Records. Deleted May '88. Catalogue no: **TRO 9059**

Alpine

GEORGETOWN GIRL
Tracks: / Georgetown girl.
7" Single: Released Sep '85, on Hive, Catalogue no: **HIVE 5**
12" Single: Released Sep '85, on Hive, Catalogue no: **12HIVE 5**

Alston

TRY AGAIN
Tracks: / Try again / Get a little closer to the phone.
7" Single: Released Apr '85, on Sonet, by Sonet Records. Catalogue no: **SON 2280**

Alston, Frank

SUPERLOVER
Tracks: / Superlover.
12" Single: Released Aug '86, on Move, Catalogue no: **MS 13**

Alston, Gerald

ACTIVATED
Tracks: / Activated / Activated (version).
7" Single: Released Mar '89, on Motown, by BMG Records (UK). Catalogue no: **ZB 42681**
12" Single: Released Mar '89, on Motown, by BMG Records (UK). Catalogue no: **ZT 42682**
CD 5": Released Mar '89, on Motown, by BMG Records (UK). Catalogue no: **ZT 42682**

TAKE ME WHERE YOU WANT TO
Tracks: / Take me where you want to / Still in love with loving you.
7" Single: Released Dec '88, on Motown, by BMG Records (UK). Catalogue no: **ZB 42577**
12" Single: Released Dec '88, on Motown, by BMG Records (UK). Catalogue no: **ZT 42578**

Alta Moda

JULIAN
Tracks: / Julian / My millionaire / Julian (the final mix) (Only on 12" single.) / Julian (acoustic mix) (Only on 12" single.).
Note: Taken from the album Alta Moda on President -- PTLS 1096.
7" Single: Released Aug '88, on President, by President Records. Catalogue no: **PT 577**
12" Single: Released Jul '89, on President, by President Records. Catalogue no: **PT 12 577**

ALTERED IMAGES - BRING ME CLOSER (Released on Epic)

Altar Boys

BE BOP A LULA
Tracks: / Be bop a lula / Isn't it about time.
7" Single: Released Nov '82, on Sundance, by Sundance Records. Catalogue no: **SUND 002**

YOU REALLY GOT ME
Tracks: / You really got me.
7" Single: Released May '83, on Sundance, by Sundance Records. Catalogue no: **SUND 4**

Altar Ego

WAR
Tracks: / War.
7" Single: Released Sep '86, on Round World Discs, Catalogue no: **RWD 001**

Alterations

MY FAVOURITE ANIMALS
Tracks: / My favourite animals
7" Single: Released '86, on Beat-The-System, Catalogue no: **PAINT 01**

Altered Images

BRING ME CLOSER (see panel above)
Tracks: / Bring me closer.
7" Pic: Released Jun '83, on Epic, by CBS Records. Catalogue no: **WA 3398**
7" Single: Released May '83, on Epic, by CBS Records. Catalogue no: **A 3398**
12" Single: Released May '83, on Epic, by CBS Records. Catalogue no: **TA 3398**
12" Pic: Released Jun '83, on Epic, by CBS Records. Catalogue no: **WTA 3398**

DAY'S WAIT
Tracks: / Day's wait / Who cares.
7" Single: Released May '81, on Epic, by CBS Records. Deleted May '86. Catalogue no: **EPC 1167**

DEAD POP STARS
Tracks: / Dead pop stars / Sentimental
7" Single: Released 28 Mar '81, on Epic, by CBS Records. Catalogue no: **EPC A 1023**

DON'T TALK TO ME ABOUT LOVE (see panel below)
Tracks: / Don't talk to me about love / Last goodbye.
7" Single: Released Mar '83, on Epic, by CBS Records. Deleted '86. Catalogue no: **A 3083**

GREATEST ORIGINAL HITS
7" EP: Released Mar '83, on Epic, by CBS Records. Catalogue no: **EPC A 2617**

ALTERED IMAGES - DON'T TALK TO ME ABOUT LOVE (Released on Epic)

Altered Images - Happy Birthday (Released on Epic)

HAPPY BIRTHDAY (See panel above)
Tracks: / Happy birthday / So we go whispering / I could be happy / Dead pop stars / Day's way.
7" Single: Released '81, on Epic, by CBS Records. Catalogue no: **EPC A 1522**
Cassingle: Released Sep '82, on Epic, by CBS Records. Deleted '85. Catalogue no: **EPCA 40-2617**
12" Single: Released Oct '81, on Epic, by CBS Records. Deleted Oct '82. Catalogue no: **EPCA13 1522**

HAPPY BIRTHDAY (OLD GOLD)
Tracks: / Happy birthday.
7" Single: Released Jan '89, on Old Gold, by Old Gold Records. Catalogue no: **OG 9663**

I COULD BE HAPPY (See panel below)
Tracks: / I could be happy / Insects.
7" Single: Released 11 Dec '81, on Epic, by CBS Records. Catalogue no: **EPC A 1834**

LOVE TO STAY
Tracks: / Love to stay.
7" Single: Released Jul '83, on Epic, by CBS Records. Deleted '86. Catalogue no: **A 3582**

PINKY BLUE (SINGLE)
Tracks: / Pinky blue / Think that it might / Jump, jump.
7" Single: Released May '82, on Epic, by CBS Records. Deleted May '85. Catalogue no: **EPCA 2426**
12" Single: Released May '82, on Epic, by CBS Records. Deleted May '85. Catalogue no: **EPCA 132426**

SEE THOSE EYES
Tracks: / See those eyes / I've missed my train.
7" Single: Released 27 Mar '82, on Epic, by CBS Records. Catalogue no: **EPC A 2198**

SURPRISE ME
Tracks: / Surprise me / bring me closer.
7" Single: Released '83, on Epic, by CBS Records. Catalogue no: **A 3398**

Altered States (group)

DROWNING CHILDREN
Tracks: / Drowning children.
12" Single: Released Oct '88, on Ediesta, Catalogue no: **CALC 068T**

LOWLIFE
Tracks: / Low life.
12" Single: Released Feb '88, on Ediesta, Catalogue no: **CALC 046**

Alternative

IN NOMINE PATRI
Tracks: / In nomine patri.
7" Single: on Crass, by Crass Records. Catalogue no: **221984/8**

Alternative ...

ALTERNATIVE TENTACLES SAMPLER
7" Single: Released Jul '89, on Alternative Tentacles, by Alternative Tentacles Records. Catalogue no: **VIRUS 76**

Alternative Attack

NO TURNIN' BACK
Tracks: / No turnin' back.
7" Single: Released 11 Jun '87, on Loony Tunes, by Loony Tunes Records. Catalogue no: **TUNE 003**

Alternative Radio

CHANGE OF HEART
Tracks: / Change of heart / Butterflies in the rain.
12" Single: Released 22 Aug '88, on PRT, by Castle Communications Records. Catalogue no: **PYT 15**
7" Pic: Released 22 Aug '88, on PRT, by Castle Communications Records. Catalogue no: **PYS 15**

FIRST NIGHT (SINGLE)
Tracks: / First night / Emotional disaster.
7" Single: Released May '86, on Cold Harbour, by Cold Harbour Records. Catalogue no: **COLD 1001**

STRANGERS IN LOVE
Tracks: / Strangers in love / Summer '85.
7" Single: Released Jul '86, on Towerbell, Catalogue no: **TOW 92**

SWING OUT
Tracks: / Swing out / Everybody wants to be loved.
7" Pic: Released 20 Apr '88, on PRT, by Castle Communications Records. Catalogue no: **PYS 8**
12" Pic: Released 20 Apr '88, on PRT, by Castle Communications Records. Catalogue no: **PYT 8**

VALLEY OF EVERGREEN
Tracks: / What a dream / Valley of evergreen / Summer 85.
Note: extra track on 12" single "What a dream"
7" Single: Released Jan '87, on Cold Harbour, by Cold Harbour Records. Catalogue no: **COLD 3**
12" Single: Released Jan '87, on Cold Harbour, by Cold Harbour Records. Catalogue no: **COLD 3T**

Alternative TV

COMMUNICATE
Tracks: / Communicate / Obsessions.
7" Single: Released Sep '81, on I.R.S, Deleted Sep '84. Catalogue no: **PFP 1009**

LOVE & SEX
Tracks: / Love & sex.
12" Single: Released Jun '86, on Noiseville, Catalogue no: **V 002T**

MY BABY'S LAUGHING
Tracks: / My babys laughing / I look at her eyes / I had love in my hands.
7" Single: Released Aug '87, on Anagram, by Cherry Red Records. Catalogue no: **ANA 36**

WELCOME TO THE END OF FUN
Tracks: / Welcome to the end of fun.
12" Single: Released Mar '86, on Noiseville, Catalogue no: **V 001T**

Althia and Donna

UPTOWN TOP RANKING
Tracks: / Uptown top ranking.
7" Single: Released Jan '78, on Lightning, Catalogue no: **LIG 506**

Altitude

SIX NINE SHUFFLE
Tracks: / Six nine shuffle / Rhythm in blues.
7" Single: Released Feb '81, on Champagne Records, Deleted '88. Catalogue no: **FUNKY 2**

Alton and Johnny

HANG ON IN THERE BABY
Tracks: / Hang on in there baby.
7" Single: Released Jan '80, on Polydor, by Polydor Ltd. Deleted Jan '85. Catalogue no: **POSP 118**

Alton, Roy

DON'T GAMBLE WITH LOVE
Tracks: / Don't gamble with love.
12" Single: Released Oct '83, on Sunburn, by Orbitone Records. Catalogue no: **SBD 39**

GIRL I LOVE YOU
Tracks: / Girl I love you.
12" Single: Released Jul '83, on Sunburn, by Orbitone Records. Catalogue no: **SBD 35**

Altered Images - I Could be Happy (Released on Epic)

IF YOU WANT ME
Tracks: / If you want me / If you want me (part 2).
12" Single: Released Jun '82, on Island, by Island Records. Deleted '85. Catalogue no: **12WIP 6790**
7" Single: Released Jun '82, on Island, by Island Records. Deleted '85. Catalogue no: **WIP 6790**

IRON LADY
Tracks: / Iron lady.
12" Single: Released May '82, on Sunburn, by Orbitone Records. Catalogue no: **SBD 07**

MEDLEY
Tracks: / Medley.
12" Single: Released Jan '89, on W.E.M. International, Catalogue no: **W 0011**

MY MISTAKE
Tracks: / My mistake / Please don't make me cry.
12" Single: Released Nov '83, on Sunburn, by Orbitone Records. Catalogue no: **SUD 40**

OH, IT'S A LONG STORY
Tracks: / Oh, it's a long story.
12" Single: Released Sep '88, on W.E.M. International, Catalogue no: **WOO 11**

STAY ALIVE
Tracks: / Stay alive.
7" Single: Released Aug '85, on Sunburn, by Orbitone Records. Catalogue no: **SBD 50**

TELL THEM
Tracks: / Tell them.
12" Single: Released May '83, on Sunburn, by Orbitone Records. Catalogue no: **SBD 17**

WE SHALL OVERCOME
Tracks: / We shall overcome.
12" Single: Released Jan '85, on Sunburn, by Orbitone Records. Catalogue no: **SBD 48**

Alveoli

HOW MANY SUGARS
Tracks: / How many sugars.
12" Single: Released Jun '85, on Paladin, Catalogue no: **PALS 103 12**
7" Single: Released Jun '85, on Paladin, Catalogue no: **PALS 103**

Alvie

I'LL GO TO
Tracks: / I'll go to.
7" Single: Released Aug '83, on 46 Records (Germany), Catalogue no: **5101**

Alvin, Dave

FOURTH OF JULY
Tracks: / Fourth of July / You got me.
7" Single: Released May '87, on Demon, by Demon Records. Catalogue no: **D 1049**

Always, Billy

BACK ON TRACK
Tracks: / Back on track / Back on track (club version) / Back on track (hip hop mix) (Only on 12".) / Back on track (inst) (Only on 12".).
12" Single: Released Oct '88, on Epic, by CBS Records. Deleted 17 Apr '89. Catalogue no: **653113 6**
7" Single: Released Oct '88, on Epic, by CBS Records. Deleted 17 Apr '89. Catalogue no: **653113 7**
12" Single: Released Oct '88, on Epic, by CBS Records. Catalogue no: **653113 8**

Always (group)

ARIEL ATLAS
Tracks: / Dreams of leaving / Morning heights / Heavens / Flying display, The.
12" Single: Released Oct '86, on El, by Cherry Red Records. Catalogue no: **GPO 16 T**

METROLAND
Tracks: / Metroland / Arcade, The / W.C..
12" Single: Released Mar '87, on El, by Cherry Red Records. Catalogue no: **GPO 27 T**

THAMES VALLEY LEATHER CLUB
Tracks: / Thames Valley leather club / Amateur detection.
10" single: Released 14 Mar '88, on El, by Cherry Red Records. Catalogue no: **GPOT 34**

Always The Now

FROM DAWN TILL DUSK
Tracks: / From dawn till dusk.
7" Single: Released Jun '83, on Mayday, Deleted '84. Catalogue no: **SRT 4K5 115**

Aly

KISS IN THE DARK
Tracks: / Kiss in the dark.
7" Single: Released Nov '82, on Raffia,

Deleted '83. Catalogue no: **RAF 002**

YOU WERE MY EVERYTHING
Tracks: / You were my everything.
7" Single: Released Nov '82, on Raffia, Deleted '83. Catalogue no: **RAF 003**

Amanda

CRY OUT IN THE NIGHT
Tracks: / Cry out in the night.
12" Single: Released Aug '87, on Rise, Catalogue no: **RISET 5**

Amara, Adrian

DIAMONDS
Tracks: / Diamonds.
7" Single: Released Aug '84, on Diamonds, by President Records. Catalogue no: **PT 529**

Amayenge

PEEL SESSIONS:AMAYENGE
12" Single: Released Feb '89, on Strange Fruit, by Strange Fruit Records. Catalogue no: **SFPS 067**

Amazing Bavarian

LIBERTY BELL
Tracks: / Liberty bell / Colonel Bogey.
7" Single: Released Dec '81, on Penthouse, by Penthouse Records. Catalogue no: **PENT 11**

Amazing Noel Bon Band

GRANDMA GOT RUN OVER BY A REINDEER
Tracks: / Grandma got run over by a reindeer / Lonely.
7" Single: Released Nov '83, on A2B, Catalogue no: **ATB 001**

Amazulu

ALL OVER THE WORLD
Tracks: / All over the world / Moonlight romance (dub) / After tonight (On 12" only).
12" Single: Released Nov '86, on Island, by Island Records. Deleted Jul '87. Catalogue no: **12IS 310**
7" Single: Released Nov '86, on Island, by Island Records. Catalogue no: **IS 310**

CAIRO
Tracks: / Cairo.
7" Single: Released Feb '83, on Towerbell, Catalogue no: **TOW 35**
12" Single: Released Feb '83, on Towerbell, Catalogue no: **12 TOW 35**

DON'T YOU JUST KNOW IT
Tracks: / Don't you just know it.
12" Single: Released Nov '85, on Island, by Island Records. Deleted Jun '87. Catalogue no: **12IS 233**
7" Single: Released Nov '85, on Island, by Island Records. Deleted Jul '87. Catalogue no: **IS 233**

EXCITABLE
Tracks: / Excitable.
7" Pic: Released Aug '85, on Island, by Island Records. Deleted Jun '87. Catalogue no: **ISP 201**
12" Single: Released Aug '85, on Island, by Island Records. Deleted Jun '87. Catalogue no: **12IS 201**
12" Single: Released Aug '85, on Island, by Island Records. Deleted Jun '87. Catalogue no: **12ISX 201**
7" Single: Released Aug '85, on Island, by Island Records. Deleted Jun '87. Catalogue no: **IS 201**

MONTEGO BAY
Tracks: / Montego bay / Only love.
7" Single: Released Aug '86, on Island, by Island Records. Catalogue no: **IS 293**
12" Single: Released Aug '86, on Island, by Island Records. Deleted Jul '87. Catalogue no: **12IS 293**

MONY MONY
Tracks: / Mony mony / Mony mony / Mony mony instrumental.
12" Single: Released Sep '87, on EMI, by EMI Records. Deleted 31 Jul '88. Catalogue no: **12EM 32**
7" Single: Released Oct '87, on EMI, by EMI Records. Deleted Apr '88. Catalogue no: **EMP 32**
7" Single: Released Sep '87, on EMI, by EMI Records. Deleted 31 Jul '88. Catalogue no: **EM 32**

MOONLIGHT ROMANCE
Tracks: / Moonlight romance.
7" Single: Released Oct '84, on Island, by Island Records. Deleted Jul '87. Catalogue no: **IS 182**
12" Single: Released Oct '84, on Island, by Island Records. Deleted Jun '87. Catalogue no: **12IS 182**

SMILEY STYLEE
Tracks: / Smiley stylee.
7" Single: Released Jul '83, on Towerbell, Catalogue no: **TOW 40**

THINGS THE LONELY DO, THE
Tracks: / Things the lonely do / Sez who.
12" Single: Released Mar '86, on Island, by Island Records. Deleted Jul '87. Catalogue no: **12ISG 267**
7" Single: Released Mar '86, on Island, by Island Records. Deleted '87. Catalogue no: **IS 267**
7" Pic: Released Mar '86, on Island, by Island Records. Deleted '87. Catalogue no: **ISP 267**
12" Single: Released Mar '86, on Island, by Island Records. Deleted '87. Catalogue no: **12IS 267**

TO GOOD TO BE FORGOTTEN
Tracks: / Too good to be forgotten / Too good to be forgotten (megamix) (On 12" only) / Too good to be forgotten (hitmix) (On 12" only) / Sez who.
12" Single: Released Jun '86, on Island, by Island Records. Catalogue no: **12ISD 284**
7" Single: Released May '86, on Island, by Island Records. Deleted '89. Catalogue no: **IS 284**
7" Pic: Released Jun '86, on Island, by Island Records. Deleted '87. Catalogue no: **ISP 284**

WONDERFUL WORLD, BEAUTIFUL PEOPLE
Tracks: / Wonderful world, beautiful people / Wonderful world, beautiful people (Instrumental) / Wonderful world, beautiful people (Radio version).
7" Single: Released 7 Dec '87, on EMI, by EMI Records. Deleted 31 Jul '88. Catalogue no: **EMX 38**
12" Single: Released 28 Nov '87, on EMI, by EMI Records. Deleted 31 Jul '88. Catalogue no: **12 EM 38**
12" Single: Released 7 Dec '87, on EMI, by EMI Records. Deleted 31 Jul '88. Catalogue no: **12 EMX 38**
7" Single: Released 28 Nov '87, on EMI, by EMI Records. Deleted 31 Jul '88. Catalogue no: **EM 38**

Amazulu, Annie

SUGAR SUGAR
Tracks: / Sugar sugar.
12" Single: Released Sep '89, on Imperative, Catalogue no: **TIV 001**
7" Single: Released Sep '89, on Imperative, Catalogue no: **7TIV 0001**

Ambar

LOVE MANIAC
Tracks: / Love maniac / Love maniac (part 2).
7" Single: Released Feb '80, on Polydor, by Polydor Ltd. Deleted '83. Catalogue no: **POSP 120**

Ambassador

LIFE'S RIDDLE
Tracks: / Life's riddle.
12" Single: Released Mar '85, on Dubplate, Catalogue no: **OZE 01**

Ambassador 277

POP UP MAN, THE
Tracks: / Pop up man, The / Valediction.
10" single: Released 14 Mar '88, on El, by Cherry Red Records. Catalogue no: **GPOT 37**

Ambassadors Of Funk

ANOTHER SIDE TO YOU
Tracks: / Another side to you / Ambassadors megamix.
12" Single: Released Mar '89, on Living Beat, by Living Beat Records. Catalogue no: **SMASH 4**
7" Single: Released Apr '89, on Living Beat, by Living Beat Records. Catalogue no: **7SMASH 4**

JAMAICAN HOUSE REVENGE
Tracks: / Jamaican house revenge.
12" Single: Released Oct '89, on Living Beat, by Living Beat Records. Catalogue no: **SCAM 2**

MY MIND'S MADE UP (Featuring rap by Greg Edwards)
Tracks: / My mind's made up / Just a groove / Everybody (Only on 12" version.).
7" Single: Released Nov '88, on Living Beat, by Living Beat Records. Catalogue no: **7 SMASH 1**
12" Single: Released Nov '88, on Living Beat, by Living Beat Records. Catalogue no: **SMASH 1**

Ambatone

PARTY TIME
Tracks: / Party time / Saxaphone party.
12" Single: Released Aug '86, on Firm (1), Catalogue no: **FR 222**

Amber

DY-NO-MITE
Tracks: / Dy-no-mite / Take your time.
7" Single: Released May '80, on EMI, by EMI Records. Deleted May '85. Catalogue no: **EMI 5072**

Ambience

MISS YOU
Tracks: / Miss you / Gone.
7" Single: Released Aug '86, on Mr.Sam, by Mr.Sam Music. Catalogue no: **SAS 105**

Ambient

DREAM
Tracks: / Dream.
12" Single: Released 5 Jun '89, on Gee Street, by Gee Street Records. Catalogue no: **UNKNOWN**

Ambitious Beggars

MAN IN A SUIT
Tracks: / Man in a suit.
7" Single: Released Jan '88, on Whippet Shed, Catalogue no: **WHIPPET 001**

WELCOME
Tracks: / Welcome.
12" Single: Released Nov '88, on Ugly Man, by Ugly Man Records. Catalogue no: **UGLY 10T**

Ambitious Lovers

LOVE OVERLAP
Tracks: / Love overlap (7" edit) / It only has to happen once / Love overlap (stretched out-long mix) (12" only) / Love overlap (stuck in love mix) (12" only).
12" Single: Released 3 Oct '88, on Virgin, by Virgin Records. Catalogue no: **VST 1128**
7" Single: Released 3 Oct '88, on Virgin, by Virgin Records. Catalogue no: **VS 1128**

Ambrosia

BIGGEST PART OF ME
Tracks: / Biggest part of me / Living on my own.
7" Single: Released May '80, on Warner Bros., by WEA Records. Deleted May '83. Catalogue no: **K 17611**

HOW CAN YOU LOVE ME
Tracks: / How can you love me / Fool like me.
7" Single: Released May '82, on Warner Bros., by WEA Records. Catalogue no: **K 17933**
7" Pic: Released May '82, on Warner Bros., by WEA Records. Catalogue no: **K 17933P**

Amebix

ENEMY, THE
Tracks: / Enemy, The.
7" Single: Released Sep '82, on Spiderleg, Catalogue no: **SDL 6**

WINTER
Tracks: / Winter.
7" Single: Released Feb '83, on Spiderleg, Catalogue no: **SDL 10**

Amen Corner

BEND ME SHAPE ME
Tracks: / Bend me shape me.
7" Single: Released 17 Jan '68, on Deram, by London Records. Deleted Jan '71. Catalogue no: **DM 172**
7" Single: Released Oct '80, on Decca, by Decca Records. Deleted '88. Catalogue no: **F 13897**

BEND ME SHAPE ME (OLD GOLD)
Tracks: / Bend me shape me.
7" Single: Released Oct '83, on Old Gold, by Old Gold Records. Catalogue no: **OG 9354**

GIN HOUSE BLUES
Tracks: / Gin house blues.
7" Single: Released 26 Jul '67, on Deram, by London Records. Catalogue no: **DM 136**

HALF AS NICE (OLD GOLD)
Tracks: / Half as nice.
7" Single: Released Jan '85, on Old Gold, by Old Gold Records. Catalogue no: **OG 9469**

HELLO SUZIE
Tracks: / Hello Susie.
7" Single: Released 25 Jun '69, on Immediate, Catalogue no: **IM 081**

HIGH IN THE SKY
Tracks: / High in the sky.
7" Single: Released 31 Jul '68, on Deram, by London Records. Catalogue no: **DM 197**

(IF PARADISE IS) HALF AS NICE
Tracks: / If paradise is half as nice.
7" Single: Released 29 Jan '69, on Immediate, Catalogue no: **IM 073**
7" Single: Released 14 Feb '76, on Immediate, Catalogue no: **IMS 103**

WORLD OF BROKEN HEARTS
Tracks: / World of broken hearts.
7" Single: Released 11 Oct '67, on Deram, by London Records. Catalogue no: **DM 151**

America (group)

BORDER
Tracks: / Border / Sometimes lovers.
7" Single: Released Jul '83, on Capitol, by EMI Records. Deleted '88. Catalogue no: **CL 301**

HORSE WITH NO NAME, A
Tracks: / Horse with no name, A.
7" Single: Released Dec '71, on Warner Bros., by WEA Records. Deleted '74. Catalogue no: **K 16128**

HORSE WITH NO NAME, A (OLD GOLD)
Tracks: / Horse with no name, A./ Ventura highway.
7" Single: Released Sep '85, on Old Gold, by Old Gold Records. Catalogue no: **OG 9525**

VENTURA HIGHWAY
Tracks: / Ventura Highway.
7" Single: Released 25 Nov '72, on Warner Bros., by WEA Records. Catalogue no: **K 16219**

YOU CAN DO MAGIC
Tracks: / You can do magic.
7" Single: Released 6 Nov '82, on Capitol, by EMI Records. Catalogue no: **CL 264**

American Breed

BEND ME SHAPE ME
Tracks: / Bend me shape me.
7" Single: Released 7 Feb '68, on Stateside, by EMI Records. Catalogue no: **SS 2078**

American Buzz

QUEEN OF ILLUSION
Tracks: / Queen of illusion.
7" Single: Released Jul '84, on Plaza, by Plaza Records. Catalogue no: **PLAZA 010**
12" Single: Released Jul '84, on Plaza, by Plaza Records. Catalogue no: **PLAZA T 010**

American Dance Band

SWEET SWEET MUSIC
Tracks: / Sweet sweet music / Get it on.
12" Single: Released May '83, on DJM, Catalogue no: **DJR 1**
7" Single: Released May '83, on DJM, Catalogue no: **DJS 1**

American Express

COLUMBIA SUNRISE
Tracks: / Columbia sunrise / To the limit / Into Stella.
12" Single: Released Jun '82, on Superville, Deleted Jun '85. Catalogue no: **SUP 001**

American Fade

I'M ALIVE
Tracks: / I'm alive.
12" Single: Released Feb '83, on Proto, by Proto Records. Catalogue no: **ENAT 105**
7" Single: Released Mar '83, on Proto, by Proto Records. Catalogue no: **ENA 105**

American Girls

AMERICAN GIRLS (SINGLE)
Tracks: / American girls.
12" Single: Released Aug '86, on I.R.S, Catalogue no: **IRMT 117**
7" Single: Released Aug '86, on I.R.S, Catalogue no: **IRM 117**

American Heroes

(JUST) WALKAWAY
Tracks: / (Just) walkaway.
7" Single: Released Aug '87, on GFM, Catalogue no: **GFM 114**
12" Single: Released Aug '87, on GFM, Catalogue no: **GFMT 114**

American Ruse

I NEED YOU (SONIC REDUCTION)
Tracks: / I need you (sonic reduction) / Death by the gun.
7" Single: Released Aug '89, on Shakin' Street, Catalogue no: **YEAH HUP 003**

Americans

DISNEYWORLD
Tracks: / Disneyworld / Love bombing.
7" Single: Released Feb '82, on Eagle (West Germany), by Bear Family Records (Germany). Catalogue no: **ERS 013**

Ameritz

WE SHOULD BE TOGETHER
Tracks: / We should be together / Love will take us higher.
7" Single: Released Jul '82, on Lucky Seven, Deleted '85. Catalogue no: **LUCKY**

001

Ames, Bob

NOBODY BUT ME
Tracks: / Nobody but me / When the sun shines.
7" Single: Released Jun '82, on JSO, Deleted Jun '87. Catalogue no: **EAT 14**

Ames Brothers

NAUGHTY LADY OF SHADY LANE
Tracks: / Naughty lady of Shady Lane.
7" Single: Released 4 Feb '55, on H.M.V., by EMI Records. Catalogue no: **B 10800**

Amiet, Julie

MUSIC IS OUR FREEDOM
Tracks: / Music is our freedom.
7" Single: Released Jun '83, on Precious Organisation, by Precious Organisation. Catalogue no: **AVE 5**

TONIGHT
Tracks: / Tonight.
7" Single: Released Sep '81, on Precious Organisation, by Precious Organisation. Catalogue no: **AVE 1**

Amin Peck

GIRLS ON ME
Tracks: / Girls on me / Anxiety / Coda.
12" Single: Released Jun '82, on Connection, by Connection Records. Catalogue no: **CONT 8204**

LOVE DISGRACE
Tracks: / Love disgrace.
7" Single: Released Mar '82, on Connection, by Connection Records. Catalogue no: **CON 8201**

Amion

I HEAR YOU KNOCKING
Tracks: / I hear you knocking / Pizza walk.
12" Single: Released 23 May '87, on Uptown Records, by Uptown Records. Catalogue no: **12 ORT**
7" Single: Released 23 May '87, on Uptown Records, by Uptown Records. Catalogue no: **7 URT**

Amir

LINES OF LOVE
Tracks: / Lines of love.
12" Single: Released Feb '87, on Pink Pop, Catalogue no: **POP 003**

Amlak

CHRISTMAS IS HERE
Tracks: / Christmas is here.
7" Single: Released Dec '83, on Roots Music, Catalogue no: **RM 3**
12" Single: Released Dec '83, on Roots Music, Catalogue no: **12 RAM 3**

Ammonites

DRESSED TO KILL
Tracks: / Dressed to kill / Big eaters.
7" Single: Released Feb '81, on Red Rat, Deleted Feb '84. Catalogue no: **RRR 402**

Amnesia

IBIZA
Tracks: / Ibiza.
7" Single: Released Mar '89, on Debut, by Skratch Records. Catalogue no: **DEBT 3069**
12" Single: Released Mar '89, on Debut, by Skratch Records. Catalogue no: **DEBTX 3069**

IT'S A DREAM
Tracks: / It's a dream / It's a reality.
12" Single: Released Oct '89, on Debut, by Skratch Records. Catalogue no: **DEBTX 3082**

Amoo, Chris

NO CHOIR OF ANGELS
Tracks: / No choir of angels / Love talk.
7" Single: Released Mar '84, on EMI, by EMI Records. Catalogue no: **EMI 5455**

THIS MUST BE LOVE
Tracks: / This must be love / You'll never know what you're missing.
7" Single: Released Apr '81, on Precision (1), Deleted Apr '86. Catalogue no: **PAR 118**

Ampage

D-DAY
Special: Released Dec '87, on Iron Works (USA), by Azra International (USA). Catalogue no: **IW 1025**

Amphibious

TWIGHLIGHT SMILE
Tracks: / Twighlight smile.

7" Single: Released Sep '82, on Crammed Discs, by Crammed Discs. Catalogue no: **A 001**

Amps, Kym

YOU DON'T KNOW MY NAME
Tracks: / You don't know my name.
7" Single: Released Feb '85, on Division, Catalogue no: **DVN 501**

Amuzement Park

GROOVE YOUR BLUES AWAY
Tracks: / Groove your blues away.
12" Single: Released Aug '82, on Satril, by Satril Records. Catalogue no: **12 SAT 501**
7" Single: Released Aug '82, on Satril, by Satril Records. Catalogue no: **7 SAT 501**

Amy

SMALL TALK
Tracks: / Small talk / I'm the best thing that happened to me.
7" Single: Released Aug '80, on Earlobe, by Earlobe Records. Deleted '83. Catalogue no: **ELS 2**

Ana

SHY BOYS
Tracks: / Shy boy / Love is the winner.
12" Single: Released Jul '87, on Epic, by CBS Records. Catalogue no: **650858 6**
7" Single: Released Aug '87, on Epic, by CBS Records. Catalogue no: **65058 7**

Anabas

BARRICADES
Tracks: / Barricades / Dream dance.
7" Single: Released Nov '83, on Flame On, Catalogue no: **FLAME 3**

Analysis

SURFACE TENSION/CONNECTIONS
7" Single: Released Nov '81, on Survival (1), by Survival Records. Catalogue no: **SUR 003**

Anaxagorou, James

LITTLE BALLERINA
Tracks: / Little ballerina / Make believe.
7" Single: Released Oct '81, on Anaza, Deleted Oct '84. Catalogue no: **JADV 100**

And All Because The

IF YOU RISK NOTHING
Tracks: / If you risk nothing.
7" Single: Released Jan '88, on Sweet Release, Catalogue no: **SWEET 2**

NOT THAT KIND OF GIRL
Tracks: / Not that kind of girl.
12" Single: Released Jun '89, on Paint It Red, Catalogue no: **RED 002**

And Also The Trees

CRITICAL DISTANCE, THE
Tracks: / Critical distance, The / Scythe and spade, The / Renegade, The (Original version by Ton ton Macoutes).
12" Single: Released Jun '87, on Reflex, by Reflex Records. Catalogue no: **12 RE 12**

HOUSE OF THE HEART
Tracks: / House of heart.
7" Single: Released May '88, on Reflex, by Reflex Records. Catalogue no: **RE 014**
12" Single: Released May '88, on Reflex, by Reflex Records. Catalogue no: **12RE 014**
CD 5": Released May '88, on Reflex, by Reflex Records. Catalogue no: **RE 014 CD**

LADY D'ARBANVILLE
Tracks: / Lady D'Arbanville.
CD 5": Released Jun '89, on Reflex, by Reflex Records. Catalogue no: **REO 15 CD**
12" Single: Released 27 Feb '89, on Reflex, by Reflex Records. Catalogue no: **12 RE 15**

ROOM LIVES IN LUCY, A 3 Track EP
Tracks: / Room lives in Lucy, A.
12" Single: Released Jan '85, on Reflex, by Reflex Records. Catalogue no: **12 RE 8**

SECRET SEA, (THE)
Tracks: / Secret sea, The.
12" Single: Released Jun '84, on Reflex, by Reflex Records. Catalogue no: **12 RE 6**
7" Single: Released May '84, on Reflex, by Reflex Records. Catalogue no: **RE 3**

SHALETOWN
Tracks: / Shaletown / L'unica strada.
12" Single: Released Nov '87, on Reflex, by Reflex Records. Catalogue no: **12 RE 13**

SHANTELL
Tracks: / Shantell.
7" Single: Released Nov '84, on Reflex, by Reflex Records. Catalogue no: **FS 9**

And Indians

OPERA OF LOVE
Tracks: / Opera of love.
7" Single: Released May '84, on A Record Company, Catalogue no: **ARC 001**

And So To Bed (group)

JUST DESSERTS
Tracks: / Just desserts / Plaindom.
7" Single: Released Aug '87, on Timebox, Catalogue no: **TARDIS 005**

And Why Not

RESTLESS DAYS (SHE SCREAMS OUT LOUD)
7" Single: Released Jul '89, on Island, by Island Records. Catalogue no: **IS 426**
CD 5": Released Jul '89, on Island, by Island Records. Catalogue no: **CID 426**

CARL ANDERSON - BUTTERCUP (Released on CBS)

12" Single: Released Jul '89, on Island, by Island Records. Catalogue no: **12IS 426**
Cassingle: Released Jul '89, on Island, by Island Records. Catalogue no: **CIS 426**

Anderson, Andy

WAR PEACE
Tracks: / War peace.
12" Single: Released May '89, on Sure Spin, Catalogue no: **SPN 009**

Anderson, Angry

CALLING
Tracks: / Calling.
7" Single: Released Feb '89, on Music For Nations, by Music For Nations Records. Catalogue no: **YUM 116**
12" Single: Released Feb '89, on Music For Nations, by Music For Nations Records. Catalogue no: **12 YUM 116**

SUDDENLY
Tracks: / Suddenly.
7" Single: Released Nov '88, on Food For Thought, by Music For Nations Records. Catalogue no: **YUM 113**

Anderson, Bill

MISTER PEEPERS
Tracks: / Mister peepers / How married are you mary ann.
7" Single: Released May '81, on Bulldog Records, by President Records. Deleted May '86. Catalogue no: **BD 21**

Anderson, Carl

BUTTERCUP (see panel above)
Tracks: / Buttercup (radio edit) / Amour / Buttercup / Magic.
12" Single: Released '87, on CBS, by CBS Records. Catalogue no: **MKHAN 45**
7" Single: Released '87, on CBS, by CBS Records. Catalogue no: **KHAN 45**

BUTTERCUP (OLD GOLD)
Tracks: / Buttercup.
12" Single: Released Nov '87, on Old Gold, by Old Gold Records. Catalogue no: **OG 4026**

Anderson, Dean

DON'T STOP
12" Single: Released Oct '87, on Trax (USA), Catalogue no: **TX 149**

Anderson, Gregory

MY LADY
Tracks: / My lady.
12" Single: Released Mar '89, on New World, by President Records. Catalogue no: **NW 001**

Anderson, Harley

WHATEVER YOU BELIEVE
Tracks: / Whatever you believe (studio version) / Whatever you believe (live) / Deep is my yearning (Only on 12" version.).
12" Single: Released Nov '88, on Epic, by CBS Records. Deleted 17 Apr '89. Catalogue no: **PEEPST 1**
7" Single: Released Nov '88, on Epic, by CBS Records. Deleted 17 Apr '89. Catalogue no: **PEEPS 1**

Anderson, Ian

Biographical details: For 20 years Ian Anderson led Jethro Tull to international triumphs. Formed at the tail-end of psychedelia in 1968, the band has survived all the changing faces of the rock scene to become part of the fabric of British music. Anderson's first solo album, Walk Into Light -- released in 1983 -- features arrangements well outside the Jethro Tull formula: "I needed to get off the treadmill for a few months," he said at the time. (Chrysalis Records, 1983.).

FLY BY NIGHT
Tracks: / Fly by night / End game.
7" Single: Released '83, on Chrysalis, by Chrysalis Records. Deleted '87. Catalogue no: **CHS 2746**

Anderson, John

BIG BANDS ARE BACK
Tracks: / Big bands are back.
7" Single: Released Jun '84, on Emerald, by Emerald Records. Deleted '88. Catalogue no: **MOD 004**

CAGE OF FREEDOM
Tracks: / Cage of freedom / Workers' dance.
12" Single: Released Dec '84, on CBS, by CBS Records. Catalogue no: **TX 4862**
7" Single: Released Dec '84, on CBS, by CBS Records. Catalogue no: **A 4862**

GLENN MILLER MEDLEY, THE
Tracks: / Glenn Miller medley, The.
12" Single: Released Nov '85, on Priority, by Priority Records. Deleted Oct '87. Catalogue no: **12GLEN 1**
7" Single: Released Nov '85, on Priority, by Priority Records. Deleted Oct '87. Catalogue no: **GLEN 1**

NON-STOP COPS
Tracks: / Non-stop cops / Glenn Miller Medley, The.
12" Single: Released Jul '87, on Priority, by Priority Records. Deleted Sep '89. Catalogue no: **12POLICE 1**
7" Single: Released Jul '87, on Priority, by Priority Records. Catalogue no: **POLICE 1**

SWINGIN'
Tracks: / Swingin'.
7" Single: Released Jul '83, on Warner Bros., by WEA Records. Catalogue no: **W 9788**

Anderson, Jon

ALL IN A MATTER OF TIME
Tracks: / All in a matter of time / Spider.
7" Single: Released Jun '82, on Polydor, by Polydor Ltd. Deleted Jun '85. Catalogue no: **POSP 465**

EASIER SAID THAN DONE
Tracks: / Easier said than done.
7" Single: Released Nov '85, on Elektra (USA), by Elektra Records (USA). Deleted Jan '88. Catalogue no: **EKR 31**
12" Single: Released Nov '85, on Elektra (USA), by Elektra Records (USA). Deleted Jan '88. Catalogue no: **EKR 31 T**

HOLD ON TO LOVE
Tracks: / Hold on to love / Sundancing / In a lifetime (extra track on 12".).
CD 5": Released 6 Jun '88, on Epic, by CBS Records. Deleted Jan '89. Catalogue no: **651514 2**
7" Single: Released May '88, on Epic, by CBS Records. Deleted Jan '89. Catalogue

no: 651514 7
12" Single: Released May '88, on Epic, by CBS Records. Deleted Jan '89. Catalogue no: **651514 6**

IS IT ME
Tracks: / Is it me / Top of the world (glass bead song) / For you (12" only).
12" Single: Released 15 Aug '88, on Epic, by CBS Records. Deleted 17 Apr '89. Catalogue no: **652947 6**
CD 5": Released 15 Aug '88, on Epic, by CBS Records. Deleted 17 Apr '89. Catalogue no: **652947 2**
7" Single: Released 15 Aug '88, on Epic, by CBS Records. Deleted 17 Apr '89. Catalogue no: **652947 7**

SOME ARE BORN
Tracks: / Some are born / Days.
7" Single: Released Oct '80, on Atlantic, by WEA Records. Deleted Oct '83. Catalogue no: **K 11619**

SURRENDER
Tracks: / Surrender / Spider.
7" Single: Released Apr '82, on Polydor, by Polydor Ltd. Deleted '85. Catalogue no: **POSP 393**

TAKE YOUR TIME
Tracks: / Take your time / Heart of the matter.
7" Single: Released Jan '81, on Atlantic, by WEA Records. Deleted Jan '84. Catalogue no: **K11641**

Anderson, Laurie

Biographical details: Laurie was born in 1950; a composer, singer, violinist and performance artist, she was a resident of the lower Manhatten loft scene in the early 1970's, began as a sculptor and presented a 12 hour long audio-visual experience. *The life and times of Joseph Stalin* at the Brooklyn Academy of Music in 1973. Her eight minute single *O Superman* (from Big Science) was voted most likely to clear dance floors by the brain damaged disco generation in the UK, but reached No.2 here anyway in 1982. Her 1983 album *Mr Heartbreak* is a good introduction to her work for the fainthearted. Much of her work is part of the spectacular *United States*, recorded live in 1984, issued on five discs or four tapes with 76 titled sections, using multi tracking synthesisers, bagpipes, digital electric violin, backing vocalists and much else. There are numerous themes in Anderson's work but no arguments. She appears to be obsessed by the passing of time, about dreams, technology and its threat, communication, language and about her status and function as an artist. (Donald Clarke, July 1988)
This American singer, multi-instrumentalist and performance artist shot to prominence in 1981 with her eight minute single *O Superman*. Originally released by New York indie label One Ten Records, it was picked up by Warner Bros. and became an underground success in the States but shot to No. 2 in Britain. Nobody was really sure whether this stunning single was the greatest record ever made or just an enjoyable one off novelty. British listeners seemed to decide the latter, for the record was on the chart for a mere six weeks, one of the shortest ever totals for a No. 2 hit. Her *Big science* album entered the Top 30 the following year, but Anderson has been unable to regain the interest caused by the highly original *O Superman*. (Bob MacDonald, 1984).

BIG SCIENCE (SINGLE)
Tracks: / Big science / Example 22.
7" Single: Released Nov '82, on Warner Bros., by WEA Records. Deleted Nov '85. Catalogue no: **K 17941**

LANGUAGE IS A VIRUS FROM OUTER SPACE
Tracks: / Language is a virus from outer space (edit) / White.
12" Single: Released May '86, on Warner Bros., by WEA Records. Deleted Jun '87. Catalogue no: **W 8701T**
7" Single: Released May '86, on Warner Bros., by WEA Records. Deleted Jun '87. Catalogue no: **W 8701**

LET X=X
Tracks: / Let X=X.
7" Single: Released Jun '82, on Warner Bros., by WEA Records. Catalogue no: **K 179562**

O SUPERMAN
Tracks: / O superman.
7" Single: Released Oct '81, on Warner Bros., by WEA Records. Deleted Jun '87. Catalogue no: **K 17870**

Anderson, Leroy

Biographical details: This American orchestra, led by Leroy Anderson, reached No. 24 on the UK charts in 1957 with their only hit single *Forgotten Dreams*, composed by Anderson. (BM '84).

FORGOTTEN DREAMS
Tracks: / Forgotten dreams.
7" Single: Released 28 Jun '57, on Brunswick, by Decca Records. Catalogue no: **05485**

Anderson, Lynn

ROSE GARDEN (OLD GOLD)
Tracks: / Rose garden / You're my man.
7" Single: Released Jun '84, on Old Gold, by Old Gold Records. Catalogue no: **OG 9397**

ROSE GARDEN (SINGLE)
Tracks: / Rose garden / Snow bird.
7" Single: Released Apr '82, on CBS, by CBS Records. Catalogue no: **CBS 7069**
7" Single: Released 22 Feb '71, on CBS, by CBS Records. Catalogue no: **CBS 5360**

Anderson, Michael

LOVERS HARMONY
Tracks: / Lover's harmony.
12" Single: Released Mar '83, on JD, Catalogue no: **JD 010**

Anderson, Moira

HOLY CITY
Tracks: / Holy City, The.
7" Single: Released 27 Dec '69, on Decca, by Decca Records. Catalogue no: **F 12989**

Anderson, Ricky

I DON'T WANT TO LOSE YOUR LOVE
Tracks: / I don't want to lose your love.
7" Single: Released Aug '83, on Creole, by Creole Records. Catalogue no: **CR 59**

NITE SPOT
Tracks: / Nite spot.
7" Single: Released Nov '84, on Creole, by Creole Records. Catalogue no: **CR 69**

Anderson, Stuart

BONNIE WEE JEANNIE MCCALL
Tracks: / Bonnie wee Jeannie McCall.
7" Single: Released May '89, on Scotdisc, by Scotdisc Records. Catalogue no: **ITV 75481**

Anderson Bruford

BROTHER OF MINE
Tracks: / Brother of mine / Themes: sound / Attention / Soul warrior / Vultures (in the sky).
CD 3": Released Jun '89, on Arista, by BMG Records (UK). Catalogue no: **162379**
CD 5": Released Jun '89, on Arista, by BMG Records (UK). Catalogue no: **662379**
10" single: Released Jun '89, on Arista, by BMG Records (UK). Catalogue no: **260018**
12" Single: Released Jun '89, on Arista, by BMG Records (UK). Catalogue no: **612379**
7" Single: Released Jun '89, on Arista, by BMG Records (UK). Catalogue no: **112379**
7" Single: Released Jun '89, on Arista, by BMG Records (UK). Catalogue no: **112444**
Cassingle: Released Jun '89, on Arista, by BMG Records (UK). Catalogue no: **410017**

Andersons

BOOGIE WOOGIE BUGLE BOY
Tracks: / Boogie woogie bugle boy.
7" Single: Released May '83, on President, by President Records. Catalogue no: **PT 516**

Andi Sex Gang

IDA-HO
Tracks: / Ida-ho.
12" Single: Released Feb '85, on Illuminated, Catalogue no: **ILL 5312**
7" Single: Released Feb '85, on Illuminated, Catalogue no: **ILL 53**

LES AMANTS D'UN JOUR
Tracks: / Les amants d'un jour.
12" Single: Released Sep '84, on Illuminated, Catalogue no: **ILL 52**

NAKED AND THE DEAD
Tracks: / Naked and the dead, The / You don't know me / Quick and the dead, The.
12" Single: Released Sep '86, on Revolver, by FM-Revolver Records. Catalogue no: **12 REV 27**

SEVEN WAYS TO KILL A MAN
Tracks: / Seven ways to kill a man.
7" Single: Released Nov '88, on Jungle, by Jungle Records. Catalogue no: **JUNG 42**
12" Single: Released Nov '88, on Jungle, by Jungle Records. Catalogue no: **JUNG 42T**

Andrew, Elvis

JUST A LONELY MAN
Tracks: / Just a lonely man.
12" Single: Released Oct '83, on Antigua's, Catalogue no: **ANT 035**

Andrew, Simon

CALL ME NOW (DON'T)
Tracks: / Call me now (Don't) / So confused.
7" Single: Released Sep '86, on Epic, by CBS Records. Catalogue no: **650102 7**
12" Single: Released Sep '86, on Epic, by CBS Records. Catalogue no: **650102 6**

SO CONFUSED
Tracks: / So confused.
7" Single: Released Oct '85, on Ideal Music, by Ideal Music Records. Catalogue no: **IDEAL 2**
12" Single: Released Oct '85, on Ideal Music, by Ideal Music Records. Catalogue no: **IDEALT 2**

Andrews, Barry

ROSSMORE ROAD
Tracks: / Rossmore Road / Win a night out with a well known paranoiac.
7" Single: Released Sep '80, on Virgin, by Virgin Records. Deleted Sep '84. Catalogue no: **VS 378**
7" Single: Released Jun '81, on Virgin, by Virgin Records. Deleted Jun '84. Catalogue no: **VS 428**

Andrews, Chris

AMAZING GRACE
Tracks: / Amazing grace.
7" Single: Released Apr '79, on Klub, by Klub Records. Catalogue no: **KLUB 02**

SOMETHING ON MY MIND
Tracks: / Something on my mind.
7" Single: Released 14 Apr '66, on Decca, by Decca Records. Catalogue no: **F 22365**

STOP THAT GIRL
Tracks: / Stop that girl.
7" Single: Released 25 Aug '66, on Decca, by Decca Records. Catalogue no: **F 22472**

TO WHOM IT CONCERNS
Tracks: / To whom it concerns.
7" Single: Released 2 Dec '65, on Decca, by Decca Records. Catalogue no: **F 22285**
7" EP: Released Oct '84, on Scoop 33, by Pickwick Records. Catalogue no: **7SR 5051**

WHATCHA GONNA DO NOW
Tracks: / Whatcha gonna do now.
7" Single: Released 2 Jun '66, on Decca, by Decca Records. Catalogue no: **F 22404**

YESTERDAY MAN
12" Pic: Released Mar '88, on PRT, by Castle Communications Records. Catalogue no: **PYT 6**
7" Pic: Released Mar '88, on PRT, by Castle Communications Records. Catalogue no: **PYS 6**
7" Single: Released Sep '63, on Decca, by Decca Records. Catalogue no: **F 12236**

YESTERDAY MAN (OLD GOLD)
Tracks: / Yesterday man.
7" Single: Released Sep '85, on Old Gold, by Old Gold Records. Catalogue no: **OG 9527**

Andrews, Eamonn

SHIFTING WHISPERING SANDS
Tracks: / Shifting, whispering sands.
7" Single: Released 20 Jan '56, on Parlophone, by EMI Records. Catalogue no: **R 4106**

Andrews, Elaine

IN THE BEGINNING
Tracks: / In the beginning.
7" Single: Released Apr '79, on Klub, by Klub Records. Catalogue no: **KLUB 17**

Andrews, Harvey

GOLDEN PENNIES THEME
Tracks: / Golden pennies theme.
7" Single: Released Nov '85, on Telebell, Catalogue no: **TVP 6**

MARGARITA (SINGLE)
Tracks: / Margarita / Long ago.
7" Single: Released Oct '80, on Polydor, by Polydor Ltd. Deleted Oct '83. Catalogue no: **POSP 178**

ME MOM
Tracks: / Me mom / We were there.
7" Single: Released Jul '83, on Dingle's, by Dingle's Records. Catalogue no: **SID 335**

WRITER OF SONGS
Tracks: / Writer of songs.
12" Single: Released May '86, on Modtone, Catalogue no: **ADU 12**
7" Single: Released May '86, on Modtone, Catalogue no: **ADU 1**

Andrews, Janine

PLEASE DONT GO
Tracks: / Please don't go / Got to have you for myself.
7" Single: Released 10 Oct '87, on Carrere, Catalogue no: **CAR 420**

Andrews, Julie

Biographical details: Julie Andrews was born Julia Elizabeth Wells in 1935 in Walton-on-Thames, Surrey. She performed in Music Halls in the family act, in a London Show *Starlight Roof* in 1947, on radio (especially in series 'Educating Archie' with ventriloquist Peter Brough's dummy). Her very English voice was ideal for typical British musical roles: played Polly Brown in NYC prod. of 'The Boy Friend' in 1954, then was a major hit in Lerner & Loewe's 'My Fair Lady', in New York in 1956 and London in '58; then as Queen Guinevere in their 'Camelot' in 1960. The film of 'My Fair Lady' in 1964 used Audrey Hepburn instead, whose singing voice had to be dubbed by Marni Nixon, but Andrews starred the same year in Walt Disney's film 'Mary Poppins' (Oscar for best actress). Many other films incl. 'Sound Of Music' '65 (one of the biggest grossers of all time), 'Thoroughly Modern Millie' '67, 'Star!' '68 (playing Gertrude Lawrence). Her USA TV variety series flopped '73; she had a hit Las Vegas night club act '76. Second husband, director Blake Edwards, once described her image as so sweet that people think she probably has violets between her legs; she challenged that image in later, less successful films, wearing a badge that said 'Mary Poppins is a Junkie'. (Donald Clarke, 21 July 1988)..

LE JAZZ HOT
Tracks: / Le jazz hot / Shady dame from Seville.
7" Single: Released Apr '82, on Polydor, by Polydor Ltd. Deleted Apr '85. Catalogue no: **POSP 438**

LOVE ME TENDER (SINGLE)
7" Single: Released Aug '83, on Peach River, Deleted '84. Catalogue no: **BBPR 5**

Andrews, Mark

BIG BOY (SINGLE)
Tracks: / Big boy / In a jam.
7" Single: Released Mar '80, on A&M, by A&M Records. Deleted Mar '83. Catalogue no: **AMS 7514**

LAID ON A PLATE
Tracks: / Laid on a plate / West one.
7" Single: Released May '80, on A&M, by A&M Records. Deleted '83. Catalogue no: **AMS 7525**

Andrews, Paul

GET IN THE DANCE
Tracks: / Get in the dance.
12" Single: Released Dec '87, on Y & D, Catalogue no: **YDDO 115**

Andrews Sisters

Biographical details: The close-harmony vocal trio from Minneapolis, Minnesota was one of the biggest acts of the 1940s, now rivalling Glenn Miller and Vera Lynn for period nostalgia; LaVerne, Maxene and Patti were born 1915-20; LaVerne was a contralto (died 1967), Maxene sang harmony, Patti lead. They had 90 hits on USA Decca (now MCA) 1938-51, taking up where the Boswell Sisters left off and inspiring '50s groups like the McGuire Sisters; they sold 60 million records, No. 1 hits including *'Bei Mir Bist Du Schon'* (1938), *'Rum And Coca-Cola'* (1945), *'I can dream, can't I?'* (1949); 23 hits with Bing Crosby (*'Pistol Packin' Mama'*, *'Don't Fence Me In'*); they also recorded with Guy Lombardo, Ernest Tubb, Carmen Miranda, etc. and appeared in many films. Bette Midler's top ten hit *'Boogie Woogie Bugle Boy'* in 1973 was a cover of their 1943 one. Patti and Maxene appeared in Broadway show *Over Here* in the mid-'70s; Maxene had a heart attack in 1982 after 11 concerts in Chicago, followed by heart by-pass operation; made her first solo album in 1985: *Maxene* on the Bainbridge label had a sleeve note by Midler. (Donald Clarke, 21 July 1988)..

BOOGIE WOOGIE BUGLE BOY
Tracks: / Boogie woogie bugle boy.
7" Single: Released Jul '82, on Revival, Catalogue no: **REV 6018**
7" Single: Released Nov '83, on Old Gold, by Old Gold Records. Catalogue no: **OG 9388**

Andros, Dede

MASTER OF THE GAME
Tracks: / Master of the game.
7" Single: Released Aug '84, on BBC, by BBC Records & Tapes. Deleted '87. Catalogue no: **RESL 157**

Andy, Bob

Biographical details: Bob Andy (Keith Anderson) is a Jamaican singer and songwriter whose exquisite *Songbook* album for Studio One, compiling sides made for that label in the mid-'60s, was considered one of the finest bodies of work in the island's brief history of recording. He sang in the rocksteady group the Pendragons, went solo and almost immediately hit with the diasporic *'I've Got To Go back Home'* (Peter Tosh and Bunny Wailer singing on harmony); many hits since then included a duet with Marcia Griffiths on Nina Simone's *'Young Gifted And Black'* in 1970. he now records on his own I-Anka label. (Donald Clarke, 21 July 1988).

CHERRY
Tracks: / Cherry.
12" Single: Released Sep '88, on I-Anka, by I-Anka Records. Catalogue no: **DKAA 001**

HONEY
Tracks: / Honey / Going home.
12" Single: Released Jul '83, on I-Anka, by I-Anka Records. Deleted '84. Catalogue no: **AV 001**

JUST FOR A TIME
Tracks: / Just for a time / Life.

12" Single: Released Aug '86, on Anka, Catalogue no: **AV 003**

SUPER POWERS
Tracks: / Super powers / Dark clouds.
12" Single: Released Jul '87, on I-Anka, by I-Anka Records. Catalogue no: **AV 004D**

Andy & Chris

UNREST WORK & PLAY (EP)
Tracks: / Unrest, work & play.
7" Single: Released Nov '82, on Art House, Catalogue no: **AH 1**

Andy, Horace

AIN'T NO LOVE
Tracks: / Ain't no love.
12" Single: Released Jan '84, on Tads, Catalogue no: **TRD 2284**

COOL & DEADLY
Tracks: / Cool & deadly / Deadly version.
12" Single: Released Oct '83, on Tads, Catalogue no: **TADS 23983**

CUS CUS
Tracks: / Cus cus.
12" Single: Released Jan '85, on Scom, Catalogue no: **BD 010**

DEBE DEBE SOUND
Tracks: / Debe debe sound.
12" Single: Released Oct '88, on World Enterprise, Catalogue no: **WED 76**

ELEMENTARY
Tracks: / Elementary / Primary.
12" Single: Released Apr '85, on Rough Trade, by Rough Trade Records. Catalogue no: **RTT 162**

ETERNAL LOVE
Tracks: / Eternal love.
12" Single: Released Apr '84, on Tads, Catalogue no: **TRD 298**

FEVER
Tracks: / Fever.
7" Single: Released May '89, on Studio One, Catalogue no: **UNKNOWN**

GATEMAN
Tracks: / Gateman.
12" Single: Released Aug '85, on Fashion, by Fashion Records. Catalogue no: **FAD 036**

GET DOWN
Tracks: / Get down.
12" Single: Released Jul '85, on Rough Trade, by Rough Trade Records. Catalogue no: **RTT 172**

GUIDING STAR
Tracks: / Guiding star.
12" Single: Released May '88, on Angstar, by Angstar Records. Catalogue no: **CGDD 110**

GUN SHOT
Tracks: / Gunshot.
12" Single: Released Sep '84, on Taxi (1), Catalogue no: **Unknown**

HOLLY HOLLY
Tracks: / Holly holy.
12" Single: Released Sep '88, on Redman International, Catalogue no: **RED 34**

HYPOCRITES
Tracks: / Hypocrite / Diplomatic dance / Hypocrite (A SIDE OF 12" SINGLE) / Diplomatic Don (B SIDE OF 12" SINGLE).
12" Single: Released May '86, on Fashion, by Fashion Records. Catalogue no: **FAD 041**

I WANT YOUR LOVE
Tracks: / I want your love.
12" Single: Released Sep '88, on Stone Rock, Catalogue no: **MH 222**

I'M IN LOVE
Tracks: / I'm in love.
7" Single: Released May '82, on Oval, by Oval Records. Catalogue no: **OVAL 1010**

LOVE HANGOVER
Tracks: / Love hangover / Serious thing.
12" Single: Released Jul '82, on Solid Groove, Catalogue no: **SG 014 12**

MUST HAVE TO GET IT
Tracks: / Must have to get it.
12" Single: Released May '87, on Live & Love, Catalogue no: **LLD 38**

ONE MORE NIGHT
Tracks: / One more night.
12" Single: Released Nov '85, on Money Disc, Catalogue no: **MDL 400**

PROBLEM TIMES
Tracks: / Problem times.
12" Single: on Burning Sounds, by Burning Sounds Records. Deleted May '88. Catalogue no: **BSD 024**

RAMM DANCEMASTER
Tracks: / Ramm dancemaster.
12" Single: Released Jul '85, on Phil Pratt, Catalogue no: **PP 0019**

Angel Chorus - Devil On My Shoulder (Released on 10 Records)

SWEET MUSIC
Tracks: / Sweet music.
12" Single: Released Nov '83, on Music Hawk, Catalogue no: **MHD 11**

USER
Tracks: / User / User (version).
12" Single: Released Feb '86, on Music Hawk, Catalogue no: **MH 16**

WATCH YOUR STEP
Tracks: / Watch your step / Strange thing.
12" Single: Released Feb '86, on Ragin' Lion Music, Catalogue no: **RL 004**

YOU ARE MY ANGEL
Tracks: / You are my angel.
12" Single: Released Jul '84, on Tads, Catalogue no: **TRD 13118**

Andy, Patrick

COW HORN CHALICE
Tracks: / Cow horn chalice.
7" Single: Released Oct '84, on Ujama, Catalogue no: **Unknown**

CRY FOR ME
Tracks: / Cry for me.
12" Single: Released Nov '85, on Crystal, by President Records. Catalogue no: **CR 007**

DON'T WORRY YOURSELF
Tracks: / Don't worry yourself.
12" Single: Released Jan '85, on Jedi, Catalogue no: **JJ 206**

GET UP,STAND UP
Tracks: / Get up stand up / Regular heartbreaker.
12" Single: Released Aug '84, on Greensleeves, by Greensleeves Records. Catalogue no: **GRED 154**

NEAT SI SWEET
Tracks: / Neat si sweet / Bicycle move.
12" Single: Released Mar '85, on Tonos, Catalogue no: **TON 003**

PRETTY ME
Tracks: / Pretty me.
12" Single: Released Nov '84, on Jedi, Catalogue no: **JJ 213**

STING ME A STING,SHOCK ME A SHOCK
Tracks: / Sting me a sting, shock me a shock / Every posse get ready.

12" Single: Released Mar '85, on Greensleeves, by Greensleeves Records. Catalogue no: **GRED 172**

STRUGGLE
Tracks: / Struggle.
12" Single: Released Jul '87, on Simba, Catalogue no: **SIM 009**

Andy T

WEARY OF THE FLESH(EP)
Tracks: / Weary of the flesh.
7" Single: Released Nov '82, on Crass, by Crass Records. Catalogue no: **221984/4**

Aneka

Biographical details: Despite appearing on "Top Of The Pops" with kimono and Japanese wig, Aneka was, in fact, a Scottish folk singer usually known as Mary Sandeman.
Deciding to record a pop single purely for fun, she cut a Eurodisco record and entitled *"Japanese Boy"* For the German - based Hansa company, best known for its Boney M hits.
The song went to No.1 in the UK and was also a sizeable Continental hit. Several follow-ups were tried, but Sandeman soon returned to her Gaelic folk singing-Aneka had only been a hobby.
(Bob MacDonald, 1988)..

HEART TO BEAT
Tracks: / Heart to beat / Starshine.
7" Single: Released Feb '83, on Ariola, by BMG Records (UK). Catalogue no: **ARO 295**

JAPANESE BOY
Tracks: / Japanese boy / I lost my heart to a starship trooper.
Note: Double 'A' side
7" Single: Released Sep '82, on Hansa, by Hansa Records. Catalogue no: **HANSA 5**
7" Single: Released Apr '87, on Old Gold, by Old Gold Records. Catalogue no: **OG 9710**

LITTLE LADY
Tracks: / Little lady / Chasing dreams.
7" Single: Released 7 Nov '81, on Hansa, by Hansa Records. Catalogue no: **HANSA 8**

OOH SHOOBY DOO DOO LANG
Tracks: / Ooh shooby doo doo lang / Could it last a little longer.
7" Single: Released Sep '82, on Hansa, by Hansa Records. Catalogue no: **HANSA 13**

ROSE ROSE I LOVE YOU
Tracks: / Rose Rose I love you / My Johnny (kneels and kissed me).

7" Single: Released '33, on Ariola, by BMG Records (UK). Deleted '86. Catalogue no: **ARO 307**

Angel

20TH CENTURY FOXES
Tracks: / 20th century foxes / Can you feel it.
7" Single: Released Jun '80, on Casablanca, by PolyGram UK Ltd. Deleted Jun '83. Catalogue no: **CAN 193**

DO IT
Tracks: / Do it.
7" Single: Released Nov '85, on Rainbow, by Rainbow Records. Catalogue no: **RBR 2**
12" Single: Released Nov '85, on Rainbow, by Rainbow Records. Catalogue no: **RBRT 2**

DRIVING (DOWN)
Tracks: / Driving (down) / Driving (up).
7" Single: Released Aug '82, on Teddy Bear Records, Deleted '86. Catalogue no: **BEAR 001**

IT'S GONNA COME BACK TO YOU
Tracks: / It's gonna come back to you / Tomorrow night.
7" Single: Released Jun '86, on Rainbow, by Rainbow Records. Catalogue no: **RBR 8**
12" Single: Released Jun '86, on Rainbow, by Rainbow Records. Catalogue no: **RBRT 8**

Angel Beat City

AROUND
Tracks: / Around.
12" Single: Released Mar '89, on Brilliant, by Brilliant Records. Catalogue no: **BRN 001T**

Angel Chorus

DEVIL ON MY SHOULDER (See adjacent panel)
Tracks: / Devil on my shoulder / Can't you see / Devil on my shoulder (dub).
7" Single: Released Jan '86, on 10 Records, by Virgin Records. Deleted '86. Catalogue no: **TEN 90**
12" Single: Released Jan '86, on 10 Records, by Virgin Records. Deleted '86. Catalogue no: **TEN 90-12**

Angel City

AM I EVER GONNA SEE YOUR FACE AGAIN
Tracks: / Am I ever gonna see your face again / Shadow boxer.
7" Single: Released Aug '80, on Epic, by CBS Records. Deleted '83. Catalogue no: **EPC 8792**

COMIN' DOWN
Tracks: / Comin' down / No exit.
7" Single: Released May '80, on CBS, by CBS Records. Deleted '83. Catalogue no: **CBS 8538**

NO SECRETS
Tracks: / No secrets / Wasted sleepless nights / Darkroom.
7" Single: Released Dec '80, on Epic, by CBS Records. Deleted Dec '85. Catalogue no: **EPC 8962**

Angel Eek

LOOK AT ME NOW
Tracks: / Look at me now.
7" Single: Released Mar '83, on Playfar, by Playfar Records. Catalogue no: **ESM 204**

Angel Love

HEARTACHE
Tracks: / Heartache / Heartache (instrumental).
12" Single: Released Feb '89, on TEL Productions, Catalogue no: **TEL 2222**

SAY NO TO A.I.D.S. AND DRUGS
Tracks: / Say no to A.I.D.S. and drugs / Say no to A.I.D.S. and drugs / Say no to A.I.D.S. and drugs.
7" Single: Released 12 May '89, on TEL Productions, Catalogue no: **TEL 2223**

Angel, Ronnie

CUDDLE UP
Tracks: / Cuddle up / I got love.
7" Single: Released '82, on Arista, by BMG Records (UK). Deleted '87. Catalogue no: **BELL 1504**

WHITE SPORTS COAT AND A PINK CARNATION
Tracks: / White sports coat / Rock 'n' rollin' man.
7" Single: Released '82, on Arista, by BMG Records (UK). Deleted '87. Catalogue no: **BELL 1501**

Angel Witch

ANGEL WITCH (SINGLE)
Tracks: / Angel Witch / Gorgon.
7" Single: Released Oct '82, on Bronze, by Bronze Records. Deleted Oct '85. Catalogue no: **BRO 108**

GOODBYE
Tracks: / Goodbye.
7" Single: Released Jul '85, on Killerwatt, by Killerwatt Records. Deleted '87. Catalogue no: **KIL 3001**

LOSER
Tracks: / Loser / Suffer / Doctor Phibes.
7" EP: Released May '81, on Bronze, by Bronze Records. Deleted May '84. Catalogue no: **BRO 121**

SWEET DANGER
Tracks: / Sweet danger / Hadies paradise / Flight nineteen.
7" Single: Released 7 Jun '80, on EMI, by EMI Records. Catalogue no: **EMI 5064**
12" Single: Released May '80, on EMI, by EMI Records. Deleted May '83. Catalogue no: **12 EMI 5064**

Angelettes

DON'T LET HIM TOUCH YOU
Tracks: / Don't let him touch you.
7" Single: Released 13 May '72, on Decca, by Decca Records. Catalogue no: **F 13284**

Angelic Upstarts

BRIGHTON BOMB
Tracks: / Brighton bomb.
12" Single: Released Jun '85, on Gas, Catalogue no: **GM 3010**

BURGLAR, THE
Tracks: / Burglar, The.
7" Single: Released Jul '83, on Anagram, by Cherry Red Records. Deleted '88. Catalogue no: **ANA 11**

DIFFERENT STROKES
Tracks: / Different strokes / Different dub.
7" Single: Released Oct '81, on Zonophone, by EMI Records. Deleted Oct '84. Catalogue no: **Z 25**

ENGLAND
Tracks: / England / Stick's diary.
7" Single: Released Nov '80, on Zonophone, by EMI Records. Deleted Nov '83. Catalogue no: **Z 12**

ENGLAND'S ALIVE
Tracks: / England's alive.
12" Single: Released 23 Jul '88, on Skunx, Catalogue no: **MENSIX 1**

I UNDERSTAND
Tracks: / I understand / Never come back / Heath's lament (on 12" only).
7" Single: Released May '81, on Zonophone, by EMI Records. Deleted May '84. Catalogue no: **Z 22**
12" Single: Released May '81, on Zonophone, by EMI Records. Deleted May '84. Catalogue no: **12 Z 22**

I'M AN UPSTART
Tracks: / I'm an upstart / Never 'ad nothing.
7" Single: Released 21 Apr '79, on Warner Bros., by WEA Records. Catalogue no: **K 17354**
Cassingle: Released Apr '81, on WEA, by WEA Records. Deleted Apr '86. Catalogue no: **SPC 2**

KIDS ON THE STREET
Tracks: / Kids on the street / Sun never shines.
7" Single: Released 7 Feb '81, on Zonophone, by EMI Records. Catalogue no: **Z 16**

LAST NIGHT ANOTHER SOLDIER
Tracks: / Last night another soldier.
7" Single: Released 2 Aug '80, on EMI, by EMI Records. Catalogue no: **Z 7**

MACHINE GUN KELLY
Tracks: / Machine gun Kelly.
12" Single: Released Jul '85, on Picasso, by Picasso Records. Catalogue no: **PIKT 001**

NEVER 'AD NOTHIN'
Tracks: / Never 'ad nothin'.
7" Single: Released 3 Nov '79, on Warner Bros., by WEA Records. Catalogue no: **K 17476**

NOT JUST A NAME
Tracks: / Not just a name / Leech.
7" Single: Released Sep '83, on Anagram, by Cherry Red Records. Deleted '88. Catalogue no: **ANA 13**
12" Single: Released Sep '83, on Anagram, by Cherry Red Records. Deleted '88. Catalogue no: **12 ANA 13**

OUT OF CONTROL
Tracks: / Out of control / Shotgun solution.
7" Single: Released 9 Feb '80, on Warner Bros., by WEA Records. Catalogue no: **K 17558**

SOLIDARITY
Tracks: / Solidarity.
12" Single: Released May '83, on Anagram, by Cherry Red Records. Deleted '88. Catalogue no: **12 ANA 07**
7" Single: Released May '83, on Anagram, by Cherry Red Records. Deleted '88. Catalogue no: **ANA 7**

TEENAGE WARNING (SINGLE)
Tracks: / Teenage warning.
7" Single: Released Aug '79, on WEA, by WEA Records. Catalogue no: **K 17426**

WE GOTTA GET OUT OF THIS PLACE (SINGLE)
Tracks: / We gotta get out of this place / Unsung heroes.
7" Single: Released Mar '80, on WEA, by WEA Records. Deleted '82. Catalogue no: **K 17576**

WOMAN IN DISGUISE
Tracks: / Woman in disguise / Lust for glory.
12" Single: Released Nov '82, on Anagram, by Cherry Red Records. Deleted '88. Catalogue no: **12 ANA 03**
7" Single: Released Nov '82, on Anagram, by Cherry Red Records. Deleted '88. Catalogue no: **ANA 3**

Angelo, Bobby

BABY SITTIN'
Tracks: / Baby sittin'.
7" Single: Released 10 Aug '61, on H.M.V., by EMI Records. Catalogue no: **POP 892**

Angelo, Don

BIETCLE MOVE
Tracks: / Bietcle move.
12" Single: Released Oct '84, on R & M, Catalogue no: **Unknown**

LOVING STICK
Tracks: / Loving stick.
12" Single: Released Feb '89, on Manzie, Catalogue no: **MAN 003**

MAMPIE SIZE
Tracks: / Mampie size.
7" Single: Released Nov '88, on Waterhouse, Catalogue no: **UNKNOWN**

REGGAE MUSIC WE WANT
Tracks: / Reggae music we want / Petty robber.
12" Single: Released Feb '66, on Unity Sound, Catalogue no: **UN 011**

Angels

Biographical details: The Angels were a vocal trio from New Jersey consisting of two sisters Barbara and Jiggs plus another girl Peggy. The group formed in 1961, and achieved two US Top 40 hits with *"'Til"* and *"Cry Baby Cry"*. The big one came in the autumn of '63 when they hit No.1 with *"My Boyfriend's Back"*, a song written by Richard Gottehrer (later known for his production work with Blondie and the Go-Gos), Gerald Goldstein and Robert Fieldman. Britain, by this time, was caught up in Beatlemania and was no longer interested in theirs rapidly dating early Sixties girl-group sound, unless it was produced by Phil Spector. The record had just one week on the UK Top 50, at No.50. The girls could only manage one more American success before the Beatles conquered that country too..

MY BOYFRIEND'S BACK
Tracks: / My boyfriend's back.
7" Single: Released 3 Oct '63, on Mercury (EMI), Catalogue no: **AMT 1211**

Angels In Aspic

DRIVE ME TO THE CENTRE OF MAXIMUM PLEASURE
Tracks: / Drive me to the centre of maximum pleasure.
12" Single: Released Apr '89, on Suspended Jelly, Catalogue no: **SJR 2**

JUST SOME KIND OF GROOVY MAYHEM
Tracks: / Just some kind of groovy mayhem / Riding on a ghost train.
12" Single: Released Sep '88, on Suspended Jelly, Catalogue no: **SJR 1**

Angels One Five

CUT AND DRY
Tracks: / Cut and dry / Countdown.
7" Single: Released Nov '82, on Galaxy (1), by Galaxy Records. Deleted Nov '85. Catalogue no: **GAL 005**

Angie

DON'T LET IT BREAK YOUR HEART
Tracks: / Don't let it break your heart / Idiot laughter.
7" Single: Released Jun '84, on Lamborghini, by Lamborghini Records. Catalogue no: **LMG 12**

Angry Flowers

HEAVEN WHEN YOU SMILE
Tracks: / Heaven when you smile.
7" Single: Released 5 Mar '88, on Exile, Catalogue no: **EX 7010**

Angus

PAPA DON'T FREAK
Tracks: / Papa don't freak.
12" Single: Released Jul '87, on Megaton, Catalogue no: **MEGATON 2.19**

Anhrefn

BE NESA 89
Tracks: / Be nesa 89.
7" Single: Released 13 Sep '88, on Anhrefn, Catalogue no: **ANHREFN 015**

EDRYCH AR Y RUDE BOYS
Tracks: / Edrych ar y rude boys.
12" Single: Released Jul '89, on Released Emotions, Catalogue no: **UNKNOWN**

Animal Farm

MODEL SOLDIER
Tracks: / Model soldier.
7" Single: Released Mar '84, on Rot, by Rot Records. Catalogue no: **ASS 7**

Animal Hysteria

JINGLE BELLS
Tracks: / Jingle bells.
7" Single: Released Dec '83, on Look, by Look Records. Catalogue no: **LKSP 6789**

Animal Logic

SOMEDAY WE'LL UNDERSTAND
Tracks: / Someday we'll understand / Lopsy Lu.
12" Single: Released Jul '89, on Virgin, by Virgin Records. Catalogue no: **ALT 11**
CD 5": Released Sep '89, on Virgin, by Virgin Records. Catalogue no: **ALSCD 11**
7" Single: Released Jul '89, on Virgin, by Virgin Records. Catalogue no: **AL 11**

THERE'S A SPY IN THE HOUSE OF LOVE
Tracks: / There's a spy / Someone to come home to / Night owls.
7" Single: Released Feb '89, on Virgin, by Virgin Records. Catalogue no: **AL 10**
CD 5": Released Feb '89, on Virgin, by Virgin Records. Catalogue no: **ALTSCD 10**
12" Single: Released Feb '89, on Virgin, by Virgin Records. Catalogue no: **ALT 10**

Animal Magic

DOO DOO DOOLEY
Tracks: / Doo doo dooley.
7" Single: Released Apr '83, on Sniff, Catalogue no: **SNIF 1**

GET IT RIGHT
Tracks: / Get it right.
12" Single: Released Feb '82, on Record Shack, by Record Shack Records. Catalogue no: **SPORT 52**
7" Single: Released Feb '82, on Record Shack, by Record Shack Records. Catalogue no: **SPORT 5**

STANDARD MAN
Tracks: / Standard man.
7" Single: Released May '82, on Recreational, by Revolver Records. Catalogue no: **SPORT 8**

WELCOME TO THE MONKEY HOUSE
Tracks: / Welcome to the monkey house.
7" Single: Released Sep '81, on EMI, by EMI Records. Deleted Sep '84. Catalogue no: **EMI 5240**
12" Single: Released Nov '81, on EMI, by EMI Records. Catalogue no: **12EMI 5240**

Animal Magnet

BABY CLOTHES
Tracks: / Baby clothes / Bamba.
12" Single: Released Jun '82, on EMI, by EMI Records. Deleted '85. Catalogue no: **12EMI 5310**
7" Single: Released Jun '82, on EMI, by EMI Records. Deleted '85. Catalogue no: **EMI 5310**

Animal Nightlife

Biographical details: Having established themselves as London night club favourites, Animal Nightlife -- Billy Chapman, Len Chignoli, Flid, Andy Polaris and Paul Waller -- scored a minor hit in 1983 with the jazzy pop single Native Boy. Due to record company and personnel difficulties almost a year went by before a second single was issued: Mr Solitaire, another well-made jazz-influenced record, reached No 25 in October, '84, featuring the backing vocals of David Joseph (ex-Hi Tension and solo chart artist) and Jam/Style Council maestro Paul Weller (not to be confused with the band's own drummer, Paul Waller). (Bob MacDonald, 1984.)

ANIMAL NIGHTLIFE - MR. SOLITARE (Released on Island)

ALWAYS YOUR HUMBLE SLAVE
Tracks: / Always your humble slave (7" edit) (On all versions) / Badlands (On all versions) / Always your humble slave (Big Bang) (12" & CD only) / Always your humble slave (gold diggers of 88) (12" only) / Boys with the best intentions (CD only).
12" Single: Released Mar '88, on 10 Records, by Virgin Records. Catalogue no: **TENX 213**
CD 5": Released Aug '88, on 10 Records, by Virgin Records. Catalogue no: **TENCD 213**
7" Single: Released Mar '88, on 10 Records, by Virgin Records. Catalogue no: **TEN 213**

BOY WITH THE BEST INTENTIONS
Tracks: / Boy with the best intentions.
7" Single: Released Sep '87, on 10 Records, by Virgin Records. Deleted May '88. Catalogue no: **TEN 185**
12" Single: Released Sep '87, on 10 Records, by Virgin Records. Deleted May '88. Catalogue no: **TENT 185**

LOVE IS JUST THE GREAT PRETENDER 'UNDRESSING'
Tracks: / Love is just the great pretender undressing.
12" Single: Released Jul '85, on Island, by Island Records. Deleted '87. Catalogue no: **12ISX 200**
7" Set: Released Jun '85, on Island, by Island Records. Catalogue no: **AN 1**
7" Pic: Released Jul '85, on Island, by Island Records. Catalogue no: **ISP 200**
7" Single: Released Nov '82, on Inner Vision, Deleted Nov '85. Catalogue no: **IVLA 2881**
7" Single: Released Jun '85, on Island, by Island Records. Catalogue no: **IS 200**

MIGHTY HANDS OF LOVE
Tracks: / Mighty hands of love.
7" Single: Released Mar '83, on Inner Vision, Catalogue no: **IVLA 3190**
12" Single: Released Mar '83, on Inner Vision, Catalogue no: **IVLA 13-3190**

MR. SOLITAIRE (see panel above)
Tracks: / Mr. Solitaire / Lazy afternoon.
7" Pic: Released Jul '84, on Island, by Island Records. Catalogue no: **ISP 193**
Cassingle: Released Oct '84, on Island, by Island Records. Catalogue no: **CIS 193**
7" Single: Released Jul '84, on Island, by Island Records. Catalogue no: **IS 193**

NATURE BOY (UPTOWN)
Tracks: / Nature boy (uptown).
7" Single: Released Aug '83, on Inner Vision, Deleted '86. Catalogue no: **A 3584**

PREACHER, PREACHER
Tracks: / Preacher preacher.
7" Single: Released Sep '85, on Island, by Island Records. Catalogue no: **IS 245**

PREACHER PREACHER REMIX
Tracks: / Preacher preacher (remix).
12" Single: Released Oct '85, on Island, by Island Records. Deleted '87. Catalogue no **12ISX 245**

Animals

Biographical details: The Animals had their roots in an early Sixties jazz trio, the Alan Price Combo. They became the Animals when Burdon and Valentine were recruited in 1962. Having gigged around their native Newcastle, they cut their own EP and sold five hundred copies. Pop producer Mickie Most, who had recently returned from being a recording star in South Africa, was impressed and brought them down to London

Success was immediate. The band remade /'Baby Let Me Follow You Down"D, a track from Bob Dylan's debut album, and called it /'Baby Let Me Take You Home"D. It reached No.21. In a move that was as obvious as it was brilliant, they followed that initial hit with a version of the very next track on the Dylan album. The traditional blues number /'House Of The Rising Sun"D proved perfect for the Animals' bluesy style. It shot to No.1 not only in Britain but also in the States, wherethe Beatles were leading the famous British invasion. Burdon's passionate vocals combined with the eerie organ arrangement of Alan Price, made it quite unlike anything else being played on pop radio at the time. In this regard, it broke an important barrier in Britain by being over four minutes in length, far longer than the conventional 2:30 - 3 minute pop single (though in America an edited version was usually played). /'House Of The Rising Sun's"D all - time classic status was reaffirmed in 1972 and 1982, when it hit the British Top 30 for the second and third times. Having made the major contributions to the appeal of "House", Burdon and Price wrote its follow-up themselves. "I'm Crying" reached No.8 in the UK and No.19 in the US. The Animals' self-titled debut LP established the group as one of the greatest white exponents of black rhythm and blues; it featured a mix of originals and blues standards, all sung convincingly and powerfully by Burdon. Having become international stars in '64, they continued in '65 withthe hits /'Don't Let Me Be Misunderstood"D, "Bring It On Home To Me" and /'We've Gotta Get Out Of This Place"D, all Top 10 in Britain and Top 40 in America. About this time, Price quit the group, citing not only musical differences but manic fear of flying. He went on to have hits in the Sixties and Seventies with the Alan Price Set, with Georgie Fame and as a solo artist. The Animals continued having hits for year without Price but, following the departure of John Steel in '66 the group broke up. Burdon embarked on a solo career but, on record company insistence used the billing Eric Burdon and the Animals'. Hits followed for a couple of years, "San Franciscan Nights" being the biggest on both sides of the Atlantic. In 1970, as one of the greatest white r'n'b singers, he teamed up with US soul act War for a one-off American hit. Meanwhile Chas Chandler, having been Jimi Hendrix's manager, was about to guide Slade to the top. The Animals have released two reunion albums, in 1977 and 1983, but neither were of any great musical value. (Bob McDonald 1984)

British R&B band, formed in Newcastle in 1960 as the Alan Price Combo: vocalist/keyboardist Price was born in 1942 in County Durham; the others were Hilton Valentine on guitar, John Steel on drums, Bryan 'Chas' Chandler on bass. Their wild stage act after Eric Burdon was recruited as lead singer suggested a new name. They backed visiting USA blues artists (gig with Sonny Boy Williamson issued on LP in '70's); they were a success in London early in 1964 as the demand for British R&B was an alternative to the Mersey sound. Produced by Mickie Most, they raided Bob Dylan's first LP for *Baby let me follow you down* retitled *Baby let me take you home*), and the traditional *House of the rising sun*, a four minute single (unheard of then) which helped inspire Dylan to go electric. The latter was a transatlantic No. 1 and their hits remain '60's classics. Price left, became a MOR pop star; Chandler later entered management with Jimi Hendrix, later with Slade; the Animals' reunions were not too successful, only Burden still having the stage presence that gave them their name (see his solo listing). (Donald Clarke, July 1988)l.

BABY LET ME TAKE YOU HOME
Tracks: / Baby let me take you home.
7" Single: Released 16 Apr '64, on Columbia, by EMI Records. Catalogue no: **DB 7247**

BRING IT ON HOME TO ME
Tracks: / Bring it on home to me.
7" Single: Released 8 Apr '65, on Columbia, by EMI Records. Catalogue no: **DB 7539**

DON'T BRING ME DOWN
Tracks: / Don't bring me down.
7" Single: Released 2 Jun '66, on Decca, by Decca Records. Catalogue no: **F 12407**

DON'T LET ME BE MISUNDERSTOOD
Tracks: / Don't let me be misunderstood.
7" Single: Released 4 Feb '65, on Columbia, by EMI Records. Catalogue no: **DB 7445**

HOUSE OF THE RISING SUN (SINGLE)
Tracks: / House of the rising sun / Don't let me be misunderstood / I'm crying.
7" Single: Released Sep '82, on RAK Replay, by EMI Records. Catalogue no: **RR 1**
7" Pic: Released Sep '82, on RAK Replay, by EMI Records. Deleted Sep '88. Catalogue no: **RRP 1**

7" Single: Released 25 Jun '64, on Columbia, by EMI Records. Catalogue no: **DB 7301**
7" Single: Released Apr '83, on EMI (France), by EMI Records. Catalogue no: **2C 008 91569**

I'M CRYING
Tracks: / I'm crying.
7" Single: Released 17 Sep '64, on Columbia, by EMI Records. Catalogue no: **DB 7354**

INSIDE LOOKING OUT
Tracks: / Inside looking out.
7" Single: Released 17 Feb '66, on Decca, by Decca Records. Catalogue no: **F 12332**

IT'S MY LIFE
Tracks: / It's my life.
7" Single: Released 28 Oct '65, on Columbia, by EMI Records. Catalogue no: **DB 7741**

WE'VE GOTTA GET OUT OF THIS PLACE
Tracks: / We've gotta get out of this place.
7" Single: Released 15 Jul '65, on Columbia, by EMI Records. Catalogue no: **DB 7639**

Animals & Men

NEW AGE
Tracks: / New age.
7" Single: Released May '82, on T.W., by T.W. Records. Catalogue no: **HIT 101**

Animotion

CALLING IT LOVE
Tracks: / Calling it love / Way into your heart / Room to move / Ground zero.
7" Single: Released Jul '89, on Mercury, by Phonogram Ltd. Catalogue no: **MER 300**
12" Single: Released Jul '89, on Mercury, by Phonogram Ltd. Catalogue no: **MERX 300**

I ENGINEER
Tracks: / I engineer / Essence / I engineer (remix) (Extra track on 12" only) / Obsession (remix) (Extra track on 12" only).
7" Single: Released Apr '86, on Philips, by Phonogram Ltd. Deleted '87. Catalogue no: **PH 40**
12" Single: Released Apr '86, on Philips, by Phonogram Ltd. Deleted '87. Catalogue no: **PH 4012**

OBSESSION (SINGLE)
Tracks: / Obsession.
12" Single: Released Apr '85, on Mercury, by Phonogram Ltd. Deleted '87. Catalogue no: **PH 3412**
7" Single: Released Apr '85, on Mercury, by Phonogram Ltd. Deleted '87. Catalogue no: **PH 34**

ROOM TO MOVE
Tracks: / Room to move / Obsession.
12" Single: Released May '89, on Mercury, by Phonogram Ltd. Deleted Oct '89. Catalogue no: **MERX 282**
CD 5": Released May '89, on Mercury, by Phonogram Ltd. Deleted Oct '89. Catalogue no: **MERCD 282**
7" Single: Released May '89, on Mercury, by Phonogram Ltd. Deleted Oct '89. Catalogue no: **MER 282**

Anka, Paul

Biographical details: Paul was born in 1941 in Canada of Syrian parents; as a singer, songwriter and entrepreneur, he began as a teen idol and proved to be more than just a pretty face. He buttonholed record exucs while on Hollywood holiday; ABC's Don Costa signed him up and *Diana* was a USA No.1 in 1957, a world-wide hit selling nine million by 1961, said to have been written for a baby-sitter nine years older than he was. He had other hits; wrote Buddy Holly's *It doesn't matter anymore* in 1958; *Puppy love* in 1960 was a mawkish ballad dedicated to Anka's then girl friend Annette. He made several films notably D Day epic *The longest day* in '62 (also wrote the title song). Left ABC for RCA as newer stars eclipsed him, but shrewdly bought his own masters (since periodically re-issued) and acrried on with TV and cabaret work along with writing *Johnny's theme* for Carson Tonight TV show; his translation of French singer-songwriter Claude Francois' lyric save *My way* to Frank Sinatra (and Sid Vicious and many others). Anka's own top 40 USA hits have continued into the 80's. (Donald Clarke, July 88)8.

ALL OF A SUDDEN MY HEART SINGS
Tracks: / All of a sudden my heart sings.
7" Single: on Columbia, by EMI Records. Catalogue no: **DB 4241**

CRAZY LOVE
Tracks: / Crazy love.
7" Single: on Columbia, by EMI Records. Catalogue no: **DB 4110**

DIANA (OLD GOLD)
Tracks: / Diana / You are my destiny.
7" Single: Released '88, on Old Gold, by Old Gold Records. Catalogue no: **OG 9077**

DIANA (SINGLE)
Tracks: / Diana.
7" Single: Released Aug '57, on Columbia, by EMI Records. Deleted Aug '62. Catalogue no: **DB 3980**

HELLO YOUNG LOVERS
Tracks: / Hello young lovers.
7" Single: on Columbia, by EMI Records. Catalogue no: **DB 4504**

HOLD ME 'TIL THE MORNING COMES
Tracks: / Hold me 'til the morning comes.
7" Single: Released Jul '87, on CBS, by CBS Records. Catalogue no: **A 3434**

I LOVE YOU BABY
Tracks: / I love you baby.
7" Single: on Columbia, by EMI Records. Catalogue no: **DB 4022**

IT'S TIME TO CRY
Tracks: / It's time to cry.
7" Single: on Columbia, by EMI Records. Catalogue no: **DB 4390**

LONELY BOY
Tracks: / Lonely boy.
7" Single: on Columbia, by EMI Records. Catalogue no: **DB 4324**
7" Single: on Old Gold, by Old Gold Records. Catalogue no: **OG 9078**

LONELY BOY (OLD GOLD)
Tracks: / Lonely boy / Put your head on my shoulder.
7" Single: Released '88, on Old Gold, by Old Gold Records. Catalogue no: **OG 9078**

LOVE ME WARM AND TENDER
Tracks: / Love me warm and tender.
7" Single: on RCA, by BMG Records (UK). Catalogue no: **RCA 1276**

MIDNIGHT
Tracks: / Midnight.
7" Single: Released Sep '58, on Columbia, by EMI Records. Deleted '61. Catalogue no: **DB 4172**

PUPPY LOVE
Tracks: / Puppy love.
7" Single: on Columbia, by EMI Records. Catalogue no: **DB 4434**

PUT YOUR HEAD ON MY SHOULDER
Tracks: / Put your head on my shoulder.
7" Single: on Columbia, by EMI Records. Catalogue no: **DB 4355**

SECOND CHANCE
Tracks: / Second chance.
7" Single: Released Jul '87, on CBS, by CBS Records. Catalogue no: **A 3652**

STEEL GUITAR AND A GLASS OF WINE, A
Tracks: / Steel guitar and a glass of wine, A.
7" Single: on RCA, by BMG Records (UK). Catalogue no: **RCA 1292**

TELL ME THAT YOU LOVE ME
Tracks: / Tell me that you love me.
7" Single: on Columbia, by EMI Records. Catalogue no: **DB 4022**

YOU ARE MY DESTINY
Tracks: / You are my destiny.
7" Single: on Columbia, by EMI Records. Catalogue no: **DB 4063**

YOU'RE HAVING MY BABY
Tracks: / You're having my baby / Papa.
7" Single: Released Jul '74, on United Artists, by EMI Records. Deleted Nov '88. Catalogue no: **UP 35713**

Ankh

STILL LIFE BEFORE SUCCESS
Tracks: / Still life before success.
7" Single: on WW, Catalogue no: **ANKH 1**

Ann & Sonia

FROM MY HEART
Tracks: / From my heart.
7" Single: Released May '88, on BB, Catalogue no: **BBS 201**
12" Single: Released May '88, on BB, Catalogue no: **BBD 201**

HEY LITTLE BOY
Tracks: / Hey little boy / Start all over again.
12" Single: Released Sep '88, on BB, Catalogue no: **BBD 210**
12" Single: Released Jan '87, on BB, Deleted '88. Catalogue no: **BBD 190**

WAY YOU LOVE ME, THE
12" Single: Released Feb '89, on B.B. Music, Catalogue no: **BBD 222**

Anna

LIKE THEY DO IN THE MOVIES
Tracks: / Like they do in the movies / Movies.
7" Single: Released Aug '81, on RCA, by BMG Records (UK). Deleted Aug '84. Catalogue no: **RCA 101**

NOTHING CAN MAKE ME FEEL (THE WAY YOU DO)
Tracks: / Nothing can make me feel (the way you do) / Love in command.
7" Single: Released Aug '86, on No-Go, Deleted '87. Catalogue no: **GO 2**

SYSTEM'S BREAKING DOWN
Tracks: / System's breaking down / System's breaking down (part 2).
7" Single: Released May '82, on RCA, by BMG Records (UK). Deleted '85. Catalogue no: **RCA 213**
12" Single: Released May '82, on RCA, by BMG Records (UK). Deleted '85. Catalogue no: **RCAT 213**

Annabas

START OF OUR LIVES, THE
Tracks: / Start of our lives, The / Romance.
12" Single: Released May '85, on Armadillo, by Red Rhino Records. Deleted '87. Catalogue no: **ARS 001T**
7" Single: Released '85, on Armadillo, by Red Rhino Records. Deleted '87. Catalogue no: **ARS 001**

Annabel

CINDERELLA
Tracks: / Cinderella / Safety in numbers.
7" Single: Released Oct '82, on A&M, by A&M Records. Catalogue no: **AMS 8257**

I KNOW HOW LOVE GOES
Tracks: / I know how love goes / Elecronic toys.
7" Single: Released Aug '82, on A&M, by A&M Records. Deleted Aug '85. Catalogue no: **AMS 8240**

TELL HIM
Tracks: / Tell him / All night TV.
7" Single: Released Jun '82, on A&M, by A&M Records. Deleted Jun '85. Catalogue no: **AMS 8230**

Annabella

DON'T DANCE WITH A STRANGER
Tracks: / Don't dance with a stranger.
7" Single: on RCA, by BMG Records (UK). Catalogue no: **PB 40377**
12" Single: on RCA, by BMG Records (UK). Catalogue no: **PT 40378**

FEVER (SINGLE)
Tracks: / Fever / War boys (rough & tough mix).
7" Single: Released Apr '86, on RCA, by BMG Records (UK). Catalogue no: **PB 40541**
12" Single: Released Apr '86, on RCA, by BMG Records (UK). Catalogue no: **PT 40542**

WAR BOYS
Tracks: / War boys.
12" Single: Released Feb '86, on RCA, by BMG Records (UK). Catalogue no: **PT 40542**
7" Single: Released Feb '86, on RCA, by BMG Records (UK). Catalogue no: **PB 40541**

Anne, Dee

PRIVATE NUMBER
Tracks: / Private number / Billy the Kid.
7" Single: Released Sep '80, on WEA, by WEA Records. Deleted '83. Catalogue no: **K 18328**

Anne, Shirley

GROWING UP IS HARD (SINGLE)
Tracks: / Growing up is hard.
7" Single: on Greenhill, by Greenhill Records. Catalogue no: **GHI 001**

LITTLE DONKEY
7" Single: Released Dec '87, on HHO (Henry Hadaway Organisation), by Henry Hadaway Organisation. Catalogue no: **HAD 1**

PAL OF MY CRADLE DAYS
Tracks: / Pal of my cradle days / Young girl at heart.
7" Single: Released Feb '86, on Greenhill, by Greenhill Records. Catalogue no: **GMI 1005**

Annerley, Cindy

ANSWERS ON A POSTCARD PLEASE
Tracks: / Answers on a postcard please / Give or take a small heartache / Without you there is no me.

7" Single: Released Jan '82, on Lunar (Ireland), by Lunar Records (Ireland). Deleted Jan '85. Catalogue no: **MOON 3**

Annette

DREAM 17
Tracks: / Dream 17.

7" Single: Released Dec '88, on RCA, by BMG Records (UK). Deleted Aug '89. Catalogue no: **PB 42561**
12" Single: Released Dec '88, on RCA, by BMG Records (UK). Catalogue no: **PT 42562**

I'M ALONE
Tracks: / I'm alone.
12" Single: on New Talents, Catalogue no: **NT 002**

MARTIN ANSELL - EIGHTH WONDER (Released on Island)

Annette B

I NEED YOU NOW
Tracks: / I need you now / I need you now (inst).
12" Single: Released Mar '88, on Greensleeves, by Greensleeves Records. Catalogue no: **UKMC 28**

Annihilated

PATH TO DESTRUCTION
Tracks: / Path to destruction.
12" Single: Released Oct '86, on Annihilated, Catalogue no: **BREW 1**

Annis

OFFER ME
Tracks: / Offer me / Don't play your game.
7" Single: Released Feb '80, on GTO, Deleted Feb '83. Catalogue no: **GT 226**

Anorexia

ANOREXIA
7" EP: Released '86, on Slim, Deleted '87. Catalogue no: **BRS 001**

Anorexic Dread

TRACEY'S BURNING
Tracks: / Tracey's burning.
12" Single: on Criminal Damage, Catalogue no: **CRI 12114**

Another Cinema

HALLUCINATION SPIRES
Tracks: / Hallucination Spires.
12" Single: Released May '85, on Altered States, by Altered States Records. Catalogue no: **AST 001**
7" Single: Released Feb '88, on Altered States, by Altered States Records. Deleted '88. Catalogue no: **AS 001**

MIDNIGHT BLUE OCEANS
Tracks: / Midnight blue oceans.
7" Single: Released Jun '85, on Altered States, by Altered States Records. Deleted '88. Catalogue no: **AS 002**
12" Single: Released Jun '85, on Altered States, by Altered States Records. Deleted '88. Catalogue no: **AST 002**

Another Pretty Face

WHAT EVER HAPPENED TO THE WEST?
Tracks: / What ever happened to the west? / Goodbye 1970's.
7" Single: Released Feb '80, on Virgin, by Virgin Records. Deleted '83. Catalogue no: **VS 320**

Another Sunny Day

I'M IN LOVE WITH A GIRL WHO DOESN'T KNOW I EXIST
Tracks: / I'm in love with a girl who doesn't know I exist.
7" Single: Released Jun '88, on Sarah, Catalogue no: **SARAH 007**

WHAT'S HAPPENED
Tracks: / What's happened.
7" Single: Released Apr '89, on Sarah, Catalogue no: **SARAH 16**

Another Time...

ANOTHER TIME, ANOTHER PLACE
original soundtrack
Tracks: / Another time, another place: *Various artists.*
12" Single: Released '86, on T. E. R., by That's Entertainment Records. Catalogue no: **TER 12 007**

Ansell, Martin

EIGHTH WONDER (see panel above)
Tracks: / Eighth wonder / Infidel (for Chrissie).
7" Single: on Island, by Island Records. Catalogue no: **IS 218**
12" Single: on Island, by Island Records. Catalogue no: **12IS 218**

Ansil Meditation

QUIET WOMAN
Tracks: / Quiet woman / Reggae crazy.
12" Single: Released Dec '85, on Paradise, Catalogue no: **PDRS 514**

Ant, Adam

Biographical details: Adam & The Ants had been Britain's best-selling group of 1981, so it came as no surprise when their leader, Londoner Adam Ant -- real name Stuart Goddard -- announced the following year that he was disbanding the group to pursue a solo career. Retaining his songwriting partner Marco Perroni, his first single, Goody Two Shoes, gave him a No 1 to add to the two he had gained with the Ants. Both that single and its follow-up, Friend Or Foe, were, with their primeval beat and egocentric themes, in similar vein to the previous group material. In 1983 Ant achieved his first US Top Twenty success, with Goody Two Shoes, but he found the American market hard to crack and later releases were not so well received. Strip might have been a major transAtlantic winner, had it not been for its less than subtle lyrics, which both British and American radio stations were reluctant to play. Puss 'n' Boots and Apollo 9 later kept him in the public eye. (Bob MacDonald, 1984.)
Adam Ant was born Stuart Leslie Goddard in 1954 in London. The punk rock/new wave star of the early 1980's was an art student/semi pro bassist inspired by the '76 punk explosion to form band The Ants. He played a small part in Derek Jarman's *Jubillee* film in 1978 (with Toyah), made Nazi references in lyrics and had six different lineups, but finally appointed ex-Sex Pistols manager Malcolm McLaren as a 'consultant', who poached the Ants - Dave Barbe, drums; Mathew Ashman, guitar; Lee Gorman, bass to back his protege Annabella Lwin in Bow Wow Wow, leaving Adam a 'noble savage' image of facepaint and frills. Updating Gary Glitter's double drum kit sound with a dash of Burundi rhythms, Adam and writing partner Marco Pirroni (ex-Models) had seven top 10 hits '80-1 which were of absolutely no consequence, but the videos directed by Mike Mansfield (later by Adam himself) depicted him as highwayman, pirate, armoured knight and later became popular on MTV in the USA. He had a few more hits but was more successful as a director of videos. His music was described by a USA magazine as 'Stereo Review' as 'profoundly defiant drivel' but he was a millionare at 30. (Donald Clarke, July 1988)
Adam & The Ants cut a number of singles in the late Seventies and won support from John Peel. McLaren (who always claims to have suggested Adam's pirate image), became their manager but then persuaded some of the band's key members to leave to form Bow Wow Wow. At the beginning of 1980 Adam formed a new line-up comprising 'Marco, Merrick, Terry Lee, Gary Tibbs and yours truly" (as shouted repeatedly in "Antrap"), and rapidly perfected his primeval rhythms and swashbuckling lyrics. The act's singles chart debut came in August of that year, when *Kings Of The Wild Frontier* achieved a minor placing. This was the vital toehold they needed. The next record *Dog Eat Dog* reached No. 4 followed by the *Antmusic* anthem at No. 2.
In 1981 they were the biggest act in Britain, scoring a string of Top 3 singles including two no. 1's *Stand And Deliver* and *Prince Charming*, plus simultaneous success with much of Adam's old matrial. *Kings Of The Wild Frontier* was the biggest selling album of the year. Each single was backed with a stunning promotional video, an important ingredient in the Ants' success. The following year saw Adam disband his ants and opt for a solo career, although his writing partnership with Marco continued.(Bob MacDonald)..

ANT MUSIC
Tracks: / Ant music / Fall in.
7" Single: Released Dec '80, on CBS, by CBS Records. Deleted '83. Catalogue no: **CBS 9352**

ANT MUSIC EP B-sides
Tracks: / Ant music / Friends / Kick / Physical.
7" EP: Released Mar '82, on Do-It, by Do-It Records. Deleted '85. Catalogue no: **DUN 20**

ANT MUSIC (OLD GOLD)
Tracks: / Ant music / Stand and deliver.
7" Single: Released Jan '88, on Old Gold, by Old Gold Records. Catalogue no: **OG 9739**

ANT RAP
Tracks: / Ant rap / Friends.
7" Single: Released Dec '81, on CBS, by CBS Records. Deleted '84. Catalogue no: **A 1738**

APOLLO 9
Tracks: / Apollo 9 / 'B' side baby.
7" Single: Released Sep '84, on CBS, by CBS Records. Catalogue no: **A 4719**

CAR TROUBLE
Tracks: / Car trouble / Kick.
7" Single: Released Feb '81, on Do-It, by Do-It Records. Deleted '88. Catalogue no: **DUN 10**

DESPERATE BUT NOT SERIOUS
Tracks: / Desperate but not serious / Why do girls like horses.
7" Single: Released Nov '82, on CBS, by CBS Records. Deleted '85. Catalogue no: **A 2892**

DEUTSCHER GIRLS
Tracks: / Deutscher girls / Plastic surgery.
7" Single: Released Feb '82, on E.G., by E.G. Records. Deleted '88. Catalogue no: **EGO 5**

DOG EAT DOG (see panel below)
Tracks: / Dog eat dog / Physical (you're so).
7" Single: Released Oct '80, on CBS, by CBS Records. Deleted '83. Catalogue no: **CBS 9039**

FRIEND OR FOE (SINGLE)
Tracks: / Friend or foe.
7" Single: Released Sep '82, on CBS, by CBS Records. Deleted '85. Catalogue no: **A 2736**

FRIENDS
Tracks: / Friends / Kicks / Physical.
7" Single: Released Feb '82, on Do-It, by Do-It Records. Deleted '88. Catalogue no: **DUN 20**

GOODY TWO SHOES
Tracks: / Goody two shoes.
7" Single: Released '87, on CBS, by CBS Records. Deleted '87. Catalogue no: **A 2367**

KINGS OF THE WILD FRONTIER (SINGLE)
Tracks: / Kings of the wild frontier.
7" Single: Released Aug '80, on CBS, by CBS Records. Deleted '83. Catalogue no: **CBS 8877**

NINE TO FIVE
Tracks: / Nine to five / Jerusalem.
7" Single: on E.G., by E.G. Records. Catalogue no: **EGO 8**

PRINCE CHARMING (SINGLE)
Tracks: / Prince Charming.
7" Single: Released Sep '81, on CBS, by CBS Records. Deleted '84. Catalogue no: **A 1408**

PUSS 'N' BOOTS
Tracks: / Puss 'n' boots.
7" Single: Released Oct '83, on CBS, by CBS Records. Deleted '86. Catalogue no: **A 3614**

STAND AND DELIVER
Tracks: / Stand and deliver / Be my guest.
7" Single: Released May '81, on CBS, by CBS Records. Deleted '84. Catalogue no: **A 1065**

STRIP (SINGLE)
Tracks: / Strip / Your, your, yours.
12" Single: on CBS, by CBS Records. Catalogue no: **TA 3589**
7" Single: Released May '88, on CBS, by CBS Records. Catalogue no: **A 3589**
7" Pic: on CBS, by CBS Records. Catalogue no: **WA 3589**

VIVE LE ROCK (SINGLE)
Tracks: / Vive le rock.
7" Single: Released Jul '85, on CBS, by CBS Records. Deleted '88. Catalogue no: **A 6367**
12" Single: on CBS, by CBS Records. Catalogue no: **TA 6367**

YOUNG PARISIANS
Tracks: / Young Parisians / Lady.
7" Single: Released Nov '80, on Decca, by Decca Records. Deleted '88. Catalogue no: **F 13803**

YOUNG PARISIANS (RE-RELEASE
Tracks: / Young Parisians.
12" Single: Released Jul '89, on Damaged Goods, Catalogue no: **FNARR 7**

ZEROX
Tracks: / Zerox / Whip, The.
7" Single: Released Feb '81, on Do-It, by Do-It Records. Deleted '88. Catalogue no

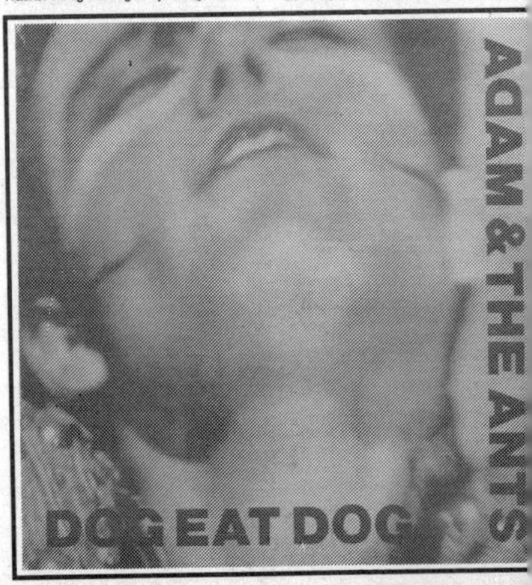

ADAM ANT - DOG EAT DOG (Released on CBS)

)UN 8

Antena, Isabelle

.AYING ON THE SOFA
racks: / Laying on the sofa.
" **Single:** Released 15 Aug '87, on Les isques Du Crepuscule(Belgium), by Les isques Du Crepuscule(Belgium). Catague no: **7TWI 809**

E POISSON DES MERS DU SUD
racks: / Le poisson des mers du sud.
2" **Single:** Released Aug '87, on Les Disues Du Crepuscule(Belgium), by Les Disues Du Crepuscule(Belgium). Catalogue): **TWI 820**

EASIDE WEEKEND
racks: / Seaside weekend.
' **Single:** Released Feb '86, on Les Disues Du Crepuscule(Belgium), by Les Disues Du Crepuscule(Belgium). Catalogue): **7TWI 601**
2" **Single:** Released Feb '86, on Les Disues Du Crepuscule(Belgium), by Les Disues Du Crepuscule(Belgium). Catalogue): **TWI 601**

Antenna

-BOP
acks: / B-bop / Mummy's not at home night.
" **Single:** on Mercury, by Phonogram Ltd. atalogue no: **PH 812**
' **Single:** on Mercury, by Phonogram Ltd. atalogue no: **PH 8**

OY FROM IPANEMA, THE
acks: / Boy from Ipanema, The.
Single: on T.W., by T.W. Records. Catague no: **TWI 074**

Anthony, Billie

IIS OLE HOUSE
acks: / This ole house.
Single: on Columbia, by EMI Records. talogue no: **DB 3519**

nthony, Carlton

GHTWALK
acks: / Nightwalk / Nightwalk (version).
" **Single:** Released May '86, on Water unt, Catalogue no: **WMT 3**

nthony, Charles

REAKTHROUGH
cks: / Breakthrough.
Single: on Button, by Musical Characters cords. Catalogue no: **BTN 106**

nthony, Chris

IANCES ARE GONE
cks: / Chances are gone / Chances are e (inst).
Single: Released May '86, on Unit 7, by ensleeves Records. Deleted '88. Catae no: **UNST 2**

nthony, Michael

'N'T MAKE ME WAIT FOR LOVE
cks: / Don't make me wait for love.
Single: Released Nov '88, on T.B.Sharp, alogue no: **UNKNOWN**

nthony, Mike

UISING IN LOVE
ks: / Cruising in love.
Single: Released Jul '89, on Merger, alogue no: **MER 003**

EN YOUR HEART
ks: / Open your heart.
Single: Released Jan '89, on Merger, alogue no: **MER 002**

Y CAN'T WE LIVE TOGETHER
ks: / Why can't we live together / Let it ove.
ingle: on Ariola, by BMG Records (UK). alogue no: **ARO 293**
Single: on Ariola, by BMG Records . Catalogue no: **AROD 293**

nthony, Miki

WASN'T FOR THE REASON AT I LOVE YOU
ks: / If it wasn't for the reason that I love

ingle: on Bell, Catalogue no: **BELL**

thony, Pad

RROT AND ONION
s: / Carrot and onion.
Single: on CSA, by CSA Records. ted '88. Catalogue no: **12CSA 508**

MPION BUBBLER
s: / Champion bubbler.
Single: Released Jul '87, on Greenes, by Greensleeves Records. Catae no: **GRED 143**

IEY PROBLEM
s: / Money problem.
ingle: Released Jul '87, on Reggae . Catalogue no: **UNKNOWN**

VORLD WITHOUT YOU
s: / No world without you / Loving stylee (Tonto irie).
12" **Single:** Released Sep '86, on Wheely Connexion, Catalogue no: **WWD 001**

RESPECT YOU
Tracks: / Respect you.
12" **Single:** Released Mar '85, on Greensleeves, by Greensleeves Records. Catalogue no: **GRED 171**

WHAT'S YOUR NAME
Tracks: / What's your name / Running man.
12" **Single:** on Right Track, Catalogue no: **RTD 001**

Anthony, Pat

MOVING FORWARD
Tracks: / Moving forward / Moving forward (version).
12" **Single:** Released Jun '87, on Super Power, Catalogue no: **SPD 8**

Anthony, Patrick

KUSUPENG
Tracks: / Kusupeng.
12" **Single:** on R & M, Catalogue no: **UNKNOWN**

Anthony, Peter

SONG FOR FESCON
Tracks: / Song for Fescon.
7" **Single:** on Clay, by Clay Records. Deleted '88. Catalogue no: **CLAY 20**

Anthony, Ray

Biographical details: This American orchestra leader first became known as a trumpeter in the Glenn Miller and Jimmy Dorsey bands. He hit No 7 on the UK chart in 1953 with *Dragnet*. After duetting with Frank Sinatra on a 1955 US Top Twenty hit, *Melody Of Love*, he reached the American Top Ten in '59 with his version of Henry Mancini's *Peter Gunn* theme, outstripping Duane Eddy. (Bob MacDonald, 1984.)
Ray Anthony was born in 1922 in Pennsylvania. He played trumpet with Glenn Miller and Jimmy Dorsey in the '40's, then had his own band with an unusual lineup: one trumpet, one French horn, five reeds, three rhythm. After US Navy service 1942-6, his more convential dance band was the most successful Miller imitator in the early '50's, playing very well indeed and benefitting form the excellent technology of Capitol Records, at the time the most innovative and up to date in the world. Hit singles 1950-54 included *Dragnet*, TV cop show theme; co written pop novelty *The bunny hop*; single *Dancing in the dark* won award as best dance band record in '53. He was married to actress Mamie Van Doren. He bought the Billy May Band in 1954, hiring Sam Donahue to front it. He led smaller combos, had a band in Las Vegas in 1980, formed Big Bands in the '80's to furnish the traditional sound to school, radio. (Donald Clarke, July 1988).

DRAGNET
Tracks: / Dragnet.
7" **Single:** on Capitol, by EMI Records. Catalogue no: **CL 13983**

Anthony, Richard

Biographical details: A French national who was born in Egypt, Richard Anthony -- real name Richard Anthony Btesh -- recorded I"Peggy Sue"D in 1959, making him one of the first French singers to test the rock 'n' roll market. In 1962 he scored a massive hit at home with I"J'Entends Siffler Le Train"D, a French version of the American song I"Five Hundred Miles Away From Home"D. After achieving a modest chart success in Britain with Walking Alone he made the UK Top Twenty in 1964 with Rodgers and Hammerstein's If I Loved You, from Carousel. (Bob MacDonald, 1984.).

IF I LOVED YOU
Tracks: / If I loved you.
7" **Single:** on Columbia, by EMI Records. Catalogue no: **DB 7235**

WALKING ALONE
Tracks: / Walking alone.
7" **Single:** on Columbia, by EMI Records. Catalogue no: **DB 7133**

Anthony, Tad

BOMB, THE
Tracks: / Bomb, The.
12" **Single:** Released Jul '87, on Bounty Hunter Records, Catalogue no: **UNKNOWN**

Anthony & The Camp

WHAT I LIKE
Tracks: / What I like / What I like (inst).
7" **Single:** Released Jun '86, on Warner Bros., by WEA Records. Catalogue no: **W 8730**
12" **Single:** Released Jun '86, on Warner Bros., by WEA Records. Deleted Jun '87. Catalogue no: **W 8730T**

Anthrax

Biographical details: New York thrash band comprising of vocalist Joey Belladonna, Frank Bello, Charlie Bonante, Ian "Not" Scott and Dan Spitz. Having already released a mini LP Armed And Dangerous, the group signed to a major label, Island records. By the time of their third album Among The Living in 1987, Anthrax had broekn into the UK Top 40 with the single I Am The Law. (P.Williams 7/88).

ANTHRAX: INTERVIEW PICTURE DISC
7" **Pic:** Released 16 Jun '89, on Baktabak, by Baktabak Records. Catalogue no: **BAK 2134**

ANTI-SOCIAL
Tracks: / Anti-social / Parasite / Le-sect.
7" **Pic:** Released 13 Mar '89, on Island, by Island Records. Catalogue no: **CIS 409**
CD 5": Released 13 Mar '89, on Island, by Island Records. Catalogue no: **CIDX 409**
7" **Single:** Released 6 Mar '89, on Island, by Island Records. Catalogue no: **IS 409**
12" **Single:** Released 6 Mar '89, on Island, by Island Records. Catalogue no: **12 IS 409**

CAPITALISM IS CANNIBALISM
7" **EP:** on Crass, by Crass Records. Catalogue no: **CRASS 221984**

I AM THE LAW
Tracks: / Bud. E. Luvbomb and Satan's lounge band / I am the law.
7" **Single:** Released Feb '87, on Island, by Island Records. Deleted Jul '87. Catalogue no: **LAW 1**
12" **Single:** Released Feb '87, on Island, by Island Records. Catalogue no: **12IS 316**

I AM THE LAW (LIVE)
Tracks: / I am the law (live).
12" **Single:** on Island, by Island Records. Deleted Jun '88. Catalogue no: **ISX 316**

I'M THE MAN
Tracks: / I'm the man / Caught in the mosh / I am the law (live).
12" **Single:** Released Jul '87, on Island, by Island Records. Deleted Dec '88. Catalogue no: **12IS 338**
7" **Pic:** on Island, by Island Records. Deleted Jun '88. Catalogue no: **ISP 338**
7" **Single:** Released Jul '87, on Island, by Island Records. Deleted Jun '88. Catalogue no: **IS 338**

INDIANS
Tracks: / Indians / Sabbath bloody sabbath / Taint.
7" **Single:** Released 13 Jun '87, on Island, by Island Records. Deleted Jun '88. Catalogue no: **IS 325**
7" **Pic:** Released 13 Jun '87, on Island, by Island Records. Catalogue no: **ISP 325**
Cassingle: Released Jul '87, on Island, by Island Records. Deleted Jun '88. Catalogue no: **CIS 325**
12" **Single:** Released 13 Jun '87, on Island, by Island Records. Catalogue no: **12IS 325**

MAD HOUSE
Tracks: / Madhouse / A.I.R. / God save the Queen.
12" **Single:** Released '88, on Island, by Island Records. Deleted Dec '88. Catalogue no: **12ISB 285**
12" **Pic:** Released May '86, on Island, by Island Records. Deleted Jul '87. Catalogue no: **12ISP 285**
12" **Single:** Released Sep '86, on Island, by Island Records. Deleted Apr '89. Catalogue no: **12IS 285**

MAKE ME LAUGH
Tracks: / Make me laugh / Anti social (live) / Friggin' in the riggin' (Available on 12" only.).
12" **Single:** Released Jul '88, on Island, by Island Records. Deleted Dec '88. Catalogue no: **12IS 379**
7" **Single:** Released Jul '88, on Island, by Island Records. Catalogue no: **IS 379**

THEY'VE GOT IT ALL WRONG
Tracks: / They've got it all wrong.
7" **Single:** on Small Wonder, by Small Wonder Records. Catalogue no: **SMALL 27**

Anti Establishment

ANTI MEN
Tracks: / Anti men / Misunderstood.
7" **Single:** on Glass, by Glass Records. Deleted '83. Catalogue no: **GLASS 023**

FUTURE GIRL
Tracks: / Future girl / No trust.
7" **Single:** Released '82, on Glass, by Glass Records. Deleted '83. Catalogue no: **GLASS 002**

Anti Group

BIG SEX, THE
Tracks: / Big sex, The.
7" **Single:** Released Aug '87, on Sweatbox, by Sweatbox Records. Catalogue no: **OX 11**
12" **Single:** Released Aug '87, on Sweatbox, by Sweatbox Records. Catalogue no: **SOX 11**

HA ZULU
Tracks: / Ha zulu.
12" **Single:** Released Jan '86, on Sweatbox, by Sweatbox Records. Catalogue no: **SOX 009**

Anti Pasti

Biographical details: This British male band typified the brand of anarchic rock which filled much of the indie charts in the early and mid-80's. Their album *"The Last Call"* got to No 31 on the national LP chart in '81. Later that year they teamed up with the Exploited for a single called *"Don't Let 'Em Grind You Down"*. Other 45s included *"Let Them Free"*, *"Six Guns"* and *"Caution In The Wind"*. (Bob MacDonald, 1984.).

CAUTION IN THE WIND (SINGLE)
Tracks: / Caution in the wind / Last train to nowhere / Blind faith.
7" **Single:** Released Sep '82, on Rondelet Music, by Rondelet Music & Records. Catalogue no: **ROUND 26**

EAST TO THE WEST
Tracks: / East to the west.
7" **Single:** Released May '82, on Rondelet Music, by Rondelet Music & Records. Catalogue no: **ROUND 18**
7" **Single:** Released Jun '82, on Rondelet Music, by Rondelet Music & Records. Deleted '85. Catalogue no: **ROUND 18**

FOUR SORE POINTS
Tracks: / Four sore points.
7" **Single:** Released Nov '80, on Rondelet Music, by Rondelet Music & Records. Catalogue no: **ROUND 2**

LET THEM FREE
Tracks: / Let them free / Another dead soldier/Hell.
7" **Single:** Released Jan '81, on Rondelet Music, by Rondelet Music & Records. Catalogue no: **ROUND 5**

SIX GUNS
Tracks: / Six guns / Call the army.
7" **Single:** Released Oct '81, on Rondelet Music, by Rondelet Music & Records. Catalogue no: **ROUND 10**

Anti Social

MADE IN ENGLAND
Tracks: / Made in England / Back street.
7" **EP:** Released Jul '82, on Lightbeat, Catalogue no: **SOCIAL 1**

TOO MANY PEOPLE
Tracks: / Too many people.
7" **Single:** Released Oct '82, on Beat-The-System, Deleted '88. Catalogue no: **FIT 2**

Anti-Cimex

DISTRAUGHT
Tracks: / Distraught.
12" **Single:** Released 6 Jun '87, on Skysaw, by Skysaw Records. Catalogue no: **SKY 5**

Antidote

DESTROY FASCISM
Tracks: / Destroy fascism.
7" **Single:** Released 5 May '87, on Loony Tunes, by Loony Tunes Records. Catalogue no: **TUNE 002**

Antietam

UNTIL NOW
Tracks: / Until now.
7" **Single:** Released Sep '86, on Homestead, Catalogue no: **HMS 059**

Antilles

LET'S SHAKE
Tracks: / Let's shake / Simon's melody.
7" **Single:** Released Feb '82, on Ice, by Ice Records. Deleted Feb '87. Catalogue no: **ICE 53**
12" **Single:** Released Feb '82, on Ice, by Ice Records. Deleted Feb '87. Catalogue no: **ICET 53**

Antilles (group)

I'VE GOT TO HAVE YOU
Tracks: / I've got to have you.
12" **Single:** Released Apr '83, on Creole, by Creole Records. Catalogue no: **CR 1251**
7" **Single:** Released Apr '83, on Creole, by Creole Records. Catalogue no: **CR 51**

Anti-Nowhere League

Biographical details: One of the last out-and-out British punk bands to chart, the Anti-Nowhere League -- Animal, Magoo, P.J. and Winston -- spent most of 1981 touring the London area. Their debut single, a 100 mph version of Ralph McTell's 1975 smash Streets Of London, became an indie favourite that crossed over to the national chart in early '82, peaking at No 48. Ten thousand copies were seized by the police on an obscenity charge. Later that year the band chalked up two further minor hits plus a Top Thirty album. It seemed that while the Human League were absent from the charts there was room for another League: but this League's attitude to humans was succinctly expressed by the title of their second single, *"Hate People"* (Bob MacDonald, 1984.).

FOR YOU
Tracks: / For you.
7" **Single:** Released Jul '87, on WXYZ, Catalogue no: **ABCD 6**

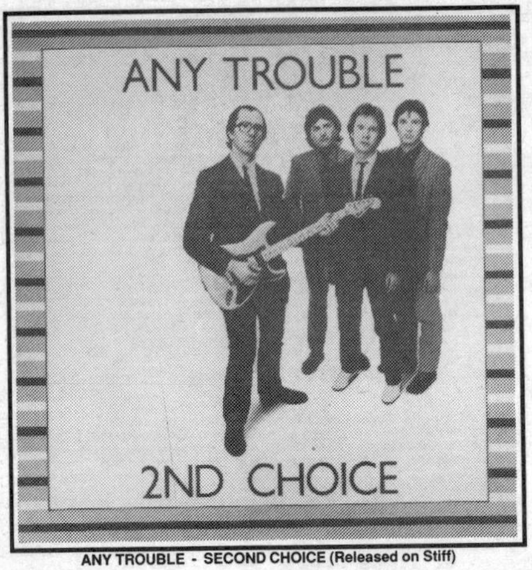

ANY TROUBLE - SECOND CHOICE (Released on Stiff)

I HATE PEOPLE
Tracks: / I hate people.
7" Single: Released Jul '87, on WXYZ, Catalogue no: **ABCD 2**

OUT ON THE WASTELAND
Tracks: / Out on the wasteland / We will survive / Queen and country.
7" Pic: Released Dec '84, on ABC (indie), Catalogue no: **ABCS 004P**
7" Single: Released Dec '84, on ABC (indie), Catalogue no: **ABCS 004**
12" Single: Released Dec '84, on ABC (indie), Catalogue no: **ABCS 004T**

STREETS OF LONDON
Tracks: / Streets of London.
7" Single: Released Nov '88, on WXYZ, Catalogue no: **ABCD 1**

WOMAN
Tracks: / Woman / Rocker.
7" Pic: Released Jun '82, on WXYZ, Catalogue no: **ABCDP 4**
7" Single: Released Jun '82, on WXYZ, Catalogue no: **ABCD 4**

Antisect

OUT FROM THE VOID
Tracks: / Out from the void.
7" Single: Released Oct '85, on Endangered Musik, Catalogue no: **EDR 4**

Anti-System

DEFENCE OF THE REALM
Tracks: / Defence of the realm.
7" EP: Released Jun '83, on Paragon, Catalogue no: **PAX 11**

STRANGE LOVE
Tracks: / Strange love.
7" Single: Released Apr '85, on Reconciliation, Catalogue no: **RECONCILE 3**

Antlers

IT LOOKS LIKE REINDEER
Tracks: / It looks like reindeer / You can change my world.
7" Single: Released Dec '82, on Kingdom, by Kingdom Records. Catalogue no: **KV 8011**

Antonia

LA BAMBA
Tracks: / La bamba.
7" Single: Released Oct '83, on Calibre, Deleted '85. Catalogue no: **CAB 117**
12" Single: Released Oct '83, on Calibre, Deleted '85. Catalogue no: **CABL 117**

Antoniou, Tony

CAN'T GIVE YOU ALL MY LOVE
Tracks: / Can't give you all my love.
12" Single: Released Jul '86, on Adventures In Clubland, Catalogue no: **AICT 4**
7" Single: Released Jul '86, on Adventures In Clubland, Catalogue no: **AIC 4**

SEND IN THE NIGHT
Tracks: / Send in the night.
7" Single: Released Jul '84, on Spartan, Catalogue no: **SP 12**

STREET SOUND
Tracks: / Street sound / Sound on sound.
12" Single: Released Dec '82, on Elite Records, by Elite Records. Deleted '84. Catalogue no: **DAZZ 17**

Antony, David

MY LADY DIANA
Tracks: / My lady Diana / When boy meets girl.
7" Single: Released May '81, on Pinnacle, by Pinnacle Records. Deleted May '84. Catalogue no: **THOMO 81**

Antz Avenue

CHEERS CLUB, THE
Tracks: / Cheers club, The.
7" EP: Released Nov '85, on Boulevard, by Boulevard Records. Catalogue no: **BR 5**

Anusia

IMAGINATION
Tracks: / Imagination.
12" Single: on Metropolis (France), by Island Records. Catalogue no: **CART 254**
7" Single: Released Oct '82, on Metropolis (France), by Island Records. Catalogue no: **CAR 254**

Anvil

MAKE IT UP TO YOU
Tracks: / Make it up to you.
7" Single: Released Jun '83, on Noir, by Noir Records. Catalogue no: **MET 002**
12" Single: Released Jun '83, on Noir, by Noir Records. Catalogue no: **MET 12 002**

STEAMIN
Tracks: / Steamin'.
7" Single: Released Aug '82, on Noir, by Noir Records. Catalogue no: **MET 001**
12" Single: Released Aug '82, on Noir, by Noir Records. Catalogue no: **MET 12 001**

Anxiety, Annie

AS I LIE IN YOUR ARMS
Tracks: / As I lie in your arms.
12" Single: Released Jul '87, on One Little Indian, by One Little Indian Records. Catalogue no: **12TP 6**

HIER ENCORE
Tracks: / Hier encore.
7" Single: Released Feb '88, on One Little Indian, by One Little Indian Records. Catalogue no: **TP 13**
12" Single: Released 5 Mar '88, on One Little Indian, by One Little Indian Records. Catalogue no: **12TP 13**

Any Day Now

I'LL BE WAITING
Tracks: / I'll be waiting / Under your spell.
7" Single: Released Oct '86, on A&M, by A&M Records. Deleted '87. Catalogue no: **AM 355**

SHOW ME THE WAY (GRAND GROOVE)
Tracks: / Show me the way (Grand groove) / Shock tactics / Show me the way (No Derek) (On 12" version only).
7" Single: Released Apr '86, on A&M, by A&M Records. Deleted '88. Catalogue no: **AM 310**
12" Single: Released Apr '86, on A&M, by A&M Records. Deleted '88. Catalogue no: **AMY 310**

Any Trouble

GIRLS ARE ALWAYS RIGHT
Tracks: / Girls are always right / No idea.
7" Single: Released Sep '80, on Stiff, by Stiff Records. Catalogue no: **BUY 94**

I'LL BE YOUR MAN
Tracks: / I'll be your man.
12" Single: Released Sep '83, on EMI-America, by EMI Records. Catalogue no: **EA 163**
7" Single: Released Sep '83, on EMI-America, by EMI Records. Catalogue no: **EA 163**

NICE GIRLS
Tracks: / Nice girls.
7" Single: Released Jan '83, on Stiff, by Stiff Records. Catalogue no: **BUY 74**
7" Single: Released Feb '80, on Stiff, by Stiff Records. Catalogue no: **BUY 74**

OPEN FIRE
Tracks: / Open fire.
7" Single: Released Jun '84, on EMI-America, by EMI Records. Catalogue no: **EA 173**

SECOND CHOICE (see panel top left)
Tracks: / Second choice / The name of the game.
7" Single: Released Jun '80, on Stiff, by Stiff Records. Catalogue no: **BUY 79**

TOUCH AND GO
Tracks: / Touch and go.
7" Single: Released May '83, on EMI-America, by EMI Records. Catalogue no: **EA 154**
12" Single: Released May '83, on EMI-America, by EMI Records. Catalogue no: **12 EA 154**

TROUBLE WITH LOVE
Tracks: / Trouble with love / She'll belong to me.
7" Single: Released Jul '81, on Stiff, by Stiff Records. Catalogue no: **BUY 119**

YESTERDAY'S LOVE
Tracks: / Yesterday's love / Nice girls.
7" Single: Released Mar '80, on Stiff, by Stiff Records. Deleted '83. Catalogue no: **BUY 74**

Anya

ONE WORD
Tracks: / One word.
7" Single: Released Apr '87, on Rocket, by Rocket Records. Deleted Dec '87. Catalogue no: **BLAST 2**
12" Single: Released Apr '87, on Rocket, by Rocket Records. Deleted Dec '87. Catalogue no: **BLAST 212**

Anyways

CONFESSION
Tracks: / Confession.
7" Single: Released 10 Oct '87, on Notown, Catalogue no: **NO 001**

AOA

WHO ARE THEY TRYING TO CON
Tracks: / Who are they trying to con.
12" Single: Released May '85, on Children Of The Revolution, by Revolver Records. Catalogue no: **COR 4**

Apartment

CAR
Tracks: / Car / Winter.
7" Single: Released Mar '80, on Heartbeat, by Mainline Records. Deleted '83. Catalogue no: **PULSE 7**

Apartments

ALL YOU WANTED
Tracks: / All you wanted / Sunset Hotel / What's the morning for (Extra track on 12" only) / Black road shines, The (Extra track on 12" only).
7" Single: Released Mar '86, on Rough Trade, by Rough Trade Records. Catalogue no: **RT 188**
12" Single: Released Mar '86, on Rough Trade, by Rough Trade Records. Catalogue no: **RTT 188**

SHYEST TIME, THE
Tracks: / Shyest time, The.
12" Single: Released '88, on Glass, by Glass Records. Catalogue no: **GLASS 12055**
7" Single: Released '88, on Glass, by Glass Records. Catalogue no: **GLASS 055**

APB

CHAIN REACTION
Tracks: / Chain reaction.
7" Single: Released Jul '81, on Oily, by Oily Records. Catalogue no: **SLICK 6**

DANCEABILITY
Tracks: / Danceability / Crazy day rainy day / Palace filled with love.
12" Single: Released Apr '84, on Albion, by Albion Records. Catalogue no: **12ION 160**

MISSING YOU ALREADY
Tracks: / Missing you already / Best of our love / Boy, you're not so great.
7" Single: Released 10 Oct '87, on Red River, Catalogue no: **YTHAN 6**
12" Single: Released Apr '89, on Red River, Catalogue no: **YTHANT 6**

ONE DAY
Tracks: / One day.
7" Single: Released Aug '83, on Oily, by Oil Records. Catalogue no: **SLICK 10**
12" Single: Released Aug '83, on Oily, b Oily Records. Catalogue no: **SLICK 1210**

OPEN YOUR EYES
Tracks: / Open your eyes / Sunset song.
7" Single: Released Apr '86, on Red Rive Catalogue no: **YTHAN 3**
12" Single: Released Apr '86, on Red Rive Catalogue no: **YTHANT 3**

PALACE FILLED WITH LOVE
Tracks: / Palace filled with love / All your li with me.
7" Single: Released Apr '82, on Oily, by Oil Records. Catalogue no: **SLICK 8**

RAINY DAY
Tracks: / Rainy day.
7" Single: Released Oct '82, on Oily, by Oi Records. Catalogue no: **SLICK 9**

SHOOT YOU DOWN
Tracks: / Shoot you down.
7" Single: Released Oct '81, on Oily, by Oi Records. Catalogue no: **SLICK 7**

SOMETHING TO BELIEVE IN
Tracks: / Something to believe in.
7" Single: Released Oct '85, on Red Rive Catalogue no: **YTHAN 2**
12" Single: Released Oct '85, on Red Rive Catalogue no: **YTHANT 2**

SUMMER LOVE
Tracks: / Summer love.
12" Single: Released Jul '85, on Red Rive Catalogue no: **YTHANT 1**
7" Single: Released Jul '85, on Red Rive Catalogue no: **YTHAN 1**

WHAT KIND OF GIRL
Tracks: / What kind of girl.
12" Single: Released Jun '84, on Albion, Albion Records. Catalogue no: **12ION 16**
7" Single: Released Jun '84, on Albion, Albion Records. Catalogue no: **ION 160**

Aphrodisiac

YOUR LOVE
Tracks: / Your love.
12" Single: Released Feb '89, on Groove (USA), Catalogue no: **NG 006**
7" Single: Released Sep '89, on Champi by Champion Records. Catalogue **CHAMP 216**
12" Single: Released Sep '89, on Cha pion, by Champion Records. Catalogue **CHAMP 12216**

Aphrodite's Child

Biographical details: Vangelis (Papat nassiou), Demis Roussos and Lucas Sic as got together around 1963 and in '68 th scored a massive hit throughout the Co nent and Scandinavia with an English l guage adaptation of a 17th century Germ tune, Rain And Tears. The single was rat less well received in Britain, peaking at 30 -- it was their only UK hit. Two memb of the trio progressed to international s stardom: the high-pitched wail of Rouss sold truckloads of albums throughout rope during the 70's, while Vangelis w perfecting his instrumental wizadry, cu nating in Chariots Of Fire. (Bob MacDon 1984.)

A Greek pop trio formed in 1963: Lu Sideras, Demis Roussos (later succes solo) and Evangelos Papathanassiou (la with Jon Anderson as Jon & Vangelis, later famous as film composer). All pla several instruments. Greece was more sistant to Anglo USA pop style at this t than any other country in Europe; on t way to London in 1968 they were signe Philips by Piere Sberre in Paris, who duced *Rain and tears*: the 17th century man sung in English was a massive h France, No. 2 in Italy, No. 3 in Turkey, m top 10 in Belgium, Netherlands, Spain, banon; No. 30 UK; did not make the G Top 20; more hits followed until they mid-70's. Vangelis' synthesised film m has made him very rich: music from *Cha of fire* topped many charts in 1981. He sued by EMI on behalf of Stavros Logar over similarity of *Chariot* theme to latter's theme *City of violets*; EMI lost in '87. (Do Clarke, July 1988).

RAIN AND TEARS
Tracks: / Rain and tears.
7" Single: on Mercury, by Phonogram Catalogue no: **MF 1039**

Apocalypse

TEDDY
Tracks: / Teddy / Release.
12" Single: Released Sep '82, on Jamm Catalogue no: **12 CREAT 5**
7" Single: Released Sep '82, on Jamm Catalogue no: **CREATE 5**

Apocalypse Jive

LIFE (THE OUTCOME)
Tracks: / Life (the outcome).
7" Single: Released Nov '82, on Comp by Company Records. Catalogue no

820911

Apollinaires

ENVY THE LOVE
Tracks: / Envy the love / Give it up.
12" Single: Released '83, on Chrysalis, by Chrysalis Records. Deleted '87. Catalogue no: **CHS TT 1222**
7" Single: Released '83, on Chrysalis, by Chrysalis Records. Deleted '87. Catalogue no: **CHS TT 22**

FEELING'S GONE, THE
Tracks: / Feeling's gone, The / Feeling's back, The / Feelings gone, The (dance mix) (Only on 12" version.) / Bongo medley (extremely long version) (Only on 12" version.).
7" Single: Released '83, on Two-Tone, by Chrysalis Records. Deleted '87. Catalogue no: **CHS TT 20**
12" Single: Released '83, on Chrysalis, by Chrysalis Records. Deleted '87. Catalogue no: **CHS TT 1220**

Apollo 11

ONE SMALL STEP
Tracks: / One small step.
12" Single: Released '88, on Debut, by Skratch Records. Catalogue no: **DEBTX 3041**

Apollo 100

JOY (JESU, JOY OF MAN'S DESIRING)
Tracks: / Joy (Jesu, joy of man's desiring) / Can can.
7" Single: Released Nov '80, on Young Blood, by Young Blood Records. Deleted Nov '83. Catalogue no: **YB 97**

Apollonia 6

SEX SHOOTER
Tracks: / Sex shooter.
7" Single: Released Oct '84, on Warner Bros., by WEA Records. Catalogue no: **929 182 7**

Apology For Innocence

ACROSS THE WIRE
Tracks: / Across the wire / Days alone.
7" Single: Released May '82, on Illusive, Catalogue no: **AF 11**
12" Single: Released May '82, on Illusive, Catalogue no: **12 AF 11**

A-Pop

ART OF PERSUASION
Tracks: / Art of persuasion (radio mix) / Rock and roll.
12" Single: Released Oct '86, on Jungle, by Jungle Records. Catalogue no: **JUNG 25T**
7" Single: Released Oct '86, on Jungle, by Jungle Records. Catalogue no: **JUNG 25**

Apostles

CURSE OF THE CREATURE
Tracks: / Curse of the creature.
7" Single: Released Jun '84, on Pigs For Slaughter, Catalogue no: **PFS 1**
7" Single: Released Jun '84, on Scum, Catalogue no: **SCUM 3**

DEATH TO WACKY POP
Tracks: / Death to wacky pop.
7" Single: Released May '88, on Fight Back, Catalogue no: **FIGHT 9**

RISING FROM THE ASHES
Tracks: / Rising from the ashes.
7" Single: Released Dec '83, on Scum, Catalogue no: **SCUM 2**

SMASH THE SPECTACLE
Tracks: / Fifth apostle, The.
7" EP: Released Mar '85, on Mortarhate, by Mortarhate Records. Catalogue no: **MORT 9**

Appice, Carmine

BE MY BABY
Tracks: / Be my baby / I'll leave it up to you.
7" Single: Released Feb '82, on Riva, by Riva Records. Catalogue no: **RIVA 32**

Apple Boutique

LOVE RESISTANCE
Tracks: / Love resistance.
7" Single: Released Mar '88, on Creation, by Creation Records. Catalogue no: **CRE 052**
12" Single: Released Mar '88, on Creation, by Creation Records. Catalogue no: **CRE 052T**

Apple Junior

JAILHOUSE RAINDROPS
Tracks: / Jailhouse raindrops.
12" Single: Released Jul '89, on Hill Crest, Catalogue no: **HCR 011**

Apple Mosaic

HONEY IF
Tracks: / Honey if / Mary Hell / Me, myself and I (Extra track on 12").
7" Single: Released Jul '87, on MDM, by MDM Communications. Deleted May '88. Catalogue no: **MDM 22**
12" Single: Released Jul '87, on MDM, by MDM Communications. Deleted May '88. Catalogue no: **MDM 22-12**

VELVET AVENUE
Tracks: / Velvet Avenue / One more step to go / Never see his face (Available on 12" only.).
7" Single: Released Sep '87, on MDM, by MDM Communications. Deleted May '88. Catalogue no: **MDM 23**
12" Single: Released Sep '87, on MDM, by MDM Communications. Deleted May '88. Catalogue no: **MDM 23-12**

Applejacks

Biographical details: Coming from Solihull, the Applejacks were one of the endless groups that rode the crest of British Beat boom in 1964. They attracted a lot of publicity by having a female bassist, in those days a complete novelty. Megan Davies was the sister of Kinks frontman Ray Davies and beat her brother's group to the charts by five months. *Tell me when* reached No.7 in the spring of '64 and was followed by a Lennon/McCartney song *Like dreamers do* which peaked No. 20. The Applejacks were a lightweight combo who were rather thin on talent and, just as the Kinks were getting their string of Top 10 his underway, this act were having their third and final chart success. They are not to be confused with an American outfit called the Applejacks, who had a couple of US Top 40 hits in the late fifties. (Bob MacDonald, 1988).

LIKE DREAMERS DO
Tracks: / Like dreamers do.
7" Single: on Decca, by Decca Records. Catalogue no: **F 11916**

TELL ME WHEN
Tracks: / Tell me when / Baby Jane.
7" Single: Released May '82, on Decca, by Decca Records. Deleted '88. Catalogue no: **F 11833**

TELL ME WHEN/JUST LIKE EDDIE
Tracks: / Tell me when / Just like Eddie.
7" Single: Released Oct '83, on Old Gold, by Old Gold Records. Catalogue no: **OG 9583**

THREE LITTLE WORDS
Tracks: / Three little words.
7" Single: on Decca, by Decca Records. Catalogue no: **F11981**

Applewhite, Charlie

BLUE STAR
Tracks: / Blue star.
7" Single: on Brunswick, by Decca Records. Catalogue no: **05416**

Appreciations

I CAN'T HIDE IT
Tracks: / I can't hide it / Stronger than her love / I never knew / Little togetherness.
7" EP: Released Jan '85, on Soul Supply, by Soul Supply Records. Catalogue no: **7SS 104**

April

BOYS COME AND GO
Tracks: / Boys come and go.
12" Single: Released Apr '85, on Record Shack, by Record Shack Records. Catalogue no: **SOHOT 40**
7" Single: Released Apr '85, on Record Shack, by Record Shack Records. Catalogue no: **SOHO 40**

April, Helen

HOUSEWIVES CHOICE
Tracks: / Housewives choice / Housewives choice (pt 2).
7" Single: Released Oct '81, on A&M, by A&M Records. Deleted Oct '84. Catalogue no: **AMS 8168**

April love

LA BLONDE
Tracks: / La blonde / Stay with me now.
7" Single: Released May '80, on Ariola, by BMG Records (UK). Deleted May '83. Catalogue no: **ARO 230**

April Moon

RECKLESS HEART
Tracks: / Reckless heart / Let the music shine in you.
7" Single: Released May '84, on Red Bus, by Red Bus Records. Catalogue no: **RBUS 92**

April Showers

ABANDONED SHIP
Tracks: / Abandoned ship.
7" Single: Released Jun '84, on Big Star, by Chrysalis Records. Catalogue no: **CHS 2787**
12" Single: Released Jun '84, on Big Star, by Chrysalis Records. Catalogue no: **CHS 12 2787**

April Wine

ALL OVER TOWN
Tracks: / All over town / Crash and burn.
7" Single: Released Jan '81, on Capitol, by EMI Records. Deleted Jan '84. Catalogue no: **CL 16181**

ARCADIA - ELECTION DAY (Released on EMI)

I LIKE TO ROCK
Tracks: / I like to rock / Rock 'n' roll is a vicious game / Before the dawn / Roller.
7" Single: on Capitol, by EMI Records. Catalogue no: **CL 16121**

JUST BETWEEN YOU AND ME
Tracks: / Just between you and me / Big city girls.
7" Single: on Capitol, by EMI Records. Catalogue no: **CL 16184**

LADIES MAN
Tracks: / Ladies man / Oowatanite / Get ready for love (Only available on 12" single.) / I like to rock (Only available on 12" single.).
12" Single: Released Aug '80, on Capitol, by EMI Records. Deleted '83. Catalogue no: **12CL 16164**
7" Single: Released Aug '80, on Capitol, by EMI Records. Deleted '83. Catalogue no: **CL 16164**

SIGN OF THE GYPSY QUEEN
Tracks: / Sign of the gypsy queen / Crash and burn.
7" Single: Released May '81, on Capitol, by EMI Records. Deleted May '84. Catalogue no: **CL 205**

Aqua Regia

NEW YORK CITY SMILE ON ME
Tracks: / New York city smile on me.
12" Single: Released Jun '89, on Irdia, Catalogue no: **IRDAQR 5**

Aquarian Dream

YOU'RE A STAR
Tracks: / You're a star.
7" Single: Released '88, on Elektra, by Elektra Records (UK). Catalogue no: **LV 7**

Aquila

FALL
Tracks: / Fall / Threatened.
7" Single: Released Oct '82, on Graphic, by Graphic Records. Catalogue no: **G001**

Aquizim

AFRICAN CONNECTION
Tracks: / African connection / African voyage.
12" Single: Released Aug '83, on Ariwa Sounds, by Ariwa Sounds. Catalogue no: **ARI 1025**

AFRICAN DREAM
Tracks: / African dream / English girl.
12" Single: Released Oct '82, on Jah Shaka, Catalogue no: **JS 826**

KUNTE KINTE
Tracks: / Kunte kinte.
12" Single: Released Feb '83, on Ariwa Sounds, by Ariwa Sounds. Catalogue no: **ARI 1015**

TIME OF MY LIFE
Tracks: / Time of my life, The / Sheila.
12" Single: Released Sep '82, on Ariwa Sounds, by Ariwa Sounds. Catalogue no: **ARI 007**

TRUE TRUE LOVING
Tracks: / True true loving / Concrete slaveship.
12" Single: Released May '82, on Ariwa Sounds, by Ariwa Sounds. Catalogue no: **ARID 1005**

Arabeque

TIME TO SAY GOODBYE
Tracks: / Time to say goodbye.
12" Single: Released Nov '85, on ZYX (Germany), Catalogue no: **ZYX 5330**

Aragorn

BLACK ICE
Tracks: / Black ice / Noonday.
7" Single: Released Feb '81, on Neat, by Neat Records. Deleted '88. Catalogue no: **NEAT 07**

Aran, Duncan

TEACH ME HOW TO DANCE
Tracks: / Teach me how to dance / I saw a star.
7" Single: Released Apr '81, on Pulsar, by Lismor Records. Catalogue no: **PUS 102**

Arawaks

JUST WHEN I NEEDED YOU MOST
Tracks: / Just when I needed you most.
12" Single: on Burning Sounds, by Burning Sounds Records. Deleted May '88. Catalogue no: **BSD 039**

Arbeid Adelt

DAG DAT HET ZONLICH NIET MEER SCHEEN, DE
Tracks: ./ Dag det het zonlich niet meer scheen, De.
7" Single: Released Aug '82, on Parsley (Belgium), Catalogue no: **PP 018**

Arc

WAR OF THE RING
Tracks: / War of the ring.
7" Single: Released Nov '81, on Slipped Discs, by Slipped Discs Records. Catalogue no: **SD 001**

Arcadia

ELECTION DAY (see panel above)
Tracks: / Election day / She's moody and grey, she's mean and she's res.
7" Single: Released Oct '85, on EMI, by EMI Records. Catalogue no: **NSR 1**
12" Single: Released Oct '85, on EMI, by EMI Records. Catalogue no: **12 NSR 1**

ELECTION DAY (CRYPTIC CUT)
Tracks: / Election day (cryptic cut).
Note: Cryptic cut - no voice
12" Single: Released Nov '85, on EMI (Odeon), by EMI Records. Deleted '87. Catalogue no: **12NRSA 1**

FLAME, THE
Tracks: / Flame / Flame game / Election day (Extra track on 12" only).
7" Single: Released Jul '86, on EMI (Odeon), by EMI Records. Deleted '87. Catalogue no: **NSR 3**
12" Single: Released Jul '86, on EMI (Odeon), by EMI Records. Deleted '87. Catalogue no: **12 NSR 3**

PROMISE, THE
Tracks: / Promise, The / Rose Arcana / Promise, The (ext) (Extra track on 12" only).
7" Single: Released Jan '86, on EMI (Odeon), by EMI Records. Deleted '87. Catalogue no: **NSR 2**

12" Single: Released Jan '86, on EMI (Odeon), by EMI Records. Deleted '87. Catalogue no: **12 NSR 2**

Arcadians

WITH ALL OUR LOVING
Tracks: / With all our loving.
7" Single: Released Dec '84, on Les Disques Du Crepuscule(Belgium), by Les Disques Du Crepuscule(Belgium). Catalogue no: **7TWI 440**

Arcainians

CHRISTMAS IN JAMAICA
Tracks: / Christmas in Jamaica / Christmas in Jamaica (dub).
12" Single: Released Jan '86, on Jama, Catalogue no: **JADC 0025**

Arch

AS QUIET AS
Tracks: / As quiet as.
12" Single: Released Jun '87, on Anything But, Catalogue no: **ABR 016**

STAY LAY
12" Single: Released '89, on Anything But, Catalogue no: **ABR 024**

Arch Criminals

HANG
Tracks: / Hang.
12" Single: Released May '88, on Fight Back, Catalogue no: **FIGHT 8**

Archangel, Natalie

MR PERFECT FOR ME
Tracks: / Mr. Perfect for me / Let's make love.
7" Single: Released Aug '87, on CBS, by CBS Records. Catalogue no: **650939 7**
12" Single: Released Aug '87, on CBS, by CBS Records. Catalogue no: **650939 6**

Archar, Zehn

CHARM CITY BLUES
Tracks: / Charm city blues / Suburbia hard.
7" Single: Released Apr '80, on Omegalphia, Deleted '83. Catalogue no: **40591/2**

Archer, Robyn

STAR IS TORN , A
Tracks: / Star is torn, A.
7" EP: Released Aug '82, on Cube, Catalogue no: **HBUG 92**

Archer, Yvonne

AIN'T NOBODY
Tracks: / Ain't nobody.
12" Single: Released Dec '84, on Freedom Sounds, Catalogue no: **VG 013**

Archies

Biographical details: Despite the fact that they never really existed, the Archies logged eight weeks at No. 1 in Britain in 1969 with *Sugar sugar*, the ultimate bubblegum record. No other One Hit Wonder has ever had as many weeks at no. 1 with their solitary hit. The Archies was a childrens' TV cartoon series and the musicians who played under that name were session players. Lead vocalist Ron Dante was simultaneously enjoying hit status as lead singer on the Cuff-Links *Tracy*. He also became associated with Barry Manilow. Co-writer Andy Kim had a smash single in his own right in 1974 called *Rock me gently*. No One Hit Wonders in the States. *Sugar sugar* was preceded by *Bang shang a lang* (No.22) and followed by *Jingle jangle* (No. 10) and *Who's your baby* (No.40). (Bob MacDonald, 1988).

SUGAR SUGAR
Tracks: / Sugar sugar / Sugar and spice / Jingle jangle.
7" Single: Released Jul '82, on Old Gold, by Old Gold Records. Catalogue no: **OG 9084**
7" Single: on RCA, by BMG Records (UK). Catalogue no: **RCA 1872**
12" Single: Released Jul '87, on Debut, by Skratch Records. Catalogue no: **DEBTX 3030**
7" Single: Released Jul '87, on Debut, by Skratch Records. Catalogue no: **DEBT 3030**

Architects Of Disaster

CUCUMBER SANDWICH
Tracks: / Cucumber sandwich.
7" Single: Released Nov '82, on Neuter, Catalogue no: **NEU 1**

Ardoin, Lawrence

ZYDECO
Special: Released '88, on Arhoolie (USA), by Arhoolie Records (USA). Catalogue no: **C 1091**

Areeba-reeba

PEANUT VENDOR, THE
Tracks: / Peanut vendor (fiesta mix) / Peanut vendor (hornpella mix) / Peanut vendor (extended fiesta mix) (12" only) / Peanut vendor (percussia mix) (12" only) / Peanut vendor (bonus beat) (12" only).
7" Single: Released Aug '88, on MCA, by MCA Records. Deleted 1 Jul '89. Catalogue no: **MCA 1270**
12" Single: Released Aug '88, on MCA, by MCA Records. Catalogue no: **MCAT 1270**

Areety, Colin

LOVE AND PAIN
Tracks: / Love and pain / Midnight disco train.
7" Single: Released Dec '82, on Troubador, Catalogue no: **TRUB 5**

Arena

BACK A YARD
Tracks: / Back a yard.
12" Single: Released Jul '82, on City Boy, Catalogue no: **CB 002**

BLOW MY MIND
Tracks: / Blow my mind / In love.
12" Single: Released Nov '82, on City Boy, Catalogue no: **CBD 003**

LOVE IS HERE
Tracks: / Love is here.
12" Single: Released Jan '84, on City Boy, Catalogue no: **CBD 005**

TURN AROUND
Tracks: / Turn around.
12" Single: Released Apr '83, on City Boy, Catalogue no: **CBD 004**

Argent

Biographical details: This four-piece British group was formed in 1969 by former Zombie Rod Argent. A track from their eponymous debut album, a song called /Lair'D, became an American top 10 hit for Three Dog Night in 1971. Argent introduced their third album /All Together Now'D with a transatlantic top 5 single in their own right, /Hold Your Head Up'D. After a second UK top 20 single, /God Gave Rock And Roll To You'D, the band went into commercial decline. Russ Ballard quit in 1974 and pursued a solo career. While being relatively unsuccessful as a performer, he established an astonishing reputation as a song-writer, and composed numerous hits over the following decade. Among the acts who have charted in the UK and/or US with his songs are Rainbow, Santana, America, Frida and Agnetha, to name just five. The band folded in 1976 and Rod Argent commenced a solo career encompassed various diverse activities. (Bob MacDonald, 1984).

GOD GAVE ROCK & ROLL TO YOU
Tracks: / God gave rock'n'roll to you.
7" Single: Released Nov '88, on Epic, by CBS Records. Catalogue no: **EPC 1243**

HOLD YOUR HEAD UP
Tracks: / Hold your head up.
7" Single: Released Jul '82, on Old Gold, by Old Gold Records. Catalogue no: **OG 9187**
7" Single: Released Jul '87, on Epic, by CBS Records. Catalogue no: **EPC 7786**

TRAGEDY
Tracks: / Tragedy.
7" Single: Released Nov '88, on Epic, by CBS Records. Catalogue no: **EPC 8115**

Argent, Rod

BABY DON'T YOU CRY NO MORE
Tracks: / Baby don't you cry no more / Teenage years.
7" Single: Released Sep '88, on MMC, by MMC Records. Deleted Jun '89. Catalogue no: **MMCS 1**

Ariel Fix

TAKE IT FROM HERE
Tracks: / Take it from here / Somewhere.
7" Single: Released May '81, on Island, by Island Records. Deleted May '84. Catalogue no: **WIP 6698**

Arista Funksters

ARISTA FUNKSTERS
Tracks: / Baby not tonight: *Various artists* / Song for Jeremy: *Various artists* / Red piper: *Various artists* / Saturday night: *Various artists*.
12" Single: Released Sep '81, on Arista, by BMG Records (UK). Catalogue no: **ARIST 12430**

Arizona Smoke Revue

ALL FALL DOWN
Tracks: / All fall down / Border song.
7" Single: Released Mar '81, on Rola, by Rola Records. Catalogue no: **R 007**

DON'T LOOK BACK
Tracks: / Don't look back / Further along.
7" Single: Released Sep '81, on Rola, by Rola Records. Catalogue no: **R 010**
7" Single: Released Feb '82, on Rola, by Rola Records. Deleted Feb '87. Catalogue no: **R 008**

FACTORY
Tracks: / Factory / Last day of July.
7" Single: Released Apr '82, on Rola, by Rola Records. Catalogue no: **R 011**

MOHAMMEDS RADIO
Tracks: / Mohammed's radio.
7" Single: Released Apr '83, on Rola, by Rola Records. Catalogue no: **R 013**

JOAN ARMATRADING - ALL THE WAY FROM AMERICA (Released on A & M)

SMOKIN'
Tracks: / Smokin' / Morning sky / Feeling lazy / Worksong / Sam old man.
7" EP: Released Aug '80, on Avada, Catalogue no: **AVEP 108**

Ark

LISTEN UP
Tracks: / Listen up.
7" Single: Released Aug '88, on Rough Trade, by Rough Trade Records. Catalogue no: **RTT 229**

Ark Royal

Biographical details: The ship's company and Royal Marine band of H.M.S Ark Royal had a minor Christmas hit in 1978 with their rendition of /The Last Farewell'D. It peaked at No.46, 44 places lower than the original 1975 version by Roger Whittaker. (Bob MacDonald).

LAST FAREWELL, THE
Tracks: / Last farewell, The.
7" Single: Released Dec '78, on BBC, by BBC Records & Tapes. Catalogue no: **RESL 61**

Arka

IN PARADISUM
Tracks: / In paradisum.
12" Single: Released Apr '87, on One G, by One G.Productions. Catalogue no: **ONEG 001T**

Arlana

YOU CAN'T KEEP BREAKING MY HEART
Tracks: / You can't keep breaking my heart.
12" Single: Released Aug '83, on Hitman, Catalogue no: **HM 002**

Ar-Log

CARMARTHEN OAK
Tracks: / Carmarthen oak / Llongau Carnarfon.
7" Single: Released Nov '80, on Dingle's, by Dingle's Records. Catalogue no: **SID 224**

Armalite

LIVING ON THE EDGE
Tracks: / Living on the edge
.
7" Single: Released Apr '84, on Sonar, by Sonar Records. Catalogue no: **SON 3**

Armando

CONFUSION
Tracks: / Confusion.

12" Single: Released Nov '87, on Westbrook (USA), Catalogue no: **AGWB 4**

Armando, Don

I'M AN INDIAN TOO
Tracks: / I'm an Indian too / Deputy of love.
7" Single: Released Sep '82, on Island, by Island Records. Deleted Sep '85. Catalogue no: **WIP 6557**
7" Single: Released Jan '80, on Cobra, Deleted '83. Catalogue no: **COB 4**
12" Single: Released Sep '82, on Island, by Island Records. Deleted Sep '85. Catalogue no: **12WIP 6557**

Armatrading, Joan

Biographical details: Joan Armatrading was born in 1950 in St Kitts, West Indies, and emigrated to Birmingham in 1956. The singer/songwriter's first album was a duet with Pam Nestor, *Whatever's for us* in 1974; her debut solo album was *back to the night* in 1975. Her 1976 album *Joan Armatrading*, was described by producer Glyn Johns as the best he'd ever worked on. She doesn't need big hits; her albums are among the best in the genre, and they just keep on selling. (Donald Clarke, August '88)
Joan Armatrading was born in St Kitts, West Indies, and emigrated to Birmingham with her family at the age of eight. In the early seventies she cut her first album *Whatever's for us* - a collaboration with Pam Nestor. Going fully solo in the middle of the decade, her second album *Back to the night* won sufficient acclaim to build up a cult following. Teaming up with mega-producer Glyn Johns (famed for his work with the Stones, Who, Eagles and many others), Armatrading issued a self-titled third album in 1976. This LP transformed into a major artist, logging six months on the album chart and yielding a top 21 single *Love and affection*. The fact that this was her first foray into either chart, combined with the LP's simple *Joan Armatrading* title led many new fans to believe that this was a debut album - they only later became aware of her previous platters.
Love and affection was an extraordinarily individual single, in a diffrent musical category from anything else in the charts at the time. Armatrading was to wait until 1980 for her next chart single, but it did not matter; the intervening albums *Show some emotion* and *To the limit* continued her unique fusion of sparsely arranged accoustic funk, passionate but uncluttered love songs, perceptive lyrics and deep vocals, and were well received..
Cutting the tie with Glyn Johns, she enlisted Richard Gottehrer to produce her 1980 album *Me myself I*. The title track was a hit single in Britain, while the album continued to widen her audience in both the UK and the US. Subsequent albums *Walk under ladders* and *The key*, produced by Steve Lillywhite, have continued the musical pattern, though a rockier, electric-based feel has gradually been worked in. In 1983 *Drop the pilot* reached No.11 in the singles chart, the closest Armatrading has come to repeating the top 10 success of *Love and affection*. (Bob Mac Donald, 1985)..

ALL THE WAY FROM AMERICA (see panel above)
Tracks: / All the way from America / Is it tomorrow yet.
7" Single: Released Sep '80, on A&M, by A&M Records. Catalogue no: **AMS 7552**

COMPACT HITS: JOAN ARMATRADING
Tracks: / Love and affection / All the way from America / Flight of the wild geese / Willow.
CD 5": Released Apr '88, on A&M, by A&M Records. Deleted Apr '88. Catalogue no: **AMCD 903**

DROP THE PILOT
Tracks: / Drop the pilot / Business is business.

7" Single: Released Feb '83, on A&M, by A&M Records. Deleted '86. Catalogue no: **AMS 8306**

I'M LUCKY
Tracks: / I'm lucky.
7" Single: Released Sep '81, on A&M, by A&M Records. Catalogue no: **AMS 8163**

JESSE
Tracks: / Jesse / Don Juan / Love and affection (Extra track in 12" & double pack only) / Willow (Extra track in 12" only).
7" Single: Released Sep '86, on A&M, by A&M Records. Deleted '88. Catalogue no: **AM 350**
7" Set: Released Sep '86, on A&M, by A&M Records. Deleted Mar '88. Catalogue no: **AMS 350**
12" Single: Released Sep '86, on A&M, by A&M Records. Deleted '88. Catalogue no: **AMY 350**

KIND WORDS (AND A REAL GOOD HEART)
Tracks: / Kind words (and a real good heart) / Figure of speech.
12" Single: Released Apr '86, on A&M, by A&M Records. Deleted '88. Catalogue no: **AMY 315**
7" Single: Released Apr '86, on A&M, by A&M Records. Deleted '88. Catalogue no: **AM 315**

LIVING FOR YOU
Tracks: / Living for you / Innocent request.
12" Single: Released Aug '88, on A&M, by A&M Records. Deleted Feb '89. Catalogue no: **AMY 460**
CD 5": Released Aug '88, on A&M, by A&M Records. Catalogue no: **AMCD 460**
7" Single: Released Aug '88, on A&M, by A&M Records. Deleted Feb '89. Catalogue no: **AM 460**

LONELY LADY
Tracks: / Lonely lady.
7" Single: Released Jun '82, on Cube, Catalogue no: **BUG 93**

LOVE AND AFFECTION
Tracks: / Love and affection / Help yourself.
7" Single: Released '88, on A&M, by A&M Records. Catalogue no: **AMS 7249**

ME MYSELF I (SINGLE)
Tracks: / Me myself I.
7" Single: Released Jun '80, on A&M, by A&M Records. Deleted '82. Catalogue no: **AMS 7527**

NO LOVE
Tracks: / No love / Dollars.
7" Single: Released Jan '82, on A&M, by A&M Records. Catalogue no: **AMS 8179**

REACH OUT
Tracks: / Reach out / Rivers on fire.
7" Single: Released Jul '86, on A&M, by A&M Records. Deleted '87. Catalogue no: **AM 338**

ROSIE
Tracks: / Rosie / How cruel.
7" Single: Released Feb '80, on A&M, by A&M Records. Catalogue no: **AMS 7506**

SHOUTING STAGE, THE (SINGLE)
Tracks: / Shouting stage, The / I really must be going / He wants her (Available on 12" only).
CD 5": Released Jul '88, on A&M, by A&M Records. Catalogue no: **AMCD 449**
7" Single: Released Jul '88, on A&M, by A&M Records. Deleted Feb '89. Catalogue no: **AM 449**
12" Single: Released Jul '88, on A&M, by A&M Records. Deleted Feb '89. Catalogue no: **AMY 449**

SIMON
Tracks: / Simon / He wants her.
7" Single: Released Oct '82, on A&M, by A&M Records. Deleted Oct '84. Catalogue no: **AMS 7541**

STRONGER LOVE
Tracks: / Stronger love / Devil I know, The.
7" Single: Released 7 Nov '88, on A&M, by A&M Records. Catalogue no: **AM 482**

TEMPTATION
Tracks: / Temptation.
7" Single: Released Mar '85, on A&M, by A&M Records. Deleted '88. Catalogue no: **AM 238**
12" Single: Released Feb '85, on A&M, by A&M Records. Deleted '88. Catalogue no: **AMY 238**

THINKING MAN
Tracks: / Thinking man.
7" Single: Released May '85, on A&M, by A&M Records. Deleted '88. Catalogue no: **AM 250**

WHEN I GET IT RIGHT
Tracks: / When I get it right / Crying.
7" Single: Released Oct '81, on A&M, by A&M Records. Deleted '85. Catalogue no: **AMS 8180**

Armenta

I WANNA BE WITH YOU
Tracks: / I wanna be with you.
Cassingle: Released Nov '83, on Savoir Faire, Catalogue no: **FAIT 005**
7" Single: Released Nov '83, on Savoir Faire, Catalogue no: **FAIS 005**

Armoury Show

CASTLES IN SPAIN
Tracks: / Castles in Spain / Gathering, A / Ring those bells (Extra track on 12" only).
7" Single: Released Aug '84, on Parlophone, by EMI Records. Deleted '87. Catalogue no: **R 6079**
7" Single: Released Jan '86, on Parlophone, by EMI Records. Catalogue no: **R 6109**
12" Single: Released Aug '84, on Parlophone, by EMI Records. Deleted '87. Catalogue no: **12R 6079**
12" Single: Released Jan '86, on Parlophone, by EMI Records. Catalogue no: **12 R 6109**

GLORY OF LOVE
Tracks: / Glory of love.
12" Single: Released Jul '85, on EMI, by EMI Records. Catalogue no: **12RA 6098**

NEW YORK CITY
Tracks: / New York City / Whirlwind.
7" Single: Released Apr '87, on Parlophone, by EMI Records. Deleted Jul '87. Catalogue no: **R 6153**
12" Single: Released Apr '87, on Parlophone, by EMI Records. Deleted 31 Jul '88. Catalogue no: **12R 6153**

NEW YORK CITY (DANCE VERSION)
Tracks: / New York City (Dance version) / New York City (New York a go go version).
12" Single: Released Apr '87, on Parlophone, by EMI Records. Catalogue no: **12 RX 6153**

WE CAN BE BRAVE AGAIN
Tracks: / We can be brave again.
7" Single: Released Jan '85, on Parlophone, by EMI Records. Deleted '88. Catalogue no: **R 6087**

Armstrong, Herbie

HERE COMES THE NIGHT
Tracks: / Here comes the night / Back against the wall.
7" Single: Released May '86, on Making Waves, by Celtic Music. Catalogue no: **SURF 111**

JOSIE
Tracks: / Josie / Do you.
7" Single: Released Jan '83, on MMC, by MMC Records. Catalogue no: **MMC 061**

REAL REAL GONE
Tracks: / Real real gone.
7" Single: Released Aug '81, on Avatar, by Avatar Record Corporation. Catalogue no: **AAA 108**

SAVE THE LAST DANCE FOR ME
Tracks: / Save the last dance for me / Do you.
7" Single: Released Mar '84, on MMC, by MMC Records. Catalogue no: **MMC 602**
7" Single: on PRT, by Castle Communications Records. Catalogue no: **7P 281**

Armstrong, Janet

TWO HEARTS IN PAIN
Tracks: / Two hearts in pain / Exploitation.
7" Single: Released Jan '82, on Silent (1), by Silent Records. Deleted Jan '85. Catalogue no: **SSH 1**

Armstrong, Kevin

HOW THE WEST WAS WON
Tracks: / How the west was won.
7" Single: Released May '82, on Oval, by Oval Records. Catalogue no: **OVAL 302**

Armstrong, Louis

Biographical details: ARMSTRONG, Louis When 'Satchmo' died in 1971, he was one of the best-known, best loved entertainers in the world, but many people had forgot (if they ever knew) that he was one of the most important stars in the history of popular music, having invented much of it. He traditionally gave his birth date as the fourth of July 1900, but was probably born a couple of years earlier; he may not have known when he was born, and may have fibbed about his age to avoid the draft during WW1. He came from utter poverty in New Orleans, where he was put in the Coloured Waif's Home for firing a pistol in the air on the fourth of July (USA Independence Day); he learned to play the cornet there. He played in local bands and was invited to Chicago in 1923 to play second cornet to King Oliver in his Creole Jazz Band, which made the first important jazz records that year, preserving the New Orleans style. Pushed by his then-wife, pianist Lillian Hardin, to strike out on his own, he joined Fletcher Henderson's band in New York for a year; it was just a good ragtimey dance band then, but he set it on fire and set New York on its ear. Back in the Midwest in 1925, as the new technology of electrical recording was being adopted, he made the first of his small group recordings, leading studio groups called the Hot Five and the Hot Seven, later editions including pianist Earl Hines; these records changed popular music forever, astonishing every musician who heard them. He set the soloist free from the constraints of the New Orleans style once and for all and did it with such complete mastery that he remains one of the most influential musicians of the century, rivalled only by Charlie Parker and John Coltrane. By the late 1920s he was an enormously popular theatre entertainer, and for the next 20 years he made delightful pop records with his travelling big band; the band itself was not up to much, but there was something magical on every record, and his singing was almost as influential as his playing. In the late '40s he began to play and record again with small groups; the famous Town Hall concert in New York in 1947 (with Hines, Jack Teagarden and other stars) was so successful that the big band was abandoned for good. The best of his later records include the small-group sides made for Victor and USA Decca (now MCA) during that period and a handful on CBS from the '50s, including *Ambassador Satch* (live on world tour) and albums of songs by W.C.Handy.

FAITHFUL HUSSAR, THE
Tracks: / Faithful hussar, The.
7" Single: Released Jul '56, on Philips, by Phonogram Ltd. Deleted Jul '61. Catalogue no: **PB 604**

HELLO DOLLY (SINGLE)
Tracks: / Hello dolly.
7" Single: Released Apr '64, on London-American, Deleted Apr '69. Catalogue no: **HLR 9878**

MACK THE KNIFE
Tracks: / Mack the knife.
7" Single: Released Nov '59, on Philips, by Phonogram Ltd. Deleted Nov '64. Catalogue no: **PB 967**

SUNSHINE OF LOVE
Tracks: / Sunshine of love.
7" Single: Released Jun '68, on Stateside, by EMI Records. Deleted Jun '73. Catalogue no: **SS 2116**

TAKE IT SATCH
Tracks: / Take it Satch / Tiger rag / Mack the knife / Faithful hussar, The / Back o' town blues.
7" EP: Released Jun '56, on Philips, by Phonogram Ltd. Deleted Jun '61. Catalogue no: **BBE 12035**

TAKES TWO TO TANGO
Tracks: / Takes two to tango.
7" Single: Released Dec '52, on Brunswick, by Decca Records. Deleted Dec '57. Catalogue no: **04995**

THEME FROM THE THREEPENNY OPERA
Tracks: / Theme from the threepenny opera.
7" Single: Released Apr '56, on Philips, by Phonogram Ltd. Deleted Apr '61. Catalogue no: **PB 574**

WHAT A WONDERFUL WORLD (OLD GOLD)
Tracks: / What a wonderful world / Cabaret.
7" Single: Released Dec '88, on Old Gold, by Old Gold Records. Catalogue no: **OG 9419**

WHAT A WONDERFUL WORLD (SINGLE)
Tracks: / What a wonderful world.
7" Single: Released Feb '68, on H.M.V., by EMI Records. Deleted Feb '73. Catalogue no: **POP 1615**
7" Single: Released Mar '88, on A&M, by A&M Records. Catalogue no: **AM 435**
12" Single: Released Mar '88, on A&M, by A&M Records. Catalogue no: **AMY 435**

WHAT A WONDERFUL WORLD/HELLO DOLLY
Tracks: / What a wonderful world / Hello Dolly.
7" Single: Released Jul '86, on MCA, by MCA Records. Deleted '86. Catalogue no: **MCA 706**

Armstrong, Vanessa

PRESSING ON
Tracks: / Pressing on.
7" Single: Released 14 May '88, on Jive, by Zomba Records. Deleted '88. Catalogue no: **JIVE 168**
12" Single: Released 14 May '88, on Jive, by Zomba Records. Deleted '88. Catalogue no: **JIVET 168**

Army

ARMY LIFE
Tracks: / Army life.
12" Single: Released Sep '81, on EMI, by EMI Records. Deleted Sep '84. Catalogue no: **12EMI 5226**

Army Of Lovers

LOVE ME LIKE A LOADED GUN
Tracks: / Love me like a loaded gun / Love me like a loaded gun (dub).
7" Single: Released Aug '88, on Sonet, by Sonet Records. Catalogue no: **SON 7**
12" Single: Released Aug '88, on Sonet, by Sonet Records. Catalogue no: **SONL 7**

Arnau, Brenda

ELECTRA FLASH
Tracks: / Electra flash / Dance electra flash.
7" Single: Released Jun '80, on Pye, Deleted Jun '83. Catalogue no: **7P 185**

Arnie's Love

Biographical details: Arnie's Love are one of the numerous anonymous, faceless acts to have made the disco/dance charts. 'I'm Out Of Your Life' scored a minor national chart placing in late 1983, having been issued by Morgan Khan's Streetwave label, an outlet for many club favourites in the Eighties. (BM 84).

I'M OUT OF YOUR LIFE
Tracks: / I'm out of your life.
7" Single: Released Nov '83, on Streetwave, Deleted '86. Catalogue no: **WAVE 9**

NATURAL WISH
Tracks: / Natural wish / Natural wish (inst).
7" Single: Released Mar '86, on PRT, by Castle Communications Records. Catalogue no: **7P 351**
12" Single: Released Mar '86, on PRT, by Castle Communications Records. Catalogue no: **12P 351**

Arnold, Billy Boy

Biographical details: ARNOLD, Billy Boy Blues singer, guitarist, harmonica player, born in 1935 in Chicago. He worked as a child with Bo Diddley in a washboard trio at parties, etc; later with all the Chicago greats; recorded under his own name from 1954 and toured Europe in the '70s. Donald Clarke 21 July 1988.

I WISH YOU WOULD
Tracks: / I wish you would.
7" Single: Released Jul '80, on Charly, by Charly Records. Deleted '87. Catalogue no: **CTD 117**

SUPERHARPS
12" Single: Released Oct '88, on Red Lightnin', by Red Lightning Records. Deleted Jun '89. Catalogue no: **RLEP 0027**

Arnold, Eddy

Biographical details: Born in West Tennessee in 1918, Eddy Arnold became the most successful artist in the history of country music. Arnold's most triumphant year came relatively early in his lengthy career. Having turned professional in 1943, he dominated the fledgling country charts in 1948 with four back-to-back monster hits: 'I'll Hold You In My Heart', 'Bouquet Of Roses'/'Texarkana Baby', 'Any Time' and 'Just A Little Lovin' (Will Go A Long Long Way)'. Further No.1s on the Billboard country chart included 'I Wanna Play House With You' (1951) and 'Cattle Call' (1955), amongst others. Arnold's forte was the slow rambling country and western ballad. While his music was perfect for his own market, however, he was unable to sell it in any great quantities to the world outside. Like many of country music's biggest stars, he never crossed over to the pop market, with the exception of his mid-Sixties winner 'Make The World Go Away', a transatlantic Top 10 hit. A couple of smaller pop hits followed it up, but Arnold always stuck to the style and the audience he knew best. In 1966 Eddy Arnold was awarded one of the highest accolades in his field, being elected to the Country Music Association Hall of Fame. (Bob McDonald 1984)
Eddy Arnold was born in 1918 near Henderson, in the state of Tennessee; he was later aptly billed 'The Tennessee Plowboy'. He is one of the first to cross over to the pop charts. He first performed on radio in 1936, travelled with the Grand Ole Opry's Camel Caravan '41-2 entertaining servicemen; signed with RCA in 1944: his first manager was Tom Parker, later the evil crook who held Elvis Presley in his choking grasp. The hits began in 1948 and the crossovers began immediately with *Bouquet of roses*; he had 70 top 20 entries in Billboard's country chart between the years of 1949 and 1969 and was said to have

sold 70 million records by 1980. Always a smooth balladeer who co-wrote many songs, he was so popular that some country music people accused him of selling out. (Donald Clarke, July 1988)g.

I WANT TO GO WITH YOU
Tracks: / I want to go with you.
7" Single: Released May '66, on RCA, by BMG Records (UK). Deleted May '71. Catalogue no: **1519**

IF YOU WERE MINE MARY
Tracks: / If you were mine Mary.
7" Single: Released Jul '66, on RCA, by BMG Records (UK). Deleted Jul '71. Catalogue no: **1529**

MAKE THE WORLD GO AWAY
Tracks: / End of the world / Make the world go away.
7" Single: Released Oct '86, on Old Gold, by Old Gold Records. Catalogue no: **OG 9619**
7" Single: Released Feb '66, on RCA, by BMG Records (UK). Deleted Feb '71. Catalogue no: **1496**

Arnold, P.P.

Biographical details: P.P. Arnold was born in Los Angeles, but settled in Britain in 1966 when she arrived here as a member of the Ikettes, Ike and Tina Turner's backing group. The Turners were flopping in their native land with /River Deep Mountain High'D but were in demand in Britain in the wake of the single's big UK success. Arnold recorded a Cat Stevens song /The First Cut Is The Deepest'D and took it to no.18 on the British charts. (Exactly ten years later Rod Stewart was to take the song to no.1). Her first cut was the biggest. A year later, in the summer of '68, she hit the top 30 with /Angel Of The Morning'D, but her pleasant voice failed to grace the charts again, at least in her own name. An album called /Kafunta'D aroused little interest, despite being produced by Mick Jagger and Steve Marriott. She has subsequently pursued a career as a session singer, and is still active in the music business. (Bob MacDonald).

ANGEL OF THE MORNING
Tracks: / Angel of the morning.
7" Single: Released Apr '82, on Immediate, Catalogue no: **IM 067**

ELECTRIC DREAMS
Tracks: / Electric dreams.
7" Single: Released Aug '84, on 10 Records, by Virgin Records. Deleted '86. Catalogue no: **TEN 29**
12" Single: Released Aug '84, on 10 Records, by Virgin Records. Deleted '86. Catalogue no: **TEN 29-12**

FIRST CUT IS THE DEEPEST, THE
Tracks: / First cut is the deepest / Speak to me.
7" Single: Released Dec '82, on Immediate, Catalogue no: **IMS 047**

FIRST CUT IS THE DEEPEST, THE (OLD GOLD)
Tracks: / First cut is the deepest, The.
7" Single: Released Jan '85, on Old Gold, by Old Gold Records. Catalogue no: **OG 9464**

(IF YOU THINK) YOU'RE GROOVY
Tracks: / (If you think) you're groovy.
7" Single: Released Jan '68, on Immediate, Deleted '71. Catalogue no: **IM 061**

LITTLE PAIN, A
Tracks: / Little pain, A.
7" Single: Released Sep '85, on 10 Records, by Virgin Records. Deleted '86. Catalogue no: **TEN 70**
12" Single: Released Sep '85, on 10 Records, by Virgin Records. Deleted '86. Catalogue no: **TEN 70-12**

SUPERGRASS
Tracks: / Supergrass / Inside man.
7" Single: Released Dec '85, on Island, by Island Records. Catalogue no: **IS 257**

TIME HAS COME, THE
Tracks: / Time has come, The.
7" Single: Released Aug '67, on Immediate, Deleted Aug '72. Catalogue no: **IM 055**

Aroma Di Amore

KOUDE OORLOG
Tracks: / Koude oorlog.
12" Single: Released Jun '84, on Play It Again Sam(Belgium), by Play It Again Sam (Belgium). Catalogue no: **BIAS 005**

VOOR DE DOOD
Tracks: / Voor de dood.
12" Single: Released 1 May '85, on Play It Again Sam(Belgium), by Play It Again Sam (Belgium). Catalogue no: **BIAS 006**

ZONDER OMZIEN
Tracks: / Zonder omzien.
12" Single: Released Jan '86, on Play It Again Sam(Belgium), by Play It Again Sam (Belgium). Catalogue no: **BIAS 021**

Arpeggio

LOVE AND DESIRE
Tracks: / Love and desire.
7" Single: Released Mar '79, on Polydor, by Polydor Ltd. Deleted Mar '84. Catalogue no: **POSP 40**

Arriba

PEANUT VENDOR
Tracks: / Peanut vendor / Fair winds.
7" Single: Released Nov '82, on EMI, by EMI Records. Deleted Nov '85. Catalogue no: **EMI 5357**
12" Single: Released Nov '82, on EMI, by EMI Records. Deleted Nov '85. Catalogue no: **12EMI 5357**

Arrington, Steve

DANCIN' IN THE KEY OF LIFE (SINGLE)
Tracks: / Dancin' in the key of life.
7" Single: Released Jun '85, on Atlantic, by WEA Records. Catalogue no: **A 9534**
12" Single: Released Jun '85, on Atlantic, by WEA Records. Deleted Jun '87. Catalogue no: **A 9534 T**

FEEL SO REAL
Tracks: / Feel so real / Willie Mae.
7" Single: Released Apr '85, on Atlantic, by WEA Records. Deleted Jun '87. Catalogue no: **A 9576**
12" Single: Released Apr '85, on Atlantic, by WEA Records. Deleted Jan '88. Catalogue no: **A 9576 T**

HUMP TO THE BUMP
Tracks: / Hump to the bump / Nobody can be you.
12" Single: Released Mar '84, on Atlantic, by WEA Records. Catalogue no: **A 6963 T**

JAMMIN' NATIONAL ANTHEM, THE (SINGLE)
Tracks: / Jammin' National Anthem, The / Racial jammin'.
7" Single: Released Apr '86, on Atlantic, by WEA Records. Catalogue no: **A 9428**
12" Single: Released Apr '86, on Atlantic, by WEA Records. Catalogue no: **A 9428 T**

STONE LOVE (RADIO EDIT)
Tracks: / Stone love (radio edit) / Trouble.
7" Single: Released Oct '87, on EMI-Manhattan, by EMI Records. Catalogue no: **MT 30**
12" Single: Released Oct '87, on EMI-Manhattan, by EMI Records. Deleted Apr '88. Catalogue no: **12 MT 30**

Arrival

FRIENDS
Tracks: / Friends.
7" Single: Released Jan '70, on Decca, by Decca Records. Deleted Jan '75. Catalogue no: **F 12986**

I WILL SURVIVE
Tracks: / I will survive.
7" Single: Released Jun '70, on Decca, by Decca Records. Deleted Jun '75. Catalogue no: **F 13026**

ONLY LOVE
Tracks: / Only love / What a way to go.
7" Single: Released Aug '82, on CBS, by CBS Records. Deleted Aug '85. Catalogue no: **A 2654**

TELL HIM
Tracks: / Tell him / He makes me feel.
7" Single: Released May '82, on Kaleidoscope (USA), by Kaleidoscope (USA). Deleted '85. Catalogue no: **KROA 2306**

Arrogant

EGO
Tracks: / Ego / So near, so far.
7" Single: Released Feb '81, on Rocket, by Rocket Records. Deleted Jan '86. Catalogue no: **XPRES 43**

Arrogant Adams

I'M GOOD LOOKING
Tracks: / I'm good looking / I'm number one / Good company.
7" Single: Released Jan '82, on RCA, by BMG Records (UK). Deleted Jan '85. Catalogue no: **SUPER 45 2**

Arrow

GROOVE MASTER
Tracks: / Groove master / Acid soca house.
7" Single: Released Jun '88, on Mango, by Island Records. Deleted Apr '89. Catalogue no: **IS 369**
12" Single: Released Jun '88, on Mango, by Island Records. Deleted Apr '89. Catalogue no: **12IS 369**

HOT HOT HOT
Tracks: / Hot hot hot / Money money.
7" Single: Released Jun '84, on Chrysalis, by Chrysalis Records. Catalogue no: **ARROW 1**
12" Single: Released Jun '84, on Chrysalis, by Chrysalis Records. Catalogue no: **ARROX 1**

LONG TIME
Tracks: / Long time.
Cassingle: Released Aug '85, on London Records, by London Records. Catalogue no: **LONMC 70**
7" Single: Released Jun '85, on London Records, by London Records. Catalogue no: **LON 70**
12" Single: Released Jun '85, on London Records, by London Records. Catalogue no: **LONX 70**

LONG TIME THE HOT MIXTURE
Tracks: / Long time the hot mixture.
12" Single: Released Jun '88, on Arrow, Catalogue no: **ARROW 030**

O' LA SOCA (SINGLE)
Tracks: / O' la soca (jam fierce remix) / O' la soca (Afro soca acid dub) / O' la soca.
7" Single: Released Jul '89, on Mango, by Island Records. Catalogue no: **MNG 710**
12" Single: Released Jul '89, on Mango, by Island Records. Catalogue no: **12 MNG 710**

Arrows

MY LAST NIGHT WITH YOU
Tracks: / My last night with you.
7" Single: Released Feb '75, on RAK, by EMI Records. Deleted Feb '80. Catalogue no: **RAK 189**

TALK TALK
Tracks: / Talk talk / Easy street.
7" Single: Released Feb '86, on A&M, by A&M Records. Deleted '88. Catalogue no: **AM 298**
12" Single: Released Feb '86, on A&M, by A&M Records. Deleted '88. Catalogue no: **AMY 298**

TOUCH TOO MUCH, A
Tracks: / Touch too much, A.
7" Single: Released May '74, on RAK, by EMI Records. Deleted May '79. Catalogue no: **RAK 171**

Arrowsmith, Eugenie

DANCING IN MY HEART
Tracks: / Dancing in my heart / Talk talk about.
7" Single: Released Feb '86, on 10 Records, by Virgin Records. Deleted '86. Catalogue no: **TEN 95**
12" Single: Released Feb '86, on 10 Records, by Virgin Records. Deleted May '88. Catalogue no: **TEN 95-12**

PROMISES
Tracks: / Promises / Try.
7" Single: Released Apr '86, on 10 Records, by Virgin Records. Deleted May '88. Catalogue no: **TEN 107**
12" Single: Released Apr '86, on 10 Records, by Virgin Records. Deleted '89. Catalogue no: **TENY 107**

Arsenal

MANIPULATOR
Tracks: / Manipulator.
7" Single: Released Dec '88, on Blast First, by Blast First Records. Catalogue no: **BFFP 35**

WE'RE BACK (WHERE WE BELONG)
Tracks: / We're back (where we belong) / Spot the ball.
7" Single: Released Jul '89, on Dover, by Chrysalis Records. Catalogue no: **DEIN 1**
12" Single: Released Jul '89, on Dover, by Chrysalis Records. Catalogue no: **DEINX 1**

Arsenal F.C.

GOOD OLD ARSENAL
Tracks: / Good old Arsenal.
7" Single: Released May '71, on Pye, Deleted May '76. Catalogue no: **7N 45067**

Art Company

GET IT OUT OF YOUR HEAD
Tracks: / Get it out of your head.
7" Single: Released Jul '84, on Epic, by CBS Records. Catalogue no: **A 4619**

ONE CUP OF COFFEE
Tracks: / One cup of coffee / All day all night.
7" Single: Released Oct '87, on Polydor, by Polydor Ltd. Catalogue no: **POSP 890**
12" Single: Released Oct '87, on Polydor, by Polydor Ltd. Catalogue no: **POSPX 890**

SUSANNAH
Tracks: / Susannah / 17th floor.
7" Single: Released Apr '81, on Epic, by CBS Records. Catalogue no: **A 4174**
12" Single: Released Apr '84, on Epic, by CBS Records. Catalogue no: **TA 4174**

Art In The Dark

ART IN THE DARK
Tracks: / Art in the dark.
12" Single: Released Sep '85, on Press, by Compendium Int.Records. Catalogue no: **P 2013**

Art Objects

SHOWING OFF TO IMPRESS THE GIRLS
Tracks: / Showing off to impress the girls.
7" Single: Released '81, on Heartbeat, by Mainline Records. Catalogue no: **PULSE 10**

Art Of Noise

Biographical details: Group made up of producers Anne Dudley, J.J. Jeczalik and Gary Lanagan. Although they have hits in their own right, notably the 1985 UK Top 10 hit Close (To The Edit), the trio have found greater success in collaborations with Duane Eddy (Peter Gunn), Max Headroom (Paranoimia) and Tom JOnes (Kiss). (P.Williams 7/89).

BEAT BOX
Tracks: / Beat box / Diversions 1 & 2.
7" Single: Released Mar '84, on ZTT, by ZTT Records. Deleted Apr '88. Catalogue no: **ZTIS 108**

CLOSE (TO THE EDIT)
Tracks: / Close (to the edit).
7" Pic: Released Feb '85, on ZTT, by ZTT Records. Catalogue no: **PZTPS 1**
7" Single: Released Oct '84, on ZTT, by ZTT Records. Deleted Jul '87. Catalogue no: **ZTPS 1**
12" Single: Released Nov '84, on ZTT, by ZTT Records. Catalogue no: **12 ZTPS 1**

DRAGNET
Tracks: / Dragnet / Dragnet (aon mix).
Cassingle: Released Jul '87, on China, by Polydor Ltd. Catalogue no: **WOK 14 MC**
7" Single: Released Jul '87, on China, by Polydor Ltd. Catalogue no: **WOK 14**
12" Single: Released Jul '87, on China, by Polydor Ltd. Catalogue no: **WOKX 14**

DRAGNET '88
Tracks: / Dragnet 88 / Dragnet 88 (12" mix / Dragnet (Arthur Baker house mix) / Actor art.
7" Single: Released Feb '88, on China, by Polydor Ltd. Catalogue no: **CHINA 4**
12" Single: Released Feb '88, on China, by Polydor Ltd. Catalogue no: **CHINAX 4**

INTO BATTLE WITH
7" EP: Released Oct '83, on ZTT, by ZTT Records. Deleted Jun '88. Catalogue no: **ZTIS 100**

INTO TROUBLE
Tracks: / Into trouble.
7" Single: Released May '85, on Ying Yang Yum, Catalogue no: **YYY 001**

KISS
Tracks: / Kiss / E.F.L. / Kiss (battery mi (Only on the 12" version and CD single) Ode to Don Jose (Only on 12" remix ver sion.).
12" Single: Released Oct '88, on China, b Polydor Ltd. Deleted 31 May '89. Catalogue no: **CHIXR 11**
CD 5": Released Oct '88, on China, by Polydor Ltd. Catalogue no: **CHICD 11**
7" Single: Released Oct '88, on China, b Polydor Ltd. Deleted 30 May '89. Catalogue no: **CHINA 11**
12" Single: Released Oct '88, on China, b Polydor Ltd. Deleted 31 May '89. Catalogue no: **CHINX 11**

KISS (REMIX)
Tracks: / Kiss (remix) / Ode to Don Jose.
12" Single: Released Oct '88, on China, b Polydor Ltd. Catalogue no: **CHXR 11**

LEGACY
Tracks: / Legacy / Opus 111.
7" Single: Released Oct '86, on China, b Polydor Ltd. Catalogue no: **WOK 11**
12" Single: Released Oct '86, on China, b Polydor Ltd. Catalogue no: **WOKX 11**

LEGS
12" Single: Released Oct '85, on China, b Polydor Ltd. Catalogue no: **WOKX 5**
7" Single: Released Oct '85, on China, b Polydor Ltd. Catalogue no: **WOK 5**

MOMENTS IN LOVE
Tracks: / Moments in love / Love beat.
7" Single: Released 30 May '87, on ZTT, b ZTT Records. Deleted Dec '88. Catalogu no: **WEEP 1**
7" Pic: Released Mar '85, on ZTT, by Z Records. Catalogue no: **PZTPS 2**
7" Single: Released Mar '85, on ZTT, b ZTT Records. Deleted Apr '88. Catalog no: **ZTPS 2**
12" Single: Released 30 May '87, on ZT by ZTT Records. Catalogue no: **WEEPS 1**
12" Single: Released Mar '85, on ZTT, ZTT Records. Catalogue no: **12 ZTPS 2**

PARANOIMIA
Tracks: / Paranoimia / Why me.
7" Single: Released May '86, on China, Polydor Ltd. Catalogue no: **WOK 9**
12" Single: Released May '86, on China, Polydor Ltd. Catalogue no: **WOKX 9**

PARANOIMIA '89
Tracks: / Paranoimia '89 / Locus classic
7" Single: Released Mar '89, on China, Polydor Ltd. Deleted Oct '89. Catalogue r **CHINA 14**
12" Single: Released Mar '89, on China, Polydor Ltd. Deleted Oct '89. Catalogue r **CHINX 14**
CD 5": Released Mar '89, on China, Polydor Ltd. Catalogue no: **CHICD 14**
12" Single: Released Mar '89, on China, Polydor Ltd. Deleted Oct '89. Catalogue

HIXP 14

ETER GUNN
acks: / Peter Gunn / Something always
appens.
Single: Released May '68, on London
ecords, by London Records. Catalogue no:
LW 10191
" Single: Released Mar '86, on China, by
olydor Ltd. Catalogue no: WOKX 6
Single: Released Mar '86, on China, by
olydor Ltd. Catalogue no: WOK 6

EBO
acks: / Yebo / Dan Dare (On 7", CD and
HINX 18 only) / To add to the confusion (On
th 12"s and CD only) / Yebo (remix) (On
HIXR 18 only) / Yebo (Mbaguanga mix)
n 12" and CD only).
" Pic: Released Aug '89, on China, by
lydor Ltd. Catalogue no: CHIXP 18
" Single: Released 31 Jul '89, on China,
Polydor Ltd. Catalogue no: CHINX 18
" Single: Released Aug '89, on China, by
lydor Ltd. Catalogue no: CHIXR 18
Single: Released 31 Jul '89, on China, by
lydor Ltd. Catalogue no: CHINA 18
5": Released 31 Jul '89, on China, by
lydor Ltd. Catalogue no: CHICD 18

Art School

MOTION EXPLOSION
acks: / Emotion explosion / Hold on tight.
Single: Released Nov '82, on RAK, by
I Records. Deleted Nov '85. Catalogue
RAK 343
" Single: Released Nov '82, on RAK, by
I Records. Deleted Nov '85. Catalogue
12RAK 343

VIN' YOU
acks: / Loving you.
Single: Released Apr '83, on RAK, by
I Records. Catalogue no: RAK 356

Arte Noir

RICAN CONNECTION
cks: / African connection.
Single: Released May '81, on EMI, by
I Records. Deleted May '84. Catalogue
EMI 5198
Single: Released May '81, on EMI, by
I Records. Deleted May '84. Catalogue
12 EMI 5198

rtery

TERWARDS (SINGLE)
cks: / Afterwards.
Single: Released Nov '81, on Armaged-
, by Armageddon Records. Catalogue
AS 026

ABAMA SONG
cks: / Alabama song.
Single: Released Nov '83, on Red Flame
by Red Flame Records. Catalogue no:
B 25
Single: Released Nov '83, on Red
me (1), by Red Flame Records. Cata-
e no: RFB 2512

G MACHINE
cks: / Big machine.
Single: Released May '84, on Golden
vn, Catalogue no: GD 1202

OWN, THE
cks: / Clown, The.
Single: Released Aug '82, on Red Flame
by Red Flame Records. Catalogue no:
704

AMONDS IN THE MINE FIELD
cks: / Diamonds in the mine field.
Single: Released Oct '84, on Golden
vn, Catalogue no: GD 704
Single: Released Oct '84, on Golden
vn, Catalogue no: GD 1204

DE, THE
cks: / Slide, The.
Single: Released Jun '82, on Red
ne (1), by Red Flame Records. Cata-
e no: RF 1201

BALANCED
cks: / Unbalanced.
Single: Released Nov '80, on Aardvark,
ardvark Records. Catalogue no: STEAL

thur

CKING WITH THE DOGGIES
ks: / Rocking with the doggies.

ingle: Released Jul '83, on Lampost,
logue no: WOOF 1

thur, Tony

NATHAN'S ZOO
ks: / Johnathan's zoo / Let's all go to the

ingle: Released Feb '80, on Pye,
ed Feb '83. Catalogue no: 7P 165

thur two stroke

O WHO SONG
ks: / Who who song / I'm not sorry.
ingle: Released Jan '81, on Satellite,
ted Jan '84. Catalogue no: KAK 1

Artists

PLAYING GAMES
Tracks: / Playing games / Girl who has nothing.
7" Single: Released May '83, on Bulrush, by Bulrush Records. Catalogue no: **BULA 1**

Artists Mean

LOVE
Tracks: / Love.
7" Single: Released Mar '83, on Social, Catalogue no: **SOC 1**

Artists United

SUN CITY (SINGLE)
Tracks: / Sun city.
7" Single: Released Nov '85, on EMI-Manhattan, by EMI Records. Catalogue no: **MT 7**
12" Single: Released Nov '85, on EMI-Manhattan, by EMI Records. Catalogue no: **12 MT 7**

A's

WHO'S GONNA SAVE THE WORLD
Tracks: / Who's gonna save the world / Artificial love.
7" Single: Released Jan '80, on Arista, by BMG Records (UK). Deleted Jan '85. Catalogue no: **ARIST 324**

As Seen On TV

SUMMER HOLIDAY
Tracks: / Summer holiday / We don't talk anymore.
7" Single: Released Jun '83, on Empire Records, Catalogue no: **HAM 2**

A.S.A.P.

SILVER AND GOLD
Tracks: / Silver and gold (7" only.) / Blood brothers (7" only.) / Silver and gold (12" remix) (Not on 7".) / Blood brothers (alt. version) (Not on 7".) / Fighting man (Not on 7".).
CD 5": Released Oct '89, on EMI, by EMI Records. Catalogue no: **203 542 2**
CD 5": Released Oct '89, on EMI, by EMI Records. Catalogue no: **CDEM 107**
7" Single: Released Oct '89, on EMI, by EMI Records. Catalogue no: **EM 107**
7" Single: Released Oct '89, on EMI, by EMI Records. Catalogue no: **203 542 7**
7" Single: Released Oct '89, on EMI, by EMI Records. Catalogue no: **EMG 107**
7" Single: Released Oct '89, on EMI, by EMI Records. Catalogue no: **203 542 8**
12" Single: Released Oct '89, on EMI, by EMI Records. Catalogue no: **12EMP 107**
12" Single: Released Oct '89, on EMI, by EMI Records. Catalogue no: **203 542 0**
12" Single: Released Oct '89, on EMI, by EMI Records. Catalogue no: **12EMPD 107**
12" Single: Released Oct '89, on EMI, by EMI Records. Catalogue no: **203 556 6**
12" Single: Released Oct '89, on EMI, by EMI Records. Catalogue no: **203 542 6**
12" Single: Released Oct '89, on EMI, by EMI Records. Catalogue no: **12EM 107**

Ash 48

ASH 48
Tracks: / Ash 48 (remix) / 137 disco heaven.
12" Single: Released Jan '86, on Sedition, by Sedition Records. Catalogue no: **EDITX 3306**

ASH 48 (PART 2)
12" Single: Released Oct '85, on Sedition, by Sedition Records. Catalogue no: **EDITL 3306**

Ash, Daniel

BURNING SKIES
Tracks: / Burning skies.
7" Single: Released May '83, on Situation 2, by Beggars Banquet Records. Catalogue no: **SIT 21**
12" Single: Released May '83, on Situation 2, by Beggars Banquet Records. Catalogue no: **SIT 21T**

THERE'S ONLY ONE
Tracks: / There's only one.
12" Single: Released Sep '82, on Beggars Banquet, by Beggars Banquet Records. Deleted Jan '88. Catalogue no: **BEG 85T**

TONES ON TAIL
Tracks: / Tones on tail.
7" EP: Released Apr '82, on 4AD, by 4AD Records. Catalogue no: **BAD 203**

Ash, Leslie

DON'T CALL ME BABY (I'M A WOMAN)
Tracks: / Don't call me baby (I'm a woman).
7" Single: Released May '86, on Jive, by Zomba Records. Catalogue no: **JIVE 108**
12" Single: Released May '86, on Jive, by Zomba Records. Catalogue no: **JIVET 108**

Ashanti Waugh

PARTY TIME LOVING
Tracks: / Party time loving.
12" Single: Released Jun '83, on Youth In Progress, Catalogue no: **YP 003**

Ashantie, Congo

BIG SHOT
Tracks: / Big shot / Put it out.
7" Single: Released Jun '81, on Pre, by Charisma Records. Deleted Jun '84. Catalogue no: **PRE 15**

Ashantis

LIFE COULD BE A DREAM
Tracks: / Life could be a dream.
12" Single: Released Feb '83, on Tree Roots, Catalogue no: **VG 1001**

Ashaye

MICHAEL JACKSON MEDLEY
Tracks: / Michael Jackson medley.
7" Single: Released Oct '83, on Record Shack, by Record Shack Records. Catalogue no: **SOHO 10**
12" Single: Released Oct '83, on Record Shack, by Record Shack Records. Catalogue no: **SOHOT 10**

Ashcroft & Avant

CARTOON
Tracks: / Cartoon.
12" Single: Released Oct '88, on Deep Cut, Catalogue no: **KNI 01**

Asher D

BRUTALITY
Tracks: / Brutality.
12" Single: Released Jan '88, on Music Of Life, by Music Of Life Records. Catalogue no: **NOTE 11**

RAGAMUFFIN HIP-HOP (SINGLE)
Tracks: / Ragamuffin hip-hop.
12" Single: Released Aug '87, on Music Of Life, by Music Of Life Records. Catalogue no: **NOTE 5**

SUMMERTIME
Tracks: / Summertime.
12" Single: Released Sep '88, on Music Of Life, by Music Of Life Records. Catalogue no: **NOTE 19**

WE'RE THE CHAMPIONS
Tracks: / We're the champions.
12" Single: Released Sep '89, on Music Of Life, by Music Of Life Records. Catalogue no: **NOTE 28**

Asher, Granti

COME INTO MY LIFE
Tracks: / Come into my life.
12" Single: Released Mar '88, on Pioneer, by Word Records (UK). Catalogue no: **PI 66**

TOUCH DEM DEEP
Tracks: / Touch dem deep.
12" Single: Released Aug '88, on BP International, Catalogue no: **BP 21**

Asher, John

LET'S TWIST AGAIN
Tracks: / Let's twist again.
7" Single: Released Nov '75, on Creole, by Creole Records. Deleted Nov '80. Catalogue no: **CR 112**

Asher, Ras Imru

MARSHALL
Tracks: / Marshall.
12" Single: Released Jun '82, on Jah Shaka, Catalogue no: **KMD 001**

Ashes Of Rose

SILK NOOSE TIGHTENS
Tracks: / Silk noose tightens.
7" Single: Released Sep '87, on Tito, Catalogue no: **ASH 001**

Ashes & Stars

GOING HOME (2 parts)
Tracks: / Going home (2 parts).
7" Single: Released Nov '82, on Satril, by Satril Records. Catalogue no: **SAT 502**
12" Single: Released Nov '82, on Satril, by Satril Records. Catalogue no: **12 SAT 502**

Ashford & Simpson

BABIES
Tracks: / Babies / Outta the world.
7" Single: Released Apr '85, on Capitol, by EMI Records. Deleted '88. Catalogue no: **CL 355**

COUNT YOUR BLESSINGS
Tracks: / Count your blessings / Side effect.
7" Single: Released Aug '86, on Capitol, by EMI Records. Deleted '88. Catalogue no: **CL 422**
12" Single: Released Aug '86, on Capitol, by EMI Records. Deleted '88. Catalogue no: **12 CL 422**

HAPPY ENDING
Tracks: / Happy ending / Handkerchief.
7" Single: Released Jan '81, on Warner Bros., by WEA Records. Deleted Jan '84. Catalogue no: **K 17738**

HIGH RISE (SINGLE)
Tracks: / High rise.
7" Single: Released Aug '83, on Capitol, by EMI Records. Deleted Jan '88. Catalogue no: **CL 304**
12" Single: Released Jul '83, on Capitol, by EMI Records. Deleted '88. Catalogue no: **12 CL 304**

IT SEEMS TO HANG ON
Tracks: / It seems to hang on.
7" Single: Released Nov '78, on Warner Bros., by WEA Records. Deleted Nov '83. Catalogue no: **K 17237**

LOVE DON'T MAKE IT RIGHT
Tracks: / Love don't make it right / Bourgie bourgie.
7" Single: Released Sep '80, on Warner Bros., by WEA Records. Deleted '83. Catalogue no: **K 17679**

SOLID (SINGLE)
7" Single: Released Oct '84, on Capitol, by EMI Records. Deleted Aug '89. Catalogue no: **CL 345**
12" Single: Released Mar '85, on Capitol, by EMI Records. Deleted '88. Catalogue no: **12CLX 345**

STREET CORNER
Tracks: / Street corner / Make it work again.
7" Single: Released Nov '82, on Capitol, by EMI Records. Deleted Nov '85. Catalogue no: **CL 242**
12" Single: Released Nov '82, on Capitol, by EMI Records. Deleted Nov '85. Catalogue no: **12CL 242**

TIME TALKING
Tracks: / Time talking / Time talking (ext mix) (Extra track on 12" only) / Flying / Flying (inst).
7" Single: Released Mar '86, on EMI, by EMI

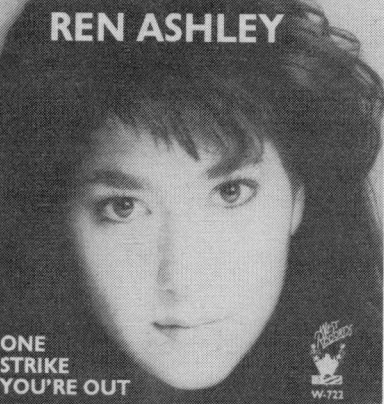

Records. Deleted Jul '87. Catalogue no: **EMI 5555**
12" Single: Released Mar '86, on EMI, by EMI Records. Catalogue no: **12 EMI 5555**

Ashington, Carl

PHOTO IN A FRAME
Tracks: / Photo in a frame.
7" Single: Released Aug '87, on WBL (White Bell), by White Bell Records. Catalogue no: **WBL/CA 001**

SUGAR PIE HONEYBUNCH
Tracks: / Sugar pie honeybunch / Sugar pie honeybunch (version).
7" Single: Released Jan '89, on Cabe, Catalogue no: **CABE 001**
12" Single: Released Jan '89, on Cabe, Catalogue no: **CABE 001T**

TOY TO A CHILD, A (A Christmas Ballad)
Tracks: / Toy to a child, A / Toy to a child (instrumental), A.
7" Single: Released Oct '87, on WBL (White Bell), by White Bell Records. Catalogue no: **WBL/CA 003**

WHY
Tracks: / Why.
Note: 'Why' is an old Anthony Newley song revived in an up-tempo reggae/disco type version.
7" Single: Released Sep '87, on WBL (White Bell), by White Bell Records. Catalogue no: **WBL/CA 002**

Ashley, Paul

RUN
7" Single: Released Oct '87, on Fon, by FON Records. Catalogue no: **PAW 13**

Ashley, Ren

ONE STRIKE YOUR OUT
Tracks: / One strike you're out / Take my heart home.
7" Single: Released '86, on West Records, Catalogue no: **W 772**

Ashman

DUGGU DUGGU
Tracks: / Duggu duggu.
7" Single: Released Jun '88, on BP International, Catalogue no: **BP 18**

Ashnti, Roy

AFRICAN BLOOD
Tracks: / African blood.
10" single: Released Aug '88, on On-U-Sound, by On-U-Sound Records. Catalogue no: **ONUDP 8**

Ashton & Hayes

RESURRECTION SHUFFLE
Tracks: / Resurrection shuffle / Resurrection shuffle.
7" Single: Released Jan '71, on Capitol, by EMI Records. Deleted Jan '76. Catalogue no: **CL 15665**
7" Single: Released May '83, on Safari, by Safari Records. Catalogue no: **SAFE 55**
12" Single: Released May '83, on Safari, by Safari Records. Catalogue no: **SAFELS 55**

Ashton, Tony

SATURDAY NIGHT & SUNDAY MORNING
Tracks: / Saturday night & Sunday morning.
7" Single: Released Jul '88, on Trax, by Filmtrax Records. Deleted Aug '89. Catalogue no: **TRA1**

Asia

Biographical details: Asia represent one of the most carefully contrived projects in the history of rock. Their story began in 1980 when Yes decided to disband. Long-serving member Steve Howe and Buggle Geoff Downes (recruited by the group mere months before) were looking for outlets for their musicianship, now that their band was folded. Howe met & teamed up with John Wetton and then suggested that Downes join them in a new group. Wetton had, at various times played with Family, King Crimson, Roxy Music and Uriah Heep. The quartet was completed in 1981 when Carl Palmer, one third of Emerson, Lake and Palmer(and another former Crimson) joined the band. A supergroup had been assembled. With unashamed calculation, the four set about making an LP that would be 99% certain of US success, one that would be ideally suited for rock and AOR (adult oriented rock) radio in the States. They even reportedly, hired a professional American radio consultant to advise them while recording. Rock critics en masse were pre-judging the record, arguing that, in an age of new and exciting techno-rock, this amalgamation of old seventies megastars was a total irrelevance. When the *'Asia'* LP was released in April 82 the reviews were predictable. But if the band had aimed squarely at the USA, even they could not have forseen the sheer scale of their success. Asia held the no.1 spot on the Billboard album chart for nine weeks and ended up as America's biggest selling album for 1982. It's first two tracks, *'Heat Of The Night'* and *'Only Time Will Tell'* were both top 20 singles. The group was less well received in their native country, though it should be noted that *'Asia'* was a steady but unspectacular seller, remaining on the UK top 100 albums for 36 weeks. A supergroup whose four superstars had all previously had more success in the UK than the US, now had there position reversed. 1983's follow-up *f"Alpha"D* was a weaker version of the same formula and consequently a little less successful. Shortly after its release, bassist and lead vocalist John Wetton departed, to be replaced by Greg lake. So it came to be that two-thirds of ELP were now reunited. Such are the personnel sagas of rock supergroups. (Bob MacDonald)..

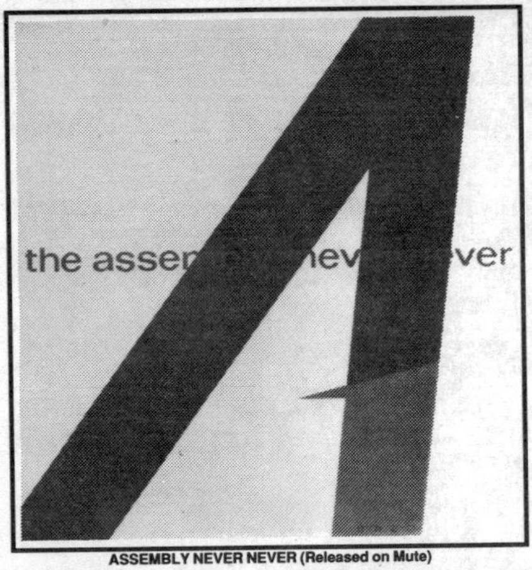

ASSEMBLY NEVER NEVER (Released on Mute)

DON'T CRY
Tracks: / Don't cry.
7" Single: Released Aug '83, on Geffen, by Geffen Records (USA). Deleted '86. Catalogue no: **A 3580**

HEAT OF THE MOMENT
Tracks: / Heat of the moment / Time again.
7" Single: Released Jul '82, on Geffen, by Geffen Records (USA). Deleted Jul '87. Catalogue no: **GEF A2494**

ONLY TIME WILL TELL
Tracks: / Only time will tell / Ride easy.
7" Single: Released Aug '82, on Geffen, by Geffen Records (USA). Deleted Aug '87. Catalogue no: **GEF A2228**

SOLE SURVIVOR
Tracks: / Sole survivor / Here comes the feeling.
7" Single: Released Oct '82, on Geffen, by Geffen Records (USA). Deleted Oct '85. Catalogue no: **GEF A2884**

Asinovi, Jon

DREAM REGGAE MUSIC
Tracks: / Dream reggae music / Dub for you.
7" Single: Released Aug '83, on Edit, Deleted '87. Catalogue no: **ED 002**

A.S.K.

KISS AND TELL
Tracks: / Kiss and tell (Original version) / Kiss and tell (Detroit Techno style) / Kiss and tell (Detroit techno edit) / Kiss and tell (Radio edit) / Love mix / Kiss and tell (New York style) (12CLX 505 only.).
7" Single: Released Oct '88, on Capitol, by EMI Records. Deleted Jun '89. Catalogue no: **CL 505**
12" Single: Released Nov '88, on Capitol, by EMI Records. Deleted Jun '89. Catalogue no: **12CLX 505**
12" Single: Released Oct '88, on Capitol, by EMI Records. Deleted Jun '89. Catalogue no: **12CL 505**

Askendea, Judah

RASTA TELL YOU
Tracks: / Rasta tell you.
7" Single: Released May '89, on Studio One, Catalogue no: **UNKNOWN**

Aslan

LOVING ME LATELY
Tracks: / Loving me lately / Run like the devil / Gallery, The (Track available on 12" only.).
7" Single: Released Jan '88, on EMI, by EMI Records. Deleted Nov '88. Catalogue no: **EM 39**
12" Single: Released Jan '88, on EMI, by EMI Records. Deleted Nov '88. Catalogue no: **12EM 39**

PLEASE DON'T STOP
Tracks: / Please don't stop / Please don't stop (extended) (the glossy mix) (on 12" only.) / Please don't stop (7" version) / Please don't stop (extended) (the Hank mix) (on 12" only.) / Can't hold back.
7" Single: Released Sep '87, on EMI, by EMI Records. Deleted Apr '88. Catalogue no: **EM 27**
12" Single: Released Sep '87, on EMI, by EMI Records. Deleted Apr '88. Catalogue no: **12EM 27**

THIS IS
Tracks: / This is / Courier, The (dangerous games) / Something's wrong (Extra track on 12" version only.).
7" Single: Released 7 Mar '88, on EMI, by EMI Records. Deleted Nov '88. Catalogue no: **EM 48**
12" Single: Released 7 Mar '88, on EMI, by EMI Records. Deleted Nov '88. Catalogue no: **12EM 48**

THIS IS ASLAN
Tracks: / This is... / Please don't stop.
7" Single: Released Jul '86, on Reekus, by Reekus Records. Catalogue no: **RKS 016**
12" Single: Released Jul '86, on Reekus, by Reekus Records. Catalogue no: **RKST 016**

Asmo

TRIP ON THIS
Tracks: / Trip on this.
12" Single: Released '88, on Bolts, by Bolts Records. Catalogue no: **NUTSX 103**

A.S.P.

BOYS WILL BE BOYS
Tracks: / Boys will be boys / Oh Kevin.
7" Single: Released May '82, on Carrere, Deleted May '85. Catalogue no: **CAR 234**

Aspey, Gary

DON'T GET MARRIED GIRL
Tracks: / Don't get married girl.
7" Single: Released Jul '81, on Dingle's, by Dingle's Records. Catalogue no: **SID 232**

Aspeys

COME ON HOME
Tracks: / Come on home.
7" Single: Released Jul '82, on Dingle's, by Dingle's Records. Catalogue no: **SID 234**

Assassins

JOEY
Tracks: / Joey.
12" Single: Released Oct '89, on Rough Trade, by Rough Trade Records. Catalogue no: **RTT 227**

Assembly

Biographical details: Vince Clarke and E.C. Radcliffe are the nucleus of a flexible studio project called the Assembly, which aims to feature a different lead vocalist with each release. Clarke had become famous through his songwriting and technical wizardry with Depeche Mode and then Yazoo, his partnership with Alison 'Alf' Moyet folde inthe summer of 1983. Clarke then got t work on his new idea and soon came up wit the single *"Never Never"*. This was in a sim lar vein to Yazoo material in terms of melod and synthesised backing, but featured th singing of the previously underrated Unde tones frontman Feargal Sharkey. *'Neve Never'* shot quickly into the top 5 in th autumn of 83. What Clarke could not hav forseen, however is that it would be up staged by one of his old songs-while *'Neve Never'* was on its way up , after peaking a No.4 the Flying Pickets version of *'Only Yo* was storming up the charts, ready to tak Christmas No. 1 honours. Having had tw simultaneous records in the Top 10, Clark then became silent. Over a year went b before the next product by the Assembl (Bob MacDonald)..

NEVER NEVER (see panel left)
Tracks: / Never never / stop/start.
7" Single: Released Nov '83, on Mute, b Mute Records. Catalogue no: **TINY 1**
12" Single: Released Nov '83, on Mute, b Mute Records. Catalogue no: **12 TINY 1**

Assistants

DOWN AT THE SUPERSTORE
Tracks: / Down at the superstore / Half da closing.
7" Single: Released Oct '82, on BBC, BBC Records & Tapes. Deleted '87. Cat logue no: **RESL 122**

Associates

Biographical details: Billy Mackenzie a Alan Rankine were a cabaret outfit in th native Scotland in 1976. Over the next f years they experimented with various gro line-ups, finally reverting to a duo but w backing musicians. Their debut LP *"T Affectionate Punch"* came out in 1980 a received wide acclaim in the rock press. series of indie single hits and 1981's *"Fou Drawer Down"* album further enhanced th 'Press Darlings' status. 1982 saw the lease of *"Party Fears Two"*, a single th combined the latest aspects of British ro vocalising, with a catchy keyboard hook. reached No.9 on the national charts and w followed by *"Club Country"* at No.13. B were issued on their own eponymous lab which also released the pair's third albu *"Sulk"*, a Top 10 LP. Having cracked b singles and album charts for the first time '82, the Associates failed to consolidate t following year. Alan Rankine quit, leavi Mackenzie to form a new Associates gro The new line-up's first singles, *"Those F Impressions"* and *"Waiting For The L Boat"*, scored minor chart placings in 19 (Bob MacDonald)
Scottish new wave group formed in Dund by Billy McKenzie (vocals) and Alan Rank (guitar, bass, keyboards) who met in 197 a cabaret group. They added bassist chael Dempsey (ex-Cure) and Austral John Murphy on drums; after a string independent singles, the original duo sig to Warner Bros. had a top 10 UK hit *Party fears two) and other minor hits: vol releationship split the group in 1983; a solo single Ice cream factory* MacKe readopted the group name with new pers nel: Steve Reid and Ian Mackintosh, guita L Howard Hughes, keyboards; Robe Soave, bass for commercial seamless '8 pop. (Donald Clarke, July 1988).

18 CARAT LOVE AFFAIR
Tracks: / 18 carat love affair / Love hang / Voluntary wishes.
7" Single: Released Aug '82, on Associa Deleted Aug '87. Catalogue no: **ASC 3**
12" Single: Released Aug '82, on Ass ates, Deleted Aug '87. Catalogue no: **A 3T**

A
Tracks: / A / Would I... bounce back.
7" Single: Released Oct '81, on Fiction Fiction Records. Deleted Oct '84. Catalo no: **FICS 12**
12" Single: Released Oct '81, on Fiction Fiction Records. Deleted Oct '84. Catalo no: **FICSX 13**

AFFECTIONATE PUNCH
Tracks: / Affectionate punch / You w wrong.
7" Single: Released Aug '80, on Fiction Fiction Records. Deleted Aug '83. Catalo no: **FICS 11**

BREAKFAST
Tracks: / Breakfast.
7" Single: Released Jan '85, on WEA WEA Records. Deleted '88. Catalogue **YZ 28**

CLUB COUNTRY
Tracks: / Club country / It's you ag Ultragyceptemol.
7" Single: Released May '82, on As ates, Deleted May '87. Catalogue no: **A**
12" Single: Released May '82, on As ates, Deleted May '87. Catalogue no: **A T**

COUNTRY BOY
Tracks: / Country boy / Just can't say goodbye.
7" Single: Released Jan '89, on WEA, by WEA Records. Catalogue no: **YZ 329**
12" Single: Released Jan '89, on WEA, by WEA Records. Catalogue no: **YZ 329 T**

HEART OF GLASS
Tracks: / Heart of glass / Her only wish / Breakfast (On CD only.) / Those first impressions (On CD only.).
CD 5": Released Sep '88, on WEA, by WEA Records. Catalogue no: **YZ 310CD**
7" Single: Released Sep '88, on WEA, by WEA Records. Catalogue no: **YZ 310**
12" Single: Released Sep '88, on WEA, by WEA Records. Catalogue no: **YZ 310T**

KITCHEN PERSON
Tracks: / Kitchen person / An even whiter car.
7" Single: Released Nov '82, on Situation 2, by Beggars Banquet Records. Catalogue no: **SIT 7**
12" Single: Released Nov '82, on Situation 2, by Beggars Banquet Records. Catalogue no: **SIT 7T**

MATTER OF GENDER
Tracks: / Matter of gender / Even dogs in the wild.
7" Single: Released Nov '82, on Fiction, by Fiction Records. Deleted Nov '85. Catalogue no: **FICS 16**
12" Single: Released Nov '82, on Fiction, by Fiction Records. Deleted Nov '85. Catalogue no: **FICSX 16**

MESSAGE OBLIQUE SPEECH
Tracks: / Message oblique speech.
7" Single: Released Nov '82, on Situation 2, by Beggars Banquet Records. Catalogue no: **SIT 10**
12" Single: Released Nov '82, on Situation 2, by Beggars Banquet Records. Catalogue no: **SIT 10T**

PARTY FEARS TWO
Tracks: / Party fears two / It's better this way.
7" Single: Released Feb '82, on Associates, Deleted Feb '87. Catalogue no: **ASC 1**

PEEL SESSIONS: ASSOCIATES
CD 5": Released Oct '89, on Strange Fruit, by Strange Fruit Records. Catalogue no: **SFPSCD 075**
12" Single: Released Oct '89, on Strange Fruit, by Strange Fruit Records. Catalogue no: **SFPS 075**

Q QUARTERS
Tracks: / Q quarters / Kissed.
7" Single: Released Jul '81, on Situation 2, by Beggars Banquet Records. Catalogue no: **SIT 4**

TAKE ME TO THE GIRL
Tracks: / Take me to the girl.
10" single: Released Nov '85, on WEA, by WEA Records. Catalogue no: **YZ 47 TE**
7" Single: Released Oct '85, on WEA, by WEA Records. Catalogue no: **YZ 47**
12" Single: Released Oct '85, on WEA, by WEA Records. Catalogue no: **YZ 47 T**

TELL ME EASTER'S ON FRIDAY
Tracks: / Tell me Easter's on friday.
12" Single: Released Nov '82, on Situation 2, by Beggars Banquet Records. Catalogue no: **SIT 1T**

THOSE FIRST IMPRESSIONS
Tracks: / Those first impressions / Thirteen feelings.
7" Single: Released Jun '84, on WEA, by WEA Records. Deleted '87. Catalogue no: **YZ 6**

WAITING FOR THE LOVEBOAT
Tracks: / Waiting for the loveboat.
7" Single: Released Sep '84, on WEA, by WEA Records. Deleted '87. Catalogue no: **YZ 16**

WHITE CAR IN GERMANY
Tracks: / White car in Germany / Associate.
7" Single: Released Nov '82, on Situation 2, by Beggars Banquet Records. Catalogue no: **SIT 11**
12" Single: Released Nov '82, on Situation 2, by Beggars Banquet Records. Catalogue no: **SIT 11T**

Association

Biographical details: The Association were a six-man vocal harmony group who sang straightforward late Sixties pop but with tinges of flower power. Hailing from California, their first big hit was *"Along Comes Mary"* in the summer of 1966. This reached No.7 on the US charts despite alleged drug references. It was followed by the No.1 smash *"Cherish"*. Questions were again asked about the next single *"Pandora's Golden Heebie Jeebies"*, a smaller hit and their last on Valiant Records before switching to Warner Bros. Once with this major company, their records became totally conventional love songs. *"Windy"* was their biggest single, logging four weeks at No. 1 in the US in the summer of '67. It was followed by two more Top Tenners, *"Never My Love"* and *"Everything That Touches You"*. The Association's final American Top 40 record, *"Time For Livin"*, was their only hit in Britain, where the commercial pop market was already well catered for. (Bob MacDonald).
A USA soft rock harmony group formed in 1965 by Russ Giguere on guitar; Brian Cole on bass (died in 1972 of drugs); Terry Kirkman, winds; Gary Alexander on guitar; Jim Yester on guitar and sax; Ted Bluechtel on drums. There were some personnel changes; they had a dozen chart hits in the USA but began to dry up late '60's; songs are still staples on easy-listening radio. Perhaps a cult band that peaked too soon: success may have stifled a sense of humour similar to that of Yester's brother Jerry's group, the Lovin' Spoonful. (Donald Clarke, July 1988)e.

NEVER MY LOVE
Tracks: / Never my love / Windy.
7" Single: Released Jul '82, on Old Gold, by Old Gold Records. Deleted Jul '88. Catalogue no: **OG 9095**

TIME FOR LIVING
Tracks: / Time for living.
7" Single: Released May '68, on Warner Bros., by WEA Records. Deleted May '73. Catalogue no: **WB 7195**

Assyne

CALL IT A DAY
Tracks: / Call it a day / Ask me no question.
7" Single: Released Apr '83, on Zone To Zone, by Zone To Zone Records. Catalogue no: **ZON 02**

LEAVING
Tracks: / Leaving.
7" Single: Released Oct '83, on Zone To Zone, by Zone To Zone Records. Catalogue no: **ZON 05**

Astaire

ANGLIA REMIX VOL.2
Tracks: / Angie remix.
12" Single: Released Nov '85, on ZYX (Germany), Catalogue no: **ZYX 5248**

BORN TO DANCE (SINGLE)
Tracks: / Born to dance.
7" Single: Released Oct '83, on Passion, by Skratch Records. Catalogue no: **PASH 09**
12" Single: Released Oct '83, on Passion, by Skratch Records. Catalogue no: **PASH 09(12)**

FIRE IN MY HEART
Tracks: / Fire in my heart / Fire in my heart (inst).
12" Single: Released Jun '86, on Passion, by Skratch Records. Catalogue no: **PASH 57(12)**

FIRE ME UP
Tracks: / Fire me up / Fire me up (inst).
12" Single: Released Feb '86, on Passion, by Skratch Records. Catalogue no: **PASH 52(12)**

IN THE NAME OF LOVE
Tracks: / In the name of love.
12" Single: Released Feb '85, on Passion, by Skratch Records. Catalogue no: **PASH 41(12)**

LOVE TRAP
Tracks: / Love trap.
12" Single: Released Feb '84, on Passion, by Skratch Records. Catalogue no: **PASH 19(12)**

POWER OF LOVE, THE
Tracks: / Power of love, The.
12" Single: Released Oct '84, on Passion, by Skratch Records. Catalogue no: **PASH 36(12)**

RIVAL LOVE
Tracks: / Rival love / Rival love (version).
12" Single: Released Oct '88, on Passion, by Skratch Records. Catalogue no: **PASH 84(12)**

TURN ME ON AGAIN
Tracks: / Turn me on again / Turn me on again (inst).
12" Single: Released Jul '87, on Passion, by Skratch Records. Catalogue no: **PASH 74(12)**

WHAT HAVE I GOT TO LOSE
12" Single: Released Nov '86, on Passion, by Skratch Records. Catalogue no: **PASH 65(12)**

Astley, John

JANE'S GETTING SERIOUS
Tracks: / Jane's getting serious / Animal, The.
7" Single: Released 10 Oct '87, on Atlantic, by WEA Records. Deleted Jul '88. Catalogue no: **A 9258**

PUT THIS LOVE TO THE TEST
Tracks: / Put this love to the test / Bin there, done that.
7" Single: Released Sep '88, on WEA, by WEA Records. Catalogue no: **A 9027**
12" Single: Released Sep '88, on WEA, by WEA Records. Catalogue no: **A 9027T**

Astley, Rick

Biographical details: Originally singer with the group FBI, Astley was spotted by Hit Factory producers Stock, Aitken and Waterman and launched in Britain in 1987 with the single Never Gonna Give You Up. Not only did it reach No.1 in both the UK and US, but it also became the best selling record of that year. Another American No.1, Together Forever, followed in 1988, as did the release of his first self-penned single She Wants To Dance With Me. (P.Williams 7/88).

HOLD ME IN YOUR ARMS (SINGLE)
Tracks: / Hold me in your arms / I don't wanna be your lover / Hold me in your arms (extended version) (on CD single only.) / Rick's hit mix (CD only) / Hold me in your arms (on CD only.).
CD 5": Released Feb '89, on RCA, by BMG Records (UK). Deleted Jul '89. Catalogue no: **PD 42616**
7" Single: Released Jan '89, on RCA, by BMG Records (UK). Catalogue no: **PB 42615**
12" Single: Released Feb '89, on RCA, by BMG Records (UK). Deleted Aug '89. Catalogue no: **PT 42630**
12" Single: Released Jan '89, on RCA, by BMG Records (UK). Catalogue no: **PT 42616**
Special: Released Jan '89, on RCA, by BMG Records (UK). Deleted May '89. Catalogue no: **PT 42632**
Special: Released Feb '89, on RCA, by BMG Records (UK). Catalogue no: **PB 42629**

IT WOULD TAKE A STRONG, STRONG MAN
Tracks: / It would take a strong, strong man / It would take a strong, strong man (inst) / It would take a strong, strong man (Matt's jazzy guitar mix) / You move me.
Note: Track taken from his debut album, released in the U.S. only. No U.K. release planned.
12" Single: Released Sep '88, on RCA (USA), Catalogue no: **86961 RD**

NEVER GONNA GIVE YOU UP
Tracks: / Never gonna give you up / Never gonna give you up (inst).
CD 5": Released Jun '89, on RCA, by BMG Records (UK). Catalogue no: **PD 42639**
7" Single: Released Jul '87, on RCA, by BMG Records (UK). Catalogue no: **PB 41447**
12" Single: Released Jul '87, on RCA, by BMG Records (UK). Catalogue no: **PT 41447**

SHE WANTS TO DANCE WITH ME
Tracks: / She wants to dance with me / It would take a strong strong man (on 12" & CD only).
CD 5": Released Sep '88, on RCA, by BMG Records (UK). Deleted Jul '89. Catalogue no: **PD 42190**
Cassingle: Released Sep '88, on RCA, by BMG Records (UK). Catalogue no: **PV 42190**
7" Single: Released Sep '88, on RCA, by BMG Records (UK). Deleted Aug '89. Catalogue no: **PB 42189**
12" Single: Released Oct '88, on RCA, by BMG Records (UK). Catalogue no: **PT 42190R**
12" Single: Released Sep '88, on RCA, by BMG Records (UK). Catalogue no: **PT 42190**

TAKE ME TO YOUR HEART
Tracks: / Take me to your heart / I'll be fine / Hit mix (Only on 12" version (PT 42582)).
Note: The hit mix featured on the special 12" version, features 6 Rick Astley hits segued into a six minute Megamix. Tracks include Never gonna give you up, Whenever you need somebody, Together forever, My arms keep missing you, She wants to dance with me and Take me to your heart.
CD 5": Released Nov '88, on RCA, by BMG Records (UK). Deleted Jul '89. Catalogue no: **PD 42574**
7" Single: Released Dec '88, on RCA, by BMG Records (UK). Deleted May '89. Catalogue no: **PB 42593**
7" Single: Released Nov '88, on RCA, by BMG Records (UK). Catalogue no: **PB 42573**
12" Single: Released Dec '88, on RCA, by BMG Records (UK). Deleted Aug '89. Catalogue no: **PT 42582**
12" Single: Released Nov '88, on RCA, by BMG Records (UK). Catalogue no: **PT 42574**

TOGETHER FOREVER
Tracks: / Together forever / I'll never set you free.
Cassingle: Released 19 Feb '88, on RCA, by BMG Records (UK). Deleted May '89. Catalogue no: **PB 41817C**
7" Single: Released Feb '88, on RCA, by BMG Records (UK). Deleted Aug '89. Catalogue no: **PB 41817**
12" Single: Released Feb '88, on RCA, by BMG Records (UK). Catalogue no: **PT 41818**

WHEN I FALL IN LOVE
Tracks: / When I fall in love / My arms keep missing you.
7" Single: Released Dec '87, on RCA, by BMG Records (UK). Deleted Aug '89. Catalogue no: **PB 41683**
12" Single: Released Dec '87, on RCA, by BMG Records (UK). Catalogue no: **PT 41684**

WHENEVER YOU NEED SOMEBODY (SINGLE)
Tracks: / Whenever you need somebody / Whenever you need somebody (instrumental).
Cassingle: Released Oct '87, on RCA, by BMG Records (UK). Catalogue no: **PB 41567C**
7" Single: Released Oct '87, on RCA, by BMG Records (UK). Deleted Aug '89. Catalogue no: **PB 41567**
12" Single: Released Oct '87, on RCA, by BMG Records (UK). Catalogue no: **PT 41568**

Astley, Tyrone

JUST ANOTHER RUMOUR
Tracks: / Just another rumour (inst).
12" Single: Released Feb '87, on Nightmare Gold, Catalogue no: **NGR 5**

Astley, Virginia

ABAO AQU
Tracks: / Abao aqu.
10" single: Released Jan '82, on Why-Fi, by Why-Fi Records. Catalogue no: **WHYD 8**

DARKNESS HAS REACHED IT'S END
Tracks: / Darkness has reached it's end.
7" Single: Released Nov '85, on Elektra (USA), by Elektra Records (USA). Catalogue no: **YZ 53**
12" Single: Released Nov '85, on Elektra (USA), by Elektra Records (USA). Catalogue no: **YZ 53T**

LOVE'S A LONELY PLACE TO BE
Tracks: / Love's a lonely place to be.
7" Single: Released Jan '83, on Why-Fi, by Why-Fi Records. Catalogue no: **WFI 001**
12" Single: Released Jan '83, on Why-Fi, by Why-Fi Records. Catalogue no: **WFIT 001**

MELT THE SNOW (EP)
Tracks: / Melt the snow.
12" Single: Released Feb '85, on Rough Trade, by Rough Trade Records. Catalogue no: **RTT 158**

SOME SMALL HOPE
Tracks: / So like Dorian (On 12" only) / Summer long since past, A.
7" Single: Released Feb '87, on WEA, by WEA Records. Deleted Jan '88. Catalogue no: **YZ 107**
12" Single: Released Feb '87, on WEA, by WEA Records. Deleted Jan '88. Catalogue no: **YZ 107T**

TENDER
Tracks: / Tender.
7" Single: Released Sep '85, on Elektra (USA), by Elektra Records (USA). Deleted '86. Catalogue no: **EKR 21**
12" Single: Released Sep '85, on Elektra (USA), by Elektra Records (USA). Catalogue no: **EKR 21 T**

Astra

WAKE UP TO MY LOVE
Tracks: / Wake up to my love (ballroom mix) / Wake up to my love (bathroom mix) / Wake up to my love (bedroom mix).
7" Single: Released Jul '86, on Adventures In Clubland, Catalogue no: **AIC 3**
12" Single: Released Jul '86, on Adventures In Clubland, Catalogue no: **AICT 3**

Astrakhan

POWER OF TOUCH, THE
Tracks: / Power of touch, The.
7" Single: Released Mar '89, on Guntalk, Catalogue no: **GUN 001FF**

Astro-Knight

FROM ELVIS BY PROXY
Tracks: / From Elvis by proxy.
7" Single: Released 10 Jun '89, on Misteri, Catalogue no: **AKNS 1**

Astronauts

BYE BYE GIRL
Tracks: / Bye bye girl.
12" Single: Released Jun '82, on Thunderbolt, by Magnum Music Group. Deleted '89. Catalogue no: **TBD 01**

DARLING JAMAICA
Tracks: / Darling Jamaica.
7" Single: Released Oct '83, on Thunderbolt, by Magnum Music Group. Deleted '89. Catalogue no: **TBD 06**

I'M YOUR ASTRONAUT
Tracks: / I'm your astronaut / Commander Incredible.
7" Single: Released Apr '82, on Stiff, by Stiff Records. Catalogue no: **BUY 145**

MEK WE JAM

Tracks: / Mek we jam.
10" single: Released Aug '82, on Pama, by Pama Records. Catalogue no: **PMD 3218**

PRANKSTERS IN REVOLT (EP)
Tracks: / Pranksters in revolt.
7" Single: Released Oct '80, on Bugle, Catalogue no: **BLAST 5**

PRETTY ISLAND
Tracks: / Pretty island.
12" Single: Released May '83, on Thunderbolt, by Magnum Music Group. Deleted '89. Catalogue no: **TBB 02**

Aswad

Biographical details: One of Britain's foremost reggae bands, Aswad released their debut self-titled album in 1976. After much gigging, a second LP /'Hulet'D finally came out in 1980. After switching from Island to CBS they released /'New Chapter'D in 81 and /'Not Satisfied' D their first chart album in 82. Aswad's story has been one of hard gigging and gradually building up greater support with each LP release. 1984 saw themmake their long overdue singles chart debut, with two minor hits /'Chasing For The Breeze'D and '54-46 (Was My Number)'. (Bob MacDonald)..

54-46(WAS MY NUMBER)
Tracks: / 54-46 (was my number).
7" Single: Released Sep '84, on Island, by Island Records. Catalogue no: **IS 170**
12" Single: Released Sep '84, on Island, by Island Records. Deleted Jul '87. Catalogue no: **12IS 170**

BABYLON
Tracks: / Babylon / Behold.
12" Single: Released Apr '81, on Island, by Island Records. Deleted Apr '84. Catalogue no: **12 WIP 6693**

BEAUTY'S ONLY SKIN DEEP
Tracks: / Beauty is only skin deep / Smokey blues / Beauty is only skin deep (version) (Only on 12" and CD.) / 54-46 (that's my number) (Only on CD single.).
CD 5": Released Mar '89, on Mango, by Island Records. Catalogue no: **CIDMX 105**
7" Single: Released Apr '89, on Mango, by Island Records. Catalogue no: **MNGG 105**
7" Single: Released 20 Mar '89, on Mango, by Island Records. Catalogue no: **MNG 105**
12" Single: Released Apr '89, on Mango, by Island Records. Catalogue no: **12 MNX 105**
12" Single: Released 20 Mar '89, on Mango, by Island Records. Catalogue no: **12 MNG 105**

BUBBLING
Tracks: / Bubbling.
12" Single: Released Oct '85, on Simba, Catalogue no: **12 SIM 101**

CHASING FOR THE BREEZE
Tracks: / Chasing for the breeze / Gave you my love.
7" Single: Released Mar '84, on Island, by Island Records. Catalogue no: **IS 160**
12" Single: Released Mar '84, on Island, by Island Records. Catalogue no: **12ISX 160**

DON'T TURN AROUND
Tracks: / Don't turn around / Woman.
7" Pic: Released '88, on Island, by Island Records. Deleted Apr '89. Catalogue no: **ISP 341**
7" Single: Released '88, on Island, by Island Records. Deleted Dec '88. Catalogue no: **ISD 341**
7" Single: Released Feb '88, on Mango, by Island Records. Deleted Apr '89. Catalogue no: **IS 341**
12" Single: Released Feb '88, on Mango, by Island Records. Deleted Apr '89. Catalogue no: **12IS 341**

GIVE A LITTLE LOVE
Tracks: / Give a little love / Gimme some (dub) / Chasin' the breeze (Track on 12" single.).
7" Single: Released May '88, on Mango, by Island Records. Deleted Apr '89. Catalogue no: **ISG 358**
7" Single: Released 14 May '88, on Mango, by Island Records. Deleted Dec '88. Catalogue no: **IS 358**
12" Single: Released 14 May '88, on Mango, by Island Records. Deleted Dec '88. Catalogue no: **12IS 358**

HOOKED ON YOU
Tracks: / Hooked on you (version).
12" Single: Released Feb '87, on Simba, Catalogue no: **SIMT 104**

KOOL NOH
Tracks: / Kool noh / Free Azania.
12" Single: Released Dec '85, on Simba, Catalogue no: **SIM 102**

MESSAGE, THE
Tracks: / Message, The / Set them free.
12" Single: Released Sep '88, on Mango, by Island Records. Catalogue no: **12IS 383**

NEED YOU BY MY SIDE
Tracks: / Need you by my side.
12" Single: Released Dec '84, on World Enterprise, Catalogue no: **WER/D 119**

NEED YOUR LOVE (EACH & EVERY DAY)
Tracks: / Need your love (each and every day) / Rainfall, sunshine.
7" Single: Released Mar '85, on Island, by Island Records. Catalogue no: **IS 214**
12" Single: Released Dec '84, on Island, by Island Records. Deleted '87. Catalogue no: **12IS 214**

ASWAD - ON AND ON (Released on Mango)

ON AND ON (see panel above)
Tracks: / On and on (Available on 7" and CD only) / Feelings / International melody (Only on CD single.) / On and on (dancehall mix) (Available on 12" and CD only) / Beauty's only skin deep (skin deep mix) (Available on CD only).
CD 5": Released 2 May '89, on Mango, by Island Records. Catalogue no: **CIDM 708**
CD 5": Released 2 May '89, on Mango, by Island Records. Catalogue no: **MNCD 708**
7" Set: Released 2 May '89, on Mango, by Island Records. Catalogue no: **MNGB708**
7" Pic: Released 24 Jul '89, on Mango, by Island Records. Catalogue no: **MNGP 708**
Cassingle: Released Jun '89, on Mango, by Island Records. Catalogue no: **MCT 708**
7" Single: Released 2 May '89, on Mango, by Island Records. Catalogue no: **MNG 708**
12" Single: Released 2 May '89, on Mango, by Island Records. Catalogue no: **12 MNG 708**

PASS THE CUP
Tracks: / Pass the cup / Girl's got to know.
7" Single: Released May '82, on CBS, by CBS Records. Deleted May '85. Catalogue no: **A 2391**
12" Single: Released May '82, on CBS, by CBS Records. Deleted May '85. Catalogue no: **A13 2391**

PULL UP
Tracks: / Pull up / Dub up.
7" Single: Released Jun '86, on Simba, Catalogue no: **SIM 103**
12" Single: Released Jun '86, on Simba, Catalogue no: **12 SIM 103**

RAINBOW CULTURE
Tracks: / Rainbow culture / Covenant (dub).
7" Single: Released Jan '80, on Island, by Island Records. Deleted Jan '85. Catalogue no: **WIP 6575**
12" Single: Released Jan '80, on Island, by Island Records. Deleted Jan '85. Catalogue no: **12WIP 6575**

ROOTS ROCKIN'
Tracks: / Roots rockin'.
7" Single: Released Jun '83, on Simba, Catalogue no: **SM 005**
12" Single: Released Jun '83, on Simba, Catalogue no: **12SM 005**

SET THEM FREE
Tracks: / Set them free / Message, The.
7" Single: Released Jul '88, on Mango, by Island Records. Deleted Apr '89. Catalogue no: **IS 383**
12" Single: Released Jul '88, on Mango, by Island Records. Deleted Apr '89. Catalogue no: **12IS 383**

SET THEM FREE (REMIX)
Tracks: / Set them free (remix).
12" Single: Released '88, on Island, by Island Records. Deleted Apr '89. Catalogue no: **12 ISX 383**

SMOKEY BLUES
Tracks: / Smokey blues.
7" Single: Released Oct '88, on Mango, by Island Records. Catalogue no: **IS 398**
12" Single: Released Oct '88, on Mango, by Island Records. Catalogue no: **12IS 398**

WARRIOR CHARGE
Tracks: / Warrior charge / Dub charge.
7" Single: Released Sep '80, on Island, by Island Records. Deleted Sep '84. Catalogue no: **WIP 6646**
7" Single: Released Sep '80, on Island, by Island Records. Deleted Sep '84. Catalogue no: **12WIP 6646**

WAYS OF THE LORD
Tracks: / Ways of the Lord / Lord of the dub.
7" Single: Released Sep '81, on CBS, by CBS Records. Deleted Sep '84. Catalogue no: **CBSA 1653**

Asylum

LEOPARDS
7" Single: Released Jan '88, on Waterfront, by Waterfront Music. Catalogue no: **DAMP 057**

Atack

DON'T WIND ME UP
Tracks: / Don't wind me up / Can't get over you.
7" Single: Released Mar '82, on Limo, Deleted '85. Catalogue no: **LIM 08**

Atavistic

EQUILIBRIUM
Tracks: / Equilibrium.
7" Single: Released Jul '87, on Loony Tunes, by Loony Tunes Records. Catalogue no: **TUNE 007**

A.T.F.

DANCING IN THE SHADOWS
Tracks: / Dancing in the shadows / Nobody else but you.
7" Single: Released Jul '81, on Epic, by CBS Records. Deleted '85. Catalogue no: **EPC A 1378**

Athletico Spizz 80

CENTRAL PARK
Tracks: / Central park.
7" Single: Released Oct '80, on Polydor, by Polydor Ltd. Deleted '83. Catalogue no: **POSP 182**

HOT DESERTS
Tracks: / Hot deserts / Legal proceedings.
7" Single: Released Aug '80, on A&M, by A&M Records. Deleted '83. Catalogue no: **AMS 7550**

Atkins

FEEL IT, DON'T FIT IT
Tracks: / Feel it don't fit it / Love is growing stronger.
7" Single: Released Apr '82, on Warner Bros., by WEA Records. Deleted Apr '85. Catalogue no: **K 17935**

Atkins, Chet

Biographical details: Born in Tennessee in 1924, Chet Atkins successfully combined careers as musician, producer and executive. Learning to play fiddle and then guitar, he signed to RCA Records in 1946. He established himself as a leading session guitarist, moved to Nashville in 1950 and helped make the town the centre of country music. During the early fifties Atkins was living a double life, he became artists and repertoire assistant to RCA's Steve Sholes while simultaneously commencing a solo recording career. His debut album /'Gallopin' shoes'D was the first of numerous strong selling country LP's that dotted his career. In the mid-fifties he played sessions with RCA's new signing Elvis Presley, he was soon assigned by the companyto supervise Elvis's recording career. In 1960 he became RCA's head of NashvilleA & R. As well as steering the careers of many fledgling country singers who were to become major artists, he played on many of their records himself, together with pianist Floyd Cramer. Atkin's guitar and Cramer's piano characterised many country records of the period. By both playing on so many Nashville hits and supervising the artists involved, Atkins became all powerful. He created the Nasville Sound- the familiar pedal steel guitars, the massed strings. The style evolved not only from traditional country, but also from Atkin's interests in jazz androck. Having been responsible for such a distinctive sound, however, he became less and less interested in progression. The Nashville establishment grew more and more conservative in a attempt to preserve their musical trademark. Their output becane samey. Having gained further promotion within his record company. Atkins was elected to the Country Music Association Hall of Fame in 1973. As guitarist, writer, producer, executive and above all, catalyst, he was the man most resposible for bringing about RCA's dominance of the US country charts. He was an important figure in the careers of Elvis Presley, Jim Reeves, Charley Pride, Jerry Reed and numerous others. As far as UK recognition is concerned, Chet Atkins scored three top 20 albums in the early sixties, also a minor chart single called /'Teensville'D..

TEENSVILLE
Tracks: / Teensville.
7" Single: Released Mar '60, on RCA, by BMG Records (UK). Deleted Mar '65. Catalogue no: **RCA 1174**

Atkinson, Rowan

Biographical details: Star of BBC TV's *'Not The Nine O'Clock News'*, a satirical show that always included a high musical element, Rowan Atkinson proceeded in the early eighties to pursue a career as one of Britain's top one-man comedians. His album *'Live In Belfast'* reached No. 44 in 1981, a respectable placing for a comedy LP though not the top 5 status that he was able to achieve as part of the *'Nine O'Clock'* team. Atkinson's ultra-flexible facial features and hands have made him an engaging visual performancer. (Bob MacDonald)..

I BELIEVE
Tracks: / I believe / Kana.
7" Single: Released 28 Nov '87, on Polydor, by Polydor Ltd. Catalogue no: **POSP 899**

Atkinson, 'Sweet Pea'

DON'T WALK AWAY
Tracks: / Don't walk away / Dance or die.
7" Single: Released Aug '82, on Island, by Island Records. Deleted Aug '85. Catalogue no: **WIP 6808**
12" Single: Released Aug '82, on Island, by Island Records. Deleted Aug '85. Catalogue no: **12WIP 6808**

SOMEONE COULD LOSE A HEART TONIGHT
Tracks: / Someone could lose a heart tonight / It's an attack / Carry me back to old Morroco.
7" Single: Released Nov '82, on Island, by Island Records. Deleted Nov '85. Catalogue no: **WIP 6837**
12" Single: Released Nov '82, on Island, by Island Records. Deleted Nov '85. Catalogue no: **12WIP 6837**

Atlanta Rhythm Section

Biographical details: This group of Atlanta studio musicians released their debut eponymous album in 1972. Two years on, their second set /'Back Up Against The Wall"D yielded the US Top 40 single /'Doraville"D. For a three year period, from 1977-9, thier brand of soft adult rock brought American radio and album success. The LPs /'Rock 'n' Roll Alternative"D and /'Champagne Jam"D were strong sellers, and the band chalked up five top 20 singles. The last of these, a remake of late Sixties hit /'Spooky"D, was a piece of deja vu for guitarist Cobb; he had played on the original version by Classic IV. /'Spooky"D was the Section's only taste of British chart success, peaking at No.48 in the autumn of '79. (Bob MacDonald)..

ALIEN
Tracks: / Alien / Southern exposure.
7" Single: Released Nov '81, on CBS, by CBS Records. Deleted Nov '84. Catalogue no: **A 1701**

IMAGINARY LOVER

Tracks: / Imaginary lover / So into you.
7" Single: Released Apr '80, on Polydor, by Polydor Ltd. Deleted '83. Catalogue no: **POSP 130**

INDIGO PASSIONS
Tracks: / Indigo passions / Born ready.
7" Single: Released Jan '80, on Polydor, by Polydor Ltd. Deleted Jan '85. Catalogue no: **POSP 103**

SPOOKY
Tracks: / Spooky.
7" Single: Released Oct '79, on Polydor, by Polydor Ltd. Deleted Oct '84. Catalogue no: **POSP 74**

Atlantic Starr

4-LEAF CLOVER
Tracks: / 4 leaf clover.
7" Single: Released Oct '83, on A&M, by A&M Records. Deleted '88. Catalogue no: **AMS 155**
12" Single: Released Oct '83, on A&M, by A&M Records. Deleted '88. Catalogue no: **AMX 155**

ALWAYS
Tracks: / Always / Always (inst).
7" Single: Released 30 May '87, on Warner Bros., by WEA Records. Catalogue no: **W 8455**
12" Single: Released 30 May '87, on Warner Bros., by WEA Records. Catalogue no: **W 8455T**

CIRCLES
Tracks: / Circles / Does it matter.
7" Single: Released Nov '82, on A&M, by A&M Records. Deleted Nov '85. Catalogue no: **AMS 8218**

COMPACT HITS: ATLANTIC STARR
Tracks: / Secret lovers / Circles / Touch a four leaf clover / Silver shadow.
CD 5": Released Apr '88, on A&M, by A&M Records. Deleted Feb '89. Catalogue no: **AMCD 907**

FREAK-A-RISTIC
Tracks: / Freak a ristic.
7" Single: Released Apr '85, on A&M, by A&M Records. Deleted '88. Catalogue no: **AM 245**
12" Single: Released Apr '85, on A&M, by A&M Records. Deleted '88. Catalogue no: **AMY 245**

GIMME YOUR LOVIN'
Tracks: / Gimme your lovin'.
7" Single: Released Sep '78, on A&M, by A&M Records. Deleted Sep '83. Catalogue no: **AMS 7380**

IF YOUR HEART ISN'T IN IT
Tracks: / If your heart isn't in it / Let's start it over / Stand up (Extra track on 12" only).
Cassingle: Released Aug '88, on A&M, by A&M Records. Deleted 1 Aug '88. Catalogue no: **AMC 319**
7" Single: Released May '86, on A&M, by A&M Records. Deleted '88. Catalogue no: **AM 319**
12" Single: Released May '86, on A&M, by A&M Records. Deleted '88. Catalogue no: **AMY 319**

LET THE SUN IN
Tracks: / Let the sun in / Females / All in the name of love (12" only).
7" Single: Released Oct '87, on Warner Bros., by WEA Records. Catalogue no: **W 8145**
12" Single: Released Oct '87, on Warner Bros., by WEA Records. Catalogue no: **W 8145 T**

LOVE ME DOWN
Tracks: / Love me down / You're the one.
7" Single: Released Aug '82, on A&M, by A&M Records. Deleted Aug '85. Catalogue no: **USAF 1224**

ONE LOVE
Tracks: / One love.
7" Single: Released Aug '85, on A&M, by A&M Records. Deleted '88. Catalogue no: **AM 273**
12" Single: Released Aug '85, on A&M, by A&M Records. Deleted '88. Catalogue no: **AMY 273**

ONE LOVER AT A TIME
Tracks: / I'm in love / One lover at a time.
7" Single: Released Aug '87, on Warner Bros., by WEA Records. Deleted Jul '88. Catalogue no: **W 8327**
12" Single: Released Aug '87, on Warner Bros., by WEA Records. Deleted Jul '88. Catalogue no: **W 8327 T**

SECRET LOVERS
Tracks: / When love calls / Secret lovers.
7" Single: Released Feb '86, on A&M, by A&M Records. Deleted '87. Catalogue no: **AM 307**
12" Single: Released Feb '86, on A&M, by A&M Records. Deleted '87. Catalogue no: **AMY 307**

SECRET LOVERS (OLD GOLD)
Tracks: / Secret lovers / Silver shadow.
12" Single: Released Nov '88, on Old Gold, by Old Gold Records. Catalogue no: **OG 4089**

SILVER SHADOW
Tracks: / Silver shadow / Cool calm collected / Cool calm collected (LP version remix) / Cool calm collected (US club mix).
7" Single: Released Sep '85, on A&M, by A&M Records. Deleted '88. Catalogue no: **AM 260**
7" Single: Released Aug '86, on A&M, by A&M Records. Deleted '87. Catalogue no: **AM 336**
12" Single: on A&M, by A&M Records. Deleted Aug '88. Catalogue no: **AMYE 260**
12" Single: Released Aug '86, on A&M, by A&M Records. Deleted '87. Catalogue no: **AMY 336**

Atlantics

PASSION BLUE
Tracks: / Passion blue / 7 roads to heaven.
7" Single: Released May '86, on Delightful, by Delightful Records. Deleted '88. Catalogue no: **FUL 04**

STACKS OF SOUL
Tracks: / Stacks of soul / Stacks of soul (part 2).
7" Single: Released Oct '81, on Mean, by Mean Records. Deleted Oct '84. Catalogue no: **MEAN 6**
12" Single: Released Nov '81, on Mean, by Mean Records. Deleted '84. Catalogue no: **12MEAN 6**

WHITE HORSES
Tracks: / White horses / White horses (version).
7" Single: Released Sep '89, on Bass, by Champion Records. Catalogue no: **BSS 8**
12" Single: Released Sep '89, on Bass, by Champion Records. Catalogue no: **BSS 128**

Atlantis People

STORMY WEATHER
Tracks: / Stormy weather / No such thing.
7" Single: Released Feb '80, on Ice, by Ice Records. Deleted '83. Catalogue no: **GUY 33**
12" Single: Released Feb '80, on Ice, by Ice Records. Deleted '83. Catalogue no: **GUY 33-12**

Atmosfear

Biographical details: Atmosfear, an all-male British disco band, hit No. 46 on the charts in 1979 with *'Dancing In Outer Space'D*. Subsequent club-oriented singles hace included *'Invasion'D*, *'Motivation'D* and *'What Do We Do'D*. (Bob MacDonald)..

DANCING IN OUTER SPACE
Tracks: / Dancing in outer space.
7" Single: Released Nov '79, on MCA, by MCA Records. Deleted Nov '84. Catalogue no: **MCA 543**

INTERPLAY
Tracks: / Interplay.
12" Single: Released Oct '81, on Elite Records, by Elite Records. Deleted '83. Catalogue no: **DAZZ 8**

INVASION
Tracks: / Invasion.
7" Single: Released Jul '81, on MCA, by MCA Records. Catalogue no: **MCA 734**
12" Single: Released Jul '81, on MCA, by MCA Records. Catalogue no: **MCAT 734**

MOTIVATION
Tracks: / Motivation / Extract.
7" Single: Released Mar '80, on MCA, by MCA Records. Deleted '83. Catalogue no: **MCA 580**

PERSONAL COLUMN
Tracks: / Personal column / Dancing in outer space.
12" Single: Released Mar '86, on Elite Records, by Elite Records. Deleted '88. Catalogue no: **DAZZ 47**

TELEPATHY
Tracks: / Telepathy.
12" Single: Released Dec '84, on Elite Records, by Elite Records. Deleted '86. Catalogue no: **DAZZ 35**

WHAT DO WE DO
Tracks: / What do we do / What do we do (club mix) / Xtra special.
7" Single: Released Aug '83, on Chrysalis, by Chrysalis Records. Catalogue no: **CHS 2730**
12" Single: Released Aug '83, on Chrysalis, by Chrysalis Records. Catalogue no: **CHS 12 2730**

WHAT'S HAPPENING (HORNET MIX)
Tracks: / What's happening.
12" Single: Released Jan '89, on Black Market, Catalogue no: **12CHIL 10**

WHEN TONIGHT IS OVER
Tracks: / When tonight is over.
7" Single: Released Jun '84, on Elite Records, by Elite Records. Deleted '86. Catalogue no: **DAZZ 317**
12" Single: Released Mar '84, on Elite Records, by Elite Records. Deleted '86. Catalogue no: **DAZZ 31**

XTRA SPECIAL
Tracks: / Xtra special.
12" Single: Released Apr '82, on Elite Records, by Elite Records. Deleted '84. Catalogue no: **DAZZ 12**

Atom Kraft

QUEEN OF DEATH
Tracks: / Queen of death / Protector / Demolition / Funeral pyre / Mode III.
12" Single: Released Oct '86, on Neat, by Neat Records. Catalogue no: **NEAT 55 12**

Atomic Rooster

Biographical details: British group Atomic Rooster were formed at the beginning of the seventies. Vincent Crane had played keyboards on *'Fire'* the 1968 No. 1 by the Crazy World Of Arthur Brown. The new band's debut LP had just one week on the charts in 1970 at No. 49. Their next set *'Death Walks Behind You'* hit the Top 20 the following year to be quickly succeeded by *'In Hearing Of Atomic Rooster'*. 1971 also yielded two hit 45's : *'Tomorrow Night'* reached No. 11, to be bettered by *'The Devil's Answer'* at No. 4. However, many other bands were also doing the same kind of riff-laden rock material, and Atomic Rooster floundered. Cann and Hammond went on to form an unsuccessful band called Hard Stuff. (Bob MacDonald)..

DEVILS' ANSWER (OLD GOLD)
Tracks: / Devil's answer.
7" Single: Released Jun '84, on Old Gold, by Old Gold Records. Catalogue no: **OG 9391**

DEVILS' ANSWER (SINGLE)
Tracks: / Devil's answer / Tomorrow night / Can't take no more.
Cassingle: Released '87, on B & C, by Trojan Records. Deleted May '88. Catalogue no: **BCS 21**
7" Single: Released Jul '71, on B & C, by Trojan Records. Deleted '76. Catalogue no: **CB 157**
7" Single: on Mooncrest, by Trojan Records. Deleted May '88. Catalogue no: **MOON 52**

PLAY IT AGAIN
Tracks: / Play it again / Start to live.
7" Single: Released Oct '81, on Polydor, by Polydor Ltd. Deleted Oct '84. Catalogue no: **POSP 334**
12" Single: Released Oct '81, on Polydor, by Polydor Ltd. Deleted Oct '84. Catalogue no: **POSPX 334**

TOMORROW NIGHT
Tracks: / Tomorrow night.
7" Single: Released Feb '71, on B & C, by Trojan Records. Deleted '76. Catalogue no: **CB 131**

TOMORROW NIGHT (OLD GOLD)
Tracks: / Tomorrow night / Devils answer / Natural born bugie.
CD 5": Released 24 Apr '89, on Old Gold, by Old Gold Records. Catalogue no: **OG 6136**

Atrix

TREASURE ON THE WASTELAND
Tracks: / Treasure on the wasteland / Graphite pile.
7" Single: Released Jan '81, on Double Dee, Deleted Jan '84. Catalogue no: **DDEE 8**

A.T.'s

COME 'ERE
Tracks: / Come 'ere / One more for the road.
7" Single: Released Aug '80, on Rialto (1), by Rialto Records. Deleted '83. Catalogue no: **TREB 120**

LEAVING ALONE
Tracks: / Leaving home / Too young girl.
7" Single: Released Oct '82, on Rialto (1), by Rialto Records. Deleted Oct '85. Catalogue no: **TREB 127**

Attack

ATTACK
Tracks: / Attack: *Various artists.*
7" EP: Released Jun '88, on Jungle Hop, Catalogue no: **JHL 105**
CD 5": Released Jun '88, on Jive, by Zomba Records. Catalogue no: **JIVECD 174**

DON'T YOU BELIEVE IN MAGIC
Tracks: / Don't you believe in magic.
7" Single: Released Jul '81, on Limo, Deleted Jul '84. Catalogue no: **LIMO 4**

MURDER IN THE SUBWAY
Tracks: / Murder in the subway.
7" Single: Released Sep '82, on No Future, Deleted '87. Catalogue no: **01 17**

OOIN' IN THE MOONLIGHT
Tracks: / Ooin' in the moonlight.
7" Single: Released Jul '82, on Towerbell, Catalogue no: **TOW 23**

TODAYS GENERATION
Tracks: / Today's generation.
7" Single: Released Jul '82, on No Future, Deleted '87. Catalogue no: **01 7**

Attaco Decente

I DON'T CARE HOW LONG IT TAKES
Tracks: / I don't care how long it takes.
CD 5": Released Sep '88, on All Or Nothing, Catalogue no: **AONCD 004**
7" Single: Released Sep '88, on All Or Nothing, Catalogue no: **AON 004**
12" Single: Released Sep '88, on All Or Nothing, Catalogue no: **AON 004T**

TROJAN HORSE
Tracks: / Trojan horse / Storms clear the air.
7" Single: Released Mar '84, on Timber, Deleted '85. Catalogue no: **TMBR 1**

WILL OF ONE, THE
Tracks: / Will of one, The / One mountain, one checkpoint, one chance.
CD 5": Released '88, on All Or Nothing, Catalogue no: **AONCD 003**
7" Single: Released '88, on All Or Nothing, Catalogue no: **AON 003**
12" Single: Released '88, on All Or Nothing, Catalogue no: **AONT 003**

Attila The Stockbroker

COCKTAILS (EP)
Tracks: / Cocktails / Contributory negligence / Night I slept with seething wells / Fifth column.
7" EP: Released Oct '82, on Cherry Red, by Cherry Red Records. Deleted '87. Catalogue no: **CHERRY 46**

RADIO RAP
12" Single: Released Aug '84, on Cherry Red, by Cherry Red Records. Deleted '87. Catalogue no: **12 CHERRY 82**

Attila's Brides

WOOLY BULLY
Tracks: / Wooly bully / Running out of time.
7" Single: Released May '80, on A&M, by A&M Records. Deleted May '85. Catalogue no: **AMS 8202**

Attractions

ARMS RACE
Tracks: / Arms race / Lonesome little town.
7" Single: Released Dec '80, on F-Beat, by F-Beat Records. Deleted Dec '85. Catalogue no: **XX10**

Attrition

HAYDN REMIX
Tracks: / Haydn remix.
12" Single: Released Oct '88, on Antler, by Antler Records (Belgium). Catalogue no: **ANT 089**

HAYLON
Tracks: / Haylon.
12" Single: Released '89, on Antler, by Antler Records (Belgium). Catalogue no: **ANT 015**

MONKEY IN A BIN
Tracks: / Monkey in a bin.
12" Single: Released Mar '84, on Uniton Records, Catalogue no: **UNITON 1984-1**

SHRINKWRAP
Tracks: / Shrinkwrap / Pendulum turns.
12" Single: Released May '85, on Third Mind, by Third Mind Records. Catalogue no: **TMS 04**

TURN TO GOLD
Tracks: / Turn to gold.
12" Single: Released Apr '89, on Antler, by Antler Records (Belgium). Catalogue no: **ANT 101**

VOICE OF GOD, THE
Tracks: / Voice of God, The.
12" Single: Released Dec '84, on Third Mind, by Third Mind Records. Catalogue no: **TMS 03**

Atuma

LAWD ME GOD
Tracks: / Lawd me god / Night has a thousand eyes, The.

7" Single: Released Aug '89, on Arista, by BMG Records (UK). Catalogue no: **NEWTAR 0013**
12" Single: Released Aug '89, on Arista, by BMG Records (UK). Catalogue no: **NEWTAR 001312**

Au Pairs - Diet It's Obvious (Released on 021 Records)

Atwell, Winifred

Biographical details: Born in Trinidad, Winifred Atwell began playing the piano at the age of four. She attempted a classical career but later decided to concentrate on playing in a boogie style. She made her first broadcast in 1947 and cut her first records in 1951. On the suggestion of Decca Records she went in search of a worn-out piano that would emit a tinny sound. The one she found was, apparently, sitting in a Battersea junk shop with a price of 50 shillings. Little can the proprietor have known that the instrument would be the star attraction of two No 1 hits plus many other Top Ten tunes. Atwell's Britannia Rag hit the Top Five in early '53, to be followed by Coronation Rag and Flirtation Waltz. The tinny sound was proving amazingly popular and was making her a favourite on radio, TV and cabaret. Let's Have A Party, a medley of old favourites aimed at the Christmas market, hit No 2 at the end of '53, her fourth and biggest hit so far. The formula was repeated the following Christmas with even greater results: Let's Have Another Party was No 1 for five weeks, becoming the first British chart-topper by a black artist and the only medley ever to hit the top.

A second No 1, The Poor People Of Paris, came in 1956. The hits kept on coming until the end of the decade, when yet another medley, Piano Party, gave Atwell her final chart record. It was perhaps symbolic that this final hit fell off the chart in January 1960: this style belonged to the 50's and had already been sustained for eight years, no mean achievement. Winifred Atwell and her "other piano" -- as she always called it -- continued to be in great cabaret demand. She died in March 1983.

(Bob MacDonald, 1984.)

The pop pianist was born in Trinidad in 1914 and died in Australia in 1983. She studied classical music and played recitals at age six; she turned to pop in London and was a popular act all through the '50's. *Black and white rag* was a big hit (written in 1908 by ragtime composer George Botsford) and established gimmick of tinny 'old time piano sound: the 'other piano' became part of the act. Knees-up medleys began with *Let's have a party* in 1953. Tours, classical concerts etc. made her one of UK's best paid stars.

(Donald Clarke, July 1988) .

BRITANNIA RAG
Tracks: / Britannia rag.
7" Single: Released Dec '52, on Decca, by Decca Records. Deleted '57. Catalogue no: **F 10015**

CORONATION RAG
Tracks: / Coronation rag.
7" Single: Released May '53, on Decca, by Decca Records. Deleted '58. Catalogue no: **F 10110**

FLIRTATION WALTZ
Tracks: / Flirtation waltz.
7" Single: Released Aug '53, on Decca, by Decca Records. Deleted '58. Catalogue no: **F 10181**

LEFT BANK
Tracks: / Left bank.
7" Single: Released Jul '56, on Decca, by Decca Records. Deleted '61. Catalogue no: **F 10762**

LET'S HAVE A BALL
Tracks: / Let's have a ball.
7" Single: Released Dec '57, on Decca, by Decca Records. Deleted '62. Catalogue no: **F 10956**

LET'S HAVE A DING-DONG
Tracks: / Let's have a ding-dong.
7" Single: Released Nov '55, on Decca, by Decca Records. Deleted '60. Catalogue no: **F 10634**

LET'S HAVE A PARTY
Tracks: / Let's have a party.
7" Single: Released Dec '53, on Philips, by Phonogram Ltd. Deleted '58. Catalogue no: **PB 213**

LET'S HAVE ANOTHER PARTY
Tracks: / Let's have another party.
7" Single: Released Nov '54, on Philips, by Phonogram Ltd. Deleted '59. Catalogue no: **PB 268**

LET'S ROCK'N'ROLL
Tracks: / Let's rock 'n' roll.
7" Single: Released Feb '57, on Decca, by Decca Records. Deleted '62. Catalogue no: **F 10852**

MAKE IT A PARTY
Tracks: / Make it a party.
7" Single: Released Sep '56, on Decca, by Decca Records. Deleted '61. Catalogue no: **F 10796**

POOR PEOPLE OF PARIS
Tracks: / Poor people of Paris, The.
7" Single: Released Mar '56, on Decca, by Decca Records. Deleted '61. Catalogue no: **F 10681**

PORT AU PRINCE
Tracks: / Port au Prince.
7" Single: Released May '56, on Decca, by Decca Records. Deleted '61. Catalogue no: **F 10727**

RACHMANINOV 18TH VARIATION (On a theme by Paganini)
Tracks: / Rachmaninov 18th variation.
7" Single: Released Jun '54, on Philips, by Phonogram Ltd. Deleted '59. Catalogue no: **PB 234**

SUMMER OF THE SEVENTEENTH DOLL
Tracks: / Summer of the seventeenth doll.

7" Single: Released Jul '59, on Decca, by Decca Records. Deleted '64. Catalogue no: **F 11143**

Au Pairs

DIET (See panel above)
Tracks: / Diet / It's obvious.
7" Single: Released '80, on 021 Records, by Avatar Record Corporation. Catalogue no: **OTO 4**

INCONVENIENCE
Tracks: / Inconvenience / Pretty boys.
Cassingle: Released Jul '81, on Human (2), Catalogue no: **MAN 2**
7" Single: Released Jul '81, on Human (2), Catalogue no: **HUM 8**
12" Single: Released Aug '81, on Human (2), Deleted Aug '84. Catalogue no: **HUM 12 8**

YOU
Tracks: / You.
7" Single: Released Jun '81, on 021 Records, by Avatar Record Corporation. Deleted '83. Catalogue no: **OTO 1**

Auclair, Philippe

RED SHOES WALTZ, THE
Tracks: / Red shows waltz, The / Goodbye again / Green park.

10" single: Released 14 Mar '88, on El, by Cherry Red Records. Catalogue no: **GPOT 35**

Audio

LOVE ON YOUR MIND
Tracks: / Love on your mind.
7" Single: Released Apr '83, on Rex (1), by Decca Records. Catalogue no: **EURO 1**

Audio Force Crew

RAPPERS DELIGHT
Tracks: / Rappers delight.
12" Single: Released Jun '88, Catalogue no: **MII 15 1001**

Aufgang

SOLID GLASS SPINE
7" Single: Released Jun '84, on Criminal Damage, Catalogue no: **CRI 112**

THINK IN TO YOU
Tracks: / Think in to you.
12" Single: Released Oct '84, on Criminal Damage, Catalogue no: **CRI 12123**

Augins, Charles

BABY I NEED YOUR LOVING
Tracks: / Baby I need your loving / Baby dub.
7" Single: Released Nov '82, on Malaco, by Malaco Records (UK). Deleted '88. Catalogue no: **MAL 004**
12" Single: Released Nov '82, on Malaco, by Malaco Records (UK). Deleted '88. Catalogue no: **MAL 12 004**

Augustine, Nat

EGO
Tracks: / Ego / I'll rescue you.
7" Single: Released Aug '86, on A&M, by A&M Records. Deleted Mar '88. Catalogue no: **AM 329**
12" Single: Released Aug '86, on A&M, by A&M Records. Deleted Mar '88. Catalogue no: **AMY 329**

SUMMER IS HERE AGAIN
Tracks: / Summer is here again.
7" Single: Released Jul '85, on Debut, by Skratch Records. Catalogue no: **DEBT 06**
12" Single: Released Jul '85, on Debut, by Skratch Records. Catalogue no: **DEBT 06(12)**

THAT GIRL
Tracks: / That girl / Underneath the sheets.
7" Single: Released Aug '87, on Breakout, by A&M Records. Deleted Feb '89. Catalogue no: **USA 609**
12" Single: Released Apr '87, on Breakout, by A&M Records. Deleted Feb '89. Catalogue no: **USAT 609**

Aural Exciters

CHINESE RAP
Tracks: / Chinese rap.
12" Single: Released Apr '83, on Move, Catalogue no: **MV 1201**

Aural John

REASON
Tracks: / Reason.
12" Single: Released May '83, on Joint Effort, Catalogue no: **JE 5001**

Aurora

I'LL BE YOUR FANTASY
Tracks: / I'll be your fantasy / If I really knew.
7" Single: Released Mar '83, on Aurora, Catalogue no: **RAM 9**

Aurra

HAPPY FEELING
Tracks: / Happy feeling.
7" Single: Released Jul '85, on 10 Records, by Virgin Records. Deleted May '88. Catalogue no: **TEN 54**
12" Single: Released Jul '85, on 10 Records, by Virgin Records. Deleted May '88. Catalogue no: **TEN 54-12**

IN THE MOOD
Tracks: / In the mood / You're the only one.
12" Single: Released 20 Jun '80, on Salsoul, Deleted '83. Catalogue no: **SAL 12 3**

LIKE I LIKE IT (REMIX) (SINGLE)
Tracks: / Like I like it (remix) / I love myself.
7" Single: Released Jun '86, on 10 Records, by Virgin Records. Deleted '89. Catalogue no: **TEN 126**

LIKE I LIKE IT (SINGLE)
Tracks: / Like I like it.
7" Single: Released '85, on 10 Records, by Virgin Records. Deleted May '88. Catalogue no: **TEN 45**
12" Single: Released '85, on 10 Records, by Virgin Records. Catalogue no: **TEN 45-12**

LITTLE LOVE, (A)
Tracks: / Little love, A / Make up your mind / Checking out.
12" Single: Released Jun '82, on Battersea, Catalogue no: **BATTL 1**

NASTY DISPOSITION
Tracks: / Nasty disposition / Are you single.
12" Single: Released May '81, on Salsoul, Deleted May '84. Catalogue no: **SALT 9**

WHEN I COME HOME
Tracks: / When I come home / Who are you.
7" Single: Released Sep '80, on Salsoul, Deleted Sep '83. Catalogue no: **SALT 5 12**

YOU AND ME TONIGHT
Tracks: / You and me tonight / You and me tonight (inst) / Keep on dancing (On TEN 7112 only) / You and me tonight (midnight mix) (On TEN 7113 only).
7" Single: Released Apr '86, on 10 Records, by Virgin Records. Deleted May '88. Catalogue no: **TEN 71**
12" Single: on 10 Records, by Virgin Records. Catalogue no: **TEN 71-13**
12" Single: Released Apr '86, on 10 Records, by Virgin Records. Catalogue no: **TEN 71-12**

YOU AND ME TONIGHT (OLD GOLD)
Tracks: / You and me tonight / Like I like it.
12" Single: Released 28 Mar '89, on Old Gold, by Old Gold Records. Catalogue no: **OG 4106**

Ausgang

HEAD ON
Tracks: / Head on / Sink into your luck / If that's your bat / I'm leaving you.
12" Single: Released Dec '84, on Criminal Damage, Catalogue no: **CRI 12124**

HERE IT COMES
Tracks: / Here it comes.
12" Single: Released Oct '85, on Heavy Metal, by FM-Revolver Records. Catalogue no: **12VHF 21**

TEACHING OF WEB (4 TRACK EP)
Tracks: / Teaching of web.
12" Single: Released Feb '84, on Criminal Damage, Catalogue no: **CRI 12109**

Austin, David

KISS AND TELL
Tracks: / Kiss and tell / Kiss and tell (instr.).
7" Single: Released Jul '85, on Parlophone, by EMI Records. Catalogue no: **R 6102**
12" Single: Released Jul '85, on Parlophone, by EMI Records. Catalogue no: **12R 6102**

THIS BOY LOVES THE SUN
Tracks: / This boy loves the sun.
7" Single: Released Aug '84, on Parlophone, by EMI Records. Catalogue no: **R 6077**
12" Single: Released Aug '84, on Parlophone, by EMI Records. Deleted '86. Catalogue no: **12R 6077**

TURN TO GOLD
Tracks: / Turn to gold.
7" Single: Released May '84, on Parlophone, by EMI Records. Catalogue no: **R 6068**
12" Single: Released May '84, on Parlophone, by EMI Records. Catalogue no: **12R 6068**

Austin, Michel

OUT TONIGHT
Tracks: / Out tonight.
7" Pic: Released Oct '84, on Chrysalis, by Chrysalis Records. Catalogue no: **MICKP 1**
7" Single: Released Oct '84, on Chrysalis, by Chrysalis Records. Catalogue no: **MICK 1**
12" Single: Released Oct '84, on Chrysalis, by Chrysalis Records. Catalogue no: **MICKX 1**

Austin, Patti

Biographical details: Quincy Jones, producer of the world's biggest ever album 'Thriller', cities Pattie Austin as his favourite

singer. The two have worked extensively together, with Austin singing backing vocals on many of the stars records that Jones has produced and with Jones producing her own work. The first Patti Austin album 'End Of A Rainbow' was issued in 1976, to be followed in'77 by Havana Candy and in '80 by 'Body Language'. The first LP to make a real impact was 1981's 'Every Home Should Have One', a slow but steady seller in her native US. It appeared that not every British home had one, for it managed just one week on the UK album chart, at no.99. Austin did score a British top 20 single that year, however, singing lead on Quincy Jones,'Razzamatazz. In 1982 she teamed with another of Jones stalwart singers, James Ingram, for a 45 entitled 'Baby Come To Me'. The record proved to be a sleeper smash. having hovered in the being used regularly on a TV series. It hit no.1 in February to be deposed by the Jones-produced 'Billie Jean' by Michael Jackson. The success of 'Baby' crossed the Atlantic, and the song hit no.11 in the UK. Patti Austin's dual career is continuing apace. (BM 84)
Soul singer, born in 1950 in California. Began as a child, went to Europe with Quincy Jones at age nine, already a trouper; established as a studio performer at 17, sessioning with Paul Simon, Billy Joel, George Benson, Roberta Flack etc. Made her own jazz influenced albums on CTI (1976-80), continued sessioning, linked again with Jones: lead vocal on his smash hit (The Dude) won a Grammy in 1982. The title track was a hit from her album *Every home should have one* in 1981 on Jones Qwest label; it also included a duet with James Ingram *Baby come to me*, becmae theme on TV's soap opera *General hospital* made No.1 in the USA, no 11 in the UK; their second duet *How do you keep the music playing* from film *Best friends* was nominated for best song Oscar. Second solo album on Qwest called *It's gonna be special* in USA 1984, eponymous Patti Austin in UK, then *Getting away with murder* in 1985. She has still to gain the stardom her voice deserves. (Donald Clarke, July 1988).

BABY COME TO ME
Tracks: / Baby come to me / Solero.
7" Single: Released Feb '83, on Warner Bros., by WEA Records. Deleted '86. Catalogue no: **K 15005**
12" Single: Released Feb '83, on Warner Bros., by WEA Records. Catalogue no: **K 15005T**

DO YOU LOVE ME
Tracks: / Do you love me / Solero.
7" Single: Released Aug '81, on Qwest (USA), by Qwest Records (USA). Deleted Aug '84. Catalogue no: **K 17838**

EVERY HOME SHOULD HAVE ONE (SINGLE)
Tracks: / Every home should have one / Genie.
7" Single: Released May '80, on Qwest (USA), by Qwest Records (USA). Deleted May '83. Catalogue no: **K 17874**

GIRL USED TO BE ME, THE
Tracks: / Girl used to be me, The.
7" Single: Released Oct '89, on GRP, by GRP Records (USA). Catalogue no: **GRP 30277**

HEAT OF HEAT, THE
Tracks: / Heat of heat, The / Hot in the heat of love / All behind us now (Extra track on 12" only).
7" Single: Released Mar '86, on Warner Bros., by WEA Records. Catalogue no: **W 8798**
12" Single: Released Mar '86, on Warner Bros., by WEA Records. Catalogue no: **W 8798T**

HOW DO YOU KEEP THE MUSIC PLAY
Tracks: / How do you keep the music play.
7" Single: Released May '83, on Warner Bros., by WEA Records. Catalogue no: **W 9618**
12" Single: Released May '83, on Warner Bros., by WEA Records. Catalogue no: **W 9681T**

I CAN'T STOP
Tracks: / I can't stop / Body language.
7" Single: Released Sep '80, on CTI (1), by Polydor Ltd. Deleted Sep '83. Catalogue no: **CTSP 15**

Austin, Rockin' Johnny

CITY LIGHTS
Tracks: / City lights.
7" Single: Released Jun '81, on Nervous, by Nervous Records. Catalogue no: **NER 004**

MEETS THE FEDS
Tracks: / Meets the feds.
7" Single: Released Jun '81, on Nervous, by Nervous Records. Catalogue no: **NEP001**

Australia (group)

OLD ENGLAND (FOR MOM)
Tracks: / Old England (for Mom).
7" Single: Released Apr '83, on Magic (1), by Submarine Records. Catalogue no: **MAGIC 6**

Australian Crawl

BOYS LIGHT UP
Tracks: / Boys light up.
7" Single: Released Jan '84, on Geffen, by Geffen Records (USA). Catalogue no: **A 4104**
12" Single: Released Jan '84, on Geffen, by Geffen Records (USA). Catalogue no: **TA 4104**

DOWNHEARTED
Tracks: / Downhearted / Letter from Zimbabwe.
7" Single: Released Feb '83, on EMI, by EMI Records. Catalogue no: **EMI 5365**

RECKLESS
Tracks: / Reckless / White limbo.
7" Single: Released Feb '84, on Geffen, by Geffen Records (USA). Catalogue no: **A 4243**
12" Single: Released Feb '84, on Geffen, by Geffen Records (USA). Catalogue no: **TA 4243**

Austyn, Heather

BAD ATTITUDE
Tracks: / Bad attitude.
7" Single: Released 20 Mar '89, on Urban, by Polydor Ltd. Deleted Oct '89. Catalogue no: **URB 33**
12" Single: Released 20 Mar '89, on Urban, by Polydor Ltd. Deleted Oct '89. Catalogue no: **URBX 33**

Ausweis

A VICTIMES
Tracks: / A victimes.
12" Single: Released Nov '85, on Chainsaw, Deleted '88. Catalogue no: **TEXT 8**

JOURS DE HAINE
Tracks: / Jours de haine.
12" Single: Released May '86, on Ediesta, Deleted '88. Catalogue no: **CALC 1**

Auto Da Fe

ALL IS YELLOW (HOT, HOT, HOT)
Tracks: / All is yellow (hot hot hot).
7" Single: Released Feb '85, on Spartan, Catalogue no: **SP 18**
12" Single: Released Feb '85, on Spartan, Catalogue no: **12SP 18**

MAGIC MOMENTS
Tracks: / Magic moments.
7" Single: Released Dec '85, on Spartan, Catalogue no: **SP 128**

MAN OF MINE
Tracks: / Man of mine.
7" Single: Released Apr '83, on Rewind, Catalogue no: **REWIND 14**

NOVEMBER NOVEMBER
Tracks: / November November / For rich people.
7" Single: Released Oct '83, on Rewind, Catalogue no: **REWIND 15**

SOMETHING'S GOTTEN HOLD OF MY HEART
Tracks: / Something's gotten hold of my heart.
7" Single: Released Apr '84, on Rewind, Catalogue no: **REW 18**

Autograph

TURN UP THE RADIO
Tracks: / Turn up the radio / Thrill of love / Fever line.
7" Single: Released Mar '85, on RCA, by BMG Records (UK). Catalogue no: **RCA 483**
12" Single: Released Mar '85, on RCA, by BMG Records (UK). Catalogue no: **RCAT 483**

Automatic Diamini

CRAZY SUPPER, THE
7" EP: Released Jun '86, on D for Drum, Catalogue no: **DLAM 1**

I DON'T KNOW YOU BUT...
Tracks: / I don't know you but....
7" Single: Released Mar '87, on D for Drum, Catalogue no: **DLAM 2**

ME & MY CONSCIENCE
Tracks: / Me & my conscience

7" Single: Released 21 Nov '87, on Idea, by Idea Records. Catalogue no: **IDEA 009**
12" Single: Released 21 Nov '87, on Idea, by Idea Records. Catalogue no: **IDEAT 009**

Automatic Slim

SPOONFUL, THE
Tracks: / Spoonful, The.
7" Single: Released 19 Sep '87, on Square One, Catalogue no: **SQUARE 022**

Automation

DANCING IN OUTER SPACE 84 RAP
Tracks: / Dancing in outer space 84 rap.
12" Single: Released Sep '84, on Jungle Rhythm, Catalogue no: **SWEAT 2**

Autopilot

ESCAPING FROM A MAZE
Tracks: / Escaping from a maze / New terrain.
7" Single: Released Jan '81, on Chrysalis, by Chrysalis Records. Deleted Jan '84. Catalogue no: **CHS 2483**

Autumn

MY LITTLE GIRL
Tracks: / My little girl.
7" Single: Released Sep '71, on Pye, Deleted '76. Catalogue no: **7N 45090**

Auty, Peter

WALKING IN THE AIR
Tracks: / Walking in the air.
7" Single: Released Dec '85, on Stiff, by Stiff Records. Deleted '88. Catalogue no: **LAD 1**

Avalon, Frankie

Biographical details: Born in Philadelphia in 1940, Frankie Avalon was one of the many stereotyped teen idols who took over the American charts in the late fifties, during the gap between the rock'n'roll heyday and the arrival of the Beatles. Despite his contrived image, Avalon did possess talent - in fact he won a talent contest at the age of six, and grew up as a trumpet playing child prodigy. Discovered by Chacellor Records, he recorded a couple of flop singles. It was third time lucky for 17 year old Frankie: he hit No.7 on the Billboard charts in early '58 with *Dede Dinah*, a moronic, singalong, nasal record on which he pinched his nose to obtain the right sound. This began a two year string of Top 10 hits, the biggest of which was *Venus*, a five week US No.1. A second chart topper *Why* was a Christmas winner in 1959, but from then on the winning streak went into decline. Avalon was never a major star in Britain, where the likes of Cliff and Marty Wilde were satifying the teen market. His best showing *Venus* peaked at No. 16 and Anthony Newly covered *Why* and stole the UK No.1 honours. During the Sixties and Seventies, Avalon pursued various showbusiness activities, including singing in return to the pop spotlight by appearing for four minutes in the blockbusting movie *Grease*. His performance of the song *Beauty school dropout* was a highlight of the film and its soundtrack album, one of the all time best selling LPs. (Bob MacDonald).
One of the biggest and one of the worst of the teen idols of the period when Elvis Presley was in the army, Buddy Holly was dead etc, soon washed away by the Beatles. Born in 1940 in Philadelphia, he played trumpet on TV guest spots as a child; signed by music publishers to the new local Chancellor label, with constant access to locally based American Bandstand TV show, he had 24 hits 1958-1962. *Venus* was No. 1 for five weeks in the USA, reaching No. 16 in the UK; a contender for one of the all time worst records ever made. In 1960 he was eclipsed by Tommy Rydell, another Philadelphian (and somewhat better singer) on the rival Cameo label. He made *Carpetbagger's* in 1962, his role too small to be mentioned in film reference books, he floated up in *Grease* in 1978. *The idolmaker* in 1980 profiled Chancellor's Bob Marcucci, who with Peter DeAngelis pulled strings for Avalon. (Donald Clarke, July 1981).

DON'T THROW AWAY ALL THOSE TEARDROPS
Tracks: / Don't throw away all those teardrops.
7" Single: Released Apr '60, on H.M.V., by EMI Records. Deleted '65. Catalogue no: **POP 727**

GINGERBREAD
Tracks: / Gingerbread.
7" Single: Released Sep '58, on H.M.V., by EMI Records. Deleted '63. Catalogue no: **POP 517**

VENUS
Tracks: / Venus.
7" Single: Released Apr '59, on H.M.V., by EMI Records. Deleted '64. Catalogue no: **POP 603**

VENUS (OLD GOLD)
Tracks: / Venus / Why.
7" Single: Released Jul '82, on Old Gold, by Old Gold Records. Deleted Jul '88. Catalogue no: **OG 9160**

WHY
Tracks: / Why.
7" Single: Released Jan '60, on H.M.V., by EMI Records. Deleted '65. Catalogue no: **POP 688**

Avant Gardeners

DEADWOOD STAGE
Tracks: / Deadwood stage / John priest / Where are my hormones.
7" Single: Released Dec '83, on Speed, Catalogue no: **SPEED 11**

Avenger

TOO WILD TO TAME
Tracks: / Too wild to tame / On the rocks.
7" Single: Released Oct '88, on Neat, by Neat Records. Catalogue no: **NEAT 31**

Avengers (group)

OH BABY
Tracks: / Oh baby.
7" Single: Released Jul '84, on MCA, by MCA Records. Catalogue no: **PAN 4**

Avenue 'B' Boogie Band

BUMPER TO BUMPER
Tracks: / Bumper to bumper (part 1) / Bumper to bumper (part 2).
12" Single: Released Apr '80, on Salsoul, Deleted Apr '83. Catalogue no: **SAL 12-2**

Average Buss Cue

WHENEVER I'M WITH YOU
Tracks: / Whenever I'm with you.
7" Single: Released Mar '84, on Swagman, Catalogue no: **CY**

Average White Band

Biographical details: AVERAGE WHITE BAND A UK soul/funk band formed in 1972 by Scottish musicians, named after their collective obsession with black music. Original lineup: bassist/vocalist Alan Gorrie, guitarist Onnie McIntyre, drummer Robbie McIntosh, Roger Ball on sax and keyboards, Malcolm 'Molly' Duncan on trumpet; Mike Rosen on guitar and trumpet, replaced by Hamish Stuart on guitar and vocals. McIntosh had worked for Brian Auger; he died in a drug accident and was replaced by Steve Ferrone, also ex-Auger and the group's first black sideman. Their best work was produced by Arif Mardin at Atlantic. They relocated to USA West Coast, soon confused fans with switch to disco producer and guest guitarist Richie Stotts with punk Mohican hairstyle, recruited from New York punks Plasmatics for *Cupid's In Fashion* in 1982. *Benny & Us* was with Ben E King Band members sessioned, especially Dundee Horns; Gorrie's first solo album *Sleepless Nights* in 1985 seemed to signal the end. Donald Clarke 21 July 1988
Formed in 1972, the Average White Band hailed from Glasgow and were all previously experienced. They first came to public attention when supporting Eric Clapton at his comeback Rainbow concert in January 1973. After recording a debut album called *Show you hand* for MCA, they transferred to Atlantic Records, where they were given a heavy American push. As *Average White Band* album, produced by the legendary Arif Mardin, was taking off in the states, the band's drummer Robbie McIntosh died of an accidental heroin overdose to be replaced by Steve Ferrone. That album hit the top of the US album charts in early simultaneous US No.1 single. Both single and album reached No.6 in their native Britain. The Average White Band were hardly what their name implied - they played and sounded like Black Soul musicians and achieved one of the most authentic white versions of the black man's funk in the history of pop music. The successful groove was repeated on the *Cut the cake* album, the title track becoming another US Top 10 single. Having moved permanently to Los Angeles, the group continued the formula but with less effect. Having enjoyed enormous success at an early stage, they could only now repeat themselves and began a gradual decline in their American chart fortunes. 1980 brought them a brief resurgence in the form of a UK Top 20 single *Let's go round again* from the album *Shine*. Having been more successful in the States than at home, the positions were echelons of the British album chart. The Average White Band have continued to release competent product, but can no longer capture the sheer vitality of *Pick up the pieces*. (Bob MacDonald).

CUT THE CAKE (SINGLE)
Tracks: / Cut the cake.
7" Single: Released Jun '75, on Atlantic, by WEA Records. Deleted '80. Catalogue no: **K 10605**

FOR YOU FOR LOVE
Tracks: / For you for love / Help is on the way.
7" Single: Released Jun '80, on RCA, by BMG Records (UK). Deleted '85. Catalogue no: **AWB 2**
12" Single: Released Jun '80, on RCA, by BMG Records (UK). Deleted '85. Catalogue no: **AWB 12 2**

I BELIEVE
Tracks: / I believe.
7" Single: Released Sep '82, on RCA, by BMG Records (UK). Catalogue no: **RCA 274**
12" Single: Released Sep '82, on RCA, by BMG Records (UK). Catalogue no: **RCAT 274**

LET'S GO ROUND AGAIN (PT 1)
Tracks: / Let's go around again (Pt 1) / Love of your own.
7" Single: Released Apr '80, on RCA, by BMG Records (UK). Deleted '85. Catalogue no: **AWB 1**

12" Single: Released Apr '80, on RCA, by BMG Records (UK). Deleted '85. Catalogue no: **AWB 12 1**

PICK UP THE PIECES
Tracks: / Pick up the pieces.
7" Single: Released Feb '75, on Atlantic, by WEA Records. Deleted '80. Catalogue no: **K 10489**

PICK UP THE PIECES (OLD GOLD)
Tracks: / Pick up the pieces.
7" Single: Released Jul '81, on RCA Golden Grooves, by BMG Records (UK). Catalogue no: **GOLD 514**

QUEEN OF MY SOUL
Tracks: / Queen of my soul.
7" Single: Released Sep '76, on Atlantic, by WEA Records. Deleted '81. Catalogue no: **K 10825**

WALK ON BY
Tracks: / Walk on by.
7" Single: Released Jun '79, on RCA, by BMG Records (UK). Deleted '84. Catalogue no: **XC 1087**

WHEN WILL YOU BE MINE
Tracks: / When will you be mine.
7" Single: Released Jul '79, on RCA, by BMG Records (UK). Deleted '84. Catalogue no: **XB 1096**

YOU'RE MY NUMBER 1
Tracks: / You're my number 1 / Theater of excess.
7" Single: Released Jul '82, on RCA, by BMG Records (UK). Catalogue no: **RCA 250**
12" Single: Released Jul '82, on RCA, by BMG Records (UK). Catalogue no: **RCAT 250**

Aviator

ALL YOUR LOVE IS GONE
Tracks: / All your love is gone / Wood wharf gumbo.
7" Single: Released Jul '80, on Harvest (1), by EMI Records. Deleted '83. Catalogue no: **HAR 5208**

Avo 8

BIG CAR
Tracks: / Big car / Fame / It's a game (on 12" only.).
7" Single: Released Sep '89, on Cherry Red, by Cherry Red Records. Catalogue no: **CHERRY 102**
12" Single: Released Sep '89, on Cherry Red, by Cherry Red Records. Catalogue no: **12 CHERRY 102**

IS THIS THE END
Tracks: / Is this the end.
12" Single: Released '88, on Avo Records. Catalogue no: **AR 001**

Avons

DIRTY AND CONTROVERSIAL
Tracks: / Dirty and controversial.
12" Single: Released Sep '86, on Letharge. Catalogue no: **ARGE 11**

FOUR LITTLE HEELS
Tracks: / Four little heels.
7" Single: Released Sep '60, on Columbia, by EMI Records. Deleted '65. Catalogue no: **DB 4522**

RUBBER BALL
Tracks: / Rubber ball.
7" Single: Released Jan '61, on Columbia, by EMI Records. Deleted '66. Catalogue no: **DB 4569**

SEVEN LITTLE GIRLS SITTING IN THE BACK SEAT
Tracks: / Seven little girls sitting in the back seat.
7" Single: Released Nov '59, on Columbia, by EMI Records. Deleted '64. Catalogue no: **DB 4363**

WE'RE ONLY YOUNG ONCE
Tracks: / We're only young once.
7" Single: Released Jul '60, on Columbia, by EMI Records. Deleted '65. Catalogue no: **DB 4461**

WHY DID YOU FALL IN LOVE
Tracks: / Why did you fall in love.
7" Single: Released Sep '83, on Nectar, by Nectar Music. Catalogue no: **NRS 2**

Axe

I CAN'T HELP MYSELF
Tracks: / I can't help myself / Let me know.
7" Single: Released 20 Jun '80, on MCA, by MCA Records. Deleted '83. Catalogue no: **MCA 611**

Axeman

AFRICA
Tracks: / Africa / Blacker silk.
12" Single: Released Sep '86, on Fashion, by Fashion Records. Catalogue no: **FAD 046**

NO SKIN UP
Tracks: / No skin up.
12" Single: Released Mar '86, on Fashion, by Fashion Records. Catalogue no: **FAD 037**

TAKE IT DOWN LOW
Tracks: / Take it down low / Singing in a dance hall / Safer with you.
12" Single: Released Mar '87, on Fashion, by Fashion Records. Catalogue no: **FAD 047**

Axis

LADY
Tracks: / Lady / Messiah.
7" Single: Released Oct '81, on Metal Minded, by Neat Records. Catalogue no: **MM1 AX 1047**

ROLLING WITH RAI
Tracks: / Rolling with Rai.
12" Single: Released Mar '89, on Gee Street, by Gee Street Records. Catalogue no: **GEET 018**

WEDDING BELL
Tracks: / Wedding bell / And the truth.
7" Single: Released May '82, on JSO, Deleted '87. Catalogue no: **EAT 8**

Axis Point

RED HOT & BLUE
Tracks: / Red hot & blue.
7" Single: Released Mar '80, on RCA, by BMG Records (UK). Deleted '83. Catalogue no: **PB 5229**

Axton, Hoyt

Biographical details: Born in Oklahoma, Hoyt Axton is an artist based in country music but also combining elements of folk and rock. His mother Mae Axton co-wrote *Heartbreak Hotel*,Elvis's legendary first hit, and indeed her son is better known for his writing even though he has recorded over fifteen albums. He co-wrote *Greenback Dollar*, a US top 30 hit for the Kingston Trio in 1963. A song about drug abuse *The Pusher* was recorded by Steppenwolf and featured on the *Easy Rider* soundtrack LP. Other winners include *Joy To The World*, the biggest ever hit for Three Dog Night (six weeks at US no.1 slot in 1971) plus *No No Song*, a US No. 3 single for Ringo Starr in '75. Success on this scale has always encluded Axton has an artist, either in Britain or the States. His only chart single in the UK is *Della And The Dealer*, an comical piece that reached No. 48 in 1980. (Bob MacDonald). The singer, songwriter and actor was born in 1938 in Oklahoma; his mother Mae Boron Axton wrote *Heartbreak hotel*, also country hits. Hoyt made first record in Nashville in 1957, served in the US Navy, moved to West Coast; worked bars and coffee houses and made folk and blues records for Vee Jay. Wrote hits *Greenback dollar, Kingston trio, The pusher* for Steppenwolf and others for Three Dog Night etc; other songs recorded by John Denver, Waylon Jennings, Glen Campbell. He recorded for CBS, Capitol, A&M with excellent backing but his own work never acquired more than a deserved cult following. He moved to MCA in 1977, had minor country hits; formed his own Jeremiah label in 1978, named after the bullfrog in his song *Joy to the world*; had biggest hits with *Della & the dealer, Rusty old halo* in '79. Became actor with TV guest parts, films including *Et* ('83), *Gremlins* ('84). (Donald Clarke, July 1988).

DELLA AND THE DEALER
Tracks: / Della and the dealer / Gotta keep rollin'.
7" Single: Released Jun '80, on Young Blood, by Young Blood Records. Deleted '85. Catalogue no: **YB 0082**
12" Single: Released Mar '80, on Young Blood, by Young Blood Records. Deleted Mar '83. Catalogue no: **YB GOLD 82**

EVERYBODY'S GOIN' ON THE ROAD (SINGLE)
Tracks: / Everybody's goin' on the road / Battle of New Orleans.
7" Single: Released Nov '81, on Young Blood, by Young Blood Records. Deleted Nov '84. Catalogue no: **YB 120**

HOTEL RITZ
Tracks: / Hotel Ritz / Evangelina.
7" Single: Released Jul '80, on Young Blood, by Young Blood Records. Deleted '83. Catalogue no: **YB 92**

WILD BULL RIDER
Tracks: / Wild bull rider / Torpedo.
7" Single: Released Sep '80, on Young Blood, by Young Blood Records. Deleted '83. Catalogue no: **YB 101**

Axxess

OWLS
Tracks: / Owls.
7" Single: Released Aug '83, on Lamborghini, by Lamborghini Records. Catalogue no: **LMG 3**

Axxis

KINGDOM OF THE NIGHT (SINGLE)
Tracks: / Kingdom of the night / Young souls / Kings made of steel (12" & CD only.).
CD 5": Released Aug '89, on Parlophone, by EMI Records. Catalogue no: **CDR 6225**
CD 5": Released Aug '89, on Parlophone, by EMI Records. Catalogue no: **147 460 2**
7" Pic: Released Aug '89, on Parlophone, by EMI Records. Catalogue no: **147 460 0**
7" Pic: Released Aug '89, on Parlophone, by EMI Records. Catalogue no: **RPD 6225**
7" Single: Released Aug '89, on Parlophone, by EMI Records. Catalogue no: **R 6225**
7" Single: Released Aug '89, on Parlophone, by EMI Records. Catalogue no: **147 460 7**
12" Single: Released Aug '89, on Parlophone, by EMI Records. Catalogue no: **147 460 6**
12" Single: Released Aug '89, on Parlophone, by EMI Records. Catalogue no: **12R 6225**

Ayers, Kevin

MONEY MONEY MONEY
Tracks: / Money money money / Stranger in blue suede shoes.
7" Single: Released Nov '80, on Harvest (1), by EMI Records. Deleted Nov '83. Catalogue no: **HAR 5198**

MY SPEEDIN' HEART
Tracks: / My speedin' heart.
7" Single: Released Jul '83, on Charly, by Charly Records. Catalogue no: **CYZ 7 107**

STEPPIN' OUT
Tracks: / Steppin' out.
7" Single: Released May '86, on Illuminated, Catalogue no: **LEV 71**

Ayers, Roy

Biographical details: Roy Ayers is an American funk vocalist, whose records are designed to appeal to regular clubgoers rather than the wider pop audience. In 1978 he made the national pop chart for the first time with 'Get On Up, Get On Down', peaking at no.41. The following year saw him reach no.43 with 'Heat Of The Beat', a duet with Wayne Henderson on which Ayers sang and played vibrophone and Henderson played trumpet. His third chart single 'Don't Stop The Feeling' hit no.56 in 1980. All three 45s charted solely on the strength of disco reaction, and received virtually no radio plays. (BM 84).

CAN'T YOU SEE ME
Tracks: / Can't you see me / Love will bring us back together / Sweet tears.
7" Single: Released Sep '87, on Urban, by Polydor Ltd. Catalogue no: **URB 6**
12" Single: Released Sep '87, on Urban, by Polydor Ltd. Catalogue no: **URBX 6**

CRACK IN THE MIRROR (WAKE UP)
Tracks: / Crack in the mirror (wake up) / Spirit of dodo 89.
12" Single: Released Sep '89, on Ichiban, by Ichiban Records (UK). Catalogue no: **12 PO 33**

DON'T STOP THE FEELING
Tracks: / Don't stop the feeling / Don't hide your love.
7" Single: Released Jan '80, on Polydor, by Polydor Ltd. Deleted '85. Catalogue no: **STEP 9**
7" Single: Released Feb '80, on Polydor, by Polydor Ltd. Deleted '85. Catalogue no: **STEP 6**
12" Single: Released Jan '80, on Polydor, by Polydor Ltd. Deleted '85. Catalogue no: **STEPX 9**

FAST MONEY
Tracks: / Fast money / Black family.
12" Single: Released Sep '88, on Ichiban, by Ichiban Records (UK). Catalogue no: **12 PO 14**

GET ON UP, GET ON DOWN
Tracks: / Get on up, get on down.
7" Single: Released Sep '78, on Polydor, by Polydor Ltd. Deleted '83. Catalogue no: **AYERS 7**

HEAT OF THE BEAT
Tracks: / Heat of the beat / No deposit, no return.
7" Single: Released Jan '79, on Polydor, by Polydor Ltd. Deleted '84. Catalogue no: **POSP 16**

IN THE DARK (SINGLE)
Tracks: / In the dark.
7" Single: Released Nov '84, on CBS, by CBS Records. Catalogue no: **A 4855**
12" Single: Released Nov '84, on CBS, by CBS Records. Catalogue no: **TA 4855**

POO POO LALA
Tracks: / Poo poo la la / Compadre / Running away (on 12" only).
12" Single: Released Feb '85, on CBS, by CBS Records. Deleted '86. Catalogue no: **TA 6087**
7" Single: Released Feb '85, on CBS, by CBS Records. Catalogue no: **A 6087**

RUNNING AWAY
Tracks: / Running away / Can't you see me.
12" Single: Released Mar '80, on Polydor, by Polydor Ltd. Deleted '80. Catalogue no: **POSPX 135**

SILVER VIBRATIONS (SINGLE)
Tracks: / Silver vibrations.
12" Single: Released Jul '83, on Uno Melodic, Catalogue no: **UM 1 T**
7" Single: Released Jul '83, on Uno Melodic, Catalogue no: **UM 1**

SOMETIMES BELIEVE IN YOURSELF
Tracks: / Sometimes believe in yourself / Can you dance / Thank you, thank you.
7" Single: Released Oct '80, on Polydor, by Polydor Ltd. Deleted Oct '83. Catalogue no: **POSPX 186**

SUAVE
Tracks: / Suave / And then we were one.
12" Single: Released 1 May '89, on Ichiban, by Ichiban Records (UK). Catalogue no: **12PO 23**

TURN ME LOOSE
Tracks: / Turn me loose / Ooh.
7" Single: Released Apr '82, on Polydor, by Polydor Ltd. Deleted Apr '85. Catalogue no: **POSP 427**
12" Single: Released Apr '82, on Polydor, by Polydor Ltd. Deleted Apr '85. Catalogue no: **POSPX 427**

Ayre Rayde

SOCK IT TO ME
Tracks: / Sock it to me.
7" Single: Released Jun '86, on Cherry Red, by Cherry Red Records. Deleted '87. Catalogue no: **DANCE 2**
12" Single: Released Jun '86, on Cherry Red, by Cherry Red Records. Deleted '87. Catalogue no: **12 DANCE 2**

Ayres, Pam

Biographical details: The comical poetry of Pam Ayres, satirising the everyday lives of ordinary folk, shot her to TV stardom in the mid-Seventies. I"Some Of Me Poems And Songs"D capitalised on her fame, reaching No.13 on the album chart with 14 weeks on the list, in 1976. The formula was repeated later in the year, but with less success: I"Some More Of Me Poems And Songs"D peaked at No.23 with a six-week run. Ayres has not graced the album chart since, but her nauseating or refreshing way with words (depending on taste) has continued to sell well in book form throughout her native Britain. (Bob McDonald 1984).

PLEASE WILL YOU TAKE YOUR CHILDREN
Tracks: / Please will you take your children.
7" Single: Released Nov '81, on Honest Penny, Catalogue no: **HP 001**

AYS

TWELVE INCHES OF AYS
Tracks: / Twelve inches of AYS.
12" Single: Released May '88, on Mortarhate, by Mortarhate Records. Catalogue no: **MORT 27**

A-Z & The Girl Guides

LOVE IS BLIND
Tracks: / Love is blind.
7" Single: Released Feb '85, on Mordent, Catalogue no: **DMOR 3**

Azana

RUNAWAY WOMAN
Tracks: / Runaway woman / Runaway woman (version).
12" Single: Released Apr '87, on UK Bubblers, by Greensleeves Records. Deleted '88. Catalogue no: **UKMC 24**

Azare

LOVE'S GONE
Tracks: / Love's gone.
7" Single: Released May '85, on TVM, Catalogue no: **TVM 101**

Aznavour, Charles

Biographical details: Born in Paris in 1924, Aznavour had just turned 50 when he scored his only British No 1. He became a star in France in the mid-50's and has remained popular there ever since. A prolific composer, he is said to have written or co-written at least 500 songs. His biggest hit in his own country was La Mama (1964) which sold a million copies solely in France. Ten years later The Old-Fashioned Way gave him his first UK chart hit, peaking at No 38. He was then commissioned to write the theme song for the TV series The Seven Faces Of Women and came up with She, a joint composition with British journalist Herbert Kretzmer. Sung in his usual slushily romantic manner, She rocketed to the top slot in its second week on the UK chart and remained in pole position for four weeks. Two Top Thirty albums immediately followed. After 1974, however, he failed to continue to win over British record buyers. When K-Tel issued His Greatest Love Songs in 1980 it enjoyed just one week on the LP chart at No 73, a blunt signal of lack of interest. But Charles Aznavour does remain in the top league of middle-of-the-road entertainers and he managed to achieve international

recognition from a very insular base: France has the most parochial and isolated music business in Western Europe. (Bob MacDonald, 1984.)
A singer, songwriter and actor born in Paris in 1924, of Armenian family who had fled Turkish massacres in 1915. First audition at age nine; family restaurant closed following German occupation of Paris, he began acting on tour. Teamed with actor Pierre Roche by a nervous announcer, who introduced them as double act; they began writing songs during nine-year partnership. First hit *J'ai bu I have drunk* followed by a flood of songs recorded by Mistinguette, Maurice Chavalier, Edith Piaf, etc. He first visited the USA in 1948 without a visa: We owed our entry permit to the judge's love of *Finian's rainbow* (which Aznavour had translated into French). He went solo in 1950, encouraged by Piaf and others to interpret his own songs; he has become perhaps the biggest french star, singing in both French and English, warmth and angst in onstage performance called the epitome of French romance; he has also played roles in many films. (Donald Clarke, July 1988)o.

IN TIMES TO BE (SINGLE)
7" Single: Released Apr '83, on Barclay, by Decca Records. Catalogue no: **BA 3**

OLD FASHIONED WAY, THE
Tracks: / Old fashioned way, The.
7" Single: Released Aug '73, on Barclay, by Decca Records. Deleted '78. Catalogue no: **BAR 20**

SHE (SINGLE)
Tracks: / She.
7" Single: Released Jun '74, on Barclay, by Decca Records. Deleted '79. Catalogue no: **BAR 26**

Aztec Camera

Biographical details: This Scottish band are very much dominated by frontman Roddy Frame, vocalist, guitarist and songwriter. Originally formed in January 1980 while still at school, they released their first single "Just Like Gold" in March 1981. The record that began attracting attention was their '82 single, the Sixties-inflected "Pillar To Post". The band scored their first minor hit in early '83 with "Oblivious", from the debut album "High Land Hard Rain". The highly melodic next single failed when issued that May - hardly a sensible time to release a song called "Walk Out To Winter". Later in the year they were snapped up by WEA, having previously recorded for Postcard and Rough Trade, and the new company promptly re-issued "Oblivious" and made it into a Top 20 hit. In 1984 the "Knife" album and its first single "All I Need Is Everything" both charted respectably, but Roddy Frame's nifty songs and group's acttractive acoustic-based sound probably have greater sales potential than thus far achieved. (Bob McDonald 1984).

ALL I NEED IS EVERYTHING
Tracks: / All I need is everything.
7" Single: Released Aug '84, on WEA, by WEA Records. Catalogue no: **AC 1**
12" Single: Released Aug '84, on WEA, by WEA Records. Deleted '86. Catalogue no: **AC 1T**

DEEP AND WIDE AND TALL
Tracks: / Deep and wide and tall / Bad education / More than a law.
CD 5": Released Sep '88, on WEA, by WEA Records. Deleted Jul '88. Catalogue no: **YZ 154CD**
7" Single: Released Sep '87, on WEA, by WEA Records. Deleted Jul '88. Catalogue no: **YZ 154**
12" Single: Released Sep '87, on WEA, by WEA Records. Deleted Jul '88. Catalogue no: **YZ 154T**

HOW MEN ARE
Tracks: / How men are / Red flag, The / Killermont street (live) (Only on 12".) / Pillar to post (live) (On 12" only.).
CD 5": Released May '88, on WEA (Holland), by WEA Records. Catalogue no: **2480282**
7" Single: Released Jan '88, on WEA, by WEA Records. Catalogue no: **YZ 668**
12" Single: Released Jan '88, on WEA, by WEA Records. Catalogue no: **YZ 668T**

JUST LIKE GOLD (SINGLE)
7" Single: Released Mar '81, on Postcard, Deleted '82. Catalogue no: **POSTCARD 81/3**

MATTRESS OF WIRE
7" Single: Released Jul '81, on Postcard, Catalogue no: **POSTCARD 81/8**

OBLIVIOUS
Tracks: / Oblivious / Orchard girl.
7" Single: Released Jan '83, on Rough Trade, by Rough Trade Records. Catalogue no: **RT 122**
12" Single: Released Jan '83, on Rough Trade, by Rough Trade Records. Catalogue no: **RT 122T**

OBLIVIOUS (RE-ISSUE)
Tracks: / Oblivious.
7" Single: Released Nov '83, on WEA, by WEA Records. Deleted '86. Catalogue no: **AZTEC 1**

PILLAR TO POST
Tracks: / Pillar to post / Queen's tattoo.
7" Single: Released Aug '82, on Rough Trade, by Rough Trade Records. Catalogue no: **RT 112**

SOMEWHERE IN MY HEART
Tracks: / Somewhere in my heart / Everybody is a number one / Down the dip (Available on 12" single only.) / Jump (Available on 12" only) / Walk out on winter (CD only) / Still on fire (CD only).
CD 5": Released Apr '88, on WEA, by WEA Records. Catalogue no: **YZ 181 CD**
7" Single: Released Apr '88, on WEA, by WEA Records. Catalogue no: **YZ 181**
12" Single: Released Apr '88, on WEA, by WEA Records. Catalogue no: **YZ 181T**

STILL ON FIRE
Tracks: / Still on fire.
7" Single: Released Nov '84, on WEA, by WEA Records. Catalogue no: **AC 2**
12" Single: Released Nov '84, on WEA, by WEA Records. Deleted '86. Catalogue no: **AC 2T**

WALK OUT TO WINTER
Tracks: / Walk out to winter.
7" Single: Released May '83, on Rough Trade, by Rough Trade Records. Catalogue no: **RT 132**
12" Single: Released May '83, on Rough Trade, by Rough Trade Records. Catalogue no: **RTT 132**

WORKING IN A GOLDMINE
Tracks: / Working in a goldmine.
CD 5": Released Jul '88, on WEA, by WEA Records. Catalogue no: **YZ 7199CD**
7" Single: Released Jul '88, on WEA, by WEA Records. Catalogue no: **YZ 7199**
12" Single: Released Jul '88, on WEA, by WEA Records. Catalogue no: **YZ 7199TW**
12" Single: Released Jul '88, on WEA, by WEA Records. Catalogue no: **YZ 7199T**

Azymuth

Biographical details: This all-male Brazilian instrumental group reached No 19 in early 1980 with their only UK chart record, Jazz Carnival. The single broke in the discos and received little airplay. (Bob MacDonald, 1984.)
A Brazilian jazz trio formed in 1972: keyboardist/writer/producer Jose Roberto Bertrami (aka Ze Roberto), percussionist Ivan Conti (aka Mamao), bassist Alex Malheiros, all born in 1946. Bertrami worked in Sao Paulo clubs in the mid '60's with Flora Purim and percussionist Airto playing progressive bossa novas. Went to Rio in 1967 and formed a samba trio, played in popular club Canacao; he met Mamao playing in rock band The Youngsters; they found Malheiros playing in bowling alley. They gigged and sessioned seperately for five years while working on a style described as samba dioda (crazy samba): a blend of Brazilian rhythms and jazz funk. The first Azymuth album was the soundtrack to a film about racing driver Emerson Fittipaldi in 1973, written by Bertrami; Several of their albums are available in the USA from the fantasy group. *Flame* includes guest Purim; 1985's *Spectrum* includes several famous Rio samba drummers, baiao rhythms of north east Brazil, covers of songs by Marvin Gaye, Antonio Carlos Jobim; *Jazz carnival* was a hit in the UK. (Donald Clarke, July 1988)f.

DEAR LIMMERTZ
Tracks: / Dear Limmertz / Papa song.
7" Single: Released 28 Nov '80, on Mile Stone, Deleted '83. Catalogue no: **MSP 102**
12" Single: Released Oct '80, on Mile Stone, Deleted Oct '83. Catalogue no: **MRC 102**

JAZZ CARNIVAL (SINGLE)
Tracks: / Jazz carnival.
7" Single: Released Jan '80, on Milestone, by Ace Records. Deleted '85. Catalogue no: **MRC 101**

Azzam, Bob

MUSTAPHA
Tracks: / Mustapha.
7" Single: Released May '60, on Decca, by Decca Records. Deleted '65. Catalogue no: **F 21235**

B

The following information was taken from the Music Master database on October 20th, 1989.

B-52'S

Biographical details: This American rock band consist of Kate Pierson, Fred Schneider, Keith Strickland, Cindy Wilson and Ricky Wilson. They are named after the slang term for the smooth, high, puffed out hairstyles worn by the group's two women at the time of their formation in 1976. Their bizarre band of punk first came to the attention of the music business in '78, when they issued a weird but amusing single *Rock Lobster*. It became a fashionable record in Britain after receiving heavy airplay by influential DJ John Peel. The excitement and novelty surrounding the single had worn off a little by the time of its belated UK release a year later, but it still managed to reach No. 37 on the chart. Simultaneously they went to No. 22 on the UK album chart with their self-titled debut LP, produced by Island Records' famous founder Chris Blackwell. By this time they had toured in the States supporting Talking Heads, the band who had originally discovered them and with whom they shared a love for the quirky, left-field aspects of rock music.
1980 saw the B-52's cement their popularity in Australis, a nation that had given them greater recognition than the mere cult following they enjoy in the US and UK. That year they released their second LP *Wild Planet*. In '82 they returned once more to their link with Talking Heads, when the Heads' David Byrne produced their mini-album *Mesopotamia*.

CHANNEL Z
Tracks: / Channel Z / Junebug.
7" Single: Released Sep '89, on Warner Bros., by WEA Records. Catalogue no: **W 2831**
CD 5": Released Sep '89, on Warner Bros., by WEA Records. Catalogue no: **W 2831 CD**
12" Single: Released Sep '89, on Warner Bros., by WEA Records. Catalogue no: **W 2831 T**

FUTURE GENERATION
Tracks: / Future generation.
7" Set: Released Apr '83, on Island, by Island Records. Catalogue no: **ISD 107**
7" Single: Released Apr '83, on Island, by Island Records. Catalogue no: **IS 107**

GIVE ME BACK MY MAN (See panel above)
Tracks: / Give me back my man / Give me back my man (version).
7" Single: Released Jul '80, on Island, by Island Records. Deleted '85. Catalogue no: **WIP 6579**
7" Single: Released Sep '81, on Island, by Island Records. Deleted Jul '87. Catalogue no: **WIP 6727**

PLANET CLAIRE
Tracks: / Planet Claire.
7" Single: Released Jul '81, on Island, by Island Records. Catalogue no: **WIP 6551**

ROCK LOBSTER
Tracks: / Rock lobster / Planet Claire / Song for a future generation (featured on 12" & double pack only) / Give me back my man* (*=Extra track on 12" only) / 52 Girls (+=Extra track on double pack only).
7" Set: Released Apr '86, on Island, by Island Records. Deleted Jul '87. Catalogue no: **BFTD 1**
7" Pic: Released May '86, on Island, by Island Records. Catalogue no: **BFGR 1**
7" Single: Released Jul '79, on Island, by Island Records. Deleted '84. Catalogue no: **WIP 6506**
7" Single: Released Apr '86, on Island, by Island Records. Deleted '87. Catalogue no: **BFT 1**
12" Single: Released Apr '86, on Island, by Island Records. Catalogue no: **12BFT 1**

STROBELIGHT
Tracks: / Strobelight / Dirty back road.
7" Single: Released Nov '80, on Island, by Island Records. Deleted Nov '83. Catalogue no: **WIP 6665**

WIG
Tracks: / Wig / Summer of love / Song for a future generation (Track on 12" only.).
7" Pic: Released 20 Jun '87, on Island, by Island Records. Catalogue no: **BFTT 2**
Cassingle: Released Jul '87, on Island, by Island Records. Deleted Jun '88. Catalogue no: **BFTC 2**
7" Single: Released 6 Jun '87, on Island, by Island Records. Deleted Apr '88. Catalogue no: **BFT 2**
12" Single: Released 6 Jun '87, on Island, by Island Records. Deleted Apr '88. Catalogue no: **12BFT 2**

B 52's - Give Me Back My Man (Released on Island)

B, Annette

CASANOVA
Tracks: / Casanova / Casanova (P.A Mix).
7" Single: Released Jan '87, on Greensleeves, by Greensleeves Records. Catalogue no: **UKMC 20**

GIVE HER THE LOVE THAT'S RIGHT
Tracks: / Give her the love that's right / Give her the love that's right (version).
12" Single: Released 13 Jun '87, on UK Bubblers, by Greensleeves Records. Catalogue no: **UKMC 26**

I FOUND LOVE
Tracks: / I found love / I found love (version).
12" Single: Released Sep '86, on UK Bubblers, by Greensleeves Records. Deleted '88. Catalogue no: **UKMC 16**

YOU'LL NEVER GET TO HEAVEN
12" Single: Released Feb '89, on Ariwa Sounds, by Ariwa Sounds. Catalogue no: **ARIWA 84**

B., Asha

OUT OF AFRICA
Tracks: / Out of Africa.
7" Single: Released Oct '88, on Quartz, by Quartz Records. Catalogue no: **QUARTZ 001**

B B Band

DUKE, THE
Tracks: / Duke, The / Wanrantanra.
7" Single: Released Jan '83, on AVM, by AVM Records. Deleted '87. Catalogue no: **GIN 1**

B B & Q Band

GENIE (SINGLE)
Tracks: / Genie.
7" Single: Released Jun '85, on Cool Tempo, by Chrysalis Records. Deleted '86. Catalogue no: **COOL 110**
12" Single: Released Jun '85, on Cool Tempo, by Chrysalis Records. Catalogue no: **COOLX 110**

I'LL CUT YOU LOOSE
Tracks: / I'll cut you loose / Starlette.
7" Single: Released Sep '81, on Capitol, by EMI Records. Deleted '84. Catalogue no: **12 CL 220**

(I'M A) DREAMER
Tracks: / I'm a dreamer.
7" Single: Released Sep '86, on Cool Tempo, by Chrysalis Records. Deleted '89. Catalogue no: **COOL 132**

MINUTES AWAY
Tracks: / Minutes away.
12" Single: Released Aug '85, on Cool Tempo, by Chrysalis Records. Catalogue no: **COOLX 112**
7" Single: Released Aug '85, on Cool Tempo, by Chrysalis Records. Catalogue no: **COOL 112**

ON THE BEAT
Tracks: / On the beat / Don't say goodbye / Love is what we should do.
7" Single: Released Jul '81, on Capitol, by EMI Records. Deleted '86. Catalogue no: **CL 202**
12" Single: Released Jul '81, on Capitol, by EMI Records. Deleted '86. Catalogue no: **12CL 202**

RICOCHET
Tracks: / Genie / Dreamer / Genie.
12" Single: Released Sep '87, on Cool Tempo, by Chrysalis Records. Catalogue no: **COOLX 154**
7" Single: Released Sep '87, on Cool Tempo, by Chrysalis Records. Catalogue no: **COOL: 154**

B Boat

BUT MY BROTHER HE DID
Tracks: / But my brother he did / Found myself with you / Married man, lawyer's house / Limo for Jeremy.
12" Single: Released May '89, on Ship, Catalogue no: **BBOAT 1**

B Boys

START WREKKIN'
Tracks: / Start wrekkin' / Start wrekkin' (demolition version).
7" Single: Released Jul '87, on Debut, by Skratch Records. Catalogue no: **DEBT 3029**
12" Single: Released Jul '87, on Debut, by Skratch Records. Catalogue no: **DEBTX 3029**

B, Bubble

ROCK IT
Tracks: / Rock it.
12" Single: Released Feb '89, on PLJ Records, Catalogue no: **PLJ 005**

B. Bumble & The

NUT ROCKER
Tracks: / Nut rocker / Happy organ / Pipeline.
7" Single: Released Apr '83, on EMI (France), by EMI Records. Catalogue no: **2C 008 93392**
7" Single: Released Aug '82, on Old Gold, by Old Gold Records. Deleted Jul '88. Catalogue no: **OG 9080**
7" Single: Released Aug '82, on Blast From The Past, by Creole Records. Catalogue no: **CR 186**
7" Single: Released Feb '85, on EMI Golden 45's, by EMI Records. Catalogue no: **G45 40**

B, Charles

LACK OF LOVE
Tracks: / Lack of love / Lack of love (ivory mix).
7" Single: Released '89, on Desire, by Desire Records. Catalogue no: **WANT 13**
12" Single: Released '89, on Desire, by Desire Records. Catalogue no: **WANTX 13 R**
12" Single: Released '89, on Desire, by Desire Records. Catalogue no: **WANTX 13**

B, Colin

DON'T YOU KNOW
Tracks: / Don't you know.
12" Single: Released Sep '89, on White Label (1), Catalogue no: **PZS 001**

B, Derek

BAD YOUNG BROTHER
Tracks: / Bad young brother / Good groove.
12" Single: Released Apr '88, on Tuff Audio, Deleted Oct '88. Catalogue no: **DRKB 112**
12" Single: Released May '88, on Tuff Audio, Deleted Oct '88. Catalogue no: **DRKBX 112**
CD 5": Released May '88, on Tuff Audio, Deleted Oct '88. Catalogue no: **DRKCD 112**
7" Single: Released Apr '88, on Tuff Audio, Deleted Oct '88. Catalogue no: **DRKB 1**

GET DOWN
Tracks: / Get down.
12" Single: Released Aug '87, on Music Of Life, by Music Of Life Records. Catalogue no: **NOTE 7**

GOODGROOVE
Tracks: / Good groove.
7" Single: Released 20 Feb '88, on Music Of Life, by Music Of Life Records. Catalogue no: **7 NOTE 12**
12" Single: Released 20 Feb '88, on Music Of Life, by Music Of Life Records. Catalogue no: **NOTE 12**

ROCK THE BEAT
Tracks: / Rock the beat.
12" Single: Released May '87, on Music Of Life, by Music Of Life Records. Catalogue no: **NOTE 3**

WE'VE GOT THE JUICE
Tracks: / We've got the juice / We've got the juice (Freshly squeezed mix) (Available on 12" only) / Power move*.
CD 5": Released Jun '88, on Phonogram, by Phonogram Ltd. Deleted Feb '89. Catalogue no: **DRKCD 2**
12" Single: Released Jun '88, on Phonogram, by Phonogram Ltd. Deleted 31 Jul '89. Catalogue no: **DRKDJ 212**
7" Single: Released Jun '88, on Phonogram, by Phonogram Ltd. Deleted Feb '89. Catalogue no: **DRKB 2**
12" Single: Released Jun '88, on Phonogram, by Phonogram Ltd. Deleted Feb '89. Catalogue no: **DRKBX 2**
12" Single: Released Jun '88, on Phonogram, by Phonogram Ltd. Deleted Feb '89. Catalogue no: **DRKB 212**

B, Eric & Rakim

AS THE RHYME GOES ON
Tracks: / As the rhyme goes on / Chinese arithmetic.
7" Single: Released 24 May '88, on 4th &

DEREK B - BAD YOUNG BROTHER (Released on Tuff Audio)

Broadway, by Island Records. Deleted Aug '88. Catalogue no: **BRW 106**
12" Single: Released 24 May '88, on 4th & Broadway, by Island Records. Deleted Aug '88. Catalogue no: **12 BRW 106**

ERIC B FOR PRESIDENT
Tracks: / Eric B for president.
12" Single: Released Aug '86, on Cool Tempo, by Chrysalis Records. Catalogue no: **COOLX 129**

FOLLOW THE LEADER (SINGLE)
Tracks: / Follow the leader / Follow the leader (dub) / Follow the leader (extended mix)* / Follow the leader (Accapella).
Note: * Only available on the 12" version. "A magnum on the microphone murdering all other M.C's. Rakim unleashes an explosive rap over the colossal base line being layed down by Eric B, taking hip hop into a new direction.
CD 5": Released Jul '88, on MCA, by MCA Records. Catalogue no: **DMCA 1256**
7" Single: Released Jul '88, on MCA, by MCA Records. Catalogue no: **MCAB 1256**
7" Single: Released Jun '88, on MCA, by MCA Records. Catalogue no: **DOPE 1**
7" Single: Released Jun '88, on MCA, by MCA Records. Catalogue no: **MCA 1256**
12" Single: Released Jun '88, on MCA, by MCA Records. Catalogue no: **MCAT 1256**
12" Single: Released Jun '88, on MCA, by MCA Records. Catalogue no: **DOPE (T) 1**

I KNOW YOU GOT SOUL
Tracks: / I know you got soul.
7" Single: Released 6 Jun '87, on Cool Tempo, by Chrysalis Records. Catalogue no: **COOL 146**
12" Single: Released 6 Jun '87, on Cool Tempo, by Chrysalis Records. Catalogue no: **COOLX 146**

I KNOW YOU GOT SOUL (REMIX)
Tracks: / I know you got soul / I know you got soul (Double trouble remix) / I know you got soul (acapella).
7" Single: Released Feb '88, on Cool Tempo, by Chrysalis Records. Catalogue no: **COOLR 146**
12" Single: Released Feb '88, on Cool Tempo, by Chrysalis Records. Catalogue no: **COOLRX 146**

MICROPHONE FIEND
Tracks: / Microphone fiend.
CD 5": Released Oct '88, on MCA, by MCA Records. Catalogue no: **DMCA 1300**
7" Single: Released Oct '88, on MCA, by MCA Records. Deleted 1 Jul '89. Catalogue no: **MCA 1300**
12" Single: Released Oct '88, on MCA, by MCA Records. Catalogue no: **MCAT 1300**

MOVE THE CROWD
Tracks: / Move the crowd / Move the crowd (album mix) / Move the crowd (wild bunch mix) / Extended beat.
7" Single: on 4th & Broadway, by Island Records. Deleted Jun '88. Catalogue no: **BRW 88**
12" Single: Released Feb '88, on 4th & Broadway, by Island Records. Deleted Jun '88. Catalogue no: **12 BRW 88**

PAID IN FULL
7" Single: Released Oct '87, on 4th & Broadway, by Island Records. Deleted Apr '88. Catalogue no: **BRW 78**
12" Single: Released '88, on 4th & Broadway, by Island Records. Deleted Dec '88. Catalogue no: **12 BRX 78**
12" Single: Released Oct '87, on 4th & Broadway, by Island Records. Catalogue no: **12 BRW 78**

R, THE
Tracks: / R, The.
CD 5": Released 30 Jan '89, on MCA, by MCA Records. Catalogue no: **CMCA 1303**
7" Single: Released 30 Jan '89, on MCA, by MCA Records. Deleted 1 Jul '89. Catalogue no: **MCA 1303**
12" Single: Released 30 Jan '89, on MCA, by MCA Records. Catalogue no: **MCAT 1303**
CD 3": Released Feb '89, on MCA, by MCA Records. Catalogue no: **DMCA 1303**

B. Fats

B. FATS, THE
Tracks: / B-Fats, The / B-Fats, The (Dub Inst) / B-Fats, The (Edit).
7" Single: Released Sep '87, on Champion, by Champion Records. Catalogue no: **CHAMP 57**
12" Single: Released Aug '87, on Champion, by Champion Records. Catalogue no: **CHAMP 1257**

B, Freddy

WE'RE BACK Y'ALL
Tracks: / We're back y'all.
12" Single: Released 28 Sep '87, on Tuff City (USA), Catalogue no: **TUF 128020**

B, Holly

NO LIES
Tracks: / No lies / We're the wildcats.
7" Single: Released Feb '80, on Pye, Deleted Feb '83. Catalogue no: **7P 164**

B, Jenny

SEXY EYES
Tracks: / Sexy eyes.
12" Single: Released Sep '88, on Power Pakk, Catalogue no: **PP 1T**
12" Single: Released Jul '88, on White Label (1), Catalogue no: **PP 1**

B, McBuzz

SEQUEL, THE
Tracks: / Sequel, The.
12" Single: Released Jul '89, on Play Hard, by Play Hard Records. Catalogue no: **DEC 016**

B., Macka

DREAD A WHO SHE LOVE
Tracks: / Dread a who she love.
12" Single: Released Sep '89, on Ariwa Sounds, by Ariwa Sounds. Catalogue no: **ARI 92**

UNEMPLOYMENT BLUES
12" Single: Released Feb '89, on Ariwa Sounds, by Ariwa Sounds. Catalogue no: **ARI 85**

B, Maka

LOVE IT JAMAICA
Tracks: / Love it Jamaica / Love it Jamaica (version).
12" Single: Released Aug '88, on Black Scorpio, Catalogue no: **BS 018**

B Mania

BACK IN THE USSR
Tracks: / Back in the USSR / Love game.
7" Single: Released Aug '87, on Epic, by CBS Records. Catalogue no: **USSR 1**
12" Single: Released Aug '87, on Epic, by CBS Records. Catalogue no: **USSR T1**

B Project

WAR THEME FROM ROCKY IV
Tracks: / War theme from Rocky IV / War, the fanfare.
7" Single: Released Mar '86, on Certain, by Certain Records. Catalogue no: **ACERT 7**
12" Single: Released Mar '86, on Certain, by Certain Records. Catalogue no: **12 ACERT 7**

B, Stevie

SPRING LOVE COME BACK TO ME
Tracks: / Spring love come back to me.
12" Single: Released Jul '88, on LMR, Catalogue no: **LMR 4002**

B. Team

ALL BECAUSE (I LOVE YOU)
Tracks: / All because (I love you).
7" Single: Released Feb '87, on Mainfeature, by Mainfeature Records. Catalogue no: **ASM 001**

B Three

PEACE
Tracks: / Peace.
12" Single: Released Nov '88, on Transatlantic, by Transatlantic Records. Catalogue no: **TRANS 001**

B, Tina

NOTHING'S GONNA COME EASY
Tracks: / Nothing's gonna come easy.
7" Single: Released Jan '85, on Atlantic, by WEA Records. Catalogue no: **A 9603**

Babakoto

JUST TO GET BY
Tracks: / Just to get by / Dream world.
7" Single: Released Sep '88, on MCA, by MCA Records. Catalogue no: **KOT 3**
7" Single: Released Feb '88, on MCA, by MCA Records. Catalogue no: **KOT 1**
12" Single: Released Sep '88, on MCA, by MCA Records. Catalogue no: **KOTT 3**
12" Single: Released Feb '88, on MCA, by MCA Records. Catalogue no: **12 KOT 1**

LOVE HAS GOT A HOLD ON ME
Tracks: / Love has got a hold on me / Special lady.
7" Single: Released Mar '87, on Mr.Sam, by Mr.Sam Music. Catalogue no: **SAS 107**

MAGIC POTION
Tracks: / Magic potion / Can't come back / Magic potion (ext. mix)* / Magic potion (7" version)*.
Note: John, Julian, Steve, Mike and another Julian are the five young imps who arguably had last year's biggest radio hit "Just to Get By", on their own independent label. Their return to Radio land with their first full-scale release on MCA Records. "Magic Potion" is another piece of plastic cut and tailor made for the measurements and requirements of daytime Radio 1, with the support of Radio and TV being gathered up as I live and breathe. Wide eyed and at the ready, these cheeky chappies are pumping up the tyres on the transit van and are packing their sleeping bags for a PA tour around Britain and the word around our way is that Babakoto are to support Wet Wet Wet on their summer tour. (MCA Records, June 88)
* extra track on 12" version
7" Single: Released Jun '88, on MCA, by MCA Records. Catalogue no: **KOT 2**
12" Single: Released Jun '88, on MCA, by MCA Records. Catalogue no: **KOTT 2**

Babayaga

WHICH WAY
Tracks: / Which way / Hiawatha.
CD 5": Released Jun '89, on Fly, by Fly Records. Deleted Aug '89. Catalogue no: **FLEASC 2**
7" Single: Released Jun '89, on Fly, by Fly Records. Deleted Sep '89. Catalogue no: **FLEA 2**

Babies

I'M FALLING
Tracks: / I'm falling / Time on my hands / Do it nice (Extra track on 12" only) / Jack the lad (Available on 12" only) / Bitch or angel (Extra track on 12" only).
7" Single: Released Oct '86, on Pow Wop, Deleted '87. Catalogue no: **BABY 7**
12" Single: Released Oct '86, on Pow Wop, Deleted '87. Catalogue no: **BABY 12**

Babs, Alice

Biographical details: Alice Babs was a rare example of a Swedish singer achieving British chart glory in pre-Abba days. But she had to be content with just a week: After You've Gone peaked at No 43 in 1963. (Bob MacDonald, 1984.)
Born Alice Nilson in 1924 in Kalmar, Sweden, Babs has been a film and TV star in Europe, touring for some years with a trio including Sven Asmussen. She had a Uk hit in 1963 with *After You've Gone*, and recorded with Duke Eillington the same year, later singing in his Sacred Concerts, as well as at the 1975 Newport Jazz Festival. Ellington said 'Alice Babs is a composer's dream, for with her he can forget all the limitations and just write his heart out'. (Donald Clarke 23 August 1988).

AFTER YOU'VE GONE
Tracks: / After you've gone.
7" Single: Released Aug '63, on Fontana, by Phonogram Ltd. Deleted '66. Catalogue no: **TF 409**

Babson, Monty

DID YOU EVER SEE A DREAM WALKING
Tracks: / Did you ever see a dream walking? / Pennies from heaven.
7" Single: Released May '82, on Mr.Sam, by Mr.Sam Music. Deleted '85. Catalogue no: **HOS 22**

ONE FOR MY BABY (AND ONE MORE FOR THE ROAD)
Tracks: / One for my baby.
7" Single: Released Aug '85, on Mr.Sam, by Mr.Sam Music. Catalogue no: **SAS 102**

Baby Amphetamine

CHERNOBYL BABY (Who needs the government)
Tracks: / Chernobyl baby (who needs the government) / Cheque it out.
7" Single: Released Apr '87, on Creation, by Creation Records. Catalogue no: **CRE 041**
12" Single: Released Apr '87, on Creation, by Creation Records. Catalogue no: **CRE 041T**

NO RESPECT
Tracks: / No respect.
12" Single: Released 19 Sep '87, on Spectec, Catalogue no: **SPEC 001**

Baby Ford

BEACH PUMP
Tracks: / Beach pump.
7" Single: Released Nov '89, on Rhythm King, by Mute Records. Catalogue no: **BFORD 6**
12" Single: Released Nov '89, on Rhythm King, by Mute Records. Catalogue no: **12BFORD 6**

CHIKKI CHIKKI AHH AHH
Tracks: / Chikki chikki ahh ahh.
7" Single: Released Oct '88, on Rhythm King, by Mute Records. Catalogue no: **7 BFORD 2**
12" Single: Released Nov '88, on Rhythm King, by Mute Records. Catalogue no: **BFORD 2**

CHIKKI REMIX
Tracks: / Chikki chikki.
12" Single: Released 23 Jan '89, on Rhythm King, by Mute Records. Catalogue no: **LBFORD 002**
12" Single: Released 19 Dec '88, on Rhythm King, by Mute Records. Catalogue no: **RBFORD 002**

CHILDREN OF THE REVOLUTION
Tracks: / Children of the revolution.
CD 5": Released Jul '89, on Rhythm King, by Mute Records. Catalogue no: **BFORD 4 CD**
7" Single: Released May '89, on Rhythm King, by Mute Records. Catalogue no: **BFORD 4**
12" Single: Released May '89, on Rhythm King, by Mute Records. Catalogue no: **BFORD 4 T**

OOCHY KOOCHY(F.U.BABY YEAH YEAH)
Tracks: / Oochy koochy(F.U.baby yeah yeah) / Flowers.
CD 5": Released Sep '88, on Rhythm King, by Mute Records. Catalogue no: **BFORD 1CD**
7" Single: Released Jul '88, on Rhythm King, by Mute Records. Catalogue no: **BFORD 1**
12" Single: Released Oct '88, on Rhythm King, by Mute Records. Catalogue no: **RBFORD 001**
12" Single: Released 14 Aug '88, on Rhythm King, by Mute Records. Catalogue no: **12 BFORD 1**

Baby Go Boom

LIFE (CAN BE A HURTFUL THING)
Tracks: / Life (can be a hurtful thing) / Perfect thing / Life (can be a hurtful thing)(US remix) (Extra track on 12" only).
7" Single: Released May '84, on Inner Vision, Deleted '86. Catalogue no: **IVS 1**
7" Single: Released Mar '86, on Island, by Island Records. Deleted Jul '87. Catalogue no: **IS 248**
12" Single: Released May '84, on Inner Vision, Deleted '86. Catalogue no: **IVST 1**
12" Single: Released Mar '86, on Island, by

Island Records. Catalogue no: **12IS 248**

Baby Lemonade

SECRET GOLDFISH, THE
Tracks: / Secret goldfish, The.
7" Single: Released 30 May '87, on Narodnik, by Narodnik Records. Catalogue no: **NRK 004**

Baby 'n' The Monsters

I'D RATHER NOT
Tracks: / I'd rather not / Stood.
7" Single: Released Oct '81, on Mean, by Mean Records. Catalogue no: **MEAN 5**

Baby O

IN THE FOREST
Tracks: / In the forest.
7" Single: Released Jul '80, on Calibre, Deleted '83. Catalogue no: **CAB 505**

Baby Tuckoo

MONY MONY
Tracks: / Mony mony / Baby's rocking tonight.
7" Single: Released Mar '84, on Albion, by Albion Records. Catalogue no: **TUCK 001**

ROCK ROCK
Tracks: / Rock rock.
12" Single: Released May '86, on Music For Nations, by Music For Nations Records. Catalogue no: **12 KUT 120**

TEARS OF A CLOWN, THE
Tracks: / Tears of a clown / Over you / Lights go down, The (Available on 12" only).
7" Single: Released Aug '86, on Fun After All, by Music For Nations Records. Catalogue no: **FAA 105**
12" Single: Released Aug '86, on Fun After All, by Music For Nations Records. Catalogue no: **12 FAA 105**

Babyface

IT'S NO CRIME
Tracks: / It's no crime / It's no crime (instrumental).
CD 5": Released Aug '89, on MCA, by MCA Records. Catalogue no: **DMCAT 1366**
7" Single: Released Aug '89, on MCA, by MCA Records. Catalogue no: **MCA 1366**
12" Single: Released Aug '89, on MCA, by MCA Records. Catalogue no: **MCAT 1366**

Babylon 5

ALPHA OMEGA
Tracks: / Alpha omega / Chunky chicken.
12" Single: Released Dec '88, on Cheque This, by Cheque This Records. Catalogue no: **ABB 199**

LAST SUPPER, THE
Tracks: / Last supper, The.
12" Single: Released Jun '89, on Cheque This, by Cheque This Records. Catalogue no: **CTT 2**

Babymen

FOR KING WILLY
Tracks: / For King Willy.
12" Single: Released Aug '87, on One Little Indian, by One Little Indian Records. Catalogue no: **12TP 3**
12" Single: Released Feb '87, on One Little Indian, by One Little Indian Records. Catalogue no: **TP 3**

Babys

Biographical details: Led by British vocalist and bassist John Waite, the Babys -- other members were Tony Brock, Mike Corby and Walt Stocker -- were more successful in America than the UK. Their breakthrough hit, ľIsn't It Time?"D, a dramatic pop/rock single in a style that was to be better done by the likes of Meat Loaf and Styx, hit No 13 in the US at the end of 1977 but could only crawl to No 45 in Britain despite heavy promotion. The group never charted again in the UK but scored another No 13 on the other side of the Atlantic in '79 with ľEvery Time I Think Of You"D. Following the demise of the Babys, John Waite scored solo success, his 1984 winner Missing You beginning with the line ľEvery time I think of you..."D. (Bob MacDonald, 1984.).

ISN'T IT TIME
Tracks: / Isn't it time.
7" Single: Released Jan '78, on Chrysalis, by Chrysalis Records. Deleted '81. Catalogue no: **CHS 2173**

TRUE LOVE TRUE CONFESSIONS
Tracks: / True love true confessions / Broken heart / Money.
7" Single: Released Jan '80, on Chrysalis, by Chrysalis Records. Deleted Jan '85. Catalogue no: **CHS2398**

Baby's Got A Gun

SUICIDE GIRL
Tracks: / Suicide girl.
12" Single: Released Apr '87, on McDonald Brothers, Catalogue no: **JOCK 12 02**

Babysitters

I WANNA BE ON THE TV
Tracks: / I wanna be on the TV.
7" Single: Released Jun '85, on FM, by FM-Revolver Records. Catalogue no: **VHF 11**

LIVE AT THE MARQUEE
Tracks: / Live at the Marquee (EP) / Picking up the blues / Can you hear it / Overkill / Big girls / Frank Bough.
12" Single: Released Nov '86, on Killerwatt, by Killerwatt Records. Deleted '87. Catalogue no: **KIL-12-2**

Bacall, Warren

BRIEF ENCOUNTER
Tracks: / Brief encounter.
7" Single: Released Oct '84, on Pilot, by New Music Enterprises. Catalogue no: **TAIL 1**

CRYSTAL TEARS
Tracks: / Crystal tears / Another tear.
7" Single: Released Mar '85, on Pilot, by New Music Enterprises. Catalogue no: **TAIL 2**

LIONS AND TIGERS
Tracks: / Lions and tigers.
7" Single: Released Oct '82, on Stagecoach, Deleted Oct '85. Catalogue no: **MAIL 37**

Baccara

Biographical details: Some summers there is a particular record doing very well on the Continent which British holidaymakers enjoy and bring over to the UK charts in the early autumn. The 1977 example was ľYes Sir, I Can Boogie"D, a catchy piece of Europop by two Spanish girls called Baccara. Having been a big European hit the single reached No 1 in Britain in October and Baccara became both the first female duo ever to top the UK chart and the first-ever Spanish act the lead the list. And, strangely, the No 2 that week was also by a female vocal duo, France's La Belle Epoque. In 1978 Baccara achieved one more Top Tenner, ľSorry, I'm A Lady"D, plus a Top Thirty eponymous LP, before they faded into the Spanish sunset. (Bob MacDonald, 1984.).

FANTASY BOY
Tracks: / Fantasy boy / Touch me.
7" Single: Released May '89, on Loading Bay, Catalogue no: **7LBAY 4**
12" Single: Released May '89, on Loading Bay, Catalogue no: **LBAY 4**

SORRY I'M A LADY
Tracks: / Sorry I'm a lady.
7" Single: Released Jan '78, on RCA, by BMG Records (UK). Deleted '81. Catalogue no: **PB 5555**

YES SIR, I CAN BOOGIE
Tracks: / Yes sir, I can boogie / Sorry, I'm a lady.
7" Single: Released Sep '77, on RCA, by BMG Records (UK). Catalogue no: **PB 5526**
7" Single: Released Jul '81, on RCA Golden Grooves, by BMG Records (UK). Catalogue no: **GOLD 501**
7" Single: Released Apr '87, on Old Gold, by Old Gold Records. Catalogue no: **OG 9708**

Bacharach, Burt

Biographical details: Born in Kansas City in 1929, Burt Bacharach graduated in music at McGill University in Montreal and then became a piano accompanist to middle-of-the-road ballad singers. In the late 50's he took up songwriting and when he met lyricist Hal David one of the great partnerships in pop music history was formed. The pair were immediately successful, particularly with two songs: The Story Of My Life took country singer Marty Robbins to No 15 on the US charts and Perry Como hit No 4 with Magic Moments. In Britain success was still more striking. A cover version of The Story Of My Life by UK singer Michael Holliday went to No 1 only to be dethroned by Como, the first time two consecutive British chart-toppers had been written by the same songwriters. Breaking temporarily from David to write the Drifters' US Top Twenty single Please Stay, with Bob Hilliard, Bacharach discovered a singer called Dionne Warwick who was singing backing vocals on a Drifters session. Something clicked and this up-and-coming singer became the main 60's vehicle for Bacharach and David's songs. Don't Make Me Over was the first, reaching No 21 in America in 1963. During the rest of the decade Warwick had six big American hits with their material: Anyone Who Had A Heart, Walk On By, Message To Michael, I Say A Little Prayer, Do You Know The Way To San Jose? and This Girl's In Love With You -- and those are just the ones which made the Top Ten. Yet though Warwick was their protegee and drew more heavily from their talents that any other artist, Bacharach and David's greatest achievement was the sheer diversity of acts who recorded their songs. Of the hits listed, for example, Anyone Who Had A Heart was a British No 1 for Cilla Black, Walk On By has been successfully covered by Isaac Hayes and the Stranglers, Message To Martha was a UK hit for Adam Faith, I Say A Little Prayer was made even more famous by Aretha Franklin, This Guy's In Love With You was a smash for Herb Alpert... To emphasise the point the pair have achieved six British No 1s, each by a different act, and have thus written chart-toppers for more acts than any other partnership. Bacharach's intricate, well-rounded melodies were perfectly matched by David's imaginative love lyrics which were romantic without being sugary or trivial. They began the 70's with two more American No 1s, B.J. Thomas's Raindrops Keep Falling On My Head and the Carpenters' Close To You. This was followed by the Fifth Dimension's One Less Bell To Answer, No 2 in the US. Success then tailed off and the legendary partnership ended. David became immersed in the administrative side of the music business and was elected head of the American Society of Composers, Authors and Publishers (ASCAP), one of the US equivalents of Britain's Performing Rights Society. Bacharach's career went into bottom gear for almost a decade until, in 1981, he enjoyed a revival of fortunes as Christopher Cross took Arthur's Theme (Best That You Can Do), written by Bacharach with three colleagues -- including his wife, Carole Bayer Sager -- to No 1 in the States. In the mid-80's a recording reunion of Bacharach and Dionne Warwick took place. As a recording artist he enjoyed a British Top Five single in 1965 with Trains And Boats And Planes and has had two high-charting albums. These employed an orchestra and chorus performing his arrangements of his songs, which often differed considerably from the arrangements he used on the well-known hit versions. In recent years Bacharach has sometimes been mistakenly placed in an easy listening category by pop historians: they have tended to forget the enormous influence he has had on pop music's songwriting and arrangement techniques. (Bob MacDonald, 1984.)
One of the most successful songwriters of recent decades was born in 1928 in Kasas City, Missouri; he is also a pianist, arranger, conducter and vocalist in what a record company once called an earnest, rumpled baritone. He acompanied singers on the piano, touring with Marlene Dietrich 1958-63. At Paramount studios in 1957 he had met lyricist Hal David, younger brother of Mack David; Bacharch wrote *Baby, It's You* for the Shirelles with Mack (covered on the Beatles' first album), but soon teamed with Hal for a long series of hits by Perry Como, Cilla Black, Jackie DeShannon, Sandie Shaw, Gene Pitney, Jack Jones, The Carptenters and others, but most of all for Dionne Warwick (one of the biggest: *Do you Know The Way To San Jose.* Bacharach had his own hit single with *Trains And Boats And Planes.* In the mid-'70s the Bacharach/David team ran out of steam, but Bacharach bounced back with his second wife, songwriter Carole Bayer Sager, writing morehits such as the 1986 USA chart-toppers *That's What Friends Are For* for Warwick and friends, and *On My Own,* for Patti Labelle and Michael McDonald. (Donald Clarke 23 August 1988).

TRAINS AND BOATS AND PLANES
Tracks: / Trains and boats and planes.
7" Single: Released May '65, on London Records, by London Records. Deleted '68. Catalogue no: **HL 9968**

Bach-a-Telle

GET BACK TO BACH
Tracks: / Get back to Bach / Japanese nights.
7" Single: Released May '83, on Paro, by Paro Records. Catalogue no: **PARO 6**

Bachelet, Pierre

MUSIC FROM THE STORY OF O
Tracks: / Music from the story of O.
7" Single: Released Dec '83, on Byron Lane, Catalogue no: **BYRL 01**

Bachelor Pad

ALL HASH & COCK
12" Single: Released Oct '88, on Warhola Sound, by Warhola Sound Records. Catalogue no: **WST 005 MINS**

DO IT FOR FUN
7" Single: Released 20 Feb '88, on Warhola Sound, by Warhola Sound Records. Catalogue no: **WS 004 MINS**
12" Single: Released 20 Feb '88, on Warhola Sound, by Warhola Sound Records. Catalogue no: **WST 004 MINS**

Bachelors

Biographical details: Formed in Dublin in 1953 while barely into their teens, Stokes and the Clusky brothers started as a harmonica trio. In the early Sixties they turned their attention to singing and became the Bachelors, undeterred by the fact that they were all married. Running totally against the tide of Beatlemania and Merseybeat, they began a string of hits with MoR standards, starting in 1963 with ľCharmaine"D. Three of their Top 10 singles - ľCharmaine"S, "Diane"D (their only No. 1) and ľRamona"D - were all songs that had started life in the Twenties as sheet music favourites. Other hits such as ľI Believe"D and ľNo Arms Can Ever Hold you"D dated from the early to mid Fifties.
The Bachelors' image suited their music - they were clean-cut, cosy and forever smiling. They represented the ideal alternative for record buyers who continued until the summer of '67 and included two more girl's name titles, ľMarie"D and ľMarta"D plus a shrewdly timed cover version of Simon & Garfunkel's US No. 1 ľSound Of Silence"D. The Bachelors achieved six Top 40 hits in America: the first of these, ľDiane"D was the only one to hit the Top 10. Album-wise, their first British chart album was also their biggest. ľThe Bachelors And 16 Great Songs"D reached No. 2 with 44 weeks on the chart. the longest charting of several compilations was 1969's ľWorld Of The Bachelors"D.
They are now firm favourites on the cabaret circuit, where they mix nostalgia with comedy. (Bob MacDonald)..

6 TRACK HITS: BACHELORS
Tracks: / Sound of silence, The / Marie / Hello Dolly / Me with all your heart / Marta / Mame.
7" EP: Released Sep '83, on Scoop 33, by Pickwick Records. Catalogue no: **7SR 5021**

CAN I TRUST YOU
Tracks: / Can I trust you.
7" Single: Released Jul '66, on Decca, by Decca Records. Deleted '69. Catalogue no: **F 12417**

CHARMAINE (SINGLE)
Tracks: / Charmaine / Ramona.
7" Single: Released Jan '63, on Decca, by Decca Records. Deleted '66. Catalogue no: **F 11559**
7" Single: Released Mar '82, on Decca, by Decca Records. Deleted '88. Catalogue no: **F 13766**

DIANE
Tracks: / Diane.
7" Single: Released Jan '64, on Decca, by Decca Records. Deleted '88. Catalogue no: **F 11799**

DIANE/I BELIEVE
Tracks: / Diane / I believe.
7" Single: Released Oct '83, on Old Gold, by Old Gold Records. Deleted Jul '88. Catalogue no: **OG 9356**

FARAWAY PLACES
Tracks: / Faraway places.
7" Single: Released Jul '63, on Decca, by Decca Records. Deleted '66. Catalogue no: **F 11666**

HELLO DOLLY
Tracks: / Hello dolly.
7" Single: Released Jan '66, on Decca, by Decca Records. Deleted '69. Catalogue no: **F 12309**

I BELIEVE
Tracks: / I believe.
7" Single: Released Mar '64, on Decca, by Decca Records. Deleted '88. Catalogue no: **F11857**

I WOULDN'T TRADE YOU FOR THE WORLD
Tracks: / I Wouldn't trade you for the world.
7" Single: Released Aug '64, on Decca, by Decca Records. Deleted '67. Catalogue no: **F 11949**

IN THE CHAPEL IN THE MOONLIGHT
Tracks: / In the chapel in the moonlight.
7" Single: Released Oct '65, on Decca, by Decca Records. Deleted '68. Catalogue no: **F 12256**

MARIE
Tracks: / Marie.
7" Single: Released May '65, on Decca, by Decca Records. Deleted '68. Catalogue no: **F 12156**

MARTA
Tracks: / Marta.
7" Single: Released Aug '67, on Decca, by Decca Records. Deleted '70. Catalogue no: **F 22634**

NO ARMS CAN EVER HOLD YOU
Tracks: / No arms can ever hold you.
7" Single: Released Dec '64, on Decca, by Decca Records. Deleted '67. Catalogue no: **F 12034**

OH HOW I MISS YOU
Tracks: / Oh how I miss you.
7" Single: Released Apr '67, on Decca, by Decca Records. Deleted '70. Catalogue no: **F 22592**

RAMONA
Tracks: / Ramona.
7" Single: Released Jun '64, on Decca, by Decca Records. Deleted '67. Catalogue no: **F 11910**

SOUND OF SILENCE, THE

Tracks: / Sound of silence, The.
7" Single: Released Mar '66, on Decca, by Decca Records. Deleted '69. Catalogue no: **F 12351**

SUFFER LITTLE CHILDREN
Tracks: / Suffer little children / Dear father in Heaven.
7" Single: Released Nov '81, on President, by President Records. Catalogue no: **PT 500**

TRUE LOVE FOR EVER MORE
Tracks: / True love for ever more.
7" Single: Released Apr '65, on Decca, by Decca Records. Deleted '68. Catalogue no: **F 12108**

WALK WITH FAITH IN YOUR HEART
Tracks: / Walk with faith in your heart.
7" Single: Released Dec '66, on Decca, by Decca Records. Deleted '69. Catalogue no: **F 22523**

WHISPERING
Tracks: / Whispering.
7" Single: Released Aug '63, on Decca, by Decca Records. Deleted '66. Catalogue no: **F 11712**

Bachman-Turner

Biographical details: This Canadian group -- Randy and Robbie Bachman, Fred Turner and Blair Thornton -- were formed in 1972 by Randy Bachman and Fred Turner. Bachman had also been the founder of Guess Who?, a group who enjoyed enormous success on the American charts in 1969 and 1970: surprisingly, as that outfit's lead guitarist and songwriter, he quit when they were at the height of their popularity. BTO originally consisted of Turner and three Bachman brothers, Randy, Robbie and Tim. The latter quit early on, to be replaced by guitarist Thornton. In 1974 they hit the US Top Thirty with the single /'Let It Ride"D (No 23), followed by /'Takin' Care Of Business"D (No 12). The band's third LP, Not Fragile, featured a third Top Thirty single: /'You Ain't Seen Nothing Yet"D was the finest example of their brand of poppy heavy metal and took them to No 1. It was also their first UK hit, reaching No 2. The follow-up single, /'Roll On Down The Highway"D, did reasonably well in both countries and the group were established as firm concert favourites. But they repeated their winning formula too often and record sales dropped off. Randy Bachman left in 1977. (Bob MacDonald, 1984.)
A Canadian hard-rock band formed in the early 1970s by Randy Bachman after leaving his first group Guess Who at the height of their success. He made a solo LP, produced for former Guess Who Singer Chad Allen, formed duo Brave Belt with him for two albums, then formed the new group with drummer Robbie Bachman, bassist C.F. 'Fred' Turner, joined by Tim Bachman replacing Allan. Their name and gearwheel logo were borrowed from a trucking magazine and led to 'working-class rock' label. The overtly commercial outfit had a good chart run on Mercury, then ran it into the ground with personnel changes and a switch to MCA. Randy Bachman did another unsuccessful solo album, formed Ironhorse in 1979, wrote songs with Beach Boys' Carl Wilson, re-formed Guess Who for a tour etc. (Donald Clarke 23 August 1988).

FOR THE WEEKEND
Tracks: / For the weekend.
7" Single: Released Sep '84, on Compleat (USA), by Compleat Entertainment Corp.(USA). Deleted '86. Catalogue no: **CLT 6**

ROLL ON DOWN THE HIGHWAY
Tracks: / Roll on down the highway.
7" Single: Released Feb '75, on Mercury, by Phonogram Ltd. Deleted '78. Catalogue no: **6167 071**

YOU AIN'T SEEN NOTHING YET (SINGLE)
Tracks: / You ain't seen nothing yet / Roll on down the highway.
7" Single: Released Nov '74, on Mercury, by Phonogram Ltd. Deleted '77. Catalogue no: **6167 025**
7" Single: Released Oct '84, on Mercury, by Phonogram Ltd. Deleted Mar '88. Catalogue no: **CUT 109**

Back Bite Band

THRU THE MIDDLE OF THE HOUSE
Tracks: / Thru the middle of the house.
7" Single: Released Oct '84, on Savoir Faire, Catalogue no: **FAIS 009**

Back To Back

PERFECT GIRL
Tracks: / Perfect girl.
7" Single: Released Oct '88, on Vendetta, Catalogue no: **VE 7009**

Bad Boy Bill

JACK IT ALL NIGHT LONG
Tracks: / Jack it all night long.
12" Single: Released Sep '87, on DJ Int.(USA), Catalogue no: **DJ 894**

MEGA MIX
Note: (House) A megamix which also features Julian 'Jumpin' Perez. Essential purchase for all 'House' accounts!
12" Single: Released Nov '87, on DJ Int.(USA), Catalogue no: **DJ 946**

Bad Boy Eugene

BAD BOY EUGENE
Tracks: / Bad boy Eugene.
12" Single: Released Feb '88, on Organik, Catalogue no: **ORG 87/11**

Bad Boys

LET'S MOVE, LET'S GROOVE
Tracks: / Let's move, let's groove.
12" Single: Released Sep '89, on Idlers (USA), Catalogue no: **WAR 053**

Bad Boys Blue

YOU'RE A WOMAN
Tracks: / You're a woman.
7" Single: Released Oct '86, on Zaytron, Deleted '87. Catalogue no: **ZAY 1**
12" Single: Released Oct '86, on Zaytron, Deleted '87. Catalogue no: **12ZAY 1**

Bad Brains

I AND I SURVIVE
Tracks: / I and I survive / Destroy Babylon.
12" Single: Released Mar '83, on Food For Thought, by Music For Nations Records. Catalogue no: **YUMT 101**

I LOVE JAH
Tracks: / Bad brains / Sailin' on / Big takeover.
12" Single: Released Jun '82, on Alternative, Deleted '88. Catalogue no: **VIRUS 13**

Bad Breed Band

HEY LITTLE GIRL
Tracks: / Hey little girl.
12" Single: Released Apr '83, on Bad Breed, Catalogue no: **BREED 001**

Bad Caesar

BABY, THE RAIN MUST FALL
Tracks: / Baby, the rain must fall.
7" Single: Released Feb '89, on Jil, Catalogue no: **JIL 01**

DADDY'S BEEN WORKING
Tracks: / Daddy's been working / Demon lover, The.
7" Single: Released 13 Jun '87, on GFM, Catalogue no: **GFM 113**
12" Single: Released 13 Jun '87, on GFM, Catalogue no: **GFMT 113**

Bad Company

Biographical details: Bad Company Uk blues-rock group named after a 1972 western movie, formed in '73 by ex-Free members Paul Rodgers on piano and vocals and Simon Kirke on drums, who recruited Mick Ralphs on guitar and piano from Mott the Hoople and Boz Burrell on bass from King Crimson. Straight ahead macho rock swagger was successful, steady rather than spectacular success with shrewd management of Led Zep supremo Peter Grant, on whose label Swan Song they come out in USA; like most groups they became progressively more predictable. Rodgers' solo *Cut Loose* on Atlantic in 1984 confirmed split; he teamed with Led Zep guitarist Jimmy Page in The Firm; Kirke played in litle-known Wildlife; Burrell sessioned, notably with ex-Family man Roger Chapman; After Ralphs' solo *Take This* in 1985 he re-formed Bad Company with ex-Ted Nugent Brian Howe replacing Rogers for Fame And Fortune in 1986. (Donald Clarke 23 August 1988)
This British band were formed in 1973, rising out of the ashes of the highly successful rock group Free. Kirke and Rogers had been in that band, Ralphs had just enjoyed Top 3 success with *All the young dudes* as part of Mott The Hoople and Burrell had had a brief spell in King Crimson. Named after a Robert Benton movie, Bad Company's records were immediately popular. Their self titled debut LP was a huge success in both the UK and the US and its single *I can't get enough* went Top 5 in the States and Top 20 in Britain. 1975's *Straight shooter* repeated the winning formula with its selection of unoriginal but tightly played rock tracks and Paul Rodgers' powerful vocals. It also featured their best remembered single *Feel like makin' love* which reached No.20 in Britain, No. 10 in the US. Their '76 set *Run with the pack* was again well received, but subsequent albums have simply retreaded old ground with less and less conviction. With a world tour every two years, the group remained a top concert attraction however and the albums continued to sell to the heavy metal hard core. *Desolation angels* album yielded another US Top 20 single 1979's *Rock 'n' roll fantasy.* After the release of 1982's *Rugh diamonds* the band split. (Bob MacDonald)e.

CAN'T GET ENOUGH
Tracks: / Can't get enough.
7" Single: Released Jun '74, on Island, by Island Records. Deleted '77. Catalogue no: **WIP 6191**

FAME & FORTUNE(SINGLE)
Tracks: / Fame and fortune.
7" Single: Released Feb '87, on Atlantic, by WEA Records. Deleted Jan '88. Catalogue no: **A 9296**

FEEL LIKE MAKIN' LOVE
Tracks: / Feel like makin' love.
7" Single: Released Aug '75, on Island, by Island Records. Deleted '78. Catalogue no: **WIP 6242**

GOOD LOVIN' GONE BAD
Tracks: / Good lovin' gone bad.
7" Single: Released Mar '75, on Island, by Island Records. Deleted '78. Catalogue no: **WIP 6223**

THIS LOVE
Tracks: / This love / Tell it like it is / Burning up (Extra track on 12" only) / Fame and fortune (on 12" only).
7" Single: Released Nov '86, on Atlantic, by WEA Records. Deleted Jan '88. Catalogue no: **A 9355**
12" Single: Released Nov '86, on Atlantic, by WEA Records. Deleted Jan '88. Catalogue no: **A 9355 T**

Bad Dream Fancy Dress

CURRY CRAZY
Tracks: / Curry crazy / Up the King of Luxembourg.
10" single: Released 14 Mar '88, on El, by Cherry Red Records. Catalogue no: **GPOT 33**

FLAIR
Tracks: / Flair / You wind me up / Flair (extended mix) (Only on 12" single.).
7" Single: Released 4 Sep '89, on El, by Cherry Red Records. Catalogue no: **GPO 42**
12" Single: Released 4 Sep '89, on El, by Cherry Red Records. Catalogue no: **GPO 42 T**

SUPREMES, THE
Tracks: / Supremes, The / Choirboys gas.
7" Single: Released Nov '88, on El, by Cherry Red Records. Catalogue no: **GPO 41**

Bad English

FORGET ME NOT
Tracks: / Forget me not / Lay down / Rockin' horse (Only on CD and 12" single.).
CD 5": Released Aug '89, on Epic, by CBS Records. Catalogue no: **655 089 2**
7" Single: Released Aug '89, on Epic, by CBS Records. Catalogue no: **655 089 7**
12" Single: Released Aug '89, on Epic, by CBS Records. Catalogue no: **655 089 6**

Bad Girls

CONGA
Tracks: / Conga / It's not the rock.
7" Single: Released Nov '81, on Spinach, by Spinach Records. Deleted '86. Catalogue no: **SPIN 002**

LITTLE BIT OF LOVE
Tracks: / Little bit of love.
7" Single: Released Feb '82, on Spinach, by Spinach Records. Deleted Feb '87. Catalogue no: **SPIN 003**

TEACH ME TO BOOGIE
Tracks: / Teach me to boogie / It's not the rock.
7" Single: Released Jun '81, on Spinach, by Spinach Records. Deleted Jun '84. Catalogue no: **SPIN 001**

Bad Manners

Biographical details: Formed in London in 1980 this nine-piece band -- Doug Trendle (Buster Bloodvessel), Louis Alphonso, Winston Bazoomies, Brian Chew-It, David Farren, Gus "Hot Lips" Herman, Chris Vane, Andrew "Marcus Absent" Marson and Martin Stewart -- enjoyed rapid success with their deput single, Ne-Ne-Na-Na-Na-Nu-Nu, climbing to No 28 and having a prolonged run on the Top Seventy-Five. The Group relied heavily on a zany image and as the title of their first album, Ska 'n' B, suggested, their music was very much part of the then much-talked-about ska revival. It has to be said that on both counts they were bettered by Madness. Unlike Madness their act was centred on a frontman. Seventeen-stone Buster Bloodvessel wore ludicrous costumes made to look even more ridiculous by his totally bald head and cheeky face. The appropriately-named second single, Lip Up Fatty, reached No 15 and the next one, Special Brew, fared better still, peaking at No 3 at the end of 1980, while Looney Tunes was their second Top Forty album. Their peak year was 1981, with a remake of Can Can becoming a monster party hit that summer and reaching No 3, the band's joint biggest hit. This piece of pomp and romp was followed by one of Bad Manners' more serious musical offerings, Walking In The Sunshine, a No 10 single taken from the Top Twenty LP Gosh, It's Bad Manners. Then came a couple of relative flops, after which Buster and the boys came back with a surefire cover of a 1964 smash: My Girl Lollipop, with its silly words and party feel, was perfect fodder for the Bad Manners style and restored them to the Top Ten. But the resurgence was short-lived -- Samson And Delilah could only crawl to No 58, another single, That'll Do Nicely, flopped altogether and an album, Forging Ahead, managed just one week on the chart at No 78. It seemed the public had tired of the somewhat gimmicky sound of Bad Manners. (Bob MacDonald 1984)
A ska revival band formed in London in 1980: first lineup was Buster Bloodvessel (Douglas Trendle) on lead vocalists; Gus 'Hot Lips' Herman, trumpet; Andrew 'Marcus Absent' Marson and Chris Kane, Saxes; David Farren, bass; Winston Bazoomies (Alan Sayag) on harmonica; Brian Chew-It (Tuitt) on drums; Louis Alphonzo (Cook) on guitar; Martin Stewart, keyboards. Together since schooldays, their appeal centered around Trendle, shaven headed heavyweight whose cartooned head became band's logo; his penchant for outrageous costumes, being photographed in a vat of baked beans etc. soon brought press attention. Instrumentally they were tight, and they were fun: hits included *Special Brew* (ode to Carlsberg lager), *Lorraine* (to blow-up doll), *Can Can* (Offenbach rip-off with Buster in a tutu) etc. They attracted crowds on a USA tour despite the fact that most of their records hadn't even been released there and they're probably still playing somewhere. (Donald Clarke 23 August 1988).

BUONA SERA
Tracks: / Buona sera / Don't be angry / New one / No respect.
7" Single: Released Nov '81, on Magnet, by WEA Records. Deleted '84. Catalogue no: **MAG 211**

CAN CAN
Tracks: / Can can / Armchair disco.
7" Single: Released Nov '85, on Magnet, by WEA Records. Catalogue no: **MAG 190**
7" Single: Released Jan '87, on Old Gold, by Old Gold Records. Catalogue no: **OG 9668**
12" Single: Released Jan '87, on Old Gold, by Old Gold Records. Catalogue no: **OG 4014**

GONNA GET ALONG WITHOUT YOU NOW
Tracks: / Gonna get along with you now.
7" Single: Released Jul '89, on Blue Beat, Catalogue no: **BBSP 004**
12" Single: Released Jul '89, on Blue Beat, Catalogue no: **BBLS 004**

GOT NO BRAINS
Tracks: / Got no brains / Psychedelic Eric.
7" Single: Released May '82, on Magnet, by WEA Records. Deleted '85. Catalogue no: **MAG 216**

JUST A FEELING
Tracks: / Just a feeling / No respect / Suicide.
7" EP: Released Mar '81, on Magnet, by WEA Records. Deleted '84. Catalogue no: **MAG 187**

LIP UP FATTY
Tracks: / Lip up Fatty / Night bus to Dalston.
7" Single: Released Aug '80, on Magnet, by WEA Records. Deleted '83. Catalogue no: **MAG 175**

LORRAINE
Tracks: / Lorraine / Back in '60 / Here comes the major.
7" Single: Released Sep '80, on Magnet, by WEA Records. Deleted '83. Catalogue no: **MAG 181**

MY GIRL LOLLIPOP (MY BOY LOLLIPOP)
Tracks: / My girl lollipop (my boy lollipop).
7" Single: Released Jul '82, on Magnet, by WEA Records. Deleted '85. Catalogue no: **MAG 232**

NE NE NA NA NA NU NU
Tracks: / Ne ne na na na na nu nu / Holidays.
7" Single: Released Mar '80, on Magnet, by WEA Records. Deleted '83. Catalogue no: **MAG 164**

SALLY BROWN
Tracks: / Sally Brown.
7" Single: Released Aug '89, on Blue Beat, Catalogue no: **BBSP 002**
12" Single: Released Aug '89, on Blue Beat, Catalogue no: **BBSPLS 002**

SAMSON AND DELILAH
Tracks: / Samson and Delilah / Good honest man.
12" Single: Released Oct '82, on Magnet, by WEA Records. Deleted '85. Catalogue no: **12MAG 236**
7" Single: Released Oct '82, on Magnet, by WEA Records. Deleted '85. Catalogue no: **MAG 236**

SKAVILLE UK
Tracks: / Skaville UK.
12" Single: Released May '89, on Blue Beat, Catalogue no: **BBLS 001**

WALLY BADAROU - HI-LIFE (Released on 4th & Broadway)

SPECIAL BREW
Tracks: / Special brew / Ivor the engine.
7" Single: Released Sep '80, on Magnet, by WEA Records. Deleted '83. Catalogue no: **MAG 180**

SPECIAL BREW (OLD GOLD)
Tracks: / Lip up fatty / Special brew.
7" Single: Released Jan '87, on Old Gold, by Old Gold Records. Catalogue no: **OG 9670**

THAT'LL DO NICELY
Tracks: / That'll do nicely.
7" Single: Released May '83, on Magnet, by WEA Records. Deleted '86. Catalogue no: **MAG 243**

TOSSING IN MY SLEEP
Tracks: / Tossing in my sleep / Louie louie.
7" Single: Released Feb '86, on Portrait, by CBS Records. Catalogue no: **A 6953**

WALKING IN THE SUNSHINE
Tracks: / Walking in the sunshine.
7" Single: Released Sep '81, on Magnet, by WEA Records. Deleted '84. Catalogue no: **MAG 197**

Bad News

BOHEMIAN RHAPSODY
Tracks: / Bohemian rhapsody / Life with Brian.
7" Pic: Released Sep '87, on EMI, by EMI Records. Deleted Apr '88. Catalogue no: **EMP 24**
7" Single: Released Aug '87, on EMI, by EMI Records. Deleted Apr '88. Catalogue no: **EM 24**
7" Single: Released Sep '87, on EMI, by EMI Records. Deleted Apr '88. Catalogue no: **EMX 24**

CASHING IN ON CHRISTMAS
Tracks: / Cashing in on Christmas (version) / Cashing in on Christmas (let's bank mix) (On 12" single only) / Bad News.
7" Single: Released 28 Nov '87, on EMI, by EMI Records. Deleted Apr '88. Catalogue no: **EMG 36**
7" Single: Released Nov '87, on EMI, by EMI Records. Deleted Apr '88. Catalogue no: **EM 36**
12" Single: Released Nov '87, on EMI, by EMI Records. Deleted Apr '88. Catalogue no: **12 EM 36**

Bad Tune Men

DO THE SWAMP
Tracks: / Do the swamp.
7" Single: Released Jul '85, on Nonchalant, Catalogue no: **NON 1**

JAIL HEAD RACK
Tracks: / Jailhead rack.
12" Single: Released Jan '87, on Nonchalant, Catalogue no: **NON 2**

Badarou, Wally

CHIEF INSPECTOR
Tracks: / Chief inspector.
7" Single: Released Oct '85, on 4th & Broadway, by Island Records. Deleted '87. Catalogue no: **BRW 37**
12" Single: Released Nov '85, on 4th & Broadway, by Island Records. Catalogue no: **12 BRWX 37**
12" Single: Released Oct '85, on 4th & Broadway, by Island Records. Deleted Apr '88. Catalogue no: **12 BRW 37**

ECHOES
Tracks: / Countryman theme / Chief inspector.
7" Single: Released Apr '82, on Island, by Island Records. Catalogue no: **WIP 6759**

HI-LIFE (see panel above)
Tracks: / Hi-life (radio edit.) / Hi-life.
7" Single: Released Oct '86, on 4th & Broadway, by Island Records. Catalogue no: **BRW 53**

NOVELA DAS NOVE
Tracks: / Novela das nove / Chief Inspector (precinct 13) / Endless race (extra track on 12" only).
7" Single: Released Mar '86, on 4th & Broadway, by Island Records. Deleted '87. Catalogue no: **BRW 44**
12" Single: Released Mar '86, on 4th & Broadway, by Island Records. Deleted Apr '88. Catalogue no: **12 BRW 44**

Badfinger

COME AND GET IT
Tracks: / Come and get it.
7" Single: Released Jan '70, on Apple, by Apple Records. Deleted '73. Catalogue no: **APPLE 20**

DAY AFTER DAY
Tracks: / Day after day.
7" Single: Released Jan '72, on Apple, by Apple Records. Deleted '75. Catalogue no: **APPLE 40**

NO MATTER WHAT
Tracks: / No matter what.
7" Single: Released Jan '71, on Apple, by Apple Records. Deleted '74. Catalogue no: **APPLE 31**

Badge

SILVER WOMAN
Tracks: / Silver woman.
7" Single: Released Oct '81, on Metal Minded, by Neat Records. Catalogue no: **MM2**

Badi, Mark

CHANGES
Tracks: / Changes / Close your eyes.
7" Single: Released May '85, on Sour Grape, by Sour Grape Records. Deleted '87. Catalogue no: **SG 120**

Badman, Flinty

MY LOVER GONE
Tracks: / My lover gone.
12" Single: Released Jul '89, on Unity, Catalogue no: **FEA 017**

PRETTY GAL
Tracks: / Pretty gal.
12" Single: Released 8 May '89, on Unity, Catalogue no: **FEA 010**

STUSH
Tracks: / Stush.
7" Single: Released Apr '89, on Jetstar, by Jetstar Records. Catalogue no: **HR 03**

Badoo

I GOT LOVE IN THE MORNING
Tracks: / I got love in the morning / Loneliness.
12" Single: Released Nov '82, on Jah Congo, Catalogue no: **YC 002**

Badowski, Henry

HENRY'S IN LOVE
Tracks: / Henry's in love / Lamb to the slaughter.
7" Single: Released Jun '81, on A&M, by A&M Records. Deleted Jun '84. Catalogue no: **AMS 8135**

MY FACE
Tracks: / My face / Four more seasons.
7" Single: Released Feb '80, on A&M, by A&M Records. Deleted Feb '83. Catalogue no: **AMS 7503**

Baez, Joan

Biographical details: Born in New York in 1941, Joan Baez moved to Boston with her family after leaving school. She taught herself to sing and play guitar and proceeded to make a striking impact at the first Newport Folk Festival in 1959. She met Bob Dylan, a fellow up-and-coming young folk singer, and their two careers became intertwined. As well as developing a deep personal relationship the two toured together. Baez was heavily influenced by Dylan's style of social and political commentary and she began to incorporate her strongly-held views -- mainly against war the the draft -- into her own songs. The album Joan Baez In Concert, issued in 1962, received enthusiastic cult acceptance. As the Dylan-led folk protest movement grew, Baez's music became accepted by a wider audience. In '64 Joan Baez In Concert, Vol 2, was a strong seller, reaching No 8 in Britain with 19 weeks on the chart. Britain was becoming very responsive to her work and '65 saw her score her first UK hit singles, none of the three doing as well in her native America. The Dylan influence was clearly displayed by the choice of two of the songs, We Shall Overcome (No 26) and It's All Over Now, Baby Blue (No 22). But the big one was the middle hit of the three: Baez's record of Phil Ochs' album track, There But For Fortune, took her into the British Top Ten. Although a competent and supple acoustic guitarist, her main strength was her pure, crystal-clear voice. Her singing was technically superb but, being untrained, had an added passion. It was rewarded by no less than three further Top Ten albums in 1965, making Baez one of the biggest-selling American acts in Britain that year. Back at home the politically-motivated singer was making headlines with her pacifist activities. As well as refusing to pay that portion of her taxes estimated to be spent on arms and warfare she founded California's Institute for the Study of Non-Violence. Having been a regular participant in civil rights and peace demonstrations, she narried fellow campaigner David Harris in 1968. Both were embroiled in draft-resistance activities, she being sent to prison for two 10-day terms, he being jailed for three years. In 1971, the year Harris and Baez were divorced, she scored her biggest hit on either side of the Atlantic. The Night They Drove Old Dixie Down was her most commercial single, reaching No 3 in the States, No 6 in Britain. Though continuing her involvement in politics by becoming an active member of Amnesty International, her music was becoming less political. The Diamonds And Rust set, in 1975, saw her moving into the jazz-rock area, with backing by the Crusaders: it was a strong seller at home but not in Britain, where record sales since Dixie have eluded her. Never enamoured of the trappings of stardom, Baez continued quietly to record and tour. (Bob MacDonald, 1984.)

Born in 1941 in Staten Island, New York, she sang at the Newport Folk Festival in 1959, and her first albums on Vanguard were a revelation after many years of neglect of folk music in the USA, featuring a silvery voice, her own guitar accompaniment and traditional Child ballads. Her eighth album *Joan* in 1969 was an unwise attempt at art-song treatment arranged by Peter Schickele; she was an early advocate of her friend Bob Dylan and made a two record set of his songs *Any Day Now*. She founded Institute for the Study of Non-Violence '65, became an active opponent of the Vietnam war and was arrested at demo; married student leader David Harris in 1968 (later jailed for resisting the draft; son Gabriel born '69; they separated '71). Single *The Night They Drove Ol' Dixie Down* (song by Robbie Robertson) was top five in the USA in 1972.
The American right hated her, but only fools doubted her sincerity and her honesty: she was a heroine of terrible times without even trying. Her albums became increasinly political until she retunred to more commercial product, confessing frankly that she needed the money, changing labels to A&M for *Diamonds And Rust* in 1975: an uneven album with an excellent title song about her relationship with Dylan, others by her sister Mimi Farina, Jackson Browne etc. She joined Dylan's Rolling Thunder tour, appeared in his overlong home movie Renaldo and Clara; switched labels to Portrait. With no record contract for several years, she denied being blacklisted for politics in Regan era: 'I don't think they would care whether I was a communist or a fascist (if) I would commit myself to making platinum singles'. First USA album in eight years was *Recently* in 1987, with songs by U2, Dire Straights, Peter Gabriel: *I haven't been a folk singer for 15 years.* She thinks she has a sense ofhumour, but it is obvious; her phrasing, like that of Linda Ronstadt, leaves something to be desired: she is no swinger, but like Ronstadt, she has few peers when she is handling material which suits her. (Donald Clarke 23 August 1988).

FAREWELL ANGELINA (SINGLE)
Tracks: / Farewell Angelina.
7" Single: Released Dec '65, on Fontana, by Phonogram Ltd. Deleted '68. Catalogue no: **TF 639**

IT'S ALL OVER NOW BABY BLUE
Tracks: / It's all over now baby blue.
7" Single: Released Sep '65, on Fontana, by Phonogram Ltd. Deleted '68. Catalogue no: **TF 604**

NIGHT THEY DROVE OLD DIXIE DOWN (SINGLE)
Tracks: / Night they drove old Dixie down, The / There but for fortune.
7" Single: Released Oct '71, on Vanguard, by Start Records Ltd.. Deleted '74. Catalogue no: **VS 35138**
7" Single: Released Jan '83, on Flashback, by Mainline Records. Catalogue no: **FBS 12**

PACK UP YOUR SORROWS
Tracks: / Pack up your sorrows.
7" Single: Released Jul '66, on Fontana, by Phonogram Ltd. Deleted '69. Catalogue no: **TF 727**

THERE BUT FOR FORTUNE
Tracks: / There but for fortune.
7" Single: Released Jul '65, on Fontana, by Phonogram Ltd. Deleted '68. Catalogue no: **TF 587**

WE SHALL OVERCOME
Tracks: / We shall overcome.
7" Single: Released May '65, on Fontana, by Phonogram Ltd. Deleted '68. Catalogue no: **TF 564**

Baez, Tony

TELL ME WHY
Tracks: / Tell me why.
CD 5": Released Jul '89, on WEA, by WEA Records. Catalogue no: **YZ 425CD**
7" Single: Released Jul '89, on WEA, by WEA Records. Catalogue no: **YZ 425**
12" Single: Released Jul '89, on WEA, by WEA Records. Catalogue no: **YZ 425T**

Bagatelle

DON'T SAY NO
Tracks: / Don't say no / Golden days.
7" Single: Released May '86, on Roxy (1), Catalogue no: **TEASE 3**

LOVE IS THE REASON
Tracks: / Love is the reason / Always on your mind.
7" Single: Released Sep '81, on Polydor, by Polydor Ltd. Deleted Sep '84. Catalogue no: **POSP 331**

OUTRAGEOUS
Tracks: / Outrageous / Going back to Ireland.
7" Single: Released Jan '82, on Polydor, by Polydor Ltd. Deleted '85. Catalogue no: **POSP 389**

SECOND VIOLIN
Tracks: / Second violin / Getting what's mine.
7" Single: Released May '81, on Polydor, by Polydor Ltd. Deleted May '84. Catalogue no: **POSP 271**

SUMMER IN DUBLIN
Tracks: / Summer in Dublin / Highway blues.
7" Single: Released Jun '82, on Polydor, by Polydor Ltd. Deleted Jun '85. Catalogue no: **POSP 445**
7" Single: Released Nov '80, on Polydor, by Polydor Ltd. Deleted '83. Catalogue no: **2078111**

TRUMP CARD
Tracks: / Trump card / Turn the heat on.
7" Single: Released Jan '81, on Polydor, by Polydor Ltd. Deleted Jan '84. Catalogue no: **POSP 213**

Bagga Puss & Curfew

PARTY INNA CHELSEA
Tracks: / Party inna Chelsea / Party inna Chelsea (version).
12" Single: Released Aug '86, on Street Beat (USA), Catalogue no: **TNT 007**

Baghdad Five

LOVIN' AFFECTION
Tracks: / Lovin' affection.
7" Single: Released Jan '84, on Risky, Catalogue no: **RR 2511**

Bailey, Admiral

BUM USE
Tracks: / Bum use.
12" Single: Released 31 Jul '89, on Live & Love, Catalogue no: **LLD 131**

DONE (PART II)
Tracks: / Done (part II).
12" Single: Released Jun '89, on Sir Coxsone, Catalogue no: **BD 8910**

RETURN OF SLENG TENG
Tracks: / Return of sleng teng / Science.
12" Single: Released 7 Aug '89, on Jammy's, Catalogue no: **HD/JAM 002**

Bailey & Bridges

COME AND GET MY LOVE
Tracks: / Come and get my love.
Note: Pic bag
7" Single: Released Apr '87, on Rhythm King, by Mute Records. Catalogue no: **LEFT 6**
12" Single: Released Apr '87, on Rhythm King, by Mute Records. Catalogue no: **LEFT 6T**

Bailey, Errol

DANCE TO REGGAE MUSIC
Tracks: / Dance to reggae music.
12" Single: Released Oct '83, on Foundation, Catalogue no: **TF 007**

Bailey, James

I'M YOUR SUGAR
Tracks: / I'm your sugar (dub mix).
12" Single: Released Feb '87, on Willow Tree, Catalogue no: **WTL 03**

Bailey, Jordan

DON'T WORRY BE HAPPY
Tracks: / Don't worry be happy / You build me up.
7" Single: Released 19 Sep '88, on Mango, by Island Records. Deleted Apr '89. Catalogue no: **IS 396**
12" Single: Released 19 Sep '88, on Mango, by Island Records. Deleted Apr '89. Catalogue no: **12IS 396**

Bailey, Philip

EASY LOVER
Tracks: / Easy lover / Woman.
12" Single: Released Mar '85, on CBS, by CBS Records. Deleted '86. Catalogue no: **TA 4195**
7" Single: Released Mar '85, on CBS, by CBS Records. Catalogue no: **A 4195**

ECHO MY HEART
Tracks: / Echo my heart / Take this with you / Walking on the Chinese wall (extra track on 12" only) / Children of the ghetto (extra track on 12" only).
12" Single: Released Jul '86, on CBS, by CBS Records. Deleted '86. Catalogue no: **TA 7293**
7" Single: Released Jul '86, on CBS, by CBS Records. Deleted '86. Catalogue no: **A 7293**

STATE OF THE HEART
Tracks: / State of the heart / Take this with you.
7" Single: Released May '86, on CBS, by CBS Records. Deleted '86. Catalogue no: **A 7086**
12" Single: Released May '86, on CBS, by CBS Records. Deleted '86. Catalogue no: **TA 7086**

TWINS
Tracks: / Twins / Twins (instrumental) / Twins (extended mix) (Only on 12" and CD single.) / Twins (acapella) (Only on 12" and CD single.) / Twins (dub mix) (Only on 12" and CD single.).
12" Single: Released Mar '89, on Epic, by CBS Records. Deleted Oct '89. Catalogue no: **654519 6**
CD 5": Released Mar '89, on Epic, by CBS Records. Deleted Oct '89. Catalogue no: **654519 2**
7" Single: Released Mar '89, on Epic, by CBS Records. Deleted Oct '89. Catalogue no: **654519 7**

WALKING ON THE CHINESE WALL
Tracks: / Walking on the chinese wall / Woman I know / Trapped.
7" Single: Released May '85, on CBS, by CBS Records. Deleted '88. Catalogue no: **A 6202**

Bailey, Razzy

Biographical details: Bailey, Razzy The country/pop singer was born in 1939 in Alabama. He formed his first band in his teens and spent almost 20 years on the honky-tonk circuit; he was produced by Freddie Weller at ABC Records in 1969, but recorded for several labels and wrote hit songs for others (Dicky Lee's *9,999,999 Tears* in 1976) before having his own successes on RCA from 1978, more recently on MCA. (Donald Clarke 23 August 1988).

SHE LEFT LOVE ALL OVER ME
Tracks: / She left love all over me / Blaze of glory.
7" Single: Released Apr '82, on RCA, by BMG Records (UK). Deleted Apr '85. Catalogue no: **RCA 204**

Baily, Marcie

PLANNING TO GO
Tracks: / Planning to go / Man can't hold a woman, A.
12" Single: Released Aug '86, on Technique, Catalogue no: **WRT 07**

Baines, Murray

ON MY OWN
Tracks: / On my own.
12" Single: Released Jun '86, on Joe Frazer, Catalogue no: **BT 004**

SECRET LOVER
Tracks: / Secret lover / Loving mood.
12" Single: Released Feb '86, on Joe Frazer, Catalogue no: **BT 003**

Baiser

SUMMER BREEZE
Tracks: / Summer breeze.
7" Single: Released Jun '84, on Malaco, by Malaco Records (UK). Deleted '88. Catalogue no: **MAL 024**
12" Single: Released Jun '84, on Malaco, by Malaco Records (UK). Deleted '88. Catalogue no: **MAL 12 024**

Baisiks

THINK ABOUT THAT
Tracks: / Think about that.
7" Single: Released Apr '82, on Musician Survival, Catalogue no: **MSR 001**

Baiza, Joe

CERTAIN WAY
Tracks: / Certain way / Chasing.
12" Single: Released Aug '87, on SST (USA), by SST Records (USA). Catalogue no: **SST 109**

Bake

GET UP GET OUT
Tracks: / Get up get out.
12" Single: Released '88, on Playlist, Catalogue no: **PLAY 4**

Baker, Adrian

CRAZY ABOUT YOU
Tracks: / Crazy about you / Lovemaker.
7" Single: Released Jan '82, on Polo, by Polo Records. Deleted Jan '85. Catalogue no: **POLO 3**

DON'T WORRY BABY
Tracks: / Don't worry baby / Happy Birthday Brian Wilson.
7" Single: Released Jul '81, on Polo, by Polo Records. Deleted '85. Catalogue no: **POLO 11**

ENDLESS SUMMER
Tracks: / Endless summer / Summertime city.
7" Single: Released 6 Feb '89, on Ariola, by BMG Records (UK). Catalogue no: **112 082**

HIGH TIME
Tracks: / High time.
7" Single: Released Feb '81, on Polo, by Polo Records. Deleted '84. Catalogue no: **POLO 7**
12" Single: Released Feb '81, on Polo, by Polo Records. Deleted '84. Catalogue no: **POLO 12-7**

I GET AROUND
Tracks: / I get around.
7" Single: Released Aug '85, on Creole, by Creole Records. Catalogue no: **MX 1**
12" Single: Released Aug '85, on Creole, by Creole Records. Catalogue no: **12 MX 1**

SHERRY
Tracks: / Sherry.
7" Single: Released Jul '75, on Magnet, by WEA Records. Deleted '78. Catalogue no: **MAG 34**

Baker, Anita

Biographical details: Baker, Anita The beautiful soul singer from Detroit was formely the lead singer with a group called Chapter 8. She began having solo hits in the USA black chart in the early '80s and swept into the top ten of the national USA pop chart in '86 with *Sweet Love* and has followed that with success after success. Her fame looks like lasting as long as she wants it. (Donald Clarke 23 August 1988).

CAUGHT UP IN A RAPTURE
Tracks: / Mystery / Caught up in the rapture.
7" Single: Released Jan '87, on Elektra (USA), by Elektra Records (USA). Deleted Jan '88. Catalogue no: **EKR 49**
12" Single: Released Jan '87, on Elektra (USA), by Elektra Records (USA). Deleted Jan '88. Catalogue no: **EKR 49 T**

GIVING YOU THE BEST THAT I GOT
Tracks: / Giving you the best that I got / Good enough / Sweet love (live) (Only on 12") / Watch your step (live) (Only on CD single.).
CD 5": Released Sep '88, on Elektra, by Elektra Records (UK). Catalogue no: **EKR 79CD**
7" Single: Released Sep '88, on Elektra, by Elektra Records (UK). Catalogue no: **EKR 79**
12" Single: Released Sep '88, on Elektra, by Elektra Records (UK). Catalogue no: **EKR 79T**

BINKEY BAKER - TOE KNEE BLACK BURN (Released on 101)

JUST BECAUSE
Tracks: / Just because / Moondance / Sweet love (Only on 12" single.).
CD 5": Released Feb '89, on Elektra, by Elektra Records (UK). Catalogue no: **EKR 87CD**
7" Single: Released Jan '89, on Elektra, by Elektra Records (UK). Catalogue no: **EKR 87**
12" Single: Released Jan '89, on Elektra, by Elektra Records (UK). Catalogue no: **EKR 87 T**

SAME OLE LOVE
Tracks: / Same ole love / Been so long.
7" Single: Released 30 May '87, on Elektra (USA), by Elektra Records (USA). Deleted Jul '88. Catalogue no: **ERK 57**
12" Single: Released 30 May '87, on Elektra (USA), by Elektra Records (USA). Deleted Jul '88. Catalogue no: **ERK 57 T**

SWEET LOVE
Tracks: / Sweet love / No one in the world / Watch your step (Extra track on 12" only) / Same ole love (live) (Extra track on Double-pack only) / You bring me joy (live) (Extra track on Double-pack only) / Watch your step (inst) (Extra track on Double-pack only).
7" Set: Released Oct '86, on Elektra (USA), by Elektra Records (USA). Catalogue no: **EKR 44 TX**
7" Single: Released Jun '86, on Elektra (USA), by Elektra Records (USA). Deleted Sep '87. Catalogue no: **EKR 44**
12" Single: Released Jun '86, on Elektra (USA), by Elektra Records (USA). Deleted Sep '87. Catalogue no: **EKR 44 T**

Baker, Arthur

IT'S YOUR TIME
Tracks: / It's your time.
CD 5": Released May '89, on Breakout, by A&M Records. Catalogue no: **USACD 654**
Cassingle: Released May '89, on Breakout, by A&M Records. Catalogue no: **USATC 654**
7" Single: Released May '89, on Breakout, by A&M Records. Catalogue no: **USA 654**
12" Single: Released May '89, on Breakout, by A&M Records. Catalogue no: **USAT 654**

MESSAGE IS LOVE, THE
Tracks: / Message is love, The / Message is love, The (version).
CD 5": Released Sep '89, on Breakout, by A&M Records. Catalogue no: **USACD 668**
7" Single: Released Sep '89, on Breakout, by A&M Records. Catalogue no: **USA 668**
12" Single: Released Sep '89, on Breakout, by A&M Records. Catalogue no: **USAT 668**

TALK IT OVER
Tracks: / Talk it over / Talk it over (midnight mix).
CD 5": Released Jul '89, on A&M, by A&M Records. Catalogue no: **USACD 655**
7" Single: Released Jul '89, on A&M, by A&M Records. Catalogue no: **USA 655**
12" Single: Released Jul '89, on A&M, by A&M Records. Catalogue no: **USAT 655**

WE GOT TO COME TOGETHER
Tracks: / We got to come together.
12" Single: Released Jul '88, on Minimal 4, Catalogue no: **CR 7877**

Baker, Bart

COME BACK
Tracks: / Come back / In the city.
7" Single: Released Sep '80, on Carrere, Deleted '83. Catalogue no: **CAR 162**

Baker, Binkey

HEAVEN SENT
Tracks: / Heaven sent / Toodlepip.
7" Single: Released Feb '81, on Edge, Deleted Feb '84. Catalogue no: **EDGE 7**

TOE KNEE BLACK BURN (see panel above)
Tracks: / Toe knee black burn / Rainy day in Brighton / I was a teenage video widow.
7" Single: Released Dec '82, on 101, Deleted Dec '87. Catalogue no: **1CUR 5**
7" Single: Released '78, on Stiff, by Stiff Records. Catalogue no: **BUY 41**

Baker, Carrol

Biographical details: Baker, Carrol was born in Nova Scotia; her father was a well-known old-time fiddler. Canadian success began on the gaity label in the early '70s; she recorded for RCA from '76 and became Canada's top country singer, popular in the UK since appearing at the Wembley Country Music Festival in 1977-8. *It Always Hurts Like The First Time* reached the USA country chart in 1985. (Donald Clarke 23 August 1988).

IT ALWAYS HURTS LIKE THE FIRST TIME
Tracks: / It always hurts like the first time.
7" Single: Released Mar '86, on Tembo, by Tembo Records. Catalogue no: **TML 113**

Baker, Cheryl

IF PARADISE IS HALF AS NICE
Tracks: / If paradise is half as nice.
7" Single: Released Aug '87, on WEA, by WEA Records. Deleted Jul '88. Catalogue no: **YZ 152**
12" Single: Released Aug '87, on WEA, by WEA Records. Deleted Jul '88. Catalogue no: **YZ 152T**

Baker, Chet

Biographical details: Baker, Chet The American trumpeter was born in Oklahoma in 1929; he died in Amsterdam in 1988 in a fall from a hotel room window. In the early '50s Charlie Parker told Miles Davis, 'You'd better watch out. There's a little white cat on the West Coast who's gonna eat you up.' In fact Baker never learned to read music well and had as much in common with Bix Beiderbecke as with Davis. But he achieved national fame with the Gerry Mulligan quartet in 1952, then led his own group with the excellent Russ Freeman on piano '53-4; his light, wistful tone and laid-back lyricism was at the centre of the West Coast 'cool jazz' scene; his occasional singing was derided by critics, but the meticulous reissue of his complete Pacific Jazz recordings by the USA Mosaic label in limited-edition box sets show the records to have much more than a period charm. Chet on Riverside is a beautiful set made in 1959 with Bill Evans on piano, others including an ecellenty rhythm section (no vocals). He was one of the most tragic victims of narcotics in popular music; he was beaten by hoodlums in San Fransisco in 1968, losing his teeth; he never beat the habit, yet he recovered and his playing since the mid-'70s was as lovely as ever. His death was thought to be a drug related accident. (Donald Clarke 23 August 1988).

ALMOST BLUE
Tracks: / Almost blue.
12" Single: Released 24 Jul '89, on RCA, by BMG Records (UK). Catalogue no: **PT 49371**

NO PROBLEM
CD 5": Released '88, on Impetus, by Sweet Folk All Records. Catalogue no: **SCCD 31131**

Baker, Dave

GLOW OF LOVE
Tracks: / Glow of love / Everybody needs love.
7" Single: Released Jan '81, on Black Jack. Deleted Jan '84. Catalogue no: **BJD 4507**

Baker, George

PALOMA BLANCA (SINGLE)
Tracks: / Paloma blanca.
7" Single: Released Sep '75, on Warner Bros., by WEA Records. Deleted '78. Catalogue no: **K 16541**

Baker, Hylda

YOU'RE THE ONE THAT I WANT
Tracks: / You're the one that I want.
7" Single: Released Sep '78, on Pye. Deleted '81. Catalogue no: **7 N 46121**

Baker, Laverne

Biographical details: Baker, Laverne The rhythm & blues singer was born in 1929 in Chicago. She began at 17 as 'Little Miss Sharecropper', was spotted by bandleader Fletcher Henderson; she recorded for CBS and King but achieved her greatest success on the young Atlantic label, unfortunately during her era of the white cover: she had 18 crossovers to the USA pop chart, but her biggest hit *Tweedle Dee* was beaten in the chart by Georgia Gibbs' cover. Baker later moved to Japan. Most of her Atlantic hits are on the Charly reissue. (Donald Clarke 23 August 1988).

TWEEDLE DEE
Tracks: / Tweedle dee / Jim Dandy / Bumble bee.
7" EP: Released Jul '82, on Revival. Catalogue no: **REV 6007**

Baker, Lloyd

BISI
Tracks: / Bisi.
7" Single: Released May '82, on Sunburn, by Orbitone Records. Catalogue no: **SBD 06**

Baker, Michael

DON'T YOU WANT MY LOVIN
Tracks: / Don't you want my lovin'.
12" Single: Released Mar '84, on SMP (2). Catalogue no: **PASH 1223**

Bakerloo Junction

MY LAGAN SOFTLY FLOWING (SINGLE)
Tracks: / My lagan softly flowing / Flowers of manchester.
7" Single: Released Nov '87, on Mint, by Emerald Records. Deleted '88. Catalogue no: **CHEW 59**

REMEMBER GREEN
Tracks: / Remember green / Black velvet band.
7" Single: Released Dec '82, on Mint, by Emerald Records. Deleted '88. Catalogue no: **CHEW 78**

WINDS OF CHANGE
Tracks: / Winds of change / Porter.
7" Single: Released Jun '82, on Mint, by Emerald Records. Deleted '88. Catalogue no: **CHEW 65**

Balaam & The Angel

DAY AND NIGHT
Tracks: / Day and night.
7" Single: Released Sep '85, on Chapter 22, by Chapter 22 Records. Catalogue no: **CHAP 37**
12" Single: Released Sep '85, on Chapter 22, by Chapter 22 Records. Catalogue no: **CHAP 373**

I LOVE THE THINGS YOU DO TO ME
Tracks: / I love the things you do to me / You're in the way of my dreams / Things you know (on 12" only) / As tears go by (Extra track on 12" only.).
7" Single: Released 19 Sep '87, on Virgin, by Virgin Records. Deleted May '88. Catalogue no: **VS 993**
12" Single: Released 19 Sep '87, on Virgin, by Virgin Records. Deleted May '88. Catalogue no: **VS 993-12**

I TOOK A LITTLE
Tracks: / I took a little / Long time lovin' you / Big city fun time girl (Available on 12" only.) / Would I die for ... (Available on 12" only.).
CD 5": Released Sep '89, on Virgin, by Virgin Records. Catalogue no: **VSCD 1213**
7" Single: Released Sep '89, on Virgin, by Virgin Records. Catalogue no: **VS 1213**
12" Single: Released Sep '89, on Virgin, by Virgin Records. Catalogue no: **VSTX 1213**
12" Single: Released Sep '89, on Virgin, by Virgin Records. Catalogue no: **VST 1213**
12" Single: Released Sep '89, on Virgin, by Virgin Records. Catalogue no: **VSP 1213**

LIGHT OF THE WORLD
Tracks: / Light of the world / Day and night / She knows (Extra track on 12" only) / Love (Extra track on 12" only) / Family and friends.
7" Single: Released Aug '86, on Virgin, by Virgin Records. Deleted May '88. Catalogue no: **VS 890**
12" Single: Released Aug '86, on Virgin, by Virgin Records. Catalogue no: **VS 890-12**

LIVE FREE OR DIE (SINGLE)
Tracks: / Live free or die (7" only) / Eagle (On 12" only) / Complete control (On 12" only) / Live free or die (Texas redbeard mix) (On 12" only).
7" Single: on Virgin, by Virgin Records. Catalogue no: **VS 1124**
12" Single: Released 30 Aug '88, on Virgin, by Virgin Records. Catalogue no: **VST 1124**

LOVE ME
Tracks: / Love me.
12" Single: Released Apr '85, on Chapter 22, by Chapter 22 Records. Catalogue no: **220022**

SHE KNOWS
Tracks: / She knows / Dreams wide awake / Sister moon (extra track on double-pack only) / Warm again (extra track on double-pack only) / 2 into 1 (extra track on 12" only) / Darklands (extra track on 12" only).
7" Set: Released Mar '86, on Virgin, by Virgin Records. Deleted '86. Catalogue no: **VSD 842**
7" Single: Released Mar '86, on Virgin, by Virgin Records. Deleted '89. Catalogue no: **VS 842**
12" Single: Released Mar '86, on Virgin, by Virgin Records. Deleted '86. Catalogue no: **VS 842-12**

SLOW DOWN
Tracks: / Slow down / Walk away / Travel on (Extra track on 12" only) / In the morning * (*=extra track on 12" only).
7" Single: Released Jun '86, on Virgin, by Virgin Records. Deleted '86. Catalogue no: **VS 864**
12" Single: Released Jun '86, on Virgin, by Virgin Records. Deleted '89. Catalogue no: **VS 864-12**

SOMETHING SPECIAL
Tracks: / Something special / I feel love / Let it happen (Extra track on 12") / You took my soul (Extra track on 12").
7" Single: Released Jun '87, on Virgin, by Virgin Records. Deleted May '88. Catalogue no: **VS 970**
12" Single: Released Jun '87, on Virgin, by Virgin Records. Deleted May '88. Catalogue no: **VS 970-12**

WORLD OF LIGHT
Tracks: / World of light.
7" Single: Released Mar '84, on True Friends. Catalogue no: **TF 004**
7" Single: Released Nov '84, on Chapter 22, by Chapter 22 Records. Catalogue no: **22 001**

Balance

RUSSIAN TRAIN
Tracks: / Russian train / River ghosts.
7" Single: Released Jun '87, on Siren, by Virgin Records. Deleted May '88. Catalogue no: **SRN 39**
12" Single: Released Jun '87, on Siren, by Virgin Records. Deleted May '88. Catalogue no: **SRN 39-12**

Balancing Act

CAN YOU GET TO THAT
Tracks: / Can you get to that.
7" Single: Released 12 Jun '89, on I.R.S. Catalogue no: **EIRS 116**
12" Single: Released 12 Jun '89, on I.R.S. Catalogue no: **EIRST 116**

Balcony

REDDER THAN BURNING COALS
Tracks: / Redder than burning coals.
12" Single: Released Feb '87, on Pink Pop. Catalogue no: **POP 002**

SURPRISE AFTER SURPRISE
Tracks: / Surprise after surprise / Lizard hunt.
7" Single: Released Aug '82, on Praxis (1). Catalogue no: **TM 2**

Balcony Dogs

BALCONY DOGS (SINGLE)
Tracks: / Balcony dogs / McHelicopter (Only on 12") / Rings of Saturn / Fat pocket justice (Only on the 12" version.).
7" Single: Released 12 Aug '88, on Bloodline, by Island Records. Deleted Apr '89. Catalogue no: **IS 394**
12" Single: Released 12 Aug '88, on Bloodline, by Island Records. Deleted Apr '89. Catalogue no: **12 IS 394**

WHEELS OF FORTUNE
Tracks: / Wheels of fortune / Einstein / Creole country (part 2).
7" Single: Released Jan '89, on Bloodline, by Island Records. Catalogue no: **IS 401**
12" Single: Released Jan '89, on Bloodline, by Island Records. Catalogue no: **12 IS 401**

Baldry, Long John

Biographical details: Long John Baldry, an outstanding white British blues singer, was a prominent member of two groups in the mid-60's, the Hoochie Coochie Men and Steampacket, an outfit which included, at various times, Elton John, Elkie Brooks and Rod Stewart. Having enjoyed little commercial success, Baldry forsook the blues and recorded a pseudo-Walker Brothers big ballad written by pop songwriters Tony Macauley and John McLeod. Let The Heartaches Begin was an instant winner and the appropriately named Long John -- at more than 6ft 6in -- became the tallest artist ever to hit No 1. Heartaches dethroned the Foundations' Baby, Now That I've Found You, another song penned by the two Macs. Commercial pop music was not Baldry's long-term bag, however, and further success was short-lived. The biggest of his three other hits was Mexico, peaking at No 15 in 1968. He returned to the blues in the 70's, but without success. (Bob MacDonald, 1984.) The 6'7" R&B singer was born in London in 1941. He began in folk clubs, toured Europe with Jack Elliot in the late '50s, turned to R&B and joined Alexis Korner's Blues Incorporated, then with Cyril Davies in the All Stars, later Brian Auger's Steampacket, still later in Bluesology with pianist Reg Dwight, who grew up to be Elton John. He turned to pop(*Let The Heartaches Begin* was a no.1 UK hit '67) but later his album *It Ain't Easy* in 1971 yielded his hit *Don't Try To Lay No Boogie-Woogie On The King Of Rock'n'Roll* produced by Rod Stewart. He became a naturalised Canadian. Revival of *You've Lost That Lovin' Feelin'* a duet with Kathi MacDonald, was a minor USA hit in '79. (Donald Clarke 23 August 1988)
Long John Baldry was a white British blues singer who was a prominent member of two groups in the mid-Sixties, one called the Hoochie Coochie Men and the other called Streampacket. The latter outfit included, at various times Elton John, Elkie Brooks and Rod Stewart. Having enjoyhed no success, Baldry forsook the blues and recorded a pseudo-Walker Brothers big ballad written by pop songwriters Tony Macaulay and John McLeod. *Let the heartaches begin* was an instant winner and the appropriately nicknamed Long John Baldry became the tallest artist ever to hit No. 1 - his height measured over six and a half feet. *Heartaches* dethroned the Foundations *Baby now that I've found you*, another song penned by the two Macs. Commercial pop music was not Baldry's bag, however and further successes were short lived. The biggest of his three other hits were *Mexico*, peaking at No. 15 in 1968. He returned to the blues in the Seventies, but without success. (Bob MacDonald).

IT'S TOO LATE
Tracks: / It's too late.
7" Single: Released Jan '69, on Pye. Deleted '72. Catalogue no: **7 N 17664**

LET THE HEARTACHES BEGIN (SINGLE)
Tracks: / Let the heartaches begin / Mexico.
7" Single: Released Nov '67, on Pye. Deleted '70. Catalogue no: **7 N 17385**
7" Single: Released Jan '89, on Old Gold, by Old Gold Records. Catalogue no: **OG 9481**
7" Single: Released Jan '83, on Flashback, by Mainline Records. Catalogue no: **FBS 13**

MEXICO
Tracks: / Mexico / Let the heartaches begin.
7" Single: Released Oct '68, on Pye. Deleted '71. Catalogue no: **7 N 17563**
7" Single: Released Jun '86, on PRT, by Castle Communications Records. Catalogue no: **7P 356**

WHEN THE SUN COMES SHININ' THRU
Tracks: / When the sun comes shinin' thru.
7" Single: Released Sep '68, on Pye. Deleted '71. Catalogue no: **7 N 17593**

Baldwin, Clive

HIS MAJESTY THE BABY
Tracks: / His majesty the baby.
7" Single: Released Jun '83, on Pantoni. Catalogue no: **PA 006**

Balearic Beach

BALEARIC BEACH
12" Single: Released '89, on Subway, by Subway Records. Catalogue no: **SUB052**

Balham Alligators

LET'S DANCE
Tracks: / Let's dance / Balham stwo step.
7" Single: Released Dec '85, on Mays, by Mays Records. Catalogue no: **ING 12**
7" Single: Released Aug '87, on Special Delivery, by Topic Records. Deleted '89. Catalogue no: **SPEC 45001**

OH MARIE
Tracks: / Oh Marie / Sacre bleu.
7" Single: Released Aug '84, on Sweet Heart. Catalogue no: **SH 001**

Bali

LOVE TO LOVE YOU BABY
Tracks: / Love to love you baby / Body heat / Love to love you baby (land of Oz mix) (Available on 12", cat. no. YRTX 26 only.).
7" Single: Released Feb '89, on Circa, by Virgin Records. Catalogue no: **YR 26**
12" Single: Released Feb '89, on Circa, by Virgin Records. Catalogue no: **YRTX 26**
12" Single: Released Feb '89, on Circa, by Virgin Records. Catalogue no: **YRT 26**

PATEL RAP
Tracks: / Patel rap.
7" Single: Released Sep '89, on Multitone, by Multitone Records/Savera. Catalogue no: **7BHA 3**
12" Single: Released Sep '89, on Multitone, by Multitone Records/Savera. Catalogue no: **12BHA 3**

Ball, Dave

RARE TEMPO
Tracks: / Rare tempo.
12" Single: Released 1 May '85, on Scarface. Catalogue no: **SCAR 009T**

Ball, Kenny

Biographical details: Born in Ilford in 1931, Kenny Ball took up the trumpet at the age of 16. Having played in various jazz bands, he formed Kenny Ball & His Jazzmen in 1958. Riding the crest of the early 60's trad jazz boom, Ball and his band scored a string of hit singles, beginning with Cole Porter's Samantha in early 1961. Their biggest success came at the end of that year when Midnight In Moscow went to No 2 in both Britain and, surprisingly, America. There were no further US hits but they continued at home with three more Top Tenners, March Of The Siamese Children, The Green Leaves Of Summer and Sukiyaki, which charted in advance of the original Japanese version by Kyu Sakamoto. In 1964, when Beatlemania was at its height and the trad boom was abating, the hits tailed off. Ball could no longer achieve success in either the singles chart or the albums list, where he had had a No 1 in '62 with a collaborative Best of Ball, Barber & Bilk (Chris and Acker respectively) plus a No 4 LP with Kenny Ball's Golden Hits. A very brief return to the charts came in summer '67 with a minor hit version of the Beatles' When I'm Sixty-Four. (Bob MacDonald, 1984.)
The jazz trumpeter and bandleader born in 1931 in Ilford was one of the most successful during the trad boom: of 14 hits in the UK, three were top tens; *Midnight In Moscow* also reached no.2 in the USA. He is more highly regarded than that by some jazz fans, however; in their recent book 'The Jazz Companion', Ian Carr, Digby Fairweather and Brian Priestley gave Ball a longer entry than Chet Baker, and why not? Trad or 'dixieland' people, however talented, usually get short shrift in reference books. He toured the Soviet Union in 1985. (Donald Clarke 23 August 1988).

ACAPULCO 1922
Tracks: / Acapulco 1922.
7" Single: Released Aug '63, on Pye Jazz Today. Deleted '66. Catalogue no: **7 NJ 2067**

CASABLANCA
Tracks: / Casablanca.
7" Single: Released Apr '63, on Pye Jazz Today. Deleted '66. Catalogue no: **7 NJ 2064**

CLAP TRAP
Tracks: / Clap trap.
7" Single: Released Jul '82, on Mont, by Mont Music Records. Catalogue no: **MM 101**

GREENLEAVES OF SUMMER, THE
Tracks: / Green leaves of summer.
7" Single: Released May '62, on Pye Jazz Today. Deleted '65. Catalogue no: **7 NJ 2054**

HELLO DOLLY (SINGLE)
Tracks: / Hello Dolly.
7" Single: Released Jun '64, on Pye Jazz Today. Deleted '67. Catalogue no: **7 NJ 2071**

I STILL LOVE YOU ALL
Tracks: / I Still love you all.

7" Single: Released May '61, on Pye Jazz Today, Deleted '64. Catalogue no: **7 NJ 2042**

I WANNA BE LIKE YOU
Tracks: / I wanna be like you.
7" Single: Released Oct '83, on PRT, by Castle Communications Records. Catalogue no: **7P 289**

MARCH OF THE SIAMESE CHILDREN
Tracks: / March of the Siamese children.
7" Single: Released Feb '62, on Pye Jazz Today, Deleted '65. Catalogue no: **7 NJ 2051**

MIDNIGHT IN MOSCOW
Tracks: / Midnight in Moscow.
7" Single: Released Nov '61, on Pye Jazz Today, Deleted '64. Catalogue no: **7 NJ 2049**

MIDNIGHT IN MOSCOW (OLD GOLD)
Tracks: / Midnight in Moscow / Cast your fate to the wind.
7" Single: Released Jul '82, on Old Gold, by Old Gold Records. Catalogue no: **OG 9087**

PAY OFF, THE
Tracks: / Pay off, The.
7" Single: Released Oct '62, on Pye Jazz Today, Deleted '65. Catalogue no: **7 NJ 2061**

RONDO
Tracks: / Rondo.
7" Single: Released Jun '63, on Pye Jazz Today, Deleted '66. Catalogue no: **7 NJ 2065**

SAMANTHA
Tracks: / Samantha.
7" Single: Released Feb '61, on Pye Jazz Today, Deleted '64. Catalogue no: **7 NJ 2040**

SO DO I
Tracks: / So do I.
7" Single: Released Aug '62, on Pye Jazz Today, Deleted '65. Catalogue no: **7 NJ 2056**

SOAP (SINGLE)
Tracks: / Soap / You're bound to feel like a monkey.
7" Single: Released Nov '80, on AMI, by AMI Records. Deleted Nov '83. Catalogue no: **AIS 109**

SOMEDAY
Tracks: / Someday.
7" Single: Released Aug '61, on Pye Jazz Today, Deleted '64. Catalogue no: **7 NJ 2047**

SUKIYAKI
Tracks: / Sukiyaki.
7" Single: Released Jan '63, on Pye Jazz Today, Deleted '66. Catalogue no: **7 NJ 2062**

SUNSHINE
Tracks: / Sunshine / Scorpio.
7" Single: Released Dec '84, on American Phonogram, by American Phonogram Int.. Catalogue no: **APKB**

WHEN I'M 64
Tracks: / When I'm sixty four.
7" Single: Released Jul '67, on Pye, Deleted '70. Catalogue no: **7 N 17348**

Ball, Michael

FIRST MAN YOU REMEMBER, THE
Tracks: / First man you remember, The / Mermaid song / Love changes everything (original cast version) (Only on 12" and CD single.).
7" Single: Released Sep '89, on Really Useful Records, by Really Useful Group. Catalogue no: **RUR 6**
12" Single: Released Sep '89, on Really Useful Records, by Really Useful Group. Catalogue no: **RURX 6**

LOVE CHANGES EVERYTHING
Tracks: / Love changes everything.
12" Single: Released Jan '89, on Really Useful Records, by Really Useful Group. Catalogue no: **RUR X 3**
CD 5": Released Jan '89, on Really Useful Records, by Really Useful Group. Catalogue no: **RURCD 3**
7" Single: Released Jan '89, on Really Useful Records, by Really Useful Group. Catalogue no: **RUR 3**

Ballard, Dave

SUGAREE
Tracks: / Sugaree / You got the right string.
7" Single: Released Nov '82, on PHAB, by PHAB Records. Deleted Nov '85. Catalogue no: **PHAB 1**

Ballard, Hank

Biographical details: Ballard, Hank The soul singer and songwriter was born in 1936 in Detroit. He grew up in Alabama, but later worked on a Ford assembly line; at 16 he joined the Royals, who soon changed their name to the Midnighters, to avoid confusion with King labelmates the Five Royales. They had three huge hits in 1954: *Work With Me Annie, Sexy Ways, Annie Had A Baby*; Johnny Otis wrote answer lyrics *Roll With Me Henry* for Etta James and a watered-down white cover was a no.1 pop hit by Georgia Gibbs in 1955, Otis, James and ballard splitting royalties. Ballard invented *The Twist* (derived fom a 1955 Clyde McPhatter hit *What 'cha Gonna Do*); released on the B-side of his first Hot 100 pop chart entry *Teardrops On Your Letter* in 1959 (the group now called Hank Ballard and the Midnighters), *Twist* became a hit; they failed to turn up for an appearance on Dick Clark's American Bandstand TV show and Clark had unknown Chubby Checker cover it note-for-note for a no.1 pop hit, but Ballard's made the top 30 while his *Finger-Poppin' Time* made the top ten. His career later faltered, but he's never been away long: one of the most influential artists of all put on a stunning show in London in 1986, enterprisingly recorded by Charly to match the hits compilation. (Donald Clarke 23 August 1988).

LET'S GO, LET'S GO, LET'S GO
Tracks: / Twist, The (ext.version) / Let's go, let's go, let's go.
12" Single: Released Jul '85, on Charly, by Charly Records. Deleted '88. Catalogue no: **CYZ 113**
12" Single: Released Jan '87, on Charly, by Charly Records. Catalogue no: **CYZ 118**

Ballard, Russ

HERE COMES THE HURT
Tracks: / Here comes the hurt / Breakdown.
7" Single: Released Jan '81, on Epic, by CBS Records. Deleted Jan '84. Catalogue no: **EPC 9489**

I WILL BE THERE
Tracks: / I will be there / Madman.
7" Single: Released Mar '81, on Epic, by CBS Records. Deleted Mar '84. Catalogue no: **EPC A 1067**

TWO SILHOUETTES
Tracks: / Two silhouettes / Living without you.
7" Single: Released Jun '84, on EMI-America, by EMI Records. Catalogue no: **EA 175**

VOICES, THE
Tracks: / Voices / Living without you.
7" Single: Released Feb '85, on EMI-America, by EMI Records. Deleted Jun '89. Catalogue no: **EA 185**

Ballistic Kisses

DOMESTIC SERVANTS
Tracks: / Domestic servants / Black and broke / Five O'clock world.
12" Single: Released Jan '82, on Don't Fall Off The Mountain, by Don't Fall Off The Mountain Records. Catalogue no: **Y 13**

FIVE O'CLOCK WORLD
Tracks: / Five o'clock world / Samuria toys.
7" Single: Released Apr '82, on Ensign, by Ensign Records. Deleted '83. Catalogue no: **ENY 227**
12" Single: Released Apr '82, on Ensign, by Ensign Records. Deleted '83. Catalogue no: **ENYT 227**

SHARECROP THE NIGHT
Tracks: / Sharecrop the night / After hours.
12" Single: Released Feb '84, on Don't Fall Off The Mountain, by Don't Fall Off The Mountain Records. Catalogue no: **Y 20**

Ballot, Errol

WICKED AND WILD
Tracks: / Wicked and wild.
12" Single: Released Nov '85, on Unity Sound, Catalogue no: **UN 002**

Bally

LUCIFER IN POWDER FORM
Tracks: / All woman nice / Lucifer in powder form.
12" Single: Released Dec '86, on Hot Vinyl, Catalogue no: **HVT 32**

Ballyhoo

MAN ON THE MOON
Tracks: / Man on the moon / Loving you.
7" Single: Released Nov '81, on Blue Chip, by Blue Chip Records. Deleted Nov '84. Catalogue no: **BC 106**

Balsara

DO-RE-MI
Tracks: / Do-Re-Mi / Lonely goatherd / My favourite things / Edelweiss.
7" Single: Released Jul '81, on EMI, by EMI Records. Deleted '85. Catalogue no: **ODO 104**

Baltimora

TARZAN BOY
Tracks: / Tarzan boy.
7" Single: Released Aug '85, on Columbia, by EMI Records. Catalogue no: **DBX 9102**
7" Single: Released May '85, on Columbia, by EMI Records. Catalogue no: **DB 9102**
12" Single: Released May '85, on Columbia, by EMI Records. Catalogue no: **12DB 9102**
12" Single: Released Aug '85, on Columbia, by EMI Records. Catalogue no: **12DBX 9102**

Bam Bam

GIVE IT TO ME
Tracks: / Give it to me (double trouble extended remix).
7" Single: Released 20 Feb '88, on Serious, by Serious Records. Catalogue no: **OUS 10**
12" Single: Released Mar '88, on Serious, by Serious Records. Catalogue no: **OUSX 10**
12" Single: Released Nov '87, on Westbrook (USA), Catalogue no: **BBWB 105**

GIVE IT TO ME (ACID REVENGE MIX)
Tracks: / Give it to me (acid revenge mix) / Give it to me (version).
12" Single: Released Apr '88, on Serious, by Serious Records. Catalogue no: **OUXX 10**

NECK TATTOO
Tracks: / Neck tattoo / Cautious navigations / Glory.
7" Single: Released Jan '89, on Great, Catalogue no: **GREAT 2**
12" Single: Released Jan '89, on Great, Catalogue no: **GREAT 2 T**

POLKA DOT
Tracks: / Polka dot.
7" Single: Released May '82, on Vox Populi, Deleted '83. Catalogue no: **OP 001**

SCRAPING OFF THE SHINE
Tracks: / Scraping off the shine / Colin McKeerer sings / Presley.
7" Single: Released Nov '87, on Great, Catalogue no: **GREAT 01**
12" Single: Released Nov '87, on Great, Catalogue no: **GREAT 01T**

SPEND THE NIGHT
Tracks: / Spend the night / Spend the night (dub mix) / Spend the night (house mix).
12" Single: Released Mar '89, on Desire, by Desire Records. Catalogue no: **WANTX 15**

WHERE'S YOUR CHILD
Tracks: / Where's your child / Where's your child (suck mix).
7" Single: Released Nov '88, on Desire, by Desire Records. Catalogue no: **WANT 7**
12" Single: Released Nov '88, on Desire, by Desire Records. Catalogue no: **WANTX 7**

Bambaataa, Afrika

Biographical details: Afrika Bambaataa is the founding father and spiritual leader of America's Hip Hop movement, which was born in the mid-Seventies and led to the scratching and breakdance crazes of the early and mid-Eighties. With his Soul Sonic Force backing group, he first entered the British charts in 1982 with the *Planet Rock* single. In 1984 he scored with *Renegades Of Funk* and a duet with Godfather of Soul James Brown called *Unity*. He has not obtained a major hit on either side of the Atlantic and may never do so, but has nonetheless proved an influential man and one of the most engaging cult figures in the history of black music. (Bob MacDonald).

BAMBAATAA'S THEME(ASSAULT ON PRECINCT 13)
Tracks: / Bambaataa's theme (assault on precinct 13) / Tension.
12" Single: Released Aug '86, on WEA (International), by WEA Records. Deleted Jan '88. Catalogue no: **U 8663T**

LOOKING FOR THE PERFECT BEAT
Tracks: / Looking for the perfect beat / Bonus beat.
12" Single: Released Jul '84, on 21 Records, by Polydor Ltd. Catalogue no: **POSPX 561**

PLANET ROCK
Tracks: / Planet rock.
7" Single: Released Aug '82, on 21 Records, by Polydor Ltd. Deleted '85. Catalogue no: **POSP 497**
12" Single: Released Jul '84, on 21 Records, by Polydor Ltd. Catalogue no: **POSPX 497**

RECKLESS (Fon Force remix)
Tracks: / Reckless / Mind body and soul.
Note: Featuring UB 40
12" Single: Released 7 Mar '88, on EMI, by EMI Records. Deleted Jan '89. Catalogue no: **12 EMXS 41**
12" Single: Released Feb '88, on EMI, by EMI Records. Deleted Nov '88. Catalogue no: **12EM 41**
CD 5": Released Feb '88, on EMI, by EMI Records. Deleted 31 Jul '88. Catalogue no: **CDEM 41**
7" Single: Released Feb '88, on EMI, by EMI Records. Deleted Nov '88. Catalogue no: **EM 41**
12" Single: Released Mar '88, on EMI, by EMI Records. Deleted Jan '89. Catalogue no: **12EMX 41**

RENEGADES OF FUNK
Tracks: / Renegades of funk.
7" Single: Released Mar '84, on Tommy Boy, by Polydor Ltd. Deleted '87. Catalogue no: **AFR 1**

SHO NUFF FUNKY
Tracks: / Sho nuff funky / Tell me when you need it again (vocal mix 1) / Tell me when you need it again (inst. mix 3) (Available on 12" only) / Sho nuff funky (funking all night mix) / Tell me when you need it again (vocal mix 2).
Note: Featuring Slug-Go. Remix produced by Dakeyne of DMC Ltd. 1988 original sound recording(s) made by EMI Records Ltd.
7" Single: Released May '88, on EMI, by EMI Records. Catalogue no: **2025877**
7" Single: Released May '88, on EMI, by EMI Records. Deleted Jun '89. Catalogue no: **EM 57**
12" Single: Released May '88, on EMI, by EMI Records. Deleted Nov '88. Catalogue no: **12EM 57**
12" Single: Released '88, on EMI, by EMI Records. Deleted Nov '88. Catalogue no: **12EMXS 57**
12" Single: Released May '88, on EMI, by EMI Records. Deleted Nov '88. Catalogue no: **2025866**
12" Single: Released May '88, on EMI, by EMI Records. Deleted Nov '88. Catalogue no: **2027026**
12" Single: Released 16 May '88, on EMI, by EMI Records. Deleted Nov '88. Catalogue no: **12EMX 57**

SHOUT IT OUT
Tracks: / Shout it out / Sho nuff funky.
Note: Artist's full name: Side a) Afrika Bambaataa & Family featuring "Slug Go" with lead vocals by Afrika Bambaataa, Roland Smith, Kid Dust and Harmony. Side b) Afrika Bambaataa, Kid Dust, Harmony and Tayshan.
12" Single: Released 14 Mar '88, on EMI, by EMI Records. Deleted '88. Catalogue no: **12 BAM 1**

UNITY (PART 1 - THE THIRD COMING)
Tracks: / Unity (part 1 - the third coming).
7" Single: Released Sep '84, on Tommy Boy, by Polydor Ltd. Deleted '87. Catalogue no: **AFR 2**

Bambi Slam

BAMP-BAMP
Tracks: / Hit me with your hairbrush / Awful flute song (first half), The ((Available on 12" only)).
7" Single: Released Feb '87, on Product Inc., Catalogue no: **PROD 2.7**
12" Single: Released Feb '87, on Product Inc., Catalogue no: **PROD 2.12**

DON'T IT MAKE YOU FEEL
Tracks: / Don't it make you feel.
7" Single: Released May '87, on Product Inc., Catalogue no: **7PROD 8**
12" Single: Released May '87, on Product Inc., Catalogue no: **12 PROD 8**

HAPPY BIRTHDAY
Tracks: / Happy birthday.
7" Single: Released Feb '88, on Product Inc., Catalogue no: **7PROD 13**
12" Single: Released Feb '88, on Product Inc., Catalogue no: **12PROD 13**

LONG TIME COMING
Tracks: / Long time coming / I & I / Shame of the sick (Only on the 12" version.) / Sad psycho (Only on the 12" version.).
7" Single: Released Sep '88, on Blanco Y Negro, by Blanco Y Negro Records. Catalogue no: **NEG 36**
12" Single: Released Sep '88, on Blanco Y Negro, by Blanco Y Negro Records. Catalogue no: **NEG 36 T**

Bam-Boo

GIVE YOUR LOVE TO ME
Tracks: / Give your love to me / Love dreams.
7" Single: Released Aug '83, on Funzone, Catalogue no: **FUN 3**
12" Single: Released Aug '83, on Funzone, Catalogue no: **FUNT 3**

IT'S ALL IN YOUR MIND
Tracks: / It's all in your mind.
12" Single: Released Aug '87, on Fourth Floor (USA), Catalogue no: **FF 487**

Bamboo Blue

SCARLET ON A THURSDAY
Tracks: / Scarlet on a Thursday / Hat culture.
7" Single: Released Nov '82, on Variety, Deleted '83. Catalogue no: **BBVY 403**

Bamboo Fringe

DORIAN GRAY
Tracks: / Dorian Gray.
7" Single: Released Jun '83, on Probe Plus, by Probe Plus Records. Catalogue no: **PP 4**

Bamboola

BILLY HART
Tracks: / Billy Hart / Window.
7" Single: Released May '86, on Plastic Head, by Plastic Head Records. Catalogue

no: **PLASS 004**

Bamboos

WITH WHICH TO LOVE YOU
Tracks: / With which to love you.
7" Single: Released Jan '88, on Citadel (UK), by Citadel Records. Catalogue no: **CIT 034**

Banana Boat Company

HURTING NEVER STOPS, THE
Tracks: / Hurting never stops, The.
7" Single: Released Sep '86, on La Fillette, Catalogue no: **LAFX 01**

Banana Man

KILL A SOUND BOY
Tracks: / Kill a sound boy.
7" Single: Released Nov '88, on Taurus, Catalogue no: **UNKNOWN**

Bananamen

CRUSHER, THE
Tracks: / Crusher, The.
7" Single: Released Jul '83, on Big Beat, by Ace Records. Deleted '88. Catalogue no: **NS 88**

Bananarama

Biographical details: Sarah Dallin, Siobhan Fahey and Keren Woodward were sharing a flat in London, nurturing hopes of forming a group, when they were invited by ex-Sex Pistols Paul Cook and Steve Jones to do backing vocals and percussion with their new project the Professionals. In 1981 Cook produced Bananarama's first single, Aie A Mwana, an unusual piece of tribal-influenced pop that became a critics' favourite. Following this, the girls received a second offer to perform backing vocals, this time from Fun Boy Three, who had just broken away from the Specials and were about to record a debut album. The combination of all-male vocal trio and an all-female vocal trio proved a winner. As well as the Fune Boy Three album selling strongly, the single It Ain't What You Do, It's The Way That You Do It surged to No 4. This remake of a pre-rock 'n' roll ditty was credited to "Fun Boy Three and Bananarama"; the roles were reversed next time round with "Bananarama and Fun Boy Three" scoring a No 5 with Really Saying Something, another old song. Having been helped by the Funboys, Bananarama then teamed with Imagination producers/co-writers Tony Swain and Steve Jolley. Shy Boy, another Top Five single, was the immediate result. After a less well-received effort, Cheers Then, at the end of 1982, the trio bounced back in 1983 with a fourth Top Five single Na Na Hey Hey Kiss Him Goodbye (which climbed four places higher than the original by Steam) and a debut album, Deep Sea Skiving. Cruel Summer hit No 8 later in the year, to be followed in '84 by Robert de Niro's Waiting (No 3) and belated Stateside success with Cruel Summer. The hits have continued to follow. Well established as a lightweight pop singles group, Bananarama's vocals are perfectly suited to the gently danceable Swain and Jolley sound. (Bob MacDonald, 1984.).

AIE A MWANA
Tracks: / Aie a mwana.
7" Single: Released Sep '81, on Deram, by London Records. Catalogue no: **DM 446**
12" Single: Released Sep '81, on Deram, by London Records. Catalogue no: **DMX 446**

CHEERS THEN
Tracks: / Cheers then / Girl about town.
7" Single: Released Nov '82, on London Records, by London Records. Catalogue no: **NANA 3**
12" Single: Released Nov '82, on London Records, by London Records. Catalogue no: **NANX 3**

CRUEL SUMMER
Tracks: / Cruel summer.
7" Single: Released Jul '83, on London Records, by London Records. Catalogue no: **NANA 5**
12" Single: Released Jul '83, on London Records, by London Records. Catalogue no: **NANX 5**

CRUEL SUMMER '89 (see panel on right)
Tracks: / Cruel summer '89 / Venus (the greatest remix) / I heard a rumour (Only on 12" and CD single.) / Venus (remix) (Only on 12" and CD single.).
CD 5": Released 30 May '89, on London Records, by London Records. Catalogue no: **NANCD 19**
Cassingle: Released 30 May '89, on London Records, by London Records. Catalogue no: **NCS 19**
7" Single: Released 30 May '89, on London Records, by London Records. Catalogue no: **NANA 19**
12" Single: Released 30 May '89, on London Records, by London Records. Catalogue no: **NANX 19**

DO NOT DISTURB
Tracks: / Do not disturb.
7" Pic: Released Aug '85, on London Records, by London Records. Catalogue no: **NANPD 9**
7" Single: Released Aug '85, on London Records, by London Records. Catalogue no: **NANA 9**
12" Single: Released Aug '85, on London Records, by London Records. Catalogue no: **NANX 9**

HELP
Tracks: / Help / Love in the factory.
12" Single: Released Feb '89, on London Records, by London Records. Catalogue no: **LONX 222**
7" Single: Released Feb '89, on London Records, by London Records. Catalogue no: **LON 222**

HOTLINE TO HEAVEN
Tracks: / Hotline to heaven.
12" Single: Released Oct '84, on London Records, by London Records. Catalogue no: **NANX 8**
7" Single: Released Oct '84, on London Records, by London Records. Catalogue no: **NANA 8**

I CAN'T HELP IT
Tracks: / I can't help it / Ecstasy.
7" Single: Released Dec '87, on London Records, by London Records. Deleted Oct '88. Catalogue no: **NANA 15**
CD 5": Released Feb '88, on London Records, by London Records. Deleted Oct '88. Catalogue no: **NANCD 15**
7" Single: Released '87, on London Records, by London Records. Deleted Feb '89. Catalogue no: **NAN 15**
12" Single: Released Dec '87, on London Records, by London Records. Catalogue no: **NANXR 15**

I HEARD A RUMOUR
Tracks: / I heard a rumour / Clean cut boy (Party size) / I heard a rumour (Horoscope mix) (Track on 12" version only.) / I heard a rumour (Dub) (Track on 12" version only.).
7" Single: Released Jul '87, on London Records, by London Records. Deleted Oct '88. Catalogue no: **NANA 13**
12" Single: Released Jul '87, on London Records, by London Records. Deleted Oct '88. Catalogue no: **NANX 13**
7" Single: on London Records, by London Records. Deleted Oct '88. Catalogue no: **NANXR 13**

I WANT YOU BACK
Tracks: / I want you back / Bad for me / Amnesia (Theme from the 'Roxy') (Available on 12" only.) / I can't help it / Love in the first degree / Some girls / I heard a rumour.
7" Single: Released Mar '88, on London Records, by London Records. Deleted Feb '89. Catalogue no: **NANA 16**
CD 5": Released Mar '88, on London Records, by London Records. Deleted Jul '89. Catalogue no: **NANCD 16**
10" single: Released Apr '88, on Megamix (USA), Catalogue no: **HI NRG**
7" Single: Released Apr '88, on Megamix (USA), Catalogue no: **NANG 16**
12" Single: Released Mar '88, on London Records, by London Records. Catalogue no: **NANX 16**

LOVE IN THE FIRST DEGREE
Tracks: / Love in the first degree / Mr. Sleaze / Mr. Sleaze (rare groove remix).

BANANARAMA - SHY BOY (Released on London Records)

7" Single: Released 24 Oct '87, on London Records, by London Records. Deleted Oct '88. Catalogue no: **NANXR 14**
7" Single: Released 19 Sep '87, on London Records, by London Records. Deleted Oct '88. Catalogue no: **NANA 14**
12" Single: Released 19 Sep '87, on London Records, by London Records. Deleted Oct '88. Catalogue no: **NANX 14**

LOVE, TRUTH AND HONESTY
Tracks: / Love, truth and honesty / Strike it rich / I want you back (Extra track on CD 5").
CD 5": Released Sep '88, on London Records, by London Records. Catalogue no: **NANCD 17**
7" Single: Released Oct '88, on London Records, by London Records. Deleted May '89. Catalogue no: **NANB 17**
12" Single: Released Oct '88, on London Records, by London Records. Deleted May '89. Catalogue no: **NANXR 17**
12" Single: Released Sep '88, on London Records, by London Records. Deleted May '89. Catalogue no: **NANX 17**
7" Single: Released Oct '88, on London Records, by London Records. Catalogue no: **NANP 17**
7" Single: Released Sep '88, on London Records, by London Records. Deleted May '89. Catalogue no: **NANA 17**

MORE THAN PHYSICAL
Tracks: / More than physical.
7" Single: Released Aug '86, on London Records, by London Records. Catalogue no: **NANA 11**
12" Single: Released Aug '86, on London Records, by London Records. Catalogue no: **NANX 11**

NANA HEY HEY KISS HIM GOODBYE
Tracks: / Na na hey hey (kiss him goodbye) / Tell tale signs.
7" Single: Released Feb '83, on London Records, by London Records. Catalogue no: **NANA 4**
12" Single: Released Feb '83, on London Records, by London Records. Catalogue no: **NANX 4**

NATHAN JONES
Tracks: / Nathan Jones / Once in a lifetime / Nathan Jones (extended mix) (Only on 12".) / Nathan Jones (instrumental dub mix) (Only on 12".).
Note: Cover version of the Supremes' classic 'Nathan Jones'. Produced by Stock, Aitken & Waterman.
7" Single: Released Nov '88, on London Records, by London Records. Deleted 26 Jun '89. Catalogue no: **NANA 18**
12" Single: Released Nov '88, on London Records, by London Records. Deleted 26 Jun '89. Catalogue no: **NANX 18**
Special: Released Nov '88, on London Records, by London Records. Catalogue no: **NANB 18**
12" Single: Released Nov '88, on London Records, by London Records. Deleted May '89. Catalogue no: **NANXR 18**
CD 5": Released Nov '88, on London Records, by London Records. Catalogue no: **NANCD 18**

REALLY SAYING SOMETHING
Tracks: / Really saying something / Give us back our cheap fares.
7" Single: Released Apr '82, on Deram, by London Records. Catalogue no: **NANA 1**
12" Single: Released Apr '82, on Deram, by London Records. Catalogue no: **NANX 1**

ROBERT DE NIRO'S WAITING
Tracks: / Robert De Niro's waiting / Push.
7" Single: Released Apr '84, on Decca, by Decca Records. Deleted '88. Catalogue no: **NANX 6**
7" Single: Released Apr '84, on Decca, by Decca Records. Deleted '88. Catalogue no: **NANA 6**

ROUGH JUSTICE
Tracks: / Rough justice / Live now.
7" Single: Released May '84, on London Records, by London Records. Deleted '87. Catalogue no: **NANA 7**

SHY BOY (see panel above)
Tracks: / Shy boy / Don't call us.
Note: For information write to: Mel O'Brien 60 Parker Street London WC2
7" Single: Released Jun '82, on London Records, by London Records. Catalogue no: **NANA 2**
12" Single: Released Jun '82, on London Records, by London Records. Catalogue no: **NANX 2**

TRICK OF THE NIGHT
Tracks: / Tricky mix / Set on you (This track on 12" version only.).
12" Single: Released Jan '87, on London Records, by London Records. Deleted Sep '87. Catalogue no: **NANX 12**
7" Single: Released Jan '87, on London

BANANARAMA - CRUEL SUMMER '89 (Released on London Records)

Records, by London Records. Deleted Sep '87. Catalogue no: NANA 12

VENUS
Tracks: / Venus / White train / More than physical (Double pack only) / Scarlet (**=extra track on double pack only).
12" Single: Released May '86, on London Records, by London Records. Catalogue no: **NANX 10**
12" Single: Released '86, on London Records, by London Records. Deleted Feb '89. Catalogue no: **NAXRR 10**
7" Set: Released Aug '86, on London Records, by London Records. Catalogue no: **NANDP 11**
7" Single: Released May '86, on London Records, by London Records. Catalogue no: **NANA 10**

Banbarra

SHACK UP
Tracks: / Shack up.
7" Single: Released Jul '85, on Stateside, by EMI Records. Deleted '86. Catalogue no: **STATES 1**
12" Single: Released Jul '85, on Stateside, by EMI Records. Catalogue no: **12STATES 1**

Band

Biographical details: Formed as a group in the late 50's, Jamie "Robbie" Robertson, Rick Danko, Levon Helm, Garth Hudson and Richard Manuel began life as the Hawks, the backing band for Toronto-based rock 'n' roller Ronnie Hawkins. Helm was from Arkansas, the others from Canada. With Hawkins they hit the US Top Thirty with the single Mary Lou. After leaving him in the early 60's they played in New York with white blues singer John Hammond Jr, whose father was the famous Columbia Records executive who had signed Bop Dylan. They got to meet Dylan in 1965, at a time when he was looking to progress from folk-rock to a harder, electric sound. With each of the five players being multi-instrumentalists, Dylan realised he had found the perfect backing group with whom to ferment his new sound. They became simply Bob Dylan & The Band. The new teams's first collaboration on record was the single Can You Please Crawl Out Your Window?, a No 17 hit in the UK but, surprisingly, only a minor hit in the States. The Band also played on some tracks on Dylan's 1966 megaclassic album Blonde On Blonde, at the same time winning rave reviews with him on tour. Their driving rhythm section were the perfect live foil for Dylan's vocals. In July '66 Dylan was injured in a motorcycle crash so the group moved to Woodstock to make music with him while he recovered. The tapes of these sessions became one of the world's most talked-about bootleg recordings and Columbia Records eventually released them officially as The Basement Tapes in 1975. The cross-fertilisation between the man and his band was growing ever stronger during the mid to late-60's, as exemplified by two '68 releases, Dylan's John Wesley Harding and the Band's first record under their own name, Music From The Big Pink. Although Pig Bink failed to chart in Britain, it was internationally recognised as an excellent album, bringing together many diverse styles while still sounding controlled and coherent. Its single, The Weight, was, conversely, bigger in the UK than the US. The eclectic sound of the Band -- driving country-rock featuring soulful vocals -- was continued on 1969's self-titled album, to be followed by Stage Fright, the title track of which told of the traumas of being a touring band. After 1971's less exciting Cahoots, the Band took what turned out to be a four-year break from recording new material. When they returned with the Northern Lights - Southern Cross set in '75 it was to a lukewarm reception. Islands, in '77, was the Band's last album before they folded. The decided to go out with a bang by staging The Last Waltz in San Francisco, their last-ever concert. It featured Bob Dylan, Ronnie Hawkins, Neil Young, Van Morrison, Eric Clapton, Joni Mitchell, Neil Diamond and Muddy Waters, a galaxy of musicians with whom they had at one time or another been associated. The last waltz was issued as a triple album and a very fine film. In Britain the Band never enjoyed the same record sales as Dylan: four of their albums did chart, but only briefly. They did, however, score a Top Twenty single in 1970 with Rag Mama Rag and Joan Baez had a transAtlantic Top Ten hit in '71 with The Day They Drove Old Dixie Down, originally recorded by the Band and written by their all-important songwriter, Robbie Robertson. (Bob MacDonald, 1984.)
This USA rock band is easily one of the most influential of all time: Jaime 'Robbie' Robertson (born 1943) on guitar, Garth Hudson (born 1937) on organ, Richard Manuel (born 1943, a suicide in 1986) on piano and vocals, Rick Danko (born 1942) on bass and vocals, and Levon Helm (born 1942) on drums and vocals. All were originally Canadians except Helm, from Arkansas. They were hired as a backup group for rockabilly Ronnie Hawkins (also from Arkansas), this association lasting on and off until c. 1963. Usually called the Hawks, they toured all over North America, playing bars and dance halls which were often gloomy, soaking up the culture of the prairies. They met Bob Dylan and after his motorcycle accident in mid '66 retired with him to a rural house called Big Pink near Woodstock, New York; rehearsal of new songs there resulted in rock's first important bootleg *The great white wonder* (from plain sleeve): called *The basement tapes* when finally issued by CBS in 1975). Robertson's growing confidence as a songwriter possibly influenced Dylan, who described him as a guitar genius. Word of mouth from George Harrison and Eric Clapton prepared fans for the Band's astonishing debut album *Music from big pink* in 1968 with songs including Dylan's *I shall be released*, Dylan-Manuel's *Tears of rage*, Dylan-Danko's *This wheel's on fire*, the traditional *Long black veil* and Robertson's instant classic *The weight*. The next album *The cripple creek, Rag mama rag, Across the great divide* and one of his finest, *The night they drove dixie down* written for Helm to sing. These two albums alone saw them described as 'the only band that could have warmed up the crowd for Abraham Lincoln'. *Rock of ages* was a two-disc live set, *Moondog Matinee* covers of favourited rock'n'roll songs; they also made *Planet waves* and *Before the flood* with Dylan; they quit while they were ahead in 1976 with a joyous concert party and multiple album *The last waltz*, with guest Hawkins, Rebennack and many others. The film (by Martin Scorsese) and album also includes specially made segments with teh Staple Singers and Emmylou Harris.

RAG MAMA RAG
Tracks: / Rag mama rag.
7" Single: Released Apr '70, on Capitol, by EMI Records. Deleted '73. Catalogue no: **CL 15629**

WEIGHT, THE
Tracks: / Weight, The.
7" Single: Released Sep '68, on Capitol, by EMI Records. Deleted '71. Catalogue no: **CL 15559**

Band Aid

DO THEY KNOW IT'S CHRISTMAS?
Tracks: / Do they know it's Christmas / One year on (feed the world).
7" Pic: Released Nov '87, on Mercury, by Phonogram Ltd. Deleted Mar '88. Catalogue no: **FEEDP 1**
7" Single: Released Nov '87, on Mercury, by Phonogram Ltd. Deleted Mar '88. Catalogue no: **FEED 1**
12" Single: Released Nov '87, on Mercury, by Phonogram Ltd. Deleted Mar '88. Catalogue no: **FEED 112**

Band AKA

Biographical details: Nothing to do with Special AKA, Band AKA are a black American soul group of 10 members. They first charted in 1982 with the jazzy soul single Grace (No 41) and followed it the next year with a Top Thirty hit, Joy. Both written and produced by J. James Jarrett, they were accompanied by albums, respectively Band AKA and Men Of The Music. (Bob MacDonald, 1984.).

GRACE
Tracks: / Grace / Grace (part 2).
7" Single: Released May '82, on Epic, by CBS Records. Deleted '85. Catalogue no: **EPC A 2376**
12" Single: Released May '82, on Epic, by CBS Records. Deleted '85. Catalogue no: **EPCA 13-2376**

IF YOU WANT TO HEAR
Tracks: / If you want to hear.
7" Single: Released Apr '83, on Epic, by CBS Records. Catalogue no: **A 3370**
12" Single: Released Apr '83, on Epic, by CBS Records. Catalogue no: **TA 3370**

JOY
Tracks: / Joy.
7" Single: Released Mar '83, on Epic, by CBS Records. Deleted '85. Catalogue no: **EPC A 3145**

JOY (OLD GOLD)
Tracks: / Joy / Grace.
12" Single: Released Jul '88, on Old Gold, by Old Gold Records. Catalogue no: **OG 4070**

WHEN YOU BELIEVE IN LOVE
Tracks: / When you believe / Funk on.
7" Single: Released Jul '82, on Epic, by CBS Records. Deleted Jul '87. Catalogue no: **A 2602**

Band of Angels

ACCEPT MY INVITATION
Tracks: / Accept my invitation.
7" Single: Released Oct '83, on Soul Supply, by Soul Supply Records. Catalogue no: **7SS 101**
12" Single: Released Oct '83, on Soul Supply, by Soul Supply Records. Catalogue no: **12SS 101**

Band Of Glory

DOWN BY THE SEA
Tracks: / Down by the sea / Sweet sweet lover.
7" Single: Released Jul '82, on V-Tone, Catalogue no: **VTONE 008**

Band of Gold

IN LOVE AGAIN (MEDLEY)
Tracks: / In love again (medley).
7" Single: Released Jan '85, on RCA, by BMG Records (UK). Catalogue no: **RCA 469**
12" Single: Released Jan '85, on RCA, by BMG Records (UK). Catalogue no: **RCAT 469**

LOVE SONGS ARE BACK AGAIN (SINGLE)
Tracks: / Love songs are back again.
7" Single: Released Jul '84, on RCA, by BMG Records (UK). Deleted '87. Catalogue no: **RCA 428**

THIS IS OUR TIME
Tracks: / This is our time.
7" Single: Released Jun '85, on RCA, by BMG Records (UK). Catalogue no: **PB 40161**
12" Single: Released Jun '85, on RCA, by BMG Records (UK). Catalogue no: **PT 40162**

Band Of Holy Joy

EVENING WORLD
Tracks: / Evening world.
12" Single: Released Nov '89, on Rough Trade, by Rough Trade Records. Catalogue no: **RTT 233**

HAD A MOTHER WHO WAS PROUD
Tracks: / Had a mother who was proud.
12" Single: Released Oct '85, on Flim Flam, Catalogue no: **HARP 1T**

ROSEMARY SMITH
Tracks: / Rosemary Smith.
7" Single: Released Jan '88, on Flim Flam, Catalogue no: **HARP 6**
12" Single: Released Jan '88, on Flim Flam, Catalogue no: **HARP 6T**

TACTLESS
Tracks: / Tactless.
7" Single: Released Oct '88, on Rough Trade, by Rough Trade Records. Catalogue no: **RT 223**
12" Single: Released Oct '88, on Rough Trade, by Rough Trade Records. Catalogue no: **RTT 223**

WHO SNATCHED THE BABY
Tracks: / Who snatched the baby.
7" Single: Released Oct '86, on Flim Flam, Catalogue no: **HARP 4**
12" Single: Released Oct '86, on Flim Flam, Catalogue no: **HARP 4T**

Band of Outsiders

I WISH I WAS YOUR KID
Tracks: / I wish I was your kid.
12" Single: Released Sep '85, on Flicknife, by Flicknife Records. Catalogue no: **FLST 030**

Band Of The Black

DANCE OF THE CUCKOOS
Tracks: / Dance of the cuckoos.
7" Single: Released Dec '75, on Spark, by Spark Records. Deleted '78. Catalogue no: **SRL 1135**

PAPA'S GOT A BRAND NEW BAGPIPE
Tracks: / Papa's got a brand new bagpipe.
12" Single: Released Oct '83, on Sunny, by Sunny Records. Catalogue no: **12 BAG 1**
7" Single: Released Oct '83, on Sunny, by Sunny Records. Catalogue no: **BAG 1**

SANDS OF TIME
Tracks: / Sands of time / Dream of peace.
7" Single: Released Oct '82, on Sunny, by Sunny Records. Catalogue no: **EON 104**

SCOTCH ON THE ROCKS
Tracks: / Scotch on the rocks / Dance of the cuckoos.
7" Single: Released May '84, on RK, by RK Records. Deleted '86. Catalogue no: **RK 1040**

SCOTCH ON THE ROCKS (SINGLE)
Tracks: / Scotch on the rocks.
7" Single: Released Aug '75, on Spark, by Spark Records. Deleted '78. Catalogue no: **SRL 1128VIVA SCOTLAND**
Tracks: / Viva Scotland / Marching on tarten.
7" Single: Released Apr '82, on RK, by RK Records. Deleted '84. Catalogue no: **RK 1038**

Banda Banda

BANDA BANDA
Tracks: / Banda banda.
7" Single: Released May '89, on Divas Records, Catalogue no: **DIVAS 002**

Banda Black Rio

MISS CHERYL
Tracks: / Miss Cheryl / Nelissa / Subindo o morro / Amor natural.
7" Single: Released Dec '80, on RCA, by BMG Records (UK). Deleted Dec '95. Catalogue no: **PB 9637**
12" Single: Released Jan '81, on RCA, by BMG Records (UK). Deleted Jan '84. Catalogue no: **PC 9637**

Bandana

HOME COOKIN'
Tracks: / Home cookin' / Nothing can change this love.
7" Single: Released Sep '81, on Dakota, Deleted '84. Catalogue no: **DAK 1**
12" Single: Released Sep '81, on Dakota, Deleted '84. Catalogue no: **12 DAK 1**

SENORITA (HOLIDAY GIRL)
Tracks: / Senorita (holiday girl) / Wish you were here.
7" Single: Released Jun '86, on Tembo, by Tembo Records. Catalogue no: **TML 116**

Bandera

CRUSIN' DOWN
Tracks: / Crusin' down (On 7" only) / Crusin' down (Spanish version) (On 7" only) / Crusin' down (club mix) (On 12" only) / Crusin' down (bonus mix) (On 12" only) / Crusin' down (7" edit) (On 12" only) / Crusin' down (dub version) (On 12" only).
7" Single: Released Aug '89, on Island, by Island Records. Catalogue no: **IS 434**
12" Single: Released Aug '89, on Island, by Island Records. Catalogue no: **12 IS 434**

Bandez, Annie

AS I LIE IN YOUR ARMS
Tracks: / As I lie in your arms / Down by the station.
12" Single: Released 10 Oct '87, on One Little Indian, by One Little Indian Records. Catalogue no: **12TP 6**

Bandoo, Rolin

EXCLUSIVE LOVE
Tracks: / Exclusive love.
12" Single: Released Oct '89, on R.H.B., Catalogue no: **RHB 002T**

Bandy, Moe

Biographical details: Bandy, Moe The honky-tonk country singer was born in 1944 in Meridian, Mississippi. His grandfather had worked on the railroad with Jimmie Rodgers. Moe had a TV series with his own band in San Antonio, Texas; he went solo in 1972 and his national USA country hits began in 1974 with *I Just Started Hatin' Cheatin' Songs Today': for a while he specialised in cheatin' songs, including Honky Tonk Amnesia, It Was Always So Easy To Find An Unhappy Woman* and *Doesn't Anybody Make Love At Home Anymore*. Following an appearance with Joe Stampley at Wembley in London they formed a duo; Moe & Joe have had hit albums and singles and have always been popular in the UK.

WHERE'S THE DRESS?
Tracks: / Where's the dress / Wild life sanctuary.
7" Single: Released Aug '84, on CBS, by CBS Records. Catalogue no: **A 4641**

Bandzi

ZIG ZAG
Tracks: / Zig zag / Solid security.
7" Single: Released Dec '82, on Flipdisc, Catalogue no: **OOPS 11**

Bandzilla

DON'T TOUCH THAT DIAL
Tracks: / Don't touch that dial / Blue movies.
7" Single: Released May '87, on Rainbow, by Rainbow Records. Catalogue no: **RBR 14**

Bane, Honey

BABY LOVE
Tracks: / Baby love / Mass production.
7" Single: Released Apr '81, on Zonophone, by EMI Records. Deleted '84. Catalogue no: **Z 19**

DIZZY DREAMERS
Tracks: / Dizzy dreamers / Ongoing situation.
7" Single: Released Feb '83, on Zonophone, by EMI Records. Catalogue no: **Z 36**

I WISH I COULD BE ME
Tracks: / I wish I could be me / Childhood prince.
7" Single: Released Jun '82, on Zonophone, by EMI Records. Deleted Jun '85. Catalogue no: **Z 32**

The Bangles - In Your Room (Released on CBS)

12" Single: Released Jun '82, on Zonophone, by EMI Records. Deleted Jun '85. Catalogue no: **12Z 32**

JIMMY (LISTEN TO ME)
Tracks: / Jimmy (listen to me) / Negative exposure.
7" Single: Released May '81, on Zonophone, by EMI Records. Deleted May '84. Catalogue no: **Z 23**

TURN ME ON TURN ME OFF
Tracks: / Turn me on turn me off / In dreams / Negative exposure / Ain't nobody's business.
7" Single: Released Jan '81, on Zonophone, by EMI Records. Deleted '84. Catalogue no: **Z 15**

YOU CAN BE YOU
Tracks: / You can be you.
7" Single: Released Oct '81, on Crass, by Crass Records. Catalogue no: **521 984/1**

Bang

YOU'RE THE ONE
Tracks: / You're the one / Don't burn down the bridge.
CD 5": Released Apr '89, on RCA, by BMG Records (UK). Catalogue no: **PD 42716**
7" Single: Released Apr '89, on RCA, by BMG Records (UK). Catalogue no: **PB 42717**
7" Single: Released Mar '89, on RCA, by BMG Records (UK). Catalogue no: **PB 42715**
7" Single: Released May '89, on RCA, by BMG Records (UK). Catalogue no: **PB 42719**
12" Single: Released Apr '89, on RCA, by BMG Records (UK). Catalogue no: **PT 42720**
12" Single: Released Mar '89, on RCA, by BMG Records (UK). Catalogue no: **PT 42716**

Bang Gang

NICE 'N' SLEAZY
Tracks: / Nice 'n' sleazy.
7" Single: Released Oct '88, on Product Inc., Catalogue no: **EZEE 1**
12" Single: Released Oct '88, on Product Inc., Catalogue no: **EZEE 1T**

Bang Orchestra

SAMPLE THAT
Tracks: / Sample that (short house mix).
7" Single: Released Oct '86, on Geffen, by Geffen Records (USA). Deleted Jun '87. Catalogue no: **GEF 8**
12" Single: Released Oct '86, on Geffen, by Geffen Records (USA). Deleted Jun '87. Catalogue no: **GEF 8T**

Bang The Party

BANG BANG YOU'RE MINE
Tracks: / Bang bang you're mine.
12" Single: Released Jul '89, on Warriors, Catalogue no: **WAF 010**

GLAD ALL OVER
Tracks: / Glad all over.
12" Single: Released 19 Sep '87, on Kool Kat, by Kool Kat Records. Catalogue no: **WDT 100**

YOUR BODY
Tracks: / Your body.
12" Single: Released Jul '88, on Warriors Dance, by Warriors Dance Records. Catalogue no: **WAF 004**

Banger, Ed

KINNEL TOMMY
Tracks: / Kinnel Tommy.
7" Single: Released Sep '83, on Rabid, by Rabid Records. Catalogue no: **TOSH 106**

Bangles

Biographical details: Bangles, The The all-girl pop group formed in Los Angeles in 1981 consists of Susanna Hoffs and Vicki Peterson, guitars with Debbi Peterson on drums and Michael Steele on bass; all sing. They are skilled players of mainstream post-beatle pop; the answer to the question 'Will They Do Anything New' was apparently answered by their bubblegummish hit *Walk Like An Egyptian*, an inconsequential bit of fluff. (Donald Clarke 23 August 1988).

BE WITH YOU
Tracks: / Be with you / Let it go / In your room (extended remix).
CD 5": Released 12 Jun '89, on CBS, by CBS Records. Deleted Oct '89. Catalogue no: **BANGS D6**
CD 5": Released May '89, on CBS, by CBS Records. Deleted Oct '89. Catalogue no: **BANGS C6**
7" Pic: Released 5 Jun '89, on CBS, by CBS Records. Deleted Oct '89. Catalogue no: **BANGSP 6**
7" Single: Released May '89, on CBS, by CBS Records. Deleted Oct '89. Catalogue no: **BANGS 6**
12" Single: Released May '89, on CBS, by CBS Records. Deleted Oct '89. Catalogue no: **BANGS T6**

ETERNAL FLAME (See adjacent panel)
Tracks: / Eternal flame / What I meant to say / Walk like an Egyptian (12" dance mix) (on 12" only) / Bangles (hit mix) (On BANGS Q5 only.).
CD 5": Released 30 Jan '89, on CBS, by CBS Records. Deleted Oct '89. Catalogue no: **BANGS C5**
7" Single: Released 23 Jan '89, on CBS, by CBS Records. Deleted Oct '89. Catalogue no: **BANGS 5**
12" Single: Released 23 Jan '89, on CBS, by CBS Records. Deleted Oct '89. Catalogue no: **BANGS T5**
12" Single: Released 30 Jan '89, on CBS, by CBS Records. Deleted 10 Jul '89. Catalogue no: **BANGS Q5**

FOLLOWING
Tracks: / Following.
7" Single: Released Apr '87, on CBS, by CBS Records. Catalogue no: **BANGS Q2**

GOING DOWN TO LIVERPOOL
Tracks: / Going down to Liverpool / Let it go.
7" Single: Released Jun '85, on CBS, by CBS Records. Catalogue no: **A 7255**
12" Single: Released Jun '85, on CBS, by CBS Records. Catalogue no: **TA 7255**

HAZY SHADE OF WINTER
Tracks: / Hazy shade of winter (remix) / She's lost you.
CD 5": Released Feb '88, on CBS, by CBS Records. Deleted Jan '89. Catalogue no: **BANGS C3**
7" Pic: Released Feb '88, on Def Jam, Deleted Aug '88. Catalogue no: **BANGS P3**
7" Single: Released Feb '88, on Def Jam, Deleted Aug '88. Catalogue no: **BANGS 3**
7" Single: Released 1 Feb '88, on CBS, by CBS Records. Deleted Jun '88. Catalogue no: **BANGS Q3**
12" Single: Released Feb '88, on Def Jam, Deleted Aug '88. Catalogue no: **BANGS T3**

HERO TAKES A FALL
Tracks: / Hero takes a fall / Where were you when I needed you / Real world / I'm in line / How is the air up there.
7" Single: Released Jan '85, on CBS, by CBS Records. Deleted '87. Catalogue no: **A 4527**

IF SHE KNEW WHAT SHE WANTS
Tracks: / If she knew what she wants / Angels don't fall in love / Hero takes a fall (Extra track on double pack only) / James (Extra track on double pack only).
7" Set: Released May '86, on CBS, by CBS Records. Deleted '86. Catalogue no: **DA 7062**
7" Single: Released May '86, on CBS, by CBS Records. Deleted '86. Catalogue no: **A 7062**
12" Single: Released May '86, on CBS, by CBS Records. Catalogue no: **TA 7062**

I'LL SET YOU FREE
Tracks: / I'll set you free / Watching the sky.
CD 5": Released Sep '89, on CBS, by CBS Records. Catalogue no: **BANGS C7**
7" Single: Released Sep '89, on CBS, by CBS Records. Catalogue no: **BANGS 7**
12" Single: Released Sep '89, on CBS, by CBS Records. Catalogue no: **BANGS T7**

IN YOUR ROOM (See panel above)
Tracks: / In your room / Bell jar / Hazy shade of winter (remix) (Only on 12" & CD single.).
CD 5": Released Oct '88, on CBS, by CBS Records. Deleted 17 Apr '89. Catalogue no: **BANGS C4**
12" Pic: Released Oct '88, on CBS, by CBS Records. Deleted 17 Apr '89. Catalogue no: **BANGS P4**
7" Single: Released Nov '88, on CBS, by CBS Records. Deleted 10 Jul '89. Catalogue no: **BANGS Q4**
7" Single: Released Oct '88, on CBS, by CBS Records. Deleted 17 Apr '89. Catalogue no: **BANGS 4**
12" Single: Released 21 Nov '88, on CBS, by CBS Records. Deleted 10 Jul '89. Catalogue no: **BANGS R4**
12" Single: Released Oct '88, on CBS, by CBS Records. Deleted 17 Apr '89. Catalogue no: **BANGS T4**

MANIC MONDAY
Tracks: / Manic Monday / In a different light / Going down to Liverpool (Extra track on 12" only) / Dover beach (Extra track on 12" only).
7" Single: Released Nov '85, on CBS, by CBS Records. Catalogue no: **QA 6796**
7" Single: Released Nov '85, on CBS, by CBS Records. Catalogue no: **A 6796**
12" Single: Released Nov '85, on CBS, by CBS Records. Catalogue no: **TX 6796**

WALK LIKE AN EGYPTIAN
Tracks: / Walk like an Egyptian / Not like you.
7" Single: Released Sep '86, on CBS, by CBS Records. Catalogue no: **650071 7**

WALKING DOWN YOUR STREET
Tracks: / Return post.
7" Single: Released Dec '86, on CBS, by CBS Records. Catalogue no: **BANGS 1**
12" Single: Released Nov '86, on CBS, by CBS Records. Catalogue no: **BANG G1**

Banjax

FISHING SONG, THE
Tracks: / Fishing song, The / You, you, you.
7" Single: Released Jun '82, on EMI, by EMI Records. Deleted '85. Catalogue no: **EMI 5286**

Bank Robbers

JENNY
Tracks: / Jenny.
7" Single: Released May '83, on Good Vibration, by Good Vibrations Records. Catalogue no: **TUBE 1**

Bank Statement

THROWBACK
Tracks: / Throwback / Thursday 12th / This is love.
CD 5": Released 24 Jul '89, on Virgin, by Virgin Records. Catalogue no: **VSCD 1200**
7" Single: Released 24 Jul '89, on Virgin, by Virgin Records. Catalogue no: **VS 1200**
12" Single: Released 24 Jul '89, on Virgin, by Virgin Records. Catalogue no: **VST 1200**

Banks, Bessie

GO NOW
Tracks: / Go now / It sounds like my baby.
Note: An original Tiger recording. Arranged by Gerry Sherman. Produced by Jerry Leiber & Mike Stoller. This release C 1987 Charly Records Ltd.
7" Single: Released May '87, on Charly, by Charly Records. Deleted May '87. Catalogue no: **CYZ 7120**

Banks, Bosca

BAM BAM BOLERO
Tracks: / Bam bam bolero / Bam bam bolero (part 2).
12" Single: Released Aug '83, on Roke, Catalogue no: **ROK 12-21**

Banks, Donald

STATUS QUO
Tracks: / Status quo.
7" Single: Released Oct '85, on 4th & Broadway, by Island Records. Deleted '87. Catalogue no: **BRW 36**
12" Single: Released Oct '85, on 4th & Broadway, by Island Records. Deleted '87. Catalogue no: **12 BRW 36**

Banks, Tony

Biographical details: Tony Banks is one third of the legendary British rock group Genesis. He plays keyboards and has the lowest public profile of the trio. While in between band projects, he recorded his first solo album "A Curious Feeling" in 1979. Less

The Bangles - Eternal Flame (Released on CBS)

accessible than Genisis records, this keyboards-centred work could only manage a five-week chart run, peaking No. 21.
In 1983 Banks issued two simultaneous albums - /'The Fugitive"D plus an LP of music from the film /'The Wicked Lady"D. (Bob MacDonald)..

FOR A WHILE
Tracks: / For a while / Curious feeling.
7" Single: Released May '80, on Charisma, by Virgin Records. Deleted May '83. Catalogue no: **CB 365**

SHORT CUT TO SOMEWHERE
Tracks: / Short cut to somewhere / Smilin' Jack Casey / K2 (12" only).
7" Single: Released Oct '86, on Charisma, by Virgin Records. Catalogue no: **CB 426**
12" Single: Released Oct '86, on Charisma, by Virgin Records. Catalogue no: **CB 426-12**

WICKED LADY
Tracks: / Wicked lady.
7" Single: Released May '83, on Atlantic, by WEA Records. Catalogue no: **A 9825**

Banna Man

SOUND BOY STYLE
Tracks: / Sound boy style.
7" Single: Released May '89, on Progressive. Catalogue no: **UNKNOWN**

Banna Spar

CHANGES COMING
Tracks: / Changes coming.
7" Single: Released Sep '82, on Oraima, by Kingdom Records. Catalogue no: **SPTX/CUS1429**

Banned

LITTLE GIRL
Tracks: / Little girl.
7" Single: Released Dec '77, on Harvest (1), by EMI Records. Deleted '80. Catalogue no: **HAR 5145**

Banned From U.N.C.L.E.

CLOCKWORK ORANGE
Tracks: / Clockwork orange, A.
7" Single: Released Jun '85, on AMF, Catalogue no: **AMF 1**

Banton, George

FAITHFUL AND TRUE
Tracks: / Faithful and true / My girl.
12" Single: Released Oct '85, on Londisc, by Londisc Records. Catalogue no: **LDR 035**

SOCA MEDLEY
Tracks: / Soca medley.
12" Single: Released Oct '84, on Londisc, by Londisc Records. Catalogue no: **LDR 032**

Banton, Pato

ABSOLUTE PERFECTION
Tracks: / Absolute perfection.
7" Single: Released Sep '87, on Greensleeves, by Greensleeves Records. Catalogue no: **GRE 220**
12" Single: Released Sep '87, on Greensleeves, by Greensleeves Records. Catalogue no: **GRED 220**

BAD MAN & WOMAN
Tracks: / Bad man & woman / Bad man & woman (dub mix).
12" Single: Released Oct '86, on Movin' Music. Catalogue no: **MMD 002**

BOSS, THE
Tracks: / Boss, The.
12" Single: Released Jul '85, on Fashion, by Fashion Records. Catalogue no: **FAD 027**

DOG IS A MAN'S BEST FRIEND, A
Tracks: / Dog is a man's best friend, A / Dog is a man's best friend, A (version).
12" Single: Released 13 Jun '87, on UK Bubblers, by Greensleeves Records. Catalogue no: **UKMC 25**

MASH UP THE TELLY
Tracks: / Mash up the telly.
12" Single: Released Sep '85, on UK Bubblers, by Greensleeves Records. Deleted '87. Catalogue no: **UKMC 8**

SECRET THUNDERBIRD DRINKER
Tracks: / Secret thunderbird drinker / Don't sniff coke.
12" Single: Released May '86, on UK Bubblers, by Greensleeves Records. Deleted '88. Catalogue no: **UKMC 12**

Bantu

ENGLAND TO HER SONGS
Tracks: / England to her songs.
7" Single: Released Aug '85, on Peninsula, by Prism Records. Catalogue no: **BANTU 4U**

VIEW OF JERUSALEM (EP)
Tracks: / View of Jerusalem.
7" Single: Released Aug '86, on Wounded Knee, by Waterfall Records. Catalogue no: **WKN 1**

Banyon, John O'

LOVE YOU LIKE I NEVER LOVED BEFORE
Tracks: / Love you like i never loved before / She's not for you.
7" Single: Released May '81, on Elektra, by Elektra Records (UK). Deleted May '86. Catalogue no: **K 12528**

Banzai

RUNAWAY
Tracks: / Runaway.
7" Single: Released Oct '81, on Groove PR, by Beggars Banquet Records. Catalogue no: **GP 105**
12" Single: Released Oct '81, on Groove PR, by Beggars Banquet Records. Catalogue no: **P 105T**

TOKYO NIGHTS
Tracks: / Tokyo nights / East west.
7" Single: Released Mar '82, on Stingray. Deleted '85. Catalogue no: **STZ 1**

Bappi Bappi, K

MOVIN' ON
Tracks: / Movin' on / Tell me.
7" Single: Released Jul '86, on B&L, Catalogue no: **KBL 001**
12" Single: Released Jul '86, on B&L, Catalogue no: **12KBL 001**

Baptiste, Denise

WEAK AT THE KNEES (PART 2)
Tracks: / Weak at the knees (part 2).
12" Single: Released Jul '83, on Gi Gi, Catalogue no: **GG 01**

Barb

I WANT MY MONEY BACK
Tracks: / I want my money back / Sugar cane.
7" Single: Released Dec '83, on Magnet, by WEA Records. Catalogue no: **BARB 10**
12" Single: Released Dec '83, on Magnet, by WEA Records. Catalogue no: **12 BARB 10**

TELL ME WHY
Tracks: / Tell me why / Sugar cane.
7" Single: Released Sep '83, on Magnet, by WEA Records. Catalogue no: **MAG 248**
12" Single: Released Sep '83, on Magnet, by WEA Records. Catalogue no: **12 MAG 248**

YEAH
Tracks: / Yeah / Camel's back.
7" Single: Released May '84, on Magnet, by WEA Records. Catalogue no: **BARB 11**
12" Single: Released May '84, on Magnet, by WEA Records. Catalogue no: **12 BARB 11**

Barb & Stroke

THESE BOOTS ARE MADE FOR WALKING
Tracks: / These boots are made for walking / Sorcery.
7" Single: Released Nov '81, on Balaclava, by Balaclava Records. Deleted Nov '84. Catalogue no: **HELME 2**

Barbary Coast

HEARTS ON FIRE (ROCK MIX)
Tracks: / Hearts on fire (rock mix).
7" Single: Released Apr '84, on MDE, by MDE Records. Catalogue no: **BCAJ 001**

Barber, Chris

Biographical details: Barber, Chris The trombonist and trad jazzband leader was born in Welwyn Garden City in 1930. He joined the Ken Colyer band and took it over in 1954. It was the first UK combo to appear on the Ed Sullivan TV show in the USA in 1959.
Their big transatlantic hit was *Petite Fleur*, a song by Sidney Bechet; ironically Barber did not play on it; it was a solo vehicle for clarinettist Monty Sunshine, who used a pretty vibrato similar to that of Bechet. Sunshine (born in 1928 in London) and Barber played in films including 'Look Back In Anger; Barber's various lineups remained popular with jazz fans, and he also recorded with Dr John (Mac Rebbenack)
(Donald Clarke 23 August 1988)
Born in Welwyn Garden City in 1930, Chris Barber formed his first band in 1949 with himself on trombone.
This was the instrument he was to make his own. His new 1954 band included Lonnie Donegan on guitar and banjo and became a regular fixture at Humphrey Lyttelton's club in Oxford Street. In early '56 he scored a Top 10 hit on both sides of the Atlantic without anyone really knowing - the Chris Barber Band included in their act a skiffle on washboard and it was this outfit who played on Donegan's *Rock Island line* single. Once this 45 had become a major success, Donegan left Barber to begin his own string of hits. Chris Barber's jazz band scored a smash single in their own right in 1959 with *Petite fleur*, reaching No. 3 in the UK and No. 5 in the US. They never returned to the Top 20 in either country, but instead rode the early Sixties jazz boom with a series of UK hit albums. After charting with three LPs in the Autumn of 1960, Barber teamed with clarinet star Acker Bilk in '61 for a couple of big selling duet albums. Even more successful was the triumvirate LP *Best of Ball, Barber and Bilk*, a No. 1 album in 1962. While ot having the sinlges sales of Ball and Bilk, Barber kept busy by developing his interest in the blues. A number of American blues artists toured Britain with Barber's band and he helped to organise an important blues festival. While playing a mean jazz trombone, Chris Barber was also a quietly influential figure on Britain's burgeoning rhythm and blues scene. (Bob MacDonald).

LONESOME
Tracks: / Lonesome.
7" Single: Released Oct '59, on Columbia, by EMI Records. Deleted '62. Catalogue no: **DB 4333**

MUSIC FROM THE LAND OF DREAMS (SINGLE)
Tracks: / Music from the land of dreams.
7" Single: Released Oct '85, on Sonet, by Sonet Records. Catalogue no: **SON 2293**

PETITE FLEUR (SINGLE)
Tracks: / Petite fleur.
7" Single: Released Feb '59, on Pye Jazz Today. Deleted '62. Catalogue no: **NJ 2026**

REVIVAL
Tracks: / Revival.
7" Single: Released Jan '62, on Columbia, by EMI Records. Deleted '65. Catalogue no: **SCD 2166**

Barber, Frank

DALLAS
Tracks: / Dallas / Knots Landing.
7" Single: Released Jan '80, on BBC, by BBC Records & Tapes. Deleted 31 Aug '88. Catalogue no: **RESL 87**

GLENN MILLER TODAY
Tracks: / Glenn Miller today / Trad disco medley.
12" Single: Released Aug '81, on PRT, by Castle Communications Records. Deleted Aug '84. Catalogue no: **12P 220**
7" Single: Released Aug '81, on PRT, by Castle Communications Records. Deleted Aug '84. Catalogue no: **7P 220**

GLENN MILLER TODAY (VOL 2)
Tracks: / Glenn Miller today (vol 2) / Count Basie medley.
12" Single: Released Jan '83, on PRT, by Castle Communications Records. Catalogue no: **12P 258**
7" Single: Released Jan '83, on PRT, by Castle Communications Records. Catalogue no: **7P 258**

Barbra & Neil

YOU DON'T BRING ME FLOWERS
Tracks: / You don't bring me flowers.
7" Single: Released Nov '78, on CBS, by CBS Records. Deleted '81. Catalogue no: **CBS 6803**

Barclay, Bill

AIN'T GONNA DRINK NO MORE
Tracks: / Ain't gonna drink no more / Passing show.
7" Single: Released May '81, on G & M, by G&M Tapes & Records. Deleted May '86. Catalogue no: **GMS 035**

I AIN'T GONNA DRINK ANYMORE
Tracks: / I ain't gonna drink anymore.
7" Single: Released May '81, on G & M, by G&M Tapes & Records. Catalogue no: **MS 035**

Barclay James Harvest

Biographical details:
Formed in Manchester in 1967, Barclay James Harvest -- Les Holroyd, John Lees, Mel Pritchard and Stewart Wolstenholme -- signed to a new label, Harvest, reportedly named after them.
Their debut self-titled LP was issued in 1970, followed by the critically-acclaimed Once Again album in 1971. Despite press praise the group could not crack the album chart until 1974's Barclay James Harvest Live, which reached No 40.
The band's combination of soft rock and orchestral classical music has always found more favour in Continental Europe than in their native Britain, particularly in West Germany, where they are major stars.
Their two mid-70's albums, Time Honoured Guests and Octoberon, continued the formula, to be followed in '77 by Gone To Earth, which contained the much-played Hymn. Barclay James Harvest continued to release albums with consistent regularity, all going down a storm in Germany and usually having very brief chart runs in Britain.
They have had three minor UK hit singles, Life Is For Living, Love On The Line and a live EP. In 1982 the quartet achieved their highest album placing -- No 15 -- with A Concert For The People (Berlin), an LP which best sums up their position and status among German rock fans. (Bob MacDonald, 1984.).

CAPRICORN
Tracks: / Capricorn / Berlin.
7" Single: Released May '80, on Polydor, by Polydor Ltd. Deleted May '85. Catalogue no: **POSP 140**

HE SAID LOVE
Tracks: / He said love / On the wings of love / Hymn (live) (Available on 12" only).
7" Single: Released Nov '86, on Polydor, by Polydor Ltd. Deleted Aug '87. Catalogue no: **POSP 834**
12" Single: Released Nov '86, on Polydor, by Polydor Ltd. Deleted Aug '87. Catalogue no: **POSPX 834**

JUST A DAY AWAY
Tracks: / Just a day away.
7" Pic: Released May '83, on Polydor, by Polydor Ltd. Catalogue no: **POPPZ 585**
7" Single: Released May '83, on Polydor, by Polydor Ltd. Catalogue no: **POSP 585**

LIFE IS FOR LIVING
Tracks: / Life is for living / Shades of B. Hill.
7" Single: Released Nov '80, on Polydor, by Polydor Ltd. Deleted '83. Catalogue no: **POSP 195**

LIVE EP
Tracks: / Rock and roll star / Medicine man (part 1) / Medicine man (part 2).
7" EP: Released Apr '77, on Polydor, by Polydor Ltd. Deleted '80. Catalogue no: **2229 198**

LOVE ON THE LINE
Tracks: / Love on the line / Alright get down boogie.
7" Single: Released Jan '80, on Polydor, by Polydor Ltd. Deleted '83. Catalogue no: **POSP 97**

Bardo

Biographical details:
Stephen Fischer and Sally-Ann Triplett followed the typical pattern of British Eurovision Song Contest entrants. They were formed in 1982, immediately before the Song for Europe heats on BBC TV as the vehicle for one of the chosen eight songs.
They were made to sound as much as possible like the previous year's contest winners Bucks Fizz. One Step Further reached No 2 on the charts and came seventh in the contest final: they never graced the charts again. Sally-Ann Triplett had known what to expect, however -- she had been through it all before as a member of Britain's 1980 nonentities Prima Donna
. (Bob MacDonald, 1984.).

HANG ON TO YOUR HEAT
Tracks: / Hang on to your heat / I'll write you a letter.
7" Single: Released Jan '83, on Epic, by CBS Records. Catalogue no: **EPC A 2903**

ONE STEP FURTHER
Tracks: / One step further / Lady of the night.
7" Single: Released Apr '82, on Epic, by CBS Records. Deleted '85. Catalogue no: **EPC A 2265**

TALKING OUT OF LINE
Tracks: / Talking out of line / Always thinking of you.
7" Single: Released Jun '82, on Epic, by CBS Records. Deleted Jun '85. Catalogue no: **EPCA 2497**

Bards

LITTLE SHIRT THAT MY MOTHER MADE FOR ME
Tracks: / Little shirt that my mother made for me / Planxty McGuire.
7" Single: Released Jul '81, on Polydor, by Polydor Ltd. Deleted '85. Catalogue no: **POSP 310**

Bare, Bobby

BETTER NOT LOOK DOWN
Tracks: / Better not look down / Wait until tomorrow.
7" Single: Released May '86, on EMI-America, by EMI Records. Catalogue no: **EA 217**

I'VE NEVER GONE TO BED WITH AN UGLY WOMAN
Tracks: / I've never gone to bed with an ugly woman / If that ain't love / Numbers / Bathroom tissue paper letter.
7" Single: Released May '81, on CBS, by CBS Records. Deleted May '85. Catalogue no: **A 1026**

NUMBERS
Tracks: / Numbers / When hippies get older.
7" Single: Released Mar '80, on CBS, by CBS Records. Deleted Mar '83. Catalogue no: **CBS 8245**

TEQUILA SHEILA
Tracks: / Tequila Sheila / Gotta get rid of this band (Available on 12" only.) / Call me the breeze / Sleep tight / Goodnight man (Available n 12" only.).
7" Single: Released Sep '81, on CBS, by CBS Records. Deleted Sep '84. Catalogue no: **A 1618**
12" Single: Released Sep '81, on CBS, by CBS Records. Deleted Sep '84. Catalogue no: **A13 1618**

Bare Essentials

REBEL TOUR
Tracks: / Rebel tour.
12" Single: Released Jul '83, on Sunburn, by Orbitone Records. Catalogue no: **SBD 30**

Barflies

LIVE AT THE MARQUEE
12" Single: Released Dec '87, on Barflies, by Barflies Records. Catalogue no: **FB 701 12**

THERE'S A FIRE
Tracks: / There's a fire.
7" Single: Released Sep '84, on Barflies, by Barflies Records. Catalogue no: **FB 401**

Barin Or Morbis

NEIGHBOURS
Tracks: / Neighbours.
12" Single: Released May '86, on Flim Flam, Catalogue no: **MORB 1T**

Bar-Kays

Biographical details: Ronnie Caldwell, Ben Cauley, Carl Cunningham, Phalin Jones and Jimmy King became famous in the mid-60's as the backing group to the great soul star Otis Redding, helping his live act to become one of the most acclaimed in the world. In 1967 they emerged from Redding's shadow to score their own hit, Soul Finger, a funky instrumental with the only vocals being a shout of "Soul finger!" Apart from doing well on the US rhythm-and-blues chart it was also a pop hit, reaching No 17 in America and No 33 in Britain. Tragically, Caldwell, Cunningham, Jones and King all died in the plane crash that killed Redding in December 1967. Some old friends and associates assembled a new Bar-Kays band in the mid-70's and scored another chart hit with Shake Your Rump To The Funk. But the series of albums which followed was merely adequate and failed to stand out from many other contemporary black groups. In 1984 the Bar-Kays had a major US black hit with Freakshow On The Dance Floor, suggesting that the Mark 2 version of the band had finally hit form. (Bob MacDonald, 1984.).

BOOGIE BODY LAND
Tracks: / Boogie body land / Running in and out of my life.
7" Single: Released Jan '81, on Mercury, by Phonogram Ltd. Deleted Jan '84. Catalogue no: **MER 56**
12" Single: Released Jan '81, on Mercury, by Phonogram Ltd. Deleted Jan '84. Catalogue no: **MERX 56**

NIGHTCRUISING
Tracks: / Nightcruising / Hit and run.
7" Single: Released Jan '82, on Mercury, by Phonogram Ltd. Deleted Jan '85. Catalogue no: **MER 89**
12" Single: Released Jan '82, on Mercury, by Phonogram Ltd. Deleted Jan '85. Catalogue no: **MERX 89**

SEXOMATIC
Tracks: / Sexomatic.
7" Single: Released Jan '85, on Club, by Phonogram Ltd. Deleted '88. Catalogue no: **JAB 10**

SEXOMATIC (OLD GOLD)
Tracks: / Sexomatic / Shake your rump to the funk.
12" Single: Released Oct '88, on Old Gold, by Old Gold Records. Catalogue no: **OG 4082**

SHAKE YOUR RUMP TO THE FUNK
Tracks: / Shake your rump to the funk.
7" Single: Released Jan '77, on Mercury, by Phonogram Ltd. Deleted '80. Catalogue no: **6167 417**

SOUL FINGER
Tracks: / Soul finger.
7" Single: Released Aug '67, on Stax, by Fantasy Inc (USA). Deleted '70. Catalogue no: **601 014**

Barker, Dave

COOL OFF WOMAN
Tracks: / Cool off woman / My conversation.
12" Single: Released May '85, on Striker Lee, Catalogue no: **BL 21**

CURIOUS
Tracks: / Curious.
12" Single: Released Apr '85, on Paradise, Catalogue no: **PDIS 510**

GET HIGH EVERYBODY
Tracks: / Get high everybody.
12" Single: Released Mar '85, on Striker Lee, Catalogue no: **BL 18**

PRISONER OF LOVE
Tracks: / Prisoner of love.
12" Single: Released Apr '84, on Sunsplash, by Sunsplash Records. Deleted '87. Catalogue no: **SNS 06**

TILL I KISS YOU
Tracks: / Till I kiss you.
12" Single: Released Mar '85, on Terminal, Catalogue no: **TM 17**

Barker, Les

NIGEL'S BLUES
Tracks: / Nigel's blues.
7" Single: Released Jun '84, on Mrs.Ackroyd, Catalogue no: **MRS 001**

Barker, Tim

LOOKING GOOD
Tracks: / Looking good.
7" Single: Released '80, on Keswick, by Loose Records. Catalogue no: **KES 001**

Barking Light

LONG GOOD FRIDAY, THE (THEME FROM)
Tracks: / Long good Friday, The (theme from).
7" Pic: Released 1 Dec '88, on Woof, Deleted Aug '89. Catalogue no: **WOOFP 2**

LONG MARCH (THEME FROM)
Tracks: / Long March, Theme from / March on.
7" Pic: Released May '89, on Total, Deleted Aug '89. Catalogue no: **WOOF P1**
7" Single: Released Jan '89, on Kennel, Deleted Aug '89. Catalogue no: **WOOF 1**

Barley Wine

THAT TRAIN
Tracks: / That train / Heavy manners.
7" Single: Released Sep '83, on Black Vinyl, Deleted '85. Catalogue no: **BV 78**

Barleycorn

LAKES OF COOLFIN, THE
Tracks: / Lakes of Coolfin, The.
7" Single: Released '88, on I&B, by I & B Records. Catalogue no: **DOS 158**

MAN YOU DON'T MEET EVERYDAY, A
Tracks: / Man you don't meet everyday, A.
7" Single: Released '88, on I&B, by I & B Records. Catalogue no: **DOS 164**

MEN BEHIND THE WIRE
Tracks: / Men behind the wire.
7" Single: Released '88, on Homespun (Ireland), by Outlet Records. Catalogue no: **HIS 27**

MY LAST FAREWELL
Tracks: / My last farewell.
7" Single: Released '88, on I&B, by I & B Records. Catalogue no: **DOS 193**

Barleypop

HOOKED ON SCOTCH
Tracks: / Hooked on scotch / Haggis song.
7" Single: Released Dec '81, on Mint, by Emerald Records. Deleted '88. Catalogue no: **CHEW 56**

Barleywine, Mr.

REGGAE MUSIC 1
Tracks: / Reggae music 1.
7" Single: Released Jan '85, on Top Dog, Deleted '86. Catalogue no: **TDR 001**

Barmy Army

SHARP AS A NEEDLE
Tracks: / Sharp as a needle / England 2 - Yugoslavia 0.
12" Single: Released 21 Nov '87, on On-U-Sound, by On-U-Sound Records. Catalogue no: **ONUDP 18**

Barnbrack

BELFAST (SINGLE)
Tracks: / Belfast.
7" Single: Released Jan '85, on Homespun (Ireland), by Outlet Records. Catalogue no: **HS 092**
12" Single: Released May '88, on Homespun (Ireland), by Outlet Records. Catalogue no: **HSC 092**

MICKEY MARLEY'S ROUNDABOUT
Tracks: / Mickey Marley's roundabout / Galway shawl / Slievenamon / Love is teasin'.
7" EP: Released Mar '84, on Homespun (Ireland), by Outlet Records. Catalogue no: **HS 075**

MY LOVELY IRISH ROSE
Tracks: / My lovely Irish rose / Irish rover, The / Goodbye Mick, goodbye Pat / Ma ma will you buy me a banana.
7" Single: Released Feb '87, on Homespun (Ireland), by Outlet Records. Catalogue no: **HS 115**

POSTMAN PAT
Tracks: / Postman Pat / Handyman song.
7" Single: Released Dec '84, on Homespun (Ireland), by Outlet Records. Catalogue no: **HS 091**

PUNCH & JUDY MAN
Tracks: / Punch and Judy man / Phil the fluter / Come back Paddy Reilly / Slattery's mounted fut.
7" Single: Released Mar '86, on Homespun (Ireland), by Outlet Records. Catalogue no: **HS 105**

WHEN I WAS A LAD
Tracks: / Old MacDonald had a farm / When I was a lad.
7" Single: Released Dec '86, on Homespun (Ireland), by Outlet Records. Catalogue no: **HS 113**

Barnes, Benny

YOU GOTTA PAY
Tracks: / You gotta pay / Be boppin' daddy.
7" Single: Released Jul '87, on Detour, by Detour Records. Catalogue no: **45-004**

Barnes, Cheryl

LOVE AND PASSION
Tracks: / Love and passion / Hello Mr W.A.M..
7" Single: Released May '80, on Polydor, by Polydor Ltd. Deleted May '83. Catalogue no: **POSP 124**
12" Single: Released May '80, on Polydor, by Polydor Ltd. Deleted May '83. Catalogue no: **POSPX 124**

Barnes, Dena

IF YOU EVER WALKED OUT OF MY LIFE
Tracks: / If you ever walked out of my life / Who am I?.
7" Single: Released Jun '80, on Grapevine (Northern Soul), by BMG Records (UK). Deleted '83. Catalogue no: **GRP 141**

Barnes, Henry

SCHOOL GIRLS Your mama won't like it
Tracks: / School girls.
7" Single: Released Jan '84, on Cougar (USA), by Cougar Records (USA). Catalogue no: **BC 500001**

Barnes, Jimmy

TOO MUCH AIN'T ENOUGH LOVE
Tracks: / Too much ain't enough love / Do or die / Working class man (12" only) / Resurrection shuffle (Available on 12" only).
7" Single: Released May '88, on Geffen, by Geffen Records (USA). Catalogue no: **GEF 38**
12" Single: Released May '88, on Geffen, by Geffen Records (USA). Catalogue no: **GEF 38T**

WORKING CLASS MAN
Tracks: / Working class man (remix) / Boys cry out for war.
7" Single: Released May '86, on Geffen, by Geffen Records (USA). Catalogue no: **GEF 3**
12" Single: Released May '86, on Geffen, by Geffen Records (USA). Catalogue no: **GEF 3T**

Barnes, J.J.

COMPETITION AIN'T NOTHING
Tracks: / Competition ain't nothing / Double cookin' / Bok to Bach.
7" Pic: Released Jul '84, on Inferno (1), by Inferno Records. Catalogue no: **PICBURN 7**
7" Single: Released May '84, on Inferno (1), by Inferno Records. Catalogue no: **BURN 7**

GUESS I'LL TRY IT AGAIN
Tracks: / Guess I'll try it again.
12" Single: Released Mar '85, on Inferno (1), by Inferno Records. Catalogue no: **12 BURN 15**

SWEET SHERRY
Tracks: / Sweet sherry.
7" Single: Released Dec '83, on Inferno (1), by Inferno Records. Catalogue no: **BURN 3**

Barnes, Richard

GO NORTH
Tracks: / Go North.
7" Single: Released Oct '70, on Philips, by Phonogram Ltd. Deleted '73. Catalogue no: **6006 039**

TAKE TO THE MOUNTAINS
Tracks: / Take to the mountains.
7" Single: Released May '70, on Philips, by Phonogram Ltd. Deleted '73. Catalogue no: **BF 1840**

Barnett, Al

IN MY DREAM
Tracks: / My life / In my dream.
12" Single: Released Nov '86, on Ade J., Catalogue no: **AJ 107**

Barnett, Henrietta

SHARE AND SHARE ALIKE
Tracks: / Share and share alike.
7" Single: Released Nov '82, on Page One, by Page One Records. Deleted Nov '85. Catalogue no: **POR 004**

Barnett, Ricky

YOU MAKE IT HAPPEN
Tracks: / You make it happen.
12" Single: Released Jun '83, on Hawkeye, by Hawkeye Records. Catalogue no: **HD 48**

Barnsley, Bill

BARNSLEY RAP
Tracks: / Barnsley rap / Dancing with Ronnie / Bosanova.
7" Single: Released May '81, on Ariola, by BMG Records (UK). Deleted May '84. Catalogue no: **NAG 1**
12" Single: Released May '81, on Ariola, by BMG Records (UK). Deleted May '84. Catalogue no: **NAGX 12 1**

Barone

SHAKE IT UP
Tracks: / Shake it up.
12" Single: Released '85, on Jungle Rhythm, Catalogue no: **SWET 4**

Barracudas

Biographical details: This British-American quartet -- David Buckley, Jeremy Gluck, Nicky Turner and Robin Wills -- formed in 1978 and changed their name to the Barracudas the following year. They gained a cult following with the single I Want My Woody Back.
The group specialised in California-style nostalgia, combining the summery surfing sound of the early 60's with the folk-rock style prominent later in that decade. This musical policy was best captured on their only chart single, Summer Fun, which reached No 37 in 1980: beginning with a tape of an American 60's commercial, it developed into an engaging Beach Boys/Jan & Dean/Byrds pastiche. The Barracudas released their first LP, Drop Out With The Barracudas, in 1981, but they were unable to break big -- nostalgia was a non-starter in an age when "futurist" was the key word.

HIS LAST SUMMER
Tracks: / His last summer / Barracuda waver / Surfers are back.
7" Single: Released Sep '80, on Zonophone, by EMI Records. Deleted Sep '83. Catalogue no: **Z8**

HOUSE OF KICKS
Tracks: / House of kicks.
12" Single: Released '83, on Flicknife, by Flicknife Records. Catalogue no: **FLEP 103**

I CAN'T PRETEND
Tracks: / I can't pretend / KGB.
7" Single: Released Jan '81, on Zonophone, by EMI Records. Deleted Jan '84. Catalogue no: **Z 17**

I WANT MY WOODY BACK
Tracks: / I want my Woody back / Subway surfin'.
7" Single: Released '79, on Cells, Catalogue no: **SELL OUT 1**

(I WISH IT COULD BE) 1965 AGAIN
Tracks: / (I wish it could be) 1965 again / Rendezvous.
7" Single: Released Nov '80, on Zonophone, by EMI Records. Deleted Nov '83. Catalogue no: **Z 11**

INSIDE MINE
Tracks: / Inside mine / Hour of degradation.
7" Single: Released '82, on Flicknife, by Flicknife Records. Catalogue no: **FLS 207**

STOLEN HEART
Tracks: / Stolen heart.
7" Single: Released '84, on Closer (France), Catalogue no: **CL 7 15**
12" Single: Released '84, on Closer (France), Catalogue no: **CL 1215**

SUMMER FUN
Tracks: / Summer fun / Chevy baby.
7" Single: Released Aug '80, on EMI, by EMI Records. Deleted '83. Catalogue no: **Z 5**

THEY SAY WE'VE CHANGED
Tracks: / They say we've changed / Laughing at you.
7" Single: Released '84, on Closer (France), Catalogue no: **CL 06**

Barratt, Ray

CAN'T TAKE IT ANY LONGER
Tracks: / Can't take it any longer
12" Single: Released Nov '88 on TR. Catalogue no: **TR 036.**

VARIETY
Tracks: / Variety.
12" Single: Released '88, on Jetstar, by

Jetstar Records. Catalogue no: **LSD 07**

WALK AWAY
Tracks: / Walk away.
12" Single: Released Feb '89 on Clouds. Catalogue no: **CLSD 007**

Barrax, Andrew

JUST CAN'T SEEM TO FORGET
Tracks: / Just can't seem to forget (instrumental) / Just can't seem to forget / Just can't seem to forget (vocal edit).
12" Single: Released Apr '86, on Expansion, Catalogue no: **EXPAND 2**

Barrell, Roland

LOVE BOAT
Tracks: / Love boat / Sitting on a hillside.
12" Single: Released '84, on Gamble, Catalogue no: **GAD 05**

Barrett, Anne

STAY
Tracks: / Stay.
7" Single: Released '84, on Loose, by Loose Records. Catalogue no: **LSE 14**

Barrett, John Paul

MOVE IT BETTER
Tracks: / Move it better / Move it better (instrumental).
CD 5": Released May '89, on Radical, by Radical Records. Catalogue no: **CDRAD 2**
7" Single: Released May '89, on Radical, by Radical Records. Catalogue no: **RADC 2**
12" Single: Released May '89, on Radical, by Radical Records. Catalogue no: **RADICAL 2**

NEVER GIVIN' UP ON YOU
Tracks: / Never givin' up on you.
7" Single: Released Dec '87, on Westside, by Westside Records. Catalogue no: **WSR 2**
12" Single: Released Dec '87, on Westside, by Westside Records. Catalogue no: **WSRT 2**

SHOULD'VE KNOWN BETTER
Tracks: / Should've known better.
7" Single: Released Oct '88, on Westside, by Westside Records. Catalogue no: **WSR 10**
12" Single: Released Oct '88, on Westside, by Westside Records. Catalogue no: **WSRT 10**

Barrett, Marcia

YOU
Tracks: / You / I'm lonely.
7" Single: Released Apr '81, on Atlantic, by WEA Records. Deleted Apr '84. Catalogue no: **K 11578**

Barrett, Syd

Biographical details: Syd Barrett, from Cambridge, was a founder member of Pink Floyd and dominated the group's early records. He wrote Arnold Layne and See Emily Play, the Floyd's two hit singles, and his childlike but sinister imagery and classy lead guitar were the foremost ingredients in their first LP, Piper At The Gates Of Dawn. However, Barrett's drug problems and unpredictable behaviour forced him to quit the group in early 1968.
Two years later he released a solo double set called The Madcap Laughs, only reaching No 40 on the chart. Far more basic than the psychedelic extravagence of Pink Floyd, this album featured backing from Floyders David Gilmour and Richard Wright.
Following this, Syd Barrett was rarely heard of again but his name is fondly remembered by the ageing hippie generation. (Bob MacDonald, 1984.)
Born Roger Barrett in 1946 in Cambridge, the singer/songwriter was a founder member of Pink Floyd, writing 10 of 11 songs on their debut album *Piper At The Gates of Dawn* in 1967; he left in April of 1968, an early casualty of too much recreational substances. His whimsical eclecticism was entirely absent from the later Floyd; his two solo albums are still highly prized by fans.
(Donald Clarke 23 August 1988)i.

PEEL SESSIONS:SYD BARRETT
CD 5": Released May '88, on Strange Fruit, by Strange Fruit Records. Catalogue no: **SFPSCD 043**
12" Single: Released Jan '88, on Strange Fruit, by Strange Fruit Records. Catalogue no: **SFPS 043**

WHERE IS THE MADCAP SYD?
Tracks: / Where is the madcap Syd?.
Special: Released Feb '89, on Stampa Alternative (Italy), Catalogue no: **SCONC 006**

Barrett, Wild Willie

HITCHHIKER & THE PUNK
Tracks: / Hitchhiker and the punk.
7" Single: Released '85, on Strike Back, by Strike Back Records. Catalogue no: **SBR 6**

I'M IN LOVE AGAIN
Tracks: / I'm in love again / What you gonna do about it.
7" Single: Released Oct '81, on Black Eye, Deleted Oct '84. Catalogue no: **DARK 6**

OLD JOE CLARK
Tracks: / Old Joe Clark / Rabbit in Boston.
7" Single: Released '83, on Carrere, Catalogue no: **CAR 266**
12" Single: Released '83, on Carrere, Catalogue no: **CART 266**

TALES FROM THE RAJ
Tracks: / Tales from the Raj.
7" Single: Released '81, on Black Eyes, Catalogue no: **DARK 4**

WE'VE GOTTA GET OUT OF THIS PLACE
Tracks: / We've gotta get out of this place.
7" Single: Released '81, on Black Eyes, Catalogue no: **DARK 3**

WRAPPING ON A MOUNTAIN
Tracks: / Wrapping on a mountain / Side sounding.
7" Single: Released '83, on Carrere, Catalogue no: **CAR 281**

Barrie, J.J

Biographical details: Canadian J.J. Barrie is a true one-hit wonder in the UK -- one chart-topper and nothing else, ever.
Tammy Wynette had hit big in 1975 with Stand By Your Man and D.I.V.O.R.C.E. so, in 1976, Barrie figured that a remake of another Wynette country hit might chart in Britain.
He recorded a husky-voiced version of No Charge, a saga of a parent-child discussion containing more sugar than a Tate and Lyle refinery. Billy Connolly, the Scottish comedian who had sent up D.I.V.O.R.C.E., wasted no time in hitting the Top Thirty with his rendition called No Chance. J.J. Barrie has released numerous singles since his one week of No 1 fame, but none have surfaced in the charts.
(Bob MacDonald, 1984.).

BUENOS DIAS SENORITA
Tracks: / Buenos dias senorita / Borsche boogie.
7" Single: Released '82, on Monarch, by Monarch Records. Catalogue no: **MON 031**

CHRISTMAS
Tracks: / Christmas / Sssscrooge xmas.
7" Single: Released '81, on Monarch, by Monarch Records. Catalogue no: **MON 028**

FORTY AND FADING
Tracks: / Forty and fading.
7" Single: Released '84, on Magic (1), by Submarine Records. Catalogue no: **MAGIC 11**

IF I COULD ONLY LOVE YOU ONCE MORE
Tracks: / If I could only love you once more.
7" Single: Released '83, on Magic (1), by Submarine Records. Catalogue no: **MAGIC 5**

I'M JUST FALLING IN LOVE AGAIN
Tracks: / I'm just falling in love again / Who told the band to pack.
7" Single: Released '82, on Monarch, by Monarch Records. Catalogue no: **MON 029**

MY SON (SINGLE)
Tracks: / My son.
7" Single: Released '83, on Magic (1), by Submarine Records. Catalogue no: **MAGIC 9**

NO CHARGE
Tracks: / No charge / It's a crying shame.
7" Single: Released Mar '81, on Chopper, Deleted Mar '84. Catalogue no: **CHOP 104**
7" Single: Released Apr '76, on Power Exchange, Deleted '79. Catalogue no: **PX 209**
7" Single: Released '85, on Magic (1), by Submarine Records. Catalogue no: **MAGIC 100**

WHERE'S THE REASON
Tracks: / Where's the reason / Lucille.
7" Single: Released '83, on Magic (1), by Submarine Records. Catalogue no: **MAGIC 1**

WHILE THE FEELINGS GOOD
Tracks: / While the feelings good.
7" Single: Released '84, on Starblend, by Starblend Records. Catalogue no: **JJB 1**

YOU CAN'T WIN 'EM
Tracks: / You can't win 'em all / Together.
7" Single: Released Jan '80, on RCA, by BMG Records (UK). Deleted Jan '85. Catalogue no: **PB 5222**

YOU CAN'T WIN 'EM ALL (SINGLE)
Tracks: / You can't win 'em all / It's only a game.
7" Single: Released Nov '80, on MCA, by MCA Records. Deleted Nov '83. Catalogue no: **MCA 658**

Barrie, Ken

Biographical details: British singer Barrie released his Postman Pat theme in the summer of 1982. It has been a children's favourite ever since and is thus a slow but steady seller. Its highest charted place was No 44 but it hovered around the bottom end of the Top Seventy-Five for many weeks and can reappear at any time, particularly at Christmas.
(Bob MacDonald, 1984)..

LAZY
Tracks: / Lazy.
7" Single: Released '84, on Go Ahead, by Go Ahead Records. Catalogue no: **GA 120**

POSTMAN PAT
Tracks: / Postman Pat / Handy man song.
7" Single: Released Jul '82, on Post Music, Deleted '85. Catalogue no: **PP 001**

Barrington, Hugo

QUICK POPULAR
Tracks: / Quick popular.
12" Single: Released Feb '89, on Jammy's, Catalogue no: **VPRD 398**

Barron Knights

Biographical details:
Musical comedy group the Barron Knights -- Barron Anthony, Butch Baker, Dave Ballinger, Duke D'Mond and Peanuts Langford -- are a British institution.
They first hit the charts in 1964 with Call Up The Groups, a medley of parodies of recent hits which did just as well as the songs that inspired it, peaking at No 3.
The successful formula was repeated on two further Top Tenners, Pop Go The Workers and Merry Gentle Pops. The Knights toured the cabaret circuits for a decade before, to the surprise of many, becoming one of the few acts to make a return from that arena to the charts.
Live In Trouble showed that their style had not changed during the intervening years -- it was another Call Up The Groups-type medley and peaked at No 7 in the autumn of 1977.
A selection of 1978's hits found themselves on A Taste Of Aggro, the Knights' Christmas smash which reached No 3. Further annual medley singles met with less success, though 1980's Never Mind The Presents did manage to hit the Top Twenty.
The group have had three three chart albums, the first, Night Gallery ('78), being most successful and peaking at No 15 with 13 weeks on the list.
Their LPs contain full-length parodies as well as the usual quickies chopped into medley form. The Barron Knights are still firm favourites in cabaret where their brand of satire -- aimed at readers of the Sun rather than those of Private Eye -- really belongs.
(Bob MacDonald, 1984.)
A UK comedy/vocal quintet formed in 1960. The original lineup hasn't changed last time we looked: Duke D'Mond, vocals; Peter Langford, guitar; Butch Baker, drums; Barron Anthony Osmond, bass; Dave Ballinger, drums. Formed in Leighton Buzzard, Bedfordshire as a straight pop group, they toured with the Beatles, Rolling Stones, etc; they found greater audience response with humour and their vocal talent allowed passable irrevent imitations of the big names.
Their first hit *Call Up The Groups*, no.3 UK in 1964) parodied the Beatles, the Dave Clark Five and Freddie and the Dreamers. When the novelty wore off they were ideally suited to the cabaret circuit.
(Donald Clarke 23 August 1988).

AN OLYMPIC RECORD
Tracks: / Olympic record, An.
7" Single: Released Oct '68, on Columbia, by EMI Records. Deleted '71. Catalogue no: **DB 8485**

BLACKBOARD JUMBLE
Tracks: / Blackboard jumble / Gobbledegook.
7" Single: Released Dec '81, on CBS, by CBS Records. Deleted '84. Catalogue no: **A 17945**

BUFFALO BILL'S LAST SCRATCH
Tracks: / Buffalo Bill's last scratch.
7" Single: Released '83, on Epic, by CBS Records. Catalogue no: **EPC A 3208**
12" Single: Released '83, on Epic, by CBS Records. Catalogue no: **EPC A 13 3208**

CALL UP THE GROUPS
Tracks: / Call up the groups.
7" Single: Released Jul '64, on Columbia, by EMI Records. Deleted '67. Catalogue no: **DB 7317**

CHURCHILL RAP,THE
Tracks: / Churchill rap, The / Loan ranger.
7" Single: Released '84, on Towerbell, Catalogue no: **TOW 54**
12" Single: Released '84, on Towerbell, Catalogue no: **12TOW 54**

COME TO THE DANCE
Tracks: / Come to the dance.
7" Single: Released Oct '64, on Columbia, by EMI Records. Deleted '67. Catalogue no: **DB 7375**

DU' WOT
Tracks: / Du' wot / Spaghetti Betty.
7" Single: Released Oct '82, on Epic, by CBS Records. Deleted Oct '85. Catalogue no: **EPC A2872**

FOOD FOR THOUGHT
Tracks: / Food for thought.
7" Single: Released Dec '79, on Epic, by CBS Records. Deleted '82. Catalogue no: **EPC 8011**

FULL CIRCLE
Tracks: / Full circle / Eye of the hurricane.
7" Single: Released '83, on CBS, by CBS Records. Catalogue no: **A 3892**

LIVE IN TROUBLE (SINGLE)
Tracks: / Live in trouble.
7" Single: Released Oct '77, on Epic, by CBS Records. Deleted '80. Catalogue no: **EPC 5752**

MERRY GENTLE POPS
Tracks: / Merry gentle pops.
7" Single: Released Dec '65, on Columbia, by EMI Records. Deleted '68. Catalogue no: **DB 7780**

MR BRONSKI MEETS MR EVANS
Tracks: / Mr. Bronski meets Mr. Evans.
7" Single: Released '85, on Spartan, Catalogue no: **SP 123**

MR. RUBIK

The Barron Knights - Never Mind The Presents (Released on Epic)

Tracks: / Mr. Rubik / Fads and changes.
7" Single: Released Sep '81, on Epic, by CBS Records. Deleted Sep '84. Catalogue no: **EPC A1596**

NEVER MIND THE PRESENTS (See panel on previous page)
Tracks: / Another brick in the wall (part two) / Day trip to Bangor / Sparrow, The / Swindon cowboy.
7" EP: Released Dec '80, on Epic, by CBS Records. Deleted '83. Catalogue no: **EPC 9070**

POP GO THE WORKERS
Tracks: / Pop go the workers.
7" Single: Released Mar '65, on Columbia, by EMI Records. Deleted '68. Catalogue no: **DB 7525**

R-R-ROCK ME FATHER CHRISTMAS
Tracks: / R-r-rock me Father Christmas / Big bad band (big bad John).
7" Single: Released Nov '86, on WEA, by WEA Records. Deleted Jan '88. Catalogue no: **YZ 92**
12" Single: Released Nov '86, on WEA, by WEA Records. Deleted Jan '88. Catalogue no: **YZ 92T**

SIT SONG, THE
Tracks: / Sit song, The / Barron's fun 40.
7" Single: Released Oct '80, on Epic, by CBS Records. Deleted '83. Catalogue no: **EPC 8994**

TASTE OF AGGRO, A
Tracks: / Taste of aggro, A.
7" Single: Released Dec '78, on Epic, by CBS Records. Catalogue no: **EPC 6829**

UNDER NEW MANAGEMENT
Tracks: / Under new management.
7" Single: Released Dec '66, on Columbia, by EMI Records. Catalogue no: **DB 8071**

Barrone, Nick

BLUES IN THE CITY
Tracks: / Blues in the city.
7" Single: Released Aug '87, on Blue August, Catalogue no: **BLUE 2**
12" Single: Released Aug '87, on Blue August, Catalogue no: **BLUE 1**

Barrow Boys

WALLY RAP
Tracks: / Wally rap.
12" Single: Released '84, on Creole, by Creole Records. Catalogue no: **CRT 71**
7" Single: Released '84, on Creole, by Creole Records. Catalogue no: **CR 71**

Barry, Claudja

CAN'T YOU HEAR MY HEARTBEAT
Tracks: / Can't you hear my heartbeat.
7" Single: Released Apr '87, on Epic, by CBS Records. Deleted Nov '87. Catalogue no: **650445 7**
12" Single: Released Apr '87, on Epic, by CBS Records. Deleted Nov '87. Catalogue no: **650445 6**

DOWN & COUNTING
Tracks: / Down & counting.
7" Single: Released Oct '86, on Epic, by CBS Records. Catalogue no: **650047 7**
12" Single: Released Oct '86, on Epic, by CBS Records. Catalogue no: **350047-6**

(I DON'T KNOW IF YOU'RE) DEAD OR ALIVE
Tracks: / (I don't know if you're) dead or alive.
12" Single: Released Jun '88, on Blue Moon (1), by Magnum Music Group. Deleted '89. Catalogue no: **BLUM 1**
7" Single: Released Jun '88, on Blue Moon (1), by Magnum Music Group. Deleted '89. Catalogue no: **7 BLUM 1**

I WILL FOLLOW HIM
Tracks: / I will follow him / Work me over.
7" Single: Released '83, on Excaliber, by Red Bus Records. Deleted '88. Catalogue no: **EXC 528**
12" Single: Released '83, on Excaliber, by Red Bus Records. Deleted '88. Catalogue no: **EXCL 528**

IF I DO IT TO YOU
Tracks: / If i do it to you / Up all night.
7" Single: Released Feb '82, on Ensign, by Ensign Records. Deleted Feb '87. Catalogue no: **ENY 223**
12" Single: Released Feb '82, on Ensign, by Ensign Records. Deleted Feb '87. Catalogue no: **ENYT 223**

TRIPPIN' ON THE MOON
Tracks: / Trippin' on the Moon.
12" Single: Released '84, on Personal, by Personal Records. Catalogue no: **12 PER 103**
7" Single: Released '84, on Personal, by Personal Records. Catalogue no: **PERS 103**

Barry, D

CRAZY FOR YOUR LOVE
Tracks: / Crazy for your love.
12" Single: Released '85, on Viking (1), Catalogue no: **VK 005**

HERE I GO AGAIN
Tracks: / Still falling (class one crew) / Here I go again.
12" Single: Released Nov '86, on Class One, Catalogue no: **CO 001**

Barry, Harry

GOD BLESS YOU
Tracks: / God bless you / In winter.
7" Single: Released '82, on Coochly St., Deleted '88. Catalogue no: **MS 7**

Barry, Joe

I'M A FOOL TO CARE
Tracks: / I'm a fool to care.
7" Single: Released Aug '61, on Mercury (EMI), Deleted '64. Catalogue no: **AMT 1149**

Barry, John

Biographical details: Born John Barry Prendergast in York in 1933, this prominent arranger/producer formed a group, the John Barry Seven, in 1957.

Two years later he was instrumental in launching the career of Adam Faith, arranging his early hits and punctuating them with a distinctive pizzicato string sound that was much copied in the early 60's.

The same week that Faith scored his second No 1 with Poor Me, the John Barry Seven hit the charts for the first time in their own right. Hit And Miss, penned by Barry, reached No 10 in the spring of 1960.

Barry never got that high again but his singles continued to chart until the final week of '63 by which time the Seven had disbanded and the John Barry Orchestra was formed. Since then he has concentrated on film and TV scores and is best known for his work on James Bond movies.

At the beginning of '72 he made a one-off return to the Top Twenty with his theme for the television series The Persuaders, at the same time scoring with his first chart album, also called The Persuaders.
(Bob MacDonald, 1984.).

BEAT FOR BEATNIKS
Tracks: / Beat for beatniks.
7" Single: Released Apr '60, on Columbia, by EMI Records. Deleted '63. Catalogue no: **DB 4446**

BLACK STOCKINGS
Tracks: / Black stockings.
7" Single: Released Dec '60, on Columbia, by EMI Records. Deleted '63. Catalogue no: **DB 4554**

BLUEBERRY HILL (SINGLE)
Tracks: / Blueberry Hill.
7" Single: Released Aug '60, on Columbia, by EMI Records. Deleted '63. Catalogue no: **DB 4480**

CUTTY SARK
Tracks: / Cutty Sark.
7" Single: Released Apr '62, on Columbia, by EMI Records. Deleted '65. Catalogue no: **DB 4806**

FROM RUSSIA WITH LOVE
Tracks: / From Russia with love.
7" Single: Released Nov '63, on Ember (1), by Bulldog Records (UK). Deleted '66. Catalogue no: **S 181**

HIT AND MISS
Tracks: / Hit and miss.
7" Single: Released Mar '60, on Columbia, by EMI Records. Deleted '63. Catalogue no: **DB 4414**

JAMES BOND THEME
Tracks: / James Bond theme.
7" Single: Released Nov '62, on Columbia, by EMI Records. Deleted '65. Catalogue no: **DB 4898**

MAGNIFICENT SEVEN, THE
Tracks: / Magnificent seven, The.
7" Single: Released Mar '61, on Columbia, by EMI Records. Deleted '64. Catalogue no: **DB 4598**

MIDNIGHT COWBOY
Tracks: / Midnight cowboy.
7" Single: Released Sep '80, on United Artists, by EMI Records. Catalogue no: **UP 634**

NEVER LET GO
Tracks: / Never let go.
7" Single: Released Jul '60, on Columbia, by EMI Records. Deleted '63. Catalogue no: **DB 4480**

PERSUADERS, THE
Tracks: / Persuaders, The.
7" Single: Released Dec '71, on CBS, by CBS Records. Deleted '74. Catalogue no: **CBS 7469**

SOMEWHERE IN TIME
Tracks: / Somewhere in time / Rhapsody on a theme by Paganini.
7" Single: Released Aug '87, on MCA, by MCA Records. Catalogue no: **MCA 1195**

WALK DON'T RUN
Tracks: / Walk don't run.
7" Single: Released Sep '60, on Columbia, by EMI Records. Deleted '63. Catalogue no: **DB 4505**

Barry, Len

Biographical details: Born in Philadelphia, Len Barry was lead singer with the Dovells in the early 60's.

They had a string of hit dance records in the States, including two Top Three smashes, Bristol Stomp and You Can't Sit Down, but none of their records charted in Britain.

As a solo artist Barry triumphed at the end of '65 with 1-2-3, an international smash which reached No 2 in the US, No 3 in the UK. Roughly halfway between between the Beatles and the Motown sound, this record has since become a disco classic.

A second UK hit, Like A Baby, (No 10), fared slightly less well at home but his next 45, Somewhere, was nowhere in Britain and No 26 in America.

After this Barry's high tenor voice had to be content with entertaining on the cabaret circuit. (Bob MacDonald, 1984.) The USA soul singer with a high tenor voice was born Leonard Borrisoff in 1942 in Philadelia; he followed in the Philly teen idol tradition, his act inspired by James Brown; he had several hits in the '60s, then turned to a smoother cabaret style.
(Donald Clarke 23 August 1988).

1-2-3
Tracks: / 1.2.3..
7" Single: Released Nov '65, on Brunswick, by Decca Records. Deleted '68. Catalogue no: **05942**

1-2-3 (OLD GOLD)
Tracks: / 1-2-3 / Rescue me / Wade in the water.
CD 5": Released 30 May '89, on Old Gold, by Old Gold Records. Catalogue no: **OG 6144**
7" Single: Released Jun '82, on Old Gold, by Old Gold Records. Catalogue no: **OG 9214**

LIKE A BABY
Tracks: / Like a baby.
7" Single: Released Jan '66, on Brunswick, by Decca Records. Deleted '69. Catalogue no: **05949**

Barry, Paul

COMPLICATED
Tracks: / Complicated (dance mix) / Complicated (club mix) / U thrill me / Complicated.
7" Single: Released Sep '87, on MCA, by MCA Records. Catalogue no: **COM 1**
12" Single: Released Aug '87, on MCA, by MCA Records. Catalogue no: **COMT 1**

Barrymore, Michael

DO THE CRAB
Tracks: / Do the crab.
7" Single: Released 20 Jun '87, on Candy (USA), by Jeree Records (USA). Catalogue no: **CDY 101**

Barth, Bobby

DON'T COME TO ME
Tracks: / Don't come to me / Sara.
7" Single: Released May '86, on Atco, by Atlantic Recording Corp.(USA). Catalogue no: **B 9549**

Bartlett & Lamb

CHRISTMAS TIME AGAIN
Tracks: / Christmas time again / Hopeless case.
7" Single: Released Dec '81, on Solid Gold (1), by Creole Records. Deleted Dec '84. Catalogue no: **SGR 113**

Bartley, Chris

I FOUND A GOODIE
Tracks: / I found a goodie.
12" Single: Released '88, on UNKNOWN, Catalogue no: **MIS 004**

Barton, Edward

BARBER BARBER CUT MY HAIR
Tracks: / Barber barber cut my hair.
12" Single: Released Nov '88, on Wooden, by Wooden Records. Catalogue no: **WOOD 005**

BARBER BARBER Z BEND
Tracks: / Barber barber cut my hair.
12" Single: Released Oct '88, on Wooden, by Wooden Records. Catalogue no: **WOOD 005**

BELLY BOX BROTHER GOB
Tracks: / Belly box brother gob.
12" Single: Released 14 Mar '88, on Wooden, by Wooden Records. Catalogue no: **WOOD 002**

ME & MINNIE
Tracks: / Me & Minnie / I've got no chicken but I got wooden chairs.
7" Single: Released Nov '86, on Wooden, by Wooden Records. Catalogue no: **WOOD 001**

Barton & Harry

MULCH
Tracks: / Mulch.
12" Single: Released Aug '84, on Fever, by Fever Records. Catalogue no: **FEV 1**

Bartram, Dave

BLACK ICE
Tracks: / Black ice / Excitement.
7" Single: Released Dec '82, on Utopia, by Utopia Records. Catalogue no: **UTO 2**

Bartz, Gary

MUSIC
Tracks: / Music / Give it your best shot.
7" Single: Released Jun '80, on Arista, by BMG Records (UK). Deleted Jun '83. Catalogue no: **ARIST 355**
12" Single: Released Jun '80, on Arista, by BMG Records (UK). Deleted Jun '83. Catalogue no: **ARIST 12355**

Bas Noir

I'M GLAD YOU CAME
Tracks: / I'm glad you came.
12" Single: Released 10 Jul '89, on Nu Groove, Catalogue no: **NG 017**
7" Single: Released 24 Jul '89, on 10 Records, by Virgin Records. Catalogue no: **TEN 282**
12" Single: Released Sep '89, on 10 Records, by Virgin Records. Catalogue no: **TENR 282**
12" Single: Released 24 Jul '89, on 10 Records, by Virgin Records. Catalogue no: **TENX 282**

MY LOVE IS MAGIC
Tracks: / My love is magic.
7" Single: Released Dec '88, on 10 Records, by Virgin Records. Catalogue no: **TEN 257**
7" Single: Released Oct '88, on Nu Groove (USA), Catalogue no: **NG 003**
12" Single: Released Dec '88, on 10 Records, by Virgin Records. Catalogue no: **TENX 257**

Base, Rob

GET ON THE DANCE FLOOR
Tracks: / Get on the dancefloor.
12" Single: Released Jan '89, on Supreme, by Supreme Records. Catalogue no: **SU PETX 139**
7" Single: Released Jan '89, on Supreme, by Supreme Records. Catalogue no: **SUPE 139**
12" Single: Released Jan '89, on Supreme, by Supreme Records. Catalogue no: **SUPET 139**

IT TAKES TWO
Tracks: / It takes two / It takes two (inst).
7" Single: Released Apr '88, on Citybeat, by Beggars Banquet Records. Catalogue no: **CBE 724**
7" Single: Released Apr '88, on Citybeat, by Beggars Banquet Records. Catalogue no: **CBX 1224**
12" Single: Released Apr '88, on Citybea[t], by Beggars Banquet Records. Catalogu[e] no: **CBE 1224**

JOY AND PAIN
Tracks: / Joy and pain / Check this out.
7" Single: Released Apr '89, on Supreme, by Supreme Records. Catalogue no: **SUP 143**
12" Single: Released Apr '89, on Supreme, by Supreme Records. Catalogue no: **WUPET 143**

Base Team

CHANGE OF HABIT
Tracks: / Change of habit / Change of hab[it] (melt down dub mix).
12" Single: Released Apr '87, on Hot Me[lt], by Hot Melt Records. Catalogue no: **12 T 010**

DANCE TO THE RHYTHM
Tracks: / Dance to the rhythm.
12" Single: Released Aug '88, on Hot Me[lt], by Hot Melt Records. Catalogue no: **12 TC**

16
7" Single: Released Aug '88, on Hot Melt, by Hot Melt Records. Catalogue no: **TCT 16**

Baseball Boys

NEVER TOLD LIES
Tracks: / Never told lies.
7" Single: Released Sep '83, on Radio, by Radio Records. Catalogue no: **RADIO 2**

Basement 5

LAST WHITE CHRISTMAS
Tracks: / Last white Christmas / Traffic dub / Paranoia claustrophobia (Only on 12" single.).
7" Single: Released Nov '80, on Island, by Island Records. Deleted '83. Catalogue no: **WIP 6654**
12" Single: Released Nov '80, on Island, by Island Records. Deleted '83. Catalogue no: **12WIP 6654**

SILICONE CHIP
Tracks: / Silicone chip / Chip butty.
7" Single: Released May '80, on Island, by Island Records. Deleted '83. Catalogue no: **WIP 6614**
10" single: Released May '80, on Island, by Island Records. Deleted '83. Catalogue no: **10WIP 6614**

Basement Boys

LOVE DON'T LIVE HERE NO MORE
Tracks: / Love don't live here no more / Love don't live here no more (Dub).
12" Single: Released 23 Apr '88, on Champion, by Champion Records. Catalogue no: **CHAMP 1274**
7" Single: Released 23 Apr '88, on Champion, by Champion Records. Catalogue no: **CHAMP 74**

Basia

NEW DAY FOR YOU
Tracks: / New day for you / Forgive and forget.
7" Single: Released Jun '87, on Portrait, by CBS Records. Deleted Nov '87. Catalogue no: **BASH 2**
12" Single: Released 13 Jun '87, on Portrait, by CBS Records. Catalogue no: **BASHT 2**

NEW DAY FOR YOU (TAKE 2)
Tracks: / New day for you / Prime time TV.
12" Single: Released Jul '87, on Portrait, by CBS Records. Catalogue no: **BASHQT 2**

PRIME TIME TV
Tracks: / Prime time TV / Freeze thaw / Freeze thaw (instrumental) / Prime time T.V. (extended mix) (on 12" version only.).
Note: * Extra tracks on 12" version only.
7" Single: Released Jul '86, on Portrait, by CBS Records. Catalogue no: **A 7276**
CD 5": Released Nov '87, on Epic, by CBS Records. Catalogue no: **CD BASH 3**
7" Single: Released Oct '87, on Epic, by CBS Records. Catalogue no: **BASH 3**
7" Single: Released Oct '87, on CBS, by CBS Records. Catalogue no: **BASH Q3**
12" Single: Released Oct '87, on CBS, by CBS Records. Catalogue no: **BASH T3**

PROMISES
Tracks: / Promises (French mix) / Give me that / Promises (ext. French mix)8 / From now on (band version) (Track on 12" and CD single.) / Astrud (CD single only).
Note: * tracks on 12" & CD single. + track on CD single.
7" Single: Released Jan '88, on Epic, by CBS Records. Deleted Aug '88. Catalogue no: **BASH 4**
CD 5": Released Jan '88, on Epic, by CBS Records. Deleted Jan '89. Catalogue no: **CD BASH 4**
10" single: Released Jan '88, on Epic, by CBS Records. Catalogue no: **BASH QT4**
7" Single: Released Jan '88, on Epic, by CBS Records. Deleted Jun '88. Catalogue no: **BASH G4**
12" Single: Released Jan '88, on Epic, by CBS Records. Deleted Aug '88. Catalogue no: **BASH T4**

RUN FOR COVER
Tracks: / Run for cover / From now on.
12" Single: Released Oct '86, on Portrait, by CBS Records. Deleted Aug '87. Catalogue no: **650158 6**
7" Single: Released Oct '86, on Portrait, by CBS Records. Deleted Aug '87. Catalogue no: **650158 7**

TIME AND TIDE (SINGLE)
Tracks: / Forgive and forget / How dare you / Time and tide (inst) / Time and tide.
7" Single: Released Feb '87, on Portrait, by CBS Records. Deleted Aug '87. Catalogue no: **BASH 1**
CD 5": Released Apr '88, on Epic, by CBS Records. Deleted Jan '89. Catalogue no: **CD BASH 5**
7" Single: Released Apr '88, on Epic, by CBS Records. Deleted Jan '89. Catalogue no: **BASH 5**
12" Single: Released Apr '88, on Epic, by CBS Records. Deleted Jan '89. Catalogue no: **BASH T5**

12" Single: Released Feb '87, on Portrait, by CBS Records. Catalogue no: **BASH 1T**

Basie, Count

Biographical details: Born William Basie in New Jersey in 1904, Count Basie learned to play the piano from his mother and then studied informally with famous pianist Fats Waller. When turning professional, he began as a pianist on the vaudeville circuit, then spent a year playing the instrument as a background to silent movies in a cinema. He then joined the Blue Devils, many of whose members went on to play in Basie's own ensemble. When the Blue Devils broke up, a large proportion of their players joined a band under the leadership of Bennie Moten. With Moten passing away in 1935, the nucleus of his band became the first Basie outfit. It was when this ensemble began recording in '37 that Basie became an enormous star in the jazz field. His band gained international recognition for its hard-swinging style and freewheeling solo playing. Throughout the Forties and Fifties, Count Basie consolidated on his reputation, always recruiting players of the highest musical calibre. Among his big band's most played numbers were *"Swingin' At The Daisy Chain"*, *"Every Tub"*, *"One O'Clock Jump"* and *"Jumpin' At The Woodside"*. He was still able to hit the US Top 30 at the start of the rock 'n' roll era, reaching No. 28 in early 1956 with *"April In Paris"*. In April 1960 he hit the UK albums Top 20 with *"Chairman Of The Board"* though most of his greatest triumphs had occured before the inception of the British charts. The Count Basie Orchestra continued its hard-driving swing aound for many more years, accompanied by the Count's spare piano style. After making a partial recovery from illness in 1980, he died in 1984 at the age of 79. (Bob MacDonald)..

CUTE
Tracks: / Cute / Li'l darlin'.
7" Single: Released Feb '81, on Vogue, by Vogue Records. Deleted Feb '84. Catalogue no: **7VJ 101**

Basil, Toni

Biographical details: When Toni Basil hit with *I*"Mickey"*D* in 1982, she was heavily made up to look like a new up-and -coming star. Her publicists did not seem particularly keen to point out that she cut her first record in 1966. In the intervening years she spent her time as a successful dancer and choreographer. She appeared as a dancer in the 1968 Monkees' movie *I*"Head"*D* and then, having taken small acting parts in *I*"Easy Rider*D*" and *I*"Five Easy Pieces*D*", choreographed and appeared in the 1973 film *I*"American Graffiti"*D*. Basil subsequently worked wtih David Bowie and Bette Midler. Always primarily interested in the visual side of the entertainment business, she became involved in the video boom of the early Eighties. The return to singing came about while making a videocassette called *I*"Word Of Mouth"*D* - this featured Basil performing a Nicky Chinn/Mike Chapman song called *I*"Mickey"*D*. The track was released as a single in the spring of '81 without success. Then the BBC showed *I*"Word Of Mouth"*D* on television, the record was repromoted, and went to No.2 almost a year after its original issue. However, Basil was not cut out for recording stardom. Although the *I*"Word Of Mouth"*D* album sold well, reaching No 15 on the LP chart, the next single *I*"Nobody"*D* could climb no higher than No. 52. Months later, in December '82, *I*"Mickey"*D* hit No.1 in the US. But Toni Basil could not follow it up in her native America, any more than she could in Britain. (Bob MacDonald)..

MICKEY
Tracks: / Mickey / Hanging around.
7" Single: Released Jan '82, on Radial Choice, by Virgin Records. Deleted May '88. Catalogue no: **TIC 4**

NOBODY
Tracks: / Nobody / Thief on the loose.
7" Single: Released May '82, on Radial Choice, by Virgin Records. Deleted '85. Catalogue no: **TIC 2**

TIME AFTER TIME
Tracks: / Time after time / You gotta problem.
7" Single: Released Sep '81, on Radial Choice, by Virgin Records. Deleted '84. Catalogue no: **TIC 612**

YOU GOTTA PROBLEM
Tracks: / You gotta problem / Time after time.
7" Single: Released Aug '81, on CBS, by CBS Records. Deleted Aug '84. Catalogue no: **TIC 6**

Basking Sharks

DIAMOND AGE
Tracks: / Diamond age.
7" Single: Released Dec '83, on Fin, by Posh Records. Catalogue no: **FIN 01**

THRILL OF THE GAME (EP)
Tracks: / Thrill of the game.
7" Single: Released Mar '83, on Small Run, Catalogue no: **SRRV 013**

Bass, Beres

GOOD TIMES
Tracks: / Good times.
12" Single: Released Jul '89, on Bass, by Champion Records. Catalogue no: **BAS 001**

Bass Boyze

LOST IN BASS
Tracks: / Lost in bass.
12" Single: Released Aug '89, on Kool Kat, by Kool Kat Records. Catalogue no: **KOOLT 505**
7" Single: Released Oct '89, on Kool Kat, by Kool Kat Records. Catalogue no: **KOOL 505**

Bass Dance

PICKAPOCKET
Tracks: / Picapocket.
12" Single: Released Nov '88, on Instinct, Catalogue no: **JANET 001 T**
7" Single: Released Nov '88, on Instinct, Catalogue no: **JANET 001**

Bass E, Count

SO FINE
Tracks: / So fine / So fine (Instrumental) / It's only a dream (Available on 12" only).
7" Single: Released Feb '89, on Citybeat, by Beggars Banquet Records. Catalogue no: **CBE 734**
12" Single: Released Feb '89, on Citybeat, by Beggars Banquet Records. Catalogue no: **CBE 1234**

Bass, Fontella

Biographical details: Bass, Fontella The soul singer with a beautiful, exciting voice was born in 1940 in St Louis, Missouri. A daughter of one of the Clara Ward Ssingers, she also plays keyboards. She was talent-spotted by Little Milton and signed with Chess/Checker; her biggest hits in the '60s included the duet *Don't Mess Up A Good Thing* with Bobby McClure and her own *Rescue Me*. Trombonist Joseph Bowie (now leads band Defunkt) was her music director; she married his brother Lester Bowie, a member of the Art Ensemble of Chicago: she is heard to excellent effect on their film soundtrack *Les Stances a Sophie* (1970) on the USA Nessa label. (Donald Clarke 23 August 1988).

RECOVERY
Tracks: / Recovery.
7" Single: Released Jan '66, on Chess, by Vogue Records. Deleted '69. Catalogue no: **CRS 8027**

RESCUE ME
Tracks: / Rescue me.
7" Single: Released Jul '85, on Chess (PRT), Deleted '88. Catalogue no: **CHES 4002**
7" Single: Released Dec '65, on Chess (PRT), Deleted '68. Catalogue no: **CRS 8023**

RESCUE ME (OLD GOLD)
Tracks: / Rescue me / Recovery / Soul of a man.
7" Single: Released Jul '84, on Old Gold, by Old Gold Records. Catalogue no: **OG 9412**
7" Single: Released Jan '89, on Old Gold, by Old Gold Records. Catalogue no: **OG 9844**

Bass Inc.

ROCK THE BOAT
Tracks: / Rock the boat.
12" Single: Released Nov '88, on Black Steel, Catalogue no: **BS 2**

Bass Invaders

HIJACK
Tracks: / Hijack (On 7" only) / Instrumental hijack (On all versions) / Hijack (tension extension) (On 12" only) / Hijack (Norman J. Cook remix) (On TENR 231 only).
7" Single: Released Jul '88, on 10 Records, by Virgin Records. Catalogue no: **TEN 231**
12" Single: Released '88, on 10 Records, by Virgin Records. Catalogue no: **TENR 231**
12" Single: Released Jul '88, on 10 Records, by Virgin Records. Catalogue no: **TENX 231**

Bass Line

WIMBLEDON BREAK POINT
Tracks: / Wimbledon break point.
7" Single: Released Jun '85, on BBC, by BBC Records & Tapes. Deleted Sep '87. Catalogue no: **RESL 172**

Bassa, Berris

COMING HOME
Tracks: / Coming home.
12" Single: Released Jan '88, on Sure Spin, Catalogue no: **SPN 003**

LOVING YOU
Tracks: / Loving you.
12" Single: Released Nov '88, on Sure Spin, Catalogue no: **SPN 008**

ROUND AND ROUND
Tracks: / Round and round.
12" Single: Released Sep '88, on Sure Spin, Catalogue no: **SPN 006**

Bassey, Shirley

Biographical details: Born in Cardiff in 1937, Shirley Bassey was the first singer to take Banana Boat Song into the British charts. Entering the list in February 1957, she was quickly beaten by Harry Belafonte but nonetheless managed to take her version to No 8. She had to wait until early '59 for her next big hit. An appearance on the TV show Sunday Night at the London Palladium helped to break As I Love You and it went to No 1 for four weeks, becoming the biggest hit of Bassey's entire career. Before the television spot, however, the disc had been in the process of flopping and a follow-up had already been released. She thus achieved two simultaneous Top Ten hits and the wide difference between the ballad As I Love You and the lightweight ditty Kiss Me, Honey Honey, Kiss Me was such that her versatility impressed both music business and public alike. After a brief lull, Bassey began a string of hits in 1960, including a double-sided chart-topper (her second and final No 1) with Reach For The Stars/Climb Every Mountain and five other Top Ten singles, As Long As He Needs Me, You'll Never Know, I'll Get By, What Now My Love? and I Who Have Nothing, all sung in the powerful, emotional voice that had become instantly recognisable. In 1965 she scored a one-off Top Ten hit in the States with the James Bond theme Goldfinger, which had peaked at No 21 at home. That success apart, she found record sales harder to achieve in the mid and late 60's due to the Beatles-led boom in new talent, and she relied instead on TV and cabaret work. Ironically, though, it was a Beatles' ballad, Something, that restored her to the Top Ten in 1970. Two further big hits followed in the early 70's but when Never Never Never fell off the chart in July '73 she never never never returned. Instead Bassey relied on albums, which she had always sold steadily, and her electric presence made stage and television performances a real draw. (Bob MacDonald, 1984.)
One of Britain's most popular singers, Shirley Bassey was born in Cardiff in 1937. Her first pro job at 16 was in the touring revue Memories of Al Jolson; discovered in 1955 by Jack Hylton, her top 10 UK hits began with *Banana Boat Song, Kiss Me Honey Honey Kiss Me* and her first no.1 *As I Love You* in 1959; other songs now associated with her include *As Long As He Needs Me* (from Oliver), *You'll Never Know, I'll Get By, Reach For The Stars* and *Climb Every Mountain* was a two sided hit. Not noted for subtlety, her real talent was on stage, with dynamic singing and extravagent gestures, her often backless, sideless and strapless gowns keeping audiences in suspense. A smash hit in New York's Persian Room in 1961 established her as a live act in the USA, but her only top 40 entry there was the top ten theme from the James Bond film 'Goldfinger' in 1965. Her later hits included *What Now My Love, I (Who Have Nothing), Big Spender,* (Cy Coleman-Dorothy Fields hit from show 'Sweet Charity'): the latter became a memorable body-grinding moment in her live act and was later found effective, playing very loud, in clearing pigeons from the runways at Liverpool airport. Her concert and cabaret appearances are still hot tickets. (Donald Clarke 23 August 1988).

ALL BY MYSELF (SINGLE)
Tracks: / All by myself / We don't cry out loud.
7" Single: Released Mar '82, on Applause, by Riva Records. Catalogue no: **APK 201**

AS I LOVE YOU (SINGLE)
Tracks: / As I love you.
7" Single: Released Dec '58, on Philips, by Phonogram Ltd. Deleted '61. Catalogue no: **PB 845**

AS LONG AS HE NEEDS ME (SINGLE)
Tracks: / As long as he needs me.
7" Single: Released Aug '60, on Columbia, by EMI Records. Deleted '63. Catalogue no: **DB 4499**

AVE MARIA
Tracks: / Ave Maria.
7" Single: Released Apr '62, on Columbia, by EMI Records. Deleted '65. Catalogue no: **DB 4816**

BANANA BOAT SONG
Tracks: / Banana boat song.
7" Single: Released Feb '57, on Philips, by Phonogram Ltd. Deleted '60. Catalogue no: **PB 668**

BIG SPENDER (SINGLE)
Tracks: / Big spender.
7" Single: Released Oct '67, on United Artists, by EMI Records. Deleted '70. Catalogue no: **UP 1192**

DIAMONDS ARE FOREVER
Tracks: / Diamonds are forever.
7" Single: Released Jan '72, on United Artists, by EMI Records. Deleted '75. Catalogue no: **UP 35263**

FAR AWAY
Tracks: / Far away.
7" Single: Released May '62, on Columbia, by EMI Records. Deleted '65. Catalogue no: **DB 4836**

FIRE DOWN BELOW
Tracks: / Fire down below.
7" Single: Released Aug '57, on Philips, by Phonogram Ltd. Deleted '60. Catalogue no: **PB 723**

FOOL ON THE HILL, THE
Tracks: / Fool on the hill, The.
7" Single: Released Jan '71, on United Artists, by EMI Records. Deleted '74. Catalogue no: **UP 35156**

FOR ALL WE KNOW
Tracks: / For all we know.
7" Single: Released Aug '71, on United Artists, by EMI Records. Deleted '74. Catalogue no: **UP 35267**

GOLDFINGER
Tracks: / Goldfinger.
7" Single: Released Oct '64, on Columbia, by EMI Records. Deleted '67. Catalogue no: **DB 7360**

GONE
Tracks: / Gone.
7" Single: Released Apr '64, on Columbia, by EMI Records. Deleted '67. Catalogue no: **DB 7248**

I AM WHAT I AM (SINGLE)
Tracks: / I am what I am.
7" Single: Released Nov '84, on Towerbell, Catalogue no: **TOW 62**

I (WHO HAVE NOTHING)
Tracks: / I (who have nothing).
7" Single: Released Sep '63, on Columbia, by EMI Records. Deleted '66. Catalogue no: **DB 7113**
7" Single: Released Jun '80, on H.M.V., by EMI Records. Deleted '83. Catalogue no: **POP 2009**

I'LL GET BY
Tracks: / I'll get by.
7" Single: Released Nov '61, on Columbia, by EMI Records. Deleted '64. Catalogue no: **DB 4737**

KISS ME HONEY HONEY KISS ME
Tracks: / Kiss me honey honey kiss me.
7" Single: Released Dec '58, on Philips, by Phonogram Ltd. Deleted '61. Catalogue no: **PB 860**

MEMORY
Tracks: / Memory / That's right / Remember / Thought I'd ring.
12" Single: Released Nov '84, on Meteor, by Magnum Music Group. Catalogue no: **MTEP 1001**

MY SPECIAL DREAM
Tracks: / My special dream.
7" Single: Released Jan '64, on Columbia, by EMI Records. Deleted '67. Catalogue no: **DB 7185**

NATALIE
Tracks: / Natalie.
7" Single: Released Oct '84, on Towerbell, Catalogue no: **TOW 60**

NEVER NEVER NEVER (SINGLE)
Tracks: / Never never never.
7" Single: Released Mar '73, on United Artists, by EMI Records. Deleted '76. Catalogue no: **UP 35490**

NO REGRETS
Tracks: / No regrets.
7" Single: Released May '65, on Columbia, by EMI Records. Deleted '68. Catalogue no: **DB 7535**

REACH FOR THE STARS
Tracks: / Reach for the stars / Climb every mountain.
7" Single: Released Jul '61, on Columbia, by EMI Records. Deleted '64. Catalogue no: **DB 4685**

SOMETHING (SINGLE)
Tracks: / Something.
7" Single: Released May '70, on United Artists, by EMI Records. Catalogue no: **UP 35125**

SOMETIMES
Tracks: / Sometimes / He needs me.
7" Single: Released Mar '84, on Towerbell, Catalogue no: **TOW 51**

THERE'S NO PLACE LIKE LONDON
Tracks: / There's no place like London / Born to sing.
7" Single: Released Jun '86, on Towerbell, Catalogue no: **TOW 90**

TO ALL THE MEN I'VE LOVED BEFORE
Tracks: / To all the men I've loved before.
7" Single: Released Mar '86, on Towerbell, Catalogue no: **TOW 87**

TONIGHT
Tracks: / Tonight.
7" Single: Released Feb '62, on Columbia, by EMI Records. Deleted '65. Catalogue no: **DB 4777**

WHAT KIND OF FOOL AM I
Tracks: / What kind of fool am I.
7" Single: Released Feb '63, on Columbia, by EMI Records. Deleted '66. Catalogue no: **DB 4974**

WHAT NOW MY LOVE (SINGLE)
Tracks: / What now my love.
7" Single: Released Aug '62, on Columbia, by EMI Records. Deleted '65. Catalogue no: **DB 4882**

(WHERE DO I BEGIN) LOVE STORY
Tracks: / (Where do I begin) love story.
7" Single: Released Mar '71, on United Artists, by EMI Records. Deleted '74. Catalogue no: **UP 35194**

WITH THESE HANDS
Tracks: / With these hands.
7" Single: Released Mar '60, on Columbia, by EMI Records. Deleted '63. Catalogue no: **DB 4421**

YOU YOU ROMEO
Tracks: / You you Romeo.
7" Single: Released Sep '57, on Philips, by Phonogram Ltd. Deleted '60. Catalogue no: **PB 723**

YOU'LL NEVER KNOW
Tracks: / You'll never know.
7" Single: Released May '61, on Columbia, by EMI Records. Deleted '64. Catalogue no: **DB 4643**

Bassix

PUMP UP THE MOTORTOWN
Tracks: / Pump up the motortown / You know how to love me.
12" Single: Released Mar '88, on Saturday, by Nightmare Records. Catalogue no: **SDY 2**
7" Single: Released Mar '88, on Saturday, by Nightmare Records. Catalogue no: **7SDY 2**

Bastard Kestrel

CHOR TRANCE
7" EP: Released 5 Mar '88, on Glum, Catalogue no: **GLUM 002**

RASERA
Tracks: / Rasera.
12" Single: Released Aug '88, on Wiiija, Catalogue no: **WIIIKIT 2**

Basti

NEW YORK SELTZER
Tracks: / New York seltzer.
12" Single: Released Feb '89, on Basti, Catalogue no: **BA 001**

Bastro

SHOOT ME A DEER
Tracks: / Shoot me a deer.
7" Single: Released Apr '89, on Homestead, Catalogue no: **HMS 137**

Basturd, Kaptain

DRINK TILL I DIE
Tracks: / Drink till I die / Eat your baby.
Note: "Kaptain Basturd and the Damnation Crew provide a varied selection of music, which cater only for the sick minded. Members include Kaptain Basturd, Astro Vomit, Fred Dread, Zac Wanquer. Also write plays, have their own magazine, Basturd Monthly and are in the middle of producing a XXX video."
7" Single: Released May '88, on Rana, Catalogue no: **PUKE 1**

Bata Drum

PASSION
Tracks: / Passion / This way.
7" Single: Released Feb '86, on Champion, by Champion Records. Catalogue no: **CHAMP 9**
12" Single: Released Feb '86, on Champion, by Champion Records. Catalogue no: **CHAMP 129**

Bataan, Joe

RAP-O, CLAP-O
Tracks: / Rap-o, clap-o / Rap-o, clap-o (part 2).
12" Single: Released Feb '80, on RCA, by BMG Records (UK). Deleted '83. Catalogue no: **RAP12-1**
7" Single: Released Feb '80, on RCA, by BMG Records (UK). Deleted '83. Catalogue no: **RAP 1**

SADIE
Tracks: / Sadie / Rap o clap o.
7" Single: Released Oct '80, on Salsoul, Deleted Oct '83. Catalogue no: **SAL 7**
12" Single: Released Oct '80, on Salsoul, Deleted Oct '83. Catalogue no: **SALT 7**

Batchelor, Johnny

MUMBLE
Tracks: / Mumble.
7" Single: Released Mar '84, on Northwood, by Northwood Records. Catalogue no: **NW 45 006**

Batchelor Pad

AN ALBUM OF JACKS
Tracks: / Album of jacks, An.
12" Single: Released 20 Jun '87, on Warhola Sound, by Warhola Sound Records. Catalogue no: **WST 003 MINS**

Bates, Martyn

LOOK OF LOVE, THE
Tracks: / Look of love, The / Adam and Eve and pinch me / May the third.
7" Single: Released Sep '87, on Cherry Red, by Cherry Red Records. Catalogue no: **CHERRY 99**
12" Single: Released Oct '87, on Cherry Red, by Cherry Red Records. Catalogue no: **12 CHERRY 99**

YOU SO SECRET
Tracks: / You so secret.
12" Single: Released Apr '89, on Integrity, Catalogue no: **IR 004**

Batfish Boys

BOMB SONG, THE
Tracks: / Bomb Song, The.
7" Single: Released Mar '87, on Batfish, Catalogue no: **USS 108**
12" Single: Released Mar '87, on Batfish Inc., Catalogue no: **USS 108 12**

CROCODILE TEARS (EP)
Tracks: / Crocodile tears.
12" Single: Released Apr '86, on Batfish, Catalogue no: **USS 105**

JUSTINE
Tracks: / Justine.
7" Single: Released Nov '86, on Batfish, Catalogue no: **USS 107**

SWAMP LIQUOR
Tracks: / Swamp liquor.
7" Single: Released Apr '85, on Batfish, Deleted '88. Catalogue no: **BF 102**
12" Single: Released Apr '85, on Batfish, Deleted '88. Catalogue no: **USS 101**

Batman

BATMAN THEME
Tracks: / Batman theme.
7" Single: Released May '88, on Bam Caruso, by Demon Records. Catalogue no: **NRIC 107**
12" Single: Released May '88, on Bam Caruso, by Demon Records. Catalogue no: **PABL 107**

BATMAN THEME, THE
Tracks: / Batman theme / Batman theme (inst).
12" Single: Released Mar '88, on WEA, by WEA Records. Catalogue no: **Y 7180T**

Bators, Stiv

HAVE LOVE WILL TRAVEL
Tracks: / Have love will travel.
12" Single: Released Aug '87, on Bomp (USA), Catalogue no: **BMP12136**

Bats

FOUR SONGS
Tracks: / Four songs.
12" Single: Released Jun '88, on Flying Nun, Catalogue no: **FNE 022**

MADE UP IN BLUE
Tracks: / Made up in blue.
12" Single: Released Oct '86, on Flying Nun, Catalogue no: **FNUK 1**

NORTH BY NORTH
Tracks: / North by north.
7" Single: Released Oct '88, on Flying Nun, Catalogue no: **FNE 22**

Batson, Slim

PUSH PUSH
Tracks: / Push push.
12" Single: Released 20 Mar '89, on Nu Edge, Catalogue no: **NE 00912**

RUNNING AWAY
Tracks: / Running away / Happy birthday.
12" Single: Released Nov '83, on Ruff Cut, Catalogue no: **RC 004**

Batson, Whitfield

I WILL ALWAYS LOVE YOU
Tracks: / I will always love you / One direction.
12" Single: Released Aug '83, on Ruff Cut, Catalogue no: **RC 002**

Batt, Mike

Biographical details: Mike Batt started life as staff songwriter at Liberty Records eventually progressing to A & R manager. Going freelance, he was responsible for various junk albums such as budget price orchestral renditions of Beatles songs. His big break came in the early Seventies when he wrote the theme song for the children's TV series 'The Wombles'. 'The Wombling Song' was a neat pop ditty, full of McCartney -type irresistable melody. As a single it reached no.4 on the chart 1974 with an impressive run of 23 weeks on the list. To promote the record, Batt assembled a phoney 'group' called the Wombles with him-self dressed as the programme's leading character Orinoco. He was at the forefront of a major marketing campaign which included not only the Womble records, but also Womble books, models, key rings, etc. When the Womble novelty was wearing off in 1975, Batt wrote the theme for the television show 'Seaside Special'. Under the title 'Summertime City', he released the song under his own name and reached no.4. Despite a series of quality singles and albums, which included some experimental orchestral arrangements, Mike Batt the artist never penetrated the charts again. Instead he became known as a writer, arranger and producer of hits for other acts. The biggest of these was 'Bright Eyes' the 'Watership Down', theme sung by Art Garfunkel. This was Britain's biggest selling single of 1979, becoming the last 45 for four years to log six weeks at no.1. In the Eighties Batt collaborated with fellow British writer Tim Rice on 'A Winter's Tale' a no.2 hit for David Essex, and then proceeded to write 'I Feel Like Buddy Holly' for Alvin Stardust. The latter epitomised Mike Batt's style - strong melodies with neat, uncluttered lyrics, twee but tasteful. Less successful was 1983's 'Zero Zero' full - length video/TV project, which attempted to put Batt back in the spotlight. His forte is behind the scenes work. (BM 84).

CHILDREN OF THE SKY
Tracks: / Children of the sky.
12" Single: Released Nov '86, on Starblend, by Starblend Records. Catalogue no: **12 ARK 1**

DRAGON DANCE
Tracks: / Dragon dance.
7" Single: Released Dec '84, on Chrysalis, by Chrysalis Records. Catalogue no: **CHS 2846**

LOSING YOUR WAY IN THE RAIN
Tracks: / Losing your way in the rain / Dead of night.
7" Single: Released Mar '80, on Epic, by CBS Records. Deleted Mar '83. Catalogue no: **EPC 8155**

LOVE MAKES YOU CRAZY
Tracks: / Love makes you crazy / Dance of the neurosurgeons.
7" Single: Released Jan '83, on Epic, by CBS Records. Catalogue no: **EPC A 3011**

SUMMERTIME CITY
Tracks: / Summertime city.
7" Single: Released Aug '75, on Epic, by CBS Records. Deleted '78. Catalogue no: **EPC 3460**

WHISPERING FOOLS
Tracks: / Whispering fools.
7" Single: Released Mar '83, on Epic, by CBS Records. Catalogue no: **EPC A 3256**

WINDS OF CHANGE
Tracks: / Winds of change / Echo foxtrot.
7" Single: Released Oct '80, on Epic, by CBS Records. Deleted Oct '83. Catalogue no: **EPC 9046**

Battiato, Alice

I TRENI DI TOZEUR
Tracks: / I treni di tozeur / Le biciclette de forli.
7" Single: Released May '84, on EMI, by EMI Records. Catalogue no: **EMI 5471**

Batwing Chaps

CRAVE
Tracks: / Crave.
7" Single: Released Jul '84, on Full Moon (1), Catalogue no: **FM 001**

Baughen, Simon

SCRATCH THAT LIGHTNING
Tracks: / Scratch that lightning.
7" Single: Released May '89, on Destiny, by Destiny Records. Catalogue no: **DES 3**

Bauhaus

Biographical details: Named after Germany's Bauhaus art movement of the Twenties, this Northampton quartet released their debut record in 1979, the 12-inch EP *"Bela Lugosi's Dead"*. A much praised session on the John Peel show helped to make it an underground classic, selling in small but steady quantities over months, even years. In November 1980 their first album *"In The Flat Field"* made a brief appearance on the national album chart, a toehold that was exploited the following year. 1981 brought the band their first two minor hit singles, *"Kick In The Eye"* and *"The Passion Of Lovers"* plus a Top 30 LP *"Mask"*. The former re-surfaced in '82 on a chart EP, to be followed by the *"Spirit"* single. Bauhaus were now cult favourites, but were criticised by the music press for being a dated rehash of both Bowie and punk. These complaints were brought to a head in late '82 when the group scored their only Top 20 single, a carbon copy cover version of Bowie's *"Ziggy Stardust"*. The

success of this record boosted their third album *"The Sky's Gone Out"* to No.4 on the LP charts. 1983 saw the group chalk up two more chart singles *"Lagartija Nick"* and *"She's In Parties"* plus the Top 20 album *"Burning From The Inside"*.
At the end of that year Bauhaus fell apart. Lead vocalist and main spokesman went on to form Dali's Car, a partnership with ex-Japan man Mick Karn.
(Bob MacDonald, 1984).

BELA LUGOSI'S DEAD
Tracks: / Bela Lugosi's dead / Boys / Dark entries (demo).
12" Single: Released Sep '86, on Small Wonder, by Small Wonder Records. Catalogue no: **TEENY 2**
CD 5": Released May '88, on Small Wonder, by Small Wonder Records. Catalogue no: **TEENY 2CD**
12" Pic: Released '87, on Small Wonder, by Small Wonder Records. Catalogue no: **TEENY 2P**

DARK ENTRIES
Tracks: / Dark entries / Terror couple kill colonel / Telegram Sam / Rosegarden funeral of sores / Crowds.
12" Single: Released Sep '83, on 4AD, by 4AD Records. Catalogue no: **BAD 312**

KICK IN THE EYE
Tracks: / Kick in the eye / Harry / Earwax / Searching for Satori.
12" Single: Released Feb '82, on Beggars Banquet, by Beggars Banquet Records. Catalogue no: **BEG 74T**
7" EP: Released Feb '82, on Beggars Banquet, by Beggars Banquet Records. Catalogue no: **BEG 74**

LARGARTIJA NICK
Tracks: / Largartija Nick / Paranoia paranoia.
12" Single: Released Jan '83, on Beggars Banquet, by Beggars Banquet Records. Catalogue no: **BEG 88T**
7" Single: Released '88, on Beggars Banquet, by Beggars Banquet Records. Catalogue no: **BEG 54**
7" Single: Released Jan '83, on Beggars Banquet, by Beggars Banquet Records. Catalogue no: **BEG 88**

PASSION OF LOVERS
Tracks: / Passion of lovers / 1-2-3-4.
7" Single: Released Jun '81, on Beggars Banquet, by Beggars Banquet Records. Catalogue no: **BEG 59**

PASSION OF LOVERS (12")
12" Single: Released Oct '83, on Beggars Banquet, by Beggars Banquet Records. Deleted Jan '88. Catalogue no: **BEG 100E**

SHE'S IN PARTIES
Tracks: / She's in parties.
12" Single: Released Apr '83, on Beggars Banquet, by Beggars Banquet Records. Catalogue no: **BEG 91T**
7" Pic: Released Aug '84, on Beggars Banquet, by Beggars Banquet Records. Deleted Jan '88. Catalogue no: **BEG 91P**
7" Single: Released Apr '83, on Beggars Banquet, by Beggars Banquet Records. Catalogue no: **BEG 91**

SINGLES 1981-1983, THE (EP)
7" EP: Released Oct '83, on Beggars Banquet, by Beggars Banquet Records. Deleted '86. Catalogue no: **BEG 100 E**

SPIRIT
Tracks: / Spirit / Terror couple kill Colonel.
7" Single: Released Jun '82, on Beggars Banquet, by Beggars Banquet Records. Catalogue no: **BEG 79**

TELEGRAM SAM
Tracks: / Telegram Sam / Rosegarden funeral of sores / Crowds.
7" Single: Released Oct '80, on 4AD, by 4AD Records. Catalogue no: **AD 17**
12" Single: Released Nov '80, on 4AD, by 4AD Records. Catalogue no: **AD 17T**

ZIGGY STARDUST
Tracks: / Ziggy Stardust.
12" Single: Released Oct '82, on Beggars Banquet, by Beggars Banquet Records. Catalogue no: **BEG 83T**
7" Single: Released Sep '82, on Beggars Banquet, by Beggars Banquet Records. Catalogue no: **BEG 83**

Baum, Bruce

MARTY FELDMAN'S EYES
Tracks: / Marty Feldman's eyes / Reflections.
7" Single: Released Jul '81, on Runaway. Deleted Jul '84. Catalogue no: **RUN 3**

Baumann, Peter

Biographical details: At 18, Berlin born Baumann joined the seminal German electronic group Tangerine Dream, with whom he recorded eight albums between 1971 and 1976 - including such landmark Lp's as *Phaedra, Stratosfear* and the soundtrack to the William Friedkin film *Sorcerer.*
Tangerine Dream toured Europe extensively and in 1977 conducted a spectacular series of American performances in conjunction with the laser light show *Laserium.*
Peter Baumann's first solo album, *Romance '76*, was released in the year of it's title. In 1977, he built his own 24 track Paragon Studio in Berlin, where he recorded a second solo LP, *Transhaemonic nights* and produced several records for other European artists.
But by 1979, Peter had decided to move to New York. In a large loft on Manhattan's East Side, Peter created an impressive combination of living and recording space, including another 24 track studio and self designed custom synthesiser unit, both built around a Newlett-Packard computer.
In this sophisticated environment, Peter recorded his debut Portrait album *Repeat repeat,* and applied similar computer processes to the making of a video of the title song. *Repeat repeat* met with widespread acclaim among lovers of progressive music. For his second album, Peter sought out a new, human and distinctively American element.
That someone was Eli Holland, a Brooklyn vocalist and lyricist whose talents won Peter over after a dozen other candidates had tried and failed.
The result of their collaboration is *Strangers in the night,* produced by Peter Baumann and ace engineer Robert Clifford.
(Arista Records, January 1984).

REPEAT REPEAT (SINGLE)
Tracks: / Repeat repeat.
7" Single: Released Sep '81, on Virgin, by Virgin Records. Deleted Sep '84. Catalogue no: **VS 446**

Baxon, Bill

SUPERMAN
Tracks: / Superman.
7" Single: Released May '81, on Roxon. Catalogue no: **ROX 813**

Baxter, Les

UNCHAINED MELODY
Tracks: / Unchained melody.
7" Single: Released May '55, on Capitol, by EMI Records. Deleted '58. Catalogue no: **CL 14257**

Baxter, Screamin' Tony

GET UP OFFA THAT THING
Tracks: / Get up offa that thing.
7" Single: Released Aug '85, on 4th & Broadway, by Island Records. Catalogue no: **BRW 9**
12" Single: Released Aug '85, on 4th & Broadway, by Island Records. Deleted Jul '87. Catalogue no: **12 BRW 9**

Bay City Rollers

Biographical details: Bay City Rollers This group was formed in Edinburgh in the late 1960s as the Saxons by brothers Derek and Alan Longmuir, on drums and bass respectively.
They were anipulated by danceband leaders Tom Paton into moneyspinning Uk teen idols, the undisputed kings of bubblegum in 1974-76, hyped into the UK top 10 by sending pictures to 10,000 addressess lifted from teen magazines, by which time the band (renamed by sticking a pin into a map of the USA) had coalesced with the Longmuirs, Stuart 'Woody' Wood and Eric Faulkner on guitars and vocalist Les McKeown, all from Edinburgh.
With some personnel changes they lasted until 1979, still popular in Japan and the USA, but they were so hot at their peak (and impossible to hate) that Nick Lowe cut a novelty cash-in *We Love The Roller.*
(Donald Clarke 23 August 1988).

ALL OF ME LOVES ALL OF YOU
Tracks: / All of me loves all of you.
7" Single: Released Oct '74, on Bell. Deleted '77. Catalogue no: **BELL 1382**

BYE BYE BABY
Tracks: / Bye bye baby.
7" Single: Released Mar '75, on Bell. Deleted '78. Catalogue no: **BELL 1409**

GIVE A LITTLE LOVE
Tracks: / Give a little love.
7" Single: Released Jul '75, on Bell, Deleted '78. Catalogue no: **BELL 1425**

I ONLY WANNA BE WITH YOU
Tracks: / I only wanna be with you.
7" Single: Released Sep '76, on Bell. Deleted '79. Catalogue no: **BELL 1493**

IT'S A GAME (SINGLE)
Tracks: / It's a game.
7" Single: Released May '77, on Bell. Deleted '80. Catalogue no: **ARISTA 108**

KEEP ON DANCING
Tracks: / Keep on dancing.
7" Single: Released Sep '71, on Bell. Deleted '74. Catalogue no: **BELL 1164**

LOVE ME LIKE I LOVE YOU
Tracks: / Love me like I love you.
7" Single: Released Apr '76, on Bell. Deleted '79. Catalogue no: **BELL 1477**

MONEY HONEY
Tracks: / Money honey.
7" Single: Released Nov '75, on Bell. Deleted '78. Catalogue no: **BELL 1461**

REMEMBER (SHA LA LA)
Tracks: / Remember (sha la la).
7" Single: Released Feb '74, on Bell. Deleted '77. Catalogue no: **BELL 1338**

SHANG A LANG
Tracks: / Shang a lang.
7" Single: Released Apr '74, on Bell. Deleted '77. Catalogue no: **BELL 1355**

SUMMERLOVE SENSATION
Tracks: / Summerlove sensation.
7" Single: Released Jul '74, on Bell, Deleted '77. Catalogue no: **BELL 1369**

YOU MADE ME BELIEVE IN MAGIC
Tracks: / You made me believe in magic.
7" Single: Released Jul '77, on Arista, by BMG Records (UK). Deleted '80. Catalogue no: **ARISTA 127**

Bayer Sager, Carole

Biographical details: The wife of the legendary composer and arranger Burt Bacharach, this American singer and songwriter is best known in Britain for her 1977 Top 10 hit ГYou're Moving Out Today"D a tongue-in-cheek account of the breaking up of a relationship.
Yet that jaunty number is quite untypical of her work..

STRONGER THAN BEFORE
Tracks: / Stronger than before / Somebody's been lying.

7" Single: Released Jul '81, on Epic, by CBS Records. Deleted '85. Catalogue no: **EPC A 1322**

Baylis, Chris

HEART OF STONE
Tracks: / Heart of stone / Closer to the heart.
7" Single: Released Oct '86, on VM, by VM Records. Catalogue no: **VM 5**
12" Single: Released Oct '86, on VM, by VM Records. Catalogue no: **VMT 5**

Bayou Brothers

SUNNY WEATHER
Tracks: / Sunny weather.
7" Single: Released Aug '83, on Dingle's, by Dingle's Records. Catalogue no: **SID 216**

YOU'VE GOT A WAY WITH YOU
Tracks: / You've got a way with you.
7" Single: Released Jun '82, on Dingle's, by Dingle's Records. Catalogue no: **SID 233**

Bazooka, Joe

DRIVE
Tracks: / Drive.
7" Single: Released Jul '89, on Play It Again Sam(Belgium), by Play It Again Sam (Belgium). Catalogue no: **BIAS 129**
CD 5": Released Jul '89, on Play It Again Sam(Belgium), by Play It Again Sam (Belgium). Catalogue no: **CDBIAS 129**
12" Single: Released Jul '89, on Play It Again Sam(Belgium), by Play It Again Sam (Belgium). Catalogue no: **12BIAS 129**

SUGAR ISLAND
Tracks: / Sugar island.
12" Single: Released Oct '88, on Play It Again Sam(Belgium), by Play It Again Sam (Belgium). Catalogue no: **BIAS 098**

Bazza Bawdy

RUN FOR YOUR LIFE
Tracks: / Run for your life.
7" Single: Released Oct '82, on Peak Records, by Peak Records. Catalogue no: **PKF 104**

BBC Radiophonic

DOCTOR WHO THEME
Tracks: / Doctor Who theme / Astronauts.
7" Single: Released Sep '80, on BBC, by BBC Records & Tapes. Deleted '83. Catalogue no: **RESL 80**

DOCTOR WHO, THEME FROM
Tracks: / Doctor Who, Theme from.
7" Single: Released Feb '64, on Decca, by Decca Records. Deleted '88. Catalogue no: **F 11837**

BBDC

KISS MY ASS
Tracks: / Kiss my ass.
7" Single: Released Oct '88, on Priority, by Priority Records. Catalogue no: **P 22**
12" Single: Released Oct '88, on Priority, by Priority Records. Deleted Sep '89. Catalogue no: **PX 22**

B-Biz-R

SUCKER FOR LOVE
Tracks: / Sucker for love.
12" Single: Released Aug '84, on Magnet, by WEA Records. Catalogue no: **12 SUCK 1**
7" Single: Released Aug '84, on Magnet, by WEA Records. Catalogue no: **SUCK 1**

BBX

STRENGTH
Tracks: / Strength / Queen and country.
12" Single: Released 13 Mar '89, on Virgin, by Virgin Records. Catalogue no: **TENX 259**
7" Single: Released 13 Mar '89, on Virgin, by Virgin Records. Catalogue no: **TEN 259**

WRITTEN WORD
Tracks: / Written word / Alright.
7" Single: Released May '89, on 10 Records, by Virgin Records. Catalogue no: **TEN 269**

B.C. & Black Satin

DO YOU WANNA DANCE
Tracks: / Do you wanna dance / Satin beat.
7" Single: Released Jun '80, on Hammer. Deleted Jun '83. Catalogue no: **HS 309**

B.C. Boyz

JUST CAN'T GIVE YOU UP
Tracks: / Just can't give you up.
12" Single: Released Oct '88, on Blue Chip, by Blue Chip Records. Catalogue no: **BLUE-CHIP 6 T**

Be Big

GUILTY
Tracks: / Guilty / Get on board / Guilty (version) (Only on 12" version.).
CD 5": Released Feb '89, on Virgin, by Virgin Records. Catalogue no: **TENCD 258**
7" Single: Released Feb '89, on Virgin, by Virgin Records. Catalogue no: **TEN 258**
12" Single: Released Sep '89, on 10 Records, by Virgin Records. Catalogue no: **12 TEN 283**
7" Single: Released Sep '89, on 10 Records, by Virgin Records. Catalogue no: **TEN 283**
12" Single: Released Feb '89, on Virgin, by Virgin Records. Catalogue no: **TENX 258**

GUILTY (REMIX)
Tracks: / Guilty (getting high, blaze your hands remix) / Guilty (got high mix) / Get on board.
12" Single: Released '89, on 10 Records, by Virgin Records. Catalogue no: **TENR 258**

Be Bop DeLuxe

Biographical details: This British band, dominated by vocalist and guitarist Bill Nelson, released their first album *"Axe Victim"* in 1974. *"Sunburst Finish"* gave them their first chart album, reaching No. 17 with 12 weeks on the list, in early '76 and yielded a Top 30 single *"Ships In The Night"*. Later in the year they issued their fourth album *"Modern Music"* and had a Top 40 EP *"Hot Valves"*.
The group were a diversemixture of early Seventies rock, heavy metal, glitter rock and futurist pop. On stage they wore suits and ties, while presenting a quietly rebellious face to the music press. This eclecticism meant that they fell between various musical stools, and remained on the fringes of the big league of rock bands without actually entering it.
Their only Top 10 LP came in 1977 with the live double set *"Live! In The Air Age"*. It was followed by 1978's less successful *"Drastic Plastic"*, then the group folded.
Their leader formed the partially accepted Bill Nelson's Red Noise, before going solo in 1980. *"Do You Dream In Colour"*, a single issued on his own Cocteau lable, was an airplay favourite but could only reach No.52. 1981's LP *"Quit Dreaming And Get On The Beam"* reached No. 7 his highest ever plaing. He has kept a low profile in the Eighties, his occasional records always being too left-field to sell in large quantities. In the autumn of '84 he released a strong rock/dance single *"Acceleration"*.
(BM 1984).

HOT VALVES EP
Tracks: / Maid in heaven / Blazing apostles / Jet silver and the dolls of venus / Bring back the spark.
7" Single: Released Nov '76, on Harvest (2), by Harvest Music. Deleted '79. Catalogue no: **HAR 5117**

PANIC IN THE WORLD
Tracks: / Panic in the world.
7" Single: Released Aug '83, on Cocteau, by Cocteau Records. Catalogue no: **COQ 7**

SHIPS IN THE NIGHT
Tracks: / Ships in the night / Maid in heaven.
7" Single: Released Apr '84, on EMI Golden 45's, by EMI Records. Catalogue no: **G45 21**
7" Single: Released Feb '76, on Harvest (2), by Harvest Music. Catalogue no: **HAR 5104**

Beach Boys

Biographical details: The Beach Boys were one of the most important American pop groups of the 60's. Formed in 1961, they comprised three brothers, Brian, Carl and Dennis Wilson, plus cousin Mike Love and friend Al Jardine, ranging in age from Carl's 14 to Mike's 20. Dennis Wilson was a keen surfer and thought it was time somebody wrote and sang about his favourite sport.

The five formed a group and eldest brother Brian wrote song simply called Surfin' With Love. The Wilsons' songwriter father took the quintet to his publishing company and eventually the song was issued on the small Candix label under the group's new name, the Beach Boys. To their complete surprise it entered the charts, hovering around the lower end of the US Hot Hundred for six weeks in early 1962. Being raised in the middle class environment of the Los Angeles suburb of Hawthorne, the lads had been able to take full advantage of the most enjoyable aspects of life in California and they injected their early singles with a carefree image of sun, surfing and cars. Now signed to the mighty Capitol label, in the wake of the toehold gained by Surfin', the Beach Boys began a historic string of American hits. The formula for the first three was the same each time: the A-sides (Surfin' Safari, Surfin' USA and Surfer Girl) were about the beach sport, while the B-sides (409, Shut Down and Little Deuce Coupe) dealt with drag racing, another popular California recreation. They were all Top Twenty hits, as were the next two 45s, Be True To Your School and Fun, Fun, Fun. Brian Wilson was gradually emerging as the group's main talent and songwriter, though Surfin' USA had been an adaptation of Chuck Berry's Sweet Little Sixteen. In addition to the Beach Boys' own hits, Brian had co-written his first No 1, a collaboration with friend Jan Berry called Surfy City, performed by Jan & Dean. This was the biggest surfing hit of all: a fitting tribute to Jan & Dean, whose pioneering efforts in the late 50's and early 60's were an acknowledged influence on the Beach Boys.

Just as pop's surfing craze had hit its peak President Kennedy was assassinated and shortly afterwards the Beatles invaded America. The USA had been in a shocked and sombe mood, broken by the arrival of a new sensation. Both these phenomena made the Beach Boys' surfing, sun and dragster songs sound suddenly irrelevant. But whereas most of the American singers and groups of the early 60's were torpedoes into obscurity by the British invasion the Beach Boys rose to the challenge and secured legendary status in the annals of rock history. Brian Wilson's first response to Beatlemania was to come up with the Beach Boys' first No 1, I Get Around. This saw the group developing a more complex sound while remaining highly commercial. Throughout the rest of '64 and '65 four further Top Tenners were obtained: When I Grow Up (To Be A Man), Dance, Dance, Dance, Help me, Rhonda (their second US No 1) and California Girls.

The Boys cracked the British market in '66. The surfing sound had been alien to British ears and only one of the surfing records had ever cracked the UK Top Fifty. After peaking at No 34 with Surfin USA, I Get Around became their second chart record and was the only one to make the Top Ten before '66. Suddenly along came Barbara Ann, Sloop John B, God Only Knows and Good Vibrations, four consecutive British Top Three hits. Having suffered a nervous breakdown in in early '65 Brian Wilson was becoming more and more introverted and more and more musically experimental. The Pet Sounds album, in 1966, was, arguably, the first "concept album". That and the Good Vibrations single saw Brian at the height of his creative powers. The single became the group's best-known classic, giving them their final American and first British chart-toppers. But whereas Pet Sounds was a huge UK seller it received a muted US response, being heavily upstaged the following year by the Beatles' experimental masterwork Sergeant Pepper. Brilliant though it was, Pet Sounds began a major decline in the Beach Boys' American fortunes and they only achieved one more US Top Ten single. As Brian became more and more wrapped up in his own troubled mind, and suffering also from partial deafness, he quit touring and was replaced on the road by Bruce Johnson. Reeling from the comparative US failure of Pet Sounds the material returned to being straightforward pop.

The group coasted through the psychedelic era as though it was not happening, with singles like Darlin' and Break Away. They remained a top act in the UK during the late 60's, while tailing off at home -- a position best exemplified by 1968's Do It Again, the second British No 1 but only No 20 in their homeland. The British success dried up in 1970. With Brian now a recluse, the rest of the band tried to mould themselves into the style of the 70's West Coast rock groups but success eluded them, until their mainman was coaxed back in 1976. They then had a one-off US Top Tenner with Rock 'n Roll Music, a Chuck Berry remake, just as Surfin USA had been, and a 10-week No 1 album in Britain with Twenty Golden Greats. Lady Lynda brought them back to the higher echelons of the UK singles chart in '79. But apart from these occasional high spots the beach Boys were merely a modestly successful recording and touring outfit.

Dennis Wilson died in 1983 at the age of 39. He drowned off the Californian coast and, on recovery of the body, was buried at sea by special dispensation from President Reagan. As the only real surfer in the Beach Boys, and as the member who had first prodded brother Brian to write a song about the subject, he had played a pivotal role in launching the career of a group whose brioght vocal harmonies and irresistible Californian pop became synonymous with the word "summer". (Bob MacDonald, 1984.)

A USA vocal/instrumental group formed in 1961, one of the classic bands of post-rock'n'roll pop. Original lineup: Brian Wilson on bass and keyboards, Carl Wilson on guitar, Dennis Wilson on drums and keyboards, vocalist Mike Love and Alan Jardine on bass and guitar. All sang. The Wilson brothers were from Hawthorne, California, near Los Angeles; Love is their cousin. They enjoyed harmonising, graduating from simple two-part Everly Brothers style to more complex Four Freshmen harmonies; they formed a group called Carl and the Passions (later title of a 1972 album), also called themselves the Pendletones at one point. Brian and Mike wrote quintessential teen anthems about cars, girls, surfing and loves; the group was the godfather of today's boring USA FM rock, yet was also a classic garage band in those far-off innocent years: starting as amateurs who loved music, they were the first to combine Chuck Berry rhythms with pretty harmony and adolescent subsject matter. Like Jan & Dean, the other famous surfers, they did not immediately give up their day jobs: Jardine left for a year to study dentistry just as their first record *Surfin'* was a regional hit. They had 24 top 50 hits 1962-66, including eight 2-sided hits, 13 top tens and three at no.1 *I Get Around, Help Me Rhonda, Good Vibrations*; *California Girls* was adapted as the theme for a UK airline commercial in the 1980s *Caledonia Girls*; their other best-known hits include *Surfin' USA, Little Deuce Coupe, Surfer Girl, Be True To Your School.* Brian also worked with Jan & Dean, co-writing their 1963 no.1 *Surf City*, he produced the Honeys, a girl vocal trio (and married one of them); he had a nervous breakdown in 1964 and no longer enjoyed playing live gigs, replaced on stage by Glen Campbell, then Bruce Johnstone.

They always did their own singing but often used session players on records; Brian became a studio wizard, and *Good Vibrations* was a technical tour-de-force at the time, as advanced in production terms as anything anybody else was doing. Other later personnel included Daryl Dragon (later of Captain & Tennille) on keyboards. Their hits compilations were enormous sellers; they were one of the few USA acts not washed away by the British Invasion of 1964. Grandiose studio projects were started but never finished; the group seemed to wallow in California-style self-indulgence; in spite of problems with drugs and alcohol, their image remained clean-cut, totally associated with their sun-drenched all-American subject matter; when President Reagan's Secretary of the Interior James Watt tried to prevent them playing at the 1983 4th of July celebrations on the Mall in Washington DC, wanting Las Vegas entertainer Wayne Newton instead, he was laughed out of court, but Dennis drowned while swimming after heavy drinking late that year. Brian may have recovered his lost genius: in 1988 he had sought help from psychology, shed his various addictions, lost 120 pounds and made his first solo album. (Donald Clarke 23 August 1988).

BARBARA ANN
Tracks: / Barbara Ann / God only knows.
7" Single: Released Mar '84, on EMI Golden 45's, by EMI Records. Catalogue no: **G45 10**
7" Single: Released Feb '66, on Capitol, by EMI Records. Deleted '69. Catalogue no: **CL 15409**

BEACH BOYS MEDLEY
Tracks: / Beach boys medley.
7" Single: Released Jul '83, on Capitol, by EMI Records. Deleted '88. Catalogue no: **CL 213**

BLUEBIRDS OVER THE MOUNTAINS
Tracks: / Bluebirds over the mountain.
7" Single: Released Dec '68, on Capitol, by EMI Records. Deleted Dec '71. Catalogue no: **CL 15572**

BREAK AWAY
Tracks: / Break away.
7" Single: Released Jun '69, on Capitol, by EMI Records. Deleted Jun '72. Catalogue no: **CL 15598**

CALIFORNIA DREAMIN'
Tracks: / California dreamin' / Lady liberty / Beach Boys ballads (Medley on 12"only.).
7" Single: Released Sep '86, on Capitol, by EMI Records. Deleted '88. Catalogue no: **CL 425**
12" Single: Released Sep '86, on Capitol, by EMI Records. Deleted '88. Catalogue no: **12CL 425**

CALIFORNIA GIRLS
Tracks: / California girls.
7" Single: Released Sep '65, on Capitol, by EMI Records. Deleted '68. Catalogue no: **CL 15409**

CALIFORNIA SAGA - CALIFORNIA
Tracks: / California saga - California.
7" Single: Released Mar '73, on Reprise, by WEA Records. Deleted Mar '76. Catalogue no: **K 14232**

COTTONFIELDS
Tracks: / Cottonfields.
7" Single: Released May '70, on Capitol, by EMI Records. Deleted May '73. Catalogue no: **CL 15640**

DANCE DANCE DANCE
Tracks: / Dance dance dance.
7" Single: Released Jan '65, on Capitol, by EMI Records. Deleted '68. Catalogue no: **CL 15370**

DARLIN'
Tracks: / Darlin'.
7" Single: Released Jan '68, on Capitol, by EMI Records. Deleted Jan '71. Catalogue no: **CL 15527**

DO IT AGAIN (SINGLE)
Tracks: / Do it again.
7" Single: Released Jul '68, on Capitol, by EMI Records. Deleted Jul '71. Catalogue no: **CL 15554**

FRIENDS (SINGLE)
Tracks: / Friends.
7" Single: Released May '68, on Capitol, by EMI Records. Deleted May '71. Catalogue no: **CL 15545**

GETCHA BACK
Tracks: / Getcha back / Male ego.
12" Single: Released Jul '85, on Caribou, by CBS Records. Catalogue no: **TA 6324**

GOD ONLY KNOWS
Tracks: / God only knows.
7" Single: Released Aug '66, on Capitol, by EMI Records. Deleted '69. Catalogue no: **CL 15459**

GOD ONLY KNOWS (RE-RELEASE)
Tracks: / God only knows / Girls on the beach / In my room.
7" Single: Released 20 Jun '80, on Capitol, by EMI Records. Deleted '83. Catalogue no: **CL 16148**

GOOD VIBRATIONS (SINGLE)
Tracks: / Good vibrations.
7" Single: Released Nov '66, on Capitol, by EMI Records. Deleted '69. Catalogue no: **CL 15475**
7" Single: Released Apr '83, on EMI (France), by EMI Records. Catalogue no: **2C 008 85379**
7" Single: Released Jun '79, on Capitol, by EMI Records. Catalogue no: **CL 16054**

HELP ME RHONDA
Tracks: / Help me Rhonda.
7" Single: Released Jun '65, on Capitol, by EMI Records. Deleted '68. Catalogue no: **CL 15392**

HERE COMES THE NIGHT
Tracks: / Here comes the night.
7" Single: Released Mar '79, on Caribou, by CBS Records. Deleted Mar '82. Catalogue no: **CRB 7204**

HEROES AND VILLAINS
Tracks: / Heroes and villains.
7" Single: Released Aug '67, on Capitol, by EMI Records. Deleted '70. Catalogue no: **CL 15510**

I CAN HEAR MUSIC
Tracks: / I can hear music.
7" Single: Released Feb '69, on Capitol, by EMI Records. Deleted Feb '72. Catalogue no: **CL 15584**

I GET AROUND
Tracks: / I get around.
7" Single: Released Jul '64, on Capitol, by EMI Records. Deleted '67. Catalogue no: **CL 15350**

KEEPIN' THE SUMMER ALIVE (SINGLE)
Tracks: / Keepin' the summer alive / Whe[n] girls get together.
7" Single: Released Jun '80, on Caribou, b[y] CBS Records. Deleted '83. Catalogue no: **CRB 8663**

KOKOMO
Tracks: / Kokomo / Tutti frutti.
7" Single: Released Nov '88, on Elektra, by Elektra Records (UK). Catalogue no: **EKR 85**
12" Single: Released Nov '88, on Elektra by Elektra Records (UK). Catalogue no: **EKR 85T**

LADY LYNDA
Tracks: / Lady Lynda.
7" Single: Released Jun '79, on Caribou, b[y] CBS Records. Deleted Jun '82. Catalogu[e] no: **CRB 7427**

LIL' BIT OF GOLD: THE BEACH BOYS
Tracks: / California girls / Help me rhonda / Wouldn't it be nice / Good vibrations.
CD 5": Released May '88, on Rhino, b[y] Creole Records. Catalogue no: **R 373001**

OH DARLING
Tracks: / Oh darling / Endless harmony.
7" Single: Released Mar '80, on Caribou, b[y] CBS Records. Deleted Mar '83. Catalogu[e] no: **CRB 8367**

ROCK & ROLL MUSIC
Tracks: / Rock and roll music.
7" Single: Released Jul '76, on Reprise, b[y] WEA Records. Deleted Jul '79. Catalogu[e] no: **K 14440**

ROCK'N'ROLL TO THE RESCUE
Tracks: / Rock 'n' roll to the rescue / Goo[d] vibrations / Rock 'n' roll to the rescue (rad[io] version) (Extra track on 12" only).
12" Single: Released Aug '86, on Capito[l], by EMI Records. Deleted '88. Catalogue n[o]: **12CL 409**
7" Single: Released Jul '86, on Capitol, b[y] EMI Records. Deleted '88. Catalogue no: **C[L] 409**

SANTA ANA WINDS
Tracks: / Santa Ana winds / Sunshine.
7" Single: Released May '80, on Caribo[u], by CBS Records. Deleted '83. Catalogue n[o]: **CRB 8633**

SLOOP JOHN B
Tracks: / Sloop John B.
7" Single: Released Jul '84, on Capitol (Ho[l]land), by EMI Records. Catalogue no: **006 86474**
7" Single: Released Apr '66, on Capitol, by EMI Records. Deleted '69. Catalogue no: **C[L] 15441**

STILL CRUISIN' (SINGLE)
Tracks: / Still cruisin' / Kokomo / Rock 'n' r[oll] to the rescue (Beach Party mix-ext. dan[ce] ver) (CD single only.) / Lady Liberty (C[D] single only.).
Note: Side two of 12" contains Beach Bo[ys] medley (Uptempo - Long version): Go[od] vibrations/Help me Rhonda/I g[et] around/Little deuse coupe/Little Honda./H[a]waii/409/Noble surfer/Dance, danc[e] dance/Shut down/Surfin' safari/Barba[ra] Ann/Surfin' U.S.A./Fun, fun, fun.
CD 5": Released Aug '89, on Capitol, by E[MI] Records. Catalogue no: **CDCL 549**
7" Single: Released Aug '89, on Capitol, [by] EMI Records. Catalogue no: **203 518 7**
CD 5": Released Aug '89, on Capitol, by E[MI] Records. Catalogue no: **203 525 2**
12" Single: Released Aug '89, on Capit[ol], by EMI Records. Catalogue no: **12CL 549**
12" Single: Released Aug '89, on Capit[ol], by EMI Records. Catalogue no: **203 525 6**
7" Single: Released Aug '89, on Capitol, [by] EMI Records. Catalogue no: **CL 549**

SUMAHAMA
Tracks: / Sumahama.
7" Single: Released Sep '79, on Caribou, [by] CBS Records. Deleted Sep '82. Catalog[ue] no: **CRB 7846**

SURFIN' SAFARI
Tracks: / Surfin' safari / Surfin' USA / Sur[fer] girl.
7" Single: Released Aug '84, on Cre[ole] (Replay), by Creole Records. Catalogue n[o]: **CR 124**

SURFIN' USA (SINGLE)
Tracks: / Surfin' USA.
7" Single: Released Aug '63, on Capitol, [by] EMI Records. Deleted '66. Catalogue no: **CL 15305**

THEN I KISSED HER

Tracks: / Then I kissed her.
7" Single: Released May '67, on Capitol, by EMI Records. Deleted '70. Catalogue no: **CL 15502**

WHEN I GROW UP (TO BE A MAN)
Tracks: / When I grow up (to be a man).
7" Single: Released Oct '64, on Capitol, by EMI Records. Deleted '67. Catalogue no: **CL 15361**

WILD HONEY (SINGLE)
Tracks: / Wild honey.
7" Single: Released Nov '67, on Capitol, by EMI Records. Deleted '70. Catalogue no: **CL 15521**

Beach Coma

SHOTGUN
Tracks: / Shotgun.
7" Single: Released Jul '84, on Baskerville, Catalogue no: **BAS 4**

Beach-la-Mar

BREAKDOWN
Tracks: / While the beat goes on / Breakdown.
7" Single: Released Dec '86, on Pure Joy, Catalogue no: **JOY 1**

Beachnuts

RAVING ON THE BEACH
Tracks: / Raving on the beach.
7" Single: Released Sep '83, on Vista Sounds, by Vista Sounds Records. Catalogue no: **JC 7003**
12" Single: Released Sep '83, on Vista Sounds, by Vista Sounds Records. Catalogue no: **JCT 7003**

Beacon, Kim

MY BLUES HAVE GONE
Tracks: / My blues have gone / Minute by minute.
7" Single: Released Feb '80, on Rialto (1), by Rialto Records. Deleted Feb '83. Catalogue no: **TREB 113**

NIGHT BIRD
Tracks: / Night bird / Ravenna.
7" Single: Released Dec '80, on Rialto (1), by Rialto Records. Deleted Dec '85. Catalogue no: **TREB 129**

Bean, Carl

I WAS BORN THIS WAY
Tracks: / I was born this way.
7" Single: Released Dec '85, on 10 Records, by Virgin Records. Deleted '86. Catalogue no: **TEN 110**
12" Single: Released Dec '85, on 10 Records, by Virgin Records. Deleted '86. Catalogue no: **TEN 110-12**

Bear, George

BEAR RAP
Tracks: / Bear rap.
7" Single: Released Nov '83, on Cambra, by Cambra Records. Deleted '88. Catalogue no: **CMB 07**

Bears

FEAR IS NEVER BONNY
Tracks: / Fear is never Bonny / None of the above / Wonderful world tonight / Neighbourhood Phrenologist."
Note: A side features The Bears. B side features Balancing Act.
12" Single: Released Oct '87, on MCA, by MCA Records. Catalogue no: **IRMT 143**

Bearz

DARWIN
Tracks: / Darwin.
7" Single: Released Apr '84, on Occult, Catalogue no: **OCC 1**

Beasley, Walter

I'M SO HAPPY (SINGLE)
Tracks: / I'm so happy / Jump on it.
7" Single: Released Jan '88, on Urban, by Polydor Ltd. Catalogue no: **URB 14**
12" Single: Released Jan '88, on Urban, by Polydor Ltd. Catalogue no: **URBX 14**

Beast

NEW MOONE
Tracks: / New moone.
12" Single: Released Dec '83, on I.D., by I.D. Records. Catalogue no: **EYE T3**
7" Single: Released Dec '83, on I.D., by I.D. Records. Catalogue no: **EYE 3**

Beastie Boys

COOKY PUSS
Tracks: / Cooky puss.
12" Single: on Rat Cage, by Southern Studios Ltd.. Catalogue no: **MOTR 26**

COOKY PUSS (EP)
Tracks: / Cooky dub / Bonus batter / Beastie revolution / Cooky puss censored.
7" EP: Released Jul '87, on Rat Cage, by Southern Studios Ltd.. Catalogue no: **MOR 26**

GIRLS
Tracks: / Girls / She's crafty.
Note: BEAST S3 & BEAST Q3 - Special packs.
12" Single: Released Sep '87, on Def Jam, Catalogue no: **BEASTQ 3**
7" Single: Released Oct '87, on Def Jam, Catalogue no: **BEASTW 3**
7" Single: Released Sep '87, on Def Jam, Catalogue no: **BEASTS 3**
7" Single: Released Sep '87, on Def Jam, Catalogue no: **BEAST 3**

HEY LADIES (Love American Style E.P.)
Tracks: / Hey ladies / Shake your rump / 33% God (Not on 7".) / Dis yourself in '89 (just do it) (Not on 7".).
CD 5": Released Jul '89, on Capitol, by EMI Records. Catalogue no: **203 448 3**
12" Single: Released Jul '89, on Capitol, by EMI Records. Catalogue no: **V 15483**
7" Single: Released Jul '89, on Capitol, by EMI Records. Catalogue no: **CL 540**
CD 5": Released Jul '89, on Capitol, by EMI Records. Catalogue no: **CDCL 540**
7" Single: Released Jul '89, on Capitol, by EMI Records. Catalogue no: **203 448 7**
12" Single: Released Jul '89, on Capitol, by EMI Records. Catalogue no: **203 448 6**
12" Single: Released Jul '89, on Capitol, by EMI Records. Catalogue no: **12CL 540**

HOLD IT,NOW HIT IT
Tracks: / Hold it, now hit it / Acapulco.
7" Single: Released May '87, on Def Jam, Catalogue no: **A 7055**
12" Single: Released May '87, on Def Jam, Deleted '86. Catalogue no: **TA 7055**

IT'S THE NEW STYLE
Tracks: / It's the new style / Paul Revere.
12" Single: Released Nov '86, on Def Jam, Deleted Aug '87. Catalogue no: **650169 6**

NO SLEEP TILL BROOKLYN
Tracks: / No sleep till Brooklyn / Posse in effect.
12" Single: Released 23 May '87, on Def Jam, Deleted Nov '87. Catalogue no: **BEASTT 1**
7" Pic: Released 23 May '87, on Def Jam, Deleted Nov '87. Catalogue no: **BEASTP 1**
7" Single: Released 23 May '87, on Def Jam, Deleted Nov '87. Catalogue no: **BEAST 1**

POLLY WOG STEW
Tracks: / Polly wog stew.
7" Single: Released Nov '82, on Rat Cage, by Southern Studios Ltd.. Catalogue no: **MOTR 21**
12" Single: on Rat Cage, by Southern Studios Ltd.. Catalogue no: **MOTR21T**

SHE'S CRAFTY
Tracks: / She's crafty / Girls / Rock hard.
Note: Picture bag.
12" Single: Released Sep '87, on Def Jam, Catalogue no: **BEASTT 3**

SHE'S ON IT
Tracks: / She's on it / Slow'n'low / Hold it, now hit it (on 12" only.).
12" Single: Released Jul '87, on Def Jam, Catalogue no: **BEASTT 2**
7" Single: Released Sep '86, on Def Jam, Deleted Aug '87. Catalogue no: **650114 7**
7" Single: Released Jul '87, on Def Jam, Catalogue no: **BEASTB 2**
7" Single: Released Jul '87, on Def Jam, Catalogue no: **BEAST 2**
12" Single: Released Sep '86, on Def Jam, Deleted Aug '87. Catalogue no: **650114 6**

(YOU GOTTA) FIGHT FOR YOUR RIGHT (TO PARTY)
Tracks: / Time to Get Ill / (You gotta) Fight for your right (to party).
7" Single: Released Feb '87, on Def Jam, Catalogue no: **650418 7**
12" Single: Released Feb '87, on Def Jam, Catalogue no: **650418 6**

Beasts Of Bourbon

HARD WORK DRIVIN' MAD
Tracks: / Hard work drivin' mad.
7" Single: Released Feb '89, on Red Eye, by Red Eye Records. Catalogue no: **RED 017B**

Beat

Biographical details: This British band formed as a quartet in Birmingham in 1978. After playing their first gigs in early '79, they added Ranking Roger, who was well versed in the reggae art of 'toasting'. This form of spoken accompaniment, in effect using speech as an extra musical instrument, was becoming popular in British reggae circles at the same time as its soul equivalent, the rap, was gaining momentum in the American discos. The group toured with the selector and, through this, met the Specials who invited them to cut a single on their newly formed 2 Tone label. A sixth member was added - 50 year old saxaphone player 'Saxa', who looked incongruous when seen in photos with his five youthful colleagues but who nonetheless became an integral part of the line-up. When the Beat's first single was released, they had the advantage of being associated with the hottest movement in British music at that time - the new multi-racial ska/early reggae revival. That debut disc was a double A side combining their much played cover of Smokey Robinson's *"Tears Of A Clown"* with *"Ranking Full Stop"*. It reached No. 6 in January 1980, contributing to 2 Tone's early 100% success rate. After this big first record, the Beat took the bold descision to leave 2 Tone, wishing to show that they did not need that fashionable label's umbrella and could stand on their own feet. They formed their own label, appropriately called Go Feet and chalked up two further Top 10 hits, *"Hands Off - She's Mine"* and *"Mirror In The Bathroom"*. Their debut album issued in May '80 was a critical and commercial winner. *"Jst Can't Stop It"* reached No. 3 on the LP chart, with 32 weeks on the list. It combined the upbeat ska sound with some sharp social and political commentary, a recipe that was to be repeated with less success over the following two years. They started 1981 with a Top 10 single *"Too Nice To Talk To"* and followed it in the Spring with a second Top 3 LP *"Wha'ppen"*. With several other 2 Tone associated acts, they featured in the film *"Dance Craze"*. But the next six singles all failed to crack the Top 20 and 1982's *"Special Beat Service"* LP also fared dissapointingly. It took a remake of a 1963 Andy Williams hit to revive their fortunes. *"Can't Get Used To Losing You"* became the Beat's biggest single of all, surging to No. 3 in 1983, with the lead vocalist sounding inriguingly similar to Williams himself. By this time keyboards player Blockhead had been added and the ailing Saxa had been replaced by Wesley Magoogan. Shortly after this smash hit, singer and guitarist Dave Wakeling quit. The band folded, with Wakeling and Ranking Roger forming a new outfit called General Public who, after scoring a minor hit in '84 with their self-titled debut single, had to work hard to gain chart acceptance. (Bob MacDonald).

A ska-revival pop group, a multi-racial Birmingham-based band formed in 1978 by Dave Wakeling on vocals and guitar, Andy Cox on guitar, David Steele on bass; played their first gigs in early '79 with drummer Everett Morton, who'd played with Joan Armatrading, and picked up 'black punk' Ranking Roger, a former drummer turned vocalist, and saxophonist Saxa, a one-time Prince Buster sideman. They toured with Specials; their first hit was their own unique version of Smokey Robinson's *Tears of A Clown* for the 2-tone label. By 1982 constant touring in USA (as The English Beat) had turned them into another new wave pop group. They lasted until 1983 with some personnel changes, theri split coinciding with the biggest hit: a cover of the Andy Williams hit *Can't Get Used To Losing You*, taken from their first (best) album. Wakeling and Roger formed USA-oriented General Public, while Steele and Cox formed Fine Young Cannibals with vocalist Roland Gift. (Donald Clarke 23 August 1988).

ACKEE 1-2-3
Tracks: / Ackee 1-2-3.
12" Single: Released '83, on Go Feet, Deleted '86. Catalogue no: **FEET 1218**
7" Single: Released '83, on Go Feet, Deleted '87. Catalogue no: **FEET 18**

BEST FRIENDS (see panel below)
Tracks: / Best friend / Stand down Margaret (dub).
7" Single: Released '82, on Go Feet, Deleted '87. Catalogue no: **FEET 3**

CAN'T GET USED TO LOSING YOU
Tracks: / Can't get used to losing you.
7" Single: Released '83, on Go Feet, Deleted '87. Catalogue no: **FEET 17**

DON'T DROP THE BEAT
Tracks: / Don't drop the beat.
12" Single: Released Jun '89, on Subway dance, Catalogue no: **SD4001**
12" Single: Released '89, on Subway, by Subway Records. Catalogue no: **SUB 066**

DOOR OF YOUR HEART
Tracks: / Door of your heart / Mirror in the bathroom (On Arista versions only) / Save it for later (On BLS 16 only) / Get a job (On Go-Feet versions only) / Drowning (On FEET 12-9 only).
7" Single: Released '82, on Arista, by BMG Records (UK). Deleted '87. Catalogue no: **FEET 9**
7" Set: Released Dec '82, on Arista, by BMG Records (UK). Deleted Dec '87. Catalogue no: **BLS 16**
7" Single: Released Jun '81, on Go Feet, Deleted Jun '84. Catalogue no: **FEET 9**
12" Single: Released Jun '81, on Go Feet, Deleted Jun '84. Catalogue no: **FEET 12-9**

DROWNING
Tracks: / Drowning / All out to get you.
7" Single: Released '82, on Go Feet, Deleted '87. Catalogue no: **FEET 6**

HAND'S OFF SHE'S MINE
Tracks: / Hand's off she's mine.
12" Single: Released '82, on Go Feet, Deleted '87. Catalogue no: **FEET 121**
7" Single: Released Feb '80, on Go Feet, Catalogue no: **FEET 1**
12" Single: Released '82, on Go Feet, Deleted '87. Catalogue no: **FEET 124**

HIT IT
Tracks: / Hit it / Which side of the bed.
7" Single: Released Dec '81, on Arista, by BMG Records (UK). Deleted '86. Catalogue no: **FEET 11**
12" Single: Released Dec '81, on Go Feet, Deleted '85. Catalogue no: **FEET 1211**

I CONFESS
Tracks: / I confess / Soul salvation.
7" Single: Released Dec '82, on Go Feet, Deleted Dec '85. Catalogue no: **FEET 16**

JEANETTE
Tracks: / Jeanette.
7" Single: Released '82, on Go Feet, Deleted '87. Catalogue no: **FEET 15**
12" Single: Released Sep '82, on Go Feet, Deleted '87. Catalogue no: **FEET 1215**

MIRROR IN THE BATHROOM
Tracks: / Mirror in the bathroom.
7" Single: Released Apr '80, on Go Feet, Catalogue no: **FEET 002**

SAVE IT FOR LATER
Tracks: / Save it for later / What's your best thing.
7" Single: Released '82, on Go Feet, Deleted '87. Catalogue no: **FEET 333**
12" Single: Released Apr '82, on Go Feet, Deleted '87. Catalogue no: **FEET 12333**

BEAT - BEST FRIENDS (Released on Go Feet)

TEARS OF A CLOWN
Tracks: / Tears of a clown / Ranking full stop.
7" Single: Released Dec '79, on Two-Tone, by Chrysalis Records. Catalogue no: **CHSTT 6**

TOO NICE TO TALK TO
Tracks: / Too nice to talk to you / Psychedelic rocker.
7" Single: Released '82, on Go Feet, Deleted '87. Catalogue no: **FEET 4**

Beat Beat Beat

BEAT IN THE STREET
Tracks: / Beat in the street.
12" Single: Released Jun '88, on Kaos, Catalogue no: **KAOS 001**

Beat Box Clever

THIS CONTAGIOUS HOUSE
Tracks: / This contagious house / This contagious house (version).
7" Single: Released Jun '88, on Priority, by Priority Records. Catalogue no: **MARV 14**
12" Single: Released Jun '88, on Priority, by Priority Records. Catalogue no: **12 MARV 14**

Beat Boys

B BOP ROCK (2 parts)
Tracks: / B bop rock.
12" Single: Released Jul '83, on I.R.S, Catalogue no: **JUICE 802**

Beat Club

SECURITY
Tracks: / Security / Security (versions).
12" Single: Released Sep '88, on Bass, by Champion Records. Catalogue no: **BSS 123**

Beat Farmers

BIGGER STONES
Tracks: / Bigger stones.
7" Single: Released Jul '85, on Demon, by Demon Records. Catalogue no: **D 1031**

POWDER FINGER
Tracks: / Powder finger / Big ugly wheels / Come sail at the church (Extra track on 12" only).
12" Single: Released Jun '86, on MCA, by MCA Records. Catalogue no: **MCAT 1067**
7" Single: Released Jun '86, on MCA, by MCA Records. Catalogue no: **MCA 1067**

Beat Freaks

NATIONAL ANTHEM, THE
Tracks: / National anthem / Government don't care (dub).
12" Single: Released Jun '86, on Supreme Int.Editions, by Supreme Int.Records. Catalogue no: **EDITION 86 11**

Beat Happening

BODY THAT THEY BUILT TO FIT THE CAR, THE
Tracks: / Body that they built to fit the car, The.
12" Single: Released Feb '88, on Line, Catalogue no: **200007**

CRASHING THROUGH
Tracks: / Crashing through.
12" Single: Released Jan '88, on 53rd & 3rd, by 53rd & 3rd Records. Catalogue no: **AGARR 15T**

HONEY POT (FLEXI)
Tracks: / Honey pot.
7" Single: Released '88, on 53rd & 3rd, by 53rd & 3rd Records. Catalogue no: **ABENDI 001**

JAMBOREE
Special: Released '88, on 53rd & 3rd, by 53rd & 3rd Records. Catalogue no: **AGAS 002F**

LOOK AROUND
Tracks: / Look around.
7" Single: Released Jan '88, on K, by K Records. Catalogue no: **L 26501**

POLLY PEREGRIN
Tracks: / Polly peregrin.
12" Single: Released Jul '88, on 53rd & 3rd, by 53rd & 3rd Records. Catalogue no: **AGARR 20T**

Beat Hotels

HEY HEY AUDACIOUS
Tracks: / Hey hey audacious.
12" Single: Released Apr '89, on Household, by Household Records. Catalogue no: **HOLD 6T**

SMILE
Tracks: / Smile.
7" Single: Released Aug '88, on Household, by Household Records. Catalogue no: **HOLD 2**

Beat, Jimmy

MAIN THEME
Tracks: / Main theme.
CD 5": Released Oct '88, on Who's That Beat, by Play It Again Sam (Belgium). Catalogue no: **WHOS 007CD**
12" Single: Released Oct '88, on Who's That Beat, by Play It Again Sam (Belgium). Catalogue no: **WHOS 007**

Beat Lads

IT'S YOU
Tracks: / It's you / It's you (bass head mix) / It's you (jazz mix) / It's you (acappella).
12" Single: Released 30 Aug '88, on 4th & Broadway, by Island Records. Catalogue no: **12 BRW 111**
7" Single: Released 30 Aug '88, on 4th & Broadway, by Island Records. Deleted Apr '89. Catalogue no: **BRW 111**

Beat Necessity

PLEASURE
Tracks: / Pleasure.
7" Single: Released Feb '82, on New Town, Deleted '83. Catalogue no: **NIP 2**

THESE NIGHTS
Tracks: / These nights.
7" Single: Released Mar '83, on New Town, Deleted '84. Catalogue no: **NTT 3**

Beat Poets

COLLABORATION EP
12" Single: Released Aug '88, on 53rd & 3rd, by 53rd & 3rd Records. Catalogue no: **AGARR 21T**

GLASGOW, HOWARD MISSOURI
Tracks: / Glasgow, Howard Missouri.
7" EP: Released 30 May '87, on 53rd & 3rd, by 53rd & 3rd Records. Catalogue no: **AGARR 9T**

REBEL SURF
Tracks: / Rebel surf / I'm branded.
7" Single: Released Jul '88, on 53rd & 3rd, by 53rd & 3rd Records. Catalogue no: **AGARR 19**

Beat Professor

BEAT PROFESSOR
Tracks: / Beat professor.
12" Single: Released Sep '88, on Subway, by Subway Records. Catalogue no: **SUB 035**

YOU'VE GOT THE BEAT
Tracks: / You've got the beat.
12" Single: Released Apr '89, on Subway, by Subway Records. Catalogue no: **SUB 055**

Beat Rodeo

EVERYTHING I'M NOT
Tracks: / Everything I'm not / New love / True / Still in Hollywood.
12" Single: Released Feb '87, on I.R.S, Catalogue no: **IRMT 131**

Beat Sharks

RUN AWAY
Tracks: / Run away.
7" Single: Released Aug '85, on Sedition/ Pure Trash, by Sedition Records. Catalogue no: **EDIT 3305**
12" Single: Released Aug '85, on Sedition/ Pure Trash, by Sedition Records. Catalogue no: **EDITL 3305**

Beat Squad

U.B.A.D.J.
Tracks: / U.B.A.D.J..
12" Single: Released Feb '89, on Blue Chip, by Blue Chip Records. Catalogue no: **BLUE CHIP 13**

Beat Street

LIGHTNING STRIKE
Tracks: / Lightning strikes.
7" Single: Released Jul '88, on RCA, by BMG Records (UK). Deleted May '89. Catalogue no: **PB 49553**

Beat Street Band

BEAT STREET
Tracks: / Beat street.
7" Single: Released Jul '83, on Legacy, by Legacy Records. Catalogue no: **LGY 3**
12" Single: Released Jul '83, on Legacy, by Legacy Records. Catalogue no: **LGYT 3**

Beat The Drum

THIS CITY
Tracks: / This city.
12" Single: Released Oct '84, on Loose, by Loose Records. Catalogue no: **LSE 16T**
7" Single: Released Oct '84, on Loose, by Loose Records. Catalogue no: **LSE 16**

TRY
Tracks: / Try / This must be love.
12" Single: Released Mar '84, on Loose, by Loose Records. Catalogue no: **LSE 6T**
7" Single: Released Mar '84, on Loose, by Loose Records. Catalogue no: **LSE 6**

Beatboy A

HONEYDRIPPER, THE
Tracks: / Please please 82 / Honeydripper.
7" Single: Released 30 May '87, on Waterloo Sunset, by Waterloo Sunset Records. Catalogue no: **RUSS 106**

Beatitudes

HOME ALONE
Tracks: / Home alone.
7" Single: Released May '87, on Exile, Catalogue no: **EX 7006**

Beatles

Biographical details: John Lennon, Paul McCartney, George Harrison and Ringo Starr were the most important group in the history of rock and pop. They were formed in their native Liverpool and gained much of their experience in Hamburg, West Germany. Both were port cities with access to the latest American rhythm-and-blues releases, both had club scenes which were more raw and gutsy that showbusiness centres such as London. While the London-based record companies were heavily pushing the white, watered-down version of rock 'n' roll during the late 50's and early 60's, there were dedicated young fans in Liverpool who were listening to the original, mainly black, versions.

In was in this climate that John Lennon had founded a group called the Quarrymen (named after the school in which they were formed) and, by 1958, had brought in friends Paul McCartney and George Harrison. They became Johnny & The Moondogs and then the Silver Beatles, by which time the combo consisted of Lennon, McCartney, Harrison, Stuart Sutcliffe and Pete Best. Having come together in Liverpool they gained vital experience in Hamburg, where they had to work long and hard to please audiences -- eventually they did so consistently, with a brand of raw, energetic rock 'n' roll.

They cut their first records in Germany in 1961 as a backing group for British artist Tony Sheridan. By the end of that year they had developed their own style, dubbed the "Liverpool sound". This was a synthesis of American black sounds -- R & B, early gospel, early Motown -- but with the added ingredients of two fine singers and emerging songwriters in Lennon and McCartney. Now down to a quartet following the departure of Sutcliffe -- who died of a brain tumour the following year -- the group were discovered by Liverpool record store manager Brian Epstein. Impressed both by their music and their strong local following, he became their manager. He took them to London, dressed them in suits instead of their previous leathers and secured a record contract with EMI's Parlophone label. They had been rejected by Decca, who later helped to make up for it by signing the Rolling Stones. Now known simply as the Beatles -- inspired by Buddy Holly's Crickets -- the four started recording with EMI in-house producer George Martin. Pete Best was dropped in favour of a new drummer, Ringo Starr (born Richard Starkey). In October 1962 their first single, Love Me Do, entered the Top Fifty. It was a slow but steady seller, peaking at No 17 in December and staying on the list for 18 weeks. The Beatles quickly consolidated on this success with Please Please Me, a No 2 hit in early '63. Like the vast majority of their subsequent hits, these songs were credited to Lennon and McCartney (who in later years wrote separately but always credited each other) and produced by George Martin.

The Beatles quickly became the biggest sensation in British showbusiness history. They did this by following a totally different path from all the singers and musicians who had gone before them. They composed their own material, thus forever diminishing the roles of the Tin Pan Alley writers. They were a self-contained musical unit, not relying on back-up singers and musicians.

In Epstein they had a manager who was not part of the music business establishment and was therefore neither able nor willing to take them down the traditional pop road, which might have stifled their creativity and freshness. In Martin they had a producer who was not a seasoned pop man but was more accustomed to working with ballad singers and comedy acts and could provide the necessary technical expertise while giving the group musical freedom in the studio. Then there were the Beatle moptops, a famous departure from the conventional male haircut. As a result of all these factors they were able to produce a completely fresh and original sound, style and image. Having dominated the British market in 1963, the group exploded onto the American scene in January and February 1964. The sensational manner of their breakthrough was due partly to astute planning by both manager and record company, but also to the assassination of President Kennedy the previous November. The USA was in a state of profound shock and depression following that event and needed a major expression of happiness and optimism: these the Beatles provided. Statistics in Britain and America -- not to mention Europe and the rest of the world -- speak for themselves. In Britain they were No 1 for a combined total of 16 weeks in 1963 and top of the album chart for an unbroken 51-week stretch from May '63 until April '64 with, first, Please Please Me and then With The Beatles. In the US three consecutive chart-topping 45s held the No 1 spot for 14 consecutive weeks in ea rly '64, including the week of 4 April when the group held the entire Top Five plus seven other positions in the Billboard Hot Hundred. Although they never repeated these monumental chart achievements, the Beatles could do no wrong from then until their official split in 1970. They made two critically-acclaimed films in '64 and '65, A Hard Day's Night and Help! In Britain they chalked up 17 No 1 singles: From Me To You, She Loves You, I Want To Hold Your Hand, Can't Buy Me Love, A Hard Day's Night, I Feel Fine, Help!, Ticket To Ride, Day Tripper/We Can Work It Out, Paperback Writer, Yellow Submarine/Eleanor Rigby, All You Need Is Love, Hello Goodbye, Lady Madonna, Hey Jude (at 7 min 10 sec the longest-ever No 1), Get Back and The Ballad Of John And Yoko. This total is equalled only by Elvis Presley. On the album chart their tally of chart-toppers stands at an unrivalled 12. This total includes all their 11 regular studio albums: Please Please Me, With The Beatles, A Hard Day's Night, Beatles For Sale, Help!, Rubber Soul, Revolver, Sergeant Pepper's Lonely Hearts Club Band, The Beatles (a double set normally called The White Album), Abbey Road and Let It Be. In addition Parlophone released some live archive tapes in 1977 under the title The Beatles At The Hollywood Bowl, to give them their twelfth No 1 LP. The American list of 20 No 1 singles includes some tracks that were not issued as singles in Britain. Yesterday, the most recorded song of all time, was in pole position for four weeks in '65 but did not come out in the UK until '76. With each single and album release the Beatles became gradually more complex, placing greater and greater demands upon the imagination and flair of George Martin. This growing musical intricacy is best demonstrated in 1967's Sergeant Pepper and 1969's Abbey Road, the latter named after the London recording studios where Martin and the band made the legendary Sergeant Pepper, the single most important statement of the psychedelic/hippie era generally considered to be the Beatles best album, and indeed, the greatest album in rock history. The death of Brian Epstein in August 1967 signalled the start of the group's disintegration. The White Album, fine though it was, was more of a compilation of individual songs and styles than a Beatles album. The process continued with the Let It Be film and the Abbey Road LP. Lennon was becoming more and more involved, both personally and musically, with his avant garde Japanese girlfriend Yoko Ono.

The complicated relationship between Lennon and McCartney, which had previously always been a wonderfully healthy catalyst, now started to grow bitter. Businesswise Apple Records was not turning out to be the Utopian record company the Beatles had hoped for when foudning it and McCartney did not want to follow his three colleagues' lead in associating with new manager Allen Klein. The Beatles officially split in the spring of 1970, with all four members embarking on solo careers.

John Lennon was murdered outside his New York home in December 1980, in front of his wife, Yoko. It is impossible to state which was the greatest of the Beatles' achievements between 1962 and 1970. Perhaps it was their '64 conquest of America, which opened the floodgates for countless other acts in the famous British Invasion. Perhaps it was their ability to maintain their musical brilliance despite the pressures of world superstardom. Perhaps it was their domination of the late 60's psychedelic era, with all its trappings, cults and sub-cultures. It is easier simply to state that they changed the course of pop and rock history so dramatically that they now seem like an impossible but marvellous dream. (Bob MacDonald 1984.)

The UK pop group was formed in 1959 in Liverpool and lasted exactly a decade, during which they spearheaded the 'British Invasion' (of the USA) and helped make permanent changes in the music business. John Winston Lennon played rhythm guitar as did James Paul McCartney, until he switched to bass; George Harrison played lead guitar. Lennon had formed a skiffle group called the Quarrymen (after his school) in 1958; the original bassist was art-school student Stuart Sutcliffe, who quit early but died in 1962 of a brain tumour possibly caused by a hooligan's kick in the head following an early gig. Drummer Pete Best joined in 1960; they were called Johnny and the Moondogs, then the Silver Beatles then the Beatles.

They played a hard apprenticeship in Hamburg clubs, playing at Liverpool's legendary Cavern Club when at home, where they were seen by Brian Epstein, who became their manager: he ran the record department in his parents' furniture store and had been asked by a fan for an early record on Polydor, made in Germany. Epstein2 got them contract with EMI's Parlophone label, whos boss was then producer George Martin; Martin insisted on a new drummer, and Best was sacked in favour of Ringo Starr (Richard Starkey) who had played with Rory and the Hurricanes.

The rest is history. They had 17 number one UK hits between 1963-69, and 21 in the USA 1964-70, plus several consecutive number one albums in both countries. Their cheekiness, their original material, their harmonies derived from skiffle and folk music and their love of basic rock'n'roll added up to a new concept: pop music for the baby-boom generation. Hamburg photographer Astrid Kirchherr had a profound effect on '60s fashion, influencing the Beatles' famous 'mop-top' or pudding basin haircuts in the early years, as well as the way they dressed; Epstein smartened them up and insisted on a certain standard of behaviour, and Lennon said later that they never would have made it without him.

Subsequently they led their generation in looking for meaning in soft drugs and Eastern philosophy; they had to quit touring because they couldn't hear themselves play and sing, so great a phenomenon was Beatlemania and the attendant screaming. Their albums were different in the UK and the USA until *Sergeant Pepper* in 1967, the first and still the most sucessful pop concept album; Martin had become 'the fifth Beatle', developing the technology of record production in order to fully realise the Beatles' ideas and becoming the most famous producer in history. They presided over an era that saw album sales become more important than singles, and rock'n'roll change to rock, with all the inflation of pretence that that implies; however, if later groups spent far more money making less successful albums, this was because record companies gambled too much money on inferior talent: nothing to do with the Beatles. In retrospect *Rubber Soul* and *Revolver* may be better albums than *Sargeant Pepper*, which showed them to be a quintessentially English group, with a large element of seaside-postcard and music-hall variety in their act. Their first two films, *A Hard Day's Night*, and *Help*, were successful; the third, *Magical Mystery Tour*, made for television, was a self-indulgent disaster, partly because Epstein wasn't there to look after them: an unhappy homosexual and out of his depth in a world of very big money, he had died of a combination of drink and drugs. After *Sergeant Pepper* they were tired of being Beatles and tired of each other; Lennon and McCartney no longer wrote together, which meant that Lennon's acerbity and McCartney's prettiness no longer softened each other.

Their Apple business empire (label, boutique, etc.) was a hippie dream that turned to disaster. The Beatles (aka *The White Album* was an indulgent two-disc set: Martin begged them to edit it to one disc, but the only thing they could agree on was not to do that. The split in 1969; their last album was released in 1970 and they couldn't finish it themselves: *Let It Be* was handed over to Phil Spector for final production. Songs from their middle period, such as *Paperback Writer*, *Day Tripper*, Paul's *Penny Lane* and John's *Strawberry Fields Forever* set a standard of intelligence in pop songs that has not been exceeded; and the songs of Lennon & McCartney, now owned by Michael Jackson, are among the most successful and best-loved bodies of work of the century. All four had separate, less successful careers; fans did not stop hoping for a reunion until Lennon's senseless murder in 1980. (Donald Clarke 23 August 1988).

26 SINGLES (THE)
Tracks: / 26 singles, The.
7" Set: Released Dec '82, on Parlophone, by EMI Records. Catalogue no: **BSC 1**

AIN'T SHE SWEET
Tracks: / Ain't she sweet.
7" Single: Released Jun '64, on Polydor, by Polydor Ltd. Deleted Jun '67. Catalogue no: **52 317**

ALL MY LOVING
Tracks: / All my loving.
7" EP: Released Feb '64, on Parlophone, by EMI Records. Catalogue no: **GEP 8891**

ALL YOU NEED IS LOVE
Tracks: / All you need is love / Baby, you're a rich man.
Cassingle: Released Jul '85, on Parlophone, by EMI Records. Deleted Oct '87. Catalogue no: **TCR 5620**
7" Single: Released Jul '67, on Parlophone, by EMI Records. Catalogue no: **R 5620**
7" Pic: Released Jul '87, on Parlophone, by EMI Records. Catalogue no: **RP 5620**
CD 3": Released Jun '89, on Parlophone, by EMI Records. Catalogue no: **CD3R 5620**
12" Single: Released Jul '87, on Parlophone, by EMI Records. Deleted Nov '88. Catalogue no: **12R 5620**

BACK IN THE USSR
Tracks: / Back in the USSR.
7" Single: Released Jun '76, on Parlophone, by EMI Records. Catalogue no: **R**

BEATLES - TWIST AND SHOUT (Released on Parlophone)

6016

BALLAD OF JOHN AND YOKO
Tracks: / Ballad of John and Yoko / Old brown shoe.
CD 3": Released Aug '89, on Parlophone, by EMI Records. Catalogue no: **CD3R 5786**
7" Pic: Released May '89, on Parlophone, by EMI Records. Catalogue no: **RP 5786**
7" Single: Released May '69, on Apple, by Apple Records. Catalogue no: **R 5786**

BEATLES EP COLLECTION (14 EP set)
Note: Contains EP's:- The Beatles Hits, Twist & Shout, The Beatles No. 1, All My Loving, Long Tall Sally, A Hard Day's Night vol. 1, A Hard Day's Night vol. 2, Beatles For Sale, Beatles For Sale No. 2, The Beatles' Million Sellers, Yesterday, Nowhere Man, Magical Mystery Tour, The Beatles.
7" Set: Released Dec '81, on Parlophone, by EMI Records. Catalogue no: **BEP 14**

BEATLES FOR SALE NO 1
7" EP: Released Apr '65, on Parlophone, by EMI Records. Catalogue no: **GEP 8931**

BEATLES FOR SALE NO 2
7" EP: Released Jun '65, on Parlophone, by EMI Records. Catalogue no: **GEP 8938**

BEATLES' HITS
7" EP: Released Sep '63, on Parlophone, by EMI Records. Catalogue no: **GEP 8880**

BEATLES: INTERVIEW PICTURE DISC COLLECTION
7" Set: Released Apr '88, on Baktabak, by Baktabak Records. Catalogue no: **BAKPAK 1004**

BEATLES MILLION SELLERS
7" EP: Released Dec '85, on Parlophone, by EMI Records. Catalogue no: **GEP 8946**

BEATLES MOVIE MEDLEY
Tracks: / Beatles movie medley / I'm happy just to dance with you.
7" Single: Released May '82, on Parlophone, by EMI Records. Catalogue no: **R 6055**

BEATLES NO 1
7" EP: Released Nov '63, on Parlophone, by EMI Records. Catalogue no: **GEP 8883**

BEATLES SINGLES COLLECTON
7" Set: Released Dec '82, on Parlophone, by EMI Records. Catalogue no: **BSCP 1**

CAN'T BUY ME LOVE
Tracks: / Can't buy me love / You can't do that.
7" Pic: Released Mar '84, on Parlophone, by EMI Records. Catalogue no: **RP 5114**
CD 3": Released Jan '89, on Parlophone, by EMI Records. Catalogue no: **CD3R 5114**
7" Single: Released Mar '84, on Parlophone, by EMI Records. Catalogue no: **R 5114**

DAY TRIPPER
Tracks: / Day tripper.
7" Single: Released Dec '65, on Parlophone, by EMI Records. Catalogue no: **R 5389**

FROM ME TO YOU
Tracks: / From me to you / Thank you girl.
7" Single: Released Apr '83, on Parlophone, by EMI Records. Catalogue no: **R 5015**
7" Pic: Released Apr '83, on Parlophone, by EMI Records. Deleted '87. Catalogue no: **RP 5015**
CD 3": Released Nov '88, on Parlophone, by EMI Records. Catalogue no: **CD3R 5015**

GET BACK
Tracks: / Get back / Don't let me down.
7" Single: Released Apr '69, on Apple, by Apple Records. Catalogue no: **R 5777**
7" Pic: Released Apr '89, on Parlophone, by EMI Records. Catalogue no: **RP 5777**
CD 3": Released Aug '89, on Parlophone, by EMI Records. Catalogue no: **CD3R 5777**

HARD DAY'S NIGHT, A (EP) VOL. 1
7" EP: Released Nov '64, on Parlophone, by EMI Records. Catalogue no: **GEP 8920**

HARD DAY'S NIGHT, A (EP) VOL. 2
7" EP: Released Dec '64, on Parlophone, by EMI Records. Catalogue no: **GEP 8924**

HARD DAY'S NIGHT, A (SINGLE)
Tracks: / Hard day's night, A / Things we said today.
CD 3": Released Feb '89, on Parlophone, by EMI Records. Catalogue no: **CD3R 5160**
7" Pic: Released Jul '84, on Parlophone, by EMI Records. Catalogue no: **RP 5160**
7" Single: Released Jul '64, on Parlophone, by EMI Records. Catalogue no: **R 5160**

HELLO GOODBYE
Tracks: / Hello goodbye / I am the walrus.
7" Pic: Released Nov '87, on Parlophone, by EMI Records. Catalogue no: **RP 5655**
CD 3": Released Jun '89, on Parlophone, by EMI Records. Catalogue no: **CD3R 5655**
7" Single: Released Nov '67, on Parlophone, by EMI Records. Catalogue no: **R 5655**

HELP (SINGLE)
Tracks: / Help / I'm down.
7" Pic: Released Jul '85, on Parlophone, by EMI Records. Catalogue no: **RP 5305**
CD 3": Released Mar '89, on Parlophone, by EMI Records. Catalogue no: **CD3R 5305**
7" Single: Released Jul '85, on Parlophone, by EMI Records. Catalogue no: **R 5305**

HEY JUDE (SINGLE)
Tracks: / Hey Jude / Revolution.
12" Pic: Released Aug '88, on Parlophone, by EMI Records. Catalogue no: **12RP 5722**
7" Single: Released Aug '88, on Parlophone, by EMI Records. Catalogue no: **R 5722**
12" Single: Released Aug '88, on Parlophone, by EMI Records. Catalogue no: **12R 5722**
7" Pic: Released Aug '88, on Parlophone, by EMI Records. Catalogue no: **RP 5722**
CD 3": Released Jul '89, on Parlophone, by EMI Records. Catalogue no: **CD3R 5722**

I FEEL FINE
Tracks: / I feel fine / She's a woman.
CD 3": Released Feb '89, on Parlophone, by EMI Records. Catalogue no: **CD3R 5200**
7" Single: Released Nov '84, on Parlophone, by EMI Records. Catalogue no: **R 5200**
7" Pic: Released Nov '84, on Parlophone, by EMI Records. Catalogue no: **PR 5200**

I WANT TO HOLD YOUR HAND
Tracks: / I want to hold your hand / This boy.
7" Pic: Released Nov '83, on Parlophone, by EMI Records. Catalogue no: **RP 5084**
CD 3": Released Jan '89, on Parlophone, by EMI Records. Catalogue no: **CD3R 5084**
7" Single: Released Nov '63, on Parlophone, by EMI Records. Catalogue no: **R 5084**

LADY MADONNA
Tracks: / Lady Madonna / Inner light, The.
7" Pic: Released 14 Mar '88, on Parlophone, by EMI Records. Catalogue no: **RP 5675**
CD 3": Released Jul '89, on Parlophone, by EMI Records. Catalogue no: **CD3R 5675**
7" Single: Released Mar '68, on Parlophone, by EMI Records. Catalogue no: **R 5675**

LET IT BE (SINGLE)
Tracks: / Let it be / You know my name (look up the number).
7" Pic: Released Mar '89, on Parlophone, by EMI Records. Catalogue no: **RP 5833**
CD 3": Released Sep '89, on Parlophone, by EMI Records. Catalogue no: **CD3R 5833**
7" Single: Released Mar '70, on Apple, by Apple Records. Catalogue no: **R 5833**

LIVE RECORDINGS (1962)
Note: 15 x 7" singles in a box with free poster. All in picture sleeves.
7" Set: Released '88, on Baktabak, by Baktabak Records. Catalogue no: **TABOKS 1001**

LONG TALL SALLY
Tracks: / Long tall Sally.
7" EP: Released Aug '64, on Parlophone, by EMI Records. Catalogue no: **GEP 8913**

LOVE ME DO
Tracks: / Love me do / P.S. I love you.
12" Single: Released Nov '82, on Parlophone, by EMI Records. Catalogue no: **12R 4949**
7" Single: Released Oct '82, on Parlophone, by EMI Records. Catalogue no: **R 4949**
7" Pic: Released Oct '82, on Parlophone, by EMI Records. Catalogue no: **RP 4949**
CD 3": Released Nov '88, on Parlophone, by EMI Records. Catalogue no: **CD3R 4949**

MAGICAL MYSTERY TOUR (SINGLE)
7" Set: Released Oct '79, on Parlophone, by EMI Records. Catalogue no: **SMMT 1**

MY BONNIE
Tracks: / My bonnie.
7" Single: Released Jun '63, on Polydor, by Polydor Ltd. Deleted Jun '66. Catalogue no: **NH 66833**

NOWHERE MAN
Tracks: / Nowhere man.
7" EP: Released Jul '66, on Parlophone, by EMI Records. Catalogue no: **GEP 8952**

PAPERBACK WRITER
Tracks: / Paperback writer / Rain.
7" Single: Released Jun '86, on Parlophone, by EMI Records. Catalogue no: **R 5452**
7" Pic: Released Jun '86, on Parlophone, by EMI Records. Catalogue no: **RP 5452**
CD 3": Released Apr '89, on Parlophone, by EMI Records. Catalogue no: **CD3R 5452**

PLEASE PLEASE ME (SINGLE)
Tracks: / Please please me / Ask me why.
CD 3": Released Nov '88, on Parlophone, by EMI Records. Catalogue no: **CD3R 4983**
7" Single: Released Jan '83, on Parlophone, by EMI Records. Catalogue no: **R 4983**
7" Pic: Released Jan '83, on Parlophone, by EMI Records. Catalogue no: **RP 4983**

SEARCHIN'
Tracks: / Searchin' / Money / Till there was you.
7" Single: Released Nov '82, on Audio Fidelity(USA), by Audio Fidelity (USA). Catalogue no: **AFS 1**

SGT.PEPPER'S LONELY HEARTS CLUB BAND (SINGLE)
Tracks: / Sgt. Pepper's lonely hearts club band.
7" Single: Released Sep '78, on Parlophone, by EMI Records. Catalogue no: **R 6022**

SHE LOVES YOU
Tracks: / She loves you / I'll get you.
7" Single: Released Sep '83, on Parlophone, by EMI Records. Catalogue no: **R 5055**
7" Pic: Released Aug '83, on Parlophone, by EMI Records. Deleted '87. Catalogue no: **RP 5055**
CD 3": Released Nov '88, on Parlophone, by EMI Records. Catalogue no: **CD3R 5055**

SOMETHING
Tracks: / Something / Come together.
7" Pic: Released Sep '89, on Parlophone, by EMI Records. Catalogue no: **RP 5814**
7" Single: Released Oct '89, on Parlophone, by EMI Records. Catalogue no: **RP 5814**
CD 3": Released Sep '89, on Parlophone, by EMI Records. Catalogue no: **CD3R 5814**
7" Single: Released Oct '69, on Apple, by Apple Records. Catalogue no: **R 5814**

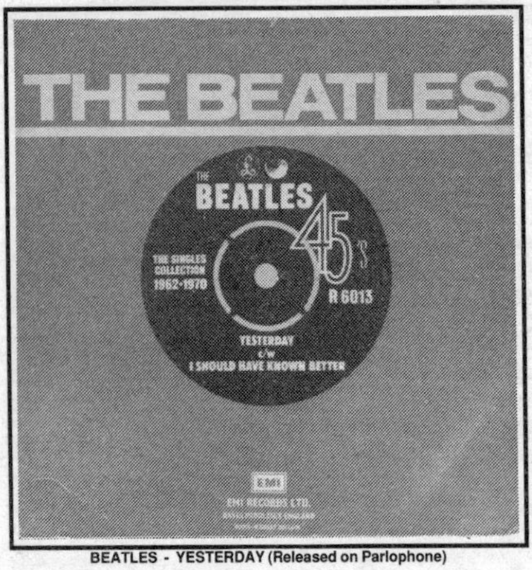

BEATLES - YESTERDAY (Released on Parlophone)

STRAWBERRY FIELDS FOREVER
Tracks: / Penny Lane / Strawberry Fields forever.
7" Pic: Released Feb '87, on Parlophone, by EMI Records. Catalogue no: **RP 5570**
CD 3": Released May '89, on Parlophone, by EMI Records. Catalogue no: **CD3R 5570**
7" Single: Released Feb '67, on Parlophone, by EMI Records. Catalogue no: **R 5570**

TICKET TO RIDE
Tracks: / Ticket to ride / Yes it is.
7" Pic: Released Apr '85, on Parlophone, by EMI Records. Catalogue no: **RP 5265**
7" Single: Released Apr '85, on Parlophone, by EMI Records. Catalogue no: **R 5265**
CD 3": Released Mar '89, on Parlophone, by EMI Records. Catalogue no: **CD3R 5265**

TONY SHERIDAN FEATURING THE BEATLES
Tracks: / Why / Cry for a shadow / Let's dance / Ya ya / What'd i say / Ruby baby / Take out some insurance / Sweet georgia brown.
7" EP: Released Dec '81, on Parlophone, by EMI Records. Catalogue no: **BEP 14**

TWIST AND SHOUT (see panel on previous page)
Tracks: / Twist and shout / Taste of honey, A / Do you want to know a secret / There's a place.
7" EP: Released '63, on Parlophone, by EMI Records. Catalogue no: **GEP 8882**

WE CAN WORK IT OUT
Tracks: / We can work it out / Day tripper.
7" Pic: Released Nov '85, on Parlophone, by EMI Records. Catalogue no: **RP 5389**
7" Single: Released Nov '85, on Parlophone, by EMI Records. Catalogue no: **R 5389**
CD 3": Released Apr '89, on Parlophone, by EMI Records. Catalogue no: **CD3R 5389**

YELLOW SUBMARINE(SINGLE)
Tracks: / Yellow submarine / Eleanor Rigby.
7" Pic: Released Aug '86, on Parlophone, by EMI Records. Catalogue no: **RP 5493**
7" Single: Released Aug '86, on Parlophone, by EMI Records. Catalogue no: **R 5493**
CD 3": Released May '89, on Parlophone, by EMI Records. Catalogue no: **CD3R 5493**

YESTERDAY (see panel above)
Tracks: / Yesterday / I should have known better.
7" Single: Released Mar '76, on Parlophone, by EMI Records. Catalogue no: **R 6013**

YESTERDAY (EP)
7" EP: Released Mar '66, on Parlophone, by EMI Records. Catalogue no: **GEP 8948**

Beatmasters

BURN IT UP
Tracks: / Burn it up
7" Single: Released Sep '88, on Rhythm King, by Mute Records. Catalogue no: **LEFT 27**
12" Single: Released Sep '88, on Rhythm King, by Mute Records. Catalogue no: **LEFT 27 T**

HEY DJ (see panel below)
Tracks: / Hey DJ / I can't dance to that music your playing / Ska train.
7" Single: Released Jul '89, on Rhythm King, by Mute Records. Catalogue no: **LEFT 034 SP**
7" Single: Released Jul '89, on Rhythm King, by Mute Records. Catalogue no: **LEFT 034**
12" Single: Released Jul '89, on Rhythm King, by Mute Records. Catalogue no: **LEFT 034 T**

ROCK DA HOUSE
Tracks: / Rock da house.
7" Single: Released Jul '87, on Rhythm King, by Mute Records. Catalogue no: **LEFT 11**
12" Single: Released Jul '87, on Rhythm King, by Mute Records. Catalogue no: **LEFT 11T**

WARM LOVE
Tracks: / Warm love.
7" Single: Released Jul '89, on Rhythm King, by Mute Records. Catalogue no: **LEFT 037**
12" Single: Released Jul '89, on Rhythm King, by Mute Records. Catalogue no: **LEFT 037T**

WHO'S IN THE HOUSE
Tracks: / Who's in the house.
12" Single: Released Mar '89, on Rhythm King, by Mute Records. Catalogue no: **LEFT 031T**
7" Single: Released Mar '89, on Rhythm King, by Mute Records. Catalogue no: **LEFT 031**

Beatnigs

TELEVISION
Tracks: / Television.
7" Single: Released Nov '88, on Alternative Tentacles, by Alternative Tentacles Records. Catalogue no: **VIRUS 71**
12" Single: Released Nov '88, on Alternative Tentacles, by Alternative Tentacles Records. Catalogue no: **VIRUS 71T**

Beatroots

UNNECESSARY WAR
Tracks: / Unnecessary war.
7" Single: Released Feb '82, on Beatroot, Catalogue no: **BR 1A**

Beats Workin'

BURN OUT DON'T FADE AWAY
Tracks: / Burn out don't fade away / Burn out don't fade away (instrumental).
7" Single: Released Apr '89, on ffrr, by London Records. Catalogue no: **FFR 26**
12" Single: Released Mar '89, on ffrr, by London Records. Catalogue no: **FFRX 26**

SURE BEATS WORKIN'
Tracks: / Sure beats workin' / Extacy / Sure beats workin' (It's a trip mix) (On 12" only) / Sure beats workin' (balearic beats) (On 12" only).
Note: "To the devotees of hip 'acid house' clubland this is the first of the new 'Balearic' sound singles so heavily featured in the press (I-D London standard etc), which is currently bringing the sounds of Ibiza so forcefully into the UK club scene. To many others this is a great house - style version of the theme from TV's whistle test show. 'Beats Workin' are 'Nicky Holloway' (who runs London's Trip Club), George Georgiou and Doug Gordon." (London records, July 1988)
12" Single: Released Jul '88, on ffrr, by London Records. Catalogue no: **FFRX 8**
7" Single: Released Jul '88, on ffrr, by London Records. Catalogue no: **FFR 8**

Beatstreet(group)

EGG ON MY FACE
7" Single: Released Nov '84, on AWA, Catalogue no: **SAW 011**

Beattie, Johnny

GLASGOW RAP
Tracks: / Glasgow rap.
7" Single: Released Nov '83, on Klub, by Klub Records. Catalogue no: **KLUB 44**

SINOOKER
Tracks: / Sinooker / Wee cock sparra, The.
7" Single: Released Nov '88, on Igus, by Klub Records. Catalogue no: **KLUB 56**

SNOOKER
Tracks: / Snooker.
7" Single: Released Nov '85, on Klub, by Klub Records. Catalogue no: **KLUB 52**

Beau Weevil

WOOLY BULLY
Tracks: / Wooly bully.
7" Single: Released Jun '82, on Forever, Catalogue no: **FORE 2**

BEATMASTERS - HEY DJ (Released on Rhythm King)

Beautiful Americans

BEAUTIFUL AMERICANS
Tracks: / Beautiful Americans.
12" Single: Released Jun '82, on Compact, Deleted Jun '85. Catalogue no: **ACTX 5**
7" Single: Released Jun '82, on Compact, Deleted Jun '85. Catalogue no: **ACT 5**

Beautiful Pea Green

CHANCE
Tracks: / Chance.
12" Single: Released Nov '84, on Rough Trade, by Rough Trade Records. Catalogue no: **BOAT 1**

POWERHOUSE
Tracks: / Powerhouse / Hammers of Islam.
7" Single: Released May '88, on Third Mind, by Third Mind Records. Catalogue no: **TMS 09**

Beautiful People

BEAUTIFUL PEOPLE
Tracks: / Beautiful people.
12" Single: Released Jan '89, on Gee Street, by Gee Street Records. Catalogue no: **GEE 5008**

LET'S GO BACK TO SAN FRANCISCO
Tracks: / Let's go back to San Francisco / Silicon city.
7" Single: Released Aug '81, on RK, by RK Records. Deleted Aug '84. Catalogue no: **RK 1035**

Beautiful South

SONG FOR WHOEVER
Tracks: / Song for whoever.
7" Single: Released Jun '89, on Go Discs, by Chrysalis Records. Catalogue no: **GOD 32**
12" Single: Released Jun '89, on Go Discs, by Chrysalis Records. Catalogue no: **GODX 32**
7" Single: Released Jun '89, on Go Discs, by Chrysalis Records. Catalogue no: **GODP 32**

YOU KEEP IT ALL IN
Tracks: / You keep it all in.
12" Single: Released Sep '89, on Go Discs, by Chrysalis Records. Catalogue no: **12 GOD 36**
7" Single: Released Sep '89, on Go Discs, by Chrysalis Records. Catalogue no: **GOD 36**

Beauty

BEAUTY (SINGLE) Various artists
Tracks: / Beauty: *Various artists.*
7" Single: Released '82, on Occult, Catalogue no: **CUS 1351**

Beauvoir, Jean

FEEL THE HEAT
Tracks: / Feel the heat / Standing in the line of fire.
7" Single: Released Aug '86, on Virgin, by Virgin Records. Deleted May '88. Catalogue no: **VS 834**
7" Single: Released Aug '86, on Virgin, by Virgin Records. Deleted May '88. Catalogue no: **VS 834-12**

GAMBLIN' MAN
Tracks: / Gamblin' man (Not on 12') / Gamblin' man (go-go mix) (CD & 12" only) / Dangerously (On all versions) / Gamblin man (African thang mix) (12" only) / Feel the heat (CD only).
7" Single: Released Mar '88, on Virgin, by Virgin Records. Catalogue no: **VS 1056**
12" Single: Released Mar '88, on Virgin, by Virgin Records. Catalogue no: **VST 1056**
CD 5": Released Aug '88, on Virgin, by Virgin Records. Catalogue no: **VSCD 1056**

MISSING THE YOUNG DAYS*
Tracks: / Crazy / Missing the young days.
12" Single: Released Jan '87, on Virgin, by Virgin Records. Deleted May '88. Catalogue no: **VS 874-12**
7" Single: Released Jan '87, on Virgin, by Virgin Records. Deleted May '88. Catalogue no: **VS 874**

Beavi & Hippy Dread

HEROES
Tracks: / Heroes / Wolf & sheep.
12" Single: Released Apr '86, on Mega, by Mega Records. Catalogue no: **MG 001**

Becaud, Gilbert

Biographical details: This MoR singer is long-standing major star in his nativ France, and normally records in his nativ tongue. A brief 1975 excursion in Englis language yielded a one-off British Top 1 single *"A Little Love And Understanding* Being part of the insular French music bus ness, however, he has stuck to his tried an tested market ever since B.M. 84.

LITTLE LOVE & UNDERSTANDING, A (OLD GOLD)
7" Single: Released Sep '85, on Old Gol by Old Gold Records. Catalogue no: **O**

9539

LITTLE LOVE & UNDERSTANDING, A (SINGLE)
Tracks: / Little love and understanding, A.
7" Single: Released Mar '75, on Decca, by Decca Records. Deleted Mar '78. Catalogue no: **F 135 37**

Beck, Jeff

Biographical details: Born in Surrey, Jeff Beck first made his name in the mid-60's when he replaced Eric Clapton in the Yardbirds. He played a prominent role on such hits as Shapes Of Things and Over Under Sideways Down. Leaving the group in December 1966 he was quickly collared by pop maestro Mickie Most to record a catchy ditty called *"Hi-Ho Silver Lining"*. Most wanted to get the song on the market before anyone else and singer-guitarist Beck was the nearest musician around at the time. Hi-Ho was not a giant hit -- it peaked at No 14 -- but it stayed on the Top Fifty for 14 weeks and established itself as a party favourite. A couple of former hits, *"Tallyman"* and *"Love Is Blue"*, followed. Beck formed his own group, including future stars Rod Stewart (vocals) and Ron Wood (bass). After hitting the Top Twenty in a duet single with Donovan, *"Goo Goo Barabajagal (Love Is Hot)"*, the group had a Top Forty LP with *"Cosa Nostra Beck-Ola"*, a hard and heavy rock album. Shortly afterwards Stewart and Wood left to join the Faces and Beck suffered a car accident which kept him out of action for 18 months. A new Jeff Beck Group emerged in 1971 and included Cozy Powell on drums. This was fairly short-lived and was followed by another brief ensemble, Jeff Beck, Tim Bogert and Carmine Appice. The trio's self-titled album hit the Top Thirty in '73. Beck's real return to form came in the mid-70's: the albums *"Blow By Blow"* and *"Wired"* featured some of his best guitar work and pleased both critics and his loyal audience, but neither were major UK sellers. A long lay-off was ended in 1980 with the album *"There And Back"*, followed by another period of inactivity. This was typical of his erratic and fragmented recording career though it did not alter his status as one of rock's most important guitarists. He had taken Eric Clapton's place in the Yardbirds and had subsequently earned himself a place alongside Clapton in the annals of rock history for his influential and creating style of playing. Jeff Beck would like to be thought of as a great guitarist, as he undoubtedly was. But many will remember him for what he calls his "albatross", that out-of-character singalong classic heard at every party, disco, jukebox and Radio One Roadshow. And as if to haunt him, *"Hi-Ho Silver Lining"* returned to the Top Twenty in 1972 and reached the lower end of the charts in 1982. (Bob MacDonald, 1984.)

Beck, Bogert, A rock trio of 1973 with guitarist Jeff Beck, bassist Tim Bogert and drummer Carmen Appice.(Donald Clarke 23 August 1988)

Beck, Jeff The guitarist was born in 1944 in Surrey with Eric Clapton; with Eric Clapton and Jimmy Page, he is one of the triumvirate of great British rock guitarists who emerged in the 1960s: all three of them played with the Yardbirds. He made commercial singles produced by Mickie Most while attempting to assemble a hard-rock unit for album work. *Truth* was made in 1968 with Rod Stewart vocals, Nicky Hopkins on piano, Mickey Waller on drums and Ron Wood on bass; it is something of a classic in Beck's fractured recording career. *Beck-Ola* in 1969 with Tony Newman replacing Waller was more of the same: Beck's slide guitar is marvelous on *All Shook Up*, but Most's production was unsuitable. Beck's next group had vocalist Bobby Tench, Max Middleton on keyboards, Clive Chaman on bass and Cozy Powell on drums; two albums *Rough And Ready* and *Jeff Beck Group* in 1971-72 lacked good songs, as did the long awaited Beck-Bogert-Appice supertrio in 1973 (with the Vanilla Fudge rhythm section of bassist Tim Bogert and drummer Carmine Appice). Beck resolved his vocalist/material problem by turning to jazz-rock fusion composed spontaneously in the studio: *Blow By Blow* in 1975 had drummer Richard Bailey, bassist Phil Chen and Middleton on keyboards; it also had Beck's voice-tube technique of channeling the guitar sound through a tube to be 'voiced' by the guitarist's mouth, a long favourite trick on stage. *Wired* in 1976 was the first collaboration with keyboardist Jan Hammer, which also included *There And Back*. Beck linked with Page and Led Zeppelin vocalist Robert Plant as the Honeydrippers, recording R&B standards for a hit 1984 album; then with Stewart for more rock-oriented *Flash* in 1985. (Donald Clarke 23 August 1988).

AMBITIOUS
Tracks: / Ambitious / Escape.
12" Single: Released Mar '86, on Epic, by CBS Records. Catalogue no: **TA 6981**
7" Single: Released Mar '86, on Epic, by CBS Records. Catalogue no: **A 6981**

FINAL PEACE
Tracks: / Final peace / Scatterbrain / Too much to lose / Led boots.
7" EP: Released Feb '81, on Epic, by CBS Records. Deleted Feb '84. Catalogue no: **EPCA 1009**

HI HO SILVER LINING
Tracks: / Hi ho silver lining / Beck's bolero / Rock my plimsoul.
7" Pic: Released Oct '82, on RAK Replay, by EMI Records. Deleted '87. Catalogue no: **RRP 3**
7" Single: Released Sep '82, on RAK Replay, by EMI Records. Catalogue no: **RR 3**
12" Single: Released Sep '82, on RAK Replay, by EMI Records. Deleted '87. Catalogue no: **12 RR 3**
7" Single: Released Mar '67, on Columbia, by EMI Records. Deleted Mar '70. Catalogue no: **DB 8151**

I'VE BEEN DRINKING
Tracks: / I've been drinking.
7" Single: Released May '73, on RAK, by EMI Records. Deleted May '76. Catalogue no: **RR 4**

LOVE IS BLUE
Tracks: / Love is blue.
7" Single: Released Feb '68, on Columbia, by EMI Records. Deleted Feb '71. Catalogue no: **DB 8359**

TALLYMAN
Tracks: / Tallyman.
7" Single: Released Aug '67, on Columbia, by EMI Records. Deleted Aug '70. Catalogue no: **DB 8227**

WILD THING
Tracks: / Wild thing / Get us all in the end / Night hawk (*=extra track on 12" only).
7" Single: Released Jul '86, on Epic, by CBS Records. Catalogue no: **A 7271**
12" Single: Released Jul '86, on Epic, by CBS Records. Catalogue no: **TA 7271**

Beck, Kenny

SHUT YOUR CRACK
Tracks: / Shut your crack.
12" Single: Released Mar '89, on White Label (1), Catalogue no: **12BECK 5**

Beck, Robin

FIRST TIME, THE
Tracks: / First time.
12" Single: Released Jul '88, on Mercury, by Phonogram Ltd. Deleted 31 Jul '89. Catalogue no: **MERX 270**
7" Single: Released Jul '88, on Mercury, by Phonogram Ltd. Deleted 31 Jul '89. Catalogue no: **MER 270**

SAVE UP ALL YOUR TEARS
Tracks: / Save up all your tears / Jealous hearts / First time.
CD 5": Released 27 Feb '89, on Phonogram, by Phonogram Ltd. Catalogue no: **CD MERCD 278**
12" Single: Released 27 Feb '89, on Phonogram, by Phonogram Ltd. Deleted Oct '89. Catalogue no: **MERX 278**
7" Single: Released 27 Feb '89, on Phonogram, by Phonogram Ltd. Deleted Oct '89. Catalogue no: **MER 278**

Beckers, Chris

KEEP ON DANCING
Tracks: / Keep on dancing.
7" Single: Released Oct '84, on Steinar, by Steinar Records (UK). Catalogue no: **STE 735**
12" Single: Released Oct '84, on Steinar, by Steinar Records (UK). Catalogue no: **STE 1235**

Becket

SOCA
Tracks: / Soca / Soca (dance mix).
7" Single: Released Aug '86, on Bumble Bee, Catalogue no: **7 BUMB 101**
12" Single: Released Aug '86, on Bumble Bee, Catalogue no: **BUMB 101**

Beckett, Chris

SHE WEARS MY RING
Tracks: / She wears my ring / Diana.
7" Single: Released Jun '81, on Homespun (Ireland), by Outlet Records. Catalogue no: **HS 046**

Beckett, Peter

I'M CRYING
Tracks: / I'm crying / High expectations.
7" Single: Released Apr '85, on MCA, by MCA Records. Catalogue no: **MCA 959**

Beckford, Keeling

BIG WHEEL (SPINNING WHEEL)
Tracks: / Big wheel (spinning wheel) / Oh Moses.
12" Single: Released Dec '82, on Vista Sounds, by Vista Sounds Records. Catalogue no: **VS 12001**

Beckford, Vincent

YOU
Tracks: / You.
12" Single: Released Jun '85, on BWB, Catalogue no: **BWB 003**

Bednarczyk, Stefan

WHEN SANTA KISSED THE FAIRY ON THE CHRISTMAS TREE
Tracks: / When Santa kissed the fairy on the Christmas tree.
7" Single: Released Nov '83, on ASV (Academy Sound & Vision), by Academy Sound & Vision Records. Deleted Jul '87. Catalogue no: **ASV 105**

Bedrock Gang

FLINTSTONES ROCK
Tracks: / Flintstone rock (part 1) / Flintstone rock (part 2) / Rub-a-dub party in bedrock. Note: * track on 12" version only.
7" Single: Released Oct '87, on Mango, by Island Records. Deleted Apr '88. Catalogue no: **IS 339**
12" Single: Released Oct '87, on Mango, by Island Records. Deleted Apr '88. Catalogue no: **12IS 339**

Bedrocks

OB LA DI OB LA DA
Tracks: / Ob la di ob la da.
7" Single: Released Jun '68, on Columbia, by EMI Records. Deleted Jun '71. Catalogue no: **DB 8516**

Bedtime Boys

NO SLEEP TILL BEDTIME
Tracks: / No sleep till bedtime.
12" Single: Released Sep '87, on Def Jim, Catalogue no: **SNOOZE 1**

Bedtime for Bonzo

EAT ME
Tracks: / Eat me.
12" Single: Released 15 May '87, on Nude Mountain, Catalogue no: **NUDE 004**

Bee, Celi

HOLD YOUR HORSES BABE
Tracks: / Hold your horses babe.
7" Single: Released Jun '78, on TK, Deleted Jun '81. Catalogue no: **TKR 6032**

Bee Gees

Biographical details: Barry Gibb and his younger non-identical twin brothers Robin and Maurice, formedas a child group in Manchester, before emigrating to Australia with their parents in 1958. In the mid-Sixties, while still in their teens, they became radio and TV favourites in Australia and established themselves as one of that country'smajor chart acts. They had taken their name from the eldest brother's initials.Australian entrepreneur Robert Stigwood figured that they would do well in their native Britain. Thus they returned in 1967, just as "Spicks and Specks" was hitting No.1 downunder. They were now a five-piece, having recruited guitarist Vince Melouney and drummer Colin Petersen. Manager Stigwood's prediction proved correct, and the group quickly achieved their first British and American hit. "New York Mining disaster 1941" made the Top 20 on both sides of the Atlantic. Written by the three brothers, it was one of the strangest debut hits in chart histroy - here was a group establishing themselves in the late Sixties pop market with a sombre, doomy piece about a catastrophe from another era. The next two singles, "To Love Somebody" and "Holiday", both made the US Top 20 but fared badly in Britain. This situation was quickly rectified by "Massachusetts," a four week UK No. 1 in the autumn of '67.It was to be their longest run at the top, though three further numbers ones were later achieved. By the end of '67 the Bee Gees were recognised as highly talented singers and songwriters. Two more UK Top Tenners, "World" and "Words", were followed by the less successful double A side"Jumbo"/"The Singer Sang His song". The group were adept at responding to the occasional stiff, and the next 45 "I've Gotta Get A Message To You" gave them their second British No. 1 and their first American Top 10 hit. It was another doom-laden song, this time about a murderer on Death Row desperate to communicate with his woman. "I Started A Joke" was an even bigger US hit, but internal frictions were now starting to emerge within the group. Few were aware that their 1969 hit "First Of May", though composed by all three Gibbs, featured only Barry and Maurice on vocals - Robin had been on holiday at the time of recording, and the others had simply gone ahead without him. This was a sympton of the animosity that was growing between Robin and his two brothers; he left and went solo, obtaining a big hit with "Saved By The Bell", but he could not sustain his success. The two sidesmen, Melouney and Petersen, also left within a short space of one another. In similar style to Robin's one-off smash, the Bee Gees duo managed oneNo.2 hit with "Don't Forget To Remember" but soon floundered. The music press had had a field day reporting every acrimonious twist and turn of the group's breakup, and the strain was showing. The Bee Gees went for over a year without a Top 40 single, either in Britain or the States; and whereas their previous five albums had all hit the UK Top 20, 1970's "Cucumber Castle" could do no better than No. 57. Failure brought the brothers back together.Barry, Maurice and Robin reformed as a trio in late '70, and scored their biggest US hit so far with "LonelyDays". Though hitting No.3 Stateside, it peaked at No.33 in Britain, and this sudden difference was even more pronounced with "How Can You Mend A Broken Heart' - this ballad was the Gibb's first American No.1 but failed to chart at all in Britain. Two 1972 singles, "My World" and "Run To Me", reached the Top 20 in both countries, but the brothers spent the next three years in the wilderness. Itseemed that the end had come; but in fact it was merely the end of their first era. That era had been full of dramatic ballads, strong story songs boldly sung and plaintively written. The second era began in 1975 and could hardly have been more different. Riding the mid-Seventies disco and sweet soul boom, the Gibbsused funky rhythms and emasculated harmony vocals to begin a historic string of danceable hits. From 1975 until the end of the decade, virtually every record was bigger in the US than the UK. While enormously popular at home, it was in the United States that the reborn trio found its greatest success. The albums "Main Course" and "Children Of The Universe". "Fanny (Be Tender With Love)" and "Love So Right" proved that the funky Bee Gees" could still come up with strong love ballads when they wanted to. One such ballad was "How Deep Is Your Love", a pivotal single in the group's career. Released at the end of '77, it had the honour of dethroning Debby Boone's "You Light Up My Life", a 10 week American No. 1. It also began a string of six consecutive Bee Gee No. 1s in the States. But most importantly, it ushered in the "Saturday Night Fever" soundtrack.iBee Gees, The UK vocal trio; brothers Barry (born 1946), Robin and Maurice Gibb (both born 1949, non-identical twins) were originally from the Isle of Man; the sons of bandleaders Hugh Gibb made their debut in a Manchester cinema when the record they were to mime as a pre-matinee attraction broke. They emigrated to Australia in 1958, were spotted by driver Bill Gates singing for change at a speedway track and named Bee Gees for Gates, local DJ Bill Goode, Brothers Gibb or Barry's initials: accounts differ. They were successful on the Festival label and returned to the UK in 1967, were launched by manager Robert Stigwood and had several classic late '60s hits with keening harmony, some songs written themselves, such as *New York Mining Disaster 1941*, *Massachusetts*. Marriages (Maurice to singer Lulu) and problems adjusting to fame caused them to split. Robin had solo hits including *Saved By The Bell*, Barry and Robin made flop rockstar film *Cucumber Castle*; a reunion in 1970 was not sucessful and they became an oldies act, apart from a number 1 USA hit with *How Can You Mend A Broken Heart*. Their second period began on Atlantic in the USA when producer Arif Mardin encouraged their R&B feel; *Jive Talkin'* was their second USA number one (Improvised from an instrumental track) and *Night On Broadway* saw Barry unleash a falsetto that soon became a trademark in their third career. They had unwittingly presaged the disco boom so Stigwell commissioned them to write songs for 'Saturday Night Fever', one of the biggest hit films of the decade; the album sold 30 million copies worldwide: three USA no.1 singles, *How Deep Is Your Love*, *Stayin' Alive* and *Night Fever*, were 3,4, & 1 respectively in the UK. Barry produced hit albums for Barbara Streisand, Dionne Warwick and Kenny Rogers, and made his own solo *Now Voyager* in 1984; they wrote for films Stayin' Alive (a sequel to Fever) and the disastrous Sgt Pepper's Lonely Heart's Club Band with Peter Frampton; they co-wrote *Chain Reaction* for Diana Ross, etc; as a trio they have carried on with their unique and popular vocal harmony and are still having hits today. Youngr brother Andy Gibb, born in 1958 in Brisbane, launched his own career with three straight USA no.1 singles in 1977-78, all written or co-written by his older brothers; he had other hits including duets with Olivia Newton-John and Victoria Principal, but died in 1988 just as he was poised for a comeback. (Donald Clarke 23 August 1988).

CRAZY FOR YOUR LOVE
Tracks: / Crazy for your love / You win again.
12" Single: Released Feb '88, on Warner Bros., by WEA Records. Catalogue no: **W 7966T**
7" Single: Released Feb '88, on Warner Bros., by WEA Records. Catalogue no: **W 7966**

DON'T FORGET TO REMEMBER
7" Single: Released Aug '69, on Polydor, by

BEE GEES - NIGHT FEVER (Released on RSO)

Polydor Ltd. Deleted Aug '72. Catalogue no: **56 343**

DON'T FORGET TO REMEMBER (OLD GOLD)
Tracks: / Don't forget to remember / First of May.
7" Single: Released Mar '86, on Old Gold, by Old Gold Records. Catalogue no: **OG 9583**

E.S.P.(SINGLE)
7" Single: Released Nov '87, on Warner Bros., by WEA Records. Deleted Jul '88. Catalogue no: **W 8139**
12" Single: Released Nov '87, on Warner Bros., by WEA Records. Deleted Jul '88. Catalogue no: **W 8139 T**

FIRST OF MAY
Tracks: / First of May.
7" Single: Released Feb '69, on Polydor, by Polydor Ltd. Deleted Feb '72. Catalogue no: **56 304**

HE'S A LIAR
Tracks: / He's a liar / He's a liar (part 2).
7" Single: Released Sep '81, on RSO, by Polydor Ltd. Deleted '84. Catalogue no: **RSO 81**

HOW DEEP IS YOUR LOVE
Tracks: / How deep is your love.
7" Single: Released Oct '77, on RSO, by Polydor Ltd. Deleted Oct '80. Catalogue no: **2090 259**

I.O.I.O
Tracks: / I.O.I.O.
7" Single: Released Mar '70, on Polydor, by Polydor Ltd. Deleted Mar '73. Catalogue no: **56 377**

I'VE GOTTA GET A MESSAGE TO YOU (OLD GOLD)
Tracks: / I've gotta get a message to you.
7" Single: Released Mar '86, on Old Gold, by Old Gold Records. Catalogue no: **OG 9585**

I'VE GOTTA GET A MESSAGE TO YOU (SINGLE)
Tracks: / I've gotta get a message to you.
7" Single: Released Aug '68, on Polydor, by Polydor Ltd. Deleted Aug '71. Catalogue no: **56 273**

JIVE TALKIN'
Tracks: / Jive talkin'.
7" Single: Released Jun '75, on RSO, by Polydor Ltd. Deleted Jun '78. Catalogue no: **2090 160**

JIVE TALKING (OLD GOLD)
Tracks: / Jive talkin' / You should be dancing.
7" Single: Released Mar '86, on Old Gold, by Old Gold Records. Catalogue no: **OG 9587**

JUMBO
Tracks: / Jumbo / Singer sang his song, The.
7" Single: Released Mar '68, on Polydor, by Polydor Ltd. Deleted Mar '71. Catalogue no: **56 242**

LIVING EYES (SINGLE)
Tracks: / Living eyes / I still love you.
7" Single: Released Jul '81, on RSO, by Polydor Ltd. Deleted '85. Catalogue no: **RSO 85**

LONELY DAYS
Tracks: / Lonely days.
7" Single: Released Dec '70, on Polydor, by Polydor Ltd. Deleted Dec '73. Catalogue no: **2001 194**

LOVE SO RIGHT
Tracks: / Love so right.
7" Single: Released Nov '76, on RSO, by Polydor Ltd. Deleted Nov '79. Catalogue no: **2090 207**

LOVE YOU INSIDE OUT
Tracks: / Love you inside out.
7" Single: Released Apr '79, on RSO, by Polydor Ltd. Deleted Apr '82. Catalogue no: **RSO 31**

MASSACHUSETTS (OLD GOLD)
Tracks: / Massachusetts / New York mining disaster (1941).
7" Single: Released Mar '86, on Old Gold, by Old Gold Records. Catalogue no: **OG 9581**

MASSACHUSETTS (SINGLE)
Tracks: / Massachusetts.
7" Single: Released Sep '67, on Polydor, by Polydor Ltd. Deleted Sep '70. Catalogue no: **56 192**

MY WORLD
Tracks: / My world.
7" Single: Released Jan '72, on Polydor, by Polydor Ltd. Deleted Jan '75. Catalogue no: **2058 185**

NEW YORK MINING DISASTER 1941
Tracks: / New York mining disaster 1941.
7" Single: Released Apr '67, on Polydor, by Polydor Ltd. Deleted Apr '70. Catalogue no: **56 161**

NIGHT FEVER (see panel above)
Tracks: / Night fever / Down the road.
7" Single: Released Apr '78, on RSO, by Polydor Ltd. Deleted Apr '81. Catalogue no: **RSO 002**

ONE (SINGLE)
Tracks: / One.
7" Single: Released Jun '89, on Warner Bros., by WEA Records. Catalogue no: **W2916**
CD 5": Released Jun '89, on Warner Bros., by WEA Records. Catalogue no: **W2916CD**
Cassingle: Released Jun '89, on Warner Bros., by WEA Records. Catalogue no: **W2916C**
12" Single: Released Jun '89, on Warner Bros., by WEA Records. Catalogue no: **W2916T**

ORDINARY LIVES
Tracks: / Ordinary lives.
12" Single: Released Mar '89, on Warner Bros., by WEA Records. Catalogue no: **W 7523 T**
Cassingle: Released Apr '89, on Warner Bros., by WEA Records. Catalogue no: **W 7523 C**
CD 5": Released Mar '89, on Warner Bros., by WEA Records. Catalogue no: **W 7523 CD**
7" Single: Released Mar '89, on Warner Bros., by WEA Records. Catalogue no: **W 7523**

RUN TO ME
Tracks: / Run to me.
7" Single: Released Jul '72, on Polydor, by Polydor Ltd. Deleted Jul '75. Catalogue no: **2058 255**

SOMEONE BELONGING TO SOMEONE
Tracks: / Someone belonging to someone / Saturday Night Fever medley / Night fever.
7" Single: Released Sep '83, on RSO, by Polydor Ltd. Deleted Sep '86. Catalogue no: **RSO 96**

SPIRITS HAVING FLOWN (SINGLE)
Tracks: / Spirits (having flown) / Winds of change.
7" Single: Released Jan '80, on RSO, by Polydor Ltd. Deleted Jan '83. Catalogue no: **RSO 52**

STAYIN' ALIVE
Tracks: / Stayin' alive.
7" Single: Released Feb '78, on RSO, by Polydor Ltd. Deleted Feb '81. Catalogue no: **2090 267**

TO LOVE SOMEBODY
Tracks: / To love somebody.
7" Single: Released Jul '67, on Polydor, by Polydor Ltd. Deleted Jul '70. Catalogue no: **56 178**

TOMORROW TOMORROW
Tracks: / Tomorrow tomorrow.
7" Single: Released Jun '69, on Polydor, by Polydor Ltd. Deleted Jun '72. Catalogue no: **56 331**

TOO MUCH HEAVEN
Tracks: / Too much heaven.
7" Single: Released Nov '78, on RSO, by Polydor Ltd. Deleted Nov '81. Catalogue no: **RSO 25**

TRAGEDY
Tracks: / Tragedy.
7" Single: Released Feb '79, on RSO, by Polydor Ltd. Deleted Feb '82. Catalogue no: **RSO 27**

WORDS
Tracks: / Words.
Note: See under Gibb, Robin
7" Single: Released Jan '68, on Polydor, by Polydor Ltd. Deleted Jan '71. Catalogue no: **56 229**

WORLD
Tracks: / World.
7" Single: Released Nov '67, on Polydor, by Polydor Ltd. Deleted Nov '70. Catalogue no: **56 220**

YOU SHOULD BE DANCING
Tracks: / You should be dancing.
7" Single: Released Jul '76, on RSO, by Polydor Ltd. Deleted Jul '79. Catalogue no: **2090 195**

YOU WIN AGAIN
Tracks: / You win again / Backtafunk.
12" Pic: Released Sep '87, on Warner Bros., by WEA Records. Deleted Jul '88. Catalogue no: **W 8351TP**
Cassingle: Released Sep '87, on Warner Bros., by WEA Records. Deleted Jul '88. Catalogue no: **W 8351C**
12" Single: Released Sep '87, on Warner Bros., by WEA Records. Catalogue no: **W 8351T**
7" Single: Released Sep '87, on Warner Bros., by WEA Records. Catalogue no: **W 8351**

Bee Vamp

OUR EYES MET ACROSS THE DISCO FLOOR
Tracks: / Our eyes met across the disco floor / Jungle fever.
12" Single: Released Jun '82, on Red Flame (1), by Red Flame Records. Catalogue no: **RF 1202**

VALIUM GIRLS
Tracks: / Valium girls.
7" Single: Released Dec '81, on Monsters In Orbit. Deleted '83. Catalogue no: **TV EYE 012**

Beef

HEAD EXPLODING EXPERIENCE
Tracks: / Head exploding experience.
7" Single: Released Aug '89, on Artlos, Catalogue no: **RAT 002**
12" Single: Released Aug '89, on Artlos, Catalogue no: **12RAT 002**

STOP THE PIGEON
Tracks: / Stop the pigeon.
7" Single: Released Mar '89, on Artlos, Catalogue no: **RAT 001**

Beefeater

NEED A JOB
Tracks: / Need a job / Soapy soutar strikes back / When a drum beats (CD single only.) / On the shore (CD single only.).
12" Single: Released Oct '88, on Wetspots, by Wetspots Records. Catalogue no: **WET 004T**

Beer, Mark

PRETTY
Tracks: / Pretty.
7" Single: Released Mar '81, on Rough Trade, by Rough Trade Records. Catalogue no: **RT 070**

Beer, Phil

DANCE WITH ME
Tracks: / Dance with me / Fairweathe friend.
7" Single: Released Aug '80, on Avada Catalogue no: **AVS 101**

Beeta

MEMORIES
Tracks: / Memories / Foreign land.
7" Single: Released Feb '85, on Omega Catalogue no: **OMG 001**

Beethoven

MY DEMISE
Tracks: / My demise / Foolish pride.
7" Single: Released Feb '80, on RCA, b BMG Records (UK). Deleted Feb '83. Cata logue no: **PB 5223**

YOU'RE THE ONE
Tracks: / You're the one / Hollywood kisses
7" Single: Released Apr '80, on RCA, b BMG Records (UK). Deleted Apr '83. Cat logue no: **PB 5250**

Beethoven (Reggae)

HIM GOOLIE GOOLIE MAN, DEM E
Tracks: / Him goolie goolie man.
12" Single: Released May '89, on Setant Catalogue no: **SET 1**

Beethoven's Kiss

WONDER OF YOU, THE
Tracks: / Wonder of you, The / Don't brea it.
7" Single: Released Jul '89, on Akashi Catalogue no: **AK 0001**

Beeto, Papa

GOLD CHAIN MONKEY
Tracks: / Gold chain monkey.
12" Single: Released Jul '89, on Carro Catalogue no: **BW 2172**

Before The War

BEFORE THE WAR
Tracks: / Before the war.
7" Single: Released 12 Jun '89, on Ste hawk, by Supertrack/EMI. Catalogue r **SHK 2**

Beggar & Co

Biographical details: Having evolved fro various soul outfits, British funk band Begg and Co hit the Top 20 in early 1981 w *"(Somebody) Help Me Out"*. Their horn se tion backed Spandau Ballet later in the ye and helped give them a British Top 3 sma andan international dance hit with *"Cha No. 1 (I Don't Need This Pressure On)"* sequel entitled *"Mule (Chant No.2)"* ca out in Beggar and Co's own name, a peaked at No. 37 in the autumn of '81. S sequent releases, such as Decemb 1981's"Monument" LP and July 198 single *"Anybody See My Trial"*, have fou a club audience but have not crossed ov to the pop charts. (Bob MacDonald 1984

LIFE
Tracks: / Life / Life (instrumental).
12" Single: Released Jun '86, on Total Co trol, by Total Control Records. Catalogue **12TOTO 9**
7" Single: Released Jun '86, on Total Co trol, by Total Control Records. Catalogue **TOTO 9**

MULE (CHANT NO.2)
Tracks: / Mule (chant no.2).
7" Single: Released Sep '81, on RCA, BMG Records (UK). Deleted Sep '84. Ca logue no: **RCA 130**

SOMEBODY HELP ME OUT
Tracks: / Somebody help me out / Ris sun.
12" Single: Released Feb '81, on Ensign Ensign Records. Deleted Feb '84. Ca logue no: **ENYT 201**
7" Single: Released Feb '81, on Ensign Ensign Records. Deleted Feb '84. Ca logue no: **ENY 201**

WE ALL WORK OUT
Tracks: / We all work out / Got to get aw
12" Single: Released Jun '82, on RCA, BMG Records (UK). Deleted Jun '85. C logue no: **RCAT 233**
7" Single: Released Jun '82, on RCA BMG Records (UK). Deleted Jun '85. C logue no: **RCA 233**

Beggar's Opera

CLASSICAL GAS
Tracks: / Classical gas / Autobahn.
7" Single: Released Oct '80, on Pho gram, by Phonogram Ltd. Deleted Oct Catalogue no: **CUT 108**

Beginning Of The End

FUNKY NASSAU
Tracks: / Funky Nassau.
12" Single: on WEA, by WEA Reco Deleted Jul '88. Catalogue no: **K 10021**
7" Single: Released Feb '74, on Atlantic

WEA Records. Deleted Feb '77. Catalogue no: **K 10021**

Begley, Philomena

OLD CROSS OF ARBOE
Tracks: / Old cross of Arboe.
7" Single: Released '88, on Homespun (Ireland), by Outlet Records. Catalogue no: **HIS 18**

ONE LOVE AT A TIME
Tracks: / One love at a time / Real men don't make quiche.
7" Single: Released Feb '87, on Ritz, by Ritz Records. Catalogue no: **RITZ 171**

SENTIMENTAL OLD YOU
Tracks: / Sentimental old you.
7" Single: Released '88, on Ritz, by Ritz Records. Catalogue no: **RITZ 080**

WAY OLD FRIENDS DO
Tracks: / Way old friends do, The / Heart to heart salesman.
7" Single: Released Apr '84, on Ritz, by Ritz Records. Catalogue no: **RITZ 065**

Behaviour Red

KE KE KE KE KE
Tracks: / Ke ke ke ke ke.
7" Single: Released Apr '82, on Dining Out, by Dining Out Records. Catalogue no: **TUX 21**

Behemoth

DEATHWINGS
Tracks: / Deathwings / Vengence.
7" Single: Released Apr '84, on Bullet Continental, by Neon Records. Catalogue no: **CONT 1**

Beki

OUT OF THE DARKNESS
Tracks: / Out of the darkness.
12" Single: Released Mar '86, on Communicate, Catalogue no: **12LITTLE 5**
12" Single: Released Mar '86, on Communicate, Catalogue no: **12LITTLE 5P**
Cassingle: Released Mar '86, on Communicate, Catalogue no: **CLITTLE 5**
7" Single: Released Mar '86, on Communicate, Catalogue no: **LITTLE 5**

Bel Airs

THERE'S ALWAYS SOMETHING THERE TO REMIND ME
Tracks: / There's always something there to remind me / Ooh baby.
7" Single: Released Nov '82, on Ensign, by Ensign Records. Deleted Nov '85. Catalogue no: **ENY 228**

Bel Canto

BLANK SHEETS
Tracks: / Blank sheets.
7" Single: Released May '88, on Crammed Discs, by Crammed Discs. Catalogue no: **CRAM 15457**

DREAMING GIRL
Tracks: / Dreaming girl.
7" Single: Released Jan '88, on Crammed Discs, by Crammed Discs. Catalogue no: **CRAM 15457**

WHITE OUT CONDITION (SINGLE)
Tracks: / White out condition.
7" Single: Released Aug '88, on Crammed Discs, by Crammed Discs. Catalogue no: **CRAM 19457**

Belafonte, Harry

Biographical details: Born in Harlem, New York in 1927, Harry Belafonte moved to Jamaica at the age of eight, before returning to the USA at the age of 13. After three years in the US Navy, he enrolled at the American Negro Theatre Workshop. He later starred in the films *"Bright Road"*, *"Carmen Jones"*, *"Island In The Sun"* and *"The World, The Flesh And The Devil"*. His first American Top 40 record came in late 1956, when he took *"Jamaica Farewell"* to No. 14. Having developed a love of folk songs, he recorded the traditional *"Banana Boat Song"* and took it to No. 5. It also gave Belafonte his first UK hit, reaching no. 2. Its famous 'Day-O' chant became a universal singalong favourite, inspiring a host of simultaneous cover versions. One of these, by the Tarriers, peaked at No. 4 in the US, one place higher than Belafonte. Other American hit versions included those by the Fontane Sisters, Steve Lawrence and Sarah Vaughan, plus a parody by Stan Freberg. In Britain, *"Banana Boat Song"* was Shirley Bassey's first hit, peaking at No. 8. Later in '57 *"Mama Look At Bubu"* reached No. 11 in the US, to be followed by *"Island In The Sun"* which hit No. 3 in the UK. Together with his albums *"Calypso"* and *"Belafonte Sings Of The Carribean"*, these hits were earning him the title King Of The Calypso'. His biggest UK success came in late 1957. *"Mary's Boy Child"* had reached No. 12 on the US charts the previous Christmas. RCA records released it in Britain in October 1957, well in advance. It reached No. 1 over a month before Christmas and stayed there until January 1958, its 7-week run at the top remaining the longest ever by a song with a Christmas theme. It was the first record to sell a million in Britain alone and returned to the chart at both of the following Yuletides. A 1978 version by Boney M was a monster hit, giving the song a second Christmas at No. 1. But much like Boney M all those years later, Belafonte's star faded a little after this massive success. His Us hits had already dried up and he only managed two more in Britain - *"Little Bernadette"* (No. 16) and another Nativity song *"Son Of Mary"* (No. 18). Then, as if to demonstrate that he no longer needed hit singles, he scored a massive American album success with his double set *"Belafonte At Carnegie Hall"*. Belafonte remains active in showbusiness. A form of salute to him hit the charts in the summer of 1981, when Dutch singer Lobo took the medley *"The Carribean Disco Show"* into the UK Top 10. (Bob MacDonald).

The singer, actor and producer was born in 1927 in New York City. He lived in Jamaica, came back to the USA at 13; he played a lead in the Oscar Hammerstein musical 'Carmen Jones' in 1954, tried pop singing and ran a restaurant in Greenwich Village. Then he discovered folk music and was signed by RCA in 1955. His first two albums were big hits, but the third, *Calypso* in 1956, was the first pop album to sell a million copies, including hit singles *Jamaica Farewell* and *Banana Boat Song* (aka *Day-O*, *Star-O*). He helped the careers of Odetta, Hugh Masekela, Miriam Makeba; recorded with Len Horne (Porgy & Bess in 1959) and Nana Mouskouri. 24 albums charted in the USA 1956-70, all but one in the top ten. He was a natural success on TV, made films including 'Island In The Sun' (controversial in 1957 for interracial theme) and 'Odds Against Tomorrow' (1959). He was active in the civil right movements, a director of the Southern Christian Leadership Conference, etc; he produced Lorraine Hansberry's play 'To Be Young, Gifted and Black' in 1969. He recorded for CBS in the late '70s; In 1988 his first album since 1981 was heavily influenced by African pop. (Donald Clarke 23 August 1988).

BANANA BOAT SONG (OLD GOLD)
Tracks: / Banana boat song / Mary's boy child.
7" Single: Released Oct '86, on Old Gold, by Old Gold Records. Catalogue no: **OG 9601**

BANANA BOAT SONG (SINGLE)
Tracks: / Banana boat song.
7" Single: Released Mar '57, on H.M.V., by EMI Records. Deleted Mar '60. Catalogue no: **POP 308**

DAY O
Tracks: / Day O / Day O (version) / Jumpin' the line (Only on 12").
7" Single: Released Jul '88, on Geffen, by Geffen Records (USA). Catalogue no: **GEF 42**
12" Single: Released Jul '88, on Geffen, by Geffen Records (USA). Catalogue no: **GEF 42T**

HOLE IN THE BUCKET
Tracks: / Hole in the bucket.
7" Single: Released Sep '61, on RCA, by BMG Records (UK). Deleted '64. Catalogue no: **RCA 1247**

ISLAND IN THE SUN
Tracks: / Island in the sun.
7" Single: Released Jun '57, on RCA, by BMG Records (UK). Deleted Jun '60. Catalogue no: **RCA 1007**

ISLAND IN THE SUN (OLD GOLD)
Tracks: / Island in the sun / Scarlet ribbons.
7" Single: Released Nov '86, on Old Gold, by Old Gold Records. Catalogue no: **OG 9640**

LITTLE BERNADETTE
Tracks: / Little Bernadette.
7" Single: Released Aug '58, on RCA, by BMG Records (UK). Deleted Aug '61. Catalogue no: **RCA 1072**

MARY'S BOY CHILD
Tracks: / Mary's boy child.
7" Single: Released Nov '57, on RCA, by BMG Records (UK). Deleted Nov '60. Catalogue no: **RCA 1022**

SCARLET RIBBONS
Tracks: / Scarlet ribbons.
7" Single: Released Sep '57, on H.M.V., by EMI Records. Deleted Sep '60. Catalogue no: **POP 360**

SON OF MARY
Tracks: / Son of Mary, The.
7" Single: Released Nov '58, on RCA, by BMG Records (UK). Deleted Nov '61. Catalogue no: **RCA 1084**

WE ARE THE WAVE
Tracks: / We are the wave / Skin to skin (Duet with Jennifer Warnes.).
Note: B-side, Skin to Skin, is a duet with Jennifer Warnes. (P) 1988 original sound recording made by EMI-Manhattan records, a division of Capitol Records Inc.
7" Single: Released Jun '88, on EMI-Manhattan, by EMI Records. Deleted Nov '88. Catalogue no: **MT 44**

Belew, Adrian

BIG ELECTRIC CAT
Tracks: / Big electric cat.
10" single: Released Jun '82, on Island, by Island Records. Catalogue no: **10 WIP 6791**

Belfairs

DRY BONES
Tracks: / Dry bones.
7" Single: Released Apr '82, on Channel Music, Catalogue no: **CHAN 002**

Belfegore

BELFEGORE
Tracks: / Belfegore.
12" Single: Released Jan '84, on Pure Freude, Deleted '85. Catalogue no: **PF 32 CK 16**

Belgian Bitch

SAME TIME, SAME FACE
Tracks: / Same time, same face / Can't say no to you / Michelle.
7" Single: Released Jun '82, on Out Of Town, Catalogue no: **HOOT 2**

Belgique

CASABLANCA
Tracks: / Casablanca / TV screens.
7" Single: Released Jun '82, on Out Of Town, Catalogue no: **HOOT 5**

Belgrano, Matt

HERE'S LOOKING AT YA
Tracks: / Here's looking at you.
7" Single: Released Nov '86, on Musik, Catalogue no: **MUK 2**
12" Single: Released Nov '86, on Musik, Catalogue no: **12 MUK 2**

Belgravia

TALKING STRANGERS
Tracks: / Talking strangers.
7" Single: Released Feb '82, on Phantom, by Mean Records. Catalogue no: **PHAN 2**

Believe It Or Not

I LIKE IT
Tracks: / I like it.
12" Single: Released Jun '88, on Subway, by Subway Records. Catalogue no: **SUB 027**

Beliner Meisterschaft

ZEITGEIST
Tracks: / Zeitgeist.
12" Single: Released '88, on Subway, by Subway Records. Catalogue no: **SUB 021**

Bell, Archie

Biographical details: Born in Houston, Texas, Archie Bell and his backing trio, the Drells, had a US No 1 in 1968 with the largely instrumental *"Tighten Up"*. Under the wing of Kenny Gamble and Leon Huff, the producers later responsible for the Philly disco sound, Archie Bell & The Drells scored another dance hit with *"I Can't Stop Dancing"*. This reached No 9 and was followed by 1969's *"There's Gonna Be A Showdown"* (No 21). Bell never had another American Top Forty single but he enjoyed British chart success in the 70's. The first UK hit, *"Here I Go Again"*, reached No 11 in '72. Signing to Philadelphia in the mid-70's, he had a second Top Twenty success in Britain with *"Soul City Walk"* in 1976. (Bob MacDonald, 1984.).

ANY TIME IS RIGHT
Tracks: / Any time is right / Harder and harder.
12" Single: Released Aug '81, on Beckett, Deleted Aug '84. Catalogue no: **BKSL 1**
7" Single: Released Aug '81, on Beckett, Deleted Aug '84. Catalogue no: **BKS 1**

DON'T LET LOVE GET YOU DOWN
Tracks: / Don't let love get you down / Where will you go when the party's over.
7" Single: Released Jun '86, on Portrait, by CBS Records. Deleted '86. Catalogue no: **A 7254**

EVERYBODY HAVE A GOOD TIME
Tracks: / Everybody have a good time.
7" Single: Released Jun '77, on Philadelphia Int., by EMI Records. Deleted '80. Catalogue no: **PIR 5179**

HERE I GO AGAIN
Tracks: / Here I go again.
7" Single: Released Sep '72, on Atlantic, by WEA Records. Catalogue no: **K 10210**

HERE I GO AGAIN (OLD GOLD)
Tracks: / Here I go again / Tighten up.
7" Single: Released Jul '72, on Old Gold, by Old Gold Records. Deleted Jul '82. Catalogue no: **OG 9096**

LOOK BACK OVER YOUR SHOULDER
Tracks: / Look back over your shoulder / Look back over your shoulder(Instrumental version).
12" Single: Released Mar '87, on Nightmare, by Nightmare Records. Catalogue no: **MARE 16**
7" Single: Released Mar '87, on Nightmare, by Nightmare Records. Catalogue no: **MARES 16**

SOUL CITY WALK
Tracks: / Soul city walk.
7" Single: Released May '76, on Philadelphia Int., by EMI Records. Deleted '79. Catalogue no: **PIR 4250**

THERE'S GONNA BE A SHOW-DOWN
Tracks: / There's gonna be a showdown.
7" Single: Released Jan '73, on Atlantic, by WEA Records. Deleted '76. Catalogue no: **K 10263**

Bell, Beckie

LET ME KNOW
Tracks: / Let me know.
Note: Pic bag
12" Single: Released Apr '87, on Carrere, Catalogue no: **CART 410**

Bell, Crawford

ANGELINE
Tracks: / Angeline / Littlest cowboy rides again.
7" Single: Released Jan '81, on Homespun (Ireland), by Outlet Records. Catalogue no: **HS 040**

EVERYTHING'S A WALTZ
Tracks: / Everything's a waltz / She has my heart.
7" Single: Released Sep '81, on Homespun (Ireland), by Outlet Records. Catalogue no: **HS 050**

IT'S HARD TO BE HUMBLE
Tracks: / It's hard to be humble / Tequilia Sheila / Last cheater's waltz.
7" Single: Released Oct '82, on Homespun (Ireland), by Outlet Records. Deleted Oct '85. Catalogue no: **HS 037**

SIOUX CITY SUE
Tracks: / Sioux city Sue / Down the trail of aching hearts.
7" Single: Released Feb '83, on Homespun (Ireland), by Outlet Records. Catalogue no: **HS 062**

STAY A LITTLE LONGER
Tracks: / Stay a little longer / Peace of mind.
7" Single: Released Feb '82, on Homespun (Ireland), by Outlet Records. Catalogue no: **HS 056**

Bell, Eric

LONELY MAN
Tracks: / Lonely man / Anyone seen my baby.
7" Single: Released Nov '81, on Mr.Sam, by Mr.Sam Music. Deleted Nov '84. Catalogue no: **HOS 16**

Bell, Freddy

GIDDY UP A DING DONG (OLD GOLD)
Tracks: / Giddy up a ding dong.
7" Single: Released Jan '85, on Old Gold, by Old Gold Records. Catalogue no: **OG 9483**

GIDDY UP A DING DONG (ORIGINAL)
Tracks: / Giddy up a ding dong.
78 rpm: Released '56, on Mercury (Pye), Deleted '58. Catalogue no: **MT 122**

Bell & James

LIVIN' IT UP (FRIDAY NIGHT)
Tracks: / Living it up (Friday night).
7" Single: Released Mar '79, on A&M, by A&M Records. Deleted '82. Catalogue no: **AMS 7424**

Bell, Jim

PITTER PATTER
Tracks: / Pitter patter / Beat goes on.
7" Single: Released Aug '81, on FX, Deleted '84. Catalogue no: **FX 5**
7" Single: on Target, by Target Records. Catalogue no: **TAR 002**

TIME TICKING AWAY
Tracks: / Time ticking away.
7" Single: Released Mar '85, on Jet, by Jet Records. Catalogue no: **JET 7045**
12" Single: Released Mar '85, on Jet, by Jet Records. Catalogue no: **JET 12045**
12" Single: Released Jun '84, on Target, by Target Records. Catalogue no: **TAR 005**

Bell, Lloyd

SHE WILL BE WAITING
Tracks: / She will be waiting.
12" Single: Released Nov '82, on Copasetic, by Copasetic Records. Catalogue no: **COPDIS 7**

Bell, Madelaine

Biographical details: Bell, Madelaine is a fine singer who was born in 1942 in Newark, New Hersey, sang in a gospel group at 14, toured the UK in 'Black Nativity' show in 1962 and was subsequently based here. She became a cabaret singer on the club circuit and signed with EMI; later with Philips. She joined the session group Blue Mink in 1969, had hit with first single *Melting Pot*, stayed with them while signing solo to RCA and continuing as a session sisnger. In the late '70s she was broadcasting with the BBC Radio Orchestra/Radio Big Band, and has many fans despite never really hitting the big time. (Donald Clarke 23 August 1988).

EAST SIDE, WEST SIDE
Tracks: / East side, West side / Love finds a way to get through.
7" Single: Released Apr '82, on Deb, by Deb Records. Catalogue no: **DEB 104**

I'M NOT REALLY ME WITHOUT YOU
Tracks: / I'm not really me without you / Without you.
7" Single: Released Jan '82, on Deb, by Deb Records. Catalogue no: **DEB 102**

Bell, Maggie

Biographical details: Born in Glasgow in 1945, Maggie Bell spent the late 60's in a local group called The Power. When signing to Polydor at the end of the decade they changed their name to Stone The Crows. During the early 70's the band released four LPs and Bell's blues and soul singing won acclaim from the rock press. Their only chart album in the UK was *"Ontinuous Performance"* (sic) but while it was being recorded their guitarist, Les Harvey, was killed in an on-stage accident. They broke up in 1973, in which year Bell released a solo album entitled *"Queen Of The Night"*, produced by veteran Jerry Wexler. Her only chart success came in 1978 when she took the theme from *"Hazell"* to No 37 on the UK singles chart. In 1982 she joined B.A. Robertson to remake 1964's P.J. Proby hit *"Hold Me"*, reaching No 11. Such a level of success has otherwise eluded Bell, to the dismay of a small but loyal army of critics and fans. (Bob MacDonald, 1984.)

A singer born in 1945 in Glasgow, who first went on stage with Alex Harvey on a bet. She linked with Harvey's younger brother Les, later in Power, which was renamed Stone The Crows and had highly praised albums on Polydor, her voice being compared to that of Janis Joplin. Les Harvey was electrocuted on stage in 1972. She has done session work, was produced by Jerry Wexler, duetted with Rod Stewart and fronted Midnight Flyer in the early '80s, but has not had the commercial success her voice deserved. (Donald Clarke 23 August 1988).

CRAZY
Tracks: / Crazy / All i have to do is dream.
7" Single: Released Dec '82, on WEA, by WEA Records. Deleted Dec '87. Catalogue no: **MB 1**

GOOSE BUMPS
Tracks: / Goose bumps / Key to my heart.
7" Single: Released Sep '82, on Swansong, Catalogue no: **SSK 19428**

HAZELL
Tracks: / Hazell.
7" Single: Released Mar '78, on Swansong, Catalogue no: **SSK 19412**

Bell & Martin

TOGETHER AGAIN
Tracks: / Together again / Lonely nights.
7" Single: Released Mar '81, on Rampage (USA), Catalogue no: **RAM 48**

WHO'S KIDDING WHO?
Tracks: / Who's kidding who.
7" Single: Released Jan '83, on Deb, by Deb Records. Catalogue no: **DEB 108**

Bell, Ritchie

YOUR LOVE IS ECSTASY
Tracks: / Your love is ecstasy / Your love is ecstasy (dub).
7" Single: Released May '86, on Somar, by Somar Records. Catalogue no: **SOMAR 211011**

Bell, William

Biographical details: Born in Memphis, William Bell was an early signing to the Stax label. He scored a number of American R & B hits in the mid to late 1960's but tended to live in the shadow of his famous labelmate, Otis Redding. After Redding's death he hit the British chart for the first time, peaking at No 31 with 1968's *"Tribute To A King"*, a reference to Redding, the King of Soul. At the end of that year he hit the British Top Ten with *"Private Number"*, a duet with Judy Clay. Over the years Bell's songs have been recorded by many other artists. He enjoyed his only Top Tenner on the US pop charts in 1977, with *"Tryin' To Love Two"*. (Bob MacDonald, 1984.)

Born in 1939 in Memphis, Tennessee, this soul singer had fine hits on Stax in the early '60s but unlike other soul artists did not cross over from the R&B chart (as it was then called) to the national USA pop chart as strongly as others did, despite his fine voice. The Charly album is a good compilation of those early hits; he served in the US Army and came back in the mid-'60s with strong ballads such as *I Forget To Be Your Lover*, which did make the USA top 50. He later recorded for Mercury and finally made the USA top 10 in 1977 with *Trying To Love Two* (no.10). His songs are still covered; he later formed his own labels and had hits in the USA black chart as late as 1986. (Donald Clarke 23 August 1988).

FEELING GUILTY
Tracks: / Feeling guilty / Headline news.
7" Single: Released Feb '87, on Tout Ensemble, Catalogue no: **LUTE 10**
12" Single: Released Feb '87, on Tout Ensemble, Catalogue no: **12LUTE 10**

HEADLINE NEWS
Tracks: / Headline news.
7" Single: Released Apr '86, on Absolute, by Absolute Records. Deleted '89. Catalogue no: **LUTE 1**

I FORGOT TO BE YOUR LOVER
Tracks: / I forgot to be your lover.
7" Single: Released Oct '87, on Stax, by Fantasy Inc (USA). Catalogue no: **STAX 818**

PASSION (SINGLE)
Tracks: / Passion.
7" Single: Released Jun '86, on Tout Ensemble, Catalogue no: **LUTE 3**
12" Single: Released Jun '86, on Tout Ensemble, Catalogue no: **12 LUTE 3**

PRIVATE NUMBER See also under Judy Clay
Tracks: / Private number / Love-eye-tis / My baby specializes / Left over love.
12" Single: Released Oct '87, on Stax, by Fantasy Inc (USA). Catalogue no: **STAT 801**
7" Single: Released Mar '82, on Stax, by Fantasy Inc (USA). Catalogue no: **STAX 1001**

TRIBUTE TO A KING
Tracks: / Tribute to a king, A.
7" Single: Released May '68, on Stax, by Fantasy Inc (USA). Deleted '71. Catalogue no: **STAX 601 038**

Bella Donna

I REMEMBER
Tracks: / I remember.
12" Single: Released May '83, on Firebird, by Pinnacle Records. Catalogue no: **PIN 63T**
7" Single: Released May '83, on Firebird, by Pinnacle Records. Catalogue no: **PIN 63**

Bellamy Brothers

Biographical details: The American vocal duo of David and Howard Bellamy scored an international smash in the early summer of 1976 with the exuberant country rock-flavoured *"Let Your Love Flow"*. It reached No 1 in America and No 7 in the UK. Their eponymous album reached No 21 on the British album charts, but a similar follow-up single, *"Satin Sheets"*, failed to crack the Top Forty on either side of the Atlantic. Success then eluded the brothers until 1979, when they topped the US country chart with the cheekily-titled *"If I Said You Had A Beautiful Body Would You Hold It Against Me?"* It crossed over to No 39 on the American pop chart and then became a surprise British smash, reaching No 3. Since then the Bellamys have concentrated on the country market, but without the same crossover success. (Bob MacDonald, 1984.)

David (born 1950) and Howard (born 1946) are a USA pop/country duo from Florida. They began in a country band with their father in Tampa and served a long apprenticeship leading to a number one USA pop hit in 1976 with *Let Your Love Flow*; their *If I Said You Had A Beautiful Body Would You Hold It Against Me* was an international smash in 1979; since then they've had a strong following on the country charts. (Donald Clarke 23 August 1988).

DANCING COWBOYS
Tracks: / Dancing cowboys / Sugar daddy.
7" Single: Released Apr '80, on Curb, by BMG Records (UK). Deleted Apr '83. Catalogue no: **K 17573**

I NEED MORE OF YOU
Tracks: / I need more of you / Restless.
7" Single: Released Aug '84, on MCA, by MCA Records. Catalogue no: **MCA 899**

IF I SAID YOU HAD A BEAUTIFUL BODY (OLD GOLD)
Tracks: / If I said you had a beautiful body / Let your love flow.
7" Single: Released Sep '85, on Old Gold, by Old Gold Records. Catalogue no: **OG 9552**
7" Single: Released Aug '79, on Warner Bros., by WEA Records. Deleted '82. Catalogue no: **K 17405**

LET YOUR LOVE FLOW (SINGLE)
Tracks: / Let your love flow.
7" Single: Released Mar '76, on Warner Bros., by WEA Records. Catalogue no: **K 16690**

LOVIN' ON
Tracks: / Lovin' on / Ole faithful.
7" Single: Released Feb '80, on Curb, by BMG Records (UK). Deleted Feb '83. Catalogue no: **K 17548**

OLD HIPPIE
Tracks: / Old hippie.
7" Single: Released Oct '85, on MCA, by MCA Records. Catalogue no: **MCA 995**

SATIN SHEETS
Tracks: / Satin sheets.
7" Single: Released Aug '76, on Warner Bros., by WEA Records. Deleted '79. Catalogue no: **K 16775**

Bellamy, David

BRONTOSAURUS WILL YOU WAIT FOR ME
Tracks: / Brontosaurus will you wait for me.
7" Single: Released Apr '83, on MD, Catalogue no: **DWON 1**

SOME THINGS MUST CHANGE
Tracks: / Some things must change / What if.
7" Single: Released Dec '88, on Sealadelic, Catalogue no: **SEAL 001**
12" Single: Released Dec '88, on Sealadelic, Catalogue no: **SEAL 001T**

Belle, Jenny

I CAN LOVE YOU BETTER
Tracks: / I can love you better.
12" Single: Released Feb '89, on White Label (1), Catalogue no: **12BR 3**

Belle, Regina

GOOD LOVIN'
Tracks: / Good lovin' / This is love / You got the love / Show me the way / So many tears.
CD 5": Released Sep '89, on CBS, by CBS Records. Catalogue no: **655 230 2**
7" Single: Released Sep '89, on CBS, by CBS Records. Catalogue no: **655 230 7**
Cassingle: Released Sep '89, on CBS, by CBS Records. Catalogue no: **655 230 4**
12" Single: Released Sep '89, on CBS, by CBS Records. Catalogue no: **655 230 8**

SHOW ME THE WAY
Tracks: / Show me the way / Show me the way (inst) / How could you do it to me (*Extra track on 12" only) / Show me the way (extended mix).
12" Single: Released Jul '87, on CBS, by CBS Records. Deleted Aug '88. Catalogue no: **650 938 8**
12" Single: Released Jun '87, on CBS, by CBS Records. Deleted Aug '88. Catalogue no: **650 938 6**
7" Single: Released Jun '87, on CBS, by CBS Records. Deleted Aug '88. Catalogue no: **650 938 7**
CD 5": Released Mar '88, on CBS, by CBS Records. Deleted 10 Jul '89. Catalogue no: **650 938-2**

YOU GOT THE LOVE
Tracks: / You got the love / Gotta give it up / You got the love (dub version) / You got the love (7" version) / Show me the way (extended mix).
Note: Picture bag.
12" Single: Released Oct '87, on CBS, by CBS Records. Deleted Jun '88. Catalogue no: **REBE QT1**
7" Single: Released Sep '87, on CBS, by CBS Records. Deleted Jun '88. Catalogue no: **REBE 1**
12" Single: Released Sep '87, on CBS, by CBS Records. Deleted Jun '88. Catalogue no: **REBE T1**

Belle Stars

Biographical details: This all-girl seven-piece band were formed in early 1981, consisting of Clare, Jennie, Judy, Lesley, Miranda, Sarah Jane and Stella. They prefer to be known as Clare Belle Star, Jennie Belle Star etc., rather than by their real surnames. Prior to theis septet's emergence, four members (Judy, Miranda, Sarah Jane and Stella) were in another all-female british band, the Bodysnatchers. They had been part of the 2 Tone explosion, achieving two chart singles in 1980 with *"Let's Do Rock Steady"* and *"Easy Life"*. Signed to Stiff Records in April '81, the Belle Stars' fourth single *"Iko Iko"* gave them their first hit in the summer of '82. This singalong chant was made famous by an American all-girl group called the Dixie Cups in 1965. Unfortunately for the Belle Stars, a singer called Natasha had had the same idea at the same time and the two versions entered the UK charts in the same week. Though the Stars' version was undoubtedly superior, Natasha's rendition was more danceable and therefore won the race. She reached No. 10, while the group had to be content with No. 35. Their follow-up, a cover of Shirley Ellis' *"The Clapping Song"* (also from 1965) had no competition and reached No. 11 in the UK. Yet another remake, *"Mockingbird"*, was issued but only reached No. 51. The group were now starting to be dismissed as throwaway cover version merchants, belying the fact that in their early days they had supported numerous big names on tour. They rectified the matter by coming up with *"Sign Of The Times"* a bouncy self-penned pop song tha gave them their biggest hit, peaking No. 3 in Britain in early '83. *"Sweet Memory"* and *"Indian Summer"*, two more self-penned hits reached much lower positions and were fol lowed by *"The Entertainer"* which failed to chart at all. 1984's single *"80's Romance"* just scraped the Top 75. it seemed that the Belle Stars had to come up with stronge material, if they were to successfully com pete with many other acts performing the same type of material. (Bob MacDonald)..

80'S ROMANCE
Tracks: / 80's romance / It's me.
7" Single: Released Jun '84, on Stiff, by Stiff Records. Catalogue no: **BUY 200**
12" Single: Released Jun '84, on Stiff, by Stiff Records. Catalogue no: **SBUY 200**

ANOTHER LATIN LOVE SONG
Tracks: / Another Latin love song / Stop now / Having a good time / Miss world.
7" Single: Released Oct '81, on Stiff, by Stiff Records. Catalogue no: **BUY 130**

CLAPPING SONG (see panel below)
Tracks: / Clapping song, The / Blame.
12" Single: Released Jul '82, on Stiff, by Stiff Records. Catalogue no: **SBUY 155**
7" Pic: Released Jul '82, on Stiff, by Stiff Records. Catalogue no: **PBUY 155**

BELLE STARS - CLAPPING SONG (Released on Stiff)

BELLE STARS - THE ENTERTAINER (Released on Stiff)

7" Single: Released Jul '82, on Stiff, by Stiff Records. Catalogue no: **BUY 155**

ENTERTAINER, THE (see panel above)
Tracks: / Entertainer, The / Spider, The.
7" Single: Released Sep '83, on Stiff, by Stiff Records. Catalogue no: **BUY 187**
12" Single: Released Sep '83, on Stiff, by Stiff Records. Catalogue no: **SBUY 187**

HIAWTHA (see panel below)
Tracks: / Hiawatha / Big blonde.
7" Single: Released May '81, on Stiff, by Stiff Records. Catalogue no: **BUY 117**

IKO IKO
Tracks: / Iko iko / Reason.
7" Single: Released Jun '82, on Stiff, by Stiff Records. Catalogue no: **BUY 150**

IKO IKO (RE-ISSUE)
Tracks: / Iko iko / Las Vegas / Iko iko (12" mix) / Iko iko (bonus beats) (12" only.).
7" Single: Released May '89, on Capitol, by EMI Records. Deleted Oct '89. Catalogue no: **203 387 7**
12" Single: Released May '89, on Capitol, by EMI Records. Deleted Oct '89. Catalogue no: **203 405 6**
7" Single: Released May '89, on Capitol, by EMI Records. Deleted Oct '89. Catalogue no: **CL 537**
12" Single: Released May '89, on Capitol, by EMI Records. Deleted Oct '89. Catalogue no: **12CL 537**

INDIAN SUMMER
Tracks: / Indian summer.
12" Single: Released Jul '83, on Stiff, by Stiff Records. Catalogue no: **SBUY 185**
7" Single: Released Jul '83, on Stiff, by Stiff Records. Catalogue no: **BUY 185**

MOCKINGBIRD
Tracks: / Mockingbird.
7" Single: Released Sep '82, on Stiff, by Stiff Records. Catalogue no: **BUY 159**

SIGN OF THE TIMES (see panel bottom right)
Tracks: / Sign of the times / Madness.
7" Pic: Released Jan '83, on Stiff, by Stiff Records. Catalogue no: **PBUY 167**
7" Single: Released Nov '82, on Stiff, by Stiff Records. Catalogue no: **BUY 167**

SLICK TRICK
Tracks: / Slick trick.
7" Single: Released Jul '81, on Stiff, by Stiff Records. Catalogue no: **BUY 123**

SWEET MEMORY
Tracks: / Sweet memory.
12" Single: Released Apr '83, on Stiff, by Stiff Records. Catalogue no: **BUYIT 174**
7" Single: Released Apr '83, on Stiff, by Stiff Records. Catalogue no: **BUY 174**

WORLD DOMINATION
Tracks: / World domination / Just a minute / Rock me to the top (Extra track on 12" only).

12" Single: Released Apr '86, on Stiff, by Stiff Records. Catalogue no: **BUYIT 245**
7" Single: Released Apr '86, on Stiff, by Stiff Records. Catalogue no: **BUY 245**

Belle & The Devotions

Biographical details: Belle and the Devotions represented their native Britain in the 1984 Eurovision Song Contest. Having released a couple of flop 45's in '83, they thus became the UK's first Eurovision act of the Eighties not to be specially formed for the event. But this did not make much difference-for the third consecutive year Britain failed to make the top 5 in the contest. The BBC then decided to alter their 'Song For Europe' rules to improve the UK's chances. Indeed, so turgid was Belle And The Devotions *'Love Games'* - a Sixties Supremes pastiche in the style of *'Baby Love'* - that the Labour Party were prompted to launch a 'Better Song For Europe, as a vehicle for promoting their Euro-election campaign. At least Belle's girls had the consolation of reaching no.11 on the UK charts, ten places higher than the previous year's entry by Sweet Dreams (who?). However, rumours abounded that the group were not even singing on the single, even if this untrue, this record served to underline the lack of creativity and imagination shown by UK entrants to Eurovision in the Eighties. (Bob MacDonald)..

ALL THE WAY UP
Tracks: / All the way up.
7" Single: Released Aug '84, on CBS, by CBS Records. Catalogue no: **A 4605**

GOT TO LET YOU KNOW (SINGLE)
Tracks: / Got to let you know / Reach out for love.
12" Single: Released Aug '83, on DJM, Catalogue no: **DJR 3**
7" Single: Released Aug '83, on DJM, Catalogue no: **DJS 3**

LOVE GAMES
Tracks: / Love games / Rock me.
12" Single: Released Apr '84, on CBS, by CBS Records. Catalogue no: **TA 4332**
7" Single: Released Apr '84, on CBS, by CBS Records. Deleted Dec '85. Catalogue no: **A 4332**

LOVE LIKE THAT
Tracks: / Love like that.
7" Single: Released Jan '84, on DJM, Catalogue no: **DJS 9**

WHERE DID LOVE GO WRONG
Tracks: / Where did love go wrong.
12" Single: Released Apr '83, on DJM, Catalogue no: **DJR 10993**
7" Single: Released Apr '83, on DJM, Catalogue no: **DJS 10993**

Bellot, Errol

CHATTERBOX
Tracks: / Chatterbox.
7" Single: Released Apr '89, on Y & D, Catalogue no: **YDDO 137**

DON'T JOKE WITH LOVE
Tracks: / Don't joke with love.
12" Single: on Jet Sounds, Deleted Feb '83. Catalogue no: **JS 001**

GIMMIE
Tracks: / Gimmie.
12" Single: Released Sep '81, on S & G (2), Catalogue no: **SG 1**

IS THAT ALRIGHT GIRL
Tracks: / Is that alright girl.
12" Single: Released May '82, on S & G (2), Catalogue no: **SG 18**

SOUND IN A FURY
Tracks: / Sound in a fury / Trouble make.
12" Single: Released Jun '86, on Jah Tubbys, Catalogue no: **JT 019**

Bells

AULD LANG SYNE
Tracks: / Auld lang syne.
7" Single: Released Nov '85, on Klub, by Klub Records. Catalogue no: **KLUB 12**

HOKEY COKEY
Tracks: / Hokey cokey / Disco symphony / Auld lang syne disco.
12" Single: Released Nov '85, on Klub, by Klub Records. Catalogue no: **KLUBX 15**
7" Single: Released Nov '81, on Klub, by Klub Records. Catalogue no: **KLUB 15**

Belly

SLAP BELLY SLAP
Tracks: / Slap belly slap.
12" Single: Released Nov '88, on Wooden, by Wooden Records. Catalogue no: **WOOD 005**

Belly, Billy & Barry

THIS IS THE BIG SCAM
Tracks: / This is the big scam.
7" Single: Released 28 Nov '87, on In Tape, by In Tape Records. Catalogue no: **SIDE 001**

Belly Dance

SPITTIN' BULLETS
7" Single: Released Oct '87, on Session (Australia), Catalogue no: **SR 003**

Belmont School Choir

ROBIN SONG
Tracks: / Robin song.
7" Single: Released Dec '82, on Dakota, Catalogue no: **DAK 7**

Belmonts

TELL ME WHY
Tracks: / Tell me why / Diddle de dum / Come on little angel / How about me.
7" EP: Released '89, on Magnum Music (Import), by Magnum Music Group. Catalogue no: **EP BEL 001**

Beloved

FOREVER DANCING
Tracks: / Forever dancing / Forever dancing (remix) (Remix on HARP 7E).
12" Single: Released Jan '88, on Flim Flam, Catalogue no: **HARP 7E**
12" Single: Released Jan '88, on Flim Flam, Catalogue no: **HARP 7T**
7" Single: Released Jan '88, on Flim Flam, Catalogue no: **HARP 7**

HAPPY NOW
Tracks: / Happy now.
12" Single: Released 7 Mar '87, on Flim Flam, Catalogue no: **HARP 5T**

HUNDRED WORDS, A
Tracks: / Hundred words, A.
12" Single: Released Mar '86, on Flim Flam, Catalogue no: **HARP 2T**

LOVING FEELING

BELLE STARS - HIAWTHA (Released on Stiff)

BELLE STARS - SIGN OF THE TIMES (Released on Stiff)

Tracks: / Loving feeling / Acid love.
12" Single: Released Oct '88, on WEA, by WEA Records. Catalogue no: **YZ 311T**
CD 5": Released Oct '88, on WEA, by WEA Records. Catalogue no: **YZ 311CD**
7" Single: Released Oct '88, on WEA, by WEA Records. Catalogue no: **YZ 311**

SUN RISING, THE
Tracks: / Sun rising, The / Sun rising, The (version).
Cassingle: Released Sep '89, on WEA, by WEA Records. Catalogue no: **WX 414C**
7" Single: Released Sep '89, on WEA, by WEA Records. Catalogue no: **WX 414**
CD 5": Released Sep '89, on WEA, by WEA Records. Catalogue no: **WX 414CD**
12" Single: Released Sep '89, on WEA, by WEA Records. Catalogue no: **WX 414T**

SURPRISE ME
Tracks: / Surprise me.
7" Single: Released 13 Jun '87, on Flim Flam, Catalogue no: **HARP 7**
12" Single: Released 13 Jun '87, on Flim Flam, Catalogue no: **HARP 7T**

THIS MEANS WAR
Tracks: / This means war.
12" Single: Released Aug '86, on Flim Flam, Catalogue no: **HARP 3T**
7" Single: Released Aug '86, on Flim Flam, Catalogue no: **HARP 3**

YOUR LOVE TAKES ME HIGHER
Tracks: / Your love takes me higher / Paradise.
CD 5": Released Jan '89, on WEA, by WEA Records. Catalogue no: **YZ 357CD**
12" Single: Released Jan '89, on WEA, by WEA Records. Catalogue no: **YZ 357T**
7" Single: Released Jan '89, on WEA, by WEA Records. Catalogue no: **YZ 357**

Beltane Fire

CAPTAIN BLOOD
Tracks: / Captain Blood / Further up, further in.
7" Single: Released Dec '85, on CBS, by CBS Records. Catalogue no: **A 6780**

EXCALIBUR
Tracks: / Excalibur / Uther 11.
12" Single: Released Mar '86, on CBS, by CBS Records. Deleted '86. Catalogue no: **TX 6980**
7" Single: Released Mar '86, on CBS, by CBS Records. Deleted '86. Catalogue no: **A 6980**

Belucci, Morton

MCCALL
Tracks: / McCall.
12" Single: Released Apr '88, on Subway, by Subway Records. Catalogue no: **SUB 017**

Belva

LET ME KISS IT (WHERE IT HURTS)
Tracks: / Let me kiss it (where it hurts) / Let me kiss it (where it hurts) (version).
7" Single: Released Jun '88, on Supreme, by Supreme Records. Catalogue no: **SUPE 127**
12" Single: Released Jun '88, on Supreme, by Supreme Records. Catalogue no: **SUPET 127**

Benatar, Pat

Biographical details: Born Pat Andrejewski in New York, Pat Benatar trained as an opera singer but never attempted a classcal career, turning instead to rock. With the advantage of a fine, powerful voice, she hit the US charts at the start of the Eighties and has been consistently successful there ever since. It began with the albums *"In The Heat Of The Night"* and *"Crimes Of Passion"* which produced four Top 30 singles: *"Heartbreaker"*, *"We Live For Love"*, *"Treat Me Right"* and the Top 10 song *"Hit Me With Your Best Shot"*. Equally successful ws 1981's *"Precious Time"* LP and its Top 20 single *"Fire And Ice"*. The 1982 album *"Get Nervous"* featured *"Shadows Of The Night"* a highly dramatic power-pop single that once again hit the Top 20. But her biggest 45 so far came at the end of '83. *"Love Is A Battlefield"* co-written by Mike Chapman, gave Benatar her first Top 5 single and her first (albeit minor) hit in Britain; it was taken from her fifth consecutive US platinum album *"Live From Earth"*. Benatar's band includes her guitarist husband Neil Geraldo, who is also the main songwriter. Her brand of traditional, dramatic pop/rock is staple diet on US rock radio but, like the music of so many of her peers, finds little acceptance in the UK. A hard core of British followers will put her LP's in the chart briefly but they are not enough to make her the major star that she is at home. The distinguishing features of her hackneyed style are, firstly, the fact that she is female (still something of a novelty in her genre) and, secondly, her excellent voice. With her usual regularity and consistency, Pat Benatar issued her sixth album *"Tropico"* in the Autumn of 1984; this time the US hit single was *"We Belong"*. (Bob MacDonald).

This USA rock singer was born Pat Andrzejewski in 1953 in Brooklyn, New York. She has a good strong voice and has sold a lot of albums with her neo-heavy metal music, described by some critics as 'permanent wave music' or 'Wonder Woman produced by ZZ Top'. 'Hit Me With Your Best Shot' was a top ten USA single; she won Grammies in the early '80s. Some of her material is written by guitarist/husband Neil Geraldo. (Donald Clarke 23 August 1988).

ALL FIRED UP
Tracks: / All fired up.
7" Single: Released Jun '88, on Chrysalis, by Chrysalis Records. Catalogue no: **PAT 5**
12" Single: Released Jun '88, on Chrysalis, by Chrysalis Records. Catalogue no: **PATX 5**

DON'T WALK AWAY
Tracks: / Don't walk away / Lift 'em on up / Hell is for children (live) (12" & CD single only.) / We live for love (special mix) (12" & Cd single.).
CD 5": Released Sep '88, on Chrysalis, by Chrysalis Records. Catalogue no: **PAT CD 6**
7" Single: Released Sep '88, on Chrysalis, by Chrysalis Records. Catalogue no: **PAT 6**
12" Single: Released Sep '88, on Chrysalis, by Chrysalis Records. Catalogue no: **PATX 6**

FIRE AND ICE
Tracks: / Fire and ice / Hard to believe.
7" Single: Released Jul '81, on Chrysalis, by Chrysalis Records. Deleted Jul '84. Catalogue no: **CHSP 2529**

HEARTBREAKER
Tracks: / Heartbreaker / My clone sleeps alone.
7" Single: Released '83, on Chrysalis, by Chrysalis Records. Deleted '87. Catalogue no: **CHS 2395**

HIT ME WITH YOUR BEST SHOT
Tracks: / Promises in the dark / Fire and ice / Just like me / Precious / Hit me with your best shot.
7" Single: Released '82, on Chrysalis, by Chrysalis Records. Deleted '87. Catalogue no: **CHS 2474**
7" Single: Released May '86, on Chrysalis, by Chrysalis Records. Catalogue no: **PAT 5**
12" Single: Released May '86, on Chrysalis, by Chrysalis Records. Catalogue no: **PATX 5**

INVINCIBLE
Tracks: / Invincible / Invincible (instrumental).
12" Single: Released '86, on Chrysalis, by Chrysalis Records. Catalogue no: **PATX 3**
7" Single: Released Oct '85, on Chrysalis, by Chrysalis Records. Deleted '88. Catalogue no: **PAT 3**

LOVE IS A BATTLEFIELD
Tracks: / Love is a battlefield / Here's my heart.
7" Single: Released Jan '84, on Chrysalis, by Chrysalis Records. Deleted '87. Catalogue no: **CHS 2747**
12" Single: Released Feb '85, on Chrysalis, by Chrysalis Records. Catalogue no: **PATX 1**
7" Single: Released Feb '85, on Chrysalis, by Chrysalis Records. Catalogue no: **PAT 1**

ONE LOVE
Tracks: / One love / Wide awake in dreamland / Sex as a weapon (12" only as extra track) / Love is a battlefield (Extra track on CD only).
CD 5": Released Dec '88, on Chrysalis, by Chrysalis Records. Catalogue no: **PATCD 7**
12" Single: Released Dec '88, on Chrysalis, by Chrysalis Records. Catalogue no: **PATX 7**
7" Single: Released Dec '88, on Chrysalis, by Chrysalis Records. Catalogue no: **PAT 7**
12" Pic: Released Jan '89, on Chrysalis, by Chrysalis Records. Catalogue no: **PATXP 7**

SEX AS A WEAPON
Tracks: / Sex as a weapon / Red version.
12" Single: Released Feb '86, on Chrysalis, by Chrysalis Records. Catalogue no: **PATX 4**
7" Single: Released Feb '86, on Chrysalis, by Chrysalis Records. Catalogue no: **PAT 4**

SHADOWS OF THE NIGHT
Tracks: / Shadows of the night / Victim.
12" Single: Released '83, on Chrysalis, by Chrysalis Records. Deleted '87. Catalogue no: **CHS SP 12 2662**
7" Single: Released Feb '83, on Chrysalis, by Chrysalis Records. Catalogue no: **CHS SP 2662**
12" Single: Released Apr '82, on Chrysalis, by Chrysalis Records. Deleted Apr '85. Catalogue no: **CHS 2662**
12" Single: Released Apr '82, on Chrysalis, by Chrysalis Records. Deleted Apr '85. Catalogue no: **CHS 122662**
12" Single: Released '86, on Chrysalis, by Chrysalis Records. Catalogue no: **PATX 2**

SHADOWS OF THE NIGHT (SINGLE)

BENGY & RUMPO'S - WE LOVE BENGY (Released on Spark)

Tracks: / Shadows of the night / Victim.
7" Single: Released Jun '85, on Chrysalis, by Chrysalis Records. Deleted '88. Catalogue no: **PAT 2**
7" Single: Released '83, on Chrysalis, by Chrysalis Records. Catalogue no: **CHS 2662**

TREAT ME RIGHT
Tracks: / Treat me right / Hell is for children.
7" Single: Released Apr '81, on Chrysalis, by Chrysalis Records. Deleted Apr '84. Catalogue no: **CHS 2511**

WE BELONG
Tracks: / We belong / Suburban king / We live for love (Extra track on 12" version only).
7" Single: Released Dec '84, on Chrysalis, by Chrysalis Records. Catalogue no: **CHS 2821**
12" Single: Released Dec '84, on Chrysalis, by Chrysalis Records. Catalogue no: **CHS 122821**

WE LIVE FOR LOVE
Tracks: / We live for love / I need a lover / If you think you know how to love me.
12" Single: Released '82, on Chrysalis, by Chrysalis Records. Deleted '87. Catalogue no: **CHS 12 2403**
7" Single: Released '80, on Chrysalis, by Chrysalis Records. Deleted '85. Catalogue no: **CHS 2403**

Bendalls Box

NIGHTMARES
Tracks: / Nightmares / Games today.
7" Single: Released Apr '81, on Circus, by Circus Records. Catalogue no: **CIRC 0004**

Bendeth, David

Biographical details: Canadian vocalist and multi-instrumentalist Bendeth had a minor British hit in 1979, reaching No.44 with the single *"Feel The Real"*. It was taken from his album Adrenalin. A sequal, *"Feel The Real (Again)"*, popped up on 1981's follow-up album *"Just Dessert"*, but Bendeth did not appear on the charts again. (Bob McDonald 1984.).

BETTER BELIEVE IT
Tracks: / Better believe it / Make it play.
12" Single: Released Apr '81, on Ensign, by Ensign Records. Deleted Apr '84. Catalogue no: **ENYT 210**

FEEL THE REAL
Tracks: / Feel the real / Make it pop / Feel the real (again).
7" Single: Released May '81, on Ensign, by Ensign Records. Deleted May '86. Catalogue no: **ENY 210**
7" Single: Released Sep '79, on Sidewalk, by Sidewalk Records. Deleted '82. Catalogue no: **SID 113**

LOVE COLLECT
Tracks: / Love collect / Gold mine.
7" Single: Released Feb '81, on Ensign, by Ensign Records. Deleted Feb '86. Catalogue no: **ENY 203**
12" Single: Released Feb '81, on Ensign, by Ensign Records. Deleted Feb '86. Catalogue no: **ENYT 203**

Benelux

SWITCH
Tracks: / Switch.
7" Single: Released Aug '79, on Scope, Deleted '82. Catalogue no: **SC 4**

Bengie, Risto

SLICE OF THE CAKE
Tracks: / Slice of the cake.
12" Single: Released Feb '89, on Jammy's, Catalogue no: **VPRD 361**

Bengimani, Earl

HEALTH AND SORROW
Tracks: / Health and sorrow.
12" Single: Released Apr '82, on Negus Roots, Catalogue no: **NERT 101**

Bengy & Rumpo's

WE LOVE BENGY (see panel above)
Tracks: / We love Bengy / Rumpo's reggae.
7" Single: Released '75, on Spark, by Spark Records. Catalogue no: **SRL 1126**

Benie Man

OVER THE SEA
Tracks: / Over the sea.
12" Single: Released Apr '83, on Jah Observers, Catalogue no: **JAH 005**

Benjahman, I

HOLD ME TIGHT
Tracks: / Jah world will keep on turning.
12" Single: Released Feb '87, on Lion Kingdom, Catalogue no: **LTD 07**

Benjamin, Floella

DON'T TOUCH ME
Tracks: / Don't touch me.
7" Single: Released Oct '89, on Warm, by Warm Records. Catalogue no: **WARM 2**

REGGAE RITA
Tracks: / Reggae Rita.
7" Single: Released Apr '84, on BBC, by BBC Records & Tapes. Deleted '87. Catalogue no: **RESL 142**

Benjamin, Shani

LOOK AFTER YOU
Tracks: / Look after you / Inmates / In fine style.
12" Single: Released Apr '84, on Ariwa Sounds, by Ariwa Sounds. Catalogue no: 1? **ARISL 007**

Benjamin, Tony

GO 'PON DE LAND
Tracks: / Go' pon de land.
12" Single: Released Nov '82, on Ariwa Sounds, by Ariwa Sounds. Catalogue no: **ARI 1012**

SIT ALONE AGAIN
Tracks: / Sit alone again / Dub for company.
12" Single: Released Jul '86, on Soundgrip, Catalogue no: **SG 001**

TREASURES IN THE WORLD
Tracks: / Treasures in the world / That' love.
12" Single: Released Apr '84, on Ariwa Sounds, by Ariwa Sounds. Catalogue no: **ARI 29**

TWILIGHT SMILE
Tracks: / Twilight smile.
7" Single: Released '82, on Ample Productions, by Ample Productions. Catalogue no: **A 001**

Benjax

WAITING FOR YOU
Tracks: / Waiting for you / Itching sensation.
7" Single: Released Feb '84, on Orbitone, by Orbitone Records. Catalogue no: **ORS 3**

Bennett, Boyd

SEVENTEEN (SINGLE)
Tracks: / Seventeen.
7" Single: Released Dec '55, on Parlophone, by EMI Records. Deleted '58. Catalogue no: **R 4063**

Bennett, Brian

TOP OF THE WORLD
Tracks: / Top of the world / Soul ice.
7" Single: Released Jan '82, on DJM, Deleted Jan '85. Catalogue no: **DJS 10981**

Bennett, Carol

TEARING MY HEART APART
Tracks: / Tearing my heart apart / Tearing my heart apart (TV Edit).
12" Single: Released Nov '87, on Kool Kat, by Kool Kat Records. Catalogue no: **KOOLT 8**
7" Single: Released Nov '87, on Kool Kat, by Kool Kat Records. Catalogue no: **KOOL 8**

Bennett, Cliff

Biographical details: Cliff Bennett and the Rebel Rousers, an all-male British band, were formed in 1961. They made their living performing authentic covers of (mainly soul) songs. Despite their name they had a clean cut image. Among the artists whose songs they remade were Ray Charles, Bobby Bland and Bobby Parker. In 1964 they hit the Britiah charts for the first time with their rendition of a minor American hit by the Drifters. Considering *"One Way Love"* had peaked at No. 56 on the Billboard Hot 100, Bennett did well to spot its potential and take it to No. 9 in the UK. 1965's *"I'll Take you Home"* could do no better than No. 42 and the group had to wait another eighteen months for their third, final and biggest chart record. While the Beatles were recording the *"Revolver"* album in 1966, they allowed Bennett and the Rebel Rousers to record one of its songs. *"Got To Get You Into My Life"* entered the British cahrts in the same week (in August '66) as the Beatles' new LP. The Bennett single was even produced by Paul McCartney and peaked No. 6. Bennett's second album was the first to chart reaching No. 25 - but after the *"Drivin' Me Wild"* LP fell off the chart, Cliff and the Rebels were never seen again on either list. The Rebel Rousers folded in 1969, after which Bennett made a laughable attempt to break into the progressive rock market. (Bob MacDonald).

Born in Slough, the pop singer formed the Rebel Rousers in 1959, playing covers; had hits in the mid-'60s with band including a brass section; a 1969 lineup became progressive Toe Fat, with future Uriah Heep sidemen; he later linked with guitarist Mick Green in group Shanghai; left music c.'80. Never an innovator but his act was always good value. (Donald Clarke 23 August 1988).

GOT TO GET YOU INTO MY LIFE (SINGLE)
Tracks: / Got to get you into my life.
7" Single: Released Aug '66, on Parlophone, by EMI Records. Deleted '69. Catalogue no: **R 5489**

I'LL TAKE YOU HOME
Tracks: / I'll take you home.
7" Single: Released Feb '65, on Parlophone, by EMI Records. Deleted '68. Catalogue no: **R 5229**

ONE WAY LOVE
Tracks: / One way love.
7" Single: Released Oct '64, on Parlophone, by EMI Records. Deleted '67. Catalogue no: **R 5173**

Bennett, Errol

DON'T JOKE WITH LOVE
Tracks: / Don't joke with love.
12" Single: Released Dec '82, on Jet Sounds, Catalogue no: **JS 001**

Bennett, Jim

BUMP AND ROLL Give up the funk
Tracks: / Bump and roll (give up the funk) / Bump and roll (give up the funk) (inst.).
12" Single: Released Apr '87, on Bluebird (2), by BMG Records (UK). Catalogue no: **BRT 36**

Bennett, Joe

BLACK SLACKS
Tracks: / Black slacks / Short shorts.
7" Single: Released Jul '82, on Revival, Catalogue no: **REV 6020**

Bennett, Peter E

SEAGULL'S NAME WAS NELSON, THE
Tracks: / Seagull's name was Nelson, The.
7" Single: Released Nov '70, on RCA, by BMG Records (UK). Deleted '73. Catalogue no: **RCA 1991**

Bennett, Pinto

CAROLINA MORNIN'S
7" Single: Released Mar '88, on PT, Catalogue no: **PTL 1**

Bennett, Tony

Biographical details: Born Anthony Benedetto in New York in 1926, Bennett made his first public appearance in a church at the age of seven. After struggling for some years to make a name for himself, he won television and theatre contracts from Arthur Godfrey and Bob Hope. The early Fifties saw Tony Bennett become one of America's top singers with three massive No. 1 hits to his credit: *"Because Of You"*, *"Cold, Cold Heart"* (a song written by country legend Hank Williams) and *"Rags To Riches"*. A fourth smash *"Stranger In Paradise"* gave him his first anfd biggest British hit. It went to No. 1 in the UK in May '55, winning the race against no less than five other charted versions. it was his only British Top 10 single and indeed he was to have only one more in the States: after hitting No. 9 in the US with 1957's *"In The Middle Of An Island"*, Bennett turned to albums and cabaret. Strangely, Bennett's best known single was not a particularly big hit on either side of the Atlantic, *"I Left My Heart in San Francisco"* reached No. 19 in the US in 1962, winning the Grammy Award for record of the year. In the UK it had to wait untill the mid-Sixties before peaking No. 25; it was followed shortly afterwards by the biggest of his six British chart albums - *"A String Of Tony's Hits"* reached No. 9. A permanent member of the top league of MoR entertainers, Bennett's theme song should more appropriately be called *"I Left My Heart in The Early Fifties"* - his style could hardly be described as progressive. A graphic summary of the singer's views on the rock 'n' roll and pop music that curtailed his career was contained in a late seventies interview with Britain's 'Radio Times': America went through in the sixties what Germany went through in the Thirties. (Bob MacDonald)..

CLOSE YOUR EYES
Tracks: / Close your eyes.
7" Single: Released Sep '55, on Philips, by Phonogram Ltd. Deleted '58. Catalogue no: **PB 445**

COME NEXT SPRING
Tracks: / Come next Spring.
7" Single: Released Apr '56, on Philips, by Phonogram Ltd. Deleted '59. Catalogue no: **PB 537**

GOOD LIFE, THE
Tracks: / Good life.
7" Single: Released Jul '63, on CBS, by CBS Records. Deleted '66. Catalogue no: **AAG 153**

I LEFT MY HEART IN SAN FRANCISCO (SINGLE)
Tracks: / I left my heart in San Francisco.
7" Single: Released May '65, on CBS, by CBS Records. Deleted '68. Catalogue no: **CBS 201730**
7" Single: Released Jul '82, on Old Gold, by Old Gold Records. Catalogue no: **OG 9184**

IF I RULED THE WORLD
Tracks: / If I ruled the world.
7" Single: Released May '65, on CBS, by CBS Records. Deleted '68. Catalogue no: **CBS 201735**

STRANGER IN PARADISE
Tracks: / Stranger in paradise.
7" Single: Released Apr '55, on Philips, by Phonogram Ltd. Deleted '58. Catalogue no: **PB 420**

TILL
Tracks: / Till / Serenata.
7" Single: Released Jan '61, on Philips, by Phonogram Ltd. Deleted '64. Catalogue no: **PB 1079**

VERY THOUGHT OF YOU, THE
Tracks: / Very thought of you, The.
7" Single: Released Dec '65, on CBS, by CBS Records. Deleted '68. Catalogue no: **CBS 20201**

Benson, Gary

Biographical details: This British vocalist had a one-off UK Top 20 hit in 1975 with the melodic, romantic ballad *"Don't Throw It All Away"*. he was unable to fulfill the promise of this single, however, and career floundered. (Bob MacDonald)..

ALL CRIED OUT
Tracks: / All cried out / You brought the curtain down on me.
7" Single: Released Mar '81, on Warner Bros., by WEA Records. Deleted Mar '84. Catalogue no: **K 17773**

DON'T THROW IT ALL AWAY (SINGLE)
Tracks: / Don't throw it all away.
7" Single: Released Aug '75, on State, by State Records. Deleted '78. Catalogue no: **STAT 10**

DYING TO LIVE WITH YOU
Tracks: / Dying to live with you / What's gonna happen to us.
7" Single: Released Jan '81, on Aura Records, by Aura Records. Deleted '88. Catalogue no: **AUS 122**

Benson, George

Biographical details: Born in Pennsylvania in 1943, George Benson began learning the guitar at the age of eight. Having moved to New York, he earned respect from fellow musicians during the Sixties and early Seventies with his jazz flavoured guitar work, culminating in 1973's much praised *"White Rabbit"* album. under the name George 'Bad' Benson, he scored his first British hit single in the Autumn of '75 with *"Supership"*, which reached No. 30. George Benson's big break came in 1976 with the jazz-funk LP *"Breezin'"*. Suddenly it was apparent that this skilful guitarist was a strong singer too: *"This Masquerade"*, a remake of the Leon Russell song, became a US Top 10 from the US No. 1 album. 1977's *"In Flight"* continued the formula, giving Benson another US Top 10 album and his first UK chart album. *"Nature Boy"*, a remake of an early Sixties hit associated with Bobby Darin, was a Top 30 single in Britain. The Stevie Wonder-ish vocals of Benson were further pushed to the forefront on the next hit *"The Greatest Love Of All"*. This was the theme from the Muhammed Ali movie *"The Greatest"*. 1978's *"Weekend In L.A."* yielded a second American Top 10 single - indeed, *"On Broadway"* reached No. 7, two places higher than the Drifters had taken the song in 1963. The '79 single *"Love Ballad"* was one of the very best examples of dual talent, an excellent jazz/pop fusion showing off both vocals and guitar to best effect. The next turning point in his career came in 1980 when he teamed up with the famous producer Quincy Jones, who was fresh from his massive success with Michael Jackson's *"Off The Wall"* album. The combination of Benson and Jones made *"Give Me The Night"* a major commercial triumph - the producer's jazz-tinged, soul-inflected but ever commercial sound was just what the artist needed to complete his long-term move into the pop market. In the UK the LP reached No. 3 with 40 weeks on the chart, while the title track was Benson's first Top 10 single. In the US it was his biggest ever 45, reaching No. 4. *"Love X Love"* was a second UK Top Tenner from the album. *"Turn Your Love Around"* and *"Never Give Up On A Good Thing"* the two new hits on *"The George Benson Collection"*, conolidated on his success, with the former hitting No. 5 in the US and the latter reaching No. 14 in the UK. 1983's *"In Your Eyes"* album was once again well received and yielded several hit singles, but was the work of a stagnating artist, The title cut, a romantic ballad, gave Benson his biggest British single since *"Give Me The Night"*. He remains a major concert draw and has established a sufficiently broad following in the adult record-buying market to ensure continued high record sales. (Bob MacDonald).

He was born in 1943 in Pittsburgh, Pennsylvania, began in R&B bands and became a fine jazz guitarists influenced by Wes Montgomery. Worked and recorded with organist Jack McDuff on Prestige; recorded for CBS; when Montgomery died, his producer Creed Taylor signed Benson to A&M, then to Taylor's own CTI label; during this period he began singing and soon became a huge star as a jazz-influenced soul balladeer: he switched to Warner Brothers and *Breezin'* in 1976 became his first number one album in the USA, also winning Grammies. Taylor won a lawsuit against WB in 1988 claiming that they had helped to put him out of business by stealing Benson. Jazz fans were dismayed by Benson's funky crossover, but Benson has a family to support and blames broadcasting and the music business: 'If kids can't hear it, I don't care how good it is, you can't sell it to them'. Others like Derek Jewell felt that he played his hits in concert 'with such panache, creation and re-creation..that he is in truth a great jazzman'. (Derek Jewell) (Donald Clarke 23 August 1988).

20/20 (SINGLE)
Tracks: / 20/20.
7" Single: Released Jan '85, on Warner Bros., by WEA Records. Catalogue no: **W 9120**
12" Single: Released Jan '85, on Warner Bros., by WEA Records. Catalogue no: **W 9120 T**

BEYOND THE SEA
Tracks: / Beyond the sea / Breezin' / This masquerade (on 12" only).
7" Single: Released Apr '85, on Warner Bros., by WEA Records. Catalogue no: **W 9014**
12" Single: Released Apr '85, on Warner Bros., by WEA Records. Catalogue no: **WN 014 T**

Tracks: / Feel like makin' love.
7" Single: Released Jul '83, on Warner Bros., by WEA Records. Deleted '86. Catalogue no: **W 9551**

GIVE ME THE NIGHT (SINGLE)
Tracks: / Give me the night / Red lights.
7" Single: Released Aug '80, on Warner Bros., by WEA Records. Deleted '83. Catalogue no: **K 17673**
7" Single: Released Aug '80, on Warner Bros., by WEA Records. Catalogue no: **K 17673**

GREATEST LOVE OF ALL
Tracks: / Greatest love of all, The.
7" Single: Released Nov '80, on Arista, by BMG Records (UK). Catalogue no: **ARIST 133**
: by Old Gold Records.

IN YOUR EYES (SINGLE)
Tracks: / In your eyes / Being with you.
7" Single: Released Sep '83, on Warner Bros., by WEA Records. Catalogue no: **W 9487**

INSIDE LOVE (SO PERSONAL)
Tracks: / Inside love (so personal).
7" Single: Released Dec '83, on WEA (International), by WEA Records. Deleted '86. Catalogue no: **W 9427**

KISSES IN THE MOONLIGHT
Tracks: / Kisses in the moonlight / Open your eyes (instrumental).
7" Single: Released Jul '86, on Warner Bros., by WEA Records. Deleted Jun '87. Catalogue no: **W 8640**
12" Single: Released Jul '86, on Warner Bros., by WEA Records. Deleted Jun '87. Catalogue no: **W 8640 T**

LADY LOVE ME (ONE MORE TIME)
Tracks: / Lady love me (one more time).
7" Single: Released May '83, on Warner Bros., by WEA Records. Deleted '86. Catalogue no: **W 9614**

LATE AT NIGHT
Tracks: / Late at night / Love will come again / Welcome into my world (On 12" only).
7" Single: Released Mar '84, on WEA, by WEA Records. Catalogue no: **W 9325**
12" Single: Released Mar '84, on WEA, by WEA Records. Catalogue no: **W 9325T**

LET'S DO IT AGAIN
Tracks: / Let's do it again / Let's go.
7" Single: Released 22 Aug '88, on Warner Bros., by WEA Records. Catalogue no: **W 7780**
12" Single: Released Aug '88, on Warner Bros., by WEA Records. Catalogue no: **W 7780 T**

LOVE ALL THE HURT AWAY
Tracks: / Love all the hurt away / Whole lot of me / Hold on I'm coming.
12" Single: Released Aug '81, on Arista, by BMG Records (UK). Deleted '86. Catalogue no: **ARIST 12 428**
7" Single: Released Aug '81, on Arista, by BMG Records (UK). Deleted '86. Catalogue no: **ARIST 428**

LOVE BALLAD
Tracks: / Love ballad.
7" Single: Released Mar '79, on Warner Bros., by WEA Records. Deleted '82. Catalogue no: **K 17333**

LOVE X LOVE
Tracks: / Love x love / Off Broadway.
12" Single: Released Sep '80, on Warner Bros., by WEA Records. Catalogue no: **LV 41**
7" Single: Released Sep '80, on Warner Bros., by WEA Records. Catalogue no: **K 17699**

NATURE BOY
Tracks: / Nature boy.
7" Single: Released Jun '77, on Warner Bros., by WEA Records. Deleted '80. Catalogue no: **K 16921**

NEVER GIVE UP ON A GOOD THING
Tracks: / Never give up on a good thing / California p.m..
12" Single: Released Jan '82, on Warner Bros., by WEA Records. Catalogue no: **K 17902 T**
7" Single: Released Jan '82, on Warner Bros., by WEA Records. Catalogue no: **K 17902**

NO ONE EMOTION
Tracks: / No one emotion.
12" Single: Released Oct '85, on Warner Bros., by WEA Records. Catalogue no: **W 8863T**
7" Single: Released Oct '85, on Warner Bros., by WEA Records. Catalogue no: **W 8863**

ON BROADWAY
Tracks: / On Broadway / Love will come again.
7" Single: Released Nov '83, on Warner Bros., by WEA Records. Catalogue no: **W 9427**
12" Single: Released Nov '83, on Warner

Bros., by WEA Records. Catalogue no: **W 9427 T**

SHIVER
Tracks: / Shiver / Love is here tonight.
7" Single: Released Nov '86, on Warner Bros., by WEA Records. Deleted Jan '88. Catalogue no: **W 8523**
12" Single: Released Nov '86, on Warner Bros., by WEA Records. Deleted Sep '87. Catalogue no: **W 8523T**

SUPERSHIP
Tracks: / Supership.
7" Single: Released Oct '75, on CTI (1), by Polydor Ltd. Deleted '78. Catalogue no: **CTSP 002**

TEASER
Tracks: / Did you hear the thunder / Teaser.
7" Single: Released Jan '87, on Warner Bros., by WEA Records. Deleted Jan '88. Catalogue no: **W 8437**
12" Single: Released Feb '87, on Warner Bros., by WEA Records. Deleted Jan '88. Catalogue no: **W 8437T**

TURN YOUR LOVE AROUND
Tracks: / Turn your love around / Nature boy.
7" Single: Released Nov '81, on Warner Bros., by WEA Records. Deleted '84. Catalogue no: **K 17877**

TWICE THE LOVE (SINGLE)
Tracks: / Twice the love (guitar love mix) / Love is here tonight.
7" Single: Released Nov '88, on Warner Bros., by WEA Records. Catalogue no: **W 7665**
CD 5": Released Nov '88, on Warner Bros., by WEA Records. Catalogue no: **W 7665 CD**
12" Single: Released Nov '88, on Warner Bros., by WEA Records. Catalogue no: **W 7665 T**

WHAT'S ON YOUR MIND?
Tracks: / What's on your mind? / Turn out the lamplight.
12" Single: Released Feb '81, on Warner Bros., by WEA Records. Catalogue no: **K 17748 T**
7" Single: Released Feb '81, on Warner Bros., by WEA Records. Catalogue no: **K 17748**

Benson, Jo Jo

LOVERS' HOLIDAY
Tracks: / Lover's holiday / Picking wild mountain berries.
7" Single: Released Jul '80, on Charly, by Charly Records. Deleted '87. Catalogue no: **CTD 108**

Benson, Sharon

FIGHTING CHANCE
Tracks: / Fighting chance / When love's so right.
7" Single: Released Sep '86, on Sedition, by Sedition Records. Catalogue no: **EDIT 3315**
12" Single: Released Sep '86, on Sedition, by Sedition Records. Catalogue no: **EDITL 3315**

GET IT OVER WITH
Tracks: / Get it over with / All out of love.
7" Single: Released Sep '81, on Epic, by CBS Records. Deleted Sep '84. Catalogue no: **EPCA 1572**

IN YOUR EYES
Tracks: / In your eyes.
7" Single: Released Mar '84, on Starlite, by Titan Int. Prod.. Catalogue no: **GLO 1**

OUR LOVE'S ALIVE
Tracks: / Our love's alive.
7" Single: Released Aug '88, on Tribute, Catalogue no: **TRIB 1**
12" Single: Released Aug '88, on Tribute, Catalogue no: **12 TRIB 1**

OUR LOVE'S ALIVE (REMIX)
Tracks: / Our love alive (remix) / Our love alive (remix) (version).
7" Single: Released Jan '89, on Tribute, Catalogue no: **TRIBX 1**
12" Single: Released Jan '89, on Tribute, Catalogue no: **12 TRIBX 1**

Benson, Shaw

SECLUSION
Tracks: / Seclusion / Seclusion (instrumental).
12" Single: Released Jul '86, on Priority, by Priority Records. Deleted Nov '87. Catalogue no: **PX 13**

Benson, Vicki

EASY LOVE
Tracks: / Easy love / Lonely nights.
7" Single: Released Sep '84, on Bronze, by Bronze Records. Catalogue no: **BRO 186**
12" Single: Released Sep '84, on Bronze, by Bronze Records. Deleted '85. Catalogue no: **BROX 186**

PASSION
Tracks: / Passion / Shoot the moon (on 12" only) / Hold back the tears.
7" Single: Released Feb '85, on Bronze, by Bronze Records. Catalogue no: **BRO 189**

Bentley, Earlene

CAUGHT IN THE ACT (BENTLEY)
Tracks: / Caught in the act / He's a saint, he's a sinner.
7" Single: Released Jun '84, on Record Shack, by Record Shack Records. Catalogue no: **SOHO 23**
12" Single: Released Jun '84, on Record Shack, by Record Shack Records. Catalogue no: **SOHOT 23**
12" Single: Released Feb '88, on Record Shack, by Record Shack Records. Catalogue no: **SOHOB 3**

DON'T DELAY
Tracks: / Don't delay / Don't delay (instrumental).
7" Single: Released Nov '86, on Nightmare, by Nightmare Records. Catalogue no: **MARES 4**
12" Single: Released Nov '86, on Nightmare, by Nightmare Records. Catalogue no: **MARE 4**

I GOT YOU COVERED
Tracks: / I got you covered / I got you covered (inst).
7" Single: Released Apr '87, on Nightmare, by Nightmare Records. Catalogue no: **MARE 21**
7" Single: Released Apr '87, on Nightmare, by Nightmare Records. Catalogue no: **MARES 21**

I'M LIVING MY OWN LIFE
Tracks: / I'm living my own life.
7" Single: Released Feb '84, on Record Shack, by Record Shack Records. Catalogue no: **SOHO 14**
12" Single: Released Feb '84, on Record Shack, by Record Shack Records. Catalogue no: **SOHOT 14**

LET THE NIGHT TAKE THE BLAME
Tracks: / Let the night take the blame.
12" Single: Released Aug '86, on Rise, Catalogue no: **RISET 2**

POINT OF NO RETURN
Tracks: / Point of no return / Point of no return (dub mix).
7" Single: Released May '86, on Champion, by Champion Records. Catalogue no: **CHAMP 13**
12" Single: Released May '86, on Champion, by Champion Records. Catalogue no: **CHAMP 1213**

STARGAZING
Tracks: / Stargazing.
12" Single: Released Jan '85, on Record Shack, by Record Shack Records. Catalogue no: **SOHOT 32**

WHEN THE BOYS COME TO TOWN
Tracks: / When the boys come to town.
12" Single: Released Aug '83, on Soho (1), by Soho Records. Catalogue no: **SOHOT 8**
7" Single: Released Aug '83, on Soho (1), by Soho Records. Catalogue no: **SOHO 8**

Benton, Brook

Biographical details: Born in South Carolina, Brook Benton scored his first major success as both songwriter and singer in 1959. The first of his hits which he co-wrote was *"It's Just A Matter Of Time"* a No. 3 hit on the US charts. it began a string of hits that lasted until the arrival of the Beatles. benton was one of the artists who filled the American pop gap in the late Fifties and early Sixties, between the heyday of rock 'n' roll and the British Invasion. Backed with heavenly chorus and strings, Benton's smoky vocals provided the Top Ten hits *"So Many Ways"*, *"Kiddio"* and *"Hotel Happiness"* (an answer to Elvis' 1956 classic *"Heartbreak Hotel"*). his biggest American hit of all was 1961's novelty smash *"The Boll Weevil Song"* which reached No. 2.
This was an adaptation of an old American ditty, telling of the plight of the cotton farmer battling against the Boll Weevil bugs, small insects that can ruin a cotton crop. He also chalked up two top 10 duet hits with Dianah Washington (who died in 1963): *"Baby (You've Got What It Takes)"* and *"A Rockin' Good Way (To Mess Around And Fall In Love)"*, the latter becoming a 1984 UK smash for Shakin' Stevens and Bonnie Tyler.
Brook Benton never caught on in Britain, where the male vocalist market was already well catered for by such homegrown stars as Cliff Richard and Adam Faith. His first UK hit *"Endlessly"*, peaked at No. 28 and remained the biggest of his four chart records. From '64 onwards his American chart career floundered.
His only bright spot since then has been his one-off 1970 return to the US Top 5 with his version of *"Rainy Night In Georgia"*. In Britain however, it was left to Randy Crawford to take the song into the charts eleven years later. (Bob MacDonald).
The soul singer was born in 1931 in Camden, South Carolina. Like so many in the genre he came from a gospel music background; he began writing songs as a teenager and made hundreds of demos for Nat Cole, Roy Hamilton, Clyde McPhatter, many others, with writing collaborator Clyde Otis. First signed as a solo artist to Epic, then Mercury, he had 21 million-sellers 1959-64, plus duet hits with Dinah Washington. He later recorded for RCA, Reprise and Cotillion; had a top five in 1970 with Tony Joe White's *Rainy Day In Georgia*, but no other hits: his ballad style appealed to almost everybody, yet he missed out on greater success during the golden age of soul in the late '60s, perhaps because he was too smooth. His albums are still selling and his live act is a top attraction. (Donald Clarke 23 August 1988).

BOLL WEEVIL SONG
Tracks: / Boll weevil song.
7" Single: Released Jul '61, on Mercury (EMI), Deleted '64. Catalogue no: **AMT 1148**

ENDLESSLY (SINGLE)
Tracks: / Endlessly.
7" Single: Released Aug '59, on Mercury (EMI), Deleted '62. Catalogue no: **AMT 1043**

FOOLS RUSH IN
Tracks: / Fools rush in.
7" Single: Released Feb '61, on Mercury (EMI), Deleted '64. Catalogue no: **AMT 1121**

KIDDIO
Tracks: / Kiddio.
7" Single: Released Oct '60, on Mercury (EMI), Deleted '63. Catalogue no: **AMT 1109**

Benton, Buster

SWEET 94
Tracks: / Sweet 94.
7" Single: Released Jul '80, on Charly, by Charly Records. Deleted '87. Catalogue no: **CTD 119**

Berglund, Kristin

STEAL HIM AWAY
Tracks: / Steal him away / Hometown-shaker.
7" Single: Released May '80, on DJM, Deleted May '85. Catalogue no: **DJS 10938**

Berlin

DANCING IN BERLIN
Tracks: / Dancing in Berlin.
7" Single: Released '84, on Mercury, by Phonogram Ltd. Catalogue no: **MER 169**
12" Single: Released '84, on Mercury, by Phonogram Ltd. Catalogue no: **MERX 169**

LIKE FLAMES
Tracks: / Like flames / Trash.
CD 5": Released Feb '87, on Mercury, by Phonogram Ltd. Deleted Jul '87. Catalogue no: **MERCD 240**
7" Single: Released Feb '87, on Mercury, by Phonogram Ltd. Deleted Jul '87. Catalogue no: **MER 240**
12" Single: Released Feb '87, on Mercury, by Phonogram Ltd. Deleted Jul '87. Catalogue no: **MERX 240**

NO MORE WORDS
Tracks: / No more words / Rumour of love / Sex (I'm a...) (on 12" only).
7" Single: Released '84, on Mercury, by Phonogram Ltd. Catalogue no: **MER 160**
12" Single: Released '84, on Mercury, by Phonogram Ltd. Catalogue no: **MERX 160**

OVER 21
Tracks: / Over 21 / Waiting for the future.
7" Single: Released Feb '80, on Charisma, by Virgin Records. Deleted '83. Catalogue no: **CB 351**

SEX (I'M A...)
Tracks: / Sex (I'm a...) / Pleasure victim.
7" Single: Released '83, on Mercury, by Phonogram Ltd. Catalogue no: **TERRI 1**
12" Single: Released '83, on Mercury, by Phonogram Ltd. Catalogue no: **TERRI 12**

TAKE MY BREATH AWAY
Tracks: / Take my breath away / Radar radio / You've lost that lovin' feeling (Extra track on 12" only).
7" Single: Released Oct '86, on CBS, by CBS Records. Deleted Aug '88. Catalogue no: **A 7320**
12" Single: Released Oct '86, on CBS, by CBS Records. Deleted Aug '88. Catalogue no: **TA 7320**

YOU DON'T KNOW (SINGLE)
Tracks: / Hide away / Dancing the Berlin (remix).

7" Single: Released Nov '86, on Mercury, by Phonogram Ltd. Deleted Jul '87. Catalogue no: **MER 237**
12" Single: Released Nov '86, on Mercury, by Phonogram Ltd. Deleted Jul '87. Catalogue no: **MERX 237**

Berlin Blondes

FRAMEWORK
Tracks: / Framework / Zero song.
7" Single: Released Feb '81, on EMI, by EMI Records. Deleted Feb '84. Catalogue no: **EMI 5147**
12" Single: Released Feb '81, on EMI, by EMI Records. Deleted Feb '84. Catalogue no: **12EMI 5147**

MARSEILLES
Tracks: / Marseilles / Poet, The.
7" Single: Released '81, on Scratch, by Scratch Records. Catalogue no: **SCR 005**

SCIENCE
Tracks: / Science / Mannequin.
7" Single: Released Jan '80, on EMI, by EMI Records. Deleted Jan '85. Catalogue no: **EMI 5031**

Berlin Ritz

CRAZY NIGHTS
Tracks: / Crazy nights / You're where I belong.
7" Single: Released Apr '80, on Big Muff, Deleted Apr '83. Catalogue no: **BM 001**

Berlin Walls

NIGHT AND DAY
Tracks: / Night and day / You can't do that.
7" Single: Released '84, on La Rondie, Catalogue no: **LKI 101**

Bernadette

SING ME A SONG
Tracks: / Sing me a song.
7" Single: Released '83, on Polydor, by Polydor Ltd. Catalogue no: **POSP 586**

Berne, Jacqui

Biographical details: "Jacqui Berne's latest record 'Celebrate' is a brilliant summer - tinged dancefloor smash that combines an infectious pop melody with the essential rhythms of the baleric sound - a must for '88. it is already receiving great support from the ILR stations and the 12" is widely acclaimed in the clubs. A nationwide radio and club tour begins shortly to promote this single from a girl who always makes heads turn." (Hi-hat records, 1988)..

DON'T GET SERIOUS
Tracks: / Don't get serious / I'll be your angel.
7" Single: Released Jul '87, on Hi-Hat, by BMG Records (UK). Catalogue no: **HY 1**
12" Single: Released Jul '87, on Hi-Hat, by BMG Records (UK). Catalogue no: **HYT 1**

IT'S BEEN SO LONG
Tracks: / It's been so long / I'll never find a love.
CD 5": Released Jan '88, on Hi-Hat, by BMG Records (UK). Catalogue no: **HYCD 2**
7" Single: Released Jan '88, on Hi-Hat, by BMG Records (UK). Catalogue no: **HY 2**
12" Single: Released Jan '88, on Hi-Hat, by BMG Records (UK). Catalogue no: **HYT 2**

(NO DOUBT ABOUT IT)CELEBRATE
Tracks: / Celebrate / (No doubt about it) celebrate.
7" Single: Released Jul '88, on Hi-Hat, by BMG Records (UK). Catalogue no: **HY 4**
12" Single: Released Jul '88, on Hi-Hat, by BMG Records (UK). Catalogue no: **HYT 4**

Bernelle, Agnes

TOOTSIES
Tracks: / Tootsies / Chansonette.
7" Single: Released '85, on Imp, by Demon Records. Catalogue no: **IMP 004**

Bernhardts

I HEAR YOU CALLING
Tracks: / I hear you calling.
7" Single: Released '84, on Parlophone, by EMI Records. Catalogue no: **R 6076**

Bernstein, Elmer

Biographical details: The American orchestra led by Elmer Bernstein has been heard on many film soundtracks.
One of these was *"The Man With The Golden Arm"*, the title theme which gave the ensemble a US Top Twenty single in 1956. Four years later Bernstein scored his only British hit with *"Staccato's Theme"*, reaching No 4. (Bob MacDonald, 1984.)
One of the most prolific of American film composers was born in 1922 in New York City. His recording of his main theme from the Sinatra film 'Man With The Golden Arm' was a top 20 hit in 1955 and he won an Oscar in 1967 for his score for the Julie Andrews film 'Thoroughly Modern Millie'. (Donald Clarke 23 August 1988).

STACCATO'S THEME
Tracks: / Staccato's theme.
7" Single: Released Jan '60, on Capitol, by EMI Records. Deleted '63. Catalogue no: **CL 15101**

Berntholer

MY SUITOR
Tracks: / My suitor.

7" Single: Released '85, on Blanco Y Negro, by Blanco Y Negro Records. Catalogue no: **NEG 5**

Berry, Andrew

UNSATISFIED
12" Single: Released 20 Feb '88, on Cog Sinister, Catalogue no: **COGSIN 001**

Berry, Chuck

Biographical details: Charles Edward Berry was born on October 18th 1926 In San Jose, California. Some years later his family moved to St.Louis, Missouri where he spent his formative years. He soon developed an interest in music and we know he played guitar at school gigs and sang in the local church choir. When he left school he started training as a hairdresser but during his free time he played in clubs with a small group. In 1955 he took some recordings he had made to blues musician Muddy Waters in Chicago who arranged for him to be signed to the famous R&B label Chess Records. Berry's first release "Maybelline" immediately topped the charts and was followed by a string of successes which from both a musical and a lyrical aspect had a very influential effect on the rock'n'roll scene. He was to inspire many musicians especially the British rock stars of the sixties. Following his musical success Berry also starred in a few films. In 1959 he was sent to prison on charges of Immorality and did not resume his music career until 1964. Although he has had a few new hits, he has mainly concentrated on live performances in these years, running through his golden oldies.

Berry, Chuck. Born in 1926 in California, the guitarist, singer and songwriter was without doubt the greatest influence on rock 'n' roll until the Beatles. He grew up in St Louis, served time for armed robbery in 1944, became a hairdresser and regan recording for Chess in 1955: his *Ida Red* was renamed *Maybelline* and became his first hit; thereafter his songs about cars, girls and high school flattened the fence between R&B and pop.

John lennon said that if we needed another name for rock 'n' roll, we could call it Chuck Berry, while the Rolling Stones began as Berry imitators. His nine top 40 hits 1955-59 included *Roll Over Beethoven, Sweet Little Sixteen, Rock & Roll Music* and *Johnny B Goode*, while some of his best failed to cross over, such as the two-sided top ten R&B hit *Too Much Monkey Business/Brown Eyed Handsome Man.* He fell foul of an outmoded Federal law, transporting a minor across a state line 'for immoral purposes'; his first blatantly racist trial was thrown out, but the second sent him to prison again.

His writing dried up and he handicapped his own career by refusing to tour with a band, often hiring second-rate local backing groups, but his legend and his influence were already complete. Donald Clarke, 24 August 1988.

As well as being one of the greates of the Fifties rock 'n' rollers, Chuck Berry stands among the most influential artists in the entire history of rock music. Depending on which source of information you believe, Berry was born either in San Jose or St Louis. He was definately raised in St Louis, however and had a turmulent upbringing: three of his adolescent years were spent in a reform school for attempted robberty. During his first time at High school, he purchased his first second hand guitar and began listening to both 'race' music (the early name for rhythm and blues) and country and western. St Louis save him ready access to both genres and it was this dual influence that was to prove vital in his future role as one of the architects of rock 'n' roll. Berry graduated in cosmetology and hairdressing, the later being his major career ambition. In 1952 he formed his own group and spent three years playing his local club circuit. 1955 saw him journey to Chicago, where he managed to impress his hero, the legendary bluesman Muddy Waters. At Waters' suggestion, he went to Chess Records with rough demos of a couple of his compositions and was able to impress the label's chief Leonard Chess sufficiently to get a debut single released.

That first 45 was called *Maybellene* and was the first example of Berry's fusion of country and R&B. It was given a heavy push by the powerful disc jockey Alan Freed (who is said to have invented the term rock'n'roll), who received a dubious co-writing credit. Such an arrangement did not raise as many eyebrows then as it undoubtedly would today and what mattered at the time was that it was a fine, fresh record that put Berry at the forefront of the new rock'n'rollers. *Maybellene* logged nine weeks atop the US rhythm & blues charts and hit No.5 on the pop list, in the late summer and early autumn of '55. The next two singles *Thirty days* and *No money down* were R&B successes but failed to repeat the pop success of the first disc. They were followed by *Roll over Beethoven*, a witty account of the advent of the new music, which managed to reach No. 29 on the American pop charts. Yet the next record, a double A side combining *too much monkey business* and *Brown eyed handsome man*, again failed to consolidate and remained solely in the R&B charts.

By now Elvis Presley was storming the world, being universally hailed as the biggest artists of the new rock'n'roll and one of the biggest show business sensations of the century. Bill Haley's early string of hits and Berry's success with *Maybellene* were now being dwarfed by the exciting and outrageous achievements of the new King. Berry longed for this kind of pop adulation, but his problem was that his early discs were failing to talk about the subjects that the new young audience wanted to hear about. Although still influenced by his heroes, Muddy Waters and Louis Jordan, he began to address himself to the fads, fashions and interests of the newly affluent Youth Of America. The first result of this new policy was *School day* which recounted a day in the life of a typical yankee youngster - but the important factor was that it emphasised what took place after schools closed in the afternoon. By stressing the teenage themes of jukeboxes, dancing and romance, while retaining and improving his musical originality and excellence, Berry suddenly appealed to the mass youth market. *School day* reached No. 3 on the US pop charts in the early summer of 1957; it also save him his first UK hit, peaking at No. 24. By the end of the year he was returning to the US Top 10 with another anthem, simply called *Rock'n'roll music.*

It was followed in 1958 by two further smashes, *Sweet little sixteen* - No. 2 in the States and No. 16 in Britain, his second UK hit - and *Johnny B Goode.* One of the most important features of these instant rock'n'roll classics was that the lyrics were articulated clearly; because Berry ensured that every word could be understood. The full impact of his witty tales of teenage life reached the target audience. In addition he was becoming a major live attraction, with his concert performers; and along with many of his contemporites, he was appearing in the spate of rock films that were being made in the late fifties. In 1959 things started to tail off. Rock music was mellowing and his new hits like *Almost grown* and *Back in the USA* were each receiving a lower US chart position than the single before.

Then, later in the year, he appeared in an American court on a charge of transporting an under-age girl across State lines for sexual purposes. Berry consistenly professed his innocence and claimed that the real reason for the trial was an attempt to punish a black man; for becoming successful and famous. Reports of the whole episode vary, but it seems that the first trial was indeed terminated on the grounds of racial bias, the final outcome however, was that the black superstar began a two year jail sentence in the early Sixties. During this period of enforced inactivity, music was moving on in his absense - he was being left behind. Yet upon his release he suddenly found that he was a new hero in a country that had not previously given him much recognition: the Beatles, and the Rolling Stones were rapidly becoming the new pop sensations and both were acknowledging Chuck Berry as a key influence.

Berry had only had two relatively small hits in the UK during the Fifties and his other singles had failed to chart at all. So when the Stones sang and played numerous Berry songs in their stage act and scored their first hit single with his song *Come on* and when the Beatles recorded *Roll over Beethoven* as an album track they were introducing a man's work to a whole new audience. Meanwhile the United States' big new group, the Beach Boys, were hitting with *Surfin' USA*; this was an adaptation of *Sweet little sixteen*, with new surfing lyrics substituted. All of a sudden Berry was being hailed by the world's new superstars. What's more the song *Memphis Tennessee* (also commonly known as simply *Memphis*) was enjoying success in the form of two cover versions: Lonnie Mack reached No. 5 in the US with an instrumental rendition and a singer called Dave Berry (no relation) peaked at No. 19 on the British charts. Chuck Berry's own version of *Memphis* (coupled with *Let it rock*) then raced into the British charts and gave him a long overdue Top 10 debut in the UK in late '63. Simultaneously, he was making his first big impression on the British album charts - having first entered them in May of that year with a self-titled set, reaching No. 6 towards the end of '63. Encouraged by his new acclaim, the freed Berry returned to the recording studio and came up with three brand new hits, all reaching the Top 30 on both sides of the Atlantic during 1964: the biggest of these was *No particular place to go* which featured the same melody as *School day* but with new words, thus proving that his style had not changed at all in the intervening years. It was nevertheless a great record as there were two other singles *Nadine (is it you)* and *You never can tell*, the latter including some of his wittiest ever lyrics. After this glorious period of renewed success, his career floundered. No good new material surfaced for the rest of the Sixties. It is one of pop history's strangest ironies that this legendary rock'n'roll star, who had such a great influence on the music of the Fifties and Sixties, should suddenly have the biggest hit of his career in the early Seventies with a record totally out of keeping with the style that had made his name; but that is what happened.

An old song called *My ding a ling* had been in Berry's live set for many years under a different title. But in 1972, a new naughty live version recorded at a British arts festival went No. 1 on both sides of the Atlantic; it was his first chart topper in both the USA and UK. Despite the protestations of moral campaigner Mary Whitehouse in the latter nation, it was a runaway novelty favourite. Towards the middle of the decade Elvis Presley recorded Berry's *Promised land*; it hit the Top 20 in both Britain and America. Subsequently Chuck has recieved mixed fortunes. On the bright side, the Steve Gibbons Band took his song *Tulane* into the UK Top 20 and Berry played at the White House by personal invitation of US President Jimmy Carter. On the black side, he was given another prison sentence, this time for tax evasion. Chuck Berry has had his ups and downs but there is one permanent up that can not be changed. He is recognised all over the world as one of rock music's pioneers. Not only was he one of the greatest stars of the rock'n'roll heyday itself, but he also had a vital and direct influence on the emergence of rock's next great era - where would the Beatles and Stones have been without his legendary guitar work, songwriting and showmanship. (Bob MacDonald).

GO GO GO
Tracks: / Go go go.
7" Single: Released Jul '63, on Pye International, Deleted '66. Catalogue no: **7N 25209**

LET IT ROCK (SINGLE)
Tracks: / Let it rock / Memphis Tennessee.
7" Single: Released Oct '63, on Pye International, Deleted '66. Catalogue no: **7N 25218**

MEMPHIS TENNESSEE
Tracks: / Memphis Tennessee / No particular place to go.
7" Single: Released '83, on Old Gold, by Old Gold Records. Deleted Jul '88. Catalogue no: **OG 9296**

MY DING-A-LING
Tracks: / My ding a ling / School days / No particular place to go / Johnny B. Goode.
Note: * 12" version only.
7" Single: Released Jun '88, on Chess, by Vogue Records. Catalogue no: **GCHN 01**
7" Single: Released '84, on SMP (2), Catalogue no: **SKM 04**
12" Single: Released Jun '88, on Chess, by Vogue Records. Catalogue no: **GCHX 101**

MY DING-A-LING (OLD GOLD)
Tracks: / My ding a ling.
7" Single: Released Jan '89, on Old Gold, by Old Gold Records. Catalogue no: **OG 9845**

NADINE (IS IT YOU)
Tracks: / Nadine.
7" Single: Released Feb '64, on Pye International, Deleted '67. Catalogue no: **7N 25236**

NO PARTICULAR PLACE TO GO
Tracks: / No particular place to go / Sweet little sixteen.
7" Single: Released May '64, on Pye International, Deleted '67. Catalogue no: **7N 25242**
7" Single: Released '83, on Flashback, by Mainline Records. Catalogue no: **FBS 18**
CD 5": Released Feb '89, on Charly, by Charly Records. Catalogue no: **CDS 6**

NO PARTICULAR PLACE TO GO (OLD GOLD)
Tracks: / No particular place to go.
7" Single: Released Jan '89, on Old Gold, by Old Gold Records. Catalogue no: **OG 9843**

PROMISED LAND
Tracks: / Promised land.
7" Single: Released Jan '65, on Pye International, Deleted '68. Catalogue no: **7N 25285**

REELIN' AND ROCKIN' (SINGLE)
Tracks: / Reelin' and rockin'.
7" Single: Released Feb '73, on Chess, by Vogue Records. Deleted '76. Catalogue no: **CHESS 6145 020**

ROLL OVER BEETHOVEN (OLD GOLD)
Tracks: / Roll over Beethoven / Johnny B. Goode / Rock and roll music.
7" Single: Released Jan '89, on Old Gold, by Old Gold Records. Catalogue no: **OG 9847**

CD 5": Released 30 May '89, on Old Gold, by Old Gold Records. Catalogue no: **OG 6143**

RUN RUDOLPH RUN
Tracks: / Run Rudolph run.
7" Single: Released Dec '63, on Pye International, Deleted '66. Catalogue no: **7N 25228**

SCHOOL DAY
Tracks: / School days.
7" Single: Released Jul '57, on Columbia, by EMI Records. Deleted '60. Catalogue no: **DB 3951**

SWEET LITTLE SIXTEEN
Tracks: / Sweet little sixteen.
7" Single: Released '84, on SMP (2), Catalogue no: **SKM 05**
7" Single: Released Apr '58, on London-American, Deleted '61. Catalogue no: **HLM 8585**
7" Single: Released '85, on Chess (PRT), Deleted '88. Catalogue no: **CHES 4000**

SWEET LITTLE SIXTEEN (OLD GOLD)
Tracks: / Sweet little sixteen.
7" Single: Released Jan '89, on Old Gold, by Old Gold Records. Catalogue no: **OG 9849**

YOU NEVER CAN TELL (SINGLE)
Tracks: / You never can tell.
7" Single: Released Aug '64, on Pye International, Deleted '67. Catalogue no: **7N 25257**

Berry, Dave

Biographical details: Berry, Dave. Rock 'n' roll singer David Grundy was born in Sheffield, borrowed Chuck Berry's surname and formed The Cruisers in 1961. He signed to Decca in 1963 and his hits included covers of USA hits such as Chuck's *Memphis, Tennesee* and Arthur Crudup's *My Baby Left Me.* His stage act disguised his lack of innovation; he prowled the platform shielding his eyes, clad in black leather and trailing the microphone cable down his back. Alan Price can be seen explaining Berry's stage act to a bemused Bob Dylan in the 1965 documentary film 'Don't Look Back'; Alvin Stardust later borrowed some of Berry's gimmicks. Berry switched to brooding ballads after leaving The Cruisers and had a few more hits in the mid-60's. Donald Clarke, 24 August 1988.

Born in Sheffield, England, this rock'n'roll fan changed his surname from Grundy to Berry in the early Sixties, in recognition of his hero Chuck Berry. With his backing group, the Cruisers, the new Mr Berry scored his first success on the British charts in the autumn of 1963: Lonnie Mack had just scored a US Top 10 hit with an instrumental version of Chuck's *Memphis Tennessee*, so Dave recorded a vocal remake in an attempt to capitalise on the new fan following for Chuck inspired by the Rolling Stones and the Beatles. Shortly after it's release, the original version came out and stormed into the British Top 10, thereby upstaging Dave's cover. Nonetheless Dave managed to reach No. 19 and stayed on the list for 13 weeks, a very respectable showing for a debut hit. The next single *My baby left me* repeated the R&B formula, but only reached No. 37. In mid-1964 and 1966 with three similar hits in between. The three big ones, all curiously peaking at No. 5 on the British chart, were *The crying game, Little things* and *Mama*; the latter two were opportunistic remakes of recent American hits, which is why he failed to follow numerous other UK acts into the British Invasion. When the final hit *Mama* fell of the UK chart in '66, Berry became a regular fixture on Britain's Northern Club Circuit. He was not the worl's greatest singer and was beter known for his wacky stage presence and eccentric personality; his three year run of hit singles was the limit of his capabilities. (Bob MacDonald).

BABY IT'S YOU
Tracks: / Baby it's you.
7" Single: Released Apr '64, on Decca, by Decca Records. Deleted '67. Catalogue no: **F 11876**

CRYING GAME
Tracks: / Crying game, The / Don't gimme no lip child.
7" Single: Released Aug '64, on Decca, by Decca Records. Deleted '67. Catalogue no: **F 11937**
7" Single: Released Mar '82, on Decca, by Decca Records. Deleted '88. Catalogue no: **F 13608**

LITTLE THINGS
Tracks: / Little things.
7" Single: Released Mar '65, on Decca, by Decca Records. Deleted '68. Catalogue no: **F 12103**
7" Single: Released Mar '83, on Dakota, Catalogue no: **DAK 8**

MAMA
Tracks: / Mama.
7" Single: Released Jun '66, on Decca, by Decca Records. Deleted '69. Catalogue no:

7 F 12435

MEMPHIS TENNESSEE
Tracks: / Memphis tennessee.
7" Single: Released Sep '63, on Decca, by Decca Records. Deleted '66. Catalogue no: **F 11734**

MY BABY LEFT ME
Tracks: / My baby left me.
7" Single: Released Jan '64, on Decca, by Decca Records. Deleted '67. Catalogue no: **F 11803**

ONE HEART BETWEEN TWO
Tracks: / One heart between two.
7" Single: Released Nov '64, on Decca, by Decca Records. Deleted '67. Catalogue no: **F 12020**

THIS STRANGE EFFECT (SINGLE)
Tracks: / This strange effect.
7" Single: Released Jul '65, on Decca, by Decca Records. Deleted '68. Catalogue no: **F 12188**

Berry, Heidi

BELOW THE WAVES (SINGLE)
Tracks: / Below the waves.
CD 5": Released Apr '89, on Creation, by Creation Records. Catalogue no: **CRE 048CD**
12" Single: Released Apr '89, on Creation, by Creation Records. Catalogue no: **CRE 048T**

Berry, Mike

Biographical details: This British singer began his UK chart career in the Autumn of 1961 with *"Tribute To Buddy Holly"*, a single that peaked at No. 24. He had to wait until early 1963 for his next chart record: *"Don't You Think It's Time"* reached No. 6 and remains Berry's biggest ever hit. The next 45, *"My Little Baby"*, could do no better than No. 34. All three discs had featured his backing group, the Outlaws. Berry then faded into obscurity. Seventeen years later, he surprised the music business by bouncing back with a fourth hit. *"The Sunshine Of Your Smile"*, a gentle MoR singalong, hit No. 9 in Britain in 1980. The intervening period had been one of the longest gaps between hits in chart history.

ANNIVERSARY SONG
Tracks: / Anniversary song / Goodbye California.
7" Single: Released Feb '81, on Polydor, by Polydor Ltd. Deleted Feb '86. Catalogue no: **POSP 231**

DIANA
Tracks: / Diana / Words.
7" Single: Released Mar '81, on Polydor, by Polydor Ltd. Deleted Mar '84. Catalogue no: **POSP 232**

DON'T YOU THINK IT'S TIME
Tracks: / Don't you think it's time.
7" Single: Released Jan '63, on H.M.V., by EMI Records. Deleted '66. Catalogue no: **POP 1105**

EVERY LITTLE WHILE
Tracks: / Every little while.
7" Single: Released May '83, on Rockney, Catalogue no: **KOR 18**

HOLLY
Tracks: / Holly.
7" Single: Released Nov '85, on Switchback, Catalogue no: **MSSR 5**

IF I COULD ONLY MAKE YOU CARE
Tracks: / If I could only make you care / One more love story.
7" Single: Released Nov '80, on Polydor, by Polydor Ltd. Deleted '83. Catalogue no: **POSP 202**

MEMORIES (SINGLE)
Tracks: / Memories / Julie come back.
7" Single: Released Sep '81, on Polydor, by Polydor Ltd. Deleted '84. Catalogue no: **POSP 287**

MY LITTLE BABY
Tracks: / My little baby.
7" Single: Released Apr '63, on H.M.V., by EMI Records. Deleted '66. Catalogue no: **POP 1142**

SUNSHINE OF YOUR SMILE (SINGLE)
Tracks: / Sunshine of your smile, The.
7" Single: Released Jun '80, on Polydor, by Polydor Ltd. Catalogue no: **2059 261**

TILL WE MEET AGAIN
Tracks: / Till we meet again / Through noon and goes on.
7" Single: Released May '82, on Polydor, by Polydor Ltd. Deleted May '85. Catalogue no: **POSP 461**

TRIBUTE TO BUDDY HOLLY
Tracks: / Tribute to Buddy Holly.
7" Single: Released Oct '61, on H.M.V., by EMI Records. Deleted '64. Catalogue no: **POP 912**

TRIBUTE TO BUDDY HOLLY (OLD GOLD)
Tracks: / Tribute to Buddy Holly.
7" Single: Released Mar '87, on Old Gold, by Old Gold Records. Catalogue no: **OG 9648**

WHAT'LL I DO
Tracks: / What'll I do / Can a man love one woman.
7" Single: Released Jan '82, on Polydor, by Polydor Ltd. Deleted '85. Catalogue no: **POSP 385**

YOU'RE ALREADY GONE
Tracks: / You're already gone / Laughing and loving.
7" Single: Released Oct '87, on Break Heart, Catalogue no: **HBR 1**

Berry, Nick

EVERY LOSER WINS
Tracks: / Every loser wins / Every loser wins (instrumental).
7" Single: Released Oct '86, on BBC, by BBC Records & Tapes. Deleted 31 Aug '88. Catalogue no: **RESL 204**
12" Single: Released Oct '86, on BBC, by BBC Records & Tapes. Deleted 31 Aug '88. Catalogue no: **12 RSL 204**

Berryhill, Cyndi Lee

ME, STEVE, KIRK & KEITH
Tracks: / Me, Steve, Kirk & Keith / Baby.
7" Single: Released Sep '89, on Awareness, by Awareness Records. Catalogue no: **AWP 001**
12" Single: Released Sep '89, on Awareness, by Awareness Records. Catalogue no: **AWPX 001**

Bersin, Mike

ME AND MY LASER
Tracks: / Me and my laser / Time's up.
7" Single: Released Mar '80, on Amazon, Deleted '83. Catalogue no: **AMZ 1011**

Bertei, Adele

LITTLE LIVES, BIG LOVES (SINGLE)
Tracks: / Little lives, big love / Big sister / Every little bit hurts (Avalible on 12" only).
Note: * Extra track on 12"
12" Single: Released 25 Jul '88, on Chrysalis, by Chrysalis Records. Catalogue no: **CHS 12 3250**
7" Single: Released 25 Jul '88, on Chrysalis, by Chrysalis Records. Catalogue no: **CHS 3250**

WHEN IT'S OVER
7" Single: Released Sep '85, on Chrysalis, by Chrysalis Records. Deleted '87. Catalogue no: **CHS 2907**
12" Single: Released Sep '85, on Chrysalis, by Chrysalis Records. Deleted '87. Catalogue no: **CHS 12 2907**

Beshara

CANDI
7" Single: Released Oct '87, on Cande, Catalogue no: **CED 124**

GLORY GLORY
Tracks: / Glory glory.
12" Single: Released Jun '83, on Homespun (Ireland), by Outlet Records. Catalogue no: **HS 002**

SHADOW OF LOVE
Tracks: / Shadow of love.
12" Single: Released Nov '84, on Sub-Zero Music, by Sub-Zero Music. Catalogue no: **SZM 3**

WON'T LET YOU GO
Tracks: / Won't let you go.
12" Single: Released Jul '82, on Mass Media, Catalogue no: **MMM 12 1009**

Besserman, Martin

HIGH CLASS DINNER PARTY
Tracks: / High class dinner party.
12" Single: Released May '86, on Awesome Records, by Awesome Records. Catalogue no: **AOR 5T**
7" Single: Released May '86, on Awesome Records, by Awesome Records. Catalogue no: **AOR 5**

Best, George

IT TAKES TWO
Tracks: / It takes two.
7" Single: Released Mar '84, on Lifestyle, by Micrometro Ltd (Records). Catalogue no: **LIFE 10**
12" Single: Released Mar '84, on Lifestyle, by Micrometro Ltd (Records). Catalogue no: **LIFET 10**

Best Kept Secret

SPOTLIGHT
Tracks: / Spotlight.
12" Single: Released Sep '87, on Submission, by Submission Records. Catalogue no: **SUBX 02**

Best Way To Walk

UNBELIEVABLE
Tracks: / Unbelievable.
12" Single: Released Mar '87, on Two Bad, Catalogue no: **TWOB 1**

Bestwood, Clint

SOURMASH
Tracks: / Sourmash.
7" Single: Released '88, on Beam, by Beam Records. Catalogue no: **MM 001**

Bet Lynch's Legs

RIDERS IN THE SKY
Tracks: / Riders in the sky / High noon.
7" Single: Released '83, on Absurd, by Absurd Records. Catalogue no: **ABS 10**

SOME LIKE IT HOT
Tracks: / Some like it hot / Some don't.
7" Single: Released '83, on Absurd, by Absurd Records. Catalogue no: **ABS 11**

Better Mousetrap

ROAD TO KINGDOM COME
Tracks: / Road to kingdom come.
7" Single: Released 6 Jun '87, on Cuddly, Deleted '88. Catalogue no: **6/6/87**

Between Pictures

BIRTHDAY CARD
Tracks: / Birthday card / Down at the factory.
7" Single: Released May '81, on Applause, by Riva Records. Deleted May '84. Catalogue no: **CLAP 3**

TREAT ME LIKE AN EQUAL
Tracks: / Treat me like an equal / Life of your own.
7" Single: Released Dec '80, on Sonet, by Sonet Records. Deleted Dec '85. Catalogue no: **SON 2216**

Beverley Sisters

GREEN FIELDS
Tracks: / Green fields.
7" Single: Released Jun '60, on Columbia, by EMI Records. Deleted '63. Catalogue no: **DB 4444**

I DREAMED
Tracks: / I dreamed.
7" Single: Released Feb '57, on Decca, by Decca Records. Deleted '60. Catalogue no: **F 10832**

I SAW MOMMY KISSING SANTA CLAUS
Tracks: / I saw Mommy kissing Santa Claus.
7" Single: Released Nov '53, on Philips, by Phonogram Ltd. Deleted '56. Catalogue no: **PB 188**

LITTLE DONKEY
Tracks: / Little donkey.
7" Single: Released Jan '60, on Decca, by Decca Records. Deleted '63. Catalogue no: **F 11172**

LITTLE DRUMMER BOY
Tracks: / Little drummer boy.
7" Single: Released Feb '59, on Decca, by Decca Records. Deleted '62. Catalogue no: **F 11107**

SISTERS
Tracks: / Sisters.
7" Single: Released '85, on Hippodrome, by Hippodrome Records. Catalogue no: **HIPPO 104**
12" Single: Released '85, on Hippodrome, by Hippodrome Records. Catalogue no: **12HIPPO 104**

WILLIE CAN
Tracks: / Willie can.
7" Single: Released Apr '56, on Decca, by Decca Records. Deleted '59. Catalogue no: **F 10705**

Beverly, Frank

IF THAT'S WHAT YOU WANTED
Tracks: / If that's what you wanted.
7" Single: Released '83, on Inferno (1), by Inferno Records. Catalogue no: **HEAT 4**
7" Single: Released '83, on Neil Rushton, Catalogue no: **BURN 1**

Beverly & The ...

GREEN RAP, THE
Tracks: / Green rap, The / Eurotech.
7" Single: Released Jul '89, on CBS, by CBS Records. Catalogue no: **655150 7**

Beyond

WISH
Tracks: / Wish / Live to love another day.
7" Single: Released Jul '81, on Radioactive, Deleted Jul '84. Catalogue no: **RAD 102**

BFG

HIGHER EP, THE
7" Single: Released Oct '87, on Attica, by Attica Records. Catalogue no: **ATT 003**

PARIS
Tracks: / Paris.
12" Single: Released Jan '87, on Attica, by Attica Records. Deleted '88. Catalogue no: **BFG 001**

WESTERN SKY
Tracks: / Western Sky.
12" Single: Released May '87, on Attica, by Attica Records. Catalogue no: **ATT 002**

BG & The Mouse

BREAKER ONE FOUR
Tracks: / Breaker one four.
7" Single: Released Nov '81, on Maestro (2), by Maestro Recordings. Catalogue no: **MR 002**

DA DOO RON RON
Tracks: / Da doo ron ron / Clever boy.
7" Single: Released Jun '82, on Maestro (2), by Maestro Recordings. Catalogue no: **MR 003**

Bhaji, John

VINDALOO RAP
Tracks: / Vindaloo rap.
7" Single: Released Nov '88, on Bolts, by Bolts Records. Catalogue no: **NUTS 109**

Bhundu Boys

Biographical details: Bhundu Boys, The. The Zimbabwe pop band was formed in 1980 and had big hits there from 1982. Lead singer Biggie Tembo was a member of Robert Mugabe's Zanu during the civil war; he headed for Harare when the war was over with political feelings but traditional roots: the music blends the Mibira sound of the East African village with synthesised 'jit', a dance-hall beat relying on throbbing bass (David Mankaba), percussion (Kenny Chitsvatsva). Biggie also played guitar; all sing, incl. keyboardist Shakie Kangwela (name means Shakespeare Little Crocodile)

AFRICAN WOMAN
Tracks: / African woman / Ndoitasei (live at Wembley Stadium).
12" Single: Released Oct '87, on WEA, by WEA Records. Deleted Jul '88. Catalogue no: **YZ 164T**
7" Single: Released Oct '87, on WEA, by WEA Records. Deleted Jul '88. Catalogue no: **YZ 164**

BHUNDU BOYS & AFRICAN HERB
Tracks: / Bhundu Boys & African Herb.
12" Single: Released Oct '85, on Disc Afrique, Catalogue no: **DIS 1**

JIT JIVE
Tracks: / Jit jive / Rugare.
12" Single: Released Aug '87, on WEA, by WEA Records. Deleted Jul '88. Catalogue no: **YZ 151 T**
7" Single: Released Aug '87, on WEA, by WEA Records. Deleted Jul '88. Catalogue no: **YZ 151**

ZIVA KWAWAKABA
Tracks: / Ziva kwawakaba.
7" Single: Released Jan '88, on Discafrique Int., Catalogue no: **FWEAK 1**
12" Single: Released Jan '88, on Discafrique Int., Catalogue no: **FWEAK 001T**

Biafra, Jello

PRAISE THE LARD
Tracks: / Praise the lard.
7" Single: Released Mar '89, on Alternativ Tentacles, by Alternative Tentacles Re ords. Catalogue no: **UNKNOWN**

Bianca

WHERE THE BEAT MEETS TH STREET
Tracks: / Where the beat meets the street If she wanted to she would.
7" Single: Released Apr '84, on EMI, by E Records. Catalogue no: **EMI 5459**
12" Single: Released Apr '84, on EMI, EMI Records. Deleted '86. Catalogue n **12EMI 5459**

Biancamano

PIANO CONCERTO FOR THE MA WHO DOESN'T BELIEVE
Tracks: / Piano concerto for the man w doesn't believe.
12" Single: Released Aug '89, on Plaza, Plaza Records. Catalogue no: **12PZA 05**
7" Single: Released Aug '89, on Plaza, Plaza Records. Catalogue no: **PZA 050**

Bianco, Bonnie

WHEN THE PRICE IS YOUR LOVE
Tracks: / When the price is your love / Tr love.
7" Single: Released Feb '89, on WEA, WEA Records. Catalogue no: **YZ 367**
12" Single: Released Feb '89, on WEA, WEA Records. Catalogue no: **YZ 367T**

Bibi Den's Tshibayi

BEST AMBIANCE, THE
Tracks: / Best ambiance, The.
7" Single: Released Jan '84, on Earthwor

by Earthworks Records. Deleted '88. Catalogue no: **ET 002**

Bible

CRYSTAL PALACE
Tracks: / Crystal palace / Golden mile.
CD 5": Released Apr '88, on Chrysalis, by Chrysalis Records. Catalogue no: **BIBCD 2**
7" Single: Released Apr '88, on Chrysalis, by Chrysalis Records. Catalogue no: **BIB 2**
12" Single: Released Apr '88, on Chrysalis, by Chrysalis Records. Catalogue no: **BIBX 2**

GRACELAND (NEW VERSION)
Tracks: / Graceland.
12" Single: Released May '89, on Chrysalis, by Chrysalis Records. Catalogue no: **BIBX 4**
CD 5": Released May '89, on Chrysalis, by Chrysalis Records. Catalogue no: **BIBCD 4**
7" Single: Released May '89, on Chrysalis, by Chrysalis Records. Catalogue no: **BIB 4**
Cassingle: Released Jun '89, on Chrysalis, by Chrysalis Records. Catalogue no: **BIBMC**

GRACELANDS
Tracks: / Glory band (Live) / High wide (on 12" only.) / Slow drag down, The / Walking the ghost back home.
7" Single: Released Feb '87, on Chrysalis, by Chrysalis Records. Catalogue no: **BIB 1**
12" Single: Released Feb '87, on Chrysalis, by Chrysalis Records. Catalogue no: **BIBX 1**

HONEY BE GOOD
Tracks: / Honey be good / White feathers / Up in smoke (12" only.) / Coming of age (12" only.) / Glorybound (CD single.) / Abraham, Martin and John (CD single.).
12" Single: Released Sep '88, on Chrysalis, by Chrysalis Records. Catalogue no: **BIBX 3**
7" Single: Released Sep '88, on Chrysalis, by Chrysalis Records. Catalogue no: **BIB 3**
CD 5": Released Sep '88, on Chrysalis, by Chrysalis Records. Catalogue no: **BIBCD 3**

HONEY BE SO GOOD
Cassingle: Released Aug '89, on Chrysalis, by Chrysalis Records. Catalogue no: **BIBMC 5**
CD 5": Released Aug '89, on Chrysalis, by Chrysalis Records. Catalogue no: **BIBCD 5**
12" Single: Released Aug '89, on Chrysalis, by Chrysalis Records. Catalogue no: **BIBX 5**
7" Single: Released Aug '89, on Chrysalis, by Chrysalis Records. Catalogue no: **BIB 5**

MAHALIA
Tracks: / Mahalia / Spend spend spend / Sweetness (*= extra track on 12" only).
7" Single: Released Nov '86, on Backs, by Backs Recording Co.. Catalogue no: **NCH 11**
12" Single: Released Nov '86, on Backs, by Backs Recording Co.. Catalogue no: **12 NCH 11**

Bic

MUSICA POP
Tracks: / Musica pop.
12" Single: Released Oct '83, on Pop, by Magnet Records. Catalogue no: **BIG POP 1**
7" Single: Released Oct '83, on Pop, by Magnet Records. Catalogue no: **POP 1**

Bicat, Nick

CLEOPATRA'S
Tracks: / Cleopatra's / Electric in the city.
7" Single: Released Jan '83, on BBC, by BBC Records & Tapes. Deleted '87. Catalogue no: **RESL 128**

IRISH RM (THEME)
Tracks: / Irish RM (theme) / Major Yates fance / Haste to the wedding.
7" Single: Released Feb '83, on Ritz, by Ritz Records. Catalogue no: **RITZ 035**

Bicycle Thieves

WATERFRONT
Tracks: / Waterfront.
7" Single: Released Sep '89, on Sun Zoom Sparks, Catalogue no: **SZS 1**

Bid

REACH FOR YOUR GUNS
Tracks: / Reach for your guns / Sweet chariots / Love * (*=extra track on 12" only).
12" Single: Released Jun '86, on El, by Cherry Red Records. Catalogue no: **GPO 10 T**
7" Single: Released Jun '86, on El, by Cherry Red Records. Catalogue no: **GPO 10**

Biddu Orchestra

Biographical details: This British outfit was led by an Indian whose sole name was Biddu. In the summer of 1975 they hit No 14 on the UK chart with Summer of '42. This instrumental was followed by a couple of minor successes -- Rain Forest and Journey to The Moon -- over the next three years. Biddu was better known during the mid-70's as a producer of lightweight disco-inflected hits. He was responsible for Kung Fu Fighting, Carl Douglas's transAtlantic 1974 chart-topper, and Tina Charles 1976 UK No 1 I Love To Love (But My Baby Loves To Dance). (Bob MacDonald, 1984.).

FOUNDATION OF LOVE
Tracks: / Foundation of love / Humanity (latin house mix).
7" Single: Released 31 Jul '89, on Trax, by Filmtrax Records. Catalogue no: **7TX 10**
12" Single: Released 31 Jul '89, on Trax, by Filmtrax Records. Catalogue no: **12TX 10**

HUMANITY
Tracks: / Humanity.
7" Single: Released Apr '89, on Trax, by Filmtrax Records. Deleted Aug '89. Catalogue no: **7TX 5**
12" Single: Released Apr '89, on Trax, by Filmtrax Records. Deleted Aug '89. Catalogue no: **12TX 5**

JOURNEY TO THE MOON
Tracks: / Journey to the moon.
7" Single: Released Feb '78, on Epic, by CBS Records. Deleted '81. Catalogue no: **EPC 5910**

RAIN FOREST
Tracks: / Rain forest.
7" Single: Released Apr '76, on Epic, by CBS Records. Deleted '79. Catalogue no: **EPC 4084**

SUMMER OF '42
Tracks: / Summer of '42.
7" Single: Released Aug '75, on Epic, by CBS Records. Deleted '78. Catalogue no: **EPC 3318**

Biff Bang Pow

50 YEARS OF FUN
Tracks: / 50 years of fun / Then when I scream.
7" Single: Released Feb '84, on Creation, by Creation Records. Deleted Jul '88. Catalogue no: **CRE 003**

LOVE'S GOING OUT OF FASHION
Tracks: / Love's going out of fashion.
12" Single: Released Apr '86, on Creation, by Creation Records. Catalogue no: **CRE 024T**
7" Single: Released Apr '86, on Creation, by Creation Records. Catalogue no: **CRE 024**

SHE HAUNTS
7" Single: Released 20 Feb '88, on Creation, by Creation Records. Catalogue no: **CRE 051**
12" Single: Released 20 Feb '88, on Creation, by Creation Records. Catalogue no: **CRE 051T**

SOMEONE STOLE MY WHEELS
Tracks: / Someone stole my wheels.
12" Single: Released Nov '86, on Creation, by Creation Records. Catalogue no: **CRE 034T**
7" Single: Released Nov '86, on Creation, by Creation Records. Catalogue no: **CRE 034**

THERE MUST BE A BETTER LIFE
Tracks: / Chocolate elephant man, The.
7" Single: Released Jun '84, on Creation, by Creation Records. Deleted Jul '88. Catalogue no: **CRE 007**

WORLD'S TURNING BROUCHARD, THE
Tracks: / Death of England, The.
7" Single: Released Feb '87, on Creation, by Creation Records. Catalogue no: **CRE 038**

Big

LOOKING FOR HEROES
Tracks: / Looking for heroes / Looking for heroes (instrumental version) / Looking for heroes (12" extended version) (12" only).
7" Single: Released Jul '88, on Virgin, by Virgin Records. Catalogue no: **VS 1106**
12" Single: Released Jul '88, on Virgin, by Virgin Records. Catalogue no: **VST 1106**

Big Africa

I NEED YOU
Tracks: / I need you.
12" Single: Released Oct '88, on Leopard Music, by Leopard Music. Catalogue no: **BALMT 2**

Big Amongst Sheep

ASTRO POP
Tracks: / Astro pop.
12" Single: Released Jun '83, on Rock Solid, Catalogue no: **RSS 01**

Big Audio Dynamite

BOTTOM LINE
Tracks: / Bottom line, The / Bad.
7" Single: Released Oct '85, on CBS, by CBS Records. Catalogue no: **A 6591**
12" Single: Released Sep '85, on CBS, by CBS Records. Deleted '87. Catalogue no: **TA 6591**

C'MON EVERY BEAT BOX
Tracks: / C'mon every beatbox.
7" Single: Released Sep '86, on CBS, by CBS Records. Catalogue no: **650147 7**

CONTACT
Tracks: / Contact / In full effect / Who beats / If I were John Carpenter.
12" Single: Released Oct '89, on CBS, by CBS Records. Catalogue no: **BAAD T6**
CD 5": Released Oct '89, on CBS, by CBS Records. Catalogue no: **CD BAAD 6**
7" Single: Released Oct '89, on CBS, by CBS Records. Catalogue no: **BAAD 6**

E= MC2
Tracks: / E = MC2 / This is big audio dynamite.
7" Single: Released Mar '86, on CBS, by CBS Records. Catalogue no: **A 6963**
12" Single: Released Mar '86, on CBS, by CBS Records. Catalogue no: **TA 6963**

JUST PLAY MUSIC
Tracks: / Just play music / Just play music (ext. mix) (Track on 12".) / Much worse / Much worse (ext. mix) (track on 12") / Just play music (ext. remix)**.
Note: ** track on 12" (BAAD QT4).
7" Single: Released May '88, on CBS, by CBS Records. Deleted Jan '89. Catalogue no: **BAAD 4**
CD 5": Released 14 May '88, on CBS, by CBS Records. Deleted Jan '89. Catalogue no: **CDBAAD 4**
12" Single: Released May '88, on CBS, by CBS Records. Deleted Jan '89. Catalogue no: **BAAD T4**
12" Single: Released May '88, on CBS, by CBS Records. Deleted Jan '89. Catalogue no: **BAAD QT4**

MEDICINE SHOW
Tracks: / Medicine show / Party.
12" Single: Released May '86, on CBS, by CBS Records. Catalogue no: **TA 7181**
7" Single: Released May '86, on CBS, by CBS Records. Catalogue no: **A 7181**

OTHER 99
Tracks: / Other 99 / What happened to Eddie? / Other 99 (extended remix) (* on 12" & CD single only) / Just play music (club mix) (* on 12" single & CD single only).
Note: 'Other 99(extended remix)'and'Just play music(club mix)' available only on 12".s
CD 5": Released 25 Jul '88, on CBS, by CBS Records. Deleted Jan '89. Catalogue no: **CD BAAD 5**
7" Single: Released Aug '88, on CBS, by CBS Records. Deleted 17 Apr '89. Catalogue no: **BAAD B5**
7" Single: Released 25 Jul '88, on CBS, by CBS Records. Deleted Jan '89. Catalogue no: **BAAD 5**
12" Single: Released 25 Jul '88, on CBS, by CBS Records. Deleted Jan '89. Catalogue no: **BAAD T5**

SIGHTSEE M.C.
Tracks: / Sightsee M.C..
12" Single: Released Jul '87, on CBS, by CBS Records. Catalogue no: **BAAD T3**

V13
Tracks: / Hollywood Boulevard.
7" Single: Released Feb '87, on Barbarella, Catalogue no: **BAD 2**
12" Single: Released Feb '87, on CBS, by CBS Records. Catalogue no: **BADT 2**

Big Bam Boo

FELL OFF A MOUNTAIN
Tracks: / Fell off a mountain.
CD 5": Released Sep '88, on MCA, by MCA Records. Catalogue no: **DMCA 1265**
7" Single: Released Sep '88, on MCA, by MCA Records. Catalogue no: **MCA 1265**
12" Single: Released Sep '88, on MCA, by MCA Records. Catalogue no: **MCAT 1265**

IF YOU COULD SEE ME NOW
Tracks: / If you could see me now / I'm gone.
CD 5": Released Apr '89, on MCA, by MCA Records. Catalogue no: **DMCA 1321**
7" Single: Released Apr '89, on MCA, by MCA Records. Catalogue no: **MCA 1321**
12" Single: Released Apr '89, on MCA, by MCA Records. Catalogue no: **MCA 1321T**
12" Single: Released Sep '89, on MCA, by MCA Records. Catalogue no: **MCATG 1321**

SHOOTING FROM MY HEART
Tracks: / Shooting from my heart.
CD 3": Released Jan '89, on MCA, by MCA Records. Catalogue no: **DMCA 1281**
12" Single: Released Jan '89, on MCA, by MCA Records. Catalogue no: **MCAT 1281**
Special: Released Jan '89, on MCA, by MCA Records. Catalogue no: **MCAB 1281**
7" Single: Released Jan '89, on MCA, by MCA Records. Catalogue no: **MCA 1281**

Big Bands

50TH ANNIVERSARY OF THE BIG BANDS
7" Single: Released May '89, on Garland, Catalogue no: **GRZ 008**

Big Bang

ACID RADIO
Tracks: / Acid radio.
12" Single: Released May '89, on Rodger, Catalogue no: **RODGER 3**

VOULEZ VOUS
Tracks: / Voulez vous.
12" Single: Released Apr '89, on Total, Deleted Jul '89. Catalogue no: **SYRTR 1**
12" Single: Released Apr '89, on Total, Deleted Jul '89. Catalogue no: **SYRTR 1**
7" Single: Released Apr '89, on Total, Deleted Jul '89. Catalogue no: **SYRT 1**

Big Beat

KRAZE, THE
Tracks: / Kraze, The.
12" Single: Released Jun '88, on Big Beat, by Ace Records. Catalogue no: **BB 0002**

Big Ben Banjo Band

Biographical details: This all-male British instrumental group scored a Christmas Top Ten single in 1954, reaching No 6 in the UK charts. *"Let's Get Together"*, No 1, was a cash-in on Winifred Atwell's hit of the previous Christmas, *"Let's Have A Party"*. Both were medleys of old favourites, with Atwell's tinny piano replaced by nauseatingly catchy banjos. The band repeated the formula the following year but with less success: *"Let's Get Together Again"* reached No 18. They never appeared on the singles chart again, but reached No 20 on the UK album chart at Christmas 1960 with *"More Minstrel Melodies"*. (Bob MacDonald, 1984.).

LET'S GET TOGETHER AGAIN
Tracks: / Let's get together.
7" Single: Released Dec '55, on Columbia, by EMI Records. Deleted '58. Catalogue no: **DB 3676**

LET'S GET TOGETHER NO. 1
Tracks: / Let's get together.
7" Single: Released Dec '54, on Columbia, by EMI Records. Deleted '57. Catalogue no: **DB 3549**

Big Black

HEADACHE
Tracks: / Headache.
12" Single: Released Jun '87, on Blast First, by Blast First Records. Catalogue no: **BFFP 14**

IL DUCE
Tracks: / Il duce.
7" Single: Released Sep '86, on Homestead, Catalogue no: **HMS 042**

MODEL, THE
Tracks: / Model, The / Whore.
7" Single: Released Sep '87, on Blast First, by Blast First Records. Catalogue no: **BFFP 24**

Big Bopper

Biographical details: At 28, the Big Bopper died in the same North Dakota place crash that also killed touring partners Buddy Holly and Ritchie Valens in February 1959. Born J.P. Richardson in Texas, the Big Bopper became well known as a disc jockey in the early 50's.
The draft interrupted his broadcasting career in the middle of the decade but, on his return to radio, he staged a broadcasting marathon -- his continuous stretch of 122 hr 8 min broke the existing world record by eight minutes.
He turned to songwriting and, unintentionally, singing: his novelty smash Chantilly Lace, released in '58, reached No 6 in the US and No 12 in the UK and is now regarded as a rock 'n' roll classic.
The next 45, The Big Bopper's Wedding, was far less successful, bearing out the music business axiom that a novelty hit is hard to follow up. Towards the end of his life he encouraged a protege, Johnny Preston. Running Bear, Preston's single writted and produced by the Big Bopper, went to No 1 on both sides of the Atlantic in 1960, about a year after his death.
(Bob MacDonald, 1984.)

CHANTILLY LACE (OLD GOLD)
Tracks: / Chantilly lace.
7" Single: Released Jan '85, on Old Gold, by Old Gold Records. Catalogue no: **OG 9483**

CHANTILLY LACE (SINGLE)
Tracks: / Chantilly lace / Monkey song / Old maid.
7" Single: Released Mar '83, on Swift, by 77 Records. Catalogue no: **D45 1008**
7" Single: Released Oct '58, on Mercury (EMI), Deleted '61. Catalogue no: **AMT 1002**

Big Brother

BIG BROTHER
Tracks: / Big brother.
7" Single: Released Oct '84, on Code, by Code Records. Catalogue no: **LOB 12**

Big Chalk

IN THE COLD WINTERS NIGHT
Tracks: / In the cold winters night.
7" Single: Released Mar '83, on A & R, Catalogue no: **AR 002**

Big City Beat Band

CAN I BE YOUR FRIEND
Tracks: / Can I be your friend.
7" Single: Released Apr '88, on BCB, Catalogue no: **BCB 001**

Big Country

Biographical details: Big Country. A guitar based rock band formed in Scotland in 1981, a relief from synth groups ubiquitous at the time. Stuart Adamson, guitar and vocals; Bruce Watson, guitar; Tony Butler, bass; Mark Brzezicki, drums. Adamson came from the Skids, teamed with Watson and recruited the rhythm section hot from playing on Pete Townshend's solo LP *All The Best Cowboys Have Chinese Eyes*. *Steeltown* in 1984 entered the UK chart at no. 1; they have found favour with pop, folk and heavy metal fans with their characteristic 'bagpipe' guitar sound. *The Seer* in 1986 included guest Kate Bush. Donald Clarke, 24 August 1988..

BROKEN HEART (CD SINGLE)
Tracks: / Broken heart (thirteen valleys) / Soapy soutar strikes back / Made in heaven / When the drum beats / On the shore.
CD 5": Released Oct '88, on Mercury, by Phonogram Ltd. Catalogue no: **BIGCD 6**
CD 5": Released Nov '88, on Mercury, by Phonogram Ltd. Catalogue no: **BCCDR 6**

BROKEN HEART (THIRTEEN VALLEYS)
Tracks: / Broken heart (thirteen valleys).
12" Single: Released Oct '88, on Mercury, by Phonogram Ltd. Deleted 31 May '89. Catalogue no: **BIGC 612**
7" Single: Released Oct '88, on Mercury, by Phonogram Ltd. Deleted 31 May '89. Catalogue no: **BIGC 6**
Special: Released Oct '88, on Mercury, by Phonogram Ltd. Deleted 31 May '89. Catalogue no: **BIGCR 612**
CD 5": Released Oct '88, on Mercury, by Phonogram Ltd. Catalogue no: **BIGCD 6**

CHANGE (see panel below)
Tracks: / Change / Tracks of my tears / Crossing, The.
12" Single: Released Jun '84, on Mercury, by Phonogram Ltd. Deleted Mar '88. Catalogue no: **COUNT 412**
7" Single: Released Aug '83, on Mercury, by Phonogram Ltd. Deleted Mar '88. Catalogue no: **COUNT 4**

EAST OF EDEN
Tracks: / East of Eden.
7" Single: Released Sep '84, on Mercury, by Phonogram Ltd. Deleted '87. Catalogue no: **MER 175**
12" Pic: Released Sep '84, on Mercury, by Phonogram Ltd. Deleted '87. Catalogue no: **MERXP 175**
12" Single: Released Sep '84, on Mercury, by Phonogram Ltd. Deleted '87. Catalogue no: **MERX 175**

FIELDS OF FIRE
Tracks: / Fields of fire / Angle Park.
7" Single: Released Feb '83, on Mercury, by Phonogram Ltd. Deleted Jul '87. Catalogue no: **COUNT 2**

FIELDS OF FIRE(ALTERNATIVE MIX)
12" Single: Released Jun '84, on Mercury, by Phonogram Ltd. Deleted Jul '87. Catalogue no: **COUNT 212**

HARVEST HOME
Tracks: / Harvest home / Balcony / Flag of nations.
7" Single: Released Feb '83, on Mercury, by Phonogram Ltd. Deleted '87. Catalogue no: **COUNT 1**
12" Single: Released Jun '84, on Mercury, by Phonogram Ltd. Deleted '87. Catalogue no: **COUNT 112**

HOLD THE HEART
Tracks: / Honky tonk women / Hold the heart.
7" Single: Released Nov '86, on Mercury, by Phonogram Ltd. Deleted Jul '87. Catalogue no: **BIGC 4**
12" Single: Released Nov '86, on Mercury, by Phonogram Ltd. Deleted Jul '87. Catalogue no: **BIGCX 4**

IN A BIG COUNTRY
Tracks: / In a big country / All of us.
7" Single: Released Oct '84, on Mercury, by Phonogram Ltd. Deleted Mar '88. Catalogue no: **COUNT 3**
12" Single: Released Oct '84, on Mercury, by Phonogram Ltd. Deleted Mar '88. Catalogue no: **COUNT 312**

JUST A SHADOW
Tracks: / Just a shadow / Winter sky.
7" Single: Released Jan '85, on Mercury, by Phonogram Ltd. Deleted '86. Catalogue no: **BCO 8**
12" Single: Released Jan '85, on Mercury, by Phonogram Ltd. Catalogue no: **BCO 812**

KING OF EMOTION
Tracks: / King of emotion / Travellers, The / Starred & crossed (12" & CD only) / Not waving - drowning (CD only).
CD 5": Released Aug '88, on Mercury, by Phonogram Ltd. Catalogue no: **BIGCD 5**
7" Single: Released Aug '88, on Mercury, by Phonogram Ltd. Deleted 31 May '89. Catalogue no: **BIGC 5**
12" Single: Released Aug '88, on Mercury, by Phonogram Ltd. Deleted 31 May '89. Catalogue no: **BIGC 512**

LOOK AWAY
Tracks: / Look away / Restless natives.
7" Single: Released Mar '86, on Mercury, by Phonogram Ltd. Deleted '87. Catalogue no: **BIGC 1**
12" Single: Released Mar '86, on Mercury, by Phonogram Ltd. Deleted '87. Catalogue no: **BIGCX 1**

ONE GREAT THING
Tracks: / One great thing / Song of the south / Porroh man * (*=extra track on double pack only) / Champs (*=extra track on double pack only) / Flame of the west.
7" Set: Released Aug '86, on Mercury, by Phonogram Ltd. Deleted '87. Catalogue no: **BIGCD 3**
7" Single: Released Aug '86, on Mercury, by Phonogram Ltd. Deleted Jul '87. Catalogue no: **BIGC 3**
12" Single: Released Aug '86, on Mercury, by Phonogram Ltd. Deleted Jul '87. Catalogue no: **BIGCX 3**

BIG COUNTRY - CHANGE (Released on Mercury)

BIG DADDY - EYE OF THE TIGER (Released on Making Waves)

PEACE IN OUR TIME (LIVE)
Tracks: / Peace in our time (live) / Chance (live) / Big country, A (live) / Promised land.
12" Single: Released Feb '89, on Mercury, by Phonogram Ltd. Catalogue no: **BIGCR 712**

PEACE IN OUR TIME (SINGLE)
Tracks: / Peace in our time / Promised land / Over the border / Chance / Longest day, The.
12" Single: Released 23 Jan '89, on Phonogram, by Phonogram Ltd. Deleted 31 Jul '89. Catalogue no: **BIGC 712**
7" Single: Released 23 Jan '89, on Phonogram, by Phonogram Ltd. Deleted 31 Jul '89. Catalogue no: **BIGC 7**
12" Single: Released Jan '89, on Phonogram, by Phonogram Ltd. Deleted Oct '89. Catalogue no: **BIGCR 712**
Special: Released Jan '89, on Phonogram, by Phonogram Ltd. Deleted Oct '89. Catalogue no: **BIGCP 7**
CD 5": Released 23 Jan '89, on Phonogram, by Phonogram Ltd. Catalogue no: **BIGCD 7**

TEACHER, THE
Tracks: / Teacher, The / Home came the angel / Of the restless angel (on 12" only.).
12" Single: Released Jun '86, on Mercury, by Phonogram Ltd. Catalogue no: **BIGCX 2**
7" Single: Released Jun '86, on Mercury, by Phonogram Ltd. Catalogue no: **BIGC 2**

WHERE THE ROSE IS SOWN
Tracks: / Where the rose is sown.
12" Single: Released Nov '84, on Mercury, by Phonogram Ltd. Deleted '87. Catalogue no: **MERX 185**
7" Single: Released Nov '84, on Mercury, by Phonogram Ltd. Deleted '87. Catalogue no: **MER 185**

WONDERLAND
Tracks: / Wonderland / Giants.
7" Single: Released Jan '84, on Mercury, by Phonogram Ltd. Deleted '87. Catalogue no: **COUNT 5**
12" Single: Released Jan '84, on Mercury, by Phonogram Ltd. Deleted '87. Catalogue no: **COUNT 512**

WONDERLAND (EXT.VERSION)
Tracks: / Wonderland (extended version).
12" Single: Released Jun '84, on Mercury, by Phonogram Ltd. Catalogue no: **COUNT 512**

Big Daddy

Biographical details: Big Daddy. USA the last great unsigned '50s rock band, emerging in the early '80s: at least that's their story. Lineup: David Starns, Mark Kaniger, Tom Lee, vocals and guitars; Bob Wayne, keyboards and vocals; Gary Hoffman, drums. Their publicity said they entertained troops in Southeast Asia and were kidnapped by Laotian guerillas, who treated them well, having heard that rock 'n' roll was a Communist plot. Their debut album in 1983 included contemporary hits played in '50s style; rumours that they started in oldies bands no further east than L.A. are said to be spread by jealous record companies and by the CIA, embarrassed that their rescue took 24 years. Donald Clarke, 24 August 19887.

DANCING IN THE DARK
Tracks: / Dancing in the dark / I write the songs / Bette Davis eyes / Eye of the tiger.
7" EP: Released Mar '85, on Making Waves by Celtic Music. Deleted '88. Catalogue no: **SURF 1033**

EYE OF THE TIGER (see panel above)
Tracks: / Eye of the tiger / Star wars.
7" Single: Released Sep '84, on Making Waves, by Celtic Music. Deleted Nov '87. Catalogue no: **SURF 102**

I WRITE THE SONGS
Tracks: / I write the songs.
7" Single: Released Jun '85, on Making Waves, by Celtic Music. Catalogue no: **SURF 103**

WE SHALL NOT BE MOVED
Tracks: / We shall not be moved / Big daddy
7" Single: Released Apr '80, on Columbia by EMI Records. Deleted Apr '83. Catalogue no: **DB 9079**

Big Daddy Kane

I'LL TAKE YOU THERE
Tracks: / I'll take you there / Wrath.
7" Single: Released Dec '88, on Cold Chillin', by Cold Chillin' Records. Catalogue no: **921082 0**

RAW
Tracks: / Raw.
7" Single: Released 20 Feb '88, on Cold Chillin', by Cold Chillin' Records. Catalogue no: **W7 953**
12" Single: Released 20 Feb '88, on Cold Chillin', by Cold Chillin' Records. Catalogue no: **W7 953T**

SMOOTH OPERATOR
Tracks: / Smooth operator.
7" Single: Released Aug '89, on Warner Bros., by WEA Records. Catalogue no: **2804**

WRATH OF KANE, THE
Tracks: / Wrath of Kane, The / Rap summary.
12" Single: Released Apr '89, on Warner Bros., by WEA Records. Catalogue no: **2973 T**
7" Single: Released Apr '89, on Warner Bros., by WEA Records. Catalogue no: **2973**

Big Dee Irwin

SLOW DANCE
Tracks: / Slow dance / Slow dance (version
7" Single: Released Sep '88, on 2000 A Catalogue no: **IRWIN 1**
CD 5": Released Sep '88, on 2000 A Catalogue no: **IRWINC 1**
12" Single: Released Sep '88, on 2000 A Catalogue no: **IRWINT 1**

Big Dipper

VICTIMS OF THE PLANETS
Tracks: / Victims of the planets / Dipper delight.
12" Single: Released Sep '81, on Epic, CBS Records. Deleted '84. Catalogue no: **EPCA 13-1513**

Big Dish

BIG NEW BEGINNING

12" Single: Released Jun '85, on Virgin, by Virgin Records. Deleted '86. Catalogue no: **VS 776-12**
7" Single: Released Jun '85, on Virgin, by Virgin Records. Deleted '86. Catalogue no: **VS 776**

CHRISTINA'S WORLD
Tracks: / Everlasting faith / She say's nothing (This track only found on the 12" version.) / Slide (CD single only.) / Reverend killer / Christina's world / Prospect street.
7" Single: Released Jan '87, on Virgin, by Virgin Records. Deleted May '88. Catalogue no: **VS 928**
12" Single: Released Jan '87, on Virgin, by Virgin Records. Deleted May '88. Catalogue no: **VS 928-12**
CD 5": Released '88, on Virgin, by Virgin Records. Catalogue no: **DISH 1**

EUROPEAN RAIN
Tracks: / European rain / Voodoo baby / Time on your own (NOT on 7") / Swimmer, The (On 10" only).
7" Single: Released Jul '88, on Virgin, by Virgin Records. Catalogue no: **VS 1102**
12" Single: Released Jul '88, on Virgin, by Virgin Records. Catalogue no: **VST 1102**
10" single: Released '88, on Virgin, by Virgin Records. Catalogue no: **VSA 1102**

FAITH HEALER
Tracks: / Faith healer (On all versions) / Be my friend (On all versions) / Things fall into place (CD & 12" only) / Country song (CD only).
7" Single: Released 26 Sep '88, on Virgin, by Virgin Records. Catalogue no: **VS 1136**
CD 5": Released Oct '88, on Virgin, by Virgin Records. Catalogue no: **VSCD 1136**
12" Single: Released 26 Sep '88, on Virgin, by Virgin Records. Catalogue no: **VST 1136**

PROSPECT STREET
Tracks: / Prospect Street / From the neighbourhood.
7" Single: Released Oct '86, on Virgin, by Virgin Records. Deleted May '88. Catalogue no: **VS 913**
12" Single: Released Oct '86, on Virgin, by Virgin Records. Deleted May '88. Catalogue no: **VS 913-12**

SLIDE
Tracks: / Slide / Reverend killer / Presence (* =extra track on 12" only).
Note: Track 'Presence' available on 12" only.
7" Single: Released Aug '86, on Virgin, by Virgin Records. Deleted May '88. Catalogue no: **VS 851**
12" Single: Released Aug '86, on Virgin, by Virgin Records. Deleted '89. Catalogue no: **VS 851-12**

Big Feat

I LOVE REGGAE MUSIC
Tracks: / I love reggae music / Funk.
7" Single: Released 20 Feb '88, on Bold Reprieve (1), Catalogue no: **BRM 010**

Big Fin

CRY
Tracks: / Cry / Honey from the spoon.
7" Single: Released Aug '88, on S.A.M., by Sound & Music Studios. Catalogue no: **FINE 1**

Big Flame

CUBIST POP MANIFESTO
Tracks: / Cubist pop manifesto.
7" Single: Released Feb '87, on Ron Johnson, by Ron Johnson Records. Catalogue no: **ZRON 13**

DEBRA
Tracks: / Debra.
7" Single: Released Mar '85, on Ron Johnson, by Ron Johnson Records. Catalogue no: **ZRON 3**

POPSTARS
Tracks: / Popstars.
7" Single: Released Mar '86, on Ron Johnson, by Ron Johnson Records. Catalogue no: **ZRON 7**

SINK
Tracks: / Sink.
7" Single: Released Apr '84, on Plaque, by Red Rhino Records. Catalogue no: **PLAQUE 001**

TOUGH
Tracks: / Tough.
7" Single: Released Sep '85, on Ron Johnson, by Ron Johnson Records. Catalogue no: **ZRON 4**

TWO KAN GURU (EP)
Tracks: / Two kan guru / Sink / Sometimes / Man of few syllables / Sargasso / All the Irish / Cuba.
10" single: Released Jul '86, on Ron Johnson, by Ron Johnson Records. Catalogue no: **RERON 8**

XPZWRTX
Tracks: / XPZWRTX.
12" Single: Released Feb '87, on Ron Johnson, by Ron Johnson Records. Catalogue no: **ZRON15**

Big Fun

BLAME IT ON THE BOOGIE
Tracks: / Blame it on the boogie / Blame it on the boogie (inst).
12" Single: Released Aug '89, on Jive, by Zomba Records. Catalogue no: **JIVER 217**
Cassingle: Released 24 Jul '89, on Jive, by Zomba Records. Catalogue no: **JIVEC 217**
7" Single: Released 24 Jul '89, on Jive, by Zomba Records. Catalogue no: **JIVE 217**
12" Single: Released Aug '89, on Jive, by Zomba Records. Catalogue no: **JIVEX 217**
12" Single: Released 24 Jul '89, on Jive, by Zomba Records. Catalogue no: **JIVET 217**
CD 5": Released 24 Jul '89, on Jive, by Zomba Records. Deleted Aug '89. Catalogue no: **JIVECD 217**

LIVING FOR YOUR LOVE
Tracks: / Living for your love.
7" Single: Released Apr '89, on Jive, by Zomba Records. Deleted Aug '89. Catalogue no: **JIVE 200**
12" Single: Released Apr '89, on Jive, by Zomba Records. Deleted Aug '89. Catalogue no: **JIVET 200**

Big Gun

HEARD ABOUT LOVE
Tracks: / Heard about love.
7" Single: Released Mar '89, on Hi-Fibre, Catalogue no: **ATOH 001**

YOU'LL ALWAYS GIVE YOUR BEST
Tracks: / Basil Peironi / Don't ever go away again.
7" Single: Released Jan '87, on Hi-Fibre, Catalogue no: **BIG 001**

Big Jim

SWEET FORGET ME NOT
Tracks: / Sweet forget me not / When your old wedding ring was new.
7" Single: Released Oct '86, on Homespun (Ireland), by Outlet Records. Catalogue no: **HS 112**

Big Ken

HOOCHIE COOCHIE MAN
Tracks: / Hoochie coochie man / Harry Dean.
7" Single: Released Jul '87, on RCA, by BMG Records (UK). Deleted May '89. Catalogue no: **ANX 002**
12" Single: Released Jul '87, on RCA, by BMG Records (UK). Deleted May '89. Catalogue no: **ANXT 002**

Big Lady K

DON'T GET ME STARTED
Tracks: / Don't get me started.
12" Single: Released Sep '88, on B-Ware, by B/Ware Records. Catalogue no: **UM 003**

Big Louis

FRENCH KISS
Tracks: / French kiss.
7" Single: Released Jul '89, on Living Beat, by Living Beat Records. Catalogue no: **SCAM 1**

Big Mac

ROUGH DRIED WOMAN
Tracks: / Rough dried woman.
7" Single: Released Jul '80, on Charly, by Charly Records. Deleted '87. Catalogue no: **CTD 125**

Big Music

COLD EMOTION
Tracks: / Cold emotion / Hard rain's gonna fall.
12" Single: Released Sep '86, on RCA, by BMG Records (UK). Catalogue no: **PT 40908**
7" Single: Released Sep '86, on RCA, by BMG Records (UK). Catalogue no: **PB 40907**

Big Noise

FADE TO GREY
Tracks: / Fade to grey / I want your love / Fade to grey (extended remix) (Available on 12" only).
7" Single: Released Jun '89, on President, by President Records. Catalogue no: **PT 580**
12" Single: Released Jun '89, on President, by President Records. Catalogue no: **PT 12-580**

Big Outdoor Type

CALL YOU ON SUNDAY
Tracks: / Call you on Sunday.
7" Single: Released Jul '84, on Havasac, Catalogue no: **SAC 01**

Big Pete

ORIGINAL SLOBB, THE
Tracks: / Original slobb, The.
7" Single: Released Jul '84, on Stan Ollie, Deleted '86. Catalogue no: **SOR 1**

Big Pig

BIG HOTEL
Tracks: / Big Hotel / Devil's song.
12" Single: Released 1 Aug '88, on A&M, by A&M Records. Deleted 1 Aug '88. Catalogue no: **AMY 442**
7" Single: Released 1 Aug '88, on A&M, by A&M Records. Deleted 1 Aug '88. Catalogue no: **AM 429**

BREAKAWAY
Tracks: / Breakaway / Hellbent heaven / Breakaway (popper mix) (on 12" only.).
12" Single: Released Oct '87, on A&M, by A&M Records. Deleted Feb '89. Catalogue no: **AMY 419**
7" Single: Released Oct '87, on A&M, by A&M Records. Deleted Feb '89. Catalogue no: **AM 419**

HUNGRY TOWN
Tracks: / Hungry town / Boy wonder (baby mix).
7" Single: Released Jun '88, on A&M, by A&M Records. Deleted Feb '89. Catalogue no: **AM 409**
12" Single: Released Jun '88, on A&M, by A&M Records. Deleted Feb '89. Catalogue no: **AMY 409**

Big Red Boat

FAREWELL MY LOVELY
Tracks: / Farewell my lovely / Moon moocher.
7" Single: Released Mar '85, on Elastic Music, Catalogue no: **EM 003**

Big Self

DON'T TURN AROUND
Tracks: / Don't turn around / Jagged edges.
7" Single: Released Mar '82, on Reekus, by Reekus Records. Catalogue no: **RKS 003**

GHOST SHIRT
Tracks: / Ghost shirt / I'm keen.
7" Single: Released Mar '84, on Reekus, by Reekus Records. Catalogue no: **RKS 009**
12" Single: Released Mar '84, on Reekus, by Reekus Records. Catalogue no: **RKST 009**

REASON SMILES
Tracks: / Reason smiles.
12" Single: Released Apr '85, on Reekus, by Reekus Records. Catalogue no: **RKST 012**

SURPRISE SURPRISE
Tracks: / Surprise surprise.
7" Single: Released Sep '81, on Reekus, by Reekus Records. Catalogue no: **RKS 002**

VISION
Tracks: / Vision.
7" Single: Released Aug '85, on Reekus, by Reekus Records. Catalogue no: **RKS 014**

Big Smile

CROCODILE TEARS
Tracks: / Crocodile tears.
12" Single: Released Aug '88, on I.R.S, Catalogue no: **IRMT 170**
7" Single: Released Aug '88, on I.R.S, Catalogue no: **IRM 170**

Big Sound Authority

BAD TOWN
Tracks: / Bad town, A / Excuse me please.
7" Single: Released May '85, on MCA, by MCA Records. Catalogue no: **BSA 2**
7" Single: Released Jun '85, on Source, Catalogue no: **BSAX 2**
12" Single: Released May '85, on MCA, by MCA Records. Catalogue no: **BSAT 2**
12" Single: Released May '85, on MCA, by MCA Records. Catalogue no: **BSAC 2**

DON'T LET OUR LOVE START A WAR
Tracks: / Don't let our love start a war / Moving heaven & earth (revisited) / Family thing (on 12" only).
12" Single: Released Aug '86, on MCA, by MCA Records. Catalogue no: **BSAT 4**
7" Single: Released Aug '86, on MCA, by MCA Records. Catalogue no: **BSA 4**

THIS HOUSE (IS WHERE YOUR LOVE)
Tracks: / This house (is where your love stands) / I miss my baby.
7" Single: Released Jan '85, on Source, Deleted '88. Catalogue no: **BSA 1**

Big Stick

CRACK ATTACK
Tracks: / Crack attack / Crack attack (freakscene) (7" only.) / Crack attack (vocal mix) (12" only.) / Crack attack (I want my money back) (12" only.) / Crack attack (breakfast in Brooklyn) (12" only.) / Crack attack (dangerous) (12" only.).
12" Single: Released Apr '89, on EMI, by EMI Records. Deleted Oct '89. Catalogue no: **12EM 88**
CD 5": Released Apr '89, on EMI, by EMI Records. Deleted Oct '89. Catalogue no: **CDEM 88**
7" Single: Released Apr '89, on EMI, by EMI Records. Deleted Oct '89. Catalogue no: **EM 88**

DRAG RACING
Tracks: / Drag racing.
12" Single: Released Jun '86, on Blast First, by Blast First Records. Catalogue no: **BFFP 6**

Big Supreme

DON'T WALK
Tracks: / Don't walk / My addiction.
7" Single: Released Aug '86, on Polydor, by Polydor Ltd. Deleted Aug '87. Catalogue no: **POSP 809**
12" Single: Released Aug '86, on Polydor, by Polydor Ltd. Deleted Mar '88. Catalogue no: **POSPX 809**

LET'S TURN OUR LOVE AROUND
Tracks: / Let's turn our love around / He'll deceive.
12" Single: Released May '86, on Polydor, by Polydor Ltd. Deleted Aug '87. Catalogue no: **POSPX 791**
7" Single: Released May '86, on Polydor, by Polydor Ltd. Deleted '86. Catalogue no: **POSP 791**

PLEASE YOURSELF
Tracks: / Keep on pushing / Please yourself.
10" single: on Polydor, by Polydor Ltd. Deleted Aug '87. Catalogue no: **POSPT 840**
7" Single: Released Feb '87, on Polydor, by Polydor Ltd. Deleted Jan '88. Catalogue no: **POSP 840**
12" Single: Released Feb '87, on Polydor, by Polydor Ltd. Deleted Jan '88. Catalogue no: **POSPX 840**
7" Set: on Polydor, by Polydor Ltd. Deleted Aug '87. Catalogue no: **POSPD 840**

REMIND ME
Tracks: / Remind me / What love means / Remind me (I don't wanna see no panties) (Track on 12" Remix version only.).
12" Single: Released Apr '87, on Polydor, by Polydor Ltd. Deleted Jan '88. Catalogue no: **POSPA 861**
7" Single: Released Apr '87, on Polydor, by Polydor Ltd. Deleted Jan '88. Catalogue no: **POSP 861**
12" Single: Released Apr '87, on Polydor, by Polydor Ltd. Deleted Jan '88. Catalogue no: **POSPX 861**

Big Sur

DANCING ON THE HIGH WIRE
Tracks: / Dancing on the high wire.
12" Single: Released Aug '87, on Hands Like Feet, Catalogue no: **HLF 001**

PLEASE STAY
Tracks: / Please stay / Dancing on the high wire / Catch me I'm falling.
7" Single: Released May '88, on Hands Like Feet, Catalogue no: **HLF 001**

Big Three

Biographical details: The Big Three -- Brian Griffiths, John Gustafson and John Hutchinson -- were among the pioneers of the 60's Merseyside boom. As Cass & The Casanovas they had visited Hamburg during the early 60's along with many other Liverpool groups. Changing their name to the Big Three in 1962, they established themselves as one of the most popular and innovative of their home city's beat combos. Their first single, *"Some Other Guy"*, hit No 37 on the UK chart in the spring of 1963. They followed it with *"By The Way"*, which reached No 22 during the summer. Surprisingly, just when they appeared to be on the verge of a major breakthrough, Griffiths and Gustafson quit. Hutchinson recruited two other musicians but the new line-up failed. In early '64 there came a reminder of the Big Three's original potential when an EP, *"At The Cavern"*, hit No 6 on the separate EP chart. Recorded by the first line-up at Liverpool's legendary Cavern Club, it remains one of the best-loved legacies of the beat boom. (Bob MacDonald, 1984.)
Big Three. A Merseybeat trio, claimed to be the first beat group in Liverpool, lineup from late-'50s Cass and the Casanovas: Adrian Barber on guitar, John Gustavson on bass, Johnny Hutchinson on drums and lead vocals. They stood out from Liverpool groups in being a trio and in the drummer being the lead singer; signed by Brian Epstein they were sent to Hamburg, where Brian Griffiths replaced Barber. Signed by Decca on their return, their first single *Some Other Guy* reached the top 40; Freddy Garrity (of Freddy and the Dreamers) said it was the record that 'really typified the Mersey sound'. They didn't last long, but they were well-liked and good value as an act. Donald Clarke, 24 August 1988..

AT THE CAVERN
Tracks: / At the cavern.
7" EP: Released Jun '81, on Decca, by Decca Records. Deleted '88. Catalogue no: **DFE 8552**

BY THE WAY
Tracks: / By the way.
7" Single: Released Jul '63, on Decca, by Decca Records. Deleted '66. Catalogue no: **F 11689**

SOME OTHER GUY
Tracks: / Some other guy.
7" Single: Released Apr '63, on Decca, by

Decca Records. Deleted '66. Catalogue no: **F 11614**

Big Tom

CLONES CYCLONE
Tracks: / Clones cyclone.
7" Single: Released '88, on I&B, by I & B Records. Catalogue no: **DMC 1032**

I LOVE YOU STILL
Tracks: / I love you still.
7" Single: Released '88, on I&B, by I & B Records. Catalogue no: **DMC 1010**

OLD LOVE LETTERS
Tracks: / Old love letters.
7" Single: Released '88, on I&B, by I & B Records. Catalogue no: **DMC 1012**

RAMBLING MAN
7" Single: Released '88, on I&B, by I & B Records. Catalogue no: **UNIC 13**

TUBBERCURRY
Tracks: / Tubbercurry.
7" Single: Released '88, on I&B, by I & B Records. Catalogue no: **DMC 1033**

Big Tony

CAN'T GET ENOUGH OF YOUR LOVE BABE
Tracks: / Can't get enough of your love babe / I miss you.
7" Single: Released Jul '86, on Lisson, by PWL Records. Catalogue no: **DOLE 3**
12" Single: Released Jul '86, on Lisson, by PWL Records. Catalogue no: **DOLEQ 3**

Big Town Playboys

DOWN THE ROAD APIECE
Tracks: / Down the road apiece.
7" Single: Released Jan '86, on Pinnacle, by Pinnacle Records. Catalogue no: **DRIFT 103**

Big Trade

CALL OF VANITY
Tracks: / Call of vanity / Oasis ridge.
7" Single: Released 31 Jul '89, on 1992, Catalogue no: **1992 003**

Big Trouble

CRAZY WORLD
Tracks: / Crazy world / Trains and boats and planes / Say yes*.
Note: * track on 12" version.
CD 5": Released 13 Jun '88, on Epic, by CBS Records. Deleted Jan '89. Catalogue no: **651625 2**
7" Single: Released May '88, on Epic, by CBS Records. Deleted Jan '89. Catalogue no: **651625 7**
12" Single: Released May '88, on Epic, by CBS Records. Deleted Jan '89. Catalogue no: **651625 6**
7" Single: Released 6 Jun '88, on Epic, by CBS Records. Deleted Jan '89. Catalogue no: **651625 0**

WHEN THE LOVE IS GOOD
Tracks: / When the love is good / Last kiss, The / Lipstick.
7" Pic: Released Mar '88, on Epic, by CBS Records. Deleted Aug '88. Catalogue no: **651 492-0**
Special: Released Apr '88, on Epic, by CBS Records. Deleted Jan '89. Catalogue no: **651 442-9**
7" Single: Released Mar '88, on Epic, by CBS Records. Deleted Aug '88. Catalogue no: **651 492-7**
12" Single: Released Mar '88, on Epic, by CBS Records. Deleted Aug '88. Catalogue no: **651 492-6**

Big Twist

300 POUNDS OF HEAVENLY JOY
Tracks: / 300 pounds of heavenly joy.
7" Single: Released Jan '84, on Sonet, by Sonet Records. Catalogue no: **SON 2662**

Big View

AUGUST GRASS
Tracks: / August grass.
7" Single: Released Aug '82, on Point, Deleted '84. Catalogue no: **PT 01**

Big X Crewe

BEVERLY HILLS COP
Tracks: / Beverly Hills cop / Pizza Walk (inst) / Jack piano (Available on 12" only).
Note: * extra track on 12" version only.
12" Single: Released Oct '87, on Uptown Records, by Uptown Records. Catalogue no: **12 UTR 5**
7" Single: Released Oct '87, on Uptown Records, by Uptown Records. Catalogue no: **7UTR 5**

Big Youth

Biographical details: Big Youth. A Jamaican toaster, Manley Augustus Buchanan, the first to preach an overt Ras Tafari message in his lyrics. He began making a reputation in the early '70s, his commercial breakthrough coming with *Dread Locks Dread* in 1975, perhaps the most influential reggae album of that year. He began to produce himself and to vary his style, even singing (approximately), and his cult status has now lasted many years. Donald Clarke, 24 August 1988..

TROUBLE ON THE ROAD
Tracks: / Trouble on the road.
12" Single: Released May '87, on John Dread Production, Catalogue no: **JDPD 009**

Big Zap!

PSYCHEDELIC SHACK
Tracks: / Psychedelic shack / Zap attack.
12" Single: Released Jul '87, on Tim, by Tim Records. Catalogue no: **12 MOT 7**
7" Single: Released 13 Jun '87, on Tim, by Tim Records. Catalogue no: **MOT 7**

Bigg Ben

TODAY IN PARLIAMENT
Tracks: / Today in Parliament.
12" Single: Released Apr '89, on Completely Different, by Neat Records. Catalogue no: **DAFT 2T**
7" Single: Released Apr '89, on Completely Different, by Neat Records. Catalogue no: **DAFT 2**

Bigger Splash

DON'T BELIEVE A WORD
Tracks: / Don't believe a word / Silence.
7" Single: Released Jun '84, on A&M, by A&M Records. Deleted '85. Catalogue no: **AM 196**
12" Single: Released Jun '84, on A&M, by A&M Records. Deleted '85. Catalogue no: **AMX 196**

Bigger Than God

BIGGER THAN GOD
Tracks: / Bigger than God: *Various artists.*
12" Single: Released Feb '86, on Bunker, by Bunker Records. Catalogue no: **BUNKER 1**

Biggs, Barry

Biographical details: In the same way that the Stylistics produced sweet soul in the 70's, Jamaican singer Barry Biggs produced sweet reggae. He made gentle, lightweight singles sung in a soft, high-pitched voice. Between 1976 and 1981 he chalked up six chart singles in Britain, but only one made the Top Twenty. This was *"Sideshow"*, a No 3 hit in early '77 which featured a strong but plaintive melody. The record's distinctive muffled sound gave it a slightly eerie quality. (Bob MacDonald, 1984.)
Biggs, Barry. Mainstream Jamaican singer who had a string of crossover hitsin UK charts late '70s, with *Work All Day, Sideshow* '76; *Three Ring Circus* '77; *What's Your Sign Girl* '79; cover of Blues Busters *Wide Awake In A Dream* '81, plus albums *Mr Biggs, ... With Inner Circle, Sincerely* and *Wide Awake In A Dream*. Donald Clarke, 24 August 1988..

ALL I HAVE TO DO IS DREAM
Tracks: / All I have to do is dream.
7" Single: Released Dec '86, on Revue, by Creole Records. Catalogue no: **REV 041**

CONVERSATION
Tracks: / Wide awake in a dream.
7" Single: Released Aug '85, on Revue, by Creole Records. Catalogue no: **REV 027**

DON'T CRY BABY
Tracks: / Don't cry baby / Exclusively yours.
12" Single: Released Dec '85, on Revue, by Creole Records. Catalogue no: **REV 031T**

IF SHE WERE MINE
Tracks: / If she were mine.
7" Single: Released Jun '88, on Starlight, Catalogue no: **SLD 549**

IF YOU WANNA MAKE LOVE
Tracks: / If you wanna make love / Girl I really love you.
7" Single: Released Mar '87, on Revue, by Creole Records. Catalogue no: **REV 744**
12" Single: Released Mar '87, on Revue, by Creole Records. Catalogue no: **REV 044T**

IF YOU WERE NOT HERE
Tracks: / If you were not here.
12" Single: Released Jun '86, on Starlight, Catalogue no: **SLD 538**

ILLUSION
Tracks: / Illusion.
12" Single: Released Jul '83, on Bullet, by Bullet Records. Deleted '88. Catalogue no: **CPRD 128**

LOVE COME DOWN
Tracks: / Love come down.
7" Single: Released Feb '83, on Afrik, Catalogue no: **AF 140**

PROMISE IS A COMFORT TO A FOOL
Tracks: / Promise is a comfort to a fool.
12" Single: Released Jun '82, on Afrik, Catalogue no: **AF 02**

REFLECTION
Tracks: / Reflection.
10" single: Released Dec '82, on Mobiliser, by Jetstar Records. Catalogue no: **MM 45**

SIDESHOW
Tracks: / Sideshow / I'll be back.
7" Single: Released Aug '84, on Creole, by Creole Records. Catalogue no: **CR 65**
12" Single: Released Aug '84, on Creole, by Creole Records. Catalogue no: **CRT 65**
7" Single: Released Dec '76, on Dynamic, Deleted '79. Catalogue no: **DYN 118**

SIDESHOW ('87 MIX)
Tracks: / Sideshow (87 mix) / Wide awake in a dream / Work all day (Extra track on 12" only).
12" Single: Released May '87, on Dynamic, Catalogue no: **DYN 1218**
7" Single: Released May '87, on Dynamic, Catalogue no: **DYN 18**

THREE RING CIRCUS
Tracks: / Three ring circus.
7" Single: Released Jul '77, on Dynamic, Deleted '80. Catalogue no: **DYN 128**

WHAT'S YOUR SIGN GIRL
Tracks: / What's your sign girl.
7" Single: Released Dec '79, on Dynamic, Deleted '82. Catalogue no: **DYN 150**

WIDE AWAKE IN A DREAM
Tracks: / Wide awake in a dream.
7" Single: Released Jul '81, on Dynamic, Deleted '84. Catalogue no: **DYN 1**
12" Single: Released Jul '81, on Dynamic, Deleted '84. Catalogue no: **DYN 12-1**

WORK ALL DAY
Tracks: / Work all day.
12" Single: Released May '83, on Dynamic, Catalogue no: **DYN 1212**
7" Single: Released Aug '76, on Dynamic, Deleted '79. Catalogue no: **DYN 101**

YOU'RE MY LIFE
Tracks: / You're my life.
7" Single: Released Apr '77, on Dynamic, Deleted '80. Catalogue no: **DYN 127**

Biggs, Susan

SCENE FOR PEACE
Tracks: / Scene for peace / Ballet praetorius / Two Catalan folk songs.
7" Single: Released Jun '82, on Flight, Deleted Jun '85. Catalogue no: **XJ 2**

Biggun, Ivor

Biographical details: In 1978, at the time of his first UK chart record, it was rumoured that Ivor Biggun worked for BBC Radio One. This was never confirmed but the disc -- entitled *"Winker's Song (Misprint)"* and credited to Ivor Biggun & The Red Nosed Burglars -- was banned from the air; it reached No 22 with 12 weeks on the chart. Another, smaller, hit was *"Bras On 45 (Family Version)"* by Ivor Biggun & The D Cups, a parody on the then popular Stars on 45 medley fad, peaked at No 50. (Bob MacDonald, 1984.).

BRA'S ON 45 (FAMILY VERSION) (see panel below)
Tracks: / Bra's on 45 (family version) / Are mice electric / Richard the third.
7" Single: Released Sep '81, on Dead Badger, by Dead Badger Records. Deleted '84. Catalogue no: **BOP 6**

MAJORCA SONG, THE
Tracks: / Majorca song, The / Great big filthy disco version.
12" Single: Released 20 Jun '87, on Dead Badger, by Dead Badger Records. Catalogue no: **IVOR IT**
7" Single: Released 20 Jun '87, on Dead Badger, by Dead Badger Records. Catalogue no: **IVOR 1**

WANKERS ROCK AND ROLL
Tracks: / Wankers rock and roll / I lift up my finger / Send for Dr. Clap / Hide the sausage.
7" Single: Released Jan '81, on Beggars Banquet, by Beggars Banquet Records. Deleted Jan '84. Catalogue no: **BOP 5**

WINKER'S SONG (MISPRINT)
Tracks: / Winker's song (misprint).
7" Single: Released Sep '78, on Beggars Banquet, by Beggars Banquet Records. Deleted '81. Catalogue no: **BOP 1**

Bikaye, Zazou

GUILTY (SINGLE)
Tracks: / Guilty.
12" Single: Released Nov '88, on Crammed Discs, by Crammed Discs. Catalogue no: **CRAM 204512**

Bikini Atoll

TRIBAL RADIO
Tracks: / Tribal radio / Splinter.
7" Single: Released Jul '82, on Ready Go, Catalogue no: **EGO 3**

WALL, THE
Tracks: / Wall, The.
7" Single: Released Nov '81, on Ready Go, Catalogue no: **EGO 2**

Bilbo

SEX MACHINE
Tracks: / Relax / Sex machine.
12" Single: Released Aug '83, on All Boys, Catalogue no: **ABOYT 1**
7" Single: Released Aug '83, on All Boys, Catalogue no: **ABOY 1**

SHE'S GONNA WIN
Tracks: / She's gonna win.
7" Single: Released Aug '78, on Lightning, Deleted '81. Catalogue no: **LIG 548**

Bileams asna

SAAB TURBO
Tracks: / Passive so long / Saab turbo.
7" Single: Released May '84, on Cantio (Sweden), Catalogue no: **CS 011**

Bilk, Acker

Biographical details: Bilk, Acker. Bernard Stanley Bilk was born in 1929 in Somerset; he took up the clarinet to pass the time while in the guardhouse in Egypt in 1947, formed a band in 1958 and as Mr Acker Bilk became one of the most popular leaders during the trad. boom. A total of 11 singles and nine albums charted 1960-78, including many top tens; his own composition *Stranger On The Shore* (with strings) was no. 2 in the uK in 1961, no. 1 in the USA the next year. 'Acker' was rural English for 'mate' or 'chum'. Donald Clarke, 24 August 1988.
Born Bernard Bilk in Somerset, England in 1929, this accomplished clarinettist formed his Paramount Jazz Band in 1958. Having played in their local Bristol area and then in Dusseldorg, they scored their first British hit in early 1960. The gentle bluesy number *Summer set* entered the charts in January, strangely enough, and peaked at No. 5. It was quickly followed by a debut chart album *Seven ages of Acker*, which reached No. 6.

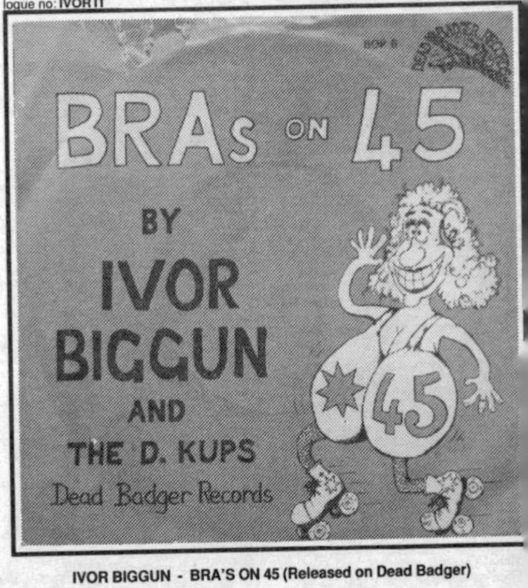

IVOR BIGGUN - BRA'S ON 45 (Released on Dead Badger)

Mr Acker Bilk (as he was known) and his Paramount Jazz Band then scored several more chart singles, including two futher top tenners, *Buona sera* and *That's my home*. Bilk became one of the most successful artists of the early sixties trad jazz boom, helped by a skilful marketing campaign and image which included two clothing trademarks - the bowler hat and the striped waistcoat. In late 1961 came the biggest success of his career. His self-penned tune *Stranger on the shore*, used at the time as the theme to a BBC Children's TV series, entered the UK chart in November of that year and stayed on the list for 55 consecutive weeks; this was a new longevity record that has only been subsequently bettered once. It peaked No. 2 but went all the way to No. 1 in the States, thus becoming Bilk's only US Top 40 hit. This classic single was credited to Mr Acker Bilk with the Leon Young String Chorale. His success on the album charts in Britain was continuing apace. In addition to his own discs he hit the Top 10 twice with *Best of Barber and Bilk* Volumues One and Two. In October 1962 *Best of Ball, Barber and Bilk* hit No. 1. These LPs were collaborations with fellow ace jazzmen Chris Barber and Kenny Ball. In 1963 the Beatles revolution torpedoed the traditional jazz merchants out of the charts. Like many of his peers, Bilk moved into cabaret and TV variety shows and in 1976, *Aria* reached No. 5 on the UK charts. The following year he scored his highest placed LP, when *Sheer magic* climbed to No.5 on the album chart. (Bob MacDonald).

ACKER'S LULLABY
Tracks: / Acker's lullaby / One more time.
7" Single: Released Jun '84, on PRT, by Castle Communications Records. Catalogue no: **7P 313**

ARIA
7" Single: Released Jun '76, on PRT, by Castle Communications Records. Catalogue no: **7N 45607**

BUONA SERA
Tracks: / Buona sera.
7" Single: Released Dec '60, on Columbia, by EMI Records. Deleted '63. Catalogue no: **DB 4544**

COLLECTION: ACKER BILK
Special: Released Sep '78, on PRT, by Castle Communications Records. Catalogue no: **11PP 605**

FIND A WAY
Tracks: / Find a way / Moment I'm with you.
7" Single: Released Sep '81, on PRT, by Castle Communications Records. Deleted '84. Catalogue no: **7 P 221**

FRANKIE AND JOHNNY
Tracks: / Frankie and Johnny.
7" Single: Released Mar '62, on Columbia, by EMI Records. Deleted '65. Catalogue no: **DB 4795**

GOODNIGHT SWEET PRINCE
Tracks: / Goodnight sweet prince.
7" Single: Released Jun '60, on Melodisc, Deleted '63. Catalogue no: **MEL 1547**

GOTTA SEE MY BABY TONIGHT
Tracks: / Gotta see my baby tonight.
7" Single: Released Jul '62, on Columbia, by EMI Records. Deleted '65. Catalogue no: **SCD 2176**

JOHN HENRY
Tracks: / John Henry.
7" Single: Released Jul '83, on PRT, by Castle Communications Records. Catalogue no: **7P 278**

LONELY
Tracks: / Lonely.
7" Single: Released Sep '62, on Columbia, by EMI Records. Deleted '65. Catalogue no: **DB 4897**

SMILE SAM SMILE
Tracks: / Smile Sam smile / Smile Sam smile (Instrumental).
7" Single: Released Jun '86, on PRT, by Castle Communications Records. Catalogue no: **7P 357**

SONG FOR GUY
Tracks: / Song for Guy / Just the way you are.
7" Single: Released Mar '80, on Piccadilly, Deleted '83. Catalogue no: **7P 169**

STARS AND STRIPES FOREVER
Tracks: / Stars and stripes forever / Creole jazz.
7" Single: Released Nov '61, on Columbia, by EMI Records. Deleted '64. Catalogue no: **SCD 2155**

STRANGER ON THE SHORE (OLD GOLD)
Tracks: / Stranger on the shore / Summer set.
7" Single: Released Jul '82, on Old Gold, by Old Gold Records. Catalogue no: **OG 9151**

STRANGER ON THE SHORE (SINGLE)
Tracks: / Stranger on the shore.
7" Single: Released Nov '61, on Columbia, by EMI Records. Deleted '64. Catalogue no: **DB 4750**

SUMMER SET
Tracks: / Summer set.
7" Single: Released Jan '60, on Columbia, by EMI Records. Deleted '63. Catalogue no: **DB 4382**

TASTE OF HONEY, A (SINGLE)
Tracks: / Taste of honey, A.
7" Single: Released Jan '63, on Columbia, by EMI Records. Deleted '66. Catalogue no: **DB 4949**

THAT'S MY HOME (SINGLE)
Tracks: / That's my home.
7" Single: Released Jul '61, on Columbia, by EMI Records. Deleted '64. Catalogue no: **DB 4673**

VERDE
Tracks: / Verde / When we were young.
7" Single: Released Jun '80, on Piccadilly, Deleted Jun '83. Catalogue no: **7P 182**

WHITE CLIFFS OF DOVER
Tracks: / White cliffs of Dover, The.
7" Single: Released Aug '60, on Columbia, by EMI Records. Deleted '63. Catalogue no: **DB 4492**

Bilko

CRAIG AND BENTLEY
Tracks: / Craig and Bentley.
7" Single: Released Apr '83, on Bilko, Catalogue no: **NYMPH 003**

Bill Stickers Banned

CHRISTMAS WRAPPING
Tracks: / Christmas wrapping / Bill Stickers Christmas rap.
7" Single: Released Dec '83, on Wombat, Deleted '84. Catalogue no: **AP 001**

Billie

NOBODY'S BUSINESS
Tracks: / Nobody's Business (Instrumental-Club Mix) / Nobody's Business.
7" Single: Released Oct '86, on Club, by Phonogram Ltd. Catalogue no: **JAB 38**
12" Single: Released Oct '86, on Club, by Phonogram Ltd. Catalogue no: **JABX 38**

Bim

BLIND LEAD THE BLIND
Tracks: / Blind lead the blind / Blind lead the blind (pt 2).
7" Single: Released Oct '82, on Swerve, Deleted Oct '85. Catalogue no: **SKID 005**

DELICIOUS
Tracks: / Delicious / Gone wrong / Favor.
7" Single: Released Jun '80, on Swerve, Deleted Jun '83. Catalogue no: **SKID 001**

FACTORY
Tracks: / Factory / Business.
7" Single: Released Mar '82, on Swerve, Deleted '85. Catalogue no: **SKID 004**

REQUEST TIME
Tracks: / Request time / Don't panic.
7" Single: Released Feb '81, on Arista, by BMG Records (UK). Deleted Feb '84. Catalogue no: **ARIST 391**

ROMANCE
Tracks: / Romance / She called me robert.
7" Single: Released May '81, on Arista, by BMG Records (UK). Deleted May '86. Catalogue no: **ARIST 409**
7" Single: Released Sep '81, on Shark, by Shark Records. Deleted '84. Catalogue no: **MAC 001**

WALLY RAP
Tracks: / Wally rap / Young and wrong.
7" Single: Released Nov '81, on Swerve, Deleted Nov '84. Catalogue no: **SKID 003**

Bimbo Jet

EL BIMBO
Tracks: / El bimbo.
7" Single: Released Jul '75, on EMI, by EMI Records. Deleted '78. Catalogue no: **EMI 2317**

Binary

MEANING, THE
Tracks: / Meaning, The.
12" Single: Released Feb '85, on Cocteau, by Cocteau Records. Catalogue no: **BTDT 94**
7" Single: Released Feb '85, on Cocteau, by Cocteau Records. Catalogue no: **BTD 94**

Bindi, Umberto

IL NOSTRO CONCERTO
Tracks: / Il nostro concerto.
7" Single: Released Nov '60, on Oriole, Deleted '63. Catalogue no: **CB 1577**

Bingo Brothers

RUSSIANS ARE COMING, THE
Tracks: / Russians are coming, The / Asleep at the wheel.
7" Single: Released Oct '86, on Bingo Brothers, Catalogue no: **SKT6K 5942**

Bingy Bunny

HUSH
Tracks: / Hush.
7" Single: Released Jun '82, on Carib Jems, Catalogue no: **CGDD 20**

LONELY WIDOW
Tracks: / Lonely widow.
12" Single: Released Jun '82, on Number 1, Catalogue no: **NR 02**

ME & JANE
12" Single: Released Jan '82, on Cha-Cha, by Cha-Cha Records. Catalogue no: **CHAD 46**

STREET LOVER
Tracks: / Street lover.
12" Single: Released Mar '82, on Cha-Cha, by Cha-Cha Records. Catalogue no: **CHAD 48**

TRAIN TO ZION
Tracks: / Train to Zion.
12" Single: Released Jul '82, on Top Ranking (1), Catalogue no: **12 TRY 2**

Binky Boy

EVERYBODY
Tracks: / Everybody.
12" Single: Released May '83, on Proto, by Proto Records. Catalogue no: **ENAT 107**
7" Single: Released May '83, on Proto, by Proto Records. Catalogue no: **ENA 107**

Bino

DREAM(FOR MY SAKE)
Tracks: / Dream.
7" Single: Released Feb '81, on Upper Class, by Chinless Prod. Records. Catalogue no: **CPS 1**

Biocar

HERO
Tracks: / Hero / Walking on water.
7" Single: Released Aug '80, on No Bad, Catalogue no: **NB 2**

Bipo

WHY
Tracks: / Why.
12" Single: Released Apr '89, on BSBI, by BSB Records. Catalogue no: **BENNT 1**
7" Single: Released Mar '89, on BSBI, by BSB Records. Catalogue no: **BENN 1**

Birdhouse

MY BIRDMAN
Tracks: / My Birdman.
7" Single: Released Jul '86, on Power House, Catalogue no: **SHOESTRING 004**

SHE REVS ME UP
Tracks: / She revs me up.
12" Single: Released Dec '87, on Vinyl Solution, by Vinyl Solution Records. Catalogue no: **VS 5**

Birdland

HOLLOW HEART (The Birdland EP)
Tracks: / Hollow heart.
7" Single: Released Mar '89, on Lazy, Catalogue no: **LAZY 13**
12" Single: Released Mar '89, on Lazy, Catalogue no: **LAZY 13 T**

PARADISE
Tracks: / Rage (12" only) / Paradise.
12" Single: Released Jun '89, on Lazy, Catalogue no: **LAZY 14T**
7" Single: Released Jun '89, on Lazy, Catalogue no: **LAZY 14**

Birds

LEAVING HERE
Tracks: / Leaving here.
7" Single: Released May '65, on Decca, by Decca Records. Deleted '68. Catalogue no: **F 12140**

Birds With Ears

MR SNEED
Tracks: / Mr. Sneed.
7" Single: Released Aug '83, on Laughing Man, Catalogue no: **BONK 1**

Birdsong, Cindy

DANCING ROOM
Tracks: / Dancing room.
12" Single: Released Dec '87, on Hi-Hat, by BMG Records (UK). Catalogue no: **CIND 1T**
7" Single: Released Dec '87, on Hi-Hat, by BMG Records (UK). Catalogue no: **CIND 1**
12" Single: Released Jan '88, on Hi-Hat, by BMG Records (UK). Catalogue no: **CIND 1TR**

Birkin, Jane

Biographical details: Jane Birkin and Serge Gainsborough scored a No. 1 hit in the UK (and several other European territories) with *"Je t'aime moi non plus"* in 1969. They never returned to the British charts, but this disc was so notorious that they secured for all time an important place in chart history. Gainsbourg, a French singer, songwriter and actor wrote the song for actress Brigitte Bardot who reportedly thought it was too erotic for her; the writer therefore decided to record it himself, in duet with his Londoner companion Jane Birkin. Set against a beautiful melody, the record featured grunts, groans and heavy breathing, in simulation of a couple making love. On the strength of this disc the couple became record and film stars in France and remained so for many years. In Britain the record was banned by the BBC, but nonetheless went to No. 2 on the Fontana label. In an extraordinary volte-face, that record company had a sudden attack of morality and handed the single over to another label, even though it was already a smash. Major Minor Records saw the record drop to No. 3 in their first week of ownership, but the following week it hit No. 1 amid the wave of controversy both within the music business and among the general public. *"Je t'aime"* thus became one of the few singles ever to drop down the charts in the week before reaching No. 1, one of the few singles to change labels while high in the charts and one of the few banned singles ever to hit the top. An opportunistic organist called Tim Mycroft hastily assembled a group called Sounds Nice and took an instrumental version of the tune to No. 18 on the British chart, so at least the BBC had something they could play. In all, *"Je t'aime... moi non plus"* logged 25 weeks on the charts. However, a mid-Seventies re-issue on the third label added a further 9 weeks to the total. Thus, with 34 appearances in all, Birkin and Gainsbourg logged more chart weeks than any other One Hit Wonder in history; and their records became the only No. 1 single to chart on three different labels. Shortly after this re-appearance, Judge Dread covered the song and took it back to the UK Top 10 - needless to say, this British comedian's rendition was also banned from airplay. The notoriety of Birkin and Gainsbourg's disc remained unequalled until 1984, when *"Relax"* by Frankie Goes To Hollywood became the next BBC-blacked 45 to climb to No. 1. This record aroused even greater controversy and enjoyed an even longer chart run - and, unlike Jane and Serge, the act in question was able to follow it up with further monster British hits. (Bob MacDonald)..

JE T'AIME
Tracks: / Je t'aime mon non plus / Jane B.
7" Single: Released Jul '69, on Fontana, by Phonogram Ltd. Deleted '72. Catalogue no: **TF 1042**
Cassingle: Released Apr '81, on WEA, by WEA Records. Deleted Apr '86. Catalogue no: **SPC 10**
7" Single: Released Oct '69, on Major Record, by The Major Record Company. Deleted '72. Catalogue no: **MM 645**
7" Single: Released Dec '74, on Antic, Deleted '77. Catalogue no: **K 11511**

Birthday Party

Biographical details: They spent the late Seventies touring around their native Melbourne under the name, the Boys Next Door. Changing their name to Birthday Party at the end of the decade, they spent much of 1980 in Britain. Their 1981 LP *"Prayers On Fire"* made them favourites amongst the UK rock papers and it went tinto the higher echelons of the British indie charts. The cult following that they were building up was enough to give them their first national chart album in 1982: *"Junkyard"* reached No. 73 and was also another indie winner. When the group moved from London to Berlin towards the end of that year, they sacked their drummer Phil Calvert. A substitute came and went, but soon guitarist Mick Harvey began playing drums and they became a four-piece. The Birthday Party continued to receive heavy radio support from John Peel, but their style of rebellious post-punk was not sufficiently commercial to win them support on a wide scale. Subsequent records by Nick Cave and the Bad Seeds took over where the Birthday Party left off. (Bob MacDonald)..

BAD SEED (SINGLE)
Tracks: / Bad seed.
12" Single: Released Feb '83, on 4AD, by 4AD Records. Catalogue no: **BAD 301**

BIRTHDAY PARTY
Tracks: / Birthday party.
12" Single: Released Jun '83, on 4AD, by 4AD Records. Catalogue no: **BAD 307**

FRIEND CATCHER
Tracks: / Friend catcher / Waving my arms / Cat man.
7" Single: Released Oct '80, on 4AD, by 4AD Records. Catalogue no: **AD 12**

MR CLARINET
Tracks: / Mr. Clarinet.
7" Single: Released Oct '81, on 4AD, by 4AD Records. Catalogue no: **AD 114**

MUTINY 1983
Tracks: / Mutiny 1983 / Jennifer's evil.
12" Single: Released Dec '83, on Mute, by Mute Records. Catalogue no: **MUTE 29**

PEEL SESSIONS:BIRTHDAY PARTY 28.4.81

CD 5": Released Aug '88, on Strange Fruit, by Strange Fruit Records. Catalogue no: **SFPSCD 020**
12" Single: Released Jan '87, on Strange Fruit, by Strange Fruit Records. Catalogue no: **SFPS 020**

PEEL SESSIONS:BIRTHDAY PARTY II
Tracks: / Big Jesus trash can / She's hit / Bully bones / Six inch gold blade.
12" Single: Released Oct '88, on Strange Fruit, by Strange Fruit Records. Catalogue no: **SFPS 058**

RELEASE THE BATS
Tracks: / Release the bats / Blast off.
7" Single: Released Aug '81, on 4AD, by 4AD Records. Catalogue no: **AD 111**

Bisca

LEARN:SUSPIRIA
Tracks: / Learn: suspiria / Tenebrae / Inferno / Deep red.
12" Single: Released Jun '89, on Vinyl Solution, by Vinyl Solution Records. Catalogue no: **STORM 5**

Biscuit, Chris

RHYMES TO KILL
Tracks: / Rhymes to kill.
12" Single: Released Feb '89, on Music Of Life, by Music Of Life Records. Catalogue no: **NOTE 24**

Biscuit, Karl

SECRET LOVE
Tracks: / Secret love.
12" Single: Released Feb '87, on Crammed Discs, by Crammed Discs. Catalogue no: **CRAM 054**

Bishop, Eddie

CALL ME
Tracks: / Darkest days (Jackie Lee) / Call me.
7" Single: Released Apr '85, on Kent, by Ace Records. Catalogue no: **TOWN 107**

Bishop, Elvin

FOOLED AROUND AND FELL IN LOVE
Tracks: / Fooled around and fell in love.
7" Single: Released May '76, on Capricorn, by Polydor Ltd. Deleted '79. Catalogue no: **2089 024**

Bishop, Randy

TWO HEARTS ON THE LOOSE
Tracks: / If I was a fool / Two hearts on the loose.
7" Single: Released Oct '85, on Aura Records, by Aura Records. Deleted '88. Catalogue no: **AUS 146**

Biss

1.2.3.4. FOR WHO? (see panel below)
Tracks: / 1.2.3.4. For who? / Robot with a rose.
7" Single: Released '82, on AVM, by AVM Records. Catalogue no: **AVM 1001**

B.I.T.B

NOCTURNAL
Tracks: / Nocturnal.
7" Single: Released Aug '82, on Blue Rhythm, Catalogue no: **CBR 2**

Bitch

FIRST BITE
Tracks: / First bite / Maggie.
7" Single: Released Jul '81, on Pinnacle, by Pinnacle Records. Deleted '85. Catalogue no: **RX 101**

Bitches Brue

LEATHER LOVE
Tracks: / Leather love / Ready for love.
12" Single: Released Mar '88, on FM, by FM-Revolver Records. Catalogue no: **12 VHF 46**

Bitches Sin

ALWAYS READY(FOR LOVE)
Tracks: / Always ready(for love) / Sign of the times.
7" Single: Released Apr '81, on Neat, by Neat Records. Catalogue no: **NEAT 09**

NO MORE CHANCES
Tracks: / No more chances.
7" Single: Released Dec '83, on QT, Catalogue no: **QT 001**
12" Single: Released Dec '83, on QT, Catalogue no: **QT 001 12**

OUT OF MY MIND
Tracks: / Out of my mind.
7" Single: Released Aug '83, on Terminal, Catalogue no: **TCAS 21**

Bite, Pete

BITE ME, I TASTE NICE
Tracks: / Bite me, I taste nice / Sex.
7" Single: Released Feb '81, on Liberty, by EMI Records. Deleted Feb '84. Catalogue no: **BP 390**

ONE MORE BITE OF MY HEART
Tracks: / One more bite of my heart / Hurt has cut me so deep / Hole in the head.
12" Single: Released Apr '84, on Loose, by Loose Records. Catalogue no: **LSE 5T**
7" Single: Released Sep '85, on Loose, by Loose Records. Catalogue no: **LSE 5**

Bite The Bullet

FINISHED WITH LOVE
Tracks: / Finished with love / Watershed / Sailors song.
12" Single: Released 8 May '89, on Jet, by Jet Records. Deleted Oct '89. Catalogue no: **654891 6**
CD 5": Released 15 May '89, on Jet, by Jet Records. Deleted Oct '89. Catalogue no: **654891 2**
7" Single: Released 8 May '89, on Jet, by Jet Records. Deleted Oct '89. Catalogue no: **654891 7**

Bitelli, Dave

FOOT IN THE DOOR
Tracks: / Foot in the door.
12" Single: Released Oct '83, on Paladin, Catalogue no: **PAL 001**

Biting Tongues

COMPRESSOR
Tracks: / Compressor.
12" Single: Released 30 May '87, on Factory (1), by Factory Records. Catalogue no: **FAC 188**

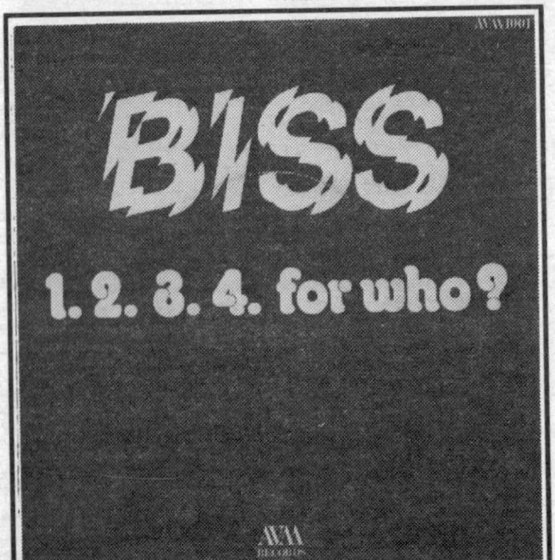

BISS - 1.2.3.4. FOR WHO ? (Released on AVM)

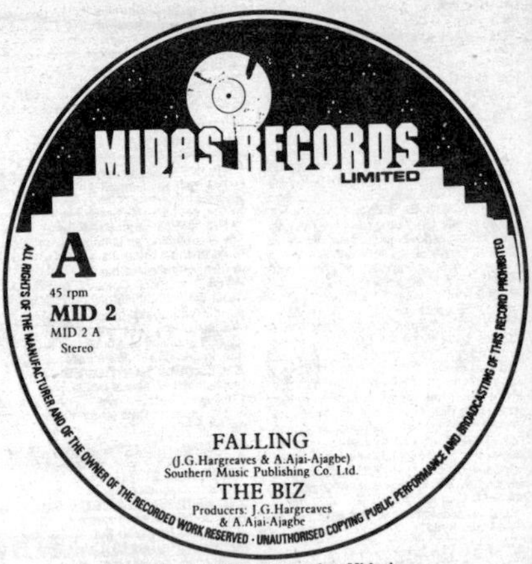

BIZ - FALLING (Released on Midas)

EVENING STATE
Tracks: / Evening State.
12" Single: Released Jun '88, on Antler, by Antler Records (Belgium). Catalogue no: **ANT 005**

TROUBLE HAND
Tracks: / Trouble hand.
12" Single: Released Nov '85, on Factory (1), by Factory Records. Catalogue no: **FAC 134**

Bits & Pieces

BITS & PIECES 86
12" Single: Released Nov '87, on Bits & Pieces (USA), Catalogue no: **BITS 86**

BITS & PIECES '87
12" Single: Released Nov '87, on Bits & Pieces (USA), Catalogue no: **BITS 87**

DON'T STOP THE MUSIC
Tracks: / Don't stop the music / Stampede.
7" Single: Released May '81, on Island, by Island Records. Deleted May '84. Catalogue no: **IPR 2049**
7" Single: Released Oct '81, on Island, by Island Records. Deleted Oct '84. Catalogue no: **WIP 6716**
12" Single: Released Oct '81, on Island, by Island Records. Deleted Oct '84. Catalogue no: **12WIP 6716**

Bitter Mousetrap

BITTER MOUSETRAP
Tracks: / Bitter mousetrap.
7" EP: Released Dec '87, on Tuff Enuff, Catalogue no: **TUFFER 01**

BIZ

FALLING (see panel above)
Tracks: / Falling / Falling (dub mix).
7" Single: Released Feb '83, on Midas, by Magnet Records. Catalogue no: **MID 2**
12" Single: Released Feb '83, on Midas, by Magnet Records. Catalogue no: **12 MID 2**

LETTERS
Tracks: / Letters.
7" Single: Released Nov '88, on Bolts, by Bolts Records. Catalogue no: **NUTS 103**
12" Single: Released Nov '88, on Bolts, by Bolts Records. Catalogue no: **NUTSX 103**

WE'RE GONNA GROOVE TONIGHT
Tracks: / We're gonna groove tonight.
7" Single: Released Jul '83, on Midas, by Magnet Records. Catalogue no: **MID 1**

Biz Internationale

STAY TRUE
Tracks: / Stay true / Just the thought of a love affair.
7" Single: Released Oct '81, on WEA, by WEA Records. Deleted Oct '84. Catalogue no: **K 19253**

Biz Markie

PICKIN' BOOGERS
12" Single: Released Oct '87, on Prism (USA), Catalogue no: **PS 2014**

Bizarre Boy's

HOP OFF YOU FROGS
Tracks: / Hop off you frogs / Electro frog.
7" Single: Released Feb '86, on Creole, by Creole Records. Catalogue no: **CR 88**

Bizarre Inc.

TECHNOLOGICAL (SINGLE)
Tracks: / Technological / Time to get funky
12" Single: Released Feb '89, on Blue Chip by Blue Chip Records. Catalogue no: **BLUE CHIP 14**

TIME TO GET FUNKY (REMIX)
Tracks: / Time to get funky (remix).
12" Single: Released Apr '89, on Blue Chip by Blue Chip Records. Catalogue no: **BLUE CHIP 14R**

Bizet Boys

RIDE 'EM CARMEN
Tracks: / Ride 'em Carmen (7" only.) / Ride 'em Carmen (Speechless) (7" only.) / Ride 'em Carmen (A Classic mix) (12" only.) / Ride 'em Carmen (Opera House mix) (12" only.) Ride 'em Carmen (3 M's much more mix (12" only.).
12" Single: Released Mar '89, on Parlo phone, by EMI Records. Catalogue no: **20 337 6**
7" Single: Released Mar '89, on Parlo phone, by EMI Records. Catalogue no: **RIDE 1**
12" Single: Released Mar '89, on Parlo phone, by EMI Records. Catalogue no: 1 **RIDE 1**
7" Single: Released Mar '89, on Parlo phone, by EMI Records..Catalogue no: **20 337 7**

Bizzy B

NIGHT CALLS, THE
Tracks: / Night calls, The.
12" Single: Released Nov '88, on Ja Street, Catalogue no: **JSR 003**

Bjoerling & Merrill

PEARL FISHERS ACT 1
Tracks: / Pearl fishers act 1.
7" Single: Released Jun '78, on RCA Re Seal, by BMG Records (UK). Catalogue n **RB 9271**

Blab Happy

FRUITS OF OUR LABOUR EP
Tracks: / Perish the thought / Fruits of o labour / Scandalized / Sullenly Sunday.
7" Single: Released Feb '89, on Wisdor Catalogue no: **WIZ 2**

Black

BIG ONE, THE
Tracks: / Big one, The / You are the one Scrapbook of ghosts (Extra track on 12").
CD 5": Released Sep '88, on A&M, by A& Records. Catalogue no: **AMCD 468**
7" Single: Released Sep '88, on A&M, A&M Records. Catalogue no: **AM 468**
12" Single: Released Sep '88, on A&M, A&M Records. Catalogue no: **AMY 468**

EVERYTHING'S COMING UP ROSES
Tracks: / Everything's coming up roses Ravel in the rain / It's not you Lady Jane. Note: Limited edition White Vinyl in gatef sleeve with booklet.
7" Single: Released Mar '87, on A&M, A&M Records. Deleted Mar '88. Catalog no: **AM 433**
12" Single: Released Mar '87, on A&M, A&M Records. Deleted Mar '88. Catalog

no: **AMY 388**
12" Single: on A&M, by A&M Records. Deleted 1 Aug '88. Catalogue no: **AMY 433**

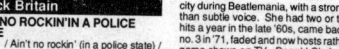

I'M NOT AFRAID
Tracks: / I'm not afraid / Have it your own way / My love.
Note: 'My love' only on 12" version
7" Single: Released Oct '87, on A&M, by A&M Records. Deleted 1 Aug '88. Catalogue no: **AM 414**
12" Single: Released Oct '87, on A&M, by A&M Records. Deleted 1 Aug '88. Catalogue no: **AMY 414**

MORE THAN THE SUN
Tracks: / More than the sun.
7" Single: Released Oct '82, on Wonderful, Deleted '83. Catalogue no: **WW 3**

NOW YOU'RE GONE
Tracks: / Now you're gone / Now you're gone (Mardi gras version).
CD 5": Released Dec '88, on A&M, by A&M Records. Catalogue no: **CDEE 491**
7" Single: Released Dec '88, on A&M, by A&M Records. Catalogue no: **AM 491**
12" Single: Released Dec '88, on A&M, by A&M Records. Catalogue no: **AMY 491**

PARADISE
Tracks: / Paradise / Dagger reel / Sometimes for the asking.
Note: * extra track on 12"
Cassingle: Released Dec '87, on A&M, by A&M Records. Deleted Feb '89. Catalogue no: **AMF 422**
CD 5": Released Dec '87, on A&M, by A&M Records. Deleted Feb '89. Catalogue no: **AMCD 422**
7" Single: Released Dec '87, on A&M, by A&M Records. Deleted Feb '89. Catalogue no: **AM 422**
12" Single: Released Dec '87, on A&M, by A&M Records. Deleted Aug '88. Catalogue no: **AMY 422**

SWEETEST SMILE
Tracks: / Sweetest smile / Sixteens / Leave yourself alone (*Extra track on 12") / Hardly star crossed lovers (*Extra track on 12").
Note: 7"single does not include 'Leave yourself alone' or 'Hardly star crossed lovers'
CD 5": Released Feb '88, on A&M, by A&M Records. Deleted Feb '89. Catalogue no: **AMCD 394**
12" Single: Released Jun '87, on A&M, by A&M Records. Deleted 1 Aug '88. Catalogue no: **AMY 394**
7" Single: Released Jun '97, on A&M, by A&M Records. Catalogue no: **AM 394**

WONDERFUL LIFE
Tracks: / Wonderful life / Life calls / Everything's coming up roses / Sometimes for the asking / Finder / Paradise / I'm not afraid / I just grew tired / Blue / Just making memories / Sweetest smile.
12" Single: Released Aug '87, on A&M, by A&M Records. Deleted Aug '88. Catalogue no: **AMY 402**
CD 5": Released May '88, on A&M (France), Catalogue no: **392 294 2**
CD 5": Released Aug '87, on A&M, by A&M Records. Deleted Feb '89. Catalogue no: **AMCD 402**
Cassingle: Released Aug '87, on A&M, by A&M Records. Catalogue no: **AMC 402**
7" Single: Released Aug '87, on A&M, by A&M Records. Deleted '88. Catalogue no: **AM 402**
7" Set: Released 22 Sep '86, on Ugly Man, by Ugly Man Records. Catalogue no: **JACK 071D**
12" Single: Released 22 Aug '86, on Ugly Man, by Ugly Man Records. Catalogue no: **JACK 001**
7"Single: Released 2 Sep '86, on Ugly Man, by Ugly Man Records. Catalogue no: **JACK 071**

YOU'RE A BIG GIRL NOW
Tracks: / You're a big girl now / Enough is enough / Reunion (Only available on AMP 480 only.).
CD 5": Released 7 Nov '88, on A&M, by A&M Records. Catalogue no: **CDEE 480**
12" Single: Released 7 Nov '88, on A&M, by A&M Records. Catalogue no: **AMY 480**
12" Single: Released Oct '88, on A&M, by A&M Records. Catalogue no: **AMP 480**
7" Single: Released 7 Nov '88, on A&M, by A&M Records. Catalogue no: **AM 480**

Black Alice

NO WARNING
Tracks: / No warning.
12" Single: Released Apr '84, on Street Tunes, by Street Tunes Records. Catalogue no: **JJ 10312**

Black Axe

HIGHWAY RIDER
Tracks: / Highway rider / Red lights.
7" Single: Released Aug '80, on Metal, by MRP Records. Deleted '83. Catalogue no: **MELT 1**

Black, Bill

Biographical details: Born in Memphis, Tennessee in 1926, Bill Black joined Memphis' Sun label in the fifties as a session bass guitar player. It was with Sun Records that the young **Elvis Presley** cut his first series of singles in 1954, before being signed by RCA in '56 and turned into a massive star. Black played with Presley in both Sun and RCA days, backing him on the vast majority of his discs between 1955 & 1958. His driving, pulsating bass was perfectly suited to Elvis' powerful singing.
Black, Bill. William Patton black was born in 1926 in Memphis, Tennessee. He played string bass in country bands, then in Elvis Presley's legendary combo from his first recording session (with Scotty Moore as Scotty & Bill); they left around 1957 because Presley was earning an unheard-of fortune and paying them peanuts. From 1959 Bill switched to electric bass and led the successful Bill Black Combo on the local Hi label, the instrumental quintet linking country music with bass-heavy Southern soul sounds of the Stax era. He retired from touring and died of a brain tumour in 1965; the group was still active under his name in the '80s. The demon compilation in the Hi series has the original hits. Donald Clarke, 24 August 1988..

DON'T BE CRUEL
Tracks: / Don't be cruel.
7" Single: Released Nov '60, on London-American, Deleted '63. Catalogue no: **HLU 9212**

WHITE SILVER SANDS
Tracks: / White silver sands.
7" Single: Released Sep '60, on London-American, Deleted '63. Catalogue no: **HLU 9090**

Black Box

FIND HIM
Tracks: / Find him.
12" Single: Released '88, on Hats, Catalogue no: **HATS 112**

RIDE ON TIME (see panel below)
Tracks: / Ride on time / Ride on time (version).
7" Single: Released Sep '89, on De Construction, by BMG Records (UK). Catalogue no: **PB 43241**
Cassingle: Released Sep '89, on De Construction, by BMG Records (UK). Catalogue no: **PK 43241**
12" Single: Released Jul '89, on De Construction, by BMG Records (UK). Deleted Sep '89. Catalogue no: **PT 43056**
CD 5": Released Sep '89, on De Construction, by BMG Records (UK). Catalogue no: **PD 43242**
CD 5": Released Aug '89, on RCA, by BMG Records (UK). Deleted Sep '89. Catalogue no: **PD 43056**
7" Single: Released Jul '89, on De Construction, by BMG Records (UK). Catalogue no: **PA 43055**
7" Single: Released Jul '89, on De Construction, by BMG Records (UK). Deleted Sep '89. Catalogue no: **PB 43055**
12" Single: Released Sep '89, on De Construction, by BMG Records (UK). Catalogue no: **PT 43242**
Cassingle: Released Aug '89, on De Construction, by BMG Records (UK). Deleted Sep '89. Catalogue no: **PK 43055**

Black Britain

AIN'T NO ROCKIN'IN A POLICE STATE
Tracks: / Ain't no rockin' (in a police state) / Cold on the streets.
7" Single: Released Mar '86, on 10 Records, by Virgin Records. Deleted May '88. Catalogue no: **TEN 106**
12" Single: Released Mar '86, on 10 Records, by Virgin Records. Deleted May '88. Catalogue no: **TENT 106**

FUNKY NASSAU
Tracks: / Funky Nassau / Runaway / Funky Nassau (extended version) (12" only) / Funky Nassau (dub version) (12" only).
7" Single: Released May '86, on 10 Records, by Virgin Records. Deleted May '88. Catalogue no: **TEN 171**
12" Single: Released May '86, on 10 Records, by Virgin Records. Catalogue no: **TENT 171**

HEROIN
Tracks: / Heroin (7" only) / King house heroin (12" only) / Heroin (acappella version) / Heroin (club version) (12" only) / Heroin (dub version) (12" only).
7" Single: Released Jul '87, on 10 Records, by Virgin Records. Catalogue no: **TEN 201**
12" Single: Released Jul '87, on 10 Records, by Virgin Records. Catalogue no: **TENT 201**

NIGHT PEOPLE
Tracks: / Night people (remix) / Night people.
7" Single: Released Mar '87, on 10 Records, by Virgin Records. Deleted May '88. Catalogue no: **TEN 133**
12" Single: Released Mar '87, on 10 Records, by Virgin Records. Deleted May '88. Catalogue no: **TENT 133**

REAL LIFE
Tracks: / Real life / Ain't no rockin' (in a police state) / Real life (Bruce's mix) (12" only) / Real life (Ted's mix) (12" only).
7" Single: Released Sep '87, on 10 Records, by Virgin Records. Deleted May '88. Catalogue no: **TEN 180**
12" Single: Released Sep '87, on 10 Records, by Virgin Records. Catalogue no: **TENT 180**

Black Cat

DANCE WITH A DOLLY
Tracks: / Dance with a dolly.
7" Single: Released Oct '83, on Peach River, Deleted '84. Catalogue no: **BBUW 9**

GONNA TYPE A LETTER
Tracks: / Gonna type a letter / Race with the devil.
7" Single: Released Aug '81, on Cheapskate, Deleted Aug '84. Catalogue no: **CHEAP 32**

QUEEN OF THE HOPILETS ROCK
Tracks: / Queen of the Hopilets rock / Rockin' chair / Black cat boogie.
7" Single: Released Feb '81, on Gale, Deleted Feb '84. Catalogue no: **MSO 2**

Black, Cilla

Biographical details: Black, Cilla. Priscilla Marie Veronica White was a hatcheck girl at the Cavern in Liverpool and swept to fame as the only girl singer to emerge from that city during Beatlemania, with a strong rather than subtle voice. She had two or three big hits a year in the late '60s, came back with a no. 3 in '71, faded and now hosts rather awful game shows on TV. Donald Clarke, 24 August 1988.
Born Priscilla White in Liverpool, this singer was discovered by red-hot Beatles manager Brian Epstein in 1963. As it turned out she was to become the second most successful of all his signings. Because many of her Liverpool admirers believed her voice sounded more black than white, Epstein felt that she should be known as Cilla Black. Like the Fab Four, she teamed with EMI's Abbey Road producer George Martin. A Lennon/McCartney song was chosen as her first record: *Love of the loved* peaked at No. 35 on the UK charts in the autumn of '63. This success was soon consolidated upon and Cilla Black's career quickly took off. For the second single it was decided to employ the conventional trick of covering a current US hit. hile Dionne Warwick was reaching No. 8 on the American charts with the Bacharach/David song *Anyone who had a heart*, Cilla recorded it and took it all the way to No. 1 in Britain. It proved the perfect vehicle for her expressive voice which, though not technically brilliant, was able to switch suddenly from gentle softness to dramatic power. After this three week chart topper, Black went one better and stayed at No. 1 for four weeks with her next 45 *You're my world*. This was another powerful love song and also gave the singer her only US Top 40 hit. After these two consecutive UK No.1's, Black never hit the very top again but continued having regular Top 10 singles until the early Seventies. One of her biggest successes was a weak version of *You've lost that lovin' feelin'* in early '65. Her rendition and the original version by the Righteous Brothers both entered the British charts in the same week, with Cilla climbing to No. 2 while the superior American version outdid her by hitting the top. Other big ones included *Suround yourself with sorrow* and *Something tells me (something is gonna happen tonight). Her biggest album was Cilla sings a rainbow* which reached No. 4 on the British LP list in 1966. Upon Epstein's death in 1967, she was managed by Bobby Willis, whom she later married. By the time her chart career slowed down in the early Seventies, Cilla Black was an established television favourite. Her vibrant and amiable personality is perfectly suited tot hat medium and it is primarily through TV that she has remained a household name in Britain. (Bob MacDonald).

ALFIE
Tracks: / Alfie.
7" Single: Released Mar '66, on Parlophone, by EMI Records. Deleted '69. Catalogue no: **R 5427**

ANYONE WHO HAD A HEART
Tracks: / Anyone who had a heart.
7" Single: Released Feb '64, on Parlophone, by EMI Records. Deleted '67. Catalogue no: **R 5101**

BABY WE CAN'T GO WRONG
Tracks: / Baby we can't go wrong.
7" Single: Released Feb '74, on EMI, by EMI Records. Deleted '77. Catalogue no: **EMI 2107**

CONVERSATIONS
Tracks: / Conversations.
7" Single: Released Jul '69, on Parlophone, by EMI Records. Deleted '72. Catalogue no: **R 5785**

FOOL AM I, A
Tracks: / Fool am I, A.
7" Single: Released Nov '66, on Parlophone, by EMI Records. Deleted '69. Catalogue no: **R 5515**

I ONLY LIVE TO LOVE YOU
Tracks: / I only live to love you.
7" Single: Released Nov '67, on Parlophone, by EMI Records. Deleted '70. Catalogue no: **R 5652**

IF I THOUGHT YOU'D EVER CHANGE YOUR MIND
Tracks: / If I thought you'd ever change your mind.
7" Single: Released Dec '69, on Parlophone, by EMI Records. Deleted '72. Catalogue no: **R 5820**

IT'S FOR YOU
Tracks: / It's for you.
7" Single: Released Aug '64, on Parlophone, by EMI Records. Deleted '67. Catalogue no: **R 5162**

I'VE BEEN WRONG BEFORE
Tracks: / I've been wrong before.
7" Single: Released Apr '65, on Parlophone, by EMI Records. Deleted '68. Catalogue no: **R 5269**

LOVE OF THE LOVED
Tracks: / Love of the love.
7" Single: Released Oct '63, on Parlophone, by EMI Records. Deleted '66. Catalogue no: **R 5065**

LOVE'S JUST A BROKEN HEART

BLACK BOX - RIDE ON TIME (Released on De Construction)

Tracks: / Love's just a broken heart.
7" Single: Released Jan '66, on Parlophone, by EMI Records. Deleted '69. Catalogue no: **R 5395**

SOMETHING TELLS ME (SOMETHING'S GONNA HAPPEN)
Tracks: / Something tells me.
7" Single: Released Nov '71, on Parlophone, by EMI Records. Deleted '74. Catalogue no: **R 5924**

STEP INSIDE LOVE
Tracks: / Step inside love.
7" Single: Released Mar '68, on Parlophone, by EMI Records. Deleted '71. Catalogue no: **R 5674**

SURPRISE SURPRISE
Tracks: / Surprise surprise / Put your heart where your love is.
7" Single: Released Dec '85, on Towerbell, Catalogue no: **TOW 81**

SURROUND YOURSELF WITH SORROW
Tracks: / Surround yourself with sorrow.
7" Single: Released Feb '69, on Parlophone, by EMI Records. Deleted '72. Catalogue no: **R 5759**

THERE'S A NEED IN ME
Tracks: / There's a need in me.
7" Single: Released Sep '85, on Towerbell, Catalogue no: **TOW 74**

WHAT GOOD AM I
Tracks: / What good am I.
7" Single: Released Jun '67, on Parlophone, by EMI Records. Deleted '70. Catalogue no: **R 5608**

YOU'RE MY WORLD
Tracks: / You're my world.
7" Single: Released May '64, on Parlophone, by EMI Records. Deleted '67. Catalogue no: **R 5133**
7" Single: Released Oct '77, on EMI, by EMI Records. Catalogue no: **EMI 2698**

YOU'VE LOST THAT LOVIN' FEELIN'
Tracks: / You've lost that lovin' feeling.
7" Single: Released Jan '65, on Parlophone, by EMI Records. Deleted '68. Catalogue no: **R 5225**

Black Cillas

SEBASTIAN
Tracks: / Sebastian.
7" Single: Released Nov '86, on Cillagram, Catalogue no: **CIG 001**

Black Earth

MOMMA'S BOY
Tracks: / Momma's boy / Prisoner of your love.
7" Single: Released Apr '88, on President, by President Records. Catalogue no: **PT 571**

THERE'LL NEVER BE ANOTHER DAY
Tracks: / There'll never be another day / Betrayed with a kiss.
7" Single: Released Dec '88, on President, by President Records. Catalogue no: **PT 566**

Black Easter

READY TO ROT
Tracks: / Ready to rot.
7" Single: Released Oct '82, on Carnage, Catalogue no: **KILL 13**

Black Flag

ANNIHILATE THIS WEEK
Tracks: / Annihilate this week.
CD 5": Released Dec '88, on SST (USA), by SST Records (USA). Catalogue no: **SSTCD 081**

FAMILY MAN (12")
Tracks: / Family man.
12" Single: Released Oct '84, on SST (USA), by SST Records (USA). Catalogue no: **SST1 2001**

JEALOUS AGAIN
Tracks: / Jealous again.
12" Single: Released Mar '83, on SST (USA), by SST Records (USA). Catalogue no: **SST 3**

NERVOUS BREAKDOWN
Tracks: / Nervous breakdown.
7" Single: Released Jul '89, on SST (USA), by SST Records (USA). Catalogue no: **SST 001**

PROCESS OF WEEDING OUT (12")
Tracks: / Process of weeding out.
12" Single: Released Mar '86, on SST (USA), by SST Records (USA). Catalogue no: **SST 037**

SIX PACK(EP)
Tracks: / Six pack.
7" Single: Released Dec '81, on Alternative Tentacles, by Alternative Tentacles Records. Catalogue no: **Unknown**

SLIP IT IN (12")
12" Single: Released Aug '84, on SST (USA), by SST Records (USA). Catalogue no: **SST 12001**

T.V.PARTY
CD 5": Released Nov '88, on SST (USA), by SST Records (USA). Catalogue no: **SSTCD 012**

Black Flames

ARE YOU MY WOMAN
Tracks: / Are you my woman / You and me (less than zero).
12" Single: Released Dec '87, on Def Jam, Deleted Jun '88. Catalogue no: **651334 6**
7" Single: Released Dec '87, on Def Jam, Deleted Jun '88. Catalogue no: **651334 7**

Black Gorilla

GIMME DAT BANANA
Tracks: / Gimme dat banana.
7" Single: Released Aug '77, on Response, by Priority Records. Deleted '80. Catalogue no: **SR 502**

Black Harmony

EVERYTHING TO ME
Tracks: / Everything to me / Stop lying.
12" Single: Released May '82, on Blue Inc, Catalogue no: **INCD 15**

LET'S BE LOVERS
Tracks: / Let's be lovers.
12" Single: Released Dec '83, on Cyprian, Catalogue no: **CYP 004**

YOU SHOULD NEVER RUN AWAY FROM LOVE
Tracks: / You should never run away from love.
12" Single: Released Apr '82, on Regal, Catalogue no: **RD 001**

Black Heroes

WE NEED A HALL OF FAME
Tracks: / We need a hall of fame.
12" Single: Released Mar '89, on White Label (1), Catalogue no: **SASH 005**

Black Ice

BLACK ICE
7" EP: Released Aug '87, on Iron Works (USA), by Azra International (USA). Catalogue no: **IW 1017**

Black, Ika

CRUCIAL WORLD
Tracks: / Crucial world.
7" Single: Released Oct '83, on Keyman, by Keyman Records. Catalogue no: **KMD 001**

SPECIAL LOVE (SINGLE)
Tracks: / Special love.
12" Single: Released Sep '86, on Keyman, by Keyman Records. Catalogue no: **KMD 003**

Black Jacks

THANK GOD FOR THE KIDS
Tracks: / Thank God for kids.
7" Single: Released Feb '89, on Black Jack, Catalogue no: **BLJ 1**

Black, Jason

I'M WALKING ALONE
Tracks: / I'm walking alone / Good good loving.
7" Single: Released Feb '81, on Beggars Banquet, by Beggars Banquet Records. Deleted Feb '84. Catalogue no: **BEG 53**

Black, Jeanne

HE'LL HAVE TO STAY
Tracks: / He'll have to stay.
7" Single: Released Jun '60, on Capitol, by EMI Records. Deleted '63. Catalogue no: **CL 15131**

Black Kiss

ORGASM, THE
Tracks: / Orgasm, The.
12" Single: Released '89, on Who's That Beat, by Play It Again Sam (Belgium). Catalogue no: **WHOS 012**

Black Lace

Biographical details: These Britons formed a group to represent the United Kingdom in the 1979 Eurovision Song Contest. their single *"Mary Ann"* was a blatant copy of Smokie's Top 5 single from the previous summer *"Oh Carol"*. The dire *"Mary Ann"* failed miserably not only in the Contest but also in the UK charts, where its No. 42 peak made it the lowest charting British Eurosong of the Seventies. Black Lace were quickly forgotten and consigned by historians to the dustbin of failed Eurovision entrants. Suddenly in the autumn of 1983, they re-emerged as a duo. *"Superman"*, a highly irritating ditty full of spoken body movement instructions, broke in Britain's northern clubs and became a national Top 10 hit. Those who hated that single were to be annoyed still further by 1984's *"Agadoo"*, a seven year-old French singalong that took many weeks to break into the Top 40 but eventually climbed to No. 2 in the UK and stayed on the chart throughout the summer and autumn. It was ideal family party fodder, a market that Black Lace were becoming adept at catering for. (Bob MacDonald)..

BLACK LACE - AGADOO (Released on Flair)

AGADOO (see panel above)
Tracks: / Agadoo / Fiddling / Supermen.
7" Single: Released May '84, on Flair, by Flair Records. Deleted Aug '89. Catalogue no: **FLA 107**
12" Single: Released May '84, on Flair, by Flair Records. Catalogue no: **FLA 107T**

CLAP CLAP SONG
7" Single: Released Jul '88, on Flair, by Flair Records. Catalogue no: **LACE 7**

DO THE CONGA
Tracks: / Do the conga.
7" Single: Released Dec '84, on Flair, by Flair Records. Catalogue no: **FLA 108**
12" Single: Released Dec '84, on Flair, by Flair Records. Catalogue no: **FLA 108T**

EL VINO COLLAPSO
Tracks: / El vino collapso.
12" Single: Released May '85, on Flair, by Flair Records. Catalogue no: **LACE 12**
7" Single: Released May '85, on Flair, by Flair Records. Catalogue no: **LACE 1**

HEY YOU
Tracks: / Hey you / Let it all go.
12" Single: Released Dec '83, on Flair, by Flair Records. Catalogue no: **FLA 106T**
7" Single: Released Dec '83, on Flair, by Flair Records. Catalogue no: **FLA 106**

HOKEY COKEY
Tracks: / Hokey cokey.
7" Single: Released Nov '85, on Flair, by Flair Records. Catalogue no: **LACE 3**
12" Single: Released Nov '85, on Flair, by Flair Records. Catalogue no: **12 LACE 3**
12" Single: Released Nov '85, on Flair, by Flair Records. Deleted Nov '87. Catalogue no: **12 LACED 3**

I AM THE MUSIC MAN
Tracks: / I am the music man / We dance we dance.
7" Single: Released Aug '89, on Flair, by Flair Records. Catalogue no: **LACE 10**

I SPEAKA DA LINGO
Tracks: / I speaka da lingo.
7" Single: Released Aug '85, on Flair, by Flair Records. Catalogue no: **LACE 2**
12" Single: Released Aug '85, on Flair, by Flair Records. Catalogue no: **12 LACE 2**

MARY ANN
Tracks: / Mary Ann.
7" Single: Released Mar '79, on EMI, by EMI Records. Deleted '82. Catalogue no: **EMI 2919**

SUPERMAN (GIOCA JOUER)
Tracks: / Superman (gioca jouer).
7" Single: Released Sep '83, on Flair, by Flair Records. Deleted '86. Catalogue no: **FLA 105**

TEARDROPS
Tracks: / Teardrops.
7" Single: Released Jul '83, on Flair, by Flair Records. Deleted Nov '87. Catalogue no: **FLA 105**
12" Single: Released Jul '83, on Flair, by Flair Records. Catalogue no: **FLA 105T**

VIVA LA MEXICO
Tracks: / So now the hurting starts / Viva la Mexico.
7" Pic: Released May '86, on Flair, by Flair Records. Deleted May '87. Catalogue no: **PLACE 4**
7" Single: Released May '86, on Flair, by Flair Records. Catalogue no: **LACE 4**

WIG-WAM BAM
Tracks: / Soaking up the sun / So now the hurting starts (Extra track on 12" version only) / Clap clap sound (Extra track on 7" double pack single only) / We dance we dance (Extra track on 7" double pack single only).
7" Set: Released Aug '86, on Flair, by Flair Records. Deleted Nov '87. Catalogue no: **LACE 55**
7" Single: Released Aug '86, on Flair, by Flair Records. Deleted Nov '87. Catalogue no: **LACE 5**
12" Single: Released Aug '86, on Flair, by Flair Records. Deleted Nov '87. Catalogue no: **12 LACE 5**

Black Mac

HOOTS MON
Tracks: / Hoots mon / Nature's way.
7" Single: Released Dec '80, on Blue Chip, by Blue Chip Records. Deleted Dec '85 Catalogue no: **BC 103**

Black, Mary

AS I LEAVE BEHIND NEIDIN
Tracks: / As I leave behind Neidin.
7" Single: Released '88, on I&B, by I & B Records. Catalogue no: **DARAS 022**

BY THE TIME IT GETS DARK (SINGLE)
Tracks: / By the time it gets dark.
7" Single: Released '88, on I&B, by I & B Records. Catalogue no: **DARAS 029**
Cassingle: Released '88, on I&B, by I & B Records. Catalogue no: **DARACS 026**

KATIE
Tracks: / Katie.
7" Single: Released '88, on I&B, by I & B Records. Catalogue no: **DARAS 026**
Cassingle: Released '88, on I&B, by I & B Records. Catalogue no: **DARACS 026**

ONCE IN A VERY BLUE MOON
Tracks: / Once in a very blue moon.
7" Single: Released '88, on I&B, by I & B Records. Catalogue no: **DARAS 028**

PAST THE POINT OF RESCUE
Tracks: / Past the point of rescue.
7" Single: Released '88, on I&B, by I & B Records. Catalogue no: **DARAS 030**
Cassingle: Released '88, on I&B, by I & B Records. Catalogue no: **DARACS 030**

Black Nasty

CUT YOUR MOTOR OFF
Tracks: / Cut you motor off / Keep on stepping.
7" Single: Released May '80, on Grapevine (Northern Soul), by BMG Records (UK). Deleted May '83. Catalogue no: **GRP 140**

Black Orchid

WONDERLICKS
Tracks: / Wonderlicks / Sweetest song, Th / Because I believe.
12" Single: Released '88, on DJM, Catalogue no: **DJR 10978**
7" Single: Released '88, on DJM, Catalogue no: **DJS 10978**

Black, Pauline

PIRATES ON THE AIRWAVES
Tracks: / Pirates of the airwaves / Pirate dance (Available on 12" only.).
12" Single: Released Apr '84, on Chrysalis, by Chrysalis Records. Catalogue no: **TUNEX 1**
7" Single: Released Apr '84, on Chrysalis, by Chrysalis Records. Catalogue no: **TUNE 1**

SHOO RA SHOO RA
Tracks: / Shoo-rah-shoo-rah / Call of the wild.
12" Single: Released '82, on Chrysalis, by Chrysalis Records. Deleted '87. Catalogue no: **CHS 122645**
7" Single: Released '82, on Chrysalis, by Chrysalis Records. Deleted '87. Catalogue no: **CHS 2645**

THREW IT AWAY
Tracks: / Threw it away / Threw it away (instrumental) (Only on 12" version.) / I can see clearly now.
12" Single: Released '83, on Chrysalis, by Chrysalis Records. Deleted '87. Catalogue no: **CHS 12 2739**
7" Single: Released '83, on Chrysalis, by Chrysalis Records. Deleted '87. Catalogue no: **CHS 2739**

Black, Peter

HOW FAR I GO
Tracks: / How far I go / My love is free.
12" Single: Released Apr '89, on Westside, by Westside Records. Catalogue no: **DJINT 8**

Black Radical Mk II

MONSOON
Tracks: / Monsoon.
7" Single: Released Jun '89, on 2 The Bone, Catalogue no: **TMS 004 R**

Black Riot

DAY IN THE LIFE, A
Tracks: / Day in the life, A / Warlock.
7" Single: Released Dec '88, on Champion, by Champion Records. Catalogue no: **CHAMP 75**
CD 5": Released Dec '88, on Champion, by Champion Records. Catalogue no: **CHAMP CD 75**
12" Single: Released Dec '88, on Champion, by Champion Records. Catalogue no: **CHAMP 1275**
12" Single: Released Dec '88, on Champion, by Champion Records. Deleted Jul '89. Catalogue no: **CHAMPR 1275**

Black Rock And Ron

BLACK ROCK AND RON
Tracks: / Black Rock & Ron / Getting large (instrumental).
12" Single: Released Feb '89, on Supreme, by Supreme Records. Catalogue no: **SUPET 141**
7" Single: Released Feb '89, on Supreme, by Supreme Records. Catalogue no: **SUPE 141**

TRUE FEELINGS
Tracks: / True feelings (Phil Harding remix).
12" Single: Released Jul '89, on Supreme, by Supreme Records. Catalogue no: **SUPET 153**

Black Roots

CHANTING FOR FREEDOM
Tracks: / Chanting for freedom.
12" Single: Released Dec '81, on Nubian, Catalogue no: **NR 00215**

FRONT LINE (7")
Tracks: / Front line / Chanting for freedom.
7" Single: Released Nov '84, on BBC, by BBC Records & Tapes. Deleted '87. Catalogue no: **RESL 148**

JUVENILE DELINQUENT
Tracks: / Juvenile delinquent.
7" Single: Released May '84, on Joy, by President Records. Catalogue no: **KIC 05**
12" Single: Released May '84, on Joy, by President Records. Catalogue no: **KIC 05T**

LET IT BE ME
Tracks: / Let it be me / Move on.
7" Single: Released Nov '87, on Nubian, Catalogue no: **NR 05**
12" Single: Released Nov '87, on Nubian, Catalogue no: **NRT 05**

MOVE ON
Tracks: / Move on / Wha them a do.
12" Single: Released Jan '83, on Silvertown, by Silvertown Records. Catalogue no: **STST 2**

SEEN YOUR FACE
Tracks: / Conman / Seen your face.
12" Single: Released Jul '86, on Nubian, Catalogue no: **NRT 03**

START AFRESH
Tracks: / Start afresh.
7" Single: Released Oct '88, on Nubian, Catalogue no: **NR 08**
12" Single: Released Oct '88, on Nubian, Catalogue no: **NRT 08**

SUZY WONG
Tracks: / Suzy Wong.
7" Single: Released Apr '87, on Nubian, Catalogue no: **NR 04**
12" Single: Released Apr '87, on Nubian, Catalogue no: **NRT 04**

ZOOM
Tracks: / Zoom / Zoom (version).
12" Single: Released Feb '89, on Nubian, Catalogue no: **NRT 9**

Black Rose

BOYS WILL BE BOYS
Tracks: / Boys will be boys / Liar.
7" Single: Released May '84, on Bullet, by Bullet Records. Deleted '88. Catalogue no: **BOL 9**

NO POINT RUNNING
Tracks: / No point running.
7" Single: Released Aug '82, on Teesbeat, by Teesbeat Records. Catalogue no: **TB 5**

ROCK ME HARD
Tracks: / Rock me hard / Need a lot of lovin' / Nightmare / Breakaway.
12" Single: Released Mar '85, on Neat, by Neat Records. Catalogue no: **NEAT 48 12**

WE GONNA ROCK YOU (EP)
Tracks: / We gonna rock you.
12" Single: Released Sep '83, on Bullet, by Bullet Records. Deleted '88. Catalogue no: **BOLT 6**

Black Russian

LEAVE ME NOW
Tracks: / Leave me now / Move together.
7" Single: Released Jan '81, on Motown, by BMG Records (UK). Deleted Jan '84. Catalogue no: **TMG 1220**

MYSTIFIED
Tracks: / Mystified / Love's enough.
7" Single: Released Aug '80, on Motown, by BMG Records (UK). Deleted Aug '83. Catalogue no: **TMG 1199**

Black Sabbath

Biographical details: Black Sabbath. A UK heavy metal band formed in 1968 as Earth, by schoolfriends Tony Iommi on guitar, Bill Ward on drums, John 'Ozzy' Osbourne on vocals, Geezer Butler on bass, all from Birmingham. They played jazz-blues fusion in Europe, renamed themselves after one of their own songs, cranked up the volume and simplified the formula to sub-Cream riffing, adopted the themes of black magic, mental illness etc. becoming common in this sort of music and despite a complete lack of any originality were extremely successful. Gerald Woodruffe played keyboards in the wings so as not to steal any spotlight; the keyboards were played by Rick Wakeman on 1973's *Sabbath Bloody Sabbath*. Iommi insisted on more keyboards and a horn section in 1976; Osbourne left for an even more mindless (but still successful) solo career; Sabbath recruited vocalist Ronnie James Dio, Vinnie Appice (Carmine's brother) replacing Ward on drums. Dio and Appice left to form Dio in 1983; Ian Gillan from Deep Purple sang on *Born Again*; there were more personnel changes; guitarist randy Rhoads was killed in an air accident and became a legend. They reformed with Osbourne for Live Aid in 1985. Donald Clarke, 24 August 1988.
All hailing from Aston, Birmingham, this quartet startet out as a blues band called Earth and then changed their name to Black Sabbath in late 1969. Early in the following year they scored their first UK chart success, with a dubut self-titled that reached No. 8. It was typical of the style that they were to persue consistently through the early seventies - out and out heavy metal combining frantically powerful guitar riffs and chords with lyrics about the occult, drugs, war, death and destruction. It was quickly followed by a second 1970 LP *Paranoid*. This became the biggest triumph of their career, sneaking a week a No. 1 on the British album chart in between chart topping runs for Simon and Garfunkel's *Bridge over troubled water*. The title track became one of the most successful heavy metal singles of all time on the British chart, peaking at No. 4; it remains one of the genre's classic cuts. The group would not achieve a second hit single until 1978 - like most British rock groups of the early Seventies they placed all their concentration on the LP market. The next three albums *Master of reality, Black Sabbath Vol 4* and *Sabbath bloody Sabbath*, continued the winning formula that were all UK Top 10 successes. They toured frequently, the trademarks of their stage show being excessive volume, simple but committed powerful playing and overtones of Black Magic. They were one of the world's foremost heavy metal acts, despite being derided by rock critics. In the late Seventies, after a period of slightly deminished success, their dynamic vocalist and frontman Ozzy Osbourne departed to commence an equally outrageous career fronting his own new band. His replacement was American singer Ronnie James Dio, who had previously been with Ritchie Blackmore's Rainbow. The new line up's 1980 album *Heaven and hell* was the biggest for several years and the band were now scoring regulat chart singles in Britain, though none made the Top 20 except for a re issue of the perennial favourite *Paranoid*. (Bob MacDonald).

BLACK SABBATH (SINGLE)
Tracks: / Paranoid / Iron man / War pigs.
CD 3": Released '88, on Special Edition, by Castle Communications Records. Catalogue no: **CD3-5**

DEVIL & DAUGHTER
Tracks: / Devil & daughter.
7" Single: Released May '89, on I.R.S, Catalogue no: **EIRS 115**
7" Single: Released Jun '89, on I.R.S, Catalogue no: **EIRSB 115**
7" Pic: Released Jul '89, on I.R.S, Catalogue no: **EIRSPD 115**
12" Single: Released May '89, on I.R.S, Catalogue no: **EIRST 115**

DIE YOUNG
Tracks: / Die young / Heaven and hell (live).
12" Single: Released Dec '80, on Vertigo, by Phonogram Ltd. Deleted '83. Catalogue no: **SAB 412**
7" Single: Released Dec '80, on Vertigo, by Phonogram Ltd. Deleted '83. Catalogue no: **SAB 4**

HARD ROAD
Tracks: / Hard road.
7" Single: Released Oct '78, on Vertigo, by Phonogram Ltd. Deleted '81. Catalogue no: **SAB 002**

HEADLESS CROSS
Tracks: / Headless cross (12" only) / Cloak and dagger / Headless cross (edit).
12" Single: Released Apr '89, on I.R.S, Catalogue no: **EIRST 107**
7" Single: Released Apr '89, on I.R.S, Catalogue no: **EIRSCB 107**
12" Single: Released Apr '89, on I.R.S, Catalogue no: **EIRSPB 107**

MOB RULES (SINGLE)
Tracks: / Mob rules / Die young.
12" Single: Released Nov '81, on Vertigo, by Phonogram Ltd. Deleted '84. Catalogue no: **SAB 512**
7" Single: Released Nov '81, on Vertigo, by Phonogram Ltd. Deleted '84. Catalogue no: **SAB 5**

NEON NIGHTS
Tracks: / Neon nights / Children of the sea.
7" Single: Released 20 Jun '80, on Vertigo, by Phonogram Ltd. Deleted '83. Catalogue no: **SAB 3**

NEVER SAY DIE (SINGLE)
Tracks: / Never say die.
7" Single: Released Jun '78, on Vertigo, by Phonogram Ltd. Deleted '81. Catalogue no: **SAB 001**

PARANOID (OLD GOLD)
Tracks: / Paranoid / Electric funeral
CD 5": Released 28 Mar '89, on Old Gold, by Old Gold Records. Catalogue no: **OG 6129**

PARANOID (SINGLE)
Tracks: / Paranoid.
7" Single: Released Aug '70, on Vertigo, by Phonogram Ltd. Deleted '73. Catalogue no: **6059 010**
7" Single: Released Jan '85, on Old Gold, by Old Gold Records. Catalogue no: **OG 9467**
7" Single: Released Sep '80, on Nems, by Castle Communications Records. Catalogue no: **BSS 101**
12" Single: Released Aug '86, on Archive 4, by Castle Communications Records. Catalogue no: **TOF 101**
7" Single: Released Sep '82, on Nems, by Castle Communications Records. Catalogue no: **NEP 1**

TURN UP THE NIGHT
Tracks: / Turn up the night
7" Single: Released Jan '82, on Vertigo, by Phonogram Ltd. Catalogue no: **SAB 6**
7" Single: Released Jan '82, on Vertigo, by Phonogram Ltd. Catalogue no: **SABP 6**
12" Single: Released Jan '82, on Vertigo, by Phonogram Ltd. Catalogue no: **SABP 6 12**

Black September

RAINBOW KISS
Tracks: / Rainbow kiss.
12" Single: Released May '86, on Lost Moments, Catalogue no: **LM 12 036**

Black, Sharon

I JUST HAD YOU ON MY MIND
Tracks: / I just had you on my mind.
12" Single: Released Jul '84, on Real Wax, Catalogue no: **RW 7115**

SLOW HAND
Tracks: / Slow hand.
12" Single: Released May '84, on Clintones, Catalogue no: **JU 81**

Black Slate

Biographical details: This large reggae band, comprising members from both Britain and Jamaica, consisted of Elroy Bailey, Anthony Brightly, Ray Carness, Keith Drummond, Chris Hanson, Herschel Holder, Rudy Holmes, Desmond Mahoney, Nicky Ridguard and Cledwyn Rogers. The title track from their first album, *"Amigo"*, was a UK Top Ten single in the autumn of 1980. An infectious, poppy reggae song, it promised much for the future, but apart from a minor follow-up hit, *"Boom Boom"*, the group were unable to enjoy sustained commercial success. Subsequent LPs included *"Sirens In The City"* and *"Six Plus One"*. (Bob MacDonald, 1984.).

AMIGO
Tracks: / Amigo / Black slate rock.
7" Single: Released Sep '80, on Ensign, by Ensign Records. Deleted '83. Catalogue no: **ENY 42**
12" Single: Released Sep '80, on Ensign, by Ensign Records. Deleted '83. Catalogue no: **ENY 4212**

BLACK SLATE DUB
Tracks: / Black Slate dub.
12" Single: Released Nov '82, on Top Ranking (1), Catalogue no: **TRY IT 2**

BOOM BOOM
Tracks: / Boom boom / Legalise holly herb.
12" Single: Released Dec '80, on Ensign, by Ensign Records. Deleted '83. Catalogue no: **ENY 4712**
7" Single: Released Dec '80, on Ensign, by Ensign Records. Deleted '83. Catalogue no: **ENY 47**

LIVE A LIFE
Tracks: / Live a life / Reggae feeling.
7" Single: Released Jul '81, on Ensign, by Ensign Records. Deleted '85. Catalogue no: **ENYT 215**

LOOK WHAT LOVE HAS DONE
Tracks: / Look what love has done / Dub pon creaction.
12" Single: Released Oct '82, on Top Ranking (1), Catalogue no: **12 TRY 4**
7" Single: Released Oct '82, on Top Ranking (1), Catalogue no: **TRY 4**

NO JUSTICE FOR THE POOR
Tracks: / No justice for the poor.
12" Single: Released May '85, on Sierra, by Sierra Records. Catalogue no: **FED 10 T**
7" Single: Released May '85, on Sierra, by Sierra Records. Catalogue no: **FED 10**

RASTA REGGAE
Tracks: / Rasta reggae / Rasta dub.
7" Single: Released May '82, on Top Ranking (1), Catalogue no: **TRY 1**
12" Single: Released May '82, on Top Ranking (1), Catalogue no: **12 TRY 1**

STICKS MAN
Tracks: / Sticks man / Rubber man in dub.
7" Single: Released Jul '82, on Top Ranking (1), Catalogue no: **TRY 2**
12" Single: Released Jul '82, on Top Ranking (1), Catalogue no: **12TRY 2**
12" Single: Released Sep '85, on Port, Catalogue no: **PORT 004**

TEARS ON MY PILLOW
Tracks: / Tears on my pillow.
12" Single: Released Sep '88, on Jetstar, by Jetstar Records. Catalogue no: **SG 049**

WISER THAN BEFORE
Tracks: / Wiser than before.
7" Single: Released May '84, on Sir George, Catalogue no: **SG 013**

Black Sorrows

CHOSEN ONES, THE
Tracks: / Chosen ones, The / Mercenary heart / Sleep through the hurricane
12" Single: Released Apr '89, on Epic, by CBS Records. Deleted Oct '89. Catalogue no: **653 044 8**
CD 5": Released Apr '89, on Epic, by CBS Records. Deleted Oct '89. Catalogue no: **653 044 2**
7" Single: Released Apr '89, on Epic, by CBS Records. Deleted Oct '89. Catalogue no: **653 044 7**

HOLD ON TO ME
Tracks: / Safe in the arms of love / Hold on to me/Kiss the motherlode(Only on 12" and

CD single.).
7" Single: Released Jun '89, on Epic, by CBS Records. Catalogue no: **6529067**
12" Single: Released Jun '89, on Epic, by CBS Records. Catalogue no: **6529068**
CD 5": Released Jun '89, on Epic, by CBS Records. Catalogue no: **6529062**
Special: Released 3 Jul '89, on Epic, by CBS Records. Catalogue no: **6429061**

Black Star

WANNA BE YOUR FRIEND
Tracks: / Wanna be your friend.
12" Single: Released '88, on World Peace, Catalogue no: **SOND 011**

Black State Choir

JIHAD
Tracks: / Jihad.
7" Single: Released Aug '88, on Brainwar, Catalogue no: **BW 001**
12" Single: Released '89, on Brainwar, Catalogue no: **BW 001**

Black Steel

DANCING THE REGGAE
Tracks: / Dancing the reggae.
12" Single: Released Jul '85, on Ariwa Sounds, by Ariwa Sounds. Catalogue no: **ARI 42**

GROOVIN' IN LOVE
Tracks: / Groovin' in love / Counsel of the father.
12" Single: Released Apr '85, on Ariwa Sounds, by Ariwa Sounds. Catalogue no: **ARI 38**

Black Symbol

LOVING JAH
Tracks: / Loving Jah / Everything has its time.
12" Single: Released Dec '82, on Black Symbol, Catalogue no: **BS 003**

SOLIDARITY
Tracks: / Tension / Solidarity.
12" Single: Released Aug '86, on Black Symbol, Catalogue no: **BS 008**

Black Uhuru

Biographical details: This trio of reggae vocalists consists of an American woman, Puma Jones and two Jamaican men, Michael Rose and Ducky Simpson. 'Uhuru' if Swahili for 'freedom'. Black Uhuru were formed in Jamaica in the mid-Seventies, stabilising with the above line-up in late '78. The following year they signed to Island Records, having teamed up with veteran reggae producers/musicians Sly Dunbar and Robbie Shakespeare. These two moves meant that they had some of the most legendary figures in the reggae fraternity behind them and were well placed for critical and commercial success. This they achieved in 1980 and '81 with the albums, *"Sinsemilla"* and *"Red"*. The latter was their first British success, climbing to No. 28 with 13 weeks on the LP chart; to tie in with this, they toured the UK for the first time. With Sly and Robbie in the backing band, Black Uhuru became one of the most acclaimed reggae acts to play Britain in the early Eighties. 1982's *"Chill Out"* album also charted and in this year they finished a European tour by playing two shows at London's Wembley Stadium as support to the Rolling Stones. By 1984 they had released two particularly catchy singles, *"Party Next Door"* and *"What Is life"*. The latter was a minor UK hit, providing further evidence of the trio's pop potential. (Bob MacDonald)..

CONQUER THE TANKER
Tracks: / Conquer the tanker.
7" Single: Released 23 May '87, on RAS (Real Authentic Sound), by Greensleeves Records. Catalogue no: **RAST 7025**

CONVICTION OR FINE
Tracks: / Conviction or fine.
12" Single: Released Jan '85, on RAS (Real Authentic Sound), by Greensleeves Records. Catalogue no: **RAS 7017**

DARKNESS
Tracks: / Darkness / Youths of Eglington.
7" Single: Released Jun '82, on Island, by Island Records. Catalogue no: **WIP 6787**
10" single: Released Jun '82, on Island, by Island Records. Catalogue no: **10 WIP 6787**

FIT YOU HAFFE FIT
Tracks: / Fit you haffe fit.
12" Single: Released Jul '85, on Taxi (1), Catalogue no: **BUT 1**

GET RICH & SWITCH
Tracks: / Get rich & switch.
12" Single: Released Jun '88, on JR, Catalogue no: **JR 10**

GREAT TRAIN ROBBERY
Tracks: / Great train robbery (dub) / Great train robbery.
7" Single: Released May '86, on RAS (Real Authentic Sound), by Greensleeves Records. Deleted '89. Catalogue no: **RAS 7018**
12" Single: Released Apr '86, on RAS (Real Authentic Sound), by Greensleeves Records. Catalogue no: **RAST 7018**

SINSEMILLA (SINGLE)
Tracks: / Sinsemilla / Guess who's coming to dinner.
12" Single: Released Jul '80, on Island, by Island Records. Deleted '83. Catalogue no: **12WIP 6626**

SPONJI REGGAE
Tracks: / Sponji reggae / Trodding.
12" Single: Released Aug '81, on Island, by Island Records. Deleted Aug '84. Catalogue no: **12WIP 6695**

WHAT IS LIFE?
Tracks: / What is life.
7" Single: Released Aug '84, on Island, by Island Records. Catalogue no: **IS 150**
12" Single: Released Aug '84, on Island, by Island Records. Deleted Jul '87. Catalogue no: **12IS 150**
12" Single: Released Oct '84, on Island, by Island Records. Catalogue no: **12ISP 150**

Black Velvet Band

OLD MAN STONE
Tracks: / Old man stone / And I'll come back (to the same ground again).
12" Single: Released Jul '89, on Mother, by Mother Records. Catalogue no: **12MUM 10**
7" Single: Released Jul '89, on Mother, by Mother Records. Catalogue no: **MUM 10**

Black, Vince

BACK OFF
Tracks: / Back off.
12" Single: Released Jun '82, on 1 Tone, Catalogue no: **ITRS 1001**

Blackburn, Tony

IT'S ONLY LOVE
Tracks: / It's only love.
7" Single: Released Mar '69, on MGM, by Polydor Ltd. Deleted '72. Catalogue no: **MGM 1467**

SO MUCH LOVE
Tracks: / So much love.
7" Single: Released Jan '68, on MGM, by Polydor Ltd. Deleted '71. Catalogue no: **MGM 1375**

Blackbyrds

DON'T KNOW WHAT TO SAY
Tracks: / Don't know what to say / Rock creek park.
12" Single: Released Feb '81, on Fantasy (1), by BMG Records (UK). Deleted Feb '86. Catalogue no: **FTCT 194**
7" Single: Released Feb '81, on Fantasy (1), by BMG Records (UK). Deleted Feb '86. Catalogue no: **FTC 194**

WALKING IN RHYTHM
Tracks: / Walking in rhythm.
7" Single: Released Sep '85, on Streetwave, Catalogue no: **SWAVE 3**
7" Single: Released May '75, on Fantasy (1), by BMG Records (UK). Deleted '78. Catalogue no: **FTC 114**

Blackett, Anthony

MY LITTLE WOMAN
Tracks: / My little woman.
12" Single: Released Oct '82, on JR, Catalogue no: **JR 001**

Blackfoot

Biographical details: An energetic rock band from the Southern United States, Blackfoot -- Charlie Hargrett, Ricky Medlocke, Jackson Spires and Greg Walker -- played traditional southern boogie rock. They were first heard on two mid-70's LPs, *"No Reservations"* and *"Flyin' High"*. But it was 1979's Strikes album that broke them into the American charts, boosted by two Top Forty singles, *"Highway Song"* (their best-known track) and *"Train Train"*. In '81 they scored their first UK success with the *"Marauder"* album, peaking at No 38 with 12 weeks on the chart; this was bettered by 1982's *"Highway Song - Blackfoot Live set"*, which reached No 14. And *"Dry County"* gave them their first British hit single -- at No 43 -- also in '82. By this time American success was diminishing: Blackfoot had proved themselves a very competent band, but there was too little to distinguish them from many similar contemporaries and predecessors. (Bob MacDonald, 1984.).

DRY COUNTY
Tracks: / Dry county.
7" Single: Released Mar '82, on Atco, by Atlantic Recording Corp.(USA). Deleted '85. Catalogue no: **K 11686**

EVERY MAN SHOULD KNOW
Tracks: / Every man should know / Highway song.
7" Single: Released Jan '81, on Atlantic, by WEA Records. Deleted Jan '84. Catalogue no: **K 11636**

FOUR FROM BLACKFOOT
Tracks: / Four from Blackfoot.
7" Single: Released Mar '82, on Atco, by Atlantic Recording Corp.(USA). Catalogue no: **K 11686 F**

GOOD MORNING
Tracks: / Good morning / Paying for it.
7" Single: Released Sep '81, on Atco, by Atlantic Recording Corp.(USA). Deleted Sep '84. Catalogue no: **K 11673**

HIGHWAY SONG (SINGLE)
Tracks: / Highway song / Rollin' and tumblin'.
7" Single: Released Aug '82, on Atco, by Atlantic Recording Corp.(USA). Catalogue no: **K 11760**

MORNING DEW
Tracks: / Morning dew.
7" Single: Released Jun '85, on Atlantic, by WEA Records. Deleted '86. Catalogue no: **B 9690**
12" Single: Released Jun '85, on Atlantic, by WEA Records. Deleted '86. Catalogue no: **B 9690 T**

ON THE RUN
Tracks: / On the run / Street fighter / Train, train.
7" Single: Released Oct '80, on Atco, by Atlantic Recording Corp.(USA). Deleted '83. Catalogue no: **K 11601**
7" Single: Released Feb '82, on Atco, by Atlantic Recording Corp.(USA). Deleted Feb '87. Catalogue no: **K 11686**

SEND ME AN ANGEL
Tracks: / Send me an angel.
7" Single: Released May '83, on Atco, by Atlantic Recording Corp.(USA). Catalogue no: **B 9880**
12" Single: Released May '83, on Atco, by Atlantic Recording Corp.(USA). Catalogue no: **B 9880 T**
7" Pic: Released May '83, on Atco, by Atlantic Recording Corp.(USA). Catalogue no: **B 9880 P**

TEENAGE IDOL
Tracks: / Teenage idol.
12" Single: Released Jul '83, on Atco, by Atlantic Recording Corp.(USA). Catalogue no: **B 9845 T**
7" Single: Released Jul '83, on Atco, by Atlantic Recording Corp.(USA). Catalogue no: **B 9845**

TRAIN TRAIN
Tracks: / Train train / Baby blue.
7" Single: Released Feb '80, on Atlantic, by WEA Records. Deleted '83. Catalogue no: **K 1147**

Blackfoot, J.

TAXI
Tracks: / Taxi / Where is love.
7" Single: Released Feb '84, on Allegience, Catalogue no: **ALES 2**

WHAT YOU DID TO ME LAST NIGHT
Tracks: / What you did to me last night / I stood on the sidewalk.
7" Single: Released Aug '84, on Allegience, Catalogue no: **ALES 6**
12" Single: Released Aug '84, on Allegience, Catalogue no: **ALES 126**

Blackfoot Sue

Biographical details: This British band -- Dave and Tom Farmer, Eddie Galga and Alan Jones -- had a No 4 UK hit with the self-penned rock single *"Standing In The Road"* in 1972, followed by a second but minor hit, *"Sing, Don't Speak"*. Subsequent singles flopped, as did their albums, *"Nothing To Hide"* and *"Gun Running"*. (Bob MacDonald, 1984.).

SING DON'T SPEAK
Tracks: / Sing don't speak.
7" Single: Released Dec '72, on Jam, Deleted '75. Catalogue no: **JAM 29**

STANDING IN THE ROAD
Tracks: / Standing in the road.
7" Single: Released Aug '72, on Jam, Deleted '75. Catalogue no: **JAM 13**

STANDING IN THE ROAD (OLD GOLD)
Tracks: / Standing in the road.
7" Single: Released Jul '82, on Old Gold, by Old Gold Records. Deleted Jul '88. Catalogue no: **OG 9037**

Blackie

FOR YOUR LOVE
Tracks: / For your love / Too much for me.
7" Single: Released Aug '80, on RAK, by EMI Records. Deleted '83. Catalogue no: **RAK 314**

MAKING A BAD BOY GOOD
Tracks: / Making a bad boy good / Can't get by without you.
7" Single: Released Jan '80, on RAK, by EMI Records. Deleted '83. Catalogue no: **RAK 304**

Blackjack

BLACK INK MIX
Tracks: / Black ink mix (part 1) / Black ink mix (part 2) / Black ink mix (part 3) (Only on 12" single.).
7" Single: Released Dec '87, on Champion, by Champion Records. Catalogue no: **CHAMP 59**
12" Single: Released Dec '87, on Champion, by Champion Records. Deleted Aug '89. Catalogue no: **CHAMP 1259**

WITHOUT YOUR LOVE
Tracks: / Without your love / Heart of mine.
7" Single: Released May '80, on Polydor, by Polydor Ltd. Deleted May '83. Catalogue no: **POSP 76**

Blackmail

BANANA BOAT SONG
Tracks: / Banana boat song / Nassau nassau.
7" Single: Released Sep '82, on Logo, by Logo Records. Deleted '85. Catalogue no: **GO 417**

Blackman, Honor

KINKY BOOTS
Tracks: / Kinky boots.
12" Single: Released Jul '83, on Cherry Red, by Cherry Red Records. Deleted '88. Catalogue no: **12 CHERRY 62**
7" Single: Released May '83, on Cherry Red, by Cherry Red Records. Catalogue no: **CHERRY 62**

Blackout

CITY, THE
Tracks: / City, The.
7" Single: Released Jan '84, on Green Flag, by Green Flag Records. Catalogue no: **GU 1**

Blackouts

EXCHANGE OF GOODS
Tracks: / Exchange of goods / Industry.
7" Single: Released Nov '81, on Situation 2, by Beggars Banquet Records. Catalogue no: **SIT 14**

Blackpool Rockers

SAN FRANCISCO DISCO DANCING SCHOOL
Tracks: / San Francisco disco dancing school / Get a proper job.
7" Single: Released Oct '82, on Sunny, by Sunny Records. Catalogue no: **EON 105**

Blackslate, Keith

DAYLIGHT COME
Tracks: / Daylight come / Kaya.
12" Single: Released May '85, on Uptempo, Catalogue no: **UT 009**

Blacksmith

GET BACK TO LOVE
Tracks: / Get back to love (radio mix) / Get back to love (swing beat mix) (Not available on 12".) / Blacksmith (Only on 12".) / Get back to love (blaze club mixes) (Not on 7".) / Get back to love (blaze dub) (Only on 12".).
Cassingle: Released Jul '89, on London Records, by London Records. Catalogue no: **MCFCS 111**
7" Single: Released Jun '89, on London Records, by London Records. Catalogue no: **F 111**
CD 5": Released Jul '89, on London Records, by London Records. Catalogue no: **FCD 111**
12" Single: Released Jun '89, on London Records, by London Records. Catalogue no: **FX 111**

Blackstock, Wayne

MR. OFFICER
Tracks: / Mr. Officer / Thanks and praise.
12" Single: Released Mar '85, on Tonos, Catalogue no: **TON 004**

Blackstone, Eddie

NEVER LET A DREAM GO BY
Tracks: / Never let a dream go by.
7" Single: Released May '83, on T.W., by T.W. Records. Deleted '85. Catalogue no: **HIT 115**

Blackstones

AIN'T SHE LOOKING FINE
Tracks: / Ain't she looking fine / Sweet dub.
12" Single: Released Nov '82, on Live & Love, Catalogue no: **LLD 210**

CREATED BY ONE
Tracks: / Created by one.
12" Single: Released Apr '82, on KG, Catalogue no: **KG 005**

FIGHTING TO THE TOP
Tracks: / Fighting to the top.
12" Single: Released Nov '83, on Easy Street, Catalogue no: **ES 003**

I SECOND THAT EMOTION
Tracks: / I second that emotion / I second that emotion (version).
12" Single: Released Dec '87, on Body Music, by Nuclear Records. Catalogue no: **BZT 11**

I'LL BE THERE
Tracks: / I'll be there (acapella) / I'll be there.
12" Single: Released May '86, on Black stones, Catalogue no: **BS 002**

I'M THE ONE FOR YOU
Tracks: / I'm the one for you.
12" Single: Released Nov '86, on Sir George, Catalogue no: **SG 041T**

IT'S ALL IN THE GAME
Tracks: / It's all in the game.
7" Single: Released Dec '81, on Riff-Raff, Catalogue no: **RFBC 7901**

JEALOUSY
Tracks: / Jealousy.
12" Single: Released May '82, on Live & Love, Catalogue no: **LLDIS 206**

LOVE I SAW IN YOU WAS JUST A MIRAGE, THE
Tracks: / Love I saw in you was just a mirage, The.
7" Single: Released May '89, on Body Music, by Nuclear Records. Catalogue no: **BZT 016**

MIGHTY LONG TIME
Tracks: / Mighty long time.
12" Single: Released Oct '84, on PRT, by Castle Communications Records. Catalogue no: **12P 319**
7" Single: Released Oct '84, on PRT, by Castle Communications Records. Catalogue no: **7P 319**

NOTHING YOU CAN DO ABOUT LOVE
Tracks: / Take another look at love / Nothing you can do about love.
12" Single: Released Apr '86, on PRT, by Castle Communications Records. Catalogue no: **12PX 328**
12" Single: Released Oct '85, on PRT, by Castle Communications Records. Catalogue no: **12P 328**
7" Single: Released Oct '85, on PRT, by Castle Communications Records. Catalogue no: **7P 328**
7" Single: Released Apr '86, on PRT, by Castle Communications Records. Catalogue no: **7PX 328**

SATURDAY NITE
Tracks: / Saturday nite.
12" Single: Released Jun '85, on Hep To Hep, Catalogue no: **HHP 002**

SOULED OUT OF LOVE
Tracks: / Souled out of love.
12" Single: Released Aug '84, on Blackstones, Catalogue no: **BS 001**

SWEET FEELINGS
Tracks: / Riding high / Sweet feelings.
12" Single: Released Feb '86, on War International, Catalogue no: **WR 11 23 507**

Blackstones, Leon

ROCKERS MEDLEY
Tracks: / Rockers medley.
12" Single: Released Jul '83, on Music Force, Catalogue no: **PRO 8782**

Blackstuff Lads

GIS A JOB
Tracks: / Gis a job / Yosser's rap.
7" Single: Released Dec '82, on State, by State Records. Catalogue no: **STAT 118**

Blackthorn

BELFAST MARATHON
Tracks: / Belfast marathon.
7" Single: Released Apr '85, on Mint, by Emerald Records. Deleted '88. Catalogue no: **CHEW 98**

Blackwell, Debbie

ONCE YOU GOT ME GOING
Tracks: / Once you got me going.
12" Single: Released Jul '86, on 10 Records, by Virgin Records. Deleted '89. Catalogue no: **TENT 151**
7" Single: Released Jul '86, on 10 Records, by Virgin Records. Deleted May '88. Catalogue no: **TEN 151**

Blackwell, Vic

LIVERPOOL BILL
Tracks: / Liverpool Bill / March of the champions.
7" Single: Released '88, on DJM, Catalogue no: **DJS 10979**

Blackwells

LOVE OR MONEY
Tracks: / Love or money.
7" Single: Released May '61, on London-American, Deleted '64. Catalogue no: **HLW 9334**

Blackwood, Vas

BOTTLE, STONE & STICKS
Tracks: / Bottle, stone & sticks / Bottle, stone & sticks (pt 2).
7" Single: Released Oct '80, on Cavalis, Deleted Oct '83. Catalogue no: **CAV 003**

Blade Runner

BACK STREET LADY
Tracks: / Back street lady.
7" Single: Released Jan '85, on Ebony (2), by Ebony Records. Catalogue no: **EBON 26**

Blades

DOWNMARKET
Tracks: / Downmarket / Truth don't hurt.
7" Single: Released Jul '86, on Reekus, by Reekus Records. Catalogue no: **RKS 017**

GHOST OF A CHANCE
Tracks: / Ghost of a chance / Real emotion.
7" Single: Released May '81, on Polydor, by Polydor Ltd. Deleted May '84. Catalogue no: **NRG 5**

Blades, Ruben

Biographical details: Blades, Ruben. A superstar in the New York City and worldwide Latin community, the singer, songwriter and bandleader was born in 1948 in Panama. He began singing in 1966, began recording in 1969 and went to New York to stay in 1973, joining Ray Berretto's band in '74 and writing hit songs other for other Latin stars; he soon worked with Willie Colon, Hector Lavoe and the Fania All Stars. His social realist lyrics, unusual then in Salsa, combined with Colon's eclectic pan-Latin music made them a new force; that collaboration lasted until 1982. Blades has made films including playing a young salsa singer in 'Crossover Dreams' in 1985; his own album *Escenas* that year included guests Linda Ronstadt and Joe Jackson. He was the subject of a channel 4 documentary by American filmmaker Robert Mugge; graduated from Harvard Law School and declared his intention of a policitical career in Panama. Donald Clarke, 24 August 1988..

MOVE ON (MUEUETE)
Tracks: / Move on (Mueuete) / Muevete.
12" Single: Released May '86, on Elektra (USA), by Elektra Records (USA). Catalogue no: **EKR 45 T**
7" Single: Released May '86, on Elektra (USA), by Elektra Records (USA). Catalogue no: **EKR 45**

Blah Blah Blah

DANCE
Tracks: / Dance.
7" Single: Released Oct '87, on The Lastest Record Company, Catalogue no: **BLAH 7999**
7" Pic: Released Oct '87, on The Lastest Record Company, Catalogue no: **BLAHP 999**
12" Single: Released Oct '87, on The Lastest Record Company, Catalogue no: **BLAH 999**

IN THE ARMY
Tracks: / In the army.
7" Single: Released Sep '82, on Absurd, by Absurd Records. Catalogue no: **ABS 1**

Blaine, Vivian

BUSHEL AND A PECK
Tracks: / Bushel and a peck, A.
7" Single: Released Jul '53, on Brunswick, by Decca Records. Deleted '56. Catalogue no: **05100**

Blaka & Bello

GANJA TREE
Tracks: / Ganja tree / Dance hall.
7" Single: Released Dec '87, on CSA, by CSA Records. Catalogue no: **CSA 514**
12" Single: Released Dec '87, on CSA, by CSA Records. Catalogue no: **12CSA 514**

Blake, Eric

BORN TO BE SPECIAL
Tracks: / Born to be special / 80's girl / Give generously.
7" Single: Released Apr '81, on Carrere, Deleted Apr '84. Catalogue no: **CAR 179**

SIN CITY
Tracks: / Sin city / Zero 6.
7" Single: Released Jun '80, on Carrere, Deleted Jun '83. Catalogue no: **CAR 141**

Blake, Howard

WALKING IN THE AIR
Tracks: / Walking in the air / Dance of the snowmen.
7" Single: Released Nov '87, on CBS, by CBS Records. Deleted Jun '88. Catalogue no: **QTA 3950**
7" Pic: Released Dec '87, on CBS, by CBS Records. Deleted Jun '88. Catalogue no: **WA 3950**
7" Single: Released Nov '87, on CBS, by CBS Records. Deleted Jun '88. Catalogue no: **GA 3950**

Blake, Paul

DANCE
Tracks: / Dance.
12" Single: Released Sep '88, on White Label (1), Catalogue no: **REV 48**

EVERY POSSE GET FLAT
Tracks: / Every posse get flat / Pink panther.
12" Single: Released Mar '85, on RAS (Real Authentic Sound), by Greensleeves Records. Catalogue no: **RAST 7011**

RUB A DUB SOLDIER
Tracks: / Rub-a-dub soldier / Scratch.
7" Single: Released May '84, on Revue, by Creole Records. Catalogue no: **REV 7008**
12" Single: Released May '84, on Revue, by Creole Records. Catalogue no: **REV 008T**

Blake, Peter

LIPSMACKIN' ROCK'N'ROLLIN'
Tracks: / Lipsmakin' rock'n'rollin'.
7" Single: Released Oct '77, on Pepper, by Pepper Records. Deleted '80. Catalogue no: **UP 36295**

Blake, Sonny

MY SPECIAL ANGEL
Tracks: / My special angel / Curiosity.
7" Single: Released May '87, on Creole, by Creole Records. Catalogue no: **CR 102**

Blakeley, Peter

CRYING IN THE CHAPEL
Tracks: / Crying in the chapel / Caterina (Not on 12".) / Crying in the chapel (jungle mix) (Not on 7".) / Crying in the chapel (jungle dub) (12" only.).
CD 5": Released Sep '89, on Capitol, by EMI Records. Catalogue no: **203 511 2**
12" Single: Released Sep '89, on Capitol, by EMI Records. Catalogue no: **203 511 6**
CD 5": Released Sep '89, on Capitol, by EMI Records. Catalogue no: **CDCL 548**
7" Single: Released Sep '89, on Capitol, by EMI Records. Catalogue no: **CL 548**
7" Single: Released Sep '89, on Capitol, by EMI Records. Catalogue no: **203 511 7**
12" Single: Released Sep '89, on Capitol, by EMI Records. Catalogue no: **12CL 548**

Blakey, Art

Biographical details: Blakey, Art. The drummer/bandleader, born in Pittsburgh in 1919, is one of the best loved jazz musicians in the world. He used the name Messengers for a 17-piece band, then an octet called the Jazz Messengers in 1947; he led a quintet in 1954 with pianist Horace Silver, who set up a Blue Note recording date, so the first Jazz Messengers date was not made under Silver's name, but under Blakey, one of the all-time great talent scouts, it has graduated more first-class musicians than any other in history: its 'hard bop' combined modern harmonies with the blues and a gospel feeling, becoming a mainstay of the Blue Note label and remains influential today. Just a few of the more famous Blakey sidemen have been Benny Golson, Freddie Hubbard, Wayne Shorter, Bobby Watson and Wynton Marsalis; in the early '80s the band included Terence Blanchard abd Donald Harrison, now co-leading their own successful combo; Jean Toussaint, now gigging and teaching in England; and new piano star Mulgrew Miller, who described Blakey as drummer/leader: 'a master of tension and release'. Blakey also toured with the Giants of Jazz in the early '70s; a Thelonious Monk trio session with Blakey and bassist Al McKibbon was made in London in '71, produced by Alan Bates on his Black Lion label. Donald Clarke, 24 August 1988..

CARAVAN
CD 3": Released '88, on Delos (USA), Catalogue no: **D/PC 2104**

Blam Blam

ROLLERCOASTING BARBIE & THE DUMB ANGELS
Tracks: / Rollercoasting Barbie & the dumb angels / Mandy is / Kids are alright, The / Touch of grey.
12" Single: Released 22 Aug '88, on Pussyface, Catalogue no: **CLT 001**

SUMMER HOLIDAY
Tracks: / Summer holiday.
7" Single: Released Jun '85, on Kak, by Kak Records. Catalogue no: **KAK 777**

Blanc, Mel

I TAUT I TAW A PUDDY TAT
Tracks: / I taut I taw a puddy tat.
Note: Tracks taken from the album "Hedllo Children Everywhere". Featuring Mel Blanc, Mandy Miller, Max Bygraves, Henry Hall.
7" Single: Released Nov '88, on EMI, by EMI Records. Deleted Aug '89. Catalogue no: **EM 82**

Blanc, Richard De

HUSH
Tracks: / Hush / Temptation.
7" Single: Released Apr '84, on Avatar, by Avatar Record Corporation. Catalogue no: **AVAT 10**

Blanchart, Dirk

COCKPIT
Tracks: / Cockpit.
7" Single: Released Jan '85, on Statik, Catalogue no: **TAK 27**
12" Single: Released Jan '85, on Statik, Catalogue no: **TAK 27/12**

DROP ME IN A CITY
Tracks: / Drop me in a city.
7" Single: Released Jun '84, on Statik, Catalogue no: **TAK 18**

I DON'T MIND IF THE SPUTNIK LANDS
Tracks: / I don't mind if the Sputnik lands.
7" Single: Released Jan '84, on Statik, Catalogue no: **TAK 9**
12" Single: Released Jan '84, on Statik, Catalogue no: **TAK 9-12**

Blancmange

Biographical details: Blancmange. UK synthesiser duo Neil Arthur and Steven Luscombe began gigging with a drum machine using audacious audio/visual effects (such as a projection screen in front of the group instead of behind it), built up a band, mixed pop and electronics until they split up in 1986. Donald Clarke, 24 August 1988.
Blancmange were one of the many British synthesiser duos to spring onto the charts in the early Eighties. Neil Arthur and Stephen Luscombe began working together in the late Seventies and released their first record in April 1980 and later supported by Grace Jones, Depeche Mode and Japan in concert. By April 1982 their experimental technopop style had gained sufficient reputation to give them their first UK chart single. The double A sided *God's kitchen/I've seen the word* reached No. 65. followed by *Feel me* which climbed to No. 46. Blancemange biggest single came in the Autumn of '82 - the highly original and amusing *Living on the ceiling* hit No. 7 on the British charts and was accompanied by a Top 30 album *Happy families.* The next single was totally different *Waves,* a gentle MOR ballad, peaked at No. 19. This title was said to represent a polite way of saying 'get stuffed' to unenthusiastic rock critics. It's UK Top 10 single *Don't tell me* was in very much the same vein as *Living on the ceiling* but in order to demonstrate their unpredictability, the pairs follow up 45 was a cover version of one of Abba's smallest hits. *The day before you came,* a highly unusual story song detailing a mundane day in the life of the love-starved individual, peaked at No. 22 on the UK charts, ten places higher than Abba had mangaged. This surprise choice of song, perfect for Neil Arthur's strong and bold voice, said a lot about the duo's attitude. They had a history of originality and would never do quite what was expected. (Bob MacDonald).

BLIND VISION
Tracks: / Blind vision.
7" Single: Released May '83, on London Records, by London Records. Deleted '86. Catalogue no: **BLANC 5**

BLIND VISION (OLD GOLD)
Tracks: / Blind vision / Living on the ceiling.
7" Single: Released May '83, on London Records, by London Records. Catalogue no: **BLANC 5**
12" Single: Released Oct '88, on Old Gold, by Old Gold Records. Catalogue no: **OG 4081**
12" Single: Released May '83, on London Records, by London Records. Catalogue no: **BLANCX 5**

DAY BEFORE YOU CAME, THE
Tracks: / Day before you came, The.
7" Single: Released Jun '84, on London Records, by London Records. Catalogue no: **BLANC 8**
7" Single: Released Jul '84, on London Records, by London Records. Catalogue no: **BLAPD 8**
12" Single: Released Jul '84, on London Records, by London Records. Catalogue no: **BLAPX 8**
12" Single: Released Jun '84, on London Records, by London Records. Catalogue no: **BLANCX 8**

DON'T TELL ME
Tracks: / Don't tell me / Get out of that.
7" Single: Released Mar '84, on London Records, by London Records. Catalogue no: **BLANC 7**
12" Single: Released Mar '84, on London Records, by London Records. Catalogue no: **BLANCX 7**

FEEL ME
Tracks: / Feel me.
12" Single: Released Jul '82, on London Records, by London Records. Deleted '85. Catalogue no: **BLANX 2**
7" Single: Released Jul '82, on London Records, by London Records. Deleted '85. Catalogue no: **BLANC 2**

GOD'S KITCHEN
Tracks: / God's kitchen / I've seen the world.
7" Single: Released Apr '82, on London Records, by London Records. Deleted '85. Catalogue no: **BLANC 1**
12" Single: Released Apr '82, on London Records, by London Records. Deleted '85. Catalogue no: **BLANX 1**

I CAN SEE IT
Tracks: / I can see it / Scream down the house.
7" Single: Released Apr '86, on London Records, by London Records. Catalogue no: **BLANC 11**
12" Single: Released Apr '86, on London

BLANCMANGE - LIVING ON THE CEILING (Released on London Records)

Records, by London Records. Catalogue no: **BLANCX 11**

LIVING ON THE CEILING (see panel above)
Tracks: / Living on the ceiling / Running thin.
12" Single: Released Oct '82, on London Records, by London Records. Catalogue no: **BLANCX 3**
7" Single: Released Oct '82, on London Records, by London Records. Catalogue no: **BLANC 3**

LIVING ON THE CEILING (OLD GOLD)
Tracks: / Living on the ceiling / Don't tell me.
7" Single: Released Oct '88, on Old Gold, by Old Gold Records. Catalogue no: **OG 9808**

LOSE YOUR LOVE
Tracks: / Lose your love.
12" Single: Released Oct '85, on London Records, by London Records. Catalogue no: **BLANX 10**

THAT'S LOVE THAT IT IS
Tracks: / That's love that it is / Vishnu.
7" Pic: Released Nov '83, on London Records, by London Records. Catalogue no: **BLAPD 6**
7" Single: Released Nov '83, on London Records, by London Records. Catalogue no: **BLANC 6**
12" Single: Released Nov '83, on London Records, by London Records. Catalogue no: **BLANCX 6**

WAVES
Tracks: / Waves / Game above my head.
7" Single: Released Feb '83, on London Records, by London Records. Deleted '86. Catalogue no: **BLANC 4**

WHAT'S YOUR PROBLEM?
Tracks: / What's your problem.
7" Single: Released Aug '85, on London Records, by London Records. Catalogue no: **BLANC 9**
12" Single: Released Aug '85, on London Records, by London Records. Catalogue no: **BLANX 9**

Bland, Billy

Biographical details: Bland, Billy. A USA R&B singer born in 1932 who had big hits in the early '60s. *Chicken Hop* included guest Sonny Terry; then *Let The Little Girl Dance* was top 10 USA. Donald Clarke, 24 August 1988.
Born in North Carolina, Billy Bland worked as a ballroom dancer before becoming a respected blues and soul singer. His output was very diverse and, in 1960 he scored his only Top 40 hit in either the US or the UK with an out of character catchy pop ditty. *Let the little girl dance* reached No. 7 in the states and No. 15 in Britain. Other singles in the Fifties and Sixties such as *Chicken in the basket, Born to be loved* and *My heart's on fire* were of high quality but failed to achieve the same success. (Bob MacDonald).

LET THE LITTLE GIRL DANCE
Tracks: / Let the little girl dance.
7" Single: Released May '60, on London Records, by London Records. Deleted '63. Catalogue no: **HL 9096**

LET THE LITTLE GIRL DANCE (OLD GOLD)
Tracks: / Let the little girl dance.
7" Single: Released Jul '82, on Old Gold, by Old Gold Records. Deleted Jul '88. Catalogue no: **OG 9019**

Bland, Bobby

Biographical details: Bland, Bobby 'Blue'. The soul/blues singer was born Robert Clavin Bland in 1930 in Rosemark, Tennessee; he is a smooth pop balladeer using a palette of blues feeling and vocal effects. His influence has been huge; he began recording in 1954; he had 37 hits in the Billboard R&B chart 1960-70, with 17 top tens; double-sided hit *That's The Way Love Is/Call On Me* made the pop chart as well. Always true to himself, his work is classic stuff from the early part of Soul's golden era. *Members Only* in 1986 on Malaco was said to be his best since the early classic days. Donald Clarke, 24 August 1988..

MEMBERS ONLY (12")
Tracks: / Members only / Straight from the shoulder / Sweet surrender.
12" Single: Released Mar '86, on Malaco, by Malaco Records (UK). Deleted '88. Catalogue no: **MAL 12 031**

SHOES
7" Single: Released Jun '85, on Kent, by Ace Records. Catalogue no: **TOWN 108**

Bland, Paula Ann

LOCOMOTION
Tracks: / Locomotion, The / Go for it.
7" Single: Released Sep '83, on Kay-Drum, by Kay-Drum Records. Catalogue no: **KRUM 103**

Blandamare, Oscar

HERE COMES THE NIGHT
Tracks: / Here comes the night / Why won't you come home.
7" Single: Released May '80, on Pye. Deleted May '83. Catalogue no: **7 P 179**

Blanket Of Secrecy

LOVE ME TOO
Tracks: / Love me too / Devil and the deep.
7" Single: Released Oct '82, on F-Beat, by F-Beat Records. Deleted '85. Catalogue no: **XX 29**

SAY YOU WILL
Tracks: / Say you will / Leather in my hand.
7" Single: Released May '82, on F-Beat, by F-Beat Records. Deleted May '85. Catalogue no: **XX 24**

Blast

SCHOOL'S OUT
Tracks: / School's out.
7" Single: Released Jul '89, on SST (USA), by SST Records (USA). Catalogue no: **SST 124**

Blast, C.L.

LAY ANOTHER LOG ON THE FIRE
Tracks: / Lay another log on the fire / Somebody shot my eagle.
12" Single: Released Feb '87, on Charly, by Charly Records. Deleted '88. Catalogue no: **CYZ 117**

Blast Furnace

CAN'T STOP THE BOY
Tracks: / Can't stop the boy.
7" Single: Released Aug '80, on Nighthawk, by Nighthawk Records (USA). Catalogue no: **HOT 4**

SOUTH OF THE RIVER
Tracks: / South of the river.
7" Single: Released Feb '79, on Nighthawk, by Nighthawk Records (USA). Catalogue no: **HOT 2**

Blasters

Biographical details: Blasters, The. An influential USA rock band, demonstrating that rock, like jazz, is now repertory music. The original 1979 lineup: Dave Alvin, guitar; Phil Alvin, vocals; John Bazz, bass and Bill Bateman, drums, later augmented by Gene Taylor on keyboards, Steve Berlin on baritone sax; Berlin later left to join Los Lobos. The legendary Lee Allen, who played sax on original Little Richard hits, has also sessioned with the Blasters. The Alvin brothers, from Downey, California, were brought up on a diet of Sun Rockabilly, Chess R&B, local heroes Eddie Cochran, Johnny and Dorsey Burnette, Jack Scott. Dave left to join X, also played with the Knitters; guitarist Hollywood Fats (Michael Mann) was recruited, but died of a heart attack, Dave returning temporarily; Phil and Dave also made solo albums. Donald Clarke, 24 August 1988..

I'M SHAKIN'
Tracks: / I'm shakin' / No other girl.
7" Single: Released Nov '82, on WEA, by WEA Records. Deleted Nov '85. Catalogue no: **XX 25**

SO LONG BABY GOODBYE
Tracks: / So long baby goodbye / American music.
7" Single: Released Jun '82, on F-Beat, by F-Beat Records. Deleted Jun '85. Catalogue no: **XX 27**

Blat Zone

MARY HAD A LITTLE JAM
Tracks: / Mary had a little jam.
7" Single: Released Mar '89, on Blip Blop, by Blip Blop Records. Catalogue no: **BLIP 39**
12" Single: Released Mar '89, on Blip Blop, by Blip Blop Records. Catalogue no: **BLIPT 39**

Blaze

CAN'T WIN FOR LOSIN'
Tracks: / Can't win for losin' / Can't win for losin' (remix) (Only on (LIC 004 R) 12" remix.).
12" Single: Released Nov '88, on Republic, by Code Records. Catalogue no: **LIC 004 R**
12" Single: Released Oct '88, on Republic, by Code Records. Catalogue no: **LICT 004**

IF YOU SHOULD NEED A FRIEND
Tracks: / If you should need a friend (friendship mix) / If you should need a friend (movin mix) / If you should need a friend (stardust mix).
7" Single: Released 10 Oct '87, on Debut, by Skratch Records. Catalogue no: **DEBTX 3032**
7" Single: Released '88, on Debut, by Skratch Records. Catalogue no: **DEBT 3032**

WHATCHA GONNA DO
Tracks: / Whatcha Gonna Do / Whatcha gonna do (dub mix).
7" Single: Released Feb '87, on Champion, by Champion Records. Catalogue no: **CHAMP 36**
12" Single: Released Feb '87, on Champion, by Champion Records. Deleted Aug '89. Catalogue no: **CHAMP 1236**

Blazin' Son

CHANT DOWN NATIONAL FRONT
Tracks: / Chant down National Front.
7" Single: Released Jul '83, on Cool Ghoul, by Cool Ghoul Records. Catalogue no: **COOL 2**

Blazing Apostles

DAY OF DESCENT, THE (see panel below)
Tracks: / Day of descent, The / Arrival.
Note: Distributor: Broken Records,37 Dollar Crescent,Kircaldy,Fife,Scotland.
7" Single: Released Mar '86, on Broken, Catalogue no: **BROKE 1**

IT'S SO EASY
Tracks: / It's so easy / Comfort.
7" Single: Released Feb '86, on KDY, by KDY Records. Catalogue no: **KDY 1**

Blaztzone

BLAST THE WALLS OUT
Tracks: / Blast the walls out.
Note: "Excellent club reaction. Superior house track with all the potential to cross over." (Supertrack, June 1988)
7" Single: Released Jun '88, on Blip Blop, by Blip Blop Records. Catalogue no: **BLIP 38**
12" Single: Released Jun '88, on Blip Blop, by Blip Blop Records. Catalogue no: **12 BLIP 38**

Bleach Boys

STOCKING CLAD NAZI DEATH
Tracks: / Stocking clad nazi death.
12" Single: Released '88, on Zombie Int., Catalogue no: **ZOMBO 10301**

Bleep

SURE BE GLAD WHEN YOU'RE DEAD
Tracks: / Sure be glad when you're dead.
12" Single: Released 13 Feb '89, on Sampler Et Sans Reproches, Catalogue no: **12 SSR 91**

Blegvad, Peter

PETTY U AND UGLY
Tracks: / Petty U and ugly.
7" Single: Released Aug '85, on Virgin, by Virgin Records. Deleted '86. Catalogue no: **VS 753**
12" Single: Released Aug '85, on Virgin, by Virgin Records. Deleted '86. Catalogue no: **VS 753-12**

SPECIAL DELIVERY
Tracks: / Special delivery.
12" Single: Released Jul '85, on Virgin, by Virgin Records. Deleted '89. Catalogue no: **VS 798-12**

Blevins, Alan

SMILE WITH US
Tracks: / Smile with us.
7" Single: Released Aug '86, on Floating World, by Floating World Records. Cata-

BLAZING APOSTLES - THE DAY OF DESCENT (Released on Broken)

logue no: **FLOAT 08**

Blind Alley

KEEP ME HANGING ON
Tracks: / Keep me hanging on / Visions.
7" Single: Released Sep '82, on Cheapskate, Deleted '85. Catalogue no: **CHEAP 100**

Blind Amongst ...

DEMENTIA AMERICANA
Tracks: / Dementia Americana.
Note: Full title of the group is Blind Amongst The Flowers.
7" Single: Released '88, on Eyas Media, by Eyas Media. Deleted '88. Catalogue no: **EYAS 499**

Blind Date

HEY DAD
Tracks: / Hey dad.
7" Single: Released Jan '86, on Mak, Catalogue no: **MAK 003**

I WISH YOU WELL
Tracks: / I wish you well / Please don't hide / You don't know what I'm talking about.
7" Single: on Acorn Records, Catalogue no: **OAK 003S**

TOO HOT TO HANDLE
Tracks: / Too hot to handle.
12" Single: Released Aug '85, on Mak, Catalogue no: **12 MAK 002**
7" Single: Released Aug '85, on Mak, Catalogue no: **MAK 002**

YOUR HEART KEEPS BURNING
Tracks: / Your heart keeps burning / Feel my love.
7" Single: Released Feb '86, on Arista, by BMG Records (UK). Catalogue no: **ARIST 642**

Blind Descent

STONE COLD AND YOU
Tracks: / Stone cold and you.
12" Single: Released Jul '89, on Probe Plus, by Probe Plus Records. Catalogue no: **PROBE M22**

Blind Idiot God

SAWTOOTH
Tracks: / Sawtooth.
12" Single: Released 8 May '89, on Enemy, Catalogue no: **EMY 12 001**

Blind Mice

TATTOOED LEGEND
Tracks: / Tattooed legend.
7" Single: Released Jun '89, on Davy Lamp, Catalogue no: **DL 11**

Blinding Tears

HEAVEN ONLY KNOWS
Tracks: / Heaven only knows / Call of the wild.
7" Single: Released Feb '87, on Riva, by Riva Records. Catalogue no: **RIVA 49**

Blipvert Big Top

MOMENT OF MUTATION
Tracks: / Moment of mutation.
7" Single: Released Apr '89, on Earworm, Catalogue no: **EAR 021**

Bliss

HOW DOES IT FEEL THE MORNING AFTER?
Tracks: / How does it feel the morning after? / Your love meant everything (live) / All across the world (live) (12" & CD single only.) / How does it feel the morning after? (live) (CD single only.).
12" Single: Released Jul '89, on Parlophone, by EMI Records. Catalogue no: **12R 6222**
7" Single: Released Jul '89, on Parlophone, by EMI Records. Catalogue no: **203 435 7**
CD 5": Released Jul '89, on Parlophone, by EMI Records. Catalogue no: **203 435 2**
CD 5": Released Jul '89, on Parlophone, by EMI Records. Catalogue no: **CDR 6222**
7" Single: Released Jul '89, on Parlophone, by EMI Records. Catalogue no: **R 6222**
12" Single: Released Jul '89, on Parlophone, by EMI Records. Catalogue no: **203 435 6**

I HEAR YOU CALL
Tracks: / I hear you call / Waited too long (12" and CD single only) / May it be on this earth / Further from the truth (CD single only).
12" Single: Released Jan '89, on Parlophone, by EMI Records. Deleted Aug '89. Catalogue no: **12R 6202**
CD 5": Released Jan '89, on Parlophone, by EMI Records. Deleted Aug '89. Catalogue no: **CDR 6202**
7" Single: Released Jan '89, on Parlophone, by EMI Records. Deleted Aug '89. Catalogue no: **R 6202**

JUST ONE LOOK
Tracks: / Just one look / De blissful.
12" Single: Released Jan '82, Deleted '85. Catalogue no: **KRT 2**
7" Single: Released Jan '82, on KR, Deleted '85. Catalogue no: **KR 2**

WON'T LET GO
Tracks: / Won't let go / Your love meant everything / Further from the truth.
12" Single: Released 19 Sep '87, on Survival (1), by Survival Records. Catalogue no: **SUR 12 037**

WON'T LET GO (2)
Tracks: / Won't let go / Sweet lovin' child / Light and shade (Not on 7".) / All across the world (live) (CD single only.).
12" Single: Released Apr '89, on Parlophone, by EMI Records. Deleted Oct '89. Catalogue no: **12R 6216**
7" Single: Released Apr '89, on Parlophone, by EMI Records. Deleted Oct '89. Catalogue no: **R 6216**
CD 5": Released Apr '89, on Parlophone, by EMI Records. Deleted Oct '89. Catalogue no: **203 346 2**
CD 5": Released Apr '89, on Parlophone, by EMI Records. Deleted Oct '89. Catalogue no: **CDR 6216**
12" Single: Released Apr '89, on Parlophone, by EMI Records. Deleted Oct '89. Catalogue no: **203 346 6**
7" Single: Released Apr '89, on Parlophone, by EMI Records. Deleted Oct '89. Catalogue no: **203 346 7**

Bliss, Edith

TWO SINGLE BEDS
Tracks: / Two single beds.
7" Single: Released Oct '80, on EMI, by EMI Records. Deleted '83. Catalogue no: **EMI 5104**

Bliss, Paul

TEAR IT UP
Tracks: / Tear it up / Someday.
7" Single: Released Oct '81, on EMI, by EMI Records. Deleted '85. Catalogue no: **EMI 5241**

Blitz

Biographical details: This all-male British band were one of the numerous anarchist post-punk groups to flood the UK independent charts in the early Eighties. Their single titles, such as *"All Out Attack"*, *"Never Surrender"* and *"Warriors"*, succinctly sum up their philosophy and style. November 1982 saw them achieve their first national chart album in Britain with *"Voice Of A Generation"*, which reached No. 27. I 1983 they released the singles, *"New Age"*, *"Telecommunications"* and *"Solar"* and the LP *"Second Empire Justice"*. (B. MacDonald)..

NEVER SURRENDER
Tracks: / Never surrender.
7" Single: Released Jul '82, on No Future, Deleted '87. Catalogue no: **01 6**

NEW AGE
Tracks: / New age / Bleed / Fatigue.
7" Single: Released Jan '83, on Future, Catalogue no: **FS 1**

SOLAR
Tracks: / Solar.
7" Single: Released Oct '83, on No Future, Catalogue no: **FS 6**
12" Single: Released Oct '83, on No Future, Catalogue no: **12 FS 6**

TELECOMMUNICATIONS (EP)
Tracks: / Telecommunication.
7" Single: Released Apr '83, on No Future, Catalogue no: **FS 3**
12" Single: Released Apr '83, on No Future, Catalogue no: **12 FS 3**

WARRIORS
Tracks: / Warriors / Youth.
7" Single: Released Jul '82, on No Future, Deleted '87. Catalogue no: **01 16**

Blitz Brothers

ROSE TATTOO
Tracks: / Rose tattoo / Walking all alone.
7" Single: Released Apr '80, on Blitz, Deleted '83. Catalogue no: **BLITZ 002**

Blitzkrieg

BURIED ALIVE
Tracks: / Buried alive.
7" Single: Released Oct '81, on Neat, by Neat Records. Deleted '88. Catalogue no: **NEAT 10**

CONCIOUS PRAYER
Tracks: / Concious prayer.
7" Single: Released Mar '83, on Sexual Phonograph, Catalogue no: **SPH 3**

LEST WE FORGET
Tracks: / Lest we forget.
7" Single: Released Jul '82, on No Future, Deleted '87. Catalogue no: **01 8**

Block

BLOCK
Tracks: / Block / Block (version).
12" Single: Released Dec '88, on Vinyl Solution, by Vinyl Solution Records. Catalogue no: **STORM 1**

Blockheads

TWIST AND SHOUT
Tracks: / Twist and shout / Take out the lead.
7" Single: Released Dec '82, on Statik, Deleted '85. Catalogue no: **STAT 28**
12" Single: Released Dec '82, on Statik, Deleted '85. Catalogue no: **STAT 2812**

Blonde On Blonde

ARE YOU MAN ENOUGH
Tracks: / Are you man enough / I want you.
7" Single: Released Jul '80, on Precision (1), Deleted '83. Catalogue no: **PAR 105**

MOVE OVER DARLING
Tracks: / Move over darling / Snapshot queen.
7" Single: Released Apr '80, on Precision (1), Deleted Apr '83. Catalogue no: **PAR 101**

Blondie

Biographical details: The most successful group to emerge from the mid-to-late-70's New York New Wave scene, Blondie comprised Debbie Harry, Clem Burke, Jimmy Destri, Nigel Harrison, Frank Infante and Chris Stein. From the moment the band released their first single in 1976, good-looking singer Debbie Harry was projected as the main selling point. Her artificial blonde hair had given the group their name and, indeed, many were led to believe that Blondie referred to her and the the men were her backing band. Harry possessed a fine, distinctive voice that was equally effective when raucously belting out punk material and when calmly singing mid-tempo pop. That first 45 was X Offender and the group at that time consisted of Harry, Burke, Destri, Stein and Gary Valentine. By '78 Valentine had been replaced by Infante and that year saw Blondie break into the UK charts, where their punky powerpop fitted in perfectly at a time when the New Wave was gaining steadily increasing commercial acceptance in Britain. Their first hit was Denis, a remake of Randy & The Rainbows' 1963 US Top Tenner Denise. It reached No 2 in the UK and was followed by the No 10 success of I'm Always Touched By Your Presence, Dear. Both tracks were included on the band's first British chart LP, Plastic Letters, which remained on the list for more than a year. At about the same time bassist Harrison joined, becoming the only Briton in an otherwise all-American group. It was the autumn '78 album Parallel Lines which turned them into one of the world's biggest acts. For this they teamed with star pop producer Mike Chapman who, with Nicky Chinn, had scored numerous successes on the British charts during the 70's and who was now turning his attention towards America. The LP's first two singles, Picture This and Hanging On The Telephone, were merely preludes for the third 45, Heart Of Glass. This ultra-commercial New Wave/disco single was ideal fodder for the Bee Gees-led disco boom and was the track that broke them in America, which had previously ignored both Blondie and punk. It went to No 1 on both sides of the Atlantic in 1979 and was followed by a second UK chart-topper, Sunday Girl, another cut from Parallel Lines which itself hit No 1 in Britain and stayed on the album chart for 105 weeks as well as being an international monster hit. The next LP, Eat To The Beat, issued in the autumn of 1979, failed to capitalise on their US breakthrough but was another UK No 1 and yielded a third British chart-topping single, Atomic. But the American lull was merely temporary, for 1980 proved to be Blondie's peak international year. A one-off partnership with disco music wizard Giorgio Moroder -- a punchy disco/rock single, Call Me, from the film American Gigolo -- was their biggest US hit, logging six weeks at the summit and also hitting the top in Britain. By the end of the year they had scored three consecutive UN No 1s (Atomic, Call Me and The Tide Is High) bringing their tally to five; three of these had been co-written by Harry who had thus become the only woman to have a hand in composing three British chart-toppers. The Tide Is High, a pop version of a reggae song written by Jamaican John Holt and originally recorded by his group, the Paragons, hit No 1 in the States in early '81, becoming Blondie's third and final single to top the charts in both America and Britain. A fourth and final US No 1 quickly followed: Rapture was the first white rapping record and the song which introduced this black technique of rhythmic speech to the American pop audience. But it was Blondie's final Top Ten hit in both Britain and the States. Debbie Harry teamed with Chic maestros Bernard Edwards and Nile Rodgers for a disastrous album, Koo Koo, released under her own name. The 1982 Blondie album, The Hunter, was a commercial disappointment and, amazingly, the group had to cancel a British tour through lack of interest and low ticket sales. This represented a remarkable reversal for a band who, only 18 months earlier, had been one of pop's hottest properties, and Blondie folded in '83. Harry continued an acting career that had begun at the beginning of the decade with the films Union City and Roadie. In their heyday Blondie sold millions of records by combining strong pop songs with elements of punk and disco and, at times, reggae and soul. And in Debbie Harry they had a good vocalist and a photogenic sex symbol. (Bob MacDonald, 1984.)

Blondie. A USA new wave group formed by vocalist Debbie Harry and guitarist Chris Stein. She recruited Stein in 1973 for the Stilettoes, with three female singers doing girl-group covers; this became Blondie the next year with Stilettoes rhythm section and made a reputation at trendy NYC punk club CBGBs; the scantily-clad peroxid e-blond Harry made a valuable visual impact and the group, named after the famous uSA comic strip recorded with a new rhythm section of Clem Burke (drums), Gary Valentine (bass) and the obligatory new-wave Farfisa organ provided by Jimmy Destri, touching all the pop-culture bases necessary in mid-'70s pop. She dabbled in film and other things, retiring in 1983 to nurse Stein through pem-

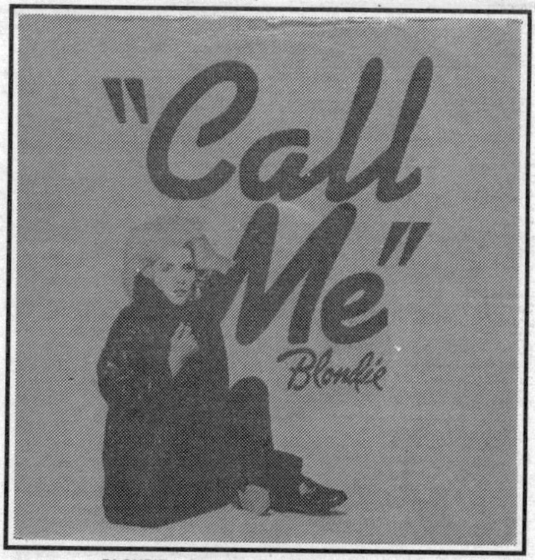

BLONDIE - CALL ME (Releasaed on Chrysalis)

phigus vulgaris, a rare debilitating disease of genetic origin, and came back in 1985 as a solo artist. Donald Clarke, 24 August 1988..

ATOMIC
Tracks: / Atomic / Die young stay pretty / Heroes (Only on 12" version.).
12" Single: Released '80, on Chrysalis, by Chrysalis Records. Catalogue no: **CHS 12 2410**
7" Single: Released Feb '80, on Chrysalis, by Chrysalis Records. Deleted '85. Catalogue no: **CHS 2410**

CALL ME (see panel on previous page)
Tracks: / Call me / Call me (instrumental) / Call me (Spanish version).
7" Single: Released Apr '80, on Chrysalis, by Chrysalis Records. Deleted '85. Catalogue no: **CHS 2414**
12" Single: Released Apr '80, on Chrysalis, by Chrysalis Records. Deleted '85. Catalogue no: **CHS 12 2514**

CALL ME (2)
Tracks: / Call me.
CD 5": Released Jan '89, on Chrysalis, by Chrysalis Records. Catalogue no: **CHSCD 3342**
7" Single: Released Jan '89, on Chrysalis, by Chrysalis Records. Catalogue no: **CHS 3342**
12" Single: Released Jan '89, on Chrysalis, by Chrysalis Records. Catalogue no: **CHS 123 342**

CALL ME (OLD GOLD)
Tracks: / Call Me / Union city blues.
7" Single: Released Feb '87, on Old Gold, by Old Gold Records. Catalogue no: **OG 9676**

DENIS
Tracks: / Denis / Contact in red square / Kung Fu girls.
7" Single: Released Feb '78, on Chrysalis, by Chrysalis Records. Catalogue no: **CHS 2204**
12" Single: Released Dec '81, on Chrysalis, by Chrysalis Records. Catalogue no: **CHS 12 2204**

DENIS 88
Tracks: / Denis 88 / Rapture (Teddy Riley remix).
7" Single: Released Nov '88, on Chrysalis, by Chrysalis Records. Catalogue no: **CHS 3328**
CD 5": Released Nov '88, on Chrysalis, by Chrysalis Records. Catalogue no: **CHS CD 3328**
12" Single: Released Nov '88, on Chrysalis, by Chrysalis Records. Catalogue no: **CHS 12 3328**

DREAMING
Tracks: / Dreaming / Sound asleep.
7" Single: Released '82, on Chrysalis, by Chrysalis Records. Deleted '87. Catalogue no: **CHS 2350**

DREAMING (OLD GOLD)
Tracks: / Dreaming / Atomic.
7" Single: Released Feb '87, on Old Gold, by Old Gold Records. Catalogue no: **OG 9680**

HANGING ON THE TELEPHONE
Tracks: / Hanging on the telephone / Will anything happen.
7" Single: Released Nov '78, on Chrysalis, by Chrysalis Records. Deleted '83. Catalogue no: **CHS 2266**

HEART OF GLASS
Tracks: / Rifle range / Heart of glass / Heart of glass (instrumental).
7" Single: Released '83, on Chrysalis, by Chrysalis Records. Deleted '87. Catalogue no: **CHS 2275**
12" Single: Released Jan '79, on Chrysalis, by Chrysalis Records. Deleted '84. Catalogue no: **CHS 12 2275**

HEART OF GLASS (OLD GOLD)
Tracks: / Heart of glass / Rapture / Tide is high, The.
12" Single: Released Jan '88, on Old Gold, by Old Gold Records. Catalogue no: **OG 4040**
7" Single: Released 27 Feb '89, on Old Gold, by Old Gold Records. Catalogue no: **OG 9678**

(I'M ALWAYS TOUCHED BY YOUR) PRESENCE DEAR
Tracks: / (I'm always touched by your) Presence dear / Poets problem / Detroit 442.
7" Single: Released May '78, on Chrysalis, by Chrysalis Records. Deleted '83. Catalogue no: **CHS 2217**
12" Single: Released '78, on Chrysalis, by Chrysalis Records. Catalogue no: **CHS 12 2217**

ISLAND OF LOST SOULS
Tracks: / Island of lost souls / Dragonfly.
7" Pic: Released May '82, on Chrysalis, by Chrysalis Records. Deleted May '85. Catalogue no: **CHSP 2608**
7" Single: Released Apr '82, on Chrysalis, by Chrysalis Records. Catalogue no: **CHS 2608**

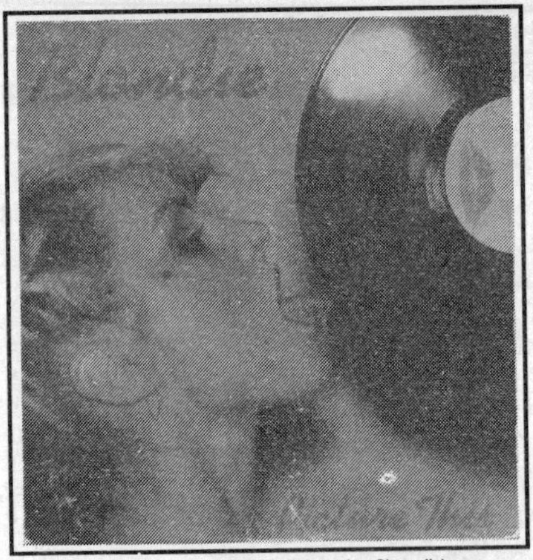

BLONDIE - PICTURE THIS (Released on Chrysalis)

PICTURE THIS (see panel above)
Tracks: / Picture this / Fade away and radiate.
7" Single: Released Aug '78, on Chrysalis, by Chrysalis Records. Deleted '83. Catalogue no: **CHS 2242**

RAPTURE
Tracks: / Rapture / Walk like me / Rapture (disco mix) (Only on 12" version.) / Live it up (disco mix) (Only on 12" version.).
7" Single: Released Jan '81, on Chrysalis, by Chrysalis Records. Deleted '86. Catalogue no: **CHS 2485**
12" Single: Released Jan '81, on Chrysalis, by Chrysalis Records. Catalogue no: **CHS 12 2485**

RIP HER TO SHREDS
Tracks: / Rip her to shreds / In the flesh.
12" Single: Released '77, on Chrysalis, by Chrysalis Records. Deleted '82. Catalogue no: **CHS 12 2180**
7" Single: Released '77, on Chrysalis, by Chrysalis Records. Deleted '82. Catalogue no: **CHS 2180**

SUNDAY GIRL
Tracks: / I know but I don't know / Sunday girl / Sunday girl (french version).
7" Single: Released May '79, on Chrysalis, by Chrysalis Records. Deleted '84. Catalogue no: **CHS 2320**
12" Single: Released Dec '81, on Chrysalis, by Chrysalis Records. Deleted '86. Catalogue no: **CHS 12 2320**

SUNDAY GIRL (OLD GOLD)
Tracks: / Sunday Girl / Hanging on the Telephone.
7" Single: Released Feb '87, on Old Gold, by Old Gold Records. Catalogue no: **OG 9674**

TIDE IS HIGH, THE (see panel below)
Tracks: / Tide is high, The / Susie & Jeffrey.
7" Single: Released Nov '80, on Chrysalis, by Chrysalis Records. Deleted '85. Catalogue no: **CHS 2465**

UNION CITY BLUE
Tracks: / Union city blues / Living in the real world.
7" Single: Released '82, on Chrysalis, by Chrysalis Records. Deleted '87. Catalogue no: **CHS 2400**

WAR CHILD
Tracks: / War child / Little Caesar / War child (extended version) (Only on 12" version.).
7" Single: Released '82, on Chrysalis, by Chrysalis Records. Deleted '87. Catalogue no: **CHS 2624**
12" Single: Released '82, on Chrysalis, by Chrysalis Records. Deleted '87. Catalogue no: **CHS 12 2624**

BLONDIE - THE TIDE IS HIGH (Released on Chrysalis)

Blondy, Alpha

Biographical details: Blondy, Alpha. A singer, composer and bandleader born in 1953 on the Ivory Coast. He led an Afro-rock band in high school, recorded reggae in Jamaica but had no money to release records, worked for Ivorian TV and began to have massive hits in 1983 with *Jah Glory*. His reggae with strong Rasta appeal includes lyrics in Dioula, French and English. Donald Clarke, 24 August 1988..

RASTA POUE
Tracks: / Rasta poue.
12" Single: Released Aug '84, on Syllart, by Earthworks Records. Deleted '88. Catalogue no: **SYLL 8312**

Blood

MEGLOMANIA
Tracks: / Meglomania.
7" Single: Released Mar '83, on No Future, Deleted '87. Catalogue no: **01 122**

STARK RAVING NORMAL
Tracks: / Stark raving normal.
7" Single: Released Oct '83, on Noise, by Dorane Records. Catalogue no: **NOY 1**

Blood Brothers

REPLICA
Tracks: / Replica.
12" Single: Released Jan '89, on Jive, by Zomba Records. Catalogue no: **JIVET 180**
7" Single: Released Jan '89, on Jive, by Zomba Records. Catalogue no: **JIVE 180**

Blood Circus

PRIMAL ROCK THERAPY
7" Single: Released Jan '89, on Glitterhouse, Catalogue no: **EFA 4473**

Blood Donor

DOCTOR?
Tracks: / Doctor.
7" Single: Released May '85, on Safari, by Safari Records. Catalogue no: **SAFE 29**

Blood & Roses

NECRO MANTRA
Tracks: / Necro mantra.
12" Single: Released Feb '83, on Kamera Deleted '88. Catalogue no: **ERA 018**

SOME LIKE IT HOT
Tracks: / Some like it hot.
7" Single: Released Jun '85, on Audiodrome, Catalogue no: **ASSAULT 1**
12" Single: Released Jun '85, on Audio drome, Catalogue no: **12 ASSAULT 1**

Blood Sisters

DO NOT SAY GOODBYE
Tracks: / Do not say goodbye / Let me love you.
7" Single: Released Jul '81, on Sound City by Sound City Records. Deleted '85. Cata logue no: **SCB 007**

MY GUY
Tracks: / My guy / Love don't come easy.
12" Single: Released Mar '82, on Soun City, by Sound City Records. Catalogue no **SCD 006**

NIGHTS ARE SO LONELY
Tracks: / Nights are so lonely.
12" Single: Released Sep '82, on Soun City, by Sound City Records. Catalogue nc **SCD 008**

RING MY BELL
Tracks: / Ring my bell.
12" Single: Released Jun '83, on Soun City, by Sound City Records. Catalogue nc **SCD 002**

Blood Sport

AGENT
Tracks: / Agent / On ice.
7" Single: Released Jan '86, on Quiet, t Quiet Records. Catalogue no: **QS 011**

CLASS STRUGGLE
Tracks: / Class struggle.
12" Single: Released Aug '85, on Quiet, b Quiet Records. Catalogue no: **QST 006**

Blood, Sweat & Tears

Biographical details: Bllod Sweat & Tear This was a jazz-rock group formed by form Bob Dylan sessioneer Al Kooper on ke boards and vocals after leaving the Blue Project. A rock quartet with Steve Katz c guitar, Jim Fielder on bass and Bobby C lomby on drums was augmented by a fou man horn section including Randy Brecke they made a huge splash at the time on CB their first album *Child Is Father To The M* in 1968 mixing brash blues-rock with Ma nard Ferguson-inspired horn arrangemen on songs by Carole King, Randy Newma others; their second (eponymous) albu and biggest hit included Laura Nyro's *Sp ning Wheel*. Kooper had left, replaced

Englishman (naturalised Canadian) David Clayton Thomas; since then there have been many albums and personnel changes: ten albums slowly sank in their billboard USA chart placings through 1976 as they became less fashionable. Donald Clarke, 24 August 1988..

NUCLEAR BLUES (SINGLE)
Tracks: / Nuclear blues / Agitato / Drowning in my own tears (Only on 12" single.).
7" Single: Released Mar '80, on MCA, by MCA Records. Deleted '83. Catalogue no: **MCA 569**
12" Single: Released Mar '80, on MCA, by MCA Records. Deleted '83. Catalogue no: **MCAT 569**

YOU'VE MADE ME SO VERY HAPPY
Tracks: / You've made me so very happy.
7" Single: Released Apr '69, on CBS, by CBS Records. Deleted '72. Catalogue no: **CBS 4116**

Blood Uncles

BEATHAG
Tracks: / Beathag / God says no / Broken town (Extra track on 12").
12" Single: Released Jul '87, on Virgin, by Virgin Records. Deleted May '88. Catalogue no: **VS 980-12**
7" Single: Released Jul '87, on Virgin, by Virgin Records. Deleted May '88. Catalogue no: **VS 980**

CRASH
Tracks: / Crash / Caravan / Never happy man.
7" Single: Released May '87, on Virgin, by Virgin Records. Deleted May '88. Catalogue no: **VS 964**
12" Single: Released May '87, on Virgin, by Virgin Records. Deleted May '88. Catalogue no: **VS 964-12**

LET'S GO CRAZY
Tracks: / Let's go crazy / Shake.
12" Single: Released Oct '87, on Virgin, by Virgin Records. Deleted May '88. Catalogue no: **VST 1015**

PETROL
Tracks: / Petrol (4-track EP).
12" Single: Released Apr '86, on Drastic Plastic, by Drastic Plastic Records. Catalogue no: **DRASTIC 1**

Bloodfire Posse

ARE YOU READY (SINGLE)
Tracks: / Are you ready / Coconut water / Every posse get flat.
7" Single: Released Aug '86, on CBS, by CBS Records. Catalogue no: **650072 7**
12" Single: Released Sep '86, on CBS, by CBS Records. Catalogue no: **650072 0**

CAN'T STOP ROCKING TONIGHT
Tracks: / Can't stop rocking tonight.
12" Single: Released Sep '88, on Synergy, Catalogue no: **SND 01**

EVERY POSSE GET FLAT
Tracks: / Every posse get flat / Pink panther.
7" Single: Released Oct '86, on CBS, by CBS Records. Catalogue no: **650184 7**
12" Single: Released Oct '86, on CBS, by CBS Records. Catalogue no: **650184 6**

Bloods

BUTTON UP
Tracks: / Button up.
7" Single: Released Apr '82, on Exit International, Catalogue no: **EXIT OTO 9**

Bloodstone

Biographical details:
The group had its beginnings in the members' school days in Missouri, USA, in the early Sixties. After failing as a vocal group during that decade, they became an instrumental band, with each of the six members playing one instrument as well as singing. They played Britain in 1972 and won much acclaim. This led them to teaming with British producer Mike Vernon, who proved ideal for the group's style, which combined soul, rock and a strong vocal harmony sound. Though the band became noticed in the UK first, it was in their native US that they hit the Top 10 with the ethereal single *Natural high*. It was only a No. 40 in Britain, where they never hit the charts again. In the States *Outside woman* became a second but similar Top 40 single. Subsequent singles and albums fared well on the US soul charts, but did not cross over to the pop listings. In 1975 Bloodstone financed their own movie *Train ride to Hollywood* which included some Fifties standards as well as the band's original material. It was of good quality but not particularly successful, a state of affairs that typified much of the group's Seventies work. (Bob MacDonald)t.

GO ON AND CRY
Tracks: / Go on and cry / Go on and cry (2).
7" Single: Released Sep '82, on Epic, by CBS Records. Deleted Sep '85. Catalogue no: **EPCA 2713**

INSTANT LOVE
Tracks: / Instant love.
7" Single: Released Jun '84, on Epic, by CBS Records. Catalogue no: **A 4574**

NATURAL HIGH (OLD GOLD)
Tracks: / Natural high.
7" Single: Released Oct '83, on Old Gold, by Old Gold Records. Catalogue no: **OG 9360**

NATURAL HIGH (SINGLE)
Tracks: / Natural high.
7" Single: Released Aug '73, on Decca, by Decca Records. Deleted '76. Catalogue no: **F 13382**

Bloody Marys

MORE SWAMP THAN ELVIS
Tracks: / More swamp than Elvis.
12" Single: Released Jul '88, on Mess, Catalogue no: **JOSS 003**

PARIS
Tracks: / Paris / Party hair.
7" Single: Released Sep '86, on Mess, Catalogue no: **MESS 001**
7" Single: Released Feb '89, on Mess, Catalogue no: **JOSS 001**

Bloom, Bobby

HEAVY MAKES YOU HAPPY
Tracks: / Heavy makes you happy.
7" Single: Released Jan '71, on Polydor, by Polydor Ltd. Deleted '74. Catalogue no: **2001 122**

MONTEGO BAY
Tracks: / Montego Bay / Try a little harder / Jungle fever.
7" Single: Released Jul '84, on Old Gold, by Old Gold Records. Catalogue no: **OG 9439**
7" Single: Released Oct '86, on Polydor, by Polydor Ltd. Deleted Mar '87. Catalogue no: **POSP 819**

MONTEGO BAY (SINGLE)
Tracks: / Montego Bay.
7" Single: Released Aug '70, on Polydor, by Polydor Ltd. Deleted '73. Catalogue no: **2058 051**

Bloomsbury Set

DRESS PARADE
Tracks: / Dress parade / Serenade / Second hand.
12" Single: Released Aug '83, on Stiletto, by Fast Forward Distribution. Catalogue no: **STLT 15**
7" Single: Released Aug '83, on Stiletto, by Fast Forward Distribution. Catalogue no: **STL 15**

HANGING AROUND WITH THE BIG BOYS
Tracks: / Hanging around with the big boys.
7" Single: Released Apr '83, on Stiletto, by Fast Forward Distribution. Catalogue no: **STL 13**
12" Single: Released Apr '83, on Stiletto, by Fast Forward Distribution. Catalogue no: **STLT 13**

SWEET EUROPEANS
Tracks: / Sweet Europeans.
7" Single: Released Nov '82, on Disques Bleu, by Disques Bleu Records. Catalogue no: **STL 10**

THIS YEAR NEXT YEAR
Tracks: / This year next year / Other side of you.
7" Single: Released May '80, on Graduate, by Graduate Records. Deleted May '85. Catalogue no: **GRAD 13**

Blotto Otto

LAST ORDERS
Tracks: / Last orders / Blotto's blues.
7" Single: Released Jul '87, on Crystal, by President Records. Catalogue no: **CR 7037**

Blow

CHANGE (MAKES YOU WANT TO HUSTLE) (featuring Belva)
Tracks: / Change (makes you want to hussle)
7" Single: Released Nov '88, on 10 Records, by Virgin Records. Catalogue no: **TEN 245**
12" Single: Released Dec '88, on 10 Records, by Virgin Records. Catalogue no: **TENR 245**
CD 5": Released '88, on 10 Records, by Virgin Records. Catalogue no: **TENCD 245**
12" Single: Released Nov '88, on 10 Records, by Virgin Records. Catalogue no: **TENX 245**

GO
Tracks: / Go
12" Single: Released '88, on 10 Records, by Virgin Records. Catalogue no: **TENR 219**
CD 5": Released '88, on 10 Records, by Virgin Records. Deleted '89. Catalogue no: **TENCD 219**
12" Single: Released May '88, on 10 Records, by Virgin Records. Catalogue no: **TENX 219**
7" Single: Released May '88, on 10 Records, by Virgin Records. Catalogue no: **TEN 219**

Blow Fly

BUSINESS DEAL
Tracks: / Business deal.
12" Single: Released Nov '83, on Red Rooster, Catalogue no: **HEN 3**

WORK YOUR BODY
Tracks: / Work your body.
7" Single: Released Oct '89, on Modo, Catalogue no: **MWS 005R**

Blow, Kurtis

Biographical details: In the week of 15th December, 1979, the Sugarhill Gang hit No. 3 in Britain with the first rapping hit *Rapper's Delight*. That same week, US soul vocalist Kurtis Blow entered the British charts with the second. *Christmas Rappin'* reached No. 30. On this record, Blow proved himself a master of the Rap, which is the art of rhythmic, rhyming speech. He helped to cement its place in black music during the early Eighties by scoring a 1980 Top 5 hit on the American soul charts with *The Breaks*, which also gave him a second (albeit minor) hit in Britain. Later releases by Blow failed to make an impression in either country. (Bob MacDonald)..

BREAKS, THE
Tracks: / Breaks, The.
12" Single: Released Sep '80, on Mercury, by Phonogram Ltd. Deleted Sep '83. Catalogue no: **BLOW 8-12**
7" Single: Released Oct '80, on Mercury, by Phonogram Ltd. Deleted '83. Catalogue no: **BLOW 8**

CHRISTMAS RAPPIN'
Tracks: / Christmas rappin' / Nervous.
7" Single: Released Dec '79, on Mercury, by Phonogram Ltd. Deleted '82. Catalogue no: **BLOW 7**

EGO TRIP
Tracks: / Eight million stories / AJ Scratch / Basketball / Under fire / I can't take it no more / Ego trip / Falling back in love again.
CD 5": Released Nov '84, on Mercury (USA), by PolyGram Rec.Inc.(USA). Catalogue no: **8224204**

IF I RULED THE WORLD
Tracks: / If I ruled the world
7" Single: Released Dec '85, on Club, by Phonogram Ltd. Deleted '87. Catalogue no: **JAB 26**
12" Single: Released Dec '85, on Club, by Phonogram Ltd. Deleted '87. Catalogue no: **JABX 26**

I'M CHILLIN'
Tracks: / I'm chillin' / Don't cha feel like making love.
12" Single: Released Oct '86, on Club, by Phonogram Ltd. Deleted Jul '87. Catalogue no: **JABX 42**
7" Single: Released Oct '86, on Club, by Phonogram Ltd. Deleted '87. Catalogue no: **JAB 42**

PARTY TIME
Tracks: / Party time / Breaks.
7" Single: Released Feb '85, on Club, by Phonogram Ltd. Catalogue no: **JAB 12**
12" Single: Released Feb '85, on Club, by Phonogram Ltd. Deleted '87. Catalogue no: **JABX 12**

THROUGHOUT YOUR YEARS
Tracks: / Throughout your years
7" Single: Released Dec '80, on Phonogram, by Phonogram Ltd. Deleted '83. Catalogue no: **BLOW 9**
12" Single: Released Dec '80, on Phonogram, by Phonogram Ltd. Deleted '83. Catalogue no: **BLOW 912**

TOUGH (SINGLE)
Tracks: / Tough / Tough (pt 2).
12" Single: Released Oct '82, on Mercury, by Phonogram Ltd. Deleted Oct '85. Catalogue no: **BLOW 1012**
7" Single: Released Oct '82, on Mercury, by Phonogram Ltd. Deleted Oct '85. Catalogue no: **BLOW 12**

Blow Monkeys

ATOMIC LULLABY
Tracks: / Atomic lullaby.
12" Single: Released Sep '84, on RCA, by BMG Records (UK). Deleted '85. Catalogue no: **RCAT 444**
7" Single: Released Sep '84, on RCA, by BMG Records (UK). Catalogue no: **RCA 444**

CELEBRATE THE DAY
Tracks: / Celebrate the day.
CD 5": Released Jun '89, on RCA, by BMG Records (UK). Catalogue no: **MONKC 6**

CHOICE
Tracks: / Choice / Oh yeah /
12" Single: Released 17 Jul '89, on RCA, by BMG Records (UK). Catalogue no: **PT 42958**
7" Single: Released Jul '89, on RCA, by BMG Records (UK). Catalogue no: **PB 42885**
CD 5": Released Jul '89, on RCA, by BMG Records (UK). Catalogue no: **PD 42886**
Cassingle: Released 10 Jul '89, on RCA, by BMG Records (UK). Catalogue no: **PK 42885**
12" Single: Released Jul '89, on RCA, by BMG Records (UK). Catalogue no: **PT 42886**

DAY AFTER YOU, THE
Tracks: / Day after you, The
10" single: Released Jun '87, on RCA, by BMG Records (UK). Catalogue no: **MONKX 6**
7" Single: Released May '87, on RCA, by BMG Records (UK). Deleted '87. Catalogue no: **MONK 6**
12" Single: Released May '87, on RCA, by BMG Records (UK). Catalogue no: **MONK T6**

DIGGING YOUR SCENE

BLOOMSBURY SET - THIS YEAR NEXT YEAR (Released on Graduate)

Tracks: / Digging your scene / I backed a winner (in you).
12" Single: Released Feb '86, on RCA, by BMG Records (UK). Catalogue no: **PT 40599**
7" Single: Released Feb '86, on RCA, by BMG Records (UK). Deleted May '89. Catalogue no: **PB 40599**

DON'T BE SCARED OF ME
Tracks: / Don't be scared of me / Superfly.
7" Single: Released Jun '86, on RCA, by BMG Records (UK). Catalogue no: **MONK 3**
12" Single: Released Jun '86, on RCA, by BMG Records (UK). Catalogue no: **MONKT 3**

FORBIDDEN FRUIT
Tracks: / Forbidden fruit.
7" Single: Released Sep '85, on RCA, by BMG Records (UK). Catalogue no: **PB 40331**
12" Single: Released Sep '85, on RCA, by BMG Records (UK). Catalogue no: **PT 40332**

GO PUBLIC
Tracks: / Go public / Rub-a-dub skank.
12" Single: Released Mar '84, on RCA, by BMG Records (UK). Catalogue no: **RCAT 398**
7" Single: Released Mar '84, on RCA, by BMG Records (UK). Catalogue no: **RCA 398**

IT DOESN'T HAVE TO BE THIS WAY
Tracks: / Ask for more / It doesn't have to be this way.
7" Single: Released Jan '87, on RCA, by BMG Records (UK). Catalogue no: **MONK 4**
12" Single: Released Jan '87, on RCA, by BMG Records (UK). Deleted May '89. Catalogue no: **MONKT 4**

IT PAYS TO BE TWELVE
Tracks: / It pays to be twelve / This is your house / Diggin' your remix.
12" Single: Released Oct '88, on RCA, by BMG Records (UK). Deleted May '89. Catalogue no: **PT 42232 R**

IT PAYS TO BELONG
Tracks: / It pays to belong / Love of which I dare not speak / Hingway (Only on 12" & CD single.) / It pays to be short (Only on CD single.).
CD 5": Released Oct '88, on RCA, by BMG Records (UK). Catalogue no: **PD 42232**
12" Single: Released Oct '88, on RCA, by BMG Records (UK). Deleted May '89. Catalogue no: **PT 42232**
7" Single: Released Oct '88, on RCA, by BMG Records (UK). Deleted May '89. Catalogue no: **PB 42231**

LIVE TODAY LOVE TOMORROW
Tracks: / Live today love tomorrow / In cold blood.
7" Single: Released Jun '82, on Parasol, by Parasol Records. Catalogue no: **PAR 1**

MAN FROM RUSSIA
Tracks: / Man from Russia / Resurrection love.
7" Single: Released Jun '84, on RCA, by BMG Records (UK). Catalogue no: **RCA 418**
12" Single: Released Jun '84, on RCA, by BMG Records (UK). Catalogue no: **RCAT 418**

OUT WITH HER
Tracks: / Out with her / Grantham groover, The.
7" Single: Released Mar '87, on RCA, by BMG Records (UK). Deleted '87. Catalogue no: **MONK 5**
12" Single: Released Mar '87, on RCA, by BMG Records (UK). Deleted '87. Catalogue no: **MONKT 5**

SLAVES NO MORE
Tracks: / Slaves no more.
Cassingle: Released Oct '89, on RCA, by BMG Records (UK). Catalogue no: **PK 43201**
12" Single: Released Oct '89, on RCA, by BMG Records (UK). Catalogue no: **PT 43204**
7" Single: Released Sep '89, on RCA, by BMG Records (UK). Catalogue no: **PT 43202**

SOME KIND OF WONDERFUL
Tracks: / Some kind of wonderful / Sweet obsession / Huckleberry (Exrta track on 12").
7" Single: Released Jul '87, on RCA, by BMG Records (UK). Catalogue no: **MONK 7**
12" Single: Released Jul '87, on RCA, by BMG Records (UK). Catalogue no: **MONKT 7**

THIS IS YOUR HOUSE
Tracks: / This is your house / This is your life (short).
Note: "This limited edition version of the current single features the ultimate acid re-mix, cunningly titled 'This is Your House'. Copies are individually numbered in a gatefold sleeve, with first editions signed by the band. 'This is Your House' has already become something of an underground club hit on white label" (RCA Records, August 1988).
12" Single: Released 8 Aug '88, on RCA, by BMG Records (UK). Deleted May '89. Catalogue no: **PT 42150R**

THIS IS YOUR LIFE
Tracks: / This is your life / This day today / Let the big bad dog eat it (Available on CD single only.).
Note: * Only available on the CD single.
CD 5": Released Jul '88, on RCA, by BMG Records (UK). Catalogue no: **PD 42150**
12" Single: Released Jul '88, on RCA, by BMG Records (UK). Deleted May '89. Catalogue no: **PT 42150**
7" Single: Released Jul '88, on RCA, by BMG Records (UK). Deleted May '89. Catalogue no: **PB 42149**

THIS IS YOUR LIFE (BASS MENT MIX)
Tracks: / This is your life (edited LP version) / This is your life (ten city short).
7" Single: Released Apr '89, on RCA, by BMG Records (UK). Catalogue no: **PT 42696**

THIS IS YOUR LIFE (EDITED LP VERSION)
Tracks: / This is your life (edited LP version) / This is your life (Ten City short).
12" Single: Released Apr '89, on RCA, by BMG Records (UK). Catalogue no: **PT 42696**
7" Single: Released Apr '89, on RCA, by BMG Records (UK). Deleted Aug '89. Catalogue no: **PB 42695**

THIS IS YOUR LIFE (TEN CITY MIX)
Tracks: / This is your life (N ten city mix) / Wait / This is your life (LP version).
12" Single: Released Apr '89, on RCA, by BMG Records (UK). Catalogue no: **PT 42698**

WICKED WAYS
Tracks: / Wicked ways / Walking the blue-beat.
7" Single: Released Apr '86, on RCA, by BMG Records (UK). Catalogue no: **PB 40703**
12" Single: Released Apr '86, on RCA, by BMG Records (UK). Catalogue no: **PB 40704**

WILD FLOWER
Tracks: / Wild flower.
7" Single: Released Jan '85, on RCA, by BMG Records (UK). Catalogue no: **RCA 477**
12" Single: Released Jan '85, on RCA, by BMG Records (UK). Catalogue no: **RCAT 477**

Blow Up

FOREVER HOLIDAY
Tracks: / Forever holiday.
12" Single: Released Oct '88, on Ediesta, Catalogue no: **CALC 066T**

FOREVER HOLIDAY (RE-RELEASE)
Tracks: / Forever holiday / Honker's cha cha.
7" Single: Released Sep '89, on Cherry Red, by Cherry Red Records. Catalogue no: **CHERRY 103**
12" Single: Released Sep '89, on Cherry Red, by Cherry Red Records. Catalogue no: **12 CHERRY 103**

GOOD FOR ME
Tracks: / Good for me.
12" Single: Released 13 Jun '87, on Creation, by Creation Records. Catalogue no: **CRE 045T**
7" Single: Released 13 Jun '87, on Creation, by Creation Records. Catalogue no: **CRE 045**

POOL VALLEY
Tracks: / Pool valley.
7" Single: Released Jul '87, on Creation, by Creation Records. Catalogue no: **CRE 049**
12" Single: Released Jul '87, on Creation, by Creation Records. Catalogue no: **CRE 049T**

Blu, Peggi

TWO CAN PLAY AT THAT GAME
Tracks: / Two can play at that game / Tender moment.
12" Single: Released 19 Sep '87, on Capitol, by EMI Records. Deleted Apr '88. Catalogue no: **12 CL 460**
7" Single: Released 19 Sep '87, on Capitol, by EMI Records. Deleted Apr '88. Catalogue no: **CL 460**

Blubberhouse

LAST SUPPER
Tracks: / Last supper, The.
12" Single: Released Nov '88, on H-T, Catalogue no: **HT 002T**

PERFUMED PAPERBACK
Tracks: / Perfumed paperback.
12" Single: Released Jan '88, on H-T, Catalogue no: **HT 001T**

Blubbery Hellbellies

PLASTIC PONY
Tracks: / Plastic pony / Bar of soap / Sex gods cometh.
12" Single: Released Nov '86, on I.D., by I.D. Records. Catalogue no: **EYE T11**

Bludgeon Meat

POTTED TROTTER
Tracks: / Potted trotter.
7" Single: Released Sep '84, on Bludgeon-Riffola, Catalogue no: **BLUD 704**

Blue

DON'T WANNA MAKE YOU CRY
7" Single: Released Jan '85, on Zuma, Catalogue no: **ZOOM 1**

GONNA CAPTURE YOUR HEART
Tracks: / Gonna capture your heart.
7" Single: Released Apr '77, on Rocket, by Rocket Records. Deleted '81. Catalogue no: **ROKN 522**

I WANNA GO TO NEW YORK
Tracks: / I wanna go to New York / Love made a fool of me.
7" Single: Released Mar '84, on Zuma, Catalogue no: **ZOOM 3**

Blue Aeroplanes

ACTION PAINTING
Tracks: / Action painting.
12" Single: Released Feb '85, on Fire, by Fire Records. Catalogue no: **FIRE 2**

BURY YOUR LOVE LIKE TREASURE
Tracks: / Bury your love like treasure.
12" Single: Released Oct '87, on Fire, by Fire Records. Catalogue no: **BLAZE 23T**

LOVER AND CONFIDANTE
Tracks: / Lover and confidante.
12" Single: Released Mar '86, on Fire, by Fire Records. Catalogue no: **FIRE 8**

NIGHT TRAX
Tracks: / Night trax.
12" Single: Released Apr '88, on Night Tracks, by Pinnacle Records. Catalogue no: **SFNT 009**

TOLERANCE
Tracks: / Tolerance / When the wave comes down.
12" Single: Released Oct '86, on Fire, by Fire Records. Catalogue no: **BLAZE 12T**
7" Single: Released Oct '86, on Fire, by Fire Records. Catalogue no: **BLAZE 12**

VEILS OF COLOUR
Tracks: / Veils of colour.
12" Single: Released May '88, on Fire, by Fire Records. Catalogue no: **BLAZE 24T**

Blue Angel

I HAVE A LOVE
Tracks: / I have a love / Can't blame me.
7" Single: Released Apr '81, on Polydor, by Polydor Ltd. Deleted Apr '84. Catalogue no: **POSP 241**

I'M GONNA BE STRONG
Tracks: / I'm gonna be strong / Anna blue.
7" Single: Released Jan '81, on Polydor, by Polydor Ltd. Deleted Jan '84. Catalogue no: **POSP 212**

Blue August Project

OXYGEN
Tracks: / Oxygen.
7" Single: Released 13 Jun '87, on Blue August, Catalogue no: **JUN 4**
12" Single: Released 13 Jun '87, on Blue August, Catalogue no: **12 JUN 4**

Blue, Babbity

DON'T MAKE ME
Tracks: / Don't make me.
7" Single: Released Feb '65, on Decca, by Decca Records. Deleted '68. Catalogue no: **F 12053**

Blue, Barry

Biographical details: Born Barry Green, this British songwriter and vocalist wrote *Sugar Me* with Lynsey de Paul in 1972. It hit No 5 in the UK. The following year the pair wrote *Dancin' On A Saturday Night* and this time Barry Blue recorded it, reaching No 2. At the end of '73 he teamed with two different co-writers and scored a No 7 hit with *Do You Wanna Dance?* Blue's two Top Ten singles were lightweight, throwaway songs aimed at the younger teenager. Both up-tempo, they were followed in '74 by a slower single, *School Love*, which peaked at No 11. After two smaller Top Thirty hits later in the year -- *Miss Hit And Run* and *Hot Shot* -- Blue's chart career ended. By this time the career of his old backing group was well underway - they were now called the Rubettes. (Bob MacDonald)..

DANCING ON A SATURDAY NIGHT
Tracks: / Dancing on a Saturday night / Morning after (the night before), The.
12" Single: Released Sep '89, on Escape, by Escape Records. Catalogue no: **AWOL T4**
7" Single: Released Jan '89, on Old Gold, by Old Gold Records. Catalogue no: **OG 9842**
7" Single: Released Sep '89, on Escape, by Escape Records. Catalogue no: **AWOL 4**
7" Single: Released Jul '82, on Old Gold, by Old Gold Records. Deleted Jun '89. Catalogue no: **OG 9031**

DANCING ON A SATURDAY NIGHT (SINGLE)
Tracks: / Dancing on a Saturday night.
7" Single: Released Jul '73, on Bell, Deleted '76. Catalogue no: **BELL 1295**

DO YOU WANNA DANCE? (OLD GOLD)
Tracks: / Do you wanna dance / Miss hit and run.
7" Single: Released Jul '82, on Old Gold, by Old Gold Records. Deleted Jul '88. Catalogue no: **OG 9026**

DO YOU WANNA DANCE (SINGLE)
Tracks: / Do you wanna dance.
7" Single: Released Nov '73, on Bell, Deleted '76. Catalogue no: **BELL 1336**

HOT SHOT
Tracks: / Hot shot.
7" Single: Released Oct '74, on Bell, Deleted '77. Catalogue no: **BELL 1379**

MISS HIT AND RUN
Tracks: / Miss hit and run.
7" Single: Released Aug '74, on Bell, Deleted '77. Catalogue no: **BELL 1364**

SCHOOL LOVE
Tracks: / School love.
7" Single: Released Mar '74, on Bell, Deleted '77. Catalogue no: **BELL 1345**

Blue Blud

RUNNING BACK
Tracks: / Running back.
12" Single: Released Jun '89, on Music For Nations, by Music For Nations Records. Catalogue no: **12KUT 133**
7" Single: Released Jun '89, on Music For Nations, by Music For Nations Records. Catalogue no: **KUT 133**

Blue Cats

WILD NIGHT
Tracks: / Wild night / Jump cat jump.
7" Single: Released Apr '81, on Charly, by Charly Records. Deleted Apr '84. Catalogue no: **CYS 1075**

Blue Danube

YOU ARE A SONG
Tracks: / You are a song / Let me hear that song again / Du bist musik.
7" Single: Released May '80, on EMI, by EMI Records. Deleted May '83. Catalogue no: **EMI 5070**

Blue Feather

Biographical details: This Dutch all-male funk band scored a British club hit in 1982 with *Let's Funk Tonight*. It also reached No. 50 on the UK pop charts and was taken from their debut album *Feather Funk*. A 1983 single *Let It Out* failed to match its predecessor's success. (Bob MacDonald)..

LET IT OUT
Tracks: / Let it out.
7" Single: Released Mar '83, on Mercury, by Phonogram Ltd. Catalogue no: **MER 136**
12" Single: Released Mar '83, on Mercury, by Phonogram Ltd. Catalogue no: **MERX 136**

LET'S FUNK TONIGHT
Tracks: / Let's funk tonight / It's love.
12" Single: Released Jul '82, on Mercury by Phonogram Ltd. Deleted '85. Catalogue no: **MERX 109**
7" Single: Released Jul '82, on Mercury, by Phonogram Ltd. Deleted '85. Catalogue no **MER 109**

Blue Haze

SMOKE GET'S IN YOUR EYES
Tracks: / Smoke gets in your eyes.
7" Single: Released Mar '72, on A&M, by A&M Records. Deleted '75. Catalogue no **AMS 891**

Blue in Heaven

ACROSS MY HEART
Tracks: / Across my heart.
12" Single: Released Sep '84, on Island, by Island Records. Deleted '87. Catalogue no **12IS 199**
7" Single: Released Sep '84, on Island, by Island Records. Catalogue no: **IS 199**

I JUST WANNA
Tracks: / I just wanna / Beating in my hea (little flower).
12" Single: Released May '86, on Island, by Island Records. Catalogue no: **12IS 278**

JULIE CRIES
Tracks: / Julie cries.
12" Single: Released Jul '84, on Island, b Island Records. Catalogue no: **12IS 12**
7" Single: Released Jul '84, on Island, by Island Records. Catalogue no: **IS 192**

Blue, Joseph

POVERTY IS WICKED
Tracks: / Poverty is wicked.
12" Single: Released Jul '89, on Hill Cres Catalogue no: **HCR 010**

Blue Light

INTO PARADISE
Tracks: / Into Paradise / I want you.
12" Single: Released 24 Jul '89, on Setanta. Catalogue no: **SET 2**

Blue Magic

Biographical details: Blue Magic. Soul vocal group. Vernon and Wendell Sawyer, Richard Pratt, Keith Beaton and Ted Mills recorded with good studio musicians, arrangers Norman Harris, Vince Montana, producer Bobby Eli, etc. at Sigma Sound (Philadelphia); resulting high-class product was leased to Atlantic. USA top 40 hits included *Sideshow* and *Three Ring Circus*, both in 1974. Donald Clarke, 24 August 1988..

ROMEO AND JULIET
Tracks: / Romeo and Juliet.
12" Single: Released Mar '89, on Def Jam. Deleted Oct '89. Catalogue no: **654 769 6**
CD 5": Released Mar '89, on Def Jam. Deleted Oct '89. Catalogue no: **654 769 2**
7" Single: Released Mar '89, on Def Jam. Deleted Oct '89. Catalogue no: **654 769 7**
7" Single: Released Mar '89, on Def Jam. Deleted Oct '89. Catalogue no: **446 819 7**

Blue Mathue

PERFECT PICTURES
Tracks: / Perfect pictures.
12" Single: Released Jan '84, on Uniton Records. Catalogue no: **U 019**

Blue Meanies

POP SENSIBILITY
Tracks: / Pop sensibility / I'm not in love with you.
7" Single: Released Sep '80, on Mercury, by Phonogram Ltd. Deleted '83. Catalogue no: **MEAN 1**

Blue Mercedes

I WANT TO BE YOUR PROPERTY
Tracks: / I want to be your property / I want to be your property (instrumental mix) / I want to be your property (Daktari mix) / I want to be your property (street latin Wolff / I want to be your property (Def 4B dishonour mix) / I want to be your property (Terence yo-you mix.
7" Single: Released Sep '87, on MCA, by MCA Records. Catalogue no: **BONA 1**
12" Single: Released Oct '87, on MCA, by MCA Records. Catalogue no: **BONAX 1**
CD 5": Released Oct '87, on MCA, by MCA Records. Catalogue no: **DBONA 1**
12" Single: Released Sep '87, on MCA, by MCA Records. Catalogue no: **BONAT 1**

LOVE IS THE GUN
Tracks: / Love is the gun / Love is the gun (street latin wolff 3 edit) / Love is the gun (Miami five o mix) (Track available on 12" version only.) / Love is the gun (Miami instrumental) (Track available on 12" single only.).
7" Single: Released Jun '88, on MCA, by MCA Records. Catalogue no: **BONA 3**
12" Single: Released Jun '88, on MCA, by MCA Records. Catalogue no: **BONAT 3**

SEE WANT MUST HAVE
Tracks: / See want must have / See want must have (funk ass mix) / See want must have (street latin wolff II mix).
12" Single: Released Feb '88, on MCA, by MCA Records. Catalogue no: **BONAX 2**
12" Single: Released Jan '88, on MCA, by MCA Records. Catalogue no: **BONA T2**
CD 5": Released Feb '88, on MCA, by MCA Records. Catalogue no: **DBONA 2**
Cassingle: Released Feb '88, on MCA, by MCA Records. Catalogue no: **BONAC 2**
7" Single: Released Jan '88, on MCA, by MCA Records. Deleted 1 Jul '89. Catalogue no: **BONA 2**

TREEHOUSE
Tracks: / Treehouse / Crunchy love affaire / Treehouse (Street Latin Wolff 4) (Only on 12".) / Treehouse (7" version).
7" Single: Released Nov '88, on MCA, by MCA Records. Deleted 1 Jul '89. Catalogue no: **BONA 4**
12" Single: Released Nov '88, on MCA, by MCA Records. Catalogue no: **BONAT 4**
CD 5": Released Nov '88, on MCA, by MCA Records. Catalogue no: **DBONA 4**

Blue Mink

Biographical details: Blue Mink -- Madeline Bell, Roger Cook, Roger Coulam, Herbie Flowers, Barry Morgan and Alan Parker -- were formed in 1969 when a group of leading British session players got together to record an instrumental album. One song they wanted to use was Melting Pot, written by Roger Cook and Roger Greenaway, who had scored a couple of Top Twenty hits in Britain in 1966 under the names David & Jonathan. This number required vocals so they recruited Cook and black American singer Madeline Bell. The song, a somewhat bland call for racial unity, was released as a single towards the end of '69 and stormed to No 3 on the UK chart. The result of this success was that Blue Mink became a leading pop singles band during the early 70's and the fronting duo of Bell and Cook became familiar faces on Britain's Top Of The Pops TV show. Hits included Good Morning Freedom, Our World and Stay With Me. Banner Man reached No 3 in Britain in 1971, equalling the success of Melting Pot. Most of the singles were written by Cook and Greenaway with the group's bassist Herbie Flowers. Their final hit was Randy, which peaked at No 9 in summer '73. Blue Mink folded in 1975. All the members were seasoned music business professionals and had other projects to go to. Bell -- who had begun her career with a one-off US Top Thirty hit in '68 -- used her fine voice on session work, commercials and jingles and had stints as a radio DJ; Cook continued writing hits for other artists and set up a base in Nashville; Coulam, Parker and Morgan concentrated on session work, the latter two running a studio in North London; Flowers also did sessions then helped to form classical/rock fusion group Sky. (Bob MacDonald, 1984.)

Blue Mink. A UK pop group of 1969-75, whose lineup of vocalists Madeline Bell and Roger Cook, bassist Herbie Flowers, drummer Barry Morgan, guitarist Alan Parker and Roger Coulam on keyboards were all-in demand session musicians, Cook having a successful songwriting partnership with Roger Greenaway. Their sudden no. 3 hit *Melting Pot*, a catchy plea for racial harmony, caught them with barely enough material to play at their own London reception. They rarely strayed from surefire commercial stuff; Bell then resumed her solo career and Flowers joined John Williams' fusion group Sky. Donald Clarke, 24 August 1988..

BANNER MAN
Tracks: / Banner man.
7" Single: Released Apr '83, on Old Gold, by Old Gold Records. Catalogue no: **OG 9275**
7" Single: Released May '71, on Regal Zonophone, by EMI Records. Deleted '74. Catalogue no: **RZ 3034**

BLUE MINK
Tracks: / Blue mink.
CD 5": Released Nov '88, on Counterpoint. Catalogue no: **CDEP 11 C**

BY THE DEVIL
Tracks: / By the devil.
7" Single: Released Mar '73, on EMI, by EMI Records. Deleted '76. Catalogue no: **EMI 2007**

GOOD MORNING FREEDOM
Tracks: / Good morning freedom.
7" Single: Released Mar '70, on Philips, by Phonogram Ltd. Deleted '73. Catalogue no: **BF 1838**

MELTING POT
Tracks: / Melting pot.
7" Single: Released Nov '69, on Philips, by Phonogram Ltd. Deleted '72. Catalogue no: **BF 1818**

MELTING POT (OLD GOLD)
Tracks: / Melting pot.
7" Single: Released Jul '82, on Old Gold, by Old Gold Records. Catalogue no: **OG 9035**

OUR WORLD
Tracks: / Our world.
7" Single: Released Sep '70, on Philips, by Phonogram Ltd. Deleted '73. Catalogue no: **6006 042**

RANDY
Tracks: / Randy.
7" Single: Released Jun '76, on EMI, by EMI Records. Deleted '76. Catalogue no: **EMI 2028**

STAY WITH ME
Tracks: / Stay with me.
7" Single: Released Nov '72, on Regal Zonophone, by EMI Records. Deleted '75. Catalogue no: **RZ 3064**

Blue Moderne

DO THAT AGAIN
Tracks: / Do that again / Blue.
12" Single: Released Sep '88, on Atlantic, by WEA Records. Catalogue no: **A 9045 T**
7" Single: Released Sep '88, on Atlantic, by WEA Records. Catalogue no: **A 9045**

THROUGH THE NIGHT
Tracks: / Through the night.
12" Single: Released Jul '86, on Sure Delight, by Sure Delight Records. Catalogue no: **SDT 2**
7" Single: Released Jul '86, on Sure Delight, by Sure Delight Records. Catalogue no: **SD 2**

Blue Murder

TALK TALK TALK
Tracks: / Talk talk talk / Mr. Soul.
7" Single: Released Jun '86, on WEA (International), by WEA Records. Catalogue no: **248 845-7**

Blue Nile

DOWNTOWN LIGHTS, THE
Tracks: / Downtown lights, The / Wires are down, The.
7" Single: Released Sep '89, on Linn, by Linn Records. Catalogue no: **LKS 3**
12" Single: Released Sep '89, on Linn, by Linn Records. Catalogue no: **LKS 312**
CD 5": Released Sep '89, on Linn, by Linn Records. Catalogue no: **LKS CD3**

I LOVE THIS LIFE
Tracks: / I love this life / Second act.
7" Single: Released Oct '81, on RSO, by Polydor Ltd. Deleted Oct '84. Catalogue no: **RSO 84**

STAY
Tracks: / Stay / Saddle the horses.
12" Single: Released Oct '84, on Linn, by Linn Records. Catalogue no: **LKS 1-12**
7" Single: Released Oct '84, on Linn, by Linn Records. Deleted '89. Catalogue no: **LKS 1**

STAY (REMIX)
Tracks: / Stay (remix) / Saddle the horses / Tinseltown in the rain / Heatwave (instrumental).
7" Set: Released '89, on Linn, by Linn Records. Catalogue no: **LKSD 1**

TINSELTOWN IN THE RAIN
Tracks: / Tinsel Town in the rain (7" only) / Heatwave (instrumental) / Tinsel Town in the rain (extended) (12" only) / Regret (12" only).
12" Single: Released Jul '84, on Linn, by Linn Records. Catalogue no: **LKS 2-12**
7" Single: Released Jul '84, on Linn, by Linn Records. Catalogue no: **LKS 2**

Blue Nut

LA ROLLS
12" Single: Released '89, on Escalator. Catalogue no: **BN 001**

Blue On Shock

HEAVEN WON HERE
Tracks: / Heaven won here.
7" Single: Released Mar '87, on Trigger Happy. Deleted '88. Catalogue no: **TH 181086**

Blue Orchids

AGENTS OF CHANCE
Tracks: / Agents of chance.
12" Single: Released Nov '82, on Rough Trade, by Rough Trade Records. Catalogue no: **RT 117T**

DISNEY BOYS
Tracks: / Disney boys.
7" Single: Released Nov '80, on Rough Trade, by Rough Trade Records. Catalogue no: **RT 065**

WORK
Tracks: / Work.
7" Single: Released Mar '81, on Rough Trade, by Rough Trade Records. Catalogue no: **RT 067**

Blue Ox Babes

APPLES AND ORANGES (THE INTERNATIONAL HOPE CAMPAIGN)
Tracks: / Apples and oranges (the international hope campaign) / Yes, lets (Available on 12" only) / Russia in winter (on 12" only.) / Pray lucky.
Note: * Only available on the 12" version.
7" Single: Released Jun '88, on Go Discs, by Chrysalis Records. Catalogue no: **GOBOB 2**
12" Single: Released Jun '88, on Go Discs, by Chrysalis Records. Catalogue no: **GOBOB 212**

THERE'S NO DECEIVING YOU
Tracks: / There's no deceiving you / Last detail, The (inst) / Take me to the river (Extra track on 12".).
Note: Produced by Pete Wingfield.
12" Single: Released Mar '88, on Go Discs, by Chrysalis Records. Catalogue no: **GOBOB 112**
7" Single: Released Mar '88, on Go Discs, by Chrysalis Records. Catalogue no: **GOBOB 1**

Blue Oyster Cult

Biographical details: This American heavy metal band consists of Eric Bloom, Albert Bouchard, Joe Bouchard, Allen Lanier and Donald "Buck Dharma" Roeser. Formed in New York in 1970, they released their first, self-titled, LP in 1972. Their third album, 1974's Secret Treaties, broke them in the States. It was followed the next year by a live double-set called On Your Feet Or On Your Knees which cemented their already strong live following and displayed their powerhouse concert appeal, featuring hard driving riffs, rhythms and vocals. Agents Of Fortune ('76) gave the band their first American top 40 single, (Don't Fear) The Reaper reaching No. 21; this remains their best-known song, although it was softer and more melodic than much of their material. In Britain the group had to wait until '78 for the single to become a hit. It reached No. 16 and has been their only UK chart single. The song is widely regarded a classic, with its catchy guitar hook, understated vocals and an atmosphere that is simultaneously summery and eerie. From the late 70's onwards, Blue Oyster Cult continued to attract a large following among the heavy metal fraternity, with their mystical and supernatural lyrics and their out-and-out hard rock style. They have never been in the rock superstar bracket, but nonetheless have a sufficiently loyal audience to ensure that each album charts respectably in both the US and UK. Their highest placed LP on the UK charts has been 1980's Cultosaurus Erectus, which peaked at No. 12. (Bob MacDonald, 1984.)

Blue Oyster Cult. A USA heavy rock band formed in the late 1960s, fluctuating lineup including Allen Lanier, guitar and keyboards; Buck Dharma (Donald Roeser), lead guitar; after various vocalists they settled for Eric Bloom, adding Bouchard brothers Joe (bass), Albert (drums, both sing); the music is basic, riff-dominated stuff with lyrics in mock-occult style; Lanier's girlfriend Patti Smith contributed material. Albert Bouchard was replaced by Rick Downey after a decade. Donald Clarke, 24 August 1988.

Formed in New York in 1970, the Blue Oyster Cult released their first self-titled LP in 1972. Their third album, 1974's *Secret treaties* broke them in the States. It was followed the next year by a live double set called *On your feet or on your knees* - this cemented their already strong live following and displayed their powerhouse concert appeal, featuring hard-driving riffs, rhythms and vocals. 1976's *Agents of fortunes* gave the band their first British chart album, peaking at No. 26 with 10 weeks on the list. It also yielded their first American Top 40 single *Don't fear the reaper*, reaching No. 12; this remains their best known song, although it was softer and more melodic than much of their material. In Britain the group had to wait until '78 for the single to become a hit. It reached No. 16 and has been their only UK chart single. The song is widely regarded as a classic, with its catchy guitar hook, understated vocals and an atmosphere that is simultaneously summery and eerie. From the late Seventies onwards, the Blue Oyster Cult have continued to attract a large following among the heavy metal fraternity, with their mystical and supernatural lyrics and their out and out hard rock style. The group have never been in the rock superstar bracket, but nonetheless have a sufficiently loyal audience to ensure that each album charts respectably in both the US and UK. Their highest placed LP on the UK charts has been 1980's *Cultosauraus erectus* which peaked at No. 12. (Bob MacDonald)B.

ASTRONOMY
Tracks: / Astronomy / Magna of illusion / (Don't fear) The reaper (Only on 12" & CD.) / Astronomy (wild mix) (Only on 12" picture bag.).
7" Single: Released Oct '88, on CBS, by CBS Records. Deleted 10 Jul '89. Catalogue no: **652 985-0**
12" Single: Released Oct '88, on CBS, by CBS Records. Catalogue no: **652985 6**
CD 5": Released Oct '88, on CBS, by CBS Records. Deleted 10 Jul '89. Catalogue no: **652 985-2**
12" Single: Released Nov '88, on CBS, by CBS Records. Deleted 10 Jul '89. Catalogue no: **652 985-8**

DEADLINE
Tracks: / Deadline / Monsters.
7" Single: Released Oct '80, on CBS, by CBS Records. Deleted Oct '83. Catalogue no: **CBS 8986**

(DON'T FEAR) THE REAPER
Tracks: / (Don't fear) the reaper.
7" Single: Released May '78, on CBS, by CBS Records. Deleted '81. Catalogue no: **CBS 6333**
7" Single: Released Jul '84, on CBS, by CBS Records. Catalogue no: **A 4584**

SHOOTING SHARK
Tracks: / Shooting shark.
7" Single: Released Jan '84, on CBS, by CBS Records. Catalogue no: **A 4117**
12" Single: Released Jan '84, on CBS, by CBS Records. Catalogue no: **TA 4117**

Blue Rhythm Boys

ROLLIN' 'N' TUMBLIN'
Tracks: / Rollin' 'n' tumblin'.
7" Single: Released Mar '84, on Backs, by Backs Recording Co.. Catalogue no: **NWEP 101**

THAT DON'T MOVE ME
Tracks: / That don't move me.
7" Single: Released Mar '84, on Backs, by Backs Recording Co.. Catalogue no: **NWER 101**

Blue Rodeo

TRY
Tracks: / Try / Piranha pool / Floating live (Extra track on 12").
7" Single: Released Sep '88, on WEA, by WEA Records. Catalogue no: **YZ 305**
12" Single: Released Sep '88, on WEA, by

WEA Records. Catalogue no: **YZ 305T**

Blue Rondo a la Turk

Biographical details: Named after a tune by jazz pianist Dave Brubeck, Blue Rondo a la Turk consisted of Moses Mount Bassie, Lloyd Bynoe, Art Collins, Geraldo D'Arbilly, Kito Poccioni, Mark Reilly, Chris Sullivan, Chris Tolera, Tholo Peter Tsegona and Daniel White. The band was formed in London in early 1981. All 10 members were based in London but they included Greeks, Brazilians and West Indians. Founder was one of the two vocalists, Chris Sullivan, a well-known figure on the London night club circuit. The single Me and Mr Sanchez reached No 40 on the UK chart in late '81, amid much music press coverage. They seemed to be heading for the big time, but they didn't make it. The next single, Klacto Ve Sedstein, could do no better than No 50 and the second album, Chewing The Fat, was the only one to make the British chart, topping out at No 80. The band split in '83 with some members remaining but shortening the name to Blue Rondo. The original outfit tried to incorporate many diverse sounds and styles, which confused their public. Born during Britain's New Romantic era, they were too unwieldy to follow bands like Spandau Ballet and Visage into the higher echelons of the charts. (Bob MacDonald, 1984.).

CARIOCA
Tracks: / Carioca.
7" Single: Released Oct '82, on Virgin, by Virgin Records. Deleted '89. Catalogue no: **VS 549**
12" Single: Released Oct '82, on Virgin, by Virgin Records. Deleted '89. Catalogue no: **VS 549-12**

HEAVENS ARE CRYING (PARTS 1 & 2)
Tracks: / Heavens are crying, The / Cities are dying.
7" Single: Released Aug '82, on Virgin, by Virgin Records. Deleted '89. Catalogue no: **VS 516**
12" Single: Released Aug '82, on Virgin, by Virgin Records. Deleted '89. Catalogue no: **VS 516-12**

KLACTOVEESEDSTEIN
Tracks: / Klactoveesedstein / Klacto (part 2).
7" Single: Released Feb '82, on Virgin, by Virgin Records. Deleted '89. Catalogue no: **VS 476**
12" Single: Released Feb '82, on Virgin, by Virgin Records. Catalogue no: **VS 476-12**

ME AND MR. SANCHEZ
Tracks: / Me and Mr. Sanchez / Sarava.
7" Single: Released Jul '81, on Virgin, by Virgin Records. Deleted '84. Catalogue no: **VS 463**
12" Single: Released Jul '81, on Virgin, by Virgin Records. Deleted '84. Catalogue no: **VS 463 12**

MR & MRS SANCHEZ
Tracks: / Me and Mr Sanchez.
7" Single: Released Nov '81, on Virgin, by Virgin Records. Deleted '84. Catalogue no: **VS 463**

Blue, Ruby

GIVE US OUR FLAG BACK
Tracks: / Give us our flag back.
7" Single: Released Jul '87, on Red Flame (1), by Red Flame Records. Catalogue no: **RF 753**

STAND TOGETHER
Tracks: / Stand together / Easy.
7" Single: Released Feb '89, on Red Flame (1), by Red Flame Records. Catalogue no: **RF 762**
12" Single: Released Feb '89, on Red Flame (1), by Red Flame Records. Catalogue no: **RF 1262**

Blue Section Two

STRANGE FASCINATION (see panel on right)
Tracks: / Strange fascination / Nothing to say.
12" Single: Released Mar '84, on EMI, by EMI Records. Deleted '87. Catalogue no: **12 EMI 5456**

Blue Toys

GOOD DAY
Tracks: / Good day.
7" Single: Released Oct '86, on Sedition, by Sedition Records. Catalogue no: **EDIT 3317**
12" Single: Released Oct '86, on Sedition, by Sedition Records. Catalogue no: **EDITL 3317**

Blue Train

LAND OF GOLD
Tracks: / Land of gold.
12" Single: Released Mar '87, on Dreamworld, by Dreamworld Records. Catalogue no: **DREAM 007T**

Blue World

HELLO DARLING
Tracks: / Hello darling.
12" Single: Released May '89, on Anagram, by Cherry Red Records. Catalogue no: **12 ANAD 48**

Blue Zone

FINEST THING
Tracks: / Finest thing / Love will wait / Finest thing (US remix) (on 12" RHTX 109 only) / Finest thing (instrumental) (on 12" RHTX 109 only).
12" Single: Released Jun '86, on Rockin' Horse, by BMG Records (UK). Catalogue no: **RHT 109**
12" Single: Released Jun '86, on Rockin' Horse, by BMG Records (UK). Catalogue no: **RHTX 109**
7" Single: Released Jun '86, on Rockin' Horse, by BMG Records (UK). Catalogue no: **RH 109**

JACKIE
Tracks: / Jackie / There was I / Chance it (Only on 3" CD single.).
12" Single: Released Sep '88, on Arista, by BMG Records (UK). Catalogue no: **611548**
CD 3": Released Sep '88, on Arista, by BMG Records (UK). Catalogue no: **661548**
7" Single: Released Sep '88, on Arista, by BMG Records (UK). Catalogue no: **111548**

LOVE WILL WAIT
Tracks: / Love will wait / There was I / Dirty tale (extra track on 12" RHTX 107 only).
12" Single: Released Mar '86, on Rockin' Horse, by BMG Records (UK). Catalogue no: **RHTX 107**
7" Single: Released Mar '86, on Rockin' Horse, by BMG Records (UK). Catalogue no: **RH 107**
12" Single: Released Mar '86, on Rockin' Horse, by BMG Records (UK). Catalogue no: **RHT 107**

ON FIRE
Tracks: / On fire / Be the sugar.
12" Single: Released Oct '87, on Arista, by BMG Records (UK). Catalogue no: **RHT 116**
7" Single: Released Oct '87, on Arista, by BMG Records (UK). Catalogue no: **RH 116**

THINKING ABOUT HIS BABY
Tracks: / Thinking about his baby / Thinking about his baby (extended) (on 12" only) / Big thing (extended version) (Track on 12") / Big thing.
Note: * 12" tracks
12" Single: Released Jan '88, on Arista, by BMG Records (UK). Deleted May '89. Catalogue no: **RHT 115**
CD 5": Released Feb '88, on Arista, by BMG Records (UK). Deleted Jul '89. Catalogue no: **RHCD 115**
7" Single: Released Jan '88, on Arista, by BMG Records (UK). Catalogue no: **RH 115**
Special: Released Feb '88, on Arista, by BMG Records (UK). Catalogue no: **RH5 115**

Blue Zoo

Biographical details: Formed in 1980, Blue Zoo -- Mike Ansell, Andy O, Tim Parry and Micky Sparrow -- first came to the attention of the rock press with their '81 single, *Love Moves In Strange Ways*. In the summer of the following year they hit the UK chart for the first time, getting to No 55 with a funky single, *I'm Your Man*. But it was the follow-up, *Cry Boy Cry*, which took them into the Top Twenty. This blend of rock and British funk reached No 13 in Britain. Subsequent singles failed, and their debut album, *Two By Two*, released in November 1983, was largely unnoticed. (Bob MacDonald, 1984.).

CRY BOY CRY
Tracks: / Cry boy cry / Off to market dub.
12" Single: Released Sep '82, on Magnet, by WEA Records. Catalogue no: **12 MAG 234**
7" Single: Released Sep '82, on Magnet, by WEA Records. Catalogue no: **MAG 234**

FORGIVE AND FORGET
Tracks: / Forgive and forget.
12" Single: Released Apr '83, on Magnet, by WEA Records. Catalogue no: **12 MAG 241**
7" Pic: Released Apr '83, on Magnet, by WEA Records. Catalogue no: **MAGS 241**
7" Single: Released Apr '83, on Magnet, by WEA Records. Catalogue no: **MAG 241**

I'M YOUR MAN
Tracks: / I'm your man / Fate.
7" Single: Released Jun '82, on Magnet, by WEA Records. Deleted '85. Catalogue no: **MAG 224**
12" Single: Released Jun '82, on Magnet, by WEA Records. Deleted '85. Catalogue no: **12MAG 224**

LOVE MOVES IN STRANGE WAYS
Tracks: / Love moves in strange ways / Chameleon waves.
7" Single: Released Sep '81, on Magnet, by WEA Records. Deleted '84. Catalogue no: **MAG 205**

LOVED ONE'S AN ANGEL
Tracks: / Loved one's an angel / These days.
7" Single: Released Jan '83, on Magnet, by WEA Records. Catalogue no: **MAG 240**
12" Single: Released Jan '83, on Magnet, by WEA Records. Catalogue no: **12 MAG 240**

SOMEWHERE IN THE WORLD THERE'S A COWBOY SMILING
Tracks: / Somewhere in the world there's a cowboy smiling.
7" Single: Released Oct '83, on Magnet, by WEA Records. Catalogue no: **MAG 250**
12" Single: Released Oct '83, on Magnet, by WEA Records. Catalogue no: **12 MAG 250**

Bluebells

Biographical details: Scottish quintet Bluebells, an all-male band, first hit the headlines in 1982 -- before they achieved a hit record -- when the famous French dance troupe of the same name took court action, claiming the group's scruffy image tarnished their reputation for chic professionalism. This action failed and the Scots retained their name. They made the British charts for the first time with *Cath*, a minor hit in early 1983. But they had to wait a year for their big breakthrough: *I'm Falling* reached No 11 in the spring of '84 and this success was consolidated by the No 8 placing of *Young At Heart*. However, a reissue of *Cath* -- coupled as a double-A-side with *Will She Always Be Waiting?* -- again failed to achieve other than minor hit status. The Bluebells' lyrics are bright, traditional pieces of pop, with a singalong feel. But there are sometimes more serious lyrics on the B-sides and LP tracks. (Bob MacDonald, 1984.)

A scottish pop group formed in 1982: vocalist Ken McCluskey, drummer David McCluskey, guitarist/vocalist Robert Hodgens, guitarist Craig Gannon. They began on the enterprising Postcard label of Glasgow and were part of the trend back to pure pop away from the synthesiser soundalikes. They had to engage in litigation with the Bluebell Girls of Paris over their name, which they won. (Donald Clarke, August 1988).

ALL I AM (IS LOVING YOU)
Tracks: / All I am (is loving you).
12" Single: Released Jan '85, on London Records, by London Records. Catalogue no: **LONX 58**
7" Single: Released Jan '85, on London Records, by London Records. Catalogue no: **LON 58**

CATH
Tracks: / Cath / All I ever said.
12" Single: Released Jan '83, on London Records, by London Records. Catalogue no: **LONX 20**
12" Single: Released Sep '84, on London Records, by London Records. Catalogue no: **LONX 54**
7" Single: Released Sep '84, on London Records, by London Records. Catalogue no: **LON 54**
7" Single: Released Jan '83, on London Records, by London Records. Catalogue no: **LON 20**

FOREVER MORE
Tracks: / Forever more.
12" Single: Released Oct '82, on London Records, by London Records. Catalogue no: **LONX 14**
7" Single: Released Oct '82, on London Records, by London Records. Catalogue no: **LON 14**

I'M FALLING
Tracks: / I'm falling / Holland.
7" Single: Released Mar '84, on London Records, by London Records. Deleted '88. Catalogue no: **LON 45**
12" Single: Released Mar '84, on London Records, by London Records. Deleted '88. Catalogue no: **LONX 45**

SUGAR BRIDGE (IT WILL STAND)
Tracks: / Sugar bridge (it will stand).
7" Single: Released Jun '83, on London Records, by London Records. Catalogue no: **LON 27**
12" Single: Released Jun '83, on London Records, by London Records. Catalogue no: **LONX 27**

WILL SHE ALWAYS BE WAITING
Tracks: / Will she always be waiting.
12" Single: Released Aug '84, on London Records, by London Records. Catalogue no: **LONX 54**
7" Single: Released Aug '84, on London Records, by London Records. Catalogue no: **LON 54**

YOUNG AT HEART
Tracks: / Young at heart.
7" Single: Released Jun '84, on London Records, by London Records. Deleted '87. Catalogue no: **LON 49**
12" Single: Released Aug '84, on London Records, by London Records. Catalogue no: **LONX 49**

Blues...

Biographical details: Blues A genre created by Americans of African descent, one of the few new art forms of modern times, also (paradoxically) a true folk music, its development complete shortly after 1900. Jazz included a greater European element, while blues remained relatively unsophisticated, accessible to untrained players and singers, whose art was in subtle but direct communication. Ex-slaves sang as they worked; the inexorable rhythm of work songs, with lyrics full of irony and earthy imagery became a commentary on daily life and love, and a relief of tension. The classic blues is a 12- bar form, three lines of four bars each; the lyric is a ouplet with the first line repeated once: each line of lyric takes about 2.5 bars, the rest of each 4-bar segment being improvised fill, sometimes vocal, usually instrumental on the singer's own guitar or piano. The form has been further developed by many artists: 13-bar blues are not uncommon; it used to be said tha sosngs such as W.C. Handy's *St Louis Blues* were not really blues, but such distinctions now seem unnecessary. Blues are contrary to European musical practice, were therefore frowned upon by educated blacks (who were also taught that polyphonic music was invented in Renaissance Europe, while Africans had practised it for centuries). Blues are played not in major or minor but in a 'blue mode'; the off-pitch 'blue notes' cannot be played on the piano and are now thought to be more or less direct from African music. The first published blues appeared in 191[illegible] (*Dallas Blues* and Handy's *Memphis Blues*) but Bill Broonzy claimed that some of h[illegible] blues dated to 1890; the first blues recor[illegible]

BLUE SECTION TWO - STRANGE FACINATION (Released on EMI)

was Mamie Smith's version of Perry Bradford's *Crazy Blues* in 1920, a suprise hit that discovered a new market. Great female blues singers included the Smiths, not related: Mamie, Clara, Trixie and Bessie, the greatest of all: Victoria Spivey, Ida Cox, Ma Rainey, many more, accompanied on piano by James P.Johnson, Fats Waller, Fletcher Henderson, many others; Louis Armstrong and other jazz greats were sidemen on records. A pattern of fractured family life resulting from slavery followed by institutionalised racism meant that male blues singers were itinerant, accompanying themselves on guitar and often recorded in the field by talent scouts and researchers; they led hard lives and often died young, such as Robert Johnson (perhaps the greatest of all), Charlie Patton and Blind Lemon Jefferson. Son House and Bukka White also came from the Mississippi Delta; Tommy Johnson, Peetie Wheatstraw and many more had a profound effect on post-war pop music decades after they died, thanks to records. Blind Boy Fuller, Sonny Terry, Brownie McGhee and Gary Davis represented the more delicate Piedmont tradition of the Southeast USA. Instrumental blues piano enjoyed a vogue in the '40s called boogie-woogie; Memphis Slim (Peter Chatman) and Roosevelt Sykes played piano and wrote and sang classic songs, with guitarists John Lee Hooker and Lightnin' Hopkins becoming legends in their own lifetimes. Musicians like Patton, Snooks Eaglin, Mance Lipsome and Mississippi John Hurt were all round entertainers, influenced as much by ragtime and other styles as by blues. Leroy Carr played piano and sang a smoother, urban style in the 1930s, influencing later black styles. The emergence of the Count Basie Band and others from Kansas City in the late 1930s gave a powerful reinjection of blues into the big-band jazz of the Swing Era; partly for this reason, post-war bop had a strong blues element for all its technical sophistication; in '50s-60s small-group 'blowing sessions' from labels like Prestige and Blue Note always included a blues: the blues is not jazz but the best jazz had blues in it. Rhythm & Blues began in the 1940s, influenced equally by the Swing Era and the blues: this black pop/party music was imitated by '50s rock 'n' rollers. Muddy Waters went to Chicago in '43; urban blues emerged as performers adopted microphones and electric guitars in order to be heard in noisy taverns: a Chicago scene of great power developed with Waters, Willie Dixon, Walter Horton, Little Walter, James Coton, Otis Rush, Howlin' Wolf, Otis Spann, J.B. Hutto, Magic Sam, Johnny Shines and many others; inspired by country blues artists of '20s-30s mentioned above, their own post-war work in Chicago was imitated in the '60s by a new generation of rock bands and singers: tours and imported records inspired a London scene that threw up Alexis Korner, John Mayall, then the Rolling Stones, thus having a profound impact on pop music of the last 20 years. Beginning in the late '50s whites in USA like Paul Butterfield, John Koerner, John Hammond and Dave Van Ronk worked hard at playing authentic blues styles: at the Newport Folk Festival in1965 folkies booed Bob Dylan, appearing with Butterfield's electric band, but accepted the band separately because they had never heard electric blues before; despite a foolishly insulting introduction from Alan Lomax, Michael Bloomfield's guitar did not fail to impress: Lomax thought he was an expert on the blues but had apparently never heard a southside Chicago tavern band. From the 1960s younger black Chicagoans like Junior Wells, Buddy Guy Jimmy Dawkins and Houndog Taylor held down the scene; B.B.King began at a Memphis radio station in the late 1940s, worked the 'chitlin circuit' for years and emerged as the most highly regarded living bluesman (Albert King and Freddie King were also highly rated; may or may not have been related). As the blues were worked to death by rock 'n' rollers (leading to heavy metal, whose lack of subtlety is a vulgar antithesis), Texans Albert Collins and Johnny Copeland and in the '80s Robert Cray (born in Georgia, raised in Washington state) have emerged as new keepers of the flame. White guitarists such as Roy Buchanan and Johnny Winter have never strayed far from the blues; in the mid-80s Otis Rush was recording again, Earl King was backed on an album by the white band Roomful of Blues; white bands like the Fabulous Thunderbirds and Kingsnake carried on with love for the music, and new black talents like Cray and Walter 'Wolfman' Washington seem to transcend the category, while Koko Taylor and Big Twist are going strong, and Lil' Ed and the Blues Imperials (two of whom are Hutto's nephews) are the latest blues sensation. (Donald Clarke 23 August 1988).

AIM FOR THE EYES
Tracks: / Aim for the eyes / Out of town.
7" Single: Released Jun '82, on Precious Organisation, by Precious Organisation. Catalogue no: **PRE 1**

BLUES EP, THE Various artists
7" Single: Released Jul '85, on Chess (PRT). Deleted '88. Catalogue no: **CHES 4008**

Blues Band

Biographical details: This British band -- Paul Jones, Tom McGuinness, Hughie Flint, Gary Fletcher and Dave Kelly -- were formed almost accidentally at the beginning of 1980, as a result of some gigs organised purely for fun. Jones had been a major star in the 60's, first as lead singer with Manfred Mann and then as a solo artist; he later took up a successful career in acting. Tom McGuinness, another former Manfred Mann member, and Hughie Flint had formed a group called simply McGuinness Flint at the start of the 70's and they had scored two British Top Five singles. The *Blues Band's Official Bootleg Album* and its follow-up, *Ready*, both issued in 1980, were enjoyable, spontaneous celebrations of the music they loved. The project came across as a hobby, in which its members were temporarily putting aside their careers to indulge themselves. Both LPs made the UK Top Forty and the band also had a minor chart EP. *Itchy Feet*, in 1981, sold a little less well, as did their '82 set, *Brand Loyalty*. May 1983's *Bye Bye Blues* heralded the end of the hobby and the musicians resumed their regular careers. (Bob MacDonald, 1984.).

BLUES BAND (EP)
Tracks: / Maggie's farm / Ain't it tuff / Diddy wah diddy / Back door man.
7" EP: Released Jul '80, on Arista, by BMG Records (UK). Deleted '83. Catalogue no: **BOOT 2**

COME ON
Tracks: / Come on / Green stuff.
7" Single: Released Nov '81, on Arista, by BMG Records (UK). Catalogue no: **BOOT 5**

FIND YOURSELF ANOTHER FOOL
Tracks: / Find yourself another fool / Sus blues.
7" Single: Released Sep '80, on Arista, by BMG Records (UK). Deleted '83. Catalogue no: **BOOT 3**

MAGGIE'S FARM
Tracks: / Maggie's farm / Ain't it tough / Diddy wah diddy / Back door man.
7" Single: Released 20 Jun '80, on Ariola, by BMG Records (UK). Deleted '83. Catalogue no: **BOOT 2**

SEEMED LIKE A GOOD IDEA AT THE TIME
Tracks: / Seemed like a good idea at the time / Rolling fog.
7" Single: Released Nov '82, on Arista, by BMG Records (UK). Deleted Nov '85. Catalogue no: **BOOT 7**

TAKE ME HOME
Tracks: / Take me home / So bad / Sus blues / Hey little girl.
7" EP: Released '82, on Arista, by BMG Records (UK). Deleted '87. Catalogue no: **BOOT 6**

WHO'S RIGHT WHO'S WRONG
Tracks: / Who's right, who's wrong.
7" Single: Released Sep '81, on Arista, by BMG Records (UK). Catalogue no: **BOOT 4**

Blues Brothers

EVERYBODY NEEDS SOMEBODY TO LOVE
Tracks: / Everybody needs somebody to love / Jailhouse rock.
7" Single: Released Oct '80, on Atlantic, by WEA Records. Deleted Oct '83. Catalogue no: **K 11625**

Blues Busters

CLOSER I GET TO YOU
Tracks: / Closer I get to you, The / Midnight.
12" Single: Released Sep '86, on Spank. Catalogue no: **SP 20**

Blues Trottoir

UN SOIR DE PLUIE
Tracks: / Un soir de pluie.
7" Single: Released 5 Mar '88, on Carrere. Catalogue no: **CAR 424**
12" Single: Released 5 Mar '88, on Carrere. Catalogue no: **CART 424**

Blues 'N' Trouble

CADILLAC
Tracks: / Cadillac.
7" Single: Released Sep '85, on Ammunition Communications, by Ammunition Communications. Catalogue no: **BNT 3**

FINE,FINE,FINE
Tracks: / Fine, fine, fine / Free to ride / Red hot.
7" Single: Released Feb '86, on Ammunition Communications, by Ammunition Communications. Catalogue no: **BNT 4**

MYSTERY TRAIN
Tracks: / Mystery train.
7" Single: Released Aug '84, on Plus One. Catalogue no: **BNT 2**

OLD TIME BOOGIE
Tracks: / Old time boogie.
7" Single: Released Oct '83, on Castle Rock. Catalogue no: **BNT 1**

Blumen Ohne Duff

FAMILY, THE
10" single: Released 30 Jun '87, on Scratch & Sniff. Catalogue no: **SS 002**

Blunsdon, Ian

CUT ME DOWN
Tracks: / Cut me down.
7" Single: Released Aug '85, on Climber, by Climber Records. Deleted '86. Catalogue no: **CLIS 2**
12" Single: Released Aug '85, on Climber, by Climber Records. Deleted '86. Catalogue no: **CLIX 2**

Blunstone, Colin

Biographical details: Blunstone, Colin. The UK singer-songwriter was born in 1954 in Hatfield; his first success as lead vocalist was with the Zombies, he left music, was tempted back by Rod Argent and Chris White, who wrote songs and produced him. He's been in and out of the charts ever since, his various projects including the session supergroup Keats in 1984. His material has often not been up to his highly regarded voice. Donald Clarke, 24 August 1988.
This British vocalist began his career in the Sixties as lead singer with the Zombies. Their famous single *She's not there* hit No. 12 in the UK and No. 2 in the US. But whereas success quickly tailed off in Britain, American record buyers save the group two further Top 10 smashes. After the Zombies had folded Blunstone inexplicably re-recorded *She's not there* under the pseudonym of Neil MacArthur; it hit No. 34 on the UK charts in 1969. Reverting to his real name, Blunstone embarked upon a solo career in the Seventies that yielded a British Top 20 single - the Denny Laine song *Say you don't mind* in 1972 - plus a couple of minor hits. His airy vocals had to then wait eight years before gracing another hit record. 1981 saw Blunstone team up with studio keyboards wizard Dave Stewart for a one-off single. It was a futurist version of the Jimmy Ruffin classic *What becomes of the broken hearted* and reached No. 13 on the UK listings. Stewart went on to have a No. 1 later in the year, but Blunstone only managed one further minor hit: a wimpy version of Smokey Robinson's *Tears of a clown* reached No. 60 in '82. (Bob MacDonald) .

CRY AN OCEAN
Tracks: / Cry an ocean / Make it easy / What becomes of the broken hearted? (Only available on 12" version).
Note: "Cry an ocean is the first down payment from Mr Blunstone's forthcoming 'Thirty Three'." (MCA May 88)
12" Single: Released May '88, on MCA, by MCA Records. Catalogue no: **IRMT 151**
7" Single: Released May '88, on MCA, by MCA Records. Catalogue no: **IRM 151**

HOW COULD WE DARE TO BE WRONG
Tracks: / How could we dare to be wrong.
7" Single: Released Feb '73, on Epic, by CBS Records. Deleted '76. Catalogue no: **EPC 1197**

I DON'T BELIEVE IN MIRACLES (SINGLE)
Tracks: / I don't believe in miracles.
7" Single: Released Nov '72, on Epic, by CBS Records. Deleted '75. Catalogue no: **EPC 8434**

MILES AWAY
Tracks: / Miles away.
7" Single: Released Sep '81, on Panache. Catalogue no: **PAN 1**

SAY YOU DON'T MIND
Tracks: / Say you don't mind.
7" Single: Released Apr '82, on Epic, by CBS Records. Catalogue no: **EPC 7765**

SHE'S NOT THERE
Tracks: / She's not there / Who fires the gun.
12" Single: Released Oct '86, on Sierra, by Sierra Records. Catalogue no: **FED 27T**
7" Single: Released Oct '86, on Sierra, by Sierra Records. Catalogue no: **FED 27**

TRACKS OF MY TEARS
Tracks: / Tracks of my tears / Last goodbye.
12" Single: Released May '82, on PRT, by Castle Communications Records. Deleted '85. Catalogue no: **12 P 236**
7" Single: Released May '82, on PRT, by Castle Communications Records. Deleted '85. Catalogue no: **7 P 236**

WHERE DO WE GO FROM HERE
Tracks: / Where do we go from here / Helen loves Paris.
12" Single: Released May '86, on Sierra, by Sierra Records. Deleted Jun '87. Catalogue no: **FED 22T**
7" Single: Released May '86, on Sierra, by Sierra Records. Deleted Jun '87. Catalogue no: **FED 22**

Blurt

FISH NEEDS A BIKE
Tracks: / Fish needs a bike / This is my Royal Wedding souvenir.
7" Single: Released May '81, on Armageddon, by Armageddon Records. Deleted May '84. Catalogue no: **AS 013**

MAN TO FLY
Tracks: / Man to fly.
7" Single: Released '88, on N L Centre. Catalogue no: **Unknown**

RUMINANT PLINTH
Tracks: / Ruminant plinth.
12" Single: Released May '82, on Red Flame (1), by Red Flame Records. Catalogue no: **RF 1206**

WHITE LINE FEVER
Tracks: / White line fever.
12" Single: Released Feb '85, on Another Side (Belgium), by Another Side Records (Belgium). Catalogue no: **SIDE 8418**

Blyth Power

CHEVY CHASE
Tracks: / Chevy Chase.
12" Single: Released Sep '85, on All The Madmen, by All The Madmen Records. Catalogue no: **MAD 9**

GOODBYE TO ALL THAT
Tracks: / Goodbye to all that.
7" Single: Released 30 Aug '88, on Midnight Music, by Midnight Music Records. Catalogue no: **DONG 38**

JUNCTION SIGNAL
Tracks: / Junction signal / Bind their kings in chains & the nobles with links of iron / Tribute to Admiral Byng (Extra track on 12" only) / Ffucke masticke room (on 12" only).
7" Single: Released May '86, on All The Madmen, by All The Madmen Records. Catalogue no: **MAD 12**
12" Single: Released May '86, on All The Madmen, by All The Madmen Records. Catalogue no: **MADT 12**

UP FROM THE COUNTRY
Tracks: / Up from the country / Tale of a cock and a bull, A / Blow the man down.
12" Single: Released 14 May '88, on Midnight. Catalogue no: **DONG 37**

B.M.O.C.

PLAY THAT FUNK
Tracks: / Play that funk.
7" Single: Released 5 Mar '88, on WEA, by WEA Records. Catalogue no: **W 7950**
12" Single: Released 5 Mar '88, on WEA, by WEA Records. Catalogue no: **W 7950T**

B-Movie

LETTER FROM AFAR
Tracks: / Letter from afar / No joy in heaven.
7" Single: Released Jan '84, on Sire (USA). Catalogue no: **SIR 4058**

NOWHERE GIRL
Tracks: / Nowhere girl.
7" Single: Released Mar '82, on Some Bizzare, by Some Bizzare Records. Deleted '87. Catalogue no: **BZZ 8**
12" Single: Released 1 Aug '89, on Play It Again Sam(Belgium), by Play It Again Sam (Belgium). Catalogue no: **LD 878**
12" Single: Released Feb '88, on Wax, by Wax Records. Catalogue no: **12 WAX 3**

POLAR OPPOSITES
Tracks: / Polar opposites / Taxi driver.
12" Pic: Released Jul '89, on Wax, by Wax Records. Catalogue no: **12 WAX 4P**
12" Single: Released Aug '88, on Wax, by Wax Records. Catalogue no: **12 WAX 4**

REMEMBRANCE DAY
Tracks: / Remembrance day / Marilyn dreams / Nowhere girl (Only available on 12" version.).
Note: Nowhere Girl is an extra track on the 12" version.
7" Single: Released Mar '87, on Wax, by Wax Records. Catalogue no: **12 WAX 2**
7" Single: Released Apr '80, on Deram, by London Records. Deleted '85. Catalogue no: **DM 437**
7" Single: Released Mar '87, on Wax, by Wax Records. Catalogue no: **7 WAX 2**

SWITCH ON SWITCH OFF
Tracks: / Switch on switch off.
7" Single: Released Sep '85, on Sire (USA). Catalogue no: **W 8933**
12" Single: Released Sep '85, on Sire (USA). Catalogue no: **W 8933T**

BMX Bandits

CAT FROM OUTER SPACE
Tracks: / Cat from outer space / Strawberry Sunday.
12" Single: Released Oct '86, on 53rd & 3rd, by 53rd & 3rd Records. Catalogue no: **AGARR 312**

E 102
Tracks: / E 102 / Sad.
7" Single: Released May '86, on 53rd & 3rd, by 53rd & 3rd Records. Catalogue no: **AGARR 3**

FIGURE FOUR
Tracks: / Figure four.
7" Single: Released Jan '88, on 53rd & 3rd, by 53rd & 3rd Records. Catalogue no: **AGARR 18**
12" Single: Released Jan '88, on 53rd & 3rd, by 53rd & 3rd Records. Catalogue no: **AGARR 18T**

SAD
Tracks: / Sad.
7" Single: Released '88, on 53rd & 3rd, by 53rd & 3rd Records. Catalogue no: **AGARR 003**

WHAT A WONDERFUL WORLD
Tracks: / Day before tomorrow, The / Johnny Alucard / Sad / What a wonderful world.
7" Single: Released Mar '89, on 53rd & 3rd, by 53rd & 3rd Records. Catalogue no: **AGARR 006**
12" Single: Released Jan '87, on 53rd & 3rd, by 53rd & 3rd Records. Catalogue no: **AGARR 612**

Bo & Generals

RICH GIRL
Tracks: / Rich girl / I know.
7" Single: Released 20 Jun '80, on Island, by Island Records. Deleted '83. Catalogue no: **WIP 6603**

Boa, Philip

CONTAINER LOVE
Tracks: / Container love.
7" Single: Released 18 Sep '89, on Polydor, by Polydor Ltd. Catalogue no: **871 448 7**
12" Single: Released 18 Sep '89, on Polydor, by Polydor Ltd. Catalogue no: **871 449 1**

FOR WHAT BASTARDS
Tracks: / For what bastards.
12" Single: Released 23 May '87, on Red Flame (1), by Red Flame Records. Catalogue no: **RF 1254**

KILL YOUR IDEALS
Tracks: / Kill your ideals / Fire / Flowers of witness.
12" Single: Released Sep '87, on Red Flame (1), by Red Flame Records. Catalogue no: **RF 1255**

Boardman, Phil

MUCH MISSED MAN
Tracks: / Much missed man / Real.
7" Single: Released Jan '82, on Mayfield, Catalogue no: **MA 103**

REAL
Tracks: / Real / Much missed man.
7" Single: Released Nov '82, on Mayfield, Deleted Nov '85. Catalogue no: **MAY 103**

Boatman, Tooter

THUNDER AND LIGHTNIN'
7" EP: Released May '88, on Rockstar (1), Catalogue no: **RSREP 2008**

Bob

CONVENIENCE
Tracks: / Convenience.
12" Single: Released Mar '89, on House of Teeth, Catalogue no: **HOT 12002**
7" Single: Released Mar '89, on House of Teeth, Catalogue no: **HOT 7002**

KIRSTY
Tracks: / Kirsty / Hippy goes fishing, The / Bandwell blues like these.
12" Single: Released May '88, on Sombrero, by Sombrero Records. Catalogue no: **SOMBRERO 2**

WHAT A PERFORMANCE
Tracks: / What a performance / Deary me / Piggery / Memory of a free lunch.
7" Single: Released Oct '87, on Sombrero, by Sombrero Records. Catalogue no: **SOMBRERO 1**

Bob, Bob, Bob And Bob

LOUD, A (EP)
Tracks: / What do they mean? / Firework display / Time to time.
12" Single: Released Sep '88, on 808 Bob, Catalogue no: **808**

Bob & Earl

Biographical details: Bobby Byrd and Earl Nelson met in 1957, when the latter joined Byrd's group, the 'Hollywood Flames'. At the end of that year, with Nelson singing lead, the 'Flames' reached no. 11 on the US charts with *Buzz-Buzz-Buzz*. Between 1957 and 1959 they cut some records as a duo under the billing 'Bob & Earl'; during this period Bob, using his alias Bobby Day, scored a US No. 2 smash with *Rockin' Robin*. In '59 Bobby Byrd was replaced by Bobby Relf and it was this Bob & earl who wrote and recorded the duo's best known song *Harlem Shuffle*, a bouncy dance favourite which only scraped the lower reaches of the US Top 50 in 1963. It failed to chart in the UK at all until 1969, when the single became a surprise British Top 10 hit on re-issue. In the meantime, using the name Jackie Lee, Nelson had scored a No. 14 hit in the States with his mid-Sixties 45 *The Duck*. The above named hits were Bob & Earl's only forays into the pop charts. This American vocal duo have had a long and active career in soul music, but their work has normally been confined to the US soul charts and has not crossed over. (Bob MacDonald).

HARLEM SHUFFLE (OLD GOLD)
Tracks: / Harlem shuffle / Duck, The.
7" Single: Released '82, on Old Gold, by Old Gold Records. Deleted '88. Catalogue no: **OG 9032**

HARLEM SHUFFLE (ORIGINAL)
Tracks: / Harlem shuffle.
7" Single: Released Mar '69, on Island, by Island Records. Deleted '72. Catalogue no: **WIP 6053**

Bob, Ken

IN DANGER
Tracks: / In danger.
12" Single: Released Jun '84, on Dynamic, Catalogue no: **DYN 1215**

Bob & Marcia

Biographical details: The Jamaican vocal duo of Bob Andy and Marcia Griffiths formed in 1969. Andy whose real name was Keith Anderson, had previously been a successful solo hit maker in Jamaica and surrounding countries. The duo recorded a poppy reggae version of Nina Simone's late Sixties plea for racial tolerance and awareness, *Young, Gifted And Black*. In the wake of reggae successes on the British charts by Johnny Nash and Desmond Dekker, the single reached No. 5 in the UK in 1970. The following year they hit No. 11 with a version of Crispian St. Peters' mid-Sixties hit *The Pied Piper*. Shortly afterwards the pair split and resumed solo careers. The prominent presence of strings on Bob & Marcia's hits made them two of the most pop-flavoured reggae singles of the early Seventies. (Bob MacDonald)..

ALWAYS TOGETHER
Tracks: / Always together.
7" Single: Released May '89, on Coxsone, Catalogue no: **UNKNOWN**

PIED PIPER
Tracks: / Pied piper.
7" Single: Released Jun '71, on Trojan, by Trojan Records. Deleted '74. Catalogue no: **TR 7818**

YOUNG, GIFTED AND BLACK
Tracks: / Young, gifted and black.
7" Single: Released Mar '70, on Harry, Deleted '73. Catalogue no: **HJ 6605**
12" Single: Released Jul '83, on Sun Set (reggae), Catalogue no: **SSRD 004**

YOUNG, GIFTED AND BLACK (OLD GOLD)
Tracks: / Young gifted and black / Pied piper.
7" Single: Released Jul '84, on Old Gold, by Old Gold Records. Catalogue no: **OG 9390**
CD 5": Released May '89, on Old Gold, by Old Gold Records. Catalogue no: **OG 6131**

Bob Sleigh

POP LOOK BACH
Tracks: / Pop looks Bach / Freestyle.
7" Single: Released Feb '88, on Enterprizes, Deleted Aug '89. Catalogue no: **109791**

Bob & Vi

KEEP LYING,I LOVE IT
Tracks: / Keep lying I love it / O boy.
7" Single: Released Feb '86, on Vindaloo, by Vindaloo Records. Catalogue no: **UGH 10**

Bobalouis

GO AHEAD
Tracks: / Go ahead / Please please me.
7" Single: Released Jan '81, on WEA, by WEA Records. Deleted Jan '84. Catalogue no: **K18372**

NOT A SECOND CHANCE
Tracks: / Not a second chance / City boys.
7" Single: Released Feb '81, on WEA, by WEA Records. Deleted '84. Catalogue no: **K 18441**

Bobbettes

MR LEE
Tracks: / Mr. Lee / I shot Mr. Lee.
7" Single: Released Jul '82, on Revival, Catalogue no: **REV 6006**

Bobby & Girls Next

NOW WE KNOW IT'S DIANA
Tracks: / Now we know it's Diana / Wedding dub.
7" Single: Released Mar '81, on Hansa, by Hansa Records. Deleted Mar '84. Catalogue no: **K 18495**

Bobby M

LET'S STAY TOGETHER
Tracks: / Let's stay together / Charlie's back beat.
7" Single: Released Jan '83, on Gordy (USA), by Motown Records (UK). Catalogue no: **TMG 1288**
12" Single: Released Jan '83, on Gordy (USA), by Motown Records (UK). Catalogue no: **TMGT 1288**

Bobby Sox

LET IT SWING
Tracks: / Let it swing.
7" Single: Released May '85, on RCA, by BMG Records (UK). Catalogue no: **PB 40127**

WAITING FOR THE MORNING
Tracks: / Waiting for the morning / Working heart.
7" Single: Released Jun '86, on Sonet, by Sonet Records. Catalogue no: **SON 2303**

Bobby'O'

I'M SO HOT FOR YOU
Tracks: / I'm so hot for you / Still hot for you.
7" Single: Released Oct '82, on O, Deleted '85. Catalogue no: **QUE 2**
12" Single: Released Oct '82, on O, Deleted '85. Catalogue no: **QUET 2**
7" Single: Released Sep '84, on BMC Imp, Catalogue no: **BMC 1016**

SHE HAS A WAY
Tracks: / She has a way.
7" Single: Released Sep '84, on BMC Imp, Catalogue no: **BMC 1511**
12" Single: Released Feb '83, on O, Deleted '85. Catalogue no: **QUEL 5**
7" Single: Released Feb '83, on O, Deleted '85. Catalogue no: **QUE 5**

Bobby's Boys

BOBBY CAN'T DANCE
Tracks: / Bobby can't dance / Bobby can't dance(dub) / Bobby can't dance(radio version).
12" Single: Released Aug '86, on Oval, by Oval Records. Catalogue no: **OVALT 34-12**

BOBBY CAN'T DANCE (RE-ISSUE)
Tracks: / Bobby can't dance / No way Jose (King size enigma mix).
7" Single: Released 13 Jun '87, on Oval, by Oval Records. Deleted Jul '88. Catalogue no: **OVAL 101**
12" Single: Released 13 Jun '87, on Oval, by Oval Records. Deleted Jul '88. Catalogue no: **OVAL 101T**

Bobo Zero

CRIME OF EMOTION
7" Single: Released Jun '85, on Safari, by Safari Records. Catalogue no: **SAFE 67**

Boddington, Karen

HOME AND AWAY
Tracks: / Home and away.
7" Single: Released Sep '89, on First Night, by First Night Records. Catalogue no: **SCORE 19**

BoDeans

DREAMS
Tracks: / Dreams / Big thing / Stella.
7" Single: Released 20 Feb '88, on Slash, by London Records. Deleted Oct '88. Catalogue no: **LASH 15**
12" Single: Released 20 Feb '88, on Slash, by London Records. Deleted Oct '88. Catalogue no: **LASHX 15**

Bodines

DECIDE
Tracks: / Decide.
12" Single: Released Mar '89, on Play Hard, by Play Hard Records. Catalogue no: **DEC 18**

GOD BLESS
Tracks: / God bless.
7" Single: Released Sep '85, on Creation, by Creation Records. Catalogue no: **CRE 016**

HEARD IT ALL
Tracks: / Heard it all / William Shatner / Clear.
7" Single: Released Aug '86, on Creation, by Creation Records. Deleted Jul '88. Catalogue no: **CRE 030**
12" Single: Released Aug '86, on Creation, by Creation Records. Deleted Jul '88. Catalogue no: **CRE 030 T**

SKANKIN QUEENS
Tracks: / Skankin queens / 1000 times / My remarkable mind.
7" Single: Released Jul '87, on Pop, by Magnet Records. Deleted Jan '88. Catalogue no: **BOD 2**
12" Single: Released Jul '87, on Pop, by Magnet Records. Deleted Jun '88. Catalogue no: **BODT 2**

SLIP SLIDE
Tracks: / Slip slide / Naming names.
12" Single: Released Sep '87, on Pop, by Magnet Records. Deleted Jun '88. Catalogue no: **BODT 3**
7" Single: Released Sep '87, on Magnet, by WEA Records. Deleted Jan '88. Catalogue no: **BOD 3**

THERESE
Tracks: / Therese (new mix) / Heard it all Pop.
12" Single: Released '87, on Creation, by Creation Records. Deleted '88. Catalogue no: **CRE 028T**
7" Single: Released '87, on Creation, by Creation Records. Deleted '88. Catalogue no: **CRE 028**
7" Single: Released Feb '87, on Pop, by Magnet Records. Deleted Jan '88. Catalogue no: **BOD 1**
12" Single: Released Feb '87, on Pop, by Magnet Records. Deleted Jun '88. Catalogue no: **BODT 1**

Body

MIDDLE OF THE NIGHT
Tracks: / Middle of the night / Middle of the night (inst).
12" Single: Released Feb '88, on MCA, by MCA Records. Catalogue no: **MCAT 1203**
7" Single: Released Feb '88, on MCA, by MCA Records. Catalogue no: **MCA 1203**

Body Heat

NO NO MR. BOOM BOOM
Tracks: / No no Mr. Boom Boom / No no Mr. Boom Boom (version).
7" Single: Released Jul '87, on Diamond, by Revolver Records. Catalogue no: **DMR 1**
12" Single: Released Jul '87, on Diamond, by Revolver Records. Catalogue no: **DMRT 1**

Body Music Mokili

BODY MUSIC
Tracks: / Body music / Motema.
7" Single: Released Oct '82, on Island, by Island Records. Catalogue no: **WIP 6822**
12" Single: Released Oct '82, on Island, by Island Records. Catalogue no: **12WIP 6822**

Bodysnatchers

EASY LIFE
Tracks: / Easy life / Too experienced.
7" Single: Released '80, on Two-Tone, by Chrysalis Records. Catalogue no: **CHS TT 12**

LET'S DO ROCK STEADY
Tracks: / Let's do rock steady / Ruder than you.
7" Single: Released Mar '80, on Two-Tone, by Chrysalis Records. Deleted '85. Catalogue no: **CHS TT 9**

Boeing Boeing

UP SHE RISES
Tracks: / Up she rises / Ocean motion.
7" Single: Released Dec '82, on Mont, by Mont Music Records. Catalogue no: **MM 104**

Bofill, Angela

Biographical details: The source of Angela's music versatility comes in varying degrees from her heritage (her father was French-Cuban and her mother Puerto Rican), her superior vocal ability (a three octave range that has been enhanced, she says, by her health food diet), and her musical influences. Her cultural backgrounds account for much of the flavour of her music but her technique comes from serious studying. After graduating Hunter College High School, Angie went on to refine her talents at the Manhattan School of Music, and then at Hartford Conservatory. Compressing the events that followed, Bofill was introduced to Arista. Accolades and awards followed the release of *Angie* and haven't stopped. (Arista Records, Feb 1983).

BREAK IT TO ME GENTLY
Tracks: / Break it to me gently / Time to say goodbye.
12" Single: Released '82, on Arista, by BMG Records (UK). Deleted '87. Catalogue no: **ARIST 12463**
7" Single: Released '82, on Arista, by BMG Records (UK). Deleted '87. Catalogue no: **ARIST 463**

HOLDING ON TO LOVE
Tracks: / Holding on to love.
7" Single: Released '82, on Arista, by BMG Records (UK). Deleted '87. Catalogue no: **ARIST 433**

HOLDING OUT FOR LOVE
Tracks: / Holding out for love / Only love.
7" Single: Released Jan '82, on Arista, by BMG Records (UK). Deleted Jan '85. Catalogue no: **ARIST 433**

TOO TOUGH (SINGLE)
Tracks: / Too tough / Rainbow inside my heart.
7" Single: Released Feb '83, on Arista, by BMG Records (UK). Catalogue no: **ARIST 515**
12" Single: Released Feb '83, on Arista, by BMG Records (UK). Catalogue no: **ARIST 12 515**

Bogaz

I'VE GOT LOVE
Tracks: / I've got love.

7" Single: Released Oct '83, on AGR, Deleted '87. Catalogue no: **AGR 2**
12" Single: Released Oct '83, on AGR, Deleted '87. Catalogue no: **12 AGR 2**

Bogdan

OH EDDIE
Tracks: / Oh Eddie / Reet petite.
7" Single: Released Jul '81, on Black Label (USA), by House Of America Records (USA). Catalogue no: **GB 003**

WHO DO YOU THINK YOU ARE?
Tracks: / Who do you think you are.
7" Single: Released Nov '81, on Brilliant, by Brilliant Records. Catalogue no: **HIT 1**

Bogle, Eric

Biographical details: Bogle, Eric. The singer-songwriter, born in 1944 in Scotland, emigrated to Australia in 1969, returning to the UK as a performer in 1982 with partner/multi-instrumentalist John Munro; his albums are highly praised and his songs have been covered by June Tabor, the Clancy Brothers, the Furies and others: the best-known is *The Band Played Waltzing Matilda*, written in 1972 after watching a military parade. Donald Clarke, 24 August 1988..

SINGING THE SPIRIT HOME (SINGLE)
Tracks: / Singing the spirit home / Australian through and through.
7" Single: Released Apr '87, on Sonet, by Sonet Records. Catalogue no: **SON 2320**

Bogshed

EXCELLENT GIRL
Tracks: / Excellent girl.
7" Single: Released Jul '87, on Shellfish, Catalogue no: **SHELF 6**

LET THEM EAT BOGSHED
Tracks: / Let them eat Bogshed.
12" Single: Released Sep '85, on Vinyl Drip, by Vinyl Drip Records. Catalogue no: **DRIP 2**

MORNING SIR
Tracks: / Morning sir.
7" Single: Released May '86, on Shellfish, Catalogue no: **SHELF 1**

TRIED AND TESTED PUBLIC SPEAKER (THE PEEL SESSION)
Tracks: / Champion love shoes / Little grafter / Morning Sir / Fastest legs / Adventure of dog / Tried and tested public speaker.
12" Single: Released Jan '87, on Shellfish, Catalogue no: **SHELF 3**

Bohannon, (Hamilton)

Biographical details: American singer and drummer Hamilton Bonahhon worked as an in-house drummer for Motown before beginning a string of solo disc hits in the mid-70's. In Britain these records started crossing over to the pop charts. He had four UK hit singles in 1975, by far the biggest being the No 6 placing of Disco Stomp. This was the only one to gain substantial airplay, for his music had its main appeal in the clubs, where the skills of a soul percussionist were perfectly suited to the disco boom. Let's Start The Dance and Let's Start To Dance Again provided Bohannon with two more minor British hits, in 1978 and 1982 respectively. He was obviously well respected in the UK: merely four months after the '75 success of Disco Stomp a British group called Hello "borrowed" the record's main hook and riff for their Top Ten single New York Groove. (Bob MacDonald, 1984.).

BOHANNON MIX
Tracks: / Bohannon mix / Disco stomp / South African man.
12" Single: Released Jan '84, on Passion, by Skratch Records. Catalogue no: **PASH 17(12)**

DISCO STOMP
Tracks: / Disco stomp.
7" Single: Released May '75, on Brunswick, by Decca Records. Deleted '78. Catalogue no: **BR 19**

DISCO STOMP (OLD GOLD CD SINGLE)
Tracks: / Disco stomp / Foot stompin' music / South African man.
CD 5": Released Nov '88, on Old Gold, by Old Gold Records. Catalogue no: **OG 6110**

FOOT STOMPIN' MUSIC
Tracks: / Foot stompin' music.
7" Single: Released Jul '75, on Brunswick, by Decca Records. Deleted '78. Catalogue no: **BR 21**

HAPPY FEELING
Tracks: / Happy feeling.
7" Single: Released Sep '75, on Brunswick, by Decca Records. Deleted '78. Catalogue no: **BR 24**

LET'S START THE DANCE
Tracks: / Let's start the dance.
12" Single: Released Jun '83, on Compleat (USA), by Compleat Entertainment Corp.(USA). Deleted '85. Catalogue no: **CLTL 1**
7" Single: Released Aug '78, on Mercury, by Phonogram Ltd. Deleted '81. Catalogue no: **6167 700**
7" Single: Released Jun '83, on Compleat (USA), by Compleat Entertainment Corp.(USA). Deleted '85. Catalogue no: **CLT 1**

LET'S START TO DANCE AGAIN (2)
Tracks: / Let's start to dance again.
12" Single: Released Jul '83, on London-American, Catalogue no: **HLX 10582**
7" Single: Released Jul '83, on London Records, by London Records. Catalogue no: **HL 10582**

LET'S START TO DANCE AGAIN (RAP)
Tracks: / Let's start to dance again(rap) / Let's start to dance again(party version).
12" Single: Released Jul '86, on Domino, by Domino Records. Catalogue no: **DOM T3**

SOUTH AFRICAN MAN
Tracks: / South African man.
7" Single: Released Feb '75, on Brunswick, by Decca Records. Deleted '78. Catalogue no: **BR 16**

WAKE UP
Tracks: / Wake up / Enjoy your day.
7" Single: Released Sep '83, on Compleat (USA), by Compleat Entertainment Corp.(USA). Deleted '85. Catalogue no: **CLT 2**
12" Single: Released Sep '83, on Compleat (USA), by Compleat Entertainment Corp.(USA). Deleted '85. Catalogue no: **CLTL 2**

Bohard

MAYBE TOMORROW
Tracks: / Maybe tomorrow / So in love are we.
12" Single: Released Apr '87, on Seahorse, Catalogue no: **12SH 2**
7" Single: Released Jan '82, on Atlantic, by WEA Records. Catalogue no: **K 11703**

QUITE A FEELING
Tracks: / Quite a feeling / Heaven.
12" Single: Released Feb '87, on Seahorse, Catalogue no: **12SH 1**
7" Single: Released Feb '87, on Seahorse, Catalogue no: **SH 1**

Bohn Legion

MAY IN BERLIN
Tracks: / May in Berlin.
7" Single: Released '88, on Stranded, by Stranded Records. Catalogue no: **XLNT 004**

Boiling Point

LET'S GET FUNKTIFIED
Tracks: / Let's get funktified.
7" Single: Released May '78, on Bang, Deleted '81. Catalogue no: **BANG 1312**

Boizee

WINTER IS
Tracks: / Winter is.
7" Single: Released Nov '82, on State, by State Records. Catalogue no: **STAT 117**

Bokoor

HIP HIP HOP
Tracks: / Hip hip hop.
12" Single: Released Dec '82, on Keynote, Catalogue no: **KEY 1**

Bolan, Marc

Biographical details: Born Mark Feld in London, he changed his name to Marc Bolan when releasing his first single in late 1965. Before then he had been a passionate mod, but now he was joining the rising flower power movement. Shortly after this first 45, The Wizard, he joined a group called John's Children who gained cult acceptance with their single, Desdemona, with Bolan as vocalist and guitarist. Then he joined forces with percussionist Steve Peregrine Took to form the duo Tyrannosaurus Rex. Their brand of acoustic folk rock, full of lines about flowers, magic and Tolkienesque mythology, featuring the distinctly tremulous voice of Bolan, made them firm underground favourites in the Britain of the late 60's. They chalked up three small UK hit singles with Debora, One Inch Rock and King Of The Rumbling Spires. But it was the titles of their two Top Twenty LPs that best sum up their style: My People Were Fair And Had Sky In Their Hair But Now They're Content To Wear Stars On Their Brows and Unicorn. In 1970 Took was replaced by Mickey Finn, with whom Bolan recorded the British Top Thirty album A Beard Of Stars, on which he began to make a transition from acoustic to electric guitar. The electrification process was rapidly accelerated late in 1970 when he shortened the name to T. Rex. At the end of the year the pair suddenly scored a smash No 2 single in the UK with Ride A White Swan, an uptempo but understated electric folk number. Delighted with his newfound stardom, Bolan added two new members to T. Rex, drummer Bill Legend and bassist Steve Currie, and decided to aim directly at the pop singles market. The first record by the new line-up was to be the biggest single of Bolan's career: Hot Love was No 1 in Britain for six weeks. Its ultra-commercial feel was heightened by its extended "La la la" fade-out, an idea inspired by the Beatles' Hey Jude. Marc Bolan became a teenybopper hero and, following the break-up of the Beatles, Britain's first major new pop star of the early 70's. The peak of his success was a 15-month period from March '71 to June '72. During this time he scored four UK No 1 singles -- Hot Love, Get It On, Telegram Sam and Metal Guru -- plus three British No 1 albums -- Electric Warrior, the Bolan Boogie compilation and a Tyrannosaurus doublepack reissue. This winning streak also brought Bolan the only US Top Forty hit of his career: Get It On was retitled Bang A Gong and reached No 10. By the time of Metal Guru the T. Rex sound had become commercial powerpop and the Tyrannosaurus style had completely disappeared. Bolan had been transformed from a cult favourite of the psychedelic era into a pop idol of the teenybop era. The fickleness of the market to which he now appealed is demonstrated by the fact that, outside the aforementioned 15-month period, he never scored a No 1 on either the singles or album charts in the UK. From late '72 his young fans began deserting him in favour of either the fresher, harder sound of Slade or the American teen appeal of the Osmonds or David Cassidy. Bolan's final Top Ten single was The Groover in summer '73. Having achieved 11 consecutive Top Tenners he never got there again. The occasional bright moment -- such as 1976's I Love To Boogie (No 13) -- showed that he remained a much-loved figure despite the now erratic quality of his recording career. Indeed his extrovert, publicity-seeking personality ensured him of continuous press coverage, whether the records were selling or not. In 1977 he proclaimed himself the forefather of the burgeoning punk rock movement. Many of Britain's New Wave bands cited him as a major influence and -- now a cult hero once more -- he was given his own weekly TV pop show, while at the same time planning a chart comeback. But it was not to be: while the television show was still running he was killed, at the age of 30. On early September morning in 1977 the Mini car driven by his girlfriend, Gloria Jones, veered off the road on a dangerous London bend and crashed into a tree. Jones survived her injuries but passenger Bolan was dead. One of the mourners at his funeral was his long-time friend David Bowie. This was a fitting tribute because, like Bowie, Bolan was one of the most influential stars of the 70's. Bolan started the glam rock movement, with many others capitalised upon. He was one of the most charismatic and engaging figures in the history of British pop. The memory of his entertaining music and likeable personality has assured him of one of the most loyal posthumous fan followings of any artist. (Bob MacDonald, 1984.)
Bolan, Marc. The pop singer and songwriter was born Marc Feld in London in 1947. He pursued a pop career as Toby Tyler, then Marc Bowland on Decca, then Marc Bolan. He joined John's Children in 1967, wrote their mini-hit 'Desdemonia', banned by the BBC. He formed an acoustic duo Tyrannosaurus Rex with percussionist Steve Peregrine-Took (1949-80); his hippie period featured distinctive, quavery vocals, fairy stories, etc. Took left, Bolan went electric and formed band T.Rex: with nonsense lyrics and relentless thumping he held the teenybopper audience for a couple of years in the early '70s, hysteria captured by Ringo Starr in semi-documentary film *Born To Boogie*. He faded; his TV series 'Marc' was a showcase for emerging punk bands and they later covered his songs, though in retrospect it seems they should have been opposed to everything he stood for. He revamped his band including girlfriend Gloria Jones, made workmanlike album *Dandy In The Underworld* and was pursuing a comeback when his car hit a tree near Putney Common in 1977.
See also listings for T . Rex (Donald Clarke, August 1988.)

CAT BLACK
Tracks: / Cat black / Jasper C. Debussy.
7" Single: Released Nov '81, on Cherry Red, by Cherry Red Records. Deleted '87. Catalogue no: **CHERRY 32**

CHRISTMAS BOP
Tracks: / Christmas bop.
7" Single: Released Dec '82, on Marc, Catalogue no: **S BOLAN 12**

DEEP SUMMER
Tracks: / Deep summer.
7" Single: Released Jul '82, on Marc On Wax, Catalogue no: **RAP 2**

LIFE'S A GAS
Tracks: / Life's a gas.
12" Single: Released Jun '82, on Marc On Wax, Catalogue no: **RAP 1**

MARC BOLAN: INTERVIEW PICTURE DISC COLLECTION
7" Set: Released Apr '88, on Baktabak, by Baktabak Records. Catalogue no: **BAKPAK 1006**

MEGAREX 1
Tracks: / Megarex 1 / Chariot choogie / Life's an elevator / Megarex 2 / Tame my tiger / Chrome sitar / Solid baby.
12" Single: Released Apr '85, on Marc On Wax, Catalogue no: **12TANX 1**
7" Pic: Released Apr '85, on Marc On Wax, Catalogue no: **PTANX 1**
7" Single: Released Apr '85, on Marc On Wax, Catalogue no: **TANX 1**

MELLOW LOVE
Tracks: / Mellow love / Foxy boy / Lunacy's back / Rock me.
7" Single: Released Feb '82, on Marc On Wax, Catalogue no: **SBOLAN 13**
12" Single: Released Feb '82, on Marc On Wax, Catalogue no: **BOLAN 13**

SAILOR OF THE HIGHWAY
Tracks: / Sailor of the highway.
7" Single: Released Jun '84, on Dakota, Catalogue no: **BUG 99**

SING ME A SONG
Tracks: / Sing me a song / Endless sleep / Lilac hand of menthol dan.
7" Single: Released Mar '81, on Rarn, Catalogue no: **MBFS 001**
12" Single: Released Jul '82, on Rarn, Catalogue no: **MBFS 001**

SUNKEN RAGS
Tracks: / Sunken rags.
7" Single: Released Jul '85, on Marc On Wax, Catalogue no: **TANX 2**
12" Single: Released Jul '85, on Marc On Wax, Catalogue no: **12TANX 2**

THINK ZINC
Tracks: / Think zinc.
7" Single: Released Jun '83, on Marc On Wax, Catalogue no: **SBOLAN 14**
12" Single: Released Jun '83, on Marc On Wax, Catalogue no: **SBOLAN 12EP**
7" Pic: Released Jun '83, on Marc On Wax, Catalogue no: **SBOLAN 14PD**

WIZARD
Tracks: / Wizard.
7" Single: Released Apr '82, on Cherry Red, by Cherry Red Records. Deleted '87. Catalogue no: **CHERRY 39**

YOU SCARE ME TO DEATH
Tracks: / You scare me to death / Cat black / Mustang ford / Hippy gumbo / Perfumed garden of Gulliver Smith, The.
CD 5": Released Jul '89, on Cherry Red, by Cherry Red Records. Catalogue no: **CDCHERRY 29**
7" Single: Released Aug '81, on Cherry Red, by Cherry Red Records. Catalogue no: **CHERRY 29**

Bollock Brothers

ACT BECAME REAL, THE
Tracks: / Act became real, The.
7" Single: Released Mar '81, on McDonald Brothers, Catalogue no: **BOLL 2**

BUNKER
Tracks: / Bunker.
7" Single: Released Apr '83, on Charly, by Charly Records. Catalogue no: **BOLL 4**

DRAC'S BACK
Tracks: / Drac's back / Horror movies.
7" Single: Released Apr '86, on Charly, by Charly Records. Deleted '87. Catalogue no: **BOLL 6**
12" Single: Released Apr '86, on Charly, by Charly Records. Catalogue no: **BOLL 6T**

HARLEY DAVIDSON
Tracks: / Harley Davidson.
12" Single: Released Sep '86, on Play It Again Sam(Belgium), by Play It Again Sam (Belgium). Catalogue no: **BIAS 036**

HORROR MOVIES
Tracks: / Horror movies / Imagine.
7" Single: Released Jan '83, on Charly, by Charly Records. Deleted '87. Catalogue no: **BOLL 5**

PRINCE AND THE SHOWGIRL
Tracks: / Prince and the showgirl.
12" Single: Released Aug '84, on Disc(Brussels), Catalogue no: **DID 127700**

ROCK AND ROLL 2001
Tracks: / Rock and roll 2001.
12" Single: Released Sep '82, on Charly, by Charly Records. Deleted '87. Catalogue no: **BOLL 3T**

SLOW REMOVAL OF VINCENT VAN GOGH'S LEFT EAR
Tracks: / Slow removal of Vincent Van Gogh's left ear.
7" Single: Released Sep '82, on Charly, by Charly Records. Deleted '87. Catalogue no: **BOLL 3**

Bolo, Yami

LOVING YOU
Tracks: / Loving you.
7" Single: Released Oct '88, on Skengdon, Catalogue no: **SKDL 084**

POVERTY & BRUTALITY
Tracks: / Poverty & brutality.
7" Single: Released May '89, on UNKNOWN, Catalogue no: **UNKNOWN**

Bolshoi

AWAY
Tracks: / Away.
12" Single: Released Mar '86, on Beggars Banquet, by Beggars Banquet Records. Catalogue no: **BEG 158T**
7" Single: Released Mar '86, on Beggars Banquet, by Beggars Banquet Records. Catalogue no: **BEG 158**

AWAY II
Tracks: / Black black black / Away.
7" Single: Released Jan '87, on Beggars Banquet, by Beggars Banquet Records. Catalogue no: **BEG 180**
12" Single: Released Jan '87, on Beggars Banquet, by Beggars Banquet Records. Catalogue no: **BEG 180T**

BOOKS ON THE BONFIRE
Tracks: / Books on the bonfire / Boss / Funny thing, A.
7" Single: Released Aug '86, on Beggars Banquet, by Beggars Banquet Records. Deleted Jun '87. Catalogue no: **BEG 170**
12" Single: Released Aug '86, on Beggars Banquet, by Beggars Banquet Records. Catalogue no: **BEG 170T**

HAPPY BOY
Tracks: / Happy boy.
7" Single: Released Oct '85, on Situation 2, by Beggars Banquet Records. Catalogue no: **SIT 40**
12" Single: Released Oct '85, on Situation 2, by Beggars Banquet Records. Catalogue no: **SIT 40T**

PLEASE
Tracks: / Please / West of London town.
12" Single: Released May '87, on Beggars Banquet, by Beggars Banquet Records. Catalogue no: **BEG 189T**
7" Single: Released May '87, on Beggars Banquet, by Beggars Banquet Records. Catalogue no: **BEG 189**

SOB STORY
Tracks: / Sob story / Port of Amsterdam / Cross town traffic.
7" Single: Released Mar '85, on Situation 2, by Beggars Banquet Records. Catalogue no: **SIT 38**
12" Single: Released Mar '85, on Situation 2, by Beggars Banquet Records. Catalogue no: **SIT 38T**

SUNDAY MORNING
Tracks: / Sunday morning / Foxes / Musak (*= Extra track on 12" only.).
7" Single: Released Oct '86, on Beggars Banquet, by Beggars Banquet Records. Deleted Jun '87. Catalogue no: **BEG 175**
12" Single: Released Oct '86, on Beggars Banquet, by Beggars Banquet Records. Deleted Jul '88. Catalogue no: **BEG 175TD**
12" Single: Released Oct '86, on Beggars Banquet, by Beggars Banquet Records. Catalogue no: **BEG 175T**

T.V. MAN
Tracks: / T.V. man / Strawberries and cream / I'm depressed (we all die) (Extra track available on 12" version only).
Note: * Extra track on 12" version only.
7" Single: Released Aug '87, on Beggars Banquet, by Beggars Banquet Records. Catalogue no: **BEG 197**
12" Single: Released Aug '87, on Beggars Banquet, by Beggars Banquet Records. Catalogue no: **BEG 197T**

Bolt Thrower

PEEL SESSIONS:BOLT THROWER
Tracks: / Forgotton existence / Attack in the aftermath / Psychological warefare / In battle there is no law.
12" Single: Released Oct '88, on Strange Fruit, by Strange Fruit Records. Catalogue no: **SFPS 056**

Bolton, Michael

DOCK OF THE BAY
Tracks: / (Sittin' on) the dock of the bay.
7" Single: Released Apr '88, on CBS, by CBS Records. Deleted Jan '89. Catalogue no: **651 387 7**
12" Single: Released Apr '88, on CBS, by CBS Records. Deleted Jan '89. Catalogue no: **651 387 8**
CD 5": Released Apr '88, on CBS, by CBS Records. Deleted Jan '89. Catalogue no: **651 387-2**

SOUL PROVIDER (SINGLE)
Tracks: / Soul provider (Only on 7" and CD single.) / Hunger, The / Soul provider (12" remix) (Only on 12" and CD single.) / Soul provider (7" edit) (Only on 12" single.) / (Sittin' on) the dock of the bay (Only on 12" and CD single.).
7" Single: Released Jul '89, on CBS, by CBS Records. Catalogue no: **654946 7**
CD 5": Released Jul '89, on CBS, by CBS Records. Catalogue no: **654946 2**
12" Single: Released Jul '89, on CBS, by CBS Records. Catalogue no: **654946 8**

THAT'S WHAT LOVE IS ALL ABOUT
Tracks: / That's what love is all about / Take a look at my face / Fool's game* (* on 12" & CD single only) / Can't hold on, can't let go (* on 12" & CD single only).
7" Single: Released '88, on CBS, by CBS Records. Deleted 17 Apr '89. Catalogue no: **651059 0**
CD 5": Released 25 Jul '88, on CBS, by CBS Records. Deleted Jan '89. Catalogue no: **651059 2**
7" Single: Released Feb '88, on CBS, by CBS Records. Deleted Jan '89. Catalogue no: **651059 7**
12" Single: Released 25 Jul '88, on CBS, by CBS Records. Deleted Jan '89. Catalogue no: **651059 8**

Bomb Party

I WANNA BE ABUSED
Tracks: / I wanna be abused.
7" Single: Released Dec '87, on Upright, by Upright Records. Catalogue no: **WPCS 001**

LIFE'S A BITCH
Tracks: / Life's a bitch.
7" Single: Released Dec '85, on Abstract, by Abstract Sounds. Catalogue no: **ABS 038**

NEW MESSIAH
Tracks: / New messiah.
7" EP: Released Jul '85, on Abstract, by Abstract Sounds. Catalogue no: **12 ABS 035**

PRETTY FACE
Tracks: / Pretty face.
7" Single: Released Dec '87, on Workers Playtime, by Upright Records. Catalogue no: **WP CF 001**

RAY GUN
Tracks: / Ray gun / Harry was a babysitter / Get lost my love / Knocking.
7" EP: Released May '85, on Abstract, by Abstract Sounds. Catalogue no: **12 ABS 032**

SUGAR SUGAR
Tracks: / Sugar sugar.
7" Single: Released Oct '88, on Normal, by Jungle Records. Deleted '89. Catalogue no: **NORMAL 93**
CD 5": Released Oct '88, on Normal, by Jungle Records. Deleted '89. Catalogue no: **NORMAL 93 CD**
12" Single: Released Oct '88, on Normal, by Jungle Records. Catalogue no: **NORMAL 93T**

WHY DON'T YOU BEHAVE
Tracks: / Why don't you behave.
7" Single: Released 31 Jul '89, on Normal, by Jungle Records. Catalogue no: **NORMAL 103S**

Bomb The Bass

BEAT DIS
Tracks: / Beat dis.
12" Single: Released Jan '88, on Misteron, Catalogue no: **DOOD 12001**
12" Single: Released Jan '88, on Misteron, Catalogue no: **DOODR 12001**

DON'T MAKE ME WAIT
Tracks: / Don't make me wait / Megablast.
7" Single: Released Aug '88, on Rhythm King, by Mute Records. Catalogue no: **DOOD 2**
12" Single: Released Aug '88, on Rhythm King, by Mute Records. Catalogue no: **DOOD 122**

I CAN'T STOP
Tracks: / I can't stop.
7" Single: Released Jun '89, on Rhythm King, by Mute Records. Catalogue no: **DOOD 004**
12" Single: Released Jun '89, on Rhythm King, by Mute Records. Catalogue no: **DOOD 12004**

MEGABLAST
Tracks: / Megablast.
7" Single: Released Apr '88, on Rhythm King, by Mute Records. Catalogue no: **DOOD 002**
12" Single: Released Apr '88, on Rhythm King, by Mute Records. Catalogue no: **DOOD 12002**

SAY A LITTLE PRAYER
Tracks: / I say a little prayer.
7" Single: Released Nov '88, on Rhythm King, by Mute Records. Catalogue no: **DOOD 3**
12" Single: Released Nov '88, on Rhythm King, by Mute Records. Catalogue no: **DOOD 123**

Bombay

BREAKING THE RULES
Tracks: / Breaking the rules.
12" Single: Released Apr '84, on Music For Nations, by Music For Nations Records. Catalogue no: **YUMT 105**

Bombers

(EVERYBODY) GET DANCIN'
Tracks: / (Everybody) get dancin'.
7" Single: Released May '79, on Flamingo, by Airwave Records (USA). Deleted '82. Catalogue no: **FM 1**

LET'S DANCE
Tracks: / Let's dance.
7" Single: Released Aug '79, on Flamingo, by Airwave Records (USA). Deleted '82. Catalogue no: **FM 4**

Bon Jovi

BAD MEDICINE
Tracks: / Bad medicine / 99 in the shade / Lay your hands on me (Only on 12" and CD single.).
12" Single: Released Sep '88, on Vertigo, by Phonogram Ltd. Deleted 31 May '89. Catalogue no: **JOV 312**
7" Single: Released Sep '88, on Vertigo, by Phonogram Ltd. Deleted 31 May '89. Catalogue no: **JOVS 3**
CD 5": Released Sep '88, on Vertigo, by Phonogram Ltd. Catalogue no: **JOVCD 3**
7" Single: Released Sep '88, on Vertigo, by Phonogram Ltd. Deleted 31 May '89. Catalogue no: **JOV 3**
12" Single: Released Sep '88, on Vertigo, by Phonogram Ltd. Deleted 31 Jul '89. Catalogue no: **JOVR 312**

BON JOVI: INTERVIEW PICTURE DISC COLLECTION
7" Set: Released Apr '88, on Baktabak, by Baktabak Records. Catalogue no: **BAKPAK 1007**

BORDERLINE
Tracks: / Borderline.
12" Single: Released Dec '88, on Mercury (Japan), Catalogue no: **15 PP56**

BORN TO BE MY BABY
Tracks: / Born to be my baby / Love for sale / Wanted dead or alive (Only on 12" version.) / Runaway (Only on CD single.) / Livin' on a prayer (Only on CD single.) / Wanted dead or alive (live) (Only on JOVR 412 12" version.).
12" Single: Released Nov '88, on Vertigo, by Phonogram Ltd. Deleted 31 May '89. Catalogue no: **JOV 412**
7" Single: Released Nov '88, on Vertigo, by Phonogram Ltd. Deleted 31 Jul '89. Catalogue no: **JOV 4**
CD 5": Released Nov '88, on Vertigo, by Phonogram Ltd. Catalogue no: **JOVCD 4**
7" Single: Released Dec '88, on Vertigo, by Phonogram Ltd. Deleted 31 May '89. Catalogue no: **JOVS 4**
12" Single: Released Nov '88, on Vertigo, by Phonogram Ltd. Deleted 31 May '89. Catalogue no: **JOVR 412**

BURNING FOR LOVE
Tracks: / Burning for love.
12" Single: Released Dec '88, on Mercury (Japan), Catalogue no: **15 PP44**

HARDEST PART IS THE NIGHT
Tracks: / Hardest part is the night.
12" Single: Released Aug '85, on Vertigo, by Phonogram Ltd. Deleted Jul '87. Catalogue no: **VERXR 22**
7" Single: Released Aug '85, on Vertigo, by Phonogram Ltd. Deleted '88. Catalogue no: **VER 22**

I'LL BE THERE FOR YOU
Tracks: / I'll be there for you / Homebound train / Wild in the streets (live) (Only on 12" single.) / Borderline (on CD single only.) / Edge of a broken heart (Available on CD only).
7" Single: Released Apr '89, on Vertigo, by Phonogram Ltd. Deleted 31 Jul '89. Catalogue no: **JOV 5**
12" Single: Released Apr '89, on Vertigo, by Phonogram Ltd. Catalogue no: **JOVR 512**
12" Single: Released Apr '89, on Vertigo, by Phonogram Ltd. Deleted 31 Jul '89. Catalogue no: **JOV 512**
7" Single: Released Apr '89, on Vertigo, by Phonogram Ltd. Deleted 31 Jul '89. Catalogue no: **JOVPB 85**
CD 5": Released Apr '89, on Vertigo, by Phonogram Ltd. Deleted Oct '89. Catalogue no: **JOVCD 5**
Cassingle: Released May '89, on Vertigo, by Phonogram Ltd. Catalogue no: **872 564 4**

IN AND OUT OF LOVE
Tracks: / In and out of love / Roulette.
12" Single: Released May '85, on Vertigo, by Phonogram Ltd. Deleted May '88. Catalogue no: **VERX 19**

LAY YOUR HANDS ON ME
Tracks: / Lay your hands on me / Bad medicine.
CD 5": Released Jul '89, on Vertigo, by Phonogram Ltd. Catalogue no: **JOVCD 6**
10" single: Released Jul '89, on Vertigo, by Phonogram Ltd. Catalogue no: **JOVP 610**
7" Single: Released Jul '89, on Vertigo, by Phonogram Ltd. Catalogue no: **JOVS 662**

LIVE TOUR EP: BON JOVI
Tracks: / Breakout / Runaway / Tokyo road / Wanted dead or alive.
Note: Four-track live tour EP, featuring three tracks recorded in Japan -- Breakout, Runaway and Tokyo Road -- and a version of Wanted DOA recorded in Detroit. Total 26 minutes on two 7" records in a gatefold sleeve.
7" EP: Released Oct '87, on Mercury (Australia), Catalogue no: **8888201**
7" Set: Released Oct '87, on Mercury (Australia), Catalogue no: **8888207**

LIVIN' ON A PRAYER
Tracks: / Livin' on a prayer / Wild in the streets / Edge of a broken heart* (*=Extra track on 12" only) / Livin' on a prayer(remix) (Extra track on 12"(VERXR 28) only).
Note: (Cat. No. 8882311 - 3 track 12" in full coulour picture sleeve, featuring two singles 'Living On A Prayer' (now deleted in the U.K.) and 'You Give Love A Bad Name' plus 'Edge Of A Broken Heart' (previously unreleased studio track).
12" Single: Released Nov '87, on Mercury (Germany), Catalogue no: **888 2311**
7" Single: Released Oct '86, on Vertigo, by Phonogram Ltd. Deleted Jul '87. Catalogue no: **VER 28**
12" Single: Released Oct '86, on Vertigo, by Phonogram Ltd. Deleted Jul '87. Catalogue no: **VERX 28**
12" Single: Released Oct '86, on Vertigo, by Phonogram Ltd. Catalogue no: **VERXR 28**

NEVER SAY GOODBYE
Tracks: / Never say goodbye / Raise your hands.
7" Single: Released Aug '87, on Vertigo, by Phonogram Ltd. Catalogue no: **JOVI 2**
12" Single: Released Aug '87, on Vertigo, by Phonogram Ltd. Catalogue no: **JOVI 212**

SHE DOESN'T KNOW ME
Tracks: / She doesn't know me / Breakout.
12" Single: Released May '84, on Vertigo, by Phonogram Ltd. Catalogue no: **VERX 11**
7" Single: Released May '84, on Vertigo, by Phonogram Ltd. Catalogue no: **VER 11**

WANTED DEAD OR ALIVE
Tracks: / Wanted dead or alive / Shot through the heart / Social Disease (Extra track on 12" version only.) / Silent night (Extra track in doublepack.) / Get ready (Extra track in doublepack.).
7" Set: Released Mar '87, on Mercury, by Phonogram Ltd. Catalogue no: **JOVR 112**
12" Single: Released Mar '87, on Mercury, by Phonogram Ltd. Catalogue no: **JOV 112**
7" Single: Released Mar '87, on Mercury, by Phonogram Ltd. Catalogue no: **JOV 1**

YOU GIVE LOVE A BAD NAME
Tracks: / You give love a bad name / Let it rock / Borderline (* =Extra track on 12" only).
7" Single: Released Jul '86, on Vertigo, by Phonogram Ltd. Deleted Jul '87. Catalogue no: **VER 26**
12" Single: Released Jul '86, on Vertigo, by Phonogram Ltd. Deleted Jul '87. Catalogue no: **VERX 26**

Bon Rock

B BOY
Tracks: / B boy / It's alright.
12" Single: Released Feb '84, on Beau-Jolly, Deleted '86. Catalogue no: **12 BJ 1002**

Bona-Riah

HOUSE OF THE RISING SUN, THE
Tracks: / House of the rising sun.
12" Single: Released 21 Nov '87, on Rise, Catalogue no: **RISET 8**

Bond

BOYS TOYS
Tracks: / Boys toys / Do you really want to hide.
12" Single: Released Apr '87, on Arista, by BMG Records (UK). Catalogue no: **RIST 9**
7" Single: Released Apr '87, on Arista, by BMG Records (UK). Catalogue no: **RIS 9**

Bond, Eddie

I GOT A WOMAN
7" EP: Released May '88, on Rockstar (1), Catalogue no: **RSREP 2002**

Bond, James (Ska)

WRITE TO PASTOR
Tracks: / Write to pastor.
12" Single: Released Jul '89, on Jetstar, by Jetstar Records. Catalogue no: **ST 10012**

Bond, Joyce

DO THE TEASY
Tracks: / Do the teasy / Dreaming of a little island.
12" Single: Released Mar '89, on Orbitone, by Orbitone Records. Catalogue no: **OR 1236**
7" Single: Released Mar '89, on Orbitone, by Orbitone Records. Catalogue no: **OR 736**

HOW SWEET IT IS TO BE LOVED BY YOU
Tracks: / How sweet it is to be loved by you.
7" Single: Released Dec '88, on Orbitone, by Orbitone Records. Catalogue no: **OR 734**
12" Single: Released Dec '88, on Orbitone, by Orbitone Records. Catalogue no: **OR 1234**

NOTHING CAN STOP ME LOVING YOU
Tracks: / Nothing can stop me loving you.
12" Single: Released Apr '88, on Orbitone, by Orbitone Records. Catalogue no: **OR 1228**
7" Single: Released May '88, on Orbitone, by Orbitone Records. Catalogue no: **OR 728**

TEARS FROM MY EYES
7" Single: Released Sep '87, on Orbitone, by Orbitone Records. Catalogue no: **OR 723**
12" Single: Released Sep '87, on Orbitone, by Orbitone Records. Catalogue no: **OR 1223**

Bond, Michael

BIGGEST HIT OF ALL
Tracks: / Biggest hit of all / I made it after all.
7" Single: Released Mar '82, on Page One, by Page One Records. Deleted '85. Catalogue no: **POR 003**

Bond, Ronnie

IT'S WRITTEN ON YOUR BODY
Tracks: / It's written on your body.
7" Single: Released May '80, on Mercury, by Phonogram Ltd. Deleted '83. Catalogue no: **MER 13**

LIVE AND LET LIVE
Tracks: / Live and let live / Ball and chain.
7" Single: Released Nov '82, on Polydor, by Polydor Ltd. Deleted Nov '85. Catalogue no: **POSP 532**

WRITTEN ON YOUR BODY
Tracks: / Written on your body / Naked in the sun.
7" Single: Released May '80, on Mercury, by Phonogram Ltd. Deleted May '85. Catalogue no: **MER 13**

Bondage, Beki

DON'T TURN AWAY
Tracks: / Don't turn away.
7" Single: Released Nov '85, on Communique, Catalogue no: **COMM 2**
12" Single: Released Nov '85, on Communique, Catalogue no: **COMM 122**
12" Pic: Released Nov '85, on Communique, Catalogue no: **LITTLE 12002P**

WHEEL OF FORTUNE, THE
Tracks: / Wheel of fortune, The.
12" Single: Released Oct '85, on Communique, Catalogue no: **122**

Bonds, Gary U.S.

Biographical details: Born Gary Anderson in Florida, USA in 1939, Gary US Bonds enjoyed two quite separate chart careers, in the early Sixties and the early Eighties. He moved with his parents to Virginia as a child and grew up singing both in church and school. In 1960 he met local recording studio owner Frank Guida, who became his producer. Bonds' first hit was not long in coming. The hard-rocking *New Orleans* hit No. 6 in the US in late 1960 and No. 16 in the UK in early '61. The next single *Not Me* was a disaster, but was quickly followed by the smash 45 *Quarter To Three*. This was his biggest success on both sides of the Atlantic: in the States it was his only chart topper, in Britain his only Top Tenner (No. 7). The following year the writers of this hit, which included Bonds and Guida, took legal action against Chubby Checker's 1962 hit *Dancin' Party*, claiming plagiarism. Bonds was unable to come up with further British hits but, in his native America he scored five more Top 40 successes in quick succession. *School Is Out* reached No. 5 and this was clearly a more popular sentiment than the follow-up: *School Is In* peaked at No. 28. The singer then adapted his rocking R&B style to suit the burgeoning Twist craze. *Dear Lady Twist* and *Twist, Twist Senora* both made the US Top 10. After *Seven Days Weekend* peaked at No. 27 in the summer of '62, the hits dried up. The name Gary US Bonds was consigned to history, but with the important footnote that his records and sound were making a great impact upon the emerging British R&B scene. Many years later, in the first week of May 1981, two unrelated but coincidental events occured simultaneously. British rock band Gillan reached a peak position of No. 17 onthe UK charts with a frantic revival of *New Orleans* while, on the US charts, *This Little Girl* by Gary US Bonds himself entered the Top 40. Suddenly the man was back in vogue. *This Little Girl* went on to peak at No. 11 in the States and reached No. 43 in Britain. it was taken from the successful new LP *Dedication*. This remarkable comeback was masterminded by ace rocker Bruce Springsteen, in collaboration with his friend Miami Steve van Zandt, were injected with the raw power and energy that Bruce had become famous for. In both the US and the UK, Bonds had made a chart resurgence after one of the longest gaps between hits in history. (Bob MacDonald)..

CROSS MY PAWS AND HOPE TO DIE
Tracks: / Cross my paws and hope to die / Marmalade song.
7" Single: Released Jan '83, on TV Records, Deleted '84. Catalogue no: **STV 1**

IT'S ONLY LOVE
Tracks: / It's only love / This little girl.
7" Single: Released Oct '81, on EMI-America, by EMI Records. Deleted '84. Catalogue no: **EA 128**

JOLE BLON
Tracks: / Jole blon.
7" Single: Released Aug '81, on EMI-America, by EMI Records. Deleted '84. Catalogue no: **EA 127**

NEW ORLEANS
Tracks: / New Orleans / High time / Little bitty pretty one.
7" Single: Released Oct '81, on Ensign, by Ensign Records. Deleted Oct '84. Catalogue no: **ENY 219**
7" Single: Released Jan '61, on Top Rank (1), Deleted '64. Catalogue no: **JAR 527**
7" Single: Released Oct '80, on Blast From The Past, by Creole Records. Catalogue no: **CR 181**

QUARTER TO THREE
Tracks: / Quarter to three.
7" Single: Released Jul '61, on Top Rank (1), Deleted '64. Catalogue no: **JAR 575**

SOUL DEEP
Tracks: / Soul deep / Bring her back.
7" Single: Released Jul '82, on EMI-America, by EMI Records. Deleted '85. Catalogue no: **EA 140**

STANDING IN THE LINE OF FIRE (SINGLE)
Tracks: / Standing in the line of fire.
7" Single: Released Jul '85, on Making Waves, by Celtic Music. Catalogue no: **SURF 106**
12" Single: Released Jul '85, on Making Waves, by Celtic Music. Catalogue no: **SURFT 106**

STAR, THE
7" Single: Released Nov '81, on Charly, by Charly Records. Deleted '88. Catalogue no: **CYX 200**

THIS LITTLE GIRL
Tracks: / This little girl.
7" Single: Released May '81, on EMI-America, by EMI Records. Deleted '84. Catalogue no: **EA 122**

Bone Orchard

JACK (SINGLE)
Tracks: / Jack.
7" Single: Released Sep '84, on Jungle, by Jungle Records. Catalogue no: **JUNG 18**

PRINCESS EPILEPSY
Tracks: / Princess epilepsy.
12" Single: Released Jun '85, on Jungle, by Jungle Records. Catalogue no: **JUNG 22T**

STUFFED TO THE GILLS
Tracks: / Stuffed to the gills.
12" Single: Released May '88, on Jungle, by Jungle Records. Catalogue no: **JUNG 8**

SWALLOWING HAVOC
12" Single: Released Apr '84, on Jungle, by Jungle Records. Catalogue no: **JUNG 15**

Bone, Richard

BEAT IS ELITE
Tracks: / Beat is elite, The.
7" Single: Released Sep '82, on Survival (1), by Survival Records. Catalogue no: **SUR 123**

DIGITAL DAYS
Tracks: / Digital days / Alien girl.
7" Single: Released Apr '82, on Survival (1), by Survival Records. Catalogue no: **SUR 006**

JOY OF RADIATION
Tracks: / Joy of radiation / Do angels dance.
12" Single: Released Feb '83, on Survival (1), by Survival Records. Catalogue no: **SUR 12 009**
7" Single: Released Feb '83, on Survival (1), by Survival Records. Catalogue no: **SUR 009**

LIVING IN PARTY TOWN
Tracks: / Living in party town / Men with secrets.
12" Single: Released Mar '84, on Survival (1), by Survival Records. Catalogue no: **SUR 12 019**

REAL THING
Tracks: / Real thing, The.
12" Single: Released Nov '84, on Survival (1), by Survival Records. Catalogue no: **SUR 12 021**

Bone Symphony

IT'S A JUNGLE OUT THERE
Tracks: / It's a jungle out there.
12" Single: Released Feb '84, on Capitol, by EMI Records. Deleted '88. Catalogue no: **12CL 322**

Bones, Elbow

Biographical details: Elbow Bones & The Racketeers, an American group, were proteges of August Darnell, alias Kid Creole. At the end of 1983 they had their first hit with *A Night In New York*, an atmospheric disco single in a similar style to that of Kid Creole & The Coconuts. On the British charts it managed the insignificant, but quaint, achievement of logging four consecutive weeks in the No 33 position. It was to go no higher and follow-ups failed to chart at all. (Bob MacDonald, 1984.).

HAPPY BIRTHDAY BABY
Tracks: / Happy birthday baby / I got you.
7" Single: Released Apr '84, on EMI-America, by EMI Records. Catalogue no: **EA 168**
12" Single: Released Apr '84, on EMI-America, by EMI Records. Catalogue no: **12EA 168**

MAMA'S IN LOVE AGAIN
Tracks: / Mama's in love again / Our love will always stand.
7" Single: Released Aug '84, on EMI-America, by EMI Records. Catalogue no: **EA 178**

NIGHT IN NEW YORK
Tracks: / Night in New York / Happy times.
7" Single: Released Jan '84, on EMI-America, by EMI Records. Deleted '87. Catalogue no: **EA 165**
12" Single: Released Nov '83, on EMI-America, by EMI Records. Catalogue no: **12 EA 165**

Boney M

Biographical details: A German-based Eurodisco group of the 1970s, created by producer Frank Farian to cash in on the dance sound pioneered by Giorgio moroder (with Donna Summer). Having written and recorded a typical example of the genre in *Baby do you wanna bump* (a continental hit with synthetic strings, minimal lyrics, relentless drumbeat) he needed a group to promote it. He advertised in trade papers and settled on a vocal quartet of Marcia Barrett, Bobby Farrell, lead singer Liz Mitchell (all from the Caribbean) and Masie Williams (from Monserrat). Backing tapes made in Munich were road-tested in discos before laying the group's vocals on top; they had nine top ten singles in the UK 1976-79, rivalling ABBA as the most commercially successful act of the time, mixing covers such as Bobby Hebb's *Sunny* with Farian's own nursery-like chants. The Jamaican nursery rhyme *Brown girl in the ring* backed with a cover of The Melodians' *Rivers of Babylon* had a 40 week run. They had four No.1 albums, played ten concerts in The USSR but did very little in the USA. Donald Clarke, 24 August 1988.producer Frank Farian to cash in on the dance sound pioneered by Giorgio Moroder (with Donna Summer). Having written and recorded a typical example of the genre in *Baby Do You Wanna Bump* (a continental hit with synthetic strings, minimal lyrics, relentless drumbeat) he needed a group to promote it, advertised in trade papers and settled on a vocal quartet of Marcia Barret, Bobby Farrell, lead singer Liz Mitchell (all from the Caribbean) and Masie Williams (from Monserrat). Backing tapes made in Munich were road-tested in discos before laying the group's vocals on top; they had nine top 10 singles in the UK 1976-79, rivalling Abba as the most commercially successful act of the time, mixing covers such as Bobby Hebb's *Sunny* with Farian's own nursery-like chants. The Jamaican nursey rhyme *Brown Girl In The Ring* backed with a cover of the Melodians' *Rivers Of Babylon* had a 40-week run. They had four no. 1 albums, played ten concerts in the USSR but did very little in the USA. Donald Clarke, 24 August 1988..

BABY DO YOU WANNA BUMP?
Tracks: / Baby do you wanna bump.
7" Single: Released May '78, on Creole, by Creole Records. Catalogue no: **CR 119**

BANG BANG LULU
Tracks: / Bang bang Lulu / Young free and single.
12" Single: Released Jul '86, on Carrere, Catalogue no: **CART 395**

BELFAST
Tracks: / Belfast.
7" Single: Released Oct '77, on Atlantic, by WEA Records. Catalogue no: **K 11020**

BROWN GIRL IN THE RING
Tracks: / Brown girl in the ring.
7" Single: Released Mar '78, on Atlantic, by WEA Records. Catalogue no: **K 11120**

CARNIVAL IS OVER
Tracks: / Carnival is over, The / Going back west.
7" Single: Released Dec '82, on Atlantic, by WEA Records. Catalogue no: **A 9973**

CHILDREN OF PARADISE
Tracks: / Children of paradise / Gadda da vida.
7" Single: Released Feb '81, on Atlantic, by WEA Records. Deleted '84. Catalogue no: **K 11637**

DADDY COOL
Tracks: / Daddy cool.
7" Single: Released Dec '76, on Atlantic, by WEA Records. Deleted '79. Catalogue no: **K 10827**

EVERYBODY WANTS TO DANCE LIKE JOSEPHINE BAKER
Tracks: / Everybody wants to dance like Josephine Baker.
7" Single: Released Oct '89, on Imperative, Catalogue no: **7TIV 002**
12" Single: Released Oct '89, on Imperative, Catalogue no: **12TIV 002**

GOTTA GO HOME
Tracks: / Gotta go home / El lute.
7" Single: Released Aug '79, on Atlantic, by WEA Records. Deleted '82. Catalogue no: **K 11351**

HOORAY HOORAY IT'S A HOLIDAY
Tracks: / Hooray hooray it's a holi-holiday.
7" Single: Released Apr '79, on Atlantic, by WEA Records. Catalogue no: **K 11279**

I'M BORN AGAIN
Tracks: / I'm born again.
7" Single: Released Dec '79, on Atlantic, by WEA Records. Deleted '82. Catalogue no: **K 11410**

JAMBO-HAKUMA-MATATA
Tracks: / Jambo hakuma matata.
7" Single: Released Sep '83, on Atlantic, by WEA Records. Catalogue no: **A 9767**

MA BAKER
Tracks: / Ma Baker.
7" Single: Released Jun '77, on Atlantic, by WEA Records. Catalogue no: **K 10965**

MARY'S BOY CHILD
Tracks: / Mary's boy child / Dancing in the streets / Oh my Lord.
7" Single: Released '78, on Atlantic, by WEA Records. Catalogue no: **K 11221**

MARY'S BOY CHILD (88 REMIX)
Tracks: / Mary's boy child (88 remix) / Rivers of Babylon (remix) (Available on 12" format only.).
7" Single: Released Dec '88, on Ariola, by BMG Records (UK). Deleted Aug '89. Catalogue no: **111 947**
12" Single: Released Dec '88, on Ariola, by BMG Records (UK). Catalogue no: **611 947**

MY FRIEND JACK
Tracks: / My friend Jack / Like a boat.
7" Single: Released Apr '80, on Atlantic, by WEA Records. Deleted '83. Catalogue no: **K 11463**

PAINTER MAN
Tracks: / Painter man / He was Steppenwolf.
7" Single: Released May '82, on Atlantic, by WEA Records. Catalogue no: **K 11255**

RASPUTIN
Tracks: / Rasputin.
7" Single: Released Oct '78, on Atlantic, by WEA Records. Deleted '81. Catalogue no: **K 11192**

RIVERS OF BABYLON
Tracks: / Rivers of Babylon / Brown girl in the ring.
7" Single: Released Jun '88, on Old Gold, by Old Gold Records. Catalogue no: **OG 9783**

SUMMER MEGA MIX, THE
Tracks: / Summer mega mix, The.
7" Single: Released Aug '89, on RCA, by BMG Records (UK). Catalogue no: **112497**
12" Single: Released Aug '89, on RCA, by BMG Records (UK). Catalogue no: **612497**

SUNNY
Tracks: / Sunny.
7" Single: Released Mar '77, on Atlantic, by WEA Records. Deleted '80. Catalogue no: **K 10892**

WE KILL THE WORLD (DON'T KILL THE WORLD)
Tracks: / We kill the world (don't kill the world) / Boonoonoonoos.
7" Single: Released Nov '81, on Atlantic, by WEA Records. Catalogue no: **K 11689**
12" Single: Released Nov '81, on Atlantic, by WEA Records. Catalogue no: **K 11689T**

YOUNG FREE & SINGLE
Tracks: / Young free and single / Chica da Silva.
12" Single: Released Mar '86, on Carrere,

Catalogue no: **CART 384**
7" Single: Released Mar '86, on Carrere, Catalogue no: **CAR 384**

Bonfire

HARD ON ME
Tracks: / Hard on me / Freedom is my belief / You're back / Ready 4 reaction.
CD 5": Released 23 Sep '89, on RCA, by BMG Records (UK). Catalogue no: **ZD 43194**
12" Single: Released Sep '89, on RCA, by BMG Records (UK). Catalogue no: **ZT 43176**
12" Single: Released Sep '89, on RCA, by BMG Records (UK). Catalogue no: **ZT 43194**
7" Single: Released Sep '89, on RCA, by BMG Records (UK). Catalogue no: **ZB 43081**
7" Single: Released Sep '89, on RCA, by BMG Records (UK). Catalogue no: **ZB 43175**

SWEET OBSESSION
Tracks: / Sweet obsession / Don't get me wrong / Angel in white(12" only).
12" Single: Released Jun '88, on RCA, by BMG Records (UK). Deleted May '89. Catalogue no: **ZT 41570 RB**
7" Single: Released Jun '88, on RCA, by BMG Records (UK). Deleted May '89. Catalogue no: **ZB 41569 B**

Bonfires In The Sky

MACHINES
Tracks: / Machines.
7" Single: Released Jun '85, on Writers Reign, by Writers Reign Records. Catalogue no: **WRS 30**

Bongo Mike

SHAVING IN A TOILET
Tracks: / Shaving in a toilet.
7" Single: Released Apr '88, on Recommended, by Recommended Records. Catalogue no: **NP 001**

Bongos

BULLRUSHES
Tracks: / Bull rushes.
7" Single: Released Dec '81, on Fetish, Catalogue no: **FE 009**
12" Single: Released Jan '82, on Fetish, Deleted Jan '85. Catalogue no: **FET 009**

IN THE CONGO
Tracks: / In the congo.
12" Single: Released May '81, on Fetish, Catalogue no: **FET 005**

MAMBO SUN
Tracks: / Mambo sun / Hunting / In the congo.
7" Single: Released Apr '82, on Fetish, Catalogue no: **FE 18**
12" Single: Released Apr '82, on Fetish, Catalogue no: **FET 18**

TELEPHOTO LENS
Tracks: / Telephoto lens.
7" Single: Released May '81, on Fetish, Catalogue no: **FET 003**

ZEBRA CLUB
Tracks: / Zebra club.
7" Single: Released Feb '82, on Fetish, Catalogue no: **FE 17**

Bongwater

BREAKING NO NEW GROUND (SINGLE)
Tracks: / Breaking no new ground.
12" Single: Released Feb '88, on Shadowline, Catalogue no: **SR 6887**

Bonham, Debbie

ON THE AIR TONIGHT
Tracks: / On the air tonight.
12" Single: Released Aug '85, on Carrere, Catalogue no: **CART 371**
7" Single: Released Aug '85, on Carrere, Catalogue no: **CAR 371**

SANCTUARY
Tracks: / Sanctuary.
7" Single: Released Jul '85, on Carrere, Catalogue no: **CAR 363**
12" Single: Released Jul '85, on Carrere, Catalogue no: **CART 363**

Bonito Star

GROOVY KIND OF LOVE
Tracks: / Groovy kind of love.
12" Single: Released May '89, on Realistic, Catalogue no: **RRO 16**

Bonk

I'M NOT UNUSUAL
Tracks: / I'm not unusual / I'm not completely unusual.
7" Single: Released Oct '82, on Ensign, by Ensign Records. Deleted Oct '85. Catalogue no: **ENY 233**

Bonnet, Graham

LIAR
Tracks: / Liar / Bad days are gone.
7" Single: Released Jun '81, on Vertigo, by Phonogram Ltd. Deleted '84. Catalogue no: **VER 2**

NIGHT GAMES
Tracks: / Night games / Out on the water.
7" Single: Released Mar '81, on Vertigo, by Phonogram Ltd. Deleted '84. Catalogue no: **VER 1**

THAT'S THE WAY THAT IT IS
Tracks: / That's the way that it is /
7" Single: Released Oct '81, on Vertigo, by Phonogram Ltd. Deleted Oct '84. Catalogue no: **VER 4**

Bonney, Graham

SUPERGIRL
Tracks: / Supergirl.
7" Single: Released Mar '66, on Columbia, by EMI Records. Deleted '69. Catalogue no: **DB 7843**

Bonnie Lou

TENNESSEE WIG WALK
Tracks: / Tennessee wig walk.
7" Single: Released Feb '54, on Parlophone, by EMI Records. Deleted '57. Catalogue no: **R 3730**

Bonny, Lauren

INVASION
Tracks: / Invasion / Dream romance.
12" Single: Released Jan '82, on S & G (2), Catalogue no: **SG 7 14**

Bonoff, Karla

Biographical details: Bonoff, Karla. This West Coast USA singer/songwriter was born in 1952. She formed Bryndle in 1969 with Wendy Waldman and Andrew Gold; they made an album which was never released. Three Bonoff songs were included in Linda Ronstadt's hit album *Hasten Down The Wind* in 1976 and she was signed by CBS; three albums charted in the USA 1977-82, but her best songs were covered by others (Bonnie Raitt, etc.) so that her own records were heard as covers (her top 20 USA hit *Personally* in 1982 was ironically not her song). She also sang on four of Waldman's albums; Waldman had the same problem, her songs covered by Marie Muldaur, Judy Collins, Kim Carnes, others. D. Clarke , August 1988..

BABY DON'T GO
Tracks: / Baby don't go / Never stop her heart.
7" Single: Released Feb '80, on CBS, by CBS Records. Deleted Feb '83. Catalogue no: **CBS 8177**

SOMEBODY'S EYES
Tracks: / Somebody's eyes.
7" Single: Released Jun '84, on CBS, by CBS Records. Catalogue no: **A 4565**

Bontempo

GOODTIMES
Tracks: / Goodtimes.
12" Single: Released Oct '87, on Pana, Catalogue no: **SHR 2022**

Bonzo Dog Band

Biographical details: Bonzo Dog Band. London band formed by art students in 1966, originally called the Bonzo Dog Doo-dah Band: Vivian Stanshall, vocalist; Neil Innes, vocals and guitar; 'Legs' Larry Smith on drums; Dennis Cowan on bass, Roger Ruskin Spear working saxes and robots; Rodney Slater on sax, Sam Spoons (Martin Stafford) on percussion, others. They provided relief in a pompous rock scene, the early act a mixture of Temperance Seven trad jazz and Spear's robots running amok, music and lyrics by Stanshall and Innes. They made singles on Parlophone, then *Gorilla* on Liberty, a dadaist riposte to the Beatles' *Sgt. Pepper*; more send-ups on *The Doughnut In Granny's Greenhouse*. They were seen in TV show 'Do Not Adjust Your Set' with fledgling Monty Python Team and in Beatles' 'Magical Mystery Tour'; Paul McCartney (as Appolo C. Vermouth) produced their only hit single *I'm The Urban Spaceman* (on Tadpoles). They split in 1969, Smith and others joining Bob Kerr's Whoopee Band (still a popular London pub act); Stanshall and Innes perpetrated individual nonsense including the Rutles (Beatle send-up with Innes and Python's Eric Idle) and Stanshall's Rawlinson End saga about loony aristocrat Sir Henry; they reformed the Bonzos for *Let's Make Up And Be Friendly* in 1972. Donald Clarke, 24 August 1988.
The group were formed in 1965 when its members were attending various London art colleges. In '67 they released their first album *Gorilla* and appeared in the Beatles *Magical mystery tour* TV film. A year later they issued a single entitled *I'm the urban spaceman* a Neil Innes-penned ditty satirising the much publicised Apollo moon missions. The disc was produced by Paul McCartney under the pseudonym 'A.C. Vermouth'; this fact was not disclosed until it was already climbing the chart, whereupon it zoomed to No. 5. It was their only UK chart single, but it was followed by two chart LPs. *Doughnut in Granny's greenhouse* and *Tadpoles*. Another acclaimed album, *Keynsham* failed to chart. The group became widely known throughout Britain because of their hilarious concert and TV appearances. Their formula was a winning combination of lyrical and musical satire, with some Twenties jazz tinges also included. The group was led by the incongruous talents of Innes and Stanshall, whose contrasting ideas made the Band truly electric and bizarre. The group broke up at the start of the Seventies. Innes teamed with fellow comedian Eric Idle to produce the Rutles, a well recived Beatles parody that came out of the late Seventies. He also gained his own TV show, *The Innes book of records*. Slater left the business. Spear became a solo live performer, touring with his *Giant kinetic wardrobe* home made robot show. The ever-eccentric Stanshall made a couple of solo albums *Men open umbrellas ahead* and *Sir Henry of Rawlinson End* and made various media appearances. Bohay-Nowell, Smith and Spoons joined Bob Kerr's Whoopee Band, a less successful Bonzo-style outfit. (Bob MacDonald).

I'M THE URBAN SPACEMAN
Tracks: / I'm the urban spaceman.
7" Single: Released Nov '68, on Liberty, by EMI Records. Deleted '71. Catalogue no: **LBF 15144**
7" Single: Released Jul '84, on EMI Golden 45's, by EMI Records. Catalogue no: **G45 33**

PEEL SESSIONS:BONZO DOG BAND
Tracks: / We're going to bring it on home / Sofa head / Tent / Monster mash.
12" Single: Released Jul '88, on Strange Fruit, by Strange Fruit Records. Catalogue no: **SFPS 051**

Boo Hoos

SUN, THE SNAKE AND THE HOO, THE (SINGLE)
Tracks: / Sun, the snake and the hoo, The.
12" Single: Released Apr '87, on Electric Eye, Catalogue no: **EES 014**

Boogie

BOOGIE Original London cast
Tracks: / Boogie: *Various artists.*
7" Single: Released May '89, on T. E. R., by That's Entertainment Records. Catalogue no: **STER 001**

Boogie Box High

GAVE IT ALL AWAY
Tracks: / Gave it all away / That's it.
7" Single: Released Sep '87, on Hardback, by Hardback Records. Catalogue no: **7 BOSS 5**
12" Single: Released Sep '87, on Hardback, by Hardback Records. Catalogue no: **BOSS 5**

JIVE TALKIN'
Tracks: / Jive talkin' / Rhythm talking (part 1).
12" Single: Released 20 Jun '87, on Hardback, by Hardback Records. Catalogue no: **BOSS 4**
7" Single: Released 20 Jun '87, on Hardback, by Hardback Records. Catalogue no: **7 BOSS 4**

NERVOUS
Tracks: / Nervous (Shep Pettibone mix) / Nervous (7" version)
7" Single: Released Aug '89, on SBK, by EMI Records. Catalogue no: **SBK 1**
12" Single: Released Aug '89, on SBK, by EMI Records. Catalogue no: **12SBKX 1**
12" Single: Released Aug '89, on SBK, by EMI Records. Catalogue no: **203 502 6**
12" Single: Released Aug '89, on SBK, by EMI Records. Catalogue no: **12SBK 1**
CD 5": Released Aug '89, on SBK, by EMI Records. Catalogue no: **CDSBK 1**
Cassingle: Released Aug '89, on SBK, by EMI Records. Catalogue no: **TSCBK 1**

Boogie Boys

DEALIN' WITH LIFE
Tracks: / Dealin' with life / Fly girl.
7" Single: Released Aug '86, on Capitol, by EMI Records. Deleted '88. Catalogue no: **CL 418**
12" Single: Released Aug '86, on Capitol, by EMI Records. Catalogue no: **12CL 418**

Boogie Brothers

BOOGALOO
Tracks: / Boogaloo.
7" Single: Released 12 Jun '89, on Unicorn Records, by Unicorn Records. Catalogue no: **PHZ 39**

Boogie Down

GHETTO MUSIC: THE BLUE PRINT OF HIP HOP (SINGLE)
Tracks: / Ghetto music: The blueprint of hip hop.
12" Single: Released Jul '89, on Jetstar, by Jetstar Records. Catalogue no: **JIVE 11871 J**

I'M STILL NO. 1
Tracks: / Essays on B.D.P.-ism / I'm still no.1 / Jimmy.
12" Single: Released 23 Jul '88, on Jive, by Zomba Records. Catalogue no: **JIVET 179**

JACK OF SPADES
Tracks: / Jack of spades.
7" Single: Released Dec '88, on Jive, by Zomba Records. Catalogue no: **JIVE 192**
12" Single: Released Dec '88, on Jive, by Zomba Records. Catalogue no: **JIVET 192**

MY PHILOSOPHY
Tracks: / My philosophy.
12" Single: Released Apr '88, on Jive, by Zomba Records. Catalogue no: **JIVET 170**
7" Single: Released Apr '88, on Jive, by Zomba Records. Catalogue no: **JIVE 170**
Special: Released '88, on Jive, by Zomba Records. Deleted '88. Catalogue no: **JIVEX 170**

WHY IS THAT
Tracks: / Why is that / Hip hop rules.
Cassingle: Released Jul '89, on Jive, by Zomba Records. Catalogue no: **JIVEC 210**
7" Single: Released Jul '89, on Jive, by Zomba Records. Catalogue no: **JIVE 210**
12" Single: Released Jul '89, on Jive, by Zomba Records. Catalogue no: **JIVET 210**

YOU MUST LEARN (IMPORT)
Tracks: / You must learn.
12" Single: Released Sep '89, on Jive (USA), by Zomba Records. Catalogue no: **12751 JD**

Boogie Man

CHANTILLY LACE
Tracks: / Chantilly lace / Boppin' shoes.
7" Single: Released Sep '82, on Polydor, by Polydor Ltd. Deleted '85. Catalogue no: **POSP 463**

Boogie Men

CURLY SHUFFLE
Tracks: / Curly shuffle / Boogie men'll get you.
12" Single: Released Jan '84, on Crash, by Satril Records. Deleted '85. Catalogue no: **12 CRA 605**

Boogie T

JULIA
Tracks: / Julia / Love of my people.
12" Single: Released Aug '86, on Hawkeye, by Hawkeye Records. Catalogue no: **HD 76**

Boo-Hooray

HEP CAT GLOSS
Tracks: / Hep cat gloss.
12" Single: Released Jun '84, on Gone, Catalogue no: **GONE 001**

REINDEER LIBERTY TV'S
Tracks: / Reindeer liberty tv's.
12" Single: Released '88, on Gone & Gone, Catalogue no: **BH 012**

Book Of Love

BOY
Tracks: / Boy / Book of love.
7" Single: Released Jun '85, on Sire (USA), Deleted Sep '87. Catalogue no: **W 8970**

I TOUCH ROSES
Tracks: / I touch roses / Lost souls / Happy day (Extra track on 12" only).
7" Single: Released Jan '86, on Sire (USA), Catalogue no: **W 8882**
12" Single: Released Jan '86, on Sire (USA), Catalogue no: **W 8882T**

Booker, Steve

GET UP STAND UP
Tracks: / Get up stand up / Up & the up.
12" Single: Released Mar '84, on Ram, by Ram Records. Catalogue no: **RAM 7008T**
7" Single: Released Mar '84, on Ram, by Ram Records. Catalogue no: **RAM 7008**

LEAN ON ME
Tracks: / Lean on me.
7" Single: Released Oct '83, on Ram, by Ram Records. Catalogue no: **RAM 7003**

Booker T

GREEN ONIONS (SINGLE)
Tracks: / Green onions / Chinese checkers.
7" Single: Released Jun '86, on Atlantic, by WEA Records. Deleted Jun '87. Catalogue no: **K 10109**
7" Single: Released Jan '85, on Old Gold, by Old Gold Records. Catalogue no: **OG 9499**
12" Single: Released Apr '80, on Atlantic, by

WEA Records. Catalogue no: **K 10109 T**

HANG 'EM HIGH
Tracks: / Hang 'em high / Over easy.
7" Single: Released 19 Sep '87, on Stax, by Fantasy Inc (USA). Catalogue no: **STAX 813**

HIP HUG HER
Tracks: / Hip hug her / Slim Jenkin's place.
7" Single: Released Mar '80, on Atlantic, by WEA Records. Deleted '83. Catalogue no: **K 11454**

SOUL CLAP '69
Tracks: / Soul clap '69.
7" Single: Released Aug '69, on Stax, by Fantasy Inc (USA). Deleted '72. Catalogue no: **STAX 127**

SOUL LIMBO (SINGLE)
Tracks: / Soul limbo / Soul clap '69.
7" Single: Released Aug '82, on Stax, by Fantasy Inc (USA). Catalogue no: **STAX 1011**
7" Pic: Released Aug '87, on Stax, by Fantasy Inc (USA). Catalogue no: **STAP 808**
12" Single: Released Aug '87, on Stax, by Fantasy Inc (USA). Catalogue no: **STAT 808**
7" Single: Released Dec '68, on Stax, by Fantasy Inc (USA). Deleted '71. Catalogue no: **STAX 102**
7" Single: Released Aug '87, on Stax, by Fantasy Inc (USA). Catalogue no: **STAX 808**

TIME IS TIGHT
Tracks: / Time is tight / Johnny, I love you.
7" Single: Released Mar '82, on Stax, by Fantasy Inc (USA). Catalogue no: **STAX 1003**
7" Single: Released Mar '80, on Stax, by Fantasy Inc (USA). Deleted Mar '83. Catalogue no: **STAX 2001**
7" Single: Released May '69, on Stax, by Fantasy Inc (USA). Deleted '72. Catalogue no: **STAX 119**
7" Single: Released Sep '85, on Old Gold, by Old Gold Records. Catalogue no: **OG 9530**
7" Single: Released 13 Jun '87, on Stax, by Fantasy Inc (USA). Catalogue no: **STAX 803**

Books

BROADCAST
Tracks: / Broadcast / Hirohito.
7" Single: Released May '80, on Logo, by Logo Records. Deleted '83. Catalogue no: **BOOK 1**

EXPERTISE (SINGLE)
Tracks: / Expertise / Bells of Fowley.
7" Single: Released Oct '80, on Logo, by Logo Records. Deleted Oct '83. Catalogue no: **BOOK 3**

Boom

WE'RE NOT CAUSIN' ANY TROUBLE (THE GANGSTER GROOVE)
Tracks: / We're not causin' any trouble (the gangster groove) / We're not causin' any trouble (part 2) / We're not causin' any trouble (part 3) (On 12" only).
7" Single: Released 22 Aug '88, on Dancetrax, by BMG Records (UK). Deleted Aug '89. Catalogue no: **DRX 1**
12" Single: Released 22 Aug '88, on Dancetrax, by BMG Records (UK). Deleted Aug '89. Catalogue no: **DRX 112**
12" Single: Released Aug '88, on Dancetrax, by BMG Records (UK). Catalogue no: **DTRAX 913**

Boom, Barry

COME FOLLOW ME
Tracks: / When you smile / Come follow me.
12" Single: Released Dec '86, on On Top, Catalogue no: **OT 001**

MAKING LOVE
Tracks: / Making love.
12" Single: Released Jul '89, on Fine Style, by Fashion Records. Catalogue no: **FS 024**

Boom, Bobby

MISTER INFORMER
Tracks: / Mister informer.
7" Single: Released Apr '84, on London Gemi, Catalogue no: **LG 003**

Boom Boom Room

HERE COMES THE MAN
Tracks: / Here comes the man / Here comes the man (remix).
7" Single: Released Jan '86, on Fun After All, by Music For Nations Records. Catalogue no: **FUN 101**
12" Single: Released Aug '86, on Epic, by CBS Records. Catalogue no: **650054 6**
7" Single: Released Aug '86, on Epic, by CBS Records. Catalogue no: **650054 7**
12" Single: Released Jan '86, on Fun After All, by Music For Nations Records. Catalogue no: **12 FUN 101**

JULIE
Tracks: / Julie / Still together / Lady Jane (on 12" only.).
Note: Picture bag. * Extra track on 12" version only.
7" Single: Released Sep '87, on Epic, by CBS Records. Catalogue no: **OOM 2**

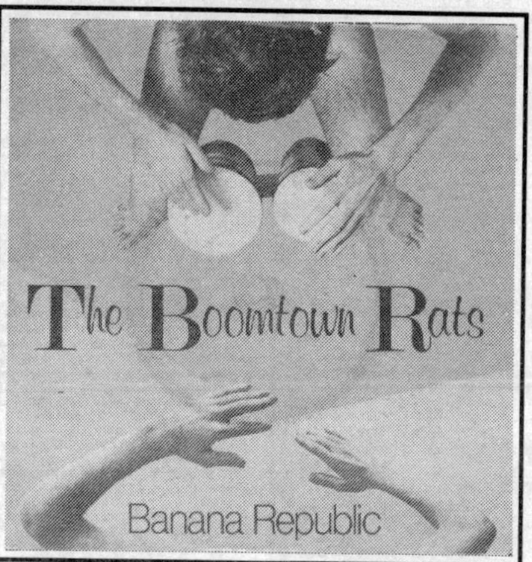

BOOMTOWN RATS - BANANA REPUBLIC (Released on Ensign)

12" Single: Released Sep '87, on Epic, by CBS Records. Catalogue no: **OOM T2**

LOVE YOUR FACE
Tracks: / Love your face / Texas blood.
7" Single: Released Jul '87, on Epic, by CBS Records. Catalogue no: **OOM 1**
7" Single: Released Jul '87, on Epic, by CBS Records. Catalogue no: **OOMQ 1**
12" Single: Released Jul '87, on Epic, by CBS Records. Catalogue no: **OOMT 1**

TAKE YOUR TIME
Tracks: / Take your time / Magic boy / Future king* (*=Extra track on 12" only).
12" Single: Released Oct '86, on Epic, by CBS Records. Catalogue no: **TA 7314**
7" Single: Released Oct '86, on Epic, by CBS Records. Catalogue no: **A 7314**

Boom Crash Opera

GREAT WALL
Tracks: / Great wall / Caught between two towns.
12" Single: Released Jul '88, on Warner Bros., by WEA Records. Catalogue no: **W 7912 T**
7" Single: Released Jul '88, on Warner Bros., by WEA Records. Catalogue no: **W 7912**

Boom, Taka

IN THE MIDDLE OF THE NIGHT
Tracks: / In the middle of the night / In the middle of the night (LP version).
7" Single: Released Jan '86, on Boiling Point, by Polydor Ltd. Catalogue no: **POSP 763**
12" Single: Released Jan '86, on Boiling Point, by Polydor Ltd. Catalogue no: **POSPX 763**

TO HELL WITH HIM
Tracks: / To hell with him.
7" Single: Released May '83, on Casablanca, by PolyGram UK Ltd. Catalogue no: **CAB 113**
12" Single: Released May '83, on Casablanca, by PolyGram UK Ltd. Catalogue no: **CABL 113**

Boomerang Gang

DOCTOR JONES
Tracks: / Doctor Jones / Inspiration.
7" Single: Released Jan '86, on WEA, by WEA Records. Catalogue no: **Y 256**

ROCK OUT WHEN YOU CLOCK IN
Tracks: / Rock out when you clock in.
7" Single: Released May '85, on Survival (1), by Survival Records. Catalogue no: **SUR 030**
12" Single: Released May '85, on Survival (1), by Survival Records. Catalogue no: **SUR 12 030**

Boomtown Rats

Biographical details: Boomtown Rats. Seminal Irish punk band formed in 1975, led by verbose Dublin vocalist Bob Geldof (born in 1954), with Johnny Fingers, keyboards; Pete Briquette, bass; Gerry Cott and Garry Roberts, guitars. Top 20 hits late '70s included *Looking After No. 1*, *She's So Modern*; then no. ones *Rat Trap* and *I Don't Like Mondays* (the last inspired by mindless murders by a San Diego schoolgirl). They lasted into the New Wave, unlike most Punk groups; Geldof was the nearest the New Wave had to a Mick Jagger figure: as an ex-freelance on a weekly music paper, he gave as good as he got in interviews. They began to decline in the '80s, later albums (out of print in 1988) regarded as perfunctory.
Geldof diversified into acting; then worked tirelessly with Ultravox's Midge Ure 1984-85 on the Band Aid project; he subsequently toured Africa and saw that the money went to famine victimes, taking no more nonsense from politicians than he had from the music press. He was knighted, his work inspiring similar projects around the world; his autobiography 'Is That All?' a best seller in 1986, probably the best book ever written by a pop star, he returned to music, refusing to cash in on charity fame. Donald Clarke, 24 August 1988.
Formed in Dublin in 1975, the band toured the Irish Republick extensively, before signing a British record deal and moving to London in '77. Their exciting live act made them one of the most talked about bands on the UK's burgeouning widely publicised punk rock scene. The fact that the group were using the British New Wave to launch their career, led many to believe that lead singer Bob Geldof became a regular favourite on TV and radio interviews that the public became aware of the group's origins.
The Rats were one of the most talented and successful bands of the Punk era, hitting the UK Top 20 with each of their first nine single releases. The first three - *Looking after No. 1, Mary of the fourth form* and *She's so modern* - were brash out and out punk rock. The fourth hit (the first one to crack the Top 10), *Like clockwork* added a new dimension and set a standard of versatility and variety that was to set them apart from most of their peers. It came from their first UK Top 10 LP *A tonic for the troops*, which had a 44 week run on the album charts. It was the third single taken from this LP that became the first New Wave No. 1: *Rat trap* was a complex mini-epic, a sort of punk answer to Bruce Springsteen in terms of rock'n'roll power and dramatic lyrics. It angrily despairing tale of working class depression combined with its musical inventiveness, took totally different from both the No. 1 singles either side of it: *Rat trap* dethroned *Summer nights* by John Travolta and Olivia Newton John and was toppled in turn by *Da ya think I'm sexy* by Rod Stewart. The follow up 45 was eight months in coming and was even more successful. *I don't like Mondays* gave the Rats a second consecutive UK No. 1 and stayed there for four weeks. The song was inspired by a recent Californian incident, when a teenage schoolgirl had opened fire on her school playground and then explained her homicidal behaviour by stating 'I don't like Mondays'. Composer Geldof was shocked by this reply as by her crime itself and wrote this dramatic single. Its accompanying video was also widely acclaimed and was influential in inspiring many up and coming British bands to make promotional videos. The single was an international hit, with the conspicuous exception of the US, where *I don't like Mondays* could only crawl to No. 73. The Rats were never particularly successful in America, in common with most other New Wave acts of the late Seventies. Punk rock never really happened in that country. This record was the subject of an unofficial ban by most US radio stations, who were wary of legal action. The schoolgirl's parents denounced the song and attempted to stifle it, believing it to be in sick taste. In Britain the group were now established as a top band, with the frontman Geldof becoming a major media star. He was highly articulate and was viewed by press, radio and TV as the leading New Wave spokesman. The Boomtown Rats looked set to continue into the early Eighties as one of the biggest acts around; but strangely the magic dissipated. The weak follow up *Diamond smiles* peaked at No. 13 heralding the beginning of the group's decline. Admittedly, their third LP *The fine art of surfacing* had a 26 week run on the UK charts, reaching No. 7; but the Rats' superstar status was beginning to diminish. They had their two final Top 10 singles at the beginning and end of 1980: *Someone's looking at you* reached No. 4 and the calypso infected *Banana republic* hit No. 3. The latter was the first sinlge from *Mondo Bongo*. This album reached No. 6, their highest ever placing on the British LP chart, but it only remained on the list for seven weeks. From '81 the group were reduced to minor hit status. Geldof starred in a movie version of Pink Floyd's *The wall*, but has subsequently kept a fairly low profile. Now a five-piece following the departure of guitarist Gerry Cott, the Boomtown Rats continued to record and perform. (Bob MacDonald, 1984).

BANANA REPUBLIC (see panel top centre)
Tracks: / Banana republic / Man at the top.
7" Single: Released Nov '80, on Ensign, by Ensign Records. Deleted '83. Catalogue no: **BONGO 1**

CHARMED LIVES
Tracks: / Charmed lives / Storm breaks.
12" Single: Released Jun '82, on Mercury, by Phonogram Ltd. Deleted '85. Catalogue no: **MERX 106**
7" Single: Released Jun '82, on Mercury, by Phonogram Ltd. Deleted '85. Catalogue no: **MER 106**

DAVE
Tracks: / Dave.
7" Single: Released Jan '85, on Mercury, by Phonogram Ltd. Catalogue no: **MER 179**

DIAMOND SMILES
Tracks: / Diamond smiles.
7" Single: Released Nov '79, on Ensign, by Ensign Records. Deleted '82. Catalogue no: **ENY 33**

DRAG ME DOWN
Tracks: / Drag me down / Icicle in the sun.
7" Single: Released May '84, on Mercury, by Phonogram Ltd. Deleted '87. Catalogue no: **MER 163**

ELEPHANT'S GRAVEYARD, THE
Tracks: / Elephant's graveyard, The / Real different.
7" Single: Released Jan '81, on Ensign, by Ensign Records. Deleted '84. Catalogue no: **BONGO 2**

HOUSE ON FIRE
Tracks: / House on fire / Europe looked ugly.
12" Single: Released Mar '82, on Mercury, by Phonogram Ltd. Deleted '85. Catalogue no: **MERX 91**
7" Single: Released Mar '82, on Mercury, by Phonogram Ltd. Deleted '85. Catalogue no: **MER 91**

I DON'T LIKE MONDAYS
Tracks: / I don't like Mondays.
7" Single: Released Jul '79, on Ensign, by Ensign Records. Deleted '82. Catalogue no: **ENY 30**

I DON'T LIKE MONDAYS (OLD GOLD)
Tracks: / I don't like Mondays / Rat trap.
7" Single: Released Jun '88, on Old Gold, by Old Gold Records. Catalogue no: **OG 9790**

LIKE CLOCKWORK
Tracks: / Like clockwork.
7" Single: Released Jun '78, on Ensign, by Ensign Records. Deleted '81. Catalogue no: **ENY 14**

LOOKING AFTER NO. 1
Tracks: / Looking after no. 1.
7" Single: Released Aug '77, on Ensign, by Ensign Records. Deleted '80. Catalogue no: **ENY 4**

MARY OF THE FOURTH FORM
Tracks: / Mary of the fourth form.
7" Single: Released Nov '77, on Ensign, by Ensign Records. Deleted '80. Catalogue no: **ENY 9**

NEVER IN A MILLION YEARS
Tracks: / Never in a million years / Don't talk to me.
7" Single: Released Dec '81, on Mercury, by Phonogram Ltd. Deleted '84. Catalogue no: **MER 87**

RAT TRAP

BOOMTOWN RATS - SOMEONE'S LOOKING AT YOU (Released on Ensign)

Tracks: / Rat trap.
7" Single: Released Oct '78, on Ensign, by Ensign Records. Deleted '81. Catalogue no: **ENY 16**

SHE'S SO MODERN
Tracks: / She's so modern.
7" Single: Released Apr '78, on Ensign, by Ensign Records. Deleted '81. Catalogue no: **ENY 13**

SOMEONE'S LOOKING AT YOU (see panel above)
Tracks: / Someone's looking at you / When the night comes.
7" Single: Released Jan '80, on Ensign, by Ensign Records. Deleted '83. Catalogue no: **EN 34**

TONIGHT
Tracks: / Tonight.
7" Single: Released Jan '84, on Mercury, by Phonogram Ltd. Catalogue no: **MER 154**
12" Single: Released Jan '84, on Mercury, by Phonogram Ltd. Catalogue no: **MERX 154**

CHARMED LIVES (SINGLE SET)
Tracks: / Charmed lives / Nothing happened today / No hiding place / Storm breaks.
7" Set: Released Jun '82, on Mercury, by Phonogram Ltd. Deleted '85. Catalogue no: **MER 1062**

Boon Squark

COME ON DADDY
Tracks: / Come on daddy / Right on.
12" Single: Released Feb '89, on Gee Street, by Gee Street Records. Catalogue no: **GEET 009**
12" Single: Released Feb '89, on Gee Street, by Gee Street Records. Catalogue no: **GEET 9**
7" Single: Released Feb '89, on Gee Street, by Gee Street Records. Catalogue no: **GEE 9**

Boone, Daniel

Biographical details: This British singer first came to public attention in 1971 when he recorded a song called *Daddy Don't You Walk So Fast*, a sugar filled number concerning a marriage break-up and its effect on the offspring. It was a slow but very steady seller, peaking at No. 17 on the UK charts by logging 15 weeks on the Top 50 total. The following year, Boone released the uptempo *Beautiful Sunday*, which he co-wrote. It peaked No. 21 in Britain, but then gave him a surprise American hit, reaching 15 on the Billboard Hot 100. But it was no good thinking he was going to score a follow-up hit - Las Vegas entertainer Wayne Newton had just made the US Top 5 with his version of *Daddy*. For the UK and US record buyers, the Daniel Boone story ends here. But in 1976 *Beautiful Sunday* became a monster hit in Japan, after being adopted as the theme to a Japanese breakfast TV programme. It sold two million copies in that country alone, becoming one of the nation's all-time biggest sellers; in addition to Boone's single, two cover versions hit the Japanese Top 10. From then on, Boone was a major artist in that country. (Bob MacDonald, 19/11/84)..

BEAUTIFUL SUNDAY
Tracks: / Beautiful Sunday.
7" Single: Released Apr '72, on Penny Farthing, by Penny Farthing Records. Deleted '75. Catalogue no: **PEN 781**

BEAUTIFUL SUNDAY (OLD GOLD)
Tracks: / Beautiful Sunday.
7" Single: Released Apr '88, on Old Gold, by Old Gold Records. Catalogue no: **OG 9007**

DADDY DON'T YOU WALK SO FAST
Tracks: / Daddy don't you walk so fast.
7" Single: Released Aug '71, on Penny Farthing, by Penny Farthing Records. Deleted '74. Catalogue no: **PEN 764**

I'M ONLY LOOKING
Tracks: / I'm only looking / Sweet conversation.
7" Single: Released Jul '82, on Swoop, Deleted Jul '87. Catalogue no: **RTLS 009**

I'VE REALLY GOT YOU
Tracks: / I've really got you / Do you believe in me.
7" Single: Released Jan '80, on WEA, by WEA Records. Catalogue no: **K 18129**

STREET FIGHTERS
Tracks: / Street fighters / Trouble in the family.
7" Single: Released Sep '86, on Swoop, Catalogue no: **RTL 006**

TOTAL REACTION
Tracks: / Total reaction / Sanctuary.
7" Single: Released Nov '83, on Brilliant, by Brilliant Records. Catalogue no: **HIT 5**

TROUBLE IN THE FAMILY
7" Single: Released Nov '81, on Swoop, Catalogue no: **RTL 006**

Boone, Debby

Biographical details: American singer Debby is the daughter of Pat Boone, whose clean-cut sound and image made him a hugely successful hitmaker in the 50's and early 60's. Debby scored only one US Top Forty single, 37 fewer than her father. But it was quite a disc: 1977's *You Light Up My Life*, written and produced by Joe Brooks, logged 10 weeks at No 1 and was the longest-running American chart-topper for more than 20 years. In the same week that this big ballad was finally dethroned it entered the British Top Fifty, where it stayed for just two weeks and peaked at only No 48. By a curious coincidence a similar phenomenon was happening in reverse: Wings' *Mull Of Kintyre* was in the midst of a nine-week run at the top of the British chart while only reaching No 33 in the States. (Bob MacDonald, 1984.).

FREE TO BE LONELY AGAIN
Tracks: / Free to be lonely again / Love put a song.
7" Single: Released Sep '80, on Warner Bros., by WEA Records. Deleted Sep '83. Catalogue no: **K 17682**

YOU LIGHT UP MY LIFE
Tracks: / You light up my life.
7" Single: Released Dec '77, on Warner Bros., by WEA Records. Deleted '80. Catalogue no: **K 17043**

Boone, Len

LOVE WON'T BE DENIED
Tracks: / Love won't be denied / Living just to love you / Love won't be denied (instrumental) (Only on 12" version.).
12" Single: Released '83, on Chrysalis, by Chrysalis Records. Deleted '87. Catalogue no: **CHS 12 2227**
7" Single: Released '83, on Chrysalis, by Chrysalis Records. Deleted '87. Catalogue no: **CHS 2227**

Boone, Pat

Biographical details: Boone, Pat. Born Charles Eugene Boone in 1934 in Jacksonville, Florida, Pat Boone was the second most successful male artist in USA pop after Elvis Presley in the late '50s. His first single *Two Hearts, Two Kisses* was first of 38 USA top 40 hits 1955-62, including 10 top 10 entries, six at no. 1. His style was distinguished by his clean-cut image; many hits were covers of black artists: Fats Domino's *Ain't That A Shame*, Ivory Joe Hunter's *I Almost Lost My Mind*, most ludicrously Little Richard's *Long Tall Sally*; ballads included *Love Letters In The Sand* and *April Love*, both chart toppers. He made several films; fade from charts was accompanied by business and marriage trouble; he turned to religion, made gospel albums and had country hits. Doanld Clarke, 24 August 1988.
Born Charles Euguene Boone in Florida in 1934, this American singer is a direct descendant of legendary frontiersman Daniel Boone. Between the start of the rock'n'roll era in the mid-Fifties and the arrival of the Beatles in the early Sixties, Pat Boone was the United States' second most successful singer after Elvis Presley. He chalked up 38 American Top 40 singles and 26 in Britain. He achieved this status by being the exact opposite of everything that Elvis stood for. (The two men were of similar age). While Presley was popularising a revolutionary new form of music down and doing so in a sexually exciting fashion, Boone was watering that music down and presenting it to the youth of America in a cleaned up version that their parents approved of. Between 1955 and 1958 he successfully combined his career as a teenage idol with that if studying at university, graduating in speech and English in the latter year. Boone's first big record came in the spring of '55, when *Two hearts* peaked at No. 16 on the US charts. It was followed by *Ain't that a shame*, his first American No. 1; it was also his first UK chart record, reaching No. 7. In both countries it outsold the original version by Fats Domino. 1956 gave him his only British No. 1: *I'll be home* was on top for five weeks and peaked at No. 4 in his home country. But it was his 1956 versions of two Little Richard hits that best summed up Boone's approach: his politely sung renditions of *Tutti frutti* and *Long tall Sally* were an embarrassment to lovers of authentic rock'n'roll; but to those youngsters who were unable or unwilling to rebel, but who still wanted to be associated with the new music. Boone represented an acceptable middle ground. His tally of six American chart toppers comprises 1955's *Ain't that a shame*, 1956's *I almost lost my mind* plus *Dont forbid me*, *Love letters in the sand* and *April love* (1957) and *Moody river* (1961). As the Fifties went on, he progressed from pseudo rock style to a string of slushy, romantic ballads. *Love letters in the sand*, his biggest US hit of all, is a good example of the latter sound. He and his astute record company were adept at finding the right songs to record, an important matter in his sustained chart success. He was also a major film and TV attraction. His final Top 10 single in both the US and UK was perhaps his best. *Speedy gonazales* was an engaging, Latin flavoured number that hit the charts in the summer of '62. The advent of Beatlemania finally killed off Boone's hit making status, but he remained active in showbusiness. However, his fundamentalist Christianity led him more and more into the field of religious performances. His daughter Debby Boone made chart history in 1977 - her single *You light up my life* became the first record for over twenty years to stay on top of the US chart for ten weeks. One of Pat Boone's 1959 hits was called *Twixt twelve and twenty*. A book of this title was published under his name (though probably ghost written): it was a manual for good, clean living and advised teenagers not to rebel against authority, for authority knew best. This wholesome attitude epitomised Boone's character, a character summarised by Dean Martin who was once quoted as saying: 'I shook hands with Pat Boone and my whole right side sobered up'. (Bob MacDonald).

AIN'T THAT A SHAME?
Tracks: / Ain't that a shame.
7" Single: Released Nov '55, on London-American, Deleted '58. Catalogue no: **HLD 8173**

APRIL LOVE
7" Single: Released Dec '57, on London-American, Deleted '60. Catalogue no: **HLD 8512**

APRIL LOVE (OLD GOLD)
Tracks: / April love.
7" Single: Released Jul '82, on Old Gold, by Old Gold Records. Deleted Jul '88. Catalogue no: **OG 9211**

DON'T FORBID ME
Tracks: / Don't forbid me.
7" Single: Released Feb '57, on London-American, Deleted '60. Catalogue no: **HLD 8370**

FOR A PENNY
Tracks: / For a penny.
7" Single: Released May '59, on London-American, Deleted '62. Catalogue no: **HLD 8855**

FRIENDLY PERSUASION (OLD GOLD)
Tracks: / Friendly persuasion.
7" Single: Released Jul '82, on Old Gold, by Old Gold Records. Catalogue no: **OG 9210**

FRIENDLY PERSUASION (SINGLE)
Tracks: / Friendly persuasion.
7" Single: Released Dec '56, on London-American, Deleted '59. Catalogue no: **HLD 8346**

GEE BUT IT'S LONELY
Tracks: / Gee but it's lonely.
7" Single: Released Dec '58, on London-American, Deleted '61. Catalogue no: **HLD 8739**

I ALMOST LOST MY MIND
Tracks: / I almost lost my mind.
7" Single: Released Aug '56, on London-American, Deleted '59. Catalogue no: **HLD 8303**

IF DREAMS COME TRUE
Tracks: / If dreams come true.
7" Single: Released Aug '58, on London-American, Deleted '61. Catalogue no: **HLD 8675**

I'LL BE HOME
Tracks: / I'll be home.
7" Single: Released Apr '56, on London-American, Deleted '59. Catalogue no: **HLD 8253**

I'LL REMEMBER TONIGHT
Tracks: / I'll remember tonight.
7" Single: Released Jan '59, on London-American, Deleted '62. Catalogue no: **HLD 8775**

I'LL SEE YOU IN MY DREAMS
Tracks: / I'll see you in my dreams.
7" Single: Released Feb '62, on London-American, Deleted '65. Catalogue no: **HLD 9504**

IT'S TOO SOON TO KNOW
Tracks: / It's too soon to know.
7" Single: Released Apr '58, on London-American, Deleted '61. Catalogue no: **HLD 8574**

JOHNNY WILL
Tracks: / Johnny will.
7" Single: Released Dec '61, on London-American, Deleted '64. Catalogue no: **HLD 9461**

LONG TALL SALLY
Tracks: / Long tall Sally.
7" Single: Released Jul '56, on London-American, Deleted '59. Catalogue no: **HLD 8291**

LOVE LETTERS IN THE SAND (OLD GOLD)
7" Single: Released Jul '82, on Old Gold, by Old Gold Records. Deleted Jul '88. Catalogue no: **OG 9209**

LOVE LETTERS IN THE SAND (SINGLE)
Tracks: / Love letters in the sand.
7" Single: Released Aug '57, on London-American, Deleted '60. Catalogue no: **HLD 8445**

MAIN ATTRACTION, THE
Tracks: / Main attraction.
7" Single: Released Oct '62, on London-American, Deleted '65. Catalogue no: **HLD 6920**

MOODY RIVER
Tracks: / Moody river.
7" Single: Released Jul '61, on London-American, Deleted '64. Catalogue no: **HLD 9350**

QUANDO QUANDO QUANDO
Tracks: / Quando, quando, quando.
7" Single: Released May '62, on London-American, Deleted '65. Catalogue no: **HLD 9543**

REMEMBER YOU'RE MINE
Tracks: / Remember you're mine / There's a goldmine in the sky.
7" Single: Released Sep '57, on London-American, Deleted '60. Catalogue no: **HLD 8479**

SPEEDY GONZALES
Tracks: / Speedy Gonzales.
7" Single: Released Jul '62, on London-American, Deleted '65. Catalogue no: **HLD 9573**

SPEEDY GONZALES (OLD GOLD)
Tracks: / Speedy Gonzales.
7" Single: Released Jul '82, on Old Gold, by Old Gold Records. Catalogue no: **OG 9213**

SUGAR MOON
Tracks: / Sugar moon.
7" Single: Released Jun '58, on London-American, Deleted '61. Catalogue no: **HLD 8640**

TWIXT TWELVE AND TWENTY
Tracks: / Twixt twelve and twenty.
7" Single: Released Jul '59, on London-American, Deleted '62. Catalogue no: **HLD 8910**

WALKING THE FLOOR OVER YOU
Tracks: / Walking the floor over you.
7" Single: Released Jun '60, on London-American, Deleted '63. Catalogue no: **HLD 9138**

WHITE CHRISTMAS
Tracks: / White Christmas.
7" Single: Released Dec '57, on London-American, Deleted '60. Catalogue no: **HLD 8520**

WHY BABY WHY
Tracks: / Why baby why.
7" Single: Released Apr '57, on London-American, Deleted '60. Catalogue no: **HLD 8404**

WITH THE WIND AND THE RAIN IN YOUR HAIR
Tracks: / With the wind and the rain in your hair.
7" Single: Released Apr '59, on London-American, Deleted '62. Catalogue no: **HLD 8824**

WONDERFUL TIME UP THERE
Tracks: / Wonderful time up there, A.
7" Single: Released Apr '58, on London-American, Deleted '61. Catalogue no: **HLD 8574**

Boonierats

MESSING EP
Tracks: / Leech reef / Flag day / Incoming / Tiresome.
12" Single: Released Jan '88, on Fillet, Catalogue no: **TF 569**

Booth, Patrick

EASIER SAID THAN DONE
Tracks: / Easier said than done.
7" Single: Released Jul '87, on Supreme, by Supreme Records. Catalogue no: **SUPE 115**
12" Single: Released Jul '87, on Supreme, by Supreme Records. Catalogue no: **SUPET 115**

Boothe, Ken

Biographical details: Born in Denham Town, Jamaica, reggae singer Boothe first became active in the Jamaican music business in the late 60's. Becoming a cult figure in Britain in the early 70's, he suddenly hit the UK national charts for the first time in the autumn of 1974 when his reggae remake of the '72 Bread hit, *Everything I Own*, went to No 1 -- 31 places higher than David Gates and his band had managed to take the song in Britain. Boothe's infectious version included amendments ("Everything I own" is inexplicably replaced by "Anything I own") and, in his Jamaican accent, he articulates the line "The finest years I ever knew is all the years I had with you". Like many acts of his genre his pop success was short-lived. A follow-up hit, *Crying Over You*, reached No 11 in Britain, then his chart career ended. He remains active in the recording studio. (Bob MacDonald, 1984.)
Boothe, Ken. A Jamaican singer with a distinctive style who emerged as a soloist at Studio One during the rock steady era, had hits in the late '60s and became something of a pin-up with teen-age girls in the reggae world; his cover of David Gate's *Everything I Own* was a UK no. 1 in 1974, after several months heading the reggae chart; the album of that name also included his no. 11 hit *Crying Over You*. Donald Clarke, 24 August 1988..

ARCHIBELLA
Tracks: / Archibella.
12" Single: Released Oct '84, on Small Acts, Catalogue no: **Unknown**

BABY I LOVE YOU TOO
Tracks: / Baby I love you too.
12" Single: Released Sep '83, on Tads, Catalogue no: **TRD 26783**

BAD RISK
Tracks: / Bad risk / Sitting on a mountain top.
7" Single: Released Aug '87, on Silverman, by Priority Records. Deleted Jan '88. Catalogue no: **SMRC 1**
12" Single: Released Aug '87, on Silverman, by Priority Records. Deleted Jan '88. Catalogue no: **12SMRC 1**

BRING IT ON HOME TO ME
Tracks: / Bring it on home to me.
12" Single: on Trojan, by Trojan Records. Deleted May '88. Catalogue no: **TROT 9092**
7" Single: on Trojan, by Trojan Records. Deleted May '88. Catalogue no: **TRO 9092**

CLASSIC TRACKS
CD 5": Released Nov '88, on Classic Tracks, Catalogue no: **CDEP 5 C**

CRYING OVER YOU
Tracks: / Crying over you.
7" Single: Released Dec '74, on Trojan, by Trojan Records. Deleted '77. Catalogue no: **TR 7944**

EVERYTHING I OWN (OLD GOLD)
Tracks: / Everything I own / Help me make it through the night / Love of the common people.
7" Single: Released Apr '83, on Old Gold, by Old Gold Records. Catalogue no: **OG 9271**
CD 5": Released 28 Mar '89, on Old Gold, by Old Gold Records. Catalogue no: **OG 6126**

EVERYTHING I OWN (SINGLE)
Tracks: / Everything I own.
7" Single: Released Sep '74, on Trojan, by Trojan Records. Deleted '77. Catalogue no: **TR 7920**
12" Single: Released Mar '87, on Trojan, by Trojan Records. Catalogue no: **CSY 3**
7" Single: Released Mar '87, on Trojan, by Trojan Records. Catalogue no: **7 CSY 3**

IF I HAD KNOWN
Tracks: / If I had known / Welfare people.
12" Single: Released Jul '83, on Greensleeves, by Greensleeves Records. Catalogue no: **GRED 122**

LOVE IS REAL
Tracks: / Love is real.
12" Single: Released Nov '84, on White Label (1), Catalogue no: **Unknown**

MAN IS A MAN, A
Tracks: / Man is a man, A / Man is a man, A (inst).
12" Single: Released Jul '88, on Greensleeves, by Greensleeves Records. Catalogue no: **GRED 224**

OH WHAT A SMILE
Tracks: / Oh what a smile / Open the door.
12" Single: Released Aug '86, on Blue Mountain, Catalogue no: **BMD 024**

SAY YOU
Tracks: / Say you.
12" Single: Released Aug '88, on Germaine, Catalogue no: **DGT 41**

TELL ME DARLING
Tracks: / Tell me darling.
12" Single: Released May '89, on Live & Love, Catalogue no: **LLD 120**

THINKING
Tracks: / Thinking / Valley of peace.
12" Single: Released Mar '84, on Greensleeves, by Greensleeves Records. Catalogue no: **GRED 140**

WHO GETS YOUR LOVE?
Tracks: / Who gets your love?.
7" Single: on Trojan, by Trojan Records. Deleted May '88. Catalogue no: **TRO 9052**

YOU'RE NO GOOD
Tracks: / You're no good.
12" Single: on Attack, Deleted '88. Catalogue no: **TACK 6**

Boothe, Patrick

DANCE ALL NIGHT
Tracks: / Dance all night / Dance all night (part 2).
7" Single: Released May '82, on Streetwave, Deleted '85. Catalogue no: **STRA 2213**
12" Single: Released May '82, on Streetwave, Deleted '85. Catalogue no: **STRA 13 2213**

NEVER KNEW LOVE LIKE THIS BEFORE
Tracks: / Never knew love like this before.
7" Single: Released Aug '82, on Streetwave, Deleted Aug '85. Catalogue no: **STRA 2596**
12" Single: Released Aug '82, on Streetwave, Deleted Aug '85. Catalogue no: **STRA 132596**

Boothill Footappers

GET YOUR FEET OUT OF MY SHOES
Tracks: / Get your feet out of my shoes / Milk train / True blues / People get ready / Chasing women.
7" Single: Released Jul '84, on Go Discs, by Chrysalis Records. Deleted '87. Catalogue no: **TAP 1**

Bootleggers

HOT MIX 1
Tracks: / Hot mix 1.
7" Single: Released Aug '87, on Polo, by Polo Records. Deleted '88. Catalogue no: **POLO 43**
12" Single: Released Aug '87, on Polo, by Polo Records. Deleted '88. Catalogue no: **POLO 12-43**

HOT MIX 2
Tracks: / Hot mix 2.
12" Single: Released Sep '87, on Polo, by Polo Records. Deleted '88. Catalogue no: **POLO 12-44**
7" Single: Released Sep '87, on Polo, by Polo Records. Deleted '88. Catalogue no: **POLO 44**

HOT MIX 3
Tracks: / Hot mix 3.
7" Single: Released Dec '88, on Bass, by Champion Records. Catalogue no: **BSS 5**
12" Single: Released Dec '88, on Bass, by Champion Records. Catalogue no: **BSS 125**

HOT MIX 4
Tracks: / Hot mix 4 / Hot mix 4 (version).
12" Single: Released Sep '89, on Bass, by Champion Records. Catalogue no: **BSS 129**
7" Single: Released Sep '89, on Bass, by Champion Records. Catalogue no: **BSS 9**

Boots For Dancing

BOOTS FOR DANCING
Tracks: / Boots for dancing / Parachute / Guitars and girl trouble.
7" Single: Released Apr '80, on Fast Products, by Fast Product Records. Deleted '83. Catalogue no: **POP 002**

OOH BOP SH'BANG
Tracks: / Ooh bop sh'bang.
7" Single: Released Apr '82, on Fast, by Fast Forward Records. Catalogue no: **WAY 100**

RAIN SONG
Tracks: / Rain song.
7" Single: Released Nov '80, on Pop Aural, Catalogue no: **POP 006**

Bootsy's Rubber Band

Biographical details: Bootsy's Rubber Band were formed in 1976 by bassist/guitarist/vocalist William 'Bootsy' Collins. This eccentric figure first came to public attention as bassist with James Brown's backing group, the 'JBs'. He was then a leading member of Parliament and Funkadelic, the twin bands formed by zany funk star George Clinton. When Collins begun to overshadow Clinton in these two combos, the latter suggested that Collins form his own ensemble. This he did, making use of some of the P/Funk players. In common with all of Clinton's activities, the Bootsy band enjoyed enourmous recognition amongst the funk fraternity, but was both too hard-sounding and too eccentric to cross over to the pop market. Their third LP *Bootsy: Player Of The year* yielded their only British hit 45: *Bootzilla* reached No. 43 in July 1978. (Bob MacDonald, 1984)..

BOOTZILLA
Tracks: / Bootzilla.
7" Single: Released Jul '78, on Warner Bros., by WEA Records. Deleted '81. Catalogue no: **K 17196**

Boottee Duke

BROADWAY
Tracks: / Broadway.
7" Single: Released Nov '86, on Hardback, by Hardback Records. Catalogue no: **7 BOSS 2**
12" Single: Released Nov '86, on Hardback, by Hardback Records. Catalogue no: **BOSS 2**

Bop

Biographical details: A jazz genre developed by black musicians in the early 1940s, the beginning of the modern era in jazz. Its name came from re-bop or be-bop, onomatopoeiac in origin from the music itself, or possibly from scat-singing. Rhythm section playing had become smoother and the technical fluency of soloists higher than ever; influenced by Lester Young, Charlie Christian, Jo Jones, Art Tatum and others, younger musicians such as Charlie Parker, Dizzy Gillespie, Kenny Clarke, Thelonius Monk, Miles Davis, Fats Navarro, Max Roach and many others jammed in Harlem clubs, improvising on the chords instead of the melody and inventing new tunes from chord structures of standards: they used altered chords and higher intervals, and insisted on using a wider range of notes (a process that has been going on in classical music for centuries).
Tempi were often furiously fast or very slow (but even when the tempo was slow the soloist often played fast, using machine-gun runs of sixteen notes).
Syncopation finally disappeared; new accents within measures, together with phrases of unusual lengths, changed even the rhythmic nature of jazz; in addition, the drum kit emerged as a musical instrumental in its own right, and the bass player often played often played on top of the beat, taking over some of the drummer's timekeeping function, whereas earlier he had more often played behind the beat, taking over some of the drummer's timekeeping function, whereas earlier he had more often played behind the beat. An intense music was created, technically brilliant, full of pride, sardonic wit and fierce joy. The scene was accompanied by attitudes and language incomprehensible to outsiders (some of this had been pioneered by Young; the zany wit of Gillespie was also important). The chromatic style of Coleman Hawkins had been influencial; he encouraged boppers, hiring them for record dates. The first bop records were made in 1944-45 by small groups on independent labels, mainly Savoy. Bop big bands were led by Gillespie and Billy Eckstine; the white bands of Boyd Raeburn and Woody Herman were heavily influenced by bop, but the development of these big bands (and of bop itself) was poorly documented on disc because of USA musicians' union strikes, which also meant that bop emerged very suddenly in the late '40s upon an unsuspecting public. There were white boppers in black combos (e.g. Reg Rodney, Joe Albany, Al Haig), but pressure on black leaders to practise Crow Jim sent them into obsurity later; many made comebacks as bop became repertory music in the '70s. Boppers often flattened the fifth note of a chord, inventing short routes between keys: Eddie Condon said, 'We don't flatten our fifths, we drink 'em' (but Igor Stravinsky had used flattened fifths in 1910). Alot of people hated it; Cab Calloway called it 'Chinese music'. Bop was not a revolution, but a further flowering of an artform already decades old; the orthodoxy is that bop was not commercially successful because it wasn't dance music, but bop was fun, and Gillespie regarded it as dance music. He formed the DeeGee label and went broke, but reissues (now on Savoy) hold up much better than the pop of the period. Bop was also very obviously black music, long before the Civil Rights era, and in any case the music business tends to mishandle anything it doesn't understand, as it did rock'n'roll a decade later. The Max Roach Quintet of 1954-55, with Cifford Brown and Harold Land (replaced by Sonny Rollins) was probably the peak of bop's perfection; modern jazz was already developed in several direction: sheer beauty came from Miles Davis's quintet of 1956, and as composers and arrangers such as Tadd Dameron, Mal Waldon, George Russell, Gil Evans and Benny Golson applied their talent to the new harmonic ideas. Independent USA labels (Prestige, Riverside and especially Blue Note) developed the blowing session, where the tenor saxophone was king, leading to further developed of the music by Sonny Rollins, John Coltrane and many others. The 'hard top' school of Art Blakey's Jazz Messengers, playing a less frenetic mucic with modern harmonies and a strong backbeat, graduated scores of fine young musicians, Milt Jackson, Horace Silver, Bobby Timmons, Lee Morgan and Herbie Hancock played modern jazz with soul, which came to be called funk, and led directly to the cliches of today's jazz-funk, but also to a renewal of interest in the roots of today's pop music..

TOO YOUNG TO KNOW
Tracks: / Too young to know.
7" Single: Released Feb '84, on EMI, by EMI Records. Catalogue no: **PAGE 1**

Bop Natives

ON THE CASE
Tracks: / On the case.
7" Single: Released Sep '81, on King (USA), Catalogue no: **KC 1**

Bop-Baroque

GREAT TEMPTATION
Tracks: / Great temptation.
7" Single: Released Oct '87, on Wye, by Wye Records. Deleted '88. Catalogue no: **TEMMBC 3**

INTERNATIONAL
Tracks: / International / Save my soul / Final kiss, The.
12" Single: Released 22 Aug '88, on Wye, by Wye Records. Deleted Feb '89. Catalogue no: **BOP 112**
7" Single: Released Jan '89, on Wye, by Wye Records. Catalogue no: **BOP 17**
7" Single: Released 22 Aug '88, on Wye, by Wye Records. Deleted Jan '89. Catalogue no: **WRC BOP 1**

Boray, Lisa

TONIGHT
12" Single: Released Oct '83, on Albion, by Albion Records. Catalogue no: **12ION 154**
7" Single: Released Oct '83, on Albion, by Albion Records. Catalogue no: **ION 154**

Border Boys

TRIBUTE, THE
Tracks: / Tribute.
12" Single: Released Nov '83, on Les Disques Du Crepuscule(Belgium), by Les Disques Du Crepuscule(Belgium). Catalogue no: **TWI 174**

Borghesia

NAKED UNIFORMED DEAD
Tracks: / Naked uniformed dead.
12" Single: Released '88, on Play It Again Sam(Belgium), by Play It Again Sam (Belgium). Catalogue no: **BIAS 86**
CD 5": Released Sep '88, on Play It Again Sam(Belgium), by Play It Again Sam (Belgium). Catalogue no: **BIAS 86CD**

SURVEILLANCE AND PUNISHMENT
Tracks: / Surveillance and punishment / Raga / Am I / Disciple.
12" Single: Released Apr '89, on Play It Again Sam(Belgium), by Play It Again Sam (Belgium). Catalogue no: **BIAS 120**

Born B.C

POWER AND PRIVILEGE
Tracks: / Power and privilege.
7" Single: Released Oct '83, on Expertise Noise & Tapes, Catalogue no: **FIRST 1**

Borsig, Alexander Von

HIROSHIMA
Tracks: / Hiroshima.
12" Single: Released Aug '83, on Supermax (Germany), Catalogue no: **6371**

Bosanquet, Reginald

DANCE WITH ME
Tracks: / Dance with me / News letter.
7" Single: Released Feb '80, on Pye, Deleted Feb '83. Catalogue no: **7P 167**

Bosca

WE'LL BE TOGETHER
Tracks: / We'll be together.
12" Single: Released May '85, on Oval, by Oval Records. Catalogue no: **OVALT 33-12**

Bose

LAY DOWN ON ME
Tracks: / Lay down on me / Como un lobo / Seems like it's midnight forever (Available on 12" single only.).
12" Single: Released Apr '88, on WEA, by WEA Records. Catalogue no: **YZ 183T**
7" Single: Released Apr '88, on WEA, by WEA Records. Catalogue no: **YZ 183**

LAY DOWN ON ME (REMIX)
Tracks: / Lay down on me (remix) / Como un lobo / Seems it's like midnight forever (Available on 12" format only.).
12" Single: Released Nov '88, on WEA, by WEA Records. Catalogue no: **YZ 322T**
12" Single: Released Nov '88, on WEA, by WEA Records. Catalogue no: **YZ 322**

Bose, Miguel

IF YOU BREAK MY HEART
Tracks: / If you break my heart.
7" Single: Released Mar '82, on Epic, by CBS Records. Deleted '85. Catalogue no: **EPCA 2124**

LIVING ON THE WIRE
Tracks: / Living on the wire / Up to the up.
7" Single: Released 20 Jun '87, on WEA (International), by WEA Records. Deleted Jan '88. Catalogue no: **X 8561**
12" Single: Released 20 Jun '87, on WEA (International), by WEA Records. Deleted Jan '88. Catalogue no: **X 8561T**

YOU CAN'T STAY THE NIGHT
Tracks: / You can't stay the night / Imagination.
7" Single: Released Jun '82, on Epic, by CBS Records. Deleted Jun '85. Catalogue no: **EPCA 2530**

Boss

DANCING IN THE U.S.A...MEDLEY
Tracks: / Dancing in the U.S.A...medley / Lonely heart.
7" Single: Released Feb '86, on WEA, by WEA Records. Deleted Sep '87. Catalogue no: **X 8838**
12" Single: Released Feb '86, on WEA, by WEA Records. Catalogue no: **X 8838 T**

FEELING
Tracks: / Feeling / Dance crazy.
7" Single: Released Sep '87, on E.G., by E.G. Records. Deleted May '88. Catalogue no: **EGO 37**
12" Single: Released Sep '87, on E.G., by E.G. Records. Deleted '89. Catalogue no: **EGLX 37**

NO MORE HEROES
Tracks: / No more heroes (7" only) / No more heroes (the MBE on mix) (12" only) / Fresh beat.
7" Single: Released Apr '88, on E.G., by E.G. Records. Catalogue no: **EGO 39**
12" Single: Released Apr '88, on E.G., by E.G. Records. Catalogue no: **EGOX 39**

RUDE BOYS ARE BACK IN TOWN
Tracks: / Rude boys are back in town / Live fast die laughing.
7" Single: Released May '80, on RAK, by EMI Records. Deleted '83. Catalogue no: **RAK 315**

WHEN THE CHIPS ARE DOWN
Tracks: / When the chips are down / War war war.
7" Single: Released Aug '80, on RAK, by EMI Records. Deleted '83. Catalogue no: **RAK 320**

Boss Beat

LET THERE BE DRUMS
Tracks: / Let there be drums / Caramba / Let there be drums (Only on 12" & CD) / Let there be drums (On 12' only) / Let there be drums (only on CD).
Note: Boss Beat relive the fast furious fun of the sixties generation with their eighties style cover version of Sanday Nelson's 'Let there be drums' originally released and a huge hit in 1961.
7" Single: Released 3 Oct '88, on Siren, by Virgin Records. Catalogue no: **SRN 91**
12" Single: Released 3 Oct '88, on Siren, by Virgin Records. Catalogue no: **SRNT 91**
CD 3": Released '88, on Siren, by Virgin Records. Catalogue no: **SRNCD 91**

Boss Brothers

CANDLE
Tracks: / Candle / Roll me over.
7" Single: Released Apr '80, on Mercury, by Phonogram Ltd. Deleted Apr '83. Catalogue no: **6007254**

HARPS OF BRETAGNE
Tracks: / Harps of Bretagne / Where are you going.
7" Single: Released Aug '80, on Mercury, by Phonogram Ltd. Deleted '83. Catalogue no: **MER 32**

WHERE ARE YOU GOING
Tracks: / Where are you going / Nicola.
7" Single: Released 20 Jul '80, on Mercury, by Phonogram Ltd. Deleted '83. Catalogue no: **MER 24**

Boss Squad

WORST SONG EVER, THE
Tracks: / Worst song ever, The.
Note: Sung by most of the football managers in the first division including Brian Clough, Jack Charlton, Bobby Robson, George Graham Et Al. Also features Saint and Greavsie and the England national team. Proceeds will go to Sport Aid '88 to save lives and build a better future for children worldwide.
7" Single: Released Apr '88, on Polydor, by Polydor Ltd. Catalogue no: **FOOTY 1**

Bossbone, Pat

BREAKAWAY MUSIC
Tracks: / Breakaway music.
12" Single: Released Apr '83, on Sunburn, by Orbitone Records. Catalogue no: **SBD 23**

LITTLE MISS HARD-TO-GET
Tracks: / Little Miss Hard to Get.
12" Single: Released Jul '83, on Sunburn, by Orbitone Records. Catalogue no: **SBD 32**

SOCA MAGIC
Tracks: / Soca magic.
12" Single: Released Mar '83, on Sunburn, by Orbitone Records. Catalogue no: **SBD 14**

Boston

Biographical details: Brad Delp, Barry Goudreau, Sib Hashian, Tom Scholz and Fran Sheehan named their band -- formed in 1975 by guitar and keyboards player Scholz -- after their home city in Massachusetts, USA. Released the following year, their debut album, called, simply, Boston, was a surprise smash, selling millions of copies in the States. They were at the forefront of a new wave of mid-70's American rock bands, which also produced hit outfits like Kansas and Foreigner. Despite the name, the group's sound was a traditional West Coast mix of powerful but melodic guitars combined with strong songs. Their album yielded a US Top 5 single, More Than A Feeling. The band cracked the UK market in early '77, with the album reaching No 11 and the single peaking at No 22. Initial success was not sustained: the long-awaited second LP, Don't Look Back, was a critical and commercial disappointment, although the title track reached No 4 in the US as a single. Boston broke up in 1979. (Bob MacDonald, 1984.)
Boston. A USA hard rock band formed by Tom Scholz (guitar, keyboards, vocals), an MIT graduate from Toledo Ohio who played nights in Boston bar bands, worked days for Polaroid and dabbled in home recordings: home-made demos (later bootleged as *We Found It In The Trash Can, Honest*) secured a contract with Epic. With Bradley Delp on vocals, Sib Hashian on drums, Barry Goudreau on guitar, Fran Sheehan on bass, all from Boston, first album *Boston* (on which Hashian's predecessor Jim Masdea also appeared) was the fastest selling debut in history, entering USA chart in 1976 and reached no. 3, with three top 40 singles; ringing harmonies, twin lead guitars and classy production by John Boylan made ideal driving music for the US male's in-car cassette deck.
The album reached no. 11 in UK and re-charted to no. 58 on budget reissue in '81. Sequel *Don't Look Back* sold only half as many copies; after a tour all except Sheehan sessioned for Sammy Hegar; Goudreau made a solo album, then formed pomp-rockers Orion The Hunter; Scholz worked on the Rockman, a gadget for obtaining overdriven guitar sound at low volumes for home recording; then *Third Stage* in 1986 was a surprise hit on MCA, with no. 1 USA single *Amanda*, Delp still on board, Masdea on drums, Scholz doing most of the rest. Donald Clarke, 24 August 1988..

AMANDA
Tracks: / My destination.
7" Single: Released Jan '87, on MCA, by MCA Records. Catalogue no: **MCA 1092**
12" Single: Released Jan '87, on MCA, by MCA Records. Catalogue no: **MCAS 1901**

CAN'TCHA SAY (YOU BELIEVE IN ME)
Tracks: / Can'tcha say (you believe in me) / Still in love / Call the engines / Launch, The.
CD 5": Released May '87, on MCA, by MCA Records. Catalogue no: **DMCA 1150**
7" Single: Released May '87, on MCA, by MCA Records. Catalogue no: **MCA 1150**
12" Single: Released May '87, on MCA, by MCA Records. Catalogue no: **MCAT 1150**

DON'T LOOK BACK (SINGLE)
Tracks: / Don't look back.
7" Single: Released Oct '78, on Epic, by CBS Records. Deleted '81. Catalogue no: **EPC 6653**

MORE THAN A FEELING
Tracks: / More than a feeling.
7" Single: Released Jan '77, on Epic, by CBS Records. Deleted '80. Catalogue no: **EPC 4658**

MORE THAN A FEELING (IMPORT)
Tracks: / More than a feeling / Foreplay / Long time.
CD 3": Released Aug '88, on Epic (USA), by CBS Records (USA). Catalogue no: **34K 02355**

MORE THAN A FEELING (OLD GOLD)
Tracks: / More than a feeling / Don't look back.
7" Single: Released May '83, on Old Gold, by Old Gold Records. Catalogue no: **OG 9299**

Boswell, Eve

PICKIN' A CHICKEN
Tracks: / Pickin' a chicken.
7" Single: Released Dec '55, on Parlophone, by EMI Records. Deleted '58. Catalogue no: **R 4082**

Botany 500

BULLY BEEF
Tracks: / Bully beef / Chill shake / My secret love.
12" Single: Released Jul '86, on Supreme Int.Editions, by Supreme Int.Records. Catalogue no: **EDITION 86 12**

Bottle Boys

BOTTLE BOYS
Tracks: / Bottle boys.
7" Single: Released Sep '84, on Sierra, by Sierra Records. Deleted Jun '87. Catalogue no: **FED 2**

Bottle Tops

I'LL NEVER DRINK AGAIN
Tracks: / I'll never drink again.
7" Single: Released Nov '87, on Young Blood, by Young Blood Records. Catalogue no: **YB SOBER 2**

Bottles

CRASH HELMET
Tracks: / Crash helmet.
7" Single: Released Jun '84, on Waterfront, by Waterfront Music. Catalogue no: **WFS 6**

Boucher, Judy

CAN'T BE WITH YOU TONIGHT
Tracks: / Can't be with you tonight.
7" Single: Released Dec '86, on Orbitone, by Orbitone Records. Catalogue no: **DR 721**
12" Single: Released Dec '86, on Orbitone, by Orbitone Records. Catalogue no: **OR 1221**

DREAMING OF A LITTLE ISLAND
Tracks: / Dreaming of a little island.
12" Single: Released Aug '85, on Orbitone, by Orbitone Records. Catalogue no: **ORB 10**

LOVELY PARADISE
Tracks: / Lovely paradise / Lovely paradise (version).
12" Single: Released May '86, on Orbitone, by Orbitone Records. Catalogue no: **DORB 14**

MY HEART IS YEARNING
Tracks: / My heart is yearning / My heart is yearning (version).
12" Single: Released Oct '86, on Orbitone, by Orbitone Records. Catalogue no: **DORB 16**

YOU CAUGHT MY EYE
Tracks: / You caught my eye.
12" Single: Released Jul '87, on Orbitone, by Orbitone Records. Catalogue no: **OR 1222**
7" Single: Released Jul '87, on Orbitone, by Orbitone Records. Catalogue no: **OR 722**

Boudoir

GO TO SLEEP MY BABY
Tracks: / Go to sleep my baby / Come on up.
7" Single: Released Nov '82, on V-Tone, Catalogue no: **VTONE 009**

Boulaye, Patti

HE'S MY GUY
Tracks: / He's my guy / Love for sale.
7" Single: Released Mar '81, on Celebrity, Deleted Mar '84. Catalogue no: **ASC 6**

I KNOW I'LL NEVER LOVE THIS WAY AGAIN
Tracks: / I know I'll never love this way again / All my love.
7" Single: Released Feb '80, on Polydor, by Polydor Ltd. Deleted Feb '83. Catalogue no: **POSP 115**

SWINGING ON A STAR
Tracks: / Swinging on a star.
7" Single: Released Oct '84, on Hollywood, by Hollywood Records. Catalogue no: **HWD 016**

THAT'S MY MAN
Tracks: / That's my man.
7" Single: Released Sep '82, on Shell, by Shell Records. Deleted '87. Catalogue no: **PB 1**

TRY ME I'M A WOMAN
Tracks: / Try me I'm a woman.
7" Single: Released Feb '83, on Shell, by Shell Records. Deleted '87. Catalogue no: **PB 4**

Boulevard

DO YOU WANNA DO THE DANCE
Tracks: / Do you wanna do the dance / Are angels flights of fancy.
7" Single: Released Jan '80, on RCA, by BMG Records (UK). Deleted Jan '85. Catalogue no: **PB 5203**

DREAM ON
Tracks: / Dream on.
7" Single: Released 16 Jan '89, on MCA, by MCA Records. Deleted 1 Jul '89. Catalogue no: **MCA 1308**
CD 5": Released 16 Jan '89, on MCA, by MCA Records. Catalogue no: **DMCA 1308**
12" Single: Released 16 Jan '89, on MCA, by MCA Records. Catalogue no: **MCAT 1308**

NEVER GIVE UP
Tracks: / Never give up / When the lights go down.
12" Single: Released May '89, on MCA, by MCA Records. Catalogue no: **MCAT 1326**
7" Single: Released May '89, on MCA, by MCA Records. Catalogue no: **MCA 1326**

Bounce The Mouse

LIKE LORRAINE
Tracks: / Like Lorraine / Sugar hate spice / man won't listen, The.
7" Single: Released Jun '89, on Big Round, Catalogue no: **BIGR 102**
12" Single: Released Jun '89, on Big Round, Catalogue no: **BIGR 102T**

WILL YOU EVER SAY?
Tracks: / Will you ever say?.
7" Single: Released Aug '88, on Mousetrap, by Mousetrap Records. Catalogue no: **BTM 1**

Bouncer, Peter

HUFF 'N' PUFF
Tracks: / Huff 'n' puff.
12" Single: Released Jul '89, on Y & D, Catalogue no: **YDD 0138**

READY FOR THE DANCE HALL TONIGHT
Tracks: / Don't test / Ready for the dance hall tonight.
12" Single: Released Dec '86, on Unity Sound, Catalogue no: **UN 023**

ROUGH NECK SOUND
Tracks: / Rough neck sound.
12" Single: Released Oct '88, on Y & D, Catalogue no: **YDDO 131**

Bouncing Czechs

I'M A LITTLE CHRISTMAS CRACKER
Tracks: / I'm a little Christmas cracker.
7" Single: Released Nov '84, on RCA, by BMG Records (UK). Catalogue no: **RCA 463**

LOOKING FOR A MAN

Tracks: / Looking for a man.
7" Single: Released Apr '82, on Pretentious, Deleted '83. Catalogue no: **JA 100**

Bouncy Bouncy

100TH MONKEY EFFECT
Tracks: / 100th monkey effect.
7" Single: Released Jan '85, on Wooltown, Catalogue no: **WOOL 1**

Bounty Hunters

COCONUT SHUFFLE
Tracks: / Coconut shuffle / Barrelhouse.
7" Single: Released 20 Jun '80, on EMI, by EMI Records. Deleted '83. Catalogue no: **RIC 112**

Bourgeois Tagg

I DON'T MIND AT ALL
Tracks: / I don't mind at all.
7" Single: Released Dec '87, on Island, by Island Records. Deleted Jun '88. Catalogue no: **IS 353**
CD 5": on Island, by Island Records. Deleted Jun '88. Catalogue no: **CID 353**
12" Single: Released Dec '87, on Island, by Island Records. Deleted Jun '88. Catalogue no: **12IS 353**

WAITING FOR THE WORLD TO TURN
Tracks: / Waiting for the world to turn / Changed.
12" Single: Released Apr '88, on Island, by Island Records. Deleted Jun '88. Catalogue no: **12IS 360**
7" Single: Released Apr '88, on Island, by Island Records. Deleted Jun '88. Catalogue no: **IS 360**

Bourgie Bourgie

BREAKING POINT
Tracks: / Breaking point / Apres ski.
7" Single: Released Feb '84, on MCA, by MCA Records. Catalogue no: **BOU 1**
12" Single: Released Feb '84, on MCA, by MCA Records. Catalogue no: **BOUT 1**

CARELESS
Tracks: / Careless / Change of attitude.
12" Single: Released Apr '84, on MCA, by MCA Records. Catalogue no: **BOUT 2**
7" Single: Released Apr '84, on MCA, by MCA Records. Catalogue no: **BOU 2**

Bovell, Dennis

BERTIE
Tracks: / Bertie / Bettah.
12" Single: Released Aug '81, on Fontana, by Phonogram Ltd. Deleted Aug '84. Catalogue no: **BOV 12**
7" Single: Released Aug '81, on Fontana, by Phonogram Ltd. Deleted Aug '84. Catalogue no: **BOV 7**

Bovver Boys

SUPERMIX PART ONE
12" Single: Released Oct '87, on Awesome (USA), Catalogue no: **AW 100**

Bow, Trevor

WOMAN
Tracks: / Woman.
12" Single: Released Dec '84, on 24 Karat, Catalogue no: **TKDM 002**

Bow Wow

YOU'RE MINE
Tracks: / You're mine / Don't cry baby.
" Single: Released Nov '83, on Heavy Metal Worldwide, by FM-Revolver Records. Catalogue no: **HM INT 2**

Bow Wow Wow

Biographical details: This British group comprised Matthew Ashman, Dave Barbarossa, Leroy Gorman and Annabella Lwin. Ashman and Barbarossa were members of an early Adam & The Ants line-up. At the suggestion of former Sex Pistols entrepreneur Malcolm McLaren they left Adam to join forces with Gorman and Lwin, a 14-year-old Burmese girl McLaren had discovered working in a London launderette. Their first single, C30, C60, C90, Go, was released in the summer of 1980. Co-written and produced by McLaren (who was also their manager), the content and promotion were typical of the man: its cheeky advocation of home taping was designed to antagonise record industry executives, who were in the midst of a major campaign to stamp out this illegal practice; and it promoted casettes and mini-cassette players, which McLaren saw as being favoured by the young of the early 80's. His adept publicity skills ensured that Bow Wow Wow were at the centre of controversy. The single reached No 34 in the UK and might have gone a lot higher but for the fact that EMI were reluctant to market or advertise it. The cassette theme continued in late '80 with the release of Your Cassette Pet, an eight-track cassette which, surprisingly, reached No 58 on the singles chart. In the following year there were three minor hit singles in Britain, plus a debut chart album entitles See Jungle! See Jungle! Go Join Your Gang Yeah City All Over! Go Ape Crazy! The cover, with young Annabella depicted nude, caused uproar and further fuel was added by the girl's mother, who claimed the entire Bow Wow Wow saga had taken place without her permission or approval. With the help of this continued publicity, Bow Wow Wow scored their first two UK Top Ten singles in 1982. Go Wild in the Country reached No 7 and I Want Candy peaked at No 9, although a well-intentioned initial experiment, of issuing this one as a one-sided single at a reduced price, failed. The album of the same name reached No 26. Annabella was now growing up. The group broke off their association with McLaren -- she said any "exploitation" had been solely for promotional and commercial reasons -- and in 1983 teamed with producer Mike Chapman for the album When The Going Gets Tough The Tough Get Going. But he was not able to give them the big hit that he gave Altered Images, another male group with an extrovert young girl singer. Bow Wow Wow had, it seemed, finished their brief, controversial career... (Bob MacDonald, 1984.)

Bow Wow Wow. UK post-punk pop group formed in 1980 by Malcolm McLaren, who swiped Adam Ant's backing group (drummer David Barbarossa, guitarist Matthew Ashman, Bassist Leigh Gorman) to back Annabella Lwin instead (born 1966 in Rangoon, Burma). She posed nude on a record cover at 15. McLaren's typical outrageousness combined with acceptable pop music amused the public for a few years. Annabella became ambitious; McLaren tried to control her behaviour by recruiting then-unkown Boy George as a potential replacement, but then dissasociated himself from the group, who recorded through 1983 attracting less and less attentionDonald Clarke, 24 August 1988.

Ashman and Barbarossa were members of an early incarnation of Adam & The Ants. At the suggestion of former Sex Pistols entrepreneur Malcolm McLaren, they parted company with Adam and joined forces with Gorman and Lwin to form Bow Wow Wow. McLaren discovered Lwin, a 14 year old Burmese born girl, working in a London laundrette. Their first single *C30, C60, C90, go* was released in the summer of 1980. Co-written and produced my McLaren (also their manager), everything about the record's content and promotion was typical of the man. Its cheeky advocation of home taping was designed to antagonise record industry, who were in the midst of a major campaign to stamp out this illegal practice. It was also designed to promote cassettes and mini-cassette players - McLaren saw these as the preferred youth media of the early Eighties (rather than vinyl Lps) and was leading a cassette movement. His adept publicity skills ensured that Bow Wow Wow were at the centre of controversy. The song reached No. 34 in the UK; it might have gone a lot higher had it not been for the fact that their record company EMI were reluctant to market the single or advertise it. The cassette theme continued in late '80 with the release of *Your cassette pet*, an eight track cassette that reached No. 58 on the singles chart, surprisingly. 1981 brought three further minor hit singles in Britain, plus a debut chart album entitled *See jungle see jungle go join your gang yeah city all over go ape crazy*. The cover of the LP caused uproar with young singer Annabella depicted nude. Further fuel wadded to the fire by the girl's mother, who claimed that the entire Bow Wow Wow saga had taken place without her permission or approval. With the help of this continued publicity, Bow Wow Wow scored their first two UK Top 10 singles in 1982. *Go wild in the country* reached No. 7 and was typical of the band's style - it featured tribal African jungle rhythms of the type that Adam Ant was performing more successfully, combined with Lwin's carefree, extroverted vocal performance. *I want candy*, a remake of a 1965 hit, peaked at No. 9. Initial UK pressings of this 45 were issued experiment failed. The album of the same name reached No. 26 on the British charts. Annabella was now growing up. The group broke off from their relationship with McLaren and the singer purged his exploitation of her, which she said had occured solely for promotional and commercial reasons. In 1983 Bow Wow Wow teamed with producer Mike Chapman on the album *When the going gets tough the tough get going*. But he was not able to give them the big hits that he gave Altered Images, another male group with a young female extrovert single. Bow Wow Wow had, it seemed, finished their brief but controversial career. (Bob MacDonald)a.

BOW WOW WOW
Tracks: / I want candy / See jungle / Go wild in the country / Chihuahua.
Cassingle: Released May '83, on RCA, by BMG Records (UK). Catalogue no: **RCXK 004**

C30 C60 C90 GO
Tracks: / C30 c60 c90 go.
12" Single: Released Jul '80, on EMI, by EMI Records. Catalogue no: **12EMI 5088**
7" Single: Released Jul '80, on EMI, by EMI Records. Catalogue no: **EMI 5088**

CHIHUAHUA
Tracks: / Chihuahua / Golly, golly, go buddy.
7" Single: Released Oct '81, on RCA, by BMG Records (UK). Catalogue no: **RCA 144**
12" Single: Released Oct '81, on RCA, by BMG Records (UK). Catalogue no: **RCAT 144**

DO YOU WANNA HOLD ME
Tracks: / Do you wanna hold me / What's the time.
7" Single: Released Feb '83, on RCA, by BMG Records (UK). Catalogue no: **RCA 314**
12" Single: Released Feb '83, on RCA, by BMG Records (UK). Catalogue no: **RCAT 314**

FOOLS RUSH IN
Tracks: / Fools rush in.
7" Single: Released Sep '82, on EMI, by EMI Records. Catalogue no: **EMI 5344**

GO WILD IN THE COUNTRY
Tracks: / Go wild in the country / I want candy.
7" Single: Released Jan '82, on RCA, by BMG Records (UK). Catalogue no: **RCA 175**
12" Single: Released Jan '82, on RCA, by BMG Records (UK). Catalogue no: **RCAT 175**

I WANT CANDY
Tracks: / I want candy
7" Single: Released May '82, on RCA, by BMG Records (UK). Catalogue no: **RCA 238**

LOUIS QUARTORZE (see panel below)
Tracks: / Louis Quartorze / Mile high club.
7" Single: Released Jul '82, on RCA, by BMG Records (UK). Catalogue no: **RCA 263**

PRINCE OF DARKNESS
Tracks: / Prince of darkness.
7" Single: Released Jul '81, on RCA, by BMG Records (UK). Catalogue no: **RCA 100**
12" Single: Released Aug '81, on RCA, by BMG Records (UK). Catalogue no: **RCAT 100**

SEE JUNGLE (JUNGLE BOY)
Tracks: / See jungle (jungle boy)
12" Single: Released Apr '82, on RCA, by BMG Records (UK). Catalogue no: **RCAT 220**
7" Single: Released Apr '82, on RCA, by BMG Records (UK). Catalogue no: **RCA 220**

WORK (NO NAH NO NO MY...)
Tracks: / Work (no nah no no my...)
7" Single: Released Mar '81, on EMI, by EMI Records. Catalogue no: **EMI 5153**
12" Single: Released Mar '81, on EMI, by EMI Records. Catalogue no: **12 EMI 5153**

YOUR CASSETTE PET
Tracks: / Your cassette pet.
7" Single: Released Dec '80, on EMI, by EMI Records. Deleted '83. Catalogue no: **WOW 1**

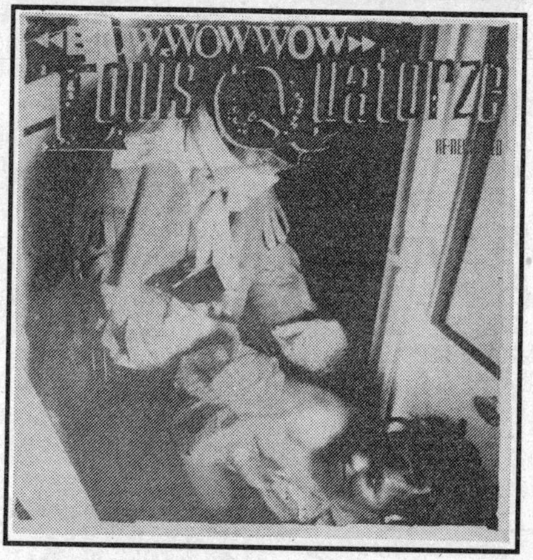

Bowie, Angie

CRYING (IN THE DARK)
Tracks: / Crying (in the dark).
7" Single: Released Oct '85, on Sierra, by Sierra Records. Deleted Jun '87. Catalogue no: **FED 17**
12" Single: Released Oct '85, on Sierra, by Sierra Records. Deleted Jun '87. Catalogue no: **FED 17T**

Bowie, David

Biographical details: The Prettiest Star, released on Philips sister label Mercury, flopped and now commands a seventy-pound price tag, not least due to the fact that Marc Bolan plays one of his most famous guitar solos on the track. This is the only official release which features both Bowie and Bolan together. Two more Mercury singles followed; I971's Memory Of A Free Festival, a number written in celebration of the Bowie-organised Beckenham Free Festival in 1969 and originally included on the Philips album. The Mercury version is notable for the inclusion of Mick Ronson on lead guitar for the first time; and Holy Holy, a very commercial single which met with very little airplay and consequently sank without trace. Should you decide to track down Bowie's three Mercury singles today you would need in excess of two hundred pounds for the three! Bowie's only album for the Mercury label marked a departure from the gentle folk-rock of the Philips lp. Now it was hard rock and themes of devils and angels and the master race. The album was of course the Man Who Sold The World, infamous for it's legendary 'drag' sleeve depicting Bowie spread across a chaise-longe attired in what seems to be a dress. In later interviews Bowie argued that it was in fact 'A man's dress'. In the USA, the drag sleeve was replaced by a somewhat ludicrous cartoon drawn by former King Bee George Underwood. The cartoon sleeve depicted a cowboy character lookingover his shoulder, standing outside a building which, in later years, was discoveredto be Cain Hill mental hospital in London where Bowie's brother Terry had been a patient for several years. The British release of the album is now one of the most famous of all rock collectables, and the price is heading for two hundred pounds. The music contained in the Man Who Sold The World was, on the whole, superb, from the haunting All The Madmen and After All, to the hard rock of the epic Width Of A Circle and Saviour Machine. The album met with little success on it's original release, but an RCA reissue in late I972 made the Top 20. Following the failure of TMWSTW, Bowie retired to his home at Haddon Hall in Bromley with new bride Angie and a posse of musicians including three friends from Hull, Mick Ronson, Trevor Bolder and Woody Woodmansey, all former members of a band called The Rats, and record producer Tony Visconti. It was here, during late 1970 and throughout 1971, that the musical foundations of two albums which were to help shape the 70's were laid. While Bowie and his band worked on the album which was to become Hunky Dory, he took lead vocals on two singles released on the B&C label, ostensibly by the band Arnold Corns who were in fact simply a bunch of Bowie's mates from the Beckenham area. The two singles are important due to the fact that they include embryonic versions of two tracks which eventually turned up on the Ziggy Stardust album, Hang On To Yourself and Moonage Daydream. As one would suspect, both singles flopped and in turn have become collectors items, as has a reissue from 1973 on the Mooncrest label. When Hunky Dory hit the streets in late 1971, most of Ziggy Stardust was in the can and the masterplan was about to begin. Hunky Dory still stands up today as one of the all time great albums, with almost every track a classic: Life On Mars, Andy Warhol, Quicksand, Bewlay Brothers (a song featuring Bowie's most complex lyric of all time), the Velvet Underground parody Queen Bitch, and the superb opening track Changes, which was taken off the album for the first single on RCA. Although Changes didn't make the charts, Bowie was now being noticed, and his increasingly flamboyant and exciting stage shows were adding to the legend. By the time Ziggy Stardust was released in February 1972, Bowie was one of the countries top live acts. Bowie gradually adopted the persona of Ziggy Stardust, the superstar cosmic rocker who became so big that the fans finally 'killed' the man. Bowie was Ziggy, Ziggy was Bowie, and Bowie/Ziggy was now a glamourous, glittering, untouchable megastar. The hits began, kicking off with Starman, then with John I'm Only Dancing, the Jean Genie, Life On Mars and Sorrow. The follow-up album, Aladdin Sane, was the fastest selling LP since the days of the Beatles. However, on July 3rd 1973, at the height of Bowiemania, David killed off the Ziggy character onstage at the Hammersmith Odeon on the last night of the Aladdin Sane tour. Bowie's announcement that "Not only is this the last show of the tour but it's the last show that we'll ever do" was taken in the wrong context by the press and rumors of Bowie's imminent retirement were greatly exagerrated. On July 4th, he arrived at the Chateau D'Heroville near Paris to record his next album, Pin-Ups. .

ABSOLUTE BEGINNERS
Tracks: / Absolute beginners (7" only) / Absolute beginners (dub mix) (On all versions) / Absolute beginners (full length version) (CD & 12" only).
7" Pic: Released Mar '86, on Virgin, by Virgin Records. Deleted '86. Catalogue no: **VSS 838**
12" Single: Released Mar '86, on Virgin, by Virgin Records. Catalogue no: **VS 838-12**
CD 3": Released '88, on Virgin, by Virgin Records. Catalogue no: **CDT 20**
12" Single: Released Mar '86, on Virgin, by Virgin Records. Deleted '89. Catalogue no: **VSG 838-12**
7" Single: Released Mar '86, on Virgin, by Virgin Records. Catalogue no: **VS 838**

ALABAMA SONG (SINGLE)
Tracks: / Alabama song / Space oddity.
12" Single: Released May '83, on RCA (Germany), Catalogue no: **PC 09854**
7" Single: Released Mar '80, on RCA, by BMG Records (UK). Deleted '83. Catalogue no: **BOW 5**

ARNOLD CORNS AND THE SPIDERS FROM MARS
Tracks: / Arnold Corns and the spiders from Mars / Hang on to yourself.
Note: David Bowie cut these three tracks in 1971, just prior to his signing with RCA. Intended as a showcase for the singing talents of Freddie Buretti, Bowie's costume designer, all three tracks (Looking For A Friend, Man In The Middle and Hang On To Yourself) are pure Bowie. Hang On To Yourself is very different to the version that ended up on Ziggy Stardust, while Looking For A Friend remains unreleased. Man In The Middle was issued twice in the 70's, firstly on B & C then two years later on Mooncrest. These two singles, and a third featuring a basic demo version of Moonage Daydream, are all scarce collectors items.
12" Single: Released May '85, on Krazy Kat, by Interstate Music. Catalogue no: **PAST 2**

ASHES TO ASHES
Tracks: / Ashes to ashes / Alabama song.
12" Single: Released Mar '86, on RCA, by BMG Records (UK). Catalogue no: **PC 9631**

ASHES TO ASHES (SINGLE)
Tracks: / Ashes to ashes / Move on.
7" Single: Released Aug '80, on RCA, by BMG Records (UK). Catalogue no: **BOW 6**

BAAL'S HYMN
Tracks: / Baal's hymn / Drowned girl, The / Remembering Marie / Dirty song, The / Ballad of the adventurers.
7" EP: Released Mar '82, on RCA, by BMG Records (UK). Deleted '85. Catalogue no: **BOW 11**
12" Single: Released Jul '83, on RCA, by BMG Records (UK). Catalogue no: **PG 45092**

BE MY WIFE
Tracks: / Be my wife.
7" Single: Released Jun '83, on RCA, by BMG Records (UK). Catalogue no: **BOW 511**

BEAUTY AND THE BEAST
Tracks: / Beauty and the beast.
7" Single: Released Jan '78, on RCA, by BMG Records (UK). Deleted '81. Catalogue no: **PB 1190**
7" Single: Released Jun '83, on RCA, by BMG Records (UK). Catalogue no: **BOW 512**

BLUE JEAN
Tracks: / Blue Jean / Dancing with the big boys.
7" Single: Released Sep '84, on EMI-America, by EMI Records. Catalogue no: **EA 181**
12" Single: Released Sep '84, on EMI-America, by EMI Records. Catalogue no: **12EA 181**

BOYS KEEP SWINGING
Tracks: / Boys keep swinging.
7" Single: Released Apr '79, on RCA, by BMG Records (UK). Catalogue no: **BOW 2**

BREAKING GLASS
Tracks: / Breaking glass.
7" Single: Released Jun '83, on RCA, by BMG Records (UK). Catalogue no: **BOW 520**

BREAKING GLASS EP
Tracks: / Breaking glass / Art decade / Ziggy Stardust.
7" EP: Released Dec '78, on RCA, by BMG Records (UK). Deleted '81. Catalogue no: **BOW 1**

CAT PEOPLE
Tracks: / Cat people / Paul's theme (jogging chase).
7" Single: Released Apr '82, on MCA, by MCA Records. Deleted '85. Catalogue no: **MCA 770**
12" Single: Released Dec '83, on MCA, by MCA Records. Catalogue no: **MCAT 770**

CHINA GIRL
Tracks: / China girl.
12" Single: Released May '83, on EMI-America, by EMI Records. Deleted Nov '88. Catalogue no: **12EA 157**
7" Single: Released May '83, on EMI-America, by EMI Records. Catalogue no: **EA 157**
7" Pic: Released May '83, on EMI-America, by EMI Records. Deleted '84. Catalogue no: **EAP 157**

DANCING IN THE STREET
Tracks: / Dancing in the street.
7" Single: Released Aug '85, on EMI-America, by EMI Records. Catalogue no: **EA 204**
12" Single: Released Aug '85, on EMI-America, by EMI Records. Deleted Nov '88. Catalogue no: **12EA 204**

DAY-IN, DAY-OUT
Tracks: / Day in, day out / Julie.
7" Single: Released Mar '87, on EMI-America, by EMI Records. Deleted Apr '88. Catalogue no: **EA 230**
12" Single: Released Mar '87, on EMI-America, by EMI Records. Deleted Apr '88. Catalogue no: **12EA 230**

DAY-IN DAY-OUT (REMIX)
Tracks: / Day in, day out (remix) / Day in, day out (ext dub mix) / Julie.
12" Single: Released Apr '87, on EMI-America, by EMI Records. Deleted Jul '87. Catalogue no: **12 EAX 230**

DIAMOND DOGS (SINGLE)
Tracks: / Diamond dogs / Holy holy.
7" Single: Released Jun '83, on RCA, by BMG Records (UK). Catalogue no: **BOW 504**
7" Single: Released Jun '74, on RCA, by BMG Records (UK). Deleted '77. Catalogue no: **APBO 0293**

DJ
Tracks: / D.J..
7" Single: Released Jul '79, on RCA, by BMG Records (UK). Deleted '82. Catalogue no: **BOW 3**
7" Single: Released Jun '83, on RCA, by BMG Records (UK). Catalogue no: **BOW 516**

DRIVE IN SATURDAY
Tracks: / Drive in saturday / Round and round.
7" Single: Released Jun '83, on RCA, by BMG Records (UK). Catalogue no: **BOW 501**
7" Single: Released Apr '73, on RCA, by BMG Records (UK). Deleted '76. Catalogue no: **RCA 2352**

FAME
Tracks: / Fame.
7" Single: Released Aug '75, on RCA, by BMG Records (UK). Deleted '78. Catalogue no: **RCA 2579**
7" Single: Released Jun '83, on RCA, by BMG Records (UK). Catalogue no: **BOW 507**

FASHION (SINGLE)
Tracks: / Fashion / Scream like a baby.
7" Single: Released Oct '80, on RCA, by BMG Records (UK). Catalogue no: **BOW 7**
12" Single: Released May '83, on RCA (Germany), Catalogue no: **PC 09638**
12" Single: Released Oct '80, on RCA, by BMG Records (UK). Catalogue no: **BOWT 7**

FASHIONS
Note: Limited edition set of ten picture discs in wallet.
7" Set: Released Nov '82, on RCA, by BMG Records (UK). Catalogue no: **BOW 100**

GOLDEN YEARS (SINGLE)
Tracks: / Golden years.
7" Single: Released Jun '83, on RCA, by BMG Records (UK). Catalogue no: **BOW 508**
7" Single: Released Oct '75, on RCA, by BMG Records (UK). Deleted '78. Catalogue no: **RCA 2640**

HEROES (SINGLE)
Tracks: / Heroes / Helden.
7" Single: Released Jun '83, on RCA, by BMG Records (UK). Catalogue no: **BOW 513**
12" Single: Released Mar '86, on RCA, by BMG Records (UK). Catalogue no: **PC 9821**
7" Single: Released Oct '77, on RCA, by BMG Records (UK). Deleted '80. Catalogue no: **PB 1121**
12" Single: Released May '83, on RCA (Germany), Catalogue no: **PC 09821**

JEAN GENIE
Tracks: / Jean Genie, The / Ziggy Stardust.
7" Single: Released Dec '72, on RCA, by BMG Records (UK). Deleted '75. Catalogue no: **RCAS 2302**
7" Single: Released Jun '83, on RCA, by BMG Records (UK). Catalogue no: **BOW 515**

JOHN I'M ONLY DANCING
Tracks: / John, I'm only dancing / Hang on to yourself.
7" Single: Released Jun '83, on RCA, by BMG Records (UK). Catalogue no: **BOW 517**
7" Single: Released Sep '72, on RCA, by BMG Records (UK). Deleted '75. Catalogue no: **RCA 2263**

JOHN I'M ONLY DANCING AGAIN
Tracks: / John, I'm only dancing again (1975) / John, I'm only dancing (1972).
7" Single: Released Dec '79, on RCA, by BMG Records (UK). Deleted '82. Catalogue no: **BOW 4**

KNOCK ON WOOD
Tracks: / Knock on wood / Panic in Detroit.
7" Single: Released Jun '83, on RCA, by BMG Records (UK). Catalogue no: **BOW 505**
7" Single: Released Sep '74, on RCA, by BMG Records (UK). Deleted '77. Catalogue no: **RCA 2466**

LAUGHING GNOME
Tracks: / Laughing gnome, The / Gospel according to Tony Day.
7" Single: Released Sep '73, on Deram, by London Records. Deleted '76. Catalogue no: **DM 123**
7" Single: Released May '82, on Decca, by Decca Records. Deleted '88. Catalogue no: **F 13924**

LET'S DANCE (SINGLE)
Tracks: / Let's dance.
12" Single: Released Mar '83, on EMI-America, by EMI Records. Deleted Aug '89. Catalogue no: **12EA 152**
Cassingle: Released Mar '83, on EMI-America, by EMI Records. Catalogue no: **TCEA 152**
7" Single: Released Mar '83, on EMI-America, by EMI Records. Catalogue no: **EA 152**

LIFE ON MARS
Tracks: / Life on Mars / Man who sold the world, The.
7" Single: Released Jun '73, on RCA, by BMG Records (UK). Deleted '76. Catalogue no: **RCA 2316**
7" Single: Released Jun '83, on RCA, by BMG Records (UK). Catalogue no: **BOW 502**

LONDON BOYS
Tracks: / London boys (P 1970) / Love you till Tuesday (P 1967) / Laughing gnome, The (P 1967) / Maid of Bond Street (P 1967).
Note: Written by David Bowie Licensed from the Decca Record Co.Ltd. Limited edition release.
12" Single: Released Aug '86, on Archive 4, by Castle Communications Records. Catalogue no: **TOF 105**
7" Single: Released Mar '82, on Decca, by Decca Records. Deleted '88. Catalogue no: **F 13579**

LOVING THE ALIEN
Tracks: / Loving the alien.
12" Pic: Released Jun '86, on EMI-America, by EMI Records. Catalogue no: **12EAP 196**
12" Single: Released May '85, on EMI-America, by EMI Records. Catalogue no: **12EA 195**
7" Single: Released May '85, on EMI-America, by EMI Records. Catalogue no: **EA 195**

MODERN LOVE
7" Single: Released Aug '83, on EMI-America, by EMI Records. Deleted Oct '87. Catalogue no: **EA 158**
12" Single: Released Aug '83, on EMI-America, by EMI Records. Deleted Oct '87. Catalogue no: **12 EA 158**

NEVER LET ME DOWN (SINGLE)
Tracks: / Never let me down.
12" Single: Released Aug '87, on EMI-America, by EMI Records. Deleted Apr '88. Catalogue no: **12EA 239**
7" Pic: Released Sep '87, on EMI-America, by EMI Records. Deleted Apr '88. Catalogue no: **EAP 239**
Cassingle: Released Aug '87, on EMI-America, by EMI Records. Deleted 31 Jul '88. Catalogue no: **TCEA 239**
7" Single: Released Aug '87, on EMI-America, by EMI Records. Deleted Apr '88. Catalogue no: **EA 239**

REBEL REBEL
Tracks: / Rebel rebel / Queen bitch.
7" Single: Released Feb '74, on RCA, by BMG Records (UK). Deleted '77. Catalogue no: **LPBO 5009**
7" Single: Released Jun '83, on RCA, by BMG Records (UK). Catalogue no: **BOW 514**

ROCK AND ROLL SUICIDE
Tracks: / Rock and roll suicide.
7" Single: Released Apr '74, on RCA, by BMG Records (UK). Deleted '77. Catalogue no: **LPBO 5021**
7" Single: Released Jun '83, on RCA, by BMG Records (UK). Catalogue no: **BOW 503**

SCARY MONSTERS (SINGLE)
Tracks: / Scary monsters (and super creeps) / Because you're young.
12" Single: Released Mar '86, on RCA, by BMG Records (UK). Catalogue no: **PB 9657**
12" Single: Released May '83, on RCA (Germany), Catalogue no: **PC 09657**
Cassingle: Released Jan '81, on RCA, by BMG Records (UK). Deleted Jan '84. Catalogue no: **BOWC 8**
7" Single: Released Jan '81, on RCA, by BMG Records (UK). Catalogue no: **BOW 8**

SORROW
Tracks: / Sorrow / Amsterdam.
7" Single: Released Jun '83, on RCA, by BMG Records (UK). Catalogue no: **BOW 519**
7" Single: Released Oct '73, on RCA, by BMG Records (UK). Deleted '76. Catalogue no: **RCA 2424**

SOUND AND VISION
Tracks: / Sound and vision.
7" Single: Released Jun '83, on RCA, by BMG Records (UK). Catalogue no: **BOW 510**
7" Single: Released Feb '77, on RCA, by BMG Records (UK). Deleted '80. Catalogue no: **PB 0905**

SPACE ODDITY (SINGLE)
Tracks: / Space oddity / Changes / Velvet goldmine.
7" Single: Released Jun '83, on RCA, by BMG Records (UK). Catalogue no: **BOW 518**
7" Single: Released Oct '75, on RCA, by BMG Records (UK). Deleted '78. Catalogue no: **RCA 2593**
7" Single: Released Sep '69, on Philips, by Phonogram Ltd. Deleted '72. Catalogue no: **BF 1801**

STARMAN
Tracks: / Starman / Suffragette city.
7" Single: Released Jun '72, on RCA, by BMG Records (UK). Deleted '75. Catalogue no: **RCA 2199**

THIS IS NOT AMERICA
Tracks: / This is not America.
7" Single: Released Jan '85, on EMI-America, by EMI Records. Catalogue no: **EA 190**
12" Single: Released Jan '85, on EMI-America, by EMI Records. Deleted Aug '89. Catalogue no: **12EA 190**

TIME WILL CRAWL (DANCE CREW MIX)
Tracks: / Time will crawl (dance crew mix) / Time will crawl (dub) / Girls (Japanese version).
12" Single: Released Jul '87, on EMI-America, by EMI Records. Catalogue no: **12 EAS 237**

TIME WILL CRAWL (SINGLE VERSION)
Tracks: / Time will crawl (single version) / Girls (single edit).
7" Single: Released 27 Jun '87, on EMI-America, by EMI Records. Deleted Oct '87 Catalogue no: **EAP 237**
7" Single: Released 13 Jun '87, on EMI America, by EMI Records. Deleted Apr '88 Catalogue no: **EA 237**
12" Single: Released 13 Jun '87, on EMI America, by EMI Records. Deleted Apr '88 Catalogue no: **12 EA 237**

TONIGHT (SINGLE)

Tracks: / Tonight / Tumble and whirl.
7" Single: Released Nov '84, on EMI-America, by EMI Records. Catalogue no: **EA 187**
12" Single: Released Nov '84, on EMI-America, by EMI Records. Catalogue no: **12EA 187**

TVC 15
Tracks: / TVC-15.
7" Single: Released May '76, on RCA, by BMG Records (UK). Deleted '79. Catalogue no: **RCA 2682**
7" Single: Released Jun '83, on RCA, by BMG Records (UK). Catalogue no: **BOW 509**

UNDERGROUND
Tracks: / Underground / Underground(instrumental).
7" Single: Released Jun '86, on EMI-America, by EMI Records. Deleted Oct '87. Catalogue no: **EA 216**
12" Single: Released Jun '86, on EMI-America, by EMI Records. Deleted Oct '87. Catalogue no: **12 EA 216**

UP THE HILL BACKWARDS
Tracks: / Up the hill backwards / Crystal Japan.
7" Single: Released Mar '81, on RCA, by BMG Records (UK). Deleted Mar '84. Catalogue no: **BOW 9**
12" Single: Released Mar '81, on RCA, by BMG Records (UK). Deleted Mar '84. Catalogue no: **BOWT 9**

WHEN THE WIND BLOWS
Tracks: / When the wind blows (7" only) / When the wind blows (instrumental) / When the wind blows (extended mix) (12" only).
12" Single: Released Oct '86, on Virgin, by Virgin Records. Catalogue no: **VS 906-12**
7" Single: Released Oct '86, on Virgin, by Virgin Records. Catalogue no: **VS 906**

WHITE LIGHT, WHITE HEAT
Tracks: / White light, white heat.
7" Single: Released Nov '83, on RCA, by BMG Records (UK). Deleted '86. Catalogue no: **RCA 372**

WILD IS THE WIND
Tracks: / Wild is the wind / Golden years.
7" Single: Released Nov '81, on RCA, by BMG Records (UK). Catalogue no: **BOW 10**
12" Single: Released Nov '81, on RCA, by BMG Records (UK). Catalogue no: **BOWT 10**
12" Single: Released Mar '86, on RCA, by BMG Records (UK). Catalogue no: **PC 9773**
12" Single: Released Jul '84, on RCA, by BMG Records (UK). Catalogue no: **PC 09773**

YOUNG AMERICANS
Tracks: / Young Americans.
7" Single: Released Mar '75, on RCA, by BMG Records (UK). Deleted '78. Catalogue no: **RCA 2523**

YOUNG AMERICANS (SINGLE)
Tracks: / Young Americans.
7" Single: Released Jun '83, on RCA, by BMG Records (UK). Catalogue no: **BOW 506**

Bown, Alan

HELP ME
Tracks: / Help me.
7" Single: Released Mar '83, on EMI, by EMI Records. Catalogue no: **EMI 5372**

Bown, Andy

ANOTHER SHIPWRECK
Tracks: / Another shipwreck / Another night without you.
7" Single: Released Feb '81, on EMI, by EMI Records. Deleted '84. Catalogue no: **EMI 2906**

MARIANNE
Tracks: / Marianne / One forward, two back again.
7" Single: Released Jun '82, on EMI, by EMI Records. Deleted '85. Catalogue no: **EMI 5312**

SAY IT WAS MAGIC
Tracks: / Say it was magic / One forward two back again.
7" Single: Released Jan '82, on EMI, by EMI Records. Deleted '85. Catalogue no: **EMI 5245**

Bowser & Blue

RAPPIN' RAMBO
Tracks: / Rappin' Rambo / Bald is beautiful.
7" Single: Released Jun '88, on Bold Reprieve (1), Catalogue no: **BRM 015**

Bowyer, Jeremy

HANDEL ARIAS
Tracks: / My God I love Thee (Hymn) / Angels ever bright and fair / How beautiful are the feet / But oh, what art can teach / Let the bright Seraphim (end s1) / Happy, Iphis, thou shalt live / Lord of our being / I know that my Redeemer liveth / Rejoice, the Lord is King (Hymn).
Note: Southwark Cathedral: Director, Harry Bramma; organ, Andrew Lumsden.
12" Single: Released '85, on Alpha, by Abbey Recording Co.Ltd.. Catalogue no: **XPS 108**

Box

MUSCLE OUT (SINGLE)
Tracks: / Muscle out.
12" Single: Released Dec '84, on Double Vision, by Double Vision Records. Catalogue no: **DVR 10**

NO TIME FOR TALK
Tracks: / No time for talk.
12" Single: Released Jan '83, on Go Discs, by Chrysalis Records. Catalogue no: **VFM 1**

OLD STYLE DROP DOWN
Tracks: / Old style drop down.
12" Single: Released May '83, on Go Discs, by Chrysalis Records. Catalogue no: **VFM 3**
7" Single: Released May '83, on Go Discs, by Chrysalis Records. Catalogue no: **VFM 2**

Box Of Frogs

AVERAGE
Tracks: / Average / Strange lands / Keep calling (Extra track on 12" only).
Note: "Extra track on 12" only
12" Single: Released Jun '86, on Epic, by CBS Records. Deleted '86. Catalogue no: **TA 7248**
7" Single: Released Jun '86, on Epic, by CBS Records. Deleted '86. Catalogue no: **A 7248**

BACK WHERE I STARTED
Tracks: / Back where I started.
7" Single: Released Jun '84, on Epic, by CBS Records. Catalogue no: **A 4562**
12" Single: Released Jun '84, on Epic, by CBS Records. Catalogue no: **TA 4562**

INTO THE DARK
Tracks: / Into the dark.
12" Single: Released Aug '84, on Epic, by CBS Records. Deleted '85. Catalogue no: **TA 4678**
7" Single: Released Aug '84, on Epic, by CBS Records. Catalogue no: **A 4678**

Box Of Toys

I'M THINKING OF YOU NOW
Tracks: / I'm thinking of you now.
7" Single: Released Aug '83, on Inevitable, by Inevitable Records. Catalogue no: **INEV 13**

PRECIOUS IS THE PEARL
Tracks: / Precious is the pearl / It goes without saying.
7" Single: Released Mar '84, on Inevitable, by Inevitable Records. Catalogue no: **INEV 15**
12" Single: Released Mar '84, on Inevitable, by Inevitable Records. Catalogue no: **INEVT 15**

Box, Robin

I AIN'T GOT YOU
Tracks: / I ain't got you.
7" Single: Released Nov '82, on Punchline, Catalogue no: **PL 003**

Box Tops

Biographical details: This American group consisted of Alex Chilton, Bill Cunningham, John Evans, Danny Smythe and Gary Talley. The five members met while in college and formed the group in 1965. Hailing from Memphis, Tennessee, they were one of the few white acts of the Sixties to score success from that City's soul studios. Their first success was the biggest : *'The Letter'*, a powerful, intense and very catchy pop single was no.1 for four week's in the States in the autumn of 1967. Six months later they hit with *'Cry like a baby'*, a bluesy single featuring electric sitar. This peaked at at No.2 in the US, No.15 in the UK. Their only other 45 to hit the top 20 on either side of the Atlantic was 1969's *'Soul deep'*, No.18 in the US. Several other records were US top 40 hits, but the Box Tops will always be remembered for *'The letter'*. Joe Cocker's remake of this song reached the US top 10 in the summer of 1970, but by this time the Box Tops had disbanded.
Box Tops, The. A white soul quintet, first called The De Villes, formed im Memphis in 1966 by vocalist/guitarist Alex Chilton, who was born there in 1950. They signed with the production team of Dan Penn and Spooner Oldham, already famous for helping to set off the golden age of soul music in Memphis and Muscle Shoals (Florence) Alabama; their first single *The Letter* was no. 1 in the USA in 1968, written by unknown Wayne Carson Thompson; their third was *Cry Like A Baby*, with a psychadelic guitar and a blue-eyed soul vocal from Chilton, reached no. 2. Known as Memphis' answer to NYC's Young Rascals, they became a purely studio creation, Smythe and Evans were replaced after the second single by Tom Boggs and Rick Allen, but Chilton was often the only member to participate in recording sessions. They had ten Hot 100 hits '67-70, with other soul heroes Tommy Cogbill and Chips Moman taking over production c.'68; another Thompson song, *Soul Deep*, was top 20 in late 1969. Chilton quit and went solo; despite much critical praise he was never as successful gain. Donald Clarke, 24 August 1988..

CRY LIKE A BABY
Tracks: / Cry like a baby / Lightning strikes / Sugar shack.
7" Single: Released Aug '82, on Blast From The Past, by Creole Records. Catalogue no: **CR 179**

CRY LIKE A BABY (ORIGINAL)
Tracks: / Cry like a baby.
7" Single: Released Mar '68, on Bell, Deleted '71. Catalogue no: **BELL 1001**

LETTER, THE
Tracks: / Letter, The.
7" Single: Released Sep '67, on Stateside, by EMI Records. Deleted '70. Catalogue no: **SS 2044**
CD 5": Released Jun '89, on Arista, by BMG Records (UK). Catalogue no: **162071**
7" Single: Released Jul '82, on Old Gold, by Old Gold Records. Catalogue no: **OG 9116**

LETTER, THE (RE-RELEASE)
Tracks: / Letter, The / Cry like a baby.
7" Single: Released Mar '82, on Juke Box (Re-issue), Deleted '85. Catalogue no: **JB 04**

SOUL DEEP
Tracks: / Soul deep.
7" Single: Released Aug '69, on Bell, Deleted '72. Catalogue no: **BELL 1068**

Box Trouble

BOX TROUBLE
Tracks: / Box Trouble.
12" Single: Released Mar '88, on Rise, Catalogue no: **RISET 12**

Box Trouble With Donna

HIT THE DECK
Tracks: / Hit the deck.
12" Single: Released Oct '87, on Rise, Catalogue no: **RISET 7**

Boxcar

FREEMASON
Tracks: / Freemason.
7" Single: Released Jul '89, on Arista, by BMG Records (UK). Catalogue no: **112499**
CD 5": Released Jul '89, on Arista, by BMG Records (UK). Catalogue no: **662499**
CD 5": Released '89, on Nettwerk, by Nettwerk Records. Catalogue no: **NET 010CD**
12" Single: Released Jul '89, on Arista, by BMG Records (UK). Catalogue no: **612499**
12" Single: Released '89, on Nettwerk, by Nettwerk Records. Catalogue no: **NET 010**

Boxcar Willie

Biographical details: This American singer has spent his career in the second division of country music, without ever breaking into the big league. His brand of humorous country enjoys more popularity in Britain than at home. His TV advertised "King of the road" compilation gave him a one-off chart album, reaching No.5 on the UK list. B.M 84
Boxcar Willie. Lecil Travis Martin, born in Texas in 1931, is a country singer affectionately known in the UK as 'Boxie'. He began semi-pro in early '50s as Marty Martin, was a pilot in the USAF, then adopted a hobo persona and a new name; after tours of Scotland and an appearance at the Wembley Festival in 1979 he finally became an overnight star. His repertoire is based on music of his idols Jimmy Rodgers, Hank Williams and Lefty Frizzell; he's also written more than 400 songs of his own. He made his USA chart debut in 1983 with *Not The Man I Used To Be*. Donald Clarke, 24 August 1988.

GOOD HEARTED WOMAN
Tracks: / Good hearted woman / Cold windy city of Chicago.
7" Single: Released Mar '81, on Big R, by Big R Records. Catalogue no: **BRS 01**

MAN I USED TO BE, THE
7" Single: Released Apr '85, on Spartan, Catalogue no: **SP 21**

WATCHING NEW LOVE GROW
Tracks: / Watching new love grow / Luther.
7" Single: Released Dec '85, on Spartan, Catalogue no: **SP 129**

Boxers

WATCH IT(DO ME A FAVOUR)
Tracks: / Watch it (do me a favour).
7" Single: Released Aug '83, on Gipsy, by Gipsy Records. Catalogue no: **GIPSY 11**
12" Single: Released Aug '83, on Gipsy, by Gipsy Records. Catalogue no: **GIPSYT 11**

Boy George

Biographical details: Boy George. George Alan O'Dowd, born in 1961 in London, is a UK pop singer, songwriter and bandleader. He almost joined Malcolm McLaren's Bow Wow Wow in 1981, but met London drummer Jon Moss and formed Culture Club, with Mikey Craig and Roy Hay; their singles and albums were enormous hits in 1982-83. George's penchant for make-up and frocks curiously innocent: they became trend setters among the New Romantics, whose only object was to have fun, and even parents approved of George. The excellent Helen Terry sang with the band, then went solo. His persona was the same off-stage as on; he was and still is an excellent talk-show guest, but he became over-exposed and his musical cleverness seemed to flag; he was still selling lots of records, especially in France and the USA, but he had also become a heroin addict, paying for this mistake by seeing musician friends Michael Rudetsky, then Mark Goldring die of drugs. But he recovered; his album *Sold* in 1987 was noticeably more mature, including songs by Lamont Dozier: he may be around for a while yet. Donald Clarke, 24 August 1988..

DON'T CRY
Tracks: / Don't cry (On BOYZ 107 only) / Leave in love (On all versions) / Don't cry (version) (Only on 12") / Don't cry (edit) (ON BOY 107 & 12" only) / Don't cry (full version) (ON CD & 12" only) / Boy called Alice, A (On CD only).
7" Single: Released '88, on Virgin, by Virgin Records. Catalogue no: **BOYZ 107**
12" Single: Released Sep '88, on Virgin, by Virgin Records. Catalogue no: **BOY 107-12**
7" Single: Released Sep '88, on Virgin, by Virgin Records. Catalogue no: **BOY 107**
CD 5": Released '88, on Virgin, by Virgin Records. Catalogue no: **BOYCD 107**

DON'T TAKE MY MIND ON A TRIP
Tracks: / Don't take my mind on a trip / Girlfriend / I go where I go (12" only).
7" Single: Released Feb '89, on Virgin, by Virgin Records. Catalogue no: **BOY 108**
12" Single: Released Feb '89, on Virgin, by Virgin Records. Catalogue no: **BOY 108-12**
CD 3": Released Mar '89, on Virgin, by Virgin Records. Catalogue no: **BOYCD 108**

EVERYTHING I OWN
Tracks: / Everything I own (7" only) / Use me / Everything I own (P. W. Botha mix) (12" only) / Everything I own (dub version) (12" only).
7" Single: Released Feb '87, on Virgin, by Virgin Records. Catalogue no: **BOY 100**
12" Single: Released Feb '87, on Virgin, by Virgin Records. Catalogue no: **BOY 100-12**

INTERVIEW FLEXIDISC
7" Single: Released '87, on Flexi, Catalogue no: **RM FLEXIDISC 1**

KEEP ME IN MIND
Tracks: / Keep me in mind (On all versions) / State of love (On 7" only) / I pray (On 12' & cassette only) / State of love (extended version) (On 12" & cassette only) / Everything I own (On cassette & picture disc only).
12" Pic: Released '88, on Virgin, by Virgin Records. Catalogue no: **BOYZ 101-12**
12" Single: Released 23 May '87, on Virgin, by Virgin Records. Catalogue no: **BOY 101-12**
7" Single: Released 23 May '87, on Virgin, by Virgin Records. Deleted May '88. Catalogue no: **BOY 101**
Cassingle: Released 20 Jun '87, on Virgin, by Virgin Records. Deleted May '88. Catalogue no: **BOYC 101-12**

LIVE MY LIFE
Tracks: / Live my life (7" version) (Not on BOY 10513) / Live my life (soul remix) (Not on BOY 10513) / Live my life (klub mix) (On BOY 10512) / Live my life (business mix) (On BOY 10513 only) / Live my life (12" club remix) (On BOY 10513 only).
12" Single: Released Feb '88, on Virgin, by Virgin Records. Catalogue no: **BOY 105-12**
7" Single: Released Feb '88, on Virgin, by Virgin Records. Catalogue no: **BOY 105**
12" Single: on Virgin, by Virgin Records. Catalogue no: **BOY 105-13**

NO CLAUSE 28
Tracks: / No Clause 28 (BOY 106 only) / No Clause 28 (beats) (BOY 106 & 106-12 only) / No Clause 28 (Emilio Pasquez space face full re-mix) (CD, BOYR 106 & BOY 10613 only) / No clause 28 (full version) (CD & BOY 106-12 only) / No clause 28 (extended 7" version) (CD & BOY 106-12 only).
Note: "No Clause 28 will be a must for fans not only for it topical message but because it culminates the best production of George's material since Culture Club...... The sleeve features a Jamie (Sex Pistols) Reid spectacular of Boy George as Noddy, but you won't need Big Ears to hear what's inside "(Virgin Records, June 1988.)
7" Single: Released Jun '88, on Virgin, by Virgin Records. Catalogue no: **BOY 106**
12" Single: Released '88, on Virgin, by Virgin Records. Catalogue no: **BOY 106-13**
12" Single: Released Jun '88, on Virgin, by Virgin Records. Catalogue no: **BOY 106-12**
7" Single: Released '88, on Virgin, by Virgin Records. Catalogue no: **BOYR 106**
CD 5": Released Aug '88, on Virgin, by Virgin Records. Catalogue no: **BOYT 106**

SOLD (SINGLE)
Tracks: / Sold / Are you too afraid / Sold (12"

version) (Not on 7") / Everything I own (go-go mix) (Not on 7").
7" Single: Released Jul '87, on Virgin, by Virgin Records. Deleted May '88. Catalogue no: **BOY 102**
Cassingle: Released Jul '87, on Virgin, by Virgin Records. Deleted May '88. Catalogue no: **BOYC 102-12**
12" Single: Released Jul '87, on Virgin, by Virgin Records. Catalogue no: **BOY 102-12**

TO BE REBORN
Tracks: / To be reborn / Where are you now?.
7" Single: Released Nov '87, on Virgin, by Virgin Records. Deleted May '88. Catalogue no: **BOY 103**
CD 5": Released Aug '88, on Virgin, by Virgin Records. Catalogue no: **CDEP 9**
12" Single: Released Nov '87, on Virgin, by Virgin Records. Deleted '89. Catalogue no: **BOY 103-12**

YOU FOUND ANOTHER GUY
Tracks: / You found another guy.
12" Single: Released Jun '89, on Virgin (USA), by Virgin Records. Catalogue no: **UNKNOWN**
7" Single: Released Jun '89, on Virgin (USA), by Virgin Records. Catalogue no: **UNKNOWN**

Boy Hairdressers

GOLDEN SHOWER
Tracks: / Golden shower.
12" Single: Released Jan '88, on 53rd & 3rd, by 53rd & 3rd Records. Catalogue no: **AGARR 12T**

Boy Meets Girl

BRING DOWN THE MOON
Tracks: / Bring down the moon / Someone's got to send out love (on CD only) / One sweet dream (CD only).
CD 5": Released Mar '89, on RCA, by BMG Records (UK). Deleted Jul '89. Catalogue no: **PD 49493**
7" Single: Released Mar '89, on RCA, by BMG Records (UK). Catalogue no: **PB 49493**
12" Single: Released Mar '89, on RCA, by BMG Records (UK). Catalogue no: **PT 49494**

EMPTY BED
Tracks: / Empty bed / Romantic poet.
7" Single: Released Aug '82, on Chromozone, Catalogue no: **CB 71**

OH GIRL
Tracks: / Oh girl.
7" Single: Released May '85, on A&M, by A&M Records. Deleted '88. Catalogue no: **AM 254**
12" Single: Released May '85, on A&M, by A&M Records. Deleted '88. Catalogue no: **AMY 254**

STORMY LOVE
Tracks: / Stormy love / Waiting for a star to fall.
CD 5": Released May '89, on RCA, by BMG Records (UK). Catalogue no: **PD 49398**
7" Single: Released May '89, on RCA, by BMG Records (UK). Catalogue no: **PB 49397**
12" Single: Released May '89, on RCA, by BMG Records (UK). Catalogue no: **PT 49398**

WAITING FOR A STAR TO FALL
Tracks: / Waiting for a star to fall / No apologies / Restless dreamer* (*Track on 12" only.).
CD 5": Released 7 Nov '88, on RCA, by BMG Records (UK). Deleted Jul '89. Catalogue no: **PD 49520**
12" Single: Released 7 Nov '88, on RCA, by BMG Records (UK). Deleted Aug '89. Catalogue no: **PT 49520**
7" Single: Released 7 Nov '88, on RCA, by BMG Records (UK). Catalogue no: **PB 49519**
12" Single: Released Nov '88, on RCA, by BMG Records (UK). Deleted Aug '89. Catalogue no: **PT 42588**

Boy Toy

TOUCH MY BODY
Tracks: / Touch my body.
12" Single: Released Apr '89, on Kaos, Catalogue no: **KAOS 014**

Boy Tronic

YOU
Tracks: / You.
7" Single: Released Feb '84, on Magic (1), by Submarine Records. Catalogue no: **MAGIC 13**
12" Single: Released Feb '84, on Magic (1), by Submarine Records. Catalogue no: **MAGIC 12/13**

Boy Wonder

JACKIN' THE BEANSTALK
Tracks: / Jackin' the beanstalk.
12" Single: Released Nov '87, on Wide Angle (USA), Catalogue no: **TTW 87126**

Boyce, Jesse

IT'S YOUR CHANCE(TO BREAK DANCE)
Tracks: / It's your chance (to breakdance).
12" Single: Released Aug '84, on Compleat (USA), by Compleat Entertainment Corp.(USA). Deleted '85. Catalogue no: **CLTL 4**

Boyce, Max

Biographical details: Welshman Boyce became one of Britain's top comedians during the 70's. He has always dealt with subjects close to Welsh hearts, most notably rugby. His *Life At Treorchy* album first entered the UK charts in the summer of 1975 and stayed there for 32 weeks. He consolidated on this popularity with his second chart LP, *We All Had Doctors' Papers*, which gave him his sole No 1 album, going to the top of the British list in November 1975. Subsequent albums continued to sell in considerable quantities, particularly *The Incredible Plan* ('76) and *I Know 'Cos I Was There* ('78). Boyce's shows, a mixture of songs and chat, remain popular on stage and television: you either love him or you can't stand him, but helps if you like Welsh rugby. (Bob MacDonald, 1984.).

RAILWAY HOTEL
Tracks: / Railway hotel / In the morning (morning of my life).
7" Pic: Released 17 Feb '88, on PRT, by Castle Communications Records. Catalogue no: **PYS 5**

Boyd, Jimmy

I SAW MOMMY KISSING SANTA CLAUS
Tracks: / I saw mommy kissing Santa Claus.
7" Single: Released Nov '53, on Columbia, by EMI Records. Deleted '56. Catalogue no: **DB 3365**

Boyd, Tom

BREAKER BREAKER
Tracks: / Breaker breaker / Foxy lady.
7" Single: Released Dec '81, on Towerbell, Deleted Dec '84. Catalogue no: **KOR 13**

Boyer, Jacqueline

TOM PILLIBI
Tracks: / Tom Pillibi.
7" Single: Released Apr '60, on Columbia, by EMI Records. Deleted '63. Catalogue no: **DB 4452**

Boyfriend Cast

IT'S NEVER TOO LATE TO FALL IN LOVE
Tracks: / It's never too late to fall in love / Won't you Charleston with me.
7" Single: Released Dec '84, on T. E. R., by That's Entertainment Records. Catalogue no: **STER 9**

Boyfriends

BOYFRIEND
Tracks: / Boyfriend / Give a little, take a little.
7" Single: Released Jan '83, on Plastic, Catalogue no: **PRES 001**

Boyo, Billy

BILLY BOYO ON THE GO
Tracks: / Billy Boyo on the go / Good the ugly and the bad.
12" Single: Released Nov '82, on Greensleeves, by Greensleeves Records. Catalogue no: **GRED 110**

Boys

Biographical details: Their debut self-titled album reached No.50 on the UK chart in October 1977. Its solitary week of glory was the group's only success-they did not achieve a hit single, and subsequent albums failed to chart. These LPs included the 1978 offering *"Alternative Chartbusters"* and *"To hell with the boys"* (1979). The band continued recording into the early Eighties. (Bob MacDonald, 1984)..

DIAL MY HEART
Tracks: / Dial my heart / Dial my heart (instrumental).
CD 5": Released Oct '88, on Motown, by BMG Records (UK). Catalogue no: **ZD 42246**
12" Single: Released Oct '88, on Motown, by BMG Records (UK). Catalogue no: **ZT 42246**
7" Single: Released Nov '88, on Motown, by BMG Records (UK). Catalogue no: **ZB 42571**
7" Single: Released Oct '88, on Motown, by BMG Records (UK). Catalogue no: **ZB 42245**

KAMIKAZE
Tracks: / Kamikaze.
7" Single: Released '80, on Safari, by Safari Records. Catalogue no: **SAFE 21**

LET IT RAIN
Tracks: / Let it rain / Lucy.
7" Single: Released Feb '81, on Safari, by Safari Records. Catalogue no: **SAFE 33**

LUCKY CHARM
Tracks: / Lucky charm / Lucky charm (version).
7" Single: Released Mar '89, on Motown, by BMG Records (UK). Catalogue no: **ZB 42687**
12" Single: Released Mar '89, on Motown, by BMG Records (UK). Catalogue no: **ZT 42688**

TERMINAL LOVE
Tracks: / Terminal love / You better move on.
7" Single: Released Jan '80, on Safari, by Safari Records. Catalogue no: **SAFE 23**

WEEKEND
Tracks: / Weekend.
7" Single: Released '81, on Safari, by Safari Records. Catalogue no: **SAFE 31**

Boy's Brigade

OLD FATHER TIME
Tracks: / Old father time.
7" Single: Released Aug '83, on Thaw, by Thaw Records. Catalogue no: **THAW 1**

PASSION OF LOVE
Tracks: / Passion of love.
7" Single: Released Feb '84, on Capitol, by EMI Records. Deleted '88. Catalogue no: **CL 324**
12" Single: Released Feb '84, on Capitol, by EMI Records. Deleted '85. Catalogue no: **12CL 324**

YOU BRING OUT THE VICAR IN ME
Tracks: / You bring out the vicar in me / Such a treasure.
7" Single: Released Apr '82, on Rocket, by Rocket Records. Deleted Apr '85. Catalogue no: **XPRES 76**

Boy's Club

I REMEMBER HOLDING YOU
Tracks: / I remember holding you.
7" Single: Released Feb '89, on MCA, by MCA Records. Deleted 1 Jul '89. Catalogue no: **MCA 1316**
CD 5": Released Feb '89, on MCA, by MCA Records. Catalogue no: **DMCA 1316**
12" Single: Released Feb '89, on MCA, by MCA Records. Catalogue no: **MCAT 1316**

Boys Don't Cry

CITIES ON TIME, THE
Tracks: / Cities on time, The.
12" Single: Released Oct '86, on Legacy, by Legacy Records. Catalogue no: **LGYT 55**
7" Single: Released Oct '86, on Legacy, by Legacy Records. Catalogue no: **LGY 55**

DON'T TALK TO STRANGERS
Tracks: / Don't talk to strangers / Pure pleasure / New Yorker.
7" Single: Released Mar '84, on Legacy, by Legacy Records. Catalogue no: **LGY 4**
12" Single: Released Mar '84, on Legacy, by Legacy Records. Catalogue no: **LGYT 4**

HEARTS BEEN BROKEN
Tracks: / Hearts been broken.
7" Single: Released Aug '86, on Legacy, by Legacy Records. Catalogue no: **LGY 60**
12" Single: Released Aug '86, on Legacy, by Legacy Records. Catalogue no: **LGYT 60**
7" Single: Released Apr '83, on Legacy, by Legacy Records. Catalogue no: **LGY 1**

I WANNA BE A COWBOY
Tracks: / I wanna be a cowboy / Turn over(I like it better that way).
12" Pic: Released May '86, on Legacy, by Legacy Records. Catalogue no: **LGYTP 28**
7" Single: Released Sep '85, on Legacy, by Legacy Records. Catalogue no: **LGY 28**
12" Single: Released Sep '85, on Legacy, by Legacy Records. Catalogue no: **LGYT 28**

LIPSTICK
Tracks: / Lipstick.
7" Single: Released Mar '85, on Legacy, by Legacy Records. Catalogue no: **LGY 21**

TURN OVER(I LIKE IT BETTER THAT WAY)
Tracks: / Turn over(I like it better that way).
12" Single: Released Jul '84, on Legacy, by Legacy Records. Catalogue no: **LGYT 13**

WHO THE AM DAM DO YOU THINK YOU AM
Tracks: / Who the am do you think you am / Cure, The.
12" Single: Released Apr '87, on Legacy, by Legacy Records. Deleted May '88. Catalogue no: **LGYT 57**
7" Single: Released Apr '87, on Legacy, by Legacy Records. Deleted May '88. Catalogue no: **LGY 57**

Boys From Syracuse

I'LL CRY FOR YOU
Tracks: / I'll cry for you.
12" Single: Released Jul '86, on New England, Catalogue no: **12BRIT 1**
7" Single: Released Jul '86, on New England, Catalogue no: **BRIT 1**

Boys From The East

BRILLIANT
Tracks: / Brilliant.
7" Single: Released Jun '87, on Final Cut, Deleted '88. Catalogue no: **FINC 001**
12" Single: Released 4 Jun '87, on Final Cut, Deleted '88. Catalogue no: **FINC 12001**

Boys In Darkness

BACK TO FRANCE
Tracks: / Back to France / Man an island.
7" Single: Released Oct '81, on Bid For Freedom, Deleted '85. Catalogue no: **BIDS 1**
7" Single: Released Nov '81, on Champagne (DJM), Deleted Nov '84. Catalogue no: **BUBL 702**
12" Single: Released Nov '81, on Champagne (DJM), Deleted Nov '84. Catalogue no: **BUBLY 702**

HEART OF DARKNESS
Tracks: / Heart of darkness.
12" Single: Released Jun '84, on Parlophone, by EMI Records. Deleted '86. Catalogue no: **12R 6069**
7" Single: Released Jun '84, on Parlophone, by EMI Records. Catalogue no: **R 6069**

Boys White Teeth

PRICES (WILL BE QUOTED)
Tracks: / Prices (will be quoted) / Trip to rio.
12" Single: Released Jul '82, on T.W., by T.W. Records. Catalogue no: **HIT 12 108**
7" Single: Released Jul '82, on T.W., by T.W. Records. Catalogue no: **HIT 108**

Boys Wonder

GOODBYE JIMMY DEAN
Tracks: / Goodbye Jimmy Dean.
7" Single: Released Jul '88, on Boys Wonder, Catalogue no: **BW 1**
12" Single: Released Aug '88, on Boys Wonder, Catalogue no: **BW 1 12**

NOW WHAT EARTHMAN
Tracks: / Now what earthman / 10 million ton headache.
7" Single: Released 13 Jun '87, on Sire (USA), Deleted Jul '88. Catalogue no: **W 8293**
12" Single: Released 13 Jun '87, on Sire (USA), Deleted Jul '88. Catalogue no: **W 8293T**

SHINE ON ME
Tracks: / Shine on me / Stop it.
12" Single: Released Oct '87, on Sire (USA), Catalogue no: **W 8195T**
7" Single: Released Oct '87, on Sire (USA), Deleted Jul '88. Catalogue no: **W 8195**

Boystown Gang

Biographical details: This mixed group of American vocalists were, as their name suggests, at the forefront of the boystown disco scene of the Eighties, later called 'high energy' music (or 'Hi-NRG). This style is perhaps best described as a gay version of the Eurovision Song Contest. Material consisted either of cover versions, or of supposedly original material that borrowed heavily from other songs: it was usually embellished with a 'pots and pans' percussion sound and amateurish production. But for all its shortcomings, the boystown genre had a significant pop appeal, allowing some of its singles to cross over from their original homosexual audience into the national disco and pop charts, especially in Britain. The Boystown Gang's output has mainly consisted of remakes. They first hit the UK pop charts with their 1981 renditin of Diana Ross' 1970 hit *"Ain't no mountain high enough"* peaking at No.46. Their only major hit was *"Can't take my eyes off you"*, a reworking of the familiar late Sixties smash. The Gang took its bland but irrestible catchy version to No.4 on the British chart, one place higher than Andy Williams had managed. They followed it with a No.50 remake of Stevie Wonder's *"Signed sealed delivered (I'm yours)"*. As 'boystown' gradually became a dated word the Gang faded. (Bob MacDonald)..

AIN'T NO MOUNTAIN HIGH ENOUGH
Tracks: / Ain't no mountain high enough.
7" Single: Released Sep '82, on Moby Dick, Catalogue no: **DICK 1**
12" Single: Released Sep '82, on Moby Dick, Catalogue no: **DICK 1T**

BRAND NEW ME
Tracks: / Brand new me.
7" Single: Released Sep '84, on Rich & Famous, Catalogue no: **7RNF 1**
12" Single: Released Sep '84, on Rich & Famous, Catalogue no: **12RNF 1**

CAN'T TAKE MY EYES OFF YOU
Tracks: / Can't take my eyes off you / Disco kicks.
12" Single: Released Jul '82, on ERC, Catalogue no: **ERCL 101**
7" Single: Released Jul '82, on ERC, Catalogue no: **ERC 101**

I JUST CAN'T HELP BELIEVIN'
Tracks: / I just can't help believing.
7" Single: Released Jul '83, on ERC, Cata-

ɔgue no: **ERC 107**
2" Single: Released Jul '83, on ERC, Cata-
ɔgue no: **ERCL 107**

ɩEMEMBER ME
racks: / Remember me / Ain't no mountain igh enough / Cruising in the streets / You o it for me.
2" Single: Released Aug '86, on Record ɜhack, by Record Shack Records. Cata-ɒgue no: **SOHOT 69**

ɩIGNED, SEALED, DELIVERED (I'M 'OURS)
racks: / Signed, sealed, delivered, I'm ours.
" Single: Released Sep '82, on ERC, Cata-ɒgue no: **ERC 102**
2" Single: Released Sep '82, on ERC, atalogue no: **ERCL 102**

'ESTER-ME, YESTER-YOU, YES-ERDAY
racks: / Yester-me, yester-you, yesterday Dance trance medley.
2" Single: Released Dec '84, on Rich & amous, Catalogue no: **12RNF 2**
" Single: Released Jan '85, on Rich & amous, Catalogue no: **7RNF 2**

Boyz On The Hill

ɩAPPITUP
racks: / Rappitup.
2" Single: Released 20 Mar '89, on ʀRRAG, Catalogue no: **WR 008**

Boyzone

AST ADVENTURE
racks: / Last adventure / Blueprint / Mara-on.
' Single: Released Dec '84, on Topland, eleted '86. Catalogue no: **JOG 1**
2" Single: Released Dec '84, on Topland, eleted '85. Catalogue no: **JOGT 1**

Brad Is Sex

RIUMPH OF THE GOOD
acks: / Triumph of the good / Hanging on Blue skies / Hard nights work / Transistor dio.
" Single: Released May '89, on Company Catalogue no: **X 333**

WINKLE TWINKLE LITTLE POP TAR
acks: / Twinkle twinkle little pop star.
Single: Released Dec '87, on Company Catalogue no: **NUMBER 001**

Bradford

DRIFT AGAIN
acks: / Adrift again.
" Single: Released 11 Sep '89, on Foun-tion, Catalogue no: **TFL 004T**

LIVERPOOL
acks: / In Liverpool / Boys will be boys / erywhere I turn.
Single: Released Jul '89, on Foundation, atalogue no: **TFL 1**
) 5": Released Jul '89, on Foundation, atalogue no: **TFL 1CD**
" Single: Released Jul '89, on Founda-ı, Catalogue no: **TFL 1T**

KIN STORM
acks: / Skin storm.
Single: Released 20 Feb '88, on Village, Village Records. Catalogue no: **VILS 101**
5": Released '88, on Village, by Village cords. Catalogue no: **VILSD 101**
' Single: Released 23 Jul '88, on Village, Village Records. Catalogue no: **VILT 101**

TTERED, TANGLED & TORN
acks: / Tattered, tangled & torn.
' Single: Released Nov '88, on Village, by age Records. Catalogue no: **VILT 104**
Single: Released Nov '88, on Village, by age Records. Catalogue no: **VILS 104**

Bradford, Terry

IERICAN LADY
cks: / American lady / When your mama es you home.
Single: Released May '81, on Carrere, eted May '84. Catalogue no: **CAR 178**

Bradley

M WHAT I AM
cks: / I am what I am / Reflective mood.
Single: Released Apr '84, on Hippo-me, by Hippodrome Records. Catalogue **HIPPO 3**

Bradley, Brian

INCE WAS BORN TODAY
cks: / Prince was born today / Nicoli.
Single: Released Sep '84, on Zodiac, by iac-Wilcox Records. Catalogue no: **ZR)**

Bradley, Jan

MA DIDN'T LIE
cks: / Mama didn't lie.
Single: on MCA, by MCA Records. alogue no: **MCAT 1258**
ingle: on MCA, by MCA Records. Cata-e no: **MCA 1258**

Bradley & The Boys

DYNA-DALL
Tracks: / Dyna-dall / Dance you bitch.
12" Single: Released Dec '84, on Hippodrome, by Hippodrome Records. Catalogue no: **12HIPP 1**
7" Single: Released Jan '85, on Hippodrome, by Hippodrome Records. Catalogue no: **7 HIPPO 1**

Bradshaw, Billy

EASY PEASY SONG
Tracks: / Easy peasy song.
Note: The Bradshaws of Barnoldswick created by Piccadilly Radio's own Buzz Hawkins. Based around Billy's catch phrase, "Yer think it's easy peasy but it's not".
7" Single: Released Feb '88, on IMS, by Polydor Ltd. Catalogue no: **BRAD 29**

Brady, Paul

Biographical details: Brady, Paul. The singer and multi-instrumentalist was born in 1947 in Northern Ireland. He played in the Irish rock circuit with Dublin-based groups, was a member of the Johnstons folk group until 1972; lived in USA for first of several stays there, and joined Planxty in 1974, replacing Christy Moore: although he did not record with them, this was regarded as one of their best line-ups. *Andy Irvine/Paul Brady* on Mulligan showcased Planxty-period repertoire impressively, and *Welcome Here Kind Stranger* was a brilliant folk album; he began writing his own songs and *Hard Station* was an accomplished debut in 1981. His work is widely admired and covered, but like a lot of good work has not received the commercial success it deserves. Donald Clarke, 24 August 1988..

BACK TO THE CENTRE (WALK THE WHITE LINE)
Tracks: / Back to the centre (walk the white line) / Airwaves / Lakes of Ponchartrain, The (Extra track on 12" only).
12" Single: Released Jun '86, on Mercury, by Phonogram Ltd. Deleted '87. Catalogue no: **MERX 224**
7" Single: Released Jun '86, on Mercury, by Phonogram Ltd. Deleted '87. Catalogue no: **MER 224**

BUSTED LOOSE
Tracks: / Busted loose / Road to the promised land.
7" Single: Released May '81, on WEA, by WEA Records. Deleted May '84. Catalogue no: **K 18779**

CRAZY DREAMS
Tracks: / Crazy dreams / Something in the atmosphere.
7" Single: Released Dec '80, on WEA, by WEA Records. Deleted Dec '85. Catalogue no: **K 18355**

DEEP IN YOUR HEART
Tracks: / Deep in your heart / Follow on / Cold cold night (Extra track on 12" only).
7" Single: Released Mar '86, on Mercury, by Phonogram Ltd. Catalogue no: **MER 216**
12" Single: Released Mar '86, on Mercury, by Phonogram Ltd. Deleted '87. Catalogue no: **MERX 216**

EAT THE PEACH
Tracks: / Eat the peach (7"version) / In case of accidents / Loving of a stranger, The / Eat the peach (12" extended mix).
7" Single: Released Mar '87, on Mercury, by Phonogram Ltd. Deleted Dec '87. Catalogue no: **MER 241**
CD 5": Released Apr '87, on Mercury, by Phonogram Ltd. Deleted Feb '89. Catalogue no: **8884642**
12" Single: Released Mar '87, on Mercury, by Phonogram Ltd. Catalogue no: **MERX 241**

ISLAND, THE
Tracks: / Island, The / Great pretender, The / Dance the romance (Extra track on 12" only).
Note: * Extra track on 12" only
7" Single: Released Sep '86, on Mercury, by Phonogram Ltd. Deleted Jul '87. Catalogue no: **MER 232**
12" Single: Released Sep '86, on Mercury, by Phonogram Ltd. Deleted Jul '87. Catalogue no: **MERX 232**

STEAL YOUR HEART AWAY
Tracks: / Steal your heart away / Soul commotion, The / Awakening, The*.
12" Single: Released 30 May '87, on Mercury, by Phonogram Ltd. Deleted Dec '87. Catalogue no: **MERX 247**
7" Single: Released 30 May '87, on Mercury, by Phonogram Ltd. Deleted Dec '87. Catalogue no: **MER 247**

Brady, Sean

DE VALERA
Tracks: / De valera.
7" Single: Released '88, on I&B, by I & B Records. Catalogue no: **CRU 009**

MOTHER ENGLANDS GIRO
Tracks: / Mother Englands giro.
7" Single: Released '88, on I&B, by I & B

BRAFA TEAM - LET'S MAKE AFRICA GREEN AGAIN (Released on Island)

Records. Catalogue no: **ADY 001**

TAOISEACH'S HOOLEY
Tracks: / Taoiseach's hooley.
7" Single: Released Mar '84, on Crubeen, Catalogue no: **CRU 001**

THATCHER SONG (SINGLE)
Tracks: / Thatcher song.
7" Single: Released Mar '84, on IMI, Catalogue no: **IMI 2001**

Brafa Team

LET'S MAKE AFRICA GREEN AGAIN (see panel above)
Tracks: / Let's make Africa green again / Let's make Africa green again (part two).
7" Single: Released Apr '85, on Island, by Island Records. Catalogue no: **BRAFA 1**
12" Single: Released Apr '85, on Island, by Island Records. Catalogue no: **12BRAFA 1**

Bragg, Billy

Biographical details: This singer and songwriter from the east end of London survived the pressure of being widely tipped as 'Brightest Hope for 1984'. During 1983 he had established himself on Britain's independent charts with the mini-album *"Life's a riot with Spy vs Spy"*. It had also given Bragg his debut entry on the UK's national LP charts. It was a collection of witty, unclutered songs delivered by one man and his guitar, placing Bragg in the folk tradition despite being the darling of the rock press. The standout cuts were *"The milkman of human kindness"* and "A new England". Bragg was originally in a Peterborough band called Riff Raff, and later spent an abortive three-month spell in the army. He consolidated his position as a solo recording artist in late '84 with *"Brewing up with Billy Bragg"* another UK chart LP. Bragg was proving a success, but his style was too far removed from conventional pop to make him the major star that some had predicted. B.M. 84
This singer/songwriter and guitarist was born in Barking in 1958. He heard the Clash, served time with the punk band Riff Raff in 1978 and took to the road solo, dubbed the *'one-man Clash'*; his 7-track mini album *Life's A Riot With Spy Vs Spy* drew attention to the pungent, topical material and staccato guitar. *Brewing Up* had 14 passionate tracks including *Island Of No Return*, a comment on the Falklands war. Bragg is not a folkie, but because of his solo nature is championed by them; he is also very political, supporting the miners' strike in 1984-5, the Labour 'Jobs For Youth' tour, and the Red Wedge tour in 1986. His first chart hits in 1985-6 included the EP *Between The Wars*, with Leon Rosselson's *World Turned Upside Down* and the old striker's anthem *Which Side Are You On?*, and *Levi Stubbs'Tears* and *Greetings To The New Brunette*, both from the album *Talking With The Taxman About Poetry*, as well as *Days Like These*. Donald Clarke, 24 August 1988..

BETWEEN THE WARS
Tracks: / Between the wars / Which side are you on / World turned upside down, The / It says here.
7" EP: Released Feb '85, on Go Discs, by Chrysalis Records. Catalogue no: **AGOEP 1**

DAYS LIKE THESE
Tracks: / Days like these / I don't need this pressure Ron / Scholarship is the enemy of romance.
7" Single: Released Dec '85, on Go Discs, by Chrysalis Records. Catalogue no: **GOD 8**

GREAT LEAP FORWARD,THE
Tracks: / Great leap forward, The.
7" Single: Released 29 Aug '88, on Chrysalis, by Chrysalis Records. Catalogue no: **GOD 23**

GREETINGS TO THE NEW BRUNETTE
Tracks: / Greetings to the new brunette / Deportees / Tattler.
Note: 5 track 12" E.P.
7" EP: Released Sep '87, on Liberation (Australia), Catalogue no: **LMD 504**
7" Single: Released Oct '82, on Go Discs, by Chrysalis Records. Deleted '85. Catalogue no: **GOD 15**

LEVI STUBB'S TEARS
Tracks: / Levi Stubb's tears / Think again / Walk away Renee / Between the wars(live) (Extra track on 12" only.).
7" Single: Released Jun '86, on Go Discs, by Chrysalis Records. Catalogue no: **GOD 12**
12" Single: Released Jun '86, on Go Discs, by Chrysalis Records. Catalogue no: **GODX 12**

NEW ENGLAND, A
Tracks: / New England, A.
7" Single: Released Jan '85, on Go Discs, by Chrysalis Records. Catalogue no: **10767**

PEEL SESSIONS:BILLY BRAGG
27.3.83
CD 5": Released Aug '88, on Strange Fruit, by Strange Fruit Records. Catalogue no: **SFPSCD 027**
12" Single: Released Jun '87, on Strange Fruit, by Strange Fruit Records. Catalogue no: **SFPS 027**

SHE'S GOT A NEW SPELL
Tracks: / She's got a new spell / Must I paint you a picture.
7" Single: Released Nov '88, on Go Discs, by Chrysalis Records. Catalogue no: **GOD 24**

WAITING FOR THE GREAT LEAP FORWARDS
Tracks: / Waiting for the great leap forwards / Wishing the days away / Sin City.
Note: Available on 7" only which contains 12 minutes of music.
7" Single: Released Aug '88, on Go Discs, by Chrysalis Records. Catalogue no: **GOD 23**

Brain

NIGHTMARES IN RED
Tracks: / Nightmare in red / Black sheep.
7" Single: Released 8 Nov '88, on Bam Caruso, by Demon Records. Catalogue no: **OPRA 063**

Brain, Brian

CULTURE
Tracks: / Culture.
12" Single: Released Dec '80, on Secret, by Secret Records. Catalogue no: **12SHH 109**

FUNKY ZOO
Tracks: / Funky zoo / Flies.

7" Single: Released Oct '82, on Secret, by Secret Records. Catalogue no: **SHH 142**
12" Single: Released Oct '82, on Secret, by Secret Records. Catalogue no: **SHH 142 12**

JIVE JIVE
Tracks: / Jive jive / Hello to the working class.
7" Single: Released Jul '82, on Secret, by Secret Records. Catalogue no: **SHH 119**

Brain Of Morbius

KILL YOUR NEIGHBOURS
12" Single: Released Mar '88, on Flim Flam, Catalogue no: **HARP 10T**

Brains

RAELINE
Tracks: / Raeline / Treason.
7" Single: Released Aug '80, on Mercury, by Phonogram Ltd. Deleted '83. Catalogue no: **MER 31**

Brains Trust

UNEARTHLY POWERS
Tracks: / Unearthly powers.
7" Single: Released Mar '84, on Trust, Catalogue no: **BTR 1**

Braithwaite, Daryl

ALL I DO
Tracks: / All I do / Promised land / Up-out.
7" Single: Released 12 Jun '89, on Epic, by CBS Records. Deleted Oct '89. Catalogue no: **653029 7**
CD 5": Released 12 Jun '89, on Epic, by CBS Records. Deleted Oct '89. Catalogue no: **653029 2**
12" Single: Released 12 Jun '89, on Epic, by CBS Records. Deleted Oct '89. Catalogue no: **653029 8**

AS THE DAYS GO BY
Tracks: / As the days go by / As the days go by (extended mix) / Down down / In my life.
7" Single: Released 30 Jan '89, on Epic, by CBS Records. Deleted 10 Jul '89. Catalogue no: **652 941-7**
CD 5": Released 30 Jan '89, on Epic, by CBS Records. Deleted 10 Jul '89. Catalogue no: **652 941-2**
12" Single: Released 30 Jan '89, on Epic, by CBS Records. Deleted 10 Jul '89. Catalogue no: **652 941-8**

Braithwaite, Norman

CAN'T FINISH THE SONG
Tracks: / Can't finish the song / Why do I go fishin'.
7" Single: Released Jul '82, on Solid, by Solid Records. Catalogue no: **STOP 002**

Brakes

BLAME IT ON THE BRAKES
Tracks: / Blame it on the brakes / Doin' life.
7" Single: Released Jan '80, on Magnet, by WEA Records. Deleted Jan '85. Catalogue no: **MAG 161**

Brambell, Wilfred

AT THE PALACE
Tracks: / At the palace.
7" Single: Released Nov '63, on Pye, Deleted '66. Catalogue no: **7 N 15588**

Brammer, Junior

I CAN'T STAND THE PAIN
Tracks: / I can't stand the pain / I can't stand the pain (version).
12" Single: Released Jul '86, on John Dread Production, Catalogue no: **JDED 006**

IF YOU SHOULD LOSE ME
Tracks: / If you should lose me.
12" Single: Released Nov '85, on High Power, Catalogue no: **HPD 0010**

Brammer, Phil

LONDON PLEASURES
Tracks: / London pleasures.
7" Single: Released Apr '82, on Paperback, Deleted '84. Catalogue no: **BOOK 1**

Brand New Heavies

GOT TO GIVE
Tracks: / Got to give (part 1) / Got to give (part 2).
7" Single: Released May '88, on Cool Tempo, by Chrysalis Records. Catalogue no: **COOL 167**
12" Single: Released May '88, on Cool Tempo, by Chrysalis Records. Catalogue no: **COOLX 167**

Brandon, Johnny

DON'T WORRY
Tracks: / Don't worry.
7" Single: Released Jul '55, on Polygon, Deleted '58. Catalogue no: **P 1163**

TOMORROW
Tracks: / Tomorrow.
7" Single: Released Mar '55, on Polygon, Deleted '58. Catalogue no: **P 1131**

Brandos

GETTYSBURG
Tracks: / Gettysburg.
7" Single: Released Sep '87, on Relativity (USA), Catalogue no: **88561-8192-7**

Brandt's, Pete Method

POSITIVE THINKING
Tracks: / Positive thinking.
7" Single: Released Jul '81, on Fried Egg, by Fried Egg Records. Deleted '87. Catalogue no: **EGG 5**

Brandy Snaps

CHRISTMAS TIME
Tracks: / Christmas time / Reggae Christmas.
7" Single: Released Nov '80, on DJM, Deleted '83. Catalogue no: **DJS 10960**

IT'S CHRISTMAS TIME
Tracks: / It's christmas time / Reggae christmas.
7" Single: Released Dec '80, on DJM, Deleted Dec '85. Catalogue no: **DJS 10960**

Braniffs

WHY SHOULD I BE LONELY
Tracks: / Why should I be lonely.
7" Single: Released Aug '85, on Mint, by Emerald Records. Deleted '88. Catalogue no: **CHEW 99**

Branigan, Laura

Biographical details: This American pop singer came to fame in 1982 with the single *"Gloria"*. This Itailian song had originally been a hit in Continental Europe in the late Seventies, but had been ignored in the UK and US, save for a minor British hit version by the irrepressible Jonathan King. When Branigan recorded it in '82 (with a different English lyric from the King version), it was a sleeper smash, eventually climbing to No.2 in the States. Her powerful voice breathed new life into this catchy song, sung in a Donna Summer vein. It was also Branigan's first UK hit, peaking at No.6 in early '83. Its follow-up *"Solitaire"* was another Top Tenner in America, though not a major British success. In 1984 she recorded another Italian song and scored another international smash. *"Self control"* reached No.4 in the US, was a huge hit, in complex structure but still with a broad pop appeal. The most extraordinary example of its success was in West Germany, where the Branigan version went to No.1 while the original Italian disc by co-writer Raffaele Riefcoli was simultaneously at the No.2. Raff's original had the disadvange of lacking the Branigan vocal performance, which was once again powerpacked. The next single *"The Lucky one"* was a Top 20 hit in the States. Her LPs are patchy in their choice of material, but her voice is good enough that, when she has the right song, Branigan will sell many singles. (Bob MacDonald)..

DEEP IN THE DARK
Tracks: / Deep in the dark / I'm not the only one / All night with me.
7" Single: Released Aug '83, on Atlantic, by WEA Records. Catalogue no: **A 9817**
12" Single: Released Aug '83, on Atlantic, by WEA Records. Catalogue no: **A 9817 T**

GLORIA
Tracks: / Gloria / I wish we could be alone.
12" Single: Released Aug '82, on Atlantic, by WEA Records. Catalogue no: **K 11759T**
7" Single: Released Aug '82, on Atlantic, by WEA Records. Catalogue no: **K 11759**

LUCKY ONE, THE
Tracks: / Lucky one.
7" Single: Released Oct '84, on Atlantic, by WEA Records. Deleted '87. Catalogue no: **A 9636**

SELF CONTROL (SINGLE)
Tracks: / Self control / Silent partners.
7" Single: Released Jun '84, on Atlantic, by WEA Records. Deleted Jun '87. Catalogue no: **A 9676**

SHATTERED GLASS
Tracks: / Shattered glass / Statue in the rain.
7" Single: Released Jul '87, on Atlantic, by WEA Records. Deleted Jul '88. Catalogue no: **A 9921**
12" Single: Released Jul '87, on Atlantic, by WEA Records. Catalogue no: **A 9921 T**

SOLITAIRE
Tracks: / Solitaire.
12" Single: Released Apr '83, on Atlantic, by WEA Records. Catalogue no: **A 9856 T**
7" Single: Released Apr '83, on Atlantic, by WEA Records. Catalogue no: **A 9856**

Brard, Patty

TENDER LOVE
Tracks: / Tender love / Mystery theme.
Note: See also listing under Eddie Kendricks.
7" Single: Released Feb '87, on Spartan, Catalogue no: **SP 144**
12" Single: Released Feb '87, on Spartan, Catalogue no: **12SP 144**

Brass Bands

MUSIC OF NEW ORLEANS The brass bands
Tracks: / Music of New Orleans: *Various artists.*
7" Single: Released May '89, on Jazzology (USA), by Jazzology Records (USA). Catalogue no: **JCE 35**

Brass Construction

Biographical details: Formed in 1975, Brass Construction hit big the following year with their debut self-titled album. Following its disco success, it became a transatlantic Top 10 seller. It was an important LP as it was one of the first to make a successful fusion between jazz and R & B, and the group were one of the pioneers of the form later known as jazz-funk. A single from the album *"Movin"* went to No. 14 in the US and No. 23 in the UK Up to and including their sixth album, 1981's *"Brass Constrution 6"*, asll their albums were simply named after the band, with the appropriate number added. None sold as well as their first outing, however. Like many acts who score major successes with their debut, they were unable to maintain their momentum. This was particularly the case in Britain, where they never entered the album chart again, after their first offering. *"Brass Construction 5"* yielded the UK Top 40 single *"Music makes you feel like dancing"*, but the LP failed to chart. Nevertheless the group continue to please their own specialist audience with albums such as 1982's "Attitudes" and 1983's *"Conversations"*, and they are still competent exponents of the music that they helped to launch. (Bob MacDonald)..

CONQUEST (SINGLE)
Tracks: / Conquest.
7" Single: Released Aug '85, on Capitol, by EMI Records. Deleted '88. Catalogue no: **CL 371**
12" Single: Released Aug '85, on Capitol, by EMI Records. Deleted '88. Catalogue no: **12CL 371**

GIVE AND TAKE
Tracks: / Give and take.
12" Single: Released Oct '85, on Capitol, by EMI Records. Deleted '88. Catalogue no: **12CL 377**
7" Single: Released Oct '85, on Capitol, by EMI Records. Deleted Jul '87. Catalogue no: **CL 377**

HA CHA CHA
Tracks: / Ha cha cha (radio version) / Ha cha cha (New York mix) / Movin' 1988 (7" version) (CD single only.) / Ha cha cha (one,two,dub) / Ha cha cha (two,two,dub) / Ha cha cha / Ha cha cha (remix) / Ha cha cha (acieed mix) (Remix version only.) / Ha cha cha (Acieeeeeed) (Remix version only.).
12" Single: Released Sep '88, on Syncopate, by EMI Records. Deleted Aug '89. Catalogue no: **12 SYR 15**
12" Single: Released 8 Aug '88, on Syncopate, by EMI Records. Deleted Aug '89. Catalogue no: **12 SYX 15**
12" Single: Released 8 Aug '88, on Syncopate, by EMI Records. Deleted Aug '89. Catalogue no: **12 SY 15**
CD 5": Released 15 Aug '88, on Syncopate, by EMI Records. Deleted Aug '89. Catalogue no: **CDSY 15**
7" Single: Released 8 Aug '88, on Syncopate, by EMI Records. Deleted Jun '89. Catalogue no: **SY 15**

HA CHA CHA (FUNKTION)
Tracks: / Ha cha cha (funktion).
7" Single: Released Feb '77, on United Artists, by EMI Records. Deleted '80. Catalogue no: **UP 36205**

INTERNATIONAL
Tracks: / International.
7" Single: Released Oct '84, on Capitol, by EMI Records. Deleted '87. Catalogue no: **CL 341**
12" Single: Released Oct '84, on Capitol, by EMI Records. Deleted '86. Catalogue no: **12CL 341**

MOVIN'
Tracks: / Movin' / Changin'.
7" Single: Released Apr '76, on United Artists, by EMI Records. Deleted '79. Catalogue no: **UP 36090**
12" Single: Released Mar '80, on Liberty, by EMI Records. Deleted Mar '83. Catalogue no: **12 UP 617**

MOVIN' - 1988
Tracks: / Movin' - 1988 (extended mix) (Track on 12" version only) / Movin' - 1988(Let's All Chant Mix) / Movin' - 1988 / Give and take / Movin' - 1988(Brass Construction reconstruction) (On 12" special only.).

7" Single: Released 16 May '88, on Syncopate, by EMI Records. Deleted Jun '89. Catalogue no: **SY 11**
CD 5": Released May '88, on Syncopate, by EMI Records. Deleted Aug '89. Catalogue no: **CDSY 11**
12" Single: Released 16 May '88, on Syncopate, by EMI Records. Deleted Aug '89. Catalogue no: **12SY 11**
Special: Released 23 May '88, on Syncopate, by EMI Records. Deleted Aug '89. Catalogue no: **12 SYX 11**

MUSIC MAKES YOU FEEL LIKE DANCING
Tracks: / Music makes you feel like dancin / Shakit.
7" Single: Released Jan '80, on United A tists, by EMI Records. Deleted '83. Catalogue no: **UP 615**

PARTYLINE
Tracks: / Partyline.
7" Single: Released Jul '84, on Capitol, b EMI Records. Deleted '87. Catalogue no: **C 335**
12" Single: Released Jun '84, on Capitol, b EMI Records. Deleted '86. Catalogue n **12CL 335**

WALKIN' THE LINE
Tracks: / Walkin' the line.
7" Single: Released May '83, on Capitol, b EMI Records. Deleted '88. Catalogue no: **C 292**
12" Single: Released May '83, on Capitc by EMI Records. Deleted '85. Catalogue n **12CL 292**

WE CAN WORK IT OUT
Tracks: / We can work it out.
12" Single: Released Jul '83, on Capitol, EMI Records. Deleted '88. Catalogue n **12CL 299**
7" Single: Released Jul '83, on Capitol, EMI Records. Deleted '88. Catalogue no: **C 299**

Brat

CHALK DUST
Tracks: / Chalk dust / Umpire strikes bac Moody.
7" Single: Released Sep '82, on Ariola, BMG Records (UK). Catalogue no: **SMAS 1**

Brat Pack

SO MANY WAYS
Tracks: / So many ways / So many wa (worldwide DJ anthem).
Note: Currently two guys and a girl, The B pack's debut is a fierce assault on the dan floor. Their rhythm track plays off one of t most popular underground beats of the pa year, updating and expanding its appeal w a wealth of sly musical references. (A& Records, 1988)
7" Single: Released 17 Oct '88, on Bre kout, by A&M Records. Catalogue no: **US 646**
12" Single: Released 17 Oct '88, on Bre kout, by A&M Records. Catalogue no: **US 646**

SO MANY WAYS (REMIX)
Tracks: / So many ways (remix) / So ma ways (version).
12" Single: Released Oct '88, on Breakc by A&M Records. Catalogue no: **USAF 6**

Bratter, Henri

MADAME LEROY
Tracks: / Madame Leroy.
7" Single: Released Jun '84, on Red B by Red Bus Records. Catalogue no: **RB 95**

Braun, Steve

LOVE COULD BE SO GOOD
Tracks: / Love could be so good / Red li districts.
12" Single: Released Jun '86, on Numa, Numa Records. Catalogue no: **NUM 15**
7" Single: Released Jun '86, on Numa, Numa Records. Catalogue no: **NU 15**

OUT TO PLAY
Tracks: / Out to play.
7" Single: Released Mar '82, on Univer Deleted '87. Catalogue no: **UNIS 1**

WHEN I SEE YOUR EYES
Tracks: / When I see your eyes / Out to p
7" Single: Released Jan '86, on Numa, Numa Records. Catalogue no: **NU 12**
12" Single: Released Jan '86, on Numa Numa Records. Catalogue no: **NUM 12**

Brave New World

SUPERHERO
Tracks: / Super hero.
7" Single: Released Jul '83, on Tris Catalogue no: **TRI 1**

Braxton, Dhar

ILLUSIONS
Note: Mantronik produced.... another ' Dance Tracks' from the big apple.
12" Single: Released Nov '87, on Sleep Rag, by Sleeping Bag Records. Catalo no: **SLX 30**

JUMP BACK (SET ME FREE)
Tracks: / Jump back (set me free) / Ju back (set me free)(backappella).
7" Single: Released May '86, on 4t Broadway, by Island Records. Deleted '88. Catalogue no: **BRW 47**
12" Single: Released May '86, on 4t Broadway, by Island Records. Deleted '88. Catalogue no: **12 BRW 47**

Brazil

NUTS FROM BRAZIL
Tracks: / Nuts from Brazil / Give your love.
7" Single: Released May '83, on Spellbound, by Spellbound Records. Catalogue no: **SPELL 1**

SLIP AWAY
Tracks: / Slip away.
7" Single: Released Aug '85, on G.A.P., Catalogue no: **GAP 002**

WHO'S GONNA LOVE YOU NOW
Tracks: / Who's gonna love you now / Head on.
7" Single: Released Oct '80, on MCA, by MCA Records. Catalogue no: **MCA 655**

Bread

Biographical details: The mainstay of Bread was its songwriter and lead vocalist Dave Gates, who had been very active in the music business long before the group's formation in 1969. Among the artists whom Gates - also a guitarist and keyboards player - had backed were Chuck Berry, Glen Campbell, Duane Eddy, Merle Haggard and Carl Perkins. Bread were initially a trio comprising Gates and two fellow singer/guitarists, James Griffin and Robb Royer. Their first album was a self titled set, issued in '69. But it was the 1970 LP *On The Waters* that gave them their breakthrough, by yielding the smash single *Make It With You*. This was their first and biggest American Top 40 single, making No. 1 for one week. it also gave them their first and biggest British hit, peaking at No. 5. This song was typical Bread - a gentle but confident, highly melodic love song, written by David Gates. Frontman Gates continued to be the source of Bread material, despite the fact the Griffin and Royer were the composers of an acclaimed movie song entitled *For All We know*, that brought success for both the Carpenters and Shirley Bassey. The public acceptance of *Make It With You*, and its follow-up US Top 10 single *It Don't Matter To Me*, inspired Bread to become a touring group rather than purely a studio ensemble. To this end, drummer Mike Botts was added to the line-up. 1971's *Manna* album yielded another strong love song *If*, which reached No. 4 on the US chart although, curiously, it flopped in Britain. By the end of that year Royer had been replaced by keyboards player Larry Knechtel, fresh from playing on Simon & Garfunkel's *Bridge Over Troubled Water* album. Bread's next LP *Baby I'm A Want You* brought forth three further American hits, all perfect examples of the group's strong, harmonic, melodic style - the title song (No. 3) *Everything I Own* (No. 5) and *Diary* (No. 15). Two of these were Top 40 hits in the UK. Their British status was cemented in the autumn of '72 by the *Best Of Bread* compilation, which reached No. 7 on the UK album chart and stayed on the listings for exactly 100 weeks. At the same time the group were enjoying a transatlantic Top 20 single with the title track from their next regular album *Guitar Man*. As usual, they managed to pluck more hit singles from the LP in America than in Britain, with *Sweet Surrender* and *Aubrey* becoming further US Top 20 hits. Despite their high position in the musical world, Bread split in 1973. This was apparently due to disagreements between Gates and Griffin. The former attempted a career as a solo artist, but without the degree of success that he had attained in the group context. Meanwhile, however, the many cover versions of his songs included two surprise British No.1 singles. *Everything I Own* hit the top in a Jamaican reggae version by Ken Boothe in the autumn of 1974; and, less than four months later, a dire spoken rendition by 'Kojak' TV star Telly Savalas of the song *If* grabbed the UK No. 1 position, something that Bread themselves had never attained. A Bread reunion was attempted in the mid-Seventies, but the now weak quality of Gates' material ensured that it was short-lived. The title track from the album *Lost Without Your Love*, a single that hit the US Top 10 and the UK Top 30, was virtually the only strong song on the comeback album. Less than a year later, another collection album - *The Sound Of Bread* - was released in Britain and went to No. 1, a reminder of the far higher standard reached by the group in their heyday. As a solo performer once again, David Gates reached No. 15 in the US charts in 1978 with his single *Goodbye Girl*. Subsequent records failed to sell in these quantities, but he does not need the money. The mass, broad appeal of his Bread classics represents perfect material for numerous MoR singers, thus ensuring Gates a steady flow of songwriter's royalties. (Bob MacDonald).
Bread. A USA soft-rock trio/quartet formed in 1969 in Los Angeles. Lineup: David Gates (born 1940 in Tulsa, Oklahoma) on vocals, guitar, keyboards, etc. and James Griffin (from Memphis) on vocals, guitar, etc. Gates had worked in Tulsa with Leon Russell, done session work and song writing; Griffin had worked with master producer Snuff Garrett, and co-wrote *For All We Know* under the name of Arthur James, an Oscar-winning song in 1970 and a top 3 hit for the Carpenters. They made six albums plus a couple of compilations, all of which charted; *Make It With You* from their second album was a no. 1 USA hit; drummer Mike Botts and keyboardist Larry Knechtel *Baby I'm A Want You* (no. 3 title track) and *Guitar Man* (no. 11 title track). There was tension between Gates and Griffin, who wanted more of his songs used; after 11 top 40 singles they split in 1973 and re-formed in 1977 for *Lost Without Your Love* (top 10 title track). Gates had three top 40 solo hits 1975-78. Donald Clarke, 24 August 1988.

BABY I'M A WANT YOU (SINGLE)
Tracks: / Baby I'm a want you.
7" Single: Released Sep '85, on Old Gold, by Old Gold Records. Catalogue no: **OG 9513**
7" Single: Released Jan '72, on Elektra, by Elektra Records (UK). Deleted '75. Catalogue no: **K 12033**

EVERYTHING I OWN
Tracks: / Everything I own.
7" Single: Released Apr '72, on Elektra, by Elektra Records (UK). Deleted '75. Catalogue no: **K 12041**

GUITAR MAN (SINGLE)
Tracks: / Guitar man.
7" Single: Released Sep '76, on Elektra (USA), by Elektra Records (USA). Catalogue no: **K 12110**
7" Single: Released Sep '72, on Elektra, by Elektra Records (UK). Deleted '75. Catalogue no: **K 12066**

IF
Tracks: / If / Sweet surrender.
7" Single: Released Sep '76, on Elektra (USA), by Elektra Records (USA). Catalogue no: **K 12222**

LOST WITHOUT YOUR LOVE (SINGLE)
Tracks: / Lost without your love.
7" Single: Released Dec '76, on Elektra, by Elektra Records (UK). Deleted '79. Catalogue no: **K 12241**

MAKE IT WITH YOU
Tracks: / Make it with you / Everything I own.
7" Single: Released Sep '76, on Elektra (USA), by Elektra Records (USA). Catalogue no: **K 12221**
7" Single: Released Aug '70, on Elektra, by Elektra Records (UK). Deleted '73. Catalogue no: **2101 010**
7" Single: Released Sep '85, on Old Gold, by Old Gold Records. Catalogue no: **OG 9512**

Break Boys

AND THE BREAK GOES ON
Tracks: / And the break goes on.
12" Single: Released May '88, on Hardcore, Catalogue no: **HAKT 15**

Break Machine

ARE YOU READY
Tracks: / Are you ready.
7" Single: Released Jul '84, on Record Shack, by Record Shack Records. Catalogue no: **SOHO 24**
12" Single: Released Jul '84, on Record Shack, by Record Shack Records. Catalogue no: **SOHOT 24**

LET'S HAVE A BREAK DANCE PARTY
Tracks: / Let's have a break dance party.
7" Single: Released May '84, on Record Shack, by Record Shack Records. Catalogue no: **SOHO 20**
12" Single: Released May '84, on Record Shack, by Record Shack Records. Catalogue no: **SOHOT 20**

STREET DANCE
Tracks: / Street dance.
12" Single: Released Jan '84, on Record Shack, by Record Shack Records. Catalogue no: **SOHOT 13**
7" Single: Released Jan '84, on Record Shack, by Record Shack Records. Catalogue no: **SOHO 13**

STREET DANCE (OLD GOLD)
Tracks: / Street dance / Break dance party.
12" Single: Released 30 Jan '89, on Old Gold, by Old Gold Records. Catalogue no: **OG 4093**

Break The Illusion

CAN YOU UNDERSTAND
Tracks: / Can you understand.
12" Single: Released Oct '89, on Play Hard, by Play Hard Records. Catalogue no: **DEC 23**

Breakers

HEADLINE NEWS
Tracks: / Headline news / Give yourself some time.
7" Single: Released Jul '80, on M.A.M, by M.A.M. Records. Deleted '83. Catalogue no: **MAMS 203**

Breakfast Band

FEELING THE FEELING
Tracks: / Feeling the feeling (version) / Feeling the feeling / Never going to leave.
12" Single: Released Jun '89, on Cane, Catalogue no: **TASSA 1T**

FUNKSTERS
Tracks: / Funksters / Such a feeling.
12" Single: Released Nov '83, on Breakfast Music, by Breakfast Music Records. Catalogue no: **12 BM 103**

SUCH A FEELING
Tracks: / Such a feeling / Dozen time dragon.
7" Single: Released Sep '82, on Breakfast Music, by Breakfast Music Records. Catalogue no: **BM 102**
12" Single: Released Sep '82, on Breakfast Music, by Breakfast Music Records. Catalogue no: **12 BM 102**

TOKYO SHUFFLE
Tracks: / Tokyo shuffle / Broadside rhumba.
12" Single: Released Mar '82, on Breakfast Music, by Breakfast Music Records. Catalogue no: **12 BM 101**
7" Single: Released Mar '82, on Breakfast Music, by Breakfast Music Records. Catalogue no: **BM 101**

Breakfast Club

NEVER BE THE SAME
Tracks: / Never be the same / Never be the same (version) / Never be the same (Shep Pettibone mix) (on 12" only.) / Never be the same (sunny side up mix) (on 12" only.).
7" Single: Released Feb '88, on MCA, by MCA Records. Catalogue no: **MCA 1220**
12" Single: Released Feb '88, on MCA, by MCA Records. Catalogue no: **MCAT 1220**

RIGHT ON TRACK
Tracks: / Right on track / Right on track (local mix).
12" Single: Released 23 May '87, on MCA, by MCA Records. Catalogue no: **MCAT 1146**
7" Single: Released 23 May '87, on MCA, by MCA Records. Catalogue no: **MCA 1146**

Breakwater

SAY YOU LOVE ME GIRL
Tracks: / Say you love me girl / Work it out.
7" Single: Released Sep '86, on Arista, by BMG Records (UK). Catalogue no: **ARIST 674**
12" Single: Released Sep '86, on Arista, by BMG Records (UK). Catalogue no: **ARIST 12 674**

Breathe

ANY TRICK (LIKE A MONKEY)
Tracks: / Make it funky (On all versions) / Any trick (like a monkey club mix) (12" only) / Don't tell me lies (12" dance mix) (Cassette only).
7" Single: Released Mar '88, on Siren, by Virgin Records. Catalogue no: **SRN 81**
12" Single: Released Mar '88, on Siren, by Virgin Records. Catalogue no: **SRNT 81**
Cassingle: Released Mar '88, on Siren, by Virgin Records. Catalogue no: **SRNC 81**

DON'T TELL ME LIES
Tracks: / Don't tell me lies (extended version) / Moments (extended version) (On Siren 1112 only) / Don't tell me lies (dance mix) / Monday morning blues (On SRN & SRNT 109 only).
CD 5": Released Apr '89, on Siren, by Virgin Records. Catalogue no: **SRNCD 109**
7" Single: Released Apr '89, on Siren, by Virgin Records. Catalogue no: **SRNX 109**
7" Single: Released Jan '86, on Siren, by Virgin Records. Deleted May '88. Catalogue no: **SIREN 11**
12" Single: Released 20 Feb '89, on Virgin, by Virgin Records. Catalogue no: **SRNT 109**
7" Single: Released 20 Feb '89, on Virgin, by Virgin Records. Catalogue no: **SRN 109**
12" Single: Released Jan '86, on Siren, by Virgin Records. Deleted Feb '89. Catalogue no: **SIREN 11-12**

HANDS TO HEAVEN
Tracks: / Hands to heaven / Life and times / Hands to heaven (radio mix) (On 12" only) / All that jazz (On CD only) / Stay (7" version) (On CD only).
Cassingle: Released '89, on Siren, by Virgin Records. Catalogue no: **SRNC 68**
CD 5": Released '88, on Siren, by Virgin Records. Catalogue no: **SRNCD 68**
12" Single: Released Jul '88, on Siren, by Virgin Records. Catalogue no: **SRNT 68**
7" Single: Released '89, on Siren, by Virgin Records. Catalogue no: **SRNL 68**
7" Single: Released Jul '88, on Siren, by Virgin Records. Catalogue no: **SRN 68**

HOW CAN I FALL
Tracks: / How can I fall / All this I should have known (On CD & 12" only) / Hands to heaven (Only on 7" version (SRNH 102)) / How can I fall (extended remix) (Only on 12" & CD) / In all honesty (U.S. remix) (on CD only).
12" Single: Released 21 Nov '88, on Siren, by Virgin Records. Catalogue no: **SRNT 102**
7" Single: Released 21 Nov '88, on Siren, by Virgin Records. Catalogue no: **SRN 102**
7" Single: Released Nov '88, on Siren, by Virgin Records. Catalogue no: **SRNH 102**
12" Single: Released 21 Nov '88, on Siren, by Virgin Records. Catalogue no: **SRNTP 102**
CD 3": Released '88, on Siren, by Virgin Records. Catalogue no: **SRNCD 102**

IN ALL HONESTY
Tracks: / In all honesty (Not on 12") / Take a little time (NOT on 12") / In all honesty (radical mix) / In all honesty (chilled out mix) / Take a little time (extended version) / In all honesty (instrumental).
7" Single: Released May '86, on Siren, by Virgin Records. Deleted May '88. Catalogue no: **SIREN 18**
12" Single: on Siren, by Virgin Records. Catalogue no: **SIREN 1813**
12" Single: Released May '86, on Siren, by Virgin Records. Deleted May '88. Catalogue no: **SIREN 1812**

JONAH
Tracks: / Jonah (On all versions) / Won't you come back (extended version) (On CD & 12" only) / Liberties of love (NOT on 12") / Jonah (extended mix) (On 12' only) / Hands to heaven (On CD only).
CD 5": Released '88, on Siren, by Virgin Records. Catalogue no: **SRNCD 95**
7" Single: Released 3 Oct '88, on Siren, by Virgin Records. Catalogue no: **SRNP 95**
7" Single: Released 30 May '87, on Siren, by Virgin Records. Catalogue no: **SRN 95**
12" Single: Released 30 May '87, on Siren, by Virgin Records. Catalogue no: **SRNT 95**
12" Pic: Released '88, on Siren, by Virgin Records. Catalogue no: **SRNTY 95**
7" Single: Released '88, on Siren, by Virgin Records. Catalogue no: **SRNB 95**

Breathers

LIVIN' IN THE AGE AGE
Tracks: / Livin' in the age age / Count on counting.
7" Single: Released Dec '80, on Diversion, by Dingle's Records. Catalogue no: **DIV 111**

Breathing Age

HERE WE GO
Tracks: / Here we go / Camera room.
7" Single: Released May '81, on Edge, Deleted May '86. Catalogue no: **EDGE 13**

Breathless

2 DAYS FROM EDEN
Tracks: / 2 days from Eden.
12" Single: Released Aug '85, on Tenor Vosa, Catalogue no: **BREATH 3**

I NEVER KNOW WHERE YOU ARE
Tracks: / I never know where you are.
12" Single: Released Oct '89, on Tenor Vosa, Catalogue no: **BREATH 8**

NAILING COLOURS TO THE WHEEL (EP)
Tracks: / Bad blood / Nailing colours to the wheel.
12" Single: Released Nov '86, on Tenor Vosa, Catalogue no: **BREATH 5**

OH YOU BABE
Tracks: / Oh you babe / You will.
7" Single: Released Oct '81, on Magnum Force, by Magnum Music Group. Deleted Oct '84. Catalogue no: **MEEP 005**

WATERLAND
Tracks: / Waterland / Second heaven.
7" Single: Released Apr '84, on Tenor Vosa, Catalogue no: **BREATH 1**

Breck, Freddy

SO IN LOVE WITH YOU
Tracks: / So in love with you.
7" Single: Released Apr '74, on Decca, by Decca Records. Deleted '77. Catalogue no: **F 13481**

Brecker Brothers

EAST RIVER
Tracks: / East River.
7" Single: Released Nov '78, on Arista, by BMG Records (UK). Deleted '81. Catalogue no: **ARIST 211**

Breekout Krew

MATT'S MOOD
Tracks: / Matt's mood / Matt's cool / Everybody break (Available on 12" only.).
7" Single: Released Nov '84, on London Records, by 10 Records. Deleted '87. Catalogue no: **LON 59**

Breen, Ann

Biographical details: Hailing from the Irish Republic, this middle-of-the-road singer released her first album in 1981. By the end of '84 she had released five LPs. She is best known for her recording of *Pal Of My Cradle Days*, a 1982 single that sold in very slow but steady quantities in Britain over the following two years, gaining very slow but steady quantities in Britain over the following two years, gaining a Top 75 placing at one point and coming close to it on several occasions.

Such consistent sales figures suggest major hit potential, which a large record company might have been able to exploit. However, Dublin's Homespun label seemed unable to capitalise. Breen remains a well-known name in the somewhat insular Irish music scene and her regular UK releases reach a small but reliable audience (Bob MacDonald)..

BLUE VIOLETS & RED ROSES
Tracks: / Blue violets & red roses
7" Single: Released Feb '83, on Homespun (Ireland), by Outlet Records. Catalogue no: **HS 063**

BREAKAWAY
Tracks: / Breakaway.
7" Single: Released Feb '85, on Homespun (Ireland), by Outlet Records. Catalogue no: **HS 094**

BY THE SILVERY LIGHT OF THE MOON
Tracks: / By the silvery light of the moon / Dear little boy of mine.
7" Single: Released Sep '82, on Homespun (Ireland), by Outlet Records. Catalogue no: **HS 059**

DEAR LITTLE BOY OF MINE
Tracks: / Dear little boy of mine / By the bright silvery light of the moon.
7" Single: Released Jul '82, on Homespun (Ireland), by Outlet Records. Deleted '85. Catalogue no: **HS 059**

DIVIDED WE FALL
Tracks: / Divided we fall / Divided we fall (instrumental).
7" Single: Released Mar '87, on Play, by Play Records. Catalogue no: **PLAY 215**

DOMINO
Tracks: / Domino (easy listening mix) / Domino (slap remix).
7" Single: Released Sep '86, on Play, by Play Records. Catalogue no: **PLAY 210**
12" Single: Released Sep '86, on Play, by Play Records. Catalogue no: **PLAY 210 T**

GENTLE MOTHER
Tracks: / Gentle mother / Bunch of violets blue.
7" Single: Released Oct '83, on Homespun (Ireland), by Outlet Records. Catalogue no: **HS 072**

GIVE ME ONE GOOD REASON
Tracks: / Give me one good reason / Tenasee waltz.
7" Single: Released May '84, on Homespun (Ireland), by Outlet Records. Catalogue no: **HS 080**

HEART YOU BREAK WILL BE YOUR OWN
Tracks: / Heart you break will be your own / Two loves.
7" Single: Released Feb '82, on Homespun (Ireland), by Outlet Records. Deleted Feb '87. Catalogue no: **H 5055**

HOLD ME IN YOUR ARMS
Tracks: / Hold me in your arms.
7" Single: Released '88, on Play (Ireland), Catalogue no: **PLAY 222**

I WISH ALL MY BABIES WERE CHILDREN
Tracks: / I wish all my babies were children.
7" Single: Released '88, on Play (Ireland), Catalogue no: **PLAY 236**

LOVE BY LOVE
Tracks: / Love by love.
7" Single: Released Sep '84, on Homespun (Ireland), by Outlet Records. Catalogue no: **HS 084**

MOONSHINER
Tracks: / Moonshiner.
7" Single: Released '88, on Play (Ireland), Catalogue no: **PLAY 231**

MY MOTHER'S PEARLS
Tracks: / My mother's pearls.
7" Single: Released '88, on Play (Ireland), Catalogue no: **PLAY 229**

OLD COUNTRY WALTZ, THE
Tracks: / Old country waltz, The.
7" Single: Released '88, on Play (Ireland), Catalogue no: **PLAY 235**

PAL OF MY CRADLE DAYS
Tracks: / Pal of my cradle days.
7" Single: Released '88, on Homespun (Ireland), by Outlet Records. Catalogue no: **HIS 52**

PAL OF MY CRADLE DAYS(SINGLE)
Tracks: / Pal of my cradle days / Love is teasin'.
7" Single: Released Mar '86, on Homespun (Ireland), by Outlet Records. Catalogue no: **HS 052**

QUE SERA SERA
Tracks: / Que sera sera.
7" Single: Released Oct '84, on Homespun (Ireland), by Outlet Records. Catalogue no: **HS 089**

SAVE THE LAST DANCE FOR ME
Tracks: / Save the last dance for me / Rustic bridge.
7" Single: Released Jan '84, on Homespun (Ireland), by Outlet Records. Catalogue no: **HS 076**

THOSE BROWN EYES
Tracks: / Those brown eyes / Love is teasin'.
7" Single: Released Jul '81, on Homespun (Ireland), by Outlet Records. Catalogue no: **HS 047**

TWO LOVES
Tracks: / Two loves / Heart you break will be your own, The.
7" Single: Released Sep '82, on Homespun (Ireland), by Outlet Records. Catalogue no: **HS 055**

WHAT A FRIEND WE HAVE IN MOTHER
Tracks: / What a friend we have in mother / Falling.
7" Single: Released Sep '82, on Homespun (Ireland), by Outlet Records. Catalogue no: **HS 053**

YOU ALWAYS HURT THE ONE YOU LOVE (SINGLE)
Tracks: / You always hurt the one you love.
7" Single: Released Jun '83, on Homespun (Ireland), by Outlet Records. Catalogue no: **HS 069**

Breeze

MIDNIGHT LADIES
Tracks: / Midnight ladies.
7" Single: Released Aug '83, on Breeze, by Pinnacle Records. Catalogue no: **BRZ 1**
12" Single: Released Aug '83, on Breeze, by Pinnacle Records. Catalogue no: **BRZX 1**

Bremner, Billy

ENDLESS SLEEP
Tracks: / Endless sleep.
7" Single: Released Feb '85, on Rock City, Catalogue no: **RCR 6**

LAUGHTER TURNS TO TEARS
Tracks: / Laughter turns to tears / Tired and emotional.
7" Single: Released Feb '82, on Stiff, by Stiff Records. Catalogue no: **BUY 143**

LOUD MUSIC IN CARS
Tracks: / Loud music in cars / Price is right.
7" Single: Released Sep '81, on Stiff, by Stiff Records. Catalogue no: **BUY 125**

LOVE GOES TO SLEEP
Tracks: / Love goes to sleep / Fire in my pocket.
12" Single: Released Apr '84, on Arista, by BMG Records (UK). Catalogue no: **ARIST 12566**
7" Single: Released Apr '84, on Arista, by BMG Records (UK). Catalogue no: **ARIST 566**

MEEK POWER
Tracks: / Meek power.
7" Single: Released Aug '82, on Demon, by Demon Records. Catalogue no: **D 1014**

SHATTERPROOF
Tracks: / Shatterproof / Look at that car / Muscle bound.
12" Single: Released Feb '84, on Arista, by BMG Records (UK). Catalogue no: **ARIST 12557**
7" Single: Released Feb '84, on Arista, by BMG Records (UK). Catalogue no: **ARIST 557**

Brenda & Rattlesnakes

I'M BORED
Tracks: / I'm bored / We're OK.
7" Single: Released Mar '80, on Active, by Active Records. Deleted '83. Catalogue no: **ACT 3**

Brenda & The...

AMALAHLE
Tracks: / Amalahle / Bongani / Weekend special (ext. version) (Only available on 12" version.).
Note: Weekend special (Ext. Version) is an extra track only available on 12" version.
12" Single: Released Mar '87, on EMI, by EMI Records. Catalogue no: **12EMI 5604**
7" Single: Released Mar '87, on EMI, by EMI Records. Catalogue no: **EMI 5604**

BONGANI
Tracks: / Bongani (remix) / Higher.
7" Single: Released Feb '86, on EMI, by EMI Records. Catalogue no: **DUDE 1**
12" Single: Released Feb '86, on EMI, by EMI Records. Catalogue no: **12DUDE 1**

CATCH A FALLING STAR
Tracks: / Shellfish samba / Catch a falling star.
12" Single: Released Oct '87, on Siren, by Virgin Records. Deleted May '88. Catalogue no: **SRN 65-12**
7" Single: Released Oct '87, on Siren, by Virgin Records. Deleted May '88. Catalogue no: **SRN 65**

D'YA HEAR ME?
Tracks: / D'ya hear me? / D'ya hear me? (ext. version) / D'ya dub? / Mandarin mooch.
7" Single: Released Feb '88, on Siren, by Virgin Records. Catalogue no: **SRN 73**
12" Single: Released Feb '88, on Siren, by Virgin Records. Catalogue no: **SRNT 73**

LET'S GO ALL THE WAY DOWN
Tracks: / Let's go all the way down.
12" Single: Released Sep '87, on Casablanca (USA), by PolyGram Rec.Inc.(USA). Catalogue no: **8269731M1**

WEEKEND SPECIAL
Tracks: / Weekend special / Weekend special (instrumental).
7" Single: Released Jul '86, on EMI, by EMI Records. Catalogue no: **DUDE 2**
12" Single: Released Jul '86, on EMI, by EMI Records. Catalogue no: **12DUDE 2**

Brendon

GIMME SOME
Tracks: / Gimme some.
7" Single: Released Mar '77, on Magnet, by WEA Records. Deleted '80. Catalogue no: **MAG 80**

Brennan, Lee

SHUT YER GOB
Tracks: / Shut yer gob.
7" Single: Released Apr '81, on Rox, by Rox Records. Catalogue no: **ROX 016**

Brennan, Rose

TALL DARK STRANGER
Tracks: / Tall dark stranger / Goodbye.
7" Single: Released Dec '61, on Philips, by Phonogram Ltd. Deleted '64. Catalogue no: **PB 1193**

Brennan, Walter

OLD RIVERS
Tracks: / Old rivers.
7" Single: Released Jun '62, on Liberty, by EMI Records. Deleted '65. Catalogue no: **LIB 55436**

Brent, Tony

CINDY OH CINDY
Tracks: / Cindy Oh Cindy.
7" Single: Released Nov '56, on Columbia, by EMI Records. Deleted '59. Catalogue no: **DB 3844**

CLOUDS WILL SOON ROLL BY, THE
Tracks: / Clouds will soon roll by, The.
7" Single: Released Feb '58, on Columbia, by EMI Records. Deleted '61. Catalogue no: **DB 4066**

DARK MOON
Tracks: / Dark moon.
7" Single: Released Jun '57, on Columbia, by EMI Records. Deleted '60. Catalogue no: **DB 3950**

GIRL OF MY DREAMS
Tracks: / Girl of my dreams.
7" Single: Released Sep '58, on Columbia, by EMI Records. Deleted '61. Catalogue no: **DB 4177**

GOT YOU ON MY MIND
Tracks: / Got you on my mind.
7" Single: Released Jan '53, on Columbia, by EMI Records. Deleted '56. Catalogue no: **DB 3226**

MAKE IT SOON
Tracks: / Make it soon.
7" Single: Released Jan '53, on Columbia, by EMI Records. Deleted '56. Catalogue no: **DB 3187**

WALKIN' TO MISSOURI
Tracks: / Walkin' to Missouri.
7" Single: Released Dec '52, on Columbia, by EMI Records. Deleted '55. Catalogue no: **DB 3147**

WHY SHOULD I BE LONELY
Tracks: / Why should I be lonely.
7" Single: Released Jul '59, on Columbia, by EMI Records. Deleted '62. Catalogue no: **DB 4304**

Bresslaw, Bernard

MAD PASSIONATE LOVE
Tracks: / Mad passionate love.
7" Single: Released Sep '58, on H.M.V., by EMI Records. Deleted '61. Catalogue no: **POP 522**

Brett, Ann & Ray

THERE'S NO MORE YOU AND ME
Tracks: / There's no more you and me.
7" Single: Released Jun '83, on A & R, Catalogue no: **AR 003**

Brett, Paul

FOREVER AUTUMN
Tracks: / Forever autumn
7" Single: Released Apr '80, on RCA, by BMG Records (UK). Deleted Apr '83. Catalogue no: **PB 5230**

Brewer, Teresa

Biographical details: Born in Ohio, USA, Teresa Brewer took up signing at a very early age and became a local child prodigy. At the age of 19, she was already a seasoned performer when she enjoyed her smash hit in 1950. *Music, Music, Music* was a US No. 1 single in that year and turned Brewer into a major star. 1952's *Till I Waltz Again With You* was another American chart-topper. The following year saw her make her film debut in *Those Redheads From Seattle* and also saw her enjoying a US Top 10 hit with *Ricochet*. In late 1954 the singer released a version of *Let Me Go Lover*. This song was a US No. 1 at the start of '55 for Joan Weber, but Brewer's rendition managed to climb to No. 6 in the States. In Britain, she easily beat the Weber competition; the single gave Brewer her first UK hit, peaking at No. 9. After three smaller American Top 20 singles, she enjoyed another enormous hit in 1956 with *A Tear Fell*. This reached No. 5 in the US, and became her biggest UK 45 by reaching No. 2. Its follow-up entitled *A Sweet Old-Fashioned Girl* was another Top Tenner on both sides of the Atlantic. After this however, success was more difficult to sustain. The chart records continued spasmodically, but she never hit the British Top 10 again and only got there once more in her native America. Even then it was with an inferior version of *You Send Me* which was outstripped by the No. 1 success of the Sam Cooke original. She enjoyed her last year of chart success in 1960. she was a conventional, run-of-the-mill Fifties singer. She possessed a good voice and was a success all the time that she found the right songs. When it was realised that rock 'n' roll and pop music were here to stay, she had to follow many of her contemporaries in moving out of the charts and into other areas of showbusiness. She continues to visit recording studios from time to time and, in 1983, released an album called *I Dig Big Band Singers*, a series of medleys combining popular numbers from the big band era. (Bob MacDonald)

HOW DO YOU KNOW IT'S LOVE
Tracks: / How do you know it's love.
7" Single: Released Jun '60, on Coral, by MCA Records. Deleted '63. Catalogue no: **Q 72396**

LET ME GO LOVER
Tracks: / Let me go lover.
7" Single: Released Feb '55, on Vogue, by Vogue Records. Deleted '58. Catalogue no: **Q 72043**

NORA MALONE
Tracks: / Nora Malone.
7" Single: Released May '57, on Vogue, by Vogue Records. Deleted '60. Catalogue no: **Q 72224**

SWEET OLD FASHIONED GIRL
Tracks: / Sweet old fashioned girl.
7" Single: Released Jul '56, on Vogue, by Vogue Records. Deleted '59. Catalogue no: **Q 72172**

TEAR FELL, A
Tracks: / Tear fell, A.
7" Single: Released Apr '56, on Vogue, by Vogue Records. Deleted '59. Catalogue no: **Q 72146**

Brian & Michael

Biographical details: This British vocal duo consisted of Brian Parrott (real name Kevin Parrott) and Michael Coleman. The pair are One Hit Wonders on the British charts, having scored one No. 1 single but nothing else ever. Their big record was written by Coleman and produced by Parrott. They billed themselves as Brian & Michael in the belief that this was commercially a more viable name than Kevin & Michael. The song was *Matchstalk Men & Matchstalk Cats & Dogs*, a tribute to the life and artistic style of the late painter L.S. Lowry. he died in February 1976 and this single was issued in December 1977. It was either a lovely or nauseating song, depending on personal taste and featured the vocal talents not only of the duo themselves but also of St. Winifred's School Choir. It was a sleeper smash in the UK taking over two months to enter the charts. BBC Radio One DJ Peter Powell, who gave the record heavy airplay, had given up hope and dropped the record from his show, but the time it cracked the Top 50 at the end of February '78. At the beginning of April, it fell from No. 3 to No. 4 and then went to the very top the following week, thus becoming one of the few chart singles to start moving downwards before hitting No. 1. Brian & Michael never hit the chart again in their own right but Parrott produced *The Sparrow*, a 197 No. 11 hit in the UK for the Ramblers,

RIAN & MICHAEL - MATCHSTALK MEN AND MATCHSTALK CATS AND DOGS (Released on PRT)

ildren's choir from the Abbey Hey Junior hool. The St. Winifred's School Choir went to have their own No. 1 hit during Christ- as 1980 with *There's No-one Quite Like andma* and thus became the only act in tish chart history whose only chart ap- arances have been on two One Hit Won- r records! Brian & Michael and the Choir eased an unsuccessful 1983 single entit- *Mama*. (Bob MacDonald)..

AMA
acks: / Mama / Time made a man out of .
Single: Released Nov '83, on RCA, by IG Records (UK). Catalogue no: **RCA 377**

ATCHSTALK MEN AND MATCH- ALK CATS AND DOGS (see nel above)
acks: / Matchstalk men and matchstalk s and dogs / Old rocking chair, The.
Single: Released Dec '77, on PRT, by stle Communications Records. Cata- ue no: **7N 46035**

ATCHSTALK MEN AND MATCH- ALK ... (OLD GOLD)
acks: / Matchstalk men and matchstalk s and dogs.
Single: Released Apr '83, on Old Gold, Old Gold Records. Catalogue no: **OG 5**

rian & Zan

MP YOUR BODY
cks: / Pump your body.
Single: Released Jul '83, on Sound Of w York (USA), by Sound Of New York cords(USA). Catalogue no: **SYN 5**
Single: Released Jul '83, on Sound Of w York (USA), by Sound Of New York cords(USA). Catalogue no: **SYNL 5**

riar

GE OF A BROKEN HEART
cks: / Edge of a broken heart / Don't et me when you're on your island / Boys back in town (on 12" only.).
Single: Released Jul '87, on PRT, by tle Communications Records. Cata- e no: **BRIAR T1**
ic: Released Aug '87, on PRT, by Castle nmunications Records. Catalogue no: **AR X1**
ic: Released Jul '87, on PRT, by Castle nmunications Records. Catalogue no: **AR 1**
ic: Released Aug '87, on PRT, by Castle nmunications Records. Catalogue no: **AR P1**

ANKIE
ks: / Frankie.
ingle: Released 21 Nov '87, on UK, by Records. Catalogue no: **UKP 003**
Single: Released 21 Nov '87, on UK, by Records. Catalogue no: **UKPT 003**

E MONKEY DON'T STOP NO OW
: "In the six years of their existence, have acquired a catalogue of admirers; vell as making a host of television ap- ances, the band has been heavily npioned at Radio 1, as well as notching over 20,000 sales of their '85 inde- ent LP debut *Too Young*. Briar's inexor- climb to chart prominence takes a new step this summer with the release of their debut A&M single, a rocking rendition of the Atlantic Soul standard *One Monkey Don't Stop No Show*, produced by long-time Briar mentor/devotee Jonathan King". (A&M Rec- ords, August 1988)
7" Single: Released Aug '88, on A&M, by A&M Records. Deleted Feb '89. Catalogue no: **AM 456**
12" Single: Released Aug '88, on A&M, by A&M Records. Deleted Feb '89. Catalogue no: **AMY 456**

ONE MORE CHANCE
Tracks: / One more chance.
7" Single: Released Aug '85, on FM, by FM-Revolver Records. Catalogue no: **VHF 14**

Brick

DAZZ
Tracks: / Dazz.
7" Single: Released Feb '77, on Bang. Deleted '80. Catalogue no: **BANG 004**

Brickell, Edie

CIRCLE
Tracks: / Circle / Plain Jane.
12" Single: Released Apr '89, on Geffen, by Geffen Records (USA). Catalogue no: **GEF 51T**
CD 5": Released Apr '89, on Geffen, by Geffen Records (USA). Catalogue no: **GEF 51CD**
7" Single: Released Apr '89, on Geffen, by Geffen Records (USA). Catalogue no: **GEF 51**

LOVE LIKE WE DO
Tracks: / Love like we do.
7" Single: Released Oct '89, on Geffen, by Geffen Records (USA). Catalogue no: **GEF 61**

WHAT I AM
Tracks: / What I am / I do / Walk on the wild side (Only on 12" version.).
CD 5": Released Feb '89, on Geffen, by Geffen Records (USA). Catalogue no: **GEF 49CD**
7" Single: Released Feb '89, on Geffen, by Geffen Records (USA). Catalogue no: **GEF 49B**
12" Single: Released Jan '89, on Geffen, by Geffen Records (USA). Catalogue no: **GEF 49 T**
7" Single: Released Jan '89, on Geffen, by Geffen Records (USA). Catalogue no: **GEF 49**

Brid Kids

CHILDREN ARE THE FUTURE
Tracks: / Children are the future.
7" Single: Released Dec '88, on BBC, by BBC Records & Tapes. Catalogue no: **RESL 232**

Bridge

BABY DON'T HOLD YOUR LOVE BACK
Tracks: / Baby don't hold your love back.
7" Single: Released Jul '85, on Atlantic, by WEA Records. Deleted '86. Catalogue no: **A 9565**
12" Single: Released Jul '85, on Atlantic, by WEA Records. Catalogue no: **A 9565 T**

INDUSTRIAL LOVE DANCE
Tracks: / Industrial love dance.
12" Single: Released May '84, on Second Vision, Catalogue no: **SV 12003**
7" Single: Released May '84, on Second Vision, Catalogue no: **SV 003**

SALT IN MY WOUNDS
Tracks: / Salt in my wounds.
12" Single: Released Aug '87, on Legacy, by Legacy Records. Catalogue no: **LGYT 58**

SHAME IS A GIRL
Tracks: / Shame is a girl / Loveless, The.
7" Single: Released Mar '87, on Backs, by Backs Recording Co.. Catalogue no: **NCH 112**

Bridges, Alicia

I LOVE THE NIGHTLIFE
Tracks: / I love the nightlife / Body heat.
12" Single: Released Aug '87, on Polydor, by Polydor Ltd. Deleted Mar '88. Catalogue no: **POSPX 879**
7" Single: Released Nov '78, on Polydor, by Polydor Ltd. Deleted '81. Catalogue no: **2066 936**
7" Single: Released Aug '87, on Polydor, by Polydor Ltd. Deleted Mar '88. Catalogue no: **POSP 879**

PLAY IT AS IT LAYS
Tracks: / Play it as it lays / Cheap affairs.
7" Single: Released Feb '80, on Polydor, by Polydor Ltd. Deleted '83. Catalogue no: **POSP 102**
12" Single: Released Feb '80, on Polydor, by Polydor Ltd. Deleted '83. Catalogue no: **POSPX 102**

Bridges, Calvin

ROSE OF SHARON
Tracks: / Rose of Sharon / Rose of Sharon (inst).
12" Single: Released Apr '87, on Bluebird (2), by BMG Records (UK). Catalogue no: **BRT 32**

Bridges, Clyde

IT'S HARD TO BE HUMBLE
Tracks: / It's hard to be humble / Y'all come back now.
7" Single: Released Nov '80, on EMI, by EMI Records. Deleted '83. Catalogue no: **EMI 5124**

Bridges, Slim

ROCKING GOOSE
Tracks: / Rockin' goose.
7" Single: Released Nov '81, on Circus, by Circus Records. Catalogue no: **CIRC 0006**

Bridgewater, Dee Dee

Biographical details: Bridgewater, Dee Dee. The USA jazz singer was born in 1950 in Memphis, Tennessee; she married trumpeter Cecil Bridgewater and went to NYC with him (later divorced). She was featured singer with the Trad Jones-Mel Lewis Band 1972-74 at the Village Vanguard, recorded with them and others, but did not make an album of her own until she was a hit in Paris in a one-woman show 'Lady Day', which she brought to London in early '87. She portrayed her own interpretation of Billie Holiday, rather than an imitation, and won praise from critics. Donald Clarke, 24 August 1988..

ONE IN A MILLION GUY
Tracks: / One in a million guy / Lonely disco dance.
7" Single: Released Nov '80, on Elektra, by Elektra Records (UK). Deleted '83. Catalogue no: **K 12490**

WHEN LOVE COMES KNOCKIN'
Tracks: / When love comes knockin' / Gun shots in the night.
7" Single: Released Jan '81, on Elektra, by Elektra Records (UK). Deleted Jan '84. Catalogue no: **K 12499**

Brigadier Jerry

Biographical details: Brigadier Jerry. A Jamaican toaster, real name Robert Russell, who emerged as the most acclaimed of mike chanters in early '80s. Along with Josie Wales and Charlie Chaplin he was one of the few to carry on the signifying tradition formerly practiced by u roy and big youth. He rarely recorded, but examples of his work were readily available via the reggae network of sound system cassettes recorded in dancehalls; his first studio album was *Jamaica Jamaica* in 1985, from the USA reggae specialists Ras. Donald Clarke, 24 August 1988..

HARD DRUGS
Tracks: / Hard drugs.
7" Single: Released Oct '88, on Pioneer Muzik, Catalogue no: **PM 014**

JAH JAH YOU PAIN
Tracks: / Jah jah you pain.
12" Single: Released Dec '82, on Jwyanza, Catalogue no: **J 24**

JAMAICA JAMAICA (SINGLE)
12" Single: Released Sep '84, on Jah Love, Catalogue no: **Not known**

MY IMAGINATION
Tracks: / My imagination.
7" Single: Released Jun '88, on Super Supreme, Catalogue no: **SPT 2**

Briggs, Billy

CHEW TOBACCO RAG
Tracks: / Chew tobacco rag.
7" Single: Released Jan '81, on United Artists, by EMI Records. Deleted Jan '84. Catalogue no: **UP 637**

Briggs, Brian

LOOKIN' OUT
Tracks: / Lookin' out.
7" Single: Released Jan '82, on Avatar, by Avatar Record Corporation. Catalogue no: **AAA 120**

NERVOUS BREAKDOWN
Tracks: / Nervous breakdown / Lifer.
7" Single: Released Jan '81, on Island, by Island Records. Deleted Jan '84. Catalogue no: **WIP 6545**

SEE YOU ON THE OTHER SIDE
Tracks: / See you on the other side / Spy vs. spy.
7" Single: Released Feb '81, on Island, by Island Records. Deleted Feb '84. Catalogue no: **WIP 6664**

Brighouse & Rastrick

Biographical details: This British brass band hail from the West Yorkshire towns of Brighouse and Rastrick, situated between Bradford and Huddersfield. They shot to national fame in late 1977 when their bright, catchy rendition of *The Floral Dance* an old standard penned by Katie Moss, reached No. 2 on the UK singles chart. It was a massive Christmas seller, staying in that position for six successive weeks. it had the mis-fortune to coincide with Britain's all-time best-selling 45, Wings' *Mull Of Kintyre/Girls School*, which held *The Floral Dance* down to No. 2 for that entire period. So successful was the band's single, that it inspired a vocal version by Terry Wogan, the BBC radio and TV personality. His single peaked at No. 21 on the UK chart. *The Floral Dance* was the band's only chart single and it was quickly followed by their sole chart LP - this was also entitled *The Floral Dance* and peaked at No. 10 with 11 weeks on the survey. They continue to issue albums regularly and are widely regarded as one of the finest ensembles in their field. At the time of their chart glory they were billed as the Brighouse & Rastrick Brass Band, though the word 'Brass' is normally omitted on later releases. All its members are male. (Bob MacDonald)..

FLORAL DANCE (SINGLE)
Tracks: / Floral dance.
7" Single: Released Nov '77, on Transatlantic, by Transatlantic Records. Deleted '80. Catalogue no: **BIG 548**

Bright, Bette

Biographical details: British singer Bright was a member of unsuccessful 70's band Deaf School before turning solo at the end of the decade. With her backing band the Illuminations she scored a solitary chart single in 1980: *Hello, I Am Your Heart* peaked at No 50 on the UK listings. Subsequent singles and a 1981 LP, *Rhythm Breaks The Ice*, failed to make impact. Her records were in a punk-influenced pop style. (Bob MacDonald, 1984.).

HELLO I AM YOUR HEART
Tracks: / Hello I am your heart / All girls lie.
7" Single: Released Mar '80, on Korova, by WEA Records. Deleted '83. Catalogue no: **KOW 3**

SOME GIRLS HAVE ALL THE LUCK (see panel on next page)
Tracks: / Some girls have all the luck / Tender touch.
7" Single: Released '81, on Korova, by WEA Records. Catalogue no: **KOW 18**

WHEN YOU WERE MINE
Tracks: / When you were mine / Soulful dress.
7" Single: Released Jul '81, on Korova, by WEA Records. Deleted '85. Catalogue no: **KOW 14**

Bright, Greg

I'M A BELIEVER
Tracks: / I'm a believer / Sweet in the leyden jar.
7" Single: Released Aug '80, on Rat Race, by Rat Race Records. Catalogue no: **RAT 5**

Bright, Len

SOMEONE MUST HAVE NAILED US TOGETHER
Tracks: / Someone must have nailed us together / Mona.
7" Single: Released Apr '86, on Empire Records, Catalogue no: **LEN 1**

Brighter

AROUND THE WORLD IN 80 DAYS
Tracks: / Around the world in 80 days.
7" Single: Released 24 Jul '89, on Sarah,

Betty Bright - Some girls have all the luck (Released on Korova)

Catalogue no: **SARAH 019**

Brightman, Sarah

Biographical details: This British singer first became known as a member of the sexy TV dance troupe 'Hot Gossip'. In late 1978 she released a single called *I Lost My Heart To A Starship Trooper*, with the billing reading as 'Sarah Brightman & Hot Gossip'. It reached no. 6 in the UK chart.
This lightweight, very commercial single was a clever confluence, designed to capitalise on two prevalent crazes of the day: the Boney M-ied Eurodisco boom and the science fiction explosion prompted by the *Star Wars* and *Close Encounters Of The Third Kind* movies. A follow-up single entitled *The Adventures Of A Love Crusader*, credited to 'Sarah Brightman & The Starship Troopers' was merely a re-run of its predecessor and could only climb to No. 53. No further chart records were forthcoming
1981 saw Brightman perform in the opening run of Andrew Lloyd Webber's *Cats* musical. This was a London theatrical adaptation of T.S. Eliot poetry.
She then appeared in Rod Argent's musical adaptation of *Masquerade*, then took the title role in the world premiere of Charles Strouse's children's opera *Nightingale*. Yet another British musical followed - Brightman appeared in Gilbert & Sullivan's *The Pirates of Penzance*.
1983 saw her working with Andrew Lloyd Webber again, this time in his new musical *Starlight Express*. She is now married to Webber. (Bob MacDonald)..

ADVENTURES OF THE LOVE CRUSADER, THE
Tracks: / Adventures of the love crusader, The.
7" Single: Released Apr '79, on Ariola, by BMG Records (UK). Deleted '82. Catalogue no: **AHA 538**

ANYTHING BUT LONELY
Tracks: / Anything but lonely.
7" Single: Released 2 May '89, on Polydor, by Polydor Ltd. Catalogue no: **RUR 5**
CD 5": Released 2 May '89, on Polydor, by Polydor Ltd. Catalogue no: **RURCD 5**
12" Single: Released 2 May '89, on Polydor, by Polydor Ltd. Deleted Oct '89. Catalogue no: **RURX 5**

HIM
Tracks: / Him.
7" Single: Released Jul '83, on Polydor, by Polydor Ltd. Deleted '86. Catalogue no: **POSP 625**

I LOST MY HEART TO A STARSHIP TROOPER
Tracks: / I lost my heart to a starship trooper.
7" Single: Released Nov '78, on Ariola, by BMG Records (UK). Deleted '81. Catalogue no: **AHA 527**

MY BOYFRIEND'S BACK
Tracks: / My boyfriend's back / Sleeping beauty.
7" Single: Released Jul '81, on Whisper, by Whisper Records. Catalogue no: **WSP 102**

NOT HAVING THAT
Tracks: / Not having that.
7" Single: Released Oct '81, on Whisper, by Whisper Records. Catalogue no: **WSP 104**

PHANTOM OF THE OPERA
Tracks: / Phantom of the opera / Overture - Phantom of the opera.
7" Single: Released Nov '85, on Polydor, by Polydor Ltd. Deleted Aug '87. Catalogue no: **POSP 800**
12" Single: Released Nov '85, on Polydor, by Polydor Ltd. Deleted Aug '87. Catalogue no: **POSPX 800**

PIE JESU
Tracks: / Pie Jesu.
7" Single: Released Mar '85, on H.M.V., by EMI Records. Deleted '88. Catalogue no: **WEBBER 1**

ROOM WITH A VIEW, A (Theme)
Tracks: / Room with a view.
7" Single: Released May '87, on Polydor, by Polydor Ltd. Deleted Jan '88. Catalogue no: **POSP 862**

UNEXPECTED SONG
Tracks: / Unexpected song.
7" Single: Released Sep '84, on RCA, by BMG Records (UK). Catalogue no: **RCA 438**

Brighton Football Club

BOYS IN THE OLD BRIGHTON BLUE, THE
Tracks: / Boys in the old Brighton blue, The.
7" Single: Released May '83, on Energy (UK), by Energy Records. Deleted '86. Catalogue no: **NRG 2**

Brightsteen, Bill

IF IT MOVES FUNK IT
Tracks: / If it moves funk it.
12" Single: Released Jul '85, on Green Pea, Catalogue no: **GP 112**
7" Single: Released Jul '85, on Green Pea, Catalogue no: **GP 17**

Brilliant

COLOURS
Tracks: / Colours.
12" Single: Released Jun '83, on Risk, Catalogue no: **RTT 105**

END OF THE WORLD, THE
Tracks: / End of the world / How high the sun / Crash the car (Extra track on 12" only) / Ruby fruit jungle (on 12" only.).
Note: Extra track on 12" only*
12" Single: Released Nov '86, on Food, by Food Records. Deleted Jun '87. Catalogue no: **FOOD 8T**
7" Single: Released Nov '86, on Food, by Food Records. Deleted Jun '87. Catalogue no: **FOOD 8**

IT'S A MAN'S MAN'S MAN'S WORLD
Tracks: / It's a man's man's man's world.
7" Single: Released Sep '85, on Food, by Food Records. Deleted Jun '87. Catalogue no: **FOOD 5**
12" Single: on Food, by Food Records. Deleted Jun '87. Catalogue no: **FOOD 5T**

LOVE IS WAR
Tracks: / Love is war / Red red groovy, The / Ruby fruit jungle (on 12" only.).
7" Single: Released Feb '86, on Food, by Food Records. Deleted Jun '87. Catalogue no: **FOOD 6**
12" Single: Released Feb '86, on Food, by Food Records. Deleted Jun '87. Catalogue no: **FOOD 6T**

SOMEBODY
Tracks: / Somebody / Burning necklace, The / Love is war (On 12" only).
7" Single: Released Jul '86, on Food, by Food Records. Deleted Jun '87. Catalogue no: **FOOD 7**
12" Single: Released Jul '86, on Food, by Food Records. Deleted Jun '87. Catalogue no: **FOOD 7T**

Brilliant Corners

BIG HIP
Tracks: / Big hip.
7" Single: Released Feb '89, on SS 20, by SS 20 Records. Catalogue no: **SS 022**

BRIAN RIX
Tracks: / Brian Rix / Trudy is a squeal.
7" Single: Released Apr '87, on SS 20, by SS 20 Records. Catalogue no: **SS 27**

DELILAH SANDS, THE
Tracks: / Delilah sands, The.
7" Single: Released Oct '87, on SS 20, by SS 20 Records. Catalogue no: **SS 28**
12" Single: Released Oct '87, on SS 20, by SS 20 Records. Catalogue no: **SS 28 T**

FRUIT MACHINE
Tracks: / Fruit machine.
12" Single: Released May '86, on SS 20, by SS 20 Records. Catalogue no: **SS 25T**
7" Single: Released May '86, on SS 20, by SS 20 Records. Catalogue no: **SS 25**

MY BABY IN BLACK
Tracks: / My baby in black.
12" Single: Released Oct '84, on SS 20, by SS 20 Records. Catalogue no: **SS 23T**

SHE'S GOT FEVER
Tracks: / She's got fever.
7" Single: Released Jan '84, on SS 20, by SS 20 Records. Catalogue no: **SS 21**

TEENAGE
Tracks: / Teenage.
7" Single: Released 5 Mar '88, on McQueen, Catalogue no: **MCQ 1**
12" Single: Released 5 Mar '88, on McQueen, Catalogue no: **MCQ 1T**

WHY DO YOU HAVE TO GO OUT WITH MEN?
Tracks: / Why do you have to go out with men?.
Note: Full title: Why do you have to go out with men when you could go out with me?
12" Single: Released Oct '88, on McQueen, Catalogue no: **MCQ 2T**
7" Single: Released Oct '88, on McQueen, Catalogue no: **MCQ 2**

Brimstone

WINNER, THE
Tracks: / Winner, The.
12" Single: Released Jun '84, on London Gemi, Catalogue no: **LG 004**

Brio

TWO SIDE TO LOVE
Tracks: / Two sides to love.
7" Single: Released Sep '86, on Essel, Deleted Nov '87. Catalogue no: **BRIO 1**

Brissett, Annette

HARD TO FIND
Tracks: / Hard to find.
12" Single: Released Aug '84, on Wackies, Catalogue no: **W 973**

Bristol, Johnny

Biographical details: Bristol, Johnny. A multi-talented soul singer, songwriter, producer and arranger from North Carolina. He helped with many Motown acts; switched to CBS as a producer when Motown moved to the West Coast; went to MGM with his own album *Hang on in there baby* in 1974, a good album with a top ten title track in then-voguish Barry White vein. Later albums were less successful. but he carried on with behind-the-scenes work. (Donald Clarke. 24th August, 1988.)

HANG ON IN THERE BABY (OLD GOLD)
Tracks: / Hang on there baby.
7" Single: Released Jul '84, on Old Gold, by Old Gold Records. Catalogue no: **OG 9449**

HANG ON IN THERE BABY (SINGLE)
Tracks: / Hang on in there baby.
7" Single: Released Aug '74, on MGM, by Polydor Ltd. Deleted '77. Catalogue no: **2006 443**

HOLD ON TO LOVE
Tracks: / Hold on to love / Loving and free.
7" Single: Released Jan '82, on Ariola, by BMG Records (UK). Deleted Jan '85. Catalogue no: **HANSA 11**

LOVE NO LONGER HAS A HOLD ON ME
Tracks: / Love no longer has a hold on me Till I see you again.
12" Single: Released Dec '80, on Ariola Hansa, by Hansa Records. Deleted Dec '85 Catalogue no: **AHA 567**

TAKE ME DOWN
Tracks: / Take me down / Rosebud.
7" Single: Released Nov '81, on Hansa, by Hansa Records. Deleted Nov '84. Catalogue no: **HANSA 9**

Britain, Chris

FOREVER
Tracks: / Forever.
7" Single: Released Jul '82, on Raffia Deleted '83. Catalogue no: **RAF 001**

British Colony

HAVE YOU SEEN ME DANCING
Tracks: / Have you seen me dancing / A often as the day breaks (on 12" only).
12" Single: Released Nov '83, on Carrere Catalogue no: **CART 296**
7" Single: Released Nov '83, on Carrere Catalogue no: **CAR 296**

British Darts Team

180
Tracks: / 180 / Bobby's theme.
7" Single: Released Apr '82, on Smile, Catalogue no: **SRO 028**

Britny Fox

GIRLSCHOOL
Tracks: / Girlschool / Kick and fight / Fun Texas (Only on 12" version and CD single
CD 5": Released Oct '88, on CBS, by CB Records. Deleted 17 Apr '89. Catalogue n **653144 2**
12" Single: Released Oct '88, on CBS, b CBS Records. Deleted 17 Apr '89. Cat logue no: **653144 6**
7" Single: Released 21 Nov '88, on CBS, CBS Records. Deleted 17 Apr '89. Cat logue no: **653144 0**
7" Single: Released Oct '88, on CBS, CBS Records. Deleted 17 Apr '89. Ca logue no: **653144 7**

LONG WAY TO LOVE
Tracks: / Long way to love / Living on th edge / Long way to love (full length versio (12" only.) / Save the weak (12" only.).
12" Single: Released Oct '88, on CBS, CBS Records. Catalogue no: **653018 6**
7" Single: Released Oct '88, on CBS, CBS Records. Catalogue no: **653018 7**
7" Pic: Released Oct '88, on CBS, by CB Records. Catalogue no: **653018 0**

Britton, Chris

ONE NINE FOR A LADY BREAKER
Tracks: / One nine for a lady breaker / O foot on the ground.
7" Single: Released Feb '82, on Logo, Logo Records. Deleted Feb '87. Catalog no: **GO 410**

Britton, Johnny

ONE THAT GOT AWAY
Tracks: / One that got away / Happy-g lucky.
7" Single: Released Feb '81, on Oddb Producti, Deleted Feb '84. Catalogue **BRIT 1**

Britton, Maggie

BRIGHT WATER
Tracks: / Bright water.
7" Single: Released Apr '80, on Songwrit Workshop, by Songwriters Workshop P lishing. Deleted '87. Catalogue no: **SW 7**

GOODSHIP EARTH
Tracks: / Goodship Earth / No secrets.
7" Single: Released Aug '80, on Piccad Deleted Aug '83. Catalogue no: **7P 191**

Brixton, Webby J

READY
Tracks: / Ready / Boy in the corner.
12" Single: Released Dec '82, on Spic web, Catalogue no: **SP 1002**

Broads

SING SING SING
Tracks: / Sing, sing, sing.
12" Single: Released Oct '83, on Proto Proto Records. Catalogue no: **ENAT 11**
7" Single: Released Oct '83, on Proto Proto Records. Catalogue no: **ENA 112**

Brock, Dave

SOCIAL ALLIANCE
Tracks: / Social alliance / Raping robot the street.

' **Pic:** Released Sep '83, on Flicknife, by licknife Records. Catalogue no: **FLS 024P**
' **Single:** Released Sep '83, on Flicknife, Flicknife Records. Catalogue no: **FLS 024**

Broken Bones

RUCIFIX
racks: / Crucifix.
' **Single:** Released '84, on Fall Out, eleted '88. Catalogue no: **FALL 025**

ECAPITATED (SINGLE)
racks: / Decapitated.
' **Single:** Released Jan '84, on Scarlet, atalogue no: **FALL 020**

EVER SAY DIE
racks: / Never say die.
2" **Single:** Released Jul '86, on Fall Out, atalogue no: **FALL 12039**

EEING THROUGH MY EYES
racks: / Seeing through my eyes.
)" **single:** Released Jun '85, on Fall Out, atalogue no: **FALL 10034**
' **Pic:** Released Jun '85, on Fall Out, eleted '88. Catalogue no: **FALL 034P**
' **Single:** Released Jun '85, on Fall Out, eleted '88. Catalogue no: **FALL 034**

RADERS IN DEATH
acks: / Traders in death.
2" **Single:** Released 13 Jun '87, on RFB ecordings, Catalogue no: **RFBSIN 4**

3roken English

OMIN' ON STRONG
acks: / Comin' on strong (fallout mix) (On D only) / Suffer in silence / Comin' on strong ire me up (long version) (On CD only).
D 5": Released May '87, on EMI, by EMI ecords. Deleted Jan '88. Catalogue no: DEM 5
" **Single:** Released May '87, on EMI, by MI Records. Deleted Apr '88. Catalogue : **12 EM 5**
Pic: Released 30 May '87, on EMI, by EMI ecords. Deleted Oct '87. Catalogue no: **MP 5**
Single: Released May '87, on EMI, by MI Records. Deleted Apr '88. Catalogue : **EM 5**

OMIN' ON STRONG (ALT VER-ON)
acks: / Comin' on strong (alt version).
Single: Released Jun '87, on EMI, by EMI ecords. Deleted Oct '87. Catalogue no: **M 5**

) YOU REALLY WANT ME BACK
acks: / Do you really want me back / nnin' out.
Single: Released Aug '88, on EMI, by I Records. Deleted Nov '88. Catalogue **EMG 69**
5": Released Aug '88, on EMI, by EMI cords. Deleted Nov '88. Catalogue no: **EM 69**
' **Single:** Released Aug '88, on EMI, by I Records. Deleted Nov '88. Catalogue **12 EMP 69**
Single: Released Jul '88, on EMI, by EMI cords. Deleted Nov '88. Catalogue no: **69**
' **Single:** Released Jul '88, on EMI, by I Records. Deleted Nov '88. Catalogue **12 EM 69**

VE ON THE SIDE
cks: / Love on the side / Deep in my art.
te: * 7" single poster bag.
Single: Released Oct '87, on EMI, by EMI cords. Deleted Jan '88. Catalogue no: **S 55**
Pic: Released Sep '87, on EMI, by EMI cords. Deleted Jan '88. Catalogue no: **P 55**
Single: Released Sep '87, on EMI, by I Records. Deleted Apr '88. Catalogue **12EM 55**
Single: Released Sep '87, on EMI, by I Records. Deleted Apr '88. Catalogue **EM 55**

3roken Glass

YLE OF THE STREET
cks: / Style of the street / Style of the eet (original mix).
Single: Released Jul '84, on Street-ve, Catalogue no: **MKHAN 17**

3roken Home

ATH OF GOG
cks: / Death of gog / China in your heart.
Single: Released May '80, on WEA, by A Records. Deleted May '85. Catalogue **K18229**

NAWAY FROM HOME
cks: / Runaway from home / Shot over

Single: Released Nov '80, on WEA, by A Records. Deleted '83. Catalogue no: **K 465**

3romley Boy Singers

RISTMAS SNOW
cks: / Christmas snow / Please don't go ay.

7" **Single:** Released Jan '82, on JPD, Deleted Jan '85. Catalogue no: **JPD 1**

Brompton Cocktail

CITY OF NIGHTMARES
Tracks: / City of nightmares.
7" **Single:** Released '88, on Blind Date, Catalogue no: **ONEBC 001**

Bron Area

DIFFERENT PHASES
Tracks: / Different phases / You would be amazed / Dancing.
12" **Single:** Released Feb '82, on Glass, by Glass Records. Deleted '83. Catalogue no: **GLASS 012**

Brondie, Ian

PURE & SIMPLE
Tracks: / Pure and simple.
12" **Single:** Released 27 Feb '89, on Sub Aqua, Catalogue no: **12 MUTE 87**
7" **Single:** Released 27 Feb '89, on Sub Aqua, Catalogue no: **MUTE 87**

Bronski Beat

Biographical details: Bronski Beat A UK pop group formed in London in 1984: vocalist Jimi Somerville, Jerry Steinbachek and Steve Bronski on keyboards and percussion. With a strong following on the gay circuit, they signed to London and to everyone's surprise became stars. Somerville quit blaming 'pressures of being a pop star', worked with new group called The Committee, then Body Politic, with saxist Richard Cole; then the Communards, whose eponymous debut album in 1986 included hit singles *You Are My World* and *Don't Leave Me This Way* (a UK no. 1 hit). Bronski, Steinbachek and John Foster carried on with original group name in less political direction: *Truthdare, Doubledare* '86 incl. hits *C'mon, C'mon, Hit That Perfect Beat.* Donald Clarke, 24 August 1988..

CHA CHA HEELS
Tracks: / Cha cha heels / My discarded men / Cha cha heels (7" remix) (Available on 12" only).
CD 5": Released May '89, on Arista, by BMG Records (UK). Catalogue no: **662 331**
12" **Single:** Released May '89, on Arista, by BMG Records (UK). Catalogue no: **612 331**
Cassingle: Released Jul '89, on Arista, by BMG Records (UK). Catalogue no: **410 140**
7" **Single:** Released May '89, on Arista, by BMG Records (UK). Catalogue no: **112 331**
12" **Single:** Released 10 Jul '89, on Arista, by BMG Records (UK). Catalogue no: **612 332**

C'MON, C'MON
Tracks: / C'mon, c'mon / Something special / Drum majors (12" only).
12" **Single:** Released Mar '86, on Forbidden Fruit, by London Records. Catalogue no: **BITEX 7**
7" **Single:** Released Mar '86, on Forbidden Fruit, by London Records. Catalogue no: **BITE 7**

HIT THAT PERFECT BEAT
Tracks: / Hit that perfect beat.
12" **Single:** Released Nov '85, on Forbidden Fruit, by London Records. Catalogue no: **BITEX 6**
7" **Single:** Released Nov '85, on Forbidden Fruit, by London Records. Deleted Sep '87. Catalogue no: **BITE 6**

I FEEL LOVE
Tracks: / I feel love / Puit d'amour / Potato fields (on 12" only) / Signs (on 12" only).
7" **Single:** Released Apr '85, on Forbidden Fruit, by London Records. Catalogue no: **BITE 4**

IT AIN'T NECESSARILY SO
Tracks: / It ain't necessarily so.
12" **Single:** Released Nov '84, on Forbidden Fruit, by London Records. Catalogue no: **BITEX 3**
7" **Single:** Released Nov '84, on Forbidden Fruit, by London Records. Catalogue no: **BITE 3**

SMALLTOWN BOY
Tracks: / Smalltown boy.
7" **Single:** Released Jun '84, on Forbidden Fruit, by London Records. Catalogue no: **BITE 1**
12" **Single:** Released Jun '84, on Forbidden Fruit, by London Records. Deleted Feb '89. Catalogue no: **BITEX 1**

THIS HEART
Tracks: / This heart / What are you going to do about it.
7" **Single:** Released Aug '86, on Forbidden Fruit, by London Records. Catalogue no: **BITE 8**
12" **Single:** Released Aug '86, on Forbidden Fruit, by London Records. Catalogue no: **BITEX 8**

WHY
Tracks: / Why.
12" **Single:** Released Sep '84, on Forbidden Fruit, by London Records. Catalogue no: **BITEX 2**

7" **Single:** Released Sep '84, on Forbidden Fruit, by London Records. Catalogue no: **BITE 2**

Bronx, Jet

AIN'T DOIN' NOTHIN'
Tracks: / Ain't doin' nothin' / I can't stand it.
7" **Single:** Released Dec '77, on Lightning, Deleted '80. Catalogue no: **LIG 507**

Bronx, MC

TOP CAT RAP
Tracks: / Top Cat rap.
12" **Single:** Released Aug '88, on 100 2 One, by 100 2 One Records. Catalogue no: **CATRAP 12 1**
7" **Single:** Released Aug '88, on 100 2 One, by 100 2 One Records. Catalogue no: **CA-TRAP 1**

Bronz

SEND DOWN AN ANGEL
Tracks: / Send down an angel / Tiger / Stranded.
7" **Single:** Released Aug '84, on Bronze, by Bronze Records. Catalogue no: **BRO 183**
12" **Single:** Released Aug '84, on Bronze, by Bronze Records. Catalogue no: **BROX 183**

Brook Brothers

Biographical details: This British vocal duo hailed from Southampton and were one of two duos who, in 1961, posed as Britain's answer to the Everly Brothers. While the Allisons were riding high with their only big hit *Are You Sure*, the Brook Brothers entered the British charts with their first and biggest hit single, entitled *Warpaint*. This was a song penned by famed American writers Barry Mann and Howard Greenfield. The Brooks followed this No. 1 hit with *Ain't Gonna Wash For A Week* the latter reaching No. 13 on the British chart. 1962 and 1963 yielded three minor hit singles, then the Brook Brothers faded into obscurity. British talent of a far more substantial nature, in the form of the Beatles-led Merseybeat boom was arriving. (Bob MacDonald)..

AIN'T GONNA WASH FOR A WEEK
Tracks: / Ain't gonna wash for a week.
7" **Single:** Released Sep '61, on Pye, Deleted '64. Catalogue no: **7 N 15369**

HE'S OLD ENOUGH TO KNOW BETTER
Tracks: / He's old enough to know better.
7" **Single:** Released Jan '62, on Pye, Deleted '65. Catalogue no: **7 N 15409**

TROUBLE IS MY MIDDLE NAME
Tracks: / Trouble is my middle name.
7" **Single:** Released Feb '63, on Pye, Deleted '66. Catalogue no: **7 N 15498**

WARPAINT
Tracks: / Warpaint.
7" **Single:** Released Apr '80, on Flashback, by Mainline Records. Catalogue no: **FBS 11**
7" **Single:** Released Mar '61, on Pye, Deleted '64. Catalogue no: **7 N 15333**

WELCOME HOME BABY
Tracks: / Welcome home.
7" **Single:** Released Sep '62, on Pye, Deleted '65. Catalogue no: **7 N 15453**

Brook, Mike

DARLING I LOVE YOU
Tracks: / Darling I love you.
12" **Single:** Released May '85, on Music Rock, Catalogue no: **ROCK 004**

Brooker, Gary

Biographical details: Brooker, Gary This singer and keyboardist from Southend came to fame with Procul Harum and was later part of Paul McCartney's Rockestra; he made solo albums from 1979, still had a soulful voice famous from *Whiter Shade Of Pale*. *Lead Me To The Water* had allstar help: George Harrison, Phil Collins, Albert Lee, Eric Clapton. Donald Clarke, 24 August 1988..

CYCLE
Tracks: / Cycle / Badlands.
7" **Single:** Released Mar '82, on Mercury, by Phonogram Ltd. Catalogue no: **MER 94**

HOME LOVIN'
Tracks: / Home lovin' / Chasing for the chop.
7" **Single:** Released May '81, on Mercury, by Phonogram Ltd. Deleted May '86. Catalogue no: **MER 70**

LEAVE THE CANDLE
Tracks: / Leave the candle / Chasing the chop.
7" **Single:** Released Jan '82, on Chrysalis, by Chrysalis Records. Deleted Jan '85. Catalogue no: **CHS 2396**

TWO FOOLS IN LOVE
Tracks: / Two fools in love.
7" **Single:** Released Apr '85, on Mercury, by Phonogram Ltd. Catalogue no: **MER 188**

Brookes, Jacqui

TRAINS AND BOATS AND PLANES
Tracks: / Trains boats and planes.
7" **Single:** Released Jan '84, on MCA, by MCA Records. Catalogue no: **MCA 855**

Brookins, Robert

OUR LIVES
Tracks: / Our lives / Incredulous.
7" **Single:** Released Jul '87, on MCA, by MCA Records. Catalogue no: **MCA 1131**
12" **Single:** Released Jul '87, on MCA, by MCA Records. Catalogue no: **MCAT 1131**

Brooklyn

HOLLYWOOD
Tracks: / Hollywood / Late again.
7" **Single:** Released May '81, on Rondelet Music, by Rondelet Music & Records. Deleted May '86. Catalogue no: **ROUND 6**

Brooklyn Brats

BROOKLYN BRATS
7" **EP:** Released Jan '86, on Iron Works (USA), by Azra International (USA). Catalogue no: **IW 1002**

Brooks

KNOW A LADY
Tracks: / Know a lady / One night stand.
7" **Single:** Released Mar '80, on Polydor, by Polydor Ltd. Deleted '83. Catalogue no: **POSP 137**

WE ARE UNITED
Tracks: / We are united / Jenny.
7" **Single:** Released Aug '80, on Polydor, by Polydor Ltd. Deleted '83. Catalogue no: **POSP 167**

WHAT A GREAT NIGHT FOR FALLING IN LOVE
Tracks: / What a great night for falling in love / Now or never.
7" **Single:** Released Jan '80, on Polydor, by Polydor Ltd. Deleted Jan '85. Catalogue no: **POSP 98**

Brooks, Dave

VOX POP
Tracks: / Vox pop / After all this time.
7" **Single:** Released Jan '83, on BBC, by BBC Records & Tapes. Deleted '87. Catalogue no: **RESL 129**

Brooks, Elkie

Biographical details: Born in Manchester in 1945, Elkie Brooks spent the Sixties in a variety of musical guises. She released a couple of flop singles in her own right, joined a dance band, worked as a jazz singer with Humphrey Lyttleton and spent periods as a session and back-up singer. In the early Seventies she fronted a short-lived 12 piece jazz-rock band called Dada. This outfit included guitarist Pete Gage, who progressed with Brooks to Vinegar Joe, a critcally acclaimed soul-rock group. Vocals in Vinegar Joe were shared by Brooks and Robert Palmer. Elkie's powerful jazzy, blues-inflected voice, combined with her dynamic stage presence, made her a cult figure; but this was not enough to put any of the band's three albums into the charts. Vinegar Joe folded in 1974, with both of its singers embarking on solo careers. Palmer eventually achieved a reasonable degree of commercial success, but he did not obtain it as early as Brooks. Elkie's first solo LP *Rich Man's Woman* was not a success, but the second certainly was. Issued in '77 *Two Days Away* reached No. 16 on the album charts in her native Britain and stayed on the list for 20 weeks. Even more importantly, it gave Brooks her first two chart singles. *Pearl's A Singer*, a bluesy, plaintive number about a girl singer who failed to make the grade and was confined to local clubs, was wonderfully paradoxical - it was this first hit single that was saving Brooks from a similar fate. What's more, it sounded quite different from anything else on the British charts at that time. It peaked at No. 8. A more conventional pop song *Sunshine After The Rain* reached No. 10. This came from the pen of famous songwriter Ellie Greenwich; the album was produced by the legendary team of Jerry Leiber and MikeStoller, who co-wrote *Pearl*. Surprisingly, Brooks never again scored a UK Top 10 single. 1978 brought *Lilac Wine* (No. 16) and *Don't Cry Out Loud* (No. 12). The latter was a hit for Melissa Manchester in the USA, a territory that Brooks has never managed to penetrate. Her album *Shooting Star* reached No. 20 on the UK chart. Far less successful was 1979's *Live And Learn* LP.
Brooks, Elkie. This UK pop singer was born Elaine Bookbinder in 1945 in Manchester; she began in the London jazz scene with Eric Delaney and Humphrey Lyttleton, and commenced a session career. She linked with guitarist Pete Gage in a 12-piece jazz/rock group, Dada, then a slimmed-down R&B outfit Vinegar Joe, sharing vocals in both with Robert Palmer. Signed to A&M as a solo in 1974, she had ten hit singles on that label, but slowly sank in the charts: A&M led her away from her reputation as one of the gutsiest UK female vocalists to the ghetto of

ELKIE BROOKS - OUR LOVE (Released on A & M)

MEL BROOKS - IT'S GOOD TO BE THE KING OF RAP (Released on Luggage)

MOR, then regarded her as washed up; she switched to Mike Heap's Legend Label for *No More The Fool* in 1986 and was back high in the charts with stronger material. Donald Clarke, 24 August 1988.

BREAK THE CHAIN
Tracks: / Break the chain (ext mix) / Break the chain (edit/the groove) / Break the chain / Groove.
CD 5": Released Apr '87, on Legend (1), by Legend Records (UK). Deleted Jun '88. Catalogue no: **CDLM 8**
7" Single: Released Feb '87, on Legend (1), by Legend Records (UK). Catalogue no: **LM 8**
12" Single: Released Feb '87, on Legend (1), by Legend Records (UK). Catalogue no: **12LM 8**

COMPACT HITS: ELKIE BROOKS
Tracks: / Pearl's a singer / Sunshine after the rain / Only love can break a heart / Nights in white satin.
CD 5": Released Aug '88, on A&M, by A&M Records. Catalogue no: **AMCD 913**

DANCE AWAY
Tracks: / Dance away / Play the way I feel.
7" Single: Released Oct '80, on A&M, by A&M Records. Deleted Oct '83. Catalogue no: **AMS 7567**

DON'T CRY OUT LOUD
Tracks: / Don't cry out loud.
7" Single: Released Nov '78, on A&M, by A&M Records. Deleted '81. Catalogue no: **AMS 7395**

FOOL IF YOU THINK IT'S OVER
Tracks: / Fool if you think it's over / Giving it up for your love.
7" Single: Released Jan '82, on A&M, by A&M Records. Deleted '85. Catalogue no: **AMS 8187**

GASOLINE ALLEY
Tracks: / Gasoline Alley / Loving arms.
7" Single: Released Jan '83, on A&M, by A&M Records. Deleted '86. Catalogue no: **AMS 8305**

I JUST CAN'T GO ON
Tracks: / I just can't go on.
7" Single: Released Feb '83, on A&M, by A&M Records. Deleted '88. Catalogue no: **AM 104**

LILAC WINE
Tracks: / Lilac wine / Live, laugh and love.
7" Single: Released Jan '78, on A&M, by A&M Records. Deleted Mar '88. Catalogue no: **AMS 7333**

LILAC WINE (OLD GOLD)
Tracks: / Lilac Wine / Don't cry out loud.
7" Single: Released Oct '88, on Old Gold, by Old Gold Records. Catalogue no: **OG 9810**

NIGHTS IN WHITE SATIN (see panel on right)
Tracks: / Nights in white satin / Lilac wine.
7" Single: Released Jul '82, on A&M, by A&M Records. Deleted '85. Catalogue no: **AMS 8235**

NO MORE THE FOOL
Tracks: / No more the fool / City lights / Blue jay (Extra track on 12" only).
Note: *=extra track on 12" only
7" Single: Released Nov '86, on Legend (1), by Legend Records (UK). Catalogue no: **LM 4**
12" Single: Released Nov '86, on Legend (1), by Legend Records (UK). Catalogue no: **12LM 4**

ONLY LOVE CAN BREAK YOUR HEART
Tracks: / Only love can break a heart.
7" Single: Released Apr '78, on A&M, by A&M Records. Deleted '88. Catalogue no: **AMS 7353**

OUR LOVE (see panel above)
Tracks: / Our love / Nothing in this world.
7" Single: Released May '82, on A&M, by A&M Records. Deleted '85. Catalogue no: **AMS 8214**

PEARL'S A SINGER
Tracks: / Pearl's a singer.
CD 5": on A&M, by A&M Records. Catalogue no: **AMC 913**
7" Single: Released Jun '85, on Old Gold, by Old Gold Records. Catalogue no: **OG 9543**
7" Single: Released Apr '77, on A&M, by A&M Records. Deleted '80. Catalogue no: **AMS 7275**

RUNAWAY, THE
Tracks: / Runaway.
7" Single: Released May '79, on A&M, by A&M Records. Deleted '82. Catalogue no: **AMS 7428**

SAIL ON
Tracks: / Sail on.
7" Single: Released Apr '88, on Legend (1), by Legend Records (UK). Catalogue no: **LM 11**
12" Single: Released Apr '88, on Legend (1), by Legend Records (UK). Catalogue no: **12LM 11**

SHAME
Tracks: / Shame.
7" Single: Released Oct '89, on Telstar, by Telstar Records (UK). Catalogue no: **STAS 2394**

SUNSHINE AFTER THE RAIN
Tracks: / Sunshine after the rain.
7" Single: Released Sep '77, on A&M, by A&M Records. Deleted '80. Catalogue no: **AMS 7306**

WARM AND TENDER LOVE
Tracks: / Warm and tender love / Thank you for the light.
7" Single: Released Oct '81, on A&M, by A&M Records. Deleted '88. Catalogue no: **AMS 8167**

WE'VE GOT TONIGHT
Tracks: / We've got tonight / Hold the dream (live) / We've got tonight (live) / Piece of my heart.
12" Single: Released Jun '87, on Legend (1), by Legend Records (UK). Catalogue no: **LM 12 009**
Cassingle: Released Jun '87, on Legend (1), by Legend Records (UK). Catalogue no: **TLM 9**
7" Pic: Released Jun '87, on Legend (1), by Legend Records (UK). Catalogue no: **L**
9
7" Single: Released Jun '87, on Legend by Legend Records (UK). Catalogue no: **009**

WHY DON'T YOU SAY IT?
Tracks: / Why don't you say it? / We all ha our dreams.
7" Single: Released May '80, on A&M. A&M Records. Deleted '83. Catalogue **AMS 7529**

WILL YOU WRITE ME A SONG
Tracks: / Will you write me a song / Giv you hope.
7" Single: Released Nov '82, on A&M A&M Records. Deleted Nov '85. Catalo no: **AMS 8266**

Brooks, Karen

I WILL DANCE WITH YOU (SINGL
Tracks: / I will dance with you.
7" Single: Released Aug '85, on Wa Bros., by WEA Records. Catalogue no **8979**

Brooks, Mel

Biographical details: This American maker and film star has long retained a figure' image despite the fact that he enjoys major international popularity. M cally, he came to public attention in 1981 his single *'It's Good To Be The King'rap.* was used to promote his movie *Histor The World - Part 1* and was produce co-written by well-known British prod Pete Wingfield. Brooks mouthed his h ous rapping lyrics over a disco-flavo backing and these verses were augme by a catchy chorus. The single was not in its own right, but paved the way for 19 *To Be Or Not To Be (The Hitler Rap).* movie *To Be Or Not To Be* was a sati account of the Nzi regime, in which Brc characteristically obtained comic mile from subjects normally outside the bou of humour. Once again he co-wrote single with Wingfield whichwas, musica virtual carbon copy of *It's Good To B King Of Rap.* The lyrics were outrageo tasteless, with Brooks adopting the pers of Hitler and recounting his experience Fuhrer. This time he enjoyed some succ with the record as well as the film and hi 12 on the British chart. Brooks claimed t 'the first Jew to make a living out of Hit (Bob MacDonald)..

IT'S GOOD TO BE THE KING OF RAP (see panel above)
Tracks: / It's good to be the king rap one) / It's good to be the king rap (part
7" Single: Released Oct '81, on Lugg by Multicord Records. Catalogue no: **02**

TO BE OR NOT TO BE (THE HITLER RAP)
Tracks: / To be or not to be (the hitler
7" Single: Released Feb '84, on Islan Island Records. Deleted '87. Catalogu **IS 158**

Brooks, Mike

ALL I NEED IS YOU
Tracks: / All I need is you.
12" Single: Released Sep '89, on P

ELKIE BROOKS - NIGHTS IN WHITE SATIN (Released on A & M)

BROS - TOO MUCH (Released on CBS)

Catalogue no: **PD 001**

BEYOND THE HILLS
Tracks: / Beyond the hills.
12" Single: Released Feb '85, on Music Rock, Catalogue no: **ROCK 002**

COME SISTER COME
Tracks: / Come sister come.
12" Single: Released Jun '83, on Coptic Lion, Catalogue no: **CLD 001**

NIGHT RAVER
Tracks: / Night raver / Hollywood style.
7" Single: Released Jun '84, on Coptic Lion, Catalogue no: **CLD 003**

Brooks, Norman

SKY BLUE SHIRT AND A RAINBOW TIE, A
Tracks: / Sky blue shirt and a rainbow tie, A.
7" Single: Released Nov '54, on London Records, by London Records. Deleted '57. Catalogue no: **L 1228**

Broomfield

DON'T COVER UP YOUR FEELINGS
Tracks: / Don't cover up your feelings (remix) / Don't cover up your feelings (ext. remix) / Don't cover up your feelings (inst) (Available on 12" single only.) / Through all the years.
CD 5": Released 6 Jun '88, on CBS, by CBS Records. Deleted Jan '89. Catalogue no: **651629 2**
7" Single: Released May '88, on CBS, by CBS Records. Deleted Jan '89. Catalogue no: **651 629 7**
12" Single: Released May '88, on CBS, by CBS Records. Deleted Jan '89. Catalogue no: **651 629 6**

SHE CAN'T GET SERIOUS
Tracks: / She can't get serious / Light up the world.
7" Single: Released Aug '88, on CBS, by CBS Records. Deleted 17 Apr '89. Catalogue no: **652924 7**
12" Single: Released Aug '88, on CBS, by CBS Records. Deleted 17 Apr '89. Catalogue no: **652924 6**

Bros

CAT AMONG THE PIGEONS
Tracks: / Cat among the pigeons / Silent night / I owe you nothing (live)* (*Not on 7".) / Love to hate you (live) (Not on 7".) / Shocked (Only on CD single.).
7" Single: Released 21 Nov '88, on CBS, by CBS Records. Deleted Jan '89. Catalogue no: **ATOM 6**
7" Single: Released Dec '88, on CBS, by CBS Records. Deleted 10 Jul '89. Catalogue no: **ATOM Q6**
7" Single: Released 28 Nov '88, on CBS, by CBS Records. Deleted 17 Apr '89. Catalogue no: **ATOM B6**
CD 5": Released Dec '88, on CBS, by CBS Records. Deleted 10 Jul '89. Catalogue no: **ATOM QC6**
CD 5": Released 21 Nov '88, on CBS, by CBS Records. Deleted Jan '89. Catalogue no: **ATOM C6**
7" Single: Released Dec '88, on CBS, by CBS Records. Catalogue no: **ATOM R6**
7" Single: Released Dec '88, on CBS, by CBS Records. Deleted 10 Jul '89. Catalogue no: **ATOM S6**
12" Single: Released Dec '88, on CBS, by CBS Records. Deleted 10 Jul '89. Catalogue no: **ATOM QT6**
12" Single: Released 21 Nov '88, on CBS, by CBS Records. Deleted Jan '89. Catalogue no: **ATOM T6**

CHOCOLATE BOX
Tracks: / Chocolate box / Life's a heartbeat.
7" Pic: Released Sep '89, on CBS, by CBS Records. Catalogue no: **ATOM M8**
Cassingle: Released Sep '89, on CBS, by CBS Records. Catalogue no: **ATOM C8**
7" Single: Released Sep '89, on CBS, by CBS Records. Catalogue no: **ATOM L8**
CD 5": Released Sep '89, on CBS, by CBS Records. Catalogue no: **CDATOM 8**
7" Single: Released Sep '89, on CBS, by CBS Records. Catalogue no: **ATOM 8**
12" Single: Released Sep '89, on CBS, by CBS Records. Catalogue no: **ATOM T8**

DROP THE BOY
Tracks: / Drop the boy / Boy is dropped, The.
12" Single: Released Mar '88, on CBS, by CBS Records. Deleted Aug '88. Catalogue no: **ATOM T3**
7" Single: Released Mar '88, on CBS, by CBS Records. Deleted Aug '88. Catalogue no: **ATOM 3**
7" Single: Released Mar '88, on CBS, by CBS Records. Deleted Aug '88. Catalogue no: **ATOM P3**
7" Single: Released Mar '88, on CBS, by CBS Records. Deleted Aug '88. Catalogue no: **ATOM B3**
Special: Released Mar '88, on CBS, by CBS Records. Deleted Aug '88. Catalogue no: **ATOM W3**

DROP THE BOY (ART MIXING)
Tracks: / Drop the boy (art mixing) / Drop the boy (shep pettibone mix) / When will I be famous / Boy is dropped, the.
CD 5": Released Mar '88, on CBS, by CBS Records. Deleted Jan '89. Catalogue no: **CDATOM 3**
12" Single: Released Mar '88, on CBS, by CBS Records. Deleted Aug '88. Catalogue no: **ATOM QT3**

I OWE YOU NOTHING
Tracks: / I owe you nothing / I owe you nothing (club mix) / I owe you nothing (the voice) / I owe you nothing (the beats).
7" Single: Released Aug '87, on CBS, by CBS Records. Deleted Jan '89. Catalogue no: **ATOM 4**
12" Single: Released Jun '88, on CBS, by CBS Records. Deleted Jan '89. Catalogue no: **ATOM TQ4**
12" Single: Released Aug '87, on CBS, by CBS Records. Deleted Jan '89. Catalogue no: **ATOM T4**
Cassingle: Released Sep '87, on CBS, by CBS Records. Deleted Jan '89. Catalogue no: **ATOM C1**
7" Single: Released Jun '88, on CBS, by CBS Records. Deleted Aug '88. Catalogue no: **ATOM Q1**

I OWE YOU NOTHING (OVER 18 MIX)
Tracks: / I owe you nothing (over 18 mix) / Nothing.
12" Single: Released 13 Jun '88, on CBS, by CBS Records. Catalogue no: **ATOM QT4**

I QUIT
Tracks: / I quit (7" and CD only) / I quit (acid drops) (7" and CD only) / I quit (turn on mix) (12" and CD only) / Big push overture (12" and CD only) / I quit (acidic mix) (Only on ATOM QT5 (12")).
12" Single: Released 16 Sep '88, on CBS, by CBS Records. Deleted 17 Apr '85. Catalogue no: **ATOM QT5**
12" Single: Released Sep '88, on CBS, by CBS Records. Deleted 17 Apr '89. Catalogue no: **ATOM T5**
7" Single: Released Sep '88, on CBS, by CBS Records. Deleted 17 Apr '89. Catalogue no: **ATOM 5**
CD 5": Released Sep '88, on CBS, by CBS Records. Deleted 17 Apr '89. Catalogue no: **CD ATOM 5**
7" Pic: Released 19 Sep '88, on CBS, by CBS Records. Deleted 17 Apr '89. Catalogue no: **ATOM P5**

TOO MUCH (see panel above)
Tracks: / Too much / Astrologically / Too much (extended version) (Only on 12" and CD single.) / Too much (Wembley mix) (Only on 12" single (ATOMW 7)).
7" Single: Released Jul '89, on CBS, by CBS Records. Catalogue no: **ATOMM 7**
12" Single: Released Jul '89, on CBS, by CBS Records. Catalogue no: **ATOM QT 7**
7" Single: Released Jul '89, on CBS, by CBS Records. Catalogue no: **ATOML 7**
CD 5": Released Jul '89, on CBS, by CBS Records. Catalogue no: **ATOMC 7**
Cassingle: Released Jul '89, on CBS, by CBS Records. Catalogue no: **ATOMCA 7**
7" Single: Released Jul '89, on CBS, by CBS Records. Catalogue no: **ATOMB 7**
7" Single: Released Jul '89, on CBS, by CBS Records. Catalogue no: **ATOM 7**
12" Single: Released Jul '89, on CBS, by CBS Records. Catalogue no: **ATOMT 7**
12" Single: Released Jul '89, on CBS, by CBS Records. Catalogue no: **ATOMW 7**

WHEN WILL I BE FAMOUS?
Tracks: / Love to hate you / When will I be famous / When will I be famous (the contender dub mix) (On 12" ATOM S2 only, in picturebag, shrinkwrapped with badge.) / Love to hate you (version) / When will I be famous (version) / Love to hate you (mix).
12" Single: Released Jul '88, on Epic (USA), by CBS Records (USA). Catalogue no: **4907826**
7" Single: Released Nov '87, on CBS, by CBS Records. Deleted Jun '88. Catalogue no: **ATOM Q2**
7" Single: Released Nov '87, on CBS, by CBS Records. Deleted Aug '88. Catalogue no: **ATOM 2**
7" Pic: Released Nov '87, on CBS, by CBS Records. Deleted Jun '88. Catalogue no: **ATOM P2**
12" Single: Released Dec '87, on CBS, by CBS Records. Deleted Jun '88. Catalogue no: **ATOM QT2**
12" Single: Released Nov '87, on CBS, by CBS Records. Deleted Aug '88. Catalogue no: **ATOM T2**
Special: Released Nov '87, on CBS, by CBS Records. Deleted Jun '88. Catalogue no: **ATOM S2**

B.R.O.T.H.E.R.

BEYOND THE 16TH PARALLEL (See panel on left)
Tracks: / Beyond the 16th parallel / S.W.A.P.O. chant / Sharpville salute (available on 12" only).
Cassingle: Released Jun '89, on 4th & Broadway, by Island Records. Catalogue no: **BRCA 139**
7" Single: Released Jun '89, on 4th & Broadway, by Island Records. Catalogue no: **BRW 139**
12" Single: Released Jun '89, on 4th & Broadway, by Island Records. Catalogue no: **12 BRW 139**

Brother Beyond

BE MY TWIN
Tracks: / Be my twin / Broken life / Be my twin (inst.) (12" only.) / Be my twin (ext.) (12" & CD single only.).
7" Single: Released Jan '89, on Parlophone, by EMI Records. Deleted Oct '89. Catalogue no: **RP 6195**
12" Single: Released Jan '89, on Parlophone, by EMI Records. Deleted Oct '89. Catalogue no: **12R 6195**
7" Single: Released Jan '89, on Parlophone, by EMI Records. Deleted Oct '89. Catalogue no: **R 6195**
CD 5": Released Jan '89, on Parlophone, by EMI Records. Deleted Oct '89. Catalogue no: **CDR 6195**
7" Single: Released Jan '89, on Parlophone, by EMI Records. Deleted Oct '89. Catalogue no: **RG 6195**

CAN YOU KEEP A SECRET
Tracks: / Can you keep a secret (Extended) / Can you keep a secret (House mix) / Can you keep a secret (House dub) / Can you keep a secret / Can you keep a secret (instrumental) / Can you keep a secret (Miami mix) / Can you keep a secret (Miami dub) (Only on special & limited edition.) / Can you keep a secret (Miami 7") (Only on special & limited edition.).
7" Single: Released Jan '88, on Parlophone, by EMI Records. Deleted 31 Jul '88. Catalogue no: **RP 6174**
7" Single: Released Dec '87, on Parlophone, by EMI Records. Deleted 31 Jul '88. Catalogue no: **R 6174**
12" Single: Released Dec '87, on Parlophone, by EMI Records. Deleted Nov '88. Catalogue no: **12 R 6174**
Special: Released Jan '88, on Parlophone, by EMI Records. Deleted Nov '88. Catalogue no: **12RX 6174**

CAN YOU KEEP A SECRET ('89 MIX)
Tracks: / Can you keep a secret ('89 mix) (Not on 12".) / Act for love (Love love mix) (Not on 7".) / Can you keep a secret ('89 ext. remix) (Not on 7".) / Can you keep a secret (Miami mix) (CD single only.) / Act for love (Love mix) (7" only.).
7" Single: Released Mar '89, on Parlophone, by EMI Records. Catalogue no: **RP 6197**
7" Single: Released Mar '89, on Parlophone, by EMI Records. Catalogue no: **R 6197**
12" Single: Released Mar '89, on Parlophone, by EMI Records. Catalogue no: **12R 6197**
CD 5": Released Mar '89, on Parlophone, by EMI Records. Catalogue no: **CDR 6197**

CHAIN GANG SMILE
Tracks: / Chain gang smile / Sometimes good sometimes bad (sometimes better).

B.R.O.T.H.E.R. - BEYOND THE 16TH PARALLEL (Released on 4th & Broadway)

Special: Released Aug '87, on Parlophone, by EMI Records. Deleted Oct '87. Catalogue no: **RS 6160**
12" Single: Released Aug '87, on Parlophone, by EMI Records. Deleted Oct '87. Catalogue no: **12RX 6160**
12" Single: Released Jul '87, on Parlophone, by EMI Records. Deleted Apr '88. Catalogue no: **12R 6160**
7" Single: Released Jul '87, on Parlophone, by EMI Records. Deleted Apr '88. Catalogue no: **R 6160**

DRIVE ON
Tracks: / Drive on (7", CD single & Cassingle only.) / Drive on (dream on) (7" & Cassingle only.) / Drive on (So strong mix) (12" & CD single only.) / Drive on (Apple mix) (12" only.) / Drive on (Auto mix) (Limited edition only.) / Drive on (Dr. Boozie's revenge mix) (Limited edition only.) / Be my twin (US remix).
12" Single: Released Oct '89, on Parlophone, by EMI Records. Catalogue no: **203 577 8**
12" Single: Released Oct '89, on Parlophone, by EMI Records. Catalogue no: **203 577 6**
12" Single: Released Oct '89, on Parlophone, by EMI Records. Catalogue no: **12RP 6233**
CD 5": Released Oct '89, on Parlophone, by EMI Records. Catalogue no: **203 577 2**
CD 5": Released Oct '89, on Parlophone, by EMI Records. Catalogue no: **CDR 6233**
Cassingle: Released Oct '89, on Parlophone, by EMI Records. Catalogue no: **203 577 4**
Cassingle: Released Oct '89, on Parlophone, by EMI Records. Catalogue no: **TCR 6233**
7" Single: Released Oct '89, on Parlophone, by EMI Records. Catalogue no: **R 6233**
7" Single: Released Oct '89, on Parlophone, by EMI Records. Catalogue no: **203 577 7**
12" Single: Released Oct '89, on Parlophone, by EMI Records. Catalogue no: **12R 6233**

HARDER I TRY, THE
Tracks: / Harder I try, The / Remember me / Harder I try (ext) (Track available on 12" single only.) / Remember me (ext) / Harder I try (Inst) (Available on 12" only.).
7" Single: Released Jul '88, on Parlophone, by EMI Records. Deleted Aug '89. Catalogue no: **R 6184**
7" Single: Released Jul '88, on Parlophone, by EMI Records. Deleted Nov '88. Catalogue no: **RP 6184**
12" Single: Released Jul '88, Deleted Aug '89. Catalogue no: **12RX 6184**
CD 5": Released Jul '88, on Parlophone, by EMI Records. Deleted Jun '89. Catalogue no: **CDR 6184**
Cassingle: Released Jul '88, on Parlophone, by EMI Records. Deleted Nov '88. Catalogue no: **TCR 6184**
7" Single: Released Jul '88, on Parlophone, by EMI Records. Deleted Nov '88. Catalogue no: **RS 6184**
12" Single: Released Jul '88, on Parlophone, by EMI Records. Deleted Aug '89. Catalogue no: **12R 6184**

HE AIN'T NO COMPETITION
Tracks: / He ain't no competition / Call me lonely / He ain't no competion (ext.) (Not on 7".) / Call me lonely (kickback mix) (Not on 7".) / He ain't no competition (inst.) / Somebody, somewhere (CD single only.) / Call me lonely (get the sun remix) (12" remix only.) / He ain't no competition (Ease the pressure rem (12" remix only.).
7" Single: Released Oct '88, on Parlophone, by EMI Records. Deleted Aug '89. Catalogue no: **R 6193**
7" Single: Released Oct '88, on Parlophone, by EMI Records. Deleted Aug '89. Catalogue no: **RP 6193**
CD 5": Released Oct '88, on Parlophone, by EMI Records. Deleted Aug '89. Catalogue no: **CDR 6193**
12" Single: Released Oct '88, on Parlophone, by EMI Records. Deleted Aug '89. Catalogue no: **12RP 6193**
12" Single: Released Nov '88, on Parlophone, by EMI Records. Deleted Aug '89. Catalogue no: **12RX 6193**
12" Single: Released Oct '88, on Parlophone, by EMI Records. Deleted Aug '89. Catalogue no: **12R 6193**
7" Single: Released Oct '88, on Parlophone, by EMI Records. Deleted Aug '89. Catalogue no: **RS 6193**

HOW MANY TIMES
Tracks: / How many times (More) (12" only) / How many times / Give it all back.
7" Single: Released Feb '87, on EMI, by EMI Records. Catalogue no: **EMI 5591**
12" Single: Released Feb '87, on EMI, by EMI Records. Catalogue no: **12EMI 5591**

HOW MANY TIMES (CD SINGLE)
Tracks: / How many times / How many times (more) / How many times (John Robie remix) / Give it all back.
CD 5": Released May '87, on EMI, by EMI Records. Catalogue no: **CDEMI 5591**

I SHOULD HAVE LIED
Tracks: / I should have lied / Act for love.
7" Single: Released Aug '86, on EMI, by EMI Records. Deleted Jul '87. Catalogue no: **EMI 5569**
12" Single: Released Aug '86, on EMI, by EMI Records. Deleted Jul '87. Catalogue no: **12EMI 5569**

Brother Choice

HOW I FEEL
Tracks: / How I feel.
7" Single: Released Jul '86, on Blue Bird (1), by Blue Sun Records (USA). Deleted Jun '88. Catalogue no: **7 BILLY 4**
12" Single: Released Jul '86, on Blue Bird (1), by Blue Sun Records (USA). Deleted Jun '88. Catalogue no: **12 BILLY 4**

Brother D

CLAPPER'S POWER
Tracks: / Clapper's power.
7" Single: Released 10 Oct '87, on Rough Trade, by Rough Trade Records. Catalogue no: **RTT 209**
12" Single: Released Oct '87, on Clappers (USA), Catalogue no: **CL 120008**

NENGEH NENGEH
Tracks: / Nengeh nengeh / Private image / Chatte chatte.
12" Single: Released Apr '86, on Blue Trac, by Blue Trac Records. Catalogue no: **BTR 002**

Brother Dee

BIGGER BOSS
Tracks: / Bigger boss / Bigger boss (dub).
7" Single: Released Nov '87, on Creole, by Creole Records. Catalogue no: **CR 4**
12" Single: Released Nov '87, on Creole, by Creole Records. Catalogue no: **CRT 4**

PRIVATE ENEMY NO 1
Tracks: / Private enemy no.1.
12" Single: Released Nov '84, on Big Brother, Deleted '87. Catalogue no: **QBR 1201**

Brother Lees

DID YOU HEAR WHAT TERRY WOGAN SAID
Tracks: / Did you hear what Terry Wogan said.
7" Single: Released Dec '82, on Go Ahead, by Go Ahead Records. Catalogue no: **GA 115**

Brother Resistance

RING DEM BELLS
Tracks: / Ring dem bells.
7" Single: Released Aug '87, on Bumble Bee, Catalogue no: **7 BUMB 108**
12" Single: Released Aug '87, on Bumble Bee, Catalogue no: **BUMB 108**

Brotherhood Of Man

Biographical details: This British two-man two-woman vocal group had two quite separate careers. The first took place in 1970, when much employed British session singer Tony Burrows sang lead on a single called *United We Stand*. the record entered the British chart, but the group whose name appeared on the label did not exist. For promotion purposes, Brotherhood Of Man therefore became a hastily assembled two-man two-woman outfit. The single reached No. 10 in the UK and No. 13 in the US. Burrows was hyperactive at the time - he also did the lead vocals on two other simultaneous hits, Edison Lighthouse's *Loves Grows (Where My Rosemary Goes)* and the Pipkins' *Gimme Dat Ding*. Both of these were Top Tenners on both sides of the Atlantic. In Britain, Brotherhood Of Man managed one more Top 30 single *Where Are You Going To My Love*. They were surprised to discover that, in the States, *United We Stand* was adopted as an anthem by the homosexual fraternity, who made both the group's name and the song's lyrics fit their cause. No more was heard of Brotherhood Of Man and the name was consigned to the pop history books. Then suddenly in 1976 they re-appeared. The new Brotherhood Of Man was a different group, but was guided by producer and co-writer Tony Hiller, the man who had co-written and produced *United We Stand*. The new ensemble took advantage of a 1976 change in the BBC rules governing entry into the British heats of the Eurovision Song Contest. The effect of this change was that the old system of a previously named star singing six songs, with the winning number determined by public postal ballot, was scrapped in favour of a panel of juries choosing both act and the song from a roster of twelve. Fear of the humiliation of loosing in these heats prevented big name artists from entering, thus making way for unknowns. Brotherhood Of Man's *Save Your Kisses For Me* was tailor-made for Eurovision - a catchy ditty about a father going to work and leaving his darling three-year-old daughter at home, sung by clones of former Contest winners Abba. The song inevitably won the Contest (held in Holland), enjoyed a six week run at the top of the UK charts, was an international smash and even reached No. 27 in the States. Ironically it was eventually knocked off the UK No. 1 position by their mentors, Abba. When a carbon copy follow-up *My Sweet Rosalie* peaked No. 30 on the British chart, it appeared that the Brotherhood were to vanish into obscurity that awaited most Eurovision winners. But the following year they came with a UK No. 8 hit in the form of *Oh Boy (The Mood I'm In)*, a cover version of an American country hit. The summer of '77 brought them a second British No. 1 with *Angelo*; in early '78 came *Figaro*, their third chart topper. Both of these lightweight numbers were clearly inspired by Abba's *Fernando* (the song that dethroned *Save Your kisses For Me*). They appeared to be back-to-back No. 1s for Brotherhood Of Man but, in fact, there was another 45 called *Highwayman* which flopped totally in the autumn of '77. After *Figaro* was toppled from the top of the British charts - once again by Abba! - the hits started to tail off. *Beautiful Lover* reached No. 15 on the UK listings and *Middle Of The Night* peaked at No. 41. Their TV-advertsied self-titled album reached No. 6 on the British LP list, but this was their last major chart success. With three chrt-toppers behind them, Brotherhood Of Man were able to make a comfortable living on the cabaret and MoR circuit, which they have continued to do for many years. They returned briefly to the British album chart at the end of 1980 and acored a minor hit single in '82 but their regular touring activities will ensure that they do not need even these spasmodic chart appearances to stay in business. (Bob MacDonald)..

ANGELO
Tracks: / Angelo.
7" Single: Released Jul '77, on Pye, Deleted '80. Catalogue no: **7 N 45699**

BEAUTIFUL LOVER
Tracks: / Beautiful lover.
7" Single: Released May '78, on Pye, Deleted '81. Catalogue no: **7 N 46071**

CRY BABY CRY
Tracks: / Cry baby cry / I don't need it.
7" Single: Released Jan '82, on EMI, by EMI Records. Deleted Jan '85. Catalogue no: **EMI 5331**

FIGARO
Tracks: / Figaro.
7" Single: Released Jan '78, on Pye, Deleted '81. Catalogue no: **7 N 46037**

HONEY DONT THROW OUR LOVE AWAY
Tracks: / Honey don't throw our love away / This is the night.
7" Single: Released Apr '80, on Dazzle, by Dazzle Records. Deleted '82. Catalogue no: **DAZS 1**

LIGHTNING FLASH
Tracks: / Lightning flash / Heartbreaker.
7" Single: Released Jul '82, on EMI, by EMI Records. Deleted '85. Catalogue no: **EMI 5309**

MIDDLE OF THE NIGHT
Tracks: / Middle of the night.
7" Single: Released Sep '78, on Pye, Deleted '81. Catalogue no: **7 N 46117**

MY SWEET ROSALIE
Tracks: / My sweet Rosalie.
7" Single: Released Jun '76, on Pye, Deleted '79. Catalogue no: **7 N 45602**

OH BOY (THE MOOD I'M IN)
Tracks: / Oh boy (the mood I'm in).
7" Single: Released Feb '77, on Pye, Deleted '80. Catalogue no: **7 N 45656**

SAVE ALL YOUR KISSES FOR ME (SINGLE)
Tracks: / Save all your kisses for me.
7" Single: Released Mar '76, on Pye, Deleted '79. Catalogue no: **7 N 45569**

SAVE YOUR KISSES FOR ME (OLD GOLD)
Tracks: / Save your kisses for me / Oh boy.
7" Single: Released Jul '82, on Old Gold, by Old Gold Records. Deleted Jul '88. Catalogue no: **OG 9127**

UNITED WE STAND
Tracks: / United we stand.
7" Single: Released Feb '70, on Deram, by London Records. Deleted '73. Catalogue no: **DM 284**

WHEN THE KISSING STOPS
Tracks: / When the kissing stops.
7" Single: Released Jun '83, on EMI, by EMI Records. Catalogue no: **EMI 5396**

WHERE ARE YOU GOING TO MY LOVE
Tracks: / Where are you going to my love.
7" Single: Released Jul '70, on Deram, by London Records. Deleted '73. Catalogue no: **DM 298**

WILL YOU LOVE ME TOMORROW?
Tracks: / Will you love me tomorrow? / Catch me, catch me if you can.
7" Single: Released Jun '80, on Dazzle, by Dazzle Records. Deleted '83. Catalogue no: **DAZS 3**

Brotherhood Of Sleep

NEW BEAT
Tracks: / New beat.
CD 5": Released Apr '89, on Subway, by Subway Records. Catalogue no: **SUB 61CD**
12" Single: Released Apr '89, on Subway, by Subway Records. Catalogue no: **SUB 061**

Brothers

Biographical details: This British male vocal group scored a one-off Top 10 single in 1977, reaching No. 8 on the UK chart with *Sing Me*, a lightweight reggae-tinged ditty. Their style was very similar to that of 'Sheer Elegance', another British male vocal outfit, who had scored the previous year with *Milky Way* and *Life Is Too Short Girl*. Sheer Elegance faded quickly into obscurity and so did the Brothers. *Sing Me* was produced by pop masters Mitch Murray and Pete Callander, who have had a hand in many UK hits. (Bob MacDonald)..

BROTHERHYMN
Tracks: / Brotherhymn.
12" Single: Released '89, on Antler, by Antler Records (Belgium). Catalogue no: **SUB 013**
12" Single: Released '88, on Subway, by Subway Records. Catalogue no: **SUB 013**

MONTEGO BAY
Tracks: / Montego Bay / Mauritius farewell.
7" Single: Released Sep '83, on Paro, by Paro Records. Catalogue no: **PARO 007**

NIGHTSCHOOL
Tracks: / Nightschool.
7" Single: Released Aug '85, on TVM, Catalogue no: **TVM 100**

SING ME
Tracks: / Sing me.
7" Single: Released Jan '77, on Bus Stop, Deleted '80. Catalogue no: **BUS 1054**

Brothers Four

Biographical details: This American vocal group consisted of Richard Foley, Bob Glick, Mike Kirkland and John Paine. They were not of course real brothers, but 'fraternity brothers' who met as contemporaries at the University Of Washington. In 1960 they scored an American smash single with *Greenfields*, reaching No. 2 on the charts. it was written by Terry Gilkyson & The Easy Roders, who had scored their own US Top 5 hit three years earlier with *Marianne*. In 1961 the Brothers Four achieved a No. 32 placing with the novelty single *Frogg*, but the thirs American Top 40 hit never came. In Britain *Greenfields* was their only chart record, peaking at No. 40. (Bob MacDonald)..

GREENFIELDS (SINGLE)
Tracks: / Green fields.
7" Single: Released Jun '60, on Philips, by Phonogram Ltd. Deleted '63. Catalogue no: **PB 1009**

Brothers Johnson

Biographical details: Brothers Johnson Session musicians with their own hitmaking band: George on vocals and guitar, Louis on bass. Quincy Jones produced their debut album *Look Out For No. 1* in 1976; it sold over a million, hit singles including *Get The Funk Out Ma Face*. They produced five more albums of their own, all of which did well, as well as playing on records by Patti Austin, George Benson, The Crusaders, The Pointer Sisters, Lee Ritenour, Grover Washington, and many others. Donald Clarke, 24 August 1988.
George and Louis Johnson entered the music business as teenagers, performing in and around their native Los Angeles, USA they established good contacts, going on to back such artists as the Supremes, Bobby Womack and David Ruffin. But their most important contact was famous producer Quincy Jones, whom they teamed with on their 1976 debut album *Look Out For No. 1* it was a major success, peaking at No. 9 on the US LP chart and staying on the list for most of the year. Its major selling point was *I'll Be Good to you*, their first and biggest American Top 40 single; it reached No. 3 *Get The Funk Out Ma Face* was also a chart 45. Still working with Jones, they consolidated their position in 1977 with their second LP *Right on Time*, another very strong Stateside seller. It yielded the No. 5 single *Strawberry Letter 23*, an acclaimed melodic soul track that also gave the brothers their first UK chart records, peaking at No. 35 1978's *Blam!!* set was a relative dissapointment, but they bounced back in 1980 with the Jones-produced *Light Up The Night* album. Quincy was, at that time enormous success as producer of Michael Jackson's blockbusting *Off The Wall* LP; the acclaim h was thus receiving gave a major fillip to th new Johnsons set. It was introduced by th *Stomp!* single, which reached No. 7 on th

US chart. In Britain it was their only Top 30 single, peaking at No. 6. This was a typical slice of Jone slickness, an immaculately produced pop/soul/disco number with broad appeal. After the success of this album, the brothers parted company to produce themselves. Their career immediately went into decline. 1981's *Winners* album hardly lived up to its title, failing to produce a big hit single on either side of the Atlantic. Since then their records have continued to perform well on US black charts, but have not crossed over to the pop listings. The Brothers Johnson remain competent vocalists and guitarists, but their brand of pop-flavoured funk is not quite as commercial as it once was. (Bob MacDonald)..

AIN'T WE FUNKIN' NOW
Tracks: / Ain't we funkin' now.
" Single: Released Sep '78, on A&M, by A&M Records. Deleted '81. Catalogue no: **AMS 7379**

DANCIN' FREE
Tracks: / Dancin' free / Do it for love / I'll be good to you.
" Single: Released Sep '81, on A&M, by A&M Records. Deleted '84. Catalogue no: **AMS 8165**
2" Single: Released Sep '81, on A&M, by A&M Records. Deleted '84. Catalogue no: **AMSX 8165**

KICK IT TO THE CURB
Tracks: / Kick it to the curb / Ain't we funkin' now?.
" Single: Released May '88, on Breakout, by A&M Records. Deleted Feb '89. Catalogue no: **USA 631**
2" Single: Released May '88, on Breakout, by A&M Records. Deleted Feb '89. Catalogue no: **USAT 631**

LIGHT UP THE NIGHT (SINGLE)
Tracks: / Light up the night / Streetwave / Free yourself (Only on 12" single.).
2" Single: Released May '80, on A&M, by A&M Records. Deleted '83. Catalogue no: **AMSP 7526**
' Single: Released May '80, on A&M, by A&M Records. Deleted '83. Catalogue no: **AMS 7526**

REAL THING, THE
Tracks: / Real thing, The.
' Single: Released Jul '81, on A&M, by A&M Records. Deleted '84. Catalogue no: **AMS 8149**

RIDE O ROCKET
Tracks: / Ride o rocket.
' Single: Released Nov '78, on A&M, by A&M Records. Deleted '81. Catalogue no: **AMS 7400**

STOMP
Tracks: / Stomp / Let's swing.
' Single: Released Feb '80, on A&M, by A&M Records. Deleted '83. Catalogue no: **AMS 7509**
2" Single: Released Feb '80, on A&M, by A&M Records. Deleted '83. Catalogue no: **AMSP 7509**
2" Single: Released Jan '87, on Old Gold, by Old Gold Records. Catalogue no: **OG 411**

STRAWBERRY LETTER 23
Tracks: / Strawberry letter 23.
' Single: Released Jul '77, on A&M, by A&M Records. Deleted '80. Catalogue no: **AMS 7297**

Brothers Jones

FOLLOW ME
Tracks: / Follow me / I always win.
Single: Released May '80, on Ovation, by Gull Records. Deleted May '85. Catalogue no: **OVS 1204**

Brothers Of Craig

COLOUR OF HEAVEN
Tracks: / Colour of heaven.
" Single: Released May '89, on UNKNOWN, Catalogue no: **DOC 1**

COLOURS OF HEAVEN
' Single: Released Mar '89, on Boc, Catalogue no: **BOC 001FF**

TOSSING AND TURNING
Tracks: / Tossing and turning.
Single: Released Aug '86, on Brotherhood, Catalogue no: **DOC 3**

Broughton, Edgar

APACHE DROPOUT
Tracks: / Apache dropout.
Single: Released Jan '71, on Harvest (1), by EMI Records. Deleted '74. Catalogue no: **HAR 5032**

OUT DEMONS OUT (SINGLE)
Tracks: / Out demons out.
Single: Released Apr '70, on Harvest (1), by EMI Records. Deleted '73. Catalogue no: **HAR 5015**

Broughtons

ALL I WANT TO BE
Tracks: / All I want to be / Meglamaster.

7" Single: Released Feb '80, on Harvest (1), by EMI Records. Deleted '83. Catalogue no: **HAR 5199**

Brown, A. J

HUMAN NATURE
Tracks: / Human nature.
7" Single: Released Dec '83, on Sun Set (reggae), Catalogue no: **HJ 5175**

JUST CAN'T GET YOU OUT OF MY MIND
Tracks: / Just can't get you out of my mind.
12" Single: Released Dec '84, on Level Vibes, by Level Vibes Records. Catalogue no: **LV 006**

TOO MANY WOMEN
Tracks: / Too many women.
12" Single: Released 31 Jul '89, on Germaine, Catalogue no: **DGT 56**

Brown, A. S

SUNSHINE FOR ME
Tracks: / Sunshine for me.
12" Single: Released Sep '85, on Level Vibes, by Level Vibes Records. Catalogue no: **LVT 008**

Brown, Al

CARIBBEAN QUEEN
Tracks: / Caribbean Queen.
12" Single: Released Nov '84, on Jedi, Catalogue no: **JJ 212**

NO SOUL TODAY
Tracks: / No soul today.
12" Single: Released Aug '84, on Ethnic, Catalogue no: **ETH 2249**

Brown, Ale

IT'S ONLY A WIND UP (MAKING YOUR MIND UP)
Tracks: / It's only a wind up (making your mind up) / Normal service.
7" Single: Released May '81, on Radioactive, Deleted May '84. Catalogue no: **RAD 104**
7" Single: Released Mar '82, on Radioactive, Catalogue no: **RAD 502**

Brown, Alex

COME ON AND SHOUT
7" Single: Released Aug '85, on Mercury, by Phonogram Ltd. Deleted '87. Catalogue no: **MER 200**

Brown, Arthur

Biographical details: Brown, Arthur. UK rock singer, a philosophy student from Yorkshire who worked in small-time R&B bands, fromed Crazy World of Arthur Brown with organist Vincent Crane, drummer Drachen Theaker, replaced by Carl Palmer. The act owed much to Screamin' Jay Hawkins, with robes, painted face, cover of *I Put A Spell On You*. *Fire* was a transatlantic hit '68 (his only USA hit); Crane and Palmer left to form Atomic Rooster; Theaker was later in Love, Palmer in Emerson, Lake and Palmer. Brown formed Kingdom Come in 1970, made albums of rock theatre, played a priest in the Who's film 'Tommy', made albums of synthesiser music c.'80, lived in Austin, Texas: a great British eccentric. Donald Clarke, 24 August 1988
Born in Yorkshire, UK, Arthur Brown tried various University courses and day jobs, before joining Vincent Crane in 1967 in forming an ensemble billed as the Crazy World Of Arthur Brown. Arthur had previously been playing in minor R&B groups. The pair penned some weird and idiosyncratic material and became popular on Britain's burgeoning underground rock scene. They became friendly with Kit Lambert, manager of the Who, who encouraged and brought out the pair's outrageous and dynamic characteristics. In the summer of '68, they released a single called *Fire*. Starting with the now famous gruffly spoken intro 'I am the God of hell-fire and I bring you.....Fire', the single combined a strong commercial song with dramatic, over-the-top delivery. It went to No. 1 in the UK and No. 2 in the US. No other hits were forthcoming, so The Crazy World Of Arthur Brown went down in the history books as One hit Wonders. brown and Crane were credited as the writers of the smash, but their success was clouded by a lawsuit. Writers Michael Finesilver and Peter Ker sued successfully to show that *Fire* was in fact based on their own song of the same name. They were then credited as co-writers, with the royalties therefore being split four ways. *The Crazy World Of Arthur Brown* album reached No. 2 with 16 weeks on the UK list. Brown's highly theatrical stage act was designed to create both the maximum excitement and publicity. Wearing garish make-up and flowing robes, he growled, sang, screamed, jumped and gyrated his way through his concerts. His most famous stage trademark was the blazing hat, which startled audiences during his performance of *Fire*. This level of dynanism could not be sustained, however and the public soon tired of his antics. Keyboards player Crane left to form 'Atomic Rooster' and the Crazy World disintegrated. Brown spent the Seventies pursuing various esoteric musical activities, but he never won fame again. (Bob MacDonald)..

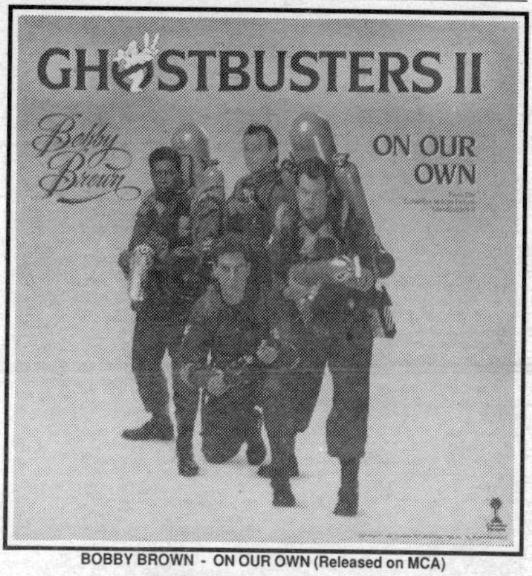

BOBBY BROWN - ON OUR OWN (Released on MCA)

FIRE
7" Single: Released Jan '74, on Track, by Polydor Ltd. Catalogue no: **2094 017**
7" Single: Released Jul '84, on Old Gold, by Old Gold Records. Catalogue no: **OG 9427**

FIRE (ORIGINAL)
Tracks: / Fire.
7" Single: Released Jun '68, on Track, by Polydor Ltd. Deleted '71. Catalogue no: **604 022**

Brown, Barry

BELLY MOVE
Tracks: / Belly move.
12" Single: Released Jun '84, on Greensleeves, by Greensleeves Records. Catalogue no: **GRED 150**

FREE AGAIN
Tracks: / Free again / Ghetto life.
12" Single: Released Dec '84, on Lix, Catalogue no: **LD 7510**

LADY
Tracks: / Lady / Love life.
12" Single: Released Dec '84, on Lix, Catalogue no: **LD 7511**

LIVING AS A BROTHER
Tracks: / Living as a brother / Caring for my sister.
12" Single: on Attack, Deleted '88. Catalogue no: **TACK 23**

OVER ME
Tracks: / Over me.
10" single: Released Jul '83, on Hitbound, Catalogue no: **JJ 125**

SEPARATION
Tracks: / Separation.
12" Single: on Attack, Deleted '88. Catalogue no: **TACK 21**

TANK YOU MAMA
Tracks: / Tank you mama.
12" Single: Released Jul '83, on Observers, Catalogue no: **OBS 001**

THEM A FIGHT
Tracks: / Them a fight.
12" Single: Released Mar '83, on Joe Gibbs, Catalogue no: **JGM 8170**

TOURIST SEASON
Tracks: / Tourist season.
12" Single: Released Jan '84, on Real Wax, Catalogue no: **JGMB 8173**

YOUR STEP
Tracks: / Your step.
10" single: Released May '83, on Hitbound, Catalogue no: **JJ 115**

Brown, B.C.

I REMEMBER
Tracks: / I remember / Spare me the pain.
7" Single: Released Nov '80, on Rocket, by Rocket Records. Deleted Nov '83. Catalogue no: **XPRES 42**

Brown, Betty

I GOT A DREAM
Tracks: / I got a dream.
12" Single: Released Jul '86, on L.I.S., Catalogue no: **MDTX 201**

Brown, Bobby

DON'T BE CRUEL (SINGLE)
Tracks: / Don't be cruel / Don't be cruel (instrumental) / Don't be cruel (radio edit) (Available on 12" single only.) / Don't be cruel (acapella).
7" Single: Released 30 Jan '89, on MCA, by MCA Records. Deleted 1 Jul '89. Catalogue no: **MCA 1310**
7" Single: Released 25 Jul '88, on MCA, by MCA Records. Catalogue no: **MCA 1268**
12" Single: Released 30 Jan '89, on MCA, by MCA Records. Catalogue no: **MCAT 1310**
CD 5": Released 30 Jan '89, on MCA, by MCA Records. Catalogue no: **CDDMCA 1310**
Cassingle: Released 6 Mar '89, on MCA, by MCA Records. Catalogue no: **MCAC 1310**
7" Single: Released Mar '89, on MCA (USA), by MCA Records (USA). Catalogue no: **MCA 238 61**
12" Single: Released 25 Jul '88, on MCA, by MCA Records. Catalogue no: **MCAT 1268**

EVERY LITTLE STEP
Tracks: / Every little step.
CD 5": Released May '89, on MCA, by MCA Records. Catalogue no: **DMCAT 1338**
7" Single: Released May '89, on MCA, by MCA Records. Catalogue no: **MCAR 1338**
12" Single: Released May '89, on MCA, by MCA Records. Catalogue no: **MCAT 1338**
7" Single: Released May '89, on MCA, by MCA Records. Catalogue no: **MCA 1338**

GIRL NEXT DOOR, A
Tracks: / Girl next door, A / Girl next door, A (inst).
7" Single: Released May '87, on MCA, by MCA Records. Catalogue no: **MCA 1153**
12" Single: Released May '87, on MCA, by MCA Records. Catalogue no: **MCAT 1153**

GIRLFRIEND
Tracks: / Girlfriend / King of stage.
7" Single: Released Apr '87, on MCA, by MCA Records. Catalogue no: **MCA 1114**
12" Single: Released Apr '87, on MCA, by MCA Records. Catalogue no: **MCAT 1114**

MY PEROGATIVE
Tracks: / My perogative / Girl next door / Girl next door (extended version) (Only on 12".) / My prerogative (extended remix) (Only on 12".) / My prerogative (instrumental) (Only on 12".).
CD 5": Released Dec '88, on MCA, by MCA Records. Catalogue no: **DMCA 1299**
7" Single: Released Nov '88, on MCA, by MCA Records. Catalogue no: **MCA 1299**
12" Single: Released Nov '88, on MCA, by MCA Records. Catalogue no: **MCAT 1299**

ON OUR OWN (see panel above)
Tracks: / On our own / On our own (rap).
CD 5": Released Jul '89, on MCA, by MCA Records. Catalogue no: **DMCAT 1350**
Cassingle: Released Jul '89, on MCA, by MCA Records. Catalogue no: **MCAC 1350**
7" Single: Released Jul '89, on MCA, by MCA Records. Catalogue no: **MCA 1350**
12" Single: Released Jul '89, on MCA, by MCA Records. Catalogue no: **MCAT 1350**

ROCK WIT'CHA (IMPORT)

Tracks: / Rock wit'cha.
12" Single: Released Sep '89, on MCA (USA), by MCA Records (USA). Catalogue no: **MCA 23951**

ROCK WIT'CHA
Tracks: / Rock Wit'cha.
CD 5": Released Sep '89, on MCA, by MCA Records. Catalogue no: **DMCAT 1367**
7" Single: Released Sep '89, on MCA, by MCA Records. Catalogue no: **MCA 1367**
12" Single: Released Sep '89, on MCA, by MCA Records. Catalogue no: **MCAT 1367**

Brown, Boe

CHINATOWN
Tracks: / Chinatown / Dancer man.
7" Single: Released Aug '86, on President, by President Records. Catalogue no: **PT 547**

SOUND THAT FUNKY HORN
Tracks: / Sound that funky horn.
7" Single: Released Sep '85, on President, by President Records. Catalogue no: **PT 540**
12" Single: Released Sep '85, on President, by President Records. Catalogue no: **PT 12 540**

Brown, Bunny

STRAWBERRY LETTER 23
Tracks: / Strawberry letter 23 / Strawberry letter 23 (pt 2).
7" Single: Released Oct '82, on EMI, by EMI Records. Deleted Oct '85. Catalogue no: **EMI 5119**
12" Single: Released Oct '82, on EMI, by EMI Records. Deleted Oct '85. Catalogue no: **12EMI 5119**

Brown, Carol

COME LOVE ME
Tracks: / Come love me / Version love.
12" Single: Released Apr '86, on Rhythm Gits, Catalogue no: **LS 006**

FEEL SO GOOD
Tracks: / Feel so good.
12" Single: Released Jan '85, on Revue, by Creole Records. Catalogue no: **REV 014T**

I WON'T HURT YOUR FEELINGS
Tracks: / I won't hurt your feelings / Whistling Willie / Little action, A / Little action, A (instrumental).
12" Single: Released Sep '87, on CSA, by CSA Records. Catalogue no: **12CSA 513**

THIS USED TO BE YOUR HOUSE
Tracks: / This used to be your house.
12" Single: Released Jun '85, on Rhythm Gits, Catalogue no: **CB 003**

YOU ARE THE ONLY LOVE
Tracks: / You are the only love.
12" Single: Released May '88, on Jimpy's International, Catalogue no: **JWH 041**

Brown, Chad

I'M SORRY
Tracks: / I'm sorry.
7" Single: Released Mar '86, on Bonaire, by Bonaire Records. Deleted '88. Catalogue no: **BON 2**

Brown, Chuck

BUSTIN' LOOSE (SINGLE)
Tracks: / Bustin' loose / Miss fine lover / Solar funk / Bussie.
7" Single: Released Mar '85, on Source, Deleted May '86. Catalogue no: **SOURCE 1**
12" Single: Released Jan '80, on Source, Deleted '83. Catalogue no: **12 SRC 101**
12" Single: Released Feb '85, on Source, Catalogue no: **12 SOURCE 1**

WE NEED SOME MONEY
Tracks: / We need some money.
12" Single: Released Aug '84, on Greyhound, by Greyhound Records. Catalogue no: **W 6**

Brown, Dana & Gerry

HARMONY
Tracks: / Harmony.
7" Single: Released Apr '89, on Captain Billy's Music, Catalogue no: **FAN 1 7**

Brown, Dee Dee

MERRY CHRISTMAS BABY
Tracks: / Merry Christmas baby / Merry Christmas baby (version).
7" Single: Released Dec '87, on Copasetic, by Copasetic Records. Catalogue no: **COP 003**

Brown, Dennis

Biographical details: This Jamaican reggae singer entered the music business while still a child, working for a time with Kingston's well-known reggae outfit, Byron Lee & The Dragonaires. by the time he was out of his teens, he had performed extensively throughout the West Indies. His first big record was 1979's *Money In My Pocket*, a strong reggae single that took him to No. 14 on the British charts. In the same year he made an unexpected appearance at the Montreux Jazz Festival. He recorded prolifically during the early Eighties, the most satisfactory output being his only UK chart album *Love Has Found Its Way* which reached No. 72 in 1982. It yielded two minor UK hit singles in the shape of the title cut and *Halfway Up Halfway Down*. Brown is a worthy artist but, like many of his peers, is still waiting for a major reggae explosion in the western world. (Bob MacDonald)..

ALL FOR ONE,ONE FOR ALL
Tracks: / All for one,one for all / All for one,one for all (version).
12" Single: Released May '86, on Charm, by Charm Records. Catalogue no: **CRT 1**

AMAGIDEON
Tracks: / Amagideon.
12" Single: Released Jul '84, on Tads, Catalogue no: **TRD 15118**

ANYWAY YOU WANT IT
Tracks: / Anyway you want it / Anyway you want it(version).
12" Single: Released Sep '86, on Tads, Catalogue no: **TRD 14786**

BIG ALL AROUND
Tracks: / Big all around / Big all around (version) / Ain't nothin' to it / Beat is military, The.
7" Single: Released Apr '89, on Greensleeves, by Greensleeves Records. Catalogue no: **GRED 238**

BLACK MAGIC WOMAN
Tracks: / Black magic woman / Sweat for you baby.
12" Single: Released Apr '84, on Phil Pratt, Catalogue no: **SS 10**

BREAKING DOWN THE BARRIERS
12" Single: Released Nov '83, on Natty Congo, Catalogue no: **NCD MO20**

DECEIVING GIRL
Tracks: / Deceiving girl.
12" Single: Released Apr '84, on Yucca Ur, by Revolver Records. Catalogue no: **YS 016**

DEEPEST LOVE
Tracks: / Deepest love / Deep music.
12" Single: Released May '86, on Natty Congo, Catalogue no: **NCDM 034**

EASY
Tracks: / Easy.
7" Single: Released Apr '89, on Frame, Catalogue no: **CSES 01**

EASY TAKE IT EASY
Tracks: / Easy take it easy.
12" Single: Released Jun '83, on Tads, Catalogue no: **TRD 21483**

EXIT,THE
Tracks: / Exit, The / Exit, The (version).
12" Single: Released Dec '85, on Unity Sound, Catalogue no: **UN 010**

FLY ME AWAY
Tracks: / Fly me away / Travelling dub.
12" Single: Released Dec '82, on Jah Shaka, Catalogue no: **SHAKA 829**

FUNNY FEELING
Tracks: / Funny feeling / Foundation.
12" Single: Released Apr '84, on Hawkeye, by Hawkeye Records. Catalogue no: **HD 007**

GO NOW
Tracks: / Go now.
7" Single: Released May '82, on Oval, by Oval Records. Catalogue no: **OVAL 1009**

HALFWAY UP HALFWAY DOWN
Tracks: / Halfway up halfway down / Weep and moan.
12" Single: Released Aug '82, on A&M, by A&M Records. Deleted '84. Catalogue no: **AMSX 8250**
7" Single: Released Aug '82, on A&M, by A&M Records. Deleted '88. Catalogue no: **AMS 8250**

HERE I COME
Tracks: / Here I come.
12" Single: Released Aug '85, on Tads, Catalogue no: **TRD 8785**

HOLD ON TO WHAT YOU GOT
Tracks: / Hold on to what you've got.
12" Single: Released Jul '82, on Power House, Catalogue no: **PH 04 A 1**

HOLD TIGHT(12")
Tracks: / Hold tight / Hold tight (version).
12" Single: Released Apr '86, on Live & Learn (USA), by Live & Learn Records (USA). Catalogue no: **LLB 008**

HOW CAN I LEAVE
Tracks: / How can I leave.
12" Single: Released Aug '84, on Real Wax, Catalogue no: **JGMD 5226**

I CAN'T STAND IT
Tracks: / I can't stand it / Too hot.
12" Single: Released Apr '84, on Joe Gibbs, Catalogue no: **JGM 8191**

I DON'T WANT TO BE
Tracks: / I don't want to be / No General.
7" Single: Released Apr '80, on Deb, by Deb Records. Deleted '83. Catalogue no: **DEB 039**

I LIKE IT LIKE THAT
Tracks: / I like it like that.
12" Single: Released Jun '83, on Yvonne's, Catalogue no: **YS 012**

IF I DIDN'T LOVE YOU
Tracks: / If I didn't love you.
12" Single: Released Dec '82, on Thompson Sound, Deleted Dec '85. Catalogue no: **TS003**

IF THIS WORLD WAS MINE
Tracks: / If this world was mine.
12" Single: Released Nov '82, on Tads, Catalogue no: **TRD 311 082**

ISRAEL
Tracks: / Israel.
12" Single: Released Nov '85, on Natty Congo, Catalogue no: **NCDM 031**

IT'S MAGIC
Tracks: / It's magic / Crazy love.
12" Single: Released Dec '84, on Greensleeves, by Greensleeves Records. Catalogue no: **GRED 167**

I'VE GOT TO FIND YOU
Tracks: / I've got to find you.
12" Single: Released Feb '82, on Black Joy, Catalogue no: **BEH 814**

LET ME DOWN EASY
Tracks: / Let me down easy.
7" Single: on Trojan, by Trojan Records. Deleted May '88. Catalogue no: **TRO 9056**

LET YOUR LOVE GO
Tracks: / Let your love go.
12" Single: Released Aug '89, on White Label (1), Catalogue no: **WR 009**
7" Single: Released Sep '89, on White Label (1), Catalogue no: **7WR 009**

LIVE AND LOVE
Tracks: / Live and love.
12" Single: Released Nov '85, on Greensleeves, by Greensleeves Records. Catalogue no: **GRED 191**

LOVE HAS FOUND ITS WAY (SINGLE)
Tracks: / Love has found it's way / Why baby why / I couldn't stand losing you (on 12" only).
7" Single: Released Jul '82, on A&M, by A&M Records. Deleted '85. Catalogue no: **AMS 8226**
12" Single: Released Jul '82, on A&M, by A&M Records. Deleted '85. Catalogue no: **AMSX 8226**

LOVE ME FOREVER
Tracks: / Love me forever.
12" Single: Released Mar '86, on Paradise, Catalogue no: **PPD 12 377**

LOVELY FEELING
Tracks: / Lovely feeling.
12" Single: Released Aug '86, on Blue Mountain, Catalogue no: **BMD 26**

LOVE'S GOTTA HOLD ON ME
Tracks: / Love's gotta hold on me.
12" Single: Released '85, on Joe Gibbs, Deleted Jun '89. Catalogue no: **JG 60079**

LOVING FEELING
Tracks: / Loving feeling.
7" Single: Released Apr '89, on Yvonne's, Catalogue no: **CSES 1**

MADONNA
Tracks: / Madonna.
7" Single: Released Aug '85, on Chartsounds, Catalogue no: **CS 00D**

MISCHIEF
Tracks: / Mischief.
12" Single: Released May '87, on Live & Learn (USA), by Live & Learn Records (USA). Catalogue no: **LLD 103**

MONEY IN MY POCKET (SINGLE)
Tracks: / Money in my pocket.
7" Single: Released Mar '79, on Lightning, Deleted '82. Catalogue no: **LV 5**

MR BOJANGLES
Tracks: / Mr. Bojangles.
12" Single: Released Jul '85, on Maccabees, Catalogue no: **unknown**

NOWHERE WILL I ROAM
Tracks: / Nowhere will I roam.
12" Single: Released Dec '84, on Time, Catalogue no: **TR 007**

OH GIRL
Tracks: / Oh girl.
12" Single: Released Sep '85, on Natty Congo, Catalogue no: **NCDM 028**
12" Single: Released Oct '82, on Natty Congo, Catalogue no: **NCDM 014**

OLE MAN RIVER
Tracks: / Ol' man river.
12" Single: Released Apr '85, on Maccabees, Catalogue no: **MPCDB 2**

PROMISED LAND
Tracks: / Promised land.
12" Single: Released Apr '83, on Simba, Catalogue no: **SM 003**

RAGGAMUFFIN'
Tracks: / Raggamuffin'.
12" Single: Released Sep '85, on Greensleeves, by Greensleeves Records. Catalogue no: **GRED 188**

REBEL WITH A CAUSE
Tracks: / Rebel with a cause.
12" Single: Released Jun '86, on Jakki, Catalogue no: **JM 468**

REVOLUTION (PART 2)
Tracks: / Revolution (part 2).
12" Single: Released Apr '85, on Taxi (1), Catalogue no: **unknown**

SENORITA
Tracks: / Senorita.
Note: "Reggae superstar Brown lifts this jaunty, medium paced ballad from this current album with its slick Willie Lindo production" (Music Week, July 1988)
12" Single: Released Jul '88, on J & W Records, Catalogue no: **JW59T**
7" Single: Released Jul '88, on J & W Records, Catalogue no: **JW59**

SLAVE DRIVER
Tracks: / Money in my pocket / Slave driver.
Note: "A classic track here in its full version from perhaps today's biggest reggae artist." (Magnum Music Group, May 1988).
12" Single: Released Jan '84, on Blue Moon (1), by Magnum Music Group. Catalogue no: **BMS 1002**

SLOW DOWN WOMAN
Tracks: / Slow down woman.
12" Single: Released Apr '85, on Greensleeves, by Greensleeves Records. Catalogue no: **GRED 175**

STEP BY STEP
Tracks: / Step by step / Stepping.
12" Single: Released May '86, on Diamond C, Catalogue no: **DB 008**

WHIP THEM JAH
Tracks: / Whip them Jah.
12" Single: Released Sep '81, on Hawkeye by Hawkeye Records. Catalogue no: **HD 3[illegible]**

YESTERDAY, TODAY AND TOMORROW
Tracks: / Yesterday, today and tomorrow.
12" Single: Released '87, on Joe Gibbs Deleted Jun '89. Catalogue no: **JG 6057**

YOU ARE
Tracks: / You are.
12" Single: Released Dec '83, on Tads Catalogue no: **TRD 111383**

YOUR LOVE GOTTA HOLD ON ME (SINGLE)
Tracks: / Your love gotta hold on me.
7" Single: Released May '83, on Joe Gibbs Catalogue no: **7 JGM 8175**
12" Single: Released Jun '83, on Joe Gibbs Catalogue no: **JGM 8175**

YOUR LOVE IS A BLESSING
Tracks: / Your love is a blessing.
12" Single: Released Nov '83, on Yvonne's Catalogue no: **YS 014**

Brown, Diana

BLIND FAITH
Tracks: / Blind faith / Blind faith (instrumental) / Blind faith (master jam) (Only on 12" single.) / Blind faith (dubwise selection) (Only on 12" single.) / Blind faith (ground beat mix (Only on 12" single.).
7" Single: Released Jul '89, on ffrr, by London Records. Catalogue no: **F 114**
12" Single: Released Jul '89, on ffrr, by London Records. Catalogue no: **FX 114**

Brown, Errol

BODY ROCKIN'
Tracks: / Body rockin' / My little girl.
CD 5": Released Sep '87, on WEA, by WEA Records. Deleted Jul '88. Catalogue no: **YZ 162CD**
12" Single: Released Sep '87, on WEA, by WEA Records. Deleted Jul '88. Catalogue no: **YZ 162 T**
7" Single: Released Sep '87, on WEA, by WEA Records. Deleted Jul '88. Catalogue no: **YZ 162**

LOVE GOES UP & DOWN
Tracks: / Love goes up & down / Thank yo[u]
CD 5": Released Jan '89, on WEA, by WEA Records. Catalogue no: **YZ 340CD**
7" Single: Released Jan '89, on WEA, by WEA Records. Catalogue no: **YZ 340**
12" Single: Released Jan '89, on WEA, by WEA Records. Catalogue no: **YZ 340T**

MAYA
Tracks: / Maya / She's my lady / Broth[er] Louie (Only on 12").
CD 5": Released 16 Sep '88, on WEA, by WEA Records. Catalogue no: **YZ 313CD**
7" Single: Released 16 Sep '88, on WEA by WEA Records. Catalogue no: **YZ 313**
12" Single: Released 16 Sep '88, on WEA by WEA Records. Catalogue no: **YZ 313T**

PERSONAL TOUCH
Tracks: / Personal touch / Why don't you [...] me.
7" Single: Released Jun '87, on WEA, by WEA Records. Deleted Jul '88. Catalogue no: **YZ 130**
12" Single: Released Jun '87, on WEA, by WEA Records. Deleted Jul '88. Catalogue no: **YZ 130T**

Brown, Foxy

ALL I NEED TO KNOW
Tracks: / All I need to know.
12" Single: Released Mar '89, on Reality, Catalogue no: **SE 001**
12" Single: Released Mar '89, on Reality, Catalogue no: **RR 128881**

FAST CAR
Tracks: / Fast car.
12" Single: Released 31 Jul '89, on Charm, by Charm Records. Catalogue no: **CRT 35**

SORRY
Tracks: / Sorry.
7" Single: Released Apr '89, on Steely & Cleevie, Catalogue no: **VPRD 446**

SWEET BABY
Tracks: / Sweet baby.
12" Single: Released Jul '89, on Techniques, Catalogue no: **WRT 40**

Brown, Gerry

IT'S ALRIGHT
Tracks: / It's alright.
7" Single: Released Apr '84, on AOR, Deleted '85. Catalogue no: **AOR 2**

MARY SAID
Tracks: / Mary said.
7" Single: Released Aug '84, on AOR, Deleted '85. Catalogue no: **AOR 1**

Brown, Glen

YOU'RE BREAKING MY HEART
Tracks: / Hi tech (dub) / You're breaking my heart.
12" Single: Released Nov '86, on Hi-Tech, by Hi-Tech Records. Catalogue no: **HT 001**

Brown, Gloria.D

MORE THEY KNOCK THE MORE I LOVE YOU, THE
Tracks: / More they knock, the more I love you, The.
7" Single: Released Jul '85, on 10 Records, by Virgin Records. Deleted '88. Catalogue no: **TEN 52**

Brown, Graham. T.

SAY WHEN
Tracks: / Say when / She's mine.
7" Single: Released Feb '87, on Capitol, by EMI Records. Deleted '88. Catalogue no: **CL 443**

TALKIN' TO IT
Tracks: / Talkin' to it.
7" Single: Released Aug '87, on Capitol, by EMI Records. Catalogue no: **CL 462**

Brown, Greg

BABY TALK
Tracks: / Baby talk.
7" Single: Released Jun '84, on Beau-Jolly, Deleted '86. Catalogue no: **BJ 1004**
12" Single: Released Jun '84, on Beau-Jolly, Deleted '86. Catalogue no: **12 BJ 1004**

CAN I GO
Tracks: / Can I go / Can I go (version).
7" Single: Released Nov '88, on Lab, Catalogue no: **7 LAB 1**
12" Single: Released Nov '88, on Lab, Catalogue no: **12LAB 1**

Brown, James

Biographical details: Brown, James. The singer, songwriter, bandleader and producer/arranger is one of the most dynamic and influential entertainers in post-war black music; a great R&B and soul artist, also admired by such modern jazzmen as Miles Davis and Anthony Braxton. Born in 1933 and raised in Georgia, he overcame poverty and prison with a southern synthesis of gospel music, vaudeville and R&B pioneers Louis Jordan and Roy Brown; legendary R&B producer Ralph Bass spotted him and recorded him with his Famous Flames initially on his Federal label, which had become part of King. King's boss Syd Nathan did not appreciate Brown, who eventually took over his own career, becoming an innovator in the black music business as well as stylistically: he made the dance hit *Do The Mashed Potatoes* on another label under his drummer's name (Nat Kendricks and the Swans) in 1960 (a top 10 R&B hit) because if King's obstinacy; he made the smash hit *Live At The Apollo* in 1960-62 because none of his studio records reflected his live act accurately. He had over 90 crossovers to the USA pop chart 1958-77, his innovative attitude and terminology included *Pap's Got A Brand New Bag* (his first UK hit, in 1965), *Cold Sweat, Say It Loud - I'm Black And I'm Proud, Make It Funky* and much else. His work was relentlessly ripped off by the inventors of disco and hip-hop; he came back in the mid-'80s with more hits, just to remind everybody who the boss was. (Donald Clarke, 24 August 1988.)
Born in Georgia, USA in 1928, James Brown's story is a true rags to riches tale. he was born into rural poverty, but went on to become one of black music's all-time legends. While still at school Brown had to augment his family's income by working as a shoeshine and newspaper boy. By the time he finished his studies, he was becoming proficient on piano, organ, bass guitar and drums. In 1954 he formed the Famous Flames, a group to back him while he sang gospel material. Brown and his ensemble attracted local acclaim and, as they did so, gradually eased out of the gospel songs in favour of secular rhythm and blues. They scored their firsat record success in '56, when the slow, impassioned *Please Please Please* became a big single in the US R&B charts. it took them two years to follow up this winner. The one that did the trick was 1958's *Try Me*, another intense piece of soul. Already Brown was displaying the committed, pleading vocal style that would make him famous. After these big R&B 45s, Brown achieved his first American Top 40 pop hit in 1960. The up-tempo *Think* was the first of 43 singles to reach this list over the next fifteen years. The second was 1961's *Bewildered*, a slow song; the third was 1962's first instrumental *Night Train*. By now James Brown and the Famous Flames were gaining the reputation of being America's hottest and most dynamic live act. The slick dance routines of the fast numbers were interwoven with the deep, impassioned soulfulness of the slow songs. Brown electrified his audiences with the sheer power and excitement of his performance. The icing on the cake was his lavish dress sense. The whole dynamic package was captured on 1962's double album *Live At The Apollo* a truly historic record that became the first R&B album to sell a million copies. It was this LP that introduced Brown to the white audience. The success of *Live At The Apollo* paved the way for his first US Top 20 single in 1963, with *Prisoner Of Love* an emotional ballad. But his real breakthrough single in the pop market was the characteristically wild *Papa's Got A Brand New Bag*. Issued in '65, it gave the star his first US Top Tenner and his first UK hit of any kind, reaching No. 25. As usual it was penned by Brown himself, who was a prolific composer as well as a workaholic recording and touring artist. Then came *I Got You (I Feel Good)*, his biggest US pop hit; it reached No. 3, his only hit to crack the Top 5 on Billboard's hot 100. It is a curious paradox that, though the frantic release schedule of James Brown earned him 43 Top 40 hits in fifteen years and many other Hot 100 entries, only six of these hit the Top 10. In Britain he has only placed nine 45s on the charts in his entire career, the biggest of these being the No. 13 position of 1966's big ballad *It's A Man's Man's Man's World*. To black America, though, he was not only the top black musical superstar but also, by the mis-Sixties, a champion of the black consciousness movement. Following Martin Luther King's assassination in 1968, he took over as the unofficial new black leader. His televised appeal for calm in the wake of the King shooting had a major impact. In that same year he dropped the Famous Flames billing for good and all subsequent discs were issued solely under the nameof James Brown. The first release under this new policy was his final American Top Tenner - *Say It Loud - I'm Black And I'm Proud* - was the untimate anthem of the conciousness movement. After this, the records became more and more homogenised and less and less interesting. Virtually every single came to be issued in Part 1/Part 2 format, a sign of Brown's growing self-indulgence and decreased imagination. Tracks such as *Let A Man Come In And Do The Popcorn* scarcely merited a first part, let alone a second. 1970's ludicrous but exciting *Get Up I feel Like Being A Sex Machine* provided a brief respite from the artistic decline. During the early Seventies his fans remained loyal, as his influence on the new generation of soul and funk acts was clearly visible. As the decade progressed, new chart names such as the Ohio Players, Kool & The Gang and Earth, Wind & Fire were citing Brown as a major source of inspiration. Brown himself became involved in the disco explosion with the tracks *Get Up Offa That Thing* and *Body Heat*. 1983 saw the release of *Bring It On*, one of his strongest latterday singles. the following year he teamed with Afrika Bambaataa for a duet single called *Unity*. This was a meeting of the Godfather of Soul with Bambaataa. Symbolically this pairing was a fine idea - the two were almost like father and son, musically. In practice it did not really work. 'Godfather of Soul' is just one of the many titles that have been bestowed on James Brown. Others include 'Mr Showbusiness', 'Mr Dynamite' and 'The Hardest Working Man In Showbusiness'. Indeed he is as keen as anybody to grant himself the accolades. He is hardly a modest man; but modesty is not a virtue you would expect to find in a master showman, something Brown has proved himself to be over and over again. From the mid-Fifties onwards, he was at the pulse of soul music. He helped to invent it, nurtured it and kept on playing it. The soul boom of the Sixties, the disco explosion of the Seventies, the dance ethic of the Eighties - these major musical phenomena all owe their place in history largely to James Brown. (Bob MacDonald)..

BODY HEAT (SINGLE)
Tracks: / Body heat (single).
7" Single: Released Jan '77, on Polydor, by Polydor Ltd. Deleted '80. Catalogue no: **2066 763**

BRING IT ON
Tracks: / Bring it on, bring it on / Today / You can't keep a good man down / Tennessee waltz / Night time is the right time / For your precious love.
7" Single: Released Mar '86, on Sonet, by Sonet Records. Catalogue no: **SON 2258**
12" Single: Released Mar '86, on Sonet, by Sonet Records. Catalogue no: **SONL 2258**

FROGGY MIX
Tracks: / Froggy mix.
7" Single: Released Apr '85, on Boiling Point, by Polydor Ltd. Catalogue no: **FROG 1**
12" Single: Released Apr '85, on Boiling Point, by Polydor Ltd. Deleted Mar '88. Catalogue no: **FROGX 1**

FUNKY MEN
Tracks: / Funky men / Mashed potatoes.
7" Single: Released May '81, on RCA, by BMG Records (UK). Deleted May '86. Catalogue no: **RCA 65**
12" Single: Released May '81, on RCA, by BMG Records (UK). Deleted May '86. Catalogue no: **RCAT 65**

GET UP, GET INTO IT, GET INVOLVED
Tracks: / Get up, get into it, get involved (pt.I) / Get up, get into it, get involved (pt.II).
7" Single: Released Mar '87, on King (USA), Catalogue no: **45-6347**

(GET UP I FEEL LIKE BEING A) SEX MACHINE (OLD GO
Tracks: / (Get up I feel like being a) sex machine.
7" Single: Released Jun '88, on Old Gold, by Old Gold Records. Catalogue no: **OG 9438**
7" Single: Released Sep '70, on Polydor, by Polydor Ltd. Catalogue no: **2001 071**
12" Single: Released Jun '85, on Boiling Point, by Polydor Ltd. Catalogue no: **POSPX 751**
7" Single: Released Jun '85, on Boiling Point, by Polydor Ltd. Catalogue no: **POSP 751**

GET UP OFFA THAT THING
Tracks: / Get up offa that thing.
7" Single: Released Sep '76, on Polydor, by Polydor Ltd. Deleted '79. Catalogue no: **2066 687**

GRAVITY (SINGLE)
Tracks: / Gravity / Gravity (dub).
7" Single: Released Oct '86, on Scotti Bros (USA), Catalogue no: **650059 7**
12" Single: Released Oct '86, on Scotti Bros (USA), Catalogue no: **650059 6**

HEY AMERICA
Tracks: / Hey America.
7" Single: Released Nov '71, on Mojo, Deleted '74. Catalogue no: **2093 006**

HOW DO YOU STOP?
Tracks: / How do you stop / Repeat the beat (faith).
7" Single: Released Apr '87, on Scotti Bros (USA), Deleted Nov '87. Catalogue no: **JAMES 1**
12" Single: Released Apr '87, on Scotti Bros (USA), Deleted Nov '87. Catalogue no: **JAMES T1**

HOW DO YOU STOP (SPECIAL EXTENDED REMIX)
Tracks: / Goliath (message house mix) / Repeat the beat (faith).
12" Single: Released Dec '86, on Scotti Bros (USA), Deleted Nov '87. Catalogue no: **JAMES Q1**

I GO CRAZY
Tracks: / I go crazy / World Cycle Inc..
7" Single: Released Jun '81, on Polydor, by Polydor Ltd. Deleted Jun '84. Catalogue no: **POSP 290**

I GOT YOU
Tracks: / I got you / Good good lovin' / Lost someone / I can't help it / You've got the power / Night train / I've got money / Dancin' little thing / Think / Three hearts in a tangle / Suds / Love don't love nobody.
7" Single: Released '83, on Polydor (Import), by Polydor Ltd. Deleted '88. Catalogue no: **2489 196**
7" Single: Released Feb '66, on Pye International, Deleted '69. Catalogue no: **7N 25350**

I GOT YOU (I FEEL GOOD)
Tracks: / I got you (I feel good) / Nowhere to run.
Note: "A&M release two vintage soul classics - James Brown's, I Got You (I Feel Good) and Martha Reeves and the Vandellas', Nowhere to run. Both songs are taken from the A&M soundtrack album to the American No.1 smash film 'Good morning Vietnam' which topped the American box office early this year. I Got You (I Feel Good) is a James Brown original and was a hit for him in 1966, and Nowhere to Run first charted for Martha Reeves in 1965. (A&M May 88)
12" Single: Released 4 Jul '88, on A&M, by A&M Records. Catalogue no: **AMY 444**
7" Single: Released 4 Jul '88, on A&M, by A&M Records. Catalogue no: **AM 444**

I'M REAL (SINGLE)
Tracks: / I'm real / Keep keepin' / Tribute* / I'm real (FF hyped up mix) (on CD single and 12" only.).
Note: Brand new 1988 material by James Brown 'I'm Real' was written and produced by US production crew Full Force. Taken from the forthcoming album "I'm real." * only on 12" and CD
12" Single: Released May '88, on Urban, by Polydor Ltd. Catalogue no: **JSBX 1**
7" Single: Released May '88, on Urban, by Polydor Ltd. Catalogue no: **JSB 1**
12" Single: Released Sep '88, on Intercord (Germany), Catalogue no: **INT 127328**
CD 5": Released May '88, on Urban, by Polydor Ltd. Catalogue no: **JSBCD 1**

IT'S A MAN'S MAN'S MAN'S WORLD
Tracks: / It's a man's man's man's world.
7" Single: Released Jun '66, on Pye International, Deleted '69. Catalogue no: **7N 25371**

IT'S A MAN'S WORLD
Tracks: / It's a man's man's man's world / Sex machine.
12" Single: Released May '86, on Konnexion, Catalogue no: **PER 128 601**

LET'S GET SERIOUS
Tracks: / Let's get serious.
12" Single: Released Oct '88, on Lucky, by Lucky Records. Catalogue no: **12LSD 101**

LIVING IN AMERICA
Tracks: / Living in America / Farewell, The.
7" Single: Released Jan '86, on Scotti Bros (USA), Catalogue no: **A 6701**
12" Single: Released Jan '86, on Scotti Bros (USA), Catalogue no: **TA 6701**

PAPA'S GOT A BRAND NEW BAG (SINGLE)
Tracks: / Papa's got a brand new bag / Get up offa that thing.
7" Single: Released Sep '65, on London Records, by London Records. Catalogue no: **HL 9990**
12" Single: Released Oct '82, on Polydor, by Polydor Ltd. Catalogue no: **POSPX 605**
12" Single: Released May '87, on Perfect, Catalogue no: **PER 12 8607**

PAYBACK MIX PART ONE, THE
Tracks: / Payback mix / Give it up or turn it loose / Keep on doing what you're doing but make it funky (Only on 12" single.) / Stone to the bone (Only on 12" single.) / Cold sweat (Only on 12" single.).
7" Single: Released Apr '88, on Urban, by Polydor Ltd. Deleted 30 May '89. Catalogue no: **URB 17**
12" Single: Released Apr '88, on Urban, by Polydor Ltd. Deleted 30 May '89. Catalogue no: **URBX 17**

PLAY BACK PART ONE, THE (REMIX)
Tracks: / Play back part one, The / Play back part one, The (version).
12" Single: Released Apr '88, on Urban, by Polydor Ltd. Catalogue no: **URBA 17**

RAPP PLAYBACK
Tracks: / Rapp playback.
12" Single: Released Jan '81, on RCA, by BMG Records (UK). Deleted '84. Catalogue no: **RCAT 28**
7" Single: Released Jan '81, on RCA, by BMG Records (UK). Deleted '84. Catalogue no: **RCA 28**

REGRETS
Tracks: / Regrets / Stone cold drag.
7" Single: Released Feb '80, on Polydor, by Polydor Ltd. Deleted '83. Catalogue no: **POSP 121**

SEX MACHINE (SINGLE)
Tracks: / Sex machine.
CD 5": Released '88, on Polydor (Germany), by Polydor Ltd. Catalogue no: **883 923-2**

SHE'S THE ONE
Tracks: / She's the one / Funky president / Funky drummer.
7" Single: Released Jan '88, on Urban, by Polydor Ltd. Catalogue no: **URB 13**
12" Single: Released Jan '88, on Urban, by Polydor Ltd. Catalogue no: **URBX 13**

SOUL POWER (PART 1)
Tracks: / Soul power (part 1) / It's a man's man's man's world / King heroin (don't mess with heroin) (Extra track on 12" only) / Don't tell it (*=Extra track on 12" only).
12" Single: Released Apr '86, on Boiling Point, by Polydor Ltd. Catalogue no: **POSPX 783**
7" Single: Released Apr '86, on Boiling Point, by Polydor Ltd. Catalogue no: **POSP**

783

STATIC
Tracks: / Static / I'm real (US remix) / Static (full force def mix) (Only on 12" and CD single.).
12" Single: Released Aug '88, on Scotti Bros (USA), Catalogue no: **JSBX2**
7" Single: Released Aug '88, on Scotti Bros (USA), Catalogue no: **JSP 2**

STAY WITH ME
Tracks: / Stay with me / Smokin' and drinkin'.
7" Single: Released Feb '81, on RCA, by BMG Records (UK). Deleted Feb '84. Catalogue no: **RCA 44**

SUPERBAD
Tracks: / Superbad (Pt. I) / Superbad (Pt. II).
7" Single: Released Mar '87, on King (USA), Catalogue no: **45-6329**

TIME TO GET BUSY
Tracks: / Time to get busy.
7" Single: Released Oct '88, on Scotti Bros (USA), Catalogue no: **4Z9 081 30**

Brown, Jim

Biographical details: Brown, Jim. USA country singer James Edward Brown was born in Arkansas in 1934. A vocal trio with his sisters Ella Maxine and Bonnie, as 'The Borwn, or 'Jim Ed, Maxine and Bonnie Brown', had many country hits and one massive crossover: their cover of the 1948 international French hit *Les Trois Cloches* (by Edith Piaf and Les Compagnons de la Chanson), called *The Three Bells*, was number one in both the pop and country charts in the USA in 1959, as well as reaching the top ten in the USA R&B and the UK pop charts. Jim went solo in 1965 and continued having country hits; *Morning* in 1970 was covered in the UK by Val Doonican. Helen Cornelius (born in 1950 in Missouri) joined his roadshow and they had duet hits from 1976-82; she became a popluar solo act on the USA country circuit and also wrote songs which have been covered by Dottsy, Lynn Anderson, Jeannie C Riley and others. Donald Clarke, 24 August 1988..

CURE FOR FEVER
Tracks: / Cure for fever.
12" Single: Released Sep '84, on Studio Worx, Deleted '87. Catalogue no: **DLP 104**

IN TIME
Tracks: / In time.
12" Single: Released Oct '83, on Midnight Rock, Deleted '87. Catalogue no: **JT 6713**

Brown, Jocelyn

I WISH YOU WOULD
Tracks: / I wish you would.
7" Single: Released Sep '84, on 4th & Broadway, by Island Records. Catalogue no: **BRW 14**
12" Single: Released Oct '84, on 4th & Broadway, by Island Records. Catalogue no: **BRWX 14**
12" Single: Released Sep '84, on 4th & Broadway, by Island Records. Deleted '87. Catalogue no: **12 BRW 14**

LOVE'S GONNA GET YOU
Tracks: / Love's gonna get you / Love's gonna get you (fun house mix).
7" Single: Released Feb '86, on Warner Bros., by WEA Records. Catalogue no: **W 8889**
12" Single: Released Feb '86, on Warner Bros., by WEA Records. Deleted Jun '87. Catalogue no: **W 8889T**

SOMEBODY ELSE'S GUY
Tracks: / Somebody else's guy.
7" Single: Released Apr '84, on 4th & Broadway, by Island Records. Catalogue no: **BRW 5**
12" Single: Released Jul '88, on Vinyl Dreams (USA), by Prelude Records (USA). Catalogue no: **VNDD 1**
12" Single: Released Apr '84, on 4th & Broadway, by Island Records. Catalogue no: **12 BRW 5**

TO THROUGH
Tracks: / To through.
7" Single: Released Aug '85, on Excaliber, by Red Bus Records. Deleted '88. Catalogue no: **EXC 1400**
12" Single: Released Aug '85, on Excaliber, by Red Bus Records. Deleted '88. Catalogue no: **EXCL 1400**

Brown, Joe

Biographical details: Brown, Joe. A UK pop singer born in 1941 in Lincolnshire. He moved to London's East End at age 2, later playing and touring with Eddie Cochran, Gene Vincent, Johnny Cash etc. Producer Jack Good put him on TV and he had 12 chart hits 1960-73, including *I'm Henry VIII I Am* (a hit in the USA by Herman's Hermits). He also did instrumentals, rare then, such as *The Switch* and *Pop Corn*. He switched to contrived pop films and also appeared with Anna Neagle in the musical *Charley Girl* in the late '60s; he formed a country-style group Brown's Home Brew with his wife Vicki in the early '70s; he's now seen on TV game shows and adverts. Donald Clarke, 24 August 1988.
Born in Lincolnshire, UK, but raised in London, Joe Brown became involved in Britain's mid-fifties skiffle boom while in his mid-teens. In 1959 he was discovered by Jack Good, the champion of British pop television. Good employed him as a backing musician on his show *Boy Meets Girl*. brown sufficiently impressed Good in his capacity to progress quickly to a solo instrumental slot and then to spot on the show as a fully fledged singer and performer. Soon he began to make records, using his backing group, the Bruvvers. Brown's first chart single was a 1960 version of the standard *Darktown Strutter's Ball*, which reached No. 34 on the UK listings. His sales were sluggish over the next two years, during which time he achieved just two more minor hits. Then in 1962, he suddenly scored what was to be the biggest hit of his career. *A Picture Of You* reached No. 2 on the British chart and is the record that he is remembered for today. It was a very catchy pop number and a fine vehicle for Brown's amiable style. Although a competent singer and guitarist, he was as much known for his lighthearted personality as his image of a loveable Cockney. His blond crewcut was instantly recognisable. Within a year he had chalked up two further major UK hits: *It Only Took A Minute* (No. 6) and *That's What Love Will Do* (No. 3). In addition his LP *A Picture Of You* went to No. 3 and remained on the British chart for 39 weeks. It was followed by the *Joe Brown - Live* set, which also hit the Top 20. However it was no coincidence that his chart success began to subside in the summer of '63, at the same time as The Beatles and Gerry And The Pacemakers were beginning to dominate the charts. brown belonged to the old school of solo male singers a la Cliff, Marty Wilde and Adam Faith. The tide was now turning in favour of new British talent dominated by groups. Since 1963 Brown has returned to the charts with two minor UK hits : 1967's Beatles cover *With A Little Help From My Friends* (No. 32) and 1973's dreary ballad *Hey Mama* (No. 33). By this time he was concerntrating on acting, a field in which he was, and still is, able to make a steady living. (Bob MacDonald)..

DARKTOWN STRUTTERS' BALL, THE
Tracks: / Darktown strutters' ball.
7" Single: Released Mar '60, on Decca, by Decca Records. Deleted '63. Catalogue no: **F 11207**

GIVE US A BREAK
Tracks: / Give us a break.
7" Single: Released Sep '83, on BBC, by BBC Records & Tapes. Deleted '87. Catalogue no: **RESL 134**

HEY MAMA
Tracks: / Hey mama / Misty mountain.
7" Single: Released Apr '73, on Ammo, Deleted '76. Catalogue no: **AMO 101**
7" Single: Released Apr '81, on TFI, Catalogue no: **TFC 1**

HIGHLAND WIDOW'S LAMENT
Tracks: / Highland widow's lament / Silent night.
7" Single: Released Sep '80, on EMI, by EMI Records. Deleted '83. Catalogue no: **EMI 5117**

IT ONLY TOOK A MINUTE
Tracks: / It only took a minute.
7" Single: Released Nov '62, on Piccadilly, Deleted '65. Catalogue no: **7 N 35082**

LITTLE CHILDREN
Tracks: / Little children / Cooky & Lila.
7" Single: Released Nov '81, on Solid Gold (1), by Creole Records. Deleted '86. Catalogue no: **SGR 105**

NATURE'S TIME FOR LOVE
Tracks: / Nature's time for love.
7" Single: Released Jun '63, on Piccadilly, Deleted '66. Catalogue no: **7 N 35129**

PICTURE OF YOU, A (SINGLE)
Tracks: / Picture of you.
7" Single: Released May '62, on Pye, Deleted '65. Catalogue no: **7 N 35047**

SALLY ANN
Tracks: / Sally Ann.
7" Single: Released Sep '63, on Piccadilly, Deleted '66. Catalogue no: **7 N 35138**

SHINE
Tracks: / Shine.
7" Single: Released Jan '61, on Pye, Deleted '64. Catalogue no: **7 N 15322**

THAT'S WHAT LOVE WILL DO
Tracks: / That's what love will do.
7" Single: Released Feb '63, on Piccadilly, Deleted '66. Catalogue no: **7 N 35106**

WHAT A CRAZY WORLD WE'RE LIVING IN
Tracks: / What a crazy world we're living in.
7" Single: Released Jan '62, on Pye, Deleted '65. Catalogue no: **7 N 35024**

WITH A LITTLE HELP FROM MY FRIENDS
Tracks: / With a little help from my friends.
7" Single: Released Jun '67, on Pye, Deleted '70. Catalogue no: **7 N 17339**

YOUR TENDER LOOK
Tracks: / Your tender look.
7" Single: Released Sep '62, on Pye, Deleted '65. Catalogue no: **7 N 35058**

Brown, June

JUNGLE BEWARE
Tracks: / Jungle beware.
12" Single: Released Feb '85, on Bolts, by Bolts Records. Deleted Jan '87. Catalogue no: **BOLTS 1**

LONDON
Tracks: / Where Is Love? / London.
7" Single: Released Jan '87, on MBS, by MBS Records. Catalogue no: **MBS 2064**

Brown, Junior

KNOCK KNOCK KNOCK
Tracks: / Knock knock knock.
12" Single: Released Apr '84, on London Gemi, Catalogue no: **LG 002**

LONG TIME ME CALL YOU
Tracks: / Long time me call you.
12" Single: Released Dec '83, on Fashion, by Fashion Records. Catalogue no: **FAD 017**

LOVE ME DARLING
Tracks: / Love me darling.
12" Single: Released Nov '85, on Natty Congo, Catalogue no: **NCDM 030**

MY DEVOTION
Tracks: / My devotion / People.
12" Single: Released Dec '82, on CSA, by CSA Records. Deleted '88. Catalogue no: **SPCSA 12001**

OH NO NOT MY BABY
Tracks: / Oh no not my baby.
12" Single: Released Oct '85, on Broadway, Catalogue no: **BY 1**

REGGAE MELODY
Tracks: / Reggae melody / Cool off.
10" single: Released Nov '82, on Roots Music, Catalogue no: **RM 002**

ROCKERS
Tracks: / Rockers / My devotion dub.
12" Single: Released Apr '82, on Solid Groove, Catalogue no: **SG 010**

SHOW THE YOUTH THE WAY
Tracks: / Show the youth the way.
12" Single: Released Dec '81, on Kingdom, by Kingdom Records. Deleted '83. Catalogue no: **KV 8021 12**

WARRIOR
Tracks: / Warrior.
12" Single: Released Apr '82, on Jah Shaka, Catalogue no: **SHAKA 22**

Brown, Laverne

I GOT THE WILL
Tracks: / I got the will / Georgia on my mind / You got your finger in my eye / That driving beat.
7" EP: Released May '81, on Big Beat, by Ace Records. Deleted '88. Catalogue no: **SW 68**

WORDS ARE IMPOSSIBLE
Tracks: / Words are impossible / Hey girl.
7" Single: Released May '82, on Chiswick-Ace, by Ace Records. Catalogue no: **DICE 6**

Brown, Leroy

IT'S ALL RIGHT
Tracks: / It's all right / It's all right (part 2).
7" Single: Released Sep '80, on Creole, by Creole Records. Deleted '83. Catalogue no: **CR 206**
12" Single: Released Sep '80, on Creole, by Creole Records. Deleted '83. Catalogue no: **CR 12-206**
7" Single: Released Sep '80, on Creole, by Creole Records. Catalogue no: **CR 206**
12" Single: Released Sep '80, on Creole, by Creole Records. Catalogue no: **CR 12-206**

TAXI
Tracks: / Taxi.
12" Single: Released Jan '85, on Revue, by Creole Records. Catalogue no: **REV 010T**

Brown, Maxine

IT'S TORTURE
Tracks: / It's torture / I got love

7" Single: Released Mar '86, on Kent, by Ace Records. Catalogue no: **TOWN 110**

Brown, Milton

FALLING FROM A GREAT HEIGHT
Tracks: / Falling from a great height / Falling from a great height (inst.).

7" Single: Released Mar '87, on Nightmare, by Nightmare Records. Catalogue no: **MARES 15**
12" Single: Released Mar '87, on Nightmare, by Nightmare Records. Catalogue no: **MARE 15**

Brown, Miquel

Biographical details: Born in Detroit, USA, Miquel Brown (pronounced 'Michael' Brown) began a successful career as an actress in 1973, spending much of her time in Britain. In '74 she appeared in the film 'Rollerball' and the London West End atage production of *Hair*, She later appeared on the British TV shows 'Seaside Special' and 'Supersonic' and the movies 'Superman' and 'Superman II'. Brown released her first single *So Many Men So Little Time* in 1983. While not a pop hit, it became an anthem in gay discos. It was in this regard particularly well received in the UK, where it was at the forefront of the burgeoning Hi-NRG scene - a boom that produced its own mini-industry of cliched po/dance records with homosexual overtones. UK magazine Record Mirror's weekly Hi-NRG specialist Top 30 showed Brown's in its higher echelons for several months. It was followed by her debut album *Manpower* and , in '84, a highly successful repetition of the *So Many Men* acclaim with the single *He's A Saint, He's A Sinner*. It was written and produced by Ian Levine and Fiachra Trench, the team responsible for the genre's greatest anthem: Evelyn Thomas' *High Energy*. Miquel Brown, a singer with strong pop potential, benefited from the great paradox of the gay clubs: that most of the homosexual hits about 'My Man', 'Him' etc., were performed by female artists. She is now permanently resident in the UK. (Bob MacDonald)..

BLACK LEATHER
Tracks: / Black leather.
12" Single: Released Sep '84, on Record Shack, by Record Shack Records. Catalogue no: **SOHOT 27**

CLOSE TO PERFECTION(SINGLE)
Tracks: / Close to perfecion.
12" Single: Released Feb '88, on Record Shack, by Record Shack Records. Catalogue no: **SOHOB 8**
12" Single: Released Aug '85, on Record Shack, by Record Shack Records. Catalogue no: **SOHOT 48**
7" Single: Released Aug '85, on Record Shack, by Record Shack Records. Catalogue no: **SOHO 48**

FOOTPRINTS IN THE SAND
Tracks: / Footprints in the sand (Inst.) / Footprints in the sand.
7" Single: Released Jan '87, on Nitemare, Catalogue no: **MARES 5**
12" Single: Released Jan '87, on Nightmare, by Nightmare Records. Catalogue no: **MARE 5**

HE'S A SAINT HE'S A SINNER
Tracks: / He's a saint, he's a sinner.
7" Single: Released Feb '84, on Record Shack, by Record Shack Records. Catalogue no: **SOHO 15**
12" Single: Released Feb '84, on Record Shack, by Record Shack Records. Catalogue no: **SOHOT 15**

ON THE RADIO
Tracks: / On the radio.
7" Single: Released Nov '85, on Record Shack, by Record Shack Records. Catalogue no: **SOHO 59**
12" Single: Released Nov '85, on Record Shack, by Record Shack Records. Catalogue no: **SOHOT 59**

SO MANY MEN SO LITTLE TIME
Tracks: / So many men so little time / Man power.
7" Single: Released Jun '83, on Record Shack, by Record Shack Records. Catalogue no: **SOHO 6**
7" Single: Released Apr '84, on Record Shack, by Record Shack Records. Catalogue no: **SOHO 17**
12" Single: Released Feb '88, on Record Shack, by Record Shack Records. Catalogue no: **SOHOB 1**
12" Single: Released Apr '84, on Record Shack, by Record Shack Records. Catalogue no: **SOHOT 17**
12" Single: Released Jun '83, on Record Shack, by Record Shack Records. Catalogue no: **SOHOT 6**

Brown, Neville

I'M A SUPERMAN
Tracks: / I'm a superman / Say forward.
12" Single: Released Mar '85, on Negus Roots, Catalogue no: **NERT 023**

Brown, Noreen

I'D RATHER GO BLIND
Tracks: / I'd rather go blind.
12" Single: Released Apr '85, on Three Kings, Catalogue no: **TK 026**

Brown, O'Chi

100% PURE PAIN
Tracks: / 100% pure pain / I just want to be loved.
7" Single: Released Jul '86, on Magnet, by WEA Records. Deleted Jan '88. Catalogue no: **MAG 296**
12" Single: Released Aug '86, on Magnet,

by WEA Records. Deleted Jan '87. Catalogue no: **MAGT 296R**
12" Single: Released Jul '86, on Magnet, by WEA Records. Deleted Jan '88. Catalogue no: **MAGT 296**

CAN'T SAY GOODBYE TO YOU
Tracks: / Can't say goodbye to you.
7" Single: Released May '88, on Angstar, by Angstar Records. Catalogue no: **CGDD 19**
12" Single: Released May '82, on Carib Jems, Catalogue no: **CGDD 19**

I GOT A FEELING
Tracks: / I got a feeling / Lady / Another broken heart (Extra track available on 12" version only.).
7" Single: Released Aug '87, on Magnet, by WEA Records. Deleted Jan '88. Catalogue no: **OCHI 5**
12" Single: Released Aug '87, on Magnet, by WEA Records. Deleted Jun '88. Catalogue no: **OCHIT 5**

LEARNING TO LIVE (WITHOUT YOUR LOVE)
Tracks: / Learning to live (without your love) / Another broken heart.
7" Single: Released Oct '87, on Magnetic Dance, by Magnet Records. Deleted '87. Catalogue no: **MAGD 7**
12" Single: Released Oct '87, on Magnetic Dance, by Magnet Records. Deleted '87. Catalogue no: **MAGDT 7**

ROCK YOUR BABY (EDIT)
Tracks: / Rock your baby (edit) / Another broken heart.
7" Single: Released Feb '87, on Magnet, by WEA Records. Deleted Jan '88. Catalogue no: **OCHI 4**
12" Single: Released Feb '87, on Magnet, by WEA Records. Deleted Jan '88. Catalogue no: **OCHIT 4**

TWO HEARTS BEATING AS ONE
Tracks: / Two hearts beating as one.
12" Single: Released Oct '86, on Magnet, by WEA Records. Deleted Jun '88. Catalogue no: **MAGT 297**
7" Single: Released Oct '86, on Magnet, by WEA Records. Deleted Jan '88. Catalogue no: **MAG 297**

UNCHAINED MELODY
Tracks: / Unchained melody / If I'm crying.
7" Single: Released Jun '84, on DBM, Catalogue no: **DBM 1**

WHENEVER YOU NEED SOMEBODY
Tracks: / Whenever you need somebody (umbungo mix) / Whenever you need somebody (pull it off mix) / Whenever you need somebody / Whenever you need somebody (on 12" single).
12" Single: Released Dec '87, on Magnet, by WEA Records. Deleted Jun '88. Catalogue no: **MAGDT 9**

WHITER SHADE OF PALE
Tracks: / Whiter shade of pale, A / When I'm crying.
7" Single: Released Sep '83, on Romantic, Catalogue no: **RR 005**
12" Single: Released Sep '83, on Romantic, Catalogue no: **RR 005T**

WHY CAN'T WE BE FRIENDS?
Tracks: / Why can't we be friends.
12" Single: Released Jul '85, on DBM, Deleted '87. Catalogue no: **12DBM 009**
7" Single: Released Jul '85, on DBM, Deleted Jan '88. Catalogue no: **DBM 009**

Brown, Patrick

ON THE RIGHT TRACK
Tracks: / On the right track.
12" Single: Released Oct '84, on Kufe, Catalogue no: **EB 003**

Brown, Paul

WE'RE HAVIN' FUN
Tracks: / We're havin' fun.
7" Single: Released Jun '84, on Carrere, Catalogue no: **CAR 311**
12" Single: Released Jun '84, on Carrere, Catalogue no: **CART 311**

Brown, Peter

BABY GETS HIGH
Tracks: / Baby gets high.
7" Single: Released Feb '83, on RCA, by BMG Records (UK). Catalogue no: **RCA 317**

CAN'T BE LOVE
Tracks: / Can't be love / Do it to me anyway / West of the North Star.
12" Single: Released 20 Jul '80, on TK, Deleted '83. Catalogue no: **TKR 13 7580**
7" Single: Released 20 Jul '80, on TK, Deleted '83. Catalogue no: **TKR 7580**

DANCE WITH ME
Tracks: / Dance with me.
7" Single: Released Jun '78, on TK, Deleted '81. Catalogue no: **TKR 6027**

DO YA WANNA GET FUNKY WITH ME
Tracks: / Do ya wanna get funky with me.
7" Single: Released May '82, on TK, Catalogue no: **CBS 8870**

7" Single: Released Feb '78, on TK, Deleted '81. Catalogue no: **TKR 6009**

LOVE IN OUR HEARTS
Tracks: / Love in our hearts / Penguins.
7" Single: Released Jan '80, on TK, Deleted Jan '85. Catalogue no: **TKR 7572**

STARGAZER
Tracks: / Stargazer / West of the north star.
7" Single: Released May '80, on TK, Deleted May '85. Catalogue no: **TKR 7579**

THEY ONLY COME OUT AT NIGHT
Tracks: / They only come out at night.
12" Single: on CBS, by CBS Records. Catalogue no: **TA 4334**
7" Single: Released Jul '87, on CBS, by CBS Records. Catalogue no: **A 4334**

Brown, Polly

Biographical details: This British pop singer came to fame in 1970 as lead singer with Pickettywitch a group who enjoyed three British hits that year. The biggest of these was *That Same Old Feeling* (No. 5). In the mid-Seventies she returned briefly to the spotlight with two further successes. She was 50% of a duo called 'Sweet Dreams', who reached No. 10 in the UK with the Abba song *Honey, Honey*. This choice of song was shrewd, in view of the fact that the Swedish quartet had recently won the Eurovision Song Contest and scored an international No. 1 with *Waterloo*. The Sweet Dreams single went 22 places higher in the British charts than Abba's own follow-up to *Waterloo*, *Ring Ring* and Abba later admited that they should have released *Honey Honey* instead of *Ring Ring*. For ten years the Sweet Dreams 45 remained the only Abba cover version to make the British Chart; Blancmange came out with the second in 1984. Polly Brown's other mid-Seventies hit was a one-off solo success called *Up In A Puff Of Smoke*. This peaked at No. 43 in the UK but then proceded to reach No. 16 in the US, her only major American success. Brown continued recording for many years, but with no further luck. Her voice and talent were simply too lightweight to sustain a prolonged chart career. (Bob MacDonald)..

BELIEVE IN ME
Tracks: / Believe in me / Never dare to love.
7" Single: Released Oct '82, on Witch, by Witch Records. Catalogue no: **POL 5**

BEWITCHED
Tracks: / Bewitched / Writing you a letter.
7" Single: Released Aug '80, on Witch, by Witch Records. Catalogue no: **POL 1**
12" Single: Released Aug '80, on Witch, by Witch Records. Catalogue no: **POL 1-12**

I'LL NEVER BE THE SAME
Tracks: / I'll never be the same / Stop and start.
7" Single: Released Feb '82, on Witch, by Witch Records. Catalogue no: **POL 3**

LOVE TO GIVE
Tracks: / Love to give / High society.
7" Single: Released Oct '81, on Mint, by Emerald Records. Deleted '88. Catalogue no: **CHEW 55**

PRECIOUS ME
Tracks: / Precious me.
7" Single: Released May '81, on Witch, by Witch Records. Catalogue no: **POL 2**

PRECIOUS TO ME
Tracks: / Precious to me / Never dared to love.
7" Single: Released May '81, on Pinnacle, by Pinnacle Records. Deleted May '84. Catalogue no: **PO 12**

UP IN A PUFF OF SMOKE
Tracks: / Up in a puff of smoke.
7" Single: Released Sep '74, on GTO, Deleted '77. Catalogue no: **GT 2**

YOU'VE GOT IT ALL
Tracks: / You've got it all / Starting all over again.
7" Single: Released Oct '81, on Rooster (Europe), by Rooster Records. Catalogue no: **ROO 101**

Brown, Randy

ARE YOU LONELY
Tracks: / Are you lonely.
12" Single: Released Jul '88, on Threeway, Catalogue no: **WAY 103 T**

WE OUGHT TO BE DOING IT
Tracks: / We ought to be doing it / Things I could do to you / You're so good (Available on 12" only.) / I wanna make love to you (Available on 12" only.) / You make me happy (Available on 12" only).
7" Single: Released Mar '80, on Casablanca, by PolyGram UK Ltd. Deleted Mar '83. Catalogue no: **CAN 190**
12" Single: Released Mar '80, on Casablanca, by PolyGram UK Ltd. Deleted Mar '83. Catalogue no: **CANL 190**

Brown, Roy

Biographical details: Brown, Roy An R&B

SAM BROWN - CAN I GET A WITNESS (Released on A & M)

singer from New Orleans (1925-81). He recorded his own *Good Rockin' Tonight* for De Luxe in 1948, covered by Wynonie Harris on King, later by Elvis Presley on Sun; *Boogie At Midnight* was a no. 3 R&B hit in 1949, then *Hard Luck Blues* was no. 1 in 1950, followed by more hits. He switched to King in 1952 and had less luck, though always a popular act; then to Imperial in 1956, teaming with Dave Bartholemew for a cover of Buddy Knox's *Party Doll* which was a no. 14 R&B hit in 1957, and reached the pop Hot 100; *Let The Four Winds Blow* was a pop top 40 the same year; he later joined the Johnny Otis review and re-formed his own band in the late '70s. Donald Clarke, 24 August 1988.

CONDOM SONG, THE
Tracks: / Condom song, The / Love is.
7" Single: Released Jul '88, on Rio, by Rio Records. Catalogue no: **RDS 4**
12" Single: Released Jul '88, on Rio, by Rio Records. Catalogue no: **72 RDS 4**

Brown, Roy 'Chubby'

I'M LOOKING SICK
Tracks: / I'm looking sick / Gossamer.
7" Single: Released Jan '82, on Really Rude, by Neat Records. Catalogue no: **FU 2**

Brown, Rula

I DON'T WANNA LIVE MY LIFE WITHOUT YOU
Tracks: / I don't wanna live my life without you / Reggae down on it.
12" Single: Released Dec '84, on Revue, by Creole Records. Catalogue no: **REV 018T**

Brown, Russ

GOTTA FIND A WAY
Tracks: / Gotta find a way.
7" Single: Released Apr '86, on 10 Records, by Virgin Records. Deleted '86. Catalogue no: **TEN 122**
12" Single: Released Sep '87, on Jump St (USA), Deleted Oct '87. Catalogue no: **JS 1001**
12" Single: Released Apr '86, on 10 Records, by Virgin Records. Deleted '86. Catalogue no: **TENT 122**

TAKE MY LOVE
Tracks: / Take my love / Got to find a way.
7" Single: Released Jun '87, on 10 Records, by Virgin Records. Deleted May '88. Catalogue no: **TEN 182**
12" Single: Released Jun '87, on 10 Records, by Virgin Records. Deleted May '88. Catalogue no: **TENT 182**

Brown, Sam

CAN I GET A WITNESS (see panel above)
Tracks: / Can I get a witness / Walking after midnight.
CD 5": Released May '89, on A&M, by A&M Records. Catalogue no: **AMCD 509**
CD 5": Released 8 May '89, on A&M, by A&M Records. Catalogue no: **CDEE 509**
Cassingle: Released May '89, on A&M, by A&M Records. Catalogue no: **AMCS 509**
7" Single: Released Jun '89, on A&M, by

BROWN SAUCE - I WANNA BE A WINNER (Released on BBC)

A&M Records. Catalogue no: **AMS 509**
7" Single: Released 8 May '89, on A&M, by A&M Records. Catalogue no: **AM 509**
12" Single: Released Jun '89, on A&M, by A&M Records. Catalogue no: **AMT 509**
12" Single: Released 8 May '89, on A&M, by A&M Records. Catalogue no: **AMY 509**
12" Single: Released Jun '89, on A&M, by A&M Records. Catalogue no: **AMT 509**

STOP (SINGLE)
Tracks: / Stop / Blue soldier.
CD 5": Released Jan '89, on A&M, by A&M Records. Catalogue no: **AMCD 440**
7" Single: Released Apr '88, on A&M, by A&M Records. Catalogue no: **AM 440**
12" Single: Released Apr '88, on A&M, by A&M Records. Catalogue no: **AMY 440**

WALKING BACK TO ME
Tracks: / Walking back to me / Tender hearts.
CD 5": Released Feb '88, on A&M, by A&M Records. Catalogue no: **AMCD 432**
7" Single: Released 29 Feb '88, on A&M, by A&M Records. Catalogue no: **AM 432**
12" Single: Released 29 Feb '88, on A&M, by A&M Records. Catalogue no: **AMY 432**

Brown Sauce

Biographical details: This British vocal group consisted of Keith Chegwin, Noel Edmonds and Maggie philbin. They were the presenters of the long-running BBC TV Saturday morning children's show "Multi-coloured Swapshop". In October 1981 they released a novelty single entitled *I Wanna Be A Winner* under the name Brown Sauce, though no attempt was made to conceal the identities of the trio. Penned by Scottish hit maker and songwriter B.A. Robertson, it was a catchy and amusing expression of the desire for success, employing numerous topical references. It proved to Robertson's last major chart success for some time. The single was a sleeper hit, peaking at No. 15 on the UK chart at the end of january '82 and staying on the list for 12 weeks. This record was a hit as the "Swapshop" programme was nearing the end of its life. When chief presenter Noel Edmonds announced his desire to leave the show, a clone programme under the name "Saturday Superstore" was devised. It was hosted by Mike Read who, like his predecessor, had become a household name through presenting BBC Radio One's weekday breakfast show. The next twelve months brought varying fortunes for the defunct Brown Sauce - Chegwin and Philbin became husband and wife, while Edmonds divorced his wife Jill. (Bob MacDonald)..

I WANNA BE A WINNER (see panel on previous page)
Tracks: / I wanna be a winner / Hello Hello.
7" Single: Released Dec '81, on BBC, by BBC Records & Tapes. Deleted '84. Catalogue no: **RESL 101**

Brown, Sharon

Biographical details: This British singer scored a huge winner in discos in 1982 with *I Specialise In Love*. This dynamite dance disc also reached No. 38 on the UK pop charts. The follow-up single *Love Don't Hurt People* did not make nearly as much impact and Brown faded from public attention. (Bob MacDonald)..

I SPECIALISE IN LOVE
Tracks: / I specialise in love / I specialise in love (instrumental).
7" Single: Released Aug '85, on Virgin, by Virgin Records. Deleted '86. Catalogue no: **VS 494**
12" Single: Released Aug '85, on Virgin, by Virgin Records. Catalogue no: **VS 494-12**

I SPECIALISE IN LOVE (OLD GOLD)
Tracks: / I specialise in love / This beat is mine.
12" Single: Released 27 Feb '89, on Old Gold, by Old Gold Records. Catalogue no: **OG 4100**

LOVE DON'T HURT PEOPLE
Tracks: / Love don't hurt people / Unexpected.
7" Single: Released Aug '82, on Virgin, by Virgin Records. Deleted '89. Catalogue no: **VS 535**
12" Single: Released Aug '82, on Virgin, by Virgin Records. Deleted '89. Catalogue no: **VS 535-12**

Brown, Shirley

BOYFRIEND (see panel on right)
Tracks: / Boyfriend / Looking for the real thing.
7" Single: Released Jul '85, on 4th & Broadway, by Island Records. Catalogue no: **BRW 31**
12" Single: Released Jul '85, on 4th & Broadway, by Island Records. Deleted '87. Catalogue no: **12 BRW 31**

LOVE FEVER
Tracks: / Love fever.
7" Single: Released Jun '85, on 4th & Broadway, by Island Records. Catalogue no: **BRW 27**
12" Single: Released Jun '85, on 4th & Broadway, by Island Records. Catalogue no: **12 BRW 27**

WOMAN TO WOMAN (SINGLE)
Tracks: / Woman to woman.
7" Single: Released Mar '82, on Stax, by Fantasy Inc (USA). Catalogue no: **STAX 1010**
7" Single: Released 13 Jun '87, on Stax, by Fantasy Inc (USA). Catalogue no: **STAX 806**

Brown, Steven

LAST RENDEZVOUS, THE
Tracks: / Last rendezvous, The.
7" Single: Released 20 Jun '87, on Play It Again Sam(Belgium), by Play It Again Sam (Belgium). Catalogue no: **BIAS 066**

ME & YOU & THE LICORICE STICK
Tracks: / Me & you & the licorice stick.
12" Single: Released Jul '87, on Sub Rosa, by Sub Rosa Records. Catalogue no: **SUB 12002 4**

Brown Sugar

GO NOW
Tracks: / Go now.
12" Single: Released Jul '83, on El Jay, Catalogue no: **LJ 02**

Brown, T. Graham

Biographical details: Brown, T Graham An interesting country/soul performer who has served a considerable aprenticeship on the road. He does not call himself Tony Brown because that name is being used by a top country producer and A&R man at MCA. T Graham has a road band called the Hardtops, and he should probably be recording with them and with the other Tony Brown: unfortunately, his debut Capitol albums are badly overproduced, with the usual too-loud and unsymathetic rock drums obviously recorded in another room and on a different track. The producer is Bud Logan. Donald Clarke, 24 August 1988..

BRILLIANT CONVERSATIONALIST (SINGLE)
Tracks: / Brilliant conversationalist.
7" Single: Released Sep '87, on Capitol, by EMI Records. Deleted Apr '88. Catalogue no: **CL 470**

POWER OF LOVE, THE
Tracks: / Power of love, The / Save that dress / Brilliant conversationalist*.
Note: *Track on 12in single only. (P) 1987 original sound recording(s) made by Capitol-Records Inc.
CD 5": Released Jun '88, on Capitol, by EMI Records. Deleted Nov '88. Catalogue no: **CDCL 494**
7" Single: Released Jun '88, on EMI, by EMI Records. Deleted Nov '88. Catalogue no: **CL 494**
12" Single: Released Jun '88, on EMI, by EMI Records. Deleted Nov '88. Catalogue no: **12CL 494**

ROCK IT BILLY
Tracks: / Rock it, Billy / Later train.
7" Single: Released May '87, on Capitol, by EMI Records. Deleted Oct '87. Catalogue no: **CL 449**

Brown, Teddy

BAD MAN WAGON
7" Single: Released '87, on UNKNOWN, Deleted Jun '89. Catalogue no: **TRI 3421**

Brown, U

ME CHAT YOU ROCK
Tracks: / Me chat you rock.
12" Single: on Trojan, by Trojan Records. Deleted May '88. Catalogue no: **TRT 9070**

OUT OF HAND
Tracks: / Out of hand.
12" Single: Released Aug '82, on Taxi (1), Catalogue no: **TX 04**

THINGS A COME UP TO GO BUMP
12" Single: Released Sep '83, on Midnight Rock, Catalogue no: **MR 014**

Brown, Veda

SHORT STOPPING
Tracks: / Short stopping.
7" Single: Released Aug '87, on Stax, by Fantasy Inc (USA). Catalogue no: **STAX 812**
7" Single: Released Mar '82, on Stax, by Fantasy Inc (USA). Catalogue no: **STAX 1007**

Brown, Vicki

CAN IT LET GO
Tracks: / Can it let go / Once again / Look at me.
Note: * 12" version only.
7" Single: Released 6 Jun '88, on Ariola, by BMG Records (UK). Deleted May '89. Catalogue no: **PB 41537**
12" Single: Released 6 Jun '88, on Ariola, by BMG Records (UK). Deleted May '89. Catalogue no: **PT 41538**

Brown, Winston

AFRICA
Tracks: / Africa.
12" Single: Released '86, on Fashion, by Fashion Records. Catalogue no: **FAD 046**

SAFER WITH YOU
Tracks: / Safer with you.
12" Single: Released 13 Jun '87, on Fine Style, by Fashion Records. Catalogue no: **FS 011**

Brown, Yvonne

MY WORLD IS EMPTY WITHOUT YOU
Tracks: / My world is empty without you / Going down.
12" Single: Released Apr '84, on Buzz Int., Catalogue no: **VIBE 3T**

Browne, Duncan

JOURNEY
Tracks: / Journey.
7" Single: Released Sep '72, on RAK, by EMI Records. Deleted '75. Catalogue no: **RAK 135**

TRAVELLING MAN, THEME FROM
Tracks: / Travelling man, Theme from / Andrea's theme.
7" Single: Released Jul '85, on Towerbell, Catalogue no: **TOW 64**

Browne, Jackson

Biographical details: Browne, Jackson. A USA singer-songwriter who was born in Heidelberg, West Germany in 1948. He began writing and performing in Los Angeles in the early '60s, where the Nitty Gritty Dirt Band recorded his songs; he went to New York in '67 and gained a residency at Andy Warhol's Dom Club; by the end of the '70s his songs had been covered by Nico, the Byrds, Tom Ruch, Bonnie Raitt, Linda Ronstadt, Moving Hearts, the Eagles and the Jackson 5: his own first single *Doctor My Eyes* was a top 10 USA hit in '72, and a UK hit by the Jacksons in '73. His wife committed suicide in 1976, casting a shadow over his album *The Pretender* that year: its title track is perhaps his best song ever (covered by Gary 'US' Bonds on his comeback *Dedication*). All of his albums have charted strongly in the USA, four in the top 10 including *Hold Out* at no. 1; four have charted in the UK, where foolish critics have characterised him as 'chilled white wine': he is an active anti-nuke campaigner, but at least he doesn't waste his time supporting miners' strikes. He has also produced some albums for Warren Zevon, David Lindley, etc. Donald Clarke, 24 August 1988.

Born in Germany but brought up in Los Angeles, this American singer, songwriter and guitarist became well known in the music business in the late Sixties as a promising up and coming young writer. His songs were recorded by such cult artists as Johnny Rivers, Nico, the Nitty Gritty Dirt band and Tom Rush. He released his first album in his own right in 1971. Under the curious title *Jackson Browne (saturate before using)*, this critically acclaimed (though commercially unsuccessful) album contained songs that had mostly already been covered by other artists; all were in a poetic country-rock vein. 1972 brought Browne to public attention via the US singles chart. *Doctor My Eyes* gave him his first Top 40 hit, climbing to No. 8. It was quickly folowed by the US No. 12 placing of *Take It Easy*, the first hit for The Eagles. Browne wrote that song in collaboration with the band's Glenn Frey, thus highlighting the similarities of two acts whose styles had much in common with one another. Both came to epitomise the folk/country-tinged sound of Seventies West Coast soft rock. It was a style that Britain was very slow to catch on to, so neither single entered the UK charts. Browne was however, compensated the following year when - of all people - the Jackson Five took *Doctor My Eyes* into the British Top 10. The sound of the Jacksons playing Jackson, was an eloquent display of the strength of Browne's writing; he has also seen his material recorded by Joan Baez and Joe Cocker, so the range is diverse. Browne's own rendition of *Take It Easy* appeared on 1973's *Fo Everyman* LP. Once again this album appealed more to the press than to the public despite his singles success. It was the '74 se *Late For The Sky* that began to break him in the States. The 1976 suicide of his wife delayed his next offering *The Pretender* until the end of that year. This LP was, for many the best achievement of his career. It combined fine playing with sharply focused lyrics, these running the gamut of persona human experiences. *The Pretende* reached No. 5 in the US and also gave Browne his first UK chart album, peaking a No. 26. The rocky *Here Come Those Tear Again* provided him with his second American Top 40 single. 1978's *Running O Empty* was an unusual semi-studio/semi-live album, recorded while on the road. The title song reached No. 11 on the US singles chart. The British public went for *Stay* which reached No. 12, becoming the only UK h single of Browne's career. This was a delightful remake of the song that had been a Sixties hit for the Hollies (Britain) and th Four Seasons (America) and originall Maurice Williams & The Zodiacs (both countries). 1980's US No. 1 LP *Hold Out* yielde two American hits in the shape of Boulevar and *That Girl Could Sing*, but was not quit the great LP that the two previous sets ha been. In 1982 he achieved his bigges American single, reaching No. 7 wit *Somebody's Baby*, a track written for the fil soundtrack *Fast Times At Rigemont High* This was a much lighter, poppier song tha his usual material. A return to norm too place with the release of *Lawyers In Lov* the first 45 from his 1983 album of the sam name, which was traditional Browne fare That fare had made Jackson Browne one America's leading pop poets - though di missed as dated by the young generatio he has a consistent following amongst thos who grew up with the late Sixties and Seve ties West Coast sound. His compassiona and understanding lyrics have assured hi of a lasting place in the American mus industry. (Bob MacDonald)..

BOULEVARD
Tracks: / Boulevard / Call it a loan.
7" Single: Released Aug '80, on Electr Deleted Aug '83. Catalogue no: **K 12466**

DISCO APOCALYPSE
Tracks: / Disco apocalypse / Boulevard.
7" Single: Released Oct '80, on Elekt Asylum, by Elektra Records (USA). Delet

SHIRLEY BROWN - BOYFRIEND (Released on 4th & Broadway)

Oct '83. Catalogue no: **K 12479**

EGO MANIAC
Tracks: / Ego maniac / Love's gonna get you.
7" Single: Released Feb '87, on Warner Bros., by WEA Records. Deleted Jan '88. Catalogue no: **W 8698**
12" Single: Released Feb '87, on Warner Bros., by WEA Records. Deleted Jan '88. Catalogue no: **W 8698T**

FOR AMERICA
Tracks: / For America / Till I go down.
7" Single: Released Feb '86, on Elektra (USA), by Elektra Records (USA). Catalogue no: **EKR 35**

IN THE SHAPE OF A HEART
Tracks: / In the shape of a heart (edited remix) / Voice.
7" Single: Released '86, on Elektra (USA), by Elektra Records (USA). Deleted Jun '87. Catalogue no: **EKR 42**

LAWYERS IN LOVE (SINGLE)
Tracks: / Lawyers in love.
7" Single: Released Jul '83, on Elektra (USA), by Elektra Records (USA). Catalogue no: **E 9826**

STAY
Tracks: / Stay.
7" Single: Released Jul '78, on Asylum, by WEA Records. Deleted '81. Catalogue no: **K 13128**

Browne, Jamie

LET'S GET SERIOUS
Tracks: / Let's get serious.
12" Single: Released Nov '88, on Lucky, by Lucky Records. Catalogue no: **LSD 101**

Browne, Sam

LET'S FACE THE MUSIC & DANCE
Tracks: / Let's face the music & dance / Stormy weather.
7" Single: Released Mar '81, on World Records, by EMI Records. Deleted Mar '84. Catalogue no: **CXT 501**

Browne, Tom

Biographical details: This American jazzy rhythm and blues vocalist and trumpeter released his debut album in 1979. The critical acclaim received by the *Browne Sugar* set paved the way for the success of his second LP, 1980's *Love Approach*. It was boosted by the single *Funkin' For Jamaica (N.Y.)*, a slice of hard, meaty funk. It was a smash No. 1 on the US soul charts, but became one of the few black music chart toppers to fail to cross over to the American pop charts - it was unable to crack even the lower reaches of the Billboard Hot 100. Pop radio in the States was unwilling to give airplay to such an uncompromisingly funky track. No such problems existed, however, in Britain. The single went to No. 10 on the UK chart. Next came the album *Magic*, which yielded a minor British hit entitled *Thighs High (Grip Your Hips And Move)*. At the end of 1981 he issued the *Yours Truly* album. Once again their was a small UK hit single, the ludicrous title being *Fungi Mama (bebopafunkadiscocalypso)*. The electicism suggested by this single's sub-title was the feature of Browne's work that made him a consistently interesting artist. 1983's *Rockin' Radio* album continued the formula, as did the 1984 LP *Tommy Gun*. He was now associated with Maurice Starr, the writer and producer who had been responsible for recent records by New Edition and the Jonzun Crew. Several tracks on the latter LP were highly derivative, 'borrowing' from a number of familiar hit records. Browne was attempting to attract a more mainstream audience, while still keeping the specialist R&B and jazz enthusiasts happy. (Bob MacDonald)..

BYE GONES
Tracks: / Bye gones.
7" Single: Released '82, on Arista, by BMG Records (UK). Deleted '87. Catalogue no: **ARIST 462**
12" Single: Released '82, on Arista, by BMG Records (UK). Deleted '87. Catalogue no: **ARIST 12462**

FUNGI MAMA
Tracks: / Fungi mama / Funkin' for Jamaica / Come for a ride.
7" Single: Released Jan '82, on Arista, by BMG Records (UK). Deleted '85. Catalogue no: **ARIST 450**
12" Single: Released Apr '82, on Arista, by BMG Records (UK). Deleted '86. Catalogue no: **ARIST 12456**
12" Single: Released Jan '82, on Arista, by BMG Records (UK). Deleted '86. Catalogue no: **ARIST 12450**

FUNKIN' FOR JAMAICA
Tracks: / Funkin' for Jamaica / Her silent smile.
7" Single: Released '82, on Arista, by BMG Records (UK). Deleted '87. Catalogue no: **ARIST 357**
12" Single: Released '82, on Arista, by BMG Records (UK). Deleted '87. Catalogue no: **ARIST 12857**

FUNKIN' FOR JAMAICA (OLD GOLD)
Tracks: / Funkin' for Jamaica / Rockin' radio.
12" Single: Released Jan '88, on Old Gold, by Old Gold Records. Catalogue no: **OG 4042**

MAGIC
Tracks: / Magic / Midnight interlude.
7" Single: Released Jan '81, on Arista, by BMG Records (UK). Catalogue no: **ARIST 387**
12" Single: Released Jan '81, on Arista, by BMG Records (UK). Catalogue no: **ARIST 12 387**

THIGHS HIGH (GRIP YOUR HIPS AND MOVE)
Tracks: / Thighs high (grip your hips and move).
7" Single: Released Oct '80, on Arista, by BMG Records (UK). Deleted '83. Catalogue no: **ARIST 367**
12" Single: Released Oct '80, on Arista, by BMG Records (UK). Deleted '83. Catalogue no: **ARIST 12367**

Browne, Yasmine

BABY I'M IN LOVE
Tracks: / Baby I'm in love.
12" Single: Released Oct '88, on West Ferry, Catalogue no: **WF 1**

Brownmark

NEXT TIME
Tracks: / Next time / Next time (inst).
7" Single: Released Mar '88, on Motown, by BMG Records (UK). Catalogue no: **ZB 41773**
12" Single: Released Mar '88, on Motown, by BMG Records (UK). Catalogue no: **ZT 41774**

Browns

Biographical details: This American vocal trio consisted of Jim Edward Brown and his sistera Maxine and Bonnie. THis family group had sung together since childhood. Hailing from Arkansas, they hit it big in 1959 when they were all in their twenties. Their version of the quasi-religious *The Three Bells* soared to the US No. 1 position in that year and also reached No. 6 in the UK. This song had originally been composed in France in 1945 as *Les Trois Cloches*, with English lyrics added three years later. The French rendition was a major success for Edith Piaf in her native France and also for a vocal group called Les Compagnons de la Chanson; the latter version was issued in the Uk in late '59 to compete with the Browns, but peaked at No. 21. In both the UK and the US, it is the Browns' recording of this gentle, sentimental song (sub titled *The Jimmy Brown Song*) that is best remembered. They never hit again in Britain but scored two follow-up successes in their native America. *Scarlet Ribbons (For Her Hair)* peaked at No. 13, then *The Old lamplighter* reached No. 5 in the spring of 1960. During the sixties Jim Ed Brown became a solo country singer, but his sisters drifted into obscurity. (Bob MacDonald)..

THREE BELLS, THE
Tracks: / Three bells, The.
7" Single: Released Sep '59, on RCA, by BMG Records (UK). Deleted '62. Catalogue no: **RCA 1140**
7" Single: Released Nov '86, on Old Gold, by Old Gold Records. Catalogue no: **OG 9653**

Brown's Gazette

BLOW ME DOWN
Tracks: / Blow me down / Jimmy kept his head.
7" Single: Released 21 Nov '87, on Crook Cassettes, by Crook Cassettes. Catalogue no: **BG 1**

Brownsville Station

SMOKIN' IN THE BOYS ROOM
Tracks: / Smokin' in the boys room.
7" Single: Released Mar '74, on Philips, by Phonogram Ltd. Deleted '77. Catalogue no: **6073 834**

Brubeck, Dave

Biographical details: Born in California in 1920, this American pianist (real name David Warren) made his name as a top concert attraction in the late Forties and early Fifties, first on college campuses and later in the United States at large. The Dave Brubeck Quartet, an instrumental jazz combo, comprised Brubeck, alto saxophone player Paul Desmond, drummer Joe Morello and bassist Eugene Wright. Of the many albums and singles released by the group, the one that they are best known for is the Desmond-penned 1961 *Take Five*. This 45 reached No. 25 in the US and No. 6 in the UK. It was their only American Top 40 hit, but they managed two follow-ups in Britain: *It's A Raggy Waltz* (No. 36) and *Unsquare Dance*, a Brubeck composition which reached No. 14. Their two big-selling LPs of the period were *Time out* and *Time Further Out*. Brubeck's distinctive and original style continued to win him much respect amongst the jazz fraternity for many years. A British tribute was paid in 1981, when one of his tracks *Blue Rondo A La Turk* became the name of a marginally successful but highly fashionable London jazz-influenced pop group. (Bob MacDonald)..

IT'S A RAGGY WALTZ
Tracks: / It's a raggy waltz.
7" Single: Released Feb '62, on Fontana, by Phonogram Ltd. Deleted '65. Catalogue no: **H 352**

TAKE FIVE (SINGLE)
Tracks: / Take five.
7" Single: Released Oct '61, on Fontana, by Phonogram Ltd. Deleted '64. Catalogue no: **H 339**
7" Single: Released Apr '83, on Old Gold, by Old Gold Records. Catalogue no: **OG 9300**

UNSQUARE DANCE
Tracks: / Unsquare dance.
7" Single: Released May '62, on CBS, by CBS Records. Deleted '65. Catalogue no: **AAG 102**

Bruce & Bongo

GEIL
Tracks: / Geil / Geil (Bruce & Bongo dub).
7" Single: Released Jun '86, on Columbia, by EMI Records. Catalogue no: **DB 9135**
12" Single: Released Jun '86, on Columbia, by EMI Records. Catalogue no: **12DB 9135**

Bruce, Ed

DIANE
Tracks: / Diane.
7" Single: Released Apr '83, on MCA, by MCA Records. Catalogue no: **MCA 810**

Bruce, Jack

Biographical details: Born in Scotland, bass guitarist Jack Bruce first became known when he joined Alexis Corner's rhythm-and-blues band Blues Incorporated in 1962. He was one of three members to leave the group the following year when he, drummer Ginger Baker and organist Graham Bond formed the Graham Bond Organisation. They became a popular attraction on the London club circuit but failed to sell records. In 1965 Bruce and Baker left Bond and Bruce had brief stints with John Mayall's Bluesbreakers and Manfred Mann. Next year he joined Baker and guitarist Eric Clapton to form Cream, the legendary rock trio who won such acclaim that all three were assured of lasting places in rock history. Bruce co-wrote their biggest UK single, 1967's I Feel Free. He was the group's vocalist, in addition to his bass duties. On Cream's break-up in '69 Baker and Clapton became part of the short-lived supergroup Blind Faith. Meanwhile Bruce recorded a solo album, Songs For A Tailor, which became his only solo British chart LP, peaking at No 6 in the autumn of that year. The 70's saw him bringing in a number of blues/rock friends to join him in recording and performing. These included Graham Bond, Dick Heckstall-Smith, John McLaughlin, Chris Spedding and Tony Williams. Combinations of such guests joined Bruce in 1971's Things We Like and Harmony Row albums. A number of rock, jazz and blues offerings kept Jack Brice's name afloat in the music business (though not the charts) for the next 10 years. Two albums with guitarist Robin Trower were issued in the early 80's. Bruce is widely acknowledged as one of rock music's best and most innovative bassists, but he will always be best remembered for his work with Cream. (Bob MacDonald, 1984.)

Born in Scotland, UK, this bass guitarist first became well-known in 1962 when he joined Alexis Korner's R&B group Blues Incorporated. He was one of three members to leave the band in '63, when Bruce, drummer Ginger Baker and organist Graham Bond formed the Graham Bond Organisation. They became a popular attraction on the London club circuit, though failing to sell records. 1965 saw Bruce and Baker quit the GBO. The former then had brief stints with John Mayall's Bluesbreakers and Manfred mann. In 1966 Bruce joined guitarist Eric Clapton in forming Cream, the legendary trio who won such acclaim that all three members were assured of lasting places in rock history. Bruce co-wrote their biggest UK single, 1967's *I Feel Free*. he was the group's vocalist, in addition to his bass duties. Upon Cream's break-up in '69, baker and Clapton became part of the short-lived supergroup Blind Faith. Meanwhile, Bruce recorded a solo album *Songs For A Tailor*, which became his only solo UK chart LP, peaking at No. 6 in the autumn of that year. The Seventies saw him bringing in a number of blues/rock friends to assist his recording and performing career. These included Graham Bond, Dick Heckstall-Smith, John Mclaughlin, Chris Spedding and Tony Williams. Various combinations of such guests joined Bruce in 1971's *Things We Like* and *Harmony Row* LPs. A number of rock, jazz and blues offerings kept Jack Bruce's name afloat in the music business (though not the charts) throughout the next ten years. Two albums with guitarist Robert Trower were issued in the early Eighties. Bruce is widely acknowledged as one of rock music's best and innovative bassists, but will always be best remembered for his work with Cream, a success that he has never been really alble to follow up. (Bob MacDonald)..

I FEEL FREE
Tracks: / I feel free / Make love.
7" Single: Released Jun '86, on Virgin, by Virgin Records. Deleted May '88. Catalogue no: **VS 875**
12" Single: Released Jun '86, on Virgin, by Virgin Records. Deleted '89. Catalogue no: **VS 875-12**

Bruce, Tommy

AIN'T MISBEHAVIN'
Tracks: / Ain't misbehavin'.
7" Single: Released May '60, on Columbia, by EMI Records. Deleted '63. Catalogue no: **DB 4453**

BABETTE
Tracks: / Babette.
7" Single: Released Feb '62, on Columbia, by EMI Records. Deleted '65. Catalogue no: **DB 4776**

BROKEN DOLL
Tracks: / Broken doll.
7" Single: Released Sep '60, on Columbia, by EMI Records. Deleted '63. Catalogue no: **DB 4498**

Bruford, Bill

HELLS BELLS
Tracks: / Hells bells / Age of info.
7" Single: Released Apr '80, on Polydor, by Polydor Ltd. Deleted '83. Catalogue no: **EGEP 1**

Bruisers

BLUE GIRL
Tracks: / Blue girl.
7" Single: Released Aug '63, on Parlophone, by EMI Records. Deleted '66. Catalogue no: **R 5042**

Brummel, Beau

HOT GEORGE
Tracks: / Hot George.
7" Single: Released Sep '82, on Moonlight, by Lithon Recording & Music Publishing. Catalogue no: **MNS 004**

Brunel

DON'T CALL US, WE'LL CALL YOU
Tracks: / Don't call us, we'll call you / Heroes.
7" Single: Released Oct '82, on Monarch, by Monarch Records. Deleted Oct '85. Catalogue no: **MON 18**

Brunning, John Band

1991
Tracks: / 1991 / Syndrum syndrome.
7" Single: Released Jun '81, on Technical, by Technical Records. Deleted Jun '84. Catalogue no: **TECS 1**

DREAM POLICE
Tracks: / Dream police / Living in the EEC.
7" Single: Released Feb '83, on Technical, by Technical Records. Catalogue no: **TECS 2**

Brunson, Tyrone

Biographical details: American bass guitarist Brunson scored a minor instrumental hit in the UK at the end of 1983. *The Smurf* referred to a style of dancing which was mildly popular in discos at the time and had nothing to do with the cartoon variety brought to the charts by Father Abraham in the late 70's! Brunson's single was taken from his album *Sticky Situation*. (Bob MacDonald, 1984.).

SMURF
Tracks: / Smurf / I need love.
7" Single: Released Dec '82, on Epic, by CBS Records. Deleted Dec '85. Catalogue no: **EPC A3024**
12" Single: Released Dec '82, on Epic, by CBS Records. Deleted Dec '85. Catalogue no: **EPC A133024**

Brush Shiels

BETTER THAN I EXPECTED BUT NOT MUCH
Tracks: / Better than I expected but not much.
7" Single: Released Aug '80, on Bruised, Catalogue no: **BRU 001**

Brussels Sound

PUMP UP THE TWIST
Tracks: / Pump up the twist.
7" Single: Released 14 Aug '89, on Sound Of Belgium, Catalogue no: **SOB 74**
12" Single: Released 14 Aug '89, on Sound

Of Belgium, Catalogue no: **SOB 124**
CD 3": Released 14 Aug '89, on Sound Of Belgium, Catalogue no: **SOBCD 34**

Brutus

EXCITATION
Tracks: / Excitation.
7" Single: Released Jul '83, on Philly World (USA), by Philly World (USA). Catalogue no: **PWS 112**
12" Single: Released Jul '83, on Philly World (USA), by Philly World (USA). Catalogue no: **PWSL 112**

Brutus, Tony

WATER PISTOL
Tracks: / Water pistol.
12" Single: Released Jan '84, on Intense, by Intense Records. Catalogue no: **INT 013**

Bruzzz

SO REAL
Tracks: / So real / So real (version).
7" Single: Released Jun '88, on Madcap, Catalogue no: **MAD 5**

Bryan, Dora

ALL I WANT FOR CHRISTMAS IS A BEATLE
Tracks: / All I want for Christmas is a Beatle.
7" Single: Released Dec '63, on Fontana, by Phonogram Ltd. Deleted '66. Catalogue no: **TF 427**

Bryant, Anita

MY LITTLE CORNER OF THE WORLD
Tracks: / My little corner of the world.
7" Single: Released Oct '60, on London-American, Deleted '63. Catalogue no: **HLL 9171**

PAPER ROSES
Tracks: / Paper roses.
7" Single: Released May '60, on London-American, Deleted '63. Catalogue no: **HLL 9144**

Bryant, Leon

JUST THE WAY YOU LIKE
Tracks: / Just the way you like / Something more.
7" Single: Released May '81, on De-Lite, Deleted May '84. Catalogue no: **DE 3**
12" Single: Released May '81, on De-Lite, Deleted May '84. Catalogue no: **DEX 3**

Bryant, Ray

IT'S MADISON TIME
Tracks: / It's Madison time / Mama didn't lie / Foot stompin' (Available on 12" only.).
7" Single: Released Jul '88, on MCA, by MCA Records. Catalogue no: **MCA 1258**
12" Single: Released Jul '88, on MCA, by MCA Records. Catalogue no: **MCAT 1258**

Brynteg School

DALIWCH YMLAEN
Tracks: / Daliwch ymlaen.
7" Single: Released '88, on Popdy, by Popdy Cyf. Catalogue no: **POPDY RP11**

Bryson, Peabo

Biographical details: This American soul singer scored a number of successes on the UK black charts during the early Eighties, but came to prominence in 1983. This is when he teamed with well-known soul vocalist Roberta Flack for a duet single *Tonight I Celebrate my Love*, a song penned by two of America's best ballad writers, Gerry Goffin and Michael Masser. it was a major soul and pop hit on both sides of the Atlantic, particularly in Britain where it reached No. 2 on the national charts, thus becoming Flack's biggest and Bryson's first UK hit. A duet album called *Born To Love* was issued. Having thereby introduced his name into the pop market, Bryson decided to consolidate on his crossover success. This he did in the US (but not the UK) with 1984's single *If Ever You're In My Arms Again* which reached No. 10 on the Billboard Hot 100. This classy, melodic single was again written by some of the best composers in the middle-of-the-road genre: Michael Masser, Tom SNow and Cynthia Weil. It was taken from Bryson's album *Straight From The Heart*, a good outlet for the pleasant vocal style that will ensure a continuation of his steady US record sales. (Bob MacDonald)..

HEAVEN ABOVE ME
Tracks: / Heaven above me.
12" Single: Released Oct '83, on Capitol, by EMI Records. Deleted '88. Catalogue no: **12CL 310**
7" Single: Released Oct '83, on Capitol, by EMI Records. Deleted Jan '88. Catalogue no: **CL 310**

LET THE FEELING FLOW
Tracks: / Let the feeling flow / Move your body.
7" Single: Released Feb '82, on Capitol, by EMI Records. Deleted Feb '87. Catalogue no: **CL 236**

SHOW AND TELL
7" Single: Released Sep '89, on Capitol, by EMI Records. Catalogue no: **CL 544**
12" Single: Released Sep '89, on Capitol, by EMI Records. Catalogue no: **12CL 544**

TONIGHT I CELEBRATE MY LOVE FOR YOU (See Flack, Roberta)
Tracks: / Tonight I celebrate my love / Love's comin' at ya / Born to love / Let the feeling flow.
7" Single: Released Jul '83, on Capitol, by EMI Records. Deleted Jan '88. Catalogue no: **CL 302**
12" Single: Released Sep '83, on Capitol, by EMI Records. Deleted '88. Catalogue no: **12 CL 302**
7" Single: Released 30 May '87, on Old Gold, by Old Gold Records. Deleted Sep '89. Catalogue no: **OG 9721**

WITHOUT YOU
Tracks: / Without you / If ever you're in my arms again / Higher you climb, The (track on 12") / Again (track on 12").
12" Single: Released Feb '88, on Elektra, by Elektra Records (UK). Catalogue no: **EKR 66T**
7" Single: Released Feb '88, on Elektra, by Elektra Records (UK). Catalogue no: **EKR 66**

BSWG Ensemble

ANIMALS WENT IN TWO BY TWO
Tracks: / Animals went in two by two, The.
7" Single: Released May '83, on International, by International Records & Tapes. Catalogue no: **INTLB 002**

JINGLE BELLS
Tracks: / Jingle bells.
7" Single: Released May '83, on International, by International Records & Tapes. Catalogue no: **INTLB 001**

B-Team

ALL I EVER WANTED
Tracks: / All I ever wanted.
7" Single: Released Sep '85, on Diamond, by Revolver Records. Catalogue no: **DIA 008**

B.T.Express

Biographical details: This American funk band consisted of the following line-up at the time of their major mid-Seventies success: Barbara Joyce Lomas, Bill Risbrook, Louis Risbrook, Dennis Rowe, Richie Thompson, Carlos Ward and Terrell Woods. B.T. stands for 'Brothers Trucking', the name of the embryonic version of the band. During the early Seventies the various memebers were in a number short-lived groups which evolved into B.T. Express. Their first single *Do It ('Til You're Satisfied)* was an American smash, reaching No. 2 on the national pop chart in late 1974. Its infectious, driving rhythm was ideal material for the exploding disco market and was quickly repeated on the '75 instrumental single *Express*. This reached No. 4 and also gave the group its first British chart record, peaking at No. 34. one more Top 40 single was forthcoming in the States, but subsequent releases were merely predictable re-workings of the same formula. It was left to others to continue the disco boom. 1980 saw the ensemble make a minor return to the UK singles chart, reaching No. 52 with the double A sided 45 *Does It Feel Good/Give Up The Funk (Let's Dance)*. (Bob MacDonald)..

DOES IT FEEL GOOD
Tracks: / Does it feel good / Give up the funk.
7" Single: Released Jul '80, on Calibre, Deleted '85. Catalogue no: **CAB 503**

EXPRESS
Tracks: / Express.
7" Single: Released Mar '75, on Pye International, Deleted '80. Catalogue no: **7N 25674**

MIDNIGHT BEAT
Tracks: / Midnight beat.
7" Single: Released Mar '81, on Excaliber, by Red Bus Records. Deleted '88. Catalogue no: **EXC 508**
12" Single: Released Mar '81, on Excaliber, by Red Bus Records. Deleted '88. Catalogue no: **EXCL 508**

THIS MUST BE THE NIGHT
Tracks: / This must be the night.
7" Single: Released Feb '83, on Record Shack, by Record Shack Records. Catalogue no: **SOHO 3**
12" Single: Released Feb '83, on Record Shack, by Record Shack Records. Catalogue no: **SOHOT 3**

Bubba Lou

LOVE ALL OVER THE PLACE
Tracks: / Love all over the place / Over you.
7" Single: Released May '80, on Silent (1), by Silent Records. Deleted May '85. Catalogue no: **SSH3**
7" Single: Released Mar '81, on Stiff, by Stiff Records. Catalogue no: **BUY 114**

Bubble Gum

BUBBLE GUM BIGGIES
Tracks: / Bubble gum biggies.
7" Single: Released Jul '80, on Flashback, by Mainline Records. Catalogue no: **FBEP 106**

Bubblegum Splash

SPLASHDOWN EP
7" EP: Released Aug '87, on Subway, by Subway Records. Catalogue no: **SUBWAY 13**

Bubblemen

BUBBLEMEN ARE COMING, THE
Tracks: / Bubblemen are coming, The / B-side, The / Bubblemen are coming, The (rapping version) (Only on 12" version.).
7" Single: Released Jun '88, on Beggars Banquet, by Beggars Banquet Records. Catalogue no: **BUB 1**
12" Single: Released Jun '88, on Beggars Banquet, by Beggars Banquet Records. Catalogue no: **BUB 1T**

Bubbler, Charmain

I SAY YES
Tracks: / I say yes.
12" Single: Released Nov '88, on Black Jack, Catalogue no: **BJ 021**

TILL I SEE YOU
Tracks: / Till I see you.
12" Single: Released Mar '89, on Black Jack, Catalogue no: **BJ 024**

Bubblerock

I CAN'T GET NO SATISFACTION
Tracks: / I can't get no satisfaction.
7" Single: Released Jan '74, on UK, by UK Records. Deleted '77. Catalogue no: **UK 53**

Bubbles

MERRY CHRISTMAS, HAPPY NEW YEAR
Tracks: / Merry Christmas, Happy New Year.
12" Single: Released Jan '89, on Record Promotions, Catalogue no: **Unknown**

Bubblies

PLEASE COME HOME FOR CHRISTMAS
Tracks: / Please come home for Christmas / Christmas story.
7" Single: Released Nov '86, on Snowbow, Catalogue no: **TVR 3**

Buchanan, Catharine

LOVE IS
Tracks: / Love is / Love is (French version) / You've gone a bit to far.
CD 5": Released Jun '88, on Arista, by BMG Records (UK). Deleted Jul '89. Catalogue no: **661500**
7" Single: Released Jun '88, on Arista, by BMG Records (UK). Catalogue no: **111500**
12" Single: Released Jun '88, on Arista, by BMG Records (UK). Catalogue no: **611500**

Buchanan, Gary

I JUST NEED YOUR LOVING
Tracks: / I just need your loving.
12" Single: Released Oct '88, on Rham, by Rham Records. Catalogue no: **RS 8803**

Buchanan, Gilly

ME NO ME
Tracks: / Me no me.
12" Single: Released Sep '85, on Toe, Catalogue no: **TOE 002**

Buchanan, Kingsley

I'LL GET AWAY (AND BE FREE)
Tracks: / I'll get away (and be free).
12" Single: Released Jun '82, on Mikey, Catalogue no: **MR 82**

Buchanan, Margo

KEEP ON
Tracks: / Keep on.
7" Single: Released Dec '86, on London Records, by London Records. Catalogue no: **LON 125**
12" Single: Released Dec '86, on London Records, by London Records. Catalogue no: **LONX 125**

Buchanan, Roy

Biographical details: Born in Arkansas, rock guitarist Buchanan made Washington D.C. his permanent base in 1962. Before this he had begin making a name in musicians' circles by playing in a number of rock 'n' roll groups, including recording sessions with Freddy Cannon and Bob Luman. In the early 70's he was pushed forward by both record company and music press as the new guitar hero. Excellent though his versatile playing was, he was hardly a household name and did not have the personality or inclination to become a rock star. He made some worthwhile albums during this period, though not achieving a great deal of chart success. His only foray into UK chartdom was the 1973 single *Sweet Dreams*, a slow and moody track that reached No 40. (Bob MacDonald, 1984.).

SWEET DREAMS
Tracks: / Sweet dreams.
7" Single: Released Mar '73, on Polydor, by Polydor Ltd. Deleted '76. Catalogue no: **2066 307**
7" Single: Released Jul '84, on Old Gold, by Old Gold Records. Deleted Jul '88. Catalogue no: **OG 9434**

YOU CAN'T JUDGE A BOOK BY THE COVER
Tracks: / You can't judge a book by the cover / Chokin' kind, The.
7" Single: Released Jul '86, on Sonet, by Sonet Records. Catalogue no: **SON 2309**

Buck, Bobby

TAKE TIME TO CARE
Tracks: / Take time to care (All royalties to leukaemia research.) / Ian,Viv & Me.
Note: All A-side royalties to leukaemia research.
7" Single: Released Mar '86, on Spartan, Catalogue no: **BOTH 1**

Buckbeats

DAYDREAM
Tracks: / Daydream / Longest night.
7" Single: Released Apr '88, on Extra, Catalogue no: **XTRA 7**
12" Single: Released Apr '88, on Extra, Catalogue no: **12XTRA 7**

Buckett, Eli

YODELLING COCKEREL
Tracks: / Yodelling cockerel.

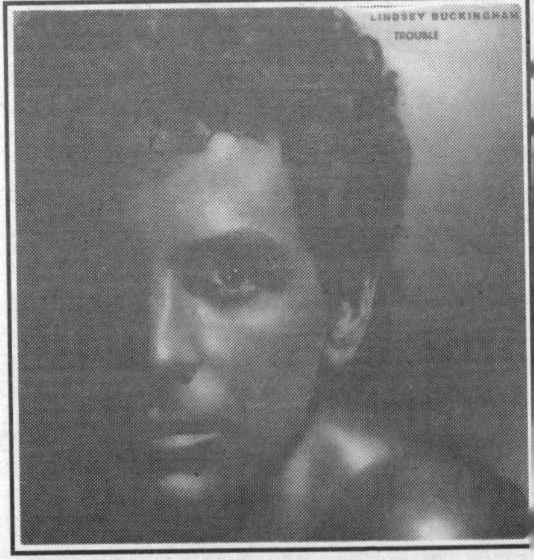

LINDSEY BUCKINGHAM - TROUBLE (Released on Mercury)

7" Single: Released Dec '87, on EB Records, by EB Records. Catalogue no: **EB 26**

Buckingham, Lindsey

Biographical details: Lindsey Buckingham recorded a 1973 album with girlfriend Stevie Nicks under the billing Buckingham Nicks before they both joined Fleetwood Mac in 1975. The input of these two Americans into a floundering British rock group transformed Mac into world superstars and produced one of the top-selling albums of all time, Rumours. By the time Buckingham released his first solo album, Law And Order, in late 1981, he was gradually reaching a position of domination of the band's musical direction. Consequently his own LP was not dissimilar to that of Mac. It yielded the catchy, slightly eerie single Trouble, which reached No 9 in the US and No 31 in the UK. Meanwhile Stevie Nicks was enjoying greater solo success with her Bella Donna album. Buckingham's next solo outing was 1984's Go Insane, which, though a good example of his gently rocking, folk-influenced style, failed to make a great impact. Fleetwood Mac continued to make best-selling albums and singles. Buckingham has now split from them, and from Nicks. (Bob MacDonald, 1984.)

This American singer and guitarist recorded a 1973 album with girlfriend Stevie Nicks under the billing "Buckingham Nicks", before they both joined Fleetwood Mac in 1975. The input of these two Americans into a floundering British rock group, transformed Mac into world superstars and produced one of the world's top-selling albums of all time *Rumours*. By the time Buckingham released his first solo album *Law And Order* in late 1981, he was graduallt reaching a position of domination in the band's musical direction. Consequently his own LP was not dissimilar to that of Mac. It yielded the catchy, slightly eerie single *Trouble*, which reached No. 9 in the US and No. 31 in the UK. Meanwhile, his former girlfirend Stevie Nicks was enjoying greater solo success wil her *Bella Donna* album. Buckingham's next solo outing was 1984's *Go Insane*, but it failed to make a great impact, although it was another good example of his gently rocking, folk-influenced pop style. (Bob MacDonald)..

GO INSANE (SINGLE)
Tracks: / Go insane / Play in the rain.
7" Single: Released Aug '84, on Mercury, by Phonogram Ltd. Deleted '85. Catalogue no: **MER 168**
12" Single: Released Aug '84, on Mercury, by Phonogram Ltd. Catalogue no: **MERX 168**

MARY LEE JONES
Tracks: / Mary Lee Jones / September song.
7" Single: Released May '82, on Mercury, by Phonogram Ltd. Deleted '85. Catalogue no: **MER 102**

TROUBLE (see panel on previous page)
Tracks: / Trouble / That's how we do it in L.A..
7" Single: Released Jan '82, on Mercury, by Phonogram Ltd. Deleted '85. Catalogue no: **MER 85**

VISITOR
Tracks: / Visitor / Satisfied mud.
7" Single: Released Mar '82, on Mercury, by Phonogram Ltd. Deleted '85. Catalogue no: **MER 96**

Buckley, Bill

MEG IS MAGIC
Tracks: / Meg is magic / Do I love you.
7" Single: Released Aug '81, on Grandstand, by Big Bear Records. Deleted '84. Catalogue no: **GRR 3**

Buckley, Michael

LOVE HAS GOT ME GOING
Tracks: / Love has got me going.
12" Single: Released 24 Jul '89, on Taurus. Catalogue no: **TRS 010**

Buckner & Garcia

PAC-MAN FEVER
Tracks: / Pac-man fever.
7" Single: Released Jun '82, on CBS, by CBS Records. Deleted Jun '85. Catalogue no: **A 2055**

Bucks Fizz

Biographical details: Bucks Fizz UK pop vocal group formed in 1980 by husband/wife management/production team of Andy Hill and Nichola Martin, with jungle-writer Hill supplying material; they hired Mike Nolan, Bobby G (for Gubby), Jay Aston and Cheryl Baker. Impressed by both girls, Martin stood down as performer. *Making Your Mind Up* won Eurovision in 1981 and the group had many hits of no consequence. Nolan was seriously injured in a coach crash in December 1984; Aston quit among tabloid revelations about hanky-panky in the group, replaced by lookalike Shelley Preston. Donald Clarke, 24 August 1988

This British vocal group consists of Jay Aston, Cheryl Baker, Bobby Gee and Mike Nolan. They were named after a fashionable cocktail drink. They were formed in early 1981 by producer Andy hill, as a vehicle to perform his Eurovision entry song *Making Your Mind Up*, a catchy pop ditty that he had penned with John Danter. He simply chose four applicants who could sing, perform simple choreography and look good and thus was founded yet another Abba clone group. He hoped to emulate the success of Britain's winning 1976, Abba copyists Brotherhood Of Man and he succeeded. *Making Your Mind Up* sailed through the UK heats and then won the Eurovision Song Contest itself. Bucks Fizz thus became the first British winners of the Contest since the Brotherhood and only the fourth ever. Like their three predecessors they took their winning entry to No. 1 on the British charts and thus became the first British entrants since the Brotherhood to even hit the Top 10. Bucks Fizz then proceeded to confound the Contest's constant critics by coming up with a further eight consecutive UK Top 20 singles. With Abba in decline and Brotherhood Of Man forgotten by record buyers, Andy Hill was able to steer his group along a consistently commercial chart path. He co-wrote and produced or co-produced the vast bulk of their output. The follow-up to *Making Your Mind Up* was the ultra-Abba-ish *Piece of The Action*, which reached No. 12; it was followed in turn byt eh mid-tempo *One Of Those Nights*, a No. 20 hit. This apparent downward trend was rapidly halted by the No. 1 success of teh next 45 *Land Of Make Believe*. This was basically aimed at the Christmas market but, because it did not actually mention the subject, it was still going strong when it hit the top in January '82. it was a children's favourite and even finished with a short poem recited by a child. The group's next single *My Camera Never lies* became their second successive British chart-topper and their third in total. it marked a departure from their previous output, in that it was more complex in structure, arrangement and production. They were now compared with Dollar, a pop duo who were adopting a similar approach under the guidance of Trevor Horn. The comparison of the two acts was heightened by the fact that they tended to have records out simultaneously - on four consecutive occassions, they entered the UK Top 40 in the same week as one another.

Hill and bucks Fizz again demonstrated considerable skill by changing course once more with their next 45: *Now Those Days Are Gone* was an acappella single and reached No. 8 on the UK chart. *If You Can't Stand The heat* and *Run For Your Life* returned to the *Camera*-style pop vein, to be followed by *When We Were Young*, a strong pop single that attempted to be slightly overdramatic. The latter number, issued in the summer of '83, was the final single in their string of consecutive UK Top 20 hits. The next singles *London Town* and *Rules Of The Game* were only minor British hits; they suffered by being further re-workings of the *My Camera Never Lies* formula and the public were growing tired of their now predictable sound.

The summer of '84 they issued the 'make or break' single *Talking n Your Sleep* - they resloved to split if the record did not end their sticky period. The group remained together because the single reached No. 15 on the British chart. It was a remake of a song that had given the Romantics a US Top 3 hit at the beginning of the year but had flopped in the UK. The Bucks Fizz disc succeeded despite its glaring inferiority to the original. To follow it up, they released their first 45 without Andy Hill - But the 'golden days are over' line in the chorus seemed appropriate. Nevertheless Bucks Fizz had lasted far longer already than most expected when they won Eurovision - they had gone on to sing many more songs than the one they were originally formed to perform. Their substantial pop appeal was displayed not only by their run of hit singles, but also by the good runs achieved by their chart albums in Britain. (Bob MacDonald)..

GOLDEN DAYS
Tracks: / Golden days.
7" Single: Released Oct '84, on RCA, by BMG Records (UK). Deleted '87. Catalogue no: **FIZ 3**

HEART OF STONE
Tracks: / Heart of stone / Here's looking at you / My camera never lies (Only on 12" single.).
Cassingle: Released Oct '88, on RCA, by BMG Records (UK). Catalogue no: **PV 42305**
7" Single: Released Oct '88, on RCA, by BMG Records (UK). Deleted Aug '89. Catalogue no: **PB 42305**
12" Single: Released Oct '88, on RCA, by BMG Records (UK). Deleted May '89. Catalogue no: **PT 42306**

I HEAR TALK (SINGLE)
Tracks: / I hear talk.
7" Single: Released Dec '84, on RCA, by BMG Records (UK). Catalogue no: **FIZ 4**
12" Single: Released Dec '84, on RCA, by BMG Records (UK). Catalogue no: **FIZT 4**

BUCKS FIZZ - MY CAMERA NEVER LIES (Released on RCA)

IF YOU CAN'T STAND THE HEAT
Tracks: / If you can't stand the heat / Stepping out.
7" Pic: Released Dec '82, on RCA, by BMG Records (UK). Catalogue no: **RCAP 300**
7" Single: Released Nov '82, on RCA, by BMG Records (UK). Catalogue no: **RCA 300**
12" Single: Released Nov '82, on RCA, by BMG Records (UK). Catalogue no: **RCAT 300**

KEEP EACH OTHER WARM
Tracks: / Give A Little Love / Keep each other warm.
7" Pic: Released Nov '86, on Polydor, by Polydor Ltd. Deleted Aug '87. Catalogue no: **POSPP 835**
7" Single: Released Nov '86, on Polydor, by Polydor Ltd. Deleted Aug '87. Catalogue no: **POSP 835**
7" Single: Released Nov '86, on Polydor, by Polydor Ltd. Deleted Aug '87. Catalogue no: **POSPG 835**
12" Single: Released Nov '86, on Polydor, by Polydor Ltd. Deleted Aug '87. Catalogue no: **POSPX 835**

LAND OF MAKE BELIEVE (SINGLE)
Tracks: / Land of make believe / Making your mind up.
7" Single: Released Nov '81, on RCA, by BMG Records (UK). Catalogue no: **RCA 163**
7" Single: Released Oct '86, on Old Gold, by Old Gold Records. Catalogue no: **OG 9617**

LONDON TOWN
Tracks: / London town.
7" Single: Released Sep '83, on RCA, by BMG Records (UK). Catalogue no: **RCA 363**
12" Single: Released Sep '83, on RCA, by BMG Records (UK). Catalogue no: **RCAT 363**

LOVE THE ONE YOU'RE WITH
Tracks: / Love the one you're with / Too hard / I hear talk (Extra track on 12" only).
Cassingle: Released '86, on Polydor, by Polydor Ltd. Deleted Mar '87. Catalogue no: **POSPC 813**
7" Single: Released '86, on Polydor, by Polydor Ltd. Deleted Mar '87. Catalogue no: **POSPA 813**
7" Single: Released Aug '86, on Polydor, by Polydor Ltd. Deleted Mar '87. Catalogue no: **POSP 813**
7" Single: Released '86, on Polydor, by Polydor Ltd. Deleted Mar '87. Catalogue no: **POSPG 813**
12" Single: Released Aug '86, on Polydor, by Polydor Ltd. Deleted Mar '87. Catalogue no: **POSPX 813**

MAGICAL
Tracks: / Magical.
7" Single: Released Aug '85, on RCA, by BMG Records (UK). Catalogue no: **PB 40367**
12" Single: Released Aug '85, on RCA, by BMG Records (UK). Catalogue no: **PT 40368**

MAKING YOUR MIND UP (SINGLE)
Tracks: / Making your mind up.
7" Single: Released Mar '81, on RCA, by BMG Records (UK). Catalogue no: **RCA 56**

MY CAMERA NEVER LIES (see panel above)
Tracks: / My camera never lies / What am i gonna do.
7" Single: Released Mar '82, on RCA, by BMG Records (UK). Catalogue no: **RCA 202**
12" Single: Released Mar '82, on RCA, by BMG Records (UK). Catalogue no: **RCAT 202**

NEW BEGINNING
Tracks: / New beginning (Mamba Seyra) / In your eyes / I need your love (Extra track on 12" only).
7" Single: Released May '86, on Polydor, by Polydor Ltd. Deleted Mar '87. Catalogue no: **POSP 794**
7" Single: Released May '86, on Polydor, by Polydor Ltd. Catalogue no: **POSPG 794**
12" Single: Released May '86, on Polydor, by Polydor Ltd. Deleted Mar '87. Catalogue no: **POSPX 794**

NOW THOSE DAYS ARE GONE (see panel on next page)
Tracks: / Now those days are gone / Takin' me higher.
7" Pic: Released Jun '82, on RCA, by BMG Records (UK). Catalogue no: **RCAP 241**
7" Single: Released Jun '82, on RCA, by BMG Records (UK). Catalogue no: **RCA 241**

ONE OF THOSE NIGHTS
Tracks: / One of those nights / Always thinking of you.
7" Single: Released Jul '82, on RCA, by BMG Records (UK). Catalogue no: **RCA 114**

PIECE OF THE ACTION
Tracks: / Piece of the action / Took it to the limit.
7" Single: Released May '81, on RCA, by BMG Records (UK). Catalogue no: **RCA 88**

RULES OF THE GAME
Tracks: / Rules of the game / When we were at war.
7" Single: Released Nov '83, on RCA, by BMG Records (UK). Catalogue no: **RCA 380**
12" Single: Released Nov '83, on RCA, by BMG Records (UK). Catalogue no: **RCAT 380**

RUN FOR YOUR LIFE
Tracks: / Run for your life.
7" Single: Released Feb '83, on RCA, by BMG Records (UK). Catalogue no: **FIZ 1**

TALKING IN YOUR SLEEP
Tracks: / Talking in your sleep.
7" Single: Released Aug '84, on RCA, by BMG Records (UK). Deleted '87. Catalogue no: **FIZ 2**

WHEN WE WERE YOUNG
Tracks: / When we were young.
7" Pic: Released Jun '83, on RCA, by BMG Records (UK). Catalogue no: **RCATP 342**
7" Single: Released Jun '83, on RCA, by BMG Records (UK). Catalogue no: **RCA 342**
12" Single: Released Jun '83, on RCA, by BMG Records (UK). Catalogue no: **RCAT 342**

YOU AND YOUR HEART OF BLUE
Tracks: / You and your heart of blue.
7" Single: Released Jun '85, on RCA, by BMG Records (UK). Catalogue no: **PB 40233**
12" Single: Released Jun '85, on RCA, by

BUCKS FIZZ - NOW THOSE DAYS ARE GONE (Released on RCA)

BMG Records (UK). Catalogue no: **PT 40234**

YOU LOVE LOVE
Tracks: / You love love.
7" Single: Released Apr '89, on RCA, by BMG Records (UK). Catalogue no: **PB 42841**

Buckwheat Zydeco

DOWN DALLAS ALLEY
Tracks: / Down Dallas Alley / Why does love got to be so sad / Make a change.
CD 5": Released Jun '89, on Island, by Island Records. Catalogue no: **CID 398**

MAKE A CHANGE
Tracks: / Make a change / In and out of my life / These things you do (Only on 12" and CD single.) / Takin' it home (Only on CD single.).
CD 5": Released 6 Mar '89, on Island, by Island Records. Catalogue no: **CID 412**
7" Single: Released 6 Mar '89, on Island, by Island Records. Catalogue no: **IS 412**
12" Single: Released 6 Mar '89, on Island, by Island Records. Catalogue no: **12 IS 412**

MARIE MARIE
Tracks: / Marie Marie / Time is tight / Buckwheat's special (Extra track on 12" only).
7" Single: Released Jul '87, on Island, by Island Records. Deleted Jun '88. Catalogue no: **IS 331**
12" Single: Released Jul '87, on Island, by Island Records. Deleted Apr '88. Catalogue no: **12IS 331**

WHY DOES LOVE GOT TO BE SO SAD
Tracks: / Why does love got to be so sad / Creole country (part 2) / Drivin' old grey (Only on 12" version.).
CD 5": Released Jan '89, on Island, by Island Records. Catalogue no: **CID 386**
7" Single: Released Jan '89, on Island, by Island Records. Catalogue no: **IS 386**
12" Single: Released Jan '89, on Island, by Island Records. Catalogue no: **12IS 386**

Budd, Julie

ROSES AND RAINBOWS
Tracks: / Roses and rainbows / Any fool could see.
7" Single: Released Feb '81, on A&M, by A&M Records. Deleted Feb '84. Catalogue no: **AMS 8117**

Budgie

Biographical details: At the time of their greatest success (1974), this British band consisted of Pete Boot, Tony Bourge and Burke Shelley. Budgie released their debut self-titled album in 1971 when they comprised Bourge, Shelley and Ray Phillips. In '74 drummer Phillips was replaced by Boot. It was with this line-up that they chalked up their first British chart LP, peaking at No. 29 with their fourth album *In For The Kill*. They got to No. 36 on the UK album chart with 1975's *Bandolier* but, by this time, the drummer had changed again, with Boot being replaced by Steve Williams. Budgie returned briefly to the LP chart with 1981's *Night Flight* and 1982's *Deliver Us From Evil*. The former yielded their only British chart single: *Keeping A Rendezvous* peaked at No. 17, by which time guitarist Bourge had quit. John Thomas was now in his shoes.
The band play hard, driving rock, but their sound has always been too cliched and repetitive to make them stars. (Bob MacDonald)..

BORED WITH RUSSIA
Tracks: / Bored with Russia / Don't cry.
7" Single: Released Sep '82, on RCA, by BMG Records (UK). Catalogue no: **RCA 271**

CRIME AGAINST THE WORLD
Tracks: / Crime against the world / Hellbender.
7" Single: Released Nov '80, on Active, by Active Records. Deleted Nov '83. Catalogue no: **BUDGE 2**

I TURNED TO STONE
Tracks: / I turned to stone.
7" Single: Released Jul '81, on RCA, by BMG Records (UK). Deleted Jul '84. Catalogue no: **BUDGE 4**

KEEPING A RENDEZVOUS
Tracks: / Keeping a rendezvous.
7" Single: Released Oct '81, on RCA, by BMG Records (UK). Deleted '84. Catalogue no: **BUDGIE 3**

Buell, Bebe

LITTLE BLACK EGG
Tracks: / Little black egg / Funtime.
7" Single: Released May '82, on Moonlight, by Lithon Recording & Music Publishing. Catalogue no: **MNS 003**

Buffallo Soldier

HI-JACKER
Tracks: / Hi jacker / Too late mama.
12" Single: Released Apr '84, on Pinnacle, by Pinnacle Records. Catalogue no: **PIN 104T**

Buffalo

BATTLE TORN HEROES
Tracks: / Battle torn heroes / Women of the night.
7" Single: Released Sep '81, on Heavy Metal, by FM-Revolver Records. Catalogue no: **HEAVY 3**

MEAN MACHINE
Tracks: / Mean machine / Rumour.
7" Single: Released Nov '82, on Heavy Metal, by FM-Revolver Records. Catalogue no: **HEAVY 15**

Buffett, Jimmy

Biographical details: Buffett, Jimmy A country-rock singer/songwriter, born in 1946 in Mobile, Alabama. He recorded in Nashville; his first album flopped and tapes of the next were lost, mysteriously rediscovered when he later hit the big time. He was a feature writer for Billboard and began recording again: *Living And Dying In 3/4 Time* was the first to make the USA pop album chart, with top 30 hit *Come Monday*. He reported that 1985 was his biggest year in concert grosses, reflecting the popularity of act: his 'I go onstage with the attitude that this is going to be my last concert, so let's all have fun and party till we drop'. Donald Clarke, 24 August 1988.

COCONUT TELEGRAPH
Tracks: / Coconut telegraph / Little Miss Magic.
7" Single: Released Feb '81, on MCA, by MCA Records. Deleted Feb '84. Catalogue no: **MCA 679**

CREOLA (SINGLE)
Tracks: / Creola.
7" Single: Released Oct '86, on MCA, by MCA Records. Catalogue no: **MCA 1093**
12" Single: Released Oct '86, on MCA, by MCA Records. Catalogue no: **MCAT 1093**

STARS FELL ON ALABAMA
Tracks: / Stars fell on Alabama / Growing older but not up.
7" Single: Released May '81, on MCA, by MCA Records. Deleted May '84. Catalogue no: **MCA 724**

VOLCANO
Tracks: / Volcano / Stranded on a sandbar.
7" Single: Released Jan '80, on MCA, by MCA Records. Deleted Jan '85. Catalogue no: **MCA 562**

Bugatti, Ramon

WHEN THE NIGHT COMES
Tracks: / When the night comes / Come on home with me tonight.
7" Single: Released Apr '80, on Motor, Deleted Apr '83. Catalogue no: **MOT 1**

Buggles

Biographical details: Geoff Downes and Trevor Horn are two Britons who formed a duo called the Buggles in 1979. They released a self produced-single *Video Killed The Radio Star*, a song written in collaboration with their friend Bruce Woolley. it shot to the top of the British charts. It was a perfect pop single - musically, it was irresistibly catchy, almost bubblegum; lyrically, the futuristic, slightly tongue-in-cheek message captured the imagination of the public. Making maximum use of new recording techniques and sounds, the record sounded fresh and exciting. It reached No. 40 in the States.
The Buggles showed all the signs of being a One Hit Wonder, but this was not the case. In early 1980 they reached No. 16 on the UK chart with *The Plastic Age*, a single in a similar vein to its predecessor. The album of the same name peaked at No. 27. In March '80 came the surprise announcement that the pair were joining the mega-rock band 'Yes'. They played on the *Drama* LP, altogether successful, however, 'yes' folded in December 1980. During their time with the group, two further Buggles singles had been issued from the album *The Plastic Age* and became minor hits. In 1981 Geoff Downes jined fellow Yes-man Steve Howe in forming the supergroup called Asia, whose debut self-titled album became America's biggest seller of 1982. Meanwhile Trevor Horn began a hugely successful career as one of Britain's top record producers. Starting with Dollar, he then moved on to ABC, Malcolm McLaren, a new 'Yes' line-up and, eventually and most importantly, Frankie Goes To Hollywood. (Bob MacDonald)..

ADVENTURES IN MODERN RECORDING
Tracks: / Adventures in modern recording / Blue nylon.
7" Single: Released Jan '82, on Carrere, Deleted '85. Catalogue no: **CAR 222**
12" Single: Released Jan '82, on Carrere, Deleted '85. Catalogue no: **CART 222**

CLEAN CLEAN
Tracks: / Clean clean / Technopop.
7" Single: Released Apr '80, on Island, by Island Records. Deleted '83. Catalogue no: **WIP 6584**

ELSTREE (see panel below)
Tracks: / Elstree / Johnny on the monorail.
7" Single: Released Oct '80, on Island, by Island Records. Deleted '83. Catalogue no: **WIP 6624**

ON TV
Tracks: / On TV / Fade away.
7" Single: Released Nov '82, on RCA, by BMG Records (UK). Deleted Nov '85. Catalogue no: **RCA 232**

PLASTIC AGE, THE
Tracks: / Plastic age, The / Island.
7" Single: Released Jan '80, on Island, by Island Records. Deleted '83. Catalogue no: **WIP 6540**

VIDEO KILLED THE RADIO STAR (see panel on next page)
Tracks: / Video killed the radio star / Kid Dynamo.
7" Single: Released Jul '81, on Island, by Island Records. Catalogue no: **WIP 6524**

Bugs

LEAVING HERE
Tracks: / Leaving here / Leave us alone / See if I care.
7" Single: Released Feb '87, on Hit (UK), Catalogue no: **WILD TURKEY1**

Buhl, J.D.

5 O'CLOCK WORLD
Tracks: / 5 o'clock world.
7" Single: Released Aug '81, on Rag Baby, Catalogue no: **BRAG 105**

Buick Circus Hour

LIFE IN CHAINS, A
Tracks: / Life in chains, A.
12" Single: Released Nov '88, on Kaleidoscope Sound, by Kaleidoscope Sound Records. Catalogue no: **KS 109**

Builders

NO MORE PROMISES
Tracks: / No more promises.
7" Single: Released Nov '84, on Tunnel, by Tunnel Records. Catalogue no: **TUN 02**

Buirski, Felicity

HEARTLESS HOTEL (see panel on next page)
Tracks: / Heartless hotel / Travelling home.
Note: As an international model, Felicity Buirski experienced first-hand the world of the beautiful and not-so-beautiful people. Many of her songs reflect on the illusions we have about the world of fame and success. More directly her compositions reflect on the illusions of love and life. Rueful, ironic, often bitter, but never without wit, Felicity is a Suzanne Vega for grown-ups. (Run River publicity 5/88)
7" Single: Released May '88, on Run River, by In-Market Ltd.. Catalogue no: **RRAS 002**

LET THERE BE LIGHT
Tracks: / Let there be light / Executioner's song.

BUGGLES - ELSTREE (Released on Island)

BUGGLES - VIDEO KILLED THE RADIO STAR (Released on Island)

7" Single: Released Sep '89, on Run River, by In-Market Ltd.. Catalogue no: **RRAS 003**

Bulgarka

MUSICA
Tracks: / Musica.
7" Single: Released Oct '88, on World Today, Catalogue no: **WT 002**

Bull, Johnny

BATTLE OF THE FALKLANDS
Tracks: / Battle of the Falklands / Red alert.
7" Single: Released Dec '82, on Victory (1), Catalogue no: **VIC 1**

Bullamakanka

DOCTOR WHO IS GONNA FIT IT
Tracks: / Doctor who is gonna fit it.
7" Single: Released Nov '83, on BBC, by BBC Records & Tapes. Deleted '87. Catalogue no: **RESL 132**

Bullaweyo

FALLING APART
Tracks: / Falling apart / Over to you.
7" Single: Released Dec '81, on Shout, by Shout Records. Catalogue no: **XS 1000**

Bullens, Cindy

HOLDING ME CRAZY
Tracks: / Holding me crazy / Trust me.
7" Single: Released Jan '80, on Casablanca, by PolyGram UK Ltd. Deleted '83. Catalogue no: **NB 2217**

TOO CLOSE TO HOME
Tracks: / Too close to home / Raincheck on romance.
7" Single: Released Jun '80, on Casablanca, by PolyGram UK Ltd. Deleted Jun '83. Catalogue no: **CAN 197**

Bullet Boys

SMOOTH UP
Tracks: / Smooth up / Badlands.
7" Single: Released Sep '89, on Warner Bros., by WEA Records. Catalogue no: **W 2876**

Bulluck, Janice

DO YOU REALLY LOVE ME
Tracks: / Do you really love me.
7" Single: Released Aug '87, on Ichiban, by Ichiban Records (UK). Catalogue no: **WCS 206**
12" Single: Released Aug '87, on Ichiban, by Ichiban Records (UK). Catalogue no: **WCST 206**

DON'T START A FIRE (SINGLE)
Tracks: / Don't start a fire.
12" Single: Released Aug '87, on Ichiban, by Ichiban Records (UK). Catalogue no: **12PO 3**

Bulpitt, Chris

GAMES OF CHANCE
Cassingle: Released Apr '84, on Cockpit, by Cockpit Records. Catalogue no: **COCKPIT 6**

FELICITY BUIRSKI - HEARTLESS HOTEL (Released on Run River)

SURFACE TENSION
Cassingle: Released Apr '84, on Cockpit, by Cockpit Records. Catalogue no: **COCKPIT 5**

SURFACE TENSION/GAMES OF CHANCE
Cassingle: Released Jul '83, on Cockpit, by Cockpit Records. Catalogue no: **COCKPIT 5/6**

Bumble, B & The

NUT ROCKER
Tracks: / Nut rocker.
7" Single: Released Jun '72, on Stateside, by EMI Records. Deleted '75. Catalogue no: **SS 2203**
7" Single: Released Apr '62, on Top Rank (1), Deleted '65. Catalogue no: **JAR 611**

NUT ROCKER (OLD GOLD)
Tracks: / Nut rocker / Bumble boogie.
7" Single: Released Nov '80, on Old Gold, by Old Gold Records. Deleted Nov '83. Catalogue no: **OG 9080**

Bumble & The Beez

MY LIFE
Tracks: / My life / Signing on.
7" Single: Released Jan '83, on Zonophone, by EMI Records. Catalogue no: **Z 37**

ROOM ABOVE
Tracks: / Room above / Blowsing.
7" Single: Released Feb '82, on Zonophone, by EMI Records. Deleted Feb '87. Catalogue no: **Z27**
12" Single: Released Feb '82, on Zonophone, by EMI Records. Deleted Feb '87. Catalogue no: **12Z27**

Bumbry, Grace

NATALIE
Tracks: / Natalie.
7" Single: Released Jun '81, on Multi-Media, Catalogue no: **MMT 3**

Bunburys

FIGHT
Tracks: / Fight / We are the Bunburys.
7" Single: Released Jan '89, on Bunbury, by Island Records. Catalogue no: **LBW 2**
12" Single: Released Jan '89, on Bunbury, by Island Records. Catalogue no: **LBWC 2**

WE'RE THE BUNBURYS
Tracks: / We're the Bunbury's / Record breakers (chapter 1).
Cassingle: Released Aug '86, on Enterprises Ltd-Island, by Island Records. Deleted Apr '89. Catalogue no: **LBWC 1**
7" Single: Released Aug '86, on Enterprises Ltd-Island, by Island Records. Deleted Jul '87. Catalogue no: **LBW 1**

Bunch Of 5's

MASTERGROOVE (WILDEBEEST MIX)
Tracks: / Mastergroove (wildebeest mix) / Mastergroove (master mix).
12" Single: Released 13 Jun '87, on Production House (1), Catalogue no: **PNT 006**

SHAK RENDEZVOUS
Tracks: / Shak rendezvous (instrumental).
12" Single: Released Jan '87, on Production House (1), Catalogue no: **PNT 002**

Bunena, Richard

ATOMIC TWIST
Tracks: / Atomic twist.
7" Single: Released Jun '82, on Survival (1), by Survival Records. Catalogue no: **SUR 123**

Bunito star

LOVERS QUARREL
Tracks: / Lover's quarrel.
12" Single: Released May '88, on New Talents, Catalogue no: **NT 004**

Bunker Kru

SET IT OFF (Bunker 88 remix)
Tracks: / Set it off / Set it off (dub).
7" Single: Released 27 Feb '88, on Champion, by Champion Records. Deleted Aug '89. Catalogue no: **CHAMPR 64**
12" Single: Released 27 Feb '88, on Champion, by Champion Records. Deleted Aug '89. Catalogue no: **CHAMPR 1264**

Bunny

SHAKE YOU BATTY
Tracks: / Shake you batty.
12" Single: Released Dec '83, on Right Sounds, by Right Sounds Records. Catalogue no: **RTA 008**

Bunny Lie Lie

BROWN EYE BABY
Tracks: / Brown eye baby / Brown eye baby (version).
12" Single: Released Nov '88, on Flash Music, Catalogue no: **FMD 008**

ITIE-TITIE GIRL
Tracks: / Itie titie girl / Righteousness.
12" Single: Released May '82, on Greensleeves, by Greensleeves Records. Catalogue no: **GRED 89**

MR DYNAMITE
Tracks: / Mr. Dynamite.
12" Single: Released Apr '83, on Greensleeves, by Greensleeves Records. Catalogue no: **GRED 116**

Bunny Rugs

LET LOVE TOUCH US NOW
Tracks: / Let love touch us now.
12" Single: Released May '82, on Black Ark, Catalogue no: **BA 601**

Buongiorno Italia

BUONGIORNO ITALIA New beginners' course in Italian
Special: Released Apr '82, on BBC Publications, by BBC Records & Tapes. Catalogue no: **Unknown**

Burdette, Joe

NEW WEST, THE
Tracks: / New West, The.
10" single: Released 16 Sep '88, on Exile, Catalogue no: **EX 10EP 06**

Burdick, Kathy

HEART BEATER
Tracks: / Heart beater.
7" Single: Released Jan '84, on Sesame, Deleted '86. Catalogue no: **SES 1**

Burdon, Eric

Biographical details: Burdon, Eric The UK rock singer, born in 1941 in Newcastle, who came to fame with The Animals, went to the USA after they split in 1966, retaining the name and drummer Brian Jenkins, and formed New Animals, who split after two albums; among replacements were Andy Summers (later in Police) and Zoot Money. He reappeared in 1970 as frontman for the black Latin-rock band War, who went on to become funk superstars. He tried heavy rock, formed Fire Dept with German musicians; never recaptured his earliest success, but never lost his vocal talent either. He published a book 'I Used To Be An Animal But I'm Alright Now' in 1986. Donald Clarke, 24 August 1988

Born in Newcastle, this British vocalist joined the Alan Price Combo in 1962.
They soon became the Animals, who became one of the most important groups to emerge from the lively R&B scene. Their most famous disc was the 1964 smash revival of the traditional blues number *House Of The Rising Sun*, a No. 1 on both sides of the Atlantic. When the Animals broke up in 1966, Burden wanted to pursue a solo career, but record company pressure led him to credit his recordings to 'Eric Burdon & The Animals'. Burdon thus recruited some new Animals.
The first single under this new arrangement was *Help Me Girl*, a No. 14 hit in Britain. In 1967 he hit the US Top 20 with the sitar-flavoured *When I Was Young* and hit the UK Top 20 with the music hall-flavoured *Good Times*. Both were reminiscences of Burdon's turbulent past. Later that year he had a trans-atlantic Top 10 hit with *San Franciscan Nights* a track that ushered in a new era for Burdon. He was falling in love with the Californian hippie lifestyle and was switching from his old blues-influenced style to a new pop sound full of 'love and peace' optimism. After this single, Burdon's records sold much better in the States than in his native Britain. *Monteray*, a single inspired by the recent Californian festival and *Sky Pilot* both hit the US Top 20. At the end of '68 Burdon's group broke up and he thus became the solo artist that he had envisaged years earlier. He only achieved a one-off success in this capacity, however. That was with 1970's *Spill The Wine*, a duet with American soul group war which reached the US No. 3 position.
The group went on to have a string of American hits in the early and mid-Seventies, but withour Eric. He drifted into obscurity, a state of affairs that would only be broken by a dull Animals revival in 1983. Burdon's post-1966 career did not represent the singer at his best. He had enjoyed his finest years in the heyday of the original Animals, when he had been hailed as Britain's greatest white blues vocalist. (Bob MacDonald)..

GOOD TIMES
Tracks: / Good times / San Fransisco nights.
7" Single: Released Nov '82, on Polydor, by Polydor Ltd. Catalogue no: **POSP 534**
7" Single: Released Sep '67, on MGM, by Polydor Ltd. Deleted '70. Catalogue no: **MGM 1344**

HELP ME GIRL
Tracks: / Help me girl.
7" Single: Released Oct '66, on Decca, by Decca Records. Deleted '69. Catalogue no: **F 12503**

RING OF FIRE
Tracks: / Ring of fire.

BUREAU - ONLY FOR THE SHEEP (Released on Bureau Productions)

7" Single: Released Jan '69, on MGM, by Polydor Ltd. Deleted '72. Catalogue no: **MGM 1461**

SAN FRANCISCAN NIGHTS (SINGLE)
Tracks: / San Franciscan nights.
7" Single: Released Oct '67, on MGM, by Polydor Ltd. Deleted '70. Catalogue no: **MGM 1359**

SKY PILOT
Tracks: / Sky pilot.
7" Single: Released Feb '68, on MGM, by Polydor Ltd. Deleted '71. Catalogue no: **MGM 1373**

WHEN I WAS YOUNG
Tracks: / When I was young.
7" Single: Released Jun '67, on MGM, by Polydor Ltd. Deleted '70. Catalogue no: **MGM 1340**

Bureau

LET ME HAVE IT
Tracks: / Let me have it / Noose.
7" Single: Released May '81, on WEA, by WEA Records. Deleted May '84. Catalogue no: **K 18753**

ONLY FOR THE SHEEP (see panel above)
Tracks: / Only for sheep / First one, The.
7" Single: Released '81, on Bureau Productions, Catalogue no: **K 18478**

Burge, Greg

SURPRISE SURPRISE
Tracks: / Surprise surprise / I can do that.
7" Single: Released Jan '86, on Casablanca, by PolyGram UK Ltd. Catalogue no: **CAN 1022**
12" Single: Released Jan '86, on Casablanca, by PolyGram UK Ltd. Catalogue no: **CANX 1022**

Burgess, Leroy

SLAUGHTERHOUSE
Tracks: / Slaughterhouse.
12" Single: Released Aug '88, on Zoo Experience, by Zoo Experience Records. Catalogue no: **ZEROO 121**

Burgon, Geoffrey

Biographical details: This British orchestra leader took his ensemble to No 48 on the UK singles chart at the beginning of 1982. Their hit was the theme from the successful British television series Brideshead Revisited, a drama series which was also popular in America. (Bob MacDonald, 1984.)
This British orchestra leader took his ensemble to No. 48 on the UK singles chart at the beginning of 1982. Their hit was *Brideshead Theme*, the music for a very successful British television series *Brideshead Revisited*. This drama serial was also very popular in the States. The theme was Burgon's only British chart record. (Bob MacDonald)..

BRIDESHEAD THEME
Tracks: / Brideshead revisited, Theme from / Finale.
7" Single: Released '81, on Chrysalis, by Chrysalis Records. Catalogue no: **CHS 2562**

Buritz

SLEEP SOFTLY MARY
Tracks: / Sleep softly Mary.
7" Single: Released '84, on Spartan, Catalogue no: **SP 13**
12" Single: Released '84, on Spartan, Catalogue no: **12SP 13**

Burke & Hodge

INDEED
Tracks: / Indeed.
7" Single: Released Aug '87, on Orchid, by Orchid Records. Catalogue no: **ORC 1**
12" Single: Released Aug '87, on Orchid, by Orchid Records. Catalogue no: **12ORC 1**

Burke, Keni

Biographical details: American funk singer Burke scored a minor British chart single in the summer of 1981 with *Let Somebody Love You*, peaking at No 59. It was taken from his album *You're The Best*. An LP the following year, *Changes*, did not live up to its name and was similar in style: competent but run-of-the-mill disco material written and produced by Burke himself. He remains active in the recording studio, continuing to serve the specialist soul market. (Bob MacDonald, 1984.).

LET SOMEBODY LOVE YOU
Tracks: / Let somebody love you.
7" Single: Released Jun '81, on RCA, by BMG Records (UK). Deleted '84. Catalogue no: **RCA 93**

RISIN' TO THE TOP (OLD GOLD)
Tracks: / Risin' to the top / Let somebody love you.
12" Single: Released 30 Jan '89, on Old Gold, by Old Gold Records. Catalogue no: **OG 4097**

RISIN' TO THE TOP (SINGLE)
Tracks: / Risin' to the top / Hang tight.
12" Single: Released Jun '82, on RCA, by BMG Records (UK). Deleted Jun '85. Catalogue no: **RCAT 252**

YOU'RE THE BEST (SINGLE)
Tracks: / You're the best / Gotta find my way back in your heart.
12" Single: Released Sep '81, on RCA, by BMG Records (UK). Deleted '84. Catalogue no: **RCAT 126**

Burke, Solomon

EVERYBODY NEEDS SOMEBODY TO LOVE
Tracks: / Everybody needs somebody to love / If you need me / Walking the dog / Jump Jack.
7" Single: Released Apr '80, on Atlantic, by WEA Records. Deleted Apr '83. Catalogue no: **ATM9**

YOU SEND ME
Tracks: / You send me.
12" Single: Released May '87, on Perfect, Catalogue no: **PER 12 806**

Burmoe Brothers

SKIN
Tracks: / Skin.
12" Single: on Some Bizzare, by Some Bizzare Records. Catalogue no: **WBY 121**

Burne, Keni

RISIN' TO THE TOP (GIVE IT ALL YOU GOT)
Tracks: / Rising to the top / Let somebody love you.
7" Single: Released Oct '87, on RCA, by BMG Records (UK). Deleted May '89. Catalogue no: **PB 49613**
7" Single: Released '83, on RCA, by BMG Records (UK). Deleted '87. Catalogue no: **RCA 354**
12" Single: Released Oct '87, on RCA, by BMG Records (UK). Catalogue no: **PT 49614**
12" Single: Released '83, on RCA, by BMG Records (UK). Deleted '87. Catalogue no: **RCAT 354**

SHAKIN'
Tracks: / Shakin' / Night riders.
7" Single: Released '82, on RCA, by BMG Records (UK). Catalogue no: **RCA 223**
12" Single: Released '82, on RCA, by BMG Records (UK). Catalogue no: **RCAT 223**

Burnett, Howard

DANCE OF THE DUCKS
Tracks: / Dance of the ducks.
7" Single: Released '81, on Smile, Catalogue no: **LAFF 002**

Burnett, T-Bone

Biographical details: Burnett, T-Bone A USA singer/songwriter born in 1945 in Texas. He produced albums, e.g. by Delbert McClinton; joined Bob Dylan's Rolling Thunder Review tour in 1975, formed the Alpha Band in 1977 with others from the tour for two albums. Sporadic solo albums since then built a cult following in the USA. He has recently toured with Richard Thompson and Elvis Costello, and produced albums by Costello and by Los Lobos. An idiosyncratic artist with a steadily impressive body of work Donald Clarke, 24 August 1988.

BABY FALL DOWN
Tracks: / Baby fall down / Art movies.
7" Single: Released '83, on Demon, by Demon Records. Catalogue no: **D 1021**

Burnett, Watty

DANCING SHOES Congo dubba
Tracks: / Dancing shoes.
12" Single: Released '82, on Dread At The Controls, Catalogue no: **DATC 007**

Burnette

RUNNING BEAR
Tracks: / Running bear / Dance, dance, dance (shall we).
7" Single: Released Feb '87, on Hot Lead, by Hot Lead Records. Deleted Nov '87. Catalogue no: **HL 21**

Burnette, Billy

IN JUST A HEARTBEAT
Tracks: / In just a heartbeat / Rockin' L.A..
7" Single: Released Feb '81, on CBS, by CBS Records. Deleted Feb '84. Catalogue no: **CBS 9591**

TEAR IT UP
Tracks: / Tear it up / Oh Susan.
7" Single: Released Jun '81, on CBS, by CBS Records. Deleted Jun '84. Catalogue no: **CBSA 1283**

WHAT'S A LITTLE LOVE BETWEEN FRIENDS
Tracks: / What's a little love between friends / Precious time.
7" Single: Released Jan '80, on Polydor, by Polydor Ltd. Deleted Jan '85. Catalogue no: **POSP 95**

Burnette, Charmaine

AM I THE SAME GIRL
Tracks: / Am I the same girl.
12" Single: Released '81, on P.R.O., Catalogue no: **PRO D 001**

Burnette, Hank C.

Biographical details: This Swedish artist is a multi-instrumentalist but a particularly dab hand at the guitar. he came to public attention in 1976 with his single *Spinning Rock boogie*, a 100 mph instrumental hit that drew affectionately upon Fifties rock 'n' roll. This exciting 45 reached No. 21 on the UK charts. he was soon forgotten again by the general public, but remained active in the recording studio, releasing several albums in the mid and late Seventies. (Bob MacDonald)..

SPINNING ROCK BOOGIE
Tracks: / Spinning rock boogie.
7" Single: Released Oct '76, on Sonet, by Sonet Records. Deleted '79. Catalogue no: **SON 2094**

Burnette, Johnny

ALL BY MYSELF
Tracks: / All by myself / Drinkin' wine.
7" Single: Released Jul '82, on Revival, Catalogue no: **REV 6014**

CLOWN SHOES
Tracks: / Clown shoes.
7" Single: Released May '62, on Liberty, by EMI Records. Deleted '65. Catalogue no: **LIB 55416**

DREAMIN'
Tracks: / Dreamin'.
7" Single: Released Sep '60, on London-American, Deleted '63. Catalogue no: **HLG 9172**

GIRLS
Tracks: / Girls.
7" Single: Released Aug '61, on London-American, Deleted '64. Catalogue no: **HLG 9388**

LITTLE BOY SAD
Tracks: / Little boy sad.
7" Single: Released Apr '61, on London-American, Deleted '64. Catalogue no: **HLG 9315**

LONESOME TRAIN
Tracks: / Lonesome train / Sweet love on my mind.
7" Single: Released Jul '82, on Revival, Catalogue no: **REV 6011**

PLEASE DON'T LEAVE ME
Tracks: / Please don't leave me / Oh baby babe.
7" Single: Released Jul '82, on Revival, Catalogue no: **REV 6012**

ROCKABILY BOOGIE
Tracks: / Rockabily boogie / Tear it up.
7" Single: Released Jul '82, on Revival, Catalogue no: **REV 6013**

TRAIN KEPT A ROLLIN
Tracks: / Train kept a rollin' / Honey hush.
7" Single: Released Jul '82, on Revival, Catalogue no: **REV 6010**

YOU'RE SIXTEEN
Tracks: / You're sixteen.
7" Single: Released Jan '61, on London-American, Deleted '64. Catalogue no: **HLG 9254**

Burnette, Rocky

Biographical details: This American singer is the son of rock 'n' roll/pop star Johnny Burnette and the nephew of rock 'n' roll/country star Dorsey Burnette. Having lost his father in 1964, Rocky had just suffered the blow of his uncle's death when he launched his own recording career in late 1979. He released an album called *The Son Of Rock And Roll* - this title was perhaps a mistake, as it was open to misunderstanding, Some thought that this title was an attempt to cash in on his father's reputation; others felt that the implication that Johnny Burnette was rock 'n' roll, was an over-extravagant tribute. In fact it was a worthy rock 'n' roll revival LP, suggesting fine talent. The album yielded the single *Tired Of Toein' The Line* a strong pop 45 full of rock 'n' roll inflections. It reached No. 58 in the UK at the end of '79; many months later, in the summer of '80, it suddenly shot into the US charts and went all the way to No. 8, a truer reflection of the record's merits. In 1981 British audiences and record buyers, who failed to give Burnette a big hit, gave immediate acceptance to the virtual carbon copy of the single in the form of *You Drive Me Carzy*, a UK No. 2 hit for fellow revivalist Shakin' Stevens. Burnette mysteriously failed to fulfil his early promise and has not been seen in the charts again. At least his one-off hit managed to equal his father's peak on the American listings. Johnny scored a series of hits, but only one made the US Top 10 and that single peaked at No. 8. (Bob MacDonald)..

BABY TONIGHT
Tracks: / Baby tonight / Boogie down in mobile, alabama.
7" Single: Released Jan '80, on EMI, by EMI Records. Deleted Jan '85. Catalogue no: **EMI 5037**

FALLIN' IN LOVE
Tracks: / Fallin' in love / Because of you.
7" Single: Released Apr '80, on EMI, by EMI Records. Deleted Apr '83. Catalogue no: **EMI 5060**

TIRED OF TOEIN' THE LINE
Tracks: / Tired of toein' the line.
7" Single: Released Oct '79, on EMI, by EMI Records. Deleted '82. Catalogue no: **EMI 2992**

Burnham, Alan

MUSIC TO SAVE THE WORLD BY
Tracks: / Music to save the world by / Science fiction.
7" Single: Released Jan '81, on Cherry Red by Cherry Red Records. Deleted '87. Catalogue no: **CHERRY 15**

Burning

THROUGH THE DARKNESS
Tracks: / Touch me / Feeling your bite.
12" Single: Released Nov '86, on Bang Bang, by Bang Bang Records. Deleted '88 Catalogue no: **12 GANG 001**

Burning Bridges

BURNING BRIDGES

Tracks: / Burning bridges: *Various artists.*
Note: Artists include Instigators, Civilised Society, Mad Parade and Pagan Babies.
7" Single: Released '88, on Wear & Tear, Catalogue no: **WAT 001**

Burning Bush

GO TO SCHOOL
Tracks: / Go to school.
12" Single: Released Jul '84, on Kongo, by Kongo Records. Catalogue no: **DP 001**

Burning Illusion

SO LONELY
Tracks: / So lonely / Worries in the dark.
12" Single: Released Dec '85, on Melody, Catalogue no: **M6 D45**

Burning Sensations

BELLY OF THE WHALE
Tracks: / Belly of the whale.
7" Single: Released Jun '83, on Capitol, by EMI Records. Deleted '88. Catalogue no: **CL 296**
12" Single: Released Jun '83, on Capitol, by EMI Records. Deleted '88. Catalogue no: **12 CL 296**

Burning Skies Of

LAST REVOLVING DOOR
Tracks: / Alone / For my eyes / Carousel / Death of the clowns / Far from the crowds / Beggarman thief / Domino / Out on the paperchase / Too late for tears / Fragments.
7" Single: Released Dec '87, on Crisis, by Prism Records. Catalogue no: **EL 3**

Burning Spear

Biographical details: Burning Spear A Jamaican visionary and singer, real name Winston Rodney, whose lorn vocal style was appropriate to the kind of protest he contemplated. He made his early reputation on the island's sound systems, then wider acclaim joining backup singers Delroy Hines and Rupert Willington on records produced by Jack Ruby; *Marcus Garvey* was so popular that its dub incarnation *Garvey's Ghost* was also issued; the preachings of Garvey were a recurrent theme in his work. His later work was self-produced, such as *Dry And Heavy, Harder Than The Beat, Hail H I M, Resistance, People Of The World.* Donald Clarke, 24 August 1988..

JAH IS MY DRIVER
Tracks: / Jah is my driver / Driver / Distance / Far over.
12" Single: Released Oct '82, on Radic, Deleted Oct '85. Catalogue no: **12 RIC 114**

MARCUS GARVEY (SINGLE)
Tracks: / Marcus Garvey.
12" Single: Released Aug '87, on Island, by Island Records. Deleted Apr '88. Catalogue no: **12IS 332**

SHE'S MINE
Tracks: / She's mine / Education.
7" Single: Released Jun '82, on Radic, Deleted Jun '85. Catalogue no: **RIC 113**

TELL THE CHILDREN
Tracks: / Tell the children.
7" Single: Released Sep '88, on Blue Moon (1), by Magnum Music Group. Catalogue no: **BMS 608**

Burning The Bridge

PERFECT LOVE
Tracks: / Perfect love / Long day's journey into love.
7" Single: Released Feb '88, on Legacy, by Legacy Records. Catalogue no: **LGY 61**
12" Single: Released Feb '88, on Legacy, by Legacy Records. Catalogue no: **LGYT 61**

Burns, George

I WISH I WAS EIGHTEEN AGAIN
Tracks: / I wish i was eighteen again / One of the mysterys of life.
7" Single: Released Jan '80, on Mercury, by Phonogram Ltd. Deleted Jan '85. Catalogue no: **MER 6**

Burns, Jake

BREATHLESS
Tracks: / Breathless / Valentine's day.
7" Single: Released Feb '87, on Jive, by Zomba Records. Deleted Jul '87. Catalogue no: **JIVE 139**

NIGHT TRACKS EP
12" Single: Released Jun '88, on Night Tracks, by Pinnacle Records. Catalogue no: **SFPS 013**

ON FORTUNE STREET
Tracks: / On fortune street.
7" Single: Released Jul '85, on Rigid Digits, by Survival Records. Catalogue no: **SRD 2**
12" Single: Released Jul '85, on Survival (1), by Survival Records. Catalogue no: **SRDT 2**

SHE GREW UP
Tracks: / She grew up / Race you to the grave.
7" Single: Released Mar '86, on Survival (1), by Survival Records. Catalogue no: **SRD 3**
12" Single: Released Mar '86, on Survival (1), by Survival Records. Catalogue no: **SRDT 3**

Burns, Ray

MOBILE
Tracks: / Mobile.
7" Single: Released Feb '55, on Columbia, by EMI Records. Deleted '58. Catalogue no: **DB 3563**

THAT'S HOW A LOVE SONG WAS BORN
Tracks: / That's how a love song was born.
7" Single: Released Aug '55, on Columbia, by EMI Records. Deleted '58. Catalogue no: **DB 3640**

Burr, Pauline

OVERLANDER
Tracks: / Overlander, The / Just a step away.
7" Single: Released Nov '87, on Silver Heart, Catalogue no: **HEART 1**

Burrell

I REALLY LIKE
Tracks: / I really like (On 7" only) / I really like (LP version) (NOT on TENX 243) / Yes (ON TENX only) / I really like (12" dub) (On 12" only) / I really like (12" dub) (On TENX 243 only) / I really like (remix) (On TENR 243 only).
7" Single: Released 3 Oct '88, on 10 Records, by Virgin Records. Catalogue no: **TEN 243**
12" Single: on 10 Records, by Virgin Records. Catalogue no: **TENR 243**
12" Single: Released 3 Oct '88, on 10 Records, by Virgin Records. Catalogue no: **TENX 243**

I'LL WAIT FOR YOU (TAKE YOUR TIME)
Tracks: / Waiting / I'll wait for you (take your time)(dance mix) (On 12" only) / I'll wait for you (take your time)(acappella) (On 12" only) / I'll dub for you (take your time) (On 12" only) / I'll wait for you (take your time) (On 7" only).
Note: "Ronald and Rheji Burrell are twins. They are from New York. They make wicked music. They caused a storm at this years DMC convention with their fierce blend of house, percussion - and their individual style of dancing." (Virgin Records May 1988.)

7" Single: Released May '88, on 10 Records, by Virgin Records. Catalogue no: **TEN 218**
12" Single: Released May '88, on 10 Records, by Virgin Records. Catalogue no: **TENX 218**

PUT YOUR TRUST IN THE MUSIC
Tracks: / Put your trust in the music / Dominate me / Put your trust in the music (version) (12" only).
CD 5": Released Feb '89, on Virgin, by Virgin Records. Catalogue no: **TENCD 264**
7" Single: Released Feb '89, on Virgin, by Virgin Records. Catalogue no: **TEN 264**
12" Single: Released Feb '89, on Virgin, by Virgin Records. Catalogue no: **TENR 264**
12" Single: Released Feb '89, on Virgin, by Virgin Records. Catalogue no: **TENX 264**

Burrell, Roland

BLOODSHOT EYES
Tracks: / Bloodshot eyes.
12" Single: Released Dec '83, on Music

Burstow Kids

CHRISTMAS TIME AGAIN
Tracks: / Christmas time again / All that you mean to me.
7" Single: Released Dec '87, on Rich, Catalogue no: **GRQ 103**

Burtnick, Glenn

FOLLOW YOU
Tracks: / Follow you / Walls come down / Abalene (On 12" only).
7" Single: Released Dec '87, on A&M, by A&M Records. Deleted 1 Aug '88. Catalogue no: **AM 421**
12" Single: Released Dec '87, on A&M, by A&M Records. Deleted 1 Aug '88. Catalogue no: **AMY 421**

HEARD IT ON THE RADIO
Tracks: / Heard it on the radio / Walls came down.
12" Single: Released 29 Feb '88, on A&M, by A&M Records. Deleted Feb '89. Catalogue no: **AMY 437**
7" Single: Released 29 Feb '88, on A&M, by A&M Records. Deleted Feb '89. Catalogue no: **AM 437**

Burton, Jenny

BAD HABITS
Tracks: / Bad habits / Let's get back to love.
7" Single: Released Jun '85, on Atlantic, by WEA Records. Deleted Sep '87. Catalogue no: **A 9583**
12" Single: Released Jun '85, on Atlantic, by WEA Records. Deleted Sep '87. Catalogue no: **A 9583 T**

DO YOU WANT IT BAD ENUFF
Tracks: / Call me anytime / Do you want it bad enuff.
7" Single: Released Jan '87, on Atlantic, by WEA Records. Deleted Jan '88. Catalogue no: **A 9343**
12" Single: Released Jan '87, on Atlantic, by WEA Records. Deleted Jan '88. Catalogue no: **A 9343 T**

REMEMBER WHAT YOU LIKE
Tracks: / Remember what you like.
12" Single: Released Mar '84, on Atlantic, by WEA Records. Catalogue no: **A 6959 T**
7" Single: Released Apr '84, on Atlantic, by WEA Records. Catalogue no: **A 6959**

Burtons

MACARTHUR PARK
Tracks: / MacArthur Park / Wuthering heights.
7" Single: Released Feb '80, on Cherry Red, by Cherry Red Records. Deleted Feb '83. Catalogue no: **CHERRY 11**

Burtussi, Ann

I'M NUMBER ONE
Tracks: / I'm number one / So selfish.
7" Single: Released Feb '83, on Speed, Catalogue no: **SPEED 14**

Burundi Black

Biographical details: In late 1971 a single entitled *Burundi Black*, by Burundi Steiphenson Black, entered the British chart. It was a slow but steady seller, peaking at No 31 but remaining in the Top Fifty for 14 weeks. The record featured drummers and chanters from the country of Burundi, with orchestral additions by Frenchman Mike Steiphenson. It stood out because of its tribal rhythms, an unusual feature for a chart record. The name of Burundi Black became fashionable to drop in 1981, the big year for British pop stars Adam & The Ants, whose style was heavily influenced by the Burundi sound and rhythms. (Bob MacDonald, 1984.).

BURUNDI BLACK
Tracks: / Burundi black.
7" Single: Released Nov '71, on Barclay, by Decca Records. Deleted '74. Catalogue no: **BAR 3**
7" Single: Released Jul '81, on Barclay, by Decca Records. Catalogue no: **BA 1**
12" Single: Released Jul '81, on Barclay, by Decca Records. Deleted Feb '89. Catalogue no: **BAX 1**

Bus Boys

BOYS ARE BACK IN TOWN
Tracks: / Boys are back in town.
7" Single: Released Apr '83, on Arista, by BMG Records (UK). Catalogue no: **ARIST 528**

Busch, Lou

Biographical details: Busch, Lou The USA piainist (1910-79) worked on the A&R staff at Capitol in the early '50s and recorded ragtimey piano as Joe ;Fingers' Carr; under his own name his instrumental *Zambesi* was a UK no. 2 in 1956. Donald Clarke, 24 August 1988..

ZAMBESI
Tracks: / Zambesi.
7" Single: Released Jan '56, on Capitol, by EMI Records. Deleted '59. Catalogue no: **CL 14504**

ZAMBESI (OLD GOLD)
Tracks: / Zambesi / Sixteen tons.
7" Single: Released Apr '87, on Old Gold, by Old Gold Records. Deleted Sep '89. Catalogue no: **OG 9719**

Bush Babies

LOVESICK
Tracks: / Lovesick / One night (livin' with you).
7" Single: Released Oct '88, on Escape, by Escape Records. Catalogue no: **AWOL 2**

Bush, Kate

Biographical details: Bush, Kate The UK vocalist and composer was born in 1958 in Surrey; Pink Floyd's Dave Gilmour was a friend who subsidised her early demos. She scored a UK no. 1 in 1978 with her first single *Wuthering Heights*: condensing the gothic Bronte novel to 3 minutes: remains an original achievement. Critics either love her or hate her; she was mercilessly satirised on TV, but every release is successful, though she aims high: her concept LP *Hounds Of Love* in 1986 was a no. 1 album, side 2 inspired by Tennyson's poem 'The Holy Grail'. *The Whole Story* compiles the hit singles. She also sang on Peter Gabriel albums. Donald Clarke, 24 August 1988.

Born in London in 1958, Kate Bush is a singer, songwriter, dancer, mime artist and pianist. By the time she left school at the age of 16, she was a competent piano player and was already writing her own songs. her precocious talent came to the attention of Pink Floyd guitarist David Gilmour, who took her under his wing and financed a professional demo tape. At the age of 17 a recording contract with EMI was secured. One would have expected to see the record company wishing to market this new young talent immediately, but instead they gave the girl an advance payment with which to go and develop her talents at their own speed. Depending on one's view, this unusual restraint by EMI either displayed artistic integrity and foresight on their part, or else was dictated by the commercially minded belief that a more mature Kate would be more successful in the long run. Either way, it was a tribute to Gilmour's negotiating skills that her contract allowed her maximum experimentation and creative freedom.
Kate spent the next two years gigging in the London area and learning to dance and mime. in the summer of 1977 she entered the studios to record her first album.
The general public were quite unaware of this history when her debut single *Wuthering eights* was released in early 1978. To many British record buyers it was a musical revelation, suddenly sprung on their ears from nowhere. Inspired by Emily Bronte's classic novel, it was a dramatic song combining operatic and rock influences, closing with a memorable guitar performance by Gilmour. But the main talking point of the record was Bush's high, ethereal voice which was, depending on personal taste, either strikingly original and fresh or nauseating to the point of aural agony. What was universally agreed upon was the disc's stunning uniqueness. It surged to the British No. 1 position, dethroning Abba in the progress and stayed there for four weeks. To EMI, this sudden fame was the fruit of their careful artist development strategy. To the public, Kate Bush was an overnight sensation.
The same week that *Wuthering Heights* hit the top slot, Bush's debut LP *The Kick Inside* entered the UK album chart. It reached No. 3 and stayed on the list for over a year. it was one of the most extraordinarily original and accomplished opening efforts in the history of British popular music. The title of the album was a reference both to the internal impulses experienced by a pregnant woman and to the energies and ambitions possessed by a young adult. These themes were typical of an album full of controversial, varied and sensitive subjects.
Coming from anyone, these thirteen songs would have been fascinating listening. Coming from this weird 19 year-old girl, they were amazingly perceptive and challenging. There were songs such as *Strange Phenomena* (the artist's personal favourite) which analysed the role of mystical and spiritual forces in everyday life and *Feel It* which, like most of the LPs love songs, was erotic and sexy while simultaneously shy and innocent. *The Man With The Child In His Eyes*, a track culled directly from her original 1975 session, became the second single and reached No. 6 in the UK. it later became a minor hit single in the States, but this was her only significant foray into the US market, a territory which has otherwise shown itself impervious to Bush's unusual talents.
Her second album *Lionheart* was released just eight months after *The Kick Inside*. In terms of both quality and success, it was a strong LP but not the masterwork that its predecessor had been. *Lionheart* reached No. 6 with 36 weeks on the UK charts. Its first single *Hammer Horror* fared dissapointingly, peaking at No. 44 in Britain - it was clearly not a commercial track and was a strange choice for a single.
The next 45 *Wow* compensated by reaching No. 14. This was partly an answer to those critics who poured scorn on her frequent use in interviews of such cliches as 'wow', 'amazing' and 'great', This single coincided with the launch of her first long-awaited national UK tour. Bush was responsible for the entire conception ofthe show, both musically and visually. Its highly theatrical combination of music, dance, costume and mime was a huge box-office and critical success and further heightened her reputation as the UK's most exciting female performer.
Well over a year elapsed between the end of the tour and the release of her next album *Never For Ever*. It was due in June 1980, but was delayed until September. This was to be an ever-growing trend for Bush in the Eighties as her work became more and more complex, she took longer and longer over it. This third LP was nonetheless another commercial triumph, entering the UK album chart at No. 1. In doing so, it became the first album by a solo female British artist ever to reach the top slot. It had been introduced by two UK Top 20 singles: *Breathing*, a weird account of a nuclear holocaust as seen through the eyes of an unborn child, was musically inaccessible but captured the mood of a recently reinvigorated nuclear disarmament movement. *Babooshka*, by contrast was one of her most catchy, poppy singles; it went to No. 5 in the UK charts and thus stands as the second biggest single of her career. The *Never For Ever* album once again displayed extraordinary diversity and

imagination in its choice of themes.
1981 brought just one single, the experimental *Sat In Your Lap*. It was a tribute to the artist's standing in the eyes of the public that such a strange offering should manage to reach No. 11 on the British chart. it was the last time that her audience would so loyally trust her artistic instincts. *Sat In Your Lap* was the first single from her fourth album - but that album was not to surface for over a year.
When *The Dreaming* LP was finally finished and isued in September '82, it entered the k album chart at No. 3. It thus became the only Top 3 album in the whole of 1982 by a solo British female artist. But this initial impact was misleading: it remained on the chart for just nine weeks, by far her lowest total. It was her first LP to fail to yield a major hit single. The inaccessible songs were hindered still further by a doomy, claustrophobic production.
Having begun her career with a No. 1 smash single, Kate Bush has now become merely a cult artist. As her music and creativity had grown more introspective and increasingly wrapped in its own weirdness, her audience had grown smaller. Such a development could hardly have pleased EMI Records, who might by this time have been wondering whether they had allowed her just a little too much freedom. That freedom meant that she spent even longer on her fifth LP. Her new customary studio hibernation extended still further, delaying the release of this next album until 1985. Bush has always resisted outside pressure on her career development. She is a totally individual and unique artist. She has not been an influential figure on other artists, but her place in pop history is assured by the fact that she is one of the most original talents that Britain has yet produced. (Bob MacDonald)..

ARMY DREAMERS
Tracks: / Army dreamers.
7" Single: Released Sep '80, on EMI, by EMI Records. Deleted Apr '88. Catalogue no: **EMI 5106**

BABOOSHKA
Tracks: / Babooshka.
7" Single: Released Jul '80, on EMI, by EMI Records. Deleted '83. Catalogue no: **EMI 5085**

BIG SKY, THE
Tracks: / Big sky, The (single mix) / Not this time / Morning fog, The (12" only).
7" Single: Released Apr '86, on EMI, by EMI Records. Deleted Oct '87. Catalogue no: **KB 4**
12" Single: Released Apr '86, on EMI, by EMI Records. Catalogue no: **12KB 4**

BREATHING
Tracks: / Breathing / Empty bullring.
7" Single: Released Apr '80, on EMI, by EMI Records. Deleted '83. Catalogue no: **EMI 5058**

CLOUDBUSTING
Tracks: / Cloudbusting.
7" Single: Released Oct '85, on EMI, by EMI Records. Deleted Aug '89. Catalogue no: **KB 2**
12" Single: Released Oct '85, on EMI, by EMI Records. Deleted Aug '89. Catalogue no: **12KB 2**

DECEMBER WILL BE MAGIC AGAIN
Tracks: / December will be magic again / Warm and soothing.
7" Single: Released Dec '80, on EMI, by EMI Records. Deleted '83. Catalogue no: **EMI 5121**

DREAMING, THE (SINGLE)
Tracks: / Dreaming, The.
7" Single: Released Aug '82, on EMI, by EMI Records. Deleted '85. Catalogue no: **EMI 5296**

EXPERIMENT IV
Tracks: / Experiment IV / Wuthering heights.
7" Single: Released Oct '86, on EMI, by EMI Records. Deleted Oct '87. Catalogue no: **KB 5**
12" Single: Released Oct '86, on EMI, by EMI Records. Deleted Oct '87. Catalogue no: **12KB 5**

HAMMER HORROR
Tracks: / Hammer horror.
7" Single: Released Nov '78, on EMI, by EMI Records. Deleted '81. Catalogue no: **EMI 2887**

HOUNDS OF LOVE
Tracks: / Hounds of love / Handsome cabin boy, The / Hounds of love (Del Palmer remix) (Extra track on 12" only) / Jig of love* (*=Extra track on 12" only).
7" Single: Released Feb '86, on EMI, by EMI Records. Deleted 31 Jul '88. Catalogue no: **KB 3**
12" Single: Released Feb '86, on EMI, by EMI Records. Deleted Aug '89. Catalogue no: **12KB 3**

KATE BUSH ON STAGE EP
Tracks: / Them heavy people / Don't push your foot on the heartbrake / James and the cold gun / L'amour looks something like you.
7" Single: Released Sep '79, on EMI, by EMI Records. Deleted '82. Catalogue no: **MIEP 2991**

MAN WITH THE CHILD IN HIS EYES
Tracks: / Man with the child in his eyes, The.
7" Single: Released Jun '78, on EMI, by EMI Records. Deleted '81. Catalogue no: **EMI 2806**

NE T'ENFUIS PAS
Tracks: / Ne t'enfuis pas.
7" Single: Released Aug '83, on EMI (Europe), by EMI Records. Catalogue no: **PM 165 1527**

RUNNING UP THAT HILL
Tracks: / Running up that hill.
12" Single: Released Aug '85, on EMI, by EMI Records. Deleted Aug '89. Catalogue no: **12KB 1**
7" Single: Released Aug '85, on EMI, by EMI Records. Deleted Aug '89. Catalogue no: **KB 1**

SAT IN YOUR LAP
Tracks: / Sat in your lap / Lord of the reedy river.
7" Single: Released Jul '81, on EMI, by EMI Records. Deleted '84. Catalogue no: **EMI 5201**

SENSUAL WORLD, THE (SINGLE)
Tracks: / Sensual world, The / Sensual world, The (Instrumental version) (12" & CD single only.) / Walk straight down the middle.
Cassingle: Released Sep '89, on EMI, by EMI Records. Catalogue no: **TCEM 102**
CD 5": Released Sep '89, on EMI, by EMI Records. Catalogue no: **EMCD 102**
7" Single: Released Sep '89, on EMI, by EMI Records. Catalogue no: **EM 102**
12" Single: Released Sep '89, on EMI, by EMI Records. Catalogue no: **12EM 102**

THERE GOES A TENNER
Tracks: / There goes a tenner / Ne t'en fui pas.
7" Single: Released Oct '82, on EMI, by EMI Records. Deleted Oct '85. Catalogue no: **EMI 5350**

WOW
Tracks: / Wow.
7" Single: Released Mar '79, on EMI, by EMI Records. Deleted '82. Catalogue no: **EMI 2911**

WUTHERING HEIGHTS
Tracks: / Wuthering heights.
7" Single: Released Nov '77, on EMI, by EMI Records. Catalogue no: **EMI 2719**

Bush, Stan

TOUCH, THE
Tracks: / Dare to be stupid / Touch, The.
7" Single: Released Nov '86, on Epic, by CBS Records. Catalogue no: **A 7318**

Bush Tetras

BOOM
Tracks: / Boom.
7" Single: Released May '81, on Fetish, Catalogue no: **FET 007**

RITUALS
Tracks: / Rituals.
12" Single: Released Dec '81, on Fetish, Catalogue no: **FE 16 EP**

Bushay, Silhouett

SO I CAN LOVE YOU
Tracks: / So I can love you.
12" Single: Released Nov '88, on Bushranger, Catalogue no: **BFM 66**

Bushido

AMONG THE RUINS
Tracks: / Among the ruins.
12" Single: Released Nov '84, on Third Mind, by Third Mind Records. Catalogue no: **TMS 02**

VOICES
Tracks: / Voices.
12" Single: Released Oct '85, on Third Mind, by Third Mind Records. Catalogue no: **TMS 05**

Bushmen

SEAT IT OUT
Tracks: / Seat it out.
12" Single: Released Jun '85, on Uptight, Catalogue no: **UPT 11**

Bushmen Don't Surf

HAPPY FACES
Tracks: / Happy faces / Ntombentle.
7" Single: Released Oct '88, on Tau Music, Catalogue no: **TAU 5001**
12" Single: Released Oct '88, on Tau Music, Catalogue no: **TAU 5001T**

Busia, Kofi

Biographical details: Kofi Busia is the 36 year-old son of Dr. K.A. Busia,a former Prime Minister of Ghana,and brother of film actress Akosua Busia(Nettle in'The Color Purple'the film by Steven Spielberg).He was inspired while watching the Live Aid concert on TVto start work on the album'Oh Africa',an album that sets out to outline some of Africa's political & historical transformations since the arrival of the 'European settlers'in music & song.Although his work is mainly to do with political protest it should not be ignored as it contains the infectious rhythms & percussive interplays that are the exciting hallmark of African music.Well worth checking out..

HOLD SOMEBODY
Tracks: / Hold somebody / N.M.Q. (Nelson Mandela Quintet).
Note: All instruments & vocals by Kofi Busia.Recorded & mixed at Keyboard Studios, London, June 1,2,3, 1987.Engineered by Oliver Hitch. Mastered at Abbey Road Studios London, June 11th.1987. Engineered by Steve Rooke.
12" Single: Released Aug '87, on African Records International, by African Rec. Int.. Catalogue no: **ANM 12281T**

Business

DAY O
Tracks: / Smash the discos / Day O.
7" Single: Released Jul '82, on Secret, by Secret Records. Catalogue no: **SHH 132**

DO A RUNNER
Tracks: / Do a runner.
12" Single: Released Apr '88, on Link, by Link Records. Catalogue no: **LINK 1201**

DRINKING AND DRIVING
Tracks: / Drinking and driving / H-bomb / Hurry up Harry (on 12" only).
7" Single: Released Dec '85, on Diamond, by Revolver Records. Catalogue no: **DIA 011**
12" Single: Released Dec '85, on Diamond, by Revolver Records. Catalogue no: **DIAEL 011**

GET OUT OF MY HOUSE
Tracks: / Get out of my house / All out tonight / Foreign girl / Outlaw.
7" Single: Released Aug '86, on Link, by Link Records. Catalogue no: **WOW 121**

GET UP
Tracks: / Get up / This is the night.
7" Single: Released Apr '81, on MCA, by MCA Records. Deleted Apr '86. Catalogue no: **MCA 2003**

HARRY MAY
Tracks: / Harry May.
7" Single: Released Jul '82, on Secret, by Secret Records. Catalogue no: **SHH 123**

Business Connection

BRING YOU DOWN
Tracks: / Bring you down / Connections.
12" Single: Released Jan '86, on Hippodrome, by Hippodrome Records. Catalogue no: **12 HIPPO 106**
7" Single: Released Jan '86, on Hippodrome, by Hippodrome Records. Catalogue no: **HIPPO 106**

Busker

HOME NEWCASTLE
Tracks: / Home Newcastle / Takin' the time.
7" Single: Released Sep '81, on EMI, by EMI Records. Deleted '84. Catalogue no: **EMI 5235**
7" Single: Released Aug '81, on Lynx, Catalogue no: **SSM 025**

Buster

SUNDAY
Tracks: / Sunday.
7" Single: Released Jun '78, on RCA, by BMG Records (UK). Deleted '81. Catalogue no: **RCA 2678**

Buster Gobsmack...

WE WANNA BE FAMOUS
Tracks: / We wanna be famous.
7" Single: Released Jul '88, on BBC, by BBC Records & Tapes. Catalogue no: **RESL 226**

Buster, Prince

Biographical details: See under **Prince Buster**.

AL CAPONE
Tracks: / Al Capone.
12" Single: Released Sep '81, on Blue Beat, Catalogue no: **DDBB 324**
7" Single: Released Sep '81, on Blue Beat, Catalogue no: **BB 324**

BIG 5
Tracks: / Big 5.
7" Single: Released Sep '81, on Prince Buster, by Melodisc Records. Catalogue no: **PB 1**
12" Single: Released Sep '81, on Prince Buster, by Melodisc Records. Catalogue no: **DDPB 1**

CLEOPATRA
Tracks: / Cleopatra.
7" Single: Released Sep '81, on Prince Buster, by Melodisc Records. Catalogue no: **PB 2**
12" Single: Released Sep '81, on Prince Buster, by Melodisc Records. Catalogue no: **DDPB 2**

JUDGE DREAD
Tracks: / Judge Dread.
12" Single: Released Sep '81, on Prince Buster, by Melodisc Records. Catalogue no: **DDPB 4**
7" Single: Released Sep '81, on Prince Buster, by Melodisc Records. Catalogue no: **PB 4**

STACK-O-LEE
Tracks: / Stack-o-lee / Stack o lee (version).
12" Single: Released Feb '89, on Gaz's, Catalogue no: **GAZ 12010**

TEN COMMANDMENTS OF MEN
Tracks: / Ten commandments of men.
12" Single: Released Sep '81, on Blue Beat, Catalogue no: **DDBB 334**
7" Single: Released Sep '81, on Blue Beat, Catalogue no: **BB 334**

WRECK A PUM PUM (SINGLE)
Tracks: / Wreck a pum pum.
7" Single: Released Sep '81, on Prince Buster, by Melodisc Records. Catalogue no: **PB 3**
12" Single: Released Sep '81, on Prince Buster, by Melodisc Records. Catalogue no: **DDPB 3**

Busters

RUDE GIRL
Tracks: / Rude girl.
7" Single: Released Mar '89, on Unicorn Records, by Unicorn Records. Catalogue no: **PHZ 37**
12" Single: Released Apr '89, on Unicorn Records, by Unicorn Records. Catalogue no: **12PHZ 37**

SOMEONE SAYS
Tracks: / Someone says.
7" Single: Released Apr '89, on Unicorn Records, by Unicorn Records. Catalogue no: **PHZ 37**

Busy Bee

SUICIDE
Tracks: / Suicide.
12" Single: Released 29 Sep '86, on Strong City (USA), by M-Low Records (USA). Catalogue no: **ST 006**

Butcher

ON THE GROUND
Tracks: / On the ground.
7" Single: Released Feb '83, on Inept, Catalogue no: **INEPT 002**

STAND AND FIGHT
Tracks: / Stand and fight.
12" Single: Released Oct '83, on Inept, Catalogue no: **INEPT 003**

Butcher, John

GOODBYE SAVING GRACE
Tracks: / Goodbye saving grace / Partners in crime.
7" Single: Released Oct '87, on Capitol, by EMI Records. Catalogue no: **CL 464**
12" Single: Released Oct '87, on Capitol, by EMI Records. Catalogue no: **12CL 464**

Butera, Sam

BIM BAM
Tracks: / Bim bam / Twinkle in your eye.
7" Single: Released Jan '81, on Capitol, by EMI Records. Deleted Jan '84. Catalogue no: **CL 16179**

Butler, Billy

RIGHT TRACK
Tracks: / Right track.
7" Single: Released Mar '85, on Skratch, by Skratch Records. Catalogue no: **SKM 09**
12" Single: Released Mar '85, on Skratch, by Skratch Records. Catalogue no: **SKM 09(12)**

Butler, Jerry

Biographical details: Butler, Jerry A soul singer born in Mississippi in 1939, he moved to Chicago at age 3. He sang in church, met Curtis Mayfield and renamed the group the Impressions, scoring a no. 11 pop hit *For Your Precious Love* in 1958. The label's billing of group as 'Jerry Butler and the Impressions' led to a rift; ex-Rooster Fred Cash replaced him, but Mayfield continued to write and arrange for Butler. Vee Jay took over the Falcon label and signed Butler as a single, letting the Impressions go; the Butler-Mayfield team had further hits including Henry Mancini's *Moon River*, helping to make it song of the year. Butler wrote solo too, contributing to Jackie Wilson and Otis Redding; his mellow ballads and cool stage style earned him the nickname of 'Iceman'. He worked with Gamble & Huff in Philadelphia for a while, continued making fine records, including guets with Gene Candler and Thelma Houston. With younger brother Billy he ran a music workshop in Chicago for young singers/musicians/writers (grads include Natalie Cole). Donald Clarke, 24 August 1988..

HE WILL BREAK YOUR HEART
Tracks: / He will break your heart.
7" Single: Released Jul '80, on Charly, by Charly Records. Deleted '87. Catalogue no: **CTD 114**

SHORTY'S GOT TO...
Tracks: / Shorty's got to...
7" Single: Released '88, on JSP, by JSP Records. Catalogue no: **JSP 4501**

Butler, Jonathan

BABY PLEASE DON'T TAKE IT
Tracks: / Baby please don't take it / Haunted by your love / Gentle love (Extra track on 12" only).
12" Single: Released May '86, on Jive, by Zomba Records. Deleted Jul '87. Catalogue no: **JIVET 120**
7" Single: Released May '86, on Jive, by Zomba Records. Deleted Jul '87. Catalogue no: **JIVE 120**

HOLDING ON
Tracks: / Holding on / Seventh Avenue South.
7" Single: Released '88, Deleted '88. Catalogue no: **JIVE 157**
12" Single: Released Oct '87, on Jive, by Zomba Records. Deleted '88. Catalogue no: **JIVET 157**

LIES
Tracks: / Lies / Haunted by you love.
CD 5": Released Jul '87, on Jive, by Zomba Records. Catalogue no: **JIVECD 141**
7" Single: Released Jul '87, on Jive, by Zomba Records. Catalogue no: **JIVE 141**
12" Single: Released Jul '87, on Jive, by Zomba Records. Catalogue no: **JIVET 141**

OVERFLOWING
Tracks: / Overflowing / Lies.
CD 5": Released May '88, on Jive, by Zomba Records. Deleted '88. Catalogue no: **JIVECD 172**
7" Single: Released 23 Apr '88, on Jive, by Zomba Records. Deleted '88. Catalogue no: **JIVE 172**
12" Single: Released 23 Apr '88, on Jive, by Zomba Records. Deleted '88. Catalogue no: **JIVET 172**

TAKE GOOD CARE OF ME
Tracks: / Take good care of me / Song for John / Thinking of you (Extra track available on 12" only.).
CD 5": Released Jan '88, on Jive, by Zomba Records. Catalogue no: **JIVECD 159**
7" Single: Released Jan '88, on Jive, by Zomba Records. Deleted '88. Catalogue no: **JIVE 159**
12" Single: Released Jan '88, on Jive, by Zomba Records. Deleted '88. Catalogue no: **JIVET 159**

THERE'S ONE BORN EVERY MINUTE
Tracks: / There's one born every minute.
CD 5": Released '88, on Jive, by Zomba Records. Deleted '88. Catalogue no: **JIVECD 187**
Special: Released '88, on Jive, by Zomba Records. Deleted '88. Catalogue no: **JIVER 187**
7" Single: Released Oct '88, on Jive, by Zomba Records. Deleted '88. Catalogue no: **JIVE 187**
12" Single: Released Oct '88, on Jive, by Zomba Records. Deleted '88. Catalogue no: **JIVET 187**

TRUE LOVE NEVER FAILS
Tracks: / True love never fails / Lies (By J.Butler) / Take me home (By J.Butler) / Love songs (On 12" only) / Candlelight and you (On 12" only).
12" Single: Released Dec '88, on Jive, by Zomba Records. Catalogue no: **JIVET 196**
CD 5": Released Jan '89, on Jive, by Zomba Records. Catalogue no: **JIVECD 196**
7" Single: Released Dec '88, on Jive, by Zomba Records. Catalogue no: **JIVE 196**

Butler, Marty

LOOKS LIKE LOVE THIS TIME
Tracks: / Looks like love this time.
7" Single: Released Jan '84, on Gipsy, by Gipsy Records. Catalogue no: **GIPSY 14**

Butler, Matthew

BRIGHT EYES
Tracks: / Bright eyes / We are the Four Tuckateers.
7" Single: Released Nov '80, on CBS, by CBS Records. Deleted Nov '83. Catalogue no: **CBS 9096**

Butler, Tara

MISCHIEF
Tracks: / Mischief.
12" Single: Released May '85, on Illuminated, Catalogue no: **ILL 5712**

UP AGAINST THE WALL
Tracks: / Up against the wall.
7" Single: Released Feb '85, on Illuminated, Catalogue no: **ILL 44**
12" Single: Released Feb '85, on Illuminated, Catalogue no: **ILL 4412**

Butterfield 8

WATERMELON MAN
Tracks: / Watermelon man / St. Lyle Drive / Rag (Only on 12".) / B on it (Only on 12".).
7" Single: Released Jun '88, on Go Discs, by Chrysalis Records. Catalogue no: **GO BUT 1**
12" Single: Released Jun '88, on Go Discs, by Chrysalis Records. Catalogue no: **GO BUT 112**

Butterscotch

DON'T YOU KNOW
Tracks: / Don't you know.
7" Single: Released May '70, on RCA, by BMG Records (UK). Deleted '73. Catalogue no: **RCA 1937**

Butthole Surfers

CREAMED CORN FROM THE SOCKET OF DAVIS EP
12" Single: Released Oct '85, on Fundamental, by Fundamental Music Records. Deleted '87. Catalogue no: **PRAY 069**

WIDOWERMAKER
Tracks: / Widower maker.
12" Single: Released Jul '89, on Blast First, by Blast First Records. Catalogue no: **BFFPO 41**
CD 5": Released Jul '89, on Blast First, by Blast First Records. Catalogue no: **BFFPO 41CD**
10" single: Released Jul '89, on Blast First, by Blast First Records. Catalogue no: **BFIPO 41**

Buy Off The Bar

MY LIFE IS LIKE A STANLEY KNIFE(EP)
7" EP: Released Jun '86, on Deng Deng Deng, Catalogue no: **DENG 2**

SECOND PEEL SESSION, THE
10" single: Released Jan '88, on Bang Bang, by Bang Bang Records. Catalogue no: **BILLY 002**

Buzby

BIRDS DANCE
Tracks: / Birds dance / Disneyland.
7" Single: Released Sep '81, on Flair, by Flair Records. Catalogue no: **FLA 102**

Buzz

MARINETTI
Tracks: / Marinetti.
12" Single: Released May '88, on Danceteria, Catalogue no: **12 DAN 002**

SEXE
Tracks: / Sexe.
12" Single: Released May '88, on Danceteria, Catalogue no: **12 DAN 008**

Buzz And The Flyers

GO CAT WILD
Tracks: / Go cat wild / Dance to the bop.
7" Single: Released Mar '81, on Hot Rock, by Hot Rock Records. Catalogue no: **HR 45 007**

Buzzcocks

Biographical details: Buzzcocks, The New wave/punk combo, formed in Manchester in 1975 by guitarist Pete Shelley and Howard Devoto, who sang and wrote lyrics. Inspired by the Sex Pistols to recruit John Maher on drums, Steve Diggle on bass; an EP on their own New Hormones got them off but Devot left to form Magazine, Diggle moving to guitar, Garth joining on bass (replaced in 1978 by Steve Garvey). *Another Music In A Different Kitchen* '77 saw Shelley's romantic/adolescent lyrics differ from prevailing concerns of punk, yet songs were still played at breakneck punk pace, like the Beatles at 78 rpm. They evolved towards Shelley's interest in avant-garde Euro rock, lost impetus and split up in 1981. Shelley had been collaborating with Buzzcock's producer Martin Rushent; Diggle and Maher formed Flag of Convenience but Shelley has been more successful as a solo. Donald Clarke, 24 August 1988

At the time of their greatest commercial success, this British punk rock band consisted of Steve Diggle, Steve Garvey, John Maher and Pete Shelley.

The Buzzcocks were formed in the summer of 1976 when guitarist Pete Shelley met vocalist Howard Devoto. Gathering other musicians around them, they played support to an anarchistic, up-and-coming punk band, the Sex Pistols. In January 1977 the Buzzcocks financed the release of their own first record, a four-track EP entitled *Spiral Scratch*. By this time they had built up a reputation as one of the leading groups in Britain's exploding New Wave of punk rock - this disc cemented that status. The four songs - *Breakdown, Time's Up, Boredom* and *Friends Of Mine* - were seminal examples of this sudden revolution in British rock. Issued only one month after the Sex Pistols' notorious appearance on the Bill Grundy TV show, this EP played an important role in the advancement of a genre and movement that was to turn the UK music business on its head. its songs and style were uncompromising and furiously energetic, providing a perfect antidote for those bored by the sophisticated, well-produced rock that had become prevalent in the early and mid-Seventies. Together with the Pistols, the Clash, the Damned and the Jam, the Buzzcocks were one of the five leading pioneers of the UK's 1976/77 New Wave/Punk rock explosion.

Despite their increasing reputation, Devoto left the band shortly after the release of the EP and began his own group 'Magazine'. Shelley took over vocal duties and the new Buzzcocks supported the Clash on their White Riot tour. Signing with United Artists Records later in '77, the Buzzcocks scored their fist chart single in February 1978. It was called *What Do I Get* and reached No. 37 on the UK listings. It was quickly followed by their debut album *Another Music In A Different Kitchen*, which peaked No. 15 with 11 weeks on the UK chart. Two more minor hit 45s, *I Don't Mind* and *Love You More*, were fast in appearing. Then, in the autumn of '78, came their biggest single *Ever Fallen In Love (With Someone You Shouldn't Have)*. This reached No. 12 and demonstrated that the group were losing their original punk-orientated cutting edge in order to move closer to pop. This policy was briefly successful - the hit was accompanied by a second UK Top 20 album *Love Bites*, plus a follow-up Top 20 single *Promises*.

They never reached either Top 20 again, however. The group's only quality release to reach the charts subsequently was the reactivated *Spiral Scratch* EP. This received its long overdue chart placing in the late summer of '79, peaking at No. 31 in Britain. Realising that the punk had gone, Shelley left the band in early '81 and the Buzzcocks folded. He embarked on a solo career which, despite continued coverage in the British rock press, failed to make much impact. (Bob MacDonald)..

ARE EVERYTHING
Tracks: / Are everything / Why she's a girl from the chainstore.
7" Single: Released Sep '80, on United Artists, by EMI Records. Deleted '83. Catalogue no: **BP 365**

EVER FALLEN IN LOVE (WITH SOMEONE YOU SHOULDN'T'VE)
Tracks: / Ever fallen in love / Ever fallen in love (with someone you shouldn't've) / Promises / Everybody's happy nowadays / Harmony in my head.
7" Single: Released Sep '78, on United Artists, by EMI Records. Deleted '81. Catalogue no: **UP 36455**

EVERYBODY'S HAPPY NOWADAYS
Tracks: / Everybody's happy nowadays.
7" Single: Released Mar '79, on United Artists, by EMI Records. Deleted '82. Catalogue no: **UP 36499**

FAB FOUR
Tracks: / Ever fallen in love (with someone you shouldn't 've?) / Promises / Everybody's happy nowadays / Harmony in my head.
7" Single: Released Oct '89, on EMI, by EMI Records. Catalogue no: **203 519 7**
CD 5": Released Oct '89, on EMI, by EMI Records. Catalogue no: **CDEM 104**
CD 5": Released Oct '89, on EMI, by EMI Records. Catalogue no: **203 519 2**
12" Single: Released Oct '89, on EMI, by EMI Records. Catalogue no: **12EM 104**
7" Single: Released Oct '89, on EMI, by EMI Records. Catalogue no: **EM 104**
12" Single: Released Oct '89, on EMI, by EMI Records. Catalogue no: **203 519 6**

HARMONY IN MY HEAD
Tracks: / Harmony in my head.
7" Single: Released Jul '79, on United Artists, by EMI Records. Deleted '82. Catalogue no: **UP 36541**

I DON'T MIND
Tracks: / I don't mind.
7" Single: Released May '78, on United Artists, by EMI Records. Deleted '81. Catalogue no: **UP 36386**

LOVE YOU MORE
Tracks: / Love you more.
7" Single: Released Jul '78, on United Artists, by EMI Records. Deleted '81. Catalogue no: **UP 36433**

PEEL SESSIONS: BUZZCOCKS
12" Single: Released Jan '88, on Strange Fruit, by Strange Fruit Records. Catalogue no: **SFPS 044**

PROMISES
Tracks: / Promises.
7" Single: Released Nov '78, on United Artists, by EMI Records. Deleted '81. Catalogue no: **UP 36471**

RUNNING FREE
Tracks: / Running free / What do you know.
7" Single: Released Nov '80, on Liberty, by EMI Records. Deleted Nov '83. Catalogue no: **BP 382**

SPIRAL SCRATCH (EP)
Tracks: / Breakdown / Time's up / Boredom / Friends of mine.
7" Single: Released Jul '81, on New Hormones, Catalogue no: **ORG 1**

STRANGE THING
Tracks: / Strange thing.
7" Single: Released Oct '80, on Liberty, by EMI Records. Deleted Oct '83. Catalogue no: **BP 371**

WHAT DO I GET
Tracks: / What do I get.
7" Single: Released Feb '78, on United Artists, by EMI Records. Deleted '81. Catalogue no: **UP 36348**

Buzzcocks Foc

SUNSET
Tracks: / Sunset.
CD 5": Released Jul '89, on Thin Line, by Thin Line Records. Catalogue no: **THIN 003 CD**
12" Single: Released Jul '89, on Thin Line, by Thin Line Records. Catalogue no: **THIN 003**

Buzzz

HIT THE ROAD JACK
Tracks: / Hit the road Jack.
7" Single: Released Jul '82, on RCA, by BMG Records (UK). Catalogue no: **RCA 248**
12" Single: Released Jul '82, on RCA, by BMG Records (UK). Catalogue no: **RCAT 248**

BY ALL MEANS - SURRENDER TO YOUR LOVE (Released on 4th & Broadway)

OBSESSION
Tracks: / Obsession / I like it like that.
7" Single: Released Nov '82, on RCA, by BMG Records (UK). Catalogue no: **RCA 281**
12" Single: Released Nov '82, on RCA, by BMG Records (UK). Catalogue no: **RCAT 281**

SORRY MY DEAR
Tracks: / Sorry my dear / Buzzy.
7" Single: Released Jan '82, on RCA, by BMG Records (UK). Catalogue no: **RCA 181**
12" Single: Released Jan '82, on RCA, by BMG Records (UK). Catalogue no: **RCAT 181**

BVO

PINK PUNKER
Tracks: / Pink punker / Kyoto.
7" Single: Released May '83, on EMI, by EMI Records. Catalogue no: **EMI 5388**

B.V.S.M.P.

ANY TIME
Tracks: / Any time (inst) / Any time.
12" Single: Released Sep '88, on Debut, by Skratch Records. Catalogue no: **DEBTX 3056**
CD 5": Released Sep '88, on Debut, by Skratch Records. Catalogue no: **BC 50-2160**
7" Single: Released Sep '88, on Debut, by Skratch Records. Catalogue no: **DEBT 3056**

I NEED YOU
Tracks: / I need you / I need you (radio instrumental) / I need you (extended vocal version) (Track on 12" version.) / I need you (radio mix) (Track on 12" version.).
7" Single: Released 14 Jul '88, on Debut, by Skratch Records. Catalogue no: **DEBT 3044**
12" Single: Released 14 Jul '88, on Debut, by Skratch Records. Catalogue no: **DEBTX 3044**

By All Means

SOMEBODY SAVE ME
Tracks: / Somebody save me / Somebody save me (LP version) / Somebody save me (garage mix) (Only on the 12" version.) / Somebody save me (emotion mix) (Only on the 12" version.) / Somebody save me (bonus beat) (Only on the 12" version.) / Somebody save me (remix).
12" Single: Released 26 Sep '88, on 4th & Broadway, by Island Records. Deleted Apr '89. Catalogue no: **12 BRW 114**
7" Single: Released 26 Sep '88, on 4th & Broadway, by Island Records. Deleted Apr '89. Catalogue no: **BRW 114**
12" Single: Released 26 Sep '88, on 4th & Broadway, by Island Records. Deleted Apr '89. Catalogue no: **12 BRX 114**

SURRENDER TO YOUR LOVE (see panel on previous page)
Tracks: / Surrender to your love / We're into this groove / Slow Jam.
12" Single: Released 24 May '88, on 4th & Broadway, by Island Records. Catalogue no: **12 BRW 102**
7" Single: Released 16 May '88, on 4th & Broadway, by Island Records. Deleted Apr '89. Catalogue no: **BRW 102**

By Chance

REVENGE
Tracks: / Revenge / Soul kitchen.
7" Single: Released May '87, on Crammed Discs, by Crammed Discs. Deleted '88. Catalogue no: **CRAM 5457**
12" Single: Released May '87, on Crammed Discs, by Crammed Discs. Catalogue no: **CRAM 54512**

Byfield, Annette

NEVER GET TO HEAVEN
Tracks: / Never get to heaven.
12" Single: Released Feb '89, on Ariwa Sounds, by Ariwa Sounds. Catalogue no: **ARI 84**

Byfield, Rockin' Jimmy

RAGING STORM
Tracks: / Raging storm / Can't jive enough.
7" Single: Released Oct '81, on Sonet, by Sonet Records. Catalogue no: **SON 2236**

STAND BACK
Tracks: / Stand back / Another chance.
7" Single: Released May '81, on Sonet, by Sonet Records. Catalogue no: **SON 2224**

YOU GOT ME AND I GOT YOU
Tracks: / You got me and I got you.
7" Single: Released Oct '82, on Sonet, by Sonet Records. Catalogue no: **SON 2247**

Byfield, Ziggy

RUNNING
Tracks: / Running / If i see you in the morning.
7" Single: Released May '80, on PVK, by PVK Records. Deleted May '85. Catalogue no: **PV 39**

Bygraves

LOVING YOU
Tracks: / Loving you.
12" Single: Released Jul '89, on Rham, by Rham Records. Catalogue no: **RS 89005**

Bygraves, Max

Biographical details: Bygraves, Max Born in 1922 in London, the British entertainer was nicknamed after legendary comic Max Miller. He made a few films, was heard on radio with Peter Brough and young Julie Andrews in 'Educating Archie'; also worked with Judy Garland. Twelve UK top 30 entries in the '50s included *Cowpuncher's Cantata*, *Heart Of My Heart*, novelty *Gilly, Gilly, Oscenfeffer, Katzenellen Bogen By The Sea*. His own song *You Need Hands* '58, recording of Leslie Bricusse number *Out Of Town* '56 won Ivor Novello awards. UK top ten hit *Fings Ain't Wot They Used T' Be* '60 was his last; after hearing his mother complain about 'beat' music, he made an album of standards produced by Cyril Stapleton: *Singalongamax* medleys began in 1971 and were of absolutely no consequence, but made a lot of mothers happy. He published autobiography 'I Wanna Tell You A Story' in 1976, was awarded OBE in 1982, hosted TV game show 'Family Fortunes' in 1983. Donald Clarke, 24 August 1988

This British singer, comedian and entertainer had the honour of being listed on Britain's first ever record chart. Published by the New Musical Express on 14th November 1952, Bygraves was at No. 11 on the inaugural list with *Cowpuncher's Cantata*, a medley single which eventually peaked at No. 6. He became a chart regular throughout the Fifties. His middle-of-the-road, easy listening hits included the Top Tenners, *Heart Of Mine*, *Gilly Gilly Ossenfeffer Katzenellen Bogen By The Sea* (!) and *Jingle Bell Rock*. But his two biggest singles on the British charts were 1955's *Meet Me On The Corner* (No. 2) and 1958's long-running double A sided success *You Need Hands/ Tulips From Amsterdam* (No. 3). *You Need hands* was an appropriate number for Bygraves to sing - he became well known on British television for his hand-flapping gestures, which were often accompanied by his catch-phrase *I Wanna Tell You A Story*.
The Sixties brought him the occasional chart single and his final hit 45 was his 1973 UK Top 20 remake of *Deck Of Cards*, the slightly sickly religious narration made famous by Wink Martindale. By this time he had started selling albums in large quantities and it was in this field that he now concerntrated his recording activities. His first successful LP was 1972's *Sing Along With Max*, which peaked No. 4 with 44 weeks on the UK listings. This proved the first in a never-ending series. The title was amended to *Singalongamax* and later came *Singalongapartysong*, *Singalongaxmas*, etc., etc. These LPs featured endless medleys of mainly familiar songs, designed to appeal to those older record buyers who did not demand a great deal of depth or imagination from their music. Vast numbers of songs were strung together, made to sound rather similar to one another and woven into a bland but effective whole. Bygraves' highest placed album was issued in 1976: *100 Golden Greats*, a double set, reached No. 3 on the British LP chart. By this time Bygraves had become an even bigger star on UK TV, including many shows featuring his (mainly nostalgic) singalongs. He continues to be a British showbusiness institution. (Bob MacDonald)..

6 TRACK HITS: MAX BYGRAVES
Tracks: / You're my everything / Gentle on my mind / Deck of cards / Walk right back / For the good times / Rolling round the world.
7" EP: Released Sep '83, on Scoop 33, by Pickwick Records. Catalogue no: **7SR 5009**

BALLAD OF DAVY CROCKETT
Tracks: / Ballad of Davy Crockett, The.
7" Single: Released Feb '56, on H.M.V., by EMI Records. Deleted '59. Catalogue no: **POP 153**

BELLS OF AVIGNON
Tracks: / Bells of Avignon.
7" Single: Released Jun '61, on Decca, by Decca Records. Deleted '64. Catalogue no: **F 11350**

BLUE EYES DON'T MAKE AN ANGEL
Tracks: / Blue eyes don't make an angel / Long long singalong.
7" Single: Released Sep '82, on Monarch, by Monarch Records. Catalogue no: **MON 033**

CONSIDER YOURSELF
Tracks: / Consider yourself.
7" Single: Released Jul '60, on Decca, by Decca Records. Deleted '63. Catalogue no: **F 11251**

COSTA DEL SOL
Tracks: / Costa del sol.
7" Single: Released Jul '85, on Lantern, Catalogue no: **LTR 7001**

COWPUNCHER'S CANTATA
Tracks: / Cowpuncher's cantata.
7" Single: Released Nov '52, on H.M.V., by EMI Records. Deleted '55. Catalogue no: **B 10250**

DECK OF CARDS (SINGLE)
Tracks: / Deck of cards.
7" Single: Released '74, on PRT, by Castle Communications Records. Catalogue no: **7N 45276**

FINGS AIN'T WHAT THEY USED TO BE
Tracks: / Fings ain't what they used to be.
7" Single: Released Mar '60, on Decca, by Decca Records. Deleted '63. Catalogue no: **F 11214**

GILLY GILLY OSSENFEFFER KATZENELLEN BOGEN
Tracks: / Gilly gilly ossenfeffer katzenellenbogen by the sea.
7" Single: Released Sep '54, on H.M.V., by EMI Records. Deleted '57. Catalogue no: **B 10734**

HEART
Tracks: / Heart.
7" Single: Released Apr '57, on Decca, by Decca Records. Deleted '60. Catalogue no: **F 10862**

HEART OF MY HEART
Tracks: / Heart of my heart.
7" Single: Released May '54, on H.M.V., by EMI Records. Deleted '57. Catalogue no: **B 10654**

I LIKE BEER
Tracks: / I like beer / Movies.
7" Single: Released Aug '80, on Piccadilly, Deleted Aug '83. Catalogue no: **7P 198**

I'VE GOTTA COLD
Tracks: / I've gotta cold / Every now and then.
7" Single: Released Feb '81, on Piccadilly, Deleted Feb '84. Catalogue no: **7P 210**

JINGLE BELL ROCK
Tracks: / Jingle bell rock.
7" Single: Released Dec '59, on Decca, by Decca Records. Deleted '62. Catalogue no: **F 11176**

KITE
Tracks: / Kite / Picking up pebbles.
7" Single: Released Feb '80, on Pye, Deleted '83. Catalogue no: **7P 158**

LITTLE TRAIN
Tracks: / Little train / Gotta have rain.
7" Single: Released Aug '58, on Decca, by Decca Records. Deleted '61. Catalogue no: **F 11096**

MEET ME ON THE CORNER
Tracks: / Meet me on the corner.
7" Single: Released Nov '55, on H.M.V., by EMI Records. Deleted '58. Catalogue no: **POP 116**

MR SANDMAN
Tracks: / Mr. Sandman.
7" Single: Released Jan '55, on H.M.V., by EMI Records. Deleted '58. Catalogue no: **B 10821**

MY UKELELE
Tracks: / My ukelele.
7" Single: Released Feb '59, on Decca, by Decca Records. Deleted '62. Catalogue no: **F 11077**

OUT OF TOWN
Tracks: / Out of town.
7" Single: Released May '56, on H.M.V., by EMI Records. Deleted '59. Catalogue no: **POP 164**

TIME,TIME,TIME
Tracks: / Time,time,time / When you were young.
7" Single: Released Jan '86, on Spartan, Catalogue no: **SP 131**

YOU NEED HANDS
Tracks: / You need hands / Tulips from Amsterdam.
7" Single: Released May '58, on Decca, by Decca Records. Deleted '61. Catalogue no: **F 11004**

YOU'RE MY EVERYTHING (SINGLE)
Tracks: / You're my everything.
7" Single: Released Feb '69, on Pye, Deleted '72. Catalogue no: **7 N 17705**

Byles, Junior

BETTER BE CAREFUL
Tracks: / Better be careful.
12" Single: Released Jun '82, on Carib Jems, Catalogue no: **CGDD 21**

Byrd, Beverly

ALL DAY & ALL OF THE NIGHT
Tracks: / All day & all of the night / We're so modern.
12" Single: Released Jun '81, on Rialto (1), by Rialto Records. Deleted Jun '84. Catalogue no: **TREBL 141**
7" Single: Released Jun '81, on Rialto (1), by Rialto Records. Deleted Jun '84. Catalogue no: **TREB 141**

Byrd, Bobby

I KNOW YOU GOT SOUL
Tracks: / Hot pants...I'm coming, coming I'm coming / I know you got soul.
7" Single: Released Aug '87, on Urban, by Polydor Ltd. Catalogue no: **URB 8**
12" Single: Released Aug '87, on Urban, by Polydor Ltd. Deleted 31 May '89. Catalogue no: **URBX 8**

Byrd, Bonnie

GOOD GIRL
Tracks: / Good girl.
7" Single: Released Mar '89, on BSBI, by BSB Records. Catalogue no: **BENN 2**
7" Single: Released Feb '89, on Wadworth Records, Catalogue no: **WAD 417**
12" Single: Released Apr '89, on BSBI, by BSB Records. Catalogue no: **BENN T2**

Byrd, Donald

Biographical details: Byrd, Donald Born in 1932 in Detroit, the trumpeter came to fame with Art Blakey's Jazz Messengers in 1955; he made a lot of very popular albums. *A New Perspective* in 1963 included *Christo Rendentor*, a hymn written and arranged by Duke Pearson, personnel including a choir: it marked Byrd's moving away from hard bop. Finally obtained a doctorate, studied law and became an ethnomusicologist, helped launch students in a funk group called Blackbyrds. He was of course accused of selling out; he has recently started recording again. Donald Clarke, 24 August 1988.

This American jazz trumpeter first came to the attention of jazz fans in the Fifties and has remained a active and respected figure ever since, by the Seventies he had become director of jazz studies at Washington's Howard University. It was while in this capacity that he took a group of his students in 1973 and formed a group called the Blackbyrds. Their aim was to experiment with Byrd's musical ideas, as a way of complementing and enhancing their studies. They suddenly broke big in 1975 with their catchy single *Walking In Rhythm*. One of the first jazz-funk fusion hits, it was perfect for the new disco era and reached No. 6 on the American pop charts. It also climbed to No. 23 in Britain. The following year they scored a second US Top 20 hit, peaking at No. 19 with *Happy Music*. When they went on tour, their itinerary included university and college lectures and demonstrations, in addition to conventional concerts. Subsequent record releases became less interesting and less successful however.
In 1981 Donald Byrd returned to the lower reaches of the UK pop charts as a solo artist. His double A sided single *Love Has Come Around/Loving You* reached No. 41, while his album *Love Byrd* peaked at No. 70. He remains active in the jazz field, often incorporating the soul and R&B tinges that gave him major success in the mid-Seventies. (Bob MacDonald)..

DOMINOES
Tracks: / Dominoes / Change (makes you want to hustle).
12" Single: Released Apr '80, on United Artists, by EMI Records. Deleted '82. Catalogue no: **12UP 622**
12" Single: Released Oct '88, on Domino, by Domino Records. Catalogue no: **DOM T**

DOMINOES(LIVE)
Tracks: / Dominoes(live) / Wind parade.
Note: DJ limited edition
12" Single: Released Mar '86, on Streetwave, Catalogue no: **SWAVE 7**

I'LL ALWAYS LOVE YOU
Tracks: / I'll always love you / Falling.
7" Single: Released Jan '82, on Elektra (USA), by Elektra Records (USA). Catalogue no: **K 12580**

LOVE FOR SALE
Tracks: / Love for sale / I love your love.
7" Single: Released Apr '82, on Elektra (USA), by Elektra Records (USA). Catalogue no: **K 13172**

LOVE HAS COME AROUND
Tracks: / Love has come around / Loving you.
12" Single: Released Sep '81, on Elektra, by Elektra Records (UK). Deleted '84. Catalogue no: **K 12559T**
7" Single: Released Sep '81, on Elektra, by Elektra Records (UK). Deleted '84. Catalogue no: **K 12559**

STAR TRIPPIN
Tracks: / Star trippin'.
12" Single: Released Nov '82, on Elektra (USA), by Elektra Records (USA). Catalogue no: **9679620 T**

Byrd, Gary

Biographical details: Byrd, Gary A soul rapper, born in Buffalo NY in 1950, he became the youngest deejay in New York City; he wrote lyrics for Stevie Wonder, played him a demo over the phone and soon recorded *The Crown*, a 10 minute celebration of black history from Egypt to Malcolm; Wonder supplying backing and joined choruses; the long track was issued on 1 only, making top ten in many countries including UK but failed in USA, through Motown, in USA, on Motown elsetop 10 in Holland, Germany, perhaps to a Motown switch in distribution. He continues to broadcast on WLIB NYC, hosting talk shows, etc., a born-again Christian, he presented 'Sweet Inspiration' series of gospel-related programmes for the BBC in 1985. Donald Clarke, 24 August 1988

This American vocalist describes himself as "Professor Of The Rap". He began a career as a disc jockey in New York City in the mid-Sixties. He eventually gained a reputation as one of the City's leading rappers, the rap being an art of rhythmic, rhyming speech popularised by black American funkers at the end of the Seventies. A long-time friend of the legendary Stevie Wonder, Byrd teamed with Wonder in 1983 for a ten-minute single entitled *The Crown*. This was a rapping epic by Byrd, with lyrics written by him, set to music composed and largely performed by Wonder. On this record Byrd recounted the history of the black man, documenting such landmarks as slavery and referring to many great people and events. The real message of the disc, however, was that it was an impassioned plea for racial unity and a bright, optimistic vision of human destiny. Credited by Gary Byrd & the G.B. Enterprise, *The Crown* was available on 12-inch single format only, being too long for a 7-inch release. it shot into the British chart in the summer of '83. By peaking at No. 6 in the UK, it became the highest placed 12-inch-only disc in the history of the larger single format. In his native America, however, Byrd's record won success on the black chart but failed to cross over to the pop listings. This was due both to radio resistance to the track's ten-minute length and to lack of radio interest in the rapping art - such seminal black singles as the Sugarhill Gang's *Rapper's Delight* and Grandmaster Flash & the Furious Five's *The Message* were not major pop hits in the US. Even in Britain, BBC radio usually substituted the full-length version with their own clumsy three-minute edit.

Having introduced himself to a new receptive UK audience, Byrd was invited by the BBC to present a new weekly gospel music show on Radio One. *Sweet Inspirations* began in March 1984, was recorded weekly in the States and broadcast late on Sunday nights. (Bob MacDonald).

CROWN, THE 2 Parts
Tracks: / Crown, The.
12" Single: Released Jul '83, on Motown, by BMG Records (UK). Catalogue no: **TMGT 1312**

RAP THE WORLD(IN YOUR LOVE)
Tracks: / Rap the world(in your love) / Rap the world(in your love)(club version).
7" Single: Released Oct '86, on In Recordings, Catalogue no: **INR 1**
12" Single: Released Oct '86, on In Recordings, Catalogue no: **INRT 1**

Byrds

Biographical details: In their heyday this American group consisted of Gene Clark, Michael Clarke, David Crosby, Chris Hillman and Roger McGuinn.

The band formed in 1964, its members individually been involved in America's burgeoning folk movement. Heavily influenced by Bob Dylan, the Byrds decided to record one of his songs as their first single. the song chosen was a recent Dylan album track *Mr Tambourine Man*, which they enlivened to create a catchy pop single. It proved a runaway debut success, surging to No. 1 in both the US and UK. It was also a musical innovation, being the first 'folk-rock' hit. While Dylan was America's most important musical act, the Beatles and the Rolling Stones were leading the field in Britain - the Byrds fused the folk style of Dylan with the melodic pop strength of the Beatles and it was a winner. One fact that was not so well known about *Mr Tambourine Man* at the time was that only one of the Byrds was really playing an instrument on it. McGuinn was aided on the record by three session players. On later releases, however, the real Byrds proved themselves to be a highly competent group of musicians.

With total predictability, the band recorded another recent Dylan album track for the follow-up single. What they had not bargained for was that singer Cher would have the same idea at the same time. The Byrds' version of *All I Really Want To Do* lost out in the States, peaking at No. 40 while Cher got to No. 15. It was a very different story in Britain where both renditions amazingly became Top 10 hits and the Byrds won, reaching No. 4 while Cher got to No. 9.

There was no competition with the next 45 *Turn! Turn! Turn!* and this Bible-inspired number gave them their second US No. 1 of 1965, reaching only No. 26 in the UK. The source of the song was another folk singer, Pete Seeger, who had adapted it in 1962 from the Book Of Ecclesiastes.

1966 brought them their final American Top 20 single with *Eight Miles high*, one of their best remembered tracks. At the time its success was slightly hindered by its drug connotations - once these were understood by radio stations, the disc received little airplay. That same year Gene Calrk departed and the group thus lost one of its three voices that made up its distinctive vocal harmony sound. As hit singles tailed off, the Byrds concentrated on albums, which continued to sell well. They began to experiment with electronic sounds and issued some fine LPs. in late '67 however, arguments about musical direction led to the departure of two more members, Michael Clarke and David Crosby. They were replaced by Kevin Kelley and Gram Parsons, with whom the Byrds recorded 1968's *Sweetheart Of The Rodeo* album. This again broke new ground, by being virtually the first country-rock record. It was a major influence on the early Seventies work of such names as the Eagles and Jackson Browne. Shortly after the album's emergence, Hillman and Parsons quit, leaving McGuinn as the only original Byrd (as, indeed, he had been on *Mr Tambourine Man*). Their replacements were Gene Parsons and Clarence White.

The early Seventies brought several more album projects, which were partially successful, plus their final British Top 20 single *Chestnut Mare*. The group folded in 1973 and McGuinn attempted to reform the original quartet. He succeeded for the duration of one reunion album, simply called *Byrds*, but it was not a worthy LP.

The trio of McGuinn, Clark & Hillman scored a one-off US Top 40 single *Don't You Write Her Off* in 1979, but failed to follow it up. In the Eighties the various ex-Byrds' careers went through the floor, with some members even finding difficulty getting record contracts. Nonetheless, for all their later troubles, the Byrds had achieved a great deal in the Sixties, virtually inventing both folk-rock and country-rock.

Sadly, Gram Parsons died of a drug overdose in September 1973. in 1983 David Crosby, who had followed his Byrds days with great success as a member of Crosby, Stills & Nash (& Young), received a five-year jail term for illegal possession of arms. (Bob MacDonald)..

6 TRACK HITS
Tracks: / Lay lady lay / Turn turn turn / Gon'back / So you want to be a rock'n'roll star / Chestnut mare / All I really want to do.
7" EP: Released Aug '83, on Scoop 33, by Pickwick Records. Catalogue no: **7SR 5016**

ALL I REALLY WANT TO DO
Tracks: / All I really want to do.
7" Single: Released Aug '65, on CBS, by CBS Records. Deleted '68. Catalogue no: **CBS 201796**

CHESTNUT MARE
Tracks: / Chestnut mare.
7" Single: Released Jul '82, on Old Gold, by Old Gold Records. Deleted Jul '88. Catalogue no: **OG 9182**

CHESTNUT MARE (SINGLE)
Tracks: / Chestnut mare.
7" Single: Released Feb '71, on CBS, by CBS Records. Deleted '74. Catalogue no: **CBS 5322**

EIGHT MILES HIGH
Tracks: / Eight miles high.
7" Single: Released May '66, on CBS, by CBS Records. Deleted '69. Catalogue no: **CBS 20267**

MR TAMBOURINE MAN (OLD GOLD)
Tracks: / Mr. Tambourine man / Turn turn turn.
7" Single: Released Jan '88, on Old Gold, by Old Gold Records. Catalogue no: **OG 9747**

MR.TAMBOURINE MAN (SINGLE)
Tracks: / Mr. Tambourine man.
7" Single: Released Jun '65, on CBS, by CBS Records. Deleted '68. Catalogue no: **CBS 201765**

TURN, TURN, TURN (SINGLE)
Tracks: / Turn turn turn.
7" Single: Released Nov '65, on CBS, by CBS Records. Deleted '68. Catalogue no: **CBS 202008**

YOU AIN'T GOIN' NOWHERE
Tracks: / You ain't goin' nowhere.
7" Single: Released Jun '68, on CBS, by CBS Records. Deleted '71. Catalogue no: **CBS 3411**

Byrnes, Edward

KOOKIE KOOKIE (LEND ME YOUR COMB)
Tracks: / Kookie kookie (lend me your comb).
7" Single: Released May '60, on Warner Bros., by WEA Records. Deleted '63. Catalogue no: **WB 5**

Byron Band

EVERY INCH OF THE WAY
Tracks: / Every inch of the way / Routine.
7" Single: Released Apr '81, on Creole, by Creole Records. Catalogue no: **CR 8**

NEVER SAY DIE
Tracks: / Never say die / Titred eyes.
7" Single: Released Jul '81, on Creole, by Creole Records. Catalogue no: **CR 12**
7" Single: Released Oct '81, on Creole, by Creole Records. Catalogue no: **CR 24**

Bystanders

98.6
Tracks: / 98.6.
7" Single: Released Feb '67, on Piccadilly, Deleted '70. Catalogue no: **7 N 35363**

Bywaters

BIG BLUE PLYMOUTH
Tracks: / Big blue Plymouth / Leg bells

7" Single: Released Dec '81, on Sire (USA), Catalogue no: **SIR 4054**
12" Single: Released Dec '81, on Sire (USA), Catalogue no: **SIR 4054T**

B-Z Party

YON TREE
Tracks: / Yon tree.
12" Single: Released '87, on Lost Moments, Catalogue no: **LM 12029**

BZN

ROCKIN' THE TROLLS
Tracks: / Rockin' the trolls / Nadja.
7" Single: Released Jan '81, on Carrere, Deleted Jan '84. Catalogue no: **CAR 171**

C

The following information was taken from the Music Master database on October 20th, 1989.

C, Henrietta

ROCKING ON THE RED BOOK
Tracks: / Rocking on the red book / Paddy field.
7" Single: Released May '80, on Back Door (Holland), Deleted May '83. Catalogue no: **DOOR 7**

C, Julie

YOU STEPPED OUT OF MY DREAMS
Tracks: / You stepped out of my dreams.
7" Single: Released Apr '89, on Sonet, by Sonet Records. Catalogue no: **SON 2324**
12" Single: Released Apr '89, on Sonet, by Sonet Records. Catalogue no: **SONL 2324T**

C, Roy

SHOTGUN WEDDING
Tracks: / Shotgun wedding / High school dropout.
7" Single: Released Jun '81, on Decca, by Decca Records. Deleted Jun '84. Catalogue no: **F 13902**

Ca Va Ca Va

Biographical details: This British group, who hailed from Bournemouth, took their name from 'ca va', the French phrase for 'that's alright'. They appeared on the scene in 1982 with a fashionable sound and image, in the mould of such bands as Duran Duran and ABC, but somehow failed to catch on. Their catchy one-off hit *Where's Romeo?* reached No. 49 on the UK singles chart, but they failed to capitalise on this toehold. All members were male. (Bob MacDonald)..

BROTHER BRIGHT
Tracks: / Brother bright / Clown.
7" Single: Released Jan '83, on Regard, Catalogue no: **RG 105**
7" Pic: Released Jan '83, on Regard, Catalogue no: **RGP 105**

BURNING BOY
Tracks: / Burning boy.
12" Single: Released May '83, on Regard, Catalogue no: **RGT 110**
7" Pic: Released Jun '83, on Regard, Catalogue no: **RGTP 110**
7" Single: Released May '83, on Regard, Catalogue no: **RG 110**

WHERE'S ROMEO?
Tracks: / Where's Romeo / See saw and sway.
7" Single: Released Aug '82, on Regard, Catalogue no: **RG 103**

Cabaret Voltaire

Biographical details: This British group consists of Richard Kirk, Stephen Mallinder and Chris Watson.
Formed in Sheffield in 1973, Cabaret Voltaire's weird style of electronic experimentation made it hard for them to obtain live work, until the advent of the 'anything goes' punk era three years later. Gradually gaining cult acceptance during the late Seventies, they began releasing albums and singles on a prolific scale. Among their LPs were a live set *Live At The YMCA* and the early Eighties studio albums, *The Voice Of America, Red Mecca* and *Hail*.
1982 brought the group their first entry into the UK national charts - albeit for one week on the Top 100 Albums at No. 98 with *12 X 45*. After this their hectic release schedule continued with such LPs as *Some Fascination*, their idiosyncratic form of rock music winning regular praise from the British music papers but little commercial success. (Bob MacDonald).
An electronic group formed in Sheffield in 1973 by bassist/lead vocalist Stephen 'Mal' Mallinder, guitarist Richard Kirk (also plays wind instruments), and Chris Watson running electronics and tapes. They were influenced by European groups like Can and Kraftwerk; their machine-like rhythms, sound collages and distorted vocals put audiences off at first, but the punk movement rendered an uncompromising stance more acceptable. They have been very prolific on several of the New Wave labels. Their musical stance was carried over to video, using audio techniques of repetition, montage and distortion to create disturbing visual images. Watson left for TV work in 1981; the others carried on and also did solo work. (Donald Clark, April 1989)n.

BRAIN TRAIN, THE
Tracks: / Brain train, The.
12" Single: Released Jun '86, on Double Vision, by Double Vision Records. Catalogue no: **DVR 21**

CRACKDOWN (SINGLE)
Tracks: / Crackdown / Just fascination.
12" Single: Released '89, on Some Bizzare, by Some Bizzare Records. Catalogue no: **CVS 112**

DON'T ARGUE
Tracks: / Don't argue / Don't argue (Who's arguing).
Cassingle: Released Jul '87, on Parlophone, by EMI Records. Catalogue no: **TCR 6157**
7" Single: Released Jul '87, on Parlophone, by EMI Records. Deleted Apr '88. Catalogue no: **R 6157**
12" Single: Released Jul '87, on Parlophone, by EMI Records. Deleted Apr '88. Catalogue no: **12R 6157**

DON'T ARGUE (DANCE MIX)
Tracks: / Don't argue (dance mix) / Don't argue (dub).
12" Single: Released Jul '87, on Parlophone, by EMI Records. Catalogue no: **12 RX 6157**

DREAM TICKET, THE
Tracks: / Dream ticket, The / Safety zone.
12" Single: on Some Bizzare, by Some Bizzare Records. Catalogue no: **CVS 212**

EDDIE'S OUT
Tracks: / Eddie's out / Walls of Jericho.
7" Single: Released Dec '81, on Rough Trade, by Rough Trade Records. Catalogue no: **RT 096**

HERE TO GO
Tracks: / Here to go (extended mix) / Here to go (space dub) / Here to go / Here to go (dub) / Here to go (live drum remix) (Available on RX 6166.) / Here to go (eleven eleven mix) (Available on RX 6166.).
Note: * tracks on RX 6166.
12" Single: Released Sep '87, on Parlophone, by EMI Records. Deleted Apr '88. Catalogue no: **12R 6166**
CD 5": Released Sep '87, on Parlophone, by EMI Records. Deleted Apr '88. Catalogue no: **CD R 6166**
Cassingle: Released Sep '87, on Parlophone, by EMI Records. Deleted Apr '88. Catalogue no: **TC-R 6166**
7" Single: Released Sep '87, on Parlophone, by EMI Records. Deleted Apr '88. Catalogue no: **R 6166**
12" Single: Released Sep '87, on Parlophone, by EMI Records. Catalogue no: **RX 6166**

HYPNOTISED
Tracks: / Hypnotised (7" only.) / Hypnotised - Gerald's vocal mix (faded) (7" & 7" special only.) / Hypnotised - Fon force mix (12" mix.) / Hypnotised -Daniel Miller mix (12" mix.) / Hypnotised - Western works mix (12" mix.) / Hypnotised - Fon force dub / Hypnotised - A guy called Gerald's music mix (Special only.) / Hypnotised - Gerald's vocal mix (Special only.).
12" Single: Released Oct '89, on Parlophone, by EMI Records. Catalogue no: **12R 6227**
CD 5": Released Oct '89, on Parlophone, by EMI Records. Catalogue no: **203 537 2**
CD 5": Released Oct '89, on Parlophone, by EMI Records. Catalogue no: **CDR 6227**
: by EMI Records.
7" Single: Released Oct '89, on Parlophone, by EMI Records. Catalogue no: **203 537 7**
7" Single: Released Oct '89, on Parlophone, by EMI Records. Catalogue no: **R 6227**
12" Single: Released Oct '89, on Parlophone, by EMI Records. Catalogue no: **203 537 0**
Special: Released Oct '89, on Parlophone, by EMI Records. Catalogue no: **12RX 6227**
12" Single: Released Oct '89, on Parlophone, by EMI Records. Catalogue no: **12RS 6227**
12" Single: Released Oct '89, on Parlophone, by EMI Records. Catalogue no: **203 537 6**
Special: Released Oct '89, on Parlophone, by EMI Records. Catalogue no: **203 537 8**

I WANT YOU
Tracks: / I want you / Drink your poison / C.O.M.A..
12" Single: Released Sep '85, on Some Bizzare, by Some Bizzare Records. Catalogue no: **CVS 5-12**
7" Single: Released Sep '85, on Some Bizzare, by Some Bizzare Records. Deleted May '88. Catalogue no: **CVS 5**

JAMES BROWN
Tracks: / James Brown / Bad self-part 1.
7" Single: Released Jan '85, on Some Bizzare, by Some Bizzare Records. Deleted '89. Catalogue no: **CVS 4**
12" Single: Released Jan '85, on Some Bizzare, by Some Bizzare Records. Catalogue no: **CVS 412**

JAZZ THE GLASS
Tracks: / Jazz the glass / Burnt to the ground.
7" Single: Released Oct '81, on Rough Trade, by Rough Trade Records. Catalogue no: **RT 085**

NAG NAG NAG
Tracks: / Nag nag nag.
7" Single: Released Jun '79, on Rough Trade, by Rough Trade Records. Catalogue no: **RT 018**

SECONDS TOO LATE
Tracks: / Seconds too late.
7" Single: Released Nov '80, on Rough Trade, by Rough Trade Records. Catalogue no: **RT 061**

SENSORIA
Tracks: / Sensoria / Cut the damn camera.
7" Single: Released Sep '84, on Some Bizzare, by Some Bizzare Records. Deleted '85. Catalogue no: **CVS 3**
12" Single: Released Sep '84, on Some Bizzare, by Some Bizzare Records. Catalogue no: **CVS 3-12**

SILENT COMMAND
Tracks: / Silent command.
7" Single: Released Nov '79, on Rough Trade, by Rough Trade Records. Catalogue no: **RT 035**

TALKOVER
Tracks: / Talkover.
7" Single: Released Jan '79, on Rough Trade, by Rough Trade Records. Catalogue no: **RT 003**

THREE MANTRAS
Tracks: / Three mantras.
12" Single: Released Apr '80, on Rough Trade, by Rough Trade Records. Catalogue no: **RT 038**

Cabell, Sly

FEELIN' FINE
Tracks: / Feelin' fine.
12" Single: Released Aug '82, on Virgin, by Virgin Records. Deleted Aug '85. Catalogue no: **VS 525 12**
7" Single: Released Aug '82, on Virgin, by Virgin Records. Deleted Aug '85. Catalogue no: **VS 525**

Cabinet

LANGUAGE AND WORDS
Tracks: / Language and words.
7" Single: Released Nov '83, on Sharp, by Sharp Records. Catalogue no: **CAL 2**

STILL TEARS
Tracks: / Still tears.
12" Single: Released Feb '83, on Sharp, by Sharp Records. Catalogue no: **CAL 1**

Cache

WHERE IS MY SUNSHINE?
Tracks: / Where is my sunshine / Jazzin' and cruisin'.
7" Single: Released Nov '81, on Groove PR, by Beggars Banquet Records. Catalogue no: **GP 111**
12" Single: Released Nov '81, on Groove PR, by Beggars Banquet Records. Catalogue no: **GP 111T**

Cacique

DEVOTED TO YOU
Tracks: / Devoted to you.
7" Single: Released May '85, on Diamond Duel, by Diamond Duel Records. Deleted Nov '87. Catalogue no: **DISC 1**
12" Single: Released May '85, on Diamond Duel, by Diamond Duel Records. Deleted Nov '87. Catalogue no: **DISCT 1**

DRESSED TO KILL
Tracks: / Dressed to kill / Dressing up mix.
7" Single: Released 23 May '87, on Point Sound, Catalogue no: **PTS 1**

Cactus World News

BRIDGE, THE
Tracks: / Bridge, The.
Cassingle: Released Sep '86, on MCA, by MCA Records. Catalogue no: **MGAWN 1080**
12" Single: Released Nov '85, on Mother, by Mother Records. Catalogue no: **12 MUM 2**
7" Single: Released Sep '86, on MCA, by MCA Records. Deleted 1 Jul '89. Catalogue no: **MCA 1080**
7" Single: Released Nov '85, on Mother, by Mother Records. Deleted Apr '88. Catalogue no: **MUM 2**

REBOUND
Tracks: / Rebound.
12" Single: Released Jun '89, on MCA, by MCA Records. Catalogue no: **MCAT 1340**
CD 5": Released Jun '89, on MCA, by MCA Records. Catalogue no: **DMCAT 1340**
7" Single: Released Jun '89, on MCA, by MCA Records. Catalogue no: **MCA 1340**

TOWN LIKE THIS
Tracks: / Town like this.
12" Single: Released Sep '89, on MCA, by MCA Records. Catalogue no: **MCAT 1364**
CD 5": Released Sep '89, on MCA, by MCA Records. Catalogue no: **DMCAT 1364**
7" Single: Released Sep '89, on MCA, by MCA Records. Catalogue no: **MCA 1364**

WORLDS APART
Tracks: / Worlds apart / Cashen bay stand.
7" Single: Released Apr '86, on MCA, by MCA Records. Catalogue no: **MCA 1040**
12" Single: Released Apr '86, on MCA, by MCA Records. Catalogue no: **MCAT 1040**

YEARS LATER
Tracks: / Years later / Hurry back / Third one live.
7" Single: Released Jan '86, on MCA, by MCA Records. Catalogue no: **MCA 1024**
12" Single: Released Jan '86, on MCA, by MCA Records. Catalogue no: **MCAT 1024**

Cadeau De Mariage

POURQUOI ES TU DEVENUE
Tracks: / Pourquoi es tu devenue.
7" Single: Released Oct '88, on Reception, by Reception Records. Catalogue no: **REC 001 F**

Cadets

JEALOUS HEART
Tracks: / Jealous heart.
Note: Eileen Read lead vocal.o
7" Single: Released Jun '65, on Pye International, Deleted Jun '68. Catalogue no: **7N 15852**

Cadillac, Vince

LOVEY DOVEY
Tracks: / Lovey dovey / Gambler.
7" Single: Released Aug '80, on Crash, by Satril Records. Deleted Aug '83. Catalogue no: **POW 1**

Cadillacs

Biographical details: A USA doo wop group formed in New York City in 1953 as the Carnations, changing their name and becoming a quintet (one girl and four boys) the next year. The original lineup included Earl 'Speedo' Carroll, who left in 1959 to join the Coasters. Their biggest hit was *Speedo*, a top 3 in the USA R&B chart, originally spelled *Speedoo* and since covered by Ry Cooder.
They were known for energy and flamboyance and were one of the first groups to practise on-stage choreography, influencing later Motown acts. (Donald Clarke, April 1989)..

BILLY
Tracks: / Billy.
7" Single: Released Sep '80, on Red Eye, by Red Eye Records. Catalogue no: **EYE 3**

CADILLAC WALK
Tracks: / Cadillac walk / Same old stuff.
7" Single: Released Oct '81, on Red Eye, by Red Eye Records. Catalogue no: **EYE 1**

Cadman, John

LHAMBRA (CAN FEEL YOUR OVE)
racks: / Alhambra (can feel your love).
' **Single:** Released May '81, on Black yes, Catalogue no: **DARK 5**

Cadogan, Susan

iographical details: This British singer ame from nowhere to public attention in 975, when she hit o. 4 on the UK singles hart with *Hurt So Good*, a gentle reggae ecord. A samey follow-up *Love Me baby* eaked at No. 22 later that year, then Caogan went back into the realms of obcurity.

AUSE YOU LOVE ME BABY
racks: / Cause you love me baby.
2" **Single:** Released Sep '84, on Haweye, by Hawkeye Records. Catalogue no: D 57

URT SO GOOD
racks: / Hurt so good / Sideshow.
' **Single:** Released Nov '86, on Old Gold, Old Gold Records. Catalogue no: **OG 62**
Single: Released Apr '75, on Magnet, WEA Records. Deleted Apr '78. Catague no: **MAG 23**

OVE ME
acks: / Love me / Careless me.
' **Single:** Released Jan '83, on Hawkeye, Hawkeye Records. Catalogue no: **HD**
2" **Single:** Released Jan '83, on Haweye, by Hawkeye Records. Catalogue no: D 43 12

OVE ME BABY
acks: / Love me baby.
Single: Released Jul '75, on Magnet, by EA Records. Deleted Jul '78. Catalogue : **MAG 36**

OVE TRILOGY
acks: / Love trilogy / Curfew.
Single: Released Jun '86, on Solid Gold , by Creole Records. Deleted '86. Cataue no: **SG 7003**
" **Single:** Released Jun '86, on Solid old (1), by Creole Records. Deleted '86. atalogue no: **SG 007**

OBODY WINS
acks: / Nobody wins / Nobody wins (vern).
' **Single:** Released Nov '86, on C & E, talogue no: **CED 103**

ECE OF MY HEART
cks: / Piece of my heart.
' **Single:** Released May '82, on Carge, Catalogue no: **CRD 109**

ACKS OF MY TEARS
cks: / Tracks of my tears.
Single: Released Jun '82, on GG'S, eted Jun '85. Catalogue no: **GG 103**
' **Single:** Released Jun '82, on GG'S, alogue no: **GG 103 12**

afe

ANT ADS
cks: / Want ads.
' **Single:** Released Oct '83, on Malaco, Malaco Records (UK). Deleted '88. talogue no: **MAL 12 012**

afe Society

LIGHT MY FIRE
cks: / Relight my fire.
' **Single:** Released Dec '84, on Passion, Skratch Records. Catalogue no: **PASH 12)**

MEBODY TO LOVE
cks: / Somebody to love / Knight rider.
Single: Released Jul '87, on Passion, Skratch Records. Catalogue no: **PASH 12)**
Single: Released Jul '87, on Passion, Skratch Records. Catalogue no: **PASH**

afferty, John

ARTS ON FIRE
cks: / Hearts on fire.
Single: Released Mar '86, on Scotti s (USA), Catalogue no: **A 6702**

THE DARK SIDE
ks: / On the dark side.
Single: Released Apr '85, on Scotti s (USA), Catalogue no: **A 4867**

ICE OF AMERICA'S SON
ks: / Voice of America's son / Dixie-
Single: Released Aug '86, on Scotti s (USA), Catalogue no: **A 7204**

affrey

R JACKY Q
ks: / Dear Jacky Q / Ain't she fine.
ingle: Released Jun '80, on Mercury, honogram Ltd. Deleted Jun '83. Catalogue no: **MER 15**

Cage

DO WHAT YOU WANNA DO
Tracks: / Do what you wanna do / Slammer.
12" Single: Released Apr '82, on Island, by Island Records. Deleted Apr '85. Catalogue no: **12WIP 6769**
7" Single: Released Apr '82, on Island, by Island Records. Deleted Apr '85. Catalogue no: **WIP 6769**

Cagliostra

LIBERA ME
Tracks: / Madmen and lovers / Libera me.
7" Single: Released Dec '86, on El, by Cherry Red Records. Catalogue no: **GPO 22**

Cahill

YOU DON'T KNOW ME
Tracks: / You don't know me / Dover.
12" Single: Released Jun '84, on Dibble, Deleted '87. Catalogue no: **DIB 5014T**
7" Single: Released Jun '84, on Dibble, Deleted '87. Catalogue no: **DIB 5014**

Cahoot

ARE YOU READY
Tracks: / Are you ready / Gimme some sign.
12" Single: Released Nov '86, on Haj, Catalogue no: **HAJ 1202**

Cain, Sheila

I'M SO SCARED
Tracks: / I'm so scared.
12" Single: Released Feb '89, on Claypot, Catalogue no: **PHD 0042**

Caine, Andrew

WHAT DO WE SAY TO EACH OTHER
Tracks: / What do we say to each other / Dance under a midnight sun.
12" Single: Released Aug '86, on Epic, by CBS Records. Catalogue no: **650037 6**
7" Single: Released Aug '86, on Epic, by CBS Records. Catalogue no: **650037 7**

WHAT KIND OF WORLD
Tracks: / What kind of world / Tearing me apart.
7" Single: Released Oct '86, on Epic, by CBS Records. Catalogue no: **CAINE 1**
7" Single: Released Oct '86, on Epic, by CBS Records. Catalogue no: **CAINE 1**
7" Single: Released Jun '85, on Epic, by CBS Records. Deleted '86. Catalogue no: **A 6343**
12" Single: Released Jun '85, on Epic, by CBS Records. Catalogue no: **TA 6343**

Caine, Daniel

A-TEAM, THEME FROM
Tracks: / A team, Theme from.
7" Single: Released Sep '84, on Indiana, by Indiana Records. Catalogue no: **B-TS 1111**

Caine, Marti

CAN I SPEAK TO THE WORLD PLEASE
Tracks: / Can I speak to the world please / Tin heart and the rebel.
7" Single: Released Mar '82, on BBC, by BBC Records & Tapes. Deleted '85. Catalogue no: **RESL 113**

I'LL NEVER SEE YOU AGAIN
Tracks: / I'll never see you again / Bitch is love.
7" Single: Released Feb '81, on BBC, by BBC Records & Tapes. Deleted Feb '84. Catalogue no: **RESL 90**

Caiola, Al

MAGNIFICENT SEVEN, THE
Tracks: / Magnificent seven, The.
7" Single: Released Jun '61, on H.M.V., by EMI Records. Deleted Jun '64. Catalogue no: **POP 889**

Caiphus Semenya

ANGELINA
Tracks: / Angelina.
7" Single: Released Jun '85, on Jive, by Zomba Records. Catalogue no: **JIVE 40**
12" Single: Released Jun '85, on Jive, by Zomba Records. Catalogue no: **JIVET 40**

Cair Paravel

WISE MAN
Tracks: / Wise man / It's okay.
7" Single: Released Apr '82, on Multi-Media, Catalogue no: **MMT 5**

Cairo

I LIKE BLUEBEAT
Tracks: / I like bluebeat.
7" Single: Released Jan '80, on Absurd, by Absurd Records. Deleted Jan '85. Catalogue no: **A7**

I WANT THAT GIRL
Tracks: / I want that girl / Hold on.
7" Single: Released Jan '89, on Citybeat, by Beggars Banquet Records. Catalogue no: **CBE 735**
CD 5": Released Jan '89, on Citybeat, by Beggars Banquet Records. Catalogue no: **CBE 1235 CD**
12" Single: Released Jan '89, on Citybeat, by Beggars Banquet Records. Catalogue no: **CBE 1235**

I WANT YOU IN MY LIFE
Tracks: / Uncle Charlie / I want you in my life / Uncle Charlie.
12" Single: Released Aug '87, on Citybeat, by Beggars Banquet Records. Catalogue no: **CBE 1215**
7" Single: Released Aug '87, on Citybeat, by Beggars Banquet Records. Deleted Jan '88. Catalogue no: **CBE 715**

MOVIE STARS
Tracks: / Movie stars / Cuthberts birthday treat.
7" Single: Released Apr '81, on Absurd, by Absurd Records. Deleted '85. Catalogue no: **ASK 15**

ON THE REBOUND
Tracks: / On the rebound.
12" Single: Released Jul '85, on Champion, by Champion Records. Deleted Aug '89. Catalogue no: **CHAMP 122**
7" Single: Released Jul '85, on Champion, by Champion Records. Deleted Jul '89. Catalogue no: **CHAMP 2**

SMOKIN'
Tracks: / Smokin' / Smokin' (Uncle Charlie remix).
12" Single: Released 14 May '88, on Citybeat, by Beggars Banquet Records. Catalogue no: **CBE 1226**
CD 5": Released 14 May '88, on Chrysalis, by Chrysalis Records. Catalogue no: **CHSCD 3204**
7" Single: Released 14 May '88, on Citybeat, by Beggars Banquet Records. Catalogue no: **CBE 726**
12" Single: Released 14 May '88, on Chrysalis, by Chrysalis Records. Catalogue no: **CHS 123204**

YOU ARE
Tracks: / You are.
12" Single: Released May '83, on Vista Sounds, by Vista Sounds Records. Catalogue no: **VSEP 601**

Cajun, R

JAMBALAYA (GRAND TEXAS)
Tracks: / Jambalaya.
7" Single: Released Sep '84, on Moonraker, by Moonraker Records. Catalogue no: **MOOS 1**

Calamites, Les

PAS LA PEINE
Tracks: / Pas la peine.
7" Single: Released Jan '85, on New Rose (1), by New Rose Records. Catalogue no: **NEW 46**

Calamity Jane

SEND ME SOMEBODY TO LOVE
Tracks: / Send me somebody to love / Don't you leave me alone too long.
7" Single: Released Nov '81, on CBS, by CBS Records. Deleted Nov '84. Catalogue no: **A 1720**

Caldwell, Bobby

ALL OF MY LOVE
Tracks: / All of my love / Catwalk.
7" Single: Released Apr '82, on Polydor, by Polydor Ltd. Deleted Apr '85. Catalogue no: **POSP 426**

COMING DOWN FROM LOVE
Tracks: / Coming down from love / Open your eyes.
7" Single: Released 20 Jul '80, on TK, Deleted '83. Catalogue no: **TKR 7577**

JAMAICA
Tracks: / Jamaica / You belong to me.
7" Single: Released Jul '82, on Polydor, by Polydor Ltd. Deleted Jul '87. Catalogue no: **POSP 476**

WHAT YOU WON'T DO FOR LOVE
Tracks: / What you won't do for love (edit
12" Single: Released 13 Jun '87, on Magnetic Dance, by Magnet Records. Deleted Jun '88. Catalogue no: **MAGDT 5**
7" Single: Released 13 Jun '87, on Magnetic Dance, by Magnet Records. Deleted Jun '88. Catalogue no: **MAGD 5**

Cale, J.J.

Biographical details: Born in Tulsa, Oklahoma in 1939, this American singer, guitarist and songwriter started playing the guitar at the age of ten. In the mid to late Fifties he played rock 'n' roll and then country music. In 1963 he wrote and recorded a song called *After Midnight*, which Eric Clapton took into the US Top 20 in late 1970. This bluesy rock number was perfect material for Clapton and was a typical example of both artists' style.
Armed with the Clapton seal of approval, the previously obscure Cale sold records in his own right during the early Seventies. The single *Crazy Mama* became his only 45 ever to make the American Top 40, reaching No. 22 in '72. It came from the album *Naturally*, a relaxed concoction of rock, country, blues and cajun music, featuring Cale's expert guitar style and somewhat lazy vocals. Regular subsequent LPs have been in a similar vein, but have not consolidated upon the commercial inroads gained by *Naturally*. One reason for this is Cale's personality, which dislikes the glare of publicity and shuns the spotlight. The artist just preferred to be accepted by the critics and retain merely a cult following. 1977 saw Eric Clapton recording another of his songs: *Cocaine* was featured on Clapton's highly successful *Slowhand* LP.
Cale did not make the UK album chart until 1976. his highest placed LP in Britain was 1982's *Grasshopper*, which reached No. 36. (Bob MacDonald).

CARRY ON
Tracks: / Carry on / Cloudy day.
7" Single: Released Oct '81, on Island, by Island Records. Deleted '85. Catalogue no: **WIP 6686**

MAMA DON'T
Tracks: / Mama don't / What do you expect.
7" Single: Released May '81, on Island, by Island Records. Deleted May '84. Catalogue no: **WIP 6697**

SHANGHAID
Tracks: / Shanghaid / Artificial paradise.
7" Single: Released Oct '89, on Silvertone, Catalogue no: **ORE 12**

Cale, John

Biographical details: One of the godfathers of subsequent developments in pop music, the vocalist, composer and multi-instrumentalist was bron in 1940 in South Wales, studied at Goldsmiths College in London and went to the USA, where he studied with Aaron Copland, then became a founder member with Lou Reed of the Velvet Underground, where his classical and avant-garde experiments influenced the music deeply. *Vintage Violence* in 1969 was his first solo album: he worked with composer Terry Riley on *The church of anthrax* and *The academy in peril* in 1971-72. *Fear* in 1974 was harder-edged rock; *June 1, 1974* found Cale reunited with Nico from the Velvets, as well as Brian Eno and Kevin Ayers. *Slow dazzle* in 1975 featured guitarist Phil Manzanera. *Guts* is a 'best of'. *Music for a new society* in 1982 was his debut on the Ze label. He also produced albums by Nico, Iggy Pop, Patti Smith, Jonathan Richman's Modern Lover's, the first Squeeze album, demos by the Police, etc. (Donald Clarke, April 1989).

DEAD OR ALIVE
Tracks: / Dead or alive / Honi soit.
7" Single: Released May '81, on A&M, by A&M Records. Deleted May '86. Catalogue no: **AMS 8130**

DYING ON THE VINE
Tracks: / Dying on the vine.
12" Single: Released Jul '85, on Beggars Banquet, by Beggars Banquet Records. Deleted Jun '87. Catalogue no: **BEG 145T**
7" Single: Released Jul '85, on Beggars Banquet, by Beggars Banquet Records. Deleted Jun '87. Catalogue no: **BEG 145**

SATELLITE WALK
Tracks: / Satellite walk
12" Single: Released Nov '85, on Beggars Banquet, by Beggars Banquet Records. Deleted Jun '87. Catalogue no: **BEG 153T**

Calendar Crowd

LISTEN TO THE HEART
Tracks: / Listen to the heart.
12" Single: Released Jun '85, on Production Line, Catalogue no: **KALE 126**

PERFECT HIDEAWAY
Tracks: / Perfect hideaway / Perfect hideaway (part 2).
7" Single: Released Dec '82, on Romantic, Catalogue no: **RR002**

Calendar, Phil

ISLAND MUSIC
Tracks: / Island music / It's late.
12" Single: Released May '85, on Revue, by Creole Records. Catalogue no: **REV 022T**

Calibre Cuts

CALIBRE CUTS
Tracks: / Calibre cuts (montage).
7" Single: Released May '80, on Calibre,

Deleted May '83. Catalogue no: **CAB 502**

California

HE'S ALMOST THERE
Tracks: / He's almost there / Three times loser.
7" Single: Released Feb '83, on RCA, by BMG Records (UK). Catalogue no: **RCA 306**

California Raisins

I HEARD IT THROUGH THE GRAPEVINE Lead vocals Buddy Miles
Tracks: / I heard it through the grapevine / Lean on me.
7" Single: Released Apr '89, on Dino Entertainment, by Dino Entertainments. Catalogue no: **GRAPE 1**

California, Randy

ALL ALONG THE WATCHTOWER
Tracks: / All along the watchtower / Killer week / Radio man / Easy love / Break out.
12" Single: Released Sep '82, on Beggars Banquet, by Beggars Banquet Records. Deleted Jan '88. Catalogue no: **BEG 82T**
7" Single: Released Sep '82, on Beggars Banquet, by Beggars Banquet Records. Deleted Jan '88. Catalogue no: **BEG 82**

HAND GUN
Tracks: / Hand gun / This is the end.
7" Single: Released May '82, on Beggars Banquet, by Beggars Banquet Records. Deleted '85. Catalogue no: **BEG 76**

JACK RABBIT
Tracks: / Jack rabbit.
12" Single: Released Jun '85, on Vertigo, by Phonogram Ltd. Catalogue no: **ERX 21**
7" Single: Released Jun '85, on Vertigo, by Phonogram Ltd. Catalogue no: **VER 21**

Call

EVERYWHERE I GO
Tracks: / Everywhere I go / Tore the old place down.
7" Single: Released May '86, on Elektra (USA), by Elektra Records (USA). Deleted Jun '87. Catalogue no: **EKR 40**
12" Single: Released May '86, on Elektra (USA), by Elektra Records (USA). Deleted Jun '87. Catalogue no: **EKR 40 T**

I DON'T WANNA
Tracks: / I don't wanna / Day or night.
12" Single: Released Jul '87, on Elektra, by Elektra Records (UK). Deleted Jan '88. Catalogue no: **EKR 60T**
12" Single: Released Jul '87, on Elektra, by Elektra Records (UK). Deleted Jul '88. Catalogue no: **EKR 60**

LET THE DAY BEGIN
Tracks: / Let the day begin / Uncovered.
7" Single: Released Aug '89, on MCA, by MCA Records. Catalogue no: **MCA 1362**
CD 5": Released Aug '89, on MCA, by MCA Records. Catalogue no: **DMCAT 1362**
12" Single: Released Aug '89, on MCA, by MCA Records. Catalogue no: **MCAT 1362**

WALLS CAME DOWN
Tracks: / Walls came down.
12" Single: Released Jul '83, on London Records, by London Records. Catalogue no: **LONX 28**
7" Single: Released Jul '83, on London Records, by London Records. Catalogue no: **LON 28**

Calling Hearts

RETURN TO BASE
Tracks: / Return to base / In the jungle.
7" Single: Released Sep '81, on Illuminated, Catalogue no: **ILL 6**

Calloways

WENT THATAWAY
Tracks: / Went thataway.
7" Single: Released Jun '84, on Wonderful World Of, by Wonderful World Of Records. Catalogue no: **WW 001**

Calmheads

SUMMERS COMING DOWN
Tracks: / Summers coming down.
12" Single: Released Jul '89, on Jericho, Catalogue no: **JR 002**

Calvert, Eddie

Biographical details: This British instrumentalist, born in Lancashire, came to be billed as 'The man with the golden trumpet'. By the time of his mid-Fifties record success, he had built up a strong reputation in the UK as a concert and radio attraction. He opened his chart career with two British No. 1s, but they were not consecutive releases and over a year elapsed between them.
The first was *Oh Mein Papa*, originally a German song written in 1948. Calvert's single was instrumental, save for a female vocal group who occasionally sang the title. It was left to leading American singer Eddie Fisher to chart with a full English translation, but the over-sentimentalism of the lyrics prevented Fisher's rendition from reaching higher than No. 9 on the UK charts. Calvert, on the other hand, remained at the top spot for nine weeks, and his disc thus remains one of Britain's eleven longest running chart-toppers of all time. It was the first No. 1 single produced by Norrie Paramor, who went on to produce a further twenty-six toppers; Paramor remains one of the two joint all-time champion producers of UK No. 1s. *Oh Mein Papa* was also the first No. 1 recorded at Britain's most successful studios, the legendary Abbey Road - approximately eighty more were to follow over the ensuing thirty years. Calvert also achieved a Top 20 placing in the States with this record.
over a year later, in May 1955, Calvert returneo to the UK No. 1 position with *Cherry Pink And Apple Blossom White*, originally a French tune. Perez Prado had just been on the top for two weeks with *Cherry*, but Calvert's version managed to hold the summit for four weeks. This tune remains the only instrumental single in the Britiah chart history to hit No. 1 in two different versions. In the USA however, Prado scored a mammoth run at the top, leaving Calvert without a look-in.
Calvert never reached the top slot again, but gained two further UK Top Tenners with 1955's *John & Julie* (No. 6) and 1958's *Mandy* (No. 9). After the latter's success, his disc popularity waned. He died in South Africa in August 1978, at the age of 56.
In 1982 a tribute was paid to him by British pop group Modern Romance, when they took a vocal version of *Cherry Pink And Apple Blossom White*to No. 15 on the UK charts. The band's trumpeter John Du prez claimed that he used the very same instrument played by Calvert on his 1955 record. Soon after the Modern Romance hit, a brighton group called the Piranhas reached the Top 20 with *Zambesi*, another tune that Calvert had charted with; no such claim, however, was made by the trumpet player of the Piranhas, one 'Boring Bob Grover' (Bob MacDonald).
The trumpet player was born in Preston in 1922 and died in South Africa in 1978. He worked with Geraldo, gigged in clubs, appeared on TV with Stanley Black and had huge hits in the early '50's including *Oh mein papa* and a copy of Perez Prado's *Cherry pink and apple blossom white*, both also charting in the USA. He also played in film soundtracks, moved to South Africa in 1968 and died there ten years later. (Donald Clarke, April 1989)n.

CHERRY PINK AND APPLE BLOSSOM WHITE
Tracks: / Cherry pink and apple blossom white.
7" Single: Released Apr '55, on Columbia, by EMI Records. Deleted Apr '58. Catalogue no: **DB 3581**

JOHN AND JULIA
Tracks: / John and Julia.
7" Single: Released Jul '55, on Columbia, by EMI Records. Deleted Jul '58. Catalogue no: **DB 3624**

LITTLE SERENADE
Tracks: / Little serenade.
7" Single: Released Jun '58, on Columbia, by EMI Records. Deleted Jun '61. Catalogue no: **DB 4105**

MANDY
Tracks: / Mandy.
7" Single: Released Feb '58, on Columbia, by EMI Records. Deleted Feb '61. Catalogue no: **DB 3956**

OH MEIN PAPA
Tracks: / Oh mein papa / Cherry pink.
7" Single: Released Dec '53, on Columbia, by EMI Records. Deleted Dec '56. Catalogue no: **DB 3337**
7" Single: Released Nov '80, on H.M.V., by EMI Records. Catalogue no: **POP 2016**

STRANGER IN PARADISE
Tracks: / Stranger in paradise.
7" Single: Released May '55, on Columbia, by EMI Records. Deleted May '58. Catalogue no: **DB 3594**

Camacho, Thelma

LOVE WILL CARRY ME HOME
Tracks: / Love will carry me home / Double or nothing.
7" Single: Released May '80, on Casablanca, by PolyGram UK Ltd. Deleted '83. Catalogue no: **CAN 195**

Camargue

HOWL OF THE PACK
Tracks: / Howl of the pack.
7" Single: Released Jun '84, on Clubland, Catalogue no: **SJP 848 A**

Cambell, Carol

BETWEEN ME AND YOU
Tracks: / Between me and you.
12" Single: Released Oct '83, on Sea View, Catalogue no: **SV 1**

Camberwell Now

GREENFINGERS
Tracks: / Greenfingers.
12" Single: Released Feb '87, on Ink, by Red Flame Records. Catalogue no: **INK 1224**

Cambria, Jacqui

SONGS FOR ALL FEELINGS
Tracks: / Songs for all feelings / Reflections.
7" Single: Released Jan '80, on Monarch, by Monarch Records. Deleted '83. Catalogue no: **MON 06**

Cambridge Buskers

DING DONG MERRILY ON HIGH
Tracks: / Ding dong merrily on high / Sweet William.
7" Single: Released Jan '81, on Polydor, by Polydor Ltd. Deleted Jan '84. Catalogue no: **POSP 191**

LAMBETH WALK
Tracks: / Lambeth walk / Recorder concer-to-finale.
7" Single: Released Jan '81, on Polydor, by Polydor Ltd. Deleted Jan '84. Catalogue no: **POSP 226**

Camel

Biographical details: At the time of their greatest success, this British band consisted of Peter bardens, Doug Ferguson, Andy Latimer and Andy Ward.
Camel were formed in 1972. During the Sixties Bardens had played in the group Them and later with then unknowns Mick Fleetwood, Peter Green and Rod Stewart. The other three members had just finished being the backing group of unsuccessful singer/songwriter Philip Goodhand Tait. Camel's debut eponymous 1973 album failed to make any impact, as did 1974's *Mirage*. The LP that made their name was 1975's *The Snow Goose*, a rock version of a children's story. This gave them their first and loongest run on the UK album chart, staying on the survey for 13 weeks. It was the archetypal Seventies concept album - a constant theme and storyline running throughout, played by long-haired, serious-minded art-rock group. The album wasso well-received that they performed it at London's Royal Albert hall.
Their next two sets, *Moon Madness* (1976) and *Rain Dances* (1977), both made the Top 20 in Britain, but no subsequent releases have made that mark or attracted more than cult acceptance. In the aftermath of the punk revolution, their style came to be regarded as passe; in addition, they were with Decca Records who, in the late Seventies and early Eighties, proved themselves to be a spent force in the record marketplace. (Bob MacDonald).
A progressive rock band formed in 1972 by keyboardist Peter Bardens, Andy Latimer on flute, guitar and vocals, bassist Doug Ferguson and drummer Andy Ward. As Brew they had backed singer/songwriter Philip Goodhand Tait. The similarity of their new name to ex-Herd hearthrob Peter Frampton's Camel didn't help their first two albums; the third, *The snow goose* a concept album suggested by Paul Gallico's children's novel, was an instrumental hit with Lattimer's flute prominent and led to an Albert Hall concert with the London Symphony Orchestra. They lasted well into the 80's with completely different personnel, Bardens guesting on some albums. (Donald Clarke, April 1989)t.

CLOAK & DAGGER MAN
Tracks: / Cloak and dagger man / Pressure point.
7" Single: Released Apr '84, on Decca, by Decca Records. Deleted '88. Catalogue no: **CAMEL 1**
12" Single: Released Apr '84, on Decca, by Decca Records. Deleted '88. Catalogue no: **CAMEX 1**

YOUR LOVE IS STRANGER THAN MINE
Tracks: / Your love is stranger than mine / Neon magic.
7" Single: Released Feb '80, on Decca, by Decca Records. Deleted '83. Catalogue no: **FR 13871**

Cameo

Biographical details: This America[n] soul/disco band consists of Larry Blackmo[n], Tomi Jenkins, Gregory johnson, Arnett Le[f]tenant and Nathan Leftenant.
Cameo issued their first album *Cardiac A[r]rest* in 1977. Their regular subsequent re[]leases in the late Seventies and early Eig[h]ties established the group as a regular fixtu[re] on the US black charts, though they neve[r] crossed over to pop listings. They score[d] their first British hit single with 1984's *She['s] Strange*, a laid-back piece of soul that i[n]cluded some spoken segments. It ju[st] scraped the UK Top 40 and was another b[ig] black chart success in their native count[ry]. (Bob MacDonald)..

ATTACK ME WITH YOUR LOVE
Tracks: / Attack me with your love.
7" Single: Released Jun '85, on Club, b[y] Phonogram Ltd. Deleted '86. Catalogue n[o]: **JAB 16**
12" Single: Released Jun '85, on Club, [by] Phonogram Ltd. Deleted '87. Catalogue n[o]: **JABX 16**

BABY, NOW THAT I'VE FOUND YOU
Tracks: / Baby, now that I've found you.
7" Single: Released Jul '83, on Loose, [by] Loose Records. Catalogue no: **LSE 2**

BACK AND FORTH
Tracks: / Back and forth / You can have t[he] world.
12" Single: Released Apr '87, on Club, [by] Phonogram Ltd. Deleted Mar '88. Catalog[ue] no: **JABX 49**
CD 5": Released '88, on Club, by Phon[o]gram Ltd. Deleted Feb '89. Catalogue [no]: **8885132**
7" Single: Released Apr '87, on Club, [by] Phonogram Ltd. Deleted Mar '88. Catalog[ue] no: **JAB 49**

CANDY
Tracks: / Candy.
12" Single: Released Nov '86, on Club, [by] Phonogram Ltd. Deleted Jul '87. Catalog[ue] no: **JABX 43**
7" Set: Released Nov '86, on Club, by P[ho]nogram Ltd. Catalogue no: **JABXD 43**
7" Single: Released Nov '86, on Club, [by] Phonogram Ltd. Deleted Jul '87. Catalog[ue] no: **JAB 43**

DON'T BE SO COOL
Tracks: / Don't be so cool / Sound table /

CAMEO - SHE'S STRANGE (Released on Club)

the one (Only on 12" single.).
7" Single: Released Aug '81, on Casablanca, by PolyGram UK Ltd. Deleted '84. Catalogue no: **CAN 1004**
12" Single: Released Aug '81, on Casablanca, by PolyGram UK Ltd. Deleted '84. Catalogue no: **CANX 1004**

FOUR FROM CAMEO (EP)
12" Single: Released May '82, on Casablanca, by PolyGram UK Ltd. Catalogue no: **CANX 1010**
7" Single: Released May '82, on Casablanca, by PolyGram UK Ltd. Catalogue no: **CAN 1010**

GOODBYE, A
Tracks: / Goodbye / I've got your image / On the one (Extra track on 12" only.) / Goodbye (long version) (Available on double-pack only.) / Just be yourself (Available on double-pack only.) / It's serious (Available on double-pack only.).
Note: On The One - only on 12" version. A Goodbye(long version)/Just Be Yourself/ It's Serious - only on 12" double pack edition.
12" Single: Released Mar '86, on Club, by Phonogram Ltd. Catalogue no: **JABX 28**
7" Set: Released Mar '86, on Club, by Phonogram Ltd. Catalogue no: **JABXD 28**
7" Single: Released Mar '86, on Club, by Phonogram Ltd. Catalogue no: **JAB 28**

HANGIN' DOWNTOWN
Tracks: / Hangin' downtown / Talkin' out the side of your neck / You're a winner (on 12" only).
7" Single: Released May '84, on Club, by Phonogram Ltd. Catalogue no: **JAB 4**
12" Single: Released May '84, on Club, by Phonogram Ltd. Catalogue no: **JABX 4**

ON THE ONE
Tracks: / On the one / Cameosis.
7" Single: Released 20 Jun '80, on Casablanca, by PolyGram UK Ltd. Deleted '83. Catalogue no: **CAN 199**

SHE'S MINE
Tracks: / Flirt (Only on 12" single.) / Knights of the sound table (Only on 12" single.) / She's mine.
7" Single: Released Sep '87, on Club, by Phonogram Ltd. Deleted Mar '88. Catalogue no: **JAB 57**
12" Single: Released Sep '87, on Club, by Phonogram Ltd. Deleted Mar '88. Catalogue no: **JABX 57**

SHE'S MINE - THE CAMEO MEGAMIX 2
Tracks: / She's mine (cameo megamix) / She's mine.
12" Single: Released Sep '87, on Club, by Phonogram Ltd. Catalogue no: **JABX R57**

SHE'S STRANGE (see panel on previous page)
Tracks: / She's strange / Groove with you.
7" Single: Released Mar '84, on Club, by Phonogram Ltd. Deleted Mar '87. Catalogue no: **JAB 2**

SHE'S STRANGE (RE-ISSUE)
Tracks: / She's strange / Love you anyway / Talkin' out the side of your neck / Tribute to Bob Marley / Groove with you / Hangin' downtown / Leve tol.
12" Single: Released Nov '85, on Club, by Phonogram Ltd. Deleted '87. Catalogue no: **JABX 25**
" EP: Released Nov '85, on Club, by Phonogram Ltd. Catalogue no: **JAB 252**
" Single: Released Nov '85, on Club, by Phonogram Ltd. Deleted '87. Catalogue no: **JAB 25**

SINGLE LIFE (SINGLE)
Tracks: / Single life / She's strange.
" Single: Released Feb '88, on Old Gold, by Old Gold Records. Catalogue no: **OG 774**
" Single: Released Sep '85, on Club, by Phonogram Ltd. Deleted '88. Catalogue no: **JABXR 21**
' Single: Released Sep '85, on Club, by Phonogram Ltd. Deleted Sep '88. Catalogue no: **JAB 21**

SKIN I'M IN
Tracks: / Skin I'm in / Honey / Cameo megamix two (Only on 12" version.).
CD 5": Released Jan '89, on Club, by Phonogram Ltd. Catalogue no: **JABCD 77**
2" Single: Released Jan '89, on Club, by Phonogram Ltd. Deleted 31 Jul '89. Catalogue no: **JABX 77**
Single: Released Jan '89, on Club, by Phonogram Ltd. Deleted 31 Jul '89. Catalogue no: **JAB 77**
2" Single: Released Jan '89, on Club, by Phonogram Ltd. Deleted 31 Jul '89. Catalogue no: **JABXR 77**

SPARKLE
Tracks: / Sparkle / I just want to be / Do it with your body / Get up.
Single: Released Jan '80, on Casablanca, by PolyGram UK Ltd. Deleted Jan '85. Catalogue no: **CSS 3202**
" Single: Released Jan '80, on Casablanca, by PolyGram UK Ltd. Deleted Jan '85. Catalogue no: **CSSL 3202**

THROW IT DOWN
Tracks: / Throw it down / Is this the way.
7" Single: Released Dec '80, on Casablanca, by PolyGram UK Ltd. Deleted Dec '85. Catalogue no: **CANL 216**

WE'RE GOING OUT TONIGHT
Tracks: / We're going out tonight / Sparkle.
7" Single: Released Apr '80, on Casablanca, by PolyGram UK Ltd. Deleted '83. Catalogue no: **CAN 204**

WORD UP
Tracks: / Word up / Urban warrior (This track only available on singles.) / Candy / Back and forth / Don't be lonely / She's mine / Fast, fierce and funny / You can have the world.
Note: Produced by Larry Blackmon. Features guest appearances by Charlie Singleton andThe Brecker Brothers.
12" Single: Released Jul '87, on Club, by Phonogram Ltd. Catalogue no: **JABXR 38**
7" Single: Released Aug '86, on Club, by Phonogram Ltd. Deleted Mar '88. Catalogue no: **JAB 38**
12" Single: Released Aug '86, on Club, by Phonogram Ltd. Catalogue no: **JABX 38**

YOU MAKE ME WORK
Tracks: / You make me work / Dkwig.
CD 5": Released Oct '88, on Club, by Phonogram Ltd. Catalogue no: **JABCD 70**
12" Single: Released Oct '88, on Club, by Phonogram Ltd. Deleted 31 May '89. Catalogue no: **JABX 70**
7" Single: Released Oct '88, on Club, by Phonogram Ltd. Deleted 31 May '89. Catalogue no: **JAB 70**
12" Single: Released Oct '88, Deleted 31 May '89. Catalogue no: **JABXR 70**

Camera Obscura

DESTITUTION
Tracks: / Destitution.
7" Single: Released Apr '83, on Small Wonder, by Small Wonder Records. Catalogue no: **SMALL 28**

Cameron

LET'S GET IT OFF
Tracks: / Let's get it off / Magic of you.
12" Single: Released Aug '80, on Salsoul, Deleted '83. Catalogue no: **SAL 12 4**

WAIT UNTIL TOMORROW
Tracks: / Wait until tomorrow / Shadows.
7" Single: Released Feb '89, on Ardent, by Ardent Records. Catalogue no: **ADS 9002**

Cameron, Andy

Biographical details: This British singer is a Scottish football fanatic. In April 1978 he hit No. 6 on the UK charts with his single *Ally's Tartan Army*. In anticipation of that summer's world cup, this enthusiastic singalong ditty in praise of the Scotland squad can, at best, be described as amateurish. Four years later, when the next world cup came round, he tried again with the single *We're On The March Again*; this time however, his efforts fell on deaf ears. (Bob MacDonald)..

ALLY'S TARTAN ARMY
Tracks: / Ally's tartan army.
7" Single: Released Apr '78, on Klub, by Klub Records. Catalogue no: **KLUB 03**

WE'RE ON THE MARCH AGAIN
Tracks: / We're on the march again / Scotland for me.
7" Single: Released Apr '82, on Klub, by Klub Records. Catalogue no: **KLUB 33**

Cameron, Chris

IS THIS LOVE
7" Single: Released Jun '85, on Steinar, by Steinar Records (UK). Catalogue no: **STE 765**
12" Single: Released Jun '85, on Steinar, by Steinar Records (UK). Catalogue no: **STE 1265**

WRITTEN IN YOUR HEART
12" Single: Released Sep '85, on Steinar, by Steinar Records (UK). Catalogue no: **STE 1285**
7" Single: Released Sep '85, on Steinar, by Steinar Records (UK). Catalogue no: **STE 785**

Cameron, Christel

GIVE ME ONE MORE CHANCE
Tracks: / Give me one more chance / Return fom exile.
12" Single: Released Jul '86, on Jam Star, Catalogue no: **JS 002**

Cameron, Debbie

STRAIGHT OR CURLY HAIR
Tracks: / Straight or curly hair / Kroller eller e.j..
7" Single: Released Apr '81, on EMI, by EMI Records. Deleted Apr '86. Catalogue no: **EMI 5173**

YOU TO ME ARE EVERYTHING
7" Single: Released Oct '84, on Artistic, by Submarine Records. Catalogue no: **SART 004**

Cameron, G.C.

HEARTS AND FLOWERS
Tracks: / Hearts and flowers.
7" Single: Released Apr '83, on Malaco, by Malaco Records (UK). Deleted '88. Catalogue no: **MAL 006**

LIVE FOR LOVE
Tracks: / Live for love / I love you.
12" Single: Released Feb '81, on Flamingo, by Airwave Records (USA). Deleted '84. Catalogue no: **FMT 11**
7" Single: Released Feb '81, on Flamingo, by Airwave Records (USA). Deleted '84. Catalogue no: **FM 11**

Cameron, Ian

POP UP THE AISLE
Tracks: / Pop up the aisle / Pop round the aisle.
7" Single: Released Jul '81, on Pip, by Pip Records. Catalogue no: **PIP 8101**

Cameron, Mary

DURISDEER
Tracks: / Durisdeer / Dumbarton's drums.
7" Single: Released 16 Sep '88, on Scotdisc, by Scotdisc Records. Catalogue no: **ITV 7s 459**

Cameron, Rafael

ALL THAT'S GOOD TO ME
Tracks: / All that's good to me / Funtown USA.
7" Single: Released Aug '81, on Salsoul, Deleted '84. Catalogue no: **SAL 10**
12" Single: Released Aug '81, on Salsoul, Deleted '84. Catalogue no: **SALT 10**

Cameron, Stuart

HOW DID YOU CHANGE YOUR MIND ?
Tracks: / How did you change your mind ?.
12" Single: Released 24 Jul '89, on Silver Heart, by Silver Heart Records. Catalogue no: **CUFF 1A**

Camillo

SAG WARUM
Tracks: / Sag warum.
7" Single: Released Apr '83, on EMI (France), by EMI Records. Catalogue no: **2C 008 232443**

Camillo, Tony Bazuka

DYNOMITE
Tracks: / Dynomite.
7" Single: Released May '75, on A&M, by A&M Records. Catalogue no: **AMS 7168**

Camino

HIGH WINDOWS
Tracks: / High windows / Devil in Miss Jones, The.
7" Pic: Released 6 Apr '88, on PRT, by Castle Communications Records. Catalogue no: **PYS 11**

Camouflage

BEE STING (featuring Mysti)
Tracks: / Bee sting.
7" Single: Released Sep '77, on State, by State Records. Deleted Sep '80. Catalogue no: **STAT 58**

GREAT COMMANDMENT, THE
Tracks: / Great commandment / Pompeii.
12" Single: Released Mar '89, on Atlantic, by WEA Records. Catalogue no: **A 9031T**
7" Single: Released Mar '89, on Atlantic, by WEA Records. Catalogue no: **A 9031**

SAMANTHA
Tracks: / Samantha / Gotta find a place in your heart.
7" Single: Released Sep '84, on Homespun (Ireland), by Outlet Records. Catalogue no: **HS 095**

Camp Sophisto

SONGS IN PRAISE OF THE REVOLUTION
Tracks: / Songs in praise of the revolution.
7" Single: Released Aug '83, on Pure Freude, Deleted '85. Catalogue no: **6446**

Campaign

TRY AGAIN
Tracks: / Try again.
7" Single: Released Apr '83, on CBS, by CBS Records. Catalogue no: **A 3180**

Campbell, Al

ALL KINDS OF PEOPLE
Tracks: / All kinds of people.
12" Single: Released May '83, on Greensleeves, by Greensleeves Records. Catalogue no: **GRED 121**

CAN'T TAKE THE PRESSURE
Tracks: / Can't take the pressure / Police in England (computerised version).
12" Single: Released Mar '86, on Greensleeves, by Greensleeves Records. Catalogue no: **GRED 197**

COLLIE HERB
Tracks: / Collie herb / Jail bait.
12" Single: Released May '85, on Jah Life, Catalogue no: **JL 009**

DANCE HALL STYLE
Tracks: / Dance hall style / Fight it down.
12" Single: Released Jun '82, on Greensleeves, by Greensleeves Records. Catalogue no: **GRED 94**

DOWN IN BABYLON
Tracks: / Down in Babylon.
12" Single: Released Jun '84, on Ethnic, Catalogue no: **ETHDD 2244**

EVERYBODY NEEDS LOVE
Tracks: / Everybody needs love.
12" Single: Released Sep '85, on Striker Lee, Catalogue no: **BL 31**

FOWARD NATTY
12" Single: Released Jun '85, on Live & Learn (USA), by Live & Learn Records (USA). Catalogue no: **LLD 002**

GEE BABY
Tracks: / Gee baby / Where were you.
12" Single: Released Nov '83, on Solomonic (1), by Solomonic Records. Catalogue no: **SS 1099**

GIMME WEH ME WANT
Tracks: / Gimme weh me want / Gimme weh me want (version).
12" Single: Released Jul '87, on Greensleeves, by Greensleeves Records. Catalogue no: **GRED 215**

GIVE ME LOVE
Tracks: / Give me love.
12" Single: Released Jan '84, on Mobiliser, by Jetstar Records. Catalogue no: **MM 70**

HOLD YOUR CORNER
Tracks: / Hold your corner / Jammys posse.
12" Single: Released Oct '86, on Jammy's, Catalogue no: **JAM 003**

I CAN'T STOP LOVING YOU
Tracks: / I can't stop loving you / I can't stop loving you (Version).
12" Single: Released May '86, on Hands & Hearts, Catalogue no: **HHD 001**

I SHOULD BE YOUR LOVER
Tracks: / I should be your lover.
12" Single: Released Oct '82, on J.B., Catalogue no: **JBD 041**

I'VE GOT TO GET YOUR LOVING
Tracks: / I've got to get your loving.
12" Single: Released Oct '82, on Music Maker, Catalogue no: **MM 001**

JUGGLING IN THE FRONT LINE
Tracks: / Juggling in the frontline.
12" Single: Released Jun '85, on FMJ, Catalogue no: **FMJ 002**

JUST MY IMAGINATION
Tracks: / Just my imagination.
12" Single: Released Dec '82, on Exclusive, Catalogue no: **EXC 601140**

LAMBS BREAD
78 rpm: Released Apr '82, on Silver Camel, Catalogue no: **SC 014**

LET ME BE THE ONE
Tracks: / Let me be the one.
12" Single: Released Sep '88, on Skengdon, Catalogue no: **SKDL 080**

LET ME INTO YOUR WORLD
Tracks: / Let me into your world.
12" Single: Released Dec '82, on Music Works, Catalogue no: **WRT 1289**

LET THEM PROSPER
Tracks: / Let them prosper.
12" Single: Released Nov '84, on Black Solidarity, Catalogue no: **UNKNOWN**

LOVE AGAIN
Tracks: / Love again.
7" Single: Released 10 Oct '87, on Mix Music, Catalogue no: **MM 001**

MASH IT ALREADY
Tracks: / Mash it already.
12" Single: Released Sep '84, Catalogue no: **UNKNOWN**

POLITICIANS
Tracks: / Politician.
12" Single: Released Jul '86, on Move, Catalogue no: **MS 12**

REALLY SMOKIN'
Tracks: / Really smokin'.
12" Single: Released Feb '85, on Fashion, by Fashion Records. Catalogue no: **FAD 025**

RIOT
Tracks: / Riot.
12" Single: Released Nov '85, on John Dread Production, Catalogue no: **JDP 004**

SHE NUH READY
Tracks: / She nuh ready.
12" Single: Released Jul '84, on Tads, Catalogue no: **TRD 15308**

STYLE & FASHION
Tracks: / Style and fashion.
12" Single: Released Aug '84, on Greensleeves, by Greensleeves Records. Catalogue no: **GRED 153**

TALK ABOUT LOVE
Tracks: / Talk about love / Diet rock.
12" Single: Released Apr '85, on Scom, Catalogue no: **BD 019**

TRY MY LOVE
Tracks: / Try my love / Official fashion.
12" Single: Released May '86, on Fashion, by Fashion Records. Catalogue no: **FAD 039**

WHEN THE LIGHTS ARE LOW
Tracks: / When the lights are low.
12" Single: Released Apr '85, on Taxi (1), Catalogue no: **UNKNOWN**

Campbell, Barbara

I'M A WOMAN
Tracks: / I'm a woman.
12" Single: on Red Rose, Catalogue no: **RR 001**

Campbell, Bill

ENDLESS LOVE
Tracks: / Endless love.
12" Single: Released Oct '81, on BB, Catalogue no: **BBD 138**

FALLING IN LOVE
Tracks: / Falling in love.
12" Single: Released Jul '89, on BB, Catalogue no: **BBD 215**

LET ME HAVE THE CHANCE
Tracks: / Guilty / Let me have the chance.
12" Single: Released Nov '86, on Backbeat, Catalogue no: **BBD 188**

ON MY OWN
Tracks: / On my own / For the love of you.
Note: See also under Valerie Harrison.
12" Single: Released May '86, on Backbeat, Catalogue no: **BBD 177**

PRIVATE NUMBER
Tracks: / Private number.
12" Single: Released Dec '88, on B.B. Music, Catalogue no: **BBD 212**

TAKE ME AND MAKE ME
Tracks: / Take me and make me.
12" Single: Released Oct '84, on Cima, Catalogue no: **CR 001**

TONIGHT I CELEBRATE MY LOVE
Tracks: / Tonight I celebrate my love / Lonely night.
12" Single: Released Oct '83, on BB, Catalogue no: **BBD 151**

WE ARE (FUNKY)
Tracks: / We are (funky) / We are (funky) part 2.
12" Single: Released Feb '86, on BB, Catalogue no: **BBD 21010**

WHO TOUCHED SHE BAM BAM
Tracks: / Who touched she bam bam.
12" Single: Released Aug '86, on Backbeat, Catalogue no: **BBD 178**

Campbell, Carol

EVERYTHING I LOVE SEEMS TO DIE
Tracks: / Everything I love seems to die.
12" Single: Released Apr '84, on Sea View, Catalogue no: **SV 4**

GOT TO LET YOU KNOW
Tracks: / Got to let you know / Got to let you know.
12" Single: Released Oct '86, on Sea View, Catalogue no: **SV 13**

I'M IN LOVE
Tracks: / I'm in love.
7" Single: Released Nov '85, on Sea View, Catalogue no: **SV 10**

IT'S REAL
Tracks: / It's real.
12" Single: Released Jan '85, on Sea View, Catalogue no: **SV 7**

LET'S KISS AND MAKE UP
Tracks: / Let's kiss and make up / It's not the same.
10" single: Released Dec '82, on Jenieves, Catalogue no: **JRR 10501**

LET'S TRY AGAIN
Tracks: / Let's try again.
12" Single: Released Aug '84, on Sea View, Catalogue no: **SV 5**

Campbell, Cornell

CONSCIOUS LOVER
Tracks: / Conscious lover.
12" Single: Released Jul '87, on Black Joy, Catalogue no: **DH 820**

HUNDRED POUNDS OF COLLIE
Tracks: / Hundred pounds of collie.
12" Single: Released Jun '82, on Black Joy, Catalogue no: **BH 821**

I AM A MAN
Tracks: / I am a man / Troddin out of Babylon.
12" Single: Released Jul '82, on Black Music, Catalogue no: **BM 704**

JAIL HOUSE CAN'T STAY EMPTY
Tracks: / Jailhouse can't stay empty.
7" Single: Released Apr '89, on Jetstar, by Jetstar Records. Catalogue no: **KCKM 4104**

LOVE THAT'S TRUE
Tracks: / Love that's true / Kingdom dub / Thunder and lightning dub.
12" Single: Released Jun '81, on Kingdom, by Kingdom Records. Deleted '83. Catalogue no: **KV 8016 12**

LOVE TRAP
Tracks: / Love trap.
12" Single: Released Apr '83, on Shuttle, Catalogue no: **SH 001**

NEVER LET IT GO
Tracks: / Never let it go.
12" Single: Released Nov '83, on Greensleeves, by Greensleeves Records. Catalogue no: **GRED 133**

UNFAIR GAME
Tracks: / Unfair game.
12" Single: Released Mar '87, on Live & Love, Catalogue no: **LLDIS 0033**

WE A BOOBLING
Tracks: / We a boobling.
12" Single: Released Oct '84, on Striker, Catalogue no: **LEE BL 01**

WHAT KIND OF WORLD ARE WE LIVING IN?
Tracks: / What kind of world are we livin' in.
12" Single: Released Jan '84, on Mobiliser, by Jetstar Records. Catalogue no: **MM 67**

YOU ARE MY LADY
Tracks: / You are my lady.
12" Single: Released Apr '83, on Guidance, Catalogue no: **VPRD 121**

YOU WALKING
Tracks: / You walking.
12" Single: Released Mar '83, on Earthquake, Catalogue no: **QH 20**

Campbell, Dudley

BAPTISM
Tracks: / Baptism.
12" Single: Released May '82, on Cartridge, Catalogue no: **CRD 108**

GETTING STRONGER
Tracks: / Getting stronger.
12" Single: Released May '82, on Cartridge, Catalogue no: **CRD 103**

Campbell, Errol

NEAREST TO MY HEART
Tracks: / Nearest to my heart.
7" Single: Released Feb '83, on Stiff, by Stiff Records. Catalogue no: **BUY 173**

Campbell, Ethna

Biographical details: This British singer entered the UK chart with her only hit in the final week of '75. *The Old Rugged Cross*, a traditional gospel song, proved a slow but steady seller -- it peaked at No 33 but spent 11 weeks in the Top Fifty, moving up and down in a seemingly endless yo-yo pattern. Campbell went on to release a couple of albums, but little has been heard of her since. (Bob MacDonald, 1984.).

OLD RUGGED CROSS, THE
Tracks: / Old rugged cross, The.
7" Single: Released Dec '75, on Philips, by Phonogram Ltd. Deleted Dec '78. Catalogue no: **6006 475**

Campbell, Glen

Biographical details: This American singer, guitarist and multi-instrumentalist is the seventh son of a seventh son and was born into a highly musical family. Already an accomplished musician by the time he let school, he spent the late Fifties and early Sixties building up his reputation in the music business, first as a number of various gigging groups and then as a session musician. His varied instrumental skills won him backup appearances on many stars' records during the early and mid-Sixties, including Frank Sinatra, Bobby Darin, Nat King Cole, the Mammas and the Papas and the Monkees. He also joined the Beach Boys on tour for a brief period, when leader Brian Wilson's troubled psyche forced him to quit the road. During the era of all these guest appearances, Campbell was simultaneously trying to make it big as a solo artist. He failed dismally in this regard for several years. It was not until 1967, when he began selecting his material himself, that he hit the American Top 40.
By The Time I Get To Pheonix, a plaintive song penned by Jim Webb, reached No. 26 on the US chart at the end of '67. This helped to establish Webb as a major composer, a status he cemented the following year with the huge success of Richard Harris' *MacArthur Park*. Webb then wroite two smash hits for Campbell - the hauntin *Wichita Lineman* reached No. 3 in the US, followed by the No. 4 success of *Galveston*. They also gave the artist his first two UK hits. Having been a bigger star in America than in Britain up to this point, Campbell scored two hits in 1970 that were much more successful in the UK than the US: *All I Have To Do Is Dream*, a duet remake with Bobbie Gentry of the Everly Brothers classic reached No. 3 in the UK and would thus prove to be the biggest British single of Campbell's career and the Jim Webb ballad *Honey Come Back* peaked at No. 4. Meanwhile back in the States, the singer was selling large quantities of albums and also making a smash movie debut, costarring with John Wayne in *True Grit*. He ended 1970 by making the Top 10 on both sides of the Atlantic with a cover version of Conway Twitty's late Fifties chart-topper *It's Only Make Believe*.
From 1971 onwards hit singles were not forthcomng for several years, however. Instead Campbell concerntrated on further film success and on US television work. A *Greatest Hits* set was issued in the autumn of '71, selling particularly well in Britain, where it logged no less than 113 weeks on the chart. He returned to the singles charts in a big way in 1975, when the catchy *Rhinestone Cowboy* gave him his first US No. 1 and reached No. 4 in the UK. This track was typical Campbell - a middle-of-the-road number rooted in country music, but also incorporating elements of rock. Another country/rock flavoured single *Southern Nights* gave him a second American No. 1 in 1977, soon after he had topped the British album chart for six weeks with the TV-advertised *20 Golden Greats* collection.
Through this continued acceptance, Glen Campbell had proved himself to be a highly durable star. As the Seventies became the Eighties, he retired from the pop market and concerntrated solely on his adult MoR following. he remains active in showbusiness, both in recording and touring terms. (Bob MacDonald).
The country/pop singer and guitarist was born in 1936 in Delight, Arkansas. With plenty of experience, he moved to L.A. in 1958 and played on the Champs smash novelty *Tequila*, also sessioning with Nat Cole, Frank Sinatra, Elvis Presley, Mamas & The Papas, Merle Haggard and others. He deputised for Brian Wilson in the Beach Boys in 1965 and made his big breakthrough in 1967 with the John Hartford song *Gentle on my mind*, then Jim Webb's *By the time I get to Phoenix*, both country hits which crossed over to the pop chart; he won Grammies, was named Entertainer of the year by the Country Music Association in 1968, and his laid back sincerety crossed over regularly: *Galveston* and *Wichita lineman* were both Webb songs. He had 12 gold and seven platinum albums in 1968-72; in the UK his 1971 greatest hits album was in the charts for 113 weeks. He also dueted with Tanya Tucker (a long personal relationship), Anne Murray, Bobbie Gentry and Rita Coolidge. He played straight roles in films, had his own TV series in the early '70's and his own golf tournament. (Donald Clarke, April 1989).

DREAM BABY
Tracks: / Dream baby.
7" Single: Released Mar '71, on Capitol, by EMI Records. Deleted Mar '74. Catalogue no: **CL 15674**

EVERYTHING A MAN COULD EVER NEED
Tracks: / Everything a man could ever need.
7" Single: Released Sep '70, on Capitol, by EMI Records. Deleted Sep '73. Catalogue no: **CL 15653**

GALVESTON
Tracks: / Galveston.
7" Single: Released May '69, on Ember (1), by Bulldog Records (UK). Deleted May '72. Catalogue no: **EMBS 263**

HOLLYWOOD SMILES
Tracks: / Hollywood smiles / Hooked on love.
7" Single: Released Sep '80, on Capitol, by EMI Records. Deleted '83. Catalogue no: **CL 16167**

HONEY COME BACK
Tracks: / Honey come back.
7" Single: Released May '70, on Capitol, by EMI Records. Deleted May '73. Catalogue no: **CL 15638**

HOUND DOG MAN
Tracks: / Hound dog man / Highwayman.
7" Single: Released Feb '80, on Capitol, by EMI Records. Deleted Feb '83. Catalogue no: **CL 16122**

IF YOU WERE MY LADY
Tracks: / If you were my lady / It's one to grow on.
7" Single: Released Oct '82, on Energy (USA), by Bulldog Records (USA). Catalogue no: **NRG 008**

IT'S ONLY MAKE BELIEVE
Tracks: / It's only make believe.
7" Single: Released Nov '70, on Capitol, by EMI Records. Deleted Nov '73. Catalogue no: **CL 15663**

JUST A MATTER OF TIME
Tracks: / Just a matter of time / Gene Autry, my hero.
7" Single: Released Mar '86, on Atlantic, by WEA Records. Catalogue no: **A 9600**

LETTING GO
Tracks: / Letting go / Face to face.
7" Single: Released Apr '84, on Compleat (USA), by Compleat Entertainment Corp.(USA). Deleted '85. Catalogue no: **CLT 3**

RHINESTONE COWBOY
Tracks: / Rhinestone cowboy / Lovelight.
7" Single: Released Oct '75, on Capitol, by EMI Records. Deleted Oct '89. Catalogue no: **CL 15824**

SOUTHERN NIGHTS (SINGLE)
Tracks: / Southern nights.
7" Single: Released Mar '77, on Capitol, by EMI Records. Catalogue no: **CL 15907**

THEY STILL DANCE TO WALTZES IN ENGLAND
Tracks: / They still dance to waltzes in England / Letter to home.
7" Single: Released May '84, on Atlantic, by WEA Records. Catalogue no: **A 9755**

TRY A LITTLE KINDNESS (SINGLE)
Tracks: / Try a little kindness.
7" Single: Released Feb '70, on Capitol, by EMI Records. Deleted Feb '73. Catalogue no: **CL 15622**

WHY DON'T WE JUST SLEEP ON IT TONIGHT
Tracks: / Why don't we just sleep on it tonight / Daisy a day, A.
7" Single: Released Feb '81, on Capitol, by EMI Records. Deleted Feb '84. Catalogue no: **CL 16182**

WICHITA LINEMAN
Tracks: / Wichita lineman.
7" Single: Released Jan '69, on Ember (1) by Bulldog Records (UK). Deleted Jan '72 Catalogue no: **EMBS 261**

WOMAN'S TOUCH
Tracks: / Woman's touch, A.
7" Single: Released Oct '82, on Atlantic, b WEA Records. Catalogue no: **799960 7**

Campbell, Gloria

ONE OF US
Tracks: / One of us.
12" Single: Released Aug '85, on Pionee International, Catalogue no: **PIDISCO 06**

TONIGHT IS MY NIGHT OUT
Tracks: / Tonight is my night out.
12" Single: Released Apr '82, on Disc Rocker, Catalogue no: **DR 01003**

Campbell, Gordon

I WOULD LOVE YOU
Tracks: / I would love you.
7" Single: Released May '85, on Holyrooc by REL Records. Deleted '87. Catalogue nc **HOLLY 001**

JUST LET ME
Tracks: / Just let me / Miss miss miss.
7" Single: Released Apr '87, on Rocket, b Rocket Records. Deleted Dec '87. Cata logue no: **BLAST 3**

WITH A WOMAN LIKE YOU
Tracks: / With a woman like you / Besic you.
7" Single: Released Jun '82, on Rel, by RE Records. Deleted Jun '85. Catalogue n **RES 009**
7" Single: Released Jul '83, on Holyrood, b REL Records. Deleted '87. Catalogue n **HOLLY 004**

YOU CAN'T ALWAYS WANT WHAT YOU GET
Tracks: / You can't always want what yo get.
7" Single: Released Oct '84, on Holyroc by REL Records. Deleted '87. Catalogue r **HOLLY 009**

Campbell, Ian

TIMES THEY ARE A-CHANGIN' (re entered twice)
Tracks: / Times they are a-changin'.
7" Single: Released Mar '65, on Transatla tic, by Transatlantic Records. Deleted M '68. Catalogue no: **SP 5**

Campbell, Jo Ann

MOTORCYLE MICHAEL
Tracks: / Motorcycle Michael.
7" Single: Released Jun '61, on H.M.V., EMI Records. Deleted Jun '64. Catalog no: **POP 873**

Campbell, Junior

Biographical details: This British guita songwriter and singer first came to fam the late sixties as a member of a Scottish p group, the Marmalade. The scored a UK 1 smash in 1969 with their rendition of highly catchy Beatles album track *Ob-l Ob-la-da*. Their other two Top 3 singles, b hits in 1970 were co-written by Campb *Reflections Of My Life* and *Rainbow*. He shortly after these successes to becom solo singer/songwriter.
In this capacity he achieved a pair of Top singles in Britain. *Hallelujah Freedom* bright pop song, reached No. 10 in 1

The following year he peaked at No. 15 with *Sweet Illusion*. Little has been heard from Junior Campbell Since. (Bob MacDonald)..

HALLELUJAH FREEDOM
Tracks: / Hallelujah freedom.
7" Single: Released Oct '72, on Deram, by London Records. Deleted Oct '75. Catalogue no: **DM 364**
7" Single: Released Oct '83, on Old Gold, by Old Gold Records. Deleted Jul '88. Catalogue no: **OG 9358**

SWEET ILLUSION
Tracks: / Sweet illusion.
7" Single: Released Jun '73, on Deram, by London Records. Deleted Jun '76. Catalogue no: **DM 387**

Campbell, Malcolm

BUCK UP
Tracks: / Buck up.
12" Single: Released Feb '82, on Solid Groove, Catalogue no: **SG 005 12**

Campbell, Pat

Biographical details: Hailing from the Irish Republic, this vocalist scored his only British chart record in lat 1969 with *The Deal*. More noteworthy than the record was the label on which it appeared. Major Minor Records had won much publicity a few weeks earlier by relieving Fontana Records of the rights to Jane Birkin & Serge Gainsbourg's *Je t'aime...moi non plus*, after the latter company had suffered a sudden attack of moral indignation over that 'obscene' disc. The surprise takeover had taken place while the record was at No. 2 on the UK charts; it had gone to No. 1 in the second week of the new label's tenure.
Pat Campbell continued recording into the Seventies but little of note was heard from hin or, for that matter, from Major Minor. *The Deal* reached No. 31 on the British listings. (Bob MacDonald)..

DEAL, THE
Tracks: / Deal, The.
7" Single: Released Nov '69, on Major Record, by The Major Record Company. Deleted Nov '72. Catalogue no: **MM 648**

Campbell, Pete

CARIBBEAN CIRCUS SHOW
Tracks: / Caribbean circus show.
12" Single: Released Mar '85, on B.B. Music, Catalogue no: **BBD 164**

HOLDING BACK THE YEARS
Tracks: / Holding back the years / Blue music.
12" Single: Released Aug '86, on PC, Catalogue no: **PC 0010**

I WANT TO WAKE UP WITH YOU
Tracks: / I want to wake up with you / I want to wake up with you (version).
12" Single: Released Aug '86, on Blackbeat, Catalogue no: **BBD 182**

LET'S MAKE A BABY
Tracks: / Let's make a baby / Blue.
12" Single: Released Nov '84, on PC, Catalogue no: **PC 2**

RED RED WINE
Tracks: / Red red wine / Sweet dancing.
12" Single: Released Oct '83, on Caribbean Echo, Catalogue no: **CBED 006**

SHAVING CREAM
Tracks: / Shaving cream (instrumental) / Shaving cream.
12" Single: Released Nov '86, on PC, Catalogue no: **PC 0012**

THIS TIME (I'M COMING HOME)
Tracks: / This time (I'm coming home).
12" Single: Released Nov '88, on B.B. Music, Catalogue no: **BBD 211**

Campbell, Ricky

DON'T BLAME ME FOR YOUR MISTAKE
Tracks: / Other side, The / Don't blame me for your mistake.
12" Single: Released Jan '87, on Time, Catalogue no: **TR 025**

Campbell, Rocky

BUONA SERA
Tracks: / Buona sera.
12" Single: Released Dec '83, on Sunburn, by Orbitone Records. Catalogue no: **SBD 43**

FATHER BEG YOUR PARDON
Tracks: / Father beg your pardon.
12" Single: Released May '82, on Cartridge, Catalogue no: **CRD 10**

LET ME DREAM
Tracks: / Let me dream

12" Single: Released Nov '88, on Lucky, by Lucky Records. Catalogue no: **LSD 008**

TOGETHER AGAIN
Tracks: / Together again.
7" Single: Released Oct '88, on Clouds, Catalogue no: **CLSD 004 7**

Campbell, Sharon

ON MY TIME
Tracks: / On my time / All time favourite thing.
7" Single: Released Feb '80, on RCA, by BMG Records (UK). Deleted '83. Catalogue no: **PB 5227**

YOU PICK ME UP
Tracks: / You pick me up.
7" Single: Released Oct '80, on RCA, by BMG Records (UK). Deleted '83. Catalogue no: **RCA 6**

Campbell, Stan

Biographical details: Soul singer Campbell was born in Coventry in 1962, and was at the centre of the city's 'two-tone' scene with Selector in the early '80s, then with Jerry Dammers' Special AKA (lead vocal on hit *Free Nelson Mandela*). His debut album on WEA in 1987 was unusual in not being overproduced, with seven originals and good covers such as the Animals' *Don't let me misunderstood* and *Crawfish* from the Elvis Presley movie *King Creole*. The album's fine rhythm sections showed a strong Latin bent. (Donald Clarke, April 1989).

CRAWFISH
Tracks: / Crawfish / Till we meet again.
7" Single: Released Mar '87, on WEA, by WEA Records. Deleted Jan '88. Catalogue no: **YZ 102**
12" Single: on WEA, by WEA Records. Deleted Jan '88. Catalogue no: **YZ 102T**

KNOCKING ON HEAVENS DOOR
Tracks: / Knocking on heavens door.
12" Single: Released Aug '87, on WEA, by WEA Records. Deleted Jul '88. Catalogue no: **YZ 150T**
7" Single: Released Aug '87, on WEA, by WEA Records. Deleted Jul '88. Catalogue no: **YZ 150**

YEARS GO BY
Tracks: / Years go by / Seven more days.
7" Single: Released May '87, on WEA, by WEA Records. Deleted Jul '88. Catalogue no: **YZ 127**
12" Single: Released May '87, on WEA, by WEA Records. Deleted Jul '88. Catalogue no: **YZ 127T**

Campbell, Trevor 'Big

DESIDERATA
Tracks: / Desiderata / Desiderata (instrumental).
7" Single: Released Dec '83, on Mint, by Emerald Records. Deleted '88. Catalogue no: **CHEW 87**

Campbell-Lyons

NAKED ROBOTS WATCHING BREAKFAST TV
Tracks: / Naked robots watching breakfast TV.
7" Single: Released Nov '81, on Public, Catalogue no: **PUB 006**

Camper Van Beethoven

GOOD GUYS AND BAD GUYS (SINGLE)
Tracks: / Good guys and bad guys.
12" Single: Released Oct '87, on Rough Trade, by Rough Trade Records. Catalogue no: **RTT 205**

LIFE IS GRAND
Tracks: / Life is grand / Love is a weed / Harmony in my head (on 12" & CD only) / Wade in the water (on 12" & CD only).
7" Single: Released 30 Aug '88, on Virgin, by Virgin Records. Catalogue no: **VS 1122**
12" Single: Released 30 Aug '88, on Virgin, by Virgin Records. Catalogue no: **VST 1122**
CD 3": Released '88, on Virgin, by Virgin Records. Catalogue no: **VSCD 1122**

TAKE THE SKINHEADS BOWLING
Tracks: / Take the skinheads bowling.
7" Single: Released Mar '87, on Rough Trade, by Rough Trade Records. Catalogue no: **RT 161**
12" Single: Released Mar '87, on Rough Trade, by Rough Trade Records. Catalogue no: **RTT 161**

Campi, Ray

BOOZE IT
Tracks: / Booze it.
7" Single: Released Jun '80, on Rollin' Rock, Catalogue no: **45 027**

CATERPILLAR
Tracks: / Caterpillar.
7" Single: Released Jul '81, on Rollin' Rock, Catalogue no: **PFE 003**

EAGER BEAVER BOY (SINGLE)
Tracks: / Eager beaver boy.
7" Single: Released Jun '80, on Rollin' Rock, Catalogue no: **45 006**

MY BABY LEFT ME
Tracks: / My baby left me.
7" Single: Released Jun '80, on Rollin' Rock, Catalogue no: **45 019**

NEWEST WAVE
Tracks: / Newest wave, The / Once is enough.
7" Single: Released Jun '80, on Rollin' Rock, Catalogue no: **45 047**
7" Single: Released May '81, on Rondelet Music, by Rondelet Music & Records. Deleted May '86. Catalogue no: **ROUND 1000**

PLAY IT COOL
Tracks: / Play it cool.
7" EP: Released Sep '81, on Rollercoaster, by Rollercoaster Records. Deleted '86. Catalogue no: **PFE 003**

ROCKIN' AT THE RITZ
Tracks: / Rockin' at the Ritz / Quit your trifelin' / How low can you feel / Tor up.
7" EP: Released '89, on Magnum Music (Import), by Magnum Music Group. Catalogue no: **RR 101**
7" Single: Released Dec '81, on Rondelet Music, by Rondelet Music & Records. Catalogue no: **ROUND 1008**

SIXTEEN CHICKS
Tracks: / Sixteen chicks.
7" Single: Released Jun '80. on Rollin' Rock, Catalogue no: **45 014**

TORE UP
Tracks: / Tore up.
7" Single: Released Jun '80, on Rollin' Rock, Catalogue no: **45 008**

Camra Chaii

DANCING AT THE EDGE
Tracks: / Dancing at the edge.
7" Single: Released 8 Apr '86, on Power Dance, Catalogue no: **PD 001**

Can

Biographical details: At the time of their sole British hit, this German band consisted of Holger Czukay, Peter Gilmore, Michael Karoli, Jaki Liebezeit, Irmin Schmidt and Rene Tinner.
Formed in 1968 by a group of classicaly and jazz-trained musicians, they released their first album *Monster Movie* the following year, featuring black American vocalist Malcolm Mooney. He left soon afterwards, to be replaced by the wild singing of Japanese vocalist Kenji 'Damo' Suzuki. Can's avant-garde electronic rock, incorporating a wide variety of influences, featured on a series of albums during the early and mid-Seventies. These releases did not sell in large quantities, but won them an underground cult following.
By the time of 1976's *Flow Motion*, Suzuki had left. None of Can's LPs made the British charts, but this album yielded their only UK chart single. The pop-flavoured *I Want More* was a slow but steady seller, peaking at No. 26 but staying on the British Top 50 for ten weeks. It was in a more commercial vein than the bulk of their material. After this success the quality of the band's work diminished.
During the early Eighties a number of successful British and American acts cited Can as a major influence. The modern music recorded by such names as New Order, the Human League and the Talking Heads owes much to the experimentation of Can and fellow German innovators Kraftwerk. While the latter group were able to capitalise on their new found acclaim, Can were not. (Bob MacDonald).
This influential German avant-garde electronic rock band was formed in 1968 in Cologne: Irmin Schmidt, keyboards: Michael Karoli, guitar, violin; Holger Czukay, bass, electronics; Jaki Liebezeit, drums, reeds; the last three also sing. Their early albums from 1970 were primitive; they discovered Damo Suzuki singing in the streets in Munich and were influenced by composer Karlheinz Stockhausen. Suzuki left around 1973; bassist Rosko Gee and Reebop Kwaku Baah on percussion were added. Czukay has pursued solo work. (Donald Clarke, April 1989)t.

I WANT MORE
Tracks: / I want more.
7" Single: Released Aug '76, on Virgin, by Virgin Records. Deleted Aug '79. Catalogue no: **VS 153**
7" Single: Released May '81, on Virgin, by Virgin Records. Deleted May '84. Catalogue no: **VS 422**
12" Single: Released May '81, on Virgin, by Virgin Records. Deleted May '84. Catalogue no: **VS 422-12**

MOONSHAKE
Tracks: / Moon shake.
12" Single: Released Mar '83, on Cherry Red, by Cherry Red Records. Deleted '87. Catalogue no: **12 CHERRY 57**

Candela

LOVE YOU MADLY
Tracks: / Love you madly.
7" Single: Released '82, on Arista, by BMG Records (UK). Deleted '87. Catalogue no: **ARIST 473**
12" Single: Released '82, on Arista, by BMG Records (UK). Deleted '87. Catalogue no: **ARIST 12473**

Candi

DANCING UNDER A LATIN MOON
Tracks: / Dancing under a Latin moon (edit) / Luna latina tu y yo / Dancing under a Latin moon (vocal club mix) (12" only.).
12" Single: Released May '89, on I.R.S, Catalogue no: **EIRST 108**
CD 5": Released May '89, on I.R.S, Catalogue no: **EIRSCD 108**
7" Single: Released May '89, on I.R.S, Catalogue no: **EIRS 108**

LOVE MAKES NO PROMISES
Tracks: / Love makes no promises.
7" Single: Released Jul '89, on I.R.S, Catalogue no: **EIRS 118**
12" Single: Released Jul '89, on I.R.S, Catalogue no: **EIRST 118**

UNDER YOUR SPELL
Tracks: / Under your spell / Dance with me (7" only.) / Under your spell (12' club mix) (12" only.) / Under your spell (trance dub mix).
7" Single: Released Mar '89, on I.R.S, Catalogue no: **EIRS 101**
12" Single: Released Mar '89, on I.R.S, Catalogue no: **EIRST 101**

Candi, Errol

SHAME SHAME SHAME
Tracks: / Shame shame shame / Shame shame shame (inst).
12" Single: Released Jul '88, on Bonnymove, by Bonnymove Records. Catalogue no: **BONT 1**
7" Single: Released Sep '88, on Bonnymove, by Bonnymove Records. Catalogue no: **BONS 1**

SMILING FACE
Tracks: / Smiling face.
12" Single: Released Sep '88, on New Talents, Catalogue no: **NT 003**

Candice

POWER OF LOVE
Tracks: / Power of love, The.
12" Single: Released Dec '88, on Clouds, Catalogue no: **CLSD 003**

Candido

Biographical details: American multi-instrumentalist Candido scored a minor one-off hit in summer 1981 when his disco single *Jingo* reached No 55 on the British chart. (Bob MacDonald, 1984.).

JINGO
Tracks: / Jingo / Dancin' & prancin'.
7" Single: Released Jul '81, on Excaliber, by Red Bus Records. Deleted Jul '84. Catalogue no: **EXC 102**
12" Single: Released Nov '86, on Streetwave, Catalogue no: **MKHAN 79**

Candle

MUSIC MACHINE, THE Children's musical, A
Tracks: / Land called love / Music machine, The / Whistle song / Smile / String song, The / Patience / Gentleness / Faith / Joy / Peace / Goodness / Love / Self-control / Kindness / Reprise.
Special: Catalogue no: **AT 2004**

Candlemass

SAMARITHAN
Tracks: / Samarithan / Solitude.
7" Single: Released Mar '88, on Axis, by Axis Records. Deleted '87. Catalogue no: **7AX 1**
12" Single: Released Mar '88, on Axis, by Axis Records. Deleted '87. Catalogue no: **12AX 1**

Candlewick Green

WHO DO YOU THINK YOU ARE?
Tracks: / Who do you think you are?.
7" Single: Released Feb '74, on Decca, by Decca Records. Deleted Feb '77. Catalogue no: **F 13480**

Candu

CRAWLING
Tracks: / Crawling / All the pretties.
7" Single: Released Mar '80, on Young Blood, by Young Blood Records. Deleted '83. Catalogue no: **YB 83**

Candy

BABY BABY I STILL LOVE YOU
Tracks: / Baby baby I still love you.
7" Single: Released Sep '83, on Speed, Catalogue no: **SPEED 17**

Candy, B

MEANING OF LIFE
Tracks: / Meaning of life.
12" Single: Released Jul '88, on Saxon Studio, Catalogue no: **SHF 005**

Candy From...

CANDY
Tracks: / Candy.
7" Single: Released Feb '83, on KA, Cata-

logue no: **KA 13**

Candy Girls

NO ONE'S GONNA LOVE YOU
Tracks: / No one's gonna love you.
12" Single: Released Sep '84, on Record Shack, by Record Shack Records. Catalogue no: **FOX 001**

Candy Man

A IT MEK
Tracks: / A it mek.
7" Single: Released Apr '89, on Jetstar, by Jetstar Records. Catalogue no: **KCKM 4101**

I BET YOU DON'T KNOW
Tracks: / I bet you don't know.
7" Single: Released Apr '89, on Jetstar, by Jetstar Records. Catalogue no: **KCKM 4103**

SUNSHINE LADY
Tracks: / Sunshine lady.
12" Single: Released Nov '88, on Dennis Star, Catalogue no: **DS 008**

Candy Roxx

SEX AND LEATHER
Tracks: / Sex and leather.
12" Single: Released Feb '85, on Sword, Catalogue no: **SWORD 12006**

Candy & The Kisses

MR CREATOR
Tracks: / Mr. Creator.
7" Single: Released Apr '85, on Kent, by Ace Records. Catalogue no: **TOWN 104**

Cannanes

NO ONE EP
Tracks: / No one.
7" Single: Released Jan '88, on K, by K Records. Catalogue no: **L 28202**

Canned Heat

Biographical details: At the time of their greatest success, this American white blues band consisted of Fito de la Parra, Bob Hite, Larry Taylor, Harry Vestine and Alan Wilson. Canned heat were formed in 1966 by blues fanatics Bob 'The Bear' Hite, Henry Vestine and Al 'Blind Owl' Wilson. Hite's nickname was due to his 19-stone weight; he also came to be known for his enthusiastic collecting of blues records. Adding Larry Taylor and Frank Cook to the original trio, the group issued their debut self-titled album in 1967. Later that year they made a successful appearance at the fondly remembered Monterey Festival.
The following year, original drummer Cook was replaced by Fito de la Parra. The new line-up broke big with the album *Boogie With Canned Heat* and its single *On The Road Again*. This pre-war song, originally asociated with the Memphis Jug Band, was given the typical Canned Heat treatment: an infectious blues style with tinges of country and rock. *Boogie With Canned Heat* was their first and biggest UK chart album, reaching No. 5 with 21 weeks on the survey. The single peaked at No. 8 in the UK, No. 16 in the US. Conversely, the early '69 follow-up 45 *Going Up The Country* was bigger in the States, reaching No. 11 while peaking at No. 19 in Britain.
1970 brought the group their biggest UK hit. The catchy, almost anthemic *Let's Work Together* took them to No. 2. In the States, the original version by its writer Wilbert Harrison was on the charts (albeit No. 32); so the Heat delayed their version until the late autumn and reached No. 26. Sadly Al Wilson died in the interim, passing away in September 1970 at the age of 27. This event gave the band a shock from which they never recovered. A catalogue of peronnel changes followed, but Canned Heatnever sold records again. By the time Bryan Ferry took a remake of *Let's Work Together* (renamed *Let's Stick Together*) into the British Top 5 in the summer of 1976, they were on the verge of folding.
A second founder member, Bob Hite, died in April 1981. He was felled by a drug-related heart attack at the age of 38. (Bob MacDonald).
A white blues band formed in 1966 by Bob 'The Bear' Hite (1945-81) and Alan 'Blind Owl' Wilson (1943-70). Hite was a record shop manager with a mania for blues, Wilson a music student; they formed a jug band in 1965, recruited drummer Bob Cook, Zappa guitarist Henry Vestine and ex-Jerry Lee Lewis bassist Larry Taylor to mix country blues with electric instruments and were a hit at Monterey in 1967. Cook was replaced by Adolpho 'Fito' de la Parra on their second album, *Boogie with Canned Heat; Living the blues* was their third; Vestine left to work with Albert Ayler, replaced by Harvey Mandel, and they played at Woodstock. Hooker'n'Heat from 1971 had them backing one of their idols, John Lee Hooker, and remains a famous album. Mandel was replaced by Vestine coming back, Taylor by Antonio de la Berreda (aka Tony Olay); but Wilson's death on the eve of their third UK tour removed his light tenor voice, a good foil for Hite's growl. They carried on in the 70's but Hite's death was the end: his 60,000+blues record collection left a further legacy by helping United Artists compile its Legendary Masters series. (Donald Clarke, April 1989)a.

GOING UP THE COUNTRY
Tracks: / Going up the country.
7" Single: Released Jan '69, on Liberty, by EMI Records. Deleted Jan '72. Catalogue no: **LBF 15169**

LET'S WORK TOGETHER
Tracks: / Let's work together / Goin' up the country / Rollin' and tumblin' (12" & CD single only) / Amphetamine Annie (CD single only).
7" Single: Released Jul '89, on Liberty, by EMI Records. Catalogue no: **EM 100**
CD 5": Released Jul '89, on Liberty, by EMI Records. Catalogue no: **CDEM 100**
CD 5": Released Jul '89, on Liberty, by EMI Records. Catalogue no: **203 478 2**
7" Single: Released Jul '89, on Liberty, by EMI Records. Catalogue no: **203 478 7**
7" Single: Released Jan '70, on Liberty, by EMI Records. Deleted Jan '73. Catalogue no: **LBF 15302**
12" Single: Released Jul '89, on Liberty, by EMI Records. Catalogue no: **203 478 6**
12" Single: Released Jul '89, on Liberty, by EMI Records. Catalogue no: **12EM 100**

ON THE ROAD AGAIN
Tracks: / On the road again / Let's work together.
7" Single: Released Apr '83, on EMI (France), by EMI Records. Catalogue no: **2C 008 93731**
7" Single: Released Jul '68, on Liberty, by EMI Records. Deleted Jul '71. Catalogue no: **LBS 15090**
7" Single: Released May '84, on EMI Golden 45's, by EMI Records. Catalogue no: **G45 24**

SUGAR BEE
Tracks: / Sugar bee.
7" Single: Released Jul '70, on Liberty, by EMI Records. Deleted Jul '73. Catalogue no: **LBF 15350**

Cannibals

CHRISTMAS ROCK 'N' ROLL
Tracks: / Christmas rock 'n' roll.
7" Single: Released Nov '85, on Hit Freebee, Catalogue no: **FREEBEE 2**

HOT STUFF
Tracks: / Hot stuff.
12" Single: Released '87, on Hit, by Hit Records. Catalogue no: **FUK 005**

LED ASTRAY
Tracks: / Led astray / Mumbo jumbo.
7" Single: Released '82, on Hit (UK), Catalogue no: **FUK 4**

Canning, Francis

BLACK AND WHITE RAG
Tracks: / Black and white rag / Root beer rag.
7" Single: Released May '87, on Mint, by Emerald Records. Deleted '88. Catalogue no: **CHEW 111**

Cannon & Ball

BOYS IN BLUE
Tracks: / Boys in blue / Big star.
7" Single: Released '83, on MFP, by EMI Records. Catalogue no: **FP 908**

EVERYBODY'S MAKING IT BIG BUT ME
Tracks: / Everybody's making it big but me / Together we'll be O.K..
7" Single: Released '82, on MFP, by EMI Records. Catalogue no: **FP 905**

HOLD ME IN YOUR ARMS
Tracks: / Hold me in your arms / Crying.
7" Single: Released '82, on MFP, by EMI Records. Catalogue no: **FP 906**

IT'S ALL IN THE GAME
Tracks: / It's all in the game.
7" Single: Released '84, on Relax, Catalogue no: **LAX 1**

LET YOUR BRACES DOWN
Tracks: / Let your braces down / Remember the stars.
7" Single: Released '81, on SRT, by SRT Records. Catalogue no: **SRTS 81433**

ROCK ON TOMMY (SINGLE)
Tracks: / Rock on Tommy / Together.
7" Single: Released '80, on SRT, by SRT Records. Catalogue no: **SRTS 80429**

WIND BENEATH MY WINGS
Tracks: / Wind beneath my wings / Melody.
7" Single: Released May '88, on First Night, by First Night Records. Catalogue no: **SCORE 16**

Cannon, Freddy

Biographical details: Born Frederick Picarielle in Massachusetts, USA, this rock 'n' roll singer was fortunate enough t make it big with his first record. The fun, rocking sound of *Tallahassee Lassie* was to prove typical of his work - his less than brilliant voice was compensated by his sheer enthusiasm. Although born too late to enjoy the fruits of the original mid-Fifties rock boom, Cannon's late Fifties/early Sixties success helped keep alive the sound of the rock 'n' roll at a time when the charts were being filled with softer, pop-flavoured records and stars. *Tallahassee Lassie* reached No. 6 in the US and No. 17 in the UK in 1959. It was followed by a no. 3 single on both sides of the Atlantic: *Way Down Yonder In New Orleans* was a revival of the twenties song. Perhaps Cannon's greatest achievement occurred in March 1960: *The Explosive Freddie Cannon* topped the UK album chart for one week that month and was the artist's only charted LP in Britain. That week was the only interruption to an otherwise un-broken 89-week No. 1 run for the *South Pacific* soundtrack album and Cannon thus became the first rock 'n' roll act to hit the top of the British LP list.
After his first two major hit singles, he had a string of minor hits in both the UK and US, but with totally different tracks being issued in the two countries. The only subsequent song to chart in both nations was *Palisades Park* another of his many titles featuring American place names. This single marked the opening of a large US fun fair. it reached No. 3 in the States in the summer of '62 and No. 20 in Britain. This was his last chart record in the UK, but he achieved two more Top 20 successes in the US before passing into rock history: 1964's *Abigail Beecher* and 1965's *Action*, the latter a US TV theme. (Bob MacDonald).
Frederick Anthony Picariello was born in 1940; he wrote *Rock'n'roll baby* with his mother, its name was changed to Tallahassee Lassie, it made the USA top ten in 1959, he quit driving a truck: with had over 20 Hot 100 entries in seven years, his rasping vocals with horns, Bo Diddley style guitar from Kenny Paulson and roaring sax section he had over 20 Hot entries in seven years. *The explosive Freddy Cannon* topped the UK album chart in 1960. (Donald Clarke, April 1989)h.

CALIFORNIA HERE I COME
Tracks: / California here I come.
7" Single: Released Mar '60, on Top Rank (1), Deleted Mar '63. Catalogue no: **JAR 309**

HEY PUNK ROCKER
Tracks: / Hey punk rocker / At the disco down.
7" Single: Released '80, on Hot Rock, by Hot Rock Records. Catalogue no: **HR45 003**

INDIANA
Tracks: / Indiana.
7" Single: Released Mar '60, on Top Rank (1), Deleted Mar '63. Catalogue no: **JAR 309**

MUSKRAT RAMBLE
Tracks: / Muskrat ramble.
7" Single: Released Apr '61, on Top Rank (1), Deleted Apr '64. Catalogue no: **JAR 548**

PALISADES PARK
Tracks: / Palisades park.
7" Single: Released Jun '62, on Stateside, by EMI Records. Deleted Jun '65. Catalogue no: **SS 101**
7" Single: Released '82, on Old Gold, by Old Gold Records. Deleted Jul '88. Catalogue no: **OG 9202**

TALLAHASSEE LASSIE
Tracks: / Tallahassee lassie.
7" Single: Released '82, on Old Gold, by Old Gold Records. Deleted Jul '88. Catalogue no: **OG 9159**
7" Single: Released Aug '59, on Top Rank (1), Deleted Aug '62. Catalogue no: **JAR 135**
7" Single: Released '82, on Blast From The Past, by Creole Records. Catalogue no: **CR 192**

URGE, THE
Tracks: / Urge, The.
7" Single: Released May '60, on Top Rank (1), Deleted May '63. Catalogue no: **JAR 369**

WAY DOWN YONDER IN NEW ORLEANS
Tracks: / Way down yonder in New Orleans / Do you wanna dance / But I do / Tallahassie lassie / Palisades park.
7" Single: Released Jan '60, on Top Rank (1), Deleted Jan '63. Catalogue no: **JAR 247**
7" Single: Released '84, on Creole (Replay), by Creole Records. Catalogue no: **CR 210**
7" Single: Released '82, on Blast From The Past, by Creole Records. Catalogue no: **CR 190**

Cantabile

BEAUTIFUL MEXICAN LADY
Tracks: / Beautiful Mexican lady / Aubade.
7" Single: Released '83, on Zonk, Deleted '85. Catalogue no: **ZNK 1**

Cantels

I WANT TO BE ALONE
Tracks: / I want to be alone.
12" Single: Released Jun '89, on Bubble, Catalogue no: **BUBBLE 001T**

Canton

PLEASE DON'T STAY
Tracks: / Please don't stay.
7" Single: Released '85, on Creole, by Creole Records. Catalogue no: **CR 84**

Canute

NO LOOKING BACK
Tracks: / No looking back.
7" Single: Released '85, on EMI, by EMI Records. Catalogue no: **TAKE 4**
12" Single: Released '85, on EMI, by EMI Records. Catalogue no: **12TAKE 4**

Capaldi, Jim

Biographical details: This British artist first found fame in the 60's as drummer with Traffic, a group widely admired for their psychedelic pop hits and, later, sophisticated fusions. Capaldi issued his first solo album, *Oh How We Danced*, in 1972, singing and drumming with back-up help from Traffic friends. Neither the LP not its single, Eve, were commercial successes. In fact none of his albums entered the charts, despite press acceptance. Capaldi did, however, score two British chart singles in the mid-70's. *It's All Up To You* reached No 27 and was followed a year later by *Love Hurts*, a pop-flavoured single in a more commercial vein than usual, which took him to No 4 in autumn '75. By this time Traffic had been officially declared defunct. (Bob MacDonald, 1984.).

CHILD IN THE STORM
Tracks: / Child in the storm / Bright fighter.
7" Single: Released '81, on Carrere, Catalogue no: **CAR 175**

I'LL KEEP HOLDING ON
Tracks: / I'll keep holding on.
7" Single: Released '84, on WEA (International), by WEA Records. Catalogue no: **U 9272**

IT'S ALL UP TO YOU (SINGLE)
Tracks: / It's all up to you.
7" Single: Released Jul '74, on Island, by Island Records. Deleted Jul '77. Catalogue no: **WIP 6198**

LIVING ON THE EDGE
Tracks: / Living on the edge / Gifts.
7" Single: Released '83, on WEA (International), by WEA Records. Catalogue no: **U 9850**

LOVE HURTS
Tracks: / Love hurts.
7" Single: Released Oct '75, on Island, by Island Records. Deleted Oct '78. Catalogue no: **WIP 6264**

LOW SPARK OF HIGH HEELED BOYS
Tracks: / Low spark of high heeled boys / Bathroom Jane.
7" Single: Released Oct '80, on Carrere, Deleted '83. Catalogue no: **CAR 167**

OLD PHOTOGRAPHS
Tracks: / Old photographs / Man with no country.
7" Single: Released Apr '81, on Carrere, Deleted Apr '84. Catalogue no: **CAR 189**

SOME COME RUNNING (SINGLE)
Tracks: / Some come running / Fabela music / Love hurts.
CD 5": Released 20 Feb '89, on Island, by Island Records. Catalogue no: **CID 391**
7" Single: Released 20 Feb '89, on Island, by Island Records. Catalogue no: **IS 391**
12" Single: Released 20 Feb '89, on Island, by Island Records. Catalogue no: **12 IS 391**

SOMETHING SO STRONG
Tracks: / Something so strong / Child in the storm / Tales of power (On 12" and CD only).
CD 5": Released Jan '89, on Island, by Island Records. Catalogue no: **CID 389**
7" Single: Released Jan '89, on Island, by Island Records. Catalogue no: **IS 389**
12" Single: Released Jan '89, on Island, by Island Records. Catalogue no: **12IS 389**

TAKE ME HOME
Tracks: / Take me home / Child in the storm / Fabela music (Only on CD single.) / Take me home (version) (Only on CD single.).
CD 5": Released 9 May '89, on Island, by Island Records. Catalogue no: **CID 419**
7" Single: Released 9 May '89, on Island, by Island Records. Catalogue no: **IS 419**
12" Single: Released 9 May '89, on Island, by Island Records. Catalogue no: **12 IS 419**

THAT'S LOVE
Tracks: / That's love / Runaway.
7" Single: Released '83, on WEA (International), by WEA Records. Catalogue no: **U 9937**
12" Single: Released '83, on WEA (International), by WEA Records. Catalogue no: **U 9937 T**

TONITE YOU'RE MINE
Tracks: / Tonite you're mine / Back at my place.
7" Single: Released '83, on WEA, by WEA Records. Catalogue no: **U 9816**

Capaldi, Phil

PARADISE
Tracks: / Paradise / Paradise (part 2).
7" Single: Released Jun '82, on Creole, by Creole Records. Deleted '85. Catalogue no: **CR 34**
12" Single: Released Jun '82, on Creole, by Creole Records. Deleted '85. Catalogue no: **CR 12 34**

Capella

HELYCOM HALIB
Tracks: / Helyom halib.
12" Single: Released Apr '89, on Music Man, Catalogue no: **MMPT 12004**
7" Single: Released Apr '89, on Music Man, Catalogue no: **MMPS 7004**

HOUSE ENERGY REVENGE
Tracks: / House energy revenge.
7" Single: Released Sep '89, on Music Man, Catalogue no: **MMPS 7009**
12" Single: Released Sep '89, on Music Man, Catalogue no: **MMPT 12009**

Capitol Pops Orchestra

BOLERO
Tracks: / Bolero / Drum battle.
7" Single: Released '84, on Sirocco, Catalogue no: **SIR 102**

Capitols

Biographical details: This USA vocal trio, earlier called the Three Caps, were all from Detroit. They were basically one hit wonders, but *Cool jerk* was a dance craze/top ten hit in 1966, still heard in discotheques. (Donald Clarke, April 1989)i.

COOL JERK (OLD GOLD)
Tracks: / Cool jerk / Cool pearl.
7" Single: Released '82, on Old Gold, by Old Gold Records. Deleted Jul '88. Catalogue no: **OG 9106**

COOL JERK (SINGLE)
Tracks: / Cool jerk / Under the moon of love / Pretty little angel eyes.
7" Single: Released '84, on Creole (Replay), by Creole Records. Catalogue no: **CR 19**
7" Single: Released Aug '87, on Creole Classics, by Creole Records. Catalogue no: **R 108**
12" Single: Released Aug '87, on Creole Classics, by Creole Records. Catalogue no: **RT 108**

Capone's Treatment,

WON'T GIVE YOU UP
Tracks: / I won't give you up.
7" Single: Released '85, on Treatment, by Treatment Records. Catalogue no: **SOB 004**

Cappella

HEYLOM HALIB
Tracks: / Heylom halib.
12" Single: Released Apr '89, on P1, Catalogue no: **508 409**
CD 5": Released Apr '89, on P1, Catalogue no: **588 410**

PUSH THE BEAT
Tracks: / Push the beat / Bauhas.
7" Single: Released Mar '88, on Fast Globe, Deleted Jul '89. Catalogue no: **FGL 1**
12" Single: Released Mar '88, on Fast Globe, Deleted Jul '89. Catalogue no: **FGL 1**

Caprice

100%
Tracks: / 100%.
7" Single: Released '85, on Lovebeat Int., Catalogue no: **LOV 1**
12" Single: Released '85, on Lovebeat Int., Catalogue no: **LOV 1T**

100% (TAKE IT TO THE MAX)
Tracks: / 100% (take it to the max) / Voices.
12" Single: Released Jan '86, on Lovebeat Int., Catalogue no: **LOV 1TX**

LOVE LETTERS
Tracks: / Love letters / Love letters (pt 2).
7" Single: Released Sep '81, on Beggars Banquet, by Beggars Banquet Records. Deleted Sep '84. Catalogue no: **BEG 64T**

Capricorn

BELLS OF LOVE
Tracks: / Bells of love / Walk in the snow.
7" Single: Released Dec '81, on Swamp, by Swamp Records. Deleted Dec '84. Catalogue no: **WAM 117**

FULL MOON MADNESS
Tracks: / Full moon madness / One more minute.
7" Single: Released May '81, on Pinnacle, by Pinnacle Records. Deleted May '84. Catalogue no: **PENT 4**

Capstick, Tony

Biographical details: This local radio DJ shot to national fame as a recording artist in his native Britain in 1981. The novelty record which gave him this sudden, short-lived prominence was a double-A-sided single, *The Sheffield Grinder/Capstick Comes Home.* Backed by the Carlton Main/Frickley Colliery Band, the disc rocketed to No 3 on the UK chart. The side that received the lion's share of the airplay was *Capstick Comes Home*, a hilariously exaggerated piece of "nostalgia" describing working class life in Northern England. It was a spoken piece augmented by a gentle brass band backing. Though a one-off hit, its success assured Capstick of regular work as a live performer. (Bob MacDonald, 1984.).

CHRISTMAS CRACKER
Tracks: / Christmas cracker / Recruited collier.
7" Single: Released Dec '81, on Epic, by CBS Records. Deleted Dec '84. Catalogue no: **EPCA 1890**

SHEFFIELD GRINDER, THE
Tracks: / Sheffield grinder, The / Capstick comes home.
7" Single: Released '81, on Dingle's, by Dingle's Records. Deleted '84. Catalogue no: **SID 27**

Captain Barkey

STAMINA MAN
Tracks: / Stamina man.
12" Single: Released Sep '89, on Living Room, Catalogue no: **LM 028**

Captain Beaky

PANTOMIME
Tracks: / Pantomime / Christ carol.
7" Single: Released Dec '80, on Polydor, by Polydor Ltd. Deleted Dec '85. Catalogue no: **POSP 207**

Captain Beefheart

LEGENDARY A & M SESSIONS
12" Single: Released '84, on A&M, by A&M Records. Deleted '88. Catalogue no: **AMY 226**

LIGHT REFLECTED OFF THE OCEANS OF THE MOON
Tracks: / Light reflected off the oceans of the moon.
12" Single: Released Sep '82, on Virgin, by Virgin Records. Deleted '85. Catalogue no: **VS 53412**

Captain Gerry Atrix

HOKEY COKEY BOOGIE
Tracks: / Hokey cokey boogie / Hokey cokey boogie (instrumental).
7" Single: Released Sep '88, on W.M., Catalogue no: **WMS 002**
12" Single: Released Sep '88, on W.M., Catalogue no: **WMX 002**

Captain Rapp

BAD TIMES (I CAN'T STAND IT)
Tracks: / Bad times (I can't stand it).
12" Single: Released '84, on Beckett, Deleted '86. Catalogue no: **BKSL 10**
12" Single: Released Sep '87, on Saturn (USA), Catalogue no: **SAT 2003**

Captain Sensible

Biographical details: This British singer (real name Ray Burns) lives a double life - he sang as a solo artist and also plays guitar with the Damned. Along with the Sex Pistols, the Clash, the Jam and the Buzzcocks, the Damned were one of the five most important groups in Britain's 1976/77 punk rock explosion. Captain Sensible was originally their bassist, but later switched to guitar.
In 1982 the Captain decided that, while continuing his group acivities, he would launch a solo career. his choice for a debut single could hardly have been more different from the Damned's style: he recorded the song *Happy Talk* from the Rogers & Hammerstein's legendary "South Pacific" soundtrack and it stormed to the UK No. 1 position. Released in June 1982 the single coincided with the announcement of Britain's military victory over Argentina in the Falklands War; the bright jelliness of *Happy Talk* was ideally suited to the nation's mood at the time and this was an undoubted factor in the record's swift success. It entered the UK chart at No. 33 and was No. 1 the following week; excepting records that have entered the charts at No. 1, thi was the biggest ever leap to the top slot in Britain. However, after two weeks at the sumit, *Happy Talk* slid downwards almost as fast as it had come up. It was in the Top 10 for just three weeks and in the Top 75 for eight weeks, both exceptionally low totals for a No. 1 single.
The follow-up *Wet!* peaked at No. 26 in Britain, but was a bigger hit in parts of Continental Europe. It was a disco-inflected number, featuring strong assistance from the good Captain's female vocal back-up trio, the Dolly Mixtures. Sensible returned to the Top 10 in 1984 with *Glad Its All Over/Damned On 45.* Although officially a double A sided hit, it was the highly catchy *Glad Its All Over* that won all the airplay - like all his dole hits, this was produced by Tony Mansfield. It reached No. 6 on the UK charts, fourteen places higher than the most successful Damned single. (Bob MacDonald)..

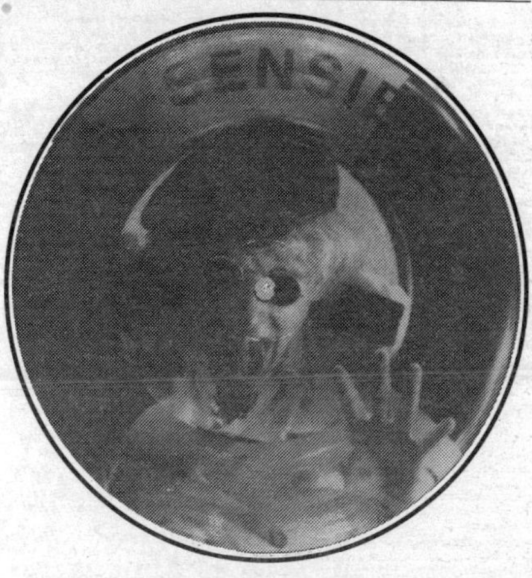

CAPTAIN SENSIBLE - CROYDON (Released on A & M)

CROYDON (see panel above)
Tracks: / Croydon / Jimi Hendrix's strat.
7" Single: Released '82, on A&M, by A&M Records. Catalogue no: **CAPP 3**

GLAD IT'S ALL OVER
Tracks: / Glad it's all over / Damned on 45.
7" Single: Released '84, on A&M, by A&M Records. Deleted '88. Catalogue no: **CAP 6**
7" Pic: Released '84, on A&M, by A&M Records. Deleted '88. Catalogue no: **CAPP 6**

HAPPY TALK
Tracks: / Happy talk / Glad it's all over.
7" Single: Released Jun '82, on A&M, by A&M Records. Deleted Jun '85. Catalogue no: **CAP 1**
7" Single: Released Oct '88, on Old Gold, by Old Gold Records. Catalogue no: **OG 9811**

JET BOY JET GIRL
Tracks: / Jet boy, jet girl.
7" Pic: Released '82, on Big Beat, by Ace Records. Deleted '88. Catalogue no: **NSP 77**
7" Single: Released '82, on Big Beat, by Ace Records. Deleted '88. Catalogue no: **NS 77**

ONE CHRISTMAS CATALOGUE
Tracks: / One Christmas catalogue.
12" Single: Released '84, on A&M, by A&M Records. Deleted '88. Catalogue no: **CAPY 8**
7" Single: Released '84, on A&M, by A&M Records. Deleted '88. Catalogue no: **CAP 8**

REVOLUTION NOW!
Tracks: / Revolution now / Coward of treason cove, The.
7" Single: Released 13 Jun '87, on A&M, by A&M Records. Deleted Mar '88. Catalogue no: **AM 395**
12" Single: Released 13 Jun '87, on A&M, by A&M Records. Deleted Mar '88. Catalogue no: **AMY 395**

SNOOKER SONG, THE
Tracks: / Snooker song, The / Midnight smoke.
7" Single: Released Apr '88, on Trax, by Filmtrax Records. Deleted Aug '89. Catalogue no: **HS1**

THERE ARE MORE SNAKES THAN LADDERS
Tracks: / There are more snakes than ladders.
7" Single: Released '84, on A&M, by A&M Records. Deleted '88. Catalogue no: **CAP 7**
12" Single: Released '84, on A&M, by A&M Records. Deleted '88. Catalogue no: **CAPX 7**

THIS IS YOUR CAPTAIN SPEAKING
Tracks: / This is your captain speaking.
7" Single: Released '81, on Crass, by Crass Records. Catalogue no: **321984/5**

TOYS TAKE OVER, THE
Tracks: / Toys take over, The.
7" Single: Released Jun '88, on Deltic, Catalogue no: **DELT 1**
12" Single: Released Jun '88, on Deltic, Catalogue no: **DELT 1 T**

WOT - NO MEAT?
Tracks: / Wot - no meat? / Strawberry dross.
7" Single: Released Aug '82, on A&M, by A&M Records. Deleted Aug '85. Catalogue no: **CAP 2**
12" Single: Released Aug '82, on A&M, by A&M Records. Deleted Aug '85. Catalogue no: **CAPP 2**
7" Single: Released '85, on Animus, by Southern Studios Ltd.. Catalogue no: **TOUCH 3**
7" Single: Released Nov '86, on Animus, by Southern Studios Ltd.. Catalogue no: **FEEL 3**

Captain Sinbad

DALLAS
Tracks: / Dallas.
12" Single: Released '85, on Mab, Catalogue no: **MAB 005**

SISTER MIRACLE
Tracks: / Sister miracle / Funny love.
12" Single: Released '83, on Rusty International, Catalogue no: **RI 006**

Captain Sky

DON'T TOUCH THAT DIAL
Tracks: / Don't touch that dial / Natural high.
7" Single: Released '83, on Philly World (USA), by Philly World (USA). Catalogue no: **PWS 107**
12" Single: Released '83, on Philly World (USA), by Philly World (USA). Catalogue no: **PWSL 107**

YOU BRING ME UP
Tracks: / You bring me up.
12" Single: Released Oct '87, on Pana, Catalogue no: **PRI 2003**

Captain & Tennille

Biographical details: This American pop duo consisted of keyboards player Daryl Dragon ('the captain') and his wife, singer Toni Tennille. By the time they became famous in 1975, they had both been in the music business for approximately a decade. At one point, both had toured together with the Beach boys, Tennille thus becoming the only ever 'Beach Girl'. The record that turned the pair into American household names was 1975's *Love Will Keep Us Together*, this was written by Neil Sedaka and Howard Greenfield, the team that had penned such famous Sedaka hits as *Oh Carol* and *Breaking Up Is hard To Do.* The Captain and Tennille's single went to the US No. 1 slot and stayed there for four weeks, thereby outflanking even Sedaka's own biggest career hits. it was followed by *The Way I Want To Touch You*, a song written by Tennille in 1973 as a loving tribute to her husband. It reached No. 4 on the US chart in late '75. Their album *Love Will Keep Us Together* was also a huge seller that year.
1976 was another golden year, with three more American Top 5 singles: *Lonely Night (angel face)*, *Shop Around* (a remake of Smokey Robinson & the Miracles' first hit) and *Muskrat Love.* In the late Seventies, however, they found the going tougher. They suffered from the effects of over-exposure on American TV and the public were growing tired of their slightly nauseating bland image. They scored two more major hits, but both were isolated successes in an otherwise slack period: 1978's *You Never Done It Like That* reached No. 10; 1980's *Do That To Me One More Time* gave them a second US No. 1. The latter was the duo's only major British

hit - the UK market was generally indifferent to their style of middle-of-the-road pop. (Bob MacDonald).
A faceless MOR vocal duo resembling the Carpenters which had seven top ten hits in the late '70's. Keyboardist Daryl Dragon is the son of conductor Carmen Dragon; Toni Tenille was classically trained on piano. Her father Frank sang with the Bob Crosby band and had a number one hit in 1935 with *In a little gypsy room*. She and Dragon were married in 1974; she made a solo album of standards in 1984 resembling Linda Ronstadt's albums with Nelson Riddle. (Donald Clarke, 1989).

DO THAT TO ME ONE MORE TIME
Tracks: / Do that to me one more time / Deep in the dark.
7" Single: Released Feb '80, on Casablanca, by PolyGram UK Ltd. Deleted Feb '83. Catalogue no: **CAN 175**

HAPPY TOGETHER
Tracks: / Happy together / Baby you still got it / No love in the morning (Only on 12" single.) / Do that to me one more time (Only on 12" single.).
12" Single: Released 20 Jul '80, on Casablanca, by PolyGram UK Ltd. Deleted '83. Catalogue no: **CANL 200**
7" Single: Released 20 Jul '80, on Casablanca, by PolyGram UK Ltd. Deleted '83. Catalogue no: **CAN 200**

KEEPING OUR LOVE WARM (SINGLE)
Tracks: / Keeping our love warm / Gentle stranger.
7" Single: Released Nov '80, on Casablanca, by PolyGram UK Ltd. Deleted Nov '83. Catalogue no: **CAN 215**

LOVE WILL KEEP US TOGETHER
Tracks: / Love will keep us together.
7" Single: Released Aug '75, on A&M, by A&M Records. Deleted Aug '78. Catalogue no: **AMS 7165**
7" EP: Released '84, on Scoop 33, by Pickwick Records. Catalogue no: **7SR 5040**

NO LOVE IN THE MORNING
Tracks: / No love in the morning / How can you be so cold / Do that to me one more time / Happy together.
7" Single: Released Apr '80, on Casablanca, by PolyGram UK Ltd. Deleted '82. Catalogue no: **CAN 191**
12" Single: Released Apr '80, on Casablanca, by PolyGram UK Ltd. Deleted '82. Catalogue no: **CANL 191**

WAY I WANT TO TOUCH YOU, THE
Tracks: / Way I want to touch you, The.
7" Single: Released Jan '76, on A&M, by A&M Records. Deleted Jan '79. Catalogue no: **AMS 7203**

YOU NEVER DONE IT LIKE THAT
Tracks: / You never done it like that.
7" Single: Released Nov '78, on A&M, by A&M Records. Deleted Nov '81. Catalogue no: **AMS 7384**

Captains Of Industry

LIFELINE
Tracks: / Lifeline.
7" Single: Released '84, on Go Discs, by Chrysalis Records. Catalogue no: **GOD 6**

Car Called James

DOWN ON YOUR KNEES
Tracks: / Down on your knees / Shock / Burning Whitemans crown.
12" Single: Released Sep '89, on Vinyl Villais, Catalogue no: **VILLIN 001T**

Car Crash

ALL PASSION SPENT
Tracks: / All passion spent.
12" Single: Released '84, on Crammed Discs, by Crammed Discs. Catalogue no: **CRAM 031**

WHIP,THE
Tracks: / Whip, The / Ghostman / T.V. shock theatre.
12" Single: Released '83, on Crammed Discs, by Crammed Discs. Catalogue no: **CRAM 028**

Car Park

LET'S DO WHAT YOU DO SO WELL
Tracks: / Let's do what you do so well / Fun city.
7" Single: Released Jul '81, on Carrere, Deleted '84. Catalogue no: **CAR 202**

Car Pets

JOHNNY WON'T HURT YOU
Tracks: / Johnny won't hurt you / Frustration paradise.
7" Single: Released Mar '80, on Beggars Banquet, by Beggars Banquet Records. Deleted Mar '83. Catalogue no: **BEG 32**

Cara, Irene

Biographical details: This American singer first made her name in 1980 when she sang the theme to and appeared in, the highly successful movie "Fame". Telling the story of an American academy teaching singing, dancing and acting to young would-be stars, the film gave Cara a No. 4 single on the US chart in the summer of '80, She followed this title song from the movie with another of the film's tracks: *Out Here On My own* gave her a US No. 19 hit. Neither song charted in Britain, despite the former gaining substantial airplay.
In 1982 an American TV serial based on the movie began running in the UK. The unexpected success of this series gave Cara a sudden British smash. *Fame* entered the UK singles chart at No. 51, shot to No. 4 the following week and, seven days later found itself at the very top. Cara's version was not actually used in the TV serial, but was far superior. her strong singing style was very similar to that of Donna Summer.
Out Here On My Own then reached No. 58 on the UK chart, but the real follow-up to *Fame* came the following year. Working with famed Italian disco producer/songwriter Giorgio Moroder (well-known ironically for his work with Donna Summer) and Moroder's Lieutenant Keith Fersey, Cara cowrote and sang *Flashdance....What A feeling*, the theme to the movie "Flashdance" starring Jennifer beals. The single and film were both smashes. The former, an irresistible pop song, logged six week at No. 1 on the US singles chart and reached No. 2 in Britain.
Cara was unable to follow this success in Britain but, in the States, she managed a further two Top 20 singles within a year; both were produced by Moroder. They were *Why ME* and *Breakdance*, the latter being America's most successful cash-in on the breakdance street craze. (Bob MacDonald).
This excellent New York City pop singer, found *Fame* by singing the title song of the film. She appeared in a Broadway musical at age eight, sang in a Madison Square Garden tribute to Duke Ellington with Roberta Flack and Sammy Davis Jr at 10, had a part in TV's *Roots* and played Coco Hernandez in *Fame* in 1980, Alan Parker's film about New York's High School for the Performing Arts which spun off a TV series. *Fame* won an Oscar for best film song, as did *Flashdance ... what a feeling*, co-written by Cara. She also wrote half of here first solo album *Anyone can see*. (Donald Clarke, April 1989)..

BREAKDANCE
Tracks: / Breakdance / Cue me up.
7" Single: Released '84, on Epic, by CBS Records. Catalogue no: **A 4427**
12" Single: Released '84, on Epic, by CBS Records. Catalogue no: **TA 4427**

DREAM,THE
Tracks: / Dream, The / Receiving.
7" Single: Released '84, on Network, by CBS Records. Catalogue no: **A 4100**
12" Single: Released '84, on Network, by CBS Records. Catalogue no: **TA 4100**

FAME
Tracks: / Fame.
7" Single: Released Jul '82, on RSO, by Polydor Ltd. Deleted Jul '85. Catalogue no: **RSO 90**

FLASHDANCE WHAT A FEELING
Tracks: / Flashdance... what a feeling.
7" Single: Released '84, on Casablanca, by PolyGram UK Ltd. Deleted 31 May '89. Catalogue no: **CAN 1016**

OUT HERE ON MY OWN
Tracks: / Out here on my own / Out here on my own (part 2).
7" Single: Released Sep '82, on Polydor, by Polydor Ltd. Deleted Sep '85. Catalogue no: **RSO 66**

Caramba

FEDORA (I'LL BE YOUR DAWG)
Tracks: / Fedora (I'll be your dawg) / Ralph & Rolph.
12" Single: Released '83, on Billco, Deleted '87. Catalogue no: **BILLT 101**
7" Single: Released '83, on Billco, Deleted '87. Catalogue no: **BILL 101**

HUBBA HUBBA ZOOT ZOOT
Tracks: / Hubba hubba zoot zoot / Donna May.
7" Single: Released Oct '82, on Epic, by CBS Records. Deleted Oct '85. Catalogue no: **EPC A 1644**

Caravan

Biographical details: At the time of their greatest success, this British band consisted of Richard Coughlan, Pye Hastings, Geoff Richardson, Dave Sinclair and Mike Wedgewood.
Formed in 1968, Caravan were originally part of British rock's late Sixties/early Seventies underground scene. The original Caravan quartet hailed from Canterbury and comprised Coughlan, hastings and Dave and Richard Sinclair. The Sinclairs left in the early Seventies, but Dave briefly rejoined the group three years later. Despite being a popular live band, Caravan failed to crack the British album chart until 1975. Even then *Cunning Stunts* had to be content with a number 50 placing. The following year *Blind Dog At St. Dustan's* peaked at No. 53 on the UK listings, their second and final chart LP. With an unstable line-up, the group continued recording and touring into the Eighties. Caravan's reputation has always been that of an avant-garde and eccentric outfit. Their sophisticated style is best described as orchestral rock, featuring strong vocals and even the occasional big band tinges. (Bob MacDonald).
A rock band formed by Richard Coughland (drums), Julian 'Pye' Hastings (guitar), David Sinclair (keyboards) and Richard Sinclair (bass), all from Canterbury, where they had played in the legendary local band Wilde Flowers in 1965-6, which also included Kevin Ayers and members of Soft Machine. Albums like *In the land of gray and pink* were progressive rock with a jazzy touch from flautist/saxophonist Jimmy Hastings, and seemed influential at the time. The Sinclair brothers left to form Hatfield and the North, Dave later returning briefly; with ex-Delivery keyboardist Steve Miller they carried on into the early '80s. (Donald Clarke, April 1989)l.

HEARTBREAKER
Tracks: / Heartbreaker / It's never too late.
7" Single: Released '80, on Kingdom, by Kingdom Records. Deleted '82. Catalogue no: **KV 8009**

KEEPING UP DEFENCES
Tracks: / Keeping up defences.
7" Single: Released '81, on Kingdom, by Kingdom Records. Deleted '83. Catalogue no: **KV 8014**

Caravelles

YOU DON'T HAVE TO BE A BABY TO CRY
Tracks: / You don't have to be a baby to cry.
7" Single: Released Aug '63, on Decca, by Decca Records. Deleted Aug '66. Catalogue no: **F 11697**

Card, Joy

SUPER STATIC MAGIC MYSTERY
Tracks: / Super static magic mystery.
12" Single: Released '84, on Wackies, Catalogue no: **W 33**

Cardenas, Luis

RUNAWAYS
Tracks: / Runaways / Still waiting / Let it out (live) (Available on 12" versions only.).
Note: Let it out (live) is an extra track on 12" version.
7" Pic: Released Aug '86, on Consolidated Allied, Catalogue no: **TOONT 1P**
7" Single: Released Aug '86, on Consolidated Allied, Catalogue no: **TOON 1**
12" Single: Released Aug '86, on Consolidated Allied, Catalogue no: **TOONT 1**

Cardiacs

BABY HEART DIRT
Tracks: / Baby heart dirt / I hold my love in my arms.
7" Single: Released Apr '89, on Alphabet, by Alphabet Business Concern. Catalogue no: **ALPH 011**
12" Single: Released Apr '89, on Alphabet, by Alphabet Business Concern. Catalogue no: **ALPH 011T**

EVENING SHOW EP: CARDIACS
Tracks: / R.E.S. / Buds and spawn / In a city lining / Is this the life / Cameras.
12" Single: Released Jul '88, on Strange Fruit, by Strange Fruit Records. Catalogue no: **SFNT 013**

IS THIS THE LIFE
Tracks: / Is this the life.
7" Single: Released Mar '88, on Alphabet, by Alphabet Business Concern. Catalogue no: **ALPH 008 SP**
12" Single: Released Mar '88, on Alphabet, by Alphabet Business Concern. Catalogue no: **ALPH 008 T**

SEASIDE TREATS
Tracks: / Consultants flower garden, The / Little man and a house / RES / To go off and things / Seaside treats.
Note: Running time is 22 minutes. "Recent IFVA video festival winner" (Jettisoundz 1988)
12" Single: Released May '86, on Jettisoundz, by Jettisoundz Records. Deleted '85. Catalogue no: **ALPH 002**

SUSANNAH'S STILL ALIVE
Tracks: / Susannah's still alive / Blind in safty & leafy in love / All his geese are swans (Only on 12".).
7" Single: Released Aug '88, on Alphabet, by Alphabet Business Concern. Catalogue no: **ALPH 009**
12" Single: Released Aug '88, on Alphabet, by Alphabet Business Concern. Catalogue no: **ALPH 009 T**

THERE'S TOO MANY IRONS IN THE FIRE
Tracks: / There's too many irons in the fire / All spectacular / Loosefish scapegrace.
12" Single: Released Aug '87, on Alphabet, by Alphabet Business Concern. Catalogue no: **ALPH 006**

Care

Biographical details: The history of the duo begins when they met in their home town of Liverpool both at the same time belonging to different groups. 'Eric's' is an important club in musical history and both Paul (playing with the Teardrop Explodes) and Ian with (Big In Japan) both made stage appearances at the club which has played host to the best bands of the the time. Five years on, Paul Simpson and Ian Broudie, under the name 'Care' are now working together. Their chemistry has sparked both to achieve their best work to date. In the intervening years, Ian formed the Original Mirrors, whose recordings and live performances won them many an admirer. He turned his hand to producing and generally acting as a mentor figure in Liverpool. He produced TV 21, Wah, and most recently Echo & The Bunnymen's single *The back of love* and LP *Porcupine* under the alias of 'Kingbird'. Paul re-emerged around two years ago as singer/guitarist with the Wild Swans, who released one remarkable single 'Revolutionary spirit' on Zoo Records, did a couple of much admired radio sessions and gave the mighty Echo & The Bunnymen something hard to follow on their pre-Christmas tour of 1982. Paul and Ian began working together last summer, and, suddenly Paul had found the perfect musical foil for his langurous, poetic lyrics and haunting voice. Fired by this, they demoed the handful of songs they'd written together and found eager interest from Arista Records to whom they signed earlier this year. One of those earlier songs became their debut single *My boyish days (drink to me)*, produced by Clive Langer and Alan Winstanley. The single became a major feature on national radio and the band went on to record several sessions for the Radio One DJ's - one of whom enthused that the Care session was his best of 1983 and how eagerly he awaited the follow up single. *My flaming sword* lived up to all expectations. The single was produced by Ian Broudie and paves the way for an album (November 1983, Arista Records).

FLAMING SWORD
Tracks: / Flaming sword, The.
7" Single: Released '83, on Arista, by BMG Records (UK). Deleted '86. Catalogue no: **KBIRD 2**
12" Single: Released '83, on Arista, by BMG Records (UK). Deleted '87. Catalogue no: **KBIRD 22**

MY BOYISH DAYS DRINK TO ME
Tracks: / My boyish days drink to me.
12" Single: Released '83, on Arista, by BMG Records (UK). Deleted '87. Catalogue no: **KBIRD 121**
7" Single: Released '83, on Arista, by BMG Records (UK). Deleted '86. Catalogue no: **KBIRD 1**

WHATEVER POSSESSED YOU
7" Single: Released '84, on Arista, by BMG Records (UK). Catalogue no: **KBIRD 3**
12" Single: Released '84, on Arista, by BMG Records (UK). Catalogue no: **KBIRD 123**

Careless Hands

LOOKING FOR A SECRET
Tracks: / Looking for a secret.
7" Single: Released '82, on Flying Kite, Catalogue no: **FKR 001**

Caresse & Sickmob

R. U. XPERIENCED?
Tracks: / R. U. Xperienced.
7" Single: Released May '89, on Temple Records, by Temple Records (2). Catalogue no: **TOPY 44S**
12" Single: Released May '89, on Temple Records, by Temple Records (2). Catalogue no: **TOPY 44**

Caretaker Race

ANYWHERE BUT HOME
Tracks: / Anywhere but home.
12" Single: Released 23 Jul '88, on Roustabout, by Roustabout Records. Catalogue no: **RST 004T**

I WISH I'D SAID THAT
Tracks: / I wish I'd said that.
12" Single: Released Jul '89, on Foundation, Catalogue no: **TFL 002T**
7" Single: Released Jul '89, on Foundation, Catalogue no: **TFL 002**

SOMEWHERE ON SEA
Tracks: / Somewhere on sea.
12" Single: Released Oct '87, on Roustabout, by Roustabout Records. Catalogue no: **RST 001 T**
7" Single: Released Oct '87, on Roustabout, by Roustabout Records. Catalogue no: **RST 001**

Carey, Tony

IT'S A FINE FINE DAY
7" Single: Released '84, on MCA, by MCA Records. Catalogue no: **MCA 873**

Cargo

DO IT
Tracks: / Do it.
12" Single: Released Jul '87, on Cargo Gold, by Cargogold Productions. Catalogue no: **CG 1024**
12" Single: Released Jun '84, on Cargo Gold, by Cargogold Productions. Catalogue no: **CG 1023**

DON'T STOP YOUR LOVE
Tracks: / Don't stop your love / Cover me.
7" Single: Released Apr '86, on WEA, by WEA Records. Catalogue no: **YZ 66**
12" Single: Released Jun '86, on Cargo Gold, by Cargogold Productions. Catalogue no: **CG 1026**
12" Single: Released Apr '86, on WEA, by WEA Records. Catalogue no: **YZ 66T**

HOLDING ON FOR LOVE
Tracks: / Holding on for love / It's your love.
7" Single: Released '82, on Zonophone, by EMI Records. Catalogue no: **Z 38**
12" Single: Released Jun '82, on Cargo Gold, by Cargogold Productions. Catalogue no: **CG 1021**
12" Single: Released '82, on Zonophone, by EMI Records. Catalogue no: **12Z 38**

JAZZ RAP
Tracks: / Jazz rap.
12" Single: Released '85, on Calibre, Deleted '86. Catalogue no: **CABL 205**
7" Single: Released '85, on Calibre, Deleted '86. Catalogue no: **CAB 205**
12" Single: Released Jun '85, on Cargo Gold, by Cargogold Productions. Catalogue no: **CG 1025**

LADY'S MAN
Tracks: / Lady's man
12" Single: Released Mar '87, on Cargo Gold, by Cargogold Productions. Catalogue no: **CG 1027**

LOVE YOU SO (WITHOUT YOU)
Tracks: / Love you so (without you) / Love you so (without you) (Istrumental)
7" Single: Released Aug '86, on Streetwave, Catalogue no: **KHAN 73**
12" Single: Released Aug '86, on Streetwave, Catalogue no: **MKHAN 73**

SUNNY LOVE AFFAIR
Tracks: / Sunny love affair / Drifter, The.
12" Single: Released Jun '81, on Cargo Gold, by Cargogold Productions. Catalogue no: **CG 1020**

TENDER TOUCH
Tracks: / Tender touch.
12" Single: Released Jun '83, on Cargo Gold, by Cargogold Productions. Catalogue no: **CG 1022**
12" Single: Released '84, on Korova, by WEA Records. Catalogue no: **KOW 33T**
7" Single: Released '84, on Korova, by WEA Records. Catalogue no: **KOW 33**

Caribbean Caper

SUNSHINE BOY
Tracks: / Sunshine boy / Hold me.
7" Single: Released '83, on Rooster (Europe), by Rooster Records. Catalogue no: **ROO 104**

Carl, President

CARAVAN OF LOVE
Tracks: / Selah.
12" Single: Released Jun '89, on Selah, Catalogue no: **DEX 008**

Carl 'That man'...

GRAND NATIONAL
Tracks: / Grand national.
12" Single: Released '84, on Big Ship, Catalogue no: **CARL 1**

Carless, Ray

TARANTULA WALK
Tracks: / Tarantula walk / New born child.
12" Single: Released Feb '81, on Ensign, by Ensign Records. Deleted '84. Catalogue no: **ENYT 204**
7" Single: Released Feb '81, on Ensign, by Ensign Records. Deleted '84. Catalogue no: **ENY 204**

Carline, Russell

EACH AND EVERY MINUTE
Tracks: / Each and every minute.
12" Single: Released Jul '89, on Nightmare, by Nightmare Records. Catalogue no: **12AXL 1**
7" Single: Released Jul '89, on Nightmare, by Nightmare Records. Catalogue no: **AXL 1**
7" Single: Released Jul '89, on Nightmare, by Nightmare Records. Catalogue no: **NTG 1**
12" Single: Released Jul '89, on Nightmare, by Nightmare Records. Catalogue no: **12NTG 1**

Carlisle, Belinda

CIRCLE IN THE SAND
Tracks: / Circle in the sand (7" mix on all versions) / Circle in the sand (seaside mood groove mix) (Not on cassette) / Circle in the sand (sandblast multi-mix) (CD & cassette only) / Circle in the sand (beach party mix) (CD & 12" only) / Heaven is a place on earth (Cassette only).
7" Single: Released Apr '88, on Virgin, by Virgin Records. Catalogue no: **VS 1074**
CD 5": Released Aug '88, on Virgin, by Virgin Records. Catalogue no: **VSCD 1074**
Cassingle: Released '99, on Virgin, by Virgin Records. Catalogue no: **VSTC 1074**
12" Single: Released Apr '88, on Virgin, by Virgin Records. Catalogue no: **VST 1074**

HEAVEN IS A PLACE ON EARTH
Tracks: / Heaven is a place on Earth / We can change / Heaven is a place on earth (heavenly version) (On CD & 12" only) / Heaven is a place on earth (acappella version) (On CD only).
7" Single: Released Dec '87, on Virgin, by Virgin Records. Catalogue no: **VS 1036**
CD 5": Released Aug '88, on Virgin, by Virgin Records. Catalogue no: **VSCD 1036**
12" Single: Released '87, on Virgin, by Virgin Records. Catalogue no: **VST 1036**

I FEEL FREE
Tracks: / I feel free / I feel free (dub version).
Note: U.S.-only release of track from her mega-selling album.
12" Single: Released Sep '88, on MCA (USA), by MCA Records (USA). Catalogue no: **MCA 23886**

I GET WEAK
Tracks: / I get weak (7" mix on all versions) / Should I let you in (On all versions) / I get weak (12" version) (Not on 7").
12" Single: Released Feb '88, on Virgin, by Virgin Records. Catalogue no: **VST 1046**
CD 5": Released Aug '88, on Virgin, by Virgin Records. Catalogue no: **VSCD 1046**
Cassingle: Released '88, on Virgin, by Virgin Records. Catalogue no: **VSTC 1046**
7" Single: Released Feb '88, on Virgin, by Virgin Records. Catalogue no: **VS 1046**

LEAVE A LIGHT ON
Tracks: / Leave a light on / Shades of Michaelangelo.
Cassingle: Released Sep '89, on Virgin, by Virgin Records. Catalogue no: **VSC 1210**
CD 3": Released Oct '89, on Virgin, by Virgin Records. Catalogue no: **VSCD 1210**
7" Single: Released Sep '89, on Virgin, by Virgin Records. Catalogue no: **VS 1210**
12" Single: Released Sep '89, on Virgin, by Virgin Records. Catalogue no: **VST 1210**

LOVE NEVER DIES
Tracks: / Love never dies / Heaven is a place on earth (live) / I feel free (live) (Only on 12" & CD) / Love never dies...(full length version) (on CD & 12" only) / Circle in the sand (live) (on CD & 12" only).
12" Single: Released Nov '88, on Virgin, by Virgin Records. Catalogue no: **VST 1150**
7" Single: Released Nov '88, on Virgin, by Virgin Records. Catalogue no: **VS 1150**
12" Single: Released Nov '88, on Virgin, by Virgin Records. Catalogue no: **VSTA 1150**
CD 3": Released Nov '88, on Virgin, by Virgin Records. Catalogue no: **VSCD 1150**

MAD ABOUT YOU
Tracks: / Mad about you / I never wanted a rich man.
7" Single: Released Feb '88, on I.R.S, Deleted 1 Jul '89. Catalogue no: **IRM 118**
CD 5": Released Aug '88, on I.R.S, Catalogue no: **DIRM 118**
12" Single: Released Feb '88, on I.R.S, Catalogue no: **IRMT 118**

WORLD WITHOUT YOU
Tracks: / World without you (7" remix) (On all versions) / Nobody owns me (On all versions) / World without you (extended worldwide mix) (NOT on 7") / World without you (panavision mix) (On CD only).
12" Single: Released 22 Aug '88, on Virgin, by Virgin Records. Catalogue no: **VST 1114**
CD 5": Released 22 Aug '88, on Virgin, by Virgin Records. Catalogue no: **VSCD 1114**
7" Single: Released '88, on Virgin, by Virgin Records. Catalogue no: **VSX 1114**
7" Single: Released 22 Aug '88, on Virgin, by Virgin Records. Catalogue no: **VS 1114**
12" Single: Released '88, on Virgin, by Virgin Records. Catalogue no: **VSTP 1114**

Carlos, Don

CAN'T WASTE TIME
Tracks: / Can't waste time / Waste dub.
10" single: Released '82, on Cha-Cha, by Cha-Cha Records. Catalogue no: **CHAD**

52

COME IN
Tracks: / Come in / Special request.
12" Single: Released '83, on Greensleeves, by Greensleeves Records. Catalogue no: **GRED 124**

DANCE GATES
Tracks: / Dance gates / 12 tribes of Israel.
12" Single: Released '83, on Rusty International, Catalogue no: **RI 007**

FIND YOURSELF A FOOL
Tracks: / Find yourself a fool.
12" Single: Released '84, on Kingdom, by Kingdom Records. Deleted '86. Catalogue no: **KV 8026 12**

FROM CREATION
Tracks: / From creation.
12" Single: Released '84, on Blacker Dread, Catalogue no: **SCOM 003**

GRIEF MY HEART
Tracks: / Grief my heart / Spread out.
12" Single: Released '83, on Ethnic, Catalogue no: **ETH 2236**

ISOBEL
Tracks: / Isobel / One morning (silly boys).
12" Single: Released '82, on Rusty International, Catalogue no: **RI 001**

JORDAN RIVER
Tracks: / Jordan river / Reason.
12" Single: Released '83, on Youth In Progress, Catalogue no: **YP 001**

MAGIC MAN
Tracks: / Magic man / Magic rhythm.
12" Single: Released '82, on Negus Roots, Catalogue no: **NERT 015**

MONEY & WOMEN
Tracks: / Money & woman / Keep on working.
12" Single: Released '83, on Shuttle, Catalogue no: **SH 008**

MR BIG MAN
Tracks: / Mr. Big Man / Runaround.
12" Single: Released '83, on Black Roots, Catalogue no: **LML 181260**

NICE TIME (LATE NIGHT BLUES)
Tracks: / Nice time (late night blues) / Get up.
12" Single: Released '83, on CSA, by CSA Records. Deleted '88. Catalogue no: **12CSA 502**

PEACE AND LOVE
Tracks: / Peace and love / Lock and key.
10" single: Released '83, on Nice'n'Nasty, Deleted '84. Catalogue no: **NN 02**

ROCK THIS HERE MUSIC
Tracks: / Rock this here music.
12" Single: Released '83, on Shuttle, Catalogue no: **SH 002**

STRICTLY CULTURE
Tracks: / Strictly culture.
12" Single: Released '85, on Scom, Catalogue no: **BD 020**

UNTRUE GIRL
Tracks: /Untrue girl
12" Single: Released '84, on EAD, Catalogue no: **GEM 009**

YOU ARE MY SUNSHINE
Tracks: / You are my sunshine.
12" Single: Released '84, on Tads, Catalogue no: **RAS 7006**

Carlton, Carl

Biographical details: This American soul singer born in Detroit in 1953, began making records while he was still a child. He achieved a number of entries on the US soul charts in the late Sixties, including *46 Drums - 1 Guitar* and *Don't Walk Away*. His discs were a little too close in imitation of young Stevie Wonder and the Motown sound to gain wider pop acceptance.
Carlton's major success on the US pop chart came late in 1974, when his rendition of *Everlasting Love* reached No. 6. This cover of the well-known song therefore remain the highest placed version on the American charts; the original hit by Robert Knight peaked at No. 13 in 1967 and the British 1968 No. 1 version by the Love Affair never charted in the States. Carlton's '74 single missed out in the UK, where the reativated Knight original had recently charted. Carlton was unable to follow up the success of *Mama Jama* in either country. (Bob MacDonald)..

SHE'S A BAD MAMA JAMA
Tracks: / She's a bad mama jama /This feeling rated zero (Available on 12" only) /
12" Single: Released Jun '81, on 20th Century, by 20th Century Records. Deleted Jun '84. Catalogue no: **TCD 2488**
7" Single: Released Jul '81, on 20th Century, by 20th Century Records. Deleted Jul '84. Catalogue no: **TC 2488**

Carlton & His Shoes

MOOD FOR LOVE
Tracks: / Mood for love / Carlton's mood.
12" Single: Released '82, on Fashion, by Fashion Records. Catalogue no: **FAD 010**

Carlton, Little Carl

COMPETITION AIN'T NOTHING
Tracks: / Competition ain't nothing / I'm not built that way.
7" Single: Released '85, on Kent, by Ace Records. Catalogue no: **TOWN 105**

Carlton, Steve

EASY
Tracks: / Easy / Back to square one / Baby's good to me (Only on 12" version.).
Note: Baby's good to me - extra track on 12".
7" Single: Released Aug '86, on RCA, by BMG Records (UK). Catalogue no: **PB 40911**
12" Single: Released Aug '86, on RCA, by BMG Records (UK). Catalogue no: **PT 40912**

KEEP ON WALKING
Tracks: / Keep on walking / Goodbye / Keep on walking (inst) (Available on 12" only.).
Note: Keep on walking (inst) is an extra track on 12".
7" Single: Released Apr '86, on RCA, by BMG Records (UK). Catalogue no: **PB 40695**
12" Single: Released Apr '86, on RCA, by BMG Records (UK). Catalogue no: **PT 40696**

Carmel

Biographical details: Carmel is a British singer whose main field is Jazz. She first began to be noticed in the autumn of 1982, when a six-track mini-album showcasing her talents was released. It included the song *Storm*, which had been issued as a single some six months earlier. Carmel hit big when *Bad Day* reached the UK Top 20 in the late summer of '83. Although the lyrics were secular, this single was, musically, in a gospel vein. This made it an unusual record to reach the upper echelons of the charts; this fact, coupled with her powerful vocal delivery, made *Bad Day* a standout single.
The next single *Willow Weep For Me* flopped, but Carmel returned to the Top 30 in Britain with *More, More, More*, an uptempo jazz-flavoured offering more typical of the artist's work. her album *The Drum Is Everything* also attained Top 30 status. She has a permanent bass player and drummer, who are often photographed with her, leading some people to the misconception that Carmel is the name of a trio rather than the name of the singer. (Bob MacDonald)..

6 TRACK EP
12" Single: Released '82, on Red Flame (2), by London Records. Catalogue no: **RFM 9**

BAD DAY
Tracks: / Bad day / Rue St. Denis.
12" Single: Released '83, on London Records, by London Records. Catalogue no: **LONX 29**
7" Single: Released '83, on London Records, by London Records. Deleted '87. Catalogue no: **LON 29**

EVERY LITTLE BIT
Tracks: / Every little bit / Crocodile poem / Every little bit (ext) (On 12" only.) / Long come liberty (On 12" only).
7" Single: Released Jan '88, on London Records, by London Records. Deleted Oct '88. Catalogue no: **LON 157**
12" Single: Released Jan '88, on London Records, by London Records. Deleted Oct '88. Catalogue no: **LONX 157**

I HAVE FALLEN IN LOVE (JE SUIS TOMBE)
Tracks: / I have fallen in love (je suis tombe) / Moving.
CD 5": Released Oct '89, on London Records, by London Records. Catalogue no: **LONCD 227**
12" Single: Released Oct '89, on London Records, by London Records. Catalogue no: **LONX 227**
Cassingle: Released Oct '89, on London Records, by London Records. Catalogue no: **LONCS 227**
7" Single: Released Oct '89, on London Records, by London Records. Catalogue no: **LON 227**

I'M NOT AFRAID OF YOU
Tracks: / I'm not afraid of you.
7" Single: Released '85, on London Records, by London Records. Catalogue no: **LON 74**
12" Single: Released '85, on London Records, by London Records. Catalogue no:

LONX 74

IT'S ALL IN THE GAME
Tracks: / It's all in the game / More, more, more / Tracks of my tears (on 12" only).
7" Single: Released Aug '87, on London Records, by London Records. Deleted Oct '88. Catalogue no: **LON 144**
CD 5": on London Records, by London Records. Deleted Oct '88. Catalogue no: **LONCD 144**
12" Single: Released Aug '87, on London Records, by London Records. Deleted Oct '88. Catalogue no: **LONX 144**

MERCY
Tracks: / Mercy / What a story.
12" Single: Released Sep '86, on London Records, by London Records. Catalogue no: **LONX 102**
7" Single: Released Sep '86, on London Records, by London Records. Deleted Sep '87. Catalogue no: **LON 102**

MORE MORE MORE
Tracks: / More more more / Hot day (version).
12" Single: Released '84, on London Records, by London Records. Catalogue no: **LONX 44**
7" Single: Released '84, on London Records, by London Records. Catalogue no: **LON 44**

MY HEART SINGS COUNTRY
Tracks: / My heart sings country.
7" Single: Released '85, on Superbad, Catalogue no: **TS 1**

SALLY
Tracks: / Sally / Hymn of love.
12" Single: Released May '86, on London Records, by London Records. Catalogue no: **LONX 90**
7" Single: Released May '86, on London Records, by London Records. Catalogue no: **LON 90**

STORM
Tracks: / Storm / Can't stand the rain.
7" Single: Released '82, on Red Flame (1), by Red Flame Records. Catalogue no: **RF 701**

WILLOW WEEP FOR ME
Tracks: / Willow weep for me / That's cool that's neat.
12" Single: Released '83, on London Records, by London Records. Catalogue no: **LONX 38**
7" Single: Released '83, on London Records, by London Records. Catalogue no: **LON 38**

Carmen

THEN HE KISSED ME
Tracks: / Then he kissed me.
12" Single: Released May '89, on Passion, by Skratch Records. Catalogue no: **PASH 1289**

Carmen, Eric

Biographical details: This American singer, painist, bassist and songwriter first came to fame in 1972 as leader of the Raspberries. This inventive Ohio rock group fused catchy pop material with dramatic, powerful rock instrumentation. Their first and biggest hit single *Go All The Way* reached No. 5 on the US chart that year. By the end of 1974 the band had chalked up two further American Top 20 hits, *I Wanna Be With ou* and *Overnight Sensation (hit record)*. None of their singles or albums charted in Britain, although the charmingly extravagant *Overnight Sensation* gained considerable UK airplay. Their final LP was paradoxically titled *Starting Over* and the Raspberries broke up in 1975. Carmen embarked upon a solo career.
He enjoyed immediate success with his early '76 single *All By Myself*, a classical-based song that signalled a move into the adult ballad field. Carmen's strong voice was well suited for this style and the single reached No. 2 thus becoming his biggest career hit in the US. It was also his only single to register in Britain, reaching No. 12. A further American hit from the *Eric Carmen* album, entitled *Never Gonna Fall In Love Again*, got to No. 11.
Carmen could have consolidated on his position and carved out a long-term niche in the Barry Manilow field; but instead, his career wavered somewhat in the late Seventies. He managed two more US Top 30 singles, *She Did It* and *Change Of Heart*, but then he slipped into obscurity. (Bob MacDonald)..

ALL BY MYSELF
Tracks: / All by myself.
7" Single: Released Apr '76, on Arista, by BMG Records (UK). Deleted Apr '80. Catalogue no: **ARISTA 42**

ALL BY MYSELF (OLD GOLD)
Tracks: / All by myself.
7" Single: Released Jul '82, on Old Gold, by Old Gold Records. Catalogue no: **OG 9122**

HUNGRY EYES
Tracks: / Hungry eyes / Where are you tonight? (on 12" only) / I've had the time of my life (* Track on 12" version only.).
12" Single: Released May '88, on RCA, by BMG Records (UK). Deleted May '89. Catalogue no: **PT 49594**
CD 5": Released Jun '89, on RCA, by BMG Records (UK). Deleted Jul '89. Catalogue no: **PD 49594**
7" Single: Released Jan '88, on RCA, by BMG Records (UK). Catalogue no: **PB 49593**

I WANT TO HEAR IT FROM YOUR LIPS
Tracks: / I want to hear it from your lips.
7" Single: Released Jan '85, on Geffen, by Geffen Records (USA). Catalogue no: **A 4956**
12" Single: Released Jan '85, on Geffen, by Geffen Records (USA). Catalogue no: **TA 4956**

MAKE ME LOSE CONTROL
Tracks: / Make me lose control / All by myself / That's rock'n'roll (Only on 12".).
CD 5": Released Sep '88, on Arista, by BMG Records (UK). Catalogue no: **661718**
7" Single: Released Sep '88, on Arista, by BMG Records (UK). Catalogue no: **111718**
12" Single: Released Sep '88, on Arista, by BMG Records (UK). Catalogue no: **611718**

Carmen, Pauli

DIAL MY NUMBER (SINGLE)
Tracks: / Dial my number.
7" Single: Released May '86, on CBS, by CBS Records. Deleted '87. Catalogue no: **A 7096**
12" Single: Released May '86, on CBS, by CBS Records. Deleted '87. Catalogue no: **TA 7096**

Carmen, Tracey

RESCUE ME
Tracks: / Rescue me / Infrafni (infra) / Summertime (Extra track on 12" only.).
12" Single: Released Jan '86, on Infrastructure, Deleted '87. Catalogue no: **INFRA 1T**
7" Single: Released Jan '86, on Infrastructure, Deleted '87. Catalogue no: **INFRA 1**

Carn, Jean

IF YOU DON'T KNOW ME BY NOW
Tracks: / If you don't know me by now.
7" Single: Released Jul '82, on Motown, by BMG Records (UK). Catalogue no: **TMG 1271**

Carnage

ALL THE SAD PEOPLE
Tracks: / All the sad people.
7" Single: Released Nov '83, on Creative Reality, Catalogue no: **REAL 5**

LIARS AND HYPOCRITES
Tracks: / Liars and hypocrites.
7" Single: Released Jul '84, on Creative Reality, Catalogue no: **REAL 6**

OUR LIFE IN THEIR HANDS
Tracks: / Our life in their hands.
7" Single: Released Jun '85, on Creative Reality, Catalogue no: **REAL 10**

Carne, Jean

AIN'T NO WAY
Tracks: / Ain't no way / Flame of love / You're a part of me (Only on 12".).
7" Single: Released Jun '88, on RCA, by BMG Records (UK). Deleted Jun '89. Catalogue no: **PB 42067**
12" Single: Released Jun '88, on RCA, by BMG Records (UK). Deleted May '89. Catalogue no: **PT 42068**

CLOSER THAN CLOSE (SINGLE)
Tracks: / Closer than close.
7" Single: Released Aug '86, on Omni (USA), by First String Records (USA). Catalogue no: **OMN 3**
12" Single: Released Aug '86, on Omni (USA), by First String Records (USA). Catalogue no: **12 OMN 3**

LET ME BE THE ONE
Tracks: / Let me be the one / Break up to make up / Closer than close (Extra track on 12".).
7" Single: Released Mar '88, on RCA, by BMG Records (UK). Deleted May '89. Catalogue no: **PB 41879**
12" Single: Released Mar '88, on RCA, by BMG Records (UK). Deleted May '89. Catalogue no: **PT 41880**

Carnegie

JO STREET MACHINE
Tracks: / Jo street machine (ext street mix) / Road machine (ext road mix).
12" Single: Released Apr '87, on Dove, Catalogue no: **JO 12-124**
7" Single: Released Apr '87, on Dove, Catalogue no: **JO 124**

Carnes, Kim

Biographical details: This American singer and songwriter, born in Los Angeles in 1945, released her debut self-titled album in 1976. Before that she had had experience as a member of a group called the New Christy Minstrels and also as a writer and performer of jingles and commercials. Her second album *Sailin'* was produced by veteran Jerry Wexler. Her first taste of chart success came in 1978, when a duet with Gene Cotton called *You're A Part Of Me* reached No. 36 on the American listings.
Carnes' breakthrough year was 1980. A duet with Kenny Rogers, *Don't Fall In Love With a Dreamer*, reached the US No. 4 position; this was a strong MoR ballad. She finally achieved solo success later that year with *More Love*, a remake of Smokey Robinson & The Miracles' 1967 hit. By peaking at No. 10, it was placed thirteen notches higher than the original on the US chart.
It Carnes was pleased with her 1980 progress, she could hardly have anticipated what was to follow in '81. Teaming with producer Val Garay, she recorded a 1975 Jackie de Shannon song *Bette Davis Eyes*. Although Kim's husky voice was similar to that of De Shannon, her new treatment of the song was far superior to the original. With its mesmerising keyboard backing track, Carnes' single had such an air of magic that it became an across-the-board smash. the record logged no less than nine weeks in the US No. 1 position and became the world's biggest selling single of 1981. Its UK peak position of No. 10 was one of its lowest on the globe; none of the singer's previous efforts had, however, charted in Britain at all. Her album *Mistaken Identity* also hit the US No. 1 slot.
Bette Davis Eyes was such a monster hit that all her subsequent discs seemed anticlimatic. The follow-up single *Draw Of The Cards* peaked at No. 28 on the Billboard Hot 100. Still more dissapointing was the next album *Voyeur*. this was a slow-selling LP and its first single reached only No. 29. In the UK, the *Voyeur* single peaked at No. 68; Britain soon forgot about the name Kim Carnes. She returned to the US Top 20 in 1984 with *What bout Me*, a single that featured the triumvirate of Carnes, James Ingram and her old friend Kenny Rogers. Having appealed to pop and rock fans with *Bette Davis Eyes*-type material, Carnes was now firmly back in the adult ballad field. (Bob MacDonald).
This very highly regarded singer and songwriter was born in 1948 in Los Angeles. Her husky, breathy vocal style was compared to Rod Stewart's, evident on her first solo hit, *More love* in 1980 (a Smokey Robinson song); but *Bette Davis eyes* (by Donna Weiss and Jackie De Shannon) the next year was number one for nine weeks in the USA, made the album *Mistaken identity* into a best seller and won a deserved Grammy. Ironically her own fine songs were most successful in cover versions, often co-written with husband David Ellingson and recorded by Anne Murray, Frank Sinatra, Barbra Streisand, Rita Coolidge and others. She was the first artists signed to the new EMI/America label. She had sung in the New Christy Minstrels; another ex-Minstrel, Kenny Rogers, made an album of Carnes/Ellinson songs called Gideon, from which *Don't fall in love with a dreamer* (a duet with Kim) was a top five hit. (Donald Clarke, April 1989)m.

ABADABADANGO
Tracks: / Abadabadango.
7" Single: Released Oct '85, on EMI-America, by EMI Records. Catalogue no: **EA 207**

BETTE DAVIS EYES (see panel below)
Tracks: / Bette Davis eyes / Miss you tonite.
7" Single: Released Apr '81, on EMI-America, by EMI Records. Catalogue no: **EA 121**

DIVIDED HEARTS
Tracks: / Divided hearts / You say you love me (but I know better).
7" Single: Released Jul '86, on EMI-America, by EMI Records. Catalogue no: **EA 218**
12" Single: Released Jul '86, on EMI-America, by EMI Records. Catalogue no: **12EA 218**

DRAW OF THE CARDS
Tracks: / Draw of the cards.
7" Single: Released Aug '81, on EMI-America, by EMI Records. Deleted Aug '84. Catalogue no: **EA 125**

JUST TO SPEND THE NIGHT WITH YOU
Tracks: / Just to spend the night with you.
CD 5": Released 30 Jan '89, on MCA, by MCA Records. Catalogue no: **DMCA 1290**
7" Single: Released 30 Jan '89, on MCA, by MCA Records. Deleted 1 Jul '89. Catalogue no: **MCA 1290**
12" Single: Released 30 Jan '89, on MCA, by MCA Records. Catalogue no: **MCAT 1290**

MISTAKEN IDENTITY (SINGLE)
Tracks: / Mistaken identity / Jamaica Sunday morning.
7" Single: Released Oct '81, on EMI-America, by EMI Records. Deleted '85. Catalogue no: **EA 129**
12" Single: Released Oct '81, on EMI-America, by EMI Records. Deleted Oct '84. Catalogue no: **12EA 129**

MORE LOVE
Tracks: / More love / Changin'.
12" Single: Released 20 Jun '80, on EMI-America, by EMI Records. Deleted '83. Catalogue no: **12EA 113**
7" Single: Released 20 Jun '80, on EMI-America, by EMI Records. Deleted '83. Catalogue no: **EA 113**

TAKE IT ON THE CHIN
Tracks: / Take it on the chin / Undertow.
7" Single: Released Nov '82, on EMI-America, by EMI Records. Deleted Nov '85. Catalogue no: **EA 147**

VOYEUR (SINGLE)
Tracks: / Voyeur / Thrill of the grill.
7" Single: Released Oct '82, on EMI-America, by EMI Records. Deleted Oct '85. Catalogue no: **EA 143**

Carnival

WAKE UP(DON'T BE SHEEP)
Tracks: / Wake up (don't be sheep).
7" Single: Released Apr '83, on Allemande, Catalogue no: **A 010**

Carnival Season

PLEASE DON'T SEND ME TO HEAVEN
Tracks: / Please don't send me to heaven / Wondering about the.
12" Single: Released Feb '87, on What Goes On, by What Goes On Records. Catalogue no: **GOES ON 12T**

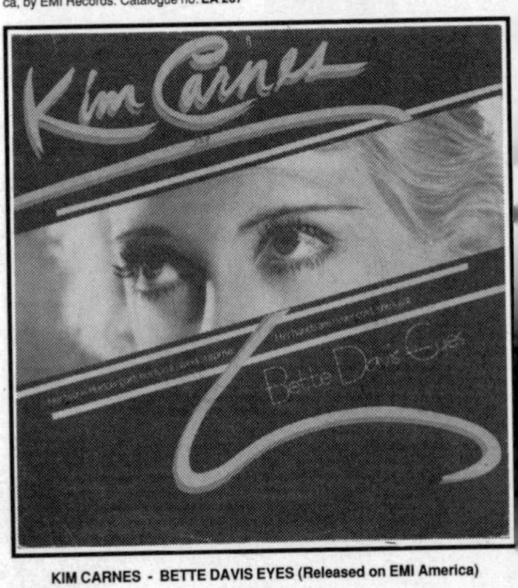

KIM CARNES - BETTE DAVIS EYES (Released on EMI America)

Carola

LOVE ISN'T LOVE
Tracks: / Love isn't love.
7" Single: Released May '83, on Towerbell, Catalogue no: **TOW 38**

RUNAWAY
Tracks: / Runaway / So far.
7" Single: Released Aug '86, on Polydor, by Polydor Ltd. Deleted Aug '87. Catalogue no: **8339 467**

Carolgees, Bob

DO ANIMALS DREAM
Tracks: / Do animals dream / Home on the range.
7" Single: Released Oct '80, on RK, by RK Records. Deleted Oct '83. Catalogue no: **RK 1032**

Carolyn

CAN'T GET IT
Tracks: / Can't get it.
7" Single: Released Feb '89, on Exel, Deleted Sep '89. Catalogue no: **EXEL 2**
12" Single: Released Feb '89, on Exel, Deleted Sep '89. Catalogue no: **12 EXEL 2**

Carosone, Renato

TORERO - CHA CHA CHA
Tracks: / Torero.
7" Single: Released Jul '58, on Parlophone, by EMI Records. Deleted Jul '61. Catalogue no: **R 4433**

Carousel

MY HEART AND I
Tracks: / My heart and i / Heart to heart.
7" Single: Released Jul '82, on CBS, by CBS Records. Deleted Jul '87. Catalogue no: **A 2545**

STRAWBERRY FAYRE
Tracks: / Strawberry fair / Evergreen / Halfpennies and farthings / September come again.
12" Single: Released Apr '89, on Cosmic English Music, Catalogue no: **CTA 102**

Carpendale, Howard

HELLO AGAIN
Tracks: / Hello again.
7" Single: Released Dec '84, on Juice, by Juice Records. Deleted '88. Catalogue no: **AA 2**

SHINE ON
Tracks: / Shine on.
7" Single: Released Jul '85, on Juice, by Juice Records. Deleted '88. Catalogue no: **AA 3**
12" Single: Released Jul '85, on Juice, by Juice Records. Deleted '88. Catalogue no: **12 AA 3**

Carpenter, Richard

IN LOVE ALONE
Tracks: / That's what I believe.
7" Single: on A&M, by A&M Records. Catalogue no: **AM 417**

Carpenter, Scott

PISTOL PACKIN' MAMA (see panel bleow)
Tracks: / Pistol packin' mama / Baby I don't care.
7" Single: Released '86, on West Records, Catalogue no: **W-724 B**

Carpenters

Biographical details: This American pop duo consisted of singer and keyboards player Richard Carpenter, born in 1946 and his sister Karen, singer and drummer, born in 1950. They were born in New Haven, Conneticut. On stage and on record they were joined by additional musicians, though the duo performed all the vocals on the records and Richard handled the arrangements.
Their family moved to Los Angeles in 1963 and the pair made masic their profession in 1967. After making local headway in a group called Spectrum, they came to the attention of superstar trumpeter and record executive Herp Alpert. he signed them to A&M Records, the label that he had cofounded in the early Sixties and massive success came to the duo within months. They recorded a Burt Bacharach/Hal David song *(They Long To Be) Close To You* and released it in the US in May 1970 - it was a No. 1 for four weeks. This single was typical of the consistently high standard of music that was to follow over the next five years: an excellent choice of song, pure and crystal clear singing by Karen, immaculate vocal harmonies by the pair, backed with just the right instrumentation. Their records would appeal to both the older middle-of-the-road audience and the younger pop market.
Close To You was the first of six consecutive US Top 3 singles. A further four hits reached that mark by the middle of the Seventies, including a second and third chart-topper: 1973's *Top Of The World* and 1975's remake of the Marvelettes' *Please Mr. Postman* (with the latter thus being a US No. 1 in both 1961 and 1975). The Carpenters were equally successful with ballads and uptempo material. Some of their hits were penned by Richard in collaboration with lyricist John Bettis, others (particularly the earlier singles) were carefully selected from other writers' catalogues. Britain was unduly selective as far as Carpenters singles were concerned, putting some in its Top 10 while confining others to lower chart positions. The duo's two biggest UK hits both reached No. 2: the beautiful 1973 ballad *Yesterday Once More* (also No. 2 in the States) and *Please Mr. Postman*. Album-wise, however, they scored two chart-toppers in Britain: *The Singles 1969-1973* logges 17 weeks at No. 1 in '74 and was listed on the chart for an amazing 115 weeks; their last great studio LP *Horizon* scaled the summit in the summer of '75.
The Carpenters had five golden years between 1970 and 1975. Their career can be divided into two distinct black and white era: they maintained a superlative standard during the first half of the Seventies but, from '76 onwards, the pair were an artistic and commercial decline. They never achieved a US Top 10 single during the latter period and managed only one in the UK, 1977's *Calling Occupants Of Interplanetary Craft*. This somewhat awkward attempt to develop a more complex sound was of little merit and the bulk of their more conventional late Seventies output was mediocre.
Sadly, Karen died in February 1983 at the age of 32. She suffered from a heart attack caused by Anorexia Nervosa. The possessor of one of popular music's finest voices had passed away. (Bob MacDonald)

CALLING OCCUPANTS OF INTERPLANETARY CRAFT
Tracks: / Calling occupants of interplanetary craft.
7" Single: Released Oct '77, on A&M, by A&M Records. Deleted Oct '80. Catalogue no: **AMS 7318**

CLOSE TO YOU (THEY LONG TO BE)
Tracks: / Close to you.
7" Single: Released Sep '70, on A&M, by A&M Records. Deleted Sep '73. Catalogue no: **AMS 800**

COMPACT HITS: THE CARPENTERS
Tracks: / (They long to be) close to you / We've only just begun / I won't last a day without you / Goodbye to love.
CD 5": Released Apr '88, on A&M, by A&M Records. Deleted Apr '88. Catalogue no: **AMCD 901**

I NEED TO BE IN LOVE
Tracks: / I need to be in love.
7" Single: Released Jul '76, on A&M, by A&M Records. Deleted Jul '79. Catalogue no: **AMS 7238**

I WON'T LAST A DAY WITHOUT YOU
Tracks: / I won't last a day without you / Goodbye to love.
7" Single: Released Jun '74, on A&M, by A&M Records. Deleted Jun '77. Catalogue no: **AMS 7111**
7" Single: Released Sep '72, on A&M, by A&M Records. Deleted Sep '75. Catalogue no: **AMS 7023**

JAMBALAYA (ON THE BAYOU) MR GUDER
Tracks: / Jambalaya.
7" Single: Released Mar '74, on A&M, by A&M Records. Deleted Mar '77. Catalogue no: **AMS 7098**

MAKE BELIEVE IT'S YOUR FIRST TIME
Tracks: / Make believe it's your first time.
7" Single: Released Oct '83, on A&M, by A&M Records. Deleted Oct '86. Catalogue no: **AM 147**

MERRY CHRISTMAS, DARLING
Tracks: / Merry Christmas darling.
7" Single: Released Jan '72, on A&M, by A&M Records. Deleted Jan '75. Catalogue no: **AME 601**

ONLY YESTERDAY
Tracks: / Only yesterday.
7" Single: Released Apr '75, on A&M, by A&M Records. Deleted Apr '78. Catalogue no: **AMS 7159**

PLEASE MISTER POSTMAN
Tracks: / Please Mr. Postman.
7" Single: Released Jan '75, on A&M, by A&M Records. Deleted Jan '78. Catalogue no: **AMS 7141**

SANTA CLAUS IS COMING TO TOWN
Tracks: / Santa Claus is coming to town.
7" Single: Released Dec '75, on A&M, by A&M Records. Deleted Dec '78. Catalogue no: **AMS 7144**

SOLITAIRE
Tracks: / Solitaire.
7" Single: Released Aug '75, on A&M, by A&M Records. Deleted Aug '78. Catalogue no: **AMS 7187**

SUPERSTAR
Tracks: / Superstar / For all we know.
7" Single: Released Sep '71, on A&M, by A&M Records. Deleted Sep '74. Catalogue no: **AMS 864**

SWEET SWEET SMILE
Tracks: / Sweet sweet smile.
7" Single: Released Feb '78, on A&M, by A&M Records. Deleted Feb '81. Catalogue no: **AMS 7327**

THERE'S A KIND OF HUSH
Tracks: / There's a kind of hush.
7" Single: Released Mar '76, on A&M, by A&M Records. Deleted Mar '79. Catalogue no: **AMS 7219**

THOSE GOOD OLD DREAMS
Tracks: / Those good old dreams / Back in my life again.
7" Single: Released Nov '81, on A&M, by A&M Records. Deleted Nov '84. Catalogue no: **AMS 8181**

TOP OF THE WORLD
Tracks: / Top of the world.
7" Single: Released Oct '73, on A&M, by A&M Records. Deleted Oct '76. Catalogue no: **AMS 7086**

TOUCH ME WHEN WE'RE DANCING
Tracks: / Touch me when we're dancing / Because we are in love.
7" Single: Released Jun '81, on A&M, by A&M Records. Deleted Jun '84. Catalogue no: **AMS 8141**

WE'VE ONLY JUST BEGUN
Tracks: / We've only just begun.
7" Single: Released Jan '71, on A&M, by A&M Records. Deleted Jan '74. Catalogue no: **AMS 813**

WITH PEN IN HAND
Tracks: / With pen in hand.
7" Single: Released 30 Apr '69, on Liberty, by EMI Records. Deleted 30 Apr '72. Catalogue no: **LBF 15166**
7" Single: Released 26 Mar '69, on Liberty, by EMI Records. Deleted 26 Mar '72. Catalogue no: **LBF 15166**
7" Single: Released 12 Mar '69, on Liberty, by EMI Records. Deleted 12 Mar '72. Catalogue no: **LBF 15166**

YESTERDAY ONCE MORE (SINGLE)
Tracks: / Yesterday once more.
7" Single: Released Jul '73, on A&M, by A&M Records. Deleted Jul '76. Catalogue no: **AMS 7073**
7" Single: Released Sep '85, on Old Gold, by Old Gold Records. Catalogue no: **OG 9541**

Carpetbaggers

SORRY
Tracks: / Sorry / Beautiful gas.
7" Single: Released Nov '82, on Page One, by Page One Records. Catalogue no: **POR 006**
7" Single: Released Nov '82, on Lucky, by Lucky Records. Deleted Nov '85. Catalogue no: **LUCKY 003**

Carpettes

HOW ABOUT ME AND YOU
Tracks: / How about me and you.
7" Single: Released Jan '78, on Small Wonder, by Small Wonder Records. Catalogue no: **SMALL 3**

LAST LONE RANGER
Tracks: / Last lone ranger / Love's so strong.
7" Single: Released Jan '81, on Beggars Banquet, by Beggars Banquet Records. Deleted Jan '84. Catalogue no: **BEG 49**

NOTHING EVER CHANGES
Tracks: / Nothing ever changes / You never realise / Frustration.
7" Single: Released Apr '80, on Beggars Banquet, by Beggars Banquet Records. Deleted '83. Catalogue no: **BEG 47**

Carpio, Teresa

STREET ANGEL
Tracks: / Street angel / It will be alright.
7" Single: Released Oct '80, on Warner Bros., by WEA Records. Deleted Oct '83. Catalogue no: **K 73006**

Carr, Joe 'Fingers'

PORTUGUESE WASHERWOMAN
Tracks: / Portuguese washerwoman.
7" Single: Released Jun '56, on Capitol, by EMI Records. Deleted Jun '59. Catalogue no: **CL 14587**

Carr, John

PENNY ARCADE
Tracks: / Penny arcade / Hold on.
7" Single: Released Dec '82, on Dual Purpose, Catalogue no: **DPR 1**

COME SHARE MY LOVE
Tracks: / Come share my love.
7" Single: Released Aug '84, on Dual Purpose, Catalogue no: **DPR 3**

IF EVER I SEE YOU AGAIN
Tracks: / If ever I see you again / Such feeling.
7" Single: Released Mar '84, on Dual Purpose, Catalogue no: **DPR 2**

Carr, Linda

HIGH WIRE
Tracks: / High wire.
7" Single: Released Jul '75, on Chelsea, Deleted Jul '78. Catalogue no: **2005 025**

HIGH WIRE (OLD GOLD)
Tracks: / High wire / Ride a wild horse.
7" Single: Released 24 Apr '89, on Old Gold, by Old Gold Records. Catalogue no: **OG 9882**

SCOTT CARPENTER - PISTOL PACKIN' MAMA (Released on West Records)

Carr, Pearl

HOW WONDERFUL TO KNOW
Tracks: / How wonderful to know.
7" Single: Released Apr '61, on Columbia, by EMI Records. Deleted Apr '64. Catalogue no: **DB 4603**

SING LITTLE BIRDIE
Tracks: / Sing little birdie.
7" Single: Released Mar '59, on Columbia, by EMI Records. Deleted Mar '62. Catalogue no: **DB 4275**

Carr, Valerie

WHEN THE BOYS TALK ABOUT THE GIRLS
Tracks: / When the boys talk about the girls.
7" Single: Released 4 Jul '58, on Columbia, by EMI Records. Deleted Jul '62. Catalogue no: **DB 4131**
7" Single: Released 18 Jul '58, on Columbia, by EMI Records. Deleted Jul '62. Catalogue no: **DB 4131**

Carr, Vikki

Biographical details: Florencia Bisenta de Casillas Martinez Cardona was born in Texas in 1941 and became a highly regarded pop singer, with hit singles and albums in the 1960's and early 70's; *It must be him* was her biggest. Later she performed in hospitals at benefits and set up a scholarship foundation for Chicano children, resuming recording in Spanish for Mexican CBS. (Donald Clarke, April 1989).

IT MUST BE HIM (OLD GOLD)
Tracks: / It must be him / Hurt.
Note: Also contains:"Hurt" by Timi Yuro
7" Single: Released Apr '87, on Old Gold, by Old Gold Records. Deleted Sep '89. Catalogue no: **OG 9722**

IT MUST BE HIM (SINGLE)
Tracks: / It must be him (Becaud/Vidalin/David).
7" Single: Released Jun '67, on Liberty, by EMI Records. Deleted Jun '70. Catalogue no: **LIB 55917**

THERE I GO
Tracks: / There I go.
7" Single: Released Aug '67, on Liberty, by EMI Records. Deleted Aug '70. Catalogue no: **LBF 15022**

Carra, Raffaella

Biographical details: This Italian singer, a media star in her native country, scored a one-off UK Top 10 single in 1978, reaching No. 9 with *Do It Do It Again*. How this dire, lightweight pop ditty, similar in standard to the B side of an unsuccessful Eurovision entry, became a British hit remains a mystery. (Bob MacDonald)..

DO IT DO IT AGAIN
Tracks: / Do it do it again.
7" Single: Released Apr '78, on Epic, by CBS Records. Deleted Apr '82. Catalogue no: **EPC 6094**

Carrack, Paul

BEAUTY IS ONLY SKIN DEEP
Tracks: / Beauty is inly skin deep / Bet you never been in love.
7" Single: Released Apr '80, on Vertigo, by Phonogram Ltd. Deleted Apr '83. Catalogue no: **PAUL 1**

DON'T SHED A TEAR
Tracks: / Don't shed a tear / Merilee / All your love is in vain (Only on 12" format.).
12" Single: Released Oct '87, on Chrysalis, by Chrysalis Records. Catalogue no: **CHS 12 3164**
7" Single: Released Oct '87, on Chrysalis, by Chrysalis Records. Catalogue no: **CHS 3164**

EVERY TIME YOU WALK IN THE ROOM
Tracks: / How long / Album medley / Every time you walk in the room / Collraine.
Note: *Album medley* on 12" only..
7" Single: Released Apr '87, on Chrysalis, by Chrysalis Records. Catalogue no: **CHS 3109**
12" Single: Released Apr '87, on Chrysalis, by Chrysalis Records. Catalogue no: **CHS 123109**

I NEED YOU
Tracks: / I need you / Call me tonight.
7" Single: Released Oct '82, on Epic, by CBS Records. Deleted Oct '85. Catalogue no: **EPC A 2874**

LITTLE UNKIND
Tracks: / Little unkind.
7" Single: Released Feb '83, on Epic, by CBS Records. Catalogue no: **EPC A 3159**

ONE GOOD REASON
Tracks: / One good reason / When you walk in the room / Button off my shirt / Give me a chance / Double it up / Don't shed a tear / Fire with fire / Here I am / Collraine / Do I figure in your life?.
CD 5": Released 30 May '88, on Chrysalis, by Chrysalis Records. Catalogue no: **CHS CD 3204**

ONE GOOD REASON (SINGLE)
Tracks: / One good reason.
12" Single: Released 30 May '88, on Chrysalis, by Chrysalis Records. Catalogue no: **CHS 12 3204**
7" Single: Released 30 May '88, on Chrysalis, by Chrysalis Records. Catalogue no: **CHS 3204**

WHEN YOU WALK IN THE ROOM
CD 5": Released May '87, on Chrysalis, by Chrysalis Records. Catalogue no: **CDE 3**

Carrasco, Joe 'King'

BUENA
Tracks: / Buena / Tuff enuff.
7" Single: Released Sep '80, on Stiff, by Stiff Records. Deleted '83. Catalogue no: **BUY 88**

DON'T LET A WOMAN
Tracks: / Don't let a woman / That's the love.
7" Single: Released Nov '82, on MCA, by MCA Records. Deleted Nov '85. Catalogue no: **MCA 803**

Carreras, Jose

SOME ENCHANTED EVENING
Tracks: / This nearly was mine / Some enchanted evening.
7" Single: Released Nov '86, on CBS, by CBS Records. Catalogue no: **650271 7**

Carringtons

ROOTED TO THE SPOT
Tracks: / Rooted to the spot / Say it isn't so (part 1) / Rockin' chair blues.
10" single: Released Dec '87, on Island, by Island Records. Catalogue no: **10IS 347**
CD 5": Released Dec '87, on Island, by Island Records. Catalogue no: **CD ISX 347**
7" Single: Released Dec '87, on Dex Discs, Catalogue no: **DEX 001**

SWELL PARTY
Tracks: / Swell party / Swell party (version).
12" Single: Released Jan '89, on Dex Discs, Catalogue no: **DEX 002 RV**

Carroll, Deana

PEOPLE ALL AROUND THE WORLD
Tracks: / People all around the world.
7" Single: Released Aug '89, on Jive, by Zomba Records. Catalogue no: **JIVE 213**
12" Single: Released Aug '89, on Jive, by Zomba Records. Catalogue no: **JIVET 213**

Carroll, Jim

Biographical details: A poet, songwriter and singer born in 1950 in NYC, he published a book of poems at age 16; he was a self-confessed heroin addict who supported his habit by hustling and writing about it. He kicked the habit on the West Coast in the mid '70's, returned to NYC and collaborated with Patti Smith on poetry, following her into rock. *Catholic Boy* includeds *People who died*, a powerful catalogue of tragedies of personal friends. (Donald Clarke, April 1989)k.

PEOPLE WHO DIED
Tracks: / People who died / I want the angel.
7" Single: Released Jun '81, on CBS, by CBS Records. Deleted Jun '84. Catalogue no: **A 1034**

Carroll, Johnny

RATTLE MY BONES
Tracks: / Rattle my bones.
7" Single: Released Jul '83, on Seville, by President Records. Catalogue no: **SEV 1029**

Carroll, Ronnie

FOOTSTEPS
Tracks: / Footsteps.
7" Single: Released Mar '60, on Philips, by Phonogram Ltd. Deleted Mar '63. Catalogue no: **PB 1004**

IF ONLY TOMORROW
Tracks: / If only tomorrow.
7" Single: Released Nov '62, on Philips, by Phonogram Ltd. Deleted Nov '65. Catalogue no: **326550 BF**

RING A DING GIRL
Tracks: / Ring a ding girl.
7" Single: Released Feb '62, on Philips, by Phonogram Ltd. Deleted Feb '65. Catalogue no: **PB 1222**

ROSES ARE RED
Tracks: / Roses are red.
7" Single: Released Aug '62, on Philips, by Phonogram Ltd. Deleted Aug '65. Catalogue no: **326532 BF**

SAY WONDERFUL THINGS
Tracks: / Say wonderful things.
7" Single: Released Mar '63, on Philips, by Phonogram Ltd. Deleted Mar '66. Catalogue no: **326574 BF**

WALK HAND IN HAND
Tracks: / Walk hand in hand.
7" Single: Released Jul '56, on Philips, by Phonogram Ltd. Deleted Jul '60. Catalogue no: **PB 603**

WISDOM OF A FOOL, THE
Tracks: / Wisdom of a fool.
7" Single: Released Mar '57, on Philips, by Phonogram Ltd. Deleted Mar '60. Catalogue no: **PB 667**

Carrot Crunchers

ON THE PHONE
Tracks: / On the phone / Hey good lookin'.
7" Single: Released Jun '88, on Far End, Catalogue no: **FNS 1**

Carrott, Jasper

Biographical details: This British comedian first came to national prominence in 1975 with a one-off hit single. It was a double A sided hit and reached No. 5 on the UK chart, logging an impressive total of 15 weeks on the Top 50. The much-played *Funky Moped* was a comical pop song that avoided the blandness of some novelty hits; on the other side was the lewd *Magic Roundabout*, a non-broadcastable parody of the popular children's TV programme. Carrott then quickly achieved a Top 10 album with *Rabbits On And On*. Subsequent LPs have also sold well.
By the end of the Seventies he had cemented his position as one of the UK's top one-man comics, a status he maintained into the next decade. Carrott is a major success on British television, although some of the more bawdy parts of his act have to be curtailed, in order to suit that medium. (Bob MacDonald)..

FUNKY MOPED
Tracks: / Funky moped / Magic roundabout.
7" Single: Released Aug '75, on DJM, Deleted Aug '78. Catalogue no: **DJS 388**

TWELVE DAYS OF CHRISTMAS, THE
Tracks: / Twelve days of Christmas, The / Local radio promotion.
12" Single: Released '88, on DJM, Catalogue no: **DJR 18002**

Cars

Biographical details: This American pop/rock band consists of Elliot Easton, Greg Hawkes, Ric Ocasek, Ben Orr and David Robinsonl.
Hailing from the Boston area, the Cars were formed in 1976. They issued their debut eponymous album in '78 and it became a huge US seller. Produced by Britain's Roy Thomas Baker (who had become well-known through his work with Queen), it incorporated elements of American FM rock and British Sixties pop. *Just What I Needed* and *My Best Friend's Girl* became American Top 40 singles. In Britain the latter song hit the charts first and did this via an unprecedented marketing ploy. In a climate in which gimmicks and novelty discs (e.g. coloured vinyl, square singles etc.) were at the height of their popularity, Elektra Records issued *My Best Friend's Girl* as the first picture disc of the rock era. The record became an instant must for UK record collectors and crashed onto the singles chart at No. 10, an extraordinary feat for an act's debut hit. It peaked at No. 3 and remains the group's biggest British single. *Just What I Needed* then became a US Top 20 hit and the album was also a steady seller.
The Cars had caused such a stir so early on in their career, that the second album *Candy-O* seemed an anticlimax. Britain lost interest in the band and their records sold erratically in the States.. High spots were marked by the success of the 1979 single *Let's Go* (No. 14 in the US) and their first American Top Tenner, 1982's *Shake it Up* (No. 4). Shortly after the latter, their lead vocalist, songwriter and creative force Ric Ocasek issued a solo LP *Beatitude*.
Suddenly in 1984, they became bigger than ever before in the States. The album *Heartbeat City* enjoyed a mammoth run on the Top 5, boosted by the success of singles entitled *You Might Think, Magic* and *Drive*. The latter became their biggest US 45, peaking at No. 3; it also returned the group's name to the British chart, reaching No. 5. The main factor behind this sudden surge was the group's brilliantly executed move into the video field, which utilised to maximum effect the promotional possibilities of MTV, America's 24-hour rock video channel. The clip for *You Might Think* was widely acclaimed as the best video of 1984. (Bob MacDonald).
A USA New Wave goup which began with songwriter/guitarist Ric Otcasek, who later dropped the 't' from his name, and session musician Ben Orr. The catalyst was David Robinson, ex-Modern Lovers/Pop/DMZ drummer: they changed their name, made demos and evolved a red/white/black colour scheme for their act. They were successful as an opening act for Bob Seger, their demos were played on the radio, they signed to Elektra and their punchy power-pop was immediately successful. Ric has recorded solo, and also worked with singer/model Bebe Buell and the avant-garde duo, Suicide. (Donald Clarke, 1989).

DRIVE
Tracks: / Drive / Stranger eyes.
7" Single: Released Aug '84, on Elektra (USA), by Elektra Records (USA). Catalogue no: **E 9706**
12" Single: Released Aug '84, on Elektra (USA), by Elektra Records (USA). Deleted Jan '88. Catalogue no: **E 9706 T**

HEARTBEAT CITY (SINGLE)
Tracks: / Heartbeat city / Why can't I have you.
7" Single: Released Sep '85, on Elektra (USA), by Elektra Records (USA). Deleted '86. Catalogue no: **EKR 3**
12" Single: Released Sep '85, on Elektra (USA), by Elektra Records (USA). Catalogue no: **EKR 3T**

I'M NOT THE ONE
Tracks: / I'm not the one (remix) / Since you're gone / Shake it up (Extra track on 12" version only.).
12" Single: Released Apr '86, on Elektra (USA), by Elektra Records (USA). Catalogue no: **EKR 38 T**
7" Single: Released Apr '86, on Elektra (USA), by Elektra Records (USA). Catalogue no: **EKR 38**

IT'S ALL I CAN DO
Tracks: / It's all I can do / Candy-o.
7" Single: Released Nov '80, on Elektra, by Elektra Records (UK). Deleted Nov '83. Catalogue no: **K 12416**

JUST WHAT I NEEDED
Tracks: / Just what I needed.
7" Single: Released Feb '79, on Elektra, by Elektra Records (UK). Deleted Feb '62. Catalogue no: **K 12312**

LET'S GO
Tracks: / Let's go.
7" Single: Released Jul '79, on Elektra, by Elektra Records (UK). Deleted Jul '62. Catalogue no: **K 12371**

MY BEST FRIEND'S GIRL
Tracks: / My best friend's girl.
7" Single: Released Nov '78, on Elektra, by Elektra Records (UK). Deleted Nov '81. Catalogue no: **K 12301**

PANORAMA (SINGLE)
Tracks: / Panorama.
7" Single: Released Nov '81, on Elektra (USA), by Elektra Records (USA). Catalogue no: **K 12583**

SINCE YOU'RE GONE
Tracks: / Since you're gone / Maybe baby.
7" Single: Released May '82, on Elektra (USA), by Elektra Records (USA). Catalogue no: **K 13177**

THINK IT OVER
Tracks: / Think it over / I'm not the one.
7" Single: Released Aug '82, on Elektra (USA), by Elektra Records (USA). Catalogue no: **K 13187**

TONIGHT SHE COMES
Tracks: / Tonight she comes.
7" Single: Released Nov '85, on Elektra (USA), by Elektra Records (USA). Catalogue no: **EKR 30**
12" Single: Released Nov '85, on Elektra (USA), by Elektra Records (USA). Catalogue no: **EKR 30 T**

TOUCH AND GO
Tracks: / Touch and go / Down boys.
7" Single: Released Oct '80, on Elektra Asylum, by Elektra Records (USA). Deleted Oct '83. Catalogue no: **K 12477**

WHY CAN'T I HAVE YOU
Tracks: / Why can't I have you / Heatrbreak city.
7" Single: Released Apr '84, on Elektra (USA), by Elektra Records (USA). Catalogue no: **E 9741**

YOU ARE THE GIRL
Tracks: / You are the girl / Ta ta wayo wayo / Tonight she comes (On 12" version only.).
7" Single: Released Sep '87, on Elektra, by Elektra Records (UK). Deleted Jul '88. Catalogue no: **EKR 63**
12" Pic: Released Sep '87, on Elektra, by Elektra Records (UK). Deleted Jul '88. Catalogue no: **EKR 63 TP**
12" Single: Released Sep '87, on Elektra, by Elektra Records (UK). Deleted Jul '88. Catalogue no: **EKR 63 T**

Carson, Des

WALTZ ACROSS TEXAS
Tracks: / Waltz across Texas / Cup of conversation.
7" Single: Released Oct '80, on Homespun (Ireland), by Outlet Records. Deleted Oct '83. Catalogue no: **HS 039**

Carstairs

IT REALLY HURTS ME GIRL
Tracks: / It really hurts me girl.
7" Single: Released Jul '80, on Inferno (1), by Inferno Records. Catalogue no: **HEAT 7**
12" Single: Released Jul '80, on Inferno (1), by Inferno Records. Catalogue no: **HEAT 7-12**

Carter

SHELTERED LIFE
Tracks: / Sheltered life.
12" Single: Released Aug '88, on Big Cat, by Big Cat Records. Catalogue no: **BBA 03**

SHERIFF FAT MAN
Tracks: / Sheriff fat man.
12" Single: Released Oct '89, on Big Cat, by Big Cat Records. Catalogue no: **ABB 100T**

Carter Brothers

SOUTHERN COUNTRY BOY
Tracks: / Southern country boy.
7" Single: Released Jul '80, on Charly, by Charly Records. Deleted '88. Catalogue no: **CTD 120**

Carter, Carlene

Biographical details: Born in 1955 in Nashville, Carlene Carter has impeccable country music credentials: the daughter of Carl Smith and June Carter, her stepfather is Johnny Cash and she was taught to play guitar by her grandmother, Maybelle Carter, of the original Carter Family. But she resists typing as a country singer. Her third husband was Nick Lowe, who helped her with her first album in 1978, on which she was backed by Grahams Parker's *The rumour*. her version of Rodney Crowell's *Never together, but close sometimes* was a minor UK hit. *Two sides to every woman* in 1979 was followed by *Musical Shapes* in 1980, produced by Lowe and including a duet with Dave Edmunds on Richard Dobson's song *Baby ride easy*. *Blue nun* in 1981 included members of Squeeze; *Do it in a heartache* made the USA country chart. *C'est si bon* in 1983 included members of Rockpile. She starred in the cast of *Pump boys & dinettes* in 1984 and made a short film seen at the London Film Festival, *Too drunk to remember*, based on a song from Musical Shapes. She was to star in the London musical *Angry housewives* in 1986, but walked out during rehearsals. (Donald Clarke, April 1989)h.

BABY RIDE EASY
Tracks: / Baby ride easy / Too bad about Sandy.
7" Single: Released Sep '80, on F-Beat, by F-Beat Records. Deleted '83. Catalogue no: **XX 8**

DO IT IN A HEARTBEAT
Tracks: / Do it in a heartbeat / Swapmeat rag.
7" Single: Released Apr '80, on Warner Bros., by WEA Records. Deleted '83. Catalogue no: **K 17597**

DO ME LOVER
Tracks: / Do me lover / If the shoe fits.
7" Single: Released Sep '81, on F-Beat, by F-Beat Records. Deleted '84. Catalogue no: **XX 16**

OH HOW HAPPY
Tracks: / Oh how happy / Billy.
7" Single: Released Oct '81, on F-Beat, by F-Beat Records. Deleted '85. Catalogue no: **XX 18**

Carter, Clarence

Biographical details: The only Carter ever to make the British charts is this blind American soul singer, guitarist and pianist. Based in Alabama, he gained a degree in music from a college there and subsequently made frequent use of Alabama's Muscle Shoals studios. Carter first began scoring American R&B hits in 1967. The following year his records began crossing over to the pop charts. *Slip Away* reached No. 6 on teh US Hot 100 and was followed by the No. 13 placing of another soulful love song *Too Weak To Fight*.
In 1970 he released *Patches*, a story song co-written by General Johnson of the Chairmen of the Board. Sincere but slightly syrupy, this told the tale of a poor boy growing up in a poor family, having to combine school with bread-winning work following the early death of his father. The kid is nicknamed 'Patches' because he can only afford to dress in rags. Carter took the song to No. 4 in the States and it became his only British hit, reaching No. 2 on the UK charts. Carter was unable to follow this success on either side of the Atlantic and his name passed into musical history. (Bob MacDonald)..

I WAS IN THE NEIGHBOURHOOD
Tracks: / I was in the neighbourhood.
7" Single: Released May '86, on Tout Ensemble, Catalogue no: **LUTE 2**
12" Single: Released May '86, on Tout Ensemble, Catalogue no: **12LUTE 2**

I'M NOT JUST GOOD I'M THE BEST
Tracks: / I'm not just good I'm the best / Kiss you all over.
12" Single: Released Jan '89, on Ichiban, by Ichiban Records (UK). Catalogue no: **12 PO 16**

MESSIN' WITH MY MIND
Tracks: / Messin' with my mind.
7" Single: Released Oct '85, on Certain, by Certain Records. Catalogue no: **ACERT 1**

PATCHES
Tracks: / Patches / Knock on wood / Letter, The.
7" Single: Released Oct '70, on Atlantic, by WEA Records. Deleted Oct '73. Catalogue no: **2091 030**
7" Single: Released Aug '82, on Blast From The Past, by Creole Records. Catalogue no: **CR 178**

STROKIN'
Tracks: / Strokin' / Watch where you stroke.
7" Single: Released Apr '88, on Ichiban, by Ichiban Records (UK). Catalogue no: **7 STROKE 1**
12" Single: Released 5 Mar '88, on Ichiban, by Ichiban Records (UK). Catalogue no: **STROKE 1**

Carter, Diane

IF YOU TAKE THE TIME
Tracks: / If you take the time.
7" Single: Released Aug '83, on T.Y.C.O.S., by T.Y.C.O.S Records. Catalogue no: **AM 232**

LITTLE BOY LOST
Tracks: / Little boy lost.
7" Single: Released Dec '83, on Beebee, Deleted '86. Catalogue no: **BUZZ 1**

Carter, Eddie

AM I WRONG AGAIN
Tracks: / Am I wrong again / Banana republic.
7" Single: Released Aug '80, on Ariola-Hansa, by Hansa Records. Deleted '83. Catalogue no: **AHA 565**

Carter, Lisa

DOCTOR'S ORDERS
Tracks: / Doctor's orders / Good medicine (instrumental).
Note: Executive producer: Don Evetts. (P) 1988 Original Sound Recording made by EMI Records Ltd.
12" Single: Released Jul '88, on EMI, by EMI Records. Deleted Nov '88. Catalogue no: **12 NHS 1**
7" Single: Released Jul '88, on EMI, by EMI Records. Deleted Nov '88. Catalogue no: **NHS 1**

Carter, Lynda

LAST SONG
Tracks: / Last song / What's a little love between friends.
7" Single: Released Sep '80, on Motown, by BMG Records (UK). Deleted Sep '83. Catalogue no: **TMG 1207**

Carter, Mike

MY TRUE LOVE
Tracks: / My true love / Let the rain fall down.
7" Single: Released Jun '84, on Button, by Musical Characters Records. Catalogue no: **BTN 117**

Carter, Nina

FOLIES BERGERE
Tracks: / Folies bergere / Sound waves.
7" Single: Released Nov '81, on Moon, by Moon Records (UK). Catalogue no: **LUNA 1**

THESE BOOTS ARE MADE FOR WALKING
Tracks: / These boots are made for walking.
7" Single: Released Mar '83, on Moon, by Moon Records (UK). Catalogue no: **LUNA 4**

Cartoons

BEEP BEEP LOVE
Tracks: / Beep beep love / Thomas Cadillac.
7" Single: Released Oct '81, on Hot, Catalogue no: **HOT 002**

GEE GEORGE
Tracks: / Gee George.
7" Single: Released Aug '83, on Stiletto, by Fast Forward Distribution. Catalogue no: **STO 001**

ONCE THE VICTOR
Tracks: / Once the victor.
7" Single: Released Jun '84, on Another Fabulous Production, Catalogue no: **CAGE 002**

Carvells

L.A. RUN, THE
Tracks: / L.A. run, The.
7" Single: Released Nov '77, on Creole, by Creole Records. Deleted Nov '80. Catalogue no: **CR 143**

Casa

15 MINUTES
Tracks: / 15 Minutes.
12" Single: Released Mar '88, on Diamond Duel, by Diamond Duel Records. Catalogue no: **DISCT 2**

Casablanca

WITH LOVE
Tracks: / With love.
7" Single: Released Mar '83, on RCA, by BMG Records (UK). Catalogue no: **RCA 324**

Casal

BEWITCHED (Embrujada)
Tracks: / Bewitched.
7" Single: Released Jul '83, on EMI, by EMI Records. Catalogue no: **EMI 5407**

Casandra

I WANNA BE THAT WOMAN
Tracks: / I wanna be that woman.
7" Single: Released Jun '88, on Pioneer International, Catalogue no: **PI 80**

Casanova Fly

CASANOVA'S RAP
Tracks: / Casanova's rap.
12" Single: Released Nov '87, on Tuff City (USA), Catalogue no: **TUF 128022**

Casanova's Revenge

LET'S WORK
Tracks: / Let's work / Can't take it / Let's work (extended mix) (Only on 12" single.).
12" Single: Released Jul '89, on RCA, by BMG Records (UK). Catalogue no: **ZT 42888**
7" Single: Released Jul '89, on RCA, by BMG Records (UK). Catalogue no: **ZB 42287**

Cascade

LET IT BE ME (SINGLE)
Tracks: / Let it be me.
7" Single: Released Nov '88, on OK, by Klub Records. Catalogue no: **OK 013**

Cascade Orchestra

SPRING RAIN
Tracks: / Spring rain / I'm the one.
12" Single: Released Nov '83, on Passion, by Skratch Records. Deleted Nov '86. Catalogue no: **PASH 12(12)**

Cascades

Biographical details: From San Diego, California, the Cascades -- John Gummoe, Eddie Snyder, Dave Stevens, Dave Wilson and Dave Zabo -- shot to brief international fame in 1963 with the wistful *Rhythm Of The Rain*, written by Gummoe. Its gentle, melodic feel was matched by the group's clean-cut image and the single reached No 3 in the US, No 5 in the UK. But the Cascades -- although they played their own instruments they were primarily known for their soft, smooth vocal harmonies -- could not follow up this smash on either side of the Atlantic, though they continued performing and recording throughout the 60's. (Bob MacDonald, 1985.)
A vocal group from San Diego, one hit wonders whose hit will not soon be forgotten: Member John Gummoe wrote *Rhythm of the rain*, a USA number 3, UK number 5 in early '63, the last flourish of pop crooning before the onlaught of the Beatles. The bleak song played on the teen-age heartbreak syndrome and cries out for a sympathetic modern cover. (Donald Clarke, April 1989).

RHYTHM OF THE RAIN
Tracks: / Rhythm of the rain / Shy girl.
7" Single: Released Jul '82, on Old Gold, by Old Gold Records. Catalogue no: **OG 9057**
7" Single: Released Feb '63, on Warner Bros., by WEA Records. Deleted Feb '66. Catalogue no: **WB 88**

Case

OH
Tracks: / Oh.
7" Single: Released Aug '83, on Suspect, Catalogue no: **SUS 1**

Case, Connie

SOONER OR LATER
Tracks: / Sooner or later / Sooner or later (part 2).
12" Single: Released Dec '82, on Vista Sounds, by Vista Sounds Records. Catalogue no: **VS 12002**

Case, Harry

NIAGARA
Tracks: / Niagara (a jealous man's dream) / Easy vamp / Magic cat.
12" Single: Released May '88, on Ichiban, by Ichiban Records (UK). Catalogue no: **12PO 9**

Case, Peter

STEEL STRINGS
Tracks: / Steel strings / Small town spree.
7" Single: Released Oct '86, on Geffen, by Geffen Records (USA). Deleted Jun '87. Catalogue no: **GEF 14**
12" Single: Released Oct '86, on Geffen, by Geffen Records (USA). Deleted Jun '87. Catalogue no: **GEF 14T**

Casey, Natalie

Biographical details: This British vocalist was just three years old when she entered the UK chart in the first week of 1984. Coinciding with the pantomime season, she reached No. 72 with her rendition of the chilren's standard *Chick Chick Chicken*. (Bob MacDonald)..

CHICK CHICK CHICKEN
Tracks: / Chick chick chicken / Natalie's disco nursery.
7" Single: Released Jan '84, on Polydor, by Polydor Ltd. Deleted Jan '87. Catalogue no: **CHICK 1**

Cash, Andrew

SMILE ME DOWN
Tracks: / Smile me down / Places / Smile me down (LP version) *.
Note: * Avaliable on 12" format only.
7" Single: Released '88, on Island, by Island Records. Deleted Apr '89. Catalogue no: **IS 342**
12" Single: Released '88, on Island, by Island Records. Deleted Apr '89. Catalogue no: **12IS 342**

Cash Crew

YOU CAN'T STOP THIS
Tracks: / You can't stop this.
12" Single: Released Jun '89, on Vinyl Solution, by Vinyl Solution Records. Catalogue no: **STORM 7**

Cash, Johnny

Biographical details: This American singer, guitarist and songwriter was born in Kingsland, Arkansas in 1932. After a spell in the US Air Force, he had a short-lived job as an electrical salesman, before joining Sun Records in Memphis in 1955. That label, owned by Sam Phillips, signed Elvis Presley at around the same time as Cash. The first record by Cash called *Cry, Cry, Cry* made the Top 10 of the US country charts. In '56 he crossed over to the pop chart, reaching No. 17 with *I Walk The Line*. Further Top 30 pop hits followed in 1958 with *Ballad Of A Teenage Queen, Guess Things Happen That Way* and *The Ways Of A Woman In Love*. All featured his distinctive, deep, doomy voice. In late '58 he switched to Columbia records a move that suggested further success. In the event however, Cash's career went into decline for several years; this slack period, which lasted throughout the early mid-Sixties, was interrupted only by 1963's *Ring Of Fire*. This song was co-written by country singer June Carter, a member of the famous Carter country music family, his future wife.
One of the main reasons for Cash's long-lasting mediocre era was his serious drug addiction, a condition that he eventually overcame with June's help. A revitalised Johnny Cash bounced back bigger than ever in 1968, when he took the unprecedented step of recording a live concert at California's Folsom Prison. The resulting album was a monster success, remaining on the US album charts for over two years. It was also the artist's first major chart record in the UK, reaching No. 8 and staying on the survey for exactly a year. Indeed, so successful was the idea that Cash did exactly the same thing in 1969. *Johnny Cash At San Quentin* was another smash LP on both sides of the Atlantic. In Britain in reached No. 2 and logged no less than 114 weeks on the listings. The album yielded the comedy single *A Boy Named Sue*, penned by Shel Silverstein. it reached No. 2 in the States, Cash's only American Top 10 pop hit and No. 4 in Britain, his first Top 20 single in the latter country. No longer was he just a country star - he was given his own US networked TV show and became an international showbusiness phenomenon.
In 1972 he achieved a second British Top 10 single with *A Thing Called Love*, a gospel-inflected record on which he was backed by the Evangel Temple Choir. Since then he has concerntrated less on recording, with only 1976's amusing *One Piece At A Time* returning him to the pop charts. he developed a substantial acting career, appearing both in movies and on television. by the early Eighties two interesting family developments had taken place; his stepdaughter Carlene Carter married Nick Lowe, thereby establishing an intriguing link between an American country music legend and a British rock star; and his daughter Rosanne Cash became a leading figure on the US country charts. (Bob MacDonald).
Born in 1932 in Arkansas, Cash began recording for Sun in 1955 with the Tennessee Two: his sepulchral voice, Luther Perkin's electric guitar and Marshall Grant's slap-bass style stayed in the country, but was also a unique sound in the heyday on Sun's rockabilly. *I walk the line* crossed over to the SUA pop chart in 1956; he joined the Grand Old Opry in 1957; his versions of *Guess things happen that way* and Jack Clement's *Ballad of a teenage queen* were country number ones in 1958; drummer W.S. Holland was added that year and stayed with Cash for 25 years. He switched to CBS in 1958 and in the early '60's was working 300 gigs a year; his honesty about problems with pills and minor brushes with the law, as well as his story songs, were ultimately a contribution to 'outlaw country' in the '60's and '70's and have helped to keep him a giant in his field.

He has championed other songwriters such as kris Kristopherson, and dueted with Bob Dylan; marriage to his second wife June Carter helped to stabilise him and kick the pill habit. They hosted a hit TV show; her daughter Carlene Carter (with Carl Smith) and his daughter Roseanne Cash (from his first marriage) became recording artists. He was one of the first to make hit live albums in prison while entertaining convicts; he guested on Emmylou Harris Lps; with Jerry Lee Lewis and Carl Perkings he made *Survivors* in 1981, their first time together in more than 20 years; with Roy Orbison they recreated the 'million-dollar quartet' on *Class of '55* in 1985 (originally with Elvis Presley), including guest spots from Dave Edmunds, John Fogerty, the Judds and Rick Waylon Jennings (his last session); *The Highwaymen* in 1985, with Waylon Jennings, Willie Nelson and Kristofferson had a number one country single in the title track. He has had 58 top 40 country hits in 25 years and 11 pop in the USA; he switched to Mercury in 1988 after CBS foolishly dropped him: he'll be around for a while yet. (Donald Clarke, April 1989)n.

6 TRACK HITS
Tracks: / Boy named Sue, A / I walk the line / Ring of fire / If I were a carpenter / Folsom Prison blues / What is truth?.
7" EP: Released Sep '83, on Scoop 33, by Pickwick Records. Catalogue no: **7SR 5015**

BARON (SINGLE)
Tracks: / Baron / I will dance with you.
7" Single: Released May '81, on CBS, by CBS Records. Deleted May '84. Catalogue no: **A 1155**

BIG LIGHT, THE
Tracks: / Big light, The / Sixteen tons.
7" Single: Released May '88, on Mercury, by Phonogram Ltd. Deleted Oct '88. Catalogue no: **MER 263**

BOY NAMED SUE (SINGLE)
Tracks: / Boy named Sue, A.
7" Single: Released Sep '69, on CBS, by CBS Records. Deleted Sep '72. Catalogue no: **CBS 4460**
7" Single: Released Apr '82, on CBS, by CBS Records. Catalogue no: **CBS 1152**
7" Single: Released Jul '82, on Old Gold, by Old Gold Records. Catalogue no: **OG 9180**

GET RHYTHM
Tracks: / Get rhythm.
7" Single: on Mercury, by Phonogram Ltd. Deleted 31 Jul '89. Catalogue no: **MER 286**

IT AIN'T ME, BABE
Tracks: / It ain't me babe.
7" Single: Released Jun '65, on CBS, by CBS Records. Deleted Jun '68. Catalogue no: **CBS 201760**

LIL' BIT OF GOLD: JOHNNY CASH
Tracks: / I walk the line / Folsom Prison blues / Guess things happen that way / Ballad of a teen.
CD 5": Released May '88, on Rhino, by Creole Records. Catalogue no: **R 373002**

NIGHT HANK WILLIAMS CAME TO TOWN, THE
Tracks: / Night Hank Williams came to town, The.
7" Single: Released Aug '87, on Mercury, by Phonogram Ltd. Catalogue no: **MER 225**

ONE PIECE AT A TIME (SINGLE)
Tracks: / One piece at a time.
7" Single: Released Jul '76, on CBS, by CBS Records. Deleted Jul '79. Catalogue no: **CBS 4287**

THING CALLED LOVE, A (OLD GOLD)
Tracks: / Thing called love, A.
7" Single: Released Jul '82, on Old Gold, by Old Gold Records. Deleted Aug '87. Catalogue no: **OG 9177**

THING CALLED LOVE, A (SINGLE)
Tracks: / Thing called love, A.
7" Single: Released Jul '72, on CBS, by CBS Records. Deleted Jul '75. Catalogue no: **CBS 7797**

WHAT IS TRUTH?
Tracks: / What is truth?.
7" Single: Released May '70, on CBS, by CBS Records. Deleted May '73. Catalogue no: **CBS 4934**

Cash Money

FIND AN UGLY WOMAN
Tracks: / Find an ugly woman.
12" Single: Released Dec '88, on Sleeping Bag, by Sleeping Bag Records. Catalogue no: **SLX 40143**

MIGHTY HARD ROCKER, THE
Tracks: / Mighty hard rocker, The

7" Single: Released 9 Jan '89, on Sleeping Bag, by Sleeping Bag Records. Catalogue no: **SBUK 5**
12" Single: Released Nov '88, on Sleeping Bag, by Sleeping Bag Records. Catalogue no: **SBUK 5T**

Cash, Rosanne

Biographical details: Born in 1955 in Memphis, Tennessee, this successful pop/country singer is one of four daughters from Johnny Cash's first marriage. She worked for CBS records in London, studied drams and signed to Arista Records in Germany in 1977, then switched to American CBS. Her album *Right or wrong* in 1979 included a hit duet with Bobby Bare on *No memories hangin' round*. She married singer/songwriter Rodney Crowell that year; he produced her second album *Seven year ache* in 1981, including two number one country singles: *My baby thinks she's a train* had harmony with Rosemary Butler and Emmylou Harris, and the album's title track went pop top 30. *Somewhere in the stars* in 1982 was followed by the biographical concept album *Rhythm and romance* in 1985, *King's record shop* in 1987 was named after a shop in Louisville, Kentucky pictured on the sleeve. (Donald Clarke, April 1989).

AIN'T NO MONEY
Tracks: / Ain't no money / Feeling.
7" Single: Released Sep '82, on Ariola, by BMG Records (UK). Deleted Sep '85. Catalogue no: **ARO 286**

I DON'T KNOW WHY
Tracks: / I don't know why / You don't want me / What you gonna do about it.
7" Single: Released Feb '86, on CBS, by CBS Records. Catalogue no: **A 6808**

SEVEN YEAR ACHE
Tracks: / Seven year ache / Raining.
7" Single: Released Jul '81, on Ariola, by BMG Records (UK). Deleted '85. Catalogue no: **ARO 263**

Cashears

EXCERPT FOR LOVE I'M VERY POOR
Tracks: / Excerpt for love I'm very poor / Excerpt for love I'm very poor (pt 2).
7" Single: Released Mar '81, on PRT, by Castle Communications Records. Deleted Mar '84. Catalogue no: **7P 212**

Cashflow

CAN'T LET LOVE PASS US BY
Tracks: / Can't let love pass us by / Can't let love pass us by (remix) (Available on 12" remix only.) / Can't let love pass us by (remix)(dub version) (Available on 12" remix only.) / I need your love / Spending money (Extra track available on 12" versions only.).
7" Single: Released Jul '86, on Club, by Phonogram Ltd. Deleted '87. Catalogue no: **JAB 33**
12" Single: Released Jul '86, on Club, by Phonogram Ltd. Catalogue no: **JABXR 33**
12" Single: Released Jul '86, on Club, by Phonogram Ltd. Deleted '87. Catalogue no: **JABX 33**

MINE ALL MINE
Tracks: / Mine all mine / Party freak / It's just a dream (Extra track on 12" version only.).
7" Single: Released May '86, on Club, by Phonogram Ltd. Deleted '87. Catalogue no: **JAB 30**
12" Single: Released May '86, on Club, by Phonogram Ltd. Deleted '87. Catalogue no: **JABX 30**
12" Single: Released May '86, on Club, by Phonogram Ltd. Deleted '87. Catalogue no: **JABXR 30**

MINE ALL MINE (OLD GOLD 12")
Tracks: / Mine all mine / Party freak.
12" Single: Released Nov '88, on Old Gold, by Old Gold Records. Catalogue no: **OG 4086**

Cashmere

CAN I (see panel on right)
Tracks: / Can I / Can I (full length).
7" Single: Released Jan '85, on 4th & Broadway, by Island Records. Catalogue no: **BRW 19**
12" Single: Released Jan '85, on 4th & Broadway, by Island Records. Deleted Jul '87. Catalogue no: **12 BRW 19**

DO IT ANY WAY YOU WANNA
Tracks: / Do it anyway you wanna.
7" Single: Released Mar '83, on Philly World (USA), by Philly World (USA). Catalogue no: **PWS 108**
12" Single: Released Mar '83, on Philly World (USA), by Philly World (USA). Catalogue no: **PWSL 108**

LET THE MUSIC TURN YOU ON
Tracks: / Let the music turn you on.
7" Single: Released Oct '83, on Philly World (USA), by Philly World (USA). Catalogue no: **PWS 114**
12" Single: Released Oct '83, on Philly World (USA), by Philly World (USA). Catalogue no: **PWSL 114**

TRY YOUR LOVIN'
Tracks: / Try your lovin'.
7" Single: Released Aug '83, on Philly World (USA), by Philly World (USA). Catalogue no: **PWS 113**
12" Single: Released Aug '83, on Philly World (USA), by Philly World (USA). Catalogue no: **PWSL 113**

WE NEED LOVE
Tracks: / We need love / Keep me up.
7" Single: Released Mar '85, on 4th & Broadway, by Island Records. Catalogue no: **BRW 22**
12" Single: Released Mar '85, on 4th & Broadway, by Island Records. Deleted '87. Catalogue no: **12 BRW 22**

Casinos

Biographical details: This quickly forgotten American vocal group scored a one-off hit single in 1967. *Then You Can Tell Me Goodbye* reached No. 6 in the US, No. 28 in the UK. All the Casinos were male. Glen Campbell returned the song to the American Top 30 in 1976 as half of a medley single. (Bob MacDonald)..

THEN YOU CAN TELL ME GOODBYE
Tracks: / Then you can tell me goodbye.
7" Single: Released Feb '67, on President, by President Records. Deleted Feb '70. Catalogue no: **PT 123**
7" Single: Released Jul '82, on Old Gold, by Old Gold Records. Catalogue no: **OG 9012**

Cassady, Linda

DUSTY RAVEN
Tracks: / Dusty raven.
7" Single: Released Nov '81, on Amigo, Catalogue no: **AMGO 001**

Cassandra

LOVE ME SWEETER TONIGHT
Tracks: / Love me sweeter tonight.
7" Single: Released Jun '82, on Red Nail, Catalogue no: **RN 0036**

Cassandra Complex

30 MINUTES OF DEATH
Tracks: / 30 minutes of death.
CD 5": Released '88, on Play It Again Sam(Belgium), by Play It Again Sam (Belgium). Catalogue no: **BIAS 112CD**
12" Single: Released '88, on Play It Again Sam(Belgium), by Play It Again Sam (Belgium). Catalogue no: **BIAS 112**

DATA KILL
Tracks: / Datakill.
12" Single: Released Jul '86, on Rouska, by Rouska Records. Catalogue no: **COME 5T**

KILL THE CHILDREN
12" Single: Released '88, on Play It Again Sam(Belgium), by Play It Again Sam (Belgium). Catalogue no: **BIAS 064T**

KILL YOUR CHILDREN
Tracks: / Kill your children.
7" Single: Released Oct '87, on Play It Again Sam(Belgium), by Play It Again Sam (Belgium). Catalogue no: **BIAS 064**
12" Single: Released Oct '87, on Play It Again Sam(Belgium), by Play It Again Sam (Belgium). Catalogue no: **BIAS 064T**

MARCH
Tracks: / March.
7" Single: Released Apr '85, on Complex (R.A.P.), Catalogue no: **CXD 001**

MOSCOW IDAHO
Tracks: / Moscow Idaho.
12" Single: Released Sep '85, on Rouska, by Rouska Records. Catalogue no: **COME 2T**

Cassel, Justin

WHO IS THE MAN
Tracks: / Who is the man / Who is the man (version).
12" Single: Released Feb '86, on Hero, Catalogue no: **HERO 026**

OLD TIME PARTY
Tracks: / Old time party.
12" Single: Released Aug '88, on UNKNOWN, Catalogue no: **MC 0002**

Cassidy, David

Biographical details: Born in New York in 1950, David Cassidy went into showbusiness at the age of 16, with the aim of becoming a successful actor. He took a part in a Broadway production a couple of years later but, when this flopped, he went to Hollywood and obtained some television work. This led him to auditioning for a singing and acting role in "The Partridge Family" TV series. he landed the role of Keith in this new American comedy programme, which was an account of the ups and downs of a widow and her five children. He found himself playing alongside his real-life stepmother Shirley Jones. The show attracted top ratings and the recording career of this imaginary family was launched in the States. *I Think I Love You* was the first single; it was a catchy pop song and went to the US No. 1 position. Cassidy was lead vocalist and proved himself to be a competent if unspectacular singer; acting was definately his forte. Further hits followed, but each peaked at a lower US chart position than the one before.
Witnessing the steady decline, Bell Records marketed Cassidy as a solo singer. his first record *Cherish* hit No. 9, but subsequent records failed to reach America's Top 20. As his career as a teen idol was on its way downwards in his native USA, the TV programme was gaining popularity in Britain. Consequently Cassidy and the family underwent the whole process again in a new country. The Partridges hit No. 3 with Neil Sedaka's *Breaking Up Is hard To Do*, four places higher on the UK chart than the 1962 original. Cassidy chalked up two british chart-toppers: *How Can I Be Sure* (1972) and the double A sided smash *Daydreamer/The Puppy Song* (1973). Like his teenybop rivals, the Osmonds, he was no longer the teenage girls' hero in the States but now attracted huge hysteria at concerts in Britain. He achieved a UK No. 1 LP in 1973 with *Dreams Are Nothin' More Than Wishes*. Frustrated by his exclusively teen following, he began an image change in late '74 and attempted to be treated more seriously as an artist. But apart from a couple more UK Top 20 hits, this policy failed. his musical career ended and Cassidy resumed an acting career, thus returning to his principal talent. (Bob MacDonald).
The son of actors Jack Cassidy and Evelyn Ward was born in 1950 in New York and followed them into TV acting. Screen Gems/Columbia, the power behind the Monkees, hired his stepmother Shirley Jones to play the adult lead in a music-orientated kids' show; he became the star of the Partridge Family, then a solo bubblegum idol; he had

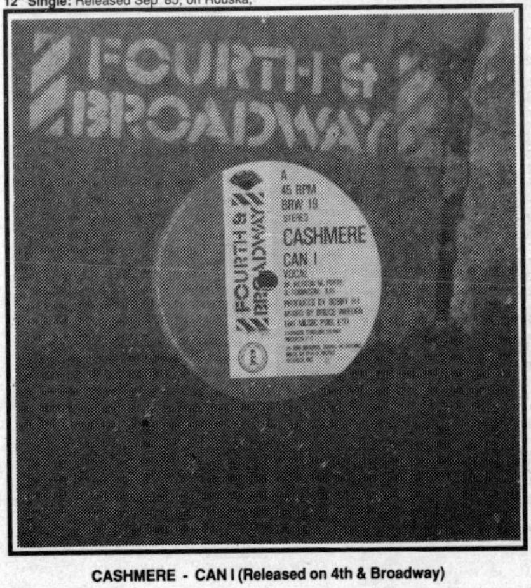

CASHMERE - CAN I (Released on 4th & Broadway)

hits in the early 70's but disappeared almost as quickly as he came. Sporadic comeback attempts have not had lasting success, although *The last kiss* made the UK Top Ten in 1985. At one point he planned a collaboration with George Michael, perhaps his 1980's counterpart. (Donald Clarke, April 1989).

COULD IT BE FOREVER
Tracks: / Could it be forever.
7" Single: Released Apr '72, on Bell, Deleted Apr '75. Catalogue no: **BELL 1224**

DARLIN'
Tracks: / Darlin'.
7" Single: Released Oct '75, on RCA, by BMG Records (UK). Deleted Oct '78. Catalogue no: **RCA 2622**

DAYDREAMER
Tracks: / Daydreamer / Puppy song, The.
7" Single: Released Oct '73, on Bell, Deleted Oct '76. Catalogue no: **BELL 1334**

EP, THE
7" Single: Released Nov '86, on Starblend, by Starblend Records. Catalogue no: **DCEP 1**
12" Single: Released Nov '86, on Starblend, by Starblend Records. Catalogue no: **12DCEP 1**

HOW CAN I BE SURE
Tracks: / How can I be sure.
7" Single: Released Sep '72, on Bell, Deleted Sep '75. Catalogue no: **BELL 1258**

HOW CAN I BE SURE (OLD GOLD)
Tracks: / How can I be sure / Could it be forever.
7" Single: Released Nov '88, on Old Gold, by Old Gold Records. Catalogue no: **OG 9834**

I WRITE THE SONGS
Tracks: / I write the songs / Get it up for love.
7" Single: Released Jul '75, on RCA, by BMG Records (UK). Deleted Jul '78. Catalogue no: **RCA 2571**

IF I DIDN'T CARE
Tracks: / If I didn't care.
7" Single: Released May '74, on Bell, Deleted May '77. Catalogue no: **BELL 1350**

I'M A CLOWN
Tracks: / I'm a clown / Some kind of summer.
7" Single: Released Mar '73, on Bell, Deleted Mar '76. Catalogue no: **MABEL 4**

LAST KISS, THE
Tracks: / Last kiss, The / Better.
7" Pic: Released Feb '85, on Arista, by BMG Records (UK). Catalogue no: **ARISD 589**
7" Single: Released Feb '85, on Arista, by BMG Records (UK). Catalogue no: **ARIST 589**
12" Single: Released Feb '85, on Arista, by BMG Records (UK). Catalogue no: **ARIST 12589**

PLEASE, PLEASE ME
Tracks: / Please, please me.
7" Single: Released Jul '74, on Bell, Deleted Jul '77. Catalogue no: **BELL 1371**

ROCK ME BABY (SINGLE)
Tracks: / Rock me baby.
7" Single: Released Nov '72, on Bell, Deleted Nov '75. Catalogue no: **BELL 1268**

ROMANCE (LET YOUR HEART GO) (SINGLE)
Tracks: / Romance (let your heart go).
7" Single: Released Apr '85, on Arista, by BMG Records (UK). Catalogue no: **ARIST 620**
12" Single: Released Apr '85, on Arista, by BMG Records (UK). Catalogue no: **ARIST 12620**

SOMEONE
Tracks: / Someone.
7" Single: Released Aug '85, on Arista, by BMG Records (UK). Catalogue no: **ARIST 626**
12" Single: Released Aug '85, on Arista, by BMG Records (UK). Catalogue no: **ARIST 12626**

Cassidy, Linda

CB WIDOW
Tracks: / CB widow / Do you still want what's left of me.
7" Single: Released Nov '81, on Amigo, Catalogue no: **AMGO 006**

Cassie

CHANGE MY IMAGE
Tracks: / Change my image.
7" Single: Released Sep '82, on AKA, Catalogue no: **AKS 101**

CATCH - 25 YEARS (Released on Stiff)

Cassiopea

SOUNDOGRAPHY, THE (SINGLE)
Tracks: / Soundography, The / Looking up.
7" Single: Released Jun '84, on Sonet, by Sonet Records. Catalogue no: **SON 2269**

Cassle

CASSLE
Special: Released Dec '83, on Azra (USA), by Azra International (USA). Catalogue no: **A 67**

Cast Of Bread

HOME
Tracks: / Home (Theme from Bread) / Red bricks.
7" Single: Released May '86, on BBC, by BBC Records & Tapes. Catalogue no: **RESL 186**

Cast Of The Bike Shed

BEHIND THE BIKE SHED
Tracks: / Behind the bike shed.
7" Single: Released Feb '85, on MCA, by MCA Records. Catalogue no: **MCA 944**

Cast of Thousands

NOTHING IS FOREVER
Tracks: / Nothing is forever (7" mix) / New tomorrow.
12" Single: Released Aug '87, on Fun After All, by Music For Nations Records. Catalogue no: **12 FAA 108**

Castanarc

THIS ISLAND LOVE
Tracks: / This island love / Heroes.
7" Single: Released Aug '89, on Pyramid, by Pyramid Records. Catalogue no: **PYR 9**
12" Single: Released Aug '89, on Pyramid, by Pyramid Records. Catalogue no: **12PYR 9**

Castaways

DREAM MAKER
Tracks: / Dream maker / Dream maker (part 2).
7" Single: Released Sep '82, on Virgin, by Virgin Records. Deleted '89. Catalogue no: **VS 540**

Castell, Lacksley

JOHNNY BROWN
Tracks: / Johnny Brown / Mrs Brown.
12" Single: Released Aug '83, on Negus Roots, Catalogue no: **NERT 019**

SPEAK SOFTLY
Tracks: / Speak softly / Take this message.
12" Single: Released Sep '82, on Negus Roots, Catalogue no: **NERT 013**

TUG-O-WAR GAMES
Tracks: / Tug-o-war games / Rise in the morning.
12" Single: Released Nov '83, on CSA, by CSA Records. Deleted '88. Catalogue no: **SPCSA 12006**

Castle, David

TEN TO EIGHT
Tracks: / Ten to eight / Finally.
7" Single: Released Feb '80, on Parachute (USA), Deleted '83. Catalogue no: **RRS 501**

Castle, Roy

Biographical details: This British television and showbusiness personality scored his only UK chart hit at Christmas 1960. *Little White Berry* reached No. 40 on the singles list. Castle's bright personality kept him in the public eye right into the Eighties, notably with his "Record Breakers" TV show.(Bob MacDonald)..

LITTLE WHITE BERRY
Tracks: / Little white berry.
7" Single: Released Dec '60, on Philips, by Phonogram Ltd. Deleted Dec '63. Catalogue no: **PB 1087**

Castleman, Boomer

HOT DAY IN THE SOUTH
Tracks: / Hot day in the south / Let's get the feeling again.
7" Single: Released Feb '80, on Monarch, by Monarch Records. Deleted Feb '83. Catalogue no: **MON 09**

Casualeers

DANCE DANCE DANCE
Tracks: / Dance dance dance.
7" Single: Released '74, on Disco Demand, Deleted '79. Catalogue no: **DDS 103**

Casuals

JESAMINE
Tracks: / Jesamine.
7" Single: Released Aug '68, on Decca, by Decca Records. Deleted Aug '71. Catalogue no: **F 22784**
7" Single: Released Oct '83, on Old Gold, by Old Gold Records. Catalogue no: **OG 9347**

TOY
Tracks: / Toy.
7" Single: Released Dec '68, on Decca, by Decca Records. Deleted Dec '71. Catalogue no: **F 22852**

Caswell, Johnny

IN THIS LAND
Tracks: / In this land
7" Single: Released Oct '81, on MCA, by MCA Records. Deleted Oct '84. Catalogue no: **MCA 733**

YOU DON'T LOVE ME ANYMORE
Tracks: / You don't love me anymore.
7" Single: Released Apr '85, on Kent, by Ace Records. Catalogue no: **TOWN 106**

Cat Club

ONE LAST KISS
Tracks: / Wild / One last kiss.
7" Single: Released Aug '87, on Jive, by Zomba Records. Catalogue no: **JIVE 155**

Catapult

SINK ME
Tracks: / Sink me.
12" Single: Released Apr '88, on September, Catalogue no: **SEPT 6T**
12" Single: Released Jan '88, on S.T.S., Catalogue no: **STS 12**

SUMMARY
Tracks: / Summary.
7" Single: Released Aug '87, on SST (USA), by SST Records (USA). Catalogue no: **SST 45**

Catch

25 YEARS (see panel on left)
Tracks: / 25 years / The end of the day.
7" Single: Released Apr '84, on Carrere, Catalogue no: **CAR 313**
7" Single: Released Jul '84, on Stiff, by Stiff Records. Catalogue no: **BUY 209**
12" Single: Released Aug '84, on Stiff, by Stiff Records. Catalogue no: **BUYIT 209**
12" Single: Released Apr '84, on Carrere, Catalogue no: **CART 313**

FIND THE LOVE
Tracks: / Find the love.
7" Single: Released Apr '85, on Stiff, by Stiff Records. Catalogue no: **BUY 222**
12" Single: Released Apr '85, on Stiff, by Stiff Records. Catalogue no: **BUYIT 222**

TIME TO MYSELF
Tracks: / Time to myself / I'm interested in you.
7" Single: Released May '81, on EMI, by EMI Records. Deleted May '84. Catalogue no: **EMI 5183**

Catch 22

FREEWAY TO PARADISE
Tracks: / Freeway to paradise / Truth conquers all.
Note: Self - 01 534 8500.
7" Single: Released Sep '86, on Plankton, by Plankton Records. Catalogue no: **PLANK 003**

GET CLOSE TO ME
Tracks: / Get close to me.
7" Single: Released Feb '85, on Rimshot, Catalogue no: **RSS 001**

MARATHON MAN
Tracks: / Marathon man.
7" Single: Released May '82, on Applause, by Riva Records. Catalogue no: **CLAP 6**

Catch, C.C.

SOUL SURVIVOR
Tracks: / Soul survivor / Midnight gambler.
7" Single: Released Aug '88, on RCA, by BMG Records (UK). Deleted May '89. Catalogue no: **PB 42173**
12" Single: Released Aug '88, on RCA, by BMG Records (UK). Deleted Aug '89. Catalogue no: **PT 42174**

Catcher

LONGEST DAY, THE
Tracks: / Longest day, The / State of the world.
7" Single: Released Jan '88, on Survival (1), by Survival Records. Catalogue no: **SUR 040**

Cateran

BLACK ALBUM, THE
Tracks: / Black album, The.
7" Single: Released Dec '88, on Imaginary, by Imaginary Records. Catalogue no: **MIRAGE 666**

LAST BIG LIE
Tracks: / Difficult days / Last big lie.
7" Single: Released Jan '87, on DDT, by D.D.T.Records. Catalogue no: **DISP 6**

Caterwaul

SHEEPS A WOLF BEHOLDEN
Tracks: / Sheep's a wolf beholden.
7" Single: Released Jun '89, on I.R.S, Catalogue no: **EIRS 111**
12" Single: Released Jun '89, on I.R.S, Catalogue no: **EIRST 111**

Cathleen

BABY ME
Tracks: / Baby me.
12" Single: Released Mar '86, on Another Side (Belgium), by Another Side Records (Belgium). Catalogue no: **SIDE 8506**

Cathy's Choir

MERRY CHRISTMAS
Tracks: / Merry Christmas
7" Single: Released Nov '80, on AMI, by AMI Records. Deleted '83. Catalogue no: **AIS 110**

Cats Can Fly

FLIPPIN' TO THE A SIDE
Tracks: / Flippin' to the A side
7" Single: Released Sep '86, on Epic, by CBS Records. Catalogue no: **650111 7**
12" Single: Released Sep '86, on Epic, by CBS Records. Catalogue no: **650111 6**

Cats UK

HOLIDAY CAMP

Tracks: / Holiday camp / Charlie's angel.
7" Single: Released Aug '80, on Magnet, by WEA Records. Deleted '83. Catalogue no: **MAG 177**

LOOKING FOR LOVE
Tracks: / Looking for love / Why did we wait so long.
7" Single: Released Jan '80, on WEA, by WEA Records. Deleted Jan '85. Catalogue no: **K 18142**

LUTON AIRPORT
Tracks: / Luton airport.
7" Single: Released Oct '79, on WEA, by WEA Records. Deleted Oct '82. Catalogue no: **K 18075**

Catsfield Steamers

HOME BOYS HOME
Tracks: / Home boys home.
7" Single: Released Jul '82, on Dandelion, Catalogue no: **D 001**

Catwax Axe Co

25 GALLONS OF PARANOIA
Tracks: / 25 gallons of paranoia.
12" Single: Released Aug '84, on Fever, by Fever Records. Catalogue no: **FEV 2**

WAX WALK
Tracks: / Wax walk / Jumbo jet.
7" Single: Released Oct '81, on Doila, Catalogue no: **CAT 001**
7" Single: Released Mar '82, on Rondelet Music, by Rondelet Music & Records. Catalogue no: **ROUND 17**

Caught In The Act

WALK ON WATER/BLIND LOVE
Tracks: / Walk on water / Blind love.
7" Single: Released Feb '86, on Works, by Works Records. Catalogue no: **TWR 107**

Caution

SHOULD I PUT MY TRUST IN YOU
12" Single: Released Dec '84, on Level Vibes, by Level Vibes Records. Catalogue no: **LV 005**

Cavaliere, Felix

ONLY A LONELY HEART SEES
Tracks: / Only a lonely heart sees / You turned me around.
7" Single: Released Apr '80, on Epic, by CBS Records. Deleted Apr '83. Catalogue no: **EPC 8312**

Cavaliers

IT'S A BEAUTIFUL GAME
Tracks: / It's a beautiful game / I.T. man.
7" Single: Released Jul '86, on El, by Cherry Red Records. Catalogue no: **GPO 11**

Cavander, Geoff

GIRLS
Tracks: / Girls / Goin' home.
7" Single: Released May '80, on Logo, by Logo Records. Deleted '83. Catalogue no: **GO 380**

Cave, Nick

IN THE GHETTO
Tracks: / In the ghetto.
7" Single: Released Jun '84, on Mute, by Mute Records. Catalogue no: **MUTE 32**

MERCY SEAT, THE (SINGLE)
12" Single: Released Jun '88, on Mute, by Mute Records. Catalogue no: **12 MUTE 052**
7" Single: Released Jun '88, on Mute, by Mute Records. Catalogue no: **MUTE 52**

OH DEANNA
Tracks: / Oh Deanna / Girl at the bottom of my glass, The.
12" Single: Released Sep '88, on Mute, by Mute Records. Catalogue no: **12 MUTE 86**
7" Single: Released Sep '88, on Mute, by Mute Records. Catalogue no: **MUTE 86**

SINGER, THE
Tracks: / Singer, The / Running scared / Black Betty (Extra track available on 12" version only.).
7" Single: Released Jun '86, on Mute, by Mute Records. Catalogue no: **7 MUTE 47**
12" Single: Released Jun '86, on Mute, by Mute Records. Catalogue no: **12 MUTE 47**

TUPELO
Tracks: / Tupelo.
7" Single: Released Aug '85, on Mute, by Mute Records. Catalogue no: **7 MUTE 38**

Cavello, Jimmy

ROCK ROCK ROCK
Tracks: / Rock rock rock / Big beat.
7" Single: Released Jul '82, on Revival, Catalogue no: **REV 6009**

Cavern

IT MIGHT AS WELL RAIN UNTIL SEPTEMBER
Tracks: / It might as well rain until September.
7" Single: Released Jun '83, on Kay-Drum, by Kay-Drum Records. Catalogue no: **KRUM 101**

NO REASON TO CRY
Tracks: / No reason to cry / Cry for you / Won't let you go.
7" Single: Released Nov '82, on KA Drum, Catalogue no: **DRUM 2**

Cayenne

Biographical details: An excellent salsa-styled band formed in London in 1979 by guitarist Robert Greenfield, also known as Roberto Campoverde. He ran a Hampstead music shop, worked in Crossbreed with guitarist John Ethridge (ex Soft Machine) and did music for the Comic Strip, the alternative comedy TV series. Other founder members of Cayenne were trumpeter Ron Carthy, who'd played with Freddy King and also formed the successful Latin-flavoured disco band Gonzales; trombonist Paul Niemen, who later formed his own band called Elephant; Bud Beadle on alto and soprano saxes, who worked with Georgie Fame and Ginger Baker; and pianist Roy Davies, who worked with Freddie King and Elton John. Recent lineups included Steve Waterman on trumpet, who played for Alison Moyet; trombonist Fayyez Virgi, also an excellent writer, who has been touring with the Jazz Warriors; and the exciting percussionist Jody Linscott, from Boston, Massachusetts, who has recorded with David Sanbourne, Pete Townshend and Robert Palmer. Many more excellent session players have taken part; this outfit deserves to be much better known, but such good music doesn't get on the radio easily. (Donald Clarke, April 1989).

CROSS THE CHANNEL FERRY
Tracks: / Cross the channel ferry.
7" Single: Released Aug '86, on Coda, by Coda Records. Catalogue no: **CODS 20**
12" Single: Released Aug '86, on Coda, by Coda Records. Catalogue no: **CODS 20T**

ROBERTO WHO? (SINGLE)
7" Single: Released '81, on Groove PR, by Beggars Banquet Records. Catalogue no: **GP 3012 7**
12" Single: Released '81, on Groove PR, by Beggars Banquet Records. Catalogue no: **GP 3012 12**

Cayne, Carol

WHAT MY LOVE CAN BRING
Tracks: / What my love can bring (Fon force edit) / What my love can bring (summer mix) / What my love can bring (dub)*.
Note: (P) 1988 original sound recording made by EMI Electrola GMBH. * track on 12" version.
CD 5": Released Jul '88, on Syncopate, by EMI Records. Deleted Nov '88. Catalogue no: **CDSY 12**
7" Single: Released Jul '88, on Syncopate, by EMI Records. Deleted Nov '88. Catalogue no: **SY 12**
12" Single: Released Jul '88, on Syncopate, by EMI Records. Deleted Nov '88. Catalogue no: **12SYX 12**
12" Single: Released Jul '88, on Syncopate, by EMI Records. Deleted Nov '88. Catalogue no: **12SY 12**

Cazazza, Monte

SOMETHING FOR NOBODY
7" Single: Released '80, on Industrial, by Industrial Records. Catalogue no: **IR 0010**

C-Bank

GET WET
Tracks: / Get wet.
12" Single: Released '83, on Elite Records, by Elite Records. Deleted '85. Catalogue no: **USDAZZ 26**

CBI

BIG TEARS
Tracks: / Big tears.
7" Single: Released Jul '87, on Radioactive, Catalogue no: **HORN 7003**
12" Single: Released Jul '87, on Radioactive, Catalogue no: **HORN 003**

CC Frost

ACE OF HEARTS
Tracks: / Ace of hearts.
7" Single: Released '82, on After Hours, Deleted '88. Catalogue no: **AFT 01**

C-Cat Trance

DREAMS OF LIVING
Tracks: / Dreams of living / Dangling on a string.
12" Single: Released Mar '84, on Ink, by Red Flame Records. Catalogue no: **INK 123**

ISHTA BIL HABUL (CREAM GALORE!)
Tracks: / Ishta bil habul (cream galore!) / Ishta bil habul (dance mix) / Ishta bil habul (edit mix).
Note: With the St. Louis Symphony Orchestra, conducted by Slatkin. Artists include Lieberman
12" Single: Released Apr '87, on Ink, by Red Flame Records. Catalogue no: **INK 12 27**

JINNIYA
Tracks: / Jinniya.
12" Single: Released Sep '88, on Ink, by Red Flame Records. Catalogue no: **INK 1235**

SCREAMING TO BE WITH YOU
Tracks: / Screaming to be with you.
12" Single: Released Oct '86, on Ink, by Red Flame Records. Catalogue no: **INK 1223**

SHE STEALS CARS
Tracks: / She steals cars.
12" Single: Released '85, on Ink, by Red Flame Records. Catalogue no: **INK 126**

YINNIYA
Tracks: / Yinniya.
12" Single: on Ink, by Red Flame Records. Catalogue no: **INK 1235**

CCCP

ORTODOSSIA II
Tracks: / Ortodossia II.
12" Single: Released '88, on Attack Punk, by Southern Studios Ltd.. Catalogue no: **AT-TACK 8**

HARD WORK
Tracks: / Hard work.
7" Single: Released Apr '89, on MCA, by MCA Records. Catalogue no: **MCA 1298**
12" Single: Released Apr '89, on MCA, by MCA Records. Catalogue no: **DMCAT 1298**

C.C.R. Crew

SLAP
Tracks: / Slap.
7" Single: Released 23 Apr '88, on Circle City, Catalogue no: **CCY 6**
12" Single: Released 23 Apr '88, on Circle City, Catalogue no: **CCYT 6**

STRETCHIN' THE PIECES
Tracks: / Sretchin' the pieces.
7" Single: Released Nov '87, on Circle City, Catalogue no: **CCY 1**
12" Single: Released Nov '87, on Circle City, Catalogue no: **CCYT 1**

CCS

Biographical details: This British blues/pop group were formed in 1970 by influential blues guitarist, vocalist and catalyst Alexis Korner. Like most of his projects, the band featured a flexible, ever-changing line-up of Korner's friends and associates from the blues world. C.C.S. stood for Collective Conciousness Society.
By the end of '71 they had chalked up three UK Top 20 singles: a dynamic, brassy version of Led Zeppelin's *Whole Lotta Love* (No. 13), a Donovan song called *Walkin'* (No. 7) and *Tap Turns On The Water* (No. 5), the latter penned by Korner with pianist John Cameron. Two smaller hits later followed; then, in 1973 C.C.S. disbanded. The extraordinary feature o the project was that it linked Korner with the commercial pop world. Known as the father of the British R&B boom, he had played a vital role in the formation of the Rolling Stones but had always shunned the spotlight himself. Now he found himself of BBC TV's *Top Of The Pops* - indeed, the C.C.S. rendition of *Whole Lotta Love* was adopted as its theme tune and used on the programme throughout the Seventies. The band's hits were produced by Britain's king of commercial pop, Mickie Most and issued on his RAK label.
Korner remained an active musician and (latterly) Radio One broadcaster until his death from lung cancer in January 1984, at the age of 55. His distinctive, deep, smokey voice and his enthusiastic musicianship was thereafter missed by many. (Bob MacDonald)..

BAND PLAYED THE BOOGIE
Tracks: / Band played the boogie.
7" Single: Released Aug '73, on RAK, by EMI Records. Deleted Aug '76. Catalogue no: **RAK 154**

BROTHER
Tracks: / Brother.
7" Single: Released Mar '72, on RAK, by EMI Records. Deleted Mar '75. Catalogue no: **RAK 126**

TAP TURNS ON THE WATER
Tracks: / Tap turns on the water.
7" Single: Released Sep '71, on RAK, by EMI Records. Deleted Sep '74. Catalogue no: **RAK 119**

WALKIN'
Tracks: / Walkin'.
7" Single: Released Feb '71, on RAK, by EMI Records. Deleted Feb '74. Catalogue no: **RAK 109**

WHOLE LOTTA LOVE
Tracks: / Whole lotta love.
7" Single: Released Oct '70, on RAK, by EMI Records. Deleted Oct '73. Catalogue no: **RAK 104**
7" Single: Released '84, on EMI Golden 45's, by EMI Records. Catalogue no: **G45 20**

CD III

SUCCESS
Tracks: / Success.
12" Single: Released '84, on Prelude, Catalogue no: **MHST 101**

Ceberano, Kate

BEDROOM EYES
Tracks: / Bedroom eyes / Katie's blues / Bedroom eyes (extended mix) (Only on 12" and CD single.).
12" Single: Released Sep '89, on London Records, by London Records. Catalogue no: **LONX 326**
Cassingle: Released Sep '89, on London Records, by London Records. Catalogue no: **LONCS 236**
7" Single: Released Sep '89, on London Records, by London Records. Catalogue no: **LON 326**
CD 5": Released Sep '89, on London Records, by London Records. Catalogue no: **LONCD 236**

YOUNG BOYS ARE MY WEAKNESS
Tracks: / Young boys are my weakness / Higher ground / Young boys are my weakness (12" version) (Only on 12" and CD single.).
Note: Voted Australian female singer of the year, this is her first UK single. The song was originally a classic track by the Commodores. Produced by Ian Curnow and Phil Harding (PWL). (London Records, July 1989)
CD 5": Released Jul '89, on London Records, by London Records. Catalogue no: **LONCD 226**
7" Single: Released Jun '89, on London Records, by London Records. Catalogue no: **LON 226**
12" Single: Released Jun '89, on London Records, by London Records. Catalogue no: **LONX 226**

Cecchetto, Claudio

GIOCA JOUER
Tracks: / Gioca jouer.
12" Single: Released '83, on Banana, Catalogue no: **FRUIT 1T**
7" Single: Released '83, on Banana, Catalogue no: **FRUIT 1**

Ced D

NO SANTA CLAUS
Tracks: / No Santa Claus.
12" Single: Released Jan '89, on Hill Top, Catalogue no: **HTD 001**

Cedar Roots

NIGHT CLUB
Tracks: / Night club.
12" Single: Released '83, on Live & Love, Catalogue no: **LLDIS 114**

Ceeja

COULD THIS BE LOVE
Tracks: / Could this be love / Hammer to m... head.
7" Single: Released Feb '87, on Noir, b... Noir Records. Catalogue no: **CHALK 3**
12" Single: Released Feb '87, on Noir, b... Noir Records. Catalogue no: **CHALK 123**

NEW BEAT CHART MEGAMIX
12" Single: Released '89, on Subway, b... Subway Records. Catalogue no: **SUB 057**

Celebration

CELEBRATION GOLD
Tracks: / Celebration gold / Celebration go... (part 2).
7" Single: Released '82, on Polo, by Po... Records. Deleted '88. Catalogue no: **POL 16**
12" Single: Released '82, on Polo, by Po... Records. Deleted '88. Catalogue no: **POL 12-16**

Celentano, Adriano

LANGUAGE OF LOVE (PRISENCO LINENSINAINCIUSOL)
Tracks: / Disc jockey / Language of love.
7" Single: Released Aug '87, on Clan, Catalogue no: **15320**

Celibate Rifles

PRETTY PICTURES
Tracks: / Pretty pictures / Kent theme.
7" Single: Released Apr '87, on Sound Shigaku Presents, Catalogue no: **SHIGS**

CELTIC RAP
Tracks: / Celtic rap, The.
7" Single: Released Sep '88, on Warwi... by Warwick Records. Catalogue no: **CF 1**
12" Single: Released Sep '88, on Warwi... by Warwick Records. Catalogue no: **CFC**

Celtic Frost

I WON'T DANCE
Tracks: / I won't dance.
12" Single: Released Feb '89, on Noise, ... Dorane Records. Catalogue no: **NOI**

094T

Centerfold

MONEY
Tracks: / Money / So distant.
7" Single: on Epic, by CBS Records. Deleted 10 Jul '89. Catalogue no: **XXXG 3**
7" Single: Released Jan '89, on Epic, by CBS Records. Deleted 10 Jul '89. Catalogue no: **XXX 3**
12" Single: Released Jan '89, on Epic, by CBS Records. Deleted 10 Jul '89. Catalogue no: **XXX T3**

MORE MONEY
Tracks: / More money / Money (dance mix) / Money (rock mix) / So distant.
CD 5": Released 30 Jan '89, on Epic, by CBS Records. Deleted 10 Jul '89. Catalogue no: **653 036-3**
CD 5": Released 16 Jan '89, on Epic, by CBS Records. Deleted 10 Jul '89. Catalogue no: **XXX C3**

Central Line

Biographical details: This all-male British band were among a spate of white soul groups who emerged in the UK in the early Eighties. They had worked at their music for some time before scoring their first chart single in early 1981 and their experience displayed itself via the tightness on this and subsequent records. They comprised Linton Beckles, Henry Defoe, Lipson Francis and Camelle Hinds.
The first UK hit was *(You Know) You Can Do It* and it reached No. 67. Later that year they hit No. 42 with *Walking Into Sunshine*, a classy soul single that logged an impressive ten weeks on the Top 75. 1982 saw the release of their debut album *Breaking Point*, which reached No. 64 on the British LP list shortly after the group had celebrated a substantial US soul hit with *Walking Into Sunshine*. Further American success was not forthcoming, however and they had to wait until 1983 for their only British Top 30 single. That was a disco version of *Nature Boy*, a song that had previously been a hit for Bobby Darin and George Benson (originally Nat King ole). Achieving only modest subsequent success, Central Line were on the verge of breaking up by the end of 1984. (Bob MacDonald)..

BETCHA GONNA
Tracks: / Betcha gonna.
7" Single: Released Feb '84, on Mercury, by Phonogram Ltd. Catalogue no: **MER 152**
12" Single: Released Feb '84, on Mercury, by Phonogram Ltd. Catalogue no: **MERX 152**

DON'T TELL ME
Tracks: / Don't tell me / Shake it up.
7" Single: Released Jan '82, on Mercury, by Phonogram Ltd. Deleted Jan '85. Catalogue no: **MER 90**
12" Single: Released Jan '82, on Mercury, by Phonogram Ltd. Deleted Jan '85. Catalogue no: **MERX 90**

NATURE BOY
Tracks: / Nature boy / Goodbye.
7" Single: Released Dec '82, on Mercury, by Phonogram Ltd. Deleted '85. Catalogue no: **MER 131**
12" Single: Released Dec '82, on Mercury, by Phonogram Ltd. Deleted '85. Catalogue no: **MERX 131**

NATURE BOY (OLD GOLD)
Tracks: / Nature boy / Walking in sunshine.
12" Single: Released 28 Mar '88, on Old Gold, by Old Gold Records. Catalogue no: **OG 4053**

STICKS AND STONES
Tracks: / Sticks and stones / Summer romance.
7" Single: Released Feb '80, on Mercury, by Phonogram Ltd. Deleted Feb '85. Catalogue no: **MER 4**
12" Single: Released Feb '80, on Mercury, by Phonogram Ltd. Deleted Feb '85. Catalogue no: **MERX 4**

SURPRISE SURPRISE
Tracks: / Surprise surprise.
7" Single: Released Mar '83, on Mercury, by Phonogram Ltd. Catalogue no: **MER 133**
12" Single: Released Mar '83, on Mercury, by Phonogram Ltd. Catalogue no: **MERX 133**

WALKING INTO SUNSHINE
Tracks: / Walking into sunshine.
7" Single: Released Aug '81, on Mercury, by Phonogram Ltd. Deleted Aug '84. Catalogue no: **MER 78**
12" Single: Released Aug '81, on Mercury, by Phonogram Ltd. Deleted Aug '84. Catalogue no: **MERX 78**

YOU CAN DO IT (YOU KNOW)
Tracks: / You can do it (you know) / We chose love.
7" Single: Released Jan '81, on Mercury, by Phonogram Ltd. Deleted Jan '84. Catalogue no: **LINE 7**
12" Single: Released Jan '81, on Mercury, by Phonogram Ltd. Deleted Jan '84. Catalogue no: **LINE 12**

YOU'VE SAID ENOUGH
Tracks: / You've said enough.
7" Single: Released Nov '82, on Mercury, by Phonogram Ltd. Deleted Nov '85. Catalogue no: **MER 117**
12" Single: Released Nov '82, on Mercury, by Phonogram Ltd. Deleted Nov '85. Catalogue no: **MERX 117**

Centrefold

DICTATOR
Tracks: / Dictator / Dictator (inst).
7" Single: Released May '87, on Carrere, Catalogue no: **CAR 412**
12" Single: Released May '87, on Carrere, Catalogue no: **CART 412**

Century Steel Band

BABY DONT WANT YOU
Tracks: / Baby don't want you / Look to the future.
7" Single: Released Dec '82, on Rough Trade, by Rough Trade Records. Deleted Dec '85. Catalogue no: **RT 1A**
7" Single: Released Dec '82, on Glasshouse, Catalogue no: **CSE 1**

FIELDS OF ATHENRY
Tracks: / Fields of Athenry.
7" Single: Released '88, on I&B, by I & B Records. Catalogue no: **CSB 103**

Cerrone

Biographical details: This French multi-instrumentalist and producer (full name Jean-Marc Cerrone) came to clubgoers' attention during the late Seventies disco boom, with his tailor-made, somewhat soulless dance records. The instrumental *Love In C Minor* reached the Top 40 pop charts in both the UK and the US in 1977. The following year he obtained a sleeper hit in Britain with *Supernature*, a catchy disco single featuring sporadic female vocals. The record was issued in March '78, entered the UK charts in July and peaked at No. 8 in August. one further hit *Je Suis Music* reached No. 39 on the British listings in 1979. (Bob MacDonald)..

CLUB UNDERWORLD
Tracks: / Club underworld.
7" Single: Released Aug '84, on Personal, by Personal Records. Catalogue no: **PERS 107**

JE SUIS MUSIC
Tracks: / Je suis music.
7" Single: Released Jan '79, on CBS, by CBS Records. Deleted Jan '82. Catalogue no: **CBS 6918**

LOVE IN 'C' MINOR
Tracks: / Love in 'C' minor.
7" Single: Released Feb '77, on Atlantic, by WEA Records. Catalogue no: **K 10895**

SUPERNATURE
Tracks: / Supernature.
7" Single: Released Jul '78, on Atlantic, by WEA Records. Deleted Jul '81. Catalogue no: **K 11089**

SUPERNATURE 86
Tracks: / Supernature 86.
7" Single: Released Aug '86, on Music Of Life, by Music Of Life Records. Catalogue no: **MOL 5**
12" Single: Released Aug '86, on Music Of Life, by Music Of Life Records. Catalogue no: **MOLIF 5**

SUPERNATURE (SINGLE)
Tracks: / Supernature.
7" Single: Released Mar '78, on Atlantic, by WEA Records. Catalogue no: **K 11089**

WHERE ARE YOU NOW
Tracks: / Where are you now.
7" Single: Released Nov '83, on Record Shack, by Record Shack Records. Catalogue no: **SOHO 13**
12" Single: Released Nov '83, on Record Shack, by Record Shack Records. Catalogue no: **SOHOT 13**

Cetera, Peter

GLORY OF LOVE
Tracks: / Glory of love / On the line.
12" Single: Released Jul '86, on Warner Bros., by WEA Records. Deleted Jan '88. Catalogue no: **W 8662T**
7" Single: Released Jul '86, on Warner Bros., by WEA Records. Catalogue no: **W 8662**

NEXT TIME I FALL, THE
Tracks: / Next time I fall, The / Holy Moly.
7" Single: Released Oct '86, on Full Moon (USA), Deleted Jan '88. Catalogue no: **W 8597**
12" Single: Released Oct '86, on Full Moon (USA), Deleted Jan '88. Catalogue no: **W 8597T**

ONE GOOD WOMAN
Tracks: / One good woman / One more story / Daddy's girl (On 12" only).
7" Single: Released Aug '88, on Warner Bros., by WEA Records. Catalogue no: **W 7824**
12" Single: Released Aug '88, on Warner Bros., by WEA Records. Catalogue no: **W 7824T**

Cha Cha At The Opera

CHA CHA AT THE OPERA
Tracks: / Cha Cha at the opera / Concerto no. 2.
7" Single: Released Nov '82, on Island, by Island Records. Deleted Nov '85. Catalogue no: **WIP 6835**
12" Single: Released Nov '82, on Island, by Island Records. Deleted Nov '85. Catalogue no: **12WIP 6835**

Chacksfield, Frank

Biographical details: This British orchestra leader, born in Battle, Sussex in 1914, was a church organist in his teens and entered the music business in his early twenties. Having formed his own band shortly before the outbreak of the Second World War, he began playing on BBC Radio while in the army, later becoming a resident arranger for the Services entertainment show *Stars In Battle Dress*. After the war he began making regular records. In 1953 he entered Britain's recently inaugurated record charts, peaking at No. 10 with *Little Red Monkey*. That single was credited to Frank Chacksfield's Tunesmiths, but subsequent discs billed the Frank Chacksfield Orchestra.
Little Red Monkey was quickly followed by his smash hit *Limelight*. Composed by Charlie Chaplin for his movie of the same name, it went to No. 2 in the UK and was also a Top Tenner in the States, where the record introduced Chacksfield as an important arranger and orchestra leader. In Britain *Limelight* remains the only single in chart history to log eight weeks at No. 2 without hitting the very top. His follow-up *Ebb-Tide* was another transatlantic Top 10 hit, but this time was bigger in the US then the UK.
The mid-Fifities rock 'n' roll explosion killed off Chacksfield's record chart career, but he remained in showbusiness right into the Eighties. His middle-of-the-road style ensured a steady audience for his performing and recording activities. Many of his later discs consisted of cover versions of contemporary pop hits. (Bob MacDonald)
Born in Battle, Sussex in 1914, the pianist, arranger, conductor made his first broadcast in 1943 and his first records in 1948; he was signed by Decca UK and did lush string arrangements well recorded with Decca's 'Ffrr' system (Full Frequency Range Recordings), the best technology around at the time. He had worldwide hits in 1953 with the theme from the Charlie Chaplin film *Limelight* and with *Ebb tide* (both now on the album *Stardust*). He was a consistent album seller for many years and continued with UK hit singles; he was music adviser to the Irish Television Service on it's formation, and in the mid '70's he took a 40 piece orchestra on a 15-date tour of Japan. (Donald Clarke, April 1989)d.

DONKEY CART
Tracks: / Donkey cart.
7" Single: Released Aug '56, on Decca, by Decca Records. Deleted Aug '59. Catalogue no: **F 10743**

EBB TIDE
Tracks: / Ebb tide.
7" Single: Released Feb '54, on Decca, by Decca Records. Deleted Feb '57. Catalogue no: **F 10122**

IN OLD LISBON
Tracks: / In old Lisbon.
7" Single: Released Feb '56, on Decca, by Decca Records. Deleted Feb '59. Catalogue no: **F 10689**

LIMELIGHT
Tracks: / Limelight.
7" Single: Released May '53, on Decca, by Decca Records. Deleted May '56. Catalogue no: **F 10106**

LITTLE RED MONKEY
Tracks: / Little red monkey.
7" Single: Released Apr '53, on Parlophone, by EMI Records. Deleted Apr '56. Catalogue no: **R 3658**

Chad Tree

SWEET JESUS BLUE EYES
Tracks: / Sweet Jesus blue eyes.
12" Single: Released Nov '86, on Hot, Catalogue no: **HOT 1229**

Chagrin D'Amour

CHACUN FAIT
Tracks: / Chacun fait.
7" Single: Released Jun '82, on Polydor, by Polydor Ltd. Deleted Jun '87. Catalogue no: **POSP 446**
12" Single: Released Jun '82, on Polydor, by Polydor Ltd. Deleted Jun '87. Catalogue no: **POSPX 446**

Chai Am

DANCE CRAZY
Tracks: / Dance crazy.
7" Single: Released Aug '85, on Illuminated, Catalogue no: **ILL 63**
12" Single: Released Aug '85, on Illuminated, Catalogue no: **12 ILL 63**

FASCINATION
Tracks: / Fascination / Far away.
7" Single: Released Aug '86, on GC, Catalogue no: **GC 01**
12" Single: Released Aug '86, on GC, Catalogue no: **GCT 01**

ME & BABY BROTHER
Tracks: / Me & baby brother.
7" Single: Released Oct '85, on Illuminated, Catalogue no: **LEV 67**
12" Single: Released Oct '85, on Illuminated, Deleted Nov '87. Catalogue no: **12LEV 67**

Chain

BANGING ON THE HOUSE CHAIN
Tracks: / Banging on the house gang.
12" Single: Released Sep '85, on Native (1), by Native Records. Catalogue no: **NTV 2**

Chain Gang

LONG TIME GONE
Tracks: / Long time gone.
12" Single: Released 30 May '87, on Idea, by Idea Records. Catalogue no: **IDT 002**

MAKING TRACKS
Tracks: / Making tracks.
7" Single: Released '88, on Supreme, by Supreme Records. Catalogue no: **EDIT 87 14**

MORE THAN A DREAM
Tracks: / More than a dream / Ridin' down the line / Long time gone / Fight for your life.
12" Single: Released Mar '87, on Troll Kitchen, by Troll Kitchen Records. Catalogue no: **WORKS 002**

Chain Reaction

DANCE FREAK
Tracks: / Dance freak.
12" Single: Released Jun '89, on Blue Chip, by Blue Chip Records. Catalogue no: **BLUEC 16**

Chainsaw

MASSACRE
Tracks: / Devil's daughter / Ballad of Mean Street / Rock 'n' roll gambler / Accident victim.
Note: Debut product from Coventry-based outfit with all the necessary ingredients. (Magnum Music May, 1988)
12" Single: Released Dec '84, on Thunderbolt, by Magnum Music Group. Catalogue no: **THBE 1.006**

Chairman Youth

UNCERTAINTY
Tracks: / Uncertainty / Business partners.
7" Single: Released Mar '81, on Last Ditch, Deleted Mar '84. Catalogue no: **TRENCH 1**

Chairmen Of The Board

Biographical details: They were formed in 1969 by the legendary Tamla Motown songwriting/producing team, Holland/Dozier/Holland. HDH had left Motown the previous year and used the Chairmen of the Board as one of the acts with which to launch their new Invictus label. The group hit big quickly, reaching No. 3 in both the US and the UK with 1970's *Give me just a little more time*. In both nations this was their first and biggest success. This uptempo single was strongly influenced by the Motown sound, but the most distinctive feature of the Chairmen's records was the nasal vocal style of lead singer General Johnson. This formula was repeated on subsequent hit singles. Most were produced though not penned, by the HDH trio. Those other hit 45s, which continued for a longer period in Britain than the States, included *You've got me dangling on a string*, *Pay the piper* and *Working on a building of love*. *Dangling on a string* reached No. 5 in the UK but peaked at No. 38 in the US. Johnson's voice and personality came through so strongly on the records, that many people thought they were by a solo artist called the ChairmAn of the Board; but

the name actually referred to a whole group and should correctly appear in the plural.
By the time the British hits ended in 1973, the group were down to a trio, following the departure of Eddie Curtis. Johnson was now concerntrating more on writing and producing for other artists. (Bob MacDonald).
A vocal group formed in 1969 by General George Johnson who had been the lead singer with Showmen, whose rock'n'roll anthem *It will stand* was their only hit (in 1961, re-entering in 1964). He refused an offer of Frankie Lymon's place in the Teenagers, and signed in 1968 with Invictus, a new label formed by ex-Motown legends Holland-Dolzier-Holland; recruited Danny Woods, Harrison Kennedy and Eddie Custis to form the Gentlemen, later renamed Chairmen of the Board. Each could handle leads, but Johnson took most of them. Their first single *Give me just a little more time* was a big international hit. Their USA top 40 teunure lasted through 1970 but their UK hits continued through 1973. Johnson wrote for others; most of them made solo albums; Johnson and Wood Johnson and Wood re-formed as Chairmen for an album in 1981 for *Success* as the Chairmen. They were influential on Style Council and Dexy's Midnight Runners, among others; *Salute the General* is a good compilation. Paul Weller remixed *Loverboy* for a UK hit in 1986; Johnson was active on USA circuits promoting the dance fad 'The Shag'. (Donald Clarke, April 1989)J.

CHAIRMAN OF THE BOARD
Tracks: / Chairman of the board.
7" Single: Released Sep '71, on Invictus, Deleted Sep '74. Catalogue no: **INV 516**

ELMO JAMES
Tracks: / Elmo James.
7" Single: Released Oct '72, on Invictus, Deleted Oct '75. Catalogue no: **INV 524**

EVERYTHING'S TUESDAY
Tracks: / Everything's Tuesday.
7" Single: Released Feb '71, on Invictus, Deleted Feb '74. Catalogue no: **INV 507**

FINDERS KEEPERS
Tracks: / Finders keepers.
7" Single: Released Jun '73, on Invictus, Deleted Jun '76. Catalogue no: **INV 530**

GIVE ME JUST A LITTLE MORE TIME
Tracks: / Give me just a little more time.
7" Single: Released Oct '84, on HDH (Holland/Dozier/Holland), by Demon Records. Catalogue no: **HDH 4511**

GIVE ME JUST A LITTLE MORE TIME (EP)
Tracks: / Give me just a little more time / You've got me dancing on a string / Everything's Tuesday.
7" Single: Released Aug '70, on Invictus, Deleted Aug '73. Catalogue no: **INV 501**
7" Single: Released Jan '80, on Inferno (1), by Inferno Records. Catalogue no: **HEAT 16**

I'M ON MY WAY TO A BETTER PLACE
Tracks: / I'm on my way to a better place.
7" Single: Released 13 Jan '73, on Invictus, Deleted 13 Jan '76. Catalogue no: **INV 527**
7" Single: Released 16 Dec '72, on Invictus, Deleted 16 Dec '75. Catalogue no: **INV 527**

LOVER BOY (MEDLEY)
Tracks: / Loverboy.
Cassingle: Released Aug '87, on EMI, by EMI Records. Deleted Oct '87. Catalogue no: **TC - SYX 4**
12" Single: Released Aug '87, on Syncopate, by EMI Records. Deleted Apr '88. Catalogue no: **12SYX 4**

LOVERBOY
Tracks: / Loverboy / Loverboy / Loverboy (instrumental) / Give me just a little more time (Extra track on double pack version only. Gatefold sleeve.) / You've got me dangling on a string (Extra track on double pack version only. Gatefold sleeve.) / Loverboy (Ian Levine remix) (Only available on 12" remix.) / Loverboy (7" version) (Only available on 12" remix.) / Loverboy (original 12" version) (Only available on 12" remix.) / Everythin's Tuesday.
12" Single: Released Aug '86, on EMI, by EMI Records. Deleted Jul '87. Catalogue no: **12EMI 5585**
7" Set: Released Aug '86, on EMI, by EMI Records. Catalogue no: **12EMID 5585**
7" Single: Released Aug '86, on EMI, by EMI Records. Catalogue no: **EMI 5585**
12" Single: Released Oct '86, on EMI, by EMI Records. Catalogue no: **12EMIX 5585**

PAY TO THE PIPER
Tracks: / Pay to the piper.
7" Single: Released May '71, on Invictus, Deleted May '74. Catalogue no: **INV 511**

WORKING ON A BUILDING OF LOVE
Tracks: / Working on a building of love.
7" Single: Released Jul '72, on Invictus, Deleted Jul '75. Catalogue no: **INV 519**

YOU'VE GOT ME DANGLING ON A STRING
Tracks: / You've got me dangling on a string / Tricked and trapped.
7" Single: Released Nov '70, on Invictus, Deleted Nov '73. Catalogue no: **INV 504**
7" Single: Released Mar '84, on HDH (Holland/Dozier/Holland), by Demon Records. Catalogue no: **HDH 452**

Chairs

HONEY I NEED A GIRL
Tracks: / Honey I need a girl.
7" Single: Released Jan '89, on Pink Halo, by Pink Halo Records. Catalogue no: **PH 003**
12" Single: Released Jan '89, on Pink Halo, by Pink Halo Records. Catalogue no: **PHOT 03**

LIKES OF YOU, THE
Tracks: / Likes of you, The / Something's happening.
12" Single: Released Mar '88, on Pink Halo, by Pink Halo Records. Catalogue no: **PH 01 T**
7" Single: Released Mar '88, on Pink Halo, by Pink Halo Records. Catalogue no: **PH 01**

Chakachas

JUNGLE FEVER
Tracks: / Jungle fever.
7" Single: Released May '72, on Polydor, by Polydor Ltd. Deleted May '75. Catalogue no: **2121 064**

JUNGLE FEVER (OLD GOLD)
Tracks: / Jungle fever.
7" Single: Released Jul '84, on Old Gold, by Old Gold Records. Catalogue no: **OG 9439**

TWIST TWIST
Tracks: / Twist twist.
7" Single: Released Jan '62, on RCA, by BMG Records (UK). Deleted Jan '65. Catalogue no: **RCA 1264**

Chakiris, George

HEART OF A TEENAGE GIRL
Tracks: / Heart of a teenage girl.
7" Single: Released Jun '60, on Triumph, Deleted Jun '63. Catalogue no: **RGM 1010**

Chakk

BIG HOT BLUES
Tracks: / Big hot blues / Cut the dust / Big hot blues (big blue mix) (Extra track on 12" version only.).
7" Single: Released May '86, on MCA, by MCA Records. Catalogue no: **FON 3**
12" Single: Released May '86, on MCA, by MCA Records. Catalogue no: **FONT 3**

IMAGINATION
Tracks: / Imagination / Imagination (instrumental) / Imagination (dub) (Extra track available on 12" version only.).
7" Single: Released Mar '86, on MCA, by MCA Records. Catalogue no: **FON 2**
12" Single: Released Mar '86, on MCA, by MCA Records. Catalogue no: **FONT 2**

MURDERER
Tracks: / Murderer / Big hot mix / Stare me out - crash mix / Cut the dust.
7" Single: Released Jun '86, on Fon, by FON Records. Catalogue no: **MCG 6006 EP**

OUT OF THE SLUSH
Tracks: / Out of the slush.
12" Single: Released Sep '84, on Double Vision, by Double Vision Records. Catalogue no: **DVR 6**

TIMEBOMB
Tracks: / Take your time (earth coming) / Just pieces (bumper bomb bonus bombbay mix bouncing beats).
7" Set: Released 30 May '87, on Fon, by FON Records. Catalogue no: **FONT 6P**
7" Single: Released Mar '87, on Fon, by FON Records. Catalogue no: **FON L 6**
12" Single: Released Feb '87, on Fon, by FON Records. Catalogue no: **FONT 6**

YOU
Tracks: / You / They say.
12" Single: Released Mar '85, on Fon, by FON Records. Catalogue no: **FONT 1**
7" Single: Released Mar '85, on Fon, by FON Records. Catalogue no: **FON 001**

Chako, Lori

GLOSSY MAGAZINES
Tracks: / Glossy magazines.
7" Single: Released Apr '83, on Boadicea, Deleted '88. Catalogue no: **GLOSS 1**

Chalice

DANGEROUS DISTURBANCES
Tracks: / Dangerous disturbances.
12" Single: Released Oct '84, on Pipe (Austria), by Cherry Red Records. Catalogue no: **Unknown**

NOBODY CAN TOUCH MY SOUL
Tracks: / Nobody can touch my soul / Back way.
7" Single: Released Feb '81, on Hansa, by Hansa Records. Deleted Feb '84. Catalogue no: **HANSA 2**

SAYONARA
Tracks: / Sayonara / Doctor doctor.
7" Single: Released Oct '87, on Bold Reprieve (1), Catalogue no: **BRM006**
7" Single: Released 10 Oct '87, on Bold Reprieve (1), Catalogue no: **BIRM 006**
12" Single: Released Oct '87, on Bold Reprieve (1), Catalogue no: **BRM006T**

WICKED INTENTION
Tracks: / Wicked intention.
12" Single: Released Apr '85, on Diamond C, Catalogue no: **VCS 0014**

Chalker, Bryan

I CAN'T READ THE THOUGHTS IN YOUR MIND
Tracks: / I can't read the thoughts in your mind.
7" Single: Released Aug '83, on Acuff-Rose, Catalogue no: **AR 004**

Challengers

HE'LL BE THERE
Tracks: / He'll be there / Streets of God.
7" Single: Released Jun '82, on Out Of Town, Catalogue no: **HOOT 6**

Challenor, Jackie

BACK ON MY FEET AGAIN
Tracks: / Back on my feet again / Never together.
7" Single: Released Sep '80, on WEA, by WEA Records. Deleted '83. Catalogue no: **K 18330**

MAMA
Tracks: / Mama / Put me down softly.
7" Single: Released May '80, on WEA, by WEA Records. Deleted May '85. Catalogue no: **K 18207**

Chalmers, Lloyd

IF LEAVING ME IS EASY
Tracks: / If leaving me is easy / Give me a little more.
7" Single: Released Nov '81, on Radioactive, Deleted Nov '84. Catalogue no: **RAD 3**
7" Single: Released Jun '82, on KR, Catalogue no: **KR 6**
12" Single: Released Jun '82, on KR, Catalogue no: **KRT 6**

IF YOU WERE HERE TONIGHT
Tracks: / If you were here tonight / Galveston Bay.
12" Single: Released Jun '86, on Sarge, Catalogue no: **SRL 7**

Chaloner, Susan

MISSING MR. MARLEY
Tracks: / Missing Mr. Marley.
7" Single: Released Apr '84, on Fearless, Deleted '87. Catalogue no: **FEA1**

Chamberlain, Richard

HI-LILI HI-LO
Tracks: / Hi lili hi lo.
7" Single: Released Feb '63, on MGM, by Polydor Ltd. Deleted Feb '66. Catalogue no: **MGM 1189**

LOVE ME TENDER
Tracks: / Love me tender.
7" Single: Released Nov '62, on MGM, by Polydor Ltd. Deleted Nov '65. Catalogue no: **MGM 1173**

THEME FROM DR KILDARE-3 STARS WILL SHINE TONIGHT
Tracks: / Dr Kildare, Theme from.
7" Single: Released Jun '62, on MGM, by Polydor Ltd. Deleted Jun '65. Catalogue no: **MGM 1160**

TRUE LOVE
Tracks: / True love.
7" Single: Released Jul '63, on MGM, by Polydor Ltd. Deleted Jul '66. Catalogue no: **MGM 1205**

Chambers, Dave

DON'T LET IT GO TO YOUR HEAD
Tracks: / Don't let it go to your head.
12" Single: Released Mar '83, on Elite Records, by Elite Records. Deleted '85. Catalogue no: **DAZZ 19**

Chameleons

AS HIGH AS YOU CAN GO
Tracks: / As high as you can go.
12" Single: Released Feb '83, on Statik, Catalogue no: **STAT 3012**

IN SHREDS
Tracks: / In shreds / Less than human.
7" Single: Released Apr '82, on Epic, by CBS Records. Deleted Apr '85. Catalogue no: **EPCA 2210**

NOSTALGIA
Tracks: / Nostalgia.
7" Single: Released Feb '85, on Statik, Catalogue no: **TAK 29**
12" Single: Released Feb '85, on Statik, Catalogue no: **TAK 2912**

PARADISE
Tracks: / Paradise / Chinatown.
7" Single: Released May '82, on Model, Catalogue no: **MOD 1**

PERSON ISN'T SAFE ANYWHERE THESE DAYS
Tracks: / Person isn't safe anywhere these days.
7" Single: Released Jun '83, on Statik, Catalogue no: **TAK 6**

SHONA TU
Tracks: / Shona tu.
7" Single: Released Apr '89, on Lamplight, by Priority Records. Catalogue no: **EAGLE 11**

SINGING RULE BRITANNIA
Tracks: / Singing Rule Britannia / While the walls close in.
7" Single: Released Aug '85, on Statik, Catalogue no: **TAK 35**
12" Single: Released Aug '85, on Statik, Catalogue no: **TAK 1235**

SWAMP THING
Tracks: / Swamp thing / John, I'm only dancing / Tears (orginal arrangement) (Extra track available on 12" only.).
7" Single: Released Aug '86, on Geffen, by Geffen Records (USA). Deleted Jun '87. Catalogue no: **GEF 10**
12" Single: Released Aug '86, on Geffen, by Geffen Records (USA). Deleted Jul '88. Catalogue no: **GEF 10T**

TEARS
Tracks: / Tars / Paradiso / Inside out (version) (Only available on 12" version.).
7" Single: Released Jun '86, on Geffen, by Geffen Records (USA). Deleted Jun '87. Catalogue no: **GEF 4**
12" Single: Released Jun '86, on Geffen, by Geffen Records (USA). Deleted Jan '88. Catalogue no: **GEF 4T**
7" Set: Released Jun '86, on Geffen, by Geffen Records (USA). Deleted Jun '87. Catalogue no: **GEF 4F**

Chamfort, Alain

MANUREVA
Tracks: / Manureva / Beguine.
7" Single: Released Mar '80, on Epic, by CBS Records. Deleted Mar '83. Catalogue no: **EPC 8497**

Champagne Kindergarten

I WANT TO MARRY HARRY WHEN I'M GROWN UP
Tracks: / I want to marry Harry when I'm grown up.
7" Single: Released Sep '85, on EMI, by EMI Records. Catalogue no: **HRH 1**

Champaign

Biographical details: This American soul band consists of Paulie Carman, Michael Day, Rena Jones, Rocky Maffitt, Michael Reed, Howard Reeder and Dana Walden; the group are named after their home town of Champaign, Illinois; in Britain their name has frequently been misspelt as 'Champagne'.
Champaigne gained prominence in 198[illegible] with their smooth, laid-back single *How 'bout Us*. After scoring on the US soul chart, it became a major pop hit, peaking at No. 12 in the US and reaching No. 5 in the UK. Two years later they bounced back with a second success in similar vein, entitled *try again*. this time, however, their soul sound failed to cross the Atlantic and Britain forgot the group. (Bob MacDonald)..

CAN YOU FIND THE TIME
Tracks: / Can you find the time / Whiplash
7" Single: Released Jul '81, on CBS, by CBS Records. Deleted '85. Catalogue no: **A 1381**
12" Single: Released Jul '81, on CBS, by CBS Records. Deleted '85. Catalogue no: **A13 1381**

HOW 'BOUT US (OLD GOLD)
Tracks: / How 'bout us / Off and on love.
7" Single: Released Sep '85, on Old Gold, by Old Gold Records. Catalogue no: **OG 9559**
7" Single: Released Nov '87, on Old Gold, by Old Gold Records. Catalogue no: **OG 4033**

HOW 'BOUT US (SINGLE)
Tracks: / How 'bout us / Spinnin'.
7" Single: Released May '81, on CBS, by CBS Records. Deleted May '84. Catalogue no: **A 1046**

Champs

Biographical details: The Champs were a band of West Coast session players who shot to fame in 1958 with their instrumental smash *Tequila*, a catchy rock 'n' roll ditty composed by saxophonist Chuck Rio. It logged five weeks at No. 1 in the US and reached No. 5 in Britain. For the next four years they released a series of singles in similar vein, but did not repeat its success. The nearest they came in the US was with the No. 30 placings of *El Rancho Rock* and *Too Much Tequila*; in the UK *Too Much Tequila* was the only subsequent single to even hit the chart and it peaked at No. 49. During this period Rio and Alden were replaced by Jimmy Seals and Dash Crofts, who found major American success in the Seventies as a duo. (Bob MacDonald).
A quintet of studio session players who hit big with the instrumental rock'n'roll novelty *Tequila*, number one for five weeks in the USA in 1959, interesting for its quasi-Latin beat. They had smaller hits until 1962; Glen Campbell, Jimmy Seals and Dash Crofts passed through after the big one. (Donald Clarke, April 1989).

TEQUILA
Tracks: / Tequila.
7" Single: Released Apr '58, on London-American, Deleted Apr '61. Catalogue no: **HLU 8580**

TEQUILA (OLD GOLD)
Tracks: / Tequila / Limbo rock.
7" Single: Released May '81, on Old Gold, by Old Gold Records. Deleted May '84. Catalogue no: **OG 9105**

TEQUILA (SINGLE)
Tracks: / Tequila / Pee Wee's dance.
7" Single: Released Sep '87, on Cool Tempo, by Chrysalis Records. Catalogue no: **COOL 152**
12" Single: Released Sep '87, on Cool Tempo, by Chrysalis Records. Catalogue no: **COOLX 152**

TOO MUCH TEQUILA
Tracks: / Too much tequila.
7" Single: Released Mar '60, on London-American, Deleted Mar '63. Catalogue no: **HLH 9052**

Champs Boys

TUBULAR BELLS
Tracks: / Tubular bells.
7" Single: Released Jun '76, on Philips, by Phonogram Ltd. Deleted Jun '79. Catalogue no: **6006 519**

Chan

CHAN THEME SHIMBA
Tracks: / Chan theme shimba.
7" Single: Released Dec '81, on CSB London, Catalogue no: **DES 1002**

Chan, Jackie

NO ONE MOVE
Tracks: / No one move.
12" Single: Released Nov '84, on Crown H.I.M., Catalogue no: **Unknown**

Chance

MODERN TV
Tracks: / Modern TV / Kitchen porter.
7" Single: Released Nov '82, on Fortune (USA), by Fortune Records (USA). Catalogue no: **FR 4001**

YOU'VE REALLY GOT A HOLD ON ME
Tracks: / You've really got a hold on me / Innocent.
7" Single: Released Aug '80, on Magnet, by WEA Records. Deleted '83. Catalogue no: **MAG 178**

Chandell, Tim

OH WHAT A SMILE CAN DO
Tracks: / Oh what a smile can do.
12" Single: Released May '82, on Orbitone, by Orbitone Records. Catalogue no: **ORB 1**

SWEETER THAN HONEY
Tracks: / Sweeter than honey / Back in my arms.
12" Single: Released Jun '82, on Freedom, Catalogue no: **VG 010**

TRUE LOVE
Tracks: / True love.
12" Single: Released May '82, on Orbitone, by Orbitone Records. Catalogue no: **ORB 4**

Chandler, E.J.

I CAN'T STAND TO LOSE YOU
Tracks: / I can't stand to lose you.
7" Single: Released Feb '80, on Destiny (Northern Soul), by Destiny Records. Catalogue no: **DS 1026**

Chandler, Gene

Biographical details: This American pop/soul singer, born in Chicago in 1937, turned professional in 1960. he surged to sudden stardom two years later with *Duke of Earl*, a single penned by three writers including Chandler under his real name Euguene Dixon. The novelty feature of this catchy song was its delightfully silly 'Dook dook dook, dook of Earl' hook. It was No. 1 for three weeks in the States but was not a hit in Britain. Such a gimick was hard to follow and the singer had to wait until 1964 for a second Top 20 hit. That was entitled *Just Be True* and reached No. 19; it was followed the next year by the No. 18 placing of *Nothing can stop me*. Both were composed by Curtis Mayfield, lead singer of the Impressions. Chandler was more consistently successful on the American R&B charts.
After five years without a Top 40 pop hit, he bounced back in 1970 with a US No. 12 single *Groovy Situation*, a sweet soul record. He made little impact during the bulk of the Seventies, but demonstrated his resilience once again in 1979. In that year he acieved his ludicrously overdue Top 40 debut in Britain with *Get Down*, a sungle that successfully cashed in on the disco boom. Conversely this was a greater hit (No. 11) in Britain than in the States, as was the UK No. 28 placing of 1980's ballad *Does she have a friend*. in between these two hits, British rock 'n' roll revival group Darts crowned the UK's sudden Chandler craze, by reaching No. 6 with their immaculate remake of *Duke Of Earl*, thus giving the song its first entry into the UK charts. (Bob MacDonald).
Born in 1940 in Chigago a soul singer whose classic hit was *Duke of Earl* in 1962: a number one on bothe black and white charts, it owed much to doo-wop with its 'dook dook dook' chorus. He benefited from the writing and production skill of Curtis Mayfield, who wrote his signature tune *Rainbow) and others. Chandler's visual gimmick was a ducal outfit including monocle, top hat, cane and cloak. Duets with Barbara Acklin and Jerry Butler were hits; he continued with occasional series of hits through the late '70's disco boom with chocolate-brown vocals on dance records and made a new album as recently as 1985. (Donald Clarke, April 1989).*

DOES SHE HAVE A FRIEND
Tracks: / Does she have a friend / Let me make love to you.
7" Single: Released Jun '80, on 20th Century, by 20th Century Records. Deleted Jun '83. Catalogue no: **TC 2451**

DUKE OF EARL (SINGLE)
7" Single: Released Jul '82, on Old Gold, by Old Gold Records. Deleted Jul '88. Catalogue no: **OG 9030**

GET DOWN
Tracks: / Get down.
7" Single: Released Feb '79, on 20th Century, by 20th Century Records. Deleted Feb '82. Catalogue no: **BTC 1040**

LOVE IS THE ANSWER
Tracks: / Love is the answer / I'm attracted to you.
12" Single: Released Aug '81, on 20th Century, by 20th Century Records. Deleted '84. Catalogue no: **TCD 2505**

NOTHING CAN STOP ME
Tracks: / Nothing can stop me.
7" Single: Released Jun '68, on Soul City, by Soul City Records. Deleted Jun '71. Catalogue no: **SC 102**

WHEN YOU'RE NUMBER 1
Tracks: / When you're number 1.
7" Single: Released Sep '79, on 20th Century, by 20th Century Records. Deleted Sep '82. Catalogue no: **TC 2411**

Chandler, George

THIS COULD BE THE NIGHT
Tracks: / This could be the night / Can't go back no more.
7" Single: Released May '82, on Polydor, by Polydor Ltd. Deleted '85. Catalogue no: **POSP 436**
12" Single: Released May '82, on Polydor, by Polydor Ltd. Deleted '85. Catalogue no: **POSPX 436**

Chanel

YOU'VE GOT A GIFT
Tracks: / You've got a gift / I'll be your girl.
7" Single: Released Apr '82, on Mass Media, Deleted Apr '85. Catalogue no: **MM 1007**
12" Single: Released Apr '82, on Mass Media, Catalogue no: **MMM 12 1007**

Chanelle

ONE MAN
Tracks: / One man.
12" Single: Released Feb '89, on Cool Tempo, by Chrysalis Records. Catalogue no: **COOLX 183**
7" Single: Released Feb '89, on Profile (USA), by Profile Records (USA). Catalogue no: **PRO 7241**
12" Single: Released 20 Mar '89, on Cool Tempo, by Chrysalis Records. Catalogue no: **COOLXR 183**
7" Single: Released Feb '89, on Cool Tempo, by Chrysalis Records. Catalogue no: **COOL 183**

Chaney, Allen

SOUND OF MUZAK
Tracks: / Sound of muzak / It is nowhere.
7" Single: Released Jan '82, on Albion, by Albion Records. Catalogue no: **ION 1027**

Change

Biographical details: Change came to prominence in 1980 when their meaty single *A Lover's Holiday* became a big dance and soul hit in the States. It proceeded to reach No. 40 on the pop chart and also sold well in Britain where it reached No. 14 on the national charts. In the latter country it was a double A sided single combining *A Lover's Holiday* with *Glow Of Love*. The next 45 *Searching* was an even stronger song and took Change to No. 11 in the UK. This track featured lead vocals by Luther Vandross, who was to become a major figure on the US soul scene in the early Eighties.
Subsequent releases attracted favourable reviews by soul critics, but it was not until 1984 that Change repeated their '80 success. They issued a single and album called *Change of Heart* in collaboration with the producing/arranging/songwriting team of Jimmy Jam and Terry Lewis, who were fresh from their success with the S.O.S. Band's single *Just be good to me*. The new Change offerings did well on the US black charts and the UK pop charts. The single reached No. 17 in Britain, where the album did unusually good business for a soul LP. (Bob MacDonald)..

ALRIGHT LET'S GO
Tracks: / Alright let's go / Part of me.
7" Single: Released Mar '85, on Cool Tempo, by Chrysalis Records. Deleted '86. Catalogue no: **COOL 107**
12" Single: Released Mar '85, on Cool Tempo, by Chrysalis Records. Catalogue no: **COOLX 107**

CHANGE OF HEART
Tracks: / Change of heart.
7" Single: Released Jun '84, on WEA, by WEA Records. Deleted Jun '87. Catalogue no: **YZ 7**

GLOW OF LOVE
Tracks: / Glow of love / It's a great affair.
7" Single: Released Nov '80, on WEA, by WEA Records. Deleted '83. Catalogue no: **K 79187**

LOVER'S HOLIDAY, A
Tracks: / Lover's holiday / Glow of love, The.
7" Single: Released Jun '80, on WEA, by WEA Records. Deleted Jun '83. Catalogue no: **K 79141**

MUTUAL ATTRACTION
Tracks: / Mutual attraction.
7" Single: Released Jun '85, on Cool Tempo, by Chrysalis Records. Catalogue no: **COOL 111**
12" Single: Released Jun '85, on Cool Tempo, by Chrysalis Records. Deleted '86. Catalogue no: **COOLX 111**

OH WHAT A FEELING
Tracks: / Oh what a feeling.
12" Single: Released Apr '85, on Cool Tempo, by Chrysalis Records. Catalogue no: **COOLX 109**
12" Single: Released Apr '85, on Cool Tempo, by Chrysalis Records. Catalogue no: **COOLX 1009**
7" Single: Released Apr '85, on Cool Tempo, by Chrysalis Records. Catalogue no: **COOL 109**

PARADISE
Tracks: / Paradise / Your move.
7" Single: Released Oct '81, on WEA, by WEA Records. Deleted '85. Catalogue no: **K 79196**

SEARCHING
Tracks: / Searching.
7" Single: Released Sep '80, on WEA, by WEA Records. Deleted Sep '83. Catalogue no: **K 79156**
7" Single: Released Sep '80, on WEA, by WEA Records. Deleted Sep '83. Catalogue no: **K 79156**

STOP FOR LOVE
Tracks: / Stop for love / Heaven of my life.
7" Single: Released Jul '81, on WEA, by WEA Records. Deleted '85. Catalogue no: **K 79217**

VERY BEST IN YOU
Tracks: / Very best in you.
7" Single: Released Jun '82, on London (Decca), by Decca International. Deleted Jun '87. Catalogue no: **LON 009**
12" Single: Released Jun '82, on London (Decca), by Decca International. Deleted Jun '87. Catalogue no: **LONX 009**

YOU ARE MY MELODY
Tracks: / You are my melody.
7" Single: Released Aug '84, on WEA, by WEA Records. Deleted Aug '87. Catalogue no: **YZ 14**

Changing Faces

I WANT YOU
Tracks: / I want you / I want you (radio edit) / I want you (dance mix).
12" Single: Released 21 Nov '88, on G.T.I. Records, by G.T.I. Music. Catalogue no: **GT 1003T**

Channel 3

I'VE GOT A GUN (SINGLE)
Tracks: / I've got a gun.
7" Single: Released Jan '84, on No Future, Deleted '87. Catalogue no: **01 11**

Channel, Bruce

Biographical details: This American singer born in Jacksonville, Texas, shot to fame in 1962 with his one-off smash *Hey! baby*. Prior to this he had made a number of unsuccessful country-tinged rock 'n' roll records, but the catchy *Hey! baby* was a pop record with a blues influence. It reached No. 1 in the US, No. 2 in the UK. One of the most memorable features of the single was its distinctive harmonica accompaniment, played by Delbert McClinton (who had to wait nineteen years for his big solo US hit - 1981's *Giving it up for your love*). When Channel played in Britain in '62, an up-and-coming group called the Beatles were his support act. They were impressed by McClinton and used a similar harmonica sound later that year on their first hit *Love Me Do*.
Channel remained active in the music business for many years, but never came up with another *Hey! baby* (a song he co-wrote). His only subsequent Top 40 hit on either side of the Atlantic was the British No. 11 placing of 1968's *Keep On*. (Bob MacDonald).
Born in 1940 in Texas, a pop singer based in country music. Like Elvis Presley, his break came on the Louisiana Hayride in the '50's; then *Hey baby* made number one in USA, two in UK in 1962 with the plaintive harmonica of Delbert McLinton, inspiring John Lennon on the Beatles *Love me do* and *Please please me*. Ironically, the Beatles swamped Channel's pop career along with many others. (Donald Clarke, April 1989).

HEY BABY
Tracks: / Hey baby.
7" Single: Released Mar '62, on Mercury (EMI), Deleted Mar '65. Catalogue no: **AMT 1171**

KEEP ON
Tracks: / Keep on.
7" Single: Released Jun '68, on Bell, Deleted Jun '71. Catalogue no: **BELL 1010**

Chanson

DON'T HOLD BACK

Tracks: / Don't hold back.
7" Single: Released Jan '79, on Ariola, by BMG Records (UK). Deleted Jan '82. Catalogue no: **ARO 140**

Chant Of Barry Flynn

SMILE AND THE KISS
Tracks: / Smile and the kiss / Big love theme.
7" Single: Released Apr '84, on Ensign, by Ensign Records. Deleted '85. Catalogue no: **ENY 511**
12" Single: Released Apr '84, on Ensign, by Ensign Records. Deleted '85. Catalogue no: **12ENY 511**

Chantays

Biographical details: Brian Carman, Bob Marshall, Bob Spickard, Warren Waters and Bob Welch had a one-off hit single in 1963 with the instrumental *Pipeline*, a memorable pop tune that rode the crest of America's Jan & Dean/Beach Boys-led surfing wave. This summery single reached No 4 in the US, No 16 in the UK. Britain was ignoring most of the hits inspired by the Californian surfing craze, as the sport was not popular here, but as the Chantays' disc had no words UK record buyers were able to judge it solely on its musical merits. The same was true of the Surfaris' instrumental 45, *Wipeout*, a transatlantic Top Five hit later that summer. By the time the Surfaris hit big, however, the Chantays were already back on the road to obscurity. (Bob MacDonald, 1985.).

PIPELINE
Tracks: / Pipeline.
7" Single: Released Apr '63, on London-American, Deleted Apr '66. Catalogue no: **HLD 9696**
7" Single: Released Jul '80, on MCA, by MCA Records. Deleted '87. Catalogue no: **MCA 702**

PIPELINE (OLD GOLD)
Tracks: / Pipeline / Wipe out.
7" Single: Released Jul '82, on Old Gold, by Old Gold Records. Catalogue no: **OG 9171**

Chantelle

DESPERATE TIME
Tracks: / Desperate time / Waiting in the park.
12" Single: Released Mar '85, on Phaze 1, Catalogue no: **PRF 1**

I LOVE EVERY LITTLE THING ABOUT YOU
Tracks: / I love every little thing about you / Over-world.
7" Single: Released Jul '86, on T-Mac, by T-Mac Records. Deleted '88. Catalogue no: **UEZS 5**

SUMMER LOVER
Tracks: / Summer lover / Summer's day.
7" Single: Released Aug '89, on V-Ram, Catalogue no: **V-RAM 0014**

Chanter Sisters

Biographical details: British vocal duo Doreen and Irene Chanter scored a one-off UK chart entry in 1976. The well-executed, melodic *Side Show* single reached No 43. It was written by Roger Cook, who also produced, and Herbie Flowers, two seasoned music business professionals who had recently come from the defunct Blue Mink. *Side Show* was taken from an album entitled *First Flight*, a misnomer as the Chanters had issued an LP called *Birds Of A Feather* as long ago as 1970: this was conveniently overlooked by Polydor Records in '76 as they wanted to market the girls as hot new talent. The duo failed, however, despite the single's promise. (Bob MacDonald, 1985.).

CAN'T STOP DANCING
Tracks: / Can't stop dancing.
7" Single: Released '79, on Safari, by Safari Records. Catalogue no: **SAFE 10**

SIDE SHOW
Tracks: / Sideshow.
7" Single: Released Jul '76, on Polydor, by Polydor Ltd. Deleted Jul '79. Catalogue no: **2058 735**

Chaos

TRIBAL WARFARE
Tracks: / Tribal warfare.
7" Single: Released May '88, on Pogar, Catalogue no: **POGAR 10**

Chaos UK

BURNING BRITAIN (EP)
Tracks: / Burning Britain.
7" Single: Released Mar '82, on Riot City, by Riot City Records. Catalogue no: **RIOT 6**

LOUD, POLITICAL AND UNCOMPROMISING
Tracks: / Loud, political and uncompromising.
7" Single: Released Jul '82, on Riot City, by Riot City Records. Catalogue no: **RIOT 12**

SINGLES EP
12" Single: Released Sep '84, on Riot City, by Riot City Records. Catalogue no: **12 RIOT 32**

Chaotic Dischord

F*CK THE WORLD
Tracks: / F**k the world.
7" Single: Released Jul '82, on Riot City, by Riot City Records. Catalogue no: **RIOT 10**

FINAL CURTAIN
Tracks: / Final curtain.
7" Single: Released Jan '84, on Riot City, by Riot City Records. Catalogue no: **12 RIOT 30**

NEVER TRUST A FRIEND (3 TRACK EP)
Tracks: / Never trust a friend.
7" Single: Released May '83, on Riot City, by Riot City Records. Catalogue no: **RIOT 22**

Chaotic Youth

SAD SOCIETY (EP)
Tracks: / Sad society.
7" Single: Released May '83, on Lightbeat, Catalogue no: **YOUTH 1**

Cha-pelle, Maria

DANCING INTO LOVE
Tracks: / Dancing into love / Dancing into love (version).
7" Single: Released Jan '89, on RCA, by BMG Records (UK). Catalogue no: **PB 42227**
12" Single: Released Jan '89, on RCA, by BMG Records (UK). Catalogue no: **PT 42228**

Chapin, Harry

Biographical details: This American singer-songwriter, born in Greenwich Village, New York, spent about a decade on the periphery of the music business before chalking up his first American hit in 1972. That song was *Taxi* and was taken from his first Elektra Records album, *Heads And Tails*. *Taxi* reached No 24 on the US charts and set the course for future Chapin output: a melodramatic narrative sung with intensity. His story songs were sometimes hightly perceptive, at other simplistically moralistic. His only British hit came in 1974 when he reached No 34 with the single *WOLD*, a No 36 hit in the States, which told the story of morning DJ on an imaginary radio station. His only US Top Twenty single was a No 1: *Cat's In The Cradle*, co-written with his wife, Sandy, told the story of a developing and changing relationship between a father and son and is his best-known track. Chapin was always far more popular in America than anywhere else and he remained an effective and well-received live performer in his home country throughout the rest of the 70's. In 1980 he achieved his fourth and final US Top Forty single (his first since Cat's In The Cradle) with the appropriately titled *Sequel*. This was a sequel to his first hit, *Taxi*, and peaked at No 23, one place higher than the '72 original. Noted for his social and humanitarian awareness, both inside and outside his musical career, Chapin made a number of substantial donations to UNICEF at various times and also undertook lengthy benefit tours in aid of the World Health Organisation. His life was tragically ended by a fatal car crash in July 1981, at the age of 38. (Bob MacDonald, 1985.).
A USA singer/songwriter (1942-81) whose brother Tom is another (Tom's lates album is on the Chicago Flying Fish label). Harry wrote songs for a Chapin Brothers album on Epic in 1978; always willing to try something new, he rented an NYC venue for the summer in 1971 instead of renting himself out as an entertainer (the band included brother Steve). He then signed with Elektra. *W*O*R*L*D* was about an aging DJ; his number one hit *Cat's in the cradle* about a father too busy to give time to his children. He mounted a Broadway show *The night that made America famous* in 1975 that was nominated for awards, and did a Hollywood revue Chapin in 1977. He was killed in a car crash, and is still sorely missed for talent and spirit of optimism. (Donald Clarke, April 1989).

REMEMBER WHEN THE MUSIC
Tracks: / Remember when the music / Northwest.
7" Single: Released May '81, on Epic, by CBS Records. Deleted May '84. Catalogue no: **EPC A 1168**

W.O.L.D.
Tracks: / W.O.L.D. / Cat's in the cradle.
7" Single: Released May '74, on Elektra, by Elektra Records (UK). Deleted May '77. Catalogue no: **K 12133**
7" Single: Released Sep '76, on Elektra (USA), by Elektra Records (USA). Deleted Jun '87. Catalogue no: **K 12224**

Chaplin, Charlie

BOYIE BOYIE
Tracks: / Boyie boyie.
12" Single: Released Nov '85, on Horseshoe, Catalogue no: **UNKNOWN**

COME BACK CHARLIE
Tracks: / Come back Charlie.
12" Single: Released Apr '86, on Winner, by Creole Records. Catalogue no: **WINT 004**

KILLER
Tracks: / Killer.
12" Single: Released Oct '84, on Power House, Catalogue no: **UNKNOWN**

MI GAL A QUESTION MI
Tracks: / Mi gal a question mi.
7" Single: Released Jan '89, on Exterminator, Catalogue no: **Unknown**

UNITY IN STRENGTH
Tracks: / Unity is strength.
12" Single: Released Apr '83, on CSA, by CSA Records. Deleted '88. Catalogue no: **SPCSA 12002**

Chapman, Toby

ALWAYS
Tracks: / Always / Give it a little time.
7" Single: Released Sep '81, on Klub, by Klub Records. Deleted '88. Catalogue no: **KLUB 31**
7" Single: Released Sep '86, on Tembo, by Tembo Records. Catalogue no: **TML 120**

THAT'S HOW HEARTS BREAK
Tracks: / That's how hearts break / Forever.
7" Single: Released Feb '87, on Tembo, by Tembo Records. Catalogue no: **TML 125**

Chapman, Tracy

BABY CAN I HOLD YOU
Tracks: / Baby can I hold you / Across the lines / Mountain O' things (12" only.).
12" Single: Released Nov '88, on Elektra, by Elektra Records (UK). Catalogue no: **EKR 82T**
7" Single: Released May '89, on Elektra, by Elektra Records (UK). Catalogue no: **UNKNOWN**
7" Single: Released Nov '88, on Elektra, by Elektra Records (UK). Catalogue no: **EKR 82**
CD 5": Released Nov '88, on Elektra, by Elektra Records (UK). Catalogue no: **EKR 82CD**

CROSSROADS (SINGLE)
Tracks: / Crossroads.
12" Single: Released Sep '89, on Elektra, by Elektra Records (UK). Catalogue no: **EKR 95 T**
7" Single: Released Sep '89, on Elektra, by Elektra Records (UK). Catalogue no: **EKR 95 X**
7" Single: Released Sep '89, on Elektra, by Elektra Records (UK). Catalogue no: **EKR 95**
CD 5": Released Sep '89, on Elektra, by Elektra Records (UK). Catalogue no: **EKR 95 CD**
Cassingle: Released Sep '89, on Elektra, by Elektra Records (UK). Catalogue no: **EKR 95 C**

FAST CAR
Tracks: / Fast car / For you / Behind the wall (* Track on 12" version only.).
7" Single: Released May '88, on Elektra, by Elektra Records (UK). Catalogue no: **EKR 73**
12" Single: Released May '88, on Elektra, by Elektra Records (UK). Catalogue no: **EKR 73T**

TALKIN' 'BOUT A REVOLUTION
Tracks: / Talkin' 'bout a revolution / If not now / She's got her ticket (CD only).
CD 5": Released 22 Aug '88, on Elektra, by Elektra Records (UK). Catalogue no: **EKR 78CD**
7" Single: Released 22 Aug '88, on Elektra, by Elektra Records (UK). Catalogue no: **EKR 78**
12" Single: Released 22 Aug '88, on Elektra, by Elektra Records (UK). Catalogue no: **EKR 78T**

Chappelle, Helen

VIDEO LOVE
Tracks: / Video love / Are you ready.
7" Single: Released May '81, on WEA, by WEA Records. Deleted May '86. Catalogue no: **K 18740**

Chaps

LEGEND OF ROBIN HOOD
Tracks: / Legend of Robin Hood / Jock the rapper.
7" Single: Released Mar '84, on Dakota, Catalogue no: **DAK 16**

RAWHIDE
Tracks: / Rawhide / Ghost riders in the sky.
7" Pic: Released Sep '82, on Stiff, by Stiff Records. Deleted Sep '85. Catalogue no: **RAWP 1**
7" Pic: Released Sep '82, on Stiff, by Stiff Records. Catalogue no: **PRAW 1**
7" Single: Released Sep '82, on Stiff, by Stiff Records. Catalogue no: **RAW 1**

Chapter 8

WE NEED LOVE (OLD GOLD)
Tracks: / We need love / I just wanna be your girl.
12" Single: Released 24 Apr '89, on Old Gold, by Old Gold Records. Catalogue no: **OG 4508**

Chapter & The Verse

ALL THIS AND HEAVEN TOO
Tracks: / All this and heaven too / Lover come back to me.
12" Single: Released Apr '89, on Rham, by Rham Records. Catalogue no: **RX 8801**
12" Single: Released Jul '88, on Rham, by Rham Records. Catalogue no: **RS 8801**

Chaquito

NEVER ON SUNDAY
Tracks: / Never on Sunday.
7" Single: Released Oct '60, on Fontana, by Phonogram Ltd. Deleted Oct '63. Catalogue no: **H 265**

Characters

LOVE TALK
Tracks: / Love talk / Where's all the love gone.
7" Single: Released Oct '86, on Characters, Catalogue no: **BEM 701**

Charade

BREAK ME
Tracks: / Break me.
12" Single: Released Aug '84, on Passion, by Skratch Records. Catalogue no: **PASH 30(12)**

CONVERSATIONS
Tracks: / Conversations / Good good feeling.
7" Single: Released May '81, on Bronze, by Bronze Records. Deleted May '84. Catalogue no: **BRO 119**

GOT TO GET TO YOU
Tracks: / Got to get to you.
12" Single: Released Aug '83, on Passion, by Skratch Records. Catalogue no: **PASH 04(12)**
7" Single: Released Aug '83, on Passion, by Skratch Records. Catalogue no: **PASH 04**

I'M THE ONE
12" Single: Released '88, on Passion, by Skratch Records. Catalogue no: **PASH 26(12)**

Charge

DESTROY THE YOUTH (EP)
Tracks: / Destroy the youth / No one knows / Can I go to heaven / Absolution.
7" Single: Released Feb '82, on Kamera, Deleted '88. Catalogue no: **ERA 003**

FASHION
Tracks: / Fashion / Ugly shadows.
7" Single: Released May '82, on Kamera, Deleted '88. Catalogue no: **ERA 007**

LUXURY
Tracks: / Luxury / Madman in the north.
7" Single: Released Sep '82, on Kamera, Deleted '88. Catalogue no: **ERA 015**

Chariot

ALL ALONE AGAIN
Tracks: / All alone again.
12" Single: Released Mar '85, on Shades, Catalogue no: **SHAD 2**

Charisma

EVERYTHING IS FINE
Tracks: / Everything is fine / Every dub.
12" Single: Released Sep '82, on King & City, Catalogue no: **KCD 006**

LOVE IS JUST AROUND THE CORNER
Tracks: / Love is just around the corner.
12" Single: Released Aug '84, on MK, Catalogue no: **MKR D 0021**

OPEN UP THE DOOR
Tracks: / Open up the door / It's a sin.
12" Single: Released Feb '82, on King & City, Catalogue no: **KCD 005**

SOMETHING ABOUT YOU
Tracks: / Something about you.
12" Single: Released Jan '85, on Neville

King, by Neville King Records. Catalogue no: **NKRD 0024**

Charity Case

SAFE IN MIND
7" Single: Released '88, on Fishdisc, Catalogue no: **F 002**

Charjan, Papa

ONE SCOTCH, ONE LAGER, ONE BREW
Tracks: / One scotch, one lager, one brew / Moany, moany.
7" Single: Released May '86, on Shuttle, Deleted Nov '87. Catalogue no: **BREW 1**
12" Single: Released May '86, on Shuttle, Deleted Nov '87. Catalogue no: **12BREW 1**

ONE SCOTCH, ONE TENNANTS, ONE BREW
Tracks: / One scotch, one tennants, one brew / One scotch, one lager, one brew / Moany, moany / Drinking spree.
12" Single: Released Jun '86, on Shuttle, Catalogue no: **12BREWT 1**

Charlene

Biographical details: Charlene Duncan, an American singer with a clear, attractive voice, recorded a song called *I've Never Been To Me for Motown* in 1977. It peaked at No 97 on the Billboard Hot Hundred and was the follow-up to two previous minor hits for the frustrated Charlene: the first had reached No 97, the second 96. In Britain *I've Never Been To Me* was even less successful for Charlene, where a version by Nancy Wilson grabbed the airplay but still failed to chart. Charlene eventually decided to drop her recording career and settled in Ilford, on the outskirts of London, with her British husband. She was working in an Ilford sweetshop in the spring of 1982 when she received a call telling her that *I've Never Been To Me* was receiving renewed US interest and airplay and had started to climb the American charts. It gathered momentum and surged to No 3 on the Hot Hundred. The word spread across the Atlantic and the record went to the very top of the UK chart, becoming Motown's only No 1 by a white artist. It was a highly melodic song sung in the first person: the title referred to the fact that the storyteller had been round the world and experienced a great deal but had "never been to me". Some found the song and the sentiment moving and highly original, others found it nauseating and twee. Either way, Charlene was a one-hit wonder. A ghastly gospel duet with Stevie Wonder called *Used To Be* was, mercifully, a turkey on both sides of the Atlantic. (Bob MacDonald, 1985.)
A white vocalist from L.A. who had a short stay at Motown, retired from music and was rediscovered working behind the counter of a sweet shop in London when the saccharine ballad *I've never been to me* was revived by a deejay in Tampa, Florida: it reached number three in the USA and number one in the UK. She was swiftly resigned by Motown who railroaded her into disco, where she was not very successful: the title cut of *Used to be*, a duet with Stevie Wonder, made the top 40 in the USA, it's lyrics allegedly too strong for airplay; the album squeezed into the USA top 200. (Donald Clarke, April 1989)c.

IF YOU TAKE AWAY THE PAIN UNTIL THE..
Tracks: / If you take away the pain until the morning.
7" Single: Released Aug '83, on Motown, by BMG Records (UK). Catalogue no: **TMG 1310**

IT AIN'T EASY COMIN' DOWN
Tracks: / It ain't easy comin' down / Ninca te ido ar mi / If i could see myself.
7" Single: Released Aug '82, on Motown, by BMG Records (UK). Catalogue no: **TMG 1272**

I'VE NEVER BEEN TO ME
Tracks: / I've never been to me / Somewhere in my life.
7" Single: Released Mar '82, on Motown, by BMG Records (UK). Catalogue no: **TMG 1260**

USED TO BE (SINGLE)
Tracks: / Used to be.
7" Single: Released Nov '82, on Motown, by BMG Records (UK). Catalogue no: **TMG 1287**

WE'RE BOTH IN LOVE WITH YOU
Tracks: / We're both in love with you.
7" Single: Released Oct '84, on Motown, by BMG Records (UK). Catalogue no: **TMG 1352**

Charles, Alex

COME ON OVER
Tracks: / Come on over / Come on over (version).
7" Single: Released Jul '87, on New York, Catalogue no: **AC 1**
12" Single: Released 30 May '87, on New York, Catalogue no: **ACT 1**

Charles, C.August

GET UP GET WITH IT
Tracks: / Get up get with it / Get up get with it (dub inst).
7" Single: Released Mar '87, on Champion, by Champion Records. Catalogue no: **CHAMP 32**
12" Single: Released Mar '87, on Champion, by Champion Records. Catalogue no: **CHAMP 1232**

Charles, Clare

TOO MUCH
Tracks: / One step closer / Too much.
7" Single: Released Jan '87, on IBE, Catalogue no: **BEP 1**

Charles, Don

WALK WITH ME MY ANGEL
Tracks: / Walk with me my angel.
7" Single: Released Feb '62, on Decca, by Decca Records. Deleted Feb '65. Catalogue no: **F 11424**

Charles, Evan

ASK YOURSELF
Tracks: / Ask yourself.
7" Single: Released Aug '82, on Naive, by Naive Records. Catalogue no: **NAV 2**

INTIMACY
Tracks: / Intimacy.
7" Single: Released May '83, on Naive, by Naive Records. Catalogue no: **NAV 6**

Charles, Julie

AS LONG AS YOU LOVE ME
Tracks: / As long as you love me.
12" Single: Released Jan '83, on Body Music, by Nuclear Records. Catalogue no: **B 777**

Charles, Kelly

REACHIN'
Tracks: / Reachin'.
7" Single: Released Sep '89, on Champion, by Champion Records. Catalogue no: **CHAMP X214**
12" Single: Released Sep '89, on Champion, by Champion Records. Catalogue no: **CHAMP X12214**

YOU'RE NO GOOD FOR ME
Tracks: / You're no good for me / You're no good for me (Dub) / You're no good for me (club) / You're no good for me (radio edit) / Classy club (dub).
7" Single: Released Sep '87, on London Records, by London Records. Catalogue no: **LON 153**
12" Single: Released Sep '87, on London Records, by London Records. Catalogue no: **LONX 153**

YOU'RE THE ONE
Tracks: / You're the one / You're the one (version).
7" Single: Released Jul '89, on Champion, by Champion Records. Catalogue no: **CHAMP 100**
12" Single: Released Jul '89, on Champion, by Champion Records. Catalogue no: **CHAMP 12100**

Charles, Kenny

TONGUE TIED
Tracks: / Tongue tied.
7" Single: Released Mar '86, on MCA, by MCA Records. Catalogue no: **MCA 1044**

Charles, Phil

JOKER, THE
Tracks: / Joker, The / Joker, The (DJ version).
7" Single: Released Sep '82, on Fun, Catalogue no: **FUN 1**

Charles, Ray

Biographical details: This American singer, pianist, arranger and songwriter is one of the most important artists in the post-war history of black music. Born Ray Charles Robinson in Georgia in 1932, he was blinded by glaucoma at the age of six and rendered an orphan while in his early teens. After moving to Seattle, Washington, he spent the early 50's playing in a trio which based its style heavily on that of Nat King Cole. It was about this time that he dropped his surname, in order to avoid confusion with star boxer Sugar Ray Robinson. During the mid to late 50's Charles developed his own highly distinctive style, fusing rhythm and blues, gospel and jazz, and helping to create soul music, a genre that exploded into fashion in the 60's. Charles' first American Top Forty hit was 1957's Swanee River Rock, which reached No 34. His big breakthrough was 1959's self-penned *What'd I Say?*, a frantic, frenetic call-and-response single which was an enormously exciting listening experience appealing to fans of rock 'n' roll, blues, gospel and jazz. It reached No 6 on the US chart and its instant classic status was confirmed by the fact that, within five years, it had become a US Top Thirty hit for Jerry Lee Lewis, Bobby Darin and Elvis Presley. Charles' next milestone record was a 1960 rendition of a 1930 Hoagy Carmichael number: *Georgia On My Mind*, a tribute to Ray's own birthplace, gave him his first US No 1 and his first UK hit of any kind. A second American chart-topper came in '61 with another classic, the highly catchy *Hit The Road, Jack*, a No 6 hit in Britain. All these achievements, though, were dwarfed by the red-hot Ray Charles' 1962 exploits. *I Can't Stop Loving You*, a country balled written by fellow hitmaker Don Gibson, was reworked by Charles and became his biggest-ever single on both sides of the Atlantic and his only single to go to No 1 in both America and Britain. It was featured on his seminal, highly influential LP *Modern Sounds In Country And Western Music*, which further enhanced his status as a bridge between white country music and the black R & B style. Its success inspired a Volume 2 follow-up the following year. By the mid-60's he had chalked up two more transAtlantic Top Ten singles -- *You Don't Know Me* and *Take These Chains From My Heart* -- plus another three US Top Tenners with *You Are My Sunshine*, *Busted* and *Cryin' Time*. By this time he had lost the raw edge that had been so much a part of his earlier work and was concentrating on ballads. During the late 60's and early 70's drug addiction marred his career; he eventually overcame this affliction. His late 70's and early 80's recordings did not break new ground but were nonetheless competent restatements of his eclectic approach that, 20 years earlier, had opened up new possibilities for countless future stars. (Bob MacDonald, 1985.)
Ray Charles Robinson was born in 1930 or 1932 in Albany, Georgia; blinded at age six by an accident, he became the most successful soul artist of all time. He went to Florida school for the blind, then to Seattle to get as far from the South as possible. He began heavily influenced by Nat 'King' Cole, like Cole leading a trio, and was the first black in the Northwest to have a TV show, with his hits in the R&B chart, but soon developed his own style: his soulful arrangement of *Things that I used to do* for Guitar Slim was a number one R&B hit in 1954; meanwhile he had signed with Atlantic and his string of originals began in 1953: *Losing hand, It should've been me, Mess around, I got a woman* (covered by Elvis Presley), *Hallelujah I love here so* and others were all R&B hits, sometimes fitting new words to gospel tunes: *Talkin' 'bout Jesus* became *Talkin' 'bout you*; Clara Ward's *This little light of mine* became *This little girl of mine*; *How Jesus died* became *Lonely Avenue*. Big Bill Broonzy said 'He's mixing the blues with the spituals. I know what's wrong ... he should be singing in a church.' But the mixture of gospel emotion, secular subject matter and smooth but honest delivery led to comic Bill Cosby's routine about Columbus going to America so he could discover Ray Charles. He used a female quartet, The Raelets; on the soulful *What kind of man are you* they carried the vocal on their own. His first LP *The great Ray Charles* in 1957 was a jazz set, with laid back instrumentals such as Horace Silver's *Doodlin'* and his own *Sweet sixteen bars*; his first top 40 pop hit was *Swanee river rock* the same year. Another jazz-oriented album, with Basie and Ellington sidemen and arrangements by Ralph Burns, Quincy Jones and others dubbed him 'The Genius'. His extended arrangement with the Raelets *What'd I say* was a hard-driving gospel style rock'n'roll hit in 1959 and he was already alegend; he switched to ABC in 1960 with an astonishing contract for a black artists then, allowing him to retain ownership of his own recordings at the end of the association; he soon had a smash number one hit with a down-home vocal on the Hoagy Carmichael evergreen *Georgia on my mind*, used in film soundtracks of *In the heat of the night* in 1969 and *George's friends* in 1982. The impulse album *Genius plus soul equals jazz* was arranged by Jones; women got the upperhand as the Raelets told hime to *Hit the road Jack*, his second number one single in 1961 charted (and was the reissue of the year in the USA in 1988), followed by the number one hit album *Modern sounds in country and western music* in 1962: his version of Don Gibson's *I can't stop loving you* hit the top of the pop, black and country charts. A sequel was a number two album the same year; he could do no wrong. His eclectic material predictably upset some critics, but he was voted best male singer five years in a row from 1961 by international jazz critics in Down Beat magazine, and won his first Grammy in 1961. He formed his own company, Tangerine in 1962, recording Louis Jordan and others, leasing the records to ABC. He packed a huge sports stadium in Paris several nights at the height of the Algerian crisis; he walked out of an Atlanta gig because the audience was segretated and played the first integrated concert in the Memphis municipal auditorium. In the mid-60's he cured himself of drug addiction and acted in a film; his hits continued to alternate between straight soul numbers and others with slushy strings setting off blues-flecked vocals and piano: there were more country songs in the top ten singles chart, including the humorous *Busted* (written by Harlan Howard); *Crying time* in 1966 won two Grammies. He had 32 top 40 pop hits altogether 1957-71 and more than 50 in the R&B chart 1951-71, and is still pleasing crowds at jazz festivals today. (Donald Clarke, April 1989).

BUSTED
Tracks: / Busted.
7" Single: Released Oct '63, on H.M.V., by EMI Records. Deleted Oct '66. Catalogue no: **POP 1221**

CRYIN' TIME
Tracks: / Crying time.
7" Single: Released Feb '66, on H.M.V., by EMI Records. Deleted Feb '69. Catalogue no: **POP 1502**

DON'T SET ME FREE
Tracks: / Don't set me free.
7" Single: Released Mar '63, on H.M.V., by EMI Records. Deleted Mar '66. Catalogue no: **POP 1133**

ELEANOR RIGBY
Tracks: / Eleanor Rigby.
7" Single: Released Jul '68, on Stateside, by EMI Records. Deleted Jul '71. Catalogue no: **SS 2120**

GEORGIA ON MY MIND (SINGLE)
Tracks: / Georgia on my mind.
7" Single: Released Dec '60, on H.M.V., by EMI Records. Deleted Dec '63. Catalogue no: **POP 792**

HERE WE GO AGAIN
Tracks: / Here we go again.
7" Single: Released Jul '67, on H.M.V., by EMI Records. Deleted Jul '70. Catalogue no: **POP 1595**

HIT THE ROAD JACK (SINGLE)
Tracks: / Hit the road Jack.
7" Single: Released Oct '61, on H.M.V., by EMI Records. Deleted Oct '64. Catalogue no: **POP 935**

I CAN'T STOP LOVING YOU
Tracks: / I can't stop loving you.
7" Single: Released Jun '62, on H.M.V., by EMI Records. Deleted Jun '65. Catalogue no: **POP 1034**

I WISH YOU WERE HERE TONIGHT
Tracks: / I wish you were here tonight.
7" Single: Released May '83, on CBS, by CBS Records. Catalogue no: **A 3407**

I WONDER WHO'S KISSING HER NOW
Tracks: / I wonder who's kissing her now / She's on the ball / Baby won't you please come home.
12" Single: Released Feb '87, on Charly, by Charly Records. Catalogue no: **CYZ 119**
7" Single: Released '87, on Charly, by Charly Records. Catalogue no: **CYZ 7 119**

MAKIN' WHOOPEE
Tracks: / Makin' whoopee.
7" Single: Released Jan '65, on H.M.V., by EMI Records. Deleted Jan '68. Catalogue no: **POP 1383**

NO ONE
Tracks: / No one.
7" Single: Released Sep '63, on H.M.V., by EMI Records. Deleted Sep '66. Catalogue no: **POP 1202**

NO ONE TO CRY TO
Tracks: / No one to cry to.
7" Single: Released Sep '64, on H.M.V., by EMI Records. Deleted Sep '67. Catalogue no: **POP 1333**

SHAKE YOUR TAIL FEATHER
Tracks: / Shake your tail feather / Minnie the moocher.
7" Single: Released Oct '80, on Atlantic, by WEA Records. Deleted Oct '83. Catalogue no: **K 11615**

TAKE THESE CHAINS FROM MY HEART
Tracks: / Take these chains from my heart.
7" Single: Released May '63, on H.M.V., by EMI Records. Deleted May '66. Catalogue no: **POP 1161**

TOGETHER AGAIN

Tracks: / Together again.
7" Single: Released Apr '66, on H.M.V., by EMI Records. Deleted Apr '69. Catalogue no: **POP 1519**

YESTERDAY
Tracks: / Yesterday.
7" Single: Released Dec '67, on Stateside, by EMI Records. Deleted Dec '70. Catalogue no: **SS 2071**

YOU DON'T KNOW ME
Tracks: / You don't know me.
7" Single: Released Sep '62, on H.M.V., by EMI Records. Deleted Sep '65. Catalogue no: **POP 1064**

YOUR CHEATIN' HEART
Tracks: / Your cheatin' heart.
7" Single: Released Dec '62, on H.M.V., by EMI Records. Deleted Dec '65. Catalogue no: **POP 1099**

Charles, Tina

Biographical details: This British singer was working as a session vocalist in 1975 when she recorded *I'm on Fire*, a catchy disco pop single released under the name of 5000 Volts. The song became a UK Top 5 hit but, inexplicably, a different girl was chosen to mime the record when the 5000 Volts group appeared on television. Several months later, in early '76, Tina Charles' solo career was launched, and it was then admitted that she had in fact been the true voice on *I'm On Fire*.
Charles promptly achieved a smash hit under her own name: *I Love To Love (But My Baby Loves To Dance)* logged three weeks at No. 1 on the British charts. It was produced by the Indian-born Biddu, a man who had previously been reponsible for Carl Douglas' 1974 international chart-topper, *Kung-Fu Fighting*. Tina was tiny but had a loud screeching voice to make up for it. With Biddu's help, she managed six further UK Top 30 hits over the following two years, including two more Top Tenners: *Dance Little Lady Dance* and *Dr Love*. After this her name was forgotten. No doubt there will be a few people who look back on Charles' ultra-bouncy singles with nostalgia, but in truth, she epitomised all that was worst in mid-Seventies British pop. (Bob MacDonald)..

DANCE LITTLE LADY
Tracks: / Dance little lady.
7" Single: Released Aug '76, on CBS, by CBS Records. Deleted Aug '79. Catalogue no: **CBS 4480**

DOCTOR LOVE
Tracks: / Doctor Love.
7" Single: Released Dec '76, on CBS, by CBS Records. Deleted Dec '79. Catalogue no: **CBS 4779**

I LOVE TO DANCE
Tracks: / I love to dance / Disco fever.
7" Single: Released Oct '82, on CBS, by CBS Records. Deleted Oct '85. Catalogue no: **CBS 5966**

I LOVE TO LOVE
Tracks: / I love to love (teenage mix) / Biddu Orchestra, The (Sunburn: Accapella, Percussion Dub are only available on the 12"(7"teena) / I love to love.
7" Single: Released Feb '76, on CBS, by CBS Records. Deleted Feb '79. Catalogue no: **CBS 3937**
7" Single: Released Aug '87, on DMC, Deleted May '89. Catalogue no: **DECK 6**
7" Single: Released Apr '82, on CBS, by CBS Records. Catalogue no: **CBS 5966**
12" Single: Released Aug '86, on Disco Mix, by DMC Records. Deleted '87. Catalogue no: **DECK 121**
12" Single: Released Aug '87, on DMC, Catalogue no: **DECK 126**
12" Single: Released Aug '86, on Disco Mix, by DMC Records. Catalogue no: **DECKS 121**
7" Single: Released Aug '86, on Disco Mix, by DMC Records. Deleted '87. Catalogue no: **DECK 1**

I LOVE TO LOVE (OLD GOLD)
Tracks: / I love to love / You set my heart on fire.
7" Single: Released 27 Feb '89, on Old Gold, by Old Gold Records. Catalogue no: **OG 9198**

I'LL GO WHERE YOUR MUSIC TAKES ME
Tracks: / I'll go where your music takes me.
7" Single: Released Mar '78, on CBS, by CBS Records. Deleted Mar '81. Catalogue no: **CBS 6062**

JUST ONE SMILE (SINGLE)
Tracks: / Just one smile / Fire down below.
7" Single: Released Mar '80, on CBS, by CBS Records. Deleted Mar '83. Catalogue no: **CBS 8301**

LOVE BUG-SWEETS FOR MY SWEET

TINA CHARLES - SECOND TIME AROUND (Released on Sonet)

Tracks: / Love bug-sweets for my sweet (medley).
7" Single: Released Oct '77, on CBS, by CBS Records. Deleted Oct '80. Catalogue no: **CBS 5680**

LOVE HUNGER
Tracks: / Love hunger.
7" Single: Released Feb '85, on Sonet, by Sonet Records. Catalogue no: **SON 2276**
12" Single: Released Feb '85, on Sonet, by Sonet Records. Catalogue no: **SONL 2276**

LOVE ME LIKE A LOVER
Tracks: / Love me like a lover.
7" Single: Released May '76, on CBS, by CBS Records. Deleted May '79. Catalogue no: **CBS 4237**

RENDEZVOUS
Tracks: / Rendezvous.
7" Single: Released May '77, on CBS, by CBS Records. Deleted May '80. Catalogue no: **CBS 5174**

ROLLIN'
Tracks: / Rollin' / Don't throw your love.
7" Single: Released Jan '81, on Polydor, by Polydor Ltd. Deleted Jan '84. Catalogue no: **POSP 218**

RUNNING INTO DANGER
Tracks: / Running into danger.
7" Single: Released Sep '85, on Sonet, by Sonet Records. Catalogue no: **SON 2287**
12" Single: Released Sep '85, on Sonet, by Sonet Records. Catalogue no: **SONL 2287**

SECOND TIME AROUND (see panel above)
Tracks: / Second time around / Played for a fool.
7" Single: Released Sep '86, on Sonet, by Sonet Records. Catalogue no: **SON 2300**

TURN BACK THE HANDS OF TIME
Tracks: / Turn back the hands of time / Night follows day.
7" Single: Released Aug '80, on Polydor, by Polydor Ltd. Deleted '83. Catalogue no: **POSP 162**

Charlesworth, Dick

BILLY BOY
Tracks: / Billy boy.
7" Single: Released May '61, on Top Rank (1), Deleted May '64. Catalogue no: **JAR 558**

Charlie

FIVE YEARS
Tracks: / Five years / Only dreaming.
7" Single: Released Apr '82, on Polydor, by Polydor Ltd. Deleted Apr '85. Catalogue no: **POSP 428**

FOR YOUR LOVE
Tracks: / For your love / I'm angry with you.
7" Single: Released Sep '81, on RCA, by BMG Records (UK). Deleted Sep '84. Catalogue no: **RCA 122**

OUR EARTH
Tracks: / Our earth / Sophie.
7" Single: Released Feb '83, on President, by President Records. Catalogue no: **PTZ 514**

PERFECT LOVE
Tracks: / Perfect love / Angry with you.
7" Single: Released Apr '81, on RCA, by BMG Records (UK). Deleted Apr '84. Catalogue no: **RCA 62**

Charlie Chalk

CHARLIE CHALK (SINGLE)
Tracks: / Charlie Chalk: *Various artists.*
7" Single: Released Aug '89, on Redrock, by Redrock Records. Catalogue no: **CHARLIE 1**

Charlie Don't Surf

MAN HIS OWN WORST ENEMY
Tracks: / Man his own worst enemy / Life time.
7" Single: Released Nov '87, on Go Metric, Catalogue no: **GM 002**

Charlie Makes The Cook

BOYS & GIRLS
Tracks: / Boys & girls.
7" Single: Released Jan '88, on Quazar, Catalogue no: **QUA 2**
12" Single: Released Jan '88, on Quazar, Catalogue no: **QUAT 2**

Charlie's Brothers

WISHING TREE
Tracks: / Wishing tree.
7" Single: Released Mar '85, on Lost Moments, Catalogue no: **LM 010**
12" Single: Released Mar '85, on Lost Moments, Catalogue no: **LM 12 010**

Charlotte

BANAKE
Tracks: / Banake / B.B. Seaton: I'm trying / Jamaica mood (This track is only available on 12" single.).
12" Single: Released 21 Nov '87, on Real Authentic Sound (See:RAS), Catalogue no: **RAST 2**

PICTURE OF A CLOWN
12" Single: Released Jun '85, on Tropical Sunset, Catalogue no: **CPP 001**

Charlottes

ARE YOU HAPPY NOW
Tracks: / Are you happy now / How can you say.
7" Single: Released Oct '88, on Molesworth, by New Leaf Records. Catalogue no: **HUNTS 5**

Charm

WALK ON THE WILD SIDE
Tracks: / Walk on the wild side / Phantastic voyage.
Note: (The ultimate house version of Lou Reed's 1973 classic-radically remixed from the Urban Acid album)
7" Single: Released Jan '89, on Urban, by Polydor Ltd. Deleted 30 Jun '89. Catalogue no: **URB 29**
12" Single: Released Jan '89, on Urban, by Polydor Ltd. Deleted 30 Jun '89. Catalogue no: **URBX 29**

Charm School

DANCER
Tracks: / Dancer / Pulling me under.
7" Single: Released Aug '87, on WEA, by WEA Records. Deleted Jul '88. Catalogue no: **YZ 139**
12" Single: Released Aug '87, on WEA, by WEA Records. Deleted Jul '88. Catalogue no: **YZ 139T**

LIFE'S A DECEIVER
Tracks: / Life's a deceiver / Your passion.
7" Single: Released Mar '85, on Zarjazz, by Zarjazz Records. Deleted May '88. Catalogue no: **JAZZ 4**
12" Single: Released Mar '85, on Zarjazz, by Zarjazz Records. Deleted May '88. Catalogue no: **JAZZ 4-12**

SUN
Tracks: / Sun.
7" Single: Released Jan '84, on Button, by Musical Characters Records. Catalogue no: **BTN 113**

Charme

GEORGY PORGY
Tracks: / Georgie Porgie.
7" Single: Released Nov '84, on RCA, by BMG Records (UK). Catalogue no: **RCA 464**

Charmers, Lloyd

GREATEST INSPIRATION
Tracks: / Greatest inspiration.
12" Single: Released Apr '83, on Sarge, Catalogue no: **CHR 1001**

OH ME, OH LADY
Tracks: / Oh me, oh lady / Colour him father.
12" Single: Released Sep '86, on Charmers, Catalogue no: **FRL 8**

Charms

DO IT FOR LOVE
Tracks: / Do it for love / Georgie porgie.
7" Single: Released Jan '80, on RCA, by BMG Records (UK). Deleted Jan '85. Catalogue no: **PC 1727**

I CAN'T LET GO
Tracks: / I can't let go / One step closer.
7" Single: Released Apr '87, on WEA (International), by WEA Records. Deleted Jan '88. Catalogue no: **X 8487**
12" Single: Released Apr '87, on WEA (International), by WEA Records. Deleted Jan '88. Catalogue no: **X 8487T**

Charney, Marlene Roots

IT'S TOO LATE
Tracks: / It's too late.
12" Single: Released Jul '85, on Esso Jaxxon, Catalogue no: **UTU 8501**

Charo

DANCE A LITTLE BIT CLOSER
Tracks: / Dance a little bit closer.
7" Single: Released Apr '78, on Salsoul, Deleted Apr '81. Catalogue no: **SSOL 101**

Chart

CHART
Tracks: / Chart.
7" Single: Released Sep '84, on The Chart, Catalogue no: **THECHART 1**

CharVoni

ALWAYS THERE
Tracks: / Always there (12" only.) / Always there (radio version) (7" only.) / Always there (intense instrumental) / Always there (intense dub mix).
7" Single: Released May '89, on Syncopate, by EMI Records. Deleted Oct '89 Catalogue no: **SY 28**
12" Single: Released Jun '89, on Syncopate, by EMI Records. Deleted Oct '89 Catalogue no: **12SYX 28**
12" Single: Released May '89, on Syncopate, by EMI Records. Deleted Oct '89 Catalogue no: **12SY 28**
12" Single: Released Jun '89, on Syncopate, by EMI Records. Deleted Oct '89 Catalogue no: **203 366 8**

Chas

FOR YOUR LOVE
Tracks: / For your love / Just say you will.
12" Single: Released Oct '86, on Expansion, Catalogue no: **EXPAND 4**

Chas & Dave

Biographical details: Chas Hodges and Dave Peacock are a British vocal and instrumental duo, whose working class comedy style took them from London's pubs to national record and TV stardom. They call their sound 'Rockney', a term derived from their blend of rock music with Cockney humour. This is also the nickname given to Mickey Burt, the duo's uncredited but ever-present drummer.
Chas & Dave's first album was released i

1975. Their first taste of chart success came in November 1978, when *Strummin'* reached No. 52 on the UK singles listings. Shortly after this they achieved their big breakthrough, when *Gertcha* was used by the Courage brewery in a successful TV beer commercial and then, on the strength of this exposure, reached No. 20 as a single. This helped the pair to become nationally known names, although it was another eighteen months before they made a further significant impact on the UK charts. That success was another Courage ad. - *Rabbit* took them into the Top 10 for the first time, despite protests from feminists about the song's alledgedly male chauvinist lyrics. A year later the duo pekaed at No. 21 with *Stars Over 45*, a medley of old music hall favourites assembled in answer to the *Stars On 45* disco medley hits. Their biggest hit came in 1982, when they reached No. 2 in Britain with *Ain't No Pleasing You*, a well-crafted pastiche of the music hall/pub singalong sound that successfully appealed both to the nostalgia market and to younger pop fans. Also in the early Eighties, they enjoyed chart success in two consecutive years, through giving uncredited musical assistance to he recording efforts of their favourite soccer team, Tottenham Hotspur. After this, the single hits dried up, but their LPs fared well on the Britiah album chart and their TV and live work kept them in business. (Bob MacDonald).

A knees up good time pub trio who first hit the big time doing TV adverts: Charles Hodges sings, plays piano and guitar and a little fiddle; Dave Peacock sings and plays guitars; Mick Burt is the drummer. Hodges played piano at 18 as a stand in at a pub rehearsal; Jerry Lee Lewis walked in and said 'What the hell do you need me for when you got him'. He worked with Joe Meek, with Ritchie Blackmore in the Outlaws, with Cliff Bennett's Rebel Rousers and with Peacock in the short lived band Black Claw in 1970; and made three albums with the cult band Heads Hands & Feet 1970-72; he rejoined Peacock in the Albert Lee Band in 1975; meanwhile Burt had played in the Rebel Rousers and gone back to plumbing. Chas & Dave decided to form a group and asked Burt to join. They had a minor hit with *Strummin'* in 1978; then an advertising agent heard them doing *Gertcha* (gotcha) in a pub and signed them for a series of TV adverts for Courage beer: *Gercha* made the UK top 20 in 1979 and became a utility catchphrase. *The sideboard song (got my beer in the sideboard here)* was followed by *Rabbit*, also used in a Courage advert; this top ten hit, a cartoonish sendup of talking wives, outraged feminists who wrote a song called *Beer belly*. They called their music and their label *Rockney* (also Burt's nickname and the name of their 1978 album). They wrote and produced singles for Tottenham Hotspur Football Club in 1981; just to show they could do anything their fine ballad *Ain't pleasin' you* reached number two in 1982, the song's timeless appeal similar to that of *You don't understand) in 1928 (recorded by James P Johnson and Bessie Smith).*

They also recorded as Oily Rags in the USA when Bob Thiele borrowed them from Atlantic to record with Teresa brewer they weren't allowed to be called Chas & Dave. They opened their own London pub in 1985 called Chas & Dave's - a courage house of course. (Donald Clarke, April 1989)n.

AIN'T NO PLEASING YOU
Tracks: / Ain't no pleasing you.
7" Single: Released Feb '82, on Rockney, Catalogue no: **KOR 14**

BEER BARREL BANJOS(ROLL OUT THE BARRELS)
Tracks: / Beer barrel banjos (roll out the barrels).
7" Single: Released Jul '83, on Rockney, Catalogue no: **KOR 10**

DIDDLUM SONG (see panel below)
Tracks: / Diddlum song / Ain't no pleasing you / Bangin' in your head.
7" Single: Released 20 Feb '88, on Bunce, Catalogue no: **7 BUN 2**

FLYING
Tracks: / Flying / Exhibition rag.
7" Single: Released Jul '87, on Bunce, Catalogue no: **7 BUN 1**

GERTCHA
Tracks: / Gertcha / Banging in your head.
7" Single: Released May '79, on EMI, by EMI Records. Deleted May '82. Catalogue no: **EMI 2947**

HALLEY'S COMET
Tracks: / Halley's comet / Brother-in-law.
7" Single: Released Jul '86, on Rockney, Catalogue no: **KOR 28**

HARRY WAS A CHAMPION
Tracks: / Harry was a champion.
7" Single: Released Nov '84, on Rockney, Catalogue no: **KOR 24**

I WONDER IN WHOSE ARMS
Tracks: / I wonder in whose arms / I miss ya girl.
7" Single: Released Sep '84, on Rockney, Catalogue no: **KOR 23**

IN SICKNESS & IN HEALTH
Tracks: / In sickness and in health.
7" Single: Released Sep '85, on BBC, by BBC Records & Tapes. Deleted Sep '87. Catalogue no: **RESL 176**

LONDON GIRLS
Tracks: / London girls.
7" Single: Released Feb '83, on Rockney, Catalogue no: **KOR 17**

LONG LONG AGO
Tracks: / Silent night / Long long ago.
7" Single: Released Nov '86, on Hodgecock Productions, Deleted '88. Catalogue no: **HOD 9**

LOVE SONG
Tracks: / Love song / That's what I like.
7" Single: Released Oct '82, on Rockney, Catalogue no: **KOR 16**

MARGATE
Tracks: / Margate / Give it gavotte.
7" Single: Released Jun '82, on Rockney, Catalogue no: **KOR 15**

CHAS & DAVE - DIDDLUM SONG (Released on Bunce)

MY MELANCHOLY BABY
Tracks: / My melancholy baby.
7" Single: Released Nov '83, on Rockney, Catalogue no: **KOR 21**

POOR OLD MR.WOOGIE
Tracks: / Poor old Mr.Woogie / Uneasy feeling.
7" Single: Released Feb '81, on Rockney, Catalogue no: **ROCKNEY 10**

RABBIT
Tracks: / Rabbit / Sideboard song.
7" Single: Released Nov '80, on Rockney, Catalogue no: **ROCKNEY 9**

ROCK'N'ROLL JAMBOREE MEDLEY
7" Single: Released Nov '85, on Rockney, Catalogue no: **KOR 25**
12" Single: Released Nov '85, on Rockney, Catalogue no: **12KOR 25**

ROMFORD RAP
Tracks: / Romford rap, The / Crackerjack theme.
7" Single: Released Mar '87, on Rainbow, by Rainbow Records. Catalogue no: **RBR 15**

SIDEBOARD SONG
Tracks: / Sideboard song.
7" Single: Released Sep '79, on EMI, by EMI Records. Deleted Sep '82. Catalogue no: **EMI 2986**

STARS OVER 45
Tracks: / Stars over 45 / Harem.
7" Single: Released Nov '81, on Rockney, Catalogue no: **KOR 12**

STRUMMIN'
Tracks: / Strummin'.
7" Single: Released Nov '78, on EMI, by EMI Records. Deleted Nov '81. Catalogue no: **EMI 2874**

THERE IN YOUR EYES
Tracks: / There in your eyes.
7" Single: Released Aug '84, on Rockney, Catalogue no: **KOR 22**

TURN THAT NOISE DOWN
Tracks: / Turn that noise down.
12" Single: Released Aug '81, on Rockney, Catalogue no: **KOR 112**
7" Single: Released Aug '81, on Rockney, Catalogue no: **KOR 11**

YOU'RE JUST IN LOVE
Tracks: / You're just in love / That's what I like.
7" Single: Released Jan '86, on Rockney, Catalogue no: **KOR 26**

Chase

OH WHAT A NIGHT
Tracks: / Oh what a night / Betcha.
7" Single: Released Nov '80, on EMI, by EMI Records. Deleted '83. Catalogue no: **EMI 5122**

Chase, Carol

THIS MUST BE MY SHIP
Tracks: / This must be my ship / It always takes a fool to fool around.
7" Single: Released Feb '80, on Casablanca, by PolyGram UK Ltd. Deleted '83. Catalogue no: **CWS 1001**

Chase, Marianne

LOVE AMNESIA
Tracks: / Love amnesia / Ghosts of love.
7" Single: Released Aug '80, on Double D, Deleted '83. Catalogue no: **DDEE 4**

Chase, Tommy

KILLER JOE (RIGHT CROSS)
Tracks: / Killer Joe / Double street.
7" Single: Released Feb '87, on Stiff, by Stiff Records. Catalogue no: **BUY 256**
12" Single: Released Feb '87, on Stiff, by Stiff Records. Catalogue no: **BUYIT 256**

Chat Show

KINGS OF CONFUSION
Tracks: / Kings of confusion / Reach.
7" Single: Released Jun '87, on Federation, by Federation Records. Deleted '88. Catalogue no: **FED 8**
12" Single: Released Jun '87, on Federation, by Federation Records. Deleted '88. Catalogue no: **FED 812**

NOISY BABY HIGH THING
Tracks: / Noisy baby high thing.
7" Single: Released 20 Feb '88, on Idea, by Idea Records. Catalogue no: **IDEA 011**
12" Single: Released 20 Feb '88, on Idea, by Idea Records. Catalogue no: **IDEAT 011**

RED SKIES
Tracks: / Red skies.
12" Single: Released Apr '86, on Tanz, Catalogue no: **TANZ 4**

SHAKE IT DOWN
Tracks: / Shake it down.
12" Single: Released Dec '86, on Federation, by Federation Records. Catalogue no: **FED 7**

Chatton

EVERYBODY'S SOMEBODY'S FOOL
Tracks: / Everybody's somebody's fool / Miss molly mandy.
7" Single: Released Feb '82, on RCA, by BMG Records (UK). Deleted Feb '87. Catalogue no: **RCA 177**

TAKE MY LOVE AND RUN
Tracks: / Take my love and run / While I'm with you now.
7" Single: Released Oct '81, on RCA, by BMG Records (UK). Deleted Oct '84. Catalogue no: **RCA 147**

Chayell

IT'S NEVER TOO HOT
Tracks: / It's never too hot.
7" Single: Released Nov '87, on Antler, by Antler Records (Belgium). Catalogue no: **ANT 069**

RIO
Tracks: / Rio.
12" Single: Released 23 Apr '88, on Subway, by Subway Records. Catalogue no: **SUB 018**

Chazer

PRACTISE MAKES PERFECT
Tracks: / Practice makes perfect.
7" Single: Released Jan '84, on Polo, by Polo Records. Deleted '88. Catalogue no: **POLO 29**
12" Single: Released Jan '84, on Polo, by Polo Records. Deleted '88. Catalogue no: **POLO 12-29**

Che

I WISH HE DIDN'T TRUST ME SO MUCH
Tracks: / I wish he didn't trust me so much / Fireflies in summer.
7" Single: Released 12 Jun '89, on Siren, by Virgin Records. Catalogue no: **SRN 115**
12" Single: Released 12 Jun '89, on Siren, by Virgin Records. Catalogue no: **SRNT 115**

TRUST
Tracks: / Trust.
7" Single: Released Jun '89, on Siren, by Virgin Records. Catalogue no: **SRN 115**
12" Single: Released Jun '89, on Siren, by Virgin Records. Catalogue no: **SRNT 115**

WHAT YOU'VE BEEN THROUGH IS LOVE(SCREAM LIKE A S
Tracks: / What you've been through is love (scream like a swift).
7" Single: Released Jan '84, on Desire, by Desire Records. Deleted '89. Catalogue no: **WANT 3**
12" Single: Released Jan '84, on Desire, by Desire Records. Deleted '89. Catalogue no: **WANTX 3**

Cheap Frills

ALMOST AWAKE
Tracks: / Almost awake.
7" Single: Released Aug '84, on Mongrel, Catalogue no: **PDIGRE 001**

Cheap Thrills

DESPAIR
Tracks: / Despair / Angeline.
7" Single: Released Feb '81, on Precision (USA), Deleted Feb '84. Catalogue no: **PAR 115**

Cheap Trick

Biographical details: This American rock band comprised, at the time of their greatest success, Bun E. Carlos, Rick Nielsen, Tom Peterson and Robin Zander.

Nielsen and Peterson worked together in the late Sixties in a number of little known bands. They formed Cheap Trick in 1972, with the above line-up evolving two years later. The quartet spent the mid-Seventies touring the States, concerntrating especially on the Midwest. Their first two albums, *Cheap Trick* and *In Color*, were both released in 1977, with the latter reaching America's album charts. By this time the band were gaining a strong reputation for their raw, exciting live concerts and were supporting such megastars as Queen and Kiss on US tours. This live sound was perfectly captured on *Cheap Trick At Budokan*, a 1979 LP release of a Japanese concert that made the group big news in both the US and UK. It even managed to steal a march on Bob Dylan, preceding by a few weels his live album recorded at the same venue. It yielded a hit single in the form of *I Want You To Reach Me*, which reached No. 7 in AMerica and No. 29 in Britain.

However, just as Cheap Trick seemed to have everything going for them, they lost

their way a little. Their next LP *Dream Police*, recorded before the success of the Budokan set, was, by contrast, a slick studio production that confused fans. 1980's *All Shook Up* produced by George Martin, proved a total dissapointment and was the last album to feature Tom Petersson who, by this time, has added an extra 's' to his surname. He was replaced on bass by Pete Comita, who was in turn replaced by Jon Brant. 1982 saw the group make a brief foray into the lower reaches of the British and American charts with their Beatles-esque single *If You Want My Love*; but *I Want You With Me* remained their only major hit 45 on either side of the Atlantic. For a short time in the late Seventies, Cheap Trick had looked set for major stardom, with critics enthusiastically citing their unusual combination of various pop, rock, punk and heavy metal styles. But this eclectic asset has perhaps also been to their disadvantage - they have fallen between musical stools and failed to win over a sufficiently loyal army of fans. (Bob MacDonald).
A USA rock band formed in 1972-74 by guitarist Rick Nielsen and bassist Tom Peterson, both from Rockford, Illinois. They first played in local band Fuse, which made an album on Epic in 1968; after working in Europe, back in Rockford they formed Cheap Trick with Brad Carlson on drums, soon recruiting vocalist Robert Zander, who had a folk background. They toured the midwest as support act, soon signed with CBS and reinvented themselves: Carlson became Bun E Carlos and Peterson added an extra 's' to his name to enhance mystique. Their second and third albums made the USA top 40 and they became superstars in Japan, where a 10-date tour in 1978 was greeted with adolescent hysteria captured on *Cheap Trick at Budokan*. The act was unusual: the diminutive, rubber-faced Nielsen in a baseball cap bounced about the stage with collection of guitars (sometimes several at once) while swarthy, bespectacled Carlos sweated behind the drum kit, Zander growing into the role of teen heart throb alongside Peterson, who was almost as pretty. Petersson left in 1980 to form a group with his wife and Nielson's song's began to slip. (Donald Clarke, April 1989)e.

DON'T BE CRUEL
Tracks: / Don't be cruel / I know what I want (live) / Ain't that a shame (12" and CD only) / California man (12" and CD only).
12" Single: Released Sep '88, on Epic, by CBS Records. Deleted 17 Apr '89. Catalogue no: **652896 6**
Special: Released 19 Sep '88, on CBS, by CBS Records. Deleted 17 Apr '89. Catalogue no: **652896 0**
7" Single: Released Sep '88, on Epic, by CBS Records. Deleted 17 Apr '89. Catalogue no: **652896 7**
CD 5": Released '88, on CBS, by CBS Records. Deleted 17 Apr '89. Catalogue no: **653005 3**
CD 5": Released Sep '88, on Epic, by CBS Records. Deleted 17 Apr '89. Catalogue no: **652896 2**

FLAME, THE
Tracks: / Flame / Through the night / Flame (album version) (Track on 12" and CD single.) / I want you to want me (Track on 12" and CD single.) / If you want my love (Track on 12" and CD single.).
CD 5": Released May '88, on Epic, by CBS Records. Deleted 10 Jul '89. Catalogue no: **651 466-2**
7" Pic: Released 6 Jun '88, on Epic, by CBS Records. Catalogue no: **651466 0**
7" Single: Released Apr '88, on Epic, by CBS Records. Deleted 10 Jul '89. Catalogue no: **651 466-7**
12" Single: Released May '88, on Epic, by CBS Records. Deleted 10 Jul '89. Catalogue no: **651 466-6**

I WANT YOU TO WANT ME
Tracks: / I want you to want me.
7" Single: Released May '79, on Epic, by CBS Records. Deleted May '82. Catalogue no: **EPC 8258**

IF YOU WANT MY LOVE
Tracks: / If you want my love / Four letter word.
7" Single: Released Jul '82, on Epic, by CBS Records. Deleted Jul '85. Catalogue no: **EPCA 2406**

I'LL BE WITH YOU TONIGHT
Tracks: / I'll be with you tonight / He's a whore / So good to see you.
7" EP: Released Apr '80, on Epic, by CBS Records. Deleted Apr '83. Catalogue no: **EPC 8355**

STOP THIS GAME
Tracks: / Stop this game / Who d'king.
7" Single: Released Oct '82, on Epic, by CBS Records. Deleted Oct '85. Catalogue no: **EPC 9071**

TONIGHT IT'S YOU
Tracks: / Tonight it's you.
7" Single: Released Feb '86, on Epic, by CBS Records. Deleted '87. Catalogue no: **A 6390**
12" Single: Released Feb '86, on Epic, by CBS Records. Deleted '87. Catalogue no: **TX 6390**

WAY OF THE WORLD
Tracks: / Way of the world / Oh candy.
7" Single: Released Feb '80, on Epic, by CBS Records. Deleted Feb '83. Catalogue no: **EPC 8114**

WORLD'S GREATEST LOVER
Tracks: / World's greatest lover / High priest of rhythmic noise.
7" Single: Released Feb '81, on Epic, by CBS Records. Deleted '84. Catalogue no: **EPC 9502**

Cheasters Peace

SNOW WHITE DOVE
Tracks: / Snow white dove / Rose, The.
7" Single: Released Nov '88, on August Records, by Scotdisc Records. Catalogue no: **GBH 765**

Cheaters

CONFIDANTE
Tracks: / Confidante.
7" Single: Released Aug '83, on Holyrood, by REL Records. Deleted '87. Catalogue no: **HOLLY 005**

GROOVIN' WITH MR. BLOE
Tracks: / Groovin' with Mr. Bloe / Can't sleep.
7" Single: Released Dec '83, on Holyrood, by REL Records. Deleted '87. Catalogue no: **HOLLY 008**
12" Single: Released Dec '83, on Holyrood, by REL Records. Catalogue no: **12 HOLLY 008**

NUTHIN' EVER HAPPENS ON SATURDAY
Tracks: / Nuthin' ever happens on Saturday / Hard work / Stop pushing.
7" Single: Released Oct '80, on Parlophone, by EMI Records. Deleted Oct '83. Catalogue no: **R 6041**

SPIRIT IN THE SKY
Tracks: / Spirit in the sky / Diplomatic.
7" Single: Released Jan '82, on Revo, Catalogue no: **ION 1028**

Cheatham, Oliver

Biographical details: Soul/disco singer Cheatham was a session man in Detroit before issuing a solo album in 1983. The first single from this LP was a major British club hit despite combining two of disco music's most over-used cliches, *Get Down* and *Saturday Night*. Nevertheless, *Get Down Saturday Night*was both a dance success and scraped into the British Top Forty. A less favourable reaction greeted further singles which, despite Cheatham's smooth, competent vocals, failed to distinguish themselves from a mass of similar products. (Bob MacDonald, 1985.).

BE THANKFUL FOR WHAT YOU'VE GOT
Tracks: / Be thankful for what you've got / Show me.
7" Single: Released Oct '87, on Champion, by Champion Records. Deleted Aug '89. Catalogue no: **CHAMP 54**
12" Single: Released Oct '87, on Champion, by Champion Records. Deleted Aug '89. Catalogue no: **CHAMP 1254**

CELEBRATE
Tracks: / Celebrate.
7" Single: Released Nov '86, on Champion, by Champion Records. Deleted Aug '89. Catalogue no: **CHAMP 25**
12" Single: Released Nov '86, on Champion, by Champion Records. Deleted Aug '89. Catalogue no: **CHAMP 1225**

GET DOWN SATURDAY NIGHT
Tracks: / Get down Saturday night / You can do it.
12" Single: Released May '88, on Old Gold, by Old Gold Records. Catalogue no: **OG 4063**

GO FOR IT (SINGLE)
Tracks: / Go for it / Go for it (version).
7" Single: Released 8 Feb '88, on Champion, by Champion Records. Catalogue no: **CHAMP 24**
7" Single: Released Feb '88, on Champion, by Champion Records. Deleted Aug '89. Catalogue no: **CHAMP 63**
12" Single: Released 8 Feb '88, on Champion, by Champion Records. Catalogue no: **CHAMP 1224**
12" Single: Released Feb '88, on Champion, by Champion Records. Deleted Aug '89. Catalogue no: **CHAMP 1263**

MAMA SAID
Tracks: / Mama said.
7" Single: Released Aug '85, on Move, Catalogue no: **MSS 3**
12" Single: Released Aug '85, on Move, Catalogue no: **MS 312**

S.O.S.
Tracks: / S.O.S. (Dub mix).
12" Single: Released May '86, on Champion, by Champion Records. Deleted Aug '89. Catalogue no: **CHAMP 1211**
7" Single: Released May '86, on Champion, by Champion Records. Catalogue no: **CHAMP 11**

TURNING POINT
Tracks: / Turning point.
7" Single: Released Nov '85, on PRT, by Castle Communications Records. Catalogue no: **MSS 6**

WISH ON A STAR
Tracks: / Wish on a star / Wish on a star (acca dub).
12" Single: Released Jun '87, on Champion, by Champion Records. Catalogue no: **CHAMP 1240**
7" Single: Released Jun '87, on Champion, by Champion Records. Deleted Jul '89. Catalogue no: **CHAMP 40**

Cheba, Eddie

LOOKING GOOD
Tracks: / Looking good.
7" Single: Released Mar '80, on Destiny, by Destiny Records. Catalogue no: **DS 3**

Check It Out

ROMEO & JULIET
Tracks: / Romeo and Juliet.
12" Single: Released Sep '88, on Stomp, by Stomp Records. Catalogue no: **STOMP 1**

Checker, Chubby

Biographical details: Hailing from Philadelphia, this singer was working as a chicken plucker before being discovered in 1959 and signed to a record company. His real name, Ernest Evans, was changed by the wife of Dick Clark, presenter of the influential American TV show American Bandstand. Mrs Clark remarked that he looked a little like Fats Domino, so be became Chubby Checker! He first scraped the American Top Forty with his 1959 single *The Class*, a novelty disc. But it was his next hit, more than a year later, which was to be the big one: *The Twist*, written by Hank Ballard, had been the B side of a '59 hit by Ballard's group, the Midnighters, and legend has it that Dick Clark asked Checker to perform it on television when Ballard failed to turn up. Checker's version hit No 1 on the US chart in September 1960 and sparked off a national craze for the song's accompanying gyratory dance. He thus became a major star and soon scored another American chart-topper, Pony Time. Checker and his US record label, Parkway, wasted no time in exploiting these two successes, keeping the former Mr Evans high on the American charts through 1961-63 with a succession of hits about various dances. The twist remained the most popular, however, with Slow Twistin' reaching No 3 and *The Twist* making US chart history by returning to No 1 in January 1962. In Britain *Let's Twist Again* was regarded as Checker's definitive disc, reaching No 2 and enjoying an extended chart life. The famous dance thrived in the UK despite being banned in some dance halls, which decried it as sexual and vulgar. With the arrival of the all-conquering Beatles, Checker's hits began to diminish. As he struggled to maintain his chart life the dances became ever more ludicrous, as shown by his final US Top Forty hit, 1965's *Let's Do The Freddie*. In Britain, however, a mid-70's twist revival resulted in a chart comeback for *Let's Twist Again/The Twist*, a specially released double-A-sided 45 that reached No 5. In the annals of pop history, Chubby Checker's name remains synonymous with the twist, a fondly-remembered fad. (Bob MacDonald, 1985.)
Ernest Evans, born in 1941 in Philadelphia, was a former chicken plucker when he was signed to Cameo-POarkway as a vocalist. His new name (after Fats Domino) was suggested by Dick Clark's wife; of his first four records, 'The Class' made the top 40 in 1959. When Hank Ballard failed to show up for a recording session for Clark's American Bandstand TV show, Checker's hastily arranged cover of Ballard's *The twist* (backed by Bandstand's resident group) shot to number one in 1960 and reached the top again the next year. He became an energetic showman and enjoyed his success, with 20 top 40 hits 1959-64. (Donald Clarke, April 1988).

DANCIN' PARTY
Tracks: / Dancin' party.
7" Single: Released Aug '62, on Columbia, by EMI Records. Deleted Aug '65. Catalogue no: **DB 4876**

JINGLE BELL ROCK
Tracks: / Jingle bell rock.
7" Single: Released Dec '62, on Cameo Parkway, Deleted Dec '65. Catalogue no: **C 205**

LETS TWIST AGAIN (SINGLE)
Tracks: / Twist, The / Lets twist again / Dancin' party / Pony Time.
7" Single: Released Apr '87, on Creole Classics, by Creole Records. Catalogue no: **CR 100**
7" Single: Released Aug '61, on Columbia, by EMI Records. Catalogue no: **DB 4691**
7" Single: Released Nov '75, on London-American, Catalogue no: **HL 10512**
12" Single: Released Apr '87, on Creole Classics, by Creole Records. Catalogue no: **CRT 100**

LIMBO ROCK
Tracks: / Limbo rock.
7" Single: Released Nov '62, on Cameo Parkway, Deleted Nov '65. Catalogue no: **P 849**

PONY TIME
Tracks: / Pony time.
7" Single: Released Mar '61, on Columbia, by EMI Records. Catalogue no: **DB 4591**

SLOW TWISTIN'
Tracks: / Slow twistin'.
7" Single: Released Apr '62, on Columbia, by EMI Records. Deleted Apr '65. Catalogue no: **DB 4808**

TEACH ME TO TWIST
Tracks: / Teach me to twist.
7" Single: Released Apr '62, on Columbia, by EMI Records. Deleted Apr '65. Catalogue no: **DB 4802**

TWIST, THE
Tracks: / Twist, The.
7" Single: Released Sep '60, on Columbia, by EMI Records. Catalogue no: **DB 4503**

WHAT DO YA SAY
Tracks: / What do ya say.
7" Single: Released Oct '63, on Cameo Parkway, Deleted Oct '66. Catalogue no: **P 806**

Checkmates Ltd

PROUD MARY
Tracks: / Proud Mary.
7" Single: Released Nov '69, on A&M, by A&M Records. Deleted Nov '72. Catalogue no: **AMS 769**

Cheeks, Judy

I STILL LOVE YOU
Tracks: / I still love you / I still love you (12" mix) (on 12" version only) / Believe.
7" Single: Released Apr '88, on Polydor, by Polydor Ltd. Catalogue no: **POSP 914**
12" Single: Released Apr '88, on Polydor, by Polydor Ltd. Catalogue no: **POSPX 914**

JUST ANOTHER LIE
Tracks: / Just another lie / I'll be waiting.
CD 5": Released Jul '88, on Polydor, by Polydor Ltd. Deleted Aug '89. Catalogue no: **PZCD 11**
7" Single: Released Jul '88, on Polydor, by Polydor Ltd. Catalogue no: **PO 11**
12" Single: Released Jul '88, on Polydor, by Polydor Ltd. Catalogue no: **PZ 11**

Cheeky

DON'T MESS AROUND
Tracks: / Don't mess around.
7" Single: Released Jul '80, on Woodbine, Catalogue no: **WSR 005**

Cheetah

SPEND THE NIGHT
Tracks: / Spend the night / I'm yours.
7" Single: Released Jun '82, on Epic, by CBS Records. Deleted Jun '85. Catalogue no: **EPCA 1646**

Cheetahs

MECCA
Tracks: / Mecca.
7" Single: Released Oct '64, on Philips, by Phonogram Ltd. Deleted Oct '67. Catalogue no: **BF 1362**

SOLDIER BOY
Tracks: / Soldier boy.
7" Single: Released Jan '65, on Philips, by Phonogram Ltd. Deleted Jan '68. Catalogue no: **BF 1383**

Chefs

24 HOURS
Tracks: / 24 hours.
7" Single: on Graduate, by Graduate Records. Deleted Jan '87. Catalogue no: **GRAD 11**

SWEETIE
Tracks: / Sweetie / Thrush / Records and tea / Boasting.
7" Single: Released Sep '80, on Attrix, by

Attrix Records. Catalogue no: **RB 10 EP**

Chegwin, Keith

GONNA BE A FOOL NO MORE
Tracks: / Gonna be a fool no more.
7" Single: Released Jun '83, on Moon, by Moon Records (UK). Catalogue no: **LUNA 5**

MORE TO LOVE
Tracks: / More to love / Night after night.
7" Single: Released Sep '81, on Secret, by Secret Records. Deleted Sep '84. Catalogue no: **SHH 121**

Chelsea

EVACUATE (SINGLE)
Tracks: / Evacuate.
7" Single: Released Nov '81, on Faulty Products, by Faulty Products Records. Catalogue no: **SF 20**

FREEMANS
Tracks: / Freemans.
7" Single: Released Sep '81, on Step Forward, by Faulty Products Records. Catalogue no: **SF 18**

GIVE ME MORE
Tracks: / Give me more.
7" Single: Released May '88, on Chelsea, Catalogue no: **CH 001**

ROCKIN' HORSE
Tracks: / Rockin' horse.
7" Single: Released Apr '81, on Faulty Products, by Faulty Products Records. Catalogue no: **SF 17**

STAND OUT
Tracks: / Stand out.
7" Pic: Released Oct '82, on Step Forward, by Faulty Products Records. Catalogue no: **SF 22**

WAR ACROSS THE NATION
Tracks: / War across the nation / High rise living.
7" Single: Released Mar '82, on Step Forward, by Faulty Products Records. Catalogue no: **SF 21**

Chelsea F.C....

BACK ON THE BALL
Tracks: / Back on the ball.
7" Single: Released Sep '84, on WEA, by WEA Records. Catalogue no: **YZ 23**

BLUE IS THE COLOUR
Tracks: / Blue is the colour / Chelsea we love you / Blue is the colour (inst.) (Only on 12" single.).
7" Single: Released Dec '87, on London Records, by London Records. Deleted Oct '88. Catalogue no: **CFC 1**
12" Single: Released Dec '87, on London Records, by London Records. Deleted Oct '88. Catalogue no: **CFCX 1**
7" Single: Released Feb '72, on Penny Farthing, by Penny Farthing Records. Catalogue no: **PEN 782**

Chemical Alice

GOODNIGHT VIENNA
Tracks: / Goodnight Vienna.
7" Single: Released May '82, on Acidic, Deleted '83. Catalogue no: **GNOME 1**

Chequers

Biographical details: This British disco group, the brainchild of writer-producer John Mathias, hit No 21 on the UK charts in the autumn of 1975 with *Rock On, Brother*, a largely instrumental single in a similar vein to Van McCoy's summer smash of a few months earlier, *The Hustle*. The Chequers achieved a second chart hit, peaking at No 32 with *Hey Miss Payne*, but later records failed to make any impact. (Bob MacDonald, 1985.).

HARD TIMES
Tracks: / Hard times.
7" Single: Released Mar '83, on EMI-Manhattan, by EMI Records. Catalogue no: **MT 102**

HEY MISS PAYNE
Tracks: / Hey Miss Payne.
7" Single: Released Feb '76, on Creole, by Creole Records. Deleted Feb '79. Catalogue no: **CR 116**

ROCK ON BROTHER
Tracks: / Rock on brother.
7" Single: Released Oct '75, on Creole, by Creole Records. Deleted Oct '78. Catalogue no: **CR 111**

Cher

Biographical details: Cherilyn La Pierre, part Cherokee Indian, was born in California. To pay for acting lessons she took up session singing and it was at a 1963 recording session that she met her future husband, Sonny Bono: they had both been brought to the studio by Phil Spector to sing backing vocals on the Ronettes' *Be My Baby*, which became an international Top Five smash. Sonny and Cher developed both a professional and personal interest in each other and their big breakthrough came in the summer of 1965 with *I Got You Babe*, a delightful love song which appealed both to the pop market and the burgeoning folk-rock movement and was a simultaneous No 1 in the US and the UK. Penned by Bono, it clearly demonstrated that he was an excellent songwriter but that Cher was the superior singer. He enjoyed only one solo hit but she had many, particularly in the States. Meanwhile they also continued their career as a duo, gaining success in the mid-60's and early 70's, with a dry spell in between. They divorced in the mid-70's, after which Cher filled many inches of newspaper gossip columns through her perceived relationships with various well-known men. In particular she had a tempestuous marriage to Gregg Allman, of Allman Brothers Band fame, which included a brief and unsuccessful recording career together. Cher made an uncredited British chart come-back in 1982, giving strong vocal assistance to Meat Loaf on his Top Five single *Dead Ringer For Love*. In terms of her solo hits, the deep and powerful voice of Cher scored a transatlantic Top Three success in 1966 with *Bang Bang (My Baby Shot Me Down)*, composed by Sonny Bono. In America, her career reached a new high in the early 70's: by '74 she had achieved three US No 1 singles, *Gypsies, Tramps And Thieves* ('71, No 4 in UK), *Half-Breed* ('73) and *Dark Lady* ('74). Her late 70's barren era was briefly rescued by the American Top Ten success of 79's *Take Me Home*. She has concentrated on acting in recent years, with considerable success, winning a 1988 Oscar as best female actress for her performanin the film Moonstruck. (Bob MacDonald)..

AFTER ALL
Tracks: / After all.
Cassingle: Released Apr '89, on Geffen, by Geffen Records (USA). Catalogue no: **GEF 52C**
12" Single: Released Apr '89, on Geffen, by Geffen Records (USA). Catalogue no: **GEF 52T**
7" Single: Released Apr '89, on Geffen, by Geffen Records (USA). Catalogue no: **GEF 52**
CD 5": Released Apr '89, on Geffen, by Geffen Records (USA). Catalogue no: **GEF 52CD**

ALL I REALLY WANT TO DO
Tracks: / All I really want to do.
7" Single: Released Aug '65, on Liberty, by EMI Records. Deleted Aug '68. Catalogue no: **LIB 66114**

BANG BANG (MY BABY SHOT ME DOWN)
Tracks: / Bang bang (my baby shot me down).
7" Single: Released Mar '66, on Liberty, by EMI Records. Deleted Mar '69. Catalogue no: **LIB 66160**
7" Single: Released Jul '84, on EMI Golden 45's, by EMI Records. Deleted '89. Catalogue no: **G45 32**

DARK LADY
Tracks: / Dark lady.
7" Single: Released Feb '74, on MCA, by MCA Records. Deleted Feb '77. Catalogue no: **MCA 101**

GYPSIES, TRAMPS AND THIEVES
Tracks: / Gypsies tramps and thieves.
7" Single: Released Nov '71, on MCA, by MCA Records. Deleted Nov '74. Catalogue no: **MU 1142**

GYPSIES, TRAMPS AND THIEVES (OLD GOLD)
Tracks: / Gypsies, tramps and thieves / Half breed / All I ever need is you.
CD 5": Released May '89, on Old Gold, by Old Gold Records. Catalogue no: **OG 6146**
7" Single: Released Jul '82, on Old Gold, by Old Gold Records. Catalogue no: **OG 9167**

HOLDIN' OUT FOR LOVE
Tracks: / Holdin' out for love.
7" Single: Released Mar '82, on Casablanca, by PolyGram UK Ltd. Deleted '85. Catalogue no: **CAN 1006**

I FEEL SOMETHING IN THE AIR
Tracks: / I feel something in the air.
7" Single: Released Aug '66, on Liberty, by EMI Records. Deleted Aug '69. Catalogue no: **LIB 12034**

I FOUND SOMEONE
Tracks: / I found someone / Dangerous times.
7" Single: Released Sep '87, on Geffen, by Geffen Records (USA). Catalogue no: **GEF 31**
12" Single: Released Sep '87, on Geffen, by Geffen Records (USA). Catalogue no: **GEF 31 T**
12" Pic: Released Oct '87, on Geffen, by Geffen Records (USA). Deleted Jul '88. Catalogue no: **GEF 31TP**

IF I COULD TURN BACK TIME
Tracks: / If I could turn back time.
7" Single: Released Jul '89, on Geffen, by Geffen Records (USA). Catalogue no: **GEF 59**
12" Single: Released Jul '89, on Geffen, by Geffen Records (USA). Catalogue no: **GEF 59 T**
Cassingle: Released Jul '89, on Geffen, by Geffen Records (USA). Catalogue no: **GEF 59 C**
CD 5": Released Jul '89, on Geffen, by Geffen Records (USA). Catalogue no: **GEF 59 CD**

IT'S TOO LATE TO LOVE ME NOW
Tracks: / It's too late to love me now / Shoppin'.
7" Single: Released Mar '80, on Casablanca, by PolyGram UK Ltd. Deleted Mar '83. Catalogue no: **CAN 185**

RUDY
Tracks: / Rudy / Do I ever cross your mind.
7" Single: Released Apr '82, on CBS, by CBS Records. Deleted Apr '85. Catalogue no: **A 2227**

SKIN DEEP
Tracks: / Skin deep / Perfection.
12" Single: Released 22 Aug '88, on Geffen, by Geffen Records (USA). Catalogue no: **GEF 44T**
CD 5": Released 22 Aug '88, on Geffen, by Geffen Records (USA). Catalogue no: **GEF 44CD**
7" Single: Released 22 Aug '88, on Geffen, by Geffen Records (USA). Catalogue no: **GEF 44**

SUNNY
Tracks: / Sunny.
7" Single: Released Sep '66, on Liberty, by EMI Records. Deleted Sep '69. Catalogue no: **LIB 12083**

WE ALL SLEEP ALONE
Tracks: / We all sleep alone / Working girl / I found someone (Extra track on CD single.).
7" Single: Released Mar '88, on Geffen, by Geffen Records (USA). Catalogue no: **GEF 35**
12" Single: Released Mar '88, on Geffen, by Geffen Records (USA). Catalogue no: **GEF 35T**
CD 5": Released Mar '88, on Geffen, by Geffen Records (USA). Catalogue no: **GEF 35CD**

Cheri

Biographical details: This Canadian vocal duo -- Roz Hunt and Amy Roslyn -- came to the attention of North American discos in the spring of 1982 with their nauseous novelty single *Murphy's Law*. The record crossed over to the US pop Top Forty and then performed even better on the British charts, where it reached No 13. More conventional disco material followed but the girls had already been written off as a one-off novelty and they were quickly forgotten. *Murphy's Law* -- which states that whatever can go wrong will go wrong -- appeared to come true for Cheri. (Bob MacDonald, 1985.).

COME & GET THESE MEMORIES
Tracks: / Come & get these memories / Starstruck.
12" Single: Released Sep '82, on Polydor, by Polydor Ltd. Deleted '85. Catalogue no: **POSPX 508**
7" Single: Released Sep '82, on Polydor, by Polydor Ltd. Deleted '85. Catalogue no: **POSP 508**

GIVE IT TO ME BABY
Tracks: / Give it to me baby / Starstruck.
7" Single: Released Nov '82, on Polydor, by Polydor Ltd. Deleted Nov '85. Catalogue no: **POSP 537**
12" Single: Released Nov '82, on Polydor, by Polydor Ltd. Deleted Nov '85. Catalogue no: **POSPT 537**

MURPHY'S LAW
Tracks: / Murphy's law / Anything is possible.
Note: See under Booker Newbury III
7" Single: Released Jun '82, on Polydor, by Polydor Ltd. Catalogue no: **POSP 459**
12" Single: Released Jun '82, on Polydor, by Polydor Ltd. Catalogue no: **POSPX 459**

WORKING GIRL
Tracks: / Working girl.
12" Single: Released Feb '83, on 21 Records, by Polydor Ltd. Catalogue no: **POSPX 563**
7" Single: Released Feb '83, on 21 Records, by Polydor Ltd. Catalogue no: **POSP 563**

Cherish

RUN TO ME Featuring Lydia Steinman
Tracks: / Run to me / Run to me (version).
7" Single: Released Jan '89, on Instant Karma, Catalogue no: **KARMA 101**
12" Single: Released Jan '89, on Instant Karma, Catalogue no: **KARMAX 101**

Cherokees

SEVEN DAFFODILS
Tracks: / Seven daffodils.
7" Single: Released Sep '64, on Columbia, by EMI Records. Deleted Sep '67. Catalogue no: **DB 7341**

Cherrelle

AFFAIR (SINGLE)
Tracks:. / Affair / New love / Affair (steamy affair mix) / Affair (street dub hip hop mix).
12" Single: Released 24 Apr '89, on Tabu, Deleted Oct '89. Catalogue no: **654 673 1**
12" Single: Released Apr '89, on Tabu, Deleted Oct '89. Catalogue no: **654 673 8**
7" Single: Released Apr '89, on Tabu, Deleted Oct '89. Catalogue no: **654 673 7**
CD 5": Released Apr '89, on Tabu, Deleted Oct '89. Catalogue no: **654 673 2**

ARTIFICIAL HEART
Tracks: / Oh no it's U again / Artificial heart.
7" Single: Released May '86, on Tabu, Deleted '87. Catalogue no: **A 7185**

EVERYTHING I MISS AT HOME
Tracks: / Everything I miss at home / Where do I run to / I didn't mean to turn you on (Only on 12" version and CD single.).
12" Single: Released Nov '88, on Tabu, Deleted 17 Apr '89. Catalogue no: **6530666**
CD 5": Released Nov '88, on Tabu, Deleted 17 Apr '89. Catalogue no: **6530662**
7" Single: Released Nov '88, on Tabu, Deleted 17 Apr '89. Catalogue no: **6530667**
12" Single: Released 28 Nov '88, on Tabu, Deleted 17 Apr '89. Catalogue no: **6530668**

I DIDN'T MEAN TO TURN YOU ON
Tracks: / I didn't mean to turn you on.
7" Single: Released Aug '84, on Tabu, Catalogue no: **A 4656**
12" Single: Released Aug '84, on Tabu, Catalogue no: **TA 4656**

SATURDAY LOVE
Tracks: / Saturday love / I didn't mean to turn you on / Saturday love (remix).
12" Single: Released Jan '86, on Tabu, Catalogue no: **TA 6829**
12" Single: Released Jan '86, on Tabu, Catalogue no: **QTA 6829**
7" Single: Released Jan '86, on Tabu, Catalogue no: **A 6829**

WILL YOU SATISFY?
Tracks: / When you look in my eyes / Will you satisfy* / Saturday love / Saturday love (remix).
12" Single: Released Feb '86, on Tabu, Catalogue no: **DTA 6927**
7" Set: Released Feb '86, on Tabu, Catalogue no: **DA 6927**
7" Single: Released Feb '86, on Tabu, Catalogue no: **A 6927**
12" Single: Released Feb '86, on Tabu, Deleted '87. Catalogue no: **TA 6927**

Cherry

MAGIC HOLIDAY
Tracks: / Magic holiday.
7" Single: Released Aug '89, on Sublime, Catalogue no: **LIME 107**
12" Single: Released Jul '89, on Sublime, Catalogue no: **LIMET 107**

Cherry Ann

ME AND YOU
Tracks: / Me and you.
12" Single: Released Mar '82, on BB, Catalogue no: **BBD 137**

Cherry, Ava

LOVE TO BE TOUCHED
Tracks: / Love to be touched / This time around.
7" Single: Released May '82, on Capitol, by EMI Records. Deleted '85. Catalogue no: **CL 243**

Cherry Black Dawn

BLUE BABY BLUE
Tracks: / Blue baby blue.
7" Single: Released Jun '84, on Cherry Black, Deleted '87. Catalogue no: **CH 1**

Cherry Blossom

OOH WEE BABY
Tracks: / Ooh wee baby / Cherry blossom blues.
7" Single: Released Sep '87, on Five O Four Records, Catalogue no: **504 SP 1**

YOU GOT ME RUNNIN
Tracks: / You got me running / Niteshade blues.

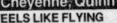

7" Single: Released Sep '87, on Five O Four Records, Catalogue no: **504 SP 2**

Cherry Bombz

HOT GIRLS IN LOVE
Tracks: / Feeline feeling / Hot girls in love.
12" Single: Released Feb '86, on Lick, by Lick Records. Catalogue no: **LIXT 3**
7" Single: Released Feb '86, on Lick, by Lick Records. Catalogue no: **LIX 3**

HOUSE OF ECSTASY
Tracks: / House of ecstasy / Declaration (On 7" only) / Countryfield inner city blues (On 12" only) / Running (back to your lover) (On 12" only).
12" Single: Released May '86, on Lick, by Lick Records. Catalogue no: **LIXT 4**
7" Single: Released May '86, on Lick, by Lick Records. Catalogue no: **LIX 4**

Cherry Boys

KARDOMAH CAFE
Tracks: / Kardomah cafe / Airs and graces.
7" Single: Released Jul '83, on Crash, by Satril Records. Deleted '85. Catalogue no: **CRA 510**

ONLY FOOLS DIE
Tracks: / Only fools die / Come the day.
7" Single: Released Nov '82, on Cherryosa, Catalogue no: **CY 2001**

SHOOT THE BIG SHOT
Tracks: / Shoot the big shot / Falling / Leave that way (on 12" only).
12" Single: Released Nov '83, on Crash, by Satril Records. Deleted '85. Catalogue no: **12 CRA 604**
7" Single: Released Nov '83, on Crash, by Satril Records. Deleted '85. Catalogue no: **CRA 604**

Cherry, Don

BAND OF GOLD
Tracks: / Band of gold.
7" Single: Released Feb '56, on Philips, by Phonogram Ltd. Deleted Feb '59. Catalogue no: **PB 549**

Cherry, Neneh

BUFFALO STANCE
Tracks: / Buffalo stance (7" only) / Buffalo stance (12" mix) (On 12" & CD only) / Buffalo stance (scratchapella) (Only on 12" & CD) / Buffalo stance (instrumental) (Only on 12" version.) / Buffalo stance (electro ski mix) (On all versions) / Give me a muthu***ing break beat (sukka mix) (On CD only).
12" Single: Released 21 Nov '88, on Circa, by Virgin Records. Catalogue no: **YRT 21**
CD 3": Released Jan '89, on Circa, by Virgin Records. Catalogue no: **YRCD 21**
12" Single: Released Jan '89, on Circa, by Virgin Records. Catalogue no: **YRTX 21**
7" Single: Released Oct '88, on Circa, by Virgin Records. Catalogue no: **YR 21**

KISSES ON THE WIND (see,panel on right)
Tracks: / Kisses on the wind / Buffalo blues.
7" Single: Released 24 Jul '89, on Circa, by Virgin Records. Catalogue no: **YR 33**
12" Single: Released 24 Jul '89, on Circa, by Virgin Records. Catalogue no: **YRTPR 33**
12" Single: Released 24 Jul '89, on Circa, by Virgin Records. Catalogue no: **YRT 33**
12" Single: Released Sep '89, on Circa, by Virgin Records. Catalogue no: **YRTX 33**
Cassingle: Released 24 Jul '89, on Circa, by Virgin Records. Catalogue no: **YRC 33**
CD 3": Released 24 Jul '89, on Circa, by Virgin Records. Catalogue no: **YRCD 33**

MANCHILD
Tracks: / Manchild / Buffalo stance (12" only.).
7" Single: Released 2 May '89, on Virgin, by Virgin Records. Catalogue no: **YR 30**
12" Single: Released 2 May '89, on Virgin, by Virgin Records. Catalogue no: **YRT 30**
CD 3": Released 2 May '89, on Virgin, by Virgin Records. Catalogue no: **YRCD 30**
12" Single: Released 2 May '89, on Virgin, by Virgin Records. Catalogue no: **YRTX 30**
Cassingle: Released 2 May '89, on Virgin, by Virgin Records. Catalogue no: **YRC 30**

Cheryl

IN YOUR SHADOW
Tracks: / In your shadow again.
7" Single: Released Jun '86, on Creole, by Creole Records. Catalogue no: **CR 92**
12" Single: Released Jun '86, on Creole, by Creole Records. Catalogue no: **CRT 92**

Chester

FOR THE TRUCKS SAKE
Tracks: / For the trucks sake.
7" Single: Released Sep '81, on Roxon, Catalogue no: **ROX 0235**

Chesterfields

ASK JOHNNY DEE
Tracks: / Ask Johnny Dee.
7" Single: Released Mar '87, on Subway, by Subway Records. Catalogue no: **SUBWAY 11**

BLAME
Tracks: / Blame.
12" Single: Released 22 Aug '88, on Household, by Household Records. Catalogue no: **HOLD 3T**
7" Single: Released 22 Aug '88, on Household, by Household Records. Catalogue no: **HOLD 3**

COMPLETELY AND UTTERLY
Tracks: / Completely and utterly.
7" Single: Released Nov '86, on Subway, by Subway Records. Catalogue no: **SUBWAY 7**

FOOL IS A MAN
Tracks: / Fool is a man.
12" Single: Released Apr '89, on Household, by Household Records. Catalogue no: **HOLD 5T**

GOODBYE, GOODBYE
Tracks: / Goodbye goodbye.
12" Single: Released 5 Mar '88, on Household, by Household Records. Catalogue no: **HOLD 1T**

GUITAR IN YOUR BATH, A
Tracks: / Guitar in your bath, A.
7" Single: Released Apr '86, on Subway Organisation, Catalogue no: **SUBWAY 003**

JANICE LONG SESSION: CHESTERFIELDS
12" Single: Released Jul '87, on Night Tracks, by Pinnacle Records. Catalogue no: **SFNT 003**

Chevalier Brothers

BABY
Tracks: / You're something else / Baby.
7" Single: Released Mar '86, on Disques Chevalier, Catalogue no: **DCG 01**
12" Single: Released Mar '86, on Disques Chevalier, Catalogue no: **DCGT 01**

BARTENDER
Tracks: / Bartender / Coco beans / On the tip of my tongue.
12" Single: Released Feb '84, on Waterfront, by Waterfront Music. Catalogue no: **WFST 005**

BUONA SERA
Tracks: / Buona sera / Clark Kent blues / Shuffling the cards (Available on 12" only.).
Note: * Extra track on 12" version only.
7" Single: Released 21 Nov '87, on Magnet, by WEA Records. Deleted Jun '88. Catalogue no: **CHEV 1**
12" Single: Released 21 Nov '87, on Magnet, by WEA Records. Deleted Jun '88. Catalogue no: **CHEVT 1**

I LIVE 'EM
Tracks: / I live 'em.
7" Single: Released Aug '84, on Mean, by Mean Records. Catalogue no: **MEAN 105**

Chevi

GE ME MORE
Tracks: / Ge me more.
7" Single: Released Aug '84, on 4th & Broadway, by Island Records. Catalogue no: **BRW 12**
12" Single: Released Aug '84, on 4th & Broadway, by Island Records. Deleted '87. Catalogue no: **12 BRW 12**

MR. D.J
Tracks: / Mr. D.J..
12" Single: Released Jan '84, on Subversive, Catalogue no: **SBD 46**

ROSALIE
Tracks: / Rosalie.
12" Single: Released Apr '83, on Sunburn, by Orbitone Records. Catalogue no: **SBD 21**

Chevron, Philip

CAPTAINS AND THE KINGS
Tracks: / Captains and the kings.
7" Single: Released Oct '83, on Imp, by Demon Records. Catalogue no: **IMP 002**

SONGS FROM BILL'S DANCEHALL
Tracks: / Songs from Bill's dancehall.
12" Single: Released Nov '81, on Mosa, by Mosa Records. Catalogue no: **MOEP 412**

Chevvy

TAKER (SINGLE)
Tracks: / Taker, The / Life on the run.
7" Single: Released May '81, on Avatar, by Avatar Record Corporation. Catalogue no: **AAA 107**

TOO MUCH LOVING
Tracks: / Too much loving / See the light.
7" Single: Released Aug '81, on Avatar, by Avatar Record Corporation. Catalogue no: **AAA 104**

Chevy D

TRAINS KEEP STEAMING
Tracks: / Trains keep steaming.
7" Single: Released Oct '89, on Living Beat, by Living Beat Records. Catalogue no: **7 SMASH 6**

Cheyanne

I'VE WAITED TOO LONG (FOR YOUR LOVE)
Tracks: / I've waited too long (for your love) (single mix) (Composers: Cheyanne/West/Robinson/Brace.) / I've waited too long (for your love) (Hypnotic inst.) (Composers: Cheyanne/West/Robinson/Brace.) / I've waited too long (for your love) (Extended mix) (Composers: Cheyanne/West/Robinson/Brace.) / I've waited too long (for your love) (Charlie 'Dee' dub) (Composers: Cheyanne/West/Robinson/Brace.).
7" Single: Released Nov '88, on Syncopate, by EMI Records. Deleted Jun '89. Catalogue no: **SY 21**
12" Single: Released Nov '88, on Syncopate, by EMI Records. Deleted Aug '89. Catalogue no: **12SY 21**

NENEH CHERRY - KISSES ON THE WIND (Rleased on Circa)

Cheyenne, Quinn

FEELS LIKE FLYING
Tracks: / Feels like flying.
7" Single: Released Jul '83, on Crazy Viking, by Crazy Vikings Records. Catalogue no: **CV 002**

Cheyne

CALL ME MR. TELEPHONE
Tracks: / Call me Mr. Telephone.
12" Single: Released Jun '85, on MCA, by MCA Records. Catalogue no: **MCAX 966**

CALL ME TELEPHONE
Tracks: / Call me telephone.
12" Single: Released '88, on Crepescule, by Island Records. Catalogue no: **TWI 532**

Chic

Biographical details: Chic are masterminded by their two key members, the New York writing/arranging/producing team of Edwards and Rogers. Both had had many years of music business experience, playing in various small-time bands, before forming Chic in 1977. They soon came up with their first big hit in the form of *Dance, dance, dance (yowsah, yowsah, yowsah)*, which reached No. 6 in both the US and UK. It began a string of superb singles that were perfect material for the late Seventies disco explosion and were enormous international hits. Along with the Bee Gees, Chic were one of the few acts to carve out a real chart career during this period, an era which through up a profusion of anonymous one-off hitmakers. The group achieved two US No. 1 smashes: spectacularly successful *Le Freak*, which sold over two million copies in the States alone and *Good Times*. in between these two single came their biggest British hit, *I Want Your Love*, which reached No.4.

The beginning of the Eighties heralded an immediate curtailment of the group's success. By this time however, Edwards and Rogers were more interested in writing and producing for other acts. Their very distinctive disco sound, which featured irresistibly catchy and repetitive melodies backed by slick, sparse rhythms, was in great demand. They provided hits for Sister Sledge, Sheila B. Devotion, Diana Ross and Carly Simon. A fallow period followed, caused by an over-exposure of their famous sound and by the failure of a dire collaboration with Blondie star Debbie Harry. Rogers bounced back with a vengeance in 1983, thanks to his work on David Bowie's brilliantly successful *Let's Dance* LP. That album made him America's hottest producer of the mid-Eighties. In the first week of January 1985, Rogers staged a complete takeover of the Top 3 singles on the Billboard chart, thanks to hits by Madonna, Duran Duran and the Honeydrippers. By now the name Chic had passed into history, although the group never officially broke up. (Bob MacDonald).

A disco band formed in 1977, one of the few in the genre which was not faceless, and became the best selling act in the history of Atlantic Records. Bassist Bernard Edwards, one of the most imitated of the era, met rhythm guitarist Nile Rodgers working in a post office, who had done everything from folk through punk and working in the Apollo house band.
They formed the Big Apple Band with ex-Patti LaBelle drummer Tony Thompson and changed it's name when audience reaction in clubs got them a record contract because a similarly named outfit had a number one hit in 1976. Norma Jean Wright and Alfa Anderson, later Luci Martin were vocalists; the band only became faceless like the rest because Edwards and Rodgers became so busy playing and producing for others. (Donald Clarke, April 1989).

26
Tracks: / 26 / Chip off the old block.
7" Single: Released Oct '82, on Atlantic, by WEA Records. Deleted Oct '85. Catalogue no: **K 11617**

DANCE DANCE DANCE Yowsah yowsah yowsah
Tracks: / Dance dance dance.
7" Single: Released Nov '77, on Atlantic by WEA Records. Deleted Nov '80. Catalogue no: **K 11038**

EVERYBODY DANCE
Tracks: / Everybody dance.
7" Single: Released Apr '78, on Atlantic by WEA Records. Deleted Apr '81. Catalogue no: **K 11097**

GOOD TIMES

Tracks: / Good times / Warm summer night, A.
12" Single: Released Mar '88, on Atlantic, by WEA Records. Catalogue no: **A 9107 T**
7" Single: Released Mar '88, on Atlantic, by WEA Records. Catalogue no: **A 9107**
7" Single: Released Jun '79, on Atlantic, by WEA Records. Deleted Jun '82. Catalogue no: **K 11310**

HANGIN
Tracks: / Hangin'.
7" Single: Released Jan '83, on Atlantic, by WEA Records. Catalogue no: **A 9898**
12" Single: Released Jan '83, on Atlantic, by WEA Records. Catalogue no: **A 9898 T**

I WANT YOUR LOVE
Tracks: / I want your love.
7" Single: Released Feb '79, on Atlantic, by WEA Records. Deleted Feb '82. Catalogue no: **LV 16**

JACK THE FREAK
Tracks: / Jack the freak / Savoir faire.
7" Single: Released Sep '87, on Raise The Roof, by Orbit Records. Catalogue no: **ROOF 3**
12" Single: Released Sep '87, on Atlantic, by WEA Records. Catalogue no: **A 9198 T**
12" Single: Released Sep '87, on Raise The Roof, by Orbit Records. Catalogue no: **ROOF T3**
7" Single: Released Sep '87, on Atlantic, by WEA Records. Deleted Jul '88. Catalogue no: **A 9198**

LE FREAK
Tracks: / Savoir faire / Chic (everybody say) / Le freak.
7" Single: Released '78, on Atlantic, by WEA Records. Deleted May '88. Catalogue no: **K 11209**
12" Single: Released Aug '86, on Atlantic, by WEA Records. Catalogue no: **K 11209 T**

MY FEET KEEP DANCIN'
Tracks: / My feet keep dancing.
7" Single: Released Dec '79, on Atlantic, by WEA Records. Deleted Dec '82. Catalogue no: **K 11415**

MY FORBIDDEN LOVER
Tracks: / My forbidden lover.
7" Single: Released Oct '79, on Atlantic, by WEA Records. Deleted Oct '82. Catalogue no: **K 11385**

Chicago
Biographical details: Formed in Chicago but shortly afterwards moving to Los Angeles, the group released their first album in 1969 under the name of Chicago Transit Authority. This was also the title of the LP itself. With the release of their second album in 1970, their name was shortened to Chicago. It was this latter effort that broke the band in both the US and UK. On the strength of its success, the first LP which had been overlooked in some quarters, was transformed into a long-running Stateside seller. As well as big album sales, 1970 also brought single success on both sides of the Atlantic: *I'm A Man* a cover version of the Spencer Davis Group's 1967 hit, went to No. 8 in the UK, one place higher than the original, while *Make Me Smile* hit the US Top 10; *25 or 6 to 4* reached the Top 10 in both countries. But whereas the band never again reached the Top 20 of the British album chart and were not to achieve another UK hit single until 1976, their American success continued with amazing consistency.
Under the auspices of their producer and manager James William Guerico, Chicago released albums at regular annual intervals, each LP simply being titled *Chicago V*, *Chicago VI*, *Chicago VII* etc. As predictable as the titles was the fact that the music contained on them was equally monotonous. With a jazz-rock sound influenced by the success of Blood, Sweat & Tears, one of America's top-selling acts of the late Sixties and early Seventies, Chicago found their niche and stayed in it, gradually moving more and more towards a middle-of-the-road version of their style, with the ballads gaining greater prominence. Their 1976 return to the UK charts came in the shape of *If You Leave Me Now*, a No. 1 in both Britain and the States. This beautiful love song was an instant classic and remains the group's best known track.
The extraordinary and tragic death of Terry Kath - he accidentally shot himself while playing with a pistol - severely diminished the group's morale and chart status during the late Seventies. His role as guitarist and lead vocalist was eventually filled by Donnie Dacus, with whom Chicago bounced back in the Eighties with the albums *Chicago 16* and *Chicago 17* and new hit singles in typical ballad form: *Hard To Say I'm Sorry* and *Hard Habit To Break*. (Bob MacDonald).
A jazz-rock septet formed in Chicago in 1967. First called the Big Thing, then Chicago Transit Authority, like Blood, Sweat & Tears they were a big rock band that used horns but ultimately had little to do with jazz. Producer James William Guercio had played bass in Dick Clark road shows and later with the Beach Boys and Blood, Sweat and Tears, also produced and directed the film *Elektra glide in blue* in 1973 which had members of Chicago in the cast; he opened Caribou Ranch studios and recorded Elton John there in 1974. Their first three albums were two-disc sets and the third was a triple; at the time they had a counterculture image: the fourth side of the first set began with chants from the 1968 Democratic National Convention, but their *Greatest hits* sets chart their evolution from anti-establishment to MOR fodder. They had a transatlantic number one hit in 1976 with a luch ballad *If you leave men now*, and more similar hits; they had dropped Guercio to produce themselves. In the early '80's CBS dropped them and they formed their own Full Moon label. Only die-hard fans can now keep track of all their albums. (Donald Clarke, April 1989).

25 OR 6 TO 4
Tracks: / 25 or 6 to 4 (remix) / One more day / Hard habit to break.
7" Single: Released Oct '86, on Warner Bros., by WEA Records. Deleted Jun '87. Catalogue no: **W 8628**
12" Single: Released Oct '86, on Warner Bros., by WEA Records. Deleted Jun '87. Catalogue no: **W 8628 T**
7" Single: Released Jul '70, on CBS, by CBS Records. Catalogue no: **CBS 5076**
12" Pic: Released Oct '86, on Warner Bros., by WEA Records. Deleted Jun '87. Catalogue no: **W 8638 TP**

25 OR 6 TO 4 (IMPORT)
Tracks: / 25 or 6 to 4 / Make me smile.
CD 3": Released Aug '88, on Columbia (USA), by CBS Records (USA). Catalogue no: **38K33193**

ALONG COMES A WOMAN
Tracks: / Along comes a woman / We can stop the hurting.
12" Single: Released Apr '85, on Full Moon (USA), Catalogue no: **W 9082 T**

BABY, WHAT A BIG SURPRISE
Tracks: / Baby, what a big surprise.
7" Single: Released Nov '77, on CBS, by CBS Records. Deleted Nov '80. Catalogue no: **A 5672**

HARD HABIT TO BREAK
Tracks: / Hard habit to break / Remember the feeling.
12" Single: Released Nov '84, on Full Moon (USA), Catalogue no: **W 9214 T**
7" Single: Released Aug '84, on Full Moon (USA), Deleted Jan '88. Catalogue no: **W 9214**

HARD TO SAY I'M SORRY
Tracks: / Hard to say I'm sorry / Think.
7" Single: Released Jul '82, on Full Moon (USA), Catalogue no: **K 79301**

HOUSE ... MEGAMIX VOL. 2
7" EP: Released Nov '87, on DJ Int.(Germany), Catalogue no: **DJ 33101445**

I DON'T WANNA LIVE WITHOUT YOUR LOVE
Tracks: / I don't wanna live without your love / I stand up.
7" Single: Released Sep '88, on WEA, by WEA Records. Catalogue no: **W 7855**
12" Single: Released Sep '88, on WEA, by WEA Records. Catalogue no: **W 7855T**

IF SHE WOULD HAVE BEEN FAITHFUL
Tracks: / If she would have been faithful / Forever full moon.
12" Single: Released 10 Oct '87, on Warner Bros., by WEA Records. Deleted Jul '88. Catalogue no: **W 8428T**
12" Single: Released 10 Oct '87, on Warner Bros., by WEA Records. Deleted Jul '88. Catalogue no: **W 8242 T**
7" Single: Released 10 Oct '87, on Warner Bros., by WEA Records. Deleted Jul '88. Catalogue no: **W 8424**

IF YOU LEAVE ME NOW (SINGLE)
Tracks: / If you leave me now / 25 or 6 to 4 / Baby what a big suprise (Available on cassingle only.) / Wishing you were here (Available on cassingle only).
7" Single: Released Oct '76, on CBS, by CBS Records. Catalogue no: **A 4603**
7" Single: Released Nov '82, on CBS, by CBS Records. Catalogue no: **A 2939**

I'M A MAN
Tracks: / I'm a man.
7" Single: Released Jan '70, on CBS, by CBS Records. Deleted Jan '73. Catalogue no: **CBS 4715**

LOOK AWAY (REMIX)
Tracks: / Look away / Come in from the night / 25 or 6 to 4 (Available on 12" only.).
CD 5": Released Dec '88, on Warner Bros., by WEA Records. Catalogue no: **W 7766CD**
12" Single: Released Dec '88, on Warner Bros., by WEA Records. Catalogue no: **W 7766T**
7" Single: Released Dec '88, on Warner Bros., by WEA Records. Catalogue no: **W 7766**

LOVE ME TOMORROW
Tracks: / Love me tomorrow / Bad advice.
7" Single: Released Nov '82, on Full Moon (USA), Catalogue no: **K 79338**

SONG FOR YOU, A
Tracks: / Song for you, A / I'd rather be rich.
7" Single: Released Aug '80, on CBS, by CBS Records. Deleted '82. Catalogue no: **CBS 8921**

STAY THE NIGHT
Tracks: / Stay the night / Only you.
7" Single: Released Jun '84, on Warner Bros., by WEA Records. Deleted '87. Catalogue no: **W 9306**

STREET PLAYER (SINGLE)
Tracks: / Street player / Window dreamin'.
7" Single: Released Apr '80, on CBS, by CBS Records. Deleted Apr '83. Catalogue no: **CBS 8040**

WILL YOU STILL LOVE ME
Tracks: / Will you still love me / Forever / Hard habit to break (Available on 12" version only.).
Note: Hard habit to break is available on 12" version only.
12" Single: Released Feb '87, on Warner Bros., by WEA Records. Deleted Jan '88. Catalogue no: **W 8439T**
7" Single: Released Feb '87, on Warner Bros., by WEA Records. Deleted Jul '88. Catalogue no: **W 8439**

YOU'RE THE INSPIRATION
Tracks: / You're the inspiration.
7" Single: Released Feb '85, on Full Moon (USA), Deleted Jun '87. Catalogue no: **W 9126**
12" Single: Released Feb '85, on Full Moon (USA), Catalogue no: **W 9126 T**

Chicago Bears

SUPERBOWL SHUFFLE
Tracks: / Superbowl (Inst. mix) / Superbowl shuffle.
Cassingle: Released Jun '86, on Phonogram, by Phonogram Ltd. Deleted '87. Catalogue no: **BOWLC 1**
7" Single: Released Jun '86, on Phonogram, by Phonogram Ltd. Deleted '87. Catalogue no: **BOWL 1**
12" Single: Released Jun '86, on Phonogram, by Phonogram Ltd. Deleted '87. Catalogue no: **BOWL 112**

Chicago House Hustlers

SHOW ME HOW TO JACK
Tracks: / Show me how to jack (dub version).
12" Single: Released Nov '86, on Spin-Off's, Catalogue no: **12 OFF 3**

Chicago Trax..

CHICAGO TRAX MEGAMIX
7" EP: Released Nov '87, on Trax (Germany), Catalogue no: **TX 33500345**

Chicanes

CRY A LITTLE
Tracks: / Cry a little / Further thoughts.
7" Single: Released Apr '81, on Dinosaur, Deleted Apr '84. Catalogue no: **DD 003**

Chicaynes

FURTHER THOUGHTS
Tracks: / Further thoughts.
7" EP: Released Jun '88, on Bam Caruso, by Demon Records. Catalogue no: **NRIC 039**

Chicken Chest

LABBA LABBA
Tracks: / Labba labba.
12" Single: Released Oct '88, on Jammy's, Catalogue no: **VPRD 341**

Chicken Ranch

HUSH
Tracks: / Hush.
7" Single: Released Sep '85, on Cannon Fodder, Catalogue no: **KIDTHATCH 85**

Chicken Shack
Biographical details: Chicken Shack were formed in Birmingham in 1965 by guitarist Stan Webb. At the time they were a trio but by 1968, when the group was living in London, Webb's two original colleagues had left and been replaced by three others: Bidwell, Perfect and Sylvester. Their first album, issued in '68, was entitled *40 blue Fingers Freshly Packed And Ready To Serve*. It was ideal material for Britain's late Sixties blues boom and reached No. 12 on the LP charts. 1969's follow-up album *OK Ken?* was in similar vein and made a brief visit to the Top 10. That same year they enjoyed their only two hit singles: *I'd Rather Go Blind*, an R&B song originally recorded by Etta James two years earlier, reached No. 14 and logges 13 weeks on the Top 50; *Tears In The Wind* peaked at No. 29.
At the end of this successful year, Perfect left the group to join her husband John McVie in Fleetwood Mac, then a blues-orientated rock outfit; she stayed with them to experience success followed by failure, followed by new heights of American and world success with the *Rumours* album.
The loss of Perfect's fine voice, together with the waning of the blues' popularity, meant the end of the band's record sales, though they remained a well-received live attraction during the early Seventies. By the time Chicken Shack folded in 1974, only Stan Webb from the '69 line-up was still there. (Bob MacDonald).
A blues band formed in Birmingham in 1965, with vocalist/guitarist Stan Webb, vocalist/pianist Christine Perfect, bassist Andy Sylvester and drummer Dave Bidwell. Like Cream, John Mayall and the early Fleetwood Mac they unearthed obscure USA blues and left room for guitar solos, and were one of the groups parodied by the Bonzo Dog Band for their earnest white approach to ethnic black music. Etta James's *I'd rather go blind* was one of their biggest hits; Perfect won a Melody Maker poll as best British female singer, though Webb was the focus of the stage act, playing solos with a 200 foot lead on his guitar. Webb carried on after she married Fleetwood Mac's John McVie and helped that group to greater success. He also played with Savoy Brown while Chicken Shack split and re-formed, and still works the London pub circuit. (Donald Clarke, April 1989).

I'D RATHER GO BLIND (OLD GOLD)
Tracks: / I'd rather go blind / Tears in the wind.
7" Single: Released Jul '82, on Old Gold, by Old Gold Records. Deleted Jul '88. Catalogue no: **OG 9201**

I'D RATHER GO BLIND (SINGLE)
Tracks: / I'd rather go blind.
7" Single: Released May '69, on Blue Horizon, by Ace Records. Deleted May '72. Catalogue no: **57 3153**

TEARS IN THE WIND
Tracks: / Tears in the wind.
7" Single: Released Sep '69, on Blue Horizon, by Ace Records. Catalogue no: **57-3160**

Chico

CONGA
Tracks: / Conga.
7" Single: Released 21 Nov '87, on Quazar, Catalogue no: **QUA 3**
12" Single: Released 21 Nov '87, on Quazar, Catalogue no: **QUAT 3**

Chico Chico

BAMBALEO
Tracks: / Bambaleo / Just shadows on the wall / If I had a hammer (Only on the 12" version.) / Bambeleo (Spanish summer mix) (Only on the 12" version.).
Note: A huge summer dance floor smash throughout Europe and a Top 20 hit in Belgium and Germany and feaures the big beat Ballearic sound of summer 1988.
12" Single: Released Sep '88, on Polydor, by Polydor Ltd. Catalogue no: **PZ 19**
7" Single: Released Sep '88, on Polydor, by Polydor Ltd. Catalogue no: **PO 19**

Chico & The Chile

NO NEWS IS BETTER THAN BAD NEWS
Tracks: / No news is better than bad news.
12" Single: on Creole, by Creole Records. Catalogue no: **CR 12 41**
7" Single: Released Oct '82, on Creole, by Creole Records. Catalogue no: **CR 41**

Chicory Tip
Biographical details: Discovered in Maidstone, Kent in 1970 by record producer Roger Easterby, Chicory Tip shot to national fame in early 1972 with a UK chart-topper called *Son Of My Father*. Over the following eighteen months, the group managed two more Top 20 singles: *What's Your Name* and *Good Grief Christina*. By the time of the latter's success, Foster had been replaced by Rod Cloutt. Although the group continued performing throughout the rest of the Seventies, their fourth hit single never came.
Son Of My Father has far greater historical importance than the group who released it. It was the first UK No. 1 to feature a synthesiser, though played by engineer Chris Thomas and not by any member of Chicory Tip. An everyday feature of pop music in

the Eighties, the synth was a total novelty in 1972 and its prominent use on *Son Of My Father* was the song's main selling point. The original German version was co-written by the man who scored a Continental hit with it, Giorgio Moroder. Chicory Tip's rendition was thus the first experience of a British No. 1 for a man who, in the late Seventies and the Eighties, was to mastermind numerous synthesised disco hits, notably UK chart-toppers for Donna Summer and Blondie. (Bob MacDonald)..

GOOD GRIEF CHRISTINA
Tracks: / Good grief Chistina.
7" Single: Released Mar '73, on CBS, by CBS Records. Deleted Mar '76. Catalogue no: **A 1258**

SON OF MY FATHER
Tracks: / Son of my father.
7" Single: Released Jan '72, on CBS, by CBS Records. Deleted '75. Catalogue no: **A 7737**

SON OF MY FATHER (OLD GOLD)
Tracks: / Son of my father / What's your name.
7" Single: Released Jul '82, on Old Gold, by Old Gold Records. Catalogue no: **OG 9003**

WHAT'S YOUR NAME
Tracks: / What's your name.
7" Single: Released May '72, on CBS, by CBS Records. Deleted May '73. Catalogue no: **A 8021**

Chief

DON'T TOUCH THE RECEIVER
Tracks: / Don't touch the receiver / Ice breaker.
7" Single: Released Aug '81, on Swamp, by Swamp Records. Deleted '84. Catalogue no: **WAM 114**

Chiefs of Relief

FREEDOM TO ROCK
Tracks: / Freedom to rock.
7" Single: Released Oct '85, on W.A.R., by W.A.R. Records. Catalogue no: **WAR 3004**
12" Single: Released Oct '85, on W.A.R., by W.A.R. Records. Catalogue no: **12 WAR 3004**

HOLIDAY
Tracks: / Holiday.
7" Single: Released Aug '84, on MCA, by MCA Records. Catalogue no: **MCA 908**
12" Single: Released Aug '84, on MCA, by MCA Records. Catalogue no: **MCAT 908**

WEEKENDS
Tracks: / Weekends / Kiss of life.
7" Single: Released Feb '87, on WEA, by WEA Records. Deleted Jan '88. Catalogue no: **YZ 109**
12" Single: Released Feb '87, on WEA, by WEA Records. Deleted Jan '88. Catalogue no: **YZ 109T**

Chiesel

SALLY GARDENS
Tracks: / Sally gardens.
7" Single: Released Sep '84, on Homespun (Ireland), by Outlet Records. Catalogue no: **HS 087**

Chiffons

Biographical details: The Chiffons were one of numerous all-girl vocal groups to hit the American and, to a lesser extent, the British charts in the early and mid-Sixties. Other US acts in the same category included the Crystals, the Angels, the Cookies, the Ronnettes and, of course, the famous Supremes. The Chiffons rocketed to fame in 1963 with their US No. 1 *He's So Fine*. Its follow-up was another bright, catchy pop ditty *One Fine Day* reached No. 5 on the American charts. Both were Top 30, though not Top 10, successes in the UK. Two smaller US Top 40 singles followed, but the hits then tailed off for the Chiffons. After a couple of years' absence, they returned to the charts with *Sweet Talkin' Guy*, which reached No. 10 in the States. In Britain it peaked at No. 31 first time round, but hen shot to No. 4 in 1972, benefiting from a record industry re-issue craze. By this time the group were still performing in the New York area but were no longer creating new hits.
As the Chiffons themselves passed into pop history, their *He's So Fine* hit remained in the public eye. The song's writer (and the group's manager) Ronald Mack successfully sued George Harrison for breach of copyright - the ex-Beatle's transatlantic 1971 chart-topper *My Sweet Lord* was ruled in court to be musically identical to the Chiffons' American No. 1, thus representing the best publicised plagiarism case of the rock ers. (Bob MacDonald).
A vocal quartet, the quintessential '60's girl group, like others in the genre an outlet for a creative writing/production team, in this case the doo-wop group, the Tokens. They had a minor hit with *Tonight's the night* in 1960, then number one on both R&B and pop charts in 1963 with *He's so fine* followed by more hits. Their last top ten was the classic *Sweet talkin' guy* in 1966; in 1971 there was litigation over the similarity of George Harrison's hit *My sweet lord* to *He's so fine*. *Sweet talkin' guy* was reissued in the UK in 1972 for a surprise top five. (Donald Clarke, April 1989)e.

HE'S SO FINE
Tracks: / He's so fine / Sweet talking guy / One fine day.
7" Single: Released May '82, on RCA, by BMG Records (UK). Deleted May '85. Catalogue no: **GOLD 545**
7" Single: Released Oct '82, on Phonogram, by Phonogram Ltd. Deleted Oct '85. Catalogue no: **CUT 115**
7" Single: Released Aug '82, on Blast From The Past, by Creole Records. Catalogue no: **CR 183**
7" Single: Released Apr '63, on Stateside, by EMI Records. Deleted Apr '66. Catalogue no: **SS 172**

ONE FINE DAY
Tracks: / One fine day / Love so fine.
7" Single: Released Aug '81, on RCA, by BMG Records (UK). Catalogue no: **GOLD 536**
7" Single: Released Jul '63, on Stateside, by EMI Records. Catalogue no: **SS 202**

SWEET TALKING GUY
Tracks: / Sweet talking guy / He's so fine.
7" Single: Released Aug '82, on Creole, by Creole Records. Deleted '87. Catalogue no: **HR 183**
7" Single: Released Mar '72, on London-American, Catalogue no: **HL 10271**
7" Single: Released May '66, on Stateside, by EMI Records. Catalogue no: **SS 512**

SWEET TALKING GUY (OLD GOLD)
7" Single: Released Jun '88, on Old Gold, by Old Gold Records. Catalogue no: **OG 9406**

Chilcott, Steve

PLANXTY IRWIN
Tracks: / Planxty Irwin.
7" Single: Released Dec '82, on Gypsy Folk, by Gypsy Folk Records. Catalogue no: **GFR 002**

Child

IT'S ONLY MAKE BELIEVE
Tracks: / It's only make believe.
7" Single: Released Jul '78, on Ariola-Hansa, by Hansa Records. Deleted Jul '81. Catalogue no: **AHA 522**

ONLY YOU (AND YOU ALONE)
Tracks: / Only you (and you alone).
7" Single: Released Apr '79, on Ariola-Hansa, by Hansa Records. Deleted Apr '82. Catalogue no: **AHA 536**

WHEN YOU WALK IN THE ROOM
Tracks: / When you walk in the room.
7" Single: Released Apr '78, on Ariola-Hansa, by Hansa Records. Deleted Apr '81. Catalogue no: **AHA 511**

Child Aid

HELP THE CHILDREN
Tracks: / Help the children.
7" Single: Released 21 Nov '87, on Identity, by Identity Records. Catalogue no: **IDEN 101**
12" Single: Released 21 Nov '87, on Identity, by Identity Records. Catalogue no: **IDENT 101**

Child, Desmond & Rouge

GOODBYE BABY
Tracks: / Goodbye baby / Imitation of love.
7" Single: Released Jan '80, on Capitol, by EMI Records. Deleted Jan '85. Catalogue no: **CL 16115**

Childish, Wild Billy

COMPANIONS IN A DEATH BOAT
Special: Released Jun '88, on Hangman, by Hangman Records. Catalogue no: **WORDUP 001**

CONVERSATIONS WITH DOCTOR X
Special: Released Jun '88, on Hangman, by Hangman Records. Catalogue no: **WORDUP 006**

MONKS WITHOUT GOD
Special: Released Jun '88, on Hangman, by Hangman Records. Catalogue no: **WORDUP 005**

POEMS FROM THE BARRIER BLOCK
Special: Released Jun '88, on Hangman, by Hangman Records. Catalogue no: **WORDUP 003**

POEMS WITHOUT RHYME
Special: Released Jun '88, on Hangman, by Hangman Records. Catalogue no: **WORDUP 004**

TO THE QUICK
Special: Released Jun '88, on Hangman, by Hangman Records. Catalogue no: **WORDUP 007**

Children

FREEDOM
Tracks: / Freedom.
12" Single: Released Nov '87, on DJ Int.(USA), Catalogue no: **DJ 951**

Children Kinder

CHILDREN KINDER ENFANTS Various artists
7" Single: Released May '85, on Sonet, by Sonet Records. Catalogue no: **SON 2281**

Children Of Seven

SOLIDARITY
Tracks: / Solidarity / Solid dub.
7" Single: Released May '80, on Stiff, by Stiff Records. Deleted May '83. Catalogue no: **SOL-1**
12" Single: Released May '80, on Stiff, by Stiff Records. Deleted May '83. Catalogue no: **SOL-112**

Children Of The Night

IT'S A TRIP
Tracks: / It's a trip.
7" Single: Released Oct '88, on Jive, by Zomba Records. Catalogue no: **JIVE 189**
12" Single: Released Oct '88, on Jive, by Zomba Records. Catalogue no: **JIVET 189**

WE PLAY SKA
Tracks: / We play ska.
12" Single: Released Apr '89, on Jive, by Zomba Records. Catalogue no: **JIVET 202**
7" Single: Released Apr '89, on Jive, by Zomba Records. Catalogue no: **JIVE 202**

Children Of The World

IF WE ONLY HAD THE TIME
Tracks: / If we only had the time / America the beautiful / God bless america.
7" Single: Released Dec '80, on Polydor, by Polydor Ltd. Deleted Dec '85. Catalogue no: **EPC 9307**

Child's Play

PLAYGROUND ROMANCE
Tracks: / Playground romance / Escape.
7" Single: Released Jul '81, on Cable, Deleted '85. Catalogue no: **VHF 1**

Childs, Toni

DON'T WALK AWAY (REMIX)
Tracks: / Don't walk away / Hush.
7" Single: Released 6 Mar '89, on A&M, by A&M Records. Catalogue no: **AM 462**
CD 5": Released 6 Mar '89, on A&M, by A&M Records. Catalogue no: **CDEE 462**
12" Single: Released 6 Mar '89, on A&M, by A&M Records. Catalogue no: **AMY 462**

STOP YOUR FUSSIN'
Tracks: / Stop your fussin'.
CD 5": Released May '89, on A&M, by A&M Records. Catalogue no: **AMYCD 508**
12" Single: Released May '89, on A&M, by A&M Records. Catalogue no: **AMY 508**
7" Single: Released May '89, on A&M, by A&M Records. Catalogue no: **AM 508**

ZIMBABWE
Tracks: / Zimbabwe (remix) / Where's the ocean.
12" Single: Released Jan '89, on A&M, by A&M Records. Catalogue no: **AMY 492**
7" Single: Released Jan '89, on A&M, by A&M Records. Catalogue no: **AM 492**

Chi-lites

Biographical details: The Chi-Lites, originally known as the Hi-Lites but amended to tie in with their home city of Chicago, were formed in the early Sixties but patiently waited until the early Seventies for major success. Under the direction of their key member, singer/songwriter/producer Eugene Record, they achieved a long run of successes on the US soul charts, many of which crossed over to the pop listings. Their irst Top 40 pop hit was the demanding, hard-hitting *(For God's Sake) Give More Power To The People*. In total contrast, the group returned to the charts shortly afterwards with the deeply soulful *Have You Seen Her*, a slow, partly spoken/partly sung narrative. This all-time classic single reached No. 3 on both sides of the Atlantic and remains their best-known track. The quartet then enjoyed a US No. 1 with 1972's *Oh Girl*.
By the end of 1973 the Chi-Lites' US pop hits had finished. On the UK charts, however, they came back with renewed vigour. 1974's *Homely Girl* reached No. 5 and they achieved four more Top 10 singles during the mid-Seventies: in addition to a smash double A sided re-issue, *Have You Seen Her/Oh Girl*, these included the ultra-soulful slowie *It's Time For Love* plus up-tempo numbers in the shape of *Too Good To Be Forgotten* and *You Don't Have To Go*. By this time, in addition to his other roles, Record was a senior executive of Brunswick Records. In the late Seventies and early Eighties, the group were unsuccessful. But, proving that they were indeed 'too good to be forgotten', they nade a comeback of sorts with 1983's danceable single *Changing For You*. (Bob MacDonald)..

ALL I WANT TO DO IS MAKE LOVE TO YOU
Tracks: / All I want to do is make love to you / Love shock.
7" Single: Released Jan '81, on 20th Century, by 20th Century Records. Deleted Jan '84. Catalogue no: **TC 2479**

CHANGING FOR YOU (SINGLE)
Tracks: / Changing for you.
12" Single: Released Jul '83, on R & B, by Red Bus Records. Catalogue no: **RBS 215T**
7" Single: Released Jul '83, on R & B, by Red Bus Records. Catalogue no: **RBS 215**

GIVE MORE POWER TO THE PEOPLE
Tracks: / Give more power to the people.
7" Single: Released Aug '71, on MCA, by MCA Records. Deleted Aug '74. Catalogue no: **MU 1138**

HARD ACT TO FOLLOW
Tracks: / Hard act to follow / Hard act to follow (inst.).
12" Single: Released Oct '85, on Certain, by Certain Records. Deleted '88. Catalogue no: **12ACERT 3**
7" Single: Released Oct '85, on Certain, by Certain Records. Deleted '88. Catalogue no: **ACERT 3**

HAVE YOU SEEN HER ?
Tracks: / Have you seen her / Homely girl / I found sunshine / Too good to be forgotten / (For God's sake) give more power to the people.
7" Single: Released Apr '81, on 20th Century, by 20th Century Records. Deleted Apr '84. Catalogue no: **TC 2481**
12" Single: Released Jun '84, on Skratch, by Skratch Records. Catalogue no: **SKI 02(12)**
7" Single: Released Jan '72, on MCA, by MCA Records. Catalogue no: **MU 1146**
7" Single: Released Jun '84, on Skratch, by Skratch Records. Catalogue no: **SKI 02**

HAVE YOU SEEN HER ?/OH GIRL
Tracks: / Have you seen her? / Oh girl.
7" Single: Released Jun '75, on Brunswick, by Decca Records. Deleted Jun '7[illegible] Catalogue no: **BR 20**

HOMELY GIRL
Tracks: / Homely girl.
7" Single: Released Mar '74, on Brunswick, by Decca Records. Deleted Mar '7[illegible] Catalogue no: **BR 9**

HOMELY GIRL (OLD GOLD C[illegible] SINGLE)
Tracks: / Homely girl / Have you seen he[r] / Oh girl.
CD 5": Released Nov '88, on Old Gold, by Old Gold Records. Catalogue no: **OG 610[illegible]**

I FOUND SUNSHINE
Tracks: / I found sunshine.
7" Single: Released Jul '74, on Brunswick, by Decca Records. Deleted Jul '77. Catalogue no: **BR 12**

IT'S TIME FOR LOVE
Tracks: / It's time for love.
7" Single: Released Sep '75, on Brunswick, by Decca Records. Deleted Sep '7[illegible] Catalogue no: **BR 25**

MAKING LOVE
Tracks: / Making love.
12" Single: Released Sep '83, on R & [B], by Red Bus Records. Catalogue no: **R[BS] 217**
7" Single: Released Sep '83, on R & B, by Red Bus Records. Catalogue no: **RBS 2[17]**

ME AND YOU (SINGLE)
Tracks: / Me and you / Tell me where it hurts.
12" Single: Released Oct '81, on 2[0th] Century, by 20th Century Records. Dele[ted] '85. Catalogue no: **TCD 132**
7" Single: Released Oct '81, on 20th Century, by 20th Century Records. Deleted '[illegible] Catalogue no: **TC 2503**

OH GIRL
Tracks: / Oh girl.
7" Single: Released May '72, on MCA, by MCA Records. Deleted May '75. Catalog[ue] no: **MU 1156**

STAY A LITTLE LONGER
Tracks: / Stay a little longer / Hi'ya.
12" Single: Released Jan '80, on P[illegible] Deleted Jan '85. Catalogue no: **12P500[5]**
7" Single: Released Jan '80, on P[illegible] Deleted Jan '85. Catalogue no: **7P5005**

TOO GOOD TO BE FORGOTTEN
Tracks: / Too good to be forgotten.
7" Single: Released Nov '74, on Brunswick, by Decca Records. Deleted Nov '77. Catalogue no: **BR 13**

TWIST (ROUND 'N' ROUND)
Tracks: / Twist (round 'n' round).
7" Single: Released Apr '83, on Philly World (USA), by Philly World (USA). Deleted Apr '86. Catalogue no: **PWS 109**

YOU DON'T HAVE TO GO
Tracks: / You don't have to go.
7" Single: Released Jul '76, on Brunswick, by Decca Records. Deleted Jul '79. Catalogue no: **BR 34**

YOU DON'T HAVE TO GO (OLD GOLD)
Tracks: / You don't have to go / Too good to be forgotten / I found sunshine.
12" Single: Released 30 May '89, on Old Gold, by Old Gold Records. Catalogue no: **OG 4119**

Chill Fac-torr

SHOUT (THE EXOTIC)
Tracks: / Shout (the exotic).
12" Single: Released Oct '83, on Philly World (USA), by Philly World (USA). Catalogue no: **PWSL 115**
7" Single: Released Oct '83, on Philly World (USA), by Philly World (USA). Catalogue no: **PWS 115**

TWIST
Tracks: / Twist.
7" Single: Released Mar '83, on Philly World (USA), by Philly World (USA). Catalogue no: **PWS 109**
12" Single: Released Mar '83, on Philly World (USA), by Philly World (USA). Catalogue no: **PWSL 109**

Chillin' Krew

TOO MUCH FUN
Tracks: / Too much fun / Krew salute (instrumental) / Too much fun (krew cut mix) (Only on 12" single.).
7" Single: Released Aug '88, on MCA, by MCA Records. Deleted 1 Jul '89. Catalogue no: **KRU 1**
12" Single: Released 22 Aug '88, on MCA, by MCA Records. Catalogue no: **KRUPR 1**
12" Single: Released Aug '88, on MCA, by MCA Records. Catalogue no: **KRUT 1**

Chilliwack

I BELIEVE
Tracks: / I believe / Living in stereo.
7" Single: Released Apr '82, on RCA, by BMG Records (UK). Deleted Apr '85. Catalogue no: **RCA 205**

MY GIRL
Tracks: / My girl / Sign here.
7" Single: Released Nov '81, on RCA, by BMG Records (UK). Deleted Nov '84. Catalogue no: **FB 1813**

Chillout, Chuck

NO DJ LIKE CHUCK
Tracks: / No DJ like Chuck.
12" Single: Released Oct '89, on Mercury, by Phonogram Ltd. Catalogue no: **MERX 301**
7" Single: Released Oct '89, on Mercury, by Phonogram Ltd. Catalogue no: **MER 301**

Chills

BLACK LEATHER JACKET
Tracks: / Black leather jacket.
12" Single: Released Feb '87, on Flying Nun, Catalogue no: **FNUK 7**

HOUSE WITH 100 ROOMS
Tracks: / House with 100 rooms.
12" Single: Released Aug '87, on Flying Nun, Catalogue no: **FNUK 11T**

LOST EP
Tracks: / Lost.
12" Single: Released Mar '86, on Flying Nun, Catalogue no: **COLD 004**

Chilly

COME TO L.A.
Tracks: / Come to L.A. / Get up.
7" Single: Released Feb '80, on Polydor, by Polydor Ltd. Deleted Feb '85. Catalogue no: **2042 137**

Chilton, Alex

DALAU LAMA
Tracks: / Dalau lama.
7" Set: Released 20 Feb '88, on New Rose (1), by New Rose Records. Catalogue no: **NEW 102**

HEY LITTLE CHILD
Tracks: / Hey little child / No more the moon shines Lorena.
7" Single: Released 20 Jun '80, on Aura Records, by Aura Records. Deleted '83. Catalogue no: **AUS 117**

MAKE A LITTLE MOVE
Tracks: / Make a little move.
7" Single: Released Dec '87, on New Rose (1), by New Rose Records. Catalogue no: **NEW 96**

NO SEX
Tracks: / No sex.
12" Single: Released May '86, on New Rose (1), by New Rose Records. Catalogue no: **12 NEW 068**

Chimes

1-2-3
Tracks: / 1-2-3 (Only on 7" and CD single.) / Underestimate (Only on 7" single.) / 1-2-3 (UK raw mix) (Only on 12" and CD single.) / Underestimate (special extended version) (Only on 12" and CD single.) / Bodyrock (demo version) (Only on 12" single.) / 1-2-3 (silent club dub) (On 655166 8 only) / 1-2-3 (gospel mix) (On 655166 8 only) / 1-2-3 (Philly mix) (On 655166 8 only).
12" Single: Released 14 Aug '89, on CBS, by CBS Records. Catalogue no: **655 166 8**
Cassingle: Released 14 Aug '89, on CBS, by CBS Records. Catalogue no: **655 166 4**
CD 5": Released Jul '89, on CBS, by CBS Records. Catalogue no: **655 166 2**
12" Single: Released Jul '89, on CBS, by CBS Records. Catalogue no: **655 166 6**
7" Single: Released Jul '89, on CBS, by CBS Records. Catalogue no: **655 166 7**

Chin, Junior

POSSE MOVE
Tracks: / Posse move.
12" Single: Released Nov '87, on Y & D, Catalogue no: **YDDO 114**

Chin, Leonard

GROOVIN'
Tracks: / Groovin'.
7" Single: Released Dec '83, on Cassia Music, Catalogue no: **CAS 002**

HOW COULD I LEAVE YOU NOW
Tracks: / How could I leave you now.
12" Single: Released Jul '85, on Cassia Music, Catalogue no: **CAS 003**

VISIONS
12" Single: Released Aug '84, on Adelphi (1), Catalogue no: **ADET 004**

WHAT MORE CAN I SAY
Tracks: / What more can I say.
12" Single: Released Feb '83, on Sanity, Catalogue no: **STY 002**

China Crisis

Biographical details: One of many acts to emerge from Liverpool during the first half of the Eighties, China Crisis first gained major attention when they supported Duran Duran in concert. Their first chart single *African And White* reached No. 45 on the UK listings in the summer of 1982, to be followed by the brief chart appearance of their debut album *Difficult Shapes And Passive Rhythms*, released on Virgin Records in November of that year. Their dreamy, understated pop sound gave them a UK No. 12 single in early '83 with the very peaceful *Christian*. The up-tempo follow-up *Tragedy and Mystery* was only a minor hit, however. Towards the end of the year the band issued a second album, *Working With Fire And Steel* which, at the beginnng of '84, yielded their firs Top 10 single - *Wishful Thinking*, another soft, relaxing record. But once again, the follow-up failed to consolidate. The sound of China Crisis is sufficiently distinctive to give them major success when the right songs are released, but their task during the mid-Eighties and beyond would be to carve out a more consistent career, in place of their previously erratic chart performance. (Bob MacDonald)..

AFRICAN AND WHITE
Tracks: / African and white / De suspicious.
7" Single: Released Aug '82, on Inevitable, by Inevitable Records. Deleted Aug '85. Catalogue no: **INEV 011**

ARIZONA SKY
Tracks: / Arizona sky (full length version) (On 12" only) / Trading in gold.
7" Single: Released Oct '86, on Virgin, by Virgin Records. Deleted May '88. Catalogue no: **VS 898**
12" Single: Released Oct '86, on Virgin, by Virgin Records. Catalogue no: **VS 898-12**

BEST KEPT SECRET
Tracks: / Instigator, The / Black man Ray (On CD only) / You did cut me (ON CD only) / Arizona sky (On CD only) / Little Italy (On 12" only) / Best kept secret / Instigator, The (Italian fuzzbox version) (On 12" only).
7" Single: Released Jan '87, on Virgin, by Virgin Records. Deleted May '88. Catalogue no: **VS 926**
12" Single: Released Jan '87, on Virgin, by Virgin Records. Catalogue no: **VS 926-12**
CD 5": Released '88, on Virgin, by Virgin Records. Catalogue no: **CRIS 92612**

CHINA CRISIS - CHRISTIAN (Released on Virgin)

BLACK MAN RAY
Tracks: / Black man Ray / Animalistic (7" only) / Animalistic (a day at the zoo mix) (CD & 12" only) / Hampton beach (CD only).
CD 3": Released Jun '88, on Virgin, by Virgin Records. Catalogue no: **CDT 15**
7" Single: Released Mar '85, on Virgin, by Virgin Records. Catalogue no: **VS 752**
12" Single: Released Mar '85, on Virgin, by Virgin Records. Catalogue no: **VS 752-12**

BLACK MAN RAY (OLD GOLD)
Tracks: / Black man ray / King in a catholic style (wake up).
7" Single: Released Nov '88, on Old Gold, by Old Gold Records. Catalogue no: **OG 9827**

CHRISTIAN (see panel above)
Tracks: / Christian / Greenacre bay / Performing seals.
7" Single: Released Jan '83, on Virgin, by Virgin Records. Catalogue no: **VS 562**
12" Single: Released Jan '83, on Virgin, by Virgin Records. Catalogue no: **VS 562-12**

CHRISTIAN (OLD GOLD)
Tracks: / Christian / Wishful thinking.
7" Single: Released Nov '88, on Old Gold, by Old Gold Records. Catalogue no: **OG 9818**
12" Single: Released 27 Feb '89, on Old Gold, by Old Gold Records. Catalogue no: **OG 4103**

HANNA HANNA
Tracks: / Hanna Hanna / Hanna Hanna (extended mix) / Here comes a raincloud / African and white.
12" Single: Released Mar '84, on Virgin, by Virgin Records. Catalogue no: **VS 665-12**
7" Single: Released Mar '84, on Virgin, by Virgin Records. Deleted '86. Catalogue no: **VS 665**

KING IN A CATHOLIC STYLE (WAKE UP)
Tracks: / King in a catholic style (wake up) / Blue sea / King in a catholic style (wake up) (extended version) (12" only).
12" Single: Released May '85, on Virgin, by Virgin Records. Catalogue no: **VS 765-12**
7" Single: Released May '85, on Virgin, by Virgin Records. Catalogue no: **VS 765**

NO MORE BLUE HORIZONS
Tracks: / No more blue horizons / No ordinary lover / Watching over burning fields.
7" Single: Released Oct '82, on Virgin, by Virgin Records. Deleted Oct '85. Catalogue no: **VS 521**
12" Single: Released Oct '82, on Virgin, by Virgin Records. Deleted Oct '85. Catalogue no: **VS 521 12**

RED LETTER DAY
Tracks: / Red letter day / Diary of a hollow horse / Strength of character (Only on 12" version.).
12" Single: Released May '89, on Virgin, by Virgin Records. Catalogue no: **VST 1188**
CD 3": Released May '89, on Virgin, by Virgin Records. Catalogue no: **VSCDX 118**
7" Single: Released May '89, on Virgin, by Virgin Records. Catalogue no: **VSE 1188**
7" Single: Released May '89, on Virgin, by Virgin Records. Catalogue no: **VS 1188**

SCREAM DOWN AT ME
Tracks: / Scream down at me.
12" Single: Released Oct '82, on Virgin, by Virgin Records. Deleted Oct '85. Catalogue no: **VS 495 12**
7" Single: Released Oct '82, on Virgin, by Virgin Records. Deleted Oct '85. Catalogue no: **VS 495**

ST. SAVIOUR'S SQUARE
Tracks: / St. Saviour's square / Back home / St. Saviour's square (version) (12" only).
12" Single: Released Mar '89, on Virgin, by Virgin Records. Catalogue no: **VST 1168**
CD 3": Released Mar '89, on Virgin, by Virgin Records. Catalogue no: **VSCD 1168**
7" Single: Released Mar '89, on Virgin, by Virgin Records. Catalogue no: **VS 1168**

TRAGEDY AND MYSTERY
Tracks: / Tragedy and mystery.
7" Single: Released May '83, on Virgin, by Virgin Records. Deleted May '86. Catalogue no: **VS 587**

WISHFUL THINKING
Tracks: / Wishful thinking / Some people I know to lead fantastic lives / This occupation (extended mix) / Some people I know to lead fantastic lives (extended mix).
7" Single: Released Jan '84, on Virgin, by Virgin Records. Deleted May '88. Catalogue no: **VS 647**
12" Single: Released Jan '84, on Virgin, by Virgin Records. Catalogue no: **VS 647-12**

WORKING WITH FIRE & STEEL (SINGLE)
Tracks: / Working with fire and steel / Fire and steel (mix) / Dockland / Forever I and I.
7" Single: Released Sep '83, on Virgin, by Virgin Records. Deleted '86. Catalogue no: **VS 620**
12" Single: Released Sep '83, on Virgin, by Virgin Records. Catalogue no: **VS 620-12**

YOU DID CUT ME
Tracks: / You did cut me.
7" Single: Released Sep '85, on Virgin, by Virgin Records. Deleted Sep '88. Catalogue no: **VS 799**

China Doll

CHINA DOLL
Tracks: / China doll / Fear of flying.
7" Single: Released Jul '88, on Breakin', by Breakin' Records. Catalogue no: **7 BRK 2**
7" Single: on Graduate, by Graduate Records. Deleted Jan '87. Catalogue no: **GRAD 12**

TURKISH DELIGHT
Tracks: / Turkish delight / Red lantern.

7" Single: Released Jun '83, on Parlophone, by EMI Records. Catalogue no: **R 6061**

China Dolls

AIN'T LOVE AIN'T BAD
Tracks: / Ain't love ain't bad / One hit wonders.
7" Single: Released Nov '82, on Speed, Catalogue no: **FIRED 1**

Chinawhite

BLOOD ON THE STREETS
Tracks: / Blood on the streets.
7" Single: Released Apr '83, on Future Earth, by Future Earth Records. Deleted '87. Catalogue no: **FER 014**

Chinese Gangster

EP
Note: EP (4 track)
7" Single: Released Feb '87, on Ted Rum, Catalogue no: **CGE 001**

Chingas, Johnny

PHONE HOME
Tracks: / Phone home.
12" Single: Released Feb '83, on CBS, by CBS Records. Catalogue no: **A 13 3121**
7" Single: Released Feb '83, on CBS, by CBS Records. Catalogue no: **A 3121**

Chinieman

ROUGH TYPE OF LIFE
Tracks: / Rough type of life.
12" Single: Released Jun '89, on Reality, Catalogue no: **REAL 001**

Chiny

TELL ME
Tracks: / Tell me.
12" Single: Released Oct '87, on J.R. Production, Catalogue no: **TKJR 16**

Chip, Kool

JAZZ IT UP (REMIX)
Tracks: / Jazz it up (remix).
12" Single: Released Jul '87, on 4th & Broadway, by Island Records. Deleted Apr '88. Catalogue no: **12 BRX 62**

JAZZ IT UP - VOCAL
Tracks: / Jazz it up / Jazz it up (dub) / Keep it mellow.
7" Single: Released 20 Jun '87, on 4th & Broadway, by Island Records. Deleted Apr '88. Catalogue no: **BRW 62**
12" Single: Released 20 Jun '87, on 4th & Broadway, by Island Records. Deleted Apr '88. Catalogue no: **12 BRW 62**

Chipmunks

Biographical details: This American 'group' were the creation of David Seville, a Californian of Armenian extraction whose real name was Ross Bagdasarian. Seville entered showbusiness in the theatrical area, then moved on to songwriting, his biggest success beign Rosemary Clooney's *Come On-A My House*, a big US smash that he co-wrote several years before its early Fifties success. In 1956 he decided to record some material himself: posing as Alfi & Harry, he reached No. 15 on the British charts that year with *The Trouble With Harry*. Though he did not compose that record, he did write the song that brought him major international fame two years later. He released *Witch Doctor* under the name of David Seville - this was an unusual novelty record, featuring an orchestra and vocals recorded at half speed then played back at normal speed. The result was an American No. 1 single; in Britain Seville peaked at No. 11, losing the battle to an opportunistic cover version by Don Lang and His Frantic Five, a UK outfit who took the song to No. 5.
Using further tape machine tricks, he invented the chipmunks, an imaginary trio of North American squirrels that were actually his own voice recorded at three incorrect speeds. *The Chipmunk Song* became AMerica's Christmas No. 1 for 1958 and was, at the time, that nation's fastest selling disc in history, shifting 3.5 million copies in five weeks. Alvin, Simon and Theodore, the names that children all over America came to know them by, were derived from the names of three Liberty Records executives. Thus was created one of the most famous children's novelty ideas of all time. The follow-up single, *Alvin's Harmonica*, reached No. 3 in the US. Then came *Ragtime Cowboy Joe* which peaked at no. 16 in the summer of '59; this was the Chipmunks' only British hit, reaching No. 11 on the UK charts. Eking out the successful gimmick for as long as possible, Seville achieved three smaller American Top 40 hits over the following three years. He died in 1972 at the age of 52. Eight years after his passing, the idea was ressurected in his absence. The albums *Chipmunk Punk* and *Urban Chipmunk*, adaptations of rock and country songs respectively, were strong Stateside sellers in the early Eighties. (Bob MacDonald)..

MY SHARONA
Tracks: / My Sharona / You may be right.
7" Single: Released Nov '80, on Mercury, by Phonogram Ltd. Deleted Nov '83. Catalogue no: **MER 43**

RAGTIME COWBOY JOE
Tracks: / Ragtime cowboy Joe.
7" Single: Released Jul '59, on London-American, Deleted Jul '62. Catalogue no: **HLU 8916**

SLEIGH RIDE
Tracks: / Sleigh ride / Chipmunk song.
7" Single: Released Dec '81, on RCA, by BMG Records (UK). Deleted Dec '84. Catalogue no: **PB 12354**

Chippington, Ted

NON-STOP PARTY HITS OF THE 50'S,60'S AND 70'S
7" Single: Released Jan '85, on Vindaloo, by Vindaloo Records. Catalogue no: **UGH 8**

SHE LOVES YOU
Tracks: / Rockin' with Rita / Wierdness oh no / She loves you.
7" Single: Released Apr '86, on WEA, by WEA Records. Deleted Jun '87. Catalogue no: **UGH 12**
12" Single: Released Apr '86, on WEA, by WEA Records. Deleted Jun '87. Catalogue no: **UGH 12T**

WANDERER, THE
Tracks: / Wanderer.
7" Single: Released Aug '87, on Vindaloo, by Vindaloo Records. Catalogue no: **UGH 15**
12" Single: Released Aug '87, on Vindaloo, by Vindaloo Records. Catalogue no: **UGH 15T**

Chips

YOU NAME IT...I'LL DO IT
Tracks: / You name it...I'll do it / Ooh...the night.
7" Single: Released Aug '80, on RCA, by BMG Records (UK). Deleted Aug '83. Catalogue no: **PB 4537**

Chiquitas

DANCE THE RHUMBA
Tracks: / Dance the rhumba.
7" Single: Released Mar '84, on Banana, Catalogue no: **FRUIT 5**

Chisholm & Spence

YOU CAN'T GET NEAR ENOUGH TO THE ONE YOU LOVE
Tracks: / You can't get near enough to the one you love / I didn't know.
7" Single: Released Jun '80, on CBS, by CBS Records. Deleted '83. Catalogue no: **CBS 8612**

Chisum, Frank

I JUST CAN'T HELP BELIEVING
Tracks: / Just can't help believing / Wooden heart / Here go / You and I.
7" EP: Released Jun '88, on Ritz, by Ritz Records. Catalogue no: **RITZ 186**
Cassingle: Released Jun '88, on Ritz, by Ritz Records. Catalogue no: **RITZC 186**

Chloe

HE IS ELECTRIC
Tracks: / He is electric.
7" Single: Released Feb '84, on Sirocco, Catalogue no: **SIR 101**

Chocolate Milk

I'M YOUR RADIO
Tracks: / I'm your radio / Would it be alright / Action speaks louder than words (Only on 12" format.).
7" Single: Released Aug '80, on RCA, by BMG Records (UK). Deleted '83. Catalogue no: **PB 2030**
12" Single: Released Aug '80, on RCA, by BMG Records (UK). Deleted '83. Catalogue no: **PC 2030**

Choice

AN OLD FASHIONED CHRISTMAS
Tracks: / Old fashioned christmas, An.
7" Single: Released Dec '82, on Weasel, by Weasel Records. Catalogue no: **WR 4004**

SWEET LITTLE INDIANS
Tracks: / After you're gone / Sweet little Indians.
12" Single: Released Jun '86, on Climax, Catalogue no: **CLIMAX 1**

Choice Treats

LOVE ON THE REBOUND
Tracks: / Love on the rebound.
7" Single: Released Jan '84, on Passion, by Skratch Records. Catalogue no: **PASH 11**
12" Single: Released Jan '84, on Passion, by Skratch Records. Catalogue no: **PASH 11(12)**

Choir

TO THE CITY TOMORROW
Tracks: / To the city tomorrow.
7" Single: Released Feb '83, on A&M, by A&M Records. Deleted '88. Catalogue no: **AM 102**

Choir Militia

SHARPEN THE KNIFE
Tracks: / Nothing that would / Sharpen the knife.
7" Single: Released Jun '86, on W.A.R., by W.A.R. Records. Catalogue no: **WAR 3006**
12" Single: Released Jun '86, on W.A.R., by W.A.R. Records. Catalogue no: **12 WAR 3006**

Choirgirls

I COULD HAVE KISSED HIM THEN
Tracks: / I could have kissed him then / It's in his kiss.
7" Single: Released Sep '82, on BK, Catalogue no: **BKRS 100**

Choo Choo Train

BRIAR ROSE, THE
Tracks: / Briar rose, The.
12" Single: Released Jul '88, on Subway, by Subway Records. Catalogue no: **SUBWAY 20T**

HIGH
Tracks: / High / Wishing on a star.
12" Single: Released Nov '88, on Subway, by Subway Records. Catalogue no: **SUBWAY 23T**
7" Single: Released Nov '88, on Subway, by Subway Records. Catalogue no: **SUBWAY 23**

Chorale

MOUNTAIN MEN
Tracks: / Mountain men.
7" Single: Released Jun '85, on Telebell, Catalogue no: **TVP4**

SAFE AND SOUND
Tracks: / Safe and sound.
7" Single: Released Jan '84, on RCA, by BMG Records (UK). Catalogue no: **RCA 371**

Chordettes

Biographical details: This American female vocal group, featuring an unstable line-up, hailed from Wisconsin. Originally formed for folk festival appearances, the Chordettes were discovered by Arthur Godfrey, a famous media talent scout. Their first record *Mr. Sandman* was a huge-selling American No. 1 in 1954. Subsequent singles, all in a highly commercial pop vein, gave the group a string of US hits during the mid to late Fifties. Their Top 20 hits included *Eddie My Love, Born To Be With You* (revived in Britain by Dave Edmunds in 1973), *Lay Down Your Arms, Just Between You And Me, Lollipop* and *Zorro*. Though they managed three Top 20 singles in the UK, their British success was lessened by competition from UK cover versions of some of their American hits.
The Chordettes' record sales tailed off in the early Sixties, by which time they had helped to open the floodgates for numerous American girl groups, including such hitmakers as the Angels, the Cookies, the Chiffons, the Ronnettes and the Crystals. (Bob MacDonald)..

BORN TO BE WITH YOU
Tracks: / Born to be with you.
7" Single: Released Aug '56, on London-American, Deleted Aug '59. Catalogue no: **HLA 8302**

LOLLIPOP
Tracks: / Lollipop.
7" Single: Released Apr '58, on London-American, Deleted Apr '61. Catalogue no: **HLA 8584**
7" Single: Released Jul '82, on Old Gold, by Old Gold Records. Catalogue no: **OG 9051**
7" Single: on WEA, by WEA Records. Deleted Jan '88. Catalogue no: **A 9310**

MR SANDMAN
Tracks: / Mr. Sandman.
7" Single: Released Dec '54, on Columbia, by EMI Records. Catalogue no: **DB 3553**
7" Single: Released Jul '82, on Old Gold, by Old Gold Records. Catalogue no: **OG 9204**

Chords

Biographical details: This British band -- Brett Ascott, Billy Hassett, Martin Mason, Chris Pope and Mick Talbot -- were one of a considerable number of bands to appear and disappear during Britain's short-lived Mod revival of 1979-80. They achieved a Top Thirty album with *So Far Away* plus five minor hit singles, the best being *Maybe Tomorrow*, which reached No 40. Coincidentally, keyboards player Talbot was also a member of the Merton Parkas, another Mod revival band which reached No 40 with their biggest single, *You Need Wheels*. The Chords faded into history but Talbot's career reached a new level in 1983. Having played on some Jam sessions he teamed up with Paul Weller, on Jam's disbandment, to form Style Council, and quickly began a Jam-like string of British Top Twenty hits. (Bob MacDonald, 1985.).

BRITISH WAY OF LIFE, THE
Tracks: / British way of life, The / Way it's got to be.
7" Single: Released Jul '80, on Polydor, by Polydor Ltd. Deleted Jul '83. Catalogue no: **2059 258**

IN MY STREET
Tracks: / In my street.
7" Single: Released Oct '80, on Polydor, by Polydor Ltd. Deleted Oct '83. Catalogue no: **POSP 185**

MAYBE TOMMOROW
Tracks: / Maybe tommorow / I don't wanna know / Hey girl.
7" Single: Released Feb '80, on Polydor, by Polydor Ltd. Deleted Feb '83. Catalogue no: **POSP 101**

NOW IT'S GONE
Tracks: / Now it's gone.
7" Single: Released Oct '79, on Polydor, by Polydor Ltd. Deleted Oct '82. Catalogue no: **2059 141**

ONE MORE MINUTE
Tracks: / One more minute / Who's killing who.
7" Single: Released May '81, on Polydor, by Polydor Ltd. Deleted May '86. Catalogue no: **POSP 270**

SOMETHING'S MISSING
Tracks: / Something's missing / This is what they want.
7" Single: Released Apr '80, on Polydor, by Polydor Ltd. Deleted Apr '83. Catalogue no: **POSP 146**

Choristers

TELL US
Tracks: / Tell us.
7" Single: Released Oct '84, on Aul Reekie, Catalogue no: **GALA 1**

Chorus

THESE STONES
Tracks: / These stones.
7" EP: Released Jun '85, on AAZ, by AAZ Records. Deleted '88. Catalogue no: **AA023**

Chose & Essence

THIS IS THE B SIDE
Tracks: / This is the B side.
12" Single: Released Jan '89, on Gee Street, by Gee Street Records. Catalogue no: **GEET 011**

Chosen

SOUND OF A DREAM
Tracks: / Sound of a dream.
12" Single: Released Apr '89, on London Ocean & Coastal, by London Ocean & Coastal. Catalogue no: **LOC 1202**
7" Single: Released Apr '89, on London Ocean & Coastal, by London Ocean & Coastal. Catalogue no: **LOC 702**

SOUND OF THE DREAM
Tracks: / Sound of the dream, The / Immaculate.
7" Single: Released Jun '89, on London Ocean & Coastal, by London Ocean & Coastal. Catalogue no: **LOC 1**
12" Single: Released Jun '89, on London Ocean & Coastal, by London Ocean & Coastal. Catalogue no: **12LOC 1**

Chosen 3

NEVER AGAIN
Tracks: / Never again.
7" Single: Released Oct '84, on Plezure, by Plezure Records. Catalogue no: **PLZ 842**
12" Single: Released Oct '84, on Plezure, by Plezure Records. Catalogue no: **PLZ 12841**

Chosen Brothers

THERE YOU ARE
Tracks: / There you are / There you are (part 2).
12" Single: Released Nov '84, on Wakies, Catalogue no: **W 974**

Chosen Few

25-30 YEARS OF LOVE

Tracks: / 25-30 years of love (Inst).
12" Single: Released Apr '86, on Kufe, Catalogue no: **KV 007**

DON'T KEEP ME WAITING
Tracks: / Don't keep me waiting.
12" Single: Released Aug '85, on Kufe, Catalogue no: **EB 006**

IN THE RAIN
Tracks: / In the rain.
12" Single: Released May '87, on Kufe, Catalogue no: **EB 008**

LA LA MEANS I LOVE YOU
Tracks: / Club mix / La la means I love you.
12" Single: Released Aug '86, on Love & Unity, Catalogue no: **VGO 1003**
12" Single: Released Nov '86, on Now Generation, Catalogue no: **NG 012**

LOVE BETWEEN A BOY AND GIRL
Tracks: / Love between a boy and girl.
12" Single: Released Feb '83, on Tree Roots, Catalogue no: **VGO 1003**

MY SWEET BABY
Tracks: / My sweet baby.
12" Single: Released May '82, on Legal Lights, by Legal Light Records. Catalogue no: **LD 012**
12" Single: Released Jun '82, on Legal Lights, by Legal Light Records. Deleted Jun '85. Catalogue no: **IDO 12**

ON THE RIGHT TRACK
Tracks: / On the right track / Tracking.
12" Single: Released Jan '84, on Kufe, Catalogue no: **EB 001**

SUNDAY MORNING
Tracks: / Sunday morning (club mix).
12" Single: Released Nov '86, on New Generation, Catalogue no: **NG 012**

TRYING TO MAKE A FOOL OF ME
Tracks: / Trying to make a fool of me.
12" Single: Released Oct '82, on Regal, Catalogue no: **RD 019**

Chow-Chow

THIS IS ABOUT LOVE
Tracks: / This is about love.
12" Single: Released Jun '88, on Antler, by Antler Records (Belgium). Catalogue no: **ANT 034**

Chris & Cosey

CONSPIRACY
Tracks: / Conspiracy.
7" Single: Released Sep '84, on International One, Catalogue no: **CT1 001**

EXOTIKA (REMIX)
Tracks: / Exotica (remix).
12" Single: Released '89, on Play It Again Sam(Belgium), by Play It Again Sam (Belgium). Catalogue no: **BIAS 105**
12" Single: Released '88, on Play It Again Sam(Belgium), by Play It Again Sam (Belgium). Catalogue no: **BIAS 075**

OBSESSION
Tracks: / Obsession.
12" Single: Released 1 Jun '87, on Play It Again Sam(Belgium), by Play It Again Sam (Belgium). Catalogue no: **BIAS 054**

OCTOBER LOVE SONG
Tracks: / October love song.
7" Single: Released May '83, on Rough Trade, by Rough Trade Records. Catalogue no: **RT 078**
12" Single: Released May '83, on Rough Trade, by Rough Trade Records. Catalogue no: **TRR 078**

SWEET SURPRISE
Tracks: / Sweet surprise.
12" Single: Released Nov '85, on Rough Trade, by Rough Trade Records. Catalogue no: **RTT 148**

TAKE FIVE
Tracks: / Take five.
Note: Take five ia an ep.
12" Single: Released 26 Jan '87, on Licensed, Catalogue no: **LD 874**

Chris-Maz

DEAR SANTA
Tracks: / Dear Santa / You've forgotten how to love me.
7" Single: Released Nov '80, on Solid Music, Deleted Nov '83. Catalogue no: **SOLID 001**

Christ On Parade

ISN'T LIFE A DREAM?
Tracks: / Isn't life a dream.
7" Single: Released Nov '86, on Mind Matter, by Mind Matter Records. Catalogue no: **THOUGHT 6**

Christ & Satan

DARK SIDE OF THE SAUSAGE EP
Tracks: / Dark side of the sausage.
Cassingle: Released Aug '89, on Magic Moments At Twilight Time, by Magic Moments At Twilight Time. Catalogue no: **MMATT 28**

Christian

I'M STILL DANCING
Tracks: / I'm still dancing.
12" Single: Released Nov '82, on Gipsy, by Gipsy Records. Deleted '84. Catalogue no: **GIPSY 8 12**
7" Single: Released Nov '82, on Gipsy, by Gipsy Records. Catalogue no: **GIPSY 8**

OH LITTLE MAMA
Tracks: / Oh little mama.
7" Single: Released '81, on Gipsy, by Gipsy Records. Deleted '83. Catalogue no: **GIPSY 3**

Christian, Barry

BOY MEETS GIRL
Tracks: / Boy meets girl / I can detect you for 100,000 miles.
7" Single: Released Sep '80, on GTO, Deleted '83. Catalogue no: **GT 280**

JUDY WILL BE THERE
Tracks: / Judy will be there / Let me know you like it.
7" Single: Released Oct '82, on Kaleidoscope Sound, by Kaleidoscope Sound Records. Deleted '85. Catalogue no: **KRLA 2799**

Christian Death

BELIEVERS OF THE UNPURE
Tracks: / Believers of the unpure.
12" Single: Released Feb '86, on Jungle, by Jungle Records. Catalogue no: **JUNG 24T**

CHRISTIAN DEATH - 7" BOX SET
7" Single: Released Sep '87, on Normal, by Jungle Records. Deleted Oct '87. Catalogue no: **NORMAL 48**

CHURCH OF NO RETURN
Tracks: / Church of no return, The.
7" Single: Released May '88, on Jungle, by Jungle Records. Catalogue no: **JUNG 40**
12" Single: Released May '88, on Jungle, by Jungle Records. Catalogue no: **JUNG 40T**

SICK OF LOVE
Tracks: / Sick of love.
7" Single: Released Sep '87, on Jungle, by Jungle Records. Catalogue no: **JUNG 35**
12" Single: Released Sep '87, on Jungle, by Jungle Records. Catalogue no: **JUNG 35T**

WHATS THE VERDICT
Tracks: / What's the verdict / This is not blasphemy.
7" Single: Released Nov '88, on Jungle, by Jungle Records. Catalogue no: **JUNG 45**
12" Single: Released Nov '88, on Jungle, by Jungle Records. Catalogue no: **JUNG 45T**

ZERO SEX
Tracks: / Zero sex.
7" Single: Released 5 Jun '89, on Jungle, by Jungle Records. Catalogue no: **JUNG 050**
12" Single: Released 5 Jun '89, on Jungle, by Jungle Records. Catalogue no: **JUNG 050T**
CD 5": Released 5 Jun '89, on Jungle, by Jungle Records. Catalogue no: **JUNG 050CD**

Christian, John

LOVE GAMES
Tracks: / Love games / Cadillac.
7" Single: Released Jan '82, on Recorded Delivery, Deleted Jan '85. Catalogue no: **RDR 004**

Christian, Neil

THAT'S NICE
Tracks: / That's nice.
7" Single: Released Apr '66, on Strike (1), by Strike Records. Deleted Apr '69. Catalogue no: **JH 301**

Christian, Roger

TAKE IT FROM ME
Tracks: / Take it from me / Alive and kicking / Take it from me (version) (On 12" only) / Take it from me (ext version) (On CD only).
Cassingle: Released Jul '89, on Island, by Island Records. Catalogue no: **CIS 427**
12" Single: Released Jul '89, on Island, by Island Records. Catalogue no: **12 IS 427**
CD 5": Released Jul '89, on Island, by Island Records. Catalogue no: **CID 427**
7" Single: Released Jul '89, on Island, by Island Records. Catalogue no: **IS 427**
CD 3": Released Jul '89, on Island, by Island Records. Catalogue no: **CIDX 427**

WORLDS APART
Tracks: / Worlds apart.
7" Single: Released Oct '89, on Island, by Island Records. Catalogue no: **IS 442**
12" Single: Released Oct '89, on Island, by Island Records. Catalogue no: **12 IS 442**
CD 5": Released Oct '89, on Island, by Island Records. Catalogue no: **CID 442**

Christiana F

FINAL CHURCH (EP)
Tracks: / Final church.
12" Single: Released Aug '83, on Supermax (Germany), Catalogue no: **6374**

Christianhound

NOT GUILTY
Tracks: / Not guilty.
12" Single: Released Jul '87, on Constrictor, by Constrictor Records (Germany). Catalogue no: **CON 00028**

Christians

BORN AGAIN (REMIX)
Tracks: / Born again / Forgotten town (US remix) / Lover's question (on 12" only).
12" Single: Released Apr '88, on Island, by Island Records. Deleted Dec '88. Catalogue no: **12IS 365**
Special: Released Apr '88, on Island, by Island Records. Deleted Apr '89. Catalogue no: **ISB 365**
7" Single: Released Apr '88, on Island, by Island Records. Deleted Dec '88. Catalogue no: **IS 365**

FORGOTTEN TOWN
Tracks: / Why waltz / Heading for a hardtime.
7" Single: Released Jan '87, on Island, by Island Records. Deleted Jun '88. Catalogue no: **IS 291**
12" Single: Released '88, on Island, by Island Records. Deleted Dec '88. Catalogue no: **12 IS 291**
CD 5": Released Feb '87, on Art & Soul, by Island Records. Deleted Jun '88. Catalogue no: **CID 291**
12" Single: Released Jan '87, on Island, by Island Records. Deleted Jul '87. Catalogue no: **12IS 291**

FORGOTTEN TOWN (REMIX)
Tracks: / Forgotten town (remix) / Why waltz / Heading for a hardtime.
12" Single: Released Feb '87, on Island, by Island Records. Deleted Apr '88. Catalogue no: **12ISX 291**

HARVEST FOR THE WORLD
Tracks: / Harvest for the world / Harvest for the world (version) (Only on 12" version.) / Small axe / People get ready.
7" Single: Released Oct '88, on Island, by Island Records. Deleted Apr '89. Catalogue no: **IS 395**
12" Single: Released Aug '88, on Island, by Island Records. Deleted Apr '89. Catalogue no: **12IS 395**

HOOVERVILLE And they promised us the world
Tracks: / Hooverville / No reason / Losing game (Not on cassette) / Born again (Extra track on cassette) / Drip drop (Extra track on cassette).
Cassingle: Released 13 Jun '87, on Island, by Island Records. Deleted Apr '88. Catalogue no: **CIS 326**
7" Single: Released 30 May '87, on Island, by Island Records. Deleted Jun '88. Catalogue no: **IS 326**
12" Single: Released 30 May '87, on Island, by Island Records. Deleted Apr '88. Catalogue no: **12IS 326**

IDEAL WORLD
Tracks: / Ideal world / Rockin' chair blues / Say it isn't so.
12" Single: Released Nov '87, on Island, by Island Records. Deleted Jun '88. Catalogue no: **12IS 347**
10" single: Released '87, on Island, by Island Records. Deleted Jun '88. Catalogue no: **10IS 347**
7" Single: Released Nov '87, on Island, by Island Records. Deleted Jun '88. Catalogue no: **IS 347**
CD 5": on Island, by Island Records. Deleted Jun '88. Catalogue no: **CID 347**

WHEN THE FINGERS POINT
Tracks: / When the fingers point.
CD 5": on Island, by Island Records. Deleted Jun '88. Catalogue no: **CIS 335**
12" Single: Released '87, on Island, by Island Records. Deleted Jun '88. Catalogue no: **12IS 335**

Christie

Biographical details: The trio were assembled by Jeff Christie in 1970 for the specific purpose of recording his song *Yellow River*. He had written it two years earlier with the Tremeloes in mind, but they turned it down. He thus decided to record it himself. With the aid of the Trems' producer Mike Smith and their record company CBS, the Christie trio took the highly catchy song to No. 1 in Britain and many other territories. It peaked at No. 23 in the States. The samey follow-up *San Bernadino* reached No. 7 on the UK charts, but it was Christies second and last significant triumph. Such a hastily consituted had not been built to last. Mike Blakely was the brother of the Tremeloes' Alan Blakely. (Bob MacDonald)..

IRON HORSE
Tracks: / Iron horse.
7" Single: Released Mar '72, on CBS, by CBS Records. Deleted Mar '75. Catalogue no: **A 7747**

SAN BERNADINO
Tracks: / San Bernadino.
7" Single: Released Oct '70, on CBS, by CBS Records. Deleted Oct '73. Catalogue no: **A 5169**

YELLOW RIVER
Tracks: / Yellow river.
7" Single: Released May '70, on CBS, by CBS Records. Catalogue no: **A 4911**
7" Single: Released Apr '83, on Old Gold, by Old Gold Records. Catalogue no: **OG 9301**

Christie, David

Biographical details: This French singer and songwriter reached No. 9 on the UK chart with a one-off hit single *Saddle Up*. Released in June 1982, it was a sleeper hit and did not hit the Top 10 until the autumn. It was hardly surprising that Christie failed to come up with a follow-up hit - *Saddle Up* was a distinctly mediocre pop/disco record and its level of success was unexpected. (Bob MacDonld)..

LIVING IT UP
Tracks: / Living it up.
7" Single: Released Nov '88, on Ocean (2), Catalogue no: **OCN 5**
12" Single: Released Nov '88, on Ocean (2), Catalogue no: **OCN 5T**

OUR TIME HAS COME
Tracks: / Our time has come / Fools only see / Heartbeat.
12" Single: Released Nov '82, on KR, Catalogue no: **KRT 15**
7" Single: Released Nov '82, on KR, Catalogue no: **KR 15**

SADDLE UP
Tracks: / Saddle up / Signals.
7" Single: Released Jun '82, on KR, Catalogue no: **KR 9**
12" Single: Released Jun '82, on KR, Catalogue no: **KRT 9**

Christie, Janice

HEATSTROKE
Tracks: / Heatstroke (dub) / Heatstroke.
7" Single: Released Jan '87, on London Records, by London Records. Catalogue no: **LON 120**
12" Single: Released Jan '87, on London Records, by London Records. Catalogue no: **LONX 120**

I'M HUNGRY FOR YOUR LOVE
Tracks: / I'm hungry for your love.
12" Single: Released Aug '86, on Affair, Catalogue no: **TART 1**

Christie, Jeff

BOTH ENDS OF THE RAINBOW
Tracks: / Both ends of the rainbow / Turn on your lovelight.
7" Single: Released Feb '80, on RK, by RK Records. Deleted Feb '83. Catalogue no: **RK 1026**

TIGHTROPE
Tracks: / Tightrope / Somebody else.
7" Single: Released Nov '80, on RK, by RK Records. Deleted '83. Catalogue no: **RK 1033**

Christie, John

HERE'S TO LOVE (AULD LANG SYNE)
Tracks: / Here's to love.
7" Single: Released Dec '76, on EMI, by EMI Records. Deleted Dec '79. Catalogue no: **2554**

Christie, Kyle

THAT SON OF YOURS
7" Single: Released Aug '88, on Gigantic, by Gigantic Records. Catalogue no: **GI 008**

Christie, Lou

Biographical details: This American singer, born in Pennsylvania, experienced a spasmodic career during the Sixties, enjoying three short bursts of success. The first took place in 1963, when he reached No. 24 on the US charts with *The Gypsy Cried* and followed it with a No. 6 hit, *Two Faces Have I*. 1966 brought Christie an American No. 1 with *Lightnin' Strikes*, an infectious rock single that was influenced

both by Motown and by the Four Seasons; it also gave him his first hit in Britain, where it peaked at No. 11. The follow-up *Rhapsody In The Rain* was another Top 20 single in the States, but suffered in the UK from a radio ban on the grounds of sexual explicitness - such a blacking has sometimes worked wonders for records but, in this case, it had the reverse effect.
The singer's third period of success came in '69, via the very catchy *I'm Gonna Make You Mine*. This single took him to No. 2 in Britain and No. 10 in America. With the exception of this record, his hits were usually written by Christie himself in collaboration with Twyla Herbert, a mystic who was twenty years his senior. Apparently Herbert predicted Christies success and regularly ha visions of his future. All the hits were sung in a high falsetto voice, in a broadly similar style to that of Frankie Valli. During the Seventies, Christie remained active in showbusiness but his records did not sell. (Bob MacDonald)..

I'M GONNA MAKE YOU MINE
Tracks: / I'm gonna make you mine.
7" Single: Released Sep '69, on Buddah, by Buddah Records Inc.(USA). Deleted Sep '72. Catalogue no: **201 057**
7" Single: Released Jan '83, on Flashback, by Mainline Records. Catalogue no: **FBS 25**

LIGHTNIN' STRIKES
Tracks: / Lightning strikes.
7" Single: Released Jul '84, on Old Gold, by Old Gold Records. Catalogue no: **OG 9447**
7" Single: Released Feb '66, on MGM, by Polydor Ltd. Deleted Feb '69. Catalogue no: **MGM 1297**

RHAPSODY IN THE RAIN
Tracks: / Rhapsody in the rain.
7" Single: Released Apr '66, on MGM, by Polydor Ltd. Deleted Apr '69. Catalogue no: **MGM 1308**

SHE SOLD ME MAGIC
Tracks: / She sold me magic.
7" Single: Released Dec '69, on Buddah, by Buddah Records Inc.(USA). Deleted Dec '72. Catalogue no: **201 073**

Christie, Pete

GOOD MORNING
Tracks: / Good morning / How much love.
7" Single: Released Jan '83, on PRT, by Castle Communications Records. Catalogue no: **7P 260**

NOCTURNE
Tracks: / Nocturne / Thank you.
7" Single: Released Nov '81, on Cheapskate, Deleted Nov '84. Catalogue no: **CHEAP 37**

Christie, Tony

Biographical details: This British singer, born Anthony Fitzgerald in Yorkshire, began a chart career in the early Seventies under the guidance of the successful writing/production team of Mitch Murray and Pete Callander. Christie sang in a middle-of-the-road style similar to that of Tom Jones and his first UK hit best sums up his sound and attitude - *Las Vegas*. It reached No. 21 in early 1971 and was followed by a British No. 2 smash, *I Did What I Did For Maria*; this was a death disc about a man who was about to meet his maker, after avenging the death of his wife. At the end of '71, Murray and Callander decided he should record *Is This The Way To Amarillo*, a song written by the famous AMerican partnership, Neil Sedaka and Howard Greenfield. This was a wise move. Though *Amarillo* peaked at No. 18 in the UK, it remained in the Top 50 for over 13 weeks; more importantly for Christies career, it reached No. 1 in half a dozen European countries. The resulting international fame ensured Christie of a steady career throughout the Seventies despite, from '72 onwards, comparatively lacklustre record sales in his native Britain. (Bob MacDonald)..

AVENUES AND ALLEYWAYS
Tracks: / Avenues and alleyways.
7" Single: Released Feb '73, on MCA, by MCA Records. Deleted Feb '76. Catalogue no: **MKS 5101**

DRIVE SAFELY DARLIN'
Tracks: / Drive safely darlin'.
7" Single: Released Jan '76, on MCA, by MCA Records. Deleted Jan '79. Catalogue no: **MCA 219**

I DID WHAT I DID FOR MARIA (SINGLE)
Tracks: / I did what I did for Maria.
7" Single: Released May '71, on MCA, by MCA Records. Deleted May '74. Catalogue no: **MK 5064**
7" Single: Released Jul '82, on Old Gold, by Old Gold Records. Catalogue no: **OG 9212**

IS THIS THE WAY TO AMARILLO
Tracks: / Is this the way to Amarillo.
7" Single: Released Nov '71, on MCA, by MCA Records. Deleted Nov '74. Catalogue no: **MKS 5073**

LAS VEGAS
Tracks: / Las Vegas.
7" Single: Released Jan '71, on MCA, by MCA Records. Deleted Jan '74. Catalogue no: **MK 5058**

WIND BENEATH MY WINGS
Tracks: / Wind beneath my wings.
7" Single: Released Jul '85, on A.1, by A.1 Records. Catalogue no: **A1 291**

Christina

DRIVE MY CAR
Tracks: / Drive my car / Don't be greedy.
7" Single: Released May '80, on Island, by Island Records. Deleted May '83. Catalogue no: **WIP 6616**

THINGS FALL APART
Tracks: / Things fall apart / It's a holiday.
7" Single: Released Dec '81, on Island, by Island Records. Deleted Dec '84. Catalogue no: **IPR 2052**

Christmas Bunch

STRONG
Tracks: / Strong.
7" Single: Released Jul '89, on Christmas Bunch, Catalogue no: **BUNCH 2**

Christmas (group)

STUPID KIDS
Tracks: / Stupid kids / Ring my bell.
12" Single: Released May '89, on I.R.S, Catalogue no: **EIRST 110**
7" Single: Released May '89, on I.R.S, Catalogue no: **EIRS 110**

Christopher, Dov

JOY IS THE WORLD
Tracks: / Joy is the world / If that ain't love.
7" Single: Released Oct '80, on Flamingo, by Airwave Records (USA). Deleted Oct '83. Catalogue no: **FM 10**

Christopher, Gavin

ONE STEP CLOSER TO YOU (SINGLE)
Tracks: / One step closer to you (inst) / One step closer to you (club mix) / Accapella plus / Short version / One step closer to you.
7" Single: Released May '86, on EMI-Manhattan, by EMI Records. Catalogue no: **MT 10**
12" Single: Released May '86, on EMI-Manhattan, by EMI Records. Catalogue no: **12 MT 10**

Christy

CRY
Tracks: / Cry.
7" Single: Released Jul '83, on Le Cam, by Le Cam Records (USA). Catalogue no: **LC 100**

Christy, David

DAVID CHRISTY MEDLEY
Tracks: / David Christy medley / Cindy Lou.
7" Single: Released Apr '85, on Record Shack, by Record Shack Records. Catalogue no: **SOHO 38**
12" Single: Released Apr '85, on Record Shack, by Record Shack Records. Catalogue no: **SOHOT 38**

Chromatics

99
Tracks: / 99 / Noise annoys.
7" Single: Released Aug '84, on PVK, by PVK Records. Catalogue no: **PV 121**

HOT STUFF
Tracks: / Hot stuff / Lookin' at the joint.
7" Single: Released May '83, on Swoop, Catalogue no: **RTL 003**

I'M A REP
Tracks: / Eat em' up / I'm a rep.
7" Single: Released Sep '86, on Grenouille, Catalogue no: **RTLS 014**

Chrome

BLOOD ON THE MOON (SINGLE)
Tracks: / Blood on the moon.
7" Single: Released Jun '81, on Don't Fall Off The Mountain, by Don't Fall Off The Mountain Records. Catalogue no: **X 6**

FIREBOMB
Tracks: / Firebomb.
7" Single: Released Apr '82, on Don't Fall Off The Mountain, by Don't Fall Off The Mountain Records. Catalogue no: **Z 17**

INWORLDS
Tracks: / Inworlds / Danger zone / In a dream.
12" Single: Released Jan '81, on Don't Fall Off The Mountain, by Don't Fall Off The Mountain Records. Catalogue no: **Y 3**

NEW AGE
Tracks: / New age / Information.
7" Single: Released Apr '80, on Beggars Banquet, by Beggars Banquet Records. Deleted '83. Catalogue no: **BEG 36**

Chrome Molly

I WANT TO FIND OUT
Tracks: / I want to find out.
7" Single: Released Mar '86, on Powerstation, by Powerstation Records. Catalogue no: **OHM 12**
7" Single: Released Mar '86, on Powerstation, by Powerstation Records. Catalogue no: **OHM 12 T**

SHOOTING ME DOWN
Tracks: / Shooting me down.
7" Single: Released Nov '88, on I.R.S, Deleted 1 Jul '89. Catalogue no: **IRM 176**
12" Single: Released Nov '88, on I.R.S, Catalogue no: **12IRM 176**

TAKE IT OR LEAVE IT
Tracks: / Take it or leave it.
12" Single: Released Aug '85, on Powerstation, by Powerstation Records. Catalogue no: **OHM 11 T**

TAKE ME I'M YOURS
Tracks: / Take me I'm yours / Don't fight dirty / Lose again (Available on 12" version only.).
7" Pic: Released Apr '88, on MCA, by MCA Records. Catalogue no: **IRMP 152**
7" Single: Released Apr '88, on MCA, by MCA Records. Catalogue no: **IRM 152**
12" Single: Released Apr '88, on MCA, by MCA Records. Catalogue no: **IRMT 152**

THANX FOR THE ANGST
Tracks: / Thanx for the angst / Living a lie / One at a time (Extra track on 12".).
7" Single: Released Mar '88, on I.R.S, Catalogue no: **IRM 158**
12" Single: Released Mar '88, on I.R.S, Catalogue no: **IRMT 158**

WHEN THE LIGHTS
Tracks: / When the lights.
12" Single: Released May '84, on Bulleon, Catalogue no: **BOLT 10**

YOU CAN HAVE IT ALL
Tracks: / You can have it all.
7" Single: Released Apr '88, on I.R.S, Catalogue no: **AMP 006**

Chron Gen

Biographical details: This British all-male rock group were one of numerous underground bands to attempt to continue the late Seventies punk era into the early Eighties. Their album *Chronic Generation* reached No. 53 on the UK LP charts in 1982. (Bob MacDonald)..

JET BOY JET GIRL
Tracks: / Jet boy jet girl / Abortions / Subway sadist.
7" Single: Released Jul '82, on Secret, by Secret Records. Deleted May '88. Catalogue no: **SHH 129**

OUTLAW
Tracks: / Outlaw / Behind closed doors - disco.
7" Single: Released Oct '82, on Secret, by Secret Records. Deleted May '88. Catalogue no: **SHH 139**

PUPPETS OF WAR
Tracks: / Puppets of war / Puppets of war (part 2).
7" Single: Released Sep '81, on Fresh, by Jetstar Records. Deleted '84. Catalogue no: **FRESH 36**

REALITY
Tracks: / Reality / Subway sadist.
7" Single: Released Sep '81, on Step Forward, by Faulty Products Records. Catalogue no: **SF 19**

Chrysanthemums

LIKE INDUSTRIOUS ELVES) WE STOPPED (Live at the London Palladium)
Tracks: / (Like industrious elves) we stopped.
12" Single: Released Mar '89, on Egg Plant (UK), by Orgone Company, The. Catalogue no: **FIVE EGGS**

MOUTH PAIN
Tracks: / Mouth pain.
7" Single: Released Mar '87, on Egg Plant (UK), by Orgone Company, The. Catalogue no: **ONE EGG**

XXXX SESSIONS, THE
12" Single: Released Apr '88, on Egg Plant (UK), by Orgone Company, The. Catalogue no: **THREE EGGS**

Chubb Rock

CAUGHT UP
Tracks: / Caught up (remix) / Caught up(instrumental) / Caught up (version).
12" Single: Released Aug '88, on Champion, by Champion Records. Catalogue no: **CHAMP 12 88**
7" Single: Released Aug '88, on Champion, by Champion Records. Catalogue no: **CHAMP 88**

YA BAD CHUBBS (CRIB MIX)
Tracks: / Ya bad Chubbs (crib mix) / Ya bad Chubbs (version).
12" Single: Released Jul '89, on Champion, by Champion Records. Catalogue no: **CHAMP 12215**
7" Single: Released Jul '89, on Champion, by Champion Records. Catalogue no: **CHAMP 215**

Chucks

LOO-BE-LOO
Tracks: / Loo-be-loo.
7" Single: Released Jan '63, on Decca, by Decca Records. Deleted Jan '66. Catalogue no: **F 11569**

Chude

YOU GAVE YOUR LOVE TO ME
Tracks: / You gave your love to me / Dub pella.
7" Single: Released Nov '87, on Cool Tempo, by Chrysalis Records. Catalogue no: **COOL 155**
12" Single: Released Nov '87, on Cool Tempo, by Chrysalis Records. Catalogue no: **COOLX 155**

Chumba Wamba

ENGLISH REBEL SONGS 1381 - 1914
Tracks: / English rebel songs 1381 - 1914.
10" single: Released Oct '88, on Agit Prop, by Agit Prop Records. Catalogue no: **PROP 003**

FIGHT THE ALTON BILL
Tracks: / Fight the Alton bill / Smash clause 28.
7" Single: Released '88, on Agit Prop, by Agit Prop Records. Catalogue no: **AGIT 003**

REVOLUTION
Tracks: / Revolution.
7" Single: Released Aug '85, on Agit Prop, by Agit Prop Records. Deleted '88. Catalogue no: **AGIT 001**

WE ARE THE WORLD (SINGLE)
Tracks: / We are the World? / State of mind.
7" Single: Released Apr '86, on Agit Prop, by Agit Prop Records. Deleted '88. Catalogue no: **AGIT 002**

Church

ALMOST WITHOUT YOU
Tracks: / Almost without you / Life speeds up.
7" Single: Released Jul '82, on Carrere, Deleted Jul '87. Catalogue no: **CAR 247**

DESTINATION
Tracks: / Destination.
CD 3": Released Dec '88, on Arista (USA), Catalogue no: **CD 33001**

DIFFERENT MAN 5 track EP
Tracks: / Different man, A.
7" Single: Released Apr '83, on Carrere, Catalogue no: **CHURCH 5**

DISENCHANTED
Tracks: / Trance ending / You've got to go (12" only) / Disenchanted.
7" Single: Released Sep '86, on Parlophone, by EMI Records. Catalogue no: **R 6139**
12" Single: Released Sep '86, on Parlophone, by EMI Records. Catalogue no: **12 R 6139**

IT'S NO REASON
Tracks: / It's no reason.
7" Single: Released Jun '84, on Carrere, Catalogue no: **CAR 336**
12" Single: Released Jun '84, on Carrere, Catalogue no: **CART 336**

TANTALIZED
Tracks: / View, The / As you will / Tantalized.
7" Single: Released Apr '86, on EMI, by EMI Records. Catalogue no: **EMI 5557**
12" Single: Released Apr '86, on EMI, by EMI Records. Catalogue no: **12 EMI 5557**

UNDER THE MILKY WAY
Tracks: / Under the milky way / Warm spell, The (track available on 12" only) / Musk.
12" Single: Released Feb '88, on Arista, by BMG Records (UK). Catalogue no: **609778**
7" Single: Released Feb '88, on Arista, by BMG Records (UK). Catalogue no: **109778**
CD 5": Released Feb '88, on Arista, by BMG Records (UK). Catalogue no: **659778**

UNGUARDED MOMENT

Tracks: / Unguarded moment.
12" Single: Released Apr '88, on Carrere, Catalogue no: **CART 425**
7" Single: Released Apr '88, on Carrere, Catalogue no: **CAR 425**
7" EP: Released Nov '82, on Metropolis (France), by Island Records. Catalogue no: **CAR 257**

Church, Joe

DON'T YOU WANNA BE MINE
Tracks: / Don't you wanna be mine.
12" Single: Released Nov '87, on Apexton (USA), by Apexton Records (USA). Catalogue no: **AP 130**

Chyna

UNFORGETTABLE
Tracks: / Unforgettable.
12" Single: Released Mar '88, on Spice Records, Catalogue no: **12 SPICE 1**
7" Single: Released Mar '88, on Spice Records, Catalogue no: **SPICE 1**

C.I.A.

DISTANT LANDS
Tracks: / Distant lands.
7" Single: Released Apr '84, on Round, Catalogue no: **PR 2**

Ciari, Claude

PLAYA, LA
Tracks: / La playa.
7" Single: Released Apr '83, on EMI, by EMI Records. Catalogue no: **2C 008 72694**

Ciccone Youth

INTO THE GROOVY
Tracks: / Burnin' up / Into the groovy.
12" Single: Released Nov '86, on Blast First, by Blast First Records. Catalogue no: **BFFP 8**

Cijay

LOVE IS LIKE AN ITCHING IN MY HEART
Tracks: / Love is like an itching in my heart.
12" Single: Released May '85, on Eden, Catalogue no: **XTCT 13**

Cimarons

BIG GIRLS DON'T CRY
Tracks: / Big girls don't cry / How can I prove myself to you / Poor people of Paris.
12" Single: Released Aug '82, on Safari, by Safari Records. Catalogue no: **SAFELS 49**
7" Single: Released Aug '82, on Safari, by Safari Records. Catalogue no: **SAFE 49**
7" Pic: Released Sep '82, on Safari, by Safari Records. Catalogue no: **SAFELX 49**

LOVE AND AFFECTION
Tracks: / Love and affection.
7" Single: Released Apr '83, on Cimarons, Catalogue no: **CIM 001**
12" Single: Released Apr '83, on Cimarons, Catalogue no: **12 CIM 001**

READY FOR LOVE
Tracks: / Ready for love / So real.
7" Single: Released Feb '81, on Charisma, by Virgin Records. Deleted Feb '84. Catalogue no: **CB 380**

WITH A LITTLE LUCK
Tracks: / With a little luck.
7" Single: Released Feb '82, on Imp, by Demon Records. Catalogue no: **IMPS 50**

Cinderella

CINDERELLA (well loved tales age up to 9)
12" Single: Released Dec '82, on Disneyland-Vista(USA), by Disneyland-Vista Records (USA). Catalogue no: **D 3908**
7" Pic: Released Dec '82, on Disneyland-Vista(USA), by Disneyland-Vista Records (USA). Catalogue no: **D 3107**
7" EP: Released Dec '82, on Disneyland-Vista(USA), by Disneyland-Vista Records (USA). Catalogue no: **D 308**

Cinderella (Group)

DON'T KNOW WHAT YOU GOT (TIL IT'S GONE)
Tracks: / Don't know what you got (til it's gone) / Fire and ice / Push, push (live) (Only on the Gatefold and CD versions) / Once around the ride (Only on gatefold sleeve.) / Long cold winter (On CD single only).
7" Pic: Released 13 Feb '89, on Vertigo, by Phonogram Ltd. Deleted Aug '89. Catalogue no: **VERP 43**
7" Single: Released 13 Feb '89, on Vertigo, by Phonogram Ltd. Deleted Aug '89. Catalogue no: **VERXG 43**
CD 5": Released 13 Feb '89, on Vertigo, by Phonogram Ltd. Catalogue no: **VERCD 43**
12" Single: Released 13 Feb '89, on Vertigo, by Phonogram Ltd. Deleted Aug '89. Catalogue no: **VERX 43**
7" Single: Released 13 Feb '89, on Vertigo, by Phonogram Ltd. Deleted Aug '89. Catalogue no: **VER 43**

GYPSY ROAD
Tracks: / Gypsy road.
12" Single: Released 28 Jul '88, on Vertigo, by Phonogram Ltd. Deleted Feb '89. Catalogue no: **VERX 40**
12" Single: Released 28 Jul '88, on Vertigo, by Phonogram Ltd. Deleted Feb '89. Catalogue no: **VERXG 40**
CD 5": Released 28 Jul '88, on Vertigo, by Phonogram Ltd. Deleted Feb '89. Catalogue no: **VERCD 40**
7" Single: Released 28 Jul '88, on Vertigo, by Phonogram Ltd. Deleted Feb '89. Catalogue no: **VER 40**

NOBODY'S FOOL
Tracks: / Nobody's fool / Shake me (live) / Galaxy blues, The.
7" Single: Released 23 May '87, on Vertigo, by Phonogram Ltd. Catalogue no: **VER 32**
12" Single: Released 23 May '87, on Vertigo, by Phonogram Ltd. Catalogue no: **VERX 32**

SHAKE ME
Tracks: / Shake me / Nightsongs / Hell on wheels.
Note: Hell on wheels is only available on 12" version.
12" Single: Released Feb '87, on Vertigo, by Phonogram Ltd. Catalogue no: **VERX 29**
7" Single: Released Feb '87, on Vertigo, by Phonogram Ltd. Catalogue no: **VER 29**

SOMEBODY SAVE ME
Tracks: / Shake me (Live) / Galaxy blues (Live) / Somebody save me / Nothin' for nothin'.
12" Single: Released Jul '88, on Mercury (Japan), Catalogue no: **15PP64**

YOU'VE GOT IT
7" Set: Released Sep '89, on Polygram Music Video, by PolyGram Video. Catalogue no: **080 098 2**

Cinderella (reggae)

MONEY MAD
Tracks: / Money mad.
12" Single: Released May '88, on Mafia/Fluxy, Catalogue no: **M&F 006**

Cindy

HAPPY TO BE
Tracks: / Happy to be.
7" Single: Released Aug '84, on Unit 7, by Greensleeves Records. Deleted '88. Catalogue no: **UNS 51**
12" Single: Released Aug '84, on Unit 7, by Greensleeves Records. Deleted '88. Catalogue no: **12 UNS 51**

MOVE OVER DARLING
Tracks: / Move over darling.
7" Single: Released Apr '83, on Big Boy, by Big Boy Records. Catalogue no: **BB 2**

PAST PRESENT FUTURE
Tracks: / Past, present and future.
7" Single: Released Feb '83, on Disques Bleu, by Disques Bleu Records. Catalogue no: **STL 9**

TERRY
Tracks: / Terry.
12" Single: Released Apr '83, on Stiletto, by Fast Forward Distribution. Catalogue no: **STLT 12**
7" Single: Released Apr '83, on Stiletto, by Fast Forward Distribution. Catalogue no: **STL 12**

Cindy & Barbie Dolls

VOICE IN THE NIGHT
Tracks: / Voice in the night / Reporter / In silence.
7" EP: Released Feb '80, on Not Major, Deleted Feb '83. Catalogue no: **NOTEM 1**

Cindy & Roy

I WANNA TESTIFY
Tracks: / I wanna testify / Changing jobs.
7" Single: Released Jan '80, on WEA, by WEA Records. Deleted Jan '85. Catalogue no: **K 79113**

Cinematics

FAREWELL TO THE PLAYGROUND
Tracks: / Farewell to the playground.
7" Single: Released Nov '82, on Cine, Catalogue no: **CINE 001**

Cinnamon

I NEED YOU NOW
Tracks: / I need you now.
12" Single: Released Mar '86, on Jive, by Zomba Records. Catalogue no: **JIVET 36**
7" Single: Released Mar '86, on Jive, by Zomba Records. Catalogue no: **JIVE 36**

Cinquetti, Gigliola

Biographical details: This Italian singer achieved two British hit singles with a decade between. Both were Eurovision Song Contest entries. The first came in 1964, when Cinquetti was in her late teens. *"Non ho l'eta per amarti"* (I'm not old enough to love you) won the contest, went to no.1 in her native Italy, and also logged an impressive total of 17 weeks on the top 50. This degree of international success ensured a long lasting showbusiness career for the singer. Exactly ten years later she almost repeated her Eurovision feat, collecting the runner up position in the 1974 contest held in Brighton. The year that Abba revoluntised the event with their driving, hard edged *"Waterloo"*, Cinquetti came second to the Swedish foursome with the traditional MOR ballad, the English translation of which was called *"Go (before you break my heart)"*. Another major European seller, *"Go"* reached no.8 on the UK charts. '74 was a rare high spot for the oft derided contest - the musical standard was better than usual, resulting in no less than four British top 20 hits, courtesy of Abba, Cinquetti, Mouth & MacNeal and Olivia Newton John. Cinquetti's contribution was the most conventional, but was nonetheless classy. (Bob Macdonald 85).

GO (BEFORE YOU BREAK MY HEART)
Tracks: / Go (before you break my heart).
7" Single: Released May '74, on CBS, by CBS Records. Deleted May '77. Catalogue no: **CBS 2294**

NON HO L'ETA PER AMARTI
Tracks: / Non ho l'eta per amarti.
7" Single: Released Apr '64, on Decca, by Decca Records. Deleted Apr '67. Catalogue no: **F 21882**

Cintron

GET AWAY
Tracks: / Get away.
7" Single: Released Jan '83, on In Rock, Catalogue no: **IR 1**

Circle Jay

NEXT MACHINE
Tracks: / Next machine.
12" Single: Released '89, on Rodger, Catalogue no: **RODGER 009**

Circles

ANGRY VOICES
Tracks: / Angry voices / Summer nights.
7" Single: Released Aug '80, on Vertigo, by Phonogram Ltd. Deleted '83. Catalogue no: **ANGRY 1**

CIRCLES
Tracks: / Circles.
7" Single: Released Jul '86, on Graduate, by Graduate Records. Deleted Jan '87. Catalogue no: **GRAD 17**

OPENING UP
Tracks: / Opening up / Billy.
7" Single: on Graduate, by Graduate Records. Deleted Jan '87. Catalogue no: **GRAD 4**

Circuit

SHELTER
Tracks: / Shelter.
7" Single: Released Apr '89, on Collision, Catalogue no: **CIR 7001**
12" Single: Released Apr '89, on Collision, Catalogue no: **CIR 12001**

STAND FOR NOTHING
Tracks: / Stand for nothing.
12" Single: Released Sep '89, on Collision, Catalogue no: **12 CR2**

Circuit Seven

MODERN STORY
Tracks: / Modern story.
7" Single: Released Sep '84, on Micro, Catalogue no: **MIC 002**

VIDEO BOYS
Tracks: / Video boys.
7" Single: Released Mar '84, on Rapp, Catalogue no: **RAPP 023459**

Circus Circus Circus

BUTCHER BITCHES
Tracks: / Butcher bitches / Chop chop chop / Six gears to heaven / Wooden man (Only on 12" single.).
7" Single: Released Mar '86, on Three, Catalogue no: **7 BB 1**
12" Single: Released Mar '86, on Three, Catalogue no: **12 BB 1**

INSIDE THE INSIDE OUT MAN
Tracks: / Inside the inside out man.
7" Single: Released 23 May '87, on BDI, Catalogue no: **BDI 1**
12" Single: Released 23 May '87, on BDI, Catalogue no: **BDI 1T**

MAGIC GIRL
Tracks: / Magic girl.
7" Single: Released Aug '87, on Sweatbox, by Sweatbox Records. Catalogue no: **OX 24**
12" Single: Released Aug '87, on Sweatbox, by Sweatbox Records. Catalogue no: **SOX 24**

THUNDER HIGH
Tracks: / Thunder high.
7" Single: Released Jul '88, on Sweatbox, by Sweatbox Records. Catalogue no: **OX 033**
12" Single: Released Jul '88, on Sweatbox, by Sweatbox Records. Catalogue no: **SOX 033**

UNDER THE LIBRARY
Tracks: / Under the library.
7" Single: Released Mar '88, on Sweatbox, by Sweatbox Records. Catalogue no: **OX 28**
12" Single: Released Mar '88, on Sweatbox, by Sweatbox Records. Catalogue no: **SOX 28**

Circus Of Poets

NOW THEN DAVOS
Tracks: / Now then davos.
7" Single: Released Aug '85, on Lambs To The Slaughter, by Prism Records. Catalogue no: **CARKEY 1**

Cirrus

ROLLIN' ON
Tracks: / Rollin' on.
7" Single: Released Sep '78, on Jet, by Jet Records. Deleted Sep '81. Catalogue no: **JET 123**

Citizens

SATISFY THE CITIZENS
Tracks: / Satisfy the citizens / TV woman.
7" Single: Released Oct '80, on Epic, by CBS Records. Deleted Oct '83. Catalogue no: **EPC 9033**
7" Single: Released Jul '80, on Cavalcade, Deleted '83. Catalogue no: **CAV 1**

Citizens Of Realm

SOMEONE ELSE'S WORLD
Tracks: / St. Malo / Someone else's world.
7" Single: Released Sep '82, on Someone Else's Music, by Someone Else's Music. Catalogue no: **SON 1**

City Boy

Biographical details: City boy were formed in 1976 and, by the end of '77, had issued three albums. They were a sophisticated pop/rock group in the 10cc mould, though not as interesting or inventive as their mentors. None of the group's LPs ever charted, buthtey managed a short-lived breakthrough in 1978 via the success of the single *5-7-0-5*. This catchy telephone song reached No. 8 in the UK and No. 27 in the US. However, a second Top 40 hit was achieved only in Britain: *What A Night* peaked at No. 39. City Boy faded into obscurity; they had been unsure whether to aim for the British or American market and had fallen between two musical stools. It is interesting to note that some of the guest musicians who played on various City Boy tracks have subsequently become major producers: Mutt Lange, Fiachra Trench, Greg Mathieson and Tim Friese-Greene all played on at least one of the group's LPs and all have achieved big success in the Eighties as producers. Another session player way Huey Lewis, who later became a huge American rock star. (Bob MacDonald)..

5-7-0-5
Tracks: / 5-7-0-5.
7" Single: Released Jul '78, on Vertigo, by Phonogram Ltd. Deleted Jul '81. Catalogue no: **6059 207**

DAY THE EARTH CAUGHT FIRE, THE (SINGLE)
Tracks: / Day the earth caught fire, The.
7" Single: Released Sep '79, on Vertigo, by Phonogram Ltd. Deleted Sep '82. Catalogue no: **6059 238**

IN LOVE
Tracks: / In love.
12" Single: Released Feb '82, on City Boy, Catalogue no: **CB 001**

LOVERS
Tracks: / Lovers / Exit the heavyweights.
7" Single: Released Nov '81, on Vertigo, by Phonogram Ltd. Deleted Nov '84. Catalogue no: **CITY 1**

NEED A LITTLE LOVING
Tracks: / Need a little loving / Bloody Sunday.
7" Single: Released Oct '80, on Vertigo, by Phonogram Ltd. Deleted Oct '83. Catalogue no: **6059363**

WHAT A NIGHT

Tracks: / What a night.
7" Single: Released Oct '78, on Vertigo, by Phonogram Ltd. Deleted Oct '81. Catalogue no: **6059 211**

City Centre

TO LOVE SOMEBODY
Tracks: / To love somebody.
7" Single: Released Aug '83, on Dingle's, by Dingle's Records. Catalogue no: **SID 215**

City Girl

DO YOU THINK I'M SEXY
Tracks: / Do you think I'm sexy.
12" Single: Released Jun '85, on Touch, by Touch Records. Catalogue no: **12TOU 21**

City Heat

CITY HEAT
Tracks: / City heat.
7" Single: Released Aug '88, on Chrysalis, by Chrysalis Records. Catalogue no: **CHS 3287**
12" Single: Released Aug '88, on Chrysalis, by Chrysalis Records. Catalogue no: **CHS 123287**

RAID, THE
Tracks: / Raid, The / Raid, The (untouchable mix) / Rendezvous, The.
12" Single: Released Apr '88, on Debut, by Skratch Records. Catalogue no: **DEBTX 3036**

City Limits Crew

FRESHER THAN EVER
Tracks: / Fresher than ever.
7" Single: Released Apr '85, on Survival (1), by Survival Records. Catalogue no: **SUR 034**
12" Single: Released Apr '85, on Survival (1), by Survival Records. Catalogue no: **SUR 12 034**

City Talk

TRICK OF THE LIGHT
Tracks: / Trick of the light.
7" Single: Released Jan '83, on Pad, by Pad Records. Catalogue no: **PAD 001**

Ciyo

COME OUT TO PLAY
Tracks: / Come out to play.
7" Single: Released Dec '88, on Ciyo, Catalogue no: **CIYO 3**

Clail, Gary

HARD LEFT
Tracks: / Hard left.
12" Single: Released Aug '88, on World, by World Records. Catalogue no: **WR 007**

Clail, Gary & Totp

HALF CUT FOR CONFIDENCE
Tracks: / Half cut for confidence.
12" Single: Released Oct '85, on On-U-Sound, by On-U-Sound Records. Catalogue no: **DP 12**

Claim

THIS PENCIL WAS OBVIOUSLY...
Tracks: / This pencil was obviously....
Note: Full title: This Pencil Was Obviously Sharpened By A Left-Handed Indian Knife Thrower.
12" Single: Released Sep '87, on Tambourine, by Tambourine Records. Catalogue no: **CUO 388**

WAIT AND SEE
Tracks: / Wait and see.
7" Single: Released Mar '89, on Esuriant, Catalogue no: **UNKNOWN**

Claire & Friends

IT'S 'ORRIBLE BEING IN LOVE (WHEN YOU'RE 8 AND A HALF)
Tracks: / It's 'orrible being in love when you're eight and a half.
7" Single: Released Jun '86, on BBC, by BBC Records & Tapes. Deleted '88. Catalogue no: **RESLP 189**

SUPERMAN
Tracks: / Rainbow / Superman.
7" Single: Released Sep '86, on BBC, by BBC Records & Tapes. Deleted Sep '87. Catalogue no: **RESL 196**
12" Single: Released Sep '86, on BBC, by BBC Records & Tapes. Deleted '88. Catalogue no: **RSL 196**

Claire, Valerie

I'M A MODEL
Tracks: / I'm a model.
7" Single: Released Jun '85, on Record Shack, by Record Shack Records. Catalogue no: **SOHO 45**
12" Single: Released Jun '85, on Record Shack, by Record Shack Records. Catalogue no: **SOHOT 45**

SHOOT ME GINO

CLANNAD - HARRY'S GAME (Released on RCA)

Tracks: / Shoot me Gino.
12" Single: Released Nov '85, on Carrere, Catalogue no: **CART 377**
7" Single: Released Nov '85, on Carrere, Catalogue no: **CAR 377**

Clamber

CHOOSE THE WAY
Tracks: / Choose the way.
7" Single: Released Mar '85, on Clamber, Catalogue no: **CLA 1**

Clan Campbell

SEVEN TEARS
Tracks: / Seven tears / Wooden heart.
7" Single: Released Nov '82, on Lochshore, by Klub Records. Catalogue no: **LOCH 605**

Clannad

Biographical details: This Irish folk band consists of Ciaran Brennan, Maire Brennam and Paul Brennan plus the Brennan's twin uncles, Noel Duggan and Padraig Duggan. Their debut album *"Clannad"* was released in Ireland in 1973, following by several subsequent LPs during the seventies and early eighties. They shot to sudden success in November 1982 when their solemn, enchanting rendition of a centuries old tradition chant was used as the theme to a popular TV series, "Harry's game". Sounding totally different to anything else on the charts at the time, *"Theme from Harry's game"* reached no.5 in the UK as a result of its television exposure. Further hit singles were not forthcoming, but their new found fame led to steady album sales; and whereas *"Theme from Harry's game"* was purely a superb vocal effort, other releases revealed the group's instrumental skills also. 1983's *"Magical ring"* LP made the UK charts, as did 1984's *"Legend"*, Clannad's musical soundtrack to a successful TV serialization of the Robin Hood story. (Bob Macdonald 85)
Irish folk group, at first singing only in Gaelic: Marie Brennan, harp, vocals; Paul Brennan, flute, guitar, keyboards; Ciaran Brennan, bass, synth; Pat Duggan, mandola, guitar; Noel Duggan, guitar and vocals. Their celtic sound slowly became more MOR as they turned to music for TV series: *Theme from Harry's game* was a top five hit in 1982, then they did the music for *Robin of Sherwood* and won a BAFTA award. Eithne Brennan joined in 1980 but was not made a profit sharing member, so she changed her name to Enya and outstripped the others's success with her first album. (Donald Clarke, April 1989)n.

ALMOST SEEMS (TOO LATE TO TURN)
Tracks: / Almost seems (too late to turn).
7" Single: Released Nov '85, on RCA, by BMG Records (UK). Catalogue no: **PB 40649**
12" Single: Released Nov '85, on RCA, by BMG Records (UK). Catalogue no: **PT 40470**

CLOSER TO YOUR HEART
Tracks: / Closer to your heart / Buachaill on eirne / Harry's game (theme from) (Track on 12" version only) / Robin (the hooded man) (Track on 12" version only).
7" Single: Released Sep '75, on RCA, by BMG Records (UK). Catalogue no: **PB 40357**
7" Single: Released Feb '86, on RCA, by BMG Records (UK). Catalogue no: **PB 40358**
12" Single: Released Sep '75, on RCA, by BMG Records (UK). Catalogue no: **PT 40358**
12" Single: Released Feb '86, on RCA, by BMG Records (UK). Catalogue no: **PT 40358**

HARRY'S GAME THEME (see panel above)
Tracks: / Harry's game (theme from) / Strayed away.
7" Single: Released Oct '82, on RCA, by BMG Records (UK). Deleted Aug '89. Catalogue no: **RCA 292**

HOURGLASS
Tracks: / Hourglass / Harry's game, Theme from.
7" Single: Released Aug '89, on RCA, by BMG Records (UK). Catalogue no: **PK 43075**
12" Single: Released Aug '89, on RCA, by BMG Records (UK). Catalogue no: **PT 43075**
CD 5": Released Aug '89, on RCA, by BMG Records (UK). Catalogue no: **PD 43075**
7" Single: Released Aug '89, on RCA, by BMG Records (UK). Catalogue no: **PB 43075**

HUNTER, THE
Tracks: / Hunter, The / Atlantic realm / Skellig (Only on CD single and 12".) / Turning tide (Only on CD single and 12".).
12" Single: Released Jan '89, on RCA, by BMG Records (UK). Catalogue no: **PT 42 610**
CD 5": Released Jan '89, on RCA, by BMG Records (UK). Catalogue no: **PD 42610**
7" Single: Released Jan '89, on RCA, by BMG Records (UK). Deleted Aug '89. Catalogue no: **PB 42 609**
7" Single: Released Jan '89, on RCA, by BMG Records (UK). Catalogue no: **PL 42 609**

I SEE RED
7" Single: Released Mar '83, on RCA, by BMG Records (UK). Catalogue no: **RCA 325**

IN A LIFETIME
Tracks: / Indoor / Northern skyline (Track on 12" version only) / New grange (Track on 12" version only) / In a lifetime.
7" Single: Released Jun '89, on RCA, by BMG Records (UK). Catalogue no: **PB 42873**
7" Pic: Released Jun '89, on RCA, by BMG Records (UK). Deleted Aug '89. Catalogue no: **PA 42995**
7" Single: Released Jan '86, on RCA, by BMG Records (UK). Catalogue no: **PB 40535**
12" Single: Released Jan '86, on RCA, by BMG Records (UK). Catalogue no: **PT 40535**

IN A LIFETIME (2)
Tracks: / In a lifetime / Something to believe in / Caislean oir (Only on 12" and CD single.) / Wild cry, The (Only on 12" and CD single.) / Atlantic realm (Only on CD single.).
12" Single: Released 30 May '89, on RCA, by BMG Records (UK). Catalogue no: **PT 42874**
7" Single: Released 30 May '89, on RCA, by BMG Records (UK). Catalogue no: **PB 42873**
CD 5": Released 30 May '89, on RCA, by BMG Records (UK). Catalogue no: **PD 42874**

NEW GRANGE
Tracks: / New grange.
7" Single: Released May '83, on RCA, by BMG Records (UK). Catalogue no: **RCA 340**

NOW IS HERE
Tracks: / Now is here.
7" Single: Released Jun '84, on RCA, by BMG Records (UK). Catalogue no: **HOOD 2**

ROBIN OF SHERWOOD
Tracks: / Robin of Sherwood (Origina Music from the TV series) / Robin (The hooded man) / Caislean oir / Now is here / Herne.
7" Single: Released May '84, on RCA, by BMG Records (UK). Deleted May '87 Catalogue no: **HOOD 1**
7" Single: Released May '86, on RCA, by BMG Records (UK). Catalogue no: **PB 40681**

SCARLET INSIDE
Tracks: / Scarlet inside / Robin the hoode man / Harry's game.
7" Single: Released Mar '85, on RCA, b BMG Records (UK). Deleted '87. Catalogue no: **PB 40033**

SOMETHING TO BELIEVE IN
Tracks: / Something to believe in / Secon nature / In a lifetime (remix) (on 12" only.).
Note: * extra track on 12" version
7" Single: Released Sep '87, on RCA, b BMG Records (UK). Deleted May '8 Catalogue no: **PB 41543**
12" Single: Released Sep '87, on RCA, b BMG Records (UK). Catalogue no: **P 41543**

WHITE FOOL
Tracks: / White fool / Many roads / Clos to your heart (track on 12" only.).
7" Single: Released Jan '88, on RCA, BMG Records (UK). Deleted May '8 Catalogue no: **PB 41703**
12" Single: Released Jan '88, on RCA, b BMG Records (UK). Deleted May '8 Catalogue no: **PT 41704**

Clanton, Jimmy

Biographical details: A pop singer born 1940, discovered by Ace Record's bo Johnny Vincent while making demos at C simo Metassa's studio with pianist Di Holler (who later wrote *Abraham, Martin John*): four USA top 40 versions in 19 71. His biggest hits are still fondly reme bered; he was swept away with ma others by the British Invasion. His top fi *Just a dream* (1958) used New Orlea players Huey 'Piano' Smith, Earl King guitar and Lee Allen on tenor; Neil Seda wrote his top ten *Venus in blue jeans*. (D nald Clarke, April 1989).

ANOTHER SLEEPLESS NIGHT
Tracks: / Another sleepless night.
7" Single: Released Jul '60, on Top Ra (1), Deleted Jul '63. Catalogue no: **J 382**

Clapham Daredevils

CHER LOUISE
Tracks: / Cher Louise.
7" Single: Released Mar '83, on Bea House Recorders, Catalogue no: **BHR 1**

Clapham South

GET ME TO THE WORLD ON TIM
Tracks: / Get me to the world on time.
7" Single: Released Dec '82, on Upri by Upright Records. Catalogue no: **YOURS 1**

Clapton, Eric

Biographical details: This British rock tarist, singer and somposer, born in Rip Surrey in March 1945, is regarded by m journalists and critics as the UK's grea ever rock guitar hero. A lover of the bl he was heavily influenced by legen bluesman Muddy Waters and by rock pioneer Chuck Berry. Clapton, in turn fluenced and inspired numerous other tists. He brought his first guitar at the of 17, and soon became engrossed in don's early/mid - sixties blues scene. joined in Yardbirds in late 1963, an up coming R&B group who took over from

Rolling Stones as the resident act at one of London's most talked about clubs. In '65 the Yardbirds moved in a commercial direction with their acclaimed single "For your love"; Capton resented this move to the pop market and left shortly after it was recorded, without waiting for it to reach the top 10 on both sides of the Atlantic. In the middle of the sixties, he achieved album chart success plus great critical acceptance as a member of John Mayall's Bluebreakers. Between late '66 and early '69, Clapton's guitar hero status reached a new level, thanks to the enormous international success of rock trio Cream; by the time the group folded, he was, to many, God for all practical purposes. In 1969 saw the appearance and rapid disappearance of the short lived, contrived supergroup Blind Faith. Clapton then recorded and toured with, the then unknown Delaney & Bonnie. In December 1970 came the release of "Layla" and other assorted love songs", released under the name of Derek & The Dominoes. That LP's centrepiece single "Layla" is one of rock music's all time classics, and remains Clapton's greatest track; it was a top 10 single twice in Britain, reaching no.7 in 1972 and no.4 in 1982. At this history suggests, Eric Clapton has always put musical integrity, as he sees it, before commercial success. Intensely disliking the pressures of stardom and its business trappings, he has never felt totally comfortable in his role as top guitar hero and during the seventies, he concentrated as much on singing and songwriting as on his instrumental skills. His first solo album was released in 1970, shortly before the "Layla" set emerged. It yielded a US top 20 single in the shape of J.J. Cale's song, "After midnight". Cale's laid back style was to have a considerable impact on Clapton's future work, as was that of Don Williams, the relaxed country singer. For a period during the early seventies, drug related health problems sent Clapton into virtual retirement. A course of acupuncture eventually cured his addiction, and he returned in triumph with the 1974 album "461 Ocean Boulevard" and the single "I shot the sheriff". The latter reached no.1 in the States and no.9 in Britain, and gave a fresh boost to the careers of both Clapton and its Jamaican composer Bob Marley, the rising reggae star whose future status and overdue recognition was undoubtedly accelerated by this successful re-working of one of his songs. From here onwards, Clapton enjoyed a fully fledged solo career and, for the first time, appeared completely contented with this position. His new found career consistency brought him years of big record sales, particulary in the US. Especially important was 1977's "Slowhand" album, which contained the US top 3 single "Lay down Sally", the beautiful ballad "Wonderful tonight" plus the J.J. Cale song "Cocaine". This gentler incarnation of the great guitar hero may have alienated some of his original worshippers, but it nonetheless kept the spotlight on one of rock music's all time legends. (Bob Macdonald 5)

Born in 1945 in Ripley, Surrey, Eric Clapton became the most famous rock guitarist in the world. He played with the Yardbirds 1964-1965, then with John Mayall's Bluebreakers; he formed the power trio Cream with Jack Bruce and Ginger Baker and became a legend playing long loud solos which were really too much weight for the blues to bear. He played on the eponymous album by the shortlived 'supergroup' Blind Faith, then sought anonymity with Delaney and Bonnie, but the two disc Derek & the Dominoes didn't fool anybody: the warm tone of his Fender Stratocaster, dubbed 'woman tone', was instantly recognisable. His first solo album Eric Clapton in 1970 included J.J. Cale's *After midnight*, and Cale's more laid-back style would be influential. Graffiti in London had already said 'CLAPTON IS GOD' in the mid '60's: not wanting that kind of adulation, he had become a heroin addict; 461 Ocean Boulevard in 1970 was named after the house in Florida where he kicked tha habit, and included Bob Marley's *I shot the sheriff*. Many albums later, his five disc (on CD) career retrospective *Crossroads* was one of the biggest hits of 1988, with 73 tracks. (Donald Clarke, April 1989).

AFTER MIDNIGHT (SINGLE)
Tracks: / After midnight / I can't stand it / What you gonna do (Available on 12" only) / Sunshine of your love*.
Note: * Only on the 12" version.
CD 5": Released 4 Jul '88, on Polydor, by Polydor Ltd. Catalogue no: **PZCD 8**
12" Single: Released 4 Jul '88, on Polydor, by Polydor Ltd. Catalogue no: **PO 8**
7" Single: Released 4 Jul '88, on Polydor, by Polydor Ltd. Deleted 30 Jun '89. Catalogue no: **PZ 8**

ANOTHER TICKET (SINGLE)
Tracks: / Another ticket / Rita Mae.
7" Single: Released Apr '81, on RSO, by Polydor Ltd. Deleted Apr '84. Catalogue no: **RSO 75**

BEHIND THE MASK
Tracks: / Grand illusion / Behind the mask.
7" Single: Released Jan '87, on Duck, by Duck Records. Deleted Jan '88. Catalogue no: **W 8461**
12" Single: Released Jan '87, on Duck, by Duck Records. Deleted Jan '88. Catalogue no: **W 8461T**

EDGE OF DARKNESS
Tracks: / Shoot out / Edge of darkness.
CD 3": Released Feb '89, on BBC, by BBC Records & Tapes. Catalogue no: **CDRSL 178**
Cassingle: Released Nov '85, on BBC, by BBC Records & Tapes. Catalogue no: **ZRSL 178**
12" Single: Released Nov '85, on BBC, by BBC Records & Tapes. Catalogue no: **12 RSL 178**
7" Single: Released Jan '86, on BBC, by BBC Records & Tapes. Catalogue no: **RESL 178**

FOREVER MAN
Tracks: / Forever man.
7" Single: Released Mar '85, on Warner Bros., by WEA Records. Deleted Mar '88. Catalogue no: **W 9069**

HOLY MOTHER
Tracks: / Holy mother / Tangled in love / Forever man (This track is available on 12" single only.) / Behind the mask (This track is available on 12" single only.).
12" Single: Released 21 Nov '87, on Duck, by Duck Records. Catalogue no: **W 8141 T**
7" Single: Released 21 Nov '87, on Duck, by Duck Records. Catalogue no: **W 8141**

I CAN'T STAND IT
Tracks: / I can't stand it / Black rose.
7" Single: Released Feb '81, on RSO, by Polydor Ltd. Deleted Feb '84. Catalogue no: **RSO 74**

I SHOT THE SHERIFF
Tracks: / Knockin' on heaven's door / I shot the sheriff.
7" Single: Released Jul '82, on RSO, by Polydor Ltd. Deleted Jul '85. Catalogue no: **RSO 88**
7" Single: Released Jul '74, on RSO, by Polydor Ltd. Catalogue no: **2090 132**
7" Single: Released Mar '86, on Old Gold, by Old Gold Records. Catalogue no: **OG 9586**

IT'S IN THE WAY THAT YOU USE IT
Tracks: / It's in the way that you use it / Bad influence / Old ways (This extra track on 12" only.) / Pretty girl (This extra track on 12" only.).
7" Single: Released Mar '87, on Duck, by Duck Records. Deleted Jan '88. Catalogue no: **W 8397**
12" Single: Released Mar '87, on Duck, by Duck Records. Deleted Jan '88. Catalogue no: **W 8397T**

I'VE GOT A ROCK & ROLL HEART
Tracks: / I've got a rock 'n' roll heart / Man in love.
7" Single: Released Jan '83, on Duck, by Duck Records. Catalogue no: **W 9780**
12" Single: Released Jan '83, on Duck, by Duck Records. Catalogue no: **W 9780T**

KNOCKIN' ON HEAVENS DOOR
Tracks: / Knockin' on heavens door.
7" Single: Released Aug '75, on RSO, by Polydor Ltd. Deleted Aug '78. Catalogue no: **2090 166**

LAY DOWN SALLY
Tracks: / Lay down Sally.
7" Single: Released Dec '77, on RSO, by Polydor Ltd. Deleted Dec '80. Catalogue no: **2090 264**

PROMISES
Tracks: / Promises.
7" Single: Released Oct '78, on RSO, by Polydor Ltd. Deleted Oct '81. Catalogue no: **RSO 21**

SHAPE YOU'RE IN
Tracks: / Shape you're in, The.
7" Single: Released Apr '83, on Duck, by Duck Records. Catalogue no: **W 9701**
12" Single: Released Apr '83, on Duck, by Duck Records. Catalogue no: **W 9701T**

SLOW DOWN LINDA
Tracks: / Slow down Linda.
7" Single: Released May '83, on Duck, by Duck Records. Catalogue no: **W 9651**
12" Single: Released May '83, on Duck, by Duck Records. Catalogue no: **W 9651T**

SWING LOW SWEET CHARIOT
Tracks: / Swing low sweet chariot.
7" Single: Released May '75, on RSO, by Polydor Ltd. Deleted May '78. Catalogue no: **2090 158**

TEARING US APART (See under Turner, Tina)
Tracks: / Tearing us apart / Hold on / Run* (*Extra track on 12").
7" Single: Released Jun '87, on WEA, by WEA Records. Deleted Jul '88. Catalogue no: **W 8299**
12" Single: Released Jun '87, on WEA, by WEA Records. Deleted Jul '88. Catalogue no: **W 8299T**
12" Pic: Released Jun '87, on WEA, by WEA Records. Deleted Jul '88. Catalogue no: **W 8299 TP**

WONDERFUL TONIGHT
Tracks: / Wonderful tonight / Cocaine.
7" Single: Released '84, on RSO (USA), by Polydor Ltd. Catalogue no: **RSO 98**
12" Single: Released Aug '87, on Polydor, by Polydor Ltd. Catalogue no: **POSPX 881**
12" Single: Released Aug '87, on Chrysalis, by Chrysalis Records. Catalogue no: **COLFX 7**
7" Single: Released Aug '87, on Polydor, by Polydor Ltd. Catalogue no: **POSP 881**

Clare, Carl St

WONDERFUL ENGLISH FOOTBALL
Tracks: / Wonderful English football / Football time.
12" Single: Released '82, on Trans Universal, Catalogue no: **TUR 004**

Clarity

WAY U MAKE ME FEEL, THE
Tracks: / Way U make me feel, The.
12" Single: Released '85, on BPOP, by BPOP Records. Deleted '86. Catalogue no: **BPOP T02**
7" Single: Released '85, on BPOP, by BPOP Records. Deleted '86. Catalogue no: **BPOP 702**

Clark, Anne

HOPE ROAD (A-Z ROUTE)
Tracks: / Hope road (A-Z route) / Poem without words / Third meeting, The / Heaven (live).
12" Single: Released '89, on 10 Records, by Virgin Records. Catalogue no: **TENT 167**

OUR DARKNESS
Tracks: / Our darkness / Sitting room.
12" Single: Released '84, on Ink, by Red Flame Records. Catalogue no: **INK 125**

SLEEPER IN METROPOLIS(EXT)
12" Single: Released '85, on Ink, by Red Flame Records. Deleted '88. Catalogue no: **INK 1213**

TRUE LOVE TALKS
Tracks: / True love talks.
12" Single: Released Mar '86, on Ink, by Red Flame Records. Catalogue no: **INK 1218**

WALLIES
Tracks: / Wallies.
12" Single: Released Sep '85, on Ink, by Red Flame Records. Catalogue no: **INK 1216**

Clark, Dave

Biographical details: A stuntman with over 40 film credits became the drummer/leader of the Dave Clark Five, an enormously popular local band in Tottenham, North London. They were seriously considered rivals to the Beatles; critics talked about a Tottenham sound as an answer to the Mersey Beat. *Glad all over* was their thumping number one hit in 1963; their compilation *Thumping great hits* was a surprise number one album in the middle of the Punk summer of 1977. Clark bought the rights to the Ready Steady Go pop show, and cashed in big when video arrived. (Donald Clarke, April 1989)a.

ANY WAY YOU WANT IT
Tracks: / Any way you want it.
7" Single: Released Oct '64, on Columbia, by EMI Records. Deleted Oct '67. Catalogue no: **DB 7377**

BITS AND PIECES
Tracks: / Bits and pieces.
7" Single: Released Feb '64, on Columbia, by EMI Records. Deleted Feb '67. Catalogue no: **DB 7210**

CAN'T YOU SEE THAT SHE'S MINE?
Tracks: / Can't you see that she's mine?.
7" Single: Released May '64, on Columbia, by EMI Records. Deleted May '67. Catalogue no: **DB 7291**

CATCH US IF YOU CAN (SINGLE)
Tracks: / Catch us if you can.
7" Single: Released Jul '65, on Columbia, by EMI Records. Deleted Jul '68. Catalogue no: **DB 7625**

COME HOME
Tracks: / Come home.
7" Single: Released May '65, on Columbia, by EMI Records. Deleted May '68. Catalogue no: **DB 7580**

DO YOU LOVE ME?
Tracks: / Do you love me?.
7" Single: Released Oct '63, on Columbia, by EMI Records. Deleted Oct '66. Catalogue no: **DB 7112**

EVERYBODY GET TOGETHER
Tracks: / Everybody get together.
7" Single: Released Mar '70, on Columbia, by EMI Records. Deleted Mar '73. Catalogue no: **DB 8660**

EVERYBODY KNOWS
Tracks: / Everybody knows.
7" Single: Released Nov '67, on Columbia, by EMI Records. Deleted '70. Catalogue no: **DB 8286**
7" Single: Released Jan '65, on Columbia, by EMI Records. Deleted Jan '68. Catalogue no: **DB 7453**

GLAD ALL OVER
Tracks: / Glad all over.
7" Single: Released Nov '63, on Columbia, by EMI Records. Deleted Nov '66. Catalogue no: **DB 7154**

GOOD OLD ROCK 'N' ROLL
Tracks: / Good old rock 'n' roll.
7" Single: Released Dec '69, on Columbia, by EMI Records. Deleted Dec '72. Catalogue no: **DB 8638**

HERE COMES SUMMER
Tracks: / Here comes summer.
7" Single: Released Jul '70, on Columbia, by EMI Records. Deleted Jul '73. Catalogue no: **DB 8689**

LIVE IN THE SKY
Tracks: / Live in the sky.
7" Single: Released Nov '68, on Columbia, by EMI Records. Deleted Nov '71. Catalogue no: **DB 8505**

LOOK BEFORE YOU LEAP
Tracks: / Look before you leap.
7" Single: Released May '66, on Columbia, by EMI Records. Deleted May '69. Catalogue no: **DB 7909**

MORE GOOD OLD ROCK 'N' ROLL
Tracks: / More good old rock 'n' roll.
7" Single: Released Nov '70, on Columbia, by EMI Records. Deleted Nov '73. Catalogue no: **DB 8724**

NO ONE CAN BREAK A HEART LIKE YOU
Tracks: / No one can break a heart like you.
7" Single: Released Feb '68, on Columbia, by EMI Records. Deleted Feb '71. Catalogue no: **DB 8342**

OVER AND OVER
Tracks: / Over and over.
7" Single: Released Nov '65, on Columbia, by EMI Records. Deleted Nov '68. Catalogue no: **DB 7744**

PUT A LITTLE LOVE IN YOUR HEART
Tracks: / Put a little love in your heart.
7" Single: Released Oct '69, on Columbia, by EMI Records. Deleted Oct '72. Catalogue no: **DB 8624**

RED BALLOON
Tracks: / Red balloon.
7" Single: Released Sep '68, on Columbia, by EMI Records. Deleted Sep '71. Catalogue no: **DB 8465**

REELIN' AND ROCKIN'
Tracks: / Reelin' and rockin'.
7" Single: Released Mar '65, on Columbia, by EMI Records. Deleted Mar '68. Catalogue no: **DB 7503**

THINKING OF YOU BABY
Tracks: / Thinking of you baby.
7" Single: Released Aug '64, on Columbia, by EMI Records. Deleted Aug '67. Catalogue no: **DB 7335**

YOU GOT WHAT IT TAKES
Tracks: / You got what it takes.
7" Single: Released Mar '67, on Columbia, by EMI Records. Deleted Mar '70. Catalogue no: **DB 8152**

Clark, Dee

Biographical details: This American singer and songwriter, born in Arkansas, achieved six American top 40 hits between 1959 and 1961. All containing strong melodies, they were some of the best black pop singles of that period. The first *"Nobody , but you"*, reached no.21 on the US charts. The second, *'Just keep it up"* hit no.18 and was his sixth and final US top 40, 1961's *"Raindrops"* which reached no.2. Having secured just one week of UK chart action in October 1959 with *"Just keep it up"*, Clark made a surprise one off comeback in 1975. His lightweight single, *"Ride a wild horse"* got to no.16 on the British charts, approximately 1 and a half decades after he slipped into obsurity; this latter success, however, failed to return him to the charts of his native country (Bob Macdonald 85).

JUST KEEP IT UP
Tracks: / Just keep it up.
7" Single: Released Oct '59, on London Records, by London Records. Deleted Oct '62. Catalogue no: **HL 8915**

RIDE A WILD HORSE
Tracks: / Ride a wild horse.
7" Single: Released Oct '75, on Chelsea, Deleted Oct '78. Catalogue no: **2005 037**

Clark, Guy

Biographical details: Born in 1941 in Texas, Guy Clark is probably the most widely admired of all the 'new country' fraterntiy, at the same time its best-kept secret. His excellent and often very funny songs have been covered by Jerry Jeff Walker, David Allen Coe, Johnny Cash, Ricky Skaggs, Bobby Bare and Dohn Conlee; the best-known is probably *L.A. freeway*, a hit for Walker) but Texas 1947 and *Desperadoes waiting for a train* are classics, while *Texas cooking* and *Homegrown tomatoes* deserve to transcend any genre. He has made a total of only five albums for RCA and WEA through 1983; his sixth in 1988 on the USA Sugar Hill label is *Old friends*. (Donald Clarke, April 1989).

GOOD LOVE AFTER BAD
Tracks: / Good love after bad / Old friends / Watermelon dream (Only on CD single.).
7" Single: Released May '89, on Mother, by Mother Records. Catalogue no: **MUM 11**
CD 5": Released May '89, on Mother, by Mother Records. Catalogue no: **MUMCD 11**

Clark, Louis

Biographical details: This British conductor and arranger is famous for his work with Britain's Royal Philharmonic Orchestra. He and they scored a huge pop hit in 1981 with *"Hooked on classics". This was a witty answer to the then prevalent medley craze that was sweeping the charts. This curious fad was led by Starsound, a Dutch studio ensemble who had just achieved two UK no.2 hits with "Stars on 45"* volumes 1 & 2. Clark took a selection of excerpts from favourite classical composers, added a disco beat, and, found that he too had a no.2 hit on his hands. Shortly afterwards *"Hooked on classics"* reached no.10 in the States. This British follow up single was *"Hooked on can can"*, a particulary silly move in view of the fact that it came mere weeks after Bad Manners Top 3 success with the same idea. Clark and the RPO thus scored only a minor hit single, as were two 1982 efforts. It was on the British album chart that they enjoyed more sustained success: 1981's *"Hooked on classics"* and 1982's *"Can't stop the classics"*, both chalked up substantial LP chart runs, backed by sonsiderable TV advertising. Albums of Queen and Police remakes were less well recieved. (Bob Macdonald 85).

GHANDI THEME
Tracks: / Ghandi (theme from) / Girl in blue.
7" Single: Released Dec '82, on RCA, by BMG Records (UK). Catalogue no: **RCA 303**

HOOKED ON CHRISTMAS
Tracks: / Viva Vivaldi.
7" Single: Released Nov '86, on Ratpack, Catalogue no: **RPC 005**
7" Single: Released Dec '82, on Jet, by Jet Records. Catalogue no: **JET 7031**

HOOKED ON CLASSICS (SINGLE)
Tracks: / Hooked on classics.
12" Single: Released Jul '81, on RCA, by BMG Records (UK). Catalogue no: **RCAT 109**
7" Single: Released Jul '81, on RCA, by BMG Records (UK). Catalogue no: **RCA 109**

HOOKED ON HOUSE
Tracks: / Hooked on house.
12" Single: Released Dec '88, on K-Tel, by K-Tel Records. Catalogue no: **ONE 6602**
7" Single: Released Dec '88, on K-Tel, by K-Tel Records. Catalogue no: **ONE 6102**

ONE DAY
Tracks: / One day.
7" Single: Released Aug '85, on Ratpack, Catalogue no: **RPC 002**

QUEEN MEDLEY
Tracks: / Bohemian rhapsody.
7" Single: Released Jun '82, on EMI, by EMI Records. Catalogue no: **EMI 5301**

STILL LIFE
Tracks: / Still life.
7" Single: Released Nov '84, on Ratpack, Catalogue no: **RPC 001**

Clark, Mary Louise

SOMETHING HERE IN MY HEART
Tracks: / Something here in my heart.
7" Single: Released Jun '85, on Mr.Sam, by Mr.Sam Music. Catalogue no: **SAS 100**

Clark, O' Neil

QUIET PLACE
Tracks: / Quiet place, A.
12" Single: Released 20 Mar '89, on Carron, Catalogue no: **CR 013**

Clark, Paula

BABY
Tracks: / Baby.
7" Single: Released 12 May '89, on Music Scene, Catalogue no: **MKS 62577**

Clark, Petula

Biographical details: This British singer, born in Epsom, Surrey in 1933, has enjoyed an extraordinarily successful and long-lasting showbusiness career. She is one of the very few stars to make the transition from child prodigy to accomplished adult performer. In a career spanning over forty years, she has won great fame both as a singer and as an actress, selling huge quantities of singles in Britain, Europe and America and making numerous television and cinema appearances.
Having studied music since early childhood, Clark was a big British radio star by the end of the Second World War. By the time of her first record hit in 1954, she had already made more than twenty films. That debut hit disc *The Little Shoemaker*, reached No. 7 on the UK chart. After three further Top 10 hits, she achieved her first No. 1 with 1961's *Sailor*, an English translation of an Austrian song. Clark's second British chart-topper came six years later, when she paced the pack with *This Is My Song*, composed by Charlie Chaplain. In between these two milestones, she chalked up two American No. 1 singles, both penned by Pye Records executive Tony Hatch: the memorable *Downtown* (No. 2 in Britain) and *My Love* (No. 4 in Britain). But the true international scale of Clark's popularity is perhaps best illustrated by the fact that two European hits recorded in 1962, *Monsieur* and *Chariot*, both sold a million copies without being Top 30 hits in either the UK or the US. The singer has often recorded in French and German as well as English.
As the hit records began to tail off in the late Sixties, Clark relied more heavily on TV, film and stage aspects of her career. In 1981 she starred as Maria in the London revival of *The Sound Of Music*. Her many movies over the forty years have included *Strwaberry Road, I Know Where I'm Going, Easy Money, Finian's Rainbow* and *Goodbye Mr. Chips* amongst numerous others. Her very first film was *A Medal For The General*, made in 1944. (Bob MacDonald).
Born in 1932 in Epsom, Surrey, the radio and film actress with the big, clear voice became one of England's best-loved pop singers, with several international hits in a row: 15 chart entries in the USA in the 1965-68 (of which *Downtown* was a number one) and 27 in the UK 1954-72 not counting re-entries. One of her best known fans was quirky Candian classical pianist Glenn Gould who wrote an essay about her. She received an ovation at the 1971 Academy Awards show singing *All we know*; she played Maria in the London Revival of the *Sound of music* and has now lived in Switzerland for many years, married to record company executive Claude Wolff. (Donald Clarke, April 1989).

ALONE
Tracks: / Alone.
7" Single: Released Nov '57, on Pye, Deleted Nov '60. Catalogue no: **N 15112**

BABY LOVER
Tracks: / Baby lover.
7" Single: Released Feb '58, on Pye, Deleted Feb '61. Catalogue no: **N 15126**

CASANOVA
Tracks: / Casanova / Chariot.
7" Single: Released May '63, on Pye, Deleted May '66. Catalogue no: **7N 15522**

DON'T SLEEP IN THE SUBWAY
Tracks: / Don't sleep in the subway.
7" Single: Released May '67, on Pye, Deleted May '70. Catalogue no: **7N 17325**

DOWN TOWN (OLD GOLD CD SINGLE)
Tracks: / Downtown / Sailor / Romeo.
CD 5": Released Nov '88, on Old Gold, by Old Gold Records. Catalogue no: **OG 6101**

DOWNTOWN '88'
Tracks: / Downtown '88'.
CD 5": Released Oct '88, on PRT, by Castle Communications Records. Catalogue no: **PYD 19**
12" Single: Released Oct '88, on PRT, by Castle Communications Records. Catalogue no: **PYT 19**
7" Pic: Released Oct '88, on PRT, by Castle Communications Records. Catalogue no: **PYS 19**

DOWNTOWN (OLD GOLD)
Tracks: / Downtown / I know a place.
7" Single: Released Jul '82, on Old Gold, by Old Gold Records. Catalogue no: **OG 9130**

DOWNTOWN (SINGLE)
Tracks: / Downtown / I know a place.
7" Single: Released Nov '64, on Pye, Deleted Nov '67. Catalogue no: **7N 15722**
7" Pic: Released Jul '87, on PRT, by Castle Communications Records. Catalogue no: **PYS 1**

DREAMING WITH MY EYES WIDE OPEN
Tracks: / Dreaming with my eyes wide open / Afterglow.
7" Single: Released Nov '82, on Scotti Bros (Germany), Deleted Nov '85. Catalogue no: **SCTA 2904**

EDELWEISS
Tracks: / Edelweiss / Darkness.
7" Single: Released Aug '81, on Epic, by CBS Records. Deleted '84. Catalogue no: **EPCA 1475**

GENTLEMEN & PLAYERS
Tracks: / Gentlemen & players.
7" Single: Released Apr '88, on Eagle (West Germany), by Bear Family Records (Germany). Catalogue no: **EAGLE 2**

I COULDN'T LIVE WITHOUT YOUR LOVE
Tracks: / I couldn't live without your love(89 mix) / Come on home.
7" Single: Released Jun '89, on Legacy, by Legacy Records. Catalogue no: **LGY 100**
7" Single: Released Jun '66, on Pye, Deleted Jun '69. Catalogue no: **7N 17133**
12" Single: Released Jun '89, on Legacy, by Legacy Records. Catalogue no: **LGYT 100**

I DON'T KNOW HOW TO LOVE HIM
Tracks: / I don't know how to love him.
7" Single: Released Jan '72, on Pye, Deleted Jan '75. Catalogue no: **7N 45112**

I KNOW A PLACE
Tracks: / I know a place.
7" Single: Released Mar '65, on Pye, Deleted Mar '68. Catalogue no: **7N 15772**

I'M COUNTING ON YOU
Tracks: / I'm counting on you.
7" Single: Released Feb '62, on Pye, Deleted Feb '65. Catalogue no: **7N 15407**

KISS ME GOODBYE
Tracks: / Kiss me goodbye.
7" Single: Released Mar '68, on Pye, Deleted Mar '71. Catalogue no: **7N 17466**

LITTLE SHOEMAKER, THE
Tracks: / Little shoemaker, The.
7" Single: Released 11 Jun '54, on Polygon, Deleted 11 Jun '57. Catalogue no: **P 1117**
7" Single: Released 25 Jun '54, on Polygon, Deleted 25 Jun '57. Catalogue no: **P 1117**

MAJORCA
Tracks: / Majorca.
7" Single: Released Mar '55, on Polygon, Deleted Mar '58. Catalogue no: **P 1146**
7" Single: Released Feb '55, on Polygon, Deleted Feb '58. Catalogue no: **P 1146**

MR ORWELL
Tracks: / Mr. Orwell.
7" Single: Released Feb '85, on PRT, by Castle Communications Records. Catalogue no: **7P 323**

MY FRIEND THE SEA
Tracks: / My friend the sea.
7" Single: Released Nov '61, on Pye, Deleted Nov '64. Catalogue no: **7N 15387**

MY LOVE
Tracks: / My love.
7" Single: Released Feb '66, on Pye, Deleted Feb '69. Catalogue no: **7N 17038**

OTHER MAN'S GRASS IS ALWAYS GREENER, THE (SINGLE)
Tracks: / Other man's grass, The.
7" Single: Released Dec '67, on Pye, Deleted Dec '70. Catalogue no: **7N 17416**

ROMEO
Tracks: / Romeo.
7" Single: Released Jul '61, on Pye, Deleted Jul '64. Catalogue no: **7N 15361**

ROUND EVERY CORNER
Tracks: / Round every corner.
7" Single: Released Oct '65, on Pye, Deleted Oct '68. Catalogue no: **7N 15945**

SAILOR
Tracks: / Sailor.
7" Single: Released Jan '61, on Pye, Deleted Jan '64. Catalogue no: **7N 15324**
7" Single: Released Mar '86, on Old Gold, by Old Gold Records. Catalogue no: **OG 9126**

SIGN OF THE TIMES
Tracks: / Sign of the times.
7" Single: Released Apr '66, on Pye, Deleted Apr '69. Catalogue no: **7N 17071**

SOMETHING MISSING
Tracks: / Something missing.
7" Single: Released Apr '61, on Pye, Deleted Apr '64. Catalogue no: **7N 15337**

SONG OF MY LIFE
Tracks: / Song of my life, The.
7" Single: Released Jan '71, on Pye, Deleted Jan '74. Catalogue no: **7N 45026**

SUDDENLY THERE'S A VALLEY
Tracks: / Suddenly there's a valley.
7" Single: Released Nov '55, on Pye, Deleted Nov '58. Catalogue no: **N 15013**

THIS IS MY SONG (OLD GOLD)
Tracks: / This is my song.
7" Single: Released Apr '83, on Old Gold, by Old Gold Records. Deleted Jul '88. Catalogue no: **OG 9288**

THIS IS MY SONG (SINGLE)
Tracks: / This is my song.
7" Single: Released 2 Feb '67, on Pye, Deleted 2 Feb '70. Catalogue no: **7N 17258**

WITH ALL MY HEART
Tracks: / With all my heart.
7" Single: Released Jul '57, on Pye, Deleted Jul '60. Catalogue no: **N 15013**

YA YA TWIST
Tracks: / Ya ya twist.
7" Single: Released 20 Sep '62, on Pye, Deleted 20 Sep '65. Catalogue no: **7N 15448**

YOU BETTER COME HOME
Tracks: / You better come home.
7" Single: Released Aug '65, on Pye, Deleted Aug '68. Catalogue no: **7N 15864**

YOU'RE THE ONE
Tracks: / You're the one.
7" Single: Released Nov '65, on Pye Deleted Nov '68. Catalogue no: **7N 15991**

Clark, Roland

RU RU ?
Tracks: / Ru ru ?.
7" Single: Released Mar '89, on Atlantic, by WEA Records. Catalogue no: **086 447**

Clark Sisters

YOU BROUGHT THE SUNSHINE INTO MY LIFE
Tracks: / You brought the sunshine into my life.
7" Single: Released Aug '83, on Westbound, by WEA Records. Catalogue no: **9810**
12" Single: Released Aug '83, on Westbound, by WEA Records. Catalogue no: **9810T**

Clark, Vivienne

IVE GOT THE BLUES
Tracks: / I've got the blues.
12" Single: Released May '82, on Go Sent, Catalogue no: **GDIS 2**

Clarke, Allan

BORN TO RUN
Tracks: / Born to run / If I were the priest.
7" Single: Released Nov '81, on Aura Records, by Aura Records. Deleted '88. Catalogue no: **AUS 129**

ONLY ONE, THE (SINGLE)
Tracks: / Only one, The.
7" Single: Released Oct '80, on Aura Records, by Aura Records. Deleted '88. Catalogue no: **AUS 101**

SHADOW IN THE STREET
Tracks: / Shadow in the street.
7" Single: Released Mar '82, on Aura Records, by Aura Records. Deleted '88. Catalogue no: **AUS 130**

SLIPSTREAM
Tracks: / Slipstream / Imagination's child.
7" Single: Released May '80, on WEA, by WEA Records. Deleted May '85. Catalogue no: **K 12442**

SOMEONE ELSE WILL
Tracks: / Someone else will / Castles in the wind.
7" Single: Released Aug '82, on Forever, Catalogue no: **FORE 3**

WALLS
Tracks: / Walls / Baby blue.
7" Single: Released Jan '81, on Aura Records, by Aura Records. Catalogue no: **AUS 125**

Clarke, Christopher

BELIEVE ME
Tracks: / Believe me / Believe me (inst).
12" Single: Released Mar '87, on T. E. R., by That's Entertainment Records. Catalogue no: **TER 12 011**

Clarke, Don

YOUNG REBEL
Tracks: / Young rebel.
10" single: Released May '83, on Top Notch, by Fashion Records. Catalogue no: **TOP 005**

Clarke, Freddie

ARE WE GOING TO MAKE IT UP
12" Single: Released May '82, on Live & Love, Catalogue no: **LLDIS 205**

NEVER GONNA CHANGE MY MIND
Tracks: / Never gonna change my mind.
12" Single: Released Aug '88, on Business, Catalogue no: **BR 01**

Clarke, John Cooper

Biographical details: This British poet, born in Manchester, emerged from the UK's new wave explosion of 1976/7 and espoused similar rebellious social and political attitudes to those of his musical colleagues. He was Britain's only punk poet, and attracted considerable attention by expressing the new wave philosophy in an art form other than music. Clarke's first record was an EP entitled *"Psycle sluts"*, released in December 1977 in a local independent label, Rabid Records. This impressive and witty debut resulted in a contract with Epic Records. His first two LPs were 1978's *"Disguise in love"* and 1979's *"Walking back to happiness"*. '79 brought his sole chart single: *"Gimmix play loud"* peaked at no.39 on the UK listings. Clarke's only significant album chart success was *"Snap crackle and bop"*, which cracked the UK top 30 and contained *"Beasley Street"*, arguably his best piece. That LP was issued in 1980, the same year that he represented the UK at the first Poetry Olympics, which took place at Poets Corner, Westminster Abbey. JCC has had books of his poetry published, has toured extensively and has appeared in the film *"Urgh a music war"*. Both his appearance - dark, untidy hair, dark spectacles, surprisingly sober jacket, collar and tie - and his voice - a slightly overstated Mancunian drawl - are distinctive. He remains an active cult figure. His lacklustre record sales demonstrate that his poetry is best appreciated live, in all its no hold barred, 100mph glory. (Bob Macdonald 85)

Punk poet. First a Bob Dylan clone, then a fixture on the Manchester punk scene, supporting local groups such as the Buzzcocks and the Fall, reading his work at frantically high speed. He appeared at the Poetry Olympics in 1980, held at Poet's Corner in Westminster Abbey. Poems on record had musical backing produced by Martin Hannett and featuring the Invisible Girls. *Psycle sluts* was his first record in 1977; he later recorded for Epic. He toured with Linto Kwesi Johnson in 1983; the tour film documentary *100 years in an open neck shirt* is also the title of a collection in book form. (Donald Clarke, April 1989).

GIMMIX! PLAY LOUD
Tracks: / Gimmix! play loud.
7" Single: Released Mar '79, on Epic, by CBS Records. Deleted Mar '82. Catalogue no: **EPC 7009**

PSYCLE SLUTS
Tracks: / Psycle sluts.
7" Single: Released Sep '82, on Rabid, by Rabid Records. Catalogue no: **TOSH 103**

Clarke, Johnny

APPLE OF MY EYE
Tracks: / Apple of my eye.
12" Single: Released Nov '84, on Hi Power, Catalogue no: **HP 003**

DO I DO I
Tracks: / Do I do I.
12" Single: Released Feb '83, on Ariwa Sounds, by Ariwa Sounds. Catalogue no: **ARI 1016**

GIVE ME LOVE
Tracks: / Give me love.
12" Single: Released Jul '82, on Cha-Cha, by Cha-Cha Records. Catalogue no: **CHAD 49**

GIVE ME YOUR LOVING
Tracks: / Give me your loving.
12" Single: Released Jun '88, on Starlight, Catalogue no: **SLD 550**

GOT TO BE STRONG
Tracks: / Got to be strong / Babylon.
12" Single: Released Mar '84, on Jah Shaka, Catalogue no: **SHAKA 842**

GUIDANCE
Tracks: / Guidance / Protection.
12" Single: Released Jul '82, on Red Nail, Catalogue no: **RN 0039**

HE'S A WALLY
Tracks: / He's a wally.
7" Single: Released Sep '82, on President, by President Records. Catalogue no: **PT 509**

I MAN COME AGAIN
Tracks: / I man come again / Give yourself a try.
12" Single: Released 27 Feb '88, on World Enterprise, Catalogue no: **WED 56**

LOVE WILL FIND A WAY
Tracks: / Love will find a way.
12" Single: Released Dec '83, on Fashion, by Fashion Records. Catalogue no: **FAD 018**

ROCKING TO THE A CLASS CHAMPIONS
Tracks: / Rocking to the A class champions / Dance hall champions.
Cassingle: Released Oct '83, on Subway Organisation, Catalogue no: **HB 005**
12" Single: Released Nov '82, on Fashion, by Fashion Records. Catalogue no: **FAD 012**

ROSIE
Tracks: / Rosie.
12" Single: Released Oct '89, on Jah Shaka, Catalogue no: **SHAKA 876**

RUDE BOY
Tracks: / Rude boy.
12" Single: Released Feb '82, on Art & Craft, Catalogue no: **ACD 15**

SWEET SENSATION
Tracks: / Sweet sensation.
12" Single: Released Aug '85, on Top Rank (2), Catalogue no: **TRK 013**

TAKE HEED
Tracks: / Take heed.
12" Single: Released Aug '82, on Black Joy, Catalogue no: **DH 819**

THANK YOU FOR THE MANY THINGS YOU'VE DONE
Tracks: / Thank you for the many things you've done / Babylon.
7" Single: Released Jan '81, on Chrysalis, by Chrysalis Records. Deleted Jan '84. Catalogue no: **CHS 2489**

TOO MUCH WAR
Tracks: / Too much war / Stop them jah.
12" Single: Released Jul '82, on Black Joy, Catalogue no: **DH 822**

YOU BETTER TRY
Tracks: / You better try.
12" Single: Released Apr '82, on Art & Craft, Catalogue no: **ACD 18**

YOU BRING ME JOY
Tracks: / You bring me joy.
12" Single: Released May '85, on Success (2), Catalogue no: **SUCCESS 180**

Clarke, Kim

SURRENDER
Tracks: / Surrender / Long time.
7" Single: Released May '80, on CBS, by CBS Records. Deleted May '83. Catalogue no: **CBS 8524**

Clarke, Rhonda

STATE OF ATTRACTION (IMPORT)
Tracks: / State of attraction.
12" Single: Released Oct '89, on UNKNOWN, Catalogue no: **4Z9 68842**

Clarke, Rick

GET BUSY
Tracks: / Get busy.
7" Single: Released Aug '88, on Wa Records, Catalogue no: **WA 2**
12" Single: Released Aug '88, on Wa Records, Catalogue no: **WAT 2**
12" Single: Released Sep '88, on Wa Records, Catalogue no: **WATR 2**

GROOVIN' ON A BASSLINE
Tracks: / Groovin' on a bassline.
12" Single: Released Sep '89, on W.A., Catalogue no: **WAT 4**

I REALLY WANT TO BE WITH YOU
Tracks: / I really want to be with you / I've been watching you.
12" Single: Released 13 Jun '87, on RCA, by BMG Records (UK). Deleted Aug '89. Catalogue no: **PT 41332**
7" Single: Released 13 Jun '87, on RCA, by BMG Records (UK). Catalogue no: **PB 41331**

IF YOU THINK YOU'RE IN LOVE
Tracks: / If you think you're in love.
12" Single: Released Dec '88, on Wa Records, Catalogue no: **WAT 3**
7" Single: Released Dec '88, on W.A., Catalogue no: **WA 3**

I'LL SEE YOU ALONG
Tracks: / I'll see you along.
12" Single: Released Apr '88, on W.A., Catalogue no: **WAT 1**

LOOKING OUT FOR YOU
Tracks: / Looking out for you.
7" Single: Released Aug '87, on RCA, by BMG Records (UK). Deleted May '89. Catalogue no: **PB 41497**
12" Single: Released Aug '87, on RCA, by BMG Records (UK). Catalogue no: **PT 41498**

LOVE WITH A STRANGER
Tracks: / Love with a stranger.
12" Single: Released Oct '85, on Local, Catalogue no: **LR 11**

PERFECT LADY
Tracks: / Perfect lady / Looking out for you.
7" Single: Released Oct '87, on RCA, by BMG Records (UK). Deleted May '89. Catalogue no: **PB 41497R**
7" Single: Released Oct '87, on RCA, by BMG Records (UK). Catalogue no: **PT 41498R**

Clarke, Robin

YOU PULL ME AROUND
Tracks: / You pull me around.
7" Single: Released Jun '84, on Blue Train, Catalogue no: **COACH 2**

Clarke, Sharon Dee

DANCE YOUR WAY OUT OF THE DOOR
Tracks: / Dance your way out of the door (dub mix) / Dance your way out of the door.
12" Single: Released Oct '86, on Arista, by BMG Records (UK). Catalogue no: **ARIST 12682**
7" Single: Released Oct '86, on Arista, by BMG Records (UK). Catalogue no: **ARIST 682**

HE'S COMING BACK
Tracks: / He's coming back (inst. mix) / He's coming back (7" mix).
12" Single: Released Mar '87, on Debut, by Skratch Records. Catalogue no: **DEBTX 3017**

SOMETHING SPECIAL
Tracks: / Something special / Something special (version).
12" Single: Released Mar '89, on Urban, by Polydor Ltd. Deleted Oct '89. Catalogue no: **URBX 31**
7" Single: Released Mar '89, on Urban, by Polydor Ltd. Deleted Oct '89. Catalogue no: **URB 31**
12" Single: Released Apr '89, on Urban, by Polydor Ltd. Deleted Oct '89. Catalogue no: **URBA 31**

Clarke, Stanley

Biographical details: This American bass guitarist, vocalist and producer, born in Philadelphia in June 1951, is at the forefront of jazz funk music. Clarke, who is a classically trained musician, began his move up the jazz ladder when he moved to New York in 1970. He spent the first half of the seventies in various bands, most notably with Chick Corea in group called Return To Forever, and also played with such well known names as Aretha Franklin and Carlos Santana. His debut eponymous album was issued in '74, and was followed by a further four solo LPs by the end of the seventies. 1980 brought Clarke his first British chart LP when *"Rocks, pebbles and sand"* reached no.42. The following year he teamed with fellow jazz funk fusionist George Duke for an album that was logically titled *"The Clarke/Duke project"*; this LP yielded the US top 20 single *"Sweet baby"*. Clarke's only taste of singles success. Typically for an artist of his genre, he puts musicanship before commercial dictates, and is content to serve his specialist market without moving over to the potentially big record sales of the broader pop audience. He is an innovative bassist, successfully projecting this instrument from an upfront position in preference to its conventional background role. (Bob Macdonald 85)

Bornin Philadelphia in 1951, the bassist and composer is one of those who can use both acoustic and electric bass, knowing the difference. Early rock experience in the late '60's was followed by gigs with Horace Silver, Joe Henderson, Pharoah Sanders and Stan Getz, then with Chick Corea's fusion group *Return to forever*.He also played some violin and cello. His own albums have charted in the USA and he is also part of the Clarke/Duke Project with pianist/composer George Duke. Influential in both jazz and rock, he also played with Jeff Beck, the New Barbarians (a Rolling Stones spin-off), and made a funk cover of Bruce Springstreen's *Born in the USA). (Donald Clarke, April 1989).*

HEAVEN SENT YOU
Tracks: / Heaven sent you.
7" Single: Released Jun '84, on Epic, by CBS Records. Catalogue no: **A 4493**

SWEET BABY
Tracks: / Sweet baby / Never judge a cover by it's book.
7" Single: Released Apr '81, on Epic, by CBS Records. Deleted Apr '86. Catalogue no: **EPC A 1123**

YOU/ME TOGETHER
Tracks: / You/me together / Rocks, pebbles and sand.
7" Single: Released Aug '80, on Epic, by CBS Records. Deleted '82. Catalogue no: **EPC 8945**

Clarke, Vince

Biographical details: Born in 1961 in Basildon, the composer and synth-studio wizard was a founder member of Depeche Mode, for whom he wrote hits but left at the height of their success. He next recruited Alison 'Alf' Moyet through a trade paper advert, named the duo Yazoo (Yaz in the USA where the Yazoo label stupidly complained about the compliment). The combination of an electronic whizz kid with melodic talent (who named Simon & Garfunkel as a favourite) and a fine girl singer steeped in jazz and blues made hit LP's *Upstairs at Eric's* named after producer, E.C. (Eric) Radcliffe, and *You and me both* in 1982-83; the first album included *Only you*, which was covered by the Flying Pickets for a UK No.1 in 1983, and also by Judy Collins, Rita Coolidge and even Richard Clayderman. He hated live work and kept a low profile. He worked with Radcliffe in the occasional group The Assembly, whose single *Never never* was a top five hit in 1983 featuring vocalist Feargal Sharkey. He produced records by the London group 'Absolute' and has band Erasure with Andy Bell. (Donald Clarke, April 1988).

ONE DAY
Tracks: / One day.
7" Single: Released Jun '85, on Mute, by Mute Records. Catalogue no: **TAG 1**
12" Single: Released Jun '85, on Mute, by Mute Records. Catalogue no: **12 TAG 1**

Clarke, Vivineo

KISS ME ONCE MORE
Tracks: / Kiss me once more.
12" Single: Released Nov '88, on Legal Lights, by Legal Light Records. Catalogue no: **LLQ 30**

Clarke, Winston

LADY YOU ARE
Tracks: / Lady you are.
12" Single: Released Sep '84, on Sir George, Catalogue no: **SG 017T**

YOUR LOVE
Tracks: / Your love.
12" Single: Released Apr '84, on Sir George, Catalogue no: **SG 007T**

Clash

Biographical details: At the time of their greatest success, this British rock group comprised Nicky 'Topper' Headon, Mick Jones, Paul Simonon and Joe Strummer. The Clash were formed in May 1976 in a squat in Shepherd's Bush, London. The founder members were Jones, Simonon, Strummer and Keith Levine; the latter quickly departed (and two years later became a founder member of John Lydon's Public Image Ltd). The first regular line up was completed by Terry Chimes. The quartet played hard hitting rock and, within months, were one of the most talked about bands in Britain's growing grass roots punk movement. In late '76 the Sex Pistols made a notorious appearance on the Bill Grundy TV show, resulting in massive publicity for this new anarchic music. The new wave explosion was on, and Britain's major record companies rushed to sign up it's leading protoagonists. The Clash joined CBS Records, and cries of sell out amongst some of the band's most loyal fans were rapidly forgotten when the first records were released. Their debut eponymous album reached no.12 on the UK charts and enjoyed a healthy run. Simultaneously they embarked on a series of dates that was dubbed the "White riot tour", with the Buzzcocks as support act. Both album and tour was historic events in terms of their influence upon the punk scene. By the end of '77 the Clash could clearly be seen as one of the five most important punk pioneers, with the Pistols, the Buzzcocks, the Damned and the Jam. Their debut single "White riot" and its follow up "Remote control" were instant classics. At the height of this frenzy, drummer Terry Chimes, disillusioned with the harsh trappings of punk, was replaced by Topper Headon. The

Clash continued to issue excellent singles and albums and survived longer than most of their peers. As the seventies gave way to the eighties, they began to make headway in the US, while cleverly avoiding losing their credibility amongst their UK fans.
This was typical of the tightrope that the group successfully walked as their career developed - diversifying their music and broadening their audience without losing sight of their original ideals; most critics agree that they never sold out.
By the end of 1982, the band had achieved 16 British hit singles without ever reaching the top 10 - a unique statistic in UK chart history, and one which demonstrates that they never been fully accepted by the pop establishment, and would still have to struggle to get their records on daytime radio.
Their nearest shots were "London calling" (no.11, 1980) and the reggae flavoured "Bankrobber" (no.12, 1980). In early '83, however, the group managed one top 10 outing in the States with "Rock the Casbah", the Clash's one off bow to danceability.
Arrests, fines, drugs and various other mishaps had fuelled the band's controversial image since their formation but, by the mid-eighties, a catalogue of personnel changes were replacing those events in the headlines.
Drummer Topper Headon was replaced by a returning Terry Chimes, who was later replaced by Peter Howard. Amusingly, vocalist Joe Strummer disappeared for a short period, just before a new album and tour. When located in Paris, he explained that he needed a rest.
(Bob Mcadonald 1985)
A punk band formed in 1976: Joe Strummer and Mick Jones on guitars and vocals, Paul Simonon on bass and Terry Chimes (Tory Crimes) on drums, replaced by Nicky 'Topper' Headon after their first three albums. Strummer's real name is John Mellors; he got his nickname busking with a ukulele.
They were figureheads of the UK punk explosion, one of the few bands to capture punk's aggressive, vitriolic energy on record, outclassing and outlasting the Sex Pistols and the rest.
From the beginning they could o savagely convincing white man's reggae. They were accused of selling out with Give em enough rope which was produced by American Sandy Pearlman at CBS's request; many regard their two disc *London calling* as their best. Legendary USA rock writer Lester Bangs toured with them in England and wrote that the English Punks were actually an incredibly polite crowd. USA tours left UK fans feeling that they were watching the Rolling Stones Mark II, but Clash went out of their way to introduce audiences to their own heroes: Bo Diddley, Mikey Dread, renegade country star Joe Ely. Headon wrote *Rock the casbah*, a big USA hit, and had become a heroin addict; there were some personnel changes and they split after *Cut the crap*
. (Donald Clarke, April 1989)I.

BANKROBBER
Tracks: / Bankrobber / Rockers galore.
7" Single: Released Sep '80, on CBS, by CBS Records. Deleted Sep '83. Catalogue no: **CBS 8323**

CALL UP, THE
Tracks: / Call up, The / Stop the world.
7" Single: Released Dec '80, on CBS, by CBS Records. Deleted Dec '83. Catalogue no: **CBS 9339**

CLASH
Tracks: / Complete control / London calling / Bank robber / Clash City Rockers.
Cassingle: Released Dec '82, on CBS, by CBS Records. Deleted Dec '85. Catalogue no: **A40-2907**

CLASH CITY ROCKERS
Tracks: / Clash city rockers.
7" Single: Released Mar '78, on CBS, by CBS Records. Deleted Mar '81. Catalogue no: **CBS 5834**

COMPLETE CONTROL
Tracks: / Complete control.
7" Single: Released Oct '77, on CBS, by CBS Records. Deleted Oct '80. Catalogue no: **CBS 5664**

COST OF LIVING, THE
Tracks: / I fought the law / Groovy times / Gates of the west / Capital radio.
7" EP: Released May '79, on CBS, by CBS Records. Deleted May '82. Catalogue no: **CBS 7324**

ENGLISH CIVIL WAR (JOHNNY COMES MARCHING HOME)
Tracks: / English civil war.
7" Single: Released Mar '79, on CBS, by CBS Records. Deleted Mar '82. Catalogue no: **CBS 7082**

HITSVILLE UK
Tracks: / Hitsville UK / Radio One.
7" Single: Released Jan '81, on CBS, by CBS Records. Deleted Jan '84. Catalogue no: **CBS 9480**

I FOUGHT THE LAW
Tracks: / I fought the law / City of the dead / Police on my back (Track on 12" and CD.) / 48 hours (Track on 12" and CD.) / 1977 (Track on 7".).
CD 5": Released Feb '88, on CBS, by CBS Records. Deleted Jan '89. Catalogue no: **CLASH C1**
12" Single: Released Feb '88, on CBS, by CBS Records. Deleted Aug '88. Catalogue no: **CLASH T1**
7" Single: Released Feb '88, on CBS, by CBS Records. Deleted Aug '88. Catalogue no: **CLASH 1**

IN HAMMERSMITH PALAIS (WHITE MAN)
Tracks: / In Hammersmith Palais (white man).
7" Single: Released Jun '78, on CBS, by CBS Records. Deleted Jun '81. Catalogue no: **CBS 6383**

KNOW YOUR RIGHTS
Tracks: / Know your rights / First night back in London.
7" Single: Released May '82, on CBS, by CBS Records. Deleted May '85. Catalogue no: **A 2309**

LONDON CALLING (SINGLE)
Tracks: / London calling / Brand new cadillac / Rudie can't fail / Street parade, The*.
Note: * extra track on 12" version.
CD 5": Released Apr '88, on CBS, by CBS Records. Deleted Jan '89. Catalogue no: **CLASH C2**
7" Single: Released Dec '79, on CBS, by CBS Records. Deleted Dec '82. Catalogue no: **CBS 8087**
7" Single: Released Apr '88, on CBS, by CBS Records. Deleted Jan '89. Catalogue no: **CLASH 2**
7" Single: Released Apr '88, on CBS, by CBS Records. Deleted Jan '89. Catalogue no: **CLASHB 2**
12" Single: Released Apr '88, on CBS, by CBS Records. Deleted Jan '89. Catalogue no: **CLASH T2**

MAGNIFICENT SEVEN, THE
Tracks: / Magnificent seven, The / Magnificent dance, The.
12" Single: Released Apr '81, on CBS, by CBS Records. Deleted Apr '84. Catalogue no: **A 12 1133**
7" Single: Released Apr '81, on CBS, by CBS Records. Deleted Apr '84. Catalogue no: **CBS 1133**

ROCK THE CASBAH
Tracks: / Rock the casbah / Long time jerk.
7" Single: Released Jun '82, on CBS, by CBS Records. Deleted Jun '85. Catalogue no: **A 2479**

ROCK THE CASBAH (IMPORT)
Tracks: / Rock the Casbah / Mustapha dance.
12" Single: Released Oct '88, on Epic (USA), by CBS Records (USA). Catalogue no: **49H 07829**

SHOULD I STAY OR SHOULD I GO
Tracks: / Should I stay or should I go / Straight to hell.
7" Single: Released Sep '82, on CBS, by CBS Records. Deleted Sep '85. Catalogue no: **A 2646**
7" Pic: Released Sep '82, on CBS, by CBS Records. Deleted Sep '85. Catalogue no: **A 112646**

THIS IS ENGLAND
Tracks: / This is England.
7" Single: Released Oct '85, on CBS, by CBS Records. Deleted Oct '88. Catalogue no: **A 6122**

THIS IS RADIO CLASH
Tracks: / This is radio clash / Radio clash.
7" Single: Released Jun '82, on CBS, by CBS Records. Deleted Jun '85. Catalogue no: **A 2429**
7" Single: Released Nov '81, on CBS, by CBS Records. Deleted Nov '84. Catalogue no: **A 1797**
CD 3": Released Dec '88, on CBS (Holland), by CBS Records. Catalogue no: **6516533**

TOMMY GUN
Tracks: / Tommy Gun.
7" Single: Released Dec '78, on CBS, by CBS Records. Deleted Dec '81. Catalogue no: **CBS 6788**

WHITE RIOT
Tracks: / White riot.
7" Single: Released Apr '77, on CBS, by CBS Records. Deleted Apr '80. Catalogue no: **CBS 5058**

Class

WINNER, THE
Tracks: / Winner, The.
12" Single: Released Jul '82, on CS, Catalogue no: **CSD 001**

Class 50

WRITING'S ON THE WALL
Tracks: / Writing on the wall.
7" Single: Released Jul '85, on Infrared (UK), by Infrared Records. Catalogue no: **IFR 104**

Class Action

WEEKEND
Tracks: / Weekend.
7" Single: Released Aug '85, on Jive, by Zomba Records. Catalogue no: **JIVE 35**
12" Single: Released Aug '85, on Jive, by Zomba Records. Catalogue no: **JIVET 35**

Class Fifty

LIVING APART (UNDER THE SAME ROOF)
Tracks: / Living apart (under the same roof) / Last chance.
7" Single: Released Mar '87, on Infrared (UK), by Infrared Records. Catalogue no: **IFR 105**

OH, WHAT A LIFE
Tracks: / Oh, what a life.
7" Single: Released Oct '84, on Infrared (UK), by Infrared Records. Catalogue no: **IFR 103**

Class Of ...

BIRTH OF ROCK'N'ROLL
Tracks: / Rock 'n' roll (fais-do-do).
7" Single: Released Jun '86, on Smash (USA), by PolyGram Rec.Inc.(USA). Deleted '87. Catalogue no: **US 1**
12" Single: Released Jun '86, on Smash (USA), by PolyGram Rec.Inc.(USA). Deleted '87. Catalogue no: **US 112**

Class War

BETTER DEAD THAN WED
Tracks: / Better dead than wed.
7" Single: Released Jul '86, on Mortarhate, by Mortarhate Records. Catalogue no: **MORT 000**

Classic

ARMAGEDDON ROCK
Tracks: / Armageddon rock / Cast your bread.
7" Single: Released Aug '80, on Sound Off, Deleted Aug '83. Catalogue no: **SOFD 009**
12" Single: Released Aug '80, on Sound Off, Catalogue no: **SOFD 009**

Classic Aid

VA PENSIERO
Tracks: / Va pensiero / Pace, pace mio dio.
Note: British Airways TV commercial theme.
7" Single: Released Feb '88, on CBS, by CBS Records. Catalogue no: **651 422 7**

Classic Black

END OF THE LINE
Tracks: / End of the line.
7" Single: Released Jun '82, on Classic Roots, Catalogue no: **CBR 003**

SUNSHINE STREET
Tracks: / Sunshine street.
12" Single: Released Sep '82, on Classic Roots, Catalogue no: **CBR 005**

WHAT IS LIFE
Tracks: / What is life.
12" Single: Released Jan '83, on Classic Black, Catalogue no: **CBR 007**

Classic Rock

WE DON'T NEED ANOTHER HERO
Tracks: / We don't need another hero / You can call me Al / We don't need another hero.
7" Single: Released Oct '87, on CBS, by CBS Records. Catalogue no: **C ROCK 1**

Classic Tracks

CLASSIC TRACKS
CD 5": Released Nov '88, on Classic Tracks, Catalogue no: **CDEP 6**

Classical Two

NEW GENERATION
Tracks: / New generation / Freak dog (She's a).
12" Single: Released 20 Jun '87, on Jive, by Zomba Records. Catalogue no: **JIVET 148**

Classics

AUDIO AUDIO
Tracks: / Audio audio / Carscapes.
7" Single: Released Apr '80, on Rocket, by Rocket Records. Deleted '83. Catalogue no: **XPRES 29**

Classics IV

SPOOKY
Tracks: / Spooky.
7" Single: Released Feb '68, on Liberty, by EMI Records. Deleted Feb '71. Catalogue no: **LBS 15051**

Classified Info

DRUG CALLED LOVE
Tracks: / Drug called love.
7" Single: Released Jul '84, on Dead Dog, by Dead Dog Records. Deleted '86. Catalogue no: **DOG 2**

Classix Nouveaux

Biographical details: Classix Nouveaux were formed in the late Seventies and gained attention in early 1981 when the New Romantic movement was at its height - but the group denied that they were part of this new British fashion/music scene.
They hit No. 43 on the UK charts with *Guilty* and, by the end of '82, had achieved a further six chart singles. However, only *It Is A Dream* (No. 11) gained major hit status.
The others all fell short of the Top 40, as did the *Night People* and *La Verite* albums. It was in other nations that the band found sustained success: they were the first Western rock band to play in Sri Lanka and also visited such diverse territories as India, Portugal and Yugoslavia.
They went behind the Iron Curtain and toured Hungary and Czechoslovakia. Particularly noteworthy has been the group's penetration of Poland: by 1985 they became the first western act to be allowed to tour there three times; and their Polish fan club has no less than 10,000 members.
Classix are dominated by their lead vocalist Sal Solo (who single-handedly wrote and produced *It Is A Dream*).
After years of absence from UK chart action he temporarily broke away from his group and scored his first solo (please pardon the pun) hit with *San Damiano (heart and soul)*. Sal Solo, whose head is forever totally shaven, reached No. 15 in Britain with this religious recordon which he was backed by a boys' choir. Needless to say, it reached No. 1 in Poland.
(Bob MacDonald)..

BECAUSE YOU'RE YOUNG
Tracks: / Because you're young.
7" Single: Released May '82, on Liberty, by EMI Records. Deleted May '85. Catalogue no: **BP 411**

END OR THE BEGINNING
Tracks: / End or the beginning.
7" Pic: Released Oct '82, on Liberty, by EMI Records. Catalogue no: **BPP 414**
7" Single: Released Oct '82, on Liberty, by EMI Records. Catalogue no: **BP 414**
12" Single: Released Oct '82, on Liberty, by EMI Records. Catalogue no: **12BP 414**

FOREVER AND A DAY
Tracks: / Forever and a day.
7" Single: Released Aug '83, on Liberty, by EMI Records. Catalogue no: **BP 419**
12" Single: Released Aug '83, on Liberty, by EMI Records. Catalogue no: **12BP 419**

GUILTY
Tracks: / Guilty / Night people.
7" Single: Released Feb '81, on Liberty, by EMI Records. Deleted Feb '84. Catalogue no: **BP 388**
12" Single: Released Feb '81, on Liberty, by EMI Records. Deleted Feb '84. Catalogue no: **12 BP 388**

INSIDE OUTSIDE
Tracks: / Inside outside.
7" Single: Released Aug '81, on Liberty, by EMI Records. Deleted Aug '84. Catalogue no: **BP 403**

IS IT A DREAM?
Tracks: / Is it a dream? / Where to go.
7" Single: Released Mar '82, on Liberty, by EMI Records. Deleted Mar '85. Catalogue no: **BP 409**
12" Single: Released Mar '82, on Liberty, by EMI Records. Deleted Mar '85. Catalogue no: **12BP 409**

NASTY LITTLE GREEN MEN
Tracks: / Nasty little green men / Test tu babies.
7" Single: Released Nov '80, on Liberty (USA), by EMI Records. Deleted Nov '8 Catalogue no: **BP 378**

NEVER AGAIN (THE DAYS TIM ERASED)
Tracks: / Never again (the days ti passed).
7" Single: Released Nov '81, on Liberty, EMI Records. Deleted Nov '84. Catalog

no: **BP 406**

NEVER NEVER COMES
Tracks: / Never never comes.
7" Single: Released Nov '83, on Liberty, by EMI Records. Catalogue no: **BP 421**
12" Single: Released Nov '83, on Liberty, by EMI Records. Catalogue no: **12BP 421**

ROBOT DANCE
Tracks: / Robot dance / 623.
7" Single: Released Aug '80, on ESP, by ESP Records. Deleted '83. Catalogue no: **ES 1**

TOKYO
Tracks: / Tokyo / Old world for sale.
7" Single: Released May '81, on Liberty, by EMI Records. Deleted May '84. Catalogue no: **BP 397**

Claudette

MINOR ON
Tracks: / That's what I like / Minor on.
7" Single: Released Oct '86, on Play, by Play Records. Catalogue no: **PLAY 211**

Claudia

DON'T GIVE UP YOUR LOVE
Tracks: / Don't give up your love.
7" Single: Released Nov '84, on Rhythmic, by Rhythmic Records. Catalogue no: **7RMIC 5**
12" Single: Released Nov '84, on Rhythmic, by Rhythmic Records. Catalogue no: **RMIC 5**

HOLD ON
Tracks: / Hold on.
7" Single: Released Jul '85, on Rhythmic, by Rhythmic Records. Catalogue no: **7RMIC 9**
12" Single: Released Jul '85, on Rhythmic, by Rhythmic Records. Catalogue no: **RMIC 9**

Clay, Judy

PRIVATE NUMBER
Tracks: / Private number / Love-eye-tis.
7" Single: Released Nov '68, on Stax, by Fantasy Inc (USA). Deleted Nov '71. Catalogue no: **STAX 101**
7" Single: Released Sep '85, on Old Gold, by Old Gold Records. Catalogue no: **OG 9532**
7" Single: Released 13 Jun '87, on Stax, by Fantasy Inc (USA). Catalogue no: **STAX 801**

Clay, Otis

LOVE BANDIT
Tracks: / Love bandit.
12" Single: Released Jul '84, on Pinnacle, by Pinnacle Records. Catalogue no: **PIN 105T**

Clay People

SAY WHAT YOU WILL EP
Tracks: / Wreaths and seashells / Hectic babble / Too much talking / Crazy fools.
12" Single: Released May '88, on Hectic, Catalogue no: **HEC 1EP**

Clay, Tiggi

WINNER GETS THE HEART
Tracks: / Winner gets the heart, The / Who shot Zorro.
7" Single: on Motown, by BMG Records (UK). Catalogue no: **TMG 1333**

Clay, Tom

WHAT THE WORLD NEEDS NOW
Tracks: / What the world needs now is love.
7" Single: Released Oct '81, on Mowest, by Motown Records (UK). Catalogue no: **MW 3013**

Clayderman, Richard

Biographical details: This French pianist sold 27 million albums in forty countries before breaking in the British market. That UK breakthrough came in late 1982 when his record company, encouraged by the recent British success of Spanish singer Julio Iglesias, launched a heavy marketing campaign for Clayderman. Over the following two years, he became an album chart regular and sold well over a million LPs. One of the few French stars to successfully break out of his country's insular music business, Clayderman's good looks and gentle piano style have charmed housewives all over the globe into buying his albums. His repertoire combines classical and popular standards with strong originals. The most notable tune from the latter catergory is *"Ballad for Adeline"*, which has become his theme number, this typifies the Clayderman technique for surrounding his relaxing piano sound with soothing strings. (Bob Macdonald 85)
Born Phillipe Pages in Paris in 1954, the pretty blonde pianist does decorated versions of light classics and pop songs and will leave no mark whatsoever on the history of music, but his TV and supermarket-promoted albums make money. He won first prize at the Paris Conservatory of Music at 16 and abandoned classical music to accompany Johnny Halliday; his first hit was *Ballade Pour Adeline*, written by producer Paul De Sunneville for his daughter; sold millions world wide. He began touring internationally in 1978 and sold nearly 3,000,000 albums in France alone in 1980. In South Africa in May 1981 four out of the five top albums were his; he broke into the UK market with sell out concerts in 1982. (Donald Clarke, April 1989).

BALLAD FOR ADELINE
Tracks: / Ballad for Adeline / Silent night / Christmas medley.
Note: This is the Christmas 1982 single, not to be confused with the other recordings (At least three albums and one single with the same title in French).
7" Single: Released Nov '82, on Delphine, by Decca Records. Catalogue no: **RC 101**

BALLADE POUR ADELINE (SINGLE)
Tracks: / Ballade pour Adeline / Walk in the woods.
Note: This is the Safari/Sonet single, not to be confused with the Delphine (Christmas1982) single (called Ballad for Adeline) or any of the eponymous albums.
7" Single: Released '79, on Safari, by Safari Records. Catalogue no: **SAFE 5**
7" Single: Released Jan '81, on Sonet, by Sonet Records. Catalogue no: **SON 2219**

BRETTS, THEME FROM
Tracks: / Bretts, Theme from / Eastenders, Theme from.
7" Single: Released Nov '87, on Decca, by Decca Records. Deleted '88. Catalogue no: **RC 110**

FEELINGS
Tracks: / Feelings.
7" Single: Released Sep '83, on Delphine, by Decca Records. Catalogue no: **RC 102**

LADY DI
Tracks: / Lady Di.
7" Single: Released Nov '83, on Delphine, by Decca Records. Catalogue no: **RC 103**

Clayson, Alan

LAST RESPECTS
Tracks: / Last respects.
7" Single: Released Dec '82, on Racket Manufacture, Catalogue no: **ARG 36**

Clayton, Lee

DREAM GOES ON
Tracks: / Dream goes on / Saturday night special.
7" Single: Released May '81, on Capitol, by EMI Records. Deleted May '84. Catalogue no: **CL 16195**

I LOVE YOU
Tracks: / I love you / Wind and rain.
7" Single: Released Jan '80, on Capitol, by EMI Records. Deleted Jan '85. Catalogue no: **CL 16108**

OH HOW LUCKY I AM
Tracks: / Oh how lucky I am / Won'y you give me one more chance.
7" Single: Released Apr '81, on Capitol, by EMI Records. Deleted '85. Catalogue no: **CL 16193**

Clayton, Merry

WHEN THE WORLD TURNS BLUE
Tracks: / When the world turns blue / Let me make you cry a little longer.
7" Single: Released Mar '80, on MCA, by MCA Records. Deleted '83. Catalogue no: **MCA 571**

YES
Tracks: / Yes / Five satins / In the still of the night.
Note: **From the Dirty Dancing soundtrack album.**
7" Single: Released Apr '88, on RCA, by BMG Records (UK). Deleted May '89. Catalogue no: **PB 49563**
12" Single: Released Apr '88, on RCA, by BMG Records (UK). Deleted May '89. Catalogue no: **PT 49564**

Claytown Troupe

HEY LORD
Tracks: / Hey Lord (7" version) (On 7" and CD only) / Hey Lord (12" version) (On 12" and CD only) / Night is ours.
CD 5": Released Aug '89, on Island, by Island Records. Catalogue no: **CID 428**
7" Single: Released Jul '89, on Island, by Island Records. Catalogue no: **IS 428**
12" Single: Released Jul '89, on Island, by Island Records. Catalogue no: **12 IS 428**

PRAYER
Tracks: / Prayer / Alabama / Chiricahau sun.
CD 5": Released 18 Apr '89, on Island, by Island Records. Catalogue no: **CID 417**
Cassingle: Released 18 Apr '89, on Island, by Island Records. Catalogue no: **CIS 417**
7" Single: Released Jun '89, on Island, by Island Records. Catalogue no: **ISS 417**
7" Single: Released 18 Apr '89, on Island, by Island Records. Catalogue no: **IS 417**
12" Single: Released 18 Apr '89, on Island, by Island Records. Catalogue no: **12 IS 417**

Clean

IN'N'NER LIVE
Tracks: / In'n'ner live.
12" Single: Released Apr '89, on Flying Nun, Catalogue no: **FNE 029**

Clean Looking Boys

SENT TO COVENTRY
Tracks: / Sent to Coventry.
7" Single: Released Oct '83, on DJM, Catalogue no: **DJW 001**

Cleaners From Venus

ILLYA KURYAKIN LOOKED AT ME
Tracks: / Illya Kuryakin looked at me.
12" Single: Released Mar '87, on Ammunition, Catalogue no: **JANGLE 1T**

LIVING WITH VICTORIA GREY
Tracks: / Living with Victoria Grey.
12" Single: Released 13 Jun '87, on Ammunition, Catalogue no: **JANGLE 2T**

Clear Cut

EAGLE EYE
Tracks: / Eagle eye / Sick and tired.
7" Single: Released Aug '81, on Recorded Delivery, Deleted '84. Catalogue no: **RDR 002**

Clegg, Johnny

Biographical details: The singer, songwriter and guitarist was born in Rochdale in 1953, lived in what is now Zimbabwe and went to South Africa at age six, where he began learning Zulu guitar and language at 14. At 16 he met street musician Sipho Mchunu, a former goatherd who'd learned to play on a home-made instrument; they played at parties and clubs, sang in Zulu and English and formed Juluka which means 'sweat' and refers to the kinds of work most people have to do for a living. Their records were international hits, with a folk-rock heat, Zulu harmonies and heart rending lyrics; they toured Europe in 1982-83, but as if having their records banned a thome wasn't enough, single-issue fanatics like the UK musicians Union also tried to ban them. Siphu gave up and Clegg formed Savuka ('we have awakened'), which plays a harder, more electric blend of Mbaqanga/township jive with international rock, all songs written or co written by Clegg including a remake of *Scatterlings of Africa*. Percussionist Dudu Zulu and drummer Derek DeBeer were also in Juluka; the band also has Steve Mabuso on keyboards, Jabu Mabuso on bass, Keith Hutchinson on keyboards and saxophone. (Donald Clarke, April 1989) .

ASIMBONANGA (MANDELA)
Tracks: / Asimbonanga / Asimbonanga / Asimbonanga (radio version)* / Berlin wall / Scatterlings of Africa (ext. mix)+ / Giyana (live)+.
Note: * extra track on 12". + tracks on CD.
CD 5": Released Feb '88, on EMI, by EMI Records. Deleted Nov '88. Catalogue no: **CDEMI 5603**
7" Single: Released Jan '88, on EMI, by EMI Records. Deleted Nov '88. Catalogue no: **EMI 5603**
12" Single: Released Jan '88, on EMI, by EMI Records. Deleted Nov '88. Catalogue no: **12EMI 5603**

GREAT HEART
Tracks: / Great heart / African sky blue / Unfazi ondali.
7" Single: Released Jul '87, on EMI, by EMI Records. Deleted Oct '87. Catalogue no: **EM 10**
12" Single: Released Jul '87, on EMI, by EMI Records. Deleted Oct '87. Catalogue no: **12 EM 10**

GREAT HEART (EXT)
Tracks: / Great heart (ext) / African sky blue (live) / Umfazi undah (live) / Africa (live).
Cassingle: Released Jul '87, on EMI, by EMI Records. Deleted Oct '87. Catalogue no: **TC-EM 10**

I CALL YOUR NAME
Tracks: / I call your name / I call your name (Track on 12".) / Scatterlings of Africa (ext) (Track on 12".) / Shine a light.
CD 5": Released 11 Apr '88, on EMI, by EMI Records. Deleted Aug '89. Catalogue no: **CDEM 56**
7" Single: Released Apr '88, on EMI, by EMI Records. Deleted Nov '88. Catalogue no: **EM 56**
12" Single: Released Apr '88, on EMI, by EMI Records. Deleted Nov '88. Catalogue no: **12EM 56**

SCATTERLINGS OF AFRICA
Tracks: / Third world child / Scatterlings of Africa / Don't walk away.
CD 5": Released May '87, on EMI, by EMI Records. Catalogue no: **CDEMI 5605**
7" Single: Released Apr '87, on EMI, by EMI Records. Deleted Apr '88. Catalogue no: **EMI 5605**
12" Single: Released Apr '87, on EMI, by EMI Records. Deleted Apr '88. Catalogue no: **12EMI 5605**

TAKE MY HEART AWAY
Tracks: / Take my heart away (edit) (7" only.) / Scatterlings of Africa / Take my heart away (LP version) (12" & CD single only.) / Siyayilanda (The Love House dub) (12" & CD single only.) / Siyayilanda (12" African House mix) (12EMX 75 only.).
CD 5": Released Oct '88, on EMI, by EMI Records. Catalogue no: **CDEM 75**
7" Single: Released Oct '88, on EMI, by EMI Records. Deleted Jun '89. Catalogue no: **EM 75**
12" Single: Released Oct '88, on EMI, by EMI Records. Deleted Aug '89. Catalogue no: **12EMX 75**
12" Single: Released Oct '88, on EMI, by EMI Records. Deleted Jun '89. Catalogue no: **12EM 75**

BOOTS CLEMENTS - I CAN'T FIND ME (Released on West Records)

Clemence, Ray

SIDE BY SIDE
Tracks: / Side by side / We're gonna win again.
7" Single: Released Dec '80, on Polydor, by Polydor Ltd. Deleted Dec '85. Catalogue no: **POSP 206**

Clements, Boots

I CAN'T FIND ME (see panel on previous page)
Tracks: / I can't find me / I keep thinking about you everyday.
7" Single: Released '86, on West Records, Catalogue no: **W-718-A**

Clemmons, Angela

B.Y.O.B. (BRING YOUR OWN BABY)
Tracks: / B.Y.O.B. (Bring your own baby) / Nothing can stop my love / B.Y.O.B. (bring your own baby (ext. version) (Only on 12".).
7" Single: Released Nov '87, on Portrait, by CBS Records. Deleted Jun '88. Catalogue no: **BYOB 1**
12" Single: Released Nov '87, on Portrait, by CBS Records. Deleted Jun '88. Catalogue no: **BYOB T1**

Clemons, Clarence

YOU'RE A FRIEND OF MINE
Tracks: / Let the music say it / You're a friend of mine.
7" Single: Released Feb '86, on CBS, by CBS Records. Catalogue no: **A 6681**
12" Single: Released Feb '86, on CBS, by CBS Records. Catalogue no: **TA 6681**

Clerc, Julien

THERE IS NO DISTANCE (SINGLE)
Tracks: / There is no distance / Wine of words.
7" Single: Released Jun '87, on 10 Records, by Virgin Records. Deleted May '88. Catalogue no: **TEN 176**

Cleveland Watkiss

SPEND SOME TIME
Tracks: / Spend some time / Spend some time (version).
CD 5": Released Apr '89, on Urban, by Polydor Ltd. Catalogue no: **URBCD 40**
7" Single: Released Apr '89, on Urban, by Polydor Ltd. Catalogue no: **URB 40**
12" Single: Released Apr '89, on Urban, by Polydor Ltd. Catalogue no: **URBX 40**

Cliche

I KNOW YOUR GAME
Tracks: / I know your game / Drawing the line.
7" Single: Released Jan '80, on Carrere, Deleted '83. Catalogue no: **CAR 133**

Click

DIZZY SPINNIN' ROUND
Tracks: / Dizzy spinnin' round.
7" Single: Released Aug '83, on New World, by President Records. Catalogue no: **NEW 3**

FREQUENCY JAM (STRAIGHT TO THE PHREEK)
Tracks: / Frequency jam (straight to the phreek) / Frequency jam (version).
7" Single: Released 31 May '88, on Phonogram, by Phonogram Ltd. Deleted Oct '88. Catalogue no: **JAB 65**
12" Single: Released 31 May '88, on Phonogram, by Phonogram Ltd. Deleted Oct '88. Catalogue no: **JABX 65**

I CAN DO WITHOUT THAT - LOSING YOU
Tracks: / I can do without that losing you.
12" Single: Released Mar '89, on Pure, Catalogue no: **PURET 22**

JUST ANOTHER MONDAY
Tracks: / Just another Monday.
7" Single: Released Nov '83, on New World, by President Records. Catalogue no: **NEW 3**
12" Single: Released Nov '83, on New World, by President Records. Catalogue no: **NEW 3EP**

Click Click

I RAGE, I MELT
Tracks: / I rage, I melt.
CD 5": Released Aug '88, on Play It Again Sam(Belgium), by Play It Again Sam (Belgium). Catalogue no: **BIAS 079CD**
12" Single: Released Jan '88, on Play It Again Sam(Belgium), by Play It Again Sam (Belgium). Catalogue no: **BIAS 079**

RUN ME DOWN (EP)
Tracks: / Run me down.
7" Single: Released '82, on Lung Function, Catalogue no: **SIGH 001**

SKRIPGLOW
Tracks: / Skripglow / Sack / Rotor babe.
12" Single: Released Feb '87, on Rorschach Testing, by Rorschach Testing Records. Catalogue no: **ROR 7**

SWEET STUFF
Tracks: / Sweet stuff.
12" Single: Released '85, on Rorschach Testing, by Rorschach Testing Records. Catalogue no: **ROR 3**
12" Single: Released Jul '86, on Rorschach Testing, by Rorschach Testing Records. Catalogue no: **ROR 3**

WET SKIN & CURIOUS EYE
Tracks: / Wet skin & curious eye.
12" Single: Released 22 Aug '88, on Licensed, Catalogue no: **LD 879**

YAKUTSKA
Tracks: / Yakutska.
12" Single: Released '89, on Play It Again Sam(Belgium), by Play It Again Sam (Belgium). Catalogue no: **BIAS 126**

Cliff, Jimmy

Biographical details: Born James Chambers in 1948, this Jamaican reggae singer and songwriter was still in his early teens when he scored a hit record in his native country. This local success led to him touring the US in 1964, where he met Chris Blackwell, who was later to become reggae's best-known entrepreneur. Backwell persuaded Cliff to move to Britain and try for success there. After painstakingly building building up a strong club following, Cliff achieved a UK No. 6 placing in 1969 with his catchy, self-penned and self-produced single *Wonderful World, Beautiful People.* It also reached No. 25 on the American charts, thus becoming one of the very few reggae records to penetrate a country which has generally shown itself to be impervious to the genre.
The newly famous Jimmy Cliff then moved closer to the pop market. 1970 saw him take the surprising step of working with British singer/songwriter Cat Stevens, who penned and produced Cliff's second UK Top Tenner *Wild World.* Simultaneously, Desmond Dekker took Cliff's own song *You can get it if you really want* to No. 2 on the British charts. Another jamaican act, the Pioneers, successfully recorded one of his songs: *Let Your Yeah Be Yeah* hit the UK No. 5 position in '71. On the strength of such hits, Cliff then took the lead role in *The Harder They Come,* a reggae movie that won worldwide critical acclaim. However, neither the film nor it's superb soundtrack album were major commercial successes and this fact signalled a decline in its star's career. He has been dubbed the first reggae superstar but, despite his enormous talent and potential, he was never able to truly claim the title - that was left to Bob Marley. After many years without a pop hit, one of Cliff's songs hit the UK chart in 1983: UB40, Britain's top reggae group, took *Many Rivers To Cross* to No. 16; it was a track from their huge-selling No. 1 album *Labour Of Love.* (Bob MacDonald)..

ALL THE STRENGTH WE GOT
Tracks: / All the strength we got / Love again.
7" Single: Released Jul '80, on WEA, by WEA Records. Deleted '83. Catalogue no: **K 79135**

ANOTHER SUMMER
Tracks: / Another summer / Saturn's kingdom.
7" Single: Released Oct '80, on Warner Bros., by WEA Records. Deleted Oct '83. Catalogue no: **K 79182**

CLASSIC TRACKS
CD 5": Released Nov '88, on Classic Tracks, Catalogue no: **CDEP 1 C**

I AM THE LIVING
Tracks: / I am the living / Gone clear.
7" Single: Released Aug '80, on Batbeat, Deleted Aug '83. Catalogue no: **K 79155**

LOVE IS ALL
Tracks: / Love is all / Originator / Roots.
7" Single: Released '83, on CBS, by CBS Records. Catalogue no: **A 3037**
12" Single: Released '83, on CBS, by CBS Records. Catalogue no: **A 13 3037**

MANY RIVERS TO CROSS
Tracks: / Many rivers to cross.
12" Single: Released '83, on Trojan, by Trojan Records. Catalogue no: **TROT 9075**

MIDNIGHT ROCKERS True Lovers
Tracks: / Midnight rockers.
7" Single: Released '82, on Oneness, Catalogue no: **ONE 002 7**
12" Single: Released '82, on Oneness, Catalogue no: **ONE 002**

PRESSURE
Tracks: / Pressure / Pressure (version) / Josey Wales.
12" Single: Released Feb '89, on Greensleeves, by Greensleeves Records. Catalogue no: **GRED 235**

REGGAE MOVEMENT
Tracks: / Reggae movement.
7" Single: Released '84, on CBS, by CBS Records. Catalogue no: **A 4636**
12" Single: Released '84, on CBS, by CBS Records. Catalogue no: **TA 4636**

REGGAE NIGHTS
Tracks: / Reggae nights / Love heights.
12" Single: Released '84, on CBS, by CBS Records. Catalogue no: **TA 3849**
7" Single: Released '84, on CBS, by CBS Records. Catalogue no: **A 3849**

ROOTS RADICAL
Tracks: / Roots radical / Rub a dub partner.
7" Single: Released Aug '82, on CBS, by CBS Records. Deleted Aug '85. Catalogue no: **CBSA 2604**

RUB A DUB PARTNER
Tracks: / Rub-a-dub partner.
12" Single: Released '82, on Oneness, Catalogue no: **ONE 001**

SPECIAL (SINGLE)
Tracks: / Special / Keep on dancing.
7" Single: Released Oct '82, on CBS, by CBS Records. Deleted Oct '85. Catalogue no: **A 2825**

VIETNAM
Tracks: / Vietnam.
7" Single: Released 14 Feb '70, on Trojan, by Trojan Records. Deleted Feb '73. Catalogue no: **TR 7722**

WE ARE ALL ONE
Tracks: / We are all one / No apology / Piece of the pie.
12" Single: Released '84, on CBS, by CBS Records. Catalogue no: **TA 4056**
7" Single: Released '84, on CBS, by CBS Records. Catalogue no: **A 4056**

WILD WORLD
Tracks: / Wild world / Hard road to travel.
7" Single: Released Aug '70, on Island, by Island Records. Deleted Aug '73. Catalogue no: **WIP 6087**
7" Single: Released 24 May '88, on Mango, by Island Records. Catalogue no: **IS 377**

WONDERFUL WORLD BEAUTIFUL PEOPLE
Tracks: / Wonderful world, beautiful people.
7" Single: Released Oct '69, on Trojan, by Trojan Records. Deleted Oct '72. Catalogue no: **TR 690**

WONDERFUL WORLD BEAUTIFUL PEOPLE (OLD GOLD)
7" Single: Released '83, on Old Gold, by Old Gold Records. Catalogue no: **OG 9269**

Cliff, Les

DEPENDING ON YOU
Tracks: / Depending on you.
12" Single: Released '84, on Sea View, Catalogue no: **Unknown**

Clifford, Buzz

Biographical details: Clifford, an American, gained a one-off novelty hit in 1961 with *Baby Sittin' Boogie*, reaching No 6 in the US and No 17 in the UK, then disappeared into obscurity as quickly as he had appeared. However, he remained in the business and in 1969 issued an album, *See Your Way Clear.* He received a sleeve credit for vocal assistance on a '75 Jo Cocker LP. At least we knew he still existed... (Bob MacDonald, Jan 1985.)
This American singer gained a one-off novelty hit in 1961 with *Baby Sittin' Boogie.* It reached No. 6 in the US and No. 17 in the UK. Typically for a gimmick disc, the artist in question dissapeared into obscurity as quickly as he had appeared. However, Clifford remained in the music business and issued an album in 1969 entitled *See Your Way Clear.* In 1975, he received a sleeve credit for vocal assistance on a Joe Cocker LP.. (Bob MacDonald)..

BABY SITTIN' BOOGIE
Tracks: / Baby sittin' boogie.
7" Single: Released Mar '61, on Fontana, by Phonogram Ltd. Deleted Mar '64. Catalogue no: **H 297**

BABY SITTIN' BOOGIE (OLD GOLD)
Tracks: / Baby sittin' boogie / Roses are red.
7" Single: Released Jul '82, on Old Gold, by Old Gold Records. Catalogue no: **OG 9076**

Clifford, Linda

Biographical details: This black American singer gained brief success during the late 70's disco boom. Initially signing to Curtom Records, owned by legendary singer and songwriter Curtis Mayfield, she chalked up a minor hit in 1978 with *If My Friends Could See Me Now*, reaching No 50 on the UK chart. The following year she hit the British Top Thirty, and scored a US club success, with one of the most deliberately dreadful covers of all time -- a disco version of *Bridge Over Troubled Water.* To impose such treatment on one of popular music's most revered classics was either courageous or foolhardy: in terms of her future career prospects it seemed to be the latter. (Bob MacDonald, January 1985.).

BRIDGE OVER TROUBLED WATER
Tracks: / Bridge over troubled water.
7" Single: Released May '79, on RSO, by Polydor Ltd. Deleted May '82. Catalogue no: **RSO 30**

IF MY FRIENDS COULD SEE ME NOW
Tracks: / If my friends could see me now.
7" Single: Released Jun '78, on Curtom, Deleted Jun '81. Catalogue no: **K 17163**

RED LIGHT
Tracks: / Red light / Ralph and Monty / Hot lunch jam.
7" Single: Released Jul '82, on RSO (USA), by Polydor Ltd. Catalogue no: **RSO 64**

RUNAWAY LOVE
Tracks: / Runaway love.
7" Single: Released Oct '84, on Cambra, by Cambra Records. Deleted '88. Catalogue no: **CRC 002**
12" Single: Released Oct '84, on Cambra, by Cambra Records. Deleted '88. Catalogue no: **CRCT 002**

SHOOT YOUR BEST SHOT
Tracks: / Shoot your best shot / If you let me.
7" Single: Released Nov '80, on RSO, by Polydor Ltd. Deleted Nov '83. Catalogue no: **RSO 69**

Clifford, Mataya

IT'S GETTING HOT
Tracks: / It's getting hot / Hotline.
7" Single: Released Aug '80, on Batbeat Catalogue no: **BBS 10 01**

Clifton, Sharon

HE'S SO SHY
Tracks: / He's so shy / Love won't wait.
7" Single: Released Nov '80, on Greensleeves, by Greensleeves Records Deleted Nov '83. Catalogue no: **NICE 112**

Climax Blues Band

Biographical details: This British group comprised, at the time of their greatest success, Colin Cooper, John Cuffley, Pete Haycock, Derek Holt and Richard Jones. Formed in 1968 -- originally as the Climax Chicago Blues Band but quickly dropping the "Chicago", probably in deference to the up-and-coming American jazz-rock outfit of the time -- they issued their first album the following year. They were initially part of Britain's late 60's blues revival, playing in a predominantly blues style but with elements of rock and jazz. By the mid-70's they were enjoyiong greater success in the States. In 1976, however, they achieved a one-off chart single in Britain with the laid-back *Couldn't Get It Right.* having reached No 10 in the UK it went to No 3 in the US the following year. Continuing to issue albums on a regular basis, CBB managed a second American Top Twenty hit in 1981 when *I Love You* peaked at No 12 on the Billboard Hot Hundred. But by this time their music was as imaginative as that single's title. (Bob MacDonald, Jan 1985.).

COULDN'T GET IT RIGHT (SINGLE)
Tracks: / Couldn't get it right.
7" Single: Released Aug '88, on Clay, by Clay Records. Deleted Aug '89. Catalogue no: **CLAY 49**
7" Single: Released Oct '76, on BTM Deleted Oct '79. Catalogue no: **SBT 105**
7" Single: Released Nov '86, on Old Gold by Old Gold Records. Catalogue no: **OG 9642**
12" Single: Released '88, on Clay, by Clay Records. Deleted Aug '89. Catalogue no: **12CLAY 49**

DANCE THE NIGHT AWAY
Tracks: / Dance the night away / Black Jack and me.
7" Single: Released Feb '81, on Warner Bros., by WEA Records. Deleted '84. Catalogue no: **K 17754**

GOTTA HAVE MORE LOVE
Tracks: / Gotta have more love / One for me and you.
7" Single: Released Nov '80, on Warner Bros., by WEA Records. Deleted '83. Catalogue no: **K 17733**

I LOVE YOU
Tracks: / I love you / Horizontalized.
7" Single: Released Jun '81, on Warner Bros., by WEA Records. Deleted Jun '84 Catalogue no: **K 17770**

LISTEN TO THE NIGHT

racks: / Listen to the night / Church.
" **Single:** Released Feb '83, on Virgin, by /irgin Records. Deleted '89. Catalogue no: **/S 576**

VINNER, THE
racks: / Winner, The.
" **Single:** Released May '89, on Total,)eleted Aug '89. Catalogue no: **CLAY 50**

Climax Orchestra

NTERACTION
racks: / Interaction.
2" **Single:** Released Nov '84, on Chal-enge, by Elite Records. Catalogue no: **ALL 10**

Climb

CAN'T FORGET
racks: / I can't forget / Your hell.
" **Single:** Released Oct '81, on RCA/Camden, by BMG Records (UK).)eleted '85. Catalogue no: **PIN 510**
" **Single:** Released Oct '82, on Rialto (1), by Rialto Records. Catalogue no: **RIA 12**
2" **Single:** Released Oct '81, on RCA/Camden, by BMG Records (UK).)eleted '85. Catalogue no: **12PIN 510**

POACHER (IS AS POACHER DOES)
racks: / Poacher (is as poacher does).
" **Single:** Released Aug '84, on Second /ision, Catalogue no: **SV 004**

TOUCH ME (HEAVEN)
racks: / Touch me (heaven) / Lower class of heaven.
" **Single:** Released Mar '82, on Pinnacle, by Pinnacle Records. Catalogue no: **PIN 511**

Clime

ALL OUR LIVES
racks: / All our lives.
" **Single:** Released Jul '84, on Tapir, Catalogue no: **TPR 01**

Climie Fisher

FACTS OF LOVE
racks: / Facts of love (Not on 12"s.) / Cold light of day / Facts of love (ext. mix) 12"s only.) / Gypsy (CD single & 12"s only.) / Memories (If I could relive your ove) (CD single only.).
CD 5": Released Sep '89, on EMI, by EMI Records. Catalogue no: **203 505 2**
CD 5": Released Sep '89, on EMI, by EMI Records. Catalogue no: **CDEM 103**
Cassingle: Released Sep '89, on EMI, by EMI Records. Catalogue no: **203 505 4**
Cassingle: Released Sep '89, on EMI, by EMI Records. Catalogue no: **TCEM 103**
" **Single:** Released Sep '89, on EMI, by EMI Records. Catalogue no: **EM 103**
" **Single:** Released Sep '89, on EMI, by EMI Records. Catalogue no: **203 505 7**
2" **Single:** Released Sep '89, on EMI, by EMI Records. Catalogue no: **203 505 0**
2" **Single:** Released Sep '89, on EMI, by EMI Records. Catalogue no: **12EMP 103**
2" **Single:** Released Sep '89, on EMI, by EMI Records. Catalogue no: **12EM 103**
2" **Single:** Released Sep '89, on EMI, by EMI Records. Catalogue no: **203 505 6**

FIRE ON THE OCEAN
racks: / Fire on the ocean / Godsend / Fire on the ocean (12" special mix) (CD single & 12" only.).
CD 5": Released Nov '89, on EMI, by EMI Records. Catalogue no: **203 584 2**
CD 5": Released Nov '89, on EMI, by EMI Records. Catalogue no: **CDEM 112**
Cassingle: Released Nov '89, on EMI, by EMI Records. Catalogue no: **203 584 4**
Cassingle: Released Nov '89, on EMI, by EMI Records. Catalogue no: **TCEM 112**
" **Single:** Released Nov '89, on EMI, by EMI Records. Catalogue no: **203 584 8**
" **Single:** Released Nov '89, on EMI, by EMI Records. Catalogue no: **EM 112**
" **Single:** Released Nov '89, on EMI, by EMI Records. Catalogue no: **203 584 7**
" **Single:** Released Nov '89, on EMI, by EMI Records. Catalogue no: **EMS 112**
2" **Single:** Released Nov '89, on EMI, by EMI Records. Catalogue no: **203 607 6**
2" **Single:** Released Nov '89, on EMI, by EMI Records. Catalogue no: **203 584 6**
2" **Single:** Released Nov '89, on EMI, by EMI Records. Catalogue no: **12EM 112**
2" **Single:** Released Nov '89, on EMI, by EMI Records. Catalogue no: **12EMX 112**

WON'T BLEED FOR YOU
racks: / I won't bleed for you / Climbing up the ladder / This is me* (*track on CD only).
CD 5": Released Aug '88, on EMI, by EMI Records. Catalogue no: **CD EM 66**
" **Single:** Released Aug '88, on EMI, by EMI Records. Deleted Jun '89. Catalogue no: **EMX 66**
" **Single:** Released Aug '88, on EMI, by EMI Records. Deleted Jun '89. Catalogue no: **EM 66**
2" **Single:** Released Aug '88, on EMI, by EMI Records. Deleted Jun '89. Catalogue no: **12 EM 66**
12" **Single:** Released Aug '88, on EMI, by EMI Records. Deleted Jun '89. Catalogue no: **12 EMXS 66**
12" **Single:** Released Aug '88, on EMI, by EMI Records. Deleted Jun '89. Catalogue no: **12 EMX 66**

KEEPING THE MYSTERY ALIVE
Tracks: / Keeping the mystery alive / Nothing but a feeling.
7" **Single:** Released Mar '87, on EMI, by EMI Records. Deleted Oct '87. Catalogue no: **CLF 1**
12" **Single:** Released Mar '87, on EMI, by EMI Records. Deleted Oct '87. Catalogue no: **12 CLF 1**

LOVE CHANGES EVERYTHING
Tracks: / Love changes everything / Love changes everything (ext. mix) / Love changes everything (house mix) / Never close the show / Rise to the occasion (ext. hip hop mix) (Cassingle only.).
CD 5": Released Feb '88, on EMI, by EMI Records. Deleted Aug '89. Catalogue no: **CDEM 47**
7" **Pic:** Released Mar '88, on EMI, by EMI Records. Deleted Nov '88. Catalogue no: **EMPD 47**
Cassingle: Released Mar '88, on EMI, by EMI Records. Deleted Nov '88. Catalogue no: **TCEM 47**
7" **Single:** Released Aug '87, on EMI, by EMI Records. Deleted Apr '88. Catalogue no: **EMX 15**
7" **Single:** Released Feb '88, on EMI, by EMI Records. Deleted 31 Jul '88. Catalogue no: **EMP 47**
7" **Single:** Released Aug '87, on EMI, by EMI Records. Deleted Apr '88. Catalogue no: **EM 15**
7" **Single:** Released Feb '88, on EMI, by EMI Records. Deleted Nov '88. Catalogue no: **EM 47**
12" **Single:** Released Aug '87, on EMI, by EMI Records. Deleted Apr '88. Catalogue no: **12EM 15**
12" **Single:** Released Feb '88, on EMI, by EMI Records. Deleted Nov '88. Catalogue no: **12EM 47**

LOVE LIKE A RIVER
Tracks: / Love like a river / Love changes (everything) / Love like a river (dance mix) (12" only.) / Haunted house (12" only.).
CD 5": Released Dec '88, on EMI, by EMI Records. Catalogue no: **CDEM 81**
7" **Single:** Released Dec '88, on EMI, by EMI Records. Deleted Oct '89. Catalogue no: **EM 81**
7" **Single:** Released Dec '88, on EMI, by EMI Records. Deleted Aug '89. Catalogue no: **EMP 81**
12" **Single:** Released Dec '88, on EMI, by EMI Records. Deleted Oct '89. Catalogue no: **12EMX 81**
12" **Single:** Released Dec '88, on EMI, by EMI Records. Deleted Aug '89. Catalogue no: **12EM 81**

RISE TO THE OCCASION
Tracks: / Rise to the occasion / Love changes (everything) / This is me / Never let a chance go by / Rise to the occasion (special dance mix) (12" only) / Mental block (Only on 12" version.) / Rise to the occasion (hip-hop mix) (12" only).
CD 5": Released Nov '87, on EMI, by EMI Records. Deleted Aug '89. Catalogue no: **CDEM 33**
7" **Single:** Released 30 Nov '87, on EMI, by EMI Records. Deleted Nov '88. Catalogue no: **EMX 33**
7" **Single:** Released Oct '87, on EMI, by EMI Records. Deleted Jan '89. Catalogue no: **EM 33**
12" **Single:** Released Feb '88, on EMI, by EMI Records. Deleted Nov '88. Catalogue no: **12EMS 33**
12" **Single:** Released Oct '87, on EMI, by EMI Records. Deleted Jan '89. Catalogue no: **12 EMX 33**

THIS IS ME
Tracks: / This is me / This is me (this is it mix) (Track on 12" 12EMX 58 only.) / This is me (12" version) (Track on 12" 12EM 58 only.) / Far across the water.
CD 5": Released May '88, on EMI, by EMI Records. Deleted Aug '89. Catalogue no: **CDEM 58**
7" **Single:** Released May '88, on EMI, by EMI Records. Deleted Aug '89. Catalogue no: **EMG 58**
7" **Single:** Released May '88, on EMI, by EMI Records. Deleted Nov '88. Catalogue no: **EM 58**
12" **Single:** Released May '88, on EMI, by EMI Records. Deleted Aug '89. Catalogue no: **12EMX 58**
12" **Single:** Released May '88, on EMI, by EMI Records. Deleted Nov '88. Catalogue no: **12EM 58**
7" **Single:** Released Aug '86, on EMI, by EMI Records. Deleted '88. Catalogue no: **EMI 5578**
12" **Single:** Released Aug '86, on EMI, by EMI Records. Deleted '88. Catalogue no: **12EMI 5578**

Clinch

SWEETHEARTS
Tracks: / Sweethearts / Vancouver white-caps.
7" **Single:** Released Jan '81, on UNKNOWN, Catalogue no: **JIG 4**

Clinch, Matt

POSITIVE VIBRATIONS (A GOOD BUS TO RIDE)
Tracks: / Positive vibrations.
7" **Single:** Released Oct '85, on Strange, by Strange Records. Catalogue no: **WIERD 4**
12" **Single:** Released Oct '85, on Strange, by Strange Records. Catalogue no: **WIERD 4T**

Cline, Patsy

Biographical details: Born Virginia Hensley in Winchester, Virginia, USA, this country singer first came to prominence in New York rather than Nashville. This was in 1957, when she won the influential "Arthur Godfrey talent scout show" on television. *"Walkin' after midnight"*, the song she sang on the programme, became a rapid hit, reaching no.12 on the US pop chart. The remainer of the fifties saw Cline consolidate her position in the country market. Her emotional voice was perfect for the tearjerking ballads that she regularly recorded. By the early sixties, Cline was America's top female country singer and the undisputed "Queen of the weepies". She began to cross over to the US pop charts on a more consistent basis: *" I fall to pieces"* reached no.12 and *"Crazy"* - her biggest pop hit - got to no,9 in 1961; the following year saw her reach no.14 with the wonderfully heartbreaking *"She got you"*. The latter became Cline's first British hit, albeit no.43. Later in '62 she collected her second and final UK chart single, peaking at no.31 with *"Heartaches"*, a respectable showing in view of Britain's long lasting resistance to country and western music. Cline's career was still high gear when she died in a plane crash in March 1963 at the age of 30. Her music lived on, and her name is still treated with great respect today. In 1973 she was posthumously elected to the Country Music Hall of Fame. (Bob Macdonald 85)
Virginia Petterson Hensley, born in Virginia in 1932, was killed in a plane crash in 1963, but not before becoming the first female country star to cross over to the pop chart and the first to challenge Kitty Wells as the Queen of Country Music. Cline was her first husband's name; she signed to Four Star Records in 1954 and was restricted in her choice of material to songs published by them. She appeared on Arthur Godfrey's Talent Scout TV show in January 1957, sang *Walkin' after midnight* and the record went to 5 country, top 20 pop. She switched to USA Decca (now MCA) but had problems with her old contract until 1960. *I fall to pieces* was number one country, top 10 pop in 1961, then she was badly injured in a car crash; but more hits followed. Her records have been dubbed with those of Jim Reeves to make ghoulish duet hits. Loretta Lynn made an album of Cline songs and saw that the Cline role was prominent in her own biopic *Coal miner's daughter*; since then there has been a Cline biopic that was highly rated. (Donald Clarke, April 1989).

CRAZY
Tracks: / Crazy / Walking after midnight.
7" **Single:** Released Mar '87, on MCA, by MCA Records. Catalogue no: **MCA 1137**

HEARTACHES
Tracks: / Heartaches.
7" **Single:** Released Nov '62, on Brunswick, by Decca Records. Deleted Nov '65. Catalogue no: **05878**

SHE'S GOT YOU
Tracks: / She's got you.
7" **Single:** Released Apr '62, on Brunswick, by Decca Records. Deleted Apr '65. Catalogue no: **05866**

Cline, Tammy

Biographical details: A British country singer from Yorkshire. She worked in a factory, sang in a pub with a local band, the Falcons and married guitarist Rod Boulton; later formed her own Southern Comfort Band. She's made several appearances at Wembley, was named Best British Female Country Vocalist each year '80-84, and represented the UK at the International Fan Fair Show in Nashville in 1980 and the International Country & Western Music Association Awards Gala in Galveston, Texas in 1984. She lives in Humberside since the pointless government revision of local boundaries in the mid '70's, but insists she's still in Yorkshire. (Donald Clarke, April 1989)a.

I WISH I'D WROTE THAT SONG
Tracks: / I wish I'd wrote that song.
7" **Single:** Released Sep '83, on President, by President Records. Catalogue no: **PT 519**

LOVE IS A PUZZLE
Tracks: / Love is a puzzle / My heart strings along.
7" **Single:** Released Mar '82, on CBS, by CBS Records. Deleted '85. Catalogue no: **A 2076**

Clinton, George

Biographical details: This American vocalist, instrumentalist, composer and producer -- born in Ohio in 1940 -- specialises in zany, experimental funk. His first US chart success was 1967's *I Wanna Testify*, by his group, the Parliaments. After this hit he dissolved the band and formed two separare combos, Parliament and Funkadelic. Membership was interchangeable and both acts were outlets for Clinton's weird ideas. The second half of the 70's brought US hits for Parliament with *Tear The Roof Off The Sucker (Give Up The Funk)* and *Flashlight*, plus a big success in both the US and UK for Funkadelic with *One Nation Under A Groove*. The early 80's saw Clinton releasing solo records. At the end of '82 *Loopzilla* became a minor British hit single. But his most notable 45 during this period was *Atomic Dog*, a major hit on the American black charts. This disc was typical of most of his work: ludicrous lyrics immersed in uncompromisingly funky rhythm tracks, garnished with electronic experimentation. Like most of Clinton's activities, it enjoyed enormous recognition among punk followers but was too hard sounding and eccentric for major pop success. (Bob MacDonald,1985.)
George Clinton, composer, arranger, producer and vocalist, was born in North Carolina in 1940, and eventually presided over a complex of R&B groups called Parliament and Funkadelic, with hit albums under those names, later under his own. He formed a vocal quintet called the Parliaments in 1955; they scuffled for some years with little success, recorded in 1964 for Motown (who did not release the records but tried to keep the name); finally had some R&B hits (*I Wanna Testify* went top 20 pop in USA 1967). Clinton then shifted into high gear, renamed himself Dr Funkenstein (aka Maggot Overlord), recorded as Funkadelic (the backup group); influnced by '60s rock bands and Sly Stone, he had a long string of hit albums when the word 'funk' still meant something, with a black wit (in both senses), a zany stage act and titles like *Free Your Mind And Your Ass Will Follow* (1970), *Standing On The Verge Of Getting It On* (1974), others as Parliament (*The Clones Of Dr Funkenstein* 1976, etc). Sucess led to spin-off albums by bassist Willian 'Bootsey' Collins and his Rubber Band, keyboardist Junie Morrison, vocal groups Parlets and Brides of Funkenstein and others, until Clinton's funk empire collapsed in a multiplicity of labels and spin-offs, whereupon the unstoppable Clinton recorded under his own name from '82 . See also listings for groups/individuals named. (Donald Clarke 15.5.87).

DO FRIES GO WITH THAT SHAKE
Tracks: / Do fries go with that shake / Pleasures of exhaustion (do it till you drop) / Scratch medley (Extra track on 12" version).
7" **Single:** Released Apr '86, on Capitol, by EMI Records. Deleted '88. Catalogue no: **CL 402**

DOUBLE OH-OH
Tracks: / Double oh oh.
7" **Single:** Released Jul '85, on Capitol, by EMI Records. Deleted '88. Catalogue no: **CL 363**
12" **Single:** Released Jul '85, on Capitol, by EMI Records. Deleted '88. Catalogue no: **12CL 363**

LOOPZILLA
Tracks: / Loopzilla / Pot sharing tots.
7" **Single:** Released Dec '82, on Capitol, by EMI Records. Deleted Dec '85. Catalogue no: **CL 271**
12" **Single:** Released Dec '82, on Capitol, by EMI Records. Deleted Dec '85. Catalogue no: **12CL 271**

WHY SHOULD I DOG U OUT
Tracks: / Why should I dog U out / Why should I dog U out (part 2).
CD 5": Released Jul '89, on Paisley Park (USA), by WEA Records. Catalogue no: **922557 7**
7" **Single:** Released 31 Jul '89, on Paisley Park (USA), by WEA Records. Catalogue no: **W 7557**
12" **Single:** Released 31 Jul '89, on Pais-

ley Park (USA), by WEA Records. Catalogue no: **W 7557T**

Clique Afrique

CLIQUE AFRIQUE
Tracks: / Clique Afrique.
7" Single: Released Jul '82, on PRT, by Castle Communications Records. Deleted Jul '85. Catalogue no: **7P 245**
12" Single: Released Jul '82, on PRT, by Castle Communications Records. Deleted Jul '85. Catalogue no: **12P 245**

Clock Dva

4 HOURS
Tracks: / 4 hours.
7" Single: Released May '81, on Fetish, Catalogue no: **FET 008**

ACT, THE
Tracks: / Act, The.
12" Single: Released Mar '89, on Interfisch, Catalogue no: **EFA 1708**

FOUR HOURS
Tracks: / Four hours.
12" Single: Released Nov '85, on Double Vision, by Double Vision Records. Catalogue no: **DVR 18**

HACKER, THE
Tracks: / Hacker, The.
12" Single: Released Dec '88, on Interfisch, Catalogue no: **EFA 1701**

RESISTANCE
Tracks: / Resistance.
12" Single: Released Apr '83, on Polydor, by Polydor Ltd. Catalogue no: **POSPX 578**
7" Single: Released Apr '83, on Polydor, by Polydor Ltd. Catalogue no: **POSP 578**

SON OF SONS
Tracks: / Son of sons / IMD, Theme from / Don't (it's taboo) / Noises in limbo.
7" Single: Released May '82, on Polydor, by Polydor Ltd. Deleted May '85. Catalogue no: **POSP 437**
12" Single: Released May '82, on Polydor, by Polydor Ltd. Deleted May '85. Catalogue no: **POSPX 437**

Clockhouse

VANISHING POINT
Tracks: / Vanishing point.
7" Single: Released Sep '83, on Picturesque, by Picturesque Records. Catalogue no: **PIC 01**

Clocks and Clouds

HAVE A HEART (FOR THE CHILDREN)
Tracks: / Have a heart (for the children) / Couch potato boogie.
7" Single: Released Jun '89, on Ha Ha, Catalogue no: **HAHA 100B**

Clockwork

DON'T LEAVE ME LONELY AT CHRISTMAS
Tracks: / Don't leave me lonely at Christmas / Count of four / Waiting for your love.
7" Single: Released Nov '81, on Magpie, by Interstate Music. Deleted Nov '84. Catalogue no: **MAG 213**

Clockwork Criminals

YOUNG AND BOLD
Tracks: / Young and bold.
7" Single: Released Jul '83, on Ace, by Ace Records. Deleted Jun '88. Catalogue no: **ACE 038**

Clockwork Soldiers

WET DREAMS
Tracks: / Wet dreams.
7" Single: Released Mar '84, on Red Rhino, by Red Rhino Records. Catalogue no: **ASS 5**

Clooney, Rosemary

Biographical details: This American singer, born in Kentucky, began her career in duet with her sister Betty. In 1949 Rosemary was discovered by Mitch Miller of Columbia Records, who launched her as a mjor solo artist. The early Fifties were golden years for both Clooney and Miller. She had a string of hits, with him as producer. Working not only with Clooney but also with other top singers such as Frankie Laine, Guy Mitchell and Johnnie Ray, Miller became America's king of middle-of-the-road music; he represented the old school of popular music that the rock 'n' roll revolution was soon to rebel against.
The record that gave Clooney major stardom was 1951's *Come on-a my house*, a huge-selling US No. 1. The following year brought further hits with *Tenderly*, *Botch-a-me* and *Half as much*. The singer's early successes predated the British record charts, but *Half as much* had the honour of being listed on the first ever UK chart, published by the New Musical Express in 14th November 1952: it was at No. 6 that week and eventually peaked at No. 3. Clooney's success continued into the mid-Fifties with the US No. 1 *Hey there!* (No. 4 in the UK), the UK No. 1 *Mambo Italiano* (No. 10 in the US) and *This ole house*.
The latter topped the charts on both sides of the Atlantic and was an uptempo, jolly interpretaion of a song originally written as an epitaph for a dead mountain hunter. The song achieved a second UK No. 1 placing in 1981, courtesy of Shakin' Stevens.
Married to film star Jose Ferrer, Clooney also enjoyed movie stardom in the Fifties: amongst others, she appeared with Bing Crosby in "White Christmas" and with Bob Hope in "Here come the girls".
After her final big hit record - 1957's *Mangos* - Clooney's star gradually faded. (Bob MacDonald).
One of the biggest pop stars of the early '50's, with a warm, always clear and musical voice, Rosie began as a duo with sister Betty in the Tony Pastor band, went solo, signed with Columbia (CBS-USA) and had 24 hits in four years. *Come on a my house* was a number one for six weeks in 1951: written some years earlier for a Broadway play by Ross Bagdasarian, who later became David Seville and discovered Chipmunks, its bouncy arrangement featured an amplified harpsichord played by pianist Stan Freeman, as did several other CBS hits of the period, including *Too old to cut the mustard*, a duet by Rosie and Marlene Dietrich.
Other Clooney hits included *Sisters*, a duet with Betty; *You're just in love* was a duet with Guy Mitchell, and her other number ones were *Hey there* (from *Pajama Game*, *This ole house* and the Hank Williams song *Half as much*. She also recorded with Duke Ellington and the vocal group the Hi-Lo's, and switched labels to record with Bing Crosby, Les Brown and others.
She's made a splendid comeback on Concord Jazz in the 80's, backed by first rate jazzmen including Scott Hamilton and Woody Herman.
(Donald Clarke, April 1989).

HALF AS MUCH
Tracks: / Half as much.
78 rpm: Released Nov '52, on Columbia, by EMI Records. Deleted Nov '55. Catalogue no: **DB 3129**

HEY THERE
Tracks: / Hey there.
78 rpm: Released Sep '55, on Philips, by Phonogram Ltd. Deleted Sep '58. Catalogue no: **PB 494**

MAMBO ITALIANO
Tracks: / Mambo Italiano.
78 rpm: Released Dec '54, on Philips, by Phonogram Ltd. Deleted Dec '57. Catalogue no: **PB 382**

MAN
Tracks: / Man.
78 rpm: Released Feb '54, on Philips, by Phonogram Ltd. Deleted Feb '57. Catalogue no: **PB 220**

MANGOS
Tracks: / Mangos.
78 rpm: Released Apr '57, on Philips, by Phonogram Ltd. Deleted Apr '60. Catalogue no: **PB 671**

THIS OLE HOUSE
Tracks: / This ole house.
78 rpm: Released Oct '54, on Philips, by Phonogram Ltd. Deleted Oct '57. Catalogue no: **PB 336**

WHERE WILL THE BABY'S DIMPLE BE
Tracks: / Where will the baby's dimple be.
78 rpm: Released May '55, on Philips, by Phonogram Ltd. Deleted May '58. Catalogue no: **PB 428**

Close

EVERYTIME I TRY TO SAY GOODBYE
Tracks: / Everytime I try to say goodbye / Right time.
CD 5": Released Sep '89, on MCA, by MCA Records. Catalogue no: **DMCAT 1351**
7" Single: Released Sep '89, on MCA, by MCA Records. Catalogue no: **MCA 1351**
12" Single: Released Sep '89, on MCA, by MCA Records. Catalogue no: **MCAT 1351**

Close Lobsters

GOING TO HEAVEN TO SEE IF IT RAINS
Tracks: / Pathetic trivia / Going to heaven to see if it rains.
7" Single: Released Oct '86, on Fire, by Fire Records. Catalogue no: **BLAZE 15**
12" Single: Released Oct '86, on Fire, by Fire Records. Catalogue no: **BLAZE 15T**

JANICE LONG SESSION: CLOSE LOBSTERS
12" Single: Released Apr '88, on Night Tracks, by Pinnacle Records. Catalogue no: **SFNT 008**

LET'S MAKE PLANS
Tracks: / Let's make plans.
12" Single: Released Jul '87, on Fire, by Fire Records. Catalogue no: **BLAZE 22T**

NATURE THING
Tracks: / Nature thing.
7" Single: Released Mar '89, on Fire, by Fire Records. Catalogue no: **BLAZE 34**
12" Single: Released Mar '89, on Fire, by Fire Records. Catalogue no: **BLAZE 34 T**

NEVER SEEN BEFORE
Tracks: / Never seen before.
7" Single: Released Mar '87, on Fire, by Fire Records. Catalogue no: **BLAZE 20**
12" Single: Released Mar '87, on Fire, by Fire Records. Catalogue no: **BLAZE 20T**

WHAT IS THERE TO SMILE ABOUT
Tracks: / What is there to smile about.
7" Single: Released Sep '88, on Fire, by Fire Records. Catalogue no: **BLAZE 25**
CD 5": Released Sep '88, on Fire, by Fire Records. Catalogue no: **BLAZE 25CD**
12" Single: Released 30 Aug '88, on Fire, by Fire Records. Catalogue no: **BLAZE 25T**

Close Rivals

SHORT SHARP KICK IN THE TEETH
Tracks: / Short sharp kick in the teeth / You've got to make mistakes.
7" Single: Released Apr '81, on Hyped, Catalogue no: **BMRB 52**

Closed For Filming

PREJUDICE
Tracks: / Prejudice.
7" Single: Released Mar '84, on G.A.P., Catalogue no: **GAP 83**

Cloud

Biographical details: This all-male British band enjoyed just one week of chart glory with their 1981 single *All night long/Take it to the top*. Both tracks on this double A sided single were instrumentals and reached No. 72 on the UK Top 75 Singles chart. Other releases, both before and after this minor hit, failed to make any impact. *Bob MacDonald)..

ALL NIGHT LONG
Tracks: / All night long / Take it to the top.
12" Single: Released Jan '81, on Champagne Records, Deleted Jan '84. Catalogue no: **FUNKY 1**
7" Single: Released Jan '81, on Champagne Records, Deleted Jan '84. Catalogue no: **FUNK 1**
7" Single: Released Oct '80, on Flashback, by Mainline Records. Catalogue no: **FLASH 001**

STEPPIN OUT WITH YOU
Tracks: / Steppin' out with you / Rico Rico.
7" Single: Released Jan '83, on Rygel, Catalogue no: **RY 7**
12" Single: Released Jan '83, on Rygel, Catalogue no: **RYG 7**

Clouds

TRANQUIL
Tracks: / Tranquil.
7" Single: Released Jan '88, on Subway, by Subway Records. Catalogue no: **SUBWAY 12**
12" Single: Released Jan '88, on Subway, by Subway Records. Catalogue no: **SUBWAY 12T**

Clout

Biographical details: This South African all-girl group consisted of Cindi Alter, Bones Brettell, Jennie Garson, Inge Herbst, Sandie Robbie and Lee Tomlinson. One of the top bands in their native country, Clout achieved a one-off smash in Britain with *'Substitute'*. This extremely catchy 1978 version of a *Righteous Brothers* LP track reached No.2 in the UK chart. It was a perfect pop single and, like the bulk of Clout's output, occupied the middle ground between sing-along pop and hard rock. By being South African and by being an all-female band, Clout were quite a novelty in the UK charts. This fact probably did them more harm than good, and their subsequent British releases failed to make an impact: their version of Eric Clapton's *'Let It Grow'* flopped, and **Russ Ballard's** *'Since You've Been Gone'* became a hit for **Rainbow** but not for Clout. They remained stars in their home country early into the eighties, before splitting up.
[Bob Macdonald, 30.1.85].

PORTABLE RADIO
Tracks: / Portable rdio / Gonna get it to you.
7" Single: Released Aug '80, on EMI, by EMI Records. Deleted Aug '83. Catalogue no: **EMI 5099**

SUBSTITUTE
Tracks: / Substitute.
7" Single: Released Jun '78, on Carrere, Deleted Jun '81. Catalogue no: **EMI 2788**

WISH I WERE LOVING YOU
Tracks: / Wish I were loving you / Gimme love.
7" Single: Released Apr '83, on EMI, by EMI Records. Deleted '85. Catalogue no: **EMI 5162**

Cloven Hoof

OPENING RITUAL
Tracks: / Opening ritual.
Note: 4 track EP.
7" Single: Released Oct '82, on Cloven H', Catalogue no: **TOA 1402**

Clox

AGEING AGENT
Tracks: / Ageing agent / You belong to me.
7" Single: Released Jan '84, on B Flat, Deleted '85. Catalogue no: **FLAT 3**

ANIMALS CAME, THE
Tracks: / Animals came, The / Mountain to Mohammed.
7" Single: Released Oct '85, on B Flat, Deleted '85. Catalogue no: **FLAT 5**

FOLLOW ME
Tracks: / Follow me / Into the water / This.
7" Single: Released Jun '85, on B Flat, Deleted '85. Catalogue no: **FLAT 4**

Club House

Biographical details:
When Michael Jackson's single *Billie Jean* reached No. 1 in Britain, America and around the world in 1983, a number of disco DJs discovered certain similarities between its rhythm and overall sound and those of Steely Dan's 1973 US biggie *Do it again*. They began playing the two records together and this gave Silvio Pozzoli, an Italian session singer based in Milan, the idea of recording his own soundalike medley of the songs. He released the record under the name Clubhouse and *Do it again - Billie Jean* reached No. 11 on the UK chart. In the States, he suffered from competition by a rival rendition.
He tried for a follow-up hit with a coupling of Stevie Wonder's *Superstition* and Chic's *Good Times*, a strange decision in view of the fact that the originals of these two songs were not at all similar. The single did not repeat its predecessor's success and Pozzoli returned to session singing. (Bob MacDonald)..

DO IT AGAIN
Tracks: / Do it again / Billie Jean.
7" Single: Released Jul '83, on Island, by Island Records. Deleted Jul '86. Catalogue no: **IS 132**

I'M A MAN
Tracks: / I'm a man / Ye ke ye ke.
7" Single: Released Jul '89, on Music Man, Catalogue no: **MMPS 7003**
12" Single: Released Jul '89, on Music Man, Catalogue no: **MMPT 7003**

SUPERSTITION
Tracks: / Superstition / Good times.
7" Single: Released Dec '83, on Island, by Island Records. Deleted Dec '86. Catalogue no: **IS 147**

Club Karibe

CHRISTMAS MERRY CHRISTMAS
Tracks: / Christmas merry christmas.
7" Single: Released 21 Nov '87, on RCA, by BMG Records (UK). Deleted May '89. Catalogue no: **PB 41619**
12" Single: Released 21 Nov '87, on RCA, by BMG Records (UK). Deleted May '89. Catalogue no: **PT 41620**

Club Nouveau

IT'S A COLD COLD WORLD
Tracks: / It's a cold cold world / Better way.
7" Single: Released May '88, on WEA, by WEA Records. Catalogue no: **W 8101**
12" Single: Released May '88, on WEA, by WEA Records. Catalogue no: **W 8101T**

JEALOUSY
Tracks: / Lust / Jealousy (instrumental).
7" Single: Released Nov '86, on Warner Bros., by WEA Records. Deleted Jul '88. Catalogue no: **W 8551**
12" Single: Released Nov '86, on Warner Bros., by WEA Records. Deleted Jul '88. Catalogue no: **W 8551T**

LEAN ON ME
Tracks: / Lean on me / Pump it up / Lean on me.
7" Single: Released Feb '87, on Warner Bros., by WEA Records. Deleted Jul '88. Catalogue no: **W 8430**
12" Single: Released Feb '87, on Warner Bros., by WEA Records. Deleted Jul '88. Catalogue no: **W 8430 T**

Club Tango

F.T.N
Tracks: / F.T.N. / Get the picture.
7" Single: Released Nov '81, on Dining Out, by Dining Out Records. Catalogue no: **TUX 15**

PERFORMANCE
Tracks: / Performance.
7" Single: Released Jun '81, on Dining Out, by Dining Out Records. Catalogue no: **TUX 7**

Clubb Shott

STEPPIN' OUT WITH MANIAC
Tracks: / Steppin' out with maniac / Clubb rhythm.
7" Single: Released Apr '85, on Street Level, by Creole Records. Catalogue no: **CR 76**
12" Single: Released Apr '85, on Street Level, by Creole Records. Catalogue no: **CRT 76**

Clubsound

AND GOD CREATED WOMAN
Tracks: / And god created woman / We're doing fine.
7" Single: Released Dec '84, on Mint, by Emerald Records. Deleted '88. Catalogue no: **CHEW 97**

AUNTY SADIE SAYS
Tracks: / Aunty Sadie says (aerobics version) / Auntie Sadie says / Auntie Sadie says (version).
7" Single: Released Nov '86, on Mint, by Emerald Records. Deleted '88. Catalogue no: **CHEW 108**

ROCK'N'ROLL YOU'RE BEAUTIFUL
Tracks: / Rock n roll you're beautiful / Give me a road.
7" Single: Released Nov '87, on Mint, by Emerald Records. Deleted '88. Catalogue no: **CHEW 91**

WAY OLD FRIENDS DO, THE
Tracks: / Way old friends do, The / Mad fighter, The.
7" Single: Released Oct '83, on Mint, by Emerald Records. Deleted '88. Catalogue no: **CHEW 84**

Clyde, Alan

ANYTHING CAN HAPPEN
Tracks: / I wish it was you / Anything can happen.
7" Single: Released Jun '86, on Carrere, Catalogue no: **CAR 391**
12" Single: Released Jun '86, on Carrere, Catalogue no: **CART 391**

Clyde Valley Stompers

Biographical details: This all-male British band had been in existence for over a decade before they achieved their one-off hit single in 1962. In the years following the end of the Second World War, Britiah jazz enthusiasts had benefited from the increased availability of American jazz discs and, discovering previously unheard styles of their favourite music, had formed bands up and down the UK. THis trend eventually led to the 'trad jazz' boom of the early Sixties, a phenomenon that filled an otherwise lacklustre period in British popular music prior to the arrival of the Beatles. One such band was the Clyde Valley Stompers - they reached No. 25 on the UK chart in the late summer of '62 with *Peter & The Wolf.* They were unable to follow up this instrumental hit and soon returned to their tried and trusted live circuit. Many years after breaking up, the Stompers recorded a reunion LP in 1981. (Bob MacDonald)..

PETER AND THE WOLF
Tracks: / Peter and the wolf.
7" Single: Released Aug '62, on Parlophone, by EMI Records. Deleted Aug '65. Catalogue no: **R 4928**

Clydesiders

MAYBE SOMEDAY
Tracks: / Maybe someday.
7" Single: Released Nov '85, on Klub, by Klub Records. Catalogue no: **KLUB 51**

MY LOVE IS LIKE A RED RED ROSE
Tracks: / My love is like a red red rose.
7" Single: Released May '83, on Klub, by Klub Records. Catalogue no: **KLUB 39**

SAILING HOME (SINGLE)
Tracks: / Sailing home / Land I have left, The.
7" Single: Released Jul '82, on Lochshore, by Klub Records. Catalogue no: **LOCH 604**

SCOTLAND'S JIM WATT
Tracks: / Scotland's Jim Watt.
7" Single: Released Apr '81, on Lochshore, by Klub Records. Catalogue no: **LOCH 601**

WE'VE LIVED IN A DREAM
Tracks: / We've lived in a dream.
7" Single: Released Sep '84, on Klub, by Klub Records. Catalogue no: **KLUB 46**

WILD MOUNTAIN THYME (SINGLE)
Tracks: / Wild mountain thyme / Home to the Kyles.
7" Single: Released Nov '83, on Klub, by Klub Records. Catalogue no: **KLUB 42**

CO2

SEX IN THE MOVIES
Tracks: / Sex in the movies / Oh Jackie.
7" Single: Released Apr '82, on Galaxy (1), by Galaxy Records. Catalogue no: **GAL 002**

Coast To Coast

Biographical details: This seven-piece British group, comprising five men and two women, were led by male vocalist Sandy Fontaine. They enjoyed a short but sweet period of success in 1981. Their remake of *(Do) the hucklebuck* reached No. 5 on the UK chart and stayed on the list for 15 weeks. It was a lively revival of one of many dance craze hits by Chubby Checker - he had reached No. 14 on the US chart in 1960, but the song had never been a British hit before. For their follow-up, Coast To Coast recorded *Let's jump the broomstick*, a Brenda Lee hit for 1961 and took it to No. 28 on the British chart. However, their *Coasting* LP flopped, as did subsequent singles. The group's brand of rock 'n' roll revivalism was well exhausted but, in the event, the market gap aused by the decline of Showaddywaddy was filled by Shakin' Stevens rather than Coast To Coast. (Bob MacDonald)..

BABY WHY LET GO
Tracks: / Baby why let go / Your mama's back.
7" Single: Released Oct '81, on Polydor, by Polydor Ltd. Deleted Oct '84. Catalogue no: **POSP 353**

BELL
Tracks: / Bell / How can I be sure.
7" Single: Released May '82, on Polydor, by Polydor Ltd. Deleted May '85. Catalogue no: **POSP 451**

BIM BAM
Tracks: / Bim bam.
7" Single: Released Mar '85, on Orbit, by Orbit Records. Catalogue no: **TRIP 5**

COASTING (SINGLE)
Tracks: / Coasting / Born to rock'n'roll.
7" Single: Released Aug '81, on Polydor, by Polydor Ltd. Deleted '84. Catalogue no: **POSP 303**

DANCE ON
Tracks: / Dance on / Baby can't you see.
7" Single: Released Jan '83, on Polydor, by Polydor Ltd. Deleted Jan '85. Catalogue no: **POSP 382**

DO THE HUCKLEBUCK
Tracks: / Do the hucklebuck / Telephone baby.
7" Single: Released Jan '81, on Polydor, by Polydor Ltd. Deleted Jan '84. Catalogue no: **POSP 214**

LET'S JUMP THE BROOMSTICK
Tracks: / Let's jump the broomstick / Rollercoaster rock.
7" Single: Released May '81, on Polydor, by Polydor Ltd. Deleted May '84. Catalogue no: **POSP 249**

Coasters

Biographical details: The most successful line-up of this American vocal group consisted of Carl Gardner, Cornel Gunter, Billy Guy and Will 'dub' Jones. The name of the group was derived from the fact that they were based in Los Angeles on the West Coast.
The Coasters were formed in 1955 from the nucleus of another L.A. group, the Robins, who had included Carl Gardner and Bobby Nunn in their line-up. Gardner and Nunn were teamed with two more singers, Billy Guy and Leon Hughes and renamed the Coasters. In 1957 they hit big with *Searchin'*, reaching No. 3 in the US and No. 30 in the UK; the flipside *Young Blood* also made the American Top 10 in its own right. A year elapsed before the group's next big hit, by which time Hughes and Nunn had been replaced by Cornel Gunter and Will 'dub' Jones. It was this foursome who sang on the Coasters' run of classic hits between 1958 and 1961. The group were masterminded by the writing/producing team of Jerry Leiber and Mike Stoller, a brilliant pair whose previous writing credits had included Elvis Presley's 1956 classic *Hound Dog*. With the accent on humour, Leiber and Stoller gave the Coasters a series of witty songs that satirised various aspects of the lives of young (especially black) Americans. Maximum entertainment was guaranteed by the effective use of the quartet's contrasting voices. The coasters' biggest successes were *Yakety Yak* (No. 1 in US, No. 12 in UK), *Charlie Brown* (No. 2 in US, No. 6 in UK) and *Poison Ivy* (No. 7 in US, No. 15 in UK).
The Amserican hits continued until 1961 but, having started to peak at much lower chart positions, Gunter quit and was replaced by Early Carroll from the Cadillacs. The group's career went into bottom gear and they eventually split from Leiber and Stoller. The dynamic duo were reunited with them in the late Sixties by, despite a return to quality, no hits were forthcoming. With an unstable line-up, the Coasters continued to tour right through the Seventies and into the Eighties. 1980 saw the Lambrettas, a British combo, hit No. 7 on the UK chart with *Poison Ivy*, thus doing even better than the original version. (Bob MacDonald).
The classic R&B vocal group began in LA as the Robins; they had a number one R&B hit in 1950 with *Double crossing blues*. They met the writing and production team of Jerry Lieber and Mike Stoller in 1953 and became the biggest act on their Spark label: seven singles included *Framed, Riot in cell block No. 9* and *Smokey Joe's cafe*. These striking humourous insights into ghetto life were all the more amazing because the writers were white, but Lieber and Stoller saw the universal relevance of the themes. Atlantic bought their catalogue; lead singer Carl Gardner and bass Bobby Nunn recruited Bill Guy and Leon Hughes and changed their name to the Coasters, after their West Coast origin (their former colleagues lost out, their management disapproving of the Atlantic signing). The Coasters made the R&B top 10 first time with *Down in Mexico* in 1956; *Searchin'/Young blood* was a no. 1 R&B hit, 3 and 8 respectively on the pop chart in 1957. Hughes, more dancer than singer, had been replaced by Young Jessie, then Cornel Gunter; Nunn gave way to Will 'Dub' Jones; this lineup made the classics *Yakety Yak) (no.1 pop), Charlie Brown* (2), *Along came Jones* (9), *Poison ivy* (7): these were aural cartoons, with witty sax interjections by King Curtis. A stylistic innovation from the beginning was the warm bass voice uttering witty or doleful comment that entered the language of the era, as in *Charlie Brown*: 'Why is ev'rybody always pickin' on me?' and *Yakety Yak*: 'Don't talk back'. The hits sounded razor sharp, meticulously made with scores of edits in each one. Earl 'Spedoo' Carroll (ex Cadillacs) replaced Gunter in 1961; they had a total of 19 Hot 100 pop hits including *Let's go get stoned* in 1965. The hits stopped when Leiber and Stoller split up, though they had a minot hit in 1971 with a cover of the Clovers' *Love potion No. 9.* No less than Curtis Mayfield said they were 'my biggest inspiration'. Many versions of the group worked revival shows, led by Nunn, Gardner or Hughes with Guy and Jones pairing. (Donald Clarke, April 1989).

CHARLIE BROWN
Tracks: / Charlie Brown.
7" Single: Released Mar '59, on London-American, Deleted Mar '62. Catalogue no: **HLE 8819**

CHARLIE BROWN (OLD GOLD)
Tracks: / Charlie Brown / Poison Ivy.
7" Single: Released Nov '80, on Old Gold, by Old Gold Records. Deleted '83. Catalogue no: **OG 9056**
7" Single: Released Jul '82, on Old Gold, by Old Gold Records. Catalogue no: **OG 9056**

POISON IVY
Tracks: / Poison ivy / Charlie Brown.
7" Single: Released Oct '59, on London-American, Deleted Oct '62. Catalogue no: **HLE 8938**

SEARCHIN'
Tracks: / Searchin'.
7" Single: Released Sep '57, on London-American, Deleted Sep '60. Catalogue no: **HLE 8450**

YAKETY YAK
Tracks: / Yakety yak / Charlie Brown.
7" Single: Released Aug '82, on Blast From The Past, by Creole Records. Catalogue no: **CR 192**
7" Single: Released Aug '58, on London-American, Deleted Aug '61. Catalogue no: **HLE 8665**

YAKETY YAK (OLD GOLD)
Tracks: / Yakety yak / Along came Jones.
7" Single: Released Jul '82, on Old Gold, by Old Gold Records. Catalogue no: **OG 9089**

Coati Mundi

ME NO POP I
Tracks: / Me no pop I / Que pasa.
12" Single: Released May '81, on Island, by Island Records. Deleted May '84. Catalogue no: **12 WIP 6711**
7" Single: Released Jun '81, on Island, by Island Records. Deleted Jun '84. Catalogue no: **WIP 6711**

Cobalt

MANIPULATION GENETIQUE
Tracks: / Manipulation genetique.
12" Single: Released 20 Feb '88, on Antler, by Antler Records (Belgium). Catalogue no: **SUB 005**

Cobb, Joyce

DIG THE GOLD
Tracks: / Dig the gold / Don't be mad at me.
7" Single: Released Feb '80, on Hi-Cream, by Demon Records. Deleted '83. Catalogue no: **HCS 103**

HOW GLAD I AM
Tracks: / How glad I am / That's what love will do.
7" Single: Released Nov '80, on High Cream, Deleted Nov '83. Catalogue no: **HCS 105**

IT REALLY DOESN'T MATTER
Tracks: / It really doesn't matter / Let the music play.
7" Single: Released Oct '81, on Hi-Cream, by Demon Records. Deleted '85. Catalogue no: **HCS 106**

Cobham, Billy

Biographical details: Born in Panama in 1944, the drummer and composer has been a leader in the fusion movement. After military service he played with Horace Silver and others; he played in Isaac Hayes' *Shaft* soundtrack. He formed a fusion band called Dreams 1969-70, recorded with Miles Davis, then John McLaughlin and his Mahuvishnu Orchestra. His own bands included Airto and David Sancious. He recorded for Elektra with a quartet called Billy Cobham's Glass Menagerie in the early '80's. He has had a big impact on jazz/rock. (Donald Clarke, April 1989) .

SAME OLE LOVE
Tracks: / Same ole love / Juggler, The / Mozaik *.
Note: * Extra track on 12" format.
7" Single: Released Oct '87, on GRP (USA), by GRP Records (USA). Catalogue no: **GRPS 91040**
12" Single: Released Oct '87, on GRP (USA), by GRP Records (USA). Catalogue no: **GRPMS 91040**

Cochran, Eddie

Biographical details: This American singer, guitarist and songwriter, born in Oklahoma City, was one of the true greats of rock 'n' roll. Both before and after his early death, his popularity was greater in Britain than at home.
Eddie Cochran entered the music business in 1954 while only in his mid-teens. By this time he had taught himself to play guitar and had moved with his family to Los Angeles. He started playing in a Hillbilly style, but was inspired in '55 to switch to rock 'n' roll, after seeing a live concert by the young Elvis presley. The next vital stage in the Cochran story came in '56 when he met Jerry capehart, a young songwriter who was living in the same suburb of L.A. Capehart became Cochran's manager and close friend and was his writing and production partner on many of Eddie's recordings. 1957 was the year of the singer's first breakthrough: he made a short but superb appearance in *The Girl Can't Help It*, a rock 'n' roll movie and achieved his first US hit with *Sittin' in the balcony.*
This apparent twin success proved to be a false start. Over a year elapsed before Cochran's next Top 40 hit, but what a classic it was: *Summertime Blues* was so witty in tis lyrics, so exciting in its guitar talent and so enthusiastic in its overall execution, that it suggested a talent almost on a par with Chuck Berry. The song became Cochran's first UK hit, peaking at No. 18 and reached No. 8 in the US. Surprisingly, the was the only Stateside Top Tenner that he ever had - from early '59 onwards he was severely underrated in his home country, as America lessened its taste for rock 'n' roll in favour of the lighter pop sounds of such stars as Paul Anka and Frankie Avalon. *C'mon Everybody*, another seminal Cochran classic, hit No. 6 in Britain but only No. 35 in America and was his final US Top 40 single.
After further film work, he arrived in Britain for his first UK tour in early 1960, accompanied by fellow hard rocker Gene Vincent. These live shows and television appearances greatly enhanced Cochran's British reputation. Fully satisfied with the tour, Cochran was about to leave the UK and head for Hollywood when tragedy struck.

On Easter Day 1960, he was killed in a car crash at the age of 21. He was on his way from Bristol to London Airport, when a tyre burst at Chippenham, Wiltshire, causing the hired car to career 120 yards and hit a lamp standard. Among those injured were Gene Vincent and Eddie's girlfriend, songwriter Sharon Sheeley. With almost unbelievable irony, the deceased star had just recorded his new single, entitled *Three Steps To Heaven*. British record buyers gave him a posthumous No. 1 with the song and begun to put his name in the album charts for the first time.
Cochran's death can truly be termed a tragedy because the artist was at the height of his creative powers. A studio innovator, he was one of the very first to use multi-tracking techniques. But his greatest contribution to rock was his highly influential guitar style: among the numerous British stars to be directly inspired by him were Jeff Beck, Ritchie Blackmore and Jimmy Page. Successful UK cover versions of the great man's material have included Showaddywaddy's *Three Steps To Heaven* (No. 2 in 1975) and the Sex Pistols' *Somethin' Else* and *C'mon Everybody* (both No. 3 in 1979). It is a great pity that many American music fans barely remember the name of Eddie Cochran. (Bob MacDonald).
Born Eddie Cochrane in 1938, he was among the best of the original white rock'n'rollers of the '50's, and like Buddy Holly and Gene Vincent, more popular in the UK than at home. He was killed in a car crash in the UK in 1960. He dropped the 'e' from his name to work with Hank Cochran (no relation) as the Cochran brothers; Hank left for a career in country music and after two unsuccessful singles Eddie signed with Liberty: the hits began in 1957. He was a better singer than most contempories, a good guitar player who co-wrote many songs (with Jerry Capehart) and had an early grasp of studio technology. He was at home with electric blues *Milk cow blues*, anthemic rock'n'roll *Summertime blues*, or teen pop *Teresa*, *Teenage heaven*, *Sittin' in the balcony*. The hits were mostly recorded in Hollywood with expert help (black LA session musicians such as drummer Earl Palmer had an unsung role in the period's pop). *Summertime blues* stands with some of Chuck Berry's definitive teenage comment: 'I called my congressman and he said, quote,/"I'd like to help you son, but you're too young to vote". (Donald Clarke, April 1989).

C'MON EVERYBODY (SINGLE)
Tracks: / C'mon everybody / Skinny Jim (Track on 12" & CD single only.) / Jeannie, Jeannie, Jeannie* (Track on 12" & CD single only.) / Don't ever let me go.
Note: * Extra track on 12"and CD single
7" Single: Released Feb '88, on Liberty, by EMI Records. Deleted Aug '89. Catalogue no: **EDDIE 501**
CD 5": Released Feb '88, on Liberty, by EMI Records. Deleted 31 Jul '88. Catalogue no: **CDEDDIE 501**
7" Single: Released Mar '59, on London-American, Deleted Mar '62. Catalogue no: **HLU 8792**
12" Single: Released Feb '88, on Liberty, by EMI Records. Deleted Nov '88. Catalogue no: **12 EDDIE 501**

HALLELUJAH I LOVE HER SO
Tracks: / Hallelujah I love her so.
7" Single: Released Jan '60, on London-American, Deleted Jan '63. Catalogue no: **HLW 9022**

JEANNIE, JEANNIE, JEANNIE
Tracks: / Jeannie, Jeannie, Jeannie.
7" Single: Released Nov '61, on London-American, Deleted Nov '64. Catalogue no: **HLG 9460**

LIL' BIT OF GOLD: EDDIE COCHRAN
Tracks: / Summertime blues / Something else / C'mon everybody / Nervous breakdown.
CD 5": Released May '88, on Rhino, by Creole Records. Catalogue no: **R 373005**

LONELY
Tracks: / Lonely.
7" Single: Released Nov '60, on London-American, Deleted Nov '63. Catalogue no: **HLG 9196**

MORE SIDES OF EDDIE COCHRAN
7" EP: Released May '88, on Rockstar (1), Catalogue no: **RSREP 2010**

MY WAY (SINGLE)
Tracks: / My way.
7" Single: Released Apr '63, on Liberty, by EMI Records. Deleted Apr '66. Catalogue no: **LIB 10088**

ON TOUR
7" EP: Released May '88, on Rockstar (1), Catalogue no: **RSREP 2013**

PINK PEG SLACKS
7" EP: Released May '88, on Rockstar (1), Catalogue no: **RSREP 2009**

RARE ITEMS
7" EP: Released May '88, on Rockstar (1), Catalogue no: **RSREP 2012**

SKINNY JIM
Tracks: / Skinny Jim / Half loved.
7" Single: Released Dec '79, on Rockstar (1), Catalogue no: **SP 3002**

SOMETHIN' ELSE (SINGLE)
Tracks: / Something else / Boll weevil song / Nervous breakdown / I remember.
12" Single: Released Apr '88, on Liberty, by EMI Records. Deleted Nov '88. Catalogue no: **12 EDDIE 502**
7" Single: Released Apr '88, on Liberty, by EMI Records. Deleted Aug '89. Catalogue no: **EDDIE 502**
7" Single: Released Oct '59, on London-American, Deleted Oct '62. Catalogue no: **HLU 8944**

SUMMERTIME BLUES (SINGLE)
Tracks: / Summertime blues / Twenty flight rock.
7" Single: Released Nov '58, on London-American, Deleted Nov '61. Catalogue no: **HLU 8702**
7" Single: Released May '84, on EMI Golden 45's, by EMI Records. Catalogue no: **G45 19**
7" Single: Released Apr '68, on London Records, by London Records. Deleted Apr '71. Catalogue no: **LBF 15071**

SWEETIE PIE
Tracks: / Sweetie pie.
7" Single: Released Oct '60, on London-American, Deleted Oct '63. Catalogue no: **HLG 9196**

THREE STEPS TO HEAVEN
Tracks: / Three steps to heaven / Cut across shorty.
7" Single: Released May '60, on London-American, Deleted May '63. Catalogue no: **HLG 9115**
7" Single: Released Sep '79, on United Artists, by EMI Records. Catalogue no: **UP 36520**

TWENTY FLIGHT ROCK
Tracks: / Twenty flight rock / Teenage cutie.
7" Single: Released Mar '80, on United Artists, by EMI Records. Catalogue no: **UP 618**

WEEKEND
Tracks: / Weekend.
7" Single: Released Jun '61, on London-American, Deleted Jun '64. Catalogue no: **HLG 9362**

WEST COAST ROCKABILLIES
7" EP: Released May '88, on Rockstar (1), Catalogue no: **RSREP 2014**

WHAT'D I SAY
Tracks: / What'd I say / Milk cow blues.
7" Single: Released Sep '79, on Rockstar (1), Catalogue no: **RSPSP 3001**

Cochran, Jack Waukeen

MAMA
Tracks: / Mama / I don't wanna be lonely.
7" Single: Released Jan '82, on Rondelet Music, by Rondelet Music & Records. Deleted '85. Catalogue no: **ROUND 1005**

MAMA DON'T YOU THINK I KNOW
Tracks: / Mama don't you think I know.
7" Single: Released Oct '81, on Rondelet Music, by Rondelet Music & Records. Catalogue no: **ROUND 1005**

Cochran, Jackie Lee

BOP TOWN
Tracks: / Bop town / Mystery train.
7" Single: Released Jun '80, on Rollin' Rock, Catalogue no: **45 002**

Cochran, Mal

GIRLS IN ROOM 418
Tracks: / Girls in room 418 / Maybe i'm a fool.
7" Single: Released Feb '80, on RCA, by BMG Records (UK). Deleted Feb '85. Catalogue no: **PB 5228**

HOW DO YOU TALK TO GIRLS
Tracks: / How do you talk to girls / Hold back the night.
7" Single: Released Sep '81, on EMI, by EMI Records. Deleted '84. Catalogue no: **EMI 5228**

Cochran, Tom

BOY INSIDE THE MAN
Tracks: / Boy inside the man.
7" Single: Released Jan '87, on Capitol, by EMI Records. Catalogue no: **CL 429**
12" Single: Released Jan '87, on Capitol, by EMI Records. Catalogue no: **12CL 429**

Cochrane, Brenda

AUTOMATICALLY YOURS
Tracks: / Automatically yours / Automatically yours (acid remix).
7" Single: Released Nov '88, on Dazzle, by Dazzle Records. Catalogue no: **DAZ 004**
12" Single: Released Nov '88, on Dazzle, by Dazzle Records. Catalogue no: **12DAZ 0004**

DO YOU BELIEVE IN LOVE
Tracks: / Do you believe in love / You belong to me.
7" Single: Released Nov '87, on Dazzle, by Dazzle Records. Deleted '88. Catalogue no: **DAZ 001**

Cochrane, Nigel

DON'T TURN YOUR BACK ON THE ONE YOU LOVE
Tracks: / Don't turn your back on the one you love / Say it ain't so.
7" Single: Released Sep '82, on Arista, by BMG Records (UK). Catalogue no: **ARIST 489**
7" Single: Released May '85, on Telebell, Catalogue no: **TVP 1**

Cock Robin

JUST AROUND THE CORNER
Tracks: / Just around the corner / Open book.
7" Single: Released May '87, on CBS, by CBS Records. Deleted Nov '87. Catalogue no: **650824 7**
12" Single: Released 23 May '87, on CBS, by CBS Records. Deleted Nov '87. Catalogue no: **650821 6**

PROMISE YOU MADE, THE
Tracks: / Promise you made, The / Have you any sympathy.
7" Single: Released May '86, on CBS, by CBS Records. Catalogue no: **A 6764**
12" Single: Released May '86, on CBS, by CBS Records. Catalogue no: **TA 6764**

THAT'S WHEN YOUR HEART IS WEAK
Tracks: / That's when your heart is weak / Peace on earth.
12" Single: Released Aug '86, on CBS, by CBS Records. Catalogue no: **650029 6**
7" Single: Released Aug '86, on CBS, by CBS Records. Catalogue no: **650029 7**

Cock Sparrer

ENGLAND BELONGS TO ME
Tracks: / England belongs to me.
7" Single: Released Nov '82, on Carrere, Catalogue no: **CAR 255**

RUNNING RIOT
Tracks: / Running riot.
12" Single: Released Jun '89, on Damaged Goods, Catalogue no: **FNARR 5**

Cockatoos

BROKEN HEART
Tracks: / Broken heart / Love's not there any more.
7" Single: Released Oct '83, on Page One, by Page One Records. Catalogue no: **POR 014**

Cockburn, Bruce

Biographical details: Canadian singer-songwriter born in 1945. His debut album in 1970 on Epic was folky; then more than a dozen low-key albums gradually moved to an electrified rock sound; the lyrics evolved from fashionably mystical and ecological through religious (born again Christian in 1974) to political. His first five albums won awards to Canada but had little impact outside. He seemed to find maturity in ninth LP *Dancing in the dragon's jaws* in 1979, with African, reggae and jazz influence felt; it was his first to chart in the USA. He moved to the city from a rural retreat and formed a band, whose lineup in 1985 was Chi Sharp, percussion; Miche Pouliot, drums; Fergus Marsh, bass; and adopted a more progressive, urban style. His overtly anti-American foreign policy *If I had a rocket launcher* did him no harm in the rock business south of the border. His music resembled Dire Straits lean yet muscular rock. (Donald Clarke, April 1989).

HIGH WINDS, WHITE SKY
CD 5": Released Feb '85, on True North (USA), Catalogue no: **WTNT 3**

IF I HAD A ROCKET LAUNCHER
Tracks: / If I had a rocket launcher.
7" Single: Released Jun '35, on Spindrift, by Celtic Music. Catalogue no: **DRIFT 102**

RUMOURS OF GLORY (SINGLE)
Tracks: / Rumours of glory / You get bigger as you go.
7" Single: Released Oct '80, on RCA, by BMG Records (UK). Deleted Oct '83. Catalogue no: **FB 1795**

WANDERING WHERE THE LIONS ARE
Tracks: / Wandering where the lions are / After the rain.
7" Single: Released May '80, on RCA, by BMG Records (UK). Deleted May '83. Catalogue no: **FB 1786**

Cocker, Joe

Biographical details: This British singer, born John Robert Cocker in Sheffield, achieved his first UK chart single in May 1968. Before that he had participated in various small-time groups, developing a soulful, bluesy vocal style that was stongly influenced by the voice of his hero, Ray Charles. Cocker's aforementioned debut success was *Marjorine*, which reached No. 48 on the British listings. This toehold was fully exploited with the release of the follow-up single, issued in the autumn of '68: *With A Little Help From My Friends* was a UK No. 1. This Beatles song had first appeared the previous year on the Fab Four's *Sgt. Pepper* LP - but it had been sung by Ringo Starr in a *Yellow Submarine*-type singalong style; and hit cover versions by the Young Idea and Joe Brown had treated the song in the same manner. But Cocker completely re-defined it, giving the number a slow, powerful, out-and-out blues interpretation that made maximum use of his heartbreaking rhythm and blues voice and gave us the most imaginative remake of a Lennon/McCartney composition that has ever been recorded.
A successful appearance at the legendary Woodstock festival in the summer of '69 lead to a meeting with Leon Russell, a charismatic all-round musician. Russell wrote Cocker's single *Delta lady*, a UK Top 10 hit that autumn and organised a massive extravaganza of over forty musicians to play an extended series of shows around the States - the "Mad Dogs And Englishmen" tour, as it was billed, turned Russell into a star but did little for Cocker's reputation. After a brief run of American hits, which included a Top 10 remake of the Boxtops' *The Letter* plus a No. 11 placing for his reading of *Cry Me A River*, Cocker endured a series of personal and emotional problems that were largely drug-related. In 1975 he made a one-off comeback with the US Top 5 single *You Are So Beautiful*. Further returns to prominence have been often anticipated, but only delivered once: an MoR movie theme *Up Where We Belong*, on which he duetted with American singer Jennifer Warnes, gave him his first US No. 1 in late 1982 and also reached the Top 10 in Britain, his first chart entry in the UK for twelve-and-a-half years. (Bob MacDonald).
A British legend and a fine white soul singer with an unforgettable voice, born in 1944 in Sheffield. He formed his first band in 1959 but worked as a gas fitter; he finally moved to London and co-wrote *Marjorine* with keyboardist Chris Stainton for a minor hit; then had a UK number one with Lennon/McCartney's *With a little help from my friends*, Jimmy Page and Stevie Winwood guesting on the record. An album of that title on A&M went top 40 in the USA; he appeared at Woodstock in 1968; Joe Cocker in 1969 with Leon Russell and the Grease Band did well. The two disc souvenir of the Mad Dogs & Englishmen tour was a big hit in 1970 (included USA top ten hit *The Letter*), but the tour left Cocker broke and sick (from too much drink); Russell had put the show together (which was also filmed) and just about stole it. Since then his career has been up and down; he's recorded for Asylum, then Capitol; he became well known for throwing up on stage, but his albums usually chart in the USA, and there will always be fans of that rough-edged voice. (D.Clarke, 1989).

DELTA LADY
Tracks: / Delta lady.
7" Single: Released Sep '69, on Regal Zonophone, by EMI Records. Deleted Sep '72. Catalogue no: **RZ 3024**
7" Single: Released Aug '82, on Cube, Catalogue no: **BAK 9**

DON'T YOU LOVE ME ANYMORE
Tracks: / Don't you love me anymore / Te[ll] me there's a way / All our tomorrows / With a little help from my friends (Track on 12 and CD single only.).
12" Single: Released May '88, on Capitol, by EMI Records. Deleted Nov '88. Catalogue no: **12CL 493**
CD 5": Released May '88, on Capitol, by EMI Records. Deleted Nov '88. Catalogue no: **CDCL 493**
7" Single: Released 23 May '88, on Capitol, by EMI Records. Deleted Nov '88. Catalogue no: **CL 493**
7" Single: Released Apr '86, on Capitol, by EMI Records. Deleted Oct '87. Catalogue no: **CL 404**
12" Single: Released Apr '86, on Capitol, by EMI Records. Deleted '88. Catalogu[e]

JOE COCKER - LET IT BE (Released on Cube Records)

no: **12CL 404**

I'M SO GLAD I'M STANDING HERE TODAY
Tracks: / I'm so glad I'm standing here today.
7" Single: Released Apr '83, on MCA, by MCA Records. Catalogue no: **MCA 741**

JOE COCKER (EP)
Tracks: / With a little help from my friends / Marjorine / Letter, The / Delta lady (live).
CD 3": Released '88, on Special Edition, by Castle Communications Records. Catalogue no: **CD3-8**

LET IT BE (see panel above)
Tracks: / Let it be / Marjorine.
7" Single: Released '81, on Cube Records, Catalogue no: **BUG 91**

LETTER, THE
Tracks: / Letter, The.
7" Single: Released Jul '70, on Regal Zonophone, by EMI Records. Deleted Jul '73. Catalogue no: **RZ 3027**

LOVE LIVE ON
Tracks: / Love live on / My way to you.
7" Single: Released Dec '87, on MCA, by MCA Records. Catalogue no: **MCA 129**
12" Single: Released Dec '87, on MCA, by MCA Records. Catalogue no: **MCAS 129**

MARJORINE
Tracks: / Marjorine.
7" Single: Released May '68, on Regal Zonophone, by EMI Records. Deleted May '71. Catalogue no: **RZ 3006**

SHELTER ME
Tracks: / Shelter me / One more time / If you have love, give me some (Extra track on 12" only.).
7" Single: Released Mar '86, on Capitol, by EMI Records. Deleted '88. Catalogue no: **CL 362**
12" Single: Released Mar '86, on Capitol, by EMI Records. Catalogue no: **12CL 362**

SWEET LITTLE WOMAN
Tracks: / Sweet little woman / Look what you've done.
7" Single: Released Jun '82, on Island, by Island Records. Catalogue no: **WIP 6708**
12" Single: Released Jun '82, on Island, by Island Records. Catalogue no: **12WIP 6708**

UNCHAIN MY HEART (ROCK DANCE MIX)
Tracks: / Unchain my heart. / Unchain my heart .(rock dance mix) / Unchain my heart .(LP version) (available on 12" only) / One, The (LP version) (available on 12" only)
CD 5": Released Oct '87, on Capitol, by EMI Records. Deleted Nov '88. Catalogue no: **CDCL 465**
7" Single: Released Oct '87, on Capitol, by EMI Records. Deleted 31 Jul '88. Catalogue no: **CL 465**
12" Single: Released Oct '87, on Capitol, by EMI Records. Deleted 31 Jul '88. Catalogue no: **12 CL 465**

WITH A LITTLE HELP FROM MY FRIENDS (SINGLE)
Tracks: / With a little help from my friends / Delta lady.
7" Single: Released Oct '68, on Regal Zonophone, by EMI Records. Deleted Oct '71. Catalogue no: **RZ 3013**
7" Single: Released Aug '82, on Cube, Catalogue no: **BAK 9**
7" Single: Released Jul '82, on Old Gold, by Old Gold Records. Catalogue no: **OG 9232**
12" Single: Released Sep '86, on Archive 4, by Castle Communications Records. Catalogue no: **TOF 109**

YOU CAN LEAVE YOUR HAT ON
Tracks: / You can leave your hat on - single version / You can leave your hat on - instrumental uncut strip mix.
7" Single: Released Jun '86, on Capitol, by EMI Records. Deleted '88. Catalogue no: **CL 413**
12" Single: Released Jun '86, on Capitol, by EMI Records. Deleted '88. Catalogue no: **12CL 413**

Cockerel Chorus

NICE ONE CYRIL
Tracks: / Nice one Cyril.
7" Single: Released Feb '73, on Young Blood, by Young Blood Records. Deleted Feb '76. Catalogue no: **YB 1017**

Cockney Rebel

Biographical details: At the time they were simply known as Cockney Rebel, this British band consisted of Jean Paul Crocker, Stuart Elliot, Steve Harley, Milton Reame James and Paul Jeffreys.
Cockney Rebel were formed in 1973 by vocalist Steve Harley, who advertsied for musicians and obtained the above line-up. With a background in journalism, Harley was an adept self-publicist and quickly built up a 'buzz' in the UK music press about his new group. Their first album was entitled *The Human Menagerie*, but it was their second LP - 1974's *The Psychomodo* - that broke them big, reaching No. 8 on the British album chart and staying on the list for 20 weeks. That same year the group achieved two Top 10 singles: *Judy Teen* and *Mr. Soft* were quirky and highly original pop songs.
Just when it seemed that the world was their oyster, Cockney Rebel suffered an acrimonious break-up. Crocker, James and Jeffreys left. Harley told the press that he would soon be back with 'the biggest band in one world'. With three new members, the group returned under the billing 'Steve Harley & Cockney Rebel' in early '75. They immediately scored a British No. 1 single with *Make Me Smile (Come Up And See Me)*. But once again they failed to live up to their early promise and the hits tailed off at the end of '76. (Bob MacDonald)..

BADMAN
Tracks: / Badman / New song.
7" Single: Released Feb '80, on EMI, by EMI Records. Deleted Feb '83. Catalogue no: **EMI 5035**

Cockney Rejects

Biographical details: The Cockney Rejects chalked up six small hit singles on the British chart between December 1979 and November 1980. Curiously, three of these peaked at No. 65. The most successful was *The Greatest Cockney Ripoff*, which reached No. 21. By the spring of '81, they had achieved three Top 30 LPs. They were then quickly forgotten. The trouble was that they arrived two or three years after the original punk explosion and the Rejects' brash, undisciplined chanting and instrument bashing was merely a repetition of a style that had been better perormed by others in 1976/7/8. (Bob MaDonald)..

EASY LIFE
Tracks: / Easy life / Motorhead / Hang 'em high.
7" Single: Released Mar '81, on Zonophone, by EMI Records. Deleted Mar '84. Catalogue no: **Z 20**

FLARES N SLIPPERS
Tracks: / Flares and slippers.
7" Single: Released Jan '79, on Small Wonder, by Small Wonder Records. Catalogue no: **SMALL 19**

GREATEST COCKNEY RIP OFF
Tracks: / Greatest cockney rip off / Hate of the city.
7" Single: Released May '80, on Zonophone, by EMI Records. Catalogue no: **Z2**

I'M FOREVER BLOWING BUBBLES
Tracks: / I'm forever blowing bubbles / West side.
7" Single: Released May '80, on EMI, by EMI Records. Deleted May '83. Catalogue no: **Z4**

I'M NOT A FOOL
Tracks: / I'm not a fool.
7" Single: Released Dec '79, on EMI, by EMI Records. Deleted Dec '82. Catalogue no: **EMI 5008**

ON THE STREETS AGAIN
Tracks: / On the streets again / Lomdob.
7" Single: Released May '81, on Zonophone, by EMI Records. Deleted May '84. Catalogue no: **Z 21**

TILL THE END OF THE DAY
Tracks: / Till the end of the day / Rock & roll dream.
7" Single: Released Dec '65, on Pye, Deleted '68. Catalogue no: **7N 15981**
7" Single: Released Nov '82, on AKA, Catalogue no: **AKS 102**

WE ARE THE FIRM (SINGLE)
Tracks: / We are the firm.
7" Single: Released Oct '80, on EMI, by EMI Records. Deleted Oct '83. Catalogue no: **Z10**

WE CAN DO ANYTHING
Tracks: / We can do anything.
7" Single: Released Jul '80, on EMI, by EMI Records. Deleted Jul '83. Catalogue no: **Z6**

Cockney & Westerns

SHE'S NO ANGEL
Tracks: / She's no angel / Had me a real good time.
7" Single: Released Aug '80, on Beggars Banquet, by Beggars Banquet Records. Deleted Aug '83. Catalogue no: **BEG 39**

Co-Co

BAD OLD DAYS
Tracks: / Bad old days.
7" Single: Released Apr '78, on Ariola-Hansa, by Hansa Records. Deleted Apr '81. Catalogue no: **AHA 513**

Coco Tea

BIG BAD GIRL
Tracks: / Big bad girl.
12" Single: Released Nov '88, on Jammy's, Catalogue no: **VPRD 338**

CHRISTMAS TIME
Tracks: / Christmas time.
7" Single: Released Dec '88, on Blue Mountain, Catalogue no: **BM 014**

COME AGAIN
Tracks: / Come again.
12" Single: Released Feb '87, on Live & Love, Catalogue no: **LLDIS 0028**

DREAM LOVER
Tracks: / Dream lover.
12" Single: Released Jul '89, on Ital International, Catalogue no: **ITN 005**

I WANT TO LOVE YOU GIRL
Tracks: / I want to love you girl / Love me true.
12" Single: Released Jan '86, on Gold Disc, Catalogue no: **OH 16**

JAMAICA SWEET
Tracks: / Jamaica Sweet / Jamaica Sweet (version).
12" Single: Released Jun '87, on Skengdon, Catalogue no: **SKDL 025**

LET'S GIVE THANKS
Tracks: / Let's give thanks.
12" Single: Released Feb '89, on Jammy's, Catalogue no: **VPRD 399**

LONESOME SIDE
Tracks: / Lonesome side.
12" Single: Released Jul '88, on Live & Love, Catalogue no: **LLD 87**

LOVE IN THE MORNING
Tracks: / Love in the morning.
12" Single: Released Feb '89, on Jammy's, Catalogue no: **VPRD 397**

PRESIDENT BOTHA
Tracks: / President Botha (dub).
12" Single: Released Nov '86, on Rambo, Catalogue no: **RP 001**

PROUD TO BE BLACK
Tracks: / Proud to be black.
12" Single: Released 30 May '89, on Eclipse, Catalogue no: **HCF 101912**

REALITY
Tracks: / Reality.
7" Single: Released Jun '88, on Witty, Catalogue no: **MMD 135**

SWEET COCO TEA
Tracks: / Sweet coco tea.
12" Single: Released Sep '85, on Crystal, by President Records. Catalogue no: **CR 004**

TUNE IN
Tracks: / Tune in / Ram up every corner.
12" Single: Released Jul '86, on Jammy's, Catalogue no: **JAM 002**

UP TIGHT
Tracks: / Up tight.
12" Single: Released Oct '89, on Hawkeye, by Hawkeye Records. Catalogue no: **HD 94**

WHY TURN DOWN THE SOUND
Tracks: / Why turn down the sound.
12" Single: Released Sep '89, on Greensleeves, by Greensleeves Records. Catalogue no: **GRED 255**

Coconut Dogs

OFFICERS MESS
Tracks: / Officers mess / Germinate.
7" Single: Released May '81, on Rialto (USA), by CA Song Records (USA). Deleted May '84. Catalogue no: **TREB 136**

Coconuts

DID YOU HAVE TO LOVE ME LIKE YOU DID
Tracks: / Did you have to love me like you did / Hats off to Citizen K.
7" Single: Released Jun '83, on EMI-America, by EMI Records. Deleted Jun '86. Catalogue no: **EA 156**

TICKET TO THE TROPICS
Tracks: / Ticket to the tropics.
7" Single: Released Aug '83, on EMI-America, by EMI Records. Catalogue no: **EA 159**
12" Single: Released Aug '83, on EMI-America, by EMI Records. Catalogue no: **12 EA 159**

Cocteau Twins

Biographical details: This British duo, comprising vocalist Elizabeth Fraser and guitarist Robin Guthrie, released their first LP *Garlands* in 1982. They gained greater attention in late '83 with the emergence of their second album *Head Over Heels*, which enjoyed enormous success on the UK independent charts, plus an EP entitled *Sunburst And Snowblind*. The latter's two best tracks - *Sugar Hiccup* and *Flagstones* - were typical of the pair's style: a strangely hypnotic, esoteric sound fronted by Fraser's almost unearthly singing. Their folk-influenced music is curiously melodic but not commercial. Fraser also performed vocals on the acclaimed *Song To The Siren*, a minor 1983 hit by This Mortal Coil. The Cocteaus' first hit on the UK national charts was *Pearly - Dewdrops' drops*, which reached No. 29 in 1984. That year also saw them peak at No. 29 on the LP listings with the dreamy *Treasure* set. The duo epitomise Britain's independent label scene: consistently high placings on the indie charts, heavy late-night radio support from John Peel and a refusal to compromise their music in the name of commercialism. In their year-end voting for 1984, Peel's listeners voted more than half a dozen of the Twins' tracks into the Top 50, including No. 2 and No. 4. The Cocteaus, who are signed to 4AD Records, are noted for their shyness and their reluctance to talk to the press. (Bob MacDonald)..

AIKEA-GUINEA
Tracks: / Aikea guinea / Kookaburra / Quisquose / Rococo.
7" Single: Released Mar '85, on 4AD, by 4AD Records. Deleted '88. Catalogue no:

AD 501
12" Single: Released Mar '85, on 4AD, by 4AD Records. Catalogue no: **BAD 501**

ECHOES IN A SHALLOW BAY
Tracks: / Great spangled fritillary / Melonella / Pale clouded white / Eggs and their shells.
7" EP: Released Dec '85, on 4AD, by 4AD Records. Deleted Dec '88. Catalogue no: **BAD 511**

IN OUR ANGEL HOOD
Tracks: / In our angelhood.
7" Single: Released Oct '83, on 4AD, by 4AD Records. Catalogue no: **AD 314**
12" Single: Released Oct '83, on 4AD, by 4AD Records. Catalogue no: **BAD 314**

LOVE'S EASY TEARS
Tracks: / Love's easy tears / Those eyes, that mouth / Sigh's smell of farewell
(Extra track on 12" version.).

7" Single: Released Oct '86, on 4AD, by 4AD Records. Deleted Jan '88. Catalogue no: **AD 610**
12" Single: Released Oct '86, on 4AD, by 4AD Records. Catalogue no: **BAD 610**

LULLABIES (EP)
Tracks: / Lullabies.
7" Single: Released Sep '82, on 4AD, by 4AD Records. Catalogue no: **BAD 213**

PEARLY DEWDROPS DROPS
Tracks: / Pearly dewdrops drops / Pepper tree.
7" Single: Released Apr '84, on 4AD, by 4AD Records. Deleted Jan '88. Catalogue no: **AD 405**
12" Single: Released Apr '84, on 4AD, by 4AD Records. Catalogue no: **BAD 405**

PEPPERMINT PIG
Tracks: / Peppermint pig.
7" Single: Released Mar '83, on 4AD, by 4AD Records. Catalogue no: **AD 303**
12" Single: Released Mar '83, on 4AD, by 4AD Records. Catalogue no: **BAD 303**

TINY DYNAMITE
Tracks: / Tiny dynamite / Pink orange red / Ribbed and veined / Plain tiger / Sultitan itan.

7" EP: Released Nov '85, on 4AD, by 4AD Records. Deleted Nov '88. Catalogue no: **BAD 510**
CD 5": Released '88, on 4AD, by 4AD Records. Catalogue no: **BAD 510 CD**
12" Single: Released Nov '85, on 4AD, by 4AD Records. Catalogue no: **BAD 510**

C.O.D.

IN THE BOTTLE
Tracks: / In the bottle.
7" Single: Released May '83, on Streetwave. Deleted May '86. Catalogue no: **WAVE 2**

Code 61

DROP THE DEAL
Tracks: / Drop the deal / Drop the deal (rough percussion mix) / Drop the deal (ethnic mix) (Only on 12") / Drop the deal (Original version) (Only on 12") / Drop the deal (percussion mix) (Only on 12") / Drop the deal (Beat box mix) (Only on 12").
7" Single: Released 20 Jan '89, on ffrr, by London Records. Deleted 26 Jun '89. Catalogue no: **FFR 17**
12" Single: Released 20 Jan '89, on ffrr, by London Records. Deleted 26 Jun '89. Catalogue no: **FFRX 17**

Code Blue

BURNING BRIDGES
Tracks: / Burning bridges / Where am I.
7" Single: Released Mar '81, on Warner Bros., by WEA Records. Deleted Mar '84. Catalogue no: **K 17771**

FACE TO FACE
Tracks: / Face to face / Paint by numbers.
7" Single: Released Nov '80, on Warner Bros., by WEA Records. Deleted '83. Catalogue no: **K 17723**

Codek

ME ME ME
Tracks: / Me me me / Demo.
7" Single: Released Jan '80, on MCA, by MCA Records. Deleted '83. Catalogue no: **MCA 550**
12" Single: Released Jan '80, on MCA, by MCA Records. Deleted '83. Catalogue no: **MCAT 550**

Codjoe, Ann

LONELY NIGHTS
Tracks: / Lonely nights.
12" Single: Released May '85, on Hitbound, Catalogue no: **HSD 001**

Codling, Barbara

SWEETEST LOVE
Tracks: / Sweetest love.
12" Single: Released Jun '82, on Cartridge, Catalogue no: **CRD 105**

Cody, Tim

CIRCLE ONCE AGAIN
Tracks: / Circle once again / War goes on.
7" Single: Released Mar '86, on Towerbell, Catalogue no: **TOW 77**

DAVEY
Tracks: / Davey / Shallow land.
7" Single: Released Aug '86, on Towerbell, Catalogue no: **TOW 89**

Coffee

CASANOVA
Tracks: / Casanova.
12" Single: Released Sep '80, on De-Lite, Deleted Sep '83. Catalogue no: **MERX 38**
7" Single: Released Sep '80, on De-Lite, Deleted Sep '83. Catalogue no: **MER 38**

SHARON
Tracks: / Sharon / Day O.
12" Single: Released Aug '86, on M & R, Catalogue no: **DIS 1004**

SLIP AND DIP
Tracks: / Slip and dip / I wanna be with you.
7" Single: Released Dec '80, on De-Lite, Deleted Dec '83. Catalogue no: **DE 1**
12" Single: Released Dec '80, on De-Lite, Deleted Dec '83. Catalogue no: **DEX 1**

Cofi & The Lovetones

COUNTDOWN(HERE I COME)
Tracks: / Countdown (here I come).
12" Single: Released Feb '84, on Electricity, by Electricity Records. Catalogue no: **ELECT 3**

Cogan, Alma

Biographical details: This British singer achieved her first UK hit in the spring of 1954, reaching No. 4 with *Bell Bottom Blues*. It was the first of a string of chart successes that lasted for seven years. She chalked up twenty hits during that time, more than any other British female vocalist of her era. Yet those hits did not dominate the charts in the manner of some of her competitors: Cogan only had four Top 10 discs, all between '54 and '56.
The biggest was her 1955 No. 1 *Dreamboat*. Her most successful late Fifties outing was 1958's *Sugartime*, which peaked at No. 16. The singer's final hit was *Cowboy Jimmy Joe* in the spring of 1961. In common with most of her UK contemporaries, Cogan's appeal never crossed the Atlantic.
She sang in a middle-of-the-road style that was typical of much British chart material during the Fifties, a style that rock 'n' roll was founded to rebel against. Her distinctive traits included a much-used chuckle and a penchant for wearing extravagant dresses. Cogan died of cancer in October 1966 at the age of 34.
(Bob MacDonald).
Pop singer (1932-66) who began on stage and had chart hits 1959-61: she was popular on UK radio and TV (famous for her collection of gowns). *Just couldn't resist here with her pocket transister* was a hit in Japan, *Never do a tango with an eskimo* in Iceland. *If love were all* was said to be Noel Coward's favourite version of his song.
(Donald Clarke, April 1989).

BANJO'S BACK IN TOWN
Tracks: / Banjo's back in town.
78 rpm: Released Sep '55, on H.M.V., by EMI Records. Deleted Sep '58. Catalogue no: **B 10917**

BELL BOTTOM BLUES
Tracks: / Bell bottom blues.
78 rpm: Released Mar '54, on H.M.V., by EMI Records. Deleted Mar '57. Catalogue no: **B 10653**

BIRDS AND THE BEES, THE
Tracks: / Birds and the bees, The.
7" Single: Released Jul '56, on H.M.V., by EMI Records. Deleted Jul '59. Catalogue no: **POP 223**

COWBOY JIMMY JOE
Tracks: / Cowboy Jimmy Joe.
7" Single: Released Apr '61, on H.M.V., by EMI Records. Deleted Apr '64. Catalogue no: **DB 4607**

DREAM TALK
Tracks: / Dream talk.
7" Single: Released May '60, on H.M.V., by EMI Records. Deleted May '63. Catalogue no: **POP 728**

DREAMBOAT
Tracks: / Dreamboat / Twenty tiny fingers.
7" Single: Released Nov '80, on H.M.V., by EMI Records. Deleted '83. Catalogue no: **POP 2015**
7" Single: Released May '55, on H.M.V., by EMI Records. Deleted May '58. Catalogue no: **B 10872**

GO ON BY
Tracks: / Go on by.
78 rpm: Released Oct '55, on H.M.V., by EMI Records. Deleted Oct '58. Catalogue no: **B 10917**

I CAN'T TELL A WALTZ FROM A TANGO
Tracks: / I can't tell a waltz from a tango.
78 rpm: Released Dec '54, on H.M.V., by EMI Records. Deleted Dec '57. Catalogue no: **B 10786**

IN THE MIDDLE OF THE HOUSE
Tracks: / In the middle of the house.
7" Single: Released Nov '56, on H.M.V., by EMI Records. Deleted Nov '59. Catalogue no: **POP 261**

LAST NIGHT ON THE BACK PORCH
Tracks: / Last night on the back porch.
7" Single: Released Jan '59, on H.M.V., by EMI Records. Deleted Jan '62. Catalogue no: **POP 573**

LITTLE THINGS MEAN A LOT
Tracks: / Little things mean a lot.
78 rpm: Released Aug '54, on H.M.V., by EMI Records. Deleted Aug '57. Catalogue no: **B 10717**

NEVER DO A TANGO WITH AN ESKIMO
Tracks: / Never do a tango with an eskimo.
7" Single: Released Dec '55, on H.M.V., by EMI Records. Deleted Dec '58. Catalogue no: **POP 129**

STORY OF MY LIFE, THE
Tracks: / Story of my life.
7" Single: Released Jan '58, on H.M.V., by EMI Records. Deleted Jan '61. Catalogue no: **POP 433**

SUGARTIME
Tracks: / Sugartime.
7" Single: Released Feb '58, on H.M.V., by EMI Records. Deleted Feb '61. Catalogue no: **POP 450**

TRAIN OF LOVE
Tracks: / Train of love.
7" Single: Released Aug '60, on H.M.V., by EMI Records. Deleted Aug '63. Catalogue no: **POP 760**

TWENTY TINY FINGERS
Tracks: / Twenty tiny fingers.
7" Single: Released Dec '55, on H.M.V., by EMI Records. Deleted Dec '58. Catalogue no: **POP 129**

WE GOT LOVE
Tracks: / We got love.
7" Single: Released Dec '59, on H.M.V., by EMI Records. Deleted Dec '62. Catalogue no: **POP 670**

WHATEVER LOLA WANTS
Tracks: / Whatever Lola wants (Lola gets).
7" Single: Released Mar '57, on H.M.V., by EMI Records. Deleted Mar '60. Catalogue no: **POP 317**

WHY DO FOOLS FALL IN LOVE?
Tracks: / Why do fools fall in love.
7" Single: Released Aug '56, on H.M.V., by EMI Records. Deleted Aug '59. Catalogue no: **POP 223**

WILLIE CAN
Tracks: / Willie can.
7" Single: Released Dec '55, on H.M.V., by EMI Records. Deleted Dec '58. Catalogue no: **POP 187**

YOU ME AND US
Tracks: / You me and us.
7" Single: Released Jan '57, on H.M.V., by EMI Records. Deleted Jan '60. Catalogue no: **POP 284**

Cogan, Shaye

MEAN TO ME
Tracks: / Mean to me.
7" Single: Released Mar '60, on MGM, by Polydor Ltd. Deleted Mar '63. Catalogue no: **MGM 1063**

Cogic Choir

HE'S GOT THE WHOLE WORLD IN HIS HANDS (S)
Tracks: / He's got the whole world in his hands / You can't run from God.
7" Single: Released Nov '86, on Word (UK), by Word Records (UK). Catalogue no: **WS 110**
12" Single: Released Nov '86, on Word (UK), by Word Records (UK). Catalogue no: **WS 111**

Cognac

DON'T BOTHER TO KNOCK
Tracks: / Don't bother to knock.
7" Single: Released Apr '86, on Rise, Catalogue no: **RISE 1**
12" Single: Released Apr '86, on Rise, Catalogue no: **RISET 1**

Cohen, Izhar

A BA NI BI
Tracks: / A ba ni bi.
7" Single: Released May '78, on Polydor, by Polydor Ltd. Deleted May '81. Catalogue no: **2001 781**

OLE OLE
Tracks: / Ole ole / Blue.
7" Single: Released May '85, on PRT, by Castle Communications Records. Catalogue no: **7P 329**

Cohen, Leonard

Biographical details: This Canadian singer, songwriter and guitarist, born in Montreal in 1934, was a poet and a novelist before enjoying success as a recording artist. His most noteable literary effort was *Beautiful Losers*, a 1966 novel. With encouragement from folk singer Judy Collins, he began to concerntrate on a recording career and released his first album *Songs Of Leonard Cohen* in 1968.
This was a major success on both sides of the Atlantic; in Britain, for example, the LP logged 71 weeks on the charts. His 1969 follow-up, entitled *Songs From A Room*, was another winner. Cohen's LPs and concerts appealed to these rock and folk enthusiasts who were unimpressed by commercial pop music but too depressed to accept the 'love and peace' philosophy of the hippie culture.
Thousands of bed-sit occupants listened to his despairing tales of personal and sexual relationships and to his gloomy outlook on life in general. With guitar and the minimum of additional backing, he droned his way through a catalogue of poetry that was greatly admired by some and dismissed by many others. In Cohen's case, the term 'singer' was applied very loosely.
1971 saw him release 'Songs of love and hate', which reched No. 4 on the British chart. Subsequent albums have been less successful and have whittled down his audience to a hard core.
Particularly dissapointing was 1977's *Death Of A Ladies Man*, an unlikely collaboration with legendary producer Phil Spector. In the Eighties Cohen has kept an extremely low profile. His best known song is probably *Suzanne*, the first track on his first album.
(Bob MacDonald).
A gloomy Canadian poet who became the bard of bedsits in the 1960s: his limited voice and half-whispered delivery was just right for the lovelorn or lonely, though his lyrics are more intellegent than that sounds.
He was a member of a Montreal country group in 1954, then acquired a considerable reputation as a poet and novelist in Canada; his early songs were covered by Judy Collins and Tim Hardin.
His first album included his best known songs *Suzanne* and *Hey, That's No Way To Say Goodbye*.
Film director Robert Altman used his songs effectively in *McCabe & Mrs Miller* in 1971. He influenced people like James Taylor and Joni Mitchell; a collection of his songs by Jennifer Warnes called *Famous Blue Raincoat* was highly praised in 1986.
(Donald Clarke 1989)s.

6 TRACK HITS: LEONARD COHEN
Tracks: / Paper thin hotel / Bird on the wire / Lady Midnight / Joan of Arc / Suzanne / Hey, that's no way to say goodbye.
7" EP: Released Aug '83, on Scoop 33, by Pickwick Records. Catalogue no: **7SR 5022**

AIN'T NO CURE FOR LOVE
Tracks: / Ain't no cure for love / Jazz police / Hey, that's no way to say goodbye / So long Marianne.
CD 5": Released May '88, on CBS, by CBS Records. Deleted Jan '89. Catalogue no: **651 599 2**
7" Single: Released May '88, on CBS, by CBS Records. Deleted Jan '89. Catalogue no: **651 599 7**
12" Single: Released May '88, on CBS, by CBS Records. Deleted Jan '89. Catalogue no: **651 599 6**

DANCE ME TO THE END OF LOVE
Tracks: / Dance me to the end of love.
7" Single: Released Feb '85, on CBS, by CBS Records. Catalogue no: **A 6052**

FIRST WE TAKE MANHATTAN
Tracks: / First we take Manhattan / Sisters of mercy / Bird on the wire* / Suzanne*.
Note: * extra tracks on 12" version.

CD 5": Released 8 Feb '88, on CBS, by CBS Records. Deleted Jan '89. Catalogue no: **651 352 2**
7" Single: Released Jan '88, on CBS, by CBS Records. Deleted Aug '88. Catalogue no: **651 352 7**
12" Single: Released Jan '88, on CBS, by CBS Records. Deleted Aug '88. Catalogue no: **651 352 6**

Coil

ANAL STAIRCASE
Tracks: / Blood from the air / Ravenous / Anal staircase.
12" Single: Released Dec '86, on K 422, by K 422 Records. Catalogue no: **BOTA 121**

HOW TO DESTROY ANGELS

Tracks: / How to destroy angels.
CD 5": Released '88, on Laylah, by Laylah Records. Catalogue no: **LAY 005CD**
12" Single: Released Jun '84, on Laylah, by Laylah Records. Catalogue no: **LAY 005**

MUSIC FOR COMMERCIALS
Tracks: / Music for commercials.
12" Single: Released Jan '88, on Solar Lodge, by Solar Lodge Records. Catalogue no: **SL 1**

PANIC
Tracks: / Panic.
12" Single: Released Jun '85, on K 422, by K 422 Records. Catalogue no: **FSK 512**

Coil, Peter

SELFISH
Tracks: / Selfish.
12" Single: Released Aug '86, on Prism, by Prism Records. Catalogue no: **PSM 9T**

Colahs

HESITATION
Tracks: / Hesitation / Le bump.
7" Single: Released Sep '82, on Epic, by CBS Records. Deleted '85. Catalogue no: **EPCA 2642**

Cold Chisel

CHEAP WINE
Tracks: / Cheap wine / My turn to cry.
7" Single: Released Sep '80, on WEA, by WEA Records. Deleted Sep '83. Catalogue no: **K 7007**

FOREVER NOW
Tracks: / Forever now / No good for you.
7" Single: Released Sep '82, on Polydor, by Polydor Ltd. Deleted Sep '85. Catalogue no: **POSP 514**

YOU GOT NOTHING I WANT
Tracks: / You got nothing i want / Letter to alan.
7" Single: Released Jun '82, on Polydor, by Polydor Ltd. Deleted Jun '87. Catalogue no: **POSP 469**

Cold Crush Brothers

FEEL THE HORNS
Tracks: / Feel the horns / We can do this.
12" Single: Released Jun '88, on B.Boy Records, by Westside Records. Catalogue no: **BEBOY 1**

Cold Cut

BEATS AND PIECES
Tracks: / Beats and pieces / That greedy beat (On special 12" only (CCUT 1G)).
12" Single: Released Oct '87, on More Beats A Head Of Our Time, Catalogue no: **CCUT 1**
12" Single: Released '88, on More Beats A Head Of Our Time, Catalogue no: **CCUT 1G**

DOCTORIN' THE HOUSE
Tracks: / Doctorin' the house / Doctorin' the house (the upset remix).
12" Single: Released Feb '88, on Ahead Of Our Time, by Ahead of Our Time. Catalogue no: **CCUT 2**
7" Single: Released 5 Mar '88, on Ahead Of Our Time, by Ahead of Our Time. Catalogue no: **CCUT 2R**
7" Single: Released Feb '88, on Ahead Of Our Time, by Ahead of Our Time. Catalogue no: **CCUT 27**

MY TELEPHONE
Tracks: / My telephone / My telephone (remix).
7" Single: Released May '89, on Ahead Of Our Time, by Ahead of Our Time. Catalogue no: **CCUT 006**
CD 5": Released May '89, on Ahead Of Our Time, by Ahead of Our Time. Catalogue no: **CCUT 006CD**
12" Single: Released May '89, on Ahead Of Our Time, by Ahead of Our Time. Catalogue no: **CCUT 006 R**
12" Single: Released May '89, on Ahead Of Our Time, by Ahead of Our Time. Catalogue no: **CCUT 006T**

PEOPLE HOLD ON
Tracks: / People hold on / People hold on (remix).
12" Single: Released 23 Jan '89, on Ahead Of Our Time, by Ahead of Our Time. Catalogue no: **CCUT 005 T**
CD 5": Released 23 Jan '89, on Ahead Of Our Time, by Ahead of Our Time. Catalogue no: **CCUT 005 CD**
7" Single: Released 23 Jan '89, on Ahead Of Our Time, by Ahead of Our Time. Catalogue no: **CCUT 005**
12" Single: Released 23 Jan '89, on Ahead Of Our Time, by Ahead of Our Time. Catalogue no: **CCUT 005 R**

STOP THIS CRAZY THING
Tracks: / Stop this crazy thing / Stop this crazy thing (version).
7" Single: Released 16 Sep '88, on Ahead Of Our Time, by Ahead of Our Time. Catalogue no: **CCUT 4**
12" Single: Released 16 Sep '88, on Ahead Of Our Time, by Ahead of Our Time. Catalogue no: **CCUT 4T**

Cold Danse

CHOICE
Tracks: / Choice / No glamour in industry.
7" Single: Released Apr '84, on Xcentric Noise, by Xcentric Noise Records & Tapes. Catalogue no: **FIRTH 1**

Cold Fish

LOVE ME TODAY
Tracks: / Love me today / Strange boy.
7" Single: Released Sep '89, on CBS, by CBS Records. Catalogue no: **A 2779**

Cold Hand Band

TROPICANA
Tracks: / Tropicana / One day.
7" Single: Released Jul '82, on BK, Catalogue no: **PPC 109**
7" Single: Released Jun '83, on DJM, Catalogue no: **DJS 2**
12" Single: Released Jun '83, on DJM, Catalogue no: **DJR 2**

Cold Sensation

BELGIAN TRAIN MUSIC
12" Single: Released '89, on Subway, by Subway Records. Catalogue no: **SUB 062**

Cold War

MACHINIST
Tracks: / Machinist.
7" Single: Released Jun '83, on Namedrop Records, by Namedrop Records. Catalogue no: **NR 4**

Cold Water Problems

IT'S NEARLY TOO LATE
Tracks: / It's nearly too late.
7" Single: Released Apr '83, on Tat-R, Catalogue no: **LOVE 1**

Cole, Caren

I NEED A LOVER TONIGHT
Tracks: / I need a lover tonight (dance version) / I need a lover tonight (instrumental version) / I need a lover tonight (single version).
12" Single: Released Aug '86, on Passion, by Skratch Records. Catalogue no: **PASH 60(12)**

Cole, Cozy

Biographical details: The prominent Swing Era drummer (1909-81) recorded with everybody from Jelly Roll Morton to Benny Goodman and played in Louis Armstrong's All Stars in the early '50s. In the mid-'50s he operated a drum school with Gene Krupa; in 1958 he had a fluke number one novelty hit in the USA with *Topsy*, an old Count Basie tune written by Edgar 'Puddinghead' Battle and Eddie Durham. He toured with Jonah Jones, the ex-Cab Calloway trumpeter, another Swing Era veteran who had unexpected popular success in the '50s. (Donald Clarke 1989)]e.

TOPSY
Tracks: / Topsy.
7" Single: Released Dec '58, on London Records, by London Records. Deleted Dec '61. Catalogue no: **HL 8750**

Cole, David

YOU TAKE MY BREATH AWAY
Tracks: / You take my breath away.
7" Single: Released Dec '88, on Epic, by CBS Records. Deleted 17 Apr '89. Catalogue no: **653062 6**
7" Single: Released Oct '88, on Epic, by CBS Records. Deleted 17 Apr '89. Catalogue no: **653062 7**
12" Single: Released Oct '88, on Epic, by CBS Records. Deleted 17 Apr '89. Catalogue no: **653062 8**

Cole, Gardner

LIVE IT UP
Tracks: / Live it up / Got me curious.
7" Single: Released Jan '89, on Warner Bros., by WEA Records. Catalogue no: **W 7793**
12" Single: Released Jan '89, on Warner Bros., by WEA Records. Catalogue no: **W 7793 T**

Cole, George

Biographical details: This British 'vocalist' is far better known for his acting talents than for his contribution to the recording industry. Cole's most famous role is that of Arthur Daley in the ITV series "Minder" and it was in this guise that he reached No. 21 on the UK singles chart in the first week of 1984 with *What Are We Gonna Get 'Er Indoors*. This was a part-spoken, part-sung Christmas comedy offering, on which Cole duetted with Dennis Waterman, who plays Terry in the series. Cole's character had previously appeared on the chart some eighteen months earlier, when a novelty group called the Firm reached No. 14 in Britain with *Arthur Daley ('e's alright)*.
He has yet to emulate the disc success of Waterman who, in 1980, climbed to the UK No. 3 position with a straight pop single, *I Could Be So Good For You*. (Bob MacDonald)..

WHAT ARE WE GONNA GET 'ER INDOORS?
Tracks: / What are we gonna get 'er indoors / Quids and quavers.
7" Single: Released Dec '83, on EMI, by EMI Records. Deleted '87. Catalogue no: **MIN 101**

Cole, Jonathan

KEYS TO THE CAR
Tracks: / Keys to the car / Billy Green.
7" Single: Released Oct '80, on Rialto (1), by Rialto Records. Deleted Oct '83. Catalogue no: **TREB 123**

Cole, Jordan

LET'S MAKE THIS A VERY MERRY CHRISTMAS
Tracks: / Let's make this a very merry Christmas / Under the mistletoe.
7" Single: Released Nov '82, on Deluxe (1), Deleted Nov '85. Catalogue no: **DEL 1**

Cole, Jude

LIKE LOVERS DO
Tracks: / Like lovers do / Crying Mary.
7" Single: Released Jul '87, on Warner Bros., by WEA Records. Deleted Jan '88. Catalogue no: **W 8358**
12" Single: Released Jul '87, on Warner Bros., by WEA Records. Deleted Jan '88. Catalogue no: **W 8358 T**

Cole, Lloyd

Biographical details: A singer and songwriter born in Glasgow in 1961, who formed the Commotions in 1982. His music was reminiscent of the 1960s, influenced by Bob Dylan, Marc Bolan and the Velvet Underground, even to the sometimes pretentious lyrics: 'She looks like Eva Marie Saint in *On The Waterfront*She reads Simone de Beauvoir...' from *Rattlesnakes*. The brooding six foot cole with won fans with his matinee-idol looks, vocal urgency and infectious tunes. (Donald Clarke 1989)n.

BRAND NEW FRIEND
Tracks: / Brand new friend.
7" Single: Released Sep '85, on Polydor, by Polydor Ltd. Deleted Sep '88. Catalogue no: **COLE 4**

CUT ME DOWN - REMIX
Tracks: / Cut me down - remix / Are you ready to be heartbroken - live / Are you ready to be heartbroken (Extra track on 12" only.) / Forest fire (Extra track on 12" only.) / Perfect blue (instrumental) (Extra track on double pack only.) / Forest fire (live) (Extra track on double pack only.).
7" Set: Released Jan '86, on Polydor, by Polydor Ltd. Catalogue no: **COLEG 6**
7" Single: Released Jan '86, on Polydor, by Polydor Ltd. Catalogue no: **COLE 6**
12" Single: Released Jan '86, on Polydor, by Polydor Ltd. Catalogue no: **COLEX 6**

FOREST FIRE
Tracks: / Forest fire / Perfect blue.
CD 5": Released Apr '89, on Polydor, by Polydor Ltd. Catalogue no: **COLCD 10**
7" Single: Released Aug '84, on Polydor, by Polydor Ltd. Deleted Aug '87. Catalogue no: **COLE 2**
7" Single: Released Mar '89, on Polydor, by Polydor Ltd. Deleted Oct '89. Catalogue no: **COLE 10**
12" Single: Released Mar '89, on Polydor, by Polydor Ltd. Deleted Oct '89. Catalogue no: **COLEX 10**

FROM THE HIP EP
Tracks: / From the hip (remix) / From the hip (ext. remix) (Featured on 12" only.) / Lonely mile / Love your wife / Please.
7" Single: Released Apr '88, on Polydor, by Polydor Ltd. Catalogue no: **COLE 9**
12" Single: Released Apr '88, on Polydor, by Polydor Ltd. Catalogue no: **COLEX 9**
CD 5": Released Apr '88, on Polydor, by Polydor Ltd. Catalogue no: **COLCD 9**

JENNIFER SHE SAID
Tracks: / Jennifer she said.
CD 5": Released Dec '87, on Polydor, by Polydor Ltd. Catalogue no: **COLCD 8**
Cassingle: Released Dec '87, on Polydor, by Polydor Ltd. Deleted 30 Jun '89. Catalogue no: **COLCS 8**
7" Single: Released Dec '87, on Polydor, by Polydor Ltd. Catalogue no: **COLEG 8**
7" Single: Released Dec '87, on Polydor, by Polydor Ltd. Catalogue no: **COLE 8**
12" Single: Released Dec '87, on Polydor, by Polydor Ltd. Catalogue no: **COLEX 8**

LOST WEEKEND
Tracks: / Lost weekend.
10" single: Released Oct '85, on Polydor, by Polydor Ltd. Deleted Mar '87. Catalogue no: **COLET 5**
7" Single: Released Nov '85, on Polydor, by Polydor Ltd. Deleted Nov '88. Catalogue no: **COLE 5**

MY BAG
Tracks: / My bag / Jesus said.
7" Single: Released Sep '87, on Polydor, by Polydor Ltd. Catalogue no: **COLE 7**

MY BAG (DANCING VERSION)
Tracks: / My bag (dancing version) / Perfect skin / Jesus said.
12" Single: Released Sep '87, on Polydor, by Polydor Ltd. Catalogue no: **COLEX 7**

PERFECT SKIN
Tracks: / Perfect skin / Sea and the sand.
7" Single: Released May '84, on Polydor, by Polydor Ltd. Deleted May '87. Catalogue no: **COLE 1**

RATTLESNAKES (SINGLE)
Tracks: / Rattlesnakes.
7" Single: Released Oct '84, on Polydor, by Polydor Ltd. Catalogue no: **COLE 3**

Cole, Nat King

Biographical details: This American singer and pianist, born Nathaniel Cole in Montgomery, Alabama in 1919, began playing piano while still a small child and was highly accomplished at this instrument by the time he left school. during the mid to late Thirties, he toured parts of the States with a band in a revue, made his recording debut and formed his own trio. It was not until this period that Cole began to sing - an extraordinarily late start in view of his later acclaim as a vocalist. Legend has it that his singing career commenced unintentionally in a Hollywood night club, when asked to give an impromptu vocal vocal performance of a particular song by a member of the audience. By the late Forties, Cole had perfected his relaxed but polished singing style to such an extent that a fully fledged career in that capacity was launched and the public began to view him as a singer who also played piano. By this time Nat Cole had inserted the 'king' nickname, in recognition of the popularity that his trio had gained on the West Coast jazz scene. The threesome went their separate ways in 1948 when Cole achieved his first vocal smash hit as a solo performer.
That record was *Nature Boy*, a monster Stateside hit that ushered in a lengthy career of jazz-tinged middle-of-the-road successes. (*Nature Boy* has subsequently been a British hit for Bobby Darin, George Benson and Central Line.) Accompanied by smooth, lush orchestral movements, Cole's sound appealed to a mass audience; together with Louis Armstrong, a figure whom he much admired, Cole was one of the first black superstars. his string of hits continued throughout the Fifties and into the early Sixties, but his colour brough its occasional problems: in 1956, he wa attacked on stage by a gang of racists in Birmingham, Alabama; the following year, a national American TV series failed due to alleged discrimination by advertising agencies.
Cole, from the Fifties onwards never obtained a No. 1 record in either the US or the UK - his biggest American hits were 1955's *A Blossom Fell* and 1962's *Ramblin' Rose*; his greatest British successes were 1953's *Pretend*, 1954's *Smile* and 1957's *When I Fall In Love*. All these songs peaked at No. 2 in the respective nations. In 1962 he achieved a hit album in duet with blind British jazzman George Shearing.
Cole died of cancer in Santa Monica on 15th February 1965, at the age of 45. The world was without a man who, for a period during the Fifties, had clocked up estimated global disc sales totalling 7 million copies per year. In 1978 a TV advertised *20 Golden Greats* collection reached No. 1 on the UK album charts. By this time, his daughter Natalie Cole had carved a substantial career for herself on the American pop and soul charts. (Bob MacDonald).
Nathaniel Adams Cole (1917-65) was born in Alabama, grew up in Chicago and became an influential jazz pianist, leading an innovative trio with guitar and bass but no drums (because the drummer didn't show up for their first gig). Influenced by Earl Hines, along with Billy Kyle (who later secured a comfortable slot with Louis Armstrong's All Stars) he influenced the next generation, including Bud Powell, Horace Silver, Oscar Peterson and Bill Evans. He also recorded with other jazzmen, as on *Meets The Master Saxes*, and he began to sing occasionally, as on *Straighten Up And Fly Right* and *When I Take My Sugar To*

Tea, and finally became one of the best-loved vocalists in the history of popular music. He was not a jazz singer but a balladeer; his first number one was *Nature Boy* in 1948, a strange song by a writer called Eben Ahbez, but his mature style was reached with *Mona Lisa*, number one in 1950 and in the charts for 27 weeks. His jazz background was revived on the album *After Midnight*, which featured the trio with guest soloists Willie Smith, Harry Edison, Stuff Smith and Juan Tizol; and a bumper box of original trio tracks is planned by the American Mosaic label. All the classic Capitol albums have been reissued by EMI. *Love Is The Thing* is one of his best; an EP from it made the USA pop chart in 1957 because of *Stardust*. Nat's version revived the introduction, which hadn't been widely heard since hit records by Artie Shaw and Glenn Miller in 1940 dispensed with it. The album also includes *When I Fall In Love*, a UK hit recently after Rick Astley's ludicrously bad version even imitated Gordon Jenkins' original arrangement. This was followed in 1958 by *The Very Thought Of You*, also with Jenkins, its title track reviving the beautiful Ray Noble song originally recorded by Al Bowlley. Nat also made albums with Nelson Riddle, Billy May and Capitol producer Dave Cavanaugh (*Welcome To The Club* has Cavanaugh conducting what ammounts to the Count Basie band). (Donald Clarke 1989).

BECAUSE YOU'RE MINE
Tracks: / Because you're mine.
7" Single: Released Dec '52, on Capitol, by EMI Records. Deleted Dec '55. Catalogue no: **CL 13811**

BLOSSOM FELL, A
Tracks: / Blossom fell, A.
7" Single: Released Feb '55, on Capitol, by EMI Records. Deleted Feb '58. Catalogue no: **CL 14235**

BRAZILIAN LOVE SONG
Tracks: / Brazilian love song.
7" Single: Released Mar '62, on Capitol, by EMI Records. Deleted Mar '65. Catalogue no: **CL 15241**

CAN'T I?
Tracks: / Can't I?.
7" Single: Released Aug '53, on Capitol, by EMI Records. Deleted Aug '56. Catalogue no: **CL 13937**

DEAR LONELY HEARTS
Tracks: / Dear lonely hearts.
7" Single: Released Dec '62, on Capitol, by EMI Records. Deleted Dec '65. Catalogue no: **CL 15280**

DREAMS CAN TELL A LIE
Tracks: / Dreams can tell a lie.
7" Single: Released Jan '56, on Capitol, by EMI Records. Deleted Jan '59. Catalogue no: **CL 14513**

FAITH CAN MOVE MOUNTAINS
Tracks: / Faith can move mountains.
7" Single: Released Jan '53, on Capitol, by EMI Records. Deleted Jan '56. Catalogue no: **CL 13811**

JUST AS MUCH AS EVER
Tracks: / Just as much as ever.
7" Single: Released Nov '60, on Capitol, by EMI Records. Deleted Nov '63. Catalogue no: **CL 15163**

LET THERE BE LOVE
Tracks: / Let there be love.
7" Single: Released Jul '62, on Capitol, by EMI Records. Deleted Jul '65. Catalogue no: **CL 15257**

LET TRUE LOVE BEGIN
Tracks: / Let true love begin.
7" Single: Released Nov '61, on Capitol, by EMI Records. Deleted Nov '64. Catalogue no: **CL 15224**

LOVE ME AS IF THOUGH THERE WERE NO TOMORROW
Tracks: / Love me as though there were tomorrow.
7" Single: Released Sep '56, on Capitol, by EMI Records. Deleted Sep '59. Catalogue no: **CL 14621**

MAKE HER MINE
Tracks: / Make her mine.
7" Single: Released Oct '54, on Capitol, by EMI Records. Deleted Oct '57. Catalogue no: **CL 14149**

MIDNIGHT FLYER
Tracks: / Midnight flyer.
7" Single: Released Sep '59, on Capitol, by EMI Records. Deleted Sep '62. Catalogue no: **CL 15056**

MONA LISA
Tracks: / Mona Lisa / Kings Cross-follow Anderson.
7" Single: Released Aug '86, on Capitol, by EMI Records. Deleted Oct '87. Catalogue no: **CL 414**

MOTHER NATURE AND FATHER TIME
Tracks: / Mother nature and father time.
7" Single: Released Sep '53, on Capitol, by EMI Records. Deleted Sep '56. Catalogue no: **CL 13912**

MY ONE SIN
Tracks: / My one sin.
7" Single: Released Aug '55, on Capitol, by EMI Records. Deleted Aug '58. Catalogue no: **CL 14327**

MY PERSONAL POSSESSION
Tracks: / My personal possession.
7" Single: Released Oct '57, on Capitol, by EMI Records. Deleted Oct '60. Catalogue no: **CL 14765**

PRETEND
Tracks: / Pretend.
7" Single: Released Apr '53, on Capitol, by EMI Records. Deleted Apr '56. Catalogue no: **CL 13878**

RAMBLIN' ROSE
Tracks: / Ramblin' rose.
7" Single: Released Sep '62, on Capitol, by EMI Records. Deleted Sep '65. Catalogue no: **CL 15270**
7" Single: Released Mar '78, on Capitol, by EMI Records. Deleted '88. Catalogue no: **CL 15975**

RIGHT THING TO SAY, THE
Tracks: / Right thing to say, The.
7" Single: Released May '62, on Capitol, by EMI Records. Deleted May '65. Catalogue no: **CL 15250**

SMILE
Tracks: / Smile.
7" Single: Released Sep '54, on Capitol, by EMI Records. Deleted Sep '57. Catalogue no: **CL 14149**

SOMEWHERE ALONG THE WAY
Tracks: / Somewhere along the way.
7" Single: Released Nov '52, on Capitol, by EMI Records. Deleted Nov '55. Catalogue no: **CL 13774**

STARDUST
Tracks: / Stardust.
7" Single: Released Oct '57, on Capitol, by EMI Records. Deleted Oct '60. Catalogue no: **CL 14787**

STARDUST (RE-RELEASE)
Tracks: / Stardust / When I fall in love.
7" Single: Released Oct '82, on Capitol, by EMI Records. Deleted '85. Catalogue no: **CL 267**

TENDERLY
Tracks: / Tenderly.
7" Single: Released Apr '54, on Capitol, by EMI Records. Deleted Apr '57. Catalogue no: **CL 14061**

THAT'S YOU
Tracks: / That's you.
7" Single: Released May '60, on Capitol, by EMI Records. Deleted May '63. Catalogue no: **CL 15129**

TIME AND THE RIVER
Tracks: / Time and the river.
7" Single: Released Feb '60, on Capitol, by EMI Records. Deleted Feb '63. Catalogue no: **CL 15111**

TOO YOUNG TO GO STEADY
Tracks: / Too young to go steady.
7" Single: Released May '56, on Capitol, by EMI Records. Deleted May '59. Catalogue no: **CL 14573**

UNFORGETTABLE (SINGLE)
Tracks: / Unforgettable / Because of rain / Silent night / For a moment of your love (12" & CD only) (12" only.).
CD 5": Released Nov '88, on Capitol, by EMI Records. Deleted Aug '89. Catalogue no: **CDCL 518**
7" Single: Released Nov '88, on Capitol, by EMI Records. Deleted Oct '89. Catalogue no: **CL 518**
12" Single: Released Nov '88, on Capitol, by EMI Records. Catalogue no: **12CL 518**

WHEN I FALL IN LOVE
Tracks: / When I fall in love / Mona Lisa / Ramblin' rose / Christmas song, The / Love letters (ext. version)*.
12" Single: Released 7 Dec '87, on Capitol, by EMI Records. Deleted Nov '88. Catalogue no: **12CL 15975**
7" Single: Released Apr '57, on Capitol, by EMI Records. Deleted Apr '60. Catalogue no: **CL 14709**
CD 5": Released Dec '87, on Capitol, by EMI Records. Deleted 31 Jul '88. Catalogue no: **CDCL 15975**
7" Single: Released Dec '87, on Capitol, by EMI Records. Catalogue no: **CLS 15975**

WHEN ROCK 'N' ROLL CAME TO TRINIDAD
Tracks: / When rock 'n' roll came to Trinidad.
7" Single: Released Jul '57, on Capitol, by EMI Records. Deleted Jul '60. Catalogue no: **CL 14733**

WORLD IN MY ARMS, THE
Tracks: / World in my arms, The.
7" Single: Released Feb '61, on Capitol, by EMI Records. Deleted Feb '64. Catalogue no: **CL 15178**

YOU MADE ME LOVE YOU
Tracks: / You made me love you.
7" Single: Released May '59, on Capitol, by EMI Records. Deleted May '62. Catalogue no: **CL 15017**

Cole, Natalie

Biographical details: This American singer, born in Los Angeles in February 1950, is the daughter of Nat King Cole, the world famous singer and pianist. Natalie launched her recording career with the release of her debut album *Inseperable* in 1975, ten years after the death of her father. She was in the strange position of having to create her own musical identity and not simply be labelled as 'Nat King Cole's Daughter'; critical opinion varies as to whether, on balance, such legendary parentage is a blessing or burden for a new artist's career. In the event, Natalie's musical path was fairly similar to that of nat - beginning decisively in a distinct format (soul as opposed to her father's jazz) and then moving into the middle of the road. *Inseperable* was a major success in the States, enjoying a long run in both the soul LP and pop LP charts; it yielded the hit single *This Will Be*, which reached No. 6 on the Billboard Hot 100. Follow-up singles and albums also fared well and included two further Top 10 singles in the US: *I've Got Love On My Mind* reached No. 5 in '77 and, the following year, *Our Love* hit No. 10. However, by the start of the Eighties, Cole's move into the adult MoR market was passing through an insipid phase, as demonstrated by her dreadful 1980 single *Someone That I Used To Love*. Since then record sales have been sluggish, but she has a good enough voice to ensure a steady showbusiness career regardless of chart success. In 1983 she teamed with Johnny Mathis for a duet album entitled *Unforgettable - a tribute to Nat King Cole*. This nostalgic LP attained Top 20 status in Britain, the only major UK chart placing afforded to an artist who has always found the British market hard to penetrate. (Bob MacDonald).
The vocalist daughter of Nat 'King' Cole was born in L.A. in 1950. She made her debut at age 11 and released her first album in 1975, 10 years after Nat's death. She had six top 40 hits between 1975-80 and also made duets with Peabo Bryson, but left the pop chart only to make a strong comeback in more recent years with disco-oriented material. (Donald Clarke 1989).

CHRISTMAS SONG (CHESTNUTS ROASTING ON AN OPEN FIRE)
Tracks: / Christmas song, The / We three kings of Orient are.
7" Single: Released Dec '88, on A&M, by A&M Records. Catalogue no: **AM 487**

EVERLASTING (SINGLE)
Tracks: / Everlasting / Everlasting (12" mix) (on 12" only.) / Everlasting (dub) (on 12" only.) / Pink cadillac (7" turbo mix) (on 12" only.) / When I fall in love.
Note: Executive producer Gerry Griffith. * track on 12" & CD single. ** track on 12". + track on CD single. (P) 1987 Original Sound recordings made by Manhattan Records, a division of Capitol Records Inc.
CD 5": Released Jun '88, on EMI-Manhattan, by EMI Records. Deleted Jun '89. Catalogue no: **CDMT 46**
7" Single: Released Jun '88, on EMI-Manhattan, by EMI Records. Deleted Aug '89. Catalogue no: **MTX 46**
7" Single: Released Jun '88, on EMI-Manhattan, by EMI Records. Catalogue no: **MT 46**
12" Single: Released Jul '88, on EMI-Manhattan, by EMI Records. Deleted Aug '89. Catalogue no: **12 MTX 46**
12" Single: Released Jun '88, on EMI-Manhattan, by EMI Records. Deleted Aug '89. Catalogue no: **12 MT 46**

I LIVE FOR YOUR LOVE
Tracks: / I live for your love / I'm the one / In my reality / Jump start (deluxe dub mix).
7" Single: Released Nov '87, on EMI-Manhattan, by EMI Records. Deleted 31 Jul '88. Catalogue no: **MT 31**
12" Single: Released Nov '87, on EMI-Manhattan, by EMI Records. Deleted 31 Jul '88. Catalogue no: **12MT 31**

I LIVE FOR YOUR LOVE (RE-ISSUE)
Tracks: / I live for your love / Urge to merge, The / When I fall in love (12" & CD single only.) / Pink cadillac (turbo mix) (12MTX only.) / I wanna be that woman (12" mix) (12MTX only.).
7" Single: Released Oct '88, on EMI-Manhattan, by EMI Records. Deleted Oct '89. Catalogue no: **MT 57**
12" Single: Released Dec '88, on EMI-Manhattan, by EMI Records. Deleted Oct '89. Catalogue no: **12MTX 57**
12" Single: Released Oct '88, on EMI-Manhattan, by EMI Records. Deleted Oct '89. Catalogue no: **12MT 57**
CD 5": Released Oct '88, on EMI-Manhattan, by EMI Records. Deleted Oct '89. Catalogue no: **CDMT 57**

JUMP START
Tracks: / Jump start (deluxe dub mix) (Only on 12 MTX 50.) / Jump start (car mix) (Only on 12 MTX 50.) / More than the stars (Only on 12 MTX 50.) / Jump start (radio edit) (Only on MT 50, MT 22 & 12 MT 22.) / I wanna be that woman (12" version) (Only on CD single.) / This will be (Only on Cd single.) / Jump start (dance mix) (Only on CD single & 12 MT 50.) / I wanna be that woman (Not on CD single and 12 MTX 22.) / Pink cadillac (Only on 12 MT 50.).
CD 5": Released 1 Aug '88, on EMI-Manhattan, by EMI Records. Deleted Oct '89. Catalogue no: **CDMT 50**
7" Single: Released Aug '88, on EMI-Manhattan, by EMI Records. Catalogue no: **MT 50**
7" Single: Released Jul '87, on EMI-Manhattan, by EMI Records. Deleted Apr '88. Catalogue no: **MT 22**
12" Single: Released Jul '87, on EMI-Manhattan, by EMI Records. Deleted Apr '88. Catalogue no: **12 MT 22**
12" Single: Released Aug '87, on EMI-Manhattan, by EMI Records. Deleted Apr '88. Catalogue no: **12 MTX 22**
12" Single: Released 1 Aug '88, on EMI-Manhattan, by EMI Records. Catalogue no: **12 MT 50**

MISS YOU LIKE CRAZY
Tracks: / Miss you like crazy / Good to be back / Urge to merge (12" vocal mix) (12" & CD single only.) / I live for your love (CD single only.).
CD 5": Released Apr '89, on EMI-Manhattan, by EMI Records. Catalogue no: **CDMT 63**
7" Single: Released Apr '89, on EMI-Manhattan, by EMI Records. Catalogue no: **MT 63**
12" Single: Released Apr '89, on EMI-Manhattan, by EMI Records. Catalogue no: **12MT 63**

NOTHIN' BUT A FOOL
Tracks: / Nothin' but a fool / Joke is on you.
7" Single: Released Jul '81, on Capitol, by EMI Records. Deleted '84. Catalogue no: **CL 227**

PINK CADILLAC
Tracks: / Pink cadillac / I wanna be that woman / Pink cadillac (club vocal) (club vocal 12" version.) / I wanna be that woman* (*On club vocal 12" version.) / Pink cadillac (7" version) (on club vocal 12" version.) / Pink cadillac (turbo mix) / Jump start (radio edit) (Track on C.D. Single only.).
7" Single: Released Apr '88, on EMI-Manhattan, by EMI Records. Deleted Jun '89. Catalogue no: **MTX 35**
CD 5": Released Apr '88, on EMI-Manhattan, by EMI Records. Deleted Jun '89. Catalogue no: **CDMT 35**
12" Pic: Released 29 Feb '88, on EMI-Manhattan, by EMI Records. Deleted 31 Jul '88. Catalogue no: **12 MTP 35**
7" Single: Released 29 Feb '88, on EMI-Manhattan, by EMI Records. Deleted Jul '88. Catalogue no: **MT 35**
12" Single: Released 29 Feb '88, on EMI-Manhattan, by EMI Records. Deleted Nov '88. Catalogue no: **12MTX 35**
12" Single: Released 29 Feb '88, on EMI-Manhattan, by EMI Records. Deleted Nov '88. Catalogue no: **12MT 35**

REST OF THE NIGHT (see panel on next page)
Tracks: / Rest of the night (12" & CD single only.) / As a matter of fact (12" only.) / Someone's rocking my dreamboat / Rest of the night (edit) (Not on 12".) / Miss you like crazy (CD single only.).
CD 5": Released Jul '89, on EMI-Manhattan, by EMI Records. Catalogue no: **CDMT 69**
Cassingle: Released Jul '89, on EMI-Manhattan, by EMI Records. Catalogue no: **TCMT 69**
7" Single: Released Jul '89, on EMI-Manhattan, by EMI Records. Catalogue no: **MT 69**
12" Single: Released Jul '89, on EMI-Manhattan, by EMI Records. Catalogue no: **12MT 69**

SOMEONE THAT I USED TO LOVE
Tracks: / Someone that I used to love / Don't look back.
7" Single: Released Sep '80, on Capitol, by EMI Records. Deleted '83. Catalogue no: **CL 16166**

NATALIE COLE - REST OF THE IGHT (Released on EMI - Manhattan)

THIS WILL BE
Tracks: / This will be.
7" Single: Released Oct '75, on Capitol, by EMI Records. Deleted Oct '78. Catalogue no: **CL 15834**

Cole, Sonny

ROBINSON CRUSOE BOP
Tracks: / Robinson Crusoe bop.
7" Single: Released Jun '80, on Rollin' Rock, Catalogue no: **45 004**

Cole, Stranger

PRETTY COTTAGE
Tracks: / Pretty cottage.
7" Single: Released Jul '82, on Pama Oldies, by Pama Records. Catalogue no: **PTP 1031**

Coleman, Albert

JUST HOOKED ON COUNTRY
Tracks: / Just hooked on country / Just hooked on country (pt 2).
7" Single: Released Sep '82, on Epic, by CBS Records. Deleted Sep '85. Catalogue no: **EPCA 2597**

Coleman, Desiree

ROMANCE
Tracks: / Romance.
7" Single: Released Oct '88, on Motown, by BMG Records (UK). Catalogue no: **MOT 4617**

Coleman, Durrell

SOMEBODY TOOK MY LOVE
Tracks: / Somebody took my love / When a man loves a woman.
7" Single: Released Apr '86, on 4th & Broadway, by Island Records. Catalogue no: **BRW 46**
12" Single: Released Apr '86, on 4th & Broadway, by Island Records. Catalogue no: **12 BRW 46**

Coleman, Ray

JUKEBOX ROCK 'N' ROLL
Tracks: / Jukebox rock 'n' roll.
7" Single: Released '77, on Rollercoaster, by Rollercoaster Records. Deleted '87. Catalogue no: **RRC 2000**

Colenso Parade

DOWN BY THE BORDER
Tracks: / Down by the border.
12" Single: Released Apr '85, on Goliath, Deleted '88. Catalogue no: **SLING 002**

FONTANA EYES
Tracks: / Fontana eyes / Here comes the night.
7" Single: Released Oct '86, on Fire, by Fire Records. Catalogue no: **BLAZE 11**
12" Single: Released Oct '86, on Fire, by Fire Records. Catalogue no: **BLAZE 11T**

HALLELUJAH CHORUS
Tracks: / Hallelujah chorus / Too late for anything sacred lover.
12" Single: Released Dec '85, on Fire, by Fire Records. Catalogue no: **FIRE 7**

STANDING UP
Tracks: / Standing up.
7" Single: on Goliath, Deleted Sep '84. Catalogue no: **GOL 1**

Coll, Brian

TOWN I LOVE SO WELL
Tracks: / Town I love so well / Hometown on the foyle.
7" Single: Released '88, on Homespun (Ireland), by Outlet Records. Catalogue no: **HIS 6**

Collage

GET IN TOUCH WITH ME
Tracks: / Get in touch with me / Winners and losers / Love is for everyone (Extra track on 12") / Romeo where's Juliet.
12" Single: Released 20 Jun '87, on MCA, by MCA Records. Catalogue no: **MCAT 1128**
7" Single: Released 20 Jun '87, on MCA, by MCA Records. Catalogue no: **MCA 1128**

ROMEO WHERE'S JULIET
Tracks: / Romeo where's Juliet / Let's rock 'n' roll.
7" Single: Released Oct '86, on MCA, by MCA Records. Catalogue no: **MCA 1006**
12" Single: Released Oct '86, on MCA, by MCA Records. Catalogue no: **MCAT 1006**

ROMEO WHERE'S JULIET (OLD GOLD)
Tracks: / Romeo where's Juliet / You get the best from me.
12" Single: Released 30 May '89, on Old Gold, by Old Gold Records. Catalogue no: **OG 4116**

Collapsable Deckchairs

WILLIAM SHAKESPEARE
Tracks: / William Shakespeare.
7" Single: Released Aug '84, on Mordent, Catalogue no: **DMOR 1**

Collette

RING MY BELL
Tracks: / Ring my bell / Save yourself / Ring my bell (Ring-a-ling mix) / Ring my bell (Ding dong mix) / Save yourself (Survival mix).
CD 5": Released Apr '89, on CBS, by CBS Records. Catalogue no: **BELL C1**
7" Single: Released May '89, on CBS, by CBS Records. Catalogue no: **BELL Q1**
7" Single: Released Apr '89, on CBS, by CBS Records. Catalogue no: **BELL 1**
12" Single: Released Apr '89, on CBS, by CBS Records. Catalogue no: **BELL T1**

Collier, Mike

WAR AND REMEMBERANCE (Theme from Winds of war)
Tracks: / War and rememberance / Eine kleine steine.
7" Single: Released Sep '89, on Debut, by Skratch Records. Catalogue no: **DEBT 3081**

Collier, Norman

SINGING CHICKEN, THE
Tracks: / Singing chicken, The / I left my heart in San Francisco.
7" Single: Released Jun '88, on Tembo, by Tembo Records. Catalogue no: **TML 133**

SPACE CHICKEN
Tracks: / Smile / Space chicken.
7" Single: Released Dec '86, on Crystal, by President Records. Catalogue no: **CR 7036**

Collins, Ansell

MAKING LOVE
Tracks: / Making love.
12" Single: Released Jun '83, on Londisc, by Londisc Records. Catalogue no: **LD 003**

Collins, Barbara

I BELIEVE ANYTHING YOU SAY
Tracks: / I believe anything you say.
12" Single: Released Jul '89, on El Dorado, Catalogue no: **ED 001**

Collins, Bootsy

Biographical details: See Clinton, George for biographical details..

BODY SLAM
Tracks: / Body slam.
12" Single: Released Aug '86, on Bluebird (2), by BMG Records (UK). Catalogue no: **9299190**

PARTY ON PLASTIC
Tracks: / Party on plastic.
7" Single: Released Sep '88, on CBS, by CBS Records. Deleted 17 Apr '89. Catalogue no: **653003 7**
12" Single: Released Sep '88, on CBS, by CBS Records. Deleted 17 Apr '89. Catalogue no: **653003 6**

Collins, Dave

Biographical details: This Jamaican reggae singer shot to sudden fame in 1971 as 50% of Dave and Ansil Collins. This duo achieved a surprise smash that year with the quirky, incomprehensible but incredibly infectious *Double barrel*. This was only the second reggae single, up to that point, to hit No.1 in Britain, and was the one of the genre's few discs to penetrate the American Top 30. Another catchy single *Monkey spanner*, reached No.7 in Britain, and then the pair faded into obscurity as quickly as they had emerged. Their recording careers continued - for example, they issued an album in 1976 entitled *In the ghetto*, and Ansel (for whose forename there appears to be no fixed spelling) released a solo 1983 single *Making love*. But nobody really knew who they were, even when they were No.1. (Bob Macdonald 85).

CLASSIC TRACKS
CD 5": Released Nov '88, on Classic Tracks, Catalogue no: **CDEP 2 C**

DOUBLE BARREL
Tracks: / Double barrel / Liquidator / Django.
CD 5": Released 24 Apr '89, on Old Gold, by Old Gold Records. Catalogue no: **OG 6135**
7" Single: Released Apr '83, on Old Gold, by Old Gold Records. Catalogue no: **OG 9270**

DOUBLE BARREL (SINGLE)
Tracks: / Double barrel.
7" Single: Released Mar '71, on Techniques, Deleted Mar '74. Catalogue no: **TE 901**

GOOD LOVIN'
Tracks: / Good lovin' / Simple pleasures / Thinkin' about your body.
12" Single: Released Apr '88, on G.T.I. Records, by G.T.I. Music. Catalogue no: **GTI 001T**

LOVE TONITE
Tracks: / Love tonite.
12" Single: Released Mar '89, on White Label (1), Catalogue no: **12COLLINS 4**

LOVE UNITE
Tracks: / Love unite / Love unite (version).
7" Single: Released May '89, on G.T.I. Records, by G.T.I. Music. Catalogue no: **COLLINS 4**

MONEY CRAZY
Tracks: / Money crazy.
12" Single: Released Oct '88, on G.T.I. Records, by G.T.I. Music. Catalogue no: **GTI 002T**

MONKEY SPANNER
Tracks: / Monkey spanner.
7" Single: Released Jun '71, on Technique, Deleted Jun '74. Catalogue no: **TE 914**

Collins, Edwin

DON'T SHILLY SHALLY
Tracks: / Don't shilly shally.
7" Single: Released Jul '87, on WEA, by WEA Records. Deleted Jul '88. Catalogue no: **ACID 4**
12" Single: Released Jul '87, on WEA, by WEA Records. Deleted Jul '88. Catalogue no: **ACID 4T**

COFFEE TABLE SONG
Tracks: / Coffee table song / Judas in blue jeans.
7" Single: Released Jul '89, on Demon, by Demon Records. Catalogue no: **D 1064**
12" Single: Released Jul '89, on Demon, by Demon Records. Catalogue no: **D 1064 T**

MY BELOVED GIRL
Tracks: / My beloved girl / Clouds (fogging up my mind).
7" Single: Released Oct '87, on Elevation, Deleted Jul '88. Catalogue no: **ACID 6**
12" Single: Released Oct '87, on Elevation, Catalogue no: **ACID 6 T**

Collins, Jeff

ONLY YOU
Tracks: / Only you.
7" Single: Released Nov '72, on Polydor, by Polydor Ltd. Deleted Nov '75. Catalogue no: **2058 287**

Collins, Jo

SOMETIMES (SONG FOR MUM)
Tracks: / Sometimes (song for mum) / Sometimes (song for mum - inst).
7" Single: Released Dec '88, on Plaza, by Plaza Records. Catalogue no: **PZA 043**

Collins, Judy

Biographical details: This American singer, and guitarist, born in 1939 into a musical family, was initially trained as a classical pianist; but, by the early sixties, she had dropped this career option and developed a strong interest in folk music. This led to regular folk club dates in and around her native Colorado, an eastwood move to New York's Greenwich Village and a contract with Elektra Records. Her debut LP *A maid of constant sorrow* was released in 1962. Throughout the sixties, Collins was one of the prime movers of the folk movement - interpreting the songs of many of her finest contempories (usually before everyone else) including such names as Bob Dylan, Tom Paxton, Phil Ochs, Leonard Cohen, Joni Mitchell and Jacques Brel, and regularly performing with other folk artists at protest marches and politicial demonstrations. Her excellent musical sensibility led to Collins being hailed as a fine arranger. But her greatest asset was her pure, crystal clear voice, which was a sheer delight. Together with Joan Baez and Joni Mitchell, she was one of the three great women singers produced by the US folk boom. In both the US and UK, Collins has only ever achieved three major hit singles, but all three are classics. *Both sides now*, a Mitchell composition, hit the US chart in late 68 and the UK chart over a year later - simultaneously philosophical and very catchy, this a record that virtually everybody knows even if its title appears unfamiliar. Collins acappella version of *Amazing grace* a traditional 18th centuary hymn that she released in late 1970, logged 67 weeks on the British charts, a total bettered only Frank Sinatra's *My way* and it inspired the famous UK no.1 rendition by the Royal Scots Dragoon Guards. *Send in the clowns* penned by Stephen Sondheim, gave Collins a 1975 Top 20 hit in the States. She remains an active recording artist, still occasionally touching upon political and humanitarian topics despite a more middle of the road flavour. (Bob Macdonald 85)
The folksinger, born in Denver in 1939, began with traditional material on the Elektra label; by her third album she was recording contemporary songs by Bob Dylan, Phil Ochs and Tom Paxton. *In My Life* in 1966 was orchestrated by Joshua Rifkin, another milestone, as was *Wild Flowers*, which included her top ten hit *Both Sides Now*: with prescience or just good taste she was among the first to value the work of Joni Mitchell. Her other single hits were the 18th-century hymn *Amazing Grace* and Stephen Sondheim's *Send In The Clowns*. Stephen Stills wrote *Suite: Judy Blue Eyes* for her. She acted, and also directed a documentary about her former music teacher: 1974's *Antonia: A Woman* was nominated for an Oscar. She is still much-loved and rapturously received by fans in concert; taking good material from wherever she finds it, a 1984 album saw her covering Vince Clarke's *Only You*, a UK hit by both Yazoo and the Flying Pickets. (Donald Clarke 1989).

AMAZING GRACE (OLD GOLD)
Tracks: / Amazing grace.
7" Single: Released Sep '85, on Old Gold, by Old Gold Records. Catalogue no: **OG 9516**

AMAZING GRACE (SINGLE)
Tracks: / Amazing grace.

7" Single: Released Nov '71, on Elektra, by Elektra Records (UK). Deleted Nov '75. Catalogue no: **2101 020**
7" Single: Released Jul '81, on Elektra Asylum, by Elektra Records (USA). Catalogue no: **K 12534**

BOTH SIDES NOW (SINGLE)
Tracks: / Both sides now.
7" Single: Released Jan '70, on Elektra, by Elektra Records (UK). Deleted Jan '73. Catalogue no: **EKSN 45043**

GREAT EXPECTATIONS
Tracks: / Great expectations / Memory.
7" Single: Released May '82, on Elektra, by Elektra Records (UK). Deleted '85. Catalogue no: **K 13180**

SEND IN THE CLOWNS
Tracks: / Send in the clowns.
7" Single: Released Aug '77, on Elektra (USA), by Elektra Records (USA). Catalogue no: **K 12270**

Collins, Lewis

WHEN YOU COME HOME AGAIN
Tracks: / When you come home again.
7" Single: Released Sep '82, on Sour Grape, by Sour Grape Records. Deleted '87. Catalogue no: **SG 111**

Collins, Paul

DON'T WAIT UP FOR ME TONIGHT
Tracks: / Don't wait up for me tonight / Walk out on love.
7" Single: Released Feb '80, on CBS, by CBS Records. Deleted Feb '83. Catalogue no: **CBS 8135**

ROCK 'N' ROLL BEAT
Tracks: / Rock 'n' roll beat / Look but don't touch.
7" Single: Released May '80, on CBS, by CBS Records. Deleted May '85. Catalogue no: **CBS 8575**

Collins, Phil

Biographical details: This British singer, drummer, songwriter, songwriter and producer emerged during the early eighties as a major solo talent, while continuing his group activities. He had first come to public attention at the start of the seventies, when he became drummer with Genesis and began a successful career with them, selling large quantities of albums. In 1976 his profile increased dramatically, as he took over lead vocals duties from Peter Gabriel and rapidly reversed a decline in the band's fortunes. That year he could also be heard on records by Brand X, a new jazz rock outfit. He subsequently continued his work both with Genesis and Brand X, the former gaining huge and ever increasing success on both sides of the Atlantic. In 1981 he launched a solo career and found even greater acceptance than with his supergroup. Born in London in January 1951, Collins had just turned thirty when the *Face value* LP was released. He had also just suffered a marriage breakdown, and his emotional turmoil was fully reflected in the album's love songs and love lost songs. The passion of his vocals, the distinctiveness of his drumming, the power of his compositions and the superb assistance of the Earth, Wind & Fire horn section, all combined to produce an excellent LP that entered the UK charts at no.1 and remained a steady seller for several years. The single *In the air tonight* reached no.2 in Britain. Collins 1982 follow up album *Hello I must be going* was not quite up to the all round standard of its predecessor, but yielded his first UK charts no.1 in January 83: *You can't hurry love,* a perfect vehicle for his powerful drumming, was a straight remake of the Supremes 1966 hit, and stands as one of the few cover versions of an old classic that is arguably better than the original. 1984 brought Collins his first US chart topper with the Arif Mardin - produced slowie *Take a look at me now* the theme from the movie *Against all odds* it peaked at no.2 in the UK. A renowned workaholic, Collins has been the producer of successful records for several other artists, notably Frida (from Abba), Adam Ant and, in 1985, *Easy lover,* a Stateside smash for Philip Bailey, EW&F's lead vocalist. That same year Collins came up with his own *No jacket required* LP, his third successful solo outing, preceding by the big British single *Sussudio.* (Bob Macdonald 85)
The drummer, producer and vocalist began as a child actor, playing the Artful Dodger in Lionel Bart's *Oliver!* in 1964 (following the Small Faces' Steve Marriot in the role). He was in the art-rock band Flaming Youth, joined Genesis as a drummer and took over the vocals in 1975 when Peter Gabriel left. He played on two albums by the band's offshoot Brand X and released his first solo album *Face Value* in 1981. He was already becoming a superstar when he was turned down for a spot at the Academy Awards singing his own Oscar nominee, the theme from *Against All Odds,* because the committee had never heard of him. He played train robber *Buster* in 1987. (Donald Clarke 1989).

12" MEDLEY MEGAMIX
Note: German only limited edition, featuring 'Sussudio', 'Don't Lose My Number', 'You Can't Hurry Love' and 'Take Me Home'. Extended dance tracks, exclusive mixes.
12" Single: Released Nov '87, on WEA (Germany), by WEA Records. Catalogue no: **2586700**

12"ERS
Tracks: / Take me home / Sussudio / Who said I would / Only you know and I know / Don't lose my number / One more night.
CD 5": Released Aug '88, on Virgin, by Virgin Records. Catalogue no: **CDEP 4**

AGAINST ALL ODDS (TAKE A LOOK AT ME NOW)
Tracks: / Against all odds (take a look at me now) / Making a big mistake.
7" Single: Released '84, on Virgin, by Virgin Records. Catalogue no: **VS 674**

DON'T LET HIM STEAL YOUR HEART AWAY
Tracks: / Don't let him steal your heart away / And so to f.
7" Single: Released Mar '83, on Virgin, by Virgin Records. Deleted '89. Catalogue no: **VS 572**
12" Single: Released Mar '83, on Virgin, by Virgin Records. Catalogue no: **VS 572-12**

GROOVY KIND OF LOVE
Tracks: / Groovy kind of love / Big noise (instrumental) / Will you still be waiting? (On CD only-artist:Anne Dudley).
Note: From the film "Buster" which stars Phil Collins as the great train robber Buster Edwards.
12" Single: Released 22 Aug '88, on Virgin, by Virgin Records. Catalogue no: **VST 1117**
12" Single: Released 22 Aug '88, on Virgin, by Virgin Records. Deleted '89. Catalogue no: **VSTG 1117**
7" Single: Released 22 Aug '88, on Virgin, by Virgin Records. Catalogue no: **VS 1117**
CD 5": on Virgin, by Virgin Records. Catalogue no: **VSCD 1117**

I MISSED AGAIN
Tracks: / I missed again / I'm not moving.
7" Single: Released Mar '8, on Virgin, by Virgin Records. Deleted Mar '84. Catalogue no: **VS 402**

IF LEAVING ME IS EASY
Tracks: / If leaving me is easy.
7" Single: Released May '81, on Virgin, by Virgin Records. Deleted May '84. Catalogue no: **VS 423**

IN THE AIR TONIGHT
Tracks: / In the air tonight ('88 remix) / I missed again / In the air tonight (extended version) (12" & CD only).
CD 5": Released Jun '88, on Virgin, by Virgin Records. Catalogue no: **VSCD 102**
7" Single: Released Jan '81, on Virgin, by Virgin Records. Deleted Jan '84. Catalogue no: **VSK 102**
7" Single: Released Jun '88, on Virgin, by Virgin Records. Catalogue no: **VS 102**
12" Single: Released Jun '88, on Virgin, by Virgin Records. Catalogue no: **VST 102**

ONE MORE NIGHT
Tracks: / One more night / I like the way.
7" Single: Released Mar '85, on Virgin, by Virgin Records. Catalogue no: **VS 755**
12" Single: Released Mar '85, on Virgin, by Virgin Records. Catalogue no: **VS 755-12**

SEPARATE LIVES
Tracks: / Separate lives / Only you know and I know (7" only) / Only you know and I know (extended mix) (12" only).
12" Single: Released Nov '85, on Virgin, by Virgin Records. Catalogue no: **VS 818-12**
7" Single: Released Nov '85, on Virgin, by Virgin Records. Catalogue no: **VS 818**

SUSSUDIO
Tracks: / Sussudio / Man with the horn, the.
12" Single: Released Jan '85, on Virgin, by Virgin Records. Catalogue no: **VS 736-12**
7" Single: Released Jan '85, on Virgin, by Virgin Records. Catalogue no: **VS 736**

TAKE ME HOME
Tracks: / Take me home / We said hello goodbye.
7" Single: Released Jul '85, on Virgin, by Virgin Records. Catalogue no: **VS 777**
12" Single: Released Jul '85, on Virgin, by Virgin Records. Catalogue no: **VS 777-12**

THRU THESE WALLS
Tracks: / Thru these walls.
7" Single: Released Oct '82, on Virgin, by Virgin Records. Deleted Oct '85. Catalogue no: **VS 524**

TWO HEARTS
Tracks: / Two hearts / Robbery, The (exerpt) (7" only) / Robbery, The (full length version) (on CD & 12" only).
Note: The song was written and produced by Phil Collins and Lamont Dozier for the film 'Buster'. The video and sleeve continue the sixties theme used for the Buster soundtrack.
CD 3": Released '88, on Virgin, by Virgin Records. Catalogue no: **VSCD 1141**
7" Single: Released 14 Nov '88, on Virgin, by Virgin Records. Catalogue no: **VS 1141**
12" Single: Released 14 Nov '88, on Virgin, by Virgin Records. Catalogue no: **VST 1141**

YOU CAN'T HURRY LOVE
Tracks: / You can't hurry love / I can't believe it's true / Oddball (CD & 12" only-Home demo version of "Do you know, do you care?").
12" Single: Released Nov '82, on Virgin, by Virgin Records. Catalogue no: **VS 531-12**
7" Pic: Released Nov '82, on Virgin, by Virgin Records. Deleted '89. Catalogue no: **VSY 531**
7" Single: Released Nov '82, on Virgin, by Virgin Records. Catalogue no: **VS 531**

Collins, Rodger

YOU SEXY SUGAR PLUM (BUT I LIKE IT)
Tracks: / You sexy sugar plum (but I like it).
7" Single: Released Apr '76, on Fantasy (1), by BMG Records (UK). Deleted Apr '79. Catalogue no: **FTC 132**

Collins, Rossington

DON'T MISUNDERSTAND ME
Tracks: / Don't misunderstand me / Winners and losers.
7" Single: Released Aug '80, on MCA, by MCA Records. Deleted '83. Catalogue no: **MCA 636**

TESHAWNA
Tracks: / Teshawna / Gonna miss it when it's gone / Don't stop me now.
7" Single: Released Oct '81, on MCA, by MCA Records. Deleted Oct '84. Catalogue no: **MCAT 752**

Collins, Selah

NAH GO GIVE YOU
Tracks: / Nah go give you.
7" Single: Released 21 Apr '89, on Unity, Catalogue no: **FEA 08**

ON AND ON
Tracks: / On and on.
12" Single: Released Dec '88, on Unity, Catalogue no: **FEA 06**

Collins, Willie

WHERE YOU GONNA BE TONIGHT - EDIT
Tracks: / Where you gonna be tonight (edit) / Sticky situation.
7" Single: Released Jun '86, on Capitol, by EMI Records. Deleted '88. Catalogue no: **CL 410**
12" Single: Released Jun '86, on Capitol, by EMI Records. Deleted '88. Catalogue no: **12 CL 410**

Collister, Christine

WARM LOVE GONE COLD
Tracks: / Warm love gone cold / Cavatina (From Act 2 of the Marriage of Figaro.) / Warm love gone cold - extended version (On 12" version only.) / For Lucille (Extra track on 12" only.).
Note: Theme from the BBC-TV series "The Life And Loves Of A She Devil".
7" Single: Released Sep '86, on BBC, by BBC Records & Tapes. Deleted 31 Aug '88. Catalogue no: **RESL 199**
12" Single: Released Sep '86, on BBC, by BBC Records & Tapes. Deleted 31 Aug '88. Catalogue no: **12 RSL 199**

Colm III

CHRISTMAS TREE
Tracks: / Christmas tree / Go an' get 'em.
12" Single: Released Aug '87, on Ruby Red, by Ruby Red Records. Catalogue no: **12 LTD 444**

TAKE ME HIGH
Tracks: / You take me high.
7" Single: Released Dec '88, on Ruby Red, by Ruby Red Records. Catalogue no: **LTD 555**

Colon, Willie

Biographical details: Born in Bronx (NYC) in 1950, Colon began as a trombonist and a bandleader, but singing and songwriting soon came to the fore. He began recording at 17; his first few albums established an image as a Hispanic street punk for some years; vocalist Hector Lavoe appeared on all his albums until 1974, when he handed the band to Lavoe and produced albums with Lavoe and Rueben Blades, adding an eclectic mix of influences: one album featured lead guitarist Elliott Randall from Sha Na Na. His credits are too long to list here, including salsa ballets for TV and albums with Celia Cruz; the salsa superstar's hits in the UK are several cuts about the usual dance stuff. (Donald Clarke 1989)n.

SET FIRE TO ME - LATIN JAZZBO VERSION
Tracks: / Set fire to me - latin jazzbo version / Inferno dub.
7" Single: Released Jun '86, on A&M, by A&M Records. Deleted '87. Catalogue no: **AM 330**
12" Single: Released Jun '86, on A&M, by A&M Records. Deleted '87. Catalogue no: **AMY 330**

SHE DON'T KNOW I'M ALIVE
Tracks: / She don't know I'm alive / She don't know I"m alive (dub) / Set fire to me.
Note: Set fire to me on 12" version only.
7" Single: Released Feb '87, on A&M, by A&M Records. Deleted Mar '88. Catalogue no: **AM 380**
12" Single: Released Feb '87, on A&M, by A&M Records. Deleted Mar '88. Catalogue no: **AMY 380**

Colonel Abrams

MUSIC IS THE ANSWER
Tracks: / Music is the answer.
7" Single: Released Nov '85, on PRT, by Castle Communications Records. Catalogue no: **7P 336**
12" Single: Released Nov '85, on PRT, by Castle Communications Records. Catalogue no: **12P 336**

OVER AND OVER
Tracks: / Over and over / Speculation.
7" Single: Released Aug '86, on MCA, by MCA Records. Catalogue no: **MCA 1041**
12" Single: Released Aug '86, on MCA, by MCA Records. Catalogue no: **MCAT 1041**

TRAPPED
Tracks: / Trapped.
7" Single: Released Aug '85, on MCA, by MCA Records. Catalogue no: **MCA 997**
12" Single: Released Sep '85, on MCA, by MCA Records. Catalogue no: **MCAX 997**
12" Single: Released Aug '85, on MCA, by MCA Records. Catalogue no: **MCAT 997**

Colonel, Daddy

TAKE A TRIP
Tracks: / Take a trip.
12" Single: Released Sep '85, on UK Bubblers, by Greensleeves Records. Deleted '87. Catalogue no: **UKMC 7**

Colonel Lloydie

TENDER TOUCH (SINGLE)
Tracks: / Tender touch.
7" Single: Released Jun '88, on Starlight, Catalogue no: **SLD 547**

Colorado

Biographical details: British all-girl vocal group Colorado released a number of singles and albums through the UK's independent distribution network during the late 70's and early 80's. The only record to hit the charts was 1978's *California Dreamin,* a remake of the Mamas & Papas' 1966 hit: Colorado's salute to California peaked at No 45 in the British singles chart. (Bob MacDonald, February 1985.).

BOOGIE GRASS SATURDAY NIGHT
Tracks: / Boogie grass Saturday night / Love is like an echo.
7" Single: Released Aug '81, on Big R, by Big R Records. Catalogue no: **BRS 05**

CALIFORNIA DREAMIN'
Tracks: / California dreamin'.
7" Single: Released Oct '78, on Pinnacle, by Pinnacle Records. Deleted Oct '81. Catalogue no: **PIN 67**

GREEN FIELDS OF FRANCE PARTS 1 & 2
Tracks: / Green fields of France (part 1) / Green fields of France (part 2).
7" Single: Released May '82, on Big R, by Big R Records. Catalogue no: **BRS 09**

TENNESSEE WHISKY AND TEXAS WOMAN
Tracks: / Tennessee whisky and Texas woman / Thrill of the chase.
7" Single: Released Dec '81, on Big R, by Big R Records. Catalogue no: **BR 07**

Colorblind James

DANCE CRITTERS (REMIX)
Tracks: / Dance critters (remix) / You need somebody on your side.
12" Single: Released Oct '88, on Fundamental, by Fundamental Music Records.

Catalogue no: **PRAY 009**

PEEL SESSIONS: COLORBLIND JAMES EXPERIENCE
12" Single: Released Oct '89, on Strange Fruit, by Strange Fruit Records. Catalogue no: **SFPS 076**
CD 5": Released Oct '89, on Strange Fruit, by Strange Fruit Records. Catalogue no: **SFPSCD 076**

Colors

L.O.S.(LOVE ON SIGHT)
Tracks: / L.O.S. (love on sight).
12" Single: Released Aug '85, on 4th & Broadway, by Island Records. Catalogue no: **12 BRW 34**

PAY ME BACK MY LOVE
Tracks: / Pay me back my love / Pay me back my love-edited dub mix.
7" Single: Released Jul '86, on Prelude, Deleted '87. Catalogue no: **ZB 40797**
12" Single: Released Jul '86, on Prelude, Deleted '87. Catalogue no: **ZT 40798**

Colour Code

DANCE WITH THE TIMES
Tracks: / Dance with the times.
7" Single: Released Feb '85, on Ryker, Catalogue no: **RYK 3**
7" Single: Released Mar '85, on Ryker, Catalogue no: **RYKS 3**
12" Single: Released Feb '85, on Ryker, Catalogue no: **RYKT 3**
12" Single: Released Mar '85, on Ryker, Catalogue no: **RYKM 3**

I'VE HAD ENOUGH
Tracks: / I've had enough / I've had enough (7" mix) / It takes two.
Note: (Self-061 485 6702)
12" Single: Released Apr '87, on Zebra Int., by Zebra International Records. Deleted '87. Catalogue no: **ZBR 121**

Colour Me Pop

DON'T STOP
Tracks: / Don't stop.
7" Single: Released Aug '84, on Waterfall, by Waterfall Records. Catalogue no: **WFL 1**

GIRL WHO SHARES MY SHIRT
Tracks: / Girl who shares my shirt.
7" Single: Released Feb '84, on American Phonogram, by American Phonogram Int.. Catalogue no: **NCH 008**
12" Single: Released Nov '83, on American Phonogram, by American Phonogram Int.. Catalogue no: **BACKS 008**
12" Single: Released Feb '84, on Metalworks, by Metalworks Records. Catalogue no: **12 NCH 008**

Colour Out Of Time

SHE SPINS
Tracks: / She spins.
7" Single: Released Nov '82, on Monsters In Orbit, Deleted '84. Catalogue no: **TV EYE 005**

Colour Supplement

MICHAELANGELO
Tracks: / Michaelangelo / You're gone.
7" Single: Released Jul '82, on Headline, by Creole Records. Deleted '85. Catalogue no: **LIN 1**

Colour Vision

UNTIL TOMORROW
Tracks: / Until tomorrow.
7" Single: Released Jan '80, on Alien, Catalogue no: **ALIEN 11**

Colourbox

BABY I LOVE YOU
Tracks: / Baby I love you / Looks like we're shy one horse / Shoot out* (* extra track on 12".).
7" Single: Released May '86, on 4AD, by 4AD Records. Deleted Jan '88. Catalogue no: **AD 604**
12" Single: Released May '86, on 4AD, by 4AD Records. Catalogue no: **BAD 604**

BREAKDOWN
Tracks: / Breakdown / Tarantula.
7" Single: Released Apr '83, on 4AD, by 4AD Records. Catalogue no: **AD 304**
12" Single: Released Apr '83, on 4AD, by 4AD Records. Deleted Jul '88. Catalogue no: **BAD 304**

MIXED UP MURDER
Tracks: / Mixed up murder.
7" Single: Released Oct '83, on 4AD, by 4AD Records. Catalogue no: **AD 315**

OFFICIAL COLOURBOX WORLD CUP THEME
Tracks: / Official colourbox world cup theme.
7" Single: Released Apr '86, on 4AD, by 4AD Records. Catalogue no: **AD 605**
12" Single: Released Apr '86, on 4AD, by 4AD Records. Catalogue no: **BAD 605**

PUNCH
Tracks: / Punch.
7" Single: Released Apr '84, on 4AD, by 4AD Records. Deleted Jan '88. Catalogue no: **AD 407**
12" Single: Released Apr '84, on 4AD, by 4AD Records. Catalogue no: **BAD 407**

SAY YOU
Tracks: / Say you / Fast dump.
7" Single: Released Jul '85, on 4AD, by 4AD Records. Deleted Jan '88. Catalogue no: **AD 507**
7" Single: Released Mar '84, on 4AD, by 4AD Records. Deleted Jan '88. Catalogue no: **AD 403**
12" Single: Released Mar '84, on 4AD, by 4AD Records. Catalogue no: **BAD 403**

Colourfield

CASTLES IN THE AIR
Tracks: / Castles in the air / Love strings.
7" Single: Released Apr '85, on Chrysalis, by Chrysalis Records. Deleted Apr '88. Catalogue no: **COLF 4**

COLOUR FIELD, THE
Tracks: / Colourfield, The.
7" Single: Released Jan '84, on Chrysalis, by Chrysalis Records. Deleted Jan '87. Catalogue no: **COLF 1**
12" Single: Released '86, on Chrysalis, by Chrysalis Records. Catalogue no: **COLFX 1**

RUNNING AWAY
Tracks: / Running away / Digging it deep.
12" Single: Released Feb '87, on Chrysalis, by Chrysalis Records. Catalogue no: **COLFX 6**
7" Single: Released Feb '87, on Chrysalis, by Chrysalis Records. Catalogue no: **COLF 6**

SHE
Tracks: / She / Monkey in winter.
7" Single: Released Jul '87, on Chrysalis, by Chrysalis Records. Catalogue no: **COLF 7-2**

TAKE
Tracks: / Take.
7" Single: Released Jul '84, on Chrysalis, by Chrysalis Records. Deleted Jul '87. Catalogue no: **COLF 2**

THINGS COULD BE BEAUTIFUL
Tracks: / Things could be beautiful / Frosty morning.
7" Single: Released Jan '86, on Chrysalis, by Chrysalis Records. Catalogue no: **COLF 5**
12" Single: Released Jan '86, on Chrysalis, by Chrysalis Records. Catalogue no: **COLFX 5**

THINKING OF YOU
Tracks: / Thinking of you.
7" Single: Released Jan '85, on Chrysalis, by Chrysalis Records. Deleted '87. Catalogue no: **COLF 3**
12" Single: Released Jan '85, on Chrysalis, by Chrysalis Records. Catalogue no: **COLFX 3**

Colours

I WANNA MAKE LOVE
Tracks: / I wanna make love.
CD 5": Released Sep '89, on WEA, by WEA Records. Catalogue no: **YZ 418CD**
Cassingle: Released Sep '89, on WEA, by WEA Records. Catalogue no: **YZ 418C**
7" Single: Released Sep '89, on WEA, by WEA Records. Catalogue no: **YZ 418**
12" Single: Released Sep '89, on WEA, by WEA Records. Catalogue no: **YZ 418T**

Colt & Colby

SAVE YOUR LOVE
Tracks: / Save your love.
7" Single: Released Aug '84, on Hollywood, by Hollywood Records. Catalogue no: **HWD 007**
12" Single: Released Aug '84, on Hollywood, by Hollywood Records. Catalogue no: **12 HWD 007**

Coltrane, Robbie

NEW ORLEANS
Tracks: / New Orleans / Enough is enough.
7" Single: Released Mar '88, on Strike (2), Catalogue no: **STRK 1**
12" Single: Released Mar '88, on Strike (2), Catalogue no: **12 STRK 1**

Columbia Brothers

YOU'RE LEAVING
Tracks: / You're leaving.
7" Single: Released May '80, on Hotel, Catalogue no: **ROOM 002**

Comateens

RESIST HER
Tracks: / Resist her.
7" Single: Released Jul '84, on Virgin, by Virgin Records. Deleted '89. Catalogue no: **VS 692**

Combat 84

ORDERS OF THE DAY
Tracks: / Orders of the day.
7" Single: Released Dec '82, on Victory (1), Catalogue no: **VIC 1**

RAPIST
Tracks: / Rapist.
7" Single: Released Aug '83, on Victory (1), Catalogue no: **VIC 2**

Combe Passe

MAMA TOLD HER
Tracks: / Mama told her.
7" Single: Released Feb '83, on Crazy Viking, by Crazy Vikings Records. Catalogue no: **CV 1**
12" Single: Released Feb '83, on Crazy Viking, by Crazy Vikings Records. Catalogue no: **CVT 1**

Combo Passe

TICO TICO
Tracks: / Tico tico / Launderama.
7" Single: Released Oct '81, on 101, Deleted Oct '84. Catalogue no: **ICUR 3**

Come Alive

ON MY WAY
Tracks: / On my way.
7" Single: Released Dec '84, on Stinkfoot, Catalogue no: **SMSI 2**

Come On

GUITAR PARTY
Tracks: / Guitar party / Zero.
7" Single: Released May '84, on Albion, by Albion Records. Catalogue no: **ION 161**

HOUSEWIVES PLAY TENNIS
Tracks: / Housewives play tennis / Howard after six.
7" Single: Released Mar '81, on Aura Records, by Aura Records. Deleted '88. Catalogue no: **AUS 120**

Comfort & Joy

JINGLE BELLE RAP
Tracks: / Jingle belle rap / It's xmas.
7" Single: Released Dec '86, on DMC, Catalogue no: **DECK 4**
12" Single: Released Dec '86, on DMC, Catalogue no: **DECK 124**

Commando

HYMNE A L'AMOUR
Tracks: / Hymne a l'amour.
7" Single: Released Mar '89, on Nowyertalkin', by Nowyertalikin' Records. Catalogue no: **7TALK 6**
12" Single: Released Mar '89, on Nowyertalkin', by Nowyertalikin' Records. Catalogue no: **12TALK 6**

TELL ME
Tracks: / Tell me.
CD 5": Released Jan '89, on Nowyertalkin', by Nowyertalikin' Records. Catalogue no: **CDTALK 5**
7" Single: Released Jan '89, on Nowyertalkin', by Nowyertalikin' Records. Catalogue no: **7TALK 5**
12" Single: Released Jan '89, on Nowyertalkin', by Nowyertalikin' Records. Catalogue no: **12TALK 5**

Commentators

N-N-NINETEEN NOT OUT
Tracks: / N-n-nineteen not out.
7" Single: on VV Big, Catalogue no: **Unknown**
7" Single: Released Jun '85, on WEA, by WEA Records. Catalogue no: **OVAL 100**
12" Single: Released Jun '85, on WEA, by WEA Records. Catalogue no: **OVAL 100T**

Commercial Music

GET A JOB
Tracks: / Get a job / Love and money.
7" Single: Released Oct '88, on WEA, by WEA Records. Catalogue no: **YZ 318**
12" Single: Released Oct '88, on WEA, by WEA Records. Catalogue no: **YZ 318T**

Committee

OPEN YOUR EYES
Tracks: / Open your eyes.
12" Single: Released Aug '85, on Fire, by Fire Records. Catalogue no: **FIRE 4**

Commodores

Biographical details: Commodores At the time of their greatest success, this American soul band consisted of William King, Ron LaPread, Thomas McClary, Walter 'Clyde' Orange, Lionel Richie and Milan Williams.
The Commodores were formed in the mid-Sixties by King, McClary, Richie and Williams - all were based in Alabama. In the early Seventies, the group won the attention of Motown Records, securing a supporting role on tour with the Jackson Five, the company's red hot young stars and winning a recording contract with the label. The line up now included Orange and LaPraed. The group broke big in 1974 with the *Machine Gun* LP and, in particular, its punchy instrumental title single, which was a Top 30 hit in both the US and UK. They did not hit that mark again in Britain until '77, but success continued apace in the States with a string of hits through the mid-Seventies. The band had two distinct styles: hard, funky dance tracks such as *Slippery When Wet* and *Brick House* (the latter a US Top 5 hit) were sung by Walter Orange; while other smash singles - *Sweet Love* and *Just To Be Close To You* were slow, ultra romantic ballads penned and sung by Lionel Richie. By the late Seventies, the latter format was gaining the upper hand, giving the band their biggest singles and leading the public to think of Richie as the leader and frontman. The four prime examples of this were *Easy, Three Times A Lady, Sail On* and *Still*, all Top 10 hits on both sides of the Atlantic and all aimed straight at the emotions of the heart. In particular, *Three Times A Lady* was a US and UK chart-topper, became Motown UK's biggest hit to date (not overtaken until 1984), and took the group's international career to a new level. *Still* gave them a second American No.1.
1980 saw a lessening of the Commodores' public profile. They failed to come up with a major single and turned briefly to gospel via such tracks as *Jesus Is Love* on the *Heroes* album. They returned to secular soul and pop in 1981 with two new US Top Tenners: the uptempo *Lady (you bring me up)* and the slow *Oh No*, the latter in the usual ballad vein that was now a Richie tradition. However, while these two singles were on the charts, Richie was enjoying a mammoth nine week run at the US No.1 position with *Endless Love*, another self penned love song, on which he dueted with Diana Ross. With this huge success under his belt, coupled with another monster American No.1 written by Richie for Kenny Rogers, the way was now clear for Richie to step out as a solo star. This he did in 1982, and his incredible success contined unabated. For the group he left behind, however, the going was less easy. For example, in the same week in November 1983 that Richie reached the top of the US chart with *All Night Long (all night)*, the Commodores were struggling to crack the Top 50 with their Richie-less single. In 1984 guitarist McClary also left to pursue a solo career and was replaced by J.D.Nichols. After a barren period, the Commodores confounded their doubters in 1985 by returning to the US and UK charts with *Nightshift*, a touching and beautifully executed tribute to Jackie Wilson and Marvin Gaye, two recently deceased soul greats. (Bob Macdonald 1/2/85)
A soul group formed in 1968; they became the most successful Motown act of recent years after Stevie Wonder, with 20 hits in the Billboard Hot 100 1974-82. The original lineup of school friends from Tuskegee (Alabama). Institute included Lionel Richie, vocals and tenor sax; Milan Williams on keyboards and guitar; William King on horns and guitarist Thomas McClary, plus several others from a merger of two groups: they chose their new name from a dictionary, later joking that they were almost called the Commodes. They went to New York in 1969 and made flop singles for Atlantic; by the time of their first Motown album in 1974 (*Machine Gun*) they were a sextet including Ronald LaPread on bass and Walter 'Clyde' Orange on drums. Their instrumental hard funk was successful, but overtaken by ballads as Richie's songwriting emerged: *Just To Be Close To You, Sweet Love, Easy* and *Sail On* were top 5 in 1975-9, while *Three Times A Lady* and *Still* were number ones. He pursued solo projects, then became a solo black superstar, replaced by J.D. Nicholas; they continued to chart: their second album without Richie, *Nightshift* in 1985, had a hit title track and made Billboard's top 30 albums. (Donald Clarke 1989)-.

ANIMAL INSTINCT
Tracks: / Animal instinct.
7" Single: Released Apr '84, on Motown, by BMG Records (UK). Deleted '86. Catalogue no: **ZB 40097**
12" Single: Released Apr '84, on Motown, by BMG Records (UK). Deleted '86. Catalogue no: **ZT 40098**

BRICK HOUSE
Tracks: / Brick house / Sweet love.
7" Single: Released Oct '81, on Motown, by BMG Records (UK). Deleted '83. Catalogue no: **TMG 1086**

EASY
Tracks: / Easy / Machine gun / I feel sanctified / Brick house (Only on 12" version.).

COMMODORES - SAIL ON (Released on Motown)

7" Single: Released Aug '88, on Motown, by BMG Records (UK). Catalogue no: **ZB 41793**
7" Single: Released Oct '81, on Motown, by BMG Records (UK). Catalogue no: **TMG 1073**
12" Single: Released Aug '88, on Motown, by BMG Records (UK). Catalogue no: **ZT 41794**

FLYING HIGH
Tracks: / Flying high.
7" Single: Released Jun '78, on Motown, by BMG Records (UK). Deleted Jun '81. Catalogue no: **TMG 111**

GOIN' TO THE BANK
Tracks: / Going to the bank / Serious love.
12" Single: Released Oct '86, on Polydor, by Polydor Ltd. Deleted Aug '87. Catalogue no: **POSPX 826**
7" Single: Released Oct '86, on Polydor, by Polydor Ltd. Deleted Mar '87. Catalogue no: **POSP 826**

GRIPP
Tracks: / Gripp.
7" Single: Released Apr '89, on Polydor, by Polydor Ltd. Deleted Oct '89. Catalogue no: **871 370-7**
12" Single: Released Apr '89, on Polydor, by Polydor Ltd. Deleted Oct '89. Catalogue no: **871 691-1**

HEROES (SINGLE)
Tracks: / Heroes / Don't you be worried.
7" Single: Released Oct '86, on Motown, by BMG Records (UK). Deleted '88. Catalogue no: **TMG 1206**

JANET
Tracks: / Janet.
12" Single: Released Aug '85, on Motown, by BMG Records (UK). Deleted '88. Catalogue no: **ZT 40312**
7" Single: Released Aug '85, on Motown, by BMG Records (UK). Deleted '88. Catalogue no: **ZB 40311**

JESUS IS LOVE
Tracks: / Jesus is love / Mighty spirit.
7" Single: Released Oct '81, on Motown, by BMG Records (UK). Deleted '83. Catalogue no: **TMG 1218**

JUST TO BE CLOSE TO YOU
Tracks: / Just to be close to you.
7" Single: Released Nov '78, on Motown, by BMG Records (UK). Deleted Nov '81. Catalogue no: **TMG 1127**

LADY (YOU BRING ME UP)
Tracks: / Lady (you bring me up) / Gettin' it.
7" Single: Released Oct '81, on Motown, by BMG Records (UK). Deleted '83. Catalogue no: **TMG 1238**
12" Single: Released Oct '81, on Motown, by BMG Records (UK). Deleted '83. Catalogue no: **TMGT 1238**

LUCY
Tracks: / Lucy / Heaven knows.
7" Single: Released Oct '82, on Motown, by BMG Records (UK). Deleted '88. Catalogue no: **TMG 1282**
12" Single: Released Oct '82, on Motown, by BMG Records (UK). Deleted '84. Catalogue no: **TMGT 1282**

MACHINE GUN (SINGLE)
Tracks: / Machine gun.
7" Single: Released Aug '74, on Tamla Motown, by Motown Records (UK). Deleted Aug '77. Catalogue no: **TMG 902**

NIGHTSHIFT (SINGLE)
Tracks: / Nightshift / I keep running.
7" Single: Released Jan '85, on Motown, by BMG Records (UK). Catalogue no: **TMG 1371**
12" Single: Released Jan '85, on Motown, by BMG Records (UK). Catalogue no: **TMGT 1371**

OH NO
Tracks: / Oh no / Are you happy.
7" Single: Released Oct '81, on Motown, by BMG Records (UK). Deleted '83. Catalogue no: **TMG 1245**

OLD FASHIONED LOVE
Tracks: / Old fashioned love.
7" Single: Released Oct '81, on Motown, by BMG Records (UK). Deleted '83. Catalogue no: **TMG 1193**

ONLY YOU
Tracks: / Only you / Cebu.
7" Single: Released Sep '83, on Motown, by BMG Records (UK). Deleted '85. Catalogue no: **TMG 1317**

REACH HIGH
Tracks: / Reach high.
7" Single: Released Feb '83, on Motown, by BMG Records (UK). Deleted '85. Catalogue no: **TMG 1292**
12" Single: Released Feb '83, on Motown, by BMG Records (UK). Deleted '85. Catalogue no: **TMGT 1292**

SAIL ON
Tracks: / Sail on / Captain quick draw.
7" Single: Released Oct '81, on Motown, by BMG Records (UK). Deleted '83. Catalogue no: **TMG 1155**

STILL
Tracks: / Still.
7" Single: Released Oct '81, on Motown, by BMG Records (UK). Catalogue no: **TMG 1166**
7" Single: Released Apr '88, on Motown, by BMG Records (UK). Catalogue no: **ZB 41901**

THREE TIMES A LADY
Tracks: / Three times a lady.
7" Single: Released Apr '83, on Motown, by BMG Records (UK). Catalogue no: **TMG 1113**

TURN OFF THE LIGHTS
Tracks: / Turn off the lights / Painted picture.
7" Single: Released Nov '83, on Motown, by BMG Records (UK). Deleted '85. Catalogue no: **TMG 1322**
12" Single: Released Nov '83, on Motown, by BMG Records (UK). Deleted '85. Catalogue no: **TMGT 1322**

UNITED IN LOVE
Tracks: / United in love / Talk to me / Going to the bank (credit card mix) (On 12" only).
7" Single: Released 13 Jun '87, on Polydor, by Polydor Ltd. Catalogue no: **POSP 866**
7" Single: Released May '87, on Polydor, by Polydor Ltd. Deleted Jan '88. Catalogue no: **POSP 866**
12" Single: Released 13 Jun '87, on Polydor, by Polydor Ltd. Catalogue no: **POSPX 866**
12" Single: Released May '87, on Polydor, by Polydor Ltd. Deleted Jan '88. Catalogue no: **POSPX 866**

WHY YOU WANNA TRY ME
Tracks: / Why you wanna try me.
7" Single: Released Apr '82, on Motown, by BMG Records (UK). Deleted '84. Catalogue no: **TMG 1256**
12" Single: Released Apr '82, on Motown, by BMG Records (UK). Deleted '84. Catalogue no: **TMGT 1256**

WONDERLAND
Tracks: / Wonderland / Lovin' you.
7" Single: Released Oct '81, on Motown, by BMG Records (UK). Deleted '83. Catalogue no: **TMG 1172**

ZOO, THE Human zoo, The
Tracks: / Zoo, The.
7" Single: Released Nov '74, on Tamla Motown, by Motown Records (UK). Deleted Nov '77. Catalogue no: **TMG 924**

ZOOM (SINGLE)
Tracks: / Zoom / Too hot ta trot.
7" Single: Released Oct '81, on Motown, by BMG Records (UK). Deleted '88. Catalogue no: **TMG 1096**

Common Knowledge

VICTORIA
Tracks: / Victoria / Big fat baby.
7" Single: Released Jan '85, on Mercury, by Phonogram Ltd. Catalogue no: **MER 171**

Communal Drop

FANATICS
Tracks: / Fanatics.
12" Single: Released May '85, on WRTR, Catalogue no: **DROP 1**

Communards

DISENCHANTED
Tracks: / Disenchanted / Johnny verso / Annie* (* Extra track on 12".).
7" Single: Released May '86, on London Records, by London Records. Deleted Sep '87. Catalogue no: **LON 89**
12" Single: Released May '86, on London Records, by London Records. Catalogue no: **LONX 89**

DON'T LEAVE ME THIS WAY
Tracks: / Don't leave me this way / Sanctified.
7" Single: Released Aug '86, on London Records, by London Records. Deleted Oct '88. Catalogue no: **LON 103**
12" Single: Released '87, on London Records, by London Records. Deleted Feb '89. Catalogue no: **LOXR 103**
12" Single: Released Aug '86, on London Records, by London Records. Deleted Oct '88. Catalogue no: **LONX 103**
12" Single: Released '86, on London Records, by London Records. Deleted Feb '89. Catalogue no: **LONXR 103**

FOR A FRIEND
Tracks: / For a friend / Victims (live) / Don't leave me this way (live) (track on 12") / Heavens above (track on 12").
CD 5": Released Mar '88, on London Records, by London Records. Deleted Oct '88. Catalogue no: **LONCD 166**
7" Single: Released Feb '88, on London Records, by London Records. Deleted Oct '88. Catalogue no: **LON 166**
12" Single: Released '88, on London Records, by London Records. Deleted Feb '89. Catalogue no: **LONY 166**
12" Single: Released Feb '88, on London Records, by London Records. Deleted Oct '88. Catalogue no: **LONX 166**
12" Single: Released '88, on London Records, by London Records. Deleted Feb '89. Catalogue no: **LONZ 166**

NEVER CAN SAY GOODBYE
Tracks: / Never can say goodbye / 77, The great escape / Piece of saxophone (on 12" only.) / I do it all for love (Available on 12" only).
7" Single: Released Oct '87, on London Records, by London Records. Deleted Oct '88. Catalogue no: **LON 158**
12" Single: Released Oct '87, on London Records, by London Records. Deleted Oct '88. Catalogue no: **LONX 158**
CD 5": on London Records, by London Records. Deleted Oct '88. Catalogue no: **LONCD 158**

NIGHT, THE
Tracks: / Night, The.
12" Single: Released Nov '86, on London Records, by London Records. Catalogue no: **LONX 110**
7" Single: Released Nov '86, on London Records, by London Records. Catalogue no: **LON 110**

SO COLD THE NIGHT Remix
Tracks: / Multimix featuring don't leave me this way, The / So cold the night / Disenchanted.
12" Single: Released Dec '86, on London Records, by London Records. Catalogue no: **LONXR 110**
7" Single: Released Nov '86, on London Records, by London Records. Deleted Nov '89. Catalogue no: **LON 110**

THERE'S MORE TO LOVE
Tracks: / There's more to love / There's more to love (ext) (on 12" only) / Zing went the strings of my heart / Spanish Rap (El amor no es solo un hombre y una mujer) (Only on 12" single.) / When the boy in your heart is the boy in your arms (On CD only).
CD 5": Released Jun '88, on London Records, by London Records. Catalogue no: **LONCD 173**
12" Single: Released Jun '88, on London Records, by London Records. Deleted Feb '89. Catalogue no: **LONX 173**
12" Single: Released Jun '88, on London Records, by London Records. Deleted Feb '89. Catalogue no: **LONXR 173**
7" Single: Released Jun '88, on London Records, by London Records. Deleted Feb '89. Catalogue no: **LON 173**

TOMORROW
Tracks: / I just want let you know / Tomorrow.
12" Single: Released '88, on London Records, by London Records. Deleted Feb '89. Catalogue no: **LONT 143**
7" Single: Released Aug '87, on London Records, by London Records. Deleted Oct '88. Catalogue no: **LON 143**
7" Single: Released '88, on London Records, by London Records. Deleted Feb '89. Catalogue no: **LONR 143**
12" Single: Released Aug '87, on London Records, by London Records. Deleted Oct '88. Catalogue no: **LONX 143**
7" Single: on London Records, by London Records. Deleted Oct '88. Catalogue no: **LONB 143**

YOU ARE MY WORLD
Tracks: / You are my world / Judgement day / Czardas (Available on 12" version only.).

12" Single: Released Sep '85, on London Records, by London Records. Catalogue no: **LONX 77**
CD 5": on London Records, by London Records. Deleted Oct '88. Catalogue no: **LONFC 123**
12" Single: Released '87, on London Records, by London Records. Deleted Feb '89. Catalogue no: **LONXR 123**
12" Single: Released Feb '87, on London Records, by London Records. Deleted Oct '88. Catalogue no: **LONX 123**
7" Single: Released Sep '85, on London Records, by London Records. Catalogue no: **LON 77**
7" Single: Released Feb '87, on London Records, by London Records. Deleted Oct '88. Catalogue no: **LON 123**

Como, Perry

Biographical details: Como, Perry This American singer, born Pierino Como in Pennsylvania in 1912 was one of America's top crooners of the Forties and Fifties and enjoyed huge international sales. In a career spanning fifty years, he attained renewed record stardom in the Seventies. Como was dubbed 'the singing barber' because hairdressing was his original profession - he was already in the process of buying his own shop at the tender age of 14 and, by his early twenties, he had a well established business in Canonsburg, Pennsylvania. In 1934 he entered the music business, touring the Midwest for three years as a vocalist with the Freddie Carlone Band; following that, he had a five year stint with the better known Ted Weems Orchestra. By the mid Forties he had performed at night clubs and theatres, signed a recording contract, landed a movie contract and achieved his first million selling record. That smash hit was 1945's *Till The End of Time*, a Chopin adaptation that was a huge selling American No.1 for Como. He quickly followed it with a double A sided winner, *If I Loved You/I'm Gonna Love That Girl*, and then embarked on a string of American hits that lasted for fifteen years. When the British record charts were inaugurated in late 1952, he was soon in on the UK action, leading the list for five weeks in early '53 with *Don't Let The Stars Get In Your Eyes*. As well as his record sales, Como was hugely popular on television during the Fifties and, thanks to his top

rated TV variety show (which showcased a number of rock'n'roll and rhythm and blues acts in addition to those in the early listening genre), Como became the world's highest paid television personality. His very relaxed singing style and equally casual real life persona made him perfect for both the visual and disc media. During the rock'n'roll explosion, he included a prudent batch of uptempo pop songs in his repertoire which, though firmly in the middle of the road, were as near to rock as Como could get; an example of this was his 1956 US No.1 *Hot Diggity.* He also reached the American Top slot during this period with 1957's *Round and Round* and 1958's *Catch A Falling Star.* Britain preferred the other side of the latter disc and made *Magic Moments* No.1 for a mammoth eight weeks.
Como managed to hold own during the rock'n'roll era, but did not compete in the Beatles dominated Sixties pop years. But after a decade without major chart stardom, he returned in the early Seventies to demonstrate his durability. *It's Impossible* was a transatlantic Top Tenner in 1971. Though never returning to the US Top 10 thereafter, his UK career gained a fresh impetus in '73: he achieved long running smash singles with Don McLean's *And I Love You So* and Kris Kristofferson's *For The Good Times,* and the LP *And I Love You So* began a 109 week run on the British album chart, evantually hitting the No.1 spot. These were pretty impressive statistics for a man in his early Sixties, who was consequently far more than twice the age of many of his chart rivals. This intriguing situation occurred again at Christmas 1975, when his TV advertised *40 Greatest* collection enjoyed two runs at the top of the UK LP chart - alternating to No.1 with Queen's *A Night At The Opera.* (Bob Macdonald 1/2/85)
An all-time favorite pop singer, born in 1912 in Canonsburg, Pennsylvania. He had a barber shop in his home town, but joined the Ted Weems band in 1936; Weems broke up the band and went to war in 1942, Como signed with Victor and never looked back. He had 42 top 10 hits in the Billboard charts 1944-58; his totsl USA chart entries 1940-55 were second only to Bing Crosby's. In 1952 *Don't Let The Stars Get In Your Eyes* was one of the biggest hits ever; *Magic Moments* in 1958 was one of Bert Bacharach's first hit songs. Como appeared in a few films but the big screen did not capture his personality; he was a massive star on the smaller screen, hosting a weekly hour-long TV variety show 1955-63 of very high quality, with Ray Charles contributing arrangements of Como/guest medleys (also a choral director; the Ray Charles Singers made many albums). His relaxed informality became an affectionate joke, charming nearly every household; the format was influential on Andy Williams, and Val Doonican in the UK went so far as to borrow Charles. Como's annual Christmas show was a ratings-puller for several more years, and he commenced world tours at nearly 60; his 2-disc set *Perry Como's 40 Greatest Hits* was a UK million-seller in 1975. (Donald Clarke 1989).

AND I LOVE YOU SO (SINGLE)
Tracks: / And I love you so.
7" Single: Released Apr '73, on RCA, by BMG Records (UK). Deleted Apr '76. Catalogue no: **RCA 2346**
7" Single: Released Jul '81, on RCA Golden Grooves, by BMG Records (UK). Catalogue no: **GOLD 512**

BEST OF TIMES, THE (SINGLE)
Tracks: / Best of times, The.
12" Single: Released Jun '86, on RCA, by BMG Records (UK). Catalogue no: **PT 49852**
7" Single: Released Jun '86, on RCA, by BMG Records (UK). Catalogue no: **PB 49851**

CATCH A FALLING STAR
Tracks: / Catch a falling star.
7" Single: Released Mar '58, on RCA, by BMG Records (UK). Deleted Mar '61. Catalogue no: **RCA 1036**

CATERINA
Tracks: / Caterina.
7" Single: Released May '62, on RCA, by BMG Records (UK). Deleted May '65. Catalogue no: **RCA 1283**

CHRISTMAS DREAM
7" Single: Released Nov '84, on RCA, by BMG Records (UK). Catalogue no: **RCA 460**

DELAWARE
Tracks: / Delaware.
7" Single: Released Feb '60, on RCA, by BMG Records (UK). Deleted Feb '63. Catalogue no: **RCA 1170**

DON'T LET THE STARS GET IN YOUR EYES
Tracks: / Don't let the stars get in your eyes.
7" Single: Released Jan '53, on H.M.V., by EMI Records. Deleted Jan '56. Catalogue no: **B 10400**

FOR THE GOOD TIMES (SINGLE)
Tracks: / For the good times.
7" Single: Released Aug '73, on RCA, by BMG Records (UK). Deleted Aug '76. Catalogue no: **RCA 2402**

GLENDORA
Tracks: / Glendora.
7" Single: Released Sep '56, on H.M.V., by EMI Records. Deleted Sep '59. Catalogue no: **POP 240**

HOT DIGGITY
Tracks: / Hot diggity.
7" Single: Released May '56, on H.M.V., by EMI Records. Deleted May '59. Catalogue no: **POP 212**

I KNOW
Tracks: / I know.
7" Single: Released Jul '59, on RCA, by BMG Records (UK). Deleted Jul '62. Catalogue no: **RCA 1126**

I MAY NEVER PASS THIS WAY AGAIN
Tracks: / I may never pass this way again.
7" Single: Released May '58, on RCA, by BMG Records (UK). Deleted May '61. Catalogue no: **RCA 1062**

I THINK OF YOU
Tracks: / I think of you.
7" Single: Released May '71, on RCA, by BMG Records (UK). Deleted May '74. Catalogue no: **RCA 2075**

I WANT TO GIVE
Tracks: / I want to give.
7" Single: Released May '74, on RCA, by BMG Records (UK). Deleted May '77. Catalogue no: **LPBO 7518**

IDLE GOSSIP
Tracks: / Idle gossip.
7" Single: Released Jun '54, on H.M.V., by EMI Records. Deleted Jun '57. Catalogue no: **B 10710**

IT'S IMPOSSIBLE (SINGLE)
Tracks: / It's impossible.
7" Single: Released Jan '71, on RCA, by BMG Records (UK). Catalogue no: **RCA 2043**
7" Single: Released Sep '75, on RCA, by BMG Records (UK). Catalogue no: **RCA 2602**
7" Single: Released Oct '86, on Old Gold, by Old Gold Records. Catalogue no: **OG 9614**

JUKEBOX BABY (SINGLE)
Tracks: / Jukebox baby.
7" Single: Released Apr '56, on H.M.V., by EMI Records. Deleted Apr '59. Catalogue no: **POP 191**

KEWPIE DOLL
Tracks: / Kewpie doll.
7" Single: Released May '58, on RCA, by BMG Records (UK). Deleted May '61. Catalogue no: **RCA 1055**

LOVE MAKES THE WORLD GO ROUND
Tracks: / Love makes the world go round.
7" Single: Released Nov '58, on RCA, by BMG Records (UK). Deleted Nov '61. Catalogue no: **RCA 1086**

MAGIC MOMENTS (OLD GOLD)
Tracks: / Magic moments.
7" Single: Released Oct '86, on Old Gold, by Old Gold Records. Catalogue no: **OG 9606**

MAGIC MOMENTS (SINGLE)
Tracks: / Magic moments.
7" Single: Released Feb '58, on RCA, by BMG Records (UK). Catalogue no: **RCA 1036**
7" Single: Released Oct '81, on RCA Golden Grooves, by BMG Records (UK). Catalogue no: **GOLD 531**

MANDOLINS IN THE MOONLIGHT
Tracks: / Mandolins in the moonlight.
7" Single: Released Nov '58, on RCA, by BMG Records (UK). Deleted Nov '61. Catalogue no: **RCA 1086**

MOON TALK
Tracks: / Moon talk.
7" Single: Released Sep '58, on RCA, by BMG Records (UK). Deleted Sep '61. Catalogue no: **RCA 1071**

MORE
Tracks: / More.
7" Single: Released Sep '56, on H.M.V., by EMI Records. Deleted Sep '59. Catalogue no: **POP 240**

PAPA LOVES MAMBO
Tracks: / Papa loves mambo.
7" Single: Released Dec '54, on H.M.V., by EMI Records. Deleted Dec '57. Catalogue no: **B 10776**

TINA MARIE
Tracks: / Tina Marie.
7" Single: Released Dec '55, on H.M.V., by EMI Records. Deleted Dec '58. Catalogue no: **POP 103**

TOMBOY
Tracks: / Tomboy.
7" Single: Released Feb '59, on RCA, by BMG Records (UK). Deleted Feb '62. Catalogue no: **RCA 1111**

WALK RIGHT BACK
Tracks: / Walk right back.
7" Single: Released Dec '73, on RCA, by BMG Records (UK). Deleted Dec '76. Catalogue no: **RCA 2432**

WANTED
Tracks: / Wanted.
7" Single: Released Jun '54, on H.M.V., by EMI Records. Deleted Jun '57. Catalogue no: **B 10667**

Comolli, Phil Band

BEYOND A SHADOW OF A DOUBT
Tracks: / Beyond a shadow / Rosaline.
7" Single: Released Jul '88, on Lady London, by Lady London Records. Catalogue no: **LLR 010A**

Compagnons de la

THREE BELLS, THE
Tracks: / Three bells, The.
7" Single: Released Oct '59, on Columbia, by EMI Records. Deleted Oct '62. Catalogue no: **DB 4358**

Company

PRAIRIES ON FIRE
Tracks: / Prairies on fire.
12" Single: Released 26 Mar '87, on Prairie Jazz, Catalogue no: **PJ 002**

Company B

FASCINATED
Tracks: / Fascinated / Sascidubbed.
12" Single: Released Apr '87, on Bluebird (2), by BMG Records (UK). Catalogue no: **BRT 35**
7" Single: Released Apr '87, on Bluebird (2), by BMG Records (UK). Catalogue no: **BR 35**
12" Single: Released Feb '88, on Bluebird (2), by BMG Records (UK). Catalogue no: **BRT 48**

FASCINATED (1988 REMIX)
Tracks: / Fascinated (1988 remix) / Spin me around.
12" Single: Released Feb '88, on Bluebird (2), by BMG Records (UK). Catalogue no: **BRT 48**
7" Single: Released Feb '88, on Bluebird (2), by BMG Records (UK). Catalogue no: **BR 48**

JAM ON ME
Tracks: / Jam on me (dub) / Jam on me.
12" Single: Released Nov '86, on Bluebird (2), by BMG Records (UK). Catalogue no: **BRT 27**

PRIVATE LOVER
Tracks: / Private lover.
12" Single: Released Aug '87, on Bluebird (2), by BMG Records (UK). Catalogue no: **BRT 43**
7" Single: Released Aug '87, on Bluebird (2), by BMG Records (UK). Catalogue no: **BR 43**

Company Of State

METAL MOVE
Tracks: / Metal move.
12" Single: Released '88, on Antler, by Antler Records (Belgium). Catalogue no: **ANT 085**

Company She Keeps

MEN RESPONSIBLE, THE
Tracks: / Men responsible, The / Men responsible, The (long version) (Only on 12" version.) / Point of mystery / City of Quebec.
7" Single: Released May '88, on Cold Harbour, by Cold Harbour Records. Catalogue no: **COLD 6**
12" Single: Released May '88, on Cold Harbour, by Cold Harbour Records. Catalogue no: **COLDT 6**

WHAT A GIRL WANTS
Tracks: / What a girl wants / Little madness, A / Touch on my emotions (On 12" only) / Express interest (On 12" only).
7" Single: Released 13 Jun '87, on Cold Harbour, by Cold Harbour Records. Catalogue no: **COLD 5**
12" Single: Released 13 Jun '87, on Cold Harbour, by Cold Harbour Records. Catalogue no: **COLD 5T**

Company Two

I'M BREAKING THRU THIS
Tracks: / I'm breaking through this.
7" Single: Released Mar '89, on Tom Tom, Catalogue no: **TTT 06**

TELL IT AS IT IS
Tracks: / Tell it as it is / Tell it as it is (instrumental).
7" Single: Released Aug '89, on Tam, Catalogue no: **7TTT 010**
12" Single: Released Aug '89, on Tam, Catalogue no: **12TTT 010**

Competition

ALL STRING VEST & GRECIAN
Tracks: / All string vest & grecian / Take me to the hospital.
7" Single: Released Jun '80, on Laser, Deleted Jun '83. Catalogue no: **LAS 30**

Complaints

THERE WERE RAYS COMING OUT OF THEIR EYES
Tracks: / There were rays coming out of their.
7" Single: Released Feb '85, on Dog Breath, Catalogue no: **DOG 4**

Complexions

ANOTHER TEARDROP
Tracks: / Another teardrop / I've had enough.
7" Single: Released Jan '82, on Dakota, Deleted Jan '85. Catalogue no: **DAK 4**

Comsat Angels

AFTER THE RAIN
Tracks: / After the rain / Private party.
7" Single: Released Oct '82, on Polydor, by Polydor Ltd. Deleted Oct '85. Catalogue no: **POSP 513**

CUTTING EDGE (LIVE)
Tracks: / Cutting edge / Flying dream.
12" Single: Released Mar '87, on Island, by Island Records. Catalogue no: **ISB 312**

CUTTING EDGE, THE
Tracks: / Cutting Edge, The / Something's got to give / Our secret (Available on 12" version only.).
7" Single: Released Feb '87, on Island, by Island Records. Catalogue no: **IS 312**
12" Single: Released Feb '87, on Island, by Island Records. Deleted Jul '87. Catalogue no: **12IS 312**

DAY ONE
Tracks: / Day one / Will you stay tonight / Independence day.
7" Single: Released '84, on Jive, by Zomba Records. Catalogue no: **JIVE 73**
12" Single: Released '84, on Jive, by Zomba Records. Catalogue no: **JIVET 73**

DO THE EMPTY HOUSE
Tracks: / Do the empty house / Now I know / Red planet revisited.
7" Set: Released Oct '81, on Polydor, by Polydor Ltd. Deleted '85. Catalogue no: **POSP 359**

EYE OF A LENS
Tracks: / Eye of a lens / At sea / Another world (on 12" only) / Gone (on 12" only).
12" Single: Released Mar '81, on Polydor, by Polydor Ltd. Deleted Mar '84. Catalogue no: **POPX 242**
7" Single: Released Mar '81, on Polydor, by Polydor Ltd. Deleted Mar '84. Catalogue no: **POSP 242**

FOREVER YOUNG
Tracks: / Forever young.
7" Single: Released '85, on Jive, by Zomba Records. Catalogue no: **JIVE 111**
12" Single: Released '85, on Jive, by Zomba Records. Catalogue no: **JIVET 111**

I'M FALLING
Tracks: / I'm falling.
7" Single: Released '85, on Jive, by Zomba Records. Catalogue no: **JIVE 87**
12" Single: Released '85, on Jive, by Zomba Records. Catalogue no: **JIVES 87**

INDEPENDENCE DAY
Tracks: / Independence day / We were.
7" Single: Released Jul '80, on Polydor, by Polydor Ltd. Deleted '83. Catalogue no: **209525 7**
7" Single: Released '84, on Jive, by Zomba Records. Catalogue no: **JIVE 54**
12" Single: Released '84, on Jive, by Zomba Records. Catalogue no: **JIVET 54**

ISLAND HEART
Tracks: / Island heart / Scissors and stone.
7" Single: Released '83, on Jive, by Zomba Records. Catalogue no: **JIVE 51**
12" Single: Released '83, on Jive, by Zomba Records. Catalogue no: **JIVET 51**

IT'S HISTORY
Tracks: / It's history / Zinger.
7" Single: Released May '82, on Polydor, by Polydor Ltd. Deleted '85. Catalogue no: **POSP 432**

TOTAL WAR
Tracks: / Total war / Waiting for a miracle /

Home on the range.
7" Single: Released May '80, on Polydor, by Polydor Ltd. Deleted May '83. Catalogue no: **2059227**

WILL YOU STAY TONIGHT
Tracks: / Will you stay tonight.
7" Single: Released '83, on Jive, by Zomba Records. Catalogue no: **JIVE 46**
12" Single: Released '83, on Jive, by Zomba Records. Catalogue no: **JIVET 46**

YOU MOVE ME
Tracks: / You move me / Escape from Wilesden.
7" Single: Released '84, on Jive, by Zomba Records. Catalogue no: **JIVE 65**
12" Single: Released '84, on Jive, by Zomba Records. Catalogue no: **JIVET 65**

Con Funk Shun

Biographical details: A soul-funk dance band, formed in California in 1968 as Project Soul; they went to Memphis in 1972 and changed the name. The remarkably consistent lineup included Mike Cooper, lead vocals and guitar, and drummer Louis McCall (high school friends who started the group), plus Cedric Martin, bass; Danny Thomas, keyboards; Karl Fuller, Paul Harrell, Felton Pilate II, horns and various instruments (Pilate also does lead vocals). They backed Stax artists, then recorded for Mercury from 1976. (Donald Clarke 1989) .

BURNIN' LOVE (SINGLE)
7" Single: Released Jun '86, on Club, by Phonogram Ltd. Deleted '87. Catalogue no: **JAB 32**
12" Single: Released Jun '86, on Club, by Phonogram Ltd. Deleted '87. Catalogue no: **JABX 32**

IT'S GOT TO BE ENOUGH
Tracks: / It's got to be enough / Early morning sunshine.
7" Single: Released May '80, on Mercury, by Phonogram Ltd. Deleted '83. Catalogue no: **MER 14**

TOO TIGHT
Tracks: / Too tight / Play wid it.
7" Single: Released Jan '81, on Mercury, by Phonogram Ltd. Deleted Jan '84. Catalogue no: **MER 57**
12" Single: Released Jan '81, on Mercury, by Phonogram Ltd. Deleted Jan '84. Catalogue no: **MERX 57**

Concept

MR D.J.
Tracks: / Mr. D.J..
7" Single: Released '85, on 4th & Broadway, by Island Records. Deleted '87. Catalogue no: **BRW 40**
12" Single: Released '85, on 4th & Broadway, by Island Records. Deleted '87. Catalogue no: **12 BRW 40**

Concrete Blonde

GOD IS A BULLET
Tracks: / God is a bullet / Free / Little wing (12" only).
7" Single: Released 31 Jul '89, on I.R.S, Catalogue no: **EIRS 121**
12" Single: Released 31 Jul '89, on I.R.S, Catalogue no: **EIRST 121**

HAPPY BIRTHDAY
Tracks: / Happy birthday / Run, run, run.
CD 5": Released May '89, on I.R.S, Catalogue no: **EIRSCD 105**
7" Single: Released May '89, on I.R.S, Catalogue no: **EIRS 105**
12" Single: Released May '89, on I.R.S, Catalogue no: **EIRST 105**

TRUE
Tracks: / True / True 11.
7" Single: Released 30 May '87, on I.R.S, Catalogue no: **IRM 136**
12" Single: Released 30 May '87, on I.R.S, Catalogue no: **IRMT 136**

Concrete God

FLOOR
Tracks: / Floor.
12" Single: Released Mar '87, on Phlox, Catalogue no: **CGOD 1**

TOYTOWN STAR
Tracks: / Toytown star.
12" Single: Released Aug '87, on Phlox, Catalogue no: **CGOD 2**

Condemned 84

IN SEARCH OF THE NEW BREEN
Tracks: / In search of the new breen.
12" Single: Released Apr '87, on RFB Recordings, Catalogue no: **RFBSIN 3**

OI AIN'T DEAD
Tracks: / Oi ain't dead.
12" Single: Released Jul '86, on RFB Recordings, Catalogue no: **RFBSIN 2**
7" Single: Released Jul '86, on RFB Recordings, Catalogue no: **RFBSIN 27**

Conductor

VOICE ON THE RADIO
Tracks: / Voice on the radio / Burned alive.
7" Single: Released Mar '82, on RCA, by BMG Records (UK). Deleted '85. Catalogue no: **RCA 206**

Conen, Marcia

OB-LA-DI, OB-LA-DA
Tracks: / Ob la di ob la da (version).
12" Single: Released Dec '86, on Diamond C, Catalogue no: **DCD 011**

Coney Hatch

HEY OPERATOR
Tracks: / Hey operator.
7" Single: Released Mar '83, on Mercury, by Phonogram Ltd. Catalogue no: **HATCH 1**
12" Single: Released Mar '83, on Mercury, by Phonogram Ltd. Catalogue no: **HATCH 12**

Confeti's

SOUND OF C
Tracks: / Sound of C / Sound of C (version).
CD 5": Released 24 Apr '89, on Virgin, by Virgin Records. Catalogue no: **TENCD 261**
12" Single: Released 24 Apr '89, on Virgin, by Virgin Records. Catalogue no: **TENX 261**
7" Single: Released 24 Apr '89, on Virgin, by Virgin Records. Catalogue no: **TEN 261**
12" Single: Released '89, on Virgin, by Virgin Records. Catalogue no: **TENR 261**

Conflict

BATTLE CONTINUES
Tracks: / Battle continues.
7" Single: Released Sep '85, on Mortarhate, by Mortarhate Records. Catalogue no: **MORT 15**

FINAL CONFLICT, THE (SINGLE)
Tracks: / Final conflict, The.
12" Single: Released Nov '88, on Mortarhate, by Mortarhate Records. Catalogue no: **MORT 22**

FROM PROTEST TO RESISTANCE (SINGLE)
Tracks: / From protest to resistance.
12" Single: Released Oct '87, on Konnexion, Catalogue no: **KOMA 788029**

HOUSE THAT MAN BUILT
Tracks: / House that man built.
7" Single: Released Jun '82, on Crass, by Crass Records. Catalogue no: **CRASS 221984/1**

LIVE AT THE CENTRE IBERICO
7" Single: Released Oct '82, on Xntrix, Catalogue no: **XN 2001**
7" Single: Released '87, on Mortarhate, by Mortarhate Records. Catalogue no: **MORT 7**

NATION OF ANIMAL LOVERS
Tracks: / Nation of animal lovers.
7" Single: on Corpus Christi, by Corpus Christi Records. Catalogue no: **CHRIST 4**

SERENADE IS DEAD
Tracks: / Serenade is dead.
7" Single: Released Oct '83, on Mortarhate, by Mortarhate Records. Catalogue no: **MORT 1**

THIS IS NOT ENOUGH
Tracks: / This is not enough.
7" Single: Released Feb '85, on Mortarhate, by Mortarhate Records. Catalogue no: **MORT 8**

Congo

AT THE FEAST
Tracks: / At the feast.
12" Single: Released Jun '82, on 99, Catalogue no: **99 06EP**

Congo Ashanti Roy

AFRICAN BLOOD
Tracks: / African blood.
10" single: Released Jun '83, on LNU Sounds, Catalogue no: **LNU DP 8**

Congos

FISHERMAN
Tracks: / Fisherman / Can't come in.
7" Single: Released Mar '81, on Go Feet, Deleted Mar '84. Catalogue no: **FEET 5**

Congregation

Biographical details: A pop oddity of the early 70's, Congregation were a hastily-assembled mixed choir, all British, brought together for *Softly Whispering I Love You*, a very commercial pop song written by ace UK songwriters Roger Cook and Roger Greenaway. It was an extremely catchy and unusual record that outlived its intended 1971 Christmas novelty market to peak at No 4 in Britain in January 1972. Under the billing of the English Congregation, the single also reached No 29 in the States. (Bob MacDonald, February 1985.).

SOFTLY WHISPERING I LOVE YOU
Tracks: / Softly whispering I love you.
7" Single: Released Nov '71, on Columbia, by EMI Records. Deleted Nov '74. Catalogue no: **DB 8830**

SOFTLY WHISPERING I LOVE YOU (OLD GOLD)
Tracks: / Softly whispering I love you.
7" Single: Released Oct '83, on Old Gold, by Old Gold Records. Deleted Sep '89. Catalogue no: **OG 9382**

Congress

CONTRACT OF FAITH
Tracks: / Contract of faith / Don't think love is to blame.
7" Single: Released Mar '87, on EMI, by EMI Records. Deleted Jul '87. Catalogue no: **CONGRESS 1**
12" Single: Released Mar '87, on EMI, by EMI Records. Deleted Jul '87. Catalogue no: **12 CONGRESS 1**

GIVE IT TO ME
Tracks: / Give it to me / Fool maker.
12" Single: Released May '84, on PRT, by Castle Communications Records. Catalogue no: **12LP 305**
7" Single: Released May '84, on PRT, by Castle Communications Records. Catalogue no: **7P 305**

GOTTA GET IT
Tracks: / Gotta get it.
12" Single: Released Jun '82, on Tooti Frooti, Deleted Jun '87. Catalogue no: **TOOT 12**
7" Single: Released Jun '82, on Tooti Frooti, Deleted Jun '87. Catalogue no: **TOOT 2**

NEPTUNE
Tracks: / Neptune / Real hot.
12" Single: Released Nov '83, on PRT, by Castle Communications Records. Catalogue no: **12P 291**
7" Single: Released Nov '83, on PRT, by Castle Communications Records. Catalogue no: **7P 291**

THAT'S JAZZ (YOU SEXY THING)
Tracks: / That's jazz (you sexy thing).
7" Single: Released Sep '83, on Dancefloor, Catalogue no: **DF 7006**
12" Single: Released Sep '83, on Dancefloor, Catalogue no: **DFT 7006**

Conlee, John

Biographical details: A soulful country singer, born in 1946 and raised on a tobacco farm. His first number one country hit *Rose colored glasses* in 1978 was followed by many more hits. He struck a combination of adult subject matter and a ballad style for country music fans who now live mostly in the suburbs. His hits were on ABC, then MCA and CBS since 1986. (Donald Clarke 1989).

GOT MY HEART SET ON YOU
Tracks: / You've got a right / Got my heart set on you.
7" Single: Released Nov '86, on CBS, by CBS Records. Catalogue no: **650275 7**

Conley, Arthur

Biographical details: American soul singer Conley, from Atlanta, Georgia, was a protege of the great Otis Redding, who took him under his wing in 1965 after hearing a demo record and became his producer. After a number of unsuccessful attempts, they achieved a smash hit in early summer, '67, when they adapted a Sam Cooke song, *Yeah Man*, and called it *Sweet Soul Music*. The new version used an archetypal pop/soul arrangement and sound and namedropped a host of soul greats, including Otis himself. The intention was to create an anthem in celebration of a style of music that had found new popularity in the mid-60's and the result hit No 2 in the States and No 7 in the UK. Conley, however, was unable to establish himself as a long-term artist. His only other significant success was *Funky Street* which reached No 14 in the US but stopped at No 46 in Britain in April 1968, four months after the death of his mentor, Redding. (Bob MacDonald, February 1985.)
A soul singer from the golden age of the genre, born in 1946. His demo of *I'm a lonely stranger* was picked up by Otis Redding, who took Conley to Muscle Shoals; they re-wrote Sam Cooke's *Yeah man* and retitled *Sweet soul music* it was a number two USA pop chart hit in 1967: it gave namechecks to past and present soul stars atop a typical brassy Sax backing, and also underlined Conley's vocal similarity to the sadly departed Cooke, who had a total of seven soul chart hits and is still highly regarded. (Donald Clarke 1989).

FUNKY STREET
Tracks: / Funky street.
7" Single: Released Apr '68, on Atlantic, by WEA Records. Deleted Apr '71. Catalogue no: **583 175**

SWEET SOUL MUSIC
Tracks: / Sweet soul music.
7" Single: Released Jan '85, on Old Gold, by Old Gold Records. Catalogue no: **OG 9501**

SWEET SOUL MUSIC (SINGLE)
Tracks: / Sweet soul music / Down on Funky Street / Shake, rattle and roll (Extra track on 12").
12" Single: Released May '87, on WEA, by WEA Records. Deleted Jul '88. Catalogue no: **YZ 120T**
7" Single: Released Jul '81, on Atlantic, by WEA Records. Catalogue no: **K 10108**
7" Single: Released May '87, on WEA, by WEA Records. Deleted Jul '88. Catalogue no: **YZ 120**
7" Single: Released Apr '67, on Atlantic, by WEA Records. Deleted Apr '70. Catalogue no: **584 083**
12" Single: Released Apr '80, on Atlantic, by WEA Records. Catalogue no: **ATM 8**

Conley, Earl Thomas

CAROL
Tracks: / Carol / Too far from the heart of it all.
7" Single: Released Nov '88, on RCA, by BMG Records (UK). Deleted Aug '89. Catalogue no: **PB 49505**

WHAT SHE IS, IS A WOMAN IN LOVE
Tracks: / What she is (is a woman in love) / No chance (no dance).
Note: "This is a debut release from one of America's greatest talents". (RCA Records)
7" Single: Released Jul '88, on RCA, by BMG Records (UK). Deleted Aug '89. Catalogue no: **PB 49537**

Conn, Dean

SINCE I FELL FOR YOU
Tracks: / Since I fell for you / One more last chance.
7" Single: Released Nov '80, on A&M, by A&M Records. Deleted '83. Catalogue no: **AMS 7579**

Conn, Tony

LIKE WOW
Tracks: / Like wow.
7" Single: Released Jun '80, on Rollin' Rock, Catalogue no: **45 023**

ROCKIN' W JACKIE LEE
Tracks: / Rockin' W Jackie Lee.
7" Single: Released Jun '80, on Rollin' Rock, Catalogue no: **45 039**

Connell, Brian

WATCHING TELEVISION
Tracks: / Watching television.
7" Single: Released Aug '85, on Mr.Sam, by Mr.Sam Music. Catalogue no: **SAS 104**

Connery, Shaun

MARLENA
Tracks: / Marlena / Forum rock.
7" Single: Released Oct '80, on Young Blood, by Young Blood Records. Deleted Oct '83. Catalogue no: **YB 102**

WALKING TALKING DOLLY
Tracks: / Walking talking dolly / I think of home.
7" Single: Released Nov '80, on Young Blood, by Young Blood Records. Deleted Nov '83. Catalogue no: **YB 106**

Connolly, Billy

Biographical details: Scottish comedian Connolly achieved major fame in the mid-70's, his bawdy records and even coarser concerts gaining him a reputation as one of the nation's most entertaining one-man performers. He first cracked the British album chart in July 1974 with *Solo Concert* and soon followed it with a second long-running chart success, *Cop Yer Wack Of This*. Both featured a mix of spoken and sung comedy. November '75 further increased his public profile when *D.I.V.O.R.C.E.*, a delightful parody of the sickly Tammy Wynette hit from earlier that year, hit No 1 for one week on the UK singles chart, sandwiched between two seminal rock epics, David Bowie's *Space Oddity* and Queen's *Bohemian Rhapsody*. Another big hit album, *Get Right Intae Him*, followed immediately for Connolly. Apart from a couple of smaller parody hit singles he subsequently relied less on record sales, a sure sign of his huge acceptance as a concert and television comedian. With distinctive physical features, notably his unkempt hair and beard, and Glasgow brogue, Connolly has established himself as one of Britain's national institutions and

Scotland's foremost comedian. (Bob MacDonald, February 1985.)
Folksinger, songwriter, then comedian, born in Glasgow in 1942. He made albums with Gerry Rafferty in The Humblebums, then went solo, but the shaggy dog stories between songs got longer until they took over. He moved south c.1971, eventually playing to Scottish expatriates in USA and Far East. In Scotland 'The Big Yin' was a superstar, but not until the mid-'70s did other UK audiences appreciate (or understand!) him. He has also done straight acting. (Donald Clarke 1989)0.

D.I.V.O.R.C.E.
Tracks: / D.I.V.O.R.C.E..
7" Single: Released Nov '75, on Polydor, by Polydor Ltd. Deleted Nov '78. Catalogue no: **2058 652**

FREEDOM
Tracks: / Freedom.
7" Single: Released Jun '85, on Audiotrax, Deleted '86. Catalogue no: **ATX 10**

IN THE BROWNIES
Tracks: / In the brownies.
7" Single: Released Aug '79, on Polydor, by Polydor Ltd. Deleted Aug '82. Catalogue no: **2059 160**

NO CHANCE (NO CHARGE)
Tracks: / No chance (no change).
7" Single: Released Jul '76, on Polydor, by Polydor Ltd. Deleted Jul '79. Catalogue no: **2058 748**

SUPER GRAN
Tracks: / Super gran / Yootha's song.
7" Single: Released Feb '85, on Stiff, by Stiff Records. Catalogue no: **BUY 218**

TELL LAURA I LOVE HER
Tracks: / Tell Laura I love her / Song dfor Yootha.
7" Single: Released Nov '80, on Polydor, by Polydor Ltd. Deleted '83. Catalogue no: **POSP 201**

Connolly, Brian

HYPNOTISED
Tracks: / Hypnotised / Fade away.
7" Single: Released Mar '82, on Carrere, Deleted '85. Catalogue no: **CAR 231**

Connor, Mick

COTSWOLDS
Tracks: / Cotswolds / Good for the goose.
7" Single: Released Mar '80, on Logo, by Logo Records. Deleted '83. Catalogue no: **GO 378**

Connors, Norman

LOVIN' YOU
Tracks: / Loving you / I am your melody.
7" Single: Released 25 Apr '88, on Capitol, by EMI Records. Deleted Nov '88. Catalogue no: **CL 485**
12" Single: Released May '88, on Capitol, by EMI Records. Deleted Nov '88. Catalogue no: **12CL 485**

TAKE IT TO THE LIMIT (SINGLE)
Tracks: / Take it to the limit / Black cow.
7" Single: Released Sep '80, on Arista, by BMG Records (UK). Deleted '83. Catalogue no: **ARIST 363**

Connors, Shag

CLEANEST LITTLE PIGGY IN THE MARKET
Tracks: / Cleanest little piggy in the market / That's life.
7" Single: Released Dec '85, on Play, by Play Records. Catalogue no: **PLAY 204**

COTSWOLDS
Tracks: / Cotswolds.
7" Single: Released Nov '84, on Play, by Play Records. Catalogue no: **PLAY 154**

I'M JEALOUS OF THE FARMYARD COCKEREL
Tracks: / I'm jealous of the farmyard cockerel / Put your shoulder to the wheel.
7" Single: Released Aug '86, on Play, by Play Records. Catalogue no: **PLAY 208**

IT'S ME AGAIN MARGARET
Tracks: / It's me again Margaret / Hen house holiday.
7" Single: Released Feb '81, on Piccadilly, Deleted '84. Catalogue no: **7P 205**

LITTLE HOUSE UPON THE HILL, THE
Tracks: / Little house upon the hill, The.
7" Single: Released Jun '85, on Play, by Play Records. Catalogue no: **PLAY 202**

WATCH IT
Tracks: / Watch it.
7" Single: Released Dec '82, on A & R, Catalogue no: **AR 001**

Conoley, Denis

I LIKE YOU GIRL
Tracks: / I like you girl / Society talking.
7" Single: Released Mar '80, on GTO, Deleted Mar '83. Catalogue no: **GT 267**

Conrad, Jess

CHERRY PIE
Tracks: / Cherry pie.
7" Single: Released Jun '60, on Decca, by Decca Records. Deleted Jun '63. Catalogue no: **F 11236**

MYSTERY GIRL
Tracks: / Mystery girl.
7" Single: Released Jan '61, on Decca, by Decca Records. Deleted Jan '64. Catalogue no: **F 11315**

PRETTY JENNY
Tracks: / Pretty Jenny.
7" Single: Released Oct '62, on Decca, by Decca Records. Deleted Oct '65. Catalogue no: **F 11511**

Consort

BY THE SWORD DIVIDED
Tracks: / By the sword divided / Arnescote.
7" Single: Released Nov '83, on BBC, by BBC Records & Tapes. Deleted Sep '87. Catalogue no: **RESL 137**

MISS MARPLE THEME
Tracks: / Miss Marple theme / St Mary Mead.
7" Single: Released Dec '84, on BBC, by BBC Records & Tapes. Deleted Apr '89. Catalogue no: **RESL 153**

Consortium

ALL THE LOVE IN THE WORLD
Tracks: / All the love in the world.
7" Single: Released Jan '70, on Pye, Deleted Jan '73. Catalogue no: **7N 17635**

Conspiracy

CONSPIRACY INTERNATIONAL TWO
Tracks: / Conspiracy international two.
12" Single: Released Feb '85, on CTI (1), by Polydor Ltd. Catalogue no: **CTI 002**

Construction Crew

BREAK THE BEAT
Tracks: / Break the beat.
12" Single: Released May '88, on BPM, Catalogue no: **BP 12001**

Contact-U

DANCING INNER SPACE
Tracks: / Dancing inner space.
12" Single: Released Mar '83, on Challenge, by Elite Records. Catalogue no: **TALL 2**

ECUADOR
Tracks: / Ecuador.
12" Single: Released Aug '83, on Challenge, by Elite Records. Catalogue no: **TALL 4**

Contenders

WHERE'S HARRY
Tracks: / Where's Harry / Where's Harry (instrumental) / Where's Harry (upper crust) (12" only.).
Note: Featuring the voice of Frank Bruno and commentary by Harry Carpenter (courtesy of BBC Enterprises).t
7" Single: Released Feb '89, on Columbia, by EMI Records. Deleted Aug '89. Catalogue no: **DB 9136**
12" Single: Released Feb '89, on Columbia, by EMI Records. Deleted Aug '89. Catalogue no: **12DB 9136**

Conti, Bill

DYNASTY
Tracks: / Dynasty / Falcon Crest.
7" Single: Released Feb '83, on Arista, by BMG Records (UK). Catalogue no: **ARIST 520**

Contours

Biographical details: Contours This American group comprised Joe Billingslea, Huey Davis, Billy Gordon, Billy Hoggs, Hubert Johnson and Sylvester Potts.
In the late Fifties, the Counters were a young vocal quartet consisting of Billingslea, Gordon, Hoggs and Potts. They were joined by Johnson, a fifth vocalist who was a distant relative of R&B star Jackie Wilson. Through this connection they met Motown Records founder Berry Gordy and signed to his Gordy label. In 1962 a sixth Contour, guitarist Huey Davis was addied to the line up and that same year they shot to fame with a US Top 3 smash *Do You Love Me*, written by Berry Gordy, reached No.1 on the American R&B charts and hit No.3 on the pop charts. It failed in Britain but, twelve months later, was taken to the UK No.1 slot by Brian Poole & The Tremeloes. After the frantic dance energy of *Do You Love Me*, the Contours failed to come up with another major hit but nonetheless managed a series of minor chart entries. One of the last of these - 1966's *Just A Little Misunderstanding* - became their only UK hit, when it belatedly reached No.31 on the British chart in 1970. (Bob Macdonald 2/2/85)
A soul vocal group formed in 1958 in Detroit. Their second Motown single, the Gordy song *Do you love me*, was number one R&B, three pop in 1962 (covers by Brian Poole and the Tremeloes) and the Dave Clark Five were big hits in the UK. They had seven top 40 hits in the R&B chart 1962-7, and more recent reissues charted in the UK. (Donald Clarke 1989).

BABY HIT AND RUN
Tracks: / Baby hit and run.
7" Single: Released Oct '81, on Motown, by BMG Records (UK). Catalogue no: **TMG 886**

DO YOU LOVE ME
Tracks: / Do you love me / Money.
Note: "Currently a hot favourite with Dirty Dancing Fans, "Do You Love Me?" was a massive American hit back in 1962 when it reached number 2. On this side of the Atlantic it spawned cover versions by the Dave Clarke 5 and Brian Poole and The Tremeloes, both versions becoming top ten hits in the UK simultaneously". (RCA Records, May 1988).
7" Single: Released 31 May '88, on Motown, by BMG Records (UK). Catalogue no: **ZB 41903**
12" Single: Released 31 May '88, on Motown, by BMG Records (UK). Catalogue no: **ZT 41904**

JUST A LITTLE MISUNDERSTANDING
Tracks: / Just a little misunderstanding.
7" Single: Released Oct '81, on Motown, by BMG Records (UK). Catalogue no: **TMG 723**

Controlled Bleeding

SONGS FROM THE GRINDING WALL
Tracks: / Songs from the grinding wall.
12" Single: Released Mar '89, on Wax Trax, by Wax Trax Records. Catalogue no: **WAXUK 044**

Controllers

CRUSHED
Tracks: / Crushed.
7" Single: Released Oct '84, on MCA, by MCA Records. Deleted '85. Catalogue no: **MCA 923**
12" Single: Released Oct '84, on MCA, by MCA Records. Catalogue no: **MCAT 923**
12" Single: Released Jun '84, on Survival (1), by Survival Records. Catalogue no: **SUR 12 024**

STAY (SINGLE)
Tracks: / Stay / Undercover lover.
12" Single: Released '86, on MCA, by MCA Records. Catalogue no: **MCAT 1052**
7" Single: Released '86, on MCA, by MCA Records. Catalogue no: **MCA 1052**

Controls

DRESS, DANCE, DEMAND AND DESIRE
Tracks: / Dress, dance, demand and desire.
10" single: Released '84, on Stupid Rabbit Tapes, by Stupid Rabbit Tapes. Catalogue no: **SRT 007**

Conveniens

COMMERCIAL DANCE SONG
Tracks: / Commercial dance song / Barney Klark.
7" Single: Released '85, on Convenience (USA), by Convenience Records (USA). Catalogue no: **1101 (45003)**

Convertion

SWEET THING
Tracks: / Sweet thing.
7" Single: Released Nov '86, on Wax, by Wax Records. Catalogue no: **WAX 101**
12" Single: Released Nov '86, on Wax, by Wax Records. Catalogue no: **WAX 101T**

Convoy, Dave

FREEDOM
Tracks: / Freedom.
7" Single: Released Jul '83, on Shibui, Catalogue no: **SHS 001**

Conway Brothers

RAISE THE ROOF
Tracks: / Raise the roof.
12" Single: Released Dec '85, on 10 Records, by Virgin Records. Deleted '86. Catalogue no: **TEN 83-12**
7" Single: Released Dec '85, on 10 Records, by Virgin Records. Deleted '86. Catalogue no: **TEN 83**

TURN IT UP (SINGLE)
Tracks: / Turn it up.
7" Single: Released Jun '85, on 10 Records, by Virgin Records. Deleted '86. Catalogue no: **TEN 57**
12" Single: Released Jun '85, on 10 Records, by Virgin Records. Deleted '86. Catalogue no: **TEN 57-12**

Conway, Francie

TO THE EDGE OF TIME
Tracks: / To the edge of time.
7" Single: Released Aug '84, on Lamborghini, by Lamborghini Records. Catalogue no: **LMG 15**

Conway, Russ

Biographical details: This British pianist, Russ Conway, was born Trevor Stanford in Bristol in 1927, had a variety of jobs before attaining stardom in the mid Fifties. By far the most important of these were his periods of service in the Merchant Navy and the Royal Navy. It was while in the latter that he gained the Distinguished Service Medal and, not so happily, cut off part of his third finger of his right hand during an argument with a bread sliver. Despite this mishap and despite the fact that his Naval service had made him a proficient player of several brass instruments he chose piano as his musical outlet when entering showbusiness full time. Mr Stanford had become Mr Conway by the time he first penetrated the UK charts in late 1957. That debut hit was *Party Pops*, a No.24 single that might have gone higher had it not been for the fact that Christmas piano medleys were the traditional territory of Winifred Atwell - for example, she reached No.4 that Yuletide with *Let's Have a Ball*.
Conway really came into his own in 1959, when he achived two consecutive British No.1 singles with two self penned tunes *Side Saddle* and *Roulette*. He consolidated upon this double triumph with further hit singles and a succession of Top 10 LPs, and his winning charm and personality made him one of Britain's favourite TV performers. The hit singles continued during the early Sixties but the final one fell off the listings in January 1963, just as the Beatles revolution was getting underway - all of a sudden, Ross Conway and his ilk were passe. He remained in the entertainment business until a nervous breakdown forced him into retirement. He evantually won his battle against ill health and in the early Eighties, re-established himself in the media spotlight but without returing to the recording studio. (Bob Macdonald 2/2/85)
Self-taught pop pianist, born Trevor H. Stanford in 1927 in Bristol. He went from the Royal Navy to playing in clubs in 1955, accompanied Lita Rosa, Gracie Fields, Dorothy Squires and others; signed with EMI and had his own first hit *Party Pops* in 1957. A score of hits followed in the late '50s and he was a sell-out attraction in clubs and theatres, made first appearance at London Palladium '66. He slowed down because of ill health; recorded for Pye in 1971-2 with somewhat less success. He was the first UK entertainer to get a silver disc for album sales, with six in the top 10 albums in 1958-60. (Donald Clarke 1989)a.

ALWAYS YOU AND ME (SINGLE)
Tracks: / Always you and me.
7" Single: Released Nov '62, on Columbia, by EMI Records. Deleted Nov '65. Catalogue no: **DB 4934**

CHINA TEA
Tracks: / China tea.
7" Single: Released Aug '59, on Columbia, by EMI Records. Deleted Aug '62. Catalogue no: **DB 4337**

EVEN MORE PARTY POPS
Tracks: / Even more party pops.
7" Single: Released Nov '60, on Columbia, by EMI Records. Deleted Nov '63. Catalogue no: **DB 4535**

FINGS AINT WOT THEY USED T'BE
Tracks: / Fings ain't what they used to be.
7" Single: Released Apr '60, on Columbia, by EMI Records. Deleted Apr '63. Catalogue no: **DB 4422**

GOT A MATCH
Tracks: / Got a match.
7" Single: Released Aug '58, on Columbia, by EMI Records. Deleted Aug '61. Catalogue no: **DB 4166**

LESSON ONE
Tracks: / Lesson one.
7" Single: Released Feb '62, on Columbia, by EMI Records. Deleted Feb '65. Catalogue no: **DB 4784**

LUCKY FIVE
Tracks: / Lucky five.
7" Single: Released May '60, on Columbia, by EMI Records. Deleted May '63. Catalogue no: **DB 4457**

MORE AND MORE PARTY POPS

Tracks: / More and more party pops.
7" Single: Released Nov '59, on Columbia, by EMI Records. Deleted Nov '62. Catalogue no: **DB 4373**

MORE PARTY POPS
Tracks: / More party pops.
7" Single: Released Nov '58, on Columbia, by EMI Records. Deleted Nov '61. Catalogue no: **DB 4204**

PABLO
Tracks: / Pablo.
7" Single: Released May '61, on Columbia, by EMI Records. Deleted May '64. Catalogue no: **DB 4649**

PARTY POPS
Tracks: / Party pops.
7" Single: Released Nov '57, on Columbia, by EMI Records. Deleted Nov '60. Catalogue no: **DB 4031**

PASSING BREEZE
Tracks: / Passing breeze.
7" Single: Released Sep '60, on Columbia, by EMI Records. Deleted Sep '63. Catalogue no: **DB 4508**

PEPE
Tracks: / Pepe.
7" Single: Released Jan '61, on Columbia, by EMI Records. Deleted Jan '64. Catalogue no: **DB 4564**

ROULETTE
Tracks: / Roulette.
7" Single: Released May '59, on Columbia, by EMI Records. Deleted May '62. Catalogue no: **DB 4298**

ROYAL EVENT
Tracks: / Royal event.
7" Single: Released Mar '60, on Columbia, by EMI Records. Deleted Mar '63. Catalogue no: **DB 4418**

SIDESADDLE
Tracks: / Side saddle.
7" Single: Released Feb '59, on Columbia, by EMI Records. Deleted Feb '62. Catalogue no: **DB 4256**
7" Single: Released Jul '82, on Old Gold, by Old Gold Records. Deleted Jul '88. Catalogue no: **OG 9047**

SNOW COACH
Tracks: / Snow coach.
7" Single: Released Nov '59, on Columbia, by EMI Records. Deleted Nov '62. Catalogue no: **DB 4368**

TERRY FOX THEME
Tracks: / Terry Fox theme / Floriana.
7" Single: Released Jun '84, on Music & Media. Catalogue no: **RUSS 1**

TOY BALLOONS
Tracks: / Toy balloons.
7" Single: Released Nov '61, on Columbia, by EMI Records. Deleted Nov '64. Catalogue no: **DB 4738**

WORLD OUTSIDE, THE
Tracks: / World outside, The.
7" Single: Released Jan '59, on Columbia, by EMI Records. Deleted Jan '62. Catalogue no: **DB 4234**

Conway & Temple

YOU CAN LAY YOUR HEAD ON MY SHOULDER
Tracks: / You can lay your head on my shoulder.
7" Single: Released Jul '85, on Jive, by Zomba Records. Catalogue no: **JIVE 27**
12" Single: Released Jul '85, on Jive, by Zomba Records. Catalogue no: **JIVET 27**

Conwell, Tommy

IF WE NEVER MEET AGAIN
Tracks: / If we never meet again / Everything they say is true / If we never meet again (LP version) (Only on 12" and CD single.) / Workout (Only on 12" and CD single.).
CD 5": Released 6 Mar '89, on CBS, by CBS Records. Deleted Oct '89. Catalogue no: **654579 2**
12" Single: Released 6 Mar '89, on CBS, by CBS Records. Deleted Oct '89. Catalogue no: **654579 6**
7" Single: Released 6 Mar '89, on CBS, by CBS Records. Deleted Oct '89. Catalogue no: **654579 7**

I'M NOT YOUR MAN
Tracks: / I'm not your man / Workout / Workout (pt II).
7" Single: Released May '89, on CBS, by CBS Records. Deleted Oct '89. Catalogue no: **652 933 7**
CD 5": Released May '89, on CBS, by CBS Records. Deleted Oct '89. Catalogue no: **652 933 2**
12" Single: Released May '89, on CBS, by CBS Records. Deleted Oct '89. Catalogue no: **652 933 8**

Cooder, Ry

Biographical details: Cooder, Ry This American guitarist and vocalist, born Ryland Cooder in Los Angeles in March 1947, began his career as a session player in the Mid Sixties, and spent the rest of that decade working with a variety of noted names including Taj Mahal and Captain Beefheart.
His first self titled LP was released in 1970 and was followed by a succession of albums which, though not high charts, established Cooder as one of the most absorbing artist of the Seventies.
He won great acclaim for his inventive guitar technique, particularly his use of the 'bottleneck' style; and for his truly eclectic choice of material - he rarely wrote his own compositions, but selected his favourite numbers from such diverse genres as jazz, rhythm and blues, cajun, country, folk and rock. Cooder interpreted familiar songs in a new manner, and brought new life and recognition to forgotten but worthy treasures from the archives.
It was not until 1979's *Bop Till You Drop* album that Cooder's records began to attract significant commercial acceptance, but even then their success was considerably less, on both sides of the Atlantic, than their quality deserved.
Bop Till You Drop was his first LP to hit the chart in Britain, peaking at No.36. Its opening track *Little Sister* summed up the artist's approach - an Elvis Presley hit from the early Sixties given a totally different treatment. Equally irresistible was *Crazy 'bout an Automobile (Every Woman I Know)*, a cut from 1980's *Borderline* LP and the highlight of a successful British tour that showed off Cooder's impresssive roster of accompanying vocalist and musicians. 1980 saw him release *The Long Riders*, the first of a trio of soundtrack albums that he was commissioned to write for movies - it was followed by 1981's *Southern Comfort* and 1982's *The Border*. The latter year also saw him crack the UK Top 20 for the first time with this album *The Slide Area*. (Bob Macdonald 3/2/85)
The American guitarist, singer and bandleader has been most active as a composer of film soundtrack music for several years, but not before carving himself a legend as an activist curator of American popular music. He was born in 1947 in Los Angeles; he formed the Rising Sons with Taj Mahal, but turned to prolific session work, with Captain Beefheart, Phil Ochs, Randy Newman, The Rolling Stones and many others. He already had a cult following as a guitarist; he said later that his complete lack of track record as a recording artist would not have got him a contract in more recent times, but his albums beginning in 1970 began an exploration of Americana, with songs about the Great Depression by Woodie Guthrie, Leadbelly and Sleepy John Estes; *Boomers Story* in 1973 was about wanderers, while *Paradise & Lunch* in 1974 veered in the Rhythm and Blues direction and was his first commercial success, with Jim Keltner on drums and superb players such as bassist Red Callender, saxist Plas Johnson, Oscar Brashear on cornet and the legendary Earl Hines. Backing vocalists have included the wonderful Bobby King. Influenced by unusual tunings used by Bahamian guitarist Joseph Spence, Hawaiian guitarist Gabby Pahinui, then by Tex-Mexaccordianist Flaco Jiminez, his next album was *Chicken Skin Music* in 1976. *Jazz* in 1977 is his accurate, affectionate impression of that genre, with Callender, Hines and Brashear in the cast and songs by Bix Beiderbecke, Jelly Roll Morton, and traditional songs arranged by Spence: Cooder says the half-instrumental album is his least favorite; it took trouble to make and was not a good seller, but remains gorgeous. *Bop Till You Drop* in 1979 was the first digitally recorded rock album, with delicious covers of classics, and he has carried on in that vein . Meanwhile his friendship with film director Walter Hill led to composing and performing music for five films, plus several by other directors including Wim Wenders' *Paris, Texas* and Louis Malle's *Alamo Bay*, the latter with contributions from John Hiatt, Van Dyke Parks and Los Lobos. His LPs never had expensive promotion beacause they don't fit in pigeonholes, while the whole point is that they take in everything; he supported lesser acts in concert until the late 70's. (Donald Clarke 1989).

634 5789
Tracks: / 634 5789 / Girls from Texas.
7" Single: Released Nov '80, on Warner Bros., by WEA Records. Deleted '83. Catalogue no: **K 17713**

GET RHYTHM (SINGLE)
Tracks: / Get rhythm / Get your lies straight / Down in Hollywood.
Note: Extra track 'Down in Hollywood' on 12in only.
CD 5": Released Apr '88, on Warner Bros., by WEA Records. Catalogue no: **W 8107 CD**
10" single: Released Apr '88, on Warner Bros., by WEA Records. Catalogue no: **W 8107 TE**
7" Single: Released Apr '88, on Warner Bros., by WEA Records. Catalogue no: **W 8107**
12" Single: Released Apr '88, on Warner Bros., by WEA Records. Catalogue no: **W 8107T**

GYPSY WOMAN Alimony
Tracks: / Gypsy woman.
7" Single: Released '82, on Warner Bros., by WEA Records. Catalogue no: **K 17952**

WHICH CAME FIRST
Tracks: / Which came first.
12" Single: Released Nov '81, on Fetish. Catalogue no: **FE 14 12**
7" Single: Released '82, on Warner Bros., by WEA Records. Catalogue no: **K 17977**

Cook Da Books

CARESS ME LIKE A FLOWER
Tracks: / Caress me like a flower / Something good.
7" Single: Released '84, on 10 Records, by Virgin Records. Deleted '86. Catalogue no: **TEN 18**

LOW PROFILE
Tracks: / Low profile.
7" Single: Released '83, on Kiteland. Catalogue no: **CUSTY 123**

PIGGIE IN THE MIDDLE EIGHT
Tracks: / Piggie in the middle eight.
7" Single: Released '82, on Probe Plus, by Probe Plus Records. Catalogue no: **CUSTY 1**
12" Single: Released '82, on Probe Plus, by Probe Plus Records. Catalogue no: **CUSTY 1 12**

RICH MEN DON'T
Tracks: / Rich men don't.
7" Single: Released '82, on Kite, by Kite Records. Catalogue no: **CUSTY 122**

WOULDN'T WANNA KNOCK IT
Tracks: / Wouldn't wanna knock it.
7" Single: Released '83, on Kiteland. Catalogue no: **CUSTY 124**

YOUR EYES Rockin' at the hop
7" Single: Released '83, on Carrere. Catalogue no: **CAR 279**

Cook & Jones

JUST ANOTHER DREAM
Tracks: / Just another dream / Just another dream (part 2).
7" Single: Released May '80, on Virgin, by Virgin Records. Deleted '83. Catalogue no: **VS 353**

Cook, Norman

BLAME IT ON THE BASSLINE
Tracks: / Blame it on the bassline / Won't talk about it.
12" Single: Released Jul '89, on Go!. Catalogue no: **GODX 33**
7" Single: Released Jul '89, on Go!. Catalogue no: **GOD 33**

FOR SPACIOUS LIES
Tracks: / For spacious lies.
12" Single: Released Oct '89, on Go!. Catalogue no: **GODX 37**

WON'T TALK ABOUT IT
Tracks: / Won't talk about it / Blame it on the bassline.
7" Single: Released Jul '89, on Go beat. Catalogue no: **GOD 33**
12" Single: Released Jul '89, on Go beat. Catalogue no: **GODX 33**

Cook, Peter

Biographical details:
Cook, Peter This British comedian is best known for his long lasting association with Dudley Moore.
It was with Dud that he first hit the British charts, peaking at No.18 in the summer of 1965 with *Goodbye-ee*;
Cook also achived a small solo success that summer with *The Ballad of Spotty Muldoon* which peaked at No.34. Neither comedian ever hit the singles chart again, but they chalked up their debut British LP chart entry in '66.
By the time they hit that list for a second time ten years later, they had established themselves as one of the UK's most successful double acts, notably with their TV series 'Not Only..But Also'.
Their humour appealed to those who liked their comedy more left field than Morecambe & Wise or the Two Ronnies, but not so uncompromisingly zany as Monty Python

. That second hit album was *Derek and Clive Live* which reached No.12 and logged 25 weeks on the British chart - Derek and Clive were new persona adopted by Pete and Dud for the purpose of this excessively obscene attempt to observe British working class life. Its success generated a follow-up album *Derek and Clive Come Again*, which reached No. 18 on the UK listings.
Moore's buring desire for Hollywood stardom led to the duo splitting up, but Cook's name was kept in the public eye due to his continuing involvement with well received comedy projects, notably 1980's *The Secret Policeman's Ball*.
(Bob Macdonald 3/2/85).

BALLAD OF SPOTTY MULDOON
Tracks: / Ballad of Spotty Muldoon.
7" Single: Released Jul '65, on Decca, by Decca Records. Deleted Jul '68. Catalogue no: **F 12182**

GOODBYE-EE (Peter Cook & Dudley Moore)
Tracks: / Goodbye-ee.
7" Single: Released Jun '65, on Decca, by Decca Records. Deleted Jun '68. Catalogue no: **F 12158**

THERE AIN'T NO MORNING
Tracks: / There ain't no morning.
7" Single: Released '83, on Paramount. Catalogue no: **PARA 101**

Cook, Tony

DO WHAT YOU WANNA DO
Tracks: / Do what you wanna do.
7" Single: Released '83, on Half Moon, by Rondelet Music & Records. Catalogue no: **HM 1125**

Cooke, Brandon

EYES OF A STRANGER
Tracks: / Eyes of a stranger / Mission.
7" Single: Released Sep '86, on Mercury, by Phonogram Ltd. Deleted '87. Catalogue no: **BRAND 2**
12" Single: Released Sep '86, on Mercury, by Phonogram Ltd. Deleted '87. Catalogue no: **BRAND 212**

SHARP AS A KNIFE (ACID ATTACK)
Tracks: / Sharp as a knife (acid attack).
12" Single: Released Oct '88, on Phonogram, by Phonogram Ltd. Deleted 31 Jul '89. Catalogue no: **JABX 73**
12" Single: Released Oct '88, on Club, by Phonogram Ltd. Deleted 31 Jul '89. Catalogue no: **JABXR 73**
7" Single: Released Oct '88, on Phonogram, by Phonogram Ltd. Deleted 31 May '89. Catalogue no: **JAB 73**

SHARPE AS A KNIFE
Tracks: / Sharpe as a knife / Voices calling.
7" Single: Released May '86, on Mercury, by Phonogram Ltd. Deleted '87. Catalogue no: **BRAND 1**
12" Single: Released May '86, on Mercury, by Phonogram Ltd. Deleted '87. Catalogue no: **BRAND 112**

Cooke, Sam

Biographical details:
This American singer and ssongwriter, Sam Cooke was born in Chicago, began his career in gospel music and then moved on to become one of the golden voices of secular soul and pop. He was one of a family of eight children and was the son of a Baptist Minister.
Brought up in a strongly relgious environment, he first sang publicly in his local church at the age of nine and, while in his early teens, was a member of a young gospel group called the Highway QCs.
That ensemble was taught for a time by R.B. Robinson, a member of the Soul Stirrers, one of America's most proficient gospel acts; this connection led to Cooke joining the Stirrers in the early Fifties, taking over as lead tenor from the group's resigning frontman R.H.Harris.
The new recruit's wonderfully pure but emotive singing, combined with his good looks, not only enhanced the Soul Stirrers' already high reputation but also projected Cooke as one of black music's top teen idols.
One of their best songs was penned by him: *Touch The Hem of His Garment* contained all of his strong points- soulful vocals, impressive songwriting, plus a perceived charm that brought the gospel genre into the lives of legions of adoring girls. Here were the makings of a pop star and Cooke brought all these qualities to bear on his R&B based pop material when he left the Soul Stirrer and switched from religious to secular music in 1957.
Cooke quickly came up with his first - and biggest- US chart hit, reaching No.1 in late '57 with the beautiful *You Send Me* (this hit composed not by Sam, but by his brother Charles).
It reached No.29 in Britain, where his biggest hit proved to be *Twistin' The Night Away*, his 1962 bow to the Chubby Checker led dance craze.
Perhaps the best tribute to Sam Cooke is to glance at his other seven UK Top 30 singles: six of the hits - *You Send Me, Only Sixteen, Wonderful World, Cupid, Another Saturday Night*, and *Frankie and Johnny*, have all reached higher placings on the British charts via other artists than he himself achieved, a sure sign of his influence on popular music; and the remaining title, Chain Gang, inspired

a hit answer record in the early Eighties, *Back On The Chain Gang* by the Pretenders. Like many great black singers, Cooke had his roots in the church; but, unlike many of his contemporaries and the later stars whom he inspired, he received considerable resentment from the religious fraternity once pop stardom had occured - there were reports of the singer being booed off the stage by a disapproving audience at a Soul Stirrers' renuion concert.
Cooke was still scoring American hits in quick succession when he died in December 1964 at the ageof 33. In tragic and shady circumstances, he was shot in a Los Angeles motel by its manageress. A verdict of justifiable homicide was recorded, the woman alleging that Cooke had tried to force himself upon a girl in another room. It was a dreadul end to a great artist. But the immorality of the star was cemented by the posthumous success of *Shake*, a US Top 10 single in early '65 that featured a classic B side - *A Change Is Gonna Come* was a moving expression of the beliefs and hopes of America's growing civil rights movement. (Bob Macdonald 3/2/85)
One of the greatest of all soul singers, the first to bring the vocal techniques of gospel music straight to the pop chart. Born in 1931 in Chicago, he was shot to death in a motel in 1964 in a contreversial incident never fully explained. He sang in gospel groups from age 9, joining the Soul Stirrers in 1950; when he turned to pop in 1957 *You Send Me* went straight to number one on both pop and R&B charts. His gospel feeling and uncanny control over pitch, timbre and melisma (the direction of the vocally improvised melody) were entirely new in pop and led to 29 top 40 hits 1957-65. He had been produced by Bumps Blackwell, but signed to RCA, where slushy arrangements were produced by Hugo (Peretti) and Luigi (Creatore); his talent won out and many good records were made, but performances in black clubs, for people who knew who he was and where he came from, were different: on the RCA album *Live At The Harlem Square Club*, unreleased until 1985, he was backed by a band including King Curtis. (Donald Clarke 1989).

ANOTHER SATURDAY NIGHT
Tracks: / Another Saturday night / Soothe me / Chain gang / It's got the whole world shakin'.
7" Single: Released Jul '80, on RCA, by BMG Records (UK). Deleted '85. Catalogue no: **PE 9511**
7" Single: Released May '63, on RCA, by BMG Records (UK). Catalogue no: **RCA 1341**
7" Single: Released Apr '86, on RCA, by BMG Records (UK). Catalogue no: **PB 49849**
12" Single: Released Apr '86, on RCA, by BMG Records (UK). Catalogue no: **PT 49850**

CHAIN GANG
Tracks: / Chain gang.
CD 5": Released Jun '89, on RCA, by BMG Records (UK). Catalogue no: **PD 49455**
7" Single: Released Sep '60, on RCA, by BMG Records (UK). Deleted Sep '63. Catalogue no: **RCA 1202**

CUPID
Tracks: / Cupid.
7" Single: Released Jul '61, on RCA, by BMG Records (UK). Deleted Jul '64. Catalogue no: **RCA 1242**

FRANKIE & JOHNNY
Tracks: / Frankie and Johnny.
7" Single: Released Sep '63, on RCA, by BMG Records (UK). Deleted Sep '66. Catalogue no: **RCA 1361**

ONLY SIXTEEN
Tracks: / Only sixteen.
7" Single: Released Aug '59, on H.M.V., by EMI Records. Deleted Aug '62. Catalogue no: **POP 642**

TWISTIN' THE NIGHT AWAY (SINGLE)
Tracks: / Twistin' the night away.
7" Single: Released Mar '62, on RCA, by BMG Records (UK). Deleted Mar '65. Catalogue no: **RCA 1277**

WONDERFUL WORLD (SINGLE)
Tracks: / Chain gang / Cupid (available on 12" version only) / Change is gonna come, A (available on 12" version only) / Wonderful world.
12" Single: Released Mar '86, on RCA, by BMG Records (UK). Catalogue no: **PT 49872**
7" Single: Released Jul '60, on H.M.V., by EMI Records. Deleted Jul '63. Catalogue no: **POP 754**

YOU SEND ME (SINGLE)
Tracks: / You send me.
12" Single: Released May '87, on Perfect, Catalogue no: **PER 12 8605**
7" Single: Released Jan '58, on London-American, Deleted Jan '61. Catalogue no: **HLU 8506**
CD 5": Released Apr '87, on Topline, by Charly Records. Catalogue no: **TOP CD 507**
7" Single: Released Feb '85, on EMI Golden 45's, by EMI Records. Catalogue no: **G45 44**

Cooke, Tony

ON THE FLOOR (ROCK IT)
Tracks: / On the floor (rock it).
12" Single: Released '84, on Half Moon, by Rondelet Music & Records. Catalogue no: **HM 1134**
7" Single: Released '84, on Half Moon, by Rondelet Music & Records. Catalogue no: **HM 71134**

Cookey Monster

SPACE AGE NIGGER
Tracks: / Space age nigger / Sniffer's dub.
12" Single: Released '83, on Twinkle, by Twinkle Records. Catalogue no: **NG 2001**

Cookie Crew

BORN THIS WAY (LET'S DANCE)
Tracks: / Born this way (let's dance) / Born this way (let's dance) (version).
CD 5": Released Jan '89, on ffrr, by London Records. Catalogue no: **FFRCD 19**
7" Single: Released Dec '88, on ffrr, by London Records. Deleted 26 Jun '89. Catalogue no: **FFR 19**
12" Single: Released Jan '89, on ffrr, by London Records. Deleted 26 Jun '89. Catalogue no: **FFRXR 19**
12" Single: Released Dec '88, on ffrr, by London Records. Deleted Jul '89. Catalogue no: **FFRX 19**

COME ON AND GET SOME
Tracks: / Come and get some (jackswing mix) (Only on 7" and CD single.) / Come and get some (superfly mix) / Come and get some (cookapella & drum & bass) (Only on 12".) / Come and get some (cook instrumental mix) (Only on 12".) / Got to keep on (Danny D remix) (Only on CD single.).
12" Single: Released Jun '89, on London Records, by London Records. Catalogue no: **FX 110**
Cassingle: Released Jun '89, on London Records, by London Records. Catalogue no: **FCS 110**
CD 5": Released Jun '89, on London Records, by London Records. Catalogue no: **FCD 110**
7" Single: Released Jun '89, on London Records, by London Records. Catalogue no: **F 110**

FEMALES
Tracks: / Females.
7" Single: Released Oct '87, on Rhythm King, by Mute Records. Catalogue no: **LEFT 12**
12" Single: Released Oct '87, on Rhythm King, by Mute Records. Catalogue no: **LEFT 12 R**

GOT TO KEEP ON
Tracks: / Got to keep on / Pick up on this / Born this way (Only on 12" version.) / Got to keep on (Prince Paul dope mix) (Only on CD single.).
CD 5": Released Mar '89, on ffrr, by London Records. Catalogue no: **FFRCD 25**
Special: Released Mar '89, on ffrr, by London Records. Catalogue no: **FRXR 25**
12" Single: Released Mar '89, on ffrr, by London Records. Catalogue no: **FFRX 25**
7" Single: Released Mar '89, on ffrr, by London Records. Catalogue no: **FFR 25**

ROCK DA HOUSE
Tracks: / Rock da house (remix) US mix / Rock da house.
12" Single: Released Dec '87, on Rhythm King, by Mute Records. Catalogue no: **LEFT R 11T**

Cookies

CHAINS
Tracks: / Chains.
7" Single: Released Jan '63, on London-American, Deleted Jan '66. Catalogue no: **HLU 9634**

Cookman, Brian

MAN OVERBOARD
Tracks: / Man overboard / Everyone.
7" Single: Released '83, on Mummer, Catalogue no: **MUMSP 001**

Cool C

C IS COOL
Tracks: / C is cool.
12" Single: Released Apr '88, on Citybeat, by Beggars Banquet Records. Catalogue no: **CBE 1221**
7" Single: Released Apr '88, on Citybeat, by Beggars Banquet Records. Catalogue no: **CBE 721**

JUICE CREW DIS
Tracks: / Juice crew dis.
12" Single: Released Sep '87, on Hilltop Hustlers (USA), Catalogue no: **HTH 001**

Cool, Chris

JUST ONE LOOK
Tracks: / Just one look / Night moves.
7" Single: Released Sep '80, on RCA, by BMG Records (UK). Deleted '83. Catalogue no: **PB 5278**

Cool it Reba

MONEY FALL OUT OF THE SKY
Tracks: / Money fall out of the sky.
12" Single: Released '83, on Hannibal, by Hannibal Records. Catalogue no: **HNEP 3302**

Cool Notes

Biographical details: Cool Notes, This seven piece British band, who hail from Brixton, London, began as a reggae outfit and later switched to soul. In the former genre, they gained accepatance with *My Time*, a 1978 reggae No.1 on the specialist charts. They cracked the UK pop charts for the first time in 1984, reaching No.42 with *You're Never Too Young*, their second soul single. Another single *I Forgot*, released in late '84, was also a minor British hit. (Bob Macdonald 3/2/85).

BILLY THE KID
Tracks: / Billy the kid / Kidnap my baby.
12" Single: Released '80, on Jama, Catalogue no: **JADC 008**

HAVE A GOOD FOREVER (SINGLE)
Tracks: / Have a good forever.
7" Single: Released '85, on Abstract Dance, by Priority Records. Catalogue no: **AD 5**
12" Single: Released '85, on Abstract Dance, by Priority Records. Catalogue no: **ADT 5**

I FORGOT
Tracks: / I forgot how to love you.
7" Single: Released '84, on Abstract Dance, by Priority Records. Catalogue no: **AD 002**
12" Single: Released '84, on Abstract Dance, by Priority Records. Catalogue no: **12 AD 002**

I FORGOT HOW TO LOVE YOU
Tracks: / I forgot how to love you / Why can't we be friend.
7" Single: Released '82, on Mass Media, Catalogue no: **MMM 7002**
12" Single: Released '82, on Mass Media, Catalogue no: **MMM 12 1008**

I WANNA DANCE
Tracks: / I wanna dance / Blown it / In your car.
7" Single: Released '84, on Sour Grape, by Sour Grape Records. Deleted '87. Catalogue no: **SG 116**
12" Single: Released '84, on Sour Grape, by Sour Grape Records. Deleted '87. Catalogue no: **SGR 116**

IN YOUR CAR
Tracks: / In your car.
12" Single: Released '85, on Abstract Dance, by Priority Records. Catalogue no: **ADTR 4**
12" Single: Released '85, on Abstract Dance, by Priority Records. Deleted Nov '87. Catalogue no: **ADT 4**
7" Single: Released '85, on Abstract Dance, by Priority Records. Catalogue no: **AD 4**

INTO THE MOTION
Tracks: / Into the motion / Come on back / Look what you've done to me (Remix) (Available on 12" only).
12" Single: Released May '85, on Abstract Dance, by Priority Records. Deleted Nov '87. Catalogue no: **ADT 8**
7" Single: Released May '86, on Abstract Dance, by Priority Records. Deleted Nov '87. Catalogue no: **AD 8**

JUST GIRLS
Tracks: / Just girls / Sweet vibes.
7" Single: Released Nov '81, on Jama, Deleted Nov '84. Catalogue no: **JA 017**
12" Single: Released '82, on Jama, Catalogue no: **JADC 017**

MAGIC LOVER
Tracks: / Magic lover.
7" Single: Released Oct '88, on HHO (Henry Hadaway Organisation), by Henry Hadaway Organisation. Catalogue no: **RHA 102**
12" Single: Released Oct '88, on HHO (Henry Hadaway Organisation), by Henry Hadaway Organisation. Catalogue no: **RHA T102**

MOMENTARY VISION
Tracks: / Momentary vision / Girls night out / Your love is taking over (Extra track available on 12" version only).
7" Single: Released Oct '86, on Abstract Dance, by Priority Records. Deleted Nov '87. Catalogue no: **AD 10**
12" Single: Released Oct '86, on Abstract Dance, by Priority Records. Deleted Nov '87. Catalogue no: **ADT 10**

MORNING CHILD
Tracks: / Morning child.
12" Single: Released '82, on Mass Media, Catalogue no: **MMM 12 1011**

MY TUNE
Tracks: / My tune.
12" Single: Released '84, on Jama, Catalogue no: **JABC 0024**

SPEND THE NIGHT
Tracks: / Spend the night / Halu (spring) / I forgot (on 12" only).
7" Single: Released '85, on Abstract Dance, by Priority Records. Catalogue no: **AD 3**
12" Single: Released '85, on Abstract Dance, by Priority Records. Catalogue no: **ADTR 3**
12" Single: Released '85, on Abstract Dance, by Priority Records. Catalogue no: **ADT 3**

SUGAR SUGAR
Tracks: / Sugar sugar.
7" Single: Released May '80, on Gem, Deleted May '83. Catalogue no: **GEMS 32**

TELL ME
Tracks: / Tell me.
12" Single: Released Oct '89, on White Label (1), Catalogue no: **SDT 15**

YOU'RE NEVER TOO YOUNG
Tracks: / You're never to young / Sound of summer.
7" Single: Released Aug '84, on Abstract Dance, by Priority Records. Deleted '87. Catalogue no: **AD 001**
12" Single: Released '84, on Abstract Dance, by Priority Records. Catalogue no: **12 AD 001**

Cool, Phil

BRIDGE OVER TROUBLED WATER
Tracks: / Australians / Pope (The) / Rolf Harris / Bridge over troubled water.
7" Single: Released Nov '86, on Virgin, by Virgin Records. Deleted May '88. Catalogue no: **VS 923**
12" Single: Released Nov '86, on Virgin, by Virgin Records. Deleted '89. Catalogue no: **VS 923-12**

IT'S HARD BEING A STONE
Tracks: / It's hard being a stone.
7" Single: Released Feb '83, on Castle, by Castle Communications Records. Catalogue no: **CAS 020**

Cool Runners

I SHOULD HAVE LOVED YOU
Tracks: / I should have loved you / Satellite music.
7" Single: Released Mar '86, on Streetwave, Catalogue no: **KHAN 65**
12" Single: Released Mar '86, on Streetwave, Catalogue no: **MKHAN 65**

PLAY THE GAME
Tracks: / Play the game / Hawaiian dream.
7" Single: Released Feb '82, on MCA, by MCA Records. Deleted May '85. Catalogue no: **MCA 760**
12" Single: Released Feb '82, on MCA, by MCA Records. Deleted Feb '87. Catalogue no: **MCAT 760**

Cool Running

ROBIN HOOD OF THE GHETTO
Tracks: / Robin Hood of the ghetto.
12" Single: Released Aug '83, on Raka, Catalogue no: **R 002**

Coolah

JAH IS FOR EVERYONE
Tracks: / Jah is for everyone / Partial rhythm.
12" Single: Released Jul '82, on Pops, Catalogue no: **PBR 001**

Coolidge, Rita

Biographical details: Coolidge, Rita This American singer was born in Nashville, the capital of country music and has always incorporated a country flavour in her records, although veering further towards easy listening as her career has progressed. Her father was a Baptist minister, and she sang in religious choirs from early childhood. Her professional career began to take off as the Sixties gave way to the Seventies- she toured the States with Delaney & Bonnie & Friends and then with Joe Cocker and Leon Russell as part of the Mad Dogs and Englishmen Show, both semi-legendary tours that helped to spread Coolidge's name in the music business. She achived moderate sales with a series of albums during the early and mid-Seventies, and

also recorded with singer/songwriter Kris Kristofferson, whom he married in 1973. Coolidge's real breakthrough album was 1977's*Anytime Anywhere* - this was a big seller on both sides of the Atlantic, and yielded the international hit sisngle *We're All Alone*, a Boz Scaggs ballad that reached No.7 in the US and No.6 in the UK. The LP also contained *Higher and Higher*, a remake of a Jackie Wilson oldie that she took to No.2 in the US, four places higher than the original; and there was *Words* a Bee Gees song that gave Coolidge a British Top 30 hit.
Although apparently established as a major star, her career quickly went off the rails. She never had another major hit single, and subsequent albums failed to live up to the success of *Anytime Anywhere*. Her marriage to Kristofferson broke up. However, her smooth and pleasant voice assured her of a steady living in the music business, even without hit records. She achived a chart comeback of sorts with *All Time High*, the theme song from the 1983 James Bond movie *Octopussy*; although this single was not a major pop hit, it enjoyed an extended run at the top of the US Adult Contemporary charts. (Bob Macdonald 3/2/85)
A sultry pop singer with many hits in the '70s and still doing well. Born in 1945 in Nashville, she toured with Delaney & Bonnie, then Joe Cocker and Leon Russell (who wrote *Delta Lady* about her, a 1969 hit for Cocker.). She signed to A&M and was married for a time to Kris Kristofferson; she had 15 Billboard hits 1969-83 including duets with Kris and with Glen Campbell, as well as 13 hit albums, three with Kris. She tours incessantly from straight ahead rock shows to symphony pops; she was one third of *Trio* in 1987 with Dolly Parton and Emmylou Harris, an album that was in the USA country chart for over 80 weeks. (Donald Clarke 1989)h.

ALL TIME HIGH
Tracks: / All time high.
7" Single: Released Jun '83, on A&M, by A&M Records. Deleted Jun '86. Catalogue no: **AM 007**

CLOSER YOU GET
Tracks: / Closer you get / Take it home.
7" Single: Released Sep '81, on A&M, by A&M Records. Deleted '84. Catalogue no: **AMS 8162**

FOOL THAT I AM
Tracks: / Fool that I am / Can she keep you satisfied.
7" Single: Released Jan '81, on A&M, by A&M Records. Deleted Jan '84. Catalogue no: **AMS 8103**

HIGHER & HIGHER
Tracks: / Higher and higher.
7" Single: Released Oct '77, on A&M, by A&M Records. Deleted Oct '80. Catalogue no: **AMS 7315**

I'D RATHER LEAVE WHILE I'M IN LOVE
Tracks: / I'd rather leave while I'm in love / Can she keep you satisfied.
7" Single: Released May '81, on A&M, by A&M Records. Deleted May '84. Catalogue no: **AMS 7480**

LET'S GO DANCIN'
Tracks: / Let's go dancin' / Keep the candle burning.
7" Single: Released Mar '81, on A&M, by A&M Records. Deleted Mar '84. Catalogue no: **AMS 8119**

WE'RE ALL ALONE (OLD GOLD)
Tracks: / We're all alone.
7" Single: Released Oct '88, on Old Gold, by Old Gold Records. Catalogue no: **OG 9812**

WE'RE ALL ALONE (SINGLE)
Tracks: / We're all alone / Words.
7" Single: Released Jun '77, on A&M, by A&M Records. Deleted Jun '80. Catalogue no: **AMS 7295**

WORDS
Tracks: / Words.
7" Single: Released Feb '78, on A&M, by A&M Records. Deleted Feb '81. Catalogue no: **AMS 7330**

Coolrock, Johnnie

GOOD GIRLS
Tracks: / Good girls / Top jammer.
7" Single: Released Apr '80, on Casablanca, by PolyGram UK Ltd. Deleted Apr '83. Catalogue no: **CAN 189**

Cooper, Alice

Biographical details: Born Vincent Furnier in Detroit in 1948, Cooper caused a stir by the simple novelty of adopting a woman's name: in his heyday Alice Cooper was a name of his entire group as well as himself. In the band, formed in 1965, were Michael Bruce, Glen Buxton, Dennis Dunaway and Neal Smith. The story goes that, during a session with an Ouija board, a spirit told them "Alice Cooper is Vincent Fumier"... They were discovered during the late 60's by Frank Zappa and future manager Shep Gordon, apparently when they were the only two people left in the club during an Alice Cooper gig after the audience had walked out. During the first two years of the 70's the group attracted controversial publicity due to their outrageously violent stage show. In '71 they achieved their first US hit single with*Eighteen*. The word started to spread across the Atlantic and in February '72 the Killer album entered the UK charts. Later that year came School's Out, the rebellious Who-style album that made Alice Cooper a household name -- though many households wish it hadn't. The song became their first, and biggest, major hit, reaching No 7 in the US and going all the way to No 1 in the UK. A British Top Ten album followed and live shows attracted even more publicity, with Cooper caressing snakes, killing chickens, simulating the death of a baby and, as a finale, acting out his own death via gallows, electric chair and guillotine. But after School's Out the hits became noticeably smaller: it is interesting to note that in Britain all his nine chart singles peaked at a lower position than the one before. However, 1975 saw an upturn in Cooper's Stateside fortunes, after the entire group had been replaced. *Only Women Bleed,I Never Cry,You And Me*and*How You Gonna See Me Now?*brought him four US Top Twenty singles during the mid to late 70's, a period which saw him throw off his dependence on drink and try to adopt and Mr Nice Guy image. He later tried a return to his old style. (Bob MacDonald, February 1985.).

BED OF NAILS
Tracks: / Bed of nails / I'm your gun.
12" Pic: Released Sep '89, on Epic, by CBS Records. Catalogue no: **ALICE P3**
7" Pic: Released Sep '89, on Epic, by CBS Records. Catalogue no: **ALICE B3**
CD 5": Released Sep '89, on Epic, by CBS Records. Catalogue no: **ALICE C3**
Cassingle: Released Sep '89, on Epic, by CBS Records. Catalogue no: **ALICE M3**
7" Single: Released Sep '89, on Epic, by CBS Records. Catalogue no: **ALICE R3**
7" Single: Released Sep '89, on Epic, by CBS Records. Catalogue no: **ALICE 3**
12" Single: Released Sep '89, on Epic, by CBS Records. Catalogue no: **ALICE T3**

ELECTED
Tracks: / Elected.
7" Single: Released Oct '72, on Warner Bros., by WEA Records. Deleted '75. Catalogue no: **K 16214**

FOR BRITAIN ONLY
Tracks: / For Britain only / Under my wheels.
7" Pic: Released May '82, on Warner Bros., by WEA Records. Catalogue no: **K 17940 M**
7" Single: Released May '82, on Warner Bros., by WEA Records. Catalogue no: **K 17940**

FREEDOM
Tracks: / Freedom / Time to kill / School's out (live) (Extra track on 12".).
12" Single: Released Mar '88, on MCA, by MCA Records. Catalogue no: **MCAX 1241**
12" Single: Released Mar '88, on MCA, by MCA Records. Catalogue no: **MCAT 1241**
7" Single: Released Mar '88, on MCA, by MCA Records. Deleted 1 Jul '89. Catalogue no: **MCA 1241**

HELLO HURRAY
Tracks: / Hello hurray.
7" Single: Released Feb '73, on Warner Bros., by WEA Records. Deleted '76. Catalogue no: **K 16248**

HE'S BACK (THE MAN BEHIND THE MASK)
Tracks: / Billion Dollar babies / He's back (the man behind the mask).
7" Single: Released Oct '86, on MCA, by MCA Records. Catalogue no: **MCA 1090**
12" Single: Released Oct '86, on MCA, by MCA Records. Catalogue no: **MCAT 1090**

HOW YOU GONNA SEE ME NOW
Tracks: / How you gonna see me now.
7" Single: Released Dec '78, on Warner Bros., by WEA Records. Deleted '81. Catalogue no: **K 17270**

I AM THE FUTURE
Tracks: / I am the future / Zorro's ascent.
7" Single: Released Nov '82, on Warner Bros., by WEA Records. Deleted Nov '85. Catalogue no: **K 15004**

LOVE AT YOUR CONVENIENCE
Tracks: / Love at your convenience / Generation landslide.
7" Single: Released May '82, on Warner Bros., by WEA Records. Deleted '85. Catalogue no: **K 17914**

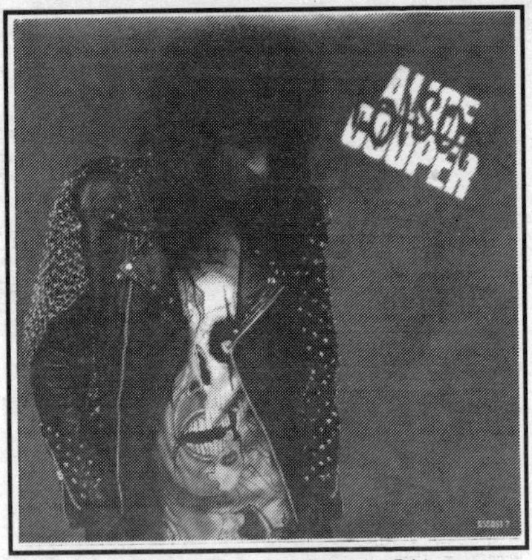

ALICE COOPER - POISON (Released on Epic)

7" Single: Released May '77, on Warner Bros., by WEA Records. Deleted '80. Catalogue no: **K 16935**
7" Single: Released Feb '82, on Warner Bros., by WEA Records. Catalogue no: **K 17914**

NO MORE MISTER NICE GUY
Tracks: / No more mister nice guy.
7" Single: Released Apr '73, on Warner Bros., by WEA Records. Deleted '76. Catalogue no: **K 16262**

POISON (see panle above)
Tracks: / Poison / Trash / Ballad of Dwight Fry (live) (Only on 12" (6550618) and CD single.) / I got a line on you (Only on CD single.) / Cold ethyl (live) (Only on 12" single (6550619)).
7" Single: Released Jul '89, on Epic, by CBS Records. Catalogue no: **6550617**
CD 5": Released Jul '89, on Epic, by CBS Records. Catalogue no: **6550612**
12" Single: Released Jul '89, on Epic, by CBS Records. Catalogue no: **6550619**
12" Single: Released Jul '89, on Epic, by CBS Records. Catalogue no: **6550618**

SCHOOL'S OUT (OLD GOLD)
Tracks: / School's out / Elected.
7" Single: Released Sep '85, on Old Gold, by Old Gold Records. Catalogue no: **OG 9519**

SCHOOL'S OUT (SINGLE)
Tracks: / School's out.
7" Single: Released Jul '72, on Warner Bros., by WEA Records. Deleted '75. Catalogue no: **K 16188**
7" Single: Released Nov '76, on Warner Bros., by WEA Records. Catalogue no: **K 16287**

SEVEN AND SEVEN IS (LIVE VERSION)
Tracks: / Seven and seven is / Generation landslide.
7" Single: Released Mar '82, on Warner Bros., by WEA Records. Deleted '85. Catalogue no: **K 17924**

TEENAGE FRANKENSTEIN
Tracks: / Teenage Frankenstein (live) / Schools out (live) / Only women bleed (This extra track on 12" only.).
7" Single: Released Mar '87, on MCA, by MCA Records. Catalogue no: **MCA 1113**
12" Single: Released Mar '87, on MCA, by MCA Records. Catalogue no: **MCAT 1113**

TEENAGE LAMENT '74
Tracks: / Teenage lament '74.
7" Single: Released Jan '74, on Warner Bros., by WEA Records. Deleted '77. Catalogue no: **K 16345**

WE'RE ALL CLONES
Tracks: / We're all clones / Model citizens.
7" Single: Released May '80, on Warner Bros., by WEA Records. Deleted May '83. Catalogue no: **K 17598**

Cooper, Amanda

DANCING QUEEN
Tracks: / Next time / Dancing queen.
7" Single: Released 24 Jul '89, on Amco, Catalogue no: **AMCO 2**

Cooper, Anthony

COCAINE
Tracks: / Cocaine.
12" Single: Released Aug '85, on Keyman, by Keyman Records. Catalogue no: **KM 001**

Cooper Clarke, John

DAY MY PAD WENT MAD, THE
Tracks: / Day my pad went mad, The / Distant relation, A.
7" Single: Released Nov '82, on Epic, by CBS Records. Deleted Nov '85. Catalogue no: **EPCA 2077**

IT MAN
Tracks: / It man / 36 hours.
7" Single: Released Jun '80, on Epic, by CBS Records. Deleted '83. Catalogue no: **EPC 8655**

NIGHT PEOPLE
Tracks: / Night people / Face behind the scream.
7" Single: Released Jun '82, on Epic, by CBS Records. Deleted Jun '85. Catalogue no: **EPCA 2521**

Cooper, D.B.

HAD ENOUGH
Tracks: / Had enough / Stand and show it.
7" Single: Released Apr '81, on Warner Bros., by WEA Records. Deleted Apr '84. Catalogue no: **K 177 75**

Cooper, Michael

TO PROVE MY LOVE
Tracks: / To prove my love / To prove my love (version).
7" Single: Released Sep '88, on WEA, by WEA Records. Catalogue no: **W 8200**
7" Single: Released Feb '88, on Warner Bros., by WEA Records. Catalogue no: **W 200**
12" Single: Released Sep '88, on WEA, by WEA Records. Catalogue no: **W 8200T**
12" Single: Released Feb '88, on Warner Bros., by WEA Records. Catalogue no: **W 200T**

Cooper, Tommy

DON'T JUMP OFF THE ROOF DAD
Tracks: / Don't jump off the roof dad.
7" Single: Released Jun '61, on Palette, Deleted '64. Catalogue no: **PG 9019**

Cope, Julian

Biographical details: Welsh-born Cope was based in Liverpool at the time of helping to form the aptly- named Crucial Three in 1977. All three members of that short-lived outfit were instrumental in reinvigorating Liverpool as a cauldron of new musical talent: Cope went on to form Teardrop Explodes, Ian McCulloch to lead Echo & The Bunnymen and Pete Wylie to lead Wah! After achieving success with the Teardrops, the temperamental Cope split with the band in late 1982. He returned a year later with a new single,*Sunshine Playroom*, a highly-inventive record displaying a surprising 10cc influence. It was too disjointed for major chart success, becoming a very minor UK hit, and a similar fate awaited its

1984 follow-up, *The Greatness And Perfection Of Love*, which peaked at No 52, and his first solo album, *World Shut Your Mouth*. Greatness And Perfection was typical Cope -- derivative 60's-style pop, highly melodic and of very fine quality. If his work is underrated it is largely due to his own erratic personality, which is distinctly uncomfortable in the glare of the spotlight. His eccentric nature has led some to dismiss him as insane and inspired others to hail him as a truly fascinating artist. His consistent praise of hero Scott Walker helped to bring the latter's name and face back in the the UK music press, but Walker did not achieve significant success any more than Cope did. (Bob MacDonald, February 1985.)
For biographical information see *Teardrop Explodes*.

5 O'CLOCK WORLD
Tracks: / 5 o'clock world / S.P.Q.R. / Reynard the fox.
7" Single: Released 7 Nov '88, on Island, by Island Records. Catalogue no: **IS 399**
12" Single: Released 7 Nov '88, on Island, by Island Records. Catalogue no: **12IS 399**
CD 5": Released Nov '88, on Island, by Island Records. Catalogue no: **CIDP 399**

CHARLOTTE ANNE
Tracks: / Charlotte Anne / Christmas mourning / Books (12" only.) / Question of temperature, A (12" only.).
12" Pic: Released Aug '88, on Island, by Island Records. Deleted Apr '89. Catalogue no: **12 ISP 380**
7" Single: Released Aug '88, on Island, by Island Records. Catalogue no: **IS 380**
12" Single: Released Aug '88, on Island, by Island Records. Deleted Apr '89. Catalogue no: **12IS 380**

CHINA DOLL (see panel below)
Tracks: / China doll / Crazy farm animal / Rail on (Only on 10", 12" and CD single.) / Desi (Only on CD single.).
10" single: Released 18 Apr '89, on Island, by Island Records. Catalogue no: **10 ISP 406**
CD 5": Released 18 Apr '89, on Island, by Island Records. Catalogue no: **CID 406**
10" single: Released 18 Apr '89, on Island, by Island Records. Catalogue no: **10 IS 406**
7" Single: Released 18 Apr '89, on Island, by Island Records. Catalogue no: **IS 406**
12" Single: Released 18 Apr '89, on Island, by Island Records. Catalogue no: **12 IS 406**

EVE'S VOLCANO (COVERED IN SIN)
Tracks: / Eve's volcano (covered in sin) / Almost beautiful child (1 & 2) / Pulsar NX (live) (Extra track on 12" version only.) / Shot down (live) (Extra track on 12" version only.) / Spacehopper.
CD 5": Released Apr '87, on Island, by Island Records. Deleted Jun '88. Catalogue no: **CID 318**
7" Single: Released Mar '87, on Island, by Island Records. Deleted Apr '88. Catalogue no: **IS 318**
12" Single: Released Apr '87, on Island, by Island Records. Catalogue no: **12 ISX 318**
12" Single: Released Mar '87, on Island, by Island Records. Deleted Apr '88. Catalogue no: **12IS 318**

GREATNESS AND PERFECTION OF LOVE
Tracks: / Greatness and perfection of love / 24a velocity crescent / Pussy free (On 12" only).
7" Single: Released Mar '84, on Mercury, by Phonogram Ltd. Catalogue no: **MER 155**
12" Single: Released Mar '84, on Mercury, by Phonogram Ltd. Catalogue no: **MERX 155**

SUN SPOTS
Tracks: / Sunspots.
12" Single: Released Feb '85, on Mercury, by Phonogram Ltd. Catalogue no: **MER 1822**

SUNSHINE PLAYROOM
Tracks: / Sunshine playroom.
7" Single: Released Nov '83, on Mercury, by Phonogram Ltd. Catalogue no: **COPE 1**
12" Single: Released Nov '83, on Mercury, by Phonogram Ltd. Catalogue no: **COPE 112**

TRAMPOLINE
Tracks: / Trampoline / Disaster / Mock turtle / Warwick the king.
7" Single: Released Jan '87, on Island, by Island Records. Catalogue no: **IS 305**
12" Single: Released Jan '87, on Island, by Island Records. Catalogue no: **12 IS 305**

WORLD SHUT YOUR MOUTH (SINGLE)
Tracks: / World shut your mouth / Umpteenth unnatural blues / I've got levitation (On 12" version only.) / Non-alignment pact (On 12" version only.) / Transporting (On 12" version only.).
7" Single: Released Oct '86, on Island, by Island Records. Catalogue no: **ISB 290**
7" Single: Released Sep '86, on Island, by Island Records. Deleted Apr '88. Catalogue no: **IS 290**
12" Single: Released Sep '86, on Island, by Island Records. Catalogue no: **12ISX 290**
12" Single: Released Sep '86, on Island, by Island Records. Deleted Apr '88. Catalogue no: **12IS 290**

Copeland, Stewart

EQUALIZER, THE
Tracks: / Equalizer, The / Equalizer (edit), The.
7" Single: Released 21 Nov '87, on I.R.S, Catalogue no: **IRM 147**
12" Single: Released 21 Nov '87, on I.R.S, Catalogue no: **IRMT 147**

KOTEJA
Tracks: / Koteja / Gone rock.
7" Single: Released Mar '85, on A&M, by A&M Records. Deleted '88. Catalogue no: **AM 242**

LOVE LESSONS
Tracks: / Love lessons / Amy (silent movies).
7" Single: Released Aug '86, on I.R.S, Catalogue no: **IRM 20**
12" Single: Released Aug '86, on I.R.S, Catalogue no: **IRMT 120**

JULIAN COPE - CHINA DOLL (Released on Island)

Copperfield, David

ARMY GAMES
Tracks: / Army games / Simple understanding.
7" Single: Released Oct '82, on CBS, by CBS Records. Deleted '85. Catalogue no: **TECS 4**

Coppin, Johnny

BELIEVE IN YOU
Tracks: / Believe in you / Run to her.
7" Single: Released Jan '80, on Red Sky, by Red Sky Records. Catalogue no: **ROO 3**

EVERYBODY KNOWS
Tracks: / Everybody knows / No going back.
7" Single: Released Jan '80, on Starward, Catalogue no: **SWS 102**

WE SHALL NOT PASS
Tracks: / We shall not pass / Can you feel it.
7" Single: Released Jan '79, on Red Sky, by Red Sky Records. Catalogue no: **ROO 1**

Cops

BABY IT'S YOU
Tracks: / Baby it's you / Downtown drinkin'.
7" Single: Released Apr '82, on Logo, by Logo Records. Catalogue no: **GO 413**

Copsey, Brian

BOYS IN LOVE
Tracks: / Boys in love / Send you my picture.
7" Single: Released Feb '81, on Chrysalis, by Chrysalis Records. Deleted Feb '84. Catalogue no: **CHS 2499**

LOVE'S MADE A FOOL OF YOU
Tracks: / Love's made a fool of you / Wendy.
7" Single: Released Jul '81, on Chrysalis, by Chrysalis Records. Deleted '85. Catalogue no: **CHS 2531**

Coptic Roots

ROOTS AND CULTURE
Tracks: / Roots and culture.
12" Single: Released Nov '85, on Axumite, Catalogue no: **AX 001**

Copy Cats

TELL THE CAPTAIN
Tracks: / Tell the captain / Getting excited.
7" Single: Released Jan '84, on Out To Lunch, by Out To Lunch Records. Catalogue no: **OTL 2**
12" Single: Released Jan '84, on Out To Lunch, by Out To Lunch Records. Catalogue no: **12 OTL 2**

Corbett, Harry H.

Biographical details: Corbett, Harry H. This British comedian played the son in 'Steptoe and Son', the BBC's long running television comedy series that documented the hilarious trials and tribulations of an elderly father and his son, struggling to earn their daily bread from the rag and bone trade. Though humorous, the programme always contained a hint of melancholy and sometimes even tragedy. The characters played by Corbett and his colleague, Wilfred Brambell, were so popular on Britain's television screens that the actors' names and faces became synonymous with those roles, regardless of their other professional activities.
The pair's 'Steptoe and son' activities were documented on disc by Pye Records, whose 1963/4 run of British chart success with the duo was lucrative (like the TV show) but brief (unlike the TV show). Three chart LPs, two chart EPs and one hit single were crammed into a period of twelve months. The most successful were the *Steptoe and Son* album and the *Facts of Life from Steptoe and Son* EP, which coincidentally, both reached No.4 and both logged 28 weeks on their respective lists. *At the Palace* peaked at No.25 on the British singles chart, logging 12 weeks on the Top 50. Harry H Corbett died in March 1982 at the age of 57, and was rejoined by his fictional father, Wilfred Brambell in January 1985. (Bob Macdonald 4/2/85).

ESPECIALLY WHEN YOU'RE YOUNG
Tracks: / Especially when you're young / Old fashioned Christmas.
7" Single: Released Sep '80, on Symbol, by Lee Lambert Records. Deleted '83. Catalogue no: **SOO 1**

OLD FASHIONED CHRISTMAS
Tracks: / Old fashioned Christmas, An / Especially when we're young.
7" Single: Released Dec '80, on Pel, Deleted '81. Catalogue no: **POO 4**

Cordell, Frank

Biographical details: Cordell, Frank This British orchestra leader was one of many such figures to score success during the pre-Beatles first decade of the British record charts. He reached No.29 in 1956 with *Sadie's Shawl* and No.44 in 1961 with *Black Bear*. (Bob Macdonald 4/2/85).

BLACK BEAR
Tracks: / Black bear, The.
7" Single: Released Feb '61, on H.M.V., by EMI Records. Deleted '64. Catalogue no: **POP 824**

SADIE'S SHAWL
Tracks: / Sadie's shawl.
7" Single: Released Aug '56, on H.M.V., by EMI Records. Deleted '59. Catalogue no: **POP 229**

Cordet, Louise

I'M JUST A BABY
Tracks: / I'm just a baby.
7" Single: Released Jul '62, on Decca, by Decca Records. Deleted Jul '65. Catalogue no: **F 11476**

Corfield, Gemma

MAD FOR IT
Tracks: / Mad for it / Laid in the USA.
12" Single: Released Aug '85, on Virgin, by Virgin Records. Catalogue no: **GEM 1**

Cori Jorsais

TAKIN' IT STRAIGHT
Tracks: / Takin' it straight / Mirror of your....
7" Single: Released Jan '83, on Metropolis (1), Catalogue no: **CAR 258**
12" Single: Released Jan '83, on Metropolis (1), Catalogue no: **CART 258**

Corina

GIVE ME BACK MY HEART
Tracks: / Give me back my heart / Give me back my heart (version).
7" Single: Released May '89, on Champion, by Champion Records. Catalogue no: **CHAMP 203**
12" Single: Released May '89, on Champion, by Champion Records. Catalogue no: **CHAMP 12203**

Corkscrew

HARD ROAD TO CALVARY
Tracks: / Square rooms / Don't play with me.
12" Single: Released Jul '82, on Glim Bim, Catalogue no: **GB 002**

Corley, Al

SQUARE ROOMS (SINGLE)
Tracks: / Square rooms.
12" Single: Released Jun '85, on Polydor, by Polydor Ltd. Catalogue no: **POSPX 747**
7" Single: Released Jun '85, on Polydor, by Polydor Ltd. Catalogue no: **POSP 747**

Cormier, Clarence

HEE HAW BREAKDOWN
Tracks: / Hee haw breakdown / Cajun waltz.
7" Single: Released Dec '82, on Swallow (USA), by Flat Town Music Co.(USA). Catalogue no: **1004**

Corn Dollies

BEING SMALL
Tracks: / Being small.
12" Single: Released Oct '87, on Medium Cool, by Medium Cool Records. Catalogue no: **MC 008T**

FOREVER STEVEN
Tracks: / Forever Steven / About to believe.
7" Single: Released Jul '87, on Farm, Catalogue no: **FARM 001**
12" Single: Released '88, on Medium Cool, by Medium Cool Records. Catalogue no: **MC 009T**

MAP OF THE WORLD
Tracks: / Map of the world.
7" Single: Released Oct '88, on Medium Cool, by Medium Cool Records. Catalogue no: **MC 017**
12" Single: Released Oct '88, on Medium Cool, by Medium Cool Records. Catalogue no: **MC 017T**

NOTHING OF YOU
Tracks: / Nothing of you.
12" Single: Released Apr '89, on Medium Cool, by Medium Cool Records. Catalogue no: **MC 020T**

SHAKE
Tracks: / Shake.
7" Single: Released Jul '88, on Medium Cool, by Medium Cool Records. Catalogue no: **MC 015**
12" Single: Released Jul '88, on Medium Cool, by Medium Cool Records. Catalogue

no: **MC 015 T**

Cornelius, Eddie

HURRY UP
Tracks: / Hurry up / That's love making in your eyes.
7" Single: Released May '86, on G&B, Catalogue no: **G & B 001**

Cornell, Don

HOLD MY HAND
Tracks: / Hold my hand.
7" Single: Released Sep '54, on Vogue, by Vogue Records. Deleted Sep '57. Catalogue no: **Q 2013**

STRANGER IN PARADISE
Tracks: / Stranger in paradise.
7" Single: Released Apr '55, on Vogue, by Vogue Records. Deleted Apr '58. Catalogue no: **Q 72073**

Cornell, Lynn

NEVER ON SUNDAY
Tracks: / Never on Sunday.
7" Single: Released Oct '60, on Decca, by Decca Records. Deleted Oct '63. Catalogue no: **F 11277**

Corniche

CHIPS
Tracks: / Chips / California hustle.
7" Single: Released May '80, on RCA, by BMG Records (UK). Deleted May '85. Catalogue no: **FB 1552**

Corns, Arnold

HANG ON TO YOURSELF
Tracks: / Hang on to yourself / Looking for a friend / Man in the middle.
12" Single: Released Apr '89, on Wax, by Wax Records. Catalogue no: **12 WAX 5**

Cornwell, Charlotte

NEVER GOING HOME
Tracks: / Never going home / Ain't happened yet.
7" Single: Released Apr '83, on CBS, by CBS Records. Catalogue no: **A 3353**

Cornwell, Hugh

ANOTHER KIND OF LOVE
Tracks: / Another kind of love / Real people / Nothing but the groove (on CD & 12" only) / Facts and figures (on CD only) / Another kind of love (another kinda mix) (On 12" only) / Where is this place, what is this thing called love? (on 12" only).
CD 5": Released Aug '88, on Virgin, by Virgin Records. Catalogue no: **VSCD 945**
7" Single: Released Apr '88, on Virgin, by Virgin Records. Catalogue no: **VS 945**
12" Single: Released Apr '88, on Virgin, by Virgin Records. Catalogue no: **VS 945-12**
CD 3": Released '88, on Virgin, by Virgin Records. Catalogue no: **VSCD 94512**

DREAMING AGAIN
Tracks: / Dreaming again (7" only) / Blue note (On all versions) / Dreaming again (full length version) (On CD & 12" only) / Getting involved (New York mix) (On CD & 12" only) / English walk, The (On CD only).
Note: "Dreaming Again is the second single to be released from Cornwell's recent album Wolf (V2420). Following on from That's Another Kind Of Love this is an even more commercial offering that is sure to achieve airplay and more media interest." (Virgin Records, July 1988).
CD 5": Released '88, on Virgin, by Virgin Records. Catalogue no: **VSCD 1093**
7" Single: Released Jun '88, on Virgin, by Virgin Records. Catalogue no: **VS 1093**
12" Single: Released Jun '88, on Virgin, by Virgin Records. Catalogue no: **VST 1093**

FACTS & FIGURES
Tracks: / Facts and figures (version).
7" Single: Released Jan '87, on Virgin, by Virgin Records. Deleted May '88. Catalogue no: **VS 922**
12" Single: Released Jan '87, on Virgin, by Virgin Records. Deleted May '88. Catalogue no: **VS 922-12**

ONE IN A MILLION
Tracks: / One in a million / Siren song.
7" Single: Released Aug '85, on Portrait, by CBS Records. Catalogue no: **A 6509**
12" Single: Released Aug '85, on Portrait, by CBS Records. Catalogue no: **TX 6509**

Coroner

PURPLE HAZE
Tracks: / Purple haze.
7" Single: Released Oct '89, Catalogue no: **7HAZE 3**

Coronets

TWENTY TINY FINGERS
Tracks: / Twenty tiny fingers.
7" Single: Released Nov '55, on Columbia, by EMI Records. Deleted Nov '58. Catalogue no: **DB 3671**

Corporation (Group)

AIN'T NOTHING BUT A HOUSE PARTY
Tracks: / Ain't nothing but a house party.
7" Single: Released Jun '89, on Pinnacle, by Pinnacle Records. Catalogue no: **KORP 1**
12" Single: Released Jun '89, on Pinnacle, by Pinnacle Records. Catalogue no: **12 KORP 1**

Corporation Of One

REAL LIFE, THE
Tracks: / Real life, The / Prayer.
7" Single: Released Apr '89, on Desire, by Desire Records. Catalogue no: **WANT 16**
12" Single: Released Jun '89, on Desire, by Desire Records. Catalogue no: **WANTX 16 R**
12" Single: Released Mar '89, on Desire, by Desire Records. Catalogue no: **WANTX 16**
12" Single: Released 20 Mar '89, on Smokin, Catalogue no: **TAI 126612**

Corrigan, Ian

GALLANT JOHN JOE
Tracks: / Gallant John Joe.
7" Single: Released '88, on Homespun (Ireland), by Outlet Records. Catalogue no: **HIS 10**

Corrosion Of

TECHNOCRACY
Tracks: / Technocracy.
12" Single: Released May '87, on Metal Blade, Catalogue no: **RR 125477**

Cortez, Dave

Biographical details: An R&B keyboard player born in Detroit in 1939. He played piano 10 years, then switched to organ. His two biggest hits were *The Happy Organ* in 1959 and *Rinky Dink* in 1962. (Donald Clarke 1989).

HAPPY ORGAN
Tracks: / Happy organ.
7" Single: Released Aug '82, on Creole, by Creole Records. Catalogue no: **CR 186**

RINKY DINK
Tracks: / Rinky dink.
7" Single: Released Aug '82, on Creole, by Creole Records. Catalogue no: **CR 184**

Corvettes

GIRLS CARS GIRLS SUN GIRLS SURF FUN GIRLS
Tracks: / Girls cars girls sun girls surf fun girls / Beach is not enough.
7" Single: Released Jul '84, on Bitchen, Catalogue no: **BIT 101**

SURF DON'T WALK
Tracks: / Surf don't walk.
7" Single: Released Jun '86, on Bitchen, Catalogue no: **BIT 100**

Cory Band

CORY BAND (SINGLE)
Tracks: / Cory Band.
7" Single: Released '80, on MGM, by Polydor Ltd. Catalogue no: **LR 4754**

STOP THE CAVALRY
Tracks: / Stop the cavalry / Longest day.
7" Single: Released Nov '81, on Stiff, by Stiff Records. Deleted Nov '84. Catalogue no: **BUY 133**

Cosgill, Doctor

BENEDICTION
Tracks: / Benediction / Douce dame.
7" Single: Released Feb '81, on Goat Bag, by Goat Bag Records. Catalogue no: **GB 003**

Cosma, Vladimir

Biographical details: Cosma, Vladimir This Hungarian orchestra leader has enjoyed just one week of British chart success. He hit No.64 in July 1979 with *David's Song* (main theme from 'Kidnapped').This was a considerable achievement for Cosma because, whatever its other qualities may be, Hungary is not noted for its penetration of the Uk record charts. (Bob Macdonald 4/2/85).

DAVID'S SONG
Tracks: / David's song.
7" Single: Released Jul '79, on Decca, by Decca Records. Deleted Jul '82. Catalogue no: **FR 13841**

SENTIMENTAL PROMENADE
Tracks: / Sentimental promenade.
7" Single: Released '83, on Palace, by Virgin Records. Catalogue no: **PS 1**

Cosmetic

SO TRANQUILIZIN (SINGLE)
Tracks: / So tranquilizin.
12" Single: Released Dec '85, on Gramavision (USA), by Grammavision Records (USA). Catalogue no: **GR 1210**

Cosmetics

CHAIN
Tracks: / Chain, The / Closures.
7" Single: Released '82, on Secret, by Secret Records. Catalogue no: **SEC 31**

COSMETIC
Tracks: / Cosmetic / New complexion.
7" Single: Released '82, on Rough Trade, by Rough Trade Records. Catalogue no: **RT 102**

CRACK, THE
Tracks: / Crack, The / Caligraphy.
12" Single: Released '82, on Illegal, by Faulty Products Records. Catalogue no: **ILS 12029**

GET READY
Tracks: / Get ready / Put it on.
7" Single: Released '82, on Rough Trade, by Rough Trade Records. Catalogue no: **RT 113**
12" Single: Released '82, on Rough Trade, by Rough Trade Records. Catalogue no: **12 RT 113**

SECRET
Tracks: / Secret.
7" Single: Released May '80, on Virgin, by Virgin Records. Deleted May '83. Catalogue no: **VS 340**

Cosmic Circle

MAGIC
Tracks: / Magic.
12" Single: Released Nov '86, on C & E, Catalogue no: **CED 104**

Costa, Don

NEVER ON SUNDAY
Tracks: / Never on Sunday.
7" Single: Released Oct '60, on London-American, Deleted Oct '63. Catalogue no: **HLT 9195**

Costa, Nikka

OUT HERE ON MY OWN
Tracks: / Out here on my own / I believe in love.
7" Single: Released Feb '82, on RCA, by BMG Records (UK). Deleted Feb '87. Catalogue no: **RCA 185**

Costandinos, Alec R

SYNERGY
Tracks: / Synergy / Pontius Pilate.
7" Single: Released Apr '80, on DJM, Deleted '82. Catalogue no: **DJS 10937**
12" Single: Released Apr '80, on DJM, Deleted '82. Catalogue no: **DJR 18010**

Co-stars

KISS ME AND MAKE UP
Tracks: / Kiss me and make up / Not ready for your love / Roll on the weekend.
7" Single: Released '85, on Individual, by Individual Records. Catalogue no: **AIRS 101**
12" Single: Released '87, on Individual, by Individual Records. Catalogue no: **AIRLP 1002**
12" Single: Released '85, on Individual, by Individual Records. Catalogue no: **AIRLT 101**

Costello, Elvis

Biographical details: Costello, Elvis This British singer, guitarist and songwriter, born Declan McManus in London in 1954, was born into a musical household, being the son of Ross McManus, a big band singer with the famous Joe Loss. After growing up with jazz and MoR influence and after playing folk, country and rock music on the pub rock circuit during the early and mid-Seventies, he was blessed with an eclectic and catholic musical experience by the time he signed with Stiff Records in 1976. This new British label was set up at the time of the New Wave/punk explosion and played an important role in its future development. The philosophy behind the new company was to provide an outlet for creative and exciting new artists who had been rejected by the major record corporations. No one fell into that category more neatly than this singer/songwriter and he quickly built up a cult following. The sheer cheek of his name change, adopting the monicker of the King of Rock, attracted the intended publicity. Fate heightened this effect dramatically because the real Elvis died two weeks after Costello's debut album *My Aim Is True* entered the UK chart. That album won ecstatic reviews in the British music press and he was soon rewarded not only with a UK Top 20 LP but also with his first UK Top 20 single *Watching The Detectives*. America also recognised his songwriting talents: by the end of '77 he had become the first British New Wave star to crack the US Top 100 Albums list and, the following year, Linda Ronstadt recorded *Allison* one of the best songs from *My Aim Is True*. Costello went on to achive substantial LP and concert success in the States, although he failed to chalk up a major US hit single.
During the late Seventies and early Eighties, Costello released a string of quality singles and albums. The LPs regularly reached the British Top 10, but only three singles attained that level of success. His varied musical tastes were reflected in his constantly shifting direction: 1979's *Armed Forces* album was in a mainstream pop/rock vein, and yielded his irresistably catchy but politically biting No.2 single *Oliver's Army*, his biggest British single; 1980's 20 track *Get Happy* LP was a rhythm and blues throwback to the Stax label's sound of the Sixties, and produced the UK No.4 single *I Can't Stand Up For Falling Down*; 1981's *Almost Blue* album was an authentic country offering recorded in Nashville, and yielded the British No.6 ballad *Good Year For The Roses*. He also wrote *Girls Talk* a UK No.4 single for Dave Edmunds in 1979. But Costello's erratic singles performance was demonstrated by the fact that he followed his *Roses* biggie with six consecutive minor hits, all of which reached the British Top 75 but fell short of the Top 40. Yet the bespectacled, distinctive face of Costello nonetheless remaines

ELVIS COSTELLO - ACCIDENT'S WILL HAPPEN (Released on Radar)

ELVIS COSTELLO - I CAN'T STAND UP FOR FALLING DOWN (Released on F Beat)

in the public ye, because his songwriting - though rarely achieving the commercial success it deserves -remains so powrful. Numbers such as *Shipbuilding*, his 1982 comment on the Falklands War, and 1984's *Peace In Our Time* have continued to cement his reputation, and have helped to place his writing ability on a par with that of Bob Dylan. (Bob Macdonald 4/2/85)
Declan Patrick McManus, born in 1954 in Paddington, is easily the most important singer/songwriter to emerge from the New Wave. As with all good singer/songwriters, his lyrics are worth listening to and fit the tunes perfectly. He is the son of Ross McManus, a big band singer with Joe Loss. He first band was the country-flavoured Flip City; he played folk clubs solo and was a computer programmer for Elizabeth Arden (the 'vanity factory' in the song *I'm not angry*). He turned up with his guitar to perform for baffled A&R men in his legendary method of auditioning; he was once arrested for busking outside a CBS convention. Deejay Charlie Gillett played early Costello tapes on his Radio London show and Costello signed with Stiff in 1977, his early work produced by Nick Lowe and singled out by critics for intensity and vitriol. He formed a backing group The Attractions which has recorded on its own. He has inevitably cooled off somewhat since his classic period; *Almost Blue* in 1981 was a lavish set of favorite country songs, produced in Nashville by the very slick Billy Sherrill, with covers of hits by Don Gibson, Gram Parsons etc. more or less straight except for a New Wave treatment of the Hank Williams classic *Why Don't You Love Me* which left it unrecognisable. He has also acted, e.g. in the UK TV series *Scully* in 1984, produced records by the Specials, Squeeze, Bluebells, Pogues; played on stage with Ricky Scaggs, Los Lobos, Richard Hell and Delbert McLinton, his own songs covered by Robert Wyatt, Dave Edmunds, George Jones etc. as well as LindaRonstadt. Generous 20-track collection *10 Bloody Marys & 10 How's Your Fathers* yield an insight into the scope of his work. *Punch The Clock* in 1983 included Wyatt's *Shipbuilding*, a Flaklands lament, with a trumpet solo by Chet Baker, as well as *Everyday I Write The Book*, his first USA top 40 hit (but all his albums charted strongly in the USA, *Armed Forces* at number 10). In 1984 he toured USA and UK solo supported by T-Bone Burnett and they went onstage together as the Coward Brothers; Burnett produced *King Of America*, which was highly praised. *Blood And Chocolate* in 1986 was produced by Lowe and a successful reunion with the Attractions. His sweep of contemporary subject matter and absorption of popular culture is matched by his lyrical talent, his work standing with that of any chronicler in popular music. He married the Pogues bassist Cait O'Riordan in 1986. (Donald Clarke 1989).

ACCIDENTS WILL HAPPEN (see panel on previous page)
Tracks: / Accidents will happen / Watching the detectives.
7" Single: Released May '79, on Radar, Deleted May '82. Catalogue no: **ADA 35**

BABY PLAYS AROUND
Tracks: / Baby plays around / Poisoned rose / Almost blue / My funny valentine.
CD 5": Released May '89, on WEA, by WEA Records. Catalogue no: **W 2949CD**
10" single: Released May '89, on WEA, by WEA Records. Catalogue no: **W 2949TE**
7" Single: Released May '89, on WEA, by WEA Records. Catalogue no: **W 2949**
12" Single: Released May '89, on WEA, by WEA Records. Catalogue no: **W 2949T**
Cassingle: Released May '89, on WEA, by WEA Records. Catalogue no: **W 2949C**

CHELSEA (I DON'T WANNA GO TO)
Tracks: / Chelsea (I don't wanna go to).
7" Single: Released Mar '78, on Radar, Deleted Mar '81. Catalogue no: **ADA 3**

CLUBLAND
Tracks: / Clubland / Clean money / Hoover factory.
7" Single: Released Dec '80, on F-Beat, by F-Beat Records. Deleted Dec '83. Catalogue no: **XX 12**

EVERYDAY I WRITE THE BOOK
Tracks: / Everyday I write the book.
12" Single: Released '83, on F-Beat, by F-Beat Records. Deleted '88. Catalogue no: **XX 32T**
7" Single: Released '83, on F-Beat, by F-Beat Records. Deleted '88. Catalogue no: **XX 32**

FROM A WHISPER TO A SCREAM
Tracks: / From a whisper to a scream / Luxembourg.
7" Single: Released Feb '81, on F-Beat, by F-Beat Records. Deleted Feb '84. Catalogue no: **XX 14**

FROM HEAD TO TOE
Tracks: / From head to toe / World of broken....
7" Single: Released '82, on F-Beat, by F-Beat Records. Deleted '88. Catalogue no: **XX 30**

GOOD YEAR FOR THE ROSES, A
Tracks: / Good year for the roses, A.
7" Single: Released Oct '81, on F-Beat, by F-Beat Records. Deleted Oct '84. Catalogue no: **XX 17**

GREEN SHIRT
Tracks: / Green shirt / Beyond belief.
7" Single: Released '85, on F-Beat, by F-Beat Records. Deleted '88. Catalogue no: **ZB 40085**
12" Single: Released '85, on F-Beat, by F-Beat Records. Deleted '88. Catalogue no: **ZT 40086**

HI FIDELITY
Tracks: / Hi fidelity.
7" Single: Released Apr '80, on F-Beat, by F-Beat Records. Deleted Apr '83. Catalogue no: **XX 3**
12" Single: Released Apr '80, on F-Beat, by F-Beat Records. Deleted Apr '83. Catalogue no: **XX 3-12**

I CAN'T STAND UP FOR FALLING DOWN (see panel above)
Tracks: / I can't stand up for falling down / Girls talk.
7" Single: Released Feb '80, on F-Beat, by F-Beat Records. Deleted Feb '83. Catalogue no: **XX 1**

I WANNA BE LOVED
Tracks: / I wanna be loved / Turning the town red.
12" Single: Released '84, on F-Beat, by F-Beat Records. Deleted '88. Catalogue no: **XX 35T**
7" Single: Released '84, on F-Beat, by F-Beat Records. Deleted '85. Catalogue no: **XX 35**

I WANT YOU
Tracks: / I want you.
7" Single: Released Oct '86, on Imp, by Demon Records. Catalogue no: **IMP 008**
10" single: Released Oct '86, on Imp, by Demon Records. Catalogue no: **IMP 008T**

I'M YOUR TOY
Tracks: / I'm your toy / Cry cry.
7" Single: Released '82, on F-Beat, by F-Beat Records. Deleted '88. Catalogue no: **XX 21**
12" Single: Released '82, on F-Beat, by F-Beat Records. Deleted '88. Catalogue no: **XX 21T**

LET THEM TALK
Tracks: / Let them talk / Keep it confidential.
12" Single: Released '83, on F-Beat, by F-Beat Records. Deleted '88. Catalogue no: **XX 33T**
7" Single: Released '83, on F-Beat, by F-Beat Records. Deleted '88. Catalogue no: **XX 33**

MAN OUT OF TIME
Tracks: / Man out of time / Town crier.
12" Single: Released '82, on F-Beat, by F-Beat Records. Deleted '88. Catalogue no: **XX 28T**
7" Single: Released '82, on F-Beat, by F-Beat Records. Deleted '88. Catalogue no: **XX 28**

NEW AMSTERDAM
Tracks: / New Amsterdam.
7" Single: Released Jun '80, on F-Beat, by F-Beat Records. Deleted Jun '83. Catalogue no: **XX 5**

OLIVERS ARMY (see panel below)
Tracks: / Olivers army / My funny valentine.
7" Single: Released Feb '79, on Radar, Deleted '85. Catalogue no: **ADA 31**

ONLY FLAME IN TOWN,THE
Tracks: / Only flame in town, The.
12" Single: Released '84, on F-Beat, by F-Beat Records. Deleted '88. Catalogue no: **XX 37T**
7" Single: Released '84, on F-Beat, by F-Beat Records. Deleted '88. Catalogue no: **XX 37**

PARTY, PARTY
Tracks: / Party, party / Imperial bedroom.
7" Single: Released Dec '82, on A&M, by A&M Records. Deleted Dec '85. Catalogue no: **AMS 8267**

PUMP IT UP
Tracks: / Pump it up.
7" Single: Released May '78, on Radar, Deleted May '81. Catalogue no: **ADA 10**

RADIO RADIO
Tracks: / Radio radio.
7" Single: Released Oct '78, on Radar, Deleted Oct '81. Catalogue no: **ADA 24**

SWEET DREAMS
Tracks: / Sweet dreams / Psycho.
7" Single: Released '81, on F-Beat, by F-Beat Records. Deleted '88. Catalogue no: **XX 19**

TOKYO STORM WARNING (PART 1)
Tracks: / Tokyo strom warning (Part 1) / Tokyo strom warning (Part II) / Black sails in the sunset (Extra track available on 12" version only).
7" Single: Released Aug '86, on Imp, by Demon Records. Catalogue no: **IMP 007**
12" Single: Released Aug '86, on Imp, by Demon Records. Catalogue no: **IMP 007T**

VERONICA
Tracks: / Veronica / You're no good / Road nobody lives in, The / Coal train.
7" Single: Released Feb '89, on Warner Bros., by WEA Records. Catalogue no: **W 755 8**
12" Single: Released Feb '89, on Warner Bros., by WEA Records. Catalogue no: **W 755 8T**
CD 5": Released Feb '89, on Warner Bros., by WEA Records. Catalogue no: **W 755 8CD**

WATCHING THE DETECTIVES
Tracks: / Watching the detectives.
12" Single: Released '85, on Stiff, by Stiff Records. Catalogue no: **BUYIT 239**
7" Single: Released Nov '77, on Stiff, by Stiff Records. Deleted Nov '80. Catalogue no: **BUY 20**

YOU LITTLE FOOL
Tracks: / You little fool / Big sister.
7" Single: Released '82, on F-Beat, by F-Beat Records. Deleted '88. Catalogue no: **XX 26**

Costello Show

BLUE CHAIR
Tracks: / American without tears No. 2 (twilight version) / Shoes without heels (This track 12" version only.).
7" Single: Released Jan '87, on Demon, by Demon Records. Catalogue no: **D 1047**
12" Single: Released Jan '87, on Demon, by Demon Records. Catalogue no: **D 1047 T**

DON'T LET ME BE MISUNDERSTOOD
Tracks: / Don't let me be misunderstood / Baby's got a brand new hair do / Get yourself another fool.
7" Single: Released Jan '86, on RCA, by BMG Records (UK). Catalogue no: **ZB 40555**
12" Single: Released Jan '86, on RCA, by BMG Records (UK). Catalogue no: **ZT 40556**

Costello, Terry

PERFECT HUMAN FACE
Tracks: / Perfect human face.

ELVIS COSTELLO - OLIVER'S ARMY (Released on Radar)

7" Single: Released Aug '83, on World Of Leisure, Deleted '84. Catalogue no: **WOL 99**

Cotgrave, Dave

LEAVE US ALONE
Tracks: / Leave us alone / Yesterday's news.
7" Single: Released Aug '88, on Bold Reprive (2), by Bold Reprive Records. Catalogue no: **7BRM 018**

Cott, Gerry

BALLAD OF THE LONE RANGER
Tracks: / Ballad of the Lone Ranger / Just like anybody else.
7" Single: Released Jan '83, on Epic, by CBS Records. Catalogue no: **EPC A 3047**

PIONEERS
Tracks: / Pioneers.
7" Single: Released Apr '83, on Epic, by CBS Records. Catalogue no: **A 3319**

Cottee, Jo

ARE THE PEOPLE CRAZY
Tracks: / Are the people crazy.
7" Single: Released Feb '85, on RCA, by BMG Records (UK). Catalogue no: **RCA 478**
12" Single: Released Feb '85, on RCA, by BMG Records (UK). Catalogue no: **RCAT 478**

TURN AWAY
Tracks: / Turn away.
7" Single: Released Oct '85, on Reluctant, Catalogue no: **RUC 18**

Cottle, Richard

BARWICK GREEN
Tracks: / Barwick Green / Old bird, The.
7" Single: Released Oct '82, on WEA, by WEA Records. Catalogue no: **ARCH 1**

Cotton, Billy

Biographical details: Cotton, Billy This British bandleader and singer, born in 1899 got his first big break in showbusiness when he played at the Regent, Brighton in 1924. His career blossomed in the late Twenties; during and after the 1939-45 war, he cemented his position as one of Britain's best known and best loved musical personalities, and became a radio and television regular. His signature tune was *Somebody Stole My Gal* and this remained his band's most famous number. Because the British record charts did not begin until 1952, Cotton's disc sales are not fairly reflected by his chart track record. His first charted disc on the newly inaugurated listings was *In A Golden Coach* which was timed to celebrate the Queen's coronation in the summer of '53, and reached No.3. *I Saw Mommy Kissing Santa Claus* took him to No.11 that Christmas and, the following year, he hit No.3 with *Friends and Neighbours*.
Accompanied by his famous band and a variety of vocalists, Cotton remained a national institution until his death in 1969 at the age of 69. His son Bill Cotton kept the family name in the public eye by enjoying a high flying career as a top BBC executive, most notably for his period in charge of light entertainment on television. (Bob Macdonald 4/2/85)
British singer and bandleader (1899-1968), enormously popular for decades. In 1923 he was introducing USA dance fads like the Black Bottom; he was at the London Astoria hotel in 1927. Popular vocalist Alan Breeze was present from 1930; the semi-hot band early '30s had Louis Armstrong clone Nat Gonella on trumpet, black American trombonist Ellis Jackson (also a fine dancer) and did its best to help keep the idea of jazz alive in Britain, but his later recording of *Begin The Beguine* was a straight version of the famous Jerry Gray arrangement for Artie Shaw: the band increadingly became a variety act during the '30s, playing theatres rather than dance halls; by the mid-'40s jazz had taken a back seat to period pop songs and comedy. After the war his radio and music hall act started each show with the catchphrase 'Wakey wakey!'. In the '50s the band did *I've Got A Lovely Bunch Of Coconuts* while pelting the audience with cotton wool balls, but the musicianship was always high and a trumpet star retained: Grisha Farfel played Harry James-styled solo spots. When UK charts were established in 1952 Cotton had top 20 hits and continued successfully on TV and radio until his death. (Donald Clarke 1989)t.

FRIENDS AND NEIGHBOURS
Tracks: / Friends and neighbours.
7" Single: Released Apr '54, on Decca, by Decca Records. Deleted Apr '57. Catalogue no: **F 10299**

I SAW MOMMY KISSING SANTA CLAUS
Tracks: / I saw mommy kissing Santa Claus.
7" Single: Released Dec '53, on Decca, by Decca Records. Deleted Dec '55. Catalogue no: **F 10206**

IN A GOLDEN COACH
Tracks: / In a golden coach.
7" Single: Released May '53, on Decca, by Decca Records. Deleted May '58. Catalogue no: **F 10058**

Cotton, Joseph

ALL OVER THE WORLD
Tracks: / All over the world.
12" Single: Released Oct '89, on Exodus, Catalogue no: **EXO 16**

CORNER SHOP
Tracks: / Corner shop.
12" Single: Released Sep '89, on Unity, Catalogue no: **FEA 021**

HALF SLIM
Tracks: / Half slim / Half slim (version).
12" Single: Released Jul '87, on Body Music, by Nuclear Records. Catalogue no: **BZT 05**

JUDGE COTTON
Tracks: / Judge Cotton.
12" Single: Released May '89, on Briggie C, Catalogue no: **BC 007**

MARK & HUG UP
Tracks: / Mark & hug up.
12" Single: Released Oct '88, on Fashion, by Fashion Records. Catalogue no: **FAD 062**

MASH UP THE FRONTLINE
Tracks: / Mash up the frontline / How me come England / Ragamuffin roll call.
12" Single: Released 27 Feb '88, on Uptempo, Catalogue no: **TEMP 019**

ME NO INNA IT
Tracks: / Me no inna it / Yuh a mi lover.
12" Single: Released 12 Aug '88, on CSA, by CSA Records. Catalogue no: **12CSA 516**

NO TOUCH THE STYLE
Tracks: / No touch the style / Cotton comes to Harlesden.
7" Single: Released 20 Jun '87, on Fashion, by Fashion Records. Catalogue no: **FAD 7048**
12" Single: Released 20 Jun '87, on Fashion, by Fashion Records. Catalogue no: **FAD 048**

PAT A FI COOK
Tracks: / Pat a fi cook.
12" Single: Released Mar '89, on Jaguar, Catalogue no: **JR 001**

TUTORING
Tracks: / Tutoring.
12" Single: Released May '89, on Jaguar, Catalogue no: **SRF 001 T**

WHAT IS THIS
Tracks: / What is this.
7" Single: Released May '89, on Fashion, by Fashion Records. Catalogue no: **FAD 064**

YUHA MI LOVER
Tracks: / Yuha mi lover (version) / Lovers in dub.
12" Single: Released Nov '86, on CSA, by CSA Records. Catalogue no: **12CSA 512**

Cotton, Josie

JIMMY LOVES MARY ANN
Tracks: / Jimmy loves Mary Ann / No pictures of Dad.
7" Single: Released Apr '84, on Elektra (USA), by Elektra Records (USA). Catalogue no: **E 9748**

JOHNNY ARE YOU QUEER
Tracks: / Johnny are you queer / Lets do the blackout.
7" Single: Released Jan '82, on Bomp International, Catalogue no: **BOMP 1**

Cotton, Mike

SWING THAT HAMMER
Tracks: / Swing that hammer.
7" Single: Released Jun '63, on Columbia, by EMI Records. Deleted Jun '66. Catalogue no: **DB 7029**

Cotton Mill Boys

GOLD WATCH AND CHAIN
Tracks: / Gold watch and chain / Devil went....
7" Single: Released May '83, on Homespun (Ireland), by Outlet Records. Catalogue no: **HS 067**

Cotton, Tom

WHO NEEDS FRIENDS?
Tracks: / Who needs friends? / Boogie Street.
7" Single: Released Mar '80, on Evolution, by Evolution Records. Deleted '83. Catalogue no: **EV 2**

Cougar, John

Biographical details: Born John Mellencamp in 1951 in Indiana, the rock singer was stuck with the name Johnny Cougar by David Bowie's manager Tony DeFries, and has since learned to laugh about it. He was influenced by black Detroit and Chicago radio stations and wrote his first song at 23. His first album *Chestnut Street incident* on MCA in 1976 was demo-quality material; label, artist and manager parted company. He began having hits in the late '70's; his music was often cliche-ridden, his sub James Dean act winning a substantial cult status, but he got better. *American fool* in 1982 was a number one album in the USA, with big hit singles *Hurts so good* and *Jack and Diane* (articulating working-class life: 'Life goes on/Long after the thrill is gone'). He produced a comeback album for his boyhood hero Mitch Ryder, *Never kick a sleeping dog* in 1983. *The lonesome jubilee* in 1987 included dobro, fiddle and accordion; he may be moving toward what might be called the new classic USA mainstream. (Donald Clarke, April 1989) .

AIN'T EVEN DONE WITH THE NIGHT
Tracks: / Ain't even done with the night / To M.G. whoever she may be.
7" Single: Released May '81, on Riva, by Riva Records. Deleted May '84. Catalogue no: **WEA 31**

HOT NIGHT IN A COLD TOWN
Tracks: / Hot night in a cold town / Tonight.
7" Single: Released Feb '81, on Riva, by Riva Records. Deleted Feb '84. Catalogue no: **RIVA 30**

THIS TIME
Tracks: / This time / Don't misunderstand.
7" Single: Released Oct '80, on Riva, by Riva Records. Deleted '83. Catalogue no: **RIVA 25**

Cougars

DOCTOR LIVINGSTONE I PRESUME?
Tracks: / Doctor Livingstone I presume?.
7" Single: Released Oct '88, on JHC International, Catalogue no: **JHC 50**
12" Single: Released Oct '88, on JHC International, Catalogue no: **12JHC 50**

SATURDAY NIGHT AT THE DUCK POND
Tracks: / Saturday night at the duck pond.
7" Single: Released Feb '63, on Parlophone, by EMI Records. Deleted Feb '66. Catalogue no: **R 4989**

Coulson, Julie

BIG TIME OPERATOR
Tracks: / Big time operator.
7" Single: Released Feb '87, on Creole, by Creole Records. Deleted May '87. Catalogue no: **CR 101**
12" Single: Released May '87, on Creole, by Creole Records. Catalogue no: **CRT 101**
7" Single: Released Oct '85, on Ecstasy, by Creole Records. Catalogue no: **XTC 15**

Coulter, Phil

Biographical details: This British songwriter and orchestra leader, who hails from Londonderry, Northern Ireland, made his name in the late Sixties when he teamed with fellow composer Bill Martin, a Scotsman. Together they penned *Puppet on a string*, Sandi Shaw's 1967 Eurovision Song Contest winner. This was the first UK entry to win the Contest since its inception in the mid-Fifties, and it hit the No.1 slot in virtually every country in Europe. The songwriting duo scored another huge success the following year with *Congratulations*, the 1968 entry sung by Cliff Richard, which was once again an international chart topper. It was pipped at the post in the actual contest in Spain, but *Congratulations* was nonetheless the biggest seller to emerge from that year's Eurovision and became and instant party singalong classic - and who remembers *La la la* by Massiel, the Spanish entry? A third British No.1 single was achieved by Martin and Coulter in 1970, when the England World Cup Squad went to the top of the charts but not on the playing field. By now Bill and Phil (as they were affectionately known in the music business) were producing as well as writing their hits. A three-year golden period from 1973-6 saw them collecting a string of hits in both capacities, most notably with the Bay City Rollers, Kenny and Slik. Although the pair were not responsible for either of the BCR's UK No.1 singles, they provided them with a US chart topper in the shape of *Saturday night* and then quickly scored a British No.1 with the Rollers clones Slik on *Forever and ever*. Perhaps the most revealing aspect of Bill and Phil's manipulative, conveyor-belt attitude was their success story with Kenny - during Kenny's chart career, Kenny changed from being a Irish singer to being a British teenybop group, but Martin and Coulter simply carried on regardless. The pair split up in the late Seventies, having been the only real challengers to the decade's ace British songwriting/producing manipulators, Nicky Chinn and Mike Chapman.
1983 saw a re-issue of *Good thing going* and *Runaway bunion*, two favourites on the UK's Northern Soul circuit performed by Coulter and his Orchestra. However, it was not this that put his name back in the chart limelight, but his hit album *Sea of tranquility*. In total contrast to his pop hits of the late Sixties and early Seventies, this was an LP of peaceful popularity in Northern Ireland led to it reaching the UK national Top 50 (in Ocotober 1984) before it had even been released on the British mainland. This was the follow-up to *Classic tranquility*, a Coulter LP that had been a major seller in the Irish Republic. (Bob MacDonald, 6th Feb 1985).

GOOD THING GOING
Tracks: / Good thing going / Runaway bunion.
7" Single: Released Mar '83, on Neil Rushton, Catalogue no: **HEAT 5**

TRANQUILITY
Tracks: / Tranquility.
7" Single: Released Oct '84, on Panther, by MCA Records. Catalogue no: **PAN 8**

Council Collective

SOUL DEEP
Tracks: / Soul deep.
12" Single: Released Dec '84, on Polydor, by Polydor Ltd. Catalogue no: **MINEX1**
7" Single: Released Dec '84, on Polydor, by Polydor Ltd. Catalogue no: **MINE 1**

Count Lorenzo

WHAT ARE YOU LOOKING AT CECIL
Tracks: / What are you looking at Cecil.
7" Single: Released Sep '84, on Shades, Catalogue no: **HADES 1**

Counterfeit

GOOD SAMARITAN
Tracks: / Good samaritan.
12" Single: Released Sep '89, on Creation, by Creation Records. Catalogue no: **CRE 068T**

Counting House

PACK YOUR BASS
Tracks: / Pack your bass / Closer.
7" Single: Released Nov '88, on Clear Cut, Catalogue no: **EASCR 1**

Country Billy

MIDNIGHT RIDER
Tracks: / Midnight rider / Six days on the road / Tequila Sheila / Sella and the dealer / Coward of the county / Tulsa time / Louisianna woman.
7" EP: Released Dec '81, on Young Blood, by Young Blood Records. Deleted Dec '84. Catalogue no: **YB 124**
12" Single: Released Dec '81, on Young Blood, by Young Blood Records. Deleted Dec '84. Catalogue no: **YB 12124**

Country Fathers

LIGHT HEADED
Tracks: / Light headed / You think it's so funny / Deep south / Lightheaded.
12" Single: Released Jan '88, on Ugly Man, by Ugly Man Records. Catalogue no: **UGLY 8T**

Country Gold

COUNTRY GOLD
Tracks: / Harper Valley PTA: *Riley, Jeannie C.* / Oh lonesome me: *Cash, Johnny* / Night life: *Nelson, Willie* / Please help me, I'm falling: *Locklin, Hank* / Sixteen tons: *La Beef, Sleepy* / Jambalaya: *Newman, Jimmy C.*.
Cassingle: Released Sep '83, on Scoop 33, by Pickwick Records. Catalogue no: **7SC 5029**
7" EP: Released Sep '83, on Scoop 33, by Pickwick Records. Catalogue no: **7SR 5029**

Country Hams

WALKING IN THE PARK WITH ELOISE
Tracks: / Walking in the park with eloise / Bridge on the river suite.
7" Single: Released Feb '82, on EMI, by EMI Records. Deleted Feb '87. Catalogue no: **EMI 2220**

Country Life Posse

FREE HORIZONS
Tracks: / Free horizons.
12" Single: Released Sep '85, on Pitch, Catalogue no: **PAT 001**

Countrymen

CONFRONTATION
Tracks: / Confrontation.
12" Single: Released Aug '82, on Jay Dee, Catalogue no: **JD 007**

I KNOW WHERE I'M GOING
Tracks: / I know where I'm going.
7" Single: Released May '62, on Piccadilly, Deleted May '65. Catalogue no: **7N 35029**

County, Jayne

SAN FRANCISCO
Tracks: / San Francisco.
12" Single: Released Nov '88, on Grapevine Communications, Catalogue no: **GV 001**

TIME MACHINE
Tracks: / Time machine.
7" Single: Released Jul '89, on Jungle, by Jungle Records. Catalogue no: **JUNG 49**

WHEN QUEENS COLLIDE
Tracks: / When queens collide.
7" Single: Released May '86, on Heighway, Catalogue no: **SAD 002**

County Line

HEROES
Tracks: / Heroes / Long way to go.
7" Single: Released Apr '86, on BBC, by BBC Records & Tapes. Deleted Sep '87. Catalogue no: **RESL 185**

County, Wayne

BERLIN
Tracks: / Berlin.
7" Single: Released '79, on Safari, by Safari Records. Catalogue no: **SAFE 13**
12" Single: Released '79, on Safari, by Safari Records. Catalogue no: **SAFELS 13**

BLATANTLY OFFENSIVE
Tracks: / Blatantly offensive.
7" Single: Released '80, on Safari, by Safari Records. Catalogue no: **WC 1**

EDDIE AND SHEENA
Tracks: / Eddie and Sheena.
7" Single: Released '79, on Safari, by Safari Records. Catalogue no: **SAFE 1**

FUCK OFF
Tracks: / F**k off.
7" Single: Released Jun '83, on Safari, by Safari Records. Catalogue no: **WCP 3**

TRYING TO GET ON THE RADIO
Tracks: / Trying to get on the radio.
7" Single: Released '79, on Safari, by Safari Records. Catalogue no: **SAFE 9**

Coup De Villes

BIG TROUBLE IN LITTLE CHINA (THEME)
Tracks: / Big trouble in little China / Pork chop express.
7" Single: Released Nov '86, on Silva Screen, by Silva Screen Records. Catalogue no: **SILVA 101**

Court Martial

GOTTA GET OUT
Tracks: / Gotta get out.
7" Single: Released Feb '82, on Riot City, by Riot City Records. Catalogue no: **RIOT 4**

NO SOLUTION
Tracks: / No solution.
7" Single: Released Jul '82, on Riot City, by Riot City Records. Catalogue no: **RIOT 11**

Courtney Melody

CAN'T GET ME OUT
Tracks: / Can't get me out.
12" Single: Released Jul '88, on Jammy's, Catalogue no: **VPRD 307**

DON'T LEAVE ME TO CRY
Tracks: / Don't leave me to cry.
7" Single: Released Jul '88, on Mossie Magnum, Catalogue no: **MM 001**

ROOTES MAN CORNER
Tracks: / Rootes man corner.
12" Single: Released Aug '88, on Redman International, Catalogue no: **VPRED 107**

Courtney-King, Barbara

PASTOURELLE
Tracks: / Pastourelle / Mirabel bridge.
7" Single: Released Feb '83, on RCA, by BMG Records (UK). Catalogue no: **RCA 308**

Cousin Rachel

BOOGIE NIGHTS
Tracks: / Boogie nights / You give me so much.
12" Single: Released Jun '88, on Supreme, by Supreme Records. Catalogue no: **SUPET 129**
7" Single: Released Jun '88, on Supreme, by Supreme Records. Catalogue no: **SUPE 129**

YOU GIVE ME SO MUCH
Tracks: / You give me so much / You give me so much (version).
7" Single: Released Jan '88, on Supreme, by Supreme Records. Catalogue no: **SUPE 121**
12" Single: Released Jan '88, on Supreme, by Supreme Records. Catalogue no: **SUPET 121**

Covay, Don

Biographical details: This American singer and songwriter, born in South Carolina, was the son of Baptist minister and was one of numerous soul singers to begin his musical career in the gospel field. But he had already switched to soul and rock by 1957 when he managed to convince Little Richard of his singing abilities. Richard gave him the chance to cut a record, but this was unsuccessful, as were all Covay's efforts for several years. His first substantial inroad into the charts occurred in 1964, when a strong rhythm and blues single entitled *Mercy mercy* reached No.35 on the US pop listings; the record creditied Don Covay and the Goodtimers, his backing group. The biggest success of his career came in 1968, when Aretha Franklin, the Queen of SOul, took his song *Chain of fools* to No.2 on the American charts. Although this smash hit proved Covay's ability as a songwriter, and displayed his vocal talents very clearly, Covay was somehow never able to consolidate on these successes. His only foray into the British charts was 1974's *It's better to have (and don't need)*, a memorable single that reached No.29. The frequent changes of record label that have dotted his career have given rise to instability, a factor that has led the significantly talented Covay to be underrated in the public mind. (6th Feb 1985, Bob MacDonald)
Soul singer and songwriter, born in 1938 in South Carolina. He began in a family gospel group, then recorded for a bewildering number of labels and had R&B hits on Atlantic 1964-70. Among his compositions was *Chain Of Fools* for Aretha Franklin.(Donald Clarke 1989).

IT'S BETTER TO HAVE (AND DON'T NEED)
Tracks: / It's better to have (and don't need).
7" Single: Released Sep '74, on Mercury, by Phonogram Ltd. Deleted Sep '77. Catalogue no: **6052 634**

SEESAW
Tracks: / Seesaw / Mercy mercy / Last night / Soul finger.
7" EP: Released Apr '80, on Atlantic, by WEA Records. Deleted '83. Catalogue no: **ATM 1**

Coventry City...

SKY BLUES GO FOR IT
Tracks: / Sky blues go for it.
7" Single: Released May '87, on Stether Music, Catalogue no: **SKB 1**

Cover girl

I'M A WINNER
Tracks: / I'm a winner.
12" Single: Released May '86, on Space Station, by Space Station Records. Catalogue no: **APOLLOT 1**

Cover Girls

INSIDE OUTSIDE
Tracks: / Inside outside / Inside outside (version).
12" Single: Released Oct '88, on Sonet, by Sonet Records. Catalogue no: **SONL 8**
7" Single: Released Oct '88, on Sonet, by Sonet Records. Catalogue no: **SON 8**

L.O.V.E
Tracks: / L.O.V.E.
7" Single: Released Nov '83, on Nectar, by Nectar Music. Catalogue no: **NRS 3**

MY HEART SKIPS A BEAT (IMPORT)
Tracks: / My heart skips a beat.
12" Single: Released Oct '89, on UNKNOWN, Catalogue no: **V 15498**

SHOW ME
Tracks: / Show me / Drumapella / Show me (nest mix) / Show me (heart-throb mix) (Mixed by Little Louie Vega for Small Wonders Productions Inc.) / Show me (Florida mix) (Mixed by The Latin Rascals and Andy "Panda" Tripoli.).
Note: Produced by Andy "Panda" Tripoli and The Latin Rascals. Edited by The Latin Ras cals for Latin Rascal Productions and Little Louie Vega for Small Wonders Productions Inc.
7" Single: Released May '87, on Magnet, by WEA Records. Deleted Jun '88. Catalogue no: **LT 1**
12" Single: Released May '87, on Magnet, by WEA Records. Deleted Jun '88. Catalogue no: **12 LT 1**

Cover up

LOVE THE ONE YOU'RE WITH
Tracks: / Feel the fire / Without an aim (Available on 12" only*).
Note: Extra tracks on 12" version only
12" Single: Released Jan '86, on Venom, Deleted '87. Catalogue no: **12COVER 1**
7" Single: Released Jan '86, on Venom, Deleted '87. Catalogue no: **COVER 1**

Covers

LOVELY DIAMOND
Tracks: / Lovely diamond / Shoot shoot.
7" Single: Released Sep '80, on Polydor, by Polydor Ltd. Deleted '83. Catalogue no: **POSP 320**

TOO HOT TO HANDLE
Tracks: / Too hot to handle / Tinted windows.
7" Single: Released Mar '81, on Polydor, by Polydor Ltd. Deleted Mar '84. Catalogue no: **POSP 233**

Covington, Julie

Biographical details: This British singer recorded her first album *Beautiful changes* in 1971. She came to prominence in 1976 as one of the four stars of *Rock follies*, a UK television series masterminded by Andy Mackay of Roxy Music fame. This documented the ups and downs of an all-girl group striving to make it big in the rock world. With its sharp, slightly controversial edge, the program attracted much press attention. The accompanying album shot straight into the UK charts at No.1, thus becoming the first ever TV soundtrack album to top the list. It enjoyed two runs at the top of the stack in '76, in the process dethroning two rock titans - Status Quo and Led Zeppelin. Both the album, which contained a collection of pop/rock songs geared towards the theme of the series, and the TV program itself were interesting and enjoyable whtn first encountered, but quickly wore thin. Thus *Rock follies of '77* peaked at No.13 on the UK album chart and achieved only a brief run; at the same time, *OK?* reached No.10, becoming the only Rock Follies hit single. By this time however, Covington's career had reached a new level - Tim Rice and Andrew Lloyd Webber, having seen her on the program, had asked her to take part in their *Evita* album.
Don't cry for me Argentina, the highly dramatic, big production number on which Covington took the role of Eva Peron, reached No.1 on the British singles chart in February 1977. However, the singer was a strangely reluctant star and seemed unwilling to appear of 'Top of the Pops' and unwilling to consolidate on her success. After one more Top 20 single, a convincing reading of Alice Cooper's US hit *Only women bleed*, her name disappeared from the charts, apparently forever. But for *Argentina* co-writer Tim Rice, there was further chart-topping success: exactly eight years after scoring his first UK No.1 single, he got there again with *I know him so well*, a February 1985 No.1 for Elaine Page and Barbara Dickson. A link therefore reaffirmed between the careers of Covington and Paige. Elaine had played the starring role in the opening run of the massively popular stage production of *Evita*, the part that Julie had played on disc back in 1977. (Bob MacDonald, 6th Feb 1985)
UK singer and actress. She became famous in *Rock Follies* in 1975, an ambitious and successful drama series with co-stars Rula Lenska and Charlotte Cornwall, and music by Roxy Music's Any MacKay. Chosen by Tim Rice and Andrew Lloyd Webber for the title role of the Evita album in 1976, she had a number one hit with *Don'y Cry For Me Argentina*, but turned down the stage role for political reasons, and disapproved of releasing the single out of context. She had a hit on Virgin with a cover of Alice Cooper's *Only Women Bleed* in 1977 and her debut album *Julie Covington* in 1978 was a strong package, with guests including Richard Thompson, Steve Winwood and John Cale. She has mostly concentrated on acting.(Donald Clarke 1989).

DON'T CRY FOR ME ARGENTINA
Tracks: / Don't cry for me Argentina.
7" Single: Released Oct '88, on MCA, by MCA Records. Catalogue no: **MCA 260**

DON'T CRY FOR ME ARGENTINA (OLD GOLD)
Tracks: / Don't cry for me Argentina.
7" Single: Released Jul '84, on Old Gold, by Old Gold Records. Catalogue no: **OG 9420**

HOUSEWIVES CHOICE
Tracks: / Housewives choice.
7" Single: Released Nov '82, on BBC, by BBC Records & Tapes. Deleted '87. Catalogue no: **RESL 123**

ONLY WOMEN BLEED
Tracks: / Only women bleed.
7" Single: Released Dec '77, on Virgin, by Virgin Records. Deleted Dec '80. Catalogue no: **VS 196**

Coward Brothers

PEOPLE'S LIMOUSINE
Tracks: / People's limousine.
7" Single: Released Jun '85, on Imp, by Demon Records. Catalogue no: **IMP 006**

Cowboy Junkies

BLUE MOON REVISITED (SONG FOR ELVIS)
Tracks: / Blue moon revisited / To love is to bury.
CD 5": Released Jun '89, on Cooking Vinyl, by Cooking Vinyl Records. Catalogue no: **FRY 011CD**
7" Single: Released Jun '89, on Cooking Vinyl, by Cooking Vinyl Records. Catalogue no: **FRY 011**
12" Single: Released Jun '89, on Cooking Vinyl, by Cooking Vinyl Records. Catalogue no: **FRY 011T**
10" single: Released Jun '89, on Cooking Vinyl, by Cooking Vinyl Records. Catalogue no: **FRYX 011**

SWEET JANE
Tracks: / Sweet Jane.
7" Single: Released Apr '89, on Cooking Vinyl, by Cooking Vinyl Records. Catalogue no: **FRY 8**
12" Single: Released Apr '89, on Cooking Vinyl, by Cooking Vinyl Records. Catalogue no: **FRY 8T**
12" Single: Released Mar '89, on Life Music, Catalogue no: **BLR 007 T**
7" Single: Released Mar '89, on Life Music, Catalogue no: **BLR 007**

Cowboy & Pisces

NO GIMME IKKY
Tracks: / No gimme ikky.
12" Single: Released Sep '89, on First Time, by First Time Records. Catalogue no: **FT 003**

Cowboys International

TODAY TODAY
Tracks: / Today today / Fixation.
7" Single: Released Feb '80, on Virgin, by Virgin Records. Deleted '83. Catalogue no: **VS 326**

Cox, Jess

BRIDGES
Tracks: / Bridges / Check it out.
7" Single: Released May '83, on Neat, by Neat Records. Catalogue no: **NEAT 26**

ONE IN A MILLION
Tracks: / One in a million / Bad time gal.
7" Single: Released Jan '84, on Neat, by Neat Records. Catalogue no: **NEAT 35**

Cox, Michael

ALONG CAME CAROLINE
Tracks: / Along came Caroline.
7" Single: Released Oct '60, on H.M.V., by EMI Records. Deleted Oct '63. Catalogue no: **POP 789**

ANGELA JONES
Tracks: / Angela Jones.
7" Single: Released Jun '60, on Triumph, Deleted Jun '63. Catalogue no: **RGM 1011**

Coxo Club Band

PARADHOUSE
Tracks: / Paradhouse / Paradhouse (remix) / Paradhouse (versions).
12" Single: Released 24 Jul '89, on Citybeat, by Beggars Banquet Records. Catalogue no: **CBE 1240**

Coyle, Peter

CIRCLE OF LIES
Tracks: / Circle of lies.
12" Single: Released Jul '87, on Ediesta, Catalogue no: **CALC 036**

Coyne, Kevin

SO STRANGE
Tracks: / So strange / Father dear father.
7" Single: Released Oct '82, on Cherry Red, by Cherry Red Records. Deleted '87. Catalogue no: **CHERRY 49**

Coyote Sisters

I'VE GOT A RADIO
Tracks: / I've got a radio.
7" Single: Released Oct '84, on Morocco

CRACK - SILLY FELLOW (Released on Bridgehouse)

(USA), by Motown Records (UK). Catalogue no: **TMG 1362**

STRAIGHT FROM THE HEART
Tracks: / Straight from the heart.
7" Single: Released Aug '84, on Morocco (USA), by Motown Records (UK). Catalogue no: **TMG 1350**
12" Single: Released Aug '84, on Morocco (USA), by Motown Records (UK). Catalogue no: **TMGT 1350**

Coyotes

SYLVIE
Tracks: / Sylvie / Daytripper.
7" Single: Released May '81, on Albany, by Albany Records. Deleted May '84. Catalogue no: **ALD 101**

Craaft

I WANNA LOOK IN YOUR EYES
Tracks: / I wanna look in your eyes / I guess you are the number one.
7" Single: Released Jun '86, on Epic, by CBS Records. Deleted '87. Catalogue no: **A 6954**

Crack

ALL OR NOTHING
Tracks: / All or nothing / I caught you out.
7" Single: Released Feb '83, on RCA, by BMG Records (UK). Catalogue no: **CRACK 1**

DON'T YOU EVER LET ME DOWN
Tracks: / Don't you ever let me down / I can't take it.
7" Single: Released Apr '82, on RCA, by BMG Records (UK). Deleted Apr '85. Catalogue no: **RCA 214**

SILLY FELLOW (see panel above)
Tracks: / Silly fellow / Fairy story.
7" Single: Released Apr '80, on Bridgehouse, Deleted '88. Catalogue no: **BHS 8**

Crack The Sky

SAFETY IN NUMBERS (SINGLE)
Tracks: / Safety in numbers.
7" Single: Released Jan '80, on Human (2), Catalogue no: **MM 116**

Cradle

IT'S TOO HIGH
Tracks: / It's too high.
7" Single: Released Apr '87, on Rough Trade, by Rough Trade Records. Catalogue no: **RT 202**
12" Single: Released Apr '87, on Rough Trade, by Rough Trade Records. Catalogue no: **RTT 202**

Craft Village Buskers

NO CHANCE TO DREAM
Tracks: / No chance to dream / Shy baby.
7" Single: Released Aug '83, on ESO, by ESO Records. Catalogue no: **ESO 0002**

Craig, Lorraine

WHERE IS THE MUSIC
Tracks: / Where is the music / Much too much.
7" Single: Released Oct '88, on BBC, by BBC Records & Tapes. Catalogue no: **RESL 228**

Craig, Mikey

I'M A BELIEVER
Tracks: / I'm a believer / Love's a demon / I'm a believer (extended mix) (on CD & 12" only).
Note: After Culture Club split, Mikey Craig purposefully kept a low profile, awaiting the right moment to unleash his unsung writing and producing talents. Now the release of his debut solo single (which is not the Monkees song), the quality of which could surprise a great many people. (Virgin, Oct 1988)
7" Single: Released Oct '88, on Virgin, by Virgin Records. Catalogue no: **VS 1131**
CD 3": Released '88, on Virgin, by Virgin Records. Catalogue no: **VSCD 1131**
12" Single: Released Oct '88, on Virgin, by Virgin Records. Catalogue no: **VST 1131**

Cramer, Floyd

Biographical details: This American pianist, born in Louisiana, began playing keyboards while a young child. After leaving school, he spent the early Fifties accompanying many stars on the *Louisiana hayride* radio programme. In 1955 he moved to Nashville and, from that time onwards, his career was guided by Chet Atkings, the prime mover in RCA Victor Records' Nashville division. Atkins teamed Cramer with the newly signed Elvis Presley. The association worked extremely well, and Cramer thus played piano on all of Elvis' historic early hits. This fact alone would have assured Floyd of an important place in musical history; but he went on to help create the distinctive 'Nashville sound' that was to become the trademark of virtually all country and western records - his simple but brilliantly infectious keyboard style, which relied on the treble end of the board to provide the rhythm, was closely imitated by hundreds of others. In addition to backing Presley, Jim Reeves and a host of others, Cramer enjoyed a brief but highly successful career as a solo chart star. This began with *Last date*, an acclaimed single that perfectly encapsulated his influential style. This entered the American charts in late 1960, becoming the first of four US Top 40 hits (all of which were instrumentals); it climbed to No.2 and stayed there for four weeks. His 1961 follow-up *On the rebound*, another self-penned single went to No.4 in the US and hit No.1 in the UK, becoming the artist's only major British hit. The next disc was *San Antonio Rose*, which reached No.8 on the American listings. Cramer continued to work as a Nashville session man through the Sixties and Seventies, and also released a large number of LP's in his own right, most of which were insubstantial restatements of his familiar style. (Bob MacDonald, 6th Feb 1985)
A country pianist, born in 1933 in Shreveport, Louisiana. He was a Nashville session player for RCA from 1955, playing on hits by the Browns, Jim Reeves, Elvis Presley (*Heartbreak Hotel*), many others. He described his distinctive piano style as 'whole-tone slur' or 'slip note'. His own hits included *Last Date*, a USA number two in 1960, and *On The Rebound*, a number four in 1961, both his own compositions. He's made more than 24 albums. (Donald Clarke 1989).

DALLAS (SINGLE)
Tracks: / Dallas / Knots landing.
7" Single: Released Jun '80, on RCA, by BMG Records (UK). Deleted Jun '83. Catalogue no: **JR 1**

HOT PEPPER
Tracks: / Hot pepper.
7" Single: Released Aug '62, on RCA, by BMG Records (UK). Deleted Aug '65. Catalogue no: **RCA 1301**

ON THE REBOUND
Tracks: / On the rebound / Boogie woogie.
7" Single: Released Jul '81, on RCA, by BMG Records (UK). Catalogue no: **GOLD 513**
7" Single: Released Apr '61, on RCA, by BMG Records (UK). Deleted Apr '64. Catalogue no: **RCA 1231**

SAN ANTONIO ROSE
Tracks: / San Antonio rose.
7" Single: Released Jul '61, on RCA, by BMG Records (UK). Deleted Jul '64. Catalogue no: **RCA 1241**

Cramps

Biographical details: A rockabilly revival band formed in 1975 in NYC: Lux Interior, vocals; 'Poison' Ivy Rorschach, guitar (both also songwriters), with Bryan Gregoryon guitar and Pam Gregory or Nick Knox (on their first record) on drums. They got TV coverage due to their stage set, including a demented version of *Surfer Bird*, the 1964 Trashmen hit, along with *Songs The Lord Taught Us* in 1980, produced by ex-Box Top Alex Chilton. They supported Police and garnered an intense cult following in Europe. Kid Congo (Brian Tristan, aka Kid Congo Powers, or just Congo Powers) replaced Bryan Gregory for *Psychedelic Jungle* in 1981. *Off The Bone* in 1983 showcased the best of their output so far as they left Miles Copeland's IRS/Illegal; they continued on shock/rockabilly course on the UK Big Beat label with *Smell Of Female* in 1983 and *A Date With Elvis* in 1986, the latter including the idie hit *Can Your Pussy Do The Dog*. (Donald Clarke 1989).

CAN YOUR PUSSY DO THE DOG
Tracks: / Can your pussy do the dog.
7" Single: Released Oct '85, on Big Beat, by Ace Records. Catalogue no: **NS 110**

CRUSHER
Tracks: / Crusher / Save it / New kind of kick.
12" Single: Released Sep '81, on A&M, by A&M Records. Deleted '84. Catalogue no: **PFSX 1008**

DRUG TRAIN
Tracks: / Drug train / Love me I can't hardly stand it.
7" Single: Released Sep '80, on Illegal, by Faulty Products Records. Deleted Sep '83. Catalogue no: **ILS 0027**

GOO GOO MUCK
Tracks: / Goo goo muck / She said.
7" Single: Released May '81, on A&M, by A&M Records. Deleted May '84. Catalogue no: **PFP 1003**

GOREHOUND
Tracks: / Gorehound / Weekend on Mars.
7" Single: Released Mar '84, on New Rose (1), by New Rose Records. Catalogue no: **NEW 33**

KISMIAZ
Tracks: / Kismiax.
12" Single: Released Jun '86, on Ace, by Ace Records. Deleted Jun '88. Catalogue no: **NEW 70**
7" Single: Released Jun '86, on Ace, by Ace Records. Deleted Jun '88. Catalogue no: **NEW 71**

WHAT'S INSIDE A GIRL
Tracks: / What's inside a girl.
Cassingle: Released Mar '87, on Big Beat, by Ace Records. Catalogue no: **CRAMP 1**
12" Single: Released Apr '86, on Big Beat, by Ace Records. Catalogue no: **NST 115**
7" Single: Released Apr '86, on Big Beat, by Ace Records. Catalogue no: **NS 115**

YOU'VE GOT GOOD TASTE
Tracks: / You've got good taste / Faster pussycat.
7" Pic: Released Mar '84, on New Rose (1), by New Rose Records. Catalogue no: **NEW 28 P**

Crane, Les

Biographical details: This American vocalist achieved a one-off spoken word hit in the early Seventies with *Desiderata*, which reached No.8 in the US in 1971 and No.7 in the UK in '72. It was also a big hit in many other territories. *Desiderata* started life as a poem in 1906, penned by US author and lawyer Max Ehrmann, who died in 1945. It is a moving and beautifully written piece, full of advice about living a happy and fulfilled life. Through a complicated series of events, it eventually came to be printed in poster form. It was discovered in this format by Fred Wever, a composer Ehrmann's work and proceed to make the record with Les Crane, who as unknown then as he is today. The finished product featured Crane reciting the text in a deep, Hollywood voice backed by a memorable tune, and interrupted occasionally by a studio choir singing the *Child of the Universe* section of the poem. This big hit single made *Desiderata* (the title means 'those things that we long for') world famous, but the artist on the record was quickly forgotton. (Bob MacDonald, 6th Feb 1985).

DESIDERATA
Tracks: / Desiderata.
7" Single: Released Feb '72, on Warner Bros., by WEA Records. Deleted Feb '75. Catalogue no: **K 16119**

Crane, Tony

FOR THE PRINCE AND HIS LADY
Tracks: / For the prince and his lady / More than words can say.
7" Single: Released May '81, on Monarch, by Monarch Records. Deleted May '84. Catalogue no: **MON 22**

Crash

ALMOST
Tracks: / Almost / My machine / On and on.
12" Single: Released Nov '86, on Remorse, Catalogue no: **LOST 4**

BRIGHT COLOURED LIGHTS
Tracks: / Bright coloured lights.
7" Single: Released Aug '87, on Remorse, Catalogue no: **LOSS 6**

DON'T LOOK NOW (NOW!)
Tracks: / Don't look now.
12" Single: Released Nov '86, on Remorse, Catalogue no: **LOST 2**

INTERNATIONAL VELVET
Tracks: / International velvet.
7" Single: Released Jun '88, on Justine, Catalogue no: **JUS 001**

SUNBURST
Tracks: / Sunburst.
7" Single: Released Mar '89, on Creation, by Creation Records. Catalogue no: **CRE 065**
12" Single: Released Mar '89, on Creation, by Creation Records. Catalogue no: **CRE 065T**

Crash Course..

SIGNALS FROM PIER
Tracks: / Signals from pier.
12" Single: Released 10 Dec '86, on LD, by LD Records. Catalogue no: **LD 001**

Crash Course In Hari

SPY, THE
Tracks: / Spy, The / Video nasty, A theme from.
7" Single: Released Jun '86, on AWA, Catalogue no: **AWA 011**

Crash Crew

2468 HERE WE ARE
Tracks: / 2468 here we are.
12" Single: Released Nov '85, on Sugarhill (USA), Catalogue no: **SHL 145**

Crass

Biographical details: This British band consists of Joy De Vivre, Phil Free, Steve Ignorant, Eve Libertine, N.A.Palmer, Penny Rimbauld and Pete Wright. These seven persons are joined by two additional members, known simply as G and Mick. In rock terminology the word 'underground' was far more fashionable in the late Sixties than in the Eighties; nevertheless Crass deserve this term, perhaps more than any other British rock history. Despite a total lack of airplay and advertising, they have consistently placed records at the top of the UK independent charts, and have also reached the national listings. All their records are issued on their own Crass label. Penny Rimbaud (who is male) owns a country farmhouse in Essex; he operates an open door policy there, and all the group's members reside in or near his home. This is very much in keeping with the band's anarchic stance. Formed by Rimbaud and Ignorant in 1978, Crass built up and maintained their following through live work. During 1980 and 1981 they released a series of singles, most notably *Nagasaki nightmare* and *Penis envy*. Playing in a totally uncompromising punk style, their philosophy was to continue the true anarchistic aims of punk rock while the original bands of the 1976/7 explosion were moving closer towards the mainstream of the rock business. Inevitably, Crass' music and political views frequently brought them into conflict with the establishment that they were out to destroy. None of their early records reached the UK national charts despite reported high sales, particularly of *Nagasaki nightmare*; and this led to allegations in some quarters that the record industry's official chart compilers, whether of their own volition or under duress, were deliberately excluding Crass discs from their statistics. What is certain is that Crass' first entry into Britain's official listings was in the late summer of 1982, when *Christ - the album* entered the LP chart at No.26; two weeks later, it fell out of the Top 100 - such a sudden and sharp decline is a statistical improbability. In 1984 a new precedent was set when police raided a record shop in Chesire and seized a number of Crass records on grounds of alleged obscenity. After passing through two courts, the eventual outcome of the case was that *Penis envy* was found to be illegal. But *Sheep farming in the Falklands*, *Whodunnit* and *Bullshit 2* were cleared, and the Judge said of them: 'They are crude, vulgar and consist to a a large extent of abusive rubbish, but they don't tend to deprave and corrupt. Bad language does not satisfy the test of obscenity, although I don't think any of us would like them in our homes'. (Bob MacDonald, 6th Feb 1985).

10 NOTES ON A SUMMER'S DAY
Tracks: / 10 notes on a summer's day.
7" Single: Released Nov '86, on Crass, by Crass Records. Catalogue no: **CATNO 6**

BLOODY REVOLUTIONS
Tracks: / Bloody revolutions / Persons unknown.
7" Single: Released Dec '80, on Crass, by Crass Records. Catalogue no: **CRASS 421984/1**

FEEDING OF THE 5,000 (SINGLE)
Tracks: / Feeding of the 5,000.
12" Single: Released Oct '81, on Crass, by Crass Records. Catalogue no: **621984**

NAGASAKI NIGHTMARE
Tracks: / Nagasaki nightmare.
7" Single: Released Oct '81, on Crass, by Crass Records. Catalogue no: **421984/5**

REALITY ASYLUM
Tracks: / Reality asylum.
7" Single: Released Dec '80, on Crass, by Crass Records. Catalogue no: **CRASS 19454 U**

SHEEP FARMING IN THE FALKLANDS
Tracks: / Sheep farming in the Falklands.
7" Single: Released May '83, on Crass, by Crass Records. Catalogue no: **CRASS 121984/3**

STATIONS OF THE CRASS (SINGLE)
Tracks: / Stations of the crass.
12" Single: Released Oct '81, on Crass, by Crass Records. Catalogue no: **521984**

Cravats

CRAVATS SING NERMINUS AND OTHER HITS
Tracks: / Cravats sing Nerminus and other hits.
12" Single: Released Aug '82, on Glass, by Glass Records. Deleted Aug '82. Catalogue no: **GLASS 021\12**

LAND OF THE GIANTS
Tracks: / Land of the giants.
12" Single: Released Feb '86, on Reflex, by Reflex Records. Catalogue no: **12 RE 10**

OFF THE BEACH
Tracks: / Off the beach / And the sun shone.
7" Single: Released Nov '81, on Small Wonder, by Small Wonder Records. Catalogue no: **SMALL 26**

RUB ME OUT
Tracks: / Rub me out.
7" Single: Released Jul '82, on Crass, by Crass Records. Catalogue no: **221984/4**

TERMINUS
Tracks: / Terminus / Little yellow froggy.
7" Single: Released Feb '82, on Glass, by Glass Records. Deleted '83. Catalogue no: **GLASS 021**

Craven, Gemma

I STILL BELIEVE IN LOVE
Tracks: / I still believe in love / Falling out of love.
7" Single: Released Jan '81, on Chrysalis, by Chrysalis Records. Deleted Jan '84. Catalogue no: **CHS 2478**

Crawford, Jimmy

I LOVE HOW YOU LOVE ME
Tracks: / I love how you love me.
7" Single: Released Nov '61, on Columbia, by EMI Records. Deleted Nov '64. Catalogue no: **DB 4717**

JIMMY THE JOKER
Tracks: / Jimmy the joker.
7" Single: Released Sep '82, on Response, by Priority Records. Catalogue no: **SR 533**

LOVE OR MONEY
Tracks: / Love or money.
7" Single: Released Jun '61, on Columbia, by EMI Records. Deleted Jun '64. Catalogue no: **DB 4633**

Crawford, Michael

COME FOLLOW THE BAND
Tracks: / Come follow the band / Colours of my life, The.
7" Single: Released '82, on Chrysalis, by Chrysalis Records. Deleted '87. Catalogue no: **CHS 2520**

MUSIC OF THE NIGHT
Tracks: / Wishing you were somehow here again.
12" Single: on Polydor, by Polydor Ltd. Deleted Aug '87. Catalogue no: **POSPX 803**
7" Single: Released Jan '87, on Polydor, by Polydor Ltd. Catalogue no: **POSP 803**

WHEN YOU WISH UPON A STAR
Tracks: / When you wish upon a star / Before the parade passes.
7" Single: Released Nov '87, on Epic, by CBS Records. Deleted Jun '88. Catalogue no: **651306 7**

Crawford, Randy

Biographical details: This American singer, born in Georgia but raised in Ohio, started out singing gospel music while growing up, and switched to secular soul and pop before beginning a full-time professional career. Her first album *Everything must change* was issued in 1976. Two further LPs were released over the following two years but, although Warner Bros. Records had high hopes for her, these records were generally overlooked. Her big breakthrough came in 1979, when she did the singing on *Street life*, a superb single by veteran jazz/soul group, the Crusaders. The record was a dance smash on both sides of the Atlantic, and reached No.5 on the UK national charts. Although the singer's name was not creditied on the disc, her inspired vocal performance was as important to the success of *Street life* as the Crusaders' instrumentation, and everybody wanted to know who she was. Randy Crawford became a star - but because *Street life* had been a much bigger pop hit in Britain than in the States, it was in the former territory that her solo career blossomed rather than in her native land. Crawford's first big album success, appropriately titled *Now we may begin*, hit the British Top 10 in the late summer of 1980 and logged 16 weeks on the charts; it yielded her biggest UK single *One day I'll fly away*, a beautifully arranged ballad that effectively displayed her distinctive voice, which had tinges of jazz, blues and soul and yet was sufficiently restrained to appeal to a broad pop audience. Although 1981's *Secret combination* LP did not contain a UK smash single on a par with the No.2 placing of *One day*, the album peaked at No.2 and logged 60 weeks on the British chart, on the strength of two smaller but equally worthy hit singles: *You might need somebody* hit No.11 in Britain, to be followed by the No.18 placing of *Rainy night in Georgia*, a tribute to her birthplace which, although an old song, had never been a UK hit before. To the disappointment of some of her fans, 1982's *Windsong* album saw Crawford moving towards the adult MoR/easy listening market, a policy that resulted in continued album sales but a lack of Top 40 singles and, artistically, the dilution of a great voice. By the time her UK record company issued *Miss Randy Crawford - the greatest hits* in 1984, she had become ideal for the cabaret circuit; its gold status reflected the esteem in which she continued to be held in Britain. (Bob MacDonald, 7th Feb 1985)
A fine soul/jazz singer born in 1952 in Georgia, more popular here than in USA: she had 11 top 75 entries in the UK 1979-84; incredibly, no hits at all in the USA Hot 100 through '84, though she sang with the Crusaders on their biggest hit *Streetlife* in 1979 and duetted with Rick Springfield. Her singles *Imagine* and *Nightline* both made the black chart in the USA in 1983 as well as charting here. (Donald Clarke 1989)e.

ALMAZ
Tracks: / Almaz / Desire.
7" Single: Released Oct '86, on Warner Bros., by WEA Records. Deleted Jan '88. Catalogue no: **W 8583**
12" Single: Released Oct '86, on Warner Bros., by WEA Records. Deleted Jan '88. Catalogue no: **W 8583T**

GETTING AWAY WITH MURDER
Tracks: / Getting away with murder / Overnight / Don't wanna be normal (Extra track available on 12" version only).
7" Single: Released Jul '86, on Warner Bros., by WEA Records. Deleted Jun '87. Catalogue no: **W 8641**
12" Single: Released Jul '86, on Warner Bros., by WEA Records. Deleted Jun '87. Catalogue no: **W 8641T**

HE REMINDS ME
Tracks: / He reminds me / Declaration of love / One day I'll fly away (Available on 12" only.).
12" Single: Released Jan '83, on Warner Bros., by WEA Records. Catalogue no: **K 17970 T**
7" Single: Released Jan '83, on Warner Bros., by WEA Records. Catalogue no: **K 17970**

HIGHER THAN ANYONE CAN COUNT
Tracks: / Higher than anyone can count / Tender falls the rain.
7" Single: Released Mar '87, on Warner Bros., by WEA Records. Deleted Jan '88. Catalogue no: **W 8423**
12" Single: Released Mar '87, on Warner Bros., by WEA Records. Deleted Jan '88. Catalogue no: **W 8423T**

IMAGINE
Tracks: / Imagine / Tender falls the rain.
7" Single: Released Jan '82, on Warner Bros., by WEA Records. Catalogue no: **K 17906**

KNOCKIN' ON HEAVEN'S DOOR
Tracks: / Knockin' on heaven's door.
7" Single: Released Sep '89, on Warner Bros., by WEA Records. Catalogue no: **W 2865**
CD 3": Released Sep '89, on Warner Bros., by WEA Records. Catalogue no: **W 2865 CD**
12" Single: Released Sep '89, on Warner Bros., by WEA Records. Catalogue no: **W 2865 T**

LAST NIGHT AT DANCELAND
Tracks: / Last night at Danceland.
7" Single: Released Jun '80, on Warner Bros., by WEA Records. Deleted Jun '83. Catalogue no: **K 17631**

LOVE THEME-THE COMPETITION
Tracks: / Love theme - the competition.
7" Single: Released Mar '81, on MCA, by MCA Records. Catalogue no: **MCA 676**

NIGHTLINE (SINGLE)
Tracks: / Nightline / Night won't last forever / Last night in danceland.
7" Single: Released Oct '83, on Warner Bros., by WEA Records. Deleted Oct '86. Catalogue no: **W 9530**

ONE DAY I'LL FLY AWAY
Tracks: / One day I'll fly away / Blue flame.
7" Single: Released Aug '80, on Warner Bros., by WEA Records. Deleted Jun '87. Catalogue no: **K 17680**
12" Single: Released Aug '80, on Warner Bros., by WEA Records. Catalogue no: **K 17680 T**

ONE DAY I'LL FLY AWAY (OLD GOLD)
Tracks: / One day I'll fly away / You might need somebody.
7" Single: Released Mar '86, on Old Gold, by Old Gold Records. Catalogue no: **OG 9571**

ONE HELLO
Tracks: / One hello.
7" Single: Released Jun '82, on Warner Bros., by WEA Records. Deleted Jun '85. Catalogue no: **K 17948**

RAINY NIGHT IN GEORGIA
Tracks: / Rainy night in Georgia.
7" Single: Released Aug '81, on Warner Bros., by WEA Records. Deleted Aug '84. Catalogue no: **K 17840**

SECRET COMBINATION (SINGLE)
Tracks: / Secret combination / Streetlife.
7" Single: Released Oct '81, on Warner Bros., by WEA Records. Deleted Oct '84. Catalogue no: **K 17872**

TENDER FALLS THE RAIN
Tracks: / Tender falls the rain / I stand accused.
7" Single: Released Nov '80, on Warner Bros., by WEA Records. Deleted '83. Catalogue no: **LV 42**

WHY
Tracks: / Why.
12" Single: Released Jan '84, on Warner Bros., by WEA Records. Catalogue no: **W 9438T**
7" Single: Released Jan '84, on Warner Bros., by WEA Records. Catalogue no: **W 9438**

YOU MIGHT NEED SOMEBODY
Tracks: / You might need somebody / You bring the sun out.
7" Single: Released May '81, on Warner Bros., by WEA Records. Deleted May '84. Catalogue no: **K 17803**

Crawford, Sandra

CAN'T BE YOUR PART-TIME LOVER
Tracks: / Can't be your part time lover (inst).
12" Single: Released Dec '86, on Star Tracks, Catalogue no: **ST 006**

Crawling Chaos

SEX MACHINE
Tracks: / Sex machine / Berlin.
7" Single: Released Mar '81, on Factory (1), by Factory Records. Catalogue no: **FAC 17**

Cray, Robert

Biographical details: The USA blues guitarist, singer and writer, born in 1953 in Columbus, Georgia, is one of the most exciting artists to emerge on the international scene in recent years, perhaps because he has paid his dues in clubs for many years. From an Army family, he went to high school in Tacoma, Washington; he formed his first band under the influence of the Beatles, but an Albert Collins concert helped decide his musical direction. He hit the road in 1974 with bassist Richard Cousins. His first album *Who's been talkin'* in 1978 was unavailable for years until reissued by Charly. The second *Bad influence* in 1983 came out on Demon in the UK, as did False Accusations in 1985: UK exposure revealed a unique blend of soul and blues, perhaps the most important establishment of a blues style since B B King. *Showdown* began as a Collins album and became an all-star guitar date which worked, charting well in the USA; and with *Strong persuader* he'd signed to a major label. Collins has covered *Phone booth* and Albert King made it a title track on a Fantasy album; Eric Clapton covered *Bad influence*. (Donald Clarke, April 1989).

ACTING THIS WAY
Tracks: / Acting this way / Laugh out loud / Acting this way (guitar version) / Smoking gun.
CD 5": Released 23 Jan '89, on Phonogram, by Phonogram Ltd. Catalogue no: **CRACD 7**
7" Single: Released 23 Jan '89, on Phonogram, by Phonogram Ltd. Deleted 31 Jul '89. Catalogue no: **CRAY 7**
12" Single: Released 23 Jan '89, on Phonogram, by Phonogram Ltd. Deleted 31 Jul '89. Catalogue no: **CRAY 712**

CHANGE OF HEART CHANGE OF MIND
Tracks: / Change of heart change of mind.
12" Single: Released Nov '85, on Demon, by Demon Records. Catalogue no: **D 1038T**

DON'T BE AFRAID OF THE DARK (SINGLE)
Tracks: / Don't be afraid of the dark / At last / Without a trace / Smoking gun.
CD 5": Released 1 Aug '88, on Phonogram, by Phonogram Ltd. Catalogue no: **CRACD 5**
7" Single: Released 1 Aug '88, on Phonogram, by Phonogram Ltd. Deleted 31 May '89. Catalogue no: **CRAY 5**
12" Single: Released 1 Aug '88, on Phonogram, by Phonogram Ltd. Deleted 31 May '89. Catalogue no: **CRAY 512**

I GUESS I SHOWED HER
Tracks: / I guess I showed her / It slipped her mind / Got to make a comeback (extra track on 12" only.) / Share what you've got, keep what you need (extra track on 12" only).
12" Single: Released Oct '86, on Mercury, by Phonogram Ltd. Deleted Jul '87. Catalogue no: **CRAY 112**
7" Single: Released Oct '86, on Mercury, by Phonogram Ltd. Deleted Jul '87. Catalogue no: **CRAY 1**

NIGHT PATROL
Tracks: / Night patrol / More than I can stand / Divided heart (Only on 12" and CD single.) / I wonder (Only on CD single.).
12" Single: Released Oct '88, on Mercury, by Phonogram Ltd. Deleted 31 May '89. Catalogue no: **CRAY 612**
CD 5": Released Oct '88, on Mercury, by Phonogram Ltd. Catalogue no: **CRACD 6**
7" Single: Released Oct '88, on Mercury, by Phonogram Ltd. Deleted 31 May '89. Catalogue no: **CRAY 6**

NOTHIN' BUT A WOMAN
Tracks: / Nothin' but a woman.
10" single: Released Aug '87, on Mercury, by Phonogram Ltd. Deleted Mar '88. Cata-

logue no: **CRAY 410**
12" Single: Released Aug '87, on Mercury, by Phonogram Ltd. Deleted Mar '88. Catalogue no: **CRAY 412**
7" Single: Released Aug '87, on Mercury, by Phonogram Ltd. Deleted Mar '88. Catalogue no: **CRAY 4**

RIGHT NEXT DOOR
Tracks: / Right next door (because of me) / New blood / Show what you got, keep what you need (Extra track on 12").
12" Single: Released 30 May '87, on Mercury, by Phonogram Ltd. Deleted Mar '88. Catalogue no: **CRAY 312**
7" Single: Released 30 May '87, on Mercury, by Phonogram Ltd. Deleted Mar '88. Catalogue no: **CRAY 3**

SMOKING GUN
Tracks: / Smoking gun / Fantasised / I guess I showed her (Available on 12" version only.) / Divided heart (Available on 12" version only.).
Note: I guess I showed her/Divided heart available on 12" version only.
7" Single: Released Feb '87, on Mercury, by Phonogram Ltd. Deleted Jul '87. Catalogue no: **CRAY 2**
12" Single: Released Feb '87, on Mercury, by Phonogram Ltd. Deleted Jul '87. Catalogue no: **CRAY 212**

Craze

LUCY
Tracks: / Lucy.
7" Single: Released Apr '80, on Harvest (1), by EMI Records. Deleted '82. Catalogue no: **HAR 5205**

MOTIONS
Tracks: / Motions / Spartans.
7" Single: Released Feb '80, on Harvest (1), by EMI Records. Deleted Feb '83. Catalogue no: **HAR 5200**

Crazy

NANI WINE (SINGLE)
Tracks: / Nani wine.
12" Single: Released Jun '89, on Hot Vinyl, Catalogue no: **HVT 53**

Crazy Albert

YIPPEE-I-AY
Tracks: / Yippee-I-ay.
7" Single: Released Nov '85, on WMWOCD, by Red Rhino Records. Catalogue no: **CRAZY 1**
12" Single: Released Nov '85, on WMWOCD, by Red Rhino Records. Catalogue no: **CRAZY 1T**

Crazy Blaze

BROKEN DREAM
Tracks: / Broken dreams / No peace for the wicked.
7" Single: Released Aug '86, on Short, Catalogue no: **Unknown**

Crazy Cats

CRAZY ROCKIN'
Tracks: / One hand loose / Ghost in a white cadillac / Sweet love on my mind / Tongue tied jill.
7" EP: Released Dec '81, on Magnum Force, by Magnum Music Group. Catalogue no: **MFEP 006**

ONE HAND LOOSE
Tracks: / One hand loose / Sweet love on my mind.
7" Single: Released Jan '82, on Magnum Force, by Magnum Music Group. Deleted '85. Catalogue no: **MFEP 006**

Crazy Elephant

GIMME GIMME GOOD LOVIN'
Tracks: / Gimme gimme good lovin'.
7" Single: Released May '69, on Major Record, by The Major Record Company. Deleted May '72. Catalogue no: **MM 609**

GIMME GIMME GOOD LOVIN' (OLD GOLD)
Tracks: / Gimme gimme good lovin'.
7" Single: Released 21 Nov '87, on Old Gold, by Old Gold Records. Catalogue no: **OG 9735**

Crazy English

CRAZY ENGLISH
Tracks: / Crazy English.
7" Single: Released Jul '82, on Cherry Hinton, Catalogue no: **CH 001**

Crazy House

BURNING RAIN
Tracks: / Burning rain / Garden of luck.
7" Single: Released Dec '87, on Chrysalis, by Chrysalis Records. Catalogue no: **CHS 3165**
12" Single: Released Dec '87, on Chrysalis, by Chrysalis Records. Catalogue no: **CHS 123165**

FIRST TIME
Tracks: / First time / We live and we learn.
7" Single: Released Jun '82, on T.W., by T.W. Records. Catalogue no: **HIT 105**

Crazy Pink Revolvers

TIMELESS SMILES
Tracks: / Timeless smiles.
12" Single: Released Jan '88, on ABC (indie), Catalogue no: **ABCS 016T**

WEDNESDAY 19.45
Tracks: / Wednesday 19.45.
7" Single: Released Nov '88, on ABC (indie), Catalogue no: **ABCS 018**
12" Single: Released Nov '88, on ABC (indie), Catalogue no: **ABCS 018T**

Crazy Trains

BETTER OFF WITHOUT YOU
Tracks: / Better off without you.
7" Single: Released Aug '84, on Spellbound, by Spellbound Records. Catalogue no: **SPELL 6**

TAXI DRIVER
Tracks: / Taxi driver.
7" Single: Released Aug '84, on Spellbound, by Spellbound Records. Catalogue no: **SPELL 8**

Crazyhead

BABY TURPENTINE
Tracks: / Baby turpentine / That kind of love / Bang bang* (*Extra track on 12") / That sinking feeling* (*Extra track on 12").
7" Single: Released Jul '87, on Food, by Food Records. Catalogue no: **FOOD 10**
12" Single: Released Jul '87, on Food, by Food Records. Catalogue no: **SNAK 10**

HAVE LOVE WILL TRAVEL
Tracks: / Have love will travel / Out on a limb (live) / Baby turpentine (live) / Snake eyes (live) / Here comes Johnny (live) (Not on 7".).
CD 5": Released Feb '89, on Parlophone, by EMI Records. Deleted Oct '89. Catalogue no: **CDSGE 2025**
7" Single: Released Feb '89, on Parlophone, by EMI Records. Deleted Oct '89. Catalogue no: **SGE 2025**
12" Single: Released Feb '89, on Parlophone, by EMI Records. Deleted Oct '89. Catalogue no: **12SGE 2025**

NIGHT TRACKS
CD 5": Released Jan '89, on Night Tracks, by Pinnacle Records. Catalogue no: **SFNT CD 018**
12" Single: Released Jan '89, on Night Tracks, by Pinnacle Records. Catalogue no: **SFNT 018**

RAGS
Tracks: / Rags / Screaming apple (On 12" & CD single only.) / Rub the Buddha / Fortune teller / Rags (ext. mix) (CD single only.).
CD 5": Released Sep '88, on Food, by Food Records. Deleted Jun '89. Catalogue no: **CDFOOD 14**
10" single: Released Sep '88, on Food, by Food Records. Deleted Jun '89. Catalogue no: **10FOOD 14**
7" Single: Released Aug '88, on Food, by Food Records. Deleted Aug '89. Catalogue no: **FOOD 14**
12" Single: Released Aug '88, on Food, by Food Records. Deleted Aug '89. Catalogue no: **12FOOD 14**
12" Single: Released Sep '88, on Food, by Food Records. Deleted Aug '89. Catalogue no: **12FOODS 14**

TIME HAS TAKEN ITS TOLL ON YOU
Tracks: / Time has taken its toll on you / Down / Time has taken its toll on you (extended version)* / Ballad of Baby Turpentine / Here comes Johnny (Available on 10" only.) / Bang bang***.
Note: *Tracks on 12in only; **track on 10in only; ***track on CD single only.
CD 5": Released Jul '88, on Food, by Food Records. Deleted Nov '88. Catalogue no: **CD FOOD 12**
10" single: Released Jun '88, on Food, by Food Records. Deleted Jun '89. Catalogue no: **10 FOOD 12**
7" Single: Released Jun '88, on Food, by Food Records. Deleted Aug '89. Catalogue no: **FOOD 12**
12" Single: Released Jun '88, on Food, by Food Records. Deleted Aug '89. Catalogue no: **12 FOOD 12**

WHAT GIVES YOU THE IDEA YOU'RE SO AMAZING BABY?
Tracks: / What gives you the idea you're so amazing baby? / Out on a limb / Snake eyes.
12" Single: Released Mar '87, on Food, by Food Records. Catalogue no: **SNAK 8**

Cream

Biographical details: This British rock band consisted of Ginger Baker, Jack Bruce and Eric Clapton. Cream were the first rock 'supergroup'. By the time they formed in the summer of 1966, all three members were regarded as virtuosos in their respective fields, having all been prime protagonists in Britain's rhythm and blues boom of the early/mid-Sixties: drummer Baker and bassist/vocalist Bruce had played with the much talked about Graham Bond Organisation, and ace guitarist Clapton had just come from John Mayall's Bluesbreakers. All had a reputation for shying away from stardom, as demonstrated by Bruce's unhappiness at playing on Manfred Mann's *Pretty flamingo* and Clapton's distaste for his work on the Yoardbirds' *For your love*, both of which had been major pop hits. The trio, named Cream because they represented the cream of Britain's musical crop, came together for musical reasons; but music business entrepreneur Robert Stigwood, who also played a part in their formation, realised that this dynamic combination of talent also had great business potential. As things turned out, both the musicians and Stigwood got their way - Cream were a huge commercial success, and attracted international acclaim for their musicianship and for their influence on rock's future development. The first LP *Fresh cream* entered the UK listings at Christmas 1966. Like their later albums, it was a Top 10 success and set the pattern for their future work: a selection a bluesy rock material laced with lengthy, improvised solos. Their second set proved to be the classic Cream album - *Disraeli gears*, issued in late '67, logged 42 weeks on the UK charts and was a huge success in the States, the latter being the nation to which the group devoted most of their strenuous touring activities. This LP showcased Cream's extraordinary talents without dwelling on the pomp and overblown virtuosity that characterised 1968's *Wheels of fire* double set and 1969's UK No.1 album *Goodbye*. The latter platter was so named because it was released as a farewell album by Cream who played their final US and UK concerts in November 1968 - though massively popular, the group's internal ego problems and musical differences led to their breakup. Cream's records and deafeningly loud shows inspired numerous musicians to jump on the heavy rock bandwagon that rode around the world in the late Sixties and early Seventies; but some critics doubt that the trio's influence was entirely beneficial, as it led to numerous subsequent players developing a penchant for 15 minute guitar solos, extended drum breaks, etc., many of which veered towards boredom and gross self-indulgence. An indisputable fact about Cream is their chart track record, which shows a string of UK Top 10 albums (including repackages compiled after their demise) and similar Stateside success. They achieved no British Top 10 single, but came close with *I feel free* (No.11), *Strange brew* (No.17) and the Eric Clapton/George Harrison composition *Badge* (No.18). They did, however, crach the US Top 10 twice, thanks to *Sunshine of your love* (No.5) and *White room* (No.6). If ego difficulties were a major factor in the termination of Cream, they rose to the surface even more quickly in Blind Faith, a 1969 supergroup that was hastily contrived, briefly successful and very short lived. Baker and Clapton were members of this quartet. Clapton then toured with Delaney and Bonnie, teamed with Duane Allman on the *Layla* classic under the guise of Derek & The Dominos, and became a solo superstar in the mid-Seventies with a more laid back musical approach. Baker formed an abortive group called Airforce with Steve Winwood, thenmoved to Nigeria and returned to Britain in the mid-Seventies to form the Baker-Gurvitz Army. Jack Bruce achieved solo LP success with 1969's *Songs for a tailor* but during the next decade, never sustained more than a cult following for his work. (Bob MacDonald, 7th Feb 1985)
The famous 'power trio' was formed in 1966, encouraged by producer/manager Robert Stigwood: Eric Clapton, guitar; Jack Bruce, bass; Ginger Baker, drums. They played blues-based material, some traditional but much of it written by Bruce with lyrics by Pete Brown. They were loud, passionate, sometimes self-indulgent; extensive improvisation in concert, unusual at the time: they were a big influence on the subsequent heavy metal genre, but perhaps we shouldn't hold that against them. They tok the USA by storm and sold 15 million records in three years, the tio format often augmented in the studio but soon exhausted. They became restless, announced the breakup in 1969 and embarked on a farewell tour. Compilation albums followed. (Donald Clarke, April 1989)6.

ANYONE FOR TENNIS ("SAVAGE SEVEN" THEME)
Tracks: / Anyone for tennis ("Savage Seven" theme).
7" Single: Released Jun '68, on Polydor, by Polydor Ltd. Deleted Jun '71. Catalogue no: **56 258**

BADGE
Tracks: / Badge / Tales of brave Ulysses / White room (Available on 12" only).
7" Single: Released Jan '82, on Polydor, by Polydor Ltd. Deleted Jan '85. Catalogue no: **RSO 91**
7" Single: Released Apr '69, on Polydor, by Polydor Ltd. Deleted Apr '72. Catalogue no: **56 315**
12" Single: Released Jan '82, on Polydor, by Polydor Ltd. Deleted Jan '85. Catalogue no: **RSOX 91**

BADGE (RE-ISSUE)
Tracks: / Badge.
7" Single: Released Oct '72, on Polydor, by Polydor Ltd. Deleted Oct '75. Catalogue no: **2058 285**

I FEEL FREE (OLD GOLD)
Tracks: / I feel free.
7" Single: Released Jul '84, on Old Gold, by Old Gold Records. Catalogue no: **OG 9423**

I FEEL FREE (SINGLE)
Tracks: / I feel free / Badge.
7" Single: Released Dec '66, on Reaction, Deleted Dec '69. Catalogue no: **591 011**
7" Single: Released Jul '86, on Polydor, by Polydor Ltd. Deleted Mar '87. Catalogue no: **POSP 812**

STRANGE BREW
Tracks: / Strange brew.
7" Single: Released Jun '67, on Reaction, Deleted Jun '70. Catalogue no: **591 015**

STRANGE BREW (OLD GOLD)
Tracks: / Strange brew.
7" Single: Released Jul '84, on Old Gold, by Old Gold Records. Deleted Jun '89. Catalogue no: **OG 9424**

SUNSHINE OF YOUR LOVE
Tracks: / Sunshine of your love.
7" Single: Released Oct '68, on Polydor, by Polydor Ltd. Deleted Oct '71. Catalogue no: **56 286**
7" Single: Released Jul '84, on Old Gold, by Old Gold Records. Catalogue no: **OG 9426**

WHITE ROOM
Tracks: / White room.
7" Single: Released Jan '69, on Polydor, by Polydor Ltd. Deleted Jan '72. Catalogue no: **56 300**

WHITE ROOM (OLD GOLD)
Tracks: / White room.
7" Single: Released Jul '84, on Old Gold, by Old Gold Records. Deleted Jun '89. Catalogue no: **OG 9425**

WRAPPING PAPER
Tracks: / Wrapping paper.
7" Single: Released Oct '66, on Reaction, Deleted Oct '69. Catalogue no: **591 007**

Creamies

CHERRY ON THE TOP
Tracks: / Cherry on the top.
7" Single: Released Mar '84, on Creamies International, Catalogue no: **IRIE 1**

Creation

Biographical details: At the time of their UK chart success, this British band comprised Bob Garner, Jack Jones, Eddie Phillips and Kenny Pickett. The Creation were formed in 1966, three of the members having previously been in an unsuccesful group called the Mark Four. The aim of the Creation was to create a pop group with a similar Mod approach to that of the Who, but who would nonetheless have a distinctive identity. By the end of '66, they had chalked up two British chart singles: *Making time* reached No.49 and *Painter man*, taken to the Top 10 by Boney M in 1979, reached No.36. Although it seemed at the time as though the group were going to be very big, their career went off the rails, and the aforementioned pair of singles represented their only British chart success. Despite the considerable publicity received by the extraordinary stage antics of lead singer Kenny Pickett, and despite Eddie Phillips' engaging technique of playing his guitar with a violin bow (a feat later made famous by Led Zeppelin's Jimmy Page), the Creation did not become the major success that their hard core of fans predicted. They were hailed by some observers as leaders of the Pop-Art rock movement; Phillips described their music as 'red with purple flashes'. After a series of personnel changes, the group folded in 1968, having had their hopes raised and then dashed. Their moderate Continental success could not have made the pill any easier to swallow for Phillips who, during the Creation's brief of rising stardom, had turned down an offer from Pete Townshend to join the Who as a second lead guitarist! (Bob MacDonald, 7th Feb 1985).

MAKING TIME
Tracks: / Making time / Uncle Bert.
7" Single: Released Jul '66, on Planet, Deleted Jul '69. Catalogue no: **PLF 116**
7" Single: Released May '84, on Edsel, by Demon Records. Catalogue no: **E 5006**

PAINTER MAN
Tracks: / Painter man.
7" Single: Released Nov '66, on Planet, Deleted Nov '69. Catalogue no: **PLF 119**

SPIRIT CALLED LOVE, A
Tracks: / Spirit called love, A / Making time / Mumbo jumbo.
7" Single: Released Apr '87, on Jet, by Jet Records. Catalogue no: **JET 7047**
12" Single: Released Apr '87, on Jet, by Jet Records. Catalogue no: **JET 12047**

Creation Rebel

BUBBLES
Tracks: / Bubbles.
12" Single: Released Jun '82, on Echo, by Echo Records. Catalogue no: **CR 002**

INDEPENDENT MAN
Tracks: / Independent man / Creation rebel.
7" Single: Released Mar '82, on On-U-Sound, by On-U-Sound Records. Catalogue no: **DP 3**

LOVE I CAN FEEL
Tracks: / Love I can feel.
7" Single: Released Jul '82, on Cherry Red, by Cherry Red Records. Deleted '87. Catalogue no: **CHERRY 41**

Creative Connection

SCRATCH MY NAME
Tracks: / Scratch my name / Baby I'm on my way / Full power remix (Extra track on 12") / Normal power remix (Extra track on 12") / Reeperbahn mix (** Extra track on 12" Reeperbahn Mix Version) / Love call mix (Extra track on 12" Reeperbahn Mix Version).
7" Single: Released Mar '86, on Conifer, Catalogue no: **CF 1000**
12" Single: Released Mar '86, on Conifer, Catalogue no: **CFZ 1000**

Creature Comfort

KAMIKAZE
Tracks: / Kamikaze.
7" Single: Released Jun '84, on Eye to Eye, Catalogue no: **EYE 101**

Creatures

Biographical details: After enjoying a run of British hit singles and albums as members of Siouxsie & The Banshees, vocalist Siouxsie Sioux and drummer Budgie formed this duo as an occasional diversion from their regular group activities. Siouxsie and her band had established themselves as one of Britain's most critically acclaimed post-punk outfits; but this side act, the Creatures, accentuated the drumming and made use of various foreign and tribal influences, to come up with a sparser sound than that of the Banshees. The duo's first product was *Mad eyed screamer*, which reached No.24 on the UK singles chart in October 1981. The Creatures surfaced more prominently in '83 when they released *Feast*, an album recorded in Hawaii. This yielded two intriguing British Top 30 singles: *Miss the girl* and *Right now*, the latter originally recorded unsuccessfully by Mel Torme in the early Sixties. Shortly after these hit records by the Creatures, Siouxsie & The Banshees achieved the biggest single of their career reaching No.3 in the UK with a version of the Beatles' *Dear Prudence*. (Bob MacDonald, 7th Feb 1985).

MAD EYED SCREAMER
Tracks: / Mad eyed screamer.
7" Single: Released Oct '81, on Polydor, by Polydor Ltd. Deleted Oct '84. Catalogue no: **POSPD 354**

MAD EYED SCREAMER (EP)
Tracks: / Mad eyed screamer / So unreal / But not them / Wild thing / Thumb.
7" EP: Released Oct '81, on Polydor, by Polydor Ltd. Deleted Oct '84. Catalogue no: **POSPG 354**

MISS THE GIRL
Tracks: / Miss the girl.
7" Single: Released Oct '81, on Polydor, by Polydor Ltd. Deleted Oct '84. Catalogue no: **SHE 1**

RIGHT NOW
Tracks: / Right now.
7" Single: Released Jul '83, on Wonderland (1), by Polydor Ltd. Deleted Jul '86. Catalogue no: **SHE 2**

STANDING THERE
Tracks: / Standing there / Divided / Solar choir (10", 12" and CD only).
CD 5": Released Sep '89, on Polydor, by Polydor Ltd. Catalogue no: **SHECD 17**
10" single: Released Sep '89, on Polydor, by Polydor Ltd. Catalogue no: **SHET 17**
7" Single: Released Sep '89, on Polydor, by Polydor Ltd. Catalogue no: **SHE 17**
7" Single: Released Sep '89, on Polydor, by Polydor Ltd. Catalogue no: **SHEP 17**
12" Single: Released Sep '89, on Polydor, by Polydor Ltd. Catalogue no: **SHEX 17**

Creatures Of Habit

DOUBLE VISION
Tracks: / Double vision / Diplomat, The.
7" Single: Released Mar '82, on Underground Music, Catalogue no: **UMA 001**

Creatures Of The Night

NO TEARS 88
Tracks: / No tears 88.
12" Single: Released '88, on Sampler Et Sans Reproches, Catalogue no: **12 SSR 8080**

Creedence Clearwater

Biographical details: This American rock band comprised brothers John and Tom Fogerty, Doug 'Cosmo' Clifford and Stu Cook. Their name was inspired by a belief in themselves (a combination of 'creed' and 'credence'), the qualities they wanted to bring to their tight, basic rock style (deep, pure and true - i.e. clear water) and a renewal of their musical selves after failing with earlier styles and names (revival). Creedence Clearwater Revival were one of the most successful groups in American rock history. Though their reign was comparatively brief - three golden years in 1969, 1970 and 1971 - they sold huge quantities of records and were one of the most exciting acts in the world. The group were formed at the end of the Fifties when three of the four were still in their early teens, and the same four members remained together under a variety of titles and styles until evolving into Creedence Clearwater Revival in 1967. The new name heralded the start of the sound that would make the group famous - an energetic, tightly played blend of rock'n'roll and R & B. The california quartet made it big in the autumn of 1968, when *Suzie Q.* hit No.11 on the US singles chart, sixteen places higher than the 1957 original by Dale Hawkins. In early '69 they achieved the first of three consecutive No.2 singles in the States, with John Fogerty's song *Proud Mary*. From that time onwards it was clear that John was totally dominant in the group, and the vast majority of their future output was penned by him; he.was also the vocalist and lead guitarist. *Proud Mary* was an instant classic and was followed by the equally superlative *Bad moon rising*, which reached No.2 in the States and No.1 in Britain. Strangely, they never hit the top slot in their native country but regularly peaked up three more US No.2 singles, in the shape of *Green river*, the double A sided *Travelin' band/Who'll stop the rain* and *Lookin' out my back door*. CCR's consistent success with singles was somewhat out of step with the pilosophy of many rock groups of their era, who preferred to concentrate on albums; but it was a fitting state of affairs, because Creedence's music was unusual for its time, being far closer to basic rock'n'roll than the psychedelic groups, the jazz-rock combos or the heavy metal bands. And yet CCR also sold LPs in massive quantities - some half a dozen of their albums passed the million-selling mark in quick succession. The best album by this prolific outfit was *Cosmo's factory*, a 1970 release that enjoyed an extended run at the top of the US album charts, and shot straight into the charts at No.1 in the UK. Personal differences within the band led to Creedence's termination. After the departure of Tom Fogerty, the three remaining members released one final album, 1972's *Mardi gras*. John Fogerty took less creative control over this project, with the result that it disgraced itself by peaking at No.12 in the States, failing to chart at all in Britain, and being ridiculed by reviewers. By the end of '72, the group were defunct. Little success greeted the various subsequent careers of Clifford, Cook and Tom Fogerty. John Fogerty launched a solo career under a false group name, the Blue Ridge Rangers, and scored a US Top 20 single with Hank Williams' song *Jambalaya (on the bayou)*; but even he found the going tough, and retired from recording in the mid-Seventies. Successful cover versions of his material have included Ike & Tina Turner's *Proud Mary* (No.4 in US in 1971) and Status Quo *Rockin' all over the world* (No.3 in UK in 1977). After almost a decade away from the limelight the solo John Fogerty made a dramatic return to the American charts in 1985, reaching the Top 10 with the album *Centerfield* and achieving a big US single with a typically straightforward and uncluttered number, *The old man down the road*. (8th Feb 1985)
A legendary USA rock band: brothers John and Tom Fogerty both from Berkeley, California, both played guitars and sang, with Doug Clifford on drums and Stu Cook on bass. They had 13 classic top 60 singles in the Billboard pop chart 1968-72, seven of them 2-sided hits and another late hit in 1976, four years after they broke up. The greatest American singles band, they were singles what The Band were on albums: a summing up of an era's American popular music. They had recorded as the Golliwogs, flop singles later collected on an album; Tom had been the centre of that group, but as Creedence John wrote and sang most of the material: without visiting the bayou he somehow invented 'swamp rock', with drive, lack of pretence and a southern flavour. Their basic rock'n'roll carved a singular niche while other bands espoused radical politics or drugs and they became a favourite of Vietnam GIs. The quality of their stuff also made classic albums, still sounding fresh as paint. A peripatetic solo artist, John has had some best-selling albums of his own in the 1980's. (Donald Clarke, April 1989)i.

BAD MOON RISING
Tracks: / Bad moon rising / Have you ever seen the rain? / Keep on chooglin' (Track on 12in single only.).
7" Single: Released Oct '81, on Fantasy (2), by Ace Records. Catalogue no: **GOLD 530**
7" Single: Released Aug '69, on Liberty, by EMI Records. Deleted Aug '72. Catalogue no: **LBF 15230**
7" Single: Released Jun '88, on Fantasy (2), by Ace Records. Catalogue no: **NS 124**
12" Single: Released Jun '88, on Fantasy (2), by Ace Records. Catalogue no: **NST 124**

BAD MOON RISING (OLD GOLD)
Tracks: / Long as I can see the light.
7" Single: Released Sep '85, on Old Gold, by Old Gold Records. Catalogue no: **OG 9569**

DOWN ON THE CORNER
Tracks: / Down on the corner.
7" Single: Released Feb '70, on Liberty, by EMI Records. Deleted Feb '73. Catalogue no: **LBF 15283**

GREEN RIVER (SINGLE)
Tracks: / Green river.
7" Single: Released Nov '69, on Liberty, by EMI Records. Deleted Nov '72. Catalogue no: **LBF 15250**

HAVE YOU EVER SEEN THE RAIN
Tracks: / Have you ever seen the rain.
7" Single: Released Mar '71, on Liberty, by EMI Records. Deleted Mar '74. Catalogue no: **LBF 15440**

LONG AS I CAN SEE THE LIGHT
Tracks: / Long as I can see the light.
7" Single: Released Sep '70, on Liberty, by EMI Records. Deleted Sep '73. Catalogue no: **LBF 15384**

PROUD MARY
Tracks: / Proud Mary.
7" Single: Released Sep '85, on Old Gold, by Old Gold Records. Catalogue no: **OG 9570**
7" Single: Released Aug '81, on Fantasy (2), by Ace Records. Catalogue no: **GOLD 521**
7" Single: Released May '69, on Liberty, by EMI Records. Deleted May '72. Catalogue no: **LBF 15223**

SWEET HITCH-HIKER
Tracks: / Sweet hitch-hiker.
7" Single: Released Jul '71, on United Artists, by EMI Records. Deleted Jul '74. Catalogue no: **UP 35261**

TRAVELLIN' BAND
Tracks: / Travellin' band.
7" Single: Released Apr '70, on Liberty, by EMI Records. Deleted Apr '73. Catalogue no: **LBF 15310**

UP AROUND THE BEND
Tracks: / Up around the bend.
7" Single: Released Jun '70, on Liberty, by EMI Records. Deleted Jun '73. Catalogue no: **LBF 15354**

Creepers

BABY'S ON FIRE
Tracks: / Baby's on fire / Another song about motor bikes.
7" Single: Released May '86, on Tape, Deleted '88. Catalogue no: **IT 033**
12" Single: Released May '86, on Tape, Deleted '88. Catalogue no: **ITT 033**

BRUTE
Tracks: / Brute.
7" Single: Released 20 Jun '87, on Red Rhino, by Red Rhino Records. Catalogue no: **RED 079**
12" Single: Released 20 Jun '87, on Red Rhino, by Red Rhino Records. Catalogue no: **REDT 079**

Creepshow

FU MAN CHU (EP)
Tracks: / Fu man chu.
12" Single: Released Aug '84, on Criminal Damage, Catalogue no: **CRI 12120**

Creme D'Cocoa

DOIN' THE DOG
Tracks: / Doin' the dog.
7" EP: Released Oct '87, on Dancefloor (USA), Catalogue no: **DF 1214**

Crenshaw, Marshall

Biographical details: A singer and songwriter born in 1954 in Detroit, he played in oldies bands in the mid '70's, then auditioned for Beatlemania on the West Coast and toured playing John Lennon. His first (eponymous) album paid homage to 30 years of pop. His third album *Downtown*, in 1985, saw him back on form, produced by T-Bone Burnette. He appeared with his band in the soundtrack of *Peggy Sue Got Married* in 1986 and played Buddy Holly in *La Bamba* in 1987. *Mary Jane & 9 Others* in 1987 confirmed his eclecticism by getting four stars in *Down Beat*. (Donald Clarke, April 1989).

CYNICAL GIRL
Tracks: / Cynical girl.
7" Single: Released Jul '82, on Warner Bros., by WEA Records. Catalogue no: **K 17971**

DISTANCE BETWEEN
Tracks: / Distance between / Someday, someway / There she goes again (Extra track on 12" version.) / Little wild one (no.5) (Extra track on 12" version.).
7" Single: Released Feb '86, on Warner Bros., by WEA Records. Catalogue no: **W 8786**
12" Single: Released Feb '86, on Warner Bros., by WEA Records. Catalogue no: **W 8786T**

SOME DAY SOME WAY
Tracks: / Someday, someway / Usual thing.
7" Single: Released Nov '82, on Warner Bros., by WEA Records. Catalogue no: **K 17995**

SOMETHINGS GONNA HAPPEN
Tracks: / Somethings gonna happen / She can't dance.
7" Single: Released May '83, on Albion, by Albion Records. Catalogue no: **ION 1029**
12" Single: Released May '83, on Albion, by Albion Records. Catalogue no: **12ION 1029**

WHENEVER YOU'RE ON MY MIND
Tracks: / Whenever you're on my mind.
7" Single: Released Jun '83, on Warner Bros., by WEA Records. Catalogue no: **W 9630**
12" Single: Released Jun '83, on Warner Bros., by WEA Records. Catalogue no: **W 9630T**

Cretons

REAL LOVE
Tracks: / Real love / Ways of the heart.
7" Single: Released Mar '80, on Planet, Deleted Mar '83. Catalogue no: **K 12433**

Cretu, Michael

SILVER WATER
Tracks: / Silver water.
7" Single: Released Jul '85, on Virgin, by Virgin Records. Deleted '86. Catalogue no: **VS 774**
12" Single: Released Jul '85, on Virgin, by Virgin Records. Deleted '86. Catalogue no: **VS 774-12**

Crew Cuts (Group)

Biographical details: This Canadian vocal group comprised Pat Barrett, Rudy Maugeri, Johnny Perkins and Ray Perkins. Originally called the Canadaires, their name was changed after they adopted a new hairstyle and image. The Crew Cuts were discovered by Bill Randle, a famous disc jockey based in Cleveland, Ohio. They shot to success in 1954 with *Sh-boom*, a Top 20 hit in both the US and UK. The success of this and subsequent records placed the quartet at the forefront of two important trends that characterised the mid-Fifties. Firstly, they were one of the most successful exponents of 'doo-wop' music, a term applied to the vocal harmony style originated by black rhythm and blues groups - while the frontman sang the lead part, his colleagues would back him by singing phrases as 'doo wop' in harmony. Second-

ly, the Crew Cuts were one of the first white acts to indulge in the practice of remaking black R & B records in a pop style - this meant that, no sooner had a disc topped the rhythm and blues listings, than a white group would hastilyh record a watered down pop version to sell to the mass market; though ethically controversial, this practice made good business sense and proved to be a vital ingredient of the rock'n'roll explosion. To follow *Sh-boom*, which they plundered from a group named the Chords, the Crew Cuts achieved another smash in the shape of *Earth angel* a song originally recorded by the Penguins. This delightful ballas, a simple portrayal of teenage romance and anxiety, took the CC's to No.3 in the US and No.4 in UK in 1955. No further hits followed in Britain but, in the USA, a series of smaller Top 20 successes kept their name on the charts until early '57. The biggest of these were *Gum drop* (No.10) and *Angels in the sky*. (Bob MacDonald, 8th Feb 1985)
A Canadian vocal group that had the first number one hit rock'n'roll record, ripping off *Sh-boom* from the Chords for an indomitably white version in 1954. They subsequently took *Earth angel* from the Penguins, but white covers soon faded as the black groups made the charts. (Donald Clarke, April 1989)e.

EARTH ANGEL
Tracks: / Earth angel.
78 rpm: Released '55, on Mercury (Oriole), Deleted '57. Catalogue no: **MB 3202**

SH-BOOM
Tracks: / Sh-boom.
78 rpm: Released '54, on Mercury (Oriole), Deleted '56. Catalogue no: **MB 3140**
7" Single: Released Aug '82, on Blast From The Past, by Creole Records. Catalogue no: **CR 180**

TWO HEARTS
Tracks: / Two hearts.
7" Single: Released Aug '84, on Pinner, Catalogue no: **PM 901**

Cribbins, Bernard

Biographical details: This British comedian was already a showbusiness success by the time he achieved recording success in 1962. That year was one of the dullest in British pop music - the charts were in limbo, stranded in time between the Fifties rock'n'roll boom, which had now lost its momentum, and the imminent arrival of the Beatles. This gap was largely filled by a flood of novelty records, and two of these were provided by Bernard Cribbins: *Hole in the ground* reached No.9 on the UK listings and was followed by *Right said Fred*, an amusing account of a carefree bunch of furniture removal men, which hit No.10. A third Cribbins hit *Gossip calypso* entered the British chart at Christmas '62 but, at that time, the Liverpool revolution was just starting to get underway, and the record peaked at No.25. Cribbins' career in the entertainment business continued apace, though he never darkened record chart doors again. He became particularly well known for telling children's stories on television and on kiddie's discs, including the tales of such famous characters as Paddington Bear and the Wombles. (Bob MacDonald, 8th Feb 1985).

GIGGLING GERTIE (SINGLE)
Tracks: / Giggling Gertie / Bleep.
7" Single: Released Oct '80, on Columbia, by EMI Records. Deleted Oct '83. Catalogue no: **DB 9088**

GOSSIP CALYPSO
Tracks: / Gossip calypso.
7" Single: Released Dec '62, on Parlophone, by EMI Records. Deleted Dec '65. Catalogue no: **R 4961**

HOLE IN THE GROUND
Tracks: / Hole in the ground / Right, said Fred.
7" Single: Released Jun '80, on H.M.V., by EMI Records. Deleted '83. Catalogue no: **POP 2003**
7" Single: Released Feb '62, on Parlophone, by EMI Records. Deleted Feb '65. Catalogue no: **R 4869**

RIGHT SAID FRED
Tracks: / Right said Fred.
7" Single: Released Jul '62, on Parlophone, by EMI Records. Deleted Jul '65. Catalogue no: **R 4923**

Cricket, Jimminy

WHEN YOU WISH UPON A STAR
Tracks: / When you wish upon a star / I've got no strings (From Pinocchio.).
7" Single: Released Aug '86, on BBC, by BBC Records & Tapes. Deleted Apr '89. Catalogue no: **RESL 197**

Crickets

Biographical details: At the time of their greatest success, this American group consisted of Jerry Allison, Buddy Holly, Joe Mauldin and Niki Sullivan. Buddy Holly ran twin careers, with some of his records being released solely under his name, and others being credited to the Crickets. The two most important members of the Crickets, Holly and Allison, began playing together as schoolfriends, with the former on vocals and guitar and the latter on drums. They formed a professional partnership in 1955 and then decided to form a group called the Crickets. By '57, the line-up of Holly, Allison, Mauldin and Sullivan had been established. A complicated chain of events led them to Norman Petty, a New Mexico studio owner and bandleader. *That'll be the day*, penned by Holly, Allison and Petty and produced by the later, became their first and biggest smash hit, reaching No.1 in both the US and UK in late '57. This perfect pop record, which was infectiously catchy and imaginatively performed, was followed by a series of hits of equal quality: *Oh boy*, *Maybe baby* and *Think it over* gave the Crickets success on both sides of the Atlantic. The group also played on early solo hits by Holly, including the big hit *Peggy Sue*. Holly and the three other Crickets split in 1958, but the singer continued using the group name with newly recruited musicians. Holly was killed in a tragic plane crash in Feb 1959 along with the Big Bopper and Richie Valens at the age of 22, and passed into legendary status. Having split from Holly mere months before his death, the old Crickets continued to function but with the numerous personnel variations. The constant nucleus of the group was Allison and vocalist/guitarist Sonny Curtis. They never achieved a hit record in the States but, in Britain, they enjoyed seven hit singles between 1959 and 1964, benefiting from a perennial Buddy Holly fervour in the UK - the Holly legacy commanded, and still commands, greater respect in Britain than in America, and the Crickets received a spin-off acceptance from this. Their biggest early Sixties single was 1962's *Don't ever change*, a Gerry Goffin/Carole King song that took them to No.5 on the UK chart. This period also saw the group touring Britain and recording with *Bobby Vee meets the Crickets* which stayed on the listing for six months; *Just for fun*, an Extended Play record by the two acts, topped the UK EP charts in May 1963. The Beatles revolution finally put paid to the Crickets' career, and they officially broke up in 1965. Attempts to revive the band in the Seventies, with musical assistance from some respected British players, met with little interest from the public. (Bob MacDonald, 8th Feb 1985)
The group formed in 1955 to back Buddy Holly: key fixtures were drummer Jerry Allison and singer/guitarist/songwriter Sonny Curtis. Curtis was a better guitarist than Holly and sometimes played lead; no hits resulted so he left. Holly was signed by Coral and the Crickets (including Holly) by Brunswick in the USA, so there were hits on two labels; the Crickets on Holly's hits in 1957 were Allison, pianist Niki Sullivan, and bassist Larry Welborn, replaced by Joe B Mauldin; Sullivan left and Holly, Allison and Mauldin toured the Uk in '58. Holly went to NYC without the Crickets; Curtis returned to join Mauldin and Allison. They recorded for Liberty; the changing lineup included Glen D Hardin on keyboards. They toured the UK with Bobby Vee and cut an album with him. They were washed away by the Beatles; Curtis recorded solo; Curtis and Allison reunited to play on Eric Clapton's debut solo album in 1970 and re-formed the Crickets, with Rick Grech and Albert Lee; later they were again a trio with Mauldin and toured with Waylon Jennings. Among Curtis's compositions were *Walk right back* a hit for the Everly Brothers. (Donald Clarke, April 1989)e.

BABY MY HEART
Tracks: / Baby my heart.
7" Single: Released May '60, on Coral, by MCA Records. Deleted May '63. Catalogue no: **Q 72395**

CRUISE IN IT
Tracks: / Cruise in it / Rock around with Ollie Vee.
7" Single: Released Jul '79, on Rollercoaster, by Rollercoaster Records. Catalogue no: **RRC 2001**

DON'T EVER CHANGE
Tracks: / Don't ever change.
7" Single: Released Jun '62, on Liberty, by EMI Records. Deleted Jun '65. Catalogue no: **LIB 55441**

DON'T TRY TO CHANGE ME
Tracks: / Don't try to change me.
7" Single: Released Jun '63, on Liberty, by EMI Records. Deleted Jun '66. Catalogue no: **LIB 10092**

LA BAMBA (THEY CALL HER)
Tracks: / La bamba.
7" Single: Released Jul '64, on Liberty, by EMI Records. Deleted Jul '67. Catalogue no: **LIB 55696**

LOVE'S MADE A FOOL OF YOU
Tracks: / Love's made a fool of you.
7" Single: Released Apr '59, on Coral, by MCA Records. Deleted Apr '62. Catalogue no: **Q 72365**

MAYBE BABY
Tracks: / Maybe baby.
7" Single: Released Mar '58, on Coral, by MCA Records. Deleted Mar '61. Catalogue no: **Q 72307**
7" Single: Released Jul '82, on Old Gold, by Old Gold Records. Catalogue no: **OG 9224**

MILLION DOLLAR MOVIE
Tracks: / Million dollar movie / Million miles apart, A / Rock and roll.
7" EP: Released Mar '80, on Rollercoaster, by Rollercoaster Records. Catalogue no: **RCEP 101**

MORE THAN I CAN SAY
Tracks: / More than I can say.
7" Single: Released May '60, on Coral, by MCA Records. Deleted May '63. Catalogue no: **Q 72395**

MY LITTLE GIRL
Tracks: / My little girl.
7" Single: Released Jan '63, on Liberty, by EMI Records. Deleted Jan '66. Catalogue no: **LIB 10067**

OH BOY
Tracks: / Oh boy.
7" Single: Released Dec '57, on Coral, by MCA Records. Deleted Dec '60. Catalogue no: **Q 72298**
7" Single: Released Jul '82, on Old Gold, by Old Gold Records. Catalogue no: **OG 9223**

THAT'LL BE THE DAY
Tracks: / That'll be the day.
7" Single: Released Sep '57, on Vogue, by Vogue Records. Deleted Sep '60. Catalogue no: **Q 72279**
7" Single: Released Jul '82, on Old Gold, by Old Gold Records. Catalogue no: **OG 9208**

THINK IT OVER
Tracks: / Think it over.
7" Single: Released Jul '58, on Coral, by MCA Records. Deleted Jul '61. Catalogue no: **Q 72329**

T-SHIRT
Tracks: / T-shirt / Holly would / Forever in mind (12" only).
CD 5": Released Sep '88, on CBS, by CBS Records. Deleted 17 Apr '89. Catalogue no: **CD TSH 1**
7" Single: Released Sep '88, on CBS, by CBS Records. Deleted 17 Apr '89. Catalogue no: **TSH 1**
12" Single: Released Sep '88, on CBS, by CBS Records. Deleted 17 Apr '89. Catalogue no: **TSH T1**

WHEN YOU ASK ABOUT LOVE
Tracks: / When you ask about love.
7" Single: Released Jan '60, on Coral, by MCA Records. Deleted Jan '63. Catalogue no: **Q 72382**

YOUR M-M-MEMORY
Tracks: / Your m-m-memory is t-t-torturing me / Three piece / Weekend, The / Forever in mind.
7" Single: Released Apr '88, on Rollercoaster, by Rollercoaster Records. Deleted Dec '88. Catalogue no: **RRC 2007**

Criddelle, Mary

DON'T HOLD BACK ON LOVE
Tracks: / Don't hold back on love.
12" Single: Released Sep '89, on Passion, by Skratch Records. Catalogue no: **PASH 1291**

Cridland, Ansel

DIZZY
Tracks: / Dizzy.
12" Single: Released Oct '88, on World Enterprise, Catalogue no: **WED 80**

Crig, Lionel

NEED TO BELONG
Tracks: / Need to belong.
7" Single: Released 12 May '89, on Jetstar, by Jetstar Records. Catalogue no: **OH 012**

Crime Fighters

BAT ATTACK
Tracks: / Bat attack (radio mix) / Bat attack (bat jazz mix) (On 7" only.) / Bat attack (deep house mix) (On 12" only.) / Bat attack (bat jazz mix instrumental) (On 12" only.) / Bat attack (bat apella mix) (On 12" only.).
CD 5": Released Sep '89, on RCA, by BMG Records (UK). Catalogue no: **PD 43136**
7" Single: Released 14 Aug '89, on RCA, by BMG Records (UK). Catalogue no: **PT 43136**
12" Single: Released 14 Aug '89, on RCA, by BMG Records (UK). Catalogue no: **PB 43135**

Crime & The City

DANGLING MAN
Tracks: / Dangling man.
12" Single: Released Jun '85, on Mute, by Mute Records. Catalogue no: **12 MUTE 36**

KENTUCKY CLICK
Tracks: / Kentucky click / Adventure / It takes two to burn.
12" Single: Released May '86, on Mute, by Mute Records. Catalogue no: **12 MUTE 46**

SHADOW OF NO MAN
Tracks: / Shadow of no man.
CD 5": Released 27 Feb '89, on Mute, by Mute Records. Catalogue no: **CD12 MUTE 94**
7" Single: Released 27 Feb '89, on Mute, by Mute Records. Catalogue no: **MUTE 94**
12" Single: Released 27 Feb '89, on Mute, by Mute Records. Catalogue no: **12 MUTE 094**

SOLUTION ON EVERY TRAIN
Tracks: / Solution on every train (Grain will bear a grain) / All must be love.
12" Single: Released Apr '88, on Mute, by Mute Records. Catalogue no: **12 MUTE 76**

Criminal Class

FIGHTING THE SYSTEM
Tracks: / Fighting the system.
7" Single: Released Nov '82, on Inferno (2), Catalogue no: **HELL 7**

Criminal Element

PUT THE NEEDLE TO THE RECORD
Tracks: / Put the needle to the record.
7" Single: Released Aug '87, on Cool Tempo, by Chrysalis Records. Catalogue no: **COOL 150**
12" Single: Released Aug '87, on Cool Tempo, by Chrysalis Records. Catalogue no: **COOLX 150**
12" Single: Released Aug '87, on Criminal (USA), by Criminal Records (USA). Deleted Oct '87. Catalogue no: **CR 12014**

Crimson Glory

DREAM DANCER
Tracks: / Dream dancer.
12" Single: Released Apr '88, on Road Runner (1), by Road Runner Records. Catalogue no: **RR 24671**

LONELY
Tracks: / Lonely.
CD 5": Released Apr '89, on Road Runner (1), by Road Runner Records. Catalogue no: **RR 24482**
7" Single: Released Apr '89, on Road Runner (1), by Road Runner Records. Catalogue no: **RR 54487**
12" Single: Released Apr '89, on Road Runner (1), by Road Runner Records. Catalogue no: **RR 24481**

Crisis

ALIENATION
Tracks: / Alienation.
7" Single: Released Nov '81, on Ardkore, Catalogue no: **CR 1004**

HOLOCAUST UK (EP)
Tracks: / Holocaust UK.
12" Single: Released Aug '82, on Dead Russian, Catalogue no: **NOTH 1**

Crisp, John

FARMER ON A BIKE
Tracks: / Farmer on a bike.
7" Single: Released Sep '82, on Ampersand, Catalogue no: **FARM 101**

LOVELY NORFOLK DUMPLINGS
Tracks: / Lovely Norfolk dumplings / Elderberry wine.
7" Single: Released Nov '82, on Ampersand, Catalogue no: **FARM 102**

Crispy Ambulance

NOT WHAT I EXPECTED
Tracks: / Not what I expected.
7" Single: Released Jun '81, on Factory (1), by Factory Records. Catalogue no: **FAC 32**

SEXUS
Tracks: / Sexus.
12" Single: Released Mar '84, on Factory Benelux, by Rough Trade Records. Catalogue no: **FBN 12**

Crispy & Co.

Biographical details: This all-male American group hit the British charts in 1975 with one of two simultaneous disco versions of

Brazil. Crispy & Co's single reached No.26 inexplicably peaking 15 places higher than the rival rendition by the Ritchie family, despite the fact that the Ritchie version was the one which became a major hit in the States, and depite the fact that the Ritchie version was unquestionably superior. The anonymous Crispy & Co achieved a second UK hit a few months later, reaching No.21 with *Get it together*, a nondescript disco offering, before fading quickly back into obscurity. (Bob MacDonald, 8th Feb 1985).

BRAZIL
Tracks: / Brazil.
7" Single: Released Aug '75, on Creole, by Creole Records. Deleted Aug '77. Catalogue no: **CR 109**

GET IT TOGETHER
Tracks: / Get it together.
7" Single: Released Dec '75, on Creole, by Creole Records. Deleted Dec '78. Catalogue no: **CR 114**

Cristian, Babette

QUESTIONS
Tracks: / Questions / In every glance.
12" Single: Released Dec '82, on Jenieves, Catalogue no: **JRR/10502**

Cristian, Chris

OH LITTLE MAMA
Tracks: / Oh little mama.
7" Single: Released Oct '81, on Gipsy, by Gipsy Records. Deleted '86. Catalogue no: **GIPSY 3**

Cristina

IS THAT ALL THERE IS
Tracks: / Is that all there is / Jungle love.
7" Single: Released Jan '80, on Island, by Island Records. Deleted Jan '83. Catalogue no: **WIP 6560**
12" Single: Released Jan '80, on Island, by Island Records. Deleted Jan '83. Catalogue no: **12WIP 6560**

Critical Mass

IN DEEPEST REBOUND
Tracks: / Shaking hands / In deepest rebound / It's gone crazy / You once said / 3 minutes in deepest rebound.
12" Single: Released 14 May '88, on Divided Kingdom, Catalogue no: **CM 1**

NO NONSENSE (GUNG-HO MIX)
Tracks: / No nonsense.
12" Single: Released Apr '88, on Kool Kat, by Kool Kat Records. Catalogue no: **KOOLT 12**

OPERATION:DREAMING OF BABYLON (EP)
Tracks: / Numbercruncher / Brainyard / Use them or lose them / Whirr.
12" Single: Released 20 Jun '87, on Timebox, Catalogue no: **TIME 002**

Critters

YOUNGER GIRL
Tracks: / Younger girl.
7" Single: Released Jun '66, on London-American, Deleted Jun '69. Catalogue no: **HL 10047**

Crocker, Barry

NEIGHBOURS
Tracks: / Neighbours / Neighbours (inst) / Chase".

7" Single: Released 23 May '87, on BBC, by BBC Records & Tapes. Catalogue no: **RESL 210**
12" Single: Released 23 May '87, on BBC, by BBC Records & Tapes. Catalogue no: **12 RSL 210**

Crocker, Brendan

WRONG DECISION
Tracks: / Wrong decision / Coconut tree / Still standing / All mixed up.
CD 5": Released Jun '89, on Silvertone, Catalogue no: **ORECD 5**
7" Single: Released Jun '89, on Silvertone, Catalogue no: **ORE 5**
12" Single: Released Jun '89, on Silvertone, Catalogue no: **ORET 5**

Crockett, Tony

QUEEN OF HEARTS
Tracks: / Queen of hearts / Plane Jane.
7" Single: Released Jul '82, on Alternative, Deleted '88. Catalogue no: **ALT 010 S**

Crocodile Harris

GIVE ME THE GOOD NEWS
Tracks: / Give me the good news / Night letters.
7" Single: Released Nov '82, on WEA, by WEA Records. Catalogue no: **K 75079**

Crocodiles

NEW WAVE GOODBYE (SINGLE)
Tracks: / New wave.
7" Single: Released Aug '81, on Aura Records, by Aura Records. Deleted '88. Catalogue no: **AUS 126**

Croft, Rachel

I KNOW SHE CARES FOR ME
Tracks: / I know she cares for me.
7" Single: Released Mar '82, on Tempo, by Warwick Records. Catalogue no: **TMPS 9020**

Croisette

LANDSLIDE
Tracks: / Landslide / Landslide instrumental.
7" Single: Released Jul '86, on Passion, by Skratch Records. Catalogue no: **PASH 59**
12" Single: Released Jul '86, on Passion, by Skratch Records. Catalogue no: **PASH 59(12)**

NOTHING BUT BLACKMAIL
Tracks: / Nothing but blackmail.
12" Single: Released '88, on Passion, by Skratch Records. Catalogue no: **PASH 66(12)**

YOU'RE A TIME WASTER
Tracks: / You're a time waster / You're a time waster (instrumental).
12" Single: Released Jul '88, on Nightmare, by Nightmare Records. Catalogue no: **MARE 54**

Croker, Brendan

DARLIN'
Tracks: / Darlin'.
7" Single: Released Jul '87, on Red Rhino, by Red Rhino Records. Catalogue no: **RED 81**

NO MONEY AT ALL
Tracks: / No money at all.
CD 5": Released Aug '89, on Silvertone, Catalogue no: **ORECD 8**
Cassingle: Released Aug '89, on Silvertone, Catalogue no: **OREC 8**
7" Single: Released Apr '89, on Silvertone, Catalogue no: **ORE 5**
12" Single: Released Apr '89, on Silvertone, Catalogue no: **ORET 5**

THAT'S THE WAY ALL MY MONEY GOES
Tracks: / That's the way all my money goes.
7" Single: Released Mar '87, on Unamerican Activities, by Unamerican Activities. Catalogue no: **SIOUX 1**

Crombie, Tony

Biographical details: This British drummer, leader of the Rockets, has a unique and honoured place in British pop history - he is credited with having the UK's first rock'n'roll band. Crombie had been a jazz drummer since the Forties, and switched to rock in th mid-Fifties. He made this move because he wanted his music to keep up to date, rather than because of any huge love for the new music. Nevertheless, it showed a far-sighted approach at a time when Britain was only just waking up to the revolution and, even then, was buying solely American rock records. Rockets' leader modelled himself on the first ever rock'n'roll giant, Bill Haley.
Unfortunately Crombie's chart life was brief in the extreme: his only UK chart record was October 1956's double A sided disc *Teach you to rock/Shortnin' bread*, which peaked at No.25. The latter track preceded the Viscounts' Top 20 version by four years. Tony Crombie & his Rockets recorded this single under the guidance of Columbia Records; A & R executive Norrie Paramor, who was one of Britain's leading record producers.
Although not yet converted to rock, this represented Paramor's first period of flirtation with the new music, the possibilities of which he did not begin to explore fully for another two years. Crombie, on the other hand, was always ready to latch onto the latest style and, convinced of the viability of the Donegan led skiffle movement, announced his intention to move into that area. His name rapidly faded from public memory. (Bob MacDonald, 8th Feb 1985).

TEACH YOU TO ROCK
Tracks: / Teach you to rock / Short'nin' bread.
7" Single: Released Oct '56, on Columbia, by EMI Records. Deleted Oct '59. Catalogue no: **DB 3822**

Crompton, Colin

GRADELY PRAYER
Tracks: / Gradely prayer / Best of order - thank you, please.
7" Single: Released Nov '80, on Columbia, by EMI Records. Deleted Nov '83. Catalogue no: **DB 9091**

Crooks

ALL THE TIME IN THE WORLD
Tracks: / All the time in the world / Banging my head.
7" Single: Released Feb '80, on Blue Print, Deleted Feb '85. Catalogue no: **BLU 2006**

Cropdusters

BANJO HILL
Tracks: / Banjo hill.
12" Single: Released Jun '88, on DDT, by D.D.T.Records. Catalogue no: **DISP 17T**

JUST GONE OUT TO START
Tracks: / Just gone out to start.
12" Single: Released Mar '89, on DDT, by D.D.T.Records. Catalogue no: **DISP 19T**

Crosby, Bing

Biographical details: This American singer, born Harry Lillis Crosby in Tacoma, Washington in 1904, gained his nickname Bing while a child; it was inspired by Bingo, the name of one of his favourite characters from *The Bingville bugle*, his favourite comic book. It became one of the most famous nicknames in history, because Bing Crosby rose to become a worldwide entertainment legend. His original intended career was law, and it was that subject that he was studying at university when he decided to quit his learning and enter show-business. Starting at the bottom of the ladder, his first big break came three years later when he was invited to join Paul Whiteman's ensemble, one of America's foremost bands. After three years with Whiteman, Crosby began to build up a reputation in Los Angeles as a solo singer.
His string of hit records began in the early Thirties, and his first million-seller *Sweet Leilani* was issued in 1937. Its success encapsulated all of Crosby's talents - his superb light baritone voice, his personable on-screen presence and, in particular, his successful marriage of the two: the song came from Crosby's movie *Waikiki wedding*, and it won the Oscar for the best film song of the year. Of Crosby's many movie appearances, the best was probably 1956's star studded *High society*. During the Forties he was a huge success on US radio, often with showbiz friends, Bob Hope and Frank Sinatra. The most important day of Crosby's career was 29 May 1942. In a Los Angeles studio on that summer's day, he recorded *White Christmas*, a song by Irving Berlin. Although written for the film *Holiday inn*, the song quickly broke out of its movie context to become the United States favourite Yuletide song. After its original 1942 success the record entered the American charts for a further eighteen Christmasses and inspired so many cover versions that it became a whole industry in itself. But for all the numerous remakes by and by an extraordinary array of artists, it was Crosby's original waxing that remained the definitive version. By the late Sixties, a quarter of a century after being recorded, it had sold 30 million copies thus becoming the world's best-selling disc of all time.
Bing's *White Christmas* maintained this honour for some fifteen years, until being overtaken in 1984 by Michael Jackson's LP *Thriller*. Crosby's performance on this single was, like the song itself brilliant in its sheer straightforward. To many people, *White Christmas* is their first thought when Bing's name is mentioned. But casual Crosby observers should not overlook three other Yuletide smashed that were recorded in the wake of the success of *White Christmas*: his versions of *Silent night*, *Oh come all ye faithful* and *Jingle bells* were multi million sellers. Indeed he recorded approximately 100 Christmas songs in his 50 year showbusiness career, ending in fine style with 1977's *Peace on Earth - little drummer boy*, an unlikely duet with David Bowie; that medley was recorded for a TV show in the final weeks of Crosby's life and became a British Top 3 hit five years later. Joseph Murrells' tome *The records that sold a million* lists over twenty Crosby million-sellers, mostly recorded during the Forties. He had the honour of being listed on the very first British record chart, published on 14 November 1952 - Crosby was No.4 that week with *Isle of Innisfree*.
Bing Crosby died in October 1977 at the age of 73; he suffered a heart attack in Madrid, Spain, minutes after indulging in one of his favouite occupations, golf. This final scene of contentment was a fitting end for a man who reportedly once told a journalist, 'If I really have accomplished just about everything I wanted to do'. One of the biggest showbusiness phenomenons of the 20th century, Crosby was the king of the crooners who dominated popular music in the pre-rock'n'roll era. (Bob MacDonald, 9th Feb 1985)
The all time great crooner, Harry Lillis Crosby (1904-77), was nicknamed as a child after a comic-strip character called Bingo who had big ears. He was the biggest selling recording artist of the first 70 years of recorded sound, and by a very wide margin. With Al Rinker (Mildred Bailey's brother) and Harry Barris, he formed a successful vaudeville act; they were hired by bandleader Paul Whiteman (the second best-selling recording artist in the entire pre-rock period) as The Rhythm Boys. Crosby's first solo was probably *I've got the girl* in 1926 with Whiteman. They left Whiteman and were booked at the Coconut Grove in Los Angeles, with the Gus Arnheim band; among the records they sang on was Duke Ellington's *Three little words*, a number one hit in 1930. Crosby's solo *I surrender dear* with Arnheim helped land his first radio show in 1931; he commissioned his theme *Where the blueof the night (meets the gold of the day)* and took a co-writing credit. He had well over 300 hit singles; German soldiers during the Second World War called him 'Der Bingle'. He began steeped in minstrelsy, influenced in terms of projection and pleasing an audience by Al Jolson, and was then influenced stylistically by jazz: Louis Armstrong, Bix Beiderbecke and Ethel Waters. (The first great jazz guitarist Eddie Land, was his personal accompanist). He added his own technique and virtually invented pop singing, with his natural insoucience, cannily informal phrasing and husky voice as opposed to the wimpish style of the period. Notes on his vocal chords produced the effect of 'singing into a rain barrel'; he called himself 'The Groaner'. In fact he was one of the first to understand the microphone, then a recent invention, and the first to sing to it as though to an individual listener. Rudy Vallee (who sang through a megaphone) said that as soon as he heard Crosby he knew that his style was outdated; the only real rival Crosby had in the early '30's was Russ Columbo, who was soon killed in an accident; in the '40's Frank Sinatra, Dick Haymes and Perry Como followed in Crosby's footstops. He broadcast for 20 years; about 2600 singles and 120 albums sold an estimated 400 million by 1975. He made over 60 films, many with first class original songs written by Johnny Burke and Jimmy Van Heusen, Nacio Herb Brown, Rodgers & Hart and others; *Holiday Inn* in 1942 had an Irving Berlin score including *White Christmas*, still one of the all time best sellers.
There was also the series of comedy musical *Road* film between 1940-62 with his close friend Bob Hope (they maintained a friendly feud until the end). He recorded for Brunswick, then switched to the new American Decca label (but the records continued to appear on Brunswick in this country). His million sellers began with *Sweet Leilani* in 1937, an Oscar winner (the gold record gimmick was only invented a few years later by RCA Victor, to honour a Glenn Miller hit); another was Bob Will's *San Antonio rose* in 1940 (with brother Bob Crosby's band); he recorded many other excellent country songs and was the first pop singer to cover them. *Swingin' on a star* in 1944 was an Oscar winner by Burke and Van Heusen from *Going my way*. Andy Williams sang in the backing group and the song was included in a songbook for school children. He recorded with the Andrews Sisters, Jolson, Les Paul, Jane Wyman (Ronald Reagan's first wife), the Ink Spots, Johnny Mercer and many others, including his son Gary and Gary's mother, Dixie Lee; and later with Rosemary Clooney and Grace Kelly (*True love* with Kelly from *High Society*, was his last chart single in 1956). His earliest records have a remarkable clarity and an obvious difference from earlier pop singing, to say nothing of good songs, many now forgotten; his many hits of the 1940s are even more relaxed, and simply do not date, not even the treacly ones, because he sounded as if he meant them. (Donald Clarke, April 1989).

AROUND THE WORLD
Tracks: / Around the world.
7" Single: Released May '57, on Brunswick, by Decca Records. Deleted May '60. Catalogue no: **05674**

CHANGING PARTNERS
Tracks: / Changing partners.
7" Single: Released Mar '54, on Brunswick, by Decca Records. Deleted Mar '57. Catalogue no: **05244**

COUNT YOUR BLESSINGS
Tracks: / Count your blessings.
7" Single: Released Jan '55, on Brunswick, by Decca Records. Deleted Jan '58. Catalogue no: **05339**

IN A LITTLE SPANISH TOWN
Tracks: / In a little Spanish town.
7" Single: Released Apr '56, on Brunswick, by Decca Records. Deleted Apr '59.

Catalogue no: **05543**

ISLE OF INNISFREE
Tracks: / Isle of Innisfree.
7" Single: Released Nov '52, on Brunswick, by Decca Records. Deleted Nov '55. Catalogue no: **04900**

PEACE ON EARTH
Tracks: / Peace on Earth / Little drummer boy / Fantastic voyage.
12" Single: Released Dec '82, on RCA, by BMG Records (UK). Catalogue no: **BOWT 12**
7" Single: Released Nov '82, on RCA, by BMG Records (UK). Catalogue no: **BOW 12**

SILENT NIGHT
Tracks: / Silent night.
7" Single: Released Dec '52, on Brunswick, by Decca Records. Deleted Dec '55. Catalogue no: **03929**

STRANGER IN PARADISE
Tracks: / Stranger in paradise.
7" Single: Released Apr '55, on Brunswick, by Decca Records. Deleted Apr '58. Catalogue no: **05410**

THAT'S WHAT LIFE IS ALL ABOUT (SINGLE)
Tracks: / That's what life is all about.
7" Single: Released Aug '75, on United Artists, by EMI Records. Deleted Aug '78. Catalogue no: **UP 35852**

TRUE LOVE (SINGLE)
Tracks: / True love / Well, did you ever.
Note: Well Did You Evah with Frank Sinatra.
7" Single: Released Nov '83, on Capitol, by EMI Records. Deleted Nov '88. Catalogue no: **CL 315**
7" Single: Released Nov '56, on Capitol, by EMI Records. Deleted Nov '59. Catalogue no: **CL 14645**

WHITE CHRISTMAS (SINGLE)
Tracks: / White christmas / God rest ye merry gentlemen.
7" Single: Released Dec '88, on MCA, by MCA Records. Catalogue no: **MCA 111**
7" Single: Released Dec '85, on MCA, by MCA Records. Deleted Dec '88. Catalogue no: **BING 1**

ZING A LITTLE ZONG
Tracks: / Zing a little zong.
7" Single: Released Dec '52, on Brunswick, by Decca Records. Deleted Dec '55. Catalogue no: **04981**

Crosby, David

Biographical details: This American singer and guitarist, born in los Angeles into a movie family, gained his musical training and experience by spending five years touring US folk clubs during the late 50's and early 60's. Indeed, his career closely mirrored the overall development of America's sixties folk movement: building a following in the clubs during the first part of the sixties, achieving success with folk-rock during the middle part and ending the 60's with country rock and Woodstock appearences. Crosby was a founder member of the Byrds, who were formed in 1964. They rocketed to fame in the summer of 65 with a transatlantic chart-topper, *Mr. Tambourine man*, though it was not widely known at the time that Roger McGuinn was the only real Byrd playing on the record: Crosby and his other three colleagues were replaced by session players for that disc. However, the real Byrds soon proved themselves to be excellent musicians, and they did play on the subsequent sngles and albums that were such an important part of the folk-rock scene. Arguments about musical direction led to Crosby's departure from the group in 1967. He quickly established himself in the public eye by enjoying great acclaim as a member of Crosby, Stills & Nash (and Young). In 1971, by which time the group had split, he hit the album charts on both sides of the Atlantic with his solo debut *If I could only reember my name*. This LP contained the usual segments of political protest that characterised Crosby, and also emphasised the softer side of his music. In 1972 he hit the album charts in duet with Graham Nash, and they continued to record and tour as a duo. After several successful CS&N reunions, Crosby's career met an unhappy interruption - he receiveda 5-year jail sentence in 1983 for illegal possession of arms, claiming in court that he had suffered from paranoia after the shooting of Lennon. (Bob Macdonald, 10.2.85).

DRIVE MY CAR
Tracks: / Drive my car.
7" Single: Released 20 Feb '89, on A&M, by A&M Records. Catalogue no: **AM 500**
12" Single: Released 20 Feb '89, on A&M, by A&M Records. Catalogue no: **AMY 500**

LADY OF THE HARBOR
Tracks: / Lady of the harbor / Drop down mama.
7" Single: Released 20 Mar '89, on A&M, by A&M Records. Catalogue no: **AM 502**
12" Single: Released 20 Mar '89, on A&M, by A&M Records. Catalogue no: **AMY 502**

Crosby, Stills & Nash

Biographical details: Formed in 1968, this rock group comprised Americans David Crosby and Stephen Stills and Graham Nash, from Britain. Crosby had been with folk-rock heroes the Byrds, Stills with hybrid rockers Buffalo Springfield and Nash was from one of the UK's leading groups, the Hollies. Although C S & N's lifespan was brief -- they split in late '70 -- their music symbolised the era for many people. Their blend of folk, country, pop and rock influences was perfect for the event that took place halfway through their existence, August 1969's legendary Woodstock festival. By this time they had added to the line-up a fourth singer/songwriter/guitarist, Neil Young, another ex-Buffalo Springfield member. The Crosby, Stills & Nash LP of 1969 was followed by the acclaimed C S N & Y album *Deja Vu*, issued in 1970, which logged more than a year on the charts on both sides of the Atlantic. *The Four-Way Street* live set, of '71, was released after the band's termination. The exuberant, catchy *Marrakesh Express* was their only British hit single, but this was followed in the States by *Suite: Judy Blue Eyes, Teach Your Children, Ohio* and *Our House*. Their biggest US single was the No 11 placing *Woodstock*, a rock treatment of Joni Mitchell's salute to the famous festival. From 1971 onwards all three members chalked up US and UK chart successes as solo artists and as members of duos and trios. The duos were Crosby & Nash and the Stills-Young Band.
C S & N reunited for an American tour in 1974 and a recording reunion occurred in '77, yielding the album *C S N* and the American No 7, *Just A Song Before I Go*, their biggest-selling 45. After several years out of the spotlight they were back in 1982 with an album, *Daylight Again*, and two US Top Twenty singles, *Wasted on The Way* and *Southern Cross*, although their highly-predictable style, a mellower retread of their familiar sound, failed to rekindle interest in Britain. Crosby's imprisonment in 1983 brought sudden end to their comeback which, though not very imaginative, had brought three great harmony voices back to the recording studio. (Bob MacDonald, February 1985.)
A vocal and instrumental supergroup formed in 1968 by ex-byrd David Crosby and ex-Buffalo Springfield Stephen Stills on guitars and vocals, and ex-Hollie Graham Nash on harmony vocals, with various people on bass and drums. They are profoundly influential on West Coast pop to this day. Their debut Crosby Stills and Nash blended breathtaking harmonies and Still's passionate love songs *Suite: Judy Blue Eyes* about his doomed romance with Judy Collins with Nash's nursery-rhymish celebrations and Crosby's hippie politicking *Wooden ships*. They added another ex-Springfielder, Neil Young, multiplying their musical options (both he and Stills played piano as well as guitar), adding another writer but also another ego. Their second public concert was at Woodstock. *Deja vu* was a more electric album; *Four way street* is a live album, released after they'd split. Reunions and olo albums (except for Young's) have not been as successful, though Stills' guitar playing is said to be underrated; Crosby became a drug addict and finally sorted himself out with the help of a year in jail in the mid-1980's. (Donald Clarke, April 1989)t.

AMERICAN DREAM (SINGLE)
Tracks: / American dream / Compass / Soldiers of peace (Available on 12" version only.).
12" Single: Released Dec '88, on Atlantic, by WEA Records. Catalogue no: **A 9003 T**
7" Single: Released Dec '88, on Atlantic, by WEA Records. Catalogue no: **A 9003**

MARRAKESH EXPRESS
Tracks: / Marrakesh express.
7" Single: Released Aug '69, on Atlantic, by WEA Records. Deleted Aug '72. Catalogue no: **584 283**

SOUTHERN CROSS
Tracks: / Southern cross / Into the darkness.
7" Single: Released Nov '82, on Atlantic, by WEA Records. Catalogue no: **K 11749**

WAR GAMES
Tracks: / War games.
7" Single: Released Jul '83, on Atlantic, by WEA Records. Catalogue no: **A 9818**
12" Single: Released Jul '83, on Atlantic, by WEA Records. Catalogue no: **A 9818 T**

WASTED ON THE WAY
Tracks: / Wasted on the way / Delta.
7" Single: Released Jun '82, on Atlantic, by WEA Records. Catalogue no: **K 11747**

Cross

COWBOYS & INDIANS
Tracks: / Cowboys and Indians / Love lies bleeding / Cowboys and Indians (full length version) (12" only) / Love lies bleeding (12" only).
CD 5": Released Aug '88, on Virgin, by Virgin Records. Deleted '89. Catalogue no: **CDEP 10**
Cassingle: Released Sep '87, on Virgin, by Virgin Records. Deleted May '88. Catalogue no: **VSTC 1007**
7" Single: Released Sep '87, on Virgin, by Virgin Records. Deleted '89. Catalogue no: **VS 1007**
12" Single: Released Sep '87, on Virgin, by Virgin Records. Catalogue no: **VST 1007**

HEAVEN FOR EVERYONE
Tracks: / Heaven for everyone / Love on a tightrope (like an animal) / Contact (Extra track on 12".).
7" Single: Released Mar '88, on Virgin, by Virgin Records. Catalogue no: **VS 1062**
12" Single: Released Mar '88, on Virgin, by Virgin Records. Catalogue no: **VST 1062**

MANIPULATOR
Tracks: / Manipulator / Stand up for love / Manipulator (extended version) (12" only).
7" Single: Released Jul '88, on Virgin, by Virgin Records. Catalogue no: **VS 1100**
12" Single: Released Jul '88, on Virgin, by Virgin Records. Catalogue no: **VST 1100**

SHOVE IT (SINGLE)
Tracks: / Shove it (Not on 12") / Rough justice (On all versions) / Shove it (extended mix) (CD & 12' only) / Shove it (metropolix) (12" only) / Cowboys and Indians (CD only).
CD 5": Released Apr '88, on Virgin, by Virgin Records. Catalogue no: **CDEP 20**
7" Single: Released Jan '88, on Virgin, by Virgin Records. Catalogue no: **VS 1026**
12" Single: Released Jan '88, on Virgin, by Virgin Records. Catalogue no: **VST 1026**

Cross, Christopher

Biographical details: Singer, songwriter and guitarist Cross had been in the music business for a decade before becoming an overnight sensation in 1980. Born in Austin, Texas, he spent the early 70's in Flash, a local band from San Antonio. After leaving them in 1973 he used the next few years finding backing musicians and developing a style with which to launch his solo career. He signed with Warner Bros in late '78 and issued his debut LP, *Christopher Cross*, at the beginning of 1980. By the end of the year the album had made him the first American pop phenomenon of the 80's. The combination of melodic songs, a good voice and the backing of many "name" musicians and vocalists, including the Doobie Brothers' Michael McDonald, the Eagles' Don Henley and guitarist Larry Carlton, added up to a powerful if unoriginal package. This was standard soft rock, perfect for programming on both rock radio and adult contemporary (MoR) radio in the States. The album yielded four US Top Twenty singles including the No 1 hit *Sailing* and the No 2 *Ride Like The Wind*. Cross swept the board at the Grammy awards in early '81 and the publicity led to his album finally cracking the British charts and staying in the listings for more than a year, although his UK singles success was far more modest that in the States. He consolidated on his position with a second American No 1, *Arthur's Theme (Best That You Can Do)*, writted with Peter Allen, Burt Bacharach and Carole Bayer Sager -- the four won an Oscar for it -- as the title theme for the Dudley Moore film *Arthur*. Less satisfactory was Cross's second LP, *Another Page*, released in 1983. Highly predictable, the songs were not nearly as memorable as on the earlier album. The first single, *All Right*, was as unimaginative as its title and it peaked at No 12 in the US despite initially crashing into the Billboard Hot 100 at 29. The album could not be described as a flop but it fell well short of the sales and longevity figures of its predecessor. Its saving grace was the touching ballad *Think Of Laura* which eventually became a US Top Ten single after television exposure on the American soap General Hospital. (Bob MacDonald, February 1985.)

A USA singer-songwriter from Texas who fronted bar bands and was signed to Warner Brothers in 1978 on the strength of his writing. His tailored-for-radio sound has been very successful since 1980, with soaring, glorious backing vocals by labelmates like Mike McDonald, Nicolette Larson and Valerie Carter. 1981 saw him win five Grammies, equaling the record for that award. A large man with a fragile, keening voice, he does not appear much in public and his success has not crossed to the UK. (Donald Clarke, April 1989)y.

ALL RIGHT
Tracks: / All right / Long world.
7" Single: Released Jan '83, on Warner Bros., by WEA Records. Catalogue no: **W 9843**
7" Single: Released Sep '83, on Warner Bros., by WEA Records. Catalogue no: **W 9474**
12" Single: Released Jan '83, on Warner Bros., by WEA Records. Catalogue no: **W 9843T**

ARTHUR'S THEME
Tracks: / Arthur's theme / Minstrel gigolo.
7" Single: Released Sep '81, on Warner Bros., by WEA Records. Deleted Jun '87. Catalogue no: **K 17847**

CHANCE AT HEAVEN
Tracks: / Chance at heaven.
7" Single: Released Jun '84, on CBS, by CBS Records. Catalogue no: **A 4524**

DEAL 'EM AGAIN
Tracks: / Deal 'em again.
7" Single: Released Jun '83, on Warner Bros., by WEA Records. Catalogue no: **W 9640**
12" Single: Released Jun '83, on Warner Bros., by WEA Records. Catalogue no: **W 9640 T**

I WILL(TAKE YOU FOREVER)
Tracks: / I will (take you forever) / Just one look / Ride like the wind (On 12" only).
7" Single: Released Aug '88, on Reprise/Slash (USA), by WEA Records. Catalogue no: **W 7795**
12" Single: Released Aug '88, on Reprise/Slash (USA), by WEA Records. Catalogue no: **W 7795T**

NEVER BE THE SAME
Tracks: / Never be the same / Light is on.
7" Single: Released Mar '82, on Warne Bros., by WEA Records. Deleted '85. Catalogue no: **K 17736**

NO TIME FOR TALK
Tracks: / No time for talk.
7" Single: Released Apr '83, on Warne Bros., by WEA Records. Catalogue no: **W 9662**
12" Single: Released Apr '83, on Warne Bros., by WEA Records. Catalogue no: **W 9662T**

RIDE LIKE THE WIND
Tracks: / Ride like the wind / Minstrel gigolo.
7" Single: Released Apr '80, on Warne Bros., by WEA Records. Deleted Apr '83. Catalogue no: **K 17582**

SAILING
Tracks: / Sailing / Light is on.
7" Single: Released Feb '81, on Warne Bros., by WEA Records. Deleted Feb '84. Catalogue no: **K 17695**

SAY YOU'LL BE MINE
Tracks: / Say you'll be mine / Poor shirley
7" Single: Released Jul '81, on Warne Bros., by WEA Records. Deleted '85. Catalogue no: **K 17659**

THAT GIRL
Tracks: / That girl / Open your heart / I really don't know anymore (Extra track on 12".).
7" Single: Released Feb '86, on Warn Bros., by WEA Records. Catalogue no: **W 8834**
12" Single: Released Feb '86, on Warn Bros., by WEA Records. Catalogue no: **W 8834T**

THINK OF LAURA
Tracks: / Think of Laura / Words of wisdom.
7" Single: Released Mar '84, on WEA, by WEA Records. Catalogue no: **W 9658**

Cross, Derrick

YOU STEPPED INTO MY LIFE
Tracks: / You stepped into my life.
12" Single: Released 8 Aug '88, on Criminal (1), by Criminal Records. Catalogue no: **BUST 9**

Cross, Henry

WILD ONE
Tracks: / Wild one / Don't call it love.
7" Single: Released Sep '87, on Sonet, by Sonet Records. Catalogue no: **SON 2329**

Cross, Jimmy

I WANT MY BABY BACK
Tracks: / I want my baby back.

7" Single: Released Mar '79, on Rollercoaster, by Rollercoaster Records. Catalogue no: **WLT 101**

Cross, Kris

SINGING BINGO
Tracks: / Singing bingo.
7" Single: Released Dec '80, on Direct Records, Catalogue no: **DODGE E1**

Cross, Sandra

GLUE ON THE PAPER
Tracks: / Glue on the paper.
12" Single: Released Apr '82, on Student, Catalogue no: **STU 009**

HARD UP BATCHELOR
Tracks: / Hard up batchelor / Hard up batchelor (version).
12" Single: Released Jul '87, on Ariwa Sounds, by Ariwa Sounds. Catalogue no: **ARI 063**

HOLDING ON
Tracks: /Holding on/ Noisy baby high thing.
7" Single: Released Apr '88, on Ariwa Sounds, by Ariwa Sounds. Catalogue no: **ARI 775**
12" Single: Released 20 Feb '88, on Ariwa Sounds, by Ariwa Sounds. Catalogue no: **ARI 075**

IT'S YOU
Tracks: / It's you.
7" Single: Released Apr '86, on Ariwa Sounds, by Ariwa Sounds. Catalogue no: **ARI 749**
12" Single: Released Apr '86, on Ariwa Sounds, by Ariwa Sounds. Catalogue no: **ARI 1249**

MY GUY
Tracks: / My guy.
12" Single: Released May '87, on Ariwa Sounds, by Ariwa Sounds. Catalogue no: **ARI 59**

MY ONLY DESIRE
Tracks: / My only desire / My only desire (version).
12" Single: Released Nov '88, on Ariwa Sounds, by Ariwa Sounds. Catalogue no: **ARI 83**

TAKE YOUR TIME
Tracks: / Take your time.
12" Single: Released Feb '89, on Ariwa Sounds, by Ariwa Sounds. Catalogue no: **ARI 87**
" Single: Released Feb '89, on Ariwa Sounds, by Ariwa Sounds. Catalogue no: **ARI 787**

YESTERDAY ONCE MORE
Tracks: / Yesterday once more.
12" Single: Released Oct '89, on Lamlight, by Priority Records. Catalogue no: **L 001**

YOU'RE LYING
Tracks: / You're lying.
12" Single: Released Dec '85, on Ariwa Sounds, by Ariwa Sounds. Catalogue no: **ARI 45**

Cross Section

WAKE UP IN THE MORNING
Tracks: / Wake up in the morning.
7" Single: Released Aug '82, on Warehouse, by Warehouse Records. Catalogue no: **L8 A 2**

Crossfire

ALIAS LOVE
Tracks: / Alias love / Magic.
7" Single: Released Jun '81, on Good Foot, by Good Foot Records (USA). Catalogue no: **GFR 002**

Crosstalk AV

QUEUE, THE
Tracks: / Queue, The.
7" Single: Released Nov '82, on Tufty Club, Deleted Oct '87. Catalogue no: **TC 1**

Crow

GEROMINO
Tracks: / Geronimo / Crow's blues.
7" Single: Released Nov '85, on WEA, by WEA Records. Catalogue no: **YZ 55**

YOUR AUTUMN OF TOMORROW
Tracks: / Your autumn of tomorrow / Uncle Funk.
7" Single: Released Jul '80, on Inferno (1), by Inferno Records. Catalogue no: **HEAT**

Crow Bar

HIPPIE PUNKS
Tracks: / Hippie punks.
7" Single: Released Jan '84, on Skinhead, Catalogue no: **SKIN 1**

Crow, Joe

COMPULSION
Tracks: / Compulsion.

7" Single: Released Oct '82, on Cherry Red, by Cherry Red Records. Deleted '87. Catalogue no: **CHERRY 48**

Crow People

CLOUD SONGS
Tracks: / Cloud songs.
12" Single: Released Aug '87, on Meantime, by Meantime Records. Catalogue no: **COX 003**

Crowd

ENGLAND
Tracks: / England / Latin quarter.
7" Single: Released May '82, on JSO, Deleted '87. Catalogue no: **EAT 16**

REAL THING
Tracks: / Real thing, The.
7" Single: Released Sep '84, on New Age, Catalogue no: **SN 001**

YOU'LL NEVER WALK ALONE
Tracks: / You'll never walk alone.
7" Single: Released Jun '85, on Spartan, Catalogue no: **BRAD 1**
12" Single: Released Jun '85, on Spartan, Catalogue no: **BRAD 112**

Crowded House

BETTER BE HOME SOON
Tracks: / Kill eye / Don't dream it's over (Recorded live at The Roxy, Los Angeles.) / Better be home soon.
CD 5": Released Jun '88, on EMI, by EMI Records. Deleted Jun '89. Catalogue no: **CDCL 498**
7" Single: Released Jun '88, on EMI, by EMI Records. Deleted Jun '89. Catalogue no: **CL 498**
12" Single: Released Jun '88, on EMI, by EMI Records. Deleted Jun '89. Catalogue no: **12CL 498**

DON'T DREAM IT'S OVER
Tracks: / Don't dream it's over / That's what I call love.
Cassingle: Released 20 Jun '87, on Capitol, by EMI Records. Deleted Apr '88. Catalogue no: **TCCL 438**
7" Single: Released Mar '87, on Capitol, by EMI Records. Deleted 31 Jul '88. Catalogue no: **CL 438**
12" Single: Released Mar '87, on Capitol, by EMI Records. Deleted 31 Jul '88. Catalogue no: **12CL 438**

SISTER MADLY
Tracks: / Sister madly / Mansion in the slums / Something so strong (live) (12" and CD Single only.).
CD 5": Released Aug '88, on Capitol, by EMI Records. Catalogue no: **CDCL 509**
7" Single: Released Aug '88, on Capitol, by EMI Records. Deleted Aug '89. Catalogue no: **CL 509**
12" Single: Released Aug '88, on Capitol, by EMI Records. Deleted Aug '89. Catalogue no: **12CL 509**

SOMETHING SO STRONG
Tracks: / Something so strong.
7" Single: Released Aug '87, on Capitol, by EMI Records. Deleted Apr '88. Catalogue no: **CL 456**
12" Single: Released Aug '87, on Capitol, by EMI Records. Deleted Apr '88. Catalogue no: **12CL 456**

WORLD WHERE YOU LIVE
Tracks: / World where you live / That's what I call love / Can't carry on (Extra track on 12".) / Something so strong / Don't dream it's over.
CD 5": Released Nov '87, on Capitol, by EMI Records. Deleted 31 Jul '88. Catalogue no: **CDCL 416**
Cassingle: Released Oct '87, on Capitol, by EMI Records. Deleted Apr '88. Catalogue no: **TCCL 416**
7" Single: Released Aug '86, on Capitol, by EMI Records. Deleted Apr '88. Catalogue no: **CL 416**
12" Single: Released Aug '86, on Capitol, by EMI Records. Deleted Apr '88. Catalogue no: **12CL 416**

Crowell, Rodney

Biographical details: A country singer/songwriter and producer, born in Texas in 1950, best known for his back up singing and guitar playing in Emmylou Harris's Hot band 1975-78 as well as his songs, of which Harris recorded more than a dozen. But he has a beautiful voice, and his albums have been underrated and may still make a breakthrough. He married Rosanne Cash in 1979 and produced her successful crossover album *Seven year ache*. His songs have been recorded by Waylon Jennings, George Jones and many others. In the early '80's he produced *Survivors* with Johnny Cash, Jerry Lee Lewis, and Carl Perkings; also albums by Bobby Bare, Guy Clark and Albert Lee. (Donald Clarke, April 1989).

HERE COMES THE 80'S
Tracks: / Here comes the 80's / Blues in the daytime.
7" Single: Released May '80, on Warner Bros., by WEA Records. Deleted May '83. Catalogue no: **K 17596**

I COULDN'T LEAVE YOU IF I TRIED
Tracks: / I couldn't leave you if I tried.
7" Single: Released 24 Apr '89, on CBS, by CBS Records. Deleted Oct '89. Catalogue no: **654935 7**

IT'S SUCH A SMALL WORLD
Tracks: / It's such a small world / Crazy baby.
7" Single: Released May '89, on CBS, by CBS Records. Catalogue no: **654 817 7**

SHAME ON THE MOON
Tracks: / Shame on the moon.
7" Single: Released Mar '82, on Warner Bros., by WEA Records. Catalogue no: **K 17919**

STARS ON THE WATER
Tracks: / Stars on the water / Aint no money.
7" Single: Released Jan '82, on Warner Bros., by WEA Records. Deleted Jan '85. Catalogue no: **K 17858**

Crowmen

DON'T BELIEVE
Tracks: / Don't believe.
12" Single: Released Nov '86, on Ultimate, by Ultimate Records. Catalogue no: **ULT 001T**

Crown Heights Affair

Biographical details: This all-male American band, comprising 8 members, achieved prominence in the mid-70's on the US soul charts. Most of their records, such as *Every beat of my heart* and *Foxy lady*, were written and produced by the team of Britt Britton and Freida Nerangis. CHA were a product of the disco boom, but their records did not cross ovedr to the higher reaches of the American pop charts. Pop success was eventually won in Britain, however, and they hit the UK national chart for the first time in 1978 with the gimmicky *Galaxy of love*, which reached no. 24. *I'm gonna love you forever* and *Dance lady dance* then became smaller hits for the black octet. 1980 brought them their only British top 10 single - the infectious *You gave me love*. However, after one more minor UK hit *You've been gone*, little more was heard of Crown Heights Affair on either side of the Atlantic. (Bob Macdonald, 14/2/85).

DANCE LADY DANCE
Tracks: / Dance lady dance.
7" Single: Released Apr '79, on Mercury, by Phonogram Ltd. Deleted Apr '82. Catalogue no: **6168 804**

GALAXY OF LOVE
Tracks: / Galaxy of love.
7" Single: Released Aug '78, on Philips, by Phonogram Ltd. Deleted Aug '81. Catalogue no: **6168 801**

I'LL DO ANYTHING
Tracks: / I'll do anything / I'll do anything (acappella) / I'll do anything (dub) (12" only.) / I'll do anything (club) (CD single only.).
7" Single: Released Nov '89, on SBK One, Catalogue no: **203 563 7**
7" Single: Released Nov '89, on SBK One, Catalogue no: **SBK 7003**
12" Single: Released Nov '89, on SBK One, Catalogue no: **203 563 6**
12" Single: Released Nov '89, on SBK One, Catalogue no: **12SBK 7003**

I'M GONNA LOVE YOU FOREVER
Tracks: / I'm gonna love you forever.
7" Single: Released Nov '78, on Mercury, by Phonogram Ltd. Deleted Nov '81. Catalogue no: **6188 808**

LOVE RIP OFF
Tracks: / Love rip off / Your love makes me hot.
7" Single: Released Oct '82, on De-Lite, Deleted Oct '85. Catalogue no: **DE 10**
12" Single: Released Oct '82, on De-Lite, Deleted Oct '85. Catalogue no: **DEX 10**

MAKE ME THE ONE
Tracks: / Make me the one / Make me the one instrumental.
7" Single: Released May '86, on Citybeat, by Beggars Banquet Records. Deleted Jun '87. Catalogue no: **CBE 704**

ROCK THE WORLD
Tracks: / Rock the world.
7" Single: Released Sep '83, on De-Lite, Catalogue no: **DE 13**
12" Single: Released Sep '83, on De-Lite, Catalogue no: **DEX 13**

SOMEBODY TELL ME WHAT TO DO
Tracks: / Somebody tell me what to do / Heart upside down.
7" Single: Released Aug '82, on De-Lite, Deleted Aug '85. Catalogue no: **DE 8**
12" Single: Released Aug '82, on De-Lite, Deleted Aug '85. Catalogue no: **DEX 8**

YOU GAVE ME LOVE
Tracks: / You gave me love / Use your body and soul.
7" Single: Released May '80, on De-Lite, Deleted May '83. Catalogue no: **MER 9**
12" Single: Released May '80, on De-Lite, Deleted May '83. Catalogue no: **MERX 9**

YOU'VE BEEN GONE
Tracks: / You've been gone.
7" Single: Released Aug '80, on De-Lite, Deleted Aug '83. Catalogue no: **MER 28**

Crows

LOVE YOU RUN, THE
Tracks: / Love you run, The / Swept away / Leaving you.
12" Single: Released Feb '88, on Survival (1), by Survival Records. Catalogue no: **SUR 12 042**

REDMAN
Tracks: / Redman.
12" Single: Released Mar '87, on Ravin', Catalogue no: **RAVE 002**

SUN WENT IN, THE
Tracks: / Sun went in, The / Round and round.
7" Single: Released Apr '86, on Ravin', Catalogue no: **RAV 7001**
12" Single: Released Apr '86, on Ravin', Catalogue no: **RAV 12001**

TAKAYAMA
Tracks: / Takayama.
12" Single: Released '87, on Survival (1), by Survival Records. Catalogue no: **SUR 12041**

Crowther, Leslie

WORLD I'D LIKE TO SEE
Tracks: / World I'd like to see.
7" Single: Released May '83, on Monarch, by Monarch Records. Catalogue no: **MON 041**

Croydon High School...

FERGIE
Tracks: / Fergie.
7" Single: Released Jul '86, on D-Sharp, by D Sharp Records. Catalogue no: **DSS 1006**

Crucial

SEND ME YOUR LOVE
Tracks: / Send me your love.
7" Single: Released May '88, on Domonique Production, Catalogue no: **CZL 001**

Crucial, Eddie

YOU ARE MY LIGHT
Tracks: / You are my light.
12" Single: Released Sep '88, on New Talents, Catalogue no: **NT 005**

Crucial Robbie

PROUD TO BE BLACK
Tracks: / Proud to be black.
12" Single: Released Aug '88, on Y & D, Catalogue no: **YDDO 130**

WEST INDIAN
Tracks: / West Indian.
12" Single: Released Feb '89, on Y & D, Catalogue no: **YDDO 136**

Crucifixion

FOX
Tracks: / Fox / Death sentence.
7" Single: Released Sep '80, on Miramar, by Miramar Records. Deleted '83. Catalogue no: **MIR 4**

MOON RISING
Tracks: / Moon rising / Green eyes / Jail bait.
7" Single: Released Jan '84, on Neat, by Neat Records. Catalogue no: **NEAT 37**

TAKE IT OR LEAVE IT (RE-ISSUE)
Tracks: / Take it or leave it / On the run.
7" Single: Released '88, on Neat, by Neat Records. Catalogue no: **NEAT 19**

Cruisers

GET A JOB
Tracks: / Get a job / I'll never let you down.
7" Single: Released Jan '81, on Harbour, by Harbour Records. Catalogue no: **HRB 11**

REBEL ED'S REBEL BOP
Tracks: / Rebel Ed's rebel bop / Ranchero.
7" Single: Released Jul '80, on Badge, by Badge Records. Catalogue no: **FLG 113**

ROCKABILLY FEVER
Tracks: / Rockabilly fever / Three nights to rock 'n' roll.
7" Single: Released Apr '81, on Feelgood, by Carlin Music Corp.. Deleted Apr '84. Catalogue no: **FLG 116**

WILDCAT ROCK
Tracks: / Wildcat rock / Easy street.
7" Single: Released Feb '81, on Feelgood, by Carlin Music Corp.. Deleted '84. Catalogue no: **FLG 114**

Cruisin' Gang

AMERICA
Tracks: / America / Radio / America instrumental.
12" Single: Released Mar '86, on ZYX (Germany). Catalogue no: **ZYX 5380**

Crusaders

Biographical details: At the time of their greatest success, this American band comprised Wilton Felder, Stix Hooper and Joe Sample. They originally came together in Texas in the early 50's, playing as the Swingsters. By the early sixties they were known as the Jazz Crusaders and consisted of the above three artists and Wayne Henderson. The quartete released their forst album *Freedom sound* in 1961, and followed it with a prolific series of LP's during the 60's. In 1970 they dropped the word "Jazz" from their title and became simply the Crusaders. This change was a recognition of the fact that they preferred to play a fusion of jazz, soul, blues and rock and not straight jazz. As their music developed in the 70's, they were recognised as pioneers of jazz-funk, a style that assumed great importance in the late 70's and early 80's, particularly in discos. This acclaim led to the group's members carving out successful subsidiary careers as session players. Henderson left the group in 1975 to pursue solo activities, whereupon they continued for eight years as a trio. Their virtuosity continued, and they often received musical assistance from fellow musicians of an equally high calibre, notable ace guitarist Larry Carlton. The band's career moved, for the first time, in a major commercial direction in 1979 - having previously been a purely instrumental outfit, they began to hire guest vocalists for certain tracks. The first and most successful example of this policy was 1979's *Street life* single, on which the superb performance of the Crusaders and Randy Crawford ensured a disco smash. The song gave the band their only substantial pop hit, reaching no.36 in the US and no.5 in the UK, and made Crawford a star, especially in Britain. Further Crusaders tracks featured vocal appearances by Bill Withers and Joe Cocker. In addition, Bobby Womack lent his vocal talents to two acclaimed singles by Felder, 1980's *Inherit the wind* and 1985's *(No matter how high I get) I'll still be looking up to you.* Drummer Stix Hooper quit in '83 to be replaced by Leon Ndugu Chancler. (Bob Macdonald, 14/2/85)
An instrumental group formed in 1957, called the Modern Jazz Sextet, then the Nite Hawks, the Jazz Crusaders in 1960 and the Crusaders from 1972, adopting the jazz rock style and popularity. They had 18 albums n the Billboard chart 1969-84, many including Wayne Henderson on trombone, Joe Sample on keyboards, Wilton Felder on reeds, Larry Carlton on guitar and Stix Hooper on drums; all are extremely busy session players as well. Guest vocalists have included Randy Crawford, Joe Cocker, Bill Withers, Nancy Wilson and B B King. (Donald Clarke, April 1989).

I'M SO GLAD I'M STANDING HERE TODAY
Tracks: / I'm so glad I'm standing here today.
7" Single: Released Sep '81, on MCA, by MCA Records. Deleted Sep '84. Catalogue no: **MCA 741**
12" Single: Released Sep '81, on MCA, by MCA Records. Catalogue no: **MCAT 741**

LAST CALL
Tracks: / Last call / Honky tonk strutting.
7" Single: Released Jan '81, on MCA, by MCA Records. Deleted Jan '84. Catalogue no: **MCA 657**
12" Single: Released Jan '81, on MCA, by MCA Records. Deleted Jan '84. Catalogue no: **MCAT 657**

NEW MOVES
Tracks: / New moves / Dead end / 1984 street life (on 12" only).
7" Single: Released Jul '84, on MCA, by MCA Records. Catalogue no: **MCA 894**

NIGHT LADIES
Tracks: / Night ladies.
7" Single: Released Apr '84, on MCA, by MCA Records. Catalogue no: **MCA 853**
12" Single: Released Apr '84, on MCA, by MCA Records. Deleted '85. Catalogue no: **MCAT 853**

SCRATCH (SINGLE)
Tracks: / Scratch.
7" Single: Released Jul '82, on MCA, by MCA Records. Catalogue no: **MCA 513**

CRUSH - TODAY'S A TOMORROW (Released on Santa Ponsa)

12" Single: Released Jul '82, on MCA, by MCA Records. Catalogue no: **MCAT 513**

STREET LIFE (OLD GOLD)
Tracks: / Street life.
12" Single: Released May '88, on Old Gold, by Old Gold Records. Catalogue no: **OG 4065**

STREET LIFE (SINGLE)
Tracks: / Street life / Hustler, The.
7" Single: Released Aug '82, on MCA, by MCA Records. Deleted Aug '85. Catalogue no: **MCA 513**
12" Single: Released Aug '82, on MCA, by MCA Records. Deleted Aug '85. Catalogue no: **MCAT 513**

THIS OLD WORLD'S TOO FUNKY FOR ME
Tracks: / This old world's too funky for me / I'm so glad / Luckenbach, Texas (Available on 12" only.).
7" Single: Released Nov '81, on MCA, by MCA Records. Deleted Nov '84. Catalogue no: **MCA 754**
12" Single: Released Nov '81, on MCA, by MCA Records. Deleted Nov '84. Catalogue no: **MCAT 754**

Crush

HE'S A REBEL
Tracks: / He's a rebel / J.F.C. 105.
7" Single: Released 20 Jun '80, on Carrere. Deleted '83. Catalogue no: **CAR 153**

TODAY'S A TOMMOROW (see panel above)
Tracks: / Today's a tommorow / On a plane to nowhere.
7" Single: Released '73, on Santa Ponsa, by Pye Records. Catalogue no: **PNS 3A**

Crush, Bobby

Biographical details: This British pianist first came to attention in late 1972 with his minor UK hit *Borsalino* and his debut self-titled album, which hit no. 15 on the British chart. He spent the rest of the seventies pursuing a successful showbiz career with out relying too heavily on record sales. He regularly appeared in traditional British outlets for family entertainment such as cabaret, variety shows and pantomime. His piano style has always been in a light melodic MoR vein, influenced by such faous names as Russ Conway and Winifred Atwell. Exactly 10 years after his first brief flurry of chart stardom, late 1982 saw Crush enjoying another encounter with the charts. *The Bobby Crush incredible double decker party*, a double album which crammed in 101 tunes, attained the lower regionsof the UK LP listings. Simultaneously, the Crush-composed *Orville's song* took Keith Harris and Orville to no.4 on the British singles chart. This children's ditty, which recounted the trials and tribulations of Harris and his duck, was typical of Crush's sphere of activity. (Bob Macdonald, 14/2/85).

BORSALINO
Tracks: / Borsalino.
7" Single: Released Nov '72, on Philips, by Phonogram Ltd. Deleted Nov '75. Catalogue no: **6006 248**

LONELY BALLERINA
Tracks: / Lonely ballerina / Slightly latin.
7" Single: Released Jun '84, on President, by President Records. Catalogue no: **PT 527**

PEPE
Tracks: / Pepe (From the film "Pepe".) / Brendan's theme.
7" Single: Released Nov '86, on President, by President Records. Catalogue no: **PT 553**

Crux

CRUX / CRASH
Tracks: / Crux / Crash.
7" Single: Released Nov '82, on No Future. Deleted '87. Catalogue no: **01 18**

Cruz, Nelson 'FFWD'

MY HOUSE
Tracks: / My house.
12" Single: Released Oct '89, on UNKNOWN. Catalogue no: **MIN 8**

Cruzados

BED OF LIES
Tracks: / Bed of lies / Chains of freedom.
7" Single: Released 20 Feb '88, on Arista, by BMG Records (UK). Deleted May '89. Catalogue no: **109488**
12" Single: Released 20 Feb '88, on Arista, by BMG Records (UK). Deleted May '89. Catalogue no: **609488**

HANGING OUT IN CALIFORNIA
Tracks: / Hanging out in California / Motorcycle girl / 1,000 miles (Extra track on 12".).
7" Single: Released Jul '86, on Arista, by BMG Records (UK). Catalogue no: **ARIST 660**
12" Single: Released Jul '86, on Arista, by BMG Records (UK). Catalogue no: **ARIST 12660**

MOTOR CYCLE GIRL
Tracks: / Motor cycle girl.
12" Single: Released Nov '86, on Arista, by BMG Records (UK). Catalogue no: **ARIST 12647**

Cry

Biographical details: The Cry comprise five members - John Watts, Mick Donnelly, David Graham, Theo Thunder and Mike Benn. The band were formed in August 1983 by John Watts.

TAKE IT ROUND AGAIN
Tracks: / Take it round again / Money goes down.
7" Single: Released May '84, on Arista, by BMG Records (UK). Catalogue no: **CRY 2**
12" Single: Released May '84, on Arista, by BMG Records (UK). Catalogue no: **CRY 122**

Cry Before Dawn

GIRL IN THE GHETTO
Tracks: / Girl in the ghetto / Tender years.
7" Single: Released Oct '87, on Epic, by CBS Records. Deleted Jun '88. Catalogue no: **WEX 1**
12" Single: Released Oct '87, on Epic, by CBS Records. Deleted Jun '88. Catalogue no: **WEX T1**

GONE FOREVER
Tracks: / Darkest night / Sentimental (This extra track on 12" only.) / Gone forever.
CD 5": Released Apr '88, on Epic, by CBS Records. Deleted Jan '89. Catalogue no: **CDGONE 2**
7" Set: Released Apr '88, on Epic, by CBS Records. Catalogue no: **GONE D2**
7" Single: Released Apr '88, on Epic, by CBS Records. Deleted Jan '89. Catalogue no: **GONE 2**
7" Single: Released May '88, on Epic, by CBS Records. Deleted Jan '89. Catalogue no: **GONE B2**
7" Single: Released Mar '87, on Epic, by CBS Records. Deleted Nov '87. Catalogue no: **GONE 1**
12" Single: Released Mar '87, on Epic, by CBS Records. Deleted Nov '87. Catalogue no: **GONE T2**

LAST OF THE SUN
Tracks: / Last of the sun / I don't care what you mean to me / I will save you / Listen to the story.
CD 5": Released 18 Sep '89, on Epic, by CBS Records. Catalogue no: **CD GONE 4**
7" Single: Released Sep '89, on Epic, by CBS Records. Catalogue no: **GONE EP4**
7" Single: Released 18 Sep '89, on Epic, by CBS Records. Catalogue no: **GONE 4**
12" Single: Released 18 Sep '89, on Epic, by CBS Records. Catalogue no: **GONE T4**
CD 3": Released Sep '89, on Epic, by CBS Records. Catalogue no: **GONE C4**

SEED THAT'S BEEN SOWN, THE
Tracks: / Seed that's been sown, The / Back to basics.
10" single: Released Aug '87, on Epic, by CBS Records. Catalogue no: **SEED QT1**
7" Single: Released Jul '87, on Epic, by CBS Records. Catalogue no: **SEEDP 1**
7" Single: Released Jul '87, on Epic, by CBS Records. Catalogue no: **SEED 1**
12" Single: Released Jul '87, on Epic, by CBS Records. Catalogue no: **SEEDT 1**

WITNESS FOR THE WORLD
Tracks: / Witness for the world / Up against the wall / Streets are paved with gold, The / When all the rest have gone.
CD 5": Released 15 May '89, on Epic, b CBS Records. Deleted Oct '89. Catalogue no: **CD GONE 3**
7" Single: Released 5 Jun '89, on Epic, b CBS Records. Deleted Oct '89. Catalogue no: **GONEG 3**
7" Single: Released 15 May '89, on Epic by CBS Records. Deleted Oct '89. Catalogue no: **GONE B3**
7" Single: Released 15 May '89, on Epic by CBS Records. Deleted Oct '89. Catalogue no: **GONE 3**
12" Single: Released 15 May '89, on Epic by CBS Records. Deleted Oct '89. Catalogue no: **GONE T3**

Cry No More

DANCING IN THE DANGER ZONE
Tracks: / Dancing in the danger zone South Africa Suite / Oh Bessie.
7" Single: Released Sep '86, on Parlophone, by EMI Records. Catalogue no: **6137**
12" Single: Released Aug '86, on Parlophone, by EMI Records. Catalogue no: **12R 6137**

PEACE IN OUR TIME
Tracks: / Peace in our time / Dear mystic man / Peace in our time (ext. mix) (1 only.).
7" Single: Released Dec '88, on Parlophone, by EMI Records. Deleted Aug '8 Catalogue no: **R 6203**
12" Single: Released Nov '88, on Parlophone, by EMI Records. Deleted Aug '8 Catalogue no: **12R 6203**

REAL LOVE
Tracks: / Cry no more ('Cry no more': (1 version)/(7" version) on single 12" only Don't leave me here.
7" Single: Released Nov '86, on Parlophone, by EMI Records. Catalogue no: **6146**
12" Single: Released Nov '86, on Parlophone, by EMI Records. Catalogue no: **12R 6146**

RECIPE FOR ROMANCE
Tracks: / Recipe for romance.
7" Single: Released Aug '87, on Parlophone, by EMI Records. Deleted Oct ' Catalogue no: **R 6165**
12" Single: Released Aug '87, on Parlophone, by EMI Records. Catalogue no: **12R 6165**

TEARS ON THE BALLROOM FLOOR
Tracks: / Forgotten now / Tears on ballroom floor.
7" Single: Released Oct '87, on EMI, EMI Records. Deleted Apr '88. Catalogue no: **R 6169**

12" Single: Released Oct '87, on EMI, by EMI Records. Deleted Apr '88. Catalogue no: **12R 6169**

Cry of the Innocent

SUSANS STORY
Tracks: / Susan's story.
12" Single: Released Jul '85, on Wild Music, Catalogue no: **FACE 1/2**

Cry Sisco

AFRO DIZZI ACT
Tracks: / Afro dizzi act / Afro dizzi act (version) / Ki ton ko.
7" Single: Released Sep '88, on Escape, by Escape Records. Catalogue no: **AWOL 1**
12" Single: Released Sep '88, on Escape, by Escape Records. Catalogue no: **AWOL TX1**
12" Single: Released Sep '88, on Escape, by Escape Records. Catalogue no: **AWOLT 1**

Cryer

SINGLE
Tracks: / Single / Second side.
7" Single: Released Jul '80, on Happy Face, by Standard Sound Productions. Deleted '83. Catalogue no: **MM 124**

Cryin' Shames

Biographical details: This all-male British pop group was one of numerous acts signed by the red-hot Decca company in the mid sixties. The group's 1966 singles *What's new pussycat* and *Please stay* were their only notable output. The latter gave the group their only chart record, it reached no.26. The combo was quickly forgotten. (Bob Macdonald, 14/2/85).

OVER MY HEAD
Tracks: / Over my head / Autumn in the city.
7" Single: Released Mar '80, on Logo, by Logo Records. Deleted Mar '83. Catalogue no: **GO 372**

PLEASE STAY
Tracks: / Please stay.
7" Single: Released Mar '66, on Decca, by Decca Records. Catalogue no: **F 12340**

PLEASE STAY (RE-ISSUE)
Tracks: / Please stay.
7" Single: Released Feb '82, on Decca, by Decca Records. Deleted '88. Catalogue no: **F 12340**

Crysanthenums

PICASSOS PROBLEM
Tracks: / Picassos problem.
12" Single: Released Jun '89, on Cordelia, by Cordelia Records. Catalogue no: **FIVEEGGS**

Crystal, Billy

YOU LOOK MARVELLOUS
Tracks: / You look marvellous (instrumental).
7" Single: Released Nov '86, on A&M, by A&M Records. Deleted '88. Catalogue no: **AM 353**
12" Single: Released Nov '86, on A&M, by A&M Records. Deleted '88. Catalogue no: **AMY 353**

Crystal, Conrad

DANCE ALL NIGHT
Tracks: / Dance all night / Dance all night (version).
7" Single: Released Oct '87, on Legal Lights, by Legal Light Records. Catalogue no: **LLD 9**

NO MONEY NO LOVE
Tracks: / No money no love.
12" Single: Released Jul '89, on Hill Crest, Catalogue no: **HCR 008**

SHE KEEPS ME WARM
Tracks: / She keeps me warm.
7" Single: Released Jan '89, on Exterminator, Catalogue no: **Unknown**
12" Single: Released Nov '88, on Black Scorpio, Catalogue no: **UNKNOWN**

TRIBUTE TO A SOUNDS BOY
Tracks: / Tribute to a sounds boy / Tribute to a sounds boy (version).
7" Single: Released Nov '87, on Legal Lights, by Legal Light Records. Catalogue no: **LLD 13**

Crystal, Lee

HIGH SCHOOL LADY
Tracks: / High school lady.
12" Single: Released Jul '89, on Pickout, Catalogue no: **PCIK 25**

Crystalite

IF MY FRIENDS COULD SEE ME NOW
Tracks: / If my friends could see me now.
12" Single: Released Oct '87, on Play House (USA), Catalogue no: **PHR 425**

Crystals

Biographical details: This Americal vocal pop group consisted of Barbara Alston, Lala Brooks, Dee Dee Kenniebrew and Pat Wright. The Crystals formed in 1961 and their career was masterminded and manipulated by Phil Spector; indeed, they were one of the acts who established him as a legendary record producer. The girls were all Brooklyn-born and in their late teens when the group started. To begin with, they comprised a quintet, the 5th being Mary Thomas. This line-up broke through at the end of '61 with *There's no other*, a single issued on Spector's Philles label that reached no.20 on the US chart. The follow-up single *Uptown* attained a no. 13 placing. In 1962 the Crystals achieved a US no.1 plus their first UK hit with the Gene Pitney-penned *He's a rebel* - but none of the group sang on this smash hit. The song was given to Spector in Los Angeles, while the group was on tour elsewhere. Instead of waiting for the girls to arrive, the producer assembled a group of session singers led by Darlene Love, and recorded and produced the song under the Crystals' banner - this action was a demonstration of Spector's dominant attitude toward his artists. The *He's a rebel* recording session also yielded a follow-up hit on the US charts: *He's sure the boy I love*. The real Crystals (minus Mary Thomas) chalked up two Top 10 hits on both sides of the Atlantic in 1963 with *Da doo ron ron* and *Then he kissed me*. By this time Spector was perfecting his famous "Wall of sound" and both singles were perfect examples of his multi-layered, richly arranged style, a style which depended far more on the producer's talents than on those of the artists. Spector dropped the Crystals in 1964, in favour of his new girl group, the Ronettes. By this time Beatlemania was sweeping the world - Spector was able to hold his own during it, but the Crystals were not, and quickly faded into obscurity. A decade after falling off the charts, the group's name resurfaced in Britain, via a 1974 re-issue of *Da doo ron ron* that reached no.15. (Bob Macdonald, 14/2/85)
A vocal quartet 'girl group' including Delores 'Lala' Brooks, Dee Dee Kennibrew and others at various times. The original lead singer was Barbara Alston. They were discovered by Phil Spector and all their records except one on his Philles label were hits 1961-64 and are classic pop of that period. (Donald Clarke, April 1989).

DA DOO RON RON
Tracks: / And then he kissed me / Da doo ron ron / He's a rebel.
7" Single: Released Oct '74, on Warner Bros., by WEA Records. Deleted Oct '77. Catalogue no: **K 19010**
7" Single: Released Aug '87, on Creole Classics, by Creole Records. Catalogue no: **CR 109**
7" Single: Released Jun '63, on London-American, Deleted Jun '66. Catalogue no: **HLU 9732**
7" Single: Released Aug '82, on Creole (Replay), by Creole Records. Catalogue no: **CR 182**
12" Single: Released Oct '87, on Creole Classics, by Creole Records. Catalogue no: **CRT 109**
12" Single: Released May '88, on Explosion, by Orbit Records. Catalogue no: **BANG 3**

HE'S A REBEL
Tracks: / He's a rebel.
7" Single: Released Nov '62, on London-American, Deleted Nov '65. Catalogue no: **HLU 9611**

I WONDER
Tracks: / I wonder.
7" Single: Released Mar '64, on London-American, Deleted Mar '67. Catalogue no: **HLU 9852**

THEN HE KISSED ME
Tracks: / Then he kissed me.
7" Single: Released Sep '63, on London-American, Deleted Sep '66. Catalogue no: **HLU 9773**

C/Siam

NIGHT AIR
Tracks: / Night air.
7" Single: Released Jun '83, on Summerhouse, by Summerhouse Records. Catalogue no: **SUM 3T**

Cuban Heels

MY COLOURS FLY
Tracks: / My colours fly.
7" Single: Released Aug '81, on Virgin, by Virgin Records. Deleted '84. Catalogue no: **VS 439**

SWEET CHARITY
Tracks: / Sweet charity.
7" Single: Released May '81, on Virgin, by Virgin Records. Deleted May '84. Catalogue no: **VS 413**

WALK ON WATER
Tracks: / Walk on water / Matthew and son.
7" Single: Released Nov '81, on Virgin, by Virgin Records. Deleted Nov '84. Catalogue no: **VS 440**

Cuban Soldiers

DANCE TO THE RHYTHM
Tracks: / Dance to the rhythm / Oh rio.
7" Single: Released Feb '82, on Radial Choice, by Virgin Records. Catalogue no: **TIC 9**

Cube

DUEL OF THE HEART
Tracks: / Duel of the heart.
7" Single: Released May '85, on Dead Volume, Deleted '88. Catalogue no: **VOL 014**
12" Single: Released May '85, on Dead Volume, Deleted '88. Catalogue no: **VOLT 014**

Cud

LOLA
Tracks: / Lola.
7" Single: Released Apr '89, on Imaginary, by Imaginary Records. Catalogue no: **MIRAGE 007**

ONLY (A PRAWN IN WHITBY)
Tracks: / Only (a prawn in Whitby).
12" Single: Released '89, on Imaginary, by Imaginary Records. Catalogue no: **MIRAGE 010**

PEEL SESSIONS:CUD
12" Single: Released Jan '88, on Strange Fruit, by Strange Fruit Records. Catalogue no: **SFPS 045**

SLACK TIME
Tracks: / Slack time.
12" Single: Released Dec '88, on Dug, Catalogue no: **DUGNI 001T**

UNDER MY HAT
Tracks: / Under my hat.
12" Single: Released 14 May '88, on Ediesta, Catalogue no: **CALC 049**

YOU'RE THE BOSS
Tracks: / You're the boss.
12" Single: Released 10 Oct '87, on Reception, by Reception Records. Catalogue no: **REC 007**

Cuddly Toys

IT'S A SHAME
Tracks: / It's a shame / Fall down.
7" Single: Released Jan '82, on Fresh, by Jetstar Records. Catalogue no: **FRESH 39**

MADMAN
Tracks: / Madman.
7" Single: Released Apr '81, on Fresh, by Jetstar Records. Catalogue no: **FRESH 10**

SOMEONES CRYING
Tracks: / Someone's crying / Rovers / Dancing glass (On 12" only) / Broken mirrors (On 12" only) / Slide (On 12" only).
7" Single: Released Feb '81, on Fresh, by Jetstar Records. Catalogue no: **FRESH 25**
12" Single: Released Feb '81, on Fresh, by Jetstar Records. Catalogue no: **FRESJ 25/12**

Cudy & Bink Band

HOME BOY (Home girls too)
7" Single: Released Apr '83, on Sound Of New York (USA), by Sound Of New York Records(USA). Catalogue no: **SNY 2**
12" Single: Released Apr '83, on Sound Of New York (USA), by Sound Of New York Records(USA). Catalogue no: **SNYL 2**

Cuff Links

Biographical details: The official line up of this US pop band was Joe Cord, Andrew Denno, Rich Dimino, Bob Gill, Dave Lavender, Pat Rizzo and Danny Valentine. In fact, none of these members appeared on the group's international hit single *Tracy*, that single was recorded by a group of session musicians and lead singer Ron Dante. Dante's voice was recorded several times on the record. The Cuff Links shot to fame in late 69 with *Tracy* and, in both the US and UK, this single entered the charts while the Archies' *Sugar sugar* was at no. 1. This was significant, because Dante also sang on the Archies' record. While everyone knew that the latter "group" was a collection of cartoon characters and that *Sugar sugar* therefore must have been recorded by session musicians, the secret took longer to come out in the case of *Tracy*. *Tracy* hit no.9 in the US and no.4 in the UK. The follow-up single *When Julie comes around* reached no.10 in Britain but only no.41 in the States. During the mid seventies Dante's career reached new heights, as he embarked upon a string of successes as Barry anilow's co-producer. The official Cuff Links, however, faded into obscurity, except for Rizzo, who was the only member able to sustain his musical career - he proceeded to play horns on records by Sly & the Family Stone, Gregg Allman and Ry Cooder. (Bob Macdonald, 14/2/85).

TRACY
Tracks: / Tracy.
7" Single: Released Nov '69, on MCA, by MCA Records. Catalogue no: **MU 1101**

TRACY (OLD GOLD)
Tracks: / Tracy / Little arrows.
7" Single: Released Jun '88, on Old Gold, by Old Gold Records. Catalogue no: **OG 9794**

WHEN JULIE COMES AROUND
Tracks: / When Julie comes around.
7" Single: Released Mar '70, on MCA, by MCA Records. Deleted Mar '73. Catalogue no: **MU 1112**

Cuffy, Claudia

DON'T GIVE UP (your love)
Tracks: / Don't give up.
12" Single: Released Oct '84, on Rhythmic, by Rhythmic Records. Catalogue no: **MIC 5**

Culbertson, Clive

I CAN'T FIGHT IT
Tracks: / I can't fight it.
7" Single: Released Aug '85, on Mint, by Emerald Records. Deleted '88. Catalogue no: **CHEW 101**

JUST A LITTLE BIT
Tracks: / Just a little bit.
7" Single: Released Mar '84, on Mint, by Emerald Records. Deleted '88. Catalogue no: **CHEW 89**

KISS ME
Tracks: / Kiss me.
7" Single: Released Jul '82, on Mint, by Emerald Records. Deleted '88. Catalogue no: **CHEW 66**

Cult

Biographical details: A new wave group formed in 1982 in Bradford as Southern Death Cult in 1984, with vocalist Ian Astbury, guitarist Billy Duffy and others. *Love* was a chart album in 1985. With echoes of Jimi Hendrix and Led Zeppelin in their songs (most of the audience had never heard the originals) and lacking some originality they still stood out in the wasteland of mid 80's pop. (Donald Clarke, April 1989)-.

EDIE (CIAO BABY)
Tracks: / Medicine train (12" and CD only) / Love removal machine (live) (12" and CD only) / Revolution (live) (CD and cassette only.) / Edie (ciao baby) / Bleeding heart graffiti (Only on cassette single.) / Li'l devil (live) (Only on CD single picture disc.).
CD 5": Released Jul '89, on Beggars Banquet, by Beggars Banquet Records. Catalogue no: **BEG 230CP**
12" Single: Released Jun '89, on Beggars Banquet, by Beggars Banquet Records. Catalogue no: **BEG 230T**
Cassingle: Released Jul '89, on Beggars Banquet, by Beggars Banquet Records. Catalogue no: **BEG 230C**
7" Single: Released Jun '89, on Beggars Banquet, by Beggars Banquet Records. Catalogue no: **BEG 230**
7" Single: Released Jun '89, on Beggars Banquet, by Beggars Banquet Records. Catalogue no: **BEG 230G**
CD 5": Released Jun '89, on Beggars Banquet, by Beggars Banquet Records. Catalogue no: **BEG 230CD**

FIRE WOMAN
Tracks: / Fire woman.
CD 5": Released 20 Mar '89, on Beggars Banquet, by Beggars Banquet Records. Catalogue no: **BEG 228 CD**
7" Single: Released 20 Mar '89, on Beggars Banquet, by Beggars Banquet Records. Catalogue no: **BEG 228**
12" Single: Released 20 Mar '89, on Beggars Banquet, by Beggars Banquet Records. Catalogue no: **BEG 228 T**

GO WEST
Tracks: / Go west / Crazy spinning circles.
7" Single: Released Jul '84, on Beggars Banquet, by Beggars Banquet Records. Catalogue no: **BEG 115**
12" Single: Released Jul '84, on Beggars Banquet, by Beggars Banquet Records. Catalogue no: **BEG 115T**

LIL' DEVIL
Tracks: / Lil' devil / Zap city / She sells sanctuary (live) (on 12" only) / Bone bag (live) (on 12" only) / Wild thing (on cassette only) / Louie Louie (on MC single only) / Phoenix (on MC single only).

CD 5": Released Apr '87, on Beggars Banquet, by Beggars Banquet Records. Deleted Jul '88. Catalogue no: **BEG 188CD**
Cassingle: Released Apr '87, on Beggars Banquet, by Beggars Banquet Records. Catalogue no: **BEG 188C**
7" Single: Released Apr '87, on Beggars Banquet, by Beggars Banquet Records. Catalogue no: **BEG 188**
12" Single: Released Apr '87, on Beggars Banquet, by Beggars Banquet Records. Catalogue no: **BEG 188T**

LOVE REMOVAL MACHINE
Tracks: / Love removal machine.
Note: Also available in double pack with Conquistador/Groove Co. Cat. no. BEG 182 D.
12" Pic: Released Feb '87, on Beggars Banquet, by Beggars Banquet Records. Catalogue no: **BEG 182TP**
7" Single: Released Feb '87, on Beggars Banquet, by Beggars Banquet Records. Catalogue no: **BEG 182**
12" Single: Released Feb '87, on Beggars Banquet, by Beggars Banquet Records. Catalogue no: **BEG 182T**

RAIN
Tracks: / Rain.
7" Single: Released Sep '85, on Beggars Banquet, by Beggars Banquet Records. Catalogue no: **BEG 147**
12" Single: Released Sep '85, on Beggars Banquet, by Beggars Banquet Records. Catalogue no: **BEG 147 T**

RESURRECTION JOE
Tracks: / Resurrection Joe.
7" Single: Released Dec '84, on Beggars Banquet, by Beggars Banquet Records. Catalogue no: **BEG 122**
12" Single: Released Dec '84, on Beggars Banquet, by Beggars Banquet Records. Catalogue no: **BEG 122 T**

REVOLUTION
Tracks: / Revolution.
7" Set: Released Jul '88, on Virgin (Australia), by Virgin Records. Catalogue no: **BEG 1882**
7" Set: Released Nov '85, on Beggars Banquet, by Beggars Banquet Records. Catalogue no: **BEG 152 D**
7" Single: Released Nov '85, on Beggars Banquet, by Beggars Banquet Records. Catalogue no: **BEG 152**
12" Single: Released Nov '85, on Beggars Banquet, by Beggars Banquet Records. Catalogue no: **BEG 152 T**

SHE SELLS SANCTUARY
Tracks: / She sells sanctuary.
7" Single: Released May '85, on Beggars Banquet, by Beggars Banquet Records. Catalogue no: **BEG 135**
12" Single: Released May '85, on Beggars Banquet, by Beggars Banquet Records. Catalogue no: **BEG 135 T**

SOLDIER BLUE
Tracks: / Soldier blue.
CD 5": Released '87, on Beggars Banquet, by Beggars Banquet Records. Deleted Jul '88. Catalogue no: **BEG 205CD**
Cassingle: Released '87, on Beggars Banquet, by Beggars Banquet Records. Deleted Jul '88. Catalogue no: **BEG 205C**
7" Single: Released '87, on Beggars Banquet, by Beggars Banquet Records. Deleted Jul '88. Catalogue no: **BEG 205**
12" Single: Released '87, on Beggars Banquet, by Beggars Banquet Records. Deleted Jul '88. Catalogue no: **BEG 205T**

SPIRIT WALKER
Tracks: / Spirit walker.
7" Single: Released Apr '84, on Situation 2, by Beggars Banquet Records. Deleted Jul '88. Catalogue no: **SIT 33**
12" Single: Released Apr '84, on Situation 2, by Beggars Banquet Records. Catalogue no: **SIT 33T**

WILDFLOWER Australian tour EP
Tracks: / Wildflower.
Note: Limited-edition EP featuring Wildflower (extended rock mix), She Sells Sanctuary(extended rock mix), Love Trooper, Horse Nation and Outlaw, recorded live in March 1987. (Cat.no. 728213) Limited edition fold-out poster sleeve (Import).
7" EP: Released Oct '87, on Virgin (Australia), by Virgin Records. Catalogue no: **VOZ 195T**
7" Set: Released Aug '87, on Beggars Banquet, by Beggars Banquet Records. Catalogue no: **BEG 195D**
7" Single: Released Nov '87, on Sire (USA), Catalogue no: **728213**

WILDFLOWER, THE
Tracks: / Wildflower / Love trooper.
CD 5": Released Aug '87, on Beggars Banquet, by Beggars Banquet Records. Deleted Jul '88. Catalogue no: **BEG 195CD**
7" Pic: Released Aug '87, on Beggars Banquet, by Beggars Banquet Records. Catalogue no: **BEG 195P**
Cassingle: Released Aug '87, on Beggars Banquet, by Beggars Banquet Records. Catalogue no: **BEG 195C**
7" Single: Released Aug '87, on Beggars Banquet, by Beggars Banquet Records. Catalogue no: **BEG 195**
12" Single: Released Aug '87, on Beggars Banquet, by Beggars Banquet Records. Catalogue no: **BEG 195TR**
12" Single: Released Aug '87, on Beggars Banquet, by Beggars Banquet Records. Catalogue no: **BEG 195T**

Cult Figures

I REMEMBER
Tracks: / I remember.
7" Single: Released Jun '81, on Rather, by Rather Records. Catalogue no: **GEAR 8**

ZIP NOLAN
Tracks: / Zip Nolan.
7" Single: Released Jun '81, on Rather, by Rather Records. Catalogue no: **GEAR 4**

Cult Mania

AMERICAN DREAM
Tracks: / American dream.
7" Single: Released Feb '83, on Elephant Rock, by Plastic Head Records. Catalogue no: **ERR 002**

BLITZ
Tracks: / Blitz.
7" Single: Released Nov '82, on Elephant Rock, by Plastic Head Records. Catalogue no: **ER 001**

Cult Maniax

AMAZING ADVENTURES OF JOHNNY THE DUCK
Tracks: / Amazing adventures of Johnny the duck and the bathtime blues / Blue baby / Village ritual / Freedom / Maniax.
7" Single: Released 13 Jun '85, on Xcentric Noise, by Xcentric Noise Records & Tapes. Catalogue no: **EIGHTH 001**
7" Single: Released Nov '84, on Xcentric Noise, by Xcentric Noise Records & Tapes. Catalogue no: **EIGHTH 1**
12" Single: Released 13 Jun '85, on Xcentric Noise, by Xcentric Noise Records & Tapes. Catalogue no: **EIGHTH 001 T**
12" Single: Released Nov '84, on Xcentric Noise, by Xcentric Noise Records & Tapes. Catalogue no: **EIGHTH 1 T**

COOL CATS DANCING
Tracks: / Cool cats dancing.
7" Single: Released Jul '84, on Xcentric Noise, by Xcentric Noise Records & Tapes. Catalogue no: **SIXTH 1**

FULL OF SPUNK EP
7" EP: Released 3 Jul '85, on Xcentric Noise, by Xcentric Noise Records & Tapes. Catalogue no: **SIXTH 001**

WHERE DO WE ALL GO
Tracks: / Where do we all go.
12" Single: Released May '85, on Xcentric Noise, by Xcentric Noise Records & Tapes. Catalogue no: **TENTH 1**

Cultural Roots

DISTANT LOVER
Tracks: / Distant lover / Class crew - Dubology, A.
12" Single: Released Nov '87, on Mango, by Island Records. Catalogue no: **12IS 348**

GHETTO RUNNING
Tracks: / Ghetto running.
12" Single: Released Apr '83, on Reggae, Catalogue no: **REG 01**

HELL A GO POP (SINGLE)
Tracks: / Hell a go pop.
12" Single: Released Jan '84, on Greensleeves, by Greensleeves Records. Catalogue no: **GRED 137**

MR. LION MAN
Tracks: / Mr. Lion man / People come a dancing.
12" Single: Released Oct '82, on Cultural Roots, by Exclusive Productions. Catalogue no: **EX 718**

REALITY
Tracks: / Reality.
12" Single: Released Oct '82, on Cultural Roots, by Exclusive Productions. Catalogue no: **EX 717**

ROUGHER YET
Tracks: / Rougher yet / Stem.
12" Single: Released May '89, on Greensleeves, by Greensleeves Records. Catalogue no: **GRED 245**

SWEET REGGAE MUSIC
Tracks: / Sweet reggae music.
12" Single: Released Jul '88, on Redman International, Catalogue no: **VPRED 101**

WHO IS THE BOSS
Tracks: / Who is the boss.
12" Single: Released May '86, on Chris's, Catalogue no: **CCR 2**

Cultural Vibe

MA FOOM BAY
Tracks: / Ma foom bay / Ma foom bay (dub version).
7" Single: Released Sep '86, on Cross-over, Catalogue no: **7 CROSS 2**

POWER
Tracks: / Power / Mind games.
12" Single: Released 30 May '87, on Hardcore, Catalogue no: **HAKT 2**

Cultural Youth

PEACE AND LOVE
Tracks: / Peace and love / Peace or dub.
12" Single: Released Nov '83, on Joe Gibbs, Catalogue no: **JGM 8187**

Culture

Biographical details: This Jamaica reggae band comprises Kenneth Lloyd Dayes, Vin Gordon, Joseph Hill, Uzziah "Sticky" Thompson and Albert Walker. Culture were first noticed in the reggae market in 1978, thanks to their album *Two sevens clash* and, in particular, its acclaimed title track, which was a review of the previous year, 1977. The album reached no.60 on the UK albums chart, no mean feat for a reggae album. Several LP's followed on various labels but, despite continued quality, none reached the charts. Culture remained one of Jamaica's most respected acts, particularly because of their incisive, politically and socially motivated lyrics and their gospel-influenced singing. (B. Macdonald, 14/2/85).

DISOBEDIENT CHILDREN
Tracks: / Disobedient children.
12" Single: Released Sep '81, on Kingdom, by Kingdom Records. Deleted '82. Catalogue no: **KV 8081 12**

FORWARD TO AFRICA
Tracks: / Forward to Africa.
12" Single: Released May '83, on Kingdom, by Kingdom Records. Deleted '84. Catalogue no: **KV 8015 12**

MONEY GIRL
Tracks: / Money girl / Dance hall style.
12" Single: Released Jun '86, on Blue Mountain, Catalogue no: **BMD 23**

PEEL SESSIONS:CULTURE
12" Single: Released May '87, on Strange Fruit, by Strange Fruit Records. Catalogue no: **SFPS 024**

Culture, Birdy

NAW GO BROCK UP
Tracks: / Naw go brock up.
12" Single: Released May '88, on Pioneer Muzik, Catalogue no: **PM 008**

Culture, Bobby

HEALTH AND STRENGTH
Tracks: / Health and strength
12" Single: Released Jul '82, on Leggo, Catalogue no: **LG 003**

Culture Clash Dance

GHETTO BLASTER
Tracks: / Ghetto blaster / Sucker M.C..
7" Single: Released 24 Jul '89, on Jive, by Zomba Records. Catalogue no: **CCDP 2**
12" Single: Released 24 Jul '89, on Jive, by Zomba Records. Catalogue no: **CCDPT 2**

LOVE FEVER
Tracks: / Love fever.
7" Single: Released Jan '88, on Jive, by Zomba Records. Catalogue no: **CCDP 1**
12" Single: Released May '89, on Jive, by Zomba Records. Catalogue no: **CCDPR 1**
12" Single: Released Jan '88, on Jive, by Zomba Records. Catalogue no: **CCDPT 1**

Culture Club

Biographical details: This British pop band comprises Boy George (aka George O'Dowd), Mikey Craig, Roy Hay and Jon Moss. Culture Club was formed in 1981. Both Boy George and Jon Moss had had links with Malcolm Maclaren, the irrepressible pop entrepreneur: George had been with Bow Wow Wow for a brief period and had been hotly tipped to become that group's frontman; Moss had played with Adam & The Ants shortly before they made it big. Prior to entering the music business George had tried hishand at a variety of jobs including fruit picking, window dressing and modelling. The newly-formed Culture Club quartet, free from MAclaren's influence, released their first two singles in the early summer of 1982. They failed to chart, but it was a totally different story with the third 45 *Do you really want to hurt me*, a gentle slice of reggae-influenced pop, rocketed to no.1 in Britain in autumn 1982. Its success ushered in a succession of smashes for the band, all written by the group, all produced by Steve Levine, a young and talented studio wizard who was at the forefront of the boom in studio computer technology. 1983 was the boom year for Culture Club. Every single they issued hit the UK Top 3 and they achieved a UK no.1 album with *Colour by numbers*. The group's success spread around the world; particularly in the States, where they were at the forefront of a spectacular new British Invasion. Trading on the androgyny and flamboyance of George, the group projected their lead singer as their spokesman and media face. He became a worldwide pin-up and, after the initial shock, even parents of the fans began to find him lovable and cute. But even more remarkable than the image was the music - each single was quite different from its predecessors. *Time (clock of the heart)* was a slick, jazz-tinged ballad, *Church of the poison mind* was an uptempo tribute to the Motown sound, *Victims* was a dramatic builder. Culture Club's biggest hit was *Karma chameleon*, a perfect pop single that became the first 45 of the 80's to log six weeks at no.1 on the UK chart; it also chalked up 3 weeks at the top in America. Although the group's output was musically unoriginal - there were no influences this side of 1975 - their singles and LP's were brilliantly conceived and executed. As soon as their musical strength and diversity diminished, they suffered a major media backlash: 1984's *Waking up with the house on fire* LP was a major artis

CULTURE CLUB - CHURCH OF THE POISON MIND (Released on Virgin

CULTURE CLUB - DO YOU REALLY WANT TO HURT ME (Released on Virgin)

CULTURE CLUB - WHITE BOY (Released on Virgin)

ic and commercial disappointment, as were its singles *The war song* and *The nedal song*. The latter peaked at no.32 in 3ritain, a major calamity in view of the band's track record of 7 consecutive top 5 singles. Stateside reaction to the album vas equally muted. It seemed that two ears of massive exposure was taking its oll. (Bob Macdonald, 15/2/85).

CHURCH OF THE POISON MIND (see panel on previous page)
racks: / Church of the poison mind / Man hake / Mystery boy (Suntori hot whiskey ong) (12" only).
" Single: Released Apr '83, on Virgin, by Virgin Records. Catalogue no: **VS 571**
2" Single: Released Apr '83, on Virgin, by Virgin Records. Catalogue no: **VS 571-12**

CHURCH OF THE POISON MIND (OLD GOLD)
racks: / Church of the poison mind / Victims.
" Single: Released Nov '88, on Old Gold, y Old Gold Records. Catalogue no: **OG 832**

O YOU REALLY WANT TO HURT ME (see panel above)
racks: / Do you really want to hurt me / Dub version (featuring Pappa Weasel) / ove is cold (you were never no good) (12" nly).
" Single: Released Sep '82, on Virgin, by irgin Records. Catalogue no: **VS 518**
2" Single: Released Sep '82, on Virgin, y Virgin Records. Catalogue no: **VS 518-2**

O YOU REALLY WANT TO HURT E (OLD GOLD)
racks: / Do you really want to hurt me / I'll umble 4 ya / Time (clock of the heart).
" Single: Released Nov '88, on Old Gold, y Old Gold Records. Catalogue no: **OG 816**
2" Single: Released 27 Feb '89, on Old old, by Old Gold Records. Catalogue no: **G 4101**

OD THANK YOU WOMAN
racks: / God thank you woman / From uxury to heartache.
" Single: Released May '86, on Virgin, by irgin Records. Deleted '86. Catalogue no: **S 861**
2" Single: Released May '86, on Virgin, y Virgin Records. Deleted '86. Catalogue o: **VS 861-12**

M AFRAID OF ME
racks: / I'm afraid of me / Murder rap ack.
' Single: Released Jun '82, on Virgin, by irgin Records. Catalogue no: **VS 509**
2" Single: Released Jun '82, on Virgin, Virgin Records. Catalogue no: **VS 509-**

'S A MIRACLE
acks: / It's a miracle / Love twist / Miss e blind (On 12" only) / Melting pot (On 2" only).
' Single: Released Mar '84, on Virgin, by rgin Records. Deleted '89. Catalogue no: **S 662**
2" Single: Released Mar '84, on Virgin, by Virgin Records. Deleted '89. Catalogue no: **VS 662-12**

KARMA CHAMELEON
Tracks: / Karma chameleon / That's the way (7" only) / I'll tumble 4 ya (12' only).
7" Single: Released Aug '83, on Virgin, by Virgin Records. Catalogue no: **VS 612**
12" Single: Released Aug '83, on Virgin, by Virgin Records. Catalogue no: **VS 612-12**

KARMA CHAMELEON (OLD GOLD)
Tracks: / Karma chameleon / It's a miracle / Miss me blind.
7" Single: Released Nov '88, on Old Gold, by Old Gold Records. Catalogue no: **OG 9822**
12" Single: Released 28 Mar '89, on Old Gold, by Old Gold Records. Catalogue no: **OG 4107**

MEDAL SONG
Tracks: / Medal song, The.
7" Single: Released Nov '84, on Virgin, by Virgin Records. Deleted '89. Catalogue no: **VS 730**
12" Single: Released Nov '84, on Virgin, by Virgin Records. Deleted '89. Catalogue no: **VS 730-12**

MOVE AWAY
Tracks: / Move away / Sexuality / Move away (extended version) (12" only) / Sexuality (tango dub remix version) (12" only).
7" Pic: Released Mar '86, on Virgin, by Virgin Records. Deleted '86. Catalogue no: **VSX 845-12**
7" Single: Released Mar '86, on Virgin, by Virgin Records. Deleted May '88. Catalogue no: **VS 845**
12" Single: Released Mar '86, on Virgin, by Virgin Records. Catalogue no: **VS 845-12**

TIME (CLOCK OF THE HEART)
Tracks: / Time (clock of the heart) / White boys can't control it / Romance beyond the alphabet (12' only).
7" Pic: Released Nov '82, on Virgin, by Virgin Records. Deleted '89. Catalogue no: **VSY 558**
7" Single: Released Nov '82, on Virgin, by Virgin Records. Catalogue no: **VS 558**
12" Single: Released Nov '82, on Virgin, by Virgin Records. Catalogue no: **VS 558-12**

VICTIMS
Tracks: / Victims / Colour by numbers / Romance revisited.
7" Single: Released Nov '83, on Virgin, by Virgin Records. Deleted '89. Catalogue no: **VS 641**
12" Single: Released Nov '83, on Virgin, by Virgin Records. Catalogue no: **VS 641-12**

WAR SONG (see panel below)
Tracks: / War song / La cancion de guerra.
7" Single: Released Sep '84, on Virgin, by Virgin Records. Deleted '89. Catalogue no: **VS 694**
12" Single: Released Sep '84, on Virgin, by Virgin Records. Deleted '89. Catalogue no: **VS 694-12**

WHITE BOY (see panel above)
Tracks: / White boy / Love twist (featuring Captain Crucial.
7" Single: Released Apr '82, on Virgin, by Virgin Records. Catalogue no: **VS 496**
12" Single: Released Apr '82, on Virgin, by Virgin Records. Catalogue no: **VS 496-12**

Culture, Jahfa

COMMANDER COMMANDO
Tracks: / Commander commando / Fatty boy.
12" Single: Released Sep '86, on Roots Connection, Catalogue no: **CON 003**

I'M GONNA MAKE SURE
Tracks: / I'm gonna make sure.
12" Single: Released Jul '88, on Commando, Catalogue no: **001 CM**

Culture, Louie

NEW DISH
Tracks: / New dish.
7" Single: Released May '89, on Supreme, by Supreme Records. Catalogue no: **UNKNOWN**

Culture, Peter

INTEGRITY
Tracks: / Integrity.
12" Single: Released Jan '89, on Silicon Squad, Catalogue no: **SSM 004**

Culture Shock

HOUSE BHANGRA
Tracks: / House Bhangra.
7" Single: Released Jun '88, on Westside, by Westside Records. Catalogue no: **HAK 13**
12" Single: Released Jun '88, on Hardcore, Catalogue no: **HAKT 13**

Culture, Smiley

COCKNEY TRANSLATION
Tracks: / Cockney translation / Roots reality / Entertainer entertainer.
7" Single: Released Dec '84, on Fashion, by Fashion Records. Catalogue no: **FAD 7009**
7" Single: Released Mar '85, on Fashion, by Fashion Records. Catalogue no: **FAD 7028**
12" Single: Released Mar '85, on Fashion, by Fashion Records. Catalogue no: **FAD 1228**
12" Single: Released Dec '84, on Fashion, by Fashion Records. Catalogue no: **FAD 020**

MR KIDNAPPER
Tracks: / Mr. Kidnapper / Supa supe.
7" Single: Released Oct '86, on Polydor, by Polydor Ltd. Deleted Aug '87. Catalogue no: **POSP 827**
12" Single: Released Oct '86, on Polydor, by Polydor Ltd. Deleted Aug '87. Catalogue no: **POSPX 827**

CULTURE CLUB - WAR SONG (Released on Virgin)

NUFF PERSONALITY
Tracks: / Nuff personality.
7" Single: Released Nov '85, on Culture, Catalogue no: **7CR 001**
12" Single: Released Nov '85, on Culture, Catalogue no: **CR 001**

POLICE OFFICER
Tracks: / Police officer.
12" Single: Released Nov '84, on Fashion, by Fashion Records. Catalogue no: **FAD 026**
12" Single: Released Nov '84, on Fashion, by Fashion Records. Catalogue no: **FAD 7012**

TV LOVER
Tracks: / T.V. lover.
12" Single: Released Apr '88, on Senator, Catalogue no: **ZZ 001**

Culture T.

WHO WEAR THE PANTS, A
Tracks: / Who wear the pants, A.
12" Single: Released Apr '88, on Wild International, Catalogue no: **WW 001**

Cumberpatch, Ken

NO TURNING BACK
Tracks: / No turning back / Sea breeze.
7" Single: Released Oct '82, on Edge, Deleted Oct '85. Catalogue no: **EDGE 3**

Cunliffe, Roger

REBECCA
Tracks: / Rebecca.
7" Single: Released Sep '83, on Voix, Deleted '84. Catalogue no: **VOX 1**

Cunningham, Earl

AFRICAN MAN
Tracks: / African man / Man from Africa.
12" Single: Released Jan '83, on Jah Shaka, Catalogue no: **SHAKA 832**

BAD BOY
Tracks: / Bad boy.
12" Single: Released Jul '83, on Struggle, Catalogue no: **ST 001**

FOOLS FALL IN LOVE
Tracks: / Fools fall in love / International.
12" Single: Released Dec '83, on Midnight Rock, Catalogue no: **MR 20**

JAILHOUSE
Tracks: / Jailhouse / Jailhouse rock.
12" Single: Released Feb '82, on Art & Craft, Catalogue no: **ACD 16**

SOCA PART 1
Tracks: / Soca part 1.
7" Single: Released Feb '85, on Hobo, Catalogue no: **HOS 027**
12" Single: Released Oct '84, on Relaxed Rabbit, by Charly Records. Catalogue no: **RR 002**

Cunningham, Gayle

PICK UP THE PHONE
Tracks: / Pick up the phone / Little child.
7" Single: Released Oct '80, on Big Fish, Deleted '83. Catalogue no: **BF 3**

Cunningham, J C

PYRAMID SONG
Tracks: / Pyramid song / I'm a lover not a fighter.
7" Single: Released Sep '80, on Scotti Bros (USA), Deleted '83. Catalogue no: **K 11559**

Cunningham, Joan

HELLO AGAIN AND GOODBYE
Tracks: / Petite fleur / Hello again and goodbye.
7" Single: Released Nov '86, on Hobo, Catalogue no: **HOS 027**

Cunningham, Larry

Biographical details: This Irish country singer has achieved just one chart record in Britain during a lengthy career. *Tribute to Jim Reeves*, a single released as a mark of respect to the recently deceased US country giant, entered the UK chart at the end of 1964.
It was a slow but steady seller, peaking at no. 40 but logging 11 weeks on the Top 50. He was backed on the single by the Mighty Avons. Cunningham's music is a blend of traditional Irish folk and American country & western, or as he once described it, Country & Irish.
(Bob Macdonald, 15/2/85).

SLANEY VALLEY
Tracks: / Slaney valley / These are my mountains.
7" Single: Released '88, on Homespun (Ireland), by Outlet Records. Catalogue no: **HIS 20**

TRIBUTE TO JIM REEVES
Tracks: / Tribute to Jim Reeves.
7" Single: Released Dec '64, on King (2), by R & B Discs Ltd. Deleted Dec '67. Catalogue no: **KG 1016**

Cupid's Inspiration

MY WORLD
Tracks: / My world.
7" Single: Released Oct '68, on Nems, by Castle Communications Records. Deleted Oct '71. Catalogue no: **56 3702**

YESTERDAY HAS GONE
Tracks: / Yesterday has gone / My world.
7" Single: Released Jun '68, on Nems, by Castle Communications Records. Deleted Jun '71. Catalogue no: **56 3500**
7" Single: Released May '87, on NB, by NB Records. Catalogue no: **NB 5**
7" Single: Released May '87, on MBS, by MBS Records. Catalogue no: **MBS 001**

Cupol

LIKE THIS FOR AGES
Tracks: / Like this for ages.
12" Single: Released Jul '80, on 4AD, by 4AD Records. Catalogue no: **BAD 9**

Cupp, Pat

I GUESS ITS MEANT THIS WAY
Tracks: / I guess it's meant this way.
7" Single: Released Jun '80, on Rollin' Rock, Catalogue no: **45 009**

LONG GONE DADDY
Tracks: / Long gone daddy / Do me no wrong.
7" Single: Released Jun '80, on Rollin' Rock, Catalogue no: **45 003**

Cure

Biographical details: This British rock group comprises Robert Smith and Lol Tolhurst plus an ever-changing band of helpers that has, at various times, included Michael Dempsey, Mathieu Hartley and Simon Gallup. The Cure were formed at the time of the 1976/7 punk explosion.
The nucleus of the band has always been vocalist and guitarist Smith, aided by his faithful helper, drummer Lol Tollhurst. 1979 saw the release of their first three singles and a debut LP, all issued on the Fiction label, for which they have recorded ever since.
The album, *Three imaginary boys*, reached no.44 on the album chart. The following year brought them their first chart single *A forest*, a claustrophobic and doomy but curiously appealiing record, hit no.31 on the British listings.
For the next three years, they remained favourites of the UK music press and continued to release music in a post-punk style similar to that of Siouxsie and the Banshees, with whom Smith has played on occasion. The Cure's music was immediately recognisable because of Smith's distinctive vocals.
They chalked up a string of minor chart singles in Britain, and hit the UK LP Top 20 with *17 seconds, Faith* and *Pornography*. In 1983 The Cure moved a little closer towards mainstream pop, and collected their first Top 20 single *The walk* and followed it with their first Top Tenner *The love cats*. 1984 saw them gain another Top 20 single in the shape of *The caterpillar*, an equally oddball but engaging item. However, sales of their LP *The top* were disappointing in view of the group's singles chart breakthrough.
(Bob Macdonald, 15/2/85)
A pop rock band formed in 1976 in Crawley, Sussex as Easy Cure, including Robert Smith, guitar and songwriter, and Lawrence Tolhurst on drums, then keyboards.
They shortened the name in 1978; guested on tour with Siouxsie & The Banshees in 1979 and played in the Banshees mould.
The band was put on hold late '82 when Smith joined the Banshees but soon resurfaced. They were a cult favourite in the USA. Tolhurst disclaimed the arty-rock label: 'I think people give too much importance to something that is entertainment, when all is said and done'.
(Donald Clarke, April 1989).

BOYS DON'T CRY (SINGLE)
Tracks: / Boys don't cry (new voice, new mix) / Pill box tails / Do the hansa (Extra track on 12".).
7" Single: Released Apr '86, on Fiction, by Fiction Records. Deleted Aug '87. Catalogue no: **FICS 24**
12" Single: Released Apr '86, on Fiction, by Fiction Records. Deleted Aug '87. Catalogue no: **FICSX 24**

CATCH
Tracks: / Catch / Breathe / Chain of flowers (Track on 12" version only.) / Kyoto song (live) (Track on 12" E.P. only.) / Night like this, A (live) (Track on 12" E.P. only.).
7" EP: Released Jul '87, on Polydor, by Polydor Ltd. Deleted 31 May '89. Catalogue no: **FICSE 26**
7" Single: Released Jul '87, on Polydor, by Polydor Ltd. Catalogue no: **FICS 26**
12" Single: Released Jul '87, on Polydor, by Polydor Ltd. Catalogue no: **FICSX 26**

CATERPILLAR, THE
Tracks: / Caterpillar, The / Happy man.
7" Single: Released Apr '84, on Fiction, by Fiction Records. Deleted Apr '87. Catalogue no: **FICS 20**

CHARLOTTE SOMETIMES
Tracks: / Charlotte sometimes.
7" Single: Released Oct '81, on Fiction, by Fiction Records. Deleted Oct '84. Catalogue no: **FICS 14**

CLOSE TO ME
Tracks: / Close to me.
10" single: Released Sep '85, on Fiction, by Fiction Records. Catalogue no: **FICST 23**
7" Single: Released Sep '85, on Fiction, by Fiction Records. Catalogue no: **FICS 23**
12" Single: Released Sep '85, on Fiction, by Fiction Records. Catalogue no: **FICSG 23**

CURE: INTERVIEW PICTURE DISC COLLECTION
7" Set: Released Apr '88, on Baktabak, by Baktabak Records. Catalogue no: **BAKPAK 1005**

FOREST, A
Tracks: / Forest, A / Another journey.
7" Single: Released Apr '80, on Fiction, by Fiction Records. Deleted Apr '83. Catalogue no: **FICS 10**
12" Single: Released Apr '80, on Fiction, by Fiction Records. Deleted Apr '83. Catalogue no: **FICSX 10**

HANGING GARDEN, THE (SINGLE)
Tracks: / Hanging gardens, The / Killing an arab / 100 years / Forest.
7" Set: Released Jun '82, on Fiction, by Fiction Records. Catalogue no: **FICG 15**
7" Single: Released Jul '82, on Fiction, by Fiction Records. Deleted Jul '85. Catalogue no: **FICS 15**

HOT HOT HOT
Tracks: / Hot hot hot (ext. remix) / Hot hot hot (7" remix) / Hey you (ext. remix).
CD 5": Released Feb '88, on Polydor, by Polydor Ltd. Catalogue no: **FIXCD 28**
12" Single: Released Feb '88, on Polydor, by Polydor Ltd. Catalogue no: **FICSX 28**

IN BETWEEN DAYS
Tracks: / In between days.
7" Single: Released Jul '85, on Fiction, by Fiction Records. Catalogue no: **FICS 22**
12" Single: on Fiction, by Fiction Records. Catalogue no: **FICSX 22**

JUST LIKE HEAVEN
Tracks: / Just like heaven / Snow in summer / Sugar girls.
Note: (Cat.no. 667934) 3-track cassette single, featuring a remix of 'Just like heaven', 'Breath' (unavailable on album) and 'A chain of flowers' (Also unavailable on album). In love packaging.
7" Pic: Released Oct '87, on Fiction, by Fiction Records. Deleted Jan '88. Catalogue no: **FICSP 27**
Cassingle: Released Nov '87, on Elektra (USA), by Elektra Records (USA). Catalogue no: **667934**
7" Single: Released Oct '87, on Fiction, by Fiction Records. Catalogue no: **FICS 27**
12" Single: Released Oct '87, on Fiction, by Fiction Records. Catalogue no: **FICSX 27**

LET'S GO TO BED
Tracks: / Let's go to bed / Just one kiss.
7" Single: Released Nov '82, on Fiction, by Fiction Records. Deleted Nov '85. Catalogue no: **FICS 17**
12" Single: Released Nov '82, on Fiction, by Fiction Records. Deleted Nov '85. Catalogue no: **FICSX 17**

LOVE CATS, THE
Tracks: / Love cats, The.
7" Single: Released Oct '83, on Fiction, by Fiction Records. Deleted Oct '86. Catalogue no: **FICS 19**

LOVE SONG
Tracks: / Lovesong / 2 late / Fear of ghosts.
CD 5": Released Aug '89, on Polydor, by Polydor Ltd. Catalogue no: **FICCD 30**
7" Set: Released Sep '89, on Polydor, by Polydor Ltd. Catalogue no: **FISCG 30**
Cassingle: Released Aug '89, on Polydor, by Polydor Ltd. Catalogue no: **FICCS 30**
7" Single: Released Aug '89, on Polydor, by Polydor Ltd. Catalogue no: **FICS 30**
12" Single: Released Aug '89, on Polydor, by Polydor Ltd. Catalogue no: **FICSX 30**

LULLABY
Tracks: / Lullaby.
7" Single: Released Apr '89, on Polydor, by Polydor Ltd. Catalogue no: **FICSP 29**
7" Single: Released Apr '89, on Polydor, by Polydor Ltd. Catalogue no: **FICS 29**
7" Single: Released Apr '89, on Polydor, by Polydor Ltd. Catalogue no: **FISG 29**
12" Single: Released Apr '89, on Polydor, by Polydor Ltd. Catalogue no: **FICSX 29**
12" Single: Released Apr '89, on Polydor, by Polydor Ltd. Catalogue no: **FICVX 29**
CD 3": Released Apr '89, on Polydor, by Polydor Ltd. Catalogue no: **FICCD 29**

PEEL SESSIONS:CURE
Note: Session material from John Peel's programme on BBC Radio 1.
CD 5": Released May '88, on Strange Fruit, by Strange Fruit Records. Catalogue no: **SFPSCD 050**
12" Single: Released May '88, on Strange Fruit, by Strange Fruit Records. Catalogue no: **SFPS 050**

PRIMARY
Tracks: / Primary.
7" Single: Released Apr '81, on Fiction, by Fiction Records. Deleted Apr '84. Catalogue no: **FICS 12**

WALK, THE (SINGLE)
Tracks: / Walk, The.
7" Single: Released Jul '83, on Fiction, by Fiction Records. Deleted Jul '86. Catalogue no: **FICS 18**

Curfew

MAKE IT UP
Tracks: / Make it up.
12" Single: Released Jan '84, on TNT Catalogue no: **TNT 005**

MERRY GO ROUND
Tracks: / Merry go round.
12" Single: Released Jul '85, on Street Bea (USA), Catalogue no: **TNT 006**

YOU KNOW
Tracks: / You know / Jah love.
12" Single: Released Oct '82, on TNT, Catalogue no: **TNT 003**

Curiosity Killed The

DOWN TO EARTH
Tracks: / Down to earth / Down to eart (instrumental) / Shallow memory (extra trac on 12").
7" Single: Released Nov '86, on Mercury by Phonogram Ltd. Deleted Mar '88. Catalogue no: **CAT 2**
12" Single: Released Nov '86, on Mercury by Phonogram Ltd. Catalogue no: **CATX 2**

FREE
Tracks: / Free / Free (inst).
7" Single: Released Sep '87, on Mercury by Phonogram Ltd. Deleted Mar '88. Catalogue no: **CAT 5**
12" Single: Released Sep '87, on Mercury by Phonogram Ltd. Deleted Mar '88. Catalogue no: **CATX 5**

MISFIT
Tracks: / Misfit / Man / Corruption (Extr track on 12".).
7" Single: Released 30 May '87, on Mercury, by Phonogram Ltd. Deleted Dec '8 Catalogue no: **CAT 4**
12" Single: Released 30 May '87, on Mercury, by Phonogram Ltd. Deleted Dec '8 Catalogue no: **CATX 4**

NAME AND NUMBER
Tracks: / Name and number / Keep c trying.
CD 5": Released Sep '89, on Mercury, b Phonogram Ltd. Catalogue no: **CATCD 6**
Cassingle: Released Sep '89, on Mercur by Phonogram Ltd. Catalogue no: **CATM 6**
7" Single: Released Sep '89, on Mercur by Phonogram Ltd. Catalogue no: **CATP 6**
7" Single: Released Sep '89, on Mercur by Phonogram Ltd. Catalogue no: **CAT 6**
12" Single: Released Sep '89, on Mercur by Phonogram Ltd. Catalogue no: **CATX 6**

ORDINARY DAY
Tracks: / Bullet / Ordinary day.
7" Single: Released Mar '87, on Mercury, b Phonogram Ltd. Deleted Dec '87. Catalogue no: **CAT 3**
12" Single: Released Mar '87, on Mercur by Phonogram Ltd. Deleted Dec '87. Catalogue no: **CATX 3**

Curley, Gary

RETURN TO ZERO
Tracks: / Return to zero.
Note: First release on the new Dar-Tek label
7" Single: Released Mar '88, on Dar-Tek, Dar-Tek Records. Catalogue no: **DTK 77**

Current 93

CROWLEY MASS
Tracks: / Crowley mass.
12" Single: Released 10 Oct '87, on Maldoror, Catalogue no: **MAL 108**

HAPPY BIRTHDAY PIGFACE CHRISTUS
Tracks: / Happy birthday pigface Christus.
12" Single: Released Jul '88, on Laylah, by Laylah Records. Catalogue no: **LAY 018**

LASHTAL
Tracks: / Lashtal.
12" Single: Released Apr '86, on Laylah, by Laylah Records. Catalogue no: **LAY 001**

RED FACE OF GOD
Tracks: / Red face of God.
12" Single: Released Mar '88, on Maldoror, Catalogue no: **MAL 088**

Currie, Cherie

MESSIN' WITH THE BOYS (SINGLE)
Tracks: / Messin' with the boys / Since you've been gone.
7" Single: Released Feb '80, on Capitol, by EMI Records. Deleted '83. Catalogue no: **CL 16119**

Curry, Tawana

LET ME SHOW YOU
Tracks: / Let me show you.
7" Single: Released Apr '89, on Republic, by Code Records. Catalogue no: **LIC 026**
12" Single: Released Apr '89, on Republic, by Code Records. Catalogue no: **LICT 026**

Curtess, Buddy

BRIDGE OVER TROUBLED WATER
Tracks: / Bridge over troubled water / Load up.
7" Single: Released Jul '87, on Mercury, by Phonogram Ltd. Deleted Mar '88. Catalogue no: **BUD 3**

DESIGN FOR ME
Tracks: / Design for me / Love me / Evil potion (Available only on 12" version.).
7" Single: Released Nov '88, on Jungle, by Jungle Records. Catalogue no: **JUNG 46**
12" Single: Released Nov '88, on Jungle, by Jungle Records. Catalogue no: **JUNG 46T**

HELLO SUZIE
Tracks: / Hot shot / Mainline (Track:'Main Line' on 12" single only.).
7" Single: Released Nov '86, on Mercury, by Phonogram Ltd. Catalogue no: **BUD 2**
12" Single: Released Nov '86, on Mercury, by Phonogram Ltd. Catalogue no: **BUD 212**

SHOOBEE BABY
Tracks: / Shoobee baby / Hypnotise me / Better be sure / Scoobeedoo (Extra track on 12".).
7" Single: Released Feb '86, on Gyrate, by Gyrate Records. Catalogue no: **GY 2**
12" Single: Released Feb '86, on Gyrate, by Gyrate Records. Catalogue no: **12GY 2**

SHOUT
Tracks: / Shout / Heart and soul.
7" Single: Released Jul '86, on Mercury, by Phonogram Ltd. Deleted '87. Catalogue no: **BUD 1**

WE CHANGE THE WORLD
Tracks: / We change the world.
7" Single: Released 21 Nov '87, on Rage, Catalogue no: **BUD 4**

Curtie & The Boom Box

BLACK KISSES NEVER MAKE YOU BLUE
Tracks: / Black kisses never make you blue.
7" Single: Released Aug '85, on RCA, by BMG Records (UK). Catalogue no: **PB 40063**
12" Single: Released Aug '85, on RCA, by BMG Records (UK). Catalogue no: **PT 40064**

Curtin, Glen

TEARS ON THE TELEPHONE
Tracks: / Tears on the telephone / Good days, bad days.
Cassingle: Released '88, on Crashed (Ireland), by Crashed Records. Catalogue no: **CARC 1**
7" Single: Released Jul '81, on Crash, by Satril Records. Deleted '85. Catalogue no: **CRA 8**

WE WILL MAKE LOVE
Tracks: / We will make love / Turn it over.
7" Single: Released May '82, on Mint, by Emerald Records. Deleted '88. Catalogue no: **CHEW 64**

Curtis, Chantal

GET ANOTHER LOVE
Tracks: / Get another love.
7" Single: Released Jul '79, on Pye, Deleted Jul '82. Catalogue no: **7P 5003**

Curtis, Clem

BABY, NOW THAT I'VE FOUND YOU
Tracks: / Baby, now that I've found you.
7" Single: Released May '87, on Opium, by Opium Records. Catalogue no: **OPIN 001**
12" Single: Released May '87, on Opium, by Opium Records. Catalogue no: **OPINT 001**

BROADWAY
Tracks: / Broadway.
7" Single: Released Aug '84, on IDM, Catalogue no: **IDM 69**
12" Single: Released Aug '84, on IDM, Catalogue no: **IDMT 69**

Curtis, Debbie

CHARLIE SO GOOD
Tracks: / Charlie so good / Anything can shake your tree.
7" Single: Released May '86, on 42nd Street, by 42nd.Street Records. Catalogue no: **ST DEB 1**

Curtis, Joe

WHAT PEOPLE SAY
Tracks: / What people say.
7" Single: Released Aug '83, on PRT, by Castle Communications Records. Catalogue no: **CLIP 12 S**
12" Single: Released Aug '83, on PRT, by Castle Communications Records. Catalogue no: **CLIP 12**

Curtis, King

IT'S GREAT TO BE RICH (EP)
Tracks: / It's great to be rich.
12" Single: Released Jun '83, on Red Lightnin', by Red Lightning Records. Deleted Jun '89. Catalogue no: **RLEP 0045**

MEMPHIS SOUL STEW
Tracks: / Memphis soul stew / Sock it to 'em JB.
12" Single: Released Apr '80, on Atlantic, by WEA Records. Catalogue no: **ATM 10**

Curtis, Mac

GRANDADDY'S ROCKIN' YOU
Tracks: / Grandaddy's rockin' you.
7" Single: Released Jun '80, on Rollin' Rock, Catalogue no: **45 016**

HOT ROCK BOOGIE
Tracks: / Hot rock boogie.
7" Single: Released Jun '80, on Hot, Catalogue no: **HR 001**

HOW COME IT
Tracks: / How come it.
7" Single: Released Apr '80, on Rollin' Rock, Catalogue no: **45 018**

HOW LOW DO YOU FEEL?
Tracks: / How low do you feel ?.
7" Single: Released Jun '80, on Rollin' Rock, Catalogue no: **45 046**

PISTOL PACKIN' MAMA
Tracks: / Pistol packin' mama.
7" Single: Released Jun '80, on Rollin' Rock, Catalogue no: **45 043**

ROCK
Tracks: / Rock.
7" Single: Released Jun '80, on Rollin' Rock, Catalogue no: **45 026**

Curtis, Paul

NO MATTER HOW I TRY
Tracks: / No matter how I try / Invisible man.
7" Single: Released Apr '82, on RCA, by BMG Records (UK). Deleted Apr '85. Catalogue no: **RCA 215**

Curtis, Sonny

I THINK I'M IN LOVE
Tracks: / I think I'm in love.
7" Single: Released Jun '85, on Songworks, Deleted '87. Catalogue no: **S1**

NOW I'VE GOT A HEART OF GOLD
Tracks: / Now I've got a heart of gold.
7" Single: Released Oct '85, on Songworks, Deleted '87. Catalogue no: **S2**

Curtis, T.C

BODYSHAKE
Tracks: / Body shake / Body shake (part 2).
12" Single: Released Dec '81, on Groove PR, by Beggars Banquet Records. Catalogue no: **GP 112T**

DANCE TO THE BEAT
Tracks: / Dance to the beat.
12" Single: Released Mar '84, on Hot Melt, by Hot Melt Records. Catalogue no: **TC 002**

GET OUT OF MY LIFE
Tracks: / Get out of my life.
12" Single: Released 20 Feb '88, on Hot Melt, by Hot Melt Records. Catalogue no: **12 TCT 15**

JACKO
Tracks: / Jacko.
Note: Remix.
12" Single: Released Sep '87, on Hot Melt, by Hot Melt Records. Catalogue no: **TCT 14**
12" Single: Released Aug '87, on Hot Melt, by Hot Melt Records. Catalogue no: **12 TCT 14**
7" Single: Released Aug '87, on Hot Melt, by Hot Melt Records. Catalogue no: **7 TCT 14**

LET'S MAKE LOVE
Tracks: / Step by step / Dance to the beat (remix).
7" Single: Released Apr '86, on Hot Melt, by Hot Melt Records. Catalogue no: **TC 005**
12" Single: Released Jul '86, on Hot Melt, by Hot Melt Records. Catalogue no: **12 TC 006**
12" Single: Released Apr '86, on Hot Melt, by Hot Melt Records. Catalogue no: **12 TC 005**
7" Single: Released Jul '86, on Hot Melt, by Hot Melt Records. Catalogue no: **7 TC 006**

LOVE GOT ME ON A MERRY GO ROUND
Tracks: / Love got me on a merry go round / What's your problem / Reunited.
12" Single: Released May '87, on Hot Melt, by Hot Melt Records. Catalogue no: **12 TC 011**

PARTY DOWN
Tracks: / Party down.
7" Single: Released Nov '82, on Romantic, Catalogue no: **RR 001**

SLAVE OF LOVE
Tracks: / Slave of love / Slave of love (dub mix).
12" Single: Released Sep '86, on Hot Melt, by Hot Melt Records. Catalogue no: **12 TC 007**
7" Single: Released Sep '86, on Hot Melt, by Hot Melt Records. Catalogue no: **14 TC 007**

SLAVE OF LOVE - FINAL COUNTDOWN MIX
Tracks: / Let's make love.
12" Single: Released Jan '87, on Hot Melt, by Hot Melt Records. Catalogue no: **15 TC 007**

SLAVE OF LOVE - REMIX
Tracks: / Slave of love (remix) / Let's make love (remix) / Body shake remix.
12" Single: Released Nov '86, on Hot Melt, by Hot Melt Records. Catalogue no: **12 14TC 007**

STRANGER
Tracks: / Stranger.
12" Single: Released Dec '88, on Hot Melt, by Hot Melt Records. Catalogue no: **12TC 18**
7" Single: Released Dec '88, on Hot Melt, by Hot Melt Records. Catalogue no: **7TC 18**

TAKE IT EASY
Tracks: / Take it easy.
7" Single: Released Jun '85, on Virgin, by Virgin Records. Deleted '86. Catalogue no: **VS 775**
12" Single: Released Jun '85, on Virgin, by Virgin Records. Deleted '86. Catalogue no: **VS 775-12**

YOU CAN'T TOUCH MY LADY
Tracks: / You can't touch my lady.
7" Single: Released Jul '89, on Hot Melt, by Hot Melt Records. Catalogue no: **7 TC 23**
12" Single: Released Jul '89, on Hot Melt, by Hot Melt Records. Catalogue no: **12 TCT 23**

YOU SHOULD HAVE KNOWN BETTER
Tracks: / You should have known better / You should have known better (dub mix).
12" Single: Released Feb '85, on Virgin, by Virgin Records. Catalogue no: **VS 754-12**
7" Single: Released Feb '85, on Virgin, by Virgin Records. Deleted '85. Catalogue no: **VS 754**

Curtis, Winston

BE THANKFUL
Tracks: / Be thankful.
12" Single: Released Jul '84, on World International, Catalogue no: **WIR 12D 503**

Curve

LOVE GOES BY
Tracks: / Love goes by / Gaigy gogue go.
7" Single: Released Sep '83, on Bright, by Bright Records. Catalogue no: **BULB 4**
12" Single: Released Sep '83, on Bright, by Bright Records. Catalogue no: **BULBT 4**

Curved Air

Biographical details: This British group comprised, at the time of their greatest success, Ian Eyre, Sonja Kristina, Francis Monkman, Florian Pilkington and Darryl Way. Curved Air released their debut album *Air conditioning* in 1970. It went on to become a major success on the UK chart, reaching no.8 and logging 21 weeks on the survey. Thegroup was fronted by singer Sonja Kristina, who played an increasingly dominant role as the band's lifespan continued. Other key members were violinist Darryl Way and keyboards/guitarist Francis Monkman. Their music was a somewhat ponderous brand of artschool rock, a style that was popular at the time but upon which Curved Air were only able to capitalise for a short time. 1971 brought the band their only hit single, but a major hit nonetheless: *Back street luv* reached no. 4 on the UK charts, and stayed there for 12 weeks. Within 12 months they had chalked up two more British top 20 albums; but despite continued recording and touring, the band never hit the charts after 1972. The band folded in the late 1970's, and revival attempts failed. The most interesting change of personnel occurred when drummer Florian Pilkington was replaced by a US musician named Stewart Copeland, later of the Police. Monkman proceeded to become a founder member of Sky and Way issued a delightful single *Little Plum* in 1982, but it failed to chart. (Bob Macdonald, 15/2/85)
A UK art-school band, with vocalist Sonja Kristina, violinist Darryl Way, Francis Monkman on keyboards and guitar, Florian Pilkington on drums (replaced in the mid-'70s by Stewart Copeland, later in the Police). Their first album *Air conditioning* in 1970 was a UK top 10; they soon passed from the charts as art-school rock passed from fashion. Monkman became a founder member of Sky with guitarist John Williams. (Donald Clarke, April 1989)m.

BACK STREET LOVE
Tracks: / Back street love / It happened today.
7" Single: Released Aug '71, on Warner Bros., by WEA Records. Deleted Aug '74. Catalogue no: **K 16092**
7" Single: Released Mar '82, on Decca, by Decca Records. Deleted '88. Catalogue no: **F 13911**

RENEGADE
Tracks: / Renegade.
7" Single: Released Jul '84, on Pearl Key, Catalogue no: **PK 07350**

Cussick, Ian

MIGHTY LOVE (THE MIGHTY MIX)
Tracks: / Mighty love.
12" Single: Released Jan '89, on Joshua, Catalogue no: **151 004**

Cut Loose

HARD WAY TO LIVE
Tracks: / Hard way to live.
7" Single: Released Jun '84, on Western, by Arhoolie Records (USA). Catalogue no: **WEST 1**

Cut The Q

CRACK DOWN
Tracks: / Crack down (extended) / Crack down (edit) / Crack down (John Crossley mix) / Crack down (parkside mix).
12" Single: Released May '89, on Submission, by Submission Records. Catalogue no: **SUBX 011**

DARKNESS
Tracks: / Darkness.
12" Single: Released Nov '88, on Submission, by Submission Records. Catalogue no: **SUBX 09**

STEREO SHOW
Tracks: / Stereo show.
12" Single: Released Oct '88, on Submission, by Submission Records. Catalogue no: **SUBX 09**

Cut-Back

DOWN TOWN
Tracks: / Down town / Down town (version).
12" Single: Released 23 Apr '88, on Legacy, by Legacy Records. Catalogue no: **LGYT 63**

Cuthbertson, Iain

I'M DEFINITELY BACK
Tracks: / I'm definitely back.
7" Single: Released Jan '81, on Thumbs Up, Catalogue no: **TU 101**

Cutler, Adge

Biographical details: This British folk co-

CUTTY - NAUGHTY TIMES (Released on Cool Tempo)

median began his career as road manager to Mr. Acker Bilk's Paramount Jazz Band. By the late 60's he had developed a folk comedy routine based on the archetypal rural image of a Somerset farmer. Together with his backing group, The Wurzels, he reached no. 45 on the British singles chart in 1967 with *Drink up thy zider.* That same year also saw Cutler & The Wurzels reach no.38 on the UK album chart. Cutler never saw chart action again after '67, but remained a popular attraction on the folk club circuit until his tragic death in a car crash in 1974. Two years later, the Wurzels stepped into the limelight and were catapulted to chart stardom - their two UK smash singles dealt with the two favourite subjects of their deceased mentor - farming and cider drinking. (Bob Macdonald, 15/2/85).

DRINK UP THY ZIDER
Tracks: / Drink up thy zider.
7" Single: Released Feb '67, on Columbia, by EMI Records. Deleted Feb '70. Catalogue no: **DB 8081**

Cutler, Ivor

PEEL SESSIONS:IVOR CUTLER
12" Single: Released Feb '89, on Strange Fruit, by Strange Fruit Records. Catalogue no: **SFPS 068**

WOMAN OF THE WORLD
Tracks: / Woman of the world.
7" Single: Released Aug '83, on Rough Trade, by Rough Trade Records. Catalogue no: **RT 145**

Cutmaster DC

BROOKLYN'S IN MY HOUSE
Tracks: / Brooklyn's in my house.
7" Single: Released Jun '86, on Cherry Red, by Cherry Red Records. Deleted '87. Catalogue no: **DANCE 3**
12" Single: Released May '86, on Cherry Red, by Cherry Red Records. Catalogue no: **12 DANCE 3**

Cutting Crew

ANY COLOUR
Tracks: / Any colour / Fear of falling.
Note: Pic bag
7" Single: Released Apr '87, on Siren, by Virgin Records. Catalogue no: **SRN 47**
12" Single: Released Apr '87, on Siren, by Virgin Records. Deleted '89. Catalogue no: **SRN 47-12**

(BETWEEN A) ROCK AND A HARD PLACE
Tracks: / (Between a) rock and a hard place / Card house / (Between a) rock and a hard place (version) (12" only).
7" Single: Released 4 Aug '89, on Virgin, by Virgin Records. Catalogue no: **SRN 108**
12" Single: Released 4 Aug '89, on Virgin, by Virgin Records. Catalogue no: **SRNT 108**
CD 3": Released 4 Aug '89, on Virgin, by Virgin Records. Catalogue no: **SRNCD 108**

(I JUST) DIED IN YOUR ARMS
Tracks: / (I just) died in your arms (On all versions) / For the longest time (Not on CD) / (I just) died in your arms (remix) (CD & 12" only) / One for the mockingbird (the Shelly Yakus remix) (CD only) / Any colour (just for you) (CD only).
7" Single: Released Jul '86, on Siren, by Virgin Records. Catalogue no: **SIREN 21**
12" Single: Released Jul '86, on Siren, by Virgin Records. Catalogue no: **SIREN 21-12**
CD 3": Released '88, on Siren, by Virgin Records. Catalogue no: **CDT 25**

I'VE BEEN IN LOVE BEFORE
Tracks: / I've been in love before (On all versions) / Life in a dangerous time (On all versions) / I've been in love before (extended) (On 12" only) / Broadcast (excerpt) (On CD only) / Any colour (all for you) (On CD only) / Don't look back (On CD only).
CD 5": Released Aug '88, on Siren, by Virgin Records. Catalogue no: **SRNCD 29**
7" Pic: Released Nov '86, on Siren, by Virgin Records. Deleted '89. Catalogue no: **SIREN P 29**
7" Single: Released Oct '87, on Siren, by Virgin Records. Catalogue no: **SIREN 29**
12" Single: Released Oct '87, on Siren, by Virgin Records. Catalogue no: **SIREN 2912**

ONE FOR THE MOCKINGBIRD
Tracks: / Mirror and a blade (live) / One for the mockingbird / (I just) died in your arms (extended remix) / One for the mockingbird (extended remix).
CD 5": Released Mar '87, on Siren, by Virgin Records. Catalogue no: **SNIK 4012**
7" Single: Released Feb '87, on Siren, by Virgin Records. Deleted May '88. Catalogue no: **SIREN 40**
12" Single: Released Feb '87, on Siren, by Virgin Records. Deleted May '88. Catalogue no: **SIREN 40-12**

SCATTERING, THE (SINGLE)
Tracks: / Scattering, The.
7" Single: Released Oct '89, on Siren, by Virgin Records. Catalogue no: **SRN 118**

Cuttty

NAUGHTY TIMES **(see panel top left)**
Tracks: / Naughty times / Naughty times (instr.).
7" Single: Released '84, on Cool Tempo, by Chrysalis Records. Catalogue no: **COOL 105**

Cyan

REMEMBER THE BEACH GIRL
Tracks: / Remember the beach girl.
7" Single: Released Sep '83, on Rialto (1), by Rialto Records. Catalogue no: **RIA 22**

Cyberia

LET ME NOW
Tracks: / Let me now.
12" Single: Released 31 Jul '89, on Avenue, Catalogue no: **AVX 101**

Cybertron

MOVE
Tracks: / Move.
12" Single: Released Sep '89, on Cybertronics, Catalogue no: **12CYB 1**

Cybotron

TURNTABLES DO IT
Tracks: / Turntables do it.
Note: "A wicked remix of the club favourite, with all the classic licks from yester-year. High powered and guaranteed to turn heads." (Supertrack, June 1988)
7" Single: Released Jun '88, on Supertrack, Catalogue no: **WDSR 101**
12" Single: Released Jun '88, on Supertrack, Catalogue no: **WDTR 101**

Cyclone

PALISADES PARK
Tracks: / Palisades Park / Crazy haze.
7" Single: Released Jan '80, on Magnet, by WEA Records. Deleted Jan '83. Catalogue no: **MAG 159**

Cymande

BRA
Tracks: / Bra.
12" Single: Released Nov '87, on J.D. (USA), Catalogue no: **JD 777**

Cymbal, Johnny

Biographical details: This American singer, who hailed from Cleveland, Ohio, hit the UK and US charts in 1963 with *Mr Bass man,* a novelty single. This was a tribute to the unsung heroes of 50's rock and roll - the bass singers, whose meaningless back-up phrases such as "bom pom pom" had enhanced countless hit records over the past decade. It was appropriate, therefore, that the bass role on Cymbal's hit was performed by one such hero, Ronald Bright; he had sung bass with the Cadillacs and on Barry Mann's immortal *Who put the bomp. Mr Bass man* reached no.16 in the States and no.24 in Britain. After thai one-off success, Johnny Cymbal was quickly forgottn by the public and, it seems, by the man himself, for when he reappeared on the US chart in 1969, he was called Derek. *Cinnamon* took Derek to no.11 in the States, but again it was a one-off. He then decided to concentrate on record production as opposed to releasing discs himself. (Bob Macdonald, 15/2/85).

MR BASSMAN (OLD GOLD)
Tracks: / Mr. Bass Man.
7" Single: Released '82, on Old Gold, by Old Gold Records. Catalogue no: **OG 9165**

MR BASSMAN (SINGLE)
Tracks: / Mr. Bass man.
7" Single: Released Mar '63, on London American, Deleted Mar '66. Catalogue no **HLR 9682**

Cymone, Andre

SURVIVIN' IN THE 80'S (SINGLE)
Tracks: / Survivin' in the 80's / What are we doin'.
7" Single: Released Jul '87, on CBS, by CBS Records. Catalogue no: **A 4328**
12" Single: on CBS, by CBS Records. Catalogue no: **TA 4328**

Cyncis

ROCK APOCALYPSE
Tracks: / Rock apocalypse.
7" Single: Released '84, on Stinkfoot Catalogue no: **SMSI 1**

Cyril Trotts to Bogna

TWO TRIPES
Tracks: / Two tripes / Yu rats / Weirdos Santa is an astronaut / They're coming t take me away.
7" Single: Released '84, on Yowsa Yowsa Catalogue no: **YY 1**
12" Single: Released '84, on Yows Yowsa, Catalogue no: **12YY 1**

Cyrnai

CHARRED BLOSSOMS
Tracks: / Charred blossoms.
12" Single: on Mind Matter, by Mind Ma ter Records. Catalogue no: **THOUGHT 3**

Czukay, Holger

COOL IN THE POOL
Tracks: / Cool in the pool / Oh Lord.
7" Single: Released '83, on EMI, by E Records. Catalogue no: **EMI 5005**

D

The following information was taken from the Music Master database on October 20th, 1989.

D, Debbie

HIT THE RAP JACK
Tracks: / Hit the rap Jack / Hit the rap Jack (version).
7" Single: Released Feb '89, on Debut, by Skratch Records. Catalogue no: **DEBT 3063**
12" Single: Released Feb '89, on Debut, by Skratch Records. Catalogue no: **DEBTX 3063**

SOUND YOUR FUNKY HORN
Tracks: / Sound your funky horn.
7" Single: Released 29 Aug '89, on Debut, by Skratch Records. Catalogue no: **DEBT 3080**
12" Single: Released 29 Aug '89, on Debut, by Skratch Records. Catalogue no: **DEBTX 3080**

D, Dolbie

ACID MANIA
Tracks: / Acid mania / Acid mania (instrumental).
12" Single: Released Jan '89, on Desire, by Desire Records. Catalogue no: **WANTX 14**

LOUD 'N' CLEAR
Tracks: / Loud 'n' clear / Loud 'n' clear (dub).
12" Single: Released May '89, on Desire, by Desire Records. Catalogue no: **WANTX 11**

D, Doris

SHINE UP
Tracks: / Shine up / Just you and me.
7" Single: Released Apr '81, on Carrere. Deleted Apr '84. Catalogue no: **CAR 187**

D, Heavy

CHUNKY BUT FUNKY
Tracks: / Chunky but funky / Chunky but funky (inst).
7" Single: Released Jul '87, on MCA, by MCA Records. Catalogue no: **MCA 1173**
12" Single: Released Jul '87, on MCA, by MCA Records. Catalogue no: **MCAT 1173**

WE GOT OUR OWN THANG
Tracks: / We got our own thang.
7" Single: Released Jul '89, on MCA, by MCA Records. Catalogue no: **MCA 23942**

D J Trotter

HOT TO TROTT
Tracks: / Hot to trott / Hot to trott (Inst.).
7" Single: Released Oct '88, on Bold Reprive (2), by Bold Reprive Records. Catalogue no: **7BRM 029**
12" Single: Released Oct '88, on Bold Reprive (2), by Bold Reprive Records. Catalogue no: **BRMT 029**

D, Lenny & Tommy

EVERYTHING BAMBOO
Tracks: / Everything bamboo / Everything bamboo (club music edit) / Everything bamboo (dub music edit).
7" Single: Released May '87, on Magnetic Dance, by Magnet Records. Deleted Jan '88. Catalogue no: **MAGD 2**
12" Single: Released May '87, on Magnetic Dance, by Magnet Records. Deleted Jun '88. Catalogue no: **MAGDT 2**

D Rail

STATION OF LOVE
Tracks: / Station of love / Station of love (instrumental).
7" Single: Released Feb '89, on Citybeat, by Beggars Banquet Records. Catalogue no: **CBE 736**
12" Single: Released Feb '89, on Citybeat, by Beggars Banquet Records. Catalogue no: **CBE 1236**

D., Shan

EVERY LITTLE STEP
Tracks: / Every little step.
12" Single: Released Oct '89, on Gunshot, Catalogue no: **CSNC 005**

D, Tas

UP & AT OM!
Tracks: / Up and at om! / They're coming to take me away.
7" Single: Released Jun '88, on Ink, by Red Flame Records. Catalogue no: **KN1 0A**
12" Single: Released Sep '88, on Deep Cut, Catalogue no: **KNI-OA**

D & The Rockets

PURE ROCK'N'ROLL
Tracks: / Pure rock 'n' roll.
7" Single: Released Oct '81, on Deb, by Deb Records. Catalogue no: **DEB 101**

D To The K

DIRECT AND LIVE
Tracks: / Direct and live.
12" Single: Released Nov '88, on BPM, Catalogue no: **BP 12004**

D & V

SNARE
Tracks: / Snare.
12" Single: Released Feb '87, on One Little Indian, by One Little Indian Records. Catalogue no: **12TP 4**

D, Vicky

THIS BEAT IS MINE
Tracks: / This beat is mine.
7" Single: Released Mar '82, on Virgin, by Virgin Records. Deleted Mar '85. Catalogue no: **VS 486**

Da Biz

ON THE BEACH
Tracks: / On the beach / This is no audition.
7" Single: Released Sep '80, on Sire, by Sire Records. Deleted '83. Catalogue no: **SIR 4045**

Da Costa, Paulino

TAJ MAHAL
Tracks: / Taj Mahal.
12" Single: Released Sep '84, on Pablo Jazz (USA), by Pablo Records (USA). Catalogue no: **5155**

Da Davo

DA DAVO
Tracks: / Da Davo.
12" Single: Released 12 Jun '87, on Play It Again Sam(Belgium), by Play It Again Sam (Belgium). Catalogue no: **BIAS 061**

Da Posse

IN THE HEAT OF THE NIGHT
Tracks: / In the heat of the night.
7" Single: Released Oct '88, on Future Records (USA), Catalogue no: **FR 1**

Da Rock

ROCK PARTY
Tracks: / Rock party / Smoke on the water.
7" Single: Released Aug '87, on DMC, Catalogue no: **DECK 7**
12" Single: Released Aug '87, on DMC, Deleted May '89. Catalogue no: **DECK 127**

D'Abo, Mike

LOVING ON A SHOESTRING
Tracks: / Loving on a shoestring / Thank you.
7" Single: Released Mar '87, on President, by President Records. Catalogue no: **PT 559**

TOMORROW'S TROUBADOR (SINGLE)
Tracks: / Tomorrow's troubador / Velvet glove.
7" Single: Released Apr '88, on President, by President Records. Catalogue no: **PT 570**

Dactyl, Terry

ON A SATURDAY NIGHT
Tracks: / On a Saturday night.
7" Single: Released Jan '73, on UK, by UK Records. Deleted Jan '76. Catalogue no: **UK21**

SEASIDE SHUFFLE
Tracks: / Seaside shuffle.
7" Single: Released Jul '72, on UK, by UK Records. Deleted Jul '75. Catalogue no: **UK 5**

D.A.D.

SLEEPING MY DAY AWAY
Tracks: / Sleeping my day away / I will.
CD 5": Released Sep '89, on WEA, by WEA Records. Catalogue no: **W 2775CD**
7" Single: Released Sep '89, on WEA, by WEA Records. Catalogue no: **W 2775**
12" Single: Released Sep '89, on WEA, by WEA Records. Catalogue no: **W 2775T**

Dada

PEARL
Tracks: / Pearl.
12" Single: Released Jan '87, on Dadisk, Catalogue no: **DADISK 1**

Daddy Freddie

AGONY JOCKEY
Tracks: / Agony jockey.
12" Single: Released Sep '89, on Blacker Dread, Catalogue no: **BD 8914**

NOW OR NEVER
Tracks: / Now or never.
12" Single: Released May '89, on Dance Vibes, Catalogue no: **DV 002**

POWER OF THE TRINITY
Tracks: / Power of the trinity.
7" Single: Released 21 Apr '89, on Briggie C, Catalogue no: **BC 005T**

Daddy Lilly

ONE OF A KIND
Tracks: / One of a kind.
12" Single: Released Sep '89, on Jetstar, by Jetstar Records. Catalogue no: **SJT 01**

SHUFFLE & DEAL
Tracks: / Shuffle & deal.
12" Single: Released Jan '89, on Redman International, Catalogue no: **VPRED 120**

Daddy Lizard

DEBI DEBI GIRL
Tracks: / Debi debi girl.
12" Single: Released Jul '88, on Jammy's, Catalogue no: **VPRD 321**

INACULATOR
Tracks: / Inaculator.
12" Single: Released Feb '89, on Digital B., Catalogue no: **VPRD 402**

JUMP SPREAD OUT
Tracks: / Jump spread out.
12" Single: Released Jul '88, on Jammy's, Catalogue no: **VPRD 323**

MOVE YUH BODY
Tracks: / Move yuh body.
12" Single: Released Jan '89, on Redman International, Catalogue no: **VPRED 121**

PACK UP AND LEAVE
Tracks: / Pack up and leave.
12" Single: Released Dec '88, on Germaine, Catalogue no: **DGT 45**

RUN GIRL RUN
Tracks: / Run girl run.
12" Single: Released Apr '88, on Techniques, Catalogue no: **WRT 28**

Daddy Rusty

FEEL SO GOOD
Tracks: / Feel so good.
12" Single: Released Sep '84, on UK Bubblers, by Greensleeves Records. Deleted '88. Catalogue no: **UKMC 3**

Daddy Sandy

RIDDLE BUBBLE
Tracks: / Riddle bubble / Vibes.
12" Single: Released Dec '84, on UK Bubblers, by Greensleeves Records. Deleted '88. Catalogue no: **UKMC 3**

Daemion

DIZZY
Tracks: / Dizzy / Human arcade.
7" Single: Released Feb '83, on Si Jenn, by Si Jenn Records. Catalogue no: **MSP 1001**

DAF

ABSOLUTELY BODY CONTROL
Tracks: / Absolutely body control.
12" Single: Released Aug '85, on Illuminated, Catalogue no: **ILL 6212**

BROTHERS
Tracks: / Brothers.
12" Single: Released Oct '85, on Illuminated, Catalogue no: **12LEV 65**
7" Single: Released Oct '85, on Illuminated, Catalogue no: **LEV 65**

DER RAUBER UND DER PRINZ
Tracks: / Der rauber und der prinz / Der Mussolini.
7" Single: Released Oct '80, on Mute, by Mute Records. Catalogue no: **MUTE 11**
12" Single: Released Oct '80, on Virgin, by Virgin Records. Catalogue no: **VS 418-12**

GOLDENES SPIELZEUG
Tracks: / Goldenes Spielziug.
12" Single: Released Nov '81, on Virgin, by Virgin Records. Deleted Nov '84. Catalogue no: **VS 44812**

KEBAB DREAMS
Tracks: / Kebab dreams / Violence.
7" Single: Released Mar '80, on Mute, by Mute Records. Catalogue no: **MUTE 005**

Dagaband

SECOND TIME AROUND
Tracks: / Second time around.
7" Single: Released Mar '83, on MHM, Catalogue no: **AM 094**

TEST FLIGHT
Tracks: / Test flight / Images.
7" Single: Released Oct '80, on Rutland, by Rutland Records. Deleted Oct '83. Catalogue no: **RX 100**

Daggermen

INTRODUCING THE DAGGERMEN
7" EP: Released Feb '86, on Empire Records, Catalogue no: **UPW 258 J**

D'Agostino, Frankie

FRANKIE
Tracks: / Frankie / Yankee doodle boy.
Note: Charity record; All proceeds to the Malcolm Sargeant cancer fund
7" Single: Released Jul '88, on Dazzle, by Dazzle Records. Catalogue no: **DAZ 003**

Daho, Etienne

STAY WITH ME
Tracks: / Stay with me / Bleu comme toi.
7" Single: Released 17 Apr '89, on Virgin, by Virgin Records. Catalogue no: **VS 1180**

Daily, E.G.

MIND OVER MATTER
Tracks: / Mind over matter / Love in the shadows.
7" Single: Released May '88, on A&M, by A&M Records. Catalogue no: **AM 436**
12" Single: Released May '88, on A&M, by A&M Records. Catalogue no: **AMY 436**
12" Single: Released Aug '87, on A&M (USA), by A&M Records (USA). Catalogue no: **SP 12246**

SAY IT, SAY IT
Tracks: / Say it, say it.
7" Single: Released Jun '86, on A&M, by A&M Records. Deleted '88. Catalogue no: **AM 313**
12" Single: Released Jun '86, on A&M, by A&M Records. Catalogue no: **AMY 313**

Daintees

ROLL ON SUMMERTIME
Tracks: / Roll on summertime.
7" Single: Released Jun '84, on Kitchenware, by Kitchenware Records. Deleted '86. Catalogue no: **SK 3**

RUNNING WATER
Tracks: / Running water.
7" Single: Released May '86, on Kitchenware, by Kitchenware Records. Catalogue no: **SKEP 1**

THERE COMES A TIME
Tracks: / There comes a time.
7" Single: on London Records, by London Records. Deleted May '89. Catalogue no: **SK 34**

Daisy Hill..

SPRAYCAN

Tracks: / Spraycan.
12" Single: Released Jun '89, on Lakeland, Catalogue no: **LKND 009**

Dakotas

CRUEL SEA, THE
Tracks: / Cruel sea.
7" Single: Released Jul '63, on Parlophone, by EMI Records. Deleted Jul '66. Catalogue no: **R 5044**

Dakrash

WASN'T I GOOD TO YA?
Tracks: / Wasn't I good to ya?* / Wasn't I good to ya? (bonus beats) (on 12" only) / Wasn't I good to ya? (12" mix) (on 12" only) / Wasn't I good to ya? (dub) (on 12" and CD only) / Wasn't I good to ya? (edit) (on 12" and CD only).
Note: *Tracks on 7in single. **Tracks on 12in single.
7" Single: Released 31 May '88, on EMI, by EMI Records. Deleted Nov '88. Catalogue no: **CL 497**
12" Single: Released 31 May '88, on EMI, by EMI Records. Deleted Nov '88. Catalogue no: **12CL 497**

Dalbello, Lisa

GONNA GET CLOSER TO YOU
Tracks: / Gonna get closer to you / Guilty by association.
7" Single: Released May '84, on Capitol, by EMI Records. Deleted '88. Catalogue no: **CL 332**
12" Single: Released May '84, on Capitol, by EMI Records. Deleted '88. Catalogue no: **12CL 332**

TALK TO ME
Tracks: / Talk to me / Talk to me (remix) / Imagination.
7" Single: Released Mar '88, on Capitol, by EMI Records. Deleted 31 Jul '88. Catalogue no: **CL 478**
12" Single: Released Mar '88, on Capitol, by EMI Records. Deleted 31 Jul '88. Catalogue no: **12CL 478**

TANGO
Tracks: / Tango / Tango dance mix / Tango (dub mix) / Why stand alone.
7" Single: Released Oct '87, on Capitol, by EMI Records. Deleted 31 Jul '88. Catalogue no: **CL 467**
12" Single: Released Oct '87, on Capitol, by EMI Records. Deleted 31 Jul '88. Catalogue no: **12CL 467**

Dale, Dick

PICK AND PLAY
Tracks: / Pick and play / Wedge, The / Hava nagila / King of the surf guitar, The.
7" Single: Released Oct '88, on Pulchwave, Catalogue no: **PSC 666**
12" Single: Released Oct '88, on Pulchwave, Catalogue no: **12PSC 666**
CD 3": Released Oct '88, on Pulchwave, Catalogue no: **PSCD 666**

Dale, Gina

GIVE ME BACK MY LOVE
Tracks: / Give me back my love / I want more love.
7" Single: Released Mar '82, on WEA, by WEA Records. Deleted '83. Catalogue no: **K 18742**

Dale & Grace

Biographical details: Dale Houston and Grace Broussard were an American vocal duo who shot to fame when both were aged 19. They came from Louisiana, and both had gained experienced by working separately in local bistros before teaming up. The record that catapulted the pair to stardom was 1963's *I'm leaving it up to you*, a remake of a late Fifties R&B hit by Don & Dewey. Dale & Grace's rendition was aimed directly at the pop market, but nevertheless retained a slightly soulful feel. It reached the US No.1 slot in November '63, and was in pole position at the time of the assassination of President Kennedy - the single thus has an indelible historical association in the minds of many Americans; it was toppled from the top by *Dominique* by the Singing Nun, a telling sign of the nation's mood in the aftermath of the shooting. In Beatles-dominated Britain, Dale & Grace could only manage a No.42 placing.
The duo reached No.8 on the US chart with their follow-up *Stop and think it over*, thus proving that they were no One Hit Wonder. However, they have yet to prove that they are no Two Hit Wonder, and quickly faded into obscurity. Donny and Marie Osmond, another starry-eyed teenage duo, revived *I'm leaving it up to you* in 1974 and took it to No.4 on the American listings; in Britain, where the song was unfamiliar to most ears, the new version hit No.2. (Bob MacDonald, 2nd March 1985).

I'M LEAVING IT UP TO YOU
Tracks: / I'm leaving it all up to you.
7" Single: Released Jan '64, on London Records, by London Records. Deleted Jan '67. Catalogue no: **HL 9807**

Dale, Jackie

OH WHY
Tracks: / Oh why / Rhythm.
12" Single: Released Jun '82, on Freedom Sounds, Catalogue no: **FS 0025**

Dale, Jim

BE MY GIRL
Tracks: / Be my girl.
7" Single: Released Oct '57, on Parlophone, by EMI Records. Deleted Oct '60. Catalogue no: **R 4343**

CRAZY DREAM
Tracks: / Crazy dreams.
7" Single: Released Jan '58, on Parlophone, by EMI Records. Deleted Jan '61. Catalogue no: **R 4376**

JUST BORN
Tracks: / Just born.
7" Single: Released Jan '58, on Parlophone, by EMI Records. Deleted Jan '61. Catalogue no: **R 4376**

SUGARTIME
Tracks: / Sugartime.
7" Single: Released Mar '58, on Parlophone, by EMI Records. Deleted Mar '61. Catalogue no: **R 4402**

Dale, Just

UNTIL YOU COME BACK TO ME
Tracks: / Until you come back to me / Duke, the.
12" Single: Released Feb '86, on Ariwa Sounds, by Ariwa Sounds. Catalogue no: **CF 002**

Dale, Ronnie

YIELD NOT TO TEMPTATION
Tracks: / Yield not to temptation.
7" Single: Released Jan '82, on Coochly St., Deleted '88. Catalogue no: **MS 3**

Dale Sisters

MY SUNDAY BABY
Tracks: / My Sunday baby.
7" Single: Released Nov '61, on Ember (1), by Bulldog Records (UK). Deleted Nov '64. Catalogue no: **S 140**

Dalek 1

DALEK I LOVE YOU
Tracks: / Dalek I love you / Happy / This is my uniform.
7" Single: Released Apr '80, on Back Door (Holland), Deleted '82. Catalogue no: **DOOR 4**

Dalek I Love You

AMBITION
Tracks: / Ambition / (I am) hot person.
7" Single: Released Sep '83, on Korova, by WEA Records. Catalogue no: **KOW 29**
12" Single: Released Sep '83, on Korova, by WEA Records. Catalogue no: **KOW 29T**

HEARTBEAT
Tracks: / Heartbeat / Astronauts have landed on the moon.
7" Single: Released Feb '81, on Back Door (Holland), Deleted Feb '84. Catalogue no: **DOOR 10**

HOLIDAY IN DISNEYLAND
Tracks: / Holiday in Disneyland.
7" Single: Released Jul '82, on Korova, by WEA Records. Catalogue no: **KOW 25**
12" Single: Released Jul '82, on Korova, by WEA Records. Catalogue no: **KOW 25T**

Daley, Derek

YOUR LOVE
Tracks: / Your love / Kingston Town.
12" Single: Released Jul '86, on Viking (1), Catalogue no: **VK 006**

Daley, Martin

ARCHITECTS OF TIME (SINGLE)
Tracks: / Architects of time / Structure.
7" Single: Released Feb '89, on PRT, by Castle Communications Records. Catalogue no: **7SLTD 004**

Daley, Tracey

EMOTION
Tracks: / Emotion.
12" Single: Released Jun '89, on Strike Force, Catalogue no: **SFD 002**

GUILTY
Tracks: / Guilty.
12" Single: Released Jun '88, on Uptempo, Catalogue no: **TEMP 025**

Dalis

ROCK STEADY
Tracks: / Rock steady.
12" Single: Released Sep '87, on Trax, by Filmtrax Records. Deleted Oct '87. Catalogue no: **TX 144**

Dali's Car

JUDGEMENT IS THE MIRROR, THE
Tracks: / Judgement is the mirror, The / High places.
7" Pic: Released Oct '84, on Paradox, by Virgin Records. Deleted '89. Catalogue no: **DOXY 1**
7" Single: Released Oct '84, on Paradox, by Virgin Records. Catalogue no: **DOX 1**
12" Single: Released Oct '84, on Paradox, by Virgin Records. Deleted '89. Catalogue no: **DOX 112**

Dallas T.R.

WHO SHOT J.R. EWING
Tracks: / Who shot J.R. Ewing / Oil bubble.
7" Single: Released Jun '80, on Young Blood, by Young Blood Records. Deleted Jun '83. Catalogue no: **YB 90**

D'Almaine, Michael

LOVE FOR LOVE
Tracks: / Love for love.
7" Single: Released Jul '83, on Monarch, by Monarch Records. Catalogue no: **MON 042**

Dalmations

DALMATIONS WITH VARIOUS ARTISTS(EP)
12" Single: Released Dec '82, on Dog Rock, by Dog Rock Records. Deleted '88. Catalogue no: **SD 102**

Dalton, Guy

NIGHT PEOPLE
Tracks: / Night people.
12" Single: Released Aug '83, on Magic (1), by Submarine Records. Catalogue no: **MAGIC 127**

YOU CAN DO MAGIC
Tracks: / You can do magic.
7" Single: Released Feb '84, on Magic (1), by Submarine Records. Catalogue no: **MAGIC 11**

Dalton, Lacy J

Biographical details: A country/rock singer and songwriter, born in 1948. She began as a folk/protest singer in the late '60's; moved to the West Coast in the early '70's and was lead singer with a psychedelic band Office using the name Jill Corston; a demo reached Billy Sherrill in Nashville in 1979 and she signed to CBS. Her gravelly bluesy voice and self-penned songs won a big following.*Can't run away from your heart* in 1985 was followed by *Highway diner*, including *Can't see me without you* written by Jonathan Cain of Heart; the album is described as populist rock like that of Bruce Springsteen. (Donald Clarke, April 1989).

FEEDIN' THE FIRE
Tracks: / Feedin' the fire / Golden memories.
7" Single: Released Jul '81, on CBS, by CBS Records. Deleted '84. Catalogue no: **A 1468**

HARD TIMES (SINGLE)
Tracks: / Hard times / Old soldier.
7" Single: Released Nov '80, on CBS, by CBS Records. Deleted Nov '83. Catalogue no: **CBS 9322**

Daltrey, Roger

Biographical details: This British singer, born and raised in London, became a household name in 1965 as lead vocalist with the Who. That group, respected as one of the world's greatest ever rock bands, had made Daltrey and his three Who colleagues living legends by 1973, the year that Daltrey launched his solo recording career. The singer's plan was to develop a subsidiary course of work that would allow him to explore material from writers other than the Who's songwriter, Pete Townshend. The first - and biggest - solo hit could not have fulfilled that aim more effectively: *Giving it all away*, a plaintive but appealing ballad, was co-written by the unknown Leo Sayer as one of Britain's leading pop singer/songwriters. Daltrey's recording was produced by Sayer's manager, the ex-pop star Adam Faith. The follow-up single was, somewhat surprising, an orchestral version of *I'm free*, a song that had originally surfaced on the Who's famous *Tommy* concept. Daltrey continued to release sporadic solo records, but they received a generally lukewarm reaction, the only exceptions being 1975's *Ride a rock horse* album (No.14 in UK) and 1980's *Without your love* single (No.20 in US, his only significant solo success there).
More illustrious than his solo singing career was his move into the acting profession. His first film role was the title part in Ken Russell's over-the-top 1975 adaption of *Tommy*. Other notable movies were *Lisztomania* and the title role in *McVicar*, the true story of an ex-criminal. Daltrey intensified his acting career when the Who folded in the early Eighties, including such parts as a role in a TV production of *The beggar's opera*. (2nd March 1985, Bob MacDonald)

AFTER THE FIRE
Tracks: / After the fire.
7" Single: Released Sep '85, on 10 Records, by Virgin Records. Deleted May '88. Catalogue no: **TEN 69**
12" Single: Released Sep '85, on 10 Records, by Virgin Records. Deleted May '88. Catalogue no: **TEN 69-12**

DON'T LET THE SUN GO DOWN ON ME
Tracks: / Don't let the sun go down on me / Heart has its reasons / Don't let the sun go down on me (ext version) (On 12" only).
7" Single: Released Jul '87, on 10 Records, by Virgin Records. Catalogue no: **TEN 202**
12" Single: Released Jul '87, on 10 Records, by Virgin Records. Catalogue no: **TENT 202**

FREE ME
Tracks: / Free me.
7" Single: Released Aug '80, on Polydor, by Polydor Ltd. Deleted Aug '83. Catalogue no: **2001 980**

GIVING IT ALL AWAY
Tracks: / Giving it all away.
7" Single: Released Apr '73, on Track, by Polydor Ltd. Deleted Apr '77. Catalogue no: **2094 110**

HEARTS ON FIRE
Tracks: / Hearts on fire / Lover's storm / Quicksilver lightning (Extra track on 12").
7" Single: Released 20 Jun '87, on 10 Records, by Virgin Records. Deleted May '88. Catalogue no: **TEN 147**
12" Single: Released 20 Jun '87, on 10 Records, by Virgin Records. Deleted May '88. Catalogue no: **TENT 147**

I'M FREE
Tracks: / I'm free.
7" Single: Released Aug '73, on Ode, Deleted Aug '76. Catalogue no: **ODS 66302**

PRIDE YOU HIDE, THE
Tracks: / Pride you hide, The / Break out / Don't talk to strangers* / Don't talk to strangers (live) / Pictures of Lily (live) (*Pictures of Lily (live) on 12" only.).
Note: 86
7" Set: Released May '86, on 10 Records, by Virgin Records. Deleted May '88. Catalogue no: **TEND 103**
7" Single: Released May '86, on 10 Records, by Virgin Records. Deleted '86. Catalogue no: **TEN 103**
12" Single: Released May '86, on 10 Records, by Virgin Records. Deleted '89. Catalogue no: **TENT 103**

UNDER A RAGING MOON (SINGLE)
Tracks: / Under a raging moon.
7" Set: Released Feb '86, on 10 Records, by Virgin Records. Deleted '86. Catalogue no: **TEND 81**
7" Single: Released Mar '86, on 10 Records, by Virgin Records. Deleted Mar '89. Catalogue no: **TEN 81**
12" Single: Released '87, on 10 Records, by Virgin Records. Deleted May '88. Catalogue no: **TENG 8112**

WALKING IN MY SLEEP
Tracks: / Walking in my sleep / Gimme some lovin' / Somebody told me.
7" Single: Released Feb '84, on WEA, by WEA Records. Catalogue no: **U 9686**
12" Single: Released Feb '84, on WEA, by WEA Records. Catalogue no: **U 9686 T**

WITHOUT YOUR LOVE
Tracks: / Without your love / Say it ain't so, Joe.
7" Single: Released Oct '80, on Polydor, by Polydor Ltd. Deleted Oct '83. Catalogue no: **POSP 181**

WRITTEN ON THE WIND
Tracks: / Written on the wind.
7" Single: Released May '77, on Polydor, by Polydor Ltd. Deleted May '80. Catalogue no: **2121 319**

Damage

CROWDED COMPANY
Tracks: / Crowded company.
7" Single: Released Jan '83, on Danger, Deleted '87. Catalogue no: **DANGER 01**

Damaris

WHAT ABOUT MY LOVE?
Tracks: / What about my love / Hooray for love.
7" Single: Released Mar '84, on CBS, by CBS Records. Catalogue no: **A 4172**
12" Single: Released Mar '84, on CBS, by CBS Records. Catalogue no: **TA 4172**

Damascus

OPEN YOUR EYES
Tracks: / Open your eyes.
12" Single: Released Apr '85, on Damascus, Catalogue no: **DAMA 1**

Damian

TIME WARP II
Tracks: / Time warp II / Fight for what you believe.
7" Single: Released Aug '88, on Jive, by Zomba Records. Catalogue no: **JIVE 182**
7" Single: Released Dec '87, on Jive, by Zomba Records. Catalogue no: **JIVE 160**
12" Single: Released Aug '88, on Jive, by Zomba Records. Catalogue no: **JIVET 182**
12" Single: Released Dec '87, on Jive, by Zomba Records. Catalogue no: **JIVET 160**

TIME WARP, THE
Tracks: / Time warp.
Cassingle: Released Jul '89, on Jive, by Zomba Records. Catalogue no: **JIVEC 209**
7" Single: Released Jul '89, on Jive, by Zomba Records. Catalogue no: **JIVE 209**
7" Single: Released Mar '86, on Sedition, by Sedition Records. Catalogue no: **EDIT 3311**
12" Single: Released Jul '89, on Jive, by Zomba Records. Catalogue no: **JIVET 209**
12" Single: Released Mar '86, on Sedition, by Sedition Records. Catalogue no: **EDITL 3311**

Damian, Michael

ROCK ON
Tracks: / Rock on.
7" Single: Released May '89, on Cypress, by Sonet Records. Catalogue no: **YY 5005**

Damned

Biographical details: The first and most important line-up of this British rock group was Captain Sensible, Brian James, Rat Scabies and Dave Vanian.
The above listed quarted were one of the five most important bands of the 1976/7 New Wave/punk explosion, together with the Sex Pistols, The Clash, The Jam and The Buzzcocks. The Damned had the distinction of being the first to sign a recording contract and the first to release an Lp. They were formed in May 1976 and signed with the newly formed independent record label, Stiff Records, in September of that year. Their first two singles, *New rose* and *Neat neat neat*, were classic punk tracks and were prime examples of the anarchistic new music that was in the process of turning the British music business on its head. The group's debut album *Damned Damned Damned*, issued in February '77, was produced by Nick Lowe. Its songs and style were uncompromising and furiously energetic, providing a perfect antidote for those bored by the sophisticated rock that had become prevalent in the early and mid-Seventies. Like the singles, it was not a major seller, largely because of the fact that punk was rejected by the bulk of the radio establishment. However, the Lp and the band's frenetic live shows quickly earned the Damned a huge street reputation.
The Damned created so much excitement in their first year of existence, that it was impossible for them to maintain the momentum. Their career quickly went off the rails. The disastrous decision to enlist Pink Floyd's Nick Mason, a member of the 'old wave', as producer of their November '77 album *Music for pleasure*, resulted in a disintegration of their street credibility and the total collapse of their sales prospects. Stiff Records dropped the group, and they eventually signed with Chiswick Records in early '79 after a confusing series of personnel changes, departures and reappearances. The most important of these were the departure of guitarist Brian James, and the transfer of Captain Sensible from bass to guitar. Scabies, Sensible and Vanian soldiered on into the Eighties with a variety of bassists, sometimes releasing great energetic records but never quite recapturing their original music. The most notable releases of this later period were 1979's *Love song* (their only UK Top 20 single), 1984's *Thanks for the night* single and 1980's *The black album*, their first foray into the British Lp Top 30. Like their bass player the band's record label was an ever-changing phenomenon. In 1982 Captain Sensible launched a solo subsidiary career, and immediately achieved a British No.1 single with an unlikely version of Rodgers & Hammerstein's *Happy talk*. Further pop singles - 1982's *Wot!* and 1984's double A sided hit *Glad it's all over/Damned on 75* - brought the good Captain the sort of chart success that was nearly always out of the reach of his group the Damned. (Bob MacDonald, 3rd March 1985)
The UK punk band, formed in 1976 by vocalist Dave Vanian, guitarist Brian James, bassist Captain Sensible (Ray Burns), and drummer Rat Scabies (Chris Miller). They played at the legendary punk festival at London's 100 Club and became the first Punks first in genre to release an album, to have a top 30 hit and to tour the USA. James was the band's writer; he left in 1978 (and was with Lords of the New Church in 1982); Sensible's solo career began in 1982; he left in '83. Meanwhile only Vanian and Scabies were constants; as Punks they were never serious rivals to the Sex Pistols or Clash, but continued finding fans. (Donald Clarke, April 1989).

ALONE AGAIN OR
Tracks: / Psychomania (Included on 12") / Eloise (Included in double pack.) / Alone again or / In dulce decorum.
7" Set: Released Apr '87, on MCA, by MCA Records. Catalogue no: **DGRIM 7**
7" Single: Released Apr '87, on MCA, by MCA Records. Catalogue no: **GRIM 7**
12" Single: Released Apr '87, on MCA, by MCA Records. Catalogue no: **GRIMT 7**

ANYTHING (SINGLE)
Tracks: / Anything / Year of the jackal, The / Thanks for the night (12" only).
10" single: Released Nov '86, on MCA, by MCA Records. Catalogue no: **GRIMX 5**
7" Single: Released Nov '86, on MCA, by MCA Records. Catalogue no: **GRIM 5**
12" Single: Released Nov '86, on MCA, by MCA Records. Catalogue no: **GRIMT 5**

DOZEN GIRLS
Tracks: / Dozen girls / Take that / Mine's a large one, landlord / Torture me.
7" Single: Released Oct '82, on Bronze, by Bronze Records. Deleted Oct '85. Catalogue no: **BRO 156**

ELOISE
Tracks: / Eloise / Temptation / Beat girl.
7" Single: Released Jan '86, on MCA, by MCA Records. Catalogue no: **GRIM 4**
12" Single: Released Jan '86, on MCA, by MCA Records. Catalogue no: **GRIMT 4**

FRIDAY 13TH (EP)
Tracks: / Disco man / Limit club, The / Billy bad breaks / Citadel.
7" EP: Released Nov '86, on Nems, by Castle Communications Records. Catalogue no: **TRY 1**

GENERALS
Tracks: / Generals / Disguise / Citadel zombies.
7" Single: Released Dec '82, on Bronze, by Bronze Records. Deleted Dec '87. Catalogue no: **BRO 159**

GIGOLO
Tracks: / Portrait.
7" Single: Released Jan '87, on MCA, by MCA Records. Catalogue no: **GRIM 6**
12" Single: Released Jan '87, on MCA, by MCA Records. Catalogue no: **GRIMT 6**

GRIMLY FIENDISH
Tracks: / Grimly fiendish / Edward the bear.
7" Single: Released Mar '85, on MCA, by MCA Records. Catalogue no: **GRIM 1**
12" Single: Released Mar '85, on MCA, by MCA Records. Catalogue no: **GRIMX 1**
12" Single: Released Mar '85, on MCA, by MCA Records. Catalogue no: **GRIMT 1**

HISTORY OF THE WORLD
Tracks: / History of the world / I believe the impossible / Sugar and spite.
7" Single: Released Oct '80, on Chiswick Records, Catalogue no: **CHIS 135**
12" Single: Released May '82, on Chiswick Records, Catalogue no: **12 CHS 135**

I JUST CAN'T BE HAPPY TODAY
Tracks: / I just can't be happy today.
7" Single: Released Dec '79, on Chiswick Records, Deleted Dec '82. Catalogue no: **CHIS 120**

IN DULCE DECORUM
Tracks: / In dulce decorum / Psychomania / In dulce decorum (dub) (on 12" only.) / In dulce decorum (ext).
7" Single: Released Oct '87, on MCA, by MCA Records. Catalogue no: **GRIM 8**
12" Single: Released Oct '87, on MCA, by MCA Records. Catalogue no: **GRIMT 8**

INTERVIEW
Note: Interview with band members.
7" Set: Released May '86, on Vlad, Catalogue no: **VLAD 666**

IS IT A DREAM?
Tracks: / Is it a dream?.
7" Single: Released Sep '85, on MCA, by MCA Records. Catalogue no: **GRIM 3**
12" Single: Released Sep '85, on MCA, by MCA Records. Catalogue no: **GRIMT 3**

LIVELY ARTS
Tracks: / Lively arts / Teenage dreams.
10" single: Released Oct '82, on Big Beat, by Ace Records. Catalogue no: **NST 80**
7" Single: Released Oct '82, on Big Beat, by Ace Records. Catalogue no: **NS 80**

LOVE SONG
Tracks: / Love song / Noise noise noise / Suicide.
7" Single: Released May '79, on Chiswick Records, Deleted May '82. Catalogue no: **CHIS 112**
7" Single: Released Feb '82, on Big Beat, by Ace Records. Catalogue no: **NS 75**

LOVELY MONEY
Tracks: / Lovely money / I think i'm wonderful.
7" Single: Released Jul '82, on Bronze, by Bronze Records. Deleted Jul '85. Catalogue no: **BRO 149**

NEW ROSE
Tracks: / New rose.
12" Single: Released Nov '85, on Stiff, by Stiff Records. Catalogue no: **BUYIT 238**

PEEL SESSIONS:DAMNED I 10.5.77
Tracks: / Sick of being sick / Stretcher case / Fan club / Feel the pain.
Note: This session was recorded by the original and best line-up of the Damned during their spell with Stiff Records.
CD 5": Released Mar '88, on Strange Fruit, by Strange Fruit Records. Catalogue no: **SFPSCD 002**
Cassingle: Released 13 Jun '87, on Strange Fruit, by Strange Fruit Records. Catalogue no: **SFPSC 002**
12" Single: Released Sep '86, on Strange Fruit, by Strange Fruit Records. Catalogue no: **SFPS 002**

PEEL SESSIONS:DAMNED II
12" Single: Released Jul '87, on Strange Fruit, by Strange Fruit Records. Catalogue no: **SFPS 040**

SHADOW OF LOVE
Tracks: / Shadow of love.
10" single: Released Jun '85, on MCA, by MCA Records. Catalogue no: **GRIMY 2**
7" Single: Released Jun '85, on MCA, by MCA Records. Catalogue no: **GRIM 2**
12" Single: Released Jun '85, on MCA, by MCA Records. Catalogue no: **GRIMX 2**

SMASH IT UP
Tracks: / Smash it up.
7" Single: Released May '79, on Chiswick Records, Deleted May '82. Catalogue no: **CHIS 116**
7" Single: Released Feb '82, on Big Beat, by Ace Records. Catalogue no: **NS 76**

THANKS FOR THE NIGHT
Tracks: / Thanks for the night / Nasty.
7" Pic: Released Apr '86, on Damned, by Damned Records. Catalogue no: **DAMNED P1**
7" Single: Released May '84, on Damned, by Damned Records. Catalogue no: **DAMNED 1**
12" Single: Released May '84, on Damned, by Damned Records. Catalogue no: **DAMNED 1T**

THERE AIN'T NO SANITY CLAUSE
Tracks: / There ain't no sanity clause / Looking at you (live) / Anti-pope (on 12" only).
7" Single: Released Nov '80, on Chiswick Records, Deleted Nov '83. Catalogue no: **CHIS 139**
7" Single: Released Dec '83, on Big Beat, by Ace Records. Deleted '88. Catalogue no: **NS 92**
12" Single: Released May '86, on Big Beat, by Ace Records. Deleted '88. Catalogue no: **NST 92**

WAIT FOR THE BLACKOUT
Tracks: / Wait for the blackout.
7" Pic: Released May '82, on Big Beat, by Ace Records. Deleted '88. Catalogue no: **NSP 74**
7" Single: Released May '82, on Big Beat, by Ace Records. Catalogue no: **NS 74**

WHITE RABBIT
Tracks: / White rabbit / Rabid over you / Seagulls.
7" Single: Released May '80, on Chiswick Records, Deleted May '83. Catalogue no: **CHIS 130**
7" Single: Released Mar '83, on Big Beat, by Ace Records. Catalogue no: **NS 85**
12" Single: Released Mar '83, on Big Beat, by Ace Records. Catalogue no: **NST 85**

Damon, Kenny

WHILE I LIVE
Tracks: / While I live.
7" Single: Released May '66, on Mercury, by Phonogram Ltd. Deleted May '69. Catalogue no: **MF 907**

Damon Silver

PUT YOUR HEAD ON MY SHOULDER
Tracks: / Put your head on my shoulder.
7" Single: Released Jun '84, on AWA, Catalogue no: **SAW 009**

Damone, Vic

Biographical details: This American singer, a New Yorker whose real name is Vito Farinola, came to prominence in the late Forties with a series of American hits, notable *Again* and *You're breaking my heart*. There was little to distinguish him from numerous other successful MOR singers of his era, although his pleasant voice was well suited to ballads. He made his big screen debut in 1951 with a leading role in *Rich, young and pretty*, but his career was then interrupted by a two-year spell in the army. On his return to showbusiness in '53, he struggled to re-establish his name. Damone's real comeback was in 1956, when he recorded *On the street where you live*, one of the stunningly successful Alan Jay Lerner/Frederick Loewe musical *My fair lady* - this took him to No.4 on the US charts and, two years later (owing to a deliberate delay by the show's producers), to No.1 in Britain. After this international smash, Damone never had another major hit on either side of the Atlantic. He remained active in the entertainment business, as demonstrated by the US No.30 placing of his 1965 single *You were only fooling (while I was falling in love)* and the UK No.44 placing of his 1981 Lp *Now!*. (Bob MacDonald, 3rd March 1985)
The Italian pop balladeer born in Brooklyn in 1928 worked as an usher at the famous Paramount Theatre, then won an Arthur Godfrey Talent Scout show at age 15 and was helped into cabaret by Milton Berle. He had hits on Mercury 1947-53, switched to CBS for a few more and sold a lot of albums. He was described by Frank Sinatra as having 'the best set of pipes in the business'. He had his own radio and TV shows, made films and later recorded for RCA; he was semi-retired into the real estate business, married to actress-singer Diahann Carroll, then had a remarkable renaissance in the UK in the early 80's: persistent plays by BBC DJ David Jacobs led to reissued albums including compilations. (Donald Clarke, April 1989)e.

AN AFFAIR TO REMEMBER
Tracks: / Affair to remember, An.
7" Single: Released Dec '57, on Philips, by Phonogram Ltd. Deleted Dec '60. Catalogue no: **PB 745**

ON THE STREET WHERE YOU LIVE
Tracks: / On the street where you live.
7" Single: Released May '58, on Philips, by Phonogram Ltd. Deleted May '61. Catalogue no: **PB 819**

ONLY MAN ON THE ISLAND, THE
Tracks: / Only man on the island, The.
7" Single: Released Aug '58, on Philips, by Phonogram Ltd. Deleted Aug '61. Catalogue no: **PB 837**

PLEASURE OF HER COMPANY
Tracks: / Pleasure of her company.
7" Single: Released May '83, on CBS, by CBS Records. Catalogue no: **A 3389**

SHE BELIEVES IN ME
Tracks: / She believes in me / Still.
7" Single: Released Jul '81, on RCA, by BMG Records (UK). Deleted '85. Catalogue no: **RCA 98**

Dan

CAN YOU DIG IT
Tracks: / Can you dig it.
7" Single: Released Dec '86, on Meantime, by Meantime Records. Catalogue no: **COX 001**

Dana

Biographical details: This Irish singer, whose real name is Rosemary Brown, was born in London in 1951 but moved with her parents to the Irish Republic at the age of two. She began her professional singing career at the age of 16 and, as an 18 year old, shot to international fame by winning the Eurovision Song Contest. *All Kinds Of Everything*, a song penned by two Dublin printers, was the first Contest win for Eire. It reached No. 1 on the charts of several countries, including Britain, where no previous Eurovision entry from a foreign country had even hit the Top 10. Both the song and the singer were sweet and sugary, but very appealing to a mass market. Dana's pure voice and innocent looks were perfect fodder for television.
Although *All Kinds Of Everything* assured Dana of a long-lasting showbusiness career, her British chart entries proved spasmodic. *Who Put The Lights Out* reached No 14 in 1971, but then she had to wait until 1975 for next hit. The catchy *Please Tell Him I Said Hello* took the singer to No 8 that year, and she reached No 4 at the end of 1975 with *It's Gonne Be A Cold Cold Christmas*. Her hot streak continued a year later with *Fairytale*, a single that peaked at No 13 and logged 16 weeks on the British Top 50. That proved to be her

final major hit, although she returned to the Top 75 in 1979 and 1982, the latter year's disc being a bouncy remake of Felice Taylor's 1967 hit *I Feel Love Comin' On*. Dana has remained a regular TV performer but, record-wise, it is perhaps a pity that her fine voice has usually been wasted on very lightweight pop material. Bob MacDonald, 3 March 1985.
Rosemary Brown, born in 1952 in Londonderry, was a convent girl who auditioned and became the for Irish entry in the Eurovision song contest at 17 and won: *All kinds of everything* was also a number one UK hit in 1970 and she had more hits through '76. She also acted in films and TV, does seaside venues and panto. (Donald Clarke, April 1989).

ALL KINDS OF EVERYTHING
Tracks: / All kinds of everything / Channel breeze.
7" Single: Released Apr '70, on Rex (1), by Decca Records. Deleted Apr '73. Catalogue no: **R 11054**
7" Single: Released May '82, on Decca, by Decca Records. Deleted '88. Catalogue no: **F 13004**

ALL KINDS OF EVERYTHING (OLD GOLD)
Tracks: / All kinds of everything.
7" Single: Released Sep '85, on Old Gold, by Old Gold Records. Catalogue no: **OG 9538**

DARIO CAN YOU GET ME INTO STUDIO 54
Tracks: / Dario can you get me into studio 54.
7" Single: Released Nov '79, on Pinnacle, by Pinnacle Records. Catalogue no: **PIN 26**

DREAM LOVER
Tracks: / Dream lover / Dance.
7" Single: Released Nov '81, on Creole, by Creole Records. Catalogue no: **CR 26**

FAIRYTALE
Tracks: / Fairytale.
7" Single: Released Oct '76, on GTO, Deleted Oct '79. Catalogue no: **GT 66**

I FEEL LOVE COMIN' ON
Tracks: / I feel love comin' on.
7" Single: Released Mar '82, on Creole, by Creole Records. Catalogue no: **CR 32**

I WANT TO STAY HERE
Tracks: / I want to stay here / Baby come back to me.
7" Single: Released Mar '86, on Ritz, by Ritz Records. Catalogue no: **RITZ 140**

IF I GIVE MY HEART TO YOU (SINGLE)
Tracks: / If I give my heart to you.
7" Single: Released Oct '85, on Ritz, by Ritz Records. Catalogue no: **RITZ 125**

IF YOU REALLY LOVE ME
Tracks: / If you really love me / Sad song.
7" Single: Released Jan '83, on Creole, by Creole Records. Catalogue no: **CR 44**

IT'S GONNA BE A COLD COLD CHRISTMAS
Tracks: / It's gonna be a cold cold Christmas.
7" Single: Released Dec '75, on GTO, Deleted Dec '78. Catalogue no: **GT 45**

LIPSTICK ON YOUR COLLAR
Tracks: / Lipstick on your collar / Baby come back to me.
7" Single: Released Nov '86, on Ritz, by Ritz Records. Catalogue no: **RITZ 159**

LITTLE THINGS MEAN A LOT
Tracks: / Little things mean a lot.
7" Single: Released Jun '85, on Ritz, by Ritz Records. Catalogue no: **RITZ 102**

NEVER GONNA FALL IN LOVE AGAIN
Tracks: / Never gonna fall in love again.
7" Single: Released Mar '76, on GTO, Deleted Mar '79. Catalogue no: **GT 55**

PLEASE TELL HIM THAT I SAID HELLO
Tracks: / Please tell him that I said hello.
7" Single: Released Jan '75, on GTO, Deleted Jan '78. Catalogue no: **GT 6**

SOMETHING'S COOKIN' IN THE KITCHEN
Tracks: / Something's cookin' in the kitchen.
7" Single: Released Mar '79, on GTO, Deleted Mar '82. Catalogue no: **GT 243**

SUMMER ROMEO
Tracks: / Summer romeo.
7" Single: Released Jun '88, on Cara, Catalogue no: **CARA 104**

TOTUS TUUS
Tracks: / Totus tuus / Cliffs of Dooneen.
7" Single: Released Mar '80, on GTO, Deleted Mar '83. Catalogue no: **GT 262**

WHO PUT THE LIGHTS OUT
Tracks: / Who put the lights out.
7" Single: Released Feb '71, on Rex (1), by Decca Records. Deleted Feb '74. Catalogue no: **R 11062**

YER MAN
Tracks: / Yer man.
7" Single: Released May '82, on Towerbell, Catalogue no: **TOW 21**

YOU NEVER GAVE ME YOUR LOVE
Tracks: / You never gave me your love / Marathon.
7" Single: Released Aug '82, on Creole, by Creole Records. Catalogue no: **CR 40**

Dana Dane

CINDERFELLA DANA DANE
Tracks: / Cinderfella Dana Dane.
12" Single: Released Aug '87, on Progressive, Catalogue no: **PRO 7151**

Dance

IN LUST
Tracks: / In lust.
12" Single: Released Aug '81, on Statik, Catalogue no: **STAT 712**

SHE LIKES TO BEAT
Tracks: / She likes to beat.
12" Single: Released Jul '80, on Gogoroo, Catalogue no: **GOGORD 03**

STAY DOWN
Tracks: / Stay down / Stay down (part 2).
7" Single: Released Apr '82, on Statik, Deleted '85. Catalogue no: **STAT 16**
12" Single: Released Apr '82, on Statik, Deleted '85. Catalogue no: **STAT 1612**

Dance Addiction

DON'T STOP
Tracks: / Don't stop.
7" Single: Released Nov '88, on Bolts, by Bolts Records. Catalogue no: **NUTS 101**
12" Single: Released Nov '88, on Bolts, by Bolts Records. Catalogue no: **NUTSX 101**

Dance Aid

GIVE GIVE GIVE
Tracks: / Give give give.
7" Single: Released Nov '87, on Supreme, by Supreme Records. Catalogue no: **SUPE 119**
12" Single: Released Nov '87, on Supreme, by Supreme Records. Catalogue no: **SUPET 119**

Dance Band

NO SOUL
Tracks: / No soul / Peter Gunn.
7" Single: Released Nov '81, on Cool King, Catalogue no: **CK 007**

STACKS OF TRACKS
Tracks: / Stacks of tracks / Do you wanna dance.
7" Single: Released May '80, on Double D, Deleted May '83. Catalogue no: **DD001**

THREE STRINGS
Tracks: / Three strings / I've got you / Barefootin'.
7" Single: Released Sep '80, on Double D, Deleted '83. Catalogue no: **DEE 5**

Dance Chapter

ANONYMITY
Tracks: / Anonymity / New dance.
7" Single: Released Dec '80, on Armageddon, by Armageddon Records. Catalogue no: **AD 18**

CHAPTER II
Tracks: / Chapter II.
7" Single: Released Nov '81, on 4AD, by 4AD Records. Catalogue no: **BAD 115**

Dance Class

SETTING MYSELF ON FIRE
Tracks: / Setting myself on fire / Night faces.
7" Single: Released Oct '82, on A&M, by A&M Records. Deleted Oct '85. Catalogue no: **AMS 8261**

YOU TALK MY HEAD OFF
Tracks: / You talk my head off / Don't you know.
7" Single: Released Aug '82, on A&M, by A&M Records. Deleted Aug '85. Catalogue no: **AMS 8243**

Dance Hall...

DANCE HALL COMBINATION
12" Single: Released Nov '84, on Striker Lee, Catalogue no: **WERM 118**

Dance In Reverse

DANCE ME TO THE FLOOR
Tracks: / Dance me to the floor.
7" Single: Released Nov '86, on Atlantic, by WEA Records. Deleted Jun '87. Catalogue no: **A 9406**
12" Single: Released Sep '86, on Atlantic, by WEA Records. Deleted Jun '87. Catalogue no: **A 9406 T**

Dance Like A Mother

PRIVATE NUMBER
Tracks: / Private number / Physical love.
7" Single: Released Jul '87, on Virgin, by Virgin Records. Deleted May '88. Catalogue no: **VS 973**
12" Single: Released Jul '87, on Virgin, by Virgin Records. Deleted May '88. Catalogue no: **VS 973-12**

YOU AIN'T SO TOUGH
Tracks: / You ain't so tough / Love or lust.
7" Single: Released Feb '87, on Virgin, by Virgin Records. Deleted May '88. Catalogue no: **VS 936**
12" Single: Released Feb '87, on Virgin, by Virgin Records. Deleted May '88. Catalogue no: **VS 936-12**

Dance Motto

TELL JACK
Tracks: / Tell Jack.
7" Single: Released Jun '87, on Rhythm King, by Mute Records. Catalogue no: **LEFT 9**
12" Single: Released Jun '87, on Rhythm King, by Mute Records. Catalogue no: **LEFT 9T**

Dance Or Die

MOVE
Tracks: / Move.
12" Single: Released Jan '89, on Madcat, by Revolver. Catalogue no: **MAD 12-5**

Dance Reaction

DISCO TRAIN
Tracks: / Disco train / Train sound.
7" Single: Released May '82, on Carrere, Catalogue no: **CAR 239**
12" Single: Released May '82, on Carrere, Catalogue no: **CART 239**

Dance Trance

DO THE DANCE
Tracks: / Do the dance / Sail away.
7" Single: Released Jul '86, on CBS, by CBS Records. Catalogue no: **A 6924**
12" Single: Released Jul '86, on CBS, by CBS Records. Catalogue no: **TA 6924**

IT TAKES TWO
Tracks: / It takes two.
7" Single: Released Feb '85, on Rollerball, Deleted '87. Catalogue no: **BALL 2**
12" Single: Released Feb '85, on Rollerball, Deleted '87. Catalogue no: **BALLT 2**

Dancette

GOING GREEN
Tracks: / Going green.
7" Single: Released Oct '82, on Bel, Catalogue no: **SSP 836**

D'Ancey, Graham Philip

LISTEN
Tracks: / Listen / Thief in the night.
7" Single: Released Jun '82, on Blue September, by Blue September Records. Catalogue no: **BSEP 007**

SACRED HEART
Tracks: / Sacred heart / Lament of the winged warrior.
7" Single: Released Apr '82, on Blue September, by Blue September Records. Catalogue no: **BSEP 005**

Dancing Bears

GOT TO GET OUT OF HERE
Tracks: / Got to get out of here.
7" Single: Released Mar '89, on UNKNOWN, Catalogue no: **BGN 001**

Dancing Did

BADGER BOYS
Tracks: / Badger boys / World's gonna end in Cheltnam.
7" Single: Released Feb '83, on Kamera, Deleted '88. Catalogue no: **ERA 017**

DANCING DID
Tracks: / Dancing Did.
7" Single: Released Oct '79, on Fruit & Veg, Catalogue no: **DID 1**

GREEN MAN & THE MARCH OF THE BUNGALOWS
Tracks: / Green man & the march of the bungalows.
7" Single: Released May '82, on Kamera, Deleted '88. Catalogue no: **ERA 008**

LOST PLATOON
Tracks: / Lost platoon / Human chicken.
7" Single: Released Nov '81, on Stiff, by Stiff Records. Catalogue no: **BUY 136**

Dancing Hoods

BLUE LETTER
Tracks: / Blue letter / Antenna's up / Pleasure.
7" Single: Released Jun '86, on Fun After All, by Music For Nations Records. Catalogue no: **FAA 104**
12" Single: Released Jun '86, on Fun After All, by Music For Nations Records. Catalogue no: **12 FAA 104**

Dancing In Exile

LIKE A TRAIN
Tracks: / Like a train.
7" Single: Released Feb '86, on Lambs To The Slaughter, by Prism Records. Catalogue no: **7 DEN 3**
12" Single: Released Feb '86, on Lambs To The Slaughter, by Prism Records. Catalogue no: **DEN 3**

Dancing With Lucy

CURE FOR LOVE
Tracks: / Cure for love / Rachael smiles.
7" Single: Released Jul '89, on Blue Zone, by Blue Zone Records. Catalogue no: **BZ 701**

Dandy Flash

MUSIC FOR DANCING
Tracks: / Music for dancing.
7" Single: Released Mar '83, on Page One, by Page One Records. Catalogue no: **POR 011**

Dandy, Jim

READY AS HELL (SINGLE)
7" Single: Released Aug '85, on FM-Revolver, by FM-Revolver Records. Catalogue no: **VHF 15**

Dane, Barbara

GIPPER GATE BLUES
Tracks: / Gipper gate blues.
Note: Trad. Jazz Band backing about the Contra Gate Scandal of 1987.
12" Single: Released '88, on Arhoolie (USA), by Arhoolie Records (USA). Catalogue no: **ARHOOLIE 1600**

Dane, Clem

U F O
Tracks: / UFO / Piano player and me, The.
7" Single: Released Apr '80, on Klub, by Klub Records. Deleted '82. Catalogue no: **KLUB 23**

Danger Youth

LADY
Tracks: / Lady.
12" Single: Released Jul '89, on Carron, Catalogue no: **BW 011**

LOST IN LOVE
Tracks: / Lost in love.
7" Single: Released 21 Apr '89, on Briggie C, Catalogue no: **BC 003T**

SIXTEEN
Tracks: / Sixteen / Sixteen (version).
12" Single: Released May '86, on Trouble Music, Catalogue no: **TM 001**

Dangermouse

TAKE IT EASY
Tracks: / Take it easy / Rhythm pattern.
12" Single: Released Mar '84, on Hot Rod, Catalogue no: **HR 003**

Dangerous, Bananas

CLOUD 9
Tracks: / Cloud 9 / Life at the woodman club.
7" Single: Released Jan '82, on Beggars Banquet, by Beggars Banquet Records. Deleted Jan '85. Catalogue no: **BEG 59**

Dangerous Girls

MAN IN THE GLASS
Tracks: / Man in the glass / M07S.
7" Single: Released Nov '80, on Human (2), Catalogue no: **HUM 1**

SAFETY IN NUMBERS
7" Single: Released Jan '80, on Human (2), Catalogue no: **MM 116**

STEP OUT
Tracks: / Step out.
7" Single: Released Apr '81, on Human (2), Catalogue no: **HUM 6**

D'Ango, Pino

MA QUALE IDEA
Tracks: / Ma quale idea / Lezione d'amour.
7" Single: Released May '82, on System, Catalogue no: **STEM 2**
12" Single: Released May '82, on System, Catalogue no: **12 STEM 2**

Dan - I

HIDDEN VALLEY
Tracks: / Hidden valley / Dennis and the spider / Action.
7" Single: Released Feb '80, on Island, by Island Records. Deleted Feb '85. Catalogue no: **WIP 6572**
12" Single: Released Feb '80, on Island, by Island Records. Deleted Feb '85. Catalogue no: **12 WIP 6572**

MONKEY CHOP

Tracks: / Monkey chop.
7" Single: Released Nov '79, on Island, by Island Records. Deleted Nov '82. Catalogue no: **WIP 6520**

Daniel

DEAREST CHARLES
Tracks: / Dearest Charles.
7" Single: Released Jul '81, on Logo, by Logo Records. Deleted Jul '84. Catalogue no: **RED 1**

Daniel, Jeffrey

AC-DC
Tracks: / AC-DC / AC-DC (part 2) / CB side (On 12" only).
7" Single: Released Mar '84, on Polydor, by Polydor Ltd. Catalogue no: **LMS 1**
12" Single: Released Mar '84, on Polydor, by Polydor Ltd. Catalogue no: **LMSX 1**

Daniel, Tim

(DON'T GIVE ME) PRESSURE
Tracks: / (Don't give me) pressure.
12" Single: Released '87, on UNKNOWN. Deleted Jun '89. Catalogue no: **SOULVT 100**

Danielle

PERFECT LOVERS
Tracks: / Perfect lovers / Winner.
7" Single: Released Jul '82, on Eagle Music, by Eagle Music Records. Deleted Jul '85. Catalogue no: **BFB 023**

Danielle, Suzanne

CHRISTMAS STOCKINGS
Tracks: / Christmas stockings.
7" Single: Released Dec '82, on Grab. Catalogue no: **GRAB 100**

Daniels, Charlie

Biographical details: This American singer, violinist and guitarist, born in North Carolina in 1937, was in his mid-Thirties when he achieved his big US breakthrough in 1973, and had been playing professionally for over fifteen years up to that point. The late Sixties and early Seventies were spent largely on session work, notably for Bob Dylan and Ringo Starr. Daniels' first solo album was released in 1970. Success came in 1973 with the US Top 10 success of *Uneasy Rider*, a novelty single released in answer to the *Easy Rider* movie and its spin off crazes. With the acceptance of this hit and of 1975's Top 30 single *The South's Gonna Do It*, he was benefitting from a mini-boom in Southern rock during the early to mid-Seventies, a period that also gave national US success to such acts as the Allman Brothers Band, Wet Willie and the Marshall Tucker Band. Daniels' pair of hits generated great demand on the concert circuit, to which his brand of tongue in cheek country rock wa ideally suited. His plump, rounded, bearded physique helped o make him a charismatic and appealing figure.
During the mid-Seventies, the Charlie Daniels Band instituted a yearly get-together of Southern combos known as the "Volunteer Jam"; these festivals were captured on a series of live albums. The Daniels Band enjoyed their biggest US - and only UK - hit in 1979 with *The Devil Went Down To Georgia*, a novelty story single that described a fiddle-playing contest between the devil and a Georgia citizen; the devil lost. Silly though the record may have been, it provided a perfect vehicle for Daniels' violin playing and his personality, and reached No 3 in America and No 14 in Britain. The eighties brought him occasional US hits, and showed his right-wing political views coming to the fore on 1980's nauseatingly patriotic *In America* (No 11) and 1982's *Still In Saigon* (No 22), singles which suited the mood of the new Reagan-ruled America. Bob MacDonald, 4 March 1985.
Guitarist, fiddler, singer and bandleader born in 1936 in North Carolina, leading a country-rock outfit. He moved to Nashville in 1967, sessioned with Bob Dylan, Ringo Starr and others and formed the Charlie Daniels Band in 1971. His annual event 'The volunteer jam' began in Nashville in early 1974, featuring top stars with his band as headliners; he soon switched from Kama Sutra to Epic and the hits have continued ever since. (Conald Clarke, April 1989).

DEVIL WENT DOWN TO GEORGIA (OLD GOLD)
7" Single: Released Jan '88, on Old Gold, by Old Gold Records. Catalogue no: **OG 9743**

DEVIL WENT DOWN TO GEORGIA, THE
Tracks: / Devil went down to Georgia, The / Jitterbuggin'.
7" Single: Released Sep '79, on Epic, by CBS Records. Deleted Sep '82. Catalogue no: **EPC 7737**
7" Single: Released Jan '88, on Old Gold, by Old Gold Records. Catalogue no: **OG 9743**

LEGEND OF WOOLY SWAMP
Tracks: / Legend of wooly swamp / Money.
7" Single: Released Oct '80, on Epic, by CBS Records. Deleted '83. Catalogue no: **EPC 9019**

STILL IN SAIGON
Tracks: / Still in Saigon / Blowing along with the wind.
7" Single: Released Jun '82, on Epic, by CBS Records. Deleted Jun '85. Catalogue no: **EPCA 2246**

UNEASY RIDER
Tracks: / Uneasy rider / Midnight lady.
7" Single: Released Apr '80, on Epic, by CBS Records. Deleted Apr '83. Catalogue no: **EPC 8337**

Daniels, Jill

RASTAFARIAN DELIGHT
Tracks: / Rastafarian delight / Crying again.
7" Single: Released Aug '82, on Jade Records, Catalogue no: **JD 3**

Daniels, Paul

WELCOME TO THE PARTY
Tracks: / Welcome to the party / Penultimate person.
7" Single: Released Apr '80, on RCA, by BMG Records (UK). Deleted Apr '83. Catalogue no: **PB 5241**

Daniels, Roly

ALMOST SOMEONE
Tracks: / Almost someone / Your eyes.
7" Single: Released Oct '80, on Mint, by Emerald Records. Deleted '88. Catalogue no: **CHEW 40**

BECAUSE I LOVE YOU
Tracks: / Because I love you / Wind beneath my wings.
7" Single: Released Sep '86, on Mint, by Emerald Records. Deleted '88. Catalogue no: **CHEW 107**

HE STOPPED LOVIN' HER TODAY
Tracks: / (When you've lost) your golden glitter / He stopped lovin' her today.
7" Single: Released Apr '84, on Mint, by Emerald Records. Deleted '88. Catalogue no: **CHEW 90**

HELLO DARLIN
Tracks: / Hello darlin.
7" Single: Released Jun '84, on Homespun (Ireland), by Outlet Records. Catalogue no: **HS 081**
7" Single: Released Sep '84, on Mint, by Emerald Records. Deleted '88. Catalogue no: **CHEW 95**

I FEEL LIKE LOVING YOU AGAIN
Tracks: / I feel like loving you again.
7" Single: Released Feb '82, on Mint, by Emerald Records. Deleted '88. Catalogue no: **CHEW 60**

I WILL LOVE YOU ALL MY LIFE
Tracks: / I will love you all my life / I don't wanna lose you.
7" Single: Released Nov '83, on Mint, by Emerald Records. Deleted '88. Catalogue no: **CHEW 86**

IT'S ALL IN THE GAME
Tracks: / It's all in the game / Sometimes when we touch.
7" Single: Released Jul '87, on Mint, by Emerald Records. Deleted '88. Catalogue no: **CHEW 114**

LAST CHEATER'S WALTZ (SINGLE)
Tracks: / Last cheater's waltz, The.
7" Single: Released Oct '81, on Mint, by Emerald Records. Deleted '88. Catalogue no: **CHEW 52**

LET'S LEAVE THE LIGHTS ON TONIGHT
Tracks: / Let's leave the lights on tonight.
7" Single: Released Apr '86, on Mint, by Emerald Records. Deleted '88. Catalogue no: **CHEW 104**

LIKE STRANGERS
Tracks: / Like strangers / I'll get over you / No one but you.
7" Single: Released Feb '83, on Mint, by Emerald Records. Deleted '88. Catalogue no: **CHEW 74**

LOVE DON'T COME ANY BETTER THAN THIS
Tracks: / Love don't come any better than this / Wonderful tonight.
7" Single: Released Apr '88, on Mint, by Emerald Records. Deleted '88. Catalogue no: **CHEW 116**

PART OF ME
Tracks: / Part of me / Seven spanish angels.
7" Single: Released Nov '87, on Mint, by Emerald Records. Deleted '88. Catalogue no: **CHEW 100**

SOMEONE I AIN'T
Tracks: / Someone I ain't.
7" Single: Released Apr '84, on Mint, by Emerald Records. Deleted '88. Catalogue no: **CHEW 92**

Dankworth, John

Biographical details: This British saxophonist and clarinettist and orchestra leader has been a part of the UK music business for three decades. Originally known as Johnny Dankworth, he has preferred to be calle John in his later years. He has often performed and recorded with his wife - the crystal clear singer, Cleo Laine. Using jazz as his bass, he has also recorded and played in various classical styles.
Dankworth first hit the British charts in 1956, when he reached No 7 with *Experiments With Mice*, his rendition of a traditional nursery rhyme. In 1961 he hit No. 9 and logged 21 weeks on the Top 50 with *African Waltz*. Though never returning to the UK charts after 1961, Dankworth's virtuosity has assured him of a steady and lucrative career ever since. Bob MacDonald, 4 March 1985.
Alto saxist, leader and composer born in 1927 in London. He formed the Johnny Dankworth Seven in 1950; vocalist Cleo Laine joined in '51 and they married in '58; he had Don Rendell on tenor in 1953 and expanded the band from that year. Since the '60's he spent more time on composing and studio work, including musicals with words by Benny Green such as *Collette* in 1979 with Cleo and scores for highly rated British films such as *Saturday night and Sunday morning, The servant* and *Morgan*. Pieces for orchestra *What the Dicken's, Zodiac variations* and *A million dollar collection* were written and recorded in the '60's; he regarded them as a trilogy and once said that he would be pleased to be judged by them: *Dickens* was a hit, bimping Stan Getz's *Jazz samba* from the UK jazz Lp chart; he received Ivor Nevello awards for *Dickens* and for *The avengers* TV theme. He converted stables at his Buckinghamshire home to music rooms and ran the Wavenden Allmusic Plan there since 1970; the musical *Side by side by Sondheim* was premiered there and went on to become a smash hit. *Fair oak fusions* is a 9-part work for cello with Julian Lloyd Webber and a small group with five reeds; *Metro* features Rod Argent. (Donald Clarke, April 1989).

AFRICAN WALTZ
Tracks: / African waltz.
7" Single: Released Feb '61, on Columbia, by EMI Records. Deleted Feb '64. Catalogue no: **DB 4590**

EXPERIMENTS WITH MICE
Tracks: / Experiments with mice.
7" Single: Released Jun '56, on Parlophone, by EMI Records. Deleted Jun '59. Catalogue no: **R 4185**

Danny Boys

DAYS OF THE WEEK
Tracks: / Days of the week.
12" Single: Released Feb '87, on Ugly Man, by Ugly Man Records. Catalogue no: **UGLY 2T**

Danny & Shirley

HEY PAULA
Tracks: / Hey Paula.
12" Single: Released Jul '82, on Black Jack, Catalogue no: **12 BJ 015**

HEY PAULA (OLD GOLD)
Tracks: / Hey baby / Hey Paula.
7" Single: Released Jul '82, on Old Gold, by Old Gold Records. Catalogue no: **OG 9099**

Danny & The Juniors

Biographical details: At the time of their major success, this American vocal group comprised lead singer Danny Rapp plus Frank Maffe, Joe Terranova and Dave White.
These four Italian Americans formed the group in their natie Philadelphia in 1957. At the start of the following year, they took the international music scene by storm with *At The Hop*, a deliriously catchy single written by White in collaboration with a friend, Johnny Madara, and a vocal coach who gloried in he appropriate of Artie Singer. *At The Hop* was No 1 for seven weeks in the States in early 1958, reached No 3 in Britain and remains one of the greatest rock 'n' roll records ever made. All four singers were in the 16-17 ae bracket at the time of this dream like success.
White wrote a samey, predictable follow-up *Rock 'N' Roll Is Here To Stay*, which reached No 19 on the US listings. However Danny & The Juniors were evidently not here to stay, and managed only two more small American Top 40 hits before disbanding in 1963. In the UK, where none of the quartet's follow-ups had hit the charts, they enjoyed a further five weeks on the listings with a 1976 re-issue of *At The Hop*, thus allowing a new generation of record buyers the chance to appreciate one of pop's most distinctive and catchy vocal sounds. Bob MacDonald, 8 March 1985.
A vocal group formed in 1955 in Philadelphia: lead Danny Rapp (1941-83), Joe Terranova, Frank Mattei and Dave White; White and John Medora wrote a smash No.1 *At the hop* (1957), typical of the period's way of diluting rock'n'roll excitement into harmless dance music. They had two more top 40 hits. (Donald Clarke, April 1989).

AT THE HOP
Tracks: / At the hop / Rock and roll is here to stay.
7" Single: Released Jul '76, on ABC Records, by MCA Records. Deleted Jul '79. Catalogue no: **ABC 4123**
7" Single: Released Jun '88, on Old Gold, by Old Gold Records. Catalogue no: **OG 9215**
7" Single: Released Jan '58, on H.M.V., by EMI Records. Deleted Jan '61. Catalogue no: **POP 436**

AT THE HOP (OLD GOLD)
Tracks: / At the hop / When / Susie darlin'.
CD 5": Released 30 May '89, on Old Gold, by Old Gold Records. Catalogue no: **OG 6148**
7" Single: Released Jun '88, on Old Gold, by Old Gold Records. Catalogue no: **OG 9215**

Danny Wilson

DAVY
Tracks: / Davy / I won't forget / Pleasure to pleasure.
7" Single: Released May '87, on Virgin, by Virgin Records. Deleted May '88. Catalogue no: **VS 965**
12" Single: Released May '87, on Virgin, by Virgin Records. Catalogue no: **VS 965-12**

DAVY (RE-ISSUE)
Tracks: / Davy (On all versions) / Living to learn (On all versions) / Aberdeen (the way it should've been) (Not on 7") / Kathleen (house mix) (Not on 7").
CD 5": Released Jun '88, on Virgin, by Virgin Records. Catalogue no: **VSCD 1095**
Cassingle: Released Jun '88, on Virgin, by Virgin Records. Catalogue no: **VSTC 1095**
7" Single: Released Jun '88, on Virgin, by Virgin Records. Catalogue no: **VS 1095**
7" Single: Released Jun '88, on Virgin, by Virgin Records. Deleted '89. Catalogue no: **VSG 1095**
12" Single: Released Jun '88, on Virgin, by Virgin Records. Catalogue no: **VST 1095**
12" Single: Released Jun '88, on Virgin, by Virgin Records. Deleted '89. Catalogue no: **VSTP 1095**

GIRL I USED TO KNOW, A
Tracks: / Girl I used to know, A / I won't forget / Pleasure to pleasure (CD & 12" only) / Mary's prayer (CD only).
CD 5": Released Aug '88, on Virgin, by Virgin Records. Catalogue no: **CDEP 12**
7" Single: Released Oct '87, on Virgin, by Virgin Records. Deleted May '88. Catalogue no: **VS 1011**
12" Single: Released Oct '87, on Virgin, by Virgin Records. Catalogue no: **VST 1011**

MARY'S PRAYER
Tracks: / Monkey's shiny day (NOT on CD & 10") / Mary's prayer (On all versions) / Monkey's shiny day (original demo version) (On CD & 10" only) / Kooks (On CD only) / Steamtrains to the milkyway (original demo version) (On 10" only) / Broken china (original demo version) (On 10" only).
CD 5": Released Aug '88, on Virgin, by Virgin Records. Catalogue no: **VSCD 934**
10" single: Released '87, on Virgin, by Virgin Records. Catalogue no: **VS 934-10**
Cassingle: Released '87, on Virgin, by Virgin Records. Catalogue no: **VSC 934-12**
7" Single: Released Feb '87, on Virgin, by Virgin Records. Catalogue no: **VS 934**
12" Single: Released Feb '87, on Virgin, by Virgin Records. Catalogue no: **VS 934-12**

SECOND SUMMER OF LOVE
Tracks: / Second summer of love / I'll be waiting / Growing emotional.
CD 3": Released Jun '89, on Virgin, by Virgin Records. Catalogue no: **VSCDX 1186**
CD 3": Released Jun '89, on Virgin, by Virgin Records. Catalogue no: **VSCD 1186**
12" Single: Released 5 Jun '89, on Virgin, by Virgin Records. Catalogue no: **VST 1186**
10" single: Released Jun '89, on Virgin, by Virgin Records. Catalogue no: **VSA 1186**

7" Single: Released 5 Jun '89, on Virgin, by Virgin Records. Catalogue no: **VS 1186**

Danny-D-Collision

PARTY PEOPLE
Tracks: / Party people.
7" Single: Released Jun '85, on Elite Records, by Elite Records. Deleted '87. Catalogue no: **DAZZ 427**
12" Single: Released Jun '85, on Elite Records, by Elite Records. Deleted '87. Catalogue no: **DAZZ 42**

Danny/Mongoose Team

BMX BOYS
Tracks: / BMX boys / Safety rap.
7" Single: Released Nov '83, on Gipsy, by Gipsy Records. Catalogue no: **GIPSY 15**

Danny/Nogoodniks

BIKE
Tracks: / Bike / Spaghetti.
7" Single: Released Dec '82, on Chrysalis, by Chrysalis Records. Catalogue no: **CHS 2667**

Danovak & Co.

CARAMBA (LET'S DO THE RUMBA)
Tracks: / Caramba (let's do the rumba) / Let me go.
7" Single: Released Jan '84, on Plaza, by Plaza Records. Catalogue no: **PLAZA 7**
12" Single: Released Jan '84, on Plaza, by Plaza Records. Catalogue no: **PLAZAT 7**

GIMME GIMME
Tracks: / Gimme gimme.
7" Single: Released Jul '87, on Plaza, by Plaza Records. Catalogue no: **PZA 029**
12" Single: Released Jul '87, on Plaza, by Plaza Records. Catalogue no: **PZA 029T**

MAGDALENA
Tracks: / Magdalena / Lucia de l'amour.
7" Single: Released Jun '85, on Plaza, by Plaza Records. Catalogue no: **PLAZA 014**

MAN WHO DOESN'T SPEAK, THE
Tracks: / Man who doesn't speak, The / Man who doesn't speak, The (inst).
7" Single: Released 23 Apr '88, on Plaza, by Plaza Records. Catalogue no: **PZA 034**
12" Single: Released 23 Apr '88, on Plaza, by Plaza Records. Catalogue no: **PZA 034T**

QUEEN OF ILLUSIONS
Tracks: / Queen of illusions / Queen of illusions (hot rock).
7" Single: Released Jul '87, on Plaza, by Plaza Records. Catalogue no: **PLAZA 024**

WHAT HAVE YOU DONE TO MY HEART
Tracks: / What have you done to my heart.
7" Single: Released Nov '82, on Plaza, by Plaza Records. Catalogue no: **PLAZA 002**
12" Single: Released Nov '82, on Plaza, by Plaza Records. Catalogue no: **PLAXZA 002T**

Danse Macabre

OH NO NOT I
Tracks: / Oh no not I.
7" Single: Released Jul '83, on Hexagon, Catalogue no: **TREK 101**

SPIRIT OF BULGARIA, THE
Tracks: / Spirit of Bulgaria, The.
12" Single: Released Apr '88, on Subway, by Subway Records. Catalogue no: **SUB 019**

Danse Society

Biographical details: A new wave band formed in Barnsley in 1979 by vocalist Steve Rawlings, drummer Pul 'Gigi' Gilmartin, guitarist Paul Nash, bassist Tim Wright and keyboardist Lyndon Scarfe. They achieved cult status thanks to John Peel, then developed back in Yorkshire away from media. Their doomladen songs allied them with Cult and the Sex Gang Children in the early '80's post-punk morass; the 6-track *Seduction* mini-album achieved a long stay in the indie chart, reaching number two, and they moved towards an electro dancefloor style. They moved from Arista and splitup in '86, Rawlings retaining the name. The others became Johnny and the Clouds. (Donald Clarke, April 1989) .

CLOCK
Tracks: / Clock.
7" Single: Released Jul '83, on Society, by Society Records. Catalogue no: **SOC 2**

DOLPHINS
Tracks: / Dolphins / These frayed edges / There is no shame in death.
12" Single: Released Aug '81, on KSV, by Kingsley Sound & Vision Records. Catalogue no: **PAX 2**

HEAVEN IS WAITING (SINGLE)
Tracks: / Heaven is waiting.
7" Single: Released Nov '83, on Arista, by BMG Records (UK). Deleted Nov '86. Catalogue no: **SOC 6**
12" Single: Released Nov '83, on Arista, by BMG Records (UK). Deleted Nov '86. Catalogue no: **SOC 12 6**

HOLD ON To what you've got
Tracks: / Hold on / Danse mood / Heaven is waiting / Dance mix.
7" Single: Released Feb '86, on Society, by Society Records. Catalogue no: **SOC 9**
12" Single: Released Feb '86, on Arista, by BMG Records (UK). Catalogue no: **SOC 129**

NO SHAME IN DEATH
Tracks: / No shame in death.
12" Single: Released Jul '83, on Society, by Society Records. Catalogue no: **SOC 121**

SAY IT AGAIN
Tracks: / Say it again.
Note: SOC 228 is limited edition club mix.
7" Single: Released Jun '85, on Society, by Society Records. Catalogue no: **SOC 8**
12" Single: Released Jun '85, on Society, by Society Records. Catalogue no: **SOC 128**
12" Single: Released Jun '85, on Society, by Society Records. Catalogue no: **SOC 228**

SOMEWHERE
Tracks: / Somewhere.
7" Single: Released Mar '83, on Society, by Society Records. Catalogue no: **SOC 4**
12" Single: Released Mar '83, on Society, by Society Records. Catalogue no: **SOC 124**

WAKE UP (SINGLE)
Tracks: / Wake up.
7" Single: Released Aug '83, on Arista, by BMG Records (UK). Deleted Aug '86. Catalogue no: **SOC 5**
12" Single: Released Aug '83, on Arista, by BMG Records (UK). Deleted Aug '86. Catalogue no: **SOC 12 5**

WE'RE SO HAPPY
Tracks: / We're so happy.
12" Single: Released Jul '83, on Society, by Society Records. Catalogue no: **SOC 123**

WOMAN'S OWN
Tracks: / Woman's own.
7" Single: Released Mar '82, on Pax, by Pax Records. Catalogue no: **SOX 5**
12" Single: Released Mar '82, on Pax, by Pax Records. Catalogue no: **POX 5**

Dansworks

SAY WHAT YOU MEAN
Tracks: / Makes you happy (do something).
7" Single: Released Nov '86, on FM-Revolver, by FM-Revolver Records. Catalogue no: **RE 33**
12" Single: Released Nov '86, on FM-Revolver, by FM-Revolver Records. Catalogue no: **12 REV 33**

Dante

FREAK IN ME
Tracks: / Freak in me / Freak in me (version) / One more time.
12" Single: Released Feb '88, on Bluebird (2), by BMG Records (UK). Catalogue no: **BR 47**

SO LONG
Tracks: / So long.
7" Single: Released Jul '85, on Cool Tempo, by Chrysalis Records. Catalogue no: **CHS 2897**
12" Single: Released Jul '85, on Cool Tempo, by Chrysalis Records. Catalogue no: **CHS12 2897**

Dante, Steven

GIVE IT UP FOR LOVE
Tracks: / Give it up for love.
7" Single: Released '86, on Cool Tempo, by Chrysalis Records. Catalogue no: **COOL 118**
12" Single: Released '86, on Cool Tempo, by Chrysalis Records. Catalogue no: **COOLX 118**

I'M TOO SCARED
Tracks: / I'm too scared.
CD 5": Released Jun '88, on Cool Tempo, by Chrysalis Records. Catalogue no: **SDCD 1**
7" Single: Released Jun '88, on Cool Tempo, by Chrysalis Records. Catalogue no: **DANTE 1**
7" Single: Released Jun '88, on Cool Tempo, by Chrysalis Records. Catalogue no: **COOL 161**
CD 5": Released Jun '88, on Cool Tempo, by Chrysalis Records. Catalogue no: **COOLCD 161**
12" Single: Released Jun '88, on Cool Tempo, by Chrysalis Records. Catalogue no: **DANTEX 1**
12" Single: Released Jun '88, on Cool Tempo, by Chrysalis Records. Catalogue no: **COOLX 161**

IMAGINATION
Tracks: / Imagination.
7" Single: Released Oct '88, on Cool Tempo, by Chrysalis Records. Catalogue no: **DANTE 2**
12" Single: Released Oct '88, on Cool Tempo, by Chrysalis Records. Catalogue no: **DANTEX 2**

JUST MY IMAGINATION
Tracks: / Just my imagination / If it makes you feel good / Just my imagination (dancin' Danny D remix).
CD 5": Released Sep '88, on Cool Tempo, by Chrysalis Records. Catalogue no: **SDCD 2**
7" Single: Released 16 Sep '88, on Cool Tempo, by Chrysalis Records. Catalogue no: **DANTE 2**
12" Single: Released 16 Sep '88, on Cool Tempo, by Chrysalis Records. Catalogue no: **DANTEX 2**

LOVE FOLLOWS
Tracks: / Love follows / Taking love to the limit.
7" Single: Released Jan '89, on Cool Tempo, by Chrysalis Records. Catalogue no: **DANTE 3**
12" Single: Released Jan '89, on Cool Tempo, by Chrysalis Records. Catalogue no: **DANTEX 3**

Dante's Voice

KICK YOUR
Tracks: / Kick your.
12" Single: Released '89, on Zaza Boem, Catalogue no: **ZZB 001**

MAGIC MUSHROOM
Tracks: / Magic mushroom.
12" Single: Released '89, on Zaza Boem, Catalogue no: **ZZB 002**

Dany

LONDON JO
Tracks: / London Jo.
7" Single: Released Sep '85, on Waterfront, by Waterfront Music. Catalogue no: **WFS 19**

Darby, Alan

CHARGE YOU UP
Tracks: / Charge you up.
7" Single: Released Mar '87, on Siren, by Virgin Records. Deleted May '88. Catalogue no: **SIREN 17**
12" Single: Released Mar '87, on Siren, by Virgin Records. Deleted May '88. Catalogue no: **SIREN 17-12**

Darby, James

SNAKE DANCE
Tracks: / Snake dance / Overlander, The.
7" Single: Released Apr '88, on President, by President Records. Catalogue no: **PT 573**

D'Arby, Terence Trent

DANCE LITTLE SISTER
Tracks: / Dance little sister (part 1) / Dance little sister (part 2).
12" Single: Released Dec '88, on Columbia (USA), by CBS Records (USA). Catalogue no: **4407887**
12" Single: Released Sep '87, on CBS, by CBS Records. Deleted Jun '88. Catalogue no: **TRENTT 3**
CD 3": Released Dec '88, on Columbia (USA), by CBS Records (USA). Catalogue no: **38K 08023**
Cassingle: Released Sep '87, on CBS, by CBS Records. Catalogue no: **TRENTC 3**
7" Single: Released Oct '87, on CBS, by CBS Records. Deleted Jun '88. Catalogue no: **TRENT Q3**
7" Single: Released Sep '87, on CBS, by CBS Records. Catalogue no: **TRENT 3**

IF YOU LET ME STAY
Tracks: / If you let me stay / Loving you is another word for lonely.
7" Single: Released Feb '87, on CBS, by CBS Records. Deleted Aug '87. Catalogue no: **TRENT 1**
12" Single: Released Feb '87, on CBS, by CBS Records. Deleted Nov '87. Catalogue no: **TRENT T1**

IF YOU LET ME STAY (IMPORT)
Tracks: / If you let me stay / If you let me stay (hardline mix) / If you let me stay (U.S. mix) / Loving you is another word for lonely.
Note: This contains the U.S. version plus an exclusive U.S. only mix & the 'Hardline' mix- also 'Loving you is another word for lonely'.
12" Single: Released Oct '88, on Columbia (USA), by CBS Records (USA). Catalogue no: **440 7450**

NEITHER FLESH NOR FISH
Tracks: / Declaration / Neither fish nor flesh / I have faith in these desolate times / It feels so good to love someone like you / I'll be alright / Billy don't fall / This side of love / Attracted to you / Roly poly / You will pay tomorrow / I don't want to bring your Gods down / And I need to be with someone tonight.
CD: Released 16 Oct '89, on CBS, by CBS Records. Catalogue no: **465809 2**

SIGN YOUR NAME
Tracks: / Sign your name / Greasy chicken / Under my thumb (12" only.) / Jumpin' Jack Flash (On 12" only) / If you all get to heaven (On 10" only) / Dance little sister (On CD picture single only).
7" Single: Released Dec '87, on CBS, by CBS Records. Deleted Jun '88. Catalogue no: **TRENT Q4**
7" Single: Released Dec '87, on CBS, by CBS Records. Deleted Jun '88. Catalogue no: **TRENT 4**
7" Pic: Released Dec '87, on CBS, by CBS Records. Deleted Jun '88. Catalogue no: **TRENT P4**
CD 5": Released Jan '88, on CBS, by CBS Records. Deleted Jan '89. Catalogue no: **TRENT C4**
10" single: Released Jan '88, on CBS, by CBS Records. Catalogue no: **TRENT G4**
12" Single: Released Dec '87, on CBS, by CBS Records. Deleted Jun '88. Catalogue no: **TRENT T4**

WISHING WELL
Tracks: / Wishing well / Elevators and hearts.
Note: TRENTQ 2 features poster bag.
12" Single: Released Jun '87, on CBS, by CBS Records. Deleted Nov '87. Catalogue no: **TRENT T2**
7" Single: Released Jun '87, on CBS, by CBS Records. Deleted Nov '87. Catalogue no: **TRENT 2**
7" Single: Released Jun '87, on CBS, by CBS Records. Deleted Nov '87. Catalogue no: **TRENTG 2**
7" Single: Released Jun '87, on CBS, by CBS Records. Deleted Nov '87. Catalogue no: **TRENTQ 2**

WISHING WELL (THE COOL IN THE SHADE MIX)
Tracks: / Wishing well / Wonderful world / Elevators and hearts.
7" Single: Released Jun '87, on CBS, by CBS Records. Deleted Nov '87. Catalogue no: **TRENT R2**

Darbyshire, Richard

AIRWAVES
Tracks: / Airwaves.
7" Single: Released Jan '82, on Arcadian Research Authority, Catalogue no: **ARA 3**

D'arc

LETTER, THE
Tracks: / Letter, The / Analysis.
7" Single: Released Jul '82, on Flying, by Flying Records. Catalogue no: **FLY 101**

Darc, Daniel

LA VILLE
Tracks: / La ville.
7" Single: Released 1 Aug '89, on Play It Again Sam(Belgium), by Play It Again Sam (Belgium). Catalogue no: **BIAS 121**

PAS SANS TE RETOURNER
Tracks: / Pas sans te retourner.
7" Single: Released 20 Feb '88, on Play It Again Sam(Belgium), by Play It Again Sam (Belgium). Catalogue no: **BIAS 084**
12" Single: Released May '88, on Play It Again Sam(Belgium), by Play It Again Sam (Belgium). Catalogue no: **BIAS 84T**

Dare

ABANDON
Tracks: / Abandon / Last time, The / Precious (Only on 12" version.) / Love is the price (Only on 12" version.).
CD 5": Released Sep '88, on A&M, by A&M Records. Catalogue no: **AMCD 470**
7" Single: Released Sep '88, on A&M, by A&M Records. Catalogue no: **AM 470**
12" Single: Released Sep '88, on A&M, by A&M Records. Catalogue no: **AMY 470**

ABANDON (REMIX)
Tracks: / Abandon / Last time, The.
Note: Dare's 54 date UK and European tour supporting the band Europe has paid off handsomely: a flood of great press reviews has supplemented the outstanding reviews of their debut album, Out of the silence. Each of Dare's singles has charted higher than its predecessor.
CD 5": Released 10 Jul '89, on A&M, by A&M Records. Catalogue no: **CDEE 519**
7" Single: Released 10 Jul '89, on A&M, by A&M Records. Catalogue no: **AM 519**
12" Single: Released 10 Jul '89, on A&M, by A&M Records. Catalogue no: **AMY 519**
7" Pic: Released 10 Jul '89, on A&M, by A&M Records. Catalogue no: **AMP 519**
7" Single: Released 10 Jul '89, on A&M, by A&M Records. Catalogue no: **AMS 519**

HEARTBREAKER
Tracks: / Heartbreaker / King of spades /

Runaway (live).
CD 5": Released Sep '89, on A&M, by A&M Records. Catalogue no: **CDEE 525**
7" Single: Released Sep '89, on A&M, by A&M Records. Catalogue no: **AM 525**
12" Single: Released Sep '89, on A&M, by A&M Records. Catalogue no: **AMY 525**

NOTHING IS STRONGER THAN LOVE
Tracks: / Nothing is stronger than love / Valentino / If looks could kill (Only on CD single.).
CD 5": Released Feb '89, on A&M, by A&M Records. Catalogue no: **CDEE 493**
7" Single: Released Feb '89, on A&M, by A&M Records. Catalogue no: **AM 493**
12" Single: Released Feb '89, on A&M, by A&M Records. Catalogue no: **AMY 493**

RAINDANCE, THE
Tracks: / Raindance, The / Return the heart / No strings attached.
CD 5": Released Apr '89, on A&M, by A&M Records. Catalogue no: **CDEE 483**
7" Single: Released Apr '89, on A&M, by A&M Records. Catalogue no: **AM 483**
12" Single: Released Apr '89, on A&M, by A&M Records. Catalogue no: **AMP 483**
12" Single: Released Apr '89, on A&M, by A&M Records. Catalogue no: **AMY 483**

Darin, Bobby

Biographical details: This American singer and songwriter, born in the Bronx, New York, was brought up by his mother and sister, his father having died before he was born. Bobby entered showbusiness in the mid-Fifties, and apparently picked his stage surname from a phone book; his real name was Walden Robert Cassotto. He surged to fame in the summer of 1958 with *Splish Splash*, a novelty rock 'n' roll single co-written by Darin and produced by Ahmet Ertegun, one of the wizards of Atlantic Records. It reached No 3 in the US, but lost out in the UK to a cover version by Britain's Charlie Drake. Later that year *Queen Of The Hop* hit the US No 9 slot, and he also reached the AMerican Top 30 with *Early In The Morning* under the pseudonym of the Rinky Dinks. These 1958 hits appeared to indicate that Darin was an entertaining but insubstantial rock 'n' roll singer. However, he quickly broadened his horizons with two contrasting smashes: *Dream Lover* and *Mack The Knife*, both issued in 1959, were his two biggest career hits in both sides of the Atlantic.
Dream Lover, penned solely by Darin, was one of his best songs and mirrored the move to more melodic pop sounds that many rock 'n' rollers were making at the end of the Fifties. It peaked at No. 2 in the States and No. 1 in Britain, where it was toppled from the top by Cliff Richard's first chart-topper - an interesting historical fact in view of Cliff's 1962 No 1 *The Young Ones*, whose tune was virtually a note for note copy of *Dream Lover*. The jazz flavoured *Mack The Knife* was an extraordinary choice of song for Darin - taken from Bertolt Brecht & Kurt Weill's *The Threepenny Opera*, it had been a US Top 40 hit for five different acts as recently as 1956, the best having been by the great Louis Armstrong. But Darin outdid them all with his '59 rendition, which was No 1 in both the US and the UK, and held the top sport for a mammouth nine weeks in the former country. *Mack The Knife* showcased his greatest qualities: his fine voice, his charismatic personality and his unpredictability. From then on, he never settled down and was constantly changing styles. His Sixties hits included *Lazy River*, a 1961 version of a Hoagy Carmichael jazz standard, a country flavoured 1962 smash entitles *Things* plus 1966's *If I Were A Carpenter*, his successful leap onto the folk-rock bandwagon. The latter song was his last major hit on either side of the Atlantic, and his career went into decline thereafter. He died of a heart attack in December 1973 at the age of 37. Dubious health had always been a factor in Darin's career, and some say that he knew he was destined to die young and therefore wanted to cram as many different styles into as short a tim as possible. This would explain his ever shifting musical persona, although his arrogant and temperamental character was probably an equal reason. He never remained in one style long enough to gather a loyal army of fans, which is why his music is underrated by many pundits and punters today. But Darin's wide ranging talents were amply displayed by such ventures as his worthy subsidiary career as an actor and his early Sixties move to Capitol Records - where he was regarded as the replacement for Frank Sinatra, who had just left the Company. Bob MacDonald, 8 March 1985.
Born in New York in 1936, the still popular singer died after heart surgery in 1973 (he had rheumatic fever as a child). He was the first big white act on Atlantic (Atco) with his own song, the amusing novelty *Splish splash* in 1956; further top 10 entries were *Queen of the hop* and *Dream lover*, followed by change to a Sinatra style for a number one smash with Kurt Weill's *Mack the knife* in 1959 and a number six with Charles Trenet's *Beyond the sea* in 1959-60. Further top tens included Tim Hardin' *If I were a carpenter*, he made films and was married to beach bunny Sandra Dee 1960-1967. His career faltered and he became Bob Darin' in 1971, singing anti-war songs. (Donald Clarke, April 1989).

BABY FACE (SINGLE)
Tracks: / Baby face.
7" Single: Released Nov '62, on London-American, Deleted Nov '65. Catalogue no: **HLK 9624**

BILL BAILEY (SINGLE)
Tracks: / Bill Bailey.
7" Single: Released Jun '60, on London-American, Deleted Jun '63. Catalogue no: **HLK 9142**

CLEMENTINE (SINGLE)
Tracks: / Clementine.
7" Single: Released Mar '60, on London-American, Deleted Mar '63. Catalogue no: **HLK 9086**

COME SEPTEMBER
Tracks: / Come September.
7" Single: Released Oct '61, on London-American, Deleted Oct '64. Catalogue no: **HLK 9407**

DREAM LOVER (OLD GOLD)
Tracks: / Dream lover / Mack the knife.
7" Single: Released Jul '82, on Old Gold, by Old Gold Records. Catalogue no: **OG 9017**

DREAM LOVER (SINGLE)
Tracks: / Dream lover.
7" Single: Released May '59, on London-American, Deleted May '62. Catalogue no: **HLE 8867**

DREAM LOVER/MACK THE KNIFE (SINGLE)(RE-ISSUE)
Tracks: / Dream lover / Mack the knife.
7" Single: Released Apr '79, on Lightning, Deleted Apr '82. Catalogue no: **LIG 9017**

EIGHTEEN YELLOW ROSES
Tracks: / Eighteen yellow roses.
7" Single: Released Jul '63, on Capitol, by EMI Records. Deleted Jul '66. Catalogue no: **CL 15306**

IF A MAN ANSWERS (SINGLE)
Tracks: / If a man answers.
7" Single: Released Oct '62, on Capitol, by EMI Records. Deleted Oct '65. Catalogue no: **CL 15272**

IF I WERE A CARPENTER (SINGLE)
Tracks: / If I were a carpenter.
7" Single: Released Oct '66, on Atlantic, by WEA Records. Deleted Oct '69. Catalogue no: **584 051**

LA MER (BEYOND THE SEA) (SINGLE)
Tracks: / La mer.
7" Single: Released Jan '60, on London-American, Deleted Jan '63. Catalogue no: **HLE 9034**

LAZY RIVER
Tracks: / Lazy river.
7" Single: Released Mar '61, on London-American, Deleted Mar '64. Catalogue no: **HLK 9303**

MACK THE KNIFE (SINGLE)
Tracks: / Mack the knife.
7" Single: Released Sep '59, on London-American, Deleted Sep '62. Catalogue no: **HLE 8939**

MULTIPLICATION
Tracks: / Multiplication.
7" Single: Released Dec '61, on London-American, Deleted Dec '64. Catalogue no: **HLK 9474**

NATURE BOY
Tracks: / Nature boy.
7" Single: Released Jul '61, on London-American, Deleted Jul '64. Catalogue no: **HLK 9375**

QUEEN OF THE HOP (SINGLE)
Tracks: / Queen of the hop.
7" Single: Released Jan '59, on London-American, Deleted Jan '62. Catalogue no: **HLE 8737**

SPLISH SPLASH (OLD GOLD)
Tracks: / Splish splash / Queen of the hop.
7" Single: Released Jul '82, on Old Gold, by Old Gold Records. Catalogue no: **OG 9088**

SPLISH SPLASH (SINGLE)
Tracks: / Splish splash.
7" Single: Released Aug '58, on London-American, Deleted Aug '61. Catalogue no: **HLE 8666**

THINGS (OLD GOLD)
Tracks: / Things.
7" Single: Released Jan '85, on Old Gold, by Old Gold Records. Catalogue no: **OG 9503**

THINGS (SINGLE)
Tracks: / Things.
7" Single: Released Jul '62, on London-American, Deleted Jul '65. Catalogue no: **HLK 9575**

YOU MUST HAVE BEEN A BEAUTIFUL BABY
Tracks: / You must have been a beautiful baby.
7" Single: Released Oct '61, on London-American, Deleted Oct '64. Catalogue no: **HLK 9429**

Dark

EINSTEIN'S BRAIN
Tracks: / Einstein's brain.
7" Single: Released Apr '81, on Fresh, by Jetstar Records. Catalogue no: **FRESH 24**

HAWAII FIVE-0
Tracks: / Hawaii five-O.
7" Single: Released Apr '81, on Fresh, by Jetstar Records. Catalogue no: **FRESH 13**

MASQUE (SINGLE)
Tracks: / Masque / War zone.
7" Single: Released Jan '82, on Fresh, by Jetstar Records. Catalogue no: **FRESH 46**

MY FRIENDS
Tracks: / My friends.
7" Single: Released Apr '81, on Fresh, by Jetstar Records. Catalogue no: **FRESH 2**

ON THE WIRES
Tracks: / On the wires / Shattered glass.
7" Single: Released Aug '81, on Fresh, by Jetstar Records. Catalogue no: **FRESH 35**

Dark Angel

MERCILESS DEATH
Special: Released Jun '88, on Metalstorm, by Azra International (USA). Catalogue no: **MS 8602**

Dark City

COME ON OVER
Tracks: / Come on over / What we had before / Come on over (extended version) (12" only).
7" Single: Released Sep '86, on Virgin, by Virgin Records. Deleted May '88. Catalogue no: **VS 891**
12" Single: Released Sep '86, on Virgin, by Virgin Records. Catalogue no: **VS 891-12**

RESCUE ME
Tracks: / Rescue me.
7" Single: Released Jun '86, on Virgin, by Virgin Records. Deleted '89. Catalogue no: **VS 869**
12" Single: Released Jun '86, on Virgin, by Virgin Records. Deleted May '88. Catalogue no: **VS 869-12**

Dark, John

OUTLAW
Tracks: / Outlaw.
7" Single: Released Jun '84, on JD, Catalogue no: **JD 01**

OUTSIDE LOOKING IN
Tracks: / Outside looking in.
12" Single: Released Jul '84, on Outlaw, Catalogue no: **12 JD 01**

SILHOUETTE
Tracks: / Silhouette.
7" Single: Released Jan '83, on Zonophone, by EMI Records. Catalogue no: **Z 35**

Dark Room

12.03
Tracks: / 12.03.
7" Single: Released '88, on Open Door, by Open Door Records. Catalogue no: **TYM 027**

Dark Secret

WHERE ARE YOU
Tracks: / Where are you.
7" Single: Released Aug '86, on MCA, by MCA Records. Catalogue no: **MCA 1055**

Dark Star

LADY OF MARS
Tracks: / Lady of mars.
7" Single: Released Aug '81, on Avatar, by Avatar Record Corporation. Catalogue no: **AAA 105**

Darken

STORMY WEATHER
Tracks: / Stormy weather.
7" Single: Released Jun '84, on Vinyl Cuts, by Vinyl Cuts Records. Catalogue no: **VC 001**

Darkness And Jive

FURNACE
Tracks: / Furnace / Guys and dolls.
7" Single: Released May '83, on Red Rhino, by Red Rhino Records. Catalogue no: **RED 27**

HOOKED ON YOU
Tracks: / Hooked on you.
7" Single: Released Nov '82, on Red Rhino, by Red Rhino Records. Catalogue no: **RED 21**

JIGSAW
Tracks: / Jigsaw.
7" Single: Released Jul '85, on Floating World, by Floating World Records. Catalogue no: **FLOAT 03**

Darko, George

Biographical details: Born in 1951 in Ghana, the guitarist and composer has become a leading artist in the high life club genre since the early '70's. He studied and played with Konimo and worked on a fusion of Konimo and George Benson; his first album with his band Bus Stop was *Friends* in 1983, including *Adoe te brofo*, a massive funk/highlife hit at home which attracted international interest: reworked in English it became *Highlife time* and the title track of his second album. Members of the band left to form own group Kantata, whose records appeared on Oval. (Donald Clarke, April 1989).

HIGH LIFE TIME (SINGLE)
Tracks: / High life time.
7" Single: Released Jun '84, on Oval, by Oval Records. Catalogue no: **OVAL 31**
12" Single: Released Jun '84, on Oval, by Oval Records. Catalogue no: **OVALT 31-12**

Darling Buds

BURST
Tracks: / Burst / Big head / Shame on you (slightlydelic version).
7" Single: Released Sep '88, on Epic, by CBS Records. Deleted 10 Jul '89. Catalogue no: **BLOND 1**
12" Single: Released Sep '88, on Epic, by CBS Records. Deleted 10 Jul '89. Catalogue no: **BLOND T1**
7" Single: Released Oct '88, on Epic, by CBS Records. Deleted 10 Jul '89. Catalogue no: **BLOND B1**
CD 5": Released Sep '88, on Epic, by CBS Records. Deleted 10 Jul '89. Catalogue no: **BLOND C1**
7" Single: Released Oct '88, on Epic, by CBS Records. Deleted 10 Jul '89. Catalogue no: **BLOND Q1**

HIT THE GROUND
Tracks: / Hit the ground / Pretty girl.
12" Single: Released Dec '88, on Epic, by CBS Records. Deleted 10 Jul '89. Catalogue no: **BLOND T2**
7" Single: Released Jan '89, on Epic, by CBS Records. Deleted 10 Jul '89. Catalogue no: **BLOND Q2**
7" Single: Released Dec '88, on Epic, by CBS Records. Deleted 10 Jul '89. Catalogue no: **BLOND 2**
CD 5": Released Dec '88, on Epic, by CBS Records. Deleted 10 Jul '89. Catalogue no: **BLOND C2**
10" single: Released Jan '89, on Epic, by CBS Records. Catalogue no: **BLOND X2**

IF I SAID
Tracks: / If I said.
7" Single: Released Feb '87, on Darling Buds, by Revolver Records. Catalogue no: **DAR 001**

IT'S ALL UP TO YOU
Tracks: / It's all up to you.
7" Single: Released '88, on Native (1), by Native Records. Catalogue no: **NTV 33**
12" Single: Released Jun '88, on Native (1), by Native Records. Catalogue no: **12 NTV 33**

LET'S GO ROUND THERE
Tracks: / Let's go round there / Turn you on / Different daze (Only on CD single & 12".) / It's all up to you (flip flop version) (Only on 7" Ep.).
7" Single: Released Apr '89, on Epic, by CBS Records. Deleted Oct '89. Catalogue no: **BLOND V3**
7" Single: Released Mar '89, on Epic, by CBS Records. Deleted Oct '89. Catalogue no: **BLOND 3**
12" Single: Released Apr '89, on Epic, by CBS Records. Deleted Oct '89. Catalogue no: **BLOND Q3**
7" EP: Released 20 Mar '89, on Epic, by CBS Records. Deleted Oct '89. Catalogue no: **BLONDE 3**
CD 5": Released Mar '89, on Epic, by CBS Records. Deleted Oct '89. Catalogue no: **BLOND C3**
12" Single: Released Mar '89, on Epic, by CBS Records. Deleted Oct '89. Catalogue no: **BLOND T3**

SHAME ON YOU
Tracks: / Shame on you.
12" Single: Released Jun '88, on Native (1), by Native Records. Catalogue no: **12 BUD 1**
7" Single: Released '88, on Native (1), by Native Records. Catalogue no: **BUD 001**
12" Single: Released 15 Feb '88, on Native (1), by Native Records. Catalogue no: **12 NTV 021**
7" Single: Released 15 Feb '88, on Native (1), by Native Records. Catalogue no: **NTV 021**

THINK OF ME
Tracks: / Think of me.
7" Single: Released Jun '88, on Native (1), by Native Records. Catalogue no: **NTV 32**
12" Single: Released Jun '88, on Native (1), by Native Records. Catalogue no: **12 NTV 32**

YOU'VE GOT TO CHOOSE
Tracks: / You've gotta choose / Mary's got to go.
7" Single: Released Jul '89, on Epic, by CBS Records. Catalogue no: **BLOND G4**
12" Single: Released Jul '89, on Epic, by CBS Records. Catalogue no: **BLOND T4**
7" Single: Released Jul '89, on Epic, by CBS Records. Catalogue no: **BLOND 4**
CD 5": Released Jul '89, on Epic, by CBS Records. Catalogue no: **BLOND C4**
Cassingle: Released Jul '89, on Epic, by CBS Records. Catalogue no: **BLOND M4**

Darlow, Simon

RUN WILD
Tracks: / Run wild / Hot (meltdown mix) / Run wild (the performance mix) (12" version.) / Hot (meltdown mix) (* = On 12" version.) / Run wild (7" version) (On 12" version.).
7" Single: Released Nov '87, on Magnet, by WEA Records. Deleted Jun '88. Catalogue no: **DARL 1**
12" Single: Released Nov '87, on Magnet, by WEA Records. Deleted Jun '88. Catalogue no: **DARLT 1**

Darrell, Guy

I'VE BEEN HURT
Tracks: / I've been hurt.
7" Single: Released Aug '73, on Santa Ponsa, by Pye Records. Deleted Aug '77. Catalogue no: **PNS 4**

Darren, James

BECAUSE THEY'RE YOUNG
Tracks: / Because they're young.
7" Single: Released Aug '60, on Pye International, Deleted Aug '63. Catalogue no: **7N 25059**

CONSCIENCE
Tracks: / Conscience.
7" Single: Released Jun '62, on Pye International, Deleted Jun '65. Catalogue no: **7N 25138**

GOODBYE CRUEL WORLD
Tracks: / Goodbye cruel world.
7" Single: Released Dec '61, on Pye International, Deleted Dec '64. Catalogue no: **7N 25116**

HER ROYAL MAJESTY
Tracks: / Her royal majesty.
7" Single: Released Mar '62, on Pye International, Deleted Mar '65. Catalogue no: **7N 25125**

Darryl Strawberry

CHOCOLATE STRAWBERRY
Tracks: / Chocolate Strawberry.
12" Single: Released Oct '87, on Macola, Catalogue no: **MRC 1041**

D-Art

PRISENCCLINENSINAINC
Tracks: / Prisencclinensinainc / Mystic warrior.
7" Single: Released Mar '87, on WEA (International), by WEA Records. Deleted Jan '88. Catalogue no: **X 8439**
12" Single: Released Mar '87, on WEA (International), by WEA Records. Deleted Jan '88. Catalogue no: **X 8439T**

Darts

Biographical details: At the time of their greatest success, this eight man one woman British group consisted of George Currie, John Drummer, Griff Fender, Bob Fish, Den Hegarty, Horatio Hornblower, Hammy Howell, Rita Ray and Thump Thompson.
This London-based combo (usually referred to as Darts rather than The Darts) claked up six British Top 10 singles in the late Seventies by specialising in tastefully executed revivals of the rock 'n' roll and doo-wap styles of the Fifties and early Sixties. Showaddywaddy, an eight man band from Leicester, seemed to have this market sewn up by the time Darts first charted in late 1977; but whereas Showaddywaddy tended to record familiar oldies (familiar, at least, to older listeners), Darts' approach was mainly to select songs that had not been UK hits before. Their first hit was *Daddy Cool - The Girl Can't Help It*, a medley single that reached No 6 on the UK listings.
1978 brought Darts a unique but frustrating achievement. Three successive singles - *Come Back My Love, Boy From New York City* and *It's Raining* - peaked at No 2, thus making the group the only act in British chart history to score three consecutive No 2 hits without, at any time in their career, reaching No 1. 1979 saw them achieve their final two Top Tenners: *Get It* and *Duke Of Earl*. The latter disc was typical of the band - a faithful and entertaining rendition of a song which, despite being an American No 1 for Gene Chandler, had never before reached the British chart. However, after this single, Darts began to lose their way, partly because of line-up changes. The Eighties brought them just one substantial hit - a 1980 remake of the Four Seasons' biggie *Let's Hang One* - their last minor hit fell off the charts in January 1981. Two months later Shakin' Stevens took over from Darts and Showaddywaddy as the King of the rock 'n; roll revivals. Bob MacDonald, 8 Mrch 1985.
Doo wop revialists formed in the UK in the mid '70's: patronage of deejay Charlie Gillett helped get a successful record contract. Bassist/leader Den Hegarty dominated colourful live act, cunning mix of revival covers and original tunes. Hegarty departed circa '79, taking the verve of the live act with him despite the vocal excellence of replacement Kenny Andrews; others quit. Their impact threatened to transcent nostalgia, but they were a revival act in the mid-80's. The music was always great fun. (Donald Clarke, April 1989)e.

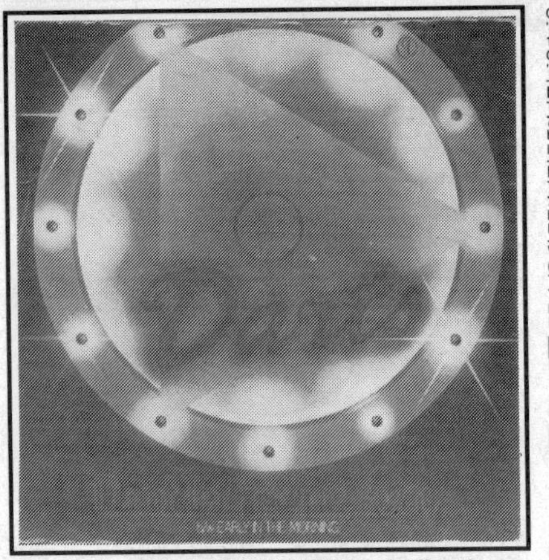

DARTS - DON'T LET IT FADE AWAY (Released on Magnet)

6 TRACK HITS
7" EP: Released Aug '84, on Scoop 33, by Pickwick Records. Catalogue no: **7SR 5046**

BLOW AWAY
Tracks: / Blow away.
7" Single: Released May '85, on Choice Cuts, by Choice Cuts Records. Deleted '86. Catalogue no: **PIG 907**
12" Single: Released May '85, on Choice Cuts, by Choice Cuts Records. Deleted '87. Catalogue no: **12 PIG 907**

BOY FROM NEW YORK CITY
Tracks: / Boy from New York City / Come back my love.
7" Single: Released Sep '81, on Magnet, by WEA Records. Deleted '84. Catalogue no: **MAG 305**
7" Single: Released May '78, on Magnet, by WEA Records. Deleted May '81. Catalogue no: **MAG 116**

CAN'T GET ENOUGH OF YOUR LOVE
Tracks: / Can't get enough of your love.
7" Single: Released Oct '79, on Magnet, by WEA Records. Deleted Oct '82. Catalogue no: **MAG 156**

CAN'T TEACH A FOOL
Tracks: / Can't teach a fool.
7" Single: Released Oct '83, on Choice Cuts, by Choice Cuts Records. Deleted '85. Catalogue no: **PIG 904**

COME BACK MY LOVE
Tracks: / Come back my love.
7" Single: Released Jan '78, on Magnet, by WEA Records. Deleted Jan '81. Catalogue no: **MAG 110**

DADDY COOL - THE GIRL CAN'T HELP IT
Tracks: / Daddy cool - the girl can't help it.
7" Single: Released Nov '77, on Magnet, by WEA Records. Deleted Nov '80. Catalogue no: **MAG 100**

DON'T LET IT FADE AWAY (see panel above)
Tracks: / Don't let it fade away / Early in the morning.
7" Single: Released Nov '78, on Magnet, by WEA Records. Deleted Nov '81. Catalogue no: **MAG 134**

DUKE OF EARL
Tracks: / Duke of Earl.
7" Single: Released Jul '79, on Magnet, by WEA Records. Deleted Jul '82. Catalogue no: **MAG 147**

GET IT
Tracks: / Get it.
7" Single: Released Feb '79, on Magnet, by WEA Records. Deleted Feb '82. Catalogue no: **MAG 140**

GROOVIN'
Tracks: / Groovin'.
7" Single: Released Jun '84, on Choice Cuts, by Choice Cuts Records. Deleted '85. Catalogue no: **PIG 906**

IT'S RAINING
Tracks: / It's raining.
7" Single: Released Aug '78, on Magnet, by WEA Records. Deleted Aug '81. Catalogue no: **MAG 126**

JUMP, CHILDREN, JUMP
Tracks: / Jump, children, jump / Green for go.
7" Single: Released Jun '81, on Magnet, by WEA Records. Deleted Jun '84. Catalogue no: **MAG 203**

LET'S HANG ON
Tracks: / Let's hang on / Cairoli.
7" Single: Released May '80, on Magnet, by WEA Records. Deleted May '83. Catalogue no: **MAG 174**

LORRAINE
Tracks: / Lorraine.
7" Single: Released Aug '82, on Sunburst, by Sunburst Records. Catalogue no: **EXP 1**
7" Single: Released Jul '83, on Choice Cuts, by Choice Cuts Records. Deleted '85. Catalogue no: **PIG 902**
12" Single: Released Aug '82, on Sunburst, by Sunburst Records. Catalogue no: **EXP 112**

MYSTERY RAGOULA
Tracks: / Mystery ragoula.
7" Single: Released Apr '83, on Choice Cuts, by Choice Cuts Records. Deleted '85. Catalogue no: **PIG 901**
12" Single: Released Apr '83, on Choice Cuts, by Choice Cuts Records. Deleted '85. Catalogue no: **12 PIG 901**

PEACHES
Tracks: / Peaches / D.I.Y. hearache.
7" Single: Released Sep '80, on Magnet, by WEA Records. Deleted Sep '83. Catalogue no: **MAG 179**

REET PETITE
Tracks: / Reet petite.
7" Single: Released Dec '79, on Magnet, by WEA Records. Deleted Dec '82. Catalogue no: **MAG 160**

WHITE CHRISTMAS/SH-BOOM (LIFE COULD BE A DREAM)
Tracks: / White Christmas / Sh'boom.
7" Single: Released Nov '80, on Magnet, by WEA Records. Deleted Nov '83. Catalogue no: **MAG 184**

Das Man Macanik

V.T.
Tracks: / V.T..
12" Single: Released 24 Jul '89, on Institute, Catalogue no: **12 INS 004**

Das Psych-Oh Rangers

HOMAGE TO THE BLESSED
Tracks: / Homage to the blessed / Essential art of communication, The / He he radical / Medea tearorists.
7" Single: Released Oct '86, on ZTT, by ZTT Records. Deleted Apr '88. Catalogue no: **ZTAS 24**
12" Single: Released Oct '86, on ZTT, by ZTT Records. Catalogue no: **12 ZTAS 24**

LOVE TERMINATOR
Tracks: / Love terminator.
CD 5": Released Jul '88, on Stress, Catalogue no: **STRESS 1 CD**
7" Single: Released Jul '88, on Stress, Catalogue no: **STRESS 1**
12" Single: Released Jul '88, on Stress, Catalogue no: **STRESS 1-12**

Dat Sound

I LIKE THE WAY YOU DO IT
Tracks: / I like the way you do it / I like the way you do it (version).
7" Single: Released 20 Mar '89, on SSR, Catalogue no: **SSR 701**
12" Single: Released 20 Mar '89, on SSR, Catalogue no: **SRR 001**

Data

BLOW
Tracks: / Blow.
12" Single: Released Feb '85, on Illuminated, Catalogue no: **ILL 4512**

FEVER OF LOVE
Tracks: / Fever of love.
7" Single: Released Jul '81, on Original, Deleted Jul '82. Catalogue no: **ABO 7**

LIVING INSIDE ME
Tracks: / Living inside me / No bungalow.
7" Single: Released Apr '85, on Illuminated, Catalogue no: **ILL 21**

RICOCHETED LOVE
Tracks: / Richocheted love / In love... DJ (Double A side).
7" Single: Released Jan '86, on Sire (USA), Catalogue no: **ENA 133**
12" Single: Released Jan '86, on Sire (USA), Catalogue no: **ENAT 133**

STOP
Tracks: / Stop.
7" Single: Released Sep '85, on Proto, by Proto Records. Catalogue no: **ENA 129**
12" Single: Released Sep '85, on Proto, by Proto Records. Catalogue no: **ENAT 129**

Data-Bank

ONE WAY EP
Tracks: / Crack dream over again / Severed from the song/ One way / Final glory.
CD 5": Released Apr '89, on Lively Arts, by New Rose Records. Catalogue no: **ARTY 7CD**

Datblygu

HUGR-GRAWTH-OG
Tracks: / Hugr-grawth-og.
7" Single: Released Feb '87, on Anhrefn, Catalogue no: **ANHREFN 008**

Datc Orchestra

JUNGLE SIGNAL
Tracks: / Jungle signal.
12" Single: Released Sep '82, on DATC, Catalogue no: **DATC 01**

Datcher, Clarke

THINGS CAN'T GET ANY WORSE
Tracks: / Things can't get any worse.
7" Single: Released Nov '84, on RAK, by EMI Records. Catalogue no: **RAK 379**

YOU FOOLED HIM ONCE AGAIN
Tracks: / You fooled him once again.
7" Single: Released Oct '81, on Blue Knight, Catalogue no: **INC 14 7**
12" Single: Released Oct '81, on Blue Knight, Catalogue no: **INC 14 12**

Dave Dee, Dozy...

BEND IT (SINGLE)
Tracks: / Bend it.
7" Single: Released Sep '66, on Fontana, by Phonogram Ltd. Deleted Sep '69. Catalogue no: **TF 746**

DON JUAN
Tracks: / Don Juan.
7" Single: Released Mar '69, on Fontana, by Phonogram Ltd. Deleted Mar '72. Catalogue no: **TF 1000**

HIDEAWAY
Tracks: / Hideaway.
7" Single: Released Jun '66, on Fontana, by Phonogram Ltd. Deleted Jun '69. Catalogue no: **TF 711**

HOLD TIGHT
Tracks: / Hold tight.
7" Single: Released Mar '66, on Fontana, by Phonogram Ltd. Deleted Mar '68. Catalogue no: **TF 671**

HOLD TIGHT (EP)
Tracks: / Hold tight / Zabadak / Legend of Xanadu / Bend it.
7" EP: Released Oct '80, on Phonogram, by Phonogram Ltd. Deleted Oct '83. Catalogue no: **CUT 105**

HOLD TIGHT (OLD GOLD)
Tracks: / Hold tight.
7" Single: Released Jan '85, on Old Gold, by Old Gold Records. Catalogue no: **OG 9472**

IN THE COVEN
Tracks: / In the coven / I can't stop wanting you.
7" Single: Released Mar '81, on Earlobe, by Earlobe Records. Deleted Mar '84. Catalogue no: **ELB S 103**

LAST NIGHT IN SOHO
Tracks: / Last night in Soho.
7" Single: Released Jul '68, on Fontana, by Phonogram Ltd. Deleted Jul '71. Catalogue no: **TF 953**

LEGEND OF XANADU
Tracks: / Legend of Xanadu.
7" Single: Released Feb '68, on Fontana, by Phonogram Ltd. Deleted Feb '71. Catalogue no: **TF 903**

LEGEND OF XANADU (OLD GOLD)
Tracks: / Legend of Xanadu.
7" Single: Released Jul '82, on Old Gold, by Old Gold Records. Deleted Jul '88. Catalogue no: **OG 9234**

OKAY
Tracks: / Okay.
7" Single: Released May '67, on Fontana, by Phonogram Ltd. Deleted May '70. Catalogue no: **TF 830**

SAVE ME
Tracks: / Save me.
7" Single: Released Dec '66, on Fontana, by Phonogram Ltd. Deleted Dec '69. Catalogue no: **TF 775**

SNAKE IN THE GRASS
Tracks: / Snake in the grass.
7" Single: Released May '69, on Fontana, by Phonogram Ltd. Deleted May '72. Catalogue no: **TF 1020**

TOUCH ME TOUCH ME
Tracks: / Touch me touch me.
7" Single: Released Mar '67, on Fontana, by Phonogram Ltd. Deleted Mar '70. Catalogue no: **TF 798**

WRECK OF THE ANTOINETTE
Tracks: / Wreck of the Antoinette.
7" Single: Released Oct '68, on Fontana, by Phonogram Ltd. Deleted Oct '71. Catalogue no: **TF 971**

YOU MAKE IT MOVE
Tracks: / You make it move.
7" Single: Released Dec '65, on Fontana, by Phonogram Ltd. Deleted Dec '68. Catalogue no: **TF 630**

ZABADAK
Tracks: / Zabadak.
7" Single: Released Oct '67, on Fontana, by Phonogram Ltd. Deleted Oct '70. Catalogue no: **TF 873**

Davey, Damien

I'M A MAN
Tracks: / I'm a man / Sounds so fine.
7" Single: Released May '87, on Passion, by Skratch Records. Catalogue no: **PASH 71**
12" Single: Released May '87, on Passion, by Skratch Records. Catalogue no: **PASH 71(12)**

Davey, Shaun

SAMSON
Tracks: / Samson / Armorica.
7" Single: Released Dec '84, on CMS, Catalogue no: **CMS 500**

David

AM I NORMAL?
Tracks: / Am I normal?.
7" Single: Released Jan '83, on Stiletto, by Fast Forward Distribution. Catalogue no: **STL 11**
12" Single: Released Jan '83, on Stiletto, by Fast Forward Distribution. Catalogue no: **STLT 11**

David, Alan

DREAMING
Tracks: / Dreaming / Always a dream.
7" Single: Released Apr '81, on EMI, by EMI Records. Deleted '85. Catalogue no: **EMI 5159**

MAIN STREET
Tracks: / Mainstreet / Heartache.
7" Single: Released Sep '81, on EMI, by EMI Records. Deleted '84. Catalogue no: **EMI 5204**

David, Anne-Marie

WONDERFUL DREAM
Tracks: / Wonderful dream, A.
7" Single: Released Apr '73, on Epic, by CBS Records. Deleted '76. Catalogue no: **EPC 1446**

David & David

AIN'T SO EASY
Tracks: / Ain't so easy / Let's just be heroes / Swimming in the ocean (Only on 12" single.).
7" Single: Released May '87, on A&M, by A&M Records. Deleted Mar '88. Catalogue no: **AM 390**
12" Single: Released May '87, on A&M, by A&M Records. Deleted Mar '88. Catalogue no: **AMY 390**

BOOMTOWN (SINGLE)
Tracks: / Boomtown / Rock for the forgotten, A.
7" Single: Released Oct '86, on A&M, by A&M Records. Deleted Mar '88. Catalogue no: **AM 348**
12" Single: Released Oct '86, on A&M, by A&M Records. Deleted Mar '88. Catalogue no: **AMY 348**

SWALLOWED BY THE CRACKS
Tracks: / Swallowed by the cracks / Alone in the big city / Swimming in the ocean (Only on 12" single.).
7" Single: Released Jan '87, on A&M, by A&M Records. Deleted Mar '88. Catalogue no: **AM 371**
12" Single: Released Jan '87, on A&M, by A&M Records. Deleted Mar '88. Catalogue no: **AMY 371**

David, F.R.

Biographical details: This French singer is known solely for his smash hit *Words*, which topped charts around Europe in late 1982 and hit No 2 in Britain in spring '83. Its eventual UK success was caused by its exposure on BBC TV's Top Of The Pops - the disc was featured on the first edition of a special Euro-slot incorporated in the programme. The Euro feature had a very brief life, although it was never clear whether or not its abolition was the producers' comment on the success of *Words*! The song was a catchy, slightly plaintive mid-tempo ballad sung in a slender, high-pitched voice. Indeed, such was Monsieur David's singing style that radio listeners all over Europe thought the single was by Madame David until seeing him. Either way, his follow-up singles, all issued on Carrere Records, plunged him back into obscurity. Bob MacDonald, 8 March 1985..

I NEED YOU
Tracks: / I need you.
7" Single: Released Sep '83, on Carrere, Catalogue no: **CAR 288**

MUSIC
Tracks: / Music.
7" Single: Released Jun '83, on Carrere, Catalogue no: **CAR 282**

PICK UP THE PHONE
Tracks: / Pick up the phone / Someone to love.
7" Single: Released Feb '83, on Carrere, Catalogue no: **CAR 260**

SAHARA NIGHTS
Tracks: / Sahara nights.
7" Single: Released Aug '86, on Epic, by CBS Records. Catalogue no: **A 7206**
12" Single: Released Aug '86, on Epic, by CBS Records. Catalogue no: **TA 7206**

THIS TIME I HAVE TO WIN
Tracks: / This time I have to win.
7" Single: Released Apr '85, on Carrere, Catalogue no: **CAR 359**
12" Single: Released Jul '85, on Carrere, Catalogue no: **CART 359**

F.R. DAVID - WORDS (Released on Carrere)

WORDS (see panel above)
Tracks: / Words / When the sun goes down.
7" Single: Released '82, on Carrere, Catalogue no: **CAR 248**

David, Ian

I MUST JUST LEAVE A KISS (SINGLE)
Tracks: / I must just leave a kiss.
7" Single: Released Sep '89, on Zonespec, Catalogue no: **DVD 1**
12" Single: Released Sep '89, on Zonespec, Catalogue no: **DVD 112**

David, Joel

BE MY VALENTINE TONIGHT
Tracks: / Be my valentine tonight / Old bones.
7" Single: Released Jan '88, on Old Gold, by Old Gold Records. Catalogue no: **OLD 2**

OLD BONES
Tracks: / Old bones / Be my valentine tonight.
CD 5": Released Jul '88, on Old, by Old Records. Catalogue no: **OLDCD 1**
7" Single: Released Jul '88, on Old, by Old Records. Catalogue no: **OLD 1**

David, John

I COULDN'T SAY NO
Tracks: / I couldn't say no / I'm giving it up.
7" Single: Released Apr '84, on Albion, by Albion Records. Catalogue no: **ION 162**

ON THE MOUNTAIN
Tracks: / On the mountain / Emma.
7" Single: Released Jul '83, on Albion, by Albion Records. Catalogue no: **ION 1051**

David & Jonathan

LOVERS OF THE WORLD UNITE (OLD GOLD)
Tracks: / Lovers of the world unite.
7" Single: Released Oct '83, on Old Gold, by Old Gold Records. Deleted Sep '89. Catalogue no: **OG 9382**

LOVERS OF THE WORLD UNITE (SINGLE)
Tracks: / Lovers of the world unite

7" Single: Released Jul '66, on Columbia, by EMI Records. Deleted Jul '69. Catalogue no: **DB 7950**

MICHELLE
Tracks: / Michelle.
7" Single: Released Jan '66, on Columbia, by EMI Records. Deleted Jan '69. Catalogue no: **DB 7800**

David, Matthew

DON'T LET LOVE GET YOU DOWN
Tracks: / Don't let love get you down.

12" Single: Released May '86, on Bluebird (2), by BMG Records (UK). Catalogue no: **BRT 23**

Davidson, Howard

VOYAGE OF THE HEROES
Tracks: / Voyage of the heroes.
7" Single: Released Oct '85, on BBC, by BBC Records & Tapes. Deleted 31 Aug '88. Catalogue no: **RESL 169**

Davidson, Jim

Biographical details: British comedian Davidson came to national fame in the mid-70's, gaining his first big break through a TV talent show. During the late Seventies and early ighties, he established himself as one of the UK's top funnymen, although there was little of originality to distinguish him from legions of other stand-up comics that had gone before. Like every comedian, Davidson had his catch-phrase - his was "Too Risky", which provided the title of one side of his sole British chart entry. This double A sided single, which reached No 52 in December 1980, also included his rendition of *White Christmas*. (Bob MacDonald, 10 March 1985.).

DEVIL WENT DOWN TO BRIXTON, THE
Tracks: / Devil went down to Brixton, The / Rock'n'roll the night away.
7" Single: Released Aug '80, on Scratch, by Scratch Records. Deleted '82. Catalogue no: **HS 407**

ENGLAND
Tracks: / I love the sun / England.
7" Single: Released Dec '86, on Sierra, by Sierra Records. Catalogue no: **FED 31**

MAGGIE
Tracks: / Maggie.
7" Single: Released Aug '85, on Relax, Catalogue no: **LAX 4**
12" Single: Released Sep '85, on Relax, Catalogue no: **LAXD 4**

MUCH TOO LATE FOR THAT
Tracks: / Much too late for that / Excerpt from Too Risky.
7" Single: Released May '81, on Scratch, by Scratch Records. Deleted May '84. Catalogue no: **SCR 004**

SILVER THREADS
Tracks: / Silver threads.
7" Single: Released Jan '85, on Relax, Catalogue no: **LAX 3**

SUPERSTAR AND THE ROADIE
Tracks: / Superstar and the roadie.
7" Single: Released Dec '81, on Rock City, Catalogue no: **RC 7002**

WHITE CHRISTMAS
Tracks: / White Christmas / Too risky.
7" Single: Released Nov '80, on Scratch, by Scratch Records. Catalogue no: **SCR 001**

Davidson, Michael

TURN IT UP
Tracks: / Turn it up.
7" Single: Released Sep '87, on Warner Bros., by WEA Records. Deleted Jul '88. Catalogue no: **W 8219**
12" Single: Released Sep '87, on Warner Bros., by WEA Records. Deleted Jul '88. Catalogue no: **W 8219 T**

Davidson, Paul

MIDNIGHT RIDER
Tracks: / Midnight rider.
7" Single: Released Dec '75, on Tropical, Deleted '78. Catalogue no: **ALO 56**

SOMEONE NEW
Tracks: / Someone new.
12" Single: Released Nov '88, on Central Zone, Catalogue no: **CZ 001**

Davidsons

LIKE AN ASTRONAUT
Tracks: / Like an astronaut.
12" Single: Released Jul '88, on Cake, by Cake Records. Catalogue no: **12 PIECE 6**
12" Single: Released Oct '88, on Native (1), by Native Records. Catalogue no: **12 NTV 35**

MUSCLE JERKS (EP)
7" EP: Released Jul '87, on Cake, by Cake Records. Catalogue no: **12 PIECE 4**

Davies, Carol

BUNNY AND THE BUBBLE
Tracks: / Bunny and the bubble.
7" Single: Released Oct '84, on EKL, Catalogue no: **EKL 79**

Davies, Craig

I DON'T WANT IT
Tracks: / I don't want it.
12" Single: Released Jul '87, on Rough Trade, by Rough Trade Records. Catalogue no: **RTT 212**

JENNIFER HOLLIDAY
Tracks: / Jennifer Holliday.
7" Single: Released Mar '88, on Rough Trade, by Rough Trade Records. Catalogue no: **RT 222**
12" Single: Released Mar '88, on Rough Trade, by Rough Trade Records. Catalogue no: **RTT 222**

Davies, Cyril

Biographical details: One of the pioneers of British blues, born in Buckinghamshire in 1932. He had played banjo in trad and skiffle, then harmonica with Alexis Korner, jamming with visiting black Americans; in the early '60's they went electric and formed Blues Incorporated: future Rolling Stones and Cream passed through; Davies left and formed his own All-Stars, taking over Screaming Lord Sutch's Savages; he employed Nicky Hopkins and others. After his death from leukemia in 1964 vocalist Long John Baldry took over most of All Stars. *Country Line Special* is a 4-track 12" EP. (Donald Clarke, April 1989)t.

COUNTRY LINE SPECIAL
Tracks: / Country line special / Chicago calling / Preachin' the blues.
7" Single: Released Jun '84, on PRT, by Castle Communications Records. Catalogue no: **7P 308**
12" Single: Released Jun '84, on PRT, by Castle Communications Records. Catalogue no: **12P 308**

Davies, Dave

Biographical details: Dave was just 17 when he shot to fame as lead guitarist with elder brother Ray's classic British rock band the Kinks. The rough-edged, driving, *You Really Got Me*, a UK No 1 and US Top Tenner that year, was the first of a string of great Kinks hits written by Ray. During a lull in the band's touring programme Dave decided to launch a subsidiary solo career and his first single, *Death Of A Clown*, stormed to No 3 in Britain in August '67, two months after the Kinks had reached No 2 with the beautiful single *Waterloo Sunset*, one of the songs which marked the now mellower, more melodic sound of the band. Although written by Dave, *Death Of A Clown* was produced by Ray and featured backing by the Kinks. His follow-up solo effort, *Susannah's Still Alive*, reached No 20 but subsequent outings, such as 1968's good but slightly cliched *Lincoln County*, flopped at a time when the group themselves were in chart decline. Dave's solo career went into cold storage, but he has subsequently made a few uninteresting and unsuccessful releases. Meanwhile he continued with the Kinks through the 70's and 80's: they had their ups and downs but built up a large following in the States, scoring one of their biggest international hits with 1983's *Come Dancing*. (Bob MacDonald, 10 March 1985.).

DEATH OF A CLOWN
Tracks: / Death of a clown.
7" Single: Released Jul '67, on Pye, Deleted '70. Catalogue no: **7N 17356**

DEATH OF A CLOWN (OLD GOLD)
Tracks: / Death of a clown / Susannah's still alive.
7" Single: Released Aug '82, on Old Gold, by Old Gold Records. Catalogue no: **OG 9128**

DOING THE BEST FOR YOU
Tracks: / Doing the best for you / Wild man.
7" Single: Released Jan '81, on RCA, by BMG Records (UK). Deleted Jan '84. Catalogue no: **PB 9620**

SUSANNAH'S STILL ALIVE
Tracks: / Susannah's still alive.
7" Single: Released Dec '67, on Pye, Deleted '70. Catalogue no: **7N 17429**

Davies, Freddie

SO LUCKY
Tracks: / So lucky / If you never went away.
7" Single: Released Mar '81, on PRT, by Castle Communications Records. Deleted Mar '84. Catalogue no: **7P 211**

Davies, Gail

Biographical details: Country music singer/songwriter born in Oklahoma in 1948. She scuffled on the road, had a writer's contract with Screen Gems and began making here own hit albums in 1978 on Lifesong, which folded; she went to Warner Brothers in 1979 and became the first female in country music to produce her own records, switching to RCA in 1984. (Donald Clarke, April 1989)n.

GIVIN' HERSELF AWAY
Tracks: / Givin' herself away / It's amazing what a little love can do.
7" Single: Released Apr '82, on Warner Bros., by WEA Records. Deleted Apr '85. Catalogue no: **K 17916**

JAGGED EDGE OF A BROKEN HEART
Tracks: / Jagged edge of a broken heart / Lion in the winter.
7" Single: Released Apr '85, on RCA, by BMG Records (UK). Catalogue no: **RCA 481**

Davies, Lesley A.

IF I TOLD YOU A LIE I'M SORRY
Tracks: / If I told you a lie I'm sorry.
12" Single: Released Dec '83, on Sea View, Catalogue no: **SV 2**

Davies, Ray (Kinks)

QUIET LIFE
Tracks: / Quiet life / Voices in the dark.
Note: From the soundtrack of the film "Absolute Beginners"
7" Single: Released May '86, on Virgin, by Virgin Records. Deleted '89. Catalogue no: **VS 865**
12" Single: Released May '86, on Virgin, by Virgin Records. Deleted '89. Catalogue no: **VS 865-12**

Davies, Richie

FLASHBACKS
Tracks: / Flashbacks.
12" Single: Released Dec '88, on Unity, Catalogue no: **FEA 04**

HOW I FEEL FOR YOU
Tracks: / How I feel for you.
12" Single: Released Apr '88, on High Power, Catalogue no: **HPD 04**

Davies, Stephanie

I'M A GIRL
Tracks: / I'm a girl (part 1) / I'm a girl (part 2).
7" Single: Released Mar '80, on Polydor, by Polydor Ltd. Deleted '83. Catalogue no: **POSP 139**

Davies, Windsor

Biographical details: This British actor became a household name during the Seventies, thanks to his domineering role in 'It Ain't Half Hot, Mum', one of BBC TV's most successful situation comedy series of that period. The shows were written by Jimmy Perry and David Croft, who were also responsible for another famous BBC army comedy, 'Dad's Army'. Perry and Croft made maximum comic use of the contrast between the programme's two most differing characters - Davies, the moustached martinet, and tiny Don Estelle, who played the long suffering Lofty. In 1975 EMI teamed the Sergeant Major and Lofty on disc: *Whispering Grass*, an evergreen song written many years earlier by Fred and Doris Fisher, was sung by Estelle with frequent spoken interruptions from Davies. It was a UK smash, and logged three weeks at No 1 in June '75. The single's success was due in no small way to the excellent voice of Estelle, who proved decisively that, were it not for his acting abilities, he could have made a good living as a singer.
As with all novelty hits, a follow-up was hard to come by, although the duo did hit No 41 on the British charts with a rendition of the Mills Brothers' early Forties smash *Paper Doll*. They even managed a Top 10 album in early '76 with *Sing Lofty*. Although Estelle released further records, none of which charted, Davies returned to where he belonged - on television screens and in theatres. Bob MacDonald, 10 March 1985..

PAPER DOLL
Tracks: / Paper doll.
7" Single: Released Oct '75, on EMI, by EMI Records. Deleted '78. Catalogue no: **EMI 2361**

WHISPERING GRASS
Tracks: / Whispering grass / Paper doll.
7" Single: Released Nov '80, on H.M.V., by EMI Records. Deleted '83. Catalogue no: **POP 2013**
7" Single: Released May '75, on EMI, by EMI Records. Deleted '78. Catalogue no: **EMI 2290**

WHISPERING GRASS (OLD GOLD)
Tracks: / Whispering grass.
7" Single: Released Oct '83, on Old Gold, by Old Gold Records. Catalogue no: **OG 9383**

Davis, Billie

HE'S THE ONE
Tracks: / He's the one.
7" Single: Released May '63, on Decca, by Decca Records. Deleted '66. Catalogue no: **F 11658**

I WANT YOU TO BE MY BABY
Tracks: / I want you to be my baby.
7" Single: Released Oct '68, on Decca, by Decca Records. Deleted '71. Catalogue no: **F 12823**
7" Single: Released Aug '72, on Decca, by Decca Records. Deleted '88. Catalogue no: **F 13334**

KISS, THE
Tracks: / Kiss, The.
7" Single: Released Dec '84, on Alternative, Deleted '88. Catalogue no: **AKISS 1**
12" Single: Released Dec '84, on Alternative, Deleted '88. Catalogue no: **AKISS 2**

TELL HIM
Tracks: / Tell him.
7" Single: Released Feb '63, on Decca, by Decca Records. Deleted '66. Catalogue no: **F 11572**
7" Single: Released Aug '85, on Old Gold, by Old Gold Records. Catalogue no: **OG 9537**

Davis Brothers

LOOKING FOR THE MONEY
Tracks: / Looking for the money / If i need anybody.
7" Single: Released Feb '80, on Charisma, by Virgin Records. Deleted Feb '85. Catalogue no: **CB 343**

Davis, Carl

CHAMPIONS THEME
Tracks: / Champions theme / Grand National.
7" Single: Released Apr '84, on Island, by Island Records. Catalogue no: **IS 161**

FEELING LOVE ON THE SIDE
Tracks: / Feeling love on the side.
12" Single: Released May '85, on Sonic Sounds, Catalogue no: **UNKNOWN**

HOLLYWOOD
Tracks: / Hollywood / Wagons roll.
7" Single: Released Jan '80, on EMI International, by EMI Records. Deleted '83. Catalogue no: **INT 592**

Davis, Carlene

BABY BUNNY
Tracks: / Baby bunny / Baby bunny (instrumental).
12" Single: Released Jul '86, on Vanessa, by Vanessa Records. Catalogue no: **VRPD 258**

BURNING UP
Tracks: / Burning up.
12" Single: Released Nov '88, on E.K.O. Records, Catalogue no: **UNKNOWN**

FIRST WORD, THE
Tracks: / First word, The.
12" Single: Released Jun '85, on Revue, by Creole Records. Catalogue no: **REV 026T**

LOVE A WOMAN SHOULD GIVE TO A MAN, A
Tracks: / Love a woman.
12" Single: Released May '84, on Moby Dick, Catalogue no: **MM 79**

REGGAE REBEL
Tracks: / Reggae rebel.
12" Single: Released 20 Feb '88, on Charm, by Charm Records. Catalogue no: **CART 14**

SANTA CLAUS
Tracks: / Santa Claus.
12" Single: Released Dec '84, on Creole, by Creole Records. Catalogue no: **CR 1243**

SWEET DREAMS
Tracks: / Sweet dreams.
12" Single: Released 22 Aug '88, on Nicole, Catalogue no: **VPRD 340**
12" Single: Released Dec '88, on Charm, by Charm Records. Catalogue no: **CRT 27**

WINNIE MANDELA
Tracks: / Winnie Mandela / One by one.
12" Single: Released 23 May '87, on Greensleeves, by Greensleeves Records. Catalogue no: **GRED 210**

WITH YOU
Tracks: / With you.
12" Single: Released Dec '84, on Nicole, Catalogue no: **VPRD 223**

WONDERING NOW
12" Single: Released May '88, on Angstar, by Angstar Records. Catalogue no: **CGDD 105**

Davis, Darlene

I FOUND LOVE (The Belated '87 Valentine)
Tracks: / I found love / I found love (premature '88 mix).
7" Single: Released Mar '87, on Serious, by Serious Records. Catalogue no: **OUSX 1**

I FOUND LOVE (RADIO MIX)
Tracks: / I found love (radio mix) / I found love (inst mix) / Dare to dance (Available on 12" version only).
Note: Dare to dance available on 12" version only.
12" Single: Released Feb '87, on Serious, by Serious Records. Catalogue no: **12OUS 1**
7" Single: Released Feb '87, on Serious, by Serious Records. Catalogue no: **7OUS 1**

Davis, Desmond

WENT DOWNTOWN
Tracks: / Went downtown.
12" Single: Released Oct '82, on Real Wax, Catalogue no: **RW 104**

Davis, James

HOLLYWOOD
Tracks: / Hollywood / Holding you close.
7" Single: Released May '80, on Active, by Active Records. Deleted May '85. Catalogue no: **ACT 6**

Davis, Janet

NEVER GONNA LET YOU GO
Tracks: / Never gonna let you go.
7" Single: Released Oct '88, on Flash Music, Catalogue no: **FID 007**

PRISONER OF LOVE
Tracks: / Prisoner of love.
12" Single: Released Jun '89, on High Power, Catalogue no: **HPD 015**

TWO TIMING LOVER
Tracks: / Two timing lover.
12" Single: Released Feb '89, on Fine Style, by Fashion Records. Catalogue no: **FS 020**

Davis, John

Biographical details: This American orchestra leader enjoyed two weeks of UK chart action in 1979 when *Ain't That Enough For You?*, by John Davis & The Monster Orchestra, peaked at No 70 on the Top Seventy-Five singles list. It was one of many disco hits of the period to feature an anonymous array of singers and musicians. (Bob MacDonald, March 1985.).

AIN'T THAT ENOUGH FOR YOU? (SINGLE)
Tracks: / Ain't that enough for you?.
7" Single: Released Feb '79, on Miracle, by Gull Records. Deleted '82. Catalogue no: **M 2**

Davis, Johnny

EXPAND YOUR MIND
Tracks: / Expand your mind.
7" Single: Released Mar '85, on Creole, by Creole Records. Catalogue no: **CR 75**

Davis, Leslie

I WON'T LET YOU DOWN
Tracks: / I won't let you down / Dry your eyes.
12" Single: Released Feb '87, on Union, Catalogue no: **UND 1111**

Davis, Mac

Biographical details: This American singer songwriter, born in Lubbock, Texas, began playing rock 'n' roll in the late Fifties. During the Sixties he worked as an executive in the record and music publishing industries, while refining his songwriting techniques. His big breakthrough came in 1969, when Elvis Presley recorded his song *In The Ghetto* and took it to the Top 3 on both sides of the Atlantic - this hit had an added significance because, in both the US and UK, it gave Elvis his biggest single for four years, and marked a career resurgence for the King after half a dozen years in the wasteland of forgettable films. Hence, *In The Ghetto* led to numerous other artists recording Davis' material. During 1969-71, other hit Davis songs included, in America, *Daddy's Little Man* (O C Smith) and *Watching Scotty Grow* (Bobby Goldsboro) and, in both America and Britain, *Don't Cry Daddy* (Elvis again) and *Something's Burning* (Kenny Rogers & the First Edition). All were in a country music vein but with a mild hint of Southern Rock; and all were sentimental while managing to stay just this side of schmaltzy.

This success led to Davis resuming his performing career and, in 1972, he landed his first - and biggest - US hit as an artist. *Baby Don't Get Hooked On Me* reached No 1 in the States and hit No 29 in Britain. This single showed that, as a performer, Davis was including a trace of humour into his act in order to offset the sentimentality. The mid-Seventies saw him enjoy three US Top 20 singles in quick succession with *One Hell Of A Woman, Stop And Smell The Roses* and *Rock 'N' Roll (I Gave You The Best Years Of My Life)*, the latter a UK hit for Kevin Johnson. He then faded into the background, to the undoubted delight of 'Rolling Stone' magazine whose "Rolling Stone Record Guide" gave every Mac Davis album a zero star rating! However, he bounced back briefly in late 1980 with the delightful *It's Hard To Be Humble*, a comedy song recorded live. This single fared notably well in Britain, where it peaked at No 27 but logged an impressive total of 15 weeks on the Top 75. Bob MacDonald, 11 March 1985..

BABY DON'T GET HOOKED ON ME
Tracks: / Baby don't get hooked on me.
7" Single: Released Nov '72, on CBS, by CBS Records. Deleted '75. Catalogue no: **CBS 8250**

CAROLINE'S STILL IN GEORGIA
Tracks: / Caroline's still in Georgia / Most of all.
7" Single: Released Apr '84, on Casablanca, by PolyGram UK Ltd. Catalogue no: **CAN 1019**

IT'S HARD TO BE HUMBLE (SINGLE)
Tracks: / It's hard to be humble.
7" Single: Released Nov '80, on Casablanca, by PolyGram UK Ltd. Deleted '83. Catalogue no: **CAN 210**

ME AND FAT BOY
Tracks: / Me and fat boy / Hooked on music.
7" Single: Released May '81, on Casablanca, by PolyGram UK Ltd. Deleted May '84. Catalogue no: **CAN 1002**

TEQUILA SHEILA
Tracks: / Tequila Sheila / It was time.
7" Single: Released Jan '81, on Casablanca, by PolyGram UK Ltd. Deleted Jan '84. Catalogue no: **CAN 219**

YOU'RE MY BESTEST FRIEND
Tracks: / You're my bestest friend / Midnight crazy.
7" Single: Released Feb '82, on Casablanca, by PolyGram UK Ltd. Deleted Feb '87. Catalogue no: **CAN 1007**

Davis, Mary

STEPPING OUT
Tracks: / Stepping out / I'm gonna love you better.
12" Single: Released 21 Nov '87, on Tabu, Catalogue no: **651256 6**
7" Single: Released 21 Nov '87, on Tabu, Catalogue no: **651256 7**

Davis, Paul

65 LOVE AFFAIR
Tracks: / 65 love affair.
7" Single: Released '82, on Arista, by BMG Records (UK). Deleted '87. Catalogue no: **ARIST 469**

COOL NIGHTS
Tracks: / Cool night / One more time for the lonely.
7" Single: Released '82, on Arista, by BMG Records (UK). Deleted '87. Catalogue no: **ARIST 449**

Davis, Phil

BLOWN IT
Tracks: / Blown it / Blown it (part 2).
7" Single: Released Mar '80, on Rocket, by Rocket Records. Deleted '83. Catalogue no: **ZPRES 27**

Davis Pinckney Pro.

TOP, BOTTOM, SIDE AND REAR
Tracks: / Top, bottom, side and rear / Top, bottom, side and rear (inst).
12" Single: Released Apr '87, on Polydor, by Polydor Ltd. Deleted Mar '88. Catalogue no: **POSPX 858**
7" Single: Released Apr '87, on Polydor, by Polydor Ltd. Deleted Aug '87. Catalogue no: **POSP 858**

YOU CAN DANCE (IF YOU WANT TO)
Tracks: / You can dance.
7" Single: Released Nov '86, on Boiling Point, by Polydor Ltd. Deleted Aug '87. Catalogue no: **POSP 836**
12" Single: Released Nov '86, on Boiling Point, by Polydor Ltd. Deleted Aug '87. Catalogue no: **POSPX 836**

Davis, Richie

CALL ME
Tracks: / Call me.
7" Single: Released 21 Apr '89, on High Power, Catalogue no: **HPD 013**

DREAM
Tracks: / Dream.
12" Single: Released Oct '89, on Power, Catalogue no: **PW 89005**

GOODBYE
Tracks: / Goodbye.
12" Single: Released Mar '89, on Unity, Catalogue no: **FEA 09**

THINKING OF ME
Tracks: / Thinking of me.
7" Single: Released Dec '88, on High Power, Catalogue no: **HPD 05**

Davis, Ronnie

LOVE I CAN FEEL
Tracks: / Love I can feel.
12" Single: Released Sep '84, on GG'S, Catalogue no: **GG 123**

PLAY ME
Tracks: / Play me.
12" Single: Released Jun '85, on Top Rank (2), Catalogue no: **TR 006**

Davis, Sammy Jnr.

Biographical details: This American singer, born in New York in 1925, came from a showbusiness family. He made his first public appearance at the age of two and, when aged eight, began touring the States with his father and uncle - Sammy Davis Snr. and Will Mastin were already a well established vaudeville duo. Sammy Jnr spent 1943-6 in the US Army, and then rejoined his two family colleagues. During the Fifties he established himself as a solo star. A serious car accident in Las Vegas interrupted his career in 1954, but he bounced back with a vengeance in '56 by starring in the Broadway production of 'Mr Wonderful'. In the meantime, his double A sided single *Something's Gotta Give/Love Me Or Leave Me*, issued in '55 hit the Top 20 on both sides of the Atlantic. He also enjoyed transatlantic success that year with another single, *That Old Black Magic*. However chart success was sporadic and modest, because the recording was just one of many strings to Davis' bow. In a showbusiness career spanning well over fifty years, his jazz-based singing activities have been augmented by his abilities as a dancer, impressionist and multi-instrumentalist.

Davis' ever grinning face has adorned many movies down the years, most notably 1959's 'Porgy And Bess' and 1964's 'Robin And The Seven Hoods'; in the latter he starred alongside Bing Crosby, Frank Sinatra and Dean Martin. He returned to the US Top 20 in 1962, peaking at No 17 with *What Kind Of Fool Am I?*. He reached No 17 again in 1964 with *The Shelter Of Your Arms* and, in '69, hit the US No 11 slot with *I've Gotta Be Me*. 1972 brought Davis his firt and only American No 1 with *The Candy Man*, a children's novelty ditty co-written by the former British pop star Anthony Newley and taken from the film 'Willie Wonka and the Chocolate Factory'. The surprise success of that single proved to be Davis' final foray into the realms of record stardom, though his career continued apace. An honoured place in showbusiness history is assured by his reputation as one of the all round great all rounders. Bob MacDonald, 14 March 1985..

ALL OF YOU
Tracks: / All of you.
7" Single: Released Dec '56, on Brunswick, by Decca Records. Deleted '59. Catalogue no: **05629**

HAPPY TO MAKE YOUR ACQUAINTANCE
Tracks: / Happy to make your acquaintance.
7" Single: Released Jun '60, on Brunswick, by Decca Records. Deleted '63. Catalogue no: **05830**

HELLO DETROIT
Tracks: / Hello Detroit.
7" Single: Released Sep '84, on Motown, by BMG Records (UK). Catalogue no: **TMG 1351**
12" Single: Released Sep '84, on Motown, by BMG Records (UK). Catalogue no: **MGT 1351**

IN A PERSIAN MARKET
Tracks: / In a Persian market.
7" Single: Released Apr '56, on Brunswick, by Decca Records. Deleted '59. Catalogue no: **05518**

LEGEND IN MY TIME
Tracks: / Legend in my time / Candy man.
7" Single: Released Nov '81, on Polydor, by Polydor Ltd. Deleted Nov '84. Catalogue no: **POSP 380**

LOVE ME OR LEAVE ME
Tracks: / Love me or leave me.
7" Single: Released Sep '55, on Brunswick, by Decca Records. Deleted '58. Catalogue no: **05428**

SOMETHING'S GOTTA GIVE
Tracks: / Something's gotta give.
7" Single: Released Jul '55, on Brunswick, by Decca Records. Deleted '58. Catalogue no: **05428**

THAT OLD BLACK MAGIC
Tracks: / That old black magic.
7" Single: Released Sep '55, on Brunswick, by Decca Records. Deleted '58. Catalogue no: **05450**

WHAT KIND OF FOOL AM I?
Tracks: / What kind of fool am I? / Gonna build a mountain.
7" Single: Released Mar '62, on Reprise, by WEA Records. Deleted '65. Catalogue no: **R 20048**

Davis, Sara

GOODBYE SCARLET
Tracks: / Goodbye Scarlet.
12" Single: Released 5 Mar '88, on September Records, Catalogue no: **SEPT 3T**

Davis, Skeeter

Biographical details: This American singer, born Mary Frances Penik in Kentucky, came to fame in 1953 as 50% of the Davis Sisters, who scored a smash hit on the US country and western charts that year with *I Forget More Than You'll Ever Know*. However, later in that same year, Bee Jay Davis, her singing partner, was killed in a car accident on the way home from a show. This calamity led to Skeeter giving up performing for several years, until persuaded back into the limelight in the late Fifties by Nashville's two leading music executives, Chet Atkins and Steve Sholes. In 1960 she hit the country charts and the US pop Top 40 with *(I Can't Help You) I'm Falling Too*, an answer to Hank Locklin's *Please Help Me, I'm Falling*, which had been an Top Tenner earlier in the year., Davis repeated the 'answer' formula in early '61 with *My Last Date (With You)*, a vocal version of Floyd Cramer's instrumental smash *Last Date*.

Davis achieved her biggest hit in 1963. *The End Of The World*, a charmingly angst-ridden love song, took her to No 2 on the US pop chart; in Britain the single reached No 18 and logged 13 weeks on the Top 50, thus becoming her only UK hit. *I Can't Stay Mad At You* provided her with a second US pop smash later in '63, reaching No 7 on the Billboard Hot 100. The Beatles revolution soon spelt the end of her pop success, however, and she relied thereafter on the country charts for success. Her records were standard products of the Nashville studios. But she upset the Nashville establishment in 1974 when she used the Grand Ole Opry, country music's most famous forum, to give vent to her views about the city's police; this led to Davis being banned from performing at the venue. Bob MacDonald, 14 March 1985..

END OF THE WORLD (OLD GOLD)
Tracks: / End of the world.
7" Single: Released Oct '86, on Old Gold, by Old Gold Records. Catalogue no: **OG 9619**

END OF THE WORLD (SINGLE)
Tracks: / End of the world.
7" Single: Released Mar '63, on RCA, by BMG Records (UK). Deleted '66. Catalogue no: **RCA 1328**

Davis, Spencer

Biographical details: This British guitarist became interested in rhythm and blues while a student at Birmingham University in the early Sixties. In early 1963, when Britain's R&B scene was rapidly building, he met three other lads from Birmingham: Pete York, and brothers Stevie & Mervyn 'Muff' Winwood. Thus the Spencer Davis Group was formed - all the members had dabbled in jazz, blues and folk, but they now devoted themselves to R&B. The following year Steve Blackwell (the founder of Island Records) discovered the Group and signed them to Fontana Records. Their first single *Dimples* flopped, but the next three were minor hits: *I Can't Stand It, Every Little Bit Hurts* and *Strong Love* all peaked in the 41 to 50 portion of the UK charts during 1964-5 and won them a grass roots following.

The roup's big breakthrough occured when Blackwell, a leading expert on Jamaican music, got them to record two singles written by Jackie Edwards, a big name on the Jamaican ska scene. These two songs, *Keep On Running* and *Somebody Help Me*, gave the group consecutive British No 1 smashes in early '66. Both were catchy and highly energetic, and were performed in the band's now perfected R&B-based pop style. These two hits clearly displayed the fact that, despite the Group's name, the key member of the quartet was its youngest member, Stevie Winwood. Although only 17 years old, he showed an astonishing maturity in his powerful lead vocals and in his keyboards and guitar playing. Bob MacDonald, 20 March 1985..

EVERY LITTLE BIT HURTS
Tracks: / Every little bit hurts.
7" Single: Released Feb '65, on Fontana, by Phonogram Ltd. Deleted '68. Catalogue no: **TF 530**

GIMME SOME LOVIN' (SINGLE)
Tracks: / Gimme some lovin'.
7" Single: Released Nov '66, on Fontana, by Phonogram Ltd. Deleted '69. Catalogue no: **TF 762**

I CAN'T STAND IT
Tracks: / I can't stand it.
7" Single: Released Nov '64, on Fontana, by Phonogram Ltd. Deleted '67. Catalogue no: **TF 499**

I'M A MAN
Tracks: / I'm a man.
7" Single: Released Jan '67, on Fontana, by Phonogram Ltd. Deleted '70. Catalogue no: **TF 785**

KEEP ON RUNNING
Tracks: / Keep on running.
7" Single: Released Dec '65, on Fontana, by Phonogram Ltd. Deleted '68. Catalogue no: **TF 632**
7" EP: Released May '78, on Island, by Island Records. Catalogue no: **IEP 10**

MR. SECOND CLASS
Tracks: / Mr. Second Class.
7" Single: Released Jan '68, on United Artists, by EMI Records. Deleted '71. Catalogue no: **UP 1203**

PRIVATE NUMBER
7" Single: Released Mar '84, on Allegience, Catalogue no: **ALES 3**

SOMEBODY HELP ME
Tracks: / Somebody help me.
7" Single: Released Mar '66, on Fontana, by Phonogram Ltd. Deleted '69. Catalogue no: **TF 679**

STRONG LOVE
Tracks: / Strong love.
7" Single: Released Jun '65, on Fontana, by Phonogram Ltd. Deleted '68. Catalogue no: **TF 571**

TIME SELLER
Tracks: / Time seller.
7" Single: Released Aug '67, on Fontana, by Phonogram Ltd. Deleted '70. Catalogue no: **TF 854**

WHEN I COME HOME
Tracks: / When I come home.
7" Single: Released Sep '66, on Fontana, by Phonogram Ltd. Deleted '69. Catalogue no: **TF 739**

Davis, Steve

GET 'EM OUT
Tracks: / Get 'em out.
7" Single: Released Mar '84, on Animus, by Southern Studios Ltd.. Catalogue no: **TOUCH 2**

Davis, Teddy

NO, NO SIN, NO SIN AT ALL
Tracks: / No, no sin, no sin at all / My heart.
12" Single: Released Nov '86, on TR, Catalogue no: **TR 029**

TABANKA
Tracks: / Tabanka / Bobby beat.
12" Single: Released Feb '86, on BB, Catalogue no: **BBD 175**

Davis, Terry

OCEANS AWAY
Tracks: / Oceans away / Davis cup (theme).

12" Single: Released Oct '86, on Tedious, by Tedious Records. Catalogue no: **TDS 202**
7" Single: Released Sep '86, on Tedious, by Tedious Records. Catalogue no: **TDS 2**

WAITING IN THE WINGS
Tracks: / Waiting in the wings.
7" Single: Released Sep '86, on Tedious, by Tedious Records. Catalogue no: **TDS 4**

Davis,Peter

LAUGHING INSIDE
Tracks: / Laughing inside / Laughing inside (Acoustive version).
7" Single: Released Feb '88, on EMI, by EMI Records. Deleted 31 Jul '88. Catalogue no: **EM 46**

Davy D

HAVE YOU SEEN DAVY?
Tracks: / Have you seen Davy? / Keep your distance.
12" Single: Released Jul '87, on Def Jam, Deleted Nov '87. Catalogue no: **650860 6**
7" Single: Released Jul '87, on Def Jam, Deleted Nov '87. Catalogue no: **650860 7**

OHH GIRL
Tracks: / Ohh girl / Clap your hands / Let's rock (Track on 12" only.).
12" Single: Released Feb '88, on Def Jam, Deleted Aug '88. Catalogue no: **651452 6**
7" Single: Released Feb '88, on Def Jam, Deleted Aug '88. Catalogue no: **651452 7**

Daw, Ali

I'M JUST A BABY
Tracks: / I'm just a baby.
7" Single: Released Oct '83, on Tristar, Catalogue no: **TRI 2**

Dawkins, Paul

COME, MY BABY
Tracks: / Baby blues.
12" Single: Released Dec '86, on Starlight, Catalogue no: **SLD 839**

Dawn

Biographical details: This American pop group consisted of lead singer Tony Orlando and his two eacking singers, Telma Hopkins and Joyce Vincent Wilson.
Orlando had enjoyed brief success in 1961 at the age of 17. His singles *Halfway To Paradise* and *Bless You* both hit the US Top 40 that year. The former was a British smash for Billy Fury, but Orlando enjoyed UK Top 10 success with the latter. After this burst of success had faded, he spent the remainder of the Sixties working in the business side of the music industry and, by 1970, had risen to a management position in Columbia Records' publishing division, April Blackwood. In that year, the tokens, a Sixties hitmaking group, prompted Orlando to record a song called *Candida*. Hopkins and Wilson, two session singers, were recruited, and the song became a transatlantic Top 10 hit, with the three singers billed as Dawn. This single set the standard for future Dawn hits - catchy pop material sung, arranged and produced in a competent, bland and highly commercial middle of the road manner. The next hit *Knock Three Times* was a giant, reaching No 1 on both sides of the Atlantic in 1971 despite its ludicrously inane lyrics. After one more UK smash with *What Are You Doing Sunday*, the trio underwent a blank period that lasted for eighteen months.
Dawn re-remerged in the Spring of 1973 with one of the biggest worldwide hits in history. *Tie A Yellow Ribbon Round The Old Oak Tree* was, like *Knock Three Times*, penned by Irwin Levine and L Russell Brown and featured equally silly words. Based on an American Civil War tale concerning the homecoming of a soldier from prison, the song's simple sentiment and irritatingly infectious tune took 'Dawn featuring Tony Orlando' (the girls now relegated to the status of background non-entities) to No 1 in the US, UK and numerous other nations, thus becoming the globe's biggest seller of the year and generating over a thousand cover versions. In Briatin, the single logged 39 consecutive weeks on the Top 50. After *Ribbon*, Orlando managed only one more significant hit in the UK - *Say, Has Anybody Seen My Sweet Gypsy Rose* - but continued to hit the US charts until 1976. He even managed a third American No 1 with 1975's *He Don't Love You (Like I Love You)*, before moving fulltime into the cabaret circuit. Bob MacDonald, 15 March 1985..

CANDIDA
Tracks: / Candida.
7" Single: Released Jul '82, on Old Gold, by Old Gold Records. Catalogue no: **OG 9120**
7" Single: Released Jan '71, on Bell, Deleted '74. Catalogue no: **BELL 1118**

KNOCK THREE TIMES
Tracks: / Knock three times.
7" Single: Released Jul '82, on Old Gold, by Old Gold Records. Catalogue no: **OG 9120**
CD 5": Released Jun '89, on Arista, by BMG Records (UK). Catalogue no: **162065**
7" Single: Released Apr '71, on Bell, Deleted '74. Catalogue no: **BELL 1146**

SAY, HAS ANYBODY SEEN MY SWEET GYPSY ROSE
Tracks: / Say, has anybody seen my sweet gypsy rose.
7" Single: Released Aug '73, on Bell, Deleted '76. Catalogue no: **BELL 1322**

SAY, HAS ANYBODY SEEN MYSWEET GYPSY ROSE (OLD GOLD)
Tracks: / Say, has anybody seen my Sweet gypsy rose.
7" Single: Released Jul '82, on Old Gold, by Old Gold Records. Catalogue no: **OG 9118**

TIE A YELLOW RIBBON
Tracks: / Tie a yellow ribbon.
7" Single: Released Mar '73, on Bell, Deleted '76. Catalogue no: **BELL 1287**
7" Single: Released Jul '82, on Old Gold, by Old Gold Records. Catalogue no: **OG 9118**

WHAT ARE YOU DOING SUNDAY
Tracks: / What are you doing Sunday?.
7" Single: Released Jul '71, on Bell, Deleted '74. Catalogue no: **BELL 1169**

WHO'S IN THE STRAWBERRY PATCH WITH SALLY
Tracks: / Who's in the strawberry patch with Sally.
7" Single: Released Apr '74, on Bell, Deleted '77. Catalogue no: **BELL 1343**

Dawn After Dark

CRYSTAL HIGH
Tracks: / Crystal high.
12" Single: Released Mar '88, on Chapter 22, by Chapter 22 Records. Catalogue no: **12CHAP 26**

GROOVE, THE
Tracks: / Groove.
12" Single: Released Oct '88, on Chapter 22, by Chapter 22 Records. Catalogue no: **12 CHAP 31**

MAXIMUM OVERDRIVE
Tracks: / Habit / Maximum overdrive.
12" Single: Released Mar '89, on Chapter 22, by Chapter 22 Records. Catalogue no: **12CHAP 40**

Dawn Chorus

I'M GOING DOWN
Tracks: / I'm going down.
7" Single: Released Oct '85, on WWOCD, Catalogue no: **DAWN 2**

TEENAGE KICKS
Tracks: / Teenage kicks.
7" Single: Released Apr '85, on WWOCD, Catalogue no: **DAWN 1**

WHEN YOU WALK IN THE ROOM
Tracks: / When you walk in the room / Lonely lips.
7" Single: Released Mar '87, on Magnet, by WEA Records. Deleted Jan '88. Catalogue no: **MAG 311**
12" Single: Released Mar '87, on Magnet, by WEA Records. Deleted Jan '88. Catalogue no: **MAGT 311**

Dawn & Christine

HOLY MOUNT ZION
Tracks: / Holy mount zion.
12" Single: on Burning Sounds, by Burning Sounds Records. Deleted May '88. Catalogue no: **BSD 032**

Dawn, Marie

YOU AND ME
Tracks: / You and me / You and me (version).
12" Single: Released Oct '88, on Ariwa Sounds, by Ariwa Sounds. Catalogue no: **ARI 69**
12" Single: Released Jul '88, on Ariwa Sounds, by Ariwa Sounds. Catalogue no: **ARI 67**

Dawn Patrol

ALL OUR YESTERDAYS
Tracks: / All our yesterdays / White coats / Prisoner / One more today
7" EP: Released Nov '81, on Dinosaur, Deleted '88. Catalogue no: **DD005/M/S**

GING GANG GOO
Tracks: / Ging gang goo / Little rabbit foo foo.
7" Single: Released Jul '89, on Red Baron, by Red Baron Records. Catalogue no: **RB 005**

Dawson

ROMPING EGOS
Tracks: / Romping egos.
7" Single: Released 31 Jul '89, on Gruff Wit, Catalogue no: **GRUFF 1**

Dawson, Cliff

SOMEHOW
Tracks: / Somehow / Somehow (part 2).
7" Single: Released Sep '82, on Half Moon, by Rondelet Music & Records. Catalogue no: **ROUND 2003**
12" Single: Released Sep '82, on Half Moon, by Rondelet Music & Records. Catalogue no: **12ROUND 2003**

Dax, Danielle

BIG HOLLOW MAN
Tracks: / Big hollow man.
12" Single: Released Jul '87, on Awesome Records, by Awesome Records. Catalogue no: **AOR 10T**
7" Single: Released Jul '87, on Awesome Records, by Awesome Records. Catalogue no: **AOR 10**

CAT HOUSE
Tracks: / Cat house.
12" Single: Released Mar '88, on Awesome Records, by Awesome Records. Catalogue no: **AOR 12T**
7" Single: Released Mar '88, on Awesome Records, by Awesome Records. Catalogue no: **AOR 12**

JANICE LONG SESSION: DANIELLE DAX
12" Single: Released Jan '88, on Night Tracks, by Pinnacle Records. Catalogue no: **SFNT 006**

WHERE THE FLIES ARE
Tracks: / Where the flies are.
7" Single: Released Oct '86, on Awesome Records, by Awesome Records. Catalogue no: **AOR 6**
12" Single: Released Oct '86, on Awesome Records, by Awesome Records. Catalogue no: **AOR 6 T**

WHITE KNUCKLE RIDE (SINGLE)
Tracks: / White knuckle ride.
12" Single: Released Apr '89, on Awesome Records, by Awesome Records. Catalogue no: **AOR 023T**
7" Single: Released Apr '89, on Awesome Records, by Awesome Records. Catalogue no: **AOR 023**

YUMMER YUMMER MAN
Tracks: / Yummer yummer man.
7" Single: Released Oct '85, on Awesome Records, by Awesome Records. Catalogue no: **AOR 3**
12" Single: Released Oct '85, on Awesome Records, by Awesome Records. Catalogue no: **AOR 3T**

Day, Arlan

I SURRENDER
Tracks: / I surrender / Woman.
7" Single: Released May '82, on Epic, by CBS Records. Deleted '85. Catalogue no: **EPCA 2036**

Day, Bobby

Biographical details: This American singer. born Robert Byrd in Texas, moved to Los Angeles as a child. He came to fame in late 1957 as a member of the Hollywood Flames - they reached No 11 on the US charts with their novelty rock 'n' roll singles *Buzz-Buzz-Buzz*. Simultaneously, he found himself on the listings as a writer - Thurston Harris hit No 6 on the US charts in late '57 with Day's song *Little Bitty Pretty One*. In 1958 Day flew up to the US No 2 slot as a solo artist with another rock 'n' roll gimmick song *Rockin' Robin*; the single peaked at No 29 in Britain. During this period, he also cut some records as a duo with fellow Hollywood Flame Earl Nelson, under the billing 'Bob & Earl'. However, it should be noted that Day was replaced in the duo by Bobby Relf in '59, and was thus not involved in Bob & Earl's Sixties hit *Harlem Shuffle* After his late Fifties flurry of chart activity, Bobby Day soon slipped into obscurity. However, two of his songs from that era subsequently became US hits for other artists. *Over And Over* gave the Dave Clark Five an American No 1 smash at Christmas 1965 - dethroning a single by the Byrds, a strange coincidence in view of Bobby's real name! *Little Bitty Pretty One* took Clyde McPhatter to No 25 in 1962 and, ten years later, gave the Jackson Five a No 13 hit. There must have been some hard core Bobby Day fans in the Jackson Family: at the same time as *Little Bitty Pretty One* was on the US chart, young Michael was enjoying solo success with his rendition of *Rockin' Robin*. Like Day, Jackson took his version to the American No 2 position; and there was yet another coincidence - Michael Jackson was born while Day's original 1958 record was on the charts. Bob MacDonald, 15 March 1985.
A singer and songwriter, born Robert Byrd in 1934 in Texas. He worked at Johnny Otis's Barrelhouse Club and wrote *Little bitty pretty one*, his own version beaten in the charts by that of Thurston Harris in 1957. He had his own six entries in Billboard's Hot 100 1957-9 including *Rock in robin*, *Over and over*. He also sang lead with the Hollywood Flames, who did beautiful ballads but had R&B hits with novelties. His songs were covered by the Dave Clark Five, The Jackson Five, etc. (Donald Clarke, April 1989).

LITTLE BITTY PRETTY ONE
Tracks: / Little bitty pretty one.
7" Single: Released Aug '82, on Blast From The Past, by Creole Records. Catalogue no: **CR 181**

ROCKIN' ROBIN (SINGLE)
Tracks: / Rockin' robin.
7" Single: Released Nov '58, on London Records, by London Records. Deleted '61. Catalogue no: **HL 8726**

Day, Doris

Biographical details: This American singer and actress, born Doris von Kappelhoff in Ohio, entered showbusiness with the ambition of becoming a famous dancer; but a leg injury put paid to those plans, so she took up singing and leter embarked on a film career. Day's huge success in both fields suggests that her leg accident was a blessing in disguise. She first sang in a band led by Ohio nightclub owner Barney Rapp, the man whose idea it was to change her name to Day. Her big break came in 1945 when she performed vocals on *Sentimental Journey*, a long running US No 1 smash for Les Brown and his Orchestra. This success led to her teaming up with another singer, Buddy Clark, for a 1947 double A sided hit, *Confess/Love Somebody*. The following year brought major solo stardom for Day - she starred in her first film "Romance On The High Seas", a movie known in Britain by the title "It's Magic", which was also the title of its smash hit song. She first hit the British record charts in the week following their inception - *My Love And Devotion* took her to the UK No 10 slot in November 1952 and, in the same month, she hit No 8 with *Sugarbush*, a duet with Frankie Laine.
The mid-Fifties saw Day achieving two monster hits with Oscar-winning songs from movies. *Secret Love* from Calamity Jane hit No 1 on both sides of the Atlantic in 1954, logging a mammouth nine weeks at the top in Britain. *Whatever Will Be, Will Be (Que Sera Sera)* from Alfred Hitchcock's "The Man Who Knew Too Much" reached No 2 in the US in 1956 and chalked up sx weeks at No 1 in Britain. Those two songs became so famous as to be regarded as all-time classics, as did her 1964 movie theme *Move Over Darling* - that number, a delightfully romantic and enticing love song, provided Day with her final major record success, reaching No 8 on the UK charts; a 1983 remake by Tracey Ullman also reached the British No 8 spot. Between *Secret Love* and *Move Over Darling*, Day enjoyed a decade of film stardom, and her periods of absence from the charts were simply a reflection of the fact that she was making the cinema her priority. Other movie successes included "Young At Heart", "By The Light Of The Silvery Moon" and "The Pyjama Game". Day hit the UK album chart for the first time in 1979 with her TV advertised *20 Golden Greats* collection. Bob MacDonald, 15 March 1985.
Pop singer and actress, born Doris Kappelhoff in 1924 in Cincinatti. She studied dancing, and turned to singing after a car crash and a broken leg at age 14. She sang with Bob Crosby in 1940 and that year went to the Les Brown band, singing on million sellers *My dreams are getting better* and *Sentimental journey*. She dueted with Buddy Clark on other big hits, then made her own series of nice pop records, including duets with Frankie Laine and Johnny Ray. Her best films (1953-57) included *Calamity Jane* (with Oscar winning ballad *Secret love*) and in 1955 *Young at heart* with Frank Sinatra and Ruth Etting biopic *Love me or leave me* with Jimmy Cagney (chart hit *I'll never stop loving you*; a soundtrack a number one album), and the *Pajama game*, a film of a Broadway musical. *Que sera sera (whatever will be will be)* also won an Oscar, from an Alfred Hitchcock movie; then she became a virgin for a series of fluffy films, mostly with Rock Hudson. She made album *Duet* with Andre Previn (trio) on Polydor in 1983. Her son Terry Melcher, from first marriage to a musician, became a prominent record producer (the Byrds) and recorded as a vocalist. (Donald Clarke, April 1989)n.

BLACK HILLS OF DAKOTA
Tracks: / Black hills of Dakota, The.
7" Single: Released Aug '54, on Philips, by Phonogram Ltd. Deleted '57. Catalogue no: **PB 287**

EVERYBODY LOVES A LOVER
Tracks: / Everybody loves a lover.
7" Single: Released Aug '58, on Philips, by Phonogram Ltd. Deleted '61. Catalogue no: **PB 843**

FULL TIME JOB
Tracks: / Full time job.
7" Single: Released Apr '53, on Philips, by Phonogram Ltd. Deleted '56. Catalogue no: **DB 3242**

IF I GIVE MY HEART TO YOU
Tracks: / If I give my heart to you.
7" Single: Released Oct '54, on Philips, by Phonogram Ltd. Deleted '57. Catalogue no: **PB 325**

I'LL NEVER STOP LOVING YOU
Tracks: / I'll never stop loving you.
7" Single: Released Oct '55, on Philips, by Phonogram Ltd. Deleted '58. Catalogue no: **PB 407**

LET'S WALK THATA-WAY
Tracks: / Let's walk thata-way.
7" Single: Released Jul '53, on Philips, by Phonogram Ltd. Deleted '56. Catalogue no: **PB 157**

LOVE ME OR LEAVE ME
Tracks: / Love me or leave me.
7" Single: Released Sep '55, on Philips, by Phonogram Ltd. Deleted '58. Catalogue no: **PB 479**

MA SAYS PA SAYS
Tracks: / Ma says pa says.
7" Single: Released Apr '53, on Philips, by Phonogram Ltd. Deleted '56. Catalogue no: **DB 3242**

MOVE OVER, DARLING
Tracks: / Deadwood stage (Extra track on 12" only.) / Move over, darling / Teachers pet.
7" Single: Released Apr '87, on CBS, by CBS Records. Deleted Nov '87. Catalogue no: **LEGS 1**
7" Single: Released Mar '64, on CBS, by CBS Records. Deleted '67. Catalogue no: **AAG 183**
12" Single: Released Apr '87, on CBS, by CBS Records. Deleted Nov '87. Catalogue no: **LEGST 1**

MY LOVE AND DEVOTION
Tracks: / My love and devotion.
7" Single: Released Nov '52, on Columbia, by EMI Records. Deleted '55. Catalogue no: **DB 3157**

READY, WILLING AND ABLE
Tracks: / Ready, willing and able.
7" Single: Released Apr '55, on Philips, by Phonogram Ltd. Deleted '58. Catalogue no: **PB 402**

SECRET DEVOTION
Tracks: / Secret devotion.
7" Single: Released Apr '54, on Philips, by Phonogram Ltd. Deleted '57. Catalogue no: **PB 230**

SECRET LOVE
Tracks: / Secret love / Que sera sera / Whatever will be will be.
7" Single: Released Jul '82, on Old Gold, by Old Gold Records. Catalogue no: **OG 9091**

SUGARBRUSH
Tracks: / Sugarbrush.
7" Single: Released Nov '52, on Philips, by Phonogram Ltd. Deleted '55. Catalogue no: **DB 3123**

VERY PRECIOUS LOVE, A
Tracks: / Very precious love, A.
7" Single: Released Jun '58, on Philips, by Phonogram Ltd. Deleted '61. Catalogue no: **PB 799**

WHATEVER WILL BE WILL BE (SINGLE)
Tracks: / Whatever will be will be.
7" Single: Released Jun '56, on Philips, by Phonogram Ltd. Deleted '59. Catalogue no: **PB 586**

Day, Morris

COLOR OF SUCCESS (SINGLE)
Tracks: / Color of success.
7" Single: Released Feb '86, on Warner Bros., by WEA Records. Catalogue no: **W 8809**
12" Single: Released Feb '86, on Warner Bros., by WEA Records. Deleted Jun '87. Catalogue no: **W 8809 T**

FISH NET
Tracks: / Fish net / Maybe.
7" Single: Released Feb '88, on Warner Bros., by WEA Records. Catalogue no: **W 8201**
12" Single: Released Feb '88, on Warner Bros., by WEA Records. Catalogue no: **W 8201T**

OAK TREE, THE
Tracks: / Oak tree, The (dance inst) / Oak tree acapella.
7" Single: Released Jan '86, on Warner Bros., by WEA Records. Catalogue no: **W 8899**
12" Single: Released Jan '86, on Warner Bros., by WEA Records. Catalogue no: **W 8899 T**

Day, Muriel

NINE TIMES OUT OF TEN
Tracks: / Nine times out of ten / Do the skunk.
7" Single: Released Aug '82, on Soul Stop, by Dawn Promotions. Catalogue no: **SS 3001**

Day, Ricky

WELCOME TO THE ISLE OF WIGHT
Tracks: / Welcome to the Isle of Wight.
7" Single: Released Jul '85, on Round, Catalogue no: **RR 3**

WE'LL MEET AGAIN
Tracks: / We'll meet again.
7" Single: Released Jun '83, on Heart, by Topic Records. Catalogue no: **H 001**

Dayglo, Johnny

FREE YOUR MIND
Tracks: / Free your mind / Free your mind (version).
12" Single: Released Oct '88, on Acid Jazz, by Acid Jazz Records. Catalogue no: **JAZID 5T**

Dayne, Taylor

DON'T RUSH ME
Tracks: / Don't rush me.
CD 5": Released Sep '88, on Arista, by BMG Records (UK). Catalogue no: **661 687**
7" Single: Released Sep '88, on Arista, by BMG Records (UK). Catalogue no: **111 687**
12" Single: Released Sep '88, on Arista, by BMG Records (UK). Catalogue no: **611 687**

I'LL ALWAYS LOVE YOU
Tracks: / I'll always love you / Where does the boy hang out? / Prove your love (on 12" only.).
12" Single: Released May '88, on Arista, by BMG Records (UK). Deleted Jul '89. Catalogue no: **611 536**
7" Single: Released May '88, on Arista, by BMG Records (UK). Catalogue no: **111 536**
CD 5": Released May '88, on Arista, by BMG Records (UK). Catalogue no: **661536**

PROVE YOUR LOVE
Tracks: / Prove your love (extended remix) / Tell it to my heart (house of hearts mix) / Upon the journey's end.
CD 5": Released Mar '88, on Arista, by BMG Records (UK). Catalogue no: **659830**

TELL IT TO MY HEART (SINGLE)
Tracks: / Tell it to my heart / Tell it to my heart (inst) (Available on 7" only) / Tell it to my heart (percapella mix) (Available on 12" only) / Tell it to my heart (dub mix) (Available on 12" only).
Note: * track on 7" only. ** tracks on 12" only.
12" Single: Released Feb '88, on Arista, by BMG Records (UK). Deleted May '89. Catalogue no: **609 616R**
7" Single: Released Jan '88, on Arista, by BMG Records (UK). Catalogue no: **109 616**
12" Single: Released Jan '88, on Arista, by BMG Records (UK). Catalogue no: **609 616**

Day's, Helen Wild

FACE THAT BROKE A THOUSAND HEARTS
Tracks: / Face that broke a thousand hearts.
7" Single: Released Sep '83, on Buzz, Catalogue no: **BUZZ 3**

Days Of 29

DESTINATION D-DAY
Tracks: / Destination D-day.
12" Single: Released Jul '85, on Braw Products, Catalogue no: **BRAWSIN 121**
12" Single: Released '88, on UNKNOWN, Catalogue no: **TH 271 284**

Days Of Grace

MY LIFE'S IN VIDEO
Tracks: / My life's in video / 21st century.
7" Single: Released Jun '82, on DJM, Deleted '85. Catalogue no: **DJS 10988**

Dayton

HOT FUN IN THE SUMMERTIME
Tracks: / Hot fun in the summertime / Eyes on you.
12" Single: Released Aug '82, on United Artists, by EMI Records. Deleted Aug '85. Catalogue no: **12UP 655**
7" Single: Released Aug '82, on United Artists, by EMI Records. Deleted Aug '85. Catalogue no: **UP 655**

SOUND OF MUSIC, THE
Tracks: / Sound of music, The / Promise me / Love you anyway.
7" Single: Released Dec '83, on Capitol, by EMI Records. Deleted '86. Catalogue no: **CL 318**

Daze

DEEP SOUTH
Tracks: / Deep South / Made in America.
7" Single: Released Jan '84, on Mynah, Catalogue no: **SDM 001**

Dazz

DEAR AUNTIE AGATHA
Tracks: / Dear Auntie Agatha / Everything's electric.
7" Single: Released Mar '81, on Polo, by Polo Records. Deleted '88. Catalogue no: **POLO 9**

EVERYTHING'S ELECTRIC
Tracks: / Everything's electric / Lady Casanova.
7" Single: Released Mar '80, on Polo, by Polo Records. Deleted '88. Catalogue no: **POLO 2**

Dazz Band

Biographical details: This American funk band, who hail from Cleveland, Ohio, consist of nine guys, eight black and one white. In similar style to another multi member soul group, Earth Wind & Fire, the Dazz Band are creatively dominated by one leader - Bobby Harris, who plays saxaphone and co-writes and co-produces their material. They began life as Bell Telephunk and then called themselves Kinsman Dazz, before settling on the Dazz Band. 'Dazz' is intended to signify the Band's musical style: a fusion of disco and jazz. This name was not an original idea, however, because an Atlanta group called Brick took a disco smash entitled *Dazz* into the US Top 3 in 1977.

After years of hard slog, Bobby Harris' outfit, signed to Motown Records, broke through in 1982 with a smash single *Let It Whip*. As well as being a US No 1 on the black charts, this slice of slightly zany hard funk managed to reach No 5 on the American pop charts, a considerable achievement for an uncompromisingly dance orientated record. *Let It Whip* was strangely ignored by the British clubs and, consequently, failed to hit the UK charts. 1983 was a lean year for the Dazz Band - they issued two LPs that year which failed to make a major impact - but they bounced back in late '84 with their insidious soul single *Let It All Blow*. This time, Britain responded positively by putting the song at No 12 on its pop charts. Bob MacDonald, 16 March 1985..

HEARTBEAT
Tracks: / Heartbeat.
7" Single: Released Jan '85, on Motown, by BMG Records (UK). Deleted '87. Catalogue no: **TMG 1368**
12" Single: Released Jan '85, on Motown, by BMG Records (UK). Deleted '87. Catalogue no: **TMGT 1368**

HOT SPOT
Tracks: / Hot spot.
7" Single: Released Jul '85, on Motown, by BMG Records (UK). Deleted '88. Catalogue no: **ZB 40307**
12" Single: Released Jul '85, on Motown, by BMG Records (UK). Deleted '88. Catalogue no: **ZT 40308**

JOYSTICK
Tracks: / To the roof / Joystick / Swoop (I'm yours) / Until you / Rock with me / Straight out of school / Now that I have you / Laughing at you / T.Mata (instrumental).
12" Single: Released Jan '84, on Motown, by BMG Records (UK). Catalogue no: **TMGT 1328**

KEEP IT LIVE
Tracks: / Let it whip / Gamble with my love / I'll keep on lovin' you / Just can't wait till the night / Shake what you got / Keep it live / Just believe in love / Can we dance / Let me love you until.
12" Single: Released Feb '83, on Motown, by BMG Records (UK). Deleted '85. Catalogue no: **TMGT 1279**
7" Single: Released Feb '83, on Motown, by BMG Records (UK). Deleted '85. Catalogue no: **TMG 1279**

LET IT ALL BLOW
Tracks: / Let it all blow.
12" Single: Released Oct '84, on Motown, by BMG Records (UK). Catalogue no: **TMGT 1361**
7" Single: Released Oct '84, on Motown, by BMG Records (UK). Catalogue no: **TMG 1361**

LET IT WHIP
Tracks: / Let it whip / Everyday love.
12" Single: Released Jun '82, on Motown, by BMG Records (UK). Deleted Jun '85. Catalogue no: **TMGT 1270**
7" Single: Released Oct '82, on Motown, by BMG Records (UK). Deleted '84. Catalogue no: **TMG 1270**

LOVE M.I.A.
Tracks: / Love M.I.A. / Place in my heart, A.
7" Single: Released Sep '86, on Geffen, by Geffen Records (USA). Deleted Jun '87. Catalogue no: **GEF 12**
12" Single: Released Sep '86, on Geffen, by Geffen Records (USA). Deleted Jun '87. Catalogue no: **GEF 12T**

ON THE ONE
Tracks: / Party right here / Cheek to cheek / On the one for fun / Don't get caught in the middle / Love song / Bad girl / Nice girls / Stay a while with me / We have more than love.
12" Single: Released Mar '83, on Motown, by BMG Records (UK). Deleted '88. Catalogue no: **TMGT 1299**
7" Single: Released Mar '83, on Motown, by BMG Records (UK). Deleted '88. Catalogue no: **TMG 1299**

SHAKE IT UP
Tracks: / Shake it up / Only love.
12" Single: Released Oct '81, on Motown, by BMG Records (UK). Deleted '83. Catalogue no: **TMGT 1213**
7" Single: Released Oct '81, on Motown, by BMG Records (UK). Deleted '83. Catalogue no: **TMG 1213**

SWOOP I'M YOURS
Tracks: / Swoop (I'm yours) / Bad girl.
7" Single: Released '84, on Motown, by BMG Records (UK). Deleted '86. Catalogue no: **TMG 1338**
12" Single: Released '84, on Motown, by BMG Records (UK). Deleted '88. Catalogue no: **TMGT 1338**

WILD AND FREE (SINGLE)
12" Single: on Geffen, by Geffen Records (USA). Deleted Jun '87. Catalogue no: **GEF 6T**

Dazzle

DAZZLE YOU
Tracks: / Dazzle you / Dazzle you (original version) / I don't want your love.
12" Single: Released Jun '89, on Jam Today, by Jam Today Records. Catalogue no: **12CHIL 14**

I DON'T WANT YOUR LOVE
Tracks: / I don't want your love.
12" Single: Released 20 Mar '89, on Jam Today, by Jam Today Records. Catalogue no: **12CHIL 11**

DBL Crew

BUST IT
Tracks: / Bust it.
7" Single: Released Jul '86, on Affair, Catalogue no: **FAIR 1**

D.B.M.

DISCO BEATLEMANIA
Tracks: / Disco beatlemania.
7" Single: Released Nov '77, on Atlantic, by WEA Records. Deleted Nov '80. Catalogue no: **K 11027**

MR PRESIDENT
Tracks: / Mr. President.
7" Single: Released Aug '70, on Fontana, by Phonogram Ltd. Deleted Aug '73. Catalogue no: **6007 022**

DB's

AMPLIFIER (SINGLE)
Tracks: / Amplifier / Ask for Jill.
7" Single: Released '82, on Albion, by Albion Records. Catalogue no: **ION 1024**

BIG BROWN EYES Baby talk
Tracks: / Big brown eyes / Baby talk.
7" Single: Released '81, on Albion, by Albion Records. Catalogue no: **ION 1010**

DYNAMITE
Tracks: / Dynamite.
7" Single: Released '81, on Albion, by Albion Records. Catalogue no: **ION 1005**

LIVING A LIE
Tracks: / Living a lie / In Spain.
7" Single: Released '82, on Albion, by Albion Records. Catalogue no: **ION 1034**

NEVERLAND
Tracks: / Neverland / pH factor.
7" Single: Released '82, on Albion, by Albion Records. Catalogue no: **ION 1030**

D.C.10's

BERMUDA
Tracks: / Bermuda / I can see through walls.
7" Single: Released Aug '80, on Certain

Euphoria, Deleted Aug '83. Catalogue no: **ACE 45-1**

D.C. & The T.B.'s

TEDDY BEAR'S PICNIC
Tracks: / Teddy bear's picnic.
7" Single: Released Nov '82, on Bear Records, Catalogue no: **BEAR 1**

D.C.L. Locomotive

KING MIDAS IN REVERSE
Tracks: / King Midas in reverse / Last black tie.
12" Single: Released Jun '84, on Reflex, by Reflex Records. Catalogue no: **12 RE 4**

D.C.S.

D.C.S. RULES BRITANIA
Tracks: / D.C.S. rules Brittania / Land of hope and glory / Bhangra lovers.
12" Single: Released Jun '89, on Multitone, by Multitone Records/Savera. Catalogue no: **12 BHA 2**

De Angelis, Nicolas

SONG FOR ANNA
Tracks: / Song for Anna / Guantanamera / Evidence of the heart.
7" Single: Released Feb '87, on London Records, by London Records. Catalogue no: **NDA 1**

De Angelo, Nino

GUARDIAN ANGEL
Tracks: / Guardian angel.
7" Single: Released '85, on Carrere, Catalogue no: **CAR 335**
12" Single: Released '85, on Carrere, Catalogue no: **CART 335**

De Blanc

MON AMOUR
Tracks: / Mon amour / Mon amour (Instrumental).
12" Single: Released Aug '87, on Diamond, by Revolver Records. Catalogue no: **DMRT 2**
7" Single: Released Jul '87, on Diamond, by Revolver Records. Catalogue no: **DMR 2**

TEMPTATION
Tracks: / Temptation / Lady's a fool.
12" Single: Released '82, on Avatar, by Avatar Record Corporation. Catalogue no: **AAA 125 T**
7" Single: Released '82, on Avatar, by Avatar Record Corporation. Catalogue no: **AAA 125**

De Burgh, Chris

Biographical details: This Irish vocalist, guitarist and songwriter released his first album *Far beyond These Castle Walls* in early 1975. His second set *Spanish Train And other Stories*, issued later that year, epitomised his style: intense narratives full of dramatic themes, accompanied by big production sound. The song *Spanish Train* was the saga of a cards game with the devil, in the style and tradition of Milton's *Paradise Lost* epic. *A Spaceman Came Travelling* was a Christmas song depicting Jesus as a visitor from outer space. Three further albums established de burgh as a cult artist and he won a significant following throughout Europe.
His small but loyal audience continued to increase in the early Eighties. He has long been on the verge of stardom, but has never quite cracked it. Chris did not make his debut on the UK album charts until the autumn of 1981, when the *Best Moves* compilation peaked at No. 65. A year later de Burgh scraped the UK Top 30 with the LP *The Getaway* and also scored his first entry on the British singles chart with a minor hit entitled *Don't Pay The Ferryman*, another piece of larger-than-life drama. When 1984's *High On Emotion* single also entered the UK Top 75, it once again seemed that he was about to become a major artist. But even this more overtly commercial single did not become a major hit. Chris de Burgh's brand of high drama rock (which has always incorporated folk and classical influences), reached an audience in many countries, but it has somehow never put him in the top league of international performers. (Bob MacDonald).
UK singer/songwriter, born in Argentine in 1948. His sweeping epic story-telling style was out of fashion before he began, but he has a firm cult following, especially in Europe and Canada. He has crept into the mainstream recently: *Into the light*, a number one hit, and his albums now include many a fine rockaballad. (Donald Clarke, April 1989).

COMPACT HITS: CHRIS DE BURGH
Tracks: / Ecstacy of flight (I love the night), The / Lady in red / Don't pay the ferryman / High on emotion.
CD 5": Released Aug '88, on A&M, by

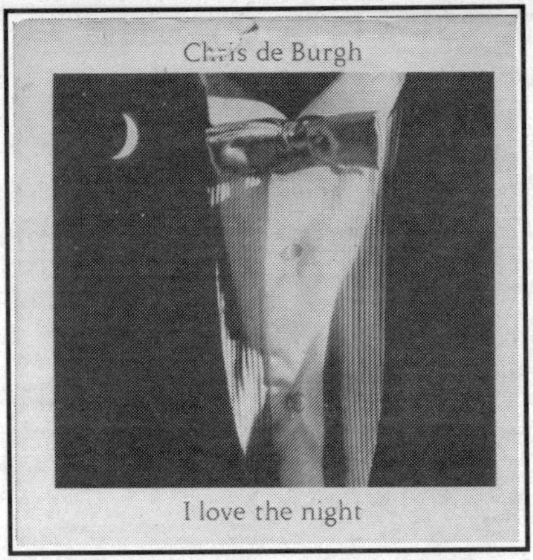

CHRIS DE BURGH - I LOVE THE NIGHT (Released on A & M)

A&M Records. Deleted Feb '89. Catalogue no: **AMCD 915**

DON'T PAY THE FERRYMAN
Tracks: / Don't pay the ferryman.
7" Single: Released Oct '82, on A&M, by A&M Records. Deleted '85. Catalogue no: **AMS 8256**

FATAL HESITATION
Tracks: / Fatal hesitation / Ecstasy of flight (I love the night).
12" Single: Released Sep '86, on A&M, by A&M Records. Deleted '87. Catalogue no: **AMY 346**
7" Single: Released Sep '86, on A&M, by A&M Records. Deleted '87. Catalogue no: **AM 346**

FIRE ON THE WATER
Tracks: / Fire on the water / Vision, The / Leader / What about me.
7" Single: Released Apr '86, on A&M, by A&M Records. Deleted '87. Catalogue no: **AM 317**
12" Single: Released Apr '86, on A&M, by A&M Records. Deleted '87. Catalogue no: **AMY 317**

GETAWAY, THE (SINGLE)
Tracks: / Getaway / Living on the island.
7" Single: Released Nov '82, on A&M, by A&M Records. Deleted '88. Catalogue no: **AMS 8268**

HIGH ON EMOTION
Tracks: / High on emotion / Much more than this.
7" Single: Released May '84, on A&M, by A&M Records. Deleted '87. Catalogue no: **AM 190**

I LOVE THE NIGHT (see panel above)
Tracks: / I love the night / Moonlight and vodka.
7" Single: Released '84, on A&M, by A&M Records. Catalogue no: **AM 202**

LADY IN RED, THE
Tracks: / Lady in red / Say goodbye to it all.
12" Single: Released Jun '86, on A&M, by A&M Records. Deleted '88. Catalogue no: **AMY 331**
7" Single: Released Jun '86, on A&M, by A&M Records. Catalogue no: **AM 331**

MISSING YOU
Tracks: / Missing you / Risen Lord, The / Last time I cried, The (CD single only.).
7" Single: Released Oct '88, on A&M, by A&M Records. Catalogue no: **AM 474**
CD 3": Released Oct '88, on A&M, by A&M Records. Catalogue no: **AMCDEE**
12" Single: Released Oct '88, on A&M, by A&M Records. Catalogue no: **AMY 474**

SAILING AWAY
Tracks: / Sailing away / Head and the heart, The.
12" Single: Released 13 Feb '89, on A&M, by A&M Records. Catalogue no: **AMY 494**
CD 5": Released 13 Feb '89, on A&M, by A&M Records. Catalogue no: **CDEE 494**
7" Single: Released 13 Feb '89, on A&M, by A&M Records. Catalogue no: **AM 494**

SHADOWS AND LIGHTS
Tracks: / Shadows and lights / Walls of silence.
7" Single: Released Aug '80, on A&M, by A&M Records. Deleted '83. Catalogue no: **AMS 7545**

SIGHT AND TOUCH
Tracks: / Sight and touch / Taking it to the top.
7" Single: Released Feb '85, on A&M, by A&M Records. Deleted '88. Catalogue no: **AM 237**

SIMPLE TRUTH (A CHILD IS BORN), THE
Tracks: / Simple truth (a child is born), The / Spirit of man, The / Head and the heart (An exclusive live version on 12" single only.).
Note: Chris De Burgh returns this Christmas with "The simple truth (A child is born)". Very much in the mould of his U.K. No.1 smash "Lady in red", "The simple truth" is not available on any De Burgh album, making it an exclusive purchase. "The simple truth" is available on 7" and 3-track 12" b/w an exclusive live version of "The head and the heart".
7" Single: Released 4 Dec '87, on A&M, by A&M Records. Deleted 1 Aug '88. Catalogue no: **AM 427**
12" Single: Released 4 Dec '87, on A&M, by A&M Records. Deleted 1 Aug '88. Catalogue no: **AMY 427**

SPACEMAN CAME TRAVELLING
Tracks: / Spaceman came travelling, A / Borderline / Ballroom of romance (remix) / Getaway (This version on 12" only.).
7" Single: Released Nov '86, on A&M, by A&M Records. Deleted Mar '88. Catalogue no: **AM 365**
7" Single: Released Nov '81, on A&M, by A&M Records. Deleted Nov '84. Catalogue no: **AMS 8182**
7" Single: Released Dec '84, on A&M, by A&M Records. Deleted '88. Catalogue no: **AM 225**

TENDER HANDS
Tracks: / Tender hands / Night on the river, A.
7" Single: Released Dec '88, on A&M, by A&M Records. Catalogue no: **AM 486**
CD 5": Released Dec '88, on A&M, by A&M Records. Catalogue no: **CDEE 486**
12" Single: Released Dec '88, on A&M, by A&M Records. Catalogue no: **AMY 486**

THIS WAITING HEART
Tracks: / This waiting heart.
7" Single: Released Sep '89, on A&M, by A&M Records. Catalogue no: **AM 528**
CD 5": Released Sep '89, on A&M, by A&M Records. Catalogue no: **AMCD 528**
12" Single: Released Sep '89, on A&M, by A&M Records. Catalogue no: **AMY 528**

TRAVELLER
Tracks: / Traveller / Eastern wind.
7" Single: Released Oct '80, on A&M, by A&M Records. Deleted Oct '83. Catalogue no: **AMS 7562**

WAITING FOR THE HURRICANE
Tracks: / Waiting for the hurricane / Broken wings.
7" Single: Released Sep '81, on A&M, by A&M Records. Deleted '84. Catalogue no: **AMS 8160**

De Castro Sisters

TEACH ME TONIGHT
Tracks: / Teach me tonight.
7" Single: Released Feb '55, on London Records, by London Records. Deleted '58. Catalogue no: **HL 8104**

De Creed, Jacquie

232 (AND A LITTLE BIT MORE)
Tracks: / 232 (and a little bit more).
7" Single: Released '85, on Polydor, by Polydor Ltd. Catalogue no: **CLIS 4**

De Danann

ALL FINE YOUNG MEN
Tracks: / All fine young men / Jigs.
7" Single: Released '88, on I&B, by I & B Records. Catalogue no: **DDS 3**

ARRIVAL OF THE QUEEN OF SHEBA
Tracks: / Arrival of the Queen of Sheba, The / Chicken reel.
7" Single: Released '83, on Cara, Deleted '84. Catalogue no: **CARA 004**

STAR SPANGLED MOLLY, THE Boys of Malin
Tracks: / Starspangled Molly / Boys of Malin.
7" Single: Released '82, on Cara, Deleted '84. Catalogue no: **CARA 003**

SWEET FORGET ME NOT
Tracks: / Sweet forget me not.
7" Single: Released '88, on I&B, by I & B Records. Catalogue no: **DDS 2**

TEDDY O' NEIL
Tracks: / Teddy O' Neil.
7" Single: Released '88, on I&B, by I & B Records. Catalogue no: **DDS 1**

De Jongh, Richard

SO EASY
Tracks: / So easy.
12" Single: Released Aug '83, on Challenge, by Elite Records. Catalogue no: **TALL 3**

De La Paz, Gil

CASA
Tracks: / Three different mixes.
12" Single: Released Aug '87, on Kool Kat, by Kool Kat Records. Catalogue no: **KOOL T6**

De La Soul

I KNOW
Tracks: / I know.
7" Single: Released Oct '89, on Big Life, by Big Life Records. Catalogue no: **BLR 13**
12" Single: Released Oct '89, on Big Life, by Big Life Records. Catalogue no: **BLR 13T**
7" Pic: Released Oct '89, on Big Life, by Big Life Records. Catalogue no: **BLR 13P**
CD 5": Released Oct '89, on Big Life, by Big Life Records. Catalogue no: **BLR 13CD**

JENIFA (TAUGHT ME)
Tracks: / Jenifa (taught me).
7" Single: Released Oct '88, on Tommy Boy, by Polydor Ltd. Catalogue no: **TB 917**

ME, MYSELF AND I
Tracks: / Me, myself and I.
7" Single: Released 27 Feb '89, on Big Life, by Big Life Records. Catalogue no: **BLR 007**
12" Single: Released Apr '89, on Big Life, by Big Life Records. Catalogue no: **BLR 007 R**
CD 5": Released Apr '89, on Big Life, by Big Life Records. Catalogue no: **BLR 007 CD**
12" Single: Released 27 Feb '89, on Big Life, by Big Life Records. Catalogue no: **BLR 007 T**

SAY NO GO
Tracks: / Say no go.
7" Single: Released Jul '89, on Big Life, by Big Life Records. Catalogue no: **BLR 010 P**
CD 5": Released Jun '89, on Big Life, by Big Life Records. Catalogue no: **BLR 10CD**
12" Single: Released Jun '89, on Big Life, by Big Life Records. Catalogue no: **BLR 010T**
7" Single: Released Jun '89, on Big Life, by Big Life Records. Catalogue no: **BLR 010**
12" Single: Released Jul '89, on Big Life, by Big Life Records. Catalogue no: **BLR 10R**

De Los Rios, Waldo

MOZART 40
Tracks: / Mozart 40 / Song of joy.
7" Single: Released Oct '88, on Old Gold, by Old Gold Records. Catalogue no: **OG**

9814

De Marchi, Suze

BIG WEDNESDAY
Tracks: / Big Wednesday / Don't go away.
7" Single: Released Jul '87, on EMI, by EMI Records. Deleted Oct '87. Catalogue no: **EM 11**
12" Single: Released Jul '87, on EMI, by EMI Records. Deleted Oct '87. Catalogue no: **12 EM11**

DRY YOUR EYES
Tracks: / Dry your eyes / Big Wednesday / Me and you* (*Track on 12" version.).
7" Single: Released 7 Mar '88, on EMI, by EMI Records. Deleted 31 Jul '88. Catalogue no: **EM 44**
12" Single: Released 7 Mar '88, on EMI, by EMI Records. Deleted 31 Jul '88. Catalogue no: **12EM 44**

YOUNG HEARTS
Tracks: / Young hearts / Biara.
7" Single: Released Apr '86, on EMI, by EMI Records. Catalogue no: **EMI 5552**
12" Single: Released Apr '86, on EMI, by EMI Records. Catalogue no: **12 EMI 5552**

De Nijs, Rob

LET LOVE BE THE ANSWER
Tracks: / Let love be the answer / Love of my life.
7" Single: Released Oct '86, on Columbia, by EMI Records. Catalogue no: **DB 9142**

De Paul, Lynsey

Biographical details: This British singer/songwriter came to fame in 1972 with *Sugar Me*, her first and biggest UK hit. This set the standard for her future hits - catchy, bland pop sung in a thin, high-pitched and (to many people) nauseating voice. *Sugar Me* was written in collaboration with Barry Blue; another song they wrote together, *Dancing On A Saturday Night*, gave Blue his first and biggest UK hit in '73. De Paul's follow-up to *Sugar Me* was *Getting A Drag*, which hit No 18. She thereafter produced her own records, in addition to writing them, and reached No 14 on the British chart with *Won't Somebody Dance With Me*, hailed by the Ivor Novello awards ceremony as the most romantic song of 1973. Her second Top Tenner as a performer occurred the following year, when she hit No 7 with her television theme *No Honestly*. However, after 1975's No 40 hit *My Man And Me*, she never returned to the UK charts as a solo artist.

De Paul's career was in sharp decline by Spring '77, when she temporarily arrested the downward slide by coming second in the Eurovision Song Contest. *Rock Bottom*, a singing, piano-playing, composing and producing collaboration with Mike Moran. The song hit No 19 on the UK listings, but its second place in the Contest was probably due more to De Paul's good looks and an imaginative stage performance than the merits of the song. *Rock Bottom* later became noteworthy for a different reason - it gave its name to a BBC Radio programme about the business side of the music industry, in which she lambusted her former manager Don Arden, accusing him of ripping her off and stating that she hoped he would 'rot in hell'. Arden denied her charges. The Eighties have not brought De Paul any success. Bob MacDonald, 24 March 1985.

UK singer/songwriter born in 1951. Her first hit was co-written with Barry blue (Ron Roker) for the vocal group the Fortunes *Storm in a teacup* in 1972; her own hit the same year was *Sugar me*, relying like all her hits on keyboard skills backing a high girlish voice and hammering home naggingly infectious hook. (Donald Clarke, April 1989)c.

GETTING A DRAG
Tracks: / Getting a drag.
7" Single: Released Dec '72, on M.A.M, by M.A.M. Records. Deleted '75. Catalogue no: **MAM 88**

MY MAN AND ME
Tracks: / My man and me.
7" Single: Released Mar '75, on Jet, by Jet Records. Deleted '78. Catalogue no: **JET 750**

NO HONESTLY (SINGLE)
Tracks: / No honestly.
7" Single: Released Nov '74, on Jet, by Jet Records. Deleted '77. Catalogue no: **JET 747**

OOH I DO
Tracks: / Ooh I do.
7" Single: Released Jun '74, on Warner Bros., by WEA Records. Deleted '77. Catalogue no: **K 16401**

ROCK BOTTOM
Tracks: / Rock bottom.
7" Single: Released Mar '77, on Polydor, by Polydor Ltd. Deleted '80. Catalogue no: **2058 859**

STRANGE CHANGES
Tracks: / Strange changes / Strange changes (pt 2).
7" Single: Released May '81, on MCA, by MCA Records. Deleted May '84. Catalogue no: **MCA 696**

SUGAR ME
Tracks: / Sugar me.
7" Single: Released Aug '72, on M.A.M, by M.A.M. Records. Deleted '75. Catalogue no: **MAM 81**

WON'T SOMEBODY DANCE WITH ME
Tracks: / Won't somebody dance with me.
7" Single: Released Oct '73, on M.A.M, by M.A.M. Records. Deleted '76. Catalogue no: **MAM 109**

De Sario, Teri

AIN'T NOTHIN' (GONNA KEEP ME FROM YOU)
Tracks: / Ain't nothin' (gonna keep me from you).
7" Single: Released Sep '78, on Casablanca, by PolyGram UK Ltd. Deleted '81. Catalogue no: **CAN 128**

CAUGHT
Tracks: / Caught / I've got a secret.
7" Single: Released Nov '80, on Casablanca, by PolyGram UK Ltd. Deleted '83. Catalogue no: **CAN 213**

DANCING IN THE STREETS
Tracks: / Dancing in the streets / Moonlight madness.
7" Single: Released Aug '80, on Casablanca, by PolyGram UK Ltd. Deleted '83. Catalogue no: **CAN 203**

YES I'M READY
Tracks: / Yes i'm ready / With your love.
7" Single: Released Jan '80, on Casablanca, by PolyGram UK Ltd. Deleted Jan '85. Catalogue no: **NB 2225**

De Shannon, Jackie

WINGS OF VICTORY
Tracks: / Wings of victory.
7" Single: Released Jun '84, on Audiotrax. Deleted '86. Catalogue no: **ATX 1**

De Stijl

ANATOMY Do the deal
Tracks: / Anatomy / Do the deal.
7" Single: Released '83, on Small Run. Catalogue no: **SRR 0009**

De Sykes, Stephanie

BORN WITH A SMILE ON MY FACE
Tracks: / Born with a smile on my face.
7" Single: Released Jul '74, on Bradley's. Deleted '77. Catalogue no: **BRAD 7409**

WE'LL FIND OUR DAY
Tracks: / We'll find our day.
7" Single: Released Apr '75, on Bradley's. Deleted '78. Catalogue no: **BRAD 7509**

De Ville, Willy

ASSASSIN OF LOVE
Tracks: / Assassin of love / Spanish Jack / Assassin of love (ext. remix) (Extra track on 12" and CD single.) / Spanish stroll (live) (extra track on 12" and CD single.) / Desparate days (live) (Extra track on CD single.).
12" Single: Released Jan '88, on Polydor, by Polydor Ltd. Catalogue no: **POSPX 904**
CD 5": Released Jan '88, on Polydor, by Polydor Ltd. Catalogue no: **POCD 904**
7" Single: Released Jan '88, on Polydor, by Polydor Ltd. Catalogue no: **POSP 904**

HEAT OF THE MOMENT
Tracks: / Heat of the moment / Pullin' my string.
7" Single: Released Sep '80, on CBS, by CBS Records. Deleted Sep '83. Catalogue no: **CBS 8526**

MIRACLE (SINGLE)
Tracks: / Miracle / I call your name / Stand by me.
7" Single: Released Nov '87, on Polydor, by Polydor Ltd. Catalogue no: **POSP 887**
12" Single: Released Oct '87, on Polydor, by Polydor Ltd. Catalogue no: **POSPX 891**
12" Single: Released Nov '87, on Polydor, by Polydor Ltd. Catalogue no: **POSPX 887**
7" Single: Released Oct '87, on Polydor, by Polydor Ltd. Catalogue no: **POSP 891**

De Wilde, Graham

FLYIN' SO FREE
Tracks: / Flyin' so free.
7" Single: Released Aug '87, on TPL, by Production League, The. Catalogue no: **7TPL 03**

DEACON BLUE - FERGUS SINGS THE BLUES (Released on CBS)

THRESHOLD
Tracks: / Threshold / Newsweek.
7" Single: Released '84, on BBC, by BBC Records & Tapes. Deleted Sep '87. Catalogue no: **RESL 143**

Deacon Blue

CHOCOLATE GIRL
Tracks: / Chocolate girl / S.H.A.R.O.N. / Dignity (live) (Track on 12" only) / Love's great fears (live) (Track on 12" only) / Very thing, The (Track on CD only).
CD 5": Released Jul '88, on CBS, by CBS Records. Deleted Jan '89. Catalogue no: **CDDEAC 6**
7" Single: Released Jul '88, on CBS, by CBS Records. Deleted Jan '89. Catalogue no: **DEAC 6**
7" EP: Released Jul '88, on CBS, by CBS Records. Deleted Jan '89. Catalogue no: **DEAC EP6**
12" Single: Released Jul '88, on CBS, by CBS Records. Deleted Jan '89. Catalogue no: **DEAC T6**

DIGNITY
Tracks: / Dignity / Suffering / Ribbons and bows.
Note: *Extra track on 12in.
12" Single: Released Jan '88, on CBS, by CBS Records. Deleted Aug '88. Catalogue no: **DEAC T4**
7" Single: Released Jan '88, on CBS, by CBS Records. Deleted Aug '88. Catalogue no: **DEAC 4**
12" Single: Released Jan '88, on CBS, by CBS Records. Deleted Nov '87. Catalogue no: **DEAC T1**
10" single: Released Jan '88, on CBS, by CBS Records. Catalogue no: **DEAC Q4**
CD 5": Released Jan '88, on CBS, by CBS Records. Deleted Jan '89. Catalogue no: **CD DEAC4**

FERGUS SINGS THE BLUES (see panel above)
Tracks: / Fergus sings the blues / Long window to love / Fergus sings the blues (extended version) / London A to Z / Back here in beano land.
CD 5": Released 8 May '89, on CBS, by CBS Records. Deleted Oct '89. Catalogue no: **CD DEAC 9**
7" Single: Released 8 May '89, on CBS, by CBS Records. Deleted Oct '89. Catalogue no: **DEAC 9**
Special: Released 8 May '89, on CBS, by CBS Records. Deleted Oct '89. Catalogue no: **DEAC GT9**
7" Set: Released May '89, on CBS, by CBS Records. Deleted Oct '89. Catalogue no: **DEAC B9**
Cassingle: Released 12 May '89, on CBS, by CBS Records. Deleted Oct '89. Catalogue no: **DEAC C9**
12" Single: Released 8 May '89, on CBS, by CBS Records. Deleted Oct '89. Catalogue no: **DEAC T9**
10" single: Released 12 May '89, on CBS, by CBS Records. Deleted Oct '89. Catalogue no: **DEAC QT9**

LOADED
Tracks: /Loaded/Long distance from just across the road/Which side are you on (12" only)/Kings of the western world(12" only).
Cassingle: Released Jun '87, on CBS, by CBS Records. Deleted Nov '87. Catalogue no: **DEAC C2**
12" Single: Released Jun '87, on CBS, by CBS Records. Deleted Nov '87. Catalogue no: **DEAC T2**
7" Single: Released Jun '87, on CBS, by CBS Records. Deleted Nov '87. Catalogue no: **DEAC 2**

LOVE AND REGRET
Tracks: / Love and regret (Only on 7" and CD single.) / Down in the flood (Only on 7" single.) / Love and regret (extended mix) (Only on 12" and CD single.) / Down in the flood (minimal mix) (Only on 12" single.) / Undeveloped heart (Only on 12" and CD single.) / Down in the flood (extended mix) (Only on CD single).
CD 5": Released Aug '89, on CBS, by CBS Records. Catalogue no: **CDDEAC 10**
12" Single: Released Aug '89, on CBS, by CBS Records. Catalogue no: **DEACT 10**
10" single: Released Aug '89, on CBS, by CBS Records. Catalogue no: **DEACQT 10**
Cassingle: Released Aug '89, on CBS, by CBS Records. Catalogue no: **DEACM 10**
7" Single: Released Aug '89, on CBS, by CBS Records. Catalogue no: **DEAC 10**

REAL GONE KID
Tracks: / Real gone kid / Little Lincoln / Real gone kid (ext.) (12" only.) / Born again (CD only.) / It's not funny anymore (CD only.).
7" Single: Released Oct '88, on CBS, by CBS Records. Deleted 17 Apr '89. Catalogue no: **DEAC 7**
CD 5": Released Oct '88, on CBS, by CBS Records. Deleted 17 Apr '89. Catalogue no: **CD DEAC 7**
12" Single: Released Oct '88, on CBS, by CBS Records. Deleted 17 Apr '89. Catalogue no: **DEAC T7**
7" Single: Released Oct '88, on CBS, by CBS Records. Deleted 17 Apr '89. Catalogue no: **DEAC EP7**
12" Single: Released Oct '88, on CBS, by CBS Records. Deleted 17 Apr '89. Catalogue no: **DEAC QT7**

WAGES DAY
Tracks: / Wages day / Take me to the place / Take the saints away / Trampoline.
12" Single: Released 20 Feb '89, on CBS, by CBS Records. Deleted 10 Jul '89. Catalogue no: **DEACT 8**
7" Single: Released 20 Feb '89, on CBS, by CBS Records. Deleted 10 Jul '89. Catalogue no: **DEAC 8**
7" EP: Released 27 Feb '89, on CBS, by CBS Records. Deleted 10 Jul '89. Catalogue no: **DEACEP 8**
CD 5": Released 20 Feb '89, on CBS, by CBS Records. Deleted 10 Jul '89. Catalogue no: **CD DEAC 8**
7" Single: Released 27 Feb '89, on CBS, by CBS Records. Catalogue no: **DEACQ 8**

WHEN WILL YOU MAKE MY TELEPHONE RING?

Tracks: / When will you make my telephone ring? / That brilliant feeling / Disneyworld* / Punch and Judy man*.
Note: * Extra tracks on 12" and CD single.
12" Single: Released Mar '88, on CBS, by CBS Records. Deleted Aug '88. Catalogue no: **DEAC T5**
CD 5": Released Mar '88, on CBS, by CBS Records. Deleted Jan '89. Catalogue no: **CD DEAC 5**
7" Single: Released Mar '88, on CBS, by CBS Records. Deleted Aug '88. Catalogue no: **DEAC 5**
Special: Released Mar '88, on CBS, by CBS Records. Deleted Aug '88. Catalogue no: **DEAC B5**

YOU MAKE MY PHONE RING
Tracks: / You make my phone ring.
12" Single: Released Aug '87, on CBS, by CBS Records. Catalogue no: **DEAC 3T**
7" Single: Released Aug '87, on CBS, by CBS Records. Catalogue no: **DEAC 3**

Deacon Judah

BEING WITH YOU
Tracks: / Being with you.
12" Single: Released Sep '89, on High Voltage, Catalogue no: **HVM 12**

Dead Beats

CHOOSE YOU
Tracks: / Choose you.
7" Single: Released 26 Jun '85, on Red Rhino, by Red Rhino Records. Deleted '88. Catalogue no: **RED 003**

CRAZY HOUND DOG
Tracks: / Crazy hound dog / Crazy when i hear the beat.
7" Single: Released Jun '82, on Sheet, Catalogue no: **BULL 5**

Dead Boys

Biographical details: A USA Punk act formed in Cleveland in 1976 by vocalist Stiv (Steve) Bators, guitarists Cheetah Chrome (Gene Connor) and Jimmy Zero, bassist Jeff Magnum and drummer Johnny Blitz. They played at CBGB's in New York and were managed by one of the owners; Young, Loud and Snotty summed them up. Bators recorded solo on Bomp and relocated to England, singing with the Wanderer's, a short-lived Punk 'supergroup', then joining ex-Damned guitarist Brian James in Lords of The New Church. (Donald Clarke, April 1989).

ALL THE WAY DOWN
Tracks: / All the way down.
12" Single: Released Aug '87, on Relativity (USA), Catalogue no: **88561-8165-1**

Dead Can Dance

GARDEN OF THE ARCANE
Tracks: / Garden of the arcane.
12" Single: Released Sep '84, on 4AD, by 4AD Records. Catalogue no: **BAD 408**

Dead Dog Limited

DEVIOUS WOMAN
Tracks: / Devious woman.
12" Single: Released Oct '86, on Island, by Island Records. Deleted Jul '87. Catalogue no: **12IS 281**
7" Single: Released Oct '86, on Island, by Island Records. Catalogue no: **IS 281**

Dead End Kids

HAVE I THE RIGHT
Tracks: / Have I the right.
7" Single: Released Mar '77, on CBS, by CBS Records. Deleted '80. Catalogue no: **CBS 4972**

Dead Kennedys

Biographical details: This American punk rock band compromised, at the time of their greatest success, Jelle Biafra, East Bay Ray, Klaus Flouride and Bruce 'Ted' Slesinger.
Formed in San Francisco in 1978, the group was materminded by vocalist Jello Biafra. In similar fashion to Britain's Crass, The Dead Kennedys' aim was to continue punk rock's original 1976/77 rebellious and outrageous ideals, at a time when many of the genre's original protagonists were moving into the rock mainstream. The DKs' geographical location fuelled their frustration - they were surrounded by the slick, professional, laid back West Coast recording scene, an establishment which punk had failed to overturn. The names of the group and its leader were, of course, designed to offend as many people as possible. In common with Crass, they formed their own record label to avoid any musical or political compromise: theirs was named Alternative Tentacles. Their debut single, issued in '79, was *California Uber Alles*, a no holds barred assault on State Governer Jerry Brown. Another single, *Holiday In Cambodia* was equally controversial.
By the time of their first album, 1980's *Fresh Fruit For Rotting Vegetables*, the Dead Kennedys had built up a sizeable underground following; particularly in Britain, where the LP reached No 33 on the national charts. The group also managed to hit the UK singles listings, peaking at No 49 with 1980's *Kill The Poor* and climbing to No 36 with 1981's *Too Drunk To Fuck*. Their uncompromisingly raw and energetic records attacked all political viewpoints - left, right and centre - and numerous other facets of modern living. In 1981 drummer Ted was replaced by D H Peligro. Late 1982 saw the release of the DKs' second LP collection of charming ditties, *Plastic Surgery Disasters*. This album showed no let-up in the group's fury, but it failed to win them any new followers. Bob MacDonald, 16 March 1985.
A USA punk act formed in San Francisco in 1978: the USA equivalent of the Sex Pistols, influenced by their late '70's tour. Lineup: Jello Biafra, vocals; East Bay Ray (aka Ray Valium), guitar; Klaus Fluoride, bass; Ted, drums. Their name alone was enough to ensure commercial failure, but they were occasionally intelligent lyrics amid the mayhem: *Nazi punks fuck off* and *Holiday in Cambodia* attacked both ends of the political spectrum. Ted was replaced by Bruce Slexinger, then by J H Pelligro. Biafra ran for mayor of San Francisco in 1979; his platform requiring businessmen to wear clown suits took him to fourth out of 10 in the poll. (Donald Clarke, April 1989)r.

BLEED FOR ME
Tracks: / Bleed for me / Life sentence.
12" Single: Released Jul '82, on Statik, Catalogue no: **STAT 2212**
7" Single: Released Jul '82, on Statik, Catalogue no: **STAT 22**

CALIFORNIA UBER ALLES
Tracks: / California uber alles.
7" Single: Released Dec '80, on Fast, by Fast Forward Records. Catalogue no: **FAST 12**

HALLOWEEN
Tracks: / Halloween.
12" Single: Released Dec '82, on Alternative, Deleted '85. Catalogue no: **STAT 2712**
7" Single: Released Dec '82, on Alternative, Deleted '88. Catalogue no: **STAT 27**

HOLIDAY IN CAMBODIA
Tracks: / Holiday in Cambodia / Police truck.
7" Single: Released Sep '81, on Cherry Red, by Cherry Red Records. Catalogue no: **CHERRY 13**
CD 5": Released Jun '88, on Cherry Red, by Cherry Red Records. Catalogue no: **CDCHERRY 13**
12" Single: Released Sep '81, on Cherry Red, by Cherry Red Records. Catalogue no: **12 CHERRY 13**

HOLIDAYS IN CAMBODIA
Tracks: / Holidays in Cambodia.
7" Single: Released Sep '81, on Cherry Red, by Cherry Red Records. Deleted '84. Catalogue no: **CHERRY 13**

IN GOD WE TRUST
Tracks: / In God we trust.
7" Single: Released Dec '81, on Statik, Catalogue no: **STAT EP 2**

KILL THE POOR
Tracks: / Kill the poor / In-sight.
CD 5": Released 13 Sep '88, on Cherry Red, by Cherry Red Records. Catalogue no: **CDCHERRY 16**
7" Single: Released Aug '81, on Cherry Red, by Cherry Red Records. Deleted '87. Catalogue no: **CHERRY 16**

TOO DRUNK TO F*CK
Tracks: / Too drunk to f*ck / Prey, The.
12" Single: Released Jun '81, on Cherry Red, by Cherry Red Records. Catalogue no: **12 CHERRY 24**
7" Single: Released Jun '81, on Cherry Red, by Cherry Red Records. Catalogue no: **CHERRY 24**

Dead Mans Shadow

ANOTHER YEAR
Tracks: / Another year.
7" Single: Released Nov '83, on Criminal Damage, Catalogue no: **CRI 105**

BOMB SCARE
Tracks: / Bomb scare / Another Hiroshima / Fighting for reality.
7" Single: Released Mar '82, on Rondelet Music, by Rondelet Music & Records. Catalogue no: **ROUND 16**

FLOWER IN THE GUN
Tracks: / Flower in the gun / Last cowboy.
7" Single: Released Nov '82, on Rondelet Music, by Rondelet Music & Records. Catalogue no: **ROUND 27**

IN MY DREAMS

DEAD OR ALIVE - COME HOME WITH ME BABY (Released on Epic)

Tracks: / In my dreams.
7" Single: Released Jun '83, on Expulsion, by Expulsion Records. Deleted '87. Catalogue no: **OUT 4**

Dead Milkmen

INSTANT CLUB HIT
Note: Collector's edition compact disc. Full colour gatefold pack.
CD 5": Released Nov '87, on Restless (USA), by Enigma Records (USA). Catalogue no: **722 312**

PUNK ROCK GIRL
Tracks: / Punk rock girl / Ringo buys a rifle / Life is shit.
12" Single: Released Feb '89, on Enigma, by Enigma Records (USA). Catalogue no: **ENVT 8**
7" Single: Released Feb '89, on Enigma, by Enigma Records (USA). Catalogue no: **ENV 8**

Dead Or Alive

Biographical details: This all male four piece British band are dominated by their lead vocalist Pete Burns. One of the many Eighties acts to emerge from the constantly creative city of Liverpool, Dead Or Alive first became noticed in 1981 through the usual channels - the independent label scene and BBC Radio One's John Peel Show. Such singles as *I'm Falling* and *The Stranger* built up the necessary cult following, but the band's breakthrough opportunities were widened when Culture Club's Boy George made sexual ambiguity an acceptable household commodity. This allowed the equally androgynous Pete Burns to get a foot in the music industry door, and his band signed with CBS Records' Epic Label in early 1983. Despite being with a major record company, Dead Or Alive continued to cultivate a controversial image. When young singer/songwriter Nick Heyward lambasted one of their singles in a music paper review, they responded by assaulting him with fire extinguishers. Burns' image combined flamboyance with a rude brashness.
DOA achieved their commercial breakthrough in spring '84 with an unlikely cover version of KC & the Sunshine Band's 1975 smash *That's The Way (I Like It)*. This set the standard for other DOA records - harsh vocals accompanied by a conventional disco beat. The Summer '84 success of *You Think You're A Man*, a UK Top 20 single by US gender bender Divine, led to Pete Burns & Co snapping up that single's producers. The first result of this partnership was *You Spin Me Round (Like A Record)*, a single issued in the autumn of '84. It entered the UK Top 75 at the beginning of December and, after ten weeks of yo-yoing around the lower regions of the chart, cracked the Top 40 in February. The single reached No 1 in March in its 15th chart week, thus becoming the slowest climbing chart-topper in history. Yet another Liverpool band had made it. Bob MacDonald, 16 March 1985.
UK New Wave band formed by vocalist Pete Burns; lineup in 1984 was keyboardist Timothy Lever, bassist Michael Percy, drummer Stephen McCoy. After his first tast of fame fronting the Mystery Girls, a legendary gig at Eric's Club in 1977 including drummer Phil Hurst, bassist Julian Cope (later of Teardrop Explodes) and guitarist Pete Wylie (later Wah), Burns formed Nightmares in Wax in 1979; by the time he changed the name to Dead Or Alive in 1980 he'd been through 30 musicians; his synthesiser/sequencer dominated cover of KC and the Sunshine Band's *That's the way (I like it)* was a number 22 hit in 1984, the chanted vocal counterpart *Keep that body strong* in a bizarre video featuring female body builders establishing a tacky image which Burns fostered in interviews. His androgynous looks and further releases aimed at the dancefloor a big gay following. (Donald Clarke, April 1989).

BABY DON'T SAY GOODBYE
Tracks: / Baby don't say goodbye.
7" Single: Released Aug '89, on Epic, by CBS Records. Catalogue no: **BURN 6**
12" Single: Released Aug '89, on Epic, by CBS Records. Catalogue no: **BURN T6**
CD 5": Released Aug '89, on Epic, by CBS Records. Catalogue no: **BURN C6**

BRAND NEW LOVER
Tracks: / Brand new lover / In too deep (live).
12" Single: Released Sep '86, on Epic, by CBS Records. Catalogue no: **650075 6**
7" Single: Released Sep '86, on Epic, by CBS Records. Catalogue no: **650075 7**
12" Single: Released Nov '87, on Epic (USA), by CBS Records (USA). Catalogue no: **4905065**

COME HOME WITH ME BABY (see panel above)
Tracks: / Come home with me baby / I'll save you all my kisses / Come home with me baby (deadhouse dub) (Only on 12" single.) / Come home with me baby (deadhouse 7" dub) (Only on 12" single.).
CD 5": Released Jul '89, on Epic, by CBS Records. Catalogue no: **BURNSC 5**
12" Single: Released Jul '89, on Epic, by CBS Records. Catalogue no: **BURNSQ 5**
12" Single: Released Jul '89, on Epic, by CBS Records. Catalogue no: **BURNST 5**
7" Single: Released Jul '89, on Epic, by CBS Records. Catalogue no: **BURNS 5**

HOOKED ON LOVE
Tracks: / Hooked on love / You spin me round (like a record).
7" Single: Released Mar '87, on Epic, by CBS Records. Catalogue no: **BURNS 2**

I'D DO ANYTHING
Tracks: / I'd do anything.
12" Single: Released Jan '84, on Epic, by CBS Records. Catalogue no: **TA 4069**
7" Single: Released Jan '84, on Epic, by CBS Records. Catalogue no: **A 4069**

I'LL SAVE YOU ALL MY KISSES
Tracks: / I'll save you all my kisses / Lover come back to me / Whirlpool / Nowhere to nowhere / I'll save you all my kisses (long wet sloppy kiss mix) (Only on BURNSQ 3.)
12" Single: Released Sep '87, on Epic, by CBS Records. Catalogue no: **BURNS T3**
7" Single: Released Sep '87, on Epic, by

CBS Records. Catalogue no: **BURNS 3**
12" Single: Released Oct '87, on Epic, by CBS Records. Catalogue no: **BURNS Q3**

I'M FALLING
Tracks: / I'm falling.
7" Single: Released Mar '81, on Inevitable, by Inevitable Records. Catalogue no: **INEV 005**

IN TOO DEEP
Tracks: / In too deep.
7" Single: Released Jun '85, on Epic, by CBS Records. Catalogue no: **A 6360**
12" Single: Released Jun '85, on Epic, by CBS Records. Catalogue no: **QTA 6360**
12" Single: Released Jun '85, on Epic, by CBS Records. Deleted '86. Catalogue no: **TA 6360**
7" Single: Released Jun '85, on Epic, by CBS Records. Catalogue no: **GA 6360**

LOVER COME BACK TO ME
Tracks: / Lover come back to me.
7" Single: Released Apr '85, on Epic, by CBS Records. Deleted '88. Catalogue no: **A 6086**

MISTY CIRCLES
Tracks: / Misty circles.
7" Single: Released May '83, on Epic, by CBS Records. Catalogue no: **A 3399**
12" Single: Released May '83, on Epic, by CBS Records. Catalogue no: **TA 3399**

MY HEART GOES BANG
Tracks: / My heart goes bang.
Note: Now deleted in U.K., great value 12" one side , 12" remix version on the flip!
12" Single: Released Nov '87, on Epic (USA), by CBS Records (USA). Catalogue no: **4905327**
7" Single: Released Sep '85, on Epic, by CBS Records. Deleted '88. Catalogue no: **A 6571**

SOMETHING IN MY HOUSE
Tracks: / D.J. hit that button / Brand new lover / Too deep.
12" Single: Released Dec '86, on Epic, by CBS Records. Catalogue no: **BURNS T1**
7" Single: Released Jan '87, on Epic, by CBS Records. Deleted Aug '87. Catalogue no: **BURNS D1**
7" Single: Released Dec '86, on Epic, by CBS Records. Catalogue no: **BURNS 1**
12" Single: Released Nov '87, on Epic (USA), by CBS Records (USA). Catalogue no: **4906750**

STRANGER, THE
Tracks: / Stranger, The.
7" Single: Released Sep '82, on Black Eyes, Catalogue no: **BE 2**

THAT'S THE WAY I LIKE IT
Tracks: / That's the way I like it / Keep that body.
7" Pic: Released Jun '83, on Epic, by CBS Records. Catalogue no: **WA 3399**
12" Single: Released Mar '84, on Epic, by CBS Records. Catalogue no: **TA 4271**
7" Single: Released Mar '84, on Epic, by CBS Records. Catalogue no: **A 4271**

TURN AROUND AND COUNT 2 TEN
Tracks: / Turn around and count 2 ten / Something in my house (inst. mix) / Turn around and count 2 ten (Pearl & Dean mix) (12" and CD only) / Turn around and count 2 ten (inst. mix) (CD single only) / Turn around and count 2 ten (disco dream mix) (special 12" only) / Then there was you (special 12" only) / Come inside (special 12" only).
CD 5": Released Aug '88, on Epic, by CBS Records. Deleted 17 Apr '89. Catalogue no: **BURNS C4**
12" Single: Released Aug '88, on Epic, by CBS Records. Deleted 17 Apr '89. Catalogue no: **BURNS T4**
7" Single: Released Aug '88, on Epic, by CBS Records. Deleted 17 Apr '89. Catalogue no: **BURNS 4**
12" Single: Released Sep '88, on Epic, by CBS Records. Deleted 17 Apr '89. Catalogue no: **BURNS Q4**

WHAT I WANT
Tracks: / What I want / Stranger.
7" Single: Released Jun '84, on Epic, by CBS Records. Catalogue no: **A 4510**
12" Single: Released Jun '84, on Epic, by CBS Records. Catalogue no: **TA 4510**

YOU SPIN ME ROUND
Tracks: / You spin me round (like a record).
Note: Deleted in the U.K., available in picture bag.
12" Single: Released Nov '87, on Epic (USA), by CBS Records (USA). Catalogue no: **4905208**
7" Single: Released Dec '84, on Epic, by CBS Records. Deleted '87. Catalogue no: **A 4861**

Dead Pan Tractor

GRUMBLE
Tracks: / Grumble.
12" Single: Released Sep '85, on Black Lagoon, by Black Lagoon Records. Deleted '88. Catalogue no: **INC 008**

Dead Wretched

CONVICTED
Tracks: / Convicted.
7" Single: Released Sep '82, on Inferno (2), Catalogue no: **HELL 5**

NO HOPE FOR ANYONE
Tracks: / No hope for anyone.
7" Single: Released Feb '82, on Inferno (2), Catalogue no: **HELL 2**

Deaf Boy

BOTTLE, THE
Tracks: / Bottle, The / New York groove.
12" Single: Released Nov '87, on Juicy Fruit, by Domino Records. Catalogue no: **JUICE 1T**
12" Single: Released Oct '88, on Domino, by Domino Records. Catalogue no: **JUICE T1**

Deaf Comet Crew

AT THE MARBLE BOY
Tracks: / At the marble boy.
12" Single: Released Mar '85, on Beggars Banquet, by Beggars Banquet Records. Deleted Jun '88. Catalogue no: **BEG 130T**

De'Allie, Adrian

MY CHERIE AMOUR
Tracks: / My cherie amour.
7" Single: Released Oct '88, on Ruff Neck Business, Catalogue no: **RL 003**

Dean, Hazell

Biographical details: This British singer, who hails from Chelmsford, spent the late Seventies and early Eighties looking for her big breakthrough. Blessed with a fine, strong voice, she worked in various small-time bands, meddling in pop and jazz. She also made a determined affort to win the British heats of the Eurovision Song Contest, but failed; in view of the low esteem in which that event is held amongst the UKpublic, it was perhaps better for Dean's long term career prospects that she failed to get through. She finally cracked the British charts in early 1984 with a double A sided single *Evergreen/Jealous Love*, which reached No 63. This record benefitted from exposure in gay discos, where the Hi-NRG dance scene was booming.

Dean's chart toehold was exploited by reactivating *Searchin' (I Gotta Find A Man)*, a single originally issued in June 1983. In June '84 it reached No 6 on the UK chart; the intervening year had seen the song build into a classic on the UK-orientated high energy scene, a scene that had been gradually expanded during the Eighties. *Searchin'* was perhaps the archetypal Hi-NRG record: a bland, Eurovision-type pop song, well sung, given a cliche 'pots and pans' percussion and production and, like the bulk of the genre's singles, featuring the word 'man' in the title. After the slow-burning *Searchin'*, Dean quickly achieved an instant and even bigger hit with *Whatever I Do (Wherever I Go)*, which went to No 4 on the British listings. Other smaller hits in the same style were *Back In My Arms (Once Again)* and *No Fool (For Love)* - these came from the studio production team compromising Matt Aitken, Mike Stock and Pete Waterman, the triumvirate who were also responsible for Divine's ultra-camp 1984 hit *You Think You're A Man* and Dead Or Alive's 1985 UK No 1 *You Spin Me Round (Like A Record)*. Bob MacDonald, 16 March 1985..

ALWAYS DOESN'T MEAN FOREVER
Tracks: / Always doesn't mean forever / Always doesn't mean forever (inst).
12" Single: Released Jun '87, on EMI, by EMI Records. Deleted Oct '87. Catalogue no: **12EM 8**
7" Single: Released Jun '87, on EMI, by EMI Records. Deleted Oct '87. Catalogue no: **EM 8**

BACK IN MY ARMS (once again)
Tracks: / Back in my arms / City nights / Back in my arms (house mix) / Back in my arms.
12" Single: Released Oct '84, on Proto, by Proto Records. Catalogue no: **ENAT 122**
7" Single: Released Oct '84, on Proto, by Proto Records. Catalogue no: **ENA 122**

E.S.P.
Tracks: / E.S.P. / Image in the mirror.
7" Single: Released Apr '86, on EMI, by EMI Records. Catalogue no: **EMI 5560**
12" Single: Released Apr '86, on EMI, by EMI Records. Catalogue no: **12 EMI 5560**

EVERGREEN
Tracks: / Evergreen / Jealous love.
7" Single: Released Feb '84, on Proto, by Proto Records. Deleted '87. Catalogue no: **ENA 114**

JEALOUS LOVE
Tracks: / Jealous love / Evergreen.
7" Single: Released Jan '84, on Proto, by Proto Records. Catalogue no: **ENA 114**
12" Single: Released Jan '84, on Proto, by Proto Records. Catalogue no: **ENAT 114**
7" Pic: Released Jan '84, on Proto, by Proto Records. Catalogue no: **ENAP 114**

LOVE PAINS
Tracks: / Love pains / More than words can say.
7" Single: Released Aug '89, on Lisson, by PWL Records. Catalogue no: **DOLE 12**
12" Single: Released Aug '89, on Lisson, by PWL Records. Catalogue no: **DOLEQ 12**
CD 5": Released Aug '89, on Lisson, by PWL Records. Catalogue no: **DOLED 12**

MAYBE (WE SHOULD CALL IT A DAY)
Tracks: / Maybe (we should call it a day) / Maybe (inst) / No fool (for love) (The Murray mix) (Track on 12") / Who's leaving who? (Bob's tambourine mix) (Only on CD single.) / Maybe (we should call it a day) (Track on 12" special only.).
Note: Produced by Stock-Aitken-Waterman. Engineered by Mark McGuire assisted by YoYo. Mixed by 'Mixmaster' Pete Hammond for PWL. **track on CD single.(P) 1988 Original sound recordings Ltd.
12" Single: Released Jun '88, on EMI, by EMI Records. Deleted Jun '89. Catalogue no: **12EM 62**
CD 5": Released Jun '88, on EMI, by EMI Records. Deleted Jun '89. Catalogue no: **CDEM 62**
7" Single: Released Jun '88, on EMI, by EMI Records. Deleted Jun '89. Catalogue no: **EM 62**
12" Single: Released Jul '88, on EMI, by EMI Records. Deleted Jun '89. Catalogue no: **12 EMX 62**
Cassingle: Released Jun '88, on EMI, by EMI Records. Deleted Nov '88. Catalogue no: **TC EM 62**

NO FOOL (FOR LOVE) (see panel below)
Tracks: / No fool (for love) / No fool (for love) (part two instr.).
12" Single: Released Feb '85, on Proto, by Proto Records. Catalogue no: **ENAT 123**
7" Single: Released Feb '85, on Proto, by Proto Records. Catalogue no: **ENA 123**
7" Pic: Released Feb '85, on Proto, by Proto Records. Catalogue no: **ENAP 123**

SEARCHIN
Tracks: / Searchin / Whatever I do (wherever I go) / Stand up (megamix) / Stand up.
12" Single: Released Oct '86, on EMI, by EMI Records. Deleted Jul '87. Catalogue no: **12EMIX 5584**
7" Single: Released Apr '84, on Proto, by Proto Records. Catalogue no: **ENA 109**
12" Single: Released Apr '84, on Proto, by Proto Records. Catalogue no: **ENAT 109**

STAND UP
Tracks: / Love ends, love parts / Whatever I do (extended) / Searching (extended) / Stand up.
Note: Extra tracks in double pack
7" Set: Released Aug '86, on EMI, by EMI Records. Catalogue no: **12 EMID 5584**
12" Single: Released Aug '86, on EMI, by EMI Records. Deleted Jul '87. Catalogue no: **12 EMI 5584**
7" Single: Released Aug '86, on EMI, by EMI Records. Deleted Jul '87. Catalogue no: **EMI 5584**

THEY SAY IT'S GONNA RAIN
Tracks: / They say it's gonna rain.
7" Single: Released Sep '85, on Parlophone, by EMI Records. Catalogue no: **R 6107**
12" Single: Released Sep '85, on Parlophone, by EMI Records. Deleted Nov '88. Catalogue no: **12R 6107**

TURN IT INTO LOVE
Tracks: / Turn it into love (7" version) / You're too good to be true / No fool (for love) (megamix) / They say it's gonna rain / Always doesn't mean forever (medley.) / Who's leaving who (medley.) / Danger / Searchin' (medley.) / Whatever I do (wherever I go) (medley.) / Turn it into love (ext. version) (12", CD single only.) / Turn it into love (Instrumental - long version) (12" only.).
7" Single: Released Sep '88, on EMI, by EMI Records. Deleted Aug '89. Catalogue no: **EM 71**
CD 5": Released Sep '88, on EMI, by EMI Records. Deleted Aug '89. Catalogue no: **CDEM 71**
12" Single: Released Sep '88, on EMI, by EMI Records. Deleted Aug '89. Catalogue no: **12EMX 71**
12" Single: Released Sep '88, on EMI, by EMI Records. Deleted Aug '89. Catalogue no: **12EM 71**

WHATEVER I DO (wherever I go)
Tracks: / Whatever I do (wherever I go).
7" Single: Released Aug '84, on Proto, by Proto Records. Catalogue no: **ENA 119**
12" Single: Released Aug '84, on Proto, by Proto Records. Catalogue no: **ENAT 119**

WHO'S LEAVING WHO?
Tracks: / Who's leaving who? / Whatever I do (wherever I go) / Who's leaving who? (Bob's tambourine mix) (Track on 12".) / Who's leaving who? (Bob's tambourine inst. mix) (Only on 12".) / Whatever I do (wherever I go)(ext. version) (Only on 12".).
7" Single: Released Mar '88, on EMI, by EMI Records. Deleted Jun '89. Catalogue no: **EM 45**
12" Single: Released Apr '88, on EMI, by EMI Records. Deleted Jun '89. Catalogue no: **12EMX 45**
12" Single: Released Mar '88, on EMI, by EMI Records. Deleted Nov '88. Catalogue no: **12EM 45**

Dean, Jamie

HEARTBREAK AVENUE
Tracks: / Heartbreak Avenue.
12" Single: Released Mar '88, on Uptown Records, by Uptown Records. Catalogue no: **12 UTR 7**
7" Single: Released Mar '88, on Uptown

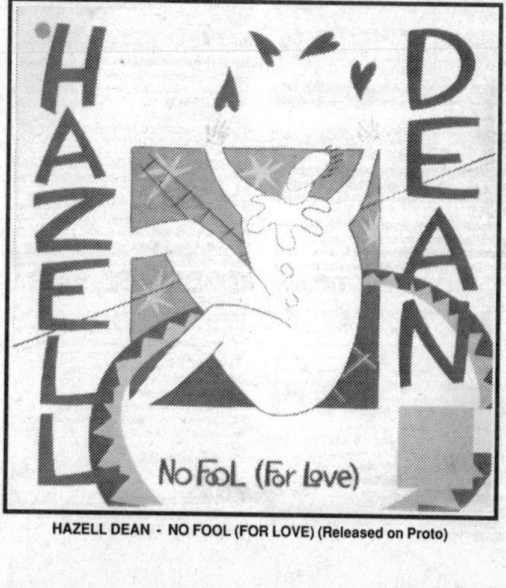

HAZELL DEAN - NO FOOL (FOR LOVE) (Released on Proto)

Records, by Uptown Records. Catalogue no: **UTR 7**

LOVE CHILD
Tracks: / Love child (New York house mix) / Love child (dance mix) / Love child (Instrumental).
12" Single: Released Nov '87, on Uptown Records, by Uptown Records. Catalogue no: **12 UTRX 1**

Dean, Jimmy

Biographical details: Enormously popular country singer in the '60's, born in 1928 in Texas; also a TV host and actor. First minor hit with the Wildcats was *Bummin' around* in 1953 on Four Star; he pioneered country music on TV, reaching network status in 1960: he signed with CBS and had collosal hit *Big bad John* in 1961: number one in both country and pop charts and won a Grammy. He retired in the mid '70's to sell sausages. (Donald Clarke, April 1989).

BIG BAD JOHN
Tracks: / Steelman / Big bad John.
7" Single: Released Oct '61, on Philips, by Phonogram Ltd. Deleted '64. Catalogue no: **PB 1187**
7" Single: Released Jan '87, on Old Gold, by Old Gold Records. Catalogue no: **OG 9399**

LITTLE BLACK BOOK
Tracks: / Little black book.
7" Single: Released Nov '62, on CBS, by CBS Records. Deleted '65. Catalogue no: **AAG 122**

Dean, Joanna

KISS THIS
Tracks: / Kiss this / I miss the money / Gimme shelter (Extra track on 12".).
Note: "Debut single from Joanna Dean, a raunchy blues/rock songstress from the southern states of the US." (Polydor, May 1988.)
7" Single: Released May '88, on Polydor, by Polydor Ltd. Catalogue no: **PO 5**
12" Single: Released May '88, on Polydor, by Polydor Ltd. Catalogue no: **PZ 5**

Dean, Johnny

SITTING AROUND MY TABLE
Tracks: / Sitting around my table.
12" Single: Released Oct '85, on Move, Catalogue no: **MS 7**

Dean, Johnson

SOMEBODY SOMEWHERE
Tracks: / Somebody, somewhere.
12" Single: Released May '89, on Mr.Modo, Catalogue no: **WMS 007T**

Dean, Letitia

SOMETHING OUTA NOTHING
Tracks: / Something outa nothing / Time square (instrumental).
12" Single: Released Oct '86, on BBC, by BBC Records & Tapes. Deleted 31 Aug '88. Catalogue no: **12 RSL 203**
7" Single: Released Oct '86, on BBC, by BBC Records & Tapes. Deleted 31 Aug '88. Catalogue no: **RESL 203**

YOU TAUGHT ME EVERYTHING I KNOW
Tracks: / You taught me everything I know / Little bit a heaven, A.
7" Single: Released Dec '88, on Rich, Catalogue no: **GRQ 105**

Dean, Mel

ZOLA ZOLA
Tracks: / Zola Zola.
7" Single: Released Jun '85, on Rubber Trumpet, Catalogue no: **MSRTR 1**

Dean, Michael Jay

STREETS AIN'T PAVED WITH GOLD
Tracks: / Streets ain't paved with gold / Because you're there.
7" Single: Released Nov '88, on Pebbles, by Pebbles Records. Catalogue no: **MJD 1**

THAT'S WHY IT'S CHRISTMAS NIGHT
Tracks: / That's why it's Christmas night / That's why it's Christmas night (instrumental).
7" Single: Released Dec '88, on Pebbles, by Pebbles Records. Catalogue no: **MJD 2**

Dean, Peter

I CAN'T GET A TICKET FOR THE WORLD CUP
Tracks: / I can't get a ticket for the world cup / Right fine, don't panic.
7" Single: Released May '86, on Portrait, by CBS Records. Deleted '86. Catalogue no: **A 7150**

Dean, Raddie

PARTY NIGHT
Tracks: / Party night.
12" Single: Released Jan '84, on Sapphire, Catalogue no: **SAP 0010**

Dean, Rick

ALLEY OOP
Tracks: / Alley oop / It's a feeling.
7" Single: Released Sep '82, on Monarch, by Monarch Records. Catalogue no: **MON 032**

Dean, Sheri

MAKE SOMEONE HAPPY
Tracks: / Make someone happy / Wizard on ice.
7" Single: Released Dec '81, on Rocket, by Rocket Records. Deleted Dec '84. Catalogue no: **XPRES 68**

Dean, Sparky

YIP YAP RABBIT
Tracks: / Yip yap rabbit / Satisfaction guaranteed.
12" Single: Released Nov '85, on UK Bubblers, by Greensleeves Records. Deleted '88. Catalogue no: **UKMC 10**

Deane, Geoff

HOLIDAY IN
Tracks: / Holiday in.
7" Single: Released Jul '85, on Record Shack, by Record Shack Records. Catalogue no: **SOHO 47**
12" Single: Released Jul '85, on Record Shack, by Record Shack Records. Catalogue no: **SOHOT 47**

NAVY LARK
Tracks: / Navylark.
12" Single: Released Apr '83, on WEA, by WEA Records. Catalogue no: **X 9863T**
7" Single: Released Apr '83, on WEA, by WEA Records. Catalogue no: **X 9863**

Deane, Geoffrey

WHAT ABOUT ROMANCE?
Tracks: / What about romance?.
7" Single: Released Oct '83, on Plastic Palm Trees, Deleted '85. Catalogue no: **PPT 1**
12" Single: Released Oct '83, on Plastic Palm Trees, Deleted '85. Catalogue no: **PPTT 1**

Deasy, Pat

YOU OUGHT TO PUT IT TO MUSIC
Tracks: / You ought to put it to music.
7" Single: Released Jul '85, on Play, by Play Records. Catalogue no: **PLAY 201**

Death By Milkfloat

ABSOLUTE NON-END, THE
Tracks: / Absolute non-end, The.
12" Single: Released Jun '88, on Ediesta, Catalogue no: **CALC 047**

T.T.Y.F.
Tracks: / T.T.Y.F..
7" Single: Released 22 Aug '88, on Constrictor, by Constrictor Records (Germany). Catalogue no: **COLL 009**

UNINFORMATION
Tracks: / Uninformation.
12" Single: Released May '89, on Vinyl Drip, by Vinyl Drip Records. Catalogue no: **SUK 6**

Death Cult

BROTHERS GRIMM
Tracks: / Brothers Grimm.
12" Single: Released Jul '83, on Situation 2, by Beggars Banquet Records. Catalogue no: **SIT 23T**

GOD'S ZOO
Tracks: / God's zoo.
12" Single: Released Nov '83, on Situation 2, by Beggars Banquet Records. Catalogue no: **SIT 29T**
7" Single: Released Nov '83, on Situation 2, by Beggars Banquet Records. Catalogue no: **SIT 29**

Death In June

...AND MURDER LOVE
Tracks: / And murder love / Come before Christ / Torture by roses.
7" Single: Released Dec '85, on New European, Catalogue no: **BADVC 73**
12" Single: Released Dec '85, on New European, Catalogue no: **BADVC 73T**

BORN AGAIN
Tracks: / Born again.
Note: CENAZ 009 is a picture disc.
12" Single: Released Jul '89, on Cenaz, by Cenaz Records. Catalogue no: **CENAZ 009**
12" Single: Released Oct '88, on Cenaz, by Cenaz Records. Catalogue no: **CEN 009**
12" Single: Released Mar '85, on New European, Catalogue no: **BADVC 69**

HEAVEN STREET
Tracks: / Heaven street.
12" Single: Released Jan '84, on New European, Catalogue no: **SA 29634**

SHE SAID DESTROY
Tracks: / She said destroy.
7" Single: Released Aug '84, on New European, Catalogue no: **BADVC 6**
12" Single: Released Aug '84, on New European, Catalogue no: **12BADVC 6**

STATE LAUGHTER
Tracks: / State laughter / Holding water.
7" Single: Released Nov '82, on New European, Catalogue no: **SA 30634**

TO DROWN A ROSE
Tracks: / To drown a rose.
10" single: Released 30 May '87, on New European, Catalogue no: **BADVC 10**

Death Pop

ROGER'S GONE MAD
Tracks: / Roger's gone mad.
7" Single: Released Sep '84, on Twinkle, by Twinkle Records. Catalogue no: **TWINK 1**

Death Sentence

DEATH AND PURE DESTRUCTION
Tracks: / Death and pure destruction.
7" Single: Released Aug '82, on Beat-The-System, Deleted '88. Catalogue no: **DEATH 1**

Deb, Debbie

WHEN I HEAR THE MUSIC
Tracks: / When I hear the music.
12" Single: Released Aug '84, on Sunny View (USA), by Sunnyview Records (USA). Catalogue no: **SUNYL 106**

DeBarge

Biographical details: A soul family vocal group. Since the Jacksons grew up Motown had searched for suitably wholesome replacements; Jermaine Jackson discovered them: a family of 10 raised single handed by their music loving mother who encouraged Bobby and Tommy to sing gospel on Detroit radio; they signed with Motown as members of disco group Switch. Then Mark DeBarge (vocals, trumpet) enlisted brothers Eldra and James (both vocals, bass), and sister Bunny in a group to play around the neighbourhood; a chance visit to Motown led to a meeting with Jackson and an on-the-spot audition to the personal interest of Berry Gordy. Their first single was released in 1978. Their candyfloss pop-soul gaining is confident but dispensible; lead singer Eldra is a Michael Jackson figure, visually and vocally similar; James was briefly married to Janet Jackson. Brother Chico Debarge signed with Motown as a solo; El went solo in 1986. (Donald Clarke, April 1989).

ALL THIS LOVE
Tracks: / All this love.
12" Single: Released Jul '83, on Motown, by BMG Records (UK). Deleted '88. Catalogue no: **TMGT 1308**
7" Single: Released Jul '83, on Motown, by BMG Records (UK). Deleted '85. Catalogue no: **TMG 1308**

DANCE ALL NIGHT
Tracks: / Dance all night / Dance all night (inst).
12" Single: Released Jul '87, on Striped Horse, by Striped Horse Records. Catalogue no: **SHR 21010**
7" Single: Released Jun '87, on Striped Horse, by Striped Horse Records. Catalogue no: **SHR 1010**

I LIKE IT
Tracks: / I like it.
7" Single: Released Mar '83, on Motown, by BMG Records (UK). Deleted '88. Catalogue no: **TMG 1296**
12" Single: Released Mar '83, on Motown, by BMG Records (UK). Deleted '88. Catalogue no: **TMGT 1296**

LOVE ALWAYS
Tracks: / Love always / Walls come tumbling down / You wear it well ((Extra track on 12" version only)).
12" Single: Released Aug '86, on Motown, by BMG Records (UK). Deleted '87. Catalogue no: **ELDT 2**
7" Single: Released Aug '86, on Motown, by BMG Records (UK). Deleted '87. Catalogue no: **ELD 2**

RHYTHM OF THE NIGHT (SINGLE)
Tracks: / Rhythm of the night / Queen of my heart.
12" Single: Released Mar '85, on Gordy (USA), by Motown Records (UK). Catalogue no: **TMGT 1376**
7" Single: Released Mar '85, on Gordy (USA), by Motown Records (UK). Catalogue no: **TMG 1376**

STOP DON'T TEASE ME
Tracks: / Stop don't tease me / Hesitated.
12" Single: Released Sep '82, on Gordy (USA), by Motown Records (UK). Catalogue no: **GF 1635**

TIME WILL REVEAL
Tracks: / Time will reveal / I'll never fall in love again.
7" Single: Released Mar '84, on Motown, by BMG Records (UK). Deleted '86. Catalogue no: **TMG 1329**
12" Single: Released Mar '84, on Motown, by BMG Records (UK). Deleted '96. Catalogue no: **TMGT 1329**

WHO'S HOLDING DONNA NOW?
Tracks: / Who's holding Donna now?.
12" Single: Released Jun '85, on Gordy (USA), by Motown Records (UK). Catalogue no: **ZT 40214**
7" Single: Released Jun '85, on Gordy (USA), by Motown Records (UK). Catalogue no: **ZB 40213**

WHO'S JOHNNY?
Tracks: / Who's Johnny? / Love me in a special way / Rhythm*.
Note: *Extra track on 12in.
12" Single: Released May '86, on Motown, by BMG Records (UK). Deleted '88. Catalogue no: **ELDT 1**
7" Single: Released May '86, on Motown, by BMG Records (UK). Deleted '88. Catalogue no: **ELD 1**

Debarge, Chico

GIRL NEXT DOOR, THE
Tracks: / Girl next door, The / You're much too fast.
7" Single: Released Mar '87, on Motown, by BMG Records (UK). Catalogue no: **ZB 41123**

TALK TO ME
Tracks: / Talk to me / If it takes all night.
12" Single: Released Oct '86, on Motown, by BMG Records (UK). Deleted '87. Catalogue no: **ZT 40888**
7" Single: Released Oct '86, on Motown, by BMG Records (UK). Delete'l '87. Catalogue no: **ZB 40887**

DeBarge, El

REAL LOVE
Tracks: / Real love / Real love (House mix) / Real love (Extended house mix).
CD 5": Released Mar '89, on Motown, by BMG Records (UK). Catalogue no: **ZD 426 86**
7" Single: Released Mar '89, on Motown, by BMG Records (UK). Catalogue no: **ZB 426 85**
12" Single: Released Mar '89, on Motown, by BMG Records (UK). Catalogue no: **ZT 426 86**

Debbie, D.J. & Pins

HULA HOOP
Tracks: / Hula hoop / Hula hoop (part 2).
7" Single: Released Aug '83, on Straight 8, Deleted '86. Catalogue no: **HOOP 1**

Deblanc, Ralph

WAYS OF THE WORLD
Tracks: / Ways of the world.
7" Single: Released Jan '84, on Avatar, by Avatar Record Corporation. Catalogue no: **AVAT 3**

Debonaires

HOOCHIE COOCHIE MAN (FROM KINGSTANDING), THE
Tracks: / Hoochie coochie man (from Kingstanding), The.
7" Single: Released Aug '89, on Dream, Catalogue no: **DRE 1**

Deborah

DANGER FOR LOVE
Tracks: / Danger for love /remix instrumental.
12" Single: Released Mar '86, on ZYX (Germany), Catalogue no: **ZYX 5392**

Debut

DEBUT 01 Various Artists
Special: Released May '84, on Debut Magazines, Catalogue no: **MAG 1**

DEBUT 02 Various Artists
Special: Released Jun '84, on Debut Magazines, Catalogue no: **MAG 2**

DEBUT 03 Various Artists
Special: Released Jul '84, on Debut Magazines, Catalogue no: **MAG 3**

DEBUT 04 Various Artists
Special: Released Aug '84, on Debut Magazines, Catalogue no: **MAG 4**

DEBUT 05 Various Artists
Special: Released Sep '84, on Debut Magazines, Catalogue no: **MAG 5**

DEBUT 06 Various Artists
Tracks: / Deeper and deeper: *Fixx* / Bal and chain: *Savage Progress* / Don't take i all away: *Roman Holiday* / Mist: *Preciou*

Few / Flesh and steel: *Flying Lizards* / Sweet thing: *Torch Song* / Killy me you're killing me: *Kantata* / Can't cloud my view: *Sunset Gun* / You are on my side: *One O'clock Gang* / Within these walls of without you: *Difford & Tilbrook* / Pretty girls make graves: *Smiths*.
Special: Released Oct '84, on Debut Magazines, Catalogue no: **MAG 6**

Debut De Soiree

NUIT DE FOILE
Tracks: / Nuit de foile.
7" Single: Released Mar '89, on PWL, by PWL Records. Catalogue no: **PWL 31**
12" Single: Released Mar '89, on PWL, by PWL Records. Catalogue no: **PWLT 31**

Deceivers

BED OF NAILS
Tracks: / Bed of nails / Flesh and blood / Don't look at me that way (Only on 12" version.).
7" Single: Released Dec '88, on Receiver, by Trojan Records. Catalogue no: **EDIT 1**
12" Single: Released Dec '88, on Receiver, by Trojan Records. Catalogue no: **12EDIT 1**

IT BREAKS MY HEART
Tracks: / It breaks my heart.
12" Single: Released Aug '89, on Sedition, by Sedition Records. Catalogue no: **12EDIT 3**
7" Single: Released Aug '89, on Sedition, by Sedition Records. Catalogue no: **EDIT 003**

Decentz

GET IN TROUBLE
Tracks: / Get in trouble.
12" Single: Released '88, on Philo (USA), by Rounder Records (USA). Catalogue no: **PH 001 EP**

Deckchairs Overboard

FIGHT FOR LOVE
Tracks: / Fight for love / Love takes over.
12" Single: Released Jan '86, on WEA, by WEA Records. Catalogue no: **U 8998 T**
7" Single: Released Jan '86, on WEA, by WEA Records. Catalogue no: **U 8998**

Decker, Diana

POPPA PICCOLINO
Tracks: / Poppa piccolino.
7" Single: Released Oct '53, on Columbia, by EMI Records. Deleted Oct '56. Catalogue no: **DB 3325**

Decorators

REBEL SONGS
Tracks: / Rebel songs.
12" Single: Released Dec '83, on Red Flame (2), by London Records. Catalogue no: **RFM 20B**

STRANGE ONE
Tracks: / Strange one.
7" Single: Released Jun '82, on Red Flame (1), by Red Flame Records. Catalogue no: **RF 705**
12" Single: Released Jun '82, on Red Flame (1), by Red Flame Records. Catalogue no: **RF 1205**

TWILIGHT VIEW
Tracks: / Twilight view.
7" Single: Released Jul '81, on New Hormones, Catalogue no: **ORG 5**

Decoupage

PUERTO RICO
Tracks: / Puerto Rico.
7" Single: Released Jan '82, on Red Bus, by Red Bus Records. Catalogue no: **RBS 207**
12" Single: Released Jan '82, on Red Bus, by Red Bus Records. Catalogue no: **RBSL 207**

Decoy

NO LOOKING BACK
Tracks: / No looking back.
7" Single: Released May '83, on Springsong, Deleted '86. Catalogue no: **DAF 2**

Dedication

PICTURES
Tracks: / Pictures / I shall sing.
7" Single: Released Nov '84, on WEA, by WEA Records. Catalogue no: **X 9261**

Dedringer

DIRECT LINE
Tracks: / Direct line / She's not ready.
7" Single: Released Jan '81, on Dindisc, by Virgin Records. Deleted Jan '84. Catalogue no: **DIN 12**

HOT LADY
Tracks: / Hot lady / Hot licks / Rock 'n' roll.
7" Single: Released Nov '82, on Neat, by Neat Records. Catalogue no: **NEAT 18**

MAXINE
Tracks: / Maxine / Innocent till proven guilty / Took a long time / We don't mind.
7" Single: Released Apr '81, on Dindisc, by Virgin Records. Deleted Apr '86. Catalogue no: **D 11**

Dee

BACK TO BACK
Tracks: / Back to back.
7" Single: Released Feb '83, on Thunderbay, Catalogue no: **TBR 012**

MOON RIVER
Tracks: / Moon river / Some girls.
7" Single: Released May '86, on Pow, by Pow Records. Catalogue no: **WOP 035**
12" Single: Released May '86, on Pow, by Pow Records. Catalogue no: **WOP 03512**

PLAY WITH FIRE
Tracks: / Play with fire / I'm bored.
7" Single: Released Apr '80, on Ariola, by BMG Records (UK). Deleted Apr '83. Catalogue no: **ARO 224**

Dee, Carolyn

MASQUERADE
Tracks: / Masquerade.
Note: Limited edition
7" Single: Released Mar '87, on Bam Caruso, by Demon Records. Catalogue no: **OPRA 062**

Dee, Dave

MY WOMAN'S MAN
Tracks: / My woman's man.
7" Single: Released Mar '70, on Fontana, by Phonogram Ltd. Deleted Mar '73. Catalogue no: **TF 1074**

Dee Jayz

ON THE LINE TONIGHT
Tracks: / On the line tonight (telethon rap) / On the line tonight (version).
Note: As featured on the ITV Telethon '88.
7" Single: Released Jun '88, on DJS, Catalogue no: **DJS 1**

Dee, Jazzy

Biographical details: This American singer achieved a one-off UK chart entry in early 1983, reaching No.53 with his danceable single *Get On Up*. As the title suggested, it would be hard to imagine a more hackneyed disco record. Jazzy Dee was quickly forgotten by clubgoers. (Bob Macdonald 11/11/85).

GET ON UP
Tracks: / Get on up.
7" Single: Released Feb '83, on Laurie, by BMG Records (UK). Catalogue no: **LRS 101**
12" Single: Released Feb '83, on Laurie, by BMG Records (UK). Catalogue no: **LRST 101**

Dee, Joey

PEPPERMINT TWIST
Tracks: / Peppermint twist.
7" Single: Released Mar '83, on Columbia, by EMI Records. Deleted Mar '86. Catalogue no: **DB 4758**

Dee, Joni

HERE COMES THE HOLIDAYS
Tracks: / Here comes the holidays / Three cheers for the sun.
7" Single: Released Jul '82, on Twist & Shout, Catalogue no: **POP 50**

Dee, Kiki

Biographical details: This British singer, born Pauline Matthews in Bradford, Yorkshire, first made musical headlines in 1970 by recording for the legendary Motown label, an unprecedented move for a white British artist. However, the association proved totally fruitless and quickly ended. Far more profitable was her 1973 decision to sign to Elton John's Rocket Label. This soon resulted in the beautiful ballad *Amoureuse*, a perfect vehicle for Dee's fine voice. It reached No 13 on the British charts in December '73, and logged 13 weeks on the Top 50; that single remains her best track. The following year, the Kiki Dee Band was launched, and Dee herself adopted a more raucous image. This period yielded UK chart singles with the hard driving rocker *I've Got The Music In Me* (No 19 in '74) and *(You Don't Know) How Glad I Am* (No 33 in '75). By the end of '75, the band had split and De was a solo artist again.
The scorching summer of 1976 saw Dee's name enjoying new heights of fame. She teamed with her old mate Elton John on a bouncy John/Taupin composition, *Don't Go Breaking My Heart*. This was the ultimate in brilliantly simple, catchy pop, and the duet disc became the world's biggest selling single of 1976. During August of that year, it was No 1 for the entire month in both the UK and the US. This astounding success should have assured Dee of a long lasting career in the superstar bracket - but things fell apart and her vocal talent, which was capable of conveying deep emotion, was wasted on a succession of weak pop material. She never returned to the American Top 40, and her only subsequent major hits in Britain were 1976's *Loving And Free* (coupled with a re-issue of *Amoureuse*) and 1981's short-lived comeback with *Star*. Superstitious observers would point out that the latter two hits both peaked at No 13 on the UK charts, as did the original 1973 release of *Amoureuse*; except for the Elton John hit, she never managed to rise above unlucky 13. However, Dee reached No 12 in the States with *I've Got The Music In Me*, and her US career did not prove any more durable. Bob MacDonald, 16 March 1985.
Pop singer, born Pauline Mathews in 1947 in Bradford. She first recorded in 1964, with a debut album on Fontana in 1968; she made history as the first British girl to sign with Tamla/Motown and also recorded for Elton John's Rocket label. There was power in reserve but her promise of a good voice did not translate into huge chart success. She appeared in the London staging of *Pump Boys and Dinettes* 1984-85; also sessioed with Yvonne Elliman, John. (Donald Clarke, April 1989).

AMOUREUSE
Tracks: / Amoureuse.
7" Single: Released Nov '73, on Rocket, by Rocket Records. Deleted Nov '76. Catalogue no: **PIG 4**

AMOUREUSE (OLD GOLD)
Tracks: / Amoureuse / Loving and free.
7" Single: Released Feb '88, on Old Gold, by Old Gold Records. Catalogue no: **OG 9775**

ANGEL EYES
Tracks: / I fall in love too easily / Stay close to you / I'll build a tower over you / Pay / We cry on / Knowing you like I do / Another day comes (another day goes) / Keep it to yourself / Good times / Angel eyes / Keep it to yourself (Only on 12" single.).
Note: A long awaited album from one of UK's favourite female stars. Featuring her new single *I fall in love too easily*, and the follow-up, the powerful and stunning performance *Stay close to you*. Produced by British Record Industry Producer of the Year (for two years running) David A. Stewart and Patrick Seymour (both of the Eurythmics), and Chris Kimsey. [EMI release sheet, April 87].
12" Single: Released Oct '87, on Columbia, by EMI Records. Deleted Apr '88. Catalogue no: **12DB 9163**
7" Single: Released Oct '87, on Columbia, by EMI Records. Deleted Apr '88. Catalogue no: **DB 9163**

ANOTHER DAY COMES/ANOTHER DAY GOES
Tracks: / Another day comes another day goes / Nightmare mix / Nightmare Dub mix.
7" Single: Released Feb '86, on Columbia, by EMI Records. Catalogue no: **DB 9122**
12" Single: Released Feb '86, on Columbia, by EMI Records. Catalogue no: **12 DB 9122**
12" Single: Released May '86, on Columbia, by EMI Records. Deleted Jul '87. Catalogue no: **12 DBX 9122**

CHICAGO
Tracks: / Chicago / Bite your lip (Get up and dance).
7" Single: Released Jun '77, on Rocket, by Rocket Records. Deleted Jun '80. Catalogue no: **ROKN 526**

FIRST THING IN THE MORNING
Tracks: / First thing in the morning.
7" Single: Released Feb '77, on Rocket, by Rocket Records. Deleted Feb '80. Catalogue no: **ROKN 520**

I FALL IN LOVE TOO EASILY
Tracks: / I fall in love too easily / Don't cry / Beyond control (Extra track on 12" only).
7" Single: Released Mar '87, on Columbia, by EMI Records. Deleted Oct '87. Catalogue no: **DB 9150**
12" Single: Released Mar '87, on Columbia, by EMI Records. Catalogue no: **12 DB 9150**

I GOT THE MUSIC IN ME
Tracks: / I got the music in me.
7" Single: Released Sep '74, on Rocket, by Rocket Records. Deleted Sep '77. Catalogue no: **PIG 12**

LOSER GETS TO WIN
Tracks: / Loser gets to win.
7" Single: Released Oct '83, on EMI, by EMI Records. Catalogue no: **EMI 5425**

LOVING AND FREE (SINGLE)
Tracks: / Loving and free / Amoureuse.
7" Single: Released Sep '76, on Rocket, by Rocket Records. Deleted Sep '79. Catalogue no: **ROKN 515**

PERFECT TIMING (SINGLE)
Tracks: / Perfect timing / There's a need.
7" Single: Released May '81, on Ariola, by BMG Records (UK). Deleted May '83. Catalogue no: **ARO 257**
12" Single: Released May '81, on Ariola, by BMG Records (UK). Deleted May '83. Catalogue no: **AROD 257**

STAR
Tracks: / Star / Give it up.
7" Single: Released '82, on Ariola, by BMG Records (UK). Deleted '87. Catalogue no: **ARO 251**

STAY CLOSE TO YOU
Tracks: / Stay close to you / Africa / We cry on / Star* (Extra track on 12 DPX 9152 only).
7" Single: Released Apr '87, on Columbia, by EMI Records. Deleted Oct '87. Catalogue no: **DB 9152**
12" Single: Released 13 Jun '87, on Columbia, by EMI Records. Catalogue no: **12 DPX 9152**
12" Single: Released Jun '87, on Columbia, by EMI Records. Catalogue no: **12DB 9152**

YOU DON'T KNOW HOW GLAD I AM
Tracks: / You don't know glad I am.
7" Single: Released Apr '75, on Rocket, by Rocket Records. Deleted Apr '78. Catalogue no: **PIG 16**

Dee Major

ROCK MY RHYME
Tracks: / Rock my rhyme / Jailbreak - powerhouse.
12" Single: Released 24 Jul '89, on Catt, by Catt Records. Catalogue no: **CATT 006**

Dee, Mike

BREAKING THE ICE
Tracks: / Breaking the ice / Passion and a twist.
7" Single: Released Nov '80, on WEA, by WEA Records. Deleted '83. Catalogue no: **K 18352**

Dee, Sandra

TEARS FALL FROM MY EYES
Tracks: / Tears fall from my eyes.
12" Single: Released Jul '82, on Ital, by Ital Records. Catalogue no: **ITD 0012**

Dee, Sugar

DANCER
Tracks: / Dancer.
12" Single: Released Jul '89, on Y & D, Catalogue no: **YDD 0139**

WORRIES IN THE DANCE
Tracks: / Worries in the dance.
12" Single: Released Jul '88, on Y & D, Catalogue no: **YDDO 125**

Dee Tees

SHAKIN' ALL OVER
Tracks: / Shakin' all over.
7" Single: Released Sep '83, on Shibui, Catalogue no: **SHS 001**
7" Single: Released Jan '85, on Shibui, Catalogue no: **SHS 002**

Dee, Tony

BELONG TO THE WILD
Tracks: / Belong to the wild.
12" Single: Released Mar '83, on Sunburn, by Orbitone Records. Catalogue no: **SBD 22**

BREAK LOOSE RUN FREE
Tracks: / Break loose, run free / Move over.
Note: Side B. Move over /Pete Watkinson.
12" Single: Released Jul '86, on Amanda, Catalogue no: **AMD 003**

DANCE TO THE MUSIC
Tracks: / Dance to the music.
12" Single: Released Jul '83, on Sunburn, by Orbitone Records. Catalogue no: **SBD 33**

DON'T MESS
Tracks: / Don't mess / No chance.
12" Single: Released Jul '86, on Whiplash, Deleted '87. Catalogue no: **WLD 004**

SOCA MELODY
Tracks: / Soca melody.
12" Single: Released Nov '82, on Sunburn, by Orbitone Records. Catalogue no: **SBD 15**

Dee, Trevor

CRY BABY CRY
Tracks: / Cry baby cry.
12" Single: Released Nov '83, on Ruff Cut, Catalogue no: **RC 006**

Dee, Wanda

BLUE EYES
Tracks: / Blue eyes / Blue eyes (Instrumental).

7" Single: Released May '86, on Lisson, by PWL Records. Catalogue no: **DOLE 1**
12" Single: Released May '86, on Lisson, by PWL Records. Catalogue no: **DOLEQ 1**

Deene, Carol

Biographical details: This British singer first hit the UK charts in the autumn of 1961. In the pre-Beatles era, many British singers achieved hits by recording rapid cover versions of American successes before the US discs were released. This opportunistic ploy was used three times over by Deene, although she never managed to crack the UK Top 20. Her first chart single *Sad Movies (Make Me Cry)* peaked at No 44 - written by John D Loudermilk, this was a quick remake of the US Top 5 smash by Sue Thompson. With horriblr predictability, Deene's next single was Thompson's own US follow-up, also penned by Loudermilk: *Norman* took Deene to No 24 on the British listings in early '62.
In the summer of '62, Deene turned to a different American hitmaker, and reached No 32 with *Johnny Get Angry* while Joanie Sommers was in the process of reaching the US Top 10. Deene's final hit was *Some People*, which peaked at No 25 on the UK charts in late 1962, by which time the Beatles were poised to revolutionise the British music scene and thus torpedo Deene and other slender talents out of the Top 50. Deene continued working, however, and still issued the occasional single in the Eighties. Bob MacDonald, 17 March 1985..

JOHNNY GET ANGRY
Tracks: / Johnny get angry.
7" Single: Released Jul '62, on H.M.V., by EMI Records. Deleted Jul '65. Catalogue no: **POP 1027**

NATIVITY SONG
Tracks: / Nativity song / Sun aint gonna shine any more.
7" Single: Released Nov '80, on Koala (USA), by Koala Records (USA). Catalogue no: **KOA 102**

NORMAN
Tracks: / Norman.
7" Single: Released Jan '62, on H.M.V., by EMI Records. Deleted Jan '65. Catalogue no: **POP 973**

SAD MOVIES
Tracks: / Sad movies.
7" Single: Released Oct '61, on H.M.V., by EMI Records. Deleted Oct '64. Catalogue no: **POP 922**
7" Single: Released Nov '61, on Polydor, by Polydor Ltd. Deleted '64. Catalogue no: **NH 66967**

SOME PEOPLE
Tracks: / Some people.
7" Single: Released Aug '62, on H.M.V., by EMI Records. Deleted Aug '65. Catalogue no: **POP 1058**

Deep Feeling

DO YOU LOVE ME
Tracks: / Do you love me.
7" Single: Released Apr '70, on Page One, by Page One Records. Deleted Apr '73. Catalogue no: **POF 165**

Deep Green

DEEP GREEN various artists
Tracks: / Deep green: *Various artists* / Save a place for me: *Various artists* / Old man and the ocean: *Various artists*.
Note: Featuring Phil Collins.
12" Single: Released Jul '87, on Bold Reprieve (1), Catalogue no: **BRMT 007**

Deep Purple

Biographical details: At the time of their greatest success, this British rock band consisted of Ritchie Blackmore, Ian Gillan, Roger Glover, Jon Lord and Ian Paice.
Deep Purple were formed in 1968 with a lineup comprising Blackmore, Lord, Paice, Rod Evans and Nick Simper. Their early sound was roughly halfway between commercial pop and the new heavy rock that was pioneered by such stars as Cream and Jimi Hendrix. Purple's first single *Hush*, penned by US singer/songwriter Joe South, was released in the summer of '68. It reached No 4 in the US but was a total failure in their native Britain. In December they reached the US No 38 position with the follow up single *Kentucky Woman*. After two American tours, vocalist Rod Evans and bassist Nick Simper were replaced by Ian Gillan and Roger Glover respectively. This line up decided to record Jon Lord's *Concerto For Group And Orchestra* and, for this purpose, they used the Royal ALbert Hall and hired one of Britain's top orchestras. The resulting publicity gave Deep Purple a toehold on the UK album charts, the project reaching No 26 in early 1970. It was at this point in the story that the classic purple era began.
Adopting a heavier rock style, the five musicians recorded the album *Deep Purple In Rock*, which set them on course for international stardom. 1970 also brought the group their first and biggest UK hit single - *Black Night* cruised to No 2. The following three years saw the band at the forefront of heavy metal music and, along with Led Zepplin and Black Sabbath, they helped to make the early Seventies the genre's classic period. Their sound was uncompromisingly deafening, energetic, macho and musically proficient; the group wrote and produced their own material. Lead guitarist Ritchie Blackmore became one of the world's leading rock axemen, and Ian Gillan's powerful and distinctive vocals were also widely acclaimed. 1971's *Fireball* and 1972's *Machine Head* both reached No 1 on the UK album charts, and they also enjoyed British Top 20 singles with *Strange Kind Of Woman* and *Fireball*. In common with most of the era's rock acts, however, they were becoming dismissive of singles and preferred to leave these to the 'commercial' pop groups; 'progressive' bands such as Purple now concentrated on the LP market. *Smoke On The Water*, the standout track on *Machine Head*, was issued as a single in the US only, more than a year after the album's release; it sold a million copies and gave them a No 4 placing on the American singles chart in the summer of '73. By this time, though, ego problems were tearing the group apart - this was perhaps not surprising for a band who performed in such an extrovert and exhibitionist style. By the end of that year, Gilland and Glover had quit; they were replaced by unknown vocalist David Coverdale and bassist Glenn Hughes, who joined the three original 1968 Purple members. Their albums, such as 1974's *Burn* and *Storm Bringer* sets, sontinued to sell well, but Blackmore dealt the group a death blow when he left in '75. He was replaced by Tommy Bolin, who died suddenly in December 1976, by which time the band was all but defunct.
After the group's demise, its key members helped to keep the heavy rock banner alive and kicking over the next decade. Blackmore fronted Rainbow, Gillan led his own self-titled band and Coverdale formed Whitesnake - all enjoyed huge success. Lord and Paice played with Whitesnake for varying lengths of time; and Glover rejoined Blackmore in Rainbow, the group with the ever-changing lineup. In 1984, the five members of the classic early Seventies Deep Purple reformed, and recorded a new album *Perfect Strangers*. The title track and *Knocking At Your Back Door* were superb, but the rest of the LP was a pale imitation of former glories; its commercial success was guaranteed. Their best compilation album was 1980's TV advertised *Deepest Purple*, which hit No 1 on the British LP list. Bob MacDonald, 18 March 1985.
UK heavy metal pioneers, originally formed in 1968 to showcase former Searchers drummer Chris Curtis as a vocalist. Backed by wealthy industrialist and first called Roundabout, the first stable lineup was guitarist Richie Blackmore, keyboardist Jon Lord, drummer Ian Paice, vocalist Rod Evans, bassist Nick Simper. Paice and Evans were ex-Maze, Lord ex-Artwoods and Simper and Lord ex-Flowerpot Men. Their first three albums did well but the Tetragrammaton label went broke; vocalist Ian Gillan and bassist Roger Glover joined and they moved from pop to heavier rock. *Deep Purple in rock* in 1970 established the formula of Gillan's wailing, high register vocals, extended instrumental breaks, solid guitar riffs from Blackmore, wild organ from Lord. After *Who de we think we are* in 1973 Gillanand Glover left. *Smoke on the water* from Machine Head became a heavy metal anthem; Vocalist David Coverdale and Glenn Hughes joined; then Blackmore left, protesting at 'funky' new musical direction away from heavy metal; he was replaced by American Tommy Bolin (ex-James Gang) but they split in 1976. Gillan bought a studio with earnings from sessioning on *Jesus Christ Superstar* in 1972 and started his own group; Glover joined Blackmore's Rainbow; Paice and Lord formed short-lived Paice Ashton Lord; Coverdale formed Whitesnake, recruited Lord and Paice in 1978 and became the most successful Purple spinoff. The group agreed to sue Rod Evans for touring with group he called Deep Purple in 1980 but did not re-form until *Perfect Strangers* in 1984, with Lord, Paice, Blackmore, Glover and Gillan, which entered UK charts at No. 5 alongside Iron Maider and scores of other young UK groups who had listened to Purple when they were spotty little kids. Some of us can't tell the difference between the young and the old heavy metal. (Donald Clarke, April 1989).

BLACK NIGHT
Tracks: / Black night / Strange kind of woman.
7" Single: Released Mar '79, on Harvest (1), by EMI Records. Catalogue no: **HAR 5178**
12" Single: Released Jun '85, on Harvest (1), by EMI Records. Deleted '87. Catalogue no: **12HAR 5233**

CALL OF THE WILD
Tracks: / Call of the wild.
7" Single: Released Feb '87, on Polydor, by Polydor Ltd. Deleted Mar '88. Catalogue no: **POSP 843**
12" Single: Released Feb '87, on Polydor, by Polydor Ltd. Deleted Aug '87. Catalogue no: **POSPX 843**
7" Pic: Released Feb '87, on Polydor, by Polydor Ltd. Deleted Aug '87. Catalogue no: **POSPP 843**

CHILD IN TIME
Tracks: / Child in time.
7" Single: Released Jul '84, on Purple-Harvest(Holland), Catalogue no: **1A 006 64519**

FIREBALL (SINGLE)
Tracks: / Fireball.
12" Single: Released Jun '85, on Harvest (1), by EMI Records. Deleted '87. Catalogue no: **12HAR 5235**

HUSH
Tracks: / Hush / Dead or alive / Bad attitude (CD+12" only).
Note: "The major resurgence in the rock market makes this a timely release from the band that arguably started it all. This is a stunning '88 recording of the track that gave them their early US breakthrough when the band had a different line-up. (Polydor Records, June 1988.)
7" Single: Released May '88, on Polydor, by Polydor Ltd. Catalogue no: **PO 4**
7" Single: Released May '88, on Polydor, by Polydor Ltd. Catalogue no: **POC 4**
12" Single: Released May '88, on Polydor, by Polydor Ltd. Catalogue no: **PZ 4**
CD 5": Released Jun '88, on Polydor, by Polydor Ltd. Deleted Oct '89. Catalogue no: **PZCD 4**

KNOCKING ON YOUR BACK DOOR
Tracks: / Knocking on your back door.
7" Single: Released Jun '85, on Polydor, by Polydor Ltd. Catalogue no: **POSP 749**
12" Single: Released Jun '85, on Polydor, by Polydor Ltd. Catalogue no: **POSPX 749**

NEVER BEFORE
Tracks: / Never before.
7" Single: Released Apr '72, on Purple, by EMI Records. Deleted Apr '75. Catalogue no: **PUR 102**

NEW LIVE AND RARE - VOL.3
Tracks: / Smoke on the water / Bird has flown / Grabsplatter.
7" Single: Released Oct '80, on Harvest (1), by EMI Records. Catalogue no: **SHEP 101**

NEW LIVE & RARE (EP)
Tracks: / Black night / Painted horse.
7" EP: Released Oct '77, on Purple, by EMI Records. Deleted '85. Catalogue no: **PUR 135**

NEW LIVE & RARE VOL.2
7" Single: Released Oct '77, on Purple, by EMI Records. Deleted Oct '80. Catalogue no: **PUR 137**

PERFECT STRANGERS (SINGLE)
Tracks: / Perfect strangers / Gypsy's kiss, A / Wasted sunsets (on 12" only) / Hungry daze (Available on 12" only).
7" Single: Released Jan '85, on Polydor, by Polydor Ltd. Catalogue no: **POSP 719**
12" Single: Released Jan '85, on Polydor, by Polydor Ltd. Catalogue no: **POSPX 719**

SMOKE ON THE WATER
Tracks: / Smoke on the water.
7" Single: Released Mar '77, on Purple, by EMI Records. Catalogue no: **PUR 132**
12" Single: Released Jun '85, on Purple, by EMI Records. Deleted Jul '87. Catalogue no: **12HAR 5236**

STRANGE KIND OF WOMAN
Tracks: / Strange kind of woman.
12" Single: Released Jun '85, on Harvest (1), by EMI Records. Catalogue no: **12HAR 5234**
7" Single: Released Feb '71, on Harvest (1), by EMI Records. Catalogue no: **HAR 5033**

Deep River Boys

THAT'S RIGHT
Tracks: / That's right.
7" Single: Released Dec '56, on H.M.V., by EMI Records. Deleted Dec '59. Catalogue no: **POP 263**

Deep Sea Jivers

DANCING AND DINING WITH THE DEEP SEA JIVERS
Tracks: / Dancing and dining with the Deep Sea Jivers.
12" Single: Released Feb '85, on Mermaid, Catalogue no: **MMD 001**

DEEP SEA JIVING
Tracks: / Deep sea jiving.
7" Single: Released Nov '86, on Mermaid, Catalogue no: **MMD 201**

Deepak and Khan

HOLLE HOLLE
Tracks: / Holle holle (7" only) / Holle holle (Not YRTX 16) / Holle holle (Indian acid trip) (On YRT 16 only) / Holle holle (no khan do) (On YRTX 16 only) / Holle holle (passage to spectrum) (On YRTX 16 only) / Holle holle (Indian acid trip radio edit) (On YRTX 16 only).
Note: "US turntable terror, Mark Kamins, slices up Calcutta and is renowned for capturing the most dangerous dancefloor in town." (Virgin, 1988)
7" Single: Released Aug '88, on Circa, by Virgin Records. Catalogue no: **YR 16**
12" Single: Released '88, on Circa, by Virgin Records. Catalogue no: **YRTX 16**
12" Single: Released Aug '88, on Circa, by Virgin Records. Catalogue no: **YRT 16**

Dees, Rick

DISCO DUCK (PART ONE)
Tracks: / Disco duck (part one).
7" Single: Released Sep '76, on RSO, by Polydor Ltd. Deleted Sep '79. Catalogue no: **2090 204**

Dees, Sam

SURVIVE
Tracks: / Survive / Fly angel fly / Survive /long version.
12" Single: Released Sep '86, on Move, Catalogue no: **MS 11**

Def Jef

ON THE REAL TIP
Tracks: / On the real tip / Give it here / On the real tip (instrumental).
12" Single: Released 6 Feb '89, on Delicious, Catalogue no: **12 BRW 123**
7" Single: Released 6 Feb '89, on Delicious, Catalogue no: **BRW 123**

Def Leppard

Biographical details: This British rock band comprises Rick Allen, Steve Clark, Phil Collen, Joe Elliott and Rick Savage.
Def Leppard were formed in Sheffield in the late Seventies, and consisted of five lads with a passion for heavy metal. One of their number, drummer Rick Allen, was barely in his mid-teens. They attracted attention from the UK media in 1979 with their self financed EP *Getcha Rocks Off* - although contrasting musically with the New Wave/Punk revolution, this record earned credibility by being released on an unknown independent label and thus fitting in with the climate of the era. The band consisted of Allen, Clark, Elliott, Savage and Pete Willis. After signing with Vertigo Records, they scored a minor UK hit single with *Wasted* in late '79. 1980 was the year of britain's great heavy metal renaissance - bands such as Iron Maiden, Saxon and Whitesnake returned the rock sounds of the early Seventies to the charts and the concert stage, after years of alienation during the punk era. Def Leppard were young and enthusiastic (although not very original), and were well able to take advantage of this new boom. Their debut album *On Through The Night* reached No 15 in Britain in 1980. However, its single *Hello America* pointed the true direction in which the group was to head.
1981's *High And Dry* album marked time - it was a competent LP, but contained little to distinguish it from a plethora of similar sounding records by other hard rock acts. It peaked at No 26 on the UK listings, and did not win them any new fans. Their masterstroke, and the turning point in their career, was their enlistment of mega-producer Robert John 'Mutt' Lange for the third album, 1983's *Pyromania*. Although he had also worked on *High And Dry*, Lange brought a new melodic feel to *Pyromania*, having learned from his worldwide success with Foreigner's album *4*. *Pyromania* was a sensational success in the States, and survived the departure of Pete Willis, one of the band's two lead guitarists; he had quit during the recording of the LP, being replaced by Phil Collen. In '83, a year when Culture Club and Duran Duran were spearheading a new British invasion of the USA, Def Leppard were the most successful UK export of all - for several weeks, *Pyromania* was America's No 2 album behind Michael Jackson's *Thriller*. The US Top 20 single *Photograph* was perhaps the best exapmle of the album's blend of hard rock and commercial melodies. Mysteriously, the LP's US suc-

cess failed to rebound to the UK - it was only a mediocre seller in their native country. There was unhappy news for Rick Allen on New Year's Eve 1984 - a road accident in the Sheffield area cost him his left arm, and doctors' attempts to re-sew it failed. Despite this event - a terrible blow for a drummer - he resolved to learn the art of one arm playing and thus continue working. Bob MacDonald, 18 March 1985.
UK heavy rock group formed in Sheffield in 1977 by vocalist Joe Elliot, bassist Rick Savage, guitarist Pete Willis; originally called Atomic Mass, they flew in the face of the punk movement, playing working men's clubs with covers of Bob Seger and Thin Lizzy; they added 15 year old drummer Rick Allen and second guitarist Steve Clark (who began composing); the new name was Elliott's idea, but others altered the spelling. They were leaders with Samson, Angelwitch, Iron Maiden in the so called New Wave of British Heavy Metal (term coined by Sounds mag) to bring HM back to the UK music scene as supergroups Judas Priest, Led Zep, Deep Purple etc. quit or went into tax exile; but when Def Leppard's debut album On through the night in 1980 made number 51 in the USA they went where the money was and became headliners. Willis left during sessions for Pyromania, replaced by Phil Collen. On New Years Eve 1984 Allen lost the use of an arm in a car crash in Sheffield; though parts for fourth album finished, release was delayed as his kit was adapted to enable him to accompany the band onstage; the others pledged to keep him in the group. The inner sleeve of Hysteria credits everybody down to the makers of Elliott's golf clubs. (Donald Clarke, April 1989)t.

ANIMAL
Tracks: / Animal / Tear it down.
7" Single: Released Jul '87, on Bludgeon-Riffola, Catalogue no: **LEP 1**
12" Single: Released Jul '87, on Bludgeon-Riffola, Deleted Feb '89. Catalogue no: **LEPX 1**

ARMAGEDDON IT
Tracks: / Armageddon it / Armageddon it (nuclear mix) (On 12"only) (*Track on 12" version.) / Ring of fire / Animal (Track on CD single.) (+Track on CD single.) / Pour some sugar on me.
CD 5": Released 28 Mar '88, on Vertigo, by Phonogram Ltd. Deleted Oct '88. Catalogue no: **LEPCD 4**
7" Single: Released 28 Mar '88, on Vertigo, by Phonogram Ltd. Deleted Oct '88. Catalogue no: **LEP 4**
12" Single: Released 28 Mar '88, on Vertigo, by Phonogram Ltd. Deleted Oct '88. Catalogue no: **LEPX 4**
Special: Released 28 Mar '88, on Bludgeon-Riffola, Deleted Oct '88. Catalogue no: **LEPP 4**
12" Single: Released Apr '88, on Bludgeon-Riffola, Catalogue no: **LEPXB 4**

BRINGING ON THE HEARTBREAK
Tracks: / Bringing on the heartbreak / You got me runnin'.
12" Single: Released Jan '82, on Vertigo, by Phonogram Ltd. Catalogue no: **LEPP 312**
7" Single: Released Jan '82, on Vertigo, by Phonogram Ltd. Catalogue no: **LEPP 3**

DEF LEPPARD: INTERVIEW PICTURE DISC
12" Single: Released '87, on Talkies, Catalogue no: **LEPPARD 1**
7" Set: Released 11 Dec '88, on Baktabak, by Baktabak Records. Catalogue no: **BAKPAK 1013**

HELLO AMERICA
Tracks: / Hello America / Good morning freedom.
7" Single: Released Feb '80, on Vertigo, by Phonogram Ltd. Deleted Feb '83. Catalogue no: **LEPP 1**

HYSTERIA (SINGLE)
Tracks: / Hysteria / Ride into the sun / Love and affection (12"only).
7" Single: Released Nov '87, on Bludgeon-Riffola, Deleted Oct '88. Catalogue no: **LEP 3**
CD 5": Released '88, on Phonogram, by Phonogram Ltd. Deleted Oct '88. Catalogue no: **LEPCD 3**
12" Single: Released Nov '87, on Bludgeon-Riffola, Deleted Oct '88. Catalogue no: **LEPX 3**
CD 5": Released '88, on Bludgeon-Riffola, Catalogue no: **28 PD 515**

LOVE BITES
Tracks: / Love bites.
Note: "This is the single which will give Def Leppard the recognition here in the U.K. to match their phenomenal standing in the States. Already being tipped as an American number one (Sugar is currently top 20). Love Bites is exactly the type of ballad which breaks across all barriers to become a massive smash. A previously unreleased live version of "Billy's Got A Gun" is on the B side of the 7" and the 12"." (Phonogram Records, June 1988).
7" Single: Released 23 Jul '88, on Bludgeon-Riffola, Deleted Oct '88. Catalogue no: **LEPG 5**
12" Single: Released 9 Jul '88, on Bludgeon-Riffola, Deleted 31 Jul '89. Catalogue no: **LEPX 5**
CD 5": Released 9 Jul '88, on Bludgeon-Riffola, Deleted Oct '88. Catalogue no: **LEPCD 5**
12" Single: Released 23 Jul '88, on Bludgeon-Riffola, Catalogue no: **LEPXB 5**
7" Single: Released 9 Jul '88, on Bludgeon-Riffola, Deleted Feb '89. Catalogue no: **LEP 5**

PHOTOGRAPH
Tracks: / Photograph / Bringing on the heartbreak.
7" Single: Released Jan '83, on Vertigo, by Phonogram Ltd. Catalogue no: **VER 5**
12" Single: Released Jan '83, on Vertigo, by Phonogram Ltd. Catalogue no: **VERX 5**

ROCK OF AGES
Tracks: / Rock of ages.
7" Single: Released Aug '83, on Vertigo, by Phonogram Ltd. Deleted Aug '86. Catalogue no: **VER 6**

ROCKET
Tracks: / Rocket / Release me / Rocket (lunar mix) / Rock of ages (live).
12" Pic: Released Feb '89, on Phonogram, by Phonogram Ltd. Catalogue no: **LEPXP 6**
12" Single: Released 30 Jan '89, on Phonogram, by Phonogram Ltd. Deleted Aug '89. Catalogue no: **LEPX 6**
7" Single: Released 30 Jan '89, on Phonogram, by Phonogram Ltd. Deleted Oct '89. Catalogue no: **LEP 6**
CD 5": Released 30 Jan '89, on Phonogram, by Phonogram Ltd. Catalogue no: **LEPCD 6**

WASTED
Tracks: / Wasted.
7" Single: Released Nov '79, on Vertigo, by Phonogram Ltd. Deleted Nov '82. Catalogue no: **6059 204**

WOMEN
Tracks: / Women.
7" Single: Released Sep '87, on Mercury (USA), by PolyGram Rec.Inc.(USA). Catalogue no: **8887577**

Default

INSPIRATION EP
7" EP: Released 5 Mar '88, on First Strike, Catalogue no: **FST 001**

Defective Turtles

FANNING FIRES
Tracks: / Fanning fires.
7" Single: Released Feb '84, on Barbel, by Barbel Records. Catalogue no: **GS 1**

Defects

SURVIVAL
Tracks: / Survival / Brutality.
7" Single: Released Apr '82, on WXYZ, Catalogue no: **ABCD 3**

SUSPICIOUS MINDS
Tracks: / Suspicious minds / Song for Mark Wynter / Know 'bout you.
7" Single: Released Jan '84, on I.D., by I.D. Records. Catalogue no: **EYE 2**

Defilm

BITTER SURPRISE
Tracks: / Bitter surprise / Telegram.
7" Single: Released Apr '86, on Portrait, by CBS Records. Deleted '86. Catalogue no: **A 7091**
12" Single: Released Apr '86, on Portrait, by CBS Records. Deleted '86. Catalogue no: **TA 7091**

I SAW YOUR DREAM
Tracks: / I saw your dream / Julia.
12" Single: Released Jan '86, on Portrait, by CBS Records. Catalogue no: **TX 6643**
7" Single: Released Jan '86, on Portrait, by CBS Records. Catalogue no: **A 6643**

Defunkt

RAZORS EDGE
Tracks: / Razors edge / Strangling me with your love.
7" Single: Released Oct '81, on Hannibal, by Hannibal Records. Catalogue no: **HNS 01**
12" Single: Released Oct '81, on Hannibal, by Hannibal Records. Catalogue no: **HNS 1201**

Dego

DANCING TIME
Tracks: / Dancing time.
12" Single: Released Mar '82, on Jetstar, by Jetstar Records. Catalogue no: **A 1 044**

OPERATION COUNTRY
Tracks: / Operation countryman.
12" Single: Released Nov '82, on Disco Rocker, Catalogue no: **DR 1004**

Deja Vu

GOING CRAZY
Tracks: / Going crazy / Waiting downtown.
12" Single: Released Jun '89, on 10 Records, by Virgin Records. Catalogue no: **TENX 275**
7" Single: Released Jun '89, on 10 Records, by Virgin Records. Catalogue no: **TEN 275**
12" Single: Released Jun '89, on 10 Records, by Virgin Records. Catalogue no: **TENR 275**
CD 3": Released Jun '89, on 10 Records, by Virgin Records. Catalogue no: **TENC 275**

MADE TO BE TOGETHER (SINGLE)
Tracks: / Made to be together / Sexy dancer.
CD 5": Released Feb '89, on Virgin, by Virgin Records. Catalogue no: **TENCD 268**
7" Single: Released Feb '89, on Virgin, by Virgin Records. Catalogue no: **TEN 268**
12" Single: Released Feb '89, on Virgin, by Virgin Records. Catalogue no: **TENX 268**

SERIOUS (SINGLE)
Tracks: / Serious (7" only) / You and me tonight (On all versions) / Serious (extended version) (On TENT 132 only) / Serious (dub version) (On 12" only) / Serious (extra beat boys mix) (On TENR 132 only).
12" Single: on 10 Records, by Virgin Records. Catalogue no: **TENT 132**
7" Single: on 10 Records, by Virgin Records. Catalogue no: **TEN 132**
12" Single: on 10 Records, by Virgin Records. Catalogue no: **TENR 132**

THAT'S WHERE YOU'LL FIND ME
Tracks: / That's where you'll find me / You and me tonight (12" only) / That's where you'll find me (album version).
12" Single: Released Feb '88, on 10 Records, by Virgin Records. Deleted '89. Catalogue no: **TENT 208**
7" Single: Released Feb '88, on 10 Records, by Virgin Records. Catalogue no: **TEN 208**

TV
Tracks: / T.V. / China doll.
7" Single: Released Aug '86, on TVR, Deleted '87. Catalogue no: **CV 1101**

Dejoney, Zena

I'VE GOT TO FIND A WAY
Tracks: / I've got to find a way.
7" Single: Released Jan '84, on Calibre, Deleted '85. Catalogue no: **CAB 121**
12" Single: Released Jan '84, on Calibre, Deleted '85. Catalogue no: **CABL 121**

Dekka Danse

IMMAGNETIZED
Tracks: / Immagnatized / Drowning by the hour.
7" Single: Released Feb '84, on CBS, by CBS Records. Catalogue no: **A 4143**
12" Single: Released Feb '84, on CBS, by CBS Records. Catalogue no: **TA 4143**

KEY FOR EVERY OCCASION
Tracks: / Key for every occasion / Malice in wonderland.
7" Single: Released Apr '82, on DJM, Deleted '85. Catalogue no: **DJS 10989**

SOUL SEPARATION
Tracks: / Soul separation.
7" Single: Released Jun '84, on CBS, by CBS Records. Catalogue no: **A 4512**
12" Single: Released Jun '84, on CBS, by CBS Records. Catalogue no: **TA 4512**

Dekker, Desmond

Biographical details: This Jamaican singer, born Desmond Dacres in Kingston, wa orphaned as a young child. He began singing professionally in the early Sixties, and spent the middle part of that decade building his reputation in his native country. He came to British prominence in 1967 with a Top 20 single *007*, which was in a 'rock steady' vein. 'Rock steady' had developed as a natural progression from other Jamaican musical forms - 'blue beat' and 'ska' - and, by the end of he Sixties, had become 'reggae'. Dekker's UK success was a result of the cult status that these forms of music enjoyed amongst British Mods and skinheads. His next UK hit, 1969's *The Israelites*, became Britain's first reggae No 1 and was also one of the few reggae records to hit the American Top 10. Despite the fact that the song's patois made it barely comprehensible to many UK and US listeners, *The Israelites* was so catchy and fresh that it earned Dekker the tag of 'first reggae superstar'. In Jamaica, it was just one of twenty or more No 1 hits for him. In Britain, it opened the flood gates for a host of other reggae artists, although most failed to sustain a lengthy chart career.

Dekker himself followed *The Israelistes* with two more UK Top Tenners: *It Mek* (No 7 in 1969) and Jimmy Cliff's *You Can Get It If You Really Want It* (No 2 in 1970). However, his chart career was too short-lived for him to truly merit his so-called superstar status , and it was left to Bob Marley in the mid-Seventies to claim the 'first reggae superstar' title. Dekker's career collapsed in 1971, when his mentor, manager, producer and co-writer, Leslie Kong, died of a heart attack at the age of 38. After moving to London, the singer enjoyed a brief revival of fortunes in 1975: a re-issue of *The Israelites* reached No 10 on the UK charts, and he followed this with a new single, a very lightweight offering entitles *Sing A Little Song*, which reached No 16. Thus, Dekker's long and pointed face, which was capable of contorting itself into a variety of amusing shapes and expressions, reappeared briefly on television. He could not come up with more hits, however, and an early Eighties comeback attempt failed. In 1984 he was declared bankrupt in a British court; he claimed that he was owed large sumes of money by the late Leslie Kong, which he had never received. This was an unhappy and undeserved predicament for

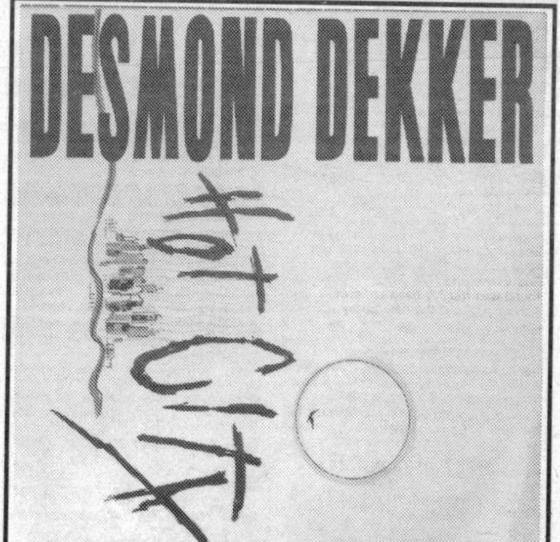

DESMOND DEKKER - HOT CITY (Released on Stiff)

a man who had played a vital role in taking Jamaica's vibrant music scene to the ears of the international pop world. Bob MacDonald, 21 March 1985.
A Jamaican singer who had a string of successes for Leslie Kong's Beverlys label 1969-70 and a total of six UK chart hits 1967-75 and has continued to perform and record at intervals. Duringthe 2-Tone phase he made albums Black and Dekker and Compass Point for Stiff, but most of the albums issued in the late '70's-80's were retrospective from the Beverlys catalogue, such as The original reggae hitsound in 1986, including *Israelites*. (Donald Clarke, April 1989).

007 (ORIGINAL)
Tracks: / 007.
7" Single: Released Jun '67, on Pyramid, by Pyramid Records. Deleted Jun '70. Catalogue no: **PYR 6004**

007 (SHANTY TOWN)
Tracks: / 007 (shanty town) / Cool collie / Judge dread in court.
7" Single: Released May '80, on Island, by Island Records. Deleted May '85. Catalogue no: **WIP 6592**

BOOK OF RULES
Tracks: / Book of rules.
7" Single: Released Mar '82, on Stiff, by Stiff Records. Catalogue no: **BUY 144**

DESMOND DEKKER
Tracks: / Desmond Dekker.
CD 5": Released Nov '88, on Counterpoint, Catalogue no: **CDEP 8 C**

DO IT RIGHT
Tracks: / Do it right.
12" Single: on Trojan, by Trojan Records. Catalogue no: **TRT 9099**
7" Single: on Trojan, by Trojan Records. Catalogue no: **TRO 9099**

HIPPOPOTAMUS
Tracks: / Hippopotamus / 007 (Shanty Town) / It mek (on 12" only).
7" Single: Released Sep '84, on Trojan, by Trojan Records. Deleted May '88. Catalogue no: **TRO 9078**
12" Single: Released Sep '84, on Trojan, by Trojan Records. Deleted May '88. Catalogue no: **TROT 9078**

HOT CITY
Tracks: / Hot city / Moving on.
7" Single: Released Aug '83, on Stiff, by Stiff Records. Catalogue no: **BUY 186**
12" Single: Released Sep '83, on Stiff, by Stiff Records. Catalogue no: **BUYIT 186**

ISRAELITES
Tracks: / Israelites / Long shot / Kick the bucket / Monkey spanner / Love of the common people.
7" Single: Released May '82, on Trojan, by Trojan Records. Deleted '85. Catalogue no: **TMX 4004**

ISRAELITES (CREOLE SINGLE)
Tracks: / Israelites / Sugar dumpling.
7" Single: Released Aug '84, on Creole (Replay), by Creole Records. Catalogue no: **CR 216**
7" Single: Released Feb '80, on Creole, by Creole Records. Catalogue no: **CR 199**
7" Single: Released May '75, on Cactus, by Creole Records. Catalogue no: **CT 57**

ISRAELITES (OLD GOLD)
Tracks: / Israelites / You can get it if you really want / 007 (CD only).
CD 5": Released Apr '89, on Old Gold, by Old Gold Records. Catalogue no: **OG 6133**
7" Single: Released Jun '88, on Old Gold, by Old Gold Records. Catalogue no: **OG 9268**

ISRAELITES (ORIGINAL ISSUE)
Tracks: / Israelites / Why fight.
7" Single: Released Apr '80, on Stiff, by Stiff Records. Deleted Apr '83. Catalogue no: **BUY 70**
12" Single: Released Apr '80, on Stiff, by Stiff Records. Deleted Apr '83. Catalogue no: **BUYIT 70**
7" Single: Released Mar '69, on Pyramid, by Pyramid Records. Deleted Mar '72. Catalogue no: **PYR 6058**

ISRAELITES (SCOOP EP)
Tracks: / Israelites / I believe / It mek / You can get it if you really want / When I'm cold / Please don't bend.
7" EP: Released Jun '84, on Pickwick, by Pickwick Records. Catalogue no: **7SR 5043**

ISRAELITES (STIFF SINGLE)
Tracks: / Israelites / Why fight?.
12" Single: Released Apr '80, on Stiff, by Stiff Records. Catalogue no: **BUYIT 70**
7" Single: Released Apr '80, on Stiff, by Stiff Records. Catalogue no: **BUY 70**

ISRAELITES (TROJAN SINGLE)
12" Single: Released May '88, on Trojan, by Trojan Records. Catalogue no: **TRO 9098**
7" Single: Released May '88, on Trojan, by Trojan Records. Catalogue no: **TRO 9098**

IT MIEK
7" Single: Released Jun '69, on Pyramid, by Pyramid Records. Deleted Jun '72. Catalogue no: **PYR 6068**

MANY RIVERS TO CROSS
Tracks: / Many rivers to cross / Pickney girl.
7" Single: Released Nov '80, on Stiff, by Stiff Records. Catalogue no: **BUY 105**

PICKNEY GAL
Tracks: / Pickney gal.
7" Single: Released Jan '70, on Pyramid, by Pyramid Records. Deleted Jan '73. Catalogue no: **PYR 6078**

SING A LITTLE SONG
Tracks: / Sing a little song.
7" Single: Released Aug '75, on Cactus, by Creole Records. Deleted Aug '78. Catalogue no: **CT 73**

WE CAN AND SHALL
Tracks: / We can and shall.
7" Single: Released Jun '81, on Stiff, by Stiff Records. Catalogue no: **BUY 116**

YOU CAN GET IT IF YOU REALLY WANT (2)
Tracks: / You can get it if you really want.
7" Single: Released Aug '70, on Trojan, by Trojan Records. Deleted Aug '73. Catalogue no: **TR 7777**
7" Single: Released Feb '87, on Bulldog Records, by President Records. Catalogue no: **BD 026**

Dekker, George

ATLANTIC ROAD
Tracks: / Atlantic road.
7" Single: Released May '85, on Safari, by Safari Records. Catalogue no: **SAFE 35**

REGGAE MAN
Tracks: / Reggae man.
12" Single: Released Sep '86, on Trojan, by Trojan Records. Deleted May '88. Catalogue no: **TROT 9089**
7" Single: Released Sep '86, on Trojan, by Trojan Records. Deleted May '88. Catalogue no: **TRO 9089**

Del Amitri

KISS THIS THING GOODBYE
Tracks: / Kiss this thing goodbye / No holding on / Slowly it's coming back (12" & CD single only).
CD 5": Released 24 Jul '89, on A&M, by A&M Records. Catalogue no: **CDEE 515**
7" Single: Released 24 Jul '89, on A&M, by A&M Records. Catalogue no: **AM 515**
12" Single: Released 24 Jul '89, on A&M, by A&M Records. Catalogue no: **AMY 515**

SENSE SICKNESS
Tracks: / Sense sickness.
7" Single: Released Aug '83, on No Strings, Catalogue no: **NOSP 1**

STONE COLD SOBER
Tracks: / Stone cold sober / Return of Maggie, The.
12" Single: Released Sep '89, on A&M, by A&M Records. Catalogue no: **AMY 527**
CD 5": Released Sep '89, on A&M, by A&M Records. Catalogue no: **CDEE 527**
7" Single: Released Sep '89, on A&M, by A&M Records. Catalogue no: **AM 527**

Del Fuego, Teresa

DON'T HANG UP
Tracks: / Don't hang up / Wonder wonder.
7" Single: Released Jul '81, on Satril, by Satril Records. Deleted Jul '84. Catalogue no: **HH 155**

Del Fuegos

I STILL WANT YOU
Tracks: / I still want you (12" only) / Don't run wild / Missing you.
12" Single: Released Jan '86, on Slash, by London Records. Catalogue no: **LASHX 6**
7" Single: Released Jan '86, on Slash, by London Records. Catalogue no: **LASH 6**

Del Lords

CHEYENNE
Tracks: / Cheyenne / River of justice / Hand to mouth (12" only).
7" Single: Released 3 Apr '89, on Enigma, by Enigma Records (USA). Catalogue no: **ENV 10**
12" Single: Released 3 Apr '89, on Enigma, by Enigma Records (USA). Catalogue no: **ENVT 10**

JUDAS KISS
Tracks: / Judas kiss / Whole lotta nothin' goin' on.
7" Single: Released Oct '88, on Enigma, by Enigma Records (USA). Catalogue no: **ENV 3**

POEM OF THE RIVER
Tracks: / Poem of the river / Get tough / Waitress (no more).
7" Single: Released 26 Jun '89, on Enigma, by Enigma Records (USA). Catalogue no: **ENV 14**
12" Single: Released 26 Jun '89, on Enigma, by Enigma Records (USA). Catalogue no: **ENVT 14**

SOLDIER'S HOME
Tracks: / Soldier's home / No waitress no more.
7" Single: Released May '86, on EMI-America, by EMI Records. Catalogue no: **EA 215**

Del Ray, Marina

I LOVE A SHARK
Tracks: / I love a shark / Lone shark.
12" Single: Released Jan '81, on Island, by Island Records. Deleted Jan '84. Catalogue no: **12 WIP 6669**
7" Single: Released Jan '81, on Island, by Island Records. Deleted Jan '84. Catalogue no: **WIP 6669**

Delahaye, Junior

LOVE
Tracks: / Love / I love you.
12" Single: Released Jul '82, on Solid Groove, Catalogue no: **SG 015**

Delaney & Bonnie

Biographical details: Delaney and Bonnie Bramlett met and married in Los Angeles in 1967, formed a legendary white blues/soul/rock entourage and had a lot of bad luck, but retain a cult following two decades later. Both had considerable experience; Bonnie had been the first white member of Ike and Tina Turner's backing group. An early LP on Stax backed by Booker T and the MGs in 1968 was not released at the time; they formed a hot band including Leon Russell and soon signed with Elektra, who failed to promote *Accept No Substitute: The Original Delaney & Bonnie*, though it had word-of-mouth going for it before it was released in 1969. By this time the group included Jim Keltner on drums, Bobby Whitlock on keyboards, Rita Coolidge on backing vocals; after they played support on a USA Blind Faith tour, Eric Clapton set up a European tour, joining it after Blind Faith split; George Harrison guested, issuing *Substitute* on Apple in UK to coincide with the tour. A live tour album *On Tour (With Eric Clapton)* went top 30 in the USA and they played on Clapton albums including *Layla* (as Derek and the Dominos). But Russell poached most of their band for a Joe Cocker tour and they never recovered their momentum. They divorced in 1972 and each recorded solo. (Donald Clarke, Sep' 88).

Delaney Bramlett and Bonnie Lynn were an American vocal duo comprising a husband/wife tem, who came to fame in 1969. They met via "Shindig", a Los Angeles-based TV show masterminded by Jack Good, and married within seven days. Prior to this, Bonnie had been a session vocalist for the famous memphis-based soul labels, Stax and Volt, and had also been the only white member of the Ikettes, the backing vocal group of Ike and Tina Turner. Delaney and Bonnie were both fine singers and, in addition to vocal duties, Delaney also played guitar. Their years of 'apprenticeship' in the music business meant that the pair had many friends and contacts on the American music scene - in 1969, they put these to good and imaginative use by assembling a flexible group called Delaney & Bonnie & Friends. The loose, ever-changing line-up of this band included future stars who were then unknown, such as Leon Russell and Rita Coolidge; also involved were Dave Mason of traffic fame and up and coming master guitarist Duane Allman. Critical acclaim greeted the ensemble's '69 album *Accept No Substitute* and, in the same year, they toured as support act to Blind Faith, the short-lived supergroup which included Eric Clapton. The unpredictable Clapton decided that he preferred Delaney & Bonnie's performances to those of Blind Faith, and he thus caused sensational headlines by knocking the Faith on the head and recording and touring with the Bramletts.
Bonnie Bramlett and Eric Clapton wrote *Comin' Home*, which gave the ensemble a UK Top 20 single in 1970. They hit the LP charts on both sides of the Atlantic that year with *On Tour*, an album released by Delaney & Bonnie & Friends featuring Eric Clapton. This LP showcased he group's eclectic concoction of white soul laced with elements of gospel, rock and country music; the fact that Clapton, the legendary guitar hero, modestly mucked in with the previously unknown duo, won huge publicity and exposure for Delaney and Bonnie. However, Leon Russell quickly ended the Friends set-up by persuading virtually the whole band to desert the duo en masse - the massed musicians joined Russell and ace vocalist Joe Cocker on the highly successful *Mad Dogs And Englishmen* tour. Delaney and Bonnie achieved two US Top 20 singles in 1971 with *Never Ending Song Of Love* (successfully covered by the New Seekers, who took the song to No 2 in the UK) and *Only You And I Know*; but the mass exodus, which coincided with marital tensions, diminished the couple's career. They were divorced, in both personal and professional terms, in 1972, whereupon both pursued unsuccessful individual careers. Bob MacDonald, 21 March 1985..

COMIN' HOME
Tracks: / Comin' home.
7" Single: Released Dec '69, on Atlantic, by WEA Records. Deleted Dec '72. Catalogue no: **584 308**

Delano, Stewart

ETERNAL LOVE
Tracks: / Eternal love.
12" Single: Released '85, on Hawkeye, by Hawkeye Records. Catalogue no: **HD 65**

Delayed Action

NEW LOVE Fire in the streets
Tracks: / New love.
7" Single: Released '82, on Cricket International, by Cricket International Records. Catalogue no: **LBW 005**
12" Single: Released '82, on Cricket International, by Cricket International Records. Catalogue no: **HOWZAT 005**

THEY SAID
Tracks: / They said / I've got to get you off my mind.
12" Single: Released '82, on Zilch, by Zilch Records. Catalogue no: **ZILCHT 9**
7" Single: Released '82, on Zilch, by Zilch Records. Catalogue no: **ZILCH 9**

Delayline

KEEP THAT SMILE
Tracks: / Keep that smile / Summer soul mix.
12" Single: Released Oct '86, on ISR, Catalogue no: **KEV 112**
7" Single: Released '85, on Big Top, by Big Top Records. Deleted '87. Catalogue no: **7DLAY 1**
12" Single: Released '85, on Big Top, by Big Top Records. Deleted '86. Catalogue no: **12DLAY 1**
7" Single: Released Oct '86, on ISR, Catalogue no: **KEV 17**

WE CAN MAKE IT
Tracks: / We can make it.
12" Single: Released '85, on Gas, Catalogue no: **GM 2010**

Del-Byzanteens

DRAFT RIOT
Tracks: / Draft riot / Sall go round the roses.
7" Single: Released '82, on Don't Fall Off The Mountain, by Don't Fall Off The Mountain Records. Catalogue no: **Z16**

MY WORLD
Tracks: / My world is empty without you / Girl's imagination / My hands are yellow.
12" Single: Released '81, on Don't Fall Off The Mountain, by Don't Fall Off The Mountain Records. Catalogue no: **Y 9**

Delegation

Biographical details: This all male British group achieved two moderate hit singles in the UK in 1977. Singing in a bland, pseudo-soul manner, their records were a rather weak imitation of the Real Thing, the group who had broken through during the previous year with a UK No 1 smash *You To Me Are Everything* and followed it with a No 2 hit *Can't Get By Without You*. Both those singles were written by Mickey Denne and Ken Gold, and produced by Gold. The Real Ting decided to compose and produce their own material in '77, so Delegation were Denne and Gold's substitute act. They had begun life as the Rumours, but switched to the name Delegation to avoid confusion with Graham Parker and the Rumour. *Where Is The Love (We USed To Know)* took them to No 22 on the UK listings in spring '77, and they reached No 49 in August with *You've Been Doing Me Wrong*. Their album *The Promise Of Love* created little interest and subsequent singles, which continued into the Eighties, met with similar apathy. Bob MacDonald, 21 March 1985..

FREE TO BE ME
Tracks: / Free to be me / I want you back.
7" Single: Released May '81, on Ariola, by BMG Records (UK). Deleted May '84. Catalogue no: **ARO 261**

HEARTACHE
Tracks: / Heartache / Stand up and reach

for the sky.
7" Single: Released Oct '80, on Ariola, by BMG Records (UK). Deleted '83. Catalogue no: **ARO 246**

IF YOU WERE A SONG
Tracks: / If you were a song.
7" Single: Released '82, on Dude, by Dude Records. Catalogue no: **DU 001**

TWELFTH HOUSE
Tracks: / Twelfth house / Singing / Dance prance boogie (12" only).
12" Single: Released Feb '81, on Ariola, by BMG Records (UK). Deleted '84. Catalogue no: **AROD 252**
7" Single: Released Feb '81, on Ariola, by BMG Records (UK). Deleted '84. Catalogue no: **ARO 252**

WHERE IS THE LOVE (WE USED TO KNOW)
Tracks: / Where is the love (we used to know).
7" Single: Released Apr '77, on State, by State Records. Deleted Apr '80. Catalogue no: **STAT 40**

YOU AND I
Tracks: / You and I / Stand up.
7" Single: Released Mar '80, on Ariola, by BMG Records (UK). Deleted '83. Catalogue no: **ARO 214**

YOU'VE BEEN DOING ME WRONG
Tracks: / You've been doing me wrong.
7" Single: Released Aug '77, on State, by State Records. Deleted Aug '80. Catalogue no: **STAT 55**

Deleru, Georges

BORGIAS, THEME FROM
Tracks: / Borgias, The (theme from).
7" Single: Released '81, on BBC, by BBC Records & Tapes. Deleted '87. Catalogue no: **RESL 106**

SILKWOOD
Tracks: / Silkwood.
7" Single: Released '84, on PRT, by Castle Communications Records. Catalogue no: **7P 309**

Delfonics

Biographical details: This American vocal group consisted of Randy Cain and brothers Wilbert and William Hart.
Hailing from Philadelphia, the three members of the Delfonics started singing together in 1961. Using the name, the 4 Guys, they added Ritchie Daniels to the line-up in '64; he was drafted into the US Army in '67, whereupon the group reverted to a trio and became the Delfonics. They came to fame in 1968 with *La La Means I Love You*, which cruised to No 4 on the US national charts. This was in a romantic, melodic, soft soul style, and subsequent releases were in similar vein. The song was penned by William Hart and Thom bell, and produced by Bell with group manager Stan Watson. *Break Your Promise, Ready Or Not Here I Come* and *You Got Yours And I'll Get Mine* all scraped the lower reaches of the American Top 40 during 1968-9, but their second and final big hit came in 1970 with *Didn't I (Blow Your Mind This Time*. This beautiful ballad hit the US No 10 slot.
Cain left the group in '71. Two substitutes were tried over the following three years, but the group's success diminished. In Britain, however, '71 was their big year. The Delfonics' 1968-70 run of US hits were uncharted in the UK; but a series of re-issues took three of them into the British listings just when the trio were fading in their native land. *Didn't I* reached No 22, *La La Means I Love You* hit No 19 and *Ready or Not Here I Come* peaked at No 41. The Delfonics were arguably ahead of their time, because they performed in a relaxed soul vein at a time when many black acts were stressing the funkier, harder uptempo side of the genre. The trio's sound influenced the sweet soul acts of the Seventies, notably the Stylistics. Bob MacDonald, 21 March 1985..

DIDN'T I (BLOW YOUR MIND THIS TIME)
Tracks: / Didn't I blow your mind.
7" Single: Released Apr '71, on Bell, Deleted Apr '74. Catalogue no: **BELL 1099**

LA LA MEANS I LOVE YOU
Tracks: / La la means I love you.
7" Single: Released Jul '71, on Bell, Deleted Jul '74. Catalogue no: **BELL 1165**

LA LA MEANS I LOVE YOU (OLD GOLD)
Tracks: / La la means I love you.
7" Single: Released '82, on Old Gold, by Old Gold Records. Deleted Jul '88. Catalogue no: **OG 9124**

READY OR NOT HERE I COME
Tracks: / Ready or not here I come.
7" Single: Released Oct '71, on Bell, Deleted Oct '74. Catalogue no: **BELL 1175**

Delgado, Junior

BUS I SKULL
Tracks: / Bus I skull.
12" Single: Released Mar '88, on Fashion, by Fashion Records. Catalogue no: **FAD 052**

COME FOLLOW ME
Tracks: / Come follow me / Come follow me (Version).
12" Single: Released Nov '86, on Jammy's, Catalogue no: **PJADIF 005**

DAY DREAMING
Tracks: / Daydreaming.
12" Single: Released Aug '88, on Fashion, by Fashion Records. Catalogue no: **FAD 057**

HOLD ON
Tracks: / Hold on (version) / Hold on.
12" Single: Released 27 Feb '88, on World Enterprise, Catalogue no: **WED 60**

HOW DO YOU FEEL
Tracks: / How do you feel?.
12" Single: Released '85, on Sweetcorn, Catalogue no: **SC 007**

IF THIS WORLD WERE MINE For love
Tracks: / If this world were mine.
12" Single: Released '82, on Progressive, Catalogue no: **JR 001**

IT TAKES TWO TO TANGO (12")
Tracks: / It takes two to tango.
12" Single: Released Mar '86, on Fashion, by Fashion Records. Catalogue no: **FAD 040**

LIVESTOCK
Tracks: / Livestock.
12" Single: Released '85, on Incredible Music, Catalogue no: **JD 007**

LOVING IN THE MORNING
Tracks: / Loving in the morning.
12" Single: Released 20 Mar '89, on Carron, Catalogue no: **BW 003**

MIDNIGHT RAVER
Tracks: / Midnight raver / 365 days.
7" Single: Released Nov '80, on Greensleeves, by Greensleeves Records. Deleted Nov '83. Catalogue no: **GRED 39**

NICE AND SWEET
Tracks: / Nice and sweet / Melody.
Note: Melody /Michael Bani Rose.
12" Single: Released Nov '86, on Incredible Music, Catalogue no: **JD 008**

PART TIME LOVER
Tracks: / Part time lover.
12" Single: Released '82, on Art & Craft, Catalogue no: **ACD 23**

PERSONALITY Rock it baby
Tracks: / Personality.
12" Single: Released '82, on Art & Craft, Catalogue no: **ACD 22**

RAGAMUFFIN YEAH
Tracks: / Ragamuffin yeah / Ragamuffin yeah dub / Closer and closer.
Note: Extra tracks on 12" version only.
12" Single: Released Sep '86, on Greensleeves, by Greensleeves Records. Catalogue no: **GRED 207**
12" Single: Released Nov '86, on Island, by Island Records. Deleted Jul '87. Catalogue no: **12IS 306**

READY OR NOT
12" Single: Released '84, on Incredible Jux, Catalogue no: **JUX IJ05**

RICH MAN POOR MAN First on Sunday
Tracks: / Rich man poor man.
12" Single: Released '82, on Live & Love, Catalogue no: **LLDIS 200**

RON COME
Tracks: / Ron come.
12" Single: Released '85, on Crystal, by President Records. Catalogue no: **CRY 001**

SUNSHINE
Tracks: / Sunshine.
12" Single: Released Dec '87, on Blue Trac, by Blue Trac Records. Catalogue no: **BTRD 014**

SWEET DARLING
Tracks: / Sweet darling.
12" Single: Released '85, on Macabeen, Catalogue no: **MPCJD 1**

TICHEN
Tracks: / Tichen.
12" Single: Released '84, on Revue, by Creole Records. Catalogue no: **REV 019T**

TIME TO WORK
Tracks: / Time to work / Let of mass.
12" Single: Released May '86, on Saxon Studio, Catalogue no: **SX 002**

TROUBLE
Tracks: / Trouble.
12" Single: Released '84, on Incredible Music, Catalogue no: **UNKNOWN**

TWICE NICE
Tracks: / Twice nice / original.
12" Single: Released Mar '86, on Legal Lights, by Legal Light Records. Catalogue no: **LEGAL 2**

WHAT A HEART
Tracks: / What a heart.
12" Single: Released '85, on Toughest, Catalogue no: **TG 001**

YOU REALLY DON'T LOVE ME
Tracks: / You really don't love me.
12" Single: Released '80, on Sound Off, Catalogue no: **SOFD 008**

Delirium Jar

TORTOISE SHELL
Tracks: / Tortoise shell.
12" Single: Released May '89, on UNKNOWN, Catalogue no: **UIA 101T**

Delite

WILD TIME
Tracks: / Wild time / Wild time (version).
12" Single: Released Sep '89, on Circa, by Virgin Records. Catalogue no: **YRT 35**
7" Single: Released Sep '89, on Circa, by Virgin Records. Catalogue no: **YR 35**

Delite, Marsha

I LIKE PLASTIC
Tracks: / I like plastic / Angel 43.
12" Single: Released Jun '82, on Red Bus, by Red Bus Records. Deleted Jun '85. Catalogue no: **RBUSL 68**
7" Single: Released Jun '82, on Red Bus, by Red Bus Records. Deleted Jun '85. Catalogue no: **RBUS 68**

Delites

LOVER
Tracks: / Lover / Tell me why.
7" Single: Released Feb '80, on Grapevine (Northern Soul), by BMG Records (UK). Deleted Feb '83. Catalogue no: **GRP 127**

Delius, Kerry

SLIPPING AWAY
Tracks: / Slipping away / They say it's gonna rain.
7" Single: Released Oct '85, on Arrival, by Blaylock Management Ltd.. Catalogue no: **PIK 17**
12" Single: Released Oct '85, on Arrival, by Blaylock Management Ltd.. Catalogue no: **12PIK 17**

THEY SAY IT'S GONNA RAIN
Tracks: / They say it's gonna rain / Dear Christine.
7" Single: Released '85, on Arrival, by Blaylock Management Ltd.. Deleted '86. Catalogue no: **PIK 16**
12" Single: Released '85, on Arrival, by Blaylock Management Ltd.. Catalogue no: **12PIK 17**
12" Single: Released '85, on Arrival, by Blaylock Management Ltd.. Deleted '86. Catalogue no: **12PIK 16**
7" Single: Released '85, on Arrival, by Blaylock Management Ltd.. Catalogue no: **PIK 17**

Deliverance

FOOLISH HEARTS
Tracks: / Foolish hearts / Face the lady.
7" Single: Released Mar '80, on Epic, by CBS Records. Deleted Mar '83. Catalogue no: **EPC 8275**

LEAVING LA
Tracks: / Leaving LA / Face the lady.
7" Single: Released Sep '80, on Epic, by CBS Records. Deleted '83. Catalogue no: **EPC 8904**

Delkass, Christine

MY MAN
Tracks: / My man.
12" Single: Released Apr '82, on PMS, Deleted '83. Catalogue no: **BEL 002**

Dell, Rod

YOU TRAPPED MY HEART
Tracks: / You trapped my heart.
7" Single: Released Jul '89, on Round, Catalogue no: **TRR 788**

Della Rosa,Georgette

D'YA WANNA
Tracks: / D'ya wanna.
12" Single: Released May '89, on Mr.Modo, Catalogue no: **WMS 006T**
7" Single: Released May '89, on Mr.Modo, Catalogue no: **WMS 006**

Dells

Biographical details: At the time of their greatest success, this American vocal group consisted of Verne Allison, Chuck Barksdale, Johnny Carter, Marvin Junior and Michael McGill.
The Dells were one of the few groups to enjoy periods of record chart success in the Fifties, Sixties and Seventies; they did this with a fairly stable lineup. They were formed in 1954 in their native Illinois after meeting and singing together at High School. They came to prominence in the American rhythm and blues market in '56 via *Oh What A Night*, which was a classic example of the doo-wap vocal style that characterised much black music during the Fifties. This single gave them a big hit on the US R&B charts, and they recorded prolifically during the rest of the decade, but with less success.
1962 brought them a minor pop hit with *Bossa Nova Bird*, but their real return to success came about in the late Sixties. Now using a vocal style similar to that of the Temptations and the Impressions, the Dells gained a string of US Top 40 pop hits during 1968-9. The two bigest singles both peaked at No 10, and were both old Dells songs: *Stay I My Corner* had previously appeared in 1965 and *Oh What A Night* was a re-recorded and updated version of their original 1956 winner. Also successful were the acclaimed *There Is* (No 20 on the US pop charts in '68) and the only British hit of the group's long career, *I Can Sing A Rainbow-Love Is Blue* - this medley single reached No 15 in the UK in '69.
The Dells always showed an ability to adapt their music to suit the direction that the soul scene was going in. If they were somewhat underrated, it is because, with the exception of their late Sixties run, their regular successes on the US R&B charts rarely crossed over to the pop listings. A good example of this fact was their 1973 single *Give Your Baby A Standing Ovation*, which was a US million seller despite peaking at No 34 in the pop field. They continued recording into the Eighties. Bob MacDonald, 22 March 1985..

ALL ABOUT THE PAPER
Tracks: / All about the paper / I touched a dream.
7" Single: Released Oct '80, on 20th Century, by 20th Century Records. Deleted '83. Catalogue no: **TC 2463**
12" Single: Released Oct '80, on 20th Century, by 20th Century Records. Deleted '83. Catalogue no: **TCD 2463**

HAPPY SONG
Tracks: / Happy song / Look at us now.
12" Single: Released Nov '81, on RCA, by BMG Records (UK). Deleted '84. Catalogue no: **TCT 133**

I CAN SING A RAINBOW
Tracks: / I can sing a rainbow.
7" Single: Released Jul '69, on Chess, by Vogue Records. Deleted Jul '72. Catalogue no: **CRS 8099**

I TOUCHED A DREAM (SINGLE)
Tracks: / I touched a dream / All about the paper.
12" Single: Released Aug '80, on 20th Century, by 20th Century Records. Deleted '82. Catalogue no: **TCD 2463**
7" Single: Released Aug '80, on 20th Century, by 20th Century Records. Deleted '82. Catalogue no: **TC 2463**

STAY IN MY CORNER
Tracks: / Stay in my corner.
7" Single: Released Jul '80, on Charly, by Charly Records. Deleted '87. Catalogue no: **CTD 110**
7" Single: Released Jul '85, on Chess (PRT), Deleted '88. Catalogue no: **CHES 4004**

YOUR SONG
Tracks: / Your song / Look at us now.
7" Single: Released Jan '81, on 20th Century, by 20th Century Records. Deleted Jan '84. Catalogue no: **TC 2478**

Delmonas

COMIN' HOME BABY
Tracks: / Comin' home baby.
7" Single: Released Dec '84, on Big Beat, by Ace Records. Deleted '88. Catalogue no: **SW 101**

HELLO WE LOVE YOU
Tracks: / Hello we love you.
7" Single: Released Dec '84, on Big Beat, by Ace Records. Deleted '88. Catalogue no: **SW 102**

SALLY-SHE-BROWN
Tracks: / Sally-she-brown.
7" Single: Released Aug '85, on Empire Records, Catalogue no: **JLM 14C**

Delneil, Mike

REFLECTIONS
Tracks: / Reflections / Caro / Without reason.
7" Single: Released Jun '79, on Silberkla, by Silberkla Records. Catalogue no: **SBK 2**

Delroy

WALK AWAY FROM LOVE
Tracks: / Walk away from love.
12" Single: Released Sep '89, on Thomas & Sons, Catalogue no: **DR 01**

Delta

TEARS DON'T SATISFY ME
Tracks: / Tears don't satisfy me / Mechanismo / Tears don't satisfy me (exterminator mix) (12" only).
7" Single: Released Jun '88, on Siren, by Virgin Records. Catalogue no: **SRN 83**
12" Single: Released Jun '88, on Siren, by Virgin Records. Catalogue no: **SRNT 83**

TOUCH THE HEART
Tracks: / Touch the heart (Inst) / Touch the heart.
12" Single: Released Nov '86, on Siren, by Virgin Records. Deleted May '88. Catalogue no: **SIREN 36-12**
7" Single: Released Nov '86, on Siren, by Virgin Records. Deleted May '88. Catalogue no: **SIREN 36**

Delta 5

MIND YOUR OWN BUSINESS
Tracks: / Mind your own business.
7" Single: Released Oct '79, on Rough Trade, by Rough Trade Records. Catalogue no: **RT 031**

POWERLINES
Tracks: / Powerlines / Heart is a lonely hunter.
7" Single: Released Jan '82, on Charisma, by Virgin Records. Deleted Jan '85. Catalogue no: **PRE 24**

SHADOW
Tracks: / Shadow / Leaving.
7" Single: Released Jun '81, on Pre, by Charisma Records. Deleted Jun '84. Catalogue no: **PRE 16**

TRY
Tracks: / Try.
7" Single: Released Nov '80, on Rough Trade, by Rough Trade Records. Catalogue no: **RT 060**

YOU
Tracks: / You.
7" Single: Released May '80, on Rough Trade, by Rough Trade Records. Catalogue no: **RT 041**

Deltas

HEART ATTACK
Tracks: / Heart attack / Spellbound.
7" Single: Released Jun '81, on Nervous, by Nervous Records. Catalogue no: **NER 005**

YOU CAN'T JUDGE A BOOK (EP)
Tracks: / You can't judge a book by the cover.
7" Single: Released Jan '89, on Raucous, Catalogue no: **RAUC 006**

Deltones

MAKE ME SMILE
Tracks: / Make me smile / Patricia Hamilton / Running around.
12" Single: Released 15 May '89, on Unicorn Records, by Unicorn Records. Catalogue no: **12 PHZ 41**

STAY WHERE YOU ARE
Tracks: / Stay where you are.
7" Single: Released Feb '89, on Unicorn Records, by Unicorn Records. Catalogue no: **PHZ 34**

Delusions Of Grandeur

LOSING MYSELF
Tracks: / Losing myself.
7" Single: Released Jul '88, on Rosie, by Rosie Records. Catalogue no: **RR 016**

Deluxe

I'VE GOT A FEELING
Tracks: / I've got a feeling / My momma and papa.
7" Single: Released Jul '88, on Unique, by Unique Records. Catalogue no: **UNQ 3**
12" Single: Released Jul '88, on Unique, by Unique Records. Catalogue no: **UNQ 3T**

JUST A LITTLE MORE
Tracks: / Just a little more.
7" Single: Released Mar '89, on Danceyard, by Danceyard Records. Catalogue no: **UNQ 5**
12" Single: Released Feb '89, on Danceyard, by Danceyard Records. Catalogue no: **UNQ 5 T**

SO GOOD (REMIX)
Tracks: / So good.
12" Single: Released Aug '89, on Unyque Artists, Catalogue no: **UNQ 106T**

YOUR LOVING DRIVES ME CRAZY
Tracks: / Your loving drives me crazy.
12" Single: Released May '88, on Unique, by Unique Records. Catalogue no: **UNQ 2**
7" Single: Released May '88, on Unique, by Unique Records. Catalogue no: **7UNQ 2**

Deluxe A

BOYS ON TV
Tracks: / Boys on TV / Friends.
12" Single: Released Jan '83, on EMI, by EMI Records. Catalogue no: **12 EMI 5354**
7" Single: Released Jan '83, on EMI, by EMI Records. Catalogue no: **EMI 5354**

Deluxe Blues Band

LIVE: DELUXE BLUES BAND
7" Single: Released Jul '81, on Hot Box, by Armageddon Records. Catalogue no: **HOT BOX 1**

Demented Are Go

HOLY HACK JACK
Tracks: / Holy hack jack / Rubber buccaneer / Don't go in the woods.
12" Single: Released Jul '86, on I.D., by I.D. Records. Catalogue no: **EYET 8**

Demestos, Johnny

LEAVE MY JELLYBABIES ALONE
Tracks: / Leave my jellybabies alone / Shanghai side street.
7" Single: Released Nov '82, on Button, by Musical Characters Records. Catalogue no: **BTN 104**

Demis

FOLLOW ME
Tracks: / Follow me / Lament.
7" Single: Released Sep '82, on Polydor, by Polydor Ltd. Deleted Sep '85. Catalogue no: **DR 2**

Demob

NO ROOM FOR YOU
Tracks: / No room for you.
7" Single: Released Nov '81, on Round Ear, Deleted '83. Catalogue no: **EAR 3**

Demolished Men

GHOST TRAIN
Tracks: / Ghost train.
7" Single: Released May '84, on Anthem, Catalogue no: **ANTHEM 2**

Demon

Biographical details: This British rock group comprises Chris Ellis, Dave Hill, Les Hunt, Mal Spooner and John Wright.
Demon were one of numerous heavy metal bands to take to the road and the studio during the early Eighties, following the genre's British renaissance in 1980. As their name suggests, they exploited one of the favourite heavy metal themes - Satan, the occult and evil. The group's debut album *Night Of The Demon* was released in 1981 and, the following year, they hit the UK national charts for the first time: *The Unexpected Guest* reached No 47 on the British albums list in August 1982. 1983 saw Demon diversifying their lyrics and adopting an anti-nucleur stance on the LP *The Plague*, with the instrumentation and arrangements also becoming a little more subtle. However, Demon are a run of the mill group, and have not really distinguished themselves from a host of other bands performing in a similar style. Bob MacDonald, 22 March 1985..

HAVE WE BEEN HERE BEFORE?
Tracks: / Have we been here before?.
7" Single: Released Jul '82, on Carrere, Catalogue no: **CAR 249**

HEART OUT OF TIME
Tracks: / Heart out of time.
12" Single: Released Mar '86, on Clay, by Clay Records. Deleted '88. Catalogue no: **PLATE 8**

ONE HELLUVA NIGHT
Tracks: / One helluva night.
7" Single: Released Mar '82, on Carrere, Catalogue no: **CAR 226**

PLAGUE, THE (SINGLE)
Tracks: / Plague, The.
7" Single: Released Aug '83, on Clay, by Clay Records. Deleted '88. Catalogue no: **CLAY 25**

RIDE THE WIND
Tracks: / Ride the wind / Ond the road.
7" Single: Released Jun '81, on Carrere, Deleted Jun '84. Catalogue no: **CAR 185**

TONIGHT THE HERO IS BACK
Tracks: / Tonight the hero is back.
7" Set: Released Apr '88, on Clay, by Clay Records. Catalogue no: **CLAY 48D**

WONDERLAND
Tracks: / Wonderland.
12" Single: Released Nov '84, on Clay, by Clay Records. Deleted '88. Catalogue no: **12 CLAY 41**
7" Single: Released Nov '84, on Clay, by Clay Records. Deleted '88. Catalogue no: **CLAY 41**

Demon Boyz

NORTHSIDE
Tracks: / Northside / Rougher than an animal.
12" Single: Released Mar '88, on Music Of Life, by Music Of Life Records. Catalogue no: **NOTE 13**

RECOGNITION (SINGLE)
Tracks: / Recognition / Lyrical culture (recognition dub).
12" Single: Released Mar '89, on Living Beat, by Living Beat Records. Catalogue no: **NOTE 26**

VIBES
Tracks: / Vibes.
12" Single: Released Nov '88, on Music Of Life, by Music Of Life Records. Catalogue no: **NOTE 22**

Demon Pact

EATEN ALIVE
Tracks: / Eaten alive / Raiders.
7" Single: Released Jan '82, on Slime, Deleted Jan '85. Catalogue no: **PACT 1**

Demon Rocka

SUGAR MY COFFEE
Tracks: / Sugar my coffee.
12" Single: Released May '89, on Unity, Catalogue no: **FEA 014**

UGLY GAL
Tracks: / Ugly gal.
12" Single: Released Mar '89, on Unity, Catalogue no: **FEA 7**

Demon Rockers

IRON LADY
Tracks: / Iron lady / Stick together.
12" Single: Released Mar '85, on Unity, Catalogue no: **UN 001**

Demus, Chaka

BAD BAD CHAKA
Tracks: / Bad bad chaka.
12" Single: Released Nov '88, on Live & Love, Catalogue no: **LLD 99**

BUBBLE
Tracks: / Bubble.
12" Single: Released Oct '89, on Penthouse, by Penthouse Records. Catalogue no: **PH 019**

GAL TEK YU TIME
Tracks: / Gal tek yu time.
12" Single: Released Nov '88, on Black Scorpio, Catalogue no: **UNKNOWN**

ORIGINAL KUFF
Tracks: / Original kuff.
12" Single: Released Feb '89, on Super Power, Catalogue no: **SPD 40**

THEM CAN'T STOP ME
Tracks: / Them can't stop me.
12" Single: Released Dec '88, on Super Power, Catalogue no: **SPD 38**

Demus, Jnr.

BOY A BOY
Tracks: / Boy a boy.
12" Single: Released 30 May '89, on Supreme, by Supreme Records. Catalogue no: **VPRD 387**

Dendy, John

SECRET LOVER
Tracks: / Secret lover / Secret lover (Instrumental).
7" Single: Released May '86, on Mainfeature, by Mainfeature Records. Catalogue no: **MAIN 001**
12" Single: Released May '86, on Mainfeature, by Mainfeature Records. Catalogue no: **MAINX 001**

Dene, Terry

Biographical details: This British singer, whose real name was Terry williams, came to fame in the UK in 1957 just as he was leaving his teens and entering his twenties. At that period in Britain's musical history, the nation had woken up to rock 'n' roll but had nothing original of its own to offer (with the exception of the skiffle acts led by Lonnie Donegan). Therefore, the UK's pop stars were pale imitators of the original American music. The country was still a year or two away from the slightly more imaginative Cliff Richard. Terry Dene was a mediocre singer whose public attention was greater than his musical contributions deserved. Indeed, he filled many newspaper columns through mishaps that were not connected with music.

Hailing from London, Dene was an early beneficiary from "6.5 Special", the BBC's first TV pop show. Regular appearances on the programme earned him three British Top 20 singles during 1957-8. In all three cases, he had to compete with rival renditions: *A White Sport Coat* reached No 18 fro Dene and No 6 for the King Brothers, *Start Movin'* reached No 15 for Dene and No 16 for US singer Sal Mineo, and *Stairway Of Love* hit No 16 for Dene while giving Michael Holliday a No 3 record. The firt and last of the three songs had originally been American chart entries for Marty Robbins. Dene could not cope with stardom - in early 1958 he was fined twice in three months: firstly for drunk and disorderly behaviour, secondly for vandalism. He was conscripted in 1959 (as usual - one year behind Elvis, his mentor), but was discharged two weeks later on medical grounds. He thus continued to attract publicity long after the hits had stopped. After eventually leaving the entertainment business, he became an evangelist. Somewhat unkindly, Decca Records issued a compilation album in 1978 entitles *I Though Terry Dene Was Dead.* Bob MacDonald, 22 March 1985.
A rock'n'roll singer born in London in 1938, noticed singing between wrestling bouts by Jack Good, signed with Decca UK and had his first hit in 1957, followed by a few more. Religious conversion in the early '60's was followed by active Evangelism and gospel albums. He played UK pubs and clubsin rock'n'roll revival in the early '80's. (Donald Clarke, April 1989).

JINGLE BELL ROCK
Tracks: / Jingle bell rock / Peace in the valley.
7" Single: Released Nov '88, on Charm, by Charm Records. Catalogue no: **C45001**

LEARNING HOW TO ROCK AND ROLL
Tracks: / Learning how to rock and roll.
7" Single: Released May '82, on Logo, by Logo Records. Catalogue no: **GO 412**
10" single: Released May '82, on Logo, by Logo Records. Catalogue no: **GOT 412**

STAIRWAY OF LOVE
Tracks: / Stairway of love.
7" Single: Released May '58, on Decca, by Decca Records. Deleted May '61. Catalogue no: **F 11016**

START MOVIN'
Tracks: / Start movin'.
7" Single: Released Jul '57, on Decca, by Decca Records. Deleted Jul '60. Catalogue no: **F 10914**

WHITE SPORTS COAT
Tracks: / White sports coat.
7" Single: Released Mar '82, on Decca, by Decca Records. Deleted '88. Catalogue no: **F 10895**

Deneb, Lenny

MUSTIQUE GIRL
Tracks: / Mustique girl / Soldiers.
12" Single: Released Dec '84, on L.E.D., Catalogue no: **LED 002**

REGGAE PARTY
Tracks: / Reggae party / Reggae party.
12" Single: Released Jul '84, on L.E.D., Catalogue no: **LED 001**

Deniz

YOU WERE THE ONE
Tracks: / You were the one / You were the one (version).
12" Single: Released 6 Mar '89, on Urban, by Polydor Ltd. Deleted Oct '89. Catalogue no: **URBX 32**
7" Single: Released 6 Mar '89, on Urban, by Polydor Ltd. Deleted Oct '89. Catalogue no: **URB 32**

Dennis, B

REGGAE MUSIC
Tracks: / Reggae music / Dub music.
12" Single: Released Jul '86, on Blakemix, Catalogue no: **BLKM 002**

Dennis D D

WHAT AM I LIVING FOR
Tracks: / What am I living for?.
12" Single: Released Jul '85, on Pioneer International, Catalogue no: **DISCO 07**

Dennis, Denzel

ENTERTAINER
Tracks: / Entertainer, The.
12" Single: Released Mar '85, on Rock'n'Groove, Catalogue no: **RNG 002**

Dennis, Jackie

LA DEE DAH
Tracks: / La de dah.
7" Single: Released Mar '58, on Decca, by Decca Records. Deleted Mar '61. Catalogue no: **F 10992**

PURPLE PEOPLE EATER
Tracks: / Purple people eater.
7" Single: Released Jun '58, on Decca, by Decca Records. Deleted Jun '61. Catalogue no: **F 11033**

ROCK YOUR LOVER

Tracks: / Rock your lover.
12" Single: Released Apr '82, on Special Request, Catalogue no: **LR 5**

Dennis, Julie

DRAINED
Tracks: / Drained.
7" Single: Released Nov '84, on Indiscreet, Catalogue no: **RITA 2**

Dennis, Stefan

DON'T IT MAKE YOU FEEL
Tracks: / Don't it make you feel / Don't it make you feel (version).
12" Single: Released Apr '89, on Sublime, Catalogue no: **LIMTX 105**
12" Single: Released Apr '89, on Sublime, Catalogue no: **LIME T105**
12" Single: Released Jun '89, on Sublime, Catalogue no: **LIMETX 105**
CD 5": Released Apr '89, on Sublime, Catalogue no: **LIMEP 105**
7" Single: Released Apr '89, on Sublime, Catalogue no: **LIME 105**

THIS LOVE AFFAIR
Tracks: / This love affair / This love affair (version).
7" Single: Released Sep '89, on Sublime, Catalogue no: **LIME 113**
12" Single: Released Sep '89, on Sublime, Catalogue no: **LIME 113T**

Dennisons

BE MY GIRL
Tracks: / Be my girl.
7" Single: Released Aug '63, on Decca, by Decca Records. Deleted Aug '66. Catalogue no: **F 11691**

WALKIN' THE DOG
Tracks: / Walking the dog.
7" Single: Released May '64, on Decca, by Decca Records. Deleted May '67. Catalogue no: **F 11880**

Denny, Sandy

Biographical details: This British singer entered the music business in the mid-Sixties, showing a deep interest in traditional British folk music at a time when the folk spotlight was firmly on the American-folk rock boom led by Bob Dylan and the Byrds. She was one of many Sixties musicians to study at a London art college and, having dabbled in nursing, began to build a reputation on the city's folk club scene. After a brief period as a member of an early incarnation of the Strawbs, Denny joined Fairport Convention in May 1968. With her input, Fairport became the UK's most acclaimed folk band. As well as contributing her own numbers (most notably *Who Knows Where The Time Goes*), she guided the group in a more traditional folk direction than the one in which they had been heading at the outset; her other main contribution was her lovely, flowing, strong voice. She chose the right songs and sang them well.
Denny left Fairport Convention in 1970 to form her own group Fotheringay. That project's self-titled album hit the UK Top 20 in the same year, but it was not artistically successful and the band quickly folded. Denny opted for a solo career, and she reached No 31 on the British chart with her 1971 album *The North Star Grassman And The Ravens*. Also in the same year, she duetted with Robert Plant on Led Zepplin's *The Battle Of Evermore*, a track from the group's legendary, untitled fourth album. Denny released two more solo albums, *Sandy* and *Like An Old Fashioned Waltz*, before rejoining Fairport in '74. She quit the group again after one album. A new solo LP *Rendezvous* was issued in 1977 but, by this time, her undiminished singing, songwriting and song-choosing talents were only reaching a small cult following. Sandy Denny met a tragic end in April 1978 at the age of 31: she fell down a flight of stairs at a friend's house and died of a brain haemorrage four days later. A sad end to a great artist. Bob MacDonald, 22 March 1985.
A folk/rock singer and songwriter, born in London in 1947, died in 1978 following a fall. She sang in folk clubs, playing her own guitar; *The original Sandy Denny* was recorded in 1967, with Tom Paxton and traditional English songs. She joined the Strawbs in 1967 and *The Strawbs featuring Sandy Denny* included the first version of her best-known song *Who knows where the time goes* later covered by Judy Collins. She joined Fairport Convention in 1968; Simon Nicol said that at the audition 'she stood out like a clean glass in a sinkful of dirty dishes'. Their albums with her set the standard for the UK genre, the sleeve of *Unhalfbricking* featuring her parents. She formed Fotheringay, named after a Scottish castle and the title of her song on the second Fairport album; the band included Trevor Lucus and Jerry Donahue, both later of Fairport, and their highly praised eponymous album was a UK top 20 hit in 1970; *Nothing more and others* was a compilation. Her solo album *North Star grassman & the ravens* in 1971 included *Sandy* in 1972 (with a David Bailey sleeve photo) and *The Bunch*, an album of rock'n'roll covers. She also sang on Led Zepelin's fourth album and in an all-star production of *Tommy*. Her best solo album was said to be *Like an old fashioned waltz* in 1973 (the title song covered by Emmylou Harris) She married Lucas, who joined Fairport; Sandy rejoined them for *Fairport Convention live* and *Rising for the moon*; her *Rendezvous* in 1977 had a stellar lineup including Stevie Winwood, Linda & Richard Thompson, Gallagher & Lyle. *Who knows where the time goes* covers her career before, during and after Fairport, over a dozen previously unreleased songs including some from the unfinished last *Fotheringay* album. (Donald Clarke, April 1989).

MAKE ME A PALLET ON YOUR FLOOR
Tracks: / Make me a pallet on the floor.
7" Single: on Mooncrest, by Trojan Records. Deleted May '88. Catalogue no: **MOON 54**

Dental Mechanic's

I'VE COME FOR MA BOY
Tracks: / I've come for ma boy / I've come for ma boy(version).
12" Single: Released Mar '88, on Goldrush, Catalogue no: **GRR 213**

LOVE ME NOW
Tracks: / Love me now / Dental mechanic's daughter, The.
7" Single: Released May '86, on Gold Rush, Catalogue no: **GRR 1**

Dentists

DOWN AND OUT IN PARIS AND CHATHAM
Tracks: / Down and out in Paris and Chatham.
7" Single: Released Jun '86, on Tambourine, by Tambourine Records. Catalogue no: **SP 006**

FUN HAS ARRIVED, THE
Tracks: / Fun has arrived, The.
12" Single: Released Apr '88, on Antler, by Antler Records (Belgium). Catalogue no: **ANT 077**

STRAWBERRIES ARE GROWING IN THE GARDEN BUT...
Tracks: / Strawberries are growing in the garden.
7" Single: Released Mar '85, on Spruck, Catalogue no: **SP 003**

WRITHING ON THE SHAGPILE
Tracks: / Writhing on the shagpile.
12" Single: Released 13 Jun '87, on Tambourine, by Tambourine Records. Catalogue no: **URINE 3**

Denton, Richard

THEME FROM THE HONG KONG BEAT
Tracks: / Theme from the Hong Kong beat.
7" Single: Released Apr '78, on BBC, by BBC Records & Tapes. Deleted Apr '81. Catalogue no: **RESL 52**

Denver, John

Biographical details: This American singer, songwriter and guitarist, born John Deutschendorf in New Mexico, was brought up in an Air Force family, and therefore spent his childhood and youth moving round the States from one school to another. His father held three world records in military aviation, but John's similar aspirations were thwarted when the USAF rejected him on grounds of shortsightedness. He took up folk singing, changed his name to Denver (inspired by the Colorado city), moved to Los Angeles and, from 1964 onwards, joined the Chad Mitchell trio, a folk music threesome. After four years with the band, they split up and Denver was faced with a large debt. It was not too long, however, before he was able to pay this - in December 1969, his song *Leavin' On A Jet Plane* gave famous folk trio Peter Paul and Mary their first ever US No 1; it was also their biggest British hit, reaching No 2 in 1970. Suddenly, Denver's name began to attract major attention and his debut album, 1969's *Rhymes And Reasons*, started to sell. 1971 brought him his first US smash as a performer: *Take Me Home, Country Roads* hit No 2, and was a typical example of his songwriting style - evoking rural America, expressing his love for natural beauty, sentimental but not twee, melodic, halfway between folk and country, and eminently remake-able. Olivia Newton-John took the song into the British Top 20 in 1973, the same year that Denver's premature *Greatest Hits* album was issued in the States - though this compilation LP contained only four US Top 40 hits, it was an excellent showcase of his talent and proved to be the marketing masterstroke that cemented his American popularity.
From '74 onwards, it was plain sailing for the bespectacled all-American boy. Denver chalked up four US No 1 singles during 1974-5. These included *Sunshine On My Shoulders, Thank God I'm A Country Boy* and *I'm Sorry*; but the biggest was *Annie's Song*. Dedicated to his wife, *Annie's Song* was both a perfect love tribute and a perfect expression of the singer's country-loving, ecology-conscious views and emotions. It was also No 1 in Britain and, amazingly, remains his only UK Top 40 single despite high album sales in Britain. Denver's highest charting LP in the UK was 1976's *Live In London*, which hit No 2. In the late Seventies, record sales dropped off on both sides of the Atlantic. Denver concentrated more on live work, made his movie debut with George Burnes in 1977's *Oh God*, and settled into the comfortable and complacent niche of being an all-round showbusiness personality. Bob MacDonald, 22 March 1985.
Country-pop singer John Henry Deutschendorf was born in New Mexico in 1943; he was briefly in a group with John Stewart, during which time each wrote his best known song: Stewart's *Daydream believer* and Denver's *Leavin' on a jet plane*. He worked with the Chad Mitchell trio for four years, went solo and struck the MOR mother lode with his clean-cut style. He has duetted with the Muppets, opera star Placido Domingo, Sylvie Vartan and Emmylou Harris. His album sales are revealing; MOR artists sell lots of albums, which sell longer than singles: he has had 21 albums in the top 200 in the USA. His sidemen in the '80's have included James Burton and Glen D Hardin. (Donald Clarke, April 1989).

ANNIE'S SONG
Tracks: / Annie's song.
7" Single: Released Aug '74, on RCA, by BMG Records (UK). Deleted Aug '77. Catalogue no: **APBO 0295**

ANNIE'S SONG (OLD GOLD)
Tracks: / Annie's song / Take me home country roads.
7" Single: Released Nov '86, on Old Gold, by Old Gold Records. Catalogue no: **OG 9633**

DON'T CLOSE YOUR EYES
Tracks: / Don't close your eyes / Wild heart looking for home.
7" Single: Released Apr '86, on RCA, by BMG Records (UK). Catalogue no: **PB 49961**

FOR YOU
Tracks: / For you / Alaska and me.
7" Single: Released 14 Nov '88, on RCA, by BMG Records (UK). Deleted Aug '89. Catalogue no: **PB 49497**

HOLD ME TIGHTLY
Tracks: / Hold me tightly.
7" Single: Released Oct '83, on RCA, by BMG Records (UK). Catalogue no: **RCA 374**

SHANGHAI BREEZES
Tracks: / Shanghai breezes / What one man can do.
7" Single: Released Nov '82, on RCA, by BMG Records (UK). Deleted Nov '85. Catalogue no: **RCA 218**

Denver, Karl

Biographical details: This British singer and guitarist enjoyed four UK Top 10 hits in a twelve-month period during 1961-2. Denver's name was consistently in the Top 40 until 1964, but the hits became smaller as the Beatles revolution got underway. His style was pseudo-country and western, at a time when British record buyers were largely unaware of authentic country music and the Dylan-led folk boom had not yet exploded into the charts. On many of his singles, Denver yodelled away in the manner of Slim Whitman.
Denver's first two Top Tenners were *Marcheta* and *Mexicali Rose* - both were ballads and both hit No 8. Then came his biggest success, which was the only one which was slightly out of keeping with his usual formula. *Wimoweh* was a Zulu chant that had first been popularised in the American Top 20 in 1952 by Pete Seeger's group, the Weavers. The Tokens took the song to the US No 1 slot at Christmas 1961 under the title *The Lion Sleeps Tonight*, which inspired Denver to rapidly record his own version; he reached No 4 on the UK chart, while the Tokens peaked at No 11. The evergreen song was a US smash in 1972 for Robert John, and a UK No 1 in '82 for Tight Fit. Denver followed his rendition with a fourth and final Top 10 single *Never Goodbye*. Subsequent singles included two more UK Top 20 hits - *A Little Love A Little Kiss* and a rendition of Bill Anderson's American hit *Still* - plus a No 32 version of *Indian Love Call*, the singer's most unashamed bow to Slim Whitman. Denver's final chart single *Love Me With All Your Heart* peaked at No 37 in the summer of '64. He should also be given credit for a big selling EP with 1962's *By A Sleepy Lagoon* plus a long run on the LP charts in the same year with his debut album, *Wimoweh*. Bob MacDonald, 24 March 1985..

BLUE WEEKEND
Tracks: / Blue weekend.
7" Single: Released Sep '62, on Decca, by Decca Records. Deleted '65. Catalogue no: **F 11505**

CAN YOU FORGIVE ME
Tracks: / Can you forgive me.
7" Single: Released Mar '63, on Decca, by Decca Records. Deleted '66. Catalogue no: **F 11608**

INDIAN LOVE CALL
Tracks: / Indian love call.
7" Single: Released Jun '63, on Decca, by Decca Records. Deleted '66. Catalogue no: **F 11674**

LITTLE LOVE A LITTLE KISS, A
Tracks: / Little love a little kiss, A.
7" Single: Released Jun '62, on Decca, by Decca Records. Deleted '65. Catalogue no: **F 11470**

LOVE ME WITH ALL YOUR HEART
Tracks: / Love me with all your heart.
7" Single: Released Jun '64, on Decca, by Decca Records. Deleted '67. Catalogue no: **F 11905**

MARCHETA
Tracks: / Marcheta.
7" Single: Released Jun '61, on Decca, by Decca Records. Deleted '64. Catalogue no: **F 11360**

MEXICALI ROSE
Tracks: / Mexicali rose.
7" Single: Released Oct '61, on Decca, by Decca Records. Deleted '64. Catalogue no: **F 11395**

MY WORLD OF BLUE
Tracks: / My world of blue.
7" Single: Released Mar '64, on Decca, by Decca Records. Deleted '67. Catalogue no: **F 11828**

NEVER GOODBYE
Tracks: / Never goodbye.
7" Single: Released Feb '62, on Decca, by Decca Records. Deleted '65. Catalogue no: **F 11431**

STILL
Tracks: / Decca.
7" Single: Released Aug '63, on Decca, by Decca Records. Deleted '66. Catalogue no: **F 11720**

WIMOWEH (OLD GOLD)
Tracks: / Wimoweh.
7" Single: Released '85, on Old Gold, by Old Gold Records. Catalogue no: **OG 9535**

WIMOWEH (SINGLE)
Tracks: / Wimoweh / Gypsy Davey.
7" Single: Released '82, on Decca, by Decca Records. Deleted '88. Catalogue no: **F 11420**

Denym

BABY IT'S LOVE
Tracks: / Baby it's love.
12" Single: Released '82, on Real Wax, Catalogue no: **RW 103**

BEAUTY
Tracks: / Beauty / Selassi.
7" Single: Released Aug '82, on Occult, Catalogue no: **CUS 1351**

Deodata

WHISTLE BUMP
Tracks: / Whistle bump / Knights of fantasy / Space dust.
7" Single: Released Jun '80, on Warner Bros., by WEA Records. Deleted Jun '83. Catalogue no: **LV 39**

Deodato

Biographical details: Eumir Deodato is a Brazilian keyboards player, arranger and producer, who was born in Rio but moved to the States in 1967. After working as an arranger for various singers, including Frank Sinatra and Aretha Franklin, he came to fame in 1973 with his jazzy version of Richard Strauss' classical movie theme from *2001, Also Sprach Zarathustra*. This single stormed to No 2 in the US and No 7 in the UK. It was a typical example of the music that was to characterise his series of albums, the first of which was released in 1973 - an orchestral fusion of jazz, funk, rock, easy listening and classical styles. Some critics hailed these LPs as inventive and experimental, while others dismissed them as amorphous collections of blandness that were suitable only as background music in supermarkets, lifts and wine bars. Deodato should certainly be given credit for often playing jazz-funk in an era before it became really fashionable.
The most lucrative period of Deodato's

career began in 1979, when he became producer for Kool And The Gang. The veteran funky soul ensemble had achieved a couple of US million-sellers in 1974, but had, strangely, found it difficult to compete during the disco boom. Just as the so-called death of disco was being proclaimed in the media, Deodato helped to turn the Gang into a major international success story. Their 1979-82 albums, *Ladies' Night, Celebrate, Something Special* and *As One*, yielded a string of hit singles, most notably the US two million selling No 1 *Celebration* and the dancefloor classic *Get Down On It*, a No 3 hit in the UK. In the wake of this success, the producer attempted to start his own hitmaking career afresh with 1982's Kool-like *Happy Hour* single plus an album of the same title; they were not a major success, however. His association with Kool & The Gang ended in 1983, whereupon the group continued their string of hits with producer Jim Bonnefond. Bob MacDonald, 24 March 1985.

Eumir De Almeida Deodato was born in 1942 in Rio De Janeiro; he plays piano and other instruments but but is best known as an arranger and composer for Frank Sinatra, Roberta Flack, Aretha Franklin and many others; and as a film composer. (Donald Clarke, April 1989)L.

ALSO SPRACH ZARATHUSTRA
Tracks: / Also sprach Zarathustra.
7" Single: Released May '73, on Creed, Deleted '76. Catalogue no: **CTI 4000**

HAPPY HOUR
Tracks: / Happy hour / Sweet magic (7" only) / Night cruiser (12"only) / Whistle bump (12" only).
12" Single: Released '82, on Warner Bros., by WEA Records. Catalogue no: **K 17960T**
7" Single: Released '82, on Warner Bros., by WEA Records. Catalogue no: **K 17960**

KEEP ON MOVING
Tracks: / Keep on moving / Whistle bump.
7" Single: Released '82, on Warner Bros., by WEA Records. Catalogue no: **K 17996**
12" Single: Released '82, on Warner Bros., by WEA Records. Catalogue no: **K 17996T**

NIGHT CRUISER
Tracks: / Night cruiser / Love magic.
7" Single: Released Oct '80, on Warner Bros., by WEA Records. Deleted Oct '83. Catalogue no: **K 17696**

WHISTLE BUMP
Tracks: / Whistle bump / Knights of fantasy / Space dust.
7" Single: Released Jun '80, on Warner Bros., by WEA Records. Deleted Jun '83. Catalogue no: **LV 39**
7" Single: Released Aug '80, on EMI, by EMI Records. Deleted Aug '83. Catalogue no: **K 17675**

Department S

Biographical details: This all-male British rock quintet came to brief fame in 1981 with two UK chart singles. The lead singer of Department S, Vaughan Toulouse, had two attributes that won him prominent coverage in the British music press - a silly name and a humerous personality. Rising from the ranks of Britain's independent label scene, they reached No 22 and logged 10 weeks on the Top 75 with *Is Vic There?*. This was a semi-novelty telephone song performed in the group's post punk style. They then signed with Stiff Records, the original punk indie label, and peaked at No 55 with their less interesting follow-up *Going Left Right*. Department S were quickly forgotten, but might have lasted longer if they had emerged in the late Seventies rather than the early Eighties. Their style sounded somewhat dated. Bob MacDonald, 24 March 1985..

GOING LEFT RIGHT
Tracks: / Going left right / She's expecting you / Is Vic there ? (On 12" only).
7" Single: Released Jul '81, on Stiff, by Stiff Records. Deleted '84. Catalogue no: **BUY 118**

I WANT MORE
Tracks: / I want more / Monte Carlos.
7" Single: Released '81, on Stiff, by Stiff Records. Catalogue no: **BUY 128**
12" Single: Released '81, on Stiff, by Stiff Records. Catalogue no: **SBUY 128**

IS VIC THERE? (SINGLE)
Tracks: / Is Vic there? / Solid gold, easy action.
7" Single: Released '81, on Demon, by Demon Records. Deleted '88. Catalogue no: **D 1003**

Depeche Mode

Biographical details: This British band comprises Andy Fletcher, Dave Gahan, Martin Gore and Alan Wilder.

Depeche Mode were formed in 1980 and took their name from a French fashion magazine - it means 'Fast Fashion'. Hailing from Basildon, Essex, they initially played with two guitars, a synthesiser and a lead vocalist; however, they soon put the guitars aside and became a totally electronic group. At that time, the quartet consisted of Fletcher, Gahan, Gore plus synth wizard and main songwriter Vince Clarke. Falling into the then fashionable 'futurist' category, they came to the attention of Daniel Miller, founder of Mute Records; he became their producer and guiding light. They first hit the British charts in April '81 with *Dreaming Of Me*, which reached No 57, but their real breakthrough single was its follow-up *New Life*, a catchy pop record that hit No 11 and logged 15 weeks on the UK Top 75. In similar vein was *Just Can't Get Enough*, which reached No 8; and they also reached the Top 10 with a highly successful debut album *Speak And Spell*.

Just as Depeche Mode seemed to have everything going their way, they suffered the potentially disastrous departure of Clarke at the end of '81. He disliked touring, an inevitable consequence of the band's success, and left to form the Yazoo duo, a highly successful collaboration with Alison Moyet. Clarke had been perceived as the group's leader, but Depeche Mode quickly surprised critics and public alike by proving they could manager very ably without him. Gore assumed the role of main songwriter, and immediately gave the band a UK No 6 hit with *See You* in early 1982. This was a melodic pop love song, but hard edged themes were later adopted in such hits as 1983's No 6 single *Everything Counts* and 1984's UK Top 20 hit *Blasphemous Rumours*. Dismissing criticism of their synthesiser sound, the electronic music and gadget gimmickry were further increased on their two 1984 British Top Tenners, *People Are People* (No 4 - their biggest hit) and *Master And Servant*. By this time, Alan Wilder was a fully integrated member of the band. Between 1981 and '84, Depeche Mode chalked up 12 British chart singles and no misses. These included one Top Tenner and two smaller hits per year (1981-3) and two Top Tenners and one smaller hit (1984). Contrary to 'Fast Fashion', consistency was the name of their game. Bob MacDonald, 24 March 1985.

A UK synthesiser group formed in Basildon in 1980 by Andy Fletcher, Marin Gore and Vince Clarke. The first two soon ditched their guitars and it became a synth band, snapped up by you labelboss Stevo for his 'new romantic' Some Bizzare, but soon escaping his clutches and signing with Mute. Clarke is a gifted commercial songwriter (see his listing) but he soon left not liking the pop lifestyle; Gore emerged as a writer and Alan Wilder joined to replace Clarke. The group is happy to remain with a tiny indie label, whose boss Daniel Miller has produced all their records, thus able to develop at their own pace. (Donald Clarke, April 1989).

BEHIND THE WHEEL
Tracks: / Behind the wheel (remix) / Route 66 / Behind the wheel / Route 66 (Megamix).
7" Single: Released 28 Dec '87, on Mute, by Mute Records. Catalogue no: **BONG 15**
Cassingle: Released 28 Dec '87, on Mute, by Mute Records. Catalogue no: **CBONG 15**
12" Single: Released 28 Dec '87, on Mute, by Mute Records. Catalogue no: **12 BONG 15**
12" Single: Released May '88, on Sire (USA), Catalogue no: **020858**

BEHIND THE WHEEL (IMPORT)
Tracks: / Behind the wheel (Beatmasters remix) / Behind the wheel (7" mix) / Route 66.
CD 5": Released Oct '88, on Intercord (Germany), Catalogue no: **INT 811854**

BEHIND THE WHEEL (REMIX)
Tracks: / Behind the wheel (remix) / Behind the wheel (remix) (Beatmasters mix) / Route 66 (casualty mix).
12" Single: Released Sep '88, on Intercord (Germany), Catalogue no: **INT 126876**

BLASPHEMOUS RUMOURS
Tracks: / Somebody / Two minute warning / Ice machine / Everything counts / Blasphemous rumours.
Note: Four live tracks, recorded on 29 September 1984 at the Empire Theatre, Liverpool, reissued in clear yellow vinyl.
12" Single: Released Sep '87, on Mute (Germany), by Mute Records. Catalogue no: **INT 126839**
7" EP: Released 29 Oct '84, on Mute, by Mute Records. Catalogue no: **7 BONG 7E**
12" Single: Released 29 Oct '84, on Mute, by Mute Records. Catalogue no: **12 BONG 7**

DEPECHE MODE: INTERVIEW PICTURE DISC
7" Set: Released Apr '88, on Baktabak, by Baktabak Records. Catalogue no: **BAKPAK 1010**
12" Single: Released '87, on Talkies, Catalogue no: **DEPECHE 1**

DREAMING OF ME
Tracks: / Dreaming of me / Ice machine.
7" Single: Released '81, on Mute, by Mute Records. Catalogue no: **MUTE 013**
CD 3": Released Aug '88, on Intercord (Germany), Catalogue no: **INT 811868**

EVERYTHING COUNTS
Note: *The limited edition series of 12" E.P.'s, now available as 6-track C.D.'s (Also ltd. edition).
7" EP: Released Oct '87, on Mute (Germany), by Mute Records. Catalogue no: **CD EP**

EVERYTHING COUNTS (LIVE)
Tracks: / Everything counts (live).
12" Single: Released 30 Jan '89, on Mute, by Mute Records. Catalogue no: **12BONG 16**
CD 5": Released Jan '89, on Mute, by Mute Records. Catalogue no: **CDBONG 16**
7" Single: Released 30 Jan '89, on Mute, by Mute Records. Catalogue no: **BONG 16**
12" Single: Released Jan '89, on Mute, by Mute Records. Catalogue no: **12LBONG 16**

EVERYTHING COUNTS (SINGLE)
Tracks: / Everything counts.
7" Single: Released 11 Jul '83, on Mute, by Mute Records. Catalogue no: **7 BONG 3**
12" Single: Released 11 Jul '83, on Mute, by Mute Records. Catalogue no: **12 BONG 3**

GET THE BALANCE RIGHT
Tracks: / Get the balance right.
Note: This version has four live tracks on the B-side, recorded at the Hammersmith Odeon on October 25th 1982. ('My secret garden', 'See you', 'Satellite' & 'Tora, Tora, Tora').
*Limitited edition series of 12" E.P.'s now available as 6-track C.D.'s (also ltd. edition).
12" Single: Released Sep '87, on Mute (Germany), by Mute Records. Catalogue no: **INT 126836**
7" Single: Released 31 Jan '83, on Mute, by Mute Records. Deleted '86. Catalogue no: **7 BONG 2**

IT'S CALLED A HEART
Tracks: / It's called a heart.
12" Single: Released May '88, on Intercord (Germany), Catalogue no: **INT 126832**
12" Single: Released 9 Sep '85, on Mute, by Mute Records. Catalogue no: **D12BONG 9**
7" Single: Released 9 Sep '85, on Mute, by Mute Records. Catalogue no: **7 BONG 9**
12" Single: Released 9 Sep '85, on Mute, by Mute Records. Catalogue no: **12 BONG 9**

JUST CAN'T GET ENOUGH
Tracks: / Just can't get enough.
Note: *Limited edition white vinyl version, in original picture sleeve.
12" Single: Released Oct '87, on Mute (Germany), by Mute Records. Catalogue no: **INT 126801***
7" Single: Released 7 Sep '81, on Mute, by Mute Records. Catalogue no: **MUTE 016**

JUST CAN'T GET ENOUGH (IMPORT)
Tracks: / Just can't get enough.
CD 5": Released Dec '88, on Intercord (Germany), Catalogue no: **INT 826801**

LEAVE IN SILENCE
Tracks: / Leave in silence / My secret garden.
7" Single: Released 16 Jun '82, on Mute, by Mute Records. Catalogue no: **7 BONG 1**
12" Single: Released 16 Jun '82, on Mute, by Mute Records. Catalogue no: **12 BONG 1**

LEAVE IN SILENCE(IMPORT)
Tracks: / Leave in silence (7" mix) / Leave in silence (12"mix) / Leave in silence (quieter mix) / Leave in silence (excerpts version) / My secret garden.
12" Single: Released Sep '87, on Mute (Germany), by Mute Records. Catalogue no: **INT 126807**
CD 5": Released Oct '88, on Intercord (Germany), Catalogue no: **INT 826807**

LITTLE 15
Tracks: / Little 15 / St. Jarna.
12" Single: Released Dec '88, on Mute, by Mute Records. Catalogue no: **12 LITTLE 15**
7" Single: Released Dec '88, on Mute, by Mute Records. Catalogue no: **LITTLE 15**
12" Single: Released Jun '88, on Intercord (Germany), Catalogue no: **INT 126832**

LOVE IN ITSELF
Tracks: / Love in itself.
Note: Four live tracks recorded at the Hammersmith Odeon (25.10.82): 'Just can't get enough', 'A photograph of you', 'Shout' and 'Photographic'. Clear yellow vinyl.*The limited edition series of 12" E.P.'s, now available as 6-track C.D.'s (also ltd. edition). Two mixes and four live tracks.
7" Single: Released 19 Sep '83, on Mute, by Mute Records. Deleted '86. Catalogue no: **7 BONG 4**
12" Single: Released Sep '87, on Mute (Germany), by Mute Records. Catalogue no: **INT 126838**
CD 5": Released Oct '87, on Mute (Germany), by Mute Records. Catalogue no: **INT 826836***

LOVE IN ITSELF (IMPORT)
Tracks: / Love in itself (long version) / Love in itself (4.39) / Love in itself / Fools (bigger mix 7.40).
CD 5": Released Oct '88, on Intercord (Germany), Catalogue no: **INT 826816**

MASTER AND SERVANT
Tracks: / Master and servant / (Set me free) remotivate me.
Note: The "slavery whip mix" with (Set Me Free) Remotivate Me and Master and Servant (instrumental) in a limited edition 12" on black-and-white marbled vinyl.
12" Single: Released 20 Aug '84, on Mute, by Mute Records. Catalogue no: **12 BONG 6**
12" Single: Released Nov '87, on Mute (Germany), by Mute Records. Catalogue no: **INT 126824**
7" Single: Released 20 Aug '84, on Mute, by Mute Records. Catalogue no: **7 BONG 6**

MASTER & SERVANT (IMPORT)
Tracks: / Master & servant (slavery whip mix) / Master & servant (voxless mix) / Master & servant (7" mix) / (Set me free) remotivate me (release mix).
CD 5": Released Oct '88, on Intercord (Germany), Catalogue no: **INT 826824**

MEANING OF LOVE (IMPORT)
Tracks: / Oberkorn.
12" Single: Released Sep '87, on Mute (Germany), by Mute Records. Catalogue no: **INT 126805**

MEANING OF LOVE (SINGLE)
Tracks: / Meaning of love / Oberkorn.
12" Single: Released 26 Apr '82, on Mute, by Mute Records. Catalogue no: **12 MUTE 022**
7" Single: Released 26 Apr '82, on Mute, by Mute Records. Catalogue no: **7 MUTE 022**

NEVER LET ME DOWN AGAIN
Tracks: / Pleasure, little treasure / Never let me down again.
12" Single: Released 24 Aug '87, on Mute, by Mute Records. Catalogue no: **12 BONG 14**
7" Single: Released 24 Aug '87, on Mute, by Mute Records. Catalogue no: **7 BONG 14**
CD 5": Released Oct '87, on Mute (Germany), by Mute Records. Catalogue no: **INT 826868**
12" Single: Released 28 Sep '87, on Pinnacle (Imports), by Pinnacle Records. Catalogue no: **INT 126869**

NEW LIFE
Tracks: / Shout / New life / See you.
7" Single: Released 13 Jun '81, on Mute, by Mute Records. Catalogue no: **MUTE 014**

NEW LIFE (IMPORT)
Tracks: / New life.
12" Single: Released Sep '87, on Mute (Germany), by Mute Records. Catalogue no: **INT 126800**
CD 5": Released Dec '88, on Intercord (Germany), Catalogue no: **INT 826800**

PEOPLE ARE PEOPLE
Tracks: / People are people / In your memory.
7" Single: Released 12 Mar '84, on Mute, by Mute Records. Catalogue no: **7 BONG 5**
12" Single: Released 12 Mar '84, on Mute, by Mute Records. Catalogue no: **12 BONG 5**

PEOPLE ARE PEOPLE (IMPORT)
CD 5": Released '88, on Intercord (Germany), Catalogue no: **INT 826820**

PERSONAL JESUS
Tracks: / Personal Jesus / Dangerous.
7" Single: Released 29 Aug '89, on Mute, by Mute Records. Catalogue no: **BONG 17**
CD 3": Released 29 Aug '89, on Mute, by Mute Records. Catalogue no: **BONG 17**

CD
12" Single: Released 29 Aug '89, on Mute, by Mute Records. Catalogue no: **12BONG 17**

QUESTION OF LUST, A
Tracks: / Question of lust, A / Christmas Island / People are people (live) (Only on 12" version) / It doesn't matter (Only on 12" version.) / Question of lust, A (minimal) (only on 12" version).
12" Single: Released 4 Apr '86, on Mute, by Mute Records. Catalogue no: **12 BONG 11**
12" Single: Released Oct '87, on Mute (Germany), by Mute Records. Catalogue no: **INT 126844**
7" Single: Released 4 Apr '86, on Mute, by Mute Records. Catalogue no: **7 BONG 11**

QUESTION OF TIME, A
Tracks: / Question of time, A / Black celebration (live) / Something to do (live) (Only on 12" version.) / Stripped (live) (Only on 12" version.).
Note: Extra track on 12" version only. *C.D EP features 'A Question Of Time' (remix and extended remix), 'Stripped', 'Black Celebration', 'Something To Do' (last three all live). 27 minutes in total).
12" Single: Released Sep '86, on Mute, by Mute Records. Catalogue no: **L 12 BONG 12**
7" Single: Released 11 Aug '86, on Mute, by Mute Records. Catalogue no: **7 BONG 12**
CD 5": Released Oct '87, on Mute (Germany), by Mute Records. Catalogue no: **INT 826850**

SEE YOU
Tracks: / See you / Now, this is fun.
12" Single: Released 29 Jan '82, on Mute, by Mute Records. Catalogue no: **12 MUTE 018**
7" Single: Released 29 Jan '82, on Mute, by Mute Records. Catalogue no: **MUTE 018**

SEE YOU (IMPORT)
Tracks: / Now, this is fun / See you.
12" Single: Released Sep '87, on Mute (Germany), by Mute Records. Catalogue no: **INT 126802**

SHAKE THE DISEASE
Tracks: / Shake the disease.
7" Single: Released 28 Apr '85, on Mute, by Mute Records. Catalogue no: **7 BONG 8**
12" Single: Released 28 Apr '85, on Mute, by Mute Records. Catalogue no: **12 BONG 8**

STRANGELOVE (EP)
Note: Five-track CD EP.
CD 5": Released Nov '87, on Mute (Germany), by Mute Records. Catalogue no: **INT 826862**

STRANGELOVE (HIGHJACK MIX)
Tracks: / Strangelove (highjack mix) / Strangelove (remix edit) / Nothing (remix).
Note: Remixed by Bomb The Bass's Tim Simenon & Mark Saunders. Also includes two remixes of the album track "Nothing".n
7" Single: Released Dec '88, on Sire (USA), Catalogue no: **727777**
12" Single: Released Dec '88, on Sire (USA), Catalogue no: **021022**
CD 3": Released Dec '88, on Sire (USA), Catalogue no: **227777**

STRANGELOVE (LIMITED)
Tracks: / Strangelove / Pimpf / Strangelove.
Note: 12" limited edition, from Germany, in bright orange vinyl.
CD 5": Released Nov '87, on Mute (Germany), by Mute Records. Catalogue no: **INT 826862**
12" Single: Released Nov '87, on Mute (Germany), by Mute Records. Catalogue no: **INT 126862**
7" Single: Released 17 Apr '87, on Mute, by Mute Records. Catalogue no: **BONG 13**
12" Single: Released 30 May '87, on Mute, by Mute Records. Catalogue no: **L 12 BONG 13**
12" Single: Released 17 Apr '87, on Mute, by Mute Records. Catalogue no: **12 BONG 13**

STRANGELOVE (SPECIAL EDITION)
Tracks: / Strangelove / Pimpf / Agent Orange.
Note: Special limited-edition, on orange vinyl, featuring four tracks -- Strangelove (two mixes), Pimpf and Agent Orange.
12" Single: Released Nov '87, on Mute (Germany), by Mute Records. Catalogue no: **INT 126866**

STRIPPED
Tracks: / Stripped / But not tonight / Breathing in fumes (Extra track available on 12" version only.) / Fly on the windscreen (Quiet Mix) (Extra track available on 12" version only.) / Black day (Extra track available on 12" version only.).
7" Single: Released 10 Feb '86, on Mute, by Mute Records. Catalogue no: **7 BONG 10**

Depth Charge Souls

PRICE OF LOVE, THE
Tracks: / Price of love, The.
7" Single: Released 21 Aug '87, on Wolf, Catalogue no: **WOLF 001**

Derek, John

HEY DUKE
Tracks: / Hey Duke / Gee ain't it funny.
7" Single: Released Jan '81, on Amigo, Deleted Jan '84. Catalogue no: **AMGO 005**

Derek & The Dominoes

Biographical details: This transatlantic British/American group consisted on Duane Allman, Eric Clapton ('Derek'), Jim Gordon, Carl Radle and Bobby Whitlock.
Eric Clapton, Britain's premier guitar hero, had an intense dislike for the pressures of stardom. He spent the Sixties playing in the Yardbirds, John Mayall's Bluesbreakers, Cream and Blind Faith and, in each case, had quit the band when they were riding high. On the second night of an American tour by Blind Faith, a contrived short-lived supergroup of UK rock stars, Clapton met the support act, Delaney & Bonnie, and soon decided to tour with them despite the fact that they were relatively unknown, and Blind Faith was therefore terminated in late 1969. In 1970, three members of Delaney & Bonnie's group - Gordon, Radle and Whitlock - joined Clapton in a new ensemble, Derek & The Dominoes; the band's name reflected the axe hero's desire for anonymity. They were initially joined by Dave Mason of Traffic fame, but he soon departed. The new combo's 1970 tour was interrupted by some Miami recording sessions, which yielded a classic double album, *Layla And Other Assorted Love Songs*. In addition to Clapton, another, newer guitar wizard was prominently featured on the project - Duane Allman, leader of the Allman Brothrs Band, proved to be the catalyst which brought the musicians together into a coherent musical package. Allman and Clapton engaged in a friendly guitar battle on the LP, which produced some of the most exhilarating rock music ever made.
Many critics rate *Layla And Other Assorted Love Songs* as the highlight of Clapton's career. It's centrepiece single *Layla*, inspired by his unrequited love for Patti Harrison, is certainly his greatest ever track. But the group's anonymity had perhaps gone too far - the single and double LP flopped on both sides of the Atlantic. This disappointment, coupled with the tragic death of Duane Allman - who was killed in a motorcycle accident at the age of 24 in October 1971 - caused Clapton to disband the Dominoes. Their second studio LP was begun but never finished. A live album was recorded but its release was delayed until '73, in the wake of the belated success of the *Layla* single: the classic track finally cracked theUK and US Top Tens in 1972. By that time, Clapton was in the middle of a drug-enforced retirement, which finally ended in 1974, when he began a long and successful solo career with a US No 1 single *I Shot The Sherriff* and began to feel more at ease in the spotlight. In order to promote a compilation album, *Layla* was re-released in Britain in 1982 and became an even bigger hit, peaking at No 4; by that time, he was married to Patti, the ex-wife of ex-Beatle George Harrison, the girl who had been the subject of the famous song. It is, however, extraordinary that the *Layla* LP never reached the UK album charts. Bob MacDobald, 25 March 1985..

LAYLA
Tracks: / Layla / Only you know and I know.
7" Single: Released Aug '72, on Polydor, by Polydor Ltd. Deleted '75. Catalogue no: **2058 130**
7" Single: Released Mar '82, on RSO, by Polydor Ltd. Deleted '85. Catalogue no: **RSO 87**
7" Single: Released Jun '88, on Old Gold, by Old Gold Records. Catalogue no: **OG 9422**
12" Single: Released Feb '88, on Old Gold, by Old Gold Records. Catalogue no: **OG 4046**
12" Single: Released Mar '82, on RSO, by Polydor Ltd. Deleted '85. Catalogue no: **RSOX 87**

Derrick & Sounds

SHAKE ME I RATTLE
Tracks: / Shake me I rattle / Sound of my music.
7" Single: Released Nov '82, on Mint, by Emerald Records. Deleted '88. Catalogue no: **CHEW 76**

Derringer, Rick

DON'T EVER SAY GOODBYE
Tracks: / Don't ever say goodbye / Timeless.
7" Single: Released Apr '80, on Blue Sky, Deleted Apr '83. Catalogue no: **SKY 8326**

Des Barres, Michael

I'M ONLY HUMAN (SINGLE)
Tracks: / I'm only human / Catchphrase.
7" Single: Released Jan '81, on Dreamland, Deleted Jan '84. Catalogue no: **DLSP 7**

OBSESSION
Tracks: / Obsession / Woman's weapon.
12" Single: Released '84, on A&M, by A&M Records. Deleted '88. Catalogue no: **AMX 183**
7" Single: Released '84, on A&M, by A&M Records. Deleted '88. Catalogue no: **AM 183**

SOMEONE SOMEWHERE IN THE NIGHT
Tracks: / Someone somewhere in the night / Five hour flight.
7" Single: Released Mar '81, on Dreamland, Deleted Mar '84. Catalogue no: **DLSP 9**

Desario, Teri

OVERNIGHT SUCCESS
Tracks: / Overnight success.
7" Single: Released Feb '85, on Epic, by CBS Records. Catalogue no: **A 5031**

Desborough School

WHY NOT BUY AN EXTRA PRESENT?
Tracks: / Why not buy an extra present?.
7" Single: Released Nov '83, on Jira, Deleted '85. Catalogue no: **JIRA 001**

Descendents

BONUS FAT
Tracks: / Bonus fat.
7" Single: Released Aug '87, on SST (USA), by SST Records (USA). Catalogue no: **SST 144**

Descloux, Lizzy

ZULU ROCK
Tracks: / Zulu rock / Sun's jive.
12" Single: Released Apr '84, on CBS, by CBS Records. Catalogue no: **TA 4359**
7" Single: Released Apr '84, on CBS, by CBS Records. Catalogue no. **A 4359**

Desert Wolves

LOVE SCATTERED LIVES
Tracks: / Love scattered lives / Stopped in my tracks / Desolation / Sunday morning.
12" Single: Released Oct '87, on Ugly Man, by Ugly Man Records. Catalogue no: **UGLY 6T**

SPEAK TO ME, ROCHELLE
Tracks: / Speak to me, Rochelle / Mexican song, The / Besottee (12" only) / Dit mai Rochelle (12" only).
7" Single: Released Jan '88, on Ugly Man, by Ugly Man Records. Catalogue no: **UGLY 9**
12" Single: Released Jan '88, on Ugly Man, by Ugly Man Records. Catalogue no: **UGLY 9T**

Deserters

ALIEN
Tracks: / Alien / Protection.
7" Single: Released Jan '82, on Capitol, by EMI Records. Deleted Jan '85. Catalogue no: **CL 225**

Desford Colliery Band

JINGLE BELLS
Tracks: / Jingle bells / Merry tijuana, A.
7" Single: Released Dec '86, on Hallamshire, Catalogue no: **BB 5302**

Desi

I WANT TO BE WITH YOU
Tracks: / I want to be with you / I'm much too shy / I want to be with you (Ext.) (Extra track on 12" version only.).
7" Single: Released Jan '86, on Certain, by Certain Records. Catalogue no: **ACERT 5**
12" Single: Released Jan '86, on Certain, by Certain Records. Catalogue no: **12 ACERT 5**
7" Single: Released Aug '72, on Decca, by Decca Records. Deleted '88. Catalogue no: **F 13334**

Desi, Dirty

BIG BATTY BETTY
Tracks: / Big batty Betty / Mi sexy.
12" Single: Released Dec '84, on D.A.D., by D.A.D. Records. Catalogue no: **DR 001**

Design 9

ROULETTE
Tracks: / Roulette.
7" Single: Released Jun '84, on Quickstep, Catalogue no: **QR 001**

Design For Living

DESIGN FOR LIVING
Tracks: / Design for living.
7" Single: Released May '84, on Anthem, Catalogue no: **ANTHEM 3**

Designer

FEELING NICE
Tracks: / Feeling nice / Besame.
12" Single: Released Mar '84, on Trindisc, by Trindisc Records. Catalogue no: **TRIN 007**
12" Single: Released Nov '83, on Trindisc, by Trindisc Records. Catalogue no: **TRIN 006**
7" Single: Released Nov '83, on Trindisc, by Trindisc Records. Catalogue no: **TRIN 003**

Desireless

JOHN
Tracks: / John / Qui peut savoir.
7" Single: Released Aug '88, on CBS, by CBS Records. Deleted 17 Apr '89. Catalogue no: **DESI 3**
12" Single: Released Sep '88, on CBS, by CBS Records. Deleted 17 Apr '89. Catalogue no: **DESIT 3**
CD 5": Released Aug '88, on CBS, by CBS Records. Deleted 17 Apr '89. Catalogue no: **CD DESI 3**

VOYAGE VOYAGE
Tracks: / Voyage voyage / Destin fragile.
Special: Released Nov '87, on CBS, by CBS Records. Catalogue no: **DESI QT1**
7" Single: Released Oct '87, on CBS, by CBS Records. Catalogue no: **DESI 1**
12" Single: Released Oct '87, on CBS, by CBS Records. Catalogue no: **DESI T1**

VOYAGE VOYAGE (REMIX)
Tracks: / Voyage voyage (remix) / Voyage voyage (britmix) (Available on 12" and CD only.) / Voyage voyage (Euro remix remix) (Available on 12" and CD only.) / Destin fragile (instrumental).
CD 5": Released May '88, on CBS, by CBS Records. Deleted Jan '89. Catalogue no: **CD DESI 2**
12" Single: Released Apr '88, on CBS, by CBS Records. Deleted Jan '89. Catalogue no: **DESI T2**
7" Single: Released Apr '88, on CBS, by CBS Records. Deleted Jan '89. Catalogue no: **DESI 2**

Desmond, Paul

Biographical details: The alto saxophonist (1924-77) was a star in the Dave Brubeck Quartet until it broke up in 1967; he wrote Brubeck's biggest hit, *Take five*. His lyrical style and light, airy tone was liked even by people who were not Brubeck fans. He recorded as a leader for Fantasy in 1954 and 1956; the quartet set *Blues in time* with Gerry Mulligan was made in 1957; *Paul Desmond Quartet live* was made in Toronto in 1975 with Ed Bickert on guitar. The complete Desmond/Jim Hall quartet tracks from two labels have been compiled in a boxed set on the American Mosaic label. He was going to write a book about the Brubeck years called *How many of you are there in the quartet* but he died of lung cancer. (Donald Clarke, April 1989)

IF IT FEELS GOOD
Tracks: / If it feels good / Have faith in your love.
7" Single: Released Mar '81, on Flamingo, by Airwave Records (USA). Deleted Mar '84. Catalogue no: **FM 14**
12" Single: Released Mar '81, on Flamingo, by Airwave Records (USA). Deleted Mar '84. Catalogue no: **FMT 14**

Desmond, Tommy

APRIL WON'T BE HERE UNTIL SEPTEMBER
Tracks: / April won't be here until September / April won't be here until September (inst).
7" Single: Released Aug '80, on Sin, by Sin Records. Catalogue no: **SIN 001**

Desperadoes

BRAZIL
Tracks: / Brazil / Don't leave me this way.
7" Single: Released Jul '81, on Charisma, by Virgin Records. Deleted '85. Catalogue no: **CB 387**

Dessus

GHETTO CHILDREN
Tracks: / Ghetto children.
7" Single: Released Jan '82, on LEJ, Catalogue no: **EJFP 9710**

Destination

MOVE ON UP
Tracks: / Move on up / Up up up / Destination's theme.
12" Single: Released '83, on Chrysalis, by Chrysalis Records. Deleted '87. Catalogue no: **CHS 12 2409**

Destiny

MARATHON, THE
Tracks: / Marathon, The / Autumn gold.
7" Single: Released Apr '84, on Windmill Music. Deleted '85. Catalogue no: **WML 1007**

Destiny Orchestra

SPRING RAIN
Tracks: / Spring rain.
7" Single: Released Oct '79, on Destiny (Northern Soul), by Destiny Records. Catalogue no: **DS 1007**

Destroy All Monsters

BORED
Tracks: / Bored.
7" Single: Released Feb '79, on Cherry Red, by Cherry Red Records. Catalogue no: **CHERRY 3**

NOBODY KNOWS
Tracks: / Nobody knows.
7" Single: Released Oct '79, on Cherry Red, by Cherry Red Records. Catalogue no: **CHERRY 9**

STRANGER THAN FICTION
Tracks: / Stranger than fiction / Stranger than fiction (version).
7" Single: Released 5 Mar '88, on Circle City, Catalogue no: **CCY 3**

Destructors

CRY HAVOC AND UNLEASH THE DOGS OF..
Tracks: / Cry havoc and unleash the dogs of....
12" Single: Released Aug '83, on Criminal Damage, Catalogue no: **CRI 12104**

FORCES OF LAW
Tracks: / Forces of law.
7" Single: Released Apr '83, on Illuminated, Catalogue no: **ILL 19**

JAILBAIT
Tracks: / Jailbait.
7" Single: Released Oct '82, on Illuminated, Catalogue no: **ILL 14**

MEANINGLESS NAMES
Tracks: / Meaningless names / AK47 / Police state / Dachau / Death squad.
7" Single: Released Jun '82, on Carnage, Catalogue no: **BOOK 2**

RELIGION THERE IS NO RELIGION
Tracks: / Religion there is no religion / Soldier boy / Agent orange / Corpse gas.
7" EP: Released Jul '82, on Carnage, Catalogue no: **KILL 2**

SENSELESS VIOLENCE
Tracks: / Senseless violence.
7" Single: Released Apr '82, on Paperback, Deleted '84. Catalogue no: **BOOK 2**

WILD THING
Tracks: / Wild thing.
12" Single: Released Jul '83, on Illuminated, Catalogue no: **ILL 1912**

Destructors V

TV EYE
Tracks: / T.V. eye.
7" Single: Released Feb '84, on Criminal Damage, Catalogue no: **CRI 108**

Details

KEEP ON RUNNING
Tracks: / Keep on running / Run ins.
7" Single: Released May '80, on Energy (UK), by Energy Records. Deleted May '83. Catalogue no: **NRG 2**

LONDON MARATHON KEEP ON RUNNING
Tracks: / London marathon keep on running / Run-ins.
7" Single: Released Mar '81, on Energy (USA), by Bulldog Records (USA). Deleted Mar '84. Catalogue no: **NRG 6**

Detroit

I HAVE A DREAM
Tracks: / I have a dream.
12" Single: Released Feb '89, on White Label (1), Catalogue no: **RSFD 001**

Detroit Emeralds

Biographical details: This American vocal group consisted of brothers Abe and Ivory Tillman plus James Mitchell.

The Detroit Emeralds first recorded in 1968 for a small local label. Singing in a soft soul style, they began to hit the US soul charts with regularity in the early Seventies with such singles as *Do Me Right*. 1972 brought the trio a pair of American Top 40 pop hits - they hit No 36 with *You Want It You Got It* and No 24 with *Baby Let Me Take You (In My Arms)*. They never returned to the US pop Top 40, but enjoyed three UK Top 40 singles in 1973. *Feel The Need In Me*, their best known track, reached No 4 on the UK listings, *You Want It You Got It* hit No 12 and *I Think Of You* peaked at No 27. The Emeralds made competent, pleasant records, but they were by no means the best of the era's sweet soul groups. Nevertheless, it is surprising that *Feel The Need In Me* was not afforded greater acceptance in their native America.

Despite the lack of US impact, *Feel The Need* enjoyed two further chart outings in Britain. The Emeralds re-recorded the song, and took the new (similar but slightly more discofied) version to No 12 on the UK listings in 1977. Six years later, a remake by Forrest hit the Top 20. The dominant member of the Emeralds was Abe Tillman, who wrote and co-produced the bulk of their material. Bob MacDonald, 25, March 1985..

DANCE SCHOOL
Tracks: / Dance school.
12" Single: Released Nov '83, on Orbit, by Orbit Records. Catalogue no: **TRIPT 3**
7" Single: Released Nov '83, on Orbit, by Orbit Records. Catalogue no: **TRIP 3**

FEEL THE NEED
Tracks: / Feel the need / J.A's rap groove UK.
12" Single: Released Jun '89, on Midas, by Magnet Records. Catalogue no: **MIDASX 1**
7" Single: Released Jun '89, on Midas, by Magnet Records. Catalogue no: **MIDAS 1**
7" Single: Released Jun '77, on Atlantic, by WEA Records. Catalogue no: **K 10945**
7" Single: Released Feb '73, on Janus, Deleted '76. Catalogue no: **6146 020**

I THINK OF YOU
Tracks: / I think of you.
7" Single: Released Aug '73, on Westbound, by WEA Records. Deleted '76. Catalogue no: **6146 104**

YOU WANT YOU GOT IT
Tracks: / You want it you got it.
7" Single: Released May '73, on Westbound, by WEA Records. Deleted '76. Catalogue no: **6146 103**

Detroit Spinners

Biographical details: The classic early Seventies lineup of this American vocal group consisted of Henry Fambrough, Billy Henderson, Pervis Jackson, Bobby Smith and Philippe Wynne. In the United States, the quintet were simply called the Spinners.

The group were originally formed in 1955 at high school, and were known as the Dominicos; they comprised Fambrough, Henderson, Jackson and Smith, plus Crathman Spencer. At the end of the Fifties, this lineup came into contact with Harvey Fuqua, the brother-in-law of Motown Records' founder Berry Gordy. They first hit the US Top 40 in 1961, reaching No 27 with *That's What Girls Are Made For* on the Tri-Phi label; they were known as the Spinners by this time. When Fuqua took the group to Motown in '65, they achieved a second US Top 40 single with *I'll ALways Love You*. Five hitless years followed, during which Spencer quit and was replaced by Edgar Edwards, who proved to be a short-lived substitute. By 1970 he had been replaced by George 'G C' Cameron; they reached the Top 20 on both sides of the Atlantic that year with *It's A Shame*, produced and co-written by Stevie Wonder. British copies of this single credited the Motown Spinners, but when they switched to Atlantic records in 1972, they became known as the Detroit Spinners in the UK; this was to avoid confusion with Britain's folk group, The Spinners.

With Cameron replaced by the superb gospel-tinged voice of Philippe Wynne, the Spinners teamed with producer/arranger Thom Bell in 1972 and came up with a classic album, *The Spinners*. Bell has a hand in writing much of the material. The album yielded two American Top Five smashes, *I'll Be Around* and *Could It Be I'm Falling Love* - these were typical of the album's smooth, immaculately sung, soul songs, and they appealed equally to soul and pop audiences. Another single, *One Of A Kind (Love Affair)* attained the US No 11 position. In late '73, *Ghetto Child* gave the group their first British Top Tenner. Thanks to lead singer Wynne and the dominant behind the scenes presence of Bell, the 1972-7 period of the Spinners made them, arguably, the best soul group of the Seventies. A 1974 duet with Dionne Warwicke on *Then Came You* gave the group their sole US No 1; and they reached No 5 with 1975's *They Just Can't Stop It (The Games People Play)* and No 2 with 1976's *The Rubberband Man*. Wynne quit in 1977 to pursue an unsuccessful solo career, and the group soon found themselves without Bell too. Apparently stranded, the Spinners found themselves another producer/arranger in Michael Zager nd made a brief comeback in 1980. They achieved a smash hit in that year with a remake of a 1966 Four Seasons hit *Working My Way Back To You*, which gave the Spinners their first British No 1 and hit No 2 in the US. They followed this with a No 4 hit on both sides of the Atlantic - a remake of Sam Cooke's *Cupid* coupled in medley form with Zager's own *I've Loved You For A Long Time*. But the resurgence was brief, and the Spinners failed to come up with another hit.

US singer Terri Wells hit the British Top 20 in 1984 with a dance-orientated version of *I'll Be Around*, a song that had mysteriously failed in the UK in 1972. Mere weeks later, in July '84, the song's original singer Philippe Wynne died of a heart attack at the age of 43. A tribute to him was paide by British soul duo David Grant and Jaki Graham, who scored a big hit in 1985 with a classy remake of *Could It Be I'm Falling In Love*. Bob MacDonald, 25 March 1985..

BODY LANGUAGE
Tracks: / Body language / With my eyes.
7" Single: Released May '80, on Atlantic, by WEA Records. Deleted '83. Catalogue no: **K 11392**

COULD IT BE I'M FALLING IN LOVE
Tracks: / Could it be I'm falling in love.
7" Single: Released Apr '73, on Atlantic, by WEA Records. Deleted '76. Catalogue no: **K 10283**
7" EP: Released Apr '77, on Atlantic, by WEA Records. Deleted '80. Catalogue no: **K 10935**

CUPID - I'VE LOVED YOU FOR A LONG TIME
Tracks: / Cupid - I've loved you for a long time.
7" Single: Released Jun '80, on Atlantic, by WEA Records. Deleted '83. Catalogue no: **K 11498**

GHETTO CHILD
Tracks: / Ghetto child.
7" Single: Released Sep '73, on Atlantic, by WEA Records. Deleted '76. Catalogue no: **K 10359**

I JUST WANT TO FALL IN LOVE
Tracks: / I just want to fall in love / Love trippin'.
7" Single: Released Oct '80, on Atlantic, by WEA Records. Deleted Oct '83. Catalogue no: **K 11624**

I'LL BE AROUND
Tracks: / I'll be around / City full of memories.
7" Single: Released Jan '83, on Atlantic, by WEA Records. Catalogue no: **A 9891**
12" Single: Released Jan '83, on Atlantic, by WEA Records. Catalogue no: **A 9891 T**

IT'S A SHAME (SINGLE)
Tracks: / It's a shame.
7" Single: Released Jun '77, on Tamla Motown, by Motown Records (UK). Deleted '80. Catalogue no: **TMG 755**
7" Single: Released Apr '88, on Motown, by BMG Records (UK). Catalogue no: **ZB 41929**
7" Single: Released Oct '80, on Motown, by BMG Records (UK). Catalogue no: **TMG 1189**

KNACK FOR ME
Tracks: / Knack for me / Can't shake this feeling.
7" Single: Released May '82, on Atlantic, by WEA Records. Deleted '85. Catalogue no: **K 11707**

LOVE IS IN SEASON
Tracks: / Love is in season / Living a little, laughing a little / Could it be I'm falling in love.
7" Single: Released Aug '85, on Atlantic, by WEA Records. Catalogue no: **A 9649**
12" Single: Released Aug '85, on Atlantic, by WEA Records. Catalogue no: **A 9649 T**

MAGIC IN THE MOONLIGHT
Tracks: / Magic in the moonlight / So far away.
12" Single: Released Nov '82, on Atlantic, by WEA Records. Catalogue no: **A 9962 T**
7" Single: Released Nov '82, on Atlantic, by WEA Records. Catalogue no: **A 9962**

PUT US TOGETHER AGAIN
Tracks: / Put us together again / Show me your magic / Right or wrong.
7" Single: Released Jan '86, on Atlantic, by WEA Records. Deleted Sep '87. Catalogue no: **B 9604**
12" Single: Deleted Sep '87. Catalogue no: **B 9604 T**
12" Single: Released Jan '86, on Atlantic, by WEA Records. Deleted Sep '87. Catalogue no: **B 9604 T**

RUBBERBAND MAN, THE
Tracks: / Rubber band man, The.
7" Single: Released Sep '76, on Atlantic, by WEA Records. Deleted '79. Catalogue no: **K 10807**

SPLIT DECISION
Tracks: / Split decision / Now that you're mine again.
7" Single: Released Sep '80, on Atlantic, by WEA Records. Deleted '83. Catalogue no: **K 11558**

WAKE UP SUSAN
Tracks: / Wake up Susan.
7" Single: Released Jan '77, on Atlantic, by WEA Records. Deleted '80. Catalogue no: **K 10799**

WORKING MY WAY BACK TO YOU
Tracks: / Working my way back to you / I'll be around / Disco ride.
7" Single: Released Feb '80, on Atlantic, by WEA Records. Deleted '83. Catalogue no: **K 11432**
7" Single: Released May '88, on Atlantic, by WEA Records. Catalogue no: **A 9071**
12" Single: Released May '88, on Atlantic, by WEA Records. Catalogue no: **A 9071 T**

YESTERDAY ONCE MORE
Tracks: / Yesterday once more / Nothing remains the same / Be my love.
12" Single: Released Mar '81, on Atlantic, by WEA Records. Deleted Mar '84. Catalogue no: **K 11564 T**
7" Single: Released Mar '81, on Atlantic, by WEA Records. Deleted Mar '84. Catalogue no: **K 11564**

Deutsch...

VERUEB DICH IN MICH
Tracks: / Verueb dich in mich / Ein bisschen Krieg.
12" Single: Released Sep '82, on Virgin, by Virgin Records. Deleted Sep '85. Catalogue no: **VS 520 12**

Deux Ex Machina

HEART OF IT ALL
Tracks: / Heart of it all.
12" Single: Released Nov '87, on DEM Productions, Catalogue no: **DEM 1**

Deval, Al

MIDNIGHT SAX
Tracks: / Midnight sax.
12" Single: Released Jun '88, on Fashion, by Fashion Records. Catalogue no: **FAD 055**

Devastation

DRAG YOU DOWN
Tracks: / Drag you down.
7" Single: Released Nov '84, on Creative Reality, Catalogue no: **REAL 8**

Devastation Run

DEVASTATION RUN
7" EP: Released Aug '87, on Iron Works (USA), by Azra International (USA). Catalogue no: **IW 1014**

Devaughan, William

BE THANKFUL FOR WHAT YOU'VE GOT
Tracks: / Be thankful for what you've got.
7" Single: Released Jul '74, on Chelsea, Deleted '77. Catalogue no: **2005 002**
7" Single: Released Sep '80, on EMI, by EMI Records. Deleted '83. Catalogue no: **EMI 5101**

CREME DE CREME
Tracks: / Creme de creme.
7" Single: Released Dec '82, on Excaliber, by Red Bus Records. Deleted '88. Catalogue no: **EXC 527**
12" Single: Released Dec '82, on Excaliber, by Red Bus Records. Deleted '88. Catalogue no: **EXCL 527**

Device

HANGING ON A HEART ATTACK
Tracks: / Hanging on a heart attack / Hanging on a heart attack (inst).
7" Single: Released Jul '86, on Chrysalis, by Chrysalis Records. Catalogue no: **CHS 2996**
12" Single: Released Jul '86, on Chrysalis, by Chrysalis Records. Catalogue no: **CHS 122996**

Deville

Biographical details: DeVille, Mink. Mink DeVille are an American rock group wh are dominated by their lead singer, guitaris and main songwriter, Willy DeVille. At th time of their only hit, the group also in cluded Thomas R Allen, Louie Erlange Bobby Leonards and Ruben Siquenza.

Willy DeVille spent the early and mic Seventies wandering around New Yor San Francisco and London, looking for mu sicians with whom to form a band. Th

above line-up was stabilised in 1977, the year that the group released their debut album. This was the time of the New Wave/punk explosion and, having been heavily involved in New York's punk club, CBGB's, Mink DeVille were placed in this category. The band's style was actually more akin to New York rhythm and blues than punk. They hit the British charts in the summer of '77 with *Spanish Stroll*, a pop/R&B hybrid single that was heavily influenced by Lou Reed. This reached No 20 in the UK and was acclaimed as one of the year's best records. However, Mink DeVille failed to come up with another hit and, to most Britons, the group's name is still associated solely with *Spanish Stroll*.
Mink DeVille's second album, 1978's *Return To Magenta*, was hailed by reviewers but ignored by record buyers, a situation that continued throughout the late Seventies and early Eighties. Capitol Records refused to release the band's third album, 1980's *Le Chat Bleu*, in the United States, until pressurised by disc jockeys and critics. Surprise string arrangements were included on this LP, but they did not help it sell. A switch to Atlantic Records and major line-up changes followed. 1983's *Where Angels Fear To Tread* LP once again displayed Willy DeVille's competent blend of R&B, rock and pop styles; but it did not provide him with a follow-up hit to *Spanish Stroll*. Bob MacDonald, 29 March 1985..

SQUEEZE YOU HOLD YOU
Tracks: / Squeeze you hold you.
12" Single: Released Apr '83, on Philly World (USA), by Philly World (USA). Catalogue no: **PWSL 110**
7" Single: Released Apr '83, on Philly World (USA), by Philly World (USA). Catalogue no: **PWS 110**

Deville, Cruella

GYPSY GIRL
Tracks: / Gypsy girl.
12" Single: Released Oct '83, on EMI, by EMI Records. Catalogue no: **12EMI 5412**
7" Single: Released Oct '83, on EMI, by EMI Records. Catalogue no: **EMI 5412**

HONG KONG SWING
Tracks: / Hong Kong swing.
7" Single: Released Aug '84, on Parlophone, by EMI Records. Deleted '87. Catalogue no: **R 6075**
12" Single: Released Aug '84, on Parlophone, by EMI Records. Deleted '87. Catalogue no: **12 R 6075**

I'LL DO THE TALKING
Tracks: / I'll do the talking.
7" Single: Released Dec '84, on CPL, Catalogue no: **CPL 5**

Deville, Mink

YOU BETTER MOVE ON
Tracks: / You better move on / She was made in heaven.
7" Single: Released Oct '81, on Atlantic, by WEA Records. Deleted '85. Catalogue no: **K 11682**

Devine, Sydney

Biographical details: This British singer, born in Cleland, near Glasgow, entered showbusiness in 1955. He spent the next twenty years building a reputation, primarily in Scotland, as a live performer. Initially a rock 'n' roll imitator, Devine later made country and western his primary style. He did not begin his recording career until the mid-Seventies, and it was this move that substantially increased his following, after two decades in the second division. He cracked the UK National charts in 1976 with *Doubly Devine*, which reached No 14 on the LP listings. Later that year, *Devine Time* entered the chart but peaked at No 49. Further album chart success was not forthcoming, but *Doubly Devine* had done its job - the LP had won Devine major concert bookings and, during the late Seventies and Eighties, he was able to make a good living with his predictable but competently executed repertoire. This included country and MOR standards such as *I Can't Stop Loving You* and *Lovesick Blues*, combined with less well known numbers such as *Favourite Memory Of Mine* and *Room Full Of Roses*. He continues to appeal to a mainly female audience, and women sometimes occupy 90% of the seats at his shows. Outside Scotland, the singer's popularity strongholds are East Anglia, Liverpool and Newcastle.
Devine's only UK chart single occurred in April 1978. *Scotland Forever* was released to capitalise on the fervour surrounding the Scottish football squad's participation in the World Cup. Unfortunately for Devine, another artist had the same idea - in the week that *Scotland Forever* peaked at No 48, Andy Cameron reached No 6 with the enthusiastically amateurish *Ally's Tartan Army*. *Scotland Forever* was re-issued in time for the 1982 World Cup, but in neither year did it help the team win. Bob MacDonald, 29 March 1985..

DAISY A DAY
Tracks: / Daisy a day / Molly darling.
7" Single: Released Sep '87, on Scotdisc, by Scotdisc Records. Catalogue no: **ITV 7S 441**

FAVOURITE MEMORY OF MINE
Tracks: / Almost persuaded / Favourite memory of mine.
7" Single: Released Nov '86, on Country House, by Scotdisc Records. Deleted Jul '88. Catalogue no: **BGC 356**
7" Single: Released Dec '83, on Country House, by Scotdisc Records. Catalogue no: **BGC 7S 356**

HOW GREAT THOU ART
Tracks: / How great Thou art.
7" Single: Released Mar '82, on Time, Catalogue no: **IMP EP 2**

LIKE STRANGERS
Tracks: / Like strangers.
7" Single: Released Oct '82, on Mint, by Emerald Records. Deleted '88. Catalogue no: **CHEW 71**

PEARLY SHELLS
Tracks: / Pearly shells.
7" Single: Released Nov '83, on Country House, by Scotdisc Records. Catalogue no: **BGC 7S 360**

SCOTLAND FOREVER
Tracks: / Scotland forever.
7" Single: Released Mar '82, on Time, Catalogue no: **IMP EP 1**
7" Single: Released Apr '78, on Philips, by Phonogram Ltd. Deleted '81. Catalogue no: **SCOT 1**

SCOTLAND WE LOVE YOU
Tracks: / Scotland we love you.
7" Single: Released Sep '84, on Scotdisc, by Scotdisc Records. Catalogue no: **7S 378**
7" Single: Released Jun '85, on August Records, by Scotdisc Records. Catalogue no: **ITVS 378**

SYDNEY DEVINE'S SING-SONG COUNTRY
7" Single: Released Nov '85, on August (USA), by Rounder Records (USA). Catalogue no: **GBH 7S 406**

Devlin, Pat

BREAK THE ICE
Tracks: / Break the ice.
7" Single: Released Jul '85, on Head To Head, Catalogue no: **HTH 001**

Devo

Biographical details: This American group consists of two sets of brothers, Bob and Jerry Casale and Bob & Mark Mothersbaugh, plus their friend Alan Myers. Devo is short for Devolution which, according to the band's philosophy, is the present state of the human race.
Devo were formed in Akron, Ohio in 1976, and released their first single *Mongloid* on their own small label in December of that year. After interest from David Bowie and cult hero Iggy Pop, the group's highly experimental and zany music began to attract attention in Britain. The UK was undergoing the punk revolution, and the music scene was opening its doors to anything new, weird and exciting. Devo also had the advantage of being signed to 'hip' record companies - their early singles were issued by Stiff Records, Britain's first New Wave independent label, and later discs were issued by Virgin Records, the company who had enhanced their street credibility by signing the Sex Pistols after the famous punk pioneers had been fired by EMI and A&M. Devo hit the UK charts in 1978 with a run of four minor hit singles. The first and biggest of these was an extraordinary, electronic, staccato remake of the Rolling Stones' classic *Satisfaction*. This reached No 41, and was followed by the No 62 placing of *Jocko Home*, the group's theme song - this contained the immortal call and response line "Q:Are we not me? A: We are Devo", which provided the title of the group's debut album. Their two other minor 1978 UK hits were *Be Stiff* and the comparatively normal (by their standards) rock single *Come Back Jonee*.
Groomed and dressed identically, and apparently sharing the same height, weight and shoe size, the quintet's robotic and emotion-less image and weird music was, in truth, gimmickry rather than valid experimentations; like all novelties, the appeal soon diminished and Devo never became a major chart act in Britain. In the States, however, where they had been ignored during the late Seventies, they scored a million selling disco smash in 1980 with *Whip It*. This long running hit reached No 14 on the US pop chart, but proved to be a one-off success. Despite major acceptance in Australia, subsequent albums and singles, including an unlikely 1982 collaboration with Jermaine Jackson, have failed to arouse much interest in the US or UK. Bob MacDonald, 29 March 1985.

Rock band formed in Ohio in 1972 by bassist and vocalist Jerry Casale, keyboardists Bob Casale and Mark Mothersbaugh, lead guitarist and vocalist Bob Mothersbaugh and drummer Allan Myers. Jerry and Mark were the main songwriters/frontmen. They took their name from a video, *The truth about de-evolution, a prize winner at the 1975 Ann Arbor Film Festival; their wacky visuals included overalls, flowerpot hats and a jerky hypnotic sound (called Robotic; their irreverent cover of the Rolling Stones Satisfaction* also brought attention.
Their greatest success was in the UK, where punk rendered the lower charts vulnerable to quirkiness. They were fun for a while. (Donald Clarke, April 1989).

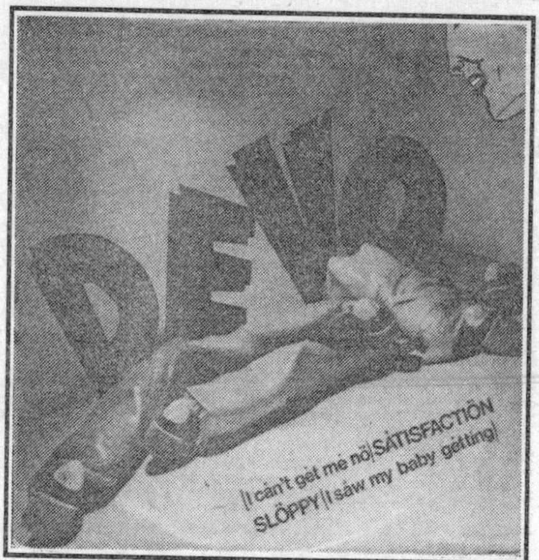

DEVO - SATISFACTION (Released on Stiff)

BE STIFF (SINGLE)
Tracks: / Be stiff.
7" Single: Released Aug '78, on Stiff, by Stiff Records. Deleted '81. Catalogue no: **BOY 2**

BEAUTIFUL WORLD
Tracks: / Beautiful world.
7" Single: Released Jan '82, on Virgin, by Virgin Records. Deleted Jan '85. Catalogue no: **VS 470**

COME BACK JONEE
Tracks: / Come back Jonee.
7" Single: Released Sep '78, on Virgin, by Virgin Records. Deleted '81. Catalogue no: **VS 223**
12" Single: Released Apr '83, on Virgin, by Virgin Records. Deleted May '88. Catalogue no: **VS 594 12**

DOCTOR DETROIT, THEME FROM
Tracks: / Doctor Detroit, Theme from.
12" Single: Released Jun '83, on MCA, by MCA Records. Catalogue no: **MCAT 822**
7" Single: Released Jun '83, on MCA, by MCA Records. Catalogue no: **MCA 822**

GIRL YOU WANT
Tracks: / Girl you want / Turn around.
7" Single: Released May '80, on Virgin, by Virgin Records. Deleted May '83. Catalogue no: **VS 350**

JOCKO HOMO
Tracks: / Jocko Homo.
7" Single: Released May '78, on Stiff, by Stiff Records. Deleted '81. Catalogue no: **DEV 1**

PEEK A BOO
Tracks: / Peek a boo.
7" Single: Released Oct '82, on Virgin, by Virgin Records. Deleted Oct '85. Catalogue no: **VS 536**
12" Single: Released Oct '82, on Virgin, by Virgin Records. Deleted Oct '85. Catalogue no: **VS 536 12**

SATISFACTION (see panel above)
Tracks: / (I can't get no) Satisfaction / Sloppy (I saw my baby getting).
7" Single: Released Apr '78, on Stiff, by Stiff Records. Deleted '81. Catalogue no: **BOY 1**

THROUGH BEING COOL
Tracks: / Through being cool.
7" Single: Released Sep '81, on Virgin, by Virgin Records. Deleted Sep '84. Catalogue no: **VS 450**

WHIP IT
Tracks: / Whip it.
7" Single: Released Nov '80, on Virgin, by Virgin Records. Deleted '83. Catalogue no: **VS 383**

WORKING IN A COALMINE
Tracks: / Working in a coalmine.
7" Single: Released Sep '81, on Virgin, by Virgin Records. Deleted Sep '84. Catalogue no: **VS 457**

Devonne

THIEF IN THE NIGHT
Tracks: / Thief In The Night.
7" Single: Released Apr '86, on Unit, Catalogue no: **TRANS 108**
12" Single: Released Apr '86, on Unit, Catalogue no: **12TRA 108**

Devonport Field Gun

COME ON YE GUNNERS
Tracks: / Come on ye gunners / You men of Devon.
7" Single: Released Jun '82, on Monarch, by Monarch Records. Catalogue no: **MON 030**

Devotion, Sheila B.

KING OF THE WORLD (SINGLE)
Tracks: / King of the world.
7" Single: Released Jun '80, on Carrere, Catalogue no: **CAR 150**
12" Single: Released Jun '80, on Carrere, Catalogue no: **CART 150**

LITTLE DARLIN' (SINGLE)
Tracks: / Little darlin' / Put it in writing.
7" Single: Released Oct '81, on Carrere, Catalogue no: **49 773**

SINGIN' IN THE RAIN
Tracks: / Singin' in the rain.
7" Single: Released Mar '78, on Carrere, Deleted Mar '81. Catalogue no: **EMI 2751**

SPACER
Tracks: / Spacer
7" Single: Released Jul '85, on Carrere, Catalogue no: **CAR 128**
12" Single: Released Jul '85, on Carrere, Catalogue no: **CART 128**
12" Single: Released Jun '84, on Carrere, Catalogue no: **CART 327**
7" Single: Released Nov '79, on Carrere, Deleted Nov '82. Catalogue no: **CAR 128**

YOU LIGHT MY FIRE
Tracks: / You light my fire.
7" Single: Released Jul '78, on Carrere, Deleted Jul '81. Catalogue no: **EMI 2828**

Dex

TAKE THE MONEY AND RUN
Tracks: / Take the money and run / Long live love.
7" Single: Released Aug '80, on Fabulous. Deleted '83. Catalogue no: **FABS 102**

Dexter, Levi

I GET SO EXCITED
Tracks: / I get so excited / Other side of midnight.
7" Single: Released Feb '82, on Fresh, by Jetstar Records. Deleted '85. Catalogue no: **FRESH 40**

Dexy's Midnight Runners

Biographical details: At the time of their greatest success, this British group comprised Billy Adams, Micky Billingham, Giorgio Kilkenny, Brian Maurice, Big Jimmy Patterson, Kevin Rowland, Seb Shelton and Paul Speare.

Dexy's Midnight Runners are dominated by their lead singer, main songwriter and public spokesman, Kevin Rowland. Since the group's inception in 1978, the remainder of the line-up has been an ever-changing phenomenon. The band enjoyed two bursts of success in the early Eighties, each featuring a vastly different eight-piece line-up and each espousing a different style of music; the linking factors were that each of the two periods produced a UK No 1 single and Top 10 album, and each featured genres of music that went against the prevalent chart trends, and therefore sounded totally fresh. Apart from Rowland, the only group member who contributed to both phases was tombone player Jimmy Patterson.

After building a controversial and exciting live reputation in 1979, Dexy's first cracked the UK singles chart in early '80 with *Dance Stance*, a No 40 hit. Consolidating on that single's refreshing brass sound, they followed it with a British No 1 smash *Geno*. This was a tribute to Geno Washington, Britain's soul club hero of the mid-Sixties, and demonstrated the group's love of passionate, communal soul music. It was followd by a further Top 10 single *There There My Dear* and a Top 10 album with their first attempt, *Searching For The Young Soul Rebels*. A series of controversies, caused largely by Rowland's rebellious and arrogant personality, accompanied this success: the group kidnapped the master tapes of the debut album until their recording contract was improved, adorned their record sleeves with some confusing and pseudo-intellectual sleeve notes, replaced press interviews with advertisements containing essays to their fans, and insulted and berated the majority of their live audiences. A period of hiatuses followed, and 1981 yielded only one UK Top 20 single, *Show Me*. With the new record deal, new personnel, a new folky image, a new folk-orientated violin-based sound and a somewhat toned down public personality, Rowland re-emerged in 1982 with the album *Too-Rye-Ay* and the smash single *Come On Eileen*. This joyous pop song was No 1 in Britain for the whole of August 1982, sold a million copies and was the UK's biggest seller of the year. They followed it with a Top 5 rendition of Van Morrison's song *Jackie Wilson Said*. Eventually, in Spring '83, *Come On Eileen* gave Dexy's a one off American smash: it reached the US No 1 slot for one week sandwiched betweeb *Billie Jean* and *Beat It*, two chart toppers by the dominant Michael Jackson. The unpredictable Rowland then proceeded to embark on a long layoff from the public eye. Bob MacDonald, 29 March 1985.

Rock band based in Birmingham ever-changing lineup fronted by volatile Kevin Rowland, formed in the post-punk period as powerful purveyors of dance music, drawing heavily on '60's soul, R & B; staunchly anti-fashionable amid the New Romantics of the early '80's. They arrived with a number one hit *Geno*, a tribute to Geno Washington. Their fusions, i.e. of black music with traditional Irish sounds, have always been interesting, and Rowland's anti-Thatcherism and run-ins with the music press haven't hurt business. (Donald Clarke, April 1989).

BECAUSE OF YOU
Tracks: / Because of you / Kathleen / Mavoureen / Sometimes theme (12" only).
12" Single: Released Oct '86, on Mercury, by Phonogram Ltd. Deleted '87. Catalogue no: **BRUSH 112**
7" Single: Released Oct '86, on Mercury, by Phonogram Ltd. Deleted '87. Catalogue no: **BRUSH 1**

BREAKING DOWN THE WALLS OF HEARTACHE
Tracks: / Breaking down the walls of heartache.

DEXY'S MIDNIGHT RUNNERS - CELTIC SOUL BROTHERS (Released on Mercury)

7" Single: Released Mar '80, on Parlophone, by EMI Records. Catalogue no: **R 6033**

CELTIC SOUL BROTHERS (see panel above)
Tracks: / Celtic soul brothers / Reminisce part one.
7" Single: Released Mar '82, on Mercury, by Phonogram Ltd. Deleted '85. Catalogue no: **DEXYS 8**

COME ON EILEEN
Tracks: / Come on Eileen / Dubious.
12" Single: Released Oct '84, on Mercury, by Phonogram Ltd. Deleted '86. Catalogue no: **DEXYS 912**
7" Single: Released Oct '84, on Mercury, by Phonogram Ltd. Deleted 31 May '89. Catalogue no: **DEXYS 9**

DANCE STANCE
Tracks: / Dance stance / There there my dear.
7" Single: Released Mar '84, on EMI Golden 45's, by EMI Records. Catalogue no: **G45 5**
7" Single: Released Jan '80, on Oddball Producti, Deleted '83. Catalogue no: **R 6028**

GENO (SINGLE)
Tracks: / Geno / Breakin' down the walls of heartache.
7" Single: Released Feb '83, on Parlophone, by EMI Records. Catalogue no: **R 6033**

JACKIE WILSON SAID
Tracks: / Jackie Wilson said.
7" Single: Released Oct '82, on Mercury, by Phonogram Ltd. Deleted '85. Catalogue no: **DEXYS 10**

KEEP IT
Tracks: / Keep it / One way love.
7" Single: Released Nov '80, on Parlophone, by EMI Records. Deleted '83. Catalogue no: **R 6042**

LIARS A TO E
Tracks: / Liars A to E / And yes we must remain the wildhearted.
7" Single: Released Nov '81, on Mercury, by Phonogram Ltd. Deleted '84. Catalogue no: **DEXYS 7**

PLAN B
Tracks: / Plan B / Soul finger.
7" Single: Released Mar '81, on Parlophone, by EMI Records. Deleted '84. Catalogue no: **R 6046**

SHOW ME
Tracks: / Show me / Soon.
7" Single: Released Jul '81, on Mercury, by Phonogram Ltd. Deleted Jul '84. Catalogue no: **DEXYS 6**

THERE, THERE MY DEAR
Tracks: / There, there my dear.
7" Single: Released Jul '80, on Late Night Feelings, by Dexy's Midnight Runners. Deleted '83. Catalogue no: **R 6038**

THIS IS WHAT SHE'S LIKE
Tracks: / This is what she's like.
12" Single: Released Nov '85, on Mercury, by Phonogram Ltd. Catalogue no: **DEXYS 1312**
7" Set: Released Nov '85, on Mercury, by Phonogram Ltd. Deleted '86. Catalogue no: **DEXYD 13**
7" Single: Released Nov '85, on Mercury, by Phonogram Ltd. Deleted '86. Catalogue no: **DEXYS 13**

Dey, Joy

CAN I TOUCH YOU
Tracks: / Can I touch you ?.
7" Single: Released May '83, on Gipsy, by Gipsy Records. Catalogue no: **GIPSY 10**

Dezzy Boy

EVERYBODY JUMP JUMP (IT'S CARNIVAL TIME)
Tracks: / Everybody jump jump (it's carnival time).
7" Single: Released Aug '89, on Nottinghill, Catalogue no: **DEZZY 1**
12" Single: Released Aug '89, on Nottinghill, Catalogue no: **DEZZY T1**

D.F.C. Team

I C LOVE AFFAIR
Tracks: / I C love affair.
12" Single: Released Sep '89, on RCA, by BMG Records (UK). Catalogue no: **PT 43044**
7" Single: Released Sep '89, on RCA, by BMG Records (UK). Catalogue no: **PB 43043**

Di Franco, Linda

MY BOXX
Tracks: / My boxx / Dance it up.
7" Single: Released May '86, on WEA, by WEA Records. Deleted Jun '87. Catalogue no: **YZ 68**
12" Single: Released May '86, on WEA, by WEA Records. Deleted Jun '87. Catalogue no: **YZ 68T**

Di Meola, Al

Biographical details: The guitarist and composer was born in 1954 in New Jersey, began on guitar at age 9 and was inspired to play fusion by hearing Miles Davis with Chick Corea. He attended Berklee in Boston and joined Corea's Return To Forever in 1974, led his own groups and toured and recorded in a guitar trio with John McLaughlin and Paco DeLucia. He plays both acoustic and electric guitars. His albums on CBS all made the top 200 USA albums; he switched to Manhattan for the acoustic solo *Cielo e terra* then formed the Al Di Meola Project, with percussionist Airto, Phil Markowtz on keyboards, Danny Gottlieb on drums and bassist Chip Jackson for *Soaring through a dream*. (Donald Clarke, April 1989)..

SPANISH EYES
Tracks: / Spanish eyes.
7" Single: Released Oct '82, on CBS, by CBS Records. Deleted Oct '85. Catalogue no: **CBS 8946**

Dial, Tony

YOU KEEP COMING ROUND
Tracks: / You keep coming round / Solo / End of the world.
7" Single: Released Jun '80, on Satril, by Satril Records. Deleted Jun '83. Catalogue no: **ABE 1**

Diamond, Greg

CREAM
Tracks: / Cream (always rises to the top).
7" Single: Released Jan '79, on Polydor, by Polydor Ltd. Deleted '82. Catalogue no: **POSP 18**

HOT BUTTERFLY
Tracks: / Hot butterfly / Hot butterfly (exit) / Fess up to the boogie / When the shit hits the fan (rocket pocket).
7" Single: Released Mar '88, on Urban, by Polydor Ltd. Catalogue no: **URB 16**
12" Single: Released Mar '88, on Urban, by Polydor Ltd. Catalogue no: **URBX 16**

Diamond Head

Biographical details: This British rock group consists of Sean Harris, Colin Kimberley, Duncan Scott and Brian Tatler.

Diamond Head began to attract attention in the heavy metal field in 1980-1 with a series of independently released singles. These included songs such as *Shoot Out The Lights* and *Play It Loud*, which coincided with the UK's heavy metal resurgence. After signing to MCA Records, they scored their first minor British chart single - *In The Heat Of The Night* reached No 67 in September 1982. This was the opening track on their first chart album *Borrowed Time*, which hit No 24 on the UK listings. All the tracks were written by vocalist/guitarist Harris and guitarist Harris and guitarist Tatler. The LP showed that this Birmingham band were a competent but run of the mill combo, with little originality to distinguish them from legions of other hard rockers.

Diamond Head's 1983 follow-up LP, *Canterbury*, showed the group branching out into more dynamic arrangements and effects, but the songs themselves were not strong enough to take the band into the top league of heavy metal acts. Bob MacDonald, 29 March 1985..

CALL ME
Tracks: / Call me / Trick or treat / Dead reckoning.
12" Single: Released Nov '82, on MCA, by MCA Records. Deleted Nov '85. Catalogue no: **DHMT 101**
7" Single: Released Nov '82, on MCA, by MCA Records. Deleted Nov '85. Catalogue no: **DHM 101**

DIAMOND LIGHTS
Tracks: / Diamond lights / We won't be back / I don't got / It's electric.
12" Single: Released Sep '81, on Windsong, by BMG Records (UK). Deleted '84. Catalogue no: **DHM 005**

IN THE HEAT OF THE NIGHT
Tracks: / In the heat of the night.
7" Single: Released Sep '82, on MCA, by MCA Records. Deleted '85. Catalogue no: **DHM 102**

PLAY IT LOUD
Tracks: / Play it loud / Waited too long.
7" Single: Released Mar '81, on UNKNOWN, Deleted Mar '84. Catalogue no: **DHM 004**

SWEET AND INNOCENT
Tracks: / Sweet and innocent / Streets of gold.
7" Single: Released Aug '80, on Media, Deleted '83. Catalogue no: **SCREEN 1**

Diamond, Jim

Biographical details: Pop vocalist born in 1953 in Glasgow. He became a club singer at 16; he formed band Bandit in 1975, but its eponymous album on Arista sunk without trace in the middle of Punk. He worked with Alexis Korner, produced Zoot Money etc., then teamed with keyboardist Tony Hymas as PhD, hitting the jackpot with ballad *I won't let you dow*, a UK number three in 1982, but Diamond contracted hepatitis and couldn't promote their album *Is it safe*. He finally embarked on a solo career, scored with another ballad *I should have known better* (number one 1984) but hasn't maintained consistency. (Donald Clarke, April 1989).

BROADWAY
Tracks: / Broadway / Second chance.
7" Single: Released Feb '89, on WEA, by WEA Records. Catalogue no: **YZ 373**

DESIRE
Tracks: / Desire / Together.
12" Single: Released Apr '86, on A&M, by A&M Records. Deleted '88. Catalogue no: **AMY 314**
7" Single: Released Apr '86, on A&M, by A&M Records. Deleted '88. Catalogue no: **AM 314**

HI HO SILVER
Tracks: / Hi ho silver / Hi ho silver (instrumental).
7" Single: Released Jan '86, on A&M, by A&M Records. Deleted Mar '88. Catalogue no: **AM 296**
12" Single: Released Jan '86, on A&M, by A&M Records. Deleted Mar '88. Catalogue no: **AMY 296**

I SHOULD HAVE KNOWN BETTER
Tracks: / I should have known better / Impossible dream, The.
7" Single: Released Oct '84, on A&M, by A&M Records. Deleted 1 Aug '88. Catalogue no: **AM 220**

I SHOULD'VE KNOWN BETTER (OLD GOLD)
Tracks: / I should've known better / Hi ho silver.
7" Single: Released Oct '88, on Old Gold, by Old Gold Records. Catalogue no: **OG 9813**

I SLEEP ALONE AT NIGHT
Tracks: / I sleep alone at night.
7" Single: Released Feb '85, on A&M, by A&M Records. Deleted '88. Catalogue no: **AM 229**

REMEMBER I LOVE YOU
Tracks: / Remember I love you.
7" Single: Released May '85, on A&M, by A&M Records. Deleted '88. Catalogue no: **AM 247**

SHOUT IT OUT
Tracks: / Shout it out / Message of chidwatch, The.
7" Single: Released 20 Jun '87, on Tembo, by Tembo Records. Catalogue no: **TML 126**
12" Single: Released 20 Jun '87, on Tembo, by Tembo Records. Deleted 31 May '89. Catalogue no: **TMLX 126**

SO STRONG
Tracks: / So strong / You'll go crazy.
7" Single: Released '88, on A&M, by A&M Records. Catalogue no: **AM 367**

YOUNG LOVE (CARRY ME AWAY)
Tracks: / Young love (carry me away) / Blue songs / Young love (Track included on limted edition cassette only.) / I should have known better (Track on limted edition cassette only.) / Remember I love you (Track on limited edition cassette only.) / Hi ho Silver (Track on limted edition cassette only.).
Special: Released Jul '86, on A&M, by A&M Records. Deleted Mar '88. Catalogue no: **AMS 332**
7" Single: Released Jul '86, on A&M, by A&M Records. Deleted '88. Catalogue no: **AM 332**

Diamond, Keith

DIP
Tracks: / Dip / You'll always be there.
12" Single: Released Oct '81, on RCA, by BMG Records (UK). Deleted Oct '84. Catalogue no: **YD 11812**

Diamond, Neil

Biographical details: This American singer, songwriter and guitarist, born in New York, moved to Memphis with his family at the age of seven, but ran away from home at 13. He ended up in Kansas City and helped to form a folk group there. In 1965, now a young adult, he was trying to earn a living as a composer in the Brill Building, New York's famous songwriting house; there he was discovered by fellow writers Jeff Barry and Ellie Greenwich, who thought that he had potential as an artist as well as a writer. His first hit *Solitary Man* entered the US Hot 100 in 1966 and, later that year, he made his US Top 10 debut with *Cherry Cherry*. Over the following twelve months, he achieved five more American Top 30 hits as a vocalist and, even more importantly, hit the big time as a composer: the Monkees recorded *I'm A Believer* and made it a long running No 1 smash on both sides of the Atlantic, and Diamond also penned their follow-up hit *A Little Bit Me, A Little Bit You*; also in '67, Lulu took his song *The Boat That I Row* into the British Top 10.
After a less glorious 1968, Diamond returned to fame as an artist in the summer of '69 with a US No 4 hit, *Sweet Caroline*. From then onwards, it was plain sailing. He cruised through the Seventies with a never ending string of hit singles and albums and, in the process, became the world's most highly paid performer. His three biggest and best Seventies hits were all in the first three years of the decade: *Cracklin' Rosie* (No 1 in US, No 3 in UK), *I Am ... I Said* (No 4 in both countries) and *Song Sung Blue* (No 1 in US, No 14 in UK) were the finest examples of Diamond's blend of folk pop and Las Vegas-style MOR; all were sung in his powerful, all-American voice. He won acclaim with two mid-Seventies albums, *Serenade* and *Beautiful Noise*, and reached the US No 1 position and the UK No 5 slot with 1978's *You Don't Bring Me Flowers*, a duet with Barbara Streisand. By now, Diamond's gradual move into the easy listening market was completed. In 1980 he starred with Sir Laurence Olivier in "The Jazz Singer", a remake of the classic 1927 Al Jolson movie. Diamond's soundtrack LP was an international smash, and contained three American Top 10 singles - *Love On The Rocks, Hello Again* and *America*. He was now established as an actor, as well as a singer and songwriter. Though very famous in Britain, it is strange to relate that he has never hit No 1 as an artist in the UK, but has got there twice as a writer: in addition to 1967's *I'm A Believer*, he penned *Red Red Wine*, a 1983 UK chart topper for UB40. There was less happy news for Diamond in 1984: he had to replace three songs and alter the cover artwork before CBS would release his *Primitive* album. It seemed that even megastars were not exempt from record company whip cracking. Bob MacDonald, 29 March 1985.
Born in 1943 in Brooklyn, Neil Diamond, like Neil Sedaka is a singer/songwriter who began with the Brill Building crowd, writing hits for Jay & The Americans, The Monkee's (*I'm a believer*) etc. and proved to have staying power: 27 of his albums charted in Billboard 1966-84 and his hits have included a duet with Barbra Streisand in 1978 on *You don't bring me flowers*. His songs have been covered by The Hollies, Elvis Presley, UB40 (a number one with *Red red wine* in the UK) and many others. *The jazz singer* in 1980 was the soundtrack of a remake the co-starred Sir Laurence Olivier; the album did well even though the film was heavily panned. *Beautiful noise* in 1976 was produced by Robbie Robertson, leading to an incongruous appearance in The Band's *Last waltz* film in 1977. (Donald Clarke, April 1989).

AMERICA
Tracks: / America / Songs of life.
7" Single: Released Apr '81, on Capitol, by EMI Records. Deleted Apr '84. Catalogue no: **CL 16197**

BE MINE TONIGHT
Tracks: / Be mine tonight / Right by you.
7" Single: Released Jul '82, on CBS, by CBS Records. Deleted Jul '85. Catalogue no: **CBS A 2580**

CRACKLIN' ROSIE
Tracks: / Cracklin' Rosie.
7" Single: Released Nov '70, on UNI, by MCA Records. Deleted '73. Catalogue no: **UN 529**

CRACKLIN' ROSIE (OLD GOLD)
Tracks: / Cracklin' Rosie / I am ... I said / Song sung blue.
CD 5": Released 30 May '89, on Old Gold, by Old Gold Records. Catalogue no: **OG 6149**

DANCING IN THE STREET
Tracks: / Dancing in the street / Jazz time.
7" Single: Released Mar '80, on CBS, by CBS Records. Deleted Mar '83. Catalogue no: **CBS 8322**

DESIREE
Tracks: / Desiree.
7" Single: Released Dec '77, on CBS, by CBS Records. Deleted '80. Catalogue no: **CBS 5869**

FOREVER IN BLUE JEANS
Tracks: / Forever in blue jeans.
7" Single: Released Mar '79, on CBS, by CBS Records. Deleted '82. Catalogue no: **CBS 7047**

HEARTLIGHT (SINGLE)
Tracks: / Heartlight.
7" Single: Released Nov '82, on CBS, by CBS Records. Deleted '85. Catalogue no: **A 2814**

HELLO AGAIN
Tracks: / Hello again / Amazed and confused.
7" Single: Released Feb '81, on Capitol, by EMI Records. Deleted '84. Catalogue no: **CL 16176**

I AM...I SAID
Tracks: / I am ... I said.
7" Single: Released May '71, on UNI, by MCA Records. Deleted '74. Catalogue no: **UN 532**

I DREAMED A DREAM
Tracks: / I dreamed a dream.
CD 5": Released Nov '87, on CBS, by CBS Records. Catalogue no: **651 201 9**
7" Single: Released Nov '87, on CBS, by CBS Records. Catalogue no: **651 201 7**

IF YOU KNOW WHAT I MEAN
Tracks: / If you know what I mean.
7" Single: Released Aug '76, on CBS, by CBS Records. Deleted '79. Catalogue no: **CBS 4398**

LOVE ON THE ROCKS
Tracks: / Love on the rocks / Acapulco.
7" Single: Released Nov '80, on Capitol, by EMI Records. Catalogue no: **CL 16173**

RAINY DAY SONG
Tracks: / Rainy day song / Be mine tonight.
7" Single: Released Feb '82, on CBS, by CBS Records. Deleted Feb '87. Catalogue no: **A 2033**

SEPTEMBER MORN
Tracks: / September morn / I'm a believer.
7" Single: Released Jan '80, on CBS, by CBS Records. Deleted Jan '85. Catalogue no: **CBS 8130**

SONG SUNG BLUE (SINGLE)
Tracks: / Song sung blue.
7" Single: Released May '72, on UNI, by MCA Records. Deleted '75. Catalogue no:- **UN 538**

STAND UP FOR LOVE
Tracks: / Stand up for love / Story of my life.
12" Single: Released Jul '86, on CBS, by CBS Records. Catalogue no: **TA 7225**
7" Single: Released Jul '86, on CBS, by CBS Records. Catalogue no: **A 7225**

SWEET CAROLINE (SINGLE)
Tracks: / Sweet Caroline (good times never seemed so good).
7" Single: Released Feb '71, on UNI, by MCA Records. Deleted '74. Catalogue no: **UN 531**

THIS TIME
Tracks: / This time / Beautiful noise / Baby can I hold you / Hooked on the memory of you.
12" Single: Released Oct '89, on CBS, by CBS Records. Catalogue no: **654 518 6**
7" EP: Released Oct '89, on CBS, by CBS Records. Catalogue no: **654 518 9**
CD 5": Released Oct '89, on CBS, by CBS Records. Catalogue no: **654 518 2**

YESTERDAY'S SONGS
Tracks: / Yesterday's songs / Guitar heaven.
7" Single: Released Nov '81, on CBS, by CBS Records. Deleted Nov '84. Catalogue no: **A 1755**

Diamond, O.J.

CRAZY WORDS
Tracks: / Crazy words.
12" Single: Released Sep '88, on John Dread Production, Catalogue no: **JDPD 011**

Diamond, Rick

IT'S ONLY PAPER THAT'S BURNING
Tracks: / It's only paper that's burning / I wanna hold you.
7" Single: Released Feb '80, on Epic, by CBS Records. Deleted '83. Catalogue no: **EPC 8269**

Diamonds

JUST CAN'T FIGURE IT OUT
Tracks: / Just can't figure it out / Keep it like it is.
7" Single: Released Apr '86, on Classy, Catalogue no: **CLASSY 2**

LITTLE DARLIN'
Tracks: / Little darlin'.
78 rpm: Released '57, on Mercury (Pye), Deleted '58. Catalogue no: **MT 148**

Diana

WHEN MUSIC HITS YOU
Tracks: / When music hits you / Feel no pain.
12" Single: Released May '82, on Oak Sound, Deleted '85. Catalogue no: **OSD 003**

Diane

MAMA LOVED JAMES DEAN
Tracks: / Mama loved James Dean / I believe.

7" Single: Released Oct '81, on OK, by Klub Records. Deleted Oct '84. Catalogue no: **OK 003**

Diaz Brothers

HERE WE GO AGAIN
Tracks: / Here we go again.
7" Single: Released Oct '88, on Bassment (USA), Catalogue no: **BASMX 1**

Diaz, Joanne

WORDS
Tracks: / Dream Bermuda.
7" Single: Released Nov '86, on Heartbreak, Deleted '87. Catalogue no: **HB 001**

Dibango, Manu

Biographical details: A singer, composer and arranger born in 1933 in the Cameroon; he also plays reeds and piano. He went to the newly independent Zaire in 1961 and stayed five years, playing with Kabaselle and The African Jazz, running a night club and playing on over 100 singles; he went to Paris with Kabaselle and made several LP's with him but determined to pursue own direction also made his own singles. His third album *Soul Makossa* became a world-wide dance-floor hit; the album was picked up by Atlantic and made number 79 on the Billboard chart, the single top 40 in 1973 and he became the first African to have an international hit. He returned to Africa as music director of Orchestre RTI, house band of Ivorian TV but has continued to tour, writing film scores and remaining an African superstar. (Donald Clarke, April 1989).

GORO CITY
Tracks: / Goro city / Reggae makossa.
12" Single: Released Jan '80, on Island, by Island Records. Deleted Jan '85. Catalogue no: **12 WIP 6556**

HAPPY FEELING (SINGLE)
Tracks: / Happy feeling / Goro city.
7" Single: Released Feb '81, on Island, by Island Records. Deleted '84. Catalogue no: **WIP 6672**
12" Single: Released Feb '81, on Island, by Island Records. Deleted '84. Catalogue no: **12WIP 6672**

MAKOSSA
Tracks: / Makossa / Gombo sauce.
12" Single: Released May '87, on Urban, by Polydor Ltd. Catalogue no: **URBX 2**
7" Single: Released May '87, on Urban, by Polydor Ltd. Deleted Jan '88. Catalogue no: **URB 2**

Dica...

IT ONLY TAKES A MINUTE
Tracks: / It only takes a minute.
12" Single: Released Nov '88, on Blue Chip, by Blue Chip Records. Catalogue no: **BLUECHIP 9 T**

Dice

I CAN'T TAKE IT
Tracks: / I can't take it / I can't take it (inst).
12" Single: Released Jan '87, on Production House (1), Catalogue no: **PNT 001**

YOU GOT ME RUNNING
Tracks: / You got me running / You got me running (inst dub mix).
12" Single: Released 13 Jun '87, on Production House (1), Catalogue no: **PNT 005**

Diced Carrots

OUR DOG ATE MY VOMIT Woof woof slurp cor lovely mix
Tracks: / Our dog ate my vomit.
12" Single: Released Mar '89, on GTO, Catalogue no: **AOURGH 1**

Dick And Bruce

BEAT THE BAT
Tracks: / Beat the bat.
12" Single: Released Mar '88, on MBS, by MBS Records. Catalogue no: **12MBS 4**
7" Single: Released Mar '88, on MBS, by MBS Records. Catalogue no: **MBS 004**

Dick & Deedee

MOUNTAIN'S HIGH, THE
Tracks: / Mountain's high, The.
7" Single: Released Oct '61, on London-American, Deleted '64. Catalogue no: **HLG 9408**

Dicken

SOLID GOLD
Tracks: / Solid gold / Beat speaks, The.
7" Single: Released Jul '86, on Mercury, by Phonogram Ltd. Deleted '87. Catalogue no: **MER 227**

Dickens, Charles

THAT'S THE WAY LOVE GOES
Tracks: / That's the way love goes.
7" Single: Released Jul '65, on Pye, Deleted '68. Catalogue no: **7 N 15887**

Dickie, Neville

ROBIN'S RETURN
Tracks: / Robin's return.
7" Single: Released Oct '69, on Major Minor, Deleted '72. Catalogue no: **MM 644**

Dickie, Tom

COMPETITION
Tracks: / Competition.
7" Single: Released May '81, on Mercury, by Phonogram Ltd. Deleted May '84. Catalogue no: **MER 69**

Dickies

Biographical details: This American band

comprised Billy Club, Karlos Kabellero, Stan Lee and Leonard Phillips.
In the later stages of the New Wave/punk revolution, the Dickies came to public attention in 1978-80 with a series of punk remakes of old classics. Because the punk phenomenon was ignored by US radio, this American's group's success was confined to the more broad minded British market. After flopping with a version of the Barry McGuire hit *Eve Of Destruction*, the Dickies scored a minor Christmas hit with their 1978 version of *Silent Night*, which reached No 47 in the UK. To those who took it too seriously, this 100 mph rendition of a traditional Christmas Carol was shocking and offensive; to those who viewed the group in the intended fun spirit, their records were delightful, entertaining and wonderfully pointless. Their sole UK Top Tenner came in Spring '79, when they hit No 7 with their romp through the children's favourite, *Banana Splits (Tra La La Song)*.
With relentless vigour, they recorded Black Sabbath's *Paranoid* and then their most ludicrously irreverent single of all, the Moody Blues' classic *Nights In White Satin*. These were minor hits and, also in '79, the Dickies scored a UK Top 20 album with *The Incredible Shrinking Dickies*. In December of that year, their idea was pirated by the UK Subs on a manic Top 40 rendition of *She's Not There*. By 1980, the novelty of the Dickies was wearing thin and, after two more very minor British hits, they passed into history. They were one of pop music's more pleasurable gimmicks. Bob MacDonald, 29 March 1985..

BANANA SPLITS (TRA LA LA SONG)
Tracks: / Banana splits (tra la la song).
7" Single: Released Apr '79, on A&M, by A&M Records. Deleted '82. Catalogue no: **AMS 7431**

FAN MAIL
Tracks: / Fan mail / I'm stuck in a pagoda with Tricia Toyota.
7" Single: Released Feb '80, on A&M, by A&M Records. Deleted '83. Catalogue no: **AMS 7504**

GIGANTOR
Tracks: / Gigantor / Bowling with Bedrock Barney.
7" Single: Released Jun '80, on A&M, by A&M Records. Deleted '88. Catalogue no: **AMS 7544**

NIGHTS IN WHITE SATIN
Tracks: / Nights in white satin.
7" Single: Released Sep '79, on A&M, by A&M Records. Deleted '82. Catalogue no: **AMS 7469**

PARANOID
Tracks: / Paranoid.
7" Single: Released Jul '79, on A&M, by A&M Records. Deleted '82. Catalogue no: **AMS 7368**

SILENT NIGHT
Tracks: / Silent night.
7" Single: Released Dec '78, on A&M, by A&M Records. Deleted '81. Catalogue no: **AMS 7403**

Dickson, Barbara

Biographical details: This British singer, who hails from Scotland, first hit the UK charts in early 1976 with *Answer Me*, a remake of a song that had been a 1953 No 1 for both David Whitfield and Frankie Laine. This reached No 9 and remained her biggest solo hit. Prior to this, she had attracted attention via her role in a Beatles-based musical, "John, Paul, George, Ringo...and Bert". It was appropriate, therefore, that her second hit came from the pens of Britain's modern masters of musical theatre, Tim Rice and Andrew Lloyd Webber. *Another Suitcase In Another Hall*gave Dickson a UK No 18 hit in early '77, and was taken from the original album version of "Evita". However, Dickson did not take part in the show's stage production when it finally opened eighteen months later. She might have wished she had done, for the singer's third chart success did not come until 1980.
After switching fromRSO to Epic Records, Dickson's flagging Career was rescued by songwriter/producer Mike Batt, who gave her a hit with *Caravan Song*, albeit No 41. This paved the way for *January February* which, with expert timing, entered the British chart in March 1980 and reached its No 11 peak in April. This was a very strong pop single with a big production, but Dickson failed to consolidate upon it. Her only subsequent major successes in the early Eighties were on the UK album listings: *The Barbara Dickson Album* reached No 7 in 1980 and the *All For A Song* compilation hit No 3 in 1982. After taking part in 1983's *Blood Brothers*, a London West End theatre production, she hit the UK No 1 slot for the first time in early '85 - *I Know Him So Well* was a duet smash with Elaine Page, penned by Tim Rice in collaboration with Benny and Bjorn of Abba fame. This archetypal theatrical love song was on top for four weeks, but once again the singer seemed unable to follow it - she did not even have her own recording contract at the time. Dickson's strong point has always been her crystal clear voice, with its superb pitch and charming quality. Yet she has never known whether to aim for the pop, soft rock or adult easy listening audience, and this has resulted in a strangely erratic career. Bob MacDonald, 29 March 1985.
Vocalist, songwriter born in 1947 in Scotland. She began in folk music and once sang in trio with Rab Noakes and Archie Fisher; she made solo albums on Decca in the early '70's, the sang Beatle songs in the Willy Russell show *John, Paul, George, Ringo and Bert* in 1973, accompanying herself on piano; it opened in Liverpool, moved to London and her beautiful voice was the best thing in it. She signed with RSO label and has had few really big hits but remains a popular club and TV act with many fans. Top 20 singles include *Answer me*, a revival of the 1956 hit by David Whitfield, and *Another suitcase, another hall* from the original album of Evita made before it opened. (Donald Clarke, April 1989).

ANOTHER SUITCASE ANOTHER HALL
Tracks: / Another suitcase in another hall.
7" Single: Released Feb '77, on MCA, by MCA Records. Deleted '80. Catalogue no: **MCA 266**

ANOTHER SUITCASE ANOTHER HALL (OLD GOLD)
Tracks: / Another suitcase in another hall.
7" Single: Released Jul '84, on Old Gold, by Old Gold Records. Catalogue no: **OG 9420**

ANSWER ME (SINGLE)
Tracks: / Answer me.
7" Single: Released Jan '76, on RSO, by Polydor Ltd. Deleted '79. Catalogue no: **2090 174**

CARAVAN SONG
Tracks: / Caravan song.
7" Single: Released Jan '80, on Epic, by CBS Records. Deleted '83. Catalogue no: **EPC 8103**
7" Single: Released May '85, on Portrait, by CBS Records. Catalogue no: **A 6169**

COMING ALIVE AGAIN
Tracks: / Coming alive again.
7" Single: Released Apr '89, on Valley, Deleted Sep '89. Catalogue no: **VYL 1**

FOR I KNOW HIM SO WELL
Tracks: / For I know him so well.
7" Single: Released Dec '84, on RCA, by BMG Records (UK). Catalogue no: **CHESS 3**
12" Single: Released Dec '84, on RCA, by BMG Records (UK). Catalogue no: **CHEST 3**

HERE WE GO
Tracks: / Here we go / Tonight.
7" Single: Released Nov '82, on Epic, by CBS Records. Deleted Nov '85. Catalogue no: **EPCA 2882**

I BELIEVE IN YOU
Tracks: / I believe in you / I know you, know me.
7" Single: Released Nov '82, on Epic, by CBS Records. Deleted Nov '85. Catalogue no: **EPC A 2305**

I DON'T BELIEVE IN MIRACLES
Tracks: / I don't believe in miracles / You don't know what you want.
7" Single: Released May '84, on Epic, by CBS Records. Catalogue no: **A 4413**

IF YOU'RE RIGHT
Tracks: / If you're right / Rivals.
7" Single: Released Apr '86, on K-Tel, by K-Tel Records. Catalogue no: **ONS 0008**

IN THE NIGHT
Tracks: / In the night / Now I don't know.
7" Single: Released Jun '80, on Epic, by CBS Records. Deleted '83. Catalogue no: **EPC 8593**

JANUARY, FEBRUARY
Tracks: / Island in the snow / January, February / Another suitcase in another hall / Answer me / Caravan song.
7" EP: Released Sep '82, on Epic, by CBS Records. Deleted '85. Catalogue no: **EPCA 40-2623**
7" Single: Released Mar '80, on Epic, by CBS Records. Deleted '83. Catalogue no: **EPC 8115**
7" Single: Released May '82, on Epic, by CBS Records. Catalogue no: **CBS 8115**

JANUARY, FEBRUARY (OLD GOLD)
Tracks: / January, February
7" Single: Released Jan '87, on Old Gold, by Old Gold Records. Catalogue no: **OG 9664**

KEEPING MY LOVE
Tracks: / Keeping my love / Find a better way.
7" Single: Released Mar '84, on Epic, by CBS Records. Catalogue no: **A 4191**

MY HEART LIES
Tracks: / My heart lies / You know it's me.
7" Single: Released Jun '81, on Epic, by CBS Records. Deleted Jun '84. Catalogue no: **EPCA 1293**

ONLY A DREAM IN RIO
Tracks: / Only a dream in Rio.
7" Single: Released 20 Feb '88, on Theobald Dickson Productions, Catalogue no: **TDPS 002**

ONLY SEVENTEEN
Tracks: / Only seventeen / You got me.
7" Single: Released Mar '81, on Epic, by CBS Records. Deleted Mar '84. Catalogue no: **EPC A 1058**

RUN LIKE THE WIND
Tracks: / Run like the wind / Forgotten time.
7" Single: Released Dec '81, on Epic, by CBS Records. Deleted Dec '84. Catalogue no: **EPCA 1858**

STILL IN THE GAME
Tracks: / Still in the game / Peter.
7" Single: Released Mar '85, on MCA, by MCA Records. Catalogue no: **MCA 955**

STOP IN THE NAME OF LOVE
Tracks: / Stop in the name of love / Find a better way.
7" Single: Released Jan '83, on Epic, by CBS Records. Catalogue no: **EPC A 3069**

TIME AFTER TIME
Tracks: / Time after time (Theme music from BBC series Animal Squad) / She moved through the fair.
7" Single: Released Sep '86, on K-Tel, by K-Tel Records. Catalogue no: **BABS 1**

Dickson, Don

PRAYING MANTIS
Tracks: / Praying mantis / Wake Up / When a man loves a woman / Andy.
12" Single: Released Mar '86, on Demon, by Demon Records. Catalogue no: **D 1041 T**

Dictators

Biographical details: At the time of their sole chart record, this American rock band consisted of Ross Funicello, Handsome Dick Manitoba, Mark Mendoza, Andy Shernoff, Ritchie Teeter and Petronius Woods.
The Dictators' first album, *The Dictators Go Girl Crazy*, was released in 1975. It made no impact, but their second LP, 1977's *Manifest Destiny*, yielded a minor UK chart single *Search And Destroy*. This was marketed as a punk rock record, at a time when the punk revolution was burgeoning in Britain. This quasi-anarchistic, contemptuous single had two runs on the UK Top 50 in the autumn of '77 - it reached No 49 in September and No 50 in October! Subsequent albums, such as 1978's *Blood Brothers*, returned the Dictators to obscurity. They remained active in the early Eighties, but few people showed interest in their inconsequential music. Bob MacDonald, 29 March 1985..

SEARCH AND DESTROY
Tracks: / Search and destroy.
7" Single: Released Sep '77, on Asylum, by WEA Records. Deleted '80. Catalogue no: **K 13091**

Did The Earth Move?

ONE IN A MILLION YOU
Tracks: / One in a million you.
7" Single: Released 20 Feb '88, on 3 Bears, by Three Bears Records. Catalogue no: **BEARS 1**

Diddley, Bo

Biographical details: This American singer, guitarist and songwriter, born Ellas McDaniel in Mississippi in 1928, is one of the most influential figures in the history of rock. He studied the classical violin for twelve years before making the guitar his primary instrument but, during his formative years, he also absorbed some very important influences from the rhythm and blues and church music spheres. In 1955 he gained a contract with Chess Records, the same label that simultaneously launched the career of Chuck Berry. Diddley soon gave the company a Top 10 success on the US R&B charts with an eponymous single, *Bo Diddley*. This seminal track incorporated all of the man's talents - an original, cheeky and witty theme and title (how many other artists had written a song about themselves?), enthusiastic vocals and, most importantly, an inventive and wildly exciting guitar style; the reverse side of the record, *I'm A Man*, was equally invigorating. Several more R&B hits followed during the remainder of the Fifties, and he also played on some of Berry's famous tracks. 1959 saw Diddley reach No 20 in the US with his novelty single *Say Man* - incredibly, this was the only pop hit of his entire career.
Diddley's influence really began to show itself in the early/mid-Sixties, particularly in Britain. Having been a part of the original mid-Fifties rock 'n' roll explosion, he played an important role in rock's next vital revolution - the Beatles-led British boom. The early repertoire of the Rolling Stones featured a host of Diddley numbers, and that up-and-coming group also helped to foster UK record buyers' interest in Chuck Berry. At about the same time, in the summer of '63, a superb version of *Bo Diddley* by the late Buddy Holly was issued and hit No 4 on the British charts. This paved the way for Diddley himself to score four UK chart albums in quick succession, plus a minor hit single with *Pretty Thing*. That song inspired the name of the Pretty Things, a British hitmaking group of the mid-Sixties. He also inspired another rising UK R&B combo, the Animals, to record *The Story Of Bo Diddley*, a lengthy and amusing account of their somewhat awkward meeting with him. Acts such as the Who and the Yardbirds also owed Diddley a considerable debt. The guitar riff on his self-titled song became one of the most imitated sounds in all of rock music, and formed the basis of many classic tracks by a variety of artists. He continued to record numerous albums during the Sixties and Seventies, but with very little success. It is very ironic that such an important figure has never enjoyed major record success as a performer on either side of Atlantic; he has always been seriously underrated in the public mind. One of his mid-Fifties R&B singles, *Who Do You Love*, became a UK Top 20 hit for Juicy Lucy in 1970, and has been covered by many other artists. Diddley still tours regularly, but is not a rich man. Bob MacDonald, 30 March 1985.
R&B singer, composer, guitarist, born Elias McDaniel in 1928 in Mississippi; one of the most influential R&B artists of the mid 50's, despite a surprisingly small number of chart entries, whose trademark 'hambone' or 'shave-and-a-haircut, six bits' beat has been imitated by countless lesser acts. He recorded for Checker/Chess 1955-74 and had eight R&B hits beginning with the two sided *Bo Diddley/I'm a man* in 1955. *Roadrunner* on Black Lion UK was made at Woodstock in the late 70.(D. Clarke 1989).

BO DIDDLEY (CD SINGLE)
Tracks: / Bo diddley / Road runner / You can't judge a book by the cover / Mona (I need you baby).
CD 5": Released Feb '89, on Charly, by Charly Records. Catalogue no: **CDS 11**

BO DIDDLEY (SINGLE)
Tracks: / Bo Diddley.
7" Single: Released Jul '85, on Chess (PRT), Deleted '88. Catalogue no: **CHES 4001**

HEY GOOD LOOKIN'
Tracks: / Hey good lookin'.
7" Single: Released Mar '65, on Chess, by Vogue Records. Deleted '68. Catalogue no: **CHESS 8000**

IT'S GREAT TO BE RICH (EP)
Tracks: / It's great to be rich.
12" Single: Released Jun '83, on Red Lightnin', by Red Lightning Records. Deleted Jun '89. Catalogue no: **RLEP 12 045**

PRETTY THING
Tracks: / Pretty thing.
7" Single: Released Oct '63, on Pye International, Deleted '66. Catalogue no: **7N 25217**

Die Doraus & Die

FRED FROM JUPITER
Tracks: / Fred from Jupiter.
7" Single: Deleted Mar '82. Catalogue no: **MUTE 019**

Die Erde

PARTY
Tracks: / Party.
12" Single: Released Jul '89, on Deutschland Strikeback, Catalogue no: **SBR 043T**

Die Haut

KARIBISCHER WESTERN
Tracks: / Karibischer western.
12" Single: Released Aug '83, on Zensor (Germany), Catalogue no: **9087**

Die Kreuzen

GONE AWAY

Tracks: / Gone away.
12" Single: Released Jul '89, on Touch & Go, by Touch & Go Records. Catalogue no: **TGEP 40**

Die Krupps

GOLDFINGER
Tracks: / Goldfinger / Zuei herzen.
7" Single: Released Jun '82, on WEA, by WEA Records. Catalogue no: **K 191390**
12" Single: Released Jun '84, on Quiet, by Quiet Records. Catalogue no: **PST 03**

MACHINERY OF JOY
Tracks: / Machinery of joy.
12" Single: Released May '89, on Mute, by Mute Records. Catalogue no: **12MUTE 101**
CD 5": Released Jun '89, on Mute, by Mute Records. Catalogue no: **CDMUTE 101**
7" Single: Released May '89, on Mute, by Mute Records. Catalogue no: **MUTE 101**

Die Monster Die

SPOCK'S BRAIN IS MISSING
Tracks: / Spock's brain is missing.
Note: Indie release on red vinyl.
7" Single: Released Oct '87, on Monkey Music, Catalogue no: **MONK 1**

Die Toten Hosen

SCHOENE BESCHERUNG
Tracks: / Schoene bescherung / Kneght ruprecat.
7" Single: Released Feb '84, on Totenkopf, Deleted '85. Catalogue no: **TOT 6**

Die Warzau

LAND OF THE FREE
Tracks: / Land of the free / Free radio Africa / Land of the free (machine mix) / I've gotta make sense.
7" Single: Released Apr '89, on Fiction Independence, Catalogue no: **WANTX 101**

WELCOME TO AMERICA
Tracks: / Welcome to America.
12" Single: Released Aug '89, on Fiction, by Fiction Records. Catalogue no: **FICSX 31**

Die Zimmermanner

ANJA
Tracks: / Anja / Anja (German version).
12" Single: Released Jan '84, on Cherry Red, by Cherry Red Records. Deleted '87. Catalogue no: **12 CHERRY 72**
7" Single: Released Jan '84, on Cherry Red, by Cherry Red Records. Deleted '87. Catalogue no: **CHERRY 72**

Die Zwei

COUNTRY BOY
Tracks: / Country boy / Fair-haired squaws / Western Union.
12" Single: Released Mar '85, on Zensor (Germany), Catalogue no: **ZSUK 02**

GRAPSCH
Tracks: / Grapsch.
12" Single: Released Apr '84, on Cherry Red, by Cherry Red Records. Deleted '87. Catalogue no: **12 EWS 2**

Died Pretty

BLUE SKY DAY
Tracks: / Blue sky day.
12" Single: Released Dec '86, on What Goes On, by What Goes On Records. Catalogue no: **GOES ON 11T**

NEXT TO NOTHING
Tracks: / Next to nothing.
12" Single: Released Nov '85, on What Goes On, by What Goes On Records. Catalogue no: **GOES ON 05T**

OUT OF MY HANDS
Tracks: / Out of my hands.
7" Single: Released Feb '89, on Au-Go-Go (Australia), by Au-Go-Go Records (Australia). Catalogue no: **K 617**

OUT OF THE UNKNOWN
Tracks: / Out of the unknown.
12" Single: Released Feb '85, on What Goes On, by What Goes On Records. Catalogue no: **GOES ON 01T**

WINTERLAND
Tracks: / Winterland.
7" Single: Released Jan '88, on Citadel (UK), by Citadel Records. Catalogue no: **CIT 035**

Diesel

GOIN' BACK TO CHINA
Tracks: / Goin' back to China / Remember the Romans.
7" Single: Released Jun '80, on Sonet, by Sonet Records. Deleted Jun '83. Catalogue no: **SON 2207**

Diesel, Johnny

DON'T NEED LOVE
Tracks: / Don't need love.

CD 5": Released Apr '89, on Chrysalis, by Chrysalis Records. Catalogue no: **CHSCD 3359**
12" Pic: Released Jul '89, on Chrysalis, by Chrysalis Records. Catalogue no: **CHSP 123359**
7" Single: Released Apr '89, on Chrysalis, by Chrysalis Records. Catalogue no: **CHS 3359**
12" Single: Released Apr '89, on Chrysalis, by Chrysalis Records. Catalogue no: **CHS 123359**

SOUL REVIVAL
Tracks: / Soul revival / Whose for better.
12" Pic: Released Aug '89, on Chrysalis, by Chrysalis Records. Catalogue no: **CHSP 123383**
7" Single: Released Jun '89, on Chrysalis, by Chrysalis Records. Catalogue no: **CHS 3383**
Cassingle: Released Jun '89, on Chrysalis, by Chrysalis Records. Catalogue no: **CHSMC 3383**
CD 5": Released Jun '89, on Chrysalis, by Chrysalis Records. Catalogue no: **CHSCD 3383**
12" Single: Released Jun '89, on Chrysalis, by Chrysalis Records. Catalogue no: **CHS 123383**

Diesel Park West

ALL THE MYTHS ON SUNDAY
Tracks: / All the myths on Sunday / Bent shattered and blue / Memo from Turner (Not on 7".) / Girl with the name, The (CD single only.).
12" Single: Released Jan '89, on Food, by Food Records. Deleted Aug '89. Catalogue no: **12FOOD 17**
CD 5": Released Jan '89, on Food, by Food Records. Deleted Aug '89. Catalogue no: **CDFOOD 17**
7" Single: Released Jan '89, on Food, by Food Records. Deleted Aug '89. Catalogue no: **FOOD 17**

HOODOO E.P., THE When the hoodoo comes (re-issue)
Tracks: / When the hoodoo comes / Fine Lilly fine / Mr. Soul (live) / Lazy me (12" only.) / Jingle jangle (CD single only.) / How strong love is (Poster Bag only.).
7" Single: Released Jul '89, on Food, by Food Records. Catalogue no: **203 436 7**
Cassingle: Released Jul '89, on Food, by Food Records. Catalogue no: **203 436 4**
CD 5": Released Jul '89, on Food, by Food Records. Catalogue no: **203 436 2**
7" Single: Released Jul '89, on Food, by Food Records. Catalogue no: **FOOD 20**
CD 5": Released Jul '89, on Food, by Food Records. Catalogue no: **CDFOOD 20**
12" Single: Released Jul '89, on Food, by Food Records. Catalogue no: **12FOOD 20**
Cassingle: Released Jul '89, on Food, by Food Records. Catalogue no: **TCFOOD 20**
12" Single: Released Jul '89, on Food, by Food Records. Catalogue no: **203 436 6**
12" Single: Released Jul '89, on Food, by Food Records. Catalogue no: **12FOODP 20**
12" Single: Released Jul '89, on Food, by Food Records. Catalogue no: **203 436 0**

JACKIE'S STILL SAD
Tracks: / Jackie's still sad / What about us / Friends and enemies / Wings of delight / Each little happy (CD single only.).
CD 5": Released Oct '88, on Food, by Food Records. Deleted Aug '89. Catalogue no: **CDFOOD 15**
7" Single: Released Oct '88, on Food, by Food Records. Deleted Aug '89. Catalogue no: **FOOD 15**
12" Single: Released Oct '88, on Food, by Food Records. Deleted Aug '89. Catalogue no: **12FOOD 15**

LIKE PRINCES DO
Tracks: / Like princes do / Wings of delight / Above these things (Not on 7".) / Endless chains (Not on 7".).
CD 5": Released Mar '89, on Food, by Food Records. Deleted Aug '89. Catalogue no: **CDFOOD 19**
12" Single: Released Mar '89, on Food, by Food Records. Deleted Aug '89. Catalogue no: **12FOOD 19**
7" Single: Released Mar '89, on Food, by Food Records. Deleted Aug '89. Catalogue no: **FOOD 19**
10" single: Released Mar '89, on Food, by Food Records. Deleted Aug '89. Catalogue no: **10FOODG 19**

WHEN THE HOODOO COMES
Tracks: / When the hoodoo comes / Above these things / Girl with the name, The ("Extra track on 12").
7" Single: Released Jul '87, on Food, by Food Records. Catalogue no: **FOOD 11**
12" Single: Released Jul '87, on Food, by Food Records. Catalogue no: **SNAK 11**

Dietrich, Marlene

Biographical details: A legend in her own lifetime, her voice, like her beautiful face, is unmistakeable. She was one of the few artists of her generation able to hold an audience in the palm of her hand from the moment she walked on stage. She was a perfectionist with an almost unique charisma.

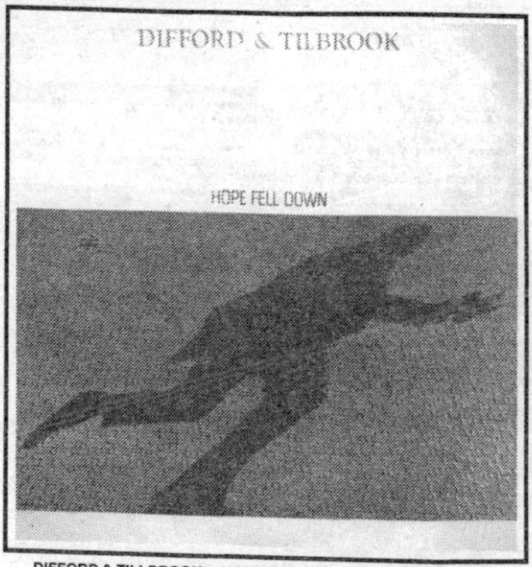

DIFFORD & TILLBROOK - HOPE FELL DOWN (Released on A & M)

LILY MARLENE (OLD GOLD)
Tracks: / Lily Marlene / Falling in love again.
7" Single: Released Jan '89, on Old Gold, by Old Gold Records. Catalogue no: **OG 9846**

Dif Juz

VIBRATING AIR
Tracks: / Vibrating air.
7" Single: Released Nov '81, on 4AD, by 4AD Records. Catalogue no: **BAD 116**

Differents

CAROLINE
Tracks: / Caroline / Be hard and boogie.
7" Single: Released Sep '82, on City, by City Records. Catalogue no: **CRO 1**
7" Single: Released Oct '82, on City, by City Records. Deleted Oct '85. Catalogue no: **CR 01**

Difford & Tillbrook

HOPE FELL DOWN
Tracks: / Hope fell down (edited verssion) / Action speaks faster (L.P. version).
7" Single: Released '84, on A&M, by A&M Records. Catalogue no: **AM 219**

LOVE'S CRASHING WAVES
Tracks: / Love's crashing waves.
7" Single: Released Jun '84, on A&M, by A&M Records. Deleted '87. Catalogue no: **AM 193**

Dig This Drill

CRANKING UP RELIGION
Tracks: / Cranking up religion.
12" Single: Released Feb '86, on Native (1), by Native Records. Catalogue no: **NTV 5**

Digance, Richard

DRINKING WITH ROSIE
Tracks: / Drinking with Rosie / Herbert the turbot.
7" Single: Released Feb '82, on Coast, by Coast Records. Catalogue no: **CODS 2**

JOURNEY
Tracks: / Journey / Halibut / Working class millionaire.
7" Single: Released Nov '80, on RCA, by BMG Records (UK). Deleted '83. Catalogue no: **RCA 11**

Diggle, Steve

SHUT OUT THE LIGHT
Tracks: / Shut out the light / 50 years of comparative wealth / Here comes the fire brigade.
7" Single: Released Feb '81, on Liberty, by EMI Records. Deleted '84. Catalogue no: **BP 389**

Digimix Hit Squad

HEY JACK
Tracks: / Hey Jack / Mean.
7" Single: Released May '88, on Digimix Music, by Digimix Music. Catalogue no: **DML 001**

Digital Dinosaurs

DON'T CALL US
Tracks: / Don't call us / Orders from the C.O..
7" Single: Released Nov '81, on Kamaflage, Deleted Nov '84. Catalogue no: **KAM 2**

Digital Emotion

GET UP ACTION
Tracks: / Get up action / Do you wanna funk.
12" Single: Released May '84, on Carrere, Catalogue no: **CART 319**

Digital pressure

GRIP OF THE GLOVE
Tracks: / Grip of the glove.
7" Single: Released Aug '85, on Fragile, Catalogue no: **FR 19**

Digital Underground

DOOWATCHYALIKE
Tracks: / Doowatchyalike / Hip-hop doll.
12" Single: Released Aug '89, on BCM Records, Catalogue no: **BCM 330 X**
CD 5": Released Aug '89, on BCM Records, Catalogue no: **BCM 330 CD**
7" Single: Released Aug '89, on BCM Records, Catalogue no: **BCM 330**

Dignitary Stylish

SLACKNESS DUN
Tracks: / Slackness dun.
12" Single: Released Nov '88, on Taurus, Catalogue no: **UNKNOWN**

Digvisdrill

SPELL SURVIVAL
Tracks: / Spell survival.
12" Single: Released Feb '87, on Native (1), by Native Records. Catalogue no: **12 NTV 19**

Dillard & Clark

AIN'T IT GOOD TO BE FREE?
Tracks: / Ain't it good to be free / Bo Diddley put the rock in rock 'n' roll.
7" Single: Released Aug '84, on New Rose (1), by New Rose Records. Catalogue no: **NEW 42**

Dillard, Rodney

SILVER DOLLAR CITY
12" Single: Released Jan '86, on Champagne (DJM), Catalogue no: **CHS 12501**

Dillinger

COCAINE
Tracks: / Cocaine.
12" Single: Released Sep '85, on Champagne (DJM), Catalogue no: **CHM 12/1001**
12" Single: Released '87, on UNKNOWN, Deleted Jun '89. Catalogue no: **CHS 501**

COCAINE IN MY BRAIN
Tracks: / Cocaine in my brain / Buckin'ham.
7" Single: Released Jul '81, on Island, by Island Records. Catalogue no: **WIP 6416**

FIVE MAN ARMY
Tracks: / Five man army / Five man dub.
7" Single: Released Feb '82, on Oak Sound. Catalogue no: **OSD 002**
12" Single: Released Feb '82, on Oak Sound. Catalogue no: **OSDD 002**

MELTING POT
Tracks: / Melting pot / Hearsay.
7" Single: Released May '81, on A&M, by A&M Records. Deleted May '84. Catalogue no: **AMS 8133**
12" Single: Released May '81, on A&M, by A&M Records. Deleted May '84. Catalogue no: **AMSP 8133**

REGGAE BEAT
Tracks: / Reggae beat / Daddy Joseph.
7" Single: Released Sep '81, on A&M, by A&M Records. Deleted '84. Catalogue no: **AMS 8156**

TRIBAL WAR (SINGLE)
Tracks: / Tribal war / War dubbing.
12" Single: Released Nov '83, on 10 Records, by Virgin Records. Deleted '86. Catalogue no: **TEN 11-12**

Dillon, Sandy

FLOWERS
Tracks: / Flowers.
7" Single: Released Aug '85, on Mainman. Catalogue no: **SANDY 1**

Dilruba

SHAAL MAR-KAY (SINGLE)
Tracks: / Shaal mar-kay.
7" Single: Released Jan '89, on Multitone, by Multitone Records/Savera. Catalogue no: **BHA 1**
12" Single: Released Nov '88, on Multitone, by Multitone Records/Savera. Catalogue no: **12 BHA 1**

Dimensions

FANTASY
Tracks: / Fantasy.
12" Single: Released Dec '88, on Warrior, by Warrior Records. Catalogue no: **WRR 12004**

Dimples

BEAUTIFUL FEELING
Tracks: / Beautiful feeling / Experimental.
12" Single: Released Aug '88, on Orbitone, by Orbitone Records. Catalogue no: **OR 1231**
12" Single: Released May '82, on Sunburn, by Orbitone Records. Catalogue no: **SBD 04**

CONFIDENTIAL
Tracks: / Confidential / Confidential (piano version).
12" Single: Released May '82, on Orbitone, by Orbitone Records. Catalogue no: **ORB 2**

Dimucci, Dion

AND THE NIGHT STOOD STILL
Tracks: / And the night stood still / Tower of love / Wanderer, The.
CD 5": Released Sep '89, on Arista, by BMG Records (UK). Catalogue no: **662408**

KING OF THE NEW YORK STREETS
Tracks: / King of the New York streets / Wanderer.
CD 5": Released 24 Jul '89, on Arista, by BMG Records (UK). Catalogue no: **662 556**
7" Single: Released 24 Jul '89, on Arista, by BMG Records (UK). Catalogue no: **112 556**
12" Single: Released 24 Jul '89, on Arista, by BMG Records (UK). Catalogue no: **612 556**

Dinah Rod & The Drains

SOMEBODY'S IN MY DRAINS
Tracks: / Somebody's in my drains.
7" Single: Released '83, on Secret, by Secret Records. Deleted May '88. Catalogue no: **SHH 146**
12" Single: Released '83, on Secret, by Secret Records. Catalogue no: **SHH 146 12**

Dinger

AIR OF MYSTERY
Tracks: / Air of mystery.
7" Single: Released '85, on Face Value. Catalogue no: **FVR 221A**

Dingo

HOUSE WITHOUT A NAME, THE
Tracks: / House without a name, The / Tell me now.
" Single: Released May '86, on Sonet, by Sonet Records. Catalogue no: **SON 2304**
12" Single: Released Sep '86, on Sonet, by Sonet Records. Catalogue no: **SONL 2304**

Dinner Ladies

MUSCLE IN THE BUD
Tracks: / Muscle in the bud / Behind glass.
7" Single: Released Sep '87, on Hannibal, by Hannibal Records. Catalogue no: **HNS 704**

Dinning, Mark

TEEN ANGEL
Tracks: / Teen angel.
7" Single: Released Mar '60, on MGM, by Polydor Ltd. Deleted '63. Catalogue no: **MGM 1053**

Dino

24/7
Tracks: / 24/7 / Night time lovekind (vocal) / Night time lovekind.
7" Single: Released 20 Mar '89, on 4th & Broadway, by Island Records. Catalogue no: **BRW 128**
12" Single: Released 20 Mar '89, on 4th & Broadway, by Island Records. Catalogue no: **12 BRW 128**

I LIKE IT
Tracks: / I like it / I like it (percapella) (On 7" only) / I like it (house vocal) (On 12" only) / I like it (sample dub) (On 12" only).
CD 5": Released Aug '89, on Island, by Island Records. Catalogue no: **CID 435**
Cassingle: Released Aug '89, on Island, by Island Records. Catalogue no: **CIS 435**
7" Single: Released Aug '89, on Island, by Island Records. Catalogue no: **IS 435**
12" Single: Released Aug '89, on Island, by Island Records. Catalogue no: **12 IS 435**

Dinosaur

GO BANG
Tracks: / Go bang.
12" Single: Released Sep '87, on Sleeping Bag, by Sleeping Bag Records. Catalogue no: **SLXO**

REPULSION
Tracks: / Repulsion.
7" Single: Released Mar '86, on Homestead. Catalogue no: **HMS 032**

Dinosaur Jnr

DINOSAUR JNR
Tracks: / Dinosaur Jnr.
CD 5": Released Dec '88, on SST (USA), by SST Records (USA). Catalogue no: **SSTCD 152**

FREAK SCENE (WHAT A MESS)
Tracks: / Freak scene (what a mess).
7" Single: Released Sep '88, on Blast First, by Blast First Records. Catalogue no: **BFFP 30**
12" Single: Released Sep '88, on Blast First, by Blast First Records. Catalogue no: **BFFP 30T**

JUST LIKE HEAVEN
Tracks: / Just like heaven.
CD 5": Released May '89, on Blast First, by Blast First Records. Catalogue no: **BFFP 047 CD**
7" Single: Released May '89, on Blast First, by Blast First Records. Catalogue no: **BFFP 047 S**
12" Single: Released Feb '89, on Blast First, by Blast First Records. Catalogue no: **BFFP 047 T**

Dinosaur L

BANGS AGAIN
Tracks: / Bangs again (remix) / Go bang (original).
7" Single: Released Jun '88, on Citybeat, by Beggars Banquet Records. Catalogue no: **CBX 1205**

GO BANG
Tracks: / Go bang.
12" Single: Released Jun '86, on Citybeat, by Beggars Banquet Records. Catalogue no: **CBE 1205**

Dinzee, Pietro

WHEN YOU GET WHAT YOU WANTED
Tracks: / When you get what you wanted.
7" Single: Released '83, on Priority, by Priority Records. Catalogue no: **P 2**
12" Single: Released '83, on Priority, by Priority Records. Catalogue no: **PX 2**

Dio

Biographical details: This heavy metal group is led and named after its American vocalist Ronnie James Dio. They released their first album in 1983. Back in 1974, Dio had been with a New York band called Elf, who had supported Deep Purple on tour. Purple's master guitarist Ritchie Blackmore left the famous rock group in '75, and used members of Elf to form his new group Rainbow. With Dio on vocals, Rainbow chalked up four UK Top 20 albums during 1975-8; the singer was then replaced in the group by Graham Bonnet. Dio moved onto Black Sabbath, where he replaced the notorious Ozzy Osbourne. Dio quit that band in November 1982, and took Sabbath drummer Vinnie Appice with him. They formed a new quartet simply called Dio, another of the members being Jimmy Bain, who had been a contemporary of Dio in Rainbow.
Dio's debut LP *Holy Diver* was issued in 1983. Predictably (in view of the group members' history), this LP was highly competent but unoriginal heavy metal. Equally predictably, it entered the UK album charts at a very high position and then fell quickly downwards - hard rock fans tended to loyally purchase albums within a short time of release, but their rejection by daytime radio resulted in a lack of crossover appeal to sustain chart momentum. 1984's *The Last In Line* LP experienced a similar sales pattern. That album yielded the group's first UK Top 40 single *Mystery*, a fine vehicle for Ronnie's powerful vocals. Bob MacDonald, 30 March 1985.
Born Ronald James Padavona, the heavy rock vocalist began forming groups in school in Portsmouth, New Hampshire and changed his name to Ronnie Dio. Ronnie and the Prophets made flop singles; in 1967 with guitarist Nick Pantas (later killed in a car crash) he formed the Electric Elves, later called just Elf.
Deep Purple's Ritchie Blackmore borrowed the group (ousting its new guitarist Steve Edwards) for Ritchie Blackmore's Rainbow in 1975 while still with Purple struck up a songwriting partnership with Dio; Rainbow became a fulltime concern. Dio left in 1979 to join Black Sabbath, where his writing was good for that group, then left it to form his own band in 1982, taking drummer Vinnie Appice with him. The new group called Dio included ex-Rainbow bassist Jimmy Bain and Irish guitarist Vivian Campbell, later adding keyboardist Claude Schnell. Dio's writing of songs rather than riffs brought the band more radio play than most in the genre. (Donald Clarke, April 1989).

HIDING THE RAINBOW
Tracks: / Hiding the rainbow.
12" Single: Released May '86, on Vertigo, by Phonogram Ltd. Deleted '87. Catalogue no: **DIOP 710**

HOLY DIVER (SINGLE)
Tracks: / Holy diver / Evil eyes / Don't talk.
7" Single: Released '83, on Vertigo, by Phonogram Ltd. Catalogue no: **DIO 1**

HUNGRY FOR HEAVEN
Tracks: / Hungry for heaven / Hide in the rainbow / Shine on the night (Extra track available on 12" version only.) / Egypt-the chains are on (Extra track available on 12" version only.).
12" Single: Released May '86, on Vertigo, by Phonogram Ltd. Deleted '87. Catalogue no: **DIO 712**
7" Single: Released Nov '85, on Vertigo, by Phonogram Ltd. Deleted '88. Catalogue no: **DIO 6**
7" Single: Released May '86, on Vertigo, by Phonogram Ltd. Deleted '87. Catalogue no: **DIO 7**
7" Set: Released May '86, on Vertigo, by Phonogram Ltd. Deleted '87. Catalogue no: **DIOEP 7**

I COULD HAVE BEEN A DREAMER
Tracks: / I could have been a dreamer / Night people / Sunset superman (Track on 12" version only.).
12" Single: Released Jul '87, on Vertigo, by Phonogram Ltd. Deleted Dec '87. Catalogue no: **DIO 812**
7" Single: Released Jul '87, on Vertigo, by Phonogram Ltd. Deleted Dec '87. Catalogue no: **DIO 8**

MYSTERY
Tracks: / Mystery.
7" Single: Released '84, on Vertigo, by Phonogram Ltd. Catalogue no: **DIO 4**
7" Pic: Released '84, on Vertigo, by Phonogram Ltd. Catalogue no: **DIOP 4**

RAINBOW IN THE DARK
Tracks: / Rainbow in the dark.
7" Single: Released '83, on Vertigo, by Phonogram Ltd. Catalogue no: **DIO 2**

ROCK'N'ROLL CHILDREN
Tracks: / Rock 'n' roll children.
7" Single: Released Aug '85, on Vertigo, by Phonogram Ltd. Deleted '88. Catalogue no: **DIO 5**

WE ROCK
Tracks: / We rock.
7" Single: Released '84, on Vertigo, by Phonogram Ltd. Catalogue no: **DIO 3**

Dion

Biographical details: This American singer, born Dion Di Mucci in the Bronx, New York, made his first professional TV appearance at the age of 15. Four years later, in 1958, he became lead singer of a vocal group, Dion and the Belmonts. They were names after Belmont Avenue, the Bronx's main thoroughfare. After flopping with their first single, they quickly began a memorable run of American hits, starting with *I Wonder Why*. This hit the US No 22 position in the summer of '58, and showed that Dion's group were adept performers of the doo-wop vocal style, a rhythm and blues singing sound that had previously been the domain of black groups. 1959's *A Teenager In Love* (No 5 in US, successfully covered in UK by Marty Wilde and Craig Douglas) and 1960's *Where Or When* (No 3 in US) made Dion and the Belmonts the top white vocal group of the rock 'n' roll era in America, although they were barely known in Britain. Tastefully using their rock and R&B influences, they were perfect purveyors of teenage angst-ridden pop.
Dion left the Belmonts in late 1960 to pursue a solo career. Although they chalked up a pair of US Top 30 singles without him, it was Dion who emerged as the star act. After a false start with the US Top 20 hit *Lonely Teenager* and some flop singles, Dion achieved his first No 1 in late '61 with the delightfully catchy *Runaround Sue*, and followed it with another classic single, *The Wanderer*, which hit the US No 2 spot. In Britain, *Runaround Sue* peaked at No 11 and *The Wanderer* went to No 10. Both were great uptempo pop records, with a rocky feel. Further UK success eluded him but, in his native America, he enjoyed a further six Top Tenners. The biggest of these were *Lovers Who Wander* (No 3) and *Ruby Baby* (No 2). It was no coincidence, however, that his final biggie *Drip Drop* (No 6) ended his chart career just as the Beatles were invading America - suddenly, Sion and his ilk were passe. However, a drugs problem was also partly to blame for Di Mucci's plunge into obscurity. After spending the mid-Sixties trying his hand at bluesy material and attempting an unsuccessful Belmonts reunion, Dion achieved a one-off comeback at the end of 1968 with *Abraham, Martin And John*. This saw him joining the folk protest movement, and it reached No 4 on the US chart. Penned by Dick Holler, this song was a tribute to three assassinated American greats: Abraham Lincoln, Martin Luther King and John F Kennedy. Dion's single failed in Britain, but a soulful 1970 rendition by Marvin Gaye hit the UK Top 10. Despite strenuous efforts, the Seventies were a totally blank period for Dion in commercial terms. It seemed that the public did not want to know Dion, the modern singer/songwriter; they only wanted to listen to the oldies, as shown by a 1976 re-issue of *The Wanderer*, which hit the UK No 16 slot, and successful 1978 remakes of Dion hits by Leif Garrett (*Runaround Sue*, No 13 in US) and Showaddywaddy (*I Wonder Why*, No 2 in UK). Bob MacDonald, 30 March 1985.
Dion DiMucci was lead singer of Dion & The Belmonts, formed in 1958 in NYC with second tenor Fred Milano, first tenor Angelo D'Aleo and baritone Carlo Mastangelo, all from the Bronx. Named after local Belmont Avenue, they had seven top 40 hits in two years with a polished image as besuited Italian-Americans hoping to equal the best of black groups: *A teenager in love* epitomised their doo wop influenced sound (covers by Craig Douglas and Marty Wilde in the UK). Dion left the group, which had two top 30 hits as a trio; he has had a successful solo career and occasionally re-united with them. (Donald Clarke, April 1989).

AND THE NIGHT STOOD STILL
Tracks: / And the night stood still / Wanderer.
CD 5": Released Jun '89, on Arista, by BMG Records (UK). Catalogue no: **662229**
7" Single: Released Jun '89, on Arista, by BMG Records (UK). Catalogue no: **112408**
12" Single: Released Jun '89, on Arista by BMG Records (UK). Catalogue no: **612408**

LONELY TEENAGER
Tracks: / Lonely teenager.
7" Single: Released Jan '61, on Top Rank (1), Deleted '64. Catalogue no: **JAR 521**

RUNAROUND SUE
Tracks: / Runaround Sue / Runaway girl.
7" Single: Released Nov '61, on Top Rank (1), Deleted '64. Catalogue no: **JAR 586**
7" Single: Released '81, on RCA, by BMG Records (UK). Catalogue no: **GOLD 526**

RUNAROUND SUE (OLD GOLD)
Tracks: / Runaround Sue / Lonely teenager.
7" Single: Released Jun '88, on Old Gold

by Old Gold Records. Catalogue no: **OG 9404**

TEENAGER IN LOVE
Tracks: / Teenager in love / I wonder why.
7" Single: Released Jun '59, on London-American, Deleted '62. Catalogue no: **HLU 8874**

TEENAGER IN LOVE (OLD GOLD)
Tracks: / Teenager in love / Where or when.
7" Single: Released Jun '88, on Old Gold, by Old Gold Records. Catalogue no: **OG 9405**

WANDERER, THE (OLD GOLD)
Tracks: / Wanderer, The / Lovers who wander.
CD 5": Released 27 Feb '89, on Old Gold, by Old Gold Records. Catalogue no: **OG 6112**
7" Single: Released Jun '88, on Old Gold, by Old Gold Records. Catalogue no: **OG 9403**

WANDERER, THE
Tracks: / Wanderer, The / Runaround Sue / Teenager in love.
7" Single: Released Feb '62, on H.M.V., by EMI Records. Deleted '65. Catalogue no: **POP 971**
7" Single: Released '81, on Laurie, by BMG Records (UK). Catalogue no: **GOLD 535**
7" Single: Released May '76, on Philips, by Phonogram Ltd. Deleted '79. Catalogue no: **6146 700**

WAY YOU DO THE THINGS YOU DO
Tracks: / Way you do the things you do, The / Hey my love.
7" Single: Released '87, on Aura Records, by Aura Records. Deleted '88. Catalogue no: **AUS 142**

WE DON'T TALK ANYMORE
Tracks: / We don't talk anymore.
7" Single: Released '83, on Aura Records, by Aura Records. Deleted '88. Catalogue no: **AUS 139**

Dionne

COME GET MY LOVIN'
Tracks: / Come get my loving.
12" Single: Released Nov '88, on Big Shot, Catalogue no: **BR 126035**
7" Single: Released Sep '89, on Citybeat, by Beggars Banquet Records. Catalogue no: **CBE 745**
12" Single: Released Sep '89, on Citybeat, by Beggars Banquet Records. Catalogue no: **CBE 1245**

Diplomats

I'LL KEEP HOLDING ON
Tracks: / I'll keep holding on.
7" Single: Released Nov '82, on Exchange, by Exchange Records. Catalogue no: **EX 1**

Dire Straits

Biographical details: This British band, at the time of their greatest success, consisted of Alan Clark, John Illsley, Mark Knopfler, Hal Lindes and Pick Withers. The band's name was inspired by the state of their financial affairs at the time of formation.

Dire Straits were founded in 1977 by singer, guitarist and songwriter Mark Knopfler. Together with drummer Withers (the most experienced of the founder members) and bassist Illsley, they pooled their resources and spent #120 on a demo version of their debut single *Sultans Of Swing*. It won airplay on Charlie Gillett's BBC Radio London show, and they quickly became one of the most talked about groups on the London pub and club circuit. In 1978 their self-titled debut album was issued, but its real success came the following year, when the polished version of *Sultans Of Swing* became a Top 10 single in both the UK and the US. Though the band's sound was unfashionable on both sides of the Atlantic, this fact worked ironically in their favour - Mark's superb songwriting, distinctive guitar style and rough, Dylan-esque vocals were like a breath of fresh air. It was clear from the outset that Mark Knopfler was, in every sense, the elader - not only did he write all the material, he later took over thr role of producer. He turned 30 years old during '79 but, despite this and his balding hair, he was a comparative newcomer to the world of full-time musicianship.

Dire Straits' follow-up LP *Communique* was released in June 1979 and, compared with its predecessor, was a musical and commercial disappointment. Its content was predictable, and David Knopfler left the band to pursue an unsuccessful solo career. Mark, who was now contributing his guitar stylings to the albums of such luminaries as Bob Dylan and Steely Dan, brought in Hal Lindes and guest keyboards playr Roy Bittan for 1980's *Making Movies* LP. The combo's career was immediately revitalised, especially on account of the beautiful ballad *Romeo And Juliet*, which was a UK Top 10 single in early '81. *Making Movies* logged over 100 weeks on the British LP chart, and was still making return visits in the mid-Eighties.

For 1982's *Love Over Gold* album, Alan Clark became Dire Straits' permanent keyboards player. This five-piece line-up took the group to even greater commercial heights, with *Love Over Gold* - consisting of five lengthy Knopfler compositions - going to No 1 in Britain and yielding the UK No 2 single *Private Investigations*. Drummer Pick Withers was replaced in 1983 by Terry Williams. 1985 saw the group back at No 1 on the UK album chart with *Brothers In Arms*. Their fanatical passion for touring - captured on the totally live 1984 LP *Alchemy - Dire Straits Live* - was summed up by their huge 1985-6 world tour, which lasted for ten months and included over 200 shows. Although Dire Straits have never been in step with the musical trends of the Eighties, the sheer talent of Mark Knopfler has made them one of the world's top concert attractions. Bob MacDonald, 21 June 1985.
A rock band formed in Deptford by former journalist and teacher turned guitarist, singer and songwriter Mark Knopfler, with bassist John Illsley, brother David Knopfler on rhythm guitar and Pick Withers on drums, named after perennial financial state. Their break came when Charlie Gillett featured them on his radio show; their eponymous debut album in 1978 epitomised their intimate sound, utterly unlike then-prevailing Punk: laconic vocals were influenced by J J Cale and Bob Dylan, and Knopfler's fluid guitar work has made him the most celebrated UK guitarist since Eric Clapton; the album included *Sultans of swing* (top 10 UK and top 5 USA), which some consider still to be their finest hour. *Communique* in 1979 was more of the same, but rivalry led to the sacking of brother Dave in 1980 (he's had a solo career with several albums), replaced by Hal Lindes while Alan Clark was added on keyboards. Meanwhile Dylan recruited Knopfler and Withers for *Slow train coming*, panned for lyrics but hailed as Dylan's best sounding album. *Love over gold* in 1983 included Tommy Mandel on keyboards and Terry Williams (ex-Rockpile) on drums. *Alchemy* is a live 2-disc souvenir; *Brothers in arms* was a number one album in the USA, with a Sting guest vocal on *Money for nothing*. Knopfler has produced albums for others, recorded solo and composed film scores. (Donald Clarke, April 1989)h.

BROTHERS IN ARMS (7" SET)
7" Set: Released Nov '85, on Vertigo, by Phonogram Ltd. Deleted '87. Catalogue no: **DSTRD 11**

BROTHERS IN ARMS (SINGLE)
Tracks: / Brothers in arms.
7" Set: Released Nov '85, on Vertigo, by Phonogram Ltd. Deleted '87. Catalogue no: **DSTRD 11**
10" single: Released Oct '85, on Vertigo, by Phonogram Ltd. Deleted '86. Catalogue no: **DSTR 1110**
7" Single: Released Oct '85, on Vertigo, by Phonogram Ltd. Deleted '87. Catalogue no: **DSTR 11**
12" Single: Released Oct '85, on Vertigo, by Phonogram Ltd. Deleted '87. Catalogue no: **DSTR 1112**

LADY WRITER
Tracks: / Lady writer.
7" Single: Released Jul '79, on Vertigo, by Phonogram Ltd. Deleted '82. Catalogue no: **6059 230**

LOVE OVER GOLD (LIVE)
Tracks: / Love over gold (live).
7" Single: Released Feb '84, on Vertigo, by Phonogram Ltd. Deleted '87. Catalogue no: **DSTRA12**

MONEY FOR NOTHING (SINGLE)
Tracks: / Money for nothing / Love over gold (live).
7" Single: Released Jun '85, on Vertigo, by Phonogram Ltd. Deleted Mar '88. Catalogue no: **DSTR 10**
7" Pic: Released Jul '85, on Vertigo, by Phonogram Ltd. Deleted '86. Catalogue no: **DSPIC 10**
12" Single: Released Jun '85, on Vertigo, by Phonogram Ltd. Deleted Mar '88. Catalogue no: **DSTR 1012**
10" single: Released Jun '85, on Vertigo, by Phonogram Ltd. Deleted '87. Catalogue no: **DSTR 1010**

PRIVATE INVESTIGATIONS
Tracks: / Private investigations / Badges, posters, stickers, T-shirts.
7" Single: Released Sep '82, on Vertigo, by Phonogram Ltd. Deleted '85. Catalogue no: **DSTR 1**

ROMEO & JULIET
Tracks: / Romeo and Juliet / Solid rock.
7" Single: Released Oct '84, on Vertigo, by Phonogram Ltd. Deleted 31 May '89. Catalogue no: **MOVIE 1**

SKATEAWAY
Tracks: / Skateaway / Expresso love.
7" Single: Released Apr '81, on Vertigo, by Phonogram Ltd. Deleted '84. Catalogue no: **MOVIE 2**

SO FAR AWAY
Tracks: / So far away / Walk of life.
10" single: Released Apr '85, on Vertigo, by Phonogram Ltd. Deleted '86. Catalogue no: **DSTR 910**
7" Single: Released Apr '85, on Vertigo, by Phonogram Ltd. Deleted Mar '88. Catalogue no: **DSTR 9**
12" Single: Released Apr '85, on Vertigo, by Phonogram Ltd. Deleted Mar '88. Catalogue no: **DSTR 912**

SULTANS OF SWING
Tracks: / Sultans of swing / Eastbound train / Southbound again.
12" Single: Released Nov '82, on Vertigo, by Phonogram Ltd. Deleted Mar '88. Catalogue no: **DSTR 312**
7" Single: Released Nov '82, on Vertigo, by Phonogram Ltd. Deleted Feb '89. Catalogue no: **6059 206**

SULTANS OF SWING (RE-RELEASE)
Tracks: / Sultans of swing / Portobello belle (live) / Romeo and Juliet (Only on CD single and 12" version.) / Money for nothing (Only on CD single and 12" version.).
CD 5": Released '88, on Vertigo, by Phonogram Ltd. Catalogue no: **DSCD 15**
7" Single: Released Nov '88, on Vertigo, by Phonogram Ltd. Deleted 31 May '89. Catalogue no: **DSTR 15**
12" Single: Released '88, on Vertigo, by Phonogram Ltd. Deleted 31 May '89. Catalogue no: **DSTR 1512**

TUNNEL OF LOVE
Tracks: / Tunnel of love / Tunnel of love (part 2).
7" Single: Released Oct '81, on Vertigo, by Phonogram Ltd. Deleted '84. Catalogue no: **MOVIE 3**

TWISTING BY THE POOL
Tracks: / Twisting by the pool / Two young lovers.
12" Single: Released Jan '83, on Vertigo, by Phonogram Ltd. Deleted 31 Jul '89. Catalogue no: **DSTR 212**
7" Single: Released Jan '83, on Vertigo, by Phonogram Ltd. Deleted 31 Jul '89. Catalogue no: **DSTR 2**

WALK OF LIFE
Tracks: / Walk of life / Two young lovers / Sultans of swing-live (Extra track on 12" version only.) / Sultans of swing (extra track on double pack only) / Eastbound train (extra track on double pack only).
12" Single: Released Dec '85, on Vertigo, by Phonogram Ltd. Deleted Jul '87. Catalogue no: **DSTR 1212**
7" Set: Released Dec '85, on Vertigo, by Phonogram Ltd. Deleted '87. Catalogue no: **DSTRD 12**
7" Single: Released Dec '85, on Vertigo, by Phonogram Ltd. Deleted Feb '89. Catalogue no: **DSTR 12**

YOUR LATEST TRICK
Tracks: / Your latest trick / Irish boy, The / Long road, The (Extra track on 12" version only.).
12" Single: Released May '86, on Vertigo, by Phonogram Ltd. Deleted '87. Catalogue no: **DSTR 1312**
7" Single: Released May '86, on Vertigo, by Phonogram Ltd. Deleted '87. Catalogue no: **DSTR 13**

Direct Drive

Biographical details: This British band consist of Peter Quinton, Helen Rogers, Mick Ward and Robert Williams.

Direct Drive first began to attract attention in UK clubs with their 1982 singles, *Don't Depend On Me* and *I'm The One*. During this period, the group included talented keyboards and synthesiser player Paul Hardcastle. He left in '83, later achieving great success as a solo artist and remixer. In that same year, Helen joined as lead vocalist. Having been discovered by one of London's leading all-round musical experts, Charlie Gillett, the band spent 1983 and 1984 consolidating their dane appeal.

Direct Drive enjoyed their first success on the UK national chart in early 1985 with *Anything?*. This catchy, light, soul single, which sounded like a slightly beefier version of the Shakatak style, reached No 67; it was penned by Quinton. Mere weeks later, Rogers found herself at No 22 in Britain in a more unlikely guise - she added a new vocal part to the original master tape of Third World's 1978 hit *Now That We've Found Love*, while it was in the process of being remixed and reworked by Hardcastle. Bob MacDonald, 21 June 1985..

ABC (FALLING IN LOVE'S NOT EASY)
Tracks: / ABC (falling in love's not easy).
7" Single: Released Apr '85, on Boiling Point, by Polydor Ltd. Catalogue no: **POSP 742**
12" Single: Released Apr '85, on Boiling Point, by Polydor Ltd. Catalogue no: **POSPX 742**

ANYTHING
Tracks: / Anything.
7" Single: Released Jan '85, on Polydor, by Polydor Ltd. Catalogue no: **POSP 728**
7" Single: Released Nov '84, on Direct Drive, by Direct Drive Records. Deleted '86. Catalogue no: **7 DRD 2**
12" Single: Released Jan '85, on Polydor, by Polydor Ltd. Catalogue no: **POSPX 728**

DON'T DEPEND ON ME
Tracks: / Don't depend on me / Time machine.
12" Single: Released Jan '82, on Oval, by Oval Records. Catalogue no: **DRIVE 20/20**

I'M THE ONE
Tracks: / I'm the one / Time's running out.
7" Single: Released Apr '82, on Oval, by Oval Records. Catalogue no: **DRIVE 21**
12" Single: Released Apr '82, on Oval, by Oval Records. Catalogue no: **DRIVE 21/12**

IN THE MIDDLE OF SPRING
Tracks: / In the middle of spring.
7" Single: Released Jul '83, on Passion, by Skratch Records. Catalogue no: **PASH 01**
12" Single: Released Jul '83, on Passion, by Skratch Records. Catalogue no: **PASH 01(12)**

NEED SOME SUNSHINE
Tracks: / Need some sunshine / Pass the paper.
12" Single: Released Nov '85, on Direct Drive, by Direct Drive Records. Deleted '86. Catalogue no: **12 DRD 3**
7" Single: Released Nov '85, on Direct Drive, by Direct Drive Records. Deleted '86. Catalogue no: **7 DRD 3**

OH YEAH
Tracks: / Oh yeah.
Note: Featuring Stan Sultzman. Limited edition.
12" Single: Released Mar '86, on Direct Drive, by Direct Drive Records. Deleted '87. Catalogue no: **GOT 1**

PASS THE PAPER
Tracks: / Pass the paper.
7" Single: Released Aug '84, on Direct Drive, by Direct Drive Records. Deleted '86. Catalogue no: **7 DRD 1**

Direct Hit

SHE DIDN'T REALLY CARE
Tracks: / She didn't really care.
7" Single: Released Mar '85, on Direct (2), Deleted '86. Catalogue no: **POP 1**

Direct Hits

MODESTY BLAISE
Tracks: / Modesty Blaise / Funny honey girl.
7" Single: Released Oct '82, on Whaam, Catalogue no: **WHAAM 07**

SNAKES AND LADDERS
Tracks: / Snakes and ladders.
12" Single: Released Jul '87, on Forbidden, Catalogue no: **TAKE 2**

Director

CHRISTMAS SOCA
Tracks: / Christmas soca / Christmas soca-instrumental.
12" Single: Released Dec '86, on Bumble Bee, Catalogue no: **BUMB 103**

Dirt

DEATH IS REALITY TODAY
Tracks: / Death is reality today.
7" Single: on Crass, by Crass Records. Catalogue no: **321984/6**

OBJECT REFUSE REJECT ABUSE
Tracks: / Object refuse reject abuse.
7" Single: Released Feb '82, on Crass, by Crass Records. Catalogue no: **CRASS 321984-6**

Dirt Band

MAKE A LITTLE MAGIC (SINGLE)
Tracks: / Make a little magic / Jas moon.
7" Single: Released Sep '80, on United Artists, by EMI Records. Deleted '83. Catalogue no: **UP 631**

Dirty Desi

SEXY LIKE A BOTTLE OF PEPSI
Tracks: / Sexy like a bottle of Pepsi.
7" Single: Released Apr '84, on Ragin' Lion Music, Catalogue no: **RL 002**

Dirty Dirt

OH WHAT A NICE PUSSY
Tracks: / Oh what a nice pussy.
12" Single: Released '88, on Subway, by Subway Records. Catalogue no: **SUB 047**

Dirty Harry

D'BOP
Tracks: / D'bop.
CD 5": Released Oct '88, on Subway, by Subway Records. Catalogue no: **SUB 015 CD**
12" Single: Released Apr '88, on Subway, by Subway Records. Catalogue no: **SUB 015**

DOUBLE B
Tracks: / Double b.
12" Single: Released Apr '89, on Subway, by Subway Records. Catalogue no: **SUB 036**

I DON'T MIND
Tracks: / I don't mind.
12" Single: Released '88, on Subway, by Subway Records. Catalogue no: **SUB 036**

Dirty Looks

LET GO
Tracks: / Let go / Accept me.
7" Single: Released May '80, on Stiff, by Stiff Records. Deleted May '83. Catalogue no: **BUY 77**

LIE TO ME
Tracks: / Lie to me / Rosario's ashes.
7" Single: Released Mar '80, on Stiff, by Stiff Records. Deleted '83. Catalogue no: **BUY 66**

TAILIN' YOU
Tracks: / Tailin' you / Automatic pilot.
7" Single: Released Oct '80, on Stiff, by Stiff Records. Deleted Oct '83. Catalogue no: **BUY 89**

Dirty Roseanna

DIRTY ROSEANNA
Tracks: / Dirty Roseanne.
12" Single: Released Mar '86, on Deep, Catalogue no: **DEEP 33003**

Dirty Strangers

BATHING BELLES
Tracks: / Bathing belles.
7" Single: Released 28 Jul '89, on UNKNOWN, Catalogue no: **TH 3**
12" Single: Released 28 Jul '89, on UNKNOWN, Catalogue no: **THT 3**

THRILL OF THE THRILL
Tracks: / Thrill of the thrill.
7" Single: Released Dec '88, on Razor, by Razor Records. Catalogue no: **RZS 113**

Dirty Work Work

LOVE YOU FEEL ME
Tracks: / Love you feel me (remix) / Nothing can hurt me now.
7" Single: Released 23 May '87, on Wire, by Wire Records. Catalogue no: **WRS 012**
12" Single: Released 23 May '87, on Wire, by Wire Records. Catalogue no: **WRMS 012**

Dis Masters

BLACK AND PROUD
Tracks: / Black and proud.
12" Single: Released Jun '89, on Sure Delight, by Sure Delight Records. Catalogue no: **SDT 8**
7" Single: Released Apr '89, on Urban Rock, Catalogue no: **UR 938**
7" Single: Released Apr '89, on Jetstar, by Jetstar Records. Catalogue no: **SDT 9**

Disc Bleu

I GOT YOUR NUMBER
Tracks: / I got your number / CT's boogie.
12" Single: Released Mar '84, on MCA, by MCA Records. Catalogue no: **PANT 1**
7" Single: Released Mar '84, on MCA, by MCA Records. Catalogue no: **PAN 1**

Discharge

Biographical details: The nucleus of this British rock band has always been vocalist Cal (rela name Kelvin Morris) and bassist Rainy.

Discharge were formed in 1978 during Britain's punk revolution. However, by the time they released their first record in 1980, the UK music press had lost interest in the genre. The original punk groups had either broken up, or else were moving into the rock mainstream. It was becoming hard for the newer bands to gain attention, and they were thus forming their own esoteric subculture in an attempt to re-establish grass roots interest. This really amounted to a recycling of the 1977-style New Wave music, but with a sharper political content.

,Discharge's debut single, a four track disc, was issued in April 1980; it was the first record released by Stoke-on-Trent's Clay label. The only Discharge single to reach the UK national chart was *Never Again*, which reached No 64 in late 1981. They cracked the British album chart in 1982, reaching No 40 with *Hear Nothing, See Nothing, Say Nothing*. Their furious, head-banging singles included such charming ditties as *Fight Back*, *State Violence* and *Price Of Silence*. By being more genuinely political and less racist than many of their punk contemporaries, Discharge managed to stay the course longer, albeit without a major success on the national charts. They remained a force on the British indie charts, thanks to singles like 1985's *Ignorance*.

With exception of Cal and Rainy, the Discharge line-up has been an ever-changing phenomenon. The only other reasonable permanent member has been drummer Garry, known solely by his Christian name.
Bob MacDonald, 21 June 1985..

DECONTROL
Tracks: / Decontrol.
7" Single: Released Jul '81, on Clay, by Clay Records. Deleted '88. Catalogue no: **CLAY 5**

FIGHT BACK
7" Single: Released Jul '81, on Clay, by Clay Records. Catalogue no: **CLAY 3**

IGNORANCE
Tracks: / Ignorance / No compromise.
12" Single: Released May '85, on Clay, by Clay Records. Deleted '88. Catalogue no: **12 CLAY 43**
7" Single: Released May '85, on Clay, by Clay Records. Deleted '88. Catalogue no: **CLAY 43**

MORE I SEE
Tracks: / More I see.
12" Single: Released May '84, on Clay, by Clay Records. Catalogue no: **12 CLAY 34**
7" Single: Released May '84, on Clay, by Clay Records. Catalogue no: **CLAY 34**

NEVER AGAIN (SINGLE)
Tracks: / Never again / Death dealers.
7" Single: Released Oct '81, on Clay, by Clay Records. Deleted '88. Catalogue no: **CLAY 6**

PRICE OF SILENCE
Tracks: / Price of silence / Born to die in the gutter.
7" Single: Released Mar '83, on Clay, by Clay Records. Deleted '88. Catalogue no: **CLAY 29**

REALITIES OF WAR
Tracks: / Realities of war.
7" Single: Released Feb '87, on Clay, by Clay Records. Deleted '88. Catalogue no: **CLAY 1**

STATE VIOLENCE
Tracks: / State violence / State control.
7" Single: Released Oct '83, on Clay, by Clay Records. Deleted '88. Catalogue no: **CLAY 14**

WARNING - H.M.GOVERNMENT
Tracks: / Warning - H.M.Government.
12" Single: Released Sep '83, on Clay, by Clay Records. Catalogue no: **PLATE 5**

WHY
Tracks: / Why.
12" Single: Released Jul '81, on Clay, by Clay Records. Catalogue no: **PLATE 2**

Disco 2000

ONE LOVE NATION
Tracks: / One love nation.
12" Single: Released Apr '88, on KLF, by KLF Communications. Catalogue no: **D 2002**

UPTIGHT
Tracks: / Uptight.
12" Single: Released 16 Jan '89, on KLF, by KLF Communications. Catalogue no: **D 2003 T**
7" Single: Released 16 Jan '89, on KLF, by KLF Communications. Catalogue no: **D 2003**

Disco Aid

GIVE GIVE GIVE
Tracks: / Give give give.
12" Single: Released Oct '86, on Total Control, by Total Control Records. Deleted Jul '87. Catalogue no: **12 GIVE 1**
7" Single: Released Oct '86, on Total Control, by Total Control Records. Deleted Jul '87. Catalogue no: **GIVE 1**

Disco Connection

BORN TO BE ALIVE
7" Single: Released Nov '83, on PRT, by Castle Communications Records. Catalogue no: **7P 294**
12" Single: Released Dec '85, on Passion, by Skratch Records. Catalogue no: **PASH 50(12)**
12" Single: Released Nov '83, on PRT, by Castle Communications Records. Catalogue no: **12P 294**
12" Single: Released Nov '85, on ZYX (Germany), Catalogue no: **ZYX 5045**

ROCK YOUR BABY
Tracks: / Rock your baby.
12" Single: Released Nov '82, on PRT, by Castle Communications Records. Deleted Nov '85. Catalogue no: **12P 251**
12" Single: Released Mar '87, on ZYX (Germany), Catalogue no: **ZYX 5007**
7" Single: Released Nov '82, on PRT, by Castle Communications Records. Deleted Nov '85. Catalogue no: **7P 251**

Disco Dog

I'M GONNA BREAK YOUR BONES
Tracks: / I'm gonna break your bones.
12" Single: Released Jan '84, on Malaco, by Malaco Records (UK). Deleted '88. Catalogue no: **MAL 12 015**

Disco Tex

GET DANCING (OLD GOLD)
Tracks: / Get dancing / I wanna dance wit'choo.
7" Single: Released 24 Apr '89, on Old Gold, by Old Gold Records. Catalogue no: **OG 9884**

GET DANCING (SINGLE)
Tracks: / Get dancing.
7" Single: Released Nov '74, on Chelsea, Deleted '77. Catalogue no: **2005 013**

I WANNA DANCE WIT'CHOO
Tracks: / I wanna dance wit'choo.
7" Single: Released Apr '75, on Chelsea, Deleted '78. Catalogue no: **2005 024**

Disco Volante

NO MOTION
Tracks: / No motion.
7" Single: Released Jul '84, on Catalyst Box, Catalogue no: **CBR 001**

Disco Zombies

HERE COMES THE BUTS
Tracks: / Here comes the buts.
7" Single: Released Jun '81, on Dining Out, by Dining Out Records. Catalogue no: **TUX 2**

TOP OF THE POPS
Tracks: / Top of the pops.
7" Single: Released '79, on Uptown Records, by Uptown Records. Catalogue no: **WIZZ 01**

Disconexion

LOVE RUSH
Tracks: / Love rush (rock cake mix) / Love rush (put on mix) / Love rush (quwazy girl mix).
12" Single: Released Apr '89, on Submission, by Submission Records. Catalogue no: **SUBX 010**

MAKE IT HAPPEN
Tracks: / Make it happen.
12" Single: Released Oct '88, on Submission, by Submission Records. Catalogue no: **SUBX 08**

Disconnection

BALI HAI
Tracks: / Bali hai.
7" Single: Released Nov '82, on Y, Catalogue no: **Y 32**
12" Single: Released Nov '82, on Y, Catalogue no: **12 Y 32**

Discount Chiefs

TRUMPETS WILL BLOW
Tracks: / Trumpets will blow.
7" Single: Released Jul '81, on Round Ear, Deleted '83. Catalogue no: **EAR 2**

Discounts

SELLING RECORDS
Tracks: / Selling records / Selling records (part 2).
7" Single: Released Aug '80, on Original, Deleted '83. Catalogue no: **AB 01**

Diskord Datkord

IDENTITY
Tracks: / Identity / Identity (version).
12" Single: Released Jul '88, on Soho Girl, Catalogue no: **12 SG 002**

Disley, Will

KEEP ON RUNNIN'
Tracks: / Keep on runnin' / Wrong side up.
12" Single: Released Aug '83, on Web, by Web Records. Catalogue no: **12 WEB 23**
7" Single: Released Aug '83, on Web, by Web Records. Catalogue no: **WEB 23**

Dislocation Dance

DISLOCATION DANCE
Tracks: / Dislocation dance.
7" Single: Released Jul '81, on New Hormones, Catalogue no: **ORG 7**

ROSEMARY
Tracks: / Rosemary.
7" Single: Released Jun '82, on New Hormones, Catalogue no: **ORG 19**

SHOW ME
Tracks: / Show me.
12" Single: Released Oct '83, on Rough Trade, by Rough Trade Records. Catalogue no: **RTT 142**

SLIP THAT DISC
Tracks: / Slip that disc.
12" Single: Released Jun '81, on New Hormones, Catalogue no: **ORG 10**

VIOLETTE
Tracks: / Violette.
7" Single: Released Jun '83, on The Music Label, Deleted '84. Catalogue no: **TML 4501**

WHAT'S GOING ON?
Tracks: / What's going on.
12" Single: Released Dec '85, on Slipped Discs, by Slipped Discs Records. Catalogue no: **SLIP 121**

YOU'LL NEVER KNOW
Tracks: / You'll never know / You can tell.
7" Single: Released Oct '82, on New Hormones, Catalogue no: **ORG 22**

Disorder

COMPLETE DISORDER
Tracks: / Complete disorder.
7" EP: Released Jun '81, on Disorder, by Heartbeat Records. Catalogue no: **ORDER 1**

DISTORTION TO DEAFNESS
Tracks: / Distortion to deafness.
7" Single: Released Dec '81, on Disorder, by Heartbeat Records. Catalogue no: **ORDER 2**

MENTAL DISORDER
Tracks: / Mental disorder.
7" EP: Released Mar '83, on Disorder, by Heartbeat Records. Catalogue no: **ORDER 4**

PERDITION (SINGLE)
Tracks: / Perdition.
12" Single: Released Sep '82, on Riot City, by Riot City Records. Catalogue no: **12 ORDER 3**

Disruptors

ALIVE IN THE ELECTRIC CHAIR
Tracks: / Alive in the electric chair.
7" Single: Released Apr '84, on Radical Change, by Backs Recording Co.. Catalogue no: **RC 8**
12" Single: Released Aug '85, on Radical Change, by Backs Recording Co.. Catalogue no: **RC 12 008**

BOMB HEAVEN
Tracks: / Bomb heaven.
7" Single: Released Apr '86, on Radical Change, by Backs Recording Co.. Catalogue no: **RC 6**

SHELTERS FOR THE RICH
Tracks: / Shelters for the rich.
7" Single: Released Jul '82, on Radical Change, by Backs Recording Co.. Catalogue no: **RC 2**

YOUNG OFFENDER
Tracks: / Young offender.
7" Single: Released Nov '81, on Radical Change, by Backs Recording Co.. Catalogue no: **RC 1**

Dissidenten

CASABLANCA
Tracks: / Casablanca.
12" Single: Released 20 Feb '88, on Fuzz, by President Records. Catalogue no: **ZZ 20019**

Distance

JUST ONE MORE KISS
Tracks: / Just one more kiss.
12" Single: Released Mar '84, on Challenge, by Elite Records. Catalogue no: **TAL 6**

Distant Cousins

I'LL BE WITH YOU
Tracks: / I'll be with you.
7" Single: Released Nov '89, on Ghetto, by CBS Records. Catalogue no: **GTG 007**
12" Single: Released Nov '89, on Ghetto, by CBS Records. Catalogue no: **GTG 007T**
12" Single: Released Jun '89, on Ghetto, by CBS Records. Catalogue no: **CTGT 005**
7" Single: Released Jun '89, on Ghetto, by CBS Records. Catalogue no: **CTG 005**

YOU USED TO

Tracks: / You used to.
7" Single: Released May '89, on Ghetto, by CBS Records. Catalogue no: **CTG 004**
12" Single: Released May '89, on Ghetto, by CBS Records. Catalogue no: **CTGT 004**
CD 5": Released May '89, on Ghetto, by CBS Records. Catalogue no: **CTGCD 004**

Distant Drums

PERFECT EYES
Tracks: / Perfect eyes.
7" Single: Released Aug '83, on Rhythmic, by Rhythmic Records. Catalogue no: **RMNS 3**

Distel, Sacha

Biographical details: This Frnach singer's only year of success on the British record charts was 1970. A self-titled album reached No 21 that year, logging 14 weeks on the LP listings. He reached No 10 on the UK singles chart with his rendition of *Raindrops Keep Falling On My Head*, the Oscar-winning Burt Bacharach/Hal David song featured in the successful movie "Butch Cassify And The Sundance Kid". The original film version was sung by B J Thomas, who took the song to the US No 1 slot in January '70. But in Britain, Distel was the clear winner. The Frenchman hit No 10 (compared with Thomas' No 38 and Bobbie Gentry's No 40), and logged a total of 27 weeks on the Top 50. In the best traditions of its writers, *Raindrops* was an agreeable piece of mass-appeal, middle of the road pop.

Distel's blank showing on the UK charts (apart from 1970) is not a trus reflection of his fame and popularity with the older British music lover, particularly during the Seventies. His albums, containing predictable selections of mainly familiar chansons d'mour, tended to sell in small quantities over a long period of time. In addition, his discs were only one part of a successful showbusiness career, which included numerous TV, cabaret, variety and concert appearances. He is one of the few artists to break out od his country's insular music business and sustain an international career. Bob MacDonald, 21 June 1985.
Jazz guitarist and singer, born in 1933 in Paris. In the '50's he played with Stan Getz, the Modern Jazz Quartet, Lionel Hampton, Dizzy Gillespie and others; by the end of the decade he was known as a classy pop singer, recording in five languages. He wrote a theme for the French film *The Seven Capital Sins*; with an English lyric by Jack Reardon it became *The Good life*, won a Grammy for best song in 1963 and was a top 20 hit for Tony Bennett. (Donald Clarke, April 1989).

IMAGINE
Tracks: / Imagine.
7" Single: Released Nov '85, on Towerbell, Catalogue no: **TOW 80**

RAINDROPS KEEP FALLING ON MY HEAD
Tracks: / Raindrops keep falling on my head.
7" Single: Released Jan '70, on Warner Bros., by WEA Records. Deleted '73. Catalogue no: **WB 7345**

STRONGER THAN BEFORE
Tracks: / Stronger than before / I just called to say I love you.
7" Single: Released Dec '85, on Towerbell, Catalogue no: **TOW 83**

Distinction

DESTINY
7" Single: Released Sep '83, on En-Ay, Catalogue no: **AM 262**

THAT'S THE WAY I LIKE IT
Tracks: / That's the way I like it.
7" Single: Released Jul '82, on Hansa, by Hansa Records. Catalogue no: **HANSA 16**
12" Single: Released Jul '82, on Hansa, by Hansa Records. Catalogue no: **HANSA 1216**

Distractions

BOYS CRY
Tracks: / Boys cry / Paracetamol paralysis.
7" Single: Released Apr '80, on Island, by Island Records. Deleted '83. Catalogue no: **WIP 6568**

IT DOESN'T BOTHER ME
Tracks: / It doesn't bother me / One way love.
7" Single: Released Jan '80, on Island, by Island Records. Deleted Jan '83. Catalogue no: **WIP 6533**

SOMETHING FOR THE WEEKEND
Tracks: / Something for the weekend / What's the use.
...sed Sep '80, on Island, by ...eleted Sep '83. Cata-

Distributors

GET RID OF THESE THINGS
Tracks: / Get rid of these things.
7" Single: Released Nov '81, on Red Rhino, by Red Rhino Records. Deleted '88. Catalogue no: **RED 009**
12" Single: Released Nov '81, on Red Rhino, by Red Rhino Records. Deleted '88. Catalogue no: **REDT 009**

LEAN ON ME
Tracks: / Lean on me.
7" Single: Released 26 Jun '85, on Red Rhino, by Red Rhino Records. Deleted '88. Catalogue no: **RED 005**

Disturbance

SNEAKIN' SNAKY
Tracks: / Sneakin' snaky / Fortune teller.
7" Single: Released Feb '80, on MCA, by MCA Records. Deleted '83. Catalogue no: **MCA 566**

Div

SEX SEX SEX
Tracks: / Sex sex sex.
12" Single: Released Feb '88, on Torso, by Torso Records. Catalogue no: **TORSO 12052**

Diva

SENTIMENTAL PROMENADE
Tracks: / Sentimental promenade.
7" Single: Released Jan '83, on Palace, by Virgin Records. Catalogue no: **PS 1**

Diversions

FATTIE BUM BUM
Tracks: / Fattie bum bum.
7" Single: Released Sep '75, on Gull, by Gull Records. Deleted '78. Catalogue no: **GULS 18**

Divine

Biographical details: This American singer, whose real name is Glen Milston, is the most outrageously camp artist ever to hit the British charts. He was given his pseudonym by John Walters, the movie director who first brought him to notoriety in the mid-Seventies with the film "Pink Flamingoes". Subsequent trashy movies included "Female Trouble" and "Polyester", and these consolidated Divine's position as one of the most over-the-top cult figures i nthe transvestite world. These grossly self-indulgent films, in which both actors and director lived out their fantasies, gave Divine the confidence to try his hand at music making in the early Eighties.

Building his reputation in the boystown clubs of Britain and Europe, Divine first hit the UK national charts in October 1983 with *Love Reaction*; this single, which shamelessly plaigarised New Order's *Blue Monday*, reached No 65. Just under a year later, he climbed to the UK No 16 slot with the catchy Hi-NRG pop single *You Think You're A Man*; but one appearance on BBC TV's Top Of The Pops, resplendent with flyaway blond locks, earrings, heavy make-up and the rest of his customary paraphernalia, convinced the corporation that he should not be invited to appear again! The success of the record was mainly due to the studio sequencer sounds employed by its producers, who later used their distinctive production trademarks on Dead Or Alive's UK No 1 *You Spin Me Round (Like A Record)*. Little artistic merit could be assigned to Divine's deep, earthy growl, which was a half-spoken/half-sung effort.

Divine's second British Top 40 hit came in 1985, when he reached No 23 with a not terribly subtle revival of the Four Seasons' *Walk Like A Man*; he then tried his hand at Sam Cooke's *Twistin' The Night Away*. Bob MacDonald, 21 June 1985..

BORN TO BE CHEAP
Tracks: / Born to be cheap / Name game.
7" Single: Released Jul '81, on Situation 2, by Beggars Banquet Records. Catalogue no: **SIT 5**

HARD MAGIC
Tracks: / Hard magic.
7" Single: Released Oct '85, on Proto, by Proto Records. Catalogue no: **ENA 131**
12" Single: Released Oct '85, on Proto, by Proto Records. Catalogue no: **ENAT 131**

HEY YOU
Tracks: / Hey you.
7" Single: Released Jan '88, on In Recordings, Catalogue no: **INR 6**
7" Single: Released Mar '88, on Dancetrax, by BMG Records (UK). Deleted Aug '89. Catalogue no: **7DTRAX 911**
12" Single: Released Jan '88, on In Recor- dings, Catalog...

DIVINE - I'M SO BEAUTIFUL (Released on Proto)

'89. Catalogue no: **12DTRAX 911**

I'M SO BEAUTIFUL (see panel above)
Tracks: / I'm so beautiful / Show me around.
7" Single: Released Sep '84, on Proto, by Proto Records. Catalogue no: **ENA 121**
12" Single: Released Sep '84, on Proto, by Proto Records. Catalogue no: **ENAT 121**

LITTLE BABY
Tracks: / Little baby (instrumental) / Little baby / Little baby (dance remix) (on 12" only).
7" Single: Released Jan '87, on In Recordings, Catalogue no: **INR 4**
12" Single: Released Feb '87, on In Recordings, Catalogue no: **INRT 4R**
12" Single: Released Jan '87, on In Recordings, Catalogue no: **INRT 4**

LOVE REACTION
Tracks: / Love reaction.
7" Single: Released Oct '83, on Design Communications, Catalogue no: **DES 4**
12" Single: Released Oct '83, on Design Communications, Catalogue no: **DEST 4**

MEDLEY
Tracks: / Medley / Native love.
12" Single: Released Feb '86, on Proto, by Proto Records. Catalogue no: **ENAT 132**
12" Single: Released Nov '86, on Receiver, by Trojan Records. Catalogue no: **REPLAY 3004**

NATIVE LOVE
Tracks: / Native love / Love reaction.
7" Single: Released Nov '82, on O, Deleted Nov '85. Catalogue no: **QUE 1**
12" Single: Released Sep '86, on Receiver, by Trojan Records. Catalogue no: **REPLAY 3001**
12" Single: Released Nov '82, on O, Deleted '85. Catalogue no: **QUEL 1**

SHAKE IT UP
Tracks: / Shake it up.
7" Single: Released Nov '83, on Design Communications, Catalogue no: **DES 5**
12" Single: Released Nov '83, on Design Communications, Catalogue no: **DEST 5**

SHOOT YOUR SHOT
Tracks: / Shoot your shot / Shake it up no.2.
12" Single: Released Feb '83, on O, Deleted '85. Catalogue no: **QUEL 4**
12" Single: Released Sep '86, on Receiver, by Trojan Records. Catalogue no: **REPLAY 3002**

TWISTIN' THE NIGHT AWAY
Tracks: / Twistin' the night away.
7" Single: Released Jun '85, on Proto, by Proto Records. Catalogue no: **ENA 127**
12" Single: Released Jun '85, on Proto, by Proto Records. Catalogue no: **ENAT 127**

WALK LIKE A MAN
Tracks: / Walk like a man.
7" Single: Released Apr '85, on Proto, by Proto Records. Catalogue no: **ENA 125**
12" Single: Released Apr '85, on Proto, by Proto Records. Catalogue no: **ENAT 125**
7" Pic: Released Apr '85, on Proto, by Proto Records. Catalogue no: **ENAP 125**

YOU THINK YOU'RE A MAN (see panel on previous page)
Tracks: / You think you're a man / Walk like a man/No. 3 / Give it up.
12" Single: Released Jun '84, on Proto, by Proto Records. Catalogue no: **ENAT 118**
12" Single: Released Sep '86, on Receiver, by Trojan Records. Catalogue no: **REPLAY 3003**
7" Single: Released Jun '84, on Proto, by Proto Records. Catalogue no: **ENA 118**

Divine Horsemen

MIDDLE OF THE NIGHT
Tracks: / Middle of the night.
12" Single: Released 13 Jun '87, on New Rose (1), by New Rose Records. Catalogue no: **NEW 87**

Divine (reggae)

IS THAT LOVE
Tracks: / Is that love.
12" Single: Released Nov '88, on GMK, Catalogue no: **GMK 001**

Divine Sounds

WHAT PEOPLE DO FOR MONEY
Tracks: / What people do for money / Dollar bill dub.
12" Single: Released Feb '86, on Streetwave, Catalogue no: **MKHAN 11**

Divinyls

BACK TO THE WALL
Tracks: / Back to the wall.
7" Single: Released Jun '88, on Chrysalis, by Chrysalis Records. Catalogue no: **CHS 3241**
12" Single: Released Jun '88, on Chrysalis, by Chrysalis Records. Catalogue no: **CHS 123241**

SCIENCE FICTION
Tracks: / Science fiction / Take a chance / Motion.
7" Single: Released May '83, on Chrysalis, by Chrysalis Records. Catalogue no: **CHS 2673**
12" Single: Released May '83, on Chrysalis, by Chrysalis Records. Catalogue no: **CHS12 2673**

Divorce Brothers

TO UNDERSTAND
Tracks: / To understand.
12" Single: Released '88, on UNKNOWN, Catalogue no: **LEFT 12001**

Dixie & Allen

COTTAGE IN THE COUNTRY
Tracks: / Cottage in the country / Before I'm over.
7" Single: Released Aug '88, on Snap Shot, Catalogue no: **SR 001**

Dixie Cups

Biographical details: This American vocal group consisted of sisters Barbara Ann and Rose Lee Hawkins and Joan Marie Johnson, who grew up singing together at school in New Orleans. They formed a trio in 1963 and, following a local talent contest, were signed to the Red Bird label, a new organisation formed by famed songwriting team Jerry Leiber and Mike Stoller. The duo gave the girls their name, Dixie Cups, but not their first hit: *Chapel Of Love* came from Jeff Barry, Ellie Greenwich and Phil Spector, who had originally written it for the Ronettes. It went to No 1 in the US in June '64 but in Beatles-dominated Britain, where home-grown talent was taking the lion's share of the business, it could only manage No 22. The follow-up single, *People Say*, reached No 12 in America and the following year an updated version of a traditional New Orleans chant, *Iko Iko*, went to No 20 in American and No 23 in the UK. (It was revived in 1982 by two simultaneous hit cover versions on the UK chart, by Natasha and by the Belle Stars.) After *Iko Iko* the Dixie Cups plunged into ob- [illegible] With Britannia ruling the waves [illegible] the Supremes and Martha & The [illegible] as giving girl groups a fresher [illegible] there was no room for the Cups. [illegible] MacDonald, June 1985.)
[illegible] ale vocal trio of the mid-'60's: Joan [illegible] Johnson, sisters Rosa Lee and Bar- [illegible] Hawkins. Discovered at a talent [illegible]
sued). His strange reluctance to do much with an obvious hit prompted Barry and Greenwich to record the Dixie Cups (originally called Little Miss and the Muffets) for an international smash in 1964. After a few more his, the chanting of a traditional New Orleans song during a lull in a recording session led to their influential last hit *Iko iko*, with simple percussive backing, call-and-response vocal. Like many girl groups, their success was brief but unforgettable. (Donald Clarke, April 1989)t.

CHAPEL OF LOVE
Tracks: / Chapel of love.
7" Single: Released Jun '64, on Pye International, Deleted '67. Catalogue no: **7N 25245**
7" Single: Released Aug '82, on Blast From The Past, by Creole Records. Catalogue no: **CR 188**

CHAPEL OF LOVE (OLD GOLD)
Tracks: / Chapel of love / Iko iko.
7" Single: Released Jul '82, on Old Gold, by Old Gold Records. Catalogue no: **OG 9083**

IKO IKO
Tracks: / Iko iko.
7" Single: Released May '65, on Red Bird, by Charly Records. Deleted '68. Catalogue no: **RB 10024**

Dixie Dregs

TAKE IT OFF THE TOP
Tracks: / Take it off the top / Belgian Tom's hat trick / Pickin' the blues.
7" Single: Released Jan '82, on Polydor, by Polydor Ltd. Deleted Jan '85. Catalogue no: **POSP 168**

Dixies

SANTA WHERE'S ME BIKE?
Tracks: / Santa where's me bike? / Mountains of Mourne.
7" Single: Released Dec '87, on Ritz, by Ritz Records. Catalogue no: **RITZ 181**

Dixo

BANG BANG
Tracks: / Bang bang / Time is tight.
7" Single: Released Oct '80, on Warner Bros., by WEA Records. Deleted Oct '83. Catalogue no: **K 18314**

Dixon, Karen

'COS I LOVE YOU BABY
Tracks: / 'Cos I love you baby.
12" Single: Released Apr '82, on Neville King, by Neville King Records. Catalogue no: **NKRD 006**

I LIKE YOUR MOVE
Tracks: / I like your move.
12" Single: Released Oct '81, on Neville King, by Neville King Records. Catalogue no: **NKRD 004**

I WANT TO BE FREE
Tracks: / I want to be free.
12" Single: Released Sep '82, on Neville King, by Neville King Records. Catalogue no: **NKRD 007**

LOVE
Tracks: / Love.
12" Single: Released Jan '85, on Neville King, by Neville King Records. Catalogue no: **NKRD 0025**

TOUCH ME BABY
Tracks: / Touch me baby.
12" Single: Released Apr '83, on NK Music, Catalogue no: **NKRD 014**

Dixon, Nigel

THUNDERBIRD
Tracks: / Thunderbird / Someone's on the loose.
7" Single: Released Feb '81, on Stiff, by Stiff Records. Deleted Feb '84. Catalogue no: **BUY 103**

Dixon, Sharon

CANDY BLUES (TALKIN'82)
Tracks: / Candy blues (talkin '82).
7" Single: Released Jul '82, on Red Rhino, by Red Rhino Records. Catalogue no: **RED 17**

HOW CAN I LOVE AGAIN?
Tracks: / How can I love again?.
12" Single: Released May '82, on Cartridge, Catalogue no: **CRD 11**

Dixon, Steve

TALKING CANDY BLUES 82
Tracks: / Talking candy blues 82.
7" Single: Released '82, on Red Rhino, by Red [illegible] '83. Cata-
[illegible]
Edge, Catalogue no: **NE 01112**

SOMETHING ABOUT YOU
Tracks: / Something about you.
12" Single: Released Dec '88, on Tee Dee, Catalogue no: **TD 003**

WOMAN OF MOODS
Tracks: / Woman of moods.
12" Single: Released Jul '88, on Groove & A Quarter, Catalogue no: **CRD 004**

Dixon, Tyrone

PRISONER OF LOVE
Tracks: / Prisoner of love.
12" Single: Released Jul '80, on Hawkeye, by Hawkeye Records. Catalogue no: **HD 24**

D.I.Y.

U DON'T HAVE 2 WORRY
Tracks: / U don't have 2 worry.
12" Single: Released May '89, on Subway, by Subway Records. Catalogue no: **SUB 60**

Diz & The Doormen

BLUECOAT MAN
Tracks: / Bluecoat man / Caldonia.
7" Single: Released Nov '82, on Ace, by Ace Records. Deleted Jun '88. Catalogue no: **NS 83**

Dizrhythmia

IT WILL ONLY END IN TEARS
Tracks: / It will only end in tears / Dizrhythmia.
7" Single: Released Jun '88, on Antilles/New Directions, by Island Records. Catalogue no: **ANN 6**

Dizzi Heights

GANGSTER BOOGIE
Tracks: / Gangster boogie / Gangster boogie (version).
12" Single: Released Aug '89, on Total/Viceroy, Catalogue no: **12VICE 3**

Dizzy Bitch

DIZZY BITCH
7" EP: Released Feb '86, on Azra (USA), by Azra International (USA). Catalogue no: **A 615**

Dizzy Heights

CHRISTMAS RAPPING
Tracks: / Christmas rapping / Unrapping.
7" Single: Released Dec '82, on Polydor, by Polydor Ltd. Deleted '85. Catalogue no: **WRAP 1**
12" Single: Released Dec '82, on Polydor, by Polydor Ltd. Deleted '85. Catalogue no: **WRAPX 1**

TO THE SOUND OF THE DRUMS AND THE BASS
Tracks: / To the sound of the drums and the bass / DIY rap track / Complete works, The.
7" Single: Released Oct '86, on Parlophone, by EMI Records. Catalogue no: **R 6138**
12" Single: Released Sep '86, on Parlophone, by EMI Records. Deleted Jul '87. Catalogue no: **12 R 6138**

WOULD I FIND LOVE?
Tracks: / Would I find love? (dub) (on 12" only) / Gospel, The (on 12" only) / Would I find love? (Instrumental) / Would I find love?.
7" Single: Released Mar '86, on Parlophone, by EMI Records. Catalogue no: **R 6126**
12" Single: Released Mar '86, on Parlophone, by EMI Records. Catalogue no: **12 R 6126**

DJ Bear

PUMP UP THE BALL
Tracks: / Pump up the ball / Pump up the ball (instrumental).
Note: "A house novelty football record, backed by Saint & Greavsie".(Supertrack, June 1988)
7" Single: Released Jun '88, on Strike (2), Catalogue no: **STRK 3**

DJ Doktor Megatrip

JOY
Tracks: / Joy.
12" Single: Released Nov '88, on Temple Records, by Temple Records (2). Catalogue no: **TOPY 40**

DJ Fast Eddie

LET'S GO
Tracks: / Let's go.
CD 5": Released May '89, on DJ International, by Westside Records. Catalogue no: [illegible]
[illegible]
national, by Westside Records. Catalogue no: **DJINX 12**
12" Single: Released May '89, on DJ International, by Westside Records. Catalogue no: **DJINT 12**

MASTERMIX
Tracks: / Mastermix.
7" Single: Released Jun '89, on Radical, by Radical Records. Catalogue no: **RADC 5**
12" Single: Released Jun '89, on Radical, by Radical Records. Catalogue no: **RADICAL 5**

YOYO GET FUNKY
Tracks: / Yoyo get funky / Yoyo get funky (version).
CD 5": Released Feb '89, on DJ International, by Westside Records. Catalogue no: **CDJIN 7**
7" Single: Released Feb '89, on DJ International, by Westside Records. Catalogue no: **DJIN 7**
12" Single: Released Feb '89, on DJ International, by Westside Records. Catalogue no: **DJINT 7**

DJ International...

DJ INTERNATIONAL ACID HOUSE MEGAJACKMIX
12" Single: Released Dec '88, on ZYX (Germany), Catalogue no: **ZYX 5973**

DJ Jack

HOTHOUSE
Tracks: / Hothouse.
7" Single: Released May '88, on Quazar, Catalogue no: **QUA 9**
12" Single: Released May '88, on Quazar, Catalogue no: **QUAT 9**

DJ Jailbreak

KATCH THE BEAT
Tracks: / Catch the beat / Starship.
7" Single: Released 22 Aug '88, on Catt, by Catt Records. Catalogue no: **CATT 3003**
12" Single: Released 22 Aug '88, on Catt, by Catt Records. Catalogue no: **CATT 003**

DJ Jazzy Jeff

BRAND NEW FUNK
Tracks: / Brand new funk / Girls ain't nothing but trouble.
12" Single: Released Dec '88, on Jive, by Zomba Records. Catalogue no: **JIVET 190**
7" Single: Released Dec '88, on Jive, by Zomba Records. Catalogue no: **JIVE 190**

GIRLS AIN'T NOTHING BUT TROUBLE
Tracks: / Girls ain't nothing but trouble (Re-Mix) / Girls ain't nothing but trouble (Original mix).
7" Single: Released Sep '86, on Champion, by Champion Records. Catalogue no: **CHAMP 18**
12" Single: Released Sep '86, on Champion, by Champion Records. Catalogue no: **CHAMP 1218**

JUST ONE OF THOSE DAYS
7" Single: Released Jun '88, on Champion, by Champion Records. Catalogue no: **CHAMP 84**
12" Single: Released Jun '88, on Champion, by Champion Records. Catalogue no: **CHAMP 12-84**

MAGNIFICENT JAZZY JEFF
Tracks: / Magnificent jazzy Jeff / Magnificent jazzy Jeff (inst' dub).
7" Single: Released Feb '87, on Champion, by Champion Records. Deleted Jul '89. Catalogue no: **CHAMP 38**
12" Single: Released Feb '87, on Champion, by Champion Records. Deleted Aug '89. Catalogue no: **CHAMP 1238**

PARENTS
Tracks: / Parents.
7" Single: Released Apr '88, on Jive, by Zomba Records. Catalogue no: **JIVE 169**
12" Single: Released Apr '88, on Jive, by Zomba Records. Catalogue no: **JIVET 169**

TOUCH OF JAZZ, A
Tracks: / Touch of jazz / Touch of jazz (street mix) / Touch of jazz (retouch mix).
7" Single: Released May '87, on Champion, by Champion Records. Catalogue no: **CHAMP 47**
12" Single: Released May '87, on Champion, by Champion Records. Catalogue no: **CHAMP 12 47**

D.J. Munch

PARTY ROCK
Tracks: / Party rock.
12" Single: Released Jul '87, on FM Dance, by FM-Revolver Records. Catalogue no: **12 VHF 39**

DJ Trouble Fezz

DRUIDS ARE HERE
Tracks: / Druids are here.
7" Single: Released Aug '82, on Whaam, Catalogue no: **WHAAM 06**

HAPPY BUT TWISTED
Tracks: / Happy but twisted.
12" Single: Released May '85, on I.R.S, Catalogue no: **MEDICS T1**

MIRACLE OF THE AGE, THE
Tracks: / Miracle of the age, The.
7" Single: Released Oct '85, on I.R.S, Catalogue no: **IRM 106**

MORE
Tracks: / Pretty little Henry.
7" Single: Released Aug '87, on I.R.S, Catalogue no: **IRM 139**

SPIRIT IN THE SKY
Tracks: / Spirit in the sky / Laughing at the pieces / Love, peace and bananas (live) (Only on 12"version) / Fried egg bad Monday (live) (on 12" version only.) / Good golly Miss Molly (live) (On 12" version only.).
7" Single: Released Apr '86, on I.R.S, Catalogue no: **IRM 113**
12" Single: Released Apr '86, on I.R.S, Catalogue no: **IRMT 113**

TWO PIECES OF CLOTH CAREFULLY STICHED TOGETHER
Tracks: / Two pieces of cloth carefully stiched together.
12" Single: Released May '87, on Illegal, by Faulty Products Records. Catalogue no: **MEDICT 2**

WATERLOO
Tracks: / Waterloo / Damaged brains / Stare crazy (On 12" version only.) / Nothing (On 12" version only.).
7" Single: Released Nov '86, on RS, Catalogue no: **IRM 125**
12" Single: Released Nov '86, on I.R.S, Catalogue no: **IRMT 125**

Doctor York

SHAKE 'N' SKATE
Tracks: / Shake and skate / Roll a rock.
12" Single: Released Sep '81, on Groove PR, by Beggars Banquet Records. Catalogue no: **GP 110T**
7" Single: Released Sep '81, on Groove PR, by Beggars Banquet Records. Catalogue no: **GP 110**

Doctors Children

GIRL WITH GREEN EYES
Tracks: / Girl with green eyes / Harvest moon / I am the son / Two fat men.
12" Single: Released Jun '87, on Buffalo (UK), by M.I.S.Records. Catalogue no: **BUFF 1**

ROSE COTTAGE, THE EP
Tracks: / Rose cottage, The / Me-Sept 24th 1983 / When I was young / Blessed is the man.
12" Single: Released Jun '86, on Upright, by Upright Records. Catalogue no: **UPT 16**

Dodd, Jegsy

ALWAYS THE BRIDESMAID
Tracks: / Always the bridesmaid / 8,000 miles away / Jewel in the flat cap, The.
12" Single: Released 20 Jun '87, on Probe Plus, by Probe Plus Records. Catalogue no: **PP 22T**

Dodd, Ken

Biographical details: This British comedian and siner, born in Liverpool, spent his late teens and early twenties entertaining in local clubs at night, while working as a salesman by day. In 1954, at the age of 22, he became a full-time professional comedian. During the Sixties and Seventies, he became one of the UK's top TV stars; his unkempt hair, protruding front teeth, tickling stick and mass-appeal but highly original humour made him a household name.

Dodd's subsidiary career as a singer began in 1960, when his debut single *Love Is Like A Violin* reached No 8 on the UK charts. This success ushered in a string of moderate hits on the British Top 50, none of which made the Top 20 until, suddenly, along came 1965's No 1 smash *Tears.* This corny 1929 ballad gave him not only Britain's most surprising hit of the year, but also the biggest. In a year dominated by the Beatles, the Stones, the Who and a host of other beat groups, Dodd managed to log five weeks atop the UK chart. He soon followed it with two more Top Tenners, *The River* and *Promises.* Smaleer, sporadic UK hits continued right through into the Eighties. Perhaps his Liverpool background gave him pop credibility!

The most remarkable thing about Dodd's long string of hits was that none were comedy records. They consisted almost entirely of romantic ballads, many of a sombre nature. His extraordinary dual career, showing two sides of Ken Dodd that could hardly have been more different, was an extraordinary showbusiness achievement, and earned him the OBE award in 1982. Bob MacDonald, 22 June 1985.

The zany comedian born in 1929 in Liverpool made his stage act with wild hair, prominent teeth, rapid-fire gags and tickling stick, he was a popular singer of romantic ballads for over 20 years: he had a top 10 in the UK with his first record *Love is like a violin* in 1960 and his most recent in 1981 with *Hold my hand.* He still works hard with his stage act, trying almost single-handed to keep theatres open all over the country. (Donald Clarke, April 1989).

BROKEN HEARTED
Tracks: / Broken hearted.
7" Single: Released Dec '70, on Columbia, by EMI Records. Deleted '73. Catalogue no: **DB 8725**

EIGHT BY TEN
Tracks: / Eight by ten.
7" Single: Released Feb '64, on Columbia, by EMI Records. Deleted '67. Catalogue no: **DB 7191**

HAPPINESS
Tracks: / Happiness.
7" Single: Released Jul '64, on Columbia, by EMI Records. Deleted '67. Catalogue no: **DB 7325**

HOLD MY HAND
Tracks: / Hold my hand / Where did the good times go.
7" Single: Released Nov '81, on Images, by Images Records. Catalogue no: **IMGS 0002**

IT'S LOVE
Tracks: / It's love.
7" Single: Released Oct '66, on Columbia, by EMI Records. Deleted '69. Catalogue no: **DB 8031**

IT'S NO SECRET
Tracks: / It is no secret / When a child is born.
7" Single: Released Dec '80, on Warwick, by Warwick Records. Catalogue no: **SW 9899**

JUST OUT OF REACH
Tracks: / Just out of reach.
7" Single: Released Nov '72, on Columbia, by EMI Records. Deleted '75. Catalogue no: **DB 8947**

LET ME CRY ON YOUR SHOULDER
Tracks: / Let me cry on your shoulder.
7" Single: Released Jan '67, on Columbia, by EMI Records. Deleted '70. Catalogue no: **DB 8101**

LITTLE WORDS
Tracks: / Little words.
7" Single: Released Nov '84, on Ritz, by Ritz Records. Catalogue no: **RITZ 090**

LOVE IS LIKE A VIOLIN
Tracks: / Love is like a violin.
7" Single: Released Jul '70, on Decca, by Decca Records. Deleted '73. Catalogue no: **F 11248**

MORE THAN LOVE
Tracks: / More than love.
7" Single: Released Aug '66, on Columbia, by EMI Records. Deleted '69. Catalogue no: **DB 7976**

NOW AND FOREVER (SINGLE)
Tracks: / Now and forever / I wish it could be yesterday today.
7" Single: Released Feb '84, on PRT, by Castle Communications Records. Catalogue no: **7P 301**

ONCE IN EVERY LIFETIME
Tracks: / Once in every lifetime.
7" Single: Released Jun '61, on Decca, by Decca Records. Deleted '64. Catalogue no: **F 11355**

PIANISSIMO
Tracks: / Pianissimo.
7" Single: Released Feb '62, on Decca, by Decca Records. Deleted '65. Catalogue no: **F 11422**

PROMISES
Tracks: / Promises.
7" Single: Released May '66, on Columbia, by EMI Records. Deleted '69. Catalogue no: **DB 7914**

RIVER, THE
Tracks: / River, The.
7" Single: Released Nov '65, on Columbia, by EMI Records. Deleted '68. Catalogue no: **DB 7750**

SO DEEP IS THE NIGHT
Tracks: / So deep is the night.
7" Single: Released Nov '64, on Columbia, by EMI Records. Deleted '67. Catalogue no: **DB 7398**

STILL
Tracks: / Still.
7" Single: Released Aug '63, on Columbia, by EMI Records. Deleted '66. Catalogue no: **DB 7094**

TEARS
Tracks: / Tears.
7" Single: Released Sep '65, on Columbia, by EMI Records. Deleted '68. Catalogue no: **DB 7659**

TEARS (OLD GOLD)
Tracks: / Tears.
7" Single: Released Jul '82, on Old Gold, by Old Gold Records. Deleted Jul '88. Catalogue no: **OG 9042**

TEARS WON'T WASH AWAY MY HEARTACHE
Tracks: / Tears won't wash away my heartache.
7" Single: Released Jul '69, on Columbia, by EMI Records. Deleted '72. Catalogue no: **DB 8600**

WHEN LOVE COMES ROUND AGAIN
Tracks: / When love comes round again.
7" Single: Released Jul '71, on Columbia, by EMI Records. Deleted '74. Catalogue no: **DB 8796**

WHEREVER YOU ARE
Tracks: / Wherever you are.
7" Single: Released Nov '75, on EMI, by EMI Records. Deleted '78. Catalogue no: **EMI 2342**

Dodds, Pete

CARDBOARD CITY
Tracks: / Cardboard city.
7" Single: Released Aug '83, on Button, by Musical Characters Records. Catalogue no: **BTN 107**

Dodge

MAKE THE BREAK
Tracks: / Make the break / When life was easy.
7" Single: Released Nov '80, on ABC Records, by MCA Records. Deleted Nov '83. Catalogue no: **ABC 3**

Dods, Marcus

PRICE AND PREJUDICE (THEME)
Tracks: / Price and prejudice (theme) / Journey to Pemberley.
7" Single: Released Jan '80, on BBC, by BBC Records & Tapes. Deleted Jan '83. Catalogue no: **RESL 77**

Dog Dog Dog

TAKE THE FEVER
Tracks: / Take the fever / Skin deep.
7" Single: Released Nov '82, on Secret, by Secret Records. Deleted Nov '85. Catalogue no: **SHH 143**

Dog Faced Hermans

BELLA - CIAO
Tracks: / Bella - Ciao / Miss O'Grady.
7" Single: Released 22 Aug '88, on Calculous, Catalogue no: **KIT 003**

HUMANS FLY
Tracks: / T.B.C..
12" Single: Released Jan '88, on Calculous, Catalogue no: **KIT 001**

NO PARTISAN
Tracks: / No partisan.
7" Single: Released Aug '88, on Calculous, Catalogue no: **KIT 3**

UNBEND
Tracks: / Unbend.
7" Single: Released Mar '87, on Demon Radge, Catalogue no: **RADGE 1**

Dogger, Bunk

PEOPLE OF ALL NATIONS
Tracks: / People of all nations / Headlining.
7" Single: Released Mar '80, on RCA, by BMG Records (UK). Deleted Mar '83. Catalogue no: **PB 5240**

YOUNG BLOOD
Tracks: / Young blood / What's on telly?.
7" Single: Released Aug '80, on RCA, by BMG Records (UK). Deleted '83. Catalogue no: **PB 5269**

Doggie, General

CHILL OUT
Tracks: / Chill out.
12" Single: Released '88, on Night Life Possie, Catalogue no: **NP 001**

Dogmatic Element

STRANGE PASSIONS
Tracks: / Strange passions.
7" Single: Released Aug '82, on Castle Co, Deleted '84. Catalogue no: **CC 001**

Dogs

RUBBISH
Tracks: / Rubbish.
7" Single: Released Aug '81, on Eagle (West Germany), by Bear Family Records (Germany). Catalogue no: **ERS 010**

Dogs D'Amour

HOW COME IT NEVER RAINS (DYNAMITE REMIX)
Tracks: / Baby glass (live) / Kirsten jet (live) (Extra track on 12" & CD singles) / How come it never rains (dynamite remix) (Extended version on CD single only).
Note: (A remixed version of the track from the album "In the Dynamite Jet Saloon")
CD 5": Released 23 Jan '89, on China, by Polydor Ltd. Catalogue no: **CHICD 13**
12" Pic: Released 23 Jan '89, on China, by Polydor Ltd. Deleted Aug '89. Catalogue no: **CHIXP 13**
7" Single: Released 23 Jan '89, on China, by Polydor Ltd. Deleted Aug '89. Catalogue no: **CHING 13**
12" Single: Released 23 Jan '89, on China, by Polydor Ltd. Deleted Aug '89. Catalogue no: **CHINX 13**
7" Single: Released 23 Jan '89, on China, by Polydor Ltd. Deleted Aug '89. Catalogue no: **CHINA 13**

I DON'T WANT YOU TO GO
Tracks: / I don't want you to go / Heroin / Ugly (Only on 12").
7" Single: Released 16 Sep '88, on China, by Polydor Ltd. Catalogue no: **CHINA 10**
12" Single: Released Oct '88, on China, by Polydor Ltd. Deleted 31 May '89. Cata-

DOGS D'AMOUR - SATELLITE KID (Released on China)

logue no: **CHIXP 10**
7" Single: Released Oct '88, on China, by Polydor Ltd. Catalogue no: **CHING 10**
12" Single: Released 16 Sep '88, on China, by Polydor Ltd. Catalogue no: **CHINX 10**

IT NEVER POURS
Tracks: / It never pours.
7" Single: Released Dec '87, on M&M, Catalogue no: **DOGS 1**

KID FROM KENSINGTON, THE
Tracks: / Kid from Kensington, The / Everything I want / State I'm in, The (12" versions only.).
7" Single: Released May '88, on China, by Polydor Ltd. Catalogue no: **CHINA 5**
12" Single: Released May '88, on China, by Polydor Ltd. Catalogue no: **CHIXP 5**
12" Single: Released May '88, on China, by Polydor Ltd. Catalogue no: **CHINX 5**
7" Single: Released May '88, on China, by Polydor Ltd. Catalogue no: **CHING 5**

SATELLITE KID (see panel on previous page)
Tracks: / Satellite kid / She thinks too much of me / Drunk like me (12" only) / Things he'd do (12" only) / As I see the poppies (CD single only).
12" Pic: Released Aug '89, on China, by Polydor Ltd. Catalogue no: **CHIXP 17**
7" Pic: Released 24 Jul '89, on China, by Polydor Ltd. Catalogue no: **CHINP 17**
7" Single: Released 24 Jul '89, on China, by Polydor Ltd. Catalogue no: **CHINA 17**
12" Single: Released 24 Jul '89, on China, by Polydor Ltd. Catalogue no: **CHINX 17**
CD 5": Released 24 Jul '89, on China, by Polydor Ltd. Catalogue no: **CHICD 17**

TRAIL OF TEARS
Tracks: / Trail of tears / Pourin' out my heart.
CD 5": Released Oct '89, on China, by Polydor Ltd. Catalogue no: **CHICD 20**
7" Single: Released Oct '89, on China, by Polydor Ltd. Catalogue no: **CHINP 20**
12" Single: Released Oct '89, on China, by Polydor Ltd. Catalogue no: **CHINX 20**
7" Single: Released Oct '89, on China, by Polydor Ltd. Catalogue no: **CHINA 20**

Doheny, Hawk

TO PROVE MY LOVE (OLD GOLD)
Tracks: / To prove my love / Nite life.
12" Single: Released Sep '88, on Old Gold, by Old Gold Records. Catalogue no: **OG 4503**

Doheny, Ned

TO PROVE MY LOVE
Tracks: / To prove my love / On the swingshift.
7" Single: Released Jan '81, on CBS, by CBS Records. Deleted Jan '84. Catalogue no: **CBS 9481**

Dokken

BURNING LIKE A FLAME
Tracks: / Burning like a flame / Lost behind the wall.
7" Single: Released Feb '88, on Elektra, by Elektra Records (UK). Catalogue no: **EKR 67**
12" Single: Released Feb '88, on Elektra, by Elektra Records (UK). Catalogue no: **EKR 67T**
12" Pic: Released 27 Feb '88, on Elektra, by Elektra Records (UK). Catalogue no: **EKR 67TP**

IN MY DREAMS
Tracks: / In my dreams / Tell the living end / Alone again (12" only).
12" Single: Released Mar '86, on Elektra (USA), by Elektra Records (USA). Deleted Jun '87. Catalogue no: **EKR 37 T**
7" Single: Released Mar '86, on Elektra (USA), by Elektra Records (USA). Catalogue no: **EKR 37**

WE'RE ILLEGAL
Tracks: / We're illegal / Paris.
7" Single: Released Apr '82, on Carrere, Deleted Apr '85. Catalogue no: **CAR 229**

Dola, Saylon

ONE GAME, THE
Tracks: / One game, The.
7" Single: Released 2 Jul '88, on Fly, by Fly Records. Catalogue no: **EAGLE 3**

Dolan, Joe

Biographical details: This irish singer came to British fame in 1969 with his smash hit *Make Me An Island.* This piece of highly commercial, middle of the road pop reached No 3 and logged 18 weeks on the UK Top 50. It was written by Albert Hammond and Mike Hazelwood, who were also responsible for other big pop hits of the era, including Leapy Lee's *Little Arrows* and the Pipkins' *Gimme Dat Ding.* H & H provided Dolan with a pair of follow-up successes - *Theresa* attained the UK No 20 position in late '69, and *You're Such A Good Looking Woman* hit No 17 in 1970.

After this, Dolan disappeared completely from the UK charts, with the exception of a brief 1977 entry with *I Need You.* Written and produced by Peter Yellowstone, this single was a wholesale theft of Demis Roussos' recent smash *Forever And Ever,* despite a promotional appearance on BBC TV's Top Of The Pops, Dolan could only reach No 43.

Though a bigger star in his native Eire than in the UK, Dolan managed to sustain a steady showbusiness career throughout the British Isles via cabaret, concert and TV work. During the eighties, he has continued to darken the doors of recording studios, notably for Ritz Records. Bob MacDonald, 23 June 1985..

COME BACK HOME
Tracks: / Come back home.
7" Single: Released Oct '84, on Ritz, by Ritz Records. Catalogue no: **RITZ 082**
12" Single: Released Oct '84, on Ritz, by Ritz Records. Catalogue no: **RITZ 12082**

I NEED YOU (SINGLE)
Tracks: / I need you.
7" Single: Released Sep '77, on Pye, Deleted '80. Catalogue no: **7 N 45702**

IT'S ONLY MAKE BELIEVE
Tracks: / It's only make believe / Let me in.
7" Single: Released May '82, on Ritz, by Ritz Records. Catalogue no: **RITZ 016**

IT'S YOU,IT'S YOU
Tracks: / It's you, it's you, its you.
7" Single: Released Feb '83, on Ritz, by Ritz Records. Catalogue no: **RITZ 001**

IT'S YOU,IT'S YOU,IT'S YOU(REMIX 85)
Tracks: / It's you, it's you, it's you.
7" Single: Released Sep '85, on Ritz, by Ritz Records. Catalogue no: **RITZ 120**

MAKE ME AN ISLAND
Tracks: / Make me an island.
7" Single: Released Jun '69, on Pye, Catalogue no: **7 N 17731**

MAKE ME AN ISLAND (OLD GOLD)
Tracks: / Make me an island / Such a good lookin' woman.
7" Single: Released Jul '82, on Old Gold, by Old Gold Records. Deleted Jul '88. Catalogue no: **OG 9129**

MORE & MORE
Tracks: / More & more / When your lover leaves you.
7" Single: Released Jul '82, on Ritz, by Ritz Records. Catalogue no: **RITZ 019**

TAKE ME I'M YOURS
Tracks: / Take me I'm yours / Hang tough.
7" Single: Released May '86, on Ritz, by Ritz Records. Catalogue no: **RITZ 147**

TERESA
Tracks: / Teresa.
7" Single: Released Nov '69, on Pye, Deleted '72. Catalogue no: **7 N 17833**

YOU'RE SUCH A GOOD LOOKING WOMAN
Tracks: / You're such a good looking woman.
7" Single: Released Feb '70, on Pye, Deleted '73. Catalogue no: **7 N 17891**

Dolby, Thomas

Biographical details: This British keyboards and synthesiser player, singer and songwriter, began to attract attention in 1981. This was a time when synthesiser technology was rapidly increasing in its importance in pop music, and Dolby, a highly skilled and knowledgeable electronic wizard, was ready to take advantage. His real name is Thomas Morgan Dolby Robertson; he chose to call himself simply Thomas Dolby, presumably because of the pioneering hi-tech connotations associated with the 'Dolby' name, although he is in no way connected with the famous monicker that appears on every hi-fi system. He cultivated the appearance of a mad scientist.

During 1981 Dolby wrote *New Toy,* a minor UK hit for the wacky Lene Lovich, and contributed his synths to Foreigner's *4* album and Joan Armatrading's *Walk Under Ladders* LP. In October of that year, he enjoyed his first chart entry in his own right - *europa And The Pirate Twins* reached No 48. 1982 saw him hit No 31 with *Windpower,* which was released on his own Venice In Peril label.

In 1983 Dolby scored an American smash with another idiosyncratic effort, *She Blinded Me With Science.* Though only a minor UK hit, it became a surprise No 5 hit in the US, where it was fuelled by an invigorating video on MTV; both the record and its accompanying promo clip featured a guest appearance from one of Britain's genuine mad professors, Dr Magnus Pike. Dolby could not consolidate upon this Stateside success, despite the simultaneous appearance of two entries on the Billboard album chart. In Britain, however, he achieved his overdue breakthrough in early 1984 with *Hyperactive;* this got to No 17, and was accompanied by an even crazier video. His album *The Flat Earth* was also a UK Top 30 item, but the erratic nature of Dolby's music meant that it was difficult for him to carve out a consistent chart career. Still, being a mate of Michael Jackson should ensure that he's kept off the streets. Bob MacDonald, 23 June 1985.

UK keyboardist born in 1958 in Egypt. He mixed love of music (piano, guitar) and passion for electronics, leading him early to synthesisers. He had widely sessioned with Lene Lovich, Foreigner, Joan Armatrading etc. and already had a reputation as a shiz kid when EMI signed him and gave him own Venice In Peril label. Joe Ely went electronic after hearing *One of our submarines;* funk ace George Clinton recorded *May the cube be with you* with him (as occasional Dolby's Cube); Joni Mitchell sought him to co-produce *Dog eat dog* when he covered her *Jungle line.* He finallyhit in UK with title track from *Hyperactive* in 1984, an astonishingly varied album. He has recorded with Ryuichi Sakamoto, Grace Jones; produced Prefab Sprout's second album, backed David Bowie on Live Aid and wrote a script for Steven Spielberg as well as composing and playing the score for Ken Russell's film *Gothic* in 1987. (Donald Clarke, April 1989)u.

AIRHEAD
Tracks: / Airhead (extended version) / Budapest by blimp (edit) / Hyperactive (7" version).
CD 5": Released Apr '88, on EMI-Manhattan, by EMI Records. Deleted Aug '89. Catalogue no: **CDMT 38**
7" Single: Released Mar '88, on EMI-Manhattan, by EMI Records. Deleted Nov '88. Catalogue no: **MT 38**
12" Single: Released Mar '88, on EMI-Manhattan, by EMI Records. Deleted Nov '88. Catalogue no: **12MT 38**

AIRWAVES
Tracks: / Airwaves / Wreck of the Fairchild.
7" Single: Released Jan '82, on EMI, by EMI Records. Deleted Jan '85. Catalogue no: **VIPS 101**

DEVIL IS AN ENGLISHMAN
Tracks: / Devil is an Englishman, The / Fantasmagoria.
12" Single: Released Feb '87, on Virgin, by Virgin Records. Deleted May '88. Catalogue no: **VS 937-12**
7" Single: Released Feb '87, on Virgin, by Virgin Records. Deleted May '88. Catalogue no: **VS 937**

EUROPA AND THE PIRATE TWINS
Tracks: / Europa and the pirate twins / Therapy / Growth / Leipzig.
7" Single: Released Oct '81, on Parlophone, by EMI Records. Deleted '84. Catalogue no: **R 6051**
12" Single: Released Oct '81, on Parlophone, by EMI Records. Deleted '84. Catalogue no: **12R 6051**

HOT SAUCE
Tracks: / Hot sauce / Salsa picante / Hot sauce (ext version) (12" & CD single only.) / Hot sauce (murder dub) (12" only.) / Salsa picante (ext mix) (12" only.) / Hot sauce (7" remix) (12" & CD single only.) / Get out of my mix (CD single only.).
CD 5": Released Jan '89, on EMI-Manhattan, by EMI Records. Deleted Aug '89. Catalogue no: **CDMT 59**
7" Single: Released Jan '89, on EMI-Manhattan, by EMI Records. Deleted Aug '89. Catalogue no: **MT 59**
12" Single: Released '88, on EMI-Manhattan, by EMI Records. Catalogue no: **V-56114**
12" Single: Released Jan '89, on EMI-Manhattan, by EMI Records. Deleted Aug '89. Catalogue no: **12MT 59**

HYPERACTIVE
Tracks: / Hyperactive.
7" Single: Released Jan '84, on Parlophone, by EMI Records. Deleted '87. Catalogue no: **R 6065**

I SCARE MYSELF
Tracks: / I scare myself / Cloudburst at shingle street / Puppet theatre (On 12" only).
7" Single: Released Mar '84, on Parlophone, by EMI Records. Deleted '87. Catalogue no: **R 6067**

MY BRAIN IS LIKE A SIEVE
Tracks: / My brain is like a sieve (Not on 12".) / My brain is like a sieve (instrumental) / My brain is like a sieve (ext. mix) (12" only.) / Ravivar fiore (Not on 7".).
CD 5": Released Aug '89, on EMI-Manhattan, by EMI Records. Catalogue no: **203 503 2**
7" Single: Released Aug '89, on EMI-Manhattan, by EMI Records. Catalogue no: **MT 71**
7" Single: Released Aug '89, on EMI-Manhattan, by EMI Records. Catalogue no: **203 503 7**
12" Single: Released Aug '89, on EMI-Manhattan, by EMI Records. Catalogue no: **12MT 71**
12" Single: Released Aug '89, on EMI-Manhattan, by EMI Records. Catalogue no: **203 503 6**
CD 5": Released Aug '89, on EMI-Manhattan, by EMI Records. Catalogue no: **CDMT 71**

RADIO SILENCE
Tracks: / Radio silence / Radio silence (part 2).
7" Single: Released Apr '82, on Venice In Peril, by EMI Records. Catalogue no: **VIPS 102**

SHE BLINDED ME WITH SCIENCE
Tracks: / She blinded me with science.
7" Single: Released Nov '82, on Venice In Peril, by EMI Records. Deleted '85. Catalogue no: **VIPS 104**
7" Single: Released Jun '83, on Venice In Peril, by EMI Records. Catalogue no: **VIPS 105**
12" Single: Released Jun '83, on Venice In Peril, by EMI Records. Catalogue no: **12 VIPS 105**

URGES
Tracks: / Urges.
7" Single: Released Feb '81, on Armageddon, by Armageddon Records. Catalogue no: **AS 007**

WINDPOWER
Tracks: / Wind power.
7" Single: Released Jul '82, on Venice In Peril, by EMI Records. Catalogue no: **VIPS 103**
12" Single: Released Jul '82, on Venice In Peril, by EMI Records. Deleted '85. Catalogue no: **12 VIPS 103**

Dolby's Cube

GET OUT OF MY MIX
Tracks: / Get out of my mix / Get on out of my mix.
12" Single: Released Oct '83, on Parlophone, by EMI Records. Catalogue no: **12R 6063**
7" Single: Released Oct '83, on Parlophone, by EMI Records. Catalogue no: **R 6063**

MAY THE CUBE BE WITH YOU
Tracks: / May the cube be with you (cubular dub mix) / Googooplexus / Cube creature caviar.
7" Single: Released Jul '85, on Parlophone, by EMI Records. Catalogue no: **R 6100**
12" Single: Released Aug '85, on EMI (Odeon), by EMI Records. Deleted '86. Catalogue no: **12RA 6100**
12" Single: Released Jul '85, on Parlophone, by EMI Records. Catalogue no: **12R 6100**

Dolce, Joe

Biographical details: This American singer and songwriter, born in Ohio, spent more than a decade striving for success before achieving his one-off novelty smash. From the mid-Sixties until the mid-Seventies, he toured around the States in various folk-orientated groups. He relocated to Australia in the late Seventies, where he founded the Joe Dolche Music Theatre. One of the characters he dreamed up for this show was a stereotype Italian whom Dolce, being of Italian-American extraction, played himself.

The Italian-style Dolce wrote, co-produced and recorded a novelty Italian language spoof called *Shaddup Your Face.* This single cruised to No 1 in Australia at the beginning of 1981. Like all the best gimmick records, it was instantly hummable and extremely irritating. Its success spread to Britain, where it held the top slot for three weeks. All novelty hits are hated by as many people as they are loved by, but *Shaddup Your Face* won particular notoriety amongst UK music fans - for the whole of the 21 days that Dolce was No 1, the frustrated No 2 record was Ultravox's epic masterwork *Vienna.*

Having taken the mickey out of Italy, and found fame in Britain via Australia, this American artist finally charted in his own country. But *Shaddup Your Face* only managed to climb halfway up the US Hot 100, and subsequent releases failed to make an impression on anyone. On the British charts, Dolce was a true One Hit Wonder - one No 1 hit and nothing else ever. Bob MacDonald, 23 June 1985..

CHRISTMAS AT OUR HOUSE
Tracks: / Christmas at our house / I saw mommy kissing Santa Claus.
7" Single: Released Dec '81, on Red Bus, by Red Bus Records. Catalogue no: **RBUS**

IF YOU WANT TO BE HAPPY
Tracks: / If you want to be happy / Ain't been missing you.
7" Single: Released Jun '81, on Epic, by CBS Records. Deleted Jun '84. Catalogue no: **A 1300**

SHADDUP YOU FACE (SINGLE)
Tracks: / Shaddup you face / Ain't in no hurry.
7" Single: Released Feb '81, on Epic, by CBS Rccords. Deleted '84. Catalogue no: **EPC 9518**

Doldinger, Klaus

BOAT
Tracks: / Boat.
7" Single: Released May '82, on WEA, by WEA Records. Deleted Sep '87. Catalogue no: **K 18852**

Dole

DREAM, THE
Tracks: / Dream, The.
12" Single: Released 1 May '85, on Play It Again Sam(Belgium), by Play It Again Sam (Belgium). Catalogue no: **BIAS 003**

HAIRCUT
Tracks: / Haircut.
7" Single: Released 14 Jun '85, on Play It Again Sam(Belgium), by Play It Again Sam (Belgium). Catalogue no: **BIAS 008**
12" Single: Released 1 May '85, on Play It Again Sam(Belgium), by Play It Again Sam (Belgium). Catalogue no: **BIAS 007**

NEW WAVE LOVE
Tracks: / New wave love.
7" Single: Released Jun '81, on Ultimate, by Ultimate Records. Catalogue no: **ULT 402**

RUMROAD
Tracks: / Rumroad / Wreckaway, The.
7" Single: Released Dec '85, on Play It Again Sam(Belgium), by Play It Again Sam (Belgium). Catalogue no: **BIAS 019**
12" Single: Released Nov '85, on Play It Again Sam(Belgium), by Play It Again Sam (Belgium). Catalogue no: **BIAS 020**

SLUMBERLAND
Tracks: / Slumberland.
7" Single: Released 19 Jan '87, on Play It Again Sam(Belgium), by Play It Again Sam (Belgium). Catalogue no: **BIAS 045**

SMALL TOWN
Tracks: / Small town.
7" Single: Released '84, on Play It Again Sam(Belgium), by Play It Again Sam (Belgium). Catalogue no: **BIAS 003**

Dolenz, Mickey

TOMORROW
Tracks: / Tomorrow / Fat Sam.
7" Single: Released Jun '83, on A&M, by A&M Records. Catalogue no: **BUGSY 1**

Doll

BURNING UP LIKE A FIRE
Tracks: / Burning up like a fire / Frozen fire.
7" Single: Released Apr '80, on Beggars Banquet, by Beggars Banquet Records. Deleted Apr '83. Catalogue no: **BEG 38**

DESIRE ME
Tracks: / Desire me.
7" Single: Released Jan '79, on Beggars Banquet, by Beggars Banquet Records. Deleted '82. Catalogue no: **BEG 11**

YOU USED TO BE MY HERO
Tracks: / You used to be my hero / Zero heroes.
7" Single: Released Jan '80, on Beggars Banquet, by Beggars Banquet Records. Deleted Jan '85. Catalogue no: **BEG 31**

Doll By Doll

CARITAS
Tracks: / Caritas / Murder on the highway / An honest woman.
7" Single: Released Sep '81, on Magnet, by WEA Records. Deleted '84. Catalogue no: **MAG 195**
12" Single: Released Sep '81, on Magnet, by WEA Records. Deleted '84. Catalogue no: **12MAG 195**

GYPSY BLOOD (SINGLE)
Tracks: / Gypsy blood / Love myself.
7" Single: Released Feb '80, on Automatic, by Automatic Records. Deleted Feb '83. Catalogue no: **K 17559**

MAIN TRAVELLED ROADS
Tracks: / Main travelled roads / Be my friend.
7" Single: Released May '81, on Magnet, by WEA Records. Deleted May '84. Catalogue no: **MAG 188**

UNDER MY THUMB
Tracks: / Under my thumb / Eternal.
7" Single: Released Aug '82, on Magnet, by WEA Records. Deleted Aug '85. Catalogue no: **MAG 229**

Dollar

Biographical details: This British vocal duo, David Van Day and Thereza Bazar, were husband and wife when they achieved their first hit in 1978. But by 1983, they had split up, in both professional and personal tems. They first came to fame in the mid-Seventies as one-third of Guys and Dolls, the three boy/three girl vocal group who enjoyed two Top 5 hits in the UK.

As Dollar, they opened their UK chart career with two No 14 hits, 1978's *Shooting Star* and 1979's *Who Were You With In The Moonlight*. But then the duo's lucky number changed from 14 to 4. Their three biggest singles all reached the British No 4 position: 1979's *Love's Gotta Hold On Me* plus two 1982 hits, *Mirro Mirro (Mon Amour)* and *Give Me Back My Heart*. By the time of the latter two songs, Dollar's production was being handled by Trevor Horn; he had come to fame in '79 as 50% of the Buggles (UK No 1 single - *Video Killed The Radio Star*) but was now seeking to establish himself as a producer. His impressive work with Dollar led to a host of hugely successful Horn assignments - ABC, Malcolm McLaren, Yes, Frankie Goes To Hollywood and the Art Of Noise all benefited from his dramatic, hi-gloss, multi-layered studio treatment. In the case of Dollar, the Horn imprint was probably more responsible for their success than the duo's merely adequate vocals.

During the Eighties, Dollar's great rivals in the ultra-commercial pop stakes were Bucks Fizz. Comparisons between the two acts were heightened by the fact that, on four consecutive occasions, they entered the UK Top 40 in the same week. Dollar's singles nearly always took a long time climbing the charts - six of their hits logged a dozen or more weeks on the listings - but they reached the high numbers evenually. However, in late 1982, they tried to take greater control of their music. The results were disasterous, and their career collapsed almost immediately. Both halves of the duo embarked on solo projects, but these were unsuccessful. In 1985 Bazar attempted a comeback with the veteran producer Arif Mardin. Bob MacDonald, 23 June 1985..

GIVE ME BACK MY HEART
Tracks: / Give me back my heart / Pink and blue.
7" Single: Released Mar '82, on WEA, by WEA Records. Catalogue no: **BUCK 3**

GIVE ME SOME KIND OF MAGIC
Tracks: / Give me some kind of magic.
7" Single: Released Sep '82, on WEA, by WEA Records. Catalogue no: **BUCK 5**

HAND HELD IN BLACK AND WHITE
Tracks: / Hand held in black and white.
7" Single: Released Aug '81, on WEA, by WEA Records. Deleted '84. Catalogue no: **BUCK 1**

HAVEN'T WE SAID GOODBYE BEFORE
Tracks: / Platinum / Haven't we said goodbye before.
7" Single: Released Nov '86, on Arista, by BMG Records (UK). Catalogue no: **DIME 2**
12" Single: Released Nov '86, on Arista, by BMG Records (UK). Catalogue no: **DIME 122**

I WANNA HOLD YOUR HAND
Tracks: / I wanna hold your hand.
7" Single: Released Nov '79, on Carrere, Deleted '82. Catalogue no: **CAR 131**

IT'S NATURES WAY (NO PROBLEM)
Tracks: / It's natures way (no problem) / Dia y noche / O l'amour (on CD single only.).
Note: This is the follow up to the top ten smash hit 'Oh l'amour' and is produced by Phil Harding, Ian Curnow and Dollar; mixed by Phil Harding for P.W.L.
CD 5": Released Jun '88, on London Records, by London Records. Catalogue no: **LONCD 179**
7" Single: Released Jul '88, on London Records, by London Records. Catalogue no: **LON 179**
12" Single: Released Jun '88, on London Records, by London Records. Catalogue no: **LONX 179**

LOVE STREET
Tracks: / Love street / I need your love.
7" Single: Released May '80, on Carrere, Deleted '83. Catalogue no: **CAR 148**

LOVE'S GOT A HOLD ON ME
Tracks: / Love's got a hold on me.

DOLLAR - TAKIN' A CHANCE ON YOU (Released on WEA)

7" Single: Released Jul '79, on Carrere, Catalogue no: **CAR 122**

MIRROR MIRROR
Tracks: / Mirror mirror / Radio.
7" Single: Released Nov '81, on WEA, by WEA Records. Deleted '84. Catalogue no: **BUCK 2**

OH L'AMOUR
Tracks: / Oh l'amour / B-beat / Who were you with in the moonlight?.
12" Single: Released Nov '87, on London Records, by London Records. Deleted Oct '88. Catalogue no: **LONX 146**
7" Single: Released Nov '87, on London Records, by London Records. Deleted Oct '88. Catalogue no: **LON 146**

RING RING
Tracks: / Ring ring / Star control.
7" Single: Released Feb '82, on Carrere, Catalogue no: **CAR 225**

SHOOTING STAR
Tracks: / Shooting star.
7" Single: Released Nov '78, on EMI, by EMI Records. Deleted '81. Catalogue no: **EMI 2871**

TAKIN' A CHANCE ON YOU (see panel above)
Tracks: / Taking a chance on you / No man's land.
7" Single: Released Oct '80, on WEA, by WEA Records. Deleted '83. Catalogue no: **K 18353**

VIDEOTHEQUE
Tracks: / Videotheque / Living a life of dreams.
7" Single: Released Jun '82, on WEA, by WEA Records. Deleted '85. Catalogue no: **BUCK 4**

WALK IN LOVE
Tracks: / Walk in love / Love tonight / If this is love (On 12" version only.).
7" Single: Released Jul '86, on Arista, by BMG Records (UK). Catalogue no: **DIME 1**
12" Single: Released Jul '86, on Arista, by BMG Records (UK). Catalogue no: **DIME 121**
7" Single: Released Jul '86, on Arista, by BMG Records (UK). Catalogue no: **DIME 1 P**

WHO WERE YOU WITH IN THE MOONLIGHT
Tracks: / Who were you with in the moonlight.
7" Single: Released May '79, on Carrere, Deleted '82. Catalogue no: **CAR 110**

YOU TAKE MY BREATH AWAY (see panel below)
Tracks: / You take my breath away / Don't

DOLLAR - YOU TAKE MY BREATH AWAY (Released on WEA)

change your life.
7" Single: Released '81, on WEA, by WEA Records. Catalogue no: **K 18423**

Dollie Deluxe

CARMEN
Tracks: / Carmen / Gimme some lovin / Na.

12" Single: Released Mar '86, on Spartan, Catalogue no: **12SP 138**
7" Single: Released Mar '86, on Spartan, Catalogue no: **SP 138**

Dollops

HERE COME THE DOLLOPS
Tracks: / Here come the Dollops.
7" Single: Released Apr '80, on Peebly, Catalogue no: **PEEB 010**

NOBODY LOVES YOU LIKE THE DOLLOPS DO
Tracks: / Nobody loves you like the Dollops do / We've got a lot of work to do.
7" Single: Released Feb '81, on Dollop, by Dollop Records. Catalogue no: **DO 1**

Dolly Dots

DO WAH DIDDY DIDDY
Tracks: / Do wah diddy diddy / Ring ring.
7" Single: Released Nov '82, on WEA, by WEA Records. Catalogue no: **X 9999**

DON'T GIVE UP
Tracks: / Don't give up / I don't wanna lose ya.
7" Single: Released Mar '84, on WEA, by WEA Records. Catalogue no: **249650 7**

LEILA (QUEEN OF SHEBA)
Tracks: / Leila (Queen of Sheba) / Writer please write me a song.
7" Single: Released Dec '81, on WEA, by WEA Records. Deleted Dec '84. Catalogue no: **K 18473**

MONEY LOVER (BITE THE DUST)
Tracks: / Money lover (bite the dust).
7" Single: Released Jul '83, on WEA, by WEA Records. Catalogue no: **249796 7**

PS I LOVE YOU
Tracks: / P.S. I love you / So that's why.
12" Single: Released Jan '82, on WEA, by WEA Records. Catalogue no: **K 18829 T**
7" Single: Released Jan '82, on WEA, by WEA Records. Catalogue no: **K 18829**

RADIO
Tracks: / Radio / Please stay.
7" Single: Released May '80, on Evolution, by Evolution Records. Deleted May '83. Catalogue no: **EV 7**

WHAT A NIGHT (PARTY NIGHT)
Tracks: / What a night (party night) / What a night (party night) (inst) / What a night (party night) (ext.) (Available on 12" only).
12" Single: Released Jul '87, on RCA, by BMG Records (UK). Deleted May '89. Catalogue no: **PT 41614**
7" Single: Released Jul '87, on RCA, by BMG Records (UK). Deleted May '89. Catalogue no: **PB 41613**

Dolly Mixtures

BABY IT'S YOU
Tracks: / Baby it's you / New look baby.
7" Single: Released '80, on Chrysalis, by Chrysalis Records. Deleted '85. Catalogue no: **CHS 2459**

BEEN TEEN
Tracks: / Been teen / Honky Honda.
7" Single: Released Nov '81, on Respond (1), by Respond Records. Deleted Nov '84. Catalogue no: **RESP 1**

EVERYTHING AND MORE
Tracks: / Everything and more.
7" Single: Released Aug '82, on Respond (1), by Respond Records. Deleted Aug '85. Catalogue no: **RESP 4**

REMEMBER THIS
Tracks: / Remember this / Listening pleasure.
7" Single: Released Jan '84, on Dead Good Dolly Platters, Catalogue no: **DMS 1**

Dolmann

HIGH SEX DRIVE (REMIX)
Tracks: / High sex drive (remix).
12" Single: Released Oct '84, on Passion, by Skratch Records. Catalogue no: **PASH 33(12)**

Dolphin Brothers

SECOND SIGHT
Tracks: / Host to the holy / Second sight.
12" Single: Released Aug '87, on Virgin, by Virgin Records. Catalogue no: **VS 997-12**
7" Single: Released Aug '87, on Virgin, by Virgin Records. Deleted May '88. Catalogue no: **VS 997**

SHINING
Tracks: / Shining / My winter / Shining (am ex mix) (12" only).
12" Single: Released Jun '87, on Virgin, by Virgin Records. Catalogue no: **VS 969-12**
7" Single: Released Jun '87, on Virgin, by Virgin Records. Deleted May '88. Catalogue no: **VS 969**

Dolphin (group)

HEY JOE
Tracks: / Hey Joe.
7" Single: Released Apr '80, on Gale, Catalogue no: **GALE 5**

Domestos, Johnny

TEN COMMANDMENTS
Tracks: / Ten commandments
.
7" Single: Released Nov '84, on Button, by Musical Characters Records. Catalogue no: **BTN 120**

Domingo, Placido

Biographical details: The world famous Spanish operatic and classical singer has never reached the UK charts in a solo capacity, but did enjoy a hit single and album in duet with John Denver.
This somewhat unlikely alliance with the American country/pop singer/songwriter occurred in 1981, when they got together to record an LP of love ballads. It reached No 26 on the British chart, and logged 21 weeks on the Top 100. It included renditions of McCartney's *Yesterday* and Denver's own evergreen *Annie's Song*. As a single, the title track *Perhaps Love* reached the UK No 46 position.

In 1985 Domingo joined forces with Sarah Brightman and Lorin Maazel for Andre Lloyd Webber's *Requiem*, thus gaining a Top 10 success on the British LP list. Bob MacDonald, 24 June 1985..

ADORO (SINGLE)
Tracks: / Adoro / El triste.
7" Single: Released Jul '82, on CBS, by CBS Records. Deleted Jul '85. Catalogue no: **CBS A 2595**

BE MY LOVE
Tracks: / Be my love / Mattinata.
7" Single: Released Jan '81, on Polydor, by Polydor Ltd. Deleted Jan '84. Catalogue no: **LOVE 1**

EL MUNDIAL
Tracks: / El mundial / El mndial (part 2).
7" Single: Released Mar '82, on Polydor, by Polydor Ltd. Deleted '85. Catalogue no: **LOVE 3**

HOSANNA
Tracks: / Hosanna / Ingemisco / From Requiem.
7" Single: Released Dec '85, on H.M.V., by EMI Records. Catalogue no: **WEBBER 2**

I COULDN'T LIVE WITHOUT YOU FOR A DAY
Tracks: / I couldn't live without you for a day.
7" Single: Released Apr '83, on CBS, by CBS Records. Catalogue no: **A 3275**

I STAND ALONE
Tracks: / I stand alone / I will paint sounds / Hasta amarte (til I loved you) (Only on 12" single.).
7" Single: Released Jul '89, on CBS, by CBS Records. Catalogue no: **GOYA 2**
Cassingle: Released Jul '89, on CBS, by CBS Records. Catalogue no: **GOYAM 2**
12" Single: Released Jul '89, on CBS, by CBS Records. Catalogue no: **GOYAT 2**
CD 5": Released Jul '89, on CBS, by CBS Records. Catalogue no: **CDGOYA 2**

MY LIFE FOR A SONG (SINGLE)
Tracks: / My life for a song.
7" Single: Released Jun '83, on CBS, by CBS Records. Catalogue no: **A 3275**

PERHAPS LOVE (SINGLE)
Tracks: / Perhaps love / Annie's song.
7" Single: Released Feb '88, on CBS, by CBS Records. Deleted Aug '88. Catalogue no: **651 439 7**
7" Single: Released Dec '81, on CBS, by CBS Records. Deleted '84. Catalogue no: **A 1905**

PIE JESU
Tracks: / Pie Jesu.
7" Single: Released Mar '85, on EMI, by EMI Records. Deleted Oct '87. Catalogue no: **WEBBER 1**
12" Single: Released Mar '85, on EMI, by EMI Records. Catalogue no: **12WEBBER 1**

STARS ARE SHINING BRIGHT, THE
Tracks: / Stars are shining bright, The / Celeste aida.

7" Single: Released Apr '81, on EMI, by EMI Records. Deleted Apr '86. Catalogue no: **EMI 5171**

PLACIDO DOMINGO - TILL I LOVED YOU (Released on CBS)

TILL I LOVED YOU(see panel above)
Tracks: / Till I loved you / Overture - Espana / Viva Espana (dance mix).
Cassingle: Released 19 Jun '89, on CBS, by CBS Records. Catalogue no: **654843 4**
7" Single: Released 24 Apr '89, on CBS, by CBS Records. Deleted Oct '89. Catalogue no: **654843 7**
12" Single: Released 24 Apr '89, on CBS, by CBS Records. Deleted Oct '89. Catalogue no: **654843 6**
CD 5": Released 24 Apr '89, on CBS, by CBS Records. Catalogue no: **654843 2**

Dominic

DRUGS MAN TYPE OF LIVING
Tracks: / Drugs man type of living.
12" Single: Released Jul '88, on Jammy's, Catalogue no: **VPRD 319**

YEAR IN JAMAICA, A
Tracks: / Year in Jamaica, A / Ragamuffin / Move over, little donkey.
12" Single: Released Nov '87, on Mango, by Island Records. Catalogue no: **12IS 349**

Dominique

THIS IS HER LIFE
Tracks: / This is her life.
12" Single: Released 21 Nov '87, on Les Disques Du Crepuscule(Belgium), by Les Disques Du Crepuscule(Belgium). Catalogue no: **TWI 754**

Dominique, Lisa

JEALOUS HEART
Tracks: / Jealous heart.
12" Single: Released 23 Apr '88, on FM-Revolver, by FM-Revolver Records. Catalogue no: **12 VHF 47**

Domino

HERE I AM (MORE THAN EVER)
Tracks: / Here I am (more than ever) / Friend, The.
12" Single: Released Apr '88, on WEA, by WEA Records. Catalogue no: **YZ 179T**
7" Single: Released Apr '88, on WEA, by WEA Records. Catalogue no: **YZ 179**

Domino, Anna

LAKE
Tracks: / Lake.
7" Single: Released Jul '87, on Les Disques Du Crepuscule(Belgium), by Les Disques Du Crepuscule(Belgium). Catalogue no: **7TWI 756**

RHYTHM
Tracks: / Rhythm.
7" Single: Released Aug '85, on Operation Afterglow, Catalogue no: **OPA 001**
12" Single: Released Aug '85, on Operation Afterglow, Catalogue no: **12 OPA 001**

SUMMER
Tracks: / Summer.
7" Single: Released Aug '86, on Factory (1), by Factory Records. Catalogue no: **FAC 158**
12" Single: Released '88, on Crepescule, by Island Records. Catalogue no: **TWI 641**
12" Single: Released Aug '86, on Factory (1), by Factory Records. Catalogue no: **FAC 158T**

TAKE THAT
Tracks: / Take that / Koo Koo / Take that (Sing it yourself mix).
12" Single: Released '88, on Crepescule, by Island Records. Catalogue no: **TWI 586**
12" Single: Released Dec '85, on Operation Afterglow, Catalogue no: **12 OPA 005**

TEMPTING
Tracks: / Tempting.
7" Single: Released Mar '88, on For A Song, Catalogue no: **7TWI 838**
12" Single: Released Mar '88, on For A Song, Catalogue no: **TWI 838**

TRUST IN LOVE
Tracks: / Trust in love.
7" Single: Released Nov '83, on Les Disques Du Crepuscule(Belgium), by Les Disques Du Crepuscule(Belgium). Catalogue no: **7TWI 177**

Domino Band

FOOL IN LOVE
Tracks: / Fool in love, A / Fool in love (Instrumental).
12" Single: Released Mar '86, on Carrere, Catalogue no: **CART 385**

Domino Effect

DOLCE VITA
Tracks: / Dolce vita / Watch the boy.
7" Single: Released Jun '81, on Stiletto, by Fast Forward Distribution. Catalogue no: **STL 1**

GETTING SERIOUS
Tracks: / Getting serious / Stateside.
7" Single: Released Oct '81, on Stiletto, by Fast Forward Distribution. Catalogue no: **STL 2**

MAN SHE WANTS
Tracks: / Man she wants / La dolce vita.
7" Single: Released May '82, on Disques Bleu, by Disques Bleu Records. Catalogue no: **STL 6**

Domino, Fats

Biographical details: This American singer, pianist and songwriter, born in New Orleans into a small family of nine children, became interested in the piano as a child. While a teenager, he suffered a factory injury which restricted the use of some of his fingers. After much perseverance, he regained full control of his wounded hand, and, at the age of 17, he played with Billy Diamond's band at the local Hideaway Club. It was Diamond who bestowed the nickname Fats upon young Antoine Domino; with the latter's 16 stone weght showing no sign of diminishing, the monicker stuck with him for his entire career. In the late Forties, when Fats Domino was just entering his twenties, the young pianist met another local bandleader named Dave Bartholemew. The two became inseparable musical colleagues and Bartholemew served as his long-term co-writer, bandleader and trumpeter.
Fats Domino's first recording session took place in December 1949. It yielded his first smash hit, aptly titled *The Fat Man*. During

the Fifties, he became a key figure in rhythm and blues music, thanks to his influential boogie-woogie piano style, his appealing voice (which somehow managed to combine the smoothness of a ballad singer with a hint of Louis Armstrong-style gruffness) and his band's infectiously rolling rhythms. He was not only an R&B great but also a rock 'n' roll pioneer, helping to lay the groundwork for the mid-Fifties rock revolution.

Domino's sales statistics wre phenomenal. Of the singles that he released between 1949 and 1960, 23 became million sellers; 17 of those were written by the Domino/Bartholemew partnership. His first major success on the US pop charts - i.e. his first record to cross over from the black to the white audience - was 1955's *Ain't That A Shame*, which reached No 10; but it was beaten to the top by a watered down No 1 cover version from the ultra-wholesome white singer Pat Boone. Nevertheless, *Ain't That A Shame* established Domino in the pop market, and the hits flowed endlessly until the early Sixties. His American Top 10 pop hits included *I'm In Love Again* (1956), *Blue Monday* (from one of his several rock 'n' roll movie appearances, "The Girl Can't Help It"), *I'm Walkin'* and *Valley Of Tears* (1957), *Whole Lotta Loving*, *I Want To Walk You Home* and *Be My Guest* (1959) and *Walking To New Orleans* (1960).

The biggest success of Domino's career was one of his few non-original hits. His 1957 smash hit *Blueberry Hill* - a song originally associated with Gene Autry in 1941 - took him to No 2 in the US; this strolling, reflective rendition of the song remains one of the greatest classics of the Fifties. In Britain, *Blueberry Hill* reached No 6, thus becoming his only UK Top Tenner; however, he chalked up 18 subsequent British hits, all of which fell short of the Top 10.

Estimates of Domino's worldwide sales figures vary between 60 million and 70 million records. The respect that he has always commanded in the rock and pop world is such that one star - Chubby Checker - was even stage named after him. On both sides of the Atlantic, Domino's final Top 40 hit was *Red Sails In The Sunset* in late 1963. His recording career went down hill, although he remained an active live performer, as shown by his long overdue UK concert debut in 1967. He never really returned to the limelight. The seventies and eighties saw him performing a less hectic schedule of concert, cabaret and film work, plus a rare return to the recording studio with 1979's critically acclaimed album *Sleeping On The Job*. Bob MacDonald, 24 June 1985.

R&B singer, pianist and bandleader, born in New Orleans in 1928; one of the earliest and most popular of the '50's rock'n'rollers: USA top 40 hits in eight years; 66 altogether in the Hot 100. His first language was French; discovered as a teenager by Dave Bartholomew, his first recording session in 1949 included the traditional *Hey la bas*, indicating the coming together of many decades of New Orleans history and musical influences *La bas* was originally a voodoo god of luck, then identified in French/Catholic Louisiana with St Peter, finally became an R&B standard. Domino's first release was a cleaned-up drug song called *The fat man* for an R&Bhit in 1950; fifth release *Every night about this time* used the piano triplet for which he became famous, showing the influence of Little Willie Littlefield. Fats became a crossover act in 1955 with *Ain't that a shame*: Pat Boone covered it for a number one pop hit, but Fats's own record made the top ten and sales of the white cover/rip off were numbered. *Blue Monday* in 1957 was featured in the film *The girl can't help it* probably the best rock'n'roll movie ever made; *I'm walkin'* was covered by teenage TV star Ricky Nelson the samehyear and was the beginning of his career in music. Most hits were Domino-Bartholomew compositions, though standards included *Blueberry Hill*, *That's the reason I'm not pleasin' you*, *Red Sails in the sunset*, Hank Williams *Jambalaya* and the Beatles *Lady Madonna*. His smoky, blues tinged voice with a trace of French accent was instantly likeable; the party-music formula perfectly captured the innocent pleasure of early pop-rock with riffing saxes, rocking tenor solo (often by Lee Allen or Herb Hardesty) and the rolling New Orleans style piano; the band rocked hard but made it sound easy. Domino is still a huge draw whenever he chooses to tour. (Donald Clarke, April 1989).

AIN'T THAT A SHAME?
Tracks: / Ain't that a shame / Fat man.
7" Single: Released Jan '57, on London-American, Deleted '60. Catalogue no: **HLU 8173**

7" Single: Released May '84, on EMI Golden 45's, by EMI Records. Catalogue no: **G45 17**

BE MY GUEST (SINGLE)
Tracks: / Be my guest.
7" Single: Released Dec '59, on London-American, Deleted '62. Catalogue no: **HLP 9005**

BIG BEAT, THE
Tracks: / Big beat, The.
7" Single: Released Mar '58, on London-American, Deleted '61. Catalogue no: **HLP 8575**

BLUE MONDAY
Tracks: / Blue monday.
7" Single: Released Mar '57, on London-American, Deleted '60. Catalogue no: **HLP 8377**

BLUEBERRY HILL (SINGLE)
Tracks: / Blueberry Hill.
7" Single: Released Apr '83, on EMI (Europe), by EMI Records. Catalogue no: **2C 008 83272**
7" Single: Released Sep '79, on United Artists, by EMI Records. Catalogue no: **UP 36524**
7" Single: Released Apr '76, on United Artists, by EMI Records. Deleted '79. Catalogue no: **UP 35797**
7" Single: Released Nov '56, on London-American, Catalogue no: **HLU 8330**
7" Single: Released Jun '84, on SMP (2), Catalogue no: **SKM 06**

COUNTRY BOY
Tracks: / Country boy.
7" Single: Released Mar '60, on London-American, Deleted '63. Catalogue no: **HLP 9073**

HONEY CHILE
Tracks: / Honey chile.
7" Single: Released Feb '57, on London-American, Deleted '60. Catalogue no: **HLU 8356**

I WANT TO WALK YOU HOME
Tracks: / I want to walk you home.
7" Single: Released Oct '59, on London-American, Deleted '62. Catalogue no: **HLP 8942**

I'M IN LOVE AGAIN
Tracks: / I'm in love again.
7" Single: Released Jul '56, on London-American, Deleted '59. Catalogue no: **HLU 8280**

I'M WALKIN'
Tracks: / I'm walking.
7" Single: Released Apr '57, on London-American, Deleted '60. Catalogue no: **HLP 8407**

IT KEEPS RAININ'
Tracks: / It keeps rainin'.
7" Single: Released Jul '61, on London-American, Deleted '64. Catalogue no: **HLP 9374**

JAMBALAYA (SINGLE)
Tracks: / Jambalaya.
7" Single: Released Mar '62, on London-American, Deleted '65. Catalogue no: **HLP 9520**

LIL' BIT OF GOLD: FATS DOMINO
Tracks: / Blueberry Hill / I'm walking / Ain't that a shame / Walking to New Orleans.
CD 5": Released May '88, on Rhino, by Creole Records. Catalogue no: **R 373007**

MARGIE
Tracks: / Margie.
7" Single: Released May '59, on London-American, Deleted '62. Catalogue no: **HLP 8942**

MY GIRL JOSEPHINE
Tracks: / My girl Josephine.
7" Single: Released Jan '61, on London-American, Deleted '64. Catalogue no: **HLP 9244**

MY TOOT TOOT
Tracks: / My toot toot / Diggy liggy lo.
7" Single: Released Aug '85, on Magnum Force, by Magnum Music Group. Catalogue no: **MFS 004**

RED SAILS IN THE SUNSET
Tracks: / Red sails in the sunset.
7" Single: Released Oct '63, on H.M.V., by EMI Records. Deleted '66. Catalogue no: **POP 1219**

SICK AND TIRED
Tracks: / Sick and tired.
7" Single: Released Jul '58, on London-American, Deleted '61. Catalogue no: **HLP 8628**

THREE NIGHTS A WEEK
Tracks: / Three nights a week.
7" Single: Released Nov '60, on London-American, Deleted '63. Catalogue no: **HLP 9198**

VALLEY OF TEARS
Tracks: / Valley of tears.
7" Single: Released Jul '57, on London-American, Deleted '60. Catalogue no: **HLP 8449**

WALKIN' TO NEW ORLEANS (SINGLE)
Tracks: / Walkin' to New Orleans / Fat man.
7" Single: Released Oct '80, on United Artists, by EMI Records. Catalogue no: **UP 36525**
7" Single: Released Jul '60, on London-American, Deleted '63. Catalogue no: **HLP 9163**

WHAT A NIGHT (SINGLE)
Tracks: / What a night.
7" Single: Released Nov '61, on London-American, Deleted '64. Catalogue no: **HLP 9456**

Don & Oli

SUPERMAN
Tracks: / Superman.
12" Single: Released May '82, on Cartridge, Catalogue no: **CRD 106**

Donaghy, Eileen

MOTHER'S LOVE, A
Tracks: / Mother's love, A.
7" Single: Released '88, on Homespun (Ireland), by Outlet Records. Catalogue no: **HIS 12**

Donaldson, Eric

CHERRY OH BABY
Tracks: / Cherry oh baby / Keep on riding.
12" Single: Released Nov '83, on Trojan, by Trojan Records. Deleted May '88. Catalogue no: **TROT 9075**
7" Single: Released Apr '84, on Dynamic, Catalogue no: **DYN 14**
7" Single: Released Nov '83, on Trojan, by Trojan Records. Deleted May '88. Catalogue no: **TRO 9075**
12" Single: Released Apr '84, on Dynamic, Catalogue no: **DYN 1214**

EASY SQUEEZE
Tracks: / Easy squeeze.
12" Single: Released Jul '84, on World Enterprise, Catalogue no: **WER/D 113**

FESTIVAL 84
Tracks: / Festival 84.
12" Single: Released Oct '84, on Stage, Catalogue no: **DSR 3025**

HOW 'BOUT MAYBE?
Tracks: / How 'bout maybe? / I've been hurt so many times.
12" Single: Released Dec '82, on Jah Congo, Catalogue no: **YC 003**

LOVE YOU FI TRUE
Tracks: / Love you fi true.
12" Single: Released Aug '88, on Serengeti, by Serengeti Records. Catalogue no: **SGTI 02**

PENNY FARTHING
Tracks: / Penny farthing.
12" Single: Released Aug '88, on Serengeti, by Serengeti Records. Catalogue no: **SGTI 01**

PROUD TO BE JAMAICAN
Tracks: / Proud to be Jamaican.
12" Single: Released Oct '84, on Stage, Catalogue no: **unknown**

Donaldson, Ian

SUN AIN'T GONNA SHINE ANYMORE
Tracks: / Sun ain't gonna shine anymore, The / U.S.A. son / All I'm asking (Track on 12" only.).
12" Single: Released Sep '87, on Legend (1), by Legend Records (UK). Catalogue no: **12LM 10**
7" Single: Released Sep '87, on Legend (1), by Legend Records (UK). Catalogue no: **LM 10**

Donegan, Lonnie

Biographical details: This British singer, guitarist and banjoist, born in Glasgow, was christened Anthony Donegan but adopted the name Lonnie in 1952, in deference to Lonnie Johnson, the noted American blues artist whom he idolised. Donegan began playing the guitar as a 15 year old during the mid-Forties; by this time, his family was based in London. Between 1949 and 1951, he underwent National Service in Army where, during his spare time, he took up banjo and also drums. Soon after discharge, he joined Ken Colyer's jazz band; in 1954 the entire combo, including Lonnie, deserted their leader and became the Chris Barber Band. With Donegan on guitar and banjo, they became a regular fixture at Humphrey Littleton's club in London's Oxford Street. The Chris Barber Band included in their act a skiffle interlude, which gave Lonnie a chance to espouse his favourite music.

Rock Island Line, a LP track recorded in 1954 featuring Donegan (guitar), Barber (string bass) and Beryl Bryden (washboard), was later issued as a single and jumped into the UK Top 10 in early '56. Even more surprisingly, it became a similar success in the US (then a rare feat for a British act), peaking at No 8 on both sides of the Atlantic. The success of this record prompted Donegan to quit Barber and begin a full-time solo career.

Donegan never looked back. He quickly became Britain's 'King of Skiffle', popularising this intriguing offshoot of jazz. The main attractions of skiffle were its sheer straightforwardness and the cheapness of the necessary instruments - washboards, tea chests and broom handles were used by numerous improvised groups up and down the UK, either as additions to or substitutes for the guitar/banjo/bass/drums line-up. This UK boom, which happened at the same time as the arrival of rock 'n' roll, found favour with rock, folk and jazz fans.

Prior to the 1958 arrival of Cliff Richard, Donegan was Britain's top homegrown act. Even after that, the hits kept on coming until late 1962. During his seven year chart life, Donegan chalked up no less than 30 UK hits; even as late as 1985, the "Guinness Book Of British Hit Singles" still ranked him as Britain's 4th biggest domestic chart act of all time, despite his 23 year absence. In 1957 he managed two consecutive UK No 1 hits, with the traditional *Cumberland Gap* and the double A sided smash *Gamblin' Man* (adapted from a Woody Guthrie number)/*Putting On The Style* (a traditional song). His status as a leading folk music expert was exemplified by his inspired choice of material, which included adaptations of songs by Leadbelly (*Rock Island Line* and *Bring A Little Water, Sylvie*), Woody Guthrie, the Carter Family and Jimmie Driftwood. His third UK No 1 single, 1960's *My Old Man's A Dustman*, confirmed that he was moving into the world of music hall comedy and showbiz variety; also in this category was *Does Chewing Gum Lose Its Flavour (On The Bed Post Overnight)*, his only American Top 5 hit. The arrival of Beatlemania immediately knocked Donegan's chart career on the head; but his TV and concert appearances kept the star of skiffle, who had inspired so many young UK musicians, in steady money. Bob MacDonald, 28 June 1985.

Born Anthony Donegan in 1931 in Glasgow, he changed his name in homage to guitarist and blues singer Lonnie Johnson. He sang and played banjo with Chris Barber's trad group and launched skiffle pratically single handed, playing onstage between sets: he plundered the USA country/folk heritage, using songs by Woody Guthrie and Leadbelly etc. for 31 top 30 UK hits 1958-1962 not counting reentries but including an EP and an album which sold so well they reached the singles chart. His *Rock Island line* was a transatlantic top ten in 1956 and inspired satires (by Stan Freberg and Jim Dale), a sure sign of his deep influence. His beat was rock-solid; the hits were well-recorded and are still listenable. (Donald Clarke, April 1989).

BATTLE OF NEW ORLEANS
Tracks: / Battle of New Orleans.
7" Single: Released Jun '59, on Pye, Deleted '62. Catalogue no: **7 N 15206**

BRING A LITTLE WATER SYLVIE
Tracks: / Bring a little water Sylvie / Dead or alive.
7" Single: Released Sep '56, on Pye, Deleted '59. Catalogue no: **N 15071**

COMANCHEROS, THE
Tracks: / Comancheros, The.
7" Single: Released Jan '62, on Pye, Deleted '65. Catalogue no: **7 N 15410**

CUMBERLAND GAP
Tracks: / Cumberland gap.
7" Single: Released Apr '57, on Pye, Deleted '60. Catalogue no: **B 15087**

DOES YOUR CHEWING GUM LOSE ITS FLAVOUR
Tracks: / Does your chewing gum lose its flavour.
7" Single: Released Feb '59, on Pye, Deleted '62. Catalogue no: **7 N 15181**

DON'T YOU ROCK ME DADDY-O
Tracks: / Don't you rock me daddy-o.
7" Single: Released Jan '57, on Pye, Deleted '60. Catalogue no: **N 15080**

FORT WORTH JAIL
Tracks: / Fort Worth jail.
7" Single: Released Jun '59, on Pye, Deleted '62. Catalogue no: **7 N 15198**

GAMBLIN' MAN
Tracks: / Gamblin' man / Putting on the style.

7" Single: Released Jun '57, on Pye, Deleted '60. Catalogue no: **N 15093**

GAMBLIN' MAN (OLD GOLD)
Tracks: / Gamblin' man / Puttin' on the style.
7" Single: Released Jul '82, on Old Gold, by Old Gold Records. Catalogue no: **OG 9131**

GRAND COULEE DAM
Tracks: / Grand Coulee dam.
7" Single: Released Apr '58, on Pye, Deleted '61. Catalogue no: **N 15129**

HAVE A DRINK ON ME
Tracks: / Have a drink on me.
7" Single: Released May '61, on Pye, Deleted '64. Catalogue no: **7 N 15354**

I WANNA GO HOME
Tracks: / I wanna go home.
7" Single: Released May '60, on Pye, Deleted '63. Catalogue no: **7 N 15267**

JACK O' DIAMONDS
Tracks: / Jack o' diamonds.
7" Single: Released Dec '57, on Pye, Deleted '60. Catalogue no: **N 15116**

LIVELY
Tracks: / Lively.
7" Single: Released Nov '60, on Pye, Deleted '63. Catalogue no: **7 N 15312**

LONESOME TRAVELLER
Tracks: / Lonesome traveller.
7" Single: Released Sep '58, on Pye, Deleted '61. Catalogue no: **N 15158**

LONNIE'S SKIFFLE PARTY
Tracks: / Lonnie's skiffle party.
7" Single: Released Nov '58, on Pye, Deleted '61. Catalogue no: **N 15165**

LORELEI
Tracks: / Lorelei.
7" Single: Released Aug '60, on Pye, Deleted '63. Catalogue no: **7 N 15275**

LOST JOHN
Tracks: / Lost John / Stewball.
7" Single: Released Apr '56, on Pye, Deleted '59. Catalogue no: **N 15036**

MICHAEL ROW THE BOAT
Tracks: / Michael row the boat / Lumbered.
7" Single: Released Aug '61, on Pye, Deleted '64. Catalogue no: **7 N 15371**

MY DIXIE DARLING
Tracks: / My dixie darling.
7" Single: Released Oct '57, on Pye, Deleted '60. Catalogue no: **N 15108**

MY OLD MAN'S A DUSTMAN
Tracks: / My old man's a dustman.
7" Single: Released Mar '60, on Pye, Deleted '63. Catalogue no: **7 N 15256**
7" Single: Released Apr '79, on Flashback, by Mainline Records. Catalogue no: **FBS 10**

PARTY'S OVER,THE
Tracks: / Party's over, The.
7" Single: Released Apr '62, on Pye, Deleted '65. Catalogue no: **7 N 15424**

PICK A BALE OF COTTON
Tracks: / Pick a bale of cotton.
7" Single: Released Aug '62, on Pye, Deleted '65. Catalogue no: **7 N 15455**

ROCK ISLAND LINE (SINGLE)
Tracks: / Rock Island line / John Henry.
7" Single: Released Mar '82, on Decca, by Decca Records. Deleted '88. Catalogue no: **F 10674**

SALLY DON'T YOU GRIEVE
Tracks: / Sally don't you grieve / Betty Betty Betty.
7" Single: Released Jul '58, on Pye, Deleted '61. Catalogue no: **N 15148**

SAL'S GOT A SUGAR LIP
Tracks: / Sal's got a sugar lip.
7" Single: Released Sep '59, on Pye, Deleted '62. Catalogue no: **7 N 15223**

SAN MIGUEL
Tracks: / San Miguel.
7" Single: Released Dec '59, on Pye, Deleted '62. Catalogue no: **7 N 15237**

SKIFFLE SESSION
Tracks: / Skiffle session.
7" Single: Released Jul '56, on Pye, Deleted '59. Catalogue no: **NJE 1017**

STEWBALL
Tracks: / Stewball.
7" Single: Released Apr '56, on Pye, Deleted '59. Catalogue no: **N 15036**

TOM DOOLEY
Tracks: / Tom Dooley.
7" Single: Released Nov '58, on Pye, Deleted '61. Catalogue no: **7 N 15172**

VIRGIN MARY
Tracks: / Virgin Mary.
7" Single: Released Dec '60, on Pye, Deleted '63. Catalogue no: **7 N 15315**

Donegan's Dancing...

DONEGAN'S DANCING SUNSHINE BAND
Tracks: / Donegan's Dancing Sunshine Band / Leaving blues.
7" Single: Released Jul '87, on Rosie, by Rosie Records. Catalogue no: **RR 015**

Donkeys

DON'T GO
Tracks: / Don't go / Living legends.
7" Single: Released Feb '81, on MCA, by MCA Records. Deleted Feb '84. Catalogue no: **MCA 682**

LET'S FLOAT
Tracks: / Let's float / Let's float (pt 2).
7" Single: Released May '81, on MCA, by MCA Records. Deleted May '84. Catalogue no: **MCA 721**

NO WAY
Tracks: / No way / You jane.
7" Single: Released May '80, on Back Door (Holland), Deleted May '85. Catalogue no: **DOOR 6**

Donnelly, Bill

MOVE OVER, LITTLE DONKEY
Tracks: / Move over, little donkey / Bill and Phil-Hush / Hush.
7" Single: Released Nov '87, on Bold Reprieve (1), Catalogue no: **BRM 008**
7" Single: Released Nov '86, on Splash, by Splash Records. Catalogue no: **CPS 1008**

Donnelly, Seamus

OLD BOG ROAD
Tracks: / Old Bog Road / Noreen Bawn.
7" Single: Released '88, on Homespun (Ireland), by Outlet Records. Catalogue no: **HIS 8**

Donner, Ral

Biographical details: This American singer, born Ralph Donner in Chicago, cut his first record in 1985 as a 15-year-old. After relocating to New York, he achieved his breakthrough in 1961 with *Girl Of My Best Friend*. This mid-tempo pop song had originally been recorded the previous year by Elvis Presley, but had been hidden away on the B side of *A Mess Of Blues*. Adopting a quasi-Elvis vocal style, Donner reached No 19 on the US charts with his rendition, on which he was backed by the Starfires.

The came Donner's biggest record - *You Don't Know What You've Got (Until You Lose It)* cruised to the US No 4 slot in the late summer of '61; it was his only British chart entry, reaching No 25 and logging 10 weeks on the Top 50. Further singles during the early Sixties, all heavily influenced by Presley, included *Please Don't Go, What A Sad Way To Love Someone* and the acclaimed *I Got Burned*; but these were only minor successes, with the exception of *She's Everything (I Wanted You To Be)*, which reached the US No 18 position in February 1962.

These records earned Donner the dubious tage of being nothing more than a competent Elvis imitator, and it was thus impossible for him to carve out a musical career in other direction. He never returned to the US Top 40, and he simply accepted his status as the No 1 artist in America's large pool of full-time Presley soundalikes. In 1981 he was the narrator, and the voice of Elvis, in the movie "This Is Elvis". Ral Donner died of cancer in April 1984, at the age of 41. Bob MacDonald, 28, June 1985.

Pop vocalist born in Chicago (1943-84) who owed his celebrity to sounding like Elvis; yet his hits hold up better than most. First hit was *Girl of my best friend*, a song of obvious hit potential which Presley had recorded but not released on a single: it went top ten in 1961. His remarkable 2-disc set *1937-1977 I've just been away for a while now* had Scotty Moore, DJ Fontana, and the Jordanaires on it. (Donald Clarke, April 1989).

DAY THE BEAT STOPPED
Tracks: / Day the beat stopped.
7" Single: Released May '83, on Thunder, Catalogue no: **TD 7801**

DON'T LET IT SLIP AWAY
Tracks: / Don't let it slip away.
7" Single: Released May '79, on Inferno (1), by Inferno Records. Catalogue no: **HEAT 3**

YOU DON'T KNOW WHAT YOU'VE GOT (SINGLE)
Tracks: / You don't know what you've got.
7" Single: Released Sep '61, on Parlophone, by EMI Records. Deleted '64. Catalogue no: **R 4820**

Donovan

Biographical details: This British singer, songwriter, guitarist and harmonica player, born Donovan Leitch in Glasgow, was roaming around southern England when his talent was discovered by his future manager, Peter eden. Unusually, Donovan was launched on UK television before achieving a hit record - it was the highly successful show "Ready Steady Go" which gave him his big break in early 1965. He was marketed as Britain's answer to Bob Dylan, and two Dylanesque debut hits quickly followed: *Catch The Wind* and *Colours* both reached No 4 on the UK singles chart during 1965. A No 1 EP with *Universal Soldier* and a No 3 album with *What's Been Did And What's Been Hid* also helped to make 1965 a golden opening year for Donovan.

The singer's problem, however, was that he looked and sounded so much like Dylan (albeit a more lightweight version) that he was written off in many quarters as a mere copyist. Therefore, in 1966, he jumped onto the psychedelic bandwagon that just beginning to gain momentum in the States. Aiming his music specifically at the American market, he achieved two smash flower power hits with the US No 1 (Sunshine Superman and the US No 2 *Mellow Yellow*. Neith song was released in Britain until it had reached its Stateside peak, but both became UK Top 10 hits eventually. These gentle, melodic, drug-influenced but highly rhythmic records were warmly received by the growing numbers of 'mind-expanding' LSD takers; the songs encapsulated both the creativity and the naivety of the era.

Donovan's hits continued on both sides of the Atlantic until 1969. *There Is A Mountain* and the incredibly catchy *Jennifer Juniper* hit the Top 10 in the UK, and *Atlantis* did the same trick in the US. 1968's *Hurdy Gurdy Man* reached the Top 5 in both countries. All were produced by Mickie Most, whose shrewd commercial attitude contrasted with the gentle-voiced artists's philosophical appraoch. This strange alliance worked sufficiently well to yield two highly acclaimed albums, *Sunshine Superman* and *A Gift From A Flower To A Garden*. After one more transatlantic Top 40 hit with the ludicrous *Goo Goo Barabajagal (Love Is Hot)*, on which he was backed by the Jeff Beck group, Donovan parted company with Most in 1969; the artist simultaneously turned his back on the drug culture and moved into another fashionable arena, that of Eastern mysticism.

During the Seventies, Donovan largely faded from the public eye. No hit singles were forthcoming, and various LP, film and theatre projects tended to reach cult circles rather than the masses. The exception was 1973's *Cosmic Wheels* album, which reached No 15 in the UK; this marked a return to Most, who also produced his 1977 comeback attempt. Bob MacDonald, 28 June 1985..

ATLANTIS
Tracks: / Atlantis.
7" Single: Released Dec '68, on Pye, Deleted '71. Catalogue no: **7 N 17660**

CATCH THE WIND (OLD GOLD)
Tracks: / Catch the wind / Colours.
7" Single: Released Nov '81, on Old Gold, by Old Gold Records. Deleted Nov '84. Catalogue no: **OG 9134**

CATCH THE WIND (SINGLE)
Tracks: / Catch the wind.
7" Single: Released Mar '65, on Pye, Deleted '68. Catalogue no: **7 N 15801**
7" Single: Released Jul '80, on PRT Flashback, Catalogue no: **FBEP 107**

COLOURS (SINGLE)
Tracks: / Colours.
7" Single: Released Jun '65, on Pye, Deleted '68. Catalogue no: **7 N 15866**

GOO GOO BARABAJAGAL (LOVE IS HOT)
Tracks: / Goo goo barabajagal (love is hot).
7" Single: Released Jul '69, on Pye, Deleted Jul '72. Catalogue no: **7N 17778**

HURDY GURDY MAN
Tracks: / Hurdy gurdy man.
7" Single: Released May '68, on Pye, Deleted '71. Catalogue no: **7 N 17537**

JENNIFER JUNIPER
Tracks: / Jennifer Juniper.
7" Single: Released Feb '68, on Pye, Deleted '71. Catalogue no: **7 N 17457**

LAY DOWN LASSIE
Tracks: / Lay down lassie.
7" Single: Released Oct '81, on Luggage by Multicord Records. Catalogue no: **LUG 03**

MELLOW YELLOW
Tracks: / Mellow yellow / Sunshine superman.
7" Single: Released Feb '67, on Pye Deleted '70. Catalogue no: **7 N 17241**
7" Single: Released Feb '85, on EMI Golden 45's, by EMI Records. Catalogue no: **G 4545**

SUNSHINE SUPERMAN (RE-ISSUE)
Tracks: / Sunshine superman / Jennifer Juniper / Wear your love like heaven (No on 7".) / Mellow yellow.
CD 5": Released Jul '89, on EMI, by EM Records. Catalogue no: **CDEM 98**
CD 5": Released Jul '89, on EMI, by EM Records. Catalogue no: **203 451 2**
7" Single: Released Jul '89, on EMI, b EMI Records. Catalogue no: **203 451 7**
12" Single: Released Jul '89, on EMI, b EMI Records. Catalogue no: **12EM 98**
12" Single: Released Jul '89, on EMI, b EMI Records. Catalogue no: **203 451 6**
7" Single: Released Jul '89, on EMI, b EMI Records. Catalogue no: **EM 98**

SUNSHINE SUPERMAN (SINGLE)
Tracks: / Sunshine superman.
7" Single: Released Dec '66, on Pye Deleted '69. Catalogue no: **7 N 17241**

THERE IS A MOUNTAIN
Tracks: / There is a mountain.
7" Single: Released Oct '67, on Pye Deleted '70. Catalogue no: **7 N 17403**

TURQUOISE
Tracks: / Turquoise.

JASON DONOVAN - SEALED WITH A KISS (Released on PWL)

7" Single: Released Nov '65, on Pye, Deleted '68. Catalogue no: **7 N 15984**

Donovan, Jason

EVERY DAY I LOVE YOU MORE
Tracks: / Every day I love you more / I guess she never loved me.
12" Single: Released Sep '89, on PWL, by PWL Records. Catalogue no: **PWLT 43**
CD 5": Released Sep '89, on PWL, by PWL Records. Catalogue no: **PWCD 43**
7" Single: Released Sep '89, on PWL, by PWL Records. Catalogue no: **PWL 43**
Cassingle: Released Sep '89, on PWL, by PWL Records. Catalogue no: **PWMC 43**

NOTHING CAN DIVIDE US
Tracks: / Nothing can divide us / Nothing can divide us (versions).
7" Single: Released Sep '88, on PWL, by PWL Records. Catalogue no: **PWL 17**
12" Single: Released Sep '88, on PWL, by PWL Records. Catalogue no: **PWLT 17**

SEALED WITH A KISS (see panel on previous page)
Tracks: / Sealed with a kiss / Just call me up.
CD 5": Released Jun '89, on PWL, by PWL Records. Catalogue no: **PWCD 39**
7" Single: Released Jun '89, on PWL, by PWL Records. Catalogue no: **PWL 39**
12" Single: Released Jun '89, on PWL, by PWL Records. Catalogue no: **PWLT 39**
Cassingle: Released Jun '89, on PWL, by PWL Records. Catalogue no: **PWMC 39**

TOO MANY BROKEN HEARTS
Tracks: / Too many broken hearts.
7" Single: Released Feb '89, on PWL, by PWL Records. Catalogue no: **PWL 32**
12" Single: Released Feb '89, on PWL, by PWL Records. Catalogue no: **PWLT 32**
CD 5": Released Feb '89, on PWL, by PWL Records. Catalogue no: **PWCD 32**

Dons

GREEN ONIONS
Tracks: / Green onions.
7" Single: Released Apr '80, on Scratch, by Scratch Records. Catalogue no: **SK 1**

Don't Ask

DESTINY
Tracks: / Destiny / You need me now.
7" Single: Released Oct '88, on Zink, Catalogue no: **ZK 1007**

Doobie Brothers

Biographical details: The most successful line-up of this American rock band were Jeff Baxter, John Hartman, Keith Knudsen, Michael McDonald, Tiran Porter and Patrick Simmons. 'Doobie' is Californian slang for a joint.

The Doobie Brothers were formed in 1970 by Hartman, Simmons, Tom Johnston and Dave Shogren. Founded in San Jose, California, the band released their eponymous debut album in '71. Following the departure of Shogren and the arrival of Porter and Michael Hossack, they made it big in late 1972 with their album *Toulouse Street* and its joyous, anathemic opening track *Listen To The Music*, which climbed to No 11 on the US Hot 100. This particular song became a long-running radio favourite, with its chorus being perfect for use in jingles.

1973 saw the Doobies consolidate upon their new-found fame with the LP *The Captain And Me*, which yielded two US Top 20 singles, *Long Train Runnin'* and *China Grove*. During the mid-Seventies, they continued in their infectious groove, which was roughly half way between the Los Angeles laziness of the Eagles and the street toughness of the Allman Brothers Band. The Doobies were noted for their excellent vocal harmonies and some powerful guitar work. The band's 1974 album *What Were Once Vices Are Now Habits* produced a 'dark horse' smash single - *Black Water* was originally issued as a B side, but became an American No 1 A side in March 1975.

The Doobie Brotehrs' line-up was an ever changing phenomenon - guitarist/vocalist Simmons was the only member who stayed the whole course from 1970 to 1982 - but two especially interesting events were the addition of two former Steely Dan players: guitarist Baxter joined in 1974, and vocalist/keyboards player McDonald arrived in '75. The input of McDonald - particularly his high, immaculate, soulful voice - gave the group even greater impetus and injected a new R&B feel. He became the focal point of the band, culminating in their most successful LP, 1979's *Minute By Minute*; this yielded the classic US No 1 single *What A Fool Believes*. Their less interesting 1980 album *One Step Closer*, which contained the American Top 5 single *Real Love*, was the band's last. Although no official split was announced in 1982, it was final year of activity. McDonald was now more interested in launching a solo career, and in contributing guest performances to other artists' work.

Despite a couple of UK Top 20 albums in the mid-Seventies, the Doobie Brothers never really caught on in Britain. Their biggest UK singles, *Listen To The Music* and *Take me In Your Arms*, both peaked at No 29; *What A Fool Believes* could only manage a No 31 placing. Bob MacDonald, 29 June 1985.

Rock band formed in 1970 in San Jose, California, where drummer John Hartman had gone to reform Moby Grape with Skip Spence, instead formed Pud with guitarist Patrick Simmons; name changed to Doobie Brothers from slang for marijuana cigarette. Their second album added extra drummer Michael Hossack and replaced Shogren with Tiran Porter; *Toulouse street* in 1972 had a solid backbeat, interlocking guitars and everyone in on the harmonies, not unlike a '70's version of Moby Grape. Later Hossack was replaced by Keith Knudson, then guitarisst Jeff 'Skunk' Baxter and keyboardist Michael McDonald (both from Steely Dan) and Johnston left due to ill-health; the new lineup hit its stride with *Minute by minute* in 1978, which yielded a USA number one *What a fool believes*. Only the tight harmonies remained of the old Doobies sound; the group rode classy AOR success on McDonald's electric keyboards and Ray Charles-inspired vocals. There were more personnel changes before they gave up. McDonald's solo career has been successful. (Donald Clarke, April 1989).

DOCTOR, THE
Tracks: / Doctor, The / Too high a price / Anything for love (12" & CD single only.).
CD 5": Released Jul '89, on Capitol, by EMI Records. Catalogue no: **203 400 2**
CD 5": Released Jul '89, on Capitol, by EMI Records. Catalogue no: **CDCL 536**
7" Single: Released Jul '89, on Capitol, by EMI Records. Catalogue no: **CL 536**
7" Single: Released Jul '89, on Capitol, by EMI Records. Catalogue no: **203 400 7**
12" Single: Released Jul '89, on Capitol, by EMI Records. Catalogue no: **12CL 536**
12" Single: Released Jul '89, on Capitol, by EMI Records. Catalogue no: **203 400 6**

LISTEN TO THE MUSIC
Tracks: / Listen to the music.
7" Single: Released Mar '74, on Warner Bros., by WEA Records. Deleted Mar '77. Catalogue no: **K 16208**

LISTEN TO THE MUSIC (OLD GOLD)
Tracks: / Listen to the music / What a fool believes.
7" Single: Released Mar '86, on Old Gold, by Old Gold Records. Catalogue no: **OG 9573**

MINUTE BY MINUTE
Tracks: / Minute by minute.
7" Single: Released Jul '79, on Warner Bros., by WEA Records. Deleted Jul '82. Catalogue no: **K 17411**

NEED A LITTLE TASTE OF LOVE
Tracks: / Need a little taste of love / I can read your mind / Doctor, The (Not on 7".).
CD 5": Released Sep '89, on Capitol, by EMI Records. Catalogue no: **CDCL 552**
CD 5": Released Sep '89, on Capitol, by EMI Records. Catalogue no: **203 535 2**
7" Single: Released Sep '89, on Capitol, by EMI Records. Catalogue no: **203 535 7**
12" Single: Released Sep '89, on Capitol, by EMI Records. Catalogue no: **203 535 6**
12" Single: Released Sep '89, on Capitol, by EMI Records. Catalogue no: **12CL 552**
7" Single: Released Sep '89, on Capitol, by EMI Records. Catalogue no: **CL 552**

ONE STEP CLOSER (SINGLE)
Tracks: / One step closer / Thank you love.
7" Single: Released Oct '82, on Warner Bros., by WEA Records. Deleted Oct '85. Catalogue no: **K 17707**

POWER
Tracks: / Power / Cape fear river.
7" Single: Released Jul '80, on Elektra Asylum, by Elektra Records (USA). Deleted '83. Catalogue no: **K 12452**

TAKE ME IN YOUR ARMS
Tracks: / Take me in your arms.
7" Single: Released Jun '75, on Warner Bros., by WEA Records. Deleted Jun '78. Catalogue no: **K 16559**

WHAT A FOOL BELIEVES
Tracks: / Minute by minute / Real love (This track on 12" version only).
Note: Featuring Michael McDonald.
7" Single: Released Feb '79, on Warner Bros., by WEA Records. Deleted Feb '82. Catalogue no: **K 17314**
7" Single: Released Jan '87, on Warner Bros., by WEA Records. Deleted Jan '88. Catalogue no: **W 8451**
12" Single: Released Jan '87, on Warner Bros., by WEA Records. Deleted Jan '88. Catalogue no: **W 8451T**

Dooleys

Biographical details: This British family group enjoyed a run of lightweight UK pop hits in the late Seventies. The driving force behind the band was not any of the five male or three female Dooleys, but producer/writer Ben Findon. In August 1977, having just enjoyed a brief but lucrative run of British chart successes with Billy Ocean, he began to provide hits for the sugary octet. The first, *Think I'm Gonna Fall In Love With You*, reached No 13.

Further Top 20 successes, *Love Of My Life* and *A Rose Has To Die*, saw the Dooleys continuing to emulate the predictable New Seekers/Brotherhood of Man school of Eurovision-style singalong MOR pop. Then, in 1979, they achieved their two biggest UK singles with a blatant Abba imitation *Wnated* (No 3) and its follow-up *The Chosen Few* (No 7). In the same year, *The Best Of The Dooleys* hit the Top 10 of the UK LP chart.

With their inane grins and ultra-bland approach, the group were only palatable to record buyers for so long. The Dooleys - even their name was irritating - struggled in the relams of minor hit status during 1980, although their morale was restored by a successful tour of Japan in the same year. By the time of their final flicker of UK chart success in October 1981, they were already heading for the well-trodden cabaret circuit. Bob MacDonald, 30 June 1985..

6 TRACK HITS: DOOLEYS
Tracks: / Honey I'm lost / I think I'm gonna fall in love with you / Don't take it lying down / Love patrol / Rose has to die, A / Wanted.
7" EP: Released Aug '84, on Scoop 33, by Pickwick Records. Catalogue no: **7SR 5047**

AND I WISH
Tracks: / And I wish.
7" Single: Released Oct '81, on GTO, Deleted Oct '84. Catalogue no: **GT 300**

BODY LANGUAGE
Tracks: / Body language.
7" Single: Released Sep '80, on GTO, Deleted Sep '83. Catalogue no: **GT 276**

CHOSEN FEW, THE (SINGLE)
Tracks: / Chosen few.
7" Single: Released Sep '79, on GTO, Deleted Sep '82. Catalogue no: **GT 258**

DANCER
Tracks: / Dancer / Face in the crowd.
7" Single: Released Nov '81, on Epic, by CBS Records. Deleted Nov '84. Catalogue no: **EPC A 1813**

DON'T TAKE IT LYING DOWN
Tracks: / Don't take it lying down.
7" Single: Released May '78, on GTO, Deleted May '81. Catalogue no: **GT 220**

FLAVOUR OF THE MONTH
Tracks: / Flavour of the month / Can't dance.
7" Single: Released Aug '83, on R'n'R, by Nimbus Records. Catalogue no: **RR 001**

HONEY I'M LOST
Tracks: / Honey I'm lost.
7" Single: Released Sep '78, on GTO, Deleted Sep '81. Catalogue no: **GT 242**

IN A RIDDLE
Tracks: / In a riddle / Going solo.
7" Single: Released Oct '80, on GTO, Deleted Oct '83. Catalogue no: **GT 283**

LOVE OF MY LIFE
Tracks: / Love of my life.
7" Single: Released Nov '77, on GTO, Deleted Nov '80. Catalogue no: **GT 110**

LOVE PATROL
Tracks: / Love patrol / Once upon a happy ending.
7" Single: Released Mar '80, on GTO, Deleted Mar '83. Catalogue no: **GT 260**

ROSE HAS TO DIE, A
Tracks: / Rose has to die, A.
7" Single: Released Sep '78, on GTO, Deleted Sep '81. Catalogue no: **GT 229**

TAKEN AT THE FLOOD
Tracks: / Taken at the flood / Secret.
7" Single: Released May '81, on GTO, Deleted May '86. Catalogue no: **GT 289**

THINK I'M GONNA FALL IN LOVE WITH YOU
Tracks: / Think I'm gonna fall in love with you.
7" Single: Released Aug '77, on GTO, Deleted Aug '80. Catalogue no: **GT 95**

WANTED
Tracks: / Wanted.
7" Single: Released Jun '79, on GTO, Deleted Jun '82. Catalogue no: **GT 249**

Doolittle Band

WHO WERE YOU THINKIN' OF
Tracks: / Who were you thinkin' of / Arizona highways.
7" Single: Released Jan '81, on CBS, by CBS Records. Deleted Jan '84. Catalogue no: **CBS 9323**

Doonican, Val

Biographical details: This Irish singer enjoyed a string of middle-of-the-road hits on the UK charts during the mid-Sixties. The first was *Walk tall*, which entered the British Top 50 in late 1964 and peaked at No.3. By early '65, he had followed it with another Top Tenner, *The special years*. 1965 was indeed a great year for him - he attained a UK No.2 album and, also, managed to reach No.1 on the EP listings. 1966 saw Doonican making headway with his opportunistic cover version of Bob Lind's self-pened US hit *Elusive butterfly*. Lind had just reached No.5 in the States with his original rendition of this touching, evocative song; *What would I be*, written by Jackie Trent, climbed to No.2. A year later, he reached No.3 with *If the whole world stopped loving*. In January 1968 Doonican became the first Irish act to reach No.1 on the British LP chart, thanks to his album *Val Doonican rocks but gently*. The title was a reference not only to his style of music, but also to the rocking chair that accompanied him whenever he set foot in a television studio or on a concert stage. During the late Sixties and early Seventies, he achieved just two more major UK hit singles, *If I knew then what I know now* and *Morning* although his albums continued to sell in copious quantities. By 1972 record sales were only a small factor in Doonican's career. His main strength became TV, where his unaffected personality and safe choice of songs met with great approval from middle-aged housewives and others. During the late Seventies and early Eighties, his Saturday night BBC TV shows attracted acclaim for the simple fact that they were broadcast live, in an era when pre-recording was the norm. *Bob MacDonald, 30th June 1985)*

Born in 1928 in Waterford, Eire, the guitarist and singer came to London in a vocal group the ramblers in 1952 and later went solo on the advice of Anthony Newly. His easy listening family favourite TV show and records were patterned after those of Perry Como in the USA even to the point of borrowing Como's arranger Ray Charles. (Donald Clarke, April 1989).

6 TRACK HITS: VAL DOONICAN
Tracks: / Leavin' on a jet plane / Little arrows / I recall a gypsy woman / Little green apples / Here you come again / You and me against the world.
7" EP: Released Sep '83, on Scoop 33, by Pickwick Records. Catalogue no: **7SR 5023**

ELUSIVE BUTTERFLY
Tracks: / Elusive butterfly.
7" Single: Released Mar '66, on Decca, by Decca Records. Deleted Mar '69. Catalogue no: **F 12358**

FRENCH WALTZ
Tracks: / French waltz / Follow me.
7" Single: Released Oct '80, on RCA, by BMG Records (UK). Deleted Oct '83. Catalogue no: **RCA 10**

HEAVEN IS MY WOMAN'S LOVE
Tracks: / Heaven is my woman's love.
7" Single: Released Mar '73, on Philips, by Phonogram Ltd. Deleted Mar '76. Catalogue no: **6028 031**

IF I KNEW THEN WHAT I KNOW NOW
Tracks: / If I knew then what I know now.
7" Single: Released Oct '68, on Pye, Deleted Oct '71. Catalogue no: **7N 17616**

IF THE WHOLE WORLD STOPPED LOVING
Tracks: / If the whole world stopped loving.
7" Single: Released Oct '67, on Pye, Deleted Oct '70. Catalogue no: **7N 17396**

I'M GONNA GET THERE SOMEHOW
Tracks: / I'm gonna get there somehow.
7" Single: Released Apr '65, on Decca, by Decca Records. Deleted Apr '68. Catalogue no: **F 12118**

LIGHT THE CANDLES
Tracks: / Light the candles / Fly away.
7" Single: Released Jun '81, on RCA, by BMG Records (UK). Deleted Jun '84. Catalogue no: **RCA 94**

MEMORIES ARE MADE OF THIS
Tracks: / Memories are made of this.

7" Single: Released Feb '67, on Decca, by Decca Records. Deleted Feb '70. Catalogue no: **F 12566**

MISSISSIPPI MUD
Tracks: / Mississippi mud / Beautiful dreamer.
7" Single: Released May '82, on RCA, by BMG Records (UK). Deleted May '85. Catalogue no: **RCA 229**

MORNING
Tracks: / Morning.
7" Single: Released Dec '71, on Philips, by Phonogram Ltd. Deleted Dec '74. Catalogue no: **6006 177**

NOW
Tracks: / Now.
7" Single: Released Jun '68, on Pye, Deleted Jun '71. Catalogue no: **7N 17534**

QUIET MOVEMENTS
Tracks: / Quiet movements / Let's take the long way around the world.
7" Single: Released Jun '81, on RCA, by BMG Records (UK). Deleted Jun '84. Catalogue no: **RCA 87**

RING OF BRIGHT WATER
Tracks: / Ring of bright water.
7" Single: Released Apr '69, on Pye, Deleted Apr '72. Catalogue no: **7N 17713**

SOUNDS GENTLE
Tracks: / Sounds gentle.
7" Single: Released Dec '69, on Pye, Deleted '74. Catalogue no: **NSPL 18321**

SPECIAL YEARS, THE
Tracks: / Special years, The.
7" Single: Released Jan '65, on Decca, by Decca Records. Deleted Jan '68. Catalogue no: **F 12049**

TWO STREETS
Tracks: / Two streets.
7" Single: Released May '67, on Decca, by Decca Records. Deleted May '70. Catalogue no: **F 12608**

WALK TALL
Tracks: / Walk tall.
7" Single: Released Oct '64, on Decca, by Decca Records. Deleted Oct '67. Catalogue no: **F 11982**

WHAT WOULD I BE
Tracks: / What would I be.
7" Single: Released Nov '66, on Decca, by Decca Records. Deleted Nov '69. Catalogue no: **F 12505**

YOU'RE THE ONLY ONE
Tracks: / You're the only one.
7" Single: Released Feb '68, on Pye, Deleted Feb '71. Catalogue no: **7N 17465**

Doonicans

FISHERWOMAN'S WAY
Tracks: / Fisherwoman's way / Chanter's song, The / Drunken pretender, The / Piper's song.
12" Single: Released Jun '87, on Probe Plus, by Probe Plus Records. Catalogue no: **PP 23T**

Doors

Biographical details: This American rock group consisted of John Densmore, Robbie Krieger, Ray Manzarek and Jim Morrison. The band's name was said to have been inspired by two inter-related literary quotations, one by William Blake, the other by Aldous Huxley. The Doors were formed in Los Angeles in 1965. Although the group wrote their material collectively, their key creative, their key creative force from the outset was singer and frontman Jim Morrison; his three colleagues proved themselves to be fine musicians, but they were essentially his backing group. The Doors' stage show wasted no time in attracting controversy - they were banned from their first important venue on account of *The end*, a frighteningly convincing portrayal of a man's personal doomsday nightmare. But *The end* was just the beginning for this group - similar epics peppered their career. The Doors' self-titled debut album was released in 1967, and it contained not only *The end* but also another highly dramatic piece, *Light my fire*. This was the song that transformed the Doors from cult status to a US national sensation. It climbed to the American No.1 position in the summer of '67, its erotic liberalism and powerful sexuality being a suitable accompaniment to the summer of love and drugs. Their second album *Strange days*, also issued in 1967, yielded two US Top 30 singles, *People are strange* and *Love me two times*. 1968 brought the Doors a second American chart-topping single *Hello-I love you* emphasised their prowess as purveyors of pure pop, which was a vital part of their career despite all the other excesses. *Hello* became a rock classic, thus weathering the hiatus of being sued by the Kinks' Ray Davies, who was quick to notice its similarity to his song *All day and all of the night*.
Meanwhile Morrison continued to be Morrison. In December 1967, a Doors concert was interrupted when he mounted an obscene and vitroilic verbal attack upon the police - the officers on duty in the arena arrested him; in March 1969, he was arrested for indecent exposure on stage. Some observers though that the enigmatic singer was a poetic genius who was driven into a world o f bleak desperation by his addiction to drink and drugs; others thought that he was mad from the outset. The group's music began to suffer in 1969 - apart from that year's American Top 3 single *Touch me*, they were on a weakish form until 1971's *L.A. Woman* album and its US hit single *Love her madly*. But by the time the LP's second hit single - the doom laden classic *Riders on the storm* - went into the charts on both sides of the Atlantic, Morrison was dead. Or was he?
Officially Morrison suffered a fatal heart attack in July 1971, at the age of 27, while residing in Paris; but subsequently, speculation that he faked his own death mounted, when it transpired that his corpse was seen only by his wife Pamela, how died from a heroin overdose in 1974, and by a doctor whose identity was never revealed. Either explanation would by totally in keeping with Jim Morrison's life history - but the former (i.e. that he really is dead) is far more likely, in view of his physical and mental excesses. In Britain, the Doors' chart performance was never spectacular. Of their singles only *Hello - I love you* made the Top 20; their highest placed LP was 1970's *Morrison hotel* which reached the UK No.12 position. In both the UK and US, however, the Doors' legendary status grew to enormous proportions during the Seventies and Eighties. The three surviving members could not live up to the legend of the group's past, and their various attempts to continue and revive the band were inevitable failures. (Bob MacDonald, 30th June 1985)
Rock band formed in Los Angeles in 1965 by vocalist/poet Jim Morrison (1943-71, whose early death was probably a good career move, and classically trained pianist Ray Manzarek, both students at UCLA film school, with guitarist Robby Krieger and drummer John Densmore. Morrison renamed the band Doors after Aldous Huxley's book about the drug experience, The Doors of Perception (Huxley borrowed it from poet William Blake). They were controvesal from the start, Morrison eventually exposing himself on stage in Miami in 1969; both police and promoters allowed themselves to be convinced that music could influence history with lines like 'They got the guns but we got the numbers' (from *Five to one*. By the time they emerged from the underground (not a tube train but a California sub-culture) songs like *Light my fire* and *Hello I love you* made good pop hits, but having become successful they must perforce have sold out, according to the same underground. In fact, without access to computers, synths, sequencers and all the junk so common today, they actually made some good old rock along the way. (Donald Clarke, April 1989)o.

END, THE
Tracks: / End, The / Delta.
7" Single: Released Jan '80, on Elektra, by Elektra Records (UK). Deleted '83. Catalogue no: **K 12400**
12" Single: Released Dec '88, on Elektra (Germany), by Elektra Records (USA). Catalogue no: **ELK 22032**

HELLO I LOVE YOU
Tracks: / Hello I love you.
7" Single: Released Feb '79, on Elektra, by Elektra Records (UK). Deleted Feb '82. Catalogue no: **K 12215**
7" Single: Released Aug '68, on Elektra, by Elektra Records (UK). Deleted Aug '71. Catalogue no: **ESKN 45037**

LIGHT MY FIRE
Tracks: / Light my fire.
7" Single: Released Sep '76, on Elektra (USA), by Elektra Records (USA). Catalogue no: **K 12227**
7" Single: Released Aug '67, on Elektra, by Elektra Records (UK). Deleted Aug '70. Catalogue no: **EKSN 45014**

RIDERS ON THE STORM
Tracks: / Riders on the storm / Light my fire.
7" Single: Released Feb '76, on Elektra (USA), by Elektra Records (USA). Catalogue no: **K 12203**
7" Single: Released Jul '81, on Elektra (USA), by Elektra Records (USA). Catalogue no: **K 12021**

RIDERS ON THE STORM (OLD GOLD)
Tracks: / Riders on the storm.
7" Single: Released Sep '85, on Old Gold, by Old Gold Records. Catalogue no: **OG 9520**

Doppelganger

COMMUNICATION BREAKDOWN
Tracks: / Communication breakdown.
12" Single: Released Apr '85, on EMI-Manhattan, by EMI Records. Catalogue no: **12 MT 1**
7" Single: Released Apr '85, on EMI-Manhattan, by EMI Records. Catalogue no: **MT 1**

MISTY EYED 33
Tracks: / Misty eyed 33 / Cover up.
7" Single: Released Dec '82, on Holyrood, by REL Records. Deleted Dec '85. Catalogue no: **HOLLY 1**

Dorchester, Des

POOR LITTLE ANGELINE
Tracks: / Poor little Angeline / Lambeth walk.
7" Single: Released Aug '83, on Dingle's, by Dingle's Records. Catalogue no: **SID 214**
7" Single: Released Jan '81, on Diversion, by Dingle's Records. Deleted Jan '84. Catalogue no: **DIV 114**

Dore, Charlie

Biographical details: This British singer and guitarist worked as a session vocalist during the latter half of the Seventies. In 1979 she launched a solo career with the LP *Where to now*. Receiving strong assistance from musician and producer Alan Tarney (who co-produced the album with Bruce Welch), it contained an unadventurous but catchy batch of country-flavoured pop songs. Amongst them was *Pilot of the airwaves*, a ditty about a radio listener asking her friendly DJ for a request. This was issued as a single but, despite predictably heavy airplay, it peaked at No.66 on the UK chart in November '79. Dore, definitely a female artist in spite of her Christian name, never returned to the British charts. But in the Spring of 1980, a re-edited and remixed version of *Pilot of the airwaves* cruised to No.13 on the American listings. Surprisingly, this was her only Stateside success too. After switching from Island to Chrysalis in 1981, she released a second album *Listen*, but this fell on deaf ears. She nosedived into obscurity, which was surprising in view of the fact that some observers had initially believed that this artist possessed considerable commercial potential in the pop and country markets. *Bob MacDonald, 1st July 1985).*

PILOT OF THE AIRWAVES
Tracks: / Pilot of the airwaves.
7" Single: Released Nov '79, on Island, by Island Records. Deleted Nov '82. Catalogue no: **WIP 6526**

WHERE TO NOW?
Tracks: / Where to now? / Fear of flying.
7" Single: Released Feb '80, on Island, by Island Records. Deleted Feb '83. Catalogue no: **WIP 6575**

YOU SHOULD HEAR
Tracks: / You should hear / Like they do it in America.
7" Single: Released Sep '81, on Chrysalis, by Chrysalis Records. Deleted Sep '84. Catalogue no: **CHS 2557**

Doreen and Country

OLD SCOTIAS DRUM
Tracks: / Old scotia's drum / Spinning wheel.
7" Single: Released May '80, on Neptune, by Lismor Records. Deleted May '85. Catalogue no: **NS 7**

Dorf, Joe

WEEKEND IN PARADISE
Tracks: / Weekend in paradise.
7" Single: Released Oct '89, on Supreme, by Supreme Records. Catalogue no: **289 221 0**
CD 5": Released Oct '89, on Supreme, by Supreme Records. Catalogue no: **289 864 2**
12" Single: Released Oct '89, on Supreme, by Supreme Records. Catalogue no: **289 212 7**

Dorian Gray

TOUCH
Tracks: / Touch.
12" Single: Released May '86, on Leeds Independent (LIL), by Revolver Records. Catalogue no: **LIL 12005**

Doris

LOVE IS FIRE
Tracks: / Love is fire.
7" Single: Released May '86, on Sonet, by Sonet Records. Catalogue no: **SON 2307**

Dormannu

DEGENERATE
Tracks: / Degenerate.
12" Single: Released Mar '85, on Illuminated, Catalogue no: **ILL 3612**

DREAD, THE
Tracks: / Dread, The.
12" Single: Released Feb '85, on Illuminated, Catalogue no: **ILL 5012**

POWDERED LOVER
Tracks: / Powdered lover.
7" Single: Released Mar '85, on Illuminated, Catalogue no: **ILL 24**

Dorothy

LOVING FEELING
Tracks: / Loving feeling / Sexual obsession.
CD 5": Released Jan '89, on Blue Guitar, by Blue Guitar Records. Catalogue no: **AZURCD 11**
7" Single: Released Jan '89, on Blue Guitar, by Blue Guitar Records. Catalogue no: **AZUR 11**
12" Single: Released Jan '89, on Blue Guitar, by Blue Guitar Records. Catalogue no: **AZURX 11**

REFLECTIONS
Tracks: / Reflections / Reflections (version).
7" Single: Released Jul '89, on Cool Tempo, by Chrysalis Records. Catalogue no: **COOL 187**
12" Single: Released Jul '89, on Cool Tempo, by Chrysalis Records. Catalogue no: **COOLX 187**

STILL WAITING
Tracks: / Still waiting / Frog prince, The.
12" Single: Released 25 Jul '88, on Blue Guitar, by Blue Guitar Records. Catalogue no: **AZURX 8**
7" Single: Released 25 Jul '88, on Blue Guitar, by Blue Guitar Records. Catalogue no: **AZUR 8**

Dorothy & Jennifer

YOU NEVER TOLD ME (LOVE HURTS)
Tracks: / You never told me (love hurts).
12" Single: Released Jan '82, on PRT, by Castle Communications Records. Deleted Jan '85. Catalogue no: **12P 228**
7" Single: Released Jan '82, on PRT, by Castle Communications Records. Deleted Jan '85. Catalogue no: **7P 228**

Dorper, Ralph

RAZORHEAD, THE
Tracks: / Razorhead, The.
12" Single: Released Jan '83, on Operation Twilight, Catalogue no: **OPT 018**

Dors, Diana

WHERE DID THEY GO?
Tracks: / Where did they go? / It's you again.
7" Single: Released Dec '81, on Nomis, by Nomis Records. Catalogue no: **NOM 1**

Dorset, Ray

KNOCKING ON HEAVENS DOOR
Tracks: / Knocking on heaven's door / Hazel eyes.
7" Single: Released Oct '81, on Stage coach, Deleted '85. Catalogue no: **TRI 101**

Dorsey, Gail Ann

JUST ANOTHER DREAM
Tracks: / Just another dream / Look wha love's got me doing again / Meet you to night.
CD 5": Released Mar '89, on WEA, b WEA Records. Catalogue no: **YZ 369CD**
7" Single: Released Mar '89, on WEA, b WEA Records. Catalogue no: **YZ 369**
12" Single: Released Mar '89, on WEA, b WEA Records. Catalogue no: **YZ 369T**

WASTED COUNTRY
Tracks: / Wasted country / Happy ending.
12" Single: Released Jul '88, on WEA, b WEA Records. Catalogue no: **YZ 194T**
7" Single: Released Jul '88, on WEA, b WEA Records. Catalogue no: **YZ 194**
CD 5": Released 22 Aug '88, on WEA, b WEA Records. Catalogue no: **YZ 194CD**

WHERE IS THE LOVE
Tracks: / Where is your love / Try it out o me / Base in your faith (12" only) / Me you tonight.
CD 5": Released Nov '88, on WEA, b WEA Records. Catalogue no: **YZ 324 CD**
7" Single: Released Nov '88, on WEA, b WEA Records. Catalogue no: **YZ 324**
12" Single: Released Nov '88, on WEA, b WEA Records. Catalogue no: **YZ 324T**

Dorsey, Lee

Biographical details: This Americ singer, born in New Orleans in 1924, w moving into his late thirties by the time achieved his first big US hit in late 1961. This extraordinarily late start was explained by his three former careers - he spent four years in the American Navy, and was also a professional boxer under the name of Kid Chocolate. While running a car business in New Orleans, he decided to try his luck at a singing career. The song that propelled Dorsey to fame was one that he co-wrote, *Ya ya*. This infectiously energetic single reached No.7 on the US charts in lat '61. In Britain, it was covered by Petula Clark, who called it *Ya Ya twist* (in recognition of the current dance craze) and took it to the UK No.14 slot in 1962. Dorsey's follow-up, *Do re mi*, was another US Top 40 hit for him. However, the Fury record label folded, which hindered his career. After a long absence, he returned to the limelight with 1965's *Ride your pony*. Now working with New Orleans' noted musician/composer/arranger/producer Allen Toussaint, Dorsey enjoyed a run of four British hits in 1966. The first two, *Get out of my life woman* and *Confusion*, failed to make the US Top 40; but he then reached No.8 on both sides of the Atlantic with the R&B classic *Working in the coalmine*. His final success was the energetic *Holy cow*, which cruised to No.6 in the UK and peaked at No.23 in the US. Subsequent records returned Dorsey from the world of international stardom to the more modest horizons of small time New Orleans fame. (Bob MacDonald, 1st July 1985)

A New Orleans R&B singer (1924-86) who worked with producer Allen Toussaint for a series of USA hits in the '60's including *Yah yah* and *Working in the coal mine*. The classic statement of the era's New Orleans sound from the two veterans was the album *Yes we can* in 1970; the title track was Dorsey's last chart entry. He guested on the debut album *I don't want to go home* in 1976 by Southside Johnny and the Asbury Jukes and made the album *Night people*, issued on ABC just as the label closed down. (Donald Clarke, April 1989).

CONFUSION
Tracks: / Confusion.
7" Single: Released May '66, on Stateside, by EMI Records. Deleted May '69. Catalogue no: **SS 506**

GET OUT OF MY LIFE WOMAN
Tracks: / Get out of my life woman.
7" Single: Released Feb '66, on Stateside, by EMI Records. Deleted Feb '69. Catalogue no: **SS 485**
7" Single: Released Mar '81, on Charly, by Charly Records. Deleted '87. Catalogue no: **CTD 129**

HOLY COW
Tracks: / Holy cow.
7" Single: Released Oct '66, on Stateside, by EMI Records. Deleted Oct '69. Catalogue no: **SS 552**

WORKING IN A COALMINE (CD SINGLE)
Tracks: / Working in a coalmine / Holy cow / Get out of my life woman / Ride your pony.
CD 5": Released Feb '89, on Charly R&B, by Charly Records. Catalogue no: **CDS 5**

WORKING IN A COALMINE (SINGLE)
Tracks: / Working in a coalmine / Ya ya / Holy cow.
7" Single: Released Aug '66, on Stateside, by EMI Records. Deleted Aug '69. Catalogue no: **SS 528**
7" Single: Released Jul '80, on Charly, by Charly Records. Deleted '87. Catalogue no: **CTD 101**
7" Single: Released Aug '84, on Creole (Replay), by Creole Records. Catalogue no: **CR 212**
7" Single: Released Jul '82, on Old Gold, by Old Gold Records. Catalogue no: **OG 9108**
7" Single: Released Jun '84, on SMP (2), Catalogue no: **SKM 07**

Dorsey, Tommy

Biographical details: This American trombonist and bandleader holds the unique and important distinction of having the first No.1 record on the world's first record sales chart. Published by Billboard magazine (still America's leading chart source) in July 1940, he was No.1 with *I'll never smile again*. To add to his triumph, he also held the US No.8 position that week with *Imagination*; his equally famous bandleading brother, Jimmy Dorsey, was No.2 with *The breeze and I*. Tommy, who first led his own orchestra in 1935, died in November 1956 at the age of 51; his elder brother passed away mere months later. After Tommy's death, the trombone player Warren Covington took over the Tommy Dorsey Orchestra. It was this set-up that scored a major hit on the British charts at the end of 1958. *Tea for two cha cha*, an updated dance version of the 1924 standard *Tea for two* reached No.3 and spent 19 weeks on the UK Top 30. In the States, the tune got to No.7. (Bob MacDonald, 1st July 1985)

Trombonist and one of the Swing Era's most successful bandleaders (1905-56). Also see biography for Dorsey Brothers. After the split from brother Jimmy he took over the band of his old friend Joe Haymes; among the excellent sidemen who passed through were trumpeters Bunny Berigan, Yank Lawson, Charlie Shavers, Max Kaminsky, Sterling Bose, Charlie Spivak, Pee Wee Erwin and Ziggy Elman; also see Buddy DeFranco on clarinet; Bud Freeman on tenor sax; Dave Tough, Buddy Rich and Louis Bellson on drums; arrangers Paul Weston, Axel Stordahl, Sy Oliver, Deane Kincaide; vocalists Edythe Wright, Jack Leanord, Dick Haymes, Connie Haines, Joe Stafford, Frank Sinatra ... The parade of talent seemed endless, and the band could play sweet or hot as well as almost any other. Dorsey was not only a talent scout, but one of the best trombonists in music, with a seamless legato, beautiful tone and phrasing; Sinatra admitted learning about phrasing and dynamics from Dorsey. The band's theme *I'm getting sentimental over you* had first been recorded in 1932 by the Dorsey Brothers band and led to Tommy's title as 'The sentimental gentlemen of swing'. There were more than 180 hits in less than 15 years, including some of the biggest of the era: *Marie* featured a vocal by Leonard against a chant by the band of a paraphrase of the lyrics; the Swing Choir device was invented by Don Redman, but Dorsey apparently got the arrangement from Doc Wheeler's Sunset Serenaders, who once cut him in a ballroom battle of the bands. *Marie* was backed with *Song of India* (from Rimsky-Korsakov) and both featured Berigan, the era's greatest white trumpeter. *Boogie woogie* was an arrangement of the Pinetop Smith classic; Sy Oliver (poached from Jimmie Lunceford) was responsible for *Opus No.1* and *On the sunny side of the street* (again using the Swing Choir effect); Oliver and Stafford say on *Yes indeed*; *Indian summer* and *All the things you are* were number one hits featuring Leonard, and *Polka dots and moonbeams, I'll never smile again, Delores, There are such things, In the blue of the evening* and many more featured Sinatra. The very name of Tommy Dorsey is synonymous with the whole era. (Donald Clarke, April 1989).

TEA FOR TWO CHA CHA
Tracks: / Tea for two cha cha.
7" Single: Released Oct '58, on Brunswick, by Decca Records. Deleted Oct '61. Catalogue no: **05757**

Dots

HELEN IN YOUR HEADPHONES
Tracks: / Helen in your headphones / Come and get it.
7" Single: Released Feb '82, on EMI, by EMI Records. Deleted May '85. Catalogue no: **EMI 5268**

Dotti & Diplomats

MADE IN HONG KONG
Tracks: / Made in Hong Kong / Making it hard enough.
7" Single: Released May '80, on Magnet, by WEA Records. Deleted May '83. Catalogue no: **MAD 171**

Double

CAPTAIN OF HER HEART
Tracks: / Captain of her heart, The.
7" Single: on Polydor, by Polydor Ltd. Deleted Mar '87. Catalogue no: **POSP 779**

DEVIL'S BALL
Tracks: / Devils ball / Megarhythm dance (Only on 12" single.).
7" Single: Released Oct '87, on Polydor, by Polydor Ltd. Catalogue no: **POSP 888**
12" Single: Released Oct '87, on Polydor, by Polydor Ltd. Catalogue no: **POSPX 888**
CD 5": Released 30 Nov '87, on Polydor, by Polydor Ltd. Catalogue no: **POCD 888**

GLIDING
Tracks: / Gliding / Lakes in the desert / Gliding (extended version).
Note: New single from Swiss techno-jazz band, taken from the album Double.
7" Single: Released May '88, on Polydor, by Polydor Ltd. Catalogue no: **POSP 903**
CD 5": Released May '88, on Polydor, by Polydor Ltd. Catalogue no: **POLD 903**
12" Single: Released May '88, on Polydor, by Polydor Ltd. Catalogue no: **POSPX 903**

Double Trouble

FEEL THE MUSIC (FEEL THE BASS)
Tracks: / Feel the music (feel the bass).
12" Single: Released 6 Feb '89, on B-Ware, by B/Ware Records. Catalogue no: **UM 005 R**
7" Single: Released 6 Feb '89, on B-Ware, by B/Ware Records. Catalogue no: **UM 005 R**
12" Single: Released Dec '88, on B-Ware, by B/Ware Records. Catalogue no: **UM 005**

JUST KEEP ROCKIN'
Tracks: / Just keep rockin' (hip house mix) / Just keep rockin' (ska house mix).
7" Single: Released Apr '89, on Desire, by Desire Records. Catalogue no: **WANT 9**
12" Single: Released Apr '89, on Desire, by Desire Records. Catalogue no: **WANTX 9**

Double Vision

NEW DAY
Tracks: / New day.
7" Single: Released Aug '84, on And, by And Records. Catalogue no: **ANDS 002**

Doug

DEBORAH
Tracks: / Deborah.
7" Single: Released Oct '82, on Shattered, Catalogue no: **OSCAR 1**

TOO BAD
Tracks: / Too bad / Move.
7" Single: Released 20 Jun '80, on Badge, by Badge Records. Deleted '83. Catalogue no: **BAD 001**

Douglas, Carl

Biographical details: This British singer and songwriter was born in Jamaica, but has been based in London throughout his adult life. Douglas had been working on the periphery of the music business for well over a decade, by the time he came to fame in 1974. The record that catapulted him to brief international stardom was the self-penned *Kung-fu fighting*. Kung Fu, the ancient Chinese martial art of self-defence, had been propelled to cinematic fame in the western world by the late actor Bruce Lee. But the Douglas disc was timed to coincide with the craze created by the TV version, which starred David Carradine. With the assistance of Indian producer/arranger/conductor Biddu, Douglas created a lightweight but infectious disco tribute to the Kung Fu phenomenon. *Kung-Fu fighting* reached No.1 in both the UK and US, and enjoyed similar popularity around the world. As usual with a novelty smash, Douglas was unable to follow it up. In Britain, he got to No.35 with the almost identical *Dance the Kung Fu*, whose only difference to its predecessor was that it exploited a dance step that had emerged in discos from the success of *Kung Fu fighting*. From 1975 onwards, the only thing that separated the singer from obscurity was *Run back*, a catchy 1977 single that reached No.25 in Britain. Subsequent singles failed. (Bob MacDonald, 1st July 1988).

DANCE THE KUNG FU
Tracks: / Dance the kung fu.
7" Single: Released Nov '74, on Pye, Deleted Nov '77. Catalogue no: **7N 45418**

KUNG FU FIGHTING
Tracks: / Kung fu fighting.
7" Single: Released Apr '79, on PRT, by Castle Communications Records. Catalogue no: **FBS 9**
7" Single: Released Aug '74, on Pye, Deleted Aug '77. Catalogue no: **7N 45377**
7" Single: Released May '89, on PRT, by Castle Communications Records. Catalogue no: **PYS 23**
12" Single: Released May '89, on PRT, by Castle Communications Records. Catalogue no: **PYT 23**

KUNG FU FIGHTING (OLD GOLD)
Tracks: / Kung fu fighting / Run back.
12" Single: Released Jul '82, on Old Gold, by Old Gold Records. Catalogue no: **OG 9136**

RUN BACK
Tracks: / Run back.
7" Single: Released Dec '77, on Pye, Deleted Dec '80. Catalogue no: **7N 46018**

STIR A LITTLE SWEETNESS IN ME
Tracks: / Stir a little sweetness in me / Hi de ho.
12" Single: Released Dec '82, on Landslide, by Landslide Records. Catalogue no: **LS 001**

Douglas, Carol

Biographical details: This American singer enjoyed a brief spell of US fame in early 1975, reaching No.11 with *Doctor's orders*. This pleasant, catchy pop song had been a UK No.7 hit for British singer Sunny in '74, but had not crossed the Atlantic. Douglas realised that the song still had potential, and simply covered it for the American market. She tried to consolidate upon this success with a series of disco-orientated albums, but she soon fell into obscurity, though not as quickly as Sunny did in Britain. Douglas managed to achieve one minow success on the UK charts. Her rendition of the Bee Gees' megahit *Night fever* crawled to No.66 in Britain in the summer of 1978. This was a pretty pointless record, because discos were quite happy to continue dancing to the original version, which was still on the charts. (Bob MacDonald, 1st July 1985).

NIGHT FEVER
Tracks: / Night fever.
7" Single: Released Jul '78, on Gull, by Gull Records. Deleted Jul '81. Catalogue no: **GULS 61**

Douglas, Craig

Biographical details: This British singer was one of the stars who occupied a gap in UK pop between the rock'n'roll era and arrival of the Beatles. Born Terence Perkins, his dream-like rise to fame started on his native Isle of Wight. Having been working as a milkman, he won a local talent contest. An appearance on Britain's *6.5 special* TV show show followed, and he made his breakthrough into the UK charts in mid-1959. Like so many of his British contemporaries, Douglas gained the majority of his hits by recording cover versions of American originals. However, he differed from many of his peers insofar as his clean-cut, wholesome image was designed to appeal to mums as well as to the pop audience. His string of rock ballad successes began with *A teenager in love*, which reached the UK No.13 slot; however, he was beaten to the Top 3 by another cover version by the already established star Marty Wilde.

Douglas had better luck with his next disc, which was a version of Sam Cooke's *Only sixteen*. This easily beat two other simultaneous versions of the song (including the original), and cruised to the UK No.1 position in the autumn of '59. During the early Sixties, his cover versions included *Pretty blue eyes, A hundred pounds of clay, When my little girl is smiling* and *Oh lonesome me*. From time to time, the singer managed to find some original unknown material to record - he hit the UK Top 10 with *The heart of a teenage girl* (1960), the touching *Time* (1961) and *Our favourite melodies* (1962). He also achieved the quaint feat of scoring four No.9 singles with a 15-month period. The Liverpool explosion knocked Douglas' (and many other stars) career on the head. He fell off the British charts for good in March 1963. After several years inmusical limbo, he moved onto the international cabaret circuit, to which he was perfectly suited; he has successfully remained there ever since. (Bob MacDonald, 1st July 1985)

A pop singer born in 1941 on the Isle of Wight. He had eleven hits 1959-63, mostly covers of American songs, before being washed away by the Beatles. (Donald Clarke, April 1989).

HEART OF A TEENAGE GIRL
Tracks: / Heart of a teenage girl.
7" Single: Released Apr '60, on Top Rank (1), Deleted Apr '63. Catalogue no: **JAR 340**

HUNDRED POUNDS OF CLAY, A
Tracks: / Hundred pounds of clay.
7" Single: Released Apr '61, on Top Rank (1), Deleted Apr '64. Catalogue no: **JAR 555**

LOVE IS A CAROUSEL
Tracks: / Love is a carousel.
7" Single: Released Aug '83, on Easy On The Ear, Deleted '85. Catalogue no: **TALE 1**

OH LONESOME ME
Tracks: / Oh lonesome me.
7" Single: Released Oct '62, on Decca, by Decca Records. Deleted Oct '65. Catalogue no: **F 11523**

OH WHAT A DAY
Tracks: / Oh what a day.
7" Single: Released Aug '60, on Top Rank (1), Deleted Aug '63. Catalogue no: **JAR 406**

ONLY SIXTEEN (OLD GOLD)
Tracks: / Pretty blue eyes / Only sixteen.
7" Single: Released Mar '87, on Old Gold, by Old Gold Records. Deleted Sep '89. Catalogue no: **OG 9682**

ONLY SIXTEEN (SINGLE)
Tracks: / Only sixteen.
7" Single: Released Aug '59, on Top Rank (1), Deleted Aug '62. Catalogue no: **JAR 159**

OUR FAVOURITE MELODIES
Tracks: / Our favourite melodies.
7" Single: Released Jun '62, on Columbia, by EMI Records. Deleted Jun '65. Catalogue no: **DB 4854**

PRETTY BLUE EYES

Tracks: / Pretty blue eyes.
7" Single: Released Jan '60, on Top Rank (1). Deleted Jan '63. Catalogue no: **JAR 268**

TEENAGER IN LOVE
Tracks: / Teenager in love.
7" Single: Released Jun '59, on Top Rank (1). Deleted Jun '62. Catalogue no: **JAR 133**

TIME
Tracks: / Time.
7" Single: Released Jun '61, on Top Rank (1). Deleted Jun '64. Catalogue no: **JAR 569**

TOWN CRIER
Tracks: / Town crier.
7" Single: Released Feb '63, on Decca, by Decca Records. Deleted Feb '66. Catalogue no: **F 11575**

WHEN MY LITTLE GIRL IS SMILING
Tracks: / When my little girl is smiling.
7" Single: Released Mar '62, on Top Rank (1). Deleted Mar '65. Catalogue no: **JAR 610**

Douglas, Duncan

FREEDOM
Tracks: / Freedom (Inst) / Freedom.
12" Single: Released Dec '86, on Live, Catalogue no: **ALIVE 3**

Douglas, K.C.

COOL DOWN AMENA
Tracks: / Cool down amena.
12" Single: Released Mar '82, on Fashion, by Fashion Records. Catalogue no: **FAD 011**

Douglas, Keith

ANGEL
12" Single: Released Nov '83, on Simba, Catalogue no: **SM 006**

BOOM
Tracks: / Boom.
12" Single: Released Dec '83, on Natty Congo, Catalogue no: **NCDM 022**

COME OVER
Tracks: / Come over.
12" Single: Released Jun '85, on Natty Congo, Catalogue no: **NCDM 024**

FRONT LINE
Tracks: / Front line.
12" Single: Released Jun '84, on Zip (1), by Zip Records. Catalogue no: **ZIP 001**

SOMETHING IN MY EYES
Tracks: / Something in my eyes.
12" Single: Released May '84, on London Gemi, Catalogue no: **LG 005**

TEACHER NEVER TAUGHT ME
Tracks: / Teacher never taught me.
12" Single: Released Oct '81, on His Majesty, Catalogue no: **HMD 015**

TRY LOVE AGAIN
Tracks: / Try love again.
12" Single: Released Dec '82, on Fashion, by Fashion Records. Catalogue no: **FAD 014**

WE'VE GOT TO BELIEVE
Tracks: / We've got to believe / Believe (dub).
12" Single: Released Mar '86, on Hot Pepper, Catalogue no: **HP 001**

YOU MOVE ME
Tracks: / You move me.
12" Single: Released May '85, on CSA, by CSA Records. Deleted '88. Catalogue no: **12CSA 505**

ZION CITY
Tracks: / Zion city / Zion height.
12" Single: Released Nov '84, on 24 Karat, Catalogue no: **KABM 001**

Douglas, Lambert

SWEET & NICE
Tracks: / Sweet & nice.
12" Single: Released Mar '89, on Charm, by Charm Records. Catalogue no: **CRT 29**

Douglas, Sir

SHEILA TEQUILA
Tracks: / Sheila Tequila / Who will be next in line / Wooley Bully / She's about a mover.
12" Single: Released Jun '81, on Chrysalis, by Chrysalis Records. Deleted Jun '84. Catalogue no: **CHS 2504**

Douglas, Tony

HOLLY HOLY
Tracks: / Holly holy / Rainy day love.
12" Single: Released Dec '83, on Natty Congo, Catalogue no: **NCDM 023**

IT'S NOT BECAUSE I DON'T LOVE YOU

WILL DOWNING - IN MY DREAMS (Released on 4th & Broadway)

Tracks: / It's not because I don't love you / It's not because I don't love you (version).
12" Single: Released Jun '86, on Love & Unity, Catalogue no: **VGO 1005**

YOUR LOVE
Tracks: / Your love.
12" Single: Released Jun '83, on Body Music, by Nuclear Records. Catalogue no: **BMDIS 12**

Doust, Barbara

IF YOU LOVE SOMEBODY
Tracks: / If you love somebody / If you love somebody (Saturday night remix) (Available on 12" only).
12" Single: Released Jun '88, on Saturday, by Nightmare Records. Catalogue no: **SDY 3**
7" Single: Released Jun '88, on Saturday, by Nightmare Records. Catalogue no: **7SDY 3**

IF YOU LOVE SOMEONE
Tracks: / If you love someone / If you love someone (version).
12" Single: Released Aug '89, on Power, Catalogue no: **PXD 090**

Dowe, Brent

DOWN HERE IN BABYLON
Tracks: / Down here in Babylon / Fancy dress.
12" Single: Released Jul '87, on RAS (Real Authentic Sound), by Greensleeves Records. Catalogue no: **RAS 7001**

Dowlands

ALL MY LOVING
Tracks: / All my loving.
7" Single: Released Jan '64, on Oriole, Deleted Jan '67. Catalogue no: **CB 1897**

Down All The Days

JUST ONE WORD
Tracks: / Just one word.
7" Single: Released Aug '83, on Outrider, by Outrider Records. Catalogue no: **JOHN 100**

Down By Law

IF YOU WANT MY LOVE
Tracks: / If you want my love.
12" Single: Released Sep '89, on Citybeat, by Beggars Banquet Records. Catalogue no: **CBE 1244**
7" Single: Released Sep '89, on Citybeat, by Beggars Banquet Records. Catalogue no: **CBE 744**

LIVING IN THE GHETTO
Tracks: / Living in the ghetto / Living in the ghetto (version).
12" Single: Released Jul '89, on Citybeat, by Beggars Banquet Records. Catalogue no: **CBE 1238**

Downes, Julia

LET SLEEPING DOGS LIE (SINGLE)
Tracks: / Let sleeping dogs lie / Helicopters.
7" Single: Released Nov '82, on Naive, by Naive Records. Catalogue no: **NAV 2**

MISSION TONITE
Tracks: / Mission tonite.
7" Single: Released Jul '83, on Naive, by Naive Records. Catalogue no: **NAV 7**

PLAYING FOR TIME
Tracks: / Playing for time.
7" Single: Released Aug '82, on Naive, by Naive Records. Catalogue no: **NAV 1**

Downing, Big Al

DOWN ON THE FARM
Tracks: / Down on the farm / Miss Lucy / Georgia slop / Yes, I'm loving you.
7" EP: Released 15 Feb '88, on Rollercoaster, by Rollercoaster Records. Catalogue no: **RCEP 105**

Downing, Don

LONELY DAYS, LONELY NIGHTS
Tracks: / Lonely days, lonely nights.
7" Single: Released Nov '73, on People, Deleted Nov '76. Catalogue no: **PEO 102**

Downing, Will

FREE
Tracks: / Free / Dancing in the moonlight / Free (Percappella) (Only on the 12" version.).
7" Single: Released 5 Sep '88, on 4th & Broadway, by Island Records. Deleted Apr '89. Catalogue no: **BRW 112**
12" Single: Released 5 Sep '88, on 4th & Broadway, by Island Records. Deleted Apr '89. Catalogue no: **12 BRW 112**

IN MY DREAMS (see panel above)
Tracks: / In my dreams (instrumental) / In my dreams (club) / In my dreams (radio) / In my dreams.
12" Single: Released 24 May '88, on 4th & Broadway, by Island Records. Deleted Apr '89. Catalogue no: **12 BRW 104**
7" Single: Released 16 May '88, on 4th & Broadway, by Island Records. Deleted Apr '89. Catalogue no: **BRW 104**

LOVE SUPREME, A
Tracks: / Love supreme, A (jazz in the house mix) / Love supreme, A (album mix) / Love supreme, A (dub in the house remix).
12" Single: Released Mar '88, on 4th & Broadway, by Island Records. Catalogue no: **12 BRW 90**
7" Single: Released '88, on 4th & Broadway, by Island Records. Deleted Dec '88. Catalogue no: **BRW 90**

LOVE SUPREME, A (REMIX)
Tracks: / Love supreme, A (remix).
12" Single: Released '88, on 4th & Broadway, by Island Records. Deleted Apr '89. Catalogue no: **12 BRX 90**

TEST OF TIME
Tracks: / Test of time / Test of time (Piano version) / Test of time (Dub version) (12" only) / Test of time (Radio version) (12" only).
7" Single: Released 15 Aug '89, on 4th & Broadway, by Island Records. Catalogue no: **BRW 146**
CD 5": Released 15 Aug '89, on 4th & Broadway, by Island Records. Catalogue no: **BRCD 146**
12" Single: Released 15 Aug '89, on 4th & Broadway, by Island Records. Catalogue no: **12 BRW 146**

WHERE IS THE LOVE
Tracks: / Where is the love / Same feeling / My one temptation (12" & CD only) / Love supreme, A.
7" Single: Released Jan '89, on 4th & Broadway, by Island Records. Catalogue no: **BRW 122**
CD 5": Released Jan '89, on 4th & Broadway, by Island Records. Catalogue no: **BRCD 122**
12" Single: Released Jan '89, on 4th & Broadway, by Island Records. Catalogue no: **12 BRW 122**

Downtown Girls

DOWNTOWN GIRLS
Tracks: / Downtown girls / Downtown girls (remix).
12" Single: Released 30 May '87, on Hardcore, Catalogue no: **HAKT 4**

Downtown Strutz

PRETTY FLAMINGO
Tracks: / Pretty flamingo / C.N.D..
7" Single: Released Dec '81, on Underworld (USA), by Apexton Records (USA). Catalogue no: **UNDY 2**

Doyle, Peter

DO YOU WANT TO MAKE LOVE
Tracks: / Do you want to make love.
7" Single: Released Jun '80, on Limelight (USA), by PolyGram Rec.Inc.(USA). Catalogue no: **BULB 1**

THIS AND THAT
Tracks: / This and that.
7" Single: Released Oct '80, on Limelight (USA), by PolyGram Rec.Inc.(USA). Catalogue no: **BULB 2**

Dozier, Lamont

Biographical details: This American singer, songwriter and producer achieved fame during the Sixties as one-third of Tamla Motown's legendary composing/producing team, Holland/Dozier/Holland. In the early Seventies, the trio found further success with their own Invictus and Hot Wax labels. From 1972 onwards, HDH wound down these famous activities, with Dozier & Brian Holland achieving a UK Top 30 hit in 1972 with *Why can't we be lovers*. Lamont Dozier launched a solo recording career in 1974, butnever managed to hit the UK charts. He did, however, achieve two US Top 30 singles in 1974 with *Trying to hold on to my woman* and *Fish ain't bitin'*. He issued a series of soulful albums during the rest of the Seventies and the Eighties. (Bob MacDonald, 1st July 1985).

COOL ME OUT
Tracks: / Cool me out / Starting over.
7" Single: Released Aug '81, on CBS, by CBS Records. Deleted '84. Catalogue no: **A 1235**

DON'T LEAVE ME
Tracks: / Don't leave me.
7" Single: Released Aug '84, on HDH (Holland/Dozier/Holland), by Demon Records. Catalogue no: **HDH 459**
12" Single: Released Aug '84, on HDH (Holland/Dozier/Holland), by Demon Records. Catalogue no: **45-9T**

MOTOR CITY (PARTS 1 & 2)
Tracks: / Motor city.
7" Single: Released Feb '84, on Demon, by Demon Records. Catalogue no: **D 1020**
12" Single: Released Feb '84, on Demon, by Demon Records. Catalogue no: **D 1020 T**

SCARLETT O'HARA
Tracks: / Scarlett O'Hara.
7" Single: Released Oct '83, on Demon, by Demon Records. Catalogue no: **D 1018**
12" Single: Released Oct '83, on Demon, by Demon Records. Catalogue no: **D 1018 T**

Dr.

SEE UNDER DOCTOR

Drafi

CAN I REACH YOU?
Tracks: / Can I reach you? / Take a look.
7" Single: Released Mar '80, on Young Blood, by Young Blood Records. Deleted '83. Catalogue no: **YB 81**

Drag

DADDY
Tracks: / Daddy.
7" Single: Released May '88, on Gigantic, by Gigantic Records. Catalogue no: **GI 002**

Dragees

SHOOT TO KILL
Tracks: / Shoot to kill.
7" Single: Released Nov '84, on Sohoho, by Sohoho Records. Catalogue no: **HOHO 1**

Dragoni Brothers

DANCE LITTLE BIRDIE
Tracks: / Dance little birdie.
7" Single: Released Sep '81, on Picador, Catalogue no: **PIC 1**

DISCO VIVA
Tracks: / Disco viva / Knees up medley.
7" Single: Released Dec '81, on Picador, Catalogue no: **PIC 2**

Dragsters

AMBITIONS
Tracks: / Ambitions / Won't bring you back.
7" Single: Released Feb '81, on Heavy Metal, by FM-Revolver Records. Deleted Feb '84. Catalogue no: **HEAVY 4**

I'M NOT AN AMERICAN
Tracks: / I'm not an American / Land of the giants.
7" Single: Released Jul '87, on Union City, Catalogue no: **SNICK 2**

ROSEMARY
Tracks: / Rosemary.
7" Single: Released Jan '88, on Union City, Catalogue no: **SNICK 8**
12" Single: Released Feb '88, on Union City, Catalogue no: **SNICK 8T**

WHERE IS THE HAMBURGER RELISH
Tracks: / Where is the hamburger relish / I wanna be an albino.
7" Single: Released Nov '86, on Union City, Catalogue no: **SNICK 1**

Drake, Charlie

MISTER CUSTER
Tracks: / Mister Custer.
7" Single: Released Oct '60, on Parlophone, by EMI Records. Deleted Oct '63. Catalogue no: **R 4701**

MY BOOMERANG WON'T COME BACK
Tracks: / My boomerang won't come back.
7" Single: Released Oct '61, on Parlophone, by EMI Records. Deleted Oct '64. Catalogue no: **R 4824**

PUCKWUDGIE
Tracks: / Puckwudgie.
7" Single: Released Jan '72, on Columbia, by EMI Records. Deleted Jan '75. Catalogue no: **DB 8829**

SPLISH SPLASH
Tracks: / Splish splash / My boomerang won't come back.
7" Single: Released Nov '80, on H.M.V., by EMI Records. Deleted '83. Catalogue no: **POP 2019**
7" Single: Released Aug '58, on Parlophone, by EMI Records. Deleted Aug '61. Catalogue no: **R 4461**

VOLARE
Tracks: / Volare.
7" Single: Released Oct '58, on Parlophone, by EMI Records. Deleted Oct '61. Catalogue no: **R 4478**

Drake, Nick

Biographical details: A singer/songwriter of the UK folk revival born in Burma in 1948; he suffered from depression and died of an accidental overdose of medication in 1974. He was recommended by Ashley Hutchings to Joe Boyd (manager of Fairport Convention, John Martyn etc.) who signed him to Island. His debut album drew comparrason with Van Morrison, but his introversion/depression deepened: only three albums were released in his lifetime, the last *Pink moon* accompanied only by his guitar and sent to the record company by post. *Life in a northern town* by Dream Academy in 1985 was dedicated to him; renewed interest led to the compilation *Heaven in a wild flower*, while *Time of no reply* included alternate takes and previously unreleased tracks, all included in the new edition (four discs) of *Fruit tree* in 1986. (Donald Clarke, April 1989).

FRUIT TREE
Note: 4 L.P. Set includes: *Time of no reply*, as well as the tree original Drake albums, *Five leaves left, Bryter Layter* and *Pink moon* in their original four colour sleeves. Re-issue.
Special: Released Aug '86, on Hannibal, by Hannibal Records. Catalogue no: **HNBX 5302**

Drama...

DO YOU LOVE ME
Tracks: / Do you love me / Been to long.
7" Single: Released Dec '82, on Orbit, by Orbit Records. Deleted Dec '85. Catalogue no: **TRIP 1**

Dramarama

IT'S STILL WARM
Tracks: / It's still warm.
7" Single: Released May '88, on New Rose (1), by New Rose Records. Catalogue no: **NEW 108**

Dramatics

I CAN'T STAND IT
Tracks: / I can't stand it / It's dramatic music.
7" Single: Released Jul '82, on Capitol, by EMI Records. Deleted Jul '85. Catalogue no: **CL 252**
12" Single: Released Jul '82, on Capitol, by EMI Records. Deleted Jul '85. Catalogue no: **12 CL 252**

IN THE RAIN
Tracks: / In the rain.
7" Single: Released Aug '87, on Stax, by Fantasy Inc (USA). Catalogue no: **STAX 809**

WHATCHA SEE IS WHATCHA GET
Tracks: / Whatcha see is whatcha get / Devil is dope, The / In the rain / And I panicked.
12" Single: Released 21 Nov '87, on Stax, by Fantasy Inc (USA). Catalogue no: **STAT 809**

Dramatis

Biographical details: This British rock band consisted of Russell Bell, Dennis Haines, Chris Payne and Cedric Sharpley. Dramatis were formed in 1979 by that year's fastest rising British superstar Gary Numan. In the autumn of '79, having just opened his UK chart career with two consecutive No.1 singles and a pair of No.1 albums, the previously unknown singer/songwriter/producer/guitarist/synthesiser wizard decided to embark upon a British tour. Dramatis became his backing band, and the itinerary was eventually extended to include Japan, Europe, Australasia and America. The musicians simply did their job and nothing more - the spectacular visual appeal of the shows did not come from them, but from the elaborate neon stage sets. By 1981 Numan had 'retired' from live performances. The redundant Dramatis decided to remain intact, however, and they released their own album in that year. Entitled *For future reference*, it was in much the same style as Numan's own bleak, robotic, futuristic work. He even sang lead vocals on the band's single *Love needs no disguise*, which became their only chart entry as a separate entity: *I can see her now* peaked at at inglorious No.57 on the British singles chart. In late 1983 Numan decided to resume live work, and re-employed Bell and Sharpley. Dramatis thus fizzled out, and their synthesised sound - which never attracted much attention without the charismatic presence of their mentor - was forgotton. (Bob MacDonald, 5th July 1985).

020-25
Tracks: / 020-25 / Curtain.
7" Single: Released Aug '81, on Rocket, by Rocket Records. Deleted '84. Catalogue no: **XPRES 61**

EX LUNA CENTA
Tracks: / Ex luna centa / Lady D.J..
12" Single: Released May '81, on Rocket, by Rocket Records. Deleted May '84. Catalogue no: **XPRES 5312**
7" Single: Released May '81, on Rocket, by Rocket Records. Deleted May '84. Catalogue no: **XPRES 53**

FACE ON THE WALL
Tracks: / Face on the wall / Pomp & Stompandstamp.
7" Single: Released Feb '82, on Rocket, by Rocket Records. Deleted '85. Catalogue no: **XPRES 69**

I CAN SEE HER NOW
Tracks: / I can see her now / One step ahead.
12" Single: Released Nov '82, on Rocket, by Rocket Records. Deleted Nov '85. Catalogue no: **XPRES 8312**
7" Single: Released Nov '82, on Rocket, by Rocket Records. Deleted Nov '85. Catalogue no: **XPRES 83**

NO ONE LIVES FOR EVER
Tracks: / No one lives for ever / For future reference / Take me home.
7" Single: Released Sep '81, on Rocket, by Rocket Records. Deleted '84. Catalogue no: **XPRES 63**

SHAME
Tracks: / Shame / I only find rewind.
12" Single: Released May '82, on Rocket, by Rocket Records. Deleted '85. Catalogue no: **XPRES 7912**
7" Single: Released May '82, on Rocket, by Rocket Records. Deleted '85. Catalogue no: **XPRES 79**

Draper, Rusty

Biographical details: A USA pop/country singer and actor. He had a series of hits 1953-60 including *No help wanted* and *Gambler's guitar*; his *Muleskinner blues* reached the UK chart in 1960. He had country chart hits in the '60's. He toured in plays and acted on TV in *77 Sunset strip*, *Rawhide*, *Laramie* etc. (Donald Clarke, April 1989).

MULE SKINNER BLUES
Tracks: / Mule skinner blues.
7" Single: Released Aug '60, on Mercury (EMI), Deleted Aug '63. Catalogue no: **AMT 1101**

SEVEN COME ELEVEN
Tracks: / Seven come eleven.
7" Single: Released Jul '84, on Pinner, Catalogue no: **PRM 901**

Draumur, S H

BLESS
Tracks: / Bless.
12" Single: Released Dec '88, on Lakeland, Catalogue no: **GRAMM 039**

Drayton, Leslie

DREAMER
Tracks: / Dreamer / Abstractions.
12" Single: Released Oct '87, on Expansion, Catalogue no: **EXPAND 10**

Dread, Alvin

GIRL OF MINE
Tracks: / Girl of mine.
12" Single: Released Oct '83, on Hot Line, Catalogue no: **HL 003**

PICTURE ON THE WALL
Tracks: / Picture on the wall.
12" Single: Released Feb '83, on Hot Line, Catalogue no: **HL 001**

Dread & Fred

WARRIORS STANCE
Tracks: / Warriors stance.
12" Single: Released Jun '89, on Jah Shaka, Catalogue no: **SHAKA 870**

Dread, Mikey

BREAK DOWN THE WALLS
Tracks: / Break down the walls / Wall Street rock / Jumping master / Master mind.
7" Single: Released Oct '80, on Dread, by Stiff Records. Catalogue no: **MIK 2**
12" Single: Released Oct '80, on Dread, by Stiff Records. Catalogue no: **DREAD 1**

BREAKING DOWN THE PRESSURE
Tracks: / Breaking down the pressure.
10" single: Released Dec '83, on On-U-Sound, by On-U-Sound Records. Catalogue no: **ONUDP 9**

CARAVAN OF LOVE
Tracks: / Caravan of love.
12" Single: Released Dec '87, on FASH, Catalogue no: **FID 01**

ROCKERS DELIGHT
Tracks: / Rockers delight.
7" Single: Released Jul '80, on DATC, Catalogue no: **MIK 1**

ROCKY ROAD
Tracks: / Rocky road / Sweet sixteen.
7" Single: Released May '82, on Do-It, by Do-It Records. Deleted '85. Catalogue no: **DUN 21**
12" Single: Released May '82, on Do-It, by Do-It Records. Deleted '85. Catalogue no: **DUNIT 21**

ROOTS AND CULTURE
Tracks: / Roots and culture.
12" Single: Released Mar '82, on Dread At The Controls, Catalogue no: **DATC 008**

RUB A DUB
Tracks: / Rub a dub / Heavyweight style.
7" Single: Released Sep '82, on Do-It, by Do-It Records. Deleted Sep '85. Catalogue no: **DUNE 24**

RUDE LITTLE DREAD
Tracks: / Rude little dread.
12" Single: Released Mar '86, on Dread At The Controls, Catalogue no: **DATC 86**

SUNDAY SCHOOL
Tracks: / Sunday school.
12" Single: Released Mar '83, on DATC, Catalogue no: **DATC 017**

WARNING
Tracks: / Warning.
12" Single: Released Jun '82, on Dread At The Controls, Catalogue no: **DATC 10**

Dread, Sammy

AFRICA
Tracks: / Africa.
12" Single: Released Mar '82, on Love Lite, Catalogue no: **LJ 001**

BE MINE
Tracks: / Be mine.
12" Single: Released Jul '82, on Love Light, Catalogue no: **LJ 001**

DREADLOCKS GIRL
Tracks: / Dreadlocks girl / Trinidad jam.
12" Single: Released Sep '82, on Ethnic, Catalogue no: **ETM 156**

LABOUR WARD
Tracks: / Labour ward.
12" Single: Released Feb '82, on Echo, by Echo Records. Catalogue no: **ECHO 010**

METAL DETECTOR
Tracks: / Metal detector / Security for surety.
12" Single: Released Apr '85, on Life Music, Catalogue no: **LM 001**

ONE COMBINATION
Tracks: / One combination / All will come by.
12" Single: Released Nov '82, on Capri, Catalogue no: **CPR 0182**

SALLY
Tracks: / Sally.
12" Single: Released Oct '83, on Sonic Sounds, Catalogue no: **SS 25**

TOP OF THE TOPS
Tracks: / Top of the tops / Nice and easy.
12" Single: Released Mar '82, on Jah Life, Catalogue no: **JL 004**

YOU MEAN SO MUCH TO ME
Tracks: / You mean so much to me.
12" Single: Released Oct '84, on Seven Leaves, Catalogue no: **SLD 003**

Dream Academy

INDIAN SUMMER
Tracks: / Indian summer / Heaven.
7" Single: Released Sep '87, on Blanco Y Negro, by Blanco Y Negro Records. Deleted Jul '88. Catalogue no: **NEG 27**
12" Single: Released 10 Oct '87, on Blanco Y Negro, by Blanco Y Negro Records. Deleted Jul '88. Catalogue no: **NEG 27T**

LIFE IN A NORTHERN TOWN
Tracks: / Life in a northern town / Test tape no. 3 / On the edge of forever (on 12" only).
7" Single: Released Mar '85, on Blanco Y Negro, by Blanco Y Negro Records. Deleted Jun '87. Catalogue no: **NEG 10**
12" Single: Released Mar '85, on Blanco Y Negro, by Blanco Y Negro Records. Deleted Jun '87. Catalogue no: **NEG 10T**

LOVE PARADE
Tracks: / Love parade.
12" Single: Released Aug '85, on Blanco Y Negro, by Blanco Y Negro Records. Deleted Jun '87. Catalogue no: **NEG 16T**
7" Single: Released Aug '85, on Blanco Y Negro, by Blanco Y Negro Records. Catalogue no: **NEG 16**

PLEASE PLEASE LET ME GET WHAT I WANT
Tracks: / Please please let me get what I want.
7" Single: Released Nov '85, on Blanco Y Negro, by Blanco Y Negro Records. Catalogue no: **NEG 20**
12" Single: Released Nov '85, on Blanco Y Negro, by Blanco Y Negro Records. Catalogue no: **NEG 20T**

Dream Baby Scream

IS THERE A REASON?
Tracks: / Is there a reason? / Alone with you / Love somebody.
7" Single: Released Jun '87, on So Romantik, by So Romantik Records. Catalogue no: **SAD 2**

Dream Clinic

RELOCATING FLOWERPOTS
Tracks: / Relocating flowerpots.
7" Single: Released May '88, on Primitive, by Primitive Records. Catalogue no: **PRIME 008**

Dream Factory

FASHION TOYS
Tracks: / Fashion toys.
12" Single: Released Mar '85, on Inferno (1), by Inferno Records. Catalogue no: **12 DREAM 1**
7" Single: Released Mar '85, on Inferno (1), by Inferno Records. Catalogue no: **DREAM 1**

Dream (group)

DESIRES (AT HER CLOSEST)
Tracks: / Desires (at her closest).
12" Single: Released Aug '87, on Black (1), by FM-Revolver Records. Catalogue no: **12 REV 40**

DO THE TRIP
Tracks: / Do the trip / Wonderful world / Anything (12" only).
12" Single: Released Jul '88, on Revolver,

by FM-Revolver Records. Catalogue no: **12 REV 48**
7" Single: Released Jul '88, on Revolver, by FM-Revolver Records. Catalogue no: **REV 48**

WONDERFUL WORLD
Tracks: / Wonderful world.
12" Single: Released Jun '88, on Revolver, by FM-Revolver Records. Catalogue no: **12 REV 48**

Dream III

FEEL (HOME LISTENING)
Tracks: / Feel (home listening) / Feel (stoned listening) / Feel (club listening).
12" Single: Released May '89, on Cheque This, by Cheque This Records. Catalogue no: **CTT 1**

Dream Merchants

AS THE WORLD TURNS
Tracks: / As the world turns / As the world turns (part 2).
12" Single: Released Aug '83, on Legacy, by Legacy Records. Catalogue no: **LGYT 6**
7" Single: Released Aug '83, on Legacy, by Legacy Records. Catalogue no: **LGY 6**

Dream Regime

SILVER SCREEN
Tracks: / Silver screen / Travels with my uncle.
7" Single: Released Sep '81, on CBS, by CBS Records. Deleted '84. Catalogue no: **A 1510**

Dream Sequence

FUNKIN' REBELS
Tracks: / Funkin' rebels / Uptown America.
12" Single: Released Aug '82, on Red Bus, by Red Bus Records. Catalogue no: **RBUSL 73**
7" Single: Released Aug '82, on Red Bus, by Red Bus Records. Catalogue no: **RBUS 73**

OUTSIDE LOOKING IN
Tracks: / Outside looking in / Jaqueline.
7" Single: Released Apr '82, on Red Bus, by Red Bus Records. Catalogue no: **RBUS 67**
12" Single: Released Apr '82, on Red Bus, by Red Bus Records. Catalogue no: **RBUSL 67**

Dream Syndicate

50 IN A 25 ZONE
Tracks: / 50 in a 25 zone / Drinking problem / Blood money / Lonely bull, The.
12" Single: Released Aug '87, on Big Time Records, by Big Time Records. Catalogue no: **ZT 41420**

I HAVE FAITH
Tracks: / I have faith / Now I ride alone / I ain't living long like this (12" only).
12" Single: Released Nov '88, on Virgin, by Virgin Records. Catalogue no: **ENVT 6**
7" Single: Released Nov '88, on Enigma, by Enigma Records (USA). Catalogue no: **ENV 6**

TELL ME WHEN IT'S OVER
Tracks: / Tell me when it's over / Some kinda itch / Mr. Soul / Sure thing.
12" Single: Released Dec '83, on Rough Trade, by Rough Trade Records. Catalogue no: **RTT 121**

Dream Team

BOY GEORGE
Tracks: / Boy George.
7" Single: Released Oct '84, on Hollywood, by Hollywood Records. Catalogue no: **HWD 017**

Dream Unit

FOUR WAVES (EP)
Tracks: / Four waves.
7" EP: Released Jul '83, on Northeast Music, by Northeast Music Records. Catalogue no: **OZS 01**

Dream Weavers

IT'S ALMOST TOMORROW
Tracks: / It's almost tomorrow.
7" Single: Released Feb '56, on Brunswick, by Decca Records. Deleted Feb '59. Catalogue no: **05515**

Dreaming In Colour

CALL ON ME
Tracks: / Call on me.
7" Single: Released Jan '89, on Savage, by Savage Records. Catalogue no: **7 SAV 006**
12" Single: Released Jan '89, on Savage, by Savage Records. Catalogue no: **12 SAV 006**

Dreams

BOYS, BOYS, BOYS
Tracks: / Boys, boys, boys.
7" Single: Released Apr '88, on Receiver, by Trojan Records. Catalogue no: **POINT 03**
12" Single: Released Apr '88, on Receiver, by Trojan Records. Catalogue no: **POINTX 03**

Dreams So Real

ROUGH NIGHT IN JERICHO
Tracks: / Rough night in Jericho / Love fall down / Cinnaman girl.
7" Single: Released 1 May '89, on Arista, by BMG Records (UK). Catalogue no: **1 12088**
CD 5": Released 1 May '89, on Arista, by BMG Records (UK). Catalogue no: **662-088**
12" Single: Released 1 May '89, on Arista, by BMG Records (UK). Catalogue no: **6 12088**

Dreamticket

ROBOCOP (SERIOUS MIX)
Tracks: / Robocop (serious mix).
7" Single: Released Oct '88, on Musik Tek, Catalogue no: **TEK I T2**

Dreamtime

COLD AND LONELY PLACE
Tracks: / Cold and lonely place / I know.
7" Single: Released May '89, on Pure, Catalogue no: **PURE 89/1**

SO ALIVE
Tracks: / So alive / Dreamtime.
CD 5": Released 31 Jul '89, on Beggars Banquet, by Beggars Banquet Records. Catalogue no: **BEG 229CD**
7" Single: Released 31 Jul '89, on Beggars Banquet, by Beggars Banquet Records. Catalogue no: **BEG 229**
12" Single: Released 31 Jul '89, on Beggars Banquet, by Beggars Banquet Records. Catalogue no: **BEG 229T**

Drennon, Eddie

LET'S DO THE LATIN HUSTLE
Tracks: / Let's do the latin hustle.
7" Single: Released Feb '76, on Pye International, Deleted Feb '79. Catalogue no: **7N 25702**

Drew, Alan

ALWAYS THE LONELY ONE
Tracks: / Always the lonely one.
7" Single: Released Sep '63, on Columbia, by EMI Records. Deleted Sep '66. Catalogue no: **DB 7090**

Drifters

Biographical details: The most successful of the many line-ups of this American all-male vocal group featured Doc Green, Elsbeary Hobbs, Ben E King, and Charlie Thomas. Since the formation of the Drifters in 1953, approximately 50 men have drifted in and out of the group, including a dozen lead singers - the name of the act could hardly have been more appropriate. In late 1959 a British combo called the Drifters (Cliff Richard's backing group) had to change their name to the Shadows to avoid confusion with the American group. The 1953 line-up of the Drifters featured personnel whose background was a gospel music. Lead vocalist Clyde McPhatter had enjoyed enormous success during the early Fifties as a member of Billy Ward and the Dominoes, who had become famous via their intense gospel treatment of secular rhythm-and-blues songs. The Drifters struck gold with their debut release - *Money honey* was a No.1 on the R&B charts for 11 weeks, although black records in those days were ignored by the white pop audience. 1954 brought the group another big R&B it with *Such a night* (taken to No.1 in Britain by Johnnie Ray, and later covered by Elvis Presley). Other big successes for McPhatter's Drifters included *Honey love, Whatcha gonna do* and a superb version of *White Christmas*. The Drifters career can best be divided into four sections, representing their four most important lead singers. After McPhatter (who enjoyed solo success in the late Fifties and early Sixties, and died in June 1972 at the age of 38), the second great leader was Ben E King. His brief but glorious period of success began in mid-1959 and ended in late 1960. By this time they were a totally different group , but manager George Treadwell had retained the rights to the name. The new Drifters now appealed to a broad pop audience, as well as to the R&B market. 1959's *There goes my baby* reached No.2 on the US pop chart, and it pioneered the use of strings on rhythm-and-blues records. In 1960 *Save the last dance for me* gave the group their only No.1 on the American Hot 100; it reached No.2 in Britain. The Drifter's third great lead vocalist was Rudy Lewis, who enjoyed three hitmaking years during 1961-3. The greatest Lewis led successes were *Up on the roof* and *On Broadway*, two thought-provoking 1963 US Top Tenners. Lewis died in May 1964 from a drug overdose.
Lewis' replacement was the man who proved to be the longest serving Drifter, Johnny Moore. Having first sung lead with the group in the mid-Fifties, he took them to No.4 on the US chart in 1964 with *Under the boardwalk*. However, at the end of the year, *Saturday night at the movies* gave their group their final American Top 40 hit. As far as the USA was concerned, the Drifters passed into history. They, and the various composers and producers who worked with them, would be remembered as pioneers of soul music; in particular, the Motown sound owed them a colossal debt. Suddenly, in the Seventies, Moore and the Drifters became Top 10 regulars in Britain. Using UK writers and producers, they achieved a string of lightweight pop hits. The two biggest successes were 1974's No.2 smash *Kissin' in the back row of the movies* (clearly inspired by *Saturday night at the movies*) and 1975's No.3 hit *There goes my first love* (could the lyricist have been thinking of *There goes my baby?*). However, after 1977's UK No.5 success, *You're more than a number in my little red book*, the group drifted out of the record charts and into cabaret. In the early Eighties, Moore quit the Drifters; surprisingly, Ben E King who had enjoyed sporadic solo success during the Sixties and Seventies rejoined the group. (Bob MacDonald, 6th July 1985)
Classic USA R&B soul vocal group with career spanning 30 years and at least that many members. The original lineup (to back Clyde McPhatter) included bass Bill Pinkney, Gerhard and Andrew Thrasher, tenor and baritone; all had gospel background. Their first six discs were all top 10 R&B hits 1953-55 including *Money honey* (later covered by Elvis) and 2 sided hit *Such a night/Lucille*. McPhatter was drafted; Johnny Moore sang lead by they disbanded in 1958. The manager (who owned the name) selected the Crowns to be the new Drifters: Ben E King, lead baritone; Doc Green, baritone; Charles Thomas, tenor; Elsbery Hobbs, bass and songs by Leiber & Stoller were hits: *There goes my baby, Save the last dance for me* and others before King left to go solo had a profound effect on '60s pop. Lyricist Leiber augmented songs with Brill Building material and tunes by Doc Pomus and Mort Shuman to continue the hits with Rudy Lewis singing lead on 7 top 40 hits including *Up on the roof* and *On Broadway* before his death from drugs in 1964. Moore rejoined in 1963 and now sang lead *Under the boardwalk* and *Saturday night at the movies* were their last top 40's as Motown took over black pop and the Drifters drifted into the supperclub circuit; their Atlantic contract expired in 1972. Moore bought them to the UK and used songwriters Cook-Greenaway, Barry Mason and Tony Macauley for top 10 hits *Like sister and brother, Kissin' in the back row of the movies, Down on the beach tonight* and others through '76 (none hit in the USA)..

6 TRACK HITS
Tracks: / Can I take you home little girl / Something tells me / Love games / Down on the beach tonight / Say goodbye to Angelina / Like sister and brother.
7" EP: Released Sep '83, on Scoop 33, by Pickwick Records. Catalogue no: **7SR 5013**

AT THE CLUB
Tracks: / At the club / Saturday night at the movies.
7" Single: Released Apr '65, on Atlantic, by WEA Records. Deleted Apr '68. Catalogue no: **AT 4019**
7" Single: Released Mar '72, on Atlantic, by WEA Records. Deleted Mar '75. Catalogue no: **K 10148**

BABY WHAT I MEAN
Tracks: / Baby what I mean.
7" Single: Released Feb '67, on Atlantic, by WEA Records. Deleted Feb '70. Catalogue no: **584 065**

CAN I TAKE YOU HOME LITTLE GIRL
Tracks: / Can I take you home little girl.
7" Single: Released Nov '75, on Bell, Deleted Nov '78. Catalogue no: **BELL 1462**

COME ON OVER TO MY PLACE
Tracks: / Come on over to my place / Up on the roof / I don't want to go on without you.
7" Single: Released Apr '65, on Atlantic, by WEA Records. Deleted Apr '68. Catalogue no: **AT 4023**
7" Single: Released Sep '86, on Atlantic, by WEA Records. Catalogue no: **K 10216**

DANCE WITH ME
Tracks: / Dance with me.
7" Single: Released Jan '60, on London-American, Deleted Jan '63. Catalogue no: **HLE 8988**

DOWN ON THE BEACH TONIGHT
Tracks: / Down on the beach tonight.
7" Single: Released Oct '74, on Bell, Deleted Oct '77. Catalogue no: **BELL 1381**

EVERY NITE'S A SATURDAY NIGHT WITH YOU
Tracks: / Every nite's a Saturday night with you.
7" Single: Released Sep '76, on Bell, Deleted Sep '79. Catalogue no: **BELL 1491**

HELLO HAPPINESS
Tracks: / Hello happiness.
7" Single: Released Mar '76, on Bell, Deleted Mar '79. Catalogue no: **BELL 1469**

I COUNT THE TEARS
Tracks: / I count the tears.
7" Single: Released Mar '61, on London-American, Deleted Mar '64. Catalogue no: **HLK 9287**

I'LL TAKE YOU HOME
Tracks: / I'll take you home.
7" Single: Released Oct '63, on London-American, Deleted Jan '66. Catalogue no: **HLK 9785**

I'M NOT THAT KIND OF GUY
Tracks: / I'm not that kind of guy / What am I doing falling in love with you.
7" Single: Released May '80, on Epic, by CBS Records. Deleted May '83. Catalogue no: **EPC 8559**

KISSING IN THE BACK ROW
Tracks: / Kissin' in the back row of the movies / You're more than a number in my little red book.
7" Single: Released Jun '74, on Bell, Deleted Jun '77. Catalogue no: **BELL 1358**

KISSING IN THE BACK ROW (OLD GOLD)
Tracks: / Kissing in the back row / You're more than a number....
7" Single: Released Jun '88, on Old Gold, by Old Gold Records. Catalogue no: **OG 9457**

LIKE SISTER AND BROTHER
Tracks: / Little sister and brother.
7" Single: Released Aug '73, on Bell, Deleted Aug '76. Catalogue no: **BELL 1313**

LIKE SISTER AND BROTHER (OLD GOLD)
Tracks: / Like sister and brother.
7" Single: Released Jul '82, on Old Gold, by Old Gold Records. Catalogue no: **OG 9121**

LOVE GAMES (SINGLE)
Tracks: / Love games.
7" Single: Released Feb '75, on Bell, Deleted Feb '78. Catalogue no: **BELL 1396**

SATURDAY NIGHT AT THE MOVIES
Tracks: / Saturday night at the movies / Under the boardwalk / Up on the roof (12" only) / Save the last dance for me (12" only) / At the club.
7" Single: Released Aug '82, on Blast From The Past, by Creole Records. Catalogue no: **CR 195**
7" Single: Released '74, on Atlantic, by WEA Records. Catalogue no: **K 10493**
7" Single: Released Mar '87, on Creole Classics, by Creole Records. Catalogue no: **CR 98**
12" Single: Released Mar '87, on Creole Classics, by Creole Records. Catalogue no: **CRT 98**

SATURDAY NIGHT AT THE MOVIES (OLD GOLD)
Tracks: / Saturday night at the movies / At the club.
7" Single: Released May '81, on Old Gold, by Old Gold Records. Deleted May '84. Catalogue no: **OG 9102**
7" Single: Released Jun '81, on Old Gold, by Old Gold Records. Deleted Jun '84. Catalogue no: **OG 9103**

SAVE THE LAST DANCE FOR ME (OLD GOLD)
Tracks: / Save the last dance for me.
7" Single: Released Jul '82, on Old Gold, by Old Gold Records. Catalogue no: **OG 9014**

SAVE THE LAST DANCE FOR ME (SINGLE)
Tracks: / Save the last dance for me.
7" Single: Released Apr '79, on Lightning, Deleted Apr '82. Catalogue no: **LIG 9014**
7" Single: Released Nov '60, on London-American, Deleted Nov '63. Catalogue no: **HLK 9201**
7" Single: Released '74, on Atlantic, by WEA Records. Catalogue no: **K 10110**

THERE GOES MY FIRST LOVE
Tracks: / There goes my first love.
7" Single: Released Sep '75, on Bell, Deleted Sep '78. Catalogue no:

1433

UNDER THE BOARDWALK
Tracks: / Under the boardwalk.
12" Single: Released Apr '80, on Atlantic, by WEA Records. Catalogue no: **ATM 6**
7" Single: Released Sep '64, on Atlantic, by WEA Records. Deleted Sep '67. Catalogue no: **AT 4001**

WHEN MY LITTLE GIRL IS SMILING
Tracks: / When my little girl is smiling.
7" Single: Released Apr '62, on London-American. Deleted Apr '65. Catalogue no: **HLK 9522**

YOU BETTER MOVE ON
Tracks: / You better move on / Save the last dance for me.
7" Single: Released Aug '82, on Atlantic, by WEA Records. Catalogue no: **K 11743**

YOU'RE MORE THAN A NUMBER IN MY LITTLE RED BOOK
Tracks: / You're more than a number in my little red book.
7" Single: Released Dec '76, on Arista, by BMG Records (UK). Deleted Dec '79. Catalogue no: **ARISTA 78**

Driftwood

RAINBOW WATERS
Tracks: / Rainbow waters.
7" Single: Released Jan '80, on UNKNOWN, Catalogue no: **JIG 1**

Drill

BANG OUR 'EADS TOGETHER
Tracks: / Bang our 'eads together / Piccadilly.
7" Single: Released Apr '80, on RCA, by BMG Records (UK). Deleted '83. Catalogue no: **PB 5236**

GOTTA GO
Tracks: / Gotta go / 1984.
7" Single: Released Oct '80, on RCA, by BMG Records (UK). Deleted Oct '83. Catalogue no: **RCA 5296**

IF I COULD READ YOUR MIND
Tracks: / If I could read your mind / Gotta go.
7" Single: Released Aug '80, on RCA, by BMG Records (UK). Catalogue no: **PB 5274**

Dring, Carl

FRESH START
Tracks: / Fresh start / Rodeo do do.
7" Single: Released Nov '81, on RCA, by BMG Records (UK). Deleted '84. Catalogue no: **RCA 153**

Drinking Electricity

CRUISING MISSILES
Tracks: / Cruising missiles.
7" Single: Released Nov '80, on Pop Aural, Catalogue no: **POP 008**

GOOD TIMES
Tracks: / Good times / Colour coding.
7" Single: Released Mar '82, on Survival (1), by Survival Records. Catalogue no: **SUR 121**
7" Single: Released Mar '82, on Survival (1), by Survival Records. Catalogue no: **SUR 005**

SUBLIMINAL
Tracks: / Subliminal / Random particles.
7" Single: Released Jun '82, on Survival (1), by Survival Records. Catalogue no: **SUR 122**
7" Single: Released Jun '82, on Survival (1), by Survival Records. Catalogue no: **SUR 001**

Driscoll, Julie

Biographical details: This British singer, born in London, first came to public attention in 1965 when he joined an R&B touring group, Steampacket; at various times, the line-up of this combo included Long John Baldry, Elkie Brooks, Elton John and Rod Stewart. Prior to this, Driscoll had been working as secretary to the Yardbirds' fan club. When Steampacket folded in 1966, Driscoll released some solo singles without success. The following year, she joined forces with Steampacket's old backing band, Brian Auger & The Trinity, and became a cult favourite. An adequate but not brilliant singer, Jools (as she was often referred to) became known for her frizzy afro hair and her casual, bra-less dressing habits, which were sufficiently unusual in those days to be considered risque. In the early summer of 1968, Julie Driscoll, Brian Auger & The Trinity achieved a one-off UK smash with their rendition of Bob Dylan's *This wheel's on fire.* The combination of the singer's slightly eerie vocals, Auger's imaginatively arranged organ and piano parts, and the inspired choice of song, made this single a great pop record and one of the classics of the psychedelic era. It reached the UK No.5 position; their album *Open* climbed to No.12. However, Driscoll was not interested in fame and fortune, and she quit the group later in '68 during an American tour. She soon retired altogether from the public eye and married Keith Tippett, the jazz pianist and composer. During the Seventies and Eighties, she made occasional low-key comebacks, latterly under her married name but with an additional 's' (i.e. Tippetts). (Bob MacDonald, 7th July 1985).

OPEN
Tracks: / Open.
7" Single: Released Jun '68, on Marmalade, by Polydor Ltd. Deleted '73. Catalogue no: **608-002**

THIS WHEEL'S ON FIRE
Tracks: / This wheel's on fire.
7" Single: Released Apr '68, on Marmalade, by Polydor Ltd. Deleted Apr '71. Catalogue no: **598 006**
7" Single: Released Jul '84, on Old Gold, by Old Gold Records. Catalogue no: **OG 9427**

Driscolls

DOCTOR GOOD & HIS INCREDIBLE LIFE-SAVING SOUP
Tracks: / Doctor Good & his incredible life-saving soup.
12" Single: Released May '89, on Teatime, Catalogue no: **TEA 004T**

GIRL I WANT YOU BACK
Tracks: / Girl I want you back.
7" Single: Released '88, on Restless (1), by Restless Records. Catalogue no: **REST 003**

I HEARD A RUMOUR
Tracks: / I heard a rumour.
7" Single: Released Nov '88, on Restless (1), by Restless Records. Catalogue no: **REST 004**

Driver 67

CAR 67 (Driver 67 is "Paul Phillips")
Tracks: / Car 67.
7" Single: Released Dec '78, on Logo, by Logo Records. Deleted Dec '81. Catalogue no: **GO 336**

HEADLIGHTS (see panel below)
Tracks: / Headlights / Tail lights.
7" Single: Released '79, on Logo, by Logo Records. Catalogue no: **GO 347**

Drivers

TALK ALL NIGHT
Tracks: / Talk all night.
7" Single: Released Jul '83, on Greyhound, by Greyhound Records. Catalogue no: **GRK 701**

D'Rone, Frank

STRAWBERRY BLONDE
Tracks: / Strawberry blonde.
7" Single: Released Dec '60, on Mercury (EMI), Deleted Dec '63. Catalogue no: **AMT 1123**

Drongos For Europe

DEATH'S A CAREER (EP)
Tracks: / Death's a career.
7" EP: Released Feb '82, on Inferno (2), Catalogue no: **HELL 3**

ETERNITY
Tracks: / Eternity.
7" Single: Released Nov '82, on Inferno (2), Catalogue no: **HELL 6**

PEACE
Tracks: / Peace.
7" Single: Released Oct '81, on Drongos For Europe, Catalogue no: **DFE 001**

Drop

BOY RACERS, THE
Tracks: / Boy racers, The.
7" Single: Released Sep '88, on Medium Cool, by Medium Cool Records. Catalogue no: **MC 014**
12" Single: Released Sep '88, on Medium Cool, by Medium Cool Records. Catalogue no: **MC 014T**

Drowning Craze

HEAT
Tracks: / Heat.
7" Single: Released Feb '82, on Situation 2, by Beggars Banquet Records. Catalogue no: **SIT 16**

STORAGE CASE
Tracks: / Storage case / Damp bones.
7" Single: Released Jul '81, on Situation 2, by Beggars Banquet Records. Catalogue no: **SIT 3**

TRANCE
Tracks: / Trance / I love the fjords.
7" Single: Released Nov '81, on Situation 2, by Beggars Banquet Records. Catalogue no: **SIT 13**

Drowsy Maggie

SING AN IRISH SONG
Tracks: / Molly Malone / Sing an Irish song.
7" Single: Released Mar '87, on Starblend, by Starblend Records. Catalogue no: **STAR 11**

DRRB

MAKE IT WITH YOU
Tracks: / Make it with you.
12" Single: Released Oct '89, on Play Hard, by Play Hard Records. Catalogue no: **DEC 21**

Dru

I CAN'T LIVE WITHOUT YOU
Tracks: / I can't live without you.
12" Single: on Silver Screen, by Creole Records. Catalogue no: **MIXT 1**
7" Single: on Silver Screen, by Creole Records. Catalogue no: **MIX 1**

Drug Free America

DAY-GLO PUSSYCAT
Tracks: / Day-glo pussycat.
7" Single: Released Jul '88, on Blind Eye, Catalogue no: **BE 004**

HEAVEN AIN'T HIGH ENOUGH
Tracks: / Heaven ain't high enough.
12" Single: Released Jan '89, on Blind Eye, Catalogue no: **BE 006**

THROW A CRAZY SHAPE
Tracks: / Throw a crazy shape.
7" Single: Released Mar '88, on Blind Eye, Catalogue no: **BE 002**

Drum & Bass

I LOVE U
Tracks: / I love you.
12" Single: Released Oct '88, on Ahead Of Our Time, by Ahead of Our Time. Catalogue no: **WA 1**

Drum Theatre

EL DORADO
Tracks: / Jungle of people / El Dorado.
12" Single: Released Dec '86, on Epic, by CBS Records. Catalogue no: **EMUT 1**
7" Single: Released Dec '86, on Epic, by CBS Records. Catalogue no: **EMU 1**
12" Single: Released Dec '86, on Epic, by CBS Records. Deleted Nov '87. Catalogue no: **EMUQ 1**

HOME IS WHERE THE HEART IS
Tracks: / Home is where the heart is.
12" Single: Released Jun '86, on Epic, by CBS Records. Deleted '86. Catalogue no: **TA 7087**
7" Single: Released Jun '86, on Epic, by CBS Records. Deleted '86. Catalogue no: **A 7087**

LIVING IN THE PAST
Tracks: / Living in the past / Seventh sin / Living in the past (remix).
12" Single: Released Dec '85, on Epic, by CBS Records. Catalogue no: **TX 6798**
7" Single: Released Dec '85, on Epic, by CBS Records. Catalogue no: **A 6798**
12" Single: Released Jan '86, on Epic, by CBS Records. Catalogue no: **QTA 6798**

MOVING TARGETS
Tracks: / Moving targets(instrumental) / Seventh fine / Moving targets.
7" Single: Released Mar '87, on Epic, by CBS Records. Deleted Aug '87. Catalogue no: **EMU 2**
12" Single: Released Mar '87, on Epic, by CBS Records. Deleted Aug '87. Catalogue no: **EMUT 2**

Drumman, Footsie

TIME WILL TELL
Tracks: / Time will tell.
12" Single: Released Jan '89, on Nisis Records, Catalogue no: **NIS 001**

Drummond, Bill

KING OF JOY, THE
Tracks: / King of joy, The.
7" Single: Released Mar '87, on Creation, by Creation Records. Catalogue no: **CRE 039**
12" Single: Released Mar '87, on Creation, by Creation Records. Catalogue no: **CRE 039T**

Drummond, Daniel

PROGRAM, THE
Tracks: / Program, The.
12" Single: Released Aug '87, on DTS, Catalogue no: **DTS 12001**

Drummond, Don

CLASH & SPECIALS GO TO JAIL
Tracks: / Clash & Specials go to jail.
12" Single: Released Jul '80, on Russ, Deleted '81. Catalogue no: **NIBZ 001**

Drummond, Keith

PEOPLE OF THE WORLD
Tracks: / People of the world.
12" Single: Released Mar '83, on Carousel (1), by Carousel Records. Catalogue no: **CAR 6**

Drunken State

BAGS NOT CARRY THE COFFIN
Tracks: / Bags not carry the coffin.
12" Single: Released Jan '89, on Blast Furnace, Catalogue no: **DRUNK 101**

Drupi

Biographical details: This Italian singer, whose real name was Gian Piero Anelli, enjoyed a one-off UK chart entry at the beginning of 1974. He reached no.17 on the British chart with a melodic and slightly maudlin ballad, *Vado via.* It logged an impressive 12 weeks on the Top 50. It was rare enough for Continental acts to break into the British charts, but even more unusual for an Italian act to achieve UK recognition. Even when the disco maestro Giorgio Moroder made it big in Britain, he was based in West Germany and not in his homeland. (Bob Macdonald, 7/7/85).

VADO VIA
Tracks: / Vado via.
7" Single: Released Dec '73, on A&M, by A&M Records. Deleted Dec '76. Catalogue no: **AMS 7083**

DRIVER 67 - HEADLIGHTS (Released on Logo)

VADO VIA (OLD GOLD)
Tracks: / Vado via.
7" Single: Released Jul '82, on Old Gold, by Old Gold Records. Deleted Jul '88. Catalogue no: **OG 9154**

Drusky, Roy

Biographical details: Country pop singer/songwriter born in 1930 in Atlanta. He had recorded for Starday and CBS and written hits for others (Faron Young's *Alone with you* was a number one), finally had his own hits on MCA and Mercury after 1960. On Capitol from 1974 he had no more hit singles but highly praised albums. The title song of *Anymore* was a 1960 hit for Teresa Brewer. (Donald Clarke, April 1989).

NIGHT FLYING (SINGLE)
Tracks: / Night flying / Daddy's little cowboy.
7" Single: Released Aug '81, on Big R, by Big R Records. Catalogue no: **BRS 04**

Dry Ice

HARRY THE HIPPIE
Tracks: / Harry hippie.
7" Single: Released Oct '84, on Simple, Deleted '87. Catalogue no: **SIM 6**

D.S.

MY TOY
Tracks: / My toy / Dirty money.
7" Single: Released Feb '80, on Optimistic, by Optimistic Records. Deleted '83. Catalogue no: **OPT 002**

D.S.M.

DESTINY
Tracks: / Destiny.
12" Single: Released May '86, on Elite Records, by Elite Records. Deleted '88. Catalogue no: **DAZZ 5212**
7" Single: Released May '86, on Elite Records, by Elite Records. Deleted '88. Catalogue no: **DAZZ 527**

DESTINY (MOBSTER REMIX)
Tracks: / Destiny (mobster remix) / Destiny (mobster remix) (version).
12" Single: Released Dec '88, on Jam Today, by Jam Today Records. Catalogue no: **12 CHIL 9**

WARRIOR GROOVE (THE SAGA CONTINUES)
Tracks: / Warrior groove (the saga continues) / Warrior dub (the final chapter) / Jazz groove.
12" Single: on Virgin, by Virgin Records. Catalogue no: **DAZZ 4513**
7" Single: Released Dec '85, on Virgin, by Virgin Records. Deleted Dec '88. Catalogue no: **DAZZ 45-7**

D.S.T.

HOME OF HIP HOP
Tracks: / Home of hip hop.
7" Single: Released Aug '85, on Celluloid (USA), by Celluloid Records (USA). Catalogue no: **CEL 706**

MEAN MACHINE
Tracks: / Mean machine.
12" Single: Released Sep '84, on Carrere, Catalogue no: **CART 343**

MEGAMIX II, WHY IS IT FRESH?
Tracks: / Why is it fresh.
12" Single: Released Sep '84, on Carrere, Catalogue no: **CART 344**

DTI

KEEP THIS FREQUENCY CLEAR
Tracks: / Keep the frequency clear / Keep the frequency clear (version).
7" Single: Released Apr '88, on Premiere, by Premiere Records. Catalogue no: **ERE 501**
12" Single: Released Mar '88, on Premiere, by Premiere Records. Catalogue no: **ERET 501**

LISTEN TO THIS
Tracks: / Listen to this / Sound of money, The.
7" Single: Released Sep '88, on Premiere, by Premiere Records. Catalogue no: **ERE 503**
12" Single: Released Sep '88, on Premiere, by Premiere Records. Catalogue no: **ERET 503**

D-Train

Biographical details: This American duo came to clubgoers' attention with a series of disco hits during 1982-3. The two mwn responsible for these were James Williams, a booming soul vocalist, and Hubert Eaves III, a skilled keyboards player and producer who had previously played synthesisers on Roberta Flack & Donny Hathaway's *Back together again* single. Hailing from New York, D Train's first hit was their self-penned single *You're the one for me*, which reached the no.30 position on the UK pop chart. It was a massive dance hit, and quickly became a club classic; its modest pop success was a reflection of the fact that it did not transfer particularly well to radio airplay. Subsequent D Train hits included a discofied rendition of Bacharach's & David's standard *Walk on by*, a UK no.23 pop hit with *Music*, plus *Keep giving me love*. *You're the one* became the all-time favourite record of Britain's Paul Hardcastle, an up-and-coming disco star whose keyboards and production talents were similar to those of Eaves. Hardcastle included his own rendition of the number in a medley single, which reached no.41 on the UK pop chart in April 1984. The following year he remixed D Train's original version. (Bob Macdonald, 7/7/85).

KEEP GIVING ME LOVE
Tracks: / Keep giving me love.
7" Single: Released Jul '83, on Prelude, Deleted Jul '86. Catalogue no: **A 3497**

KEEP ON
Tracks: / Keep on / Love vibrations / You're the one for me (on 12" only).
12" Single: Released Jul '82, on Epic, by CBS Records. Deleted Jul '85. Catalogue no: **EPCA 132543**
7" Single: Released Jul '82, on Epic, by CBS Records. Deleted Jul '85. Catalogue no: **EPCA 2543**

MUSIC
Tracks: / Music.
7" Single: Released Sep '85, on Prelude, Catalogue no: **ZB 40431**
12" Single: Released Sep '85, on Prelude, Deleted May '89. Catalogue no: **ZT 40432**

MUSIC(PART 1)
Tracks: / Music (part 1).
7" Single: Released Apr '83, on Prelude, Catalogue no: **A 3332**
12" Single: Released Apr '83, on Prelude, Catalogue no: **TA 3332**

THANK YOU
Tracks: / Thank you.
12" Single: Released Jul '84, on Prelude, Catalogue no: **MHST 102**

WALK ON BY
Tracks: / Walk on by / Lucky day.
7" Single: Released May '82, on Epic, by CBS Records. Deleted May '85. Catalogue no: **A 2298**
12" Single: Released May '82, on Epic, by CBS Records. Deleted May '85. Catalogue no: **A 132298**

YOU'RE THE ONE FOR ME (SINGLE)
Tracks: / You're the one for me / Walk on by / Keep on / D train theme.
12" Single: Released Feb '82, on Epic, by CBS Records. Deleted Feb '85. Catalogue no: **A13 2016**
7" Single: Released Sep '82, on Epic, by CBS Records. Deleted '85. Catalogue no: **EPCA 40-2626**
7" Single: Released Feb '82, on Epic, by CBS Records. Deleted Feb '85. Catalogue no: **A 2016**
7" Single: Released Jul '85, on Prelude, Catalogue no: **ZB 40302**
12" Single: Released Jul '85, on Prelude, Deleted Aug '89. Catalogue no: **ZT 40302**

DTS

TRIBUTE TO MARC Medley-2 parts
Tracks: / Tribute to Marc.
7" Single: Released Oct '82, on HME (USA), Catalogue no: **AMP 001**

Du Cann, John

DON'T BE A DUMMY
Tracks: / Don't be a dummy.
7" Single: Released Sep '79, on Vertigo, by Phonogram Ltd. Deleted Sep '82. Catalogue no: **6059 241**

Duane & Co

J.B. ON THE ONE
Tracks: / J.B. on the one (edit down).
7" Single: Released Aug '87, on Serious, by Serious Records. Catalogue no: **7OUS 7**
12" Single: Released Aug '87, on Serious, by Serious Records. Catalogue no: **OUS 7**

Duanes

WE CAN'T KEEP HANGING ON
Tracks: / We can't keep hanging on / Without you.
7" Single: Released Apr '81, on Cheapskate, Deleted Apr '84. Catalogue no: **CHEAP 20**

Duart,John

MOTORBIKE
Tracks: / Motorbike / Frederika.
7" Single: Released Apr '80, on Dresden, Catalogue no: **DR 1A**

Dub Organiser

I'VE GOT A WEAPON
Tracks: / I've got a weapon.
12" Single: Released 16 Jan '89, on Play Hard, by Play Hard Records. Catalogue no: **DEC 12**

Dub Set

FLESH BEAT FEVER
Tracks: / Flesh beat fever / Onyeoch Onyegee.
7" Single: Released Jun '84, on Elektra (USA), by Elektra Records (USA). Catalogue no: **E 9730**
12" Single: Released Jun '84, on Elektra (USA), by Elektra Records (USA). Deleted '85. Catalogue no: **E 9730 T**

NAMELESS DREAD
Tracks: / Nameless dread.
7" Single: Released Sep '84, on Elektra (USA), by Elektra Records (USA). Catalogue no: **E 9693**

Dub Sex

DUB SEX
Tracks: / Dub sex.
12" Single: Released 1 Apr '87, on Skysaw, by Skysaw Records. Catalogue no: **SKY 007**

I'M NOT AFRAID
Tracks: / I'm not afraid.
12" Single: Released Nov '88, on Cut Deep, by Cut Deep Records. Catalogue no: **CUT 12003**

SWERVE
Tracks: / Swerve.
12" Single: Released Mar '89, on Cut Deep, by Cut Deep Records. Catalogue no: **CUT 12003**

UNDERNEATH, THE
Tracks: / Underneath, The / Instead of flowers.
7" Single: Released 23 Jul '88, on Cut Deep, by Cut Deep Records. Catalogue no: **CUT 001**
12" Single: Released 23 Jul '88, on Cut Deep, by Cut Deep Records. Catalogue no: **CUT 001T**

Dub Syndicate

NIGHT TRAIN
Tracks: / Night train.
12" Single: Released 14 Jul '87, on Lacer, Catalogue no: **LACERW 001**

Dubious Brothers

DON'T LAUGH AT ME
Tracks: / Don't laugh at me / Sugar daddy / Don't laugh at me (cementmix).
7" Single: Released Sep '86, on Fend For Yourself, Catalogue no: **FFY 005**
7" Single: Released Oct '86, on Fend For Yourself, Catalogue no: **FFY 006**

EGG
Tracks: / Egg, The / Save me / Protest song (cakemix) / Dance of the undertaker.
7" Single: Released Sep '86, on Fend For Yourself, Catalogue no: **FFY 004**

LIKES OF YOU
Tracks: / Likes of you, The / Protest song / Stay awake, my little emperor / Bible stories.
7" Single: Released Sep '86, on Fend For Yourself, Catalogue no: **FFY 003**

SOUTH AMERICA WELCOMES THE NAZIS
Tracks: / South America welcomes the Nazis / Lord of the flies / Bible stories / They're coming to take me away.
12" Single: Released Feb '87, on Fend For Yourself, Catalogue no: **FFY 007**

Dublin City Ramblers

RARE OULD TIMES (SINGLE)
Tracks: / Rare ould times.
7" Single: Released '88, on I&B, by I & B Records. Catalogue no: **DOS 194**

Dubliners

Biographical details: At the time of their late sixties success, this Irish folk band consisted of Ciaron Burke, Ronnie Drew, Luke Kelly, Barny McKenna and John Sheahan. The Dubliners enjoyed a brief but lucrative run of British chart success during 1967. Their version of an old pub and folk favourite, *Seven drunken nights*, took them to no.7 on the singles chart. This rowdy singalong hit contained only a 5-day week; the others being considered unsuitable for inclusion on the single. For their follow-up, the band recorded another traditional song, *Black velvet band*, and took it to the UK no.15 position. During the same year, they managed to place three albums in the British Top 30, including two Top Tenners: *A drop of the hard stuff* and *More of the hard stuff*. Despite a lack of UK chart success during the 70's and 80's, the reputation established by their late 60's records ensured that the Dubliners would enjoy a steady live following for the rest of their career. The bearded bards have continued to commit their repertoire to vinyl, and their part-serious/part-comic blend of (mainly Irish) folk songs remains a major draw at folk clubs throughout the British Isles and beyond. (Bob Macdonald, 7/85).

BLACK VELVET BAND
Tracks: / Black velvet band.
7" Single: Released Aug '67, on Major Minor, Deleted Aug '70. Catalogue no: **MM 530**

NEVER WED AN OLD MAN
Tracks: / Never wed an old man.
7" Single: Released Dec '67, on Major Minor, Deleted Dec '70. Catalogue no: **MM 551**

SEVEN DRUNKEN NIGHTS (SINGLE)
Tracks: / Seven drunken nights / Whiskey on a Sunday.
7" Single: Released Jun '80, on H.M.V., by EMI Records. Deleted '83. Catalogue no: **POP 2010**
7" Single: Released Mar '67, on Major Minor, Deleted Mar '70. Catalogue no: **MM 506**

Duchess & High School

FRIDAYS, SATURDAY & SUNDAY
Tracks: / Friday's,Saturday & Sunday.
7" Single: Released Oct '84, on RPS, Catalogue no: **RPS 1**

Duck You Sucker

LOVE IS CRIMINAL
Tracks: / Love is criminal / I'm yours, she said.
7" Single: Released Dec '84, on Magnet, by WEA Records. Catalogue no: **MAG 268**

Ducktail

ROCKIN' DADDY
Tracks: / Rockin' daddy.
7" Single: Released Jul '80, on Ducktail, Catalogue no: **DUCKU 2**

Dudek, Andre

TIBUR
Tracks: / Tibur / Swan.
7" Single: Released Feb '80, on Laser, Deleted Feb '85. Catalogue no: **LAS 23**

Duel

TELL ME WHY LOVE DIES
Tracks: / Tell me why love dies.
CD 5": Released 23 Jul '88, on Tent, by BMG Records (UK). Catalogue no: **TENTCD 7**
7" Single: Released Jul '88, on Tent, by BMG Records (UK). Catalogue no: **TENT 7**
12" Single: Released Jul '88, on Tent, by BMG Records (UK). Catalogue no: **TENTT 7**

THERE'S A LIVING TO BE MADE
Tracks: / There's a living to be made / Not my kind of love.
7" Single: Released 23 Apr '88, on Tent, by BMG Records (UK). Catalogue no: **TENT 5**
12" Single: Released 23 Apr '88, on Tent, by BMG Records (UK). Catalogue no: **TENTT 5**

Duet Emmo

OR SO IT SEEMS (SINGLE)
Tracks: / Or so it seems.
12" Single: Released Mar '83, on Mute, by Mute Records. Catalogue no: **MUTE 25**

Duff, Mary

AMAZING GRACE
Tracks: / Amazing grace / White rose o Athens, The / Beautiful Meath / Sally gar dens.
Cassingle: Released Oct '88, on Ritz, by Ritz Records. Catalogue no: **RITZC 191**
7" Single: Released Oct '88, on Ritz, by Ritz Records. Catalogue no: **RITZ 191**

DADDY'S HANDS
Tracks: / Daddy's hands / Spancil Hill.
12" Single: Released Oct '87, on Ritz, by Ritz Records. Catalogue no: **RITZ 179**

DEAR GOD
Tracks: / Dear God / Love someone like me.
7" Single: Released Apr '88, on Ritz, by Ritz Records. Catalogue no: **RITZ 184**

GOIN' GONE
Tracks: / Goin' gone.
7" Single: Released Apr '89, on Ritz, by Ritz Records. Catalogue no: **RITZ 198**

Duffo

Biographical details: This Australia singer enjoyed just one UK chart entry. occurred in March 1979, when his punk style novelty single *Give me back me bra* reached no.60. During 1979-82 he re leased a series of albums - *Duffo*, *The di appearing boy*, *Bob the barman* an *Lexicon* - which all contained his brand loony humour and Bowie-influenced rock; *The disappearing boy* featured guest vocals from Jimmy Pursey of Sham 69. (Bob Macdonald, 7/7/85).

GIVE ME BACK MY BRAIN
Tracks: / Give me back my brain.
7" Single: Released Mar '79, on Beggars Banquet, by Beggars Banquet Records. Deleted Mar '82. Catalogue no: **BEG 15**

GONNA SEND THE BOYS AROUND
Tracks: / Gonna send the boys around.
12" Single: Released Aug '85, on Yowsa Yowsa, Catalogue no: **12YY 2**

I WANT TO BE THE PILOT
Tracks: / I want to be the pilot / Falling out of the sky.
7" Single: Released Jun '82, on PVK, by PVK Records. Catalogue no: **PK 117**

WALK ON THE WILD SIDE
Tracks: / Walk on the wild side / Sitting on an egg.
7" Single: Released Oct '82, on PVK, by PVK Records. Catalogue no: **PV 104**

Duffus D

IS IT JUST A DREAM?
Tracks: / Is it just a dream? / Cheater.
12" Single: Released Dec '82, on Jay Dee, Catalogue no: **JD 009**

Duffy Brothers

IF I NEEDED YOU
Tracks: / If I needed you / Banjo boogie.
7" Single: Released Dec '82, on Marina, Catalogue no: **DBW 021**

Duffy, Patrick

TOGETHER WE ARE STRONG
Tracks: / Together we are strong.
7" Single: Released Apr '83, on Arista, by BMG Records (UK). Catalogue no: **105 007**

Duffy, Stephen 'Tintin'

I LOVE YOU
Tracks: / I love you / Love is driving me insane / I love you (the inversion) (Extra track on 12" version only) / Wednesday Jones / Icing on the cake / Kiss me.
10" single: Released Aug '86, on 10 Records, by Virgin Records. Deleted May '88. Catalogue no: **TIND 510**
12" Single: Released Feb '86, on 10 Records, by Virgin Records. Deleted '89. Catalogue no: **TEN 91-12**
7" Single: Released Feb '86, on 10 Records, by Virgin Records. Deleted '86. Catalogue no: **TEN 91**
7" Single: Released Aug '86, on 10 Records, by Virgin Records. Catalogue no: **TIN 5**
12" Single: Released Aug '86, on 10 Records, by Virgin Records. Deleted May '88. Catalogue no: **TIN 512**

ICING ON THE CAKE (see panel below)
Tracks: / Icing on the cake / Broken home / Icing on the cake (remix) (On TIN 313 only).
12" Single: on 10 Records, by Virgin Records. Catalogue no: **TIN 313**
7" Single: Released May '85, on 10 Records, by Virgin Records. Deleted May '88. Catalogue no: **TIN 3**
12" Single: Released May '85, on 10 Records, by Virgin Records. Deleted May '88. Catalogue no: **TIN 312**

KISS ME
Tracks: / Kiss me / Icing on the cake.
12" Single: Released 30 May '89, on Old Gold, by Old Gold Records. Catalogue no: **OG 4121**
7" Single: Released Feb '85, on 10 Records, by Virgin Records. Catalogue no: **TIN 2**
12" Single: Released Feb '85, on 10 Records, by Virgin Records. Catalogue no: **TIN 212**

SHE MAKES ME QUIVER
Tracks: / She makes me quiver.
12" Single: Released Sep '84, on 10 Records, by Virgin Records. Deleted '89. Catalogue no: **TEN 28-12**
7" Single: Released Sep '84, on 10 Records, by Virgin Records. Deleted '89. Catalogue no: **TEN 28**

SOMETHING SPECIAL
Tracks: / Something special / Disenchanted, The / Cocksure (Extra track on 12" version only).
7" Single: Released Apr '86, on 10 Records, by Virgin Records. Deleted '86. Catalogue no: **TEN 105**
12" Single: Released Apr '86, on 10 Records, by Virgin Records. Deleted '86. Catalogue no: **TENT 105**

UNKISS THAT KISS
Tracks: / Unkiss that kiss.
7" Single: Released Aug '85, on 10 Records, by Virgin Records. Deleted May '88. Catalogue no: **TIN 4**

Dugmore, Barry & John

IT'S GOOD WITH YOU
Tracks: / It's good with you.
7" Single: Released May '82, on JSO, Deleted '87. Catalogue no: **EAT 15**

Duke

HE'S THUNDER
Tracks: / He's thunder.
12" Single: Released Jul '87, on Hot Vinyl, Catalogue no: **HVT 43**

LOVE IS ALIVE
Tracks: / Love is alive / Take me back to Rio.
7" Single: Released Mar '80, on Epic, by CBS Records. Deleted Mar '83. Catalogue no: **EPC 8505**

Duke, George

Biographical details: This American keyboards player, singer and producer gained experience during the mid-sixties by playing in West Coast nightclubs. His career began in earnest in 1968, when he joined the band of up-and-coming violinist Jean-Luc Ponty as a jazz keyboardist. After 3 albums with Ponty, he joined Frank Zappa's Mothers of Invention and remained with the notorious madman from 1970-75; he managed to add a degree of stability to zany Zappa's work, whose music and personnel were an ever-changing phenomenon. While with Zappa, Duke mastered the new synthesiser technology and began releasing solo LP's. Duke's fusion of jazz with funk and soul, for which he later became well-known, started to emerge in 1976 while he was collaborating with drummer Billy Cobham. During 1977-79 the prolific Duke issued five solo albums within three years, on which he consolidated his funky approach. 1980 brought him his only solo entries into the UK charts: *Brazilian love affair* reached no.36 on the singles chart; meanwhile, the album of the same name, recorded in Brazil and featuring local accompanying musicians, climbed to no.33 on the UK LP listings. For his only American Top 40 single, Duke teamed up in 1981 with a fellow jazz-funk fusionist, the brilliant bassist Stanley Clarke. Their LP *The Clarke/Duke project* yielded the US no.19 hit *Sweet baby*. At the same time as *Sweet baby* was climbing the Billboard Hot 100, Duke was doing even better as a producer. A Taste of Honey's 1981 revival of *Sukiyaki* was a million-selling US no.3 hit; on this single, Duke went for a delicate, understated, summery soul sound. 1984 brought him his first US no.1 single, plus a UK no.2 as producer of Deniece Williams' *Let's hear it for the boy*. He continued to release his own classy and polished, but somewhat underrated, albums, such as 1982's *Dream on* and 1983's *Guardian of the light*. (Bob Macdonald, 7/7/85)
Keyboardist and composer born in 1946 in California. He sessioned with Don Ellis, Frank Zappa, Cannonball Adderley and co-led a group with Billy Cobham in 1975; since then he led various groups of his own and did festival, TV and film work, also producing records (a number one USA hit in 1984 with Deniece Williams' *Let's hear it for the boy*, etc. His versatile success has been mainly in a soft-fusion mode and he is best-known for the Clarke-Duke project with the bassist Stanley Clarke. (Donald Clarke, April 1989).

BRAZILIAN LOVE AFFAIR
Tracks: / Brazilian love affair.
Cassingle: Released Aug '82, on CBS, by CBS Records. Deleted Aug '85. Catalogue no: **A40 2630**
7" Single: Released Jul '80, on Epic, by CBS Records. Deleted Jul '83. Catalogue no: **EPC 8751**

I WANT YOU FOR MYSELF
Tracks: / I want you for myself / Dog man.
7" Single: Released Jan '80, on CBS, by CBS Records. Deleted Jan '85. Catalogue no: **CBS 8137**

I WILL ALWAYS BE YOUR FRIEND
Tracks: / I will always be your friend / Framed.
7" Single: Released Aug '82, on Epic, by CBS Records. Deleted Aug '85. Catalogue no: **EPCA 2661**

REACH OUT
Tracks: / Reach out.
7" Single: Released Apr '83, on Epic, by CBS Records. Catalogue no: **A 3267**
12" Single: Released Apr '83, on Epic, by CBS Records. Catalogue no: **TA 3267**

RIDE ON LOVE
Tracks: / Ride on love / Son of reach for it.
12" Single: Released May '82, on Epic, by CBS Records. Deleted May '85. Catalogue no: **EPCA 132372**
7" Single: Released May '82, on Epic, by CBS Records. Deleted May '85. Catalogue no: **EPCA 2372**

SHINE ON
Tracks: / Shine on / Positive energy.
7" Single: Released May '80, on Epic, by CBS Records. Deleted May '85. Catalogue no: **EPC A2072**
12" Single: Released May '80, on Epic, by CBS Records. Deleted May '85. Catalogue no: **132072**

Duke, James

HOLD ON
Tracks: / Hold on / Zyzafon.
CD 5": Released Aug '86, on Creole, by Creole Records. Catalogue no: **CRT 93**
7" Single: Released Aug '86, on Creole, by Creole Records. Catalogue no: **CR 93**

Duke M.C.

I DON'T CARE ANYMORE
Tracks: / I don't care anymore / Free.
12" Single: Released Apr '88, on Music Of Life, by Music Of Life Records. Catalogue no: **NOTE 15**

I'M RIFFIN'
Tracks: / I'm riffin' / English rasta.
12" Single: Released Feb '89, on Music Of Life, by Music Of Life Records. Catalogue no: **NOTE 25**
7" Single: Released Feb '89, on Music Of Life, by Music Of Life Records. Catalogue no: **7 NOTE 25**

MIRACLES
Tracks: / Miracles.
12" Single: Released Sep '88, on Music Of Life, by Music Of Life Records. Catalogue no: **12 NOTE 21**

Duke M.C. & DJ Leader

THROW YOUR HANDS IN THE AIR
Tracks: / Throw your hands in the air / Throw your hands in the air (inst).
7" Single: Released Aug '89, on Music Of Life, by Music Of Life Records. Catalogue no: **7NOTE 27**
12" Single: Released Aug '89, on Music Of Life, by Music Of Life Records. Catalogue no: **NOTE 27**

Duke & The Earl

BRUNO RAP, THE
Tracks: / Bruno rap, The.
12" Single: Released Mar '89, on Pecka Records, Catalogue no: **PPM 02**

Dukes

I'M A SURVIVOR
Tracks: / I'm a survivor / Every woman in the world.
7" Single: Released Aug '82, on WEA, by WEA Records. Catalogue no: **K 19252**

LEAVIN' IT ALL BEHIND
Tracks: / Leavin' it all behind / I'll try to help.
7" Single: Released Feb '80, on Warner Bros., by WEA Records. Deleted Feb '83. Catalogue no: **K 17551**

MYSTERY GIRL
Tracks: / Mystery girl / My simple heart.
7" Single: Released Oct '81, on WEA, by WEA Records. Deleted Oct '84. Catalogue no: **K 18867**

THANK YOU FOR THE PARTY
Tracks: / Thank you for the party / Love's fool.
7" Single: Released May '82, on WEA, by WEA Records. Deleted May '85. Catalogue no: **K 19136**

Dukes Of Stratosphear

YOU'RE A GOOD MAN ALBERT BROWN (CURSE YOU RED BARREL)
Tracks: / You're a good man Albert Brown (curse you red barrel) / Vanishing girl / Mole from the ministry, The (12" only) / My love explodes (12" only).
7" Single: Released Jul '87, on Virgin, by Virgin Records. Deleted May '88. Catalogue no: **VS 982**
7" Pic: Released Jul '87, on Virgin, by Virgin Records. Deleted '89. Catalogue no: **VSY 982**
12" Single: Released Jul '87, on Virgin, by Virgin Records. Catalogue no: **VS 982-12**

Dukley, Errol

HAPPINESS FORGETS
Tracks: / Happiness forgets.
12" Single: Released 12 May '89, on Natty Congo, Catalogue no: **NCDM 041**

Dukov, Bruce

FOR KRIESLER'S SAKE
Tracks: / For Kriesler's sake.
7" Single: Released Apr '83, on Epic, by CBS Records. Catalogue no: **A 3315**

Dumb Angels

LOVE & MERCY
Tracks: / Love & mercy.
7" Single: Released Nov '88, on Fierce, Catalogue no: **FRIGHT 033**

Dumb Blondes

STRANGE LOVE
Tracks: / Strange love.
7" Single: Released Apr '81, on Fresh, by Jetstar Records. Catalogue no: **FRESH 21**

Dumbells

GIDDY UP
Tracks: / Giddy up / Christmas dream.
7" Single: Released Jan '81, on Polydor, by Polydor Ltd. Deleted Jan '84. Catalogue no: **POSP 209**
7" Single: Released Nov '81, on Polydor, by Polydor Ltd. Catalogue no: **EGO 3**

Dummer, John

Biographical details: Dummer the drummer was an integral part of Britain's blues boom of the late 60's, although he did not receive the commercial success enjoyed by such acts as John Mayall's Bluesbreakers, Fleetwood Mac, Chicken Shack and Family. The first line-up of the John Dummer Blues Band was formed in 1967, and it continued to the end of the decade. The early 70's saw Dummer leading the Ooblee Doobloe Band. That combo folded in 1974, and he spent the mid-seventies working for

TEPHEN 'TINTIN' DUFFY - ICING ON THE CAKE(Released on 10 Records)

record companies. Dummer experienced commercial success for the first time during the late 70's, as drummer with Darts. That rock'n'roll/doo-wop band enjoyed enormous acceptance on the British charts, including three consecutive no.2 singles in 1978. 1981 saw Dummer teaming up with a previously unknown vocalist, Helen April, for a gimmicky single *Own up if you're over 25*. Recalling the people, music and sayings of the sixties, this enjoyable record received considerable airplay, particularly on BBC Radio one's Breakfast Show, but was not a hit. Dummer & April did, however, achieve a minor hit single in 1982 with a tongue-in-cheek revival of *Blue skies*; complete with a lazy whistling accompaniment; this single reached no.54. (Bob Macdonald, 8/7/85).

BLUE SKIES
Tracks: / Blue skies / Nice cup of tea.
7" Single: Released Aug '82, on Speed, Deleted Aug '85. Catalogue no: **SPEED 8**

OWN UP IF YOU'RE OVER 25
Tracks: / Own up if your're over 25.
7" Single: Released Jan '81, on Red Shadow, Catalogue no: **REDS 009**

Dummies

DIDN'T YOU USE TO USE TO BE YOU
Tracks: / Didn't you use to use to be you / Miles out to sea.
7" Single: Released Aug '80, on Cheapskate, Deleted '83. Catalogue no: **CHEAP 3**

Dumptruck

GOING NOWHERE
Tracks: / Going nowhere / Watch her fall / Things go wrong (Only on 12" single.) / Swirls around (Only on 12" single.).
Note: Produced by Hugh Jones.
12" Single: Released 10 Oct '87, on Big Time Records, by Big Time Records. Catalogue no: **ZT 4155**
7" Single: Released Sep '87, on Big Time Records, by Big Time Records. Deleted May '89. Catalogue no: **ZB 41553**
12" Single: Released Sep '87, on Big Time Records, by Big Time Records. Deleted May '89. Catalogue no: **ZT 41554**

ISLAND
Tracks: / Island / Wire / 50 miles (12" only).
Note: From the album For The Country.
12" Single: Released Jan '88, on Big Time Records, by Big Time Records. Deleted May '89. Catalogue no: **ZT 41706**
7" Single: Released Jan '88, on Big Time Records, by Big Time Records. Deleted May '89. Catalogue no: **ZB 41705**

Dumpy's Rusty Bolts

BOX HILL OR BUST
Tracks: / Box hill or bust / Got to be blues.
7" Single: Released Oct '82, on Cool King, Deleted Oct '85. Catalogue no: **CK 008**

JUST FOR KICKS
Tracks: / Just for kicks / Come ride with me.
7" Single: Released Aug '82, on Cool King, Catalogue no: **CNK 006**

Dunbar, Ernesta

CHECKING OUT
Tracks: / Checking out / Checking out (remix).
12" Single: Released Sep '87, on Hardcore, Catalogue no: **HAKT 6**

Dunbar, Valerie

ALWAYS ARGYLL
7" Single: Released Sep '81, on Klub, by Klub Records. Catalogue no: **KLUB 32**

BLUE EYES CRYING IN THE RAIN
Tracks: / Blue eyes crying in the rain / Another year passes.
7" Single: Released Jun '83, on Klub, by Klub Records. Catalogue no: **KLUB 41**

I'LL SAY FAREWELL (SINGLE)
Tracks: / I'll say farewell.
7" Single: Released Oct '82, on Klub, by Klub Records. Catalogue no: **KLUB 36**

PAL OF MY CRADLE DAYS
Tracks: / Pal of my cradle days / Auld house.
7" Single: Released Feb '82, on Klub, by Klub Records. Catalogue no: **KLUB 34**

PROUD LION RAMPANT, THE
Tracks: / Proud lion rampant, The / Back to Bonnie Scotland/Wild mountain thyme / Come by the hills.
7" Single: Released Oct '88, on Scotdisc, by Scotdisc Records. Catalogue no: **ITV 7 S 470**

ROWAN TREE
Tracks: / Rowan tree.
7" Single: Released Jun '79, on Klub, by Klub Records. Catalogue no: **KLUB 14**

SCOTLAND YOU'RE A LADY
Tracks: / Scotland you're a lady / Brahm's cradle song.
7" Single: Released Apr '80, on Klub, by Klub Records. Deleted '83. Catalogue no: **KLUB 25**

THERE WAS A MAN
Tracks: / There was a man / Star o' Rabbie Burns.
7" Single: Released Nov '83, on Klub, by Klub Records. Catalogue no: **KLUB 45**

Duncan, Anne Marie

NO TIME FOR LOVE
Tracks: / No time for love / No time for love (version).
12" Single: Released Feb '86, on Diamond, by Revolver Records. Catalogue no: **DC 0074**

Duncan, Arlene

WANNA GROOVE, I
Tracks: / I wanna groove.
12" Single: Released Jan '83, on Proto, by Proto Records. Catalogue no: **ENAT 101**

Duncan, Carey

ALL I HAVE TO DO IS DREAM
Tracks: / All I have to do is dream.
7" Single: Released Jul '81, on Decibel, Catalogue no: **DBS 7**

I'M YOUR WOMAN
Tracks: / Im your woman.
7" Single: Released Nov '80, on DB, by DB Records. Catalogue no: **DBS 3**

NOBODY'S CHILD
Tracks: / Nobody's child.
7" Single: Released Apr '82, on Double B, Catalogue no: **BB 001**

RAINING IN MY HEART
Tracks: / Raining in my heart.
7" Single: Released Jun '84, on Ritz, by Ritz Records. Catalogue no: **RITZ 070**

TURNING AWAY
Tracks: / Turning away.
7" Single: Released Jan '85, on Ritz, by Ritz Records. Catalogue no: **RITZ 094**

Duncan, Celena

DO IT
Tracks: / Do it / Feels so good to be in love again.
12" Single: Released Jun '82, on RCA, by BMG Records (UK). Deleted Jun '85. Catalogue no: **RCAT 235**
7" Single: Released Jun '82, on RCA, by BMG Records (UK). Deleted Jun '85. Catalogue no: **RCA 235**

FASTER THAN THE EYE CAN SEE
Tracks: / Faster than the eye can see (instrumental) / Faster than the eye can see.
7" Single: Released Mar '87, on Nightmare, by Nightmare Records. Catalogue no: **MARES 12**
12" Single: Released Mar '87, on Nightmare, by Nightmare Records. Catalogue no: **MARE 12**

SHINE ON
Tracks: / Shine on / You've got the love I need.
7" Single: Released Nov '81, on RCA, by BMG Records (UK). Deleted '84. Catalogue no: **RCA 156**
12" Single: Released Nov '81, on RCA, by BMG Records (UK). Deleted '84. Catalogue no: **RCAT 156**

WANT YOUR LOVE BACK, I 2 Parts
Tracks: / I want your love back.
12" Single: Released Feb '83, on RCA, by BMG Records (UK). Catalogue no: **RCAT 307**
7" Single: Released Feb '83, on RCA, by BMG Records (UK). Catalogue no: **RCA 307**

Duncan, Daryll

JAMES BROWN
Tracks: / James Brown (part 1) / James Brown (part 2).
7" Single: Released Feb '88, on Motown, by BMG Records (UK). Catalogue no: **ZB 41739**
12" Single: Released Feb '88, on Motown, by BMG Records (UK). Catalogue no: **ZT 41740**

ROCK THE HOUSE
Tracks: / Rock the house / Rock the house (inst).
7" Single: Released May '87, on Motown, by BMG Records (UK). Catalogue no: **ZB 41277**
12" Single: Released May '87, on Motown, by BMG Records (UK). Catalogue no: **ZT 41278**

Duncan, Hugo

BRADY FROM STRABANE
Tracks: / Brady of Strabane / Misty rollin' Midlands.
7" Single: Released Aug '86, on Homespun (Ireland), by Outlet Records. Catalogue no: **HS 111**

DEAR OLD GALWAY TOWN
Tracks: / Dear old Galway Town.
7" Single: Released '88, on Homespun (Ireland), by Outlet Records. Catalogue no: **HIS 77**
7" Single: Released Jul '83, on Homespun (Ireland), by Outlet Records. Catalogue no: **HS 070**

FAIRY REEL
Tracks: / Fairy reel, The / O'Hara from Tara.
7" Single: Released May '88, on Homespun (Ireland), by Outlet Records. Catalogue no: **HS 118**

IT'S MY MOTHERS BIRTHDAY TODAY
Tracks: / It's my mother's birthday today / If those lips could only speak.
7" Single: Released Mar '85, on Homespun (Ireland), by Outlet Records. Catalogue no: **HS 095**

KATIE DAVY
Tracks: / Katie Davy.
7" Single: Released '88, on Homespun (Ireland), by Outlet Records. Catalogue no: **HIS 117**

WEDDING SONG, THE (SINGLE)
Tracks: / Wedding song, The.
7" Single: Released Nov '85, on Homespun (Ireland), by Outlet Records. Catalogue no: **HS 102**

YOU'RE AS WELCOME AS THE FLOWERS IN MAY
Tracks: / I love you the best of all.
7" Single: Released Nov '86, on Homespun (Ireland), by Outlet Records. Catalogue no: **HS 114**

Duncan, Johnny

Biographical details: This American singer and guitarist, born in Tennessee, enjoyed brief British fame in 1957 while remaining unknown in his home country. His first important musical experience occurred in his early teens when he sang in a gospel quartet. He started playing guitar at the age of 16 (1947) and soon joined Bill Monroe's Blue Grass Boys, Monroe being a noted country/blues fusionist. Duncan was drafted into the US Army and, in 1953, was posted in Britain; later that year he married a British girl. He then decided to settle in the UK after his discharge. In 1956 his musical career received a boost, when he replaced the fast-rising star Lonnie Donegan as skiffle singer in the Chris Barber Band; with *Rock Island Line* becoming a transatlantic Top 10 hit, Donegan was in the process of spearheading the UK's skiffle boom. Because of his nationality and his experience in bluegrass music, Duncan's style was more authentic than Donegan's, and he therefore attracted a credibility tag. By the start of 1957, Duncan felt confident enough to leave Barber and form his own combo, Johnny Duncan & The Blue Grass Boys. Later that year, Duncan and his group achieved their first and only major UK hit - *Last train to San Fernando*, an evocative and enjoyable single, was a no.2 smash. However, the two follow-up singles, *Blue blue heartaches* and *Footprints in the snow*, both peaked at no.27, and subsequent attempts failed to make the British charts. They continued to be a successful live group for a while, but Duncan was fading into obscurity by the end of the 50's. Duncan returned to the States in the early 60's, and tried to refine and perfect his country round. From 1967 onwards, he enjoyed hits from time to time on the US country charts, but he never became one of the genre's major artists. (Bob Macdonald, 8/7/85).

BLUE BLUE HEARTACHES
Tracks: / Blue blue heartaches.
7" Single: Released Oct '57, on Columbia, by EMI Records. Deleted '62. Catalogue no: **DB 3996**

FOOTPRINTS IN THE SNOW
Tracks: / Footprints in the snow.
7" Single: Released Nov '57, on Columbia, by EMI Records. Deleted '62. Catalogue no: **DB 4029**

LAST TRAIN TO SAN FERNANDO
Tracks: / Last train to San Fernando.
7" Single: Released Jul '57, on Columbia, by EMI Records. Deleted '62. Catalogue no: **DB 3959**

Duncan, Lesley

MASTERS OF WAR
Tracks: / Masters of war / Another light goes out.
7" Single: Released Feb '82, on Korova, by WEA Records. Deleted '85. Catalogue no: **KOW 22**

Duncan, Peter

COLD AS ICE
Tracks: / Cold as ice.
7" Single: Released May '83, on Deb, by Deb Records. Catalogue no: **DEB 112**

Duncan Sisters

YOU GIVE ME SUCH A FEELING
Tracks: / You give me such a feeling / Boys will be boys.
7" Single: Released Jan '80, on EMI, by EMI Records. Deleted '83. Catalogue no: **EMS 5501**
12" Single: Released Jan '80, on EMI, by EMI Records. Deleted '83. Catalogue no: **EML 5501**

Duncans

GONNA STAY IN LOVE (SINGLE)
Tracks: / Gonna stay in love / Too damned hot.
12" Single: Released Feb '83, on Proto, by Proto Records. Catalogue no: **ENAT 103**
7" Single: Released Feb '83, on Proto, by Proto Records. Catalogue no: **ENA 103**

Dundas, David

Biographical details: This British singer, keyboards player, songwriter and commercial jingles writer came to fame in 1976 with his hit single *Jeans on*. Coming from an aristocratic background - his full title being Lord David Paul Nicholas Dundas, second son of the 5th Earl of Zetland - he started out as a composer of jingles and ditties for TV and radio commercials. His blue jeans ad proved so catchy and popular that it was decided that it should be issued as a singles. Roger Greenaway, one of Britain's top pop songwriters, helped Dundas to extend *Jeans on* to the length of a fully fledged single, and Greenaway also produced the disc. It became a singalong smash, climbing to no.3 on the UK chart during the scorching summer of 1976. In early '77 the song reached no.17 in America. Most people think of Dundas as a one-off hitmaker, but he did actually come up with one more Top 30 hit. 1977's *Another funny honeymoon*, a weak attempt to repeat the *Jeans on* sound, peaked at no.29. His albums, *David Dundas* and *Vertical hold*, failed to make any impact, and his Lordship thereafter returned to the world of commercials, where he remained successful during the eighties. (Bob Macdonald, 8/7/85).

ANOTHER FUNNY HONEYMOON
Tracks: / Another funny honeymoon.
7" Single: Released Apr '77, on Air, by Chrysalis Records. Deleted '82. Catalogue no: **CHS 2136**

JEANS ON
Tracks: / Jeans on / Sleepy Serena.
7" Single: Released Jul '76, on Air, by Chrysalis Records. Deleted '79. Catalogue no: **CHS 2094**

Dune

DANCIN'
Tracks: / Dancin' / Heatwave.
7" Single: Released Jul '82, on Ultra, by Ultra Records. Catalogue no: **ULT 1002**

Dunkley, Errol

Biographical details: This Jamaican reggae singer and producer came to fame in his native country in the early seventies, and was noted for his intense singing style. In 1972 he joined forces with another up-and-coming Jamaican vocalist, Gregory Isaacs, to form the African Museum record label. After several years of successful singles and albums at home, Dunkley began to break into the British reggae charts. This process was enhanced in 1979, when Dunkley achieved his first and only major UK pop hit. *Okay Fred*, released on the Scope label and distributed in Britain by WEA, climbed to the no.11 position. This was a lightweight, catchy reggae single but, as with so many artists of his genre, he was unable to consolidate on this penetration of the crossover market; pop radio in the Western world continued to ignore the bulk of Jamaica's rich output. His only follow-up success on the UK pop charts was a no.52 placing in February 1980 with *Sit down and cry*. During the early 80's, he remained a regular visitor to Britain's specialist reggae listings, but he later colloed down the pace. (Bob Macdonald, 8/7/85).

AUTOGRAPH
Tracks: / Autograph.
12" Single: Released Oct '85, on Scom, Catalogue no: **BD 022**

BETCHA BY GOLLY WOW
Tracks: / Betcha by golly wow.
7" Single: Released Sep '82, on CSA, by CSA Records. Catalogue no: **CSA 500**
10" single: Released Sep '82, on CSA, by CSA Records. Catalogue no: **10CSA 500**

CHILDREN OF THE NIGHT
Tracks: / Children of the night.
12" Single: Released Oct '82, on Music Hawk, Catalogue no: **MO 2**

DARLING OOH (SINGLE)
Tracks: / Darling ooh.
12" Single: Released Aug '84, on Londisc, by Londisc Records. Catalogue no: **LDR 025**

DOWN BELOW
Tracks: / Down below.
12" Single: Released Jul '80, on Success (2), Catalogue no: **SRLD 004**

GOODNIGHT MY LOVE
Tracks: / Goodnight my love / Goodnight.
12" Single: Released 27 Feb '88, on Dunks International, Catalogue no: **D 1001**

HAVE YOU EVER BEEN BAD?
Tracks: / Have you ever been bad?.
12" Single: Released Jun '82, on PD, Catalogue no: **PCDD 006**

HOW COULD I LET YOU GET AWAY?
Tracks: / How could I let you get away / Get away dub.
12" Single: Released Dec '82, on Music Hawk, Catalogue no: **MH 03**

LITTLE BIT OF LOVING
Tracks: / Little bit of lovin'.
12" Single: Released Dec '82, on King Jam, Catalogue no: **KJ 081**

LOVE IN THE HOUSE
Tracks: / Love in the house.
12" Single: Released Aug '83, on Londisc, by Londisc Records. Catalogue no: **LD 004**

LOVE IN TIME
Tracks: / Love in time.
12" Single: Released May '82, on Judah, Catalogue no: **JR 002**

LOVE LIKE THIS
Tracks: / Love like this / In the meantime.
12" Single: Released Feb '83, on King Jam, Catalogue no: **KJ 083**

MY EYES
Tracks: / My eyes.
12" Single: Released Nov '83, on Easy Street, Catalogue no: **ES 002**

MY SWEET
Tracks: / My sweet.
12" Single: Released Jul '88, on Value Gold, Catalogue no: **VCR 005**

OK FRED
Tracks: / OK Fred.
7" Single: Released Sep '79, on Scope, Catalogue no: **SC 6**

ONLY A SMILE
Tracks: / Only a smile.
12" Single: Released Nov '82, on Natty Congo, Catalogue no: **NCDM 016**

RAGAMUFFIN GONE TO JAIL
Tracks: / Ragamuffin gone to jail.
12" Single: Released Aug '87, on Value Gold, Catalogue no: **VGR 003**

SILVER RAIN
Tracks: / Silver rain.
12" Single: Released Aug '88, on Dunks International, Catalogue no: **DI 300**

SIT DOWN AND CRY
Tracks: / Sit down and cry / Peekaboo.
7" Single: Released Feb '80, on Scope, Deleted '85. Catalogue no: **SC 11**

SPECIAL GIRL
Tracks: / Special girl.
12" Single: Released Oct '83, on Mobiliser, by Jetstar Records. Catalogue no: **MOBT 001**

TOUCH ME IN THE MORNING
Tracks: / Touch me in the morning.
12" Single: Released Jul '83, on Music Hawk, Catalogue no: **MHOD 08**

YOU HAVE BEEN BAD
12" Single: Released Feb '82, on PC, Catalogue no: **PC 006**

YOUR LOVE
Tracks: / Your love.
12" Single: Released Sep '88, on Dunks International, Catalogue no: **DI 004**

Dunlap, Gene

IT'S JUST THE WAY I FEEL (SINGLE)
Tracks: / It's just the way I feel / Love dancin' / Surest things can change.
7" Single: Released Feb '81, on Capitol, by EMI Records. Deleted Feb '84. Catalogue no: **CL 16183**
12" Single: Released Feb '81, on Capitol, by EMI Records. Deleted Feb '84. Catalogue no: **12 CL 16183**

ROCK RADIO
Tracks: / Rock radio / Surest things can change.
12" Single: Released Apr '81, on Capitol, by EMI Records. Deleted '85. Catalogue no: **12CL 16186**
7" Single: Released Apr '81, on Capitol, by EMI Records. Deleted '85. Catalogue no: **CL 16186**

Dunn & Bruce Street

IF YOU COME WITH ME
Tracks: / If you come with me.
7" Single: Released May '83, on Satril, by Satril Records. Catalogue no: **SAT 503**

SHOUT FOR JOY
Tracks: / Shout for joy / Yearnin' and burnin'.
12" Single: Released Aug '82, on Satril, by Satril Records. Catalogue no: **12SAT 500**
7" Single: Released Aug '82, on Satril, by Satril Records. Catalogue no: **SAT 500**

Dunn, Clive

Biographical details: This British actor and comedian became a one hit wonder recording star in 1971, when his *Granddad* single climbed to the no.1 slot. Although only middle-aged in real life at the time, he assumed his most famous role for this single - that of the septuagenarian butcher and war veteran, Corporal Jones from BBC TV's *Dad's Army*. This highly successful sitcom began in 1967 and ran for ten years. For *Granddad*, Dunn simply exploited the age aspect of this character, and sang nostalgic verses containing thoughts of "when I was a boy"; these were interrupted by a chorus of adoring grandchildren singing "Granddad, lovely. That's what we all think of you". *Granddad* was co-written by Herbie Flowers, who was then bassist with Blue Mink, and who later helped to form Sky; the disc was produced by John Cameron and Dunn himself. Although it entered the Top 50 in November 1970, it failed to reach no.1 until after the Christmas novelty market had receded - the song hit the top in January 1971. Dunn never returned to the charts, although subsequent visits to the recording studio included a 1982 duet single with a former *Dad's Army* colleague, John Le Mesurier, called *Not much change*. There was, however, a belated no. 1 answer record to *Granddad* in December 1980. Almost a decade after the Dunn smash, *There's no-one quite like Grandma* topped the UK listings for the St. Winifred's School Choir. (Bob Macdonald, 8/7/85).

GRANDAD
Tracks: / Grandad.
7" Single: Released Sep '70, on Columbia, by EMI Records. Catalogue no: **DB 8726**
7" Single: Released Oct '83, on Old Gold, by Old Gold Records. Deleted Jun '89. Catalogue no: **OG 9383**

NOT MUCH CHANGE
Tracks: / Not much change.
7" Single: Released Sep '82, on KA, Catalogue no: **KA 7**

Dunn, Kevin

OKTYABRINA
Tracks: / Oktyabrina.
7" Single: Released Jul '81, on Armageddon, by Armageddon Records. Catalogue no: **AS 014**

Dunn Thing

STICKING TO MY GUNS
Tracks: / Sticking to my guns / Making your mind up.
12" Single: Released Dec '84, on GC, Catalogue no: **GCT 1002**
7" Single: Released Dec '84, on GC, Catalogue no: **GC 1002**

Dupree, Robbie

HOT ROD
Tracks: / Hot rod / Thin line.
7" Single: Released Aug '80, on Elektra, by Elektra Records (UK). Deleted '83. Catalogue no: **K 12472**

STEALAWAY
Tracks: / Stealaway / I'm no stranger.
7" Single: Released May '80, on Elektra, by Elektra Records (UK). Deleted May '83. Catalogue no: **K 12450**

Dupree, Simon

Biographical details: This British singer and saxophonist's real name was Derek Shulman. Together with his brothers, Phil and Ray, he came to fame at the end of 1967 with the UK Top 10 single *Kites*, credited to Simon Dupree & The Big Sound. Born in Glasgow but based in Portsmouth, they played in various small-time R'n'B groups during the mid-sixties and, in '66, were given their new name by a new manager. Complemented by several other musicians, the brothers enjoyed their first taste of chart success in August 1967, reaching no.39 on the LP chart with *Without reservations*. With Simon (Derek) on lead vocals, the melodic and dramatic *Kites* gave them a UK no.9 single a few months later; this distinctive record could perhaps be described as a piece of MoR psychedelia. It was followed by *For whom the bell tolls*, which only reached no.43. The problem was that *Kites* had given the group a quasi-cabaret image, whereas they wanted to be a blues-oriented, less commercial combo. Simon Dupree & The Big Sound folded in 1969, and the Shulman Brothers founded Gentle Giant. They released their self-titled debut album in 1970, and continued issuing LP's at regular intervals until 1980. These albums, which showcased the group's multi-iinstrumental skills, all failed to reach the UK charts but were appreciated by a loyal cult following. Like the Big Sound, Gentle Giant included the Shulmans plus a variety of accompanying musicians, most notably Gary Green, Kerry Minnear and John Weathers; Phil Shulman quit in 1973. The group could certainly be described as progressive - their weird, adventurous and diverse experimentations included rock, jazz and classical strands. (Bob Macdonald, 8/7/85).

FOR WHOM THE BELL TOLLS
Tracks: / For whom the bell tolls.
7" Single: Released Apr '68, on Parlophone, by EMI Records. Deleted '73. Catalogue no: **R 5670**

KITES (ORIGINAL)
Tracks: / Kites.
7" Single: Released Nov '67, on Parlophone, by EMI Records. Deleted '72. Catalogue no: **R 5646**

KITES (SINGLE)
Tracks: / Kites.
7" Single: Released Mar '87, on Old Gold, by Old Gold Records. Deleted Sep '89. Catalogue no: **OG 9655**
7" Single: Released '78, on EMI, by EMI Records. Deleted Oct '87. Catalogue no: **EMI 2893**

Duprez, John

OH MY PAPA
Tracks: / Oh my papa.
7" Single: Released Nov '83, on Impression, Catalogue no: **IMS 2**
12" Single: Released Nov '83, on Impression, Catalogue no: **IMST 2**

Duran Duran

Biographical details: Duran Duran (named after the film Barbarella) at the time of the greatest success consisted of Simon Le Bon (vocals), Andy Taylor (lead guitar), Roger Taylor (drums), John Taylor (bass guitar) and Nick Rhodes (keyboards). The Taylors were not related. They released their first single *Planet Earth* in Feb 1981 on EMI. It reached No.12 and logged 11 weeks on the chart. Followed by a minor hit, *Careless memories* (No.37). Duran then shot to fame with hit after hit after hit. One of their greatest triumphs was their single *Is there something I should know* (which was not on any of their albums) shot straight in at the top of the charts. They provided one more No.1 single *The reflex* a dance remix of a song on the *Seven & The Ragged Tiger* LP. Known well as a video group, they proved that status when they released their single *Wild boys*. With Simon getting eaten by a long snake like monster that looked like a willy with teeth, they shot to No.2.
Duran then announced that were going to work on separate projects for a while. The Power Station (Andy, John teamed up with Robert Palmer and Tony Thompson). Their music proved to be more of a rock standard than that of Duran. They had hits with *Some like it hot*, *Get it on* (A cover version of the T.Rex classic) and a minor hit with *Communication*. John and Andy actually played with Power Station and Duran in the legendary Live Aid concert in the States. The other spin-off group - Arcadia which included the rest of the members of Duran provided music in the opposite class to their rivals. A more matured sound which gave them a Top 10 hit with *Election day* and minor hits with *The promise* and *The flame*. Other solo projects included John Taylor acting in a one-off TV play and releasing a solo single (the theme of the raunchy film, Nine and a half weeks). Simon represented Britain in a yachting race (and consequently nearly lost his life), all members of the group married with the exception of John (who remained an eligable young bachelor) and Andy (who was already married).
The group as a whole released another Top Tenner with the theme to the James Bond film *A view to a kill* then promptly Andy quit to take up a solo career. Roger (after having a near nervous breakdown) left to spend more time with his wife. The remaining three, obviously determined to keep going, released the album and single *Notorious*. This produced hits in the lower regions of the Top 40 with *Skin trade* and *Meet el presidente*. Their music had matured, but their popularity in Britain had declined. In the States Duran mania had just begun. In one of the top music magazines, they scooped up just about every award they could. In September 1988, they released another single *I don't want your love*, followed by another album *Big*. (Karen Blackman, Oct 1988)
A pop quintet formed in Birmingham in 1978. The first stable lineup included keyboardist Nick Rhodes (real name Nicholas Bates), bassist John Taylor, drummer Roger Taylor, lead guitarist Andy Taylor (none of the Taylor's related) and London art student, vocalist Simon Le Bon. An earlier incarnation had played its first gig at 'The Rum Runner Club' (the groups name comes from the 1967 sci-fi film *Barbarella*); they were signed by EMI in 1980 after supporting Blondi on her world tour and became favourites of teeny-boppers including Princess Diana. There have been personnel changes, but last we heard some preteens were still screaming. (Donald Clarke, April 1989)I.

ALL SHE WANTS IS
Tracks: / All she wants is / All she wants is (Euro dub mix) (12DD 11 only.) / All she wants is (US Master mix) (12DDX 11 only.) / Skin trade (Parisian mix) (CD single only.) / I believe / All I need to know.
12" Single: Released Jan '89, on EMI, by EMI Records. Deleted Oct '89. Catalogue no: **12DDX 11**
7" Single: Released Dec '88, on EMI, by EMI Records. Catalogue no: **DDP 11**
CD 5": Released Dec '88, on EMI, by EMI Records. Deleted Aug '89. Catalogue no: **CDDD 11**
7" Single: Released Dec '88, on EMI, by EMI Records. Deleted Aug '89. Catalogue no: **DD 11**
12" Single: Released Dec '88, on EMI, by EMI Records. Deleted Oct '89. Catalogue no: **12DD 11**

CARELESS MEMORIES
Tracks: / Careless memories.
7" Single: Released May '81, on EMI, by EMI Records. Deleted Aug '89. Catalogue no: **EMI 5168**
12" Single: Released May '81, on EMI, by EMI Records. Catalogue no: **12 EMI 5168**

DO YOU BELIEVE IN SHAME?
Tracks: / Do you believe in shame? / Krush brothers (LSD edit) / Notorious (live) (10" & CD single only.) / God (CD single only.) / This is how a road gets made (CD single & DDB 12 only.) / Palomino (edit) (DDB 12 only.) / Drug (It's just a state of mind) (DDC 12 only.).
Special: Released Apr '89, on EMI, by EMI Records. Catalogue no: **DDB 12**
Special: Released Apr '89, on EMI, by EMI Records. Catalogue no: **DDC 12**
10" single: Released Apr '89, on EMI, by EMI Records. Catalogue no: **10DD 12**
7" Pic: Released Apr '89, on EMI, by EMI Records. Deleted Oct '89. Catalogue no: **DDPD 12**
7" Single: Released Apr '89, on EMI, by EMI Records. Catalogue no: **DD 12**
12" Single: Released Apr '89, on EMI, by EMI Records. Deleted Oct '89. Catalogue no: **12DD 12**
12" Single: Released Apr '89, on EMI, by EMI Records. Deleted Oct '89. Catalogue no: **203 353 6**
CD 3": Released Apr '89, on EMI, by EMI Records. Catalogue no: **CDDD 12**
Special: Released Apr '89, on EMI, by EMI Records. Catalogue no: **DDA 12**

GIRLS ON FILM
Tracks: / Girls on film / Faster than light.
12" Single: Released Jul '81, on EMI, by EMI Records. Catalogue no: **12 EMI 5206**
7" Single: Released Jul '81, on EMI, by EMI Records. Catalogue no: **EMI 5206**

HUNGRY LIKE THE WOLF
Tracks: / Hungry like the wolf / Careless memories (live).
7" Single: Released Jun '82, on EMI, by EMI Records. Deleted Aug '89. Catalogue no: **EMI 5295**
12" Single: Released Jun '82, on EMI, by EMI Records. Catalogue no: **12 EMI 5295**

I DON'T WANT YOUR LOVE
Tracks: / I don't want your love / I don't want your love (Album version) / I don't want your love (Big mix) (12", Special, CD Single only.).
Special: Released Sep '88, on EMI, by EMI Records. Deleted Aug '89. Catalogue no: **12YOURS 1**
CD 5": Released Sep '88, on EMI, by EMI Records. Deleted Aug '89. Catalogue no: **CDYOUR 1**
7" Single: Released Sep '88, on EMI, by EMI Records. Catalogue no: **YOUR 1**
12" Single: Released Sep '88, on EMI, by EMI Records. Deleted Jun '89. Catalogue no: **12YOUR 1**

IS THERE SOMETHING I SHOULD KNOW?
Tracks: / Is there something I should know? / Faith in this colour.
7" Single: Released Mar '83, on EMI, by EMI Records. Catalogue no: **EMI 5371**
12" Single: Released Mar '83, on EMI, by EMI Records. Catalogue no: **12 EMI 5371**

MEET EL PRESIDENTE
Tracks: / Meet El Beat (Extra track available on CD only.) / Meet El Presidente / Vertigo (do the demolition).
7" Single: Released Apr '87, on EMI, by EMI Records. Deleted Apr '88. Catalogue no: **TOUR 1**
CD 5": Released Apr '87, on EMI, by EMI Records. Deleted Nov '88. Catalogue no: **CDTOUR 1**
12" Single: Released Apr '87, on EMI, by EMI Records. Deleted Apr '88. Catalogue no: **12TOUR 1**
7" Single: Released Apr '87, on EMI, by EMI Records. Catalogue no: **TOURG 1**

MY OWN WAY
Tracks: / My own way / Like an angel.
7" Single: Released Nov '81, on EMI, by EMI Records. Catalogue no: **EMI 5254**
12" Single: Released Nov '81, on EMI, by EMI Records. Deleted '87. Catalogue no: **12 EMI 5254**

NEW MOON ON MONDAY
Tracks: / New moon on Monday / Tiger tiger.
12" Single: Released Jan '84, on EMI, by EMI Records. Deleted Jul '87. Catalogue no: **12 DURAN 1**
7" Single: Released Jan '84, on EMI, by EMI Records. Catalogue no: **DURAN 1**

NOTORIOUS (LATIN RASCALS MIX)
Tracks: / Winter marches on / Notorious (Latin rascals mix).
7" Single: Released Nov '86, on EMI, by EMI Records. Catalogue no: **12 DDNX 45**

NOTORIOUS (SINGLE)
Tracks: / Notorious.
12" Single: Released Oct '86, on EMI, by EMI Records. Deleted Oct '87. Catalogue no: **12DDN 45**
7" Single: Released Oct '86, on EMI, by EMI Records. Deleted Oct '87. Catalogue no: **DDN 45**

PLANET EARTH
Tracks: / Planet earth / Late bar.
12" Single: Released Feb '81, on EMI, by EMI Records. Catalogue no: **12 EMI 5137**
7" Single: Released Feb '81, on EMI, by EMI Records. Catalogue no: **EMI 5137**

REFLEX, THE
Tracks: / Reflex, The / (I'm looking for) cracks in the pavement / Make me smile (come up and see me) (Only on 12" single.).
7" Pic: Released May '84, on EMI, by EMI Records. Catalogue no: **12 DURANP 2**
12" Single: Released Apr '84, on EMI, by EMI Records. Catalogue no: **12 DURAN 2**
7" Single: Released Apr '84, on EMI, by EMI Records. Catalogue no: **DURAN 2**

RIO (SINGLE)
Tracks: / Rio / Chaffeur (blue silver), The.
7" Single: Released Nov '82, on EMI, by EMI Records. Catalogue no: **EMI 5346**
12" Single: Released Nov '82, on EMI, by EMI Records. Catalogue no: **12EMI 5346**

SAVE A PRAYER
Tracks: / Save a prayer / Hold back the rain.
7" Single: Released Aug '82, on EMI, by EMI Records. Catalogue no: **EMI 5327**
12" Single: Released Aug '82, on EMI, by EMI Records. Catalogue no: **12 EMI 5327**

SKIN TRADE (RADIO CUT)
Tracks: / Skin trade (radio cut) / We need you.
7" Single: Released Feb '87, on EMI, by EMI Records. Deleted Oct '87. Catalogue no: **TRADE 1**
Cassingle: Released Mar '87, on EMI, by EMI Records. Catalogue no: **TCTRADE 1**
12" Single: Released Feb '87, on EMI, by EMI Records. Deleted Oct '87. Catalogue no: **12TRADE 1**

STRANGE BEHAVIOUR TOUR '87 DISC
Note: Italian-only tour souvenir release on picture disc. Features two mixes each of Notorious and Skin Trade. Proper printed outer cover, and group photo.
12" Single: Released Nov '87, on EMI (Italy), by EMI Records. Catalogue no: **2017660**

UNION OF THE SNAKE (see panel below)
Tracks: / Union of the snake / Secret oktober.
7" Single: Released Oct '83, on EMI, by EMI Records. Deleted Jun '89. Catalogue no: **EMI 5429**
12" Single: Released Oct '83, on EMI, by EMI Records. Catalogue no: **12 EMI 5429**

VIEW TO A KILL, A
Tracks: / View to a kill, A / View to a kill, A (version).
7" Single: Released May '85, on Parlophone, by EMI Records. Catalogue no: **DURAN 007**
7" Single: Released May '85, on Parlophone, by EMI Records. Catalogue no: **DURANOO 7**
7" Single: Released May '85, on Parlophone, by EMI Records. Catalogue no: **DURAN 7**
Special: Released May '85, on Parlophone, by EMI Records. Deleted '86. Catalogue no: **DURANG 007**

WILD BOYS, THE
Tracks: / Wild boys / I'm looking for cracks in the pavement.
7" Single: Released Oct '84, on EMI, by EMI Records. Catalogue no: **DURAN 3**
12" Single: Released Oct '84, on EMI, by EMI Records. Catalogue no: **12 DURAN 3**

Duran, Eleanor

FUNKY FLUTE
Tracks: / Funky flute / Groovy gavotte II.
7" Single: Released Oct '82, on EMI, by EMI Records. Deleted Oct '85. Catalogue no: **EMI 5108**

DURAN DURAN - UNION OF THE SNAKE (Released on EMI)

Duran, Elena

MARY ROSE
Tracks: / Mary Rose / Walaichu.
7" Single: Released Jun '82, on RCA, by BMG Records (UK). Catalogue no: **RCA 237**

Durham Brothers

BLUE WATER
Tracks: / Blue water.
7" Single: Released Jun '83, on Pastafont, by Pastafont Music. Catalogue no: **PF 3020**

Durham, Judith

OLIVE TREE
Tracks: / Olive tree.
7" Single: Released Jun '67, on Columbia, by EMI Records. Deleted '72. Catalogue no: **DB 8207**

Durie, Jo

WIMBLEDON LAWNS
Tracks: / Wimbledon lawns.
7" Single: Released Jun '83, on Blue Hat, by Blue Hat Records. Catalogue no: **BHR 14**

Durrant, Buggs

BABY COME BACK
Tracks: / Baby come back / You've got to hold me tight.
7" Single: Released Feb '84, on Shoc-Wave, Catalogue no: **SRP 11A**
12" Single: Released Feb '84, on Shoc-Wave, Catalogue no: **SRP 11X**

GONNA MAKE YOUR BODY GIVE UP
Tracks: / Gonna make your body give up.
7" Single: Released Jun '82, on Shoc-Wave, Catalogue no: **SRP 10**
12" Single: Released Jun '82, on Shoc-Wave, Catalogue no: **SRP 10X**

YOU ARE GONE
Tracks: / You are gone / Disco jump.
7" Single: Released Jul '82, on Shoc-Wave, Catalogue no: **SP 0001**

Durutti Column

Debbie

DEBBIE
Tracks: / Debbie (7" and 12" B side) / Our lady of the angels.
12" Single: Released 30 May '87, on Factory (1), by Factory Records. Catalogue no: **FAC 184**

DEUX TRIANGLES
Tracks: / Deux triangles.
12" Single: Released Aug '87, on Les Disques Du Crepuscule(Belgium), by Les Disques Du Crepuscule(Belgium). Catalogue no: **FBN 10**

GREETINGS THREE
Tracks: / Greetings three.
12" Single: Released 8 Nov '86, on Materiali Sonori, Catalogue no: **MASO 70003**

LIVE AT WOMAD
Tracks: / Live at Womad.
CD 3": Released Dec '88, on Factory (1), by Factory Records. Catalogue no: **FACD 234**

SAY WHAT YOU MEAN, MEAN WHAT YOU SAY
Tracks: / Say what you mean, mean what you say.
7" Single: Released Mar '85, on Factory (1), by Factory Records. Catalogue no: **FACT 114**

TOMORROW
Tracks: / Tomorrow.
7" Single: Released Feb '86, on Factory Benelux, by Rough Trade Records. Catalogue no: **7 FBN 51**
12" Single: Released Feb '86, on Factory Benelux, by Rough Trade Records. Catalogue no: **FBN 051**

TWO TRIANGLES (EP)
Tracks: / Two triangles.
12" Single: Released Mar '82, on Factory (1), by Factory Records. Catalogue no: **FACBN 10**

WHEN THE WORLD
Tracks: / When the world.
12" Single: Released 21 Nov '87, on Factory (1), by Factory Records. Catalogue no: **FAC 194**
CD 5": Released Mar '88, on Factory (1), by Factory Records. Catalogue no: **FACD 194**
7" Single: Released 21 Nov '87, on Factory (1), by Factory Records. Catalogue no: **FAC 1947**

Dury, Ian

Biographical details: This British singer and lyricist, born in Essex in 1942, contracted polio at the age of seven, leaving him with a withered left arm and leg. After spending several years in an institution for the disabled, he attended a grammar school, and then, at the age of 17 he joined Walthamstow Art College. This led to a postgrad. course at the Royal College of Art and a career as an art teacher. It was while teaching that he hit upon the idea of forming a rock band. Thus, Kilburn & The High Roads were born. They became one of the most popular and acclaimed bands on London's pub rock circuit; during the seventies, their zany brand of rock'n'roll made Dury one of the city's most intriguing cult figures. In 1975 the group folded and, after a much changed line-up, re-emerged as Ian Dury & The Kilburns. They finished again in 1976, the same year that Ian met keyboards/guitar player Chris Jankel, who became his musical director and composer, while Ian wrote the words for the songs. 1977 was a key year for Dury. He signed with Stiff Records, the seminal new independant label designed to provide an outlet for talent rejected by the UK's major companies; he made his British chart debut with the album *New boots and panties* and formed a new band - Ian Dury & The Blockheads. *New boots and panties* remained on the British LP chart for well over a year, peaking at no.5 - it's long-running success was fuelled by Dury's 1978-79 singles chart acceptance: he hit the top 10 with *What a waste, Hit me with your rhythm stick* (no.1) and *Reasons to be cheerful, part 3*. 1979's album *Do it yourself* album shot to the no.2 slot. Although the idiosyncratic Dury's vocals were a half spoken/half sung grunt, and although he always emphasised his British working class outlook, Ian Dury & The Blockheads were a major concert attraction all over Europe. This was explained by Jankel's highly danceable rhythms and the band's proficiency.
The prevailing sounds of the era were disco and punk - Dury and his combo could appeal to both. The 80's proved less successful for Dury, although his amiable personality continued to pop up on radio and television. He signed to Polydor in 1981, but this did not return him to the Top 20 of the British charts. He formed Ian Dury & The Music Students in 1983, but played reunion gigs with the Blockheads in 1985. The early 80's, meanwhile, brought disco dividends for Chas Jankel - he co-wrote *Ai no corrida*, a transatlantic 1981 hit for Quincy Jones; and the Dury/Jankel-penned *Glad to know you*, performed by Chas, was America's no.1 dance single of 1982. (Bob Macdonald, 14/7/85)
Songwriter and bandleader born in 1942 in Essex, the most successful (deservedly) of the pub rock fraternity of the early '70's. His first band Kilburn & The High Roads went through 7 lineups in 7 years; led by Dury, who was seriously affected by polio as a child, a wildly incongruous bunch during time of glam and pomp rock.
He took a year off to write with Chaz Jankel, then formed the Blockheads, launched anthemic single *Sex & drugs & rock & roll*, then album *New boots and panties* in 1977, hailed as an instant classic, with a tribute to *Sweet Gene Vincent* and London vignettes *Billericay Dickie, Plaistow Patricia*; his outstanding writing, with a poet's ear for unlikely rhymes and an endearing sense of humour, is among the best British pop ever made, easily transcending its category. *Hit me with you rhythm stick* was Stiff's first number one single; the album *Do it yourself* was written on the road and showed it; *Laughter* in 1980 was a return to form, with Wilko Johnson replacing Jankel on guitar. *Juke box Drury* was a good Stiff compilation, the same album as *Greatest hits* on Music For Pleasure. He re-formed the original Blockheads in 1984 for a video and a single *Profoundly in love with Pandora*; he has also acted on TV and in films. (Donald Clarke, April 1989)s.

HIT ME WITH YOUR RHYTHM STICK
Tracks: / Hit me with your rhythm stick / There ain't half ben some clever bastards.
7" Single: Released Dec '78, on Stiff, by Stiff Records. Deleted '83. Catalogue no: **BUY 38**

I WANT TO BE STRAIGHT
Tracks: / I want to be straight
7" Single: Released Aug '80, on Stiff, by Stiff Records. Catalogue no: **BUY 90**

PROFOUNDLY IN LOVE WITH PANDORA
Tracks: / Profoundly in love with Pandora.
7" Single: Released Nov '85, on EMI, by EMI Records. Deleted Oct '87. Catalogue no: **EMI 5534**
7" Pic: Released Nov '85, on EMI, by EMI Records. Deleted Jul '87. Catalogue no: **EMIP 5534**

REASONS TO BE CHEERFUL
Tracks: / Reasons to be cheerful.
7" Single: Released Aug '79, on Stiff, by

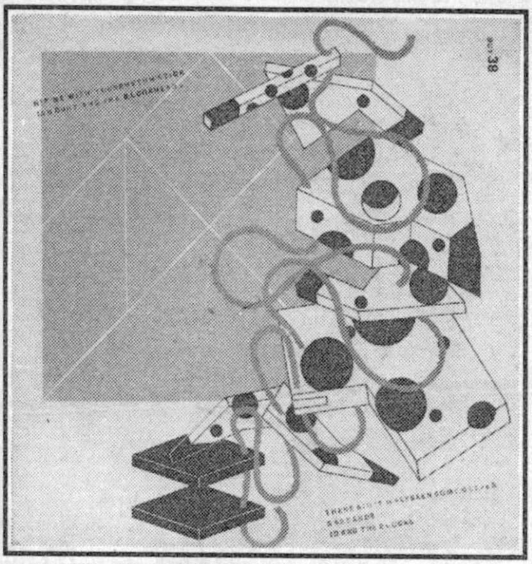

IAN DURY - HIT ME WITH YOUR RHYTHM STICK (Released on Stiff)

Stiff Records. Deleted '85. Catalogue no: **BUY 50**

SPECIAL PAUL HARDCASTLE 12" MIXES
12" Single: Released May '85, on Stiff, by Stiff Records. Catalogue no: **BUYIT 214**

SUPERMAN'S BIG SISTER
Tracks: / Superman's big sister / Funky ada.
12" Single: Released Oct '80, on Stiff, by Stiff Records. Catalogue no: **BUYIT 100**
7" Single: Released Oct '80, on Stiff, by Stiff Records. Catalogue no: **BUY 100**

WHAT A WASTE
Tracks: / What a waste / Wake up and make love with me.
7" Single: Released Nov '81, on Stiff, by Stiff Records. Catalogue no: **BUY 135**

WHAT A WASTE (ORIGINAL)
Tracks: / What a waste.
7" Single: Released Apr '78, on Stiff, by Stiff Records. Deleted '83. Catalogue no: **BUY 27**

Dusen, George Van

IT'S PARTY TIME AGAIN
Tracks: / It's party time again / It's party time again (version).
7" Single: Released Nov '88, on Britone, Catalogue no: **BT 001**

Dusseldorf, La

TINTARELLA DI
Tracks: / Tintarella Di.
7" Single: Released Dec '81, on Albion, by Albion Records. Catalogue no: **ION 1025**

Dust Devils

DROPPING WELL, THE
Tracks: / Dropping well, The.
12" Single: Released '87, on Rouska, by Rouska Records. Catalogue no: **PRO-FANE 036**

DUST DEVILS various artists
Tracks: / Dust devils: *Various artists.*
10" single: Released Sep '86, on Prophane 9, Catalogue no: **PROPHANE 9**

MOTHER SHIPTON
Tracks: / Mother Shipton.
7" Single: Released '87, on Rouska, by Rouska Records. Catalogue no: **PRO-FANE 008**

SEEDS OF THE SPOIL
Tracks: / Seeds of the spoil.
12" Single: Released Jul '86, on Rouska, by Rouska Records. Catalogue no: **COME 6T**

Dusty, Slim

Biographical details: This Australian singer achieved a one-off British smash in 1959. *A pub with no beer*, one of the year's most unexpected hits, reached no.3 and spent 15 weeks in the UK charts. The record did not manage to crack the American Top 40, and subsequent releases returned him to the obscurity of the then insular Australian music scene. It was left to fellow countryman Rolf Harris to continue flying the nation's flag in the UK charts, beginning with 1960's *Tie me kangaroo down, sport* (Bob Macdonald, 14/7/85)
Australian country singer, guitarist and songwriter, born David Gordon Kirkpatrick in 1927. He has sold more records there than anybody else, with some 70 gold and platinum records. (Donald Clarke, April 1989)d.

DUNCAN
Tracks: / Duncan (part 1) / Duncan (part 2).
7" Single: Released Feb '81, on EMI, by EMI Records. Deleted '84. Catalogue no: **EMI 5141**

PUB WITH NO BEER (OLD GOLD)
Tracks: / Pub with no beer, A / Answer.
7" Single: Released Mar '87, on Old Gold, by Old Gold Records. Deleted Sep '89. Catalogue no: **OG 9634**

PUB WITH NO BEER
Tracks: / Pub with no beer, A.
7" Single: Released Jan '59, on Columbia, by EMI Records. Deleted '64. Catalogue no: **DB 4212**

Duval, Frank

ANGEL OF MINE (SINGLE)
Tracks: / Angel of mine / Take my heart, Maria.
7" Single: Released '88, on DJM, Catalogue no: **DJS 10975**

Du - val, Ray

VIVE ROCK'N'ROLL
Special: Released '85, on Lorraine, by Ray Du-Val Records. Catalogue no: **CS 1932/4AC**

DVA

HACKED
Tracks: / Hacked.
12" Single: Released Mar '89, on Big Sex, Catalogue no: **EFA 1751**

HIGH HOLY DISCO MASS
Tracks: / High holy disco mass.
7" Single: Released Nov '82, on Polydor, by Polydor Ltd. Catalogue no: **POSP 499**
12" Single: Released Nov '82, on Polydor, by Polydor Ltd. Catalogue no: **POSPX 499**

Dwarves

LICK IT
Tracks: / Lick it.
7" Single: Released 16 Sep '88, on Ubik, Catalogue no: **CRASH 001**

Dylan, Bob

Biographical details: This American singer, songwriter, guitarist and harmonica player was born Robert Allen Zimmerman in Duluth, Minnesota in 1941. He took the name Dylan in deference to the Welsh poet Dylan Thomas. Bob Dylan was America's most important artists of the sixties, and one of the most influential figues in post-war western culture. He was raised in the Minnesota mining town of Hibbing, and his musical career began in 1959 when he joined the University of Minnesota in Minneapolis. He was there for a year, during which he adopted his new surname. The restless Bob journeyed to New Jersey in December 1960 to visit his all-time hero and musical mentor, the legendary folk singer/songwriter Woody Guthrie, who was terminally ill in hospital. Dylan decided to stay in the area, and thus settled in New York's folk haven, Greenwich Village. Dylan signed to Columbia Records in October 1961. His self-titled debut album was released in 1962. His next two LP's, *The freewheeling Bob Dylan* (1963) and *The times they are a-changing* (1964), made him the leader and key spokesman of the burgeoning folk protest movement, and he became the most articulate white champion of America's civil rights campaign. In 1965 Dylan upset his hard core folk audience by switching from acoustic to electric guitar and becoming a rock star.
However, the musical results were as brilliant as ever, and '65 represented the peak of Dylan's commercial success. He reached no. 2 in the US and no.4 in the UK with the biggest and best single of his career - the breathtaking, anathemic story song *Like a rolling stone.* In Britain *Bringing it all back home* reached no.1 on the album chart, dethroning the belated chart-topper *The freewheelin' Bob Dylan.* During that same year, he achieved five UK Top 30 singles, and scored yet another UK Top 5 album with *Highway 61 revisited.* The folk-rock boom blossomed in the summer of '65, when the Byrds' ultra-catchy two-minute rendition of Dylan's *Mr. Tambourine man* hit no.1 on both sides of the Atlantic. Although Bob never climbed to the very top of the US or UK singles charts as a performer, the Byrds' record represented his most successful single as a writer. The fact that other artists could transform his songs into such commercial singalong material, was a tribute to his melodic sensibility as well as his lyrical skills. For example, most Americans were introduced to the classic song *Blowin' in the wind* by Peter Paul & Mary, who took it to no.2 in 1963. Manfred Mann achieved a series of Dylan-penned UK pop hits, notably 1968's no.1 smash *Mighty Quinn.* 1968 was also the year of a dramatic comeback for Dylan, who had been removed from public activity by a 1966 motorbike accident. Together with his superb backing group, the Band, he showed that he had lost none of his prowess when he issued the LP *John Wesley Harding.* In Britain, this was the first in a run of four consecutive no.1 albums - it was followed by *Nashville skyline* (1969) and two 1970 sets *Self portrait* and *New morning. Nashville skyline*, recorded in the country music capital, helped to open the floodgates for America's country-rock boom of the seventies.
During the seventies, Dylan never enjoyed a US or UK Top 10 single, but was always assured of big album sales on either side of the Atlantic. Musically, his work became more erratic, although classics continued to emerge from time to time. At this time, Dylan still retained his massive following from the sixties. He finally lost this in 1979, when his transition from Judaism to "born again" Christianity failed to inspire or convince the bulk of his audience. Although God was eased out of his work in 1983, the musically indisciplined but emotionally charged voice of Bob Dylan, which had influenced a whole generation, was now preaching to comparatively few people. (Bob Macdonald, 15/7/85)
Singer-songwriter Robert Allen Zimmerman, born in 1941 in Duluth, Minnesota, became the most important figure in white rock music.
He was a rock'n'roll fan in high school, began wandering towards New York in order to visit Woody Guthrie in hospital, and played and sang in folk clubs. A review by Robert Shelton in the New York Times led to signing with CBS by John Hammond. His first album *Bob Dylan* in 1962 was standard blues and folk covers; *The freewheelin' Bob Dylan* was very different: the 13 songs were almost all his own, including *Blowin' in the wind* and *Don't think twice, it's all right* (top 10 as covered by Peter Paul & Mary); *A hard rain's a gonna fall* became an anthem. Of *Talking World War III blues* Nat Hentoff wrote that 'There's no place to hide in the talking blues ... he is able to fill all the space ... with unmistakeable originality'. *The times they are a changin'* and *Another side of Bob Dylan* began to shed the mantle of protest; his lyrics were too good for that. An electric 'folk-rock' version by the Byrds of *Mr tambourine man* was a transatlantic number one in 1965; Dylan's *Bringing it all back home* had a brilliant acoustic side including *Tambourine man, Gates of Eden, It's alright ma (I'm only bleeding, It's all over now, Baby blue*; but the electric side put him streets ahead of his contempories: savage comedy in *Maggie's farm* and *Subterranean homesick blues*, ballads *She belongs to me* and *Love minus zero* created a new era to a stroke, but purist folkies were outraged: he was booed at Newport in 1965, while his UK solo tour that year was filmed by Donn Pennebaker: *Don't look back* '67 is probably still the best rock film. *Highway 61 revisited* was all electric, including *Ballad of a thin man* with its famous line 'Something is happening here, but you don't know what it is, do you Mr Jones?'. He started a trend by recording in Nashville: *Blonde on blonde* was one of rock's first double LPs; Dylan said years later 'That's my sound. I haven't been able to succeed in getting it all the time.' 'Fans' booed and threw things at concerts on his world tour in 1966; controversy raged in 'Sing out' magazine, while Dylan said 'Folk music is a bunch of fat people.' He was badly injured in August 1966 in a motorcycle crash; he rested in Woodstock, New York and made tapes with The Band, a best-selling bootleg as *The Great White WOnder* and finally issued by CBS as *Basement tapes. John Wesley Harding* in 1968 was a shock: laid back while psychedelia was the rage, his raw voice turned smoother, with low key and acoustic backing, lyrics deeper than ever. *Nashville skyline* included a duet with Johnny Cash as well as one of Dylan's few top ten his in *Lay lady lay.*
The 2-disc *Self portrait* was a disaster and should have been edited to one disc; he described it as 'my own bootleg record, so to speak.' *New morning '70* was much tighter, but a long period of silence followed; He was rapturously received at George Harrison's *Concert for Bangla Desh* in 1971, the live 3-disc set having a whole side of Dylan. He acted in Sam Peckinpah's *Pat Garrett & Billy The Kid* in 1973, also saw writing the music including *Knockin' on heaven's door.* The first official album with The Band was *Planet waves* in 1973 is of very high quality, though it's fashionable to knock it. 2-Disc *Before the flood* was the first official Dylan live album, also with The Band; *Blood on the tracks* in 1974 is regarded by some as his best. The low key Rolling Thunder Review tour in 1975 played small local venues, including Joan Baez and many others; it included filming of *Renaldo and Clara*, a four hour home movie released in 1978 starring Dylan & Baez which lost $2 million. *Desire* in 1975 was his best seller to date. *Hard rain* was a souvenir of the tour; *Bob Dylan at Budokan* of another. *Street legal* was perhaps the last album that satisied most fans. He was The Band's special guest at their *Last waltz* finale in 1978, appearing in the film and 3-disc set. He announced that he'd become a born again Christian: *Slow train coming* with Mark Knopfler sold well, but *Saved* in 1980 is his poorest seller to date. *Shot of love* was patchy and his muse appears to have left him. *Infidels* included the Sly & Robbie rhythm section, but only 'Jokerman' was praised. *Real live* in 1984 followed another world tour, another collection of updated versions of old songs; *Empire Burlesque* in 1985 was produced by Arthur Baker and hailed as his best since *Street legal. Knocked out loaded* continued to disappoint; he recorded with Tom Petty and the Heartbreakers and with the Grateful Dead, but the power to inform the world of the late '80's which wants only mindless entertainment, is hard to find. *Biograph* is the only compilation worth having, with 52 digitally remastered tracks (18 previously unreleased) and copiously documented mostly with his own words. (Donald Clarke, April 1989).

BABY STOP CRYING
Tracks: / Baby stop crying.
7" Single: Released Jul '78, on CBS, by CBS Records. Deleted '83. Catalogue no: **CBS 6499**

BAND OF THE HAND
Tracks: / Band of the hand / Joe's death, Theme from.
12" Single: Released Aug '86, on MCA, by MCA Records. Catalogue no: **MCAT 1076**
7" Single: Released Aug '86, on MCA, by MCA Records. Catalogue no: **MCA 1076**

CAN YOU PLEASE CRAWL OUT OF YOUR WINDOW
Tracks: / Can you please crawl out of your window.
7" Single: Released Jan '66, on CBS, by CBS Records. Deleted '71. Catalogue no: **CBS 201900**

HIGHWAY '61 REVISITED (LIVE)
Tracks: / Highway '61 revisited (live) / Ain't me babe.
7" Single: Released Jan '85, on CBS, by CBS Records. Catalogue no: **A 5020**

HURRICANE
Tracks: / Hurricane.
7" Single: Released Feb '76, on CBS, by CBS Records. Deleted '81. Catalogue no: **CBS 3879**

I THREW IT ALL AWAY
Tracks: / I threw it all away.
7" Single: Released May '69, on CBS, by CBS Records. Deleted '74. Catalogue no: **CBS 4219**

I WANT YOU
Tracks: / I want you.
7" Single: Released Jul '66, on CBS, by CBS Records. Deleted '74. Catalogue no: **CBS 202258**

IS YOUR LOVE IN VAIN
Tracks: / Is your love in vain.
7" Single: Released Oct '78, on CBS, by CBS Records. Deleted '83. Catalogue no: **CBS 6718**

JOKERMAN
Tracks: / Jokerman.
7" Single: Released Jun '84, on CBS, by CBS Records. Catalogue no: **A 4055**

JUST LIKE A WOMAN
Tracks: / Just like a woman / I want you.
7" Single: Released May '82, on CBS, by CBS Records. Catalogue no: **CBS 1158**

KNOCKIN' ON HEAVEN'S DOOR
Tracks: / Knockin' on heaven's door.
7" Single: Released Oct '73, on CBS, by CBS Records. Deleted '78. Catalogue no: **CBS 1762**

LAY LADY LAY
Tracks: / Lay lady lay.
7" Single: Released Sep '69, on CBS, by CBS Records. Catalogue no: **CBS 4434**

LIKE A ROLLING STONE
Tracks: / Like a rolling stone / Gates of Eden.
7" Single: Released May '82, on CBS, by CBS Records. Catalogue no: **CBS 1181**

LIKE A ROLLING STONE (ORIGINAL)
Tracks: / Like a rolling stone.
7" Single: Released Aug '65, on CBS, by CBS Records. Deleted '70. Catalogue no: **CBS 201811**

MAGGIE'S FARM
Tracks: / Maggie's farm.
7" Single: Released Jun '65, on CBS, by CBS Records. Deleted '70. Catalogue no: **CBS 201781**

ONE OF US MUST KNOW (SOONER OR LATER)
Tracks: / One of us must know (sooner or later).
7" Single: Released Apr '66, on CBS, by CBS Records. Deleted '71. Catalogue no: **CBS 202053**

POSITIVELY FOURTH STREET
Tracks: / Positively 4th street.
7" Single: Released Oct '65, on CBS, by CBS Records. Deleted '70. Catalogue no: **CBS 201824**

RAINY DAY WOMEN NOS 12 & 35
Tracks: / Rainy day women Nos 12 & 35.
7" Single: Released May '66, on CBS, by CBS Records. Deleted '71. Catalogue no: **CBS 202307**

SILVIO
Tracks: / Silvio / When did you leave heaven? / Driftin' too far from shore (* on 12" single only).
7" Single: Released 18 Jul '88, on CBS, by CBS Records. Deleted Jan '89. Catalogue no: **651406 7**
12" Single: Released 18 Jul '88, on CBS, by CBS Records. Deleted Jan '89. Catalogue no: **651406 6**

SUBTERRANEAN HOMESICK BLUES
Tracks: / Subterranean homesick blues.
7" Single: Released Apr '65, on CBS, by CBS Records. Deleted '70. Catalogue no: **CBS 201753**

TIMES THEY ARE A-CHANGIN' (SINGLE)
Tracks: / Times they are a-changin' / Honey.
7" Single: Released May '82, on CBS, by CBS Records. Catalogue no: **CBS 1751**
7" Single: Released Apr '64, on CBS, by CBS Records. Catalogue no: **CBS 201751**

USUAL, THE
Tracks: / Usual, The / Got my mind made up / They killed him*.
7" Single: Released Oct '87, on CBS, by CBS Records. Deleted Jun '88. Catalogue no: **651 148 7**
12" Single: Released Oct '87, on CBS, by CBS Records. Deleted Jun '88. Catalogue no: **651 148 6**

WATCHING THE RIVER FLOW
Tracks: / Watching the river flow.
7" Single: Released Aug '71, on CBS, by CBS Records. Deleted '76. Catalogue no: **CBS 7329**

DYNASTY - DOES THAT RING A BELL (Released on Elektra)

WHEN THE NIGHT COMES FALLING FROM THE SKY
Tracks: / When the night comes falling from the sky.
7" Single: Released Aug '85, on CBS, by CBS Records. Deleted '86. Catalogue no: **A 6469**
12" Single: Released Aug '85, on CBS, by CBS Records. Catalogue no: **TA 6469**

YOU GOTTA SERVE SOMEBODY
Tracks: / You gotta serve somebody / Change my way of thinking.
7" Single: Released Jan '80, on CBS, by CBS Records. Deleted '83. Catalogue no: **CBS 8124**

Dyma'r Rysait

DYMA'R RYSAIT
Tracks: / Dyma'r rysait: *Various artists.*
7" Single: Released 20 Feb '88, on Artists For Animals, Catalogue no: **OFN 005**

Dynamic 3

I FEEL DYNAMIC
Tracks: / I feel dynamic.
7" Single: Released Apr '88, on Tuffgroove, Catalogue no: **TUFF 002**

Dynamic Duo

BATMAN THEME
Tracks: / Batman theme.
12" Single: Released Mar '88, on Anagram, by Cherry Red Records. Catalogue no: **12 ANA 42**

Dynamic Govenors

MUSIC USE IT
Tracks: / Music use it.
12" Single: Released 13 Feb '89, on Blapps, Catalogue no: **SEX 070**

Dynamites

LET'S DO IT TONIGHT
Tracks: / Let's do it tonight / Way that I feel.
7" Single: Released Apr '81, on Logo, by Logo Records. Deleted Apr '84. Catalogue no: **GO 399**

(WALK TALL) DO THE CRAWL
Tracks: / (Walk tall) do the crawl / Go for it.
7" Single: Released Feb '81, on Logo, by Logo Records. Deleted '84. Catalogue no: **GO 396**

Dynamix II

JUST GIVE THE D.J. A BREAK
Tracks: / Just give the D.J. a break / Straight from the jungle.
12" Single: Released Jul '87, on Cool Tempo, by Chrysalis Records. Catalogue no: **COOLX 151**
7" Single: Released Jul '87, on Cool Tempo, by Chrysalis Records. Catalogue no: **COOL 151**

Dynasty

Biographical details: This American two-man/two-woman soul band came to fame in 1979 with their transatlantic disco success *I don't wanna be a freak*. This was an answer to Chic's recent blockbusting disco classic *Le freak*. The Dynasty single fared particularly well in Britain, where it reached no.20 and logged 13 weeks on the charts. In common with Shalamar and the Whispers, Dynasty were signed to the Solar label (an acronym for Sound Of Los Angeles Records), whose key creative figure was producer/bassist/percussionist Leon Sylvers. It was he who was most responsible for Dynasty's sound, together with the group's keyboards player Kevin Spencer, who became a member of Solar's in-house rhythm section. The group found further success in 1980 with *I've just begun to love you*, a classy and bright dance single that did well on the US soul and disco charts and reached no.51 on the UK pop listings. Their albums included *Your piece of the rock* (1979), *Adventures in the land of music* (1980) and 1982's ultra-sleek *Right back at cha!*. The latter LP yielded a minor UK hit single in the spring of '83: *Does that ring a bell* reached no.53. Although they did not quite achieve the same level of success as some of the other Solar acts, Dynasty's fresh funk feel was impressive. (Bob Macdonald, 15/7/88).

DO ME RIGHT
Tracks: / Do me right / I've just begun to love you.
12" Single: Released Nov '80, on Solar Records, Deleted '83. Catalogue no: **SOT 14**
7" Single: Released Nov '80, on Solar Records, Deleted '83. Catalogue no: **SO 14**

DOES THAT RING A BELL? (see panel above)
Tracks: / Does that ring a bell? / Love in the fast lane.
7" Single: Released Apr '83, on Elektra, by Elektra Records (UK). Catalogue no: **E 9911**
12" Single: Released Apr '83, on Elektra, by Elektra Records (UK). Catalogue no: **E 9911 T**

GROOVE CONTROL
Tracks: / Groove control / Something to remember.
12" Single: Released Mar '81, on Solar (USA), by MCA Records. Deleted Mar '84. Catalogue no: **SOT 18**
7" Single: Released Mar '81, on Solar (USA), by MCA Records. Deleted Mar '84. Catalogue no: **SO 18**

I DON'T WANNA BE A FREAK (OLD GOLD)
Tracks: / I don't wanna be a freak / Music (Featuring al Hudson.).
12" Single: Released May '88, on Old Gold, by Old Gold Records. Catalogue no: **OG 4064**

I DON'T WANT TO BE A FREAK
Tracks: / I don't want to be a freak.
7" Single: Released Oct '79, on Solar Records, Deleted '82. Catalogue no: **FB 1694**

I'VE JUST BEGUN TO LOVE YOU
Tracks: / I've just begun to love you.
7" Single: Released Aug '80, on Solar Records, Deleted '85. Catalogue no: **SO 10**

LOVE IN THE FAST LANE
Tracks: / Love in the fast lane / High time.
7" Single: Released Nov '81, on Solar Records, Deleted Nov '84. Catalogue no: **K 12577**

ONLY ONE
Tracks: / Only one, The / Check it out.
12" Single: Released Jul '83, on Solar (USA), by MCA Records. Catalogue no: **E 9814 T**
7" Single: Released Jul '83, on Solar (USA), by MCA Records. Catalogue no: **E 9814**

SATISFIED
Tracks: / Satisfied / It's still a thrill.
7" Single: Released Mar '80, on Solar Records, Deleted '83. Catalogue no: **SO 3**
12" Single: Released Mar '80, on Solar Records, Deleted '83. Catalogue no: **SO 12-3**

Dynasty & Mimi

DYNASTY RAP
Tracks: / Dynasty rap / Story of the Carrington crew / Bugging animal farm, The / Story of the Carrington crew / Blake beat boy mix (12" only) / Alexis acapella (12" only).
7" Single: Released Feb '86, on Jive, by Zomba Records. Catalogue no: **CIVE 116**
12" Single: Released Feb '86, on Jive, by Zomba Records. Catalogue no: **CIVET 116**

Dynasty Of Two

STOP THIS THING
Tracks: / Stop this thing / Energy / Stop this thing (version) (Only on 12" single.).
12" Single: Released Jul '89, on RCA, by BMG Records (UK). Catalogue no: **ZT 42890**
7" Single: Released Jul '89, on RCA, by BMG Records (UK). Catalogue no: **ZB 42889**

Dynell, Johnny

JAM HOT (RUMBA ROCK)
Tracks: / Jam hot.
7" Single: Released Jun '83, on Epic, by CBS Records. Catalogue no: **A 3509**
12" Single: Released Jun '83, on Epic, by CBS Records. Catalogue no: **TA 3509**

Dyson, Ronnie

Biographical details: This American singer came to fame in 1968, while still in his teens, as one of the stars of the sensationally successful Broadway musical *Hair*. He led the cast on the show's famous opening number *Aquarius*; on its multi-million selling soundtrack album, he also took a prominent vocal role on *Able baby* and *What a piece of work is man*. Dyson's solo recording career blossomed in 1970, when he no.8 on the US Hot 100 with *(If you let me make love to you then) why can't I touch you?*, a song from the musical *Salvation*. However, his next visit to the American Top 40 did not occur until 1973, when he reachedno. 28 with *One man band (plays all alone)*. Between these two hits, he achieved his only solo entry in the British charts - *When you get right down to it* peaked at no.34 at the end of 1971. From 1974 onwards, yson was no longer a significant record seller, but he made his living in nightclubs in cabaret. His subsequent soul ballads and dance records, all of a fairly lightweight nature, included *The more you do it (the more I like it done to me)* (which reached no.62 in 1976) and *All over your face* (1983). (Bob Macdonald, 15/7/85).

ALL OVER YOUR FACE
Tracks: / All over your face / Don't need you now.
12" Single: Released Sep '83, on Cotillion (Import), by WEA Records. Catalogue no: **B 9841 T**

ONE MORE CHANCE FOR THE FOOL
Tracks: / One more chance for the fool / Foreplay.
7" Single: Released Apr '82, on Cotillion, by WEA Records. Deleted Apr '85. Catalogue no: **K 19136**

WHEN YOU GET RIGHT DOWN TO IT
Tracks: / When you get right down to it.
7" Single: Released Dec '71, on CBS, by CBS Records. Deleted '76. Catalogue no: **CBS 7449**

Dzire, DJ

BAD PLACE TO GET HIT
Tracks: / Bad place to get hit (version).
12" Single: Released Mar '89, on Furious Fish, Catalogue no: **FFD 002**

E

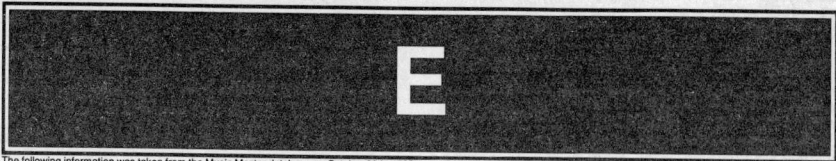

The following information was taken from the Music Master database on October 20th, 1989.

E

BAT-TRAX
Tracks: / Bat-trax.
7" Single: Released Aug '88, on Circle City, Catalogue no: **CCY 7**
12" Single: Released Aug '88, on Circle City, Catalogue no: **CCYT 7**

E, Albert

III
Tracks: / III / On and on.
7" Single: Released Nov '87, on NSF, Catalogue no: **NSF 004**

E Zee Possee

EVERYTHING BEGINS WITH AN E
Tracks: / Everything begins with an e.
12" Single: Released Feb '89, on Virgin, by Virgin Records. Catalogue no: **PROTX 112**
12" Single: Released Feb '89, on Virgin, by Virgin Records. Catalogue no: **PROT 112**

Eade, Colin

KILLER, THE
Tracks: / Killer / Aids-the killer / If in doubt leave it out / Love your life / Cry for the last time.
Note: Available from First Time Records, 12 Trewartha Road, Praa Sands, Penzance, Cornwall TR20 9ST. Tel: 0736 762826.
7" Single: Released Mar '87, on First Time, by First Time Records. Catalogue no: **CSTE 5452**

Eagles

Biographical details: At the time of their greatest success, this American band consisted of Don Felder, Glenn Frey, Don Henley, Randy Meisner and Joe Walsh. The Eagles were formed in 1971 by Frey, Henley, Meisner and guitarist Bernie Leadon. Meisner had also been a member of Poco, and Leadon had played with the Flying Burrito Brothers. The new group flew from their Californian base to London to record their self-titled debut album, which was released in 1972. With its laid-back country rock sound, it became a major success in the States, yielding three US Top 30 singles *Take it easy* (written by Frey and singer/songwriter Jackson Browne), *Witchy woman* and *Peaceful easy feeling*. The Eagles' second album, 1973's *Desperado*, did not produce any major hit singles, but consolidated their position as one of America's most important new bands of the seventies; the title track, a touching ballad, was later covered by the Carpenters and other acts. A fifth Eagle, Felder, joined the group for 1974's *On the border* album. From 1975 onwards, the Eagles could do no wrong. Their blend of vocal harmonies, ace musicianship and well-crafted melodic songs (emanating mainly from Frey & Henley) made them America's favourite purveyors of the Los Angeles soft rock sound. In that year, they enjoyed two US no.1 singles; the ballad *Best of my love* and *One of these nights* and a no.2 hit with *Lyin' eyes*. '75 also brought the group their first significant inroads into the UK market. In 1976 Leadon, overburdened by the pressure of the Eagles' growing international superstardom, was replaced by the acclaimed guitar wizard Joe Walsh. This was a somewhat unexpected move for Walsh, who had already made his name as a member of the James Gang and also a solo performer. His style was heavier than the rest of the Eagles, but the two sounds complemented each other superbly. The *Hotel California* LP was a worldwide smash; the title track was a US no. 1 and their only UK Top 10 single; and they also topped the American charts with another track, *New kid in town*. The Eagles' sixth and final studio LP *The long run* was not issued until 1979, by which time Meisner had quit and had been replaced by another ex-Poco player, Timothy Schmit. Like *Hotel California, The long run* enjoyed a long run at the top of the US album charts, but it was not as good as its predecessor. After 1980's live album, the Eagles drifted apart, although no official split was announced. Henley & Frey, the only two perennial members, both went on to achieve solo successes. (Bob Macdonald, 21/7/85)
USA West Coast rock band formed in 1971 by drummer Don Henley and guitarist Glenn Frey, with guitarist Bernie Leadon and bassist Randy Meisner. All had impeccalbe credentials, having sessioned with James Taylor, Poco, Linda Ronstadt etc. After their debut *The Eagles* and *Desperado*, Don Felder was added for *On the border; One of these nights* was Leadon's last with the band, replaced by Joe Walsh. By then they were unassailable as the USA's top band, tapping the massive AOR audience with effortless vocal and guitar harmonies. Their success was too easy for some critics and songs like *Tequila sunrise* weren't terribly relevant outside California, but commercially they could do no wrong. *Hotel California* in 1976 was their biggest success, selling 11 million worldwide. After *The long run* in 1979 they split; *Eagles live* was a souvenir. (Donald Clarke, April 1989)e.

DESPERADO (SINGLE)
Tracks: / Desperado.
7" Single: Released Jul '75, on Asylum, by WEA Records. Deleted '80. Catalogue no: **SYLL 9011**

HEARTACHE TONIGHT
Tracks: / Heartache tonight.
7" Single: Released Oct '79, on Asylum, by WEA Records. Deleted '84. Catalogue no: **K 12394**

HOTEL CALIFORNIA (OLD GOLD)
Tracks: / Hotel California / Desperado.
7" Single: Released Sep '85, on Old Gold, by Old Gold Records. Catalogue no: **OG 9511**

HOTEL CALIFORNIA (SINGLE)
Tracks: / Hotel California / Pretty maids all in a row.
12" Single: Released Sep '88, on WEA, by WEA Records. Catalogue no: **EKR 10T**
7" Single: Released Sep '88, on WEA, by WEA Records. Catalogue no: **EKR 10**

HOTEL CALIFORNIA (SINGLE 2)
Tracks: / Hotel California / Pretty maids all.
7" Single: Released Jul '81, on Elektra, by Elektra Records (UK). Catalogue no: **K 13079**

LONG RUN, THE (SINGLE)
Tracks: / Long run, The.
7" Single: Released Dec '79, on Elektra, by Elektra Records (UK). Deleted '84. Catalogue no: **K 12404**

LYIN' EYES
Tracks: / Lyin' eyes.
7" Single: Released Nov '75, on Asylum, by WEA Records. Deleted '80. Catalogue no: **AYM 548**

LYIN' EYES (OLD GOLD)
Tracks: / Lyin' eyes.
7" Single: Released Sep '85, on Old Gold, by Old Gold Records. Catalogue no: **OG 9526**

NEW KID IN TOWN
Tracks: / New kid in town.
7" Single: Released Jan '77, on Asylum, by WEA Records. Deleted '82. Catalogue no: **K 13069**

ONE OF THESE NIGHTS (SINGLE)
Tracks: / One of these nights.
7" Single: Released Aug '75, on Asylum, by WEA Records. Deleted '80. Catalogue no: **AYM 543**

PLEASE COME HOME FOR CHRISTMAS
Tracks: / Please come home for Christmas.
7" Single: Released Dec '78, on Asylum, by WEA Records. Deleted '83. Catalogue no: **K 13145**

SAD CAFE
Tracks: / Sad Cafe / Those shoes.
7" Single: Released May '80, on Asylum, by WEA Records. Deleted May '83. Catalogue no: **K 12440**

TAKE IT TO THE LIMIT
Tracks: / Take it to the limit / Seven bridges road.
7" Single: Released Mar '76, on Asylum, by WEA Records. Deleted '81. Catalogue no: **K 13029**
7" Single: Released Feb '81, on Elektra, by Elektra Records (UK). Catalogue no: **K 12504**

TAKE IT TO THE LIMIT (OLD GOLD)
Tracks: / Take it to the limit.
7" Single: Released Sep '85, on Old Gold, by Old Gold Records. Catalogue no: **OG 9510**

E.A.J. Allstars

RHYTHMS IN BLUE
Tracks: / Rhythms in blue.
7" Single: Released Feb '81, on Inferno (1), by Inferno Records. Deleted '84. Catalogue no: **RMP 2**

Ear Trumpet

BEING A DOG IS FOR LIFE
Tracks: / Being a dog is for life.
12" Single: Released Jul '89, on Sinister Groove, Catalogue no: **TAO 001**

Eargasm

THIS IS LOVERS ROCK TOO
Tracks: / This is lovers rock too / Lover's medley.
12" Single: Released Dec '86, on G Spot, Catalogue no: **GSPOT 1**

Earl 16

BEHOLD
Tracks: / Behold.
12" Single: Released Oct '89, on Sunjam, Catalogue no: **SR 009**

Earl, Robert

I MAY NEVER PASS THIS WAY AGAIN
Tracks: / I may never pass this way again.
7" Single: Released Apr '58, on Philips, by Phonogram Ltd. Deleted '63. Catalogue no: **PB 805**

MORE THAN EVER (COME PRIMA)
Tracks: / More than ever (come prima).
7" Single: Released Oct '58, on Philips, by Phonogram Ltd. Deleted '63. Catalogue no: **PB 867**

WONDERFUL SECRET OF LOVE
Tracks: / Wonderful secret of love.
7" Single: Released Feb '59, on Philips, by Phonogram Ltd. Deleted '64. Catalogue no: **PB 891**

Earland, Charles

Biographical details:
This American keyboards player came to prominence in the jazz market in 1970 with his *Black talk* album. Throughout the early Seventies, his urgent organ style attracted considerable acclaim because it broke away from the ponderous blues approach that had come to be associated with jazz organists. Adding synthesisers and electric piano to his range of instruments, Earland went disco in the mid-Seventies. In this capacity, he achieved his sole UK chart entry - *Let the music play*, which featured an unnamed male vocalist, reached No.46 on the singles chart in 1978. He continued to release albums into the Eighties, although his wavering between jazz and dance styles tended to lessen his chances of maintaining a loyal audience. (Bob MacDonald, 21.7.85).
An orgainist and compser, born in 1941 in Philadelphia. He also plays soprano sax. He started on alto-sax, played tenor at 17 with organist Jimmy McGriff, switched to organ in 1963 and has become one of the most popular organists, his walking or rolling bass lines fitting either jazz or rockish settings. (Donald Clarke, April 1989).

DOGGIE BOOGIE BABY
Tracks: / Doggie boogie baby.
12" Single: on MCA, by MCA Records. Catalogue no: **MCAT 880**
7" Single: on MCA, by MCA Records. Catalogue no: **MCA 880**

LET THE MUSIC PLAY
Tracks: / Let the music play.
7" Single: Released Aug '78, on Mercury, by Phonogram Ltd. Deleted '83. Catalogue no: **6167 703**

Earle, Steve

Biographical details: Country rock singer, songwriter, guitarist and bandleader born in 1955 in Virginia. His albums are excellent rock with a strong country flavour and country values in his very good lyrics; although slick, they manage to avoid the excesses of much of today's production. (Donald Clarke, April 1989).

BACK TO THE WALL
Tracks: / Back to the wall.
12" Single: Released Feb '89, on MCA, by MCA Records. Catalogue no: **MCAT 1319**
CD 5": Released Feb '89, on MCA, by MCA Records. Catalogue no: **DMCAT 1319**
7" Single: Released Feb '89, on MCA, by MCA Records. Deleted 1 Jul '89. Catalogue no: **MCA 1319**

COPPERHEAD ROAD (SINGLE)
Tracks: / Copperhead road.
12" Single: Released Oct '88, on MCA, by MCA Records. Catalogue no: **MCAT 1280**
CD 5": Released Oct '88, Catalogue no: **DMCA 1280**
7" Single: Released Oct '88, on MCA, by MCA Records. Deleted 1 Jul '89. Catalogue no: **MCA 1280**

FEARLESS HEART
Tracks: / Fearless heart / Little rock 'n' roller.
7" Single: Released Mar '87, on MCA, by MCA Records. Catalogue no: **MCA 1141**
12" Single: Released Mar '87, on MCA, by MCA Records. Catalogue no: **MCAT 1141**

I AIN'T EVER SATISFIED
Tracks: / I ain't ever satisfied / I love too much (Available on 12" only) / My old friend the blues.
Note: * Only available on the 12" version.
12" Single: Released 20 Jun '88, on MCA, by MCA Records. Catalogue no: **MCAT 1249**
7" Single: Released 20 Jun '88, on MCA, by MCA Records. Catalogue no: **MCA 1249**

I AIN'T NEVER SATISFIED
Tracks: / I ain't never satisfied / Nowhere Road.
12" Single: Released 23 May '87, on MCA, by MCA Records. Catalogue no: **MCAS 1162**
7" Single: Released 23 May '87, on MCA, by MCA Records. Catalogue no: **MCA 1162**

JOHNNY COME LATELY
Tracks: / Johnny come lately / Nothing but a child / Nebraska (live) (Only on 12".) / Nothing but a child (album version) (Only on 12".).
12" Single: Released Nov '88, on MCA, by MCA Records. Catalogue no: **MCAT 1301**
CD 5": Released Dec '88, on MCA, by MCA Records. Catalogue no: **DMCA 1301**
7" Single: Released Nov '88, on MCA, by MCA Records. Deleted 1 Jul '89. Catalogue no: **MCA 1301**

RAIN CAME DOWN, THE
Tracks: / Rain came down, The / I love you too much / Guitar town / No. 29.
7" Single: Released Oct '87, on MCA, by MCA Records. Catalogue no: **MCA 1209**

SOMEDAY
Tracks: / Someday / Guitar town / Good ol' boy (live) / Goodbye's all we've got left (Available on 12" version only.).
Note: Goodbye's all we got left,is an extra track available on the 12" version only.
7" Single: Released Feb '87, on MCA, by MCA Records. Catalogue no: **MCA 1123**
12" Single: Released Feb '87, on MCA, by MCA Records. Catalogue no: **MCAS 1123**

SOMEDAY (1)
Tracks: / Someday / Guitar man.
7" Single: Released Oct '86, on MCA, by MCA Records. Catalogue no: **MCA 1083**

Earls

REMEMBER THEN (OLD GOLD)
Tracks: / Remember then.

7" Single: Released Jul '82, on Old Gold, by Old Gold Records. Deleted Jul '88. Catalogue no: **OG 9019**

Early B

HISTORY OF JAMAICA
Tracks: / History of Jamaica.
12" Single: Released Oct '82, on Musical Ambassador, Catalogue no: **MA 007**

RIGHTEOUS RASTA
Tracks: / Righteous rasta / Poor man plan.
12" Single: Released Feb '83, on King Jam, Catalogue no: **KJ 098**
10" single: Released Dec '82, on King Jam, Catalogue no: **KJ 068**

Early Black

MEOW MYOO
Tracks: / Meow myoo.
7" Single: Released May '89, on Progressive, Catalogue no: **UNKNOWN**

Earons

LAND OF HUNGER
Tracks: / Land of hunger.
12" Single: Released May '84, on Island, by Island Records. Catalogue no: **12IS 167**

Earth & Fire

WEEKEND
Tracks: / Weekend / Answer me.
7" Single: Released Aug '80, on Polydor, by Polydor Ltd. Deleted '83. Catalogue no: **POSP 156**

Earth Shaker

BLONDIE GIRL
Tracks: / Blondie girl.
12" Single: Released Nov '83, on Music For Nations, by Music For Nations Records. Catalogue no: **12 KUT 107**

Earth, Wind & Fire

Biographical details:
At the time of their greatest success, this American band consisted of Philip Bailey, Larry Dunn, Johnny Graham, Ralph Johnson, Al McKay, Fred White, Maurice White, Verdine White and Andrew Woolfolk. One of the three White brothers, Maurice, was the group's founder, leader and key creative force. In common with his assistant frontman, Philip Bailey, Maurice is a singer and a drummer/percussionist. Earth, Wind & Fire were formed in Chicago in 1970. By this time, Maurice White was already an experienced session musician. Apart from his bass-playing brother Verdine, none of the early EWF cohorts lasted longer than 1973 (although guitarist Roland Bautista rejoined in 1981). The above line-up stabilised in 1975, the year of the group's major breakthrough. The song that made the band's name was *Shining star*, a dynamic Maurice White/Philip Bailey-penned single that reached the US No.1 slot in May '75; it was the opening track on their album *That's the way of the world*, which hit the top spot on the American album chart in the same month. The uplifting and electric sound of EWF brought further American smashes in 1976 with the singles *Sing a song* and *Getaway*; the double album *Gratitude* (one studio LP, one live LP) reached No.2 on the US LP listings in December '75, and *Spirit* did likewise in October '76. EWF's craftily conceived and brilliantly executed fusion of soul, rock and jazz made them one of the most exciting black groups in the business. Their joyful music was fuelled not only by White's musical creativity, but also by his interest in mystical and religious forces. Britain began to wake up to Earth, Wind & Fire in 1977, the same year that Maurice co-produced *Free*, a UK No.1 single for Deniece Williams. 1979 was a stunning year for the band - they enjoyed three consecutive transatlantic Top 10 singles, with *September*, *Boogie Wonderland* (on which they were joined by the Emotions) and *After the love has gone*. The latter two songs came from the LP *I am* - this album gave EWF the distinction of being the first act to lift five UK chart singles from the same studio album; they beat Michael Jackson to this feat by four months. 1980's *Faces* LP was a disappointment, but they made a brief recovery with the explosive dance single *Let's groove*, which hit No.3 on both sides of the Atlantic. However, their two 1983 albums were relative failures, and the band fell into abeyance. 1985 saw Philip Bailey in a highly successful alliance with Phil Collins - the pair's duet single "Easy lover" was a global pop smash. (Bob MacDonald, 21.7.85).
USA soul dance band formed in 1969 by vocalist/drummer Maurice White and his brother, bassist Verdine White. Despite its absurd name it is a musical outfit, slick in the best sense, including elements of Latin-funk beat, gospel, soul, rock etc. in a influential way. One of their first breaks was to be chosen by director Melvin Van Peebles to play in the soundtrack of *Sweet sweetback's badass song* in 1970, the first blaxploitation flick, and they've been doing well ever since. From 1973 the stable personnel included the sweet soul singer Philip Bailey, keyboardist Larry Dunn, guitarists Johnny Graham and Al McKay, Andre Woolfolk on reeds (augmented since the late '70's by the four-piece Phoenix Horns) and Ralph Johnson on drums, soon joined by a third brother Freddie White on drums. Maurice White had toured with Ramsey Lewis in the '60's, producing Lewis's hit *Sun Goddess* in 1975. (Donald Clarke, April 1989)e.

AFTER THE LOVE HAS GONE
Tracks: / After the love has gone.
7" Single: Released Jul '79, on CBS, by CBS Records. Catalogue no: **CBS 7721**

BACK ON THE ROAD
Tracks: / Back on the road / Take it to the sky.
7" Single: Released Dec '80, on CBS, by CBS Records. Deleted '85. Catalogue no: **CBS 9377**

BOOGIE WONDERLAND
Tracks: / Boogie wonderland.
12" Single: Released Jun '86, on CBS, by CBS Records. Deleted '86. Catalogue no: **TA 7253**
7" Single: Released Jun '86, on CBS, by CBS Records. Catalogue no: **A 7253**

BOOGIE WONDERLAND (OLD GOLD)
Tracks: / Boogie wonderland / Let's groove.
7" Single: Released '88, on Old Gold, by Old Gold Records. Catalogue no: **OG 9558**

BOOGIE WONDERLAND (ORIGINAL)
Tracks: / Boogie wonderland.
7" Single: Released May '79, on CBS, by CBS Records. Deleted '84. Catalogue no: **CBS 7292**

CAN'T LET GO
Tracks: / Can't let go.
7" Single: Released Dec '79, on CBS, by CBS Records. Deleted '84. Catalogue no: **CBS 8077**

FALL IN LOVE WITH ME
Tracks: / Fall in love with me / Lady sun.
12" Single: Released Jan '83, on CBS, by CBS Records. Catalogue no: **A 12 2927**
7" Single: Released Jan '83, on CBS, by CBS Records. Catalogue no: **A 2927**

FANTASY
Tracks: / Fantasy.
7" Single: Released Feb '78, on CBS, by CBS Records. Deleted '83. Catalogue no: **CBS 6056**

FANTASY (OLD GOLD)
Tracks: / Fantasy.
7" Single: Released Sep '85, on Old Gold, by Old Gold Records. Catalogue no: **OG 9556**

GOT TO GET YOU INTO MY LIFE
Tracks: / Got to get you into my life.
7" Single: Released Oct '78, on CBS, by CBS Records. Deleted '83. Catalogue no: **CBS 6553**

IN THE STONE
Tracks: / In the stone / Africano.
7" Single: Released Mar '80, on CBS, by CBS Records. Deleted '85. Catalogue no: **CBS 8252**
12" Single: Released Mar '80, on CBS, by CBS Records. Deleted '85. Catalogue no: **13-8252**

I'VE HAD ENOUGH
Tracks: / I've had enough.
7" Single: Released Feb '82, on CBS, by CBS Records. Deleted '87. Catalogue no: **CBS A 1959**

JUPITER
Tracks: / Jupiter.
7" Single: Released May '78, on CBS, by CBS Records. Deleted '83. Catalogue no: **CBS 6267**

LET ME TALK
Tracks: / Let me talk.
7" Single: Released Oct '80, on CBS, by CBS Records. Deleted '85. Catalogue no: **CBS 8982**

LET'S GROOVE
Tracks: / Let's groove / Let's groove (Instrumental).
7" Single: Released Nov '81, on CBS, by CBS Records. Deleted '86. Catalogue no: **A 1679**

LET'S GROOVE (OLD GOLD)
Tracks: / Let's groove / Boogie wonderland.
12" Single: Released Sep '87, on Old Gold, by Old Gold Records. Catalogue no: **OG 4019**

LOVE GOES ON
Tracks: / Love goes on / Faces.
7" Single: Released Feb '81, on CBS, by CBS Records. Deleted Feb '84. Catalogue no: **CBS 9521**

MAGIC MIND
Tracks: / Magic mind.
7" Single: Released Jul '78, on CBS, by CBS Records. Deleted '83. Catalogue no: **CBS 6490**

SATURDAY NITE
Tracks: / Saturday nite.
7" Single: Released Feb '77, on CBS, by CBS Records. Deleted '82. Catalogue no: **CBS 4835**

SEPTEMBER
Tracks: / September.
7" Single: Released Apr '82, on CBS, by CBS Records. Catalogue no: **CBS 6922**

SPREAD YOUR LOVE
Tracks: / Spread your love.
7" Single: Released Mar '83, on CBS, by CBS Records. Catalogue no: **A 3211**

STAR
Tracks: / Star.
7" Single: Released Oct '79, on CBS, by CBS Records. Deleted '84. Catalogue no: **CBS 7092**

STAR (OLD GOLD)
Tracks: / Star / Saturday nite / After the love is gone / I've had enough.
12" Single: Released Feb '86, on Old Gold, by Old Gold Records. Catalogue no: **OG 4008**

SYSTEM OF SURVIVAL
Tracks: / System of survival / System of survival (Percapella mix) (On 12" version only.) / Writing on the wall (On 12" version.) / System of survival (dub 1 mix) (On 12" picture bag version.) / System of survival (7" mix) (On 12" picture bad version.) / Writing on the wall (On 12" picture bad version.).
7" Single: Released Oct '87, on CBS, by CBS Records. Deleted 17 Apr '89. Catalogue no: **EWF 1**
12" Single: Released Oct '88, on CBS, by CBS Records. Deleted 17 Apr '89. Catalogue no: **EWF T1**
CD 5": Released Sep '88, on CBS, by CBS Records. Deleted 17 Apr '89. Catalogue no: **CD EWF 1**
7" EP: Released Oct '87, on Columbia (USA), by CBS Records (USA). Catalogue no: **4407475**
12" Single: Released Oct '87, on CBS, by CBS Records. Deleted 17 Apr '89. Catalogue no: **EWF QT1**
CD 5": Released Oct '88, on CBS, by CBS Records. Deleted 17 Apr '89. Catalogue no: **CDGEWF 1**

THINKING OF YOU
Tracks: / Thinking of you / Thinking of you (house mix) / Thinking of you (12" version) / Thinking of you (house mix with vocals) / Money tight.
CD 5": Released Feb '88, on CBS, by CBS Records. Deleted Jan '89. Catalogue no: **CDEWF 2**
12" Single: Released Feb '88, on CBS, by CBS Records. Deleted Aug '88. Catalogue no: **EWF T2**
7" Single: Released Feb '88, on CBS, by CBS Records. Deleted Aug '88. Catalogue no: **EWF 2**
12" Single: Released Feb '88, on CBS, by CBS Records. Deleted Aug '88. Catalogue no: **EWF QT2**

YOU
Tracks: / You / Pride.
7" Single: Released May '81, on CBS, by CBS Records. Deleted May '84. Catalogue no: **A 1204**

East Bay Ray

TROUBLE IN TOWN
Tracks: / Trouble in town.
7" Single: Released Jun '84, on Alternative Tentacles, by Alternative Tentacles Records. Catalogue no: **VIRUS 34**
12" Single: Released Apr '89, on New Rose (1), by New Rose Records. Catalogue no: **GMO 40**

East Coast Offering

DON'T YOU EVER TAKE YOUR LOVE AWAY
Tracks: / Don't you ever take your love away / Dartagnan.
12" Single: Released Aug '84, on MCA, by MCA Records. Deleted '85. Catalogue no: **MCAT 902**
7" Single: Released Aug '84, on MCA, by MCA Records. Catalogue no: **MCA 902**

East India Company

MOVE YOUR BODY
Tracks: / Move your body / Night sky.
12" Single: Released Apr '87, on Nine O Nine, by Creole Records. Catalogue no: **NINE 74**

East Of Eden

Biographical details:
At the time of their only UK hit single, this British group consisted of Jeff Allen, Dave Arbus, Ron Caines, Geoff Nicholson and Andy Sneddon. East of Eden released their debut LP *Mercator projected* in 1969. The eclectic band's second album *Snafu* gave them a brief run on the UK album charts in March 1970 - it reached No.29. They never returned to the LP listings, but enjoyed a one-off hit single in 1971: *Jig a jig*, a jolly and engaging traditional instrumental, reached the UK No.7 position. East of Eden's unusual brand of folk-influenced sounds, featuring contrasting violin and saxaphone parts, was soon forgotten in Britain; but during the mid-Seventies, the band earned a steady living in Europe and were endowed with a particularly large following in West Germany. (Bob MacDonald, 21.7.85)..

JIG A JIG
Tracks: / Jig a jig / Marcus junior.
7" Single: Released May '70, on Decca, by Decca Records. Deleted '88. Catalogue no: **F 13919**
7" Single: Released Apr '71, on Deram, by London Records. Deleted '76. Catalogue no: **DM 297**

East Of Java

BURNING SUN
Tracks: / Burning sun.
7" Single: Released Jul '84, on RCA, by BMG Records (UK). Catalogue no: **RCA 425**
12" Single: Released Jul '84, on RCA, by BMG Records (UK). Catalogue no: **RCAT 425**

DIFFERENT WORLD
Tracks: / Different world.
12" Single: Released Aug '85, on RCA, by BMG Records (UK). Catalogue no: **PT 40253**
7" Single: Released Aug '85, on RCA, by BMG Records (UK). Catalogue no: **PD 40252**

SOME PEOPLE (SAY WAR)
Tracks: / Some people (say war).
12" Single: Released Oct '84, on RCA, by BMG Records (UK). Catalogue no: **RCAT 447**
7" Single: Released Oct '84, on RCA, by BMG Records (UK). Catalogue no: **RCA 447**

TAIPO SAY DRUM
Tracks: / Taipo say drum.
7" Single: Released Jan '85, on RCA, by BMG Records (UK). Catalogue no: **RCA 447**
12" Single: Released Jan '85, on RCA, by BMG Records (UK). Catalogue no: **RCAT 447**

East Seventeen

GOOD OLD JUMBLE SALE
Tracks: / Good old jumble sale.
7" Single: Released May '83, on Goldliner, Catalogue no: **E 17**

East Side Band

1980
Tracks: / 1980 / Something strange.
7" Single: Released Jan '80, on RAK, by EMI Records. Deleted Jan '83. Catalogue no: **RAK 305**

WON'T YOU BE MINE
Tracks: / Won't you be mine / Bowery.
7" Single: Released May '81, on Black Label (USA), by House Of America Records (USA). Catalogue no: **GB 002**

East Side Torpedoes

HIGHER AND HIGHER
Tracks: / Higher and higher.
7" Single: Released 12 Sep '85, on Dead Volume, Deleted '88. Catalogue no: **VOL 015**

East Village

BACK BETWEEN PLACES
Tracks: / Between places.
12" Single: Released Oct '88, on Sub Aqua, Catalogue no: **AQUA 412**

BREAK YOUR NECK
Tracks: / Break your neck.
12" Single: Released Apr '88, on Head, Catalogue no: **HEAD 9**

CUBANS IN THE BLUE FIELD
Tracks: / Cubans in the blue field.
12" Single: Released '88, on Sub Aqua, Catalogue no: **AQUA 2T**
7" Single: Released '88, on Sub Aqua, Catalogue no: **AQUA 2**

East Wall

APPEARING IN PERSONS
Tracks: / Appearing in persons / Selfish heart (a hard time).
7" Single: Released Apr '86, on Regent, Deleted '87. Catalogue no: **REGT 1**

Eastbound Expressway

FRANTIC LOVE
Tracks: / Frantic love.
12" Single: Released May '84, on Record Shack, by Record Shack Records. Catalogue no: **SOHOT 19**
7" Single: Released May '84, on Record Shack, by Record Shack Records. Catalogue no: **SOHO 19**

KNOCK ME SENSELESS
Tracks: / Knock me senseless / Knock me senseless (Inst).
12" Single: Released Oct '86, on Passion, by Skratch Records. Catalogue no: **PASH 61(12)**
7" Single: Released Oct '86, on Passion, by Skratch Records. Catalogue no: **PASH 61**

PRIMITIVE DESIRE
Tracks: / Primitive desire.
12" Single: Released Nov '83, on Record Shack, by Record Shack Records. Catalogue no: **SOHOT 9**

RAINSTORM
Tracks: / Rainstorm / Rainstorm (Nightmare dub mix).
12" Single: Released Apr '87, on Passion, by Skratch Records. Catalogue no: **PASH 70(12)**

YOU'RE A BEAT
Tracks: / You've a beat / You're a beat(Dub version).
7" Single: Released Mar '86, on Passion, by Skratch Records. Catalogue no: **PASH 53**
12" Single: Released Mar '86, on Passion, by Skratch Records. Catalogue no: **PASH 53(12)**

Easterhouse

COME OUT FIGHTING
Tracks: / Come out fighting.
7" Single: Released 16 Jan '89, on Rough Trade, by Rough Trade Records. Catalogue no: **RT 204**
CD 5": Released Jan '89, on Rough Trade, by Rough Trade Records. Catalogue no: **CDRT 204**
12" Single: Released 16 Jan '89, on Rough Trade, by Rough Trade Records. Catalogue no: **RT T204**

COMING UP FOR AIR
Tracks: / Coming up for air / Endless march / Man alive / One more time.
7" Single: Released Mar '85, on Easterhouse, Deleted '86. Catalogue no: **EIREX 1**

INSPIRATION
Tracks: / Inspiration / Johnny I hardly knew you / Easter rising 1969 ((Extra track on 12" version only)).
12" Single: Released Apr '86, on Rough Trade, by Rough Trade Records. Catalogue no: **RTT 174**
7" Single: Released Apr '86, on Rough Trade, by Rough Trade Records. Catalogue no: **RT 174**

WHISTLING IN THE DARK
Tracks: / Whistling in the dark / Ain't that always the way / Confrontation ((Extra track on 12" version only)).
7" Single: Released Jan '86, on Rough Trade, by Rough Trade Records. Catalogue no: **RT 164**
12" Single: on Rough Trade, by Rough Trade Records. Catalogue no: **RTT 164**

YOU'RE GONNA MISS IT
Tracks: / You're gonna miss it.
7" Single: Released Jun '89, on Rough Trade, by Rough Trade Records. Catalogue no: **UNKNOWN**
12" Single: Released Jun '89, on Rough Trade, by Rough Trade Records. Catalogue no: **UNKNOWN**
CD 5": Released Jun '89, on Rough Trade, by Rough Trade Records. Catalogue no: **UNKNOWN**

Eastern Alliance

KEYS TO THE HOUSE
Tracks: / Keys to the house / Hard line girl.
7" Single: Released Jun '84, on Bronze, by Bronze Records. Catalogue no: **BRO 182**

LOVE YOU YOU BANANA
Tracks: / Love you, you banana / I'll be there.
7" Single: Released Aug '84, on Bronze, by Bronze Records. Catalogue no: **BRO 184**

Eastern Variation

BABY I LOVE YOU
Tracks: / Baby I love you / Baby I love you (version).
12" Single: Released Aug '86, on Cartridge, Catalogue no: **CRD 15**

SHEENA EASTON - 101 (Released on MCA)

Easton, Sheena

Biographical details: This British singer, born Sheena Orr in Glasgow in April 1959, first hit the UK charts in April 1980 when her debut single *Modern girl* climbed to No.56. She had previously been studying at the Royal Scottish Academy of Music and Drama and working in local clubs and pubs. In July '80 she became the subject of Esther Rantzen's BBC TV documentary *The Big Time*, which depicted Easton as a typical up-and-coming singer struggling to find stardom. This amounted to 50 minutes of peak time television exposure, and the programme gave heavy airplay to *Modern girl*. The resulting publicity meant that, by September 1980, the previously unknown Sheena Easton found herself with two simultaneous UK Top 10 singles: the infuriatingly catchy *9 to 5* peaked at no.3, and *Modern girl* got to no.8. As if that wasn't spectaclar enough, she cruised to no.1 in America in May 1981 with *Morning train (9 to 5)*; the song was retitled in the States to avoid confusion with a Dolly Parton song of the same name. Sheena then hit the Top 10 on both sides of the Atlantic with *For your eyes only*, the title song of the latest James Bond movie. Easton had quickly established herself as a mass appeal pop star in the Olivia Newton-John mould. Her voice came through to best effect on slow ballads, although she was also perfectly at home on the singalong uptempo ditties. A pleasant but hard and calculating character, Sheena opportunistically forsook her British following in favour of the lucrative lure of US stardom. While the UK hits tailed off, she enjoyed, during the early to mid-eighties, American Top 10 successes with *Telefone (long distance love affair)* and *Strut*. Based in her luxurious California home, she also experienced successful collaborations with Kenny Rogers and Prince. Sheena Easton's American acceptance was phenomenal, not because of its scale but because of its diversity - some critics argued that she achieved a series of one-offs rather than a career. By 1985 she had become the only artists in US chart history to have hit the Top 10 in all five of America's major singles charts - pop, black, dance, country and easy listening. She even managed to penetrate the Latin market, thanks to a smash duet with Luis Miguel. (Bob Macdonald, 21/7/85)
Pop singer born in 1959 in Glasgow. Her big break was being the subject of the Big Time TV show, describing the process of manufacturing a pop star after she'd been signed by EMI. She has cut her cloth to suit the prevailing style, switching from rock to ballads (pursuing the lucrative USA MOR market, for example with a duet with Kenny Rogers on a cover of Bob Seger's *We got tonight*), then enlisting Prince to redirect her to disco (*Sugar walls*, made her the first singer to have singles in Billboard's top 10 pop, black, disco, MOR and country charts, despite airplay ban.) She borrowed Madonna's street-urchin image (and producer Nile Rodgers) for the album *Do you* in 1985. (Donald Clarke, April 1989)ua.

9 TO 5
Tracks: / 9 to 5 / Moody.
7" Single: Released Jul '80, on EMI, by EMI Records. Deleted '85. Catalogue no: **EMI 5066**

101 (see panel above)
Tracks: / 101 / 101 (instrumental).
7" Single: Released Jul '89, on MCA, by MCA Records. Catalogue no: **MCA 1348**
12" Single: Released Jul '89, on MCA, by MCA Records. Catalogue no: **MCAT 1348**
CD 3": Released Jul '89, on MCA, by MCA Records. Catalogue no: **DMCA 1348**
7" Single: Released Jul '89, on MCA, by MCA Records. Catalogue no: **MCAR 1348**

ARE YOU MAN ENOUGH
Tracks: / Are you man enough / Loner.
7" Single: Released Oct '82, on EMI, by EMI Records. Deleted Oct '85. Catalogue no: **EMI 5349**

DAYS LIKE THIS
Tracks: / Days like this.
7" Single: Released 6 Mar '89, on MCA, by MCA Records. Catalogue no: **MCA 1325**
12" Single: Released Apr '89, on MCA, by MCA Records. Catalogue no: **MCA 239 32**
12" Single: Released 6 Mar '89, on MCA, by MCA Records. Catalogue no: **MCAT 1325**
7" Single: Released Apr '89, on MCA, by MCA Records. Catalogue no: **MCAR 1325**

DO IT FOR LOVE
Tracks: / Do it for love.
7" Single: Released Nov '85, on EMI, by EMI Records. Catalogue no: **EMI 5536**
12" Single: Released Nov '85, on EMI, by EMI Records. Catalogue no: **12EMI 5536**

ETERNITY
Tracks: / Eternity / Shockwaves.
7" Single: Released Sep '87, on EMI, by EMI Records. Deleted Jan '88. Catalogue no: **EM 9**
12" Single: Released Sep '87, on EMI, by EMI Records. Deleted Jan '88. Catalogue no: **12EM 9**
7" Single: Released Oct '87, on EMI, by EMI Records. Deleted Jan '88. Catalogue no: **EMP 9**

FOR YOUR EYES ONLY (SINGLE)
Tracks: / For your eyes only / Runaway.
7" Single: Released Jun '81, on EMI, by EMI Records. Deleted Jun '89. Catalogue no: **EMI 5195**

IT'S CHRISTMAS ALL OVER THE WORLD
Tracks: / It's Christmas all over the world / Thank you Santa.
7" Single: Released Nov '86, on EMI-America, by EMI Records. Deleted Oct '87. Catalogue no: **EA 225**

JUST ANOTHER BROKEN HEART
Tracks: / Just another broken heart / Savoir faire.
7" Single: Released Sep '81, on EMI, by EMI Records. Deleted '86. Catalogue no: **EMI 5232**

LOVER IN ME, THE (SINGLE)
Tracks: / Lover in me, The.
7" Single: Released Jan '89, on MCA, by MCA Records. Deleted 1 Jul '89. Catalogue no: **MCA 1289**
12" Single: Released Jan '89, on MCA, by MCA Records. Catalogue no: **MCAT 1289**
CD 5": Released Jan '89, on MCA, by MCA Records. Catalogue no: **DMCA 1289**

MACHINERY
Tracks: / Machinery / So we say goodbye.
7" Single: Released Jul '82, on EMI, by EMI Records. Deleted '87. Catalogue no: **EMI 5326**

MAGIC OF LOVE
Tracks: / Magic of love / Money back guarantee.
12" Single: Released Feb '86, on EMI, by EMI Records. Catalogue no: **12 EMI 5547**
7" Single: Released Feb '86, on EMI, by EMI Records. Catalogue no: **EMI 5547**

MODERN GIRL
Tracks: / Modern girl / Paradox.
7" Single: Released Mar '84, on EMI Golden 45's, by EMI Records. Catalogue no: **G45 3**

MODERN GIRL (ORIGINAL) (see panel below)
Tracks: / Modern girl / Paradox.
7" Single: Released Apr '80, on EMI, by

SHEENA EASTON - MODERN GIRL (Released on EMI)

EMI Records. Deleted '85. Catalogue no: **EMI 5042**

ONE MAN WOMAN
Tracks: / One man woman / Summer's over.
7" Single: Released Oct '80, on EMI, by EMI Records. Deleted '85. Catalogue no: **EMI 5114**

TAKE MY TIME (SINGLE)
Tracks: / Take my time / Calm before the storm.
7" Single: Released Feb '81, on EMI, by EMI Records. Deleted '86. Catalogue no: **EMI 5135**

WE'VE GOT TONIGHT
Tracks: / We've got tonight / You are so beautiful.
7" Single: Released Jan '83, on United Artists, by EMI Records. Catalogue no: **UP 658**

WHEN HE SHINES
Tracks: / When he shines / Right or wrong.
7" Single: Released May '81, on EMI, by EMI Records. Deleted '86. Catalogue no: **EMI 5166**

YOU COULD HAVE BEEN WITH ME (SINGLE)
Tracks: / You could have been with me / Family of one.
7" Single: Released Dec '81, on EMI, by EMI Records. Deleted '86. Catalogue no: **EMI 5252**

Eastside

MEMORIES
Tracks: / No.2 The sequel / Memories.
7" Single: Released Dec '86, on Rime, by Rime Records. Deleted '88. Catalogue no: **RIME 3**
12" Single: Released Dec '86, on Rime, by Rime Records. Deleted '88. Catalogue no: **RIM 3**

Eastside Connection

YOU'RE SO RIGHT FOR ME
Tracks: / You're so right for me.
7" Single: Released Apr '78, on Creole, by Creole Records. Deleted '83. Catalogue no: **CR 149**

Eastwood, Clint

Biographical details: This British singer and disc jockey - definitely no relation to the US film star of the same name - had his musical roots in Jamaican reggae music, although it was in Britain that he gained attention. This happened in the late seventies, with the albums *African youth, Death in the arena* and *Love and happiness*. During the 80's he came to greater prominence as half of a duo, the other half being fellow singer/DJ General Saint. Both were leading exponents of the reggae art of "toasting", a vocal format which uses rhythmic speech to convey (often political and sociological) messages. It should be noted that they were able to compose their own music, whereas many of their DJ peers simply dubbed their voices onto other artists' backing tracks. Clint Eastwood & General Saint enjoyed their first taste of chart success in February 1982, albeit no.99 on the chart list with *Too bad DJ*. They entered the British singles list forthe last time in 1984 - the catchy, melodic *Last plane (One way ticket)* peaked at no.51. (Bob Macdonald, 21/7/85).

ANOTHER ONE BITES THE DUST
Tracks: / Another one bites the dust / Young lover.
7" Single: Released Jun '81, on Greensleeves, by Greensleeves Records. Catalogue no: **OINK 1**

I TALK TO THE TREES
Tracks: / I talk to the trees.
7" Single: Released Feb '70, on Paramount, Deleted '75. Catalogue no: **PARA 3004**

KOOL & DEAD
Tracks: / Kool & dead / Kool and dead (Inst).
12" Single: Released Jun '86, on Rhino, by Creole Records. Catalogue no: **RNO 5**

LAST PLANE(ONE WAY TICKET)
Tracks: / Last plane (one way ticket) / Combination.
7" Single: Released Sep '84, on MCA, by MCA Records. Catalogue no: **MCA 910**
12" Single: Released Sep '84, on MCA, by MCA Records. Catalogue no: **MCAT 910**

MATTY GUNGA WALK
Tracks: / Matty gunga walk / Disco queen.
12" Single: Released Jul '82, on Greensleeves, by Greensleeves Records. Catalogue no: **GRED 100**

ROCK WITH ME
Tracks: / Rock with me / True vegetarian (on 12" only).
7" Single: Released Sep '83, on Greensleeves, by Greensleeves Records. Catalogue no: **OINK 5**
12" Single: Released Sep '83, on Greensleeves, by Greensleeves Records. Catalogue no: **12 OINK 5**

SHAME & SCANDAL
Tracks: / Shame and scandal.
7" Single: Released Sep '82, on Greensleeves, by Greensleeves Records. Catalogue no: **OINK 3**
12" Single: Released Sep '82, on Greensleeves, by Greensleeves Records. Catalogue no: **12OINK 3**

STOP THAT TRAIN (SINGLE)
Tracks: / Stop that train.
7" Single: Released Apr '83, on Greensleeves, by Greensleeves Records. Catalogue no: **OINK 4**
12" Single: Released Apr '83, on Greensleeves, by Greensleeves Records. Catalogue no: **12OINK 4**

TALK ABOUT RUN
Tracks: / Talk about run / Healing in the Blamyard.
12" Single: Released Dec '81, on Greensleeves, by Greensleeves Records. Catalogue no: **12OINK 2**
7" Single: Released Dec '81, on Greensleeves, by Greensleeves Records. Catalogue no: **OINK 2**

Easy Action

WE GO RACING
Tracks: / We go racing / Turn me on.
12" Single: Released Apr '84, on Sire (USA), Catalogue no: **W 9299T**
7" Single: Released Apr '84, on Sire (USA), Catalogue no: **W 9299**

Easybeats

Biographical details: An Australian beat group formed in 1963 by emigre Europeans who met at a youth hostel: rhythm guitarist George Yound, drummer Gordon 'Snowy' Fleet, lead guitarist Harry Vanda and Dick Diamonde. They had hits down uncer, came to London and were produced by Shel Talmy (Kinks, Who); Fleet left before their USA tour, replaced by Tony Cahill. They split c.1970; songwriters Vanda and Young stuck togethe: later helping Young's brothers form AC/DC. (Donald Clarke, April 1989).

FRIDAY ON MY MIND (OLD GOLD)
Tracks: / Friday on my mind / Hello, how are you?.
7" Single: Released Jun '88, on Old Gold, by Old Gold Records. Catalogue no: **OG 9548**

FRIDAY ON MY MIND (SINGLE)
Tracks: / Friday on my mind.
7" Single: Released Oct '66, on United Artists, by EMI Records. Catalogue no: **UP 1157**

HELLO HOW ARE YOU
Tracks: / Hello how are you.
7" Single: Released Apr '68, on United Artists, by EMI Records. Deleted '73. Catalogue no: **UP 2209**

Eat

AUTOGIFT EP
Tracks: / Skin / Eat eat eat / Red moon.
7" Single: Released Jan '89, on Fiction Independence, Catalogue no: **WAN 100**
12" Single: Released Jan '89, on Fiction Independence, Catalogue no: **WANTX 100**
CD 3": Released Jan '89, on Fiction Independence, Catalogue no: **WANCD 100**

PLASTIC BAG EP: BABYBOOM
Tracks: / Plastic bag: Babyboom / Mr. & Mrs. Smack / Little country.
7" EP: Released Jun '89, on Fiction, by Fiction Records. Catalogue no: **CIF 1**
CD 5": Released Jun '89, on Fiction, by Fiction Records. Catalogue no: **CIFCD 1**
12" Single: Released Jun '89, on Fiction, by Fiction Records. Catalogue no: **CIFX 1**

SUMMER IN THE CITY
Tracks: / Summer in the city / Gyrate.
7" Single: Released 31 Jul '89, on Fiction, by Fiction Records. Catalogue no: **CIF 2**
12" Single: Released 31 Jul '89, on Fiction, by Fiction Records. Catalogue no: **CIFX 2**
CD 5": Released 31 Jul '89, on Fiction, by Fiction Records. Catalogue no: **CIFCD 2**

Eat At Joe's

DON'T RUN AWAY
Tracks: / Don't run away.
7" Single: Released Nov '81, on Goldliner, Catalogue no: **EAT 1**

Eaton, Cleveland

Biographical details: This American bass guitarist and keyboards player played bass with Ramsey Lewis' band during the late 60's and early 70's. Lewis,a renowned keyboardist, also employed future Earth Wind & Fire leader Maurice White for a considerable poertion of this era. Eaton eventually went solo and issued a series of nondescript albums. He achieved his sole British chart entry in 1978 - *Bama boogie woogie*, a dreary disco offering, transferred itself from the dancefloor to the no.35 slot on the pop chart, despite a dearth of radio airplay. His LP's have includd *Half and half, Instant hip* and *Keep love alive*, all featuring his brand of jazz-funk. (Bob Macdonald, 21/7/85).

IT'S A SHAME
Tracks: / It's a shame / Cryin' tears for you.
7" Single: Released Jan '80, on Miracle, by Gull Records. Deleted '83. Catalogue no: **M 14**

E.A.V.

BA-BA-BANK ROBBERY
Tracks: / Ba-ba-bank robbery / Ba-ba-bank ubersall.
7" Single: Released Aug '86, on Columbia, by EMI Records. Deleted Jul '87. Catalogue no: **DB 9139**

Eazie Ryder

MOTORBIKIN'
Tracks: / Motorbikin'.
7" Single: on Graduate, by Graduate Records. Deleted Jan '87. Catalogue no: **GRAD 1**

Ebb, Nitzer

CONTROL I'M HERE
Tracks: / Control I'm here.
CD 5": Released Sep '88, on Mute, by Mute Records. Catalogue no: **CDMUTE 71**
12" Single: Released Oct '88, on Mute, by Mute Records. Catalogue no: **12 MUTE 71**
7" Single: Released Oct '88, on Mute, by Mute Records. Catalogue no: **MUTE 71**

HEARTS AND MINDS
Tracks: / Hearts and minds.
CD 5": Released 16 Jan '89, on Mute, by Mute Records. Catalogue no: **CDMUTE 78**
12" Single: Released 16 Jan '89, on Mute, by Mute Records. Catalogue no: **L12MUTE 78**
12" Single: Released Dec '88, on Mute, by Mute Records. Catalogue no: **12MUTE 078**
7" Single: Released 16 Jan '89, on Mute, by Mute Records. Catalogue no: **MUTE 78**

ISN'T IT FUNNY HOW YOUR BODY WORKS
Tracks: / Isn't it funny how your body works.
7" EP: Released Jan '85, on Power Of Voice, by Power Of Voice Records. Catalogue no: **NEP 1**

JOIN IN THE CHANT
Tracks: / Join in the chant.
7" Single: Released Aug '87, on Mute, by Mute Records. Catalogue no: **MUTE 64**
12" Single: Released Aug '87, on Mute, by Mute Records. Catalogue no: **12 MUTE 64**

LET YOUR BODY LEARN
Tracks: / Let your body learn / Let your body learn (inst version) / Get clean.
7" Single: Released May '86, on Power Of Voice, by Power Of Voice Records. Catalogue no: **NEB 3**
7" Single: Released Apr '87, on Mute, by Mute Records. Catalogue no: **MUTE 58**
12" Single: Released Apr '87, on Mute, by Mute Records. Catalogue no: **12 MUTE 58**

MURDEROUS
Tracks: / Murderous / Fitness to purpose.
7" Single: Released Nov '86, on Mute, by Mute Records. Catalogue no: **7 NEB 4**

SHAME
Tracks: / Shame.
7" Single: Released Aug '89, on Mute, by Mute Records. Catalogue no: **MUTE 96**
12" Single: Released Aug '89, on Mute, by Mute Records. Catalogue no: **12 MUTE 96**

WARSAW GHETTO
Tracks: / Warsaw ghetto / Warsaw ghetto (dub mix) / Warsaw ghetto (rap mix) / So bright so strong (7" version.).
12" Single: Released Oct '85, on Power Of Voice, by Power Of Voice Records. Catalogue no: **NEP 2**
12" Single: Released Mar '86, on Power Of Voice, by Power Of Voice Records. Catalogue no: **NEBX 2**

Ebeneezer

AFRICA SAYS THANK YOU
Tracks: / Africa says thank you.
12" Single: Released Dec '85, on Nadiya, Catalogue no: **NAD 02**

Eberlee

RISE TO THE TOP
Tracks: / Rise to the top.
7" Single: Released May '88, on In Tape, by In Tape Records. Catalogue no: **IT 050**
12" Single: Released May '88, on In Tape, by In Tape Records. Catalogue no: **ITTI 050**

EBN-OZN

A E I O U (SOMETIMES Y)
Tracks: / A E I O U (sometimes Y).
12" Single: Released Sep '84, on Arista, by BMG Records (UK). Catalogue no: **ARIST 12 536**
7" Single: Released Sep '84, on Arista, by BMG Records (UK). Catalogue no: **ARIST 536**

Ebony

SILLY WASN'T I
Tracks: / Silly wasn't I.
7" Single: Released Jun '89, on Mango, by Island Records. Catalogue no: **MNG 106**
12" Single: Released Jun '89, on Mango, by Island Records. Catalogue no: **12MNG 106**

Ebony Brothers

BRIGHTEN UP YOUR NIGHT
Tracks: / Brighten up your night / Touch is hot.
7" Single: Released Nov '83, on RCA, by BMG Records (UK). Catalogue no: **RCA 376**

Ebony Eyes

DON'T CALL ME, I'LL CALL YOU
Tracks: / Don't call me (I'll call you) / Don't call me (I'll call you) (dub).
12" Single: Released May '87, on Independent Soul Recordings, Catalogue no: **KEVT 3**

Ebony Rockers

STEPPIN' OUT
Tracks: / Steppin' out / Human jungle.
12" Single: Released Jan '81, on EMI, by EMI Records. Deleted Jan '84. Catalogue no: **12 EMI 5127**

Ebony Sisters

I MUST BE DREAMING
Tracks: / I must be dreaming.
12" Single: Released Sep '85, on Jama, Catalogue no: **JADC 0010**

Ebor Brass

CHINESE JUNK
Tracks: / Chinese junk.
7" Single: Released Jun '82, on Superville, Catalogue no: **SUP 002**

Eccleton & Jarrett

GREEDY GIRL
Tracks: / Greedy girl / Fling it up.
12" Single: Released Apr '84, on CF, Catalogue no: **CFD 010**

Echo & The Bunnymen

Biographical details: This British rock band consists of Pete de Freitas, Ian McCulloch, Les Pattinson and Will Sergeant. De Freitas joined the band as drummer in October 1979; when the other three men formed the group in 1978, they used a drum machine which they nicknamed "Echo" - they decided to retain the name even after the demise of Echo himself. Leader McCulloch first attracted attention in his native Liverpool in 1977. That was the year in which he was a member of The Crucial Three, a very short-lived trio who were instrumental in helping to revitalise Liverpool as acauldron of new musical talent; the other members were Julian Cope, who went on to form the Teardrop Explodes, and Pete Wylie, who became leader of Wah! Like so many of their peers in the city, Echo & the Bunnymen played their first gigs at Eric's club in Matthew Street. Their debut single *Pictures on my wall* was released in early 1979. By 1980 they were becoming the darlings of Britain's rock press, who saw the band as original and experimental despite certain similarities to the Doors. The group enjoyed their debut UK chart successes in 1980 with the single *Rescue* and the album *Crocodiles*. Since then Echo & the Bunnymen have gone from strength to strength on the British charts, while continuing to reside in credibility corner as far as the press are concerned. This combination of unpredictable music and critical acclaim has brought them Top 10 LP's with *Heaven up here* (1981), *Porcupine* (1983), and *Ocean rain* (1984) and Top 10 singles with *The Cutter* (no.8) and *The killing man* (no.9). (Bob Macdonald, 7/85)
A pst punk band of Liverpool's 'second wave' of the late 70's. vocalist/guitarist Ian McCulloch began in the Crucial Three, with Pete Wylie (later Wah!) and Julian Cope (later Teardrop Explodes); McCulloch and Cope were also in A Shallow Madness in

1978. Echo first gigged at Eric's Club in 1978, the period's equivalent of the Cavern; Echo was the name of their drum machine. They soon achieved mass popularity with unusual gigs such as A Crystal Day in 1983 (A 24 hour Liverpool event culminating in an Echo concert) and a tour of remote Scottish Islands; they were the first rock band to play at the Royal Shakespeare Company theatre in Stratford. Frontman Culloch gave good copy, rarely out of the music pressin 1985, opinionated and fiercely proud of the group and of Liverpool. (Donald Clarke, April 1989).

BACK OF LOVE
Tracks: / Back of love.
7" Single: Released May '82, on Korova, by WEA Records. Catalogue no: **KOW 24**
12" Single: Released May '82, on Korova, by WEA Records. Catalogue no: **KOW 24T**

BRING ON THE DANCING HORSES
Tracks: / Bring on the dancing horses.
12" Single: Released Oct '85, on Korova, by WEA Records. Deleted Jan '88. Catalogue no: **KOW 43T**
7" Single: Released Oct '85, on Korova, by WEA Records. Catalogue no: **KOW 43**

CROCODILES (SINGLE)
Tracks: / Crocodiles.
7" Single: Released Apr '81, on Korova, by WEA Records. Deleted '86. Catalogue no: **ECHO 1**

CUTTER, THE
Tracks: / Cutter, The / Villiers Terrace (Available on cassingle only) / Ashes to ashes (Available on cassingle only.) / Monkeys (Available on cassingle only.) / Read it in books (Available on cassingle only.).
7" Single: Released Jan '83, on Korova, by WEA Records. Deleted Jun '87. Catalogue no: **KOW 26**
12" Single: Released Jan '83, on Korova, by WEA Records. Deleted Jan '88. Catalogue no: **KOW 26T**

GAME, THE
Tracks: / Game, The.
7" Single: Released 30 May '87, on WEA, by WEA Records. Deleted Jul '88. Catalogue no: **YZ 134**
12" Single: Released 30 May '87, on WEA, by WEA Records. Deleted Jul '88. Catalogue no: **YZ 134T**

KILLING MOON
Tracks: / Killing moon.
12" Single: Released Jan '84, on Korova, by WEA Records. Deleted Jan '88. Catalogue no: **KOW 32T**
7" Single: Released Jan '84, on Korova, by WEA Records. Deleted Jun '87. Catalogue no: **KOW 32**

LIPS LIKE SUGAR
Tracks: / Lips like sugar / Rollercoaster / People are strange (Extra track on 12").
7" Single: Released Jul '87, on WEA, by WEA Records. Deleted Jul '88. Catalogue no: **YZ 144**
12" Single: Released Jul '87, on WEA, by WEA Records. Catalogue no: **YZ 144T**

NEVER STOP
Tracks: / Never stop.
7" Single: Released Jul '83, on Korova, by WEA Records. Deleted Jun '87. Catalogue no: **KOW 28**
12" Single: Released Jul '83, on Korova, by WEA Records. Deleted Jan '88. Catalogue no: **KOW 28T**

PEEL SESSIONS: ECHO & THE BUNNYMEN
Tracks: / Read it in books / Stars are stars / I bagsy yours / Villiers terrace.
12" Single: Released Oct '88, on Strange Fruit, by Strange Fruit Records. Catalogue no: **SFPS 060**
CD 5": Released Oct '88, on Strange Fruit, by Strange Fruit Records. Catalogue no: **SFPSCD 060**

PEOPLE ARE STRANGE
Tracks: / People are strange.
7" Single: Released Feb '88, on WEA, by WEA Records. Catalogue no: **YZ 175**
12" Single: Released Feb '88, on WEA, by WEA Records. Catalogue no: **YZ 175T**

PROMISE, A
Tracks: / Promise, A / Broke my neck.
12" Single: Released Jul '81, on Korova, by WEA Records. Catalogue no: **KOW 15T**
7" Single: Released Jul '81, on Korova, by WEA Records. Catalogue no: **KOW 15**

PUPPET
Tracks: / Puppet / Do it clean.
7" Single: Released Sep '80, on Korova, by WEA Records. Deleted '81. Catalogue no: **KOW 11**

RESCUE
Tracks: / Rescue.
12" Single: Released Apr '80, on Korova, by WEA Records. Catalogue no: **KOW 1T**
7" Single: Released Apr '80, on Korova, by WEA Records. Catalogue no: **KOW 1**

RESUE
Tracks: / Resue / Simple stuff.
7" Single: Released Apr '80, on Korova, by WEA Records. Deleted Apr '83. Catalogue no: **KOW 1**

SEVEN SEAS
Tracks: / Seven seas.
12" Single: Released Jun '84, on Korova, by WEA Records. Deleted Jun '87. Catalogue no: **KOW 35T**
7" Single: Released Jun '84, on Korova, by WEA Records. Deleted Jun '87. Catalogue no: **KOW 35**

SILVER
Tracks: / Silver / Angels and devils.
12" Single: Released May '84, on Korova, by WEA Records. Catalogue no: **KOW 34T**

Echo Valley Boys

HILLBILLY ROCK
Tracks: / Wash machine boogie / Breaking hearts / Dark hollow / Born with the blues.
7" EP: Released 15 Feb '88, on Rollercoaster, by Rollercoaster Records. Catalogue no: **RCEP 106**

WASH MACHINE BOOGIE
Tracks: / Wash machine boogie.
7" Single: Released Jul '79, on Rollercoaster, by Rollercoaster Records. Deleted '87. Catalogue no: **RRC 2003**

Eckstine, Billy

Biographical details: This American singer, born in Pittsburgh, Pennsylvania in 1913, took up singing at the age of 11. After his family moved to Washington DC, he developed his contrasting interests in music and football. He could not decide which of these talents would make a better career; but the choice was made for him when, after gaining an athletic scholarship to a university, he broke his collar bone. His big break as a singer came in 1939, when bandleader Earl Hines spotted him performing in a Chicago club. Eckstine became the ensemble's regular vocalist, and stayed with them for four years. During his time with Hines, Eckstine was joined on vocals by a young protege names Sarah Vaughan. When Billy formed his own band in 1944, he employed Sarah plus a host of talented musicians: his orchestra proved to be a training ground for such future jazz stars as Art Blakey, Miles Davis, Dizzy Gillespie and Charlie Parker. Billy and his band scored two smash hits in the mid-forties with *Cottage for sale* and *Prisoner of love*. The orchestra disbanded in 1947, and Eckstine became a solo recording artists and performer. During the late forties and early fifties, his baritone crooning made him one of America's top singers. His string of jazzy hits included *Everything I have is yours, Blue moon, Caravan, My foolish heart* and *I apologise* - many of these numbers were drawn from the Thirties. These American hits took place before the British charts were inaugurated, but Eckstine enjoyed a big UK chart hit at the end of '54 - *No-one but you* reached no.3. in 1959 he reached the UK no.8 position with his rendition of *Gigi*, the theme from the smash musical. In duet with Sarah Vaughan, he achieved a belated British no.17 hit in 1969 with their 1957 recording of *Passing strangers*. Mr. B, as he was known, influenced many singers with his individual style of phrasing, and was one of the first jazz vocalists to achieve a worldwide reputation. (Bob Macdonald, 22/7/85)
The American jazz-balladeer with the deep velvet voice was born William Clarence Eckstein in 1914 in Pittsburgh; he also played trumpet, valve trombone and guitar. He sang with Earl Hines 1939-43, then led one of the most influential bands of the day 1944 47 with tenor saxist/arranger Budd Johnson, sidemen at various times including Gene Ammons, Art Blakey, Miles Davies, Kenny Dorham, Dizzy Gillespie, Dexter Gordon, Fats Navarro, Lucky Thompson, Charlie Parker, singing partners Lena Horne and Sara Vaughan, arrangements by Tadd Dameron and others as well as Johnson (who by the way worked for all the most influential bands of the day--Woody Herman, Hines, Eckstine and Body Raeburn--and whose influence is underrated). This fine outfit was unsuccessful commercially: the music business didn't give a damn and musicians' union strikes hurt studio recording *Together* on Spotlite for example is an Armed Forces Network recording). Eckstine led an octet briefly then took his big beautiful voice to market and had many hits, including duets with Sassy. He is still one of the USA's favourite entertainers and there was recently a flurry of record activity in the USA: a two-disc compilation *Everything I have is yours* of 1949-57 hit tracks and a new album *Billy Eckstine sings with Benny Carter* with guest Helen Merrill (nominated for a Grammy); whether Polgram will be bothered to let the UK see them is the question. (Donald Clarke, April 1989).

GIGI
Tracks: / Gigi.
7" Single: Released Feb '59, on Mercury (EMI), Deleted '64. Catalogue no: **AMT 1018**

NO ONE BUT YOU
Tracks: / No one but you.
7" Single: Released Sep '57, on MGM, by Polydor Ltd. Deleted '62. Catalogue no: **MGM 164**

PASSING STRANGERS
Tracks: / Passing strangers.
78 rpm: Released '57, on Mercury (Pye), Deleted '58. Catalogue no: **MT 164**
7" Single: Released Mar '69, on Mercury, by Phonogram Ltd. Deleted '74. Catalogue no: **MF 1082**

Eclipse

MESSIAH
Tracks: / Messiah.
7" Single: Released Oct '82, on Clubland, Catalogue no: **SJP 832**

MICHAEL ROW THE BOAT ASHORE
Tracks: / Michael row the boat ashore.
7" Single: Released Jul '83, on Mellowdance, Catalogue no: **MD 1**

Ecosse, Kevin

WE'VE GOTTA TRY
Tracks: / We've gotta try.
7" Single: Released Jan '89, on Silverwood Records, Catalogue no: **SVR 110**

Ecstasy Club

DOING IT DEEP
Tracks: / Doing it deep.
12" Single: Released 6 Feb '89, on Swordfish, by Swordfish Records. Catalogue no: **DROP 002**

JESUS LOVES ACID
Tracks: / Jesus loves acid.
12" Single: Released '89, on Licensed, Catalogue no: **LD 8926**
7" Single: Released Nov '88, on Swordfish, by Swordfish Records. Catalogue no: **DROP 1**

Eddi

I DON'T WANT TO LOSE YOU
Tracks: / I don't want to lose you.
12" Single: Released Mar '82, on PC, Catalogue no: **PCDD 001**

Eddie

FARTHER ON DOWN THE ROAD
Tracks: / Farther on down the road / Fish 'n' chips.
7" Single: Released Apr '81, on EMI, by EMI Records. Deleted '85. Catalogue no: **EMI 5160**

Eddie, John

JUNGLE BOY
Tracks: / Jungle boy / Gay's ghost.
7" Single: Released Jul '86, on CBS, by CBS Records. Catalogue no: **A 7097**
12" Single: Released Aug '86, on CBS, by CBS Records. Catalogue no: **TA 7097**

Eddie & Sunshine

ALL I SEE IS YOU
Tracks: / All I see is you / Somewhere else in Europe.
7" Single: Released Feb '83, on Survival (1), by Survival Records. Catalogue no: **SUR 010**
12" Single: Released Feb '83, on Survival (1), by Survival Records. Catalogue no: **SUR 12 010**

PERFECT STRANGER
Tracks: / Perfect stranger.
12" Single: Released Jun '83, on Survival (1), by Survival Records. Catalogue no: **SUR 12 014**
7" Single: Released Jun '83, on Survival (1), by Survival Records. Catalogue no: **SUR 014**

THERE'S SOMEONE FOLLOWING ME
Tracks: / There's someone following me.
12" Single: Released Mar '83, on Survival (1), by Survival Records. Catalogue no: **SUR 12 018**
7" Single: Released Mar '83, on Survival (1), by Survival Records. Catalogue no: **SUR 018**

Eddie & The Hot Rods

Biographical details: A rock band formed in Southend in the mid-'70's, a link between pub rock and punk: vocalist Barrie Masters, guitarist Dave Higgs, bassist Paul Gray, drummer Steve Nicol. They were at first augmented by harmonica player Lew Lewis, whose early departure was due to the groups re-orientation towards punk; they were not genuine punks but were delighted to be adopted. Graeme Douglas from Kursaal Flyers was added on lead guitar in 1977. Douglas left; Masters disbanded and sang with the Inmates, Gray joined the Damned, then reformed Eddie & The Hot Rods with new members, sounding much like Dr Feelgoods on a live album *One story town* for Waterfront. (Donald Clarke, April 1989).

AT NIGHT
Tracks: / At night / You better run / Looking around.
7" Single: Released Mar '80, on EMI, by EMI Records. Deleted Mar '83. Catalogue no: **EMI 5052**

DO ANYTHING YOU WANNA DO
Tracks: / Do anything you wanna do.
7" Single: Released Aug '77, on Island, by Island Records. Deleted '83. Catalogue no: **WIP 6401**

FOUGHT FOR YOU
Tracks: / Fought for you.
7" Single: Released Feb '85, on Waterfront, by Waterfront Music. Catalogue no: **WFS 9**

I MIGHT BE LYING
Tracks: / I might be lying.
7" Single: Released Apr '77, on Island, by Island Records. Deleted '82. Catalogue no: **WIP 6388**

LIVE AT THE MARQUEE
Tracks: / 96 tears / Get out of Denver / Gloria / Satisfaction.
7" EP: Released Sep '76, on Island, by Island Records. Deleted '81. Catalogue no: **IEP 2**

QUIT THIS TOWN
Tracks: / Quit this town.
7" Single: Released Jan '78, on Island, by Island Records. Deleted '83. Catalogue no: **WIP 6411**

TEENAGE DEPRESSION
Tracks: / Teenage depression.
7" Single: Released Nov '76, on Island, by Island Records. Deleted '81. Catalogue no: **WIP 6354**
7" Single: Released Dec '76, on Island, by Island Records. Deleted '79. Catalogue no: **ILPS 9457**

WIDE EYED KIDS
Tracks: / Wide eyed kids / Leave us alone.
7" Single: Released Nov '80, on EMI, by EMI Records. Deleted Nov '83. Catalogue no: **EMI 5110**

Eddy, Duane

Biographical details: This American guitarist and composer, born in Corning, New York, became known as the inventor of the "twangy" guitar sound. He took up the instrument at the age of five, and moved with his family to Phoenix, Arizona just as he was entering his teens. Upon leaving school in the mid fifties, he received training from two highly respected guitarists, Al Casey and Jim Wybele. In 1957 Eddy was signed to a recording contract by Lee Hazlewood, who was a local disc jockey. Hazlewood became his record producer and co-writer, and Duane's debut single *Movin'n'groovin* was issued in '58; it was credited to Duane Eddy & The Rebels, the Rebels being his newly formed backing group. That first record was not acommercial success, but it was the first example of the Eddy sound. He and Lee hit upon the unique twangy sound by chance - Eddy played a melody on the bass strings, and it worked a treat; with the added gimmick of a flexible tremolo arm, the pair developed this novel sound into a major record-selling proposition. Eddy's breakthrough occurred later in 1958, when *Rebel rouser* reached no.6 on the US charts. With Hazlewood's astute prosuction and the Rebels' strong back-up work, Eddy achieved a string of hits which lasted till 1963. He was particularly popular in Britain, where he hit the Top 10 with *Peter Gunn theme, Shazam, Pepe, Theme from Dixie* and *Paladin*. Some of the singles were Eddy/Hazlewood compositions, while others were TV and film themes. The biggest record of his career was 1960's *Because they're young*, which was the title theme to the film in which Duane made his movie debut. Despite brief attempts to feshen his sound by adding female backing vocals (the Rebelettes), Eddy's chart career was more or less over by the time the Beatles appeared. During the late 60's and early 70's, Hazlewood dveloped a career as a singer, and achieved hits in duet with Nancy Sinatra; meanwhile, Duane enjoyed steady but unspectacular success touring round Europe. Duane did, however, manage a one-off comeback on the charts in 1975 - *Play me like you play your guitar*, a ditty penned by Britain's Tony Macaulay, reached the UK

no.9 position. (Bob Macdonald, 22/7/85)
Rock'n'roll guitarist born in New York State in 1938. He moved to Phoenix at 13, already playing; local deejay/promoter Lee Hazlewood and guitarist Al Casey helped invent the gimmick of 'twangy' sound: his instrumental hits had simple melody lines played on bass strings, heavily amplified; his second single was the top five Rebel rouser in 1958, and he toured with Dick Clark including Casey, Steve Douglas on sax, Larry Knechtel on piano, had more top 40's and a long low-key career. He produced an album by Phil Everly in 1973, had UK top ten *Play me like you play your guitar* in 1975; *You are my sunshine* on Asylum in 1977 was produced with vocals by Willie Nelson and Waylon Jennings (married to Eddy's ex-wife Jesse Colter). (Donald Clarke, April 1989).

BALLAD OF PALADIN
Tracks: / Ballad of Paladin.
7" Single: Released Aug '62, on RCA, by BMG Records (UK). Deleted '67. Catalogue no: **RCA 1300**

BECAUSE THEY'RE YOUNG
Tracks: / Because they're young.
7" Single: Released Jul '60, on London-American, Catalogue no: **HLW 9162**

BONNIE CAME BACK
Tracks: / Bonnie come back.
7" Single: Released Feb '60, on London-American, Deleted '65. Catalogue no: **HLW 9050**

BOSS GUITAR
Tracks: / Boss guitar.
7" Single: Released Feb '63, on RCA, by BMG Records (UK). Deleted '68. Catalogue no: **RCA 1329**

CANNONBALL
Tracks: / Cannonball.
7" Single: Released Jan '59, on London Records, by London Records. Deleted '64. Catalogue no: **HL 8764**

CARAVAN
Tracks: / Caravan.
7" Single: Released Oct '61, on Parlophone, by EMI Records. Deleted '66. Catalogue no: **R 4826**

DANCE WITH THE GUITAR MAN (SINGLE)
Tracks: / Dance with the guitar man.
7" Single: Released Nov '62, on RCA, by BMG Records (UK). Deleted '67. Catalogue no: **RCA 1316**

DEEP IN THE HEART OF TEXAS
Tracks: / Deep in the heart of Texas.
7" Single: Released May '62, on RCA, by BMG Records (UK). Deleted '67. Catalogue no: **RCA 1288**

DIXIE
Tracks: / Dixie.
7" Single: Released Apr '61, on London-American, Deleted '66. Catalogue no: **HLW 9324**

DRIVIN' HOME
Tracks: / Drivin' home.
7" Single: Released Sep '61, on London-American, Deleted '66. Catalogue no: **HLW 9406**

FORTY MILES OF BAD ROAD
Tracks: / Forty miles of bad world / Forty miles of bad road / Raindrops / Honky tonk.
7" Single: Released Aug '82, on Creole, by Creole Records. Catalogue no: **CB 194**
7" Single: Released Aug '82, on Blast From The Past, by Creole Records. Catalogue no: **CR 194**

FORTY MILES OF BAD ROAD (ORIGINAL)
Tracks: / Forty miles of bad road.
7" Single: Released Sep '59, on London-American, Deleted '64. Catalogue no: **HLW 8929**

KOMMOTION
Tracks: / Kommotion.
7" Single: Released Nov '60, on London-American, Deleted '65. Catalogue no: **HLW 9225**

LONELY BOY LONELY GUITAR
Tracks: / Lonely boy lonely guitar.
7" Single: Released May '63, on RCA, by BMG Records (UK). Deleted '68. Catalogue no: **RCA 1344**

PEPE
Tracks: / Pepe.
7" Single: Released Jan '61, on London-American, Deleted '66. Catalogue no: **HLW 9257**

PETER GUNN THEME
Tracks: / Peter Gunn.
7" Single: Released Jun '59, on London-American, Deleted '64. Catalogue no: **HLW 8879**

PLAY ME LIKE YOU PLAY YOUR GUITAR
Tracks: / Play me like you play your guitar.
7" Single: Released Mar '75, on GTO, Deleted '80. Catalogue no: **GT 11**

REBEL ROUSER
Tracks: / Rebel rouser / Rockin' Robin / Pony time.
7" Single: Released Aug '82, on Creole, by Creole Records. Deleted Aug '85. Catalogue no: **CR 185**
7" Single: Released Aug '82, on Creole, by Creole Records. Catalogue no: **CB 185**

REBEL ROUSER (ORIGINAL)
Tracks: / Rebel rouser.
7" Single: Released Sep '58, on London Records, by London Records. Deleted '63. Catalogue no: **HL 8669**

RING OF FIRE
Tracks: / Ring of fire.
7" Single: Released Jun '61, on London-American, Deleted '66. Catalogue no: **HLW 9370**

ROCKESTRA THEME
Tracks: / Rockestra theme / Blue city.
7" Single: Released Sep '87, on Capitol, by EMI Records. Deleted 31 Jul '88. Catalogue no: **CL 463**
12" Single: Released Sep '87, on Capitol, by EMI Records. Deleted Nov '88. Catalogue no: **12CL 463**

SHAZAM (SINGLE)
Tracks: / Shazam.
7" Single: Released Apr '60, on London-American, Deleted '65. Catalogue no: **HLW 9104**

SOME KINDA EARTHQUAKE
Tracks: / Some kinda earthquake.
7" Single: Released Dec '59, on London-American, Deleted '64. Catalogue no: **HLW 9007**

SPECIALLY FOR YOU
7" Single: Released Oct '59, on London-American, Deleted '64. Catalogue no: **HAW 2191**

YEP
Tracks: / Yep.
7" Single: Released Jul '59, on London-American, Deleted '64. Catalogue no: **HLW 8879**

YOUR BABY'S GONE SURFIN'
Tracks: / Your baby's gone surfin'.
7" Single: Released Aug '63, on RCA, by BMG Records (UK). Deleted '68. Catalogue no: **RCA 1357**

Edelman, Randy

Biographical details: This American singer, songwriter and pianist released his eponymous debut album in 1972.
As h moved into the mid seventies, Edelman's records featured back-up vocal and instrumental assistance from some of the top session musicians in the business, but his discs were totally unappreciated in his native country.
However, 1976 brought him two Top 30 singles in Britain: *Concrete and clay*, a remake of Unit Four Plus Two's 1965 UK no.1, took him to no.11; and he peaked at a surprisingly low no.25 with the acclaimed MoR ballad *Uptown uptempo woman*. Edelman's only taste of American success was as a writer rather than as a performer. Barry Manilow recorded *Weekend in New England*, another fine love ballad, and took it to the US no.10 slot in early 1977.
Edelman continued issuing albums into the 80's but, apart from a very minor UK hit single with *Nobody made me* in 1962, these offerings fell on deaf ears. Despite the clever melodies and perceptive lyrics of *Uptown uptempo woman* and *Weekend in New England* he never reaped the commercial rewards that these talents had seemed to promise.
(Bob Macdonald, 22/7/85).

BARBARA
Tracks: / Barbara / Is Mr Edelman home.
7" Single: Released Feb '82, on Rocket, by Rocket Records. Deleted '85. Catalogue no: **XPRES 73**

CARE-A-LOT
Tracks: / Care-a-lot / Care bears theme.
7" Single: Released Oct '85, on Cherry Lane, by Cherry Lane Productions. Deleted '86. Catalogue no: **PIP 714**

CONCRETE & CLAY
Tracks: / Concrete and clay.
7" Single: Released Mar '75, on 20th Century, by 20th Century Records. Deleted '80. Catalogue no: **BTC 2261**

GROWING OLDER
Tracks: / Growing older.
7" Single: Released Aug '85, on Elecstar, by Elecstar Records. Deleted '88. Catalogue no: **VCL 10**

HALF HEAVEN-HALF HEARTACHE
Tracks: / Half heaven - half heartache / Wings (London/L.A.).
7" Single: Released Sep '82, on Rocket, by Rocket Records. Catalogue no: **XPRES 86**

NOBODY MADE ME
Tracks: / Nobody made me / Is Mr. Edelman home?.
7" Single: Released Jun '82, on Rocket, by Rocket Records. Catalogue no: **XPRES 81**

PRETTY GIRLS
Tracks: / Pretty girls / Round fourteen.
7" Single: Released Nov '82, on Rocket, by Rocket Records. Catalogue no: **XPRES 87**

UPTOWN UPTEMPO WOMAN
Tracks: / Uptown uptempo woman / Concrete and clay.
7" Single: Released Sep '76, on 20th Century, by 20th Century Records. Deleted '81. Catalogue no: **BTC 2225**

UPTOWN,UPTEMPO WOMAN
Tracks: / Uptown, uptempo woman.
7" Single: Released Jan '85, on Old Gold, by Old Gold Records. Catalogue no: **OG 9488**

YOU
Tracks: / You.
7" Single: Released Jan '77, on 20th Century, by 20th Century Records. Deleted '82. Catalogue no: **BTC 2253**

Edelweiss

BRING ME EDELWEISS
Tracks: / Bring me Edelweiss / Bring me Edelweiss (version).

CD 5": Released Dec '88, on WEA, by WEA Records. Catalogue no: **YZ 353CD**
12" Single: Released Dec '88, on WEA, by WEA Records. Catalogue no: **YZ 353T**
7" Single: Released Dec '88, on WEA, by WEA Records. Catalogue no: **YZ 353**

Eden

AMERICAN DREAM
Tracks: / American dream / Lady flame.
7" Single: Released May '82, on PRT, by Castle Communications Records. Deleted May '85. Catalogue no: **PRT 7P237**

FREE
Tracks: / Free.
12" Single: Released Jun '85, on Polydor, by Polydor Ltd. Catalogue no: **EDEX 1**
7" Single: Released Jun '85, on Polydor, by Polydor Ltd. Catalogue no: **EDE 1**

Eden, John

WORKING ON THE LAND
Tracks: / Working on the land.
7" Single: Released Aug '80, on MCA, by MCA Records. Deleted '8?. Catalogue no: **MCA 627**

Edge

HEROINE (Theme from 'Captive')
Tracks: / Heroine / Heroine (mix II).
12" Single: Released Sep '86, on Virgin, by Virgin Records. Catalogue no: **VS 897-12**
7" Single: Released Sep '86, on Virgin, by Virgin Records. Catalogue no: **VS 897**

LITTLE GIRL BLUE
Tracks: / Little girl blue.
12" Single: Released Mar '86, on Volume (1), by Volume Records. Catalogue no: **VOLT 19**
7" Single: Released Mar '86, on Volume (1), by Volume Records. Catalogue no: **VOL 19**

TAKE A WALK
Tracks: / Take a walk.
7" Single: Released Sep '85, on Dead Volume, Deleted '88. Catalogue no: **VOL 016**
12" Single: Released Sep '85, on Dead Volume, Deleted '88. Catalogue no: **VOLT 016**

Edge Brothers

COCONUT GIRL
Tracks: / Coconut girl.
7" Single: Released Aug '83, on Code, by Code Records. Catalogue no: **COD 007**
12" Single: Released Aug '83, on Code, by Code Records. Catalogue no: **12 COD 007**

VIDEO
Tracks: / Video.
7" Single: Released Nov '82, on Edge, Deleted '84. Catalogue no: **EDGE 1**

Edge, Dave

NEW WORLD
Tracks: / New world.
7" Single: Released Nov '81, on Clay, by Clay Records. Deleted '88. Catalogue no: **CLAY 7**

Edinburgh Choristers

TELL US 13th Commonwealth games
Tracks: / Tell us ((13th commonwealth games commemorative song)) / Tell us (Inst).
7" Single: Released Jul '86, on PRT, by Castle Communications Records. Catalogue no: **PRT 7P**

Edison Lighthouse

Biographical details: The official line-up of this British pop group was Ray Dorey, Stuart Edwards, David Taylor and George Weyman. However, their one-off smash hit featured the lead vocals of Tony Burrows.
The previously unknown Edison Lighthouse crashed into the UK singles charts at no.12 in 1970 with *Love grows (where my Rosemary goes)*; seven days later they were at no.1 and they stayed there for five weeks
The band was really the studio creation of producer Tony Macaulay, who co-wrote the song with another of the UK's top songsmiths, Barry MAson. It was a perfect pop single - deliriously catchy, lightweight, dynamically arranged and well executed. Tony Burrows, who had enjoyed sixties success with the Ivy League and the Flowerpot men, set a new record in February 1970 by appearing three times in the same edition of "Top of the Pops" - his lead vocal talents were employed also on White Plains' *My baby loves lovin'* and Brotherhood Of Man's *United we stand*. 1970 was certainly Burrows' peak year, although he popped up again as late as 1974 on First Class' transatlantic hit *Beach baby*.
Despite the official line-up's attempts to win success in their own right, the name of Edison Lighthouse could climb no higher than no.49 with the second release *It's up to you Petula*. (Bob Macdonald, 22/7/85).

ENDEARING YOUNG CHARMS
Tracks: / Endearing young charms.
7" Single: Released Jun '81, on Greenstone, Catalogue no: **GRN 3441**

IT'S UP TO YOU PETULA
Tracks: / It's up to you Petula.
7" Single: Released Jan '71, on Bell, Deleted '76. Catalogue no: **BELL 1136**

LOVE GROWS (WHERE MY ROSEMARY GOES) (OLD GOLD)
Tracks: / Love grows (where my Rosemary goes) / It's gonna be a lonely Summer.
7" Single: Released 24 Apr '89, on Old Gold, by Old Gold Records. Catalogue no: **OG 9878**
7" Single: Released Apr '83, on Old Gold, by Old Gold Records. Deleted Jul '88. Catalogue no: **OG 9316**

LOVE GROWS (WHERE MY ROSEMARY GROWS)
Tracks: / Love grows (where my Rosemary grows).
7" Single: Released Jan '70, on Bell, Deleted '75. Catalogue no: **BELL 1091**

Edit Point

BRIGHT SIDE
Tracks: / Bright side / Bright side (part 2).
7" Single: Released Jul '81, on PVK, by PVK Records. Catalogue no: **PV 102**
12" Single: Released Jul '81, on PVK, by PVK Records. Catalogue no: **PV 102 K**

HELP YOURSELF
Tracks: / Help yourself.
7" Single: Released Nov '80, on Magnet, by WEA Records. Deleted Nov '83. Catalogue no: **MAG 200**
12" Single: Released Nov '80, on Magnet, by WEA Records. Deleted Nov '83. Catalogue no: **12MAG 200**

Editors

THOUGHT POLICE
Tracks: / Thought police.
7" Single: Released May '81, on Devil, by Devil Records. Catalogue no: **DEV 1**

Edmed, John

CRO 55Q
Tracks: / CRO 55Q.
12" Single: Released Apr '86, on Illuminated, Catalogue no: **12 LEV 69**

Edmonds, Noel

CROQUE MONSIEUR
Tracks: / Croque monsieur / Slice 2.
7" Single: Released Dec '81, on BBC, by BBC Records and Tapes. Deleted '87. Catalogue no: **RESL 107**

Edmunds, Dave

Biographical details:
This British singer, producer, and multi-instrumentalist was born in Cardiff, Wales.
After gaining much experience by playing in various local bands during the 1960's, he came to public attention at the end of 1968 as a member of the group Love Sculpture
However, they were unable to follow up

their UK Top 10 breakneck rendition of *Sabre Dance* and the group folded the following year. Edmunds concentrated on launching a solo career and, to prepare himself for his onslaught on the public, spent many months in his new Rockfield Studios in Monmouth.

Possessing an ardent interest in rock and pop history, Edmunds used this period of self imposed hibernation to teach himself how to recreate perfectly the sounds of his favourite oldies.

The first product of his labours - a remake of the 1955 Smiley Lewis *I hear you knockin'* - shot to no.1 in Britain in late 1970. It stayed at the summit over Christmas, logging six weeks at the top in all; acclaimed by critics and consumers alike, it bacame a no.4 hit in the States. Edmunds' debut solo LP *Rockpile* (named after his occasional backing group) was issued in 1971, but he did not enjoy further singles success until '73.

That year brought him two hits with tributes to Phil Spectors Wall of Sound - *Baby I love you* and *Born to be with you.* During the seventies, Edmunds produced rock'n'roll-flavoured records for a variety of acts at his own studios.

The erratic nature of his own output led to a spasmodic chart career. He made a brief appearance in the Top 30 in 1977 with the frantic *I knew the bride*, but did not make a sustained return to the listings until 1979's *Girls talk* (written by Elvis Costello), which reached no.4.

He followed this with a no.11 hit *Queen of hearts* and a Top 30 remake of *Singing the blues.*

He also played on *Cruel to be kind*, a 1979 biggie by his close friend Nick Lowe. By this time Edmunds' and Lowe's records featured the same band of musicians, Rockpile, but legal complications forced them to release product under their own names.

By the time the hassles were sorted out and Rockpile officially launched in 1980, the results were poor.

During the early 80's, Edmunds faded into the realms of minor hit status. But in his capacity as producer, he enjoyed massive success (most notably in America) with his rock and roll revival proteges, the Stray Cats (Bob Macdonald, 22/7/85)

Rock guitarist, singer and producer born in 1944 in Cardiff.

His cover of Smiley Lewis's *I hear you knockin'* was a UK number one in 1970 and made the USA top 5; he produced albums in the early '70's by Brinsley Schwarz among others, forming friendship with Brinsley bassist Nick Lowe. Edmunds was music director and appeared with David Essex in film *Stardust* 1973.

He formed band Rockpile in 1977 (also the name of one of his early solo albums) with guitarist Billy Bremner, drummer Terry Williams and Lowe; Lowe and Edmunds were part of the first Stiff tour in 1977.

He is always in demand as a producer, credits including Stray Cats, Everly Brothers, Shakin' Stevens, Jeff Beck, Fabulous Thunderbirds, Dr Feelgood etc. He appeared in Paul McCartney's film *Give my regards to Broad Street*

(Donald Clarke, April 1989)I.

ALMOST SATURDAY NIGHT
Tracks: / Almost Saturday night.
7" Single: Released Mar '81, on Swansong, Deleted '86. Catalogue no: **SSK 19424**

BABY I LOVE YOU
Tracks: / Baby I love you / Da doo ron ron / Born to be with you / Shot of rhythm and blues.
7" Single: Released Jul '80, on RCA, by BMG Records (UK). Deleted '83. Catalogue no: **PE 5243**
7" Single: Released May '82, on RCA, by BMG Records (UK). Catalogue no: **GOLD 548**
7" Single: Released Jan '73, on UNKNOWN, Deleted '78. Catalogue no: **ROC 1**

BORN TO BE WITH YOU (OLD GOLD)
Tracks: / Born to be with you / Baby I love you.
7" Single: Released Nov '88, on Old Gold, by Old Gold Records. Catalogue no: **OG 9833**

BORN TO BE WITH YOU (ORIGINAL)
Tracks: / Born to be with you.
7" Single: Released Jun '73, on UNKNOWN, Deleted '78. Catalogue no: **ROC 2**

CRAWLING FROM THE WRECKAGE
Tracks: / Crawling from the wreckage.
7" Single: Released Nov '79, on Swansong, Catalogue no: **SSK 19420**

FROM SMALL THINGS
Tracks: / From small things.
7" Single: Released '82, on Arista, by BMG Records (UK). Deleted '87. Catalogue no: **ARIST 478**

GIRLS TALK (See panel above)
Tracks: / Girls talk / Bad is bad.

Dave Edmunds - Girls Talk (Released on Swansong)

7" Single: Released Jun '79, on Swansong, Deleted '84. Catalogue no: **SSK 19418**

HIGH SCHOOL NIGHTS
Tracks: / High school nights / Porky's revenge.
7" Single: Released Jul '85, on CBS, by CBS Records. Catalogue no: **A 6277**

I HEAR YOU KNOCKING (OLD GOLD)
Tracks: / I hear you knocking / She's about a mover / Sabre dance.
Note: Double 'A' side
7" Single: Released Apr '87, on Old Gold, by Old Gold Records. Catalogue no: **OG 9711**

I HEAR YOU KNOCKING (ORIGINAL)
Tracks: / I hear you knocking.
7" Single: Released Nov '70, on M.A.M, by M.A.M. Records. Deleted '75. Catalogue no: **MAM 1**

I HEAR YOU KNOCKING (SINGLE)
Tracks: / I hear you knocking / Black Bill.
7" Single: Released Mar '84, on EMI Golden 45's, by EMI Records. Deleted Oct '89. Catalogue no: **G45 4**
7" Single: Released Apr '80, on Blue Print, Deleted '83. Catalogue no: **BLU 2010**

I KNEW THE BRIDE
Tracks: / I knew the bride.
7" Single: Released Jul '77, on Swansong, Deleted '82. Catalogue no: **SSK 19411**

ME AND THE BOYS (See panel below)
Tracks: / Me and the boys / Queen of hearts.
7" Single: Released '82, on Arista, by BMG Records (UK). Deleted '87. Catalogue no: **ARIST 471**

QUEEN OF HEARTS
Tracks: / Queen of hearts.
7" Single: Released Nov '79, on Swansong, Deleted '84. Catalogue no: **SSK 19419**

RACE IS ON
Tracks: / Race is on / I'm gonna start living again if it kills me.
7" Single: Released Jun '81, on Swansong, Deleted Jun '84. Catalogue no: **SSK 19425**

RACE IS ON, THE
Tracks: / Race is on, The.
7" Single: Released Jun '81, on Swansong, Deleted '86. Catalogue no: **SSK 19425**

SINGING THE BLUES
Tracks: / Singing the blues / Boys talk.
7" Single: Released Feb '80, on Swansong, Deleted '85. Catalogue no: **SSK 19422**

SLIPPING AWAY
Tracks: / Slipping away.
7" Single: Released Mar '83, on Arista, by BMG Records (UK). Catalogue no: **ARIST 522**
12" Single: Released Mar '83, on Arista, by BMG Records (UK). Catalogue no: **ARIST 12522**

Dave Edmunds - Me and the Boys (Released on Arista)

SOMETHING ABOUT YOU
Tracks: / Something about you.
7" Single: Released Jul '84, on Arista, by BMG Records (UK). Catalogue no: **ARIST 562**
12" Single: Released Jul '84, on Arista, by BMG Records (UK). Catalogue no: **ARIST 12 562**

WARMED OVER KISSES
Tracks: / Warmed over kisses.
7" Single: Released '82, on Arista, by BMG Records (UK). Deleted '87. Catalogue no: **ARIST 439**

Edward II

SWEDISH POLKA
Tracks: / Swedish polka / Swedish polka (version).

12" Single: Released Feb '89, on Cooking Vinyl, by Cooking Vinyl Records. Catalogue no: **FRY 007T**
7" Single: Released Feb '89, on Cooking Vinyl, by Cooking Vinyl Records. Catalogue no: **FRY 007**

Edward, Sandra

ENDLESSLY
Tracks: / Endlessly.
12" Single: Released Nov '84, on Sir George, Catalogue no: **SG 019T**

Edwards, Alton

Biographical details:
This British singer, who also has strong connections with imbabwe, enjoyed a one-off chart success in 1982.
He reached no.20 in that year with his nondescript but danceable single *I just wanna (spend some time with you)* which he cowrote. Subsequent offerings, such as 1983's *Take me* and 1984's *Everybody's watching* failed to impress.
(Bob Macdonald, 22/7/85).

I JUST WANNA (SPEND SOME TIME WITH YOU)
Tracks: / I just wanna (spend some time with you).
7" Single: Released Jan '82, on Streetwave, Deleted '87. Catalogue no: **STRA 1897**

SHINING LIGHT
Tracks: / Shining light / To have a friend.
7" Single: Released Sep '82, on CBS, by CBS Records. Deleted Sep '85. Catalogue no: **A 2767**

STRANGE WOMAN
Tracks: / Strange woman / What love.
12" Single: Released Nov '82, on CBS, by CBS Records. Deleted Nov '85. Catalogue no: **A13 2275**
7" Single: Released Nov '82, on CBS, by CBS Records. Deleted Nov '85. Catalogue no: **A 2275**

TAKE ME
Tracks: / Take me.
7" Single: Released Feb '83, on CBS, by CBS Records. Catalogue no: **A 3146**
12" Single: Released Feb '83, on CBS, by CBS Records. Catalogue no: **A 13 3146**

Edwards, Charlotte

YOU CAN'T BEAT THE FEELING
Tracks: / You can't beat the feeling / Vicious games.

Cassingle: Released Jul '89, on Mercury, by Phonogram Ltd. Catalogue no: **MERMC 297**
7" Single: Released Jul '89, on Mercury, by Phonogram Ltd. Catalogue no: **MER 297**
CD 5": Released Jul '89, on Mercury, by Phonogram Ltd. Catalogue no: **MERCD 297**
12" Single: Released Jul '89, on Mercury, by Phonogram Ltd. Catalogue no: **MERX 297**

Edwards, Dennis

DON'T LOOK ANY FURTHER
Tracks: / Don't look any further / I thought I could handle it.

7" Single: Released Jun '87, on Motown, by BMG Records (UK). Catalogue no: **TMG 1334**
12" Single: Released Jun '87, on Motown, by BMG Records (UK). Catalogue no: **TMGT 1334**

YOU'RE MY APHRODISIAC
Tracks: / You're my aphrodisiac / Shake hands (come out dancin').

12" Single: Released May '84, on Gordy

(USA), by Motown Records (UK). Catalogue no: **TMGT 1340**
7" Single: Released May '84, on Gordy (USA), by Motown Records (UK). Catalogue no: **TMG 1340**

Edwards, Devon

LAY DOWN FLAT
Tracks: / Lay down flat.
12" Single: Released Oct '84, on CF, Catalogue no: **CFD 012**

Edwards, Flaurette

SUPERWOMAN
Tracks: / Superwoman.
12" Single: Released Sep '89, on Steely & Cleevie, Catalogue no: **SCT 2**

Edwards, Idiater

LOVING SWEET DEVOTION
Tracks: / Loving sweet devotion.
12" Single: Released Nov '85, on Pressure, Catalogue no: **HAVE 2**

Edwards, Jackie

ALL SHOOK UP
Tracks: / All shook up (part 1) / All shhok up (part 2).
7" Single: Released Apr '80, on Laser, Deleted Apr '83. Catalogue no: **LAS 30**

BABY COME BACK TO ME
Tracks: / Baby come back to me.
12" Single: Released Apr '83, on Shuttle, Catalogue no: **SH 004**

BEFORE THE NEXT TEARDROP FALLS
Tracks: / Before the next teardrop falls.
12" Single: Released Aug '84, on Tim, by Tim Records. Catalogue no: **TR 001**

CARRY ON HENRY
Tracks: / Carry on Henry.
12" Single: Released Jul '82, on Starlight, Catalogue no: **SLD 523**

PEEPING JUKEBOX
Tracks: / Peeping jukebox.
12" Single: Released Jan '85, on Time, Catalogue no: **TR 8**

TELL THE TRUTH
Tracks: / Tell the truth / Man's mind.
7" Single: Released May '80, on RCA, by BMG Records (UK). Deleted May '83. Catalogue no: **PB 5238**

Edwards, Jayne

HARMONY
Tracks: / Harmony / I got it.
7" Single: Released Oct '83, on RCA, by BMG Records (UK). Catalogue no: **RCA 365**
12" Single: Released Oct '83, on RCA, by BMG Records (UK). Catalogue no: **RCAT 365**

IT SHOULD HAVE BEEN ME
Tracks: / It should have been me / Determination.
7" Single: Released Jun '84, on Profile (USA), by Profile Records (USA). Catalogue no: **RCA 412**
12" Single: Released Jun '84, on Profile (USA), by Profile Records (USA). Catalogue no: **RCAT 412**

Edwards, Jerry

I AM SOMEBODY
Tracks: / I am somebody.
12" Single: Released Apr '89, on Republic, by Code Records. Catalogue no: **LICT 021**
7" Single: Released Mar '89, on Republic, by Code Records. Catalogue no: **LIC 021**

Edwards, Jimmy

IN THE CITY
Tracks: / In the city / Five minute girl.
7" Single: Released Apr '81, on Polydor, by Polydor Ltd. Deleted Apr '84. Catalogue no: **POSP 240**

TOYS
Tracks: / Toys / Hard heart.
7" Single: Released May '80, on Polydor, by Polydor Ltd. Deleted May '83. Catalogue no: **2059240**

Edwards, Keyman

LOVE'S GOT 2 BE STRONG
Tracks: / Love's got 2 be strong / Love's got 2 be strong (house mix) / Love's got 2 be strong (key to the club mix) (on 12" only) / Love's got 2 be strong (underground mix) (on 12" only) / Love's got 2 be strong (instrumental groove mix) (on 12" only).
7" Single: Released 17 Apr '89, on 4th & Broadway, by Island Records. Catalogue no: **BRW 130**
12" Single: Released 17 Apr '89, on 4th & Broadway, by Island Records. Catalogue no: **12 BRW 130**

Edwards, O.G.

ONLY YOU
Tracks: / Only you.
12" Single: Released Mar '89, on Danceyard, by Danceyard Records. Catalogue no: **YARD T7**

Edwards, Pat

SIT DOWN POSSE
Tracks: / Sit down posse.
12" Single: Released Feb '89, on Charlie's, Catalogue no: **XCR 403**

Edwards, Rupie

Biographical details: This Jamaican reggae singer and producer was a leading studio figure in that country's music during the early seventies. In addition to his productions for other artists, he won acclaim for his own 1975 album *Dub basket.* During late 1974 and early 1975, Edwards achieved two successes on the UK singles chart. *Ire feelings (skanga)* reached no.9 despite a dearth of radio airplay; and *Lego skanga* reached no.32. (Bob Macdonald, 22/7/85).

CHILDREN OF TODAY
Tracks: / Children of today / Dub of today.
7" Single: Released 20 Jul '80, on Success (2), Deleted '83. Catalogue no: **SRLD 017**

IRE FEELINGS (SKANGA) (SINGLE)
Tracks: / Ire feelings.
7" Single: Released Nov '74, on Cactus, by Creole Records. Deleted '79. Catalogue no: **CT 38**

LEGO SKANGA
Tracks: / Lego skanga.
7" Single: Released Feb '75, on Cactus, by Creole Records. Deleted '80. Catalogue no: **CT 51**

THAT WONDERFUL SOUND
Tracks: / That wonderful sound / My little red top.
7" Single: Released May '80, on Liberty (USA), by EMI Records. Deleted May '83. Catalogue no: **BP 357**

YOU LEFT ME IN TEARS
Tracks: / You left me in tears.
12" Single: Released Mar '85, on Success (2), Catalogue no: **SUCCESS 179**

Edwards, Sandra

GIVE ME SOME EMOTION
Tracks: / Give me some emotion / I love you.
12" Single: Released Jul '86, on Soultown, Catalogue no: **SAND 12-001**

WINNER TAKES IT ALL
Tracks: / Winner takes it all, The / Jump start.
12" Single: Released Jan '88, on Bolts, by Bolts Records. Catalogue no: **BOLTS 11/12**

Edwards, Sharon

ON & OFF
Tracks: / On & off / Go.
12" Single: Released Apr '84, on Sir George, Catalogue no: **SG 006T**

Edwards, Steve

ROCK WITH ME
Tracks: / Rock with me / Club.
7" Single: Released Oct '86, on Do-It, by Do-It Records. Catalogue no: **SAE 1410**

Edwards, Tommy

Biographical details: A songwriter and singer (1922-69) who turned pro at age 9. He wrote *That chick's too young to fry* a hit for Louis Jordan. Signed by MGM he had a few minor hits including the top 20 *It's all in the game* in 1951, composed in 1912 as *Melody in F major* by banker and amateur flautist Charles Gates Dawes, later USA ice President under Calvin Coolidge; words were added by Carl Sigman in 1951. Edwards recorded it again with updated rock-aballad backing at what would have been his last MGM recording session; the new record was number one for six weeks in 1958 and eventually sold 3.5 million copies. (Donald Clarke, April 1989).

IT'S ALL IN THE GAME
Tracks: / It's all in the game.
7" Single: Released Jul '84, on Old Gold, by Old Gold Records. Catalogue no: **OG 9446**

IT'S ALL IN THE GAME (ORIGINAL)
Tracks: / It's all in the game.
7" Single: Released Oct '58, on MGM, by Polydor Ltd. Deleted '63. Catalogue no: **MGM 989**

MY MELANCHOLY BABY
Tracks: / My melancholy baby.
7" Single: Released Aug '59, on MGM, by Polydor Ltd. Deleted '64. Catalogue no: **MGM 1020**

Edwards, Vince

WHERE DOES THE LOVE GO?
Tracks: / Where does love go?.
12" Single: Released Aug '85, on Free The Spirit, Deleted '86. Catalogue no: **DACCT 2**
7" Single: Released Aug '85, on Free The Spirit, Deleted '86. Catalogue no: **DACC 2**

Edward's Voice

FALLING FROM ANOTHER HIGH BUILDING
Tracks: / Falling from another high building.
7" Single: Released Oct '82, on Edward's Voice, by Edward's Voice Records. Deleted '88. Catalogue no: **EV 001**

Eek-A-Mouse

Biographical details: This Jamaican vocalist, DJ and songwriter, whose real name is Ripton Hylton, became a leading figure on his country's reggae scene during the early eighties. He showed himself to be a witty and vivacious master of the art of toasting (the reggae equivalent of rapping). Eek-A-Mouse has used this form to great effect. His first single *Wa do dem* was later followed by *Assassinator,* which showed that Hylton was just as compulsive in his political messages as in his humour. His forceful concert persona emphasised an archetypal roots reggae approach, but his vocal style included a hint of Japanese influence. In August 1982 he managed to crack the British charts for the first time with his LP *Skidip,* which reached no.61. A growing British cult following has led to a profusion of UK releases, all highlighting his social awareness and sense of fun. (Bob Macdonald, 7/85).

ANAREXOL
Tracks: / Anarexol / Teacher.
12" Single: Released Sep '83, on Greensleeves, by Greensleeves Records. Catalogue no: **GRED 129**

CHRISTMAS A COME
Tracks: / Christmas a come / Gone water gone.
12" Single: Released Dec '81, on Greensleeves, by Greensleeves Records. Catalogue no: **GRED 74**

DEE-DI-DOO
Tracks: / Dee-di-doo / Dee-di-doo (dub mix).
7" Single: Released May '87, on Original Sounds, Catalogue no: **OS 005**
12" Single: Released Feb '89, on Original Sounds, Catalogue no: **OS 009**

DO YOU REMEMBER
Tracks: / Do you remember / Strictly the dread.
12" Single: Released May '82, on Greensleeves, by Greensleeves Records. Catalogue no: **GRED 88**

GEORGIE PORGIE
Tracks: / Georgie Porgie.
12" Single: Released Feb '82, on Echo, by Echo Records. Catalogue no: **ECHO 008**

I WANT TO KNOW
Tracks: / I want to know.
12" Single: Released Nov '83, on D-Music, Catalogue no: **DMLX 480**

MODEL SHE A MODEL
Tracks: / Model she a model / Walk and waggle.
7" Single: Released Apr '85, on Creole, by Creole Records. Catalogue no: **CR 81**
12" Single: Released Apr '85, on Creole, by Creole Records. Catalogue no: **CRT 81**

NOAH'S ARK
Tracks: / Noah's ark / My lady.
7" Single: Released Nov '80, on Greensleeves, by Greensleeves Records. Deleted '83. Catalogue no: **GRED 42**

TERRORISTS IN THE CITY
Tracks: / Terrorists in the city.
12" Single: Released Apr '83, on Greensleeves, by Greensleeves Records. Catalogue no: **GRED 109**

VIRGIN GIRL
Tracks: / Virgin girl.
7" Single: Released Feb '82, on Joe Gibbs, Catalogue no: **JGML 8144**
12" Single: Released Feb '82, on Joe Gibbs, Catalogue no: **JGML 8144 12**

WA-DO-DEM (SINGLE)
Tracks: / Wa-do-dem / Noah's ark.
12" Single: Released Sep '83, on Greensleeves, by Greensleeves Records. Catalogue no: **MOUSE 1**

WILD LIKE A TIGER
Tracks: / Wild like a tiger / Operation eradication.
12" Single: Released Nov '82, on Greensleeves, by Greensleeves Records. Catalogue no: **GRED 107**

Eezi Eezi

SAYO SAYO
Tracks: / Sayo sayo.
12" Single: Released Nov '83, on Shaka Productions, Catalogue no: **SP1**

E.F. Band

DEVIL'S EYE, THE
Tracks: / Devil's eye, The.
7" Single: Released Oct '80, on Red Ball, Catalogue no: **RR 036**

NIGHT ANGEL
Tracks: / Night angel.
7" Single: Released Apr '80, on E.F. Band, Catalogue no: **EF 1**

SELF MADE SUICIDE
Tracks: / Self made suicide.
7" Single: Released Feb '80, on Red Ball, Catalogue no: **RR 026**

Effect

ABUSING MYSELF
Tracks: / Abusing myself / Watch me dance.
7" Single: Released Nov '81, on Initial, Catalogue no: **IRS 004**

Egan, Joe

BACK ON THE ROAD
Tracks: / Back on the road / My mama told me.
7" Single: Released Feb '80, on Ariola, by BMG Records (UK). Deleted Feb '83. Catalogue no: **ARO 153**

FIVER
Tracks: / Fiver / Heat of the moment.
7" Single: Released Oct '80, on Ariola, by BMG Records (UK). Deleted Oct '83. Catalogue no: **ARO 249**

Egan, Walter

BABY LET'S RUN AWAY
Tracks: / Baby let's run away / First date, last date.
7" Single: Released Apr '81, on Edge, Deleted Apr '84. Catalogue no: **EDGE 11**

FULL MOON FIRE
Tracks: / Full moon fire.
7" Single: Released May '83, on MCA, by MCA Records. Catalogue no: **MCA 823**

Ege Bam Yasi

CIRCUMSTANCES
Tracks: / Circumstances.
12" Single: Released '87, on Survival (1), by Survival Records. Catalogue no: **SURT 036**

Eger, Lucinda

SUNSET RED
Tracks: / Sunset red.
12" Single: Released Apr '87, on Pure Trash, by Pure Trash Records. Catalogue no: **PTR 3**

Egg Hunt

ME AND YOU
Tracks: / All fall down / Me and you.
7" Single: Released Nov '86, on Dischord, by Dischord Records. Catalogue no: **DISCHORD 20**

Egypt

CRAZY HORSES (SINGLE)
Tracks: / Crazy horses.
Note: A powerful updated version of the Osmonds hit.
7" Single: Released 5 Sep '88, on H.T.D., by HTD Records. Catalogue no: **7 HTD 1**

Ehmig, Michael Dan

FOR ALL THE CHILDREN
Tracks: / For all the children.
7" Single: Released May '84, on Open Space, Catalogue no: **OS 92**

Ehrlich Bullets

MUSIC IS DEAD...LET IT ROT (EP)
Tracks: / Rasper eaze / Bathtime / Douglas dungbeetle / Oi dar.
12" Single: Released Mar '89, on Magic Moments At Twilight Time, by Magic Moments At Twilight Time. Catalogue no: **MMATT 29**

Ehrlich, John

SPILL THE WINE
Tracks: / Spill the wine.

12" Single: Released Aug '87, on Polo, by Polo Records. Deleted '88. Catalogue no: **POLO 12-42**
7" Single: Released Aug '87, on Polo, by Polo Records. Deleted '88. Catalogue no: **POLO 42**

Ei Mori

VETETTERN VIOLAT
Tracks: / Vetettern violat.

12" Single: Released 16 Sep '88, on World Today, Catalogue no: **WT 001**

Eider, Max

CONSPIRACY
Tracks: / Conspiracy.
12" Single: Released May '86, on Glass, by Glass Records. Deleted Jan '88. Catalogue no: **GLAEP 104**

Eight Eyed Spy

DIDDY WAH DIDDY
Tracks: / Diddy wah diddy / Dead you me.
7" Single: Released May '82, on Fetus Productions, by Red Rhino Records. Catalogue no: **FE 19**

Eight Hundred & Eight

LET YOURSELF GO
Tracks: / Let yourself go.
12" Single: Released Nov '88, on Creed, Catalogue no: **STATE 003**

LOUNGE
Tracks: / Lounge.
12" Single: Released Nov '88, on Creed, Catalogue no: **STATE 003**

Eight Point Five

MARY
Tracks: / Mary / I can't get you of my head.
12" Single: Released Feb '87, on Epic, by CBS Records. Deleted Aug '87. Catalogue no: **650356 6**
7" Single: Released Feb '87, on Epic, by CBS Records. Deleted Aug '87. Catalogue no: **650356 7**

Eighth Day

CALL ME UP
Tracks: / Call me up.
7" Single: Released Apr '83, on Funk America, by A&M Records. Catalogue no: **USA 1228**
12" Single: Released Apr '83, on Funk America, by A&M Records. Catalogue no: **USAF 1228**

TOO MANY COOKS (SPOIL THE BROTH)
Tracks: / Too many cooks (spoil the broth).
7" Single: Released Jun '84, on HDH (Holland/Dozier/Holland), by Demon Records. Catalogue no: **HDH 456**

Eighth Wonder

BABY BABY
Tracks: / Baby Baby / Dusted.
CD 5": Released 16 Sep '88, on CBS, by CBS Records. Deleted 17 Apr '89. Catalogue no: **CDBABE 1**
7" Single: Released 16 Sep '88, on CBS, by CBS Records. Deleted 17 Apr '89. Catalogue no: **BABE 1**
12" Single: Released Oct '88, on CBS, by CBS Records. Deleted 17 Apr '89. Catalogue no: **BABE QT1**
7" Single: Released Sep '88, on CBS, by CBS Records. Deleted 17 Apr '89. Catalogue no: **BABE P1**
12" Single: Released 16 Sep '88, on CBS, by CBS Records. Deleted 17 Apr '89. Catalogue no: **BABE T1**

CROSS MY HEART
Tracks: / Cross my heart / Let me in / Cross my heart (dance mix) / Cross my heart (house mix) / Cross my heart (instrumental).
CD 5": Released Jun '88, on CBS, by CBS Records. Deleted Jan '89. Catalogue no: **651 552 2**
7" Single: Released 13 Jun '88, on CBS, by CBS Records. Deleted Jan '89. Catalogue no: **651 552 7**
12" Single: Released 20 Jun '88, on CBS, by CBS Records. Deleted Jan '89. Catalogue no: **651 552 8**
12" Single: Released 13 Jun '88, on CBS, by CBS Records. Deleted Jan '89. Catalogue no: **651 552 6**
7" Single: Released 13 Jun '88, on CBS, by CBS Records. Deleted Jan '89. Catalogue no: **651 552 0**

I'M NOT SCARED
Tracks: / I'm not scared (disco mix) / I'm not scared / J'ai pas peur.
10" single: Released Feb '88, on CBS, by CBS Records. Deleted Jan '89. Catalogue no: **SCARE Y1**
7" Single: Released Feb '88, on CBS, by CBS Records. Deleted Jan '89. Catalogue no: **SCARE Q1**
CD 5": Released Feb '88, on CBS, by CBS Records. Deleted Jan '89. Catalogue no: **SCARE C1**
12" Single: Released Feb '88, on CBS, by CBS Records. Deleted Jan '89. Catalogue no: **SCARE T1**
7" Single: Released Feb '88, on CBS, by CBS Records. Deleted Jan '89. Catalogue no: **SCARE 1**

STAY WITH ME
7" Single: Released Sep '85, on CBS, by CBS Records. Catalogue no: **A 6594**
12" Single: Released Oct '85, on CBS, by CBS Records. Catalogue no: **QTX 6594**
12" Single: Released Sep '85, on CBS, by CBS Records. Catalogue no: **TX 6594**

WHEN THE PHONE STOPS RINGING
Tracks: / When the phone stops ringing / When the phone stops ringing (extended remix) / When the phone stops ringing (single version) / Let me in.
7" Pic: Released Nov '87, on CBS, by CBS Records. Catalogue no: **PHONE P1**
7" Single: Released Oct '87, on CBS, by CBS Records. Deleted Jan '89. Catalogue no: **PHONEW 1**
7" Single: Released Oct '87, on CBS, by CBS Records. Deleted Jan '89. Catalogue no: **PHONE 1**
12" Single: Released Oct '87, on CBS, by CBS Records. Deleted Aug '88. Catalogue no: **PHONET 1**
12" Single: Released Oct '87, on CBS, by CBS Records. Deleted Aug '88. Catalogue no: **PHONE Q1**
7" Single: Released Nov '87, on CBS, by CBS Records. Catalogue no: **ATOM 2**

WILL YOU REMEMBER
Tracks: / Having it all.
7" Single: Released Jan '87, on CBS, by CBS Records. Deleted Aug '87. Catalogue no: **650264 7**
12" Single: Released Jan '87, on CBS, by CBS Records. Deleted Aug '87. Catalogue no: **650264 6**

Eightie's Band

WE WANT A GOAL
Tracks: / We want a goal / Eightie's band.
7" Single: Released Jul '81, on JSO, Deleted '87. Catalogue no: **EAT 11**

Eighties Ladies

TURNED ON TO YOU
Tracks: / Turned on to you / Turned on to you (alternative mix).
7" Single: Released Aug '86, on Music Of Life, by Music Of Life Records. Catalogue no: **MOL 6**
12" Single: Released Aug '86, on Music Of Life, by Music Of Life Records. Catalogue no: **MOLIF 6**

Einstein

ALBERT
Tracks: / Albert / Mayday for the human race.
7" Single: Released May '80, on WEA, by WEA Records. Deleted May '85. Catalogue no: **K 18083**

FREEZE, THE
Tracks: / Freeze, The / My rhymes are smokin' / Talk like a yardie.
12" Single: Released Feb '89, on Music Of Life, by Music Of Life Records. Catalogue no: **NOTE 23**

FRIDAY NIGHT AND SATURDAY MORNING
Tracks: / Friday night, Saturday morning.
7" Single: Released Jul '88, on Music Of Life, by Music Of Life Records. Catalogue no: **7 NOTE 17**
12" Single: Released Jul '88, on Music Of Life, by Music Of Life Records. Catalogue no: **NOTE 17**

Einsturzende Neubauten

DURSTIGES TIER (EP)
12" Single: Released Aug '83, on Zick Zack (Germany), Deleted '84. Catalogue no: **6343**

YU GUNG
Tracks: / Yu gung / Seele brent sand.
12" Single: Released Mar '85, on Some Bizzare, by Some Bizzare Records. Catalogue no: **BART 12**

Ejected

HAVE YOU GOT 10P?
Tracks: / Have you got 10p?.
7" Single: Released Sep '82, on Riot City, by Riot City Records. Catalogue no: **RIOT 14**

NOISE FOR THE BOYS (EP)
7" Single: Released Feb '83, on Riot City, by Riot City Records. Catalogue no: **RIOT 19**

EK.1

AS ONE
Tracks: / As one / Summers end / As one (Inst.).
7" Single: Released Mar '86, on Be There, by Be There Records. Catalogue no: **BT 001**

Eko Eko

I CAN'T TAKE THE HURT AGAIN
Tracks: / I can't take the hurt again.
12" Single: Released Jun '84, on Red Bus, by Red Bus Records. Catalogue no: **RBUSL 98**
7" Single: Released Jun '84, on Red Bus, by Red Bus Records. Catalogue no: **RBUS 98**

El Chicano

LET ME DANCE WITH YOU
Tracks: / Let me dance with you / Do you want me (on 12" only).
7" Single: Released Aug '84, on Streetwave, Catalogue no: **KHAN 24**
12" Single: Released Aug '84, on Streetwave, Catalogue no: **MKHAN 24**

El Coco

COCOMOTION
Tracks: / Cocomotion / Let's get it together.
7" Single: Released Jan '78, on Pye International, Deleted Jan '81. Catalogue no: **7N 25761**
12" Single: Released Sep '87, on Matra (Canada), Catalogue no: **SPEC 1291**

LET'S GET IT TOGETHER
Tracks: / Let's get it together / Cocomotion '79.
12" Single: Released May '80, on AVI (USA), by AVI Record Production Inc.(USA). Deleted '83. Catalogue no: **AVISL 109**

El Debarge

HEART IS NOT SO SMART, THE
Tracks: / Heart is not so smart / Share my world.
7" Single: Released Nov '85, on Motown, by BMG Records (UK). Catalogue no: **ZB 40497**
12" Single: Released Nov '85, on Motown, by BMG Records (UK). Catalogue no: **ZT 40498**

YOU WEAR IT WELL
Tracks: / You wear it well.
12" Single: Released Aug '85, on Motown, by BMG Records (UK). Deleted '87. Catalogue no: **ZT 40346**
7" Single: Released Aug '85, on Motown, by BMG Records (UK). Catalogue no: **ZB 40345**

El Seven

MAGNIFICO
Tracks: / Magnifico.
7" Single: Released Mar '81, on Pop Records International, Catalogue no: **POP 000**

RADIO TOKYO
Tracks: / Radio Tokyo / Turn out the light.
7" Single: Released Jun '80, on Pop Records International, Deleted '82. Catalogue no: **POP 001**

El Sonido

OYE COLUMBIA
Tracks: / Oye Columbia / Mi Melodia.
12" Single: Released Mar '87, on Banana, Catalogue no: **BAN 120T**

El Trains

ACTION STYLE
Tracks: / Action style.
7" Single: Released Jul '85, on W.A.R., by W.A.R. Records. Catalogue no: **WAR 3002**
12" Single: Released Jul '85, on W.A.R., by W.A.R. Records. Catalogue no: **12 WAR 3002**

Elaine & Derick

HOW MANY TIMES CAN WE SAY?
Tracks: / How many times can we say?.
12" Single: Released Nov '85, on BB, Catalogue no: **BBD 169**

Elaine & Ellen

FILL ME UP
Tracks: / Fill me up / You made me do it.
7" Single: Released May '80, on Ovation, by Gull Records. Deleted '83. Catalogue no: **OVS 1205**

El-Bee 'N' Tee

OVER LIKE A FAT RAT 88 mix
Tracks: / Over like a fat rat.
7" Single: Released Jul '88, on UNKNOWN, Catalogue no: **ZER 00121**

Elbert, Donnie

Biographical details: This American singer and producer first found success in 1957, when his single *What can I do* was a minor hit on the US pop chrts. This introduced people his ear-catching falsetto vocals, but other singers subsequently found greater success with this style than Elbert himself. He spent the sixties traipsing around clubs and recording studios on both sides of the Atlantic, and had to wait till 1970 for his next significant success - in that year *I can't get over losing you* was a US soul hit. In late 1971 the high-voiced Mr. Elbert found himself with an American Top 20 pop hit with a disco remake of the Supremes' 1964 classic *Where did our love go*. After reaching the US no.15 slot, this track climbed to no.8 in Britain in early '72. Repeating the winning formula, he quickly achieved another transatlantic hit with a cover version of another Holland/Dozier/Holland-penned oldie from the Motown vaults: *I can't help myself*, originally recorded by the Four Tops, got to no.22 for Elbert in the US, and climbed to no.11 in the UK. A less familiar song, *Little piece of leather* was released as a rapid follow-up but was not a major success. Elbert continued recording through the seventies, but faded into obscurity. (Bob Macdonald, 26/7/85).

I CAN'T HELP MYSELF
Tracks: / I can't help myself.
7" Single: Released Feb '72, on Avco-Embassy, Deleted '77. Catalogue no: **6105 009**

LITTLE PIECE OF LEATHER
Tracks: / Little piece of leather.
7" Single: Released Apr '72, on London-American, Deleted '77. Catalogue no: **HL 10370**

WHERE DID OUR LOVE GO
Tracks: / Where did our love go.
7" Single: Released Jan '72, on London-American, Deleted '77. Catalogue no: **HL 10352**

YOU DON'T HAVE TO BE A STAR
Tracks: / You don't have to be a star / At the club / Free.
7" Single: Released Jul '81, on Sugarhill (USA), Deleted '88. Catalogue no: **SH 107**
12" Single: Released Jul '81, on Sugarhill (USA), Catalogue no: **SHL 107**

Eleanor Rigby

I WANT TO SLEEP WITH YOU
Tracks: / I want to sleep with you.
7" Single: Released Apr '85, on Waterloo Sunset, by Waterloo Sunset Records. Catalogue no: **RUSS 101**

KISS ME QUICKLY IT'S CHRISTMAS
Tracks: / Kiss me quickly it's Christmas / Mad Christmas.
7" Single: Released Nov '86, on Waterloo Sunset, by Waterloo Sunset Records. Catalogue no: **RUSS 104**

TAKE ANOTHER SHOT OF MY HEART
Tracks: / Take another shot of my heart / 1995.
7" Single: Released Sep '87, on Waterloo Sunset, by Waterloo Sunset Records. Catalogue no: **RUSS 102**

Elected

PRESS THE BUTTON
Tracks: / Press the button.
7" Single: Released Dec '83, on Riot City, by Riot City Records. Catalogue no: **RIOT 28**

Electra

JIBARO (COME ON LET'S GO) Balearic house anthem, The
Tracks: / Jibaro (ying yang mix) (12" (FFRRX 9) only.) / Jibaro (spectrum mix) (12" (FFRRX 9) only.) / Jibaro (English version) (Only on normal 12" version.) / Jibaro (Spanish version) (Only on normal 12" version.) / Future, The / Future, The (Edition 2) / Future, The.
7" Single: Released Nov '88, on ffrr, by London Records. Deleted May '89. Catalogue no: **FFX 9**
7" Single: Released Nov '88, on ffrr, by London Records. Deleted May '89. Catalogue no: **FFRXR 9**
12" Single: Released Nov '88, on ffrr, by London Records. Deleted May '89. Catalogue no: **FFRRX 9**
12" Single: Released 23 Jul '88, on ffrr, by London Records. Deleted May '89. Catalogue no: **FFRX 9**
7" Single: Released 23 Jul '88, on ffrr, by London Records. Deleted May '89. Catalogue no: **FFR 9**

Electribe 101

TALKING WITH MYSELF
Tracks: / Talking with myself / Talking with myself (instrumental).
7" Single: Released Nov '88, on Club, by Phonogram Ltd. Deleted 31 Jul '89. Catalogue no: **JAB 74**
12" Single: Released Nov '88, on Club, by Phonogram Ltd. Deleted 31 Jul '89. Catalogue no: **JABXR 74**
12" Single: Released Nov '88, on Club, by Phonogram Ltd. Deleted 31 Jul '89. Catalogue no: **JABX 74**

TELL ME WHEN THE FEVER ENDED
Tracks: / Tell me when the fever ended / Tell me when the fever ended (instrumental).
CD 5": Released Oct '89, on Mercury, by Phonogram Ltd. Catalogue no: **MERCD 310**
CD 5": Released Sep '89, on Mercury, by

Phonogram Ltd. Catalogue no: **HIPCD 2**
7" Single: Released Sep '89, on Mercury, by Phonogram Ltd. Catalogue no: **HIP 2**
12" Single: Released Oct '89, on Mercury, by Phonogram Ltd. Catalogue no: **MERX 310**
7" Single: Released Oct '89, on Mercury, by Phonogram Ltd. Catalogue no: **MER 310**
12" Single: Released Sep '89, on Mercury, by Phonogram Ltd. Catalogue no: **HIP 212**

Electric Arc

HONKY TONK RAP
Tracks: / Honky tonk rap / Just another song.
7" Single: Released Sep '83, on Red Bus, by Red Bus Records. Catalogue no: **RBUS 83**

Electric Bluebirds

BACK ON THE TRAIN
Tracks: / Stranger's just a friend, A / Back on the train.
7" Single: Released Sep '86, on Making Waves, by Celtic Music. Catalogue no: **SURF 119**

MONEY'S ALL GONE, THE
Tracks: / Money's all gone, The.
7" Single: Released Oct '86, on Making Waves, by Celtic Music. Catalogue no: **SURF 122**

TELL IT LIKE IT IS
Tracks: / Tell it like it is / Wake me, shake me.
7" Single: Released Jun '86, on Making Waves, by Celtic Music. Deleted Nov '87. Catalogue no: **SURF 117**

Electric Ceilidh Band

CEANN TRAIGH GHRUINHEARD
Tracks: / Ceann traigh ghruinheard.
12" Single: Released Mar '84, on Raucous, Catalogue no: **ECB 1**

Electric Chairs

SO MANY WAYS
Tracks: / So many ways.
7" Single: Released '79, on Safari, by Safari Records. Catalogue no: **SAFE 18**

Electric Eels

AGITATED
Tracks: / Agitated.
7" Single: Released Jan '79, on Rough Trade, by Rough Trade Records. Catalogue no: **RT 008**

DON'T WANNA GO TO MOSCOW
Tracks: / Don't wanna go to Moscow / Wild dream.
7" Single: Released Mar '80, on Rocket, by Rocket Records. Deleted '83. Catalogue no: **XPRES 28**

Electric Funk

ON A JOURNEY
Tracks: / On a journey.
12" Single: Released Nov '82, on Epic, by CBS Records. Deleted Nov '85. Catalogue no: **EPC A132299**
7" Single: Released Nov '82, on Epic, by CBS Records. Deleted Nov '85. Catalogue no: **EPC A2299**

Electric Guitars

GENGHIS KHAN
Tracks: / Genghis Khan.
12" Single: Released Oct '82, on Stiff, by Stiff Records. Catalogue no: **BUYIT 161**

HEALTH
Tracks: / Health.
7" Single: Released Jul '81, on Fried Egg, by Fried Egg Records. Deleted '87. Catalogue no: **EGG 12**

LANGUAGE PROBLEMS
Tracks: / Language problems / Night bears.
7" Single: Released May '82, on Stiff, by Stiff Records. Catalogue no: **BUY 148**
12" Single: Released May '82, on Stiff, by Stiff Records. Catalogue no: **BUYIT 148**

WOLFMAN TAP
Tracks: / Wolfman tap.
12" Single: Released May '83, on Naive, by Naive Records. Catalogue no: **12 NAV 5**
7" Single: Released May '83, on Naive, by Naive Records. Catalogue no: **NAV 5**

WORK
Tracks: / Work / Don't wake the baby.
7" Single: Released Oct '81, on Recreational, by Revolver Records. Catalogue no: **SPORT 4**

Electric Mind

PICK ME UP (CAN WE GO)
Tracks: / Pick me up (can we go).
12" Single: Released Jul '83, on Passion, by Skratch Records. Catalogue no: **PASH 03(12)**
7" Single: Released Jul '83, on Passion, by Skratch Records. Catalogue no: **PASH 03**

Electric Prunes

Biographical details: At the time of their two hit singles, this American rock group consisted of Jim Lowe, Preston Ritter, Mark Tulin and Ken Williams. The Electric Prunes came from Seattle, but based their recording activities in los Angeles. After spending a couple of years building up their experience, they came to fame in early 1967 with *I had too much to dream last night*, a druggy gimmick single that reached no.11 on the US charts. Much of the credit for the record's success was due to the combo's producer, who used studio tricks to produce a sound that was both rocky and slightly avant-garde. It fitted in well with the spirit of the times, and was quickly followed by a smaller hit with *Get me to the world on time*, which peaked at no.27. The songs did not do as well in Britain. The Prunes' 1967 LP *Mass in F minor* was one of rock's early concept albums, but was by no means a classic. By the end of the year, the group had undergone a wholesale change of personnel. The non-entities who comprised the new group were unable to find their feet, and the Prunes folded altogether in 1969. (Bob Macdonald, 26/7/88)
USA psychedelic rock group formed in Seattle c 1966, originally in the vein of contempory groups such as Them, The Seeds, The Music Machine etc. They signed with Reprise and their second single *I had too much to dream last night* became a classic of the genre; a completely new lineup took over the name and contract to make stuff like *Mass in F Minor* an electric rock mass sung in Latin, the new group's first and last album chart entry in 1968. Best work of first lineup is on *Long day's flight* on Edsel. (Donald Clarke, April 1989).

GET ME TO THE WORLD ON TIME
Tracks: / Get me to the world on time.
7" Single: Released May '67, on Reprise, by WEA Records. Deleted '72. Catalogue no: **RS 20564**

I HAD TOO MUCH TO DREAM LAST NIGHT
7" Single: Released Mar '79, on Radar, Catalogue no: **ADA 16**
7" Single: Released Feb '67, on Reprise, by WEA Records. Deleted '72. Catalogue no: **RS 20532**

Electric Shock

DON'T TALK ABOUT SEX
Tracks: / Don't talk about sex.
12" Single: Released 20 Feb '88, on Antler, by Antler Records (Belgium). Catalogue no: **SUB 008**

Electric Slacks

ELECTRIC BLUES
Tracks: / Electric blues.
7" Single: Released Jun '85, on Fundamental, by Fundamental Music Records. Catalogue no: **PRAY 1**

Electric Smoke

FREAK IT OUT
Tracks: / Freak it out.
7" Single: Released May '83, on Nite Life, Deleted '85. Catalogue no: **LIFE 3**

Electricity All Stars

ELECTRICITY MEDLEY various artists
Tracks: / Electricity medley / Cheated by a painted love.
12" Single: Released Mar '85, on Passion, by Skratch Records. Catalogue no: **PASH 42(12)**

Electro Gnome

ELECTRIC GNOME DANCE
Tracks: / Electric gnome dance.
7" Single: Released Nov '82, on EMI, by EMI Records. Deleted Nov '85. Catalogue no: **EMI 5355**

Electro Hippies

PEEL SESSIONS:ELECTRO HIPPIES
12" Single: Released Jul '87, on Strange Fruit, by Strange Fruit Records. Catalogue no: **SFPS 042**

Electronic Circus

DIRECT BLINDS
Tracks: / Direct blinds / La chorale.
7" Single: Released Mar '81, on Scratch, by Scratch Records. Deleted Mar '84. Catalogue no: **SCR 002**

Electronic Ensemble

IT HAPPENED THEN
Tracks: / It happened then.
7" Single: Released Oct '80, on Superstition, Deleted '82. Catalogue no: **SR 002**

Electronicas

Biographical details: This Belgian all-male studio band enjoyed a smash hit right across Europe in the summer of 1981 with their *Bird dance*. This infuriatingly catchy instrumental ditty, which was accompanied by a ridiculous disco and party dance routine, was the perfect novelty record to appeal to holidaymakers of all ages, from kids to grandparents. As in previous years, Britons returning from continental vacations bought up copious quantities of that summer's Eurohits, in an attempt to relive the atmosphere of their holiday. But the Electronicas' original *Bird dance* had to be content with a no.22 placing. In the tough world of the music business, a British music producer called Ray Levy and some cohorts entered a studio and rushed a cover version onto the UK market. The British rendition, billed as *The birdie song (birdie dance)* by the Tweets, flew to no.2 and stayed in the charts for 23 weeks. (Bob Macdonald, 26/7/85).

ORIGINAL BIRD DANCE
Tracks: / Original bird dance / Rattle waltz.
7" Single: Released Sep '81, on Polydor, by Polydor Ltd. Deleted '86. Catalogue no: **POSP 360**

PUSSYCAT DANCE
Tracks: / Pussycat dance / De vrijbuiter.
7" Single: Released Dec '81, on Polydor, by Polydor Ltd. Deleted Dec '84. Catalogue no: **POSP 373**

Electrotunes

THIS AIN'T LOVE
Tracks: / This ain't love / Body work.
7" Single: Released Jan '80, on Cobra, Deleted Jan '85. Catalogue no: **COB 5**

E'Leesa

I DO BELIEVE
Tracks: / I do believe.
12" Single: Released Oct '88, on Bassment (1), by Westside Records. Catalogue no: **BASMX 2**
7" Single: Released Oct '88, on Westside, by Westside Records. Catalogue no: **BASM 2**

WHERE DID YOUR LOVE GO?
Tracks: / Where did your love go?.
12" Single: Released Nov '87, on Bassment (USA), Catalogue no: **BM 0071**

Elegants

LITTLE STAR
Tracks: / Little star.
7" Single: Released Sep '58, on H.M.V., by EMI Records. Deleted '63. Catalogue no: **POP 520**

Element

KISS OF LIFE, THE
Tracks: / Kiss of life, The / Dead of night.
7" Single: Released May '89, on Clubland, Catalogue no: **SJP 859**

Elements Band

I WANNA DANCE
Tracks: / I wanna dance / Get up stand up.
12" Single: Released Feb '86, on ADA, Catalogue no: **DAD 003**

Elephant Talk

ASK
Tracks: / Ask.
7" Single: Released Mar '84, on Fragile, Catalogue no: **FRA 1**

Elevation

CRAZY RICOCHET
Tracks: / Crazy ricochet.
7" Single: Released Jan '81, on Polydor, by Polydor Ltd. Deleted Jan '84. Catalogue no: **POSP 220**

TRAITOR
Tracks: / Traitor.
7" Single: Released Oct '85, on Illuminated, Catalogue no: **LEV 66**
12" Single: Released Oct '85, on Illuminated, Catalogue no: **12LEV 66**

Eleventh Hour

GOING STRONG
Tracks: / Going strong / Going strong dub.
7" Single: Released Jan '82, on Loppylugs, Deleted '87. Catalogue no: **LOPPY 6**

Elfman, Danny

GRATITUDE
Tracks: / Gratitude / Tough as nails.
7" Single: Released May '85, on MCA, by MCA Records. Catalogue no: **MCA 943**
12" Single: Released May '85, on MCA, by MCA Records. Catalogue no: **MCAT 943**

Elgart, Larry

Biographical details: Sax player Larry and his brother, trumpeter Les, had wide Swing Era experience and led dance bands. Their most successful period was when they were together on CBS in the mid-'50's and again in the mid '60's with dance music for older folks. Larry Elgart & His Manhattan Swing Orchestra charted on RCA 1982-3 in the USA. (Donald Clarke, April 1989).

HOOKED ON SWING (SINGLE)
Tracks: / Hooked on swing / Hooked on big bands.
7" Single: Released Oct '82, on RCA, by BMG Records (UK). Catalogue no: **RCA 246**
12" Single: Released Oct '82, on RCA, by BMG Records (UK). Catalogue no: **RCAT 246**

Elgins

Biographical details: This American vocal group consisted of Johnny Dawson, Saundra Edwards, Robert Fleming, Norman McClean and Cleotha Miller. The Elgins enjoyed a brief run of modest US success in 1966. Signed to the Motown company, their records were written and produced by the stunningly successful Tamla team, Holland/Dozier/Holland. However, HDH's magic touch with such acts as the Supremes and the Four Tops did not rub off quite so profitably on these particular charges. The Elgins, who had previously recorded as the Emeralds and the Downbeats, got halfway up the Hot 100 with their pop/soul single *Heaven must have sent you*. Other chart entries included *Put yourself in my place* and *Darling baby*. As far as US record buyers were concerned, the Elgins quickly passed into obscurity. But suddenly in 1971, *Heaven must have sent you* became a Top 3 smash in Britain. Previously unknown in the UK, this reactivated single was belatedly recognised as a fine example of the legendary Motown sound. The equally tuneful *Put yourself in my place* then proceeded to reach the UK no.28 position. By this time the Elgins, who were still an active live unit, had been joined by Yvonne Allen, who replaced the group's previous principal singer Saundra Edwards. (Bob Macdonald, 27/7/85).

HEAVEN MUST HAVE SENT YOU
Tracks: / Heaven must have sent you.
7" Single: Released Oct '81, on Motown, by BMG Records (UK). Catalogue no: **TMG 771**

PUT YOURSELF IN MY PLACE
Tracks: / Put yourself in my place.
7" Single: Released Oct '71, on Tamla Motown, by Motown Records (UK). Deleted '76. Catalogue no: **TMG 787**

Eliakim

I SEE HIM
Tracks: / I see him.
7" Single: Released Jan '88, on Superrealism, Catalogue no: **ISM 001**

Elias

TOM HARK
Tracks: / Tom Hark / Ray ry.
7" Single: Released Jul '82, on Old Gold, by Old Gold Records. Deleted Jul '88. Catalogue no: **OG 9048**

Elite

YOU DON'T CARE ABOUT I
Tracks: / You don't care about me / Silly grin.
7" Single: Released Jan '83, on State, by State Records. Catalogue no: **STAT 119**
12" Single: Released Jan '83, on State, by State Records. Catalogue no: **STATT 119**

Elixia

SOHO PHAZE
Tracks: / Soho phaze.
12" Single: Released May '83, on Record Shack, by Record Shack Records. Catalogue no: **SOHOT 4**
7" Single: Released May '83, on Record Shack, by Record Shack Records. Catalogue no: **SOHO 4**

Elkin, Gilly

JUST ANOTHER NIGHT
Tracks: / Just another night / Call on me baby.
7" Single: Released Jan '83, on Hit (UK), Catalogue no: **HIT 0001**

LOVING ON THE RUN
Tracks: / Loving on the run.
7" Single: Released Jul '83, on Mantabridge, Catalogue no: **MTB 002**

Elle

GIVE IT TO ME
Tracks: / Give it to me / Dupes.
7" Single: Released Aug '89, on Rham, by Rham Records. Catalogue no: **RS 8906**

YVONNE ELLIMAN - IF I CAN'T HAVE YOU (Released on RSO)

12" Single: Released Jul '89, on Rham, by Rham Records. Catalogue no: **RS 8906**

Ellert

SOMETHING TO TALK ABOUT
Tracks: / Something to talk about / I wanna believe in love / Something to talk about (dance mix) (on 12" only) / Something to talk about (extended mix) (on 12" only).
Note: Written by hit pop duo Climie Fisher and produced by Phil Harding and Ian Curnow, this lively and very catchy dance/pop should be a successful debut for this Dutchman, Ellert Driessen." (Music Week, July 1988)
12" Single: Released Jun '88, on RCA, by BMG Records (UK). Deleted May '89. Catalogue no: **PT 42078**
7" Single: Released Jun '88, on RCA, by BMG Records (UK). Deleted May '89. Catalogue no: **PB 42077**

WHEN THE NIGHT BEGINS (SINGLE)
Tracks: / When the night begins / Sing your own song / When the night begins (extended mix) (Track on 12" only.) / Who can say (track on 12" only.).
7" Single: Released 31 Oct '88, on RCA, by BMG Records (UK). Deleted May '89. Catalogue no: **PB 42229**
12" Single: Released 31 Oct '88, on RCA, by BMG Records (UK). Catalogue no: **PT 422230**

Ellery Bop

FIRE IN REFLECTION
Tracks: / Fire in reflection / Blind / Calling.
12" Single: Released May '85, on Desire, by Desire Records. Deleted '89. Catalogue no: **WANTX 2**

HIT THE MOON
Tracks: / Hit the moon / One true way.
7" Single: Released Apr '82, on Base Ideas, by Base Ideas Records. Catalogue no: **BASE 001**

RINGING
Tracks: / Ringing / Fight and desire.
7" Single: Released Apr '82, on Base Ideas, by Base Ideas Records. Catalogue no: **BASE 002**

WE DENY
Tracks: / We deny.
10" single: Released Jul '82, on Base Ideas, by Base Ideas Records. Catalogue no: **BASE 003**

Elliman, Yvonne

HELLO STRANGER
Tracks: / Hello stranger.
7" Single: Released May '77, on RSO, by Polydor Ltd. Deleted '82. Catalogue no: **RSO 2090 236**

I CAN'T GET YOU OUT OF MY MIND
Tracks: / I can't get you out of my mind.
7" Single: Released Aug '77, on RSO, by Polydor Ltd. Deleted '82. Catalogue no: **RSO 2090 251**

I DON'T KNOW HOW TO LOVE HIM
Tracks: / I don't know how to love him.
7" Single: Released Jan '72, on MCA, by MCA Records. Deleted '77. Catalogue no: **MMKS 5077**

IF I CAN'T HAVE YOU (see panel above)
Tracks: / If I can't have you / Good sign.
7" Single: Released May '78, on RSO, by Polydor Ltd. Deleted '83. Catalogue no: **2090 266**

LOVE ME
Tracks: / Love me.
7" Single: Released Nov '76, on RSO, by Polydor Ltd. Deleted '81. Catalogue no: **RSO 2090 205**

Ellington, Duke

Biographical details: Edward Kennedy "Duke" Ellington was the greatest composer in the history of jazz, and one of the genre's most accomplished bandleaders and pianists. Although fellow American orchestra leaders such as Glenn Miller, Jimmy Dorsey and Tommy Dorsey were bigger household names and greater record sellers, and although such figures as Louis Armstrong had a stronger public personality, the Duke's pervasive musical influence and amazing consistency made him easily one of the all-time greats. Duke Ellington moved from his native Washington to New York in 1923. During the next fifteen crucial years, he gradually assembled one of the slickest and most innovative ensembles that the burgeoning jazz world had seen. He possessed an uncanny ability to develop his players' strong points and to squeeze every last drop of talent from them, thus bringing out skills that the musicians never knew they had. Having become a regular recording artist as well as a live attraction, Ellington hired a compositional collaborator in 1939, who remained a trusted lieutenant until 1967 - Billy Strayhorn co-wrote several great pieces with Ellington, and received sole composer's credit on the 1941 song *Take the A train.* During the early forties, the Duke was probably at the very peak of his career. The war then proceeded to disrupt all of America's big bands; and although Ellington remained popular through the forties and early fifties, it was not till 1956 that he began to regain his former musical greatness. A particularly noteworthy item during the fifties was his acclaimed *Such sweet thunder.* Swinging through the 60's in fine form, Ellington did not begin to go downhill till 1971. He died in May 1974; exactly 3 years later, Stevie Wonder reached no.1 in America and no.2 in Britain with his tribute single *Sir Duke.*·Ellington only chalked up two chart entries in Britain. On the UK singles chart (which was inaugurated in 1952), he reached no.7 in early '54 with *Skin deep.* On the British album listings (started in 1958), he got to no.11 in 1961 with *Nut cracker suite.* (Bob Macdonald, 28/7/85)
Edward Kennedy Ellington (1899-1974) was a pianist, bandleader, arranger and composer; he was all of these things at once, rather that wearing several hats, which made him one of the greatest composers of the century. He led a band of unruly geniuses long after big bands were no longer big business so that he could hear his own music the day after he wrote it. Born into a middle-class family in Washington DC, he went to New York twice looking for work, successful on his second trip; The Washingtonians was led by Elmer Snowden in 1923 but within a couple of years was Ellington's band playing his music. The band became famous through broadcasts from the Cotton Club 1927-31; trumpeter Bubby Miley and trombonist Joe 'Tricky' Sam Nanton practised a growling style, probably borrowed from King Oliver, which together with the Club's floor shows have it the 'Jungle Band' identity and sound. Ellington had considered a career as an artist; he discovered a talent for tone colour and began to create a unique body of composition and wrote specifically for his own men, so that his band from the beginning had a sensual beauty and an identity as a band that others lacked. Between 1926-30 *East St Louis toodle oo* was recorded eight times on six labels with different arrangements each time as the young composer experimented. On *Mood indigo* in 1930, the classic sound of the melody played by a blend of Nanton, Barney Bigard on clarinet and trumpeter Artie Whetsol showed the formidable skill of a born arranger/composer. The band had already been billed for years as Duke Ellingon & His Famous Orchestra in 1939, when Ben Webster on tenor sax and Jimmy Blanton on bass joined, along with Ellington's amanuensis Billy Strayhorn (1915-67), like Duke a composer and arranger: their work together was so seamless that later they often could not recall who had written what. Webster was the first authoriative tenor stylist in the band, while Blanton was among a handful of the most influential musicians in the history of jazz before his early death from TB. The band began recording for Victor in early 1940 and the flood of masterpieces up to the infamous 1943 musicians unions' strike against the record companies has never been equaled. *The great Ellington units* compiles the small group tracks from 1940\41, some of the most beautiful chamber music ever recorded, especially the Johnny Hodges sides: Strayhorn wrote beautiful erotic ballads for Hodges sunsuous alto sax, and the sessions included the first appearance of the riff that would be used in Ellington's *Happy go lucky local* and borrowed in a few years for the early R&B classic *Night train.* By the end of the '40's hard times were setting in for big bands and many critics were writing Duke off, but in 1956 he played at the Newport Jazz Festival and almost started a riot with the 20-year-old arrangement *Diminuendo in blue* and *Crescendo in blue*: Paul Gonsalves on tenor was supposed to play a bridge between the two parts, but played 27 choruses and had the audience dancing in the aisles. Ellington made the cover of Time magazine and the Newport album the top 15 of the Billboard pop album chart, his status as elder statesmen of American music never again in doubt. He also wrote extended compositions, film soundtracks and works for the musical stage, much of this never recorded or even assembled properly; he was always most interested in the work at hand: once his friends presented him with a beautifully bound book of his compositions, he made a gracious speech of thanks and walked away leaving the book behind. New albums are still coming out in the USA from the private stock or from broadcasters' vaults, loving produced by his son Mercer, by Stanley Dance and/or archivist Jerry Valburn; among the late masterpieces/recent reissues are the *New Orleans suite,* 1970, *Far east suite* (1966) and *...And his mother called him Bill* (1967), a tribute to Strayhorn, who sent his last composition *Blood count* to the band from the hosptial where he lay dying of cancer. (Donald Clarke, April 1989)s.

SKIN DEEP
Tracks: / Skin deep.
7" Single: Released Mar '54, on Philips, by Phonogram Ltd. Deleted '59. Catalogue no: **PB 243**

Ellington, Ray

LONG BLACK NYLONS
Tracks: / Long black nylons.
7" Single: on Northwood, by Northwood Records. Catalogue no: **NW 45 003**

MADISON, THE
Tracks: / Madison, The.
7" Single: Released Nov '62, on Ember (1), by Bulldog Records (UK). Catalogue no: **S 102**

Elliot

PRETENDING TO CARE
Tracks: / Pretending to care.
7" Single: Released 5 Mar '88, on Music For Nations, by Music For Nations Records. Catalogue no: **FAA 110**
12" Single: Released 5 Mar '88, on Music For Nations, by Music For Nations Records. Catalogue no: **12 FAA 110**

Elliot, Ian

FAKE ALL YOUR DREAMS
Tracks: / Fake all your dreams.
7" Single: Released Dec '82, on Office Box, Catalogue no: **EBO 2**
12" Single: Released Dec '83, on Office Box, Catalogue no: **EBO T2**

Elliot, Ken

ROCKABOOGIE
Tracks: / Rockaboogie / Body music.
7" Single: Released Jan '80, on RCA, by BMG Records (UK). Deleted '83. Catalogue no: **PB 5207**

Elliott, Bern

MONEY
Tracks: / Money.
7" Single: Released Nov '63, on Decca, by Decca Records. Catalogue no: **F 11770**

NEW ORLEANS
Tracks: / New Orleans.
7" Single: Released Mar '64, on Decca, by Decca Records. Deleted '69. Catalogue no: **F 11852**

Elliott, Jack

Biographical details: Born Elliott Charles Adnopez in 1931, a folksinger, songwriter and guitarist, aka Ramblin' Jack, the singing cowboy from Brooklyn. He ran away from home (a 45,000-acre ranch in the middle of Flatbush) to join the rodeo, soon met Woody Guthrie and toured with him until Woody said that Jack 'sound more like me than I do'. he spent the mid-'50's in Europe, acquiring a large following which had never been able to hear Guthrie; he played with Derroll Adams in London and other places, and was a considerable influence on UK music. He also toured with the Weavers, recorded with Johnny Cash and Tom Rush; like Arlo Guthrie he is major link between a bygone age and today's folk scene. (Donald Clarke, April 1989).

MAKIN' ME HAPPY
Tracks: / Makin' me happy.
7" Single: Released May '83, on Rubber, by Mawson & Wareham Music. Catalogue no: **ADUB 18**

Elliott, Kenneth

ONLY LOVE
Tracks: / Only love / Performer.
7" Single: Released Apr '80, on RCA, by BMG Records (UK). Deleted '82. Catalogue no: **PB 5245**

Ellis, Alton

AND I LOVE HER
Tracks: / And I love her / Chatty people.
7" Single: Released Dec '81, on Island, by Island Records. Deleted Dec '84. Catalogue no: **12 WIP 6748**

BABY I LOVE YOU
Tracks: / Baby I love you.
12" Single: Released Oct '83, on Treasure Isle, Catalogue no: **TRE 009**

BAMMY IN MY TIME
Tracks: / Bammy in my time.
12" Single: Released Jul '85, on All Tone, Catalogue no: **AT 003**

BETTER EXAMPLE
Tracks: / Better example.
12" Single: Released Nov '88, on All Tone, Catalogue no: **AT 010**

FOREVER AND EVER
Tracks: / Forever and ever / Jamaican rock.
12" Single: Released Mar '84, on Skynote, Catalogue no: **SKYDD 12**

GIMME YOUR LOVE
Tracks: / Gimme your love.
12" Single: Released Oct '85, on Jah Life, Catalogue no: **JL 013**

HARRY J & ALL STARS/ALTON ELLIS
CD 5": Released Nov '88, on Counterpoint, Catalogue no: **CDEP 6 C**

I CAN'T STAND IT
Tracks: / I can't stand it.
12" Single: Released Dec '83, on Treasure Isle, Catalogue no: **TRE 011**

I DON'T KNOW WHY
Tracks: / I don't know why / Iron rock special.
12" Single: Released Apr '86, on All Tone, Catalogue no: **AT 004**

LIVE AND LOVE
Tracks: / live and love / Live and love (version).
12" Single: Released Sep '86, on Magnificent Master Blaster, Catalogue no: **12**

MMB 4

LOVE IS TOPS
Tracks: / Love is tops.
7" Single: Released Apr '83, on Body Music, by Nuclear Records. Catalogue no: **BMDIS 8**

STICK BY THE RULE
Tracks: / Stick by the rule.
12" Single: Released Nov '88, on Natty Congo, Catalogue no: **NCDM 045**

TELEPHONE LINE
Tracks: / Telephone line.
12" Single: Released Aug '83, on Cypron, Catalogue no: **CYP 03**

TOO LATE TO TURN BACK NOW
Tracks: / Too late to turn back now.
12" Single: Released Nov '82, on Fashion, by Fashion Records. Catalogue no: **FAD 013**

WISE BIRD
Tracks: / Wise bird.
7" Single: Released May '83, on Bluebird (2), by BMG Records (UK). Catalogue no: **BR 2**

YOU'RE SO SWEET
Tracks: / You're so sweet.
12" Single: Released Jul '88, on Eastern, Catalogue no: **EA 2040**

Ellis, Beggs & Howard

BAD TIMES
Tracks: / Bad times / One tongue.
7" Single: Released 14 Aug '88, on RCA, by BMG Records (UK). Deleted May '89. Catalogue no: **PB 42041**
12" Single: Released 14 Aug '88, on RCA, by BMG Records (UK). Deleted May '89. Catalogue no: **PT 42042**
CD 5": Released Jun '89, on RCA, by BMG Records (UK). Catalogue no: **PD 42042**

BIG BUBBLES, NO TROUBLES (SINGLE)
Tracks: / Big bubbles, no troubles / Rock me / Hungry man (Available on CD only).
Note: * Only available on CD single.
10" single: Released Jul '88, on RCA, by BMG Records (UK). Deleted May '89. Catalogue no: **PT 42090X**
7" Single: Released Feb '89, on RCA, by BMG Records (UK). Deleted Aug '89. Catalogue no: **PB 42089**
12" Single: Released Jul '88, on RCA, by BMG Records (UK). Catalogue no: **PT 42090R**
12" Single: Released Jun '88, on RCA, by BMG Records (UK). Catalogue no: **PB 42090**
12" Single: Released Jun '88, on RCA, by BMG Records (UK). Catalogue no: **PT 42090**
CD 5": Released Jun '88, on RCA, by BMG Records (UK). Catalogue no: **PD 42090**

BUBBLES (DANCE MIX)
Tracks: / Bubbles (dance mix) / Bubbles (instrumental).
7" Single: Released Apr '89, on RCA, by BMG Records (UK). Catalogue no: **PB 42788**

WHERE DID TOMORROW GO
Tracks: / Where did tomorrow go / Nobody knows.
7" Single: Released Nov '88, on RCA, by BMG Records (UK). Deleted Aug '89. Catalogue no: **PB 42317**
12" Single: Released Nov '88, on RCA, by BMG Records (UK). Deleted Aug '89. Catalogue no: **PT 42318**
CD 5": Released Nov '88, on RCA, by BMG Records (UK). Deleted Jul '89. Catalogue no: **PD 42318**

Ellis, Hortense

FIRST CUT
Tracks: / First cut.
12" Single: Released Oct '89, on Pickout, Catalogue no: **PICK 27**

UNEXPECTED PLACES
Tracks: / Unexpected places / Wooden heart.
12" Single: Released Jun '82, on Burning Sounds, by Burning Sounds Records. Catalogue no: **BRD 045**

Ellis, Joanne

QUEEN OF THE WORLD
Tracks: / Queen of the world / You make me feel so cross.
7" Single: Released Oct '82, on Magnet, by WEA Records. Deleted Oct '85. Catalogue no: **MAG 182**

Ellis, Mark

CRAZY LOVE
Tracks: / Crazy love.
12" Single: Released Mar '83, on EAB, Catalogue no: **EA 001**

Ellis, Michael

ALL MY LOVE FOR YOU
Tracks: / All my love for you.
10" single: Released Feb '87, on Big One Records, by Big One Records. Catalogue no: **VBIG 2**
12" Single: Released Feb '87, on Big One Records, by Big One Records. Catalogue no: **VVBIG 2**

MEMORIES OF YOU
Tracks: / Memories of you.
12" Single: Released Sep '88, on White Label (1), Catalogue no: **PP 2**

SUPER LOVE
Tracks: / Super love.
12" Single: Released Aug '87, on Big One Records, by Big One Records. Catalogue no: **VVBIG 6**

Ellis, Nick

MY MORRIS MINOR
7" Single: Released Mar '89, on Ellis Design & Advertising, by Ellis Design & Advertising. Catalogue no: **UNKNOWN**

Ellis, Noel

DANCING PARTNER
Tracks: / Dancing partner / Dreadlocks time.
12" Single: Released Aug '86, on VIP (2), Catalogue no: **VIP 002**
12" Single: Released Dec '83, on Jam Can, Catalogue no: **JC 001**

GENESIS TO REVELATIONS
Tracks: / Genesis to revelation.
12" Single: Released Jun '84, on All Tone, Catalogue no: **AT 001**

Ellis, Paul

RUNAROUND SUE
Tracks: / Runaround Sue / Runaround Sue (version).
12" Single: Released Dec '88, on Opium, by Opium Records. Catalogue no: **OPINT 27**
7" Single: Released Dec '88, on Opium, by Opium Records. Catalogue no: **OPIN 27**

Ellis, Ron

HERE COMES SUMMER
Tracks: / Here comes summer / Hot California nights.
7" Single: Released Jun '81, on Rox, by Rox Records. Catalogue no: **ROX 011**

Ellis, Shirley

Biographical details: This American singer, born in New York, gained entry into showbiz by winning an amateur talent contest at the city's Apollo Theatre. She came to fame in 1964 with *The nitty gritty*, which reached no.8 on the US charts. This was followed by two 1965 hits, *The name game* and *The clapping song*, which was the only one to register in Britain. All three were soul-tinged gimmicks - perfect party music. However, subsequent singles were only minor US hits and despite Broadway appearances, Ellis eventually retired from entertainment. The three songs were all written by Lincoln Chase, Shirley's husband and manager. He had previously been an unsuccessful recording artist, but had penned some 50's hits for other artists, notably *Such a night*, a UK no.1 for Johnnie Ray, and later covered by Elvis Presley, and also *Jim Dandy* (a 1957 US hit for LaVern Baker). *The clapping song* was revived in 1982 by the Belle Stars, a British all-girl group who took the song to the UK no.11 position. (Bob Macdonald, 28/7/85).

CLAPPING SONG (OLD GOLD)
Tracks: / Clapping song, The.
7" Single: Released Jul '82, on Old Gold, by Old Gold Records. Deleted Jul '88. Catalogue no: **OG 9161**

CLAPPING SONG, THE
Tracks: / Clapping song, The.
7" EP: Released Jul '78, on MCA, by MCA Records. Deleted '81. Catalogue no: **MCEP 1**
7" Single: Released May '65, on London-American, Deleted '70. Catalogue no: **HLR 9961**

Ellison, Lorraine

Biographical details: A soul singer from Philadelphia. She sang gospel with her sisters in high school; the Ellison Singers performed at the Festival of Two Worlds in Italy in 1964 and Lorraine signed solo to Mercury; *I dig you baby* was an R&B hit; the next year on Warner Brothers *Stay with me* reached the pop Hot 100, still regarded as a classic of the genre for its sheer intensity. *Heart be still* also made the charts in 1969, but she never did it again, despite the high regard of soul connoisseurs and good choice of material. (Donald Clarke, April 1989).

ELMO & PATSY - GRANDMA GOT RUN OVER BY A REINDEER (Released on Stiff)

STAY WITH ME
Tracks: / Only your love / Try (just a little bit harder) / I'm gonna cry 'til my tears run dry / I want to be loved / Hurt came back again, The / Stay with me / You don't know nothing about love / You're easy on my mind / No matter how it all turns out / Good love / Heart be still.
7" Single: Released Jul '81, on Warner Bros., by WEA Records. Catalogue no: **K 16001**

Ellison, Willie

LOVE'S GOT A HOLD ON YOU
Tracks: / Love's got a hold on you / Love out of reach.
7" Single: Released Sep '80, on Red Bus, by Red Bus Records. Deleted Sep '83. Catalogue no: **RBUS 57**
12" Single: Released Sep '80, on Red Bus, by Red Bus Records. Deleted Sep '83. Catalogue no: **RBUSL 57**

WIDE WORLD
Tracks: / Wide world / Chained lover.
7" Single: Released Mar '80, on Red Bus, by Red Bus Records. Deleted Mar '83. Catalogue no: **RBUS 50**

Elmo & Patsy

GRANDMA GOT RUN OVER BY A REINDEER (see panel above)
Tracks: / Grandma got run over by a reindeer / Christmas.
7" Single: Released '80, on Stiff, by Stiff Records. Catalogue no: **BUY 99**

E.L.O.

Biographical details: At the time of their greatest success, this British band comprised Bev Bevan, Melvyn Gayle, Kelly Groucutt, Mik Kaminski, Jeff Lynne, Hugh Macdowell and Richard Tandy. The group is commonly referred to as ELO. ELO was born out of the ashes of the Move, who was one of Britain's leading pop groups of the late 60's and early 70's. That group's driving force had been the richly talented musician Roy Wood; Jeff Lynne, on vocals and guitar, joined in 1970. When the Move terminated in 1972, Wood and Lynne launched the Electric Light Orchestra with the intention of moving away from the Move's singles-oriented pop sound into a deeped and broader style; they wanted to merge the sounds of a classical orchestra with those of a rock band. However, the two men's musical and personal differences precipitated an early rupture - Wood took two ELO players, plus five new recruits, and formed Wizzard; meanwhile, Lynne became the sole leader and key creative force of ELO, eventually achieving and exceeding all his musical and commercial aims. After hitting the UK Top 10 in summer 1972 with the single *10358 overture*, ELO's first Wood-less hit was 1973's *Roll over Beethoven*, a quasi-classical remake of the Chuck Berry standard; this reached the no.6 position. After a disappointing 1974, the group settled to a stable line-up (which included two cellists and a violinist) and began to make major headway in the States. The Lennon-esque *Can't get it out of my head*, from the *Eldorado* LP, hit the US Top 10 in early '75 and was followed in early '76 by the similarly successful *Evil woman*. This American acceptance rebounded to the band's native Britain, where record buyers woke up again. *A new world record*, issued at the end of 1976, broke the ELO into a huge commercial commodity around the globe. With Jeff Lynne now totally confident in his role as songwriter producer and dominant leader, this album contained the perfect crystallisation of the group's symphonic, big-sounding and above all melodic pop/rock. Heavily influenced by the Beatles, Lynne's singles and albums were often of epic dimensions. During 1977-9 they sold truckloads of LP's, *A new world record*, *Out of the blue*, and *Discovery*, and international singles flowed thick and fast. During the final month of 1979, ELO shed their violinist and cellists and became a four-piece unit; they did, however, retain the use of their 30-piece string backup section. 1980 brought them their only UK no.1 single with *Xanadu*, a collaboration with Olivia Newton-John - this was one of several ELO contributions to the movie of that name. 1981 returned them to the top of the British album charts with *Time*, which featured their last really big single *Hold on tight*. 1983's *Secret message* LP fared relatively dissapointingly, and Lynne put ELO in abeyance while he turned to outside projects. (Bob Macdonald, 26/7/85)
A pop band formed in 1971 by guitarist/vocalist Jeff Lynne and Roy Wood (who quit in 1972) from the ashes of the Move, adding Bev Bevan on drums. They are all from Birmingham. They had an elaborate stage act in the style of lat Beatle experiments, fusing classical instruments to a rock rhythm section. Their repertoire was of no real distinction despite Lynn's knack of writing catchy pop singles; he regained some credibility working with Dave Edmunds in1983-4 and ELO came back in 1986 after a long layoff with shows for Birmingham charities and a new album, *Balance of power*, with a harder, stripped-down sound. (Donald Clarke, April 1989).

10538 OVERTURE
Tracks: / 10538 overture / Roll over Beethoven.
7" Single: Released May '84, on EMI Golden 45's, by EMI Records. Catalogue no: **G45 22**

10538 OVERTURE (ORIGINAL)
Tracks: / 10538 overture.
7" Single: Released Jul '72, on Harvest (1), by EMI Records. Deleted '77. Catalogue no: **HAR 5053**

ALL OVER THE WORLD (SINGLE)
Tracks: / All over the world.
7" Single: Released Aug '80, on Jet, by Jet Records. Deleted '85. Catalogue no: **JET 195**

CALLING AMERICA
Tracks: / Calling America / Caught in a trap.
7" Single: Released Feb '86, on Epic, by CBS Records. Catalogue no: **A 6844**
12" Single: Released Feb '86, on Epic, by

E.L.O. - Shine a Little Love (Released on Jet)

CBS Records. Catalogue no: **QTA 6844**

CONFUSION
Tracks: / Confusion / Last train to London.
7" Single: Released Nov '79, on Jet, by Jet Records. Deleted '84. Catalogue no: **JET 166**

DIARY OF HORACE WIMP
Tracks: / Diary of Horace Wimp.
7" Single: Released Jul '79, on Jet, by Jet Records. Deleted '84. Catalogue no: **JET 150**

DON'T BRING ME DOWN
Tracks: / JET 153.
7" Single: Released Sep '79, on Jet, by Jet Records. Deleted '84. Catalogue no: **JET 153**

DON'T WALK AWAY
Tracks: / Don't walk away / Across the border.
7" Single: Released Nov '80, on Jet, by Jet Records. Deleted '85. Catalogue no: **JET 7004**

ELECTRIC LIGHT ORCHESTRA EP
7" EP: Released Dec '78, on Jet, by Jet Records. Deleted '83. Catalogue no: **ELO 1**

EVIL WOMAN
Tracks: / Evil woman.
7" Single: Released Jan '76, on Jet, by Jet Records. Deleted '81. Catalogue no: **JET 764**

GETTING TO THE POINT
Tracks: / Getting to the point / Secret lives.
7" Single: Released Jul '86, on Epic, by CBS Records. Catalogue no: **A 7317**
12" Single: Released Jul '86, on Epic, by CBS Records. Catalogue no: **TA 7317**

HOLD ON TIGHT
Tracks: / Hold on tight / When time stood still.
7" Single: Released Aug '81, on Jet, by Jet Records. Deleted '86. Catalogue no: **JET 7011**

I'M ALIVE
Tracks: / I'm alive / Drum dreams.
7" Single: Released May '80, on Jet, by Jet Records. Deleted '85. Catalogue no: **JET 195**

LIVIN' THING
Tracks: / Livin' thing.
7" Single: Released Nov '76, on Jet, by Jet Records. Deleted '81. Catalogue no: **UP 36184**

MA MA MA BELLE
Tracks: / Ma ma ma belle.
7" Single: Released Mar '74, on Warner Bros., by WEA Records. Deleted '79. Catalogue no: **K 16349**

MR. BLUE SKY
Tracks: / Mr. Blue sky.
7" Single: Released Jan '78, on Jet, by Jet Records. Deleted '83. Catalogue no: **UP 36342**

ROCKARIA
Tracks: / Rockaria.
7" Single: Released Feb '77, on Jet, by Jet Records. Deleted '82. Catalogue no: **UP 36209**

ROCK'N'ROLL IS KING
Tracks: / Rock 'n' roll is king.
7" Single: Released Jun '83, on Jet, by Jet Records. Catalogue no: **A 3500**
12" Single: Released Jun '83, on Jet, by Jet Records. Catalogue no: **TA 3500**

ROLL OVER BEETHOVEN
Tracks: / Roll over Beethoven.
7" Single: Released Jan '73, on Harvest (1), by EMI Records. Deleted '78. Catalogue no: **HAR 5063**

SHINE A LITTLE LOVE
Tracks: / Shine a little love / Jungle.
7" Single: Released May '79, on Jet, by Jet Records. Deleted '84. Catalogue no: **JET 144**

SHOWDOWN
Tracks: / Showdown.
7" Single: Released Oct '73, on Harvest (1), by EMI Records. Deleted '78. Catalogue no: **HAR 5077**
7" Single: Released Mar '79, on Harvest (1), by EMI Records. Catalogue no: **HAR 5179**

SO SERIOUS
Tracks: / So serious / Matter of fact, a / Matter of fact, A (alternative lyrics) ((Extra track on 12" version only)).
12" Single: Released Apr '86, on Epic, by CBS Records. Deleted '86. Catalogue no: **TA 7090**
7" Single: Released Apr '86, on Epic, by CBS Records. Deleted '86. Catalogue no: **A 7090**

STRANGE MAGIC
Tracks: / Strange magic.
7" Single: Released Jul '76, on Jet, by Jet Records. Deleted '81. Catalogue no: **JET 779**

SWEET TALKIN' WOMAN
Tracks: / Sweet talkin' woman.
7" Single: Released Oct '78, on Jet, by Jet Records. Deleted '83. Catalogue no: **JET 121**

TELEPHONE LINE
Tracks: / Telephone line.
7" Single: Released May '77, on Jet, by Jet Records. Deleted '82. Catalogue no: **UP 36254**

TICKET TO THE MOON
Tracks: / Ticket to the moon / Here is the news.
7" Single: Released Jan '82, on Jet, by Jet Records. Deleted '87. Catalogue no: **JET 7018**

TURN TO STONE
Tracks: / Turn to stone.
7" Single: Released Nov '77, on Jet, by Jet Records. Deleted '82. Catalogue no: **UP 36313**

TWILIGHT
Tracks: / Twilight.
7" Single: Released Oct '81, on Jet, by Jet Records. Catalogue no: **JET 7015**

WAY LIFE'S MEANT TO BE
7" Single: Released Mar '82, on Jet, by Jet Records. Catalogue no: **JET 7201**

WILD WEST HERO
Tracks: / Wild west hero.
7" Single: Released Jun '78, on Jet, by Jet Records. Deleted '83. Catalogue no: **JET 109**

Eloy

FOOLS
Tracks: / Fools / Heartbeat.
7" Single: Released Nov '83, on Heavy Metal Worldwide, by FM-Revolver Records. Catalogue no: **HMINT 1**
7" Pic: Released Nov '83, on Heavy Metal Worldwide, by FM-Revolver Records. Catalogue no: **HMPD 1**

Elphick, Kenny

RAINBOW
Tracks: / Rainbow.
7" Single: Released Sep '84, on Flamingo, by Airwave Records (USA). Catalogue no: **FL 198**

SATURDAY
Tracks: / Saturday / Traveller.
7" Single: Released Mar '84, on Flamingo, by Airwave Records (USA). Catalogue no: **FL 197**

Elphick, Michael

GOTCHA
Tracks: / Gotcha.
7" Single: Released 10 Oct '87, on A.1, by A.1 Records. Catalogue no: **A1 302**
12" Single: Released 10 Oct '87, on A.1, by A.1 Records. Catalogue no: **12 A1 302**

Elstar, Jon

I SEE YOU COMIN' (I WANT TO RUN AWAY)
Tracks: / I see you comin' (I want to run away) / I see you comin' (I want to run away)(Inst).
7" Single: Released Sep '85, on Trojan, by Trojan Records. Deleted May '88. Catalogue no: **JON 1**

Elvis Brothers

FIRE IN THE CITY
Tracks: / Fire in the city / Full speed straight ahead.
7" Single: Released Feb '84, on Portrait, by CBS Records. Catalogue no: **A 4135**

Ely, Joe

Biographical details: Country rock singer born in 1947 in Texas. He recorded with the acoustic country band the Flatlanders, with singer/songwriters Jimmy Dale Gilmore and Butch Hancock, described as a 'kind of missing link' in West Texas music; their album made in Nashville *One road more* in 1971 was not released until 1980 on Charly.
Ely formed his own band and built a reputation in Texas for mixture of Tex-mex, honky tonk, blues, a rock'n'roll touch: Texas music. The band included steel guitarist Lloyd Maines, later on Mercury in the Maines Brothers Band.
He signed to MCA in 1977 and made five albums but failed to make a breakthrough in the USA because his music fits none of the categories which radio programers rely on.
He was discovered by the Clash, who featured him as a guest on a UK tour; he toured in Linda Ronstadt's backup group, then produced *High res* in 1984: synth technology harnessed to C&W roots.
He made what would have been his seventh album on MCA but chose to leave the label, it's come out as *Lord of the highway* on Demon.
(Donald Clarke, April 1989).

DALLAS
Tracks: / Dallas / Hard livin'.
7" Single: Released Jun '81, on MCA, by MCA Records. Deleted Jun '84. Catalogue no: **MCA 729**

FINGERNAILS
Tracks: / Fingernails / Suckin' a big bottle of gin / Standin' at the Big Hotel.
7" EP: Released Mar '80, on MCA, by MCA Records. Deleted Mar '83. Catalogue no: **MCA 579**

MUSTA NOTTA GOTTA LOTTA (SINGLE)
Tracks: / Musta notta gotta lotta / Wishin' for you.
7" Single: Released Apr '81, on MCA, by MCA Records. Deleted '85. Catalogue no: **MCA 688**

Elysium

CAROUSEL
Tracks: / Carousel.
12" Single: Released 10 Feb '86, on Crisis, by Prism Records. Catalogue no: **EL 002RR**

Emanon

FRESH BEATS
Tracks: / Fresh beats / Susie.
12" Single: Released Aug '87, on Urban, by Polydor Ltd. Catalogue no: **URBX 9**
7" Single: Released Aug '87, on Urban, by Polydor Ltd. Catalogue no: **URB 9**

Emanuel, Robert

FOR YOUR LOVING GIRL
Tracks: / For your loving girl / Love affair can't done.
7" Single: Released 7 Aug '89, on John Dread Production, Catalogue no: **JDP 16**

Emanuele

REFUGE
Tracks: / Refuge.
12" Single: Released Mar '89, on Oadge, Catalogue no: **SE 001**

Emerald, Steve

I LEARN'T ABOUT WOMAN FROM HER
Tracks: / I learn't about women from her.
7" Single: Released Feb '83, on The Alien, Deleted '84. Catalogue no: **CATD 9**

MICHAEL CARMICHAEL OF CLARE
Tracks: / Michael Carmichael of Clare.
7" Single: Released Dec '82, on The Alien, Deleted '83. Catalogue no: **CATD 9**

Emeralds

AIN'T EASY
Tracks: / Ain't easy.
12" Single: Released Oct '84, on Bad Gong, Catalogue no: **UNKNOWN**

Emergency

POINTS OF VIEW (EP)
Tracks: / Point of view.
7" Single: Released Mar '83, on Riot City, by Riot City Records. Catalogue no: **RIOT 21**

Emerson

SOMETHING SPECIAL
Tracks: / Something special / Stars in Hollywood.
7" Single: Released Dec '83, on Neat, by Neat Records. Catalogue no: **NEAT 34**

Emerson, Keith

Biographical details: This British keyboards player, composer and arranger, who originally came from Worthing, began his musical career in 1963 as a member of Gary Farr & The T-Bones. Until their termination in 1967, this combo's raw R'n'B sound enjoyed a strong following on the club circuit; the group also made several appearances on British television, but were not capable of selling records.
He enjoyed greater success from 1967 till 1970, as a member of the Nice. Upon that ensemble's break up in '70, he formed Emerson, Lake & Palmer, who achieved huge success with their lavish brand of classical pomp-rock. In 1976, during a long period of ELP inactivity, Emerson had his sole solo entry on the UK charts, reaching no.21 on the singles list with a lively rendition of Meade Lux Lewis' *Honky tonk train blues*. When the trio split in late 1978, Emerson concentrated on solo work - he wrote and recorded two film scores, *Inferno* (1980) and *Nighthawks* (1981, starring Sylvester Stallone). Thereafter he kept a low profile, while Lake and Palmer enjoyed success with Asia.
This was a strange state of affairs, because Keith was generally regarded as ELP's driving force - he was certainly one of the pioneers of the synthesiser and with his dynamic and extravagant disc and concert performances, helped to broaden the horizons of rock music. It was all quite a change from his sixties day job as a Worthing bank clerk.
(Bob Macdonald, 28/7/85).

I'M A MAN
Tracks: / I'm a man / Nighthawks.
7" Single: Released Apr '81, on MCA, by MCA Records. Deleted Apr '86. Catalogue no: **MCA 697**

TAXI RIDE
Tracks: / Taxi ride / Mater tenebrarum.
7" Single: Released Oct 1980, on Atlantic,

by WEA Records. Deleted Oct '81. Catalogue no: **K 11611**

UP THE ELEPHANT & ROUND THE CASTLE
Tracks: / Up the elephant & round the castle.
7" Single: Released Dec '83, on Red Bus, by Red Bus Records. Catalogue no: **RBUS 85**

WE THREE KINGS
Tracks: / We three kings of Orient are.
7" Single: Released Dec '88, on E.R., by Priority Records. Deleted Sep '89. Catalogue no: **KEITH 1**

Emerson, Lake & Palmer

Biographical details: This British group consisted of Keith Emerson, Greg Lake and Carl Palmer and was commonly referred to as ELP. Prior to ELP's formation in 1970, all three players had gained much experience on the UK music scene. Emerson, who was instrumental in founding the band, was an important member of the Nice. Lake was a founder member of King Crimson. Palmer had played with Cris Farlowe, The Crazy World Of Arthur Brown and Atomic Rooster. After making their debut at the 1970 Isle Of Wight festival, ELP released their debut album in November that year - *Emerson, Lake & Palmer* was a strong seller, reaching no.4 and logging 28 weeks on the chart. Their second album *Tarkus* reached no.1 in Britain in June 1971. The trio became a major attraction on both sides of the Atlantic, thanks to their grandiose fusion of classical music with rock. The group's driving force was Emerson, who not only amazed audiences with his dexterity on a grand piano, but was also one of the pioneers of the synth., he combined his musical precision with a flair for stage antics, such as knifing his keyboards and vaulting over the organ. Lake performed any vocals, and played guitar and bass, as well as producing the records. Palmer was the drummer and percussionist. All three musicians contributed to the writing; in addition they sometimes adapted the work of classical composers, such as *Pictures at an exhibition* by Mussorgsky. In an era when rock music was dominated by skilful musicianship and pompous exhibitionism, ELP combined these qualities superbly, and sailed through the early 70's with flying colours. Their albums, *Trilogy* (1972), *Brain salad surgery* (1973) and *Welcome back my friends....* (1974) were all top 10 hits in the UK and US. However, between '74 and '77, they took a long break from recording and touring (during which Lake scored a smash solo hit with *I believe in Father Christmas*, and Emerson released *Honky tonk train blues*) - and when they came back, they found they epitomised the kind of "old wave" that the new UK punk music was rebelling against, and that America had found many new rock bands of its own. After one hit LP with *Works* - which yielded the UK no.2 single *Fanfare for the common man*, and it was their only hit 45 on account of the fact that they rarely released singles during their heyday - they drifted downhill and split up in 1978. After the failure of his new band PM, Palmer became a founder member of the successful supergroup Asia. Lake eventually joined him. (Bob Macdonald, 29/7/85)
A progressive/techno rock band formed in 1970 by keyboardist Keith Emerson (ex Nice), bassist/vocalist Greg Lake, and ex-Atomic Rooster drummer Carl Palmer. Their stuff was commercially successful but soon dated; touring with 36 tons of equipment in 1973, they were taking music in a direction that was soon unprofitable in more ways than one. Emerson later wrote film scores; Lake recorded solo, then joined Asia, the supergroup Palmer had joined when his own group PM foundered; Emerson and Lake re-formed with ex-Jeff Beck/Whitesnake drummer Cozy Powell for Emerson Lake & Powell in 1986. (Donald Clarke, April 1989).

FANFARE FOR THE COMMON MAN
Tracks: / Fanfare for the common man.
7" Single: Released Jun '77, on Atlantic, by WEA Records. Catalogue no: **K 10946**

PETER GUNN
Tracks: / Peter Gunn / knife edge.
7" Single: Released Jan '80, on Atlantic, by WEA Records. Deleted '83. Catalogue no: **K 11416**

Emerson Lake & Powell

TOUCH AND GO
Tracks: / Touch and go / Learning to fly / Locomotion, The ((Extra track on 12" version only)).
12" Single: Released Jun '86, on Polydor, by Polydor Ltd. Deleted Mar '87. Catalogue no: **POSPX 804**
7" Single: Released Jun '86, on Polydor, by Polydor Ltd. Deleted '87. Catalogue no: **POSP 804**

Emery, Dick

YOU ARE AWFUL
Tracks: / You are awful.
7" Single: Released Jan '73, on Pye, Deleted '76. Catalogue no: **7N 45202**

EMF

ANTI-BELLUM
Tracks: / Anti bellum.
7" Single: Released Apr '81, on RCA, by BMG Records (UK). Deleted Apr '84. Catalogue no: **RCA 61**

ROUGH POTENTIAL
Tracks: / Rough potential / Rough potential (version).
12" Single: Released Aug '89, on Greedy Beat, Catalogue no: **GRREDT 10**

Emily

IRONY
Tracks: / Irony.
7" Single: Released Jan '88, on Creation, by Creation Records. Catalogue no: **CRE 050**
12" Single: Released Jan '88, on Creation, by Creation Records. Catalogue no: **CRE 050T**

Emm, M.D.

GET HIP TO THIS
Tracks: / Get hip to this.
7" Single: Released Mar '89, on Republic, by Code Records. Catalogue no: **LIC 022**
12" Single:.Released Mar '89, on Republic, by Code Records. Catalogue no: **LICT 022**

Emma

DON'T MAKE ME CHOOSE
Tracks: / Don't make me choose / Only love.
12" Single: Released Aug '87, on RCA, by BMG Records (UK). Catalogue no: **EMMAT 2**
7" Single: Released Aug '87, on RCA, by BMG Records (UK). Catalogue no: **EMMA 2**

FIND A WAY
Tracks: / Find a way / Find a way (inst).
7" Single: Released Sep '86, on RCA, by BMG Records (UK). Catalogue no: **PB 40954**
12" Single: Released Sep '86, on RCA, by BMG Records (UK). Catalogue no: **PT 40955**

Emmanuel, David

GIVING IT UP FOR LOVE
Tracks: / Giving it up for love.
7" Single: Released Jul '83, on White Lodge, by White Lodge Records. Catalogue no: **WL 1**

WAR CRY
Tracks: / War cry.
7" Single: Released Feb '87, on In Recordings, Catalogue no: **INR 5**
12" Single: Released Feb '87, on In Recordings, Catalogue no: **INRT 5**

WHEN I FALL IN LOVE
Tracks: / When I fall in love / Stir it around.
7" Single: Released Dec '83, on White Lodge, by White Lodge Records. Catalogue no: **WL 2**

Emmanuel, Eli

TURNING POINT
Tracks: / Turning point / Sarene.
12" Single: Released Dec '82, on Silver Camel, Catalogue no: **SC 020**

Emmanuel, Judy

IF YOU WANT ME
Tracks: / If you want me.
12" Single: Released Oct '89, on Blue Mountain, Catalogue no: **BMD 071**

Emmanuel, Marie-Anne

MERRY CHRISTMAS AND HAPPY NEW YEAR
Tracks: / Merry Christmas & happy New Year / Merry Christmas & happy new year (part 2).
7" Single: Released Nov '84, on Button, by Musical Characters Records. Catalogue no: **BTN 118**

Emmanuel, Robert

DON'T GET WEARY
Tracks: / Don't get weary.
12" Single: Released Jul '82, on Black Roots, Catalogue no: **BRD 01**

GOT TO GET YOUR LOVE
Tracks: / Got to get your love.
12" Single: Released Mar '84, on Black Roots, Catalogue no: **BR 181263**

SOUL MAGIC
Tracks: / Soul magic.
7" Single: Released Jun '88, on Uptempo, Catalogue no: **TEMP 024**

Emmanuelle

GHETTO BLASTER
Tracks: / Ghetto blaster / Ghetto blaster (instrumental).
7" Single: Released Feb '89, on Synchronicity, by OBE Records. Catalogue no: **EMM 3**
12" Single: Released Feb '89, on Synchronicity, by OBE Records. Catalogue no: **EMM 312**

RADIO SHOW
Tracks: / Radio show / Aquarium.
12" Pic: Released Oct '88, on Beach Ocean Disque, Catalogue no: **12S LPLTD 001**
7" Single: Released Oct '88, on Beach Ocean Disque, Catalogue no: **7S LTD 001**
CD 5": Released Oct '88, on Beach Ocean Disque, Catalogue no: **CD5 SPLTD 001**

Emma's Boogie Band

CROSSROADS
Tracks: / Crossroads.
7" Single: Released Apr '84, on Gutta (Sweden), by Gutta Records (Sweden). Catalogue no: **GUTS 1006**

Emotion Pictures

THEY SAY SPACE IS COLD
Tracks: / They say space is cold / Rescue remedy.
7" Single: Released '81, on Cherry Red, by Cherry Red Records. Deleted '87. Catalogue no: **CHERRY 14**

Emotional Play

STRANGER IN MY HOME
Tracks: / Stranger in my home.
12" Single: Released May '83, on Edible Music, Catalogue no: **EM 003**

Emotions (Group)

BEST OF MY LOVE
Tracks: / Best of my love / Lady Marmalade / Disco lady / Indian summer / Best of my love.
12" Single: Released Feb '86, on Old Gold, by Old Gold Records. Catalogue no: **OG 4009**
7" Single: Released Sep '77, on CBS, by CBS Records. Deleted '80. Catalogue no: **CBS 5555**

FLOWERS
Tracks: / Flowers / Best of my love / I don't wanna to lose your love / Me for you / You've got the right to know / We go through changes / Special part / No plans for tomorrow / How can you stop loving someone / God will take care of you.
12" Single: Released Jul '86, on Streetwave, Catalogue no: **SWAVE 10**

MISS YOUR LOVE
Tracks: / Miss your love / I can't wait to make you mine.
12" Single: Released May '85, on Motown, by BMG Records (UK). Catalogue no: **ZT 40114**
7" Single: Released May '85, on Motown, by BMG Records (UK). Catalogue no: **ZB 40113**

EMPD

I'M HOUSIN'
Tracks: / I'm housin'.
7" Single: Released Feb '89, on Sleeping Bag, by Sleeping Bag Records. Catalogue no: **SBUK 7**
12" Single: Released Feb '89, on Sleeping Bag, by Sleeping Bag Records. Catalogue no: **SBUK 7 T**

Empire

HOT SEAT
Tracks: / Hot seat / All these things.
7" Single: Released Sep '81, on White Line, by White Line Records. Deleted '87. Catalogue no: **D/E 004**

MY IMAGINATION
Tracks: / My imagination / Big city / My imagination (ext).
Note: (P) 1988 original sound recording (s) made by EMI Records Ltd. Producer Richard James Burgess.
7" Single: Released '88, on Parlophone, by EMI Records. Deleted Nov '88. Catalogue no: **RP 6185**
12" Single: Released Jul '88, on Parlophone, by EMI Records. Deleted Nov '88. Catalogue no: **12RX 6185**
12" Single: Released Jul '88, on Parlophone, by EMI Records. Deleted Nov '88. Catalogue no: **12R 6185**
7" Single: Released '88, on Parlophone, by EMI Records. Deleted Nov '88. Catalogue no: **R 6185**

TALK FREE
Tracks: / Talk free / Talk free (ext. version) / Give me some time.
12" Single: Released Jan '88, on Parlophone, by EMI Records. Deleted 31 Jul '88. Catalogue no: **12R 6175**
7" Single: Released Jan '88, on Parlophone, by EMI Records. Deleted 31 Jul '88. Catalogue no: **R 6175**

THIS IS MY WORD
Tracks: / This is my word / This is my word (extended version) / Behind closed doors / This is my word (7" version).
7" Single: Released May '88, on Parlophone, by EMI Records. Catalogue no: **R 6179**
12" Single: Released May '88, on Parlophone, by EMI Records. Catalogue no: **12R 6179**

Empire State

EMPIRE STATE
12" Single: Released 11 May '88, on Priority, by Priority Records. Deleted 24 Jun '87. Catalogue no: **12 EMPIREF 1**

Employees

PLAY WITH FIRE
Tracks: / Play with fire.
7" Single: Released Jun '88, on Antler, by Antler Records (Belgium). Deleted '88. Catalogue no: **ANT 015**

En Route

WASTING MY TIME
Tracks: / Wasting my time / I've got that feeling / I wanna talk to you / Do it the French way / It don't make you a woman / Liar.
12" Single: Released Apr '80, on RCA, by BMG Records (UK). Deleted '83. Catalogue no: **SUPER 45**

Enchantment

FEEL LIKE DANCIN'
Tracks: / Feel like dancin'.
7" Single: Released Apr '85, on Prelude, Catalogue no: **MHS 104**

SETTIN' IT OUT
Tracks: / Settin' it out / Are you ready for love.
7" Single: Released Jan '81, on RCA, by BMG Records (UK). Deleted Jan '84. Catalogue no: **RCA 32**
12" Single: Released Jan '81, on RCA, by BMG Records (UK). Deleted Jan '84. Catalogue no: **RCAT 32**

End To End

ARE YOU GONNA BE MY LOVER
Tracks: / Are you gonna be my lover.
12" Single: Released May '89, on White Label (1), Catalogue no: **TS 3**

CONFUSION
Tracks: / Confusion.
12" Single: Released Aug '88, on Sure Delight, by Sure Delight Records. Catalogue no: **SDT 7**

Endgames

FIRST LAST FOR EVERYTHING
Tracks: / First last for everything / First last for everything (pt 2).
7" Single: Released Oct '82, on Mercury, by Phonogram Ltd. Catalogue no: **GAME 2**

WE FEEL GOOD
Tracks: / We feel good / Through darkness.
12" Single: Released Apr '82, on Mercury, by Phonogram Ltd. Deleted Apr '85. Catalogue no: **GAME 12**
7" Single: Released Apr '82, on Mercury, by Phonogram Ltd. Deleted Apr '85. Catalogue no: **GAME 1**

Endless Waves

WHO PUT THE BOMP
Tracks: / Who put the bomp.
7" Single: Released Sep '84, on Meteor, by Magnum Music Group. Catalogue no: **MTS 001**
12" Single: Released Sep '84, on Meteor, by Magnum Music Group. Catalogue no: **MTS 1001**

Enemy

FALLEN HERO
Tracks: / Fallen hero.
7" Single: Released Mar '82, on Fall Out, Deleted '88. Catalogue no: **FALL 001**

LAST BUT NOT LEAST (SINGLE)
Tracks: / Last but not least.
7" Single: Released May '84, on Rot, by Rot Records. Catalogue no: **ASS 9**

LAST RITES
Tracks: / Last rites.
7" Single: Released Jul '83, on Fall Out, Catalogue no: **FALL 014**

PUNK'S ALIVE
Tracks: / Punk's alive.
7" Single: Released Aug '82, on Fall Out, Catalogue no: **FALL 004**

STRIKE
Tracks: / Strike.
7" Single: Released Nov '84, on Rough Trade, by Rough Trade Records. Catalogue no: **RT 151**
12" Single: Released Nov '84, on Rough Trade, by Rough Trade Records. Catalogue no: **RTT 151**

Energy

RADIO RADIO-O
Tracks: / Radio radio-o / Rebel with a cause.
7" Single: Released Aug '86, on Aros, by Priority Records. Catalogue no: **PYR 3**

Enfield, Harry

LOADSAMONEY (DOIN' UP THE HOUSE)
Tracks: / Loadsamoney (doin' up the house).
7" Single: Released Apr '88, on Mercury, by Phonogram Ltd. Deleted Oct '88. Catalogue no: **DOSH 1**
12" Single: Released Apr '88, on Mercury, by Phonogram Ltd. Deleted Oct '88. Catalogue no: **DOSH 112**

Engelbert

IT'S EASY TO LOVE, IT'S NOT EASY TO LIVE TOGETHER
Tracks: / It's easy to love, it's not easy to live together / Royal affair.
7" Single: Released Jan '81, on Epic, by CBS Records. Deleted Jan '84. Catalogue no: **EPC 9353**

Engine Room

WILD TIMES
Tracks: / Wild times.
7" Single: Released Sep '84, on Arista, by BMG Records (UK). Catalogue no: **ARIST 587**
12" Single: Released Sep '84, on Arista, by BMG Records (UK). Catalogue no: **ARIST 12587**

YOUR KISS IS A WEAPON
Tracks: / Your kiss is a weapon / Fall of the house of U.
7" Single: Released Feb '85, on Arista, by BMG Records (UK). Catalogue no: **ARIST 593**
12" Single: Released Feb '85, on Arista, by BMG Records (UK). Catalogue no: **ARIST 12593**
7" Pic: Released Feb '85, on Arista, by BMG Records (UK). Catalogue no: **ARIST 593**

Engineers

POMPEII LOVERS
Tracks: / Pompeii lovers.
12" Single: Released Aug '87, on Waterfront, by Waterfront Music. Catalogue no: **WFT 32**

England

LONDON STORY
Tracks: / London story.
7" Single: Released Jun '84, on Jet, by Jet Records. Catalogue no: **A 7042**

VICTORIANA
Tracks: / Victoriana.
7" Single: Released Nov '83, on Jet, by Jet Records. Catalogue no: **JET 7041**

England Dan

I'D REALLY LOVE TO SEE YOU TONIGHT
Tracks: / I'd really love to see you tonight.
7" Single: Released Sep '76, on Atlantic, by WEA Records. Deleted '79. Catalogue no: **K 10810**

I'M IN IT FOR LOVE
Tracks: / I'm in it for love / Who's lonely now.
7" Single: Released Mar '80, on Atlantic, by WEA Records. Deleted '83. Catalogue no: **K 11452**

LOVE IS THE ANSWER
Tracks: / Love is the answer.
7" Single: Released Jun '79, on Big Tree (USA). Deleted '82. Catalogue no: **L 11296**

England Football Team

ALL THE WAY
Tracks: / All the way / All the way (instrumental) / All the way (extended mix) (Track on 12" version) / All the way (on your head mix) (Track on 12" version).
7" Single: Released 9 May '88, on MCA, by MCA Records. Catalogue no: **GOAL 1**
12" Single: Released 9 May '88, on MCA, by MCA Records. Catalogue no: **GOALT 1**
12" Single: Released Apr '88, on MCA, by MCA Records. Catalogue no: **MCAT 1250**
7" Single: Released Apr '88, on MCA, by MCA Records. Catalogue no: **MCA 1250**

BACK HOME
7" Single: Released Apr '70, on Pye. Deleted '73. Catalogue no: **7N 17920**

THIS TIME (SINGLE) (we'll get it right)
Tracks: / This time / National anthem / Abide with me.
7" Pic: Released Mar '82, on Englander. Catalogue no: **ER 1P**
7" Single: Released Mar '82, on Englander. Catalogue no: **ER 1**

WE'VE GOT THE WORLD AT OUR FEET
Tracks: / When we are far from home / We've got the whole world at our feet.
12" Single: Released May '86, on Columbia, by EMI Records. Catalogue no: **12 DBP 9128**
7" Single: Released Mar '86, on Columbia, by EMI Records. Catalogue no: **DB 9128**

England, Natasha

STAY WITH ME
Tracks: / Stay with me.
7" Single: Released Nov '85, on Towerbell. Catalogue no: **TOW 75**

England Sisters

HEARTBEAT
Tracks: / Heartbeat.
7" Single: Released Mar '60, on H.M.V., by EMI Records. Deleted '63. Catalogue no: **POP 710**

England Supporters

OH SWEET ENGLAND
Tracks: / Oh sweet England.
Note: Picture disc: plus package incl. badge, rosette etc.
7" Single: Released Apr '86, on Peak Records, by Peak Records. Catalogue no: **PRIDE 1**

OH SWEET ENGLAND (1982 RELEASE)
Tracks: / Oh sweet England / England.
7" Single: Released Apr '82, on Peak Records, by Peak Records. Catalogue no: **PPC 103**

England Under Snow

STUPID SEPTEMBER
Tracks: / Stupid September / Elephant ride, The / Only for ourselves (On 12" version only.) / And the problem (On 12" version only.) / Stanley (On 12" version only.).

Note: 5 - tracks: 12" lasts 20 minutes. 7" and 12" have complementary sleeves.
7" Single: Released Sep '87, on Snow Company, by Snow Company Records. Catalogue no: **OPUS 5 A**
12" Single: Released Sep '87, on Snow Company, by Snow Company Records. Catalogue no: **OPUS 5**

English...

ENGLISH GARLAND Topic sampler no.8
Tracks: / Robin Hood and the tanner: *Harris, Roy/Notts Alliance & Roger Watson* / Breakdown, The: *High Level Ranters* / Blanchland races: *High Level Ranters* / Six jolly miners: *Arthur, Dave & Toni* / Snow it melts the soonest, The: *Briggs, Anne* / Fox jumps over the parson's gate, The: *Bellamy, Peter* / Molecatcher, The: *Wrigley, Bernard* / Thousands or more: *Oak* / Barley and the rye, The: *Bellamy, Peter with Barry Dransfield fiddle* / Cuckoo, The: *Briggs, Anne* / Lark in the morning, The: *Arthur, Dave & Toni with Barry Dransfield Fiddle* / Gee whoa, Dobbin: *Wrigley, Bernard & Wilf Darlington* / Jack the horse courser: *Wrigley, Bernard & Wilf Darlington* / Roving round the County Tyrone: *Webb, Peta* / Bonny green woods, The: *Harris, Roy & Muckram Wakes* / Hexhamshire lass, The: *Gelfellon, Tom & The High Level Ranters* / Scan's polkas: *Oak*.
12" Single: Released '81, on Topic, by Topic Records. Catalogue no: **12TS 221**

English Air

HEY HEY(SUCH IS LIFE)
Tracks: / Hey hey (such is life).
7" Single: Released '85, on Wye, by Wye Records. Deleted '88. Catalogue no: **DC 005**

JULY MARCH
Tracks: / July March / English air.
7" Single: Released '83, on Paradise. Catalogue no: **PAR 1002**

English, Barbara Jean

BETTER IF YOU DON'T GET TO KNOW ME
Tracks: / Better if you don't get to know me.
7" Single: Released May '89, on Blue Chip, by Blue Chip Records. Catalogue no: **BLUE CHIP 17**
12" Single: Released May '89, on Blue Chip, by Blue Chip Records. Catalogue no: **BLUE CHIP 17 T**

EXPERIENCE (SINGLE)
Tracks: / Experience.
12" Single: Released Aug '89, on Blue Chip, by Blue Chip Records. Catalogue no: **BLUEC 21**

English Boy On The

MAN IN YOUR LIFE, THE
Tracks: / Man in your life, The.
7" Single: Released Dec '87, on New Rose (1), by New Rose Records. Catalogue no: **NEW 101**
12" Single: Released Dec '87, on New Rose (1), by New Rose Records. Catalogue no: **NEW 100**

English Boys

RUSSIANS ARE COMING
Tracks: / Russians are coming, The / TV girl.
7" Single: Released Apr '80, on Red Bus, by Red Bus Records. Deleted '83. Catalogue no: **RBUS 52**

English Chamber

MONSIGNOR QUIXOTE
Tracks: / Monsignor Quixote / Windmills or giants.
Note: Conducted by Anton Garcia Abril.
7" Single: on Red Bus, by Red Bus Records. Catalogue no: **RBUS 2207**

English Country Blues

DON'T TAKE LOVE
Tracks: / Don't take love.
7" Single: Released '83, on Rogue, by Rogue Records. Catalogue no: **FMSS 102**

English Dogs

MAD PUNX & ENGLISH DOGS
Tracks: / Mad punx & English Dogs.
12" Single: Released '83, on Clay, by Clay Records. Catalogue no: **PLATE 6**

METALMORPHOSIS (EP)
Tracks: / Nightmare of reality / Absolution / Let the killing begin.
12" Single: Released May '86, on Under One Flag, by Music For Nations Records. Catalogue no: **12 FLAG 101**

TO THE END OF THE EARTH
Tracks: / To the end of the earth.
12" Single: Released '84, on Rot, by Rot Records. Catalogue no: **ASS 17**

English Evenings

I WILL RETURN
Tracks: / I will return / White mask.
12" Single: Released '85, on Safari, by Safari Records. Catalogue no: **SAFELS 65**
7" Single: Released '85, on Safari, by Safari Records. Catalogue no: **SAFE 65**

TEAR YOU DOWN
Tracks: / Tear you down.
7" Single: Released '84, on Safari, by Safari Records. Catalogue no: **SAFE 64**
12" Single: Released '84, on Safari, by Safari Records. Catalogue no: **SAFELS 64**

THOSE BRILLIANT TEENS
Tracks: / Those brilliant teens.
7" Single: Released Jan '87, on GFM. Catalogue no: **GFM 106**
12" Single: Released Jan '87, on GFM. Catalogue no: **GFMT 106**

TOUCH
Tracks: / Touch / Final supper, The.
12" Single: Released '84, on Safari, by Safari Records. Catalogue no: **SAFELS 59**
7" Single: Released '84, on Safari, by Safari Records. Catalogue no: **SAFE 59**

WHAT'S THE MATTER WITH HELEN
Tracks: / What's the matter with Helen.
7" Single: Released '83, on Safari, by Safari Records. Catalogue no: **SAFE 57**

English, Junior

BETWEEN YOU AN ME
Tracks: / Between you and me.
12" Single: Released '84, on International English. Catalogue no: **IE 004**

DADDY'S HOME
Tracks: / Daddy's home / Way we were, The.
12" Single: Released '82, on Exclusive. Catalogue no: **EXC 601121**

EQUAL LOVE
Tracks: / Equal love / Weeping night.
12" Single: Released '83, on Sunsplash, by Sunsplash Records. Deleted '87. Catalogue no: **SNSW 01**

HEY BABY
Tracks: / Hey Baby / High Society.
12" Single: Released Mar '86, on International English. Catalogue no: **IE 006**

I'M CHECKING OUT
Tracks: / I'm checking out / Ready to learn.
12" Single: Released Mar '84, on International English. Catalogue no: **IE 02**

LONELINESS
Tracks: / Loneliness.
12" Single: Released Sep '85, on U Mat. Catalogue no: **UM 001**

NEVER TOO LATE
12" Single: Released Apr '85, on International English. Catalogue no: **IE 005**

ONLY SIXTEEN
Tracks: / Only sixteen / You're my fire.
7" Single: on PRT, by Castle Communications Records. Catalogue no: **7P 303**
12" Single: on PRT, by Castle Communications Records. Catalogue no: **12P 303**

SAY THAT YOU'LL STAY
Tracks: / Say that you'll stay.
12" Single: Released May '89, on W.A.. Catalogue no: **WAT 4**
12" Single: Released 20 Mar '89, on White Label (1). Catalogue no: **IE 11**

SHE DON'T LET NOBODY
Tracks: / She don't let nobody / She don't let nobody (version).
12" Single: Released 23 May '87, on International English. Catalogue no: **IE 008**

TEARS OF A CLOWN
Tracks: / Tears of a clown.
12" Single: Released '84, on Ruff Cut. Catalogue no: **RC 009**

YOU ARE MY EVERYTHING
Tracks: / You are my everything.
12" Single: Released '84, on International English. Catalogue no: **IE 03**

English McCoy

DAYS OF DOUBT
Tracks: / Days of doubt.
7" Single: Released Feb '89, on Nowyertalkin', by Nowyertalikin' Records. Catalogue no: **7 TALK 2**

GIVE ME SOMETHING TO BELIEVE IN
Tracks: / Give me something to believe in / Breakin' down.
7" Single: Released Sep '88, on Nowyertalkin', by Nowyertalikin' Records. Catalogue no: **7 TALK 2**
12" Single: Released Sep '88, on Nowyertalkin', by Nowyertalikin' Records. Catalogue no: **12 TALK 2**

English, Scott

BRANDY
Tracks: / Brandy.
7" Single: Released Oct '71, on Horse, by Trojan Records. Deleted '74. Catalogue no: **HOSS 7**

English Sub-titles

TANNOY
Tracks: / Tannoy / Cars on fire.
7" Single: Released '81, on Glass, by Glass Records. Deleted '83. Catalogue no: **GLASS 007**

Enid

FOOL
Tracks: / Fool / Tico.
7" Single: Released 20 Jul '80, on Pye. Deleted '83. Catalogue no: **7P 187**

GOLDEN EARRINGS
Tracks: / Golden earrings / 665-The great bean.
7" Single: Released Oct '80, on EMI, by EMI Records. Deleted Oct '83. Catalogue no: **EMI 5109**

HEIGH HO
Tracks: / Heigh ho / Twinkle twinkle little star.
7" Single: Released Oct '81, on Bronze, by Bronze Records. Deleted '85. Catalogue no: **BRO 134**

ITCHYCOO PARK
Tracks: / Itchycoo Park.
12" Single: Released Sep '86, on Sedition, by Sedition Records. Catalogue no: **EDITL 3314**
7" Single: Released Sep '86, on Sedition, by Sedition Records. Catalogue no: **EDIT 3314**

THEN THERE WERE NONE
Tracks: / Then there were none / Letters from America.
7" Single: Released '82, on RAK, by EMI Records. Catalogue no: **RAK 349**

Enigma

Biographical details: This all-male British band lived up to their name - nobody knew who they were and nobody cared. In May 1981 a Dutch studio aggregation called Starsound reached no.2 on the British charts (and later hit no.1 in America) with a disco medley single entitled *Stars on 45*; this consisted of a series of soundalike versions of old, (mainly Beatles), favourites, set to the insistent beat of a drum machine. Its success prompted a bunch of British studio musicians calling themselves Enigma, to rush onto the market place with a medley of recent disco hits. *Ain't no stoppin'* cruised to the UK no.11 position. The title referred to to the single's opening snippet, a rendition of McFadden & Whitehead's 1979 classic *Ain't no stoppin' us now*. It was easy for observers to criticise the Enigma single, because it was an opportunistic cash-in that pandered to the lowest common denominator; but at least these anonymous musicians should have been given credit for being the first Starsuond imitators to jump on the bandwagon. They were quickly followed by many others - by August 1981, they had been joined on the UK charts by a host of other medley merchants including Tight Fit, Gidea Park, Lobo, Startrax and the Royal Philharmonic Orchestra. During August, Enigma entered the chart with their own follow-up medley - *I love music* (another medley of disco numbers, beginning with the O'Jays' song of that name) reached the no.25 position. By the end of the year, Enigma had faded from the charts, along with most of the other medley maniacs. (Bob Macdonald, 29/7/85).

AIN'T NO STOPPING-DISCO MIX 81
Tracks: / Ain't no stopping - disco mix '81.
12" Single: Released '81, on Creole, by Creole Records. Catalogue no: **CR 12 9**
7" Single: Released '81, on Creole, by Creole Records. Catalogue no: **CR 9**

I LOVE THE MUSIC
Tracks: / I love the music.
12" Single: Released '81, on Creole, by Creole Records. Catalogue no: **CR 12 14**
7" Single: Released '81, on Creole, by Creole Records. Catalogue no: **CR 14**

WHICH WAY IS UP
Tracks: / Which way is up / Car wash / Pull up to the bumper / Shake your body / Space ride.
12" Single: Released Mar '87, on Debut, by Skratch Records. Catalogue no: **DEBTX 3018**

Ennis, Ethel

MOON WAS YELLOW, THE
Tracks: / Moon was yellow, The / Night club.
7" Single: Released Jul '87, on RCA, by BMG Records (UK). Deleted May '89. Catalogue no: **PB 49701**

Eno, Brian

Biographical details: This British keyboards and synthesiser player, composer, producer and vocalist, who was born in Woodbridge, Suffolk, began his musical career in late 1970 as a founder member of Brian Ferry's Roxy Music. Eno played synths (in those days, a novelty) with the band, who came to fame in 1972. The following year, however, the eccentric musician began to steal the spotlight from Ferry; the resulting ego problems and personality clash led to Eno quitting the group in July '73. He quickly began a solo career, which he interwove with a series of interesting collaborations with other artists. 1973's *No pussyfooting* LP was the first album featuring his most famous collaborator - the King Crimson guitarist/mainman, Robert Fripp. 1974's *Here come the warm jets* reached N.26 on the UK album chart, and was one of Eno's more accessible works. He also released the acclaimed but unsuccessful single (in fact, he never reached the UK singles charts as a solo performer) *Seven deadly Finns*, which amounted to a precognition of the punk era. In early 1975, while recuperating from a road accident, he began to research and develop a brainchild that he dubbed 'ambient music'. Experimenting with various fusions of classical, electronic and avant-garde styles, the idiosyncratic Eno transformed background muzak into a serious art form and took it to a higher plane. Although this music was not a commercial commodity as far as the solo Eno was concerned, it worked brilliantly during 1977-9, when he teamed with David Bowie for three albums: *Low*, *Heroes* and *Lodger* were austere, harsh LP's, and provided Bowie with the most controversial music of his career. All reached the British Top 5. While continuing to release examples of his ambient music throughout his career, Eno began a fruitful partnership with the freaky American rock band, Talking Heads. His production of their albums *More songs about buildings and food* (1978), *Fear of music* (1979) and *Remain in light* (1980), helped to bring the group to international prominence; he co-wrote their single *Once in a lifetime*, which was a UK Top 20 hit in early '81.
While that single was charting, he enjoyed critical acclaim and moderate commercial success with *My life in the bush of ghosts* - this album was a duet with the Head's leader David Byrne, and was a wierd excursion into the realms of African music. 1984 saw Eno co-producing Ireland's favourite rock group, U2. Their LP *The unforgettable fire* reached the UK No.1 position, and spawned the Top 3 single *Pride (In the name of love)*. For Brian, this represented an unusual liaison with conventional, guitar-based rock. (Bob MacDonald, 2.8.85).
Keyboardist and composer born in Sulfolk in 1948. He was a founder member of Roxy Music, one of the first to use the synthesiser, left Roxy after two albums and became a guru of pop avant-garde, like John Cage as important for his example as for what he actually did, but also with pop success as procuder/collaborator with others. His accessible *Here come the warm jets* in 1974 was a number 26 album. His work with King Crimson guitarist Robert Fripp began with *No pussyfooting* and *Evening star*, using Eno's tape-delay system. Recovering from a road accident he invented 'ambient music', raising Muzak to a somewhat highter level: he formed the Obscure mail-order-only label, associated with E.G.; Editions EG was formed in 1981 and many albums became more widely available. He kept his hand in high-class pop, teaming with David Bowie for three albums 1977-79 and with Talking Heads '78-80 for three, also the critically praised African-inspired album *My life in the bush of ghosts* with Heads' David Byrne ('found' voices manipulated electronically). He co-produced U2's *The unforgettable fire* in 1984. (Donald Clarke, April 1989).

ANOTHER GREEN WORLD (SINGLE)
Tracks: / Another green world.
CD 3": Released Feb '89, on Virgin, by Virgin Records. Catalogue no: **CDT 41**

JEZEBEL SPIRIT
Tracks: / Jezebel spirit / Very very hungry / Regiment (on 12" only).
7" Single: Released May '81, on Polydor, by Polydor Ltd. Deleted May '84. Catalogue no: **EGO 1**
12" Single: Released May '81, on Polydor, by Polydor Ltd. Deleted May '84. Catalogue no: **EGOX 1**

Enormous Room

100 DIFFERENT WORDS
Tracks: / 100 different words.
12" Single: Released Sep '86, on Sharp, by Sharp Records. Catalogue no: **CAL 5**

I DON'T NEED YOU
Tracks: / I don't need you / Melanie and Martin.
7" Single: Released Jul '86, on Medium, Catalogue no: **MC 1**

Enthusiasts

COLUMN BRIGADE
Tracks: / Column brigade.
7" Single: Released Aug '82, on Out Of Town, Catalogue no: **HOOT 10**

Entwistle, John

TOO LATE THE HERO (SINGLE)
Tracks: / Too late the hero / Comin' back.
7" Single: Released Sep '81, on WEA, by WEA Records. Catalogue no: **K 79249**

Enya

EVENING FALLS
Tracks: / Evening falls / Oiche chiun (silent night) / Morning glory (Available on 12" format only.).
CD 5": Released Dec '88, on WEA, by WEA Records. Catalogue no: **YZ 356CD**
12" Single: Released Dec '88, on WEA, by WEA Records. Catalogue no: **YZ 356T**
7" Single: Released Dec '88, on WEA, by WEA Records. Catalogue no: **YZ 356**

I WANT TOMORROW
Tracks: / I want tomorrow / Celts, The.
7" Single: Released Feb '87, on BBC, by BBC Records & Tapes. Deleted Apr '89. Catalogue no: **RESL 201**

ORINOCO FLOW
Tracks: / Orinoco flow / Out of the blue / Smaotin (Only on 12" version and CD single.).
CD 5": Released Oct '88, on WEA, by WEA Records. Catalogue no: **YZ 312 CD**
7" Single: Released Oct '88, on WEA, by WEA Records. Catalogue no: **YZ 312**
12" Single: Released Oct '88, on WEA, by WEA Records. Catalogue no: **YZ 312 T**

STORMS IN AFRICA
Tracks: / Storms in Africa / Storms in Africa (part 1) / Kelts, The (Only on 12" version.) / Aldebaran (Only on 12" version.).

CD 5": Released Feb '89, on WEA, by WEA Records. Catalogue no: **YZ 368 CD**
Cassingle: Released Feb '89, on WEA, by WEA Records. Catalogue no: **YZ 368 C**
12" Single: Released Feb '89, on WEA, by WEA Records. Catalogue no: **YZ 368 T**
CD 3": Released Jun '89, on WEA, by WEA Records. Catalogue no: **YZ 368 CDX**
7" Single: Released Feb '89, on WEA, by WEA Records. Catalogue no: **YZ 368**

Eon

INFINTY
Tracks: / Infinty / Infinty (version) / Something stronger.
12" Single: Released Apr '89, on Vinyl Solution, by Vinyl Solution Records. Catalogue no: **STORM 4**

LIGHT COLOUR SOUND
Tracks: / Light colour sound.
12" Single: Released Dec '88, on Vinyl Solution, by Vinyl Solution Records. Catalogue no: **STORM 3**

Epee MD

IT'S MY THING
Tracks: / It's my thing / You're a customer / It's my thing (dub) (On 12" single only.).
12" Single: Released Nov '87, on Cool Tempo, by Chrysalis Records. Catalogue no: **COOLX 156**
7" Single: Released Nov '87, on Cool Tempo, by Chrysalis Records. Catalogue no: **COOL 156**

Epic Soundtracks

JELLY BABIES
Tracks: / Jelly babies.
7" Single: Released Sep '81, on Rough Trade, by Rough Trade Records. Catalogue no: **RT 084**

RAIN RAIN RAIN
Tracks: / Rain, rain, rain / Ghosttrain.
7" Single: Released Jul '82, on Rough Trade, by Rough Trade Records. Catalogue no: **RT 104**

Epileptics

1970S
7" Single: Released Jan '82, on Spiderleg, Catalogue no: **SPL 1**

LAST BUS TO DEBDEN
7" Single: Released Oct '81, on Spiderleg, Catalogue no: **SPL 2**

E.P.M.D.

BECAUSE I'M HOUSING
Tracks: / Because I'm housing.
7" Single: Released 23 Jan '89, on Sleeping Bag, by Sleeping Bag Records. Catalogue no: **SBUK 007**
12" Single: Released 23 Jan '89, on Sleeping Bag, by Sleeping Bag Records. Catalogue no: **SBUK 007 T**

SO WHATCHA SAYIN'
Tracks: / So whatcha sayin'.
7" Single: Released Jul '89, on Fresh, by Jetstar Records. Catalogue no: **SBUK 011**
12" Single: Released Jul '89, on Fresh, by Jetstar Records. Catalogue no: **SBUK 011T**
12" Single: Released Jul '89, on Fresh, by Jetstar Records. Catalogue no: **FRE 80133**

STRICTLY BUSINESS (SINGLE)
Tracks: / Strictly business / Strictly business(dub).
7" Single: Released Aug '88, on Cool Tempo, by Chrysalis Records. Catalogue no: **COOL 172**
12" Single: Released Aug '88, on Cool Tempo, by Chrysalis Records. Catalogue no: **COOLX 172**

EQ

GOODBYE LOVE
Tracks: / Goodbye love.
12" Single: Released Sep '85, on Atlantic, by WEA Records. Catalogue no: **A 9577 T**
7" Single: Released Sep '85, on Atlantic, by WEA Records. Deleted '86. Catalogue no: **A 9577**

Equa

IN THE RED
Tracks: / In the red.
12" Single: Released Dec '83, on Fox, Catalogue no: **FOX 1**

Equals

Biographical details:
This British pop group consisted of Dervin & Lincoln Gordon (twins), Eddy Grant, John Hall and Pat Lloyd. The latter two members were born in London; the Gordon brothers were born in Jamaica, but emigrated to Britain during childhood; Grant was born in Guyana, but moved to London with his parents in 1960. The Equals were formed in London in 1965. The simple fact that they were racially mixed brought them considerable attention, for this was a novelty at the time. The three black and two white lads gained a recording deal the following year, purely on the strength of a demo version of *Baby come back*. This song was written by Grant, who turned out to be their key songwriter, principal creative force and lead guitarist. *Baby come back*, a lightweight fusion of pop and soul music, was so catchy that it became a major hit in West Germany in 1967. After spending much time working in continental Europe, their reputation began to rebound to Britain - *Unequalled Equals* reached No.10 on the UK album chart in November '67 (the same month that a similar sounding racially mixed combo, the Foundations, hit No.1 in the singles chart). The Equals first cracked the British singles chart in early 1968, reaching No.44 with *I get so excited*. By this time, the success of *Baby come back* was spreading to Belgium and Holland. The UK could hold out no longer, and the song finally topped the British listings in July '68. Their next few singles relegated the group to minor hit status. They returned to the UK Top 10 in the summer of '69 with *Viva Bobby Joe*. After further hiccups, they achieved a third and final Top Tenner in early 1971 with *Black skin blue-eyed boys* - this was yet another catchy, enthusiastic pop composition from the pen of Mr. Grant. Eddy quit the Equals in 1971 to pursue a solo career as a producer and artist. After years out of the public eye, he finally returned to the UK charts as a solo star in 1979, and continued in his hitmaking ways through the early Eighties. Having struggled in vain after Grant's departure, the other Equals finally called it a day in the late Seventies. (Bob MacDonald, 2.8.85)..

6 TRACK HITS
Tracks: / Baby come back / Softly softly / Viva Bobby Joe / I won't be there / Black skinned blue-eyed boys / Michael and his slipper tree.
7" EP: Released Sep '83, on Scoop 33, by Pickwick Records. Catalogue no: **7SR 5007**

BABY COME BACK (OLD GOLD)
Tracks: / Baby come back.
7" Single: Released Jul '82, on Old Gold, by Old Gold Records. Deleted Jul '88. Catalogue no: **OG 9021**

BABY COME BACK (SINGLE)
Tracks: / Baby come back.
7" Single: Released May '68, on President, by President Records. Deleted '71. Catalogue no: **PT 135**

BLACK SKINNED BLUE-EYED BOYS
Tracks: / Black skinned blue-eyed boys.
7" Single: Released Dec '70, on President, by President Records. Deleted '73. Catalogue no: **PT 325**

BLACK SKINNED BLUE-EYED BOYS (OLD GOLD)
Tracks: / Black skinned blue-eyed boy.
7" Single: Released Jul '82, on Old Gold, by Old Gold Records. Deleted Jul '88. Catalogue no: **OG 9033**

FUNKY LIKE A TRAIN
Tracks: / Funky like a train / Born yal.
7" Single: Released Sep '87, on Club, by Phonogram Ltd. Deleted Oct '88. Catalogue no: **JAB 58**

FUNKY LIKE A TRAIN (EXTENDED VERSION)
Tracks: / Funky like a train (extended version) / Born ya! / Funky like a train (LP version).
12" Single: Released Sep '87, on Club, by Phonogram Ltd. Deleted Oct '88. Catalogue no: **JABX 58**

I GET SO EXCITED
Tracks: / I get so excited.
7" Single: Released Feb '68, on President, by President Records. Deleted '71. Catalogue no: **PT 180**

LAUREL AND HARDY
Tracks: / Laurel and Hardy.
7" Single: Released Aug '68, on President, by President Records. Deleted '71. Catalogue no: **PT 200**

MICHAEL AND THE SLIPPER TREE
7" Single: Released Apr '69, on President, by President Records. Deleted '72. Catalogue no: **PT 240**

NO PLACE TO GO
Tracks: / No place to go.
12" Single: Released Jul '83, on Moggie, by Moggie Records. Catalogue no: **12MOG 1**
7" Single: Released Jul '83, on Moggie, by Moggie Records. Catalogue no: **MOG 1**

RUB-A DUB
Tracks: / Rub-a-dub.
7" Single: Released Dec '69, on President, by President Records. Deleted '72. Catalogue no: **PT 275**

SOFTLY SOFTLY
7" Single: Released Nov '68, on President, by President Records. Deleted '71. Catalogue no: **PT 222**

VIVA BOBBY JOE
Tracks: / Viva Bobby Joe.
7" Single: Released Jul '69, on President, by President Records. Deleted '72. Catalogue no: **PT 260**

VIVA BOBBY JOE (OLD GOLD)
Tracks: / Viva Bobby Joe / I can't let you go.
7" Single: Released Jul '82, on Old Gold, by Old Gold Records. Deleted Jul '88. Catalogue no: **OG 9025**

Equators

BABY COME BACK
Tracks: / Baby come back / Georgie.
7" Single: Released Oct '80, on Stiff, by Stiff Records. Catalogue no: **BUY 95**
12" Single: Released Oct '80, on Stiff, by Stiff Records. Catalogue no: **BUYIT 95**

DREAMING
Tracks: / Dreaming.
7" Single: Released Mar '85, on Philharmonics, Catalogue no: **EQ 101**

IF YOU NEED ME
Tracks: / If you need me / So what's new.
7" Single: Released May '81, on Stiff, by Stiff Records. Catalogue no: **BUY 113**
12" Single: Released May '81, on Stiff, by Stiff Records. Catalogue no: **BUYIT 113**

Erasure

CHAINS OF LOVE (IMPORT 2)
Tracks: / Chains of love / Chains of love (remix) / Don't suppose.
CD 3": Released Aug '88, on Intercord (Germany), Catalogue no: **INT 811863**

CHAINS OF LOVE (REMIX)
Tracks: / Chains of love (remix).
CD 5": Released Jun '88, on Mute, by Mute Records. Catalogue no: **CD MUTE 83**
7" Single: Released Jun '88, on Mute, by Mute Records. Catalogue no: **MUTE 83**
12" Single: Released Jun '88, on Mute, by Mute Records. Catalogue no: **12 MUTE 83**

CHAINS OF LOVE(IMPORT)
Tracks: / Chains of love(12" mix) / Chains of love (remix) / Don't suppose / Good, the bad, The / Chains of love (Shep Pettibone mix).
Note: 6-track EP containing 2 unreleased Shep Pettibone mixes brand new to the UK.
12" Single: Released Oct '88, on Sire (USA), Catalogue no: **020953**

CIRCUS (LIVE 3)
Tracks: / Circus, Live 3.
Note: Third in a series of 3 special 12" versions of their top 10 single. Tracks as U.K. release, but in limited edition grey vinyl and including a free slipcase for all 3 volumes. Different live tracks to versions 1 and 2.
7" EP: Released Oct '87, on Mute (Germany), by Mute Records. Catalogue no: **INT 126873**

CIRCUS, THE
Tracks: / If I could (Only on 12" single.) / Spiralling (Only on 12" single.) / Circus / Victim of love.
7" Single: Released Sep '87, on Mute, by Mute Records. Catalogue no: **MUTE 66**
12" Single: Released Oct '87, on Mute, by Mute Records. Catalogue no: **MUTE 66TB**
12" Single: Released Sep '87, on Mute, by Mute Records. Catalogue no: **12 MUTE 66**
12" Single: Released Oct '87, on Mute, by Mute Records. Catalogue no: **3MUTE 66TB**
7" EP: Released Sep '87, on Mute (Germany), by Mute Records. Catalogue no: **INT 126871**

CIRCUS, THE (LIVE) (EP)
Tracks: / Circus, The / Victim of love.
Note: Aswell as the Circus and Victim of Love, there are two additional live tracks.
7" EP: Released Oct '87, on Mute (Germany), by Mute Records. Catalogue no: **INT 126872**

CRACKERS INTERNATIONAL
Tracks: / Stop / Hardest part / Knocking on your door / She won't be home.
7" Single: Released Nov '88, on Mute, by Mute Records. Catalogue no: **MUTE 93**
12" Single: Released Nov '88, on Mute, by Mute Records. Catalogue no: **12 MUTE 93**
CD 3": Released Feb '89, on Intercord (Germany), Catalogue no: **INT 826901**
CD 5": Released Dec '88, on Mute, by Mute Records. Catalogue no: **CDMUTE 93**

CRACKERS LTD
CD 5": Released 19 Dec '88, on Mute, by Mute Records. Catalogue no: **LCDMUTE 093**

CRACKERS REMIX
12" Single: Released Dec '88, on Mute, by Mute Records. Catalogue no: **L12 MUTE 93**

DRAMA
Tracks: / Drama.
CD 5": Released Sep '89, on Mute, by Mute Records. Catalogue no: **CDMUTE 89**
7" Single: Released Sep '89, on Mute, by Mute Records. Catalogue no: **MUTE 89**
12" Single: Released Sep '89, on Mute, by Mute Records. Catalogue no: **12MUTE 89**
Cassingle: Released Oct '89, on Mute, by Mute Records. Catalogue no: **CMUTE 89**

HEAVENLY ACTION
Tracks: / Heavenly action / Don't say no / My heart so blue.
Note: Original picture-sleeve, three-track 12", available for a limited period on clear yellow vinyl.
12" Single: Released Nov '87, on Mute (Germany), by Mute Records. Catalogue no: **INT 126834**
12" Single: Released Nov '85, on Mute, by Mute Records. Catalogue no: **12 MUTE 42**
Special: Released Nov '85, on Mute, by Mute Records. Catalogue no: **D12MUTE 42**
7" Single: Released Nov '85, on Mute, by Mute Records. Catalogue no: **7 MUTE 42**

IT DOESN'T HAVE TO BE (REMIX)
Tracks: / It doesn't have to be / In the hall of the mountain king / Who needs love like that (remix) (Available only on 12" version) / It doesn't have to be / Who needs love (on 12" only) / Gimme gimme gimme / Circus, The* / Heavenly action.
Note: Special limited-edition remix featuring It Doesn't Have to Be, Heavenly Action and In the Hall of the Mountain King.
7" EP: Released Sep '87, on Mute, by Mute Records. Catalogue no: **2MUTE 56T**
CD 5": Released Mar '87, on Mute, Catalogue no: **CDMUTE 56**
12" Single: Released Nov '87, on Mute (Germany), by Mute Records. Catalogue no: **INT 126859**
12" Single: Released Mar '87, on Mute, by Mute Records. Catalogue no: **L12 MUTE 56**
12" Single: Released Feb '87, on Mute, by Mute Records. Catalogue no: **12 MUTE 56**
7" Single: Released Feb '87, on Mute, by Mute Records. Catalogue no: **MUTE 56**

LITTLE RESPECT, A
Tracks: / Little respect, A / Like Zsa Zsa Gabor.
CD 5": Released Sep '88, on Mute, by Mute Records. Catalogue no: **CD MUTE 85**
12" Single: Released Sep '88, on Mute, by Mute Records. Catalogue no: **12 MUTE 85**
7" Single: Released Sep '88, on Mute, by Mute Records. Catalogue no: **MUTE 85**

OH L'AMOUR
Tracks: / Oh l'amour / March on down the line / Gimme gimme gimme.
Note: Original version in picture sleeve.
CD 5": Released Dec '88, on Intercord (Germany), Catalogue no: **INT 826 840**
12" Single: Released Apr '86, on Mute, by Mute Records. Catalogue no: **12 MUTE 45**
12" Single: Released Nov '97, on Mute (Germany), by Mute Records. Catalogue no: **INT 126840**
7" Single: Released Apr '86, on Mute, by Mute Records. Catalogue no: **MUTE 45**

OH L'AMOUR (REMIX)
Tracks: / Oh l'amour (remix).
Note: Limited-edition pressing with an otherwise unavailable German vocal version of the single.
12" Single: Released Nov '87, on Mute (Germany), by Mute Records. Catalogue no: **INT 126848**

SHIP OF FOOLS
Tracks: / Ship of fools / River deep, mountain high.
CD 5": Released 20 Feb '88, on Mute, by Mute Records. Catalogue no: **CD MUTE 74**
Cassingle: Released 20 Feb '88, on Mute, by Mute Records. Catalogue no: **CMUTE 74**
12" Single: Released 20 Feb '88, on Mute, by Mute Records. Catalogue no: **12 MUTE 74**
7" Single: Released 20 Feb '88, on Mute, by Mute Records. Catalogue no: **MUTE 74**

SOMETIMES
Tracks: / Sexuality / Sometimes / Senseless / Say what (Only on CD single.).
Note: Now only available from Germany, this 12" has the original sleeve and features Sometimes (shiver mix), Sexuality (private mix) and Senseless (CD mix).
CD 5": Released Dec '88, on Intercord (Germany), Catalogue no: **INT 826 854**
7" Single: Released Nov '86, on Mute, by Mute Records. Catalogue no: **MUTE 51**
12" Single: Released Nov '87, on Mute (Germany), by Mute Records. Catalogue no: **INT 126855**
12" Single: Released '11, on Mute, by Mute Records. Deleted '86. Catalogue no: **12 MUTE 51**

VICTIM OF LOVE
Tracks: / Victim of love / Soldier's return, The / If I could.
Note: Special limited-edition remix featuring Victim of Love, The Soldier's Return andIf I Could.
7" Pic: Released Jun '87, on Mute, by Mute Records. Catalogue no: **L12 MUTE 61**
12" Single: Released Nov '87, on Mute (Germany), by Mute Records. Catalogue no: **INT 126867**
12" Single: Released May '87, on Mute, by Mute Records. Catalogue no: **12 MUTE 61**
7" Single: Released May '87, on Mute, by Mute Records. Catalogue no: **MUTE 61**

WHO NEEDS LOVE LIKE THAT?
Tracks: / Who needs love like that? / Push me, shove me.
12" Single: Released Nov '87, on Mute (Germany), by Mute Records. Catalogue no: **INT 126833**
12" Single: Released Aug '85, on Mute, by Mute Records. Catalogue no: **12 MUTE 40**
7" Single: Released Aug '85, on Mute, by Mute Records. Catalogue no: **7 MUTE 40**

Erazerhead

APE MAN
Tracks: / Ape man.
7" Single: Released Jul '81, on Test Pressing, by Test Pressing Records. Catalogue no: **TP 4**

LIVE AT THE KLUB FOOT (EP)
Tracks: / Live at the Klub Foot.
7" Single: Released Jan '83, on Flicknife, by Flicknife Records. Catalogue no: **FLS 211**

SHELL SHOCK
7" Single: Released May '82, on Flicknife, by Flicknife Records. Catalogue no: **FLS 208**

SUMMERTIME
Tracks: / Summertime / Tonight.
7" Single: Released Apr '84, on Flicknife, by Flicknife Records. Catalogue no: **FLS 027**

WEREWOLF
Tracks: / Werewolf.
7" Single: Released Apr '83, on Flicknife, by Flicknife Records. Catalogue no: **FLS 218**

Erehwon

HEEL
Tracks: / Heel / Tiny goddess.
7" Single: Released Sep '80, on Harvest (1), by EMI Records. Deleted '83. Catalogue no: **HAR 5213**

Eric & Good Good

FUNKY
Tracks: / Funky / Funky (version).
7" Single: Released Sep '89, on Equinox, by Equinox Records. Catalogue no: **EQN 2**
12" Single: Released Sep '89, on Equinox, by Equinox Records. Catalogue no: **12 EQUN 2**

GOOD GOOD FEELING
Tracks: / Good good feeling.
CD 5": Released May '89, on Equinox, by Equinox Records. Deleted Jul '89. Catalogue no: **EQNCDS 1**
7" Single: Released May '89, on Equinox, by Equinox Records. Deleted Jul '89. Catalogue no: **EQN 1**
12" Single: Released May '89, on Equinox, by Equinox Records. Deleted Jul '89. Catalogue no: **12 EQN 1**

NUMBER ONE
Tracks: / Number one / Give it to me one more time / Number one (extended version) (*Track on 12" version) / Number one (baritone mix).
7" Single: Released 3 May '88, on MCA, by MCA Records. Catalogue no: **MCA 1247**
12" Single: Released 3 May '88, on MCA, by MCA Records. Catalogue no: **MCAT 1247**

Eric & The Vikings

HURTING
Tracks: / Hurting / My baby ain't no plaything / In the pocket / Say it isn't so.
12" Single: Released 23 May '87, on Kool Kat, by Kool Kat Records. Catalogue no: **KOOLT 5**
7" Single: Released 23 May '87, on Kool Kat, by Kool Kat Records. Catalogue no: **KOOL 5**

Erica

TONIGHT TONIGHT
Tracks: / Tonight tonight / Tonight tonight (instrumental).
12" Single: Released Nov '82, on Sanity, Catalogue no: **STY 003**

Ericksen, Joe

HIGH SCHOOL SWEETHEARTS
Tracks: / High school sweethearts.
7" Single: Released Jul '83, on Joy Kick, Catalogue no: **KIC 01**
12" Single: Released Jul '83, on Joy Kick, Catalogue no: **KIC 01T**

Erickson, Roky

CREATURE WITH THE ATOM BRAIN
Tracks: / Creature with the atom brain / Wind and more.
7" Single: Released Aug '80, on CBS, by CBS Records. Deleted '83. Catalogue no: **CBS 8888**

MINE MINE MIND
Tracks: / Mine mine mind / Bloody hammer.
7" Single: Released Oct '82, on CBS, by CBS Records. Deleted Oct '85. Catalogue no: **CBS 9055**

Ericson, Joe

TAKE YOUR TIME
Tracks: / Take your time.
7" Single: Released Jul '83, on Steinar, by Steinar Records (UK). Catalogue no: **STE 711**
12" Single: Released Jul '83, on Steinar, by Steinar Records (UK). Catalogue no: **STE 1211**

Ericsson, Lena

BARNDOMSJUL
Tracks: / Barndomsjul.
7" Single: Released Nov '82, on Phontastic (Sweden), Catalogue no: **PHONT 7208**

CHRISTMAS TREE
Tracks: / Christmas tree.
7" Single: Released Nov '82, on Phontastic (Sweden), Catalogue no: **PHONT 7209**

Erikson, Roky

BEAST, THE
Tracks: / Beast, The / Heroin.
12" Single: Released Apr '86, on One Big Guitar, by One Big Guitar Records. Catalogue no: **OBG 004 T**

TWO TWISTED TALES
Tracks: / Two twisted tales.
7" Single: Released Jun '88, on Five Hours Back, Catalogue no: **TICK 001**

YOU DON'T LOVE ME YET
Tracks: / You don't love me yet.
12" Single: Released 27 Feb '88, on Fundamental, by Fundamental Music Records. Catalogue no: **PRAY 007**

Erogenous Zones

SAY IT'S NOT SO
Tracks: / Say it's not so.
7" Single: Released May '81, on Safari, by Safari Records. Catalogue no: **SAFE 36**

Erotic Dissidents

I WANNA BE LOVED BY YOU
Tracks: / I wanna be loved by you.
12" Single: Released Jun '89, on Subway dance, Catalogue no: **SD 4004**

MOVE YOUR ASS AND FEEL THE BEAT
Tracks: / Move your ass and feel the beat.
CD 5": Released Jul '88, on Subway, by Subway Records. Catalogue no: **SUB 010CD**
12" Single: Released 27 Feb '88, on Subway, by Subway Records. Catalogue no: **SUB 010**

MOVE YOUR ASS AND FEEL THE BEAT (REMIX)
Tracks: / Move your ass and feel the beat (remix).
12" Single: Released '88, on Subway, by Subway Records. Catalogue no: **SUB 010R**

SHAKE YOUR HIPS
Tracks: / Shake your hips.
CD 5": Released Oct '88, on Subway, by Subway Records. Catalogue no: **SUB 033 CD**
12" Single: Released Aug '88, on Subway, by Subway Records. Catalogue no: **SUB 033**

Erotic Drum Band

CREAM DREAM
Tracks: / Cream dream.
12" Single: Released Mar '85, on Street Level, by Creole Records. Catalogue no: **CRT 74**

LOVE DISCO STYLE
Tracks: / Erotic drum band.
7" Single: Released Jun '79, on Scope, Deleted '82. Catalogue no: **SC 1**

POP POP SHOOWAH
Tracks: / Pop pop shoowah / Touch me where it's hot.
7" Single: Released Sep '80, on Carrere, Deleted '83. Catalogue no: **CAR 164**

Errol

WANT YOU GIRL
Tracks: / Want you girl.
12" Single: Released Sep '89, on White, Catalogue no: **12EMH 1**

Ersatz

SMILE IN SHADOW
Tracks: / Smile in shadow.
7" Single: Released Jan '81, on Leisure Sounds, by Leisure Sounds Records. Catalogue no: **SRS 32**

Erskine-Hill, Mark

BLOODSHED
Tracks: / Bloodshed.
12" Single: Released Oct '87, on E-H1, by E-H.1 Records. Catalogue no: **EHI 004**

FLY AWAY
Tracks: / Fly away.
7" Single: Released Jun '85, on E-H1, by E-H.1 Records. Catalogue no: **MEH 1**

MONDAY
Tracks: / Monday / No one stops.
7" Single: Released Feb '86, on E-H1, by E-H.1 Records. Catalogue no: **1 EHI 2**

SHE'S A VERY LONELY GIRL
Tracks: / She's a very lonely girl / Through the trees.
7" Single: Released May '86, on E-H1, by E-H.1 Records. Catalogue no: **EHI 003**

Eruption

Biographical details:
With Precious Wilson on vocals, this Jamaican band came to fame in 1978 with their rendition of *I can't stand the rain*. The song was originally an American soul and pop hit for Ann Peebles in 1973; the punchy Eruption version, aimed at both the dancefloor and the pop charts, reached No.5 in Britain and No.18 in the States. Although originally from Jamaica via the USA, Eruption were based in West Germany where they were part of Frank Farian's production line. Farian was the man behind the success of Boney M, and Wilson sang backing vocals on some of their hits. Despite the stridence of Precious' singing, Eruption's discs had to live in Boney M's shadow and the group was thus unable to enjoy a real career. After a 1979 success with *One way ticket* (No.9 in UK), Eruption drifted into obscurity. During the early Eighties, Wilson enjoyed solo success in West Germany as a slick soul singer. (Bob MacDonald, 2.8.85)..

JOY TO THE WORLD
Tracks: / Joy to the world / Time.
7" Single: Released Dec '82, on Red Bus, by Red Bus Records. Catalogue no: **RBUS 75**

ONE WAY TICKET
Tracks: / One way ticket.
7" Single: Released Apr '79, on Atlantic-Hansa, by WEA Records. Deleted '82. Catalogue no: **K 11266**

WHERE DO I BEGIN
Tracks: / Where do I begin / Broke away / Snap.
12" Single: Released Oct '86, on FM-Revolver, by FM-Revolver Records. Catalogue no: **12 VHF 31**

Escalator

LET'S MAKE SOME NOISE (EVERYBODY IN THE HOUSE)
Tracks: / Let's make some noise / Ride the escalator.
12" Single: Released Oct '86, on Elite Records, by Elite Records. Deleted '88. Catalogue no: **DAZZ 60**

Escalators

BEACH BOYS
Tracks: / Beach boys.
7" Single: Released Aug '85, on Rococo, Catalogue no: **COCO 1**

MONDAY
Tracks: / Monday.
7" Single: Released Jul '83, on Big Beat, by Ace Records. Deleted '88. Catalogue no: **NS 87**

SOMETHING'S MISSING
Tracks: / Something's missing.
7" Single: Released Mar '83, on Big Beat, by Ace Records. Catalogue no: **NS 86**

Escape

AMSTERDAM
Tracks: / Amsterdam / Girl in the film box.
7" Single: Released Sep '83, on Mercury, by Phonogram Ltd. Catalogue no: **SCAPE 1**
12" Single: Released Sep '83, on Mercury, by Phonogram Ltd. Catalogue no: **SCAPE 112**

NO GO
Tracks: / No go.
7" Single: Released Sep '82, on Volatile, by Prism Records. Catalogue no: **FIRE 1**

RUSSIAN LADY
Tracks: / Russian lady.
12" Single: Released Jun '84, on Mercury, by Phonogram Ltd. Catalogue no: **PH 312**

Escape Club

BREATHING
Tracks: / Breathing / Don't touch me.
7" Single: Released Jul '83, on Bright, by Bright Records. Catalogue no: **BULB 3**

HARD WAY, THE
Tracks: / Hard way, The / I will be there / Push, The (extra track in double pack) / 100 years (Extra track in double pack)).
7" Set: Released Oct '86, on Parlophone, by EMI Records. Deleted Jul '87. Catalogue no: **RD 6143**
7" Single: Released Oct '86, on Parlophone, by EMI Records. Catalogue no: **R 6143**
12" Single: Released Oct '86, on Parlophone, by EMI Records. Deleted Jul '87. Catalogue no: **12 R 6143**

I WILL BE THERE
Tracks: / I will be there / Money and guns.
7" Single: Released Mar '86, on EMI, by EMI Records. Catalogue no: **EMI 5548**
12" Single: Released Mar '86, on EMI, by EMI Records. Catalogue no: **12 EMI 5548**

RESCUE ME
Tracks: / Rescue me / In my town.
7" Single: Released Sep '85, on EMI, by EMI Records. Catalogue no: **EMI 5528**
12" Single: Released Sep '86, on EMI, by EMI Records. Catalogue no: **12 EMI 5528**

SHAKE FOR THE SHEIK
Tracks: / Shake for the Sheik / Working for the fat man.
CD 5": Released Feb '89, on Atlantic, by WEA Records. Catalogue no: **U 7723 CD**
7" Single: Released Feb '89, on Atlantic, by WEA Records. Catalogue no: **U 7723**
12" Single: Released Feb '89, on Atlantic, by WEA Records. Catalogue no: **U 7723 T**

WHERE ANGELS CRY
Tracks: / Where angels cry / Tonight (for the poor boy).
7" Single: Released Jun '86, on Parlophone, by EMI Records. Catalogue no: **R 6132**
12" Single: Released Jun '86, on Parlophone, by EMI Records. Catalogue no: **12 R 6132**

WILD WILD WEST (SINGLE)
Tracks: / Wild wild west / We can run.
7" Single: Released Aug '88, on Atlantic, by WEA Records. Catalogue no: **U 7928**
12" Single: Released Aug '88, on Atlantic, by WEA Records. Catalogue no: **U 7928 T**

Escorts

Biographical details:
At the time of their only UK chart entry, this British beat group consisted of Mike Gregory, John Kinrade, Johnny Sticks and Terry Sylvester. The Escorts were one of the numerous combos to emerge from the Liverpool scene in the wake of the Beatles' meteoric rise to success. With the standard two guitars, bass and drums line-up, they enjoyed enormous local popularity and were certainly one of the city's niftiest groups. The Escorts' sole foray into the British charts occured in July 1964, when *The one to cry* crawled to No.49. Their acclaimed version of *Dizzy Miss Lizzy* failed to chart, as did their later efforts. They faded into obscurity amidst several personnel changes, and even Paul McCartney's production touch on the 1966 single *From head to toe* could not rescue the group. There was better luck in store for lead singer Terry Sylvester, who replaced Graham Nash in the Hollies, when Graham left to become thirty three and a third per cent of Crosby, Stills & Nash in 1968. (Bob MacDonald, 2.8.85).
A pop band, one of the best 'second division' Merseybeat groups, formed in 1961, with bassist Mike Gregory, rhythm guitarist Terry Sylvester, drummer Pete Clark, guitarist John Kinrade. Their cover of Larry Williams' *Dizzy Miss Lizzy* was a regional USA hit, especially in Texas, but they couldn't tour there to promote it. With better luck they might have become a major force, but they split in 1966. (Donald Clarke, April 1989).

ONE TO CRY, THE
Tracks: / One to cry.
7" Single: Released Jul '64, on Fontana, by Phonogram Ltd. Deleted '67. Catalogue no: **TF 474**

E.S.G.

YOU'RE NO GOOD
Tracks: / You're no good.
7" Single: Released Jun '81, on Factory (1), by Factory Records. Catalogue no: **FAC 34**

Eskimos & Egypt

COLD, THE
Tracks: / Cold, The.
7" Single: Released Jun '88, on Village, by Village Records. Catalogue no: **VILS 002**

E-Smoove

DOWN THE DRAIN
Tracks: / Down the drain.
12" Single: Released Nov '88, on Future Sounds, Catalogue no: **FSR 1007**

ESP

IT'S YOU
Tracks: / It's you / It's you (versions).
12" Single: Released Aug '89, on DJ Int/Westside, Catalogue no: **DJINT 14**

TELL ME
Tracks: / Tell me / Illusion confusion.
7" Single: Released Mar '86, on WDTC, Catalogue no: **WDTC 1**

Esperanto

LOVE'S THE GAME
Tracks: / Love's the game / Trust.
7" Single: Released Sep '87, on Anxious, by Anxious Records. Deleted May '89. Catalogue no: **ANX 001**
12" Single: Released Sep '87, on Anxious, by Anxious Records. Deleted May '89. Catalogue no: **ANXT 001**

SECRETS
Tracks: / Secrets.
12" Single: Released Mar '89, on Anxious, by Anxious Records. Catalogue no: **NERVT 4**

Espionage

SOUND OF BREAKING HEARTS
7" Single: Released Apr '83, on A&M, by A&M Records. Deleted '88. Catalogue no: **AM 105**
12" Single: Released Apr '83, on A&M, by A&M Records. Deleted '88. Catalogue no: **AMX 105**

Esposito, Joe 'Bean'

DOWN IN YOUR SOUL
Tracks: / Down in your soul / Down in your soul (Instr. Mix) / Down in your soul (Dub mix).
12" Single: Released Mar '86, on Teldec (1), by ASV (Academy Sound & Vision). Catalogue no: **620542**

Esposito, Tony

KALIMBA DE LUNA
Tracks: / Kalimba de luna.
7" Single: Released Nov '84, on Red Bus, by Red Bus Records. Catalogue no: **RBUS 102**
12" Single: Released Nov '84, on Red Bus, by Red Bus Records. Catalogue no: **RBUSL 102**
12" Single: Released Oct '84, on Carrere, Catalogue no: **CART 351**

PAPA CHICO
Tracks: / Papa Chico (version).
7" Single: Released Sep '87, on In Disc, Catalogue no: **BLU 1**
12" Single: Released Sep '87, on In Disc, Catalogue no: **BLUT 1**

Essence

CAT, THE
Tracks: / Cat, The (remix) / Confusion / Happiness, The / Cat, The (extended version).
12" Single: Released Jun '86, on Midnight Music, by Midnight Music Records. Catalogue no: **DONG 24**

ENDLESS LAKES
Tracks: / Endless lakes.
12" Single: Released Jul '85, on Midnight Music, by Midnight Music Records. Catalogue no: **DONG 14**

MIRAGE, A
Tracks: / Mirage, A / Lollipop / Tricked.
12" Single: Released 20 Feb '88, on Midnight Music, by Midnight Music Records. Catalogue no: **DONG 33**

OIL IN MY LAMP
Tracks: / Oil in my lamp / Brown eyed girl.
7" Single: Released Sep '80, on North Of Watford, by North Of Watford Records. Catalogue no: **N 703**

ONLY FOR YOU
Tracks: / Only for you.
12" Single: Released Oct '88, on Midnight Music, by Midnight Music Records. Catalogue no: **DONG 41**

REFLECTED DREAM, A
12" Single: Released Oct '88, on Midnight Music, by Midnight Music Records. Catalogue no: **DONG 40**

Essential Bop

ELOQUENT SOUNDS(EP)
7" Single: Released Nov '80, on Monopause, Catalogue no: **MOAN 101**

Essential Logic

AEROSOL BURNS
Tracks: / Aerosol burns.
7" Single: Released Jun '78, on Cells, Catalogue no: **SELL 1**

EUGENE
Tracks: / Eugene / Tame the neighbours.
7" Single: Released Nov '80, on Rough Trade, by Rough Trade Records. Catalogue no: **RT 050**

FANFARE IN THE GARDEN
Tracks: / Fanfare in the garden / Captain.
7" Single: Released Jun '81, on Rough Trade, by Rough Trade Records. Catalogue no: **RT 074**

MUSIC IS A BETTER NOISE
Tracks: / Music is a better noise / Moontown.
7" Single: Released Feb '81, on Rough Trade, by Rough Trade Records. Catalogue no: **RT 053**

POPCORN BAY
7" Single: Released Oct '79, on Rough Trade, by Rough Trade Records. Catalogue no: **RTO 29**

Essex

EASIER SAID THAN DONE
Tracks: / Easier said than done.
7" Single: Released Aug '63, on Columbia, by EMI Records. Deleted '66. Catalogue no: **DB 7077**

Essex, David

Biographical details:
This British singer, songwriter, actor and film star was born David Cook in Plaistow, London. He became interested in music at the age of 12, and played in his first group two years later. In 1963, at the age of 16, he launched a solo singing career and changed his name to Essex. After several years of struggling, he turned to acting and gained various small-time parts in theatre. He made his first movie appearances in 1970 and, at about the same time, won the leading role in a play called *The Fantastics*. Essex's major breakthrough in showbusiness occured in 1971, when he landed the central role of Jesus in the London West End stage production of *Godspell*. The freshness and vitality of this much talked about musical, and of Essex's performance in it, earned him the part of Jim McLain in the rock'n'roll revival movie *That'll be the day* (1973); his co-star was Ringo Starr. These stage and screen successes led to David resuming his singing career. The fictional rock star he had portrayed in *That'll be the day* became a reality, for Essex embarked upon a long string of UK chart successes. Teaming with American producer Jeff Wayne, David achieved ten UK Top 40 singles and three UK Top 10 albums between 1973 and '76. All of the ten hits were penned by Essex, but Wayne's musical and technical knowledge helped to propel his vocal career into the realms of teen idol superstardom. The first was 1973's jerky, echo-filled *Rock on*, which hit No.3; this was the only one to cross the Atlantic - it peaked at No.5 on the Billboard Hot 100 (and went to No.1 on the alternative Cashbox chart). Then came two British No.1 smashes - *Gonna make you a star* (1974) and *Hold me close* (1975). During this period, Essex starred in the sequel to *That'll be the day*, *Stardust*. From 1977 onwards David's chart career was erratic, for the simple reason that his diverse talents did not allow him to concentrate solely on being a pop star. Apart from 1983's UK No.2 smash, *A winter's tale*, all his big later hits were spin-offs from other projects: *Oh what a circus* (1978) came from the Rice/Lloyd Webber blockbuster *Evita*, in which he played Che Guevara; *Silver dream machine* (1980) was the theme from his movie *Silver dream racer*, *Me and my girl (Night-clubbing)* (1982) charted on the back of his well-received BBC TV talent spotting series *The David Essex Showcase*; and *Tahiti* (1983) was the forerunner of a 1985 Wet End musical that David conceived himself - *Mutiny!* attracted a lukewarm press reaction but, as usual, the Essex combination of impish, charming looks and charismatic talent won the day. (Bob MacDonald, 3.8.85).
Pop singer and teen star born in 1947 in London. Ten singles as a singer flopped; a sideways move to theatre and repertory, bit parts in forgotten films led to a big break: he was cast from 600 to play Jesus in *Godspell* in London in late 1971. He also starred in the well received film *That'll be the day* in 1973 as a '50's rocker and wrote *Rock on* for the film, his first hit. After a string of pop hits he returned to the stage in 1978 to play Che Guevera in Tim Rice and Andrew Lloyd Webber's *Evita*. He had a 1984 total of 17 UK top 40 singles, numerous gold albums and a Grammy

DAVID ESSEX - CITY LIGHTS (Released on CBS)

DAVID ESSEX - ON MY BIKE (Released on Mercury)

nomination (for *Rock on*): unusual in combining pop with serious acting, but fans still predominantly young and female. (Donald Clarke, April 1989).

6 TRACK HITS
Tracks: / Rollin stone / Ooh darlin / America / Stay with me baby / Turn me loose / Cool out tonight.
7" EP: Released Sep '83, on Scoop 33, by Pickwick Records. Catalogue no: **7SR 5017**

AMERICA
Tracks: / America.
7" Single: Released May '74, on CBS, by CBS Records. Deleted '77. Catalogue no: **CBS 2176**

BACK IN ENGLAND FOR CHRISTMAS
Tracks: / Back in England for Christmas.
7" Single: Released Nov '86, on Lamplight, by Priority Records. Deleted Nov '87. Catalogue no: **LAMP 11**
12" Single: Released Nov '86, on Lamplight, by Priority Records. Catalogue no: **12 LAMP 11**

BE BOP A LULA
Tracks: / Be bop a lula / Secret lover.
7" Single: Released May '81, on Mercury, by Phonogram Ltd. Deleted May '84. Catalogue no: **MER 72**

BRAVE NEW WORLD
Tracks: / Brave new world.
7" Single: Released Oct '78, on CBS, by CBS Records. Deleted '81. Catalogue no: **CBS 6705**

CITY LIGHTS (see panel above)
Tracks: / City lights / St. Amie.
7" Single: Released Mar '76, on CBS, by CBS Records. Deleted '79. Catalogue no: **CBS 4050**

COMING HOME
Tracks: / Coming home.
7" Single: Released Oct '76, on CBS, by CBS Records. Deleted '79. Catalogue no: **CBS 4486**

COOL OUT TONIGHT
Tracks: / Cool out tonight.
7" Single: Released Sep '77, on CBS, by CBS Records. Deleted '80. Catalogue no: **CBS 5495**

DAVID ESSEX
Tracks: / Gonna makeyou a star / Hold me close / Rock on / Stardust.
Cassingle: Released Dec '82, on CBS, by CBS Records. Deleted Dec '85. Catalogue no: **A40-2910**

FALLING ANGELS RIDING
Tracks: / Falling angels.
7" Single: Released Jan '85, on Mercury, by Phonogram Ltd. Catalogue no: **ESSEX 6**

FISHING FOR THE MOON
Tracks: / Fishing for the moon / Zulu warrior.
7" Single: Released Mar '84, on Phonogram, by Phonogram Ltd. Catalogue no: **ESSEX 3**

FREEDOM
Tracks: / Freedom.
7" Single: Released Oct '85, on Lamplight, by Priority Records. Catalogue no: **LAMP 2**

FRIENDS
Tracks: / Friends / Welcome.
7" Single: Released May '85, on Lamplight, by Priority Records. Catalogue no: **LAMP 12**

GONNA MAKE YOU A STAR
Tracks: / Gonna make you a star.
7" Single: Released Oct '74, on CBS, by CBS Records. Deleted '77. Catalogue no: **CBS 2492**
7" Single: Released Sep '85, on Old Gold, by Old Gold Records. Catalogue no: **OG 9553**

HEART ON MY SLEEVE
Tracks: / Heart on my sleeve / I don't want to go to the disco.
7" Single: Released Jan '81, on Mercury, by Phonogram Ltd. Deleted Jan '84. Catalogue no: **MER 55**

HOLD ME CLOSE
Tracks: / Hold me close.
7" Single: Released Sep '75, on CBS, by CBS Records. Deleted '78. Catalogue no: **CBS 3572**

HOT LOVE (SINGLE)
Tracks: / Hot love / Rock and roll me.
7" Single: Released Jun '80, on Mercury, by Phonogram Ltd. Deleted '83. Catalogue no: **HOT 11**

IF I COULD
Tracks: / If I could.
7" Single: Released Dec '75, on CBS, by CBS Records. Deleted '78. Catalogue no: **CBS 3776**

IMPERIAL WIZARD (SINGLE)
Tracks: / Imperial wizard.
7" Single: Released Mar '79, on Mercury, by Phonogram Ltd. Deleted '82. Catalogue no: **6007 202**

LAMPLIGHT
Tracks: / Lamplight.
7" Single: Released Nov '73, on CBS, by CBS Records. Deleted '76. Catalogue no: **CBS 1902**

LOOK AT THE SUN SHINING
Tracks: / Look at the sun shining.
7" Single: Released Jun '88, on Priority, by Priority Records. Catalogue no: **LAMP 3**

MAGICIAN, THE
Tracks: / Magician, The / Life support system.
7" Single: Released Sep '81, on Mercury, by Phonogram Ltd. Deleted '84. Catalogue no: **MER 82**

ME AND MY GIRL
Tracks: / Me and my girl / Sleeping with the director.
7" Single: Released Jun '82, on Mercury, by Phonogram Ltd. Deleted Jun '85. Catalogue no: **MER 107**

MISSING YOU (MAGIC)
Tracks: / Missing you (magic).
7" Single: Released Oct '89, on Lamplight, by Priority Records. Catalogue no: **LAMP 7**

MYFANWY
Tracks: / Myfanwy / Love theme / Myfanwy (love theme) / Myfanwy (long version).
CD 5": Released May '87, on Arista, by BMG Records (UK). Deleted Jul '89. Catalogue no: **RISCD 11**
7" Single: Released Oct '87, on Arista, by BMG Records (UK). Catalogue no: **RIS 11**
12" Single: Released Oct '87, on Arista, by BMG Records (UK). Deleted May '89. Catalogue no: **RIST 11**

OH WHAT A CIRCUS
Tracks: / Oh what a circus.
7" Single: Released Oct '78, on Mercury, by Phonogram Ltd. Deleted '81. Catalogue no: **6007 185**

ON MY BIKE (see panel above)
Tracks: / On my bike / Swim against the flow.
7" Single: Released '80, on Mercury, by Phonogram Ltd. Catalogue no: **MER 47**

RACE
Tracks: / Race / Suzuki warlord.
7" Single: Released 20 Jul '80, on Mercury, by Phonogram Ltd. Deleted '83. Catalogue no: **BIKE 2**

RIVER, THE
Tracks: / River, The.
7" Single: Released Oct '88, on Lamplight, by Priority Records. Deleted Sep '89. Catalogue no: **LAMP 4**

ROCK ON
Tracks: / Rock on / Zone, The.
12" Single: Released Jun '89, on CBS, by CBS Records. Deleted Oct '89. Catalogue no: **6549488**

ROCK ON '88'
Tracks: / Rock on '88'.
7" Single: Released Jan '89, on Lamplight, by Priority Records. Deleted Aug '89. Catalogue no: **LAMP 5**
12" Single: Released Jan '89, on Lamplight, by Priority Records. Deleted Aug '89. Catalogue no: **12LAMP 5**

ROCK ON (89 REMIX)
Tracks: / Rock on / Zone, The.
7" Single: Released Jun '89, on CBS, by CBS Records. Catalogue no: **654 948 0**
7" Single: Released May '89, on CBS, by CBS Records. Catalogue no: **654 948 7**
CD 5": Released May '89, on CBS, by CBS Records. Catalogue no: **654 948 2**
12" Single: Released May '89, on CBS, by CBS Records. Catalogue no: **654 948 6**

ROCK ON (SINGLE)
Tracks: / Rock on.
7" Single: Released Aug '73, on CBS, by CBS Records. Deleted '76. Catalogue no: **CBS 1693**

ROLLIN' STONE
Tracks: / Rollin' stone.
7" Single: Released Jul '75, on CBS, by CBS Records. Deleted '78. Catalogue no: **CBS 3425**

SILVER DREAM MACHINE
Tracks: / Silver dream machine.
7" Single: Released Apr '80, on Mercury, by Phonogram Ltd. Deleted '83. Catalogue no: **BIKE 1**

SMILE, THE
Tracks: / Smile, The / Slave.
7" Pic: Released May '83, on Mercury, by Phonogram Ltd. Catalogue no: **ESSEP 1**
7" Single: Released May '83, on Mercury, by Phonogram Ltd. Catalogue no: **ESSEX 1**
12" Single: Released May '83, on Mercury, by Phonogram Ltd. Catalogue no: **ESSEX 112**

STARDUST
Tracks: / Stardust.
7" Single: Released Dec '74, on CBS, by CBS Records. Deleted '77. Catalogue no: **CBS 2828**

STAY WITH ME BABY
Tracks: / Stay with me baby.
7" Single: Released Mar '78, on CBS, by CBS Records. Deleted '81. Catalogue no: **CBS 6063**

SUN AIN'T GONNA SHINE ANYMORE, THE
Tracks: / Sun ain't gonna shine anymore, The.
CD 5": Released Jul '89, on Lamplight, by Priority Records. Catalogue no: **LAMPCDS 6**
12" Single: Released May '89, on Lamplight, by Priority Records. Catalogue no: **12LAMP 6**
7" Single: Released May '89, on Lamplight, by Priority Records. Deleted Sep '89. Catalogue no: **LAMP 6**

SUNSHINE GIRL
Tracks: / Sunshine girl / Don't leave me this way.
7" Single: Released Jul '81, on Mercury, by Phonogram Ltd. Deleted '85. Catalogue no: **MER 77**

SWEETHEARTS
Tracks: / Sweethearts / Hold on me.
7" Single: Released Mar '82, on Mercury, by Phonogram Ltd. Deleted '85. Catalogue no: **MER 100**

TAHITI
Tracks: / Tahiti / Hell.
7" Single: Released Aug '83, on Mercury, by Phonogram Ltd. Deleted '86. Catalogue no: **BOUNT 1**

WHISPER
Tracks: / Whisper / You're in my heart / Down again / Fishing for the moon / Ears of the city, The / Love, oh love / Moonlight dancing / Love is a stranger / Winter's tale, A / Two runaways.
7" Single: Released '83, on Mercury, by Phonogram Ltd. Deleted '88. Catalogue no: **MERH 34**

WINTERS TALE, A
Tracks: / Winter's tale, A / Verity.
7" Single: Released Dec '82, on Mercury, by Phonogram Ltd. Deleted '85. Catalogue no: **MER 127**

WORLD
Tracks: / World / I who am I.
7" Single: Released Jan '80, on Liberty, by EMI Records. Deleted '83. Catalogue no: **UP 605**

GLORIA ESTEFAN - DON'T WANT TO LOSE YOU (Released on Epic)

YOU'RE IN MY HEART
Tracks: / You're in my heart / Come on little darling.
7" Single: Released Nov '83, on Mercury, by Phonogram Ltd. Catalogue no: **ESSEX 2**

Essex, Mike

THANKS
Tracks: / Thanks / Thanks, Theme from.
Note: First Time Music, 12 Trewartha Rd, Praa Sands, Penzance, Cornwall, TR20 9ST. Telephone: 762826 (Penzance).
7" Single: Released Mar '87, on First Time, by First Time Records. Catalogue no: **FTM 5451**

Esson, Aston

I'LL GET OVER IT
Tracks: / I'll get over it / I'll get over it (II).
12" Single: Released Oct '86, on Fine Style, by Fashion Records. Catalogue no: **FS 005**

Estefan, Gloria

1-2-3
Tracks: / 1-2-3 / Surrender / 1-2-3 (ext) (12" & CD single only.) / 1-2-3 (dub) (12" & CD single only.) / Primitive love (CD single only.) / 1,2,3 (dancing by number mix) (Only on 12" picture bag version.) / Anything for you (English version) (Only on 12" picture bag version.) / Anything for you (Spanish version) (Only on 12" picture bag version.).
12" Single: Released Oct '88, on Epic, by CBS Records. Deleted 17 Apr '89. Catalogue no: **652958 8**
7" Single: Released Oct '88, on Epic, by CBS Records. Deleted 17 Apr '89. Catalogue no: **652958 7**
CD 5": Released Oct '88, on Epic, by CBS Records. Deleted 17 Apr '89. Catalogue no: **652958 2**
7" Single: Released Oct '88, on Epic, by CBS Records. Deleted 17 Apr '89. Catalogue no: **652958 0**
12" Single: Released Nov '88, on Epic, by CBS Records. Deleted 17 Apr '89. Catalogue no: **652928 1**

ANYTHING FOR YOU (SINGLE)
Tracks: / Anything for you (English version) / Anything for you (Spanish version) / Anything for you (English/Spanish version) / Megamix - rhythm is gonna get you / Conga / Doctor Beat / Betcha say that / Bad boy.
Note: 12" and 7" singles are picture bag editions.
12" Single: Released 20 Jun '88, on Epic, by CBS Records. Deleted Jan '89. Catalogue no: **651673 9**
7" Single: Released 20 Jun '88, on Epic, by CBS Records. Deleted 17 Apr '89. Catalogue no: **651673 7**
CD 5": Released 20 Jun '88, on Epic, by CBS Records. Deleted 17 Apr '89. Catalogue no: **651673 2**

BETCHA SAY THAT
Tracks: / Betcha say that / Betcha say that (dub version) / Love toy / Betcha say that/ love toy / Megamix-rhythm is gonna get you, The / Conga / Doctor Beat / Bad boy.
7" Single: Released Oct '87, on Epic, by CBS Records. Deleted Aug '88. Catalogue no: **651125 7**
12" Single: Released Oct '87, on CBS, by CBS Records. Deleted Aug '88. Catalogue no: **651125 9**
12" Single: Released Oct '87, on Epic, by CBS Records. Deleted Aug '88. Catalogue no: **651125 8**

CAN'T STAY AWAY FROM YOU
Tracks: / Can't stay away from you / Let it loose / Bold boy (remix) (12" only) / Rhythm is gonna get you (Only on CD single.) / Surrender (remix) (Only on CD single.).
CD 5": Released May '88, on Epic, by CBS Records. Deleted 10 Jul '89. Catalogue no: **651 444-2**
7" Pic: Released Feb '89, on Epic, by CBS Records. Deleted 10 Jul '89. Catalogue no: **653 195-7**
7" Single: Released May '88, on Epic, by CBS Records. Deleted 10 Jul '89. Catalogue no: **651 444-7**
12" Single: Released 30 Jan '89, on Epic, by CBS Records. Deleted 10 Jul '89. Catalogue no: **651 444-8**
12" Single: Released May '88, on Epic, by CBS Records. Deleted Oct '89. Catalogue no: **651444 9**
7" Single: Released Feb '89, on Epic, by CBS Records. Deleted 10 Jul '89. Catalogue no: **653 195-0**
7" Single: Released May '88, on Epic, by CBS Records. Catalogue no: **651444 0**

DON'T WANNA LOSE YOU (see panel above)
Tracks: / Don't want to lose you / Words get in the way.
12" Single: Released Jul '89, on Epic, by CBS Records. Catalogue no: **655 054 1**
7" Single: Released Jul '89, on Epic, by CBS Records. Catalogue no: **655 054 0**
12" Single: Released Jul '89, on Epic, by CBS Records. Catalogue no: **655 054 8**
CD 5": Released Jul '89, on Epic, by CBS Records. Catalogue no: **655 054 2**
Cassingle: Released Jul '89, on Epic, by CBS Records. Catalogue no: **655 054 4**
7" Single: Released Jul '89, on Epic, by CBS Records. Catalogue no: **655 054 9**

OYE MI CANTO (HEAR MY VOICE)
Tracks: / Oye mi canto (hear my voice) (Only on 7" and CD single.) / Conga / Oye mi canto (hear my voice) (12" pablo mix) (Only on 12" single.) / Oye mi canto (hear my voice) (pablo dub mix) (Only on 12" single.) / Oye mi canto (hear my voice) (album version) (Only on CD single.) / Rhythm is gonna get you (Only on CD single.).
12" Single: Released Sep '89, on Epic, by CBS Records. Catalogue no: **655287 6**
CD 5": Released Sep '89, on Epic, by CBS Records. Catalogue no: **655287 2**
12" Pic: Released Sep '89, on Epic, by CBS Records. Catalogue no: **655287 8**
Cassingle: Released Sep '89, on Epic, by CBS Records. Catalogue no: **655287 4**
Cassingle: Released Sep '89, on Epic, by CBS Records. Catalogue no: **655287 5**
7" Single: Released Sep '89, on Epic, by CBS Records. Catalogue no: **655287 7**

RHYTHM IS GONNA GET YOU
Tracks: / Rhythm is gonna get you / Rhythm is gonna get you (dub mix) / Give it up.
7" Single: Released Feb '88, on Epic, by CBS Records. Deleted Aug '88. Catalogue no: **650805 7**
12" Single: Released Feb '88, on Epic, by CBS Records. Deleted Nov '87. Catalogue no: **650805 8**

RHYTHM IS GONNA GET YOU (RE-ISSUE)
Tracks: / Rhythm is gonna get you / Give it up / Rhythm is gonna get you (dub mix) (Only on 12" version.) / Conga (dance mix) (Only on CD single.).
CD 5": Released Dec '88, on Epic, by CBS Records. Deleted 10 Jul '89. Catalogue no: **654 514-2**
7" Single: on Epic, by CBS Records. Deleted 10 Jul '89. Catalogue no: **654 514-9**
7" Single: Released Dec '88, on Epic, by CBS Records. Deleted 10 Jul '89. Catalogue no: **654 514-0**
7" Single: on Epic, by CBS Records. Deleted 10 Jul '89. Catalogue no: **654 534-7**
7" Single: Released Dec '88, on Epic, by CBS Records. Deleted 10 Jul '89. Catalogue no: **654 514-7**
12" Single: on Epic, by CBS Records. Deleted 10 Jul '89. Catalogue no: **654 514-8**
12" Single: Released Dec '88, on Epic, by CBS Records. Deleted 10 Jul '89. Catalogue no: **654 514-6**

Estelle, Don

ECOUTEZ MA CHANSON
Tracks: / Ecoutez ma chanson.
7" Single: Released Oct '83, on Lofty, by Monarch Records. Catalogue no: **SLR 104**

GOODBYE
Tracks: / Goodbye / Rule Britannia.
7" Single: Released Mar '82, on Lofty, by Monarch Records. Catalogue no: **SLR 103**

LITTLE DONKEY
Tracks: / Little donkey / Auld lang syne.
7" Single: Released Nov '82, on Lofty, by Monarch Records. Catalogue no: **SLR 102**

ROSE MARIE
Tracks: / Rose Marie / Beautiful dreamer.
7" Single: Released Apr '81, on Lofty, by Monarch Records. Catalogue no: **SLR 101**

Esterine, Thomas

HELLO
Tracks: / Hello.
7" Single: Released Oct '88, on Danceyard, by Danceyard Records. Catalogue no: **ANGE 2**
12" Single: Released Oct '88, on Danceyard, by Danceyard Records. Catalogue no: **ANGE T2**

Estus, Deon

1-2-3
Tracks: / 1-2-3.
7" Single: Released Aug '87, on Geffen, by Geffen Records (USA). Deleted Jul '88. Catalogue no: **GEF 25**
12" Single: Released Aug '87, on Geffen, by Geffen Records (USA). Deleted Jul '88. Catalogue no: **GEF 25T**

HEAVEN HELP ME
Tracks: / Heaven help me / Love can't wait / Me or the rumours.
CD 5": Released Apr '89, on Polydor, by Polydor Ltd. Catalogue no: **871 539-2**
7" Single: Released May '89, on Polydor, by Polydor Ltd. Deleted Oct '89. Catalogue no: **MIKAG 2**
7" Single: Released Apr '89, on Polydor, by Polydor Ltd. Deleted Oct '89. Catalogue no: **MIKA 2**
12" Single: Released Apr '89, on Polydor, by Polydor Ltd. Deleted Oct '89. Catalogue no: **MIKAZ 2**

LOVE HURTS
Tracks: / Love hurts.
7" Single: Released Mar '84, on Legacy, by Legacy Records. Catalogue no: **LGY 11**
12" Single: Released Mar '84, on Legacy, by Legacy Records. Catalogue no: **LGYT 11**

ME OR THE RUMOURS
Tracks: / Me or the rumours / Love can't wait.
7" Single: Released Jul '88, on Mika, by Mika Records. Catalogue no: **MIKA 1**
12" Single: Released Jul '88, on Mika, by Mika Records. Catalogue no: **MIKAZ 1**

MY GUY, MY GIRL (see Stewart, Amii/Deon Estus)
7" Single: Released Nov '85, on Sedition, by Sedition Records. Catalogue no: **EDIT 3310**

SPELL (SINGLE)
Tracks: / Spell.
7" Single: Released Jul '86, on Geffen, by Geffen Records (USA). Catalogue no: **GEF 5**
12" Single: Released Jul '86, on Geffen, by Geffen Records (USA). Deleted Jun '87. Catalogue no: **GEF 5T**

Esty, Kim

COME ON
Tracks: / Come on.
7" Single: Released Aug '89, on Power, Catalogue no: **ZAK 2**

Etc Etc

SCANNING THE CROWDS (CASS 45)
Tracks: / Scanning the crowds.
7" Single: Released Aug '82, on Blue Rhythm, Catalogue no: **CBR 3**

Eternal Triangle

NOTHING BUT A FRIEND
Tracks: / Nothing but a friend.
7" Single: Released May '84, on Situation 2, by Beggars Banquet Records. Catalogue no: **SIT 34**
12" Single: Released May '84, on Situation 2, by Beggars Banquet Records. Catalogue no: **SIT 34T**

ONLY IN THE NIGHT
Tracks: / Only in the night / Remote con-

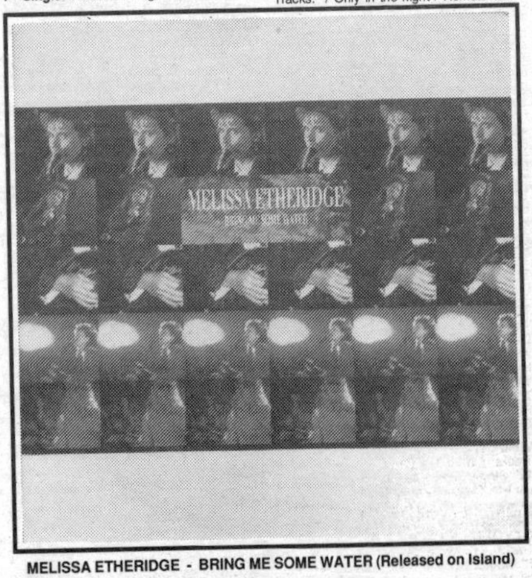

MELISSA ETHERIDGE - BRING ME SOME WATER (Released on Island)

trol.
7" Single: Released Apr '84, on Situation 2, by Beggars Banquet Records. Catalogue no: **SIT 30**
12" Single: Released Apr '84, on Situation 2, by Beggars Banquet Records. Catalogue no: **SIT 30T**

Eternity

ASHRAM HOUSE
Tracks: / Ashram house.
12" Single: Released Oct '88, on Gee Street, by Gee Street Records. Catalogue no: **GEE 12004**

Etheridge, Melissa

BRING ME SOME WATER (see panel on previous page)
Tracks: / Bring me some water / Occasionally / I want you (Only on 12".).
CD 5": Released 27 Feb '89, on Island, by Island Records. Catalogue no: **CID 393**
7" Single: Released Feb '89, on Island, by Island Records. Catalogue no: **IS 393**
12" Single: Released Feb '89, on Island, by Island Records. Deleted Apr '89. Catalogue no: **12IS 393**

DON'T YOU NEED
Tracks: / Don't you need / Precious pain.
Note: "An exceptionally talented singer/songwriter. Her deft accoustic accompaniment supports her strong voice." (Music Week, July 1988)
7" Single: Released 16 May '88, on Island, by Island Records. Deleted Apr '89. Catalogue no: **IS 376**
12" Single: Released 16 May '88, on Island, by Island Records. Deleted Apr '89. Catalogue no: **12IS 376**

NO SOUVENIRS
Tracks: / No souvenirs / No souvenirs (live) / Brave and crazy life (On 12" and CD only).
CD 5": Released Jul '89, on Island, by Island Records. Catalogue no: **CID 431**
7" Single: Released Jul '89, on Island, by Island Records. Catalogue no: **IS 431**
12" Single: Released Jul '89, on Island, by Island Records. Catalogue no: **12 IS 431**

SIMILAR FEATURES
Tracks: / Similar features / I want you / Don't you need (Avaliable on 12" format only.).
7" Single: Released Apr '88, on Island, by Island Records. Deleted Dec '88. Catalogue no: **IS 356**
12" Single: Released Apr '88, on Island, by Island Records. Deleted Dec '88. Catalogue no: **12IS 356**

Ethiopians

Biographical details: This band is actually Jamaican - the name is derived from their Rastafarian religion, a belief which teaches its followers to regard Ethiopia as Zion and worship it's most famous leader, Hailer Selassie, as God. The Ethiopians enjoyed a solitary chart entry in 1967 - the men reached no.40 with their cult single *Train to Skaville*. This was one of the classics of the "rock steady" genre, the forerunner of reggae; the Jamaican "rude boy" scene had, by 1967, spread to many kids in Britain - the UK popularity of such records as *Train to Skaville* was fuelled by repeated plays in such haunts as Brixton's Ram Jam Club. The Ethipoians remained a popular attraction on the Jamaican reggae scene throughout the 70's. Their albums included *Woman capture man* (1970) and *Slave call* (1977). They continued in the 80's with *The whip.* and *Solid as a rock.* (Bob Macdonald, 8/85).

PIRATE
Tracks: / Pirate.
12" Single: Released Oct '86, on Trojan, by Trojan Records. Deleted May '88. Catalogue no: **TROT 9085**

SOLID AS A ROCK
Tracks: / Solid as a rock / You're my baby.
12" Single: Released Mar '84, on Success (2), Catalogue no: **SUCCESS 174**

TRAIN TO SKAVILLE
Tracks: / Train to skaville / Hold them / Doctor Dick.
7" Single: Released Mar '8?, on Island, by Island Records. Deleted '83. Catalogue no: **WIP 6596**
7" Single: Released Sep '67, on Rio, by Rio Records. Deleted '70. Catalogue no: **RIO 130**

WHIP, THE
Tracks: / Whip, The.
12" Single: Released Nov '83, on Treasure Isle, Catalogue no: **TRE 010**

Etkind, Annabel

OXYGENE PART 4
Tracks: / Oxygene (part IV).
7" Single: Released Nov '83, on Lifestyle, by Micrometro Ltd (Records). Catalogue

E.U. - E.U. FREEZE (Released on 4th & Broadway)

no: **LIFE 3**

Eton Crop

BUNDLE OF BUCKS..., A
Tracks: / Bundle of bucks, A.
12" Single: Released Apr '87, on Ediesta, Catalogue no: **CALC 020**

GAY BOYS ON THE BATTLEFIELD (EP)
12" Single: Released May '84, on Bigger Bank Balance, Catalogue no: **BALANCE 1**

PEEL SESSIONS:ETON CROP
12" Single: Released Nov '88, on Strange Fruit, by Strange Fruit Records. Catalogue no: **SFPS 063**

YES PLEASE, BOB (7")
Tracks: / Yes please, Bob.
7" Single: Released Nov '86, on Ediesta, Catalogue no: **CALC 12**

Etoria, Tony

I CAN PROVE IT
Tracks: / I can prove it.
7" Single: Released Jun '77, on GTO, Deleted '80. Catalogue no: **GT 89**

SO FAR SO GOOD
Tracks: / So far so good / Move it out.
7" Single: Released Jan '80, on Cobra, Deleted Jan '83. Catalogue no: **COB 6**

E.U.

DA'BUTT
Tracks: / Da'butt / Da'butt (B Boy dub) / Da'butt (radio mix) (Track on 12" version only) / Da'butt (Ext.soundtrack version/Marcus Miller mix) (Track on 12" version only).
Note: From the School Daze soundtrack. (P) 1988 original sound recording(s) made by EMI-Manhattan Records, a division of Capitol Records Inc.
7" Single: Released Jul '88, on EMI-Manhattan, by EMI Records. Deleted Jun '89. Catalogue no: **MT 43**
12" Single: Released Jul '88, on EMI-Manhattan, by EMI Records. Deleted Jun '89. Catalogue no: **12MT 43**

E.U.FREEZE (see panel above)
Tracks: / E.U. freeze / E.U. freeze (instr.).
7" Single: Released Apr '85, on 4th & Broadway, by Island Records. Catalogue no: **GOGO 3**
12" Single: Released Apr '85, on 4th & Broadway, by Island Records. Deleted '87. Catalogue no: **12 GOGO 3**

TASTE OF YOU LOVE
7" Single: Released Jun '89, on Virgin (USA), by Virgin Records. Catalogue no: **UNKNOWN**
12" Single: Released Jun '89, on Virgin (USA), by Virgin Records. Catalogue no: **UNKNOWN**

Eugene & Syncopators

GREAT ROMANTIC
Tracks: / Great romantic / Kitten kicker.
7" Single: Released Mar '81, on Rocket, by Rocket Records. Deleted Mar '84. Catalogue no: **XPRES 50**

KEEP YOUR PECKER UP
Tracks: / Keep your pecker up / Gorgeous girl.
7" Single: Released Jun '81, on Swamp, by Swamp Records. Deleted Jun '84. Catalogue no: **WAM 113**

SOMETHING ON YOUR SHOE
Tracks: / Something on your shoe / Knock-kneed Nellie.
7" Single: Released Nov '81, on Swamp, by Swamp Records. Deleted Nov '84. Catalogue no: **WAM 116**

Eurasiantea

LIBERTY(DANCE WITH ME)
Tracks: / Liberty(dance with me).
7" Single: on Telscot, by Telscot Records. Catalogue no: **TEL 21**

Eurogliders

CAN'T WAIT TO SEE YOU
Tracks: / Can't wait to see you / I like to hear it.
7" Single: Released Jun '86, on CBS, by CBS Records. Catalogue no: **A 7139**

CITY OF SOUL
Tracks: / City of soul / When the stars come out.
7" Single: Released Jan '86, on CBS, by CBS Records. Catalogue no: **A 6774**
12" Single: Released Jan '86, on CBS, by CBS Records. Catalogue no: **TA 6774**

HEAVEN
Tracks: / Heaven / It't the way.
7" Single: Released Dec '84, on CBS, by CBS Records. Catalogue no: **A 4622**
12" Single: Released Dec '84, on CBS, by CBS Records. Catalogue no: **TX 4622**

Euro-k

ACTION MAN
Tracks: / Action man.
7" Single: Released Sep '84, on Dork, by Dork Records. Catalogue no: **UROK 4**

Europe

FINAL COUNTDOWN, THE (SINGLE)
Tracks: / Final countdown / On broken wings / Carrie (Only on 3"CD single.).
7" Single: Released Oct '86, on Epic, by CBS Records. Deleted Aug '87. Catalogue no: **A 7127**
12" Single: Released Oct '86, on Epic, by CBS Records. Deleted Aug '87. Catalogue no: **TA 7127**
CD 3": Released Sep '88, on Victor (Japan), Catalogue no: **VDPS 1002**

LET THE GOOD TIMES ROCK
Tracks: / Let the good times rock / Never say die / Carrie (Only on CD single and 12".) / Seven doors hotel (Only on Cd single and 12".).
CD 5": Released 13 Mar '89, on Epic, by CBS Records. Deleted Oct '89. Catalogue no: **CDEUR 5**
7" Single: Released 13 Mar '89, on Epic, by CBS Records. Deleted Oct '89. Catalogue no: **EUR 5**
12" Single: Released 13 Mar '89, on Epic, by CBS Records. Deleted Oct '89. Catalogue no: **EURT 5**

OPEN YOUR HEART
Tracks: / Open your heart / Just the beginning / Rock the night (Only on 12" & CD single.) / Lyin' eyes (Only on 12" & CD single.).
CD 5": Released Oct '88, on Epic, by CBS Records. Deleted 17 Apr '89. Catalogue no: **CDEUR 4**
7" Single: Released Nov '88, on Epic, by CBS Records. Deleted 17 Apr '89. Catalogue no: **EUR B4**
7" Single: Released Oct '88, on Epic, by CBS Records. Deleted 17 Apr '89. Catalogue no: **EUR 4**
7" Single: Released Oct '88, on Epic, by CBS Records. Deleted 17 Apr '89. Catalogue no: **EUR Q4**
12" Single: Released Oct '88, on Epic, by CBS Records. Deleted 17 Apr '89. Catalogue no: **EUR T4**

ROCK THE NIGHT
Tracks: / Rock the night / Seven doors hotel / Storm wind (Available on 12" version only.) / Wings of tomorrow (Available on 12" version only.).
Note: Extra tracks on 12" version only.
7" Single: Released Feb '87, on Epic, by CBS Records. Deleted Aug '87. Catalogue no: **EUR Q1**

SUPERSTITIOUS
Tracks: / Superstitious / Lights and shadows.
Note: * Only available on the 12" and CD version.
CD 5": Released Aug '88, on Epic, by CBS Records. Deleted 17 Apr '89. Catalogue no: **CDEUR 3**
7" Single: Released 22 Aug '88, on Epic, by CBS Records. Deleted 17 Apr '89. Catalogue no: **EUR C3**
7" Single: Released 14 Aug '88, on Epic, by CBS Records. Deleted 17 Apr '89. Catalogue no: **EUR Q3**
7" Single: Released Aug '88, on Epic, by CBS Records. Deleted 17 Apr '89. Catalogue no: **EUR 3**
12" Single: Released Aug '88, on Epic, by CBS Records. Deleted 17 Apr '89. Catalogue no: **EUR T3**

European Sun

ANSWER ME
Tracks: / Answer me.
7" Single: Released Sep '84, on Iguana (1), by Iguana Records. Catalogue no: **HRSL 001**

European Toys

I AM CREATOR
Tracks: / I am creator.
7" Single: Released Jul '83, on Subversive, Catalogue no: **SUB 008**

KOREA
Tracks: / Korea.
12" Single: Released Jun '84, on JKO, Catalogue no: **12JKO 107**
12" Single: Released '88, on Backs, by Backs Recording Co.. Catalogue no: **12 NCH 9**

Europeans

ANIMAL SONG
Tracks: / Animal song / Someone's changing.
7" Single: Released Sep '82, on A&M, by A&M Records. Deleted '85. Catalogue no: **AMS 8245**
12" Single: Released Sep '82, on A&M, by A&M Records. Deleted '85. Catalogue no: **AMSX 8245**

EUROPEANS
Tracks: / Europeans.
7" Single: Released Jul '79, on Heartbeat, by Mainline Records. Catalogue no: **PULSE 2**

VOCABULARY
Tracks: / Animal song / A.E.I.O.U. / Voice on the telephone / American people / Falling / Recognition / Innocence / Spirit of youth / Modern homes / Kingdom come.
7" Single: Released Nov '83, on A&M, by A&M Records. Deleted Nov '88. Catalogue no: **AMLX 68558**

Eurythmics

Biographical details: Annie Lennox and Dave Stewart, one of the foremost duos of the 80's, were the driving force behind the Tourists between 77 and 80. As 2/5 of that 5-piece band, they came to fame in 1979 and quickly achieved five chart singles. Dave and Annie had originally met in a restaurant, where Lennox had been working as a waitress and cabaret singer; prior to this, she had studied piano and flute at the Royal Academy of music. Following the Tourists' breakup in 1980, the pair took the name of "Eurythmics", and released their debut LP as a duo in October 1981 - *In the garden* was not a commercial success. In 1983 they suddenly cruised into top gear, having perfected their modern pop sound, which was sophisticated but danceable. By the end of the year, they had chalked up four superb, contrasting UK Top 10 singles with *Sweet dreams, Love is a stranger, Who's that girl* and *Right by your side*. The first of these went on to become an American no.11, and was also the title of their second album. By early 1984, the album *Touch* had reached no.1 on the British LP listings and spawned the UK & US Top 10 singles *Here comes the rain again*. At the end of '84, they hit the British no.4 position with *Sexcrime (1984)*. This was the theme track from their soundtrack LP, which they were commissioned to write and record for a cinema adaptation of the Orwell novel *1984*. However, to their chagrin, they discovered that the movie makers had already booked a second soundtrack and the Eurythmics' music barely got a look-in during the film. The group rapidly put this melee behind them by achieving a British no.1 single *There must be an angel (playing with my heart)*, featuring guest harmonica by Stevie Wonder. This song featured one of Lennox' most soaring vocal performances, whose emotional yet controlled lead singing was always one of the key ingredients in the duo's success. (Bob Macdonald, 3/8/85)

Pop duo: David Allan Stewart (born in 1952 in Sunderland) on guitars, keyboards, vocals; and vocalist Annie Lennox (born in Aberdeen in 1954). Stewart began as a folkie in the mid '60's, met Lennox waitressing in a Hampstead restaurant in 1977 and they formed the Tourists for three albums and some hits. The group split in 1980 but Stewart and Lennox carried on together. Debut LP *In the garden* was made in Germany with guests including Holger Czukay and Marcus Stockhausen, a blend of psychedelia and mildly avant-garde electronics; *Sweet dreams (are made of this)* established them with two big hit singles and clever videos emphasising Lennox's androgynous appeal. They landed the plum job of scoring film *1984*; problems with producers led to the music being shelved, but Virgin shoved it on the soundtrack album anyway. Stewart was in demand as a producer; he worked with Tom Petty, Feargal Sharkey, Bob Dylan; Lennox's marriage to a Hare Krishna devotee didn't last; she had a cameo role in the big flop film *Revolution* in 1985. They are still one of the best and brightest UK pop acts, thanks to Stewart's melodies and technique, Lennox's blue eyed soul and looks. (Donald Clarke, April 1989)a.

BEETHOVEN (I LOVE TO LISTEN TO)
Tracks: / Beethoven (I love to listen to) / Heaven / Beethoven (I love to listen to) dance mix / Beethoven (I love to listen to) extended.
7" Single: Released 10 Oct '87, on RCA, by BMG Records (UK). Deleted May '89. Catalogue no: **DA 11**
12" Single: Released 10 Oct '87, on RCA, by BMG Records (UK). Deleted May '89. Catalogue no: **DAT 11**

BELINDA
Tracks: / Belinda / Heartbeat, heartbeat.
7" Single: Released Aug '81, on RCA, by BMG Records (UK). Deleted Aug '84. Catalogue no: **RCA 115**

CHILL IN MY HEART
Tracks: / Chill in my heart / Chill in my heart (acoustic) / Chill in my heart (dance mix) / Do you want to break up / Here comes the rain again (live).
Note: " 7" and 12" and C.D. all feature a live acoustic version of 'You Have Placed A Chill In My Heart' as performed by Dave and Annie on Friday Night Live". (RCA Records, May 1988).
7" Single: Released 31 May '88, on RCA, by BMG Records (UK). Deleted Aug '89. Catalogue no: **DA 16**
12" Single: Released 31 May '88, on RCA, by BMG Records (UK). Deleted Aug '89. Catalogue no: **DAT 16**

HERE COMES THE RAIN AGAIN
Tracks: / Here comes the rain again.
7" Pic: Released Jan '84, on D & A, by BMG Records (UK). Catalogue no: **DAP 5**
7" Single: Released Jan '84, on D & A, by BMG Records (UK). Catalogue no: **DA 5**
12" Single: Released Jan '84, on D & A, by BMG Records (UK). Catalogue no: **DAT 5**

I NEED A MAN
Tracks: / I need a man / I need you.
CD 5": Released 5 Mar '88, on RCA, by BMG Records (UK). Catalogue no: **DA 15CD**
7" Single: Released 5 Mar '88, on RCA, by BMG Records (UK). Deleted May '89. Catalogue no: **DA 15**
12" Single: Released 5 Mar '88, on RCA, by BMG Records (UK). Deleted May '89. Catalogue no: **DAT 15**

EURYTHMICS -SWEET DREAMS ARE MADE OF THIS (Released on RCA)

IT'S ALRIGHT (BABY'S COMING BACK)
Tracks: / It's alright (baby's coming back) / Conditioned soul / Late notification.
7" Single: Released Jan '86, on RCA, by BMG Records (UK). Catalogue no: **PB 40375**
12" Single: Released Jan '86, on RCA, by BMG Records (UK). Deleted '87. Catalogue no: **PT 40376**

JULIA
Tracks: / Julia.
7" Single: Released Jan '85, on Virgin, by Virgin Records. Deleted '89. Catalogue no: **VS 734**
12" Single: Released Jan '85, on Virgin, by Virgin Records. Deleted '86. Catalogue no: **VS 734-12**

LOVE IS A STRANGER
Tracks: / Love is a stranger / Monkey monkey.
7" Pic: Released Sep '82, on D & A, by BMG Records (UK). Catalogue no: **DAP 1**
7" Single: Released Sep '82, on D & A, by BMG Records (UK). Deleted May '89. Catalogue no: **DA 1**
12" Single: Released Sep '82, on D & A, by BMG Records (UK). Deleted May '89. Catalogue no: **DAT 1**

MIRACLE OF LOVE
Tracks: / When tomorrow comes (live) / Who's that girl (Live track on 12" version only.).
7" Single: Released Nov '86, on D & A, by BMG Records (UK). Catalogue no: **DA 9**
12" Single: Released Nov '86, on D & A, by BMG Records (UK). Deleted May '89. Catalogue no: **DAT 9**

MISSIONARY MAN
Tracks: / Missionary man / Last time, The (live).
7" Single: Released Feb '87, on D & A, by BMG Records (UK). Deleted May '89. Catalogue no: **DA 10**
12" Single: Released Feb '87, on D & A, by BMG Records (UK). Deleted May '89. Catalogue no: **DAT 10**

NEVER GONNA CRY AGAIN
Tracks: / Never gonna cry again / Lesinestre.
7" Single: Released Jul '81, on RCA, by BMG Records (UK). Deleted '82. Catalogue no: **RCA 68**

REVIVAL
Tracks: / Revival / Precious / Revival (ET mix).
CD 5": Released 14 Aug '89, on RCA, by BMG Records (UK). Catalogue no: **DACD 17**
7" Single: Released 14 Aug '89, on RCA, by BMG Records (UK). Catalogue no: **DA 17**
12" Single: Released Sep '89, on RCA, by BMG Records (UK). Catalogue no: **DAT 18**
12" Single: Released 14 Aug '89, on RCA, by BMG Records (UK). Catalogue no: **DAT 17**

RIGHT BY YOUR SIDE
7" Single: Released Oct '83, on D & A, by BMG Records (UK). Catalogue no: **DA 4**
12" Single: Released Oct '83, on D & A, by BMG Records (UK). Catalogue no: **DAT 4**

SEXCRIME (1984)
Tracks: / Sexcrime (1984) (7" & 12" only) / Sexcrime (1984) (extended remix) (CD & 12" only) / Julia (extended mix) (CD only) / I did it just the same (On all versions).
7" Single: Released Oct '84, on Virgin, by Virgin Records. Catalogue no: **VS 728**
12" Single: Released Oct '84, on Virgin, by Virgin Records. Catalogue no: **VS 728-12**
CD 3": Released '88, on Virgin, by Virgin Records. Catalogue no: **CDT 22**

SHAME
Tracks: / Shame / I've got a lover (back in Japan) / Shame (dance mix).
Note: * extra track on 12" version.
7" Single: Released Dec '87, on Arista, by BMG Records (UK). Deleted May '89. Catalogue no: **DA 14**
12" Single: Released Dec '87, on Arista, by BMG Records (UK). Deleted May '89. Catalogue no: **DAT 14**

SISTERS ARE DOIN' IT FOR THEMSELVES
Tracks: / Sisters are doin' it for themselves.
7" Single: Released Oct '85, on RCA, by BMG Records (UK). Deleted May '89. Catalogue no: **PB 40339**
12" Single: Released Oct '85, on RCA, by BMG Records (UK). Deleted '87. Catalogue no: **PT 40340**

SWEET DREAMS (ARE MADE OF THIS) (see panel above)
Tracks: / Sweet dreams (are made of this) / I could give you (a mirror).
7" Single: Released Jan '83, on RCA, by BMG Records (UK). Deleted '87. Catalogue no: **DA 2**
12" Single: Released Jan '83, on RCA, by BMG Records (UK). Deleted Aug '89. Catalogue no: **DAT 2**

THERE MUST BE AN ANGEL (PLAYING WITH MY HEART)
Tracks: / There must be an angel (playing with my heart).
12" Single: Released Jun '85, on RCA, by BMG Records (UK). Catalogue no: **PT 40248**
7" Single: Released Jun '85, on RCA, by BMG Records (UK). Catalogue no: **PB 40247**

THIS IS THE HOUSE
Tracks: / This is the house / Home is where / Take me to your heart.
12" Single: Released Apr '82, on RCA, by BMG Records (UK). Catalogue no: **RCAT 199**
7" Single: Released Apr '82, on RCA, by BMG Records (UK). Catalogue no: **RCA 199**

THORN IN MY SIDE
Tracks: / Thorn in my side / In this town.
Note: Extra track on 12" version not known
12" Single: Released Aug '86, on D & A, by BMG Records (UK). Deleted May '89. Catalogue no: **DAT 8**
7" Single: Released Aug '86, on D & A, by BMG Records (UK). Deleted May '89. Catalogue no: **DA 8**

WALK, THE
Tracks: / Walk, The / Morning (Only on 12") / Invisible hands (Only on 12") / Step on the beast.
7" Single: Released Jun '82, on RCA, by BMG Records (UK). Catalogue no: **RCA 230**
12" Single: Released Jul '82, on RCA, by BMG Records (UK). Catalogue no: **RCAT 230**

WHEN TOMORROW COMES
Tracks: / When tomorrow comes / Take your pain away.
7" Single: Released May '86, on D & A, by BMG Records (UK). Catalogue no: **DA 7**
12" Single: Released May '86, on D & A, by BMG Records (UK). Catalogue no: **DAT 7**

WHO'S THAT GIRL
Tracks: / Who's that girl / You take some lentils.
12" Single: Released Jul '83, on D & A, by BMG Records (UK). Deleted May '89. Catalogue no: **DAT 3**
7" Single: Released Jul '83, on D & A, by BMG Records (UK). Catalogue no: **DA 3**

WOULD I LIE TO YOU
Tracks: / Would I lie to you / Here comes that sinking feeling.
7" Single: Released Apr '85, on RCA, by BMG Records (UK). Catalogue no: **PB 40101**
12" Single: Released Apr '85, on RCA, by BMG Records (UK). Deleted May '89. Catalogue no: **PT 40102**

YOU HAVE PLACED A CHILL IN MY HEART
Tracks: / You have placed a chill in my heart.
12" Single: Released Jun '88, on RCA, by BMG Records (UK). Deleted Aug '89. Catalogue no: **DAT 16**

Eva

BOY, A GIRL AND NEW YORK, A
Tracks: / Boy, a girl and New York, A.
7" Single: Released Jul '88, on In Tape, by In Tape Records. Catalogue no: **IT 055**
12" Single: Released Jul '88, on In Tape, by In Tape Records. Catalogue no: **ITTI 055**

EVARADOS
Tracks: / Evarados.
12" Single: Released '88, on John Dread Production, Catalogue no: **JDPD 10**

Evan & The MBT Band

SOMEDAY WE'LL BE TOGETHER
Tracks: / Someday we'll be together.
7" Single: Released Jul '85, on MBT, Catalogue no: **EVAN 7**
12" Single: Released Jul '85, on MBT, Catalogue no: **EVAN 12**

Evans, A

MARCHING ON
Tracks: / Marching on.
12" Single: Released Oct '85, on Yardbeat, Catalogue no: **YB 002**

Evans, Deborah

RESPECT
Tracks: / Respect.
7" Single: Released Nov '81, on CBS, by CBS Records. Deleted Nov '84. Catalogue no: **A 1715**

Evans, Don

GONNA CARE FOR YOU
Tracks: / Gonna care for you.
12" Single: Released Jul '85, on Move, Catalogue no: **MS 2**

Evans, John

BOY NAMED BEN, A
Tracks: / Boy named Ben, A / Book of my life.
7" Single: Released Dec '85, on City, by City Records. Deleted Nov '87. Catalogue no: **BEN 1**

Evans, Junior

GIMME LITTLE LOVING
Tracks: / Gimme little love / Cold outside.
12" Single: Released Nov '85, on Must Dance, Catalogue no: **MD 007**

Evans, Maureen

BIG HURT, THE
Tracks: / Big hurt, The.
7" Single: Released Jan '60, on Oriole, Deleted '63. Catalogue no: **CB 1533**

I LOVE HOW YOU LOVE ME
Tracks: / I love how you love me.
7" Single: Released Feb '64, on Oriole, Deleted '67. Catalogue no: **CB 1906**

LIKE I DO (OLD GOLD)
Tracks: / Like I do / I love how you love

me.
7" Single: Released Jan '88, on Old Gold, by Old Gold Records. Catalogue no: **OG 9757**

LIKE I DO (SINGLE)
Tracks: / Like I do.
7" Single: Released Nov '62, on Oriole, Deleted '65. Catalogue no: **CB 1763**

LOVE KISSES AND HEARTACHES
Tracks: / Love kisses and heartaches.
7" Single: Released Mar '60, on Oriole, Deleted '63. Catalogue no: **CB 1540**

PAPER ROSES
Tracks: / Paper roses.
7" Single: Released Jun '60, on Oriole, Deleted '63. Catalogue no: **CB 1550**

Evans, Paul

Biographical details: This American singer and songwriter, who hailed from Queens, New York, gained his breakthrough in 1958. In that year, the Kalin Twins took *When*, co-written by Evans, to no.5 in America and no.1 in Britain; it was a ridiculously catchy ditty. Evans did not, however, write his own first hit *Seven little girls sitting in the back seat*; backed by a female vocal duo called The Curls, he got to no.9 in the US with this novelty record. This song was covered in Britain by the Avons, who took it to no.3 as opposed to Evans' no.25. A few months later, in 1960, Evans enjoyed two more US Top 20 hits with *Midnite special* and *Happy-go-lucky me*. The biggest hit of Paul's writing career occurred in 1962, when his co-penned *Roses are red* became an American no.1 smash for Bobby Vinton and a UK no.3 hit for Ronnie Carroll. During the rest of the 60's and 70's, Evans spent his time composing comercials and jingles for TV and radio, and performing in clubs and cabaret. Suddenly in the late 70's, Paul made an unexpected comeback on the British charts. *When* was revived by Showaddywaddy, who took the song to no.3 in 1977. In early 1979, almost 19 years after his last performing hit, Evans reached no.6 with *Hello, this is Joanie (the answering machine song)*. (Bob Macdonald, 4/8/85).

HELLO THIS IS JOANIE (The telephone answering machine song)
Tracks: / Hello this is Joanie.
7" Single: Released Dec '78, on Spring, Deleted '81. Catalogue no: **2066 932**

MIDNIGHT SPECIAL
Tracks: / Midnight special.
7" Single: Released Mar '60, on London-American, Deleted '63. Catalogue no: **HLL 9045**

SEVEN LITTLE GIRLS SITTING IN THE BACK SEAT
Tracks: / Seven little girls sitting in the back seat.
7" Single: Released Nov '59, on London-American, Deleted '62. Catalogue no: **HLL 8968**

Evans, Tyrone

LONESOME LAD
Tracks: / Lonesome lad.
12" Single: Released Feb '83, on Black Music, Catalogue no: **BM 706**

WAR INTERNATIONAL
Tracks: / War international.
12" Single: Released Apr '83, on Shuttle, Catalogue no: **SH 003**

Evans, Victor Romero

AT THE CLUB
Tracks: / At the club / Poor boy.
7" Single: Released May '81, on Epic, by CBS Records. Deleted May '84. Catalogue no: **EPCA 1169**

I NEED A GIRL TONIGHT
Tracks: / I need a girl tonight / Two timing.
7" Single: Released Sep '81, on Epic, by CBS Records. Deleted Sep '84. Catalogue no: **EPC A1647**
12" Single: Released Sep '81, on Epic, by CBS Records. Deleted Sep '84. Catalogue no: **EPCA 13 1647**

MISS ATTRACTIVE
Tracks: / Miss Attractive / Keep on pressing your doorbell.
7" Single: Released Mar '82, on Epic, by CBS Records. Deleted '85. Catalogue no: **EPCA 2170**
12" Single: Released Mar '82, on Epic, by CBS Records. Deleted '85. Catalogue no: **EPCA13-2170**

ONE FOR MY BABY
Tracks: / One for my baby.
12" Single: Released Aug '83, on Special Agent, Catalogue no: **LR 7**

SPECIAL REQUEST
Tracks: / Special request.
12" Single: Released Sep '82, on Special Request, Catalogue no: **LR 6**

Evasions

Biographical details: The anonymous men and women who comprised this British band achieved a one-off UK chart entry in summer 1981. *Wikka wrap* (ie Whicker rap) reached the no.20 position. Borrowing disco segments from Chic and other artists, this single parodied the veteran British TV reporter and presenter Alan Whicker, whose long-running documentary series regularly exposed different cultures, peoples, events and fads around the globe. The Whicker soundalike on the disc carried out an in-depth investigation into the wacky world of funk, rapping and clubbing. Many past dance hits got a mention. (Bob Macdonald, 4/8/85).

JOCK'S RAP (THE PASSAGE)
Tracks: / Jock's rap.
7" Single: Released Dec '82, on Groove PR, by Beggars Banquet Records. Catalogue no: **GP 114**
12" Single: Released Dec '82, on Groove PR, by Beggars Banquet Records. Catalogue no: **GP114 T**

WIKKA WRAP
Tracks: / Wikka wrap / All wrapped up.
7" Single: Released Jul '81, on Groove PR, by Beggars Banquet Records. Catalogue no: **GP 107**
12" Single: Released Jul '81, on Groove PR, by Beggars Banquet Records. Catalogue no: **GP 107 T**

Evens, Don

TELLING ME
Tracks: / Telling me.
12" Single: Released May '85, on Technics, Catalogue no: **WR 1987**

Event Band

WHAT'S MY LINE
Tracks: / What's my line.
7" Single: Released Jul '82, on Mayhem, by International Records & Tapes. Catalogue no: **HEM 1**

Eventually

CULTURE MUSIC EP
12" Single: Released Aug '85, on Friendly Musicians, Catalogue no: **FM 1**

Ever

CAROUSEL
Tracks: / Carousel.
7" Single: Released Nov '88, on Play Room Discs, by Play Room Discs. Catalogue no: **PLAYD 005-7**

Ever Red

HOT NUMBER
Tracks: / Hot number.
12" Single: Released Oct '88, on Supertone, Catalogue no: **STR 007**

Everage, Dame Edna

NEIGHBOURS
Tracks: / Neighbours / Spooky Christmas / Neighbours (caring and sharing mix) (on 12" only.) / Shout (parts 1 & 2)* (*On 12" only.).
7" Single: Released 21 Nov '88, on Epic, by CBS Records. Deleted 17 Apr '89. Catalogue no: **EDNA 1**
12" Single: Released 28 Nov '88, on Epic, by CBS Records. Deleted 17 Apr '89. Catalogue no: **EDNA T1**
Special: Released 28 Nov '88, on Epic, by CBS Records. Deleted 17 Apr '89. Catalogue no: **EDNA B1**

Everett, Betty

Biographical details: This American singer, born in Mississippi, came to public attention in 1963 with her single *You're no good*. Written by Clint Ballad Jr, this song was well received in the R&B market and reached No.51 on the US pop chart. In Britain ther was a smash cover version by the Swinging Blue Jeans; it became a US No.1 for Linda Ronstadt in 1975, the same year that Linda Lewis scored a British Top Tenner witha remake of Everett's 1964 biggie *It's in his kiss (The shoop shoop song)*. Everett also made the grade with two other 1964 singles, *Getting ighty crowded* (which reached No.29 in the UK in early '65) and *Let it be me*. The latter was a duet with the famous Chicago soul singer Jerry Butler - their revival of the old Everly Brothers hit reached No.5 on the American pop chart, two places higher than Don & Phil had managed. The versatile Everett, whose repertoire ranged from bluesy soul to catchy pop, performed her soulful vocals on several more US R&B chart hits during the rest of the Sixties; but she did not return to the pop Top 40 until 1969 when she reached No.26 with *There'll come a time*. She gradually faded from the public eye during the early Seventies. (Bob MacDonald, 4th August 1985)
Soul singer born in 1939 in Mississippi. She moved to Chicago in 1957, began recording on local labels in 1960; *You're no good* was covered in the UK by the Swinging Blue Jeans, later in the USA by Linda Ronstadt for a number one in 1975. Everett's biggest hit was *The shoop shoop song (it's in his kiss)* in 1964 (revived by Linda Lewis in 1975 for a top 10 UK hit). Duets with Jerry Butler filled two albums. Vee-Jay folded in 1967; she recorded for ABC, Uni and Fantasy, but never was as successful as she deserved to be. (Donald Clarke, April 1989).

GETTING MIGHTY CROWDED
Tracks: / Getting mighty crowded / Shoop shoop song.
7" Single: Released Jan '65, on Fontana, by Phonogram Ltd. Deleted '68. Catalogue no: **TF 520**
7" Single: Released Jul '80, on Charly, by Charly Records. Deleted '87. Catalogue no: **CTD 104**

IT'S IN HIS KISS
Tracks: / It's in his kiss.
7" Single: Released Oct '68, on President, by President Records. Deleted '71. Catalogue no: **PT 215**

Everett, Kenny

Biographical details: Born Maurice Cole, this British disc jockey and comedian came to fame in the mid-Sixties during the UK's pirate radio era. In the days before the BBC woke up to pop music and launched Radio One, Everett's loony personality and audacious presentation were perfectly suited to the pioneering spirit of the pop pirate stations. After making his name at Radio London (whose closure was forced by the Government in August 1967), he had a brief spell on the BBC Light Programme before Radio One was inaugurated in September '67. After establishing himself on weekend shows, he was unceremoniously sacked by Radio One. The ostensible reason that was given to the press was that they disapproved of certain comments that he made about the Minister of Transport's wife; in fact it because he spoke to the press about BBC affairs, thus breaking an undertaking given in his contract. He was eventually allowed back onto Radio One and also took his turn at presenting Top of the Pops. But in 1974, shortly after the advent of UK independent local radio, he joined Capital Radio. It was while working at London's commercial pop station that he reached No.32 on the UK singles chart with *Captain Kremnen (Retribution)* - this 1977 single, featured the voice of Kenny and the many instrumental talents of former Manfred Mann player Mike Vickers, capitalised on on the his program's most popular fictional characters. A second, much bigger, hit for Everett occurred in 1983, and was also based on one of his imagined personalities - *Snot rap*, featuring the legendary Sid Snot, reached the UK No.9 position. By this time, Everett was firmly back in the BBC fold (again!). He transferred from Capital to Radio Two in 1981, and his popular TV show which featured the crazy Ken in a huge variety of disguises switched from ITV to BBC television. (Bob MacDonald, 4th August 1985).

CAPTAIN KREMMEN (RETRIBUTION)
Tracks: / Captain Kremmen (retribution).
7" Single: Released Nov '77, on DJM, Deleted '80. Catalogue no: **DJS 10810**

SNOT RAP
Tracks: / Snot rap / Snot rap (part 2).
7" Single: Released Mar '83, on RCA, by BMG Records (UK). Catalogue no: **KEN 1**
12" Single: Released Mar '83, on RCA, by BMG Records (UK). Catalogue no: **KENT 1**

SNOT RAP 2
Tracks: / Snot rap 2.
7" Single: Released Feb '85, on RCA, by BMG Records (UK). Catalogue no: **KEN 2**
12" Single: Released Feb '85, on RCA, by BMG Records (UK). Catalogue no: **KENT 2**

Everett, Rupert

GENERATION OF LONLINESS
Tracks: / Generation of lonliness / Blood under the bridge.
7" Single: Released May '87, on Chrysalis, by Chrysalis Records. Catalogue no: **CHS 3138**
12" Single: Released May '87, on Chrysalis, by Chrysalis Records. Catalogue no: **CHS 123138**

Everette, Leon

OVER
Tracks: / Over / Don't feel like the Lone Ranger.

7" Single: Released Mar '92, on RCA, by BMG Records (UK). Deleted '85. Catalogue no: **RCA 187**

Everly Brothers

Biographical details: Don & Phil Everly, born in Kentucky, were one of America's most successful duos of all time, and indeed one of the most successful acts of all time, period. Also falling into this category were Simon & Garfunkel, who were directly influenced by the Everlys. The Brothers' immaculate vocal harmonies and twin guitar sounds made them one of the most distinctive musical forces of the late Fifties and early Sixties. Don & Phil were born into a country music environment. Their parents were successful local performers, with their own radio show; as soon as the two boys were old enough (Don - 8 years old and Phil - 6), they became part of the family act. They were thus already very experienced by the time they achieved their first hit record twelve years later (1957). Having aroused interest from their music business via their parents' contacts, they were teamed up with ace Nashville guitarist Chet Atkins and songwriter Boudleaux Bryant; the latter wrote most of their early hits, often in conjunction with his wife Felice. The first hit was the classic single *Bye bye love*, one of the freshest and most contagious records of 1957; it surged to No.2 in the US and No.6 in the UK. The equally infectious follow-up, *Wake up little Susie*, fared even better - it became their first American No.1 and climbed to No.2 in Britain. From then on, it was plain sailing on both sides of the Atlantic. The two biggest smashes of their career were the ultra-melodic *All I have to do is dream* (1958, backed by the Roy Orbison penned *Claudette*) and *Cathy's clown* (1960, a self-penned triumph) both singles were No.1 for five weeks in the States and seven weeks in Britain. In the US, they also hit the top slot with 1958's *Bird dog*; in the UK, they claimed the summit with two consecutive 1961 releases, *Walk right back* and *Temptation*.
The key to the Everly Brothers' success was the shrewdness of their musical direction - they steered a pure pop course, usually inclining towards the country-and-western market but simultaneously managing to appeal to rhythm-and-blues followers. And the girls screamed. A combination of factors pushed their career into decline from 1962 onwards: they included the advent of the Beatles revolution; the Brothers' conscription into the US Marines; and increasing friction between the Everlys and their associated arrangers and musicians and, eventually between the Brothers themselves. The hit records continued, but reached much lower chart positions (apart from a brief 1965 highlight with their self-penned UK No.2 hit *The price of love*; the hits had stopped altogether by 1968. After an on-stage row and final split (1973), Don and Phil stumbled through the rest of the Seventies with two undistinguished and unsuccessful solo careers. (Bob MacDonald, 4th August 1985)
Vocal duo Don and Phil were both born in Kentucky; parents Ike and Margaret were well-known on radio, Ike in particular as a black-influenced guitarist in the same mould as Sam McGee and Merle Travis. The sons joined them on radio shows in the mid-'40's, then went to Nashville writing songs for Aduff-Rose (Don's *Thou shalt not steal* was a number 14 country hit for Kitty Wells in 1954). They made a country single for CBS *Keep on lovin' me*, then went to Archie Bleyer's Cadence label with Felice and Boudleaux Bryant's *Bye bye love* in 1957 and the excitement was unbelievable: USA record shops were being asked for it before anyone had heard it; the sudden smash hit put country harmony on the pop chart and gave Nashville a new lease on life as rock'n'oll seemed to be taking over, and made the brothers legends in their own lifetimes. They had six top 10 hits in the country chart 1957-59 and 25 top 40 pop hits 1957-64. Their second album *Songs our daddy taught us* did not even chart, but paid dues to roots with lovely versions of traditional songs before hectic stardom took over completely. They switched to WB after a dispute with Cadence over royalties, then to RCA in 1972; *Stories we could tell* and *Pass the chicken and listen* on RCA had a backup band including Warren Zevon and Waddy Wachtel. By then both had personal problems; the violent split came when Phil smashed a guitar on stage and walked out; Don announced 'The Everly Brothers died ten years ago'. They both wrote songs and recorded solo; they got back together in 1983. Popular as ever in UK, they will not talk about the split. (Donald Clarke, April 1989).

6 TRACK HITS: EVERLY BROTHERS
Tracks: / All I have to do is dream / Wake up little Susie / Bye bye love / Bird dog / Problems / Till I kissed you.
7" EP: Released Sep '83, on Scoop 33, by

Pickwick Records. Catalogue no: **7SR 5000**

ALL I HAVE TO DO IS DREAM
Tracks: / All I have to do is dream / Claudette.
7" Single: Released May '58, on London-American, Deleted '61. Catalogue no: **HLA 8618**
7" Single: Released Jun '88, on Old Gold, by Old Gold Records. Catalogue no: **OG 9062**

ALL I HAVE TO DO IS DREAM (OLD GOLD)
Tracks: / All I have to do is dream / Bye bye love / Wake up little Susie.
CD 5": Released 27 Feb '89, on Old Gold, by Old Gold Records. Catalogue no: **OG 6111**

BIRD DOG
Tracks: / Bird dog.
7" Single: Released Sep '58, on London-American, Deleted '61. Catalogue no: **HLA 8685**

BROTHER JUKE BOX (SINGLE)
Tracks: / Brother juke box / Never like this.
7" Single: Released Nov '85, on Sundown, by Magnum Music Group. Catalogue no: **SDS 001**

BYE BYE LOVE(OLD GOLD SERIES)
Tracks: / Bye bye love / I wonder if i care as much.
7" Single: Released Jul '82, on Old Gold, by Old Gold Records. Catalogue no: **OG 9060**

BYE BYE LOVE (SINGLE)
Tracks: / Bye bye love.
7" Single: Released Jul '57, on London-American, Deleted '60. Catalogue no: **HLA 8440**

CATHY'S CLOWN
Tracks: / Cathy's clown / Temptation.
7" Single: Released Sep '60, on Warner Bros., by WEA Records. Deleted '63. Catalogue no: **WB 1**
7" Single: Released Jul '82, on Old Gold, by Old Gold Records. Catalogue no: **OG 9069**
7" Single: Released Dec '83, on Warner Bros., by WEA Records. Catalogue no: **WB 1**

CRYING IN THE RAIN
Tracks: / Crying in the rain.
7" Single: Released Jan '62, on Warner Bros., by WEA Records. Deleted '65. Catalogue no: **WB 56**

DEVOTED TO YOU
Tracks: / Devoted to you.
7" Single: Released Nov '83, on Impression, Catalogue no: **IMS 1**
12" Single: Released Nov '83, on Impression, Catalogue no: **IMST 1**

DON'T WORRY BABY
Tracks: / Don't worry baby / Born yesterday / Wings of a nightingale.
CD 5": Released Apr '89, on Mercury, by Phonogram Ltd. Deleted Oct '89. Catalogue no: **MERCD 280**
7" Single: Released Apr '89, on Mercury, by Phonogram Ltd. Deleted 31 Jul '89. Catalogue no: **MER 280**

FERRIS WHEEL
Tracks: / Ferris wheel.
7" Single: Released Jul '64, on Warner Bros., by WEA Records. Deleted '67. Catalogue no: **WB 135**

GIRL SANG THE BLUES, THE
Tracks: / Girl sang the blues.
7" Single: Released Oct '63, on Warner Bros., by WEA Records. Deleted '66. Catalogue no: **WB 109**

GONE GONE GONE (SINGLE)
Tracks: / Gone gone gone.
7" Single: Released Dec '64, on Warner Bros., by WEA Records. Deleted '67. Catalogue no: **WB 146**

HOW CAN I MEET HER
Tracks: / How can I meet her.
7" Single: Released May '62, on Warner Bros., by WEA Records. Deleted '65. Catalogue no: **WB 67**

I'LL NEVER GET OVER YOU
Tracks: / I'll never get over you.
7" Single: Released Aug '65, on Warner Bros., by WEA Records. Deleted '68. Catalogue no: **WB 5639**

IT'S BEEN NICE
Tracks: / It's been nice.
7" Single: Released Jun '63, on Warner Bros., by WEA Records. Deleted '66. Catalogue no: **WB 99**

IT'S MY TIME
Tracks: / It's my time.
7" Single: Released May '68, on Warner Bros., by WEA Records. Deleted '71. Catalogue no: **WB 7192**

LET IT BE ME
Tracks: / Let it be me / Since you broke my heart.
7" Single: Released Feb '60, on London-American, Deleted '63. Catalogue no: **HLA 9039**
7" Single: Released Jul '82, on Old Gold, by Old Gold Records. Deleted Jul '88. Catalogue no: **OG 9066**

LIKE STRANGERS
Tracks: / Like strangers / Should we tell him.
7" Single: Released Dec '60, on London-American, Deleted '63. Catalogue no: **HLA 9250**
7" Single: Released Jul '82, on Old Gold, by Old Gold Records. Deleted Jul '88. Catalogue no: **OG 9068**

LIL' BIT OF GOLD: THE EVERLY BROTHERS
Tracks: / Wake up little Susie / Bird dog / Let it be me / All I have to do is dream.
CD 5": Released May '88, on Rhino, by Creole Records. Catalogue no: **R 373008**

LOVE IS STRANGE
Tracks: / Love is strange.
7" Single: Released Oct '65, on Warner Bros., by WEA Records. Deleted '68. Catalogue no: **WB 5649**

LUCILLE
Tracks: / Lucille / So sad (to watch good love go bad).
7" Single: Released Sep '60, on Warner Bros., by WEA Records. Deleted '63. Catalogue no: **WB 19**

MUSKRAT
Tracks: / Muskrat / Don't blame me.
7" Single: Released Oct '61, on Warner Bros., by WEA Records. Deleted '64. Catalogue no: **WB 50**

NASHVILLE, TENNESSEE, NOVEMBER 9, 1955
Tracks: / Keep a' lovin' me / Sun keeps shining, The / If her love isn't true (Previously unissued.) / That's the life I have to live (Previously unissued).
Note: Original CBS recordings.
7" EP: Released Sep '82, on Bear Family, by Bear Family Records (Germany). Catalogue no: **BFE 15075**

NO ONE CAN MAKE MY SUNSHINE SMILE
Tracks: / No one can make my sunshine smile.
7" Single: Released Oct '62, on Warner Bros., by WEA Records. Deleted '65. Catalogue no: **WB 79**

ON THE WINGS OF A NIGHTINGALE
Tracks: / On the wings of a nightingale.
7" Single: Released Sep '84, on Mercury, by Phonogram Ltd. Catalogue no: **MER 170**

POOR JENNY
Tracks: / Poor Jenny / Take a message to mary.
7" Single: Released May '59, on London-American, Deleted '62. Catalogue no: **HLA 8863**
7" Single: Released Jul '82, on Old Gold, by Old Gold Records. Deleted Jul '88. Catalogue no: **OG 9064**

PRICE OF LOVE, THE
Tracks: / Price of love, The / Crying in the rain.
7" Single: Released May '65, on Warner Bros., by WEA Records. Deleted '68. Catalogue no: **WB 161**
7" Single: Released Jul '82, on Old Gold, by Old Gold Records. Deleted Jul '88. Catalogue no: **OG 9072**

PROBLEMS
Tracks: / Problems / Love of my life.
7" Single: Released Jan '59, on London-American, Deleted '62. Catalogue no: **HLA 8781**
7" Single: Released Jul '82, on Old Gold, by Old Gold Records. Deleted Jul '88. Catalogue no: **OG 9063**

SO IT WILL ALWAYS BE
Tracks: / So it will always be.
7" Single: Released Mar '63, on Warner Bros., by WEA Records. Deleted '66. Catalogue no: **WB 94**

SO SAD
Tracks: / So sad / Lucille.
7" Single: Released Jul '82, on Old Gold, by Old Gold Records. Deleted Jul '88. Catalogue no: **OG 9070**

STORY OF ME
Tracks: / Story of me.
7" Single: Released Nov '84, on Mercury, by Phonogram Ltd. Catalogue no: **ER 185**

TAKE A MESSAGE TO MARY
Tracks: / Take a message to Mary.
7" Single: Released Jun '59, on London-American, Deleted '62. Catalogue no: **HLA 8863**

TEMPTATION
Tracks: / Temptation.
7" Single: Released Jun '61, on Warner Bros., by WEA Records. Deleted '64. Catalogue no: **WB 42**

THAT'LL BE THE DAY
Tracks: / That'll be the day.
7" Single: Released May '65, on Warner Bros., by WEA Records. Deleted '68. Catalogue no: **WB 158**

(TIL) I KISSED YOU
Tracks: / Till I kissed you.
7" Single: Released Sep '59, on London-American, Deleted '62. Catalogue no: **HLA 8934**

TILL I KISSED YOU
Tracks: / Till I kissed you / Bird dog / Oh what a feeling.
7" Single: Released 21 Nov '87, on Old Gold, by Old Gold Records. Catalogue no: **OG 9735**
7" Single: Released Jul '82, on Old Gold, by Old Gold Records. Deleted Jul '88. Catalogue no: **OG 9065**

WAKE UP LITTLE SUSIE
Tracks: / Wake up little Susie / Maybe tomorrow.
7" Single: Released Nov '57, on London-American, Deleted '60. Catalogue no: **HLA 8498**
7" Single: Released Jul '82, on Old Gold, by Old Gold Records. Catalogue no: **OG 9061**

WALK RIGHT BACK
Tracks: / Walk right back / Ebony eyes.
7" Single: Released Feb '61, on Warner Bros., by WEA Records. Deleted '64. Catalogue no: **WB 33**
7" Single: Released Jul '82, on Old Gold, by Old Gold Records. Catalogue no: **OG 9071**

WHEN WILL I BE LOVED?
Tracks: / When will I be loved / Be bop a lula.
7" Single: Released Jul '60, on London-American, Deleted '63. Catalogue no: **HLA 9157**
7" Single: Released Jul '82, on Old Gold, by Old Gold Records. Deleted Jul '88. Catalogue no: **OG 9067**

YOU'RE JUST WHAT I WAS LOOKING FOR
Tracks: / You're just what I was looking for.
7" Single: Released Jul '82, on Revival, Catalogue no: **BONUS 1**

Everly, Don

LET'S PUT OUR HEARTS TOGETHER
Tracks: / Let's put our hearts together / So sad.
7" Single: Released Aug '81, on Polydor, by Polydor Ltd. Deleted Aug '84. Catalogue no: **POSP 315**

Everly, Phil

DARE TO DREAM AGAIN
Tracks: / Dare to dream again / Lonely day, lonely night.
7" Single: Released Mar '81, on Epic, by CBS Records. Deleted Mar '84. Catalogue no: **EPC 9575**

LOUISE (SINGLE)
Tracks: / Louise / Sweet Suzanne.
7" Single: Released Nov '82, on Capitol, by EMI Records. Deleted '85. Catalogue no: **CL 266**

OH BABY OH
Tracks: / Oh baby oh / God bless older ladies.
7" Single: Released Jun '83, on Capitol, by EMI Records. Deleted '88. Catalogue no: **CL 294**

SHE MEANS NOTHING TO ME (Phil Everly and Cliff Richard)
Tracks: / She means nothing to me / Man and woman.
7" Single: Released Jan '83, on Capitol, by EMI Records. Deleted '88. Catalogue no: **CL 276**

SWEET PRETENDER
Tracks: / Sweet pretender.
7" Single: Released Apr '83, on Capitol, by EMI Records. Deleted '88. Catalogue no: **CL 285**

Everton Football Club

BOYS IN BLUE
Tracks: / Boys in blue.
7" Single: Released Jun '84, on PRT, by Castle Communications Records. Catalogue no: **EFC 1**

EVERYBODY'S CHEERING THE BLUES
Tracks: / Everybody's cheering the blues / Only 90 minutes away.
7" Single: Released Apr '86, on Columbia, by EMI Records. Catalogue no: **DB 9115**
7" Pic: Released Apr '86, on Columbia, by EMI Records. Catalogue no: **DBP 9115**

HERE WE GO
Tracks: / Here we go.
Note: Official Everton F.C. record 1985.
7" Single: Released May '85, on Columbia, by EMI Records. Catalogue no: **DB 9106**

SPIRIT OF THE BLUES
Tracks: / Spirit of the blues.
7" Single: Released Apr '84, on Direct (1), Catalogue no: **PH 1**

Every New Dead Ghost

ASCENSION
Tracks: / Ascension.
12" Single: Released Dec '88, on Plastic Head, by Plastic Head Records. Catalogue no: **PLASS 008**

Everything But The Girl

Biographical details: Tracey Thorn and Ben Watt are a publicity-shy British duo who came to public attention in 1982, via the UK music press and BBC Radio One's John Peel show. With both members being university students and also pursuing solo musical careers, Everything But The Girl was a part time occupation; in addition, Thorn was also one-third of a group called the Marine Girls. The plaintive voice of Thorn won particular acclaim for a beautiful 1982 solo single, *Plain sailing.* With Tracey on vocals and Ben on guitar, vocals and piano, Everything But The Girl went to the forefront of a mini-jazz-pop boom on the UK music scene. They first cracked the British charts in the summer of 1984, when their gentle jazzy soul single *Each and every one* reached No.28. It would certainly have gone higher, had they not turned down a Top of the Pops appearance - the TV invitation clashed directly with their final exams, and their refusal was typical of their general reluctance to promote themselves and their work. The duo's totally artistic attitude, which gave little or no thought to commercial considerations, did however manage to spawn a UK Top 20 LP with *Eden.* Also in 1984, they reached the lower regions of the singles chart with *Mine* and *Native land.* Their first 1985 single was called *When alls well.* (5th August 1985)
UK pop duo formed by vocalist Tracey Thorn and guitarist Ben Watt, students at Hull U. studying English and drams. They shared radical politics and a liking for folk and jazz. Both signed to the Cherry Red label and recorded solo; they collaborated with Robert Wyatt on an EP *Summer into winter.* Working as a duo they turned down a *Top of the pops* commitment. Their stuff is a gentle agitpop/jazz/folk vein; they record with session players and tour with ever changing back up. They were the first western group to play in Moscow in six years in 1985; at home they confirmed ideological soundness by playing benefits during miner's strike. *Baby the stars shine bright* in 1986 was a smooth and lushly orchestrated album. Their claim to be the antithesis of pop stardom is supported by their eclectic influences of John Martyn, Cole Porter and Antonio Carlos Jobim.
(Donald Clarke, April 1989).

ANGEL
Tracks: / Angel.
7" Single: Released May '85, on Blanco Y Negro, by Blanco Y Negro Records. Deleted '86. Catalogue no: **NEG 15**
12" Single: Released May '85, on Blanco Y Negro, by Blanco Y Negro Records. Deleted Jun '87. Catalogue no: **NEG 15T**

COME ON HOME
Tracks: / Come on home / Draining the bar / I fall to pieces (Extra track on 12" version only.).
7" Single: Released Jul '86, on Blanco Y Negro, by Blanco Y Negro Records. Deleted Jun '87. Catalogue no: **NEG 21**
12" Single: Released Jul '86, on Blanco Y Negro, by Blanco Y Negro Records. Deleted Jan '88. Catalogue no: **NEG 21T**

DON'T LEAVE ME BEHIND
Tracks: / Don't leave me behind / Alfie / Where's the playground (extra track on 12" version only).
12" Single: Released Sep '86, on Blanco Y Negro, by Blanco Y Negro Records. Deleted Jan '88. Catalogue no: **NEG 23T**
7" Single: Released Sep '86, on Blanco Y Negro, by Blanco Y Negro Records. Deleted Jun '87. Catalogue no: **NEG 23**

DRIVING
Tracks: / Driving.
7" Single: Released Sep '89, on Blanco Y Negro, by Blanco Y Negro Records. Catalogue no: **NEG 40**
CD 5": Released Sep '89, on Blanco Y Negro, by Blanco Y Negro Records. Catalogue no: **NEG 40CD**
Cassingle: Released Sep '89, on Blanco Y

Negro, by Blanco Y Negro Records. Catalogue no: **NEG 40C**
12" Single: Released Sep '89, on Blanco Y Negro, by Blanco Y Negro Records. Catalogue no: **NEG 40T**

EACH AND EVERYONE
Tracks: / Each and everyone.
12" Single: Released May '84, on Blanco Y Negro, by Blanco Y Negro Records. Deleted Jun '87. Catalogue no: **NEG 1T**
7" Single: Released May '84, on Blanco Y Negro, by Blanco Y Negro Records. Catalogue no: **NEG 1**

I ALWAYS WAS YOUR GIRL
Tracks: / I always was your girl / Hang out the flags / Home from home (Avaliable on 12" format only).
CD 5": Released Mar '88, on Blanco Y Negro, by Blanco Y Negro Records. Catalogue no: **NEG 33 CD**
7" Single: Released Mar '88, on Blanco Y Negro, by Blanco Y Negro Records. Catalogue no: **WEA NEG 33**
12" Single: Released Mar '88, on Blanco Y Negro, by Blanco Y Negro Records. Catalogue no: **NEG 33T**

I DON'T WANT TO TALK ABOUT IT
Tracks: / I don't want to talk about it / Oxford Street / Shadow on a harvest moon (on 12" only).
Note: * Only available on the 12" version.
7" Single: Released Jul '88, on Blanco Y Negro, by Blanco Y Negro Records. Catalogue no: **NEG 34**
12" Single: Released Jul '88, on Blanco Y Negro, by Blanco Y Negro Records. Catalogue no: **NEG 34T**

LOVE IS HERE WHERE I LIVE
Tracks: / Love is here where I live / Living on a honeycomb / How about me (Only on 12") / Each and everyone (Only on 12").
12" Single: Released 16 Sep '88, on Blanco Y Negro, by Blanco Y Negro Records. Catalogue no: **NEG 37T**
7" Single: Released 16 Sep '88, on Blanco Y Negro, by Blanco Y Negro Records. Catalogue no: **NEG 37**

MINE
Tracks: / Mine.
7" Single: Released Jul '84, on Blanco Y Negro, by Blanco Y Negro Records. Deleted '87. Catalogue no: **NEG 3**

NATIVE LAND
Tracks: / Native land.
12" Single: Released Sep '84, on Blanco Y Negro, by Blanco Y Negro Records. Deleted Jun '87. Catalogue no: **NEG 6T**
7" Single: Released Sep '84, on Blanco Y Negro, by Blanco Y Negro Records. Deleted '85. Catalogue no: **NEG 6**

NIGHT AND DAY
Tracks: / Night and day / Feeling dizzy / On my mind.
CD 5": Released Mar '89, on Cherry Red, by Cherry Red Records. Catalogue no: **CD CHERRY 37**
12" Single: Released Dec '85, on Cherry Red, by Cherry Red Records. Deleted '87. Catalogue no: **12 CHERRY 37**
7" Single: Released Mar '89, on Cherry Red, by Cherry Red Records. Catalogue no: **CHERRY 37**
12" Single: Released Mar '89, on Cherry Red, by Cherry Red Records. Catalogue no: **12 CHERRY 37**

THESE EARLY DAYS
Tracks: / These early days / Died in the grain.
7" Single: Released Feb '88, on Blanco Y Negro, by Blanco Y Negro Records. Catalogue no: **NEG 30**
12" Single: Released Feb '88, on Blanco Y Negro, by Blanco Y Negro Records. Catalogue no: **NEG 30T**

THESE EARLY DAYS (REMIX)
Tracks: / These early days (remix) / Dyed in the grain / No place like home (Only available on CD single.) / Another day another dollar (Only available on CD single.).
CD 5": Released Dec '88, on Blanco Y Negro, by Blanco Y Negro Records. Catalogue no: **NEG 39 CD**
7" Single: Released Dec '88, on Blanco Y Negro, by Blanco Y Negro Records. Catalogue no: **NEG 39**
12" Single: Released Dec '88, on Blanco Y Negro, by Blanco Y Negro Records. Catalogue no: **NEG 39 T**

Evie

JUST STAY THE NIGHT
Tracks: / Just stay the night.
7" Single: Released May '88, on Blatant, Deleted Sep '89. Catalogue no: **BLAT 7 4**
12" Single: Released May '88, on Blatant, Deleted Sep '89. Catalogue no: **BLAT 12 4**

Ex

1936
Tracks: / 1936.
7" Single: Released Aug '86, on Ron Johnson, by Ron Johnson Records. Catalogue no: **ZRON 11**

1936 - SPANISH REVOLUTION
Tracks: / 1936 - Spanish Revolution.
7" Set: Released 16 Jan '89, on Ex, Catalogue no: **EX 28/29**

Ex, Alerta

RED DANCE PACKAGE (EP)
12" Single: Released Jan '84, on CNT, Catalogue no: **CNT 017**

Ex Pistols

LAND OF HOPE & GLORY
Tracks: / Land of hope and glory / Flowers of Romansk.
7" Single: Released Jan '85, on Cherry Red, by Cherry Red Records. Catalogue no: **PISTOL 76**
7" Pic: Released Jan '85, on Cherry Red, by Cherry Red Records. Deleted '87. Catalogue no: **PISTOL 76P**
12" Single: Released Jan '85, on Cherry Red, by Cherry Red Records. Catalogue no: **12 PISTOL 76**

Excalibur

HOT FOR LOVE
Tracks: / Hot for love / Early in the morning / Come on and rock / Death's door.
12" Single: Released 14 Aug '88, on Clay, by Clay Records. Catalogue no: **PLATE 9**

Excel

WHAT WENT WRONG
Tracks: / What went wrong / Janita.
7" Single: Released Feb '80, on Polydor, by Polydor Ltd. Deleted Feb '83. Catalogue no: **POSP 110**

Excel, Melodious Myles

BE THERE
Tracks: / Be there.
12" Single: Released Feb '89, on Legit, Catalogue no: **JW 534 48**

Excelsius

DING DONG DISCO
Tracks: / Ding dong disco / Ding dong disco (part 2).
7" Single: Released Jan '82, on SRT, by SRT Records. Catalogue no: **SRTS 81434**

Exception

JUMP WITH IT
Tracks: / Jump with it / Jump with it (Dub mix).
12" Single: Released Oct '86, on Supreme, by Supreme Records. Catalogue no: **SUPET 109**

SLAP YOU BACK
Tracks: / Slap you back / Slap you back (dub mix).
7" Single: Released Feb '86, on Citybeat, by Beggars Banquet Records. Deleted Jun '87. Catalogue no: **CBE 701**
12" Single: Released Feb '86, on Citybeat, by Beggars Banquet Records. Catalogue no: **CBE 1201**

Exchange

AND NOW SHE'S GONE
Tracks: / And now she's gone / Alien.
7" Single: Released Feb '87, on Yellow Brick Road, by Yellow Brick Road Records. Catalogue no: **YBR 2**

GIVE ME THE MUSIC
Tracks: / Give me the music.
7" Single: Released Oct '85, on PRT, by Castle Communications Records. Catalogue no: **7P 334**
12" Single: Released Oct '85, on PRT, by Castle Communications Records. Catalogue no: **12P 334**

Exciter

FEEL THE KNIFE
Tracks: / Feel the knife.
12" Single: Released Jun '85, on Music For Nations, by Music For Nations Records. Catalogue no: **12 KUT 113**

Exciters

REACHING FOR THE BEST
Tracks: / Reaching for the best.
7" Single: Released Oct '75, on 20th Century, by 20th Century Records. Deleted '78. Catalogue no: **BTC 1005**

TELL HIM
Tracks: / Tell him.
7" Single: Released Feb '63, on United Artists, by EMI Records. Deleted '66. Catalogue no: **UP 1011**

Excused Boots

JUST MY LUCK
Tracks: / Just my luck.
7" Single: Released May '89, on Fly, by Fly Records. Deleted Sep '89. Catalogue no: **FLEA 1**

EXECUTIVES - SHY LITTLE GIRL (Released on Attrix)

CD 5": Released May '89, on Fly, by Fly Records. Deleted Aug '89. Catalogue no: **FLEASC 1**
12" Single: Released May '89, on Fly, by Fly Records. Deleted Sep '89. Catalogue no: **FLEAT 1**

Executive

CELEBRATE YOUR LOVE
Tracks: / Celebrate your love / Just save your love for me.
12" Single: Released May '84, on Personal, by Personal Records. Catalogue no: **12 PER 102**
7" Single: Released May '84, on Personal, by Personal Records. Catalogue no: **PERS 102**

Executive Slacks

ROCK'N'ROLL
Tracks: / Rock and roll.
12" Single: Released Aug '86, on Play It Again Sam(Belgium), by Play It Again Sam (Belgium). Catalogue no: **BIAS 035**

Executives

DIANA
Tracks: / Diana.
7" Single: Released Apr '82, on Creole, by Creole Records. Catalogue no: **CR 29**

SHY LITTLE GIRL
Tracks: / Shy little girl / Never go home / I got rabies / Terror in the parking lot.
7" EP: on Attrix, by Attrix Records. Catalogue no: **RB 05 EP**

Exhibit 4

HIGH TECHNOLOGY
Tracks: / High technology / Machines of war.
7" Single: Released Mar '82, on Underground Music, Catalogue no: **UND 727**

Exhibit B

IT'S HYPOTHETICAL
Tracks: / It's hypothetical / Who killed the smile / Nobody's business (Extra track on 12" version only) / Other side, The (Extra track on 12" version only).
12" Single: Released Sep '86, on Grove Street, Catalogue no: **EXB 1**
7" Single: Released Sep '86, on Grove Street, Catalogue no: **EXBS 1**

WHO KILLED THE SMILE
Tracks: / Who killed the smile / It's hypothetical / Nobody's business.
12" Single: Released May '86, on Exhibit, Catalogue no: **EXB 1**

Exile

GIVE ME ONE MORE CHANCE
Tracks: / Give me one more chance.
7" Single: Released Jan '85, on Epic, by CBS Records. Catalogue no: **A 5022**

HANG ON TO YOUR HEART (SINGLE)
Tracks: / Hang on to your heart / She likes her lovin'.
7" Single: Released Dec '85, on Epic, by CBS Records. Catalogue no: **A 6532**

HEART AND SOUL
Tracks: / Heart and soul.
7" Single: Released Sep '81, on RAK, by EMI Records. Deleted '84. Catalogue no: **RAK 333**

HOW COULD THIS GO WRONG
Tracks: / How could this go wrong.
7" Single: Released May '79, on RAK, by EMI Records. Deleted '82. Catalogue no: **RAK 293**

I COULD GET USED TO YOU
Tracks: / I could get used to you.
7" Single: Released Apr '86, on Epic, by CBS Records. Catalogue no: **7149**

KISS YOU ALL OVER
Tracks: / Kiss you all over.
7" Single: Released Aug '78, on RAK, by EMI Records. Deleted '81. Catalogue no: **RAK 279**

SHE'S TOO GOOD TO BE TRUE
Tracks: / She's too good to be true / Promises promises.
7" Single: Released Dec '87, on Epic, by CBS Records. Deleted Jun '88. Catalogue no: **651314 7**

WOKE UP IN LOVE
Tracks: / Woke up in love.
7" Single: Released Jun '84, on Epic, by CBS Records. Catalogue no: **A 4404**

Exile In The Kingdom

FREEDOM
Tracks: / Freedom.
7" Single: Released Jan '85, on Prophet, Catalogue no: **PROFEX 8**

Exit

FOOL FOR FASHION
Tracks: / Fool for fashion / I can't get it out of my head.
7" Single: Released Dec '80, on RCA, by BMG Records (UK). Deleted Dec '85. Catalogue no: **PB 5298**

HERE TODAY GONE TOMORROW
Tracks: / Here today and gone tomorrow / One sweet day.
7" Single: Released 31 Oct '87, on JB Records, by JB Records. Catalogue no: **JB 2001**

ON THE LEVEL
Tracks: / On the level / Make love with the lights on.
7" Single: Released Mar '80, on RCA, by BMG Records (UK). Deleted Mar '83. Catalogue no: **PB 5237**

PLANETOID PASSION
Tracks: / Planetoid passion / Social graces.
7" Single: Released Sep '83, on Red Beret, Catalogue no: **REB 1**

WAITING IN THE WINGS
Tracks: / Waiting in the wings / Trouble with love.
7" Single: Released 5 Mar '88, on JB Records, by JB Records. Catalogue no: **JB 2002**

Exit 13

FIELDS OF JOY

Tracks: / Fields of joy / Dark room.
7" Single: Released Nov '85, on Squad, Catalogue no: **SQA 013**

OVER THE BRIDGE
Tracks: / Over the bridge.
7" Single: Released Oct '86, on Squad, Catalogue no: **SQA 014**

PERFECT DREAM EP, THE
Tracks: / Perfect dream.
12" Single: Released Sep '87, on Squad, Catalogue no: **SQA 015**

Exit Condition

BITE DOWN HARD
Tracks: / Bite down hard.
7" Single: Released Jul '89, on Pusmort, by Pusmort Records. Catalogue no: **PUS 007 04**

Exit Visa

BREAKDOWN
Tracks: / Breakdown / Fools in the night.
7" Single: on Infrared (UK), by Infrared Records. Catalogue no: **IFR 102**

FOOLS IN THE NIGHT
Tracks: / Fools in the night / Never on a good day.
7" Single: Released Jun '83, on Infrared (UK), by Infrared Records. Catalogue no: **IFR 101**

Exit-Stance

CRIMES AGAINST HUMANITY
Tracks: / Crimes against humanity.
7" Single: Released Jun '84, on Fight Back, Catalogue no: **FIGHT 4**

ESTHETICS
Tracks: / Esthetics.
7" Single: on Exit Stance, Catalogue no: **ES 002**

WHILE BACKS ARE TURNED
Tracks: / While backs are turned.
7" Single: Released May '88, on Mortarhate, by Mortarhate Records. Catalogue no: **MORT 11**

Exodus

ENGLISH BLACK BOYS
12" Single: Released Apr '80, on Factory (1), by Factory Records. Catalogue no: **FAC 11**

Exotica Maximus

PAINT IT BLACK
Tracks: / Paint it black / Western fields.
12" Single: Released Aug '83, on MVM, by MVM Records. Catalogue no: **12 MVM 2**
7" Single: Released Aug '83, on MVM, by MVM Records. Deleted '84. Catalogue no: **MVM 2**

YOUNGER NOW
Tracks: / Younger now / Shout.
7" Single: Released Jan '83, on Flux, Catalogue no: **FLUX 183**

Expandis

MYSTIC MAN
Tracks: / Mystic man.
12" Single: Released Aug '83, on Rocket, by Rocket Records. Catalogue no: **ESP 112**
7" Single: Released Aug '83, on Rocket, by Rocket Records. Catalogue no: **ESP 1**

Expelled

DREAMING
Tracks: / Dreaming.
7" Single: Released Apr '82, on Riot City, by Riot City Records. Catalogue no: **RIOT 8**

GOVERMENT CITY
7" EP: Released Dec '82, on Riot City, by Riot City Records. Catalogue no: **RIOT 17**

MAKE IT ALONE
Tracks: / Make it alone.
7" Single: Released Oct '82, on Riot City, by Riot City Records. Catalogue no: **RIOT 17**

SINGLES, THE (EP)
12" Single: Released Sep '84, on Riot City, by Riot City Records. Catalogue no: **12 RIOT 33**

Explained Emma

UNECESSARY STRAIN
Tracks: / Unnecessary strain / Fathers day.
7" Single: Released Mar '85, on Pig Posse, Catalogue no: **POSSE 101**

Explainer

...HORSE
...His horse / His horse (version).
...Released Jun '87, on Char-... **CRDT 20**

...ih man.
...g '82, on Sunburst, by Sunburst Records. Catalogue no: **EXP 112**
7" Single: Released Aug '82, on Sunburst, by Sunburst Records. Catalogue no: **EXP 1**

SOCA ALL NIGHT
Tracks: / Soca all night.
12" Single: Released Feb '89, on Charlie's, Catalogue no: **ECR 404**

Explaires

SYMPATHY
Tracks: / Sympathy.
7" Single: Released Mar '80, on Rockburgh, Deleted '82. Catalogue no: **ROCS 222**

TO SEE YOU
Tracks: / To see you / Frequency.
7" Single: Released Feb '82, on Zoo, Catalogue no: **CAGE 007**

Exploding Seagulls

JOHNNY RUNS
Tracks: / Johnny runs.
7" Single: Released Jul '81, on Fried Egg, by Fried Egg Records. Deleted '87. Catalogue no: **EGG 8**

Exploited

Biographical details: This British punk rock band consisted of Gary, Big John, Dru Stix and Wattie. The Exploited first started recording in 1980, and were one of the wave of groups who attempted to resurrect the 1976-7 spirit of the punk explosion in the wake of declining interest from the UK music press and record buyers. Fronted by lead vocalist Wattie, whose spiky locks were striking to say the least, their music was anarchic and uncompromising. Their brash, 100mph, ultra-noisy style attracted a loyal army of fans despite, being larely ignored by the mainstream pop media. The Exploited first cracked the UK charts in the summer of '81, when *Dogs of war* reached No.63 on the singles chart and *Punks not dead* got to No.20 on the LP list. After their next single *Dead cities* won them an appearance on BBC TV's Top of the Pops in October 1981, the program's producer received a flood of letters from disapproving viewers; the 'song' reached No.31 on the charts. After further minor hit singles with *Don't let 'em grind you down* (in collaboration with fellow punk group Anti-Pasti) and *Attack* the Exploited collected a second UK Top 20 album with 1982's *Troops of tomorrow*. However, their subsequent raucous rantings were so unoriginal that they stretched the loyalty of even their most ardent supporters. The Exploited became the Forgotton. (Bob MacDonald, 5th August 1985).

ARMY LIFE
Tracks: / Army life.
7" Single: Released Oct '80, on Exploited, Catalogue no: **EXP 1001**
7" Single: Released Apr '81, on Secret, by Secret Records. Deleted '88. Catalogue no: **SH 112**

ATTACK
Tracks: / Attack / Alternatives.
7" Single: Released Jul '82, on Secret, by Secret Records. Deleted May '88. Catalogue no: **SHH 130**

COMPUTERS DON'T BLUNDER
Tracks: / Computers don't blunder / Addiction.
7" Single: Released Oct '82, on Secret, by Secret Records. Deleted May '88. Catalogue no: **SHH 140**

DEAD CITIES
Tracks: / Dead cities / Punk's not dead / Army life / Barmy army.
7" Single: Released Jul '82, on Secret, by Secret Records. Catalogue no: **SSH 120**
12" Single: Released Aug '86, on Archive 4, by Castle Communications Records. Catalogue no: **TOF 107**

DOGS OF WAR
Tracks: / Dogs of war / Blown to bits.
7" Single: Released Apr '81, on Virgin, by Virgin Records. Catalogue no: **SSH 110**

DON'T LET 'EM GRIND YOU DOWN (EP)
7" Single: Released Oct '81, on Superville, Catalogue no: **EXP 1003**

EXPLOITED BARMY ARMY
Tracks: / Exploited barmy army.
7" Single: Released Apr '81, on Secret, by Secret Records. Catalogue no: **SH 113**

JESUS IS DEAD
Tracks: / Drug squad man / Privacy invasion / Jesus is dead / Politician.
12" Single: Released Aug '86, on Rough Justice, by Music For Nations Records. Catalogue no: **12 KORE 102**

PUNK'S ALIVE
Tracks: / Punk's alive.
12" Single: Released 23 Jul '88, on Skunx, Catalogue no: **EXPX 1**

RIVAL LEADER
Tracks: / Rival leaders.
7" Single: Released Oct '83, on Pax, by Pax Records. Catalogue no: **PAX 15**

WAR NOW
Tracks: / War now.
12" Single: Released Apr '88, on Music For Nations, by Music For Nations Records. Catalogue no: **12 KORE 103**

Y.O.P.
Tracks: / Y.O.P..
12" Single: Released Aug '82, on Secret, by Secret Records. Deleted Aug '85. Catalogue no: **SHH 136 12**

Explorers

VENUE DE MILO
Tracks: / Venus de Milo.
7" Single: Released Jun '85, on Virgin, by Virgin Records. Deleted '89. Catalogue no: **VS 779**
12" Single: Released Jun '85, on Virgin, by Virgin Records. Deleted '89. Catalogue no: **VS 779-12**

Explorers Of The Nile

WE ARE ALL EGYPTIANS
Tracks: / We are all Egyptians.
12" Single: Released '88, on Antler, by Antler Records (Belgium). Catalogue no: **SUB 025**

WE'RE ALL EGYPTIANS
Tracks: / We're all Egyptians.
12" Single: Released '88, on Subway, by Subway Records. Catalogue no: **SUB 025**

Explosivo

VOLARE
Tracks: / Volare / Latin express.
12" Single: Released Jan '82, on CBS, by CBS Records. Deleted Jan '85. Catalogue no: **13-1935**
7" Single: Released Jan '82, on CBS, by CBS Records. Deleted Jan '85. Catalogue no: **A 1935**

Expose

COME GO WITH ME
Tracks: / Come go with me / December.
7" Single: Released Mar '87, on Arista, by BMG Records (UK). Catalogue no: **RIS 7**
12" Single: Released Mar '87, on Arista, by BMG Records (UK). Catalogue no: **RIST 7**

EXPOSED TO LOVE
Tracks: / Exposed to love / Exposed to love (dub).
12" Single: Released Apr '86, on Arista, by BMG Records (UK). Catalogue no: **ARIST 12659**

LET ME BE THE ONE
Tracks: / Let me be the one / Love is our destiny / Jamaican woman / Jamaican woman (version) / Let me be the one (remix) / Love is our destiny* / Point of no return (megamix) / Come go with me (megamix) (Track on special CD version.) / Exposed to love (Only on 12".).
12" Single: Released Nov '87, on Arista, by BMG Records (UK). Deleted May '89. Catalogue no: **RIST 45**
CD 5": Released Dec '87, on Arista, by BMG Records (UK). Deleted Jul '89. Catalogue no: **RISCD 45**
7" Single: Released Nov '87, on Arista, by BMG Records (UK). Deleted May '89. Catalogue no: **RIS 45**

POINT OF NO RETURN
Tracks: / Point of no return / Extra extra.
7" Single: Released Jul '87, on Arista, by BMG Records (UK). Catalogue no: **RIS 22**
12" Single: Released Jul '87, on Arista, by BMG Records (UK). Deleted May '89. Catalogue no: **RIST 22**

SEASONS CHANGE
Tracks: / Seasons change / December / Seasons change (megamix) (Extra track on 12").
7" Single: Released Mar '88, on Arista, by BMG Records (UK). Catalogue no: **109 742**
12" Single: Released Mar '88, on Arista, by BMG Records (UK). Catalogue no: **609 742**

TWIN CITY RIDE
Tracks: / Twin city ride / Lonely nights.
7" Single: Released Oct '80, on Dazzle, by Dazzle Records. Deleted Oct '83. Catalogue no: **DAZS 5**

WHAT YOU DON'T KNOW
Tracks: / What you don't know / What you don't know (version) / What you don't know (Atomic edit).
7" Single: Released 24 Jul '89, on Arista, by BMG Records (UK). Catalogue no: **112 354**
CD 5": Released 24 Jul '89, on Arista, by BMG Records (UK). Catalogue no: **662 354**
Cassingle: Released Sep '89, on Arista, by BMG Records (UK). Catalogue no: **410 080**
7" Single: Released Sep '89, on Arista, by BMG Records (UK). Catalogue no: **112 540**
7" Single: Released Sep '89, on Arista, by BMG Records (UK). Catalogue no: **112 450**
12" Single: Released 24 Jul '89, on Arista, by BMG Records (UK). Catalogue no: **612 354**

Ex-Post-Facto

DANCING CHILD
Tracks: / Dancing child.
7" Single: Released Nov '83, on Probe Plus, by Probe Plus Records. Catalogue no: **PP 7**
12" Single: Released Nov '83, on Probe Plus, by Probe Plus Records. Catalogue no: **PP 7T**

OCEANIC EXPLORERS (EP)
12" Single: Released Nov '82, on Probe Plus, by Probe Plus Records. Catalogue no: **PP 3**

Exposure

EXPERIENCE (EP)
12" Single: Released Apr '83, on Abstract, by Abstract Sounds. Catalogue no: **12 ABS 015**

INSTITUTION
Tracks: / Institution.
7" Single: Released Jun '84, on Statik, Catalogue no: **TAK 17**
12" Single: Released Jun '84, on Statik, Catalogue no: **TAK 1712**

LIEF DES LIED
Tracks: / Lief des lied.
12" Single: Released Sep '84, on Statik, Catalogue no: **TAK 23-12**
7" Single: Released Sep '84, on Statik, Catalogue no: **TAK 23**

LOVERS ROCK
Tracks: / Lover's rock / Curtain wall.
7" Single: Released Jul '82, on Abstract, by Abstract Sounds. Catalogue no: **ABS 010**

SOUND SYSTEM
Tracks: / Sound system / Hey you.
7" Single: Released Mar '82, on Abstract, by Abstract Sounds. Catalogue no: **ABS 006**

STILL THE WIND BLOWS STILL
Tracks: / Still the wind blows still.
7" Single: Released May '85, on Statik, Catalogue no: **TAK 20**
12" Single: Released May '85, on Statik, Catalogue no: **TAK 20/12**

Expressos

BY TONIGHT
Tracks: / By tonight / Ta ta.
7" Single: Released Sep '80, on WEA, by WEA Records. Deleted '83. Catalogue no: **K 18336**

HEY GIRL
Tracks: / Hey girl.
7" Single: Released Jun '80, on WEA, by WEA Records. Deleted '83. Catalogue no: **K 18246**

KISS YOU ALL OVER
Tracks: / Kiss you all over / End.
7" Single: Released May '81, on WEA, by WEA Records. Deleted May '84. Catalogue no: **K 18736**

TANGO IN MONO
Tracks: / Tango in mono / Thumbs on the ground.
7" Single: Released Mar '81, on WEA, by WEA Records. Deleted '84. Catalogue no: **K 18431**

Ex-Sample

AND SO IT GOES
Tracks: / And so it goes.
12" Single: Released Nov '87, on Wide Angle (USA), Catalogue no: **TTW 87133**

Extasis

PSYCHEDELIC JACK
Tracks: / Psychedelic jack.
12" Single: Released 14 Aug '88, on Acid Jazz, by Acid Jazz Records. Catalogue no: **JAZID 3T**

External Menace

YOUTH OF TODAY (EP)
7" Single: Released Feb '83, on Beat-The-System, Deleted '88. Catalogue no: **MENACE 1**

Extra T's

FLASH BOOGIE
Tracks: / Flash boogie.
12" Single: Released Jan '84, on Sunny View (USA), by Sunnyview Records (USA).

Catalogue no: **SUNYL 101**

Extras

BOOMERANG, THE
Tracks: / Boomerang, The.
7" Single: Released Oct '83, on Dancefloor, Catalogue no: **DF 7007**
12" Single: Released Oct '83, on Dancefloor, Catalogue no: **DFT 7007**

HAVEN'T BEEN FUNKED ENOUGH
Tracks: / Haven't been funked enough / Soap opera rap.
12" Single: Released Jan '83, on T.M.T., by T.M.T. Productions. Deleted '87. Catalogue no: **TMTT 1**

I CAN'T KEEP STILL
Tracks: / I can't keep still.
12" Single: Released Mar '83, on Dancefloor, Catalogue no: **DFT 7001**
7" Single: Released Mar '83, on Dancefloor, Catalogue no: **DF 7001**

WATCHER, THE
Tracks: / Watcher, The.
7" Single: Released Jun '84, on Audiotrax, Deleted '86. Catalogue no: **ATX 3**

Extreme Noise Terror

PEEL SESSIONS:EXTREME NOISE TERROR
12" Single: Released Apr '88, on Strange Fruit, by Strange Fruit Records. Catalogue no: **SFPS 048**

Extremes

CARCRASH MUSIC
Tracks: / Carcrash music / Violent hour / Explode / PS / Salome / Valentine's day.
12" Single: Released 20 Feb '88, on Destiny, by Destiny Records. Catalogue no: **EMD 002**

EASY MY DUST
Tracks: / Easy my dust.
7" Single: Released Aug '87, on Destiny, by Destiny Records. Catalogue no: **DES 001**

Extrol

E.S.P.
Tracks: / E.S.P..
12" Single: Released Dec '83, on Red Rooster, Catalogue no: **HEN 2**

Eye Do It

I LOST MY MIND
Tracks: / I lost my mind / Invisisbility.
7" Single: Released Mar '84, on No Rip Off, Catalogue no: **YAW 2**

Eye To Eye

AM I NORMAL?
Tracks: / Am I normal? / Midnight insomnia.
7" Single: Released Sep '80, on Automatic, by Automatic Records. Deleted '83. Catalogue no: **K 17688**

LIFE IN MOTION
Tracks: / Life in motion / Progress ahead.
7" Single: Released May '82, on Automatic, by Automatic Records. Deleted '85. Catalogue no: **K 17938**

STEP OUT
Tracks: / Step out / Burning world.
7" Single: Released Oct '80, on Flamingo, by Airwave Records (USA). Deleted Oct '83. Catalogue no: **FM 9**
12" Single: Released Oct '80, on Flamingo, by Airwave Records (USA). Deleted Oct '83. Catalogue no: **FM 12-9**

Eyedance

HILBRE ISLAND
Tracks: / Hilbre island / Life's mean / Only one, The.
12" Single: Released Sep '88, on Kick Ass, by Kick Ass Records. Catalogue no: **ASS 1**

Eyeless in Gaza

INVISIBILITY
Tracks: / Invisibility / Three kittens / Plague of years.
12" Single: Released Apr '81, on Cherry Red, by Cherry Red Records. Deleted '87. Catalogue no: **CHERRY 20**

KISS THE RAIN GOODBYE
Tracks: / Kiss the rain goodbye.
12" Single: Released Jun '86, on Cherry Red, by Cherry Red Records. Catalogue no: **12 CHERRY 93**

NEW RISEN
Tracks: / New risen.
12" Single: Released May '83, on Cherry Red, by Cherry Red Records. Catalogue no: **12 CHERRY 63**
7" Single: Released May '83, on Cherry Red, by Cherry Red Records. Catalogue no: **CHERRY 63**

OTHERS
Tracks: / Others / Jane dancing / Ever present.
7" Single: Released Nov '81, on Cherry Red, by Cherry Red Records. Deleted '87. Catalogue no: **CHERRY 31**

SUNBURSTS IN
Tracks: / Sunbursts in.
12" Single: Released Jan '84, on Cherry Red, by Cherry Red Records. Deleted '87. Catalogue no: **12 CHERRY 74**
7" Single: Released Jan '84, on Cherry Red, by Cherry Red Records. Catalogue no: **CHERRY 74**

VEIL LIKE CALM
Tracks: / Veil like calm / Taking steps.
7" Single: Released Nov '82, on Cherry Red, by Cherry Red Records. Deleted Nov '85. Catalogue no: **CHERRY 47**

WELCOME NOW
Tracks: / Welcome now.
12" Single: Released Oct '85, on Cherry Red, by Cherry Red Records. Catalogue no: **12 CHERRY 92**
7" Single: Released Oct '85, on Cherry Red, by Cherry Red Records. Catalogue no: **CHERRY 92**

Eyelids

PASSAGE FROM JUDEA
Tracks: / Passage from Judea.
7" Single: Released Jan '82, on Idyllic, by Idyllic Records. Catalogue no: **EJSP 9752**

Ezeke

CHRISTMAS BLUES
Tracks: / Christmas blues / Christmas blues (version).
12" Single: Released Dec '86, on Orbitone, by Orbitone Records. Catalogue no: **OR 1220**
7" Single: Released Dec '86, on Orbitone, by Orbitone Records. Catalogue no: **OR 720**

F

The following information was taken from the Music Master database on October 20th, 1989.

F*** Geez

HERE'S THE F*** GEEZ
Tracks: / Here's the f*** geez.
7" Single: Released Jun '88, on Jungle Hop, Catalogue no: **JHL 106**

Fab Five Freddy

UNE SAL HISTOIRE
Tracks: / Une sal histoire.
12" Single: Released May '83, on Celluloid (USA), by Celluloid Records (USA). Catalogue no: **CYZ 106**

Fab Food

NEVER ALONE
Tracks: / Never alone.
7" Single: Released Jun '81, on Smile, Deleted '88. Catalogue no: **SRO 21**
7" Single: Released Jun '81, on Smile, Deleted Jun '84. Catalogue no: **SR 021**

Fabares, Shelly

JOHNNY ANGEL
Tracks: / Johnny angel.
7" Single: Released Apr '62, on Pye International, Deleted '65. Catalogue no: **7N 25132**

Fabian

Biographical details: This American singer and actor, was born in Philadelphia in 1943, was one of the most manufactured and least talented teen idols in pop history. He is often quoted as the archetypal example of a talentless youngster being manipulated, packaged and sold to millions purely on account of his looks and image. The career of Fabian (whose real name is Fabiano Forte) was launched in introduced to the Philadelphia-based label by Frankie Avalon, who had himself just as he was turning 16, Fabian achieved his first US Top 40 single with *I'm a man*. By the end of the year, with the help of continued exposure from America's leading TV pop presenter Dick Clark, he had chalked up three US Top 10 hits *Turn me loose, Tiger* and *Hound dog man*. The latter song was also the title theme from his debut Hollywood movie. His acting abilities were no greater than his singing skills. Despite enjoying US Top 10 albums with *Hold that tiger* and *Fabulous Fabian*, the lad's popularity soon suffered a sharp decline. By mid-1960 he was a has been. All he had really been was a semi-substitute for Elvis, while Presley was in the army. However, as if to answer his constant critics, Fabia managed to sustain an undistinguished but steady career in films during the Sixties and Seventies, gradually shifting from the cinema to made-for-TV work. A surprisingly shrewd businessman, he was still active in 1985 - in August of that year, he was instrumental in organising and hosting a major American telecast, *Fabian's good time rock'n'roll*. Fabian's only foray into the British charts occurred in March 1960, and even then it was only for one week. In the week that the UK music industry published its first Top 50, Fabian was listed at No.46 with *Hound dog man*. His British track record was a truer reflection of his talents than his UK chart performance; but he has managed to survive in showbusiness. (Bob MacDonald, 10th August 1985)
USA pop singer of the late '50's, born Fabiano Forte in 1943 in Philadelphia, whence Dick Clark's Bandstand Matinee was broadcast and where the Chancellor label was located. Fabian and his friend Frankie Avalon couldn't sing for beans, but the teen idol genre was invented for them; the spotty kid with the pompadour mouthing *I'm a man* was ludicrous, but there was a lot of money involved. (Donald Clarke, April 1989)t.

HOUND DOG MAN
Tracks: / Hound dog man.
7" Single: Released Mar '60, on H.M.V., by EMI Records. Deleted '63. Catalogue no: **POP 695**

TIGER
Tracks: / Tiger.
7" Single: Released Jul '82, on Revival, Deleted '88. Catalogue no: **REV 6017**

Fabrique, Tina

ALIVE WITH LOVE
Tracks: / Alive with love.
7" Single: Released Apr '84, on Electricity, by Electricity Records. Deleted '88. Catalogue no: **TRIC 7**
12" Single: Released Apr '84, on Electricity, by Electricity Records. Deleted '88. Catalogue no: **TRICT 7**

Fabulous Five

JAMAICAN WOMAN
Tracks: / Jamaican woman.
12" Single: Released Nov '87, on Stage, Catalogue no: **SR 30**

OOH AAH
Tracks: / Ooh aah / Dreadlocks in moonlight.
7" Single: Released Aug '82, on Island, by Island Records. Deleted Aug '85. Catalogue no: **IPR 2056**

YOU SAFE
Tracks: / You safe.
12" Single: Released Apr '85, on Sunburn, by Orbitone Records. Catalogue no: **SBD 49**

Fabulous Poodles

BIONIC MAN
Tracks: / Bionic man / Pink City twist.
7" Single: Released Feb '80, on Blue Print, Deleted '83. Catalogue no: **BLU 2007**

STOMPIN' WITH THE CAT
Tracks: / Stompin' with the cat / Anna Rexia.
7" Single: Released Oct '80, on Blue Print, Deleted Oct '83. Catalogue no: **BLU 2015**

Fabulous Pop Tarts

NEW YORK CITY BEAT
Tracks: / New York City beat.
7" Single: Released Oct '85, on PRT, by Castle Communications Records. Deleted '88. Catalogue no: **PERS 3903**
12" Single: Released Oct '85, on PRT, by Castle Communications Records. Deleted '88. Catalogue no: **12PER 3903**

Fabulous Pythons

RICO LAMENTE
Tracks: / Rico Lamente / Johnny rocker.
7" Single: Released Jul '82, on Chiswick Records, Deleted '88. Catalogue no: **DICE 12**

Fabulous Thunderbirds

Biographical details: USA blues band formed in Austin, Texas in 1975. Personnel in 1987 was founder members vocalist/harmonica Kim Wilson and guitarist Jimmie Vaughan (Stevie Ray Vaughan's older brother); bassist Preston Hubbard and drummer Fran Christina came from the excellent Boston band Roomful of blues, replacing Keith Ferguson and Mike Buck. Keyboardist Junior Brantley joined in '85 and left in '86 for Roomful: the traffic in sidemen is two-way now. The T Birds had made six albums through '87, most of them of Chrysalis originally and not well promoted; the band's mix of Chicago blues, Louisiana R&B and a dash of Tex-Mex gets little airplay on sanitised USA radio, but fans eagerly await each release. *T.Bird Rhythm* was produced by Nick Lowe, *Tuff enough* by Dave Edmunds. (Donald Clarke, April 1989).

CHERRY PINK AND APPLE BLOSSOM WHITE
Tracks: / Cherry pink and apple blossom white / I believe I'm in love.
7" Single: Released Apr '81, on Chrysalis, by Chrysalis Records. Deleted Apr '84. Catalogue no: **CHS 2512**

CRAWL
Tracks: / Crawl / Last call for alcohol.
7" Single: Released Apr '80, on Chrysalis, by Chrysalis Records. Deleted '83. Catalogue no: **CHS 2422**

STAND BACK
Tracks: / Stand back / It takes a big man to cry.
7" Single: Released Jul '87, on Epic, by CBS Records. Catalogue no: **650981 7**

SUGAR COATED LOVE
Tracks: / Sugar coated love / Los Fabulosos Thunderbirds.
7" Single: Released May '80, on Chrysalis, by Chrysalis Records. Deleted May '83. Catalogue no: **CHS 2440**

TUFF ENUFF (SINGLE)
Tracks: / Tuff enuff / Look at that.
12" Single: Released Oct '86, on Epic, by CBS Records. Deleted '88. Catalogue no: **TA 6967**
7" Single: Released Oct '86, on Epic, by CBS Records. Deleted '88. Catalogue no: **A 6967**

Fabulous Wonderfuls

BEING IN LOVE
Tracks: / Being in love.
7" Single: Released Nov '81, on Eagle (London), by Eagle (London) Records. Deleted '88. Catalogue no: **ERS 014**

Face

PARADISE
Tracks: / Paradise / Why.
7" Single: Released Nov '83, on Wimp, by Wimp Records. Deleted '88. Catalogue no: **WIMP 007**

WHERE'S THE SENSE IN LOVING YOU
Tracks: / Where's the sense in loving you.
7" Single: Released May '84, on Wimp, by Wimp Records. Deleted '88. Catalogue no: **WIMP 010**

WHO ARE WE
Tracks: / Who are we (instrumental).
7" Single: Released Dec '86, on Face, by Face Records & Music. Deleted '88. Catalogue no: **ANIMAL 1**

Face Bway English

GIMME DE MONEY
Tracks: / Gimme de money.
12" Single: Released Aug '88, on Night Life Possie, Catalogue no: **NLP 004**

Face, George

SINCE I MET YOU BABY
Tracks: / Since I met you baby.
12" Single: Released Jan '84, on Dancebeat, Catalogue no: **DBD 1320**

Face of Concern

RIGHT
Tracks: / Right / Next time / You win, I lose.
12" Single: Released Jul '86, on Press, by Compendium Int.Records. Deleted '88. Catalogue no: **P 1205**

SAFE
Tracks: / Safe.
12" Single: Released Jun '85, on Press, by Compendium Int.Records. Catalogue no: **P 1206**

Face To Face

10-9-8
Tracks: / 10-9-8 / Heaven on earth.
7" Single: Released Jun '84, on Epic, by CBS Records. Deleted '88. Catalogue no: **A 4368**
12" Single: Released Jun '84, on Epic, by CBS Records. Deleted '88. Catalogue no: **TA 4368**

FACE
Tracks: / Back to back / Save the day / Dreams and promises / Right now I need you.
12" Single: Released Sep '87, on RCA, by BMG Records (UK). Catalogue no: **PT 41418**
7" Single: Released Sep '87, on RCA, by BMG Records (UK). Catalogue no: **PB 41418**

TELL ME WHY
Tracks: / Tell me why / Shake the world.
7" Single: Released Mar '86, on Epic, by CBS Records. Deleted '88. Catalogue no: **A 6883**
12" Single: Released Mar '86, on Epic, by CBS Records. Deleted '88. Catalogue no: **TA 6883**

Faces

Biographical details: The line-up of this British rock band was Kenny Jones, Ronnie Lane, Ian McLagan, Rod Stewart and Ron Wood. Jones, Lane and McLagan had found fame in the Sixties as members of the Small Faces. That group's leader Steve Marriott quit in early 1969, leaving the other three in a directionless state. They brought in Stewart and Wood from Jeff Beck's group and, after realising that the new recruits were taller than the existing three members, shortened their name to the Faces. Wood switched from bass (his instrument in the Beck days) to guitar; Stewart became the vocalist and frontman. The Faces' debut album *First step* reached No.45 on the UK LP chart in April 1970. The follow-up set *Long player* climbed to No.31. But it was in early 1972 that they really found their recording feet: the raunchy but loose *Stay with me* reached No.6 on the British single chart, and got to No.17 in America; *A nod's as good as a wink ... to a blind horse* reached No.2 on the UK LP listings. In early 1973 they enjoyed a rapid UK No.1 LP with the poorly reviewed ,ooh la la, and collected a No.2 single with *Cindy incidentally. Ooh la la* was the Faces' final studio album. They had two problems which impaired their career heavily overshadowed that of the band. Bassist Lane quit in 1973 to pursue a partially successfu solo stint (accompanied by his own band, Slim Chance); he was replaced by a Japanese player, Tetsu Yamauchi (ex Free). They enjoyed two more UK Top 2C singles, but were gradually disintergrating. The Faces officially terminated in 1975 Jones joined the Who as a drummer, following the death of Keith Moon; Wood guested with the Rolling Stones in 1975 and eventually became a full-time member Stewart of course, continued to be a solc superstar. (Bob MacDonald, 11th Augus 1985)
Rock group formed from Small Faces afte Steve Marriott left to form Humble Pie. Bassist Ronnie Lane, drummer Kenny Jones and Ian McLagen on keyboards Jeff Beck outcasts vocalist Rod Stewart and guitaris Ron Wood. Stewart replaced Marriott as writer and his partnership with Wooc proved fruitful; Stewart's solo career had already begun and his hit *Maggie May* (no.1 both UK/USA) didn't hurt. They were deservedly well-loved band but by '75 they came a poor second to Stewart's sol career; Lane left to form Slim Chance fc an album; Wood made solo albums an became a temporary Rolling Stone fc tours in 1976; with Stewart in tax exil Jones and McLagen took part in a brie Small Faces reunion, then Jones replace Keith Moon in the Who. McLagen also re corded solo. There was a reunion at the f nale of Stewart's Wembley gig in 1986 Wood's affliction with muscular scleros saw him active in ARMS, an all star mus cal fundraising venture; the disease was i remission in the mid-'80's. (Donald Clarke April 1989)v.

CINDY INCIDENTALLY
Tracks: / Cindy incidentally / Skewi (mend the fuse).
7" Single: Released Feb '73, on Warne Bros., by WEA Records. Deleted '76. Cata logue no: **K 16247**

FACES(E.P.)
Tracks: / Memphis / You can make m dance sing or anything / Stay with me Cindy incidentally.
7" EP: Released Jun '77, on Riva, by Riv Records. Deleted '80. Catalogue no: **RIV 8**

I HAVEN'T STOPPED DANCIN YET
Tracks: / I haven't stopped dancing yet.
12" Single: Released Oct '85, on Long I land Sound, Deleted '88. Catalogue n **XSN 1003**

POOL HALL RICHARD
Tracks: / Pool hall Richard / I wish it wou rain.
7" Single: Released Dec '73, on Warn Bros., by WEA Records. Deleted '76. Cat logue no: **K 16341**

SEARCHING
Tracks: / Searching.
12" Single: Released Aug '86, on L.I.S., Deleted '88. Catalogue no: **MTDX 401**

STAY WITH ME
Tracks: / Stay with me.
7" Single: Released Dec '71, on Warner Bros., by WEA Records. Deleted '74. Catalogue no: **K 16136**

YOU CAN MAKE ME DANCE SING OR ANYTHING
Tracks: / You can make me dance sing or anything.
7" Single: Released Dec '74, on Warner Bros., by WEA Records. Deleted '77. Catalogue no: **K 16294**

Facey, Sonia

TOGETHER
Tracks: / Together.
12" Single: Released Jun '84, on Ethnic, Catalogue no: **ETH 2245**

Fachin, Eria

SAVIN' MYSELF
Tracks: / Savin' myself.
12" Single: Released 31 Oct '87, on Saturday, by Nightmare Records. Catalogue no: **STD 1**
7" Single: Released 31 Oct '87, on Saturday, by Nightmare Records. Catalogue no: **7STD 1**

YOUR LOVE JUST CAME TOO LATE
Tracks: / Your love just came too late.
7" Single: Released Aug '89, on Power, Catalogue no: **ZAK 1**

Fact

ALWAYS THERE
Tracks: / Always there.
12" Single: Released Nov '86, on Tollhaus, Catalogue no: **TH 007**

Faction

EAGLE HAS LANDED, THE
Tracks: / Eagle has landed, The.
12" Single: Released '89, on Third Mind, by Third Mind Records. Catalogue no: **TMS 042**

LISTEN BUDDY
Tracks: / Listen buddy / Space bazor.
Cassingle: Released Mar '88, on Crook Cassettes, by Crook Cassettes. Catalogue no: **FAZER 01**
Cassingle: Released Nov '87, on Crook Cassettes, by Crook Cassettes. Catalogue no: **FA O**

Factor 33

NO PAIN NO GAIN
Tracks: / No pain no gain / Soul breaking.
7" Single: Released Apr '84, on Stage One, Deleted '88. Catalogue no: **SLIDE 1**

Factory

HOLD OUT
Tracks: / Hold out.
7" Single: Released Oct '86, on Strike Back, by Strike Back Records. Catalogue no: **SBR 10**
12" Single: Released Oct '86, on Strike Back, by Strike Back Records. Catalogue no: **SBR 10T**

YOU ARE THE MUSIC
Tracks: / You are the music.
7" Single: Released Mar '83, on F. Earth, Deleted '88. Catalogue no: **FER 011**

Factory Classical...

FACTORY CLASSICAL SAMPLER
CD 5": Released Sep '89, on Factory (1), by Factory Records. Catalogue no: **FACD 276**

Factory Poems

INFANT SOLDIER
Tracks: / Infant soldier / Up and rise.
7" Single: Released Nov '81, on Ryme Time, by Lismor Records. Deleted Nov '84. Catalogue no: **WRS 803**

Fad Gadget

BACK TO NATURE
Tracks: / Back to nature / Box, The.
7" Single: Released Oct '79, on Mute, by Mute Records. Catalogue no: **MUTE 002G**

COLLAPSING NEW PEOPLE
Tracks: / Collapsing new people / Spoil the child.
7" Single: Released Jan '84, on Mute, by Mute Records. Catalogue no: **MUTE 30**
12" Single: Released Jan '84, on Mute, by Mute Records. Catalogue no: **12 MUTE 030**

FIRESIDE FAVOURITES
Tracks: / Fireside favourites / Insecticide.
7" Single: Released Sep '80, on Mute, by Mute Records. Catalogue no: **MUTE 9**

FOR WHOM THE BELL TOLLS
Tracks: / For whom the bell tolls / Love parasite.
7" Single: Released Jan '83, on Mute, by Mute Records. Catalogue no: **MUTE 26**
12" Single: Released Jan '83, on Mute, by Mute Records. Catalogue no: **12 MUTE 026**

I DISCOVER LOVE
Tracks: / I discover love / Lemmings on lovers rock.
7" Single: Released Oct '83, on Mute, by Mute Records. Catalogue no: **7 MUTE 28**
12" Single: Released Oct '83, on Mute, by Mute Records. Catalogue no: **12 MUTE 28**

KING OF THE FLIES
Tracks: / King of the flies / Plain clothes.
7" Single: Released Apr '82, on Mute, by Mute Records. Catalogue no: **MUTE 21**
12" Single: Released Apr '82, on Mute, by Mute Records. Catalogue no: **12 MUTE 021**

LIFE ON THE LINE
Tracks: / Life on the line / 4M.
7" Single: Released Sep '82, on Mute, by Mute Records. Catalogue no: **MUTE 24**
12" Single: Released Sep '82, on Mute, by Mute Records. Catalogue no: **12 MUTE 024**

MAKE ROOM
Tracks: / Make room / Lady shave.
7" Single: Released Mar '81, on Mute, by Mute Records. Catalogue no: **MUTE 12**

ONE MAN'S MEAT
Tracks: / One man's meat / Sleep.
7" Single: Released May '84, on Mute, by Mute Records. Catalogue no: **MUTE 33**
12" Single: Released May '84, on Mute, by Mute Records. Catalogue no: **12 MUTE 033**

RICKY'S HAND (see panel bottom left)
Tracks: / Ricky's hand / Handshake.
7" Single: Released '80, on Mute, by Mute Records. Catalogue no: **MUTE 006**

SATURDAY NIGHT SPECIAL
Tracks: / Saturday night special.
7" Single: Released Jan '82, on Mute, by Mute Records. Catalogue no: **MUTE 17**

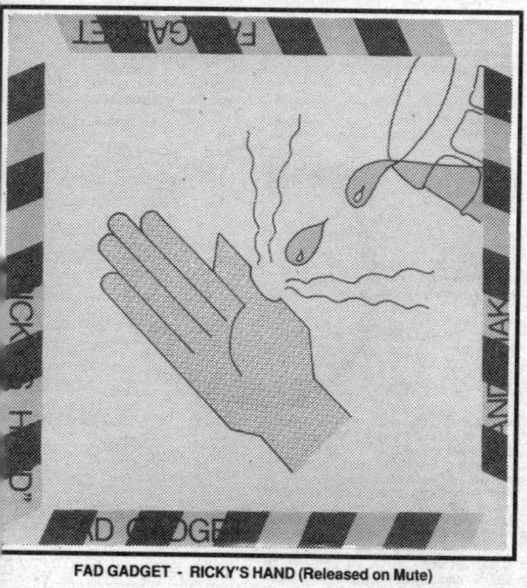

FAD GADGET - RICKY'S HAND (Released on Mute)

Fad, J.J.

SUPERSONIC
Tracks: / Supersonic / Supersonic (version).
7" Single: Released Jul '88, on Atlantic, by WEA Records. Catalogue no: **A 9328**
12" Single: Released Jul '88, on Atlantic, by WEA Records. Catalogue no: **A 9328 T**
12" Single: Released Aug '88, on Dream Team, Catalogue no: **DTR 632**

Fadela, Chaba

N'SEL FIK
Tracks: / N'sel fik.
7" Single: Released Nov '87, on Factory (1), by Factory Records. Catalogue no: **FAC 197**
12" Single: Released Nov '87, on Factory (1), by Factory Records. Catalogue no: **FACT 197 T**

N'SEL FIK (89 MIX)
Tracks: / Nsel fik (89 mix) / Nghir menek.
12" Single: Released Jul '89, on Mango, by Island Records. Catalogue no: **12 MNG 713**

Fagan, Bevin 'Bagga'

WISHING ON A STAR
Tracks: / Wishing on a star / Blah, blah, blah.
7" Single: Released Mar '80, on EMI, by EMI Records. Deleted Mar '83. Catalogue no: **RIC 108**
12" Single: Released Mar '80, on EMI, by EMI Records. Deleted Mar '83. Catalogue no: **12 RIC 108**

Fagan, Michael

GOD SAVE THE QUEEN
Tracks: / God save the Queen.
7" Single: Released May '83, on Charly, by Charly Records. Deleted '85. Catalogue no: **7 CYX 205**

Fagen, Donald

Biographical details: Fagen and Walter Becker were the composing duo behind Steely Dan. Fagen's solo album, like the later Steely Dan LPs, is remarkable for its engineering: *Nightfly* includes Larry Carlton, Rick Derringer, Randy Brecker, Hugh McCracken (B.B. King sidesman) and many others. (Donald Clarke, March 1988.)
This American keyboardist, horn player, singer and songwriter helped to form the acclaimed jazz-rock group Steely Dan in 1972. With his partner Walter Becker, he led Steely Dan to huge success through the Seventies. They became known as th ultimate purveyors of clinical studio perfectionism, and did not tour. Steely Dan folded at the start of the Eighties; by this time, Fagen had assumed an increasingly dominant role. Fagen made his solo debut in the autumn of 1982 with the brilliant LP *The nightfly*. Using an all-star cast of musicians, he conceived and created a jazzy, laid back pop rock album that managed to combine superb playing and American life. The album's eshilarating opening track, *IGY (what a beautiful)* reached No.26 as a single on the US charts. The LP was a Top 20 seller in the States, but had to be content with a No.44 placing in Britain. Fagen was mightly slow to issue a follow-up album. (Bob MacDonald, 11th August 1985).

CENTURY'S END
Tracks: / Century's end / Shangai confidential / Nightfly, The (Only on CD.) / Goodbye look, The (Only on CD.).
CD 5": Released Apr '88, on Warner Bros., by WEA Records. Catalogue no: **W 7972 CD**
7" Single: Released Apr '88, on Warner Bros., by WEA Records. Catalogue no: **W 7972**
12" Single: Released Apr '88, on Warner Bros., by WEA Records. Catalogue no: **W 7972T**

I.G.Y.
Tracks: / I.G.Y. / Walk between raindrops.
7" Single: Released Nov '82, on Warner Bros., by WEA Records. Deleted '88. Catalogue no: **W 9900**

NEW FRONTIER
Tracks: / New frontier / Maxine.
7" Single: Released Jan '83, on Warner Bros., by WEA Records. Deleted '88. Catalogue no: **W 9792**
12" Single: Released Jan '83, on Warner Bros., by WEA Records. Deleted '88. Catalogue no: **W 9792 T**

RUBY BABY
Tracks: / Ruby baby / Walk between raindrops.
7" Single: Released Apr '83, on Warner Bros., by WEA Records. Deleted '88. Catalogue no: **W 9674**

Fagin, Joe

BACK WITH THE BOYS
Tracks: / Back with the boys / Get it right / That's livin' alright (Extra track available on 12" version only.) / Breakin' away (Extra track available on 12" version only.).
7" Single: Released Mar '86, on Towerbell, Deleted '88. Catalogue no: **TOW 84**
12" Single: Released Mar '86, on Towerbell, Deleted '88. Catalogue no: **TOWT 84**

BREAKIN' AWAY
Tracks: / Breakin' away / That's livin' alright.
7" Single: Released Jan '84, on Towerbell, Deleted '88. Catalogue no: **TOW 46**

LOVE HANGS BY A THREAD (SINGLE)
Tracks: / Love hangs by a thread.
7" Single: Released Sep '85, on Towerbell, Deleted '88. Catalogue no: **TOW 72**

MONEY MONEY
Tracks: / Money money.
7" Single: Released Jun '84, on Towerbell, Deleted '88. Catalogue no: **TOW 53**

NUMBER ONE (SAVIN' FACE)
Tracks: / Number one (savin' face).
7" Single: Released Apr '85, on Towerbell, Catalogue no: **TOW 46**
12" Single: Released Apr '85, on Towerbell, Deleted '88. Catalogue no: **TOW T 46**

PRIDE OF MERSEYSIDE
Tracks: / Pride of Merseyside / Don't care much anymore.
7" Pic: Released Mar '87, on GFM, Catalogue no: **GFMP 110**
7" Single: Released Mar '87, on GFM, Catalogue no: **GFM 110**
12" Single: Released Mar '87, on GFM, Catalogue no: **GFMX 110**
12" Single: Released Mar '87, on GFM, Catalogue no: **GFMT 110**

STOWAWAY
Tracks: / Stowaway / Paradise bound.
7" Single: Released May '81, on Tamarin, Deleted May '84. Catalogue no: **TAM 1**

THAT'S LIVIN' ALRIGHT
Tracks: / That's livin' alright.
7" Pic: Released 20 Apr '88, on PRT, by Castle Communications Records. Catalogue no: **PYS 9**

WHY DON'T WE SPEND THE NIGHT
Tracks: / Why don't we spend the night / Mr. Rag man.
7" Single: Released Feb '80, on Polydor, by Polydor Ltd. Deleted '83. Catalogue no: **POSP 125**
7" Single: Released Mar '84, on Towerbell, Deleted '88. Catalogue no: **TOW 48**

Faint, Richard

ON THE ASSEMBLY LINE
Tracks: / On the assembly line / Still believing.
7" Single: Released Jan '82, on Tadpole, Deleted Jan '85. Catalogue no: **TAD 99**

Fair Deal

ALBION MARKET THEME
Tracks: / Albion Market theme.
7" Single: Released '85, on Columbia, by EMI Records. Deleted '88. Catalogue no: **DB 9114**

Fair Warning

ROCKING AT THE SPEED OF LIGHT
Tracks: / Rocking at the speed of light.
12" Single: Released Apr '88, on Areba, by Areba Records. Catalogue no: **ERA 002**

Fair Weather

NATURAL SINNER
Tracks: / Natural sinner.
7" Single: Released Jul '70, on RCA, by BMG Records (UK). Deleted '73. Catalogue no: **RCA 1977**

Fair, Yvonne

Biographical details: Here was a fiery woman, if ever there was one! American Yvonne Fair came to fame in 1976 with a one-off hit, *It Should Have Been Me*. Her dramatic interpretation of this quaintly ludicrous song, in which a member of a church wedding congregation interrupts the proceedings to proclaim that she ought to have been the bride, stormed to No 5 on the British charts. In her home country it only rose to No 85 on the Hot Hundred but fared well on the soul chart. The track was taken from her only notable album, *The Bitch Is Black* (presumably an answer to Elton John's hit, *The Bitch Is Back*). Fair's rendition of *It Should Have Been Me* was produced by the song's co-writer, Norman Whitfield. The famous Motown man, who always exploited his material to the full, also produced two earlier versions: Kim Weston originally recorded it in 1963 and Gladys Knight & The Pips took it into the American Top Forty in 1968. (Bob MacDonald, August 1985.).

IT SHOULD HAVE BEEN ME
Tracks: / It should have been me.
7" Single: Released '81, on Motown, by BMG Records (UK). Deleted '88. Catalogue no: **TMG 1013**

Fairchild, Barbara

Biographical details: Country singer and songwriter born in 1950 in Arkansas. Her songs were recorded by Loretta Lynn, Liz Anderson, Conway Twitty; her own hits began in 1970 and she has made many fans in the UK since 1979. (Donald Clarke, April 1989)h.

ANSWER GAME, THE (SINGLE)
Tracks: / Answer game, The / Bye bye love.
7" Single: Released '82, on RCA, by BMG Records (UK). Deleted '88. Catalogue no: **RCA 188**

JUST OUT RIDING AROUND
Tracks: / Just out riding around / You burned me so bad.
7" Single: Released Jun '86, on Capitol, by EMI Records. Deleted '88. Catalogue no: **CL 411**

Fairey Engineering

LISTEN WITH MOTHER THEME
Tracks: / Listen with mother theme.
7" Single: Released '83, on Mont, by Mont Music Records. Deleted '88. Catalogue no: **MM 105**

Fairground Attraction

CLARE
Tracks: / Clare / Game of love / Do you want to know a secret.
7" EP: Released 23 Jan '89, on RCA, by BMG Records (UK). Deleted Aug '89. Catalogue no: **PB 42643**
CD 5": Released Jun '89, on RCA, by BMG Records (UK). Deleted Jul '89. Catalogue no: **PD 42608**
7" Single: Released Jan '89, on RCA, by BMG Records (UK). Deleted Aug '89. Catalogue no: **PB 42607**
12" Single: Released Jan '89, on RCA, by BMG Records (UK). Deleted Aug '89. Catalogue no: **PT 42608**

FIND MY LOVE
Tracks: / Find my love / Watching the party / You send me (Only on 12".) / Ay fond kiss (Only on 12".).
Note: "A sprightly ballad with a folk element. A decent followup to their No 1 single." (Music Week, July 1988)
CD 5": Released Jul '88, on RCA, by BMG Records (UK). Deleted Jul '89. Catalogue no: **PD 42080**
7" Single: Released Jul '88, on RCA, by BMG Records (UK). Deleted Aug '89. Catalogue no: **PB 42079**
12" Single: Released Jul '88, on RCA, by BMG Records (UK). Deleted May '89. Catalogue no: **PT 42080**

PERFECT
Tracks: / Perfect / Mythology / Falling Backwards (Extra track on 12" and CD single.) / Mystery train (Extra track on 12" and CD single.).
CD 5": Released Mar '88, on RCA, by BMG Records (UK). Deleted May '89. Catalogue no: **PD 41846**
7" Single: Released Mar '88, on RCA, by BMG Records (UK). Catalogue no: **PB 41845**
12" Single: Released Mar '88, on RCA, by BMG Records (UK). Catalogue no: **PT 41846**

SMILE IN A WHISPER, A
Tracks: / Smile in a whisper, A / Winter rose / Walking after midnight (12" & CD single.) / Trying times (12" & CD single.).
Note: += track on all formats *= track on 12" and CD onlyv
CD 5": Released Nov '88, on RCA, by BMG Records (UK). Deleted Jul '89. Catalogue no: **PD 42250**
7" Single: Released Nov '88, on RCA, by BMG Records (UK). Deleted May '89. Catalogue no: **PB 42249**
12" Single: Released Nov '88, on RCA, by BMG Records (UK). Catalogue no: **PT 42250**

Fairport Convention

Biographical details: The most successful of the many line-ups of this British folk-rock group featured Sandy Denny, Ashley Hutchings, Dave Mattacks, Simon Nicol, Dave Swarbrick and Richard Thompson. During their 12 year existence, from 1967-79, 20 performers drifted in and out of the band. Pete Frame's excellent *Rock family trees* tome lists 15 different Fairport line-ups. During the Eighties, various combinations of musicians have staged an annual reunion. The name of the group was chosen because it was the name of Nicol's house - he was one of the founder members. Fairport Convention were the most influential folk group in Britain's post-war history. In addition to Nicol, the other founder players included singer Judy Dyble (replaced in May 1968 by Sandy Denny), bassist Hutchings, drummer Martin Lamble (who was killed in June 1969, when the group's van was involved in a motorway accident), Ian Mathews (a singer who later formed his own group, Mathews' Southern Comfort, and hit No.1 with Woodstock) and singer/guitarist Thompson (who found cult success in the Seventies and Eighties, as a solo artist and in conjunction with his now-divorced-wife Linda). Fairport Convention's eponymous debut album was released in June 1968. The Fairports' first chart LP was *Unhalfbricking*, which reached the UK No.12 position in 1969. This curiously titled album yielded their only hit single - *Si tu dois partir*, a rendition of Bob Dylan's *If you gotta go, go now*, reached No.21 in Britain. The classic but short lived Fairport line-up (listed at the top) then proceeded to record the group's best and most successful album *Liege and lief*. As well as contributing her own numbers, Sandy Denny guided the band in a more traditional folk direction than the one in which they had been heading at the outset; but her main contribution was her lovely, flowing, crystal-clear voice. *Liege and lief* included Sandy's highly charged rendition of the traditional folk ballad *Matty Groves*. The Fairports played a stunning fusion of folk and rock, and were a sort of unofficial British answer to the Byrds or the Band. Folk purists screamed with anguish but the Convention helped to introduce folk music to a whole new young audience, and paved the way for Steeleye Span and a host of less-well known acts. The early Seventies saw another succession of personnel changes, including the departures of Denny and Thompson. But during the Seventies, the group soldiered on - despite erratic quality and declining commercial success, there were many memorable musical moments. Violinist/vocalist Swarbrick became the backbone of the band, and was the longest serving member. Already a folk verteran before joining FC in 1969, he stayed with them until the 1979 break-up. Sandy Denny who had briefly rejoined the group in the mid-Seventies, met a tragic end in April 1978; at the age of 31: she fell down a flight of stairs at a friend's house and died of a brain haemorrhage four days later. Thus, no Fairport reunion has ever been truly complete. (Bob MacDonald, 11th August 1985)
Folk-rock band formed in 1966 in London by Ashley Hutchings, Simon Nicol and Richard Thompson, guitars and vocals, with drummer Martin Lamble (1949-69), vocalist Judy Dyble and Ian Mathews. They were named after Nicol's home. *What we did on our holidays* in 1968 introduced Sandy Denny (replacing Dybie) and emphasised Thompson's development as a writer (e.g. *Meet on a ledge*). Mathews left to pursue a solo career, though playing on some tracks on *Unhalfbricking* which also included fiddeler Dave Swarbrick, who then joined full time. Dave Mattacks joined for *Liege & Lief* in 1969, the first full flowering of English folk-rock, but the landmark caused a schism in the group; Hutchings was keen to pursue this direction and left to form Steeleye Span, while Denny formed the short lived Fotheringay. Bassist Dave Pegg joined for *Full house* in 1970. Thompson left in 1971 and they were a quartet for a while; *Rosie* in 1973 includied guest Denny, Thompson, and Ralph McTell, guitarists Trevor Lucus (Denny's husband) and Jerry Donahue joined for *Fairport 9*. Denny is on *Fairport live Convention*. Mattacks was replaced by Bruce Rowland. They seemed to split in '77; Pegg joined Jethro Tull and Nicol worked as a duo, but joyous annual reunions have been recorded. (Donald Clarke, April 1989).

MEET ON THE LEDGE
Tracks: / Meet on the ledge / Sigh beg sigh more / John Barleycorn*.
7" Single: Released 23 May '87, on Island, by Island Records. Deleted Mar '88. Catalogue no: **IS 324**
12" Single: Released 23 May '87, on Island, by Island Records. Deleted Jun '88. Catalogue no: **12IS 324**

RUBBER BAND
Tracks: / Rubber band / Bonny black hare.
7" Single: Released Mar '80, on Simons, Deleted '83. Catalogue no: **PMW 1**

SI TU DOIS PARTIR
Tracks: / Si tu dois partir.
7" Single: Released Jul '69, on Island, by Island Records. Deleted '72. Catalogue no: **WIP 6064**

Fairweather-Low, Andy

Biographical details: British singer, guitarist and songwriter Fairweather-Low had a brace of British Top Ten hits in the mid-70's. He had first come to fame in the late 60's as leader of Amen Corner, purveyors of lightweight but eminently listenable pop singles. As the 60's became the 70's he took a handful of ex-Corner members with him and formed a group called Fair Weather and they enjoyed a one-off British Top Tenner in summer 1970 with *Natural Sinner*, written by Fairweather-Low. By the end of the following year they had split up. After a long period out of the limelight, Andy Fairweather-Low launched his solo career in 1974. His two hit singles, both of an oddball nature, were the catchy *Reggae Tune* (which reached the UK No 10 position in '74) and the strangely infectious morning-after-the-night-before reflection *Wide-Eyed And Legless* (which hit No 6 in early '76). None of his albums made the British charts, but the title track of *La Booga Rooga* became a minor 1976 hit in Britain for the unknown Surprise Sisters. Fairweather-Low's thin, high but interesting voice returned thereafter to obscurity. He became virtually inactive, save for an unsuccessful 1980 album, *Megashebang*. (Bob MacDonald, 1985.).

BOSSA NOVA
Tracks: / Bossa nova / House of blue lights.
7" Single: Released Aug '86, on Stiff, by Stiff Records. Catalogue no: **BUY 252**
12" Single: Released Aug '86, on Stiff, by Stiff Records. Catalogue no: **BUYIT 252**

HARD HAT BOOGIE
Tracks: / Hard hat boogie / Bingerama.
7" Single: Released Oct '80, on Warner Bros., by WEA Records. Deleted Oct '83. Catalogue no: **K 17683**

REGGAE TUNE
Tracks: / Reggae tune.
7" Single: Released Sep '74, on A&M, by A&M Records. Deleted '77. Catalogue no: **AMS 7129**

WIDE-EYED AND LEGLESS
Tracks: / Wide-eyed and legless / Reggae tune / Spider diving / La booga rooga / Dancing in the dark / My bucket's got a hole in it.
7" EP: Released '84, on Scoop 33, by Pickwick Records. Deleted '88. Catalogue no: **7SR 5038**

WIDE-EYED AND LEGLESS (SINGLE)
Tracks: / Wide eyed and legless.
7" Single: Released Dec '75, on A&M, by A&M Records. Deleted '78. Catalogue no: **AMS 7202**

Faith, Adam

Biographical details: Born Terence Nelhams in Acton, London in 1940, this British singer is a rare example of an apparently lightweight vocalist developing other talents once the his stopped coming - he proceeded to enjoy success and an actor, manager and producer. As a school leaver, his main ambition was to become a film editor. He had two spells of employment with Rank Screen Services, interrupted by his first attempt to be a pop star (inspired by the Lonnie Donegan skiffle craze). His second stab was more successful, thanks to the exposure on the 'Drumbeat' TV series and the 'Beat girl' teen film, and thanks to songwriter Les Vandyke and arranger John Barry. With Vandyke composing most of his hits, and Barry arranging them, Faith became one of Britain's top pop stars of the early Sixties. Both of his first two hits were No.1 smashes - the 19 year old lad topped the UK charts with the classic *What do you want* in December 1959, and snatched the summit in March 1960 with the similar sounding *Poor me*. He never returned to the very top, but managed a further 11 UK Top 20 singles by the end of 1962. Faith sang this catchy pop fodder in a distinctive hiccuping style, exaggerating the Buddy Holly sound. The other main selling point (apart form the singers' blond good looks) was Barry's arrangements, which punctuated the records with an unusual pizzicato sting sound that was much copied in the early Sixties.
From 1963 onwards, the Beatles revolution steadily diminished Faith's chart prowess; by 1966, the year of his final minor hit, he had dropped his singing career and turned to acting. After a couple of low-key years in repertory theatre, he set his sights upon acting for films and television. He returned to being a household name in Britain during the early Seventies, when he played the title role in the UK television series *Budgie*. In 1972 he discovered the young singer/songwriter Leo Sayer and became his manager. The following year, Faith produced the debut solo LP by the who's Roger Daltrey - this yielded the UK Top 5 hit *Giving it all away*, which was co-written by Sayer and helped to pave the way for the latter's highly successful international career. After recovering from a serious car accident, Faith released an unsuccessful LP called *I survive* in 1974; but he has made no further attempts to stage a recording comeback. In addition to managing Leo Sayer, his subsequent activities have included major movie roles in *Stardust* with David Essex and *McVicar* with Roger Daltrey in 1979. (Bob MacDonald, 12th August 1985)
UK pop singer. Discovered singing skiffle by Jack Good and had his first hits in 1959. Even by '50's pop standards he had a weak voice; lavish arrangements by John Barry and his hiccough-style singing (recalling Buddy Holly) made him a teen idol, second only to Cliff Richard in popularity, and he couldn't have been as band as his American equivalents Fabian and Frankie Avalon. He spotted the star potential of Sandie Shaw; two members of the backing group the Roulettes went on to become Argent and Faith was one of the few UK pop stars to switch successfully to acting. (Donald Clarke, April 1989)s.

AS YOU LIKE IT
Tracks: / As you like it.
7" Single: Released May '62, on Parlophone, by EMI Records. Deleted '65. Catalogue no: **R 4896**

BABY TAKE A BOW
Tracks: / Baby take a bow.
7" Single: Released Dec '62, on Parlophone, by EMI Records. Deleted '65. Catalogue no: **R 4964**

CHERYL'S GOIN' HOME
Tracks: / Cheryl's goin' home.
7" Single: Released Oct '66, on Parlophone, by EMI Records. Deleted '69. Catalogue no: **R 5516**

DON'T THAT BEAT ALL
Tracks: / Don't that beat all.
7" Single: Released Aug '62, on Parlophone, by EMI Records. Deleted '65. Catalogue no: **R 4930**

DON'T YOU KNOW IT
Tracks: / Don't you know it.
7" Single: Released Jul '61, on Parlophone, by EMI Records. Deleted '64. Catalogue no: **R 4807**

EASY GOING ME
Tracks: / Easy going me.
7" Single: Released Apr '61, on Parlophone, by EMI Records. Deleted '64. Catalogue no: **R 4766**

FIRST TIME, THE
Tracks: / First time.
7" Single: Released Jul '63, on Parlophone, by EMI Records. Deleted '66. Catalogue no: **R 5061**

HOW ABOUT THAT
Tracks: / How about that.
7" Single: Released Sep '60, on Parlophone, by EMI Records. Deleted '63. Catalogue no: **R 4689**

I LOVE BEING IN LOVE WITH YOU
Tracks: / I love being in love with you.
7" Single: Released May '64, on Parlophone, by EMI Records. Deleted '67. Catalogue no: **R 5138**

IF HE TELLS YOU
Tracks: / If he tells you.
7" Single: Released Mar '64, on Parlophone, by EMI Records. Deleted '67. Catalogue no: **R 5109**

LONELY PUP (IN A CHRISTMAS SHOP)
Tracks: / Lonely pup (in a christmas shop).
7" Single: Released Nov '60, on Parlophone, by EMI Records. Deleted '63. Catalogue no: **R 4708**

LONESOME
Tracks: / Lonesome.
7" Single: Released Jan '62, on Parlo

phone, by EMI Records. Deleted '65. Catalogue no: **R 4864**

MESSAGE TO MARTHA (KENTUCKY BLUEBIRD)
Tracks: / Message to Martha (Kentucky bluebird).
7" Single: Released Nov '64, on Parlophone, by EMI Records. Deleted '67. Catalogue no: **R 5201**

POOR ME
Tracks: / Poor me.
7" Single: Released Jan '60, on Parlophone, by EMI Records. Deleted '63. Catalogue no: **R 4623**

SOMEONE ELSE'S BABY
Tracks: / Someone else's baby.
7" Single: Released Apr '60, on Parlophone, by EMI Records. Deleted '63. Catalogue no: **R 4591**

SOMEONE'S TAKEN MARIA AWAY
Tracks: / Someone's taken Maria away.
7" Single: Released Jun '65, on Parlophone, by EMI Records. Deleted '68. Catalogue no: **R 5289**

STOP FEELING SORRY FOR YOURSELF
Tracks: / Stop feeling sorry for yourself.
7" Single: Released Feb '65, on Parlophone, by EMI Records. Deleted '68. Catalogue no: **R 5235**

THIS IS IT
Tracks: / This is it / Who am I?.
7" Single: Released Feb '61, on Parlophone, by EMI Records. Deleted '64. Catalogue no: **R 4735**

TIME HAS COME, THE
Tracks: / Time has come, The.
7" Single: Released Oct '61, on Parlophone, by EMI Records. Deleted '64. Catalogue no: **R 4837**

WALKIN' TALL
Tracks: / Walkin' tall.
7" Single: Released Jul '63, on Parlophone, by EMI Records. Deleted '66. Catalogue no: **R 5039**

WE ARE IN LOVE
Tracks: / We are in love.
7" Single: Released Dec '63, on Parlophone, by EMI Records. Deleted '66. Catalogue no: **R 5091**

WHAT DO YOU WANT
Tracks: / What do you want / How about that.
7" Single: Released Nov '59, on Parlophone, by EMI Records. Deleted '62. Catalogue no: **R 4591**
7" Single: Released '83, on Old Gold, by Old Gold Records. Deleted Jul '88. Catalogue no: **OG 9384**

WHAT DO YOU WANT (SINGLE)
Tracks: / What do you want / Poor me.
7" Single: Released '77, on EMI, by EMI Records. Deleted Apr '88. Catalogue no: **EMI 2691**

WHAT NOW
Tracks: / What now.
7" Single: Released Jan '63, on Parlophone, by EMI Records. Deleted '66. Catalogue no: **R 4990**

WHEN JOHNNY COMES MARCHING HOME
Tracks: / When Johnny comes marching home / Made you.
7" Single: Released Jun '60, on Parlophone, by EMI Records. Deleted '63. Catalogue no: **R 4665**

Faith Brothers

COUNTRY OF THE BLIND
Tracks: / Country of the blind / Eventide.
7" Single: Released '85, on Siren, by Virgin Records. Deleted May '88. Catalogue no: **SIREN 2**
12" Single: Released '85, on Siren, by Virgin Records. Deleted May '88. Catalogue no: **SIREN 2-12**

EVENTIDE(A HYMN FOR CHANGE)
Tracks: / Eventide (a hymn for change).
7" Single: Released '85, on Siren, by Virgin Records. Deleted May '88. Catalogue no: **SIREN 9**
12" Single: Released '85, on Siren, by Virgin Records. Deleted May '88. Catalogue no: **SIREN 9-12**

STRANGER ON HOME GROUND
Tracks: / Stranger on home ground.
7" Single: Released '85, on Siren, by Virgin Records. Deleted May '88. Catalogue no: **SIREN 4**
12" Single: Released '85, on Siren, by Virgin Records. Deleted May '88. Catalogue no: **SIREN 4-12**

THAT'S JUST THE WAY IT IS WITH ME
Tracks: / That's just the way it is with me / Different kind of wonderful, A / Letter to the times, A.
7" Single: Released Mar '87, on Siren, by Virgin Records. Deleted May '88. Catalogue no: **SRN 42**
12" Single: Released Mar '87, on Siren, by Virgin Records. Deleted May '88. Catalogue no: **SRN 42-12**

WHISTLING IN THE DARK
Tracks: / Whistling in the dark / Easter Parade.
7" Single: Released Mar '86, on Siren, by Virgin Records. Deleted May '88. Catalogue no: **SIREN 13**
12" Single: Released Mar '86, on Siren, by Virgin Records. Deleted May '88. Catalogue no: **SIREN 13-12**

Faith, George

OLD FASHIONED LOVE
Tracks: / Old fashioned love.
12" Single: Released '84, on Londisc, by Londisc Records. Catalogue no: **LDR 033**

SAY YOU,SAY ME
Tracks: / Say you, say me / Say you, say me (Version).
12" Single: Released Jan '86, on Top Rank (2), Catalogue no: **TRD 023**

TO LOVE SOMEBODY
Tracks: / To love somebody / Lovesome.
12" Single: Released '83, on Foundation, Catalogue no: **TF 11**

Faith Global

CODED WORLD
Tracks: / Coded world / Love seems lost.
7" Single: Released Jul '82, on Survival (1), by Survival Records. Deleted Jul '85. Catalogue no: **SUR 124**

EARTH REPORT
Tracks: / Earth report.
7" Single: Released '83, on Survival (1), by Survival Records. Deleted '88. Catalogue no: **SUR 124**

Faith, Hope & Charity

JUST ONE LOOK
Tracks: / Just one look.
7" Single: Released Jan '76, on RCA, by BMG Records (UK). Deleted '79. Catalogue no: **RCA 2632**

Faith, Horace

BLACK PEARL
Tracks: / Black pearl.
7" Single: Released Sep '70, on Trojan, by Trojan Records. Deleted '73. Catalogue no: **TR 7790**

Faith No More

ANNE'S SONG
Tracks: / Anne's song / Anne's song (dance mix) / Greed.
7" Pic: Released Apr '88, on Slash, by London Records. Deleted Feb '89. Catalogue no: **LASHP 18**
7" Single: Released Apr '88, on Slash, by London Records. Deleted Oct '88. Catalogue no: **LASH 18**
12" Single: Released Apr '88, on Slash, by London Records. Deleted Oct '88. Catalogue no: **LASHX 18**

WE CARE A LOT (SINGLE)
Tracks: / Perfect day / Marguerite / We care a lot.
7" Single: Released Jan '88, on Slash, by London Records. Deleted Oct '88. Catalogue no: **LASH 17**
12" Single: Released Jan '88, on Slash, by London Records. Deleted Oct '88. Catalogue no: **LASHX 17**

Faith, Percy

Biographical details: There are certain tunes that everyone knows, even if they are unaware of the title, artist or composer, and even if they possess little material knowledge of any kind. Tunes in this category include *The blue Danube*, *Greensleeves* .... and Percy Faith & His Orchestra's recording of Max Steiner's *Theme from a summer place*. Faith, a Canadian arranger, conductor and orchestra leader, was born in Toronto in 1908. He became staff arranger for the Canadian Broadcasting Company in the mid-Thirties, and moved to the States in 1940. He later became a musical director of Columbia Records, the company for whom he recorded his two monster hits. During the early Fifties, he increased his popularity on US radio and television, and backed Tony Bennett on some of the singer's big hits. 1953 saw Fith topping the US charts in his own right with *Moulin rouge*, the theme from the Jose Ferrer movie of the same name; it gave Faith the biggest US hit of the year. In Britain, the tune was a No.1 for Mantovani & His Orchestra. Percy's second smash, the aforementioned *Theme from a summer place*, was the biggest US hit of 1060 - during its nine-week run atop the American charts, it became a British No.2 hit and eventually logged 30 weeks of th UK listings. It was such a smash that it became far more famous than the forgettable film for which it was written. Percy Faith died in February 1976 at the age of 67. (Bob MacDonald, 12th August 1985)
Arranger, conductor and composer (1908-76) and one of the most talented in the instrumental genre called 'light music' in the UK, and which came to be called 'mood music' in the USA. He intended to be a concert pianist but his hands were damaged in a fire; he conducted on the radio in his native Canada (Robert Farnon played trumpet in the orchestra) and moved to the USA in 1940; he recorded for RCA and from 1950 for CBS, where he was on the A&R staff, backing Rosemary Clooney, Tony Bennett, Johnny Mathis etc. He had two number one hits: *Delicado* in 1952 (a tune by a Brazilian bandleader) and *Theme from Moulin Rouge* the next year (vocal by Felicia Saunders). Among his film scores was a good one for one of the worst movies of all time, *The oscar* in 1966, which yielded *Maybe September*, a pop song recorded by Bennett. He pioneered instrumental recordings of Broadway scores beginning with *Kismet*; he made over 60 albums for CBS and they all made money. His instrumental albums in the early '50's were among the best of their kind, his arrangements full of inner voicings and beautiful writing for woodwinds, but as the decade wore on Muzak became commonplace and then rock'n'roll happened: Faith was relegated to the schlock market. His best stuff has been out of print for decades; it is a terrible irony that his third number one hit, they syrupy *Theme from a summer place* with its absurd kling-kling-kling piano, was the biggest record of 1960 in the USA. (Donald Clarke, April 1989).

SUMMER PLACE
Tracks: / Summer place, A (theme from) / Our winter love.
7" Single: Released '82, on Old Gold, by Old Gold Records. Catalogue no: **OG 9059**

THEME FROM 'A SUMMER PLACE'
Tracks: / Summer place, A (theme from).
7" Single: Released Mar '60, on Philips, by Phonogram Ltd. Deleted '63. Catalogue no: **PB 989**

Faithful

WHAT HAPPENED TO OUR LOVE?
Tracks: / What happened to our love?.
7" Single: Released Oct '88, on Runt, Catalogue no: **RUNT 1**
12" Single: Released Oct '88, on Runt, Catalogue no: **RUNTX 1**

Faithfull, Marianne

Biographical details: This British singer and actress, born in Hampstead, London in 1946, received her showbusiness breakthrough purely by chance and totally unsought. In 1964, while still a 17 year old convent schoolgirl, she went to a showbiz launch party witt her student boyfriend, who happened to be a friend of Peter Asher of Peter & Gordon. She was spotted by Andrew Loog Oldham, the Rolling Stones' manager and producer, who thought that she had a very photogenic appearance. Questions about her vocal abilitty seemed to have been secondary in Oldham's mind; fortunately, it turned out that she could indeed sing. In conjunction with Oldham, Mick Jagger and Keith Richard wrote her first single *As tears go by*. The combination of her delicate voice, her similarly appealing blonde looks, the touchingly reflective song and the Stones spiralling popularity, made the record a UK Top 10 hit in late 1964; it also reached No.22 in America, although the Stones own version did better in 1966. 1965 was an excellent year for Faithfull - Jackie de Shannon's *Come and stay with me*, John D. Loudermilk's *This little bird* and a song called *Summer nights* wll made the UK Top 10 and the US Top 40. Her first two albums both reached the British Top 20. However, from 1966 onwards, Faithfull never returned to any of those lists. Her personal life also went downhill - she suffered a marital breakup, and then began a tempestuous relationship with Jagger, which filled thousands of gossip column inches. She dropped her singing career in the late Sixties and turned to acting. After appearing on stage and screen with such names as Glenda Jackson, Oliver Reed and Nicol Williamson, she was nearly killed by a drug overdose. Having parted company with Jagger, she spent the early Seventies romancing various celebrities and suffuring from a heroin addiction. The drug problem was cured in 1973, and she gradually resumed low-key recording and to give her wide coverage. The 1979 album *Broken English* yielded a minor UK hit single with the critically acclaimed *Ballad of Lucy Jordan*. During the early Eighties, the albums *Dangerous acquaintances* and *A child's adventure* showed that her now deeper voice had taken on a new weight, reflecting the trials and tribualations of her life. (Bob MacDonald, 12th August 1985)
The quintessential female '60's pop singer, blonde and beautiful, born in 1946 in Hampstead. She was discovered at a party by Andrew Loog Oldham; the Rolling Stones wrote her debut hit *As tears go by* released when she was 18. Her affair with Mick Jagger and subsequent drug addiction was news; they went to Australia together while he worked on the flop film *Ned Kelly*, she took an overdose and he saved her life. She co-wrote Stones songs like *Sister morphine*; her acting was well recieved in films and on the stage. Her early hit albums were not bad; her comebacks have nct set the world on fire although she has probably become a more interesting singer. She deserves credit just for surviving. (Donald Clarke, April 1989),.

AS TEARS GO BY (SINGLE).
Tracks: / As tears go by / Come and stay with me.
7" Single: Released Aug '64, on Decca, by Decca Records. Deleted '67. Catalogue no: **F 11923**
7" Single: Released '83, on Old Gold, by Old Gold Records. Catalogue no: **OG 9335**
7" Single: Released 20 Jun '87, on Island, by Island Records. Deleted Apr '88. Catalogue no: **IS 323**

MARIANNE FAITHFULL - BALLAD OF LUCY JORDAN (Released on Island)

7" Single: Released '80, on Decca, by Decca Records. Deleted '88. Catalogue no: **F 13890**
12" Single: Released 20 Jun '87, on Island, by Island Records. Deleted Apr '88. Catalogue no: **12IS 323**

BALLAD OF LUCY JORDAN (see panel on previous page)
Tracks: / Ballad of Lucy Jordan / Brain drain.
7" Single: Released Nov '79, on Island, by Island Records. Deleted '82. Catalogue no: **WIP 6491**

BROKEN ENGLISH (SINGLE)
Tracks: / Broken English / What's the hurry / Sister morphine.
7" Single: Released Jan '80, on Island, by Island Records. Deleted Jan '83. Catalogue no: **WIP 6542**
12" Single: Released Jun '82, on Island, by Island Records. Deleted Jun '85. Catalogue no: **MF 100**

COME AND STAY WITH ME
Tracks: / Come and stay with me.
7" Single: Released Feb '65, on Decca, by Decca Records. Deleted '68. Catalogue no: **F 12075**

IS THIS WHAT I GET FOR LOVING YOU
Tracks: / Is this what I get for loving you.
7" Single: Released Mar '67, on Decca, by Decca Records. Deleted '70. Catalogue no: **F 22524**

SUMMER NIGHTS (SINGLE)
Tracks: / Summer nights.
7" Single: Released Jul '65, on Decca, by Decca Records. Deleted '68. Catalogue no: **F 12162**

SWEETHEART
Tracks: / Sweetheart / Over here.
7" Single: Released Dec '81, on Island, by Island Records. Deleted Dec '84. Catalogue no: **WIP 6752**

THIS LITTLE BIRD
Tracks: / This little bird.
7" Single: Released May '65, on Decca, by Decca Records. Deleted '68. Catalogue no: **F 12162**

YESTERDAY
Tracks: / Yesterday.
7" Single: Released Nov '65, on Decca, by Decca Records. Deleted '68. Catalogue no: **F 12268**

Falco

Biographical details: An Austrian vocalist, born Johann Hozel in 1957, trying for international success. His first single *All Vienna* was cult favourite after being banned because of line 'All Viena is on heroin today'. His first album *Einzelhaft (Incarcerated)* included the international hit *Der Kommisar*, he signed to WEA International in 1986. (Donald Clarke, April 1989).

BODY NEXT TO BODY
Tracks: / Body next to body.
12" Single: Released Jan '88, on WEA, by WEA Records. Catalogue no: **U 8100T**
7" Single: Released Jan '88, on WEA, by WEA Records. Catalogue no: **U 8100**

EMOTIONAL (SINGLE)
Tracks: / Der Komissar / Kiss of Kathleen Turner, The / Emotional.
12" Single: Released Apr '87, on WEA (International), by WEA Records. Catalogue no: **U 8439 T**
7" Single: Released Apr '87, on WEA (International), by WEA Records. Catalogue no: **U 8439**

JEANNY
Tracks: / Rock me Amadeus (extended '86 edit) (Extra track on 12" version only.) / Girl is missing (German language version).
7" Single: Released Jul '86, on A&M, by A&M Records. Deleted '87. Catalogue no: **AM 333**
12" Single: Released Jul '86, on A&M, by A&M Records. Deleted '87. Catalogue no: **AMY 333**

JUNGE ROEMER (SINGLE)
Tracks: / Junge roemer.
12" Single: Released '84, on A&M, by A&M Records. Deleted '88. Catalogue no: **AMX 286**
7" Single: Released '84, on A&M, by A&M Records. Deleted '88. Catalogue no: **AM 186**

ROCK ME AMADEUS US Version
Tracks: / Rock me Amadeus / Urban tropical / Rock me amadeus (salieri mix) (Extra track only on 12"version.).
7" Single: Released Mar '86, on A&M, by A&M Records. Deleted '87. Catalogue no: **AM 278**
12" Single: Released Mar '86, on A&M, by A&M Records. Deleted '88. Catalogue no: **AMYE 278**

SOUND OF MUSIK(THE)
Tracks: / Sound of musik, The/Single edit / Sound of musik, The/Rock 'n' Roll soul edit.
7" Single: Released Sep '86, on WEA, by WEA Records. Deleted Jun '87. Catalogue no: **U 8591**
12" Single: Released Sep '86, on WEA, by WEA Records. Deleted Jun '87. Catalogue no: **U 8591T**

VIENNA CALLING
Tracks: / Vienna calling / Americas.
12" Single: Released May '86, on A&M, by A&M Records. Deleted '88. Catalogue no: **AMY 318**
7" Single: Released May '86, on A&M, by A&M Records. Deleted '88. Catalogue no: **AM 318**

Falco, Tav

DROP YOUR MASK
Tracks: / Drop your mask.
7" Single: Released Mar '87, on New Rose (1), by New Rose Records. Catalogue no: **NEW 086**

PANTHER BURNS
Tracks: / Drifting heart / Poor man / Running wild / Two little puppies & one old shaggy hound / Ditch digging / She's the one to blame / Ode to Shetar / Little mixed up, A.
7" Set: Released Jan '88, on New Rose (1), by New Rose Records. Catalogue no: **NR 335**

Falcon, Billy

BLUE SMOKE
Tracks: / Blue smoke / Rocks in his head.
7" Single: Released May '80, on MCA, by MCA Records. Deleted May '85. Catalogue no: **MCA 587**

Falem Foundation

TURBO REGGAE
Tracks: / Turbo reggae.
12" Single: Released '85, on Solid Music, Catalogue no: **SM 001**

Falkirk Childrens

IT'S CHRISTMAS
Tracks: / It's Christmas.
7" Single: Released '83, on Klub, by Klub Records. Catalogue no: **KLUB 43**

Fall

Biographical details: The most successful of the many line-ups of this British rock band consisted of Karl Burns, Kay Carroll, Paul Hanley, Steve Hanley, Marc Riley, Craig Scanlon and Mark Smith. This was the team that performed on their first UK chart album, 1982's *Hex enduction hour*. However, since the group's formation in early 1977, only vocalist Mark Smith has survived the ever-changing line-up; while he has always remained their perpetual frontman, his two longest serving sidekicks have been drummer Karl Burns and guitarist Mark Riley. Hailing from Manchester in those seminal early days of the punk scene, the Fall issued their first record in 1978 - this was an EP entitled *Bingo master's breakout*, and it was soon followed by their debut single *It's the new thing*. 1979 saw the release of the band's first LP *Live at the witch trials*. By the end of the following year, they had firmly established themselves as one of the most uncompromising acts in the business - with their disdainful attitude towards the entertainment industry, they continued to develop their raucous and intense music while giving little or no thought to its commercial viability. They became stalwarts of Britain's burgeoning indie label scene, and were given consistent support by BBC Radio One's prime supporter of the New Wave, John Peel. With these solid credentials, the Fall were able to survive as a touring and recording unit into the Eighties despite the decline of punk. They did not make their UK chart debut until 1982, when the *Hex enduction hour* LP reached a modest No.71 placing. Smith and his cohorts have never become a signigicant unhummable bitterness of 1983's *Perverted by language* album to the cynical catchiness of 1984's *Creep* single, have continued to appeal to a small but dedicated audience of journalists and fans (Bob MacDonald, 16th August 1985)
New wave group formed in 1977 in Manchester by vocalist Mark E Smith, the only constant factor in lineup changes. First releases showcased atonal vocals from Smith and uncompromising guitar-based backing that owed nothing to fashion. The group was championed by deejay John Peel (of course); fans considered best work to be first LP *Live at the witch trials* and the Peel sessions, but they confounded fans by rarely playing recorded material on stage, allowing Smith free rein to rant. Compilation *Hip priests and kamerades* is required listening for interested parties. (Donald Clarke, April 1989)I.

BULBS
Tracks: / Bulbs.
7" Single: Released '87, on Beggars Banquet, by Beggars Banquet Records. Deleted Jul '88. Catalogue no: **BEG 120**

CAB IT UP
Tracks: / Cab it up / Dead beat descendant / Kurious oranj / Hit the north.
7" Single: Released Jun '89, on Beggars Banquet, by Beggars Banquet Records. Catalogue no: **BEG 226**
12" Single: Released Jun '89, on Beggars Banquet (USA), Catalogue no: **BEG 226T**

CREEP
Tracks: / Creep, The.
12" Pic: Released '84, on Beggars Banquet, by Beggars Banquet Records. Deleted Jun '87. Catalogue no: **BEG 116TP**
7" Single: Released '84, on Beggars Banquet, by Beggars Banquet Records. Catalogue no: **BEG 116**
12" Single: Released '84, on Beggars Banquet, by Beggars Banquet Records. Catalogue no: **BEG 116T**

CRUISERS CREEK
Tracks: / Cruisers creek.
7" Single: Released '85, on Beggars Banquet, by Beggars Banquet Records. Catalogue no: **BEG 150**
12" Single: Released '85, on Beggars Banquet, by Beggars Banquet Records. Catalogue no: **BEG 150T**

DRAYGO'S GUILT
Tracks: / Draygo's guilt.
12" Single: Released '84, on Beggars Banquet, by Beggars Banquet Records. Catalogue no: **BEG 120E**

HEY, LUCIANI
Tracks: / Shoulder pads / Hey, Luciani.
7" Single: Released Nov '86, on Beggars Banquet, by Beggars Banquet Records. Catalogue no: **BEG 176**
12" Single: Released Nov '86, on Beggars Banquet, by Beggars Banquet Records. Catalogue no: **BEG 176T**

HIT THE NORTH (PART 2)
Tracks: / Hit the north (part 2) / Australians in Europe (Only on 12" version.) / Northerns in Europe (Only on 12" version.).
7" Pic: Released Oct '87, on Beggars Banquet, by Beggars Banquet Records. Catalogue no: **BEG 200 P**
7" Single: Released Oct '87, on Beggars Banquet, by Beggars Banquet Records. Catalogue no: **BEG 200**
12" Single: Released Oct '87, on Beggars Banquet, by Beggars Banquet Records. Catalogue no: **BEG 200 T**

HIT THE NORTH, PART 4
Tracks: / Hit the north (part 4) / Hit the north (part 5) / Hit the north (part 1).
12" Single: Released Jul '87, on Beggars Banquet, by Beggars Banquet Records. Catalogue no: **BEG 200TR**

JERUSALEM
Tracks: / Jerusalem / Acid priest 2088 / Big new prinz / Wrong place right time.
7" Set: Released Nov '88, on Beggars Banquet, by Beggars Banquet Records. Catalogue no: **FALL 2 B**
CD 3": Released Nov '88, on Beggars Banquet, by Beggars Banquet Records. Catalogue no: **FALL 2 CD**

LIE, DREAM OF A CASINO SOUL
Tracks: / Lie, dream of a casino soul / Fantastic life.
7" Single: Released Nov '81, on Kamera, Deleted '84. Catalogue no: **ERA 001**

LIVING TOO LATE
Tracks: / Living too late / Hot after shave bop / Living too long.
12" Single: Released Jul '86, on Beggars Banquet, by Beggars Banquet Records. Catalogue no: **BEG 165 T**

LOOK NOW
Tracks: / Look now / Into CB.
7" Single: Released Apr '82, on Kamera, Deleted Apr '85. Catalogue no: **ERA 004**

MARQUIS CHA CHA
Tracks: / Marquis cha cha / Room to live.
7" Single: Released Dec '82, on Kamera, Deleted '85. Catalogue no: **ERA 014**

MR. PHARMACIST
Tracks: / Mr. Pharmacist / Lucifer over Lancashire / Auto tech pilot (Extra track on 12" version only.).
7" Single: Released Aug '86, on Beggars Banquet, by Beggars Banquet Records. Catalogue no: **BEG 168**
12" Single: Released Aug '86, on Beggars Banquet, by Beggars Banquet Records. Catalogue no: **BEG 168 T**

OH BROTHER
Tracks: / Oh brother.
7" Single: Released '84, on Beggars Banquet, by Beggars Banquet Records. Catalogue no: **BEG 110**
12" Single: Released '84, on Beggars Banquet, by Beggars Banquet Records. Catalogue no: **BEG 110T**

PEEL SESSIONS:FALL 27.11.78
Cassingle: Released 13 Jun '87, on Strange Fruit, by Strange Fruit Records. Catalogue no: **SFPSC 028**

ROLLIN' DANNY
Tracks: / Rollin' Danny.
7" Single: Released '85, on Beggars Banquet, by Beggars Banquet Records. Catalogue no: **BEG 134**
12" Single: Released '85, on Beggars Banquet, by Beggars Banquet Records. Catalogue no: **BEG 134T**

SLATES
Tracks: / Fall.
10" single: Released May '81, on Rough Trade, by Rough Trade Records. Catalogue no: **RT 071**

THERE'S A GHOST IN MY HOUSE
Tracks: / There's a ghost in my house / Sleep debt / Snatches / Haf found Bormann / Mark'll sink us all.
Cassingle: Released May '87, on Beggars Banquet, by Beggars Banquet Records. Catalogue no: **BEG 187C**
7" Single: Released May '87, on Beggars Banquet, by Beggars Banquet Records. Deleted Jun '88. Catalogue no: **BEG 187 H**
7" Single: Released Apr '87, on Beggars Banquet, by Beggars Banquet Records. Catalogue no: **BEG 187**
12" Single: Released May '87, on Beggars Banquet, by Beggars Banquet Records. Catalogue no: **BEG 187T**

VICTORIA
Tracks: / Victoria.
Cassingle: Released Jan '88, on Beggars Banquet, by Beggars Banquet Records. Catalogue no: **BEG 206C**
7" Single: Released Jan '88, on Beggars Banquet, by Beggars Banquet Records. Catalogue no: **BEG 206**
12" Single: Released Jan '88, on Beggars Banquet, by Beggars Banquet Records. Catalogue no: **BEG 206T**

Fallen Angels

AMPHETAMINE BLUES
Tracks: / Amphetamine blues.
7" Single: Released Feb '84, on Fall Out Catalogue no: **FALL 022**

CLOUDS
Tracks: / Clouds / Losing my reasons That's the way life's supposed to be (Only available on 12" version.).
7" Single: Released Nov '88, on Jungle by Jungle Records. Catalogue no: **JUNC 41**
12" Single: Released Nov '88, on Jungle by Jungle Records. Catalogue no: **JUNC 41T**

HEY SUSIE
Tracks: / Hey Susie.
7" Single: Released Nov '86, on Jungle by Jungle Records. Catalogue no: **JUN 28**

INNER PLANET LOVE
Tracks: / Inner planet love.
7" Single: Released Jun '84, on Fall Ou Deleted '88. Catalogue no: **FALL 027**
12" Single: Released Jun '84, on Fall Ou Catalogue no: **FALL 12027**

TEENAGE
Tracks: / Teenage.
7" Single: Released Mar '89, on Jungle, b Jungle Records. Catalogue no: **JUNG 47**

Fallout

SALAMI TACTICS(EP)
Tracks: / Salami tactics.
7" Single: Released Jan '83, on Mou Too Small To Fight, Catalogue no: **F2**

Fallout Club

WONDERLUST
Tracks: / Wonderlust.
7" Single: Released Oct '81, on Hap Birthday, Deleted '88. Catalogue no: **UR 1**
12" Single: Released Oct '81, on Hap Birthday, Deleted '88. Catalogue no: **U 127**

Fallover Twenty Four

PESSIMISTIC MAN
Tracks: / Pessimistic man.
7" Single: Released Nov '88, on Ugly Ma by Ugly Man Records. Catalogue **UGLY 12**

Faltermeyer, Harold

AXEL F
Tracks: / Axel F / Shoot out.
Note: Reissued.
Cassingle: Released Mar '85, on MCA, MCA Records. Deleted '88. Catalogue **MCAC 949**
7" Single: Released Oct '87, on MCA, MCA Records. Catalogue no: **MCA 949**

12" Single: Released Oct '87, on MCA, by MCA Records. Catalogue no: **MCAX 949**
12" Single: Released Mar '85, on MCA, by MCA Records. Deleted '88. Catalogue no: **MCAT 949**

FLETCH THEME
Tracks: / Fletch theme.
7" Single: Released Aug '85, on MCA, by MCA Records. Deleted '88. Catalogue no: **MCA 991**

'TOP GUN' ANTHEM
Tracks: / Memories / 'Top Gun' anthem.
7" Single: on CBS, by CBS Records. Deleted 10 Jul '89. Catalogue no: **650 270-0**
7" Single: Released Nov '86, on CBS, by CBS Records. Catalogue no: **650 270-7**

Faltskog, Agnetha

Biographical details: This swedish singer was just turning 18 when she became a recording star in her native country. The record that took her to the top of the Swedish charts was the self-penned *I was so in love*, released in 1968. The success of this song and of her two follow-up hits, *Without you* and *If tears were gold*, meant that, by the end of the Sixties, she was one of Sweden's leading artists. She was also beginning to get very friendly with a singer, musician and songwriter called Bjorn Ulvaeus. The couple married in 1971, an event which helped to sow the seeds of Abba. In early 1979, in the midst of Abba's stunning era of being one of the all-time most successful showbusiness phenomena, Anna (as she was often called) and Bjorn announced their divorce. When the quartet ground to an unofficial halt in late 1982, Faltskog set about resuming a solo career. Using Mike Chapman, one of the top international producers of the Seventies, whe released the album *Wrap your arms around me* in June 1983. With its pleasant selection of sophisticated pop material from a variety of writers, and its predictably polished performances, the LP was a moderate but not spectacular success. It's biggest single in Britain was *The heat is on*, which could only climb to No.36; in the States, only the punchy Russ Ballard-penned *Can't shake loose* could crack the Top 40. Thereafter, Agnetha took a long break from the public eye. The public had to manage without that emotional but controlled voice and those heavenly blonde looks. (Bob MacDonald, 16th August 1985).

CAN'T SHAKE LOOSE
Tracks: / Can't shake loose.
7" Pic: Released Oct '83, on Epic, by CBS Records. Deleted '88. Catalogue no: **WA 3812**
7" Single: Released Oct '83, on Epic, by CBS Records. Deleted '88. Catalogue no: **A 3812**

HEAT IS ON
Tracks: / Heat is on.
7" Pic: Released May '83, on Epic, by CBS Records. Catalogue no: **WA 3436**
7" Single: Released May '83, on Epic, by CBS Records. Catalogue no: **A 3436**

I WASN'T THE ONE (WHO SAID GOODBYE)
Tracks: / If I wasn't the one (who said goodbye) / If you need somebody tonight.
7" Single: Released May '88, on WEA, by WEA Records. Catalogue no: **YZ 177**
12" Single: Released May '88, on WEA, by WEA Records. Catalogue no: **YZ 177T**

LAST TIME, THE
Tracks: / Last time, The / Are you gonna throw it all away.
7" Single: Released Jan '88, on WEA, by WEA Records. Catalogue no: **YZ 170**
12" Single: Released Jan '88, on WEA, by WEA Records. Catalogue no: **YZ 170T**

LET IT SHINE
Tracks: / Let it shine / Maybe it was magic.
12" Single: Released Jul '88, on WEA, by WEA Records. Catalogue no: **YZ 300T**
7" Single: Released Jul '88, on WEA, by WEA Records. Catalogue no: **YZ 300**

WAY YOU ARE, THE
Tracks: / Way you are, The / Fly like an eagle.
7" Single: Released Nov '86, on Sonet, by Sonet Records. Catalogue no: **SON 2317**

WRAP YOUR ARMS AROUND ME (SINGLE)
Tracks: / Wrap your arms around me / Take good care of your children.
7" Single: Released Jul '83, on Epic, by CBS Records. Deleted '88. Catalogue no: **A 3622**
12" Single: Released Jul '83, on Epic, by CBS Records. Deleted '88. Catalogue no: **TA 3622**

Fame, Georgie

Biographical details: This British singer, keyboards player and songwriter was born Clive Powell in Lancashire. In 1959, at the age of 16, he moved to London and was spotted by Larry Parnes, a showbusiness entrepreneur who was currently enjoying success with Billy Fury and Marty Wilde. Having re-christened those two stars, Parnes came up with a similarly eye-catching and ridiculous stage name for young Clive - he became Georgie Fame. However, the teenage pianist did not live up to his new surname for several years. After a spell in Fury's backing group, the Blue Flames, Georgie broke away from Fury and took the Blue Flames with him. That was in late 1961. Early in the following year, Georgie Fame & The Blue Flames secured a residency at London's Flamingo Club in Soho. They gradually built up a cult following in that increasingly important musical haunt, thanks to the group's electic blend of various blues, jazz and Carribbean styles, and thanks also to the burgeoning popularity of the general London rhythm-and-blues scene. Georgie's first taste of chart success occurred in late 1964, when an aptly titled LP *Fame at last* entered the UK Top 20. Then, in January '65, came the smash success of the first hit single - *Yeh yeh* surged unexpectedly to the UK No.1 position. With Fames's vocals heavily influenced by US R&B singer Mose Allison, there were further British hits in store for Fame and the Flames. After achieving smaller successes plus a second No.1 with 1966's Fame-penned *Get away*, Georgie disbanded the Blue Flames and opted for a big band sound. This yielded his third UK No.1 and only US Top Tener in the shape of *The ballad on Bonnie & Clyde*, a slice of watered down, middle-of-the-road jazz (1968). As the Sixties became the Seventies, Fame drifted out of the record charts and into the steadier, less exciting world of cabaret and television. A 1971 duet with fellow singer/keyboardist/ex-bluesman Alan Price brought forth a UK No.11 hit with the irritaing *Rosetta*, but the remainder of the Seventies saw George banished permanently from the charts and toying with TV commercials, radio jingles, Blue Flames revivals and further cabaret and club work. (Bob MacDonald, 16th August 1985)
Singer and keyboardist, born Clive Powell in 1943 in Leigh. He was renamed by impresario Larry Parnes on joining Billy Fury's backing group the Blue Flames, retaining both name and group when Fury quit rock'n'roll for ballads in 1962 (though Fury once fired Fame for refusing to stick to simple rock'n'roll piano). At London's Flamingo Club black USA servicemen were among the customers: 'GIs would come up and say, Hey man have you heard Mose Allison? Eddie Jefferson? Booker T? They even lent me their own records so I could hear it for myself.' Fame aquired a Hammond organ in 1962 and the influence of Jimmy Smith crept in. He had hit albums and a number one single *Yeh yeh* in 1964. He left the band in '66, sang with a big band, worked with strings and ballads on CBS, had a two year partnership in the late '60's with former Animal Alan Price as Fame and Price Together in TV and cabaret and on a hit record *Rosetta*; he worked on TV jingles, worked in Europe and re-formed the Flames in 1974; he tours with a Hoagy Carmichael song show *Stardust road*; he packed Ronnie Scott's for a week in 1986 and starred that year in *Swingin' on 10th Avenue*, a celebration of George Gershwin's music with the LSO at the Royal Albert Hall. 'Really what I've been doing is rehearsing for 25 years.' As a result he is never short of work. (Donald Clarke, April 1989)t.

BALLAD OF BONNIE & CLYDE
Tracks: / Ballad of Bonnie and Clyde.
7" Single: Released Dec '67, on CBS, by CBS Records. Deleted '70. Catalogue no: **CBS 3124**
7" Single: Released Sep '85, on Old Gold, by Old Gold Records. Catalogue no: **OG 9554**

BECAUSE I LOVE YOU
Tracks: / Because I love you.
7" Single: Released Mar '67, on CBS, by CBS Records. Deleted '70. Catalogue no: **CBS 202587**

DRIP DROP
Tracks: / Drip drop / One morning in may.
7" Single: Released Jul '81, on Bald Eagle, Deleted Jul '84. Catalogue no: **BE 181**

GET AWAY
Tracks: / Get away.
7" Single: Released Jun '66, on Columbia, by EMI Records. Deleted '69. Catalogue no: **DB 7946**

GIVE A LITTLE MORE
Tracks: / Give a little more / Give a little more (part 2).
7" Single: Released Aug '80, on Piccadilly, Deleted '83. Catalogue no: **7P 194**

HONG KONG BLUES
Tracks: / Hong kong blues / Old music master.
7" Single: Released Feb '82, on Bald Eagle, Deleted Feb '87. Catalogue no: **BEE 182**

HURRICANE
Tracks: / Huricane.
7" Single: Released Aug '82, on My Records, Deleted Aug '85. Catalogue no: **MY 001**

IN THE MEANTIME
Tracks: / In the meantime.
7" Single: Released Mar '65, on Columbia, by EMI Records. Deleted '68. Catalogue no: **DB 7494**

LIKE WE USED TO BE
Tracks: / Like we used to be.
7" Single: Released Jul '65, on Columbia, by EMI Records. Deleted '68. Catalogue no: **DB 7633**

PEACEFUL
Tracks: / Peaceful.
7" Single: Released Jul '69, on CBS, by CBS Records. Deleted '72. Catalogue no: **CBS 4295**

ROSETTA
Tracks: / Rosetta.
7" Single: Released Sep '85, on Old Gold, by Old Gold Records. Catalogue no: **OG 9554**
7" Single: Released Jul '84, on CBS, by CBS Records. Catalogue no: **A 4599**
7" Single: Released Apr '71, on CBS, by CBS Records. Deleted '74. Catalogue no: **CBS 7108**

SAMBA
Tracks: / Samba / Willow King.
12" Single: Released Oct '86, on Ensign, by Ensign Records. Catalogue no: **ENYX 605**
7" Single: Released Oct '86, on Ensign, by Ensign Records. Catalogue no: **ENY 605**

SEVENTH SON
Tracks: / Seventh son.
7" Single: Released Dec '69, on CBS, by CBS Records. Deleted '72. Catalogue no: **CBS 4659**

SITTING IN THE PARK
Tracks: / Sitting in the park.
7" Single: Released Dec '66, on Columbia, by EMI Records. Deleted '69. Catalogue no: **DB 8096**

SOMETHING
Tracks: / Something.
7" Single: Released Oct '65, on Columbia, by EMI Records. Deleted '68. Catalogue no: **DB 7727**

SUNNY
Tracks: / Sunny.
7" Single: Released Sep '66, on Columbia, by EMI Records. Deleted '69. Catalogue no: **DB 8015**

TRY MY WORLD
Tracks: / Try my world.
7" Single: Released Sep '67, on CBS, by CBS Records. Deleted '70. Catalogue no: **CBS 2945**

YEAH YEAH
Tracks: / Yeah yeah / Getaway.
7" Single: Released May '80, on RSO, by Polydor Ltd. Deleted May '83. Catalogue no: **RSO 58**

YEH YEH
Tracks: / Get away / Yeh yeh.
7" Single: Released Mar '86, on Old Gold, by Old Gold Records. Catalogue no: **OG 9588**
7" Single: Released Dec '64, on Columbia, by EMI Records. Deleted '67. Catalogue no: **DB 7428**

Famille

DANCER
Tracks: / Dancer.
12" Single: Released Nov '82, on Chequers, by Chequers Records. Deleted '87. Catalogue no: **CR 001**

LOST IN PARADISE
Tracks: / Lost in paradise / Your stuff.
7" Single: Released Feb '85, on BPOP, by BPOP Records. Deleted '86. Catalogue no: **BPOP 701**
12" Single: Released Feb '85, on BPOP, by BPOP Records. Deleted '86. Catalogue no: **BPOP T01**

Family

Biographical details: At the time of their greatest success, this British rock band comprised Roger Chapman, Poli Palmer, Rob Townsend, John Weider and Charlie Whitney. The three mainstays of the group were Chapman (the intense, gravel voiced singer) Townsend (on drums) and Whitney (on guitar), all of whom were with the combo from their 1967 formation until their 1973 termination. The fourth and fifth members were an ever-changing phenomenon - several 'name' players passed through the ranks, including Rick Grech (who left to join the Blind Faith supergroup), John Wetton (who latter found success with King Crimson, Uriah Heep, Roxy Music and Asia), Jim Cregan (who later played with Cockney Rebel and Rod Stewart) and Tony Ashton (formerly of Ashton, Gardner & Dyke). With Chapman and Whitney composing the bulk of the material, Family were a much talked about and very distinctive part of the British progressive rock scene of the late Sixties and early Seventies. They first reached the UK charts in 1968 with the album *Music in a dolls house*, and followed it with the acclaimed Top 10 LP *Family entertainment*. Then came the most successful Family line-up (listed at the top), which was responsible for two more UK Top 10 albums *A song for me* (1970) and *Anyway* (also 1970). Family managed to keep a shrewd eye on the British singles chart: between 1969 and '72, they chalked up one hit 45 per year - *No mule's fool, Strange band, In my own time* (a No.4 smash) and *Burlesque* all made the Top 30. But various problems, including hassles with US promoters and the vagaries of Chapman's idiosyncratic personality, prevented the band from cracking the American market. Realising that they could go no further, Family called it a day in October '73. Chapman and Whitney then formed Streetwalkers, a similar sounding bluesy rock group who enjoyed modest success in the mid-Seventies. (Bob MacDonald, 16th August 1985)
Progressive rock band evolved from a Leicester R&B band, renamed in 1966 by USA producer Kim Fowley, with whom they made demos. Changing lineup included vocalist Roger Chapman, guitarist John 'Charlie' Whitney, initially Rick Grech on bass; their first album *Music in a dolls house* in 1968 was an outstanding 'underground album of the year' of the year, with spooky production effects and Chapman's natural vibrato. John Wetton added vocal harmony to *Fearless* in 1971, perhaps their best album overall and the first to chart in the USA; the band split in 1973. Their inventiveness and enthusiasm combined with bad luck to keep them from the top. Chapman and Whitney formed Streetwalkers (again with a shifting cast) for five albums; Whitney left music and Chapman had success in Europe with a band called the Shortlist. (Donald Clarke, April 1989)).

BURLESQUE
Tracks: / Burlesque / My friend the sun.
7" Single: Released Sep '72, on Reprise, by WEA Records. Deleted '75. Catalogue no: **K 14196**
7" Single: Released Jan '82, on Rebecca, by Rebecca Records. Catalogue no: **BEC 577**

IN MY OWN TIME
Tracks: / In my own time.
7" Single: Released Jul '71, on Reprise, by WEA Records. Deleted '74. Catalogue no: **K 14090**

NO MULE'S FOOL
Tracks: / No mule's fool.
7" Single: Released Nov '69, on Reprise, by WEA Records. Deleted '72. Catalogue no: **RS 27001**

PEEL SESSIONS:FAMILY
CD 5": Released Nov '88, on Strange Fruit, by Strange Fruit Records. Catalogue no: **SFPSCD 061**
12" Single: Released Nov '88, on Strange Fruit, by Strange Fruit Records. Catalogue no: **SFPS 061**

SCREAM OF PASSION, THE
Tracks: / Scream of passion, The.
7" Single: Released Nov '85, on Warner Bros., by WEA Records. Catalogue no: **W 8953**

STRANGE BAND
Tracks: / Strange band.
7" Single: Released Aug '70, on Reprise, by WEA Records. Deleted '73. Catalogue no: **RS 27009**

Family Affair

UNDER THE SUN, MOON AND STARS
Tracks: / Under the sun, moon and stars / Return to Montego Bay.
7" Single: Released Nov '80, on Bellaphon, Deleted Nov '83. Catalogue no: **BPS 005**
12" Single: Released Nov '80, on Bellaphon, Deleted Nov '83. Catalogue no: **BPSL 005**

Family Brown

I'M GONNA GETCHA

Tracks: / I'm gonna getcha.
12" Single: Released Apr '84, on Buzz Int., Catalogue no: **VIBE 4T**

Family Cat

TOM VERLAINE
Tracks: / Tom Verlaine.
7" Single: Released Jul '89, on Bad Girl, Catalogue no: **BGRLT 001**
12" Single: Released Jul '89, on Bad Girl, Catalogue no: **12BGRLT 001**

Family Dogg

WAY OF LIFE
Tracks: / Way of life.
7" Single: Released May '69, on Bell, Deleted '72. Catalogue no: **BELL 1055**

Family Fodder

BIG DIG
Tracks: / Big dig.
7" Single: Released May '82, on Fresh, by Jetstar Records. Catalogue no: **FRESH 42**

CORAL
Tracks: / Coral.
7" Single: Released Nov '82, on Jungle, by Jungle Records. Catalogue no: **JUNG 4**

DEBBIE HARRY
Tracks: / Debbie Harry.
7" Single: Released Apr '81, on Fresh, by Jetstar Records. Catalogue no: **FRESH 15**

PLAYING GOLF
Tracks: / Playing golf.
7" Single: Released Apr '81, on Fresh, by Jetstar Records. Catalogue no: **FRESH 1**

SAVOIR-FAIRE
Tracks: / Savoir-faire.
7" Single: Released May '83, on Crammed Discs, by Crammed Discs. Deleted '88. Catalogue no: **CRAM 2457**
7" Single: Released Apr '81, on Fresh, by Jetstar Records. Catalogue no: **FRESH 22**

SCHIZOPHRENIA PARTY
Tracks: / Schizophrenia party / Schizophrenia party (part 2).
12" Single: Released Sep '81, on Fresh, by Jetstar Records. Catalogue no: **FRESH 37 12**

SUNDAY GIRLS
Tracks: / Sunday girls.
7" Single: Released Apr '81, on Fresh, by Jetstar Records. Catalogue no: **FRESH 9**

WARM
Tracks: / Warm.
7" Single: Released Apr '81, on Fresh, by Jetstar Records. Catalogue no: **FRESH 8**

Family love

DECISION
Tracks: / Decision.
12" Single: Released Feb '82, on Inner City, Catalogue no: **IC 113**

HOOKED ON YOU
Tracks: / Hooked on you.
12" Single: Released Jun '83, on Firehouse, Catalogue no: **FH 002**

RELUCTANT LOVER
Tracks: / Reluctant lover.
12" Single: Released Apr '85, on Rock'n'Groove, Catalogue no: **RNG 003**

Family Ness

FAMILY NESS: ELSPETH & ANGUS MEET THE NESSIES
Special: Released Aug '84, on Tempo, by Warwick Records. Catalogue no: **TTS 9842**
Special: Released Aug '84, on Tempo, by Warwick Records. Catalogue no: **TTS 9843**

YOU'LL NEVER FIND A NESSIE IN THE ZOO
Tracks: / You'll never find a Nessie in the zoo.
7" Single: Released Oct '84, on BBC, by BBC Records & Tapes. Deleted 31 Aug '88. Catalogue no: **RESL 155**

Family Reunion

AULD LANG SYNE
Tracks: / Auld lang syne.
7" Single: Released Dec '82, on Romantic, Catalogue no: **RR 003**

Famous Imposter

WOULD ANYTHING CHANGE
Tracks: / Would anything change.
12" Single: Released Jul '86, on Children Of The Revolution, by Revolver Records. Catalogue no: **COR 7**

Famous Names

HOLIDAY ROMANCE
Tracks: / Holiday romance / Talk it out.
7" Single: Released Jan '81, on Trident, Deleted Jan '84. Catalogue no: **TR 001**

Famous Potatoes

I LIKE CHICKEN PIE
Tracks: / I like chicken pie / Chicken reel stomp.
7" Single: Released Aug '84, on Waterfront, by Waterfront Music. Catalogue no: **WFS 8**

Fanatics

SURBURBAN LOVE SONGS
Tracks: / Surburban love songs.
12" Single: Released Mar '89, on Chapter 22, by Chapter 22 Records. Catalogue no: **12CHAP 38**

Fancy

CHINESE EYES
Tracks: / Chinese eyes.
7" Single: Released Jun '85, on Personal, by Personal Records. Catalogue no: **PERS 3902**
12" Single: Released Jun '85, on Personal, by Personal Records. Catalogue no: **12 PER 3902**

SLICE ME NICE
Tracks: / Slice me nice.
7" Single: Released Apr '87, on Greyhound, by Greyhound Records. Catalogue no: **GRY 10**

Fanny & Danny

SECOND HAND RAG
Tracks: / Seven quid a week / Daydreamers' rock & roll club.
7" Single: Released Jul '81, on Zilch, by Zilch Records. Deleted Jul '84. Catalogue no: **ZILCH 6**
7" Single: Released Jul '81, on Aggro, by Chantel Records. Catalogue no: **AG 2**

Fans

COME ON THE FOREST
Tracks: / Come on the forest.
7" Single: Released Jan '80, on Soccer, by Humber Records. Catalogue no: **SRSP 001**

GIVING ME THAT LOOK
Tracks: / Giving me that look.
7" Single: Released Jul '81, on Fried Egg, by Fried Egg Records. Deleted '87. Catalogue no: **EGG 3**

I'M A FAN NOT A MORON
Tracks: / Net fever / I'm a fan not a moron.
7" Single: Released Jan '86, on Persuasion, Catalogue no: **ST ED 1**

OLE OLE OLE The name of the game
Tracks: / Ole ole (the name of the game).
7" Single: Released Sep '87, on Extra, Catalogue no: **XTRA 1**
12" Single: Released Sep '87, on Extra, Catalogue no: **12XTRA 1**

TRUE
Tracks: / True / Death wish.
7" Single: Released Jan '81, on Albion, by Albion Records. Catalogue no: **ION 1004**

YOU DON'T LIVE HERE
Tracks: / You don't live here.
7" Single: Released Jul '81, on Fried Egg, by Fried Egg Records. Deleted '87. Catalogue no: **EGG 10**

Fantasia

EVERGREEN
Tracks: / Evergreen.
12" Single: Released Jan '84, on Passion, by Skratch Records. Catalogue no: **PASH 16(12)**

GO BACK TO THE START
Tracks: / Go back to the start.
7" Single: Released Jun '89, on Chrysalis, by Chrysalis Records. Catalogue no: **CHS 3343**
12" Single: Released Jun '89, on Chrysalis, by Chrysalis Records. Catalogue no: **CHS 123343**

TONIGHT'S THE PARTY
Tracks: / Tonight's the party / Emily's party.
7" Single: Released Oct '88, on Chrysalis, by Chrysalis Records. Catalogue no: **CHS 3300**
12" Single: Released Oct '88, on Chrysalis, by Chrysalis Records. Catalogue no: **CHS 123300**

Fantastic Four

B.Y.O.F. (BRING YOUR OWN FUNK)
Tracks: / B.Y.O.F. (Bring your own funk).
7" Single: Released Feb '79, on Atlantic, by WEA Records. Deleted '82. Catalogue no: **LV 14**

Fantastic Something

IF SHE DOESN'T SMILE (it'll rain)
Tracks: / If she doesn't smile.
7" Single: Released May '83, on Cherry Red, by Cherry Red Records. Deleted '87. Catalogue no: **CHERRY 61**

Fantastics

Biographical details: The obscurity and anonymity of this American all-male vocal group is such that one assumes that their name meant 'fantastic' in the sense of fanciful or not real, rather than in the sense of excellent or fabulous. Their only taste of chart success occurred in 1971, when they reached No.9 in the UK with the catchy *Something, something new*. The song was not a hit in America. This is explained by the fact that it came from the assorted writing and production talents of Roger Cook, Roger Greenaway and Tony Macaulay, three Britons who concentrated on providing ultra-commercial pop fodder for the UK market. The same crew proceeded to resurrect the career of a much more famous American male vocal group, The Drifters, and gave them a string of UK (but not US) hits during 1973-7 that were similar in style to *Something old something new*; so it is probable that the Fantastics record was the inspiration for the Drifters' Seventies success. What's more, the chorus of the single provided disc jockeys and radio stations with some handy material for jingles and commercials. (Bob MacDonald, 17th August 1985).

SOMETHING OLD, SOMETHING NEW (EP)
Tracks: / Something old, something new / I fell in love last night at the disco / What I did for love / All in love is fair.
7" EP: Released Jan '83, on Stagecoach, Catalogue no: **BANG 2**

SOMETHING OLD, SOMETHING NEW
7" Single: Released Nov '80, on Creole (Replay), by Creole Records. Deleted '83. Catalogue no: **CR 197**
7" Single: Released Mar '71, on Bell, Deleted '74. Catalogue no: **BELL 1141**

SOMETHING OLD, SOMETHING NEW (OLD GOLD)
7" Single: Released 24 Apr '89, on Old Gold, by Old Gold Records. Catalogue no: **OG 9876**

Fantastique

MAMA TOLD ME
Tracks: / Mama told me.
12" Single: Released Jun '84, on Carrere, Catalogue no: **CART 317**

Fantasy

I WANT WHAT I WANT
Tracks: / I want what I want.
12" Single: Released Sep '86, on Affair, Catalogue no: **TART 2**

Fantasy 10

BIG BANG, THE
Tracks: / Big bang, The.
7" Single: Released Jun '87, on Greyhound, by Greyhound Records. Catalogue no: **GRY 12**

Fantoms

FIVE FOOT TWO
Tracks: / Five foot two / Idle star.
7" Single: on Magnum Force, by Magnum Music Group. Catalogue no: **MFS 002**

HEARTS OF STONE
Tracks: / Hearts of stone.
7" Single: Released Apr '83, on Ear To Ear, by Oakwood Records. Catalogue no: **GRIN 1**

Far Corporation

FIRE AND WATER
Tracks: / Life on the inside / Fire and water.
7" Single: Released May '86, on Arista, by BMG Records (UK). Catalogue no: **ARIST 662**
12" Single: Released May '86, on Arista, by BMG Records (UK). Catalogue no: **ARIST 12662**

SEBASTAIN
Tracks: / Sebastain.
7" Single: Released Aug '87, on Arista, by BMG Records (UK). Catalogue no: **RIS 28**
12" Single: Released Aug '87, on Arista, by BMG Records (UK). Catalogue no: **RIST 28**

STAIRWAY TO HEAVEN
Tracks: / Stairway to heaven.
7" Single: Released Oct '85, on Arista, by BMG Records (UK). Catalogue no: **ARIST 639**
12" Single: Released Oct '85, on Arista, by BMG Records (UK). Deleted '87. Catalogue no: **ARIST 12639**

YOU ARE THE WOMAN
Tracks: / No one else will do / You are the woman.
7" Single: Released Feb '86, on Arista, by BMG Records (UK). Catalogue no: **ARIST 650**
12" Single: Released Feb '86, on Arista, by BMG Records (UK). Catalogue no: **ARIST 12650**

Faraway stars

DISHONEST
Tracks: / Dishonest.
7" Single: Released May '83, on Runaway, Deleted '85. Catalogue no: **RUN 501**

JEALOUS
Tracks: / Jealous / Dishonest.
7" Single: Released May '82, on Runaway, Deleted '85. Catalogue no: **RUN 501**

Fardon, Don

Biographical details: This British singer who originated from Coventry, started his career as a member of a local group called the Sorrows during the early Sixties. During the middle part of the decade, he fronted Don Fardon & The Soul Machine, a vibrant live combo who worked around the UK club circuit. Stepping out as a solo artist, Fardon reached the American Top 20 in 1968 with John D Loudermilk's song *Indian Reservations (lament of the Cherokee Reservation Indian)*. This bluesy pop single, which commemorated the 1791 saga of the Cherokee Indians who were forcibly removed from their Georgian homeland, was later picked up by the modern Indians of Salt Lake City for use in their civil rights campaign. The song's history is strange. Fardon failed to achieve a hit in his native Britain in 1968, but it surged to the UK No.3 position when it was re-issued in 1970. It was then recorded by an American group, the Raiders, who took it to the US No.1 slot in 1971. Apart from one smaller UK hit, *Indian Reservation* was Fardon's only real claim to fame on either side of the Atlantic. He moved onto the cabaret circuit and devoted his energies to touring around Europe. (Bob MacDonald, August 1985).

BELFAST BOY
Tracks: / Belfast boy.
7" Single: Released Apr '70, on Young Blood, by Young Blood Records. Deleted '73. Catalogue no: **YB 1010**

INDIAN RESERVATION
Tracks: / Indian reservation.
7" Single: Released Jul '82, on Old Gold, by Old Gold Records. Deleted Jul '88. Catalogue no: **OG 9034**
7" Single: Released Oct '70, on Young Blood, by Young Blood Records. Deleted '73. Catalogue no: **YB 1015**
7" Single: Released Aug '84, on Young Blood, by Young Blood Records. Catalogue no: **YB 0087**

Fardon, Lee

BEAT SINCERE
Tracks: / Straight to the heart / Beat sincere, The.
7" Single: Released May '86, on Chord, by Chord Records. Deleted '88. Catalogue no: **CHORDS 2**

GAMES PEOPLE PLAY (SINGLE 7")
Tracks: / Treason in the heart / Games people play.
7" Single: Released Dec '86, on Chord, by Chord Records. Deleted '88. Catalogue no: **CHORDS 4**

STORIES OF ADVENTURE (SINGLE)
Tracks: / Stories of adventure.
7" Single: Released Aug '81, on Aura Records, by Aura Records. Deleted '88. Catalogue no: **AUS 128**

TOGETHER IN THE HEAT
Tracks: / Together in the heat / Turn out the light.
7" Single: Released Jun '82, on Aura Records, by Aura Records. Deleted '88. Catalogue no: **AUS 132**

Farenji, Leo

FUTURE GENERATION
Tracks: / Future generation / Future generation (inst).
7" Single: Released Feb '88, on In Touch, by In Touch Records. Catalogue no: **RORY 718**
12" Single: Released Feb '88, on In Touch, by In Touch Records. Catalogue no: **RORY 18**

Farewell Party

FAREWELL PARTY
Tracks: / Farewell party.
7" Single: Released Dec '87, on Country House, by Scotdisc Records. Catalogue no: **BGC 7S 446**

Farida Inernational

SECURITY (BITAKHON)
Tracks: / Security.
12" Single: Released Feb '89, on SSR, Catalogue no: **12SSR 93**

Farley 'Jackmaster' Funk

AS ALWAYS

Tracks: / As always / As always (version).
12" Single: Released Oct '88, on Champion, by Champion Records. Catalogue no: **CHAMP 12 90**
7" Single: Released Oct '88, on Champion, by Champion Records. Catalogue no: **CHAMP 90**

FREE AT LAST
Tracks: / Free at last / Free at last (version).
7" Single: Released Sep '89, on Champion, by Champion Records. Catalogue no: **CHAMP 217**
12" Single: Released Sep '89, on Champion, by Champion Records. Catalogue no: **CHAMP 12217**
CD 5": Released Sep '89, on Champion, by Champion Records. Catalogue no: **CHAMPCD 217**

LOVE CAN'T TURN AROUND
Tracks: / Love can't turn around / Love can't turn around (dub).
12" Single: Released Aug '86, on London Records, by London Records. Catalogue no: **LONX 105**
7" Single: Released Aug '86, on London Records, by London Records. Catalogue no: **LON 105**

THINK
Tracks: / Think / Think (version).
7" Single: Released Jul '89, on Champion, by Champion Records. Deleted Aug '89. Catalogue no: **CHAMP 210**
12" Single: Released Jul '89, on Champion, by Champion Records. Deleted Aug '89. Catalogue no: **CHAMP 12210**

Farlowe, Chris

Biographical details: Born John Henry Deighton in London, Farlowe was just 16 when, in 1957, he won the All-England Skiffle Championship as frontman of the John Henry Skiffle Group. But the combo never made any records and when the Lonnie Donegan-led skiffle craze died down the rechristened Chris Farlowe formed the Thunderbirds in 1962. With his harsh, gutsy voice, plus the group's authentic rhythm-and-blues sound, they quickly gained a residency at London's Flamingo Club, in Soho, and won substantial popularity on the city's burgeoning R & B scene. The Thunderbirds remained Farlowe's live band throughout most of the 60's, though they often failed to accompany him into the studio, where session musicians were generally used. The group had an ever-changing and erratic existence but were notable in featuring, at one time or another, such future big-name players as Albert Lee, Dave Greenslade and Carl Palmer. After enhancing his cult following with two 1965 singles, the controversial Buzz With The Fuzz and Stormy Monday Blues, Farlowe cracked the UK charts for the first time in early '66 when *Think*, written by Mick Jagger and Keith Richard, reached No 37. Being friendly with the Rolling Stones soon brought a bigger reward for Farlowe: *Out Of Time*, a song from the Stones' *Aftermath* album, reached the British No 1 position in July '66. Farlowe's version was given a dramatic production by Jagger himself, who helped to mould the single into a rock classic. Over the following 18 months Farlowe placed four more singles on the UK Top Fifty but all fell short of the Top Thirty. Partly because he was always most at home on the London club circuit, Farlowe was never quite able to fulfil his promise as a recording star and *Out Of Time* remained his only major hit. Its 1975 reisuue prompted him to form a new band -- including Albert Lee -- and resume touring. During the early 70's he had divided his time between Colloseum, for whom he performed vocals on two successful LPs, *Atomic Rooster* and his own London shop selling military memorabilia. (Bob MacDonald, August 1985.)
Singer and guitarist born in 1940 in Essex. He played in a skiffle group which won an all England championship in 1957 and led semi-pro Thunderbirds beat group in the early '60's; after other activities he had hits on Andrew Loog Oldham's Immediate label in 1966-67 including *Out of time*, written by the Rolling Stones; he sang well and grittily, but the club scene that fostered Thunderbirds had gone by the late '60's; he had a WWII memorabilia stall. He sang with Colosseum, then Atomic Rooster, then was a shopkeeper in Islington. *Out of time* charted again on reissue on 1975; he formed a new band including ex-Thunderbird guitarist Albert Lee, then left music again. Having sold his shop, gone to the USA and returned in 1983, he spent 30 days in jail, refusing to pay rates on the shop in protest against left-wing policies of the Republic of Islington, and made a brand new album in the mid '80's. (Donald Clarke, April 1989).

HANDBAGS AND GLADRAGS
Tracks: / Handbags and gladrags.
7" Single: Released Dec '67, on Immediate, Deleted '69. Catalogue no: **IM 065**

LET THE HEARTACHES BEGIN
Tracks: / Let the heartaches begin.
7" Single: Released Oct '82, on CBS, by CBS Records. Catalogue no: **A 2894**

LIVING AIN'T EASY WITHOUT YOU
Tracks: / Living ain't easy without you.
7" Single: Released Oct '83, on Taurus, Catalogue no: **BN 451**

MOANIN'
Tracks: / Moanin'.
7" Single: Released Jun '67, on Immediate, Deleted '69. Catalogue no: **IM 056**

MY WAY OF GIVING
Tracks: / My way of giving.
7" Single: Released Feb '67, on Immediate, Deleted '69. Catalogue no: **IM 041**

OUT OF TIME (SINGLE)
Tracks: / Out of time / My way of giving.
7" Single: Released Sep '75, on Immediate, Deleted '78. Catalogue no: **IMS 101**
7" Single: Released Oct '82, on Immediate, Catalogue no: **IMS 201**
7" Single: Released Jun '66, on Immediate, Deleted '69. Catalogue no: **IM 035**
7" Single: Released Jan '85, on Old Gold, by Old Gold Records. Catalogue no: **OG 9468**
7" Single: Released Jun '80, on Virgin, by Virgin Records. Catalogue no: **SV 102**

RIDE ON BABY
Tracks: / Ride on baby.
7" Single: Released Oct '66, on Immediate, Deleted '69. Catalogue no: **IM 038**

THINK
Tracks: / Think.
7" Single: Released Jan '66, on Immediate, Deleted '69. Catalogue no: **IM 023**

Farm

BODY AND SOUL
Tracks: / Body and soul / Colonels and heroes.
7" Single: Released Jun '89, on foresight, Catalogue no: **FR 2301**

HEARTS AND MINDS
Tracks: / Hearts and minds.
12" Single: Released Nov '84, on Skysaw, by Skysaw Records. Catalogue no: **END 1**

SOME PEOPLE
Tracks: / Standing together / Sign of the times (Extra track on 12" version only) / Moroccan (Extra track on 12" version only).
7" Single: Released Sep '86, on Blaze, Catalogue no: **BLAZE 13**
12" Single: Released Sep '86, on Blaze, Catalogue no: **BLAZE 13 T**

STEPS OF EMOTION
Tracks: / Steps of emotion / Memories.
7" Single: Released Nov '85, on Admiralty, Catalogue no: **PRA 1**
12" Single: Released Nov '85, on Admiralty, Catalogue no: **PRAT 1**

Farm Life

SUSIE'S PARTY
Tracks: / Susie's party.
7" Single: Released Feb '82, on Dining Out, by Dining Out Records. Catalogue no: **TUX 19**

Farmer's Boys

Biographical details: This British pop quartet first attracted attention in 1982 with independently-released singles *I Think We Need Help* and the quirky *Whatever Is He Like?* After signing with EMI they made their first appearances on the British charts in 1983 with *Muck It Out* and *For You*, and their debut album, *Get Out And Walk*, was issued in October of that year. In keeping with their name, the group had a slightly countrified sound and released strong pop music which was bright and melodic. But although they were frequent visitors to the UK Top Seventy-Five singles chart they never managed to climb into the Top Forty. Even a carefully-timed summer remake of Cliff Richard's rural hit *In The Country* could only crawl to No 44. The problem lay in the fact that their style was not sufficiently fashionable and that their music, though sounding pleasant on the radio, was not sufficiently striking to inspire large sales. Realising that they were unlikely to jump the final hurdle to major success, the Farmer's Boys split up in the summer of 1985. (Bob MacDonald, August 1985.).

FOR YOU
Tracks: / For you.
7" Single: Released Jul '83, on EMI, by EMI Records. Deleted '86. Catalogue no: **EMI 5401**

I THINK WE NEED HELP
Tracks: / I think we need help / Squit on waap.
7" Single: Released Apr '82, on Waap, Catalogue no: **WAAP 3**

IN THE COUNTRY
Tracks: / In the country.
7" Pic: Released Aug '84, on EMI, by EMI Records. Catalogue no: **FABP 2**
7" Single: Released Aug '84, on EMI, by EMI Records. Deleted '87. Catalogue no: **FAB 2**
12" Single: Released Aug '84, on EMI, by EMI Records. Deleted '87. Catalogue no: **12 FAB 2**

MORE THAN A DREAM
Tracks: / More than a dream / Country line.
7" Single: Released Dec '82, on Backs, by Backs Recording Co.. Deleted '85. Catalogue no: **NCH 003**
7" Single: Released Jan '83, on EMI, by EMI Records. Catalogue no: **EMI 5367**

MUCK IT OUT (Demo)
Tracks: / Muck it out.
7" Set: Released Jul '83, on EMI, by EMI Records. Catalogue no: **EMID 5401**
7" Pic: Released Jun '83, on EMI, by EMI Records. Catalogue no: **EMIP 5380**

PHEW WOW
Tracks: / Phew wow.
7" Single: Released Oct '84, on EMI, by EMI Records. Catalogue no: **FAB 3**
12" Single: Released Oct '84, on EMI, by EMI Records. Deleted '86. Catalogue no: **12 FAB 3**

WHATEVER IS HE LIKE
Tracks: / Whatever is he like.
7" Single: Released Jul '82, on Backs, by Backs Recording Co.. Catalogue no: **NCH 001**

Farnham, John

AGE OF REASON EXTENDED (SINGLE)
Tracks: / Age of reason.
12" Single: Released '88, on RCA, by BMG Records (UK). Deleted Aug '89. Catalogue no: **PT 42168**

AGE OF REASON (SINGLE)
Tracks: / Age of reason.
CD 5": Released Jun '89, on Wheatley, by BMG Records (UK). Deleted Jul '89. Catalogue no: **PD 42168**

PRESSURE DOWN
Tracks: / Let me out / Pressure down.
7" Single: Released Aug '87, on Wheatley, by BMG Records (UK). Catalogue no: **RCA 5000**
12" Single: Released Aug '87, on Wheatley, by BMG Records (UK). Catalogue no: **RCAT 5000**

TWO STRONG HEARTS
Tracks: / Two strong hearts / It's a long way to the top if you wanna....
CD 5": Released Feb '89, on RCA, by BMG Records (UK). Deleted Jul '89. Catalogue no: **PD 42304**
7" Single: Released Feb '89, on RCA, by BMG Records (UK). Deleted Aug '89. Catalogue no: **PB 42303**
12" Single: Released Feb '89, on RCA, by BMG Records (UK). Deleted Aug '89. Catalogue no: **PT 42304**

YOU'RE THE VOICE
Tracks: / You're the voice / Going going gone / Help (live version) / Reasons* (*Extra track on cassette).
Cassingle: Released Jun '87, on RCA, by BMG Records (UK). Catalogue no: **PB 41093C**
7" Single: Released Feb '87, on RCA, by BMG Records (UK). Catalogue no: **PB 41093**
12" Single: Released Feb '87, on RCA, by BMG Records (UK). Deleted May '89. Catalogue no: **PT 41094**

Farrar, John

CAN'T HOLD BACK
Tracks: / Can't hold back / It'll be me babe.
7" Single: Released Jan '81, on CBS, by CBS Records. Deleted Jan '84. Catalogue no: **CBS 9420**

Farrell, Bobby

HAPPY SONG
Tracks: / Happy song.
7" Single: Released Jan '85, on Carrere, Catalogue no: **CAR 354**
12" Single: Released Jan '85, on Carrere, Catalogue no: **CART 354**

Farrell, Joe

NIGHT DANCING
Tracks: / Night dancing.
7" Single: Released Dec '78, on Atlantic, by WEA Records. Deleted '81. Catalogue no: **LV 2**

Farrell, John

RIDING ON AN ANGELS WING
Tracks: / Riding on an angels wing / Dark ruler / Net.
7" Single: Released Dec '83, on Pressco-lor, Deleted '87. Catalogue no: **ERN 1**

Farrow, Gene

Biographical details: British singer Farrow had two small successes on the UK singles chart in 1978. They were aimed squarely at the dancefloor at a time when the disco boom made extraordinary inroads into the pop listings despite, in Farrow's case, a dearth of radio play. The first of the two discs was *Move Your Body*, which crept into the Top Forty, but the resulting appearance on BBC TV's Top of the Pops failed to lift it any higher, and *Don't Stop Now* stopped at No 71. Both singles were credited to Gene Farrow & The G.F. Band. Subsequent Farrow efforts fell on deaf ears and unwilling feet, although he kept trying into the early 80's. (Bob MacDonald, August 1985.).

DON'T STOP NOW
Tracks: / Don't stop now.
7" Single: Released Aug '78, on Magnet, by WEA Records. Deleted '81. Catalogue no: **MAG 125**

MOVE YOUR BODY (SINGLE)
Tracks: / Move your body.
7" Single: Released Jan '78, on Magnet, by WEA Records. Catalogue no: **MAG 109**

UNIQUE MYSTIQUE
Tracks: / Unique mystique / I go to pieces.
7" Single: Released Jan '82, on Rialto (1), by Rialto Records. Catalogue no: **RIA 4**
12" Single: Released Nov '81, on Rialto (1), by Rialto Records. Catalogue no: **12 RIA 4**

Fascinating Aida

GET KNOTTED
Tracks: / Get knotted.
7" Single: Released Jan '85, on BBC, by BBC Records & Tapes. Deleted '87. Catalogue no: **RESL 161**

LIEDER
Tracks: / Lieder.
7" Single: Released Oct '87, on First Night, by First Night Records. Catalogue no: **SCORE 12**

Fascination

DRIVE, THE
Tracks: / Drive, The.
12" Single: Released Oct '87, on Play House (USA), Catalogue no: **PHR 422**

OUT TO GET YOU
Tracks: / Out to get you.
7" Single: Released Mar '84, on Banana, Catalogue no: **FRUIT 2**
12" Single: Released Mar '84, on Banana, Catalogue no: **FRUIT 2T**

SHINE MY LOVE
Tracks: / Shine my love.
12" Single: Released Dec '84, on Banana, Catalogue no: **FRUIT 13T**

Fascinations

GIRLS ARE OUT TO GET YOU
Tracks: / Girls are out to get you.
7" Single: Released Jul '71, on Mojo, Deleted '74. Catalogue no: **2092 004**

Fascinators

BLUE MOVIES
Tracks: / Blue movies / Monochrome moan.
7" Single: Released Jun '81, on Penthouse, by Penthouse Records. Deleted Jun '84. Catalogue no: **PENT 9**

I'M INTO SOMETHING GOOD
Tracks: / I'm into something good / Don't stop now.
7" Single: Released May '81, on Penthouse, by Penthouse Records. Deleted May '84. Catalogue no: **PENT 6**

Fashanu, Justin

DO IT COS' YOU LIKE IT
Tracks: / Do it cos' you like it / Heaven on earth.
7" Single: Released Dec '81, on Rondelet Music, by Rondelet Music & Records. Catalogue no: **ROUND 14**
12" Single: Released Dec '81, on Rondelet Music, by Rondelet Music & Records. Catalogue no: **12 ROUND 14**

Fashion

Biographical details: The most successful line-up of this British band has been Dik Davis, Dee Hrris, John Mulligan and Marlon Recchi. Fashion were formed in Birmingham in 1978 and comprised Davis, Mulligan and a guitarist/vocalist known as Luke. Towards the end of that year, they released their debut single *Steady Eddie steady*, and 1979 saw the release of the group's first LP *Product perfect*. At this time, they were an ostentatious punk band;

but following the departure of Luke, who returned to his previous role as a performer on the French folk circuit, Fashion entered a period of ever-changing line-ups and styles. A stability of sorts was established in 1982, when the band began to achieve UK chart success. The Davis/Harris/Milligan/Recchi combination shot to the No.10 position with the album *Fabrique* - this LP saw them developing their danceable, jazzy, electro-funk sound. It contained two minor hit singles, *Streetplayer (Mechanik)* (their best known track) and *Love shadow*. Fashion's next minor UK hit single occurred in 1984, when *Eye talk* reached the No.69 position. By this time, Harris had been replaced by Troy Tate (ex-Teardrop Explodes), who had in turn been replaced by vocalist Alan Darby. The band seemed unable to translate their cult following into major chart success, largely because Fashion were a part-time project and the various musicians all had assorted outside commitments. (Bob MacDonald, 18th August 1985).

DREAMING
Tracks: / Dreaming / White line fever.
7" Single: Released Apr '84, on Epic, by CBS Records. Catalogue no: **A 4327**
12" Single: Released Apr '84, on Epic, by CBS Records. Catalogue no: **TA 4327**

I TALK
Tracks: / I talk.
12" Single: Released Jan '84, on Epic, by CBS Records. Catalogue no: **TA 4106**
7" Single: Released Jan '84, on Epic, by CBS Records. Catalogue no: **A 4106**

LOVE SHADOW
Tracks: / Love shadow / Let's play dirty / Let's play dirty centrefold.
7" Single: Released Aug '82, on Arista, by BMG Records (UK). Deleted '85. Catalogue no: **ARIST 483**
12" Single: Released Aug '82, on Arista, by BMG Records (UK). Deleted '86. Catalogue no: **ARIST 12483**

MOVE ON
Tracks: / Move on / Move on (audio extra) (Only on 12" version.).
7" Single: Released '83, on Arista, by BMG Records (UK). Deleted '86. Catalogue no: **ARIST 440**
12" Single: Released '83, on Arista, by BMG Records (UK). Deleted '86. Catalogue no: **ARIST 12440**

SOMETHING IN YOUR PICTURE
Tracks: / Something in your picture / Motor drive (Only on 12" version.) / Smokey dialogue (Only on 12" version.).
7" Single: Released '83, on Arista, by BMG Records (UK). Deleted '86. Catalogue no: **ARIST 472**
12" Single: Released '83, on Arista, by BMG Records (UK). Deleted '86. Catalogue no: **ARIST 12472**

STREETPLAYER (MECHANIK)
Tracks: / Streetplayer (mechanik).
7" Single: Released Apr '82, on Arista, by BMG Records (UK). Deleted '85. Catalogue no: **ARIST 456**

YOU IN THE NIGHT
Tracks: / You in the night.
7" Single: Released Aug '84, on Epic, by CBS Records. Catalogue no: **DA 4502**
7" Single: Released Jun '84, on De Stijl, by CBS Records. Catalogue no: **A 4502**
12" Single: Released Jun '84, on De Stijl, by CBS Records. Catalogue no: **TA 4502**

Fashion, Chris

EETEE WE LOVE YOU
Tracks: / Eetee we love you.
7" Single: Released Dec '82, on State, by State Records. Catalogue no: **STAT 117**

Fassbender - Russell

STAY
Tracks: / Stay / Comment ca va.
7" Single: Released May '81, on CBS, by CBS Records. Deleted May '84. Catalogue no: **A 1111**

Fassbender, Susan

MERRY GO ROUND
Tracks: / Merry go round / Reasons.
7" Single: Released Sep '81, on CBS, by CBS Records. Deleted Sep '84. Catalogue no: **A 1619**

TWILIGHT CAFE
Tracks: / Twilight cafe.
7" Single: Released Jan '81, on CBS, by CBS Records. Deleted '84. Catalogue no: **CBS 9468**

Fast Eddie

ACID THUNDER
Tracks: / Acid thunder.
7" Single: Released Sep '88, on DJ International, by Westside Records. Catalogue no: **DJ 961**

CAN U STILL DANCE
Tracks: / Can U still dance.
7" Single: Released Oct '88, on DJ International, by Westside Records. Catalogue no: **DJ 958**

GIT ON UP
Tracks: / Git on up / Git on up (Rocky Jones mix) / Git on up (LP mix).
CD 5": Released Oct '89, on DJ, Catalogue no: **655 366 2**
7" Single: Released Oct '89, on DJ, Catalogue no: **655 366 7**
12" Single: Released Oct '89, on DJ, Catalogue no: **655 366 6**

HIP HOUSE
Tracks: / Hip house / Hip house (nightmare mix) (Only on 12" version.) / Hip house (deep mix) (Only on 12" version.) / Hip house (LP version) (Only on 12" version.) / I can dance.
CD 5": Released Jan '89, on DJ International, by Westside Records. Catalogue no: **CCDJIN 5**
7" Single: Released Dec '88, on DJ International, by Westside Records. Catalogue no: **DJIN 5**
12" Single: Released Dec '88, on DJ International, by Westside Records. Catalogue no: **DJINT 5**

HIP HOUSE (REMIX)
Tracks: / Hip house (remix).
12" Single: Released 20 Mar '89, on DJ International, by Westside Records. Catalogue no: **DJINX 5**

Fast Radio

UNDER MY THUMB
Tracks: / Under my thumb.
7" Single: Released Apr '83, on Excaliber, by Red Bus Records. Deleted '88. Catalogue no: **EXC 530**

Fastbacks

IN THE WINTER
Tracks: / In the winter.
7" Single: Released Oct '88, on Subway, by Subway Records. Catalogue no: **SUBWAY 024**

WRONG WRONG WRONG
Tracks: / Wrong wrong wrong.
7" Single: Released Jun '89, on Subway, by Subway Records. Catalogue no: **SUBWAY 26**

Faster Pussycat

DON'T CHANGE THAT SONG
Tracks: / Don't change that song / Cat house.
7" Single: Released Sep '87, on Elektra, by Elektra Records (UK). Catalogue no: **TKR 22**
7" Single: Released Sep '87, on Elektra, by Elektra Records (UK). Deleted Jul '88. Catalogue no: **EKR 62**
12" Single: Released Sep '87, on Elektra, by Elektra Records (UK). Catalogue no: **EKR 62 T**

Fastway

Biographical details: This British rock band consists of 'Fast' Eddie Clarke, Dave King, Jerry Shirley and Pete Way. Fastway were formed in 1982 by 'Fast' Eddie and Pete Way, hence the name. Eddie had spent the previous six years in Motorhead, but quit the notorious headbangers in the summer of '82 on account of his dissatisfaction with the outside activities of the band's most famous member, Lemmy. Pete had been a founder member of UFO in 1969, and had stuck with them through thick and thin for thirteen years. Jerry had experienced almost as long a stint with Humble Pie. By contrast, vocalist Dave King was a novice. Fastway's stated aim was to capture the early excitement of Led Zeppelin so their music was bound to be derivative. Their eponymous debut album did indeed sound remarkably similar to their mentors, but this did not prevent it from being readily accepted by heavy metal fans. However, in view of Fastway's apparent 'supergroup' status, it was surprising that the band's only taste of UK singles chart success was *Easy livin'*, which crept to No.74 in April 1983. The second Fastway album *All fired up* continued in similar vein, although it did not set the world aflame. (Bob MacDonald, 18th August 1985).

ALL FIRED UP
Tracks: / All fired up / Hurtin' me.
7" Single: Released Jun '84, on CBS, by CBS Records. Catalogue no: **A 4503**
12" Single: Released Jun '84, on CBS, by CBS Records. Catalogue no: **TA 4503**

EASY LIVIN
Tracks: / Easy living.
7" Single: Released Mar '83, on CBS, by CBS Records. Catalogue no: **A 3196**
12" Single: Released Mar '83, on CBS, by CBS Records. Catalogue no: **A 13 3196**

FINE LINE, A
Tracks: / Fine line / Change of heart.
7" Single: Released 20 Feb '88, on GWR, by GWR Records. Catalogue no: **GWR 8**

STRANGER, THE
Tracks: / Stranger, the / Hurtin' me.
7" Single: Released May '84, on CBS, by CBS Records. Catalogue no: **A 4370**

WE BECOME ONE
Tracks: / We become one.
7" Single: Released Jun '83, on CBS, by CBS Records. Catalogue no: **A 3480**
12" Single: Released Jun '83, on CBS, by CBS Records. Catalogue no: **TA 3480**

WORLD WAITS FOR YOU, THE (SINGLE)
Tracks: / World waits for you, The.
7" Single: Released Jan '86, on CBS, by CBS Records. Catalogue no: **A 6804**
12" Single: Released Jan '86, on CBS, by CBS Records. Catalogue no: **TA 6804**

Fat Boys

ARE YOU READY FOR FREDDY?
Tracks: / Are you ready for Freddy?.
CD 5": Released Apr '89, on Urban, by Polydor Ltd. Catalogue no: **887 894-2**
7" Single: Released Apr '89, on Urban, by Polydor Ltd. Deleted Oct '89. Catalogue no: **URB 35**
12" Single: Released Apr '89, on Urban, by Polydor Ltd. Deleted Oct '89. Catalogue no: **URBX 35**

FALLING IN LOVE
Tracks: / Falling in love / Protect yourself / My nuts medley.
Note: 'My nuts medley' on 12" version only.

7" Single: Released Oct '87, on Urban, by Polydor Ltd. Catalogue no: **URB 10**
12" Single: Released Oct '87, on Urban, by Polydor Ltd. Catalogue no: **URBX 10**

JAIL HOUSE RAP
Tracks: / Stick em / Jailhouse rap.
7" Single: Released Apr '85, on WEA, by WEA Records. Catalogue no: **U 9123**
12" Single: Released Apr '85, on WEA, by WEA Records. Catalogue no: **U 9123 T**

LOUIE LOUIE
Tracks: / Louie Louie / All day lover / Louie Louie (CD version) (Only on CD single.) / Twist, The (Only on CD single.).
CD 5": Released Oct '88, on Urban, by Polydor Ltd. Catalogue no: **URBCD 26**
7" Single: Released Oct '88, on Urban, by Polydor Ltd. Catalogue no: **URB 26**
12" Single: Released Oct '88, on Urban, by Polydor Ltd. Catalogue no: **URBX 26**

SEX MACHINE
Tracks: / Beatbox is rockin' / Sex machine.
7" Single: Released May '86, on Atlantic, by WEA Records. Catalogue no: **A 8674**
12" Single: Released May '86, on Atlantic, by WEA Records. Deleted Jan '88. Catalogue no: **U 8674 T**

TWIST, THE
Tracks: / Twist, The (yo twist) / Twist, The (buffapella) (Available on 7" single only.) / Twist, The (twist so def version) / Yo twist (7" version) / Twist, The (yell for more) (Available on 12" single only.) / Wipe out (Available on CD single only.) / Falling in love.
Note: The brand new single from the Fat Boys is a rap version of the Chubby Checker classic "The Twist" featuring Chubby himself on lead vocals.
CD 5": Released Jun '88, on Urban, by Polydor Ltd. Deleted Oct '89. Catalogue no: **URCD 20**
7" Single: Released Jun '88, on Urban, by Polydor Ltd. Deleted 30 May '89. Catalogue no: **URB 20**
12" Single: Released Jun '88, on Urban, by Polydor Ltd. Deleted 30 May '89. Catalogue no: **URBX 20**

WIPEOUT (Fat Boys &The Beach Boys)
Tracks: / Wipe out / Crushin' / Wipe out (wave I version) (On 12" and cassette single.) / Crushin' (Marley Marlmix) (12" only) / Wipe out (wave II version) (Only on 12" single.) / Rock ruling.
Cassingle: Released Aug '87, on Urban, by Polydor Ltd. Deleted 30 May '89. Catalogue no: **URBC 5**
7" Single: Released Aug '87, on Urban, by Polydor Ltd. Catalogue no: **URB 5**
12" Single: Released Aug '87, on Urban, by Polydor Ltd. Deleted 30 May '89. Catalogue no: **URBX 5**

Fat & Frantic

LAST NIGHT MY WIFE HOOVERED MY HEAD
Tracks: / Last night my wife hoovered my head / It's you.
CD 5": Released Aug '89, on Total/Icy, Catalogue no: **FATD 1**
7" Single: Released Aug '89, on Total/Icy, Catalogue no: **FATS 1**

Fat Lady Sings

ARCLIGHT
Tracks: / Arclight / Behind your back / Fear and favour (12" only).
7" Single: Released Sep '89, on Fourth Base, Catalogue no: **TFLS 3**
12" Single: Released Sep '89, on Fourth Base, Catalogue no: **12 TFLS 3**

BE STILL
Tracks: / Be still.
7" Single: Released 5 Mar '88, on Harbour Sound, Catalogue no: **HSS 1**

FEAR AND FAVOUR
Tracks: / Fear and favour.
7" Single: Released Dec '86, on Good Vibration, by Good Vibrations Records. Catalogue no: **FLS 1**

Fat Larry's Band

Biographical details: Led by the overweight Larry James, this all-male American funk band chalked up three minor UK hit singles in the late Seventies. *Center city* (1977), *Boogie down* (1979 under the billing of FLB) and *Looking for love tonight* (1979) were all products of the disco boom, and were all aimed at the punters' dancing feet rather than their ears. After several years' absence, and while remaining relatively unknown in their native country, Fat Larry's Band suddenly surged back to life with a one-off UK pop smash. *Zoom*, an archetypal pop celebration of being young and in love, zoomed to No.2 on the British charts in October 1982. It was an uncharacteristic track from Fat Larry's chart LP *Breakin' out*. Despite a 1983 attempt to create another *Zoom* with the single *Don't let it go to your head* Fat Larry's Band were quickly forgotten again. (Bob MacDonald, 18th August 1985).

ACT LIKE YOU KNOW
Tracks: / Act like you know.
7" Single: Released Apr '82, on Virgin, by Virgin Records. Deleted Apr '85. Catalogue no: **VS 491**
12" Single: Released Apr '82, on Virgin, by Virgin Records. Deleted Apr '85. Catalogue no: **VS 491 12**

BOOGIE TOWN
Tracks: / Boogie town.
7" Single: Released Mar '79, on Fantasy (1), by BMG Records (UK). Deleted Mar '82. Catalogue no: **FTC 168**

CENTER CITY
Tracks: / Center city.
7" Single: Released Jul '77, on W.M.O.T.(USA), by Virgin Records. Deleted '80. Catalogue no: **K 10951**

GOLDEN MOMENT
Tracks: / Golden moment / Video.
7" Single: Released Nov '82, on Virgin, by Virgin Records. Deleted Nov '85. Catalogue no: **VS 514**
12" Single: Released Nov '82, on Virgin, by Virgin Records. Deleted Nov '85. Catalogue no: **VS 51412**

HERE COMES THE SUN
Tracks: / Here comes the sun / Love alive.
7" Single: Released Jan '80, on Fantasy (1), by BMG Records (UK). Deleted Jan '83. Catalogue no: **FTC 185**
12" Single: Released Jan '80, on Fantasy (1), by BMG Records (UK). Deleted Jan '83. Catalogue no: **12FTC 185**

LOOKING FOR LOVE TONIGHT
Tracks: / Looking for love tonight.
7" Single: Released Aug '79, on W.M.O.T.(USA), by Virgin Records. Deleted '82. Catalogue no: **FTC 179**

NICE
Tracks: / Which one should I choose / Nice.
7" Single: Released May '86, on Omni (USA), by First String Records (USA). Catalogue no: **OMN 2**
12" Single: Released May '86, on Omni (USA), by First String Records (USA). Catalogue no: **12 OMN 2**

STAND UP
Tracks: / Party after midnight / Can't keep my hands to myself / Play with me / Stand up / You've waited too long / Dirty words / You gotta help yourself.
7" Single: Released Nov '80, on Fantasy (1), by BMG Records (UK). Deleted '85. Catalogue no: **F 9699**

ZOOM
Tracks: / Zoom / House party / Traffic stop.

pers (On 12" only).
7" Single: Released '82, on Virgin, by Virgin Records. Catalogue no: **VS 546**
12" Single: Released '82, on Virgin, by Virgin Records. Catalogue no: **VS 546-12**

ZOOM (CD SINGLE)
Tracks: / Zoom / Don't let it go to your head(remix) / Act like you know / Straight from the heart(remix).
CD 3": Released '88, on Virgin, by Virgin Records. Catalogue no: **CDT 31**

Fatal Attraction

ALL THE WORLD OVER
Tracks: / All the world over / Go ahead, The.
7" Single: Released Jun '88, on Kick Back, by Kick Back Records. Catalogue no: **KR 1**

Fatal Charm

CHRISTINE
Tracks: / Christine / Paris.
7" Single: Released Feb '81, on Fatal Charm, Deleted Feb '84. Catalogue no: **FATAL 1**

IMAGES OF FIRE
Tracks: / I'm sure not in tune with it / City of dreams (Extra track on 12" version only) / Images of fire.
7" Single: Released Aug '86, on Native (1), by Native Records. Catalogue no: **NTV 8**
12" Single: Released Aug '86, on Native (1), by Native Records. Catalogue no: **NTV 12008**

KING OF COMEDY
Tracks: / King of comedy.
7" Single: Released Apr '85, on Carrere, Catalogue no: **CAR 358**
12" Single: Released Apr '85, on Carrere, Catalogue no: **CART 358**

LUCILLE
Tracks: / Lucille.
7" Single: Released Feb '87, on Native (1), by Native Records. Catalogue no: **NTV 20**
12" Single: Released Feb '87, on Native (1), by Native Records. Catalogue no: **NTV 12020**

SUMMER SPIES
Tracks: / Summer spies / Final door, The.
7" Single: Released Feb '87, on Carrere, Catalogue no: **CAR 340**
12" Single: Released Dec '84, on Carrere, Catalogue no: **CART 340**

YOU KNOW (YOU'LL NEVER BELIEVE)
Tracks: / You know (you'll never believe).
7" Single: Released Sep '85, on Carrere, Catalogue no: **CAR 372**
12" Single: Released Sep '85, on Carrere, Catalogue no: **CART 372**

Fatal Gift

WATCH, THE
Tracks: / Watch, The.
7" Single: Released Oct '84, on Yucca Ur, by Revolver Records. Catalogue no: **FG 184**

Fatal Microbes

VIOLENCE GROWS
Tracks: / Violence grows.
7" Single: Released '79, on Small Wonder, by Small Wonder Records. Catalogue no: **SMALL 20**

Fatback

Biographical details: At the time of their greatest success, this American soul band comprised Richard Cornwell, Bill Curtis, Johnny Flippin, Johnny King, Earl Shelton and George Williams. At the beginning of the Eighties, they dropped the word 'Band' and became known simply as Fatback. The Fatback Band came to fame in the mid-Seventies with a series of singles that were successful on the American black charts and British pop listings. All were aimed directly at the burgeoning disco market, and they included *Yum yum (gimme some)*, *Party time*, *Night fever* (they thought of that title well before the Bee Gees), *Double dutch* and the cult club favourite *Wicky wacky*. The above line-up were responsible for the 1976 album *Raising hell*, which reached the UK Top 20 and spawned the Band's two biggest UK singles" (*Are you ready) Do the bus stop* (No.18) and the ultra-classy, mainly instrumental streetwise stormer *(Do the) Spanish hustle* (No.10). Having helped to lay the groundwork for hip hop, rapping and various other modern manifestations of black music, Fatback's own success was slightly more sporadic from 1978 onwards. They surfaced occasionally with tracks like *Backstrokin'* and *I found lovin'*. By 1983 the group had dropped their brass section and put synthesisers and other gadgetry in its place. The title track from the Band's 1983 LP *Is this the future* was a social commentary rap, and became a long-standing cult favourite in UK discos and on London's fast-growing soul radio. (Bob MacDonald, 18th August 1985).

ALL NITE PARTY
Tracks: / All nite party / Party pella.
7" Single: Released Apr '88, on Start, by Start Records Ltd.. Catalogue no: **STS 2**
12" Single: Released Apr '88, on Start, by Start Records Ltd.. Catalogue no: **STSX 2**

(ARE YOU READY) DO THE BUS STOP
Tracks: / Are you ready do the bus stop / Wicky wacky.
7" Single: Released Dec '75, on Polydor, by Polydor Ltd. Deleted '78. Catalogue no: **2066 637**
12" Single: Released Nov '82, on Polydor, by Polydor Ltd. Deleted Nov '85. Catalogue no: **POSOX 601**

DO THE SPANISH HUSTLE
Tracks: / Do the Spanish hustle.
7" Single: Released Feb '76, on Polydor, by Polydor Ltd. Deleted '79. Catalogue no: **2066 656**

DOUBLE DUTCH
Tracks: / Double Dutch.
7" Single: Released Mar '77, on Spring, Deleted '80. Catalogue no: **2066 777**

GIRLS ON MY MIND
Tracks: / Girls on my mind.
7" Single: Released May '85, on Atlantic, by WEA Records. Deleted '88. Catalogue no: **FBACK 1**

GIRL IS FINE(SO FINE)
Tracks: / Girl is fine.
7" Single: Released Apr '83, on Spring, Catalogue no: **POSP 590**
12" Single: Released Apr '83, on Spring, Catalogue no: **POSPX 590**

I FOUND LOVIN'
Tracks: / I found lovin'.
7" Single: Released Sep '86, on Important, Catalogue no: **TAN 10**
7" Single: Released Jun '84, on Master Mix, Catalogue no: **CME 8401**
12" Single: Released Jun '84, on Master Mix, Catalogue no: **12 CME 8401**
12" Single: Released Jun '86, on Important, Catalogue no: **TANT 10**

I FOUND LOVIN'(THE LONDON BOYS MIX)
Tracks: / Anthem (Live), The / I found lovin' (The London boys mix).
12" Single: Released Aug '86, on Important, Catalogue no: **TANRT 10**

IS THIS THE FUTURE (SINGLE)
Tracks: / Is this the future.
7" Single: Released Oct '85, on Important, Catalogue no: **TAN 7**
12" Single: Released Oct '85, on Important, Catalogue no: **TANT 7**

KOOL WHIP
Tracks: / Kool whip / Concrete jungle.
7" Single: Released Sep '81, on Polydor, by Polydor Ltd. Deleted '84. Catalogue no: **POSP 321**
12" Single: Released Sep '81, on Polydor, by Polydor Ltd. Deleted '84. Catalogue no: **POSPX 321**

LET'S DO IT AGAIN
Tracks: / Let's do it again / Chillin' out / Hot box (on 12" only).
7" Single: Released Jan '81, on Spring, Deleted Jan '84. Catalogue no: **POSP 196**
12" Single: Released Jan '81, on Spring, Deleted Jan '84. Catalogue no: **POSPX 196**

LOVER UNDER COVER
Tracks: / Lover under cover.
7" Single: Released Jun '85, on Atlantic, by WEA Records. Deleted '86. Catalogue no: **A 9638**
12" Single: Released Jun '85, on Atlantic, by WEA Records. Catalogue no: **A 9638 T**

NIGHT FEVER
Tracks: / Night fever.
7" Single: Released Aug '76, on Spring, Deleted '79. Catalogue no: **2066 706**

PARTY TIME
Tracks: / Party time.
7" Single: Released May '76, on Polydor, by Polydor Ltd. Deleted '79. Catalogue no: **2066 682**

RHYTHM OF THE NIGHT
Tracks: / Rhythm of the night / Naughty dancer.
7" Single: Released 20 Jun '87, on Groove & Move, by Groove & Move Records. Catalogue no: **GMT 002**
12" Single: Released 20 Jun '87, on Groove & Move, by Groove & Move Records. Catalogue no: **GMT 12002**

SHE'S MY SHINING STAR
Tracks: / She's my shining star / Hip so slick.
7" Single: Released Jan '82, on Polydor, by Polydor Ltd. Deleted Jan '85. Catalogue no: **POSP 494**
12" Single: Released Jan '82, on Polydor, by Polydor Ltd. Deleted Jan '85. Catalogue no: **POSPX 494**

SUNSHINE LADY
Tracks : / Sunshine lady / Gotta get my hands on some (money)
7" Single: Released Jun '87, on Master Mix, Catalogue no: **CHE 8415**
12" Single: Released Jun '87, on Master Mix, Catalogue no: **12 CHE 8415**

TAKE IT ANY WAY YOU WANT IT
Tracks: / Take it any way you want it / Lady groove.
7" Single: Released Jun '81, on Polydor, by Polydor Ltd. Deleted Jun '84. Catalogue no: **POSP 283**
12" Single: Released Jun '81, on Polydor, by Polydor Ltd. Deleted Jun '84. Catalogue no: **POSPX 283**

YUM YUM GIMME SOME
Tracks: / Yum yum gimme some.
7" Single: Released Sep '75, on Polydor, by Polydor Ltd. Deleted '78. Catalogue no: **2066 590**

Fatback Band

For details see under **Fatback**

Fate

WON'T STOP
Tracks: / Won't stop (extended) (On 12" version only.) / I can't stand losing you.
7" Single: Released Oct '87, on EMI, by EMI Records. Deleted Jan '88. Catalogue no: **EM 25**
12" Single: Released Oct '87, on EMI, by EMI Records. Deleted Jan '88. Catalogue no: **12 EM 25**

Fathead

CHAMPION
Tracks: / Champion.
12" Single: Released Apr '83, on Greensleeves, by Greensleeves Records. Catalogue no: **GRED 118**

IT'S ME
Tracks: / It's me / Wha dat.
12" Single: Released Jan '83, on Greensleeves, by Greensleeves Records. Catalogue no: **GRED 108**

RAT TRAP
Tracks: / Rat trap / Come me a come.
12" Single: Released Oct '82, on Greensleeves, by Greensleeves Records. Catalogue no: **GRED 103**

Father Abraham

CHRISTMAS IN SMURFLAND
Tracks: / Christmas in Smurfland.
7" Single: Released Dec '78, on Decca, by Decca Records. Catalogue no: **F 13819**

DIPPETY DAY
Tracks: / Dippety day.
7" Single: Released Sep '78, on Decca, by Decca Records. Deleted '81. Catalogue no: **F 13798**

SMURF SONG, THE
Tracks: / Smurf song, The.
7" Single: Released Jun '78, on Decca, by Decca Records. Deleted '81. Catalogue no: **F 13759**

Father Abraphart

LICK A SMURP FOR CHRISTMAS (ALL FALL DOWN)
Tracks: / Lick a smurp for Christmas (all fall down).
7" Single: Released Dec '78, on Magnet, by WEA Records. Deleted '81. Catalogue no: **MAG 139**

Father Christmas

LAST CHRISTMAS
Tracks: / Last Christmas.
7" Single: Released Dec '84, on Go For It, Catalogue no: **GFI 001**

MERRY CHRISTMAS EVERYBODY
Tracks: / Merry Christmas everybody / Merry Christmas (instrumental).
7" Single: Released Oct '88, on Kunzel, by Gemini Enterprises. Catalogue no: **KUN 2**

Fats Comet

BOP BOP
Tracks: / Bop bop.
12" Single: Released Aug '88, on World, by World Records. Catalogue no: **WR 001**

DEE JAY'S DREAM
Tracks: / Dee Jay's dream.
12" Single: Released Aug '88, on World, by World Records. Catalogue no: **WR 004**

DON'T FORGET THAT BEAT
Tracks: / Don't forget that beat / Freak out.
12" Single: Released May '85, on Rough Trade, by Rough Trade Records. Catalogue no: **RRT 157**

ROCHESTER
Tracks: / Rochester.
12" Single: Released Jan '87, on World, by World Records. Catalogue no: **WR 006**

STORMY WEATHER
Tracks: / Stormy weather.
12" Single: Released Jun '85, on Rough Trade, by Rough Trade Records. Catalogue no: **RTT 159**

Fat's Garden

EVERY NOW AND THEN
Tracks: / Every now and then.
12" Single: Released Nov '88, on Laylah, by Laylah Records. Catalogue no: **TEMPLE 001T**

Faust

EXTRACTS FROM FAUST PARTY 3
Tracks: / Extracts from Faust party 3.
7" Single: Released Mar '80, on Recommended, by Recommended Records. Catalogue no: **RRI 15**

Fauves

TORTURED SOUL
Tracks: / Tortured soul.
7" Single: Released '88, on Rodger, Catalogue no: **RODGER 001**

Fawn, Charlie

ALWAYS SOMETHING THERE TO REMIND ME
Tracks: / Always something there to remind me / Post for a generation.
7" Single: Released Feb '80, on Hansa, by Hansa Records. Deleted Feb '83. Catalogue no: **K 17566**

Fax Yourself

SUNSHINE '89
Tracks: / Sunshine 89 (extended mix) (Only on 12" single.) / Sunshine 89 (original 12" mix) (Only on 12" single.) / Sunshine 89 (radio mix) / Techno jam.
7" Single: Released Aug '89, on Sound Of Belgium, Catalogue no: **SOB 77**
12" Single: Released Aug '89, on Sound Of Belgium, Catalogue no: **SOB 127**

Faze One

GOOD FRIENDS
Tracks: / Good friends / Pleasure seekers.
7" Single: Released 30 May '87, on Westside, by Westside Records. Catalogue no: **WSR 1**
12" Single: Released 30 May '87, on Westside, by Westside Records. Catalogue no: **WSRT 1**

LAYIN' DOWN A BEAT
Tracks: / Stronger than strong.
7" Single: Released Sep '86, on Streetwave, Catalogue no: **UKN 1**
12" Single: Released Sep '86, on Streetwave, Catalogue no: **UKHAN 1**

MELLOW DOWN
Tracks: / Mellow down
7" Single: Released Apr '88, on Westside, by Westside Records. Catalogue no: **WSR 6**
12" Single: Released Apr '88, on Westside, by Westside Records. Catalogue no: **WSRT 6**

Fear of Darkness

FEAR OF DARKNESS
Tracks: / Fear of darkness.
12" Single: Released Aug '84, on Heartbeat, by Mainline Records. Catalogue no: **FEAR 001**

LAY ME DOWN
Tracks: / Lay me down.
12" Single: Released 20 Jun '87, on Sugar Shack, by Sugar Shack Records. Catalogue no: **FOD 003**

Fear of Falling

LIKE A LION
Tracks: / Like a lion.
12" Single: Released May '83, on Excellent, by Survival Records. Catalogue no: **XR 7**

Fear Of Flying

BALANCING ACT
Tracks: / Balancing act / Tears fall.
7" Single: Released Oct '82, on RCA, by BMG Records (UK). Deleted '85. Catalogue no: **RCA 278**

Fear Of The Dark

THIS IS THE BLUES
Tracks: / This is the blues.
7" Single: Released Feb '86, on Lambs To The Slaughter, by Prism Records. Catalogue no: **7 FOD 3**
12" Single: Released Feb '86, on Lambs To The Slaughter, by Prism Records. Catalogue no: **FOD 3**

Fearless Four

PROBLEMS OF THE WORLD
Tracks: / Problems of the world.
7" Single: Released Apr '84, on WEA, by WEA Records. Catalogue no: **9669840**

ROCKIN'IT
Tracks: / Rockin' it.
12" Single: Released Jun '83, on Y, Catalogue no: **YT 105**
12" Single: Released Sep '83, on NYC, Deleted '85. Catalogue no: **NYCX 102**

Fearon, Phil

Biographical details: This British singer, guitarist, bassist, keyboardist, songwriter, arranger and producer came to fame in 1983 as the driving force of Galaxy - the records were credited either to Galaxy featuring Phil Fearon or Phil Fearon & Galaxy. To all intents and purposes, Phil Fearon is Galaxy; the only other contributors are his drumming brother, two sugary backing singers called Julie and Dorothy, plus Dorothy's sax playing brother. All Phil's work is recorded at his 24-track home studio at Kensal Rise in north-west London. In pre-Galaxy days, Fearon was a member of two successful British soul bands of the late Seventies, Hi-Tension and Kandidate. The latter act tended towards sweeter soul sounds, and their biggest single was 1979's *I don't want to lose you*, which reached the UK No.11 position. Fearon launched Galaxy in 1982 with *Head over heels*, a funky single that was well received in the clubs. He cracked the UK national charts the following year - the ultra-catchy *Dancing tight* cruised to No.4, and was ensued by two smaller hits, *Wait until tonight (my love)* and the smoochy ballad *Fantasy real*. 1984 saw him return to the UK Top 10 with *What do I do* and *Everybody's laughing* - these continued his nifty fusion of pop and soul music, and were designed to sound equally at home on the radio and on the dancefloor. The debut album, simply entitled *Phil Fearon & Galaxy*, was issued in the summer of '84 and reached the British Top 10. However, the more modest success of the 1985 singles *You don't need a reason* and *This kind of love* suggested that the public was growing tired of his now predictable sound. (Bob MacDonald, 18th August 1985).

AIN'T NOTHING BUT A HOUSE PARTY
Tracks: / Burning all my bridges / Ain't nothing but a house party.
7" Single: Released Nov '86, on Ensign, by Ensign Records. Catalogue no: **PF 2**
12" Single: Released Nov '86, on Ensign, by Ensign Records. Catalogue no: **PFX 2**

EVERYBODY'S LAUGHING
Tracks: / Everybody's laughing.
12" Single: Released Jun '84, on Ensign, by Ensign Records. Deleted '87. Catalogue no: **12ENY 514**
7" Pic: Released Jun '84, on Ensign, by Ensign Records. Deleted '85. Catalogue no: **PENY 514**
7" Single: Released Jun '84, on Ensign, by Ensign Records. Deleted '87. Catalogue no: **ENY 514**

FANTASY REAL
Tracks: / Fantasy real.
7" Single: Released Oct '83, on Ensign, by Ensign Records. Deleted '85. Catalogue no: **ENY 507**
12" Single: Released Oct '83, on Ensign, by Ensign Records. Catalogue no: **12ENY 507**

I CAN PROVE IT
Tracks: / Il gurnata / I can prove it.
7" Single: Released Jul '86, on Chrysalis, by Chrysalis Records. Catalogue no: **PF 1**
12" Single: Released Jul '86, on Chrysalis, by Chrysalis Records. Catalogue no: **PFX 1**

NOTHING IS TOO GOOD FOR YOU
Tracks: / Nothing is too good for you / You've still got my love.
12" Single: Released Jul '87, on Ensign, by Ensign Records. Catalogue no: **PF 312**
7" Single: Released Jul '87, on Ensign, by Ensign Records. Catalogue no: **PF 3**

THIS KIND OF LOVE (SINGLE)
Tracks: / This kind of love.
7" Single: Released Jul '85, on Ensign, by Ensign Records. Deleted '86. Catalogue no: **ENY 521**
12" Single: Released Aug '85, on Ensign, by Ensign Records. Deleted '87. Catalogue no: **12XENY 521**
12" Single: Released Jul '85, on Ensign, by Ensign Records. Deleted '87. Catalogue no: **12ENY 521**

WHAT DO I DO?
Tracks: / What do I do / Pina colada.
7" Single: Released Mar '84, on Ensign, by Ensign Records. Deleted '85. Catalogue no: **ENY 510**
12" Single: Released Mar '84, on Ensign, by Ensign Records. Catalogue no: **12ENY 510**

WHAT DO I DO (OLD GOLD)
Tracks: / What do I do? / I can prove it.
12" Single: Released 28 Aug '89, on Old Gold, by Old Gold Records. Catalogue no: **OG 4133**

Feathers, Charlie

Biographical details: A singer, guitarist and songwriter born in 1932 in Mississippi, a legendary rockabilly who never made big time. He went to Memphis at 18, hung around at Sun and first recorded for subsidiary Flip, then on Meteor, King, Kay, Walmay, Philips International 1956-59 in country and rockabilly styles, gaining status but few sales. He carried on; his single on *Rollin' rock' gained him a date at London's Rainbow Theatre in 1977, recorded by EMI's Harvest label. (Donald Clarke, April 1989)*.

THAT CERTAIN FEMALE
Tracks: / That certain female.
7" Single: Released Jun '80, on Rollin' Rock, Catalogue no: **45 025**

Features

GO NOW
Tracks: / Go now / Make me wanna.
7" Single: Released Jun '80, on Double Dee, Deleted Jun '83. Catalogue no: **D DEE 003**

Federation

TAKIN' UMBRAGE
Tracks: / Takin' umbrage.
7" Single: Released 11 Jul '88, on Club, by Phonogram Ltd. Deleted Feb '89. Catalogue no: **GROW 1**
12" Single: Released 11 Jul '88, on Club, by Phonogram Ltd. Deleted Feb '89. Catalogue no: **GROWX 1**

Feed Your Head

YOUR KINGDOM IS CALLING
Tracks: / Your kingdom is calling / Who's driving / When the north wind blows / Sun is shining, The.
7" Single: Released Feb '89, on Crucial Climate, Catalogue no: **CC 001**

Feedback

SIMPLY MAGIC
Tracks: / Simply magic / Simply magic (magic mix).
7" Single: Released Jul '87, on Production House (1), Catalogue no: **PN 007**
12" Single: Released Jul '87, on Production House (1), Catalogue no: **PNT 007**

SO FINE
Tracks: / So fine / Feedback of the mind.
7" Single: Released May '87, on Production House (1), Deleted Nov '87. Catalogue no: **PN 003**
12" Single: Released Mar '87, on Production House (1), Deleted Jan '88. Catalogue no: **PNT 003**

Feehan, Tim

WHERE'S THE FIRE
Tracks: / Where's the fire.
7" Single: Released Jan '87, on Scotti Bros (USA), Deleted Aug '87. Catalogue no: **SCT 650321**

Feel

I'D LIKE TO
Tracks: / I'd like to.
7" Single: Released Jan '83, on Buddah, by Buddah Records Inc.(USA). Catalogue no: **BDS 499**

Feelabeelia

FEEL IT
Tracks: / Feel it.
7" Single: Released Sep '84, on Interdisc, by Interdisc Records. Catalogue no: **IN-11**

Feelies

EVERYBODY'S GOT SOMETHING TO HIDE
Tracks: / Everybody's got something to hide / Original love.
7" Single: Released Jan '80, on Stiff, by Stiff Records. Catalogue no: **BUY 65**

NO ONE KNOWS
Tracks: / No one knows.
12" Single: Released Dec '86, on Rough Trade, by Rough Trade Records. Catalogue no: **RTT 180**

RAISED EYEBROWS
Tracks: / Raised eyebrows.
7" Single: Released Sep '79, on Rough Trade, by Rough Trade Records. Catalogue no: **RT 024**

Feelin' James

FEELIN' JAMES Various artists
Tracks: / Feelin' James: *Various artists*.
12" Single: Released Nov '87, on TD (USA), Catalogue no: **TD 802**

Feet Inc.

LOVE
Tracks: / Love.
12" Single: Released May '89, on Vinyl Lab, Catalogue no: **VL 005T**

Fehlfarben

14 TAGE
Tracks: / 14 tage / Feuer an bord
12" Single: Released Jun '82, on EMI, by EMI Records. Deleted Jun '85. Catalogue no: **12EMI 5306**

Fehlmann, Thomas

READY MADE
Tracks: / Ready made.
7" Single: Released Feb '87, on Transglobal/Rhythm King, by Mute Records. Catalogue no: **TYPE 2**
12" Single: Released Feb '87, on Transglobal/Rhythm King, by Mute Records. Catalogue no: **TYPE 2T**

Fehlmans Readymade

7" Single: Released Mar '87, on Transglobal/Rhythm King, by Mute Records. Catalogue no: **TYPER 2**
12" Single: Released Mar '87, on Transglobal/Rhythm King, by Mute Records. Catalogue no: **TYPER 2T**

Feiten, Larsen

WHO'LL BE THE FOOL TONIGHT
Tracks: / Who'll be the fool tonight / Further notice.
7" Single: Released Sep '80, on WEA, by WEA Records. Deleted '83. Catalogue no: **K 17686**

Felder, Wilton

Biographical details: This American saxophonist, bass guitarist and composer has been a member of the Crusaders since their formation (as the Swingsters) in the early Fifties. During the Sixties and Seventies, the individual members of the band carved out successful subsidiary careers as in-demand session players. With his dual instrumental skills, Felder has played on hit records by Randy Crawford, the Four Tops, Marvin Gaye, Seals & Crofts and Steely Dan, to name a mere handful. As yet another sideline to the Crusaders' work, Felder released his debut solo album in 1978. It was entitled *We all have a star*, and was followed in 1980 by *Inherit the wind*. This latter set featured some guest vocals from veteran soul singer Bobby Womack - with Bobby's assistance, the inspiring title track became a smash single on the US soul chart and a Top 40 pop hit in Britain. The two teamed up again in 1985, and went to No.2 on the US soul listings with the intense ballad *(No matter how high I get) I'll still be looking up to you*. This was a track from Felder's *Secrets* album; in the intervening period, he had issued a 1983 LP called *Gentle fire*. These solo albums continued the Crusaders' classy fusion of jazz, blues and soul, and indeed featured considerable assistance from the group's other members; but they also allowed Felder greater freedom to explore his personal musical whims. (Bob MacDonald, 19th August 1985).

I WILL STILL BE LOOKING UP TO YOU
Tracks: / I will still be looking up to you.
7" Single: Released Jan '85, on MCA, by MCA Records. Catalogue no: **MCA 919**
12" Single: Released Jan '85, on MCA, by MCA Records. Catalogue no: **MCAT 919**

INHERIT THE WIND (SINGLE)
Tracks: / Inherit the wind / Until the morning comes.
7" Single: Released Nov '80, on MCA, by MCA Records. Deleted '83. Catalogue no: **MCA 646**
12" Single: Released Oct '80, on MCA, by MCA Records. Deleted Oct '83. Catalogue no: **MCAT 646**

INSIGHT
Tracks: / Insight / You know who I am.
7" Single: Released Jan '81, on MCA, by MCA Records. Deleted Jan '84. Catalogue no: **MCA 665**
12" Single: Released Jan '81, on MCA, by MCA Records. Deleted Jan '84. Catalogue no: **MCAT 665**

Feldon, Barbara

99
Tracks: / 99.
7" Single: Released Oct '83, on Au-Go-Go (Australia), by Au-Go-Go Records (Australia). Catalogue no: **ANDA 99**

Feliciano, Jose

Biographical details: This American singer, guitarist, multi-instrumentalist and composer was born in Puerto Rico, but moved to New York with his family (he was one of nine children) at a very early age. He was born blind but, as with Stevie Wonder, this did not prevent him from developing his musical talents at a young age, in fact it probably spurred him on. He made his first public appearance on the accordion as a nine-year-old, then took up the guitar. At 18 he became a resident performer at the folk clubs and coffee houses of New York's famous Greenwich Village. This soon led to a recording contract, and his debut single - a self penned effort called *Everybody do the click* was released in late 1964. During the mid-Sixties, he concentrated on Spanish language discs and consequently became a major star throughout Latin America. By the time of his 1968 breakthrough in the States and Europe, he had become an acoustic guitar virtuoso, a master of at least five other instruments and as many languages. The record that shot Feliciano to recognition in the international pop hemisphere was the 1968 version of the Doors' classic *Light my fire*. Although it was released only a year after the original, his highly expressive voice and fresh Latin arrangement made the new rendition sufficiently different to garner a smash hit. It reached No.3 in the US; in Britain, where the Doors version had fallen on mainly deaf ears despite its later status as a rock classic, Jose obtained a No.6 placing. The *Feliciano* LP also reached the UK No.6 position, and logged 36 weeks on the charts. On both sides of the Atlantic, however, he managed one more Top 40 single. During the Seventies, singles were of no importance to his career, but his albums sold in steady, reliable quantities; he maintained his stature via concert and television appearances and by devoting much of his energy to his Latin American market base. In many critics' opinions, Feliciano never fully exploited the artistic potential of his eclectic rock, soul, jazz and latin influences; he was too content to settle into the role of a comfortable middle-of-the-road performer. His 1981 decision to sign with Motown's Latino subsidiary failed to win him any new followers; but his existing fans continued to cry along to his ultra-weepy ballads and his emotional interpretations of other artists' material. (Bob MacDonald, 19th August 1985)
Singer and songwrite and guitarist born blind in Puerto Rico in 1945. He grew up in NYC's Spanish Harlem. He has remained popular in Central and South America, but in 1968 his treatment of the Door's hit *Light my fire*, combining soul, Latin and folk-rock, was a number four in Billboard and won two Grammies including Best New Artist. He acted and wrote music for TV, sessioned with John Lennon and Joni Mitchell and recorded for Motown in 1980. (Donald Clarke, April 1989)o.

AND THE SUN WILL SHINE
Tracks: / And the sun will shine.
7" Single: Released Oct '69, on RCA, by BMG Records (UK). Deleted '72. Catalogue no: **RCA 1871**

CALIFORNIA DREAMING
Tracks: / California dreaming.
CD 5": Released Jun '89, on RCA, by BMG Records (UK). Catalogue no: **PD 49459**

EVERYBODY LOVES ME
Tracks: / Everybody loves me / Drought is over.
7" Single: Released Oct '81, on Motown, by BMG Records (UK). Deleted Oct '84. Catalogue no: **TMG 1244**

I SECOND THAT EMOTION
Tracks: / I second that emotion / Free me from my freedom.
7" Single: Released May '82, on Motown, by BMG Records (UK). Deleted '85. Catalogue no: **TMG 1264**

I WANNA BE WHERE YOU ARE
Tracks: / I wanna be where you are / Let's make love on the telephone.
7" Single: Released Jan '82, on Motown, by BMG Records (UK). Deleted Jan '85. Catalogue no: **TMG 1252**

LIGHT MY FIRE (SINGLE)
Tracks: / Light my fire / Que sera sera.
7" Single: Released Sep '68, on RCA, b BMG Records (UK). Deleted '71. Catalogue no: **RCA 1715**
7" Single: Released Jan '89, on Old Gol by Old Gold Records. Catalogue no: **O 9855**

LONELY TEARDROPS
Tracks: / Lonely teardrops.
7" Single: Released May '83, on Motow by BMG Records (UK). Catalogue no: **TM 1305**

NEVER GONNA CHANGE
Tracks: / Never gonna change / Ibiza Never gonna change (12" only.).

7" Single: Released Mar '89, on Columbia, by EMI Records. Deleted Aug '89. Catalogue no: **DB 9174**
12" Single: Released Mar '89, on Columbia, by EMI Records. Deleted Aug '89. Catalogue no: **12DB 9174**

SAMBA PA TI
Tracks: / Samba pa ti.
7" Single: Released Oct '82, on Latino (USA), by Motown Records (UK). Catalogue no: **TMG 1281**

SOMBRA PARTIT
Tracks: / Sombra partit / No hay sambra que mi cubra.
7" Single: Released Oct '82, on Motown, by BMG Records (UK). Deleted Oct '85. Catalogue no: **TMG 276**

Feline Jive

KISS'N'TELL
Tracks: / Kiss 'n' tell.
7" Single: Released Feb '87, on Massive, by Massive Records. Catalogue no: **MR 1 V**

Felix, Julie

Biographical details: This American folk singer and guitarist moved to Britain during the musical protest movement of the mid-Sixties, presumably after seeing the excellent reception afforded to Joan Baez in the UK. Felix achieved nationwide exposure via the unlikely medium of David Frost's BBC TV show *The Frost report* on which she sang one number per week. These ranged from the standard folk fare of Bob Dylan and Woody Guthrie to the irritating triteness of *Going to the zoo*. But recording success eluded her in the Sixties, save for a brief appearnace on the UK Top 30 with the 1966 album *Changes*. With Mickie Most as producer, Felix eventually enjoyed a couple of hit singles in 1970. The first was *If I could (el Condor Pasa)*. Simon & Garfunkel had adapted this traditional Peruvian number and included it on their recently released blockbuster LP *Bridge over troubled water*, but there were no plans for the S&G track to be issued as a single, so Most and Julie seized the opportunity. Julie's version peaked at No.19, and spent an impressive 11 weeks in the UK Top 50; this led to Simon & Garfunkel's rendition being released in the States, where it reached No.18. Felix managed a UK No.22 hit with another single *Heaven is here*, but then drifted into obscurity. She remained active, however, and continued to tour folk clubs and release occasional albums through into the Eighties. (Bob MacDonald, 19th August 1985).

DANCE WITH ME
Tracks: / Dance with me.
7" Single: Released Oct '83, on Gipsy, by Gipsy Records. Catalogue no: **GIPSY 12**

HEAVEN IS HERE
Tracks: / Heaven is here.
7" Single: Released Oct '70, on RAK, by EMI Records. Deleted '73. Catalogue no: **RAK 105**

IF I COULD (EL CONDOR PASA)
Tracks: / If i could (el condor pasa).
7" Single: Released Apr '70, on RAK, by EMI Records. Deleted '73. Catalogue no: **RAK 101**

YOKO
Tracks: / Yoko.
7" Single: Released Jan '84, on Gipsy, by Gipsy Records. Catalogue no: **GIPSY 12**

Fellas

DUH...WHADAYAMEAN?
Tracks: / Duh...Whadayamean?.
7" Single: Released Oct '88, on DJ World Records (USA). Catalogue no: **DJW 103**

Fellini, Suzanne

LOVE ON THE PHONE
Tracks: / Love on the phone / Bad boy.
7" Single: Released Mar '80, on Casablanca, by PolyGram UK Ltd. Deleted '83. Catalogue no: **CAN 187**

Felo De Se

VAZ
Tracks: / Vaz / Fantasia / Walking in circles / Cosmic glitter pixie dance / Crystal gold.
12" Single: Released Oct '89, on Space Dust Records, by Space Dust Records. Catalogue no: **FEL 001**

Felony

FANATIC
Tracks: / Fanatic.
7" Single: Released Apr '83, on Scotti Bros (USA). Catalogue no: **A 3109**

Felt

BALLAD OF THE BAND
Tracks: / Ballad of the band / I didn't mean to hurt you / Candles in a church (Track on 12" version only) / Ferdinand magellan (Track on 12" version only).
7" Single: Released May '86, on Creation, by Creation Records. Catalogue no: **CRE 027**
12" Single: Released May '86, on Creation, by Creation Records. Catalogue no: **CRE 027 T**

FEMME FATALE - SKAT (Released on Graduate)

FINAL RESTING OF THE ARK, THE
Tracks: / Final resting of the ark, The.
7" Single: Released Jul '87, on Creation, by Creation Records. Catalogue no: **CRE 048**
12" Single: Released Jul '87, on Creation, by Creation Records. Catalogue no: **CRE 048T**

MEXICAN BANDITS
Tracks: / Mexican bandits / Soft as lace.
7" Single: Released Mar '84, on Cherry Red, by Cherry Red Records. Deleted '87. Catalogue no: **CHERRY 78**

PENELOPE TREE+
Tracks: / Preacher in New England, A / Penelope tree.
7" Single: Released Jul '86, on Cherry Red, by Cherry Red Records. Catalogue no: **CHERRY 59**
12" Single: Released Jun '83, on Cherry Red, by Cherry Red Records. Catalogue no: **12 CHERRY 59**'

PRIMITIVE PAINTERS
Tracks: / Primitive painters.
CD 5": Released 13 Aug '88, on Cherry Red, by Cherry Red Records. Catalogue no: **CD CHERRY 89**
12" Single: Released Aug '85, on Cherry Red, by Cherry Red Records. Catalogue no: **12 CHERRY 89**

RAIN OF CRYSTAL SPIRES
Tracks: / Rain of crystal spires / I will die with my head / Gather up your wings and fly (Track on 12" version only) / I will die with my head in flames (Track on 12" version only) / Sandman's on the rise again (Track on 12" version only).
7" Single: Released Sep '86, on Creation, by Creation Records. Catalogue no: **CRE 032**
12" Single: Released Sep '86, on Creation, by Creation Records. Catalogue no: **CRE 032 T**

SOMETHING SENDS ME TO SLEEP
Tracks: / Something sends me to sleep.
7" Single: Released '81, on Cherry Red, by Cherry Red Records. Deleted '87. Catalogue no: **CHERRY 26**

SPACE BLUES
Tracks: / Space blues.
Note: Available on 12" and also as a limited edition 7" for just 0.99p.
7" Single: Released '88, on Creation, by Creation Records. Catalogue no: **CRE 060**
12" Single: Released '88, on Creation, by Creation Records. Catalogue no: **CRE 060T**

SUNLIGHT BATHED THE GOLDEN GLOW
Tracks: / Sunlight bathed the golden glow.
7" Single: Released Jul '84, on Cherry Red, by Cherry Red Records. Deleted '87. Catalogue no: **CHERRY 81**
12" Single: Released Jul '84, on Cherry Red, by Cherry Red Records. Deleted '87. Catalogue no: **12 CHERRY 81**

TRAILS OF COLOURS DISSOLVE
Tracks: / Trails of colours dissolve / My face is on fire.
7" Single: Released Sep '82, on Cherry Red, by Cherry Red Records. Deleted '87. Catalogue no: **CHERRY 45**

Feminine Touch

I GAVE YOU MY HEART
Tracks: / I gave you my heart.
12" Single: Released Sep '82, on King & City. Catalogue no: **KCD 007**

Femme Fatale

FALLING IN AND OUT OF LOVE
Tracks: / Falling in and out of love.
CD 5": Released 23 Jan '89, on MCA, by MCA Records. Catalogue no: **DMCA 1309**
7" Single: Released 23 Jan '89, on MCA, by MCA Records. Deleted 1 Jul '89. Catalogue no: **MCA 1309**
12" Single: Released 23 Jan '89, on MCA, by MCA Records. Catalogue no: **MCAT 1309**
Special: Released Jan '89, on MCA, by MCA Records. Catalogue no: **MCATR 1309**

SKAT (see panel above)
Tracks: / Skat / One fine day.
7" Single: on Graduate, by Graduate Records. Catalogue no: **GRAD 14**

WAITING FOR THE BIG ONE
Tracks: / Waiting for the big one.
7" Single: Released Oct '88, on MCA, by MCA Records. Deleted 1 Jul '89. Catalogue no: **MCA 1286**
12" Single: Released Oct '88, on MCA, by MCA Records. Catalogue no: **MCATR 1286**

Fender, Freddy

Biographical details: A Tex-Mex, country and rockabilly singer and songwriter, born Baldemar Huerta in 1937 in Texas. He spoke only Spanish until he was a teenager, and worked picking vegetables and cotton. He began playing Texas honky tonks '56-9 and made records for many small labels, rockabilly titles and songs in Spanish, including an early version of his best known song *Wasted days and wasted nights*, which reached the Cash Box Top 100. But then he was arrested and spent three years in prison for possession of marijuana. He worked clubs in New Orleans in the later '60's; finally an update of *Before the next teardrop falls* performed in English and Spanish led to a big pop and country hit in 1975. CMA Single Of The Year, and he was ACM Top New Male Vocalist, followed by further pop country hits in the '70's. (Donald Clarke, April 1989).

BEFORE THE NEXT TEARDROP FALLS (OLD GOLD)
7" Single: Released Jul '82, on Old Gold, by Old Gold Records. Deleted Jul '88. Catalogue no: **OG 9217**

Fender, Joyce

MR D.J.
Tracks: / Mr. D.J. / Mr. D.J. (instrumental) / Mr. D.J. (extended) (Only on 12" and CD single.) / Mr. D.J. (radio edit).
CD 5": Released May '89, on Motown, by BMG Records (UK). Catalogue no: **ZD 42772**
7" Single: Released May '89, on Motown, by BMG Records (UK). Catalogue no: **ZB 42771**
12" Single: Released May '89, on Motown, by BMG Records (UK). Catalogue no: **ZT 42772**

Fendermen

Biographical details: Phil Humphrey and Jim Sundquist were two American guitarists who achieved a one-off hit in 1960. *Mule skinner blues* was a remake of a tune thatl was first made famous by pioneered country singer, Jimmie Rodgers. The Fendermen took it to No.5 in the States and No.32 in Britain. They could not, however, live up to the promise of this single, and immediately returned to the land of obscurity. (Bob MacDonald, 23rd August 1985).

MULE SKINNER BLUES
Tracks: / Mule skinner blues / Love you so.
7" Single: Released Aug '60, on Top Rank (1), Deleted '63. Catalogue no: **JAR 395**
7" Single: Released Jul '82, on Revival. Catalogue no: **REV 6004**

Fenton, David

FRESH AIR
Tracks: / Fresh air / Buried snow.
7" Single: Released Aug '83, on Razor, by Razor Records. Catalogue no: **RZS 106**

Fenton, George

BERGERAC THEME
Tracks: / Bergerac theme.
7" Single: Released Oct '85, on Food For Thought, by Music For Nations Records. Catalogue no: **YUM 110**

OUT
Tracks: / Out.
7" Single: Released Aug '83, on EMI, by EMI Records. Catalogue no: **EMI 5416**

PIVARI
Tracks: / Pivari / Time of waiting, A.
7" Pic: Released Jun '88, on PRT, by Castle Communications Records. Catalogue no: **PYS 13**

Fenton, Peter

MARBLE BREAKS IRON BENDS
Tracks: / Marble breaks iron bends.
7" Single: Released Nov '66, on Fontana, by Phonogram Ltd. Deleted '69. Catalogue no: **TF 748**

Fenton, Shane

CINDY'S BIRTHDAY
Tracks: / Cindy's birthday.
7" Single: Released Jul '62, on Parlophone, by EMI Records. Deleted '65. Catalogue no: **R 4921**

I'M A MOODY GUY (SINGLE)
Tracks: / I'm a moody guy.
7" Single: Released Oct '61, on Parlophone, by EMI Records. Deleted '64. Catalogue no: **R 4827**

IT'S ALL OVER NOW
Tracks: / It's all over now.
7" Single: Released Apr '62, on Parlophone, by EMI Records. Deleted '65. Catalogue no: **R 4883**

WALK AWAY
Tracks: / Walk away.
7" Single: Released Feb '62, on Parlophone, by EMI Records. Deleted '65. Catalogue no: **R 4866**

Fentones

BREEZE AND I, THE
Tracks: / Breeze and I, The.
7" Single: Released Sep '62, on Parlophone, by EMI Records. Deleted '65. Catalogue no: **R 4937**

MEXICAN, THE
Tracks: / Mexican, The.
7" Single: Released Apr '62, on Parlophone, by EMI Records. Deleted '65. Catalogue no: **R 4899**

Fergus

BROKEN WINGS
Tracks: / Broken wings.
7" Single: Released Apr '85, on Climber, by Climber Records. Deleted '86. Catalogue no: **CLIS 1**

CAVAN BEGGARMAN
Tracks: / Cavan beggarman.
7" Single: Released Oct '80, on Rondercrest, by Rondercrest Records. Catalogue no: **ROND 5**

GOOD CLEAN FUN
Tracks: / Good clean fun.
7" Single: Released '78, on Rondercrest, by Rondercrest Records. Catalogue no: **ROND 2**

LET'S GO DANCE IN THE MOONLIGHT
Tracks: / Let's go dance in the moonlight / Cacoon tune.
7" Single: Released Sep '81, on Loopy, by Loopy Records. Catalogue no: **LOOP 1**

ROMANY HEARTS
Tracks: / Romany hearts.
7" Single: Released May '82, on Loopy, by Loopy Records. Catalogue no: **LOOP 2**

ROUNDABOUT
Tracks: / Roundabout.
7" Single: Released Jul '85, on Climber, by Climber Records. Deleted '86. Catalogue no: **CLIS 3**

Fergus, Winston

KEEP DANCING
Tracks: / Keep dancing / One day up.
12" Single: Released Mar '83, on Burning Sounds, by Burning Sounds Records. Catalogue no: **BSD 060**

ROCKERS ROCK
Tracks: / Rockers rock.
12" Single: Released Nov '83, on Three Kings, Catalogue no: **TK 002**

TOWN CALLED ALICE, A
Tracks: / Town called Alice, A (Version).
12" Single: Released Jul '86, on Hands & Hearts, Catalogue no: **HHD 003**

Ferguson, Craig

SCOTLAND (HOOCH OCH AYE)
Tracks: / Scotland (hooch och aye) / Bite / Hooch och aye - live.
7" Single: Released Oct '88, on Polydor, by Polydor Ltd. Deleted 30 May '89. Catalogue no: **PO 26**

Ferguson S

DO IT AGAIN
Tracks: / Do it again.
12" Single: Released Feb '85, on White Label (1), Catalogue no: **Unknown**

Ferguson, Sonia

ONE NIGHT STAND
Tracks: / One night stand.
12" Single: Released May '83, on Cha-Cha, by Cha-Cha Records. Catalogue no: **CLASIC 6**

Ferko String Band

ALABAMA JUBILEE
Tracks: / Alabama jubilee.
7" Single: Released Aug '55, on London Records, by London Records. Deleted '58. Catalogue no: **HL 8140**

Fermanagh Blackbirds

FERMANAGH BLACKBIRDS (Lonta Fhear Manach)
Tracks: / Ballad of Samuel Throne, The / Amhran Samuel Throne.
Note: The Fermanagh Blackbirds are a five piece band from County Fermanagh, Northern Ireland, fronted by lead singer Seamus Mac Annaidh. The band can perform all their material in either English or Irish. Contact S. Mac Annaidh, 6 Upper Celtic Park, Enniskillen, Co. Fermanagh, N. Ireland. Tel.: 0365 22886 (day), or 0365 22753 (evenings).
7" Single: Released Dec '87, on Tempest-Cuaifeach, by Tempest-Cuaifeach Records, Catalogue no: **TEMP 001**

Fernandez, Bianco

TOMORROW DOESN'T MATTER TONIGHT
Tracks: / Tomorrow doesn't matter tonight.
12" Single: Released Jun '86, on Long Island Sound, Catalogue no: **MTDX 301**

Fernandez, Luisa

LAY LOVE ON YOU
Tracks: / Lay love on you.
7" Single: Released Nov '78, on Warner Bros., by WEA Records. Deleted '81. Catalogue no: **K 17061**

Ferrante & Teicher

Biographical details: Arthur Ferrante and Louis Teicher met while studying at Julliard and began performing as a two piano act in 1947. They toured and recorded playing light classics and show music and modified pianos to produce effects such as gongs and drums. They added orchestral backing for the first time on record in the '60's and had hits with movie themes. (Donald Clarke, April 1989).

APARTMENT, THE (THEME FROM)
Tracks: / Apartment, The (Theme from).
7" Single: Released Aug '60, on London-American, Deleted '63. Catalogue no: **HLT 9164**

EXODUS (THEME FROM)
Tracks: / Exodus.
7" Single: Released Mar '61, on London-American, Deleted '64. Catalogue no: **HLT 9298**
7" Single: Released Jun '61, on H.M.V., by EMI Records. Deleted '64. Catalogue no: **POP 881**

Ferrer, Jose

WOMAN
Tracks: / Woman.
7" Single: Released Feb '54, on Philips, by Phonogram Ltd. Deleted '57. Catalogue no: **PB 220**

Ferrie, Glen

GLENFERRIE TRAM
Tracks: / Glenferrie tram.
7" Single: Released Feb '83, on Glen Ferrie, Catalogue no: **GF 001**

Ferron, Friddy

TRIBUTE
Tracks: / Tribute.
12" Single: Released Sep '84, on High Music, Catalogue no: **Unknown**

Ferry Aid

LET IT BE
Tracks: / Let it be / Let it be (Gospel version).
Note: All proceeds to Zeebrugge Disaster Fund
7" Single: Released Mar '87, on Sun-Zeebrugge Disaster Fund, Deleted '88. Catalogue no: **AID 1**

Ferry, Bryan

Biographical details: This British singer, songwriter and pianist dabbled in music (included a group called the Banshees) during the Sixties, while studying and graduating in fine art at Newcastle University and then embarking upon a teaching career. His verriding interest in music forced him to quit that job, and he formed Roxy Music at the end of 1970. The band broke through to fame and fortune in '72, and frontman Ferry decided to launch a subsidiary solo career in '73. With Roxy going from strength to strength, Bryan used his solo output to record his own interpretations of other people's standards; his original compositions were saved for the Roxy Music albums. Ferry's first effort was 1973's *These foolish things* LP, which cruised to No.5 and logged 42 weeks on the British charts. It contained oldies from such diverse sources as Bob Dylan, Smokey Robinson & The Miracles, the Rolling Stones and Lesley Gore; the opening track, a dramatic rendition of Dylan's *A hard rain's gonna fall*, became a UK Top 10 single. Ferry's equally successful 1974 album *Another time, another place* yielded UK hit singles in the shape of *The In crowd* (originally made famous in 1965 by Ramsey Lewis and Dobie Gray) and *Smoke gets in your eyes* (a 1959 smash for the Platters, composed in 1933). The contrast between the latter two songs emphasised the twin appeal of Bryan Ferry - one was dynamic, raunchy rock; the other was stylish, romantic nostalgia. He had the looks, dress sense and charisma to attact a large female fan following, and the musical power and class to command attention as a talented rock artist. Roxy Music unofficially broke up in 1976, and Ferry promptly achieved his three biggest solo UK singles. *Let's stick together* (a reworking of Canned Heat's 1970 biggie *Let's work together* reached No.4; an EP featuring a remake of the Everly Brothers' *The price of love* got to No.7; and the self-penned *This is tomorrow*, his first solo hit that was not a remake climbed to No.9. However, Ferry's solo career went into commercial decline in 1978, and he set about reforming Roxy Music. The reunited band returned to the public eye with huge success in 1979&Bryan suspended his own work. After a string of big records, Roxy went their separate ways again following 1982's *Avalon* LP. Their leader took a lengthy break from recording, and then relaunched his solo career with 1985's *Boys and girls* LP, his first since 1978. Despite the fact that it differed little from the smooth, slick, moody pop/rock sound of Roxy's later work, it entered the UK album chart at No.1. Ferry's audience was still there. (Bob MacDonald, 23rd August 1985).

DON'T STOP THE DANCE
Tracks: / Don't stop the dance.
7" Single: Released Aug '85, on E.G., by E.G. Records. Catalogue no: **FERRY 2**
12" Single: Released Aug '85, on E.G., by E.G. Records. Catalogue no: **FERRYX 2**

EXTENDED PLAY (EP)
Tracks: / Price of love, The / Shame shame shame / Heart on my sleeve / It's only love.
7" Single: Released Aug '76, on Island, by Island Records. Deleted '78. Catalogue no: **IEP 1**

HARD RAINS GONNA FALL
Tracks: / Hard rain's gonna fall.
7" Single: Released Sep '73, on Island, by Island Records. Deleted '76. Catalogue no: **WIP 6170**

HE'LL HAVE TO GO
Tracks: / He'll have to you / Carrickfergus / Windswept (12" only) / Is your love strong enough (12" only).
7" Single: Released Feb '89, on E.G., by E.G. Records. Catalogue no: **EGO 48**
12" Single: Released Feb '89, on E.G., by E.G. Records. Catalogue no: **EGOX 48**
CD 3": Released Apr '89, on E.G., by E.G. Records. Catalogue no: **EGOCD 48**

IN CROWD, THE
Tracks: / In crowd, The.
7" Single: Released May '74, on Island, by Island Records. Deleted '77. Catalogue no: **WIP 6196**

IS YOUR LOVE STRONG ENOUGH?
Tracks: / Windswept (inst) / Is your love strong enough.
7" Single: Released Mar '86, on E.G., by E.G. Records. Catalogue no: **FERRY 4**
12" Single: Released Mar '86, on E.G., by E.G. Records. Catalogue no: **FERRYX 4**

KISS AND TELL
Tracks: / Kiss and tell (Not on 12') / Zamba / Kiss and tell (dance mix) (CD & 12" only) / Kiss and tell (dub mix) (CD & 12' only).
CD 5": Released Feb '88, on Virgin, by Virgin Records. Catalogue no: **CDEP 19**
7" Single: Released Feb '88, on Virgin, by Virgin Records. Catalogue no: **VS 1034**
12" Single: Released Feb '88, on Virgin, by Virgin Records. Catalogue no: **VST 1034**

LET'S STICK TOGETHER Westside '88 remix
Tracks: / Let's stick together (7" & CD only) / Trash (On all versions) / Shame,shame,shame (On 12" only) / Angel eyes (12" mix) (On 12" only) / Sign of the times (On CD only) / Casanova (On CD only) / Let's stick together (extended remix) (On 12" only).
CD 5": Released '88, on Virgin, by Virgin Records. Catalogue no: **EGOCD 44**
7" Single: Released Jun '76, on Island, by Island Records. Deleted '79. Catalogue no: **WIP 6307**
7" Single: Released Oct '88, on E.G., by E.G. Records. Catalogue no: **EGO 44**
12" Single: Released Oct '88, on E.G., by E.G. Records. Catalogue no: **EGXO 44**

LET'S STICK TOGETHER (CD SINGLE)
Tracks: / Let's stick together / Shame shame shame / Chance meeting / Sea breezes.
CD 3": Released Jun '88, on Virgin, by Virgin Records. Catalogue no: **CDT 10**

LIMBO (LATIN MIX)
Tracks: / Limbo (latin mix) (On all versions) / Bete noire (instrumental) (On CD & 12" only) / Limbo (Brooklyn mix) (On all versions).
CD 5": Released '88, on Virgin, by Virgin Records. Catalogue no: **VSCD 1066**
7" Single: Released Jun '88, on Virgin, by Virgin Records. Catalogue no: **VS 1066**
12" Single: Released Jun '88, on Virgin, by Virgin Records. Catalogue no: **VST 1066**

PRICE OF LOVE (R&B 89 REMIX)
Tracks: / Price of love, The / Lover / Don't stop the dance (12" only) / Nocturne (12" only).
7" Single: Released Jan '89, on E.G., by E.G. Records. Catalogue no: **EGO 46**
12" Single: Released Jan '89, on E.G., by E.G. Records. Catalogue no: **EGOX 46**

PRICE OF LOVE, THE
Tracks: / Price of love, The / Lover.
CD 5": Released Feb '89, on E.G., by E.G. Records. Catalogue no: **EGOCD 46**

RIGHT STUFF, THE
Tracks: / Right stuff, The (On all versions) / Right stuff, The (Brooklyn mix) (On 7" only) / Right stuff, The (dub mix) (NOT on 7") / Right stuff, The (original mix) (On Cassette & 12" only) / Right stuff, The (long version) (On CD only).

Cassingle: Released '87, on Virgin, by Virgin Records. Catalogue no: **VSC 940-12**
CD 5": Released Aug '88, on Virgin, by Virgin Records. Catalogue no: **CDEP 8**
12" Single: Released Sep '87, on Virgin, by Virgin Records. Catalogue no: **VS 940-12**
7" Single: Released Sep '87, on Virgin, by Virgin Records. Catalogue no: **VS 940**

SIGN OF THE TIMES
Tracks: / Sign of the times.
7" Single: Released Aug '78, on Polydor, by Polydor Ltd. Deleted '81. Catalogue no: **2001 798**

SLAVE TO LOVE
Tracks: / Slave to love.
7" Single: Released Apr '85, on E.G., by E.G. Records. Catalogue no: **FERRY 1**
12" Single: Released Apr '85, on E.G., by E.G. Records. Catalogue no: **FERRYX 1**

SMOKE GETS IN YOUR EYES
Tracks: / Smoke gets in your eyes.
7" Single: Released Aug '74, on Island, by Island Records. Deleted '77. Catalogue no: **WIP 6205**

THIS IS TOMORROW
Tracks: / This is tomorrow.
7" Single: Released Feb '77, on Polydor, by Polydor Ltd. Deleted '80. Catalogue no: **2001 704**

TOKYO JOE
Tracks: / Tokyo Joe.
7" Single: Released May '77, on Polydor, by Polydor Ltd. Deleted '80. Catalogue no: **2001 711**

WHAT GOES ON
Tracks: / What goes on.
7" Single: Released May '78, on Polydor, by Polydor Ltd. Deleted '81. Catalogue no: **POSP 3**

WINDSWEPT
Tracks: / Windswept.
7" Pic: Released Nov '85, on E.G., by E.G. Records. Catalogue no: **FEREP 3**
7" Single: Released Nov '85, on E.G., by E.G. Records. Catalogue no: **FERRY 3**
12" Single: Released Nov '85, on E.G., by E.G. Records. Catalogue no: **FERRX 3**

YOU GO TO MY HEAD
Tracks: / You got to my head.
7" Single: Released Jul '75, on Island, by Island Records. Deleted '78. Catalogue no: **WIP 6234**

Fest, Manfredo

SEND IN THE CLOWNS
Tracks: / Send in the clowns.
7" Single: Released May '83, on Bluebird (2), by BMG Records (UK). Catalogue no: **BR 1**
12" Single: Released May '83, on Bluebird (2), by BMG Records (UK). Catalogue no: **BRT 1**

Fest, Mani

I WANNA GET NEXT TO YOU
Tracks: / I wanna get next to you.
12" Single: Released 31 Jul '89, on Carron, Catalogue no: **CT 001**

Festival

DON'T CRY FOR ME ARGENTINA
Tracks: / Don't cry for me Argentina / Buenos Aires.
7" Single: Released May '80, on RSO, by Polydor Ltd. Deleted May '83. Catalogue no: **RSO 60**
12" Single: Released May '80, on RSO, by Polydor Ltd. Deleted May '83. Catalogue no: **RSOX 60**

Festival Singers

HAPPY BIRTHDAY TO YOU
Tracks: / Happy birthday to you.
7" Single: Released Dec '77, on EMI, by EMI Records. Catalogue no: **EMI 2728**

Fetus Productions

ANTHEM
Tracks: / Anthem.
12" Single: Released Jul '85, on Red Rhino, by Red Rhino Records. Catalogue no: **PROD 1**

Fever

DO YOU WANT ME
Tracks: / Do you want me / One tonight.
12" Single: Released Oct '80, on Fantasy (1), by BMG Records (UK). Deleted Oct '83. Catalogue no: **FTCT 190**

Fever Tree

PIXIE SHOP, THE
Tracks: / Pixie shop, The.

7" Single: Released Sep '85, on Plan B, by Plan B Records. Catalogue no: **PBB 1**
12" Single: Released Sep '85, on Plan B, by Plan B Records. Catalogue no: **PBB 1T**

Few Shells

SOUND SENSE
Tracks: / Sound sense.
7" Single: Released Oct '84, on Loose, by Loose Records. Catalogue no: **LSE 15**
12" Single: Released Oct '84, on Loose, by Loose Records. Catalogue no: **LSE 15T**

Fflaps

FFLAPS EP
7" Single: Released '88, on Anhrefn. Catalogue no: **ANHREFN 012**

F.F.W.D.

BABY DON'T GO
Tracks: / Baby don't go / Baby don't go (dub mix).
7" Single: Released Apr '89, on Breakout, by A&M Records. Catalogue no: **USA 652**
12" Single: Released Apr '89, on Breakout, by A&M Records. Catalogue no: **USAT 652**

Fialka, Karel

Biographical details: This British singer and synthesiser player achieved a minor one-off hit in 1980. *The eyes have it* - a catchy, left field synthesised pop song - reached No.52 on the UK charts. However, it was apparently not quite catchy enough for the mass of the British public - Fialka promoted the single on 'Top of the Pops' and it was a turntable hit on Radio One, but it still could not rise into the Top 50. His *Still life* album was not as interesting as the single, and he quickly faded into obscurity. Despite later efforts, he was unable to capitalise on the technopop boom. (Bob MacDonald, 23rd August 1985).

EAT, DRINK, DANCE, RELAX
Tracks: / Eat, drink, dance, relax.
7" Single: Released 21 Nov '87, on I.R.S. Catalogue no: **IRM 148**
7" Single: Released May '83, on Carrere. Catalogue no: **CAR 271**
7" Single: Released '83, on Carrere. Catalogue no: **CAR 271**
12" Single: Released 21 Nov '87, on I.R.S. Catalogue no: **IRMT 148**

EYES HAVE IT, THE
Tracks: / Eyes have it, The / Metal urbane.
7" Single: Released May '80, on Blue Print. Deleted '83. Catalogue no: **BLU 2005**

FILE IN FORGET
Tracks: / File in forget / Exude when I'm bruised.
7" Single: Released Jul '80, on Blue Print. Deleted Jul '83. Catalogue no: **BLU 2014**

HEY MATTHEW
Tracks: / Hey Matthew / Things I saw, The.
7" Single: Released Aug '87, on I.R.S. Catalogue no: **IRM 140**
12" Single: Released Aug '87, on I.R.S. Catalogue no: **IRMT 140**

YOU BE THE JUDGE
Tracks: / You be the judge.
7" Single: Released Jul '88, on I.R.S. Catalogue no: **IRM 168**
12" Single: Released Jul '88, on I.R.S. Catalogue no: **IRMT 168**

Fiat Lux

Biographical details: This British band consisted of Dave Crickmore, Ian Nelson and Steve Wright. The name of the group was Latin for *Let there be light*. It was the first thing ever said - it's fairly timeless if God said it', explained Crickmore in an interview with Debut magazine. Hailing from Wakefield, Yorkshire, Fiat Lux were formed in 1982. Prior to this, Crickmore and Wright had studied drama together at college as well as being in a band. Ian Nelson was the younger brother of the former Be Bop Deluxe leader Bill Nelson - having impressed Bill with a demo tape, the Seventies star arranged and produced the first Fiat Lux single *Feels like winter again* and released it on his own Cocteau label. It reached Britain's indie charts, and earned the band a support slot on a Blancmange tour and a deal with Polydor Records. Fiat Lux cracked the UK naitional charts for the first time in early 1984, with a pleasant pop ballad called *Secrets*. It was quickly followed by a harder, uptempo single entitled *Blue emotion*, which obtained a No.59 placing. This chart toehold was not consolidated, though: the group's debut album *Hired history* made little impression on the public, and their next single *House of thorns* failed to enter the UK charts. The band left Polydor in early 1985, and broke up shortly afterwards. They were a classy band who didn't quite make it. (Bob MacDonald, 23rd August 1985).

BLUE EMOTION
Tracks: / Blue emotion / Sleepless nightmare.
7" Single: Released Mar '84, on Polydor, by Polydor Ltd. Deleted '84. Catalogue no: **FIAT 3**
7" Single: Released Mar '84, on Polydor, by Polydor Ltd. Deleted '84. Catalogue no: **FIATB 3**
12" Single: Released Mar '84, on Polydor, by Polydor Ltd. Catalogue no: **FIATX 3**

FEELS LIKE WINTER AGAIN
Tracks: / Feels like winter again / This illness.
7" Single: Released Mar '85, on Cocteau, by Cocteau Records. Catalogue no: **COQ 9**

SECRETS
Tracks: / Secrets.
7" Single: Released Jan '84, on Polydor, by Polydor Ltd. Deleted '87. Catalogue no: **FIAT 2**

SOLITARY LOVERS
Tracks: / Solitary lovers.
7" Single: Released Jan '85, on Polydor, by Polydor Ltd. Catalogue no: **FIAT 5**
12" Single: Released Jan '85, on Polydor, by Polydor Ltd. Catalogue no: **FIATX 5**

Fiction, Eddie

U F O
Tracks: / U F O.
7" Single: Released Sep '82, on Absurd, by Absurd Records. Catalogue no: **ABS 2**

Fiction Factory

Biographical details: Led by Kevin Patterson and Chic Medley, this all-male British band released their debut single *Ghost of love* in late 1983. Boosted by a tour supporting Paul Young, their second release *(Feels like)Heaven* became a UK Top 10 hit in early '84 - it was a very strong pop song, and was cleverly arranged so as to sound modern and synthesised without being too overtly technopop. However, success for Fiction Factory was short-lived. *Ghost of love* was reactivated, but could only manage a UK No.64 placing. The quinet's first album made little impact and, by early 1985, they had parted company with their record label (CBS) amid considerable acrimony. The group stated *(Feels like) Heaven* was a millstone round their necks, because it meant that they were 'categorised as the lates wimpy pop band'. They felt they had more to offer but, after moving to a small label, they found success even harder to come by. (Bob MacDonald, 23rd August 1985).

ALL OR NOTHING
Tracks: / All or nothing / Dreaming of someone.
7" Single: Released May '84, on CBS, by CBS Records. Catalogue no: **A 4453**
12" Single: Released May '84, on CBS, by CBS Records. Catalogue no: **TA 4453**

FEELS LIKE HEAVEN
Tracks: / Feels like heaven.
7" Single: Released Jan '84, on CBS, by CBS Records. Catalogue no: **A 3996**
12" Single: Released Jan '84, on CBS, by CBS Records. Catalogue no: **TA 3996**

GHOST OF LOVE
Tracks: / Ghost of love / Other side of love.
7" Single: Released Mar '84, on CBS, by CBS Records. Catalogue no: **A 3819**
12" Single: Released Mar '84, on CBS, by CBS Records. Catalogue no: **TA 3819**

NO TIME
Tracks: / No time.
7" Single: Released Jun '85, on Foundry. Deleted '86. Catalogue no: **FOUND 2**
12" Single: Released Jun '85, on Foundry. Deleted '86. Catalogue no: **FOUND 212**

NOT THE ONLY ONE
Tracks: / Not the only one / Let me be a part.
7" Single: Released Mar '85, on Foundry. Deleted '86. Catalogue no: **FOUND 1**
12" Single: Released Mar '85, on Foundry. Deleted '86. Catalogue no: **FOUND 112**

Fiddler, John

LOOK DON'T TOUCH
Tracks: / Look don't touch / You've got everything.
7" Single: Released Mar '80, on Harvest (1), by EMI Records. Deleted '83. Catalogue no: **HAR 5204**

Fiddlers Dram

Biographical details: This British folk band, who hailed from Kent, comprised six male musicians and a female vocalist. Their long steady and unspectacular career as a touring unit on the folk club circuit was briefly interrupted at the beginning of 1980, when their jolly singalong single *Day trip to Bangor (Didn't we have a lovely time)* shot to No.3 on the UK national charts. Like most novelty hits, it was impossible to follow-up. Fiddler's Dram's subsequent records returned them to the specialist folk market, where they carried on as before, but with better gigs. They joined the list of folk acts with one-off pop smashes to their name, a list which already included 'East of Eden', 'Ralph McTell', 'Bernie Flint' and 'Renaissance'. (Bob MacDonald, 25th August 1985).

BLACK HOLE
Tracks: / Black hole / Agony.
7" Single: Released Jul '81, on Dingle's, by Dingle's Records. Catalogue no: **SID 225**

DANCING IN THE MOONLIGHT
Tracks: / Dancing in the moonlight / Beercart lane.
7" Single: Released Aug '83, on Dingle's, by Dingle's Records. Catalogue no: **SID 221**

DAY TRIP TO BANGOR
Tracks: / Day trip to Bangor, A.
7" Single: Released Dec '79, on Dingle's, by Dingle's Records. Catalogue no: **SID 211**

LITTLE RAY OF SUNSHINE
Tracks: / Little ray of sunshine.
7" Single: Released Dec '81, on Dingle's, by Dingle's Records. Catalogue no: **SID 231**

Fidei

SNOWBLINDE
Tracks: / Snowblinde.
12" Single: Released Jul '86, on Leeds Independent (LIL), by Revolver Records. Catalogue no: **LIL 12007**

Field, Billy

Biographical details: This Australian singer became a household name in his native country during the early Eighties, thanks to his eclectic fusion of jazz, pop and middle-of-the-road styles. His voice and general appeal were perhaps best described as a combination of Barry Manilow and Tom Waits. With help from BBC disc jockey Peter Powell, he was launched into the British market in 1982. But Field's only taste of UK chart success was with the reflective ballad *You weren't in love with me*, which peaked at No.67 in June '82. Its parent LP *Bad habits* made little impression in Britain, Europe or America - Field's attempt to branch out into the internaional pop arena failed. (Bob MacDonald, 25th August 1985).

BAD HABITS (SINGLE)
Tracks: / Bad habits / You'll call it love.
7" Single: Released Aug '82, on CBS, by CBS Records. Deleted Aug '85. Catalogue no: **A 2097**

TRUE LOVE
Tracks: / True love / What a wonderful time we had.
7" Single: Released Dec '82, on CBS, by CBS Records. Catalogue no: **A 3049**

YOU WEREN'T IN LOVE WITH ME
Tracks: / You weren't in love with me / Baby, I'm easy for it.
7" Single: Released Jun '82, on CBS, by CBS Records. Deleted '85. Catalogue no: **A 2344**

Field Mice

EMMA'S HOUSE
Tracks: / Emma's house.
12" Single: Released Nov '88, on Sarah. Catalogue no: **SARAH 012**

SENSITIVE
Tracks: / Sensitive.
7" Single: Released Feb '89, on Sarah. Catalogue no: **SARAH 18**

SNOWBALL
10" single: Released 1 Sep '89, on Sarah. Catalogue no: **SARAH 402**

Fields, Ernie

IN THE MOOD
Tracks: / In the mood.
7" Single: Released Dec '59, on London Records, by London Records. Deleted '62. Catalogue no: **HL 8985**

Fields, Gracie

Biographical details: This British singer and comedienne was one of the UK's top entertainers of the Thirties and Forties. Her indelible association with the early days of BBC radio and television, and with the light relief provided by showbusiness during the dark days of the Second World War, made her a particularly special star for many Britons. She was a national institution by the time the UK record charts began in the Fifties - the bigges of her sporadic chart success occurred in 1957, when her rendition of Victor Young's *Around the world (in 80 days)* reached the UK No.8 position. *Sally* remained Fields' best known anthem. 'Our Gracie' died in September 1979. (Bob MacDonald, 25th August 1985)
Singer and comedienne (1898-1979) in Rochdale. She performed on stage in the West End, first recorded in 1928 and made the first of her 15 films in 1931. She was said to be the world's highest paid entertainer in 1939; she was beloved by 'ordinary people' in the dark pre-war days of the Depression for her broad Lancashire accent and quick informal humour. She married Italian comedian/film director Monty Banks in 1940 in the USA; on her return to the UK he was threatened with wartime internment, so they went back to the USA, taking their money with them: the UK public seemed to turn against her but a Palladium audience forgave her in 1946. She had a big international hit in 1948 with *Now is the hour*. She was semi-retired in Capri from c. 1960; her last London stage appearance was her 10th Royal Command Performance in 1978. (Donald Clarke, April 1989)
.

AROUND THE WORLD
Tracks: / Around the world.
7" Single: Released May '57, on Columbia, by EMI Records. Deleted May '60. Catalogue no: **DB 3953**

LITTLE DONKEY
Tracks: / Little donkey.
7" Single: Released Nov '59, on Columbia, by EMI Records. Deleted Nov '62. Catalogue no: **DB 4360**

SALLY (SINGLE)
Tracks: / Sally / Biggest aspidistra in the world.
7" Single: Released Jun '80, on H.M.V., by EMI Records. Deleted '83. Catalogue no: **POP 2002**

SING AS WE GO
Tracks: / Sing as we go / Wish me luck.
7" Single: Released Nov '80, on H.M.V., by EMI Records. Deleted Nov '83. Catalogue no: **POP 2022**

Fields, Kim

HE LOVES ME, HE LOVES ME NOT
Tracks: / He loves me, he loves me not.
7" Single: Released Nov '84, on Arista, by BMG Records (UK). Catalogue no: **ARIST 594**
12" Single: Released Nov '84, on Arista, by BMG Records (UK). Catalogue no: **ARIST 12594**

Fields Of The Nephilim

BLUE WATER
Tracks: / Blue water / In every dream home a heartache.
7" Single: Released 10 Oct '87, on Situation 2, by Beggars Banquet Records. Deleted Jul '88. Catalogue no: **SIT 48**
12" Single: Released 10 Oct '87, on Situation 2, by Beggars Banquet Records. Deleted Jul '88. Catalogue no: **SIT 48T**

BURNING THE FIELDS
Tracks: / Darkcell / Laura / Back in Gehenna / Trees come down.
12" Single: Released Feb '86, on Tower, by Tower Records. Catalogue no: **N 1**

MOONCHILD
Tracks: / Moonchild / Shiva.
7" Single: Released May '88, on Situation 2, by Beggars Banquet Records. Catalogue no: **SIT 52**
12" Single: Released May '88, on Situation 2, by Beggars Banquet Records. Catalogue no: **SIT 52T**

POWER
Tracks: / Power / Secrets / Tower.
12" Single: Released Aug '86, on Situation 2, by Beggars Banquet Records. Catalogue no: **SIT 42T**

PREACHER MAN
Tracks: / Preacher man / Laura 11.
7" Single: Released Mar '87, on Situation 2, by Beggars Banquet Records. Catalogue no: **SIT 46**
12" Single: Released Mar '87, on Situation 2, by Beggars Banquet Records. Catalogue no: **SIT 46T**

PSYCHONAUT LIB III
Tracks: / Psychonaut / Celebrate (second seal).
CD 5": Released Apr '89, on Situation 2, by Beggars Banquet Records. Catalogue no: **SIT 057CD**
Cassingle: Released Apr '89, on Situation 2, by Beggars Banquet Records. Catalogue no: **SIT 057C**
7" Single: Released Apr '89, on Situation 2, by Beggars Banquet Records. Catalogue no: **SIT 057**
12" Single: Released Apr '89, on Situation 2, by Beggars Banquet Records. Catalogue no: **SIT 057T**

RETURNING TO GEHENNA (SINGLE)
Tracks: / Returning to Gehenna.
7" Single: Released Jul '88, on Supporti Fonograph (Italy). Catalogue no: **SF 008**

Fields, Richard

Biographical details: This American singer, songwriter and producer came to the attention of US soul fans in the early Eighties, mainly on the strength of two tracks - *She's got papers on me*, a marital tongue-in-cheek protest featuring vocal intrusions by veteran soul artist 'Betty Wright', was quickly followed by *If it ain't one thing, it's another*. This latter song was a charming philosophical appraisal of the pressures of everyday life, and culminated (on the full-length version) in a no-holds-barred gospel rap. Another track *I've got to learn to say no*, gave Fields his only UK chart entry: it reached No.56 on the singles chart in early 1982. Somehow Dimples failed to live up to the promise of the aforementioned records. His music became a little too slick for its own good, and his success was spasmodic - he surfaced briefly on the American soul listings in 1984 with his typically cheeky single *Your wife is cheatin' on us*, and scored a soul and pop hit in 1985 as producer and co-writer of 9.9's *All of me for all of you*. (Bob MacDonald, 25th August 1985).

IF IT AIN'T ONE THING IT'S ANOTHER
Tracks: / Mr. Look so good / If it ain't one thing it's another.
7" Single: Released May '82, on Epic, by CBS Records. Deleted May '85. Catalogue no: **EPCA 2425**

I'VE GOT TO LEARN TO SAY NO
Tracks: / I've got to learn to say no / She's got papers on me.
7" Single: Released Feb '82, on Epic, by CBS Records. Deleted Feb '85. Catalogue no: **EPC A 1918**

YOUR WIFE IS CHEATIN ON US
Tracks: / Your wife is cheatin' on us.
7" Single: Released Jun '84, on RCA, by BMG Records (UK). Catalogue no: **RCA 433**
12" Single: Released Jun '84, on RCA, by BMG Records (UK). Deleted '85. Catalogue no: **RCAT 433**

Fiend

STAND ALONE
Tracks: / Stand alone.
7" Single: Released Sep '85, on Endangered Musik, Catalogue no: **EDR 1**

Fierce

PUT THAT (RECORD BACK)
Tracks: / Put that (record back) / Put that record back (version).
7" Single: Released Apr '88, on Hardback, by Hardback Records. Catalogue no: **7 BOSS 6**
12" Single: Released Apr '88, on Hardback, by Hardback Records. Catalogue no: **BOSS 6**

Fiesta

BRILLIANT
Tracks: / Brilliant.
12" Single: Released Mar '89, on VCN Records, by VCN Records. Catalogue no: **12 VCN 6**

Fifo

KLEESHAY
Tracks: / Kleeshay.
7" Single: Released May '82, on 1159, Deleted '86. Catalogue no: **11 59**

Fifteen, Sixteen...

JUST MY IMAGINATION
Tracks: / Just my imagination.
12" Single: Released Dec '88, on Jacqui, Catalogue no: **J 01**

Fifteenth

ANDELINE
Tracks: / Andeline.
12" Single: Released Apr '86, on Tanz, Catalogue no: **TANZ 3**

Fifth Column

STEEL TOWN
Tracks: / Steel town.
7" Single: Released Jul '87, on North West, Catalogue no: **NW 004**
12" Single: Released Jul '87, on North West, Catalogue no: **NW 004T**

Fifth Dimension

Biographical details: This American vocal group consisted of Billy Davis Jr, Florence LaRue, Marilyn McCoo, Lamonte McLemore and Ron Townson. The Fifth Dimension were formed in 1965 in Los Angeles, and were initially known as the Versatiles. After touring with Ray Charles and making a good impression of themselves, they became the Fifth Dimension in early 1967 and soon achieved their first US Top 40 single, reaching No.16 with *Go where you wanna go*. Their career really took off in the summer of '67, when they flew to the US No.7 position with *Up up and away* - this joyous summer celebration was penned by the then unknown Jim Webb, who rapidly became one of the top songwriters of the late Sixties. Although written about a balloon trip, it was adopted for use in air travel commercials by Trans World Air Lines, and thus became a standard. After *Up up and away*, the Fifth Dimension soared to even greater heights. *Stoned soul picnic*, written by Laura Nyro, reached No.3 on the American chart in 1968. Then came *Aquarius - Let the sunshine in*, a medly single featuring the opening and closing songs from the 1968 Broadway musical *Hair*. Released in early '69, the Dimension's record became a blockbuster of similar proportions to the show itself - it logged six weeks at the top of the US charts, and the group's album *The age of Aquarius* was also a major seller. By the end of 1969 they had chalked up a second US No.1 single with Nyro's *Wedding bell blues*. In Britain the Fifth Dimension were markedly less successful - their two American No.1 hits were their only two UK chart entries: the first reached No.11, and the second peaked at No.16. Working closely with arranger/producer Bones Howe, and selecting a shrewd repertoire of material, the Fifth Dimension's success lay in their strong vocal harmonies and the overall slickness of their records and concerts. Their music combined soul and cabaret styles. However, as the Sixties became the Seventies, critics argued that the group became less and less soulful and more and more middle-of-the-road. Nonetheless, the US hits kept on coming: they got to No.2 in late 1970 with the Bacharach/David song *One less bell to answer*, and hit the Top 10 twice in 1972 with *(Last night) I didn't get to sleep at all* and *If I could reach you*. But their final Top 40 gasp was breathed in 1973. Instead of sticking together as a cabaret act, the Fifth Dimension eventually ruptured. The husband/wife team of Marilyn McCoo and Billy Davis Jr enjoyed a US No.1 smash as a duo in 1977 with *You don't have to be a star (to be in my show)* (which reached No.7 in Britain) plus a No.15 follow-up hit with *Your love*. They then faded into obscurity (Bob MacDonald, 25th August 1985).

6 TRACK HITS
Tracks: / Puppet man / Never my love / One less bell to answer / Carpet man / Save the country / Last night I didn't get to sleep at all.
7" EP: Released Sep '83, on Scoop 33, by Pickwick Records. Catalogue no: **7SR 5025**

AQUARIUS - LET THE SUNSHINE IN
Tracks: / Aquarius - let the sunshine in.
7" Single: Released Apr '69, on Liberty, by EMI Records. Deleted Apr '72. Catalogue no: **LBF 15198**

SURRENDER
Tracks: / Surrender.
7" Single: Released Jul '83, on Buddah, by Buddah Records Inc.(USA). Catalogue no: **BDS 502**
12" Single: Released Jul '83, on Buddah, by Buddah Records Inc.(USA). Catalogue no: **BDSL 502**

UP UP AND AWAY
Tracks: / Up, up and away.
CD 5": Released Jun '89, on Arista, by BMG Records (UK). Catalogue no: **162064**

WEDDING BELL BLUES
Tracks: / Wedding bell blues.
7" Single: Released Jan '70, on Liberty, by EMI Records. Deleted Jan '73. Catalogue no: **LBF 15288**

Fifth Of Heaven

I WANT YOU
Tracks: / I want you / Just a little more (remix).
12" Single: Released 23 Oct '89, on Mixout, Catalogue no: **12FOH 2**

JUST A LITTLE MORE
Tracks: / Just a little more / Just a little more (surrender mix) (Only available on 12".) / Song for Bert.
7" Single: Released May '89, on Mixout, Catalogue no: **7FOH 1**
12" Single: Released May '89, on Mixout, Catalogue no: **12 FOH 1**

Fifty Fantastics

GOD'S GOT RELIGION
Tracks: / God's got religion.
7" Single: Released Jun '81, on Dining Out, by Dining Out Records. Catalogue no: **TUX 5**

Fifty Four - Fourty

OOH LA LA
Tracks: / Ooh la la / Every drop of your love / Ooh la la (version) (Only on 12") / Every drop of your love (version) (Only on 12").
7" Single: Released 19 Sep '88, on Mango, by Island Records. Deleted Apr '89. Catalogue no: **IS 392**
12" Single: Released 19 Sep '88, on Mango, by Island Records. Catalogue no: **12IS 392**

Fifty Hertz...

THIS RADIO STATION
Tracks: / This radio station.
7" Single: Released May '83, on Prairie Dust (USA), by Prairie Dust Records (USA). Catalogue no: **PR 011**

Fifty Second Street

ARE YOU RECEIVING ME?
Tracks: / Make up your mind / Are you receiving me? (On 7" only) / Are you receiving me? (extended remix) (On 12" only) / Are you receiving me? (over and out mix) (On 12" only).
12" Single: on 10 Records, by Virgin Records. Catalogue no: **TENR 163**
7" Single: Released Aug '87, on 10 Records, by Virgin Records. Catalogue no: **TEN 163**
12" Single: Released Aug '87, on 10 Records, by Virgin Records. Deleted May '88. Catalogue no: **TENT 163**

CAN'T AFFORD
Tracks: / Can't afford.
12" Single: Released Nov '84, on Factory (1), by Factory Records. Catalogue no: **FAC 118**

COOL AS ICE
Tracks: / Cool as ice.
7" Single: Released Mar '83, on Factory (1), by Factory Records. Catalogue no: **FBN 20**

I CAN'T LET YOU GO
Tracks: / I can't let you go / I can't let you go (jazz style) / I can't let you go (M & M style) (Extra track on 12" version only.) / I can't let you go (Timmy Regisford mix) (Extra track on 12" version only.) / Tell me (how it feels).
7" Single: Released Feb '86, on 10 Records, by Virgin Records. Deleted May '88. Catalogue no: **TEN 114**
12" Single: Released Feb '86, on 10 Records, by Virgin Records. Deleted '89. Catalogue no: **TEND 114-12**

I'LL RETURN
Tracks: / I'll return / Jamaica boy.
7" Single: Released Jun '87, on 10 Records, by Virgin Records. Deleted May '88. Catalogue no: **TEN 136**
12" Single: Released Jun '87, on 10 Records, by Virgin Records. Deleted '89. Catalogue no: **TENT 136**

LOOK INTO MY EYES
Tracks: / Look into my eyes.
7" Single: Released Aug '82, on Factory (1), by Factory Records. Catalogue no: **FAC 59**
12" Single: Released Jan '82, on Factory (1), by Factory Records. Deleted Jan '85. Catalogue no: **FAC 59 12**

SAY YOU WILL
Tracks: / Say you will / Say you will (radio edit) (Only on TENX 215) / I will wait (NOT on TENR 215) / I will wait (radio edit) (Only on TENX 215) / I will wait (version) (Only on 7") / I will wait for you (Only on TENR 215) / Something's going on (Only on TENR215) / Tell me (how it feels) (Only on TENR 215).
CD 5": Released '88, on 10 Records, by Virgin Records. Deleted '89. Catalogue no: **TENCD 215**
7" Single: Released May '88, on 10 Records, by Virgin Records. Catalogue no: **TEN 215**
12" Single: Released '88, on 10 Records, by Virgin Records. Catalogue no: **TENR 215**
12" Single: Released May '88, on 10 Records, by Virgin Records. Catalogue no: **TENX 215**

TELL ME HOW IT FEELS
Tracks: / Tell me how it feels (On TEN 7412 only) / Tell me how it feels (extended) / Tell me how it feels (dub) / Tell me how it feels (M + M stylee) (On TEN 7413 only).
7" Single: Released Oct '85, on 10 Records, by Virgin Records. Deleted May '88. Catalogue no: **TEN 74**
12" Single: on 10 Records, by Virgin Records. Catalogue no: **TEN 74-13**
12" Single: Released Oct '85, on 10 Records, by Virgin Records. Catalogue no: **TEN 74-12**

TELL ME HOW IT FEELS (OLD GOLD)
Tracks: / Tell me how it feels
12" Single: Released 28 Mar '89, on Old Gold, by Old Gold Records. Catalogue no: **OG 4110**

YOU'RE MY LAST CHANCE
Tracks: / You're my last chance/ I'm available
7" Single: Released Jan '86, on 10 Records, by Virgin Records. Deleted May '88. Catalogue no: **TEN 89**
12" Single: Released Jan '86, on 10 Records, by Virgin Records. Deleted May '88. Catalogue no: **TEN 89-12**
12" Single: Released Jan '86, on 10 Records, by Virgin Records. Deleted May '88. Catalogue no: **TEND 89-12**

Fifty Third Card

RITUAL SWAY
Tracks: / Ritual sway / Straw in the wind / Walk free.
7" Single: Released Oct '88, on Wildshine, Catalogue no: **WILDSHINE 1**

SWEET CHARITY
Tracks: / Sweet charity.
12" Single: Released Jun '89, on Wildshine, Catalogue no: **WILDSHINE 2**

Fifty Third & Third

CHICK A BOOM (DON'T YA JES LOVE IT)
Tracks: / Chick a boom (don't ya jes love it).
7" Single: Released Aug '75, on UK, by UK Records. Deleted Aug '78. Catalogue no: **2012 002**

Fifty Three Bus

HORIZONTAL DANCING
Tracks: / Horizontal dancing.
7" Single: Released Jun '84, on Custom Car, Catalogue no: **S 83 CUS**

Fifty/Fifty

MEMORIES LINGER
Tracks: / Memories linger / Just can't win.
7" Single: Released Nov '82, on PRT, by Castle Communications Records. Catalogue no: **7P 253**
12" Single: Released Nov '82, on PRT, by Castle Communications Records. Catalogue no: **12P 253**

TALK TOO MUCH
Tracks: / Talk too much.
7" Single: Released Apr '83, on PRT, by Castle Communications Records. Catalogue no: **7P 270**
12" Single: Released Apr '83, on PRT, by Castle Communications Records. Catalogue no: **12P 270**

Fight Back

FIGHT BACK (EP)
Tracks: / Fight back: *Various artists*.
7" EP: Released Feb '89, on Endangered Musik, Catalogue no: **EDR 006**

File Under Pop

HEATHROW
Tracks: / Heathrow.
7" Single: Released Jan '79, on Rough Trade, by Rough Trade Records. Catalogue no: **RT 011**

Filler

NO AIMS NO DESIRES
Tracks: / No aims no desires.
7" Single: Released May '89, on Pigboy, Catalogue no: **PIG 001**

Fillipponio

ALL ARREMBAGGIO
Tracks: / All arrembaggio / Let's go for it.
12" Single: Released May '84, on Eden, Catalogue no: **XTCT 7**

Filmcast

WORLD OF LIGHTS
Tracks: / World of lights / Distant heart.
7" Single: Released Apr '84, on True Friends, Catalogue no: **TF 004**

Filmstars

GREATEST STORY EVER TOLD
Tracks: / Greatest story ever told / So glad America loves him / Angels with dirty faces.
7" EP: Released Apr '80, on EMI, by EMI Records. Deleted Apr '83. Catalogue no: **EMI 5059**

HERE IN L.A.
Tracks: / Here in L.A. / So hollywood.
7" Single: Released Feb '80, on EMI, by EMI Records. Deleted Feb '85. Catalogue no: **EMI 5038**

Final Academy

NIGHT CAFE
Tracks: / Night cafe.
7" Single: Released Oct '83, on Spectec, Catalogue no: **SPEC 005**

Final Assault

MESSENGER OF GOD
Special: Released Dec '86, on Azra (USA), by Azra International (USA). Catalogue no: **A 26**

FINE YOUNG CANNIBALS - GOOD THING (Released on London Records)

Final Dinners

YOUR ISLAND
Tracks: / Your island.
7" Single: Released 30 Jun '85, on Slow Death By St, Catalogue no: **CAV 019**

Final Eclipse

BIRDSONG
Tracks: / Birdsong.
7" Single: Released '81, on Heartbeat, by Mainline Records. Catalogue no: **PULSE 11**

Final Frame

MASK, THE Falls away
Tracks: / Mask, The.
7" Single: Released Jun '84, on Skeleton, by Skeleton Records. Catalogue no: **PIK VP 1**

Fine Next Time

BENEATH THE HOUSES
Tracks: / Beneath the houses.
7" Single: Released Mar '86, on Stiff, by Stiff Records. Catalogue no: **BUY 248**

Fine Quality

AAH DANCE
Tracks: / Aah dance.
7" Single: Released Feb '82, on Sugarhill (USA), Deleted Feb '87. Catalogue no: **SH 110**
12" Single: Released Feb '82, on Sugarhill (USA), Deleted Feb '87. Catalogue no: **SHL 110**

Fine Young Cannibals

BLUE
Tracks: / Blue.
7" Set: Released Oct '85, on London Records, by London Records. Catalogue no: **LONDP 79**
7" Single: Released Oct '85, on London Records, by London Records. Catalogue no: **LON 79**
12" Single: Released Oct '85, on London Records, by London Records. Catalogue no: **LONX 79**

DON'T LOOK BACK
Tracks: / Don't look back / You never know / Don't look back (12" mix) (Only on 12" and CD single.).
CD 5": Released Jul '89, on London Records, by London Records. Catalogue no: **LONCD 220**
Cassingle: Released Jul '89, on London Records, by London Records. Catalogue no: **LONCS 220**
7" Single: Released Jul '89, on London Records, by London Records. Catalogue no: **LON 220**
12" Single: Released Aug '89, on London Records, by London Records. Catalogue no: **LONXG 220**
12" Single: Released Jul '89, on London Records, by London Records. Catalogue no: **LONX 220**

EVER FALLEN IN LOVE
Tracks: / Ever fallen in love / Couldn't care more.
CD 5": on London Records, by London Records. Catalogue no: **886 115-2**
CD 5": Released Apr '87, on London Records, by London Records. Deleted Oct '88. Catalogue no: **LONCD 121**
Cassingle: Released Apr '87, on London Records, by London Records. Deleted May '89. Catalogue no: **LONCS 121**
7" Single: Released Mar '87, on London Records, by London Records. Deleted Sep '87. Catalogue no: **LON 121**
12" Single: Released Mar '87, on London Records, by London Records. Catalogue no: **LONX 121**

FUNNY HOW LOVE IS
Tracks: / Motherless girl / Funny how love is.
7" Single: Released Mar '86, on London Records, by London Records. Catalogue no: **LON 88**
12" Single: Released Mar '86, on London Records, by London Records. Catalogue no: **LONX 88**

GOOD THING (see panel above)
Tracks: / Good thing / Social security / Good thing (nothing like the single) (on 12" and CD single only.) / She drives me crazy (monie love mix) (on CD only).
CD 5": Released Apr '89, on London Records, by London Records. Catalogue no: **LONCD 218**
10" single: Released Apr '89, on London Records, by London Records. Catalogue no: **LONT 218**
7" Single: Released Apr '89, on London Records, by London Records. Catalogue no: **LONB 218**
7" Single: Released Apr '89, on London Records, by London Records. Catalogue no: **LON 218**
12" Single: Released Apr '89, on London Records, by London Records. Catalogue no: **LONX 218**
Special: Released Apr '89, on London Records, by London Records. Catalogue no: **LONXR 218**

JOHNNIE COME HOME
Tracks: / Johnnie come home / Good times and bad.
7" Single: Released May '85, on London Records, by London Records. Catalogue no: **LON 68**
12" Single: Released May '85, on London Records, by London Records. Catalogue no: **LONX 68**

SHE DRIVES ME CRAZY
Tracks: / She drives me crazy / Pull the sucker off / Tired of getting pushed around (Extra track on CD only).
Note: The 12" LONXE 199 features a rapping treatment by Monie Love.
CD 5": Released Jan '89, on London Records, by London Records. Catalogue no: **886 3612**
CD 5": Released Dec '88, on London Records, by London Records. Catalogue no: **LONCD 199**
7" Single: Released Dec '88, on London Records, by London Records. Catalogue no: **LON 199**
12" Single: Released Jan '89, on London Records, by London Records. Deleted 26 Jun '89. Catalogue no: **LONXR 199**
12" Single: Released '89, on London Records, by London Records. Catalogue no: **LONXE 199**
12" Single: Released Dec '88, on London Records, by London Records. Deleted 26 Jun '89. Catalogue no: **LONT 199**
12" Single: Released Dec '88, on London Records, by London Records. Catalogue no: **LONX 199**

SUSPICIOUS MINDS (see panel below)
Tracks: / Suspicious minds / Prick up your ears.
7" Single: Released Jan '86, on London Records, by London Records. Catalogue no: **LON 82**
12" Single: Released Jan '86, on London Records, by London Records. Catalogue no: **LONX 82**

YOU DRIVE ME MENTAL
Tracks: / You drive me mental.
7" Single: Released Feb '89, on Hit (UK), Catalogue no: **SNOT 2**

Fine Young Things

CANDY MAN
7" Single: Released Nov '86, on ISR, Catalogue no: **KEV 2**
12" Single: Released Nov '86, on ISR, Catalogue no: **KEV 2T**

IT SHOULD HAVE BEEN ME
Tracks: / It should have been me / Candy man (remix).

FINE YOUNG CANNIBALS - SUSPICIOUS MINDS (Released on London Records)

Note: Featuring Mervlyn.
12" Single: Released Feb '87, on Electricity, by Electricity Records. Deleted '88. Catalogue no: **TRICT 101**

Finesse

FEEL IT
Tracks: / Feel it / Inside your head.
7" Single: Released Apr '82, on CBS, by CBS Records. Deleted Apr '85. Catalogue no: **A 2169**
12" Single: Released Apr '82, on CBS, by CBS Records. Deleted Apr '85. Catalogue no: **A 132169**

TOGETHER 2 parts
Tracks: / Together.
7" Single: Released Aug '83, on Intense, by Intense Records. Catalogue no: **INTS 009**

TONIGHT WILL LAST FOREVER
Tracks: / Tonight will last forever.
7" Single: Released Sep '84, on Tudor, Catalogue no: **FIN 1**
12" Single: Released Sep '84, on Tudor, Catalogue no: **FINT 1**

Finest Ingredients

DJ MEGAMIX, VOL 1
12" Single: Released Oct '87, on Megamix (USA), Catalogue no: **DJMM 001**

Fingerprintz

BEAT ESCAPE
Tracks: / Beat escape.
7" Single: Released Sep '81, on Virgin, by Virgin Records. Deleted Sep '84. Catalogue no: **VS 452**
12" Single: Released Sep '81, on Virgin, by Virgin Records. Deleted Sep '84. Catalogue no: **VS 452 12**

HOUDINI LOVE
Tracks: / Houdini love / All about you.
7" Single: Released Oct '80, on Virgin, by Virgin Records. Deleted Oct '83. Catalogue no: **VS 375**

SHADOWED
Tracks: / Shadowed.
7" Single: Released Jun '81, on Virgin, by Virgin Records. Deleted Jun '84. Catalogue no: **VS 420**

Fingers Inc'

CAN YOU FEEL IT
Tracks: / Can you feel it / My house.
7" Single: Released Nov '88, on Desire, by Desire Records. Catalogue no: **WANT 6**
12" Single: Released Nov '88, on Desire, by Desire Records. Catalogue no: **WANTX 6**

DISTANT PLANET
Tracks: / Distant planet.
12" Single: Released Jan '88, on Jack Trax, Catalogue no: **12JTRAX 8**

LOVE OF MY OWN
Tracks: / Love of my own.
12" Single: Released Nov '87, on Alleviated Music(USA), Catalogue no: **ML 2205**

SO GLAD
Tracks: / So glad.
12" Single: Released Apr '88, on Jack Trax, Catalogue no: **7 JTX 12**

Fingertips

BE YOUNG, BE FOOLISH, BE HAPPY
Tracks: / Be young, be foolish, be happy / Geronimo / Love is a serious business (Extra track on 12" only).
7" Single: Released May '87, on Priority, by Priority Records. Deleted Jan '88. Catalogue no: **LOOT 3**
12" Single: Released May '87, on Priority, by Priority Records. Deleted Jan '88. Catalogue no: **12 LOOT 3**

BILLY
Tracks: / Party / Billy.
7" Single: Released Aug '86, on Absolute, by Absolute Records. Catalogue no: **LOOT 2**

Fini Tribe

ANIMAL FARM
Tracks: / Animal farm.
12" Single: on One Little Indian, by One Little Indian Records. Deleted Oct '89. Catalogue no: **TP 12031**

CURLING & STRETCHING ep
Tracks: / Curling & stretching.
12" Single: Released Aug '84, on Fire, by Fire Records. Catalogue no: **LT 1001**
12" Single: Released '88, on Finiflex, Catalogue no: **FT 001**

DE TESTIMONY
Tracks: / De testimony.
12" Single: Released Oct '88, on Fini Tribe, Catalogue no: **FT 002**

ELECTROLUX EP
Tracks: / Electrolux.

12" Single: Released Jan '89, on Finiflex, Catalogue no: **FT 004**

I WANT MORE (ROW, ROW, ROW THE MIX)
Tracks: / Idiot strength / I want more (row, row, row the mix).
12" Single: Released Aug '87, on Wax Trax, by Wax Trax Records. Catalogue no: **WAXUK 027**

LET THE TRIBE GROW
Tracks: / De Testimony / Let the tribe grow.
12" Single: Released Oct '86, on Cathexis, by Cathexis Records. Catalogue no: **CRF 611**

MAKE IT ETERNAL
Tracks: / Make it eternal / Make it eternal (version) / Little visitors.
12" Single: Released 5 Mar '88, on Wax Trax, by Wax Trax Records. Catalogue no: **WAXUK 028**

NOISE LUST & FUN
Special: Released Dec '88, on Finiflex, Catalogue no: **FTLP 001X**
Special: Released Dec '88, on Finiflex, Catalogue no: **FTLP 001F**

ZULUS
Tracks: / Zulus.
12" Single: Released '88, on Finiflex, Catalogue no: **FT 003**

Fink Brothers

MUTANTS IN MEGACITY 1
Tracks: / Mutants in megacity 1.
7" Single: Released Jan '85, on Zarjazz, by Zarjazz Records. Deleted May '88. Catalogue no: **JAZZ 2**
12" Single: Released Jan '85, on Zarjazz, by Zarjazz Records. Deleted May '88. Catalogue no: **JAZZ 2-12**

Finlay, Karen

LICK IT
Tracks: / Lick it.
12" Single: Released Dec '88, on Sampler Et Sans Reproches, Catalogue no: **SSR 89**

TALES OF TABOO
Tracks: / Tales of taboo.
12" Single: Released Feb '88, on Cramboy, Catalogue no: **PWAI 049**

Finlayson, Willy

BEYOND THE BLUE HORIZON
Tracks: / Beyond the blue horizon / This time I'll sing better.
7" Single: Released 5 Mar '88, on Cara, Catalogue no: **CARA 102**

ON THE AIR TONIGHT
Tracks: / After the fall / On the air tonight.
7" Single: Released Sep '86, on PRT, by Castle Communications Records. Catalogue no: **7P 302**
12" Single: Released Sep '86, on PRT, by Castle Communications Records. Catalogue no: **12P 302**

SKYE BOAT SONG, THE
Tracks: / Skye boat song.
7" Single: Released Nov '85, on PRT, by Castle Communications Records. Catalogue no: **7P 321**

Finn, Lee

CAT ALL NIGHT
Tracks: / Cat all night.
7" Single: Released Jun '80, on Rollin' Rock, Catalogue no: **45 024**

Finn, Tim

CARVE YOU IN MARBLE
Tracks: / Hole in my heart / Carve you in marble.
7" Single: Released Jul '86, on Virgin, by Virgin Records. Deleted '89. Catalogue no: **VS 866**
12" Single: Released Jul '86, on Virgin, by Virgin Records. Deleted '89. Catalogue no: **VS 866-12**

FRACTION TOO MUCH FRICTION
Tracks: / Fraction too much friction / Below the belt.
7" Single: Released Apr '84, on Epic, by CBS Records. Catalogue no: **A 3932**

HOW'M I GONNA SLEEP
Tracks: / How'm I gonna sleep / Cruel black crow / Six months in a leaky boat (12" only.).
CD 5": Released Jul '89, on Capitol, by EMI Records. Catalogue no: **CDCL 542**
CD 5": Released Jul '89, on Capitol, by EMI Records. Catalogue no: **203 314 2**
7" Single: Released Jul '89, on Capitol, by EMI Records. Catalogue no: **CL 542**
7" Single: Released Jul '89, on Capitol, by EMI Records. Catalogue no: **203 314 7**
12" Single: Released Jul '89, on Capitol, by EMI Records. Catalogue no: **203 314 6**
12" Single: Released Jul '89, on Capitol, by EMI Records. Catalogue no: **12CL 542**

NO THUNDER NO FIRE NO CAR
Tracks: / Searching for the streets / No thunder no fire no car.
7" Single: Released Mar '86, on Virgin, by Virgin Records. Deleted '86. Catalogue no: **VS 849**

Fiona

LIVING IN A BOYS WORLD
Tracks: / Keeper of the flame / Living in a boys world.
7" Single: Released May '86, on Atlantic, by WEA Records. Catalogue no: **A 9432**

TALK TO ME
Tracks: / June / Talk to me.
7" Single: Released May '85, on Atlantic, by WEA Records. Catalogue no: **A 9572**

Fiorillo, Elisa

FORGIVE ME FOR DREAMING
Tracks: / Forgive me for dreaming / More than love / How can I forget you*.
Note: *Only on the 12" version.
7" Single: Released Jun '88, on Chrysalis, by Chrysalis Records. Catalogue no: **CHS 3251**
12" Single: Released Jun '88, on Chrysalis, by Chrysalis Records. Catalogue no: **CHS 123251**

HOW CAN I FORGET YOU?
Tracks: / How can I forget you.
7" Pic: Released Jan '88, on Chrysalis, by Chrysalis Records. Catalogue no: **ELISA P1**
7" Single: Released Feb '88, on Chrysalis, by Chrysalis Records. Catalogue no: **ELISA 1**
12" Single: Released Feb '88, on Chrysalis, by Chrysalis Records. Catalogue no: **ELISAX 1**

Fire Brigade

SHANGALI
Tracks: / Shangali.
7" Single: Released May '84, on Fox Hole, by Fox Hole Records. Catalogue no: **FHRS 01**

Fire & Desire

AIN'T NOTHING
Tracks: / Ain't nothing.
7" Single: Released Oct '86, on Hot Melt, by Hot Melt Records. Catalogue no: **DETAIL 1**
12" Single: Released Oct '86, on Hot Melt, by Hot Melt Records. Catalogue no: **12 DETAIL 1**

Fire Engines

BIG GOLD DREAM
Tracks: / Big gold dream.
7" Single: Released Nov '81, on Pop Aural, Deleted '82. Catalogue no: **POP 013**
12" Single: Released Nov '81, on Pop Aural, Deleted '82. Catalogue no: **POP 013 12**

CANDY SKIN
Tracks: / Candy skin / Meet whiplash.
7" Single: Released May '81, on Pop Aural, Deleted '82. Catalogue no: **POP 010**

GET UP AND USE ME
Tracks: / Get up and use me.
7" Single: Released 1 Feb '80, on Codex, Deleted '81. Catalogue no: **CODEX CDX 1**

Fire Next Time

I CAN'T GO BACK
Tracks: / I can't go back / Tumbling walls / Picket line ('Picket line' on 12" only.).
Note: * = Extra track on 12" only
7" Single: Released Apr '87, on Flying Nun, Deleted Jan '88. Catalogue no: **FNT 1**
12" Single: Released Apr '87, on Flying Nun, Deleted Jan '88. Catalogue no: **FNTX 1**

STAY WITH ME NOW
Tracks: / Stay with me now / Will I end up like they did? / Each time that you walk the truth inside you moves (Track on 12" and CD single.) / Broken promised land (Extra track on CD single.).
CD 5": Released Mar '88, on Polydor, by Polydor Ltd. Catalogue no: **FNTCD 2**
7" Single: Released Mar '88, on Polydor, by Polydor Ltd. Catalogue no: **FNTG 2**
7" Single: Released Mar '88, on Polydor, by Polydor Ltd. Catalogue no: **FNT 2**
12" Single: Released Mar '88, on Polydor, by Polydor Ltd. Catalogue no: **FNTX 2**

TOO CLOSE
Tracks: / Too close / Tears are nothing new / Hearts' anthem (Available on 12" only) / Gentle curve (Available on CD.).
CD 5": Released Jul '88, on Polydor, by Polydor Ltd. Catalogue no: **FNTCD 3**
7" Single: Released Jul '88, on Polydor, by Polydor Ltd. Catalogue no: **FNT 3**
12" Single: Released Jul '88, on Polydor, by Polydor Ltd. Catalogue no: **FNTX 3**

Fire On Blonde

STOP AND THINK
Tracks: / Stop and think (Instrumental).
7" Single: Released Aug '86, on Atlantic, by WEA Records. Deleted Jun '87. Catalogue no: **A 9402**
12" Single: Released Aug '86, on Atlantic, by WEA Records. Deleted Jun '87. Catalogue no: **A 9402 T**

Fireball XL5

MAN WITH NO NAME
Tracks: / Man with no name.
7" Single: Released May '85, on Northwood, by Northwood Records. Catalogue no: **NWSL 52**

ROCKIN SHOES
Tracks: / Rockin' shoes.
7" Single: on Northwood, by Northwood Records. Catalogue no: **NWEP M102**

Fireballs

QUITE A PARTY
Tracks: / Quite a party.
7" Single: Released Jul '61, on Pye International, Deleted Jul '64. Catalogue no: **7N 25092**

Firebrand

NEVER FELT THIS WAY BEFORE
Tracks: / Never felt this way before.
7" Single: Released May '85, on What Records, Catalogue no: **WR 71**

Firefall

HEADED FOR A FALL
Tracks: / Headed for a fall / Just what you need.
7" Single: Released May '80, on Atlantic, by WEA Records. Deleted May '83. Catalogue no: **K 11483**

LOVE THAT GOT AWAY
Tracks: / Love that got away / Business is business.
7" Single: Released Aug '80, on Atlantic, by WEA Records. Deleted '83. Catalogue no: **K 11552**

STAYING WITH IT
Tracks: / Staying with it / Dreamers.
7" Single: Released Feb '81, on Atlantic, by WEA Records. Deleted Feb '84. Catalogue no: **K 11658**

Firefly

LOVE IS GONNA BE ON YOUR SIDE
Tracks: / Love is gonna be on your side.
7" Single: Released Jan '82, on Excaliber, by Red Bus Records. Deleted Jan '85. Catalogue no: **EXC 506**
12" Single: Released Jan '82, on Excaliber, by Red Bus Records. Deleted Jan '85. Catalogue no: **EXCL 506**

STAY No time
Tracks: / Stay.
12" Single: Released May '85, on Break, Catalogue no: **BREAK 308590**

Firefox

FIRE
Tracks: / Stand up (for what you believe in).
7" Single: Released Jan '86, on Atlantic, by WEA Records. Catalogue no: **A 9494**
12" Single: Released Jan '86, on Atlantic, by WEA Records. Catalogue no: **A 9494 T**

IF YOU GOTTA GO GO NOW
Tracks: / If you gotta go go now.
7" Single: Released Nov '82, on Shell, by Shell Records. Deleted '87. Catalogue no: **PB 2**

Firehose

SOMETIMES
Tracks: / Rhymin' spielin' / She paints pictures / Sometimes.
Note: 'On their first twelve inch fIREHOSE slaps back the facts with two new songs and the track title.' (SST Records)
12" Single: Released Jun '88, on SST (USA), by SST Records (USA). Catalogue no: **SST 131**

Firewater

CRAZY
Tracks: / Crazy / Saving up my nights.
7" Single: Released Apr '86, on Sundown, by Magnum Music Group. Catalogue no: **SDS 003**

Firing Squad

NIGHT MANOEUVRES
Tracks: / Night manoeuvres / Big red car.
7" Single: Released Aug '81, on Shattered, Catalogue no: **SHAT 5**

Firm

ALL THE KINGS HORSES
Tracks: / All the kings horses / Fortune hunter.
7" Single: Released Apr '86, on Atlantic, by WEA Records. Catalogue no: **A 9458**

ARTHUR DALEY 'E'S ALRIGHT
Tracks: / Arthur Daley 'e's alright.
7" Single: Released Jun '82, on Bark, by Bark Records. Catalogue no: **HID 1**

BRAVO COSTA BRAVA
7" Single: Released Aug '85, on Bark, by Bark Records. Catalogue no: **BARK 1**

CASH IN HAND
Tracks: / Cash in hand / Two time loser.
7" Single: Released Nov '82, on Bark, by Bark Records. Catalogue no: **HID 2**

FLOB-A-DOB-A-LONG-A-BILL 'N' BEN
Tracks: / Flob-a-dob-a-long-a-Bill 'n' Ben / Snookered.
7" Single: Released Oct '88, on Bark, by Bark Records. Catalogue no: **FLOWER 1**

LONG LIVE THE NATIONAL
Tracks: / Long live the National.
7" Single: Released May '83, on Bark, by Bark Records. Catalogue no: **HID 3**

STAR TREKKIN'
Tracks: / Star Trekkin' / Dub trek.
7" Single: Released 23 May '87, on Bark, by Bark Records. Catalogue no: **TREK 1**

SUPER HEROES
Tracks: / Super heroes.
7" Single: Released Sep '87, on Bark, by Bark Records. Catalogue no: **SUPER 1**
12" Single: Released Sep '87, on Bark, by Bark Records. Catalogue no: **SUPER T1**

Firmament

FESTIVAL OF FROTHY MUGGAMENT
Tracks: / Festival of Frothy Muggament / Maxence cup.
7" Single: Released Jul '81, on Armageddon, by Armageddon Records. Catalogue no: **AS 017**

First Choice

ARMED & EXTREMELY DANGEROUS
Tracks: / Armed & extremely dangerous.
7" Single: Released May '73, on Bell, Deleted May '76. Catalogue no: **BELL 1297**

LET NO MAN PUT US UNDER
Tracks: / Let no man put asunder.
7" Single: Released Jun '87, on Serious, by Serious Records. Catalogue no: **7OUS 3**
12" Single: Released Jun '87, on Serious, by Serious Records. Catalogue no: **OUS 3**

First Church

DEBBYDID
Tracks: / Debbydid.
7" Single: Released Jun '85, on Off-Beat (1), Catalogue no: **OFF BEAT 2**

First Circle

CAN'T FIND A LOVE
Tracks: / Can't find a love.
12" Single: Released Sep '87, on EMI-America, by EMI Records. Catalogue no: **V 19264**

MIRACLE WORKERS
Tracks: / Miracle worker (radio edit) / Miracle worker (dub version) / Can't find a love (On 12" only).
7" Single: Released May '87, on EMI-America, by EMI Records. Deleted Oct '87. Catalogue no: **EA 232**
12" Single: Released May '87, on EMI-America, by EMI Records. Deleted Apr '88. Catalogue no: **12 EA 232**
12" Single: Released 23 May '87, on EMI-America, by EMI Records. Deleted Apr '88. Catalogue no: **12 EAX 232**

First Class

Biographical details: This British studio vocal group consisted of Tony Burrows, John Carter, Del John and Chas Mills. First Class were formed in 1974 as a vehicle for recording a particular song that they and UK Records owner Jonathon King agreed was a potential biggie. The song was *Beach baby*, a nostalgic Beach Boys - inspired number that could be described as the archetypal teenage summer love celebration. With the help of some session musicians plus the production of John Carter, the four singers embellished the song with a big vocal and instrumental sound, in keeping with its joyous mood. The voice that stood out amongst the vocal harmonies was that of Tony Burrows, one of the UK's leading session singers of the lated Sixties and early Seventies - he had previously sung lead on hits by the Flowerpot Men, Edison Lighthouse, White Plains, Brotherhood Of Man and the Pipkins. *Beach baby* reached No.13 on the British chart in the summer of '74, and then proceeded to hit No.4 in the States. Over the next few years, the faceless group attempted to achieve further success with sporadic releases, but failed. *Beach baby* remained a one-off classic. (Bob MacDonald, 25th August 1985).

BEACH BABY
Tracks: / Beach baby / Bobby dazzler / Surf queen.
7" Single: Released Jun '74, on UK, by UK Records. Deleted Jun '77. Catalogue no: **UK 66**
7" Single: Released Jul '82, on Old Gold, by Old Gold Records. Catalogue no: **OG 9097**
7" Single: Released May '82, on Sunny, by Sunny Records. Catalogue no: **EON 102**

GIMME LITTLE SIGN
Tracks: / Gimme little sign.
7" Single: Released Jul '83, on Sunny, by Sunny Records. Catalogue no: **EON 106**

SMARTY PANTS
Tracks: / Smarty pants.
7" Single: Released Aug '73, on Bell, Deleted Aug '76. Catalogue no: **BELL 1324**

First Cut

GOT TO GET CLOSE TO YOU
Tracks: / Got to get close to you.
12" Single: Released Aug '84, on Hot Rod, Catalogue no: **HR 002**

First Cuts Are..

FIRST CUTS ARE THE DEEPEST, THE
Note: Incl. Yr Anrefn/Elfyn Presli
7" EP: Released Mar '87, on Words Of Warning, Catalogue no: **WOW 2**

First Division

WHERE THE ACTION IS
Tracks: / Where the action is / Telephone number.
7" Single: Released Apr '84, on Panther, by MCA Records. Catalogue no: **PAN 3**

First Light

Biographical details: *Horse with no name*, the 1972 hit by America, was an unlikely choice of song for First Light. But that was the song that brought this British vocal and instrumental funk duo to attention in UK clubs in 1982. It was followed by *A.M.*; then, in 1983 came their first entry into the UK national charts - *Explain the reasons* reached No.65. First Light's eponymous debut LP was released in August of that year; two of its tracks, *Daybreak* and the aforementioned *A.M.*, were later re-done by Paul Hardcastle in a successful medley. Hardcastle, who played keyboards and synthesisers, was 50% of First Light; the other half was vocalist Derek Green. Paul's confusing career also included an early spell with another cult disco set, Direct Drive. Hardcastle and Green's second UK chart single was *Wish you were here* which peaked at No.71 in January 1984. However, First Light never released any more records, because Paul became immersed in a fast-growing solo career as a performer, producer and remixer, culminating in 1985's international chart-topper *19*. (Bob MacDonald, 25th August 1985).

A.M
Tracks: / A.M.
7" Single: Released Nov '82, on Oval, by Oval Records. Catalogue no: **FLIGHT 23**
12" Single: Released Nov '82, on Oval, by Oval Records. Catalogue no: **FLIGHT 23/12**

DON'T BE MISTAKEN
Tracks: / Don't be mistaken / Horse with no name.
7" Single: Released May '82, on Oval, by Oval Records. Deleted '85. Catalogue no: **FLIGHT 22-12**

EXPLAIN THE REASON
Tracks: / Explain the reason.
7" Single: Released May '83, on London Records, by London Records. Catalogue no: **LON 26**
12" Single: Released May '83, on London Records, by London Records. Catalogue no: **LONX 26**

HORSE WITH NO NAME
Tracks: / Horse with no name, A / Don't be mistaken.
7" Single: Released Jun '82, on Oval, by Oval Records. Catalogue no: **FLIGHT 22**
12" Single: Released Jun '82, on Oval, by Oval Records. Catalogue no: **FLIGHT 12 22**

LOVING YOU
Tracks: / Loving you / No way out.
CD 5": Released May '89, on Premiere UK, Catalogue no: **CDSGT 1**
7" Single: Released May '89, on Premiere UK, Catalogue no: **SGT 1**
12" Single: Released May '89, on Premiere UK, Catalogue no: **SGT 121**

WISH YOU WERE HERE
Tracks: / Wish you were here.
7" Single: Released Jan '84, on London Records, by London Records. Catalogue no: **LON 43**
12" Single: Released Jan '84, on London Records, by London Records. Catalogue no: **LONX 43**

First Love

THINGS ARE NOT THE SAME
Tracks: / Things are not the same / Without you (extended version) / Can I be with you tonight.
7" Single: Released Feb '85, on 10 Records, by Virgin Records. Deleted '89. Catalogue no: **TEN 43**
12" Single: Released Feb '85, on 10 Records, by Virgin Records. Deleted '89. Catalogue no: **TEN 43-12**

First Offence

NIGHT THE PUNKS TURNED UGLY
Tracks: / Night the punks turned ugly.
7" Single: Released Sep '83, on Chaos, by Backs Recording Co.. Catalogue no: **CHS 1**

Fischer-Z

BIG DRUM
Tracks: / Big drum / Camera (Live), The.
7" Single: Released Apr '88, on Arista, by BMG Records (UK). Catalogue no: **109704**
12" Single: Released Apr '88, on Arista, by BMG Records (UK). Catalogue no: **609704**

CUTTER'S LULLABY
Tracks: / Cutter's lullaby / You'll never find Brian here.
7" Single: Released May '81, on Liberty, by EMI Records. Deleted May '84. Catalogue no: **BP 398**

LIMBO
Tracks: / Limbo / Rat man.
7" Single: Released Sep '80, on Liberty, by EMI Records. Deleted '83. Catalogue no: **BP 360**

MARLIESE
Tracks: / Marliese / Right hand men.
7" Single: Released Feb '81, on Liberty, by EMI Records. Deleted Feb '84. Catalogue no: **BP 387**

PERFECT DAY, THE
Tracks: / Perfect day / Marguerite.
7" Single: Released Feb '88, on Arista, by BMG Records (UK). Catalogue no: **109396**
12" Single: Released Feb '88, on Arista, by BMG Records (UK). Deleted May '89. Catalogue no: **609396**

SAY NO
Tracks: / Say no / Psychojazz shuffle.
7" Single: Released 12 Jun '89, on Arista, by BMG Records (UK). Catalogue no: **112301**
CD 5": Released 12 Jun '89, on Arista, by BMG Records (UK). Catalogue no: **662301**
12" Single: Released 12 Jun '89, on Arista, by BMG Records (UK). Catalogue no: **612301**

SO LONG
Tracks: / So long / Hiding.
7" Single: Released Mar '80, on United Artists, by EMI Records. Deleted Mar '83. Catalogue no: **BP 342**

WORKER, THE
Tracks: / Worker, The.
7" Single: Released May '79, on United Artists, by EMI Records. Deleted May '82. Catalogue no: **UP 36509**

Fish

COCKS
Tracks: / Cocks.
7" Single: Released Sep '82, on Communication, Catalogue no: **AM 031**

STATE OF MIND
Tracks: / State of mind (edited version) (Not on CD single.) / Voyeur, The (I like to watch) / State of mind (Presidential mix) (Not on 7" or Cassingle.).
Cassingle: Released Oct '89, on EMI, by EMI Records. Catalogue no: **TCEM 109**
CD 5": Released Oct '89, on EMI, by EMI Records. Catalogue no: **CDEM 109**
CD 5": Released Oct '89, on EMI, by EMI Records. Catalogue no: **203 562 2**
12" Pic: Released Oct '89, on EMI, by EMI Records. Catalogue no: **12EMPD 109**
12" Pic: Released Oct '89, on EMI, by EMI Records. Catalogue no: **203 562 0**
7" Single: Released Oct '89, on EMI, by EMI Records. Catalogue no: **203 562 7**
Cassingle: Released Oct '89, on EMI, by EMI Records. Catalogue no: **203 562 4**
7" Single: Released Oct '89, on EMI, by EMI Records. Catalogue no: **EM 109**
12" Single: Released Oct '89, on EMI, by EMI Records. Catalogue no: **203 562 6**
12" Single: Released Oct '89, on EMI, by EMI Records. Catalogue no: **12EM 109**

Fish, Bob

HOTEL
Tracks: / Hotel / Like lovers do.
7" Single: Released Jul '82, on Magnet, by WEA Records. Deleted Jul '85. Catalogue no: **MAG 227**

NO CHANCE
Tracks: / No chance / Like lovers do.
7" Single: Released Oct '81, on Magnet, by WEA Records. Deleted Oct '84. Catalogue no: **MAG 199**

Fish Hildas

HOW I ITCH TO STITCH MY PITCH
Tracks: / How I itch to stitch my pitch.
7" Single: Released '88, on Fishdisc, Catalogue no: **F 001**

Fish Turned Human

ANIMAL MAGNETISM
Tracks: / Animal magnetism.
7" Single: Released Sep '81, on Detour, by Detour Records. Catalogue no: **DEEP 2**

Fishbone

FREDDIE'S DEAD
Tracks: / Freddie's dead / It's a wonderful life (gonna have a good time) / Freddie's dead (Zeoniq mix) (CD single & Picture Disc only.) / Freddie's dead (edit) (CD single & Picture Disc only.) / I like to hide behind my glasses (CD single single.).
7" Single: Released Sep '88, on Epic, by CBS Records. Deleted 17 Apr '89. Catalogue no: **FSH 1**
CD 5": Released Oct '88, on Epic, by CBS Records. Deleted 17 Apr '89. Catalogue no: **CD FSH 1**
12" Pic: Released Sep '88, on Epic, by CBS Records. Deleted 17 Apr '89. Catalogue no: **FSH P1**
12" Single: Released Sep '88, on Epic, by CBS Records. Deleted 17 Apr '89. Catalogue no: **FSH T1**

MA AND PA
Tracks: / Ma and pa / Bonin in the boneyard / I like to hide behind my glasses / In the name of swing (Only on CD single.).
7" Pic: Released 6 Mar '89, on Epic, by CBS Records. Catalogue no: **FSHP 2**
CD 5": Released 20 Mar '89, on Epic, by CBS Records. Catalogue no: **CPFSH 2**
7" Single: Released 6 Mar '89, on Epic, by CBS Records. Deleted Oct '89. Catalogue no: **FSH 2**
12" Single: Released 6 Mar '89, on Epic, by CBS Records. Deleted Oct '89. Catalogue no: **FSHT 2**

Fisher, Danny

TAKIN' MA LAGER TAE MALAGA
Tracks: / Takin' ma lager tae malaga.
7" Single: Released Apr '82, on Heavenly Sound Productions, Catalogue no: **HSP 5**

Fisher, Eddie

Biographical details: This American singer, born in Philadelphia, began his vocal career during his teens by singing on local radio stations. During the late Forties, as Fisher was entering his twenties, he procured a residency at New York's Copacabana club. Having already gained television exposure via a TV talent contest, Fisher was on course for stardom - he achieved it on a huge scale in the early Fifties. 1952 brought Fisher his first US smash hits, in the shape of *Anytime, Tell me why, Lady of Spain* and *Wish you were here*. In 1953 Eddie chalked up two No.1 hits on the fledgling British charts, with *Outside of heaven* and *I'm walking behind you*, the latter number also topped the American listings. Both hits were produced by bandleader Hugo Winterhalter, who was a regular collaborator with Fisher. During this period Fisher was the highest paid TV star in the world, as well as being one of the top recording artists. His clean-cut handsome looks, good voice and pleasant personality meant that he had all the requirements of the era's leading crooners. 1954 brought him further US No.1 hits with *Oh mein papa* (a UK No.1 for trumpeter Eddie Calvert) and *I need you now*. Two years later, he starred alongside his then wife, actress Debbie Reynolds, in the film *Bundle of joy*. Buy something else was also happening in 1956 - Elvis Presley was in the process of leading the rock'n'roll explosion and thereby torpedoing the likes of Fisher out of the record charts. Eddie's final Top Tenner on both sides of the Atlantic was *Cindy, oh Cindy*, which made its mark in late '56. Carrie Fisher, the daughter of Eddie Fisher and Debbie Reynolds, became a star in the late Seventies and early Eighties, thanks to her role in the blockbusting George Lucas movies, *Star wars* and *The empire strikes back*. Reynolds was not Eddie's only famous spouse - he was also one of the many husbands of actress Elizabeth Taylor. (Bob MacDonald, 26th August 1985)

Pop singer born in 1928 in Philadelphia, a fine tenor voice with distinctive colour. He joined Eddie Cantor's radio show in 1949 and was an instant hit; pictures of him in US Army uniform 1952-53 didn't hurt. He was one of the biggest stars of the early '50's, with 35 top 40 hits in the USA 1950-1956, 19 in the top 10, and continued hitting the Top 100 until 1967. He was especially good at show tunes; the *Junky 'dungaree' doll* was a top ten in 1955, but the other side was a very good version of *Everybody's got a home but me* from *Pipe dream*; it also made the top 20. He married Debbie Reynolds and later left her for Elizabeth Taylor, a big mistake; comedians later had Jacqueline Onassis saying that the American people would forgive her for anything, unless she married Eddie Fisher. (Donald Clarke, April 1989).

CINDY OH CINDY
Tracks: / Cindy Oh Cindy.
7" Single: Released Nov '56, on H.M.V., by EMI Records. Deleted Nov '59. Catalogue no: **POP 273**

DOWNHEARTED
Tracks: / Downhearted.
7" Single: Released May '53, on H.M.V., by EMI Records. Deleted May '56. Catalogue no: **B 10450**

EVERYTHING I HAVE IS YOURS
Tracks: / Everything I have is yours.
7" Single: Released Jan '53, on H.M.V., by EMI Records. Deleted Jan '56. Catalogue no: **B 10398**

I NEED YOU NOW
Tracks: / I need you now.
7" Single: Released Oct '54, on H.M.V., by EMI Records. Deleted Nov '57. Catalogue no: **B 10755**

I'M WALKING BEHIND YOU
Tracks: / I'm walking behind you.
7" Single: Released May '53, on H.M.V., by EMI Records. Deleted May '56. Catalogue no: **B 10489**

OH MEIN PAPA
Tracks: / Oh mein papa.
7" Single: Released Jan '54, on H.M.V., by EMI Records. Deleted Jan '57. Catalogue no: **B 10614**

OUTSIDE OF HEAVEN
Tracks: / Outside of heaven.
7" Single: Released Jan '53, on H.M.V., by EMI Records. Deleted Jan '56. Catalogue no: **B 10362**

WEDDING BELLS
Tracks: / Wedding bells.
7" Single: Released Mar '55, on H.M.V., by EMI Records. Deleted Mar '58. Catalogue no: **B 10839**

WISH YOU WERE HERE
Tracks: / Wish you were here.
7" Single: Released Nov '53, on H.M.V., by EMI Records. Deleted Nov '56. Catalogue no: **B 10564**

Fisher, Mark

LOVE SITUATION
Tracks: / Love situation.
7" Single: Released Jun '85, on Total Control, by Total Control Records. Deleted Jun '88. Catalogue no: **TOCO 3**

Fisher, Morgan

GENEVA
Tracks: / Geneva / Roll away the stone 79.
7" Single: Released Aug '79, on Pinnacle, by Pinnacle Records. Catalogue no: **CHERRY 5**

HAPPY AGAIN
Tracks: / Happy again / Lord of the full moon.
7" Single: Released Dec '84, on Cherry Red, by Cherry Red Records. Deleted '87. Catalogue no: **CHERRY 85**

UN HOMME ET UNE FILLE
Tracks: / Un homme et une fille / Silent zone.
7" Single: Released Sep '83, on Cherry Red, by Cherry Red Records. Deleted '87. Catalogue no: **CHERRY 70**

Fisher, Sue

CHRISTENING
Tracks: / Christening, The.
7" Single: Released Jul '82, on Wembley, by International Records & Tapes. Catalogue no: **CC 22**

Fisher, Toni

BIG HURT, THE
Tracks: / Big hurt, The.
7" Single: Released Feb '60, on Top Rank (1), Deleted Feb '63. Catalogue no: **JAR 261**

Fission

MILLER LITE

Tracks: / Private Dick / Miller lite.
7" Single: Released Nov '86, on Streetwave, Catalogue no: **UKN 4**
12" Single: Released Nov '86, on Streetwave, Catalogue no: **UKHAN 4**

PRIVATE DICK
Tracks: / Private dick / Miller lite.
12" Single: Released Oct '86, on Spacematic, Deleted '87. Catalogue no: **XING 111**
7" Single: Released Oct '86, on Spacematic, Deleted '87. Catalogue no: **XINGS 111**

YOUNG GUNS
Tracks: / Young guns / Word / My DJ beats (12" only).
Note: * extra track on 12"
7" Single: Released Jan '88, on Identity, by Identity Records. Catalogue no: **IDEN 102**
12" Single: Released Jan '88, on Identity, by Identity Records. Catalogue no: **IDENT 102**

Fist

COLLISION COURSE
Tracks: / Collision course / Law of the jungle.
7" Single: Released Jan '81, on MCA, by MCA Records. Deleted Jan '84. Catalogue no: **MCA 663**

FOREVER AMBER
Tracks: / Forever amber / Turn out the light.
7" Single: Released Aug '80, on MCA, by MCA Records. Deleted '82. Catalogue no: **MCA 640**

NAME RANK AND SERIAL NUMBER
Tracks: / Name rank and serial number / You'll never get me up in one of those.
7" Single: Released Apr '80, on Neat, by Neat Records. Deleted Apr '83. Catalogue no: **NEAT 04**
7" Single: Released 20 Jul '80, on MCA, by MCA Records. Deleted '83. Catalogue no: **MCA 615**

WANDERER
Tracks: / Wanderer / Too hot.
7" Single: Released Nov '82, on Neat, by Neat Records. Catalogue no: **NEAT 21**

Fits

ACHILLES HEEL
Tracks: / Achilles heel / Action.
7" Single: Released Apr '84, on Masterchord, by Masterchord Records & Tapes. Deleted '86. Catalogue no: **FIT 1**

ACTION
Tracks: / Action.
7" Single: Released 3 Jul '85, on Trapper, Catalogue no: **FIT 001**

BURIAL
Tracks: / Burial / Straps.
7" Single: Released Jan '82, on Rondelet Music, by Rondelet Music & Records. Deleted '85. Catalogue no: **ROUND 13**

FACT AND FICTION
Tracks: / Fact and fiction.
7" Single: Released 23 Sep '85, on Trapper, Catalogue no: **FIT 002**

FACT OR FICTION
12" Single: Released Nov '85, on Trapper, Catalogue no: **FIT 3**

LAST LAUGH
Tracks: / Last laugh.
7" Single: Released Dec '82, on Rondelet Music, by Rondelet Music & Records. Catalogue no: **ROUND 30**

THINK FOR YOURSELF BURIAL
Tracks: / Think for yourself burial.
7" Single: Released Dec '81, on Rondelet Music, by Rondelet Music & Records. Catalogue no: **ROUND 13**

Fitzbooth, Ella

DOWN IN POVERTY
Tracks: / Down in poverty.
12" Single: Released Nov '82, on Natty Congo, Catalogue no: **NCDM 015**

Fitzgerald, Ella

Biographical details: This American singer is commonly referred to as the First Lady of Jazz. Born in Newport News, Virginia in 1918, she ran away from home at the age of 16 to compete in a talent contest. In the following year (1935), she became the resident singer with Chick Webb's orchestra. It was in this capacity that she achieved her first big-selling record *A tisket, a tasket* - this adaptation of an old nursery rhyme was recorded in New York in 1938. Fitzgerald embarked upon a solo career in 1940 and, over the next 25 years, became a living legend. Her pitch, diction and phrasing were as close to perfection as any jazz singer has ever reached. Whether scatting a jazz standard or calmly interpreting a middle-of-the-road ballad, she transformed her repertoire into a serene sequence of vererable vignettes. The main criticism levelled at her was that her sheer coolness and imperturbaility meant boredom for some listeners - Ella put technical brilliance before emotion. Fitzgerald was with Decca until the late Fifties, but then switched to Verve Records, a label founded by her manager Norman Granz. Many aficionados argued that she reached her artistic peak during this later period. 1960 was certainly a successful year in disc terms: the singer reached the pop Top 40 on both sides of the Atlantic with her distinctive rendition of the standard *Mack the knife*; in Britain, she gained Top 20 successes with three EP's and three LP's during 1960. Between 1958 and 1964, she chalked up five UK Top 40 singles. Ella's remarkable voice was still holding up well when she turned 60 years old in 1978, and was used by Memorex in their commercials for blank tape. That climatic last note broke the glass, but was withstood intact by the cassette! In his epic 1983 rap *The crown*, Gary Byrd suggested that you should 'Sing like Ella and make them guess, Is it you or is it Memorex'. (Bob MacDonald, 26th August 1985)
One of the century's favourite singers. She was an orphan,born in 1918; she won talent contests and joined Chick Webb in 1934 (he adopted her) and had a big hit with the rhythmic novelty *A tisket a tasket* in 1938. She fronted the band after Webb died in 1939, went solo in 1942 and toured with JATP from 1946. The question of whether she's a jazz singer is pointless; she transcends category. She had hits in the Billboard charts on USA Decca (now MCA) 1940-51 including three with the Ink Spots and one with Louis Jordan, but soon switched to Norman Granz's labels and has been selling albums ever since: it was rare for two records sets to chart in the '50's but hers did. She made several films of which the best known is *Pete Kelly's blues*; the soundtrack album in 1955 was shared with Peggy Lee. (Donald Clarke, April 1989)r.

BUT NOT FOR ME
Tracks: / But not for me.
7" Single: Released Oct '59, on H.M.V., by EMI Records. Deleted Oct '62. Catalogue no: **POP 657**

CAN'T BUY ME LOVE
Tracks: / Can't buy me love.
7" Single: Released Apr '64, on Verve, Deleted Apr '67. Catalogue no: **VS 519**

DESAFINADO
Tracks: / Desafinado.
7" Single: Released Nov '62, on Verve, Deleted Nov '65. Catalogue no: **VS 502**

EVERYTIME WE SAY GOODBYE
Tracks: / Every time we say goodbye / Manhattan.
7" Single: Released Mar '88, on Honeybee, by Stylus Music Records. Catalogue no: **HONEY 5**
7" Single: Released May '80, on Verve, Deleted May '83. Catalogue no: **200901-7**
12" Single: Released Mar '88, on Honeybee, by Stylus Music Records. Catalogue no: **HONEY 5 12**

HOW HIGH THE MOON
Tracks: / How high the moon.
7" Single: Released Oct '60, on H.M.V., by EMI Records. Deleted Oct '63. Catalogue no: **POP 782**

MACK THE KNIFE
Tracks: / Mack the knife.
7" Single: Released Apr '60, on H.M.V., by EMI Records. Deleted Apr '63. Catalogue no: **POP 736**

SUMMERTIME
Tracks: / Summertime / Every time we say goodbye / Mack the knife.
7" Single: Released Jun '89, on Polydor, by Polydor Ltd. Catalogue no: **PO 48**
12" Single: Released Jun '89, on Polydor, by Polydor Ltd. Catalogue no: **PZ 48**

SWINGIN' SHEPHERD BLUES
Tracks: / Swingin' shepherd blues.
7" Single: Released May '58, on H.M.V., by EMI Records. Deleted May '61. Catalogue no: **POP 486**

Fitzgerald, Patrick

PERSONAL LOSS
Tracks: / Personal loss.
7" Single: Released Sep '82, on Red Flame (1), by Red Flame Records. Catalogue no: **RF 708**

TONIGHT
Tracks: / Tonight.
7" Single: Released Apr '84, on Red Flame (1), by Red Flame Records. Catalogue no: **FSEP 001**

Fitzgerald, Scott

GO
Tracks: / Go / Go (version).
12" Pic: Released 30 Mar '88, on PRT, by Castle Communications Records. Catalogue no: **PYT 10**
7" Pic: Released 30 Mar '88, on PRT, by Castle Communications Records. Catalogue no: **PYS 10**

IF I HAD WORDS
Tracks: / If I had words.
7" Single: Released Jul '84, on EMI (Holland), by EMI Records. Catalogue no: **1A 006 60276**

LOVE IS LOVE IS LOVE
Tracks: / Love is love is love.
7" Single: Released Jan '85, on Young Blood, by Young Blood Records. Catalogue no: **YB 0085**

MONTEGO BAY
Tracks: / Montego Bay.
7" Single: Released Jul '80, on Creole, by Creole Records. Catalogue no: **CR 203**

Fitzpatrick, Gene

KINGDOM I CALL HOME
Tracks: / Kingdom I call home.
7" Single: Released Sep '82, on Homespun (Ireland), by Outlet Records. Catalogue no: **HS 060**

LET THE REST OF THE WORLD GO BY
Tracks: / Let the rest of the world go by.
7" Single: Released Jan '83, on Homespun (Ireland), by Outlet Records. Catalogue no: **HS 064**

VIVA IRELAND
Tracks: / Viva Ireland.
7" Single: Released Mar '82, on Lismor, by Lismor Records. Deleted '88. Catalogue no: **LISP 2008**

Fitzroy, Eddie

PRETTY WOMAN
Tracks: / Pretty woman.
12" Single: Released Mar '81, on Attack, Catalogue no: **TACK 26**

Fitzroy, Edi

CHANT IT TO THE RHYTHM
Tracks: / Chant it to the rhythm.
12" Single: Released Jul '82, on Musical Ambassador, Catalogue no: **MAPD 001**

PRINCESS BLACK
Tracks: / Princess Black.
12" Single: Released Oct '84, on Pama, by Pama Records. Catalogue no: **PMD 3244**

Five

NEXT TIME
Tracks: / Next time / Clean living.
Note: Available by mail order for 3.29 plus 60p p&p from: 29 Bath Street, Edinburgh, EH15 1HB.
12" Single: Released Aug '87, on Five, Deleted '88. Catalogue no: **FIVE 5/1**

Five-0-One

LET THE NIGHT TAKE THE BLAME
Tracks: / Let the night take the blame.
12" Single: Released Jul '85, on Fanfare, by Captain Billy's Music. Catalogue no: **12 FAN 4**
7" Single: Released Jul '85, on Fanfare, by Captain Billy's Music. Catalogue no: **FAN 4**

WE ARE INVINCIBLE
Tracks: / We are invincible.
7" Single: Released Jun '84, on ERC, Catalogue no: **ERC 113**

Five Go Down To The

FIVE GO DOWN TO THE SEA
Tracks: / Five go down to the sea.
7" Single: Released Mar '83, on Kabuki, Catalogue no: **KAFIVE 5**

GLEE CLUB, THE
Tracks: / Glee club, The.
12" Single: Released Sep '84, on Abstract, by Abstract Sounds. Catalogue no: **12 ABS 027**

HAWKING
Tracks: / Hawking.
7" Single: Released Aug '85, on Creation, by Creation Records. Deleted Jul '88. Catalogue no: **CRE 021**
12" Single: Released Aug '85, on Creation, by Creation Records. Deleted Jul '88. Catalogue no: **CRE 021T**

Five Go Mad In Europe

DECADENCE
Tracks: / Decadence.
12" Single: Released Jul '84, on Criminal Damage, Catalogue no: **CRI 12117**

Five Guys Named Moe

FAIR VAN
Tracks: / Fair van.
12" Single: Released Feb '89, on Moe, Catalogue no: **MOE 001**

Five Happy Fellas

IT'S ILLEGAL, IT'S IMMORAL OR IT MAKES YOU FAT
Tracks: / It's illegal, it's immoral or it makes you fat / Party.
7" Single: Released Nov '82, on Crash, by Satril Records. Deleted '83. Catalogue no: **CRA 502**

Five Letters

CRAZY MAN
Tracks: / Crazy man / Yellow nights.
7" Single: Released Mar '81, on Earlobe, by Earlobe Records. Deleted '87. Catalogue no: **ELBS 102**

Five Miles To Midnight

CHOICES
Tracks: / Choices / Alternatives / Face / Tree growing wrong / Avoid the surgery / Victims of the carnivores.
12" Single: Released Aug '81, on Pax, by Pax Records. Catalogue no: **PAX 1**

Five Or Six

ANOTHER REASON
Tracks: / Another reason / Trial.
7" Single: Released '81, on Cherry Red, by Cherry Red Records. Deleted '87. Catalogue no: **CHERRY 19**

FOUR FROM FIVE OR SIX
Tracks: / This is for the moment / Think / Rushes / Theme.
12" Single: Released Oct '82, on Cherry Red, by Cherry Red Records. Deleted '87. Catalogue no: **12 CHERRY 43**

POLAR EXPLOSION
Tracks: / Polar explosion.
12" Single: Released Oct '81, on Cherry Red, by Cherry Red Records. Deleted '87. Catalogue no: **12 CHERRY 23**

Five Sapphires

DUKE OF EARL
Tracks: / Duke of Earl.
7" Single: Released Feb '79, on Warner Bros., by WEA Records. Catalogue no: **K 17307**

ONCE IN A WHILE
Tracks: / Once in a while.
7" Single: Released May '79, on Warner Bros., by WEA Records. Catalogue no: **K 17360**

Five Smith Brothers

Biographical details: This British vocal group enjoyed just one week of UK chart glory. In July 1955, back in the days when only a Top 20 was published, the quintet hit No.20 with *I'm In Favour Of Friendship*. It would appear that the British record buying public were not in favour of the Five Smith Brothers. Mr and Mrs. Smith's five little boys, as they became known on album titles, continued to parade their brand of music and comedy on the live circuit, concentrating particularly on Scottish and Irish audiences. (Bob McDonald 4/85).

I'M IN FAVOUR OF FRIENDSHIP
Tracks: / I'm in favour of friendship.
7" Single: Released Jul '55, on Decca, by Decca Records. Deleted Jul '58. Catalogue no: **F 10527**

Five Special

JUST A FEELING
Tracks: / Just a feeling.
7" Single: Released Jan '82, on Elektra, by Elektra Records (UK). Catalogue no: **K 12588**
12" Single: Released Jan '82, on Elektra, by Elektra Records (UK). Catalogue no: **K 12588T**

Five Star

ALL FALL DOWN
Tracks: / All fall down / First Avenue.
7" Single: Released Apr '85, on RCA, by BMG Records (UK). Catalogue no: **PB 40039**
12" Single: Released Apr '85, on RCA, by BMG Records (UK). Catalogue no: **PT 40040**

ANOTHER WEEKEND
Tracks: / Another weekend / Mews, The / Another weekend (extended remix)* / Another weekend (dub mix) (.12" only)
Apart from being remixed, 'Another Weekend' is backed with the Five Star hit-mix as constructed by Dakeyne of The Disco Mix Club featuring nine hits and all wrapped up in a magnificent poster bag". (RCA Records, May 1988).
7" Single: Released May '88, on RCA, by

BMG Records (UK). Deleted May '89. Catalogue no: **PB 42081**
12" Single: Released May '88, on RCA, by BMG Records (UK). Deleted May '89. Catalogue no: **PT 42082**

CAN'T WAIT ANOTHER MINUTE
Tracks: / Can't wait another minute.
7" Single: Released Apr '86, on Tent, by BMG Records (UK). Deleted Apr '89. Catalogue no: **PB 40697**

FIND THE TIME
Tracks: / Find the time / Sky.
7" Single: Released Jul '86, on Tent, by BMG Records (UK). Catalogue no: **PB 40799**
12" Single: Released Jul '86, on Tent, by BMG Records (UK). Catalogue no: **PT 40800**

IF I SAY YES
Tracks: / If I say yes / Let me down easy / Can't wait another minute / Say goodbye / Crazy / Winning.
12" Single: Released Nov '86, on RCA, by BMG Records (UK). Catalogue no: **PT 40982**
7" Single: Released Nov '86, on RCA, by BMG Records (UK). Catalogue no: **PB 40981**

LAST TAKEOVER
Tracks: / Last takeover.
7" Single: Released Aug '85, on RCA, by BMG Records (UK). Catalogue no: **PB 40353**
12" Single: Released Aug '85, on RCA, by BMG Records (UK). Catalogue no: **PT 40354**

LET ME BE THE ONE
Tracks: / Let me be the one / Beat 47 / Love games (on 12" only).
12" Single: Released Jul '85, on RCA, by BMG Records (UK). Catalogue no: **PT 40194**
7" Single: Released Jul '85, on RCA, by BMG Records (UK). Catalogue no: **PB 40193**

LET ME BE YOURS
Tracks: / Let me be yours / Let me be yours (remix) (Track on 12" version.) / Someone's in love (dub) (On 12" only.) / Can't wait another minute+ (+Track on CD single.).
12" Single: Released Nov '88, on RCA, by BMG Records (UK). Deleted Aug '89. Catalogue no: **PT 42344**
CD 5": Released Nov '88, on RCA, by BMG Records (UK). Deleted Jul '89. Catalogue no: **PD 42344**
7" Single: Released Nov '88, on RCA, by BMG Records (UK). Deleted Aug '89. Catalogue no: **PB 42343**

PROBLEMATIC
Tracks: / Problematic.
7" Single: Released Oct '83, on Tent, by BMG Records (UK). Catalogue no: **TENTT 4**
7" Single: Released Oct '83, on Tent, by BMG Records (UK). Catalogue no: **TENT 4**

RAIN OR SHINE
Tracks: / Rain or shine.
7" Single: Released Aug '86, on Tent, by BMG Records (UK). Deleted May '89. Catalogue no: **PB 40901**
12" Single: Released Aug '86, on Tent, by BMG Records (UK). Deleted May '89. Catalogue no: **PT 40902**

ROCK MY WORLD
Tracks: / Rock my world.
12" Single: Released Aug '88, on RCA, by BMG Records (UK). Deleted May '89. Catalogue no: **PT 42146**
7" Single: Released Jul '88, on RCA, by BMG Records (UK). Deleted May '89. Catalogue no: **PB 42145**

R.S.V.P.
Tracks: / R.S.V.P..
7" Single: Released Nov '85, on Tent, by BMG Records (UK). Catalogue no: **PB 40445**
12" Single: Released Nov '85, on Tent, by BMG Records (UK). Deleted May '89. Catalogue no: **PT 40446**

SLIGHTEST TOUCH
Tracks: / Slightest touch.
12" Single: Released Apr '87, on RCA, by BMG Records (UK). Deleted Aug '89. Catalogue no: **PT 41266**

SOMEWHERE SOMEBODY
Tracks: / Somewhere somebody / Have a good time.
12" Single: Released 21 Nov '87, on RCA, by BMG Records (UK). Deleted May '89. Catalogue no: **PT 41662**
7" Single: Released 21 Nov '87, on RCA, by BMG Records (UK). Deleted May '89. Catalogue no: **PB 41661**

STAY OUT OF MY LIFE
Tracks: / Stay out of my life / How dare you stay out of my life / If I say yes(Lew Hahn US dub mix) (on 12" version only).
7" Single: Released Jan '87, on RCA, by BMG Records (UK). Catalogue no: **PB 41131**
12" Single: Released Jan '87, on Tent, by BMG Records (UK). Catalogue no: **PT 41132**

STRONG AS STEEL
Tracks: / Strong as steel / Man, The / Can't wait another minute.
12" Single: Released Sep '87, on RCA, by BMG Records (UK). Deleted May '89. Catalogue no: **PT 41566**
Cassingle: Released Nov '78, on RCA, by BMG Records (UK). Deleted May '89. Catalogue no: **PB 41565C**
7" Single: Released Sep '87, on RCA, by BMG Records (UK). Deleted May '89. Catalogue no: **PB 41565**

SYSTEM ADDICT
Tracks: / System addict / Pure energy / Winning.
12" Single: Released Jan '86, on Tent, by BMG Records (UK). Deleted May '89. Catalogue no: **PT 40516**
CD 5": Released Jun '89, on Tent, by BMG Records (UK). Deleted May '89. Catalogue no: **PD 42647**
7" Single: Released Jan '86, on Tent, by BMG Records (UK). Deleted May '89. Catalogue no: **PB 40515**

THERE'S A BRAND NEW WORLD
Tracks: / There's a brand new world / U / Rescue me (Only on 12".).
12" Single: Released Sep '88, on RCA, by BMG Records (UK). Deleted May '89. Catalogue no: **PT 42236**
CD 5": Released Jun '89, on RCA, by BMG Records (UK). Deleted Jul '89. Catalogue no: **PD 42236**
7" Single: Released Sep '88, on RCA, by BMG Records (UK). Deleted May '89. Catalogue no: **PB 42235**

WHENEVER YOU'RE READY
Tracks: / Whenever you're ready.
7" Single: Released Aug '87, on Tent, by BMG Records (UK). Deleted May '89. Catalogue no: **PB 41477**
12" Single: Released Aug '87, on Tent, by BMG Records (UK). Deleted May '89. Catalogue no: **PT 41478**

WITH EVERY HEARTBEAT
Tracks: / With every heartbeat / Sound sweet / Let me be yours / With every heartbeat (dub).
7" Single: Released Mar '89, on RCA, by BMG Records (UK). Catalogue no: **PB 42693 G**
CD 5": Released Mar '89, on RCA, by BMG Records (UK). Deleted Jul '89. Catalogue no: **PD 42694**
Cassingle: Released Apr '89, on RCA, by BMG Records (UK). Catalogue no: **PK 42693**
7" Single: Released Mar '89, on RCA, by BMG Records (UK). Catalogue no: **PB 42693**
12" Single: Released Mar '89, on RCA, by BMG Records (UK). Catalogue no: **PT 42694**

Five TA

ANGEL (SINGLE)
Tracks: / Angel.
7" Single: Released May '84, on Torch Productions, by Torch Productions Records. Catalogue no: **JOW 1**
12" Single: Released May '84, on Torch Productions, by Torch Productions Records. Catalogue no: **JOWX 1**

HEAVEN
Tracks: / Heaven / Ting the bell.
7" Single: Released Nov '86, on Arista, by BMG Records (UK). Catalogue no: **VTA 3**
12" Single: Released Nov '86, on Arista, by BMG Records (UK). Catalogue no: **VTA 123**

LOW RIDER
Tracks: / Low rider (mezcal mix) / Law of the jungle, The.
12" Single: Released Apr '87, on Arista, by BMG Records (UK). Deleted '87. Catalogue no: **VTA 124 R**

MY BRILLIANT CAREER
Tracks: / My brilliant career / Ring the bell.
7" Single: Released Jun '86, on Arista, by BMG Records (UK). Catalogue no: **VTA 2**
12" Single: Released Jun '86, on Arista, by BMG Records (UK). Catalogue no: **VTA 122**

Five Thirty

CATCHER IN THE RYE
Tracks: / Catcher in the rye.
12" Single: Released Oct '85, on Other, by Waterfall Records. Catalogue no: **12 OTH 2**

WEIGHT OF THE WORLD
Tracks: / Weight of the world.
12" Single: Released Nov '85, on Other, by Waterfall Records. Catalogue no: **OTH 2**

Five Thousand Volts

DOCTOR KISS KISS
Tracks: / Doctor Kiss Kiss.
7" Single: Released Jul '76, on Philips, by Phonogram Ltd. Deleted Jul '79. Catalogue no: **6006 533**

I'M ON FIRE
Tracks: / I'm on fire.
7" Single: Released Sep '75, on Philips, by Phonogram Ltd. Deleted Sep '78. Catalogue no: **6006 464**

Five Year Plan

HIT THE BOTTLE
Tracks: / Hit the bottle.
7" Single: Released 8 Nov '88, on Breaking Down, Catalogue no: **BREAK 003**

NOTHING WILL GO WRONG
Tracks: / Nothing will go wrong / Brand new car / Give me a lifetime / Something to make you laugh.
12" Single: Released May '86, on Breaking Down, Catalogue no: **BREAK 001**

Fixx

Biographical details: This British band consists of Cy Cumin, Rupert Greenall, Jamie West-Oram and Adam Woods. Initially calling themselves the Portraits, the group were formed in London at the beginning of 1980. They changed their name to the Fixx after the arrival of guitarist West-Oram, who brought many fresh ideas with him. They managed to interest producer Rupert Hine in their songs and style, and the Fixx and Hine thus began a long-lasting collaboration; lead singer Curnin wrote the lyrics, and the music was composed collectively by the band. The Fixx cracked the UK charts for the first time in the spring of 1982, reaching No.54 with their single *Stand or fall*; this melancholy song was followed by another minor hit, *Red skies*. Both tracks came from the band's debut album *Shuttered room*, which got to No.54 on the British LP list. However, towards the end of the year, *Stand or fall* made a minor impression on the American Hot 100. This toehold signalled the way that the group's career was heading. In 1983 British acts mounted a major assault on the US charts, a phenomenon which statiscally surpassed the famous Breatles-led British Invasion of 1964. The Fixx became part of it, reaching No.20 with the haunting single *Saved by zero* and climbing to No.4 with the quirky and catchy *One thing leads to another*, these came from the LP *Reach the beach*. 1984's *Phantoms* album yielded the US No.15 single *Are we ourselves?*. Although their sound was basically, British techno-pop, their songs were not quite melodic or hook-laden enough to distinguish them from a mass of other UK acts in the same genre - hence their lack of major success in Britain. But the Americans warmed to the group's rock'n'roll tinges. (Bob MacDonald, 26th August 1985)
A UK new wave group formed by vocalist Cy Curnin and Adam Woods, recruiting Rupert Greenall on keyboards, Charlie Barrett on bass and guitarist Jamie West-Oram. They recorded for 101 as the Fix, then signed to MCA, who added an 'x'. Musicianship and fashionable good looks got first album *Shuttered room* an 18 month stay on the USA charts despite political content (anti-nuke etc); *Reach the beach* made the USA top ten albums, whereupon they concentrated on that market. Barrett left in 1982, replaced by Alfie Agius, then by Danny K Brown. They became archetypal new wave of second British invasion. (Donald Clarke, April 1989).

ARE WE OURSELVES
Tracks: / Are we ourselves.
7" Single: Released '84, on MCA, by MCA Records. Catalogue no: **FIXX 8**

DRIVEN OUT
Tracks: / Driven out / Shred of evidence / Flow, The (Available on 12" and CD only).
7" Single: Released Jul '89, on RCA, by BMG Records (UK). Catalogue no: **PV 49495**
CD 5": Released Mar '89, on RCA, by BMG Records (UK). Deleted Jul '89. Catalogue no: **PD 49496**
7" Single: Released Mar '89, on RCA, by BMG Records (UK). Catalogue no: **PB 49495**
12" Single: Released Mar '89, on RCA, by BMG Records (UK). Catalogue no: **PT 49496**

I WILL
Tracks: / I will.
7" Single: Released '85, on MCA, by MCA Records. Catalogue no: **FIXX 9**
12" Single: Released '85, on MCA, by MCA Records. Catalogue no: **FIXXT 9**

LESS CITIES MORE MOVING PEOPLE
Tracks: / Less cities more moving people.
12" Single: Released '84, on MCA, by MCA Records. Catalogue no: **FIXXT 7**
7" Single: Released '84, on MCA, by MCA Records. Catalogue no: **FIXX 7**

LOST PLANES
Tracks: / Lost planes / I've been there before.
7" Single: Released Apr '81, on Polydor, by Polydor Ltd. Deleted Apr '86. Catalogue no: **CLUB 101**

RED SKIES
Tracks: / Red skies / Is it by instinct.
7" Single: Released Jul '82, on MCA, by MCA Records. Deleted Jul '85. Catalogue no: **FIXX 3**
12" Single: Released Jul '82, on MCA, by MCA Records. Deleted Jul '85. Catalogue no: **FIXXT 3**

SECRET SEPARATION
Tracks: / Secret separation / Sense the adventure / Rediscover (Extra track on 12" version only).
7" Single: Released Jun '86, on MCA, by MCA Records. Catalogue no: **FIXX 10**
12" Single: Released Jun '86, on MCA, by MCA Records. Catalogue no: **FIXXT 10**

SOME PEOPLE
Tracks: / Some people / I found you.
7" Single: Released Feb '82, on MCA, by MCA Records. Deleted Feb '87. Catalogue no: **FIXX 1**

STAND OR FALL
Tracks: / Stand or fall / Strain.
7" Single: Released Apr '82, on MCA, by MCA Records. Deleted Apr '85. Catalogue no: **FIXX 2**

Fizzbombs

SIGN ON THE LINE
Tracks: / Sign on the line / Lines that, The.
7" Single: Released 30 May '87, on Narodnik, by Narodnik Records. Catalogue no: **NRK 003**

SURFIN' WINTER
Tracks: / Surfin' winter.
12" Single: Released May '88, on Calculous, Catalogue no: **KIT 002T**
7" Single: Released Apr '88, on Calculous, Catalogue no: **KIT 002**

Flack, Roberta

Biographical details: This American singer and pianist, born in Asheville, North Carolina in 1937, had the benefit of a very musical parentage: her father was a jazz musician, and her mother was a classical pianist and church organist. Roberta was a skilled pianist by the time she entered her teens; by the time she left her teenage years, she was in the process of gaining degrees in music and education from Howard Univsity, Washington D.C. Roberta then had a spell as a teacher, during which she augmented her income by accompanying opera singers in restaurants. In 1967, the year that she turned 30, she finally began a full-time performing career, singing and playing jazz and soul music in Washington clubs. Flack released her debut album *First take* in 1969, and it aroused a reasonable amount of interest. 1971 saw her begin a sporadic but fruitful collaboration with the brilliantly talented singer/pianist/arranger Donny Hathaway, who was also a former Howard student. Their rendition of Carole King's *You've got a friend* reached No.29 on the US charts, while James Taylor was simultaneously enjoying a No.1 hit with the same song.
Flack's career suddenly spiralled in the spring of 1972, when a track from her 1969 LP became a smash single - her ethereal, tender rendition of *The first time ever I saw your face*, a ballad penned by British folk singer/songwriter Ewan MacColl, went to No.1 in America for six weeks after being featured in the Clint Eastwood film *Play Misty for me*; it reached No.14 in Britain. Later that year Flack teamed again with Hathaway for the single *Where is love*, which climbed to No.5 in the US and No.29 in the UK. Roberta never stayed winin the confines of one genre. Her beautiful, delicat voice sang material that combined soul, jazz, MoR, blues, pop and classical influences. Slow ballads were her forte, although she was sometimes accused of striving for technical perfection at the expense of emotion and warmth. 1973 brought the singer her second US No.1 smash - her rendition of *Killing me softly with his song* made the number an instant standard, and held the top slot for five weeks; it reached No.6 in Britain. Her third and final American chart-topper, the infectious *Feel like makin' love*, made its mark in 1974. Flack's subsequent solo career was rather dull and lifeless, and

her major artistic and commercial triumphs were saved for her duets with male vocalists. She and Hathaway reached the US No.2 position with 1978's ultra-romantic springtime smash *The closer I get to you*, and obtained a No.3 placing in Britain in 1980 with an archive uptempo recording, *Back together again*. Between the two hits, however, there was tragedy - Donny Hathaway committed suicide in January 1979. (Bob MacDonald, 31st August 1985)

One of the USA's favourite singers since the '70's jazz influenced pop rather than soul, born in 1937 in North Carolina. Discovered by Les McCann who took her to Atlantic for 13 chart albums 1970-82 including No.1. album *First take*, which included *The first time I ever saw your face*, written by Ewen McColl: number one in the USA for six weeks in 1972 after being featured in the Clint Eastwood film *Play Misty for me*, first of 11 top 40 singles including duets with Donny Hathaway and Peabo Bryson (after Hathaway's untimely death). Another hit album was called *Chapter two* while *Killing me softly* in 1973 brought her second number one single with the title track; the album won three Grammies altogether. (Donald Clarke, April 1989).

BACK TOGETHER AGAIN
Tracks: / Back together again / Only heaven can wait.
7" Single: Released '80, on Atlantic, by WEA Records. Catalogue no: **K 11481**
12" Single: Released '80, on Atlantic, by WEA Records. Catalogue no: **K 11481 T**

CLOSER I GET TO YOU, THE
7" Single: Released May '78, on Atlantic, by WEA Records. Deleted May '81. Catalogue no: **K 11099**

DON'T MAKE ME WAIT TOO LONG
Tracks: / Don't make me wait too long.
7" Single: Released Aug '80, on Atlantic, by WEA Records. Deleted Aug '83. Catalogue no: **K 11555**

FEEL LIKE MAKING LOVE (SINGLE)
Tracks: / Feel like making love.
7" Single: Released Aug '74, on Atlantic, by WEA Records. Deleted Aug '77. Catalogue no: **K 10467**

FIRST TIME I EVER SAW YOUR FACE
Tracks: / First time ever I saw your face / Killing me softly with his song.
7" Single: Released '84, on Atlantic, by WEA Records. Catalogue no: **K 10845**
7" Single: Released '72, on Atlantic, by WEA Records. Catalogue no: **K 10161**

KILLING ME SOFTLY WITH HIS SONG
Tracks: / Killing me softly with his song.
7" Single: Released Feb '73, on Atlantic, by WEA Records. Deleted Feb '76. Catalogue no: **K 10282**

KILLING ME SOFTLY WITH HIS SONG (OLD GOLD)
Tracks: / Killing me softly with his song / First time ever I saw your face, The.
7" Single: Released Jun '88, on Old Gold, by Old Gold Records. Catalogue no: **OG 9524**

LOVE IS A WAITING GAME
Tracks: / Love is a waiting game / Back together again.
12" Single: Released '81, on Atlantic, by WEA Records. Catalogue no: **LV 45**
7" Single: Released '81, on Atlantic, by WEA Records. Catalogue no: **K 11586**

MAKING LOVE
Tracks: / Making love / Jesse.
7" Single: Released '82, on Atlantic, by WEA Records. Catalogue no: **K 11715**
12" Single: Released '82, on Atlantic, by WEA Records. Catalogue no: **K 11715 T**

UH-UH OOH-OOH LOOK OUT(HERE IT COMES)
Tracks: / Uh uh ooh ooh look out (here it comes).
7" Single: Released Jun '89, on Atlantic, by WEA Records. Catalogue no: **A 8941**
12" Single: Released Jun '89, on Atlantic, by WEA Records. Catalogue no: **A 8941T**
Cassingle: Released Jun '89, on Atlantic, by WEA Records. Catalogue no: **A 8941C**

WHERE IS THE LOVE
Tracks: / Where is the love.
7" Single: Released Aug '72, on Atlantic, by WEA Records. Deleted Aug '75. Catalogue no: **K 10202**

WHERE IS THE LOVE (OLD GOLD)
Tracks: / Where is the love.
7" Single: Released Jan '85, on Old Gold, by Old Gold Records. Catalogue no: **OG 9502**

YOU ARE MY HEAVEN
Tracks: / You are my heaven / I'll love you forever.
7" Single: Released Jan '80, on Atlantic, by WEA Records. Deleted '83. Catalogue no: **K 11414**

Flag of Convenience

EXILES
Tracks: / Exiles.
12" Single: Released Aug '88, on MCM (1), Catalogue no: **MCM 002**

LIFE ON THE TELEPHONE
Tracks: / Life on the telephone.
7" Single: Released Sep '82, on Sire (USA), Catalogue no: **SIR 4057**

NEW HOUSE
Tracks: / New house.
7" Single: Released Apr '86, on MCM (1), Catalogue no: **MCM 186**

SHOULD I EVER GO DEAF
Tracks: / Should I ever go deaf.
12" Single: Released Oct '87, on Sure Delight, by Sure Delight Records. Catalogue no: **SDT 3**
12" Single: Released Oct '87, on MCM (2), by MCM Records. Catalogue no: **MCM 001Flair**

CHASIN' THE RAIN
Tracks: / Chasin' the rain.
7" Single: Released Jun '88, on Champion, by Champion Records. Catalogue no: **CHAMP 80**
12" Single: Released Jun '88, on Champion, by Champion Records. Deleted Aug '89. Catalogue no: **CHAMP 12-80**

G.Q.
Tracks: / G.Q. / G.Q. (version).
7" Single: Released Mar '88, on Champion, by Champion Records. Catalogue no: **CHAMP 68**
12" Single: Released Mar '88, on Champion, by Champion Records. Catalogue no: **CHAMP 1268**

Flairck

EAST WEST EXPRESS
Tracks: / East West express.
7" Single: Released Mar '83, on Polydor, by Polydor Ltd. Catalogue no: **POSP 568**

TRICK OF THE NIGHT
Tracks: / Seven card tango / Trick of the night, A.
7" Single: Released Jan '87, on Columbia, by EMI Records. Deleted Jul '87. Catalogue no: **DB 9134**

Flame

ON THE STRENGTH
Tracks: / On the strength / On the strength (extended version) / On the strength (House is surrounded mix).
12" Single: Released Aug '89, on Epic, by CBS Records. Catalogue no: **655 238 6**
CD 5": Released Aug '89, on Epic, by CBS Records. Catalogue no: **655 238 2**
7" Single: Released Aug '89, on Epic, by CBS Records. Catalogue no: **655 238 7**

THIS TIME TOMORROW
Tracks: / This time tomorrow.
12" Single: Released Sep '89, on Anxious, by Anxious Records. Catalogue no: **NERVT 8**
CD 5": Released Sep '89, on Anxious, by Anxious Records. Catalogue no: **CDNERV 8**
7" Single: Released Sep '89, on Anxious, by Anxious Records. Catalogue no: **NERV 8**

X-STREAMS
Tracks: / X-streams / Built for guilt.
7" Single: Released Jun '89, on Anxious, by Anxious Records. Catalogue no: **NERV 005**
12" Single: Released Jun '89, on Anxious, by Anxious Records. Catalogue no: **NERVT 005**

Flames

YOUR LOVE IS SLIPPIN AWAY
Tracks: / Your love is slippin' away / That's what you told me.
7" Single: Released Jan '83, on Masquerade, Catalogue no: **MASQ 2**
12" Single: Released Nov '82, on Thrust, Deleted Nov '85. Catalogue no: **RUFF 3**

Flamin' Groovies

SHAKE SOME ACTION
Tracks: / Shake some action.
7" Single: Released Aug '87, on ABC (indie), Catalogue no: **ABCS 015**

Flaming Ember

WESTBOUND NO.9
Tracks: / Westbound no.9.
7" Single: Released Jan '85, on HDH (Holland/Dozier/Holland), by Demon Records. Catalogue no: **HDH 4512**

Flaming Hands

BREAK DOWN AND CRY
Tracks: / Break down and cry / Cross my heart.
7" Single: Released Feb '86, on Sierra, by Sierra Records. Deleted Jun '87. Catalogue no: **FED 20**
12" Single: Released Feb '86, on Sierra, by Sierra Records. Deleted Jun '87. Catalogue no: **FED 20T**

Flaming Lips

DRUG MACHINE
Tracks: / Drug machine.
7" Single: Released Jun '89, on Glitterhouse, Catalogue no: **EFA 40153**

Flaming Mussolinis

DIFFERENT KIND OF LOVE
Tracks: / Different kind of love / Angels fall down / Different kind of remix / Prime time T.V. / Freeze thaw / Criticize (single version) / Criticize (critical edit) / Criticize (acapella) / Criticize (Critical dub).
Note: *Available on 12" only.
7" Single: Released Nov '87, on Epic, by CBS Records. Deleted Jun '88. Catalogue no: **MUZ 2**
12" Single: Released Nov '87, on Epic, by CBS Records. Deleted Jun '88. Catalogue no: **MUZ T2**

GIRL ON A TRAIN
Tracks: / Girl on a train / Green monkey fever.
7" Single: Released Aug '87, on Epic, by CBS Records. Catalogue no: **MUZ 1**
12" Single: Released Aug '87, on Epic, by CBS Records. Catalogue no: **MUZT 1**

MASUKA DAN
Tracks: / Masuka Dan / Street garden.
12" Single: Released May '86, on Portrait, by CBS Records. Deleted '86. Catalogue no: **TA 7105**
7" Single: Released May '86, on Portrait, by CBS Records. Deleted '86. Catalogue no: **A 7105**

MY CLEOPATRA
Tracks: / My Cleopatra / Privilege.
7" Single: Released Jan '86, on Portrait, by CBS Records. Catalogue no: **A 6833**
12" Single: Released Jan '86, on Portrait, by CBS Records. Catalogue no: **TX 6833**

SWALLOW GLASS
Tracks: / Swallow glass / Movie girl.
7" Single: Released Jun '86, on Portrait, by CBS Records. Catalogue no: **A 6497**

Flamingo Express

HONEYMOON IN SPAIN
Tracks: / Honeymoon in Spain.
7" Single: Released Jul '83, on Monarch, by Monarch Records. Catalogue no: **MON 004**

Flamingos

BOOGALOO PARTY
Tracks: / Boogaloo party / Jenny take a ride.
7" Single: Released Oct '80, on Phonogram, by Phonogram Ltd. Deleted Oct '83. Catalogue no: **CUT 114**
7" Single: Released Jun '69, on Philips, by Phonogram Ltd. Deleted Jun '72. Catalogue no: **BF 1786**

IT'S GOTTA BE BAD
Tracks: / It's gotta be bad / Sometimes.
7" Single: Released May '82, on Cambridge, by Cambridge Records. Deleted '84. Catalogue no: **ULT 1001**

THIS HEAT
Tracks: / This heat.
12" Single: Released Aug '85, on Rorschach Testing, by Rorschach Testing Records. Catalogue no: **ROR 4**

Flanders, Michael

LITTLE DRUMMER BOY
Tracks: / Little drummer boy.
7" Single: Released Feb '59, on Parlophone, by EMI Records. Deleted Feb '62. Catalogue no: **R 4528**

Flash

ALLEYCAT
Tracks: / Alleycat / Caroline.
7" Single: Released May '80, on Shock Rock (Ireland), by Outlet Records. Deleted '83. Catalogue no: **SRS 503**

KEEP ON ROLLING
Tracks: / Keep on rolling / Keep on rolling (instrumental).
7" Single: Released Oct '81, on Epic, by CBS Records. Deleted Oct '84. Catalogue no: **EPCA 1641**

Flash And The Furious

FLASH IT TO THE BEAT
Tracks: / Flash it to the beat.
12" Single: Released Nov '87, on Bozo Meko (USA), Catalogue no: **BM 001**

Flash Cats

XMAS WISH
Tracks: / Xmas wish / In the bleak midwinter.
7" Single: Released Dec '82, on Lark, Deleted Dec '85. Catalogue no: **LS 2**

Flash, Diana

MY GOLLY ONE
Tracks: / My golly one.
7" Single: Released Nov '88, on T.B.Sharp, Catalogue no: **UNKNOWN**

SAVING ON MY LOVE
Tracks: / Saving on my love / My love (version).
12" Single: Released May '86, on Hawkeye, by Hawkeye Records. Catalogue no: **HD 74**

Flash & The Pan

Biographical details: The nucleus of Flash & The Pan is Harry Vanda & George Young, two Australian singers/musicians/songwriters/producers. These two gentlemen first became famous as the backbone of the Easybeats, their nation's premier group of the Sixties; masterminded John Paul Young's (no relation) international 1978 hit *Love is in the air*. Their songs have been recorded by many British and American stars. Flash & The Pan were born in 1976. The Aussie band, which has usually contained five men including Vanda & Young, achieved a minor UK hit with their highly original 1978 single *And the band played on (Down among the dead men)* - this reached the UK No.54 position, and was a refreshing piece of novelty pop in much the same way that the Buggles' *Video killed the radio star* was, a year later. But while Flash & The Pan remained very big down under, the fact that it has always been a part-time project has impaired their prospects of major international success. The band's third album *Headlines* yielded the 1983 UK Top Tenner *Waiting for a train* - with Steve Wright's nasal vocals plus the group's usual combination of a quirky hook and an infectious rhythm, this single obtained a No.7 placing on the British listings. As far as UK record buyers were concerned Flash & The Pan had two enjoyable one-off hits, in 1978 and 1983; but they have achieved more consistent success in Scandinavia, where they have always been very popular, and of course Australia. (Bob MacDonald, 31st August 1985).

AND THE BAND PLAYED ON (DOWN AMONG THE DEAD MEN)
Tracks: / And the band played on.
7" Single: Released Aug '78, on Ensign, by Ensign Records. Deleted Aug '81. Catalogue no: **ENY 15**

AYLA
Tracks: / Ayla / Your love is strange / Ayla (disco mix)* (* on CD single only) / Ayla (outta town mix)* (* on CD single only).
12" Single: Released 27 Jun '88, on Epic, by CBS Records. Deleted Jan '89. Catalogue no: **651120 6**
CD 5": Released 18 Jul '88, on Epic, by CBS Records. Deleted Jan '89. Catalogue no: **651120 2**
7" Single: Released 27 Jun '88, on Epic, by CBS Records. Deleted Jan '89. Catalogue no: **651120 7**

MEDIA MAN
Tracks: / Media man / Make your own cross.
7" Single: Released 20 Jul '80, on Ensign, by Ensign Records. Deleted '83. Catalogue no: **ENY39**

WAITING FOR A TRAIN
Tracks: / Waiting for a train.
7" Single: Released May '83, on Easybeat, Catalogue no: **EASY 1**

WAITING FOR A TRAIN 89
Tracks: / Waiting for a train.
12" Single: Released Jan '89, on Cha-Cha, by Cha-Cha Records. Catalogue no: **CHATT 1**
CD 5": Released Jan '89, on Cha-Cha, by Cha-Cha Records. Catalogue no: **CDCHAS 1**
7" Single: Released Jan '89, on Cha-Cha, by Cha-Cha Records. Catalogue no: **CHAS 1**

Flat Tops

ROCK'N'ROLL ROMEOS
Tracks: / Rock'n'roll romeos
7" Single: Released Nov '81, on Mean, by Mean Records. Deleted Nov '84. Catalogue no: **MEAN 7**

Flatbackers

BUZZ GOING ROUND
Tracks: / Buzz going round
7" Single: Released Jan '81, on Red Shadow, Deleted Jan '84. Catalogue no: **REDS 007**

PUMPING IRON
Tracks: / Pumping iron / Kid from Kid-

brooke.
7" Single: Released Aug '80, on Red Shadow, Deleted '83. Catalogue no: **REDS 005**

SERENADE OF LOVE
Tracks: / Serenade of love / Try a little harder.
7" Single: Released Apr '81, on Deram, by London Records. Deleted '85. Catalogue no: **DM 440**

Flatmates

HAPPY ALL THE TIME
Tracks: / Happy all the time.
Note: 12" version includes 4 extra tracks
7" Single: Released Mar '87, on Subway, by Subway Records. Catalogue no: **SUBWAY 9**
12" Single: Released Mar '87, on Subway, by Subway Records. Catalogue no: **SUBWAY 9T**

HEAVEN KNOWS
Tracks: / Heaven knows.
CD 5": Released Sep '88, on Subway, by Subway Records. Catalogue no: **SUBWAY 21 CD**
7" Single: Released Sep '88, on Subway, by Subway Records. Catalogue no: **SUBWAY 21**
12" Single: Released Sep '88, on Subway, by Subway Records. Catalogue no: **SUBWAY 21 T**

I COULD BE IN HEAVEN
Tracks: / I could be in heaven.
7" Single: Released Sep '86, on Subway, by Subway Records. Catalogue no: **SUBWAY 6**

JANICE LONG SESSION: FLATMATES
12" Single: Released May '88, on Night Tracks, by Pinnacle Records. Catalogue no: **SFNT 011**

SHIMMER
Tracks: / Shimmer.
12" Single: Released 5 Mar '88, on Subway, by Subway Records. Catalogue no: **SUBWAY 17T**
7" Single: Released 5 Mar '88, on Subway, by Subway Records. Catalogue no: **SUBWAY 17**

YOU'RE GONNA CRY
Tracks: / You're gonna cry.
12" Single: Released Jul '87, on Subway, by Subway Records. Catalogue no: **SUBWAY 14T**
7" Single: Released Jul '87, on Subway, by Subway Records. Catalogue no: **SUBWAY 14**

Flatt, Lester

Biographical details: Born in 1914 in Tennessee, Lester Flatt became famous via his association with Earl Scruggs. The duo was formed in 1948, after both had been members of Bill Monroe's Blue Grass Boys. A noted country/blues fusionist and bluegrass pioneer, Monroe's seminal band proved to be a valuable training ground for the pair's later career. With Flatt on acoustic guitar and vocals and Scruggs on banjo (an instrument on which he was a virtuoso, thanks to his unusual three-finger style). The duo initially called themselves the Foggy Mountain Boys. In 1949 they recorded their now famous instrumental showcase single *Foggy mountain breakdown*. 1962 brought Flatt & Scruggs one of their biggest success on the American country-and-western charts, *Ballad of Jet Clampett*, this was the theme from the television series *Beverly Hillbillies*. Their only appearance on the UK pop charts occurred in 1967 - a '65 re-recording (whose sales were combined for chart purposes) of *Foggy mountain breakdown* reached No.39; the tune also made minor waves of the US pop listings during this period. This sudden success was duo to the fact tahat the music was used as the theme for the movie *Bonnie & Clyde*. Flatt & Scruggs parted company in 1969. The latter formed a touring band playing folk-rock and country-rock, and played concerts with artists of a much younger generation, while Flatt stayed within the confines of bluegrass. Lester Flatt died in Nashville in May 1979 at the age of 64. (Bob MacDonald, 31st August 1985)
Bluegrass guitarist and singer (1914-79) who worked in textile mills, turned pro, worked with Charlie Monroe, then for Bill Monroe's Bluegrass Boys from 1944, where he met Earl Scruggs (born in 1924), one of the all-time great banjo players. They left Monroe in 1948 and co-led their own legendary outfit until 1969, when Flatt left. The sundering of the team was a terrible irony: they were unknown outside country music until the late '50's, when the folk revival discovered them at festivals; only long after that were they no longer playing bluegrass, to Flatt's annoyance. Scruggs formed the Earl Scruggs Review with his multi-instrumentalist sons; Flatt remained a bluegrass stalwart. (Donald Clarke, April 1989).

FOGGY MOUNTAIN BREAKDOWN
Tracks: / Foggy mountain breakdown.
7" Single: Released Nov '65, on CBS, by CBS Records. Deleted Nov '68. Catalogue no: **CBS 3038**

Flavin, Mick

JENNIFER JOHNSTON AND ME
Tracks: / Jennifer Johnston and me / You'll be home.
7" Single: Released May '89, on Ritz, by Ritz Records. Catalogue no: **RITZ 200**
Cassingle: Released May '89, on Ritz, by Ritz Records. Catalogue no: **RITZC 200**

Flax, Fogwell

ONE NINE FOR SANTA
Tracks: / One nine for Santa / Cheers to you at Christmas.
7" Single: Released Dec '81, on EMI, by EMI Records. Deleted Dec '84. Catalogue no: **EMI 5255**

Flee-Rekkers

GREEN JEANS
Tracks: / Green jeans.
7" Single: Released May '60, on Triumph, Deleted May '63. Catalogue no: **RGM 1008**

Fleetwood Mac

Biographical details: Much like the Bee Gees, Fleetwood Mac had two separate and distinct periods of success - the first was during the late Sixties and was based in Britain; the second started on the other side of the Atlantic in the mid-Seventies, with a radically changed sound and image, and propelled the group to worldwide megastardom. The group was originally formed in 1967 by guitarist/vocalist/songwriter Peter Green, who enlisted drummer Mick Fleetwood and bassist John McVie and thus derived the band's name (although McVie was initially reluctant to join, and almost didn't). The classic and most successful line-up of the late Sixties featured Green, Fleetwood and McVie plus Danny Kirwan and Jeremy Spencer; these five men (all British) stayed together from August 1968 till May 1970. After a long period of numerous personnel changes, the second classic Mac line-up emerged in January 1975, and stayed intact into the Eighties: three Britons (Fleetwood, McVie and wife Christine McVie) were augmented by an American duo (lindsey Buckinham and Stevie Nicks). The first Fleetwood Mac were at the forefront of Britain's late Sixties blues boom. Their eponymous debut album, released in 1968, reached No.4 and logged 37 weeks on the UK LP chart. Further LP successes with *Mr Wonderful, Pious bird of good omen* and *Then play on* were accompanied by even greater acceptance on the UK singles chart: 1969 brought a No.1 smash with the entrancing, now legendary instrumental *Albatross*, followed by two No.2 hits with *Man of the world* and *Oh well* - all three tracks were written by Green. His departure in 1970 left a major hole in the band - after one mainly instrumental album, his unique talent went into retirement for several years, before he re-emerged in 1979 with a series of low-key solo releases. Spencer joined a religious sect in 1971, leaving another major gap. By this time, former Chicken Shack singer Christine Perfect (who had just become Christine McVie) had joined Fleetwood Mac. From 1970 till 1975, a succession of personnel changes dogged the band. Of all the players who came and went, the most notable was US guitarist/singer Bob Welch, who later enjoyed solo success on the American charts. During this transitional period, Fleetwood Mac faded into obscurity in the UK (apart from a 1973 re-issue of *Albatross*, which flew to No.2) but gradually built up a live following in the States. The American influence reached its completion in 1975 with the arrival of a previously unknown US boyfriend/girlfriend duo, Lindsey Buckingham and Stevie Nicks. With a new Californian rock sound, combining excellent vocal harmonies, irresistible melodies and fine individual performances, the new Fleetwood Mac gradually became a worldwide phenomenon. The 1975 *Fleetwood Mac* album reached the US No.1 position a year after release, fuelled by a series of hit singles. 1977's *Rumours* LP - recorded while all the band members were breaking off romantic relationships - became one of the biggest sellers of all time. 1979's *Tusk* and 1982's *Mirage* were also hugely successful. (Bob MacDonald, 2nd Sept 1985)
A UK Blues band in the '60's; a USA AOR/rock band in the '70's. The lineup included John McVie, guitarist Peter Green and drummer Mick Fleetwood, who all left John Mayall's Bluesbreakers in 1967. Green left in 1970, replaced by McVie's wife, Christine Perfect (ex Chicken Shack). They had relocated to the USA West Coast and recruited Lindsay Buckingham and Stephanie 'Stevie' Nicks, a boy/girl guitar/vocal duo who first appeared on *Fleetwood Mac* in 1975: they continued with a new success. *Rumours* in 1976 sold 25 million world-wide; *Tusk* was much less successful, perhaps overproduced by Buckingham. The relationships in the band failed (McVies, Buckingham/Nicks), fueling rumours, but various combinations of these wrote 12 songs for *Tango in the night*, one of their best. Buckingham left that year (he never liked touring), replaced by Rick Vito and Billy Burnette on guitars and vocals. (Donald Clarke, April 1989).

ALBATROSS (SINGLE)
Tracks: / Albatross / Man of the world / Black magic woman (On 12" & CD only.) / Love that burns (On 12" & CD only.).
12" Single: Released 13 Feb '89, on CBS, by CBS Records. Catalogue no: **654613 8**
CD 5": Released 6 Feb '89, on CBS, by CBS Records. Deleted 10 Jul '89. Catalogue no: **654 613-2**
7" Single: Released 6 Feb '89, on CBS, by CBS Records. Deleted 10 Jul '89. Catalogue no: **654 613-7**
12" Single: Released 6 Feb '89, on CBS, by CBS Records. Deleted 10 Jul '89. Catalogue no: **654 613-6**

ALBATROSS (SINGLE) (2)
Tracks: / Albatross.
7" Single: Released Dec '68, on Blue Horizon, by Ace Records. Deleted Dec '71. Catalogue no: **57 3145**
7" Single: Released May '73, on CBS, by CBS Records. Deleted May '76. Catalogue no: **CBS 8306**

AS LONG AS YOU FOLLOW
Tracks: / As long as you follow / Oh well / Goldust woman (CD only).
12" Single: Released Nov '88, on Warner Bros., by WEA Records. Catalogue no: **W 7644T**
CD 5": Released Dec '88, on Warner Bros., by WEA Records. Catalogue no: **W 7644 CD**
7" Single: Released Nov '88, on Warner Bros., by WEA Records. Catalogue no: **W 7644**

BIG LOVE
Tracks: / Big love / You & I (part1).
7" Single: Released Mar '87, on WEA, by WEA Records. Deleted Jul '88. Catalogue no: **W 8398**

BLACK MAGIC WOMAN (SINGLE)
Tracks: / Black magic woman.
7" Single: Released Apr '68, on Blue Horizon, by Ace Records. Deleted Apr '71. Catalogue no: **57 3138**

DON'T STOP
Tracks: / Don't stop.
7" Single: Released Apr '77, on Warner Bros., by WEA Records. Deleted '80. Catalogue no: **K 16930**

DREAMS
Tracks: / Dreams.
7" Single: Released Jul '77, on Warner Bros., by WEA Records. Deleted '80. Catalogue no: **K 16969**

EVERYWHERE
Tracks: / Everywhere / When I see you again.
12" Single: Released 27 Feb '88, on WEA, by WEA Records. Catalogue no: **W 8143T**
7" Single: Released 27 Feb '88, on WEA, by WEA Records. Catalogue no: **W 8143**

EVERYWHERE (IMPORT)
Tracks: / Everywhere.
Note: Limited edition with 3 extra tracks.
CD 5": Released Oct '88, on WEA (Germany), by WEA Records. Catalogue no: **920907 2**

FAMILY MAN
Tracks: / Family man / Down endless street.
12" Single: Released Nov '87, on Warner Bros., by WEA Records. Catalogue no: **W 8114 T**
7" Single: Released Nov '87, on Warner Bros., by WEA Records. Catalogue no: **W 8114**

FARMER'S DAUGHTER
Tracks: / Farmer's daughter / Dreams.
7" Single: Released Feb '81, on Warner Bros., by WEA Records. Deleted Feb '84. Catalogue no: **K 17746**

GO YOUR OWN WAY
Tracks: / Go your own way.
7" Single: Released Feb '77, on Warner Bros., by WEA Records. Deleted Feb '80. Catalogue no: **K 16872**

GREEN MANALISHI (WITH THE TWO PRONGED CROWN)
Tracks: / Green manalishi.
7" Single: Released May '70, on Reprise, by WEA Records. Deleted May '73. Catalogue no: **RS 27007**

GYPSY
Tracks: / Gypsy.
7" Single: Released Sep '82, on Warner Bros., by WEA Records. Deleted '85. Catalogue no: **K 17997**

HOLD ME
Tracks: / Hold me / No questions asked / I loved another woman (live).
12" Single: Released Feb '89, on Warner Bros., by WEA Records. Catalogue no: **W 7528T**
CD 5": Released Feb '89, on Warner Bros., by WEA Records. Catalogue no: **W 7528CD**
7" Single: Released Feb '89, on Warner Bros., by WEA Records. Catalogue no: **W 7528**

ISN'T IT MIDNIGHT
Tracks: / Isn't it midnight / Mystified / Say you love me* / Gypsy*.
Note: * Only on the 12" version.
7" Single: Released Jun '88, on Warner Bros., by WEA Records. Catalogue no: **W 7860**
12" Single: Released Jun '88, on Warner Bros., by WEA Records. Catalogue no: **W 7860 T**

LITTLE LIES
Tracks: / Ricky / Little lies.
Cassingle: Released Aug '87, on Warner Bros., by WEA Records. Deleted Jul '88. Catalogue no: **W 8291C**
7" Single: Released Aug '87, on Warner Bros., by WEA Records. Deleted Jul '88. Catalogue no: **W 8291**
12" Single: Released Aug '87, on Warner Bros., by WEA Records. Deleted Jul '88. Catalogue no: **W 8291 T**

MAN OF THE WORLD
Tracks: / Man of the world.
7" Single: Released Apr '69, on Immediate, Deleted Apr '72. Catalogue no: **IM 080**

NEED YOUR LOVE SO BAD
Tracks: / Need your love so bad.
7" Single: Released Jul '68, on Blue Horizon, by Ace Records. Deleted Jul '71. Catalogue no: **57 3139**

NOT THAT FUNNY
Tracks: / Not that funny / Save me a place.
7" Single: Released Mar '80, on Warner Bros., by WEA Records. Deleted '83. Catalogue no: **K 17577**

OH DIANE
Tracks: / Oh Diane / Only over you.
7" Single: Released Dec '82, on Warner Bros., by WEA Records. Deleted '85. Catalogue no: **FLEET 1**

OH WELL
Tracks: / Oh well.
7" Single: Released Oct '69, on Reprise, by WEA Records. Deleted Oct '72. Catalogue no: **RS 27000**

RHIANNON
Tracks: / Rhiannon.
7" Single: Released Mar '78, on Reprise, by WEA Records. Deleted '81. Catalogue no: **K 14430**

SARA
Tracks: / Sara.
7" Single: Released Dec '79, on Warner Bros., by WEA Records. Deleted '82. Catalogue no: **K 17533**

SAY YOU LOVE ME
Tracks: / Say you love me.
7" Single: Released Nov '76, on Reprise, by WEA Records. Deleted Nov '79. Catalogue no: **K 14447**

SEVEN WONDERS
Tracks: / Seven wonders / Book of miracles.
12" Pic: Released Jun '87, on Warner Bros., by WEA Records. Deleted Jul '88. Catalogue no: **W 8317TP**
7" Single: Released Jun '87, on Warner Bros., by WEA Records. Deleted Jul '88. Catalogue no: **W 8317**
12" Single: Released Jun '87, on Warner Bros., by WEA Records. Deleted Jul '88. Catalogue no: **W 8317T**

THINK ABOUT ME
Tracks: / Think about me / Honey hi.
7" Single: Released May '80, on Warner Bros., by WEA Records. Deleted May '85. Catalogue no: **K 17614**

TUSK (SINGLE) (see panel on next page)
Tracks: / Tusk / Never make me cry.
7" Single: Released Oct '79, on Warner Bros., by WEA Records. Deleted '82. Catalogue no: **K 17468**

YOU MAKE LOVING FUN
Tracks: / You make loving fun.
7" Single: Released Oct '77, on Warner

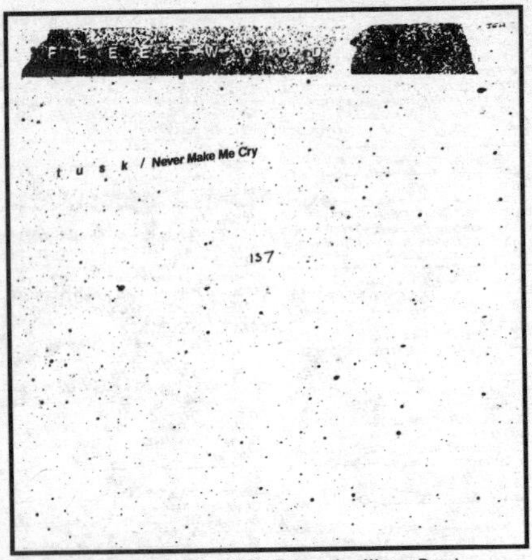

FLEETWOOD MAC - TUSK (Released on Warner Bros.)

Bros., by WEA Records. Deleted '80. Catalogue no: **K 17013**

Fleetwood, Mick

YOU WERN'T IN LOVE
Tracks: / You weren't in love / Amerley.
7" Single: Released Sep '81, on RCA, by BMG Records (UK). Deleted '84. Catalogue no: **RCA 118**

Fleetwoods

Biographical details: This American vocal group consisted of Gretchen Diane Christopher, Barbara Ellis and Gary Troxel. Initially calling themselves Two Girls and a Guy, the three members met at Olympia High School, Washington State. It was while at school that they discovered that their three voices harmonised beautifully. They perfected an imaginative way of singing and arranging their material, which led to them writing a catchy ballad, *Come softly to me.* As the Fleetwoods, the three 19 year olds achieved every teenager's dream in 1969, when *Come softly to me* - their very first record - shot to No.1 in America and stayed there for four weeks; it reached No.6 in Britain, where it was also a hit for Frankie Vaughan & The Kaye Sisters. Although *Come softly to me* was their only UK success, the Fleetwoods enjoyed a second US chart-topper in 1959 with their version of De Wayne Blackwell's song *Mr Blue.* But the trio's soft, close harmony style lost its novelty in 1960, and *Outside my window* and *Runaround* cracked the US Top 40 but not the Top 20. 1961's *Tragedy* returned them briefly to the high echelonsof the American listings; but after further smaller hits, they finally said goodbye to the US Top 40 in 1963 with their aptly titled *Goodnight my love. Come softly to me,* now a standard, became a UK hit for the New Seekers in late 1972. (Bob MacDonald, 2nd Sept 1985).

COME SOFTLY TO ME
Tracks: / Come softly to me.
7" Single: Released Apr '59, on London Records, by London Records. Deleted '62. Catalogue no: **HL 8841**

Fleetwood's Zoo

I WANT YOU BACK
Tracks: / I want you back.
7" Single: Released Oct '83, on RCA, by BMG Records (UK). Catalogue no: **RCA 360**

Fleming, George

I'M GONNA TELL
Tracks: / I'm gonna tell / Shake, The.
7" Single: Released Sep '80, on Rollercoaster, by Rollercoaster Records. Catalogue no: **RRC 2005**

Fleming, Luther

OOH BABY
Tracks: / Ooh baby.
12" Single: Released Aug '81, on Double L, Catalogue no: **LL 0003**

Flemming, Rochelle

LOVE ITCH
Tracks: / Love itch.
12" Single: Released Mar '86, on Streetnoise, Catalogue no: **12SLN 1**
7" Single: Released Mar '86, on Streetnoise, Catalogue no: **7SLN 1**

Flesh

2ND CHOICE, THE
Tracks: / 2nd choice, The / Sell yourself.
7" Single: Released Mar '86, on London Records, by London Records. Catalogue no: **LON 87**
12" Single: Released Mar '86, on London Records, by London Records. Catalogue no: **LONX 87**

MY BOY LOLLIPOP
Tracks: / My boy lollipop.
7" Single: Released Jul '80, on Dancing, Deleted '82. Catalogue no: **DI 001**

YOU CAN'T HELP
Tracks: / You can't help / Sentimental Sunday.
7" Single: Released Sep '85, on London Records, by London Records. Catalogue no: **LON 72**
12" Single: Released Sep '85, on London Records, by London Records. Catalogue no: **LONX 72**

Flesh & Fell

ANGER
Tracks: / Anger / Hunger.
12" Single: Released Nov '85, on Scarface, Catalogue no: **SCAR 18T**

Flesh For Lulu

BABY HURRICANE
Tracks: / Baby hurricane.
7" Single: Released Oct '85, on Statik, Catalogue no: **TAK 37**
12" Single: Released Oct '85, on Statik, Catalogue no: **TAK 37 - 12**

I GO CRAZY
Tracks: / I go crazy / Crash / Baby, baby, baby, baby, baby (Only on 12").
12" Single: Released Oct '88, on Beggars Banquet, by Beggars Banquet Records. Catalogue no: **BEG 221T**
7" Single: Released Oct '88, on Beggars Banquet, by Beggars Banquet Records. Catalogue no: **BEG 221**

IDOL
Tracks: / Sleeping dogs / Life of crime (Extra track on 12" version only) / Spaceball ricochet (Extra track on 12" version only).
7" Single: Released Nov '86, on Beggars Banquet, by Beggars Banquet Records. Deleted Jan '88. Catalogue no: **BEG 177**
12" Single: Released Nov '86, on Beggars Banquet, by Beggars Banquet Records. Catalogue no: **BEG 177T**

POSTCARDS FROM PARADISE
Tracks: / Postcards from paradise / Im not like everybody else / Sometimes good guys don't wear white* (*Extra track on 12").
7" Single: Released Jun '87, on Beggars Banquet, by Beggars Banquet Records. Catalogue no: **BEG 193**
12" Single: Released Jun '87, on Beggars Banquet, by Beggars Banquet Records. Catalogue no: **BEG 193T**

SIAMESE TWIST
Tracks: / Siamese twist / Dumbest thing / Blue sky / Idol.
7" Single: Released Mar '87, on Beggars Banquet, by Beggars Banquet Records. Deleted Jan '88. Catalogue no: **BEG 184**
Cassingle: Released May '87, on Beggars Banquet, by Beggars Banquet Records. Catalogue no: **BEG 184 C**
12" Single: Released May '87, on Beggars Banquet, by Beggars Banquet Records. Catalogue no: **BEG 184T**

SUBTERRANEANS
Tracks: / Subterraneans / Why me / Endless sleep / Ten foot tall.
7" Single: Released Jun '84, on Polydor, by Polydor Ltd. Catalogue no: **FFL 1**

Flesh Puppets

DEADLINE
Tracks: / Deadline.
7" Single: Released 14 Jun '85, on Plague, Catalogue no: **CAV 018**

SCARECROW
Tracks: / Scarecrow.
7" Single: Released 17 Feb '86, on Plague, Catalogue no: **PLG 002**

Flesh Volcano

SLUT
Tracks: / Slut.
12" Single: Released Apr '88, on Some Bizzare, by Some Bizzare Records. Catalogue no: **SLUT 001**

Fleshtones

GIRL FROM BALTIMORE
Tracks: / Girl from Baltimore / Feel the heat.
7" Single: Released May '81, on A&M, by A&M Records. Deleted May '84. Catalogue no: **PFP 1004**

RIGHT SIDE OF A GOOD THING
Tracks: / Right side of a good thing.
7" Single: Released Jul '83, on I.R.S, Catalogue no: **PFP 1018**

SHADOW LINE
Tracks: / Shadow line / All around the world.
7" Single: Released Mar '82, on I.R.S, Deleted '85. Catalogue no: **PSP 1012**

Fletcher, Charlie

I SEE BLUE
Tracks: / I see blue / Goodbye Mr. America.
7" Single: Released Feb '81, on Buddah, by Buddah Records Inc.(USA). Deleted '84. Catalogue no: **BDS 495**

Fletcher, Guy

BERTHA
Tracks: / Bertha (Theme fom the BBC-TV series.) / Mrs. Tupp.
7" Single: Released Sep '86, on BBC, by BBC Records & Tapes. Deleted 31 Aug '88. Catalogue no: **RESL 200**

Fletcher, Lorna

JUST THE TWO OF US
Tracks: / Just the two of us / Sandra.
12" Single: Released Mar '83, on Virgo, Catalogue no: **VG 012**

F.L.E.X.

WHY DID YOU DO IT
Tracks: / Why did you do it / Move to the machine.
12" Single: Released Feb '87, on GC, Catalogue no: **CGT 06**

YOU LOSE
Tracks: / You lose / Believe it / Hate jazz / Chance, A.
Note: Doublepack.
7" Set: Released Mar '87, on Peart, by Peart Records. Catalogue no: **JNR 5326**

Flic

FUZZIN THE TRACKS MEDLEY
Tracks: / Fuzzin' the tracks medley.
7" Single: Released Aug '84, on Towerbell, Catalogue no: **TOW 58**

Flicknife

FLICKNIFE SAMPLER EP
Tracks: / Flicknife sampler EP.
7" Single: Released Aug '89, on Flicknife, by Flicknife Records. Catalogue no: **FLSP 02**

Flicks

LOOK, THE
Tracks: / Look, The.
7" Single: Released Sep '82, on Flying, by Flying Records. Catalogue no: **FLY 102**

Flightt, K.C.

LET'S GET JAZZY
Tracks: / Let's get jazzy.
Note: (House) One of this week's better house releases...
12" Single: Released Nov '87, on TMT (USA), Catalogue no: **TMT 001**

Flik Spatula

BOZOS
Tracks: / Bozos / Monroe / Twilight zone / Freak power.
12" Single: Released 23 Apr '88, on Hag, by Primitive Records. Catalogue no: **PRAG 1**

Flim & The BB's

TUNNEL (SINGLE)
Tracks: / Tunnel.
7" Single: on T.Y.C.O.S., by T.Y.C.O.S Records. Catalogue no: **AM 458**

Flint

ROCKET LOVE
Tracks: / Rocket love / Teacher teacher.
7" Single: Released Feb '81, on Jay Boy, by President Records. Deleted Feb '84. Catalogue no: **BOY 116**

THIS SIDE OF MIDNIGHT
Tracks: / This side of midnight / Love be a shining star.
7" Single: Released Mar '80, on Jay Boy, by President Records. Deleted '83. Catalogue no: **BOY 115**

Flint, Berni

Biographical details: This British singer, guitarist and songwriter shot to brief fame in the UK in 1977 after his successful appearances on one of Britain's top TV talent contests. *I don't want to put a hold on you,* a subtly plaintive and understated folk song with a catchy melody, zoomed to No.3 on the charts and seemed to promise much for Flint's future. But Berni (who spelt his Christian name without an 'e' in those days) could only reach No.48 with his bland follow-up single *Southern comfort.* The album *I don't want to put a hold on you,* produced by Mike Berry & Hal Sharper peaked at No.37 on the UK LP listings. Flint never returned to the British charts, although he was assured of a steady living on the cabaret circuit and in summer seasons at seaside variety shows. His occasional returns to the recording studio included a 1983 children's singalong *Daisy a day,* creditied to Bernie Flint & The Kids. (Bob MacDonald, 2nd Sept 1985).

DAISY A DAY
Tracks: / Daisy a day / Foolish affair.
7" Single: Released Nov '83, on Sumatra, by Sumatra Records. Catalogue no: **SUM 3**

DON'T LAUGH AT ME
Tracks: / Don't laugh at me / Woman in love.
7" Single: Released May '80, on EMI, by EMI Records. Deleted May '85. Catalogue no: **EMI 5069**

I DON'T WANT TO PUT A HOLD ON YOU (SINGLE)
Tracks: / I don't want to put a hold on you.
7" Single: Released Mar '77, on EMI, by EMI Records. Deleted '80. Catalogue no: **EMI 2599**

ONLY ME
Tracks: / Only me / Caroline and me.
7" Single: Released Feb '80, on EMI, by EMI Records. Deleted '83. Catalogue no: **EMI 5021**

SOUTHERN COMFORT
Tracks: / Southern comfort.
7" Single: Released Jul '77, on EMI, by EMI Records. Deleted '80. Catalogue no: **EMI 2621**

Flint, Michael

ROCKING DOLLY
Tracks: / Rocking Dolly / Crowd awe.
12" Single: Released Apr '86, on Ranking Joe Universal, Catalogue no: **RJ 0012**

Flintlock

Biographical details: The summer of 1976 was famous in Britain for the drought - not only in terms of the weather, but also in terms of the record charts. The teenybopper era was on the wane, many of the established rock bands were regarded as stale and predictable, and punk rock had not yet injected its much needed energy and excitement. Flintlock were a typical example of the desperate attempts that the record industry made to find another teenage sensation, to follow the phenomenal successes of acts like the Osmonds, David Cassidy and the Bay City Rollers. Such efforts threw up Flintlock and a host of other all-male British groups in 1976 - with the notable exception of Slik's Midge Ure, groups like Buster, Flintlock, Our Kid and Slik were short on talent and long on manufactured looks. All faded into oblivion after their very brief flirtation with the charts. Flintlock's only chart entry was *Dawn*, a single written and produced by Mike Holoway Sr; it reached the UK No.30 position in June '76. The only notable thing about the record was the fact that it represented an early success for the Pinnacle company. The band's albums, *On the way*, *Hot from the look* and *Tears'n'cheers*, fell on deaf ears. (Bob MacDonald, 2nd Sept 1985).

DAWN
Tracks: / Dawn.
7" Single: Released May '76, on Pinnacle, by Pinnacle Records. Deleted '79. Catalogue no: **P 9419**

Flip

I'LL BE THERE
Tracks: / I'll be there.
7" Single: Released Aug '85, on Satril, by Satril Records. Catalogue no: **SAT 520**

PLAGUE OF HEARTS
Tracks: / Plague of hearts.
7" Single: Released Aug '84, on Arista, by BMG Records (UK). Catalogue no: **ARIST 582**

Flip, Candy

LOVE IS LIFE
Tracks: / Love is life.
7" Single: Released Sep '89, on Debut, by Skratch Records. Catalogue no: **DEBT 3079**
12" Single: Released 29 Aug '89, on Debut, by Skratch Records. Catalogue no: **DEBTX 3079**

Flipper

HA HA HA
Tracks: / Ha ha ha.
7" Single: Released Jan '82, on Alternative, Deleted '88. Catalogue no: **VIRUS 8**

Flirtations

EARTHQUAKE
Tracks: / Earthquake.
12" Single: Released Oct '83, on Siam, Catalogue no: **IANT 101**
7" Single: Released Oct '83, on Siam, Catalogue no: **IAN 101**
12" Single: Released Aug '89, on Rumour, Catalogue no: **RUMAT 3**

READ ALL ABOUT IT
Tracks: / Read all about it / Nightmare dub mix.
12" Single: Released Nov '86, on Passion, by Skratch Records. Catalogue no: **PASH 67(12)**

Flirts

ALL YOU EVER THINK OF IS SEX
Tracks: / All you ever think of is sex.
7" Single: Released Nov '86, on Epic, by CBS Records. Catalogue no: **650293 7**
12" Single: Released Jan '87, on Epic, by CBS Records. Deleted Aug '87. Catalogue no: **650293 6**

JUKEBOX Don't put another dime
Tracks: / Jukebox.
12" Single: Released Nov '82, on O, Deleted '85. Catalogue no: **QUEL 3**
7" Single: Released Nov '82, on O, Deleted '85. Catalogue no: **QUE 3**

MISS YOU
Tracks: / Miss you / Voulez vous.
7" Single: Released Aug '86, on Epic, by CBS Records. Catalogue no: **650069 7**
12" Single: Released Aug '86, on Epic, by CBS Records. Catalogue no: **650069 6**

PASSION
Tracks: / Passion.
7" Single: Released Apr '83, on O, Deleted '85. Catalogue no: **QUE 6**
7" Single: Released Apr '83, on O, Deleted '85. Catalogue no: **QUEL 6**

YOU AND ME
Tracks: / You and me.
12" Single: Released May '86, on Epic, by CBS Records. Catalogue no: **TA 6760**
7" Single: Released May '86, on Epic, by CBS Records. Catalogue no: **A 6760**

Flix

HITCH
Tracks: / Hitch / Beautiful day.
7" Single: Released May '80, on Hurricane (1), Deleted May '83. Catalogue no: **FIRE 9**

Float Up CP

JOY'S ADDRESS
Tracks: / Joy's address / Desert heart.
12" Single: Released Jul '84, on Rough Trade, by Rough Trade Records. Catalogue no: **RTT 150**
7" Single: Released Jul '84, on Rough Trade, by Rough Trade Records. Catalogue no: **RT 150**

Floaters

Biographical details: When the Floaters' *Float on* relieved Brotherhood Of Man's *Angelo* of the UK No.1 spot in August 1977, it was difficult for observers to decide whether the charts had been rescued in the nick of time, or whether they had been dragged deeper into the mire. The Floaters, a soul band from Detroit, were a one-off phenomenon on both sides of the Atlantic - they never managed to come up with a hit follow-up to *Float on*, which reached No.2 in the States and No.1 in Britain. They did, however, manage to shift some copies of their self-titled LP, which climbed to No.10 in the US and No.17 in the UK. If *Float on* was intended to be a novelty hit, it certainly worked; if it was intended to be taken seriously, it ranks as one of the laughable discs of all time! Interrupting a melodic and irritatingly hummable soul ballad, the four Floaters (Ronnie, Charles, Paul and Larry) took turns at introducing themselves and informing the world of their Zodiac sign and their tastes in women. These ranged from the ridiculous (the Cancerian Larry liked 'a woman that loves everything and everybody') to the hysterical (the Libran Charles liked 'a woman who carries herself like Miss Universe'). (Bob MacDonald, 2nd Sept 1985).

FLOAT ON
Tracks: / Float on.
7" Single: Released Jul '77, on ABC Records, by MCA Records. Deleted '80. Catalogue no: **ABC 4187**
7" Single: Released Jul '82, on Old Gold, by Old Gold Records. Catalogue no: **OG 9218**

Flock Of Seagulls

Biographical details: This British band consists of Frank Maudsley, Paul Reynolds plus brothers Ali & Mike Score. Their name was inspired by Richard Bach's book 'Jonathan Livingston Seagull'. Founded by lead vocalist/keyboardist/guitarist Mike Score in early 1980, A Flock Of Seagulls were one of the numerous groups to emerge from the reinvigoraged city of Liverpool during the early Eighties. Mike was origianally a hairdresser, and Frank was his employee. 1982 was the breakthrough year for A Flock Of Seagulls, but their success happened in America first; it then migrated back to Britain. This US acceptance happened on account of two factors - their early single *Telecommunication* was a big success in rock discos across North America; and they played a US support tour with Squeeze, after which their videos began to receive valuable exposure on the nation's burgeoning cable rock music channel, MTV. The catchy, classy *I ran*, which had only been a minor hit in Britain, sprinted to No.9 on the US charts. Word spread back to their native land and, by the end of '82, they had reached the UK Top 10 with the irresistible *Wishing (I I had a photograph of you)*. A Flock Of Seagulls played the fashionable technopop music of the time, but demonstrated a strong sense of traditional pop melody. Strangely, the band failed to truly consolidate upon their 1982 success. They did not return to the Top 10 on either side of the Atlantic, despite the quality of such singles as *Space age love song* and *Transfer affection*. *The more you live, the more you love* was a slow-burning UK hit in the summer of 1984, ultimately peaking at No.26; but the follow-up single *Never again (The dancer)* flopped. (Bob MacDonald, 2nd Sept 1985)
New wave group formed in Liverpool in 1979 by brothers Mike and Ali Score, keyboards/vocals and drums. Lead guitarist Paul Reynolds and bassist Frank Maudsley made up a group inspired by Jonathan Livingston Seagull, which says a lot. They were successful in the USA because of exposure on MTV for ex-hairdresser Mike's wilder styles; they split in 1986. (Donald Clarke, April 1989).

COLLECTION OF TEN 7" SINGLES
Tracks: / Telecommunication / Intro / Modern love / You can run / D.N.A. I ran / Pick me up / Space age love song / Windows / Wishing (if had a photograph of you) / Committed / Nightmares / Rosenmontag / Transfer affection / I ran (so far away) (live) / It's not me talking / Tanglimara / Never again (The dancer) / Living in Heaven / More you live, the more you love, The / Lost control.
7" Set: Released Jun '85, on Jive, by Zomba Records. Catalogue no: **AFOS 1**

COLLECTION OF TEN 12" SINGLES
Tracks: / Telecommunication / Intro / Modern love / You can run / D.N.A. I ran / Pick me up / Space age love song / Windows / Wishing (if had a photograph of you) / Committed / Nightmares / Rosenmontag / Transfer affection / I ran (so far away) (live) / It's not me talking / Tanglimara / Never again (the dancer) / Living in Heaven / More you live, the more you love, The / Lost control.
Special: Released Jun '85, on Jive, by Zomba Records. Catalogue no: **AFLOCK 1**

HEARTBEAT LIKE A DRUM
Tracks: / Heartbeat like a drum.
7" Single: Released Feb '86, on Jive, by Zomba Records. Catalogue no: **JIVE 113**
12" Single: Released Feb '86, on Jive, by Zomba Records. Catalogue no: **JIVET 113**

I RAN
Tracks: / I ran (so far away) / Pick me up / Messages (Only on 12" single.).
7" Single: Released Mar '82, on Jive, by Zomba Records. Catalogue no: **JIVE 14**
7" Pic: Released Mar '82, on Jive, by Zomba Records. Catalogue no: **JIVEP 14**
12" Single: Released Mar '82, on Jive, by Zomba Records. Catalogue no: **JIVET 14**

IT'S NOT ME TALKING
Tracks: / It's not me talking / Tanglimara / Traveller.
7" Single: Released Mar '83, on Cocteau, by Cocteau Records. Catalogue no: **COQT 3**
7" Single: Released Aug '83, on Jive, by Zomba Records. Catalogue no: **JIVE 47**
12" Single: Released Aug '83, on Jive, by Zomba Records. Catalogue no: **JIVET 47**

MODERN LOVE IS AUTOMATIC
Tracks: / Modern love is automatic / Telecommunication.
12" Single: Released Nov '81, on Jive, by Zomba Records. Catalogue no: **JIVET 8**
7" Single: Released Nov '81, on Jive, by Zomba Records. Catalogue no: **JIVE 8**

MORE YOU LIVE THE MORE YOU LOVE, THE
Tracks: / More you live the more you love, The.
7" Pic: Released Jun '84, on Jive, by Zomba Records. Catalogue no: **JIVEP 62**
7" Single: Released Jun '84, on Jive, by Zomba Records. Catalogue no: **JIVE 62**
12" Single: Released Jun '84, on Jive, by Zomba Records. Catalogue no: **JIVET 62**

NEVER AGAIN (THE DANCER)
Tracks: / Never again (the dancer).
7" Single: Released Sep '84, on Jive, by Zomba Records. Catalogue no: **JIVE 78**
12" Single: Released Sep '84, on Jive, by Zomba Records. Catalogue no: **JIVET 78**

NIGHTMARES
Tracks: / Nightmares.
7" Single: Released Apr '83, on Jive, by Zomba Records. Catalogue no: **JIVE 33**
7" Pic: Released Apr '83, on Jive, by Zomba Records. Catalogue no: **JIVEP 33**
12" Single: Released Apr '83, on Jive, by Zomba Records. Catalogue no: **JIVET 33**

SPACE AGE LOVE SONG
Tracks: / Space age love song / Windows / Standing in the doorway.
7" Single: Released May '82, on Jive, by Zomba Records. Catalogue no: **JIVE 17**
7" Pic: Released May '82, on Jive, by Zomba Records. Catalogue no: **JIVEP 17**
12" Single: Released May '82, on Jive, by Zomba Records. Catalogue no: **JIVET 17**

TELECOMMUNICATION
Tracks: / Telecommunication / Intro.
7" Single: Released Sep '81, on Jive, by Zomba Records. Catalogue no: **JIVE 4**
7" Single: Released Jan '82, on Jive, by Zomba Records. Catalogue no: **JIVE 12**
12" Single: Released Jan '82, on Jive, by Zomba Records. Catalogue no: **JIVET 12**
12" Single: Released Sep '81, on Jive, by Zomba Records. Catalogue no: **JIVET 4**

TRANSFER AFFECTION
Tracks: / Transfer affection.
7" Pic: Released Jul '83, on Jive, by Zomba Records. Catalogue no: **JIVEP 41**
7" Single: Released Jun '83, Catalogue no: **JIVE 41**
12" Single: Released Jun '83, on Jive, by Zomba Records. Catalogue no: **JIVET 41**

WHO'S THAT GIRL (SHE'S GOT IT)
Tracks: / Who's that girl (she's got it).
7" Single: Released Oct '85, on Jive, by Zomba Records. Catalogue no: **JIVE 106**
12" Single: Released Oct '85, on Jive, by Zomba Records. Catalogue no: **JIVET 106**

WISHING (IF I HAD A PHOTOGRAPH OF YOU)
Tracks: / Wishing (If I had a photograph of you).
7" Single: Released Oct '82, on Jive, by Zomba Records. Catalogue no: **JIVE 25**
7" Single: Released 24 Apr '89, on Old Gold, by Old Gold Records. Catalogue no: **OG 9893**
12" Single: Released Oct '82, on Jive, by Zomba Records. Catalogue no: **JIVET 25**

Flood

COLD COLD WORLD
Tracks: / Cold cold world.
7" Single: Released Dec '84, on Midnight Music, by Midnight Music Records. Catalogue no: **DING 7**

Florentines

MAN OF MINE
Tracks: / Man of mine / Lose that long face / Whisper not / Get out of town.
12" Single: Released Mar '87, on El, by Cherry Red Records. Catalogue no: **GPO 25 T**

Flores, Rosie

CRYING OVER YOU
Tracks: / Crying over you / Midnight to moonlight.
7" Single: Released Jul '88, on WEA, by WEA Records. Catalogue no: **W 8250**

Florida

CITY RACES
Tracks: / City races.
7" Single: Released Jun '85, on Musik, Catalogue no: **MRFS 1**

Florida Sun

DON'T WANNA LOVE ANYMORE
Tracks: / Don't wanna love anymore.
7" Single: Released Jul '85, on Sparkle, Catalogue no: **SPK 2**

HONEY BE
Tracks: / Honey be / My baby's so fine.
7" Single: Released Apr '88, on Tembo, by Tembo Records. Catalogue no: **TML 132**

HURT Featuring Ronnie Harwood
Tracks: / Hurt / Again.
7" Single: Released Jun '87, on Tembo, by Tembo Records. Catalogue no: **TML 128**

IF DREAMS COME TRUE
Tracks: / If dreams come true.
7" Single: Released Feb '85, on Sparkle, Catalogue no: **SPK 1**

I'M SORRY
Tracks: / I'm sorry / Florida rock.
7" Single: Released Mar '86, on Sparkle, Catalogue no: **SPK 3**

Floride, Klaus

SHORTENING BREAD
Tracks: / Shortening bread / Drowning cowboy.
12" Single: Released May '82, on Alternative Tentacles, by Alternative Tentacles Records. Deleted May '85. Catalogue no: **VIRUS 12**

Flotsam & Jetsam

FLOTZILLA
Tracks: / Flotzilla.
12" Single: Released Dec '87, on Road Runner (1), by Road Runner Records. Catalogue no: **RR 125471**

SATURDAY NIGHT'S ALRIGHT FOR FIGHTING
Tracks: / Saturday nights alright for fighting.
7" Single: Released Nov '88, on Road Runner (1), by Road Runner Records. Catalogue no: **RR 24531**

Flourgan

BAD BOY TUNE
Tracks: / Bad boy turne.
12" Single: Released Jan '89, on Scom, Catalogue no: **BD 8804**

BOUNCE
Tracks: / Bounce.
12" Single: Released Nov '88, on Live & Love, Catalogue no: **LLD 92**

BUBBLIN' TIME
Tracks: / Bubblin' time.
12" Single: Released Oct '88, on Kickers Prod., Catalogue no: **K 519255**

COM MED MEK WE GO DWEET
Tracks: / Com med mek we go dweet.
12" Single: Released Oct '88, on Kickers Prod., Catalogue no: **K 381955**

DON INNA TOWN
Tracks: / Don inna town.
12" Single: Released Feb '89, on Blue Mountain, Catalogue no: **BMD 044**

GET UP, STAND UP AND DANCE
Tracks: / Get up, stand up and dance.
12" Single: Released Apr '89, on Sir Coxsone, Catalogue no: **BD 8909**

GONE WITH THE TROPHY
Tracks: / Gone with the trophy.
12" Single: Released Feb '89, on Steely & Cleevie, Catalogue no: **VPRD 415**

GO SIT DOWN
Tracks: / Go sit down.
12" Single: Released May '89, on Super Power, Catalogue no: **SPD 43**

HOL A SPLIFF

Tracks: / Hol a spliff.
12" Single: Released Aug '87, on Technique, Catalogue no: **WRT 19**

JAMMING
Tracks: / Jamming.
12" Single: Released Sep '88, on Hawkeye, by Hawkeye Records. Catalogue no: **HD 92**

LIVE GOOD
Tracks: / Live good.
12" Single: Released Dec '88, on Germaine, Catalogue no: **DGT 43**

MI LOVE MI GIRL BAD
Tracks: / Mi love mi girl bad.
7" Single: Released Oct '88, on T.B.Sharp, Catalogue no: **TBT 1**

NAH GO SWITCH
Tracks: / Nah go switch.
12" Single: Released Nov '88, on Steely & Cleevie, Catalogue no: **VPRD 349**

PEACE
Tracks: / Peace.
12" Single: Released Jan '89, on Exterminator, Catalogue no: **VPRD 388**

SHOCK OUT YU SELF
Tracks: / Shock out yu self.
12" Single: Released Nov '88, on Digital B., Catalogue no: **VPRD 364**

SWEET REGGAE MUSIC
Tracks: / Sweet reggae music.
12" Single: Released Sep '89, on Living Room, Catalogue no: **LM 029**

TURN AND STAB
Tracks: / Turn and stab.
7" Single: Released 21 Apr '89, on Greensleeves, by Greensleeves Records. Catalogue no: **GRED 240**

WHEEL AND TURN
Tracks: / Wheel and turn.
12" Single: Released May '89, on Greensleeves, by Greensleeves Records. Catalogue no: **GRED 240**

Flouride, Klaus

SHORTNING BREAD
Tracks: / Shortnin' bread.
12" Single: Released May '82, on Alternative, Deleted '88. Catalogue no: **VIRUS 12**

Flowchart

ASK THE BOSS
Tracks: / Ask the boss.
7" Single: Released Nov '84, on Greyhound, by Greyhound Records. Catalogue no: **GRP 102**
12" Single: Released Apr '83, on Greyhound, by Greyhound Records. Catalogue no: **GRPT 102**

Flower Pornoes

FLOWER PORNOES
Tracks: / Flower pornoes.
10" single: Released 30 Jun '87, on Scratch & Sniff, Deleted '88. Catalogue no: **SS 001**

Flowerpot Men

Biographical details: This British vocal group consisted of Tony Burrows, Perry Ford and Neil Landon. But the trio were really the brainchild of John Carter and Ken Lewis, who wrote and produced their only hit record. All five men had previously been members of the hitmaking group, the Ivy League. In August 1967, while Scott McKenzie was No.1 in the UK with *San Francisco (Be sure to wear flowers in your hair)* and the world was experiencing the amazingly beautiful 'summer of love', the Flowerpot Men entered the chart with their blatantly cynical cash-in *Let's go to San Fransicco.* This delightfully lightweight and catchy ditty reached the UK No.4 position. For the next few months, they toured all over the country to exploit the success of the single. After the failure of their follow-ups - *Am I losing you, Young birds fly* and *A walk in the sky* - they knocked the project on the head. The ubiquitous Burrows proceeded to sing on hits by Edison Lighthouse, White Plains, Brotherhood Of Man, the Pipkins and First Class. The latter group's solo hit, 1974's *Beach baby,* also featured the voice of John Carter - Carter's real name is John Shakespeare, and he has subsequently made an excellent living by doing music for commercials and jingles. Lewis has followed a similar road. Billy Davidson, who toured with the Flowerpot Men but did not perform on their hit, proceeded to co-write one of Brotherhood Of Man's 1970 hits, *Where are you going my love.* (Bob MacDonald, 2nd Sept 1985).

ALLIGATOR BAIT
Tracks: / Alligator bait.
12" Single: Released Mar '87, on Aminita, Catalogue no: **COMPOST 03**

JANICE LONG SESSION: FLOWERPOT MEN
12" Single: Released Jan '88, on Night Tracks, by Pinnacle Records. Catalogue no: **SFNT 007**

JO'S SO MEAN
Tracks: / Jo's so mean.
12" Single: Released Nov '84, on Compost, Deleted '86. Catalogue no: **COMPOST 1**

LET'S GO TO SAN FRANCISCO (SINGLE)
Tracks: / Let's go to San Francisco.
7" Single: Released Aug '67, on Deram, by London Records. Deleted '70. Catalogue no: **DM 142**

SAN FRANCISCO (OLD GOLD)
Tracks: / San Francisco.
7" Single: Released Jul '82, on Old Gold, by Old Gold Records. Catalogue no: **OG 9010**

WALKING ON GILDED SPLINTERS
Tracks: / Walking on gilded splinters.
12" Single: Released Nov '85, on Aminita, Catalogue no: **COMPOST 02**
7" Single: Released Nov '85, on Aminita, Catalogue no: **COMPOST 702**

Flowers For Agatha

FREEDOM CRUISE
Tracks: / Freedom cruise.
12" Single: Released Jan '86, on Leeds Independent (LIL), by Revolver Records. Catalogue no: **LIL 12003**

THICKEST HEAD
Tracks: / Thickest head.
7" Single: Released 1 Jul '85, on Off-Beat (1), Catalogue no: **O 8010**

YOUNG FOOLISH OLD AND STUPID
Tracks: / Young foolish old and stupid.
12" Single: Released Aug '86, on Leeds Independent (LIL), by Revolver Records. Catalogue no: **LIL 12008**

Flowers, Herbie

BURLINGTON BURTIE
Tracks: / Burlington Burtie / Big George.
7" Single: Released Jul '81, on EMI, by EMI Records. Deleted Jul '84. Catalogue no: **EMI 5170**

I LOVE 'ER
Tracks: / I love her.
7" Single: Released Jan '83, on Magic (1), by Submarine Records. Catalogue no: **MAGIC 2**

JUST FOR YOU
Tracks: / Just for you / Whale.
7" Single: Released Jan '81, on EMI, by EMI Records. Deleted Jan '84. Catalogue no: **EMI 5130**

TUBA SMARTIES
Tracks: / Tuba smarties / Bathroom song.
7" Single: Released Dec '81, on Ariola, by BMG Records (UK). Deleted Dec '84. Catalogue no: **ARO 273**

Flowers In The Dustbin

LICK MY CRAZY COLOURS
Tracks: / Lick my crazy colours / Continuing tragedy of Mr Smith, The
7" Single: Released Apr '87, on Cold Harbour, by Cold Harbour Records. Catalogue no: **COLD 1002**
12" Single: Released Nov '86, on Cold Harbour, by Cold Harbour Records. Catalogue no: **COLD 1002 T**

NAILS IN THE HEART
Tracks: / Nails in the heart.
7" Single: Released Sep '85, on Mortarhate, by Mortarhate Records. Catalogue no: **MORT 16**

Flowers Of The Past

FUHRER, THE
Tracks: / Fuhrer, The.
7" Single: Released Aug '83, on Memorial, Catalogue no: **MEM 1**

Flowershop

TEN FOOT TALL
Tracks: / Ten foot tall / Faraway.
7" Single: Released Oct '88, on Molesworth, by New Leaf Records. Catalogue no: **HUNTS 4**

Floy Joy

FRIDAY NIGHT
Tracks: / Friday night / Friday night (version).
7" Single: Released Mar '86, on Virgin, by Virgin Records. Deleted '86. Catalogue no: **VS 848**
12" Single: Released Mar '86, on Virgin, by Virgin Records. Deleted '86. Catalogue no: **VS 848-12**

UNTIL YOU COME BACK TO ME
Tracks: / Until you come back to me.
12" Single: Released Oct '84, on Virgin, by Virgin Records. Deleted '85. Catalogue no: **VS 716-12**

WEAK IN THE PRESENCE OF BEAUTY (SINGLE)
Tracks: / Weak in the presence of beauty.
12" Single: Released Jun '86, on Virgin, by Virgin Records. Deleted '86. Catalogue no: **VS 833-12**
7" Single: Released Jun '86, on Virgin, by Virgin Records. Deleted '86. Catalogue no: **VS 833**

Floyd

MINUTE BY MINUTE
Tracks: / Minute by minute.
7" Single: Released Jun '85, on Compact Organisation, Deleted '86. Catalogue no: **ACT 15**
12" Single: Released Jun '85, on Compact Organisation, Deleted '86. Catalogue no: **ACTX 15**

SEAL SONG, THE
Tracks: / Seal song, The.
7" Single: Released Oct '85, on Compact Organisation, Deleted '86. Catalogue no: **ACT 18**

Floyd, Bobby

OH NO
Tracks: / Oh no.
12" Single: Released Oct '86, on Musical Ambassador, Catalogue no: **MAPD 003**

Floyd, Eddie

Biographical details: This American singer and songwriter, born in Montgomery, Alabama, joined a gospel-influenced group called the Falcons in 1956. The intense style of this Detroit-based outfit was a sound preparation for his later career in soul music. Floyd sang lead on their only US Top 40 pop hit *You're so fine,* which reached No.17 in 1959. He left the Falcons in 1962 to pursue a solo career. Floyd made a vital career move in 1966, when he signed with Memphis' seminal Stax label, one of the most important centres of Sixties soul. Stax had a distinctive sound was the MGs' guitarist Steve Cropper, and it was with Cropper that Floyd co-wrote his classic single *Knock on wood.* This raucous song gave Eddie a No.1 success on the US R&B charts in late 1966, and reached No.28 on the American pop listings; in Britain, it climbed to No.19 and logged 18 weeks on the chart during 1967 - its longevity reflected its popularity at parties and discotheques. The singer also helped to write material for other Stax artists, notably *634-5789 (Soulsville, U.S.A.)* which was a US No.13 hit for Wilson Pickett in 1966. Floyd's own recording successes, apart from *Knock on wood,* included *Raise your hand* and *Things get better* (both UK chart entries in '67) and *I've never found a girl (to love me like you do)* (a US hit in '68). At the end of 1968, he reached No.17 on the US chart with his rendition of the Sam Cooke evergreen *Bring it on home to me.* Eddie faded into obscurity during the Seventies, despite his flirtations with reggae and modern disco styles. However, *Knock on wood* lived on - it was a UK Top 10 hit for David Bowie in 1974, and reached new heights of popularity in 1979 when Amii Stewart transformed it into a worldwide disco and pop smash. Stewart's rendition was a two-million-selling No.1 in the States, and got to No.6 in Britain, where it returned to the Top 40 in remixed form in 1985. Floyd's own attepts to cash in on the disco boom had failed, but Amii had done the job for him! (Bob MacDonald, 2nd Sept 1985)
Soul singer, born in 1935 in Alabama. He joined the Falcons vocal group in Detroit, which soon included Wilson Pickett; then signed as a solo with Stax, where he had 12 Hot 100 entries 1966-1970 and carried on having hits in black charts through the '70's. Also a notable songwriter; his *634-5789* was covered by Ry Cooder. (Donald Clarke, April 1989)o.

BEAT SONG
Tracks: / Beat song / London.
7" Single: Released Aug '80, on I-Spy, Deleted '82. Catalogue no: **SEE 9**

FROM YOUR HEAD TO YOUR TOES
Tracks: / From your head to your toes / She likes the soaps / Soul is back again.
12" Single: Released May '88, on Ichiban, by Ichiban Records (UK). Catalogue no: **12PO 10**

KNOCK ON WOOD
Tracks: / Knock on wood.
7" Single: Released Jan '85, on Old Gold, by Old Gold Records. Catalogue no: **OG 9498**
7" Single: Released Feb '67, on Atlantic, by WEA Records. Deleted '70. Catalogue no: **584041**
7" Single: Released Aug '87, on Stax, by Fantasy Inc (USA). Catalogue no: **STAX 807**
12" Single: Released Nov '87, on Stax, by Fantasy Inc (USA). Catalogue no: **STAT 807**

RAISE YOUR HAND
Tracks: / Raise your hand.
7" Single: Released Mar '67, on Stax, by Fantasy Inc (USA). Deleted '70. Catalogue no: **601001**

THINGS GET BETTER
Tracks: / Things get better.
7" Single: Released Aug '67, on Stax, by Fantasy Inc (USA). Deleted '70. Catalogue no: **601016**

Fluffies

GARBAGE HEADS
Tracks: / Garbage heads.
7" Single: Released Feb '89, on Chorley, Catalogue no: **FRC 1**

KIDDING MYSELF GARBAGE HEAD
Tracks: / Kidding myself garbage head.
7" Single: Released Jan '88, on Chorley, Catalogue no: **FCR 1**

FLYING LIZARDS - MONEY (Released on Virgin)

Flux Of Pink Indians

NEW SMELL
Tracks: / New smell / Taking a liberty.
12" Single: Released Aug '87, on One Little Indian, by One Little Indian Records. Catalogue no: **12TPEP 1**
7" Single: Released Oct '81, on Crass, by Crass Records. Catalogue no: **321984/2**
12" Single: Released Mar '87, on One Little Indian, by One Little Indian Records. Catalogue no: **12TP 6**

TAKING A LIBERTY
Tracks: / Taking a liberty.
7" Single: Released Mar '85, on Spiderleg, Catalogue no: **SDL 16**

VISION
Tracks: / Vision.
12" Single: Released 23 May '87, on One Little Indian, by One Little Indian Records. Catalogue no: **12TP 9**

Flyin' Spiderz

CITY BOY
Tracks: / City boy / I don't wanna go.
7" Single: Released Jun '87, on R2, by R2 Records. Catalogue no: **RTU 0002**

Flying Burrito

ALMOST SATURDAY NIGHT
Tracks: / Almost saturday night.
7" Single: Released Jan '84, on MCA, by MCA Records. Catalogue no: **MCA 868**

Flying Colour

DEAR FRIEND
Tracks: / Dear friend / Look my way.
7" Single: Released Feb '87, on Sound & Shigaku Presents, Catalogue no: **SHIGS 1**

ABSTRACT ARTS
Tracks: / Abstract arts.
7" Single: Released Jul '81, on No, Deleted '83. Catalogue no: **NO 1**

Flying Lizards

DIZZY MISS LIZZY
Tracks: / Dizzy Miss Lizzy.
7" Single: Released Oct '84, on Statik, Catalogue no: **TAK 25**
12" Single: Released Oct '84, on Statik, Catalogue no: **TAK 25/12**

LOVERS AND OTHER STRANGERS
Tracks: / Lovers and other strangers.
7" Single: Released Jun '81, on Virgin, by Virgin Records. Deleted Jun '84. Catalogue no: **VS 421**

MONEY (see panel on previous page)
Tracks: / Money / Money B.
7" Single: Released Aug '79, on Virgin, by Virgin Records. Deleted '82. Catalogue no: **VS 276**

MONEY (OLD GOLD)
Tracks: / Money / T.V..
7" Single: Released Nov '88, on Old Gold, by Old Gold Records. Catalogue no: **OG 9828**

MOVE ON UP
Tracks: / Move on up / Portugal.
7" Single: Released Oct '82, on Virgin, by Virgin Records. Deleted Oct '85. Catalogue no: **VS 381**

SEX MACHINE
Tracks: / Sex machine.
7" Single: Released Aug '84, on Statik, Catalogue no: **TAK 19**
12" Single: Released Aug '84, on Statik, Catalogue no: **TAK 19-12**

T.V.
Tracks: / T.V..
7" Single: Released Feb '80, on Virgin, by Virgin Records. Deleted '83. Catalogue no: **VS 325**

Flying Padovanis

WESTERN PASTA
Tracks: / Western pasta.
7" Single: Released Apr '81, on Demon, by Demon Records. Deleted '88. Catalogue no: **D 1006**

Flying Pickets

Biographical details: Communists being No.1 at Christmas might sound like a strange idea, but that is what happened in Britain in 1983. The Flying Pickets, six left-wing male singers whose concerts interspersed political material with cover versions of old standards, held the top slot for five weeks in December '83 and January '84 with their rendition of Yazoo's *Only you*. The Flying Pickets were formed in 1980, and first attracted major public attention at the 1982 Edinburgh Festival. The name of the group referred to a UK trade union term coined by the National Union of Mineworkers' Arthur Scargill, and it immediately identified the singers with their political views. However, it was not these that made the Pickets famous, but their acappella versions of familiar pop songs. They stormed to stardom at the end of '83 with their virtually instrument-free rendering of *Only you*. They thus earned a very nice sum of money for its writer Vince Clarke, and helped to transform his song into one of the great standards of the Eighties, ripe for recording by every middle-of-the-road singer under the sun. For their follow-up single, the Flying Pickets reached the UK No.7 position with *When you're young and in love* - this treatment of Van McCoy's Sixties composition climbed six places higher than the Marvelettes' version; appropriately, it was a hit during the springtime. The Pickets reached the UK Top 20 with their *Lost boys* LP, but their chart success then tailed off. *So close* flopped altogether, and their dire attempt at the Eurythmics' *Who's that girl?* had to be content with being the Christmas No.71 of 1984 - rather less glorious than having the Christmas No.1. The acappella novelty had worn off. (Bob MacDonald, 2nd Sept 1985).

ONLY YOU
Tracks: / Only you / Disco down.
7" Single: Released Nov '83, on 10 Records, by Virgin Records. Deleted '86. Catalogue no: **TEN 14**

SO CLOSE (see panel below)
Tracks: / So close / Wideboy.
7" Single: Released Jun '84, on 10 Records, by Virgin Records. Deleted May '88. Catalogue no: **TEN 24**

FLYING PICKETS - SO CLOSE (Released on 10 Records)

TAKE MY BREATH AWAY
Tracks: / Roubles & dimes / Take my breath away.
7" Single: Released Nov '86, on Creole, by Creole Records. Catalogue no: **CR 94**

WHEN YOU'RE YOUNG AND IN LOVE
Tracks: / When you're young and in love / Monica engineer.
7" Single: Released Apr '84, on 10 Records, by Virgin Records. Deleted '87. Catalogue no: **TEN 20**

WHO'S THAT GIRL
Tracks: / Who's that girl / Remember this.
7" Single: Released Apr '84, on 10 Records, by Virgin Records. Catalogue no: **GIRL 1**
12" Single: Released Apr '84, on 10 Records, by Virgin Records. Catalogue no: **GIRL 112**

Flying Saucers

ROCK WITH ME BABY
Tracks: / Rock with me baby / Let's rock.
7" Single: Released Feb '82, on EMI, by EMI Records. Deleted Feb '87. Catalogue no: **EMI 5264**

SOME LIKE IT HOT (SINGLE)
Tracks: / Some like it hot / Bye bye baby.
7" Single: Released Mar '81, on EMI, by EMI Records. Deleted Mar '84. Catalogue no: **EMI 5144**

TEENAGE BOOGIE
Tracks: / Teenage boogie / Beer, bourbon and wine.
7" Single: Released Mar '81, on Harbour, by Harbour Records. Catalogue no: **HRB 12**

Flynn Brothers

FLYNN BROTHERS - TIME AND CHANCE (Released on NJ)

TIME AND CHANCE (see panel above)
Tracks: / Land all dressed in living green / As far as / Inherit the wind / John Parfit.
Note: Available from N. J. Records James Flynn, 26 Southcroft Road, Tooting, London London SW17
7" EP: Released May '86, on N.J., by N.J. Records. Catalogue no: **NJ 1**

Flys

WHAT WILL MOTHER SAY
Tracks: / What will mother say / Undercover agent zero.
7" Single: Released May '80, on Parlophone, by EMI Records. Deleted May '83. Catalogue no: **R 6036**

SIXTEEN DOWN
Tracks: / Sixteen down / Night creatures / Lois lane / Today belongs to me.
7" Single: Released Feb '80, on Parlophone, by EMI Records. Deleted Feb '85. Catalogue no: **R6030**

FM

AMERICAN GIRLS
Tracks: / American girls / That girl / American girls (remix).
7" Single: Released Aug '86, on Portrait, by CBS Records. Catalogue no: **650036 7**
12" Single: Released Aug '86, on Portrait, by CBS Records. Catalogue no: **650036 6**

BAD LUCK
Tracks: / Bad luck / This could be the last time / Hurt is where the heart is (Only on 12", CD and EP single.) / Bad luck (extended version) (Only on 12" and CD single.).
7" EP: Released Jul '89, on Epic, by CBS Records. Catalogue no: **655 031 0**
CD 5": Released Jul '89, on Epic, by CBS Records. Catalogue no: **655 031 2**
7" Pic: Released Jul '89, on Epic, by CBS Records. Catalogue no: **655 031 9**
Cassingle: Released Jul '89, on Epic, by CBS Records. Catalogue no: **655 031 4**
7" Single: Released Jun '89, on Epic, by CBS Records. Catalogue no: **655 031 7**
12" Single: Released Aug '89, on Epic, by CBS Records. Catalogue no: **655 031 8**
12" Single: Released Jun '89, on Epic, by CBS Records. Catalogue no: **655 031 6**

FROZEN HEART
Tracks: / Frozen heart / Love lasts forever / Other side of midnight, The (Only available on 12" version.) / Addicted to love (Only available on 7" Gatefold sleeve/double pack.) / Hot legs (Only available on 7" Gatefold sleeve/double pack.).
7" Single: Released Feb '87, on Portrait, by CBS Records. Catalogue no: **DIDGE 1**
12" Single: Released Feb '87, on Portrait, by CBS Records. Deleted Aug '87. Catalogue no: **DIDGE T1**

LET LOVE BE THE LEADER
Tracks: / Let love be the leader / Let love be the leader (live version) / I belong to the night (87 version).
7" Pic: Released 20 Jun '87, on Portrait, by CBS Records. Deleted Nov '87. Catalogue no: **MERVP 1**
7" Single: Released 20 Jun '87, on Portrait, by CBS Records. Deleted Nov '87. Catalogue no: **MERV 1**
12" Single: Released 20 Jun '87, on Portrait, by CBS Records. Deleted Nov '87. Catalogue no: **MERVT 1**
12" Single: Released Jun '87, on Portrait, by CBS Records. Deleted Nov '87. Catalogue no: **MERVB 1**

LOVE WAS DYING
Tracks: / Love was dying / Captured.
7" Single: Released Jun '86, on Portrait, by CBS Records. Catalogue no: **A 7233**
12" Single: Released Jun '86, on Portrait, by CBS Records. Catalogue no: **TA 7233**

SOMEDAY (YOU'LL COME RUNNING)
Tracks: / Someday (you'll come running) / Alibi / Obsession / Someday (you'll come running) (extended versio / Every time we touch.
7" EP: Released Sep '89, on Epic, by CBS Records. Catalogue no: **DINK G1**
7" EP: Released 18 Sep '89, on Epic, by CBS Records. Catalogue no: **DINK B1**
CD 5": Released 18 Sep '89, on Epic, by CBS Records. Catalogue no: **DINK CD1**
12" Pic: Released Sep '89, on Epic, by CBS Records. Catalogue no: **DINK M1**

7" Single: Released 18 Sep '89, on Epic, by CBS Records. Catalogue no: **DINK 1**
12" Single: Released 18 Sep '89, on Epic, by CBS Records. Catalogue no: **DINK T1**

THAT GIRL
Tracks: / That girl / American girls.
7" Single: Released Mar '86, on Portrait, by CBS Records. Catalogue no: **A 7005**

Focus

Biographical details: At the time of their greatest success, this Dutch band consisted of Jan Akkerman, Cyril Havermans, Thijs Van Leer and Pierre Van Der Linden. Focus were formed in Amsterdam in 1969, initially as the backing musicians for that city's production of the sensational stage musical, *Hair*. The group stuck together, and became one of the few acts from Holland to break into the UK and US market-places. Backed by the various members' impressive musical education and training, they fused elements of progressive rock, jazz and classical music into an extraordinarily eclectic cross-fertilisation. The group traded on the virtuosity of their two key, long serving players - Akkerman played the guitar as if his life depended on it, while Van Leer was a maestro on keyboards, flute and occasional vocal (although much of their work was purely instrumental). Strangely, Focus' only two UK hit singles climbed the charts simultaneously: the rocky instrumental *Sylvia* reached No.4 in early '73, while *Hocus pocus* (which featured a curious yodelling effect) peaked at No.20. The latter track obtained a No.9 placing in the USA. The band's biggest album in No.2. During 1972-4, they also charted strongly with *Focus 3*, Focus at the Rainbow and *Hamburger concerto*. In the late Seventies, guitarist Philip Catherine replaced Akkerman; but by this time, much of the record-buying world had lost interest in Focus, and they had to look closer to home for their success. Akkerman and Van Leer have both released many solo albums down the years. (Bob MacDonald, 2nd August 1985).

HOCUS POCUS
Tracks: / Hocus pocus.
7" Single: Released Dec '72, on Polydor, by Polydor Ltd. Deleted '75. Catalogue no: **2001 211**
7" Single: Released Jul '84, on EMI (Holland), by EMI Records. Catalogue no: **1A 006 26768**

SYLVIA
Tracks: / Sylvia / Hocus pocus.
7" Single: Released Mar '73, on Polydor, by Polydor Ltd. Deleted '76. Catalogue no: **2001 402**
7" Single: Released Feb '85, on EMI Golden 45's, by EMI Records. Catalogue no: **G 4539**
7" Single: Released Mar '87, on Old Gold, by Old Gold Records. Deleted Sep '89. Catalogue no: **OG 9696**

Foetus

BEDROCK
Tracks: / Bedrock / Diabolus in musica / Shut / Rattlesnake insurance
7" EP: Released 13 Jun '87, on Some Bizzare, by Some Bizzare Records. Catalogue no: **WOMBFAN 13**
7" EP: Released May '87, on Self Immolation, by Some Bizzare Records. Catalogue no: **WOMBFAN 13**

CALAMITY CRUSH
Tracks: / Calamity crush.
12" Single: Released Oct '84, on Self Immolation, by Some Bizzare Records. Catalogue no: **FAT 11 12**

CUSTOM BUILT FOR CAPITALISM
Tracks: / Custom built for capitalism.
12" Single: Released Mar '82, on Self Immolation, by Some Bizzare Records. Catalogue no: **WOMBSUSC 125**

FINELY HONED MACHINE
Tracks: / Finely honed machine.
12" Single: Released Feb '85, on Self Immolation, by Some Bizzare Records. Catalogue no: **WOMBUNC 712**

RAMROD
Tracks: / Ramrod.
12" Single: Released 10 Oct '87, on Some Bizzare, by Some Bizzare Records. Catalogue no: **WOMBPIG 12 12**

WASH IT ALL OFF
Tracks: / Wash it all off.
12" Single: Released Jan '85, on Self Immolation, by Some Bizzare Records. Catalogue no: **WOMBFGH 812**

Foffo Spearjig

TIE YOUR LACES TIGHT
Tracks: / Tie your laces tight.
7" Single: Released Mar '83, on Eccentric, Deleted '87. Catalogue no: **UBET 1003**

Fogelberg, Dan

Biographical details: This American singer, guitarist and songwriter, born in Illinois, began his musical career in the late Sixties by playing folk music. He then relocated to Los Angeles and became a competent session player, and also toured with Van Morrison. After moving again, this time to Nashville, Fogelberg released his debut labum *Home free*. His second LP, 1974's *Souvenirs*, was produced by Joe Walsh and featured backing vocals from various members of the Eagles plus Graham Nash. Fogelberg first cracked the US Top 40 singles listings with his 1975 effort *Part of the plan*, which reached No.31. The next significant landmark in his career occurred in 1978, when he issued a successful duet LP with lookalike singer/flautist Tim Weisberg. *Twin sons of different mothers*. This yielded a version of the Hollies-associated song *Tell me to my face*. With his following having also been enhanced by tours as support to the Eagles, Fogelberg achieved his biggest American (and only British) hit single in 1980 with *Longer* - this simple ballad reached No.2 in the US and a lowly No.59 in the UK. Over the following two years, he chalked up three more US Top 10 singles - *Same old Lang Syne, Hard to say* and *Leader of the band* all featured his usual blend of well-crafted melodies, lush arrangements and gentle singing. His style came somewhere between soft rock and MoR. In particular, the moving *Same old Lang Syne* became a regular airplay favourite during the New Year season. Though largely unknown in Britain, Dan has continued to sell albums and singles in very respectable quantities in his native US. His later successes have included *Run for the roses* (No.18 in 1982, from the LP *The innocent age*) and *The language of love* (No.13 in 1984, from the LP *Windows and walls*) (Bob MacDonald, 2nd Sept 1985)

Singer/songwriter, born in 1951 in Peoria, Ill. His first album was made in Nashville, a typically polite country debut; he turned more rockish, his guitar playing influenced by Joe Walsh. By the late '70s he was more successful, his songwriting stronger; his bluegrass - flavoured *Exiles* maintained a high standard from a near-recluse who once cancelled several important live dates and spent 18 months in the '70's session-ing with others. Typed as a soft-rock balladeer by his hit USA singles, he has stayed with the same label for 15 years, done a lot of different things and matured at his own pace. (Donald Clarke, April 1989).

BEGGAR'S GAME
Tracks: / Beggar's game / Along the road (On EPC 8154 only) / Gypsy wind (On 10" only).
7" Single: Released Apr '80, on Epic, by CBS Records. Deleted Apr '83. Catalogue no: **EPC 8554**
7" Single: Released Jan '80, on Epic, by CBS Records. Deleted Jan '85. Catalogue no: **EPC 8154**

HARD TO SAY
Tracks: / Hard to say / Innocent age, The.
7" Single: Released Oct '81, on Epic, by CBS Records. Deleted Oct '84. Catalogue no: **EPCA 1635**

LANGUAGE OF LOVE
Tracks: / Language of love / Windows and walls.
7" Single: Released Apr '84, on Epic, by CBS Records. Catalogue no: **A 4237**

LEADER OF THE BAND
Tracks: / Leader of the band / Times like these.
7" Single: Released Apr '82, on Epic, by CBS Records. Deleted Apr '85. Catalogue no: **EPCA 2908**

LONGER
Tracks: / Longer / Along the road.
7" Single: Released Jan '80, on CBS, by CBS Records. Deleted Jan '83. Catalogue no: **CBS 8230**
7" Single: Released Mar '80, on Full Moon (1), Deleted '83. Catalogue no: **EPC 8230**

SAME AULD LANG SYNE
Tracks: / Same Auld Lang Syne / Hearts and crafts.
7" Single: Released Nov '81, on Epic, by CBS Records. Deleted Nov '84. Catalogue no: **EPC A 1787**

Fogerty, John

EYE OF THE ZOMBIE
Tracks: / Eye of the zombie.
7" Single: Released Oct '86, on Warner Bros., by WEA Records. Deleted Jun '87. Catalogue no: **W 8657**
12" Single: Released Oct '86, on Warner Bros., by WEA Records. Deleted Jun '87. Catalogue no: **W 8657T**

Foghat

THIRD TIME LUCKY
Tracks: / Third time lucky / Somebody's been sleeping in my bed.
7" Single: Released Mar '80, on Island, by Island Records. Deleted Mar '83. Catalogue no: **WIP 6582**

Fogle, Adeen

BAKED A CAKE
Tracks: / Baked a cake / You are always on my mind.
7" Single: Released Dec '84, on Eureka, Catalogue no: **EURA 1**

Fogli, Riccardo

FOR LUCIA
Tracks: / For Lucia.
7" Single: Released Apr '83, on Ariola, by BMG Records (UK). Catalogue no: **ARO 297**

Foldy, Peter

SCHOOL OF LOVE
Tracks: / School of love / Love city.
7" Single: Released Dec '80, on Earlobe, by Earlobe Records. Deleted Dec '85. Catalogue no: **ELS 3**

Foley, Connie

HOME OF DONEGAL
Tracks: / Home of Donegal.
7" Single: Released '88, on Homespun (Ireland), by Outlet Records. Catalogue no: **HIS 3**

Foley, Ellen

Biographical details: This American singer, born and brought up in St Louis, moved to New York in 1972 to begin her showbusiness career. Although she began singing with a local rock band, Big Jive, her primary ambition at this time was to be an actress. After working in various off-Broadway show and after being part of the touring National Lampoon Show, and she went into television and appeared in soap operas such as *Search for tomorrow* and *One life to live*. Foley's recording career began in 1977, when she was reunited with two fellow ex-Lampooners, singer Meat Loaf and songwriter/keyboardist/arranger Jim Steinman. She sang background vocals on four of the seven tracks on the classic 1977 album *Bat out of hell*. This epic masterwork was a major hit on both sides of the Atlantic; in Britain, it remained on the LP charts every week from 1978 until 1985. The album was a perfect vehicle for Ellen's fiery vocals as well as Meat Loaf's, and their extended duet on *Paradise by the dashboard light* (a US Top 40 single) was breathtakingly frenetic. Foley also became the co-star of Mr Loaf's live shows. After further acting work, including the starring role in a Broadway revival of *Hair*, she launched a solo singing career in 1979, a career which has never really lived up to the promise of her Meat Loaf work. Her hard rocking debut album *Night out*, produced by Ian Hunter and Mick Ronson and featuring material from a wide variety of sources, peaked at No.68 in Britain. 1981's *Spirit of St Louis* LP, which was produced and masterminded by her then boyfriend Mick Jones of the Clash, reached No.57 in Britain but failed to crack the US Top 200 Albums chart. This somewhat bizarre, heavily European album, was followed in 1983 by the disappointing *Another breath*. Foley has never enjoyed a solo Top 40 single on either side of the Atlantic. Ellen is a vehement and vivacious vocalist who had not fulfilled her true potential. (Bob MacDonald, 3rd Sept 1985).

JOHNNY & MARY
Tracks: / Johnny and Mary.
7" Single: Released Mar '83, on Epic, by CBS Records. Catalogue no: **EPC A 3236**

SAD SONG
Tracks: / Sad song / Don't let go.
7" Single: Released May '80, on Epic, by CBS Records. Deleted '83. Catalogue no: **EPC 8561**

SHATTERED PALACE
Tracks: / Shattered palace / Beautiful waste of time.
7" Single: Released Feb '81, on Epic, by CBS Records. Deleted Feb '84. Catalogue no: **EPC 9522**

STUPID GIRL
Tracks: / Stupid girl / Young lust.
7" Single: Released Feb '80, on Epic, by CBS Records. Deleted '83. Catalogue no: **EPC 8122**

TORCHLIGHT
Tracks: / Torchlight / Game of man.
7" Single: Released Apr '81, on Epic, by CBS Records. Deleted Apr '84. Catalogue no: **EPC A 1160**

Folk Devils

BEAUTIFUL MONSTER
Tracks: / Beautiful monster.
7" Single: Released Aug '84, on Ganges, Catalogue no: **RAY 2**
12" Single: Released Aug '84, on Ganges, Catalogue no: **RAY 2T**

BEST PROTECTION, THE
Tracks: / Best protection, The / Your mistake / Third stroke, The.
12" Single: Released 13 Jun '87, on Situation 2, by Beggars Banquet Records. Catalogue no: **SIT 47T**

FIRE AND CHROME
Tracks: / Fire and chrome.
12" Single: Released Jul '85, on Karbon, by Karbon Records. Catalogue no: **KAR 601T**

HANK TURNS BLUE
Tracks: / Hank turns blue.
7" Single: Released Mar '84, on Ganges, Catalogue no: **RAY 1**

Fontaine, Claudia

NATURAL HIGH
Tracks: / Natural high / Let's love.
7" Single: Released Jun '81, on Decca, by Decca Records. Deleted Jun '84. Catalogue no: **F 13905**
12" Single: Released Jun '81, on Decca, by Decca Records. Deleted Jun '84. Catalogue no: **FX 13905**

Fontaine, Roy

ONE IS A LONELY NUMBER
Tracks: / One is a lonely number / One is a lonely number (Inst).
7" Single: Released Jul '86, on Abstract Dance, by Priority Records. Catalogue no: **AD 9**
12" Single: Released Jul '86, on Abstract Dance, by Priority Records. Catalogue no: **ADT 9**

Fontaine Sisters

DEAREST FATHER & MOTHER
Tracks: / Dearest father & mother.
12" Single: Released May '89, on Mixdown, Catalogue no: **MIXD 003**

HEARTS OF STONE
Tracks: / Hearts of stone / Seventeen.
7" Single: Released May '81, on Revival, Deleted May '84. Catalogue no: **REV 6008**

Fontana, Wayne

Biographical details: This British singer, born Glyn Ellis in Manchester, worked as a trainee telephone engineer before coming famous as the star member of Wayne Fontana & the Mindbenders. Appropriately, he recorded for the Fontana label.

With the Beatles having just exploded onto the national pop scene, young Wayne released his first record in June 1963 - he was one of numerous young hopefuls who were inspired to try their luck during that period. Some of the members of his Manchester based backing group had dropped out at the last minute, so he recruited some new players (including Eric Stewart, who achieved even greater fame in the Seventies as a member of 10cc) and christened them the Mindbenders. The first single was no success, but the second, *Hello Josephine*, crept to No 46 on the UK chart. Just over a year later, in late 1964, Fontana (still only in his late teens) and the Mindbenders were able to transform their chart toehold into major success: they recorded the infectious *Um Um Um Um Um Um*, which had been a US No 5 hit for Major Lance earlier in the year but had not made much impression in the UK. Written by Curtis Mayfield, this song took Fontana to the UK No 5 position. In 1965 Wayne achieved his biggest hit with *Game Of Love* - this cruised to No 2 in Britain and, as part of the British invasion, became a No 1 smash in the States.

Their next two singles were markedly less successful and, with Fontana and the Mindbenders blaming each other, the vocalist and the group parted company at the end of '65. While the combo hit No 2 on both sides of the Atlantic with *A Groovy Kind Of Love*, their ex-leader gained two UK Top 20 hits with *Come On Home* and Graham Gouldman's *Pamela Pamela*.

Fontana then wedded a young fan and faded into oblivion, although he did pop up from time to time on various revival shows and tours. Bob MacDonald, 3.9.85.
UK pop singer, born Glyn Ellis in 1945 in Manchester, leader of beat group the Mindbenders. They were derivative of USA music and split up in 1965 after a few hits; Fontana went solo and soon retired except oldies shows, especially in the USA; the group had hits of their own before splitting, and guitarist Eric Stewart later turned into 10CC with Graham Gouldman, who'd been a later Mindbender. (Donald Clarke, April 1989).

COME ON HOME
Tracks: / Come on home.
7" Single: Released Apr '66, on Fontana, by Phonogram Ltd. Deleted '69. Catalogue no: **TF 684**

GAME OF LOVE (SINGLE)
Tracks: / Game of love.
7" Single: Released Feb '65, on Fontana, by Phonogram Ltd. Deleted '68. Catalogue no: **TF 535**
7" Single: Released Jul '82, on Old Gold, by Old Gold Records. Catalogue no: **OG 9266**

GOODBYE BLUEBIRD
Tracks: / Goodbye bluebird.
7" Single: Released Aug '66, on Fontana, by Phonogram Ltd. Deleted '69. Catalogue no: **TF 737**

HELLO JOSEPHINE
Tracks: / Hello Josephine.
7" Single: Released Jul '63, on Fontana, by Phonogram Ltd. Deleted '66. Catalogue no: **TF 404**

IT WAS EASIER TO HURT HER
Tracks: / It was easier to hurt her.
7" Single: Released Dec '65, on Fontana, by Phonogram Ltd. Deleted '68. Catalogue no: **TF 642**

JUST A LITTLE BIT TOO LATE
Tracks: / Just a little bit too late.
7" Single: Released Jun '65, on Fontana, by Phonogram Ltd. Deleted '68. Catalogue no: **TF 579**

PAMELA PAMELA
Tracks: / Pamela, Pamela.
7" Single: Released Dec '66, on Fontana, by Phonogram Ltd. Deleted '69. Catalogue no: **TF 770**
7" Single: Released Jan '85, on Old Gold, by Old Gold Records. Catalogue no: **OG 9473**

STOP LOOK AND LISTEN
Tracks: / Stop look and listen.
7" Single: Released May '64, on Fontana, by Phonogram Ltd. Deleted '67. Catalogue no: **TF 451**

UM UM UM UM UM UM
Tracks: / Um, um, um, um, um, um.
7" Single: Released Apr '64, on Fontana, by Phonogram Ltd. Deleted '67. Catalogue no: **TF 497**

Foo Foo Lammar, Frank

FOO FOO'S NETBALL TEAM
Tracks: / Foo foo's netball team / Love you being around.
7" Single: Released Oct '80, on Columbia, by EMI Records. Deleted Oct '83. Catalogue no: **DB 9085**

Fools

PSYCHO CHICKEN
Tracks: / Psycho chicken (clucked) / Psycho chicken (beeped).
7" Single: Released Apr '80, on EMI, by EMI Records. Deleted Apr '83. Catalogue no: **EA 110**

RUNNING SCARED
Tracks: / Running scared / Alibi.
7" Single: Released May '81, on America, by Musidisc Records (France). Deleted May '84. Catalogue no: **EA 123**

TALK TO LORETTA
Tracks: / Talk to Loretta / Coming home with me.
7" Single: Released Nov '81, on EMI-America, by EMI Records. Deleted '84. Catalogue no: **EA 132**

Fools Dance

FOOLS AND DANCE
Tracks: / Fools dance.
7" Single: Released Aug '86, on Prism, by Prism Records. Catalogue no: **LTS 18**

THEY'LL NEVER KNOW
Tracks: / They'll never know / Empty hours.
7" Single: Released 10 Oct '87, on Lambs To The Slaughter, by Prism Records. Catalogue no: **LTS 22**

Foote, Wayne

UNCOOL
Tracks: / Uncool / Son of uncle.
7" Single: Released Oct '86, on Blanco Y Negro, by Blanco Y Negro Records. Catalogue no: **NEG 22**
12" Single: Released Oct '86, on Blanco Y Negro, by Blanco Y Negro Records. Deleted Jun '87. Catalogue no: **NEG 22T**

Forbert, Steve

Biographical details: This American singer, songwriter, guitarist and harmonica player first attracted attention in late 1978 with his highly impressive debut album *Alive On Arrival*. Although he was written off in many quarters as merely the latest Bob Dylan soundalike, Forbert's songs were strong enough to merit attention in their own right. Combining emotional sensitivity and refreshing honesty with some good tunes, *Alive On Arrival* received a cult following in the States; this spread to Britain after strong support from some journalists and disc jockeys, notably American born Paul Gambacini. The LP's songs ranged from the articulate advice of the up-tempo *Thinkin'* to the tender remorse of the slow ballad *It Isn't Gonna Be That Way*. The album reached No 56 in Britain in June 1979, and was soon followed by the No 54 placing of the *Jackrabbit Slim* LP. This latter set yielded his only US Top 40 single, *Romeo's Tune* (No 11).
Despite all these promising happenings, Forbert quickly drifted into obscurity. His material became weaker and weaker. Even if he had kept the standard up, it is doubtful that he would have become a major star in the early Eighties - his music, style and approach would have found far greater acceptance during the singer/songwriter era of the early Seventies. Bob MacDonald, 3.9.85.
Singer/songwriter born in 1955 in Mississippi. He was a critical and cult favourite between 1978-82, but there was no room for the singer/songwriter genre then, ironically making a comeback in the late '60's. (Donald Clarke, April 1989).

GET WELL SOON
Tracks: / Get well soon / Visitor.
7" Single: Released Sep '80, on Epic, by CBS Records. Deleted Sep '83. Catalogue no: **EPC 8995**

LONELY GIRL
Tracks: / Lonely girl / Rain.
7" Single: Released Nov '80, on Epic, by CBS Records. Deleted Nov '83. Catalogue no: **EPC 8983**

ROMEO'S TUNE
Tracks: / Romeo's tune / Sadly sorta like a soap opera.
7" Single: Released Apr '81, on Epic, by CBS Records. Deleted Apr '84. Catalogue no: **EPC A 1123**

RUNNING ON LOVE
Tracks: / Running on love / Mexico.
7" Single: Released Sep '88, on Geffen, by Geffen Records (USA). Catalogue no: **GEF 45**
12" Single: Released Sep '88, on Geffen, by Geffen Records (USA). Catalogue no: **GEF 45T**

SAY GOODBYE TO LITTLE JOE
Tracks: / Say goodbe to little Joe / Darn right.
7" Single: Released Mar '80, on Epic, by CBS Records. Deleted '83. Catalogue no: **EPC 8342**

SWEET LOVE THAT YOU GIVE
Tracks: / Sweet love that you give / Make it all so real.
7" Single: Released Jan '80, on Epic, by CBS Records. Deleted Jan '85. Catalogue no: **EPC 8124**

WHEN YOU WALK IN THE ROON
Tracks: / When you walk in the room / I don't know.
7" Single: Released Jun '82, on Epic, by CBS Records. Deleted Jun '85. Catalogue no: **EPCA 2464**

Forbes, Bill

TOO YOUNG
Tracks: / Too young.
7" Single: Released Jan '60, on Columbia, by EMI Records. Deleted '63. Catalogue no: **DB 4386**

Forbidden

LIVE AT THE DYNAMO
12" Single: Released Sep '89, on Music For Nations, by Music For Nations Records. Catalogue no: **12FLAG 108**

Force

EYE TO EYE
Tracks: / Tomorrow may never come (This extra track on 12" version only) / Amigo (This extra track on 12" version only).
7" Single: Released Jan '87, on Valentino, Deleted Jan '88. Catalogue no: **B 9478**
12" Single: Released Jan '87, on Valentino, Deleted Jan '88. Catalogue no: **B 9478 T**

FAMINE ETHIOPIA
Tracks: / Famine Ethiopia / S.O.S..
12" Single: Released Dec '84, on Mab, Catalogue no: **MAB 001**

MISSION IMPOSSIBLE
Tracks: / Mission Impossible / Microphone mania.
12" Single: Released Feb '89, on Vinyl Lab, Catalogue no: **VL 004**

MUSIC
Tracks: / Music.
12" Single: Released Mar '80, on Destiny, by Destiny Records. Catalogue no: **DS 2**

SHOUT
Tracks: / Shout / Change your heart.
7" Single: Released Sep '87, on Atlantic, by WEA Records. Deleted Jul '88. Catalogue no: **B 2423**

TOMORROW MAY NEVER COME
Tracks: / Tomorrow may never come / I heard the sound.
7" Single: Released Apr '87, on Valentino, Deleted Jan '88. Catalogue no: **B 9452**

TRICK OF LIGHT
Tracks: / Trick of light / Right side of the street.
7" Single: Released Feb '82, on Zilch, by Zilch Records. Deleted Feb '87. Catalogue no: **ZILCH 10**

Force 8

FIESTA
Tracks: / Fiesta.
7" Single: Released Aug '85, on New Merseysound, Deleted '87. Catalogue no: **FORCE 2**
12" Single: Released Aug '85, on New Merseysound, Deleted '87. Catalogue no: **12FORCE 2**

Force 10

ONE AND ONLY
Tracks: / One and only.
7" Single: Released Jul '83, on Monarch, by Monarch Records. Catalogue no: **MON 043**

Force Dimension

DUST
Tracks: / Dust.
12" Single: Released '88, on K K, by Play It Again Sam (Belgium). Catalogue no: **KK 027**

TENSION - MENTHOL - 200FA
Tracks: / Tension - menthol - 200fa.
12" Single: Released Oct '89, on KKUK, Catalogue no: **KK 028**

Force M.D.'s

FORGIVE ME GIRL
Tracks: / Forgive me girl.
7" Single: Released Oct '84, on Tommy Boy, by Polydor Ltd. Catalogue no: **IS 207**
12" Single: Released Oct '84, on Tommy Boy, by Polydor Ltd. Deleted '87. Catalogue no: **12IS 207**

HERE I GO AGAIN
Tracks: / Here I go again / Itchin' for a scratch.
7" Single: Released Jun '86, on Island, by Island Records. Catalogue no: **IS 286**
12" Single: Released Jun '86, on Island, by Island Records. Deleted Jul '87. Catalogue no: **12IS 286**

LOVE IS A HOUSE
Tracks: / Love is a house / Love is a house (inst).
7" Single: Released Jul '87, on Warner Bros., by WEA Records. Deleted Jul '88. Catalogue no: **U 8252**
12" Single: Released Jul '87, on Warner Bros., by WEA Records. Deleted Jul '88. Catalogue no: **U 8252 T**

TEARS
Tracks: / Tears.
7" Single: Released Feb '85, on Tommy Boy, by Polydor Ltd. Catalogue no: **IS 195**
12" Single: Released Feb '85, on Tommy Boy, by Polydor Ltd. Deleted '87. Catalogue no: **12IS 195**

TENDER LOVE (SINGLE)
Tracks: / Tender love.
7" Single: Released Jan '86, on President, by President Records. Catalogue no: **PT 551**
12" Single: Released Mar '86, on Tommy Boy, by Polydor Ltd. Deleted Jul '87. Catalogue no: **12 ISX 269**

Forcefield

SMOKE ON THE WATER
Tracks: / Shine it on me / Smoke on the water.
12" Single: Released Feb '87, on President, by President Records. Catalogue no: **PT 12-551**

Forcefield II

HEARTACHE
Tracks: / Heartache / I lose again (instrumental version).
Note: Side 1 taken from the album The Talisman on President Records -- PTLS 1095. Side 2 taken from the compact disc of the same title -- PCOM 1095 -- but not included on the album.
7" Single: Released Aug '88, on President, by President Records. Catalogue no: **PT 578**

Ford, Andy

GROOVY KIND OF LOVE
Tracks: / Groovy kind of love.
7" Single: Released Aug '84, on Tabitha, by Tabitha Records. Catalogue no: **TAB 6**

TEENAGE LOVE
Tracks: / Teenage love.
7" Single: Released Jan '84, on Tabitha, by Tabitha Records. Catalogue no: **TAB 5**

Ford, Barry

I WANNA REACH OUT AND TOUCH YOU
Tracks: / I wanna reach out and touch.
12" Single: Released Apr '84, on Albion, by Albion Records. Catalogue no: **12PEA 001**

RADIO ACTIVE
Tracks: / Radio active / Dub active.
7" Single: Released Nov '82, on Albion, by Albion Records. Catalogue no: **ION 1039**
12" Single: Released Nov '82, on Albion, by Albion Records. Catalogue no: **12ION 1039**

Ford, Clinton

FANLIGHT FANNY
Tracks: / Fanlight Fanny.
7" Single: Released Mar '62, on Oriole, Deleted '65. Catalogue no: **CB 1706**

OLD SHEP
Tracks: / Old shep.
7" Single: Released Oct '59, on Oriole, Deleted '62. Catalogue no: **CB 1500**

RUN TO THE DOOR
Tracks: / Run to the door.
7" Single: Released Jan '67, on Piccadilly, Deleted '69. Catalogue no: **7N 35361**

TOO MANY BEAUTIFUL GIRLS
Tracks: / Too many beautiful girls.
7" Single: Released Aug '61, on Oriole, Deleted '64. Catalogue no: **CB 1623**

Ford, Emile

Biographical details: This British singer was actually born in Nassau, Bahamas, but moved with his family to London during childhood. After leaving school, he became a regular performer in London coffee bars and eventually won a talent contest at Soho Fair. With his backing group, he shot to stardom in 1959 with his first record - *What Do You Want To Make Those Eyes At Me For?* by Emile Ford & The Checkmates was Britain's Christmas No 1 of 1959, and logged six weeks at the summit. This singalong rendition of a 1916 song was so catchy that it turned Ford into an instant household name; his voice was pleasant but not particularly special, and he owed much of the success to the producer and arranger. As well as the being the No 1 record that took Britain from the Fifties into the Sixties, *What Do You Want To Make Those Eyes At Me For?* was notable insofar as it was the first big hit by a black UK rock artist.
There were two more British Top 10 singles for Ford. Frank Loesser's 1948 song *On A Slow Boat To China* took Emile to No 3 in early 1960 and, at the end of the year, he achieved a No 4 hit with *Counting Teardrops*. After his final UK chart success in 1962, Ford relocated to Sweden where he was able to sustain a reasonably successful career for several years, before disappearing into obscurity altogether. When one of Britain's daily newspapers tracked Emile down in the early Eighties, he described himself as a 'man on the run' with large debts and major financial hassles. He thus had good reasons to be *Counting Teardrops* - or, to quote the title of one of his smaller hits, *What Am I Gonna Do?*. Bob MacDonald, 3.9.85..

COUNTING TEARDROPS
Tracks: / Counting teardrops.
7" Single: Released Dec '60, on Pye, Deleted '63. Catalogue no: **7N 15314**

HALF OF MY HEART
Tracks: / Half of my heart.
7" Single: Released May '61, on Piccadilly, Deleted '64. Catalogue no: **7N 35003**

I WONDER WHO'S KISSING HER NOW

Tracks: / I wonder who's kissing her now.
7" Single: Released Mar '62, on Piccadilly, Deleted '65. Catalogue no: **7N 35033**

ON A SLOW BOAT TO CHINA
Tracks: / On a slow boat to China.
7" Single: Released Feb '60, on Pye, Deleted '63. Catalogue no: **7N 15245**

THEM THERE EYES
Tracks: / Them there eyes.
7" Single: Released Sep '60, on Pye, Deleted '63. Catalogue no: **7N 15282**

WHAT AM I GONNA DO
Tracks: / What am I gonna do.
7" Single: Released Mar '61, on Pye, Deleted '64. Catalogue no: **7N 15331**

WHAT DO YOU WANT TO MAKE THOSE EYES AT ME FOR
Tracks: / What do you want to make those eyes at me for.
7" Single: Released Oct '59, on Pye, Deleted '62. Catalogue no: **7N 15225**
7" Single: Released Jul '82, on Old Gold, by Old Gold Records. Catalogue no: **OG 9143**

YOU'LL NEVER KNOW WHAT YOU'RE MISSING
Tracks: / You'll never know what you're missing.
7" Single: Released May '60, on Pye, Deleted '63. Catalogue no: **7N 15268**

Ford, Frankie

Biographical details: R&B singer born in 1940 in Louisiana, a white teenager selected by the New Orleans Ace label for Elvis Presley/Ricky Nelson type stardowm; *Sea cruise* was an existing track by Huey 'Piano' Smith and the Clowns with Smith's vocal removed and Ford's substituted. It was his only hit, but he still has his fans. (Donald Clarke, April 1989)i.

SEA CRUISE
Tracks: / Sea cruise / Twist, The / Dance with me.
7" Single: Released Aug '82, on Blast From The Past, by Creole Records. Catalogue no: **CR 193**

Ford, Gerry

LORD I'D FORGOTTEN
Tracks: / Lord I'd forgotten / Easy.
7" Single: Released Jun '81, on Big R, by Big R Records. Catalogue no: **BRS 03**

Ford, Jed

BOSS O' THE BLACK
Tracks: / Boss o' the black / Willie Thorne, king of the maximum break.
7" Single: Released May '86, on BBC, by BBC Records & Tapes. Deleted Sep '87. Catalogue no: **RESL 187**

Ford, John T.

WHAT YOU GONNA DO
Tracks: / What you gonna do / Tell me something new.
Note: Pic bag
7" Single: Released Apr '87, on Splash, by Splash Records. Catalogue no: **CPS 10**

Ford, Lita

CLOSE MY EYES FOREVER
Tracks: / Close my eyes forever / Under the gun.
12" Single: Released May '89, on RCA, by BMG Records (UK). Catalogue no: **PT 49410**
12" Single: Released May '89, on RCA, by BMG Records (UK). Catalogue no: **PT 49380**
7" Single: Released May '89, on RCA, by BMG Records (UK). Catalogue no: **PB 49409**
CD 5": Released 15 May '89, on RCA, by BMG Records (UK). Catalogue no: **PD 49409**
7" Single: Released 22 May '89, on RCA, by BMG Records (UK). Catalogue no: **PB 49379**
12" Single: Released May '89, on RCA, by BMG Records (UK). Catalogue no: **PA 49396**

GOTTA LET GO
Tracks: / Gotta let go.
12" Single: Released Apr '84, on Vertigo, by Phonogram Ltd. Catalogue no: **VERX 10**
7" Single: Released Apr '84, on Vertigo, by Phonogram Ltd. Catalogue no: **VER 10**

KISS
Tracks: / Kiss.
7" Single: Released May '88, on RCA, by BMG Records (UK). Catalogue no: **PB 49575**
12" Single: Released May '88, on RCA, by BMG Records (UK). Catalogue no: **PT 49576**

KISS ME DEADLY
Tracks: / Kiss me deadly / Broken dreams / Kiss me deadly (inst) (12" only).
7" Pic: Released Dec '88, on RCA, by BMG Records (UK). Catalogue no: **PA 49503**
7" Pic: Released Jul '88, on RCA, by BMG Records (UK). Deleted May '89. Catalogue no: **PB 49575P**
7" Single: Released Nov '88, on RCA, by BMG Records (UK). Deleted Aug '89. Catalogue no: **PB 49501**
7" Single: Released Apr '88, on RCA, by BMG Records (UK). Catalogue no: **PB 49575**
12" Single: Released Apr '88, on RCA, by BMG Records (UK). Catalogue no: **PT 49576**

Ford, Martyn

LET YOUR BODY GO DOWNTOWN
Tracks: / Let your body go downtown.
7" Single: Released May '77, on Mountain, Deleted '80. Catalogue no: **TOP 26**

Ford, Pennye

CHANGE YOUR WICKED WAYS
Tracks: / Change your wicked ways.
7" Single: Released Oct '84, on Total Experience, Catalogue no: **RCA 503**

DANGEROUS (see panel below)
Tracks: / Dangerous / Change your wicked ways.
7" Single: Released Apr '85, on Total Experience, Catalogue no: **FB 49975**
12" Single: Released Apr '85, on Total Experience, Deleted '87. Catalogue no: **FT 49976**

Ford, Tennessee Ernie

Biographical details: This American singer, born Ernest Jennings Ford in Bristol, Tennessee in 1919, worked as a radio announcer in Pasadena before joining the US Air Force in 1941. Upon his return to civilian life, he became a singer in a local Pasadena quartet, where he was heard by a Capitol Records executive on his car radio in 1948 and quikly signed to a solo contract. The following year, he achieved a success on the US country and western charts with *Mule Train*.
Ford soon began to attract more and more notice with his deep, rich, growling bass voice and his handsome looks. 1950 brought him a C&W No 1 with the self-penned *Shotgun Boogie* plus a further success with *I'll Never Be Free*. The latter record was a duet with Kay Starr and, althoug it reached No 4 on the US C&W charts, his choice of singing partner showed that he was setting his sights beyond the confines of country music.
In the mid-Fifties, Ernie did indeed move into the pop arena by scoring three major international pop hits. *Give Me Your Word* was No 1 for seven weeks in Britain in 1955. In the same year, *Ballad Of Davy Crockett* gave him a US No 5 hit (and later went to No 3 in the UK). Then came the sensationally successful *Sixteen Tons*, released in late 1955, which was No 1 for eight weeks in the States and four weeks in Britain. Written and originally recorded by C&W star Merle Travis in 1947, *Sixteen Tons* could best be described as a cynical singalong - Travis, a coal miner's son, transformed his father's experiences and philosophies into an infectiously catchy song. Lines like 'Another day older and deeper in debt' and 'I owe my soul to the company store' could either be regarded as humorous or bitter. Either way, Ford's thumping rockabilly rendition was one of the fastest selling records in US chart history.
1956 saw Ford commence his own national television show, which lasted until 1961. During this period he faded from the pop limelight, but concentrated more on his religious recordings. By closing each of his TV programmes with a hymn, he ensure steady sales for his 1956 *Hymns* LP, which actually became the biggest selling album in Capitol's history. He recorded approximately 20 inspirational albums for the company in total. By the early Seventies, Ford was in semi-retirement. Bob MacDonald, 3.9.85..

BALLAD OF DAVY CROCKET
Tracks: / Ballad of Davy Crockett, The.
7" Single: Released Jan '56, on Capitol, by EMI Records. Deleted '59. Catalogue no: **CL 14506**

EARLY STOMPIN, SIDES
7" EP: Released Feb '88, on Muleskinner, Catalogue no: **MSEP 10.001**

GIVE ME YOUR WORD
Tracks: / Give me your word.
7" Single: Released Jan '55, on Capitol, by EMI Records. Deleted '58. Catalogue no: **CL 14005**

SIXTEEN TONS (SINGLE)
Tracks: / Sixteen tons / Zambesi.
Note: Also contains:"Zambesi" by Lou Busch
7" Single: Released Jan '56, on Capitol, by EMI Records. Deleted '59. Catalogue no: **CL 14500**
7" Single: Released Apr '87, on Old Gold, by Old Gold Records. Deleted Sep '89. Catalogue no: **OG 9719**

Forde, Aiden

YOUNGSTERS OF BRITAIN
Tracks: / Youngsters of Britain / Nobody knows you (when you're down and out).
7" Single: Released May '88, on Accolade, by Accolade Music. Catalogue no: **YOB 1**

Forde, Charmaine

HEROES
Tracks: / Heroes / Heroes (slow version).
7" Single: Released Mar '88, on Revue, by Creole Records. Catalogue no: **REV 745**
12" Single: Released Mar '88, on Revue, by Creole Records. Catalogue no: **REV 045T**

Fordham, Julia

COMFORT OF STRANGERS, THE
Tracks: / Comfort of strangers, The (7" only) / I wish / Waiting for a miracle (12" only) / Comfort of strangers, The (extended version) (CD & 12" only) / Few too many (CD only).
CD 5": Released Aug '88, on Virgin, by Virgin Records. Catalogue no: **YRCD 11**
7" Single: Released 21 Mar '88, on Circa, by Virgin Records. Catalogue no: **YR 11**
12" Single: Released 21 Mar '88, on Circa, by Virgin Records. Catalogue no: **YRT 11**

HAPPY EVER AFTER
Tracks: / Happy ever after / My lover's keeper / My mistake (Not on 7") / Comfort of strangers, The (On CD only) / Waiting for miracles (On 10" only).
Note: 'HAPPY EVER AFTER' is the stunning new single from the debut album 'JULIA FORDHAM' (circa4). Julia Fordham's songs are statements of her time. Tough and tender, tender but tough, love, anger, resignation and resistance jolt the social concience." (VIRGIN RECORDS, JUNE 1988).O
CD 5": Released '88, on Virgin, by Virgin Records. Catalogue no: **YRCD 15**
10" single: Released '88, on Virgin, by Virgin Records. Catalogue no: **YRX 15**
7" Single: Released Jun '88, on Virgin, by Virgin Records. Catalogue no: **YR 15**
12" Single: Released Jun '88, on Virgin, by Virgin Records. Catalogue no: **YRT 15**

LOCK AND KEY
Tracks: / Lock and key.
CD 5": Released Aug '89, on Circa, by Virgin Records. Catalogue no: **YRC 36**
7" Single: Released Aug '89, on Circa, by Virgin Records. Catalogue no: **YR 36**
12" Single: Released Aug '89, on Circa, by Virgin Records. Catalogue no: **YRT 36**
CD 3": Released Aug '89, on Circa, by Virgin Records. Catalogue no: **YRCD 36**

WHERE DOES THE TIME GO
Tracks: / Where does the time go / My little secret / Behind closed doors (on 12" only.).
CD 5": Released Apr '89, on Circa, by Virgin Records. Catalogue no: **YRCD 23**
7" Single: Released Apr '89, on Circa, by Virgin Records. Catalogue no: **YRB 23**
7" Single: Released Feb '89, on Circa, by Virgin Records. Catalogue no: **YR 23**
12" Single: Released Feb '89, on Circa, by Virgin Records. Catalogue no: **YRT 23**

WOMAN OF THE 80'S
Tracks: / Woman of the 80's (7" & 10" only) / Behind closed doors (On all versions) / Woman of the 80's (album version) (On CD & 12" only) / Happy ever after (On CD & 10" only) / Woman of the 80's (radio version) (On CD & 12" only) / My little secret (On 10" only).
CD 5": Released 26 Sep '88, on Circa, by Virgin Records. Catalogue no: **YRCD 17**
10" single: Released '88, on Circa, by Virgin Records. Catalogue no: **YRTX 17**
7" Single: Released 26 Sep '88, on Circa, by Virgin Records. Catalogue no: **YR 17**
12" Single: Released 26 Sep '88, on Circa, by Virgin Records. Catalogue no: **YRT 17**

Foreign Bodies

GOING BANANAS
Tracks: / Going bananas.
7" Single: Released Feb '83, on GC, Catalogue no: **GCT 1**

Foreign Legion

TRENCH LINE
Tracks: / Trench line.
7" Single: Released Jul '86, on Rent A Racket, Catalogue no: **RR 001**

Foreign Press

CLIMBING
Tracks: / Climbing / Remember you / Oper secret.
12" Single: Released Aug '82, on Music International, by Music International Records. Catalogue no: **12 M 10016**

Foreigner

Biographical details: This UK/US alliance of musicians has always been led by British lead guitarist/keyboardist Mick Jones and American lead vocalist Lou Gramm, who are also the band's writers. From the time of their formation in New York in 1976 until 1978, the band comprised three Britons (Jones, Dennis Elliott and Ian MacDonald) and three Americans (Gramm, Ed Gagliard and Al Greenwood). in 1979 they consisted of four Britons and two Americans because Gagliardi was replaced by U bassist Rick Wills. From 1981 onwards the sextet was slimmed down to a quartet comprising three Britons (Jones, Elliott and Wills) plus one Yank (Gramm).
Prior to Foreigner's formation, most of the members had gained considerable musical experience. The ultra-professional group spent a year rehearsing and recording the self-titled debut album, which was released in 1977. Coming hard on the heels of Boston's not dissimilar debut smash LP, *Foreigner* received an ecstatic reception from American record buyers, climbing to No and staying on the LP chart for most of the year; it spawned the US Top 10 single

PENNYE FORD - DANGEROUS (Released on Total Experience)

Feels Like The First Time and *Cold As Ice.* 1978's *Double Vision* LP was equally successful, yielding a pair of million-selling US Top 3 singles, *Hot Blooded* and the title track. Together with Boston, Kansas and the Cars, Foreigner had spearheaded a new breed of Adult Orientated Rock audiences. In Britain, however, this new school of music enjoyed only modest success - UK rock fans, immersed in the New Wave/punk rock explosion, derided what they saw as a tired retread of the established Old Wave.

1979's *Head Games* LP was marginally less successful, in both commercial and musical terms. A depleted Foreigner re-emerged in 1981 with the album called *4*, the title referring both to the number of musicians now in the band and to the number of LPs thus far released. *4* contained two classic singles - *Urgent* featured a guest sax solo by the famous Junior Walker and confirmed Gramm as one of rock's finest vocalists; *Waiting For A Girl Like You* was a perfectly crafted and lushly arranged ballad, which put the band into the British Top 10 for the first time as well as spending a record setting 10 weeks i nthe US No 2 position (without ever reaching No 1!). *4* was the group's most successful LP yet, enjoying an extended run at the top of the American album chart.

After a lengthy absence from the public eye (a typical state of affairs for this perfectionist band), Foreigner unleashed the *Agent Provocateur* LP at the end of 1984. In February '85 the masterpiece single *I Want To Know What Love Is*, a mini-epic featuring the gueast vocal chords of the New Jersey Mass Choir, was No 1on both sides of the Atlantic. *Agent Provocateur* was a worldwide winner and, notably, their first No 1 album in Britain - the expatriate Jones was particularly pleased that he had finally won real acceptance in his home country. Bob MacDonald, 3.9.85.

A AOR supergroup formed in NYC in 1976 by Brits guitarist Mick Jones (ex Spooky Tooth), multi instrumentalist Ian McDonald and drummer Dennis Elliott (both ex-King Crimson); and Americans keyboardist Al Greenwood, bassist Ed Gagliardi and vocalist Lou Gramm. Rick Wills (another Brit, ex-Peter Frampton, Roxy Music, Small Faces) replaced Gagliardi; Greenwood and McDonald departed soon after and their fourth album in 1981 had the mix right: experienced musicians doing well as purveyors of USA radio rock. (Donald Clarke, April 1989).

BLUE MORNING BLUE DAY
Tracks: / Blue morning blue day.
7" Single: Released Feb '79, on Atlantic, by WEA Records. Deleted '82. Catalogue no: **K 11236**

COLD AS ICE
Tracks: / Cold as ice.
7" Single: Released Jul '78, on Atlantic, by WEA Records. Deleted '81. Catalogue no: **K 10986**

COLD AS ICE (REMIX)
Tracks: / Cold as ice.
7" Single: Released Jun '85, on Atlantic, by WEA Records. Deleted '88. Catalogue no: **A 9539**

DON'T LET GO
Tracks: / Don't let go / Fool for you anyway.
7" Single: Released Mar '82, on Atlantic, by WEA Records. Catalogue no: **K 11718**

FEELS LIKE THE FIRST TIME
Tracks: / Feels like the first time.
7" Single: Released May '78, on Atlantic, by WEA Records. Deleted '81. Catalogue no: **K 11086**

HEAD GAMES (SINGLE)
Tracks: / Head games / Do what you like.
7" Single: Released Mar '80, on Atlantic, by WEA Records. Deleted '83. Catalogue no: **K 11417**

HOT BLOODED
Tracks: / Hot blooded.
7" Single: Released Oct '78, on Atlantic, by WEA Records. Deleted '81. Catalogue no: **K 1167**

I DON'T WANT TO LIVE WITHOUT YOU
Tracks: / I don't want to live without you / Face to face / Urgent (Track on CD single.).
CD 5": Released 14 May '88, on Atlantic, by WEA Records. Catalogue no: **A 9101 CD**
7" Single: Released 14 May '88, on Atlantic, by WEA Records. Catalogue no: **A 9101**
12" Single: Released 14 May '88, on Atlantic, by WEA Records. Catalogue no: **A 9101 T**

I WANT TO KNOW WHAT LOVE IS
Tracks: / I want to know what love is.
7" Single: Released Nov '84, on Atco, by Atlantic Recording Corp.(USA). Catalogue no: **A 9596**
12" Single: Released Nov '84, on Atco, by Atlantic Recording Corp.(USA). Deleted Jan '88. Catalogue no: **A 9596 T**

I'LL GET EVEN WITH YOU
Tracks: / I'll get even with you / Blinded by science.
7" Single: Released Sep '80, on Atlantic, by WEA Records. Deleted '83. Catalogue no: **K 11602**

JUKE BOX HERO
Tracks: / Jukebox hero / I'm gonna win.
7" Single: Released Oct '81, on Atlantic, by WEA Records. Deleted '84. Catalogue no: **K 11678**

SAY YOU WILL
Tracks: / Say you will / Night to remember, A.
7" Single: Released 21 Nov '87, on Atlantic, by WEA Records. Catalogue no: **A 9269**
12" Single: Released 21 Nov '87, on Atlantic, by WEA Records. Catalogue no: **A 9169 T**

THAT WAS YESTERDAY
Tracks: / That was yesterday / Two different worlds.
7" Single: Released Apr '85, on Atlantic, by WEA Records. Deleted '88. Catalogue no: **A 9571**

URGENT
Tracks: / Urgent / Girl on the moon.
7" Single: Released Aug '81, on Atlantic, by WEA Records. Deleted '84. Catalogue no: **K 11665**
7" Single: Released May '82, on Atlantic, by WEA Records. Deleted '85. Catalogue no: **K 11728**

WAITING FOR A GIRL LIKE YOU
Tracks: / Waiting for a girl like you / Feels like the first time / Cold as ice.
7" Single: Released Dec '81, on Atlantic, by WEA Records. Catalogue no: **K 11696**

WOMEN
Tracks: / Women / Modern day.
7" Single: Released May '80, on Atlantic, by WEA Records. Deleted May '83. Catalogue no: **K 11456**

Forest Hillbillies

MUNSTERS, THE
Tracks: / Munsters, The.
7" Single: Released May '88, on Gaz's, Catalogue no: **GAZ 007**
12" Single: Released May '88, on Gaz's, Catalogue no: **GAZ 12007**

Forever Reaction

B.E.D. '34
Tracks: / B.E.D. '34.
12" Single: Released Jun '84, on Streetwave, Catalogue no: **MKHAN 18**

Formations

AT THE TOP OF THE STAIRS
Tracks: / At the top of the stairs.
7" Single: Released Jul '71, on Mojo, Deleted '74. Catalogue no: **2027 001**

Formby, George

Biographical details: One of Britain's most fondly remembered 20th century entertainers, George Formby achieved just one entry into the British record charts, which did not begin until 1952. His voice and ukelele featured on the double-A-sided single *Happy-Go-Lucky Me/Banjo Boy*, which reached the No 40 position in 1960. His best-known record was *When I'm Cleaning Windows* and other cheeky offerings included *My Ukelele, I Told My Baby With My Ukelele, I'm The Ukelele Man* and *With My Little Ukelele In My Hand.* (Bob MacDonald, September 1985.)

A singing comedian and ukulele player, born George Hoy Booth in 1904 in Wigan, son of a famous Edwardian comedian. He was a star of music hall and 22 successful films, playing an amiable dope who got the girl in the end. He died in 1961. (Donald Clarke, April 1989).

HAPPY GO LUCKY ME
Tracks: / Happy go lucky me.
7" Single: Released Jul '60, on Pye, Deleted '63. Catalogue no: **7N 15269**

Formosa

METAL GURU
Tracks: / Metal guru.
7" Single: Released Mar '88, on Awesome Records, by Awesome Records. Catalogue no: **AOR 14**
12" Single: Released Mar '88, on Awesome Records, by Awesome Records. Catalogue no: **AOR 14T**

Formula One

DREAMWORLD
Tracks: / Dreamworld.
7" Single: Released May '83, on West Coast, Catalogue no: **WCR 0001**

Forray, Andy

DRAGS BACK
Tracks: / Drags back.
7" Single: Released '82, on Arista, by BMG Records (UK). Deleted '87. Catalogue no: **BAT 13**

Forrest

Biographical details: John Forrest is an American singer based in Holland, who enjoyed three UK hit singles in 1983. The first and biggest was *Rock The Boat*, a remake of the Hues Corporation's pioneering 1974 disco/pop classic. Forrest simply updated the record, retaining the overall structure and arrangement but transforming the rhythm and feel to make it fit into the contemporary '83 dance scene. Impressively, he managed to climb to the UK No 4 position, thereby outdoing the original version by two places.

Sticking to the same formula, Forrest then released a cover version of the Detroit Emeralds' *Feel The Need In Me* (1973) and took it to No 17 on the British pop chart. But when he tried his luck with unfamiliar material, he faded into obscurity - *One Lover (Don't Stop The Show)* peaked at No 67 in September '83 and 1984's *She's So Divine* flopped altogether.

Forrest's remakes were probably the inspiration behind Eddy & The Soul Band's *Theme From 'Shaft') - this Dutch-American cover ersion of Isaac Hayes' 1971 hit reached the British Top 20 in 1985. Bob MacDonald, 4.9.85..*

FEEL THE NEED IN ME
Tracks: / Feel the need in me.
7" Single: Released May '83, on CBS, by CBS Records. Catalogue no: **A 3411**
12" Single: Released May '83, on CBS, by CBS Records. Catalogue no: **TA 3411**

ONE LOVER (DON'T STOP THE SHOW)
Tracks: / One lover (don't stop the show) / Comin'.
7" Single: Released Sep '83, on CBS, by CBS Records. Deleted '86. Catalogue no: **A 3734**

ROCK THE BOAT
Tracks: / Rock the boat / Loving you.
7" Single: Released Feb '83, on CBS, by CBS Records. Catalogue no: **A 3163**
12" Single: Released Feb '83, on CBS, by CBS Records. Catalogue no: **A 13 3163**

SHE'S SO DIVINE
Tracks: / She's so divine.
7" Single: Released Aug '84, on CBS, by CBS Records. Catalogue no: **A 4629**
12" Single: Released Aug '84, on CBS, by CBS Records. Catalogue no: **TA 4629**

Forrest, Jackie

SHOW ME HOW TO LOVE
Tracks: / Show me how to love.
7" Single: Released Mar '83, on Neil Rushton, Catalogue no: **791001**

Forsey, Keith

TAKE ME TO THE PILOT
Tracks: / Take me to the pilot / Hold on.
7" Single: Released Jan '82, on Carrere, Deleted Jan '85. Catalogue no: **CAR 221**

Forsyth, Bruce

SOUND OF CHRISTMAS, THE
Tracks: / Sound of Christmas, The / I'm glad I'm the man I am.
7" Single: Released Nov '80, on Rampage (USA), Deleted Nov '83. Catalogue no: **RAM 45**

Forte, Joanna

JIMMY'S HI-FI
Tracks: / Jimmy's hi-fi.
7" Single: Released Nov '81, on Eagle (London), by Eagle (London) Records. Deleted Nov '84. Catalogue no: **ERS 011**

ONE OF THE CHOSEN FEW
Tracks: / One of the chosen few / Eye witness.
7" Single: Released Mar '81, on Eagle (London), by Eagle (London) Records. Deleted Mar '84. Catalogue no: **ERS 007**

Fortunate Sons

HAMMERHEAD
Tracks: / Hammerhead.
12" Single: Released Jul '87, on Bam Caruso, by Demon Records. Catalogue no: **PABL 087**

SOMETIMES YOU WIN
Tracks: / Sometimes you win / Me and my uncle.
7" Single: Released Jun '86, on Bam Caruso, by Demon Records. Catalogue no: **NRIC 043**

Fortune, Lance

BE MINE
Tracks: / Be mine.
7" Single: Released Feb '60, on Pye, Deleted '63. Catalogue no: **7N 15240**

LOVE I HAVE FOR YOU, THE
Tracks: / Love I have for you, The.
7" Single: Released May '60, on Pye, Deleted '63. Catalogue no: **7N 15260**

Fortunes

Biographical details: At the time of their greatest success this British pop group consisted of Rod Allen, Andy Brown, David Carr, Glen Dale and Barry Pritchard. Formed in Birmingham in 1964, during an era when British beat combos were springing up like mushrooms, the Fortunes were fortunate enough to have their debut single, *Caroline*, adopted as the theme tune of the pioneering pop pirate radio station, Radio Caroline. With the help of this daily exposure they eventually broke into the national charts in 1965 with two consecutive smashes: Roger Cook and Roger Greenaway's *You've Got Your Troubles* reached No 2 and Les Reed and Barry Mason's *Here It Comes Again* cruised to No 4. Thanks to the Beatles-led British invasion, these records were also Top Thirty hits in America. The Fortunes specialised in strong harmony vocals and inoffensive singalong pop which, combined with a smart, clean-cut appearance, meant their music appealed to the mums and dads as well as the younger fans. After achieving a 1966 hit with *This Golden Ring*, the group languished without chart success for several years until suddenly, in 1971, they hit No 15 on the US listings with *Here Comes That Rainy Day Feeling Again.* This led to a revival of the Fortunes in Britain: the predictably jolly and melodic *Freedom Come, Freedom Go* and *Storm In A Teacup* were back-to-back UK Top Tenners. There had been personnel changes during the intervening years but the sound was the same. The Fortunes certainly lived up to their name when they recorded *It's The Real Thing* jingle for Coca-Cola. After the hits dried up again in 1972 the group entertained a steady living on the cabaret circuit. (Bob MacDonald, September 1985.).

FREEDOM COME, FREEDOM GO
Tracks: / Freedom come, freedom go.
7" Single: Released Sep '71, on Capitol, by EMI Records. Deleted '74. Catalogue no: **CL 15693**

HERE IT COMES AGAIN
Tracks: / Here it comes again.
7" Single: Released Oct '65, on Decca, by Decca Records. Deleted '68. Catalogue no: **F 12243**

STORM IN A TEACUP
Tracks: / Storm in a teacup.
7" Single: Released Jan '72, on Capitol, by EMI Records. Deleted '75. Catalogue no: **CL 15707**

THIS GOLDEN RING
Tracks: / This golden ring.
7" Single: Released Feb '66, on Decca, by Decca Records. Deleted '69. Catalogue no: **F 12321**

YOU'VE GOT YOUR TROUBLES
Tracks: / You've got your troubles.
7" Single: Released Jul '80, on Decca, by Decca Records. Deleted '88. Catalogue no: **F 13891**
7" Single: Released Jul '65, on Decca, by Decca Records. Deleted '68. Catalogue no: **F 12173**

YOU'VE GOT YOUR TROUBLES (OLD GOLD)
Tracks: / You've got your troubles.
7" Single: Released Oct '83, on Old Gold, by Old Gold Records. Catalogue no: **OG 9326**

Forty Eight Chairs

SNAP IT AROUND
Tracks: / Snap it around.
7" Single: Released Sep '82, on Absurd, by Absurd Records. Catalogue no: **ABS 3**

Forty Five King

KING IS HERE, THE
Tracks: / King is here, The / 900 No., The.
7" Single: Released Jul '89, on Filmtrax, by Filmtrax Records. Catalogue no: **DRX 9**
12" Single: Released Mar '89, on Filmtrax, by Filmtrax Records. Catalogue no: **DRX 912**

Forty Five's

SECRETS AND WHISPERS
Tracks: / Secrets and whispers / Driving / Little honda.
7" Single: Released Sep '81, on 45, by 45 Records. Catalogue no: **ONE 45**

Forty Four Max

PUSH AND SHOVE
Tracks: / Push and shove.
12" Single: Released Sep '89, on Gold Key, Catalogue no: **12 PO 31**

Forty Nine Americans

WONDER EP
7" Single: Released Mar '80, on No Bad, Catalogue no: **NB 4**

Foster & Allen

Biographical details: These two Irishmen perform folk and middle-of-the-road standards in a warm and tranquil manner. In early 1982, shortly after their fellow countrymen the Furies had scored a surprise UK Top Twenty hit with *When You Were Sweet Sixteen*, Foster & Allen got there with *A Bunch Of Thyme*. Both acts emerged on the Ritz label. *A Bunch Of Thyme*, a traditional folk song, contained words that the BBC might have banned had they not been slightly disguised by Foster & Allen's Irish brogue... but the duo's subsequent British chart hits were tamer. They included *Old Flames*, the pre-World War 1 number *Maggie* (No 27), *I Will Love You All My Life* (No 49) and *Just For Old Time's Sake* (No 47). They also enjoyed a Top Thirty success on the LP chart with a compilation album. (Bob MacDonald, September 1985.).

AFTER ALL THESE YEARS (SINGLE)
Tracks: / After all these years / Rose of Allandale.
7" Single: Released Jun '85, on Ritz, by Ritz Records. Catalogue no: **RITZ 106**

BUNCH OF THYME (SINGLE)
Tracks: / Bunch of thyme.
7" Single: Released Feb '82, on Ritz, by Ritz Records. Catalogue no: **RITZ 005**

GOLDEN YEARS, THE
Tracks: / Golden years, The.
7" Single: Released '88, on I&B, by I & B Records. Catalogue no: **CMR 72**

I WILL LOVE YOU ALL MY LIFE
Tracks: / I will love you all my life.
7" Single: Released Oct '83, on Ritz, by Ritz Records. Catalogue no: **RITZ 056**

I'LL NEVER STOP WANTING YOU
Tracks: / I'll never stop wanting you.
7" Single: Released Sep '89, on Stylus, by Stylus Music Records. Catalogue no: **SMC 989**

JUST FOR OLD TIMES SAKE
Tracks: / Just for old times sake.
7" Single: Released Jun '84, on Ritz, by Ritz Records. Catalogue no: **RITZ 066**

MAGGIE (SINGLE)
Tracks: / Maggie / Willows.
7" Single: Released Jan '83, on Ritz, by Ritz Records. Catalogue no: **RITZ 025**

OLD FLAME
Tracks: / Old flame.
7" Single: Released Aug '82, on Ritz, by Ritz Records. Catalogue no: **RITZ 028**

PART OF ME
Tracks: / Part of me / Black sheep.
7" Single: Released Oct '87, on Ritz, by Ritz Records. Catalogue no: **RITZ 178**

REMINISCING (SINGLE)
Tracks: / Reminiscing.
7" Single: Released Oct '86, on Honeybee, by Stylus Music Records. Catalogue no: **HONEY 2**

WE WILL MAKE LOVE
Tracks: / We will make love.
7" Single: Released Oct '84, on Ritz, by Ritz Records. Catalogue no: **RITZ 086**

WHEN I DREAM
Tracks: / When I Dream / Green fields round Ferbane / Maggie / Will I love you all my life.

7" Single: Released May '86, on Ritz, by Ritz Records. Catalogue no: **RITZ 126**

WHEN MY BLUE MOON TURNS GOLD
Tracks: / When my blue moon turns to gold again / Morning glory.
7" Single: Released 30 May '87, on Ritz, by Ritz Records. Catalogue no: **RITZ 174**

Foster, David

BEST OF ME (SINGLE)
Tracks: / Best of me, The.

7" Single: Released Jul '86, on Atlantic, by WEA Records. Deleted Jun '87. Catalogue no: **A 9420**

ST.ELMO'S FIRE LOVE THEME
Tracks: / St. Elmo's fire love theme.
7" Single: Released Oct '85, on Atlantic, by WEA Records. Catalogue no: **A 9528**

Foster, Gina

LOVE IS A HOUSE
Tracks: / Take me away / One kiss (Available on 12" and CD only) / Love is a house.
CD 5": Released Sep '89, on RCA, by BMG Records (UK). Catalogue no: **PD 43074**
7" Single: Released 19 Jun '89, on RCA, by BMG Records (UK). Catalogue no: **PB 42747**
CD 5": Released 19 Jun '89, on RCA, by BMG Records (UK). Catalogue no: **PD 42748**
7" Single: Released Sep '89, on RCA, by BMG Records (UK). Catalogue no: **PB 43073**
12" Single: Released Sep '89, on RCA, by BMG Records (UK). Catalogue no: **PT 43074**
12" Single: Released 19 Jun '89, on RCA, by BMG Records (UK). Catalogue no: **PT 42748**

Foster, Ian

OUT FOR THE COUNT
Tracks: / Out for the count.
7" Single: Released Aug '87, on MCA, by MCA Records. Catalogue no: **MCA 1183**
12" Single: Released Aug '87, on MCA, by MCA Records. Catalogue no: **MCAT 1183**

TELL ME IT'S TRUE
Tracks: / Tell me it's true / Tell me it's true (instrumental).
12" Single: Released May '86, on MCA, by MCA Records. Catalogue no: **MCAT 1025**
7" Single: Released May '86, on MCA, by MCA Records. Catalogue no: **MCA 1025**

Foster, Jerry

DON'T LET GO
Tracks: / Don't let go / Memories to cling to.
7" Single: Released Dec '81, on Sonet, by Sonet Records. Deleted Dec '84. Catalogue no: **SON 2237**

FOOL FOR YOU MAMA
Tracks: / Fool for you mama / Put it on me strong.
7" Single: on Range, by Range Records. Catalogue no: **RANS 72**

Foster, Mick

BLACK SHEEP, THE
Tracks: / Black sheep / Bluebell polka.
7" Single: Released Apr '88, on Honeybee, by Stylus Music Records. Catalogue no: **HONEY 6**

Foster, Royden

SHINE YOUR LOVE
Tracks: / Shine your love.
12" Single: Released 31 Jul '89, on Entente, Catalogue no: **ENT 0017**

Fote

SHAKING THE HOUSE
Tracks: / Shaking the house.
7" Single: Released Nov '81, on Le Rey, by Le Rey Records. Catalogue no: **LR 03**

Foton

BAMBOO CURTAIN
Tracks: / Bamboo curtain.
7" Single: Released May '83, on Feltwain, by Pinnacle Records. Catalogue no: **PIN 33**
12" Single: Released May '83, on Feltwain, by Pinnacle Records. Catalogue no: **PIN 33T**

Fotostat

FOTOSTAT
Tracks: / Fotostat.
7" Single: Released Nov '82, on Sour Grape, by Sour Grape Records. Deleted '87. Catalogue no: **SG 112**

Foundation

WISE UP
Tracks: / Wise up.
7" Single: Released Sep '85, on Breakout, by A&M Records. Catalogue no: **WISE 1**
12" Single: Released Sep '85, on Breakout, by A&M Records. Catalogue no: **WISE 112**

Foundation Choir

TAKE A CHANCE
Tracks: / Take a Chance / Happy in the glory way.
7" Single: Released Dec '85, on Millenium, by Millenium Records. Catalogue no: **PWP 1000**

Foundations

Biographical details: At the time of their UK No 1 hit, this British pop group consisted of Eric Allandale, Pat Burke, Clem Curtis, Mike Elliott, Tony Gomez, Tim Harris, Peter Macbeth and Alan Warner. Shortly afterwards, saxophonist Elliott departed , and lead vocalist Curtis was replaced by Colin Young. Like their similar sounding contemporaries, The Equals, the Foundations were a London-based racially mixed group.
Founded in early 1967, the Foundations soon came to the attention of Pye Records' in house songwriter/producer Tony Macaulay. Together with John McLeod, he wrote their first record *Baby Now That I've Found You* - it reached the UK No 1 position in November '67, and was dethroned by another Macaulay/McLeod composition, *Let The Heartaches Begin* by Long John Baldry. In early '68, *Baby Now That I've Found You* climbed to No 11 in the States.
The two Macs' further hit songs for the Foundations included *Back On My Feet Again, Any Old Time You're Lonely And Sad* and *In The Bad Bad Old Days*. All were in a highly commercial vein, and extracted the most marketable elements of soul music for the benefit of pop audiences. But when Macaulay and Manfred Mann's singer Mike D'Abo co-wrote *Build Me Up Buttercup* for the Foundations, the fruits of its UK and US Top 3 success were marred by a successful plagiarism suit from the composer of another song.
The group's final taste of chart status was *Born To Live And Born To Die*, which crept to the UK No 46 position in September 1969. A year later, the foundations died a natural death and the members drifted into obscurity. Bob MacDonald, 4.9.85
A pop soul multi racial group formed in London in 1967, signed by Pye's Tony Macauley to sing and play his songs. The original lineup showed an unusual range in age, born between 1928 and 1948. They had several big hits, charting in the USA, and split in 1970. Vocalist Clem Curtis has since led New Foundations lineups in UK clubs. (Donald Clarke, April 1989)a.

BABY, NOW THAT I'VE FOUND YOU
Tracks: / Baby, now that I found you / Build me up buttercup.
Note: Pic bag
12" Single: Released Apr '89, on PRT, by Castle Communications Records. Catalogue no: **PYT 24**
7" Single: Released Jul '67, on Pye, Deleted '70. Catalogue no: **7N 17366**
7" Single: Released Apr '89, on PRT, by Castle Communications Records. Catalogue no: **PYS 24**
7" Single: Released Apr '79, on PRT, by Castle Communications Records. Catalogue no: **FBS 6**
7" Single: Released Apr '87, on PRT, by Castle Communications Records. Catalogue no: **7P 372**
7" Single: Released Jun '84, on Old Gold, by Old Gold Records. Catalogue no: **OG 9407**
12" Single: Released Apr '87, on PRT, by Castle Communications Records. Catalogue no: **12P 372**

BACK ON MY FEET AGAIN
Tracks: / Back on my feet again.
7" Single: Released Jan '68, on Pye, Deleted '71. Catalogue no: **7N 17417**

BORN TO LIVE AND BORN TO DIE
Tracks: / Born to live and born to die.
7" Single: Released Sep '69, on Pye, Deleted '72. Catalogue no: **7N 17809**

BUILD ME UP BUTTERCUP
Tracks: / Build me up buttercup.
7" Single: Released Nov '68, on Pye, Deleted '71. Catalogue no: **7N 17638**

IN THE BAD BAD OLD DAYS
Tracks: / In the bad bad old days (before you loved me).
7" Single: Released Mar '69, on Pye, Deleted '72. Catalogue no: **7N 17809**

Fountainhead

ANGEL
Tracks: / Angel / Leaving it all behind / I like it like that*.
Note: * extra track on 12"
7" Single: Released Jul '88, on China, by Polydor Ltd. Catalogue no: **CHINA 7**
12" Single: Released Jul '88, on China, by Polydor Ltd. Catalogue no: **CHINX 7**

FEEL IT NOW
Tracks: / Feel it now / Open up China.
7" Single: Released May '86, on China, by Polydor Ltd. Catalogue no: **WOK 7**
12" Single: Released May '86, on China, by Polydor Ltd. Catalogue no: **WOKX 7**

RHYTHM METHOD
Tracks: / Rhythm method.
12" Single: Released Sep '85, on Fountain Of Youth, Catalogue no: **12FTN 001**
7" Single: Released Jul '86, on China, by Polydor Ltd. Catalogue no: **WOK 10**
12" Single: Released Jul '86, on China, by Polydor Ltd. Catalogue no: **WOKX 10**

SO GOOD NOW
Tracks: / Heart and soul / So good now.
12" Single: Released Jan '87, on China, by Polydor Ltd. Catalogue no: **WOKX 13**
7" Single: Released Jan '87, on China, by Polydor Ltd. Catalogue no: **WOK 13**

SOMEONE LIKE YOU
Tracks: / Someone like you / Price you've got to pay / Future days (Extra track on 12" version.) / Someone like you (rhythm method) (dub version) (Only available on C.D. single).
7" Single: Released 27 Feb '88, on China, by Polydor Ltd. Catalogue no: **CHINA 2**
CD 5": Released Apr '88, on China, by Polydor Ltd. Catalogue no: **CHICD 2**
12" Single: Released 27 Feb '88, on China, by Polydor Ltd. Catalogue no: **CHINAX 2**

Four...

FOUR ON THE FLOOR EP Various artists
7" EP: Released Feb '80, on Big Beat, by Ace Records. Deleted '88. Catalogue no: **SW 57**

Four Aces

Biographical details: This American vocal group consisted of leader Al Alberts plus Dave Mahoney, Lou Silvestri and Sol Vocarro. The Four Aces were formed by Alberts in 1949, and they were based in Pensylvania. They came to fame in 1951 with*It's A Sin (It's No Sin)*, a song which provided a simultaneous American smash for both the Aces and singer Eddy Howard. The Four Aces waxing was self financed but it led to a contract with Decca Records. The group's status was then cemented by-*Tell Me Why*, a huge hit co-written by Alberts. The mid-Fifties brought the Four Aces major chart success on both sides of the Atlantic with *Three Coins In The Fountain,Mr.Sandman*and*Stranger In Paradise*, all were made equally famous by other acts, for during this era, there was often fierce competition between rival versions of one song. The quartet enjoyed a freer run, however, with their 1955 hit*Love Is A Many Splendoured Thing*. This was a long running No.1 in the States and a No.2 in Britain, thus providing the group with their greatest success in both countries. It was also their last major triumph - the onslaught of rock'n'roll made life difficult for Alberts & co. Notwithstanding lack of later chart action, the Four Aces golden run between 1951 and 55 ensured that they would be able to earn a long-lasting showbusiness living through regular live work. (Bob Macdonald 4.85)
USA vocal quartet. They paid for their own first record *It's no sin* on an obscure label; it was picked up by USA Decca and sold a million. They sold 20 million records, with accent on the upper register, and had 20 top 40 hits 1951-6, though the shuffle beat of their ballads became monotonous. Some hits were typical street corner group fodder: *The gang that sang heart of my heart, Wedding bells are breaking up that old gang of mine*; was another film theme, their only number one (for 6 weeks) *Love is a many splendoured thing*. (Donald Clarke, April 1989).

FRIENDLY PERSUASION
Tracks: / Friendly persuasion.
7" Single: Released Jan '57, on Brunswick, by Decca Records. Deleted '60. Catalogue no: **05623**

LOVE IS A MANY SPLENDOURED THING
Tracks: / Love is a many splendoured thing.
7" Single: Released Nov '55, on Brunswick, by Decca Records. Deleted '58. Catalogue no: **05480**

MR. SANDMAN
Tracks: / Mr. Sandman.
7" Single: Released Jan '55, on Brunswick, by Decca Records. Deleted '58. Catalogue no: **05355**

STRANGER IN PARADISE
Tracks: / Stranger in paradise.
7" Single: Released May '55, on Brunswick, by Decca Records. Deleted '58. Catalogue no: **05418**

THREE COINS IN THE FOUNTAIN
Tracks: / Three coins in the fountain.
7" Single: Released Jul '54, on Brunswick, by Decca Records. Deleted '57. Catalogue no: **05308**
7" Single: Released Jul '84, on Old Gold, by Old Gold Records. Deleted Jul '88. Catalogue no: **OG 9417**

WOMAN IN LOVE
Tracks: / Woman in love.
7" Single: Released Oct '56, on Brunswick, by Decca Records. Deleted '59. Catalogue no: **05589**

WORLD OUTSIDE, THE
Tracks: / World outside, The.

7" Single: Released Jan '59, on Brunswick, by Decca Records. Deleted '62. Catalogue no: **05773**

Four Away

WANDERER
Tracks: / Wanderer / Leaving by the back door.
7" Single: Released May '86, on President, by President Records. Catalogue no: **PT 545**

Four Brothers

MAKOROTO
Tracks: / Makoroto.
7" Single: Released Jun '83, on Earthworks, by Earthworks Records. Deleted '88. Catalogue no: **DIG 002**

UCHANDIFUNGA
Tracks: / Uchandifunga.
12" Single: Released Feb '89, on Cooking Vinyl, by Cooking Vinyl Records. Catalogue no: **FRY 5T**

Four Bucketeers

BUCKET OF WATER SONG
Tracks: / Bucket of water song / Smello.
7" Single: Released May '80, on CBS, by CBS Records. Deleted '83. Catalogue no: **CBS 8383**

WATER IS WONDERFUL
Tracks: / Water is wonderful / Raspberry rock.
7" Single: Released Feb '81, on CBS, by CBS Records. Deleted '84. Catalogue no: **CBS 9514**

Four Came Home

FOUR CAME HOME
Tracks: / Four came home / Passion of ice. Note: Double 'A' side
7" Single: Released May '87, on Wounded Knee, by Waterfall Records. Catalogue no: **WKN 2**

Four Corners Of The

CUT THE BEAT
Tracks: / Cut the beat.
12" Single: Released Aug '84, on Jungle Rhythm, Catalogue no: **SWET 1**

MILLION TO ONE, A
Tracks: / Million to one, A.
12" Single: Released Jan '85, on Jungle Rhythm, Catalogue no: **SWET 3**

STANDING ON THE CORNER
Tracks: / Standing on the corner / DJ dub.
7" Single: Released Nov '83, on Red Bus, by Red Bus Records. Catalogue no: **RBUS 84**

Four Design

TALL PEOPLE
Tracks: / Tall people.
7" Single: Released Jun '85, on Official, by Official Records. Catalogue no: **OFFA 2**

Four Esquires

LOVE ME FOREVER
Tracks: / Love me forever.
7" Single: Released Jan '58, on London-American, Deleted '61. Catalogue no: **HLO 8533**

Four Hundred Blows

BEAT THE DEVIL
Tracks: / Beat the devil.
7" Single: Released Jul '82, on Concrete Productions, Catalogue no: **CPROD 002**

BREAKDOWN
Tracks: / Breakdown / Jive 69.
12" Single: Released Mar '85, on Illuminated, Catalogue no: **ILL 5612**
12" Single: Released Apr '86, on Illuminated, Catalogue no: **12 LEV 64**

DECLARATION OF INTENT
Tracks: / Declaration of intent.
12" Single: Released Feb '85, on Illuminated, Catalogue no: **ILL 3012**

G.I.
Tracks: / G.I..
12" Single: Released Mar '86, on Saderal, by Saderal Records. Catalogue no: **SLS 12002**

GROOVE JUMPING
Tracks: / Groove jumping.
12" Single: Released Feb '85, on Illuminated, Catalogue no: **ILL 4812**

LET THE MUSIC PLAY
Tracks: / Let the music play.
7" Single: Released Jan '87, on KR, Catalogue no: **KR 01**
12" Single: Released Jan '87, on KR, Catalogue no: **KRT 01**

MOVIN'
Tracks: / Movin'.
12" Single: Released May '85, on Illuminated, Catalogue no: **ILL 6112**
7" Single: Released May '85, on Illuminated, Catalogue no: **ILL 61**

PRESSURE
Tracks: / Pressure.
12" Single: Released Mar '85, on Illuminated, Catalogue no: **ILHL 3412**

RETURN OF THE DOG, THE
Tracks: / Return of the dog, The.
12" Single: Released Feb '85, on Illuminated, Catalogue no: **ILL 2712**

RUNAWAY
Tracks: / Runaway.
7" Single: Released Sep '85, on Illuminated, Catalogue no: **LEV 64**
12" Single: Released Sep '85, on Illuminated, Catalogue no: **12LEV 64**

Four In A Row

CRAZY KIND OF LOVE
Tracks: / Crazy kind of love.
7" Single: Released 31 Oct '87, on Disco Tex, Catalogue no: **DT 20**

Four Kings

LOVING YOU IS NO DISGRACE
Tracks: / Loving you is no disgrace.
7" Single: Released Apr '81, on Fresh, by Jetstar Records. Catalogue no: **FRESH 11**

PRESENT FOR JESUS
Tracks: / Present for Jesus.
7" Single: Released Jan '81, on Tyger, Deleted '82. Catalogue no: **TYG 5**

ROCK'N'ROLL
Tracks: / Rock and roll.
7" Single: Released '79, on Fresh, by Jetstar Records. Catalogue no: **PURL 2**

Four Knights

I GET SO LONELY
Tracks: / I get so lonely.
7" Single: Released Jan '54, on Capitol, by EMI Records. Deleted '57. Catalogue no: **CL 14076**

Four Lads

Biographical details: Canadian/USA vocal group formed in Toronto. They went to NYC, signed to CBS as a backing group and backed Johnny Ray on 2-sided mega-hit *Cry*/ *The Little White Cloud That Cried* in 1951. Their own biggest hits were *No, Not Much!* and *Moments To Remember* (both written by Al Stillman, who also wrote *Chances Are* and *It's Not For Me To Say* for Johnny Mathis), and *Standing On The Corner* from the musical *The Most Happy Fella*. (Donald Clarke 1989).

STANDING ON THE CORNER
Tracks: / Standing on the corner.
7" Single: Released Apr '60, on Philips, by Phonogram Ltd. Deleted '63. Catalogue no: **PB 1000**

Four Million

FRENCH GIRLS
Tracks: / Ice box / Same thing (Available on 12" only.) / Mrs. Brown (12" only) / French girls.
7" Single: Released Jan '87, on Summerhouse, by Summerhouse Records. Catalogue no: **SUMS 2**
12" Single: Released Jan '87, on Summerhouse, by Summerhouse Records. Catalogue no: **SUMS 002T**

SAVE YOU
Tracks: / Save you.
12" Single: Released Oct '88, on Summerhouse, by Summerhouse Records. Catalogue no: **SUMS 7**

Four Of Us

DRAG MY BAD NAME DOWN
Tracks: / Drag my bad name down / Fool for temptation / Washington down.
7" Single: Released Apr '89, on CBS, by CBS Records. Catalogue no: **FOUR 2**
CD 5": Released Apr '89, on CBS, by CBS Records. Catalogue no: **FOURCD 2**
10" single: Released Apr '89, on CBS, by CBS Records. Catalogue no: **FOUR QT2**
12" Single: Released Apr '89, on CBS, by CBS Records. Catalogue no: **FOURT 2**

I JUST CAN'T GET ENOUGH
Tracks: / I just can't get enough / Hit it in the back-bone / I just can't get enough (the throw-off mix) (12" & CD single only.) / I've got a job (12" & CD single only.).
7" Single: Released Oct '88, on CBS, by CBS Records. Catalogue no: **FOUR 1**
7" EP: Released 6 Feb '89, on CBS, by CBS Records. Catalogue no: **FOUR EP1**
CD 5": Released Oct '88, on CBS, by CBS Records. Catalogue no: **FOURC 1**
12" Single: Released Feb '89, on CBS, by CBS Records. Catalogue no: **FOUR QT1**
12" Single: Released Oct '88, on CBS, by CBS Records. Catalogue no: **FOUR T1**

MARY
Tracks: / Mary / I've got a job / One strong hammer (Only on 12" and CD single.) / Washington down (Only on CD single.) / Kill you (10" & EP only.) / One strong hammer (EP only.).
Cassingle: Released 26 Jun '89, on CBS, by CBS Records. Catalogue no: **FOUR M3**
7" EP: Released 26 Jun '89, on CBS, by CBS Records. Catalogue no: **FOUR EP3**
CD 5": Released 12 Jun '89, on CBS, by CBS Records. Catalogue no: **FOURC 3**
10" single: Released 19 Jun '89, on CBS, by CBS Records. Catalogue no: **FOUR QT3**
12" Single: Released 12 Jun '89, on CBS, by CBS Records. Catalogue no: **FOURT 3**
7" Single: Released 3 Jul '89, on CBS, by CBS Records. Catalogue no: **FOUR B3**
7" Single: Released 12 Jun '89, on CBS, by CBS Records. Catalogue no: **FOUR 3**

Four on Four

FOUR ON FOUR
7" Single: Released Oct '84, on Big Beat, by Ace Records. Deleted '88. Catalogue no: **SW 100**

Four Out Of Five

MODERN MAN
Tracks: / Modern man / Opus ten.
7" Single: Released Nov '80, on Epic, by CBS Records. Deleted Nov '83. Catalogue no: **EPC 9312**

Four Pennies

Biographical details: This British pop group consisted of Alan Bush, Fritz Fryer, Lionel Morton and Mike Wilsh. The Four Pennies came from Blackburn, Lancashire, and were initially maed after their lead singer - the Lionel Morton Four. In late 1963 they greatly impressed record producer Johnny Franz; he signed them up, and they became the Four Pennies. Drummer Alan Bush had previously played with Joe Brown's Bruvvers and Johnny Kidd's Pirates. The Pennies first hit the British charts in January 1964 -*Do You Want Me To*reached No.47. Their next single, a somewhat mawkish ballad entitled*Juliet*, enjoyed one week at No.1 in May 64. The Four Pennies never hit the Top 10 again, but reached the 11-20 portion of the chart twice more in 64 with Fryer's*I Found Out The Hard Way*and a traditional pre-rock'n'roll song,*Black Girl*. Also in same year,*Spin With The Pennies*and*Two Sides Of The Four Pennies*gave the group top 20 successes on the EP and Lp listings respectively. Despite their musicianship and songwriting abilities, they were somehow unable to sustain their career. Unlike so many of their contemporaries, the Pennies did not conquer America, and they only acheived two more British hits after 1964: Buffy Sainte-Marie's*Until It's Time For You To Go*in 65, and*Trouble Is My Middle Name*in early 66. Obscurity then became the Pennies middle name: they moved briefly onto the cabaret circuit and then broke up. During the 70's, Morton became a familiar face on childrens television. (Bob Macdonald 4.85)
UK pop group of the mid-'60s, all from Lancashire: Lionel Morton, vocals, rhythm guitar; Fritz Fryer, guitar; Mike Wilsh, piano; Alan Buck, drums. Vocally strong group had a number one single *Juliet* in 1964 written by Morton, once a choir boy at Blackburn Cathederal. (Donald Clarke 1989)o.

BLACK GIRL
Tracks: / Black girl.
7" Single: Released Oct '64, on Philips, by Phonogram Ltd. Deleted '67. Catalogue no: **BF 1366**

DO YOU WANT ME TO
Tracks: / Do you want me to.
7" Single: Released Jan '64, on Philips, by Phonogram Ltd. Deleted '67. Catalogue no: **PB 1296**

I FOUND OUT THE HARD WAY
Tracks: / I found out the hard way.
7" Single: Released Jul '64, on Philips, by Phonogram Ltd. Deleted '67. Catalogue no: **BF 1349**

JULIET
Tracks: / Juliet.
7" Single: Released Aug '82, on Old Gold, by Old Gold Records. Catalogue no: **OG 9251**
7" Single: Released Apr. '64, on Philips, by Phonogram Ltd. Deleted '67. Catalogue no: **BF 1322**

TROUBLE IS MY MIDDLE NAME
Tracks: / Trouble is my middle name.
7" Single: Released Feb '66, on Philips, by Phonogram Ltd. Deleted '69. Catalogue no: **BF 1469**

UNTIL IT'S TIME FOR YOU TO GO
Tracks: / Until it's time for you to go.
7" Single: Released Oct '65, on Philips, by Phonogram Ltd. Deleted '68. Catalogue no: **BF 1435**

Four Perfections

I'M NOT STRONG ENOUGH
Tracks: / I'm not strong enough.
7" Single: Released Apr '83, on Neil Rushton, Catalogue no: **BURN 1**
12" Single: Released Apr '83, on Neil Rushton, Catalogue no: **10 BURN 1**

Four Preps

Biographical details: This American vocal group consisted of Bruce Belland, Ed Cobb, Marvin Inabett and Glen Larson. The Four Preps were four clean cut lads who formed at Hollywood High School. They shot to fame in early 1958 with 26 Miles (Santa Catalina), a US No.2 smash. Penned by Belland and Larson, the song propelled the Preps to the forefront of a mini-boom in white West Coast vocal groups, most of which comprised kids from privileged backgrounds. The same pair composed the follow-up hit*Big Man*, which reached No.3 in the US and No.2 in the UK (their only major British hit). After reaching No.21 in Autumn '58 with*Lazy Summer Night*on the American listings, they drew a blank in 1959. The Four Preps bounced back in 1960 with three more US Top 30 hits:*Down By The Station*,*Got A Girl*and*More Money For You And Me*. The latter was a novelty medley, containing parodies of recent hits; this single displayed the groups strong sense of humour, an ever-present feature of their live shows. After 1962 the group faded into history, but the career of bass singer Ed Cobb was far from over. He became one of the prime movers of the LA Garage scene - this was an underground scene in which up-and-coming groups would use garages and other primitive recording and rehearsal environments, in order to train themselves for chart stardom (hopefully). One such combo was the Standells, who were closely guided by Cobb; they hit No.11 on the US charts in 1966 with*Dirty Water*. In the late 60's, Gloria Jones acheived a minor hit on the US R & B charts with Cobb's song-*Tainted Love*(which, during the 70's became a massive disc on the underground Northern Soul scene). In one of pop music's stranger episodes, this relatively obscure song was recorded in 1981 by British technopop duo Soft Cell - it not only launched the pair's career, but became Britain's biggest selling single of the year, and was a smash hit around the world. In the composer's native America,*Tainted Love*-logged 43 weeks on the Billboard Hot 100, an all-time record. No-one was more surprised than Cobb himself. (Bob Macdonald 4/85)
Vocal group formed at Hollywood High School. Lineup: Bruce Belland, Glen Larson, Ed Cobb, Mary Ingram. With 13 Hot 100 entries 1956-64, they were the era's equivalent of today's California soft-rock; their pretty harmonising may have been an influence on the Beach Boys. (Donald Clarke 1989).

BIG MAN
Tracks: / Big man.
7" Single: Released Jun '58, on Capitol, by EMI Records. Deleted '61. Catalogue no: **CL 14873**

GOT A GIRL
Tracks: / Got a girl.
7" Single: Released May '60, on Capitol, by EMI Records. Deleted '63. Catalogue no: **CL 15128**

MORE MONEY FOR YOU AND ME
Tracks: / More money for you and me (medley).
7" Single: Released Nov '61, on Capitol, by EMI Records. Deleted '64. Catalogue no: **CL 15217**

Four Seasons

Biographical details: The Sixties line-up of the American pop group consisted of Tommy De Vito, Bob Gaudio, Nick Massi and Frankie Valli. The mid-seventies line-up of the band (which should, more accurately, have been called the Six Seasons) comprised Gaudio and Valli plus Don Ciccone, John Paiva, Gerry Polci and Lee Shapiro. In 1964 the only Steside groups to withstand the challenge of the Beatles were the Beach Boys and the Four Seasons. In 1960 Valli and friends met Bob Crewe, a writer and producer who then introduced them to his protege, Bob Gaudio. The three crucial elements of the Four Seasons story came together in a cohesive whole in 1962: the falsetto voice of Valli, the production of of Crewe and the songs of Crewe and Gaudio. The group stormed to stardom with *Sherry* and *Big Girls Don't Cry*. They both held the top position on the American chart for five consecutive weeks - the former in September/October 62, the latter in November/December. Between 1962 and 68, a further 22 singles made the US top 30. *Rag Doll*gave the group their

biggest British hit of the 60's by reaching No.2. Frankie Valli thus launched a successful solo subsidiary career. By the late 60's the group had split with Bob Crewe, and their decision to sign to Mowest Records, a new Motown subsidiary, failed to arrest their commercial decline. By 1975 the Four Seasons had been well and truly consigned to the history books. But suddenly, in that year, things started happening again. Frankie Valli chalked up a solo US No.1 with a ballad smash *My Eyes Adored You*; *The Night*, an overlooked gem from their Mowest period, became a top 10 smash (mainly due to it's popularity on the UK Northern Soul scene). The time was right for a comeback - with a new Warner Brothers contract and a new line-up (still featuring Valli and Gaudio but now incorporating the complementary, lower vocals of singing drummer Gerry Polci), the revamped Four Seasons recorded an acclaimed album, *Who Loves You*. The infectious title track became a Top 10 hit on both sides of the Atlantic, and was followed by a No.1 smash in both the US and UK (the groups first in the latter nation): December 63 *Oh What A Night* was a gloriously catchy single. In 1977 the group finally folded for good and Valli became a full time solo artist once again. He enjoyed an American No.1 and worldwide monster hit in 78 with Barry Gibb's title theme from the blockbusting movie Grease, but his career then took an immediate nosedive.
Vocal quartet formed in Newark, New Jersey in 1956 by lead singer Frankie Valli, with Tommy DeVito and Hank Majewski (replaced by Nick Massi, who was replaced by Joey Long in 1965), and Nick DeVito, guitar. Ex-Royal Teen Bob Gaudio on piano replaced Nick DeVito, leading to a crucial elaboration of their doo-wop based sound; Bob Crewe of Swan Records signed them in 1960 and co-wrote with Gaudio (who'd written the Royal Teens *Short Shorts*, a big '58 hit): they highlighted Valli's 3-octave voice. Their upbeat first single for the black Vee Jay label *Sherry* with Valli's falsetto lead got airplay on black stations before their appearance on *American Bandstand* revealed Italian-Americans. *Sherry, Big Girls Don't Cry, Walk Like A Man* and *Rag Doll* were all number one '65-6; with the Beach Boys they were the only name group to retain their popularity during the British Invasion, even scoring in the UK with 9 top 40 entries. They tried to go progressive after *Sgt Pepper*, but *Genuine Imitation Life Gazette* in 1969 was an expensive flop. Valli went more or less solo on Motown's Mowest label, then re-formed with new personnel for a comeback on the disco boom, with drummer and joint lead vocalist Gerry Polci, Don Ciccone on bass (ex-Critters), guitarist John Paiva and keyboardist Lee Shapiro now on Warner Brothers: *Who Loves You* was a top 40 album in 1975, Valli's biggest since 1964. (Donald Clarke 1989)o.

AIN'T THAT A SHAME
Tracks: / Ain't that a shame.
7" Single: Released Jun '63, on Stateside, by EMI Records. Deleted '66. Catalogue no: **SS 194**

BIG GIRLS DON'T CRY
Tracks: / Big girls don't cry / Big girls don't cry (version).
7" Single: Released Jan '63, on Stateside, by EMI Records. Deleted '66. Catalogue no: **SS 145**
12" Single: Released Oct '88, on RCA, by BMG Records (UK). Catalogue no: **ZT 42287**
7" Single: Released Oct '88, on RCA, by BMG Records (UK). Catalogue no: **ZB 42287**
7" Single: Released Dec '88, on Platinum Music, by Prism Leisure. Catalogue no: **FOURPROMO**

BIG GIRLS DON'T CRY (OLD GOLD)
Tracks: / Big girls don't cry.
7" Single: Released Apr '83, on Old Gold, by Old Gold Records. Catalogue no: **OG 9277**

DOWN THE HALL
Tracks: / Down the hall.
7" Single: Released Aug '77, on Warner Bros., by WEA Records. Deleted '80. Catalogue no: **K 16982**

HARMONY
Tracks: / Harmony.
7" Single: Released May '79, on Warner Bros., by WEA Records. Catalogue no: **K 17072**

I'VE GOT YOU UNDER MY SKIN
Tracks: / I've got you under my skin.
7" Single: Released Apr '83, on Old Gold, by Old Gold Records. Deleted Jul '88. Catalogue no: **OG 9279**
7" Single: Released Sep '66, on Philips, by Phonogram Ltd. Deleted '69. Catalogue no: **BF 1511**

LETS HANG ON
Tracks: / Let's hang on.
7" Single: Released Nov '65, on Philips, by Phonogram Ltd. Deleted '68. Catalogue no: **BF 1439**
7" Single: Released Apr '83, on Old Gold, by Old Gold Records. Deleted Jul '88. Catalogue no: **OG 9278**

OH WHAT A NIGHT
Tracks: / Oh what a night.
CD 5": Released Dec '88, on Platinum Music, by Prism Leisure. Catalogue no: **CDS 277**
7" Single: Released Jan '76, on Warner Bros., by WEA Records. Deleted '79. Catalogue no: **K 16688**

OH WHAT A NIGHT (OLD GOLD)
7" Single: Released Apr '83, on Old Gold, by Old Gold Records. Deleted Jul '88. Catalogue no: **OG 9282**

OPUS 17 (DON'T YOU WORRY 'BOUT ME)
Tracks: / Opus 17 (don't you worry 'bout me).
7" Single: Released Jun '66, on Philips, by Phonogram Ltd. Deleted '69. Catalogue no: **BF 1493**

RAG DOLL
Tracks: / Rag doll.
7" Single: Released Apr '83, on Old Gold, by Old Gold Records. Deleted Jul '88. Catalogue no: **OG 9280**
7" Single: Released Aug '64, on Philips, by Phonogram Ltd. Deleted '67. Catalogue no: **BF 1347**

RHAPSODY
Tracks: / Rhapsody.
7" Single: Released Jun '77, on Warner Bros., by WEA Records. Deleted '80. Catalogue no: **K 16932**

SHERRY
Tracks: / Sherry.
7" Single: Released Oct '62, on Stateside, by EMI Records. Deleted '65. Catalogue no: **SS 122**

SHERRY (OLD GOLD)
Tracks: / Sherry.
7" Single: Released Apr '83, on Old Gold, by Old Gold Records. Catalogue no: **OG 9276**

SILVER STAR
Tracks: / Silver star.
7" Single: Released Apr '76, on Warner Bros., by WEA Records. Deleted '79. Catalogue no: **K 16742**

TELL IT TO THE RAIN
Tracks: / Tell it to the rain.
7" Single: Released Jan '67, on Philips, by Phonogram Ltd. Deleted '70. Catalogue no: **BF 1538**

WE CAN WORK IT OUT
Tracks: / We can work it out.
7" Single: Released Nov '76, on Warner Bros., by WEA Records. Deleted '79. Catalogue no: **K 16845**

WHO LOVES YOU (CD SINGLE)
Tracks: / Who loves you.
CD 5": Released Dec '88, on Platinum Music, by Prism Leisure. Catalogue no: **CDS 278**

WHO LOVES YOU (SINGLE)
Tracks: / Who loves you.
7" Single: Released Sep '75, on Warner Bros., by WEA Records. Deleted '78. Catalogue no: **K 16602**
7" Single: Released Apr '83, on Old Gold, by Old Gold Records. Catalogue no: **OG 9281**

WORKIN' MY WAY BACK TO YOU
Tracks: / Working my way back to you.
7" Single: Released Mar '66, on Philips, by Phonogram Ltd. Deleted '69. Catalogue no: **BF 1474**

Four Skins

Biographical details: This all-male British rock group came to infamy in 1981. This was a time when the original punk bands of the mid/late 70's had either broken up or moved into the rock mainstream; and the new acts who were hitting the British charts were drawn largely from the New Romantic scene, including such groups as Spandau Ballet, Duran Duran and Visage. This left a hard core of punk fans, who were now relying on underground and distinctly unfashionable groups to supply them with required dose of anarchy. The diminished but lingering punk scene, once the mainstay of the British music press, now attracted the attention of just one publication, Sounds. This paper began to publicise a new sub-culture of the genre, known as Oi! This quasi-revolutionary movement had Strength Through Oi! as it's main slogan, and it soon became decidedly unpleasant.
One of the leading Oi! bands were the Four Skins, whose unashamed racism caused a violent riot in July 81. When they appeared at a pub in London's Southall district (an area populated mainly by Asian immigrants), they caused furious battles between their skinhead followers and the local population. This was just one of a wave of riots that swept across English cities during that month. There was a complex variety of causes, but Oi! was cited as being one of them. The Four Skins managed to make a UK chart debut in spring 82: they reached No.80 on the Top 100 album list with *The Good The Bad And The Four Skins*. 1983's *A Fistful Of Four Skins* contained equally virulent political and socialogical ranting, performed on an energetic and monotonous procession of short, sharp 'songs'. (Bob Macdonald 5/4/85).

LOW LIFE
Tracks: / Low life.
7" Single: Released Oct '82, on Secret, by Secret Records. Deleted May '88. Catalogue no: **SHH 141**

ONE LAW FOR THEM
Tracks: / One law for them.
7" Single: Released Jul '81, on Clockwork Fun, Deleted '88. Catalogue no: **CF 101**

YESTERDAYS HEROES
Tracks: / Yesterdays heroes.
7" EP: Released Dec '81, on Secret, by Secret Records. Catalogue no: **SHH 125**

Four Squares

GATES OF HELL
Tracks: / Gates of hell.
7" Single: Released Aug '83, on New World, by President Records. Catalogue no: **NEW 2**

Four Tops

Biographical details: This American vocal group consists of Renaldo Benson, Abdul 'Duke' Fakir, Lawrence Payton and Levi Stubbs. The quartet's line-up has not changed since their formation in 1954; they are therefore one of the longest lasting line-ups in the worldwide history of the entertainment business. The Four Tops were founded in Detroit, initially calling themselves the Four Aims. They served a ten year apprenticeship in the music industry before their 1964 breakthrough. It was Motown's Berry Gordy who finally delivered the goods. He teamed them with his company's in-house writing/producing triumvirate, Holland/Dozier/Holland. The Tops soon reaped the rewards, storming to No.11 on the US charts in autumn 64 with the powerful, pounding *Baby I Need Your Loving*.
After a slight hiccup, they surged to America's No.1 slot in Summer 65 with *I Can't Help Myself*. From then on it was plainsailing for HDH and the Tops. Stubb's bold, dramatic and emotive lead vocals, the group's superb harmony work and HDH's soulful pop songs added up to a potent package. The crowning glory of the Four Tops career came in late 1966. *Reach Out I'll Be There* hit No.1 on both sides of the Atlantic, and became and all time classic. Reach Out clearly established the Tops as one of the finest acts on Motown, the company that was on it's way to becoming the all-time No.1 black music label. The quartet were particlularly succesful in Britain. They gave Tamla it's first UK chart topper with *Reach Out*, became the first act to top the British album charts and, with the same LP - 1968's Greatest Hits - became the first act to top the UK LP listings with a hits collection. After such later HDH hits as *Standing In The Shadows Of Love* and *Bernadette*, the Tops found themselves without HDH, who quit Motown in 1968. Gordy teamed the Tops with the Supremes for the 1971 hit remake of Ike & Tina Turner's *River Deep Mountain High* but it was not enough to prevent the group leaving the company. The Tops flourished briefly in post-Tamla days with *Keeper Of The Castle* and 1973's US million seller *Ain't No Woman Like The One I Got*, but seven years bad luck started in 1974. They returned to fame in late 1981 with *When She Was My Girl* which reached No.11 in America and No.3 in Britain. In a career spanning nearly thirty years, the Four Tops have given the world so much powerful, emotive and soulful pop music. (Bob Macdonald 4/85)

Soul vocal quartet formed as the Four Aims in 1953 in Detroit, with the same lineup more than 35 years later: lead Levi Stubbs, Abdul 'Duke' Fakir, Renaldo 'Obie' Benson, Lawrence Payton. No record success despite spells on Chess, Red Top, Columbia, Riverside. Payton's cousin Billy Davis had written hits for Jackie Wilson (with whom Stubbs had sung in Royals before joining 3 other Tops); he introduced them to co-writer Berry Gordy, who signed them up. First release *Breaking Through* on Motown's Workshop label was a jazz LP in the Hi-Los vein, but the backed Motown stars on hits and teamed with Eddie and Brian Holland and Lamont Dozier, the fast rising Motown writing/production team: *Baby I Need Your Loving* was a smash pop chart debut that set the pattern. Fourth single *I Can't Help Myself* was number one in 1965; their seventh USA top 40 hit *Reach Out I'll Be There* was their finest moment, a transatlantic number one in 1966. They moved to ABC-Dunhill as Motown moved to the West Coast; H-D-H formed their own Invictus label; they lost consistency but on the disco-oriented Casablanca label in 1981 with West Coast producer David Wolfert and white soul session players: they'd listened hard and incorporated elements of contemporary black music without compromising their glorious vocal blend. (Donald Clarke 1989)1.

7 ROOMS OF GLOOM
Tracks: / Seven rooms of gloom.
7" Single: Released Jun '67, on Tamla Motown, by Motown Records (UK). Deleted '70. Catalogue no: **TMG 612**
7" Single: Released Apr '88, on Motown, by BMG Records (UK). Catalogue no: **ZB 41905**

BABY I NEED YOUR LOVING
Tracks: / Baby I need your loving / Yesterday's dreams.
CD 5": Released Jun '89, on Motown, by BMG Records (UK). Catalogue no: **ZD 41947**
7" Single: Released Apr '82, on Motown, by BMG Records (UK). Catalogue no: **TMG 978**
12" Single: Released Apr '82, on Motown, by BMG Records (UK). Catalogue no: **TMGT 978**

BACK TO SCHOOL AGAIN
Tracks: / Back to school again / Rock-a-hula-lula.
7" Single: Released Jun '82, on RSO, by Polydor Ltd. Deleted '85. Catalogue no: **RSO 89**

BERNADETTE
Tracks: / Bernadette.
7" Single: Released Mar '67, on Tamla Motown, by Motown Records (UK). Deleted '70. Catalogue no: **TMG 601**
7" Single: Released Mar '72, on Tamla Motown, by Motown Records (UK). Deleted '75. Catalogue no: **TMG 803**
7" Single: Released Apr '85, on Motown, by BMG Records (UK). Catalogue no: **TMG 995**
12" Single: Released Apr '85, on Motown, by BMG Records (UK). Catalogue no: **TMGT 995**

DO WHAT YOU GOTTA DO
Tracks: / Do what you gotta do.
7" Single: Released Sep '69, on Tamla Motown, by Motown Records (UK). Deleted '72. Catalogue no: **TMG 710**

DON'T WALK AWAY
Tracks: / Don't walk away / I'll never ever leave again.
12" Single: Released Dec '81, on Casablanca, by PolyGram UK Ltd. Deleted Dec '84. Catalogue no: **CANX 1006**
7" Single: Released Oct '81, on Casablanca, by PolyGram UK Ltd. Deleted '84. Catalogue no: **CAN 1006**

I CAN'T HELP MYSELF
Tracks: / I can't help myself.
7" Single: Released Mar '70, on Tamla Motown, by Motown Records (UK). Deleted '73. Catalogue no: **TMG 732**
7" Single: Released Jul '65, on Tamla Motown, by Motown Records (UK). Deleted '68. Catalogue no: **TMG 515**
7" Single: Released Mar '83, on Motown, by BMG Records (UK). Catalogue no: **TMG 1120**

I JUST CAN'T WALK AWAY
Tracks: / I just can't walk away.
7" Single: Released Oct '83, on Motown, by BMG Records (UK). Deleted '85. Catalogue no: **TMG 1321**
12" Single: Released Oct '83, on Motown, by BMG Records (UK). Deleted '85. Catalogue no: **TMGT 1321**

IF I WERE A CARPENTER
Tracks: / If I were a carpenter.
7" Single: Released Mar '68, on Tamla Motown, by Motown Records (UK). Deleted '71. Catalogue no: **TMG 647**

I'LL TURN TO STONE
Tracks: / I'll turn to stone.
7" Single: Released Oct '81, on Motown, by BMG Records (UK). Deleted '83. Catalogue no: **TMG 829**

I'M IN A DIFFERENT WORLD
Tracks: / I'm in a different world.
7" Single: Released Nov '68, on Tamla

FOUR TOPS - SUN AIN'T GONNA SHINE, THE (Released on Arista)

Motown, by Motown Records (UK). Deleted '71. Catalogue no: **TMG 675**

INDESTRUCTIBLE (SINGLE)
Tracks: / Indestructible / Are you with me / Indestructible (versions) / Next time (Only on 7" picture disc.).
7" Single: Released 14 Aug '88, on Arista, by BMG Records (UK). Catalogue no: **111510**
7" Single: Released Feb '89, on Arista, by BMG Records (UK). Catalogue no: **112 074**
7" Single: Released Sep '88, on Arista, by BMG Records (UK). Deleted May '89. Catalogue no: **111 717**
12" Single: Released Sep '88, on Arista, by BMG Records (UK). Deleted May '89. Catalogue no: **611 717**
CD 5": Released Feb '89, on Arista, by BMG Records (UK). Catalogue no: **162 074**
CD 5": Released 14 Aug '88, on Arista, by BMG Records (UK). Catalogue no: **661717**
7" Pic: Released Mar '89, on Arista, by BMG Records (UK). Catalogue no: **112 151**
12" Single: Released Feb '89, on Arista, by BMG Records (UK). Catalogue no: **612 160**
12" Single: Released Feb '89, on Arista, by BMG Records (UK). Catalogue no: **612 074**
12" Single: Released 14 Aug '88, on Arista, by BMG Records (UK). Deleted May '89. Catalogue no: **611510**

IT'S ALL IN THE GAME (SINGLE)
Tracks: / Simple game / It's all in the game.
7" Single: Released Apr '88, on Motown, by BMG Records (UK). Catalogue no: **ZB 41907**
7" Single: Released May '70, on Tamla Motown, by Motown Records (UK). Deleted '73. Catalogue no: **TMG 736**
7" Single: Released Oct '81, on Motown, by BMG Records (UK). Deleted '83. Catalogue no: **TMG 965**

IT'S THE SAME OLD SONG
Tracks: / It's the same old song.
7" Single: Released Sep '65, on Tamla Motown, by Motown Records (UK). Deleted '68. Catalogue no: **TMG 528**

JUST SEVEN NUMBERS (CAN STRAIGHTEN OUT MY LIFE)
Tracks: / Just seven numbers.
7" Single: Released May '71, on Tamla Motown, by Motown Records (UK). Deleted '74. Catalogue no: **TMG 770**

KEEPER OF THE CASTLE (SINGLE)
Tracks: / Keeper of the castle.
7" Single: Released Nov '72, on Probe. Deleted '75. Catalogue no: **PRO 575**

LOCO IN ACAPULCO
Tracks: / Loco in Acapulco / Four of us, The / Loco in Acapulco (body mix) (Only on 12" version (611 850)).
12" Single: Released Jan '89, on Arista, by BMG Records (UK). Catalogue no: **611916**
CD 5": Released Dec '88, on Arista, by BMG Records (UK). Catalogue no: **661850**
7" Single: Released Nov '88, on Arista, by BMG Records (UK). Catalogue no: **111850**
Special: Released Jan '89, on Arista, by BMG Records (UK). Deleted May '89. Catalogue no: **111850X**
12" Single: Released Dec '88, on Arista, by BMG Records (UK). Catalogue no: **611850**
12" Single: Released Nov '88, on Arista, by BMG Records (UK). Catalogue no: **611730**
Special: Released Jan '89, on Arista, by BMG Records (UK). Catalogue no: **11197**

LOVING YOU IS SWEETER THAN EVER
Tracks: / Loving you is sweeter than ever.
7" Single: Released Jul '66, on Tamla Motown, by Motown Records (UK). Deleted '69. Catalogue no: **TMG 568**

REACH OUT AND TOUCH
Tracks: / Reach out and touch (somebody's hand).
7" Single: Released Oct '81, on Motown, by BMG Records (UK). Deleted '83. Catalogue no: **TMG 836**

REACH OUT, I'LL BE THERE
Tracks: / Reach out I'll be there / Standing in the shadows of love.
7" Single: Released Oct '66, on Tamla Motown, by Motown Records (UK). Deleted '69. Catalogue no: **TMG 579**
7" Single: Released May '88, on Motown, by BMG Records (UK). Catalogue no: **ZB 41943**
7" Single: Released Oct '81, on Motown, by BMG Records (UK). Catalogue no: **TMG 1049**
12" Single: Released May '88, on Motown, by BMG Records (UK). Catalogue no: **ZT 41944**

SAD HEARTS
Tracks: / Sad hearts / I believe in you and me.
7" Single: Released Jul '82, on Casablanca, by PolyGram UK Ltd. Catalogue no: **CAN 1012**
12" Single: Released Jul '82, on Casablanca, by PolyGram UK Ltd. Catalogue no: **CANX 1012**

SEVEN ROOMS OF GLOOM
Tracks: / Seven rooms of gloom / If I were a carpenter.
7" Single: Released Oct '80, on Motown, by BMG Records (UK). Deleted Oct '83. Catalogue no: **TMG 958**

SIMPLE GAME
Tracks: / Simple game / Still water.
7" Single: Released Sep '71, on Tamla Motown, by Motown Records (UK). Deleted '74. Catalogue no: **TMG 785**
7" Single: Released Oct '81, on Tamla Motown, by Motown Records (UK). Deleted '83. Catalogue no: **TMG 972**

STANDING IN THE SHADOWS OF LOVE
Tracks: / Standing in the shadows of love.
7" Single: Released Jan '67, on Tamla Motown, by Motown Records (UK). Deleted '70. Catalogue no: **TMG 589**

STILL WATER (LOVE)
Tracks: / Still water.
7" Single: Released Oct '70, on Tamla Motown, by Motown Records (UK). Deleted '73. Catalogue no: **TMG 752**

SUN AIN'T GONNA SHINE, THE (see panel on left)
Tracks: / Sun ain't gonna shine, The / Loco in Acapulco.
12" Single: Released 24 Jul '89, on Arista, by BMG Records (UK). Catalogue no: **612 252**
7" Single: Released 24 Jul '89, on Arista, by BMG Records (UK). Catalogue no: **112 252**
7" Single: Released 24 Jul '89, on Arista, by BMG Records (UK). Catalogue no: **112 378**
Cassingle: Released Aug '89, on Arista, by BMG Records (UK). Catalogue no: **409 995**
CD 5": Released 24 Jul '89, on Arista, by BMG Records (UK). Catalogue no: **662 252**

SWEET UNDERSTANDING LOVE
Tracks: / Sweet understanding love.
7" Single: Released Nov '73, on Probe. Deleted '76. Catalogue no: **PRO 604**

TONIGHT I'M GONNA LOVE YOU ALL OVER
Tracks: / Tonight I'm gonna love you all over / From a distance.
7" Single: Released Feb '82, on Casablanca, by PolyGram UK Ltd. Catalogue no: **CAN 1008**
12" Single: Released Feb '82, on Casablanca, by PolyGram UK Ltd. Catalogue no: **CANX 1008**

WALK AWAY RENEE
Tracks: / Walk away Renee.
7" Single: Released Dec '67, on Tamla Motown, by Motown Records (UK). Deleted '70. Catalogue no: **TMG 634**
7" Single: Released Oct '81, on Motown, by BMG Records (UK). Catalogue no: **TMG 1011**

WALK WITH ME TALK WITH ME DARLING
Tracks: / Walk with me talk with me.
7" Single: Released Aug '72, on Tamla Motown, by Motown Records (UK). Deleted '75. Catalogue no: **TMG 823**

WHAT IS A MAN
Tracks: / What is a man.
7" Single: Released May '69, on Tamla Motown, by Motown Records (UK). Deleted '72. Catalogue no: **TMG 698**

WHEN SHE WAS MY GIRL
Tracks: / When she was my girl / Something to remember.
7" Single: Released Dec '81, on Casablanca, by PolyGram UK Ltd. Deleted '84. Catalogue no: **CAN 1005**
12" Single: Released Dec '81, on Casablanca, by PolyGram UK Ltd. Deleted '84. Catalogue no: **CANX 1005**

YESTERDAY'S DREAMS (SINGLE)
Tracks: / Yesterday's dreams.
7" Single: Released Aug '68, on Tamla Motown, by Motown Records (UK). Deleted '71. Catalogue no: **TMG 665**

YOU KEEP RUNNING AWAY
Tracks: / You keep running away.
7" Single: Released Oct '67, on Tamla Motown, by Motown Records (UK). Deleted '70. Catalogue no: **TMG 623**

YOUR SONG
Tracks: / Your song / I'm here again.
7" Single: Released Jun '84, on Calibre. Deleted '86. Catalogue no: **CAB 124**
12" Single: Released Jun '84, on Calibre. Deleted '86. Catalogue no: **CABL 124**

Fourmost

Biographical details: This British pop group consisted of Billy Hatton, Dave Lovelady, Mike Millward and Brian O'Hara.
The Fourmost were formed in 1959 and, during the early Sixties, became one of the most popular combos on the fast growing Liverpool scene. Brian Epstein offered to manage them, but they initially turned him down. They reconsidered their decision, however, when they saw one of his other charges, the Beatles, leading a huge Merseybeat revolution. As with the Fab Four, Epstein got the Fourmost signed to Parlophone Records with George Martin as producer. Lennon & McCartney provided them with their first two hits, *Hello Little Girl* and *I'm In Love*; the first reached the UK No 9 position, the second got to No 17, although both probably sold on the strength pf the composers' spiralling reputations as much as on their somewhat insunstantial quality. A few months later, in spring 1964, the Fourmost achieved their biggest hit with *A Little Loving* (No 6).
The Fourmost's live act always emphasised their strong bent towards comedy - their impersonations of pop stars and their general stage antics were, however, excluded from their discs by George Martin, who recorded them as a straight pop group. It was left to the Barron Knights to score the comedy hits.
The Fourmost soon went into a decline. After *A Little Loving*, they only enjoyed three more UK chart entries - the biggest of these, a cover of the Four Tops' debut American hit *Baby I Need Your Lovin'*, peaked at No 24 at the end of 1964. Their slide was acclerated by the ill health of lead singer/guitarist Mike Millward, who died of leukaemia in 1965 at the age of 23. He was replaced by Joey Bower, who had actually helped to get the group off the ground in '59. But there were no more chart hits in store - having held down a lengthy variety engagement at the London Palladium, they moved into cabaret on a full-time basis. Bob MacDonald, 4.9.85.
Merseybeat group of the '60s: lead guitar Brian O'Hara, rhythm guitar Mike Millward, drummer Dave Lovelady, bassist Billy Hatton. First known as the Four Jays, then the Four Mosts, they signed with Brian Epstein and had 3 top 20 hits with their first 3 singles 1963-4:*Hello Little Girl* and *I'm In Love* were lesser-known Lennon/McCartney songs, and a few more hits followed. Comic stage routines enabled them to switch to cabaret when the hits stopped; they suffered as a band through George Martin's insistence on recording them as a straightg pop band, while Barron Knights later found popularity with a similar brand of humour. (Donald Clarke 1989)a.

BABY I NEED YOUR LOVIN'
Tracks: / Baby I need your lovin'.
7" Single: Released Nov '64, on Parlophone, by EMI Records. Deleted '67. Catalogue no: **R 5194**

GIRLS GIRLS GIRLS
Tracks: / Girls girls girls.
7" Single: Released Dec '65, on Parlophone, by EMI Records. Deleted '68. Catalogue no: **R 5379**

HELLO LITTLE GIRL
Tracks: / Hello little girl.
7" Single: Released Sep '63, on Parlophone, by EMI Records. Deleted '66. Catalogue no: **R 5056**

HOW CAN I TELL HER
Tracks: / How can I tell her.
7" Single: Released Aug '64, on Parlophone, by EMI Records. Deleted '67. Catalogue no: **R 5157**

I'M IN LOVE
Tracks: / I'm in love.
7" Single: Released Dec '63, on Parlophone, by EMI Records. Deleted '66. Catalogue no: **R 5078**

LITTLE LOVING, A
Tracks: / Little loving, A.
7" Single: Released Apr '64, on Parlophone, by EMI Records. Deleted '67. Catalogue no: **R 5128**

Fourteen Iced Bears

COME GET ME
Tracks: / Come get me.
7" Single: Released Apr '88, on Sarah. Catalogue no: **SARAH 005**

INSIDE (EP)
Tracks: / Bluesuit / Cut / Inside.
12" Single: Released Nov '86, on Frank. Catalogue no: **COPPOLA 101**

LIKE A DOLPHIN
Tracks: / Balloon song / Train song / Lie to choose / Like a dolphin.
12" Single: Released Feb '87, on Frank. Catalogue no: **CAPRA 202**

MOTHER SLEEP
Tracks: / Mother sleep.
12" Single: Released May '89, on Thunderball. Catalogue no: **12 TBL 2**

SLEEP
Tracks: / Sleep.
7" Single: Released Apr '89, on Thunderball. Catalogue no: **7TBL 2**
12" Single: Released Apr '89, on Thunderball. Catalogue no: **12TBL 2**

Fourteen Karat Soul

THIS BOY
Tracks: / This boy / Rapt aint too proud to beg (Available on 12" only.) / Wonderer, The.
12" Single: Released Nov '87, on Disc Afrique. Catalogue no: **KARA T1**
7" Single: Released Nov '87, on Disc Afrique. Catalogue no: **KARA 1**

Fourteen-Eighteen

GOOD-BYE-EE (SINGLE)
Tracks: / Goodbye-ee.
7" Single: Released Nov '75, on Magnet, by WEA Records. Deleted '78. Catalogue no: **MAG 48**

Fourth Generation

AIN'T NOBODY
Tracks: / Ain't nobody.
12" Single: Released Feb '89, on White Label (1), Catalogue no: **JDPD 014**

LET'S GET IT RIGHT
Tracks: / Let's get it right.
12" Single: Released Jul '89, on Soul Train, Catalogue no: **STD 15**

Fourth Party

LIVING IN THE ZOO
Tracks: / Living in the zoo.
7" Single: Released Oct '83, on Pip Pip Pop, Catalogue no: **PACKAGE 1**

Fowler, Barbara

COME AND GET MY LOVIN'
Tracks: / Come and get my lovin'.
12" Single: Released Sep '84, on Master Mix, Catalogue no: **CHE 840S**

Fowler, Chuck

MYSTERY TRAIN
Tracks: / Mystery train / Rockabye boogie.
7" Single: Released 20 Jul '80, on Rockburgh, Deleted '83. Catalogue no: **ROCS 227**

Fowler, Pete

ONE HEART ONE SONG
Tracks: / One heart one song.
7" Single: Released May '82, on Oval, by Oval Records. Catalogue no: **OVAL 1005**

Fowley, Kim

Biographical details: (b 21 July '42, Manila) Singer, songwriter, producer born in Manila in 1942 with a long, incredibly varied career. He worked in L.A. in the late '50s with Phil Spector, sang in black vocal group the Jayhawks, worked as a deejay in Boise, Idaho and produced the first records by Paul Revere and the Raiders in 1959, then West Coast novelties including *Alley Oop* by the Hollywood Argyles for a number one hit in 1960. He continued producing, sang on Frank Zappa's *Freak Out* album (*Mothers Of Invention*) and co-produced Jonathon Richman with John Cale. He made many albums and released singles under various names, was also a dancer, an actor, published poetry, etc. (Donald Clarke 1989).

1989 - WAITING AROUND FOR THE NEXT TEN YEARS
Tracks: / 1989 - waiting around for the next ten years / 1987 - Lost like a lizard in the snow.
7" Single: Released Jan '80, on Island, by Island Records. Deleted '83. Catalogue no: **WIP 6555**

Fox (Band)

ELECTRO PEOPLE
Tracks: / Electro people / If you don't want my peaches.
7" Single: Released Feb '82, on BBC, by BBC Records & Tapes. Deleted '87. Catalogue no: **RESL 115**

IMAGINE ME IMAGINE YOU
Tracks: / Imagine me imagine you.
7" Single: Released May '75, on GTO, Deleted '78. Catalogue no: **GT 21**

ONLY YOU CAN
Tracks: / Only you can.
7" Single: Released Feb '75, on GTO, Deleted '78. Catalogue no: **GT 8**

SET ME FREE
Tracks: / Set me free / Never / Where have all the boys gone.
12" Single: Released Mar '86, on Malaco, by Malaco Records (UK). Deleted '88. Catalogue no: **MAL 12 032**

S-S-S SINGLE BED
Tracks: / S-s-s single bed.
7" Single: Released Oct '76, on GTO, Deleted '79. Catalogue no: **GT 57**

Fox, Frizzby

PRETTY BOYS
Tracks: / Pretty boys / Cut me loose.
7" Single: Released Jul '86, on Hippodrome, by Hippodrome Records. Catalogue no: **HIPPO 109**
12" Single: Released Jul '86, on Hippodrome, by Hippodrome Records. Catalogue no: **12HIPPO 109**

Fox In Socks

SOUND PATTERNS
Tracks: / Sound patterns.
7" Single: Released Sep '82, on Gesticulation, Catalogue no: **GEST 001**

Fox, June

FRANKIE
Tracks: / Frankie.
12" Single: Released Sep '87, on C & E, Catalogue no: **CED 119**

MEANT TO BE
Tracks: / Meant to be.
12" Single: Released Nov '83, on Clair, Catalogue no: **CLAIR 010**

Fox, Noosha

Biographical details: Having enjoyed three UK hit singles plus a UK Top 10 album during 1975-6 as leader of her group Fox, this British singer launched a solo career in 1977 after the band's termination. Its success proved to be somewhat limited - Noosha achieved just one small hit single, *Georgina Bailey*, which reached the UK No 31 position in December 1977.
Georgina Bailey was the musical brainchild of two key members of the old Fox group, guitarist/songwriter/producer Kenny Young and his cohort Herbie Armstrong. Highlighting Noosha Fox's irritatingly thin but subtly seductive voice, *Georgina Bailey* was a suggestive narrative with a quasi-French sound. Noosha drifted into obscurity, and her career was not resurrected by her two 1981 singles, *More Than Molecules* and *Hot As Sun*. Bob MacDonald, 4.9.85..

GEORGINA BAILEY
Tracks: / Georgina Bailey.
7" Single: Released Nov '77, on GTO, Deleted '80. Catalogue no: **GT 106**

HOT AS SUN
Tracks: / Hot as sun.
7" Single: Released Jul '81, on Earlobe, by Earlobe Records. Deleted '87. Catalogue no: **ELBS 105**

MORE THAN MOLECULES
Tracks: / More than molecules / Odd peculiar strange.
7" Single: Released Jan '81, on Earlobe, by Earlobe Records. Deleted '83. Catalogue no: **ELBS 101**

Fox, Samantha

AIM TO WIN
Tracks: / Aim to win / Holiday / Aim To Win (extended) / Holding.
7" Single: Released Apr '86, on Genie, Catalogue no: **GEN 3**
7" Pic: Released May '86, on Genie, Catalogue no: **GENP 3**
7" Single: Released Apr '84, on Lamborghini, by Lamborghini Records. Catalogue no: **LMG 10**

DO YA DO YA (WANNA PLEASE ME)
Tracks: / Do ya do ya (wanna please me) / Never gonna fall in love again / Do ya do ya (wanna please me) (vision mix) / Do ya do ya (wanna please me) (dance mix) (Only on 12".).
12" Single: Released Jul '86, on Jive, by Zomba Records. Deleted '88. Catalogue no: **FOXYR 2**
7" Single: Released Jun '86, on Jive, by Zomba Records. Deleted Nov '87. Catalogue no: **FOXY 2**
12" Single: Released Jun '86, on Jive, by Zomba Records. Deleted '88. Catalogue no: **FOXYT 2**
Special: Released '88, on Jive, by Zomba Records. Deleted '88. Catalogue no: **FOXYS 1**

HOLD ON TIGHT
Tracks: / Hold on tight.
Special: Released '88, on Jive, by Zomba Records. Deleted '88. Catalogue no: **FOXY S 3**
7" Single: Released Aug '86, on Jive, by Zomba Records. Deleted Nov '87. Catalogue no: **FOXY 3**
12" Single: Released Aug '86, on Jive, by Zomba Records. Deleted '88. Catalogue no: **FOXYT 3**

HOLDING
Tracks: / Holding (dub mix) / Holding / Holding (dub mix).
12" Single: Released Oct '86, on Genie, Catalogue no: **12 GEN 8**
12" Pic: Released Nov '86, on Genie, Catalogue no: **GENP 8**
7" Single: Released Oct '86, on Genie, Catalogue no: **GEN 8**

I ONLY WANNA BE WITH YOU
Tracks: / I only wanna be with you / Concession.
7" Single: Released Dec '88, on Jive, by Zomba Records. Catalogue no: **FOXYX 11**
CD 5": Released Jan '89, on Jive, by Zomba Records. Catalogue no: **FOXYCD 11**
7" Single: Released Jan '89, on Jive, by Zomba Records. Catalogue no: **FOXYS 11**
12" Single: Released Dec '88, on Jive, by Zomba Records. Catalogue no: **FOXYT 11**

I PROMISE YOU
Tracks: / I promise you / Suzie don't leave me with your boyfriend.
12" Single: Released Oct '87, on Jive, by Zomba Records. Deleted '88. Catalogue no: **FOXYT 7**

SAMANTHA FOX - I WANNA HAVE SOME FUN (Released on Jive)

7" Single: Released Oct '87, on Jive, by Zomba Records. Deleted Nov '87. Catalogue no: **FOXY 7**

I SURRENDER (TO THE SPIRIT OF THE NIGHT)
Tracks: / I surrender / Best is yet to come, The.
Special: Released '88, on Jive, by Zomba Records. Deleted '88. Catalogue no: **FOXY X**
7" Single: Released Jul '87, on Jive, by Zomba Records. Deleted Nov '87. Catalogue no: **FOXY G6**
12" Single: Released Jul '87, on Jive, by Zomba Records. Deleted '88. Catalogue no: **FOXT 6**

I WANNA HAVE SOME FUN (see panel above)
Tracks: / I wanna have some fun / Out of our hands / Love don't grow on trees.
CD 5": Released Apr '89, on Jive, by Zomba Records. Catalogue no: **FOXYCD 12**
12" Single: Released Apr '89, on Jive, by Zomba Records. Catalogue no: **FOXYT 12**
12" Pic: Released '89, on Jive, by Zomba Records. Catalogue no: **FOXYS 12**
7" Pic: Released May '89, on Jive, by Zomba Records. Catalogue no: **FOXYZ 12**
7" Single: Released '89, on Jive, by Zomba Records. Catalogue no: **FOXYX 12**
7" Single: Released Apr '89, on Jive, by Zomba Records. Catalogue no: **FOXY 12**
12" Single: Released May '89, on Jive, by Zomba Records. Catalogue no: **FOXYR 12**

I'M ALL YOU NEED
Tracks: / Want you to want me / Touch me (I want your body) (Extra track on 12" version only.) / Do ya do ya (wanna please me) (Extra track on 12" version only.) / Hold on tight (Extra track on 12" version only.).
7" Single: Released Nov '86, on Jive, by Zomba Records. Deleted Nov '87. Catalogue no: **FOXY 4**
12" Single: Released Nov '86, on Jive, by Zomba Records. Deleted '88. Catalogue no: **FOXYT 4**

LOVE HOUSE
Tracks: / Love house.
12" Single: Released Oct '88, on Jive, by Zomba Records. Catalogue no: **FOXYT 10**
CD 5": Released '88, on Jive, by Zomba Records. Deleted '88. Catalogue no: **FOXY CD10**
7" Single: Released Oct '88, on Jive, by Zomba Records. Deleted '88. Catalogue no: **FOXY 10**

NAUGHTY GIRLS
Tracks: / Naughty girls / Dream city.
12" Single: Released Apr '88, on Jive, by Zomba Records. Deleted '88. Catalogue no: **FOXYT 9**
Special: Released '88, on Jive, by Zomba Records. Deleted '88. Catalogue no: **FOXYS 9**
Special: Released '88, on Jive, by Zomba Records. Deleted '88. Catalogue no: **FOXYR 9**
7" Single: Released Apr '88, on Jive, by Zomba Records. Deleted '88. Catalogue no: **FOXY 9**

NOTHING'S GONNA STOP ME NOW
Tracks: / Nothing's gonna stop me now / Dream city / Want you to want me* (Extra track on 12" only).
Note: (Cat.No. 620781 - Collectors' edition in white vinyl. Picture bag).
7" Pic: Released 30 May '87, on Jive, by Zomba Records. Catalogue no: **FOXY 5P**
12" Single: Released Nov '87, on Jive (Germany), by Zomba Records. Catalogue no: **620781**
12" Single: Released May '87, on Jive, by Zomba Records. Catalogue no: **FOXY 5T**
7" Single: Released May '87, on Jive, by Zomba Records. Deleted Nov '87. Catalogue no: **FOXY 5**

NOTHING'S GONNA STOP ME NOW (CLUB MIX)
Tracks: / Nothing's gonna stop me now (club mix) / Dream city.
12" Single: Released 20 Jun '87, on Jive, by Zomba Records. Catalogue no: **FOXYR 5**

TOUCH ME (SINGLE)
Tracks: / Touch me / I'm all you need.
12" Single: Released Mar '86, on Jive, by Zomba Records. Catalogue no: **FOXYR 1**
12" Single: Released Mar '86, on Jive, by Zomba Records. Catalogue no: **FOXYT 1**
7" Single: Released Mar '86, on Jive, by Zomba Records. Catalogue no: **FOXY 1**
12" Single: Released Mar '86, on Jive, by Zomba Records. Catalogue no: **FOXYS 1**

TRUE DEVOTION
Tracks: / True devotion / Even in the darkest hour / I surrender (Available on 12" only.) / Touch me (Available on 12" only.).
7" Single: Released Nov '87, on Jive, by Zomba Records. Deleted '88. Catalogue no: **FOXY 8**
Special: Released Nov '87, on Jive, by Zomba Records. Deleted '88. Catalogue no: **FOXY X8**
12" Single: Released Nov '87, on Jive, by Zomba Records. Deleted '88. Catalogue no: **FOXY T8**

Fox The Fox

PRECIOUS LITTLE DIAMOND
Tracks: / Precious little diamond / Man on the run.
12" Single: Released Jun '86, on Epic, by CBS Records. Deleted Jun '88. Catalogue no: **TA 6911**
7" Single: Released Jun '86, on Epic, by CBS Records. Catalogue no: **A 6911**

Fox & The Hound

FOX AND THE HOUND Various artists
Tracks: / Best of friends: *Fox & The Hound* / Lack of education: *Various artists* / Huntin' man: *Various artists* / Goodbye may seem forever: *Various artists* / Appreciate the lady: *Various artists*.
12" Single: Released Dec '82, on Disneyland-Vista(USA), by Disneyland-Vista Records (USA). Catalogue no: **D 3823**
Special: Released Dec '82, on Disneyland Vista(USA), by Disneyland-Vista Records (USA). Catalogue no: **D 3106**

BRUCE FOXTON - FREAK (Released on Arista)

Foxton, Bruce

Biographical details: British bass guitarist, singer and songwriter Foxton launched a solo career in 1983 after six years of stardom with The Jam. Paul Weller's autumn '82 decision to terminate the pioneering New Wave band at the height of their popularity was a source of surprise and resentment for Foxton. Although Foxton was the most photogenic of the trio he had always lived in the musical shadow of Weller's songwriting and socio-political prowess. Could he make it on his own?

The solo career began promisingly enough, with the powerhouse single *Freak* climbing to No 23 in Britain in summer '83. But after that each single was less successful than its predecessor: the melodic *This Is The Way* peaked at 56, *It Makes Me Wonder* stopped at 74 and *SOS (My Imagination)* flopped altogether. And his debut solo album, *Touch Sensitive*, made little impact, despite a major UK tour with his own four-piece band. By early 1985 Foxton had parted company with his record label, Arista. So far his material was simply not strong enough to stand out from the vast array of weekly pop and rock releases. (Bob MacDonald, September 1985.).

FREAK (see panel above)
Tracks: / Freak / Writing on the wall.
7" Single: Released '83, on Arista, by BMG Records (UK). Deleted '86. Catalogue no: **BFOX 1**
12" Single: Released '83, on Arista, by BMG Records (UK). Deleted '86. Catalogue no: **BFOX 121**

IT MAKES ME WONDER
Tracks: / It makes me wonder / Trying to forget you.
12" Single: Released Apr '84, on Arista, by BMG Records (UK). Deleted '87. Catalogue no: **BFOX 3**

PLAY THIS GAME TO WIN
Tracks: / Play this game to win / Welcome to the hero / Living in a dreamworld.
12" Single: Released Nov '86, on Harvest (1), by EMI Records. Catalogue no: **12 HAR 5239**
7" Single: Released Nov '86, on Harvest (1), by EMI Records. Catalogue no: **HAR 5239**

S.O.S. (MY IMAGINATION)
Tracks: / S.O.S (my imagination).
7" Single: Released Jul '84, on Arista, by BMG Records (UK). Catalogue no: **BFOX 4**
12" Single: Released Jul '84, on Arista, by BMG Records (UK). Catalogue no: **BFOX 124**

THIS IS THE WAY
Tracks: / This is the way.
7" Single: Released '83, on Arista, by BMG Records (UK). Deleted '86. Catalogue no: **BFOX 2**
12" Single: Released '83, on Arista, by BMG Records (UK). Deleted '86. Catalogue no: **BFOX 122**

Foxx, Charlie & Inez

Biographical details: Born in North Carolina, Inez Foxx gained early musical experience as a member of local church choirs. In 1959, aged 17, she moved to New York to try for a break in show business, struggling for several years before gaining a recording contract in 1963. But her first disc was worth waiting for: *Mockingbird*, a children's song newly adapted by Inez and brother Charlie reached No 7 on the US chart in '53. Charlie performed guitar and vocal accompaniment on *Mockingbird* and was also her manager and many of the records were credited to Inez & Charlie Foxx. Inez first cracked the UK chart in the summer of '64 with the gimmicky single *Hurt By Love*, which reached No 40. *Mockingbird*, whose quirky appeal had been ignored by British record buyers in 1963, finally crawled to No 34 in 1969. (It was revived in 1974 by Carly Simon & James Taylor, who took it to No 5 in the US and No 34, again, in the UK.) Most people remember Inez & Charlie Foxx solely for *Mockingbird*, their only significant success. During the 60's Inez' potentially emotional and stirring voice was wasted on such trivial ditties as *Hi Diddle Dee* and the US R & B chart hit *Count The Days*. She was rarely as soulful as she could have been. (Bob MacDonald, September 1985.).

HURT BY LOVE
Tracks: / Hurt by love.
7" Single: Released Jul '64, on Sue, by Island Records. Deleted '67. Catalogue no: **WI 323**

MOCKINGBIRD (SINGLE)
Tracks: / Mockingbird.
7" Single: Released Feb '85, on EMI Golden 45's, by EMI Records. Catalogue no: **G 4536**
7" Single: Released Jul '64, on United Artists, by EMI Records. Deleted '67. Catalogue no: **UP 2269**

Foxx, John

Biographical details: This British synthesiser player, singer and composer directly inspired two acts who proceeded to enjoy far greater success with his ideas than Foxx himself did. He was a founder member of Ultravox, and his leadership role was assumed by Midge Ure when Foxx quit the band to go solo in 1979; Ure led the group to great heights in the Eighties. And when Gary Numan shot to superstardom in 1979 with two consecutive No 1 singles, he cited John Foxx as his main influence.

Born and raised in Chorley, Lancashire, Foxx moved to london in 1974 and soon formed Ultravox. John (whose real name is Dennis Leigh) loved messing around with tape recorders and gadgets, and quickly became interested in the new synthesiser technology. During the mid to late Seventies, Ultravox built up a strong cult following, although none of their records were commercially successful. Foxx's decision to go solo in 1979 was inspired by a desire to exert the maximum influence over his already idiosyncratic output.

John's debut LP *Metamatic* was released in early 1980, and reached No 18 on the British album chart. This suggested that Numan's high praise was paying off; but in fact, Foxx never really transformed his continued cult status into stardom. 1981's *The Garden* LP peaked at No 24. During 1980-83, he obtained a succession of minor UK hit singles: *Underpass*, *No-one Driving*, *Burning Car*, *Miles Away*, *Europe - After The Rain*, *Endlessly* and *Your Dress* all landed in the 31-75 area of the charts. His unassuming public personality and generally low profile contrasted charply with Numan's charismatic image, and John was probably content to remain at this level of moderate success. In addition, much of his earlier solo work was a little too bleak, even for electronic enthusiasts. Bob MacDonald, 4.9.85..

BURNING CAR
Tracks: / Burning car.
7" Single: Released Jul '80, on Metal Beat, by Virgin Records. Deleted '83. Catalogue no: **VS 360**

DANCING LIKE A GUN
Tracks: / Dancing like a gun.
12" Single: Released Oct '81, on Virgin, by Virgin Records. Deleted '85. Catalogue no: **VS 459-12**
7" Single: Released Oct '81, on Virgin, by Virgin Records. Deleted '85. Catalogue no: **VS 459**

ENDLESSLY
Tracks: / Endlessly / Young man.
7" Single: Released Jul '83, on Virgin, by Virgin Records. Deleted '86. Catalogue no: **VS 543**

EUROPE AFTER THE RAIN
Tracks: / Europe after the rain.
7" Single: Released Aug '81, on Virgin, by Virgin Records. Deleted '84. Catalogue no: **VS 393**

MILES AWAY
Tracks: / Miles away / Long time.
7" Single: Released Nov '80, on Metal Beat, by Virgin Records. Deleted '83. Catalogue no: **VS 382**

NO-ONE DRIVING (see panel below)
Tracks: / No-one driving / Glimmer / Mr. No / This city.
7" Set: Released Mar '80, on Metal Beat, by Virgin Records. Deleted '83. Catalogue no: **VS 338**

UNDERPASS
Tracks: / Underpass / Film 1.
7" Single: Released Jan '80, on Metal Beat, by Virgin Records. Deleted '83. Catalogue no: **VS 318**

YOUR DRESS
Tracks: / Your dress / Garden / Woman on the stairway / Lifting sky / Annexe.
7" Single: Released Sep '83, on Virgin, by Virgin Records. Deleted '86. Catalogue no: **VS 615**

Foxy Feeling

FOXY FEELING
Tracks: / Foxy feeling / What would I do without you.
7" Single: Released Apr '80, on Chips, Deleted '83. Catalogue no: **CHI 102**

Fra Lippo Lippi

ANGEL
Tracks: / Angel.
7" Single: Released Aug '87, on Virgin, by Virgin Records. Deleted May '88. Catalogue no: **VS 986**
12" Single: Released Aug '87, on Virgin, by Virgin Records. Deleted May '88. Catalogue no: **VS 986-12**

COME SUMMER
Tracks: / Come summer.
7" Single: Released Jul '86, on Virgin, by Virgin Records. Deleted '86. Catalogue no: **VS 877**
12" Single: Released Jul '86, on Virgin, by Virgin Records. Deleted '86. Catalogue no: **VS 877-12**

EVERYTIME I SEE YOU
Tracks: / Every time I see you / Heather on the hall, The / True story (Extra track on 12" version only).
12" Single: Released Apr '86, on Virgin, by Virgin Records. Deleted '86. Catalogue no: **VS 854-12**
7" Single: Released Apr '86, on Virgin, by Virgin Records. Deleted '86. Catalogue no: **VS 854**

MINOX
Tracks: / Minox.
7" Single: Released 10 Sep '85, on Lacer, Catalogue no: **LACER 007**

SAY SOMETHING
Tracks: / Say something.
12" Single: Released Jan '84, on Uniton Records, Catalogue no: **U 023**

SHOULDN'T HAVE TO BE LIKE THAT
Tracks: / Shouldn't have to be like that / Distance between us, The / Say something.
12" Single: Released Jan '86, on Virgin, by Virgin Records. Deleted '86. Catalogue no: **VS 831-12**
7" Single: Released Jan '86, on Virgin, by Virgin Records. Deleted '86. Catalogue no: **VS 831**

SOME PEOPLE
Tracks: / Some people / Even tall trees bend / Come summer (Extra track on 12" version.).
7" Single: Released Oct '87, on Virgin, by Virgin Records. Deleted '89. Catalogue no: **VS 1009**
12" Single: Released Oct '87, on Virgin, by Virgin Records. Catalogue no: **VST 1009**

Fracture

SIGN, A
Tracks: / Sign.
7" Single: Released Aug '82, on Shock, Catalogue no: **SHOCK 1**

Fraggle Rock

ALL AROUND THE WORLD
Tracks: / All around the world.
7" Single: Released May '85, on RCA, by BMG Records (UK). Catalogue no:

JOHN FOXX - NO - ONE DRIVING (Released on Metal Beat)

FRAGG 1

FRAGGLE ROCK (SINGLE)
Tracks: / Fraggle rock.
7" Pic: Released Jan '84, on RCA, by BMG Records (UK). Catalogue no: **RCAP 389**
7" Single: Released Jan '84, on RCA, by BMG Records (UK). Catalogue no: **RCA 389**

Fragile Friends

NOVELTY WEARS OFF, THE
Tracks: / Novelty wears off, The.
7" Single: Released Jul '85, on KC, Catalogue no: **CT 1**

PAPER DOLL
Tracks: / Paper doll.
7" Single: Released Feb '85, on KC, Catalogue no: **KC 001**

Fraise, Renzo

12 ENGEL STREET
Tracks: / 12 engel street / Los angeles / Blue streel / Good and plenty / Chameleon.
12" Single: Released May '80, on Pye, Deleted May '85. Catalogue no: **12P5016**

Frame By Frame

LIES
Tracks: / Lies / Think of me / Your space (Track on 12" version only) / It's a miracle (Track on 12" version only).
7" Single: Released Feb '86, on Skratch, by Skratch Records. Catalogue no: **FBF 1**
12" Single: Released Feb '86, on Skratch, by Skratch Records. Catalogue no: **FBFT 1**

Framed

GONNA TAKE YOU INTO MY LIFE
Tracks: / Gonna take you into my life.
7" Pic: Released Dec '82, on Thunderbay, Catalogue no: **TBR 020**

INTO MY LIFE
Tracks: / Into my life.
7" Single: Released Jul '83, on Thunderbay, Catalogue no: **TBR 020**

WONDERLAND
Tracks: / Wonderland.
7" Single: Released Apr '83, on Thunderbay, Catalogue no: **TBR 021**

Frampton, Peter

Biographical details: Having enjoyed success with The Herd (where he was dubbed 'The face of '68') and then Humble Pie (whom he left in 1971), this British singer, guitarist, songwriter and producer launched a solo career in 1972 with the album *Wind Of Change*.

Frampton and his backing band concentrated mainly on the American market, gradually building up a strong live following. Although he did not write classic material, he elevated his songs by the sheer potency and scope of his superb guitar work. Residing halfway between pop and rock music, he used his guitar to imaginatively convey a melody and a romantic lyric.

Frampton, the artist's 1975 album, reached No 32 on the US LP chart - this was a respectable placing but not one which truly reflected his concert appeal. The decision was thus made to release a double live album containing all his best songs. After quietly entering the US album chart in January 1976, *Frampton Comes Alive!* coolly became the world's best selling live LP of all time. It spent 10 weeks at No 1 in America, and remained on the chart for almost two years. In his native Britain, it climbed to No 6 and logged 39 weeks on the survey. The ecstatic single *Show Me The Way*, which featured a mesmerising 'talking guitar' sound, was a Top 10 hit on both sides of the Atlantic. The double LP also yielded two toher US Top 20 singles, *Baby I Love The Your Way* and *Do You Feel Like We Do*. Having been Britain's teenybop face of '68, Frampton was America's rock face of 1976.

The follow-up studio album *I'm In You* entered the US Top 200 albums chart at No 5 in June 1977, and soon reached No 2. Featuring an all star cast of guest musicians, it spawned a pair of US Top 20 singles including a No 2 hit with the title track; the UK was not quite so enthused, and gave the LP a more modest chart placing.

I'm In You proved to be Frampton's last moment of glory. When he co-starred with the Bee Gees in Robert Stigwood's 1978 movie *Sergeant Pepper's Lonely Hearts Club Band*, he had to threaten legal action in order to gain top billing - the film contract was signed during the *Frampton Comes Alive!* period, when Peter was the hottest property around; by '78, however, the Bee Gees were on top of the world, and Frampton was a yesterday man. In the event the film itself (a travesty of the Beatles' classic LP) received such a slating that he must have wished he had never been associated with it.

Further mishaps included a serious car accident, which forced him off the road for a time, plus a series of poorly received albums, *Where I Should Be, Breaking All The Rules* and *The Art Of Control*. In retrospect, *Frampton Comes Alive!* could be seen as a one-off sensation during Peter's solo career, with *I'm In You* selling mainly on the strength of its live predecessor. Bob MacDonald, 5.9.85

Guitarist born in 1950 in Beckenham. He formed the Herd in 1965, with Andy Bown, keyboards; Gary Taylor, bass; Andrew Steele, drums. After 3 flop singles Parlophone dropped them; on Fontana Howard & Blaikley orchestrated a successful blend of pop and flower power. Steele left, replaced by Henry Spinetti; Frampton, dissatisfied with teen idol status and disappointed with failure of *Sunshine Cottage* (reversion to psychedelic style), left for Humble Pie, an ill-fated supergroup, then went solo for one album, then formed Frampton's Camel for live work, whose heavy touring was finally rewarded by 2-disc *Frampton Comes Alive*, recorded at San Fransisco's Winterland, one of decade's best sellers--a number one album in the USA for 10 weeks in 1976, staying in the chart for nearly two years, certainly the biggest selling pop album ever. He was in fact still a teen idol, whether he liked it or not; he has never done that well again. He starred in Robert Stigwood/Bee Gee film *Sgt Pepper's Lonely Hearts Club Band*, a mistake. *Premonition* on Virgin updated his sound with slabs of synth, but it didn't work. (Donald Clarke 1989).

ALL EYES ON YOU
Tracks: / All eyes on you / Into view.
7" Single: Released Apr '86, on Virgin, by Virgin Records. Deleted '89. Catalogue no: **VS 847**
12" Single: Released Apr '86, on Virgin, by Virgin Records. Deleted '86. Catalogue no: **VS 847-12**

BABY I LOVE YOUR WAY
Tracks: / Baby I love your way.
7" Single: Released Sep '76, on A&M, by A&M Records. Deleted '79. Catalogue no: **AMS 7246**

CRYING
Tracks: / Crying / You know so well.
7" Single: Released Dec '85, on Virgin, by Virgin Records. Deleted '86. Catalogue no: **VS 827**
12" Single: Released Dec '85, on Virgin, by Virgin Records. Deleted '86. Catalogue no: **VS 827-12**

DO YOU FEEL LIKE WE DO
Tracks: / Do you feel like we do.
7" Single: Released Nov '76, on A&M, by A&M Records. Deleted '79. Catalogue no: **AMS 7260**

I'M IN YOU (SINGLE)
Tracks: / I'm in you.
7" Single: Released Jul '77, on A&M, by A&M Records. Deleted '80. Catalogue no: **AMS 7298**

SHOW ME THE WAY
Tracks: / Show me the way / Baby, I love your way / Penny for your thoughts / I'm in you / Wind of change / Signed, sealed, delivered, I'm yours.
7" Single: Released Oct '83, on Old Gold, by Old Gold Records. Catalogue no: **OG 9363**
7" Single: Released May '76, on A&M, by A&M Records. Deleted '79. Catalogue no: **AMS 7218**

SHOW ME THE WAY(EP)
Tracks: / Show me the way.
7" EP: Released Jun '84, on Scoop 33, by Pickwick Records. Catalogue no: **7SR 5039**

Fran & Anna

IT'S SCOTLAND FOREVER
Tracks: / It's Scotland forever.
7" Single: Released May '82, on Big R, by Big R Records. Catalogue no: **BRS 11**

SCOTTISH SINGALONG
Tracks: / Scottish singalong.
7" Single: Released May '77, on Neptune, by Lismor Records. Catalogue no: **NM 1**

France (Group)

GIVE HIM A GREAT BIG KISS
Tracks: / Give him a great big kiss.
7" Single: Released Oct '85, on Satril, by Satril Records. Catalogue no: **SAT 522**
12" Single: Released Oct '85, on Satril, by Satril Records. Catalogue no: **12SAT 522**

Frances, Phil

LAUGH IT OFF
Tracks: / Laugh it off.
12" Single: Released Jan '84, on Jama, Catalogue no: **JADC 002**

Francis, Bob

DISCO IN BRAZIL
Tracks: / Disco In Brazil / This is my life.
7" Single: Released Apr '80, on Pye, Deleted '82. Catalogue no: **7P 174**

IF I NEVER SING ANOTHER SONG
Tracks: / If I never sing another song / Wake up with an angel.
7" Single: Released Jan '81, on Pye, Deleted Jan '84. Catalogue no: **7P 208**

Francis, Connie

Biographical details: This American singer, born Concetta Franconero in New Jersey, showed leanings towards showbusiness from early childhood. By the age of 17 (1955), she had written and produced a school musical, made numerous US national television appearances and signed a recording contract. Her first taste of disc success came with *Majesty Of Love*, a 1957 duet with Marvin Rainwater.

After a few solo flops, Francis stormed to stardom in the spring of 1958 with *Who's Sorry Now*, a revival of a 1923 love ballad. This reached No 4 in the US, and went to No 1 for 6 weeks in the UK (coincidentally, dethroning Rainwater's *Whole Lotta Woman*). Later in '58, she achieved another six week UK chart topper with the double A sided single *Carolina Moon/Stupid Cupid*. The latter song, written by Neil Sedaka and Howard Greenfield, contrasted sharply with *Who's Sorry Now* - she tackeld romantic, smoochy ballads and bouncy novelty rockers with equal verve, and these two strands were to typify her whole recording career. The attractive Connie possessed a powerful and pleasant, though not fantastic voice. What she lacked in musical refinement, she made up for in energy and choice of material.

During thelate Fifties and early Sixties, in the gap between the rock 'n' roll explosion and the arrival of the Beatles. Frnacis was one of the biggest pop stars on both sides of the Atlantic and certainly the world's top female singer. Her American No 1 singles included *Everybody's Somebody's Fool* (1960), *My Heart Has A Mind Of Its Own* (1960), *Don't Break The Heart That Loves You* (1962). *My Happiness* (1959), *Lipstock On Your Collar* (1959), *Mama* (1960), *Where The Boys Are* (1961), *Together* (1961) and *Vacation* (1962) all reached the Top 10 in both the US and the UK. Several of Connie's hits were remakes of standards from the Twenties, Thirties and Forties.

Francis was not such hot property in the cinema - she made her big screen debut in the 1961 movie *Where The Boys Are*, but later admitted that she was no actress. From 1963 onwards, Francis gradually faded from the British and American charts, making way for the new era of Sixties pop talent. The singer directed her talents to MOR, cabaret and nightclub audiences around the world, and skilfully made records in a variety of different languages.

A series of traumas dogged Connie's personal life during the Seventies. In 1974, shortly after suffering a miscarriage, she was raped at knife-point in a Long Island motel room. She consequently had a nervous breakdown, became a recluse and underwent a two year course of psychiatric treatment. In 1978, while courageously attempting a showbiz comeback, the singer had $50,000 worth of jewelry stolen from a London hotel room. During the early Eighties, she continued to perform and make personal appearances, particularly in the States.

A TV advertised collection of the singer's *20 All Time Greats* reached No 1 on the British LP chart in 1977. Bob MacDonald, 5.9.85

At the age of 23, Connie Francis had peaked at the top of her success: the beginning of the Sixties showed her as one of the most demanded female singers. A whole string of worldwide hits summed up in more than 25 million sold records spread over 83 countries. In Europe, Germany turned out to be the country with the biggest crowd of followers: thousands of loyal collected her records. The German version of *Everybody's Somebody's Fool* blocked the highest chart position for months. "The phenomonal success caused her to record dozens of her songs in a foreign language." (Bear Family, 1988).

Pop singer, born Concetta Rossa Maria Franconero in 1938 in Newark, New Jersey. Perhaps the biggest-selling female recording artist of the late '50s-early '60s. *Who's Sorry Now*, a 1923 song recorded at the suggestion of her father, was first of 55 entries in the Hot 100 1958-69: an average of 7 top 40 entries a year 1958-64 included junky pop songs that stick in the mind whether we like it or not, slickly prod. with pseudo rock'n'roll beat and dominated by her big, strong, accurate voice (*Stupid Cupid* and *Lipstick On Your Collar* are good examples), but also revivals of good old songs, e.g. *My Happiness, If I Didn't Care, Among My Souvenirs* etc. Of 60-odd albums 21 charted in the USA 1960-66. She did charity work for CARE, USO, INICEF in the late '60s and sang for GIs in Vietnam; then she was a victim of rape-robbery at knifepoint in November 1974 after a performance. A comeback in 1981 was warmly received but she never really got over the awful crime. (Donald Clarke 1989).

AMONG MY SOUVENEIRS
Tracks: / Among my souvenirs.
7" Single: Released Dec '59, on MGM, by Polydor Ltd. Deleted '62. Catalogue no: **MGM 1046**

BABY'S FIRST CHRISTMAS
Tracks: / Baby's first christmas.
7" Single: Released Dec '61, on MGM, by Polydor Ltd. Deleted '64. Catalogue no: **MGM 1145**

BREAKIN' IN A BRAND NEW BROKEN HEART
Tracks: / Breakin' in a brand new broken heart.
7" Single: Released Jun '61, on MGM, by Polydor Ltd. Deleted '64. Catalogue no: **MGM 1136**

CAROLINA MOON
Tracks: / Carolina moon / Stupid cupid.
7" Single: Released Aug '58, on MGM, by Polydor Ltd. Deleted '61. Catalogue no: **MGM 985**

DON'T BREAK THE HEART THAT LOVES YOU
Tracks: / Don't break the heart that loves you.
7" Single: Released Apr '62, on MGM, by Polydor Ltd. Deleted '65. Catalogue no: **MGM 1157**

EVERYBODY'S SOMEBODY'S FOOL
Tracks: / Everybody's somebody's fool.
7" Single: Released Aug '60, on MGM, by Polydor Ltd. Deleted '63. Catalogue no: **MGM 1086**

FALLIN'
Tracks: / Falling.
7" Single: Released Nov '58, on MGM, by Polydor Ltd. Deleted '61. Catalogue no: **MGM 993**

I'LL GET BY
Tracks: / I'll get by.
7" Single: Released Oct '58, on MGM, by Polydor Ltd. Deleted '61. Catalogue no: **MGM 993**

I'M GONNA BE WARM THIS WINTER
Tracks: / I'm gonna be warm this winter.
7" Single: Released Dec '62, on MGM, by Polydor Ltd. Deleted '65. Catalogue no: **MGM 1185**

I'M SORRY I MADE YOU CRY
Tracks: / I'm sorry I made you cry.
7" Single: Released Jun '58, on MGM, by Polydor Ltd. Deleted '61. Catalogue no: **MGM 982**

JEALOUS HEART
Tracks: / Jealous heart.
7" Single: Released Jan '66, on MGM, by Polydor Ltd. Deleted '69. Catalogue no: **MGM 1293**

LIPSTICK ON YOUR COLLAR
Tracks: / Lipstick on your collar.
7" Single: Released Jul '59, on MGM, by Polydor Ltd. Deleted '52. Catalogue no: **MGM 1018**

LIPSTICK ON YOUR COLLAR (OLD GOLD)
Tracks: / Lipstick on your collar / Frankie.
7" Single: Released Jul '84, on Old Gold, by Old Gold Records. Catalogue no: **OG 9444**

MAMA
Tracks: / Mama / Robot man.
7" Single: Released May '60, on MGM, by Polydor Ltd. Deleted '63. Catalogue no: **MGM 1076**

MANY TEARS AGO
Tracks: / Many tears ago.
7" Single: Released Mar '61, on MGM, by Polydor Ltd. Deleted '64. Catalogue no: **MGM 1111**

MY CHILD
Tracks: / My child.
7" Single: Released Jun '65, on MGM, by Polydor Ltd. Deleted '68. Catalogue no: **MGM 1271**

MY HAPPINESS
Tracks: / My happiness.
7" Single: Released May '59, on MGM, by Polydor Ltd. Deleted '62. Catalogue no: **MGM 1001**

MY HEART HAS A MIND OF IT'S OWN

Tracks: / My heart has a mind of it's own.
7" Single: Released Nov '60, on MGM, by Polydor Ltd. Deleted '63. Catalogue no: **MGM 1100**

PLENTY GOOD LOVIN'
Tracks: / Plenty good lovin'.
7" Single: Released Sep '59, on MGM, by Polydor Ltd. Deleted '62. Catalogue no: **MGM 1036**

STUPID CUPID
Tracks: / Stupid cupid / Carolina moon.
7" Single: Released Jul '84, on Old Gold, by Old Gold Records. Catalogue no: **OG 9442**

TOGETHER
Tracks: / Together.
7" Single: Released Jun '61, on MGM, by Polydor Ltd. Deleted '64. Catalogue no: **MGM 1136**

VACATION
Tracks: / Vacation.
7" Single: Released Aug '62, on MGM, by Polydor Ltd. Deleted '65. Catalogue no: **MGM 1165**

VALENTINO
Tracks: / Valentino.
7" Single: Released Mar '60, on MGM, by Polydor Ltd. Deleted '63. Catalogue no: **MGM 1060**

WHERE THE BOYS ARE
Tracks: / Where the boys are / Baby roo.
7" Single: Released Mar '61, on MGM, by Polydor Ltd. Deleted '64. Catalogue no: **MGM 1121**

WHO'S SORRY NOW
Tracks: / Who's sorry now.
7" Single: Released Apr '58, on MGM, by Polydor Ltd. Deleted '61. Catalogue no: **MGM 975**

WHO'S SORRY NOW (OLD GOLD)
Tracks: / Who's sorry now / Mama.
7" Single: Released Jul '84, on Old Gold, by Old Gold Records. Catalogue no: **OG 9443**

YOU ALWAYS HURT THE ONE YOU LOVE
Tracks: / You always hurt the one you love.
7" Single: Released Dec '58, on MGM, by Polydor Ltd. Deleted '61. Catalogue no: **MGM 998**

Francis, Laurence

SEARCHING FOR AMERICA
Tracks: / Searching for America / Searching for America (version).
7" Single: Released 5 Jun '89, on Kunzel, by Gemini Enterprises. Catalogue no: **KUN 5**

Francis, Mike

FEATURES OF LOVE
Tracks: / Features of love / Upside down / Prelude reprise.
7" Single: Released May '87, on Club, by Phonogram Ltd. Deleted Dec '87. Catalogue no: **JAB 52**
12" Single: Released May '87, on Club, by Phonogram Ltd. Deleted Mar '88. Catalogue no: **JABX 52**

Francis, N

POOR ME NATTY DREAD
Tracks: / Countryman / Natty dread (version) / Poor me natty dread.
12" Single: Released Jan '87, on Mi Music, Catalogue no: **MONE 3**

Francis, Steve

LETS HAVE A ROCK 'N' ROLL PARTY
Tracks: / Let's have a rock 'n' roll party / High class roller.
12" Single: Released '88, on Debut, by Skratch Records. Catalogue no: **DEBT 03(12)**

Francis, Stu

I COULD HAVE CRUSHED A GRAPE
Tracks: / I could have crushed a grape / Fat lipped boogie.
7" Single: Released Jan '82, on Lunar (Ireland), by Lunar Records (Ireland). Deleted Jan '85. Catalogue no: **MOON 4**

OOH I COULD CRUSH A GRAPE
Tracks: / Ooh I could crush a grape / Told a fib.
7" Single: Released Jan '85, on Tembo, by Tembo Records. Catalogue no: **TML 105**
7" Single: Released Nov '83, on Topaz, Deleted '85. Catalogue no: **TPZ 50**

Francis, Winston

CALIFORNIA DREAMING
Tracks: / California dreaming / Only you.
12" Single: Released Jan '81, on Black Jack, Catalogue no: **BJD 4508**

COTTAGE IN NEGRIL, A
Tracks: / Cottage in Negril (Time: 3 mins 25 secs.) / Shame on you (Time: 4 mins 05 secs).
Note: The 12" version has an extra track: "A cottage in Negril (style dub version)"; time 7 mins 01 secs.
12" Single: Released 20 Feb '88, on Magnet, by WEA Records. Deleted Jun '88. Catalogue no: **COTT 1**
7" Single: Released 20 Feb '88, on Magnet, by WEA Records. Deleted Jun '88. Catalogue no: **COT 1**

GROOVY KIND OF LOVE, A
Tracks: / Groovy kind of love / Inna de groove.
12" Single: Released May '86, on Falcon, Catalogue no: **FAL 003**

HOLDING YOU BACK
Tracks: / Holding you back / Go find yourself a fool.
12" Single: Released Feb '87, on Wambesi, Catalogue no: **Unknown**

TONIGHT
Tracks: / Tonight.
12" Single: Released Feb '82, on Red Nail, Catalogue no: **RN 0034**

YOU'RE MY EVERYTHING
Tracks: / You're my everything / You're my everything (version).
7" Single: Released Aug '89, on Arista, by BMG Records (UK). Catalogue no: **112570**
12" Single: Released Aug '89, on Arista, by BMG Records (UK). Catalogue no: **612570**

Francois, Claude

TEARS ON THE TELEPHONE
Tracks: / Tears on the telephone.
7" Single: Released Jan '76, on Bradley's, Deleted '79. Catalogue no: **BRAD 7528**

Francois, Ron

IF YOU LOVE ME
Tracks: / If you love me / I like it.
7" Single: Released Jun '82, on CBS, by CBS Records. Deleted Jun '85. Catalogue no: **A 2322**
12" Single: Released Jun '82, on CBS, by CBS Records. Deleted Jun '85. Catalogue no: **A 132322**

Frank Chickens

BLUE CANARY
Tracks: / Blue canary.
7" Single: Released Oct '85, on Kaz, by Kaz Records. Catalogue no: **KAZ 20**
12" Single: Released Oct '85, on Kaz, by Kaz Records. Catalogue no: **KAZ 20T**

DO THE KARAOKE
Tracks: / Do the karaoke.
7" Single: Released Jun '89, on Flying, by Flying Records. Catalogue no: **SYZZLE 2**

WE ARE NINJA
Tracks: / We are ninja.
7" Single: Released Jan '84, on Kaz, by Kaz Records. Catalogue no: **KAZ 10**
12" Single: Released Jan '84, on Kaz, by Kaz Records. Catalogue no: **KAZ 10T**

YELLOW TOAST
Tracks: / Yellow toast.
12" Single: Released Aug '87, on Flying Lecords, Catalogue no: **SIZZLE 112**
7" Single: Released Aug '87, on Flying Lecords, Catalogue no: **SIZZLE 1**

Frank, Nanette

CAN'T BE YOUR PART TIME LOVER
Tracks: / Can't be your part time lover.
7" Single: Released Apr '87, on Total Control, by Total Control Records. Deleted Oct '87. Catalogue no: **TOCO 12**
12" Single: Released Apr '87, on Total Control, by Total Control Records. Deleted Oct '87. Catalogue no: **12 TOCO 12**

Frank, Stanley

LOVE LIKE A HAMMER
Tracks: / Love like a hammer / Hot and new.
7" Single: Released Apr '81, on A&M, by A&M Records. Deleted Apr '86. Catalogue no: **AMS 8123**

Frankie

SWEETHEART
Tracks: / Sweetheart / Don't stop.
7" Single: Released Apr '81, on RCA, by BMG Records (UK). Deleted '85. Catalogue no: **RCA 64**

WHO THE AM DO YOU THINK YOU AM
Tracks: / Who the am do you think you am / Who the am do you think you am (instrumental).
7" Single: Released Mar '88, on Legacy, by Legacy Records. Catalogue no: **LGY 62**
12" Single: Released Mar '88, on Legacy, by Legacy Records. Catalogue no: **LGYT 62**

Frankie B

PRESSURE ME
Tracks: / Pressure me.
12" Single: Released Aug '85, on Ital Stuff, Catalogue no: **CB 001**

Frankie B. All

FRUITY
Tracks: / Fruity / Scratch me back.
12" Single: Released May '86, on Ital Stop, Catalogue no: **IS 001**

Frankie Goes To...

Biographical details: This British band consists of Peter Gill, Holly Johnson, Brian Nash, Mark O'Toole and Paul Rutherford. The group took their name from the headline of an article about Frank Sinatra in America's showbusiness magazine, Variety.

Frankie Goes To Hollywood were formed in Liverpool in 1982. They emerged from that famous city's cauldron of new musical talent, which had been reinvigorated over the preceding few years. During the late Seventies, Holly had played in a hot local band called Big in Japan, and Paul had been with the Spitfire Boys and the Opium Eaters. After the foundation of FGTH, the five lads won notable media support from BBC Radio One's John Peel and from Channel 4's television rock show, "The Tube". After appearing on that programme, they were signed by record producer Trevor Horn to his new ZTT label.

Although the Frankie boys wrote their own material, the role of Horn and his assistant producers and engineers in crafting the group's sound and style was absolutely crucial. A true master of modern studio technology, Horn (whose previous credits included the Buggles, Dollar, ABC and Malcolm McLaren) added layer upon layer of banked sounds to the group's recordings, often spending a month on just one song. The first ZTT release was Frankie's *Relax*, which entered the UK Top 75 Singles chart in November 1983.
Having hovered around the bottom half of the chart for several weeks before Christmas, *Relax* stormed into the Top 10 in January '84. In the week that *Relax* reached No 6, BBC breakfast time DJ Mike Read blacked the disc, citing its 'overtly obscene' lyrics and sleeve. Just as this pulsating pop/dance single was poised to hit the UK No 1 slot, the Corporation announced a total airplay ban.
The ensuing wave of publicity and controversy transformed Frankie Goes To Hollywood into THE British sensation of 1984. *Relax* was No 1 for five weeks, chalked up 48 consecutive weeks on the chart (the third longest unbroken run in history) and sold 1.8 million copies in the UK alone. (It was also No 1 across Europe and, eventually, a Top Tenner in the States.) Frankie fever reached its UK peak during the summer months: *Two Tribes* became the first single for six years to nail down the No 1 spot for nine weeks, *Relax* shot back up to No 2, and a crafty T-Shirt campaign kept the streets flooded with the group's slogans. Such marketing tactics, the brainchild of ZTT's brilliant publicist Paul Morley, were a vital part of the phenomenon, as were the band's controversial videos.

Various versions and remixes of the political pop protest song *Two Tribes* sold a combined total of 1,5 million UK copies, and were followed by a third chart-topper for Frankie in December, *The Power Of Love*. By hitting the top notch, this ballad gave FGTH the honour of becoming the first act to equal Gerry & The Pacemakers' 1963 heat of reaching the UK No 1 position with each of their first three single releases. The band's debut album, a double set entitles *Welcome To The Pleasuredome*, had an initial ship out of 1.1 million units, thus breaking all previous British records for advance orders. A remixed version of the title track was issued as a single in 1985, but disgraced itself by peaking at No 2 on the UK charts. Bob MacDonald, 5.9.85.

POWER OF LOVE
Tracks: / Power of love, The.
7" Single: Released Nov '84, on ZTT, by ZTT Records. Catalogue no: **ZTAS 5**
12" Single: Released Dec '84, on ZTT, by ZTT Records. Catalogue no: **XZTAS 5**
12" Single: Released Nov '84, on ZTT, by ZTT Records. Catalogue no: **12 ZTAS 5**

RAGE HARD
Tracks: / Rage hard / (Don't lose what's left) of your mind / Suffragette city (Extra track on picture bag 12" only).
12" Single: Released Aug '86, on ZTT, by ZTT Records. Deleted Jul '87. Catalogue no: **ZTD 22**
7" Single: Released Aug '86, on ZTT, by ZTT Records. Deleted Apr '88. Catalogue no: **ZTAS 22**
12" Single: Released '86, on ZTT, by ZTT Records. Deleted Jun '88. Catalogue no: **12 ZTB**
CD 5": Released '86, on ZTT, by ZTT Records. Deleted Jun '88. Catalogue no: **ZCID 22**
12" Single: Released '86, on ZTT, by ZTT Records. Deleted Jun '88. Catalogue no: **12 ZTX 22**
12" Single: Released Aug '86, on ZTT, by ZTT Records. Catalogue no: **12 ZTAS 22**
12" Single: Released '86, on ZTT, by ZTT Records. Deleted Jun '88. Catalogue no: **12 ZTS 22**
12" Single: Released Aug '86, on ZTT, by ZTT Records. Catalogue no: **12 ZTAQ 22**
12" Single: Released '86, on ZTT, by ZTT Records. Deleted Jun '88. Catalogue no: **12 TAX 22**

RELAX
Tracks: / Relax.
12" Single: Released Feb '89, on ZTT, by ZTT Records. Catalogue no: **601096**
7" Pic: Released Aug '84, on ZTT, by ZTT Records. Catalogue no: **12 PZTAS 1**

RELAX (MOVE)
Tracks: / Relax / Ferry cross the Mersey (on 12" only) / One September Monday.
7" Single: Released Nov '83, on ZTT, by ZTT Records. Catalogue no: **ZTAS 1**

RELAX SEX MIX (FUCK)
Tracks: / Relax.
12" Single: Released Nov '83, on ZTT, by ZTT Records. Catalogue no: **2 ZTAS 1**

TWO TRIBES
Tracks: / Two tribes (carnage mix) (Available on 12" only.).
12" Single: Released Jun '84, on ZTT, by ZTT Records. Catalogue no: **12 TAS 3**
7" Pic: Released Jun '84, on ZTT, by ZTT Records. Catalogue no: **PZTAS 3**
7" Single: Released Jun '84, on ZTT, by ZTT Records. Deleted Jun '88. Catalogue no: **ZTAS 3**
12" Single: Released '88, on ZTT, by ZTT Records. Deleted Dec '88. Catalogue no: **12 ZTS 3**
12" Single: Released Aug '84, on ZTT, by ZTT Records. Catalogue no: **XZIP 1**
12" Single: Released Feb '89, on ZTT, by ZTT Records. Catalogue no: **601325**
12" Single: Released Jul '84, on ZTT, by ZTT Records. Catalogue no: **XZTAS 3**

WAR (HIDE YOURSELF)
Tracks: / War (hide yourself).
7" Pic: Released Jul '84, on ZTT, by ZTT Records. Deleted Jun '88. Catalogue no: **WARTZ 3**

WARRIORS (of the wasteland)
Tracks: / Warriors (of the wasteland).
12" Single: Released Mar '87, on ZTT, by ZTT Records. Catalogue no: **12 ZTAX 26**
Cassingle: Released Nov '86, on ZTT, by ZTT Records. Deleted Jul '87. Catalogue no: **CTIS 25**
12" Single: Released Nov '86, on ZTT, by ZTT Records. Deleted Jun '88. Catalogue no: **12 ZTX 25**
7" Single: Released Nov '86, on ZTT, by ZTT Records. Deleted Apr '88. Catalogue no: **ZTAS 25**

WATCHING THE WILDLIFE (Cassette Single))
Tracks: / Watching the wildlife / Orchestral wildlife / Hotter wildlife / Waves / One bit / 2 bit / Condom mix, The.
Cassingle: Released Mar '87, on ZTT, by ZTT Records. Catalogue no: **CTIS 26**

WATCHING THE WILDLIFE
Tracks: / Watching the wildlife / Die letzen tage der nesheit mix / Waves.
7" Single: Released Feb '87, on ZTT, by ZTT Records. Deleted Apr '88. Catalogue no: **ZTAS 26**
12" Single: Released Mar '87, on ZTT, by ZTT Records. Deleted Jun '88. Catalogue no: **12 ZTX 26**
12" Single: Released Mar '87, on ZTT, by ZTT Records. Deleted Apr '88. Catalogue no: **12 ZTE 26**

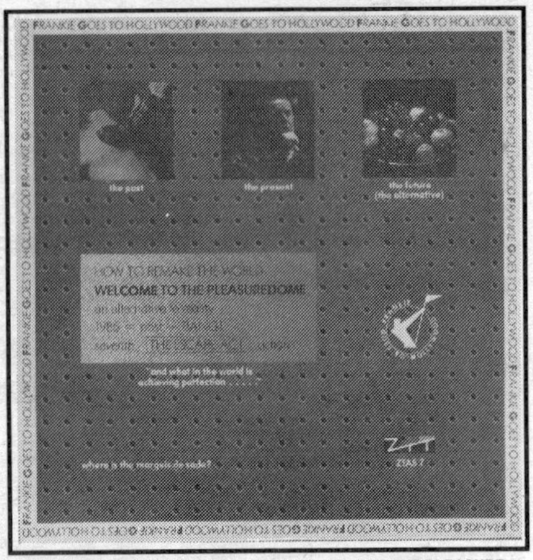

FRANKIE GOES TO HOLLYWOOD - WELCOME TO THE PLEASURE DOME (Released on ZTT)

WELCOME TO THE PLEASURE DOME (see panel above)
Tracks: / Welcome to the pleasure dome / Get it on.
7" Single: Released Mar '85, on ZTT, by ZTT Records. Deleted Apr '88. Catalogue no: **ZTAS 7**
12" Single: Released Apr '85, on ZTT, by ZTT Records. Catalogue no: **12 XZTAS 7**
12" Single: Released Mar '85, on ZTT, by ZTT Records. Catalogue no: **12 ZTAS 7**

Frankie & the Hit Men

I'LL HOLD ON
Tracks: / I'll hold on.
7" Single: Released Mar '83, on Neil Rushton. Catalogue no: **HEAT 8**

IT'S A GAME
Tracks: / It's a game.
7" Single: Released Jan '84, on Debonaire. Catalogue no: **DEB 001**
7" Single: Released Feb '84, on Nouveau Music. Catalogue no: **NMS 6**

Frankie/Classicals

WHAT SHALL I DO?
Tracks: / What shall I do.
7" Single: Released '74, on Disco Demand. Deleted '88. Catalogue no: **DDS 101**

Frankies

YO YO
Tracks: / Yo yo / Holiday magic.
7" Single: Released Jan '81, on Human (2). Catalogue no: **HUM 2**

Franklin, Aretha

Biographical details: This American singer, pianist and songwriter is generally referred to as the Queen of Soul - or, to quote the title of her best LP, *Lady Soul*. According to Billboard magazine, she is the only artist in US chart history to have had at least one single peak at every position on the American Top 10. She got to No 1 with *Respect*, No 2 with *Chain Of Fools* and *Spanish Harlem*, No 3 with Until You Come Back To Me and *Freeway Of Love*, No 4 with *Baby I Love You*, No 5 with *Since You've Been Gone* and *Daydreaming*, No 6 with *The House That Jack Built*, No 7 with *Think*, No 8 with *A Natural Woman*, No 9 with *I Never Loved A Man (The Way I Love You)* and *Rock Steady* and No 10 with *I Say A Little Prayer*. No other act has done this. This bizarre feat may seem like an arbitrary fluke; but it neatly summarises the scale of Aretha Franklin's US success, which is not always fully recognised on the other side of the Atlantic.

Born in Memphis in 1942, Aretha is the daughter of the crusading Baptist preacher, the Rev. C L Franklin, himself a regular recorder of harmonising LPs. He gave her much encouragement in her formative musical years, as did several gospel singers who were regular visitors to the family household. Sam Cooke, in particular, persuadeed Aretha to follow his switch from gospel to secular R&B music. She first cracked the US Top 40 in November 1961 with *Rock-A-Bye Your Baby With A Dixie Melody*. However, her 1960-66 spell with Columbia Records did not produce anything spectacular in musical or commercial terms.

She then made the crucial career decision to switch to Atlantic Records, who quickly proved that they fully understood the potency of her voice. She was immediately teamed with the company's veteran in-house producer Jerry Wexler and given the backing of a first class band of studio musicians. Her career exploded - during an 18-month period from early 1967 until late 1968, she chalked up nine consecutive US Top 10 singles. The two most brilliant classics, *Respect* and *I Say A Little Prayer*, also became her only two British Top Tenners. Hailed as the greatest female singer in the history of black music, she combined the inspirational intensity of gospel, the sparcity of the blues and the passion of soul. She was also a mean piano player. Her material was drawn from many sources including herself and then husband/manager Ted Waite, who co-wrote *Since You've Been Gone* and *Think*.

After a couple of less productive years, Franklin began a second hot streak in late 1970 with Ben E King's *Don't Play That Song*, a US million-seller. During 1971-2 Aretha notched up four consecutive American Top 10 singles with *Bridge Over Troubles Water,*, *Spanish Harlem*, *Rock Steady* and *Daydreaming*.

From 1975 onwards, Aretha's career went into the doldrums; the late Seventies disco era was not for her. Just when it seemed that she was a spent force, the singer bounced back in the early Eighties. *Jump To It* and *Get It Right* were solid successes and, in 1985, *Freeway Of Love* became her 20th No 1 on the US black charts. She had thus achieved more No 1 black hits than any other artist, indeed three more than her nearest rival James Brown. Bob MacDonald, 5.9.85.

Born in 1942 in Memphis, the daughter of Rev. C. L Franklin, a famous gospel singer, the Queen of soul had had more million selling singles than any other woman in the history of recorded sound, with 60 sides in Billboard's Hot 100 1961-82. She recorded for CBS 1961-66 and was highly regarded, but when she switched to Atlantic and was sent by Jerry Wexler to record in Memphis at Stax her real personality was discovered, with 5 Top 10 hits in 1967 alone: *I never loved a man (the way I love you)*, *Respect*, No. 1, *Baby I love you*, *(You make me feel like) a natural woman*, *Chain of fools*. Her sales fell off; *Amazing grace* was her triumphant return, recorded live in Los Angeles in 1972 with Rev. James Cleveland and winning her eigth Grammy. Her personal life has not been happy; she is reclusive (afraid to fly and dislikes interviews; she had switched to Arista and unhappy there, but solved the problems and came back with the huge hit album *Who's zoomin' who* in 1985. (Donald Clarke, July 1989)e.

AIN'T NOBODY EVER LOVED YOU
Tracks: / Ain't nobody ever loved you / Integrity / Ain't nobody ever loved you (dub mix) / (Percappella) integrity.
7" Single: Released Jul '86, on Arista, by BMG Records (UK). Catalogue no: **ARIST 667**
12" Single: Released Jul '86, on Arista, by BMG Records (UK). Catalogue no: **ARIST 12667**

ANGEL
Tracks: / Angel.
7" Single: Released Sep '73, on Atlantic, by WEA Records. Deleted '76. Catalogue no: **K 10346**

ANOTHER NIGHT
Tracks: / Love me forever / School days / Together again.
12" Single: Released Feb '86, on Arista, by BMG Records (UK). Catalogue no: **ARIST 12657**
7" Single: Released Feb '86, on Arista, by BMG Records (UK). Catalogue no: **ARIST 657**
7" Single: Released Feb '86, on Arista, by BMG Records (UK). Catalogue no: **ARIST 22657**

BABY I LOVE YOU
Tracks: / Baby I love you.
7" Single: Released Aug '67, on Atlantic, by WEA Records. Deleted '70. Catalogue no: **584 127**

CAN'T RUN YOU LOOSE
Tracks: / Can't run you loose / United together.
7" Single: Released Apr '81, on Arista, by BMG Records (UK). Deleted '85. Catalogue no: **ARIST 12395**

CHAIN OF FOOLS
Tracks: / Chain of fools / Satisfaction.
7" Single: Released Dec '67, on Atlantic, by WEA Records. Deleted '70. Catalogue no: **584 157**

DON'T PLAY THAT SONG
Tracks: / Don't play that song.
7" Single: Released Aug '70, on Atlantic, by WEA Records. Deleted '73. Catalogue no: **2091 027**

FREEWAY OF LOVE
Tracks: / Freeway of love / Until you say you love me / Jump to it (Extra track on 12" version only.) / Freeway of love (Pink Cadillac Mix) / Freeway of love (rock Mix) / Freeway of love (7" Version) / Until you say you love me.
7" Single: Released Apr '86, on Arista, by BMG Records (UK). Catalogue no: **ARISTA 22624**
CD 5": Released Jun '89, on Arista, by BMG Records (UK). Catalogue no: **162052**
7" Single: Released Apr '86, on Arista, by BMG Records (UK). Catalogue no: **ARIST 624**
12" Single: Released May '86, on Arista, by BMG Records (UK). Catalogue no: **ARIST 12624**

GET IT RIGHT (SINGLE)
Tracks: / Get it right.
7" Single: Released Jul '85, on Arista, by BMG Records (UK). Deleted '88. Catalogue no: **ARIST 624**

HOLD ON I'M COMING
Tracks: / Hold on I'm coming / Kind of man / I can't turn you louse.
7" Single: Released '82, on Arista, by BMG Records (UK). Deleted '87. Catalogue no: **ARIST 442**
12" Single: Released '82, on Arista, by BMG Records (UK). Deleted '87. Catalogue no: **ARIST 12442**

I KNEW YOU WERE WAITING (FOR ME)
Tracks: / I knew you were waiting (for me).
12" Single: Released Jan '87, on Epic, by CBS Records. Catalogue no: **DUET 2T**
7" Single: Released Jan '87, on Epic, by CBS Records. Deleted Aug '87. Catalogue no: **DUET 2**

I SAY A LITTLE PRAYER
Tracks: / I say a little prayer / Respect.
7" Single: Released 27 Feb '89, on Old Gold, by Old Gold Records. Catalogue no: **OG 9102**
7" Single: Released May '68, on Atlantic, by WEA Records. Deleted '71. Catalogue no: **584 206**

IT ISN'T, IT WASN'T, IT AIN'T NEVER GONNA BE
Tracks: / It isn't, it wasn't, it ain't never gonna be.
Cassingle: Released Sep '89, on Arista, by BMG Records (UK). Catalogue no: **410093**
12" Single: Released Aug '89, on Arista, by BMG Records (UK). Catalogue no: **612545**
12" Single: Released Sep '89, on Arista, by BMG Records (UK). Catalogue no: **612683**
7" Single: Released Aug '89, on Arista, by BMG Records (UK). Catalogue no: **112545**
CD 5": Released Sep '89, on Arista, by BMG Records (UK). Catalogue no: **662545**

IT'S JUST YOUR LOVE
Tracks: / It's just your love / Love me right.
12" Single: Released 24 Apr '89, on Old Gold, by Old Gold Records. Catalogue no: **OG 4511**

JIMMY LEE
Tracks: / Jimmy Lee / You need my love tonight / Aretha megamix (Only available on 12" version.) / Angel cries, An / Jimmy Lee (dub).
Note: Aretha megamix is only available on 12" version.
CD 5": Released Mar '87, on Arista, by BMG Records (UK). Catalogue no: **RICD 6**
12" Single: Released Feb '87, on Arista, by BMG Records (UK). Catalogue no: **RIST 6**
7" Single: Released Feb '87, on Arista, by BMG Records (UK). Catalogue no: **RIS 6**

JUMP TO IT (OLD GOLD)
Tracks: / Jump to it / Love me right / If she don't want your lovin' / This is for real / It's just for love / I wanna make it up to you / It's your thing / Just my day dream / Get it right.
12" Single: Released 25 Apr '88, on Old Gold, by Old Gold Records. Catalogue no: **OG 4057**

JUMP TO IT (SINGLE)
Tracks: / Jump to it / Just my daydream.
12" Single: Released '82, on Arista, by BMG Records (UK). Deleted '87. Catalogue no: **ARIST 12479**
7" Single: Released '82, on Arista, by BMG Records (UK). Deleted '87. Catalogue no: **ARIST 479**

JUMPIN' JACK FLASH
Tracks: / Jumpin' Jack Flash / Integrity.
12" Single: Released Oct '86, on Arista, by BMG Records (UK). Catalogue no: **ARIST 12678**
7" Single: Released Oct '86, on Arista, by BMG Records (UK). Catalogue no: **ARIST 678**

LOVE ME RIGHT
Tracks: / Love me right / It's just your love.
7" Single: Released Jan '83, on Arista, by BMG Records (UK). Catalogue no: **ARIST 500**
12" Single: Released Jan '83, on Arista, by BMG Records (UK). Catalogue no: **ARIST 12 500**

NATURAL WOMAN You make me feel like a
Tracks: / (You make me feel) a natural woman / Never loved a man (the way I love you) / Do right woman, do right man (Extra track on 12" version only.).
12" Single: Released May '86, on Atlantic, by WEA Records. Catalogue no: **A 9409 T**
7" Single: Released May '86, on Atlantic, by WEA Records. Deleted Jun '87. Catalogue no: **A 9409**

OH HAPPY DAY
Tracks: / Oh happy day / Lords' prayer, The.
Note: With Mavis Staples.
12" Single: Released Feb '88, on Arista, by BMG Records (UK). Deleted May '89. Catalogue no: **609 780**
7" Single: Released Feb '88, on Arista, by BMG Records (UK). Deleted May '89. Catalogue no: **109780**

RESPECT
Tracks: / Respect / Do right woman, do right man / Rock steady (12" only).
12" Single: Released Jun '87, on Atlantic, by WEA Records. Catalogue no: **YZ 121 T**
7" Single: Released Jun '87, on Atlantic, by WEA Records. Deleted Jul '88. Catalogue no: **YZ 121**
7" Single: Released Jun '67, on Atlantic, by WEA Records. Deleted '70. Catalogue no: **584 115**

ROCKALOTT
Tracks: / Rockalott / Look at the rainbow.
7" Single: Released Jun '87, on Arista, by BMG Records (UK). Catalogue no: **RIS 20**
12" Single: Released Jun '87, on Arista,

by BMG Records (UK). Catalogue no: **RIST 20**

SAY A LITTLE PRAYER
Tracks: / I say a little prayer / Revival.
7" Single: Released Jul '82, on Old Gold, by Old Gold Records. Catalogue no: **OG 9103**

SINCE YOU'VE BEEN GONE
Tracks: / Since you've been gone.
7" Single: Released Dec '67, on Atlantic, by WEA Records. Deleted '70. Catalogue no: **584 157**

SPANISH HARLEM
Tracks: / Spanish harlem.
7" Single: Released Oct '71, on Atlantic, by WEA Records. Deleted '74. Catalogue no: **2091 138**

THINK
Tracks: / Think / Respect.
7" Single: Released Oct '82, on Atlantic, by WEA Records. Deleted Oct '85. Catalogue no: **K 11614**
7" Single: Released May '68, on Atlantic, by WEA Records. Deleted '71. Catalogue no: **584 186**

THROUGH THE STORM
Tracks: / Through the storm / Come to me / Oh happy day.
12" Single: Released Apr '89, on Arista, by BMG Records (UK). Catalogue no: **612185**
CD 5": Released Apr '89, on Arista, by BMG Records (UK). Catalogue no: **162185**
7" Pic: Released Jun '89, on Arista, by BMG Records (UK). Catalogue no: **112377**
Cassingle: Released Apr '89, on Arista, by BMG Records (UK). Catalogue no: **409957**
7" Single: Released Apr '89, on Arista, by BMG Records (UK). Catalogue no: **112185**

UNITED TOGETHER
Tracks: / United together / Can't turn you loose.
7" Single: Released Feb '81, on Arista, by BMG Records (UK). Deleted '84. Catalogue no: **ARIST 395**

UNTIL YOU COME BACK TO ME
Tracks: / Until you come back to me / If you don't think.
7" Single: Released Feb '74, on Atlantic, by WEA Records. Deleted '77. Catalogue no: **K 10399**

WHAT A FOOL BELIEVES
Tracks: / What a fool believes / School days.
7" Single: Released Dec '80, on Arista, by BMG Records (UK). Deleted '83. Catalogue no: **ARIST 377**
12" Single: Released Dec '80, on Arista, by BMG Records (UK). Deleted '83. Catalogue no: **ARIST 12377**

WHO'S ZOOMING WHO (SINGLE)
Tracks: / Who's zoomin' who? / Sweet bitter love.
12" Single: Released Nov '85, on Arista, by BMG Records (UK). Catalogue no: **ARIST 12633**
7" Single: Released Nov '85, on Arista, by BMG Records (UK). Catalogue no: **ARIST 633**

Franklin, Rodney

Biographical details: This American keyboards player and singer enjoyed a one-off, unexpected UK Top 10 single in 1980 with *The Groove*. This jolly little piano workout, which featured no words, was a disco smash that climbed to No 7 on the pop chart. Its parent album, *You'll Never Know* reached No 64 on the British LP chart. Franklin had spent much of the Seventies building up his live reputation. Although rooted in jazz, he also incorporated soul and pop influences into his music. After 1980 he failed to come up with another *Groove*, but his 1982 album *Learning To Love* (produced by bass boss Stanley Clarke) was a fine vehicle for his ever expressive keyboards style and his surprisingly warm singing. Bob MacDonald, 5.9.85..

GROOVE, THE
Tracks: / Groove, The.
7" Single: Released Sep '80, on CBS, by CBS Records. Deleted '83. Catalogue no: **CBS 8529**

GROOVE, THE (OLD GOLD)
Tracks: / Groove / In the bush / Check out the groove / Strut your funky stuff.
7" Single: Released Sep '85, on Old Gold, by Old Gold Records. Deleted Jul '88. Catalogue no: **OG 9562**
12" Single: Released Feb '86, on Old Gold, by Old Gold Records. Catalogue no: **OG 4004**

HILL STREET BLUES
Tracks: / Hill Street blues / Mensaje de dios.
7" Single: Released Dec '81, on CBS, by CBS Records. Deleted Dec '84. Catalogue no: **A 1827**

Franklin, Venessa

MY MIND (IMPORT)
Tracks: / My mind.
Note: Mega hot dance track set to burn the dance floors.
12" Single: Released Nov '87, on Peppermint (USA), Catalogue no: **PM 176**

MY MIND (SINGLE)
Tracks: / My mind / Never give up.
12" Single: Released Feb '88, on Citybeat, by Beggars Banquet Records. Catalogue no: **CBE 1220**
7" Single: Released Feb '88, on Citybeat, by Beggars Banquet Records. Catalogue no: **CBE 720**

Franklyn, Fiona

BUSTED UP ON LOVE
Tracks: / Busted up on love.
7" Single: Released Jan '85, on Virgin, by Virgin Records. Deleted '89. Catalogue no: **VS 726**
12" Single: Released Jan '85, on Virgin, by Virgin Records. Deleted '89. Catalogue no: **VS 726-12**

Franks, Peter

IF I DIDN'T LOVE YOU
Tracks: / If I didn't love you.
12" Single: Released 20 Mar '89, on Body Music, by Nuclear Records. Catalogue no: **BZT 022**

SMILE
Tracks: / Smile.
12" Single: Released Dec '88, on Angella Records, Catalogue no: **PF 002**

SOON COME
Tracks: / Soon come.
7" Single: Released Oct '88, on Angella Records, Catalogue no: **ANGBP 001**

Frantic

CRAZZY
Tracks: / Crazzy.
12" Single: Released Jul '89, on Awesome Records, by Awesome Records. Catalogue no: **AOR 15T**

Frantic Elevators

HOLDING BACK THE YEARS
Tracks: / Holding back the years.
7" Single: Released Nov '82, on No Waiting, Deleted '84. Catalogue no: **NW 1**

Frantic Flintstones

BEDROCK
Tracks: / Bedrock / Hot head baby / Let's go somewhere / Sugar Daddy.
12" Single: Released Dec '87, on Raucous, Catalogue no: **RAUC 002**

YABBA DABBA DOO
Tracks: / Yabba dabba doo.
7" Single: Released Sep '89, on Raucous, Catalogue no: **RAUC 007**

Frantique

STRUT YOUR FUNKY STUFF
Tracks: / Strut your funky stuff.
7" Single: Released Aug '79, on Philadelphia Int., by EMI Records. Deleted '82. Catalogue no: **PIR 7728**

Frantix

SO DAMNED UGLY
Tracks: / In my town / So damned ugly.
7" Single: Released Nov '86, on Payola, by Payola Records. Catalogue no: **PAYOLA 1**

Fraser, Philip

MRS. JONES
Tracks: / Mrs. Jones / Missing you.
7" Single: Released '88, on Hands & Heart, Catalogue no: **HP 006**

WISH IT WAS ME
12" Single: Released Oct '88, on Bun Gem, Catalogue no: **BG 0024**

Frasier, Joe

WON'T YOU COME HOME
Tracks: / Won't you come home.
12" Single: Released Jul '89, on Jetstar, by Jetstar Records. Catalogue no: **LCD 002**

Fray, Everton

COOLIE LOVER
Tracks: / Coolie lover.
12" Single: Released Dec '87, on FASH, Catalogue no: **FID 02**

Frazer, Dean

GIRLFRIEND
Tracks: / Girlfriend.
12" Single: Released Feb '88, on Brixton Productions, Catalogue no: **BP 14**

MAGNET AND STEEL
Tracks: / Magnet and steel.
12" Single: Released Feb '89, on Dennis Star, Catalogue no: **DS 004**

NICE
Tracks: / Nice.
7" Single: Released Oct '84, on Beverly, Catalogue no: **TR 006**

REDEMPTION SONG
Tracks: / Redemption song / Redemption song (band version).
7" Single: Released Sep '84, on Island, by Island Records. Deleted '87. Catalogue no: **IS 196**
12" Single: Released Sep '84, on Island, by Island Records. Deleted '87. Catalogue no: **12IS 196**

YOU ARE
Tracks: / You are.
12" Single: Released Apr '84, on Tads, Catalogue no: **TRD 98**

Frazer, Phillip

BLOOD OF THE SAINT
Tracks: / Blood of the saint.
12" Single: Released Oct '82, on Silver Camel, Catalogue no: **SCLP 0124**

DANCING TIME
Tracks: / Dancing time.
12" Single: Released Nov '85, on Saxon Studio, Catalogue no: **SS 851**

REGGAE EXPLOSION
Tracks: / Reggae explosion.
12" Single: Released Jul '85, on Rockers Forever, Catalogue no: **UNKNOWN**

RUNNING AROUND
Tracks: / Running around.
12" Single: Released Jan '85, on Negus Roots, Catalogue no: **NERT 026**

SIREN, THE
Tracks: / Siren, The.
12" Single: Released Sep '84, on Rosie Solidarity, Catalogue no: **UNKNOWN**

TONIGHT
Tracks: / Tonight.
12" Single: Released Oct '84, on Corner Store, Catalogue no: **UNKNOWN**

Frazier, Bernice

USE ME
Tracks: / Use me.
12" Single: Released Mar '89, on BSBI, by BSB Records. Catalogue no: **BENNT 4**
7" Pic: Released Nov '88, on PRT, by Castle Communications Records. Catalogue no: **PYS 17**
7" Single: Released Mar '89, on BSBI, by BSB Records. Catalogue no: **BENN 4**
12" Single: Released Nov '88, on PRT, by Castle Communications Records. Catalogue no: **PYT 17**

WILL YOU BE THE ONE
Tracks: / Will you be the one.
12" Single: Released Jul '85, on Streetwave, Catalogue no: **MKHAN 47**

Frazier, Billy

BILLY WHO?
Tracks: / Billy who? / Billy who? (part 2).
7" Single: Released Nov '80, on Champagne Records, Deleted '83. Catalogue no: **FIZZ 503**
12" Single: Released Nov '80, on Champagne Records, Deleted '83. Catalogue no: **FIZY 5003**

Frazier Chorus

DREAM KITCHEN
Tracks: / Dream kitchen / Down.
12" Single: Released Nov '88, on Virgin, by Virgin Records. Catalogue no: **VST 1145**
7" Single: Released Nov '88, on Virgin, by Virgin Records. Catalogue no: **VS 1145**
CD 3": Released 30 Jan '89, on Virgin, by Virgin Records. Catalogue no: **VSCD 1145**

SLOPPY HEART
Tracks: / Sloppy heart / Typical / Storm / Anarchy in the UK / Spoonhead.
12" Single: Released Jun '89, on Virgin, by Virgin Records. Catalogue no: **STX 1192**
12" Single: Released Oct '87, on 4AD, by 4AD Records. Catalogue no: **BAD 708**

SLOPPY HEART (2)
Tracks: / Sloppy heart / Anarchy in the UK / Spoonhead.
7" Single: Released 26 Jun '89, on Virgin, by Virgin Records. Catalogue no: **VS 1192**
12" Single: Released 26 Jun '89, on Virgin, by Virgin Records. Catalogue no: **VST 1192**
CD 3": Released Jun '89, on Virgin, by Virgin Records. Catalogue no: **VSCD 1192**

TYPICAL
Tracks: / Typical / String
7" Single: Released Feb '89, on Virgin, by Virgin Records. Catalogue no: **VS 1174**
12" Single: Released Feb '89, on Virgin, by Virgin Records. Catalogue no: **VST 1174**
CD 3": Released Feb '89, on Virgin, by Virgin Records. Catalogue no: **VSCD 1174**

Freak Brothers

FREAK TO THE BEAT
Tracks: / Freak to the beat.
CD 5": Released Dec '88, on Subway, by Subway Records. Catalogue no: **SUB 039CD**
12" Single: Released Oct '88, on Subway, by Subway Records. Catalogue no: **SUB 039**

Freake, Syd

BUM BITES
Tracks: / Bum bites.
7" Single: Released Dec '82, on Sparky Lapwing, Deleted '83. Catalogue no: **AM 044**

Freberg, Stan

Biographical details: Born in 1926 in Pasadena, the radio comic and funny voice man became a satirist of popular music in the 50's, making crisply produced send-ups with Billy May handling the musical side, and the nonsense holds up well today. He quit when he thought that the music was too bad to be sent up; he went into advertising and his radio commercials were just as funny as the records. (Donald Clarke, July 1989) .

OLD PAYOLA ROLL BLUES
Tracks: / Old payola roll blues.
7" Single: Released May '60, on Capitol, by EMI Records. Deleted '63. Catalogue no: **CL 15122**

ROCK ISLAND LINE
Tracks: / Rock island line.
7" Single: Released Jul '56, on Capitol, by EMI Records. Deleted '59. Catalogue no: **CL 14608**

SH-BOOM
Tracks: / Sh'boom.
7" Single: Released Nov '54, on Capitol, by EMI Records. Deleted '57. Catalogue no: **CL 14187**

Fred

ALL RIGHTS RESERVED
Tracks: / All rights reserved / Marie / Reac-to-lighting.
7" Single: Released Mar '82, on Tyger, Deleted '83. Catalogue no: **TYG 7**

Fred, John

Biographical details: This American singer, harmonica player, songwriter, producer and bandleader was born John Fred Gourrier, in Baton Rouge, Louisiana. During the early Sixties, he gathered together seven other musicians and formed John Fred & his Playboy Band. After building a reputation in Louisiana, they shot to stardom in early 1968 with *Judy In Disguise (With Glasses)*. This novelty smash was a tongue-in-cheek response to the Beatles' *Lucy In The Sky With Diamonds*, but nontheless stood up as a great pop record in its own right. It was written and produced by John Fred in conjunction with his saxophonist Andrew Bernard and it highlighted the Band's big, brassy, no-holds-barred sound. *Judy In Disguise (With Glasses)* reached No 1 in the States and No 3 in Britain. It was their only hit, and they soon faded into obscurity once more. But their raunchy fun style was responsible for several other high quality releases, and John Fred long remained a respected bandleader and vocalist in his local Louisiana. Bob MacDonald, 5.9.85.
A vocalist and bandleader born in 1941 in Louisiana, he cut his first record in 1958 with Fats Domino's band while still in high school, and *Shirley* by John Fred and the Playboys reached the Billboard Hot 100. *Judy in disguise (with glasses)* was a successful piece of bubblegum in 1967, No. 1 in USA and No. 3 UK. He led a pop-soul band covering James Brown, Wilson Pickett etc, toured Europe, went psychedelic but had now more hits. (D. Clarke, 1989).

JUDY IN DISGUISE (WITH GLASSES)
Tracks: / Judy in disguise / Seven little girls

sitting in the back seat / Mr. Bass man / When the lights go out.
7" Single: Released Jul '82, on Old Gold, by Old Gold Records. Deleted Jul '88. Catalogue no: **OG 9058**
7" Single: Released Jan '68, on Pye International, Deleted '71. Catalogue no: **7N 25442**
7" Single: Released Aug '82, on Blast From The Past, by Creole Records. Catalogue no: **CR 187**

Freddie Goes To...

RELAPSE Don't ban it
Tracks: / Relapse.
7" Single: Released Jan '85, on Yum Yum Tum, Deleted '86. Catalogue no: **YUM 1**

Freddie & The Dreamers

Biographical details: This British beat group consisted of leader Freddie Garrity plus Pete Birrell, Roy Crewsdon, Berni Dwyer and Derek Quinn.
Following the national UK chart breakthroughs of the Beatles and Gerry and the Pacemakers in early 1963, Freddie & The Dreamers were one of the first combos on Britain's exploding beat scene to take advantage of the chart possibilities of this new revolution of talent. Hailing from Manchester rather than Liverpool, Garrity had sung part-time with a local skiffle group during the late Fifties. Freddie & The Dreamers were formed in 1959, and their leader worked as a milkman while the combo were building their local reputation in the early Sixties.
Their first hit, *If You Gotta Make A Fool Of Somebody* surged to No 3 on the British chart in the summer of '63; it was quickly followed by *I'm Telling You Know*, an ultra-commercial pop offering co-written by Garrity and hot songwriter Mitch Murray - this climbed to No 2. The equally catchy *You Were Made For Me* then reached No 3, rounding off a golden 1983 for Freddie & the Dreamers on the British charts. What's more, their self-titled debut album got to No 5 and logged an eventual total of 26 weeks on the LP listings; and they landed an appearance in the 1963 movie "What A Crazy World".
1964 was slightly less successful, until the end of the year when *I Understand* (a revival of a Four Tunes/G Clefs oldie) reached the UK No 5 position. However, when their zany concert act was given exposure on American television in 1965, *I'm Telling You Know* became a belated US No 1 smash. The Americans also like Garrity's 'Freddie' dance, which sparked off a mini-phenomenon in dance halls. *Do The Freddie* reached No 18 on the US chart, and was promptly covered by that King of silly dance crazes, Chubby 'Twist' Checker, although the Dreamers had a bigger hit.
By the end of 1965, however, chart success had ended for Freddie & The Dreamers on both sides of the Atlantic. But their comical stage shows, which gave full vent to the members' infectious senses of humour, stood them in good stead for the cabaret circuit, pantomime and, after the break-up of the group at the end of the Sixties, children's television for Garrity and Birrell. Bob MacDonald, 6.9.85
UK beat group formed in Manchester in 1959: vocalist was former milkman Freddie Garity, with Derek Quinn on lead guitar, Roy Crewsdon on rhythm guitar, Bernie Dwyer and Pete Birrell on drums and bass. Hits included 5 in the USA in 1965 including *I'm telling you now* at No. 1. Garrity and Birrell were also active in children's TV. (Donald Clarke, July 1989)n.

I LOVE YOU BABY
Tracks: / I love you baby.
7" Single: Released May '64, on Columbia, by EMI Records. Deleted '67. Catalogue no: **DB 7286**

I UNDERSTAND
Tracks: / I understand.
7" Single: Released Nov '64, on Columbia, by EMI Records. Deleted '67. Catalogue no: **DB 7381**

IF YOU GOTTA MAKE A FOOL OF SOMEOBODY
Tracks: / If you gotta make a fool of somebody.
7" Single: Released May '63, on Columbia, by EMI Records. Deleted '66. Catalogue no: **DB 7032**

I'M TELLING YOU NOW
Tracks: / You were made for me.
7" Single: Released Aug '63, on Columbia, by EMI Records. Deleted '66. Catalogue no: **DB 7068**

JUST FOR YOU
Tracks: / Just for you.
7" Single: Released Jul '64, on Columbia, by EMI Records. Deleted '67. Catalogue no: **DB 7322**

LITTLE YOU, A
Tracks: / Little you, A.
7" Single: Released Apr '65, on Columbia, by EMI Records. Deleted '68. Catalogue no: **DB 7526**

OVER YOU
Tracks: / Over you.
7" Single: Released Feb '64, on Columbia, by EMI Records. Deleted '67. Catalogue no: **DB 7214**

THOU SHALT NOT STEAL
Tracks: / Thou shalt not steal.
7" Single: Released Nov '65, on Columbia, by EMI Records. Deleted '68. Catalogue no: **DB 7720**

YOU WERE MADE FOR ME
Tracks: / You were made for me.
7" Single: Released Nov '63, on Columbia, by EMI Records. Deleted '66. Catalogue no: **DB 7147**

YOU WERE MADE FOR ME (RE-RELEASE)
Tracks: / You were made for me / I'm telling you now.
7" Single: Released Mar '82, on Juke Box (Re-issue), Deleted '85. Catalogue no: **JB 017**

Fredericks

CLOSER I GET TO YOU
Tracks: / Closer I get to you, The / Closer I get to you, The (version).
12" Single: Released 20 Jun '87, on People, Catalogue no: **PU 001**

DON'T STOP DON'T LET GO
Tracks: / Don't stop don't let go / Don't stop don't let go (version).
12" Single: Released Nov '87, on People Unite, by People Unite Records. Catalogue no: **PU 020 T**

END OF THE LINE
Tracks: / End of the line / Baseline wilderness.
12" Single: Released Dec '88, on People, Catalogue no: **PU 003**

Fredericks, Bill

JACK (LEGS) DIAMOND, RACKATEER AND GANGSTER
Tracks: / Jack (legs) diamond, rackateer and gangster.
12" Single: Released Nov '85, on Touch, by Touch Records. Catalogue no: **12TOU 01**
7" Single: Released Nov '85, on Touch, by Touch Records. Catalogue no: **TOU 1**

LOVERS QUESTION
Tracks: / Lovers question / Page 2.
7" Single: Released Dec '80, on Hammer, Deleted Dec '85. Catalogue no: **HVS 313**

TOO BUSY THINKING 'BOUT MY BABY
Tracks: / Too busy thinking 'bout my baby.
7" Single: Released Mar '83, on Unigram, Catalogue no: **UN 777**
12" Single: Released Mar '83, on Unigram, Catalogue no: **UNT 777**

YOU'LL NEVER FIND ANOTHER LOVE LIKE MINE
Tracks: / You'll never find... / Jukebox girl.
12" Single: Released 20 Jun '87, on Sedition, by Sedition Records. Catalogue no: **EDITL 3328**
7" Single: Released 20 Jun '87, on Sedition, by Sedition Records. Catalogue no: **EDIT 3328**

Fredericks, Dee

LOOK BEFORE YOU LEAP
Tracks: / Look before you leap.
7" Single: Released Nov '82, on Royal, Catalogue no: **JBS 100**

Free

Biographical details: At the time of their greatest success, this British rock band consisted of Andy Fraser, Simon Kirke, Paul Kossoff and Paul Rodgers. They were given early encouragement by Britain's seminal blues/rock catalyst Alexis Korner, who suggested their name.
Free were formed in 1968, when bassist Fraser was only just turning 16. He had previously had a brief spell in John Mayall's Bluesbreakers, and the other three (none of whom were yet 20) had come from various small-time bands. They were inspired by the burgeoning blues-rock boom that was taking place in Britain at the time, spearheaded by such groups as Cream and Fleetwood Mac. Their debut albums was entitled *Tons Of Sobs* and the second set was simply called *Free*. The came 1970's *Fire And Water* LP, which contained the classic single *All Right Now*.
Written by Fraser and Rodgers, *All Right Now* surged to No 2 in Britain, No 4 in the States and into Top Tens all over the world. *Fire And Water* was a big success on international album charts, reaching No 2 in Britain. A perfect rock, pop and dance single, *All Right Now* was one of the most widely acclaimed tracks ever produced by the UK record indusrty. Its success seemed to create ego problems within the band, and they split up in early 1971 after *My Brother Jake*.

After the failure of the members' various own projects, Free reformed in 1972, although the group's work was frequently disrupted by guitarist Kossoff's drug problems and by further internal friction. But with the distinctive vocals of Rodgers sounding as good as ever, they stayed intact long enough to enjoy UK Top 20 successes with the single *Little Bit Of Love* and the LP *Free At Last*. Kossoff, the son of actor David Kossoff, was then forced to quit permanently; he eventually died of drug-related heart failure in March 1976 at the age of 25, while on a flight to New York.
After achieving success in early 1973 with the *Heartbreaker* album and its classic UK Top 10 single *Wishing Well*, Free folded for good in June of that year. The members who stayed in the public eye were Kirke and Rodgers, who promptly formed the highly successful Bad Company. And while Free passed into the history books, *All Right Now* lived on - it returned to the British Top 20 in the summer of 1973 (just after the band's termination) and again in 1978. It fluttered around in the lower reaches of the Top 75 in 1982. Bob MacDonald, 6.9.85.
A UK blues/rock group formed in London in 1968: guitarist Paul Kossoff (1950-1976), vocalist Paul Rodgers, Andy Fraser and Simon Kirke on bass and drums. All were experienced, but drugs and egos caused constant problems; although their albums are highly rated by rock fans in retrospect, they did not live up to their commerical potential. Biggest hit was *All right now*, (No. 4 USA, No. 2 UK); Rodgers and Kirke formed Bad Company in 1974; Also see solo listing for Kossoff. (Donald Clarke, July 1989).

ALL RIGHT NOW
Tracks: / All right now.
7" Single: Released Jun '70, on Island, by Island Records. Deleted '73. Catalogue no: **WIP 6082**

FREE (EP)
Tracks: / All right now / My brother Jake / Wishing well.
7" Single: Released Feb '78, on Island, by Island Records. Deleted '81. Catalogue no: **IEP 6**

LITTLE BIT OF LOVE
Tracks: / Little bit of love, A.
7" Single: Released May '72, on Island, by Island Records. Deleted '75. Catalogue no: **WIP 6129**

MY BROTHER JAKE
Tracks: / My brother Jake.
7" Single: Released Aug '63, on Island, by Island Records. Deleted '66. Catalogue no: **WIP 6100**

WISHING WELL
Tracks: / Wishing well / Woman.
7" Single: Released May '85, on Island, by Island Records. Catalogue no: **IS 221**
7" Single: Released Jan '73, on Island, by Island Records. Deleted '76. Catalogue no: **WIP 6146**
12" Single: Released May '85, on Island, by Island Records. Deleted '87. Catalogue no: **12IS 221**

Free Expression

CHILL OUT
Tracks: / Chill out / Save the last dance for me.
7" Single: Released Feb '81, on Vanguard, by Start Records Ltd.. Deleted Feb '84. Catalogue no: **VS 5019**

Free Russell

I'VE GOT A SONG FOR YOU
Tracks: / I've got a song for you.
12" Single: Released Nov '83, on Half Moon, by Rondelet Music & Records. Catalogue no: **HM 1133**

Free Style

FREESTYLE
Tracks: / Freestyle: *Various artists*.
12" Single: Released 13 Feb '89, on BPM, Catalogue no: **BP 12005**

I WANT YOU
Tracks: / I want you / Fantasy.
7" Single: Released Jul '82, on Swift, by 77 Records. Catalogue no: **BIRD 2**

Free Zone

LARGE AS LIFE
Tracks: / Large as life.
12" Single: Released Jan '88, on Cheep, Catalogue no: **CHEEP 005**

Freedom Sons

FOUR GREEN FIELDS
Tracks: / Four green fields / Spancil Hill.
7" Single: Released '88, on Homespun (Ireland), by Outlet Records. Catalogue no: **HIS 21**

JAMES CONNOLLY
Tracks: / James Connolly / Connolly was there.
7" Single: Released '88, on Homespun (Ireland), by Outlet Records. Catalogue no: **HIS 22**

KEVIN BARRY
Tracks: / Kevin Barry.
7" Single: Released '88, on Homespun (Ireland), by Outlet Records. Catalogue no: **HIS 28**

Freeez

Biographical details: Led by John Rocca, Freeez were one of a wave of British funk bands that emerged during the early Eighties. They first achieved success in June 1980, reaching No 49 on the UK singles chart with *Keep In Touch*. The recording was financed by Rocca and released on Calibre Records; this label was started by Pye's disco svengali Morgan Khan as an outlet for mainly American soul tracks, and *Keep In Touch* was one of its first UK-originated successes.
After switching to the Beggars Banquet label, Freeez suddenly shot into the higher echelons of the British charts in early 1981: the *Southern Freeez* single cruised to No 8, while the album of the same name climbed to No 17. A follow-up single *Flying High* reached No 35.
This brief but very impressive burst of success was followed by two years of obscurity, during which their singles failed to make any impact. Then, in the summer of 1983, Freeez made yet another sudden reappearance. *I O U*, written and produced by New York's ace electric/funk/dance producer Arthur Baker and mixed with the help of leading club DJ John 'Jellybean' Benitez, surged to the UK No 2 position and stayed there for three weeks. This irresistible single was followed by the equally danceable but elss catchy *Pop Goes My Love*, which got to No 26.
Once again, Freeez were then frozen out of the British charts. However, Rocca proceeded to enjoy a solo No 1 on the US dance chart with *I Want It To Be Real*, a song built around a line from *I O U*. At the beginning of 1985, he re-emerged under the Pink Rhythm billing with the mellow soul single *Melodies Of Love*, which was a favourite on the London soul scene. Bob MacDonald, 9.9.85.

ALONE
Tracks: / Alone.
7" Single: Released Jan '82, on Beggars Banquet, by Beggars Banquet Records. Deleted Jan '88. Catalogue no: **BEG 70**
12" Single: Released Jan '82, on Beggars Banquet, by Beggars Banquet Records. Deleted Jan '88. Catalogue no: **BEG 70T**

ANTI-FREEEZ (SINGLE)
Tracks: / Anti-freeez.
7" Single: Released Oct '81, on Beggars Banquet, by Beggars Banquet Records. Deleted Jan '88. Catalogue no: **BEG 66**
12" Single: Released Oct '81, on Beggars Banquet, by Beggars Banquet Records. Deleted Jan '88. Catalogue no: **BEG 66T**

FLYING HIGH
Tracks: / Flying high.
12" Single: Released Apr '81, on Beggars Banquet, by Beggars Banquet Records. Deleted Jan '88. Catalogue no: **BEG 55T**
7" Single: Released Apr '81, on Beggars Banquet, by Beggars Banquet Records. Deleted Jan '88. Catalogue no: **BEG 55**

I.O.U.
Tracks: / I.O.U..
12" Single: Released Jun '83, on Beggars Banquet, by Beggars Banquet Records. Catalogue no: **BEG 96T**
7" Single: Released Jun '83, on Beggars Banquet, by Beggars Banquet Records. Catalogue no: **BEG 96**
7" Single: Released Dec '86, on Citybeat, by Beggars Banquet Records. Deleted Jan '88. Catalogue no: **CBE 709**
12" Single: Released Dec '86, on Citybeat, by Beggars Banquet Records. Catalogue no: **CBE 1209**

KEEP IN TOUCH
Tracks: / Keep in touch / Keep in touch (part 2).
12" Single: Released Jun '80, on Calibre, Deleted '83. Catalogue no: **CABL 103**
7" Single: Released Jun '80, on Calibre, Deleted '83. Catalogue no: **CAB 103**

ONE TO ONE
Tracks: / One to one.
7" Single: Released Jun '82, on Beggars Banquet, by Beggars Banquet Records.

Deleted Jan '88. Catalogue no: **BEG 78**
12" Single: Released Jun '82, on Beggars Banquet, by Beggars Banquet Records. Deleted Jan '88. Catalogue no: **BEG 78T**

POP GOES MY LOVE
Tracks: / Pop goes my love / Scratch goes my dub / No need for greed.
7" Single: Released Oct '83, on Beggars Banquet, by Beggars Banquet Records. Deleted '86. Catalogue no: **BEG 98**

SOUTHERN FREEEZ (7" RADIO MIX)
Tracks: / Southern Freeez (inst) / Southern freeez.
7" Single: Released May '87, on Total Control, by Total Control Records. Deleted Jan '88. Catalogue no: **TOCO 14**
12" Single: Released May '87, on Total Control, by Total Control Records. Deleted Jan '88. Catalogue no: **12 TOCO 14**

SOUTHERN FREEEZ (SINGLE)
Tracks: / Southern freeez.
7" Single: Released Feb '81, on Beggars Banquet, by Beggars Banquet Records. Catalogue no: **BEG 51**
12" Single: Released Feb '81, on Beggars Banquet, by Beggars Banquet Records. Catalogue no: **BEG 51T**

TRAIN OF THOUGHT
Tracks: / Train of thought.
12" Single: Released Jul '85, on Beggars Banquet, by Beggars Banquet Records. Deleted Jun '87. Catalogue no: **BEG 141T**
7" Single: Released Jul '85, on Beggars Banquet, by Beggars Banquet Records. Deleted '86. Catalogue no: **BEG 141**

Freehold

XHABBA E TARA
Tracks: / Xhabba e tara / XT rhythm.
7" Single: Released Jul '81, on PRT, by Castle Communications Records. Deleted '84. Catalogue no: **HELMET 1**

Freelancer

ALL THE TIME IN THE WORLD
Tracks: / All the time in the world / Running.
7" Single: Released Sep '80, on RCA, by BMG Records (UK). Deleted '83. Catalogue no: **PB 5277**

Freeman, Bobby

Biographical details: A USA R&B singer who played piano and sang, born in 1940 in San Francisco. Biggest hit was his own *Do you wanna dance* in 1958, which sums up that era of USA pop as well as anything. (Donald Clarke, July 1989).

DO YOU WANNA DANCE? (SINGLE)
Tracks: / Do you wanna dance / Big fat woman.
7" Single: Released Jul '82, on Revival, Catalogue no: **REV 6003**

Freeman, Dave

CALIFORNIA FREEWAY
Tracks: / California freeway / Jane.
7" Single: Released Aug '80, on DJM, Deleted '82. Catalogue no: **DJS 101401**

Freeman, Evelyn

DIDN'T IT RAIN?
Tracks: / Didn't it rain.
7" Single: Released Apr '83, on EMI (France), by EMI Records. Catalogue no: **2C 008 91099**

Freeman, Ken

TRIPODS - OPENING THEME
Tracks: / Tripods - opening theme.
7" Single: Released Oct '85, on BBC, by BBC Records & Tapes. Deleted 31 Aug '88. Catalogue no: **RESL 158**

Freestyle Express

FREESTYLE
Tracks: / Freestyle.
7" Single: Released May '84, on Sunny View (USA), by Sunnyview Records (USA). Catalogue no: **SUNY 104**
12" Single: Released May '84, on Sunny View (USA), by Sunnyview Records (USA). Catalogue no: **SUNYL 104**

Freestyle Orchestra

DON'T TELL ME
Tracks: / Don't tell me (7" only.) / Don't tell me (Bonus beats) / Don't tell me (club version) (12" only.) / Don't tell me (Garage dub) (12" & special only.) / Don't tell me (sunrise club mix) (Special only.) / Don't tell me (sunrise dub mix).
7" Single: Released Sep '89, on SBK One, Catalogue no: **203 530 7**
12" Single: Released Sep '89, on SBK One, Catalogue no: **203 530 6**
7" Single: Released Sep '89, on SBK One, Catalogue no: **SBK 7002**
12" Single: Released Sep '89, on SBK One, Catalogue no: **12SBK 7002**
Special: Released Nov '89, on SBK One, Catalogue no: **203 591 6**
Special: Released Nov '89, on SBK One, Catalogue no: **SBKX 7002**

Freeway

DANNY BOY
Tracks: / Danny boy / Don't hide the slide.
7" Single: Released Dec '88, on Frontier, by Frontier Records. Catalogue no: **FTR 3**

Freeze Frame

FOXHOLE
Tracks: / Foxhole.
7" Single: Released Jan '84, on Inevitable, by Inevitable Records. Catalogue no: **INEV 14**
12" Single: Released Jan '84, on Inevitable, by Inevitable Records. Catalogue no: **INEVT 14**

TODAY TOMORROW
Tracks: / Today tomorrow.
7" Single: Released Aug '85, on Inevitable, by Inevitable Records. Catalogue no: **ZB 40305**
12" Single: Released Aug '85, on Inevitable, by Inevitable Records. Catalogue no: **ZT 40306**

TOUCH
Tracks: / Touch.
7" Single: Released Feb '85, on Inevitable, by Inevitable Records. Catalogue no: **INEV 18**
7" Single: Released Aug '82, on Crackin' Up, by Crackin' Up Records. Catalogue no: **CRAK 2**
12" Single: Released Feb '85, on Inevitable, by Inevitable Records. Catalogue no: **INEVT 18**

YOUR VOICE
Tracks: / Your voice.
7" Single: Released Jul '83, on Inevitable, by Inevitable Records. Catalogue no: **INEV 12**

Frehley, Ace

INTO THE NIGHT
Tracks: / Into the night / Fracture too / Breakout.
7" Single: Released 30 Jun '87, on WEA, by WEA Records. Deleted Jul '88. Catalogue no: **A 9255**
12" Single: Released 30 Jun '87, on WEA, by WEA Records. Deleted Jul '88. Catalogue no: **A 9255 T**

Freight Train

MAN'S LAUGHTER
Tracks: / Man's laughter.
7" EP: Released Jun '88, on Bam Caruso, by Demon Records. Catalogue no: **NRIC 031**

Freiheit

KEEPING THE DREAM ALIVE
Tracks: / Keeping the dream alive / Land of fantasy, The / Keeping the dream alive (extended) (On 12" only.).
12" Single: Released 28 Nov '88, on CBS, by CBS Records. Deleted 17 Apr '89. Catalogue no: **652989 6**
CD 5": Released 21 Nov '88, on CBS, by CBS Records. Deleted 17 Apr '89. Catalogue no: **652989 2**
7" Single: Released 21 Nov '88, on CBS, by CBS Records. Deleted 17 Apr '89. Catalogue no: **652989 7**

KISSED YOU IN THE RAIN
Tracks: / Kissed you in the rain / Moonlight / Kissed you in the rain (Extended version) / Baby it's you / Romancing in the dark (Only on EP.) / Keeping the dream alive (Only on EP.) / Every time (Only on EP.).
12" Single: Released Feb '89, on CBS, by CBS Records. Deleted Oct '89. Catalogue no: **652 9888**
7" EP: Released 27 Feb '89, on CBS, by CBS Records. Deleted Oct '89. Catalogue no: **652 9880**
CD 5": Released 13 Feb '89, on CBS, by CBS Records. Deleted Oct '89. Catalogue no: **652 9882**
7" Single: Released Feb '89, on CBS, by CBS Records. Deleted Oct '89. Catalogue no: **652 9887**

Freiwillige

AMERICAN SECTOR, THE
Tracks: / American sector, The.
12" Single: Released 17 Oct '87, on Ediesta, Catalogue no: **CALC 032**

French (Group)

RIVER FLOWS EAST, THE
Tracks: / River flows east, The.
7" Single: Released Sep '82, on Sanguine, Catalogue no: **SAN 104**

French Impression

BREAKING LOVE
Tracks: / Breaking love / Water from the moon.
7" Single: Released Mar '85, on Steinar, by Steinar Records (UK). Catalogue no: **STE 755**
12" Single: Released Mar '85, on Steinar, by Steinar Records (UK). Catalogue no: **STE 1255**

GET UP AND DANCE
Tracks: / Get up and dance.
12" Single: Released Jul '85, on Steinar, by Steinar Records (UK). Catalogue no: **STE 1265**
7" Single: Released Jul '85, on Steinar, by Steinar Records (UK). Catalogue no: **STE 765**

French Impressionists

SANTA BABY
Tracks: / Santa baby / Jingle bell rock.
7" Single: Released Dec '82, on Operation Twilight, Catalogue no: **OPT 020**

French, Paul

HALFWAY HOTEL
Tracks: / Halfway hotel / Like a stone.
7" Single: Released Feb '85, on Flying, by Flying Records. Catalogue no: **FLY 110**

IT'S CHRISTMAS
Tracks: / It's Christmas / Nativity.
7" Single: Released Dec '83, on Flying, by Flying Records. Catalogue no: **FLY 105**

THIS HOUSE IS YOUR HOUSE
Tracks: / This house is your house.
12" Single: Released 20 Feb '88, on Rise, Catalogue no: **RISET 10**

French, Robert

GIRL NOWADAYS
Tracks: / Girl nowadays.
12" Single: Released Sep '83, on Joe Gibbs, Catalogue no: **JGM 8184**

LITTLE MORE TIME, A
Tracks: / Little more time, A.
7" Single: Released May '89, on Music Works, Catalogue no: **UNKNOWN**

MEET ME BY THE RIVER
Tracks: / Meet me by the river / Moyees Skank.
12" Single: Released May '85, on Real Wax, Catalogue no: **RW 007**

MR BABYLON
Tracks: / Mr. Babylon.
12" Single: Released Apr '84, on EAD, Catalogue no: **GEM 011**

MY BABY
Tracks: / My baby / Pretending lover.
12" Single: Released Sep '84, on Londisc, by Londisc Records. Catalogue no: **LD 014**

NATURAL LADY
Tracks: / Natural lady.
12" Single: Released Jan '85, on Sweetcorn, Catalogue no: **Unknown**

NICE TIME
Tracks: / Nice time.
12" Single: Released Jun '84, on TG Productions, Catalogue no: **ASF 242**

ON THE DANCE FLOOR
Tracks: / On the dance floor.
12" Single: Released Nov '83, on Joe Gibbs, Catalogue no: **JGM 8186**

PUMPEE SWEETIE
Tracks: / Pumpee sweetie.
12" Single: Released Nov '83, on Reggae Sound, Catalogue no: **VPRD 144**

SATISFACTION GUARANTEED
Tracks: / Satisfaction guaranteed.
12" Single: Released Aug '85, on Top Rank (2), Catalogue no: **TRK 011**

SECRET LOVER
Tracks: / Secret lover / Joe Frazier returns.
12" Single: on Lightning, Catalogue no: **VPRD 147**

SETTLE DOWN GIRL
Tracks: / Settle down girl.
12" Single: Released Dec '84, on White Label (1), Catalogue no: **Unknown**

SOMETHING ON MY MIND
Tracks: / Something on my mind / Help yourself.
12" Single: Released May '85, on Uptempo, Catalogue no: **UT 010**

TOO YOUNG
Tracks: / Too young.
7" Single: Released 4 Feb '89, on Blue Mountain, Catalogue no: **BMD 042**

Frenzy

I SEE RED
Tracks: / I see red / Whose life.
12" Single: Released Jul '86, on I.D., by I.D. Records. Catalogue no: **EYET 7**
7" Single: Released Jul '86, on I.D., by I.D. Records. Catalogue no: **EYE 7**

ROBOT RIOT
Tracks: / Robot riot.
12" Single: Released Nov '84, on Nervous, by Nervous Records. Catalogue no: **12 NEP 002**

WHO'S LOVING YOU
Tracks: / Who's loving you? / Who's loving you? (instrumental).
12" Single: Released Feb '86, on Debut, by Skratch Records. Catalogue no: **DEBT 11(12)**

Frequency

BILLS
Tracks: / Bills.
7" Single: Released Feb '83, on Hard Times, Deleted '86. Catalogue no: **HT 100**

Fresh

SUMMER IN THE CITY
Tracks: / Love life.
7" Single: Released Aug '87, on Jive, by Zomba Records. Catalogue no: **JIVE 154**
12" Single: Released Aug '87, on Jive, by Zomba Records. Catalogue no: **JIVET 154**

Fresh 4

WISHING ON A STAR
Tracks: / Wishing on a star.
7" Single: Released Sep '89, on 10 Records, by Virgin Records. Catalogue no: **TEN 297**
12" Single: Released Sep '89, on 10 Records, by Virgin Records. Catalogue no: **TENX 297**

Fresh, Doug E

ALL THE WAY TO HEAVEN
Tracks: / All the way to heaven / Nuthin' / All the way to heaven (Inst) (Available on 12" version only) / Nuthin' (inst) (Available on 12" version only).
12" Single: Released Jul '86, on Cool Tempo, by Chrysalis Records. Catalogue no: **COOLX 119**
7" Single: Released Jul '86, on Cool Tempo, by Chrysalis Records. Catalogue no: **COOL 119**

JUST HAVING FUN
Tracks: / Just having fun.
12" Single: Released Dec '85, on Streetwave, Catalogue no: **MKHAN 64**

SHOW, THE
Tracks: / Show, The.
7" Single: Released Nov '85, on Cool Tempo, by Chrysalis Records. Deleted '88. Catalogue no: **COOL 116**

Fresh Face

HUERO DANCING
Tracks: / Huero dancing.
12" Single: Released Apr '83, on Satril, by Satril Records. Catalogue no: **12 SAT 505**

Fresh Ski Dames

KICKIN' IT LIVE
Tracks: / Kickin' it live / Stay bad.
7" Single: Released 10 Apr '89, on Mango Street, by Island Records. Catalogue no: **IS 407**
12" Single: Released 10 Apr '89, on Mango Street, by Island Records. Catalogue no: **12IS 407**

Freshies

Biographical details: *I'm In Love With The Girl On A Certain Manchester Megastore Checkout Desk* was one of the longest and silliest titles ever to reach the British charts. This catchy pop ditty climbed to No 54 in February 1981 for the Freshies, and was the only taste of success for this all-male Manchester band. The song had originally been conceived as *I'm In Love With The Girl On The Virgin Manchester Megastore Checkout Desk*, but this was balcked by the BBC on the grounds that it advertised the trade name of the leading UK record chain.
Before and after the aforementioned single, the Freshies released several other singles in a post-punk, tongue-in-cheek pop vein. The best known of these was *I Can't Get 'Bouncing Babies' By The Teardrop Explodes*, a tearjerking tribute to the Liverpool band's second single which the Freshies had discovered to be unobtainable. MUSIC MASTER is happy to report that *Bouncing Babies* IS currently available o nthe Teardrop Explodes' *Kilimanjaro* album. So perhaps the Freshies will now release a single entitled *I Have Now Found 'Bouncing Babies' By The Teardrop Explodes Because I've Looked It Up In MUSIC MASTER* - but unfortunately, the BBC will probably ban it on advertising grounds!. Bob MacDonald, 9.9.85..

DANCING DOCTORS
Tracks: / Dancing doctors.
7" Single: Released Oct '81, on Pinnacle, by Pinnacle Records. Catalogue no: **RP 508**

FASTEN YOUR SAFETY BELTS
Tracks: / Fasten your safety belts / Best

we can do.
7" Single: Released Aug '82, on Stiff, by Stiff Records. Catalogue no: **BUY 158**

I CAN'T GET BOUNCING BABIES...
Tracks: / I can't get bouncing babies by The Teardrop Explodes / Tell her I'm ill.
Note: Full title: I can't get bouncing babies by The Teardrop Explodes
7" Single: Released Jun '81, on MCA, by MCA Records. Deleted Jun '84. Catalogue no: **MCA 725**

I'M IN LOVE WITH THE GIRL (On a certain Manchester megastore checkout desk)
Tracks: / I'm in love with the girl on a certain Manchester megastore.
7" Single: Released Feb '81, on MCA, by MCA Records. Deleted '84. Catalogue no: **MCA 670**

OH GIRL
Tracks: / Oh girl.
7" Single: Released Jul '80, on Razz, by Razz Records. Catalogue no: **RAZZ 7**

WRAP UP THE ROCKETS
Tracks: / Wrap up the rockets / Gonna get better / Tell her I'm ill.
12" Single: Released May '81, on MCA, by MCA Records. Deleted May '84. Catalogue no: **MCAT 693**
7" Single: Released Apr '81, on MCA, by MCA Records. Deleted '85. Catalogue no: **MCA 693**

YELLOW SPOT
Tracks: / Yellow spot / If it's news.
7" Single: Released Aug '80, on Razz, by Razz Records. Catalogue no: **RAZZ 6**

Freshman

YOU'VE NEVER HEARD ANYTHING
Tracks: / You've never heard anything.
7" Single: Released Oct '79, on Release (Ireland), Catalogue no: **RL 975**

Fretton, Matt

Biographical details: This British singer enjoyed a one-off UK chart entry in the summer of 1983, when *It's So High* reached No 50 on the singles listings. Subsequent pop/rock efforts, including *Dance It Out* and *It's All Over (Don't Say You're In Love)*, failed to consolidate upon this chart toehold. Bob MacDonald, 9.9.85
Matt Fretton was born on 15th March 1965 in Hillingdon, Middlesex. His musical training started at school where he learnt to play classical guitar and violin. He gave up the violin and started playing electric guitar in a school punk band called The Desks. Matt started writing his own material during this time eventually deciding to do everything himself, and while still at school, played his first major London solo date at the ICA rock week in May 1981. Following this, Matt played the round of London clubs, eventually securing a support slot on a nationwide tour with The Eurythmics. During 1982 Matt toured with King Crimson, The Boomtown Rats, The Gang Of Four and Depeche Mode; headlined at The Venue and played several one-off concerts with people like The Thompson Twins and Tears For Fears. From the Depeche Mode tour, Matt received a large volume of fan mail and already has a sizeable fan club. Matt was chosen to record a session for Peter Powell's radio show and made his all-important TV debut on the Oxford Road Show. His first single was called *It's So High* released by Chrysalis Records. (Julia Marcus, Chrysalis, 1984).

DANCE IT UP
Tracks: / Dance it up / Dance it up (acapella version).
7" Single: Released '83, on Chrysalis, by Chrysalis Records. Deleted '87. Catalogue no: **MATT 2**

IT'S ALL OVER (DON'T SAY YOU'RE IN LOVE)
Tracks: / It's all over (don't say you're in love).
7" Single: Released Apr '84, on Chrysalis, by Chrysalis Records. Catalogue no: **MATT 3**
12" Single: Released Apr '84, on Chrysalis, by Chrysalis Records. Catalogue no: **MATTX 3**

IT'S SO HIGH
Tracks: / It's so high / Love's sad memory.
7" Single: Released May '83, on Chrysalis, by Chrysalis Records. Catalogue no: **MATT 1**
12" Single: Released May '83, on Chrysalis, by Chrysalis Records. Catalogue no: **MATTX 1**

PALPITATING HEART
Tracks: / Palpitating heart / Caution to the wind.
12" Single: Released Sep '86, on IDK, by IDK Records. Catalogue no: **12 IDK 5001**
7" Single: Released Sep '86, on IDK, by IDK Records. Catalogue no: **IDK 5001**

Freud

FREUD Film soundtrack: composed by Jerry Goldsmith
12" Single: Released Jan '84, on CF, Catalogue no: **CF 008**

Freud, James

MODERN GIRL
Tracks: / Modern girl / Mean modultor.
7" Single: Released Feb '82, on Carrere, Deleted '85. Catalogue no: **CAR 224**

Freur

Biographical details: This British band consists of Jake Bowie, Bryn Burrows, Carl Hyde, Rick Smith, Alfie Thomas and John Warwicker le Breton. In keeping with the electronic and futuristic nature of their music, the group initially decided to draw attention to their highly original stance by not having a conventional name - they used a weird symbol to denote their identity; but in the interests of practicality, this was gradually supplanted by the name Freur.
Hailing from Cardiff, Freur achieved a one-off UK chart entry in the spring of 1983 with *Doot Doot* - this single reached No 59. Containing few intelligible words, the aesthetically entrancing *Doot Doot* was one of the year's most inventive records. Nothing quite like it had been heard before, or indeed, since. Several foreign television companies used it as thematic or background music, and the single made the band a particularly popular attraction in Italy.
Subsequent Freur singles, including *Matters Of The Heart, Runaway, Riders In The Night* and *Devil And Darkness*, failed to match up to the quality or quirkiness of *Doot Doot*, and as British record buyers had failed to make the latter track a major hit, it was no surprise that these subsequent records failed to reach the UK charts. Bob MacDonald, 9.9.85.

DOOT DOOT
Tracks: / Doot doot / Runaway / Riders in the night / Film of the same name (theme from) / Tender surrender / Matters of the heart / My room / Whispering steam machine / All too much.
Note: Freur, who are also known by a logo for a name, have completed their debut album written and produced by the band with help from John Hudson, includes their best known single "Doot doot".
7" Single: Released Jan '84, on CBS, by CBS Records. Catalogue no: **A 4073**
12" Single: Released Jan '84, on CBS, by CBS Records. Catalogue no: **TA 4073**

LOOK IN THE BACK FOR ANSWERS
Tracks: / Look in the back for answers.
7" Single: Released Feb '85, on CBS, by CBS Records. Catalogue no: **A 4983**
12" Single: Released Feb '85, on CBS, by CBS Records. Catalogue no: **TX 4983**

MATTERS OF THE HEART
Tracks: / Matters of the heart.
12" Single: Released Jun '83, on CBS, by CBS Records. Catalogue no: **TA 3456**
7" Single: Released Jun '83, on CBS, by CBS Records. Catalogue no: **A 3456**

RIDERS IN THE NIGHT
Tracks: / Riders in the night / Innocence / This is the way I like to live my life.
7" Single: Released Apr '84, on CBS, by CBS Records. Catalogue no: **A 4333**
12" Single: Released Apr '84, on CBS, by CBS Records. Catalogue no: **TA 4333**

Frey, Glenn

HEAT IS ON, THE
Tracks: / Heat is on, The.
7" Single: Released Jan '85, on MCA, by MCA Records. Catalogue no: **MCA 941**
12" Single: Released Jan '85, on MCA, by MCA Records. Catalogue no: **MCAT 941**

SMUGGLERS BLUES
Tracks: / Smugglers blues.
7" Single: Released Jun '85, on BBC, by BBC Records & Tapes. Deleted Sep '87. Catalogue no: **RESL 170**
12" Single: Released Jun '85, on BBC, by BBC Records & Tapes. Deleted Sep '87. Catalogue no: **12 RSL 170**

SOUL SEARCHIN'
Tracks: / Soul searchin'.
7" Single: Released 16 Jan '89, on MCA, by MCA Records. Deleted 1 Jul '89. Catalogue no: **MCA 1294**
CD 5": Released 16 Jan '89, on MCA, by MCA Records. Catalogue no: **DMCA 1294**
12" Single: Released 16 Jan '89, on MCA, by MCA Records. Catalogue no: **MCAT 1294**

TRUE LOVE
Tracks: / True love / Working man.
7" Single: Released Sep '88, on MCA, by MCA Records. Deleted 1 Jul '89. Catalogue no: **MCA 1284**
CD 5": Released Oct '88, on MCA, by MCA Records. Catalogue no: **DMCA 1284**
12" Single: Released Oct '88, on MCA, by MCA Records. Catalogue no: **MCAT 1284**

YOU BELONG TO THE CITY
Tracks: / You belong to the city / I got love.
7" Single: Released Mar '86, on MCA, by MCA Records. Catalogue no: **MCA 1008**
12" Single: Released Mar '86, on MCA, by MCA Records. Catalogue no: **MCAT 1008**

Fricke, Janie

Biographical details: The Nashville session singer who became a star in her own right, born in 1952 in Indiana. She has sung on over 1600 records, including work with Dolly Parton, Elvis Presley, Loretta Lynn, Crystal Gayle and Johnny Cash (*The cowboy and the lady); her work with Johnny Duncan on the No. 1 country hit Stranger* in 1976 led to a CBS contract and her own hits began. She was named best new female vocalist '78-79 and top female vocalist 82-4 by the country music business in the USA; having toured with Alabama and working with producer Bob Montgomery, in the '80's she moved from ballads into a country-rock sound, but her 1988 album *Saddle the wind* was a return to straight country. (Donald Clarke, July 1989) .

ALWAYS HAS ALWAYS WILL
Tracks: / Don't put it past my heart / Always has always will.
7" Single: Released Nov '86, on CBS, by CBS Records. Catalogue no: **650273 7**

BLUE SKY SHINING
Tracks: / Blue sky shining / It's raining too.
7" Single: Released Jun '81, on CBS, by CBS Records. Deleted Jun '84. Catalogue no: **A1146**

DO ME WITH LOVE
Tracks: / Do me with love / Heart.
7" Single: Released Oct '81, on CBS, by CBS Records. Deleted '85. Catalogue no: **A 1731**

ENOUGH OF EACH OTHER
Tracks: / Enough of each other / Down to my last broken heart.
7" Single: Released Jan '81, on CBS, by CBS Records. Deleted Jan '84. Catalogue no: **CBS 9396**

TELL ME A LIE
Tracks: / Tell me a lie / Love have mercy.
7" Single: Released Mar '84, on CBS, by CBS Records. Catalogue no: **A 3848**

Frida

Biographical details: This Swedish singer rocketed to international superstardom in the mid-Seventies as 25% of ABBA. Unlike her three colleagues in the globe conquering pop group, Frida was born in Norway rather than Sweden. After the untimely death of her 21 year old mother, she moved to Sweden at the age of two (1947) under the care of her grandmother; this emigration removed Anni-Frid Synni Lyngstad (the child's full name) of the stigma of her stranged father being an officer in the occupying German forces during wartime Norway.
Anni-Frid first began to sing in public at the age of ten. By the time she was 20, she was already married and starting a family - and beginning to win talent contests. She made her national TV debut in September 1967, an event which prompted her to move to the centre of the Swedish music business, Stockholm. It was during the late Sixties that, while building her career as a pop singer and cabaret performer, she met Benny Andersson of top Swedish rock group, The Hep Stars. The pair began living together in 1970, and the seeds of Abba were starting to be sown.
In 1981, just as Abba were nearing the end of their stunning era of being one of the all time most successful showbusiness phenomena, Frida and Benny split up. A similar experience had recently happened to British rock star Phil Collins; realising that they were undergoing the same emotions, Collins agreed to produce Frida's first English language solo LP. *Something's Going On* was released in September 1982, and reached No 18 on the British album chart; it featured an all star cast of songwriters and musicians, although the overall quality was somewhat lacklustre. One track, *I Know There's Something Going On*, rose above the album to become an international hit single; penned by ace writer Russ Ballard and with a very similar feel to Phil's own hit *In The Air Tonight*, it was only a minor hit in Britain, but eventually reached No 13 in the States after a tortuous climb up to the US Hot 100.
After the promise of *I Know There's Something Going On*, Frida's solo career seemed to disintegrate. *Shine*, a 1984 single and album, was widely ignored on account of the music's mediocre quality. She managed to reach No 45 on the UK chart with *Time*, a duet single with B A Robertson based on Abba's *Arrival* track. Bob MacDonald, 9.9.85.

HERE WE'LL STAY
Tracks: / Here we'll stay.
7" Single: Released Jun '83, on Epic, by CBS Records. Catalogue no: **A 3435**

I KNOW THERE'S SOMETHING GOING ON
Tracks: / I know there's something going on / Threnody.
7" Single: Released Aug '82, on Epic, by CBS Records. Deleted '85. Catalogue no: **A 2603**

TIME
Tracks: / Time.
7" Single: Released Dec '83, on Epic, by CBS Records. Deleted '86. Catalogue no: **A 3983**

TO TURN TO STONE
Tracks: / To turn to stone / I got something.
7" Single: Released Oct '82, on Epic, by CBS Records. Deleted Oct '85. Catalogue no: **EPCA 2863**

Friday

STRANGERS IN THE NIGHT
Tracks: / Strangers in the night / End, the.
12" Single: Released Aug '86, on Riversmeet, Catalogue no: **12RMR 1**
7" Single: Released Aug '86, on Riversmeet, Catalogue no: **RMR 1**

Friday, Gavin

EACH MAN KILLS THE THING HE LOVES (SINGLE)
Tracks: / Each man kills the thing he loves (Wilde) / Extract from the ballad of Reading Gaol / Each man (instrumental).
CD 5": Released Mar '89, on Island, by Island Records. Catalogue no: **CID 408**
12" Single: Released Mar '89, on Island, by Island Records. Catalogue no: **12IS 408**
7" Single: Released Mar '89, on Island, by Island Records. Catalogue no: **IS 408**

YOU CAN'T ALWAYS GET WHAT YOU WANT
12" Single: Released Aug '87, on Baby, by New Rose Records. Catalogue no: **BABY 010**
7" Single: Released Aug '87, on Baby, by New Rose Records. Catalogue no: **BABY 009**

YOU TAKE AWAY THE SUN
Tracks: / You take away the sun / Next thing to murder, The / Love is just a word (On 12" and CD only) / You take away the sun (version) (On CD only).
7" Single: Released Jul '89, on Island, by Island Records. Catalogue no: **IS 430**
12" Single: Released Jul '89, on Island, by Island Records. Catalogue no: **12 IS 430**
CD 5": Released Jul '89, on Island, by Island Records. Catalogue no: **CID 430**

Fridge

BRAND NEW REVOLUTION
Tracks: / Brand new revolution / Painting my heart black.
7" Single: Released May '85, on Young Blood, by Young Blood Records. Catalogue no: **1 UP**

COME ON COME ON
Tracks: / Come on come on.
7" Single: Released Nov '85, on Young Blood, by Young Blood Records. Catalogue no: **YB 0093**

Friedman, Dean

Biographical details: Friedman, Dean This American singer, songwriter, guitarist and keyboardist hails from New Jersey. His first taste of success came in 1977 when he hit No.26 on the US chart with his summery pop single *Ariel*. Slightly reminiscent of the Hollies' *Carrie-Anne*, *Ariel* became a turntable hit and cult favourite in Britain in early 1978, but failed to penetrate the charts.
Friedman never returned to the US Top 40, but got there twice in the UK during late '78. The ultra-slushy ballad *Lucky Stars* on which he duetted with the uncredited singer Denise Marsa, shot to No.3 and *Lydia* reached No.31. Both songs came from Friedman's albums *Well, Well Said The Rocking Chair*, which climbed to No.21 on the UK LP listings. With a distinctive and plaintive (and to some listeners, irritating) voice and a homely style of romantic songwriting he was tipped for a big future by man y UK observers. But instead, he promptly faded into obscurity.
Friedman was forced by legal complications and arguments to take a two year break from recording. When he returned in 1982 with the album *Rumpled Romeo*, he met with no success. During the mid-Eigh-

ties, he spent much time playing gigs in Britain and recording for independent UK labels. (Bob Macdonald 9/9/85).

HEY LARRY
Tracks: / Hey Larry / I will never leave you.
7" Single: Released Apr '82, on Epic, by CBS Records. Deleted Apr '85. Catalogue no: **EPC A2274**

I DIDN'T MEAN TO MAKE YOU CRY
Tracks: / I didn't mean to make you cry.
7" Single: Released Jun '85, on Hi Rise, Catalogue no: **HR 1**

LAKELANDS, THE
Tracks: / Lakelands, The.
7" Single: Released Dec '83, on Peach River, Deleted '85. Catalogue no: **BBPR 10**

LUCKY STARS
Tracks: / Lucky stars.
7" Single: Released Sep '78, on Lifesong, Deleted '81. Catalogue no: **LS 402**

LYDIA
Tracks: / Lydia.
7" Single: Released Nov '78, on Lifesong, Deleted '81. Catalogue no: **LS 403**

SUMMER HOLIDAY
Tracks: / Summer holiday.
7" Single: Released 23 Jul '88, on RCA, by BMG Records (UK). Deleted May '89. Catalogue no: **111624**
12" Single: Released 23 Jul '88, on RCA, by BMG Records (UK). Deleted Jun '89. Catalogue no: **611624**

WOMAN OF MINE
Tracks: / Woman of mine.
7" Single: Released Jun '78, on Lifesong, Deleted '81. Catalogue no: **LS 401**

Friendly Fires

ARKANSAS
Tracks: / Arkansas.
7" Single: Released 23 Jan '87, on Dead Bug, Deleted '88. Catalogue no: **DB 002**

Friendly Hopefuls

TRIBUTE TO THE PUNKS OF '76
Tracks: / Tribute to the punks of '76.
7" Single: Released Sep '81, on Abstract, by Abstract Sounds. Catalogue no: **BS 004**

Friendly Persuasion

TRIBUTE TO KAREN CARPENTER, A
Tracks: / Tribute to Karen Carpenter, A / Only yesterday.
7" Single: Released Jun '86, on Button, by Musical Characters Records. Catalogue no: **BTN 123**

Friends

FAR AND AWAY
Tracks: / Burning bridges / Far and away.
12" Single: Released Aug '87, on Summerhouse, by Summerhouse Records. Catalogue no: **SUMS 4**

IT'S GETTING LOUDER
Tracks: / It's getting louder.
7" Single: Released Nov '86, on Summerhouse, by Summerhouse Records. Catalogue no: **SUMS 1**

MEDDLIN' WITH SHALAMAR
Tracks: / Meddlin' with Shalamar.
12" Single: Released May '83, on Challenge, by Elite Records. Catalogue no: **TALL 1**
7" Single: Released May '83, on Challenge, by Elite Records. Catalogue no: **ALL 1**

NIGHT WALKER
Tracks: / Night walker.
7" Single: Released Nov '83, on Rock Shop, Catalogue no: **RSR 002**

Friends Again

Biographical details: Friends Again This British band consisted of Neil Cunningham, James Grant, Stuart Kerr, Paul McGeechan and Chris Thompson.
With the individual members having gained their musical apprenticeships during the punk era of the late Seventies, Friends Again were formed in Glasgow in 1982. Their debut single *Honey At The Core* were released on their own independent Moonboot label in that year and reactivated in spring '83 after the band had signed with Phonogram. They followed this with *Sunkissed* and then, in style to that of China Crisis, and was also reminsiscent of Al Stewart's *Year of The Cat - State of Art* garnered substantial airplay, but failed to crack the UK national charts.
The group's only taste of chart success occurred in August 1984, when *The Friends Again EP* (containing *Lullaby On Board, Wand You Wave* and *Thank You For Being An Angel*, crept up to No.59 on the UK singles list. Their first and only LP *Trapped and Unwrapped* was issued in October '84. They split up in 1985. (Bob Macdonald 10/9/85).

FRIENDS AGAIN (EP)
Tracks: / Lullaby on board / Wand you wave / Thank you for being an angel.
7" Single: Released Aug '84, on Mercury, by Phonogram Ltd. Deleted '87. Catalogue no: **FA 1**

HONEY AT THE CORE
Tracks: / Honey at the core / Snowboot.
7" Single: Released May '83, on Moonboot, Catalogue no: **MOON 1**
7" Single: Released May '84, on Mercury, by Phonogram Ltd. Catalogue no: **MER 156**
12" Single: Released May '84, on Mercury, by Phonogram Ltd. Catalogue no: **MERX 156**

SUNKISSED
Tracks: / Sunkissed.
7" Single: Released Aug '83, on Moonboot, Catalogue no: **MOON 2**
12" Single: Released Aug '83, on Moonboot, Catalogue no: **MOON 212**

Friends In Public

DANCEFLAW
Tracks: / Danceflaw / What's your life like.
12" Single: Released Jul '82, on Champagne Records, Deleted Jul '85. Catalogue no: **BUBLY 703**
7" Single: Released Jul '82, on Champagne Records, Deleted Jul '85. Catalogue no: **BUBL 703**

Friends & Lovers

THAT'S WHAT FRIENDS ARE FOR
Tracks: / That's what friends are for.
12" Single: Released Feb '82, on S & G (2), Catalogue no: **SG 16**

Friends Of The Family

3 FATMEN (ON A BICYCLE)
Tracks: / 3 fat men (on a bicycle).
12" Single: Released '88, on Ediesta, Deleted '88. Catalogue no: **CALC 039T**
7" Single: Released Jul '87, on Ediesta, Deleted '88. Catalogue no: **CALC 039**

ROTTEN TO THE CORE
Tracks: / Rotten to the core / Honey.
7" Single: Released Feb '87, on Ediesta, Deleted '88. Catalogue no: **CALC 17**
12" Single: Released Feb '87, on Ediesta, Deleted '88. Catalogue no: **CALC 17T**

Frighty

FUNNY DREAMS
Tracks: / Funny dreams.
12" Single: Released Jul '87, on Y & D, Catalogue no: **YDDO 111**

LIFE
Tracks: / Life / Feel so good.
7" Single: Released Dec '88, on Y & D, Catalogue no: **7YDD 0132**
12" Single: Released Dec '88, on Y & D, Catalogue no: **YDDO 132**

MAXIMUM
Tracks: / Maximum.
12" Single: Released Apr '88, on Y & D, Catalogue no: **YDDO 121**

WHY
Tracks: / Why.
12" Single: Released Sep '89, on Off-Beat (1), Catalogue no: **OFFBEAT 1201**

Frijid Pink

Biographical details: Frijid Pink This American band consisted of Tom Beaudry, Kelly Green, Rich Stevers and Gary Thompson.
Emerging from the same late Sixties Detroit scene that produced such cult favourites as the Stooges and MC5. Frijid Pink stormed to stardom in 1970 with their smash remake of *House of The Rising Sun*. This traditional blues song had become famous in 1964 when Alan Price's arrangement for the Animals had gone to No.1 on both sides of the Atlantic. Frijid Pink lacked Price's stunning organ part, but nonetheless retained the bluesy earthiness of the Animals' rendition; the new version cruised to No.7 in the States and No.4 in Britain, an impressive achievement in view of the public's familiarity with the six year old epic version by the Animals. After *House Of The Rising Sun*, Frijid Pink was greeted with instant obscurity. They released several unsuccessful albums, the last of which appeared in 1975; these showed the band steadily shifting from blues rock to mainstream rock. (Bob Macdonald 10/9/85).

HOUSE OF THE RISING SUN
Tracks: / House of the rising sun.
7" Single: Released Feb '70, on Deram, by London Records. Deleted '73. Catalogue no: **DM 288**
7" Single: Released Sep '85, on Old Gold, by Old Gold Records. Catalogue no: **OG 9533**

Fripp, Robert

Biographical details: Fripp, Robert. As a solo artist, this British guitarist, keyboardist, mellotron player, singer, composer and producer did not release his debut album until 1979 - *Exposure* spent just one week on the UK album chart, reaching No.71 in May of that year. But he first became famous in 1969 as founder and leader of King Crimson. He remained the mainman of that successful group until 1974, when he finally decided to terminate the band after a never ending series of personnel changes - indeed, no Crimson album between 1969-1974 featured the same line up as its predecessor, so Fripp's tenacity was astounding.
During the Seventies, the eccentric Robert embarked upon a variety of of often esoteric projects. 1973 saw him begin a spasmodic collaboration with Brian Eno - the first album by this partneship was entitled *No Pussyfooting*. Fripp's other idiosyncratic, avant garde undertakings included guest appearances on a couple of David Bowie albums, the production of Peter Gabriel's 1978 LP and Daryl Hall's 1980 solo set, plus a 1982 collaboration with Police guitarist Andy Summers on the *I Advance Masked* LP. Fripp launched a reformed King Crmson in 1981, although the new band did not attain the level of previous KC successes.
In the mid-Eighties, Robert issued a second album with Summers, *Betwitched* and he remixed and reissued the *Exposure* LP, which had undoubtedly been one of his most accomplished works, thanks partly to the abundance of guest stars including Eno, Gabriel, Hall, Barry Andrews, Phil Collins, Peter Hammill and Narada Michael Walden. Fans of Robert's so called 'Frippertronics' also welcomed his 1981 album *Let The Power Fall* (Bob Macdonald 10/9/85)
The guitarist, composer, bandleader and teacher was bron in 1946 in Dorset. With Michael and Pete Giles on drums and bass he made a pop LP in 1968 (*The cheerful insanity of Giles, Giles and Fripp* on Deram). With Michael Giles, multi-instrumentalist Ian McDonald, Greg Lake on bass and vocals he formed the art-rock band King Crimson in 1969; that band carried on for years with many changes of personnel, Fripp the only constant factor. King Crimson spin-offs included Emerson, Lake & Palmer and Yes, while Fripp's sessioning and other activities have been too exhaustive to list here. He combines electronics with classical technique, often playing while seated; during his work with Brian Eno in the mid-70's his tape-delay system developed into 'Frippertonics' for tours and albums. *Robert Fripp and the league of crafty guitarists* is from Fripp's master classes of 1986 at Claymont Court, West Virginia, also on video. (Donald Clarke, July 1989).

NETWORK
Tracks: / North Star (Vocal-Daryl Hall) / Water music 1 (Taped voice-J.G. Bennett) / God save the King / Under heavy manners (Vocal-David Byrne) / Here comes the flood (Vocal-Peter Gabriel).
10" single: Released Jan '87, on E.G., by E.G. Records. Catalogue no: **EGMLP 4**

Frizzell, David

I'M GONNA HIRE A WINO TO DECORATE...
Tracks: / I'm gonna hire a wino to decorate....
7" Single: Released Sep '82, on Warner Bros., by WEA Records. Catalogue no: **K 15002**

Froggatt, Raymond

DON'T LET ME CRY AGAIN
Tracks: / Don't let me cry again.
7" Single: Released May '83, on Astra, by Astra Records. Catalogue no: **ESM 405**

JETTIN'
Tracks: / Don't let me cry again.
7" Single: Released Nov '86, on Lots More Music, Catalogue no: **RPC 004**

Froggits

DOCTOR JAZZ
Tracks: / Doctor Jazz
7" Single: Released Jun '87, on Tembo, by Tembo Records. Catalogue no: **TML 129**

Frogs

SUGAR CANE
Tracks: / Sugar cane.
12" Single: Released May '82, on Sunburn, by Orbitone Records. Catalogue no: **SBD 05**

Frogs, Freddy

CRAZY LITTLE MAMA
Tracks: / Crazy little mama
7" Single: Released Feb '81, on Hertford, Deleted Feb '84. Catalogue no: **HER 2**

From 52nd Street

LOOK INTO MY EYES
12" Single: Released Aug '82, on Factory (1), by Factory Records. Catalogue no: **FAC 5912**

Froman, Jane

I WONDER
Tracks: / I wonder.
7" Single: Released Jun '55, on Capitol, by EMI Records. Deleted '58. Catalogue no: **CL 14254**

Front 242

ENDLESS RIDDANCE
Tracks: / Endless riddance.
CD 5": Released 14 Aug '88, on Red Rhino (Europe), by Red Rhino Europe. Catalogue no: **MK 003CD**
12" Single: Released 12 Nov '86, on Mask (Germany), by Mask Records (Germany). Catalogue no: **MK 003**

HEADHUNTER
Tracks: / Headhunter.
CD 5": Released Oct '88, on Red Rhino, by Red Rhino Records. Catalogue no: **RRECD 6**
7" Single: Released Oct '88, on Red Rhino, by Red Rhino Records. Catalogue no: **RRE 6**
12" Single: Released Oct '88, on Red Rhino, by Red Rhino Records. Catalogue no: **RRET 6**

INTERCEPTION
Tracks: / Interception.
CD 5": Released 14 Aug '88, on Red Rhino (Europe), by Red Rhino Europe. Catalogue no: **RRET 002CD**
7" Single: Released 17 Nov '86, on Red Rhino (Europe), by Red Rhino Europe. Catalogue no: **RRE 003**
12" Single: Released Nov '86, on Red Rhino (Europe), by Red Rhino Europe. Catalogue no: **RRET 003**

MASTER HIT (REMIX)
Tracks: / Master hit (remix).
12" Single: Released Nov '87, on Wax Trax, by Wax Trax Records. Catalogue no: **WAX 036**

NEVER STOP
Tracks: / Never stop.
12" Single: Released Mar '89, on Red Rhino (Europe), by Red Rhino Europe. Catalogue no: **RRET 8**
CD 5": Released Apr '89, on Red Rhino (Europe), by Red Rhino Europe. Catalogue no: **RRECD 8**
7" Single: Released Apr '89, on Red Rhino (Europe), by Red Rhino Europe. Catalogue no: **RRE 8**

NO SHUFFLE
Tracks: / No shuffle / Body to body.
7" Single: Released Feb '86, on Himalaya, Catalogue no: **OPA 13**
12" Single: Released Feb '86, on Himalaya, Catalogue no: **12OPA 013**

POLITICS OF PRESSURE
Tracks: / Politics of pressure.
12" Single: Released 12 Nov '86, on Mask (Germany), by Mask Records (Germany). Catalogue no: **MK 004**
CD 5": Released 14 Aug '88, on Red Rhino (Europe), by Red Rhino Europe. Catalogue no: **MK 004CD**

PRINCIPLES
Tracks: / Principles.
7" Single: Released May '82, on New Dance, Catalogue no: **ND 002**

TWO IN ONE
Tracks: / Two in one.
12" Single: Released 4 Feb '86, on 242, Catalogue no: **ND 009**
CD 5": Released Oct '88, on 242, Catalogue no: **ND 009CD**

U MEN
Tracks: / U men.
7" Single: Released May '82, on New Dance, Catalogue no: **ND 005**

Front Line Orchestra

DON'T TURN YOUR BACK ON ME
Tracks: / Don't turn your back on me / No entry.
12" Single: Released Nov '81, on Ice, by Ice Records. Deleted '84. Catalogue no: **ICET 50**
7" Single: Released Nov '81, on Ice, by Ice Records. Deleted '84. Catalogue no:

FRUITS OF PASSION - LOVE'S GLORY (Released on Siren)

ICET 50
7" Single: Released Nov '81, on Ice, by Ice Records. Deleted '84. Catalogue no: **ICE 50**

Frontline Assembly

DIGITAL TENSION DEMENTIA
Tracks: / Digital tension dementia.
12" Single: Released Nov '88, on Third Mind, by Third Mind Records. Catalogue no: **TMS 11**
CD 3": Released Nov '88, on Third Mind, by Third Mind Records. Catalogue no: **TMSCD 11**

NO LIMIT
Tracks: / No limit (damaged goods mix).
CD 5": Released '89, on Third Mind, by Third Mind Records. Catalogue no: **TMSCD 043**
12" Single: Released '89, on Third Mind, by Third Mind Records. Catalogue no: **TMS 043**

Frost, Kid

TERMINATOR
Tracks: / Terminator (vocal mix) / Terminator (instrumental).
12" Single: Released Feb '86, on ZYX (Germany), Catalogue no: **ZYX 5360**

Frosty

I NEED LOVE NOW
Tracks: / I need love now.
12" Single: Released 28 Sep '87, on Tommy Boy, by Polydor Ltd. Catalogue no: **TB 906**

Frozen Ghost

SHOULD I SEE
Tracks: / Should I see / Suspended humanation.
7" Single: Released Jul '87, on WEA (International), by WEA Records. Deleted Jan '88. Catalogue no: **U 8409**

Frugivores

MOTH INTO THE FLAME
Tracks: / Moth into the flame / Scales.
7" Single: Released 23 May '87, on Coda, by Coda Records. Catalogue no: **CODS 23**

Fruit Bats

UNTIL THE MONEY FALLS OUT OF THE SKY
Tracks: / Until the money falls out of the sky / Charlatan.
7" Single: Released Jan '89, on Backs, by Backs Recording Co.. Catalogue no: **NCH 114**

Fruit Of Life

ARE YOU CONSERVATIVE
Tracks: / Are you conservative.
12" Single: Released 27 Feb '88, on Subway, by Subway Records. Catalogue no: **SUB 007**

NOT AFRAID TO DANCE
Tracks: / Not afraid to dance.
12" Single: Released Dec '87, on Antler, by Antler Records (Belgium). Catalogue no: **SUB 004**

Fruits of Passion

ALL I EVER WANTED
Tracks: / All I ever wanted / Ambition.
7" Single: Released Mar '85, on Siren, by Virgin Records. Deleted '86. Catalogue no: **SIREN 1**

EVERYTHING I EVER WANTED
Tracks: / Everything I ever wanted / Everything I had.
12" Single: Released Aug '86, on Siren, by Virgin Records. Deleted '89. Catalogue no: **SIREN 26-12**
7" Single: Released Aug '86, on Siren, by Virgin Records. Deleted May '88. Catalogue no: **SIREN 26**

KISS ME NOW
Tracks: / Kiss me now / Place in the heart, A.
7" Single: Released May '86, on Siren, by Virgin Records. Deleted May '88. Catalogue no: **SIREN 19**
12" Single: Released May '86, on Siren, by Virgin Records. Deleted May '88. Catalogue no: **SIREN 19-12**

LOVE'S GLORY (see panel above)
Tracks: / Love's glory / You broke my heart.
12" Single: Released Mar '86, on Siren, by Virgin Records. Deleted May '88. Catalogue no: **SIREN 14-12**
7" Single: Released Mar '86, on Siren, by Virgin Records. Deleted May '88. Catalogue no: **SIREN 14**

NO MORE TEARS
Tracks: / Nothing but a prayer / Kissing me (ext) (Extra track on 12" version only.) / No more tears.
7" Single: Released Nov '86, on Siren, by Virgin Records. Deleted May '88. Catalogue no: **SIREN 30**
12" Single: Released Nov '86, on Siren, by Virgin Records. Deleted May '88. Catalogue no: **SIREN 30-12**

Fry Dee

QUICK MONEY
Tracks: / Quick money.
12" Single: Released '89, on Rodger, Catalogue no: **RODGER 005**

FSK

CANNONBALL YODEL
Tracks: / Cannonball yodel.
12" Single: Released Jul '88, on Ediesta, Catalogue no: **CALC 057**

Fudge, Mickie

IF WE STOP
Tracks: / If we stop / If you can, I can.
7" Single: Released May '84, on PRT, by Castle Communications Records. Catalogue no: **7P 299**

Fukumura, Hiroshi

HUNT UP WIND (SINGLE)
Tracks: / Hunt up wind / Captain Caribe.
7" Single: Released Oct '80, on Champagne Records, Deleted Oct '83. Catalogue no: **FIZZ 502**
12" Single: Released Oct '80, on Champagne Records, Deleted Oct '83. Catalogue no: **FIZY 5002**

Full Circle

WORKIN' UP A SWEAT
Tracks: / Working up a sweat / Workin' up a sweat dub version.
12" Single: Released Feb '87, on EMI-America, by EMI Records. Deleted Oct '87. Catalogue no: **12EA 229**
7" Single: Released Feb '87, on EMI-America, by EMI Records. Deleted Oct '87. Catalogue no: **EA 229**

Full Effect

THIS IS HOUSE MUSIC
Tracks: / This is house music / It's raw.
7" Single: Released Jun '88, on Bass, by Champion Records. Catalogue no: **BSS 1**
12" Single: Released Jun '88, on Bass, by Champion Records. Catalogue no: **BSS 121**

Full Force

AIN'T MY TYPE OF HYPE
Tracks: / Ain't my type of hype (7" version) (On 7" & CD.) / Hype (instrumental) (On 7" only.) / Ain't my type of hype (12" version) (On 12" & CD single.) / Type rider (F.F.Smoove Hype Mix) (On 12" & CD single.) / Beats, drums hype (Beat 'em up mix) (On 12" only.) / Alice I want you just for me (On CD single only.).
12" Single: Released 21 Aug '89, on CBS, by CBS Records. Catalogue no: **655075 8**
CD 5": Released 21 Aug '89, on CBS, by CBS Records. Catalogue no: **655075 2**
7" Single: Released 21 Aug '89, on CBS, by CBS Records. Catalogue no: **655075 0**

ALICE I WANT YOU JUST FOR ME
Tracks: / Alice I want you just for me / Alice /Erol's favourite.
7" Single: Released Dec '85, on CBS, by CBS Records. Catalogue no: **A 6640**
12" Single: Released Dec '85, on CBS, by CBS Records. Catalogue no: **TA 6640**

ALICE I WANT YOU JUST FOR ME (CLD GOLD)
Tracks: / Alice I want you just for me / Alice / Errols theme / I wonder if I take you home.
12" Single: Released Jul '88, on Old Gold, by Old Gold Records. Catalogue no: **OG 4068**

LOVE IS FOR SUCKERS (LIKE ME AND YOU)
Tracks: / Love is for suckers (like me and you) / Sucker punch / Sucker punch (12" version.) / Suckers (On 12" version only.) / Audition (trust me), The (On 12"version only.).
7" Single: Released Oct '87, on CBS, by CBS Records. Catalogue no: **65112 7**
12" Single: Released Oct '87, on CBS, by CBS Records. Catalogue no: **651192 6**

TAKE CARE OF HOMEWORK
Tracks: / Take care of homework.
7" Single: Released Oct '88, on Columbia, by EMI Records. Catalogue no: **44 081 28**

TEMPORARY LOVE THING, THE
Tracks: / Temporary love thing / Temporary bow legged theatre.
7" Single: Released Sep '86, on CBS, by CBS Records. Catalogue no: **A 7267**
12" Single: Released Sep '86, on CBS, by CBS Records. Catalogue no: **TA 7267**

UNSELFISH LOVER
Tracks: / Unselfish lover / Have you kissed your child lately.
7" Single: Released Feb '86, on CBS, by CBS Records. Catalogue no: **6929**

Full Hip

ACID IN THE HOUSE
Tracks: / Acid in the house.
12" Single: Released '89, on Rodger, Catalogue no: **RODGER 004**

Full House (Group)

COMMUNICATE
Tracks: / Communicate / Communicate (remix).
12" Single: Released Nov '87, on Epic, by CBS Records. Deleted Jun '88. Catalogue no: **FULL T1**

COMMUNICATE (CLUB MIX)
Tracks: / Communicate (club mix) / Communicate (edit) / Communicate (dub).
7" Single: Released Nov '87, on Epic, by CBS Records. Catalogue no: **651038 1**

Full Metal Jacket

I WANNA BE YOUR DRILL INSTRUCTOR
Tracks: / I wanna be your drill instructor / Sniper.
7" Single: Released Sep '87, on Warner Bros., by WEA Records. Catalogue no: **W 8187**
7" Plc: Released Sep '87, on Warner Bros., by WEA Records. Catalogue no: **W 8186TP**
12" Single: Released Sep '87, on Warner Bros., by WEA Records. Catalogue no: **W 8187T**

Full Time Men

FAST IS MY NAME
Tracks: / Fast is my name.
12" Single: Released Oct '86, on Homestead, Catalogue no: **SHIF 1 T**

Full Wood

STOP AND THINK ME OVER
Tracks: / Stop and think me over.
12" Single: Released Dec '84, on Freedom Sounds, Catalogue no: **FSD 020**

Fuller, Bobby

Biographical details: Fuller, Bobby Hailing from El Paso in Texas, this American singer and musicians came to fame in 1966 as leader of the Bobby Fuller Four. The rock'n'roll quartet reached No.9 in the US and No.33 in the UK with their rendition of Sonny Curtis' *I Fought The Law. Love's Made a Fool Of You* then proceeded to reach No.26 on the American charts, but it missed out in Britain on account of the fact that the song had already been a UK hit for Buddy Holly and the Crickets.
Bobby and his band (which included his brother, Randy Fuller) combined rough and ready vocal harmonies with a raunchy and slightly carefree rhythmic style. Alas, they were unable to build upon their two 1966 hits - mere weeks later, in July of that year, Bobby Fuller committd suicide at the age of 22. His three former colleagues returned to obscurity in Texas.
To mark the fact that Bobby was a keen Buddy Holly fan, Rockhouse Records issued a collection of *Memories of Buddy Holly* by Fuller in 1984. It served as a tribute to both of the deceased artists. (Bob Macdoandl 10.9.85)
This Texas singer and songwriter (1943-66) formed the Bobby Fuller Four in El Paso with his brother Randy, DeWayne Quirico and Jim Reese; he became a cult classic following his mysterious death in a freak car crash. Surviving recordings disclose the influence of Buddy Holly with an admix of Tex Mex and country rock; his biggest hit *I fought the law* was written by Sonny Curtis, for a USA top 10 in 1966. (Donald Clarke, July 1989) .

I FOUGHT THE LAW
Tracks: / I fought the law.
Note: Double A sided single.
7" Single: Released Apr '66, on London-American, Deleted '69. Catalogue no: **HL 10030**

LOVE'S MADE A FOOL OF YOU
Tracks: / Love's made a fool of you.
7" Single: Released Sep '84, on Rockhouse, by Rockhouse Records (Holland). Catalogue no: **SP 8413**

Fun Boy Three

Biographical details: Fun Boy Three This British band conisted of Lynval Golding, Terry Hall and Neville Staples.
As members of the seven piece Specials, these three gentlemen enjoyed seven consecutive UK Top 10 singles plus two UK Top 10 albums between 1979 and 1981. After the seventh - and biggest - smash single *Ghost Town* which topped the British chart for three weeks in July '81, the aforementioned trio took the cold step of breaking away while the Specials were at their peak. This was due to dissension within the group, and to the fact that the three leavers wanted to free themselves from the musical grip of the Specials' dominant creative force, Jerry Dammers.
The Fun Boy Three continued the Specials' sharp political and sosciological commentary, but moved away from the ska sound and veered closer towards mainstream pop. Their debut single - a condemnation of Thatcher's Britain called *The Lunatics (have taken over the asylum)* - reached the UK No.20 position at the end of 1981. In early '82, they gave a boost to the up and coming female vocal trio Bananarama, by hiring the women as back up singers on their self-titled debut LP. As well as the album climbing to No.7 on the British charts, the FB3/Bananarama alliance spawned two consecutive Top 5 singles with remakes of singalong oldies, *It Ain't What You Do, It's The Way That You Do It* and *Really Saying Something.* During this period, Golding recovered from an unprovoked and near fatal knife attack in a night club.
After further UK Top 20 hits with *The Telephone Always Rings* and Gershwin's *Summertime*, the Fun Boy Three released their second album *Waiting* in early 1983. Produced by David Byrne of America's Talking Heads, this nonetheless British sounding LP was melodic, accomplished, witty and satirical. *Tunnel of Love* and *Our Lips Ar*

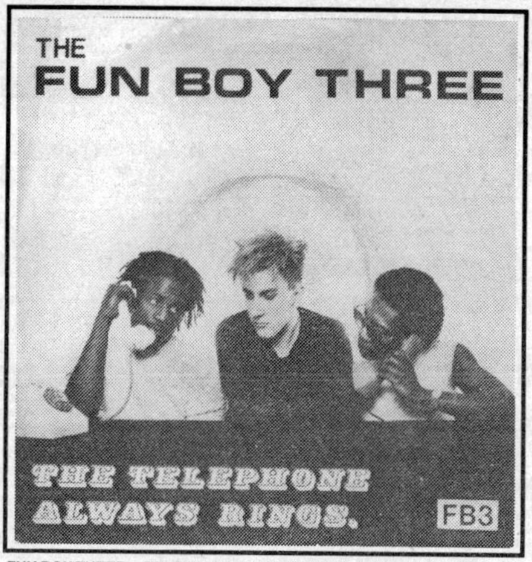

FUN BOY THREE - TELEPHONE ALWAYS RINGS (Released on Chrysalis)

Sealed. The latter was a remake of the Go-Gos' US hit of 1981 - Hall and the Go-Gos' Jane Wiedlin had written the song together while the Go-Gos were supporting the Specials on a Uk tour.

True to from, Fun Boy Three split up in the summer of 1983 while on the crest of a wave. Hall formed a new group, the Colourfield, and enjoyed further success; Golding and Staples became Sunday Best, but little was heard from them. (Bob Macdonald 11/9/85).

LUNATICS (HAVE TAKEN OVER THE ASYLUM), THE
Tracks: / Lunatics, The / Faith hope and charity.

7" Single: Released Nov '81, on Chrysalis, by Chrysalis Records. Deleted '86. Catalogue no: **CHS 2563**
12" Single: Released Nov '81, on Chrysalis, by Chrysalis Records. Deleted '86. Catalogue no: **CHS 12 2563**

MORE I SEE (THE LESS I BELIEVE)
Tracks: / More I see (the less I believe).
7" Single: Released '83, on Chrysalis, by Chrysalis Records. Catalogue no: **CHS 2664**
12" Single: Released Dec '82, on Chrysalis, by Chrysalis Records. Deleted Dec '85. Catalogue no: **CHS 12-2664**

OUR LIPS ARE SEALED
Tracks: / Our lips are sealed / Our lips are sealed (Urdu version).

12" Single: Released Apr '83, on Chrysalis, by Chrysalis Records. Deleted '85. Catalogue no: **FUNBX 1**
7" Single: Released Apr '83, on Chrysalis, by Chrysalis Records. Deleted '85. Catalogue no: **FUNB 1**

OUR LIPS ARE SEALED (OLD GOLD)
Tracks: / Our lips are sealed / Tunnel of love / Lunatics, The.
12" Single: Released Jan '88, on Old Gold, by Old Gold Records. Catalogue no: **OG 4038**

SUMMERTIME
Tracks: / Summertime / Summer of '82.
7" Single: Released Aug '83, on Chrysalis, by Chrysalis Records. Deleted Jan '84. Catalogue no: **CHS 2629**

12" Single: Released Jul '82, on Chrysalis, by Chrysalis Records. Deleted '87. Catalogue no: **CHS 12 2629**

T'AINT WHAT YOU DO (IT'S THE WAY THAT YOU DO IT)
Tracks: / T'aint what you do (it's the way that you do it) / Funrama theme, The / Funrama theme (extended version) (Only on the 12" version.).

7" Single: Released Feb '82, on Chrysalis, by Chrysalis Records. Deleted '87. Catalogue no: **CHS 2570**
12" Single: Released Feb '82, on Chrysalis, by Chrysalis Records. Deleted '87. Catalogue no: **CHS 12 2570**

TELEPHONE ALWAYS RINGS (see panel above)
Tracks: / Telephone always rings, The / Alibi, The.
7" Single: Released May '82, on Chrysalis, by Chrysalis Records. Deleted '87. Catalogue no: **CHS 2609**
12" Single: Released May '82, on Chrysalis, by Chrysalis Records. Deleted '87. Catalogue no: **CHS 12 2609**

TUNNEL OF LOVE, THE
Tracks: / Tunnel of love / Lunacy legacy, The.
7" Single: Released '83, on Chrysalis, by Chrysalis Records. Catalogue no: **CHS 2678**
12" Single: Released '83, on Chrysalis, by Chrysalis Records. Deleted '87. Catalogue no: **CHS 12 2678**

Fun & Frenzy

FALLEN DOWN IN LOVE
Tracks: / Fallen down in love.
7" Single: Released May '84, on Broiler, Catalogue no: **BR 1**

Fun Fun

BAILA BOLERO
Tracks: / Happy station / Baila bolero.
7" Single: Released Aug '87, on Carrere, Catalogue no: **CAR 416**
12" Single: Released Aug '87, on Carrere, Catalogue no: **CART 416**

Fun Patrol

RIGHT WAY TO BE WRONG, THE
Tracks: / Right way to be wrong, The.
12" Single: Released 30 May '87, on Thrush, by Thrush Records. Catalogue no: **THRUSH 5**

Funeral Directors

CORPSE GRINDER
Tracks: / Corpse grinder / Lonely hill.
7" Single: Released Oct '82, on Hell Apostal, Catalogue no: **AM 050**

Funeral Parade

FUNERAL PARADE(EP)
Tracks: / Funeral parade.
7" Single: Released Feb '83, on SRT, by SRT Records. Catalogue no: **SRTS 82CUS 1452**

Funhouse

BED OF NAILS
Tracks: / Bed of nails.
7" Single: Released May '84, on Flux, Catalogue no: **FXS 007**

Funk Deluxe

I SURRENDER
Tracks: / I surrender.
12" Single: Released Jun '89, on Tam Tam, Catalogue no: **TTT 007**

THIS TIME
Tracks: / This time / This time (dub version).
12" Single: Released Jun '86, on Streetwave, Catalogue no: **MKHAN 14**

Funk Masters

Biographical details: Funk Masters *It's Over* was a one of UK chart entry for the anonymous men andwomen who comprised this British disco band. *It's Over*, a catchy midtempo soul/pop single, climbed to No.8 in the scorching summer of 1983. Previous and subsequent offerings failed to cross over from the dancefloor to the pop charts. (Bob Macdonald 11/9/85).

BOUWKOOL
Tracks: / Bouwkool.
12" Single: Released Nov '82, on Master Funk, Catalogue no: **MF 003**

IT'S OVER
Tracks: / It's over.
7" Single: Released Oct '84, on Master Funk, Catalogue no: **7MF 004**
12" Single: Released Oct '84, on Master Funk, Catalogue no: **MF 004**

LOVE MONEY (see also "Kool, Bo 'Money we love'")
Tracks: / Love money / Money we love.
12" Single: Released Oct '81, on Tania Music, by Tania Music Records. Catalogue no: **TAN 001**

MERRY CHRISTMAS
Tracks: / Merry Christmas / Merry Christmas.
7" Single: Released Nov '84, on Master Funk, Catalogue no: **7MF 006**
12" Single: Released Nov '84, on Master Funk, Catalogue no: **MF 006**

SHAKE YOUR BODY DOWN
Tracks: / Shake your body down.
12" Single: Released 20 Feb '88, on Master Funk, Catalogue no: **TWD 1955**

Funkadelic

Biographical details: See Clinton, George for biographical details.
At the time of their brief success on the UK pop charts during the late Seventies, this American band consisted of Jerome Brailey, George Clinton, Raymond Davis, Ron Ford, Mullin Franklin, Larry Fratangelo, Mike Hampton, Tyrone Lempkin, Bobby Lavis, Walter Morrison, Cordell Mosson, Gary Shider, Calvin Simon and Bernard Worrell. The group's ever flexible line up was led and masterminded by vocalist/instrumentalist/composer/producer George Clinton, who formed the band as an alter ego for his group Parliament in 1969. His intention was to fuse the emerging black funk sound with the white rock world's psychedelic movement, hence the name Funkadelic. Clinton's 'P-Funk' organisation subsequently spawned such acts as Bootsy's Rubber Band, the P.Funk All Stars, the Brides of Frankenstein and Azpp, many of whose performers were interchangeable.
Funkadelic released their eponymous debut LP in 1970 and followed it with albums like *Free Your Mind And You Ass Will Follow, Maggot Brain, Cosmic Slop, America Eats Its Young* and *Standing On The Verge of Getting It On.* Their bizarre titles summarised their content. Ludicrous lyrics were immersed in outrageously funky rhythm tracks, garnished with white rock influences and packaged in a fantasy land of eccentric science fiction and flamboyant stage costumes. As the Seventies progressed, the ensemble received enormous recognition amongst funk following, but was both too hard sounding and too weird to cross over to major pop success.
However, *One Nation Under a Groove* proved to be an exception for Funkadelic. After Parliament had achieved US Top 20 pop hits with *Tear The Roof Off The Sucker (Give Up Th Funk)* and *Flash Light*, the insidiously infectious *One Nation Under a Groove* was released in late 1978 and became a No.9 pop hit in the UK and reached No.28 in the US. *One Nation Under a Groove* was perfect for the disco boom, which was just reaching its peak at that time. Thanks to the single's extended run atop the American soul charts, it became a US million seller; the album of the same name penetrated the lower regionss of the British LP chart.
Subsequent Funkadelic albums included *Uncle Jam Wants You* and *The Electric Spanking of War Babies.* During the early Eighties, Clinton's major influence on modern black music displayed itself via the success of such hot new funk rock fusionists as Prince and Rick James. (Bob Macdonald 11/9/85).

ELECTRIC SPANKING OF WAR BABIES (SINGLE)
Tracks: / Electric spanking of war babies.
7" Single: Released Apr '81, on Warner Bros., by WEA Records. Deleted '85. Catalogue no: **K 17786**
12" Single: Released Apr '81, on Warner Bros., by WEA Records. Deleted '85. Catalogue no: **K 17786T**

KNEE DEEP
Tracks: / Knee deep.
7" Single: Released Jan '80, on Warner Bros., by WEA Records. Deleted Jan '85. Catalogue no: **K 17494**

ONE NATION UNDER A GROOVE
Tracks: / One nation under a groove.
7" Single: Released '78, on Warner Bros., by WEA Records. Deleted '81. Catalogue no: **K 17246**

Funkapolitan

AS THE TIME GOES BY (see panel below)
Tracks: / As the time goes by / As the time goes by (rap).
7" Single: Released Aug '81, on London Records, by London Records. Deleted '84. Catalogue no: **LON 001**

IN THE CRIME OF LIFE
Tracks: / In the crime of life / War.
7" Single: Released Apr '82, on London (Decca), by Decca International. Deleted Apr '85. Catalogue no: **LON 002**
12" Single: Released Apr '82, on London (Decca), by Decca International. Deleted Apr '85. Catalogue no: **LONX 002**

RUN, RUN, RUN
Tracks: / Run, run, run / Time and space.
7" Single: Released Jun '82, on London (Decca), by Decca International. Deleted Jun '85. Catalogue no: **LON 006**
12" Single: Released Jun '82, on London

FUNKAPOLITAN - AS TIME GOES BY (Released on London Records)

(Decca), by Decca International. Deleted Jun '85. Catalogue no: **LONX 006**

Funkcrew

BREAKING HEARTS
Tracks: / Breaking hearts / Work hard work / Ghosts in the machinery (On 12" version only.).
7" Single: Released Oct '86, on Sophisticated Noise, by Sophisticated Noise Records. Catalogue no: **KREW 1**
12" Single: Released Oct '86, on Sophisticated Noise, by Sophisticated Noise Records. Catalogue no: **12 KREW 1**

Funkmasters

HAVE YOU GOT THE TIME
Tracks: / Have you got the time / Have you got the time (version).
7" Single: Released Nov '84, on Master Funk, Catalogue no: **7MF 008**
12" Single: Released Jul '87, on Master Funk, Catalogue no: **MS 008**
12" Single: Released Nov '84, on Master Funk, Catalogue no: **MF 008**
7" Single: Released Jul '87, on Master Funk, Catalogue no: **7MS 008**

Funkmeister

DEBAUCH MIX, THE
Tracks: / Debauch mix, The.
12" Single: Released Jan '85, on Ryker, Catalogue no: **RYKP 2**
7" Pic: Released Jan '85, on Ryker, Catalogue no: **RYKM 2**

WAR DANCE
Tracks: / War dance.
7" Single: Released Jan '85, on Ryker, Catalogue no: **RYK 2**
12" Single: Released Jan '85, on Ryker, Catalogue no: **RYKT 2**

Funkrew

BAD BAD BOY
Tracks: / Bad bad boy.
7" Single: Released Mar '88, on Arista, by BMG Records (UK). Catalogue no: **109 756**
12" Single: Released Mar '88, on Arista, by BMG Records (UK). Catalogue no: **609 756**

GOTTA BE STRONG
Tracks: / Gotta be strong / Gotta be strong (gospel version) / Ghost in the machine (Extra track on 12".).
12" Single: Released 20 Jun '87, on Arista, by BMG Records (UK). Catalogue no: **RIST 10**
7" Single: Released 20 Jun '87, on Arista, by BMG Records (UK). Catalogue no: **RIS 10**

Funky Christmas Band

FUNKY CHRISTMAS
Tracks: / Funky Christmas.
12" Single: Released Nov '85, on J & J, Catalogue no: **JJR 121**

Funky Four plus One

THATS THE JOINT
Tracks: / That's the joint.
12" Single: Released Dec '81, on Sugarhill (USA), Deleted Dec '84. Catalogue no: **SHL 108**
7" Single: Released Dec '81, on Sugarhill (USA), Deleted Dec '84. Catalogue no: **SH 108**

Funky Worm

HUSTLE (TO THE MUSIC)
Tracks: / Hustle (to the music) / Hustle (to the music)(version).
7" Single: Released Jul '88, on Fon, by FON Records. Catalogue no: **FON 15**
12" Single: Released Jul '88, on Fon, by FON Records. Catalogue no: **FON 15T**

SPELL, THE
Tracks: / Spell, The / Mental spell / Hustle (to the music) (CD single only.).
CD 5": Released Nov '88, on Fon, by FON Records. Catalogue no: **FON 16 CD**
7" Single: Released Nov '88, on Fon, by FON Records. Catalogue no: **FON 16**
12" Single: Released Nov '88, on Fon, by FON Records. Catalogue no: **FON 16T**

U PLUS ME = LOVE
Tracks: / U plus me = love.
CD 5": Released Apr '89, on Fon, by FON Records. Catalogue no: **FON 19CD**
7" Single: Released Apr '89, on Fon, by FON Records. Catalogue no: **FON 19**
12" Single: Released Apr '89, on Fon, by FON Records. Catalogue no: **FON 19T**

Funtopia

BEAUTIFUL PEOPLE
Tracks: / Beautiful people.
12" Single: Released 9 Jan '89, on Gee Street, by Gee Street Records. Catalogue no: **GEET 5008**

FREEDOM
Tracks: / Freedom / Freedom (remix).
12" Single: Released 6 Feb '89, on Gee Street, by Gee Street Records. Catalogue no: **GEET 014**
7" Single: Released 6 Feb '89, on Gee Street, by Gee Street Records. Catalogue no: **GEE 014**
12" Single: Released May '89, on Gee Street, by Gee Street Records. Catalogue no: **GEET 014 R**

Fur Bible

PLUNDER THE TOMBS
Tracks: / Plunder the tombs.
12" Single: Released Nov '85, on New Rose (1), by New Rose Records. Catalogue no: **NEW 61**

Furay, Richie

I STILL HAVE DREAMS
Tracks: / I still have dreams / Headin' south.
7" Single: Released Jan '80, on Elektra, by Elektra Records (UK). Deleted '83. Catalogue no: **K 12413**

Fureys

Biographical details: Fureys, This Irish family folk band consists of brothers Eddie, Finbar, George and Paul Furey augmented by family friend Davey Arthur. Davey was brought into the fold at the age of 15 when he stayed at th Fureys' family house for a period - the lad's father and the late Ted Furey taught him to play a variety of musical instruments and he remained an honorary family member from then onwards. Hailing from a suburb of Dublin, the Fureys & Davey Arthur embarked upon their full time musical career in 1980. By the end of the following year, they had chalked up a suprise UK Top 20 hit with *When You Were Sweet Sixteen*, a revival of a standard that dated back to 1898. In April '82 the band had a second but much smaller British chart success with *I Will Love You (Every Time When We Are Gone)*, which reached No.54. By the time of this second hit, Ritz Records had managed to place another Eire folk act, Foster & Allen, in the Uk Top 20.

With the help of producer Phil Coulter (a former pop songwriter.producer.svengali), the Fureys continued to release singles and albums of traditional fare, all performed with examplary musicianship. Their generally tranquil style did not make further forays into the British pop charts, but they became an increasisngly popular attraction on the concert and club circuits particularly in West Germany. (Bob Macdonald 11/9/85).

ANNIVERSARY SONG
Tracks: / Anniversary song.
7" Single: Released Sep '82, on Ritz, by Ritz Records. Catalogue no: **RITZ 032**

DREAMING MY DREAMS
Tracks: / Dreaming my dreams / Paddy in Paris.
7" Single: Released May '87, on Ritz, by Ritz Records. Catalogue no: **RITZ 172**
7" Single: Released Jun '85, on Ritz, by Ritz Records. Catalogue no: **RITZ 098**

FIRST LEAVES OF AUTUMN, THE
Tracks: / First leaves of autumn / Sitting alone.
7" Single: Released Sep '86, on Ritz, by Ritz Records. Catalogue no: **RITZ 151**

GREEN FIELDS OF FRANCE
Tracks: / Green fields of France / Evening falls.
7" Single: Released Jul '82, on Ritz, by Ritz Records. Catalogue no: **RITZ 017**

I WILL LOVE YOU (EV'RY TIME WHEN WE ARE GONE)
Tracks: / I will love you (ev'ry time when we are gone).
7" Single: Released Apr '82, on Ritz, by Ritz Records. Deleted '85. Catalogue no: **RITZ 012**

LOVELY IN LONDON
Tracks: / Lovely in London / Lament.
7" Single: Released Dec '87, on Cara, Catalogue no: **CARA 101**

MY OWN ROSCOMMON TOWN (Fureys & Shannon)
Tracks: / My own Roscommon Town.
7" Single: Released '88, on I&B, by I & B Records. Catalogue no: **CMR 82**

NOW IS THE HOUR (FAREWELL)
Tracks: / Now is the hour.
7" Single: Released May '83, on Ritz, by Ritz Records. Catalogue no: **RITZ 045**

RED ROSE CAFE (Fureys & Davey Arthur)
Tracks: / Irish eyes / Sitting alone / Red rose cafe.
Cassingle: Released Sep '87, on Ritz, by Ritz Records. Catalogue no: **RITZC 176**
7" Single: Released Sep '87, on Ritz, by Ritz Records. Catalogue no: **RITZ 176**

SCARLET RIBBONS
Tracks: / Scarlet ribbons.
7" Single: Released Nov '84, on Ritz, by Ritz Records. Catalogue no: **RITZ 087**

STEAL AWAY(7")
Tracks: / Steal away.
7" Single: Released Oct '83, on Ritz, by Ritz Records. Catalogue no: **RITZ 055**

WHEN YOU WERE SWEET SIXTEEN (SINGLE)
Tracks: / When you were sweet sixteen.
7" Single: Released Aug '81, on Ritz, by Ritz Records. Catalogue no: **RITZ 003**

Furious Apples

ENGINEERING
7" Single: Released Nov '83, on Sonar, by Sonar Records. Catalogue no: **SON 2**

Furious Pig

I DON'T LIKE YOUR FACE
Tracks: / I don't like your face.
7" Single: Released Mar '81, on Rough Trade, by Rough Trade Records. Catalogue no: **RT 064**
12" Single: Released Feb '81, on Rough Trade, by Rough Trade Records. Catalogue no: **RTT 064**

Furlong, Michael

SAVIN' THE BEST FOR YOU
Tracks: / Savin' the best for you.
12" Single: Released Aug '88, on Music For Nations, by Music For Nations Records. Catalogue no: **12 KUT 128**
7" Single: Released Aug '88, on Music For Nations, by Music For Nations Records. Catalogue no: **KUT 128**

Furniture

BRILLIANT MIND
Tracks: / Brilliant mind / To Gus.
7" Single: Released Apr '86, on Stiff, by Stiff Records. Catalogue no: **BUY 251**
12" Single: Released Apr '86, on Stiff, by Stiff Records. Catalogue no: **BUYIT 251**

DANCING THE HARD BARGAIN
Tracks: / Dancing the hard bargain / Robert Nightman's story.
12" Single: Released Apr '84, on Survival (1), by Survival Records. Catalogue no: **SUR 12 023**
7" Single: Released Apr '84, on Survival (1), by Survival Records. Catalogue no: **SUR 023**

I CAN'T CRACK
Tracks: / I can't crack / Switch off / Pause / Broken mix.
12" Single: Released May '85, on Premonition, by Survival Records. Catalogue no: **PREM 3**

LOVE YOUR SHOES
Tracks: / Love your shoes / Turnuspeed / Me and you and the name (On 12" version only.).
12" Single: Released Oct '86, on Stiff, by Stiff Records. Catalogue no: **BUYIT 254**
7" Single: Released Oct '86, on Stiff, by Stiff Records. Catalogue no: **BUY 254**

LOVEMONGERS, THE
Tracks: / Love mongers,The / Talking kittens / I can't crack (On 12" version only.).
7" Single: Released Feb '86, on Premonition, by Survival Records. Catalogue no: **PREM 5**
12" Single: Released Feb '86, on Premonition, by Survival Records. Catalogue no: **12PREM 5**

SLOW MOTION KISSES
Tracks: / Slow motion kisses / Forty hours in a day / Brilliant mind (On CD only.) / She gets out the scrapbook (On CD only.).
CD 5": Released Oct '89, on Arista, by BMG Records (UK). Catalogue no: **662 648**
7" Single: Released Sep '89, on Arista, by BMG Records (UK). Catalogue no: **112 648**
12" Single: Released Sep '89, on Arista, by BMG Records (UK). Catalogue no: **612 648**

YOUR BRILLIANT MIND
Tracks: / Your brilliant mind.
7" Single: Released Sep '84, on Survival (1), by Survival Records. Catalogue no: **SUR 028**
12" Single: Released Sep '84, on Survival (1), by Survival Records. Catalogue no: **SUR 12 028**

Furple

BURPLE
Tracks: / Burple.
7" Single: Released 24 May '84, on Turning Purple, Catalogue no: **YNOT 2**

Furry Dice

RUBI DON'T TAKE YOUR LOVE TO TOWN
Tracks: / Rubi don't take your love to town / K.G.B..
7" Single: Released Sep '81, on White Line, by White Line Records. Deleted '84. Catalogue no: **WHLS 001**

Fury

RIVER DEEP MOUNTAIN HIGH
Tracks: / River deep, mountain high.
12" Single: Released Mar '83, on Jet, by Jet Records. Catalogue no: **JET 7035**

Fury, Billy

Biographical details: The British singer and songwriter, Billy Fury, was born Ronald Wycherley in Liverpool in 1941. During childhood, he sufered from rheumatic fever, an affliction which left him with a damaged heart. After leaving school he got a job on the Mersy tugboats and it was during this period that he obtained his suprise break in showbusiness: in late 1958 a national package show organised by showbusiness impresario/promoter Larry Parnes was visiting a loval venue, and Marty Wilde was topping the bill. Young Ronald managed to hustle his way into the singer's dressing room, where he impressed Wilde and Parnes so much with his songs and style that he was immediately added to the bill. Having been responsible for the stagename of Marty Wilde, Parnes promptly dreamt up the Billy Fury monicker for the newly acquired youngster.
Fury's first single, the self penned *Maybe Tomorrow* was released in February 1959 and reached No.18 on the UK charts. After a few less successful efforts, he chalked up his first Top Tenner with *Colette* in spring 1960. Billy then issued his debut LP - many critics cite *The Sound of Fury* as the greatest rock'n'roll record ever made by a British artist. It was not a spctacular commercial success, however, and Decca Records prodded him to tone down his raw rock stance and adapt his music and image to suit the mellower pop tastes that had now become fashionable. Thus, the songwriting side of his talent (which had been responsible for the whole of *The Sound of Fury*) was subsequently ignored, versions of American songs. His quasi-rebellious image was transformed into that of a clean cut balladeer.
Fury's chart career really got into its stride in the summer of '61, when his superior rendition of Tony Orlando's US hit *Halfway To Paradise* cruised to the UK No.3 position. The follow up *Jealously* written during the Twenties, gave Billy his biggest ever hit by reaching No.2 - it is a curious fact that his evantual total of 29 UK hit singles never included a No.1; only Elton John, who has never reached the very top as a solo artist, has chalked up more British hits without enjoying a No.1 success.
When the Beatles revolutionised the UK pop scene in 1963, many of the established stars were immediately torpedoed out of the charts and onto the cabaret circuit. Fury, however, managed to stay the course, partly because of the sheer strength of his talent and partly because he came from the now charmed city of Liverpool.But his melodramatic interpretations of big ballads sounded more and more dated as the beat boom progressed. 1965's *In Thoughts Of You* was Fury's final UK Top Tenner and he faded from the charts altogether in '66. He moved predictably into cabaret, but his future activities were impaired by recurring health problems. These meant that the Seventies were a quiet decade for Billy - apart from an appearance in the 1973 rock'n'roll movie *That'll Be The Day*, he spent his life on a remote farm in Wales pursuing his interests in horses and ornithology.
In January 1983, just as he was staging a modest chart comeback, Billy Fury died of a heart attack at the age of 41. (Bob Macdonald 12/9/85)
Born Ronald Wycherly in 1941 in Liverpool, this British rocker was sacked from jobs in his teens because of punch ups; he had surgery for heart trouble caused by childhood rheumatic fever in 1967 and died in 1983. His first hit was *Maybe tomorrow* in 1959; called the 'greatiest, sexist, most angst-ridden Brit-rocker of them all, he was one of the biggest names in UK pop in the first half of the '60's. (Donald Clarke, July 1989).

BE MINE TOGETHER
Tracks: / Be mine together / No trespassers.
7" Single: Released Oct '81, on Polydor by Polydor Ltd. Deleted '85. Catalogue no **POSP 355**

BECAUSE OF LOVE
Tracks: / Because of love.

7" Single: Released Oct '62, on Decca, by Decca Records. Deleted '65. Catalogue no: **F 11508**

COLETTE
Tracks: / Colette.
7" Single: Released Mar '60, on Decca, by Decca Records. Deleted '63. Catalogue no: **F 11200**

DEVIL OR ANGEL
Tracks: / Devil or angel.
7" Single: Released Nov '82, on Polydor, by Polydor Ltd. Deleted '85. Catalogue no: **POSP 528**

DO YOU REALLY LOVE ME TOO
Tracks: / Do you really love me too.
7" Single: Released Jan '64, on Decca, by Decca Records. Deleted '67. Catalogue no: **F 11792**

DON'T WORRY
Tracks: / Don't worry.
7" Single: Released Apr '61, on Decca, by Decca Records. Deleted '64. Catalogue no: **F 11334**

FORGET HIM
Tracks: / Forget him.
7" Single: Released Jun '83, on Polydor, by Polydor Ltd. Deleted '86. Catalogue no: **POSP 558**

GIVE ME YOUR WORD
Tracks: / Give me your word.
7" Single: Released Aug '66, on Decca, by Decca Records. Deleted '69. Catalogue no: **F 12459**

HALFWAY TO PARADISE
Tracks: / Halfway to paradise / Last night was made for love.
7" Single: Released May '61, on Decca, by Decca Records. Deleted '64. Catalogue no: **F 11349**

HALFWAY TO PARADISE (OLD GOLD)
Tracks: / Halfway to paradise.
7" Single: Released Oct '83, on Old Gold, by Old Gold Records. Catalogue no: **OG 9329**

I WILL
Tracks: / I will.
7" Single: Released Apr '64, on Decca, by Decca Records. Deleted '67. Catalogue no: **F 11888**

I'D NEVER FIND ANOTHER YOU
Tracks: / I'd never find another you.
7" Single: Released Dec '61, on Decca, by Decca Records. Deleted '64. Catalogue no: **F 11409**

I'LL NEVER QUITE GET OVER YOU
Tracks: / I'll never quite get over you.
7" Single: Released Feb '66, on Decca, by Decca Records. Deleted '69. Catalogue no: **F 12325**

I'M LOST WITHOUT YOU
Tracks: / I'm lost without you.
7" Single: Released Jan '65, on Decca, by Decca Records. Deleted '68. Catalogue no: **F 12048**

IN SUMMER
Tracks: / In summer.
7" Single: Released Jul '63, on Decca, by Decca Records. Deleted '66. Catalogue no: **F 11701**

IN THOUGHTS OF YOU
Tracks: / In thoughts of you.
7" Single: Released Jul '65, on Decca, by Decca Records. Deleted '68. Catalogue no: **F 12178**

IT'S ONLY MAKE BELIEVE
Tracks: / It's only make believe.
7" Single: Released Jul '64, on Decca, by Decca Records. Deleted '67. Catalogue no: **F 11939**

JEALOUSY
Tracks: / Jealousy.
7" Single: Released Sep '61, on Decca, by Decca Records. Deleted '64. Catalogue no: **F 11384**

LAST NIGHT WAS MADE FOR LOVE
Tracks: / Last night was made for love.
7" Single: Released May '62, on Decca, by Decca Records. Deleted '65. Catalogue no: **F 11458**

LETTER FULL OF TEARS
Tracks: / Letter full of tears.
7" Single: Released Mar '62, on Decca, by Decca Records. Deleted '65. Catalogue no: **F 11437**

LIKE I'VE NEVER BEEN GONE
Tracks: / Like I've never been gone.
7" Single: Released Feb '63, on Decca, by Decca Records. Deleted '66. Catalogue no: **F 11582**

LOVE OR MONEY
Tracks: / Love or money / Love sweet love.
7" Single: Released Sep '82, on Polydor, by Polydor Ltd. Deleted '85. Catalogue no: **POSP 488**

MARGO
Tracks: / Margo.
7" Single: Released Jun '59, on Decca, by Decca Records. Deleted '62. Catalogue no: **F 11128**

MAYBE TOMORROW
Tracks: / Maybe tomorrow.
7" Single: Released Feb '59, on Decca, by Decca Records. Deleted '62. Catalogue no: **F 11102**

ONCE UPON A DREAM (SINGLE)
Tracks: / Once upon a dream.
7" Single: Released Jul '62, on Decca, by Decca Records. Deleted '65. Catalogue no: **F 11485**

RUN TO MY LOVIN' ARMS
Tracks: / Run to my lovin' arms.
7" Single: Released Sep '65, on Decca, by Decca Records. Deleted '68. Catalogue no: **F 12230**

SOMEBODY ELSE'S GIRL
Tracks: / Somebody else's girl.
7" Single: Released Oct '63, on Decca, by Decca Records. Deleted '66. Catalogue no: **F 11744**

SUZANNE IN THE MIRROR(EP)
Tracks: / Suzanne in the mirror / Times are changing / Lady / Certain things.
7" EP: Released Jul '85, on Magnum Force, by Magnum Music Group. Catalogue no: **MFEP 009**

THAT'S LOVE
Tracks: / That's love.
7" Single: Released May '60, on Decca, by Decca Records. Deleted '63. Catalogue no: **F 11237**

THOUSAND STARS, A
Tracks: / Thousand stars, A.
7" Single: Released Jan '61, on Decca, by Decca Records. Deleted '64. Catalogue no: **F 11311**

WHEN WILL YOU SAY I LOVE YOU
Tracks: / When will you say I love you.
7" Single: Released May '63, on Decca, by Decca Records. Deleted '66. Catalogue no: **F 11655**

WONDROUS PLACE
Tracks: / Wondrous place.
7" Single: Released Sep '60, on Decca, by Decca Records. Deleted '63. Catalogue no: **F 11267**

Furyo

LEGACY
Tracks: / Legacy.
12" Single: Released Oct '84, on Anagram, by Cherry Red Records. Deleted '88. Catalogue no: **12 ANA 24**

Fuse

GRAND PRIX
Tracks: / Grand prix / Double steel.
12" Single: Released Apr '81, on CTI (1), by Polydor Ltd. Deleted '85. Catalogue no: **CTSPX 16**
7" Single: Released Apr '81, on CTI (1), by Polydor Ltd. Deleted '85. Catalogue no: **CTSP 16**

Futura

FEELIN' HOT
Tracks: / Feelin' hot.
12" Single: Released Feb '83, on Graffitti, by Rialto Records. Catalogue no: **12 GRAFT 1**

Futura 2000

ESCAPADES OF FUTURA 2000
Tracks: / Escapades of futura 2000.
7" Single: Released May '83, on Celluloid (USA), by Celluloid Records (USA). Catalogue no: **CYZ 104**
12" Single: Released May '83, on Celluloid (USA), by Celluloid Records (USA). Catalogue no: **CYZ 104**

Future

HOMETOWN GIRLS
Tracks: / Hometown girls / Quicksilver mail.
7" Single: Released Oct '82, on Paro, by Paro Records. Catalogue no: **PAROS 2**

WAR OF THE ROSES
Tracks: / War of the roses / Main attraction.
7" Single: Released Apr '86, on 10 Records, by Virgin Records. Deleted '86. Catalogue no: **TEN 119**

Future Daze

HOUSE ON THE HILL
Tracks: / House on the hill / Silent room.
7" Single: Released Jun '82, on Polydor, by Polydor Ltd. Deleted Jun '85. Catalogue no: **POSP 455**

FUZZBOX - SELF (Released on WEA)

IN THIS DREAM
Tracks: / In this dream / Don't let go.
12" Single: Released Apr '82, on Polydor, by Polydor Ltd. Deleted Apr '85. Catalogue no: **POSPX 422**
7" Single: Released Apr '82, on Polydor, by Polydor Ltd. Deleted Apr '85. Catalogue no: **POSP 422**

VENUS
Tracks: / Venus.
7" Single: Released Oct '82, on Polydor, by Polydor Ltd. Catalogue no: **POSP 516**

Future Games

WUNDERLUST
Tracks: / Wanderlust.
12" Single: Released Mar '88, on Abstract, by Abstract Sounds. Catalogue no: **12 ABS 048**

Future Heroes

ANTMANIA
Tracks: / Antmania / Hold on.
7" Single: Released Jun '82, on Eagle (London), by Eagle (London) Records. Deleted Jun '85. Catalogue no: **BSB 020**

Future Primitives

RUNNING AWAY
Tracks: / Running away / Last sunset.
7" Single: Released Jul '81, on Illuminated, Catalogue no: **ILL 5**

Future Shock

SANTA LEFT US MICHROCHIPS FOR CHRISTMAS
Tracks: / Santa left us microchips for Christmas.
7" Single: Released Nov '80, on Whisper, by Whisper Records. Catalogue no: **WSP 101**

Future Shock (Group)

GOSPEL TRUTH
Tracks: / Gospel truth / Don't temper me / New age dawning (on 12" only.).
7" Single: Released Apr '89, on Priority, by Priority Records. Catalogue no: **P 24**
12" Single: Released Mar '89, on QDA, by QDA Associates. Catalogue no: **UNKNOWN**
7" Single: Released Mar '89, on QDA, by QDA Associates. Catalogue no: **UNKNOWN**
12" Single: Released Apr '89, on Priority, by Priority Records. Catalogue no: **PX 24**

Future World Orchestra

MIRACLES
Tracks: / Miracles.
7" Single: Released Jul '84, on Cambra, by Cambra Records. Deleted '88. Catalogue no: **CMB 04**

Futures

AIN'T NO TIME FOR NOTHING
Tracks: / Ain't no time for nothing / Easy money.
12" Single: Released Sep '88, on Old Gold, by Old Gold Records. Catalogue no: **OG 4502**

Futurhythm

ANTI MATTER
Tracks: / Anti matter.
Note: Distributed by Esoteric 33 Barberry House, Shannon Road, Kings Norton. Birmingham,B38 9BX. Telephone.021-458-7503.
7" Single: Released Mar '82, on Exoteric, by Esoteric Records. Catalogue no: **EX 1**

Fuze

FALKLAND SOUND
Tracks: / Falkland sound.
7" Single: Released Sep '82, on Relentless, Catalogue no: **RS 100**

Fuzzbox

INTERNATIONAL RESCUE
Tracks: / International rescue / Raining champagne / Barbarella / Love is the slug (CD single only).
CD 5": Released Feb '89, on WEA, by WEA Records. Catalogue no: **YZ 347 CD**
7" Single: Released Jan '89, on WEA, by WEA Records. Catalogue no: **YZ 347**
12" Single: Released Jan '89, on WEA, by WEA Records. Catalogue no: **YZ 347 T**

PINK SUNSHINE
Tracks: / Pink sunshine / What's the point.
CD 5": Released May '89, on WEA, by WEA Records. Catalogue no: **YZ 401CD**
7" Single: Released Jun '89, on WEA, by WEA Records. Catalogue no: **YZ 401B**
7" Single: Released May '89, on WEA, by WEA Records. Catalogue no: **YZ 401**
7" Single: Released Jun '89, on WEA, by WEA Records. Catalogue no: **YZ 401B**
12" Single: Released May '89, on WEA, by WEA Records. Catalogue no: **YZ 401T**

SELF (see panel above)
Tracks: / Self / Wait and see / Bohemian rhapsody (12" only).
CD 5": Released 24 Jul '89, on WEA, by WEA Records. Catalogue no: **YZ 408CD**
Cassingle: Released 24 Jul '89, on WEA, by WEA Records. Catalogue no: **YZ 408C**
7" Single: Released 24 Jul '89, on WEA, by WEA Records. Catalogue no: **YZ 408**
12" Single: Released 24 Jul '89, on WEA, by WEA Records. Catalogue no: **YZ 408T**

Fuzztones

BAD NEWS TRAVELS FAST
Tracks: / Bad news travels fast / Green slime / Strychine / As time's gone.
12" Single: Released Jul '86, on ABC (indie), Catalogue no: **ABCS 011T**

HURT ON HOLD
Tracks: / Hurt on hold / Jack the ripper / I can't control myself.
7" Single: Released 5 Jun '89, on Situation 2, by Beggars Banquet Records. Catalogue no: **SIT 058**
12" Single: Released 5 Jun '89, on Situation 2, by Beggars Banquet Records. Catalogue no: **SIT 058T**

NINE MONTHS LATER
Tracks: / Nine months later / Girl you captivate me / Cheyenne rider / Greatest love in the world.
12" Single: Released Apr '88, on Music

Maniac, Catalogue no: **MM 013 S**

NINE MONTHS LATER (RE-RELEASE)
Tracks: / Nine months later.
10" single: Released 28 Aug '89, on Situation 2, by Beggars Banquet Records. Catalogue no: **SIT 061P**
7" Single: Released Oct '89, on Situation 2, by Beggars Banquet Records. Catalogue no: **SIT 061**
12" Single: Released Oct '89, on Situation 2, by Beggars Banquet Records. Catalogue no: **SIT 061T**

SHE'S WICKED
Tracks: / She's wicked.
7" Single: Released Aug '85, on ABC (indie), Catalogue no: **ABCS 006**
12" Single: Released Aug '85, on ABC (indie), Catalogue no: **ABCS 006T**

FV's

MR TAMBOURINE MAN
Tracks: / Mr. Tambourine man.
7" Single: Released Sep '81, on Smile, Catalogue no: **SRO 35**

F.X.

FREAK
Tracks: / Freak.
7" Single: Released Jun '88, on Madcap, Catalogue no: **MAD 4**

Fyre, M.C.

IT'S MY RHYTHM
Tracks: / It's my rhythm.

12" Single: Released Sep '88, on DTI, Catalogue no: **MAC 003**

G

The following information was taken from the Music Master database on October 20th, 1989.

G., Anne

IF SHE KNEW
Tracks: / If she knew.
7" Single: Released 21 Apr '89, on Atlantic, by WEA Records. Catalogue no: **086445**

G A'S

BREATHLESS
Tracks: / Breathless / Heartache / Hostage.
7" Single: Released Feb '82, on Polydor, by Polydor Ltd. Deleted Feb '87. Catalogue no: **POSP 411**

IGNORE ME
Tracks: / Ignore me / Do it, don't tell me.
7" Single: Released May '81, on Polydor, by Polydor Ltd. Deleted May '86. Catalogue no: **POSP 264**

IT SHOWS IN YOUR FACE
Tracks: / It shows in your face / Tomorrow.
7" Single: Released Nov '80, on Polydor, by Polydor Ltd. Deleted Nov '83. Catalogue no: **POSP 192**

TINY B
Tracks: / Tiny B.
7" Single: Released Oct '87, on Expansion, Catalogue no: **EXRG 1**

TREATMENT
Tracks: / Treatment / Getting mighty crowded (Only on 12" single.) / That's it.
7" Single: Released Aug '81, on Polydor, by Polydor Ltd. Deleted '84. Catalogue no: **POSP 296**
12" Single: Released Aug '81, on Polydor, by Polydor Ltd. Deleted '84. Catalogue no: **POSPX 296**

G, Bobby

BIG DEAL
Tracks: / Big deal / I want to say.

7" Single: Released Oct '84, on BBC, by BBC Records & Tapes. Deleted '87. Catalogue no: **RESL 151**
7" Single: Released Sep '86, on Polydor, by Polydor Ltd. Deleted Aug '87. Catalogue no: **POSP 810**
12" Single: Released Nov '84, on BBC, by BBC Records & Tapes. Deleted '87. Catalogue no: **12RSL 151**
12" Single: Released Sep '86, on Polydor, by Polydor Ltd. Deleted Mar '87. Catalogue no: **POSPX 810**

G For Giraffe

SCIENTIFIC
Tracks: / Scientific / Guilty.
7" Single: Released Dec '83, on Amidisque, by Amidisque Records. Catalogue no: **CF 004**

G. I. Orange

FIGHT AWAY THE LOVER (see panel below)
Tracks: / Fight away the lover / Every single day.
7" Single: Released Jun '84, on EMI, by EMI Records. Catalogue no: **EMI 5477**

G, Kenny

Biographical details: Kenny G's second album for Arista *G-Force* shows the young saxaphone virtuoso making music that's right in the contemporary pocket. Lending his hitmaking expertise to the album is Kashif (known for his writing and producing for George Benson, Evelyn King, Howard Johnson and others, as well as his own records) who acts as *G-Force's* executive producer. The album's first single *Hi, how ya doin'* features a vocal by Barry Johnson of Lenny White's band. A native of Seattle, Washington, Kenny Gorelick became fascinated with the saxophone when he saw a musician playing the instrument on 'The Ed Sullivan Show' in America. He toured Europe in 1974 when his high school band won the International High School Jazz Festival. Already, he was beginning to play professionally in local stage shows: at the age of 17, he was enjoying the first standing ovations for his soloing with Barry White's Love Unlimited Orchestra.
Enrolled in the University of Washington, where he would graduate Phi Beta Kappa and Magna Cum Laude in accounting, Kenny studied by day, joined the University jazz band and gigged around town in the evenings as a member of a popular band called **Cold, Bold & Together** which scored a no.11 R&B hit in Seattle. At 20 Kenny was not only playing in but also contracting orchestra groups for visiting performers. About the time of his graduation from college, mutual friends in another northwest-based funk bands, Pleasure brought Kenny's name to Jeff Lorber's attention when one of their members withdrew from playing with Lorber. Since then three and a half years ago, Kenny has been commuting from Seattle to Portland for rehearsals and wowing audiences with his outstanding horn work. It was the enthusiastic audience and critical response to Kenny's solo turns with Lorber that led to Arista asking Kenny to make an album of his own - *Kenny G* - which made the top 10 on Billboard's jazz chart, and received considerable pop, R&B and adult contemporary airplay as well. (Arista Press Office, March 1984).

CHAMPAGNE
Tracks: / Champagne / What does it take (to win your love) / Hi, how ya doin? (Extra track available on 12" version only).
7" Single: Released Nov '86, on Arista, by BMG Records (UK). Catalogue no: **ARIST 686**
12" Single: Released Nov '86, on Arista, by BMG Records (UK). Catalogue no: **ARIST 12686**

DON'T MAKE ME WAIT FOR LOVE
Tracks: / Don't make me wait for love / Midnight motion / Virgin Island / Japan.
7" Single: Released Sep '87, on Arista, by BMG Records (UK). Deleted May '89. Catalogue no: **RIS 37**
12" Single: Released Sep '87, on Arista, by BMG Records (UK). Deleted May '89. Catalogue no: **RIST 37**

HI HOW YA DOIN'
Tracks: / Hi, how ya doin? / What does it take (to win your love).
7" Single: Released Mar '84, on Arista, by BMG Records (UK). Catalogue no: **ARIST 561**
12" Single: Released Mar '84, on Arista, by BMG Records (UK). Catalogue no: **ARIST 12561**

HI HOW YA DOIN' (OLD GOLD)
Tracks: / Hi, how ya doin?.
12" Single: Released Jul '89, on Old Gold, by Old Gold Records. Catalogue no: **OG 4058**

HI HOW YA DOIN' (REMIX)
Tracks: / Hi, how ya doin?.
7" Pic: Released Aug '84, on Arista, by BMG Records (UK). Catalogue no: **ARISD 574**
7" Single: Released Jun '84, on Arista, by BMG Records (UK). Catalogue no: **ARIST 574**
12" Single: Released Jun '84, on Arista, by BMG Records (UK). Catalogue no: **ARIST12574**

LOVE ON THE RISE
Tracks: / Love on the rise.
12" Single: Released May '85, on Arista, by BMG Records (UK). Catalogue no: **ARIST 12618**
7" Single: Released May '85, on Arista, by BMG Records (UK). Catalogue no: **ARIST 618**

SILHOUETTE
Tracks: / Silhouette / Home / Looking for a way to let go (Only on 12".).
7" Single: Released Oct '88, on Arista, by BMG Records (UK). Catalogue no: **111832**
CD 5": Released Nov '88, on Arista, by BMG Records (UK). Catalogue no: **661832**
12" Single: Released Oct '88, on Arista, by BMG Records (UK). Catalogue no: **611832**

SONGBIRD
Tracks: / Songbird / Midnight motion / Songbird (ext.).
7" Single: Released May '87, on Arista, by BMG Records (UK). Catalogue no: **RIS 18**
7" Single: Released Jul '87, on Arista, by BMG Records (UK). Catalogue no: **RISTX 18**
12" Single: Released May '87, on Arista, by BMG Records (UK). Catalogue no: **RIST 18**

WHAT DOES IT TAKE
Tracks: / What does it take (to win your love) / Songbird.
7" Single: Released Mar '88, on Arista, by BMG Records (UK). Deleted May '89. Catalogue no: **109 843**
7" Single: Released Aug '86, on Arista, by BMG Records (UK). Deleted '89. Catalogue no: **ARIST 672**

G, Lorna

DIDN'T I TELL YOU
Tracks: / Didn't I tell you.
12" Single: Released Jul '87, on Ariwa Sounds, by Ariwa Sounds. Catalogue no: **ARI 062**

G. Men

DARK TRAIN
Tracks: / Dark train / Left out / Gotta go.
7" Single: Released May '82, on Cro-Magnon, Catalogue no: **CROW 1**

G., Ragga

BAD BOY CLICK
Tracks: / Bad boy click.
12" Single: Released Jul '89, on High Power, Catalogue no: **HPD 016**

Gabby

BOOTS
Tracks: / Boots.
7" Single: Released Jul '84, on London Records, by London Records. Catalogue no: **LON 53**
12" Single: Released Jul '84, on London Records, by London Records. Catalogue no: **LONX 53**

Gaberlunzie

SAM THE SKULL
Tracks: / Sam the skull / Glasgow Dan.
7" Single: Released Oct '81, on Klub, by Klub Records. Catalogue no: **KLUB 22**

Gable, Bill

GO AHEAD AND RUN
Tracks: / Go ahead and run / Three levels of Nigeria, The / There were signs.
12" Single: Released Jul '89, on Private, Catalogue no: **612498**

Gable Hall School

REGGAE CHRISTMAS
Tracks: / Reggae Christmas.
7" Single: Released '75, on Trojan, by Trojan Records. Deleted May '88. Catalogue no: **TR 7943**

Gable, Nicci

I DON'T GIVE A DAMN
Tracks: / I don't give a damn.
7" Single: Released '88, on Passion, by Skratch Records. Catalogue no: **PASH 35**
12" Single: Released Oct '84, on Passion, by Skratch Records. Catalogue no: **PASH 35(12)**

STRANGE DESIRE
Tracks: / Strange desire.
12" Single: Released May '84, on Passion, by Skratch Records. Catalogue no: **PASH 27(12)**

Gabor, B.B.

LASER LOVE
Tracks: / Laser love.
7" Single: Released Sep '79, on Blue Print, Catalogue no: **BLU 2003**

METROPOLITAN LIFE
Tracks: / Metropolitan life.
7" Single: Released May '80, on Blue Print, Catalogue no: **BLU 2012**

NYET NYET SOVIET
Tracks: / Nyet nyet soviet / Moscow drug club.
7" Single: Released Mar '80, on Blue Print, Catalogue no: **BLU 2009**

SOVIET JEWELLRY
Tracks: / Soviet jewellry.
7" Single: Released May '79, on Pye, Catalogue no: **7N 46197**

Gabriel, Peter

Biographical details: This British singer and songwriter, born in London, helped to form Genesis with a bunch of fellow Charterhouse Public School pupils in the late sixties. During the first half of the seventies, Gabriel led the band to UK and international success with his intense and distinctive vocals plus his idiosyncratic stage theatrics; he also wrote most of their best material. In 1975 he made a surprise decision to quit the group and pursue a solo career. Many observers doubted the ability of either Gabriel or the remaining Genesis members to carry on successfully without

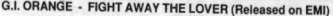

G.I. ORANGE - FIGHT AWAY THE LOVER (Released on EMI)

each other; but in the event, both flourished - drummer Phil Collins took over the role of lead singer and brought Genesis to new heights of worldwide appeal, while Peter became one of the rock world's most unpredictable yet consistently interesting artists. The artist was certainly consistent with his LP titles, which were almost invariably called *Peter Gabriel*. The first was released in 1977 - it cruised to no. 7 and logged 19 weeks on the UK chart; in the States, the album reached no. 38 with 17 weeks on the chart. The critically acclaimed LP yielded an uplifting allegorical single *Solsbury Hill*, which reached the UK no. 13 position. The second album, released in '78, was produced by Robert Fripp - the combination of two eccentrics in one studio made the LP less accessible and less successful but intriguingly experimental. Gabriel's 1980 album brought him his biggest commercial rewards to date in Britain. It knocked Paul McCartney off the top of the LP charts and spawned the brilliant no. 4 single *Games without frontiers*, which could be interpreted as a jolly singalong or as an anti-nationalistic diatribe; less subtle but equally effective was *Biko*, a tribute to the deceased South African activist, which was another UK Top 40 single. The 4th Peter Gabriel LP (entitled *Security* in the US) was issued in 1982, reached no. 6 in the UK, and yielded his first American Top 40 single *Shock the monkey* - this song showed the visually conscious Gabriel adapting himself to the new video age and winning heavy airplay on America's 24-hour MTV channel. During this period, he was instrumental in organising and financing the World of Music, Arts and Dance Festival (WOMAD), an exciting global gathering of creative talent. Such cultural exchanges were typical of Gabriel's own work, which has always been adventurous but never so esoteric as to lose his audience; like Kate Bush, he has always known the difference between genuine experimentation and wilfully obscure drivel. (Bob MacDonald 13.8.85)
The British pop singer and songwriter was born in 1950; he co-founded and starred in the art-rock group Genesis through their first seven Lp's, then went solo. His first four albums were all called *Peter Gabriel* and all went Top 10; the third (including *Biko* was a No. 1. In 1983 a double live set did well, followed by the instrumental *Birdy* in 1985 and *So* in 1986, including duet *Don't give up* with Kate Bush. He was a prime mover in WOMAD, the annual international World of Music, Arts and Dance Festival, first financed partly by reunion concert with Genesis. Now he has built the high-tech but user friendly Real World Studios in Wiltshire, where he records himself as well as the likes of Tabu Ley and Youssou N'Dour. (Donald Clarke, July 1989).

BIG TIME
Tracks: / Big time / Curtains / Big Time (extended version) (12" & CD only) / No self control (CD only) / Across the river (CD only).
CD 5": Released Apr '87, on Virgin, by Virgin Records. Catalogue no: **GAIL 312**
7" Single: Released Mar '87, on Virgin, by Virgin Records. Catalogue no: **PGS 3**
12" Single: Released Mar '87, on Virgin, by Virgin Records. Catalogue no: **PGS 312**
CD 3": Released '89, on Virgin, by Virgin Records. Catalogue no: **PGT 312**

BIKO
Tracks: / Biko / No more apartheid / I have the touch ('85 remix) (On CD only) / Jez kommit die flut.
CD 5": Released '88, on Virgin, by Virgin Records. Catalogue no: **CDPGS 612**
Cassingle: Released '88, on Virgin, by Virgin Records. Catalogue no: **PGSC 612**
7" Single: Released Sep '80, on Virgin, by Virgin Records. Deleted '81. Catalogue no: **CB 370**
7" Single: Released Nov '87, on Virgin, by Virgin Records. Catalogue no: **PGS 6**
12" Single: Released Aug '80, on Virgin, by Virgin Records. Deleted '83. Catalogue no: **CB 37012**
12" Single: Released '88, on Virgin, by Virgin Records. Catalogue no: **PGS 612**

DON'T GIVE UP
Tracks: / Don't give up / In your eyes (special mix) / This is the picture (excellent birds) (12" only).
7" Single: Released Oct '86, on Virgin, by Virgin Records. Catalogue no: **PGS 2**
12" Single: Released Oct '86, on Virgin, by Virgin Records. Catalogue no: **PGS 212**

GAMES WITHOUT FRONTIERS
Tracks: / Games without frontiers / Start, The / I don't remember.
7" Single: Released Feb '80, on Charisma, by Virgin Records. Deleted '83. Catalogue no: **CB 354**

I DON'T REMEMBER
Tracks: / I don't remember / Solsbury Hill / Kiss of life (12" only).
7" Single: Released Jul '83, on Charisma, by Virgin Records. Deleted '84. Catalogue no: **GAB 1**
12" Single: Released Jul '83, on Charisma, by Virgin Records. Catalogue no: **GAB 12**

I HAVE THE TOUCH
Tracks: / I have the touch / Across the river.
7" Single: Released Dec '82, on Charisma, by Virgin Records. Catalogue no: **CB 405**

NO SELF CONTROL
Tracks: / No self control.
7" Single: Released May '80, on Charisma, by Virgin Records. Deleted '83. Catalogue no: **CB 360**

RED RAIN
Tracks: / Red rain / Ga-ga (I go swimming) (instrumental) / Walk through the fire (On cassette & 12" only).
7" Single: Released Jun '87, on Virgin, by Virgin Records. Catalogue no: **PGS 4**
Cassingle: Released '87, on Virgin, by Virgin Records. Catalogue no: **PGSC 412**
12" Single: Released Jun '87, on Virgin, by Virgin Records. Catalogue no: **PGS 412**

SHAKIN' THE TREE
Tracks: / Shakin' the tree / Old tucson / Sweeping the leaves (Only on 12" version.).
12" Single: Released May '89, on Virgin, by Virgin Records. Catalogue no: **VSCD 1167**
12" Single: Released May '89, on Virgin, by Virgin Records. Catalogue no: **VST 1167**
7" Single: Released May '89, on Virgin, by Virgin Records. Catalogue no: **VS 1167**

SHOCK THE MONKEY
Tracks: / Shock the monkey / Soft dog (On SHOCK 1 only) / Soft dog (instrumental) (On Shock 122 only).
12" Single: Released Sep '82, on Charisma, by Virgin Records. Deleted '89. Catalogue no: **SHOCK 12**
7" Pic: Released Oct '82, on Charisma, by Virgin Records. Catalogue no: **SHOCK 122**
7" Single: Released '82, on Charisma, by Virgin Records. Catalogue no: **SHOCK 1**

SLEDGEHAMMER
Tracks: / Sledgehammer (NOT on 12") / John has a headache (On 7" only) / Don't break his rhythm (NOT on 7") / I have the touch ('85 remix) (NOT on 7") / Sledgehammer (dance mix) (On 12" only) / Biko (12" extended version) (On 12" only).
7" Single: Released Apr '86, on Virgin, by Virgin Records. Catalogue no: **PGS 1**
12" Single: Released '86, on Virgin, by Virgin Records. Catalogue no: **PGS 113**
12" Single: Released Apr '86, on Virgin, by Virgin Records. Deleted '89. Catalogue no: **PGS 112**
CD 3": Released '88, on Virgin, by Virgin Records. Catalogue no: **CDT 4**

SOLSBURY HILL
Tracks: / Solsbury hill / Moribund the burgermeister / Solsbury hill (live) (CD only).
7" Single: Released Apr '77, on Charisma, by Virgin Records. Deleted '80. Catalogue no: **CB 301**
CD 3": Released '88, on Virgin, by Virgin Records. Catalogue no: **CDT 33**

SOLSBURY HILL (OLD GOLD)
Tracks: / Solsbury hill / Games without frontiers.
7" Single: Released Jun '88, on Old Gold, by Old Gold Records. Catalogue no: **OG 9265**

WALK THROUGH THE FIRE
Tracks: / Walk through the fire / Race, The / I have the touch.
7" Single: Released Jun '84, on Virgin, by Virgin Records. Deleted '89. Catalogue no: **VS 689**
12" Single: Released '84, on Virgin, by Virgin Records. Catalogue no: **VS 689-12**

Gabrieli Brass

NEW FOREST
Tracks: / New forest / Hills and valleys.
7" Single: Released Sep '82, on Cube, Catalogue no: **BUG 94**

Gad, Jennifer

JAH JAH, A
Tracks: / Jah Jah, A.
12" Single: Released Nov '88, on Flag, Catalogue no: **FLG 105**

NATTY NAH RUN
Tracks: / Natty nah run / Babylon must fall.
12" Single: Released Oct '86, on Slag, Catalogue no: **SLG 102**

Gad, Pablo

CRISIS TIME
Tracks: / Crisis time / Saddest mistake.
12" Single: Released Oct '81, on His Majesty, Catalogue no: **HMD 010**

GUN FEVER
Tracks: / Gun fever / Fever (dub).
12" Single: Released Oct '81, on Form, Catalogue no: **FORM D 001**

HARD TIMES (SINGLE)
Tracks: / Hard times / Lighter shade of black.
12" Single: Released Oct '81, on His Majesty, Catalogue no: **HMD 011**

KING OF KINGS
Tracks: / King of kings / Lord of Lords.
12" Single: Released Jun '86, on Jah Shaka, Catalogue no: **SHAKA 853**

MEET ME ON THE CORNER
Tracks: / Meet me on the corner.
12" Single: Released Feb '83, on CD Presents, by CD Presents. Catalogue no: **CDJ 001**

NURSERY RHYME
Tracks: / Nursery rhyme / Bubbling Angelo.
12" Single: Released Oct '81, on Form, Catalogue no: **FORM D 003**

PROPHET BOB MARLEY,THE
Tracks: / Prophet Bob Marley, The / In dub.
12" Single: Released Aug '83, on CDJ, Catalogue no: **CDJ 004**

SPRING IN THE AIR
Tracks: / Spring in the air / Spring in the air (Version).
12" Single: Released Feb '86, on Try A Ting, Catalogue no: **TAT 100**

THROW YOUR DREAMS
Tracks: / Throw your dreams.
12" Single: on Burning Sounds, by Burning Sounds Records. Deleted May '88. Catalogue no: **BSD 015**

WHO'S THE TERRORIST
Tracks: / Who's the terrorist.
7" Single: Released Jul '87, on Rhythm King, by Mute Records. Catalogue no: **LEFT 14**
12" Single: Released Jul '87, on Rhythm King, by Mute Records. Catalogue no: **LEFT 14T**

Gaddis, Mark

YOUR LOVE HAS BEEN MY KEEPER
Tracks: / Your love has been my keeper / Don't go looking for love.
7" Single: Released Apr '80, on Ovation, by Gull Records. Deleted '82. Catalogue no: **OV 1203**

Gadgets

WE HAD NO WAY OF KNOWING
Tracks: / We had no way of knowing / Acid bath.
7" Single: Released Jun '83, on Glass, by Glass Records. Deleted '83. Catalogue no: **GLASS 026**
12" Single: Released Jun '83, on Glass, by Glass Records. Deleted Jun '83. Catalogue no: **GLASS 1206**

Gaelforce Orchestra

DUMBARTON DRUM
Tracks: / Dumbarton's drums / Old rustic bridge.
7" Single: Released Nov '86, on Lismor, by Lismor Records. Deleted '88. Catalogue no: **LISP 2011**

Gaffa

MAN WITH MOTIVE
Tracks: / Man with motive.
7" Single: Released Aug '80, on Gaffa'n' Products, Deleted '80. Catalogue no: **ZZZZS 003**

Gaffer

GAFFER, THE
Tracks: / Gaffer, The / Without someone to love.
7" Single: Released Mar '82, on Eagle (London), by Eagle (London) Records. Deleted '88. Catalogue no: **BSB 017**

Gage, Yvonne

Biographical details: This American singer achieved a one-off taste of UK chart success in the summer of 1984, when her enjoyable soul single *Doin' it in a haunted house* reached no. 45. This came from her *Virginity* album. The little-known Gage's other singles, such as *Garden of Eve* (1982), and *Lover of my dreams* (1984), failed to make any impact. (Bob Macdonald, 13/9/85).

DOIN' IT IN A HAUNTED HOUSE
Tracks: / Doin' it in a haunted house.
7" Single: Released Jun '84, on Epic, by CBS Records. Catalogue no: **A 4519**
12" Single: Released Jun '84, on Epic, by CBS Records. Catalogue no: **TA 4519**

GARDEN OF EVE
Tracks: / Garden of eve / Tonight I wanna love you.
7" Single: Released Jan '82, on Atlantic, by WEA Records. Deleted '84. Catalogue no: **K 11708**
12" Single: Released Jan '82, on Atlantic, by WEA Records. Deleted '84. Catalogue no: **K 11708T**

LOVER OF MY DREAMS
Tracks: / Lover of my dreams.
7" Single: Released Apr '84, on Pinnacle, by Pinnacle Records. Catalogue no: **PIN 102**
12" Single: Released Apr '84, on Pinnacle, by Pinnacle Records. Catalogue no: **PIN 102T**

Galas, Diamanda

DOUBLE-BARREL PRAYER
Tracks: / Double barrel prayer / Maladiction / Double-barrel prayer.
12" Single: Released 23 Apr '88, on Mute, by Mute Records. Catalogue no: **12 MUTE 75**

Galaxy

Biographical details: To all intents and purposes, this British "band" is Phil Fearon, the talented singer/guitarist/bassist/keyboardist/songwriter/arranger/producer. The records have been credited either to Galaxy featuring Phil Fearon or Phil Fearon & Galaxy. The only other contributors are his drumming brother, two sugary backing singers called Dorothy and Julie and Dorothy's sax-playing brother. Galaxy's records are recorded at Fearon's 24-track home studio at Kensal Rise in north-west London. Having previously played with two successful British soul bands of the late seventies, Hi Tension and Kandidate, Fearon launched Galaxy in 1982. The funky first single *Head over heels* was well received in the clubs. Galaxy cracked the UK national charts the folling year - the ultra-catchy *Dancing tight* cruised th no. 4, and was ensued by two smaller hits, *Wait until tonight (my love)* and the smoochy ballad-type *Fantasy real*. 1984 saw Fearon and Galaxy return to the top 10 with *What do I do* and *Everybody's laughing* - these continued his nifty fusion of pop and soul, and were designed to sound equally at home on the radio and on the dance floor. The debut album, simply entitled *Phil Fearon & Galaxy* was issued in the summer of '84 and reached the British top 10. However, the more modest success of the 1985 singles *You don't need a reason* and *This kind of love*, suggested that the public were growing tired of the now predictable Galaxy sound. (Bob MacDonald, 13.9.85).

BOOK OF RULES
Tracks: / Book of rules.
7" Single: Released Apr '79, on Sidewalk, by Sidewalk Records. Catalogue no: **12YSID 103**

DANCING TIGHT
Tracks: / Dancing tight.
7" Single: Released Apr '83, on Ensign, by Ensign Records. Deleted '85. Catalogue no: **ENY 501**
12" Single: Released Apr '83, on Ensign, by Ensign Records. Deleted '85. Catalogue no: **12ENY 501**

DANCING TIGHT (OLD GOLD)
Tracks: / Dancing tight / Everybody's laughing.
12" Single: Released 30 Jan '89, on Old Gold, by Old Gold Records. Catalogue no: **OG 4094**

HEAD OVER HEELS
Tracks: / Head over heels.
7" Single: Released Aug '82, on Ensign, by Ensign Records. Deleted '83. Catalogue no: **ENY 229**
12" Single: Released Aug '82, on Ensign, by Ensign Records. Deleted '84. Catalogue no: **ENYT 229**

PRIVATE COLLECTION
Tracks: / Private collection.
7" Single: Released Nov '82, on Galaxy (1), by Galaxy Records. Catalogue no: **GAL 004**

WAIT UNTIL TONIGHT
Tracks: / Wait until tonight.
7" Single: Released Jul '83, on Ensign, by Ensign Records. Deleted '85. Catalogue no: **ENY 503**
12" Single: Released Jul '84, on Ensign, by Ensign Records. Deleted '85. Catalogue no: **12ENY 503**

YOU DON'T NEED A REASON
Tracks: / You don't need a reason.
7" Single: Released Jun '85, on Ensign, by Ensign Records. Deleted '86. Catalogue no: **ENY 517**
12" Single: Released Jun '85, on Ensign, by Ensign Records. Deleted '87. Catalogue

no: **12ENY 517**

Galdez, Claudio

WATER GARDEN
Tracks: / Water garden / Water garden (dub instrumental).
12" Single: Released Mar '87, on Production House (1), Deleted Nov '87. Catalogue no: **PNT 004**

Galdez, Dorothy

NEVER TOO LATE
Tracks: / Never too late.
7" Single: Released Aug '86, on A&M, by A&M Records. Deleted '87. Catalogue no: **AM 339**
12" Single: Released Aug '86, on A&M, by A&M Records. Deleted '87. Catalogue no: **AMY 339**

Gale, Erica

AIN'T GONNA LOSE MY HEAD
Tracks: / Ain't gonna lose my head.
7" Single: Released Dec '83, on Cassia Music, Catalogue no: **CAS 001**

JUST FOR A MOMENT
Tracks: / Just for a moment.
12" Single: Released Jul '82, on Ital, by Ital Records. Catalogue no: **ITD 0103**

WHERE ARE THEY NOW
Tracks: / Where are they now.
12" Single: Released Feb '82, on Ital, by Ital Records. Catalogue no: **SAN 0022**

Gale, Philip

JUDY IN THE SCHOOL FOR JIVING
Tracks: / Judy in the shcool for jiving / Mascara.
7" Single: Released Jun '80, on Blue Print, Deleted Jun '83. Catalogue no: **BLU 2011**

Gall, France

ELLA, ELLE L'A
Tracks: / Ella elle l'a / Dancing brave.
7" Single: Released Jul '88, on WEA, by WEA Records. Catalogue no: **YZ 197**
12" Single: Released Jul '88, on WEA, by WEA Records. Catalogue no: **YZ 197T**

ELLA ELLE L'A (REMIX)
Tracks: / Ella elle l'a.
CD 5": Released Oct '88, on WEA, by WEA Records. Catalogue no: **YZ 316 CD**
7" Single: Released Oct '88, on WEA, by WEA Records. Catalogue no: **YZ 316**
12" Single: Released Oct '88, on WEA, by WEA Records. Catalogue no: **YZ 316 T**

Gallagher, Joe

THAT'S MY GIRL
Tracks: / That's my girl.
7" Single: Released Jul '88, on Rhesus, by Rhesus Records. Catalogue no: **JOE 1**

Gallagher & Lyle

Biographical details: Benny Gallagher and Graham Lyle were both born in Largs in the Strathclyde area of Scotland. After playing together in various local groups, they moved to London during the late 60's, where they had a brief spell as staff writers for Apple Records. In 1969 they became founder mèmbers of the pop/folk/country group McGuinness Flint, where the pair's vocal, guitar and songwriting skills became the backbone of the band. By the time the two left the group in autumn 1971, they had penned two UK top 5 singles for McGuinness Flint; *When I'm dead and gone* and *Malt and barley blues.* Between 1974 and 1974 Gallagher and Lyle released four albums as a duo; during this prolific period they also found time to become short-stay members of Ronnie Lane's Slim Chance. None of the four LP's enjoyed commercial success, but the duo gradually builу up a solid live reputation. Both performers played a variety of instruments in addition to guitar. 1976 suddenly brought major success for the duo. Their *Breakaway* album, issued in January, reached no. 6 on the UK album chart in March and stayed on the listings for most of the year; it yielded a pair of hit singles, both of which also peaked at no. 6 - the sophisticated romance of *I wanna stay with you* wasfollowed by the delightfully understated ballad *Heart on my sleeve.* Simultaneously, the pair's profile was additionally heightened by the fact that Art Garfunkel recorded the title track from *Breakaway* and used it as the title of his own album. The touching song became a US Top 40 single for Garfunkel, while Gallagher & Lyle obtained similar success on the UK Top 40. After their hot year, the duo slipped back in 1977. Their folky harmony vocals and melodic pop songs were no longer in such demand. *Love on the airwaves* peaked at no. 19 on the UK album listings, but they never returned to the charts after 1977, although Elkie Brooks scored a minor UK hit with her 1979 version of *The runaway.* With their material growing weaker, Gallagher & Lyle finally split up, their last album being released in '79. Benny Gallagher faded into obscurity, but Graham Lyle enjoyed a new lease of songwriting life in 1984. He cowrote Tina Turner's international smash *What's love got to do with it,* which hit no. 3 in Britain, no. 1 in the States and won the Grammy award for Record of the Year. Having penned a US no. 1, he then proceeded to co-write a UK no. 1 with Jim Diamond *I should have known better.* In summer 1985m Lyle was back in the charts on both sides of the Atlantic with Turner's hugely successful film theme *We don't need another hero (Thunderdome).* (Bob Macdonald, 13/9/85).

BREAKAWAY (SINGLE)
Tracks: / Breakaway.
7" Single: Released Sep '76, on A&M, by A&M Records. Deleted '79. Catalogue no: **AMS 7245**

EVERY LITTLE TEARDROP
Tracks: / Every little teardrop.
7" Single: Released Jan '77, on A&M, by A&M Records. Deleted '80. Catalogue no: **AMS 7274**

HEART ON MY SLEEVE
Tracks: / Heart on my sleeve.
7" Single: Released May '76, on A&M, by A&M Records. Deleted '79. Catalogue no: **AMS 7227**

I WANNA STAY WITH YOU
Tracks: / I wanna stay with you.
7" Single: Released Feb '76, on A&M, by A&M Records. Deleted '79. Catalogue no: **AMS 7211**

I WANNA STAY WITH YOU (OLD GOLD)
Tracks: / I wanna stay with you / Heart on my sleeve.
7" Single: Released Jul '82, on Old Gold, by Old Gold Records. Catalogue no: **OG 9150**

LIVING ON THE BREADLINE
Tracks: / Living on the breadline / Take the money and run.
7" Single: Released Aug '80, on Mercury, by Phonogram Ltd. Deleted '82. Catalogue no: **MER 33**

YOU PUT THE HEART BACK IN THE CITY
Tracks: / You put the heart back in the city / Fifteen summers / Heart on my sleeve (Track on 12" version only.).
7" Single: Released May '88, on A&M, by A&M Records. Deleted Feb '89. Catalogue no: **AM 443**
12" Single: Released May '88, on A&M, by A&M Records. Deleted Feb '89. Catalogue no: **AMY 443**

Gallagher, Peter

BABY
Tracks: / Baby / However dark the night.
7" Single: Released Apr '81, on A&M, by A&M Records. Deleted Apr '84. Catalogue no: **AMS 8125**

Gallagher, Rory

Biographical details: This Irish guitarist, vocalist and composer gained early experience playing in showbands before forming Taste in 1966. After achieving moderate success on record and a healthy reputation in concert, the trio broke up at the end of 1970. Their leader launched a solo career in '71, and quickly proved that his time with Taste had been a valuable training period for his fast growing status as a blues-rock guitar hero. Throughout the seventies, Rory Gallagher and his backing musicionas maintained their reputation via never-ending, hard-slogging international touring. Yet despite Rory's loyal live following, he never quite broke into the realms of superstardom. He was always around on the music scene, and no UK or European rock fan was unaware of him, but his dynamic guitar technique did not really spread beyond his hard-core army of fans. Of his 10 British chart albums between 1971 and 1982, only two made the top 30: 1972's *Live in Europe* reached no. 9 and logged 15 weeks on the listings, and 1973's *Blue print* got to no. 12. He never attached any importance to the release of 45's, and consequently never penetrated the UK singles chart. Always avoiding the trappings of the pop limelight, Gallagher consistently refused to compromise his bluesy style although, as he went into the early 80's, he was criticised in some quarters for repetition and lack of adventure. Bob MacDonald, 13.9.85.
Blues guitarist, born in 1949 in Ireland. He played in the Fontana Showband, later called the Impact; then trio Taste with bass and drums and has performed mostly in that format, playing high-octane guitar and providing raw, adequate vocals. He added a keyboardist c.1974 but reverted to trio format. He remained faithful to the blues, eschewing gimmicks; he also sessioned with Mike Vernon, Muddy Waters, Jerry Lee Lewis and Lonnie Donegan. (Donald Clarke, July 1989).

BIG GUNS
Tracks: / Big guns / Devil made me do it, The.
7" Single: Released '82, on Chrysalis, by Chrysalis Records. Deleted '87. Catalogue no: **CHS 2612**

SHADOW PLAY
Tracks: / Shadow play / Brute force & ignorance / Moonchild / Souped up ford.
10" single: Released '83, on Chrysalis, by Chrysalis Records. Deleted '87. Catalogue no: **CXP 2281**

WAYWARD CHILD
Tracks: / Wayward child / Keychain.
7" Single: Released Aug '80, on Chrysalis, by Chrysalis Records. Deleted '82. Catalogue no: **CHS 2453**

Gallant, Patsy

FROM NEW YORK TO L.A.
Tracks: / From New York to L.A..
7" Single: Released Sep '77, on EMI, by EMI Records. Deleted '80. Catalogue no: **EMI 2620**

Gallard, Regan

WE'VE BEEN AWAY
Tracks: / We've been away / Pasta song.
7" Single: Released May '81, on Penthouse, by Penthouse Records. Deleted May '84. Catalogue no: **PENT 5**

Galley Slaves

JACK IN THE BOX
Tracks: / Jack in the box.
7" Single: Released '88, on Round Black Records, Catalogue no: **ROWING 001**

Galliano

FREDERIC LIE'S STILL
Tracks: / Frederic lies's still.
7" Single: Released Jul '88, on Acid Jazz, by Acid Jazz Records. Catalogue no: **JAZZID 1**
12" Single: Released Jul '88, on Acid Jazz, by Acid Jazz Records. Catalogue no: **JAZZID 1T**

Galloway, Leata

WITH EVERY BEAT OF MY HEART
Tracks: / With every beat of my heart.
CD 5": Released 19 Sep '88, on CBS, by CBS Records. Deleted 17 Apr '89. Catalogue no: **652991 2**
7" Single: Released Sep '88, on CBS, by CBS Records. Deleted 17 Apr '89. Catalogue no: **652991 7**
12" Single: Released Sep '88, on CBS, by CBS Records. Deleted 17 Apr '89. Catalogue no: **652991 6**

Galvin, Jimmy

IF IT TAKES A MIRACLE
Tracks: / If it takes a miracle.
7" Single: Released Jan '88, on Kudos, Catalogue no: **LOAD 2**
12" Single: Released Jan '88, on Kudos, Catalogue no: **LOAD 2T**

Galwad Ar Hol...

GALWAD AR HOL FILWYR BYFFOA CYMRU
Tracks: / Galwad ar hol filwyr byffoa cymru: *Various artists.*
7" EP: Released Aug '86, on Anhrefn, Catalogue no: **ANHREFN 006**

Galway, James

Biographical details: This Irish flautist was already established as the world's top virtuoso on his instrument, by the time he first penetrated the UK pop charts in 1978. His one-off smash single *Annie's song* was a remake of John Denver's 1974 tribute to his wife Ann. Denver had reached no. 1 with his original vocal version, and Galway's beautiful instumentalrendition almost repeated that feat by climbing to no. 3, thus becoming the only song in UK chart history to hit the Top 3 in both vocal and instumental recordings. The arrival of *Annie's song* in the British singles chart sent two of Galway's catalogue LP's into the album chart - *The magic flute of James Galway* and *The man with the golden flute.* RCA then had the bright idea of issuing a showcase compilation LP entitled *James Galway plays songs for Annie,* which reached no. 7 and logged 40 weeks on the UK listings. The artist's subsequent charted albums included *Songs of the seashore* and *The James Galway collection.* In 1980 he teamed with veteran UK singer Cleo Laine on the album *Sometimes when we touch* - it climbed to no. 15 and chalked up 14 weeks on the British listings. James Galway, who bounced back fighting fit from a near-fatal car accident, possesses a degree of virtuosity and international popularity that has completely trancended many popular misconceptions and won over a broad cross-section of the public. In common with such stars as Laine, Placido Domingo, Luciano Pavarotti and John Williams, Galway's personality and affability have taken the unnecessary seriousness out of so-called "serious music". (Bob Macdonald, 14/9/85).

ANNIE'S SONG
Tracks: / Annie's song.
7" Single: Released May '78, on RCA, by BMG Records (UK). Deleted '81. Catalogue no: **RB 5085**

BABY ELEPHANT WALK
Tracks: / Baby elephant walk.
7" Single: Released Nov '84, on RCA, by BMG Records (UK). Catalogue no: **RCA 466**

BRENDON CHASE
Tracks: / Brendon Chase / Theme and incidental music.
7" Single: Released Feb '81, on RCA, by BMG Records (UK). Deleted Feb '84. Catalogue no: **RE 5318**

CARNIVAL IS OVER
Tracks: / Carnival is over / How, where, when.
7" Single: Released May '81, on RCA, by BMG Records (UK). Deleted May '86. Catalogue no: **RB 5352**

I STARTED A JOKE
Tracks: / I started a joke / Brian Boru's march.
7" Single: Released Jan '81, on RCA, by BMG Records (UK). Deleted Jan '84. Catalogue no: **RB 5135**

PACHELBEL CANON, THE (SINGLE)
Tracks: / Pachelbel canon, The / How, where, when?.
7" Single: Released May '81, on RCA, by BMG Records (UK). Deleted May '84. Catalogue no: **RCA 79**

WAYWARD WIND (SINGLE)
Tracks: / Wayward wind, The / Smoky pines.
7" Single: Released Oct '82, on RCA, by BMG Records (UK). Deleted '85. Catalogue no: **RCA 282**

Gama, Armando

WHEN LOVE HAS GONE
Tracks: / When love has gone.
7" Single: Released Jun '83, on WEA, by WEA Records. Catalogue no: **X 9801**

Gambit Of Shame

NO BOUNDS
Tracks: / No bounds.
7" Single: Released Dec '82, on Gambit Of Shame, Catalogue no: **DHE 7009**

Gamble, Loni

COULD IT BE LOVE
Tracks: / Could it be love.
7" Single: Released Jan '84, on DJM, Catalogue no: **DJS 7**
12" Single: Released Jan '84, on DJM, Catalogue no: **DJR 7**

Gambler

IT NEVER FELT LIKE THIS
Tracks: / It never felt like this / Double indemnity.
7" Single: Released 20 Jul '80, on EMI-America, by EMI Records. Deleted '83. Catalogue no: **EA 114**

Games To Avoid

NECKSPOTS
Tracks: / Neckspots.
7" Single: Released Feb '83, on Very Mouth, Catalogue no: **EAT 1**

Gamma

DIRTY CITY
Tracks: / Dirty city / Ready for action.
7" Single: Released Mar '81, on Elektra, by Elektra Records (UK). Deleted Mar '84. Catalogue no: **K 12517**

RIGHT THE FIRST TIME
Tracks: / Right the first time / Condition yellow.
7" Single: Released Nov '82, on Elektra, by Elektra Records (UK). Deleted Nov '85. Catalogue no: **K 12165**

SOMETHING IN THE AIR
Tracks: / Something in the air / May day.
7" Single: Released Oct '80, on Electra, Deleted Oct '83. Catalogue no: **K 12480**

Gammer

WILL THE NEW BABY
Tracks: / Will the new baby / Grandad, you've got me under your smell.
7" Single: Released Oct '82, on Gammer, by Gammer Records. Deleted '85. Catalogue no: **GAMMA 5**

12" Single: Released Jul '82, on Gammer, by Gammer Records. Deleted Feb '89. Catalogue no: **GAMMERT 5**

Gammons, Pete

ON THE BEACH
Tracks: / On the beach / Shark attack.
7" Single: Released Jun '88, on Priority, by Priority Records. Catalogue no: **ORB 1**
7" Single: Released Jul '88, on Nite Out, by Nite Out Records. Catalogue no: **OTB 1**
12" Single: Released Jun '88, on Priority, by Priority Records. Catalogue no: **12 ORB 1**
12" Single: Released Jul '88, on Nite Out, by Nite Out Records. Catalogue no: **12 OTB 1**

Gamson, David

SUGAR SUGAR
Tracks: / Sugar sugar.
7" Single: Released Dec '81, on Rough Trade, by Rough Trade Records. Catalogue no: **RTL 88**

Ganderton, Ron

GIGGLE AMIDST THE TEARS
Tracks: / Giggle amidst the tears / Smothered in love.
7" Single: Released Nov '82, on Centridge, Catalogue no: **CENT 2**

Gang Bang Band

GANG BANG BAND
Tracks: / Gang bang band.
12" Single: Released Aug '87, on Quiet, by Quiet Records. Catalogue no: **TROOPS 2**

Gang Green

LIVING LOVING MAID
Tracks: / Living loving maid.
12" Single: Released Jul '88, on Road Runner (1), by Road Runner Records. Catalogue no: **RR 24631**

Gang Of Four

Biographical details: The first and most successful line up of this British band consisted of Dave Allen, Hugo Burnham, Andy Gill and Jon King. The Gang of Four were formed in Leeds in 1978, the year after they had originally met up at university where all but Allen were studying. With their sparse brand of politically tinged rock, they moved into the burgeoning independent label scene and released their debut record (an EP) on the critically acclaimed Fast Product label. With the help of exposure on BBC Radio One's John Peel Show, combined with good reviews in the UK music press, the gang signed with EMI in 1979. *At home he's a tourist* gave The Gang of Four their first taste of UK chart success in June '79, but it would probably have bettered its no. 58 peak had the band nost lost the chance of appearing on "Top of the Pops" - they refused to alter a reference in the song to contraceptives. *Entertainment*, the group's debut LP, reached the UK no. 45 position in the autumn of that year. During the early '80's, the Gang Of Four continued to penetrate the lower reaches of the British singles and LP charts, but never broke through to Top 40 status. Their post-punk style remained uncompromising yet danceable; the Gang gave little regard to commercial dictates. Their frequent tours on both sides of the Atlantic were interrupted in July 1981, when bassist Allen walked out on the band in the midst of some American dates; he was eventually replaced by Sarah Lee. Their 1982 single *I love a man in a uniform* made promising chart ripples, but its progress was impaired by the fact that it coincided with the Falklands war and was thus deemed unsuitable. The Gang Of Four broke up in late 1984, having never quite translated their big cult following into major success. (Bob MacDonald, 14.9.85)
A UK punk/new wave band formed in Leeds in 1977 by students Jon King, vocals; Hugo Burnham, drums; Andy Gill, guitar; Dave Allen, bass. Allen quit during a US tour in 1981; Busta Cherry Jones depped. later Sara Lee (ex-Robert Fripps League Of Gentlemen); Burnham was sacked and the gang of two split c.'84. Allen formed moderately successful Shriekback; Burnham formed short-lived Illustrated Man. (Donald Clarke, July 1989) .

AT HOME HE'S A TOURIST
Tracks: / At home he's a tourist.
7" Single: Released May '82, on EMI, by EMI Records. Deleted '85. Catalogue no: **EMI 2956**

CALL ME UP
Tracks: / Call me up / I will be a good boy.
7" Single: Released Jun '82, on EMI, by EMI Records. Deleted Jun '85. Catalogue no: **EMI 5320**

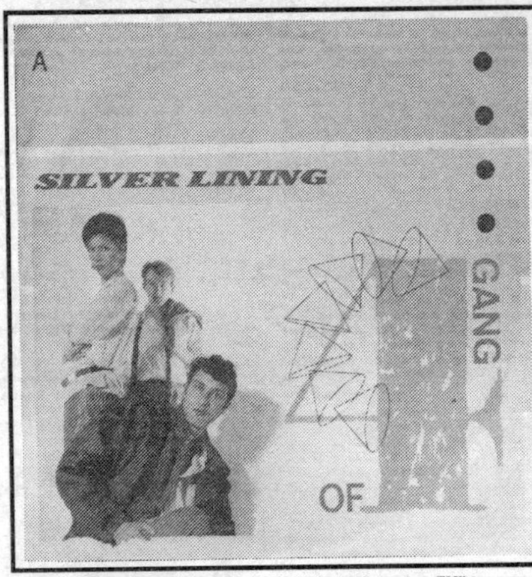

GANG OF FOUR - SILVER LINING (Released on EMI)

CHEESEBURGER
Tracks: / Cheeseburger / Paralysed.
7" Single: Released May '81, on EMI, by EMI Records. Deleted May '84. Catalogue no: **EMI 5177**

DAMAGED GOODS
Tracks: / Damaged goods / Armalite rifle / Love like anthrax.
7" EP: Released Aug '80, on EMI, by EMI Records. Deleted '83. Catalogue no: **FAST 5**

I LOVE A MAN IN A UNIFORM
Tracks: / I love a man in a uniform / World at fault.
7" Single: Released Nov '82, on EMI, by EMI Records. Deleted Nov '85. Catalogue no: **EMI 5299**
12" Single: Released Nov '82, on EMI, by EMI Records. Deleted Nov '85. Catalogue no: **12EMI 5299**

IS IT LOVE
Tracks: / Is it love.
12" Single: Released Aug '83, on EMI, by EMI Records. Catalogue no: **12EMI 5418**
7" Single: Released Aug '83, on EMI, by EMI Records. Catalogue no: **EMI 5418**

LORD MAKE ME A COWBOY
Tracks: / Lord make me a cowboy.
7" Single: Released Aug '82, on Vinyl Records, Catalogue no: **VINYL 16**

OUTSIDE THE TRAINS DON'T RUN ON TIME
Tracks: / Outside the trains don't run on time / He'd send in the army.
7" Single: Released Apr '80, on Zonophone, by EMI Records. Deleted '82. Catalogue no: **Z1**

PEEL SESSIONS:GANG OF FOUR
Cassingle: Released 13 Jun '87, on Strange Fruit, by Strange Fruit Records. Catalogue no: **SFPSC 008**
12" Single: Released Oct '86, on Strange Fruit, by Strange Fruit Records. Catalogue no: **SFPS 008**

SILVER LINING (see panel above)
Tracks: / Silver lining / Independence.
7" Single: Released Nov '83, on EMI, by EMI Records. Catalogue no: **EMI 5440**

TO HELL WITH POVERTY
Tracks: / To hell with poverty / Capital (it fails us now).
7" Single: Released Jun '81, on EMI, by EMI Records. Deleted Jun '84. Catalogue no: **EMI 5193**
12" Single: Released Jun '81, on EMI, by EMI Records. Deleted Jun '84. Catalogue no: **12EMI 5193**

WHAT WE ALL WANT
Tracks: / What we all want / History's bunk.
12" Single: Released Feb '81, on EMI, by EMI Records. Deleted Feb '84. Catalogue no: **12 EMI 5146**
7" Single: Released Feb '81, on EMI, by EMI Records. Deleted Feb '84. Catalogue no: **EMI 5146**

Ganges Orchestra

DREAM
Tracks: / Dream / Ganga: Meditasian.
12" Single: Released Mar '83, on Indipop, by Indipop Records. Catalogue no: **IND 11**

Gangsters

SOMETHING GOING ON '89'
Tracks: / Something going on / Got to give it up / Logical man / If the gangsters say jack, you jack.
12" Single: Released Feb '89, on SE 1, by Hard Times Productions. Catalogue no: **12HTP 4**

WE ARE THE GANGSTERS
Tracks: / We are the gangsters / Wooly bully.
7" Single: Released Jan '88, on Big Bear, by Big Bear Records. Deleted '88. Catalogue no: **BB 26**

Gangsters Of House

ALIEN INVASION, THE
Tracks: / Alien invasion, The / Alien invasion, The (version) / Acid by the nano-second / Acid by the nano-second (version).
12" Single: Released Jul '88, on SE 1, by Hard Times Productions. Catalogue no: **12HTP 2**

GANGSTERS OF HOUSE E.P.
12" Single: Released Feb '89, on SE 1, by Hard Times Productions. Catalogue no: **12HTP 4**

OW!
Tracks: / Ow!.
12" Single: Released Oct '88, on SE 1, by Hard Times Productions. Catalogue no: **12HTP 3**

SOMETHING GOING ON, (THERE WAS)
Tracks: / Something going on.
7" Single: Released Mar '88, on SE 1, by Hard Times Productions. Catalogue no: **7HTP 1**
12" Single: Released Mar '88, on SE 1, by Hard Times Productions. Catalogue no: **12HTP 1**

Gangway

MY GIRL AND ME
Tracks: / My girl and me / Do you remember / Once bitten twice shy (Only on 12" and CD single.) / Scream.
CD 5": Released Jun '88, on London Records, by London Records. Deleted Feb '89. Catalogue no: **LONCD 182**
12" Single: Released Jun '88, on London Records, by London Records. Deleted Feb '89. Catalogue no: **LONX 182**
7" Single: Released Jun '88, on London Records, by London Records. Deleted Feb '89. Catalogue no: **LON 182**
7" Single: Released Nov '86, on Irmgardz, Catalogue no: **IZ 1**

OUT ON THE REBOUND FROM LOVE
Tracks: / Out on the rebound from love.
7" Single: Released Nov '85, on Irmgardz, Catalogue no: **JRMGS 114**

Gannon, Mick

LADY DIANA
Tracks: / Lady Diana / It's your life.
7" Single: Released Apr '81, on Smile, Catalogue no: **SRO 30**

Ganpot, David

GIVIN' IT UP FOR LOVE
7" Single: Released Mar '83, on Osceola, by Osceola Records. Catalogue no: **OSC 5**

Ganzheit

BRAINS TO THE WALL
Tracks: / Brains to the wall.
12" Single: Released Nov '86, on Ediesta, Catalogue no: **CALC 9**

HAMMER
Tracks: / Hammer.
12" Single: Released 20 Feb '88, on Ediesta, Catalogue no: **CALC 028**

SPECTACULAR TIMES
Tracks: / Spectacular times.
12" Single: Released Nov '88, on Ediesta, Catalogue no: **CALC 065T**

Gap Band

Biographical details: This American funk band consists of three brothers: Charles, Robert and Ronnie Wilson. Hailing from Tulse, the Gap Band released their self-titled debut LP in 1977. Their albums were imaginatively titled *Gap Band II*, *Gap Band III* and *Gap Band IV*; the trend was not broken until 1983, when their new offering was called *Gap Band V - Jammin'*. The Wilson's brand of hard funk began enjoying major success in the early '80's. The Band embarked upon a string of singles which regularly hit the US soul charts and the UK pop listings. Their first and biggest British success was the semi-novelty disco smash *Oops upside your head*, which was the anthem for the crazy rowing dance; it reached no. 6 in the summer of 1980. Within twelve months, the group had notched up a further four UK chart singles: *Party lights*, the contagiously funky *Burn rubber on me (Why you wanna hurt me)*, *Humpin'* and *Yearnin' for your love*. 1982's *Gap Band IV* contained three brilliantly executed singles, which all reached the Top 3 on the American soul listings: the hard driving *Early in the morning* was followed by *You dropped a bomb on me* (not issued as a single in Britain, due to the Falklands war), and the downtempo *Outstanding*. *Gap Band V - Jammin'* suggested hints of a more pop-oriented direction; the two British hits from the album were the gently catchy *Someday* (featuring the ubiquitous Stevie Wonder on harmonica and guest vocals) and the calypso-flavoured singalong attempt *Jammin' in America*. (Bob Macdonald, 14/9/85)
A USA funk band formed early '70's by the Wilson brothers Ronnie (trumpet, keyboards), Charles (lead vocals, keyboards) and Robert (bass). They named the band after the intitial letters of three local streets and had over 25 hits in the USA black chart 1977-87. (Donald Clarke, July 1989) .

BIG FUN
Tracks: / Big fun / Big fun (serious dub mix).
7" Single: Released Nov '86, on Total Experience, Deleted May '89. Catalogue no: **FB 49779**
12" Single: Released Nov '86, on Total Experience, Deleted May '89. Catalogue no: **FT 49780**

BOYS ARE BACK IN TOWN
Tracks: / Boys are back in town / Steppin' / I don't believe you want to get up / Oops upside your head.
12" Single: Released Feb '80, on Mercury, by Phonogram Ltd. Deleted Feb '85. Catalogue no: **MERX 2**
7" Single: Released Feb '80, on Mercury, by Phonogram Ltd. Deleted '83. Catalogue no: **MER 2**

BURN RUBBER ON ME (WHY YOU WANNA MAKE ME BLUE)
Tracks: / Burn rubber on me (why you wanna make me blue) / Nothing comes to sleepers.
7" Single: Released Dec '80, on Mercury, by Phonogram Ltd. Deleted '83. Catalogue no: **MER 52**
12" Single: Released Dec '80, on Mercury, by Phonogram Ltd. Deleted '83. Catalogue no: **MERX 52**

EARLY IN THE MORNING
Tracks: / Early in the morning / I'm in love.
7" Single: Released Jun '82, on Mercury, by Phonogram Ltd. Deleted '85. Catalogue no: **MER 97**
12" Single: Released Jun '82, on Mercury, by Phonogram Ltd. Deleted '85. Catalogue no: **MERX 97**

GOING IN CIRCLES
Tracks: / Going in circles / Keep holding or / Disrespect.
12" Single: Released Apr '87, on Total Experience, Deleted '87. Catalogue no: **FT 49716**
7" Single: Released Apr '87, on Total Ex-

perience, Deleted '87. Catalogue no: **FB 49715**

HOW MUSIC CAME ABOUT (BOP B DA B DA DA)
Tracks: / How music came about (bop b da b da da) / I owe it to myself.
7" Single: Released Feb '87, on Total Experience, Deleted '87. Catalogue no: **FB 49755**
12" Single: Released Feb '87, on Total Experience, Deleted '87. Catalogue no: **FT 49756**

HUNTING
Tracks: / Hunting.
7" Single: Released Apr '81, on Mercury, by Phonogram Ltd. Deleted '84. Catalogue no: **MER 63**
12" Single: Released Apr '81, on Mercury, by Phonogram Ltd. Deleted '84. Catalogue no: **MERX 63**

I'M GONNA GIT YOU SUCKA
Tracks: / I'm gonna git you sucka / I'm gonna git you sucka (ext) / Tripped out (dub) (Available on 12" only) / Tripped out (ext) (Available on 12" only) / I'm gonna git you (sugar shack) (Only on 12" (612095)).
Note: The Gap Bands first single with Arista was penned by Norman Whitfield and comes from the movie 'I'm Gonna Git You Sucka' a pastiche of seventies 'black' movies.Mixed by Frankie Knuckles of Def Mix Productions.

7" Single: Released 6 Feb '89, on Arista, by BMG Records (UK). Catalogue no: **112016**
12" Single: Released Feb '89, on Arista, by BMG Records (UK). Catalogue no: **612062**
12" Single: Released 6 Feb '89, on Arista, by BMG Records (UK). Catalogue no: **162016**
12" Single: Released 27 Feb '89, on Arista, by BMG Records (UK). Catalogue no: **612095**
CD 5": Released 27 Feb '89, on Arista, by BMG Records (UK). Catalogue no: **662016**
12" Single: Released 6 Feb '89, on Arista, by BMG Records (UK). Catalogue no: **612016**

I'M READY (IF YOU'RE READY)
Tracks: / I'm ready (if you're ready).
12" Single: Released Oct '83, on Total Experience, Catalogue no: **X 004**
7" Single: Released Oct '83, on Total Experience, Catalogue no: **TE 004**

JAMMIN' IN AMERICA
Tracks: / Jammin' in America.
7" Single: Released Jun '84, on Total Experience, Deleted '87. Catalogue no: **TE 6**

OOPS UPSIDE YOUR HEAD
Tracks: / Oops upside your head.
7" Single: Released Jul '80, on Mercury, by Phonogram Ltd. Deleted '83. Catalogue no: **MER 22**
12" Single: Released Jul '80, on Mercury, by Phonogram Ltd. Deleted '83. Catalogue no: **MERX 22**

OOPS UPSIDE YOUR HEAD ('87 MIX)
Tracks: / Oops upside your head / Oops uppercut.
Cassingle: Released Jun '87, on Club, by Phonogram Ltd. Deleted Feb '89. Catalogue no: **JABM 54**
7" Single: Released Jun '87, on Club, by Phonogram Ltd. Deleted Oct '88. Catalogue no: **JAB 54**
12" Single: Released Jun '87, on Club, by Phonogram Ltd. Deleted Oct '88. Catalogue no: **JABX 54**

OOPS UPSIDE YOUR HEAD (OLD GOLD)
Tracks: / Oops upside your head / Burn rubber on me.
12" Single: Released 28 Aug '89, on Old Gold, by Old Gold Records. Catalogue no: **OG 4132**

OUTSTANDING
Tracks: / Outstanding.
7" Single: Released Jan '83, on Total Experience, Deleted '86. Catalogue no: **TEX 01**
Single: Released Jan '83, on Total Experience, Catalogue no: **TE 001**

PARTY LIGHTS
Tracks: / Party lights / Baba baba boogie.
12" Single: Released Sep '80, on Mercury, by Phonogram Ltd. Deleted '83. Catalogue no: **MERX 37**
Single: Released Sep '80, on Mercury, by Phonogram Ltd. Deleted '83. Catalogue no: **MER 37**

PARTY TRAIN
Tracks: / Party train / Outstanding club.
Single: Released 31 Oct '87, on Phonogram, by Phonogram Ltd. Deleted Oct '88. Catalogue no: **JAB 62**
" Single: Released Nov '87, on Club, by Phonogram Ltd. Deleted Oct '88. Catalogue no: **JABX 62**

SOMEDAY
Tracks: / Someday / Shake a leg / Outstanding (On 12" only).
7" Single: Released Feb '83, on Total Experience, Deleted '86. Catalogue no: **TE 5**

THAT'S HOW MUSIC CAME ABOUT
Tracks: / That's how music came about / I owe it to myself / Bop-b-da-b-da da (that's how music came about) (Available on 12" only.).
7" Single: Released Feb '87, on Total Experience, Deleted '87. Catalogue no: **FB 49755**
12" Single: Released Feb '87, on Total Experience, Deleted '87. Catalogue no: **FT 49756**

YEARNING FOR YOUR LOVE
Tracks: / Yearning for your love / Ooops upside your head.
7" Single: Released Jun '81, on Mercury, by Phonogram Ltd. Deleted '84. Catalogue no: **MER 73**
12" Single: Released Jun '81, on Mercury, by Phonogram Ltd. Deleted '84. Catalogue no: **MERX 73**

YOU DROPPED A BOMB ON ME
Tracks: / You dropped a bomb on me / Lonely like me.
12" Single: Released Sep '82, on Mercury, by Phonogram Ltd. Deleted Sep '85. Catalogue no: **MERX 114**
7" Single: Released Sep '82, on Mercury, by Phonogram Ltd. Deleted Sep '85. Catalogue no: **MER 114**

Garage

SAVED BY THE BELL
Tracks: / Saved by the bell.
12" Single: Released Sep '84, on Drum, Catalogue no: **RUN 5**

Garbo

DANCING STRANGE
Tracks: / Dancing strange.
7" Single: Released Apr '83, on Rarn, Catalogue no: **RARN 201**

Garbo Talks

SUMMER BREEZE
Tracks: / Summer breeze / Prayer for you.
7" Single: Released Sep '88, on Destiny, by Destiny Records. Catalogue no: **DEST 001**

Garden

NEGATIVE ALLEGORY
Tracks: / Negative allegory.
7" EP: Released Jul '87, on Gogs House, Catalogue no: **GOG 1**

Garden Band

SPONGE
Tracks: / Sponge / Touch of the sun.
7" Single: Released Dec '88, on Lapwing, by Lapwing Records. Catalogue no: **LAP S 001**

Garden Of Eden

GARDEN OF EDEN
Tracks: / Garden of Eden / Garden of Eden (version).
CD 5": Released Nov '88, on Sonet, by Sonet Records. Catalogue no: **PEPD 2**
7" Single: Released Nov '88, on Sonet, by Sonet Records. Catalogue no: **PEPS 2**
12" Single: Released Nov '88, on Sonet, by Sonet Records. Catalogue no: **PEPV 2**

SERPENT IN THE GARDEN
Tracks: / Serpent in the garden.
7" Single: Released Jan '89, on Pepper, by Pepper Records. Catalogue no: **PEP 2**

Gardeniatalogue no:

CHIQUITA LINDA
Tracks: / Chiquita Linda.
7" Single: Released Oct '85, on London Records, by London Records. Catalogue no: **LON 78**
12" Single: Released Oct '85, on London Records, by London Records. Catalogue no: **LONX 78**

Gardiner, Boris

Biographical details: This Jamaican organist and bass guitarist achieved a one-off success on the UK charts in 1970. His instrumental single *Elizabethan reggae* reached no. 14 in March of that year - this was a memorable reggae rendition of the old standard *Elisabeth serenade*, which had previously been a minor UK hit for the Gunter Kallman choir. Gardner's single was produced by the influential Jamaican music business executive and performer Byron Lee. During the rest of the seventies, Gardner remained a part of his country's music scene but kept a fairly low profile. As well as his own recordings, he played on sessions by such artists as The Heptones and Max Romeo. (Bob MacDonald Sept 1988).

CLASSIC TRACKS
CD 5": Released Nov '88, on Counterpoint. Catalogue no: **CDEP 9 C**

ELIZABETHAN REGGAE
Tracks: / Elizabethan reggae.
7" Single: Released Jan '70, on Duke, by Melodisc Records. Deleted '73. Catalogue no: **DU 39**
7" Single: Released Apr '83, on Old Gold, by Old Gold Records. Deleted Jul '88. Catalogue no: **OG 9272**

I WANT TO WAKE UP WITH YOU
Tracks: / I want to wake up with you.
12" Single: Released Jul '86, on Revue, by Creole Records. Catalogue no: **REV 033T**
7" Single: Released Jul '86, on Revue, by Creole Records. Catalogue no: **REV 733**

LET'S KEEP IT THAT WAY
Tracks: / Let's keep it that way / Let's keep it this way (Instrumental).
7" Single: Released Oct '85, on Londisc, by Londisc Records. Catalogue no: **7 LDR 017**
12" Single: Released Sep '86, on Londisc, by Londisc Records. Catalogue no: **12 LDR 017**

MEANING OF CHRISTMAS
Tracks: / Meaning of Christmas.
7" Single: Released Nov '86, on Revue, by Creole Records. Catalogue no: **REV 740**
12" Single: Released Dec '84, on Revue, by Creole Records. Catalogue no: **REV 020T**
12" Single: Released Nov '86, on Revue, by Creole Records. Catalogue no: **REV 040T**

MY COMMANDING WIFE
Tracks: / My commanding wife.
7" Single: Released Jul '89, on Charm, by Charm Records. Catalogue no: **CR 32**
12" Single: Released May '89, on Charm, by Charm Records. Catalogue no: **CRT 32**

SHE'S EVERYTHING I'M DREAMING OF
Tracks: / She's everything I'm dreaming of.
12" Single: Released Oct '88, on WKS. Catalogue no: **VPRD 331**

THIS OLD HOUSE
Tracks: / This old house / Simple silly fight.
12" Single: Released Jul '88, on WKS, Catalogue no: **VPRD 296**
7" Single: Released 21 Nov '87, on RCA, by BMG Records (UK). Deleted May '89. Catalogue no: **PB 41635**
12" Single: Released 21 Nov '87, on RCA, by BMG Records (UK). Deleted May '89. Catalogue no: **PT 41636**

YOU MAKE ME FEEL BRAND NEW
Tracks: / You make me feel brand new / Elizabethan reggae.
12" Single: Released Sep '86, on Trojan, by Trojan Records. Deleted May '88. Catalogue no: **TROT 9088**
7" Single: Released Sep '86, on Trojan, by Trojan Records. Deleted May '88. Catalogue no: **TRO 9088**

YOU'RE EVERYTHING TO ME
Tracks: / You're everything to me / Last night.
7" Single: Released Sep '86, on Revue, by Creole Records. Catalogue no: **REV 735**
12" Single: Released Sep '86, on Revue, by Creole Records. Catalogue no: **REV 035T**

Gardiner, Paul

Biographical details: This British bass guitarist was a protege of Gary Numan. He was a founder member of Numan's Tubeway Army in 1977, and remained Numan's most loyal sidekick through to the early Eighties. When Numan, the previously unknown singer/songwriter/producer/guitarist/synth esiser wizard, shot to stardom in 1979, the Tubeway Army monicker was dropped in favour of a solo Gary Numan billing; but Gardiner carried on playing on the records and live shows, in an admittedly ancillary role to the ultra-dominant Numan. The four-man Dramatis was also used as a backing band. By 1981 Numan had retired from live performances. That was the year when Gardiner achieved a one-off chart entry under his own name - *Stormtrooper in drag*, which reached no. 49 on the UK singles chart, featured Numan on guest vocals and was hardly a radical departure from Gary's own bleak, robotic and futuristic work. By the time Gary launched his Numa label in July 1984, Paul Gardiner had tragically died. As a tribute to Paul, the first record re4leased on the new label (catalogue no. NU 1) was Gardiner's *Venus in furs* single. (Bob Macdonald, 14/9/85).

STORMTROOPER IN DRAG
Tracks: / Stormtrooper in drag.
7" Single: Released Jul '81, on Beggars Banquet, by Beggars Banquet Records. Deleted Jan '88. Catalogue no: **BEG 61**

VENUS IN FURS
Tracks: / Venus in furs.
7" Single: Released Jul '84, on Numa, by Numa Records. Catalogue no: **NU 1**
12" Single: Released Jul '84, on Numa, by Numa Records. Catalogue no: **NUM 1**

Gardner & Boult

MAGIC EYES
Tracks: / Magic eyes / One love behind.
7" Single: Released Jan '80, on Gem, Deleted Jan '83. Catalogue no: **GEMS 16**

Gardner, Joanna

WATCHING YOU
Tracks: / Watching you / Pick up the pieces.
7" Single: Released May '85, on Polydor, by Polydor Ltd. Catalogue no: **POSP 744**
12" Single: Released May '85, on Polydor, by Polydor Ltd. Catalogue no: **POSPX 744**

Gardner, Willie

IMATION
Tracks: / Imation.
7" Single: Released Sep '81, on Virgin, by Virgin Records. Catalogue no: **VS 438**

Garfunkel, Art

Biographical details: This American singer, arranger and actor enjoyed his first taste of success in 1957 under the pseudonym Tom Graph. *Hey, schoolgirl* by Tom & Jerry reached no. 59 on the US Top 100 in that year, "Jerry" being Paul Simon. After this one-off foray into the charts, the two teenagers returned to school before re-emerging in 1966 as the world-famous Simon and Garfunkel duo. Following the 1970 break-up of the partnership, Arthur pursued a brief career in films: *Catch-22* (already in progress before the split) was followed by *Carnal knowledge* (1971). Garfunkel (born in Forest Hill in the New York borough of Queens) issued his debut solo album *Angel Clare* in 1973. It charted well on both sides of the Atlantic, and yielded the US Top 10 single *All I know*. Leaving lengthy gaps between LP releases, Art did not resurface until the autumn of 1975 - but it was worth the wait. The *Breakaway* album reached no. 7 in both the US and UK, and spawned a British no. 1 smash with his rendition of the Thirties standard *I only have eyes for you*. (The title song was written by Britain's Gallagher and Lyle, who simultaneously used it as the title of their own LP. *Breakaway* producer Richard Perry, in a 1982 interview with BBC Radio One, described the LP as his personal favourite amongst all the many successful albums that he has produced. Garfunkel's occasional reunions with Simon included *My little town* (on *Breakaway*) and a revival of Sam Cooke's *(What a) wonderful world* (a 1978 American Top 20 hit that featured vocals by Garfunkel, Simon and James Taylor). 1979 brought Art the biggest British hit of his career with a song that was written and produced by former Wombles mastermind Mike Batt - *Bright eyes*, lifted from the animated movie adaptation of Richard Adams' *Watership Down*, logged six weeks at the top of the UK charts and also hit no. 1 in several other European territories. Yet despite becoming Britain's best-selling single of the year, *Bright eyes* failed to even enter the Hot 100 in his native US. The high, pure, crystal-clear voice of Garfunkel had stuck with carefully selected and lushly produced ballads throughout the '70's. But the formula finally flopped in 1981, when the *Scissors cut* LP peaked at no. 51 in Britain and failed to crack the UD Top 200 albums chart. With Paul Simon's career also in the doldrums, the duo reunited in late 1981 for a massive free concert in New York's Central Park in front of 400,000 nostalgic fans. This resulted in a double album, video and tour. Garfunkel relaunched his solo career in the mid-Eighties. (Bob MacDonald, 15/9/85)
The pop singer and actor had gained international fame with Paul Simon in Simon & Garfunkel, whose split was caused partly by Garfunkel's decision to pursue an acting career, making his debut in *Catch 22* in 1970, and partly because Simon had been writing all their material and chafed at being only half the act. Garfunke's *Breakaway* in 1975 included Simon's song *My little town*; *Watermark* in 1977 had a hit cover of Sam Cooke's *Wonderful world* (singing with Simon and James Taylor); *Scissors cut* in 1981 was lushly over-produced, with songs by Jim Webb, Andrew Gold and Steven Bishop. His version of the evergreen *I only have eyes for you* was a top 20 hit in the USA, No. 1 in the UK in 1975; *The animals' Christmas* in 1986 with gospel/pop crooner Amy Grant, written by Webb, tells the story of the Nativity from the animals' point of view. He has one of the purest voices in pop. (Donald Clarke, July 1989) .

BRIGHT EYES
Tracks: / Bright eyes.
7" Single: Released Mar '79, on CBS, by CBS Records. Deleted '82. Catalogue no: **CBS 6947**

I ONLY HAVE EYES FOR YOU
Tracks: / I only have eyes for you.
7" Single: Released Sep '75, on CBS, by CBS Records. Deleted '78. Catalogue no: **CBS 3575**

SCISSORS CUT (SINGLE)
Tracks: / Scissors cut / So easy to begin.
7" Single: Released Sep '81, on CBS, by CBS Records. Deleted Sep '84. Catalogue no: **A 1708**

SINCE I DON'T HAVE YOU
Tracks: / Since I don't have you.
7" Single: Released Jul '79, on CBS, by CBS Records. Deleted '82. Catalogue no: **CBS 7371**

SO MUCH IN LOVE
Tracks: / So much in love / Slow breakup / What a wonderful world / I only have eyes for you.
CD 5": Released Mar '88, on CBS, by CBS Records. Deleted Jan '89. Catalogue no: **651 450 2**
7" Single: Released Feb '88, on CBS, by CBS Records. Deleted Aug '88. Catalogue no: **651 450 7**
12" Single: Released Feb '88, on CBS, by CBS Records. Deleted Aug '88. Catalogue no: **651 450 6**

WHEN A MAN LOVES A WOMAN
Tracks: / When a man loves a woman / King of Tonga.
7" Single: Released May '88, on CBS, by CBS Records. Deleted Jan '89. Catalogue no: **651 632 7**

Gargoyles

MADMEN FROM THE PLANET
Tracks: / Madmen from the planet.
7" Single: Released 15 Mar '87, on Reasonable, by Reasonable Records. Catalogue no: **JRR 002**

MAGNIFICENT CHURCH, THE
Tracks: / Magnificent church, The.
7" Single: Released 10 Oct '87, on Reasonable, by Reasonable Records. Catalogue no: **JRR 003**

Gariad, Heb

CANEUON O'R DE
Tracks: / Caneuon o'r de.
7" Single: Released Jun '88, on Anhrefn, Catalogue no: **ANHREFN 013**

Garland, Judy

Biographical details: This American actress and singer, born Frances Gumm in South Dakota in 1922, was the youngest of three daughters of vaudeville performers Frank & Ethel Gumm. She toured with her family in vaudeville from the age of three onwards, and was signed up by MGM Pictures at the age of 12. The precocious youngster made her screen debut for the company in *Every Sunday*, a 20 minute piece in which she appeared alongside the similarly youthful and equally talented Deanna Durbin. MGM realised that the two girls were incompatible on screen, but made the mistake of letting Durbin slip from their rosters; they kept Garland, however, and supervised her spectacular movie career until 1950. Judy's first major film was 1936's *Pigskin parade*; it was followed over the next three years by a whole host of pictures, including several with Mickey Rooney. Then came her most famous film *The Wizard Of Oz*, made in 1939 while its star was just 16 years old. Directed by Victor Fleming, *The wizard of Oz* won several Academy Awards including an Oscar for Judy for distinguished service to the cinema. The Harold Arlen/Yip Harburg song *Over the rainbow* became a worldwide standard, resulting in a million-selling disc for Judy and numerous cover versions. Even in the eighties, *The wizard of Oz* is still a stalwart item on Christmas television schedules and the Matchbox pop group reached the UK Top 20 with their 1980 version of *Over the rainbow*. Most people immediately think of this song and this film whenever Judy Garland's name is mentioned. During and after the Second World War, her many musical movies included *Babes on Broadway*, *Girl Crazy*, *Meet me in St. Louis* and *Easter parade*. 1950's *If you feel like singing* was her final film for MGM. A nervous breakdown forced her to pull out of *Annie get your gun*. Having recovered, Garland returned to showbusiness in the summer of 1951 with an acclaimed debut performance at the London Palladium. Her Hollywood renaissance came in 1954, when she starred with James Mason in Warner Brothers' *A star is born*. From that musical movie came Judy's hit single *The man that got away*, which reached the UK no. 18 position in June 1955. Her clear powerful voice penetrated the Top 20 of the UK album chart in 1962 with her double LP *Judy at Carnegie Hall* - more importantly, it was a no. 1 smash on the American album listings. With songs ranging from 1913 vintage to the 1954 variety, *Judy at Carnegie Hall* amply demonstrated Garland's ability to entertain as a singer outside the cinematic environment. Judy Garland's final concert took place in July 1968. She died in London in June 1969 at the age of 47, the pressures of showbusiness finally defeating her. Her daughter Liza Minelli followed in her career footsteps, and was particularly noticed for her 1972 movie *Cabaret*(Bob MacDonald, 15/8/85)
Frances Gumm (1922-69) became a legendary child star, but had no childhood; she is still one of the greatest stars in 20th Century showbiz. She made over 30 films, including *Wizard of Oz* in 1939 (*Over the rainbow*), *For me and my gal* in 1942 with Gene Kelly *Meet me in St Louis* in 1944, *Easter parade* in 1948 with Fred Astaire and *Summer stock* in 1950 with Kelly again: there were hit songs from most of these and her hit records began when Billboard began printing charts in 1940, in 1940, when she was still a teenager. It was George Jessel who named her Garland. *A Star is born* in 1954 with James Mason was perhaps the best film either of them made. Her nervous energy and insecurity led to problems with alcohol and pills; her Carnegie Hall concert in 1961 was a triumphant comeback: the double set topped the album chart in the USA for 13 weeks. Despite her well known health problems, her sudden death in London shocked the public; legend has it that when she died a tornado touched down in Kansas. Liza Minnelli is her daughter by the film director Vincent Minnelli, and has carried on in her larger than life tradition. (Donald Clarke, July 1989).

MAN THAT GOT AWAY, THE
Tracks: / Man that got away, The.
7" Single: Released Jun '55, on Philips, by Phonogram Ltd. Deleted '58. Catalogue no: **PB 366**

Garlow, Clarence

BON TON ROOLA (SINGLE)
Tracks: / Bon ton roola / My sweet honey bee.
7" Single: Released Dec '82, on Bally Hoo (USA), Catalogue no: **BH 1019**

ROUTE 90
Tracks: / Route 90 / Crawfishin'.
Note: This just has to be one of the best black rock 'n' roll records ever made. Recorded in the same year as Elvis' first ('That's All Right' - 1954), these records couldn't be more different. However, both were seminal building blocks for the exploding new rock 'n' roll scene of the day. This legendary Texan guitarist/singer was a steady influence on the blues/R&B scene and this superb coupling was recorded on the West Coast and features the exciting and tightly cooking band ofMaxwell Davis. (Detour Records).
7" Single: Released Jul '87, on Detour, by Detour Records. Catalogue no: **45-003**

Garner,Gigi

CITY BOY
Tracks: / City boy / Surrender.
7" Single: Released Aug '82, on Runaway, Deleted '85. Catalogue no: **RUN 504**

HEART BREAKER
Tracks: / Heartbreaker.
7" Single: Released Mar '82, on Runaway, Deleted '85. Catalogue no: **GIG 1**

LOVE HURTS
Tracks: / Love hurts / If lovin' was easy.
7" Single: Released Jul '82, on Runaway, Deleted '85. Catalogue no: **RUN 2**

REFLECTIONS OF MY LIFE
Tracks: / Reflections of my life.
7" Single: Released Apr '83, on Safari, by Safari Records. Catalogue no: **SAFE 53**

Garner,Kate

LOVE ME LIKE A ROCKET
Tracks: / Love me like a rocket.
12" Single: Released Oct '83, on Regard, Catalogue no: **RGT 112**
7" Single: Released Oct '83, on Regard, Catalogue no: **RG 112**

Garon, Jesse

ADAM FAITH EXPERIENCE
Tracks: / Adam Faith experience.
7" Single: Released Jan '88, on Speed, Catalogue no: **SPEED 001**
12" Single: Released Jan '88, on Speed, Catalogue no: **SPEED 001T**

AND IF THE SKY SHOULD FALL
Tracks: / And if the sky should fall.
7" Single: Released '88, on Velocity, Catalogue no: **SPEED 002**
12" Single: Released '88, on Velocity, Catalogue no: **SPEED 002T**

BILLY WHIZZ, THE (5 TRACK EP)
Tracks: / Billy whizz, The.
7" EP: Released 30 May '87, on Narodnik, by Narodnik Records. Catalogue no: **NRK 005T**

RAIN FELL DOWN, THE
Tracks: / Rain fell down.
7" Single: Released Mar '87, on Narodnik, by Narodnik Records. Catalogue no: **NRK 002**

SPLASHING ALONG
Tracks: / Splashing along / Presence dear.
7" Single: Released Nov '86, on Narodnik, by Narodnik Records. Catalogue no: **NRK 001**

YOU'LL NEVER BE THAT YOUNG AGAIN
Tracks: / You'll never be that young again.
12" Single: Released Jun '88, on Calculous, Catalogue no: **SPEED 2T**
7" Single: Released Jun '88, on Calculous, Catalogue no: **SPEED 2**

Garrett, Lee

YOU'RE MY EVERYTHING
Tracks: / You're my everything.
7" Single: Released May '76, on Chrysalis, by Chrysalis Records. Deleted '79. Catalogue no: **CHS 2087**

Garrett, Leif

Biographical details: This American singer and actor was born in Hollywood in 1961. It is probably just as accurate to say that his career was manufactured by Hollywood in the mid-seventies. After dabbling in nauseous teenage acting, Garrett was launched as a pop star in 1977 under the supervision of record producer Michael Lloyd. Shaun Cassidy (David's half-brother) had just been guided to yhe US no. 1 position by Lloyd with a remake of the Crystals' *Da doo ron ron*, so the opportunistic producer figured that another 1963 classic, *Surfin' USA*, would be just right for his new charge. Leif's horrendous rendition of The Beach Boys' oldie reached no. 20 in the States in '77, and was followed by a slightly less wimpy and more palatable version of Dion's *Runaround Sue*, which climbed to no. 13. Up to this point, British singles buyers remained largely impervious to the weenybopper appeal of Leif Garrett. But in early '79, his disco cash-in *I was made for dancin'* made the top 10 on both sides of the Atlantic, climbing to no. 4 in the UK. The title of the record was somewhat negated when the singer arrived in London to promote the hit - while visiting a disco, he was forced to retire from the dancefloor on the grounds of exhaustion. After achieving a smaller UK Top 40 success with a dreadful revamp of the Detroit Emeralds' *Feel the need*, Leif never returned to the Top 40 on either side of the Atlantic. By the time he celebrated his 18th birthday, he was already in the land of obscurity - where he was able to compare thoughts on th[e] vagaries of plastic stardom with his ol[d] mate Shaun Cassidy. (Bob Macdonald, 16/9/85).

LEIF GARRETT - I WAS MADE FOR DANCING (Released on Scott Bros.(USA))

FEEL THE NEED
Tracks: / Feel the need.
7" Single: Released Apr '79, on Scot[t] Bros (USA), Deleted '82. Catalogue no: **K 11274**

I WAS MADE FOR DANCING (se[e] panel above)
Tracks: / I was made for dancing / Livin[g] without your love.
7" Single: Released Jan '79, on Sco[tt] Bros (USA), Deleted '82. Catalogue no: **11202**

SAME GOES FOR YOU (SINGLE)
Tracks: / Same goes for you / Give in.
7" Single: Released Mar '80, on Sco[tt] Bros (USA), Deleted '83. Catalogue no: **11449**

WHEN I THINK OF YOU
Tracks: / When I think of you / Singing the rain.
7" Single: Released Feb '80, on Sco[tt] Bros (Germany), Deleted Feb '83. Catalogue no: **K 11438**

YOU HAD TO GO AND CHANGE O[N] ME
Tracks: / You had to go and change on m[e] / Rowena.
7" Single: Released Jan '81, on Sc[ott] Bros (Germany), Deleted Jan '84. Catalogue no: **K 11639**

Garrett, Siedah

K.I.S.S.I.N.G.
Tracks: / K.I.S.S.I.N.G. / Taboo.
12" Single: Released May '88, on Warn[er] Bros., by WEA Records. Catalogue no: **7928T**
CD 5": Released Jun '88, on Warner Bro[s.] by WEA Records. Catalogue no: **W 79[28] CD**
7" Single: Released May '88, on Warn[er] Bros., by WEA Records. Catalogue no: **7928**

Garrett,Winston

BIG BAD BOY
Tracks: / Big bad boy / Work up yourself
12" Single: Released Dec '84, on C[...] Sound, Catalogue no: **OSD 17**

Garrick, David

DEAR MRS.APPLEBEE
Tracks: / Dear Mrs.Applebee.
7" Single: Released Sep '66, on Piccad[illy] Deleted '69. Catalogue no: **7N 35335**

LADY JANE
Tracks: / Lady Jane / Let's go somewhe[re]
7" Single: Released Jun '66, on Piccad[illy] Deleted '69. Catalogue no: **7N 35317**

Garry

BRAND NEW HAIRCUT
Tracks: / Brand new haircut / Urban roc[k]billy.
7" Single: Released Feb '83, on Sin C[...]

by Sin City Records. Catalogue no: **SIN 1**

Garvey, Nick

TAKE A LOOK OVER MY SHOULDER
Tracks: / Take a look over my shoulder.
7" Single: Released Jul '82, on Virgin, by Virgin Records. Deleted '85. Catalogue no: **VS 504**

Garwood, Patrick

HURTING ME
Tracks: / Hurting me / Revolutionaries.
12" Single: Released Nov '81, on Cha-Cha, by Cha-Cha Records. Catalogue no: **CHAD 42**

Gary, John

YOURS
Tracks: / Yours.
7" Single: Released Sep '84, on RCA, by BMG Records (UK). Catalogue no: **RCA 439**

Gary O

WATCHING YOU
Tracks: / Watching you.
12" Single: Released Oct '85, on Arista, by BMG Records (UK). Catalogue no: **ARIST 12636**
7" Single: Released Oct '85, on Arista, by BMG Records (UK). Catalogue no: **ARIST 636**

Gary's Gang

Biographical details: The boom in disco music reached its peak on the UK charts in early 1979. So what better time could there be to release a record called *Keep on dancin*? That's what Gary's Gang did, and how very insipid and lightweight the single turned out to be. But it got feet moving on the dancefloor, and that was the most important factor at that time - it reached no. 8 on the British chart, and was followed by a similar sounding no. 49 hit called *Let's love dance tonight*. Rumours that Gary Glitter was the main voice and mastermind of Gary's Gang were scotched when it transpired that the band were American. After a gap of more than three years, the lads made a brief return to chartdom - *Knock me out* reached the no. 45 position in November 1982. (Bob Macdonald, 16/9/85).

KEEP ON DANCING
Tracks: / Keep on dancing / Let's love dance tonight.
7" Single: Released Feb '79, on CBS, by CBS Records. Deleted '82. Catalogue no: **CBS 7109**

KEEP ON DANCING (OLD GOLD)
Tracks: / Keep on dancing.
12" Single: Released Nov '87, on Old Gold, by Old Gold Records. Catalogue no: **OG 4025**

KNOCK ME OUT
Tracks: / Knock me out / Knock me out (instrumental).
7" Single: Released Oct '82, on Arista, by BMG Records (UK). Catalogue no: **ARIST 499**
12" Single: Released Oct '82, on Arista, by BMG Records (UK). Catalogue no: **ARIST 12499**

LET'S LOVE DANCE TONIGHT
Tracks: / Let's love dance tonight.
7" Single: Released Feb '79, on CBS, by CBS Records. Deleted '82. Catalogue no: **CBS 7328**

Gaskin

I'M NO FOOL
Tracks: / I'm no fool.
7" Single: Released Apr '81, on Rondelet Music, by Rondelet Music & Records. Catalogue no: **ROUND 7**

MONY MONY
Tracks: / Mony mony / Queen of hams.
7" Single: Released Jun '82, on Rondelet Music, by Rondelet Music & Records. Catalogue no: **ROUND 21**

Gatecrashers

YOU CAN'T DO THAT TO ME
Tracks: / You can't do that to me / Cash for my bits.
7" Single: Released Sep '81, on Bluff Tunes, by Independent Records. Deleted '86. Catalogue no: **GATE 1**

Gates, David

Biographical details: This American singer, songwriter, guitarist, keyboardist and producer was born in Tulsa, Oklahoma in 1939. His name is indelibly associated with seventies soft rock group Bread, but he was actually very active in the music business long before the band's formation in 1969. While in high school, he formed a band which included another future star, Leon Russell. Gates was also a member of a group which backed visiting rock 'n' roll stars in their local concerts. He then moved to Los Angeles to become a session performer and arranger, backing such artists as Glen Campbell, Duane Eddy and Merle Haggard. Despite their high position in the musical world, Bread split in 1973. This was apparently due to disagreements between Gates and fellow member James Griffin. David launched a solo career in the same year, releasing the logically titled LP *First*. This did not match the degree of success that he had attained in the group context, but he fared better in 1975's *Never let her go* album which yielded a US top 30 single with the title track. Meanwhile the many cover versions of his Bread songs included two surprise British no. 1 singles. *Everything I own* hit the top in a Jamaican reggae version by Ken Boothe in the autumn of 1974; and less than four months later, a dire spoken rendition by Kojak TV star Telly Savalas of the sonf *If* grabbed the UK no. 1 position, something that Bread themselves had never attained. A Bread reunion was attemped in the mid-seventies, but the now predictable nature of Gates' material and the band's sound ensured it was short lived. As a solo performer once again, David Gates reached no. 15 on the US charts in 1978 with his single *Goodbye girl*; later in the year, *Took the last train* reached no. 30 in the States and no. 50 in Britain (his only solo hit single in Britain). Gates was continuing his tradition of gentle but confident, highly melodic love songs, which he sang in his clear but delicate tenor voice. Subsequent records failed to sell in these quantities, but Gates does not need the money. The mass, broad appeal of his Bread classics represents perfect material for numerous MoR singers, thus ensuring him of a steady flow of songwriter's royalties. (Bob Mcdonald, 16/9/85).

COME HOME FOR CHRISTMAS
Tracks: / Come home for Christmas / It's what you say.
7" Single: Released Nov '82, on Arista, by BMG Records (UK). Catalogue no: **ARIST 446**

FALLING IN LOVE AGAIN
Tracks: / Falling in love again / Starship ride.
7" Single: Released Feb '80, on Elektra Asylum, by Elektra Records (USA). Deleted Feb '83. Catalogue no: **K 12423**

TOOK THE LAST TRAIN
Tracks: / Took the last train.
7" Single: Released Jul '78, on Elektra, by Elektra Records (UK). Deleted '81. Catalogue no: **K 12307**

WHERE DOES THE LOVING GO
Tracks: / Where does the loving go / Chingo.
7" Single: Released May '80, on Elektra, by Elektra Records (UK). Deleted May '83. Catalogue no: **K 12349**

Gates, Pearly

ACTION
Tracks: / Action (the Tony Atkins mix) / Action (the original mix) / Action / Sweet / Action (safe sex mix).
12" Single: Released 1 Jan '88, on Funkin' Marvellous, by Steinar Records (UK). Deleted 2 Aug '89. Catalogue no: **12MARVX 9**
7" Single: Released Jul '86, on Funkin' Marvellous, by Steinar Records (UK). Deleted Jul '86. Catalogue no: **MARV 3**
7" Single: Released Jan '88, on Funkin' Marvellous, by Steinar Records (UK). Deleted Nov '87. Catalogue no: **MARV 9**
12" Single: Released Jan '88, on Funkin' Marvellous, by Steinar Records (UK). Catalogue no: **12MARV 03**
12" Single: Released Jan '88, on Funkin' Marvellous, by Steinar Records (UK). Catalogue no: **12 MARV 9**
12" Single: Released Dec '87, on Priority, by Priority Records. Deleted Dec '87. Catalogue no: **12MARVX 3**

NO TWO WAYS ABOUT IT
Tracks: / No two ways about it.
12" Single: Released Feb '87, on Nightmare Gold, Catalogue no: **NGR 3**

Gathering

RANT
Tracks: / Rant / Dust after embers.
12" Single: Released Mar '88, on Final, Catalogue no: **FINAL 1**

Gatlin, Larry

ALL THE GOLD IN CALIFORNIA
Tracks: / All the gold in California / How much is a man supposed to take.
7" Single: Released Mar '80, on CBS, by CBS Records. Deleted Mar '83. Catalogue no: **CBS 8247**

Gatwick People

WE'RE ALL BEHIND YOU FREDDIE
Tracks: / We're all behind you Freddie / We're all behind you Freddie (part 2).
7" Single: Released Mar '82, on V-Tone, Deleted '85. Catalogue no: **006**

Gaughan, Dick

Biographical details: Singer, guitarist and songwriter born in Glasgow in 1948, from a family with a long history of working-class folk-song activity. He worked with Boys of The Lough and Five Hand Reel in the '70's, while making his own albums. During the Miner's strike of 1984-5 he campaigned on behalf of miners; in the political climate it may have been overlooked that he had always sung mining and industrial songs, contributing with Harry Boardman to the High Level Ranters' pioneering anthology *The Bonnie Pit Laddie* in 1975 on Topic. He also contributed to the Woody Guthrie tribute anthology *Woody lives* in 1987 on Black Crow. (Donald Clarke, July 1989).

GAMES PEOPLE PLAY
Tracks: / Games people play / Different kind of love song.
7" Single: Released Dec '84, on CMS, Catalogue no: **CMS 300**

Gaultier, Jean Paul

HOW TO DO THAT (IN A NEW WAY)
Tracks: / How to do that (in a new way) / How to do that (in a new way) (remix) / How to do that (in a new way) (video mix) / How to do that (in a new way) (acid version).
12" Single: Released 30 Jan '89, on Mercury, by Phonogram Ltd. Deleted Aug '89. Catalogue no: **MERX 277**
CD 5": Released 30 Jan '89, on Mercury, by Phonogram Ltd. Catalogue no: **MERCD 277**
7" Single: Released 30 Jan '89, on Mercury, by Phonogram Ltd. Deleted Aug '89. Catalogue no: **MER 277**

Gavin, Eric

POVERTY LINE
Tracks: / Poverty line.
7" Single: Released Jan '84, on Towerbell, Catalogue no: **TOW 47**
7" Single: Released Dec '82, on Trial, by Trial Records. Catalogue no: **CASE 5**

Gaye Bykers On Acid

ALL HUNG UP
Tracks: / All hung up / Afternoon tea with Dave Greenfield / All hung up (rough rider mix) (12" only) / All hung up (reprisal) (12" only).
7" Single: Released Nov '87, on Virgin, by Virgin Records. Deleted May '88. Catalogue no: **VS 1027**
12" Single: Released Nov '87, on Virgin, by Virgin Records. Catalogue no: **VST 1027**

EVERYTHING'S GROOVY
Tracks: / Everything's groovy.
12" Single: Released Nov '86, on In Tape, by In Tape Records. Deleted '88. Catalogue no: **ITTI 040**
7" Single: Released Nov '86, on In Tape, by In Tape Records. Deleted '88. Catalogue no: **IT 040**

GIT DOWN
Tracks: / Git down / Tolchocked by Kenny Pride / Go go in out, in out garotschka (On 12" only).
Special: Released '87, on Virgin, by Virgin Records. Catalogue no: **VSX 1008**
7" Single: Released 10 Oct '87, on Virgin, by Virgin Records. Deleted '89. Catalogue no: **VS 1008**
12" Single: Released 10 Oct '87, on Virgin, by Virgin Records. Catalogue no: **VST 1008**

HOT THING
Tracks: / Hot thing / Rad dude / After blow there's suck (Available on 12" format only.).
12" Single: Released Dec '88, on Virgin, by Virgin Records. Catalogue no: **VST 1165**
10" single: Released Dec '88, on Virgin, by Virgin Records. Catalogue no: **VSA 1165**
7" Single: Released Dec '88, on Virgin, by Virgin Records. Catalogue no: **VS 1165**

NIGHT TRACKS EP
Tracks: / Night tracks.
12" Single: Released Jan '89, on Night Tracks, by Pinnacle Records. Catalogue no: **SFNT 010**

NOSEDIVE KARMA
Tracks: / Nosedive karma.
7" Single: Released May '87, on In Tape, by In Tape Records. Catalogue no: **IT 046**
10" single: Released May '87, on In Tape, by In Tape Records. Deleted '88. Catalogue no: **IT 04610**
12" Single: Released May '87, on In Tape, by In Tape Records. Catalogue no: **ITTI 046**

Gaye, Frankie

IT TAKES TWO
Tracks: / It takes two.
7" Single: Released Aug '89, on Nightmare, by Nightmare Records. Catalogue no: **MARE 110**

Gaye, Marvin

Biographical details: This American singer, songwriter, keyboards player, drummer and producer was one of the greatest artists in the history of black soul music. He was born in Washington DC in 1939. His father, Rev. Marvin Gaye Sr, quickly brought him into the environment of church music - the young Marvin began singing at the age of three and, as he grew older, played the organ every Sunday. Upon completion of his education, he joined the US Air Force (again at his father's instigation) - but he was soon discharged for psychological reasons. Realising that music would always be his first love, Marvin joined the rhythm and blues band Harvey And The Moonglows - his association with leader Harvey Fuqua (who was to become an important behind-the-scenes figure at Tamla Motown Records) led to him signing with Motown in 1961. 1962 brought Gaye his first entry into the US Hot 100 with *Stubborn kind of fellow*. From '63 onwards, the American Top 40 hits came thick and fast, and the following all reached the Top 10: *Pride and joy*, *How sweet it is to be loved by you* (1965), *I'll be doggone* (1965), and *Ain't that peculiar* (1965). In addition to these solo smashes, he was regularly teamed with girl Motown singers and enjoyed hit duets with Mary Wells, Kim Weston and Tammi Terrell. The latter partnership was by far the most fruitful, yielding four US Top Tenners within a 12-month period: *Your precious love*, *If I could build my whole world around you*, *Ain't nothing like the real thing*, and *You're all I need to get by* were all big hits between late '67 and late '68. Then came the biggest hit of Marvin's career. *I heard it through the grapevine*, produced and co-written by Tamla Motown's rising svengali Norman Whitfield, logged seven weeks at no. 1 on the American charts in December '68 and January '69 - not bad considering that the same song had been a US no. 2 smash for Gladys Knight & The Pips a mere 12 months earlier. Britain, which had previously been distinctly lukewarm about Gaye's talents, finally woke up and made Marvin's *Grapevine* a no. 1 smash. Many more UK hits followed. Gaye was Tamla Motown's top male singer of the Sixties. He had joined the company just as they were warming up, and had grown with them. He had achieved all this with the help of the label's in-house writers, producers and musicians, and above all, his supremely soulful voice. But having stuck with the distinctive "Motown" sound throughout the sixties, Marvin Gaye then became the first artist to lead the company to new creative territories: deeply affected by the untimely death of Tammi Terrell, Gaye did much thinking and came up with the classic 1971 album *What's going on* - largely self-written and self-produced, this stunning "social conscience" LP paved the way for the later achievements of Stevie Wonder. Marvin's later US no. 1 smashes included *Let's get it on* (1973) and *Got to give it up* (1977). His career then collapsed for five years. Switching to CBS Records, Gaye bounced back in 1982 with the brilliant *Sexual healing*. His comeback was brutally ended on 1 April 1984, when he was shot dead by his father in a family row. It was the eve of Marvin's 45th birthday. (Bob Macdonald, 16/9/85)

Marvin Pentz Gaye (1939-84) was a singer, a star of black pop and one of the greatest crossover acts of his generation. He sang in a doo-wop group the Rainbows (with Don Covay) at 15; later won a talent contest singing Harvey Fuqua's *Ten commandments of love*, (Fuqua was one of the judges). The Rainbows became the Marquees, recording for Okeh; Gaye then joined Fuqua's Moonglows, then still recording for Chess; both Gaye and Fuqua went to Detroit and ended up with Tamla Motown, both marrying sisters of Berry Gordy. Gaye was a session drummer on early hits by the Miracles; when his own hits began he was versatile: dance craze *Hitch hike*, 12 bar blues *Can I get a witness*, rocker *Baby don't you do it* together with romantic and sensual ballads such as *How sweet it is to be loved by you*. *I heard it through the grapevine* in 1968 was his first No. 1 pop hit. He had duet hits with Mary Wells and Kim Weston, then the beautiful Tammi Terell: when she died of a brain tumour in 1970 everybody was devastated. He understood that an album should be more than two hits and 10 bits of filler: he had trouble with Motown management (it is thanks partly to his efforts that other artists like Stevie Wonder got lattitude for their projects), he avoided TV, rarely performed live and sometimes didn't show up; he used drugs and had trouble with the taxmen. Many of his later albums, beginning with *What's going on* in 1971, were huge hits and are still pop masterpieces. Getting divorced from Anna Gordy after 14 years he was ordered by a judge to give her royalties onan album; he filed bandruptcy and made *Here my dear* in '79; she considered lawsuit for invasion of privacy. His second wife left him for Teddy Pendergrass. He switched to CBS with *Midnight love* in 1982, including *Sexual healing*: after many nominations he finally won a Grammy for Best R&B Performance, Male with this No. 3 pop hit, pursued by categories to the end. He was shot to death by his father, an unbalanced clergyman. He had about 60 hits in the USA pop and black charts and 27 hit albums including compilation. (Donald Clarke, July 1989) .

ABRAHAM, MARTIN & JOHN
Tracks: / Abraham, Martin and John.
7" Single: Released May '70, on Tamla Motown, by Motown Records (UK). Deleted '73. Catalogue no: **TMG 734**
7" Single: Released Oct '81, on Motown, by BMG Records (UK). Catalogue no: **TMG 1165**

AIN'T NOTHING LIKE THE REAL THING
Tracks: / Ain't nothing like the real thing.
7" Single: Released Jun '68, on Tamla Motown, by Motown Records (UK). Deleted '71. Catalogue no: **TMG 655**

AIN'T THAT PECULIAR
Tracks: / Ain't that peculiar / I'll be doggone.
7" Single: Released Apr '88, on Motown, by BMG Records (UK). Catalogue no: **ZB 41909**

EGO TRIPPING OUT
Tracks: / Ego tripping out.
7" Single: Released Oct '81, on Motown, by BMG Records (UK). Deleted '83. Catalogue no: **TMG 1168**

GOOD LOVIN' AIN'T EASY TO COME BY
Tracks: / Good lovin' ain't easy to come by.
7" Single: Released Jun '69, on Tamla Motown, by Motown Records (UK). Deleted '72. Catalogue no: **TMG 697**

GOT TO GIVE IT UP
Tracks: / Got to give it up.
7" Single: Released May '77, on Tamla Motown, by Motown Records (UK). Deleted '80. Catalogue no: **TMG 1069**
12" Single: Released Apr '85, on Motown, by BMG Records (UK). Deleted '88. Catalogue no: **TMGT 1381**
7" Single: Released Apr '85, on Motown, by BMG Records (UK). Deleted '87. Catalogue no: **TMG 1381**

HEAVY LOVE AFFAIR
Tracks: / Heavy love affair / Far cry.
12" Single: Released Oct '81, on Motown, by BMG Records (UK). Deleted '83. Catalogue no: **TMGT 1232**
7" Single: Released Oct '81, on Motown, by BMG Records (UK). Deleted '83. Catalogue no: **7MG 1232**

HOW SWEET IT IS
Tracks: / How sweet it is to be loved by you.
7" Single: Released Dec '64, on Stateside, by EMI Records. Deleted '67. Catalogue no: **SS 360**

I HEARD IT THROUGH THE GRAPEVINE (SINGLE)
Tracks: / I heard it through the grapevine.
7" Single: Released Apr '86, on Motown, by BMG Records (UK). Catalogue no: **ZB 40701**
7" Single: Released Feb '69, on Tamla Motown, by Motown Records (UK). Deleted '72. Catalogue no: **TMG 686**
7" Single: Released Oct '81, on Motown, by BMG Records (UK). Catalogue no: **TMG 923**
12" Single: Released Apr '86, on Motown, by BMG Records (UK). Deleted '87. Catalogue no: **ZT 40702**

IF I COULD BUILD MY WHOLE WORLD AROUND YOU
Tracks: / If I could build my whole world around you.
7" Single: Released Jan '68, on Tamla Motown, by Motown Records (UK). Deleted '71. Catalogue no: **TMG 635**

IT TAKES TWO
Tracks: / It takes two.
7" Single: Released Oct '81, on Motown, by BMG Records (UK). Catalogue no: **TMG 590**

JOY (PART 1)
Tracks: / Joy (part 1).
12" Single: Released Mar '83, on CBS, by CBS Records. Catalogue no: **A 13 3242**
7" Single: Released Mar '83, on CBS, by CBS Records. Catalogue no: **A 3242**

LET'S GET IT ON (SINGLE)
Tracks: / Let's get it on.
7" Single: Released Sep '73, on Tamla Motown, by Motown Records (UK). Deleted '76. Catalogue no: **TMG 868**
7" Single: Released Mar '83, on Motown, by BMG Records (UK). Catalogue no: **TMG 868**

LITTLE DARLIN' (I NEED YOU)
Tracks: / Little darling (I need you).
7" Single: Released Sep '66, on Tamla Motown, by Motown Records (UK). Deleted '69. Catalogue no: **TMG 574**

MY LOVE IS WAITING
Tracks: / My love is waiting / Rockin' after midnight.
7" Single: Released Dec '83, on CBS, by CBS Records. Catalogue no: **A 3048**
12" Single: Released Dec '83, on CBS, by CBS Records. Catalogue no: **A 13 3048**

ONCE UPON A TIME
Tracks: / Once upon a time.
7" Single: Released Jul '64, on Stateside, by EMI Records. Deleted '67. Catalogue no: **SS 316**

ONION SONG
Tracks: / Onion song, The / You are everything.
7" Single: Released Nov '69, on Tamla Motown, by Motown Records (UK). Deleted '72. Catalogue no: **TMG 715**
7" Single: Released Oct '81, on Motown, by BMG Records (UK). Deleted '83. Catalogue no: **TMG 1047**
7" Single: Released Apr '85, on Motown, by BMG Records (UK). Deleted '87. Catalogue no: **TMG 993**
12" Single: Released Apr '85, on Motown, by BMG Records (UK). Deleted '87. Catalogue no: **TMGT 993**

PRAISE
Tracks: / Praise / Funk me.
7" Single: Released Oct '81, on Motown, by BMG Records (UK). Deleted '83. Catalogue no: **TMG 1225**
12" Single: Released Oct '81, on Motown, by BMG Records (UK). Deleted '83. Catalogue no: **TMGT 1225**

SANCTIFIED LADY
Tracks: / Sanctified lady.
7" Single: Released May '85, on CBS, by CBS Records. Deleted '88. Catalogue no: **A 4894**

SAVE THE CHILDREN
Tracks: / Save the children.
7" Single: Released Dec '71, on Tamla Motown, by Motown Records (UK). Deleted '74. Catalogue no: **TMG 796**

SEXUAL HEALING
Tracks: / Sexual healing / My love is waiting / Sexual healing (instrumental).
7" Single: Released Oct '82, on CBS, by CBS Records. Deleted '85. Catalogue no: **A 2855**

SEXUAL HEALING (OLD GOLD)
Tracks: / Sexual healing / My love is waiting.
7" Single: Released Jan '88, on Old Gold, by Old Gold Records. Catalogue no: **OG 9749**
12" Single: Released Aug '88, on Old Gold, by Old Gold Records. Catalogue no: **OG 4075**

STOP, LOOK,LISTEN TO YOUR HEART
Tracks: / Stop, look, listen to your heart.
7" Single: Released Oct '81, on Motown, by BMG Records (UK). Catalogue no: **TMG 906**

TOO BUSY THINKING 'BOUT MY BABY
Tracks: / Too busy thinking 'bout my baby.
7" Single: Released Oct '81, on Motown, by BMG Records (UK). Catalogue no: **TMG 705**

TWO CAN HAVE A PARTY
Tracks: / Two can have a party.
7" Single: Released Oct '81, on Motown, by BMG Records (UK). Catalogue no: **TMG 668**

WHAT'S GOING ON? (SINGLE)
Tracks: / What's going on? / I heard it through the grapevine / Wherever I lay my heart (on 12" only).
7" Single: Released Mar '83, on Motown, by BMG Records (UK). Catalogue no: **TMG 987**
12" Single: Released Nov '83, on Motown, by BMG Records (UK). Catalogue no: **TMGT 987**

WHEREVER I LAY MY HAT
Tracks: / Wherever I lay my hat.
7" Single: Released Jul '69, on Motown, by BMG Records (UK). Catalogue no: **TMG 705**

WORLD IS X-RATED
Tracks: / World is rated X / Lonely lover / World is rated X (instrumental) (On 12"version only.).
7" Single: Released Jun '86, on Motown, by BMG Records (UK). Deleted '88. Catalogue no: **ZB 40758**
12" Single: Released Jun '86, on Motown, by BMG Records (UK). Deleted '87. Catalogue no: **ZT 40758**

YOU AIN'T LIVIN' UNTIL YOU'RE LOVIN'
Tracks: / You ain't livin' till you're lovin' / Easiest way to fall, The.
7" Single: Released Dec '69, on Tamla Motown, by Motown Records (UK). Deleted '72. Catalogue no: **TMG 681**

YOU ARE EVERYTHING
Tracks: / You are everything.
7" Single: Released May '82, on Motown, by BMG Records (UK). Catalogue no: **TMG 890**

YOU'RE ALL I NEED TO GET BY
Tracks: / You're all I need to get by.
7" Single: Released Oct '81, on Motown, by BMG Records (UK). Catalogue no: **TMG 668**
7" Single: Released Oct '68, on Tamla Motown, by Motown Records (UK). Deleted '71. Catalogue no: **TMG 668**

Gayle, Crystal

Biographical details: This American singer and guitarist, real name Brenda Gayle Webb, is the younger sister of country superstar Loretta Lynn. Loretta was a major Nashville figure during the late sixties and early seventies, and her autobiographical novel *Coalminer's daughter* later became the basis of a movie. As a young girl, Crystal used to go and see her sister perform, often joining her on stage. As a teenager she sang in her brother's country band and in her school choir. She was still at school when she signed her first recording deal. Gayle's debut single *I've cried (the blue right out of my eyes)*, penned by Lynn, became a hit on the US country chart in 1970. Crystal carved out a steady country career over the next several years - but whereas her sister pursued a somewhat unconventional career in Nashville terms, Gayle flowed with the tide. As the country capital became more sophisticated and slick, and veered closer towards mainstream MoR and pop music, so did Crystal. Her attractive long locks and friendly eyes also helped. Returning to the theme of her original 1970 success, Gayle achieved her first and biggest pop crossover success with 1977's *Don't it make my brown eyes blue*. This brilliantly understated yet sensitive single displayed her crystal-clear voice to maximum effect - it reached no. 2 in the US and no. 5 in the UK. 1978's *Talking in your sleep* was another Top 20 hit on both sides of the Atlantic. 1979 brought her a US no. 15 hit with *Half the way*, and 1980 saw Gayle reach the Top 10 of the UK LP chart with *The Crystal Gayle singles album*. Always coming through best on ballads, she returned to the US Top 10 in 1983 with *You and I*, a duet single with fellow country crossover star Eddie Rabbitt. (Bob MacDonald, 16/9/85)

Brenda Gayle Webb was born in 1951 in Kentucky; the younger sister of Loretta Lynn, she became a country-pop star in her own right. She began working in her sister's road show at 16 and her own first country chart hit in 1970; she has had many hits through to 1989, including 17 No. 1's and duets with Eddie Rabbitt and Gary Morris. Twelve of the hers have crossed over to the Billboard Hot 100 including two top tens. (Donald Clarke, July 1989)y.

6 TRACK HITS
Tracks: / If you ever change your mind / Blue side, The / Ain't no sunshine / Lovin' in these troubled times / Dancing the night away / I just can't leave your love alone.
7" EP: Released Aug '84, on Scoop 33, by Pickwick Records. Catalogue no: **7SR 5048**

BABY WHAT ABOUT YOU
Tracks: / Baby what about you / Till I gain control again.
12" Single: Released Apr '83, on Elektra, by Elektra Records (UK). Catalogue no: **E 9880T**
7" Single: Released Apr '83, on Elektra, by Elektra Records (UK). Catalogue no: **E 9880**
7" Single: Released Sep '83, on Warner Bros., by WEA Records. Catalogue no: **W 9488**

BLUE SIDE
Tracks: / Blue side / Little bit of the rain.
7" Single: Released Jan '80, on CBS, by CBS Records. Deleted Jan '85. Catalogue no: **CBS 8076**

CRY
Tracks: / Crazy in the heart / Cry.
7" Single: Released Nov '86, on Warner Bros., by WEA Records. Deleted Jun '87. Catalogue no: **W 8689**

DON'T IT MAKE MY BROWN EYES BLUE?
Tracks: / Don't it make my brown eyes blue? / Talking in your sleep.
7" Single: Released Oct '77, on United Artists, by EMI Records. Catalogue no: **UP 36307**
7" Single: Released May '84, on EMI Golden 45's, by EMI Records. Catalogue no: **G45 18**

EVERYTHING I OWN
Tracks: / Everything I own / Easier said than done.
12" Single: Released Jan '83, on Elektra, by Elektra Records (UK). Catalogue no: **E 9909T**
7" Single: Released Dec '82, on Elektra, by Elektra Records (UK). Catalogue no: **E 9909**

HALF THE WAY
Tracks: / Half the way / Room for one more.
7" Single: Released Mar '81, on CBS, by CBS Records. Deleted Mar '84. Catalogue no: **CBS A 1024**

IF YOU EVER CHANGE YOUR MIND
Tracks: / If you ever change your mind / I just can't leave your love alone.
7" Single: Released Oct '80, on CBS, by CBS Records. Deleted Oct '83. Catalogue no: **CBS 9058**

LIVIN' IN THESE TROUBLED TIMES
Tracks: / Livin' in these troubled times / Tennessee.
7" Single: Released Feb '82, on CBS, by CBS Records. Deleted Feb '87. Catalogue no: **CBS A 1680**

LOVE, CRAZY LOVE
Tracks: / Love, crazy love / Tennessee.
7" Single: Released Oct '81, on CBS, by CBS Records. Deleted Oct '84. Catalogue no: **CBSA 1681**

TALKING IN YOUR SLEEP (SINGLE)
Tracks: / Talking in your sleep.
7" Single: Released Jun '78, on United Artists, by EMI Records. Catalogue no: **UP 36422**

TOO DEEP FOR TEARS
Tracks: / Too deep for tears / Your old cold shoulder.
7" Single: Released Feb '80, on Liberty, by EMI Records. Deleted Feb '83. Catalogue no: **UP 607**

Gayle, Erica

IT'S ALRIGHT
Tracks: / It's alright.
12" Single: Released Oct '82, on Ital, by Ital Records. Catalogue no: **ITD 0015**

Gayle, Roy

UP ALL NIGHT (DOING IT)
Tracks: / Up all night (doing it).
12" Single: Released Feb '87, on Musik, Catalogue no: **MUK 5**
7" Single: Released Feb '87, on Musik, Catalogue no: **12 MUK 5**

Gaylords

NA NA NA MARIE
Tracks: / Na na na Marie.
7" Single: Released Jan '87, on Pinner Catalogue no: **PRM 904**

Gaynor, Gloria

Biographical details: This America[n] singer can justly calim to be one of th[e] most influential artists of the seventies [-] she was the original Queen of the Disco before being dethroned by Donna Summer, and she pioneered the use of extended dance mixes. The subsequen[t] explosion in disco music owed a lot to Gaynor andher producers. Born in Newark, New Jersey, Gloria made her first tentative forays into recording studios in the mid sixties. She had to wait almost a decade fo[r] her big breakthrough, and she filled these years by performing and touring in America and Europe. Then, in late 1974, came her LP *Never can say goodbye* - immaculately conceived and produced by New York engineers Tony Bongiovi, Meco Monardo and Tom Moulton (the forerunners of peop[le] like Jellybean), the whole of Side One became staple fodder for dancefloors on both sides of the Atlantic. The three segue numbers on this historic side began wi[th] *Honey bee* and followed through with a remake of The jackson Five's *Never can say goodbye* (which gave Gaynor a no. 2 sing[le] in Britain and a no. 9 in the States) and a equally danceable remake of The Four Tops' *Reach out I'll be there* (which reached no. 14 in Britain). Gloria belted out the songs with incredible power and passion; her intensity and feeling contrasted markedly with the manufactured, mechanical production. As Donner Summer's career blossomed in 1976, Gaynor's collapsed. But in 1979, she bounced back from total obscurity to achieve her biggest hit *I will survive*, a formidable feminist anthem that scorched dancefloors and radio turntables everywhere, was a two-million-selling no. 1 monster in the US and logged four weeks at the top in the UK. The yo-yo recording career of Gloria Gaynor then nosedived once again. Five years later, she was suddenly back in the UK Top 20 with *I am what I am* from the Broadway musical *La cage aux folles*. This time the singer was striking a blow for the gay community which ironically was being heavily maligned by a "born-again" Donna Summer. Gaynor may not be too worried nowadays by the spasmodic nature of her disc success - her past achievements ensure a nice income wherever she performs. (Bob Macdonald, 17/9/85).

AIN'T NO BIGGER FOOL
Tracks: / Ain't no bigger fool / Don't read me wrong.
12" Single: Released Jun '80, on Polydor, by Polydor Ltd. Deleted Jun '84. Catalogue no: **214 125 9**
7" Single: Released Jun '80, on Polydor, by Polydor Ltd. Deleted Jun '84. Catalogue no: **209 524 1**

ALL I NEED IS YOUR SWEET LOVIN'
Tracks: / All I need is your sweet lovin'.
7" Single: Released Aug '75, on MGM, by Polydor Ltd. Deleted '78. Catalogue no: **2006 531**

BE SOFT WITH ME TONIGHT
Tracks: / Be soft with me tonight / Be soft with me tonight (club mix) / If only you'd believe it / If only you'd believe it (inst).
CD 5": Released Apr '87, on Fanfare, by Captain Billy's Music. Catalogue no: **CDFAN 11**

EVERY BREATH YOU TAKE
Tracks: / Every breath you take / Don't dare call it love.
12" Single: Released Jun '86, on Stylus, by Stylus Music Records. Deleted '88. Catalogue no: **HONEY 1 12**
7" Single: Released Jun '86, on Stylus, by Stylus Music Records. Deleted '88. Catalogue no: **HONEY 1**

HOW HIGH THE MOON
Tracks: / How high the moon.
7" Single: Released Jan '76, on MGM, by Polydor Ltd. Deleted '79. Catalogue no: **2006 558**

I AM WHAT I AM
Tracks: / I am what I am / More than enough.
12" Single: Released Dec '83, on Chrysalis, by Chrysalis Records. Catalogue no: **CHS 122765**
7" Single: Released Dec '83, on Chrysalis, by Chrysalis Records. Catalogue no: **CHS 2765**

I WILL SURVIVE
Tracks: / I will survive / Honey Bee.
12" Single: Released Oct '82, on Polydor, by Polydor Ltd. Catalogue no: **POSPX 600**
7" Single: Released Feb '79, on Polydor, by Polydor Ltd. Deleted '82. Catalogue no: **2095 017**
12" Single: Released Sep '87, on Polydor (Holland), by Polydor Ltd. Catalogue no: **887036 1**

I WILL SURVIVE (OLD GOLD)
Tracks: / I will survive / Never can say goodbye.
7" Single: Released Jun '88, on Old Gold, by Old Gold Records. Catalogue no: **OG 9436**

LET ME KNOW (I HAVE THE RIGHT)
Tracks: / Let me know (I have a right).
7" Single: Released Oct '79, on Polydor, by Polydor Ltd. Deleted '82. Catalogue no: **STEP 5**

LOVE ME REAL
Tracks: / Love me real.
12" Single: Released Sep '83, on Ecstasy, by Creole Records. Catalogue no: **XTCT 4**
7" Single: Released Sep '83, on Ecstasy, by Creole Records. Catalogue no: **XTC 4**

MY LOVE IS MUSIC
Tracks: / My love is music / If I need you.
7" Single: Released Mar '85, on Carrere, Catalogue no: **CAR 357**
12" Single: Released Mar '85, on Carrere, Catalogue no: **CART 357**

NEVER CAN SAY GOODBYE (SINGLE)
Tracks: / Never can say goodbye.
7" Single: Released '74, on MGM, by Polydor Ltd. Catalogue no: **2006 463**

REACH OUT I'LL BE THERE
Tracks: / Reach out I'll be there.
7" Single: Released Mar '75, on MGM, by Polydor Ltd. Deleted '78. Catalogue no: **2006 531**

STRIVE
Tracks: / Strive / I've been waiting for you.
12" Single: Released Mar '84, on Chrysalis, by Chrysalis Records. Catalogue no: **GAYX 1**
7" Single: Released Mar '84, on Chrysalis, by Chrysalis Records. Catalogue no: **GAY 1**

Gaz

SING SING
Tracks: / Sing sing.
7" Single: Released Feb '79, on Salsoul, Deleted '82. Catalogue no: **SSOL 116**

MELLOW SAXOPHONE
Tracks: / Mellow saxaphone.
7" Single: Released Feb '82, on Fliptone, Deleted '83. Catalogue no: **FT 003**

Gazebo

I LIKE CHOPIN
Tracks: / I like Chopin.
7" Single: Released Sep '83, on Baby, by New Rose Records. Catalogue no: **BABY 4**
12" Single: Released Sep '83, on Baby, by New Rose Records. Catalogue no: **BABY 412**

MASTERPIECE
Tracks: / Masterpiece.
12" Single: Released Sep '82, on Baby, by New Rose Records. Catalogue no: **BABY 112**
7" Single: Released Sep '82, on Baby, by New Rose Records. Catalogue no: **BABY 1**

Gaz's Rebel Blues...

TRIGGER HAPPY
Tracks: / Trigger happy.
7" Single: Released Sep '83, on Risk, Catalogue no: **RISK 1**

Gazuzu

GO GO GORILLA
Tracks: / Go go gorilla.
12" Single: Released Jan '84, on Ecstasy, by Creole Records. Catalogue no: **XTCT 6**
7" Single: Released Jan '84, on Ecstasy, by Creole Records. Catalogue no: **XTC 6**

G.B. Band

ONE'S A LONELY NUMBER
Tracks: / One's a lonely number / Same old story.
7" Single: Released Feb '81, on Magnet, by WEA Records. Deleted Feb '84. Catalogue no: **MAG 186**

SMASHEROO
Tracks: / Smasheroo / Long distance.
7" Single: Released Jul '81, on Magnet, by WEA Records. Deleted '84. Catalogue no: **MAG 204**

WHEN WILL I BE LOVED
Tracks: / When will I be loved / Survival.
7" Single: Released Oct '80, on Magnet, by WEA Records. Deleted Oct '83. Catalogue no: **MAG 183**

GB Rockers

SHEREE SHEREE
Tracks: / Sheree Sheree / You.
7" Single: Released May '83, on Runaway, Deleted '85. Catalogue no: **RUN 502**

G.B.H.

Biographical details: At the time of their greatest achievement, this British rock band consisted of Colin, Jock, Ross and Wilf, all the members being known solely by their first names. GBH, which denoted the legal term Grievous Bodily Harm, sums up the band's savage and uncompromising attitude. The group were initially known as Charged GBH. The band was formed in 1980, their first performance being a prostitutes' benefit gig. Their first record was a 12" single, *Leather, bristles, studs and acne*, which was released in August 1981 on Stoke-on-Trent's Clay label. With the Uk music press having lost interest in the punk genre, and with the original punk bands having either broken up or moved into the rock mainstream, it was becoming hard for the new bands to gain attention and they were thus forming their own esoteric subculture in an attempt to re-establish grass roots interest. This really amounted to a recycling of the 1977-style New Wave music, but with a more furious socio-political content added plus a few heavy metal ingredients. In 1982 GBH made two brief appearances on the UK national charts: *No survivors* reached no. 63, and *Give me fire* peaked at no. 69. Their debut LP was called *City baby attacked by rats* - tracks like *Slit your own throat* and *Self destruct* summed up the band's sickening stance. The group made little impact on the public, although they kept releasing singles such as *Catch-23* (1983) and *Do what you do* (1984). The latter was not the same song as the Jermaine Jackson ballad! (Bob Macdonald, 17/9/85).

CATCH 23
Tracks: / Catch 23.
7" Single: Released Apr '83, on Clay, by Clay Records. Deleted '88. Catalogue no: **CLAY 22**

CHARGED
Tracks: / Charged.
7" Single: Released Aug '84, on Clay, by Clay Records. Deleted '88. Catalogue no: **CLAY 36**
12" Single: Released Aug '84, on Clay, by Clay Records. Catalogue no: **12CLAY 36**

GIVE ME FIRE
Tracks: / Give me fire / Man-trap.
7" Single: Released Nov '82, on Clay, by Clay Records. Deleted '88. Catalogue no: **CLAY 16**
7" Pic: Released Nov '82, on Clay, by Clay Records. Deleted '88. Catalogue no: **CLAY 16P**

LEATHER BRISTLES STUDS ACNE (SINGLE)
Tracks: / Leather bristles, studs, acne.
12" Single: Released Mar '84, on Clay, by Clay Records. Catalogue no: **PLATE 3**

NO SURVIVORS (SINGLE)
Tracks: / No survivors / Self destruct / Big women.
7" Single: Released Jan '82, on Clay, by Clay Records. Deleted '88. Catalogue no: **CLAY 8**

OH NO IT'S GBH AGAIN
Tracks: / Oh no it's GBH again.
12" Single: Released Sep '86, on Rough Justice, by Music For Nations Records. Catalogue no: **12 KORE 101**

SICK BOY
Tracks: / Sick boy / Slit your own throat / Am I dead yet.
7" Single: Released Jun '82, on Clay, by Clay Records. Deleted '88. Catalogue no: **CLAY 11**

WOT A BARGIN
Tracks: / Wot a bargin.
12" Single: Released Mar '88, on Music For Nations, by Music For Nations Records. Catalogue no: **12 KORE 104**

G-Clefs

Biographical details: Unfortunately for the G-Clefs' immortality aspiration, their only major hit *I understand just how you feel* was made equally famous by two other acts. The G-clefs, an all-male American vocal group, made a brief appearance on the US Top 40 in 1956 with *Ka-ding-dong* (also a Top 40 hit for the Diamonds and the Hilltoppers). *I understand* made its mark at the end of 1961, when it reached no. 9 in the States and no. 17 in Britain. Singing against a backing tune of *Auld lang syne*, the G-Clefs' rendition of *I understand* occurred seven years after the Four Tunes' version and three years before that of Freddie and the Dreamers. The G-Clefs consisted of four brothers plus a friend; the quintet hailed from Roxbury, Massachussetts. They quickly faded into the archive files. (Bob Macdonald, 17/9/85).

I UNDERSTAND
Tracks: / I understand.
7" Single: Released Nov '61, on London-American, Deleted '64. Catalogue no: **HLU 9433**

I UNDERSTAND (OLD GOLD)
Tracks: / I understand.
7" Single: Released Oct '83, on Old Gold, by Old Gold Records. Catalogue no: **OG 9361**

Geddes Axe

ESCAPE FROM NEW YORK
Tracks: / Escape from New York.
12" Single: Released Jun '83, on Bullet, by Bullet Records. Deleted '88. Catalogue no: **BOLT 4**

RETURN OF THE GODS
Tracks: / Return of the gods.
7" Single: Released May '81, on ACS, Catalogue no: **ACS 1**

SHARPEN YOUR WITS
Tracks: / Sharpen your wits / Rock & roll is the way.
7" Single: Released Aug '82, on Steel City, Deleted '86. Catalogue no: **AXE 1**

Gee, Debbie

WILL I EVER DO
Tracks: / Will I ever do / Let me try.
12" Single: Released Dec '82, on TNT, Catalogue no: **TNT 004**

Gee, Junior

CAVEMAN ROCK
Tracks: / Caveman rock.
7" Single: Released Nov '84, on Master Funk, Catalogue no: **7MF 005**

CHECK US OUT
Tracks: / Check us out.
12" Single: Released Sep '84, on Taiwan, by Tania Music Records. Catalogue no: **TWD 1948**

TERMINATOR, THE
Tracks: / Terminator, The / Terminator, The (dub edit) / Terminator, The (perfect madness mix) / Terminator (remix) (7" radio edit) (This remix only on the 12" single 12 BRWX 63) / Terminator (instrumental) (Version on the 12" single 12 BRWX 63).
Note: see also under A Team & Junior Gee
12" Single: Released Mar '87, on 4th & Broadway, by Island Records. Catalogue no: **12 BRWX 63**
12" Single: Released Feb '87, on 4th & Broadway, by Island Records. Deleted Apr '88. Catalogue no: **12 BRW 63**
7" Single: Released Feb '87, on 4th & Broadway, by Island Records. Catalogue no: **BRW 63**

Gee, Lorna

GOTTA FIND A WAY
Tracks: / Gotta find a way.
12" Single: Released Oct '85, on Ariwa Sounds, by Ariwa Sounds. Catalogue no: **ARI 46**

SING-A-LONG
Tracks: / Sing-a-long / Russian Roulette.
12" Single: Released Sep '86, on Ariwa Sounds, by Ariwa Sounds. Catalogue no: **ARI 56**

STOP CHAT
Tracks: / Stop chat.
12" Single: Released May '89, on Ariwa Sounds, by Ariwa Sounds. Catalogue no: **ARI 790**

THREE WEEKS GONE
Tracks: / Three weeks gone.
12" Single: Released Feb '85, on Ariwa Sounds, by Ariwa Sounds. Catalogue no: **ARI 37**

YOU AND ME
Tracks: / You and me.
12" Single: Released Jan '88, on Roraima, by Ariwa Sounds. Catalogue no: **ROR 002**

Gee Mr Tracey

I WISH THE WHOLE DAMN WORLD WAS IN A BOTTLE
Tracks: / I wish the whole damn world was in a bottle.
7" Single: Released Jul '85, on Backs, by Backs Recording Co.. Catalogue no: **NCH 103**

LAVA MAN
Tracks: / Lava man / Mr. Unlucky.
7" Single: Released Jan '86, on Backs, by Backs Recording Co.. Catalogue no: **NCH 106**

PERMANENT SWOON
Tracks: / Permanent swoon / I fell through the floor.
7" Single: Released Jun '86, on Backs, by Backs Recording Co.. Catalogue no: **NCH 108**

YOU MAKE MY HOUSE SHINE
Tracks: / You make my house shine / Go scuba / For my honey.
7" Single: Released Mar '85, on Backs, by Backs Recording Co.. Catalogue no: **NCH 102**

Gee, Norman

I AM YOUR MAN
Tracks: / I am your man.
12" Single: Released Feb '89, on PLJ Records, Catalogue no: **PLJ 004**

ROLL THE DICE
Tracks: / Roll the dice / It's a must.
12" Single: Released Apr '86, on Gentlesounds, Catalogue no: **GSS 003 D**

Gee Sloley

I LIKE YOUR LOVING
Tracks: / I like your loving / I like your loving (part 2).
12" Single: Released Dec '82, on Redman International, Catalogue no: **RED 003**

Gee, Spoonie

I'M ALL SHOOK UP
Tracks: / I'm all shook up / I'm all shook up (Godfather remix).
7" Single: Released 27 Feb '88, on Sure Delight, by Sure Delight Records. Cata-

logue no: **SD 5**
12" Single: Released 27 Feb '88, on Sure Delight, by Sure Delight Records. Catalogue no: **SDT 5**

Gee, Tony

ONE MINUTE MORE
Tracks: / One minute more.
7" Single: Released Jun '85, on Mass Enterprise, Catalogue no: **MISM 1**
12" Single: Released Jun '85, on Mass Enterprise, Catalogue no: **MISMT 1**

Gehmann

BMW
Tracks: / BMW / Life in G Major.
12" Single: Released Sep '86, on BGI, Catalogue no: **GP 101**

Geils, J.

CENTREFOLD
Tracks: / Centrefold / Flamethrower.
7" Single: Released Jan '82, on EMI-America, by EMI Records. Deleted Jan '85. Catalogue no: **EA 135**

I DO
Tracks: / I do / Sanctuary.
7" Single: Released Jan '83, on EMI-America, by EMI Records. Catalogue no: **EA 149**

Geisha Girls

I'M A TEAPOT
Tracks: / I'm a teapot.
7" Single: Released Sep '83, on Dog Breath, Catalogue no: **WOOF 2**

SLAVE OF LOVE
Tracks: / Slave of love.
7" Single: Released Feb '85, on Dog Breath, Catalogue no: **7DOG 1**
12" Single: Released Feb '85, on Dog Breath, Catalogue no: **12DOG 1**

Geisterfaher

MADISH AHB'ELL
Tracks: / Madish ahb'ell / Leiser tod.
7" Single: Released Jul '82, on Upright, by Upright Records. Catalogue no: **UP YOURS 3**

Geldof, Bob

Biographical details: Geldof, Bob. See under Boomtown Rats for D Clarke, 24 August 1988..

I CRY TOO
Tracks: / I cry too (Extra track on 12") / Deep in the heart of nowhere (Extra track on 12").
7" Single: Released Jun '87, on Mercury, by Phonogram Ltd. Deleted Dec '87. Catalogue no: **BOB 103**
12" Single: Released Jun '87, on Mercury, by Phonogram Ltd. Deleted Dec '87. Catalogue no: **BOBX 103**

LOVE LIKE A ROCKET
Tracks: / Love like a rocket / Tis is the world calling / Pulled apart by horses / Truly truly blue / Love like a rocket (12" mix).
CD 5": Released Feb '87, on Mercury, by Phonogram Ltd. Deleted Oct '88. Catalogue no: **BOBCD 102**

THIS IS THE WORLD CALLING
Tracks: / This is the world calling / Talk me up.
7" Single: Released Oct '86, on Mercury, by Phonogram Ltd. Deleted Dec '87. Catalogue no: **BOB 101**
12" Single: Released Oct '86, on Mercury, by Phonogram Ltd. Deleted Dec '87. Catalogue no: **BOBX 101**

Gelzer, Helen

THERE IS A SUCKER
Tracks: / Thre is a sucker / Night and day.
7" Single: Released May '80, on Pye, Deleted '83. Catalogue no: **7P 181**

Gem, Robert

NIGHTWALKER
Tracks: / Nightwalker.
7" Single: Released Jun '85, on President, by President Records. Catalogue no: **PT 534**

Gemini

ANOTHER YOU ANOTHER ME
Tracks: / Another you another me / Falling / Copy love (On 12" version only.).
7" Single: Released Oct '86, on Polydor, by Polydor Ltd. Deleted Mar '87. Catalogue no: **POSP 795**
12" Single: Released Oct '86, on Polydor, by Polydor Ltd. Deleted Mar '87. Catalogue no: **POSPX 795**

JUST LIKE THAT
Tracks: / Just like that / Live on the love.
7" Single: Released Mar '86, on Polydor, by Polydor Ltd. Deleted '86. Catalogue no: **POSP 782**
12" Single: Released Mar '86, on Polydor, by Polydor Ltd. Deleted '86. Catalogue no: **POSPX 782**

Gems

LEAVING
Tracks: / Leaving / Forever.
12" Single: Released Mar '87, on Silent (1), by Silent Records. Deleted Nov '87. Catalogue no: **12 GEM 3**

STAND UP SIT DOWN
Tracks: / Stand up sit down / Here it comes again / Stand up sit down (instrumental) (On 12" version only.).
12" Single: Released Feb '86, on Silent (1), by Silent Records. Deleted Nov '87. Catalogue no: **12 GEM 1**
7" Single: Released Feb '86, on Silent (1), by Silent Records. Deleted Nov '87. Catalogue no: **GEM 1**

WALK AWAY
Tracks: / Walk away / Wasted land.
7" Single: Released Mar '87, on Silent (1), by Silent Records. Deleted Dec '87. Catalogue no: **GEM 3**
12" Single: Released Mar '87, on Silent (1), by Silent Records. Catalogue no: **12 GEM 3**

YOUNG MANS DREAM
Tracks: / Young mans dream / Hand over fist.
12" Single: Released May '86, on Silent (1), by Silent Records. Deleted Nov '87. Catalogue no: **12 GEM 2**
7" Single: Released May '86, on Silent (1), by Silent Records. Deleted Nov '87. Catalogue no: **GEM 2**

Gender, Jesse

SHAKE, THE
Tracks: / Shake, The / Why do fools fall in love.
12" Single: Released May '89, on Greensleeves, by Greensleeves Records. Catalogue no: **GRED 243**

GIRL IN MY DREAMS
Tracks: / Girl in my dreams, The.
12" Single: Released Jun '89, on Justice, Catalogue no: **JUDIS 42**

Gene And Jim

SHAKE
Tracks: / Shake.
12" Single: Released Mar '88, on Rough Trade, by Rough Trade Records. Catalogue no: **RTT 216**
7" Single: Released Mar '88, on Rough Trade, by Rough Trade Records. Catalogue no: **RT 216**

Gene Loves Jezebel

BRUISES
Tracks: / Bruises / Punch drunk / Brando.
7" Single: Released Jul '83, on Situation 2, by Beggars Banquet Records. Catalogue no: **SIT 24**
12" Single: Released Jul '83, on Situation 2, by Beggars Banquet Records. Catalogue no: **SIT 24T**

COW
Tracks: / Cow / Someone somewhere.
12" Single: Released May '85, on Situation 2, by Beggars Banquet Records. Catalogue no: **SIT 36T**
7" Single: Released May '85, on Situation 2, by Beggars Banquet Records. Catalogue no: **SIT 36**

DESIRE(COME AND GET IT)
Tracks: / Desire(come and get it) / Message / Sapphire scavenger (On 12" version only.) / New horizons (On 12" version only.) / Desire (full length version) / Influenza (instrumental) / Sweetest Jezebel / Rhino plasty, The / Deep sound.
7" Single: Released Oct '86, on Beggars Banquet, by Beggars Banquet Records. Catalogue no: **BEG 173**
12" Single: Released Oct '86, on Beggars Banquet, by Beggars Banquet Records. Catalogue no: **BEG 173 T**
Cassingle: Released Nov '86, on Beggars Banquet, by Beggars Banquet Records. Catalogue no: **BEG 173TC**

EVERY DOOR
Tracks: / Every door.
7" Single: Released May '88, on Beggars Banquet, by Beggars Banquet Records. Catalogue no: **BEG 212**
12" Single: Released May '88, on Beggars Banquet, by Beggars Banquet Records. Catalogue no: **BEG 212T**

GORGEOUS
Tracks: / Gorgeous / Someone on the 6th floor (at the Jezebel Palace).
Note: BEG 202S is a limited edition gatefold sleeve.
CD 5": Released Nov '87, on Beggars Banquet, by Beggars Banquet Records. Deleted Jul '88. Catalogue no: **BEG 202CD**
12" Single: Released Nov '87, on Beggars Banquet, by Beggars Banquet Records. Catalogue no: **BEG 202T**
7" Single: Released Dec '87, on Beggars Banquet, by Beggars Banquet Records. Catalogue no: **BEG 202S**
7" Single: Released Nov '87, on Beggars Banquet, by Beggars Banquet Records. Catalogue no: **BEG 202**

HEARTACHE
Tracks: / Heartache / Beyond doubt / Deli babies (On 12" version only.).
7" Single: Released May '86, on Beggars Banquet, by Beggars Banquet Records. Catalogue no: **BEG 161**
12" Pic: on Beggars Banquet, by Beggars Banquet Records. Deleted Jun '87. Catalogue no: **BEG 161TP**
7" Single: Released Dec '85, on Beggars Banquet, by Beggars Banquet Records. Catalogue no: **SIT 41**
12" Single: Released Dec '85, on Beggars Banquet, by Beggars Banquet Records. Catalogue no: **SIT 41 T**
12" Single: Released May '86, on Beggars Banquet, by Beggars Banquet Records. Catalogue no: **BEG 161T**

INFLUENZA Relapse
Tracks: / Influenza / Promise.
7" Single: Released Apr '84, on Situation 2, by Beggars Banquet Records. Catalogue no: **SIT 31**

MOTION OF LOVE, THE
Tracks: / Motion of love, The.
7" Set: Released Aug '87, on Beggars Banquet, by Beggars Banquet Records. Catalogue no: **BEG 192D**
12" Single: Released Aug '87, on Beggars Banquet, by Beggars Banquet Records. Catalogue no: **BEG 192TD**

SCREAMING
Tracks: / Screaming.
12" Single: Released May '83, on Situation 2, by Beggars Banquet Records. Catalogue no: **SIT 20T**
7" Single: Released May '83, on Situation 2, by Beggars Banquet Records. Catalogue no: **SIT 20**

SHAME
Tracks: / Shame / Whole heart howl (on 7" only) / Gorgeous / Thin things.
7" Single: Released May '84, on Situation 2, by Beggars Banquet Records. Catalogue no: **SIT 35**
12" Single: Released May '84, on Situation 2, by Beggars Banquet Records. Catalogue no: **SIT 35T**

SHAVIN MY NECK
Tracks: / Shavin' my kneck.
7" Single: Released May '82, on Situation 2, by Beggars Banquet Records. Catalogue no: **SIT 18**
12" Single: Released Jun '82, on Situation 2, by Beggars Banquet Records. Catalogue no: **SIT 18T**

SWEETEST THING
Tracks: / Sweetest thing / Psycho II.
12" Single: Released Mar '86, on Beggars Banquet, by Beggars Banquet Records. Catalogue no: **BEG 156 T**
7" Single: Released Mar '86, on Beggars Banquet, by Beggars Banquet Records. Catalogue no: **BEG 156**

Gene Syndrome

25 OR 6 TO 4
Tracks: / 25 or 6 to 4 / And she's following.
7" Single: Released Oct '86, on Toadstool, by Toadstool Records. Deleted '88. Catalogue no: **GENE 2**

ROYAL VOODOO
Tracks: / Royal voodoo / Phenomenal sky.
7" Single: Released Jun '88, on Gene, Catalogue no: **GENE 3**

General Assembly

SENSITIVE MIND
Tracks: / Sensitive mind / Lovin' time.
7" Single: Released Mar '83, on Neil Rushton, Catalogue no: **DEMW 202**

General Beeny

FIT AND ROUND
Tracks: / Fit and round.
12" Single: Released Sep '88, on Josiah, Catalogue no: **KJ 005**

General, Bingie

FOR MY LOVER
Tracks: / For my lover.
12" Single: Released Sep '89, on Steely & Cleevie, Catalogue no: **VPRD 495**

General Caine

HAIRDOOZ
Tracks: / Hairdooz / Crack killed Applejack.

12" Single: Released Nov '86, on Motown, by BMG Records (UK). Deleted '87. Catalogue no: **ZT 41034**
7" Single: Released Nov '86, on Motown, by BMG Records (UK). Deleted '87. Catalogue no: **ZB 41033**

General Degree

MOTHER RULE PICKNEY
Tracks: / Mother rule pickney.
12" Single: Released Sep '89, on Mixing Lab, Catalogue no: **MXL 27**

General Diego

DEM NO LIKE THE YARDIE
Tracks: / Dem no like the yardie.
12" Single: Released Aug '88, on Supertone, Catalogue no: **STR 006**

General Echo

AFRICAN NATIONAL HEROES
Tracks: / African national heroes / Rastaman off dignity.
7" Single: Released Dec '82, on Mandingo, Deleted Dec '87. Catalogue no: **AYO 1982**

AFRIKA'S NATIONAL HERO
Tracks: / Afrika's national hero.
10" single: Released Nov '82, on Mandingo, Catalogue no: **MM 422**

HOTEL FEE
Tracks: / Hotel fee / Bathroom sex.
12" Single: Released Jan '80, on Greensleeves, by Greensleeves Records. Catalogue no: **GRED 30**

General & Killerwatt

MINDER
Tracks: / Minder.
12" Single: Released Nov '85, on Cool Ghoul, by Cool Ghoul Records. Catalogue no: **COOL 005**

General Lafayette

TRUE LOVE WILL NEVER DIE
Tracks: / True love will never die / True love will never die (version).
7" Single: Released Sep '89, on Plaza, by Plaza Records. Catalogue no: **PZA 049**
12" Single: Released Sep '89, on Plaza, by Plaza Records. Catalogue no: **PZA 049T**

General Mickey

YOU GOT THE KEY
Tracks: / You got the key.
12" Single: Released Jan '89, on High Power, Catalogue no: **HPD 07**

General, Mikey

DANCE HALL VIBES
Tracks: / Dance hall vibes / Margaret.
12" Single: Released Oct '86, on Digikal, by Fashion Records. Catalogue no: **DIG 002**

DO FOR LOVE
Tracks: / Do for love.
7" Single: Released 21 Apr '89, on Briggie C, Catalogue no: **BC 004T**

I SAY NO
Tracks: / I say no / Rose ann.
12" Single: Released Dec '85, on MGR, Catalogue no: **MGR 3**

KUFF'N DEM
Tracks: / Kuff'n dem.
12" Single: Released Mar '87, on Digikal, by Fashion Records. Catalogue no: **DIG 005**

SINGER WITH THE FLAVOUR
Tracks: / Singer with flavour.
12" Single: Released Jun '85, on Jah Life, Catalogue no: **JLO 11**

SOUND DOCTOR
Tracks: / Sound doctor / Jump and shout.
12" Single: Released Dec '85, on Fashion, by Fashion Records. Catalogue no: **FAD 043**

General Public

FAULTS AND ALL
Tracks: / Faults and all / Taking the day off.

12" Single: Released Sep '86, on Virgin, by Virgin Records. Deleted May '88. Catalogue no: **VS 870-12**
7" Single: Released Sep '86, on Virgin, by Virgin Records. Deleted May '88. Catalogue no: **VS 870**

GENERAL PUBLIC
Tracks: / General public / Dishwasher.
7" Single: Released Mar '84, on Virgin, by Virgin Records. Deleted '87. Catalogue no: **VS 659**

TENDERNESS (see panel on next page)
Tracks: / Tenderness.
12" Single: Released Mar '85, on Virgin, by Virgin Records. Deleted '89. Catalogue no: **VS 729-12**
7" Single: Released '84, on Virgin, by Virgin Records. Catalogue no: **VS 729**

GENERAL PUBLIC - TENDERNESS (Released on Virgin)

General Slaughter

MOUTH-A-MASSEY
Tracks: / Mouth-a-massey.
12" Single: Released Jun '88, on Y & D, Catalogue no: **YDDO 127**

General Smiley

BEING WITH YOU
Tracks: / Being with you / Ghetto man.
12" Single: Released Feb '82, on Greensleeves, by Greensleeves Records. Catalogue no: **GRED 78**

General Trees

DIBI DIBI D.J.
Tracks: / Dibi dibi d.j..
12" Single: Released Nov '88, on Black Scorpio, Catalogue no: **UNKNOWN**

HORSEMAN STYLE
Tracks: / Horseman style.
12" Single: Released Sep '84, on Jammy's, Catalogue no: **UNKNOWN**

NO MONEY, NO RUN
Tracks: / No money, no run.
12" Single: Released Apr '88, on Time One, Catalogue no: **TR 023**

General Turbo

I'VE BEEN GIFTED
Tracks: / I've been gifted / General turbo.
12" Single: Released Jul '86, on Turbo, Catalogue no: **GT 001**

General Twilight

HIGHWAY LOVER
Tracks: / Highway lover / Pamela.
12" Single: Released Jan '85, on Marlon Ranks, Catalogue no: **MR 003**

Generation N

1992
Tracks: / 1992 / 1992 (version).
12" Single: Released 31 Jul '89, on Escalator, Catalogue no: **ESCA 1203**

Generation X

Biographical details: At the time oftheir greatest success, this British punk rock band consisted of Bob "Derwood" Andrews, Billy Idol, tony James and Mark Laff. The photogenic, white-haired Idol (real name William Broad) was the group's lead vocalist and frontman. They took their name from the title of a 1964 paperback about youth that was found in Idol's mother's bookshelf. Generation X were among the original wave of 1976 UK punk groups. In October of that year Idol, James and drummer John Towe were founder members of a group called Chelsea; but by December Generation X had come into being. Within a few days of their formation, they became one of the first bands to play at London's Roxy Club, a short-lived but seminal haven for the early punk bands and fans. In the autumn of 1977, with Towe having been replaced by Laff, the group entered the UK national chart with their debut single *Your generation*; it reached no. 36. This record was one of the classic statements of the new wave - it answered the Who's 1965 anthem *My generation* by declaring that the old wave of rock bands were now totally redundant. Oddly, the third single *Ready steady go* contradicted it by paying tribute to one of Britain's top TV pop shows of the Sixties. 1979 brought Generation X their only two UK Top 30 singles, both produced by Ian Hunter (ex Mott-the-Hoople): *King rocker* climbed to no. 11 and *Valley of the dolls* reached no. 23. In 1980 the band shortened their name to Gen X, in recognition of an abbreviation that was already in common usage among fans, but only the minor hit *Dancing with myself* stood between Gen X and obscurity. The group's third and final album *Kiss me deadly* (1981), flopped despite being produced by Giorgio Moroder's protege Keith Forsey. By the end of 1981 Gen X had folded. But Idol retained Forsey's services and launched a successful solo career in America under the guidance of Kiss manager William Aucoin, a career which eventually rebounded Billy into the higher echelons of the British charts. (Bob Macdonald, 18/9/85).

DANCING WITH MYSELF
Tracks: / Dancing with myself / Ugly rash / Loopy (dub) (Only on 12" version.).
7" Single: Released Nov '80, on Chrysalis, by Chrysalis Records. Deleted '85. Catalogue no: **CHS 2444**
12" Single: Released Oct '80, on Chrysalis, by Chrysalis Records. Catalogue no: **CHS 12 2444**

DANCING WITH MYSELF (2)
Tracks: / Dancing with myself / Untouchables / Rock on / King rocker.
7" Single: Released Jan '81, on Chrysalis, by Chrysalis Records. Deleted '85. Catalogue no: **CHS 2488**
12" Single: Released Jan '81, on Chrysalis, by Chrysalis Records. Catalogue no: **CHS 12 2488**

FRIDAYS ANGELS
Tracks: / Friday's angels / Trying for kicks / This heat.
7" Single: Released '79, on Chrysalis, by Chrysalis Records. Catalogue no: **CHS 2330**

KING ROCKER
Tracks: / Gimme some truth / King rocker.
7" Single: Released Jan '79, on Chrysalis, by Chrysalis Records. Catalogue no: **CHS 2261**

KING ROCKER (OLD GOLD)
Tracks: / King Rocker / Valley of the dolls.
7" Single: Released Feb '87, on Old Gold, by Old Gold Records. Catalogue no: **OG 9693**

READY STEADY GO
Tracks: / Ready steady go / No no no.
7" Single: Released Mar '78, on Chrysalis, by Chrysalis Records. Deleted '83. Catalogue no: **CHS 2207**

VALLEY OF THE DOLLS (see panel below)
Tracks: / Valley of the dolls / Shakin' all over.
7" Single: Released '79, on Chrysalis, by Chrysalis Records. Catalogue no: **CHS 2310**

WILD YOUTH
Tracks: / Wild youth / Wild dub.
7" Single: Released '82, on Chrysalis, by Chrysalis Records. Deleted '87. Catalogue no: **CHS 2189**

YOUR GENERATION
Tracks: / Your generation / Day by day.
7" Single: Released Sep '77, on Chrysalis, by Chrysalis Records. Deleted '82. Catalogue no: **CHS 2165**

Generic

FOR A FREE AND LIBERATED SA
Tracks: / For a free and liberated SA.
7" Single: Released 1 Jul '86, on Flat Earth, Deleted '88. Catalogue no: **FE 001**

SPARK INSIDE
Tracks: / Spark inside, The.
7" Single: Released 20 Feb '88, on Loony Tunes, by Loony Tunes Records. Catalogue no: **TUNE 010**

Genesis

Biographical details: The longest-lasting and most successful line-up of this British rock band has been Tony Banks, Phil Collins and Mike Rutherford. The group's name was suggested by early mentor Jonathan King because "it suggested the beginning of a new sound and feeling". Genesis was formed in 1967 while all five founder members were pupils at Charterhouse public school near Godalming, Surrey. The original quintet were keyboardist/vocalist Banks and guitarist/bassist/vocalist Rutherford (the only two members who have stayed the course throughout the band's entire history) plus lead vocalist Peter Gabriel, guitarist/vocalist Anthony Philips and drummer Chris Stewart. Genesis signed with Charisma Records in Spring 1970, and have remained with the label ever since. By the time the band issued their second Charisma LP, 1971's *Nursery cryme*, the line-up consisted of Banks, Rutherford, Gabriel and two new recruits: guitarist Steve Hackett and drummer/vocalist Phil Collins, who had grown up in showbusiness as a successful child actor. This quintet represented the first classic Genesis line-up, remaining intact till 1975. The band enjoyed their first taste of chart success in 1972 with the *Foxtrot* album. The following three LP's - *Genesis live, Selling England by the pound* and the double set *The lamb lies down on Broadway* - all made the British Top 10 and increased their international following. The band epitomised the then much-used term "progressive rock", but had the added ingredient of Gabriel's outlandish stage costumes and increasingly idiosyncratic theatrics. Gabriel also possessed an intense and distinctive voice, and wrote most of their best material. In 1975 Gabriel's shock decision to quit the group and pursue a solo career led to a widespread assumption that Genesis were finished. After exhaustive auditions to find a replacement, the rest of the band surprised press and public even more by announcing that Collins was taking over the lead vocal role. Nobody believed that the down-to-earth Phil could adequately replace the unpredictable, attention-grabbing Peter. But, confounding all expectations, he rapidly took Genesis to even greater heights of success with the albums *A trick of the tail* and *Wind and wuthering*. 1978's aptly-titled *And then there were three* LP was their first as a trio. Hackett, who had first released a solo offering in 1975, decided to pursue a full-time solo career and enjoyed reasonable success. Quashing break-up expectations yet again, the resilient Genesis undertook one of their now famous world tours (with the help of a guest drummer and additional guest guitarist, plus a huge road crew and truckloads of equipment), sold vast quantities of *And then...* and landed their first UK Top 10 single *Follow you follow me*. Finally dispensing with the grandiose and srty (many say pompous) style they had employed during the seventies, Messrs. Banks, Collins and Rutherford attacked the eighties with renewed vigour and a leaner, more rhythmic sound. *Duke* (1980), *Abacab* (1981) and *Genesis* (1983) all entered the UK album charts at no. 1 and became worldwide smashes, as did Phil's solo offerings. (Bob MacDonald, 18/9/85)
A UK art rock band who became stadium/pop biggies. They began at Charterhouse school as songwriters calling themselves Garden Wall: keyboardist Tony Banks, Michael Rutherford on guitar, bass and vocals, vocalist Peter Gabriel and guitarist Anthony Phillips. Jonathan King renamed them, godfathered pop album *From Genesis to Revelation* in 1969. They developed a theatrical stage show and began to gain a cult following with Trespass in 1970. Several drummers had passed through, finally succeeded permanently by Phil Collins; Phillips was replaced by Steve Hackett. *Nursery crymes, Foxtrot, Selling England by the pound* and *Genesis live* were folowed by double concept album *The lamb lies down on Broadway* in 1974 starring Gabriel, who then left for a solo career; they auditioned singers but decided Collins would do, hiring second drummers for tours (including Bill Bruford in 1976); they switched from costumes etc. to laser/stadium. shows. Critics havelong since given up on them, but three of their later albums were No. 1's in the UK and Top Ten in the USA. Collins became a superstar but refused to leave the group permanently. (Donald Clarke, July 1989).

3 X 3
Tracks: / Paperlate / You might recall / Me and Virgil.
7" EP: Released May '82, on Charisma, by Virgin Records. Deleted '85. Catalogue no: **GEN 1**

ABACAB (SINGLE) (see panel ojn next page)
Tracks: / Abacab / Another record.
7" Single: Released Aug '81, on Charisma, by Virgin Records. Deleted Aug '84. Catalogue no: **CB 388**

DUCHESS
Tracks: / Duchess / Open door.

GENERATION X - VALLEY OF THE DOLLS (Released on Chrysalis)

GENESIS - ABACAB (Released on Charisma)

7" Single: Released May '80, on Charisma, by Virgin Records. Deleted '83. Catalogue no: **CB 363**

FOLLOW YOU FOLLOW ME
Tracks: / Follow you follow me / Ballad of big.
7" Single: Released Mar '78, on Charisma, by Virgin Records. Deleted '81. Catalogue no: **CB 309**

FOLLOW YOU FOLLOW ME (OLD GOLD)
Tracks: / Follow you follow me / Trick of the tail.
7" Single: Released Jun '88, on Old Gold, by Old Gold Records. Catalogue no: **OG 9264**

I KNOW WHAT I LIKE (IN YOUR WARDROBE)
Tracks: / I know what I like.
7" Single: Released Apr '74, on Charisma, by Virgin Records. Deleted '77. Catalogue no: **CB 224**
7" Single: Released Jul '82, on Old Gold, by Old Gold Records. Catalogue no: **OG 9263**

ILLEGAL ALIEN
Tracks: / Illegal alien / Turn it on again (live).
7" Pic: Released Jan '84, on Charisma, by Virgin Records. Deleted '89. Catalogue no: **ALS 1**
7" Single: Released Jan '84, on Charisma, by Virgin Records. Deleted '89. Catalogue no: **AL 1**
12" Single: Released Jan '84, on Charisma, by Virgin Records. Catalogue no: **AL 112**

IN TOO DEEP
Tracks: / In too deep / Do the neurotic / In too deep (unedited version) (12" only).
7" Single: Released Aug '86, on Charisma, by Virgin Records. Catalogue no: **GENS 2**
12" Single: Released Aug '86, on Charisma, by Virgin Records. Catalogue no: **GENS 212**

INVISIBLE TOUCH (SINGLE)
Tracks: / Invisible touch / Last domino, The / Invisible touch (extended version) (On 12" only).
12" Single: Released '86, on Virgin, by Virgin Records. Catalogue no: **GENS 112**
7" Single: Released '86, on Virgin, by Virgin Records. Catalogue no: **GENS 1**

KEEP IT DARK
Tracks: / Keep it dark / Naminanu.
7" Single: Released Oct '81, on Charisma, by Virgin Records. Catalogue no: **CB 391**
12" Single: Released Oct '81, on Charisma, by Virgin Records. Deleted '89. Catalogue no: **CB 39112**

LAND OF CONFUSION
Tracks: / Land of confusion / Feeding the fire / Do the neurotic (CD only) / Land of confusion (extended remix) (CD & 12" only).
CD 5": Released Nov '86, on Virgin, by Virgin Records. Catalogue no: **SNEG 312**
7" Single: Released Nov '86, on Charisma, by Virgin Records. Catalogue no: **GENS 3**
12" Single: Released Nov '86, on Charisma, by Virgin Records. Catalogue no: **GENS 312**

MAMA
Tracks: / Mama / Gonna get better.
7" Single: Released Aug '83, on Charisma, by Virgin Records. Catalogue no: **MAMA 1**
12" Single: Released Aug '83, on Charisma, by Virgin Records. Catalogue no: **MAMA 12**

MAMA (CD SINGLE)
Tracks: / Mama (long version) / It's gonna get better (long version).
CD 3": Released Jun '88, on Virgin, by Virgin Records. Catalogue no: **CDT 5**

MAN ON THE CORNER
Tracks: / Man on the corner.
7" Single: Released Mar '82, on Charisma, by Virgin Records. Deleted '85. Catalogue no: **CB 393**

MANY TOO MANY
Tracks: / Many too many.
7" Single: Released Jul '78, on Charisma, by Virgin Records. Deleted '81. Catalogue no: **CB 315**

MISUNDERSTANDING
Tracks: / Misunderstanding / Evidence of autumn.
7" Single: Released Sep '80, on Charisma, by Virgin Records. Deleted '83. Catalogue no: **CB 369**

SPOT THE PIGEON
Tracks: / Match of the day / Pigeons / Inside and out.
CD 3": Released '88, on Virgin, by Virgin Records. Catalogue no: **CDT 40**

SPOT THE PIGEON (EP)
Tracks: / Match of the day / Pigeons / Inside and out.
7" EP: Released May '77, on Charisma, by Virgin Records. Deleted '80. Catalogue no: **GEN 001**

THAT'S ALL
Tracks: / That's all / Taking it all too hard / Firth of fifth.
12" Single: on Virgin, by Virgin Records. Catalogue no: **TATA 112**

THROWING IT ALL AWAY
Tracks: / Throwing it all away (7" only) / I'd rather be you (On all versions) / Invisible touch (live version) (12" & cassette only) / Throwing it all away (live version) (12" & cassette only).
7" Single: Released Jun '87, on Virgin, by Virgin Records. Catalogue no: **GENS 5**
Cassingle: Released '87, on Virgin, by Virgin Records. Catalogue no: **GENSC 512**
12" Single: Released Jun '87, on Virgin, by Virgin Records. Catalogue no: **GENS 512**

TONIGHT TONIGHT TONIGHT
Tracks: / Tonight tonight tonight (remix) / In the glow of the night / Paperlate (CD & 12" only) / Tonight tonight tonight (12" mix) (CD & 12" only).
7" Single: Released Mar '87, on Virgin, by Virgin Records. Catalogue no: **GENS 4**
CD 5": Released Mar '87, on Virgin, by Virgin Records. Catalogue no: **DRAW 412**
12" Single: Released Mar '87, on Virgin, by Virgin Records. Deleted May '88. Catalogue no: **GENS 412**

TURN IT ON AGAIN
Tracks: / Turn it on again / Behind the lines part 2.
7" Single: Released Mar '80, on Charisma, by Virgin Records. Deleted '83. Catalogue no: **CB 356**

YOUR OWN SPECIAL WAY
Tracks: / Your own special way / It's yourself.
7" Single: Released Feb '77, on Charisma, by Virgin Records. Catalogue no: **CB 300**

Genesis Gospel Singers

N'TUTU(SINGLE)
Tracks: / N'tutu.
7" Single: Released Feb '84, on Africagram, by Cherry Red Records. Deleted '87. Catalogue no: **ARID 1**
12" Single: Released Feb '84, on Africagram, by Cherry Red Records. Deleted '87. Catalogue no: **12 ARID 1**

Geneva

TWO MINUTES THIRTY
Tracks: / Two minutes thirty / Geneva Street.
7" Single: Released Feb '80, on Valiant, Deleted '83. Catalogue no: **ROUND 1**

Genevieve

ONCE
Tracks: / Once.
7" Single: Released May '66, on CBS, by CBS Records. Deleted '69. Catalogue no: **202061**

Genghis Khan

LOVE YOU
Tracks: / Love you.
7" Single: Released May '83, on Wabbit, Catalogue no: **WAB 63**

MEXICO
Tracks: / Mexico.
7" Single: Released '87, on Sonet, by Sonet Records. Catalogue no: **SON 2289**

MONGOL NATION
Tracks: / Mongol nation.
7" Single: Released May '83, on Wabbit, Catalogue no: **WAB 61**

Genie

HE'S A REBEL
Tracks: / He's a rebel.
7" Single: Released 21 Nov '87, on Bolts, by Bolts Records. Catalogue no: **BOLTS 9**
12" Single: Released 21 Nov '87, on Bolts, by Bolts Records. Catalogue no: **BOLTS 09/12**

Genius at Work

BIG APPLE PROD.(VOL 1)
Tracks: / Big Apple prod. (Vol 1).
12" Single: Released Nov '87, on B & W (USA), Catalogue no: **BAM 101**

BIG APPLE PROD. (VOL 2)
Tracks: / Big Apple prod. (Vol 2).
12" Single: Released Nov '87, on J&T (USA), Catalogue no: **JT 102**

BIG APPLE PROD. (VOL 3)
Tracks: / Big Apple prod. (Vol 3).
12" Single: Released Nov '87, on J&T (USA), Catalogue no: **JT 103**

Genocide

GENOCIDE (EP)
7" Single: Released '80, on Safari, by Safari Records. Catalogue no: **SAP 2**

Genocides

HONEY THAT AIN'T NO ROMANCE
Tracks: / Honey that ain't no romance.
7" Single: Released Jul '83, on Flicknife, by Flicknife Records. Catalogue no: **FLS 020**

IS THAT ALRIGHT
Tracks: / Is that alright.
7" Single: Released Oct '82, on Action, Catalogue no: **TAKE 1**

Gentle Touch

DREAM OF YOU
Tracks: / Dream of you.
7" Single: Released Nov '83, on Tristar, Catalogue no: **TRI 3**

Gentlemen Without

EONS ROLL BY
Tracks: / Eons roll by / Uchu o mamoro.
7" Single: Released 26 Sep '88, on A&M, by A&M Records. Deleted Feb '89. Catalogue no: **AM 466**
12" Single: Released 26 Sep '88, on A&M, by A&M Records. Deleted Feb '89. Catalogue no: **AMY 466**

UNCONDITIONAL LOVE(PLANET EARTH)
Tracks: / Unconditional love / Way of the dodo, The.
CD 5": Released 6 Aug '88, on A&M, by A&M Records. Catalogue no: **AMCD 448**
7" Single: Released 6 Aug '88, on A&M, by A&M Records. Deleted Feb '89. Catalogue no: **AM 448**
12" Single: Released 6 Aug '88, on A&M, by A&M Records. Deleted Feb '89. Catalogue no: **AMY 448**

Gentles, Bill

DANCE WITH ME
Tracks: / Dance with me (version).
12" Single: Released Jan '86, on Jama, Catalogue no: **JADC 0027**

EVER SINCE I MET YOU
Tracks: / Ever since I met you.
12" Single: Released Feb '82, on Echo, by Echo Records. Catalogue no: **ECHO 009**

Gentles, Errol

TELL ME WHY
Tracks: / Tell me why.
12" Single: on Attack, Deleted '88. Catalogue no: **TACK 11**

Gentlman Gerald

ANYONE FOR TENNIS
Tracks: / Anyone for tennis.
7" Single: Released Jul '81, on Dingle's, by Dingle's Records. Catalogue no: **SID 22**

Gentry, Bobbie

Biographical details: This American singer, songwriter, guitarist and dancer was born in Chickasaw County, Mississippi of Portuguese descent. Her real name was Roberta Streeter but she was inspired to change her surname by the movie "Ruby Gentry". Having dabbled in music and acting during childhood, Bobbie studied music and philosophy in Los Angeles before taking up a job as a Las Vegas nightclub dancer. Suddenly, in August 1967, the 23-year-old Gentry stormed into the US Top 40 - two weeks after entering that list, she was no. 1 with *Ode to Billy Joe* and stayed there for a further four weeks. This sombre folk/country single, which could hardly have been further removed from the music of Las Vegas, was stunning in the sparsness of its arrangement, the terseness of its melody and the moroseness of its message - Billy Joe MacAllister takes a suicide jump off the Tallahatchie Bridge, but the neighbours keep on living their lives as if nothing has happened. *Ode to Billy Joe* was Gentry's first record - her voice was accompanied by her own guitar, six violins and two cellos, and the song took barely 15 minutes of studio time to record. *Ode to Billy Joe* peaked at no. 13 in Britain, but she obtained a UK no. 1 two years later with Burt Bacharach and Hal David's *I'll never fall in love again*, a song taken from the Broadway musical *Promises Promises*. Soon afterwards, at the beginning of 1970, she duetted with Glen Campbell on a cover version of the Everly Brothers' classic *All I have to do is dream* - this reached no. 3 in Britain and no. 27 in the States. She also reached no. 31 in the States with the self-penned *Fancy* and no. 40 in the UK with *Raindrops keep fallin' on my head*. After writing and recording *Ode to Billy Joe* and other songs such as *Mississippi delta* and *Chickasaw county child*, Bobbie Gentry was hailed as a great new singer-songwriter. But as the above history shows, she was quickly whisked away into the showbiz world of TV specials and MoR cover versions, her own songwriting skills being virtually abandoned. She had left her heart in Vegas not Chickasaw, a fact confirmed by her marriage to Las Vegas magnate Bi Hurrah. (Bob MacDonald, 18/9/85)
Born Roberta Streeter in Chickasaw Country, Mississippi in 1944, she moved t California while still in high school and studied music: she played piano, guitar, bas and banjo; worked as a secretary and as dancer in Las Vegas, then sudden stormed the pop chart with a beautiful produced and recorded story song *Ode Billie Joe*, about local indifference to teenage tragedy, was No. 1 for four week in the USA, No. 13 in the UK in 1967; was arranged by Jimmy Haskell (enginee Kelly Gordon) and won several Grammie It was top ten in the USA R&B chart ar top 20 in the country chart; she won a CM award as the most promising female voca ist, but never had another hit to match Her only other USA Top 10 was in th country chart, a duet with Glen Campb on *All I have to do is dream* in 1970 (no. in UK pop chart), but that year she had chart topper in the UK with *I'll ever fall love again*. A film of *Billie Joe* was made 1976 with additional music by Michel L grand; she had a UK TV show in the la

'60's, owned a production company in L.A. and married singer Jim Stafford in 1978. (Donald Clarke, July 1989)o.

ALL I HAVE TO DO IS DREAM
Tracks: / All I have to do is dream.
7" Single: Released Dec '69, on Capitol, by EMI Records. Deleted '72. Catalogue no: **CL 15619**

I'LL NEVER FALL IN LOVE AGAIN
Tracks: / I'll never fall in love again.
7" Single: Released Aug '69, on Capitol, by EMI Records. Deleted '72. Catalogue no: **CL 15606**

ODE TO BILLY JOE
Tracks: / Ode to Billy Joe.
7" Single: Released Sep '67, on Capitol, by EMI Records. Deleted '70. Catalogue no: **CL 15511**

RAINDROPS KEEP FALLIN' ON MY HEAD
Tracks: / Raindrops keep falling on my head.
7" Single: Released Dec '69, on Capitol, by EMI Records. Deleted '72. Catalogue no: **CL 15626**

Gents

FRIDAY ON MY MIND
Tracks: / Friday on my mind.
12" Single: Released Sep '86, on Lambs To The Slaughter, by Prism Records. Catalogue no: **GN 12 T**
7" Single: Released Sep '86, on Lambs To The Slaughter, by Prism Records. Catalogue no: **GN 12**

GIVE IT TO ME
Tracks: / Give it to me / At the dance.
7" Single: Released Feb '86, on Prism, by Prism Records. Catalogue no: **GN 11**
12" Single: Released Feb '86, on Prism, by Prism Records. Catalogue no: **GN 11T**

NEW DIRECTION
Tracks: / New direction / Pink panther.
7" Single: Released May '85, on Lambs To The Slaughter, by Prism Records. Catalogue no: **GN 8**

REVENGE
Tracks: / Revenge.
7" Single: Released May '83, on Mega, by Mega Records. Catalogue no: **MEGA 1**
7" Single: Released Aug '83, on Posh, by Posh Records. Catalogue no: **POSH 007**

SCHOOLDAYS
Tracks: / School days / True stories.
7" Single: Released Jul '82, on Kosmik, by Kosmik Records. Deleted '87. Catalogue no: **KOS 6886**

SHOUT
Tracks: / Shout / Faker.
7" Single: Released Mar '85, on Lambs To The Slaughter, by Prism Records. Catalogue no: **GN 7**

STAY WITH ME
Tracks: / Stay with me.
12" Single: Released Sep '85, on Prism, by Prism Records. Catalogue no: **GN 9T**
7" Single: Released Sep '85, on Prism, by Prism Records. Catalogue no: **GN 9**

Gentz

STAND BY ME
Tracks: / Stand by me / Armageddon.
7" Single: Released Jun '83, on Shock Rock (Ireland), by Outlet Records. Catalogue no: **SRS 507**

Geordie

Biographical details: This British rock band consisted of Brian Gibson, Tom Hill, Brian Johnson and Vic Malcolm. Geordie achieved four UK hit singles between December 1972 and September 1973. *Don't do that* peaked at no 32, *All because of you* reached no 6, *Can you do it* got to no 13 and *Electric lady* landed at no 32. These hits were in a sub-Status-Quo catchy pop/rock vein and coincided with the glam rock era. None of the group's albums reached the charts, so it is probable that Geordie appealed more to the teenybopper market than to rock fans. The band's main writer was guitarist Vic Malcolm. Geordie kept issuing LP's *Hope you like it, Masters of rock, Don't be fooled by the name, Save the world* - into the mid seventies, by which time they had faded into obscurity. In 1980, however, Scottish singer Brian Johnson leapt to sudden superstardom when he performed the formidable task of replacing the late Bon Scott as leader of AC/DC. (Bob Macdonald, 18/9/85).

ALL BECAUSE OF YOU
Tracks: / All because of you.
7" Single: Released Mar '73, on EMI, by EMI Records. Deleted '76. Catalogue no: **EMI 2008**

CAN YOU DO IT
Tracks: / Can you do it.
7" Single: Released Jun '73, on EMI, by EMI Records. Deleted '76. Catalogue no: **EMI 2031**

DON'T DO THAT
Tracks: / Don't do that / Keep on rocking.
7" Single: Released Feb '81, on Red Bus, by Red Bus Records. Deleted Feb '84. Catalogue no: **RBUS 58**
7" Single: Released Dec '72, on Regal Zonophone, by EMI Records. Deleted '75. Catalogue no: **RZ 3067**

ELECTRIC LADY
Tracks: / Electric lady.
7" Single: Released Aug '73, on EMI, by EMI Records. Deleted '76. Catalogue no: **EMI 2047**

NUTBUSH CITY LIMITS
Tracks: / Nutbush City Limits / No sweat.
7" Single: Released Apr '82, on Armageddon, by Armageddon Records. Catalogue no: **AS 034**

Geordie Aid

TRY GIVING IT EVERYTHING
Tracks: / Try giving it everything.
7" Single: Released Aug '85, on Geordie Aid, Catalogue no: **HELP 01**

George & Jackie

DIANA
Tracks: / Diana.
7" Single: Released Dec '81, on Black Joy, Catalogue no: **BH 7812**

THIRD WORLD
Tracks: / Third world / Sharing the night together.
12" Single: Released Nov '82, on Black Joy, Catalogue no: **BH 825**

George, Robin

Biographical details: In 1982 this British singer, guitarist and songwriter played guitar with the short-lived Byron Band, fronted by ex-Uriah Heep singer David Byron. As a solo artists, George released the singles *Go down fighting* (1983) and *Heartline* (1984). *Heartline* was reactivated in early 1985, and gave Robin George a minor hit in both the UK and US. Mainly American in flavour despite the artist's nationality, *Heartline* was a very catchy rock track with a powerful hook and strong musicianship. The fact it was not a bigger hit was probably due to bad luck, but it promised much for the future. (Bob Macdonald, 19/9/85).

DON'T TURN AWAY
Tracks: / Don't turn away.
7" Single: Released Aug '85, on Bronze, by Bronze Records. Catalogue no: **BRO 195**
12" Single: Released Aug '85, on Bronze, by Bronze Records. Catalogue no: **BROX 195**

HEARTLINE
Tracks: / Heartline.
7" Single: Released Mar '85, on Bronze, by Bronze Records. Catalogue no: **BRO 191**
12" Single: Released Mar '85, on Bronze, by Bronze Records. Catalogue no: **BROX 191**

SPY
Tracks: / Spy.
12" Single: Released Jan '85, on Bronze, by Bronze Records. Catalogue no: **BROX 188**
7" Single: Released Jan '85, on Bronze, by Bronze Records. Catalogue no: **BRO 188**

George, Sophia

FINAL DECISION
Tracks: / Final decision / Final decision (version) / Genuine.
7" Single: Released 20 Jun '87, on Winner, by Creole Records. Catalogue no: **WINT 710**
12" Single: Released 20 Jun '87, on Winner, by Creole Records. Catalogue no: **WINT 10**

GIRLIE GIRLIE
Tracks: / Girlie girlie.
7" Single: Released Nov '85, on Winner, by Creole Records. Catalogue no: **WIN 01**
12" Single: Released Nov '85, on Winner, by Creole Records. Catalogue no: **WINT 01**

LAZY BODY
Tracks: / Can't live without you / Lazy body.
12" Single: Released Apr '86, on Winner, by Creole Records. Catalogue no: **WINT 03**
7" Single: Released Apr '86, on Winner, by Creole Records. Catalogue no: **WIN 03**

LOVE AGAIN
Tracks: / Love again / Love again (dub).
7" Single: Released Nov '87, on Winner, by Creole Records. Catalogue no: **WINT 711**
12" Single: Released Nov '87, on Winner, by Creole Records. Catalogue no: **WINT 11**

ROCKERS IN THE RAIN
Tracks: / Rockers in the rain.
12" Single: Released Nov '88, on Winner, by Creole Records. Catalogue no: **UNKNOWN**

Georgia II

AS TEARS GO BY
Tracks: / As tears go by.
7" Single: Released May '83, on PRT, by Castle Communications Records. Catalogue no: **7P 274**
12" Single: Released May '83, on PRT, by Castle Communications Records. Catalogue no: **12P 274**

FLAG, THE
Tracks: / Flag, The / Tunnel vision.
7" Single: Released Jan '83, on PRT, by Castle Communications Records. Catalogue no: **7P 257**
12" Single: Released Jan '83, on PRT, by Castle Communications Records. Catalogue no: **12P 257**

Georgia Satellites

BATTLESHIP CHAINS (KICK AND LICK REMIX)
Tracks: / Battleship chains (kick and lick remix) / Hard luck boy.
12" Single: Released Apr '87, on Elektra (USA), by Elektra Records (USA). Deleted Jul '88. Catalogue no: **EKR 58 T**
7" Single: Released Apr '87, on Elektra (USA), by Elektra Records (USA). Deleted Jul '88. Catalogue no: **EKR 58**

HIPPY HIPPY SHAKE
Tracks: / Hippy hippy shake / Hand to mouth / Powerful stuff (On 12" version only.).
7" Single: Released Jan '89, on Elektra, by Elektra Records (UK). Catalogue no: **EKR 86**
12" Single: Released Jan '89, on Elektra, by Elektra Records (UK). Catalogue no: **EKR 86 TKEEP YOUR HANDS TO YOURSELF**
Tracks: / Keep your hands to yourself / Can't stand the pain / Nights of mystery / I'm waiting for the man.
7" Single: Released Aug '87, on Elektra, by Elektra Records (UK). Deleted Jul '88. Catalogue no: **EKR 50**
12" Single: Released Aug '87, on Elektra, by Elektra Records (UK). Deleted Jul '88. Catalogue no: **EKRT 50**

SHEILA
Tracks: / Sheila / Hippy hippy shake / Battleship chains (live) (Only on 12".) / Railroad steel (live) (Only on 12".).
12" Single: Released May '89, on Elektra, by Elektra Records (UK). Catalogue no: **EKRT 89**
7" Single: Released May '89, on Elektra, by Elektra Records (UK). Catalogue no: **EKR 89**

Georgie's Revenge

BE A DEVIL
Tracks: / Be a devil / Love me.
7" Single: Released Oct '88, on Sierra, by Sierra Records. Catalogue no: **FED 45**
12" Single: Released Oct '88, on Sierra, by Sierra Records. Catalogue no: **FED 45T**

GEORGIE'S REVENGE
Tracks: / Georgie's revenge / Spend some time.
7" Single: Released 31 Oct '87, on Sierra, by Sierra Records. Catalogue no: **FED 39**
12" Single: Released 31 Oct '87, on Sierra, by Sierra Records. Catalogue no: **FED 39T**

Georgio

LOVER'S LANE
Tracks: / Lovers Lane / Lovers Lane (after hours mix) / Lovers Lane (new after hours mix) (track on 12") / Lovers Lane (club mix) / Lovers Lane (Georgio's love dance mix) (track on 12").
12" Single: Released Feb '88, on Motown, by BMG Records (UK). Catalogue no: **ZT 41612**
7" Single: Released Feb '88, on Motown, by BMG Records (UK). Catalogue no: **ZB 41611**

SEXAPPEAL (SINGLE)
Tracks: / Sexappeal / Sexappeal (instrumental).
7" Single: Released Mar '87, on Motown, by BMG Records (UK). Catalogue no: **ZB 41209**
12" Single: Released Mar '87, on Motown, by BMG Records (UK). Catalogue no: **ZT 41210**

TINA CHERRY
Tracks: / Tina Cherry.
7" Single: Released Oct '87, on Motown, by BMG Records (UK). Catalogue no: **ZB 41555**
12" Single: Released Oct '87, on Motown, by BMG Records (UK). Catalogue no: **ZT 41556**

Geraldine

HEART OF AFRICA
Tracks: / Heart of Africa, The / Thank you for tonight.
7" Single: Released Dec '83, on Magnet, by WEA Records. Catalogue no: **MAG 254**

ROSE OF ALLENDALE
Tracks: / Rose of Allendale.
7" Single: Released Dec '84, on Magnet, by WEA Records. Catalogue no: **MAG 271**

TAKE ME BACK
Tracks: / Take me back / Grab your honey and run.
7" Single: Released Mar '82, on Magnet, by WEA Records. Deleted '85. Catalogue no: **MAG 217**

WILL YOU GO LASSIE GO
Tracks: / Will you go lassie go.
7" Single: Released Oct '83, on Magnet, by WEA Records. Catalogue no: **MAG 251**

Gerard, Daniel

BUTTERFLY
Tracks: / Butterfly.
7" Single: Released Sep '71, on CBS, by CBS Records. Deleted '74. Catalogue no: **CBS 7454**

German Beat Syndrome

TANZ DER MUSSOLINI
Tracks: / Tanz der Mussolini.
12" Single: Released May '89, on V.W., Catalogue no: **VW 1002**

Germino, Mark

CAUGHT IN THE ACT OF BEING OURSELVES (SINGLE)
Tracks: / Caught in the act of being ourselves.
12" Single: Released Aug '89, on RCA, by BMG Records (UK). Catalogue no: **PT 43020**
7" Single: Released 7 Jul '89, on RCA, by BMG Records (UK). Catalogue no: **PB 49369**
CD 5": Released Aug '89, on RCA, by BMG Records (UK). Catalogue no: **PD 43020**

POLITICAL
Tracks: / Political / Oriental drag / Broken mans' lament (Extra track on 12" version only.).
12" Single: Released Mar '87, on RCA, by BMG Records (UK). Deleted '87. Catalogue no: **PT 41108**
7" Single: Released Mar '87, on RCA, by BMG Records (UK). Deleted '87. Catalogue no: **PB 41107**

Geronimo, Mark

REX BOB LOWENSTEIN
Tracks: / Rex Bob Lowenstein / Teasing we do.
7" Single: Released Apr '89, on RCA, by BMG Records (UK). Catalogue no: **PB 42769**
12" Single: Released May '89, on RCA, by BMG Records (UK). Catalogue no: **PT 42770**

Gerry & The Holograms

GERRY & THE HOLOGRAMS
Tracks: / Gerry & the holograms.
7" Single: Released Sep '82, on Absurd, by Absurd Records. Catalogue no: **ABS 4**

Gerry & The Pacemakers

Biographical details: This British beat group consisted of Gerry Marsden plus Les Chadwick, Freddy Marsden (Gerry's elder brother) and Les Maguire. For 21 years, from 1963 to 1984, Gerry & The Pacemakers held an exalted position in pop history - they were the only act ever to crack the UK no 1 position with each of their first three single releases.
The feat was finally equalled by, fittingly, another Liverpool group - Frankie goes to Hollywood. Gerry's group also held the distinction of being the first Merseybeat combo to hit the top, three weeks ahead of the Beatles.
Like the Beatles, the four members of Gerry & the Pacemakers were all born between 1940 and 1943. The Marsden brothers started playing in local rock'n'roll and skiffle groups in the late 50's, before forming their own short-lived outfit, the Mars Bars. This

name was dropped in favour of the Pacemakers, and their permanent line-up was established in 1961. When they shot to stardom in '63, they had so much in common with the Beatles in addition to city and age - both groups had gained experience by playing in Hamburg clubs, and both had shared the same manager (Brian Epstein), producer (George Martin), record company (EMI), and studio (London's Abbey Road). Moreover, the early success of Gerry & the Pacemakers helped to prove to the public and music industry that the new pop revolution was not purely a Beatles phenomenon, but there was mush other talent in Liverpool waiting to be discovered. Unlike the Fab Four, Gerry & the Pacemakers did not write their own material in the early days. Both of their first two UK no 1 smashes *How do you do it?* and *I like it* were penned by the commercial eared Mitch Murray. These similar sounding songs were in a bouncy uptempo vein, and emphasized Gerry's "cheeky Charlie" style. In total contrast *You'll never walk alone* was a big ballad the Rodgers & Hammerstein songbook. Written in 1945 for the *Carousel* musical, Gerry transformed the number into a UK classic. It rapidly became the anthem of the fast-ascending Liverpool Football Club's supporters, and within a few years, every football crowd in Britain had adopted the song. In 1964 Gerry started coming up with the hit material himself. Another new development was the British invasion of America, which the group took advantage of most notably with *Don't let the sun catch you crying*. Marsden's highly evocative 1965 song *Ferry 'cross the Mersey* was the theme for a movie in which the group starred. It was also their final top 10 hit on either side of the Atlantic. The combo broke up in 1967, occasionally reforming for revival tours. Gerry pursued a solo career encompassing cabaret, pantomime,variety shows and children's TV. He also enjoyed enjoyed a five-year run in London's West End as costar (with Anna Neagle) of the *Charlie girl* material. Six months after Frankie Goes To Hollywood matched the Pacemakers' hat-trick of chart-toppers, Gerry set a new precedent. By being the opening voice on The Crowd's all-star charity effort *You'll never walk alone*, he became the first artist to sing on two different version of a UK no 1 song. (Bob MacDonald, 19/9/85)
UK Merseybeat group signed by Brian Epstein: vocalist Gerry Marsden, pianist Les Maguire, Les Chadwick and Freddie Marsden on bass and drums set a record, hitting No. 1 with their first three releases: *How do you do it* and *I like it* (both written by Mitch Murray) revealed their rock'n'roll background; the syrupy and untypical Rodgers & Hammerstein ballad *You'll never walk alone* became a soccer anthem for some reason. They were also famous for *Don't let the sun catch you crying* (their biggest USA hit) and *Ferry cross the Mersey*, a film theme. There may have been a raunchy rocker behind Gerry's ever-sunny disposition, but he went solo in 1967, starred with Anna Neagle in *Charlie girl* on the West End stage, worked in children's TV and reformed the Pacemakers occasionally for revivals. He re-made *You'll never walk alone* in 1985 with show-boz friends as The Crowd to raise money for families of the horrific fire at Bradford Football Club; the song reached the top again. Gerry Marsden is now with a new line-up of Pacemakers and is still managing to draw the crowds on the cabaret circuit. (Donald Clarke, July 1989).

DON'T LET THE SUN CATCH YOU CRYING
Tracks: / Don't let the sun catch you crying.
7" Single: Released Apr '64, on Columbia, by EMI Records. Deleted '67. Catalogue no: **DB 7268**

FERRY ACROSS THE MERSEY (OLD GOLD)
Tracks: / Ferry 'cross the Mersey / Don't let the sun catch you crying.
7" Single: Released '83, on Old Gold, by Old Gold Records. Deleted Jul '88. Catalogue no: **OG 9373**

FERRY ACROSS THE MERSEY (SINGLE)
Tracks: / Ferry 'cross the Mersey / You'll never walk alone / Saturday night at the movies.
7" Single: Released '84, on SMP (2), Catalogue no: **SKM 08**
7" Single: Released Dec '64, on Columbia, by EMI Records. Deleted '67. Catalogue no: **DB 7437**
7" Single: Released '83, on Deb, by Deb Records. Catalogue no: **DEB 11**
7" Single: Released '82, on Blast From The Past, by Creole Records. Catalogue no: **CR 195**
7" Single: Released '82, on Columbia, by EMI Records. Catalogue no: **PMS 1002**
7" Single: Released '80, on JB, Deleted '84. Catalogue no: **JB 02**

HOW DO YOU DO IT
Tracks: / How do you do it.
7" Single: Released Mar '63, on Columbia, by EMI Records. Deleted '66. Catalogue no: **DB 4987**

I LIKE IT
Tracks: / I like it.
7" Single: Released May '63, on Columbia, by EMI Records. Deleted '66. Catalogue no: **DB 7041**

I'LL BE THERE
Tracks: / I'll be there.
7" Single: Released Mar '65, on Columbia, by EMI Records. Deleted '68. Catalogue no: **DB 7504**

I'M THE ONE
Tracks: / I'm the one.
7" Single: Released Jan '64, on Columbia, by EMI Records. Deleted '67. Catalogue no: **DB 7189**

IT'S GONNA BE ALRIGHT
Tracks: / It's gonna be alright.
7" Single: Released Sep '64, on Columbia, by EMI Records. Deleted '67. Catalogue no: **DB 7353**

OH MY LOVE
Tracks: / Oh my love / If.
7" Single: Released '83, on Deb, by Deb Records. Catalogue no: **DEB 107**

ROSE, THE
Tracks: / Rose, The / You are my everything.
7" Single: Released Sep '88, on Pacer, by Pacer Records. Catalogue no: **PACE 100**

UNCHAINED MELODY
Tracks: / Unchained melody / Girl what you doin'.
7" Single: Released '82, on Deb, by Deb Records. Catalogue no: **DEB 105**

WALK HAND IN HAND
Tracks: / Walk hand in hand.
7" Single: Released Nov '65, on Columbia, by EMI Records. Deleted '68. Catalogue no: **DB 7738**

YOU'LL NEVER WALK ALONE
Tracks: / How do you do it? / I like it / You'll never walk alone (from Carousel).
7" Single: Released '73, on EMI, by EMI Records. Catalogue no: **EMI 2086**
7" Single: Released '84, on EMI Golden 45's, by EMI Records. Deleted '86. Catalogue no: **G45 25**
7" Single: on Blast From The Past, by Creole Records. Catalogue no: **CR 195**
7" Single: Released Oct '63, on Columbia, by EMI Records. Deleted '66. Catalogue no: **DB 7126**

YOU'LL NEVER WALK ALONE (OLD GOLD)
Tracks: / You'll never walk alone.
7" Single: Released '83, on Old Gold, by Old Gold Records. Deleted Jul '88. Catalogue no: **OG 9373**

Geschlekt Akt

FOREPLAY (EP)
12" Single: Released '84, on Criminal Damage, Catalogue no: **CRI 12119**

Get Rhythm

CAIRO ROMANCE
Tracks: / Cairo romance / Attitude.
7" Single: Released Nov '88, on Hit, by Hit Records. Catalogue no: **KYR 17**

Getting The Fear

LAST SALUTE
Tracks: / Last salute.
7" Single: Released '84, on RCA, by BMG Records (UK). Catalogue no: **RCA 432**
12" Single: Released '84, on RCA, by BMG Records (UK). Catalogue no: **RCAT 432**

Getz, Stan

Biographical details: One of the greats of modern jazz, the veteran tenor saxophone of Stan Getz has occasionally graced the pop charts. In 1962 he teamed with well-known jazz guitarist Charlie Byrd, and released a bossa nova instrumental single called *Desafinado*. It reached the Top 20 on both sides of the Atlantic, as did the duo's album *Jazz samba*. The single and LP sparked off a whole bossa nova craze - literally meaning "new style", the Brazilian bossa nova was accompanied by a suddenly fashionable dance. The composer of *Desafinado., Brazil's Antonio Carlos Jobim, was also responsible for Getz's other foray into popdom. The girl from Ipanema*, which featured the sax of Getz plus a plaintive and slightly eerie vocal performance from Brazilian singer Astrud Gilberto, surged to no 5 on the American singles chart in 1964. In Britain it peaked at no 29 but had a second wind 20 years later when it got to no 55. The parent LP featured Getz in duet with Astrud's husband, Joso Gilberto, a leading singer on Brazil's bossa nova scene. Getz, always a romantic player at heart, has dabbled in a variety of jazz styles during his mammoth career. He was born in 1927, and comes from Philadelphia. His parents were Russian-Jewish immigrants, Stan's real surname being Gayetsky. He gained his first big break in the late forties with Woody Herman's band; down the years, he also played with Jimmy Dorsey, Benny Goodman and Stan Kenton. Getz's finest decade was the 60's but he was still making worthy records in the 70's. (Bob Macdonald, 19/9/85)
Born in 1927 in Philadelphia, the tenor saxist played with big-name bands while still a teenager, then was one of the Four Brothers reed section in 1947-49 that gave the Woody Herman band it's real sound, the most exciting of any white band of it's era; his solo on *Early Autumn* brought more fame: with Zoot Sims, Lee Konitz, Gerry Mulligan, Art Pepper and a few others, he led a new generation of first-class white jazz reedmen popular round the world, Getz's tone and gift for beauty making him a particularly fine ballad player. His long association with Norman Granz began in 1952; *Jazz Samba* in 1962 with guitarist Charlie Byrd introduced bossa nova and reached No. 1 on Billboard's top pop albums chart; *Getz/Gilberto* '64 with Joao Giberto and his wife Astrud reached No. 2 and included the top five hit single *The girl from Ipenema*: six hit albums in the USA pop chart in two years made him one of the era's most popular jazz musicians and won him Grammies, but when the bossa nova fad was played out the beauty of his treatment was still fresh as paint, and he's never stopped making beautiful records. (Donald Clarke, July 1989)d.

DESAFINADO
Tracks: / Desafinado.
7" Single: Released Nov '62, on H.M.V., by EMI Records. Deleted '65. Catalogue no: **POP 1061**

GIRL FROM IPANEMA, THE
Tracks: / Girl from Ipanema.
7" Single: Released Jul '64, on Verve, Deleted '67. Catalogue no: **VS 520**

Geyer, Renee

SAY I LOVE YOU
Tracks: / Say I love you / Good lovin'.

7" Single: Released Apr '82, on CBS, by CBS Records. Deleted Apr '85. Catalogue no: **A 2056**
12" Single: Released Apr '82, on CBS, by CBS Records. Deleted Apr '85. Catalogue no: **A13 2056**

Geza X

HUNGARIAN
Tracks: / Hungarian.

7" Single: Released Feb '83, on Alternative Tentacles, by Alternative Tentacles Records. Catalogue no: **VIRUS 20**

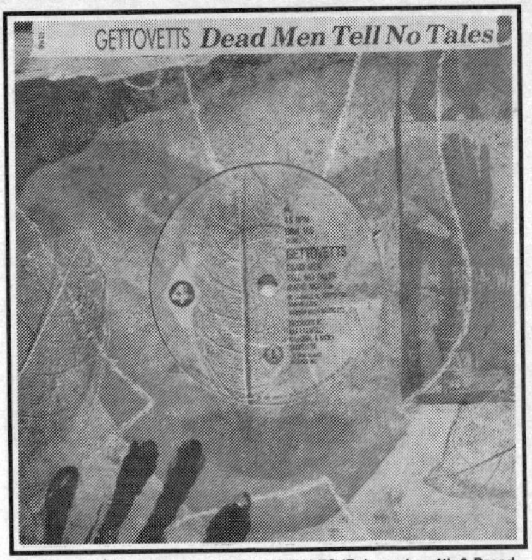

GHETTOVETTS - DEAD MEN TELL NO TALES (Released on 4th & Broadway)

G-Force

HOT GOSSIP
Tracks: / Hot gossip / Because of your love.
7" Single: Released Jun '80, on Jet, by Jet Records. Deleted Jun '83. Catalogue no: **JET 183**

SPICY
Tracks: / Spicy.
12" Single: Released May '89, on Who's That Beat, by Play It Again Sam (Belgium). Catalogue no: **WHOS 8**
CD 5": Released May '89, on Who's That Beat, by Play It Again Sam (Belgium). Catalogue no: **WHOS 008CD**

WHITE KNUCKLES
Tracks: / White knuckles / I look at you.
7" Single: Released Nov '80, on Jet, by Jet Records. Catalogue no: **JET 7005**

Ghettovetts

DEAD MEN TELL NO TALES (see panel above)
Tracks: / Dead men tell no tales / Battle call.
12" Single: Released Jun '88, on 4th & Broadway, by Island Records. Deleted Apr '89. Catalogue no: **12 BRW 105**
7" Single: Released Jun '88, on 4th & Broadway, by Island Records. Deleted Apr '89. Catalogue no: **BRW 105**

Ghost Dance

CELEBRATE
Tracks: / Celebrate.
CD 5": Released Sep '89, on Chrysalis, by Chrysalis Records. Catalogue no: **CHSCD 3402**
12" Single: Released Sep '89, on Chrysalis, by Chrysalis Records. Catalogue no: **CHS 123 402**
Cassingle: Released Sep '89, on Chrysalis, by Chrysalis Records. Catalogue no: **CHSMC 3402**
7" Single: Released Sep '89, on Chrysalis, by Chrysalis Records. Catalogue no: **CHS 3402**

DOWN TO THE WIRE
Tracks: / Down to the wire / Doctor Love / Gathering dust(live) / Blood still flows.
7" Single: Released Jun '89, on Chrysalis, by Chrysalis Records. Catalogue no: **CHS 3376**
12" Single: Released Jun '89, on Chrysalis, by Chrysalis Records. Catalogue no: **CHS12 3376**

GRIP OF LOVE
Tracks: / Grip of love / Deeper blue, A / Last train / Grip of love (a cheaper blues).
7" Single: Released Sep '86, on Karbon, by Karbon Records. Deleted '88. Catalogue no: **KAR 604**
12" Single: Released Sep '86, on Karbon, by Karbon Records. Deleted '88. Catalogue no: **KAR 604 T**

HEARTFUL OF SOUL
Tracks: / Heartful of soul / Can the can / Radar love.
12" Single: Released Jul '86, on Karbon, by Karbon Records. Catalogue no: **KAR 606 T**

RIVER OF NO RETURN
Tracks: / River of no return / Both ends burning / Yesterday again / Celebrate.
12" Single: Released Apr '86, on Karbon, by Karbon Records. Deleted '88. Catalogue no: **KAR 602 T**

WORD TO THE WISE, A (EP)
Tracks: / Holding on / Cruel light / When I call / Fools gold.
12" Single: Released Aug '87, on Karbon, by Karbon Records. Catalogue no: **KAR 608 T**

Ghost Music

LOVE YOU & LEAVE YOU
Tracks: / Love you & leave you.
7" Single: Released Mar '85, on VP, Catalogue no: **VPS 1004**

Ghost Of An

I HEAR VOICES
Tracks: / I hear voices.
7" Single: Released 13 Jun '87, on Recoil, by Prism Records. Catalogue no: **RCL 9**
12" Single: Released 13 Jun '87, on Recoil, by Prism Records. Catalogue no: **RCL 9T**

Ghost Train

HOPE AND GLORY
Tracks: / Killing time / Hope and glory.
7" Single: Released May '86, on Kingdom Come, Catalogue no: **KCR 1**

Ghostriders

BAPTISM OF FIRE
Tracks: / Baptism of fire.
12" Single: Released Jul '84, on Criminal Damage, Catalogue no: **CRI 12112**

Ghosts

MY TOWN
Tracks: / My town / I'm your man.
7" Single: Released May '80, on Arista, by BMG Records (UK). Deleted May '83. Catalogue no: **ARIST 347**

Ghosts Of Dance

GHOSTS OF DANCE
Tracks: / Ghosts of dance.
7" Single: Released Sep '82, on Plastic Canvas, Catalogue no: **PC 001**

Giant Haystacks

BABY I NEED YOU
Tracks: / Baby I need you.
7" Single: Released Jul '83, on BSB, by BSB Records. Catalogue no: **BSB 01**

IT'S OK FOR SANTA
Tracks: / It's OK for Santa / Big splash.
7" Single: Released Dec '83, on Mach 1, by Mach 1 Records. Catalogue no: **MAGIC 10**
7" Single: Released Nov '84, on Mach 1, by Mach 1 Records. Catalogue no: **MAGIC 009**

Giant Sandworms

DON'T TURN AWAY
Tracks: / Longsleeves / Don't turn away.
7" Single: Released Jan '86, on One Big Guitar, by One Big Guitar Records. Catalogue no: **OBG 001**

Giant Steps

BOOK OF PRIDE (SINGLE)
Tracks: / Book of pride / What do you want most in life.
7" Single: Released May '89, on A&M, by A&M Records. Catalogue no: **AM 510**
12" Single: Released May '89, on A&M, by A&M Records. Catalogue no: **AMY 510**

INTO YOU
Tracks: / Into you / Give it up.
Note: "Giant Steps' "Into You' follows on from their turntable hit "The World Don't Need Another Lover". Taken from their debut album "Book Of Pride", "Into You" finds the band in a melodic, tuneful mood but still holding down the soulful groove that made their first single so popular" (A&M Records, August 1988)
7" Single: Released Aug '88, on A&M, by A&M Records. Catalogue no: **AM 451**
CD 5": Released Aug '88, on A&M, by A&M Records. Catalogue no: **AMCD 451**
12" Single: Released Aug '88, on A&M, by A&M Records. Catalogue no: **AMY 451**

(WORLD DON'T NEED, THE) ANOTHER LOVER
Tracks: / (World don't need, The) another lover / Adrenaline.
12" Single: Released Oct '88, on A&M, by A&M Records. Catalogue no: **AMY 445**
7" Single: Released Oct '88, on A&M, by A&M Records. Catalogue no: **AM 445**

Gibb, Andy

Biographical details: This British singer is the younger brother of the Bee Gees. In appearance, he most closely resembles his eldest brother Barry - and it was Barry (unsoubtedly the most talented member of the family) whose writing and production skills masterminded Andy's big hits. Without Barry, and without the Bee Gee's trademark harmony vocals, Andy's own slender talent could not have succeeded. Andy Gibb was born at around the same time that the Manchester-based Gibb family emigrated to Australia in 1958. During the mid-seventies, he did what his siblings had done a decade earlier - he used Australia as a training ground before launching a showbusiness career in America and Europe. The fact that none of his successful Aussie discs were even released in the USA meant that he almost made US chart history when he did start releasing American product - between July 1977 and July 1978 *I just wanna be your everything, (Love is) thicker than water*, and the two million selling *Shadow dancing* gave Andy the rare disinction of reaching the US no. 1 slot with his first three single releases. Only the Jackson Five, who hit the American summit with their first four singles in 1970, have ever bettered this achievement. In Britain, only Gerry and the Pacemakers and Frankie goes to Hollywood have ever reached no. 1 with their first three records. The fourth Andy Gibb offering *An everlasting love* broke the sequence by peaking at no. 5 on the Billboard charts. By way of compensation, it became his forst and only Top Tenner in Britain; it seemed that UK record buyers were decidedly more sceptical about the youngest Gibb, for none of his other singles came close to the Top 10. But in the States, he sold 6 million singles in the space of eighteen months. His stunning success was fuelled by the fact that his records coincided neatly with *Saturday Night Fever* and the peak of the Bee Gees' own career. For example *Thicker than water* toppled his brothers' *Staying alive* from the top of the American charts, only to be dethroned by the trio's *Night Fever* single. From 1979 onwards, despite duets with Olivia Newton-John and Victoria Principal (!), Andy only managed one more US Top 10 hit. His 1981 single *Me without you* was his final American Top 40 entry - and it peaked at no. 40. By his 24th birthday, he was rich but obscure. (Bob Macdonald, 20/9/85).

ALL I HAVE TO DO IS DREAM
Tracks: / All I have to do is dream / Good feeling.
7" Single: Released Oct '81, on RSO, by Polydor Ltd. Deleted Oct '84. Catalogue no: **RSO 82**

DESIRE
Tracks: / Desire / Waiting for you.
7" Single: Released Feb '80, on RSO, by Polydor Ltd. Deleted Feb '83. Catalogue no: **RSO 55**

EVERLASTING LOVE, AN
Tracks: / Everlasting love.
7" Single: Released Aug '78, on RSO, by Polydor Ltd. Deleted '81. Catalogue no: **RSO 015**

I CAN'T HELP IT
Tracks: / I can't help it / Someone I ain't.
7" Single: Released May '80, on RSO, by Polydor Ltd. Deleted May '83. Catalogue no: **RSO 59**

I JUST WANNA BE YOUR EVERYTHING
Tracks: / I just wanna be your everything.
7" Single: Released Jun '77, on RSO, by Polydor Ltd. Deleted '80. Catalogue no: **2090 237**

(OUR LOVE) DON'T THROW IT ALL AWAY
Tracks: / (Our love) don't throw it all away.
7" Single: Released Jan '79, on RSO, by Polydor Ltd. Deleted '82. Catalogue no: **RSO 26**

SHADOW DANCING (SINGLE)
Tracks: / Shadow dancing.
7" Single: Released May '78, on RSO, by Polydor Ltd. Deleted '81. Catalogue no: **RSO 001**

TIME IS TIME
Tracks: / Time is time / I go for you.
7" Single: Released Jan '81, on RSO, by Polydor Ltd. Deleted Jan '84. Catalogue no: **RSO 73**

Gibb, Barry

CHILDHOOD DAYS
Tracks: / Childhood days / Moonlight madness / Cover you.
7" Single: Released 15 Aug '88, on Polydor, by Polydor Ltd. Catalogue no: **PO 15**
12" Single: Released 15 Aug '88, on Polydor, by Polydor Ltd. Catalogue no: **PZ 15**

Gibb, Maurice

HOLD HER IN YOUR HAND
Tracks: / Hold her in your hand.
7" Single: Released Sep '84, on Audiotrax, Deleted '86. Catalogue no: **AT 5**
12" Single: Released Sep '84, on Audiotrax, Deleted '86. Catalogue no: **ATX 5**

Gibb, Robin

Biographical details: This British singer, songwriter and producer is one-third of the world famous Bee Gees - he is the non-identical twin brother of Maurice and the younger brother of Barry. In 1969, having wnjoyed two years of major instrumental success, the Gibbs suffered and acrimonious break=up. Robin parted company with his brothers and obtained a big solo hit with *Saved by the bell* - written, produced and nasally sung by Robin, this big ballad reached no. 2 in Britain and was popular in several other European countries but failed in America. Another song, *August October*, was a minor UK hit for him in February 1970. In similar style to Robin's one-off smash, the depleted Bee Gees duo managed one UK no. 2 hit with *Don't forget to remember* but were soon struggling. The music press had had a field day reporting every acrimonious twist and turn of the group's rupture, and the strain was showing. Both Robin and the Bee Gees went for over a year without a Top 40 single, either in Britain or the States. Failure brought the brothers back together in late 1970 and their subsequent success was such that Robin did not bother to resume a solo career until 1983 (although he enjoyed a one-off solo US hit in 1978 with the Beatles *Oh darling*, and masterminded Jimmy Ruffin's 1980 hit *Hold on to my love*). Robin, now based in Britain again after being a tax exile in Miami, relaunched his solo work in the summer of '83 with the single *Juliet*; this was an ultra-catchy uptempo record which showed Gibb had been influenced by modern technopop trends. Extraordinarily, it failed to make the British or American charts despite being a gigantic hit all over Europe. He did manage to crack the US Top 40 with 1984's *Boys (do fall in love)*, an intriguing answer to Cyndi Lauper's *Girls just want to have fun*. (Bob Macdonald, 20/9/85).

BOYS (DO FALL IN LOVE)
Tracks: / Boys (do fall in love) / Diamonds.
12" Single: Released Jun '84, on Polydor, by Polydor Ltd. Catalogue no: **POSPX 686**
7" Single: Released Jun '84, on Polydor, by Polydor Ltd. Catalogue no: **POSP 686**

HELP ME
Tracks: / Help me.
7" Single: Released Oct '80, on RSO, by Polydor Ltd. Deleted Oct '83. Catalogue no: **RSO 65**

LIKE A FOOL
Tracks: / Possession / Like a fool.
7" Single: Released Apr '86, on Polydor, by Polydor Ltd. Catalogue no: **POSP 767**
12" Single: Released Apr '86, on Polydor, by Polydor Ltd. Catalogue no: **POSPX 767**

SAVED BY THE BELL
Tracks: / Saved by the bell / Words.
7" Single: Released Feb '88, on Old Gold, by Old Gold Records. Catalogue no: **OG 9773**

Gibber, Tony

DON'T ASK ME WHY
Tracks: / Don't ask me why / When I look in your eyes.
7" Single: Released Nov '80, on WEA, by WEA Records. Deleted '83. Catalogue no: **K 18383**

FANTASY
Tracks: / Fantasy / Why.
7" Single: Released Jan '80, on WEA, by WEA Records. Deleted Jan '85. Catalogue no: **K 18093**

Gibbons, Leroy

ADDICTED TO YOUR LOVE
Tracks: / Addicted to your love.
7" Single: Released Jan '89, on Live & Love, Catalogue no: **LLD 100**

DARLING YOU SEND ME
Tracks: / Darling you send me.
12" Single: Released Apr '88, on Pioneer Muzik, Catalogue no: **PM 003**

DAY - O
Tracks: / Day O.
12" Single: Released Aug '88, on Germaine, Catalogue no: **DGT 34**

I AM IN THE MOOD FOR LOVE
Tracks: / I am in the mood for love / Salute to all posse.
12" Single: Released Jul '88, on Jammy's, Catalogue no: **VPRD 322**

I'M IN LOVE
Tracks: / I'm in love.
12" Single: Released Mar '88, on Fashion, by Fashion Records. Catalogue no: **FAD 053**

POWER OF LOVE, THE
Tracks: / Power of love, The.
12" Single: Released Nov '88, on Charm, by Charm Records. Catalogue no: **CRT 24**

SALUTE TO ALL POSSE
Tracks: / Salute to all posse.
12" Single: Released Aug '88, on Germaine, Catalogue no: **DGT 39**

Gibbons, Steve

Biographical details: This British singer has been working on Birmingham's local rock circuit since the late Fifties, and is still going strong in the Eighites. Apart from a brief glimpse of UK national chart success in the late Seventies, Gibbons has carried on grafting through the years without the benefit of record sales. Steve's first combo, The Uglys, were formed in 1958 and remained in existence untio 1969 with various line-ups. Among the musicians who passed through the group were bassist Dave Pegg (later in Fairport Convention), keyboardist Richard Tandy (later in ELO), drummer Keith Smart (later in Wizzard), and guitarist Trevor Burton (ex-Move). Just as Burton was joining in early '69, the Uglys were transmogrified into the even more cutely named Balls. One of the founder members of the latter band was guitarist/vocalist Denny Laine (ex-Moody Blues, later with Wings). The group lasted until '71, whereupon the Steve Gibbons Band came into being; this new billing did not reflect any change of role for Gibbons, as he had been the undoubted leader of the previous groups. The Steve Gibbons Band finally hit the charts in 1977, when their revival of a latterday (1970) Chuck Berry classic *Tulane*, reached the UK no. 12 position; the group's live LP *Caught in the act* then proceeded to reach no. 22 on the British album listings. The underrated *Eddy Vortex* peaked at no. 56 on Britain's singles chart in 1978. After this, the Steve Gibbons Band did not see chart action again. The band folded in 1980, and Gibbons assembled some new players. Always a rock'n'roller first and foremost, Steve's great voice is still a strong attraction in his native Birmingham. But even the much voiced approval of Pete Townshend never made Gibbons a national star. (Bob Macdonald, 20/9/85)
A UK singer and songwriter, who had some success after 13 years in the business: he went through groups called the Dominettes, the Uglys, Balls and Idle Race; after his first album *Short stories* in 1971 he formed the Steve Gibbons Band. He may have been the Bob Seger of the UK's industrial heartland, but he's always had to swim against a tide of puerile pop. (Donald Clarke, July 1989).

A TO Z
Tracks: / A to Z / Abracadabra.
7" Single: Released Jun '81, on RCA, by BMG Records (UK). Deleted Jun '84. Catalogue no: **RCA 82**

EDDY VORTEX
Tracks: / Eddy Vortex.
7" Single: Released May '78, on Polydor, by Polydor Ltd. Deleted '81. Catalogue no: **2059 017**

LOVING ME, LOVING YOU
Tracks: / Loving me, loving you / That makes it.
7" Single: Released Jan '82, on RCA, by BMG Records (UK). Deleted Jan '85. Catalogue no: **RCA 174**

PERSONAL PROBLEM
Tracks: / Personal problems.
7" Single: Released Feb '86, on Aura Records, by Aura Records. Catalogue no: **AUS 149**

TULANE
Tracks: / Tulane.
7" Single: Released Aug '77, on Polydor, by Polydor Ltd. Deleted '80. Catalogue no: **2058 889**

Gibbs, Dave

I DON'T UNLOVE YOU
Tracks: / I don't unlove you.
7" Single: Released Dec '82, on Raffia, Deleted Dec '85. Catalogue no: **RAF 004**

Gibbs, Georgia

KISS ME ANOTHER
Tracks: / Kiss me another.
78 rpm: Released '56, on Mercury (Pye), Deleted '58. Catalogue no: **MT 110**

TWEEDLE DEE
Tracks: / Tweedle dee.
78 rpm: Released '55, on Mercury (Oriole), Deleted '56. Catalogue no: **MB 3196**

Gibbs, Leroy

REWARD ME
Tracks: / Reward me.
12" Single: Released Jan '88, on Echo, by

Echo Records. Catalogue no: **ECHO 013**

YODEL REGGAE
Tracks: / Yodel reggae.
7" Single: Released May '88, on Trojan, by Trojan Records. Catalogue no: **7 ECHO 1**
12" Single: Released '88, on Trojan, by Trojan Records. Catalogue no: **TRT 9097**
7" Single: Released '88, on Trojan, by Trojan Records. Catalogue no: **TRO 9097**
12" Single: Released May '88, on Trojan, by Trojan Records. Catalogue no: **ECHO 1**

Gibbs, Terri

SOMEBODY'S KNOCKIN'
Tracks: / Somebody's knockin' / Magic time.
7" Single: Released Mar '81, on MCA, by MCA Records. Deleted Mar '84. Catalogue no: **MCA 685**

Gibson Brothers

Biographical details: Hailing from Martinique, this family band consists of Alex, Patrick and Chris Gibson. With the help of songwriter/producer Daniel Vangarde, the Gibson Brothers commercialised the salsa and calypso sounds of the Latin/Carribean/West Indian territories and offered them to the white disco and pop markets. Chris Gibson was the gruff lead singer, but the group sounded better when all three brothers were singing in harmony. The Gibsons achieved a run of five UK hit singles between March 1979 and September 1980. *Cuba* reached no. 41, and was followed by their most pop-oriented offerings, *Ooh, what a life* (no. 10) and *Que sera mi vida (If you should go)* (no. 5). Then came a re-issue of *Cuba* on a double A-sided single with *Better do it salsa*, which climbed to no. 12; finally *Mariana* climbed to no. 11. Having milked the formula as much as they could, the Gibson Brothers faded from view in 1981. They made a very brief appearance on the British charts in 1983 with the somewhat ludicrous *My heart's beating wild (Tic tac tic tac)*, but they now rely on live work rather than recordings for their income. (Bob Macdonald, 20/9/85).

CUBA (88 REMIX)
Tracks: / Cuba (88 remix) / Cuba (88 remix) (versions).
12" Single: Released Sep '88, on Debut, by Skratch Records. Catalogue no: **DEBTX 3055**
7" Single: Released Sep '88, on Debut, by Skratch Records. Catalogue no: **DEBT 3055**

CUBA (SINGLE)
Tracks: / Cuba / Better do it salsa.
7" Single: Released Feb '80, on Island, by Island Records. Deleted '83. Catalogue no: **WIP 6561**
7" Single: Released Feb '80, on Island, by Island Records. Deleted Feb '83. Catalogue no: **WIP 6561**
7" Single: Released Mar '79, on Island, by Island Records. Deleted '82. Catalogue no: **WIP 6483**

I LEFT MY HEART IN JAMAICA
Tracks: / I left my heart in Jamaica / Limbo.
7" Single: Released Apr '82, on Epic, by CBS Records. Deleted Apr '85. Catalogue no: **A 2084**
12" Single: Released Apr '82, on Epic, by CBS Records. Deleted Apr '85. Catalogue no: **A 132084**

KEEPERS
Tracks: / Keepers.
7" Single: Released Feb '88, on Shadowline, Catalogue no: **SR 0488**

LATIN AMERICA
Tracks: / Latin America / West Indies.
7" Single: Released Oct '80, on Island, by Island Records. Deleted Oct '83. Catalogue no: **WIP 6659**
12" Single: Released Oct '80, on Island, by Island Records. Deleted Oct '83. Catalogue no: **12WIP 6659**

MARIANA
Tracks: / Mariana.
7" Single: Released Jul '80, on Island, by Island Records. Deleted '83. Catalogue no: **WIP 6617**

METROPOLIS
Tracks: / Metropolis / Because I love you.
7" Single: Released Sep '80, on Island, by Island Records. Deleted '83. Catalogue no: **12WIP 6640**
7" Single: Released Sep '80, on Island, by Island Records. Deleted '83. Catalogue no: **WIP 6640**

MY HEART'S BEATING (TIC TAC)
Tracks: / My heart's beating.
7" Single: Released Jun '83, on Stiff, by Stiff Records. Catalogue no: **BUY 184**
12" Single: Released Jun '83, on Stiff, by Stiff Records. Catalogue no: **BUYIT 184**

OOH WHAT A LIFE
Tracks: / Ooh What a life.
7" Single: Released Jul '79, on Island, by Island Records. Deleted '82. Catalogue no: **WIP 6503**

PARTY TONIGHT
Tracks: / Party tonight / B'Lola.
7" Single: Released Jul '86, on Streetwave, Catalogue no: **KHAN 68**
12" Single: Released Jul '86, on Streetwave, Catalogue no: **MKHAN 68**

QUARTIER LATIN (SINGLE)
Tracks: / Quartier latin / I-I-I-love you.
7" Single: Released Dec '81, on Epic, by CBS Records. Deleted Dec '84. Catalogue no: **EPCA 1843**

QUE SERA MI VIDA '89'
Tracks: / Que sera mi vida '89'.
7" Single: Released May '89, on Debut, by Skratch Records. Catalogue no: **DEBT 3070**
12" Single: Released May '89, on Debut, by Skratch Records. Catalogue no: **DEBTX 3070**

QUE SERA MI VIDA (IF YOU SHOULD GO)
Tracks: / Que sera mi vida.
7" Single: Released Nov '79, on Island, by Island Records. Deleted '82. Catalogue no: **WIP 6525**

Gibson, Chris

SLEEPS DARK
Tracks: / Sleeps dark / Silent gate.
7" Single: Released Mar '82, on Atmospheric, Catalogue no: **AS 1**

Gibson, Debbie

ELECTRIC YOUTH (SINGLE)
Tracks: / Electric youth / We could be together.
Cassingle: Released May '89, on Atlantic, by WEA Records. Catalogue no: **A 8919C**
CD 5": Released Apr '89, on Atlantic, by WEA Records. Catalogue no: **A 8919CD**
12" Pic: Released May '89, on Atlantic, by WEA Records. Catalogue no: **A 8919TP**
12" Single: Released Apr '89, on Atlantic, by WEA Records. Catalogue no: **A 8919T**
7" Single: Released Apr '89, on Atlantic, by WEA Records. Catalogue no: **A 8919**
12" Single: Released May '89, on Atlantic, by WEA Records. Catalogue no: **A 8919TX**

FOOLISH BEAT
Tracks: / Foolish beat / Between the lines / Shake your love (live) (on 12" only) / Out of the blue (megamix) / Shake your love (megamix) / Only in my dreams (megamix) / Only in my dreams (Dreamhouse mix).
12" Single: Released Jun '88, on Atlantic, by WEA Records. Catalogue no: **A 9059 T**
7" Single: Released Jun '88, on Atlantic, by WEA Records. Catalogue no: **A 9059**
12" Single: Released Jul '88, on Atlantic (USA), by WEA Records. Catalogue no: **086556**

LOST IN YOUR EYES
Tracks: / Lost in your eyes / Silence speaks (a thousand words).
12" Single: Released Jan '89, on Atlantic, by WEA Records. Catalogue no: **A 8970 T**
CD 5": Released Jan '89, on Atlantic, by WEA Records. Catalogue no: **A 8970 CD**
7" Single: Released Jan '89, on Atlantic, by WEA Records. Catalogue no: **A 8970**

ONLY IN MY DREAMS
Tracks: / Only in my dreams.
12" Single: Released Aug '87, on Atlantic, by WEA Records. Catalogue no: **A 9322 T**
7" Single: Released Aug '87, on Atlantic, by WEA Records. Catalogue no: **A 9322**

OUT OF THE BLUE (SINGLE)
Tracks: / Out of the blue / Fallen angel.
12" Single: Released May '88, on Atlantic, by WEA Records. Catalogue no: **A 9091 T**
7" Single: Released May '88, on Atlantic, by WEA Records. Catalogue no: **A 9091**

SHAKE YOUR LOVE
Tracks: / Shake your love / Wake up to love.
7" Single: Released Dec '87, on Atlantic, by WEA Records. Deleted Jul '88. Catalogue no: **A 9187**

STAYING TOGETHER
Tracks: / Staying together / Red hot.
7" Single: Released Oct '88, on Atlantic, by WEA Records. Catalogue no: **A 9020**
CD 5": Released Oct '88, on Atlantic, by WEA Records. Catalogue no: **A 9020 CD**
12" Single: Released Oct '88, on Atlantic, by WEA Records. Catalogue no: **A 9020 T**

WE COULD BE TOGETHER
Tracks: / We could be together / Over the wall (dub version).
CD 5": Released Jul '89, on Atlantic, by WEA Records. Catalogue no: **A 8896CD**
7" Single: Released Jul '89, on Atlantic, by WEA Records. Catalogue no: **A 8896**
12" Single: Released Jul '89, on Atlantic, by WEA Records. Catalogue no: **A 8896T**
Cassingle: Released Jul '89, on Atlantic, by WEA Records. Catalogue no: **A 8896C**
CD 5": Released Jul '89, on Atlantic, by WEA Records. Catalogue no: **756 788 7**

Gibson, Don

Biographical details: This American singer, songwriter and guitarist was born in Shelby, North Carolina. He began his full-time musical career at the age of 14 (1942), and spent the next 15 years working as a country-and-western honky tonk singer without conspicuous success. Then came the Elvis Presley phenomenon, which prompted Gibson to move towards a rockier country sound without actually becoming a rock'n'roll performer.RCA Victor's Nashville artist/producer/executive/svengali Chet Atkins was similarly striving to adapt country music in this way, and Gibson thus began working with him. Gibson came to major public attention with *Oh lonesome me*, a self-penned single which reached no. 7 on the US pop chart in 1958. Don also wrote the B side *I can't stop loving you*, which became a no. 1 smash on both sides of the Atlantic for Ray Charles in 1962. During the late fifties and early sixties Gibson chalked up a string of American hits on both the country and pop listings, many of his songs becoming standards. His style - which managed to convey lost love, loneliness and heartbreak without resorting to schmaltzy sentiment - hadan enormous influence upon Roy Orbison. The Big O often recorded Don's songs, including an entire Gibson-penned 1966 LP. Orbison's own songwriting clearly reflected the Gibson knack. Don's only substantial chart single in Britain was 1961's *Sea of heartbreak* (not his own song) which climbed to no. 14 in the UK and no. 21 in the US. Shortly afterwards he faded from the chart action, but nonetheless kept working in Nashville during the 60's and 70's. In 1980 his underrated talents were given a belated airing on the UK album chart - Warwick Records' *Country number one* LP (a reference to his song *Lonesome number one*) reached the no. 13 position. At the end of the following year, Elvis Costello reached the lower end of the UK singles chart with a remake of Gibson's *Sweet dreams* ballad. (Bob Macdonald, 20/9/85) Country pop singer and songwriter born in 1928 in North Carolina. Turned pro at age 14 on local radio; wrote his *I can't stop loving you* (for Kitty Wells), *Sweet dreams* (for Faron Young); his own version of *Sweet dreams* was a top ten country hit on MGM in 1956, but his two sided smash was *Oh lonesome me/I can't stop loving you* (No. 1 country, 7 pop in 1958) on RCA, followed by over 80 more country hits through 1970, with 14 pop crossovers. (Donald Clarke, July 1989)h.

LONESOME NUMBER ONE
Tracks: / Lonesome number one.
7" Single: Released Feb '62, on RCA, by BMG Records (UK). Deleted '65. Catalogue no: **RCA 1272**

SEA OF HEARTBREAK
Tracks: / Please help me, I'm falling (Hank Locklin) / Sea of heartbreak.
7" Single: Released Mar '84, on Pastafont, by Pastafont Music. Catalogue no: **PF 3009**
7" Single: Released Aug '61, on RCA, by BMG Records (UK). Deleted '64. Catalogue no: **RCA 1243**
7" Single: Released Oct '86, on Old Gold, by Old Gold Records. Catalogue no: **OG 9621**

SWEET SENSUOUS SENSATION
Tracks: / Sweet sensuous sensation / Stranger to me.
7" Single: Released 20 Jun '80, on Warner Bros., by WEA Records. Deleted '83. Catalogue no: **K 17624**

Gibson, Wayne

Biographical details: This British singer spent the sixties working tirelessly on the club circuit, without ever quite making the big time. He was one of the nearly men of the UK pop business. Throughout the decade, Gibson's only glimpse of chart action occurred in September 1964, when his *Kelly* single reached the UK no. 48 position. Ten years later, at the end of 1974, Gibson finally hit the British Top 20 - but his hit was a remake of the Rolling Stones' 1966 LP track *Under my thumb* (with a stronger disco beat added), thus showing that Wayne was caught in a time warp. This outrageously sexist song may not have caused too much of a stir in '66, but Gibson's rendition was still on the charts as 1974 became '75, the year that the British Parliament passed the Sex Discrimination Act. Times were moving fast, and women no longer took kindly to being told that they were under men's thumbs. By 1985 Mick Jagger was declaring that *She's the boss* - and Gibson was in the land of obscurity. (Bob Macdonald, 21/9/85).

KELLY
Tracks: / Kelly.
7" Single: Released Sep '64, on Pye, Deleted '67. Catalogue no: **7N 15680**

UNDER MY THUMB
Tracks: / Under my thumb / Yesterday's papers.
7" Single: Released Nov '74, on Disco Demand, Deleted '77. Catalogue no: **DDS 2001**
7" Single: Released Dec '83, on Kingdom, by Kingdom Records. Deleted '85. Catalogue no: **KV 8012**

Gidden, Yvonne

IN ORBIT (mega mix)
Tracks: / In orbit.
12" Single: Released Jan '84, on Electricity, by Electricity Records. Deleted '88. Catalogue no: **ELECT 2**

Gidea Park

Biographical details: This British "band" never really existed - the harmony vocals and most of the instruments were the work of Adrian Baker and his multi-tracking tricks. Baker also arranged and produced the records. The background to the brief success of Gidea Park lay in May 1981, when a Dutch studio aggregation called Starsound reached no. 2 on the British charts (and later no. 1 in America) with a disco medley *Stars on 45*; this consisted of a series of soundalike versions of old, mainly Beatles, favourites, set to the insistent disco beat of a drum machine. By August 1981, Starsound had been joined on the UK charts by a host of other medley merchants including Enigma, Tight Fit, Lobo, Startrax and even the Royal Philharmonic Orchestra. Also amongst the medley melee was Gidea Park, whose *Beach boy gold* cruised to no. 11; shortly afterward, *Seasons of gold* reached no. 28. These Beach Boys and Four Seasons imitations aroused the inevitable cries of "cash-in" among critics. But to be fair to Baker, it should be pointed out that he had scored a major UK hit as long ago as 1975 with his accurate recreation of the Seasons' *Sherry*; and his Beach Boys montage had originally been released long before Starsound, but without chart success. Indeed, the California combo were so impressed with Baker's impersonation of them that they invited him to join the group. This he did for a while - thus, while Gidea Park was charting in his native country, Adrian was on tour in the States with the Beach Boys. (Bob Macdonald, 21/9/85).

BEACH BOY GOLD
Tracks: / Beach Boy gold.
7" Single: Released May '81, on Stone, Catalogue no: **SON 2162**

BEACH BOY GOLD PART 2
Tracks: / Beach Boy gold part 2 / Summer girls.
12" Single: Released Jun '82, on Polo, by Polo Records. Deleted '88. Catalogue no: **POLO 12-22**
7" Single: Released Jun '82, on Polo, by Polo Records. Deleted '88. Catalogue no: **POLO 22**

(LAI-LO-LAH) LIMBO
Tracks: / (Lai-lo-lah) limbo / Back in '65 / (Lai-lo-lah) limbo (12" version).
7" Single: Released Jun '88, on Tiger, by Creole Records. Catalogue no: **TGR 71**
12" Single: Released Jun '88, on Tiger, by Creole Records. Catalogue no: **TGR 1**

LIGHTNIN STRIKES
Tracks: / Lightning strikes / Baby come back.
12" Single: Released Jan '82, on Polo, by Polo Records. Deleted '88. Catalogue no: **POLO 12-18**
7" Single: Released Jan '82, on Polo, by Polo Records. Deleted '88. Catalogue no: **POLO 18**

RUN BABY RUN
Tracks: / Run baby run / Don't look back.
7" Single: Released Apr '86, on Mix Factory, by Mix Factory Records. Deleted '88. Catalogue no: **MX 2**

SEASONS OF GOLD (Four Seasons medley)
Tracks: / Seasons of gold.
7" Single: Released Sep '81, on Polo, by Polo Records. Deleted '88. Catalogue no: **POLO 14**
12" Single: Released Sep '81, on Polo, by Polo Records. Deleted '88. Catalogue no: **POLO 12-14**

Gift

CRASHING DOWN
Tracks: / Crashing down.
7" Single: Released Sep '82, on Venus Catalogue no: **ORBIT 1**

Gift Horses

ROSEMARY
Tracks: / Rosemary / Learning to bring yourself down.
7" Single: Released Jul '87, on Pop, by Magnet Records. Catalogue no: **POP 161**

Gift Of Alien

CRYING IN THE RAIN
Tracks: / Crying in the rain / You're the best girl in the world.
7" Single: Released 13 Jun '87, on Blue Hat, by Blue Hat Records. Catalogue no: **BHR 52**

Gifted Children

PAINTING BY NUMBERS
Tracks: / Painting by numbers / Lichtenstein girl.
7" Single: Released May '81, on Whaam, Catalogue no: **WHAAM 01**
7" Single: Released May '81, on Whaam, Deleted May '86. Catalogue no: **WHAM 002**

Giggetty

BLACK COUNTRY CHRISTMAS
Tracks: / Black country Christmas / Lullaby.
7" Single: Released Nov '80, on Revolver, by FM-Revolver Records. Catalogue no: **REV 2**

Gigli, Suzanne

BOYS DO IT
Tracks: / Boys do it.
12" Single: Released Nov '84, on Lamborghini, by Lamborghini Records. Catalogue no: **12LSU 3**
7" Single: Released Nov '84, on Lamborghini, by Lamborghini Records. Catalogue no: **LSU 3**

Gigolo

DRY BONES
Tracks: / Dry bones.
7" Single: Released May '82, on Channel, by Channel Records. Catalogue no: **CHAN 002**

Gil, Gilberto

PALCO
Tracks: / Palco / Samba de Los Angeles.
7" Single: Released Mar '82, on WEA, by WEA Records. Deleted '85. Catalogue no: **K 79285**

TODA MENINA BAINA
Tracks: / Toda menina baina.
7" Single: Released Jul '85, on WEA, by WEA Records. Deleted '86. Catalogue no: **U 9451**
12" Single: Released Jul '85, on WEA, by WEA Records. Catalogue no: **U 9451 T**

TOUCHES PAS MON POTE
Tracks: / Toda menina baina / Polco (Extra track on 12" version only) / Touches pas mon pote.
12" Single: Released Jun '86, on WEA (International), by WEA Records. Deleted Jun '87. Catalogue no: **U 8623T**
7" Single: Released Jun '86, on WEA (International), by WEA Records. Catalogue no: **U 8623**

Gilbert, Peter

I WANT YOUR LOVE
Tracks: / I want your love.
12" Single: Released Nov '88, on Mact Records, Catalogue no: **MT 001**

Gilberto, Astrud

Biographical details: This Brazilian singer had had virtually no musical experience when she shot to brief stardom in 1964. Her husband Joao Gilberto, one of the leading figures on Brazil's bossa nova scene, was in the process of recording a bossa nova LP with himself on vocals and US tenor saxophonist Stan Getz providing the main accompaniment. For one song, *The girl from Ipanema*, it was decided that Astrud might sound suitable for some of the lyrics (she was a native of the Ipanema beach area). When the album track was issued as a single, it was in an edited form and only Astrud's section (not Joao's) could be heard. *The girl from Ipanema* was one of the year's surprise smashes, reaching no. 5 on the American chart. The untrained straightforwardness of the vocal performance was riveting - the natural quality of Astrud's voice were plaintive and slightly eerie. Although there were no further US hit singles, she became a cult figure in American jazz circles during the mid-sixties and rivalled her husband's status in their native country. In Britain *The girl from Ipanema* peaked at no. 29. Two decades later, in one of pop music's more surprising quirks, it was reissued and reached no. 55. This 1984 reappearance was due to a mini-boom in jazz that was taking place in Britain, led by such acts as Sade, Everything but the Girl and Working Week. (Bob Macdonald, 21/9/85).

GETTING OVER YOU
Tracks: / Young love of my life.
7" Single: Released Sep '84, on PRT, by Castle Communications Records. Catalogue no: **7P 317**

GIRL FROM IPANEMA, THE
Tracks: / Girl from Ipanema.
7" Single: Released Aug '84, on Verve, Deleted '87. Catalogue no: **IPA 1**

Gilbey, Chris

MOONLIGHT LADY
Tracks: / Moonlight lady / One lonely guy.
7" Single: Released Feb '80, on Laser, Deleted Feb '85. Catalogue no: **LAS 24**

Gilde Duo

TYROLEAN VAGABOND
Tracks: / Tyrolean vagabond / Snow waltz.
7" Single: Released Dec '83, on Mint, by Emerald Records. Deleted '88. Catalogue no: **CHEW 88**

Gilder, Nick

ROCK AMERICA (SINGLE)
Tracks: / Rock America / Night comes down.
7" Single: Released Nov '80, on Casablanca, by PolyGram UK Ltd. Deleted Nov '83. Catalogue no: **CAN 214**

YOU REALLY ROCK ME
Tracks: / You really rock me / Got to get out.
7" Single: Released Nov '82, on Speed, Catalogue no: **SPEED 7**

Giles, Eddie

THAT'S HOW STRONG MY LOVE IS
Tracks: / That's how strong my love is.
7" Single: Released Jul '80, on Charly, by Charly Records. Deleted '87. Catalogue no: **CTD 124**

Giles, Sheila

ALWAYS TOO LATE
Tracks: / Always too late.
7" Single: Released May '89, on Menu, Catalogue no: **MENU 4**
12" Single: Released 21 Apr '89, on Menu, Catalogue no: **MENUT 4**

Gill, Andy

DISPOSSESSION
Tracks: / Dispossession.
12" Single: Released Aug '87, on Survival (1), by Survival Records. Catalogue no: **SUR 12 039**

Gill, Johnny

CAN'T WAIT TILL TOMORROW
Tracks: / Can't wait till tomorrow / One small night.
7" Single: Released Jun '85, on Cotillion, by WEA Records. Catalogue no: **B 9646**
12" Single: Released Jun '85, on Cotillion, by WEA Records. Catalogue no: **B 9646 T**

HALF CRAZY
Tracks: / Half crazy / Super love.
7" Single: Released Sep '85, on WEA, by WEA Records. Catalogue no: **B 9611**
12" Single: Released Sep '85, on WEA, by WEA Records. Catalogue no: **B 9611 T**

Gill, Mike

FLEUR BLANCHE
Tracks: / Fleur blanche.
7" Single: Released Oct '82, on Gee Bee Music, by Gee Bee Records. Catalogue no: **GB 1001**

L.A. 84
Tracks: / L.A. 84.
7" Single: Released Oct '83, on Gee Bee Music, by Gee Bee Records. Catalogue no: **GB 1002**

Gill, Vince

TURN ME LOOSE
Tracks: / Turn me loose.
7" Single: Released Mar '85, on RCA, by BMG Records (UK). Catalogue no: **PB 49993**

Gillan

GILLAN
Tracks: / Trouble / Your sister's on my list / Vengeance / Mr.Universe / Smoke on the water.
7" Single: Released Oct '80, on Virgin, by Virgin Records. Deleted Oct '83. Catalogue no: **VS 377**

LIVING FOR THE CITY
Tracks: / Living for the city / Breaking chains.
7" Pic: Released Aug '82, on Virgin, by Virgin Records. Deleted '89. Catalogue no: **VSY 519**
7" Single: Released Aug '82, on Virgin, by Virgin Records. Deleted '89. Catalogue no: **VS 519**

LONG GONE
Tracks: / Long gone.
7" Single: Released Oct '82, on Virgin, by Virgin Records. Deleted '89. Catalogue no: **VS 537**

MUTUALLY ASSURED DESTRUCTION
Tracks: / Mutually assured destruction / Maelstrom.
7" Single: Released Feb '81, on Virgin, by Virgin Records. Deleted '84. Catalogue no: **VS 403**

NEW ORLEANS
Tracks: / New orleans.
7" Single: Released Mar '81, on Virgin, by Virgin Records. Deleted '84. Catalogue no: **VS 406**

NIGHTMARE
Tracks: / Nightmare.
7" Single: Released Oct '81, on Virgin, by Virgin Records. Deleted '84. Catalogue no: **VS 441**

NO LAUGHING IN HEAVEN
Tracks: / No laughing in heaven / Lucille / One for the road / Bad news.
7" Single: Released Jun '81, on Virgin, by Virgin Records. Deleted '84. Catalogue no: **VS 425**

RESTLESS
Tracks: / Restless.
7" Single: Released Jan '82, on Virgin, by Virgin Records. Deleted '85. Catalogue no: **VS 465**

SLEEPING ON THE JOB
Tracks: / Sleeping on the job / Higher and higher.
7" Single: Released 20 Jul '80, on Virgin, by Virgin Records. Deleted '83. Catalogue no: **VS 355**

TROUBLE
Tracks: / Trouble.
7" Single: Released Oct '80, on Virgin, by Virgin Records. Deleted '83. Catalogue no: **VS 377**

VENGEANCE
Tracks: / Vengeance / Smoke on the water.
7" Single: Released May '81, on Arista, by BMG Records (UK). Deleted May '84. Catalogue no: **BAT 12**

Gillan, Ian

Biographical details: This British rock band consisted of the following line-up at the time of their greatest success: Ian Gillan, John McCoy, Bernie Torme, Colin Towns and Mick Underwood. Ian Gillan's powerful and distinctive vocals fronted the internationally successful Deep Purple from 1961 until 1973. He quit the band in the latter year (and was replaced by the previously unknown David Coverdale), but did not form his own group till 1975. Initially known as the Ian Gillan Band, their debut album *Child in Time* was released the following year - as its title suggested, the LP borrowed heavily from the Puple era, and it was not what UK rock fans wanted to hear just at the outset of the punk era: the album peaked at no. 55 in July '76. Subsequent LP were even less successful. In late 1979, with the New Wave in its dying days, the band found their commercial feet at last. With a new line-up and a shortened name (simply Gillan), they reached no. 11 on the British album chart with *Mr. Universe.* After yet more personnel changes (resulting in the forementioned line-up), Gillan hit a hot streak during 1980-81. *Glory Road* and *Future shock* both reached the Top 3 on the UK LP listings. Two rock'n'roll remakes became UK Top 20 singles: *Trouble* (originally from Elvis Presley's 1958 film *King Creole*) got to no. 14 in 1980, and the deliriously frenetic *New Orleans* peaked at no. 17 in 1981, one place lower than Gary US Bonds had managed 20 years earlier. Ian Gillan's chosen genre - heavy metal - was now back in vogue, although the band's many cover versions showed he was leaning in a more pop-oriented direction than many of his HM peers. As always, Ian's voice glided effortlessly from a subtle soft passage to a manic screeching section - his singing was the dominant factor in the band's music. Gillan disbanded in 1983, the band's leader joining the legendary Black Sabbath.
The Sabbath liaison proved to be a short-lived affair, because the equally legendary Deep Purple reformed in 1984 with their classic line-up. Ian was the primary force that persuaded the Purple people to get back together and, at their massive summer gig at Knebworth in June '85, he declared cthat he was happier than he had ever been before in his life. (Bob Macdonald, 21/9/85).

SOUTH AFRICA
Tracks: / South Africa / John / South Africa (extended version) (12" only).
Note: "Deep Purple frontman Ian Gillan's new solo single addresses itself to the apartheid regime in South Africa. It is released in the same week as the Nelson Mandela concert takes place at Wembley Stadium......It was written by the Gillan Band's guitarist, Bernie Marsden, and produced by Ian and Bernie, with a remix by Jimbo Barton. Ian's concern over the situation in South Africa is evident within the lyrics of the song; he also wanted it released because, as he says himself, 'It's a bloody great song'." (Virgin Records, June 1988.)
7" Single: Released Jun '88, on Virgin, by Virgin Records. Catalogue no: **VS 1088**
12" Single: Released Jun '88, on Virgin, by Virgin Records. Catalogue no: **VST 1088**

Gillan, Pauline

ONE MORE TIME
Tracks: / One more time.
12" Single: Released Oct '84, on Bullet, by Bullet Records. Deleted '88. Catalogue no: **BOLT 11**

Gillan/Glover

DISLOCATED
Tracks: / Dislocated / Chet / Purple people eater (12" only).
7" Single: Released Jul '87, on 10 Records, by Virgin Records. Catalogue no: **TEN 193**
12" Single: Released Jul '87, on 10 Records, by Virgin Records. Catalogue no: **TENT 193**

SHE TOOK MY BREATH AWAY
Tracks: / She took my breath away / Cayman Island.
12" Single: Released Jan '88, on Virgin, by Virgin Records. Catalogue no: **VST 1041**
7" Single: Released Jan '88, on Virgin, by Virgin Records. Catalogue no: **VS 1041**

Gillard ,Pip

WHY CAN'T YOU LOVE ME
Tracks: / Why can't you love me.
7" Single: Released Aug '84, on Plus One, Catalogue no: **PIPS 1**

Gilles, Samantha

LET ME FEEL IT
Tracks: / Let me feel it / Let me feel it (remix).
12" Single: Released Mar '85, on Record Shack, by Record Shack Records. Catalogue no: **SOHOT 35**
7" Single: Released Nov '86, on Greyhound, by Greyhound Records. Catalogue no: **GRY 001**

Gillespie, Cherry

WHY?
Tracks: / Why? / To dance.
7" Single: Released Aug '84, on BBC, by BBC Records & Tapes. Deleted '87. Catalogue no: **RESL 156**

Gillet, Pete

HOMELESS CHILD
Tracks: / Homeless child / Homeless child (dub mix) / Homeless child (cement mix) (Only on 12" single.).
12" Single: Released Apr '88, on I.R.S, Catalogue no: **IRMT 162**
7" Single: Released Apr '88, on I.R.S, Catalogue no: **IRM 162**

Gilley, Mickey

Biographical details: A rockabilly, later a honky-tonk singer born in 1938 in Louisiana; a piano playing cousin of Jerry Lee Lewis and for many years under his shadow. He played at a Houston club through the '60s, had his own Astro record label in 1964 and had a minor hit on Paula in 1968; then suddenly four number one country hits in a row in 1974-5 on Playboy; he switched to Epic in 1979 and had well over 40 hits through to 1984, most of them in the country top 10 and 17 at No. 1. He was a co-owner of Gilley's 1971-89 (when it closed); Gilley and 'the largest honky-tonk in the world' were featured in the film *Urban cowboy* in 1980. (Donald Clarke, July 1989).

STAND BY ME
Tracks: / Stand by me / Here comes the hurt again.
7" Single: Released Oct '80, on WEA, by WEA Records. Deleted Oct '83. Catalogue no: **K 79181**

YOU DON'T KNOW ME
Tracks: / You don't know me / Jukebox argument.
7" Single: Released Oct '81, on Epic, by CBS Records. Deleted Oct '84. Catalogue no: **EPCA 1567**

Gilliam, Roberta

ALL I WANT IS MY BABY (SINGLE)
Tracks: / All I want is my baby.
12" Single: Released Jan '86, on WEA, by WEA Records. Deleted Jun '87. Catalogue no: **U 8828T**
7" Single: Released Jan '86, on WEA, by WEA Records. Catalogue no: **U 8828**

Gillies, Alasdair

BY COOL SILOAM
Tracks: / By cool Siloam's shady rill.
7" Single: Released Oct '79, on Country House, by Scotdisc Records. Catalogue no: **BGC 237**

SCOTTISH TRILOGY
Tracks: / Scottish trilogy.
7" Single: Released Jun '82, on Country House, by Scotdisc Records. Catalogue no: **BGC 311**

Gillies, Corrine

YOU DON'T KNOW WHERE YOUR INTEREST LIES
Tracks: / You don't know where your interest lies / Keep on dancing.
7" Single: Released Aug '82, on Soul Stop, by Dawn Promotions. Catalogue no: **SS 3002**

Gillies, Stuart

Biographical details: This British singer achieved a one-off UK hit in 1973, preceded and followed by total obscurity. The single was *Amanda*, a totally conventional easy listening ballad produced by veteran MoR mogul Norman Newell; it reached no. 13 on the British chart, which proved an unlucky omen for Gillies' future career. The singer might have done better if he had been around during the '60's, when this kind of artist had easier access to chart action; but glitter rock was the name of the game in '73. Still, guys with girlfriends called Amanda have ensured a trickle of catalogue sales. (Bob Macdonald, 21/9/85).

AMANDA
Tracks: / Amanda.
7" Single: Released Mar '73, on Philips, by Phonogram Ltd. Deleted '76. Catalogue no: **6006 293**

AMANDA (OLD GOLD)
Tracks: / Amanda.
7" Single: Released Jul '82, on Old Gold, by Old Gold Records. Deleted '85. Catalogue no: **OG 9255**

Gilligan

MIND GAME
Tracks: / Mind game.
7" Single: Released Apr '89, on Star Track, Catalogue no: **ST 0014**

Gilliom, Bobby

GIMME A BREAK
Tracks: / Gimme a break.
12" Single: Released Sep '83, on NYC, Deleted '85. Catalogue no: **NYCX 101**

Gilmer, Jimmy

Biographical details: This American singer and pianist was born in Chicago, spent his early years in Illinois and moved with his family to Amarillo, Texas at the age of 12 (1951). In 1959 he formed the Fireballs with three other musicians. They soon came under the wing of producer/studio owner/manager Norman Petty, who was based in New Mexico (where all the Fireballs except Gilmer were also resident). During the late Fifties, Petty had come to prominence through his close working relationship with Buddy Holly and the Crickets; and, following Holly's death in 1959, Petty used the Fireballs to help him overdub the many primitive demo tapes that the prolific Buddy had left unreleased. This tidying up and embellishment process upset many Holly historians but resulted in considerable commercial success, particularly in Britain. The Fireballs chalked up three instrumental Top 40 singles in America in their own right during 1959-61: *Torquay, Bulldog* and *Quite a party*, the latter also hit the UK Top 40. Then in 1963, they billed themselves as Jimmy Gilmer & the Fireballs (with Jimmy on lead vocals) and scored a US no. 1 smash with the catchy novelty single *Sugar shack*. This was no. 1 in America for five weeks, but peaked at no. 45 in Britain where the Beatles were spearheading a totallt different pop sound. Gilmer and his group managed a follow-up American Top 20 hit with *Daisy petal pickin'* in early 1964, before the British Invasion torpedoed them into obscurity. Contrary to expectations, however, the Fireballs made a brief comeback in 1968. Still with Gilmer on vocals, they reached the US no. 9 position with *Bottle of wine*. (Bob Macdonald, 21/9/85).

SUGAR SHACK (SINGLE)
Tracks: / Sugar shack.
7" Single: Released Nov '63, on London-American, Deleted '66. Catalogue no: **HLD 9789**

Gilmour, David

Biographical details: This British guitarist and singer began his musical career in 1966 in a local Cambridge band called Jokers Wild. In February 1968 he replaced guitarist Syd Barrett in Pink Floyd, and he remained with the legendary band until their breakup in 1983. In 1978, during a lull in the Floyd's activities, Gilmour released his debut solo album: *David Gilmour* reached no. 17 and logged nine weeks on the UK chart. '78 was indeed an important year for him - his protege Kate Bush, whose precocious talents he had discovered and nurtured several years earlier, shot to stardom. Dave Gilmour's stirring guitar style sould be heard in all its glory on the extended outro of Bush's debut single, the UK no. 1 smash *Wuthering Heights* (1979) and on Paul McCartney's *No more lonely nights* (1984). Gilmour's second solo set *About face* was issued in 1984, shortly after the termination of Pink Floyd. *About face* was not a spectacular success; neither was its first single *Blue light*, which failed to chart in Britain and only made minor rippled on the US Hot 100. In 1985 he made the UK Top 20 as co-producer of the *Dream Academy's Life in a northern town*; this single was recorded at Hook End Manor, Gilmour's home studio in Berkshire. (Bob Macdonald, 22/9/85).

LOVE ON THE AIR
Tracks: / Love on the air / Let's get metaphysical.
7" Single: Released '84, on Harvest (1), by EMI Records. Catalogue no: **HAR 5229**
12" Single: Released '84, on Harvest (1), by EMI Records. Catalogue no: **HARP 5229**

Gilreath, James

LITTLE BAND OF GOLD
Tracks: / Little band of gold.
7" Single: Released May '63, on Pye International, Deleted '66. Catalogue no: **7N 25190**

Gilroy

HOW CAN YOU SAY IT SOBER
Tracks: / How can you say it sober.
12" Single: Released '85, on Private Eye, Catalogue no: **PE 106**

Gilstrap, Jim

SWING YOUR DADDY (OLD GOLD)
Tracks: / Swing your daddy / I'm doin' fine now.
7" Single: Released 24 Apr '89, on Old Gold, by Old Gold Records. Catalogue no: **OG 9886**

SWING YOUR DADDY (SINGLE)
Tracks: / Swing your daddy.
7" Single: Released Mar '75, on Chelsea, Deleted '78. Catalogue no: **2005 021**

Giltrap, Gordon

Biographical details: This British guitarist began his career at the start of the Seventies. His debut album *Testament of time* was released in 1971, and was followed by *Giltrap* (1973) and *Visionary* (1976). During these years, he also played on various fairly unimportant sessions. Giltrap's guitar virtuosity finally received a degree of proper recognition in early 1978, when his mesmerising instrumental single *Heartsong* reached no. 21 in the UK. It was a melodic classical/rock hybrid, and became ripe fodder for use as theme music for radio and television programmes including BBC TV's Sunday night show *Holiday*. Giltrap's fourth LP *Perilous journey* reached the UK no. 29 position. His follow-up single was a remake of Fleetwood Mac's 1969 guitar-laden classic *Oh well*; but the new version made no impact on the public, and Giltrap's only return to the British charts was with a minor 1979 hit single *Fear of the dark*. The Eighties brought relative obscurity for Gordon, although he remained an active live performer. (Bob Macdonald, 22/9/85).

CHI MAI
Tracks: / Chi Mai / After the storm.
7" Single: Released '81, on PVK, by PVK Records. Catalogue no: **PV 105**

FEAR OF THE DARK (SINGLE)
Tracks: / Fear of the dark.
7" Single: Released Apr '79, on Electric, Deleted '82. Catalogue no: **WOT 29**

HEARTSONG
Tracks: / Heartsong.
7" Single: Released Jan '78, on Electric, Deleted '81. Catalogue no: **WOT 19**

HOCUS POCUS
Tracks: / Hocus pocus.
7" Single: Released Jul '81, on PVK, by PVK Records. Catalogue no: **PV 111**

MAGPIE RAG
Tracks: / Magpie rag / Gypsy Lane.
7" Single: Released Mar '81, on PVK, by PVK Records. Catalogue no: **PV 101**

SUNBURST
Tracks: / Sunburst / Headwind - the eagle.
7" Single: Released Feb '82, on PVK, by PVK Records. Catalogue no: **PVK 116**

WALTONS
Tracks: / Waltons / Birds of a feather.
7" Single: Released Apr '80, on Cube, Deleted Apr '83. Catalogue no: **BUG 89**

Giltrap, Joe

MR TAMBOURINE MAN
Tracks: / Mr. Tambourine man / When Margaret was 11.
7" Single: Released Jul '87, on Play, by Play Records. Catalogue no: **PLAY 219**

Gin Sling

HEARTBREAK
Tracks: / Heartbreak.
7" Single: Released '88, on Ginsling, Catalogue no: **GINSLING 01**

Gina

CAN'T STOP
Tracks: / Can't stop.
7" Single: Released Jun '87, on President, by President Records. Catalogue no: **PT 532**

SANTA BRING MY BABY BACK (TO ME)
Tracks: / Santa bring my baby back (to me) / Without you this Christmas.
7" Single: Released 21 Nov '87, on PRM, Catalogue no: **PRM 202**

THIS LOVE
Tracks: / This love / This love (version).
12" Single: Released Jul '82, on Judah, Catalogue no: **JR 001**

Gina X

DRIVE MY CAR
Tracks: / Drive my car.
7" Single: Released Aug '84, on Statik, Catalogue no: **TAK 21**
12" Single: Released Aug '84, on Statik, Catalogue no: **TAK 21-12**

HARLEY DAVIDSON(ENGLISH VERSION)
Tracks: / Harley Davidson (English version).
12" Single: Released Oct '84, on Statik, Catalogue no: **TAK 2612**
7" Single: Released Oct '84, on Statik, Catalogue no: **TAK 26**

NO GDM
Tracks: / No GDM / Nice mover.
12" Single: Released Mar '81, on EMI, by EMI Records. Deleted Mar '84. Catalogue no: **12 EMI 5148**
7" Single: Released Mar '81, on EMI, by EMI Records. Deleted Mar '84. Catalogue no: **EMI 5148**
7" Single: Released Mar '85, on Statik, Catalogue no: **TAK 33**
12" Single: Released Mar '85, on Statik, Catalogue no: **TAK 3312**

Gina X Performance

WEEKEND TWIST
Tracks: / Weekend twist / Nice mover.
7" Single: Released May '80, on EMI, by EMI Records. Deleted May '85. Catalogue no: **EMI 5062**

Ginger

SOMETHING WASN'T QUITE RIGHT
Tracks: / Something wasn't quite right / How good it feels tonight.
7" Single: Released Jan '81, on Eagle Music, by Eagle Music Records. Deleted Jan '84. Catalogue no: **ERS 003**

Ginger, William

TONIGHT IS MY NIGHT OUT
Tracks: / Tonight is my night out.
12" Single: Released May '82, on Disco Rocker, Catalogue no: **DR 01003**

Gingerbread

CHRISTMAS TIME
Tracks: / Christmas time.
12" Single: Released Nov '85, on RCA, by BMG Records (UK). Catalogue no: **PT 40500**
7" Single: Released Nov '85, on RCA, by BMG Records (UK). Catalogue no: **PB 40499**

Ginnette

SEA OF HEARTBREAK
Tracks: / Sea of heartbreak.
7" Single: Released Apr '83, on Pastafont, by Pastafont Music. Catalogue no: **PF 3009**

Gino Vess

PALE BLUE WINDSCREEN
Tracks: / Pale blue windscreen.
12" Single: Released Jun '84, on One Track, Catalogue no: **CAS 002**

Giorbino, Anthony

ART OF LETTING GO, THE (SINGLE)
Tracks: / Art of letting go, (The).
12" Single: Released May '88, on Strike Back, by Strike Back Records. Catalogue no: **SBR 17T**

Gipsy Kings

BAMBOLEO
Tracks: / Bamboleo / Bamboleo (version).
7" Single: Released Jul '88, on A.1, by A.1 Records. Catalogue no: **A1 305**
CD 5": Released May '89, on A.1, by A.1 Records. Deleted Jul '89. Catalogue no: **CA1 313**
7" Single: Released May '89, on A.1, by A.1 Records. Deleted Jul '89. Catalogue no: **A1 313**
12" Single: Released Jul '88, on A.1, by A.1 Records. Catalogue no: **12 A1 305**
12" Single: Released Sep '89, on A.1, by A.1 Records. Catalogue no: **12A 1313**

DJOBI DJOBA
Tracks: / Djobi djoba / Moorea.
7" Single: Released Sep '88, on A.1, by A.1 Records. Catalogue no: **A1 307**
12" Single: Released Sep '88, on A.1, by A.1 Records. Catalogue no: **12 A1 307**

MI MANERA, A
Tracks: / Mi manera, A.
12" Single: Released Mar '89, on A.1, by A.1 Records. Catalogue no: **A1 12 310**
7" Single: Released Mar '89, on A.1, by A.1 Records. Catalogue no: **A1 310**

Giraffes

ONE STEP
Tracks: / One step / For whom the bell tolls.
7" Single: Released Jul '89, on Love & Madness, Catalogue no: **LOMA 2**

PASS ME BY
Tracks: / Pass me by / Rooftop.
7" Single: Released Jan '89, on Love & Madness, Catalogue no: **LMR 1**

Girl

Biographical details: At the time of their greatest success, this British heavy metal band consisted of Phil Collen, Dave Gaynor, Gerry Laffy, Simon Laffy and Philip Lewis. Girl were one of a host of heavy metal groups to hit the UK charts in 1980, the year that the genre made a major resurgence following years in the wilderness during the punk era. Girl reached no. 33 with their debut album *Sheer greed*; the single *Hollywood tease* peaked at no. 50, although it might have been expected to fare better in view of the band's appearance on Top Of The Pops. Then followed a hiatus for Girl, during which drummer Dave Gaynor was replaced by ex-Gillan player Pete Barnacle. The new line-up could only manage a UK no. 92 placing with their 1982 album *Wasted youth*. Shortly afterwards, guitarist Phil Collen left. He joined Def Leppard halfway through the recording of Leppard's third album *Pyromania*, which turned out to be a wise move - it was one of America's best-selling albums of 1983. (Bob Macdonald, 22/9/85).

CLAPPING SONG
Tracks: / Clapping song / My boy has left me.
7" Single: Released Jul '82, on Aura Records, by Aura Records. Deleted Jul '85. Catalogue no: **AUS 118**

COME OUT
Tracks: / Come out.
12" Single: Released Feb '88, on Product Inc., Catalogue no: **12PROD 6**

DO YOU LOVE ME?
Tracks: / Do you love me? / Strawberries.
7" Single: Released Jan '80, on Jet, by Jet Records. Deleted '83. Catalogue no: **JET 169**

HOLLYWOOD TEASE
Tracks: / Hollywood tease / You really got me / My number.
7" Single: Released Apr '80, on Jet, by Jet Records. Deleted '83. Catalogue no: **JET 176**

LOVE IS A GAME
Tracks: / Love is a game / Little Miss Ann.
12" Single: Released Aug '80, on Jet, by Jet Records. Deleted '83. Catalogue no: **JET 10-191**
7" Single: Released Aug '80, on Jet, by Jet Records. Deleted '83. Catalogue no: **JET 191**

OLD DOGS

Tracks: / Old dogs / Passing clouds.
7" Single: Released Jan '82, on Jet, by Jet Records. Deleted Jan '85. Catalogue no: **JET 7019**

SHE NO RATTLE MY CAGE
Tracks: / She no rattle my cage.
7" Single: Released Jan '88, on K, by K Records. Catalogue no: **L 26500**

Girl Called Johnny

HELLO IT ISN'T ME
Tracks: / Shallow / Hello it isn't me.
7" Single: Released Nov '86, on 10 Records, by Virgin Records. Deleted May '88. Catalogue no: **TEN 144**
12" Single: Released Nov '86, on 10 Records, by Virgin Records. Deleted May '88. Catalogue no: **TENT 144**

Girl Can't Help It

BABY DOLL
Tracks: / Baby doll.
12" Single: Released Oct '82, on Virgin, by Virgin Records. Deleted '89. Catalogue no: **VS 552-12**
7" Single: Released Oct '82, on Virgin, by Virgin Records. Deleted '89. Catalogue no: **VS 552**

Girl Talk (Group)

FALLING FOR YOU
7" Single: Released Jan '87, on WEA, by WEA Records. Deleted Jan '88. Catalogue no: **YZ 88**
12" Single: Released Jan '87, on WEA, by WEA Records. Deleted Jan '88. Catalogue no: **YZ 88T**

I WILL GIVE YOU LOVE
Tracks: / I will give you love / I will give you love (inst) / Drum me up some love (inst).
12" Single: Released 13 Jun '87, on WEA, by WEA Records. Deleted Jul '88. Catalogue no: **YZ 137T**
7" Single: Released 13 Jun '87, on WEA, by WEA Records. Deleted Jul '88. Catalogue no: **YZ 137**

Girl Trouble

TARANTULA
Tracks: / Tarantula.
7" Single: Released Jan '88, on K, by K Records. Catalogue no: **L 28201**

Girls

CAN'T HELP IT BABY DOLL
Tracks: / Can't help it baby doll.
7" Single: Released Nov '82, on Virgin, by Virgin Records. Deleted Nov '85. Catalogue no: **VS 522**
12" Single: Released Nov '82, on Virgin, by Virgin Records. Deleted Nov '85. Catalogue no: **VS 52212**

Girls At Our Best

Biographical details: This British band consisted of James Alan, Judy Evans, Dave Fishel, D.Carl Harper, Rod Johnson, Gerard Swift and Alan Wakeman. Thus, despite their name, they were a predominantly male group. Hailing from Leeds, the forerunner of Girls At Our Best was a group called SOS, who were formed in the late '70s in the aftermath of the Sex Pistols' punk revolution. The Pistols helped to move the UK rock scene away from its obsession with London and put the spotlight on the provinces. In addition, of course, punk rock opened the floodgates for the independent phenomenon. Taking advantage of both developments, Girls At Our Best released their debut single *Warm girls* on a do-it-yourself basis. During the early eighties, they achieved cult status with such singles as *Politisa*, *Go for gold* and *Fast boyfriends*. But their only taste of success on the UK national charts was with their debut album *Pleasure*, which reached no. 60 in November 1981. As it turned out, it was their only LP. Featuring guest Thomas Dolby on synthesisers, it was a freaky pop platter that was entertaining in the forst instance but did not really stand up to repeated listening. After 1982's *Heaven* single, the group disintegrated. (Bob Macdonald, 22/9/88).

FAST BOYFRIENDS
Tracks: / Fast boyfriends.
7" Single: Released Oct '81, on Happy Birthday, Catalogue no: **UR 6**

GO FOR GOLD
Tracks: / Go for gold.
7" Single: Released Jun '81, on Happy Birthday, Catalogue no: **UR 4**

HEAVEN
Tracks: / Heaven.
7" Single: Released May '82, on Go Discs, by Chrysalis Records. Catalogue no: **GOD 1**

PEEL SESSIONS: GIRLS AT OUR BEST 17.2.81
12" Single: Released Jun '87, on Strange Fruit, by Strange Fruit Records. Catalogue no: **SFPS 029**

POLITICS
Tracks: / Politics.
7" Single: Released Nov '80, on Rough Trade, by Rough Trade Records. Catalogue no: **RT 055**

Girls (Group)

CLAP CLAP
Tracks: / Clap clap / My boy has left me.
7" Single: Released Jul '82, on Aura Records, by Aura Records. Deleted '88. Catalogue no: **AUS 118**

SALLY GO ROUND THE ROSES
Tracks: / Sally go round the roses.
7" Single: Released Aug '82, on Aura Records, by Aura Records. Deleted '88. Catalogue no: **AUS 134**

Girls Talkin'

GIRLS TALKIN'
Tracks: / Girls talkin' / Didn't choose love / Girls talkin' (version) (12" only).
12" Single: Released 3 Apr '89, on Virgin, by Virgin Records. Catalogue no: **TENX 254**
CD 5": Released 3 Apr '89, on Virgin, by Virgin Records. Catalogue no: **TENCD 254**
7" Single: Released 3 Apr '89, on Virgin, by Virgin Records. Catalogue no: **TEN 254**

Girlschool

Biographical details: At the time of their greatest success, this British heavy metal band consisted of Denise Dufort, Kelly Johnson, Kim McAuliffe and Enid Williams. Girlschool were one of the finest of the heavy metal groups to hit theUK charts in 1980, the year that the genre made a major resurgence following years in the wilderness during the punk era. This particular combo won extra publicity on two counts - firstly, they were protegees of the notorious Motorhead: secondly, the simple fact that they were all women was a novelty to the macho male-dominated world of hard rock. Girlschool were formed in 1978 after two of the members had been playing in a group called Painted Lady. Girlschool's debut single *Take it all away* impressed Motorhead sufficiently to invite the group to support them on tour. After signing with Bronze Records (the same label as Motorhead), they issued their first album *Demolition* in June 1980. It was readily accepted, reaching no.28 and logging 10 weeks on the UK album chart. The group achieved their first minor hit single with a remake of Gun's 1968 biggie *Race with the devil*. A cover version of Johnny Kidd's *Please don't touch* was the lead track on the *St. Valentine's Day massacre* EP, which featured Motorhead and Girlschool duetting in frenetic style - the EP brought the girls into the big league, reaching no.5 on the British singles chart. A similar position was obtained by their second album *Hit'n'run*. Bassist Enid Williams quit Girlschool in early 1982 and was replaced by Gil Weston. Although they did not repeat their 1981-style chart feats, the band continued to be one of the most popular HM acts in Britain and abroad, headbanging with the best of 'em. (Bob Macdonald, 22/9/85)
A UK heavy metal group formed in 1978 with Kim McAuliffe on rhythm guitar and vocals, Kelly Johnson on lead guitar, Enid Williams and Denise Dufort on bass and drums. They supported Motorhead on tour '80 and made an EP with them as combined 'Headgirl'. By *Play dirty* in 1983 Williams had left, replaced by Gil Weston; soon they left Bronze for Polygram with new members Chris Bonacci and Jacki Bodimead. Image change saw glitzy clothes replace denim'n'leather. They made a hit single with Gary Glitter, and by '86 had slimmed to Banacci, Dufort, Weston and McAuliffe. (Donald Clarke, July 1989)M.

C'MON LET'S GO
Tracks: / C'mon let's go / Tonight / Demolition boys.
7" Single: Released Jul '81, on Bronze, by Bronze Records. Deleted '84. Catalogue no: **BRO 126**

DON'T CALL IT LOVE
Tracks: / Don't call it love / Wild life / Don't stop.
7" Single: Released Mar '82, on Bronze, by Bronze Records. Deleted '85. Catalogue no: **BRO 144**

EMERGENCY
Tracks: / Emergency / Furniture fire.
7" Single: Released Feb '80, on Bronze, by Bronze Records. Deleted '83. Catalogue no: **BRO 89**

HIT AND RUN
Tracks: / Hit and run / Tonight / Tush (12" only).
12" Single: Released Apr '81, on Bronze, by Bronze Records. Deleted '84. Catalogue no: **BROX 118**
7" Single: Released Apr '81, on Bronze, by Bronze Records. Deleted '84. Catalogue no: **BRO 118**

I'M THE LEADER OF THE GANG (I AM)
Tracks: / I'm the leader of the gang (I am).
7" Single: Released May '86, on GWR, by GWR Records. Catalogue no: **GWR 1**
12" Single: Released May '86, on GWR, by GWR Records. Catalogue no: **GWT 1**

NOTHING TO LOSE
Tracks: / Nothing to lose / Baby doll.
7" Single: Released May '80, on Bronze, by Bronze Records. Deleted '83. Catalogue no: **BRO 95**

RACE WITH THE DEVIL (SINGLE)
Tracks: / Race with the devil.
7" Single: Released Aug '80, on Bronze, by Bronze Records. Deleted '83. Catalogue no: **BRO 100**

TAKE IT ALL AWAY
Tracks: / Take it all away.
7" Single: Released Sep '81, on City, by City Records. Catalogue no: **NIK 6**

WILDLIFE (EP)
Tracks: / Wildlife / Don't call it love / Don't stop.
7" Single: Released Apr '82, on Bronze, by Bronze Records. Deleted '85. Catalogue no: **BRO 144**

YEAH RIGHT
Tracks: / Yeah right / Hunter.
7" Single: Released Dec '80, on Bronze, by Bronze Records. Deleted Dec '85. Catalogue no: **BRO 110**

Girly

WORKING GIRL (ONE WAY LOVE AFFAIR)
Tracks: / Working girl.
12" Single: Released Nov '85, on ZYX (Germany), Catalogue no: **ZYX 5191**

Girlz

WISHING YOU WERE HERE
Tracks: / Wishing you were here.
12" Single: Released Jun '88, on Capital, Catalogue no: **V 15311**

Gist

FOOL FOR A VALENTINE
Tracks: / Fool for a valentine.
7" Single: Released Feb '83, on Rough Trade, by Rough Trade Records. Catalogue no: **RT 125**

LOVE AT FIRST SIGHT
Tracks: / Love at first sight / Light aircraft.
7" Single: Released Jun '82, on Rough Trade, by Rough Trade Records. Catalogue no: **RT 085**

THIS IS LOVE
Tracks: / This is love.
7" Single: Released Nov '80, on Rough Trade, by Rough Trade Records. Catalogue no: **RT 058**

Giuffria

CALL TO THE HEART
Tracks: / Call to the heart / Out of the blue.
7" Set: Released Mar '85, on MCA, by MCA Records. Catalogue no: **MCAS 935**
7" Single: Released Mar '85, on MCA, by MCA Records. Catalogue no: **MCA 935**
12" Single: Released Mar '85, on MCA, by MCA Records. Catalogue no: **MCAT 935**

Gladiators

CAN'T STOP RIGHTNESS
Tracks: / Can't stop rightness.
12" Single: Released May '83, on Hit-bound, Catalogue no: **JJ 114**

MASS CHARLEY
Tracks: / Mass charley.
12" Single: Released Jul '83, on Sun Set (reggae), Catalogue no: **SS RD 002**

Gladwin, Joe

WHAT HAVE THEY DONE TO MY CHRISTMAS
Tracks: / What have they done to my Christmas?.
7" Single: Released Nov '82, on Rialto (1), by Rialto Records. Catalogue no: **RIA 13**

Glaser Brothers

WEIGHT OF MY CHAINS
Tracks: / Weight of my chains / Ballad of Lucy Jordan.
7" Single: Released May '80, on Elektra, by Elektra Records (UK). Deleted May '83. Catalogue no: **K 12446**

Glaser, Jim

WHO WERE YOU THINKING OF
Tracks: / Who were you thinking of.
7" Single: Released '79, on Mint, by Emerald Records. Deleted '88. Catalogue no: **CHEW 32**

WOMAN WOMAN
Tracks: / Woman woman / I'd love to see you again.
7" Single: Released Apr '84, on Range, by Range Records. Catalogue no: **RANS 73**

Glasgow

SECRETS IN THE DARK
Tracks: / Secrets in the dark / Meet me halfway.
7" Single: Released Jan '88, on Zero 41, Catalogue no: **041 7**

STRANDED
Tracks: / Stranded / Heat of the night.
7" Single: Released May '84, on Neat, by Neat Records. Catalogue no: **NEAT 40**

Glasgow, Cheryl

EVEN NOW (I NEED YOU)
Tracks: / Even now (I need you) / Tempted.
12" Single: Released Jun '84, on Code, by Code Records. Catalogue no: **12COD 011**
7" Single: Released Jun '84, on Code, by Code Records. Catalogue no: **COD 011**

GLUED TO THE SPOT
Tracks: / Glued to the spot (instrumental) (Extra track on 12") / Glued to the spot / Losing the battle.
12" Single: Released Aug '87, on Alive, Catalogue no: **ALIVE T 5**
12" Single: Released Jan '87, on Live, Catalogue no: **ALIVE 2**
12" Single: Released Jul '87, on Live, Catalogue no: **ALIVE 5**

Glasgow, Deborah

CHAMPION LOVER
Tracks: / Champion lover / Champion lover (version).
7" Single: Released Apr '89, on Greensleeves, by Greensleeves Records. Catalogue no: **GRED 239**

DON'T STAY AWAY
Tracks: / Don't stay away / Knight in shining armour / Don't stay away (P.A.Mix/Instrumental) (Track only on 12" version).
12" Single: Released Mar '87, on UK Bubblers, by Greensleeves Records. Deleted '88. Catalogue no: **UKMC 23**
7" Single: Released Mar '87, on UK Bubblers, by Greensleeves Records. Deleted '88. Catalogue no: **7UKMC 23**

FALLING IN LOVE
Tracks: / Falling in love / Falling in love (inst).
12" Single: Released Jul '88, on UK Bubblers, by Greensleeves Records. Catalogue no: **UKMC 29**

GIVE ME THAT TOUCH
Tracks: / Give me that touch / Give me that touch (remix).
12" Single: Released Aug '89, on Greensleeves, by Greensleeves Records. Catalogue no: **GRED 252**

KNIGHT IN SHINING ARMOUR
Tracks: / Knight in shining armour / Knight in shining armour (inst).
12" Single: Released Oct '86, on UK Bubblers, by Greensleeves Records. Deleted '88. Catalogue no: **UKMC 17**

WHEN SOMEBODY LOVES YOU BACK
Tracks: / When somebody loves you back.
12" Single: Released 21 Nov '87, on UK Bubblers, by Greensleeves Records. Catalogue no: **UKMC 27**
7" Single: Released Jan '88, on UK Bubblers, by Greensleeves Records. Catalogue no: **7UKMC 27**

YOU'RE MY SUGAR
Tracks: / You're my sugar / You're my sugar (Inst).
12" Single: Released May '86, on UK Bubblers, by Greensleeves Records. Catalogue no: **UKMC 14**

Glass Beat Came

PLEASURE
Tracks: / Tell me / Pleasure.
7" Single: Released Dec '86, on Influx, by Influx Vinyls. Catalogue no: **FU 2**

Glass House

CRUMBS OFF THE TABLE
Tracks: / Crumbs off the table / Bad bill of goods.
7" Single: Released Dec '84, on HDH (Holland/Dozier/Holland), by Demon Records. Catalogue no: **HDH 458**

Glass Museum

DAY TRIPPER
Tracks: / Day tripper.
7" Single: Released Nov '83, on RGM, by RGM Records. Catalogue no: **RGM 1030**
12" Single: Released Nov '83, on RGM, by RGM Records. Catalogue no: **RGMT 1030**

FRIEND DEPARTED
Tracks: / Friend departed / Life after life.
7" Single: Released Mar '84, on RGM, by RGM Records. Catalogue no: **RGM 1040**

FUTURE
Tracks: / Future, The.
7" Single: Released Aug '83, on RGM, by RGM Records. Catalogue no: **RGM 1020**
12" Single: Released Aug '83, on RGM, by RGM Records. Catalogue no: **RGMT 1020**

Glass, Philip

Biographical details: The best known of the 'minimalist' composers was born in 1937 in Baltimore, Maryland and studied at Julliard; by the mid '60's he had composed pieces in various contemporary idioms and won awards, but wasn't satisfied with what he was doing; he got involved with Indian music and adopted its modular style and repetitive structures, becoming a part of the NYC loft scene along with Laurie Anderson and other avant-gardists. His music will either grow on you or put you to sleep; he became the first living composer to be signed to an exclusive contract by CBS since Stravinsky and Copeland, but music critics are undecided: his operas may be more a sort of static theatre than opera as we know it. He had formed the 7 piece Philip Glass Ensemble in 1968, Chatham Records in 1971 and Tomato Records in 1978; some of the records made in the '70's have been reissued by Virgin. *Glassworks* is a suite of six pieces averaging about six minutes each, played by a septet including two French horns, plus a viola section; the album is probably a good introduction to his stuff. (Donald Clarke, July 1989).

FACADE
Tracks: / Facade.
7" Single: Released May '83, on Epic, by CBS Records. Catalogue no: **A 3481**

FREEZING
Tracks: / Freezing / Lightning.
7" Single: Released May '86, on Portrait, by CBS Records. Catalogue no: **A 7166**
12" Single: Released May '86, on Portrait, by CBS Records. Catalogue no: **TA 7166**

Glass Ties

TIGHT
Tracks: / Tight / Saturday girls.
7" Single: Released Mar '82, on EMI, by EMI Records. Deleted '85. Catalogue no: **EMI 5281**

VIEWS FROM OTHER BRIDGES
Tracks: / Views from other bridges.
7" Single: Released Sep '82, on EMI, by EMI Records. Catalogue no: **EMI 5335**

YOU YOU YOU
Tracks: / You, you, you / Veiws from other bridges.
12" Single: Released Feb '83, on EMI, by EMI Records. Catalogue no: **12 EMI 5368**
7" Single: Released Feb '83, on EMI, by EMI Records. Catalogue no: **EMI 5368**

Glass Tiger

DIAMOND SUN (SINGLE)
Tracks: / Diamond sun / Suffer in silence / Do you wanna dance(with me)*.
Note: * extra track on 12" version.
CD 5": Released May '88, on EMI-Manhattan, by EMI Records. Deleted Nov '88. Catalogue no: **CDMT 40**
7" Pic: Released May '88, on EMI-Manhattan, by EMI Records. Deleted Nov '88. Catalogue no: **MTP 40**
7" Single: Released May '88, on EMI-Manhattan, by EMI Records. Deleted Nov '88. Catalogue no: **MT 40**
12" Single: Released May '88, on EMI-Manhattan, by EMI Records. Deleted Nov '88. Catalogue no: **12MT 40**

DON'T FORGET ME WHEN I'M GONE
Tracks: / Don't forget me when I'm gone / Ancient evenings / Don't forget me when I'm gone (Death Mix).
7" Single: Released Sep '86, on EMI-Manhattan, by EMI Records. Deleted Oct '87. Catalogue no: **MT13**
12" Single: Released Sep '86, on EMI-Manhattan, by EMI Records. Deleted Jan '88. Catalogue no: **12 MT 13**

MY SONG
Tracks: / My song / This island earth / My song (ext mix) (12" only.).
7" Single: Released Feb '89, on EMI-Manhattan, by EMI Records. Deleted Aug '89. Catalogue no: **MT 51**
12" Single: Released Feb '89, on EMI-Manhattan, by EMI Records. Deleted Aug '89. Catalogue no: **12MT 51**

SOMEDAY
Tracks: / Someday (dub mix) / Vanishing tribe.
7" Single: Released Jan '87, on EMI-Manhattan, by EMI Records. Deleted Jul '87. Catalogue no: **MT 17**
12" Single: Released Jan '87, on EMI-Manhattan, by EMI Records. Deleted Jul '87. Catalogue no: **12 MT 17**

Glass Torpedoes

TALL STORIES
Tracks: / Tall stories.
7" Single: Released Apr '83, on Leo Records, by Leo Records. Catalogue no: **LEO 1002**

Glasshouse

DEATH IN A ROLLS ROYCE
Tracks: / Death in a Rolls Royce / Russian roulette.
7" Single: Released Aug '82, on Coach House, Catalogue no: **ESSAR 007**

Glaxo Babies

CHRISTINE KEELER
Tracks: / Christine Keeler.
7" Single: Released Aug '79, on Heartbeat, by Mainline Records. Catalogue no: **PULSE 5**

SHAKE THE FOUNDATIONS
Tracks: / Shake the foundations / She went to pieces.
7" Single: Released Jun '80, on Heartbeat, by Mainline Records. Catalogue no: **PULSE 8**

Glazz Boy

WAYKI WAYKI
Tracks: / Wayki wayki.
12" Single: Released Apr '89, on Subway, by Subway Records. Catalogue no: **SUB 63**

Glee Club

FIVE GO DOWN TO THE SEA
Tracks: / Five go down to the sea.
12" Single: Released Aug '86, on Abstract, by Abstract Sounds. Catalogue no: **12 ABS 027**

LET MY PEOPLE TWIST!
Tracks: / Let my people twist!.
7" Single: Released Jan '87, on Ventura, Catalogue no: **VENT 1**

SOMETHING IN THE AIR
Tracks: / Something in the air.
7" Single: Released Sep '85, on Abacus, by Abacus Records. Catalogue no: **VYK 10**

Glen, Steve

DOWN AMONG THE DEAD MEN
Tracks: / Down among the dead men / I'm alright Jack.
7" Single: Released Nov '80, on Epic, by CBS Records. Deleted Nov '83. Catalogue no: **EPC 9340**

Glenn & Chris

DIAMOND LIGHTS
Tracks: / Diamond lights / Diamond lights (inst).
7" Pic: Released Apr '87, on Record Shack, by Record Shack Records. Catalogue no: **KICKG 1**
7" Pic: Released Apr '87, on Record Shack, by Record Shack Records. Catalogue no: **KICKC 1**

IT'S GOODBYE
Tracks: / It's goodbye.
7" Single: Released Aug '87, on Record Shack, by Record Shack Records. Catalogue no: **KICK 2**
12" Single: Released Aug '87, on Record Shack, by Record Shack Records. Catalogue no: **KICKT 2**

Glenn, John

BOYS OF THE COUNTY ARMAGH
Tracks: / Boys of the County Armagh / Irish eyes.
7" Single: Released '88, on Homespun (Ireland), by Outlet Records. Catalogue no: **HIS 11**

Glitter Band

Biographical details: Led by John Springate and Gerry Shephard, this British pop band also includes Brian, Eddie, Pete and Tony. After enjoying 18 months of success as the backing combo behind the ageing but highly entertaining Gary Glitter, they were launched as a separate act in their own right in early 1974. They had previously been known as the Glittermen, but were billed as the Glitter Band from '74 onwards. With shrewd timing, their debut single *Angel face* - which was very much in Gary's usual style - was released to coincide with a totally unexpected solo ballad from Gary entitled *Remember me this way*. Thus, in April 1974, Gary Glitter and the Glitter Band were cheek by jowl in the UK Top 5 with contrasting singles. As Gary reverted to his normal style and continued his historic run of British Top 10 hits, the Glitter Band lived a double life, scoring Top tenners on their own as well as with their boss. Both acts' hits were produced by Mike Leander. It was a tribute to Leander's skills and to the band's underrated musicianship that they were able to sell so many records on their own, without their characteristic frontman. It was also a tribute to the marketing men of the era, who were adept at persuading UK weenyboppers to buy vast quantities of similar sounding singles by their favourite glam rock stars. The Glitter Band's biggest hit was *Goodbye my love*, which reached the no.2 position; they also achieved two UK top 20 albums. The bubble burst for both Gary and them in 1976, and the Band were torpedoed into oblivion. But when Gary made a dramatic return to the British Top 10 at Christmas 1984, all the original Glitter Band members were back with him to share the glory. (Bob Macdonald, 22/9/85).

ANGEL FACE
Tracks: / Angel face.
7" Single: Released Jun '89, on Switchback, Catalogue no: **SW 2**
7" Single: Released Mar '74, on Bell, Deleted '77. Catalogue no: **BELL 1348**

GOODBYE MY LOVE
Tracks: / Goodbye my love / Angel face.
7" Single: Released 24 Apr '89, on Old Gold, by Old Gold Records. Catalogue no: **OG 9877**
7" Single: Released Jan '75, on Bell, Deleted '78. Catalogue no: **BELL 1395**

HEARTBEAT TO HEART
Tracks: / Heartbeat to heart / I don't want to see you tonight.
7" Single: Released Oct '82, on Cheapskate, Deleted Oct '85. Catalogue no: **CHEAP 101**

JUST FOR YOU
Tracks: / Just for you.
7" Single: Released Aug '74, on Bell, Deleted '77. Catalogue no: **BELL 1368**

LET'S GET TOGETHER AGAIN
Tracks: / Let's get together.
7" Single: Released Oct '74, on Bell, Deleted '77. Catalogue no: **BELL 1383**

LOVE IN THE SUN
Tracks: / Love in the sun.
7" Single: Released Aug '75, on Bell, Deleted '78. Catalogue no: **BELL 1437**

PEOPLE LIKE YOU AND PEOPLE LIKE ME
Tracks: / People like you and people like me.
7" Single: Released Feb '76, on Bell, Deleted '79. Catalogue no: **BELL 1471**

TEARS I CRIED, THE
Tracks: / Tears I cried, The.
7" Single: Released Apr '75, on Bell, Deleted '78. Catalogue no: **BELL 1416**

UNTIL THE NEXT TIME
Tracks: / Until the next time / Spaces.
7" Single: Released Mar '85, on Polo, by Polo Records. Deleted '88. Catalogue no: **POLO 13**

Glitter, Gary

Biographical details: This British singer and songwriter was born Paul Gadd in Banbury, Oxfordshire in 1940. Using the name Paul Raven, he released his first single *Alone in the night* in 1960. It flopped, as did all his other singles under that moniker. In 1965 he joined the production team of Britain's famed television pop show *Ready steady go*, where he met songwriter/producer Mike Leander, who was later to become a vital force in his career. After further struggles as paul Raven, he teamed up with Leander on a permanent basis and launched himself as Gary Glitter in March 1972. The first single *Rock'n'roll part 1* seemed to be going the the same way as all the Raven efforts till June, when the B side *Rock'n'roll part 2* rose to prominence and became one of the sleeper smashes of 1972. Despite the fact that *part 2* featured very little vocalising by Glitter and was mainly an instumental track, it successfully established the flamboyant image, which was ideal for the T.Rex-initiated era of '70s glam rock. The single reached no. 2 in the UK and no. 7 in the US. Although he did non sustain the American momentum, Gary Glitter quickly consolidated his British position and became one of the UK's top pop stars. 1973 was the peak year for Glitter himself and for the whole British glitter/glam rock phenomenon; by mid-75, Gary had become the only act in UK chart history to begin his chart career with 11 consecutive top 10 singles, and his feat has never been equalled. These smash hits included three no. 1's *I'm the leader of the gang (I am)*, *I love you love me love* and *Always yours* plus three no. 2's. They were written by Glitter and Leander and produced by the latter. Most of the records followed the same hand-clapping/foot-stomping/exhibitionist/teenybop pattern, which turned the ageing and podgy Gary into a most unlikely teen idol. His sequinned platform boots and tight shiny trousers were made palatablr by the fact that he never took himself very seriously. So successful was the formula that Gary's backing group, the Glitter Band, bagan their own run of top tenners in 1974. But the party was over for both acts in 1976, the year Gary announced his "retirement" (which lasted for nine months) and punk rock heralded a new era in British pop. While Glitter strove to reactivate his career, he was declared bankrupt due to his ostentatious and excessive spending - the profusion of mansions and Rolls Royces, purchased during his superstar years, finally caught up with him. Persistently recording and touring during the early eighties, and occasionally reaching the lower end of the UK charts, Gary finally achieved his 12th UK Top 10 hit in 1984 with his Yuletide romp *Another rock'n'roll Christmas* - the old Glitter Band were together again, the producer was the same and the sound hadn't changed. The 44-year-old Gary was caught in his very own tongue-in-cheek time warp. (Bob MacDonald)
Born Paul Gadd in Banbury, this UK pop singer worked as Paul Raven, then Paul Monday before becoming the king of Glam Rock in the early '70's, the Liberace of UK pop, and giving it some much needed humour. Glitter Band music was basic rock'n'roll with a heavy drumbeat, Gary cavorting in outrageous costumes, similar to T. Rex, Mud, Sweet etc. but with even less subtlety. Glam Rock was over by 1975 but Glitter retained much affection and made comebacks, also sending himself up in a soupo advert in 1985. (Donald Clarke, July 1989).

6 TRACK HITS: GARY GLITTER
Tracks: / Rock and roll / Always yours / I'm the leader of the gang / I love you love me love / Remember me this way / I didn't know I loved you.
7" EP: Released Sep '83, on Scoop 33, by Pickwick Records. Catalogue no: **7SR 5002**

ALL THAT GLITTERS
Tracks: / All that Glitters.
7" Single: Released Dec '81, on Bell, Deleted '84. Catalogue no: **BELL 1498**
12" Single: Released '82, on Arista, by BMG Records (UK). Deleted '87. Catalogue no: **BELL 12498**

ALWAYS YOURS (SINGLE)
Tracks: / Always yours.
7" Single: Released Jun '74, on Bell, Deleted '77. Catalogue no: **BELL 1359**

AND THEN SHE KISSED ME
Tracks: / And then she kissed me.
7" Single: Released Oct '81, on Bell, Deleted '84. Catalogue no: **BELL 1497**

ANOTHER ROCK 'N' ROLL CHRISTMAS
Tracks: / Another rock'n'roll Christmas.
7" Single: Released Nov '85, on MLM, Catalogue no: **RT 1**
7" Single: Released Nov '84, on Arista, by BMG Records (UK). Catalogue no: **ARIS 592**

BE MY BABY
Tracks: / Be my baby / Is this what dreams are made for.
7" Single: Released '82, on Arista, by BMG Records (UK). Deleted '87. Catalogue no: **BELL 1503**

DANCE ME UP
Tracks: / Dance me up.
7" Pic: Released Jun '84, on Arista, by BMG Records (UK). Catalogue no: **ARISD 570**
7" Single: Released Jun '84, on Arista, by BMG Records (UK). Deleted '87. Catalogue no: **ARIST 570**

DO YOU WANNA TOUCH
Tracks: / Do you wanna touch me / Hello hello I'm back again.
7" Single: Released Jan '73, on Bell, Deleted '76. Catalogue no: **BELL 1280**

DO YOU WANNA TOUCH (OLD GOLD)
7" Single: Released Jan '89, on Old Gold, by Old Gold Records. Catalogue no: **OG 9854**

DOING ALRIGHT WITH THE BOYS
Tracks: / Doing alright with the boys.
7" Single: Released Jun '75, on Bell, Deleted '78. Catalogue no: **BELL 1429**

FRONTIERS OF STYLE
Tracks: / Frontiers of style / Only way to survive, The.
7" Single: Released Dec '88, on Trax, by Filmtrax Records. Deleted Aug '89. Catalogue no: **7TX 4**

GARY GLITTER (EP)
Tracks: / I'm the leader of the gang (I am) / Rock 'n' roll part 2 / Hello hello I'm back again / Do you wanna touch me.
7" EP: Released Sep '80, on GTO, Deleted '83. Catalogue no: **GT 282**

GARY GLITTER MEDLEY
Tracks: / Gary Glitter medley.
7" Single: Released '82, on Arista, by BMG Records (UK). Deleted '87. Catalogue no: **BELL 1498**

HELLO HELLO I'M BACK AGAIN
Tracks: / Hello hello I'm back again.
7" Single: Released Apr '73, on Bell, Deleted '76. Catalogue no: **BELL 1299**

I DIDN'T KNOW I LOVED YOU Till I saw you rock'n'roll
Tracks: / I didn't know I loved you till I saw you rock'n'roll / Hard on me.
7" Single: Released Sep '72, on Bell, Deleted '75. Catalogue no: **BELL 1259**

I LOVE YOU LOVE ME LOVE
Tracks: / I love you love me love / I'm the leader of the gang (I am).
7" Single: Released Nov '73, on Bell, Deleted '76. Catalogue no: **BELL 1337**

I LOVE YOU LOVE ME LOVE (OLD GOLD)
Tracks: / I love you love me love / I'm the leader of the gang (I am) / Hello hello I'm back again.
CD 5": Released 28 Mar '89, on Old Gold, by Old Gold Records. Catalogue no: **OG 6128**
7" Single: Released 24 Apr '89, on Old Gold, by Old Gold Records. Catalogue no: **OG 9875**

IF IT TAKES ALL NIGHT LONG
Tracks: / If it takes all night long.
7" Single: Released Jan '77, on Arista, by BMG Records (UK). Deleted '80. Catalogue no: **ARISTA 85**

I'M THE LEADER OF THE GANG (I AM)
Tracks: / I'm the leader of the gang (I am).
7" Single: Released Jul '73, on Bell, Deleted '76. Catalogue no: **BELL 1321**

LITTLE BOOGIE WOOGIE IN THE BACK OF MY MIND, A
Tracks: / Little boogie woogie in the back of my mind.
7" Single: Released Jul '77, on Arista, by BMG Records (UK). Deleted '80. Catalogue no: **ARISTA 112**

LIVE ROCK 'N' ROLL
Tracks: / Live rock 'n' roll.
12" Single: Released Jul '86, on Illuminated, Catalogue no: **ILL 6012**

LOVE COMES
Tracks: / Love comes.
7" Single: Released Apr '85, on Arista, by BMG Records (UK). Catalogue no: **ARIST 615**
12" Single: Released Apr '85, on Arista, by BMG Records (UK). Catalogue no: **ARIST 12615**
7" Pic: Released Apr '85, on Arista, by BMG Records (UK). Catalogue no: **ARISD 615**

LOVE LIKE YOU AND ME
Tracks: / Love like you and me.
7" Single: Released May '75, on Bell, Deleted '78. Catalogue no: **BELL 1423**

OH YES YOU'RE BEAUTIFUL
Tracks: / Oh yes you're beautiful / Remember me this way.
7" Single: Released Nov '74, on Bell, Deleted '77. Catalogue no: **BELL 1391**
7" Single: Released 24 Apr '89, on Old Gold, by Old Gold Records. Catalogue no: **OG 9880**

PAPA OOH MOW MOW
7" Single: Released Nov '75, on Bell, Deleted '78. Catalogue no: **BELL 1451**

REMEMBER ME THIS WAY
Tracks: / Remember me this way.
7" Single: Released Mar '74, on Bell, Deleted '77. Catalogue no: **BELL 1349**

ROCK 'N' ROLL (PARTS 1 & 2)
Tracks: / Rock 'n' roll (parts 1 & 2) / I didn't know I loved you till I saw you rock'n'roll.
7" Single: Released Jan '89, on Old Gold, by Old Gold Records. Catalogue no: **OG 9850**

ROCK & ROLL PARTS 1 & 2
Tracks: / Rock 'n' roll part 1 / Rock 'n' roll part 2.
7" Single: Released Jun '72, on Bell, Deleted '75. Catalogue no: **BELL 1216**

ROCK'N'ROLL
Tracks: / Rock and roll / Not just a pretty face (on 12" only) / Oh no.
12" Single: Released Apr '85, on Illuminated, Catalogue no: **ILL 6012**
7" Single: Released Apr '85, on Illuminated, Catalogue no: **ILL 60**

ROCK'N'ROLL PART 2
Tracks: / Rock 'n' roll part 2 / I didn't know I loved you till I saw you rock'n'roll / Do you wanna touch me.
7" Single: Released 24 Apr '89, on Old Gold, by Old Gold Records. Catalogue no: **OG 6132**

ROCK'N'ROLL PART 3/4
Tracks: / Rock 'n' roll part 3/4 / Rock 'n' roll part 5 (Available on 12" only) / Rock 'n' roll part 6 (Available on 12" only).
12" Single: Released Dec '87, on RCA, by BMG Records (UK). Catalogue no: **12 GLIT 1**
7" Single: Released Dec '87, Catalogue no: **GLIT 1**

ROCK'N'ROLL PART 3,5
12" Single: Released Dec '87, on BMG Classics, by BMG Records (UK). Catalogue no: **12GLITX 1**

SHOUT SHOUT SHOUT
Tracks: / Shout shout shout.
7" Pic: Released Sep '84, on MLM, Catalogue no: **ARICV 586**

WHAT YOUR MOMMA DON'T SEE
Tracks: / What your momma don't see / I'm not just a pretty face.
7" Single: Released Nov '80, on Eagle (London), by Eagle (London) Records. Deleted Nov '83. Catalogue no: **ERS 004**

YOU BELONG TO ME
Tracks: / You belong to me.
7" Single: Released Mar '76, on Bell, Deleted '79. Catalogue no: **BELL 1473**

Globe & Pow Pow

CELEBRATE(EVERYBODY)
Tracks: / Celebrate(everybody).
7" Single: Released May '85, on Tommy Boy, by Polydor Ltd. Catalogue no: **IS 222**
12" Single: Released May '85, on Tommy Boy, by Polydor Ltd. Deleted '87. Catalogue no: **12IS 222**

Gloria

ONE DAY AT A TIME
Tracks: / One day at a time.
7" Single: Released Dec '78, on Release (Ireland), Catalogue no: **RL 873**

Glory

DOING THE BEST WITH MY LIFE
Tracks: / Doing the best with my life / Playing with fire.
7" Single: Released Aug '86, on Top Flight, Deleted '87. Catalogue no: **TPF 7001**

HEARTS WILL SING
Tracks: / Hearts will sing.
12" Single: Released Aug '87, on Riva, by Riva Records. Catalogue no: **RIVAT 51**
7" Single: Released Aug '87, on Riva, by Riva Records. Catalogue no: **RIVA 51**

Glove

Biographical details: This British rock duo is a part-time diversion for two prime movers on the UK rock scene - Siouxsie & The Banshees' bassist/multi-instrumentalist Steve Severin and the Cure's vocalist/guitarist/leader Robert Smith (who has also played with the Banshees, to help them out). The Glove were formed in 1983, and released their album *Blue sunshine* in August of that year. The opening track on the LP was quirky and catchy *Like an animal*, which was issued as a single but peaked at a surprisingly low no.52 on the UK chart. The Glove's album was not a spectacular success either, but was critically acclaimed for its experimental but melodic stance. Its multi-layered sound recalled the psychedelic and art-rock eras, yet simultaneously pointed towards new eighties trends. The LP included guest vocals by a previously unknown singer, who was billed simply as "Jeanette". The two Glove members quickly returned to their priority projects, but did not preclude the possibility of teaming up again in the future. (Bob Macdonald, 24/9/85).

LIKE AN ANIMAL
Tracks: / Like an animal.
7" Single: Released Aug '83, on Wonderland (1), by Polydor Ltd. Deleted '86. Catalogue no: **SHE 3**

Glover, Bobby

YOUR SPELL
Tracks: / Your spell / Bright skies, sunny days / It's my turn / Happy.
12" Single: Released Sep '88, on Old Gold, by Old Gold Records. Catalogue no: **OG 4507**

Glover, Roger

MASK, THE
Tracks: / Mask, The / Your so remote.
7" Single: Released Jun '84, on Polydor, by Polydor Ltd. Catalogue no: **POSP 678**

Gluck, Jeremy

LOOKING FOR A PLACE TO FALL
Tracks: / Looking for a place to fall.
12" Single: Released Sep '87, on Tuff Enuff, Catalogue no: **TUFFT 01**

THRILLING TALE OF BUFFALO BILL
Tracks: / Thrilling tale of Buffalo Bill / Looking for a place to fall / Time goes faster / One more story.
12" Single: Released Aug '87, on Tuff Enuff, Catalogue no: **T 01**

Glynn, Dominic

DOCTOR WHO
Tracks: / Doctor Who / Doctor Who (Cosmic remix).
7" Single: Released Nov '86, on BBC, by BBC Records & Tapes. Catalogue no: **RESL 193**
Cassingle: Released Nov '86, on BBC, by BBC Records & Tapes. Catalogue no: **ZRXL 193**
12" Single: Released Nov '86, on BBC, by BBC Records & Tapes. Catalogue no: **12RXL 193**

Gnass

FREE KINGS
Tracks: / Free kings / Free kings (alt. take).
7" Single: Released Nov '82, on Ffang, Catalogue no: **NAFF 001**

GNT

ONE BY ONE
Tracks: / One by one.
7" Single: Released Jul '85, on Mausoleum, by Mausoleum Records. Catalogue no: **GUTS 8406**

Go...

CASABLANCA TOUCH
Tracks: / Casablanca touch / Shanghai.
7" Single: Released Jun '82, on EMI, by EMI Records. Deleted Jun '85. Catalogue no: **EMI 5313**

Go 2

I LIKE MY OWN COMPANY
Tracks: / I like my own company / My heart bleeds.
7" Single: Released Jan '83, on Polydor, by Polydor Ltd. Catalogue no: **POSP 545**

LAND AND WATER
Tracks: / Land and water.
7" Single: Released Jul '83, on Polydor, by Polydor Ltd. Catalogue no: **GO 2**

MAN OUT OF THE JUNGLE
Tracks: / Man out of the jungle.
7" Single: Released Mar '83, on Polydor, by Polydor Ltd. Catalogue no: **GO 2**

Go (Band)

5 OZ PLAIN FLOUR
Tracks: / 5 Oz plain flour.
12" Single: Released Jul '89, on Who's That Beat, by Play It Again Sam (Belgium). Catalogue no: **WHOS 19**

Go Fundamental

FOUR TRACK EP
7" Single: Released Oct '82, on Davinci, Catalogue no: **LEO 001**

PEOPLE ON THE TOP FLOOR
Tracks: / People on the top floor / Another European.
7" Single: Released May '85, on Arista, by BMG Records (UK). Catalogue no: **ARIST 622**
12" Single: Released May '85, on Arista, by BMG Records (UK). Catalogue no: **ARISTA 12622**

Go Go Amigo

DON'T NEED IT
Tracks: / Don't need it / Sometimes.
7" Single: Released Jan '89, on Acorn (1), Catalogue no: **ACOR 3**

Go Hole

FLIGHT OF ANGELS
Tracks: / Flight of angels / Spanish fly.
7" Single: Released Aug '87, on Big Pop, Catalogue no: **GONE 1**

Go Service

IT MAKES ME REALISE
Tracks: / It makes me realise.
12" Single: Released Sep '85, on Dreamworld, by Dreamworld Records. Catalogue no: **DREAM 003**

Go West

CALL ME
Tracks: / Call me / Man in my mirror.
7" Single: Released Apr '85, on Chrysalis, by Chrysalis Records. Catalogue no: **GOW 1**
12" Single: Released Apr '85, on Chrysalis, by Chrysalis Records. Catalogue no: **GOWX 1**

DON'T LOOK DOWN-THE SEQUEL
Tracks: / Don't look down-(The sequel).
7" Single: Released Nov '85, on Chrysalis, by Chrysalis Records. Catalogue no: **GOW 3**
12" Single: Released Nov '85, on Chrysalis, by Chrysalis Records. Deleted '86. Catalogue no: **GOWX 3**

FROM BALTIMORE TO PARIS
Tracks: / From Baltimore to Paris / Little Caesar.
7" Single: Released Nov '87, on Chrysalis, by Chrysalis Records. Catalogue no: **GOW 7**
12" Single: Released Nov '87, on Chrysalis, by Chrysalis Records. Catalogue no: **GOWX 7**

GOODBYE GIRL
Tracks: / Goodbye girl / Dreamworld.
12" Single: Released Jul '85, on Chrysalis, by Chrysalis Records. Catalogue no: **GOWX 2**
7" Single: Released Jul '85, on Chrysalis, by Chrysalis Records. Catalogue no: **GOW 2**

I WANT TO HEAR IT FROM YOU
Tracks: / I want to hear it from you / Cross-fire / True colours.
7" Single: Released Apr '87, on Chrysalis, by Chrysalis Records. Catalogue no: **GOW 5**
CD 5": Released Apr '87, on Chrysalis, by Chrysalis Records. Catalogue no: **CDE 5**
7" Single: Released Apr '87, on Chrysalis, by Chrysalis Records. Catalogue no: **GOWP 5**
12" Single: Released Apr '87, on Chrysalis, by Chrysalis Records. Catalogue no: **GOWX 5**

KING IS DEAD, THE
Tracks: / King is dead, The.
7" Single: Released Aug '87, on Chrysalis, by Chrysalis Records. Catalogue no: **GOW 6**
Cassingle: Released Aug '87, on Chrysalis, by Chrysalis Records. Catalogue no: **ZGOWL 6**
12" Single: Released Aug '87, on Chrysalis, by Chrysalis Records. Catalogue no: **GOWX 6**
12" Single: Released Aug '87, on Chrysalis, by Chrysalis Records. Catalogue no: **GOWL 6**

TRUE COLOURS
Tracks: / True colours / XL 5.
7" Single: Released Nov '86, on Chrysalis, by Chrysalis Records. Catalogue no: **GOW 4**
12" Single: Released Nov '86, on Chrysalis, by Chrysalis Records. Catalogue no: **GOWX 4**

WE CLOSE OUR EYES
Tracks: / We close our eyes / Missing persons.
12" Single: on Chrysalis, by Chrysalis Records. Catalogue no: **CHS 122850**
7" Single: Released Feb '85, on Chrysalis, by Chrysalis Records. Catalogue no: **CHS 2850**

WE CLOSE OUR EYES (OLD GOLD)
Tracks: / We close our eyes / Don't look down.
12" Single: Released 28 Aug '89, on Old Gold, by Old Gold Records. Catalogue no: **OG 4134**

Goanna

SOLID ROCK
Tracks: / Solid rock / Four weeks gone.
7" Single: Released Feb '83, on WEA, by WEA Records. Catalogue no: **K 70051**

Goat

CAN'T GET BY
Tracks: / Can't get by.
12" Single: Released Nov '89, on Situation 2, by Beggars Banquet Records. Catalogue no: **SIT 63T**

REAL KAVOOM EP
12" Single: Released Jul '82, on Real Kavoom, by Jungle Records. Catalogue no: **ARK 1**

Go-Betweens

BYE BYE PRIDE
Tracks: / Bye bye pride.
7" Single: Released Aug '87, on Beggars Banquet, by Beggars Banquet Records. Deleted Jun '88. Catalogue no: **BEG 194**
12" Single: Released Aug '87, on Beggars Banquet, by Beggars Banquet Records. Catalogue no: **BEG 194T**

CATTLE & CANE
Tracks: / Cattle & cane.
7" Single: Released Feb '83, on Rough Trade, by Rough Trade Records. Catalogue no: **RT 124**

CUT IT OUT
Tracks: / Cut it out / Time in the desert / Doo wop in "A" (bam boom) (On 12" only).
7" Single: Released May '87, on Beggars Banquet, by Beggars Banquet Records. Deleted Jul '88. Catalogue no: **BEG 190**
12" Single: Released May '87, on Beggars Banquet, by Beggars Banquet Records. Catalogue no: **BEG 190T**

HAMMER THE HAMMER
Tracks: / Hammer the hammer / By chance.
7" Single: Released Jun '82, on Rough Trade, by Rough Trade Records. Catalogue no: **RT 108**

HEAD FULL OF STEAM
Tracks: / Head full of steam / Don't let him come back / Wrong road, The (Extra track available on 12" version only.).
7" Single: Released May '86, on Beggars Banquet, by Beggars Banquet Records. Deleted Jun '87. Catalogue no: **BEG 159**
12" Single: Released May '86, on Beggars Banquet, by Beggars Banquet Records. Catalogue no: **BEG 159 T**

LEE REMICK
Tracks: / Lee Remick / People say / Don't let him come back.
12" Single: Released Nov '86, on Situation 2, by Beggars Banquet Records. Catalogue no: **SIT 44T**

LOVE GOES ON
Tracks: / Love goes on / Clouds.
7" Single: Released Jan '89, on Beggars Banquet, by Beggars Banquet Records. Catalogue no: **BEG 225**

MAN O' SAND TO GIRL O' SEA
Tracks: / Man o'sand to girl o'sea.
7" Single: Released Oct '83, on Rough Trade, by Rough Trade Records. Catalogue no: **RT 114**

PEEL SESSIONS: GO BETWEENS
12" Single: Released Oct '89, on Strange Fruit, by Strange Fruit Records. Catalogue no: **SFPSCD 074**
12" Single: Released Oct '89, on Strange Fruit, by Strange Fruit Records. Catalogue no: **SFPS 074**

RIGHT HERE
Tracks: / Right here / When people are dead / Little romance, A (Only available in double pack.) / Don't call me gone (Only available in double pack.).
12" Single: Released Feb '87, on Beggars Banquet, by Beggars Banquet Records. Catalogue no: **BEG 183T**
7" Set: Released Feb '87, on Beggars Banquet, by Beggars Banquet Records. Deleted Jun '88. Catalogue no: **BEG 183D**
7" Single: Released Feb '87, on Beggars Banquet, by Beggars Banquet Records. Deleted Jan '88. Catalogue no: **BEG 183**

SPRING RAIN
Tracks: / Spring rain / Life at hand / Little Joe (Extra track available on 12" version only.).
7" Single: Released Feb '86, on Beggars Banquet, by Beggars Banquet Records. Deleted Jun '87. Catalogue no: **BEG 155**
12" Single: Released Feb '86, on Beggars Banquet, by Beggars Banquet Records. Catalogue no: **BEG 155T**

STREETS OF YOUR TOWN
Tracks: / Streets of your town / Wait until June.
CD 5": Released 23 Jul '88, on Beggars Banquet, by Beggars Banquet Records. Catalogue no: **BEG 218CD**
12" Single: Released 23 Jul '88, on Beggars Banquet, by Beggars Banquet Records. Catalogue no: **BEG 218T**
Cassingle: Released 23 Jul '88, on Beggars Banquet, by Beggars Banquet Records. Catalogue no: **BEG 218C**
7" Single: Released 23 Jul '88, on Beggars Banquet, by Beggars Banquet Records. Catalogue no: **BEG 218**

WAS THERE ANYTHING I COULD DO
Tracks: / Was there anything I could do / Rock 'n' roll friend / Mexican postcard (Only on 12" version.).
7" Single: Released Oct '88, on Beggars Banquet, by Beggars Banquet Records. Catalogue no: **BEG 219**
CD 5": Released Oct '88, on Beggars Banquet, by Beggars Banquet Records. Catalogue no: **BEG 219CD**
7" Single: Released Oct '88, on Wizz, by Sierra Records. Catalogue no: **WFI 001**
12" Single: Released Oct '88, on Beggars Banquet, by Beggars Banquet Records. Catalogue no: **BEG 219 T**

God

FOR LOVERS ONLY
Tracks: / For lovers only
7" Single: Released May '89, on Shakin' Street, Catalogue no: **YEAHHUP 002**

God Bless You

SUGAR
Tracks: / Sugar.
7" Single: Released 23 Apr '88, on Mirror (2), Catalogue no: **MIRROR 001**

God, Mother & Country

FOOT ON THE ROCK
Tracks: / Foot on the rock.
7" Single: Released Sep '85, on Kaz, by Kaz Records. Catalogue no: **KAZ 60**
12" Single: Released Sep '85, on Kaz, by Kaz Records. Catalogue no: **KAZ 60T**

God Said

OUT OF TIME
Tracks: / Out of time / House G.
7" Single: Released 23 Apr '88, on Third Mind, by Third Mind Records. Catalogue no: **TMS 08**

Godard, Vic

HEY NOW, I'M IN LOVE
Tracks: / Hey now, I'm in love / Just in time / Mr Bennett.
12" Single: Released May '82, on London Records, by London Records. Deleted '85. Catalogue no: **LONT 005**
7" Single: Released May '82, on London Records, by London Records. Deleted '85. Catalogue no: **LON 005**

HOLIDAY HYMN
Tracks: / Holiday hymn.
7" Single: Released Aug '85, on EL-Benelux, Catalogue no: **EL 4**
12" Single: Released Aug '85, on EL-Benelux, Catalogue no: **EL 4T**

SPLIT UP THE MONEY
Tracks: / Split up the money / Out of touch.
7" Single: Released Apr '80, on MCA, by MCA Records. Deleted Apr '83. Catalogue no: **MCA 585**

STAMP OF A VAMP
Tracks: / Stamp of a vamp / Hey now I'm in love.
7" Single: Released Dec '81, on Club Left, by Island Records. Deleted Dec '84. Catalogue no: **CLUB 1**

STOP THAT GIRL
Tracks: / Stop that girl / Scared.
7" Single: Released Jan '81, on Rough Trade, by Rough Trade Records. Catalogue no: **RT 068**

Godden, Carol

TASTE ME
Tracks: / Taste me / Where the cruisin' stops.
7" Single: Released Mar '80, on Monarch, by Monarch Records. Deleted Mar '83. Catalogue no: **MON 11**

Godden, Lee

IF THIS IS TRUE
Tracks: / If this is true.
7" Single: Released Jul '84, on Chart, by Monarch Records. Catalogue no: **CR 001**

NATURAL RHYTHM
7" Single: Released Oct '83, on Monarch, by Monarch Records. Catalogue no: **MON 049**

Goddo

IF TOMORROW NEVER COMES
Tracks: / If tomorrow never comes / Feelin' strange today.
7" Single: Released Apr '82, on Noir, by Noir Records. Catalogue no: **ATX 263**

Godfathers

BIRTH, SCHOOL, WORK, DEATH(SINGLE)
Tracks: / Birth, school, work, death.
7" Single: Released Feb '88, on Epic, by CBS Records. Deleted Aug '88. Catalogue no: **GFT Z1**
7" Set: Released Feb '88, on Epic, by CBS Records. Deleted Jun '88. Catalogue no: **GFT B1**
12" Single: Released Feb '88, on Epic, by CBS Records. Deleted Aug '88. Catalogue no: **GFT ZT1**
12" Single: Released Feb '88, on Epic, by CBS Records. Deleted Aug '88. Catalogue no: **GFT Q1**

CAUSE I SAID SO
Tracks: / 'Cause I said so / When am I coming down / I can only give you everything (Track on 12" single & CD single only) / Cold turkey (Track on 12" single & CD single only).
7" Single: Released 18 Jul '88, on Epic, by CBS Records. Deleted Jan '89. Catalogue no: **GFT 2**
CD 5": Released 18 Jul '88, on Epic, by CBS Records. Deleted Jan '89. Catalogue no: **CD GFT 2**
7" Single: Released Aug '88, on Epic, by CBS Records. Deleted Jan '89. Catalogue no: **GFT P2**
12" Single: Released 18 Jul '88, on Epic, by CBS Records. Deleted Jan '89. Catalogue no: **GFT T2**

LONELY MAN
Tracks: / Lonely man.
7" Single: Released 25 Oct '85, on Corporate Image, by Corporate Image Records. Deleted '88. Catalogue no: **GFTR 010**
12" Single: Released 25 Oct '85, on Corporate Image, by Corporate Image Records. Deleted '88. Catalogue no: **GFTR 010T**

LOVE IS DEAD
Tracks: / Love is dead / Angela.
12" Single: on Corporate Image, by Corporate Image Records. Catalogue no: **GFTR 040T**
7" Single: Released Feb '87, on Corporate Image, by Corporate Image Records. Catalogue no: **GFTR 040**

LOVE IS DEAD (RE-ISSUE)
Tracks: / Love is dead / Those days are over (live) / Love is dead (corporate image version) (Only on 12" and CD single.) / I'm unsatisfied (live) (Only on 12" and CD single.).
7" Pic: Released 21 Nov '88, on Epic, by CBS Records. Deleted 17 Apr '89. Catalogue no: **GFT P3**
CD 5": Released Nov '88, on Epic, by CBS Records. Deleted 17 Apr '89. Catalogue no: **CDGFT 3**
12" Single: Released Nov '88, on Epic, by CBS Records. Deleted 17 Apr '89. Catalogue no: **GFT T3**
7" Single: Released Nov '88, on Epic, by CBS Records. Deleted 17 Apr '89. Catalogue no: **GFT 3**
7" Single: Released Nov '88, on Epic, by CBS Records. Deleted 17 Apr '89. Catalogue no: **GFT G3**

NIGHT TRACKS EP
Tracks: / I want you / If I only had time / I want everything / I'm unsatisfied.
CD 5": Released Feb '89, on Strange Fruit, by Strange Fruit Records. Catalogue no: **SFNTCD 019**
12" Single: Released Feb '89, on Strange Fruit, by Strange Fruit Records. Catalogue no: **SFNT 019**

SHE GIVES ME LOVE
Tracks: / She gives me love / Walking talking Johnny Cash blues / Just because you're not paranoid doesn't mean.
CD 5": Released Apr '89, on Epic, by CBS Records. Deleted Oct '89. Catalogue no: **CDGFT 4**
7" Single: Released Apr '89, on Epic, by CBS Records. Deleted Oct '89. Catalogue no: **GFT 4**
7" Pic: Released Apr '89, on Epic, by CBS Records. Deleted Oct '89. Catalogue no: **GFTP 4**
7" Single: Released Apr '89, on Epic, by CBS Records. Catalogue no: **GFTB 4**
12" Single: Released Apr '89, on Epic, by CBS Records. Deleted Oct '89. Catalogue no: **GFFT 4**

SUNARISE
Tracks: / Sunarise.
12" Single: Released Aug '86, on Corporate Image, by Corporate Image Records. Deleted '88. Catalogue no: **GFTR 030 T**
7" Single: Released Aug '86, on Corporate Image, by Corporate Image Records. Deleted '88. Catalogue no: **GFTR 030**

THIS DAMNATION
Tracks: / This damnation.
12" Single: Released Mar '86, on Corporate Image, by Corporate Image Records. Deleted '88. Catalogue no: **GRST 020**

Godflesh

TINY TEARS (SINGLE)
Tracks: / Tiny tears.
12" Single: Released Jan '89, on Swordfish, by Swordfish Records. Catalogue no: **12FLESH 002**

Godiego

GANDHARA
Tracks: / Gandhara.
7" Single: Released Feb '80, on BBC, by BBC Records & Tapes. Deleted '83. Catalogue no: **RESL 66**

MONKEY MAGIC
Tracks: / Monkey magic / Gandhara / Thank you baby.
7" Single: Released Sep '80, on BBC, by BBC Records & Tapes. Deleted '83. Catalogue no: **RESL 81**

WATER MARGIN
Tracks: / Water margin, The.
7" Single: Released Oct '77, on BBC, by BBC Records & Tapes. Deleted '80. Catalogue no: **RESL 50**

Godley & Creme

Biographical details: Kevin Godley and Lol Creme had been art school friends before teaming up with Eric Stewart and achieving a UK no. 2 smash (and worldwide success) with 1970's *Neanderthal man* under the name Hotlegs. This British threesome blossomed into a quartet in 1972 and called themselves 10cc. Godley and Creme took the bold decision of breaking away from that highly successful band in late 1976, in order to work as a duo. At the time of splitting, Godley & Creme's stated reason was their desire to develop the Gizmo, a new instrument that they had invented. This turned out to be a small device that clamped onto the bridge of a guitar, and bowed the strings with small wheels to create an orchestral effect. In October 1977 the duo released their first post-10cc recording - it was an ambitious triple LP entitled *Consequences*. Its hefty price tag and complex pretensions contrasted markedly with the punk upheavals of the day, and the project thus peaked at no. 52 on the UK album chart. Godley & Creme's albums reverted to being single sets and became less overblown; lowever it was not their music that was to ensure them of a bumper living in the eighties, but their craftily conceived move into the burgeoning video field. After several years out of the limelight, they established themselves as Britain's foremost directors of promo video clips, most notably with their controversial 1981 piece for Duran Duran's *Girls on film* and their 1984 work with Frankie Goes To Hollywood. The duo now look upon their recording career as a part time activity, although it zoomed briefly into high gear in 1981, thanks th back-to-back Top 10 singles in the UK with *Under your thumb* and *Wedding bells*. Their highly imaginative and eye-catching visual work tended to make people forget that the pair could still create nifty pop songs when thay wanted to. Their 1985 single *Cry* gave them a Top 20 hit in Britain, and for the the first time as a duo, America.
(Bob Macdonald, 24/9/85).

10,000 ANGELS
Tracks: / 10,000 angels / Hidden heartbeat / Can't sleep / Cry**.
Note: *Included on 12" and CD singles. **Included on CD single only.
12" Single: Released 28 Mar '88, on Polydor, by Polydor Ltd. Catalogue no: **POSPX 913**
CD 5": Released 28 Mar '88, on Polydor, by Polydor Ltd. Catalogue no: **POCD 913**
7" Single: Released 28 Mar '88, on Polydor, by Polydor Ltd. Catalogue no: **POSP 913**

CRY
Tracks: / Cry / Love bombs.
7" Single: Released Aug '86, on Polydor, by Polydor Ltd. Deleted Mar '87. Catalogue no: **POSP 732**
12" Single: Released Aug '86, on Polydor, by Polydor Ltd. Deleted Mar '87. Catalogue no: **POSPX 732**

LITTLE PIECE OF HEAVEN, A
Tracks: / Little piece of Heaven, A / Bits of blue sky / Little piece of heaven (extended mix) (Available on 12" and CD only) / Rhino, rhino.
7" Single: Released Dec '87, on Polydor, by Polydor Ltd. Catalogue no: **POSP 901**
Cassingle: Released Dec '87, on Polydor, by Polydor Ltd. Deleted 30 May '89. Catalogue no: **POSPC 901**
12" Single: Released Dec '87, on Polydor, by Polydor Ltd. Catalogue no: **POSPX 901**

SAVE MOUNTAIN FOR ME
Tracks: / Save mountain for me / Welcome to breakfast TV.
7" Single: Released Oct '82, on Polydor, by Polydor Ltd. Deleted Oct '85. Catalogue no: **POSP 490**

SNACK ATTACK (2)
7" Single: Released Aug '87, on Polydor, by Polydor Ltd. Deleted Mar '88. Catalogue no: **POSP 875**
12" Single: Released Aug '87, on Polydor, by Polydor Ltd. Deleted Mar '88. Catalogue no: **POSPX 875**

SUBMARINE
Tracks: / Submarine / Marciano.
7" Single: Released Sep '80, on Polydor, by Polydor Ltd. Deleted '83. Catalogue no: **POSP 171**

UNDER YOUR THUMB
Tracks: / Under your thumb / Wedding bells.
7" Single: Released Sep '81, on Polydor, by Polydor Ltd. Deleted '84. Catalogue no: **POSP 322**

UNDER YOUR THUMB (OLD GOLD)
Tracks: / Under your thumb / Wedding bells.
7" Single: Released Mar '86, on Old Gold, by Old Gold Records. Catalogue no: **OG 9590**

Godley & Creme - Wedding Bells (Released on Polydor)

WEDDING BELLS (see panel above)
Tracks: / Wedding bells / Babies.
7" Single: Released Nov '81, on Polydor, by Polydor Ltd. Deleted '84. Catalogue no: **POSP 369**

WIDE BOY
Tracks: / Wide boy / I pity inanimate objects.
7" Single: Released Apr '80, on Polydor, by Polydor Ltd. Deleted '83. Catalogue no: **POSP 145**

Godot

SOMETHIN'S MISSING
Tracks: / Somethin's missing.
10" single: Released Aug '82, on Pinnacle, by Pinnacle Records. Catalogue no: **PIN 514 10**
7" Single: Released Aug '82, on Pinnacle, by Pinnacle Records. Catalogue no: **PIN 514**

WAIT FOR
Tracks: / Wait for / Teeth / Theme for bureaucrats.
12" Single: Released Apr '82, on Godot, Catalogue no: **GODOT 1**

God's Gift

DISCIPLINE
Tracks: / Discipline.
7" Single: Released Oct '82, on New Hormones, Catalogue no: **ORG 25**

GOD'S GIFT (EP)
12" Single: Released Jul '81, on New Hormones, Catalogue no: **ORG 14**

God's Little ...

SOUND OUT THE SYMBOLS
Tracks: / Sound out the symbols / Sea never dry.
7" Single: Released Jul '89, on Cooking Vinyl, by Cooking Vinyl Records. Catalogue no: **FRY 010**

Gods's Toys

ALL THE BORN LOSERS
Tracks: / All the born losers / I love the sound.
7" Single: Released Aug '80, on Badge, by Badge Records. Deleted '82. Catalogue no: **BAD 4**

Godwin, Peter

Biographical details: Peter Godwin gives electronic synthetic sounds a warm and human touch, drawing on classical elements and mixing them with the contemporary. As a founding member of Metro, along with Duncan Browne, Peter Godwin led that seminal group to stardom, critical acclaim and chart success in Europe with the classic *Criminal World*. The band was formed in 1977 during the heyday of the British punk scene; their first album, the self-titled *Metro* released on the Transatlantic label, was causing more than a few ripples around the world when the record company was sold, leaving Godwin and co. bereft of financial aid and unable to support the album's blossoming reputation with live work. A quick change of label found them with EMI where they were one of the first major signings for the new head of A&R, Brian Shepherd. However, a mass exodus of Metro enthusiasts from EMI left the group floundering on the rocks of record company politics.
The band bought back their second LP *Future Imperfect* (an ironic title, considering all their difficulties) and then signed to Polydor in 1981.
Metro's first single for Polydor was a remixed version of *America In My Head*.
However, by the time *America In My Head* was released, Godwin's first solo effort was just about to hit the market, which put him in the somewhat peculiar position of having to promote simultaneously his debut solo single and a Metro SP which to Peter was 12 months old.
On *Images Of Heaven* ex-Metro musician Colin Wight was featured on keyboards, Warren Cann of Ultravox on Simmons drums, and Gary Twigg on bass.
Correspondence is the title of Peter's debut solo album which is due for release in February 1984.
The Art Of Love was chosen as the first single, released in September 1983 and this insidious song has been capped by a great remix from New York's John Luongo. The follow-up, entitled *Baby's In The Mountain* is released on 20th January 1984.
This single has enjoyed a lot of success in America with a Top 5 placing in Billboard's dance chart.
(Lee Leschasin, Polydor Press Office, January 1984).

CRUEL HEART
Tracks: / Cruel heart.
12" Single: Released Nov '82, on Polydor, by Polydor Ltd. Deleted Nov '85. Catalogue no: **POSPX 525**
7" Single: Released Nov '82, on Polydor, by Polydor Ltd. Deleted Nov '85. Catalogue no: **POSP 525**

EMOTIONAL DISGUISE
Tracks: / Emotional disguise / French emotion.
7" Single: Released Feb '82, on Polydor, by Polydor Ltd. Deleted Feb '87. Catalogue no: **POSP 406**
12" Single: Released Feb '82, on Polydor, by Polydor Ltd. Deleted Feb '87. Catalogue no: **POSPX 406**

IMAGES OF HEAVEN
Tracks: / Images of heaven / Spoken images.
7" Single: Released Jun '82, on Polydor, by Polydor Ltd. Deleted Jun '85. Catalogue no: **POSP 440**
12" Single: Released Jun '82, on Polydor, by Polydor Ltd. Deleted Jun '85. Catalogue no: **POSPX 440**

Goffin, Louise

Biographical details: Singer and songwriter, the daughter of Jerry Goffin and Carole King, the famous songwriting team of the Brill Building era of the late '50's-early '60's. She has written with her father, and her mother recently returned to the recording studio. (Donald Clarke, July 1989)T.

4TH OF JULY
Tracks: / 4th of July / Day after the night before, The.
7" Single: Released Jul '88, on WEA, by WEA Records. Catalogue no: **YZ 201**
12" Single: Released Jul '88, on WEA, by WEA Records. Catalogue no: **YZ 201T**

BRIDGE OF SIGHS
Tracks: / Bridge of sighs / B-side over you.
12" Single: Released Jan '88, on WEA, by WEA Records. Catalogue no: **YZ 171T**
7" Single: Released Jan '88, on WEA, by WEA Records. Catalogue no: **YZ 171**

CARNIVAL
Tracks: / Carnival.
7" Single: Released Aug '87, on WEA, by WEA Records. Deleted Jul '88. Catalogue no: **YZ 147**
12" Single: Released Aug '87, on WEA, by WEA Records. Deleted Jul '88. Catalogue no: **YZ 147T**

IN THE MOOD
Tracks: / In the mood / Who's sleeping tonight (on 12" only) / Beside myself over you.
Note: * only available on 12" single
7" Single: Released 23 Apr '88, on WEA, by WEA Records. Catalogue no: **YZ 186**
12" Single: Released 23 Apr '88, on WEA, by WEA Records. Catalogue no: **YZ 186T**

SEND A MESSAGE
Tracks: / Send a message / Side myself over you.
12" Single: Released Sep '87, on WEA, by WEA Records. Deleted Jul '88. Catalogue no: **YZ 159 T**
7" Single: Released Sep '87, on WEA, by WEA Records. Deleted Jul '88. Catalogue no: **YZ 159**

SURRENDER
Tracks: / Surrender / I can't wait (acoustic version).
7" Single: Released 16 Sep '88, on WEA, by WEA Records. Catalogue no: **YZ 314**
12" Single: Released 16 Sep '88, on WEA, by WEA Records. Catalogue no: **YZ 314T**

Gogmagog

I WILL BE THERE
Tracks: / I will be there.
12" Single: Released Sep '85, on Food For Thought, by Music For Nations Records. Catalogue no: **YUMT 109**

Go-Go's

Biographical details:
At the time of their greatest success, this American band consisted of Belinda Carlisle, Charlotte Caffey, Gina Schock, Kathy Valentine and Jane Weidlin.
The Go-Go's were formed by Carlisle, Caffey and Weidlin in 1978. Hailing from Los Angeles, they struggled on their local club scene for a couple of years. In 1980 they turned professional, established a permanent line-up and arrived in Britain to support the Specials on tour.
Their debut single was issued on Britain's Stiff label - it was called *We got the beat* and was penned by Caffey. Weidlin compose a song called *Our lips are sealed* with the Specials' Terry Hall. Neither song aroused any interest back in the UK, but the Go-Go's began to attract a cult following back in LA.
After being rejected by the major record companies, they signed with Miles Copeland's IRS label. The idea of an all-female self-contained pop band was met with resistance not only from the big record labels but also from the then highly conservative US radio stations.
But the group's perseverance and lengthy touring finally conquered the male-dominated bastions of the American rock establishment. In late 1981, after tortuous climbs up the lower reaches of the charts, *Our lips are sealed* and *Beauty & The Beat* LP finally achieved US Top 20 status. In the early spring of 1982, this album logged six weeks at no. 1 in America while *We got the beat* became a no. 2 single.
The Go-Go's achieved the biggest-selling debut LP in US pop history, and were the first girl group of a self-contained nature to hit the top of the American album chart.
Americans thought of the Go-Go's as a new wave band but, in truth, their sound was derivative of the bast groups of the sixties and the seventies sounds of Blondie.
As the Go-Go's gradually lost their freshness, their subsequent albums *Vacation* (1982) and *Talk show* (1984) - were slightly less successful than their respective predecessors. By 1985 the group had split in two with the Go-Go's name being retained by those remaining.
British success had been extremely limited. Their only UK hit single was *Our lips are sealed* with *We got the beat* on the B side, which peaked at no. 47. *Beauty & The Beat* failed to enter the LP chart and *Vacation* peaked at no. 75. But a version of *Our lips are sealed* by the Fun Boy Three (Terry Hall's breakaway group from the Specials) reached the UK no. 7 position in 1983. (Bob MacDonald 24/9/85)
A USA all-girl new-wave quintet formed in 1978 by fashion designer turned guitarist Jane Wiedlin (born 1958 in Oconomowoc, Wisconsin), and former cheerleader/lead singer Belinda Carlisle. Originally called the Misfits, they recruited expert guitarist Charlotte Caffey to help out novice Wiedlen, whose attraction to new-wave had been via fashion.
First drummer Elissa Bello was replaced by seasoned Gina Schock in 1979; they signed with Stiff and brought their bright pop to the UK, but did better after switching to IRS. *Beauty and the beast* was No. 1 in the USA for 6 weeks in 1981. Their original bassist Margot Olavera was replaced by Kathy Valentine. Weidlin and Carlisle released solo albums. (Donald Clarke, July 1989).

GIRL OF A THOUSAND LISTS
Tracks: / Girl of a thousand lists / I think it's me.
7" Single: Released Nov '82, on I.R.S, Catalogue no: **GON 104**

OUR LIPS ARE SEALED (see panel below)
Tracks: / Our lips are sealed / We got the beat.
7" Single: Released May '82, on I.R.S, Deleted '85. Catalogue no: **GON 102**

VACATION (SINGLE)
Tracks: / Vacation / Beatnik beach.
7" Single: Released Aug '82, on A&M, by A&M Records. Deleted Aug '85. Catalogue no: **GON 103**

Go-Go's - Our Lips Are Sealed (Released on I.R.S.)

WE GOT THE BEAT
Tracks: / We got the beat / How much more.
7" Single: Released Nov '81, on A&M, by A&M Records. Deleted Nov '84. Catalogue no: **PEP 1010**
7" Single: Released May '80, on Stiff, by Stiff Records. Catalogue no: **BUY 78**

Going Red

SOME BOYS
Tracks: / Some boys / Tune Kevin's strings.
7" Single: Released Jan '81, on MCA, by MCA Records. Deleted Jan '84. Catalogue no: **MCA 673**

Going Straight

IMAGINATION
Tracks: / Imagination / Me woman.
7" Single: Released May '82, on Energy (UK), by Energy Records. Deleted May '85. Catalogue no: **NRG 007**

Gol Gappas

DINNER WITH NOUGAT
Tracks: / Dinner with nougat / St. Lucky / Chicken pox / Albert Parker / Ice cream.
12" Single: Released Apr '86, on El, by Cherry Red Records. Catalogue no: **GPO 8 T**

WEST 14
Tracks: / West 14 / Roman.
7" Single: Released Nov '86, on El, by Cherry Red Records. Catalogue no: **GPO 21**

Gold

HEARTS OF GOLD
Tracks: / Hearts of gold / Sacks of gold.
7" Single: Released 28 Nov '88, on CBS, by CBS Records. Deleted 17 Apr '89. Catalogue no: **654501 7**

HIGH TIME
Tracks: / High time / Note you left.
7" Single: Released Oct '80, on Sky-Hi, Catalogue no: **SKY 777**

LITTLE CLOSER TO FREEDOM, A
Tracks: / Little closer to freedom, A / Un peu pres des etoiles.
7" Single: Released Feb '86, on WEA (International), by WEA Records. Deleted Sep '87. Catalogue no: **X 8930**
12" Single: Released Feb '86, on WEA (International), by WEA Records. Deleted Sep '87. Catalogue no: **X 8930 T**

MIDNIGHT LIGHT
Tracks: / Midnight love / Here we go again.
7" Single: Released Jan '80, on President, by President Records. Deleted '83. Catalogue no: **PT 481**

SAIL AWAY
Tracks: / Sail away / Josy-Ann.
7" Single: Released Jun '86, on WEA (International), by WEA Records. Catalogue no: **248 688**

Gold, Andrew

Biographical details: Singer, multi-instrumentalist, songwriter and arranger Andrew Gold was born in Burbank, California and was one of the most feverishly-active musicians on the Los Angeles recording scene during the mid to late 70's. He was Linda Ronstadt's musical director and arranger and a member of her backing band. The workaholic Gold launched his own solo career in 1976 with a self-titled LP. His next album, *What's Wrong With This Picture?*, included his first hit single, *Lonely Boy*, a dramatic biographical account of a mixed-up lad's struggle from childhood to adult life which was one of 1977's most original singles, reaching No 7 in the US and No 11 in Britain. Gold's 1978 album, *All This And Heaven Too*, yielded two further UK Top Twenty singles with *Never Let Her Slip Away* (an understated but highly-effective love song which reached No 5) and *How Can This Be Love?*, but these were not hits in his native country. His style contained elements of pop, rock and middle-of-the-road, crafted with typical LA slickness, but he was somehow unable to stage a consistent penetration of the massive American soft rock market. During the early 80's his name faded into obscurity but he continued to work closely with Ronstadt and, later, with 10cc member Graham Gouldman. Gold's father was a composer, and his mother a singer. (Bob MacDonald, September 1985.).

HOW CAN THIS BE LOVE
Tracks: / How can this be love.
7" Single: Released Jun '78, on Asylum, by WEA Records. Deleted '81. Catalogue no: **K 13126**

KISS THIS ONE GOODBYE
Tracks: / Kiss this one goodbye / Make up your mind.
7" Single: Released May '80, on Elektra, by Elektra Records (UK). Deleted May '83. Catalogue no: **K 12441**

LONELY BOY
Tracks: / Lonely boy / Never let her slip away.
7" Single: Released Apr '77, on Asylum, by WEA Records. Deleted '80. Catalogue no: **K 13076**

LONELY BOY (OLD GOLD)
Tracks: / Lonely boy / Never let her slip away.
7" Single: Released Sep '85, on Old Gold, by Old Gold Records. Catalogue no: **OG 9514**

NEVER LET HER SLIP AWAY
Tracks: / Never let her slip away.
7" Single: Released Mar '78, on Asylum, by WEA Records. Deleted '81. Catalogue no: **K 13112**

THANK YOU FOR BEING A FRIEND
Tracks: / Thank you for being a friend.
7" Single: Released Oct '78, on Asylum, by WEA Records. Deleted '81. Catalogue no: **K 13135**

Gold, Angie

APPLAUSE
Tracks: / Applause / Creature of the night.
7" Single: Released Oct '86, on Passion, by Skratch Records. Catalogue no: **PASH 62**
12" Single: Released Oct '86, on Passion, by Skratch Records. Catalogue no: **PASH 62(12)**

EAT YOU UP
Tracks: / Eat you up.
7" Single: Released '88, on Passion, by Skratch Records. Catalogue no: **PASH 43**
12" Single: Released Mar '85, on Passion, by Skratch Records. Catalogue no: **PASH 43(12)**

EVERY HOME SHOULD HAVE ONE
Tracks: / Every home should have one / Let's work it out.
7" Single: Released Feb '81, on KRL, by Kaleidoscope Records (UK). Deleted Feb '84. Catalogue no: **A 1032**

THIRD FINGER LEFT HAND
Tracks: / Third finger left hand / Landslide.
7" Single: Released 20 Jun '87, on Passion, by Skratch Records. Catalogue no: **PASH 72**
12" Single: Released 20 Jun '87, on Passion, by Skratch Records. Catalogue no: **PASH 72(12)**

TIMEBOMB
Tracks: / Time bomb.
12" Single: Released Oct '85, on Passion, by Skratch Records. Catalogue no: **PASH 49(12)**
7" Single: Released '88, on Passion, by Skratch Records. Catalogue no: **PASH 49**

WHO AM I KIDDING
Tracks: / Who am I kidding / Now that the party's over.
7" Single: Released Jun '82, on Kaleidoscope Sound, by Kaleidoscope Sound Records. Deleted Jun '85. Catalogue no: **KRLA 2323**

WOMAN'S INTUITION
Tracks: / Woman's intuition / Easier said than done.
7" Single: Released Nov '81, on Kaleidoscope Sound, by Kaleidoscope Sound Records. Deleted Nov '84. Catalogue no: **KRL A1730**

Gold, Brian

GIRLS YOU CAN'T DO
Tracks: / Girls you can't do.
12" Single: Released Oct '89, on Two Friends, Catalogue no: **SIR 014**

ON AND ON
Tracks: / On and on.
12" Single: Released 31 Jul '89, on Blue Mountain, Catalogue no: **BMD 063**

Gold, David

DANCE TO THE MUSIC
Tracks: / Dance to the music / Got to dance.
12" Single: Released May '84, on Whiplash, Deleted '87. Catalogue no: **WLD 002**

Gold, Frankincense...

BUTTERSIDE DOWNS
Tracks: / Butterside downs.
12" Single: Released Oct '88, on Nuclear Blast, Catalogue no: **NW 001**

Gold, Louise

PRACTICE PRACTICE
Tracks: / Practice practice / Supersonic Sam's cosmic cafe.
7" Single: Released Apr '86, on PRT, by Castle Communications Records. Catalogue no: **7P 342**

Gold, Michelle

LOST IN LOVE
Tracks: / Lost in love.
12" Single: Released Jul '85, on Other End, Catalogue no: **12 OET 7**
7" Single: Released Jul '85, on Other End, Catalogue no: **7 OET 7**

Gold, Patti

AS LONG AS WE KEEP BELIEVING
Tracks: / As long as we keep believing.
7" Single: Released Oct '83, on Button, by Musical Characters Records. Catalogue no: **BTN 105**

DON'T TAKE IT
Tracks: / Don't take it / Perfect love song.
7" Single: Released Mar '84, on Button, by Musical Characters Records. Catalogue no: **BTN 114**

GOODBYE
Tracks: / Goodbye / Give me your word.
7" Single: Released Jan '86, on Audiotrax, Deleted '87. Catalogue no: **ATX 12**

LADY LOVES TO DANCE
Tracks: / Lady loves to dance.
7" Single: Released Sep '81, on Look, by Look Records. Catalogue no: **LK/SP 6666**

Gold Top

INTRODUCTION
Tracks: / Introduction.
12" Single: Released Jul '88, on Gee Street, by Gee Street Records. Catalogue no: **GOLD 001**

Golden Dawn

GEORGE HAMILTON'S DEAD
Tracks: / George Hamilton's dead.
7" Single: Released Aug '89, on Sarah, Catalogue no: **SARAH 17**

MY SECRET WORLD
Tracks: / My secret world.
7" Single: Released Jun '88, on Sarah, Catalogue no: **SARAH 009**

Golden Earring

Biographical details: At the time of their greatest success, this Dutch band consisted of Rinus Gerritsen, Barry Hay, George Kooymans and Cesar Zuiderwijk. With Gerritsen and Kooymans as their backbone, Golden Earring have been perennially active in the 60's, '70's and '80's. They are perhaps the Netherland's equivalent of Status Quo - long-lasting, hard-grafting pop group of the 60's turned rock band of the '70's. Their eponymous debut LP *Just Earring* was released in 1964, and was followed by imitations of the Beatles and the Byrds. One of their early members was drummer Jaap Eggermont, who quit in 1970 but made a fortune 11 years later as producer and mastermind behind the globally successful Starsound medleys. Major international acceptance has greeted Golden Earring only twice during their mammoth career. *Radar love*, a hard-driving and superbly constructed 1974 rock single, reached no.7 in the UK and no. 13 in the US; it was the opening track on the *Moontan* LP, which reached the UK no. 24 position. This success came hard on the heels of US/UK success for another Dutch rock outfit, Focus. 1983 brought Golden Earring a patiently awaited second US Top 40 single in the shape of *twilight zone* - this reached no. 10 after heavy exposure on America's fast-growing 24-hour rock cable channel MTV. They failed to consolidate upon this second breakthrough. Earring's music has always been competent but highly derivative, borrowing heavily from (mainly British) rock bastions. (Bob Macdonald, 24/9/85).

RADAR LOVE
Tracks: / Radar love / Just like Vince Taylor.
7" Single: Released Dec '73, on Track, by Polydor Ltd. Deleted '76. Catalogue no: **2094 116**
7" Single: Released Oct '77, on Polydor, by Polydor Ltd. Deleted '80. Catalogue no: **2121 335**
7" Single: Released Mar '86, on Old Gold, by Old Gold Records. Catalogue no: **OG 9582**

TWILIGHT ZONE
Tracks: / Twilight zone / King Dark.
7" Single: Released Oct '82, on Mercury, by Phonogram Ltd. Deleted Oct '85. Catalogue no: **MER 122**
12" Single: Released Oct '82, on Mercury, by Phonogram Ltd. Deleted Oct '85. Catalogue no: **MERX 122**

WHEN THE LADY SMILES
Tracks: / When the lady smiles / Orwell's year.
7" Single: Released Apr '84, on Carrere, Catalogue no: **CAR 321**
12" Single: Released Apr '84, on Carrere, Catalogue no: **CART 321**

Golden Horde

DIG THAT CRAZY GRAVE
Tracks: / Dig that crazy grave.
7" Single: Released Feb '85, on Hotwire, by Crashed Records. Catalogue no: **WAYOUT 1**

Golden Syrup

LOVERS CONCERTO
Tracks: / Lovers concerto / Don't break my heart.
7" Single: Released Oct '83, on Code, by Code Records. Catalogue no: **COD 008**
12" Single: Released Oct '83, on Code, by Code Records. Catalogue no: **12 COD 008**

Goldie

CAN'T YOU HEAR MY HEARTBEAT
Tracks: / Can't you hear my heartbeat.
7" Single: Released Feb '65, on Decca, by Decca Records. Deleted '68. Catalogue no: **F 12070**

MAKING UP AGAIN
Tracks: / Making up again.
7" Single: Released May '78, on Bronze, by Bronze Records. Deleted '81. Catalogue no: **BRO 50**

Goldman, Jean-Jacques

LA BAS (OVER THERE)
Tracks: / La bas (over there) / (Intro) a quoi tu sers / La bas (over there) (version longue) (Only on 12" version.) / Entre gris clair et gris fonce (Only on CD single.) / Entre gris clair et gris fonce (live) (Only on 12" single.).
12" Single: Released Apr '89, on Epic, by CBS Records. Catalogue no: **651 2288**
CD 5": Released Apr '89, on Epic, by CBS Records. Catalogue no: **651 2282**
7" Single: Released Apr '89, on Epic, by CBS Records. Catalogue no: **651 2287**

Goldman, Vivien

LAUNDERETTE
Tracks: / Launderette / Private armies.
7" Single: Released Aug '81, on Window, Deleted '82. Catalogue no: **WIND 1**

Goldsboro, Bobby

Biographical details: This American singer, songwriter and guitarist, born in Florida, celebrated his 21st birthday in 1962 by becoming a guitarist with Roy Orbison's group. Having moved with his family to Alabama during childhood, where he studied at high school and university, he gained initial experience in a student combo before joining Orbison. While with Roy, Bobby developed his songwriting skills and made a tentative solos bid with the single *Molly*, which became a minor US hit. His solo performing career began in earnest in early 1964, when the self-penned *See the funny little clown* surged to no. 9 on the American chart. A year later, came his next big hit, *Little things*, which reached the US no. 13 position; it was a no. 5 hit in Britain for Dave Berry, who recorded an opportunistic cover version. Goldsboro's first UK as a performer was also his biggest ever success on both sides of the Atlantic - *Honey*, a swirling death disc written by Bobby Russell, was no. 1 in America for 5 weeks in 1968 and reached no. 2 in Britain. Many listeners found the record mawkish, while others thought it poignant and moving. Amazingly, it became a UK no.2 hit all over again as a 1975 re-issue, by which time the artist had chalked up various other successes - *Watching Scotty grow* (written by Mac Davis) was a US no. 11 hit in 1971; Goldsboro's own 1973 song *Summer (the first time)* was the ultimate in romantic narratives, and reached no. 21 in the US and no. 9 in the UK; and *Hello summertime*, which started life as a TV Coke ad, was a 1974 Top 20 success in Britain. Goldsboro's style contained elements of country, pop and easy listening, and he was able to give full vent to these on his own syndicated US TV series. By the mid-seventies, the twee side of his musical character was winning the upper hand and he was getting acquainted with Las Vegas. (Bob Macdonald, 24/9/85)
Pop country singer and songwriter with a tear-jerking vocal style, born in 1941 in Florida. Some of his early songs were covered by UK artists; He had hits in the USA pop chart from 1962, including the top ten *See the funny little clown* in '64; in 1968 *Honey* was No. 1 in both country and pop charts. *With pen in hand* was a minor hit for Goldsboro, but there were three other hit versions of his song. He carried on in the country chart through '82, sometimes duetting with Del Reeves. (Donald Clarke, July 1989).

HELLO SUMMERTIME

Tracks: / Hello summertime.
7" Single: Released Aug '74, on United Artists, by EMI Records. Deleted '77. Catalogue no: **UP 35705**

HONEY
Tracks: / Honey / Danny.
7" Single: Released Apr '68, on United Artists, by EMI Records. Deleted '71. Catalogue no: **UP 2215**
7" Single: Released Feb '74, on United Artists, by EMI Records. Catalogue no: **UP 35633**

SUMMER (THE FIRST TIME) (SINGLE)
Tracks: / Summer (the first time) / Childhood - 1949.
7" Single: Released Jun '73, on United Artists, by EMI Records. Catalogue no: **UP 35558**

Goldsmith

LIFE IS KILLING ME
Tracks: / Life is killing me.
7" Single: Released Mar '83, on Bedlam, Catalogue no: **BLM 001**

Goldsmith, Glen

DREAMING
Tracks: / Dreaming / Dreaming (inst) / I won't cry (Extra track on 12").
7" Single: Released Feb '88, on RCA, by BMG Records (UK). Deleted May '89. Catalogue no: **PB 41711**
12" Single: Released Feb '88, on RCA, by BMG Records (UK). Deleted Aug '89. Catalogue no: **PT 41712**

I WON'T CRY
Tracks: / I won't cry (remix) / I won't cry (instrumental) / I won't cry (dub).
7" Single: Released Aug '87, on RCA, by BMG Records (UK). Catalogue no: **PB 41493**
12" Single: Released Aug '87, on RCA, by BMG Records (UK). Deleted May '89. Catalogue no: **PT 41494**

SAVE A LITTLE BIT
Tracks: / Save a little bit / Give your word.
7" Single: Released Aug '88, on Reproduction, Deleted May '89. Catalogue no: **PB 42147**
CD 5": Released Aug '88, on Reproduction, Deleted Jul '89. Catalogue no: **PD 42148**
12" Single: Released Aug '88, on Reproduction, Deleted May '89. Catalogue no: **PT 42148**

WHAT YOU SEE IS WHAT YOU GET (SINGLE)
Tracks: / What you see is what you get.
7" Single: Released 31 May '88, on RCA, by BMG Records (UK). Deleted May '89. Catalogue no: **PB 42075**
CD 5": Released 31 May '88, on RCA, by BMG Records (UK). Deleted Jul '89. Catalogue no: **PD 42077**
12" Single: Released 31 May '88, on RCA, by BMG Records (UK). Deleted May '89. Catalogue no: **PT 42076**

Golinski Brothers

BLOODY
Tracks: / Bloody / Toy.
7" Single: Released Feb '81, on Badge, by Badge Records. Deleted Feb '84. Catalogue no: **BAD 6**

Golson, Benny

Biographical details: Tenor saxophone/bandleader. Born in 1929, he grew up in Philadelphia with John Coltrane & the Heath brothers, and was influenced by Tadd Dameron as a composer/arranger. Coltrane took Golson's 'Stablemates' to recording sessions with the Miles Davis Quintet and Mal Waldron in 1955-6; it became a jazz classic along with 'Whisper not', 'I remember Clifford', and others. Golson and Art Farmer led the Jazztet 1959-62; his writing and studio activities included work with Peggy Lee, Lou Rawls and Nancy Wilson. Since the late 1970s he has returned to performing, including reforming the Jazztet with Farmer. (Donald Clarke 1989).

KILLER JOE RAP
Tracks: / Killer Joe rap / Walkin' and stalkin'.
12" Single: Released May '81, on CBS, by CBS Records. Deleted May '84. Catalogue no: **CBS A 12 1223**

Gomez, Ray

LOVE AT FIRST SIGHT
Tracks: / Love at first sight / World will keep on turning.
7" Single: Released Sep '80, on CBS, by CBS Records. Deleted '83. Catalogue no: **CBS 8965**

SUMMER IN THE CITY
Tracks: / Summer in the city / West Side boogie.
7" Single: Released 20 Jun '80, on CBS, by CBS Records. Deleted '83. Catalogue no: **CBS 8659**

Gomm, Ian

HOOKED ON LOVE
Tracks: / Hooked on love / Sad affair.
7" Single: Released Jan '80, on Albion, by Albion Records. Deleted Jan '83. Catalogue no: **DEL 9**

I LIKE YOU I DON'T LOVE YOU
Tracks: / I like you I don't love you / Nobody's fool.
7" Single: Released Jul '81, on Albion, by Albion Records. Catalogue no: **ION 1016**

I'M IN A HEARTACHE
Tracks: / I'm in a heartache / City style / Sad affair.
7" Single: Released Feb '83, on Albion, by Albion Records. Catalogue no: **ION 1043**

ITS GOT TO BE MAGIC
Tracks: / Its got to be magic / Play on.
7" Single: Released Sep '86, on Decal, by Charly Records. Catalogue no: **CZY 7116**

LEAVE IT TO THE MUSIC
Tracks: / Leave it to the music / Can't catch me.
7" Single: Released Nov '82, on Albion, by Albion Records. Catalogue no: **ION 1040**

SHE'LL NEVER TAKE THE PLACE OF YOU
Tracks: / She'll never take the place of you / Hole in the middle.
7" Single: Released Sep '82, on Albion, by Albion Records. Catalogue no: **ION 1026**

SLOW DANCING
Tracks: / Slow dancing / It don't help.
7" Single: Released Apr '80, on Albion, by Albion Records. Deleted Apr '83. Catalogue no: **DEL 10**

Gonads

DELILAH
Tracks: / Delilah.
7" Single: Released Feb '83, on Razor, by Razor Records. Catalogue no: **RZS 103**

PEACE ARTISTS(EP)
7" Single: Released Jul '82, on Secret, by Secret Records. Catalogue no: **SHH 134**

PURE PUNK FOR ROW PEOPLE (EP)
7" EP: Released Jul '82, on Secret, by Secret Records. Catalogue no: **SHH 131**

Gone To Earth

LIVE & BURIED
Tracks: / Live & buried.
7" Single: Released Nov '85, on Probe Plus, by Probe Plus Records. Catalogue no: **PP 15**

Gonks

GONKS ARE HERE FOR CHRISTMAS, THE
Tracks: / Gonks are here for Christmas, The.
7" Single: Released Nov '85, on WEA, by WEA Records. Catalogue no: **YZ 54**
12" Single: Released Nov '85, on WEA, by WEA Records. Catalogue no: **YZ 54T**

Gonzales, Terri

TREAT YOURSELF TO MY LOVE
Tracks: / Treat yourself to my love / Treat yourself to my love (part 2).
7" Single: Released Mar '82, on Beckett, Deleted '85. Catalogue no: **BKSL 2**

Gonzalez

DIGITAL LOVE AFFAIR
Tracks: / Digital love affair / Disco can't go on forever.
7" Single: Released Aug '80, on EMI, by EMI Records. Deleted '83. Catalogue no: **EMI 5097**
12" Single: Released Aug '80, on EMI, by EMI Records. Deleted '83. Catalogue no: **12EMI 5097**

HAVEN'T STOPPED DANCING YET
Tracks: / Haven't stopped dancing yet / Ain't no way to treat a lady.
7" Single: Released Mar '79, on Sidewalk, by Sidewalk Records. Deleted '82. Catalogue no: **SID 102**
7" Single: Released Mar '89, on Dance On Wax, Catalogue no: **DANCE 1**
12" Single: Released Jun '87, on Dance On Wax, Catalogue no: **DANCE 112**

JUST MY IMAGINATION
Tracks: / Just my imagination / Lets get it on.
12" Single: on PRT, by Castle Communications Records. Catalogue no: **12P 304**
7" Single: on PRT, by Castle Communications Records. Catalogue no: **7P 304**

PIRATES
Tracks: / Pirates.
7" Single: Released Jun '84, on Tooti Frooti, Deleted '85. Catalogue no: **7 P 314**
12" Single: Released Jun '84, on Tooti Frooti, Deleted '85. Catalogue no: **12 P 314**

Gooch, John

BRENDAN'S THEME
Tracks: / Brendan's theme / Haywire.
7" Single: Released Mar '84, on President, by President Records. Catalogue no: **PT 524**

Goochifrita, Juanita

GO FUNK YOURSELF
Tracks: / Go funk yourself.
7" Single: Released Dec '80, on EMI, by EMI Records. Deleted Dec '85. Catalogue no: **EMI 5128**
12" Single: Released Dec '80, on EMI, by EMI Records. Deleted Dec '85. Catalogue no: **12 EMI 5128**

Good Boys

KEEP HOLDING BACK YOUR LOVE
Tracks: / Keep holding back your love.
7" Single: Released Apr '89, on Hot Melt, by Hot Melt Records. Catalogue no: **7TC 22**
12" Single: Released Apr '89, on Hot Melt, by Hot Melt Records. Catalogue no: **12TC 22**

YOU KEEP HOLDING BACK YOUR LOVE FROM ME
Tracks: / You keep holding back your love from me / T.Jam - Dance to the rhythm (island mix).
12" Single: Released Jul '89, on Hot Melt, by Hot Melt Records. Catalogue no: **12TCT 22**

Good Grief (Group)

SWINGING ON A STAR
Tracks: / Swinging on a star.
7" Single: Released Oct '82, on Anytime Records, Catalogue no: **ANY 1**

Good Guys

EXTRA TERRESTRIAL SONG
Tracks: / Extra terrestial song.
7" Single: Released Dec '82, on Public, Catalogue no: **PUB 007**

Good Looks

EVERY DAY OF MY LIFE
Tracks: / Everyday of my life / What's in it for me.
7" Single: Released Apr '82, on Radioactive, Catalogue no: **RAD 503**

JIM'LL FIX IT
Tracks: / Jim'll fix it / Jim has fixed it for you.
7" Single: Released Mar '82, on Radioactive, Catalogue no: **RAD 501**

Good News (Group)

MAKIN' IT
Tracks: / Makin' it.
7" Single: Released Jun '84, on Humber, by Humber Records. Catalogue no: **HUM 52**
12" Single: Released Jun '84, on Humber, by Humber Records. Catalogue no: **12 HUM 52**

SEE THE MARINERS
Tracks: / See the mariners / Jambo.
7" Single: Released Jan '86, on Humber, by Humber Records. Catalogue no: **HUM 53**

Good Question

GOT A NEW LOVE
Tracks: / Got a new love / One more time.
7" Single: Released Oct '88, on Reprise, by WEA Records. Catalogue no: **W 7861**
12" Single: Released Oct '88, on Reprise, by WEA Records. Catalogue no: **W 7861T**

Goodacre, Tony

GUERNSEY, I'LL KEEP COMING BACK TO YOU
Tracks: / Guernsey, I'll keep coming back to you / Sarnia cherie.
7" Single: Released May '84, on Homespun (Ireland), by Outlet Records. Catalogue no: **HS 078**

Goodall, Howard

I HATE THE FRENCH
Tracks: / I hate the French / Boy in blue.
7" Single: Released Sep '80, on Columbia, by EMI Records. Deleted '83. Catalogue no: **DB 9087**

Goodbye Look

HALF THE FUN OF THE CRIME
Tracks: / Half the fun of the crime.
12" Single: Released Apr '85, on PRT, by Castle Communications Records. Catalogue no: **12 325**
7" Single: Released Apr '85, on PRT, by Castle Communications Records. Catalogue no: **7P 325**

Goodbye Mr Mackenzie

FACE TO FACE
Tracks: / Face to face.
12" Single: Released '88, on Claudestiny, Catalogue no: **MACK 001**

GOOD DEEDS AND DIRTY RAGS
Tracks: / Open your arms / Wake it up / His masters voice / Goodwill city / Candlestick park / Goodbye Mr. Mackenzie / Rattler, The / Dust / You generous thing you / Good deeds / Amsterdam (CD only.) / Calton Hill (CD only.) / Secrets (CD only.) / Knockin' on Joe (CD only.) / Strangle (On free single only.) / Extended strangle (On free single only.) / Secrets (live) (On free single only.) / Green turn red (live) (On free single only.).
Special: Released Apr '89, on Capitol, by EMI Records. Catalogue no: **ESTX 2089**
Special: Released Apr '89, on Capitol, by EMI Records. Catalogue no: **790159 0**

GOODBYE MR MACKENZIE
Tracks: / Goodbye Mr. MacKenzie / Green turn red / Knockin' on Joe (Only on 12" single.).
Note: Produced by Kevin Moloney & Terry Adams. Additional production & mix by Mack.
12" Single: Released Aug '88, on Capitol, by EMI Records. Deleted Oct '89. Catalogue no: **12CL 501**
CD 5": Released Aug '88, on Capitol, by EMI Records. Catalogue no: **CDCL 501**
7" Single: Released Aug '88, on Capitol, by EMI Records. Deleted Oct '89. Catalogue no: **CL 501**
12" Single: Released Aug '88, on Capitol, by EMI Records. Deleted Oct '89. Catalogue no: **12CLG 501**

GOODWILL CITY
Tracks: / Goodwill city / I'm sick of you / What's got into you (CD single & 12"s only.) / Insidious thing (CD single & 12" gatefold only.).
12" Single: Released Jun '89, on Capitol, by EMI Records. Catalogue no: **12CL 538**
CD 5": Released Jun '89, on Capitol, by EMI Records. Catalogue no: **CDCL 538**
CD 5": Released Jun '89, on Capitol, by EMI Records. Catalogue no: **203 419 2**
Cassingle: Released Jun '89, on Capitol, by EMI Records. Catalogue no: **TCCL 538**
Cassingle: Released Jun '89, on Capitol, by EMI Records. Catalogue no: **203 419 4**
7" Single: Released Jun '89, on Capitol, by EMI Records. Catalogue no: **CL 538**
7" Single: Released Jun '89, on Capitol, by EMI Records. Catalogue no: **203 419 7**
12" Single: Released Jun '89, on Capitol, by EMI Records. Catalogue no: **203 419 6**
12" Single: Released Jun '89, on Capitol, by EMI Records. Catalogue no: **203 419 8**
Special: Released Jun '89, on Capitol, by EMI Records. Catalogue no: **203 419 0**
12" Single: Released Jun '89, on Capitol, by EMI Records. Catalogue no: **12CLG 538**
Special: Released Jun '89, on Capitol, by EMI Records. Catalogue no: **CLX 538**

OPEN YOUR ARMS
Tracks: / Open your arms / Secrets / Amsterdam (Not on 7".) / Pleasure search (12" special & CD single only.).
7" Single: Released Nov '88, on Capitol, by EMI Records. Deleted Oct '89. Catalogue no: **CLG 513**
CD 5": Released Nov '88, on Capitol, by EMI Records. Deleted Aug '89. Catalogue no: **CDCL 513**
12" Pic: Released Nov '88, on Capitol, by EMI Records. Deleted Aug '89. Catalogue no: **12CLP 513**
12" Single: Released Nov '88, on Capitol, by EMI Records. Deleted Aug '89. Catalogue no: **12CL 513**
7" Single: Released Nov '88, on Capitol, by EMI Records. Deleted Aug '89. Catalogue no: **CL 513**
12" Single: Released Nov '88, on Capitol, by EMI Records. Deleted Aug '89. Catalogue no: **12CLG 513**

RATTLER, THE
Tracks: / Rattler, The / Here comes Deacon Brodie / Calton Hill (Not on 7".) / Drunken sailor (Not on 7".).
7" Single: Released Aug '86, on Precious Organisation, by Precious Organisation. Catalogue no: **JEWEL 2**
CD 5": Released Mar '89, on Capitol, by EMI Records. Deleted Aug '89. Catalogue no: **CDCL 522**
7" Single: Released Feb '89, on Capitol, by EMI Records. Deleted Aug '89. Catalogue no: **CL 522**
12" Single: Released Mar '89, on Capitol, by EMI Records. Deleted Aug '89. Catalogue no: **12CLG 522**
7" Single: Released Mar '89, on Capitol, by EMI Records. Catalogue no: **CLG 522**
12" Single: Released Mar '89, on Capitol, by EMI Records. Deleted Aug '89. Catalogue no: **12CLP 522**
12" Single: Released Feb '89, on Capitol,

by EMI Records. Deleted Aug '89. Catalogue no: **12CL 522**

Goodie

YOU & I
Tracks: / You & I / Do something.
12" Single: Released Feb '83, on Total Experience, Deleted May '88. Catalogue no: **TEX 003**
7" Single: Released Feb '83, on Total Experience, Deleted May '88. Catalogue no: **TE 003**

Goodies

BLACK PUDDING BERTHA
Tracks: / Black pudding Bertha.
7" Single: Released Jun '75, on Bradley's, Deleted '78. Catalogue no: **BRAD 7517**

FUNKY GIBBON
Tracks: / Funky gibbon / Sick man blues.
7" Single: Released Mar '75, on Bradley's, Deleted '78. Catalogue no: **BRAD 7504**

IN BETWEENIES
Tracks: / In betweenies / Father Christmas do not touch me.
7" Single: Released Dec '74, on Bradley's, Deleted '77. Catalogue no: **BRAD 7421**

MAKE A DAFT NOISE FOR CHRISTMAS
Tracks: / Make a daft noise for Christmas.
7" Single: Released Dec '75, on Bradley's, Deleted '78. Catalogue no: **BRAD 7533**

NAPPY LOVE
Tracks: / Nappy love / Wild thing.
7" Single: Released Sep '75, on Bradley's, Deleted '78. Catalogue no: **BRAD 7524**

Gooding, Cuba

Biographical details: This American singer came to fame in 1972 as a member of the Main Ingredient, a soul vocal group whom he had just joined as leader following the death of their original lead singer Don McPherson. Gooding quickly brought the group to greater commercial success than they had ever known before, as their sound moved in an increasingly MoR Delfonics-style sweet soul direction - the Main Ingredient's two big US hits were *Everybody plays the fool* (no. 3 in 1972, a million-seller) and *Just don't want to be lonely* (no. 10 in 1974, also a million-seller); the latter reached no. 27 in Britain. The group's third and final Top 40 single was *Happiness is just around the bend*, which peaked at no. 35 in August '74. As they faded into obscurity during the latter half of the seventies, Cuba Gooding launched a solo career which was somewhat short of meteoric. His *First album*, produced by Dennis Lambert & Brian Potter, was released in 1978. A 1983 re-recording of *Happiness is just around the bend* became a dancefloor hit in Britain, and reached no. 72 on the UK pop chart in November of that year. (Bob Macdonald, 25/9/85).

HAPPINESS IS JUST AROUND THE BEND
Tracks: / Happiness is just around the bend.
7" Single: Released Nov '83, on London Records, by London Records. Catalogue no: **LON 41**
12" Single: Released Nov '83, on London Records, by London Records. Catalogue no: **LONX 41**

Goodman, Steve

SOMETIMES LOVE FORGETS
Tracks: / Sometimes love forgets.
7" Single: Released Mar '81, on Elektra, by Elektra Records (UK). Deleted Mar '84. Catalogue no: **K 12509**

Goodwin, Ron

Biographical details: This British conductor and symphony orchestra leader scored a smash hit on Britain's newly inaugurated record chart in 1953 with *Limelight*. Composed by Charlie Chaplin for his movie of the same name, the tune took Goodwin th no. 3 and gave him a chart run of 23 weeks. The popularity of *Limelight* was such that Frank Chacksfield's orchestra had an even bigger simultaneous hit with the same tune; it was also the first Top 10 hit for singer Jimmy Young, whose vocal version was entitled *Eternally*. In October Goodwin reached the UK no. 20 position with *Blue star (The medic theme)*, but was beaten to the Top 3 by Cyril Stapleton's orchestra. The mid-50's rock'n'roll explosion killed off Goodwin's chart career, although he reached no. 49 on the LP listings in May 1970 with *Legend of the Glass mountain*. He remained in the music business right into the Eighties, his flexible but generally MoR style ensuring him of a steady audience for his performing and recording activities. In 1980 he composed a *Drake 400* concert suite - this was used by his native city of Plymouth to mark Sir Francis Drake's 1580 circumnavigation of the world. 1983 saw him conducting the RPO on the *Projections* album. In addition to his other skills, Goodwin is also a respected composer of music for movie scores. (Bob Macdonald, 25/9/85).

BLUE STAR (THE MEDIC THEME)
Tracks: / Blue star (the medic theme).
7" Single: Released Oct '55, on Parlophone, by EMI Records. Deleted '58. Catalogue no: **R 4074**

LIMELIGHT
Tracks: / Limelight.
7" Single: Released May '53, on Parlophone, by EMI Records. Deleted '56. Catalogue no: **R 3686**

Goody Goody

NUMBER ONE DEE JAY
Tracks: / Number one dee jay.
7" Single: Released Dec '78, on Atlantic, by WEA Records. Deleted '81. Catalogue no: **LV 3**

Goody, Kim

DON'T TURN AROUND
Tracks: / Don't turn around / I need time.
7" Single: Released Mar '87, on Polydor, by Polydor Ltd. Deleted Jan '88. Catalogue no: **POSP 857**

WAIT IN LINE
Tracks: / Wait in line / Giving it all.
7" Single: Released Dec '81, on Bronze, by Bronze Records. Deleted Dec '84. Catalogue no: **BRO 133**

Goom, Derek

JULIET BRAVO
Tracks: / Juliet Bravo.
7" Single: Released Oct '80, on BBC, by BBC Records & Tapes. Deleted 31 Aug '88. Catalogue no: **RESL 84**

Goombay Dance Band

Biographical details: Hailing variously from St.Lucia, Montserrat an. West Germany, this group consists of Oliver Bendt, Wendy Doorsen, Dorothy Hellings and Mario Slijngaard. They are based in West Germany. When they hit the big time in the early 80's, it was strongly rumoured that the official line-up, as seen by the public, differed somewhat from the personnel who played in the studio. Like their predecessors in the German-based pseudo-Caribbean Eurodisco market, Boney M, the band were tightly controlled by others (in their case, producer Jochen Petersen and songwriters Wolff-Eckehardt Stein & Wolfgang Jass). The Goombay Dance Band came to prominence in West Germany in 1980 with the single *Sun of Jamaica*, which was a no. 1 hit there. The group's frontman Oliver Bendt was already well into his thirties by this time; he attracted much attention on TV with his fire-eating pyrotechnics. Another of the group's big records *Seven tears*, which became a sleeper smash in Britain: in spring '82, long after its Continental success, *Seven tears* zoomed to the UK no. 1 spot. This was a novelty singalong record of such irritating proportions that it made Boney M's *Brown girl in the ring* sound positively appealing by comparison. In the wake of the single's success, the *Seven tears* album reached no.16 in Britain. However, UK record buyers could not stand the Goombay Dance Band for long - *Sun of Jamaica* proceeded to peak at no. 50, and *Rain* failed to reach the British chart at all. They drifted into obscurity,relying on cabaret dates to keep them in work. (Bob Macdonald, 25/9/88).

BORN TO WIN (SINGLE)
Tracks: / Born to win / Take me to the Caribean.
7" Single: Released Oct '82, on Epic, by CBS Records. Deleted Oct '85. Catalogue no: **EPCA 2833**

DON'T YOU CRY CAROLINE
Tracks: / Don't you cry Caroline.
7" Single: Released Dec '84, on Starblend, by Starblend Records. Catalogue no: **STAR 3**

RAIN
Tracks: / Rain / Love and tequila.
7" Single: Released Jan '81, on Epic, by CBS Records. Deleted Jan '84. Catalogue no: **EPC 9434**
7" Single: Released Jul '82, on Epic, by CBS Records. Deleted Jul '85. Catalogue no: **EPCA 2564**

SEVEN TEARS
Tracks: / Seven tears / Mama coco.
7" Single: Released Feb '82, on Epic, by CBS Records. Deleted '85. Catalogue no: **EPC A1242**

SUN OF JAMAICA (RE-RELEASE)
Tracks: / Sun of Jamaica / Alice my love.
7" Single: Released May '82, on Epic, by CBS Records. Deleted '85. Catalogue no: **EPCA 2345**

SUN OF JAMAICA (SINGLE)
Tracks: / Sun of Jamaica / Island of dreams.
7" Single: Released Jun '81, on Epic, by CBS Records. Deleted Jun '84. Catalogue no: **EPCA 1273**
7" Single: Released Mar '80, on Epic, by CBS Records. Deleted Mar '83. Catalogue no: **EPC 7947**

TYPICAL JAMAICAN MESS, A
Tracks: / Typical Jamaican mess, A / Canta Di Legua.
12" Single: Released May '86, on WEA (International), by WEA Records. Deleted Jan '88. Catalogue no: **YZ 57T**
7" Single: Released May '86, on WEA (International), by WEA Records. Deleted Sep '87. Catalogue no: **YZ 57**

Goon Squad

EIGHT ARMS TO HOLD YOU
Tracks: / Eight arms to hold you.
7" Single: Released Sep '85, on Epic, by CBS Records. Deleted '86. Catalogue no: **A 6389**
12" Single: Released Sep '85, on Epic, by CBS Records. Deleted '86. Catalogue no: **TX 6389**

Goons

Biographical details: This British comedy group consisted of Terence "Spike" Milligan, Harry Secombe and Peter Sellers. The story of the Goon show, the most acclaimed BBC radio comedy show of the 50's, began in 1951. In that year the BBC introduced the programme *Crazy people*, which starred Milligan, Secombe and Sellers plus fellow comedian Michael Bentine. The programme developed into *The Goons*, by which time Bentine had quit. With television still in the process of establishing itself as a major entertainment medium, the Goons attracted the kind of cult fervour that would not be possible for a radio comedy in the eighties. The trio's oddball humour combined surrealism and satire. In 1956 the Goons achieved two consecutive Top 5 hits on the UK singles chart, both double A sided discs: *I'm walking backwards for Christmas (Which came out in the middle of summer) c/w Bluebottle blues*, and *Bloodnock's rock'n'roll* was backed with the Milligan-penned *Ying tong song*, which became a hit all over again when re-issued in 1973. After the 50's heyday of the Goons, all three members enjoyed solo success on the UK charts. The ultra-weird Milligan, who was the Goons' main scriptwriter, assailed the nation with such multi-media projects as *Adolf Hitler - my part in his downfall*. Secombe's dual career as a comedian and as a serious crooner, plus his status as a much-loved all-round media personality, eventually won him a knighthood. Sellers' illustrious career in comedy movies was still in full swing until being abruptly terminated by his death from a heart attack in July 1980. (Bob Macdonald, 25/9/85).

BLOODNOK'S ROCK 'N' ROLL
Tracks: / Bloodnock's rock 'n' roll / I love you.
7" Single: Released Oct '75, on Decca, by Decca Records. Deleted '88. Catalogue no: **F 13609**
7" Single: Released Sep '56, on Decca, by Decca Records. Deleted '59. Catalogue no: **F 10780**

I'M WALKING BACKWARDS FOR CHRISTMAS
Tracks: / I'm walking backwards for christmas / Bluebottle blues.
7" Single: Released May '56, on Decca, by Decca Records. Deleted '59. Catalogue no: **F 10756**

YING TONG SONG
Tracks: / Ying tong song / I'm walking backwards for Christmas.
7" Single: Released Jul '73, on Decca, by Decca Records. Deleted '88. Catalogue no: **F 13414**

Gordon, Alistair

TOUCH AND GO
Tracks: / Touch & go.
7" Single: Released Jun '85, on Rainbow, by Rainbow Records. Catalogue no: **RAIN 1**

Gordon, Eric

DAY & DARKNESS
Tracks: / Day & darkness / For your love.
12" Single: Released Apr '83, on Eric (1), Catalogue no: **E 001**

JUST DO ME RIGHT
Tracks: / Just do me right.
12" Single: Released Jul '85, on NK Music, Catalogue no: **NKRD 028**

LONELY LONELY
Tracks: / Lonely lonely.
12" Single: Released Nov '84, on NK Music, Catalogue no: **NKRD 002**

Gordon, Gay

ESSENTIAL WALLY PARTY MEDLEY, THE
Tracks: Essential wally party medley, The Notes. The medley includes the following trcaks : Here we go, here we go / Can Can / Simple simon / Conga / Gay Gordons / Knees up mother brown / National anthem / Night Is Young, The /
7" Single: Released Nov '86, on Lifestyle, by Micrometro Ltd (Records). Deleted Jul '87. Catalogue no: **XY 2**

Gordon, Joe

MOONLIGHT & ROSES (SINGLE)
Tracks: / Moonlight & roses.
7" Single: Released Jun '84, on Coda, by Coda Records. Catalogue no: **ODS 5**

Gordon, Lonnie

IT'S NOT OVER (LET NO MAN PUT ASUNDER)
Tracks: / It's not over (Let no man put asunder) / Alright.
Cassingle: Released Aug '89, on Supreme, by Supreme Records. Catalogue no: **CSUPET 151**
CD 5": Released Aug '89, on Supreme, by Supreme Records. Catalogue no: **CDSUPE 151**
12" Single: Released Aug '89, on Supreme, by Supreme Records. Catalogue no: **SUPET 151**
7" Single: Released Aug '89, on Supreme, by Supreme Records. Catalogue no: **SUPE 151**
12" Single: Released Sep '89, on Supreme, by Supreme Records. Catalogue no: **SUPETX 151**
12" Single: Released Sep '89, on Supreme, by Supreme Records. Catalogue no: **SUPETZ 151**

Gordon, Michael

FEELING OF LOVE
Tracks: / Feeling of love / Feeling of love (PA mix).
12" Single: Released May '87, on Fine Style, by Fashion Records. Catalogue no: **FS 010**

LOVE IS IN THE AIR
Tracks: / Love is in the air.
7" Single: Released Mar '86, on Fine Style, by Fashion Records. Catalogue no: **FS 001**

MAGIC FEELING
Tracks: / Magic feeling / Magic instrumental.
7" Single: Released Sep '86, on Fine Style, by Fashion Records. Catalogue no: **FS 7003**
12" Single: Released Sep '86, on Fine Style, by Fashion Records. Catalogue no: **FS 003**

NOBODY ELSE BUT YOU
Tracks: / Nobody else but you.
7" Single: Released Jun '88, on Fine Style, by Fashion Records. Catalogue no: **FS 016**

READY AND WAITIN' FOR YOU
Tracks: / Ready and waiting for you (Instrumental).
12" Single: Released Dec '86, on Fine Style, by Fashion Records. Catalogue no: **FS 007**

Gordon, Noele

AFTER ALL THESE YEARS
Tracks: / After all these years / Goodbye.
7" Single: Released Jul '81, on EMI, by EMI Records. Deleted '4. Catalogue no: **EMI 5218**

Gordon, Peter

DEUTSCHE ANGST
Tracks: / Deutsche angst.
7" Single: Released May '82, on Les Disques Du Crepuscule(Belgium), by Les Disques Du Crepuscule(Belgium). Catalogue no: **7TWI 059**

Gordon, Rabbi Joseph

COMPETITION
Tracks: / Competition.
7" Single: Released Jan '85, on Bam Caruso, by Demon Records. Catalogue no: **NRIC 030**

Gordon, Robert

PICTURE OF YOU
Tracks: / Picture of you / Born to lose.
7" Single: Released Feb '80, on RCA, by BMG Records (UK). Deleted Feb '83. Catalogue no: **PB 9501**

Gordon, Roscoe

BOOTED

Tracks: / Booted / Ain't a better story told.
7" Single: Released Mar '81, on Ace, by Ace Records. Deleted Mar '84. Catalogue no: **NS 67**

JUST A LITTLE BIT
Tracks: / Just a little bit.
7" Single: Released Jul '80, on Charly, by Charly Records. Deleted '88. Catalogue no: **CTD 122**

Gordon The Moron

FIT FOR NOTHING
Tracks: / Fit for nothing.
7" Single: Released Sep '82, on Rabid, by Rabid Records. Catalogue no: **TOSH 111**

Gordon, Vin

KOJO HOY
Tracks: / Kojo hoy.
12" Single: Released May '82, on Hugo Music, Catalogue no: **VE 1008**

LIQUID HORNS
Tracks: / Liquid horns.
12" Single: on Attack, Deleted '88. Catalogue no: **TACK 10**

SEVEN ELEVEN
Tracks: / Seven eleven / In a situation.
12" Single: Released Dec '82, on Jay Dee, Catalogue no: **JD 011**

Gordons

FUTURE SHOCK
Tracks: / Future shock.
12" Single: Released Sep '88, on Flying Nun, Catalogue no: **FNE 17**

Gore, Lesley

Biographical details: This American singer had just celebrated her 17th birthday when she shot from nowhere to stardom with her American no. 1 smash *It's my party* in June 1963. She had grown up in an affluent environment, her father being a wealthy businessman, and went to an exclusive girls' school. According to legend, Lesley sang the unknown *It's my party* at a friend's birthday party, and other guests spotted the hit potential of both singer and song and persuaded her to make a demo. She was quickly picked up by Mercury Records, and became a genuine overnight sensation. Gore followed *It's my party* (incidentally, the first no. 1 for producer Quincy Jones) with a sequel record, *Judy's turn to cry*. This reached the US Top 5, as did her next 2 singles *She's a fool* and *You don't own me*. She could best be described as a solo version of a girl group - like her contemporaries such as the Supremes, the Ronettes, and the Shangri-Las, her impassioned singing was immersed in songs about teenage love and romantic angst, and garnished with a strong arrangement and production. Lesley also appeared in teen movies, including *The TAMI show, Ski party* and *Girls on the beach*. The hits got smaller after a while, and Gore never returned to the US Top 40 after 1967's *California nights*. She continued recording into the 70's without success, although a 1975 single for A&M records won substantial airplay in Britain. Lesley Gore's heyday did not really cross the Atlantic to Britain in a major way. Only two of her singles reached the UK chart - *It's my party* climbed to no. 9 and 1964's *Maybe I know* peaked at no. 20. However, in 1981, an eccentric and beautifully executed technopop rendition of *It's my party* became a British no. 1 smash for Dave Stewart & Barbara Gaskin - it logged four weeks at the top. (Bob Macdonald, 25/9/85)
Pop singer/songwriter. She was born in New Jersey in 1946, and was discovered by Quincy Jones while still in high school. Her big hits ran from 'It's my party' (no.1 in the USA, UK top ten) in 1963 to 1967. She recorded for Mowest (Motown) in 1971 and wrote songs for Fame with her brother Michael in 1980. (Donald Clarke, 1989).

IT'S MY PARTY
Tracks: / It's my party / Love on a mountain top.
7" Single: Released Jun '63, on Mercury (EMI), Deleted '66. Catalogue no: **AMT 1205**
7" Single: Released Aug '82, on Blast From The Past, by Creole Records. Catalogue no: **CR 188**

IT'S MY PARTY (OLD GOLD)
Tracks: / It's my party / My boyfriend's back.
7" Single: Released Jan '85, on Old Gold, by Old Gold Records. Catalogue no: **OG 9478**

MAYBE I KNOW
Tracks: / Maybe I know.
7" Single: Released Sep '72, on CBS, by CBS Records. Deleted Sep '75. Catalogue no: **CBS 8218**
7" Single: Released Sep '64, on Mercury, by Phonogram Ltd. Deleted '67. Catalogue no: **MF 829**

Gorehounds

BIG SPUD EP
12" Single: Released Apr '87, on Idol, Catalogue no: **12ID 1**

CARGO CULT
Tracks: / Cargo cult.
12" Single: Released 17 Oct '87, on Idol, Catalogue no: **12ID 4**

Gorl, Robert

DARLING DON'T LEAVE ME
Tracks: / Darling, don't leave me this way.
12" Single: Released Feb '84, on Mute, by Mute Records. Catalogue no: **12 MUTE 31**
7" Single: Released Feb '84, on Mute, by Mute Records. Catalogue no: **7 MUTE 31**

MIT DIR
Tracks: / Mit dir.
7" Single: Released Mar '83, on Mute, by Mute Records. Catalogue no: **7 MUTE 27**

Gorme, Eydie

Biographical details: This American singer, who hailed from New York's Bronx district, worked as vocalist with various small-time bands before beginning a solo career in 1952. During the mid to late Fifties, she achieved four US Top 40 singles, each one getting higher than its predecessor on the Billboard charts: *Too close for comfort* (no.39), *Mama, teach me to dance* (no.34), *Love me forever* (no.24) and *You need hands* (no.11). By this time Gorme had become a regular performer on Steve Allen's TV show "Tonight" - another resident on the programme was singer Steve Lawrence, whom she married in 1957. During the early 60's they continued enjoying success as separate solo acts - Eydie reached the British Top 10 in 1962 with *Yes my darling daughter* and reached the US Top 10 in'63 with a bow to the then highly popular bossa nova sound and dance - *Blame it on the bossa nova*. Under the Steve & Eydie billing, the couple achieved a UK Top 3 smash in late 1963 with *I want to stay here*. In 1964, with the Beatles revolution gathering momentum on both sides of the Atlantic, the pair were torpedoed out of the charts with their rapidly dating sound; but their cabaret style kept them in lucrative work on the concert and nightclub circuits, and they regularly appear on American television. (Bob MacDonald, 25/9/85)
Singer. Born in New York City in 1931, to a Spanish-American family, she sang on the radio at age 3. After high school she worked as an interpreter, then turned to music and obtained her first recording contract in 1953, the year that on the Steve Allen TV show she met Steve Lawrence. Her bright, clear voice and swinging style were a Godsend to writers of good songs like 'Too close for comfort', her first hit single in 1956, the year before she married Lawrence. Steve and Eydie could pull as many fans to live gigs in 1989 as the rock band Bon Jovi, but they don't bother making many albums these days as they don't get played on the radio. She has, however, recently recorded albums and singles in Spanish for the South American market, obtaining big hits. (Donald Clarke, 1989).

BLAME IT ON THE BOSSA NOVA
Tracks: / Blame it on the bossa nova.
7" Single: Released Jan '63, on CBS, by CBS Records. Deleted '66. Catalogue no: **AAG 131**

BLAME IT ON THE BOSSA NOVA (OLD GOLD)
Tracks: / Blame it on the bossa nova.
7" Single: Released Apr '83, on Old Gold, by Old Gold Records. Deleted Jul '88. Catalogue no: **OG 9302**

I WANT TO STAY HERE
Tracks: / I want to stay here.
7" Single: Released Aug '63, on CBS, by CBS Records. Deleted '66. Catalogue no: **AAG 163**

I WANT TO STAY HERE (OLD GOLD)
Tracks: / I want to stay here.
7" Single: Released Apr '83, on Old Gold, by Old Gold Records. Deleted Jul '88. Catalogue no: **OG 9302**

LOVE ME FOREVER
Tracks: / Love me forever.
7" Single: Released Jan '58, on H.M.V., by EMI Records. Deleted '61. Catalogue no: **POP 432**

YES MY DARLING DAUGHTER
Tracks: / Yes my darling daughter.
7" Single: Released Jun '62, on CBS, by CBS Records. Deleted '65. Catalogue no: **AAG 105**

Gosdin, Vern

I CAN TELL BY THE WAY YOU DANCE
Tracks: / I can tell by the way you dance / You're gonna love me tonight / My heart's in good hands.
7" Single: Released Aug '84, on Compleat (USA), by Compleat Entertainment Corp.(USA). Deleted '85. Catalogue no: **CLT 5**

Gossip Girls

LILAC DREAMS (SINGLE)
Tracks: / Lilac dreams.
7" Single: Released Aug '84, on Music In Motion, Catalogue no: **MIM 001**

Gotham City

BARRY'S HOUSE
Tracks: / Barry's house.
7" Single: Released Oct '88, on Westside, by Westside Records. Catalogue no: **WSR 8**
12" Single: Released Oct '88, on Westside, by Westside Records. Catalogue no: **WSRT 8**

Gothic Girls

GLASS BABY
Tracks: / Glass baby.
12" Single: Released Apr '84, on Backs, by Backs Recording Co.. Catalogue no: **12 NCH 10**

OUTRAGE
Tracks: / Outrage.
7" Single: Released May '83, on Backs, by Backs Recording Co.. Catalogue no: **NCH 007**

Gouldman, Graham

Biographical details: This British singer, songwriter, bassist and producer emerged from Manchester during the mid-sixties. He was a member of two local beat groups during this period but neither was successful. Instead, Gouldman made a big name for himself as a songwriter. His most notable success in this capacity was with the Yardbirds, for whom he penned three consecutive British Top 3 singles: *For your love, Heart full of soul* and *Evil hearted you*. Gouldman's other big hits of the mid-60's includes Herman's Hermits' *Listen people* and *No milk today* and the Hollies *Look through my window* and *Bus stop*. Indeed, during 1965-66, Graham's tally was six Top Tenners in Britain and four in the States. During the late 60's, he had a spell in New York working for Gerry Kasenetz and Jeff Katz's "bubblegum" pop production line. He returned to the UK in 1969. Gouldman was a founder member of 10cc in 1972 and stayed with that highly creative and internationally successful band until their termination in 1984. He co-wrote and produced all three of 10cc's UK no. 1 singles - *Rubber bullets, I'm not in love* and *Dreadlock holiday*. In 1979, just as the group were beginning their period of painful commercial decline, he embarked upon the writing and recording of the soundtrack for a movie entitled *Animalympics* - the film was a flop, but he did salvage one minor UK hit single with a quirky uptempo pop ditty called *Sunburn* (the title song from another film). 1984 saw Gouldman working with American Andrew Gold on a project that was initially dubbed *Common Knowledge*. 1985 brought Gouldman into a hastily arranged alliance with co-producer Ray Levy on the Crowd's *You'll never walk alone*; responding rapidly to the Bradford football stadium disaster, which claimed more than 50 lives in a fire, Gouldman and alevy organised and produced this all-star charity single which was no. 1 in the UK for 2 weeks. (Bob Macdonald,25/9/85).

LOVE'S NOT FOR ME
Tracks: / Love's not for me / Bionic boar.
7" Single: Released Mar '80, on Mercury, by Phonogram Ltd. Deleted Mar '83. Catalogue no: **MER 7**

SUNBURN
Tracks: / Sunburn.
7" Single: Released Jun '79, on Mercury, by Phonogram Ltd. Deleted '82. Catalogue no: **SUNNY 1**

Gowan

KEEP UP THE FIGHT
Tracks: / Keep up the fight.
7" Single: Released Apr '83, on CBS, by CBS Records. Catalogue no: **A 3360**

Gower, Huw

GUITAROPHILIA
Tracks: / Guitarophilia.
7" Single: Released 23 Jul '88, on Eisque, Catalogue no: **ENIB 001**
12" Single: Released Oct '88, on X Disque, Catalogue no: **SNIB 1**

G.Q.

DISCO NIGHTS (ROCK FREAK)
Tracks: / Disco nights (rock freak).
7" Single: Released Feb '79, on Arista, by BMG Records (UK). Deleted '82. Catalogue no: **ARIST 245**
12" Single: Released Feb '79, on Arista, by BMG Records (UK). Catalogue no: **ARIST 12245**

DISCO NIGHTS (ROCK FREAK) (OLD GOLD)
Tracks: / Disco nights (rock freak) / Unlock the funk.
12" Single: Released Jan '88, on Old Gold, by Old Gold Records. Catalogue no: **OG 4043**

GO DOWN
Tracks: / Go down / It's like that / Lies.
7" Single: Released May '80, on Arista, by BMG Records (UK). Deleted May '85. Catalogue no: **ARIST 12353**

MAKE MY DREAM A REALITY
Tracks: / Make my dream a reality.
12" Single: Released May '79, on Arista, by BMG Records (UK). Catalogue no: **ARIST 12263**
7" Single: Released May '79, on Arista, by BMG Records (UK). Catalogue no: **ARIST 263**

SHAKE
Tracks: / Shake / Skin you're in.
7" Single: Released Nov '81, on Arista, by BMG Records (UK). Catalogue no: **ARIST 427**
12" Single: Released Nov '81, on Arista, by BMG Records (UK). Catalogue no: **ARIST 12 427**

SITTING IN THE PARK
Tracks: / Sitting in the park / I do love you / Someday in your life.
12" Single: Released Jul '80, on Arista, by BMG Records (UK). Catalogue no: **ARIST 12358**
7" Single: Released Jul '80, on Arista, by BMG Records (UK). Catalogue no: **ARIST 358**

Grab Grab The Haddock

I'M USED NOW
Tracks: / I'm used now.
12" Single: Released Feb '85, on Cherry Red, by Cherry Red Records. Deleted '87. Catalogue no: **12 CHERRY 83**

LAST FOND GOODBYE
Tracks: / Last fond goodbye.
12" Single: Released Apr '85, on Cherry Red, by Cherry Red Records. Deleted '87. Catalogue no: **12 CHERRY 86**
7" Single: Released Apr '85, on Cherry Red, by Cherry Red Records. Deleted '87. Catalogue no: **CHERRY 86**

Grace

BILLY BOY
Tracks: / Billy boy / Ad mad.
7" Single: Released Feb '81, on MCA, by MCA Records. Deleted '84. Catalogue no: **MCA 667**

DOCTOR RHYTHM
Tracks: / Doctor Rhythm / Manhattan.
12" Single: Released May '84, on WEA (International), by WEA Records. Catalogue no: **U 9402 T**
7" Single: Released May '84, on WEA (International), by WEA Records. Catalogue no: **U 9402**

FIRE OF LONDON
Tracks: / Fire of London / Beatnik.
7" Single: Released Aug '80, on MCA, by MCA Records. Deleted '83. Catalogue no: **MCA 628**

MANHATTAN
Tracks: / Manhattan.
7" Single: Released Feb '84, on WEA (International), by WEA Records. Catalogue no: **249634 7**

Grace, Brendan

FATHER OF THE BRIDE
Tracks: / Father of the bride.
7" Single: Released Oct '84, on Ritz, by Ritz Records. Catalogue no: **RITZ 077**

HUMOURS OF IRELAND
Tracks: / Humours of Ireland.
7" Single: Released Mar '83, on Bottler, Catalogue no: **BO 21**

Grace & Favour

ON THE REBOUND
Tracks: / On the rebound.
7" Single: Released Sep '82, on Playfar, by Playfar Records. Catalogue no: **ESM 78201**

Grace, Janey Lee

HEARTBEAT RADIO
Tracks: / Heartbeat radio / Don't give your love to anyone.
7" Single: Released Oct '88, on Supertrack, Catalogue no: **DIAM 1**

Graces

LAY DOWN YOUR ARMS
Tracks: / Lay down your arms / Out in the fields / Should I let you in (CD only).
12" Single: Released Sep '89, on A&M, by A&M Records. Catalogue no: **AMY 526**
CD 5": Released Sep '89, on A&M, by A&M Records. Catalogue no: **CDEE 526**
7" Single: Released Sep '89, on A&M, by A&M Records. Catalogue no: **AM 526**

Gracie, Charlie

Biographical details: This American singer and guitarist was one of the first and most talented of the wave of post-Presley rock'n'rollers who came to fame in the late 50's via the springboard of Dick Clark's American TV show *American bandstand*. Born Charles Graci (the 'e' was added later) in Philadelphia in 1936, he was already a recording artist by the time he reached his mid-teens. When he came to prominence in 1957, he was well versed in playing many of the formative styles that had just caused the rock'n'roll explosion. The record that made Gracie a star was *Butterfly*, a somewhat tame rock'n'roll number that simultaneously became one of the first hits for Andy Williams. Both versions reached no. 1 in the States; Williams also hit the top in Britain, but Gracie peaked at no. 12. Charlie's follow-up was *Fabulous*, a close imitation of Elvis' *Don't be cruel*, which reached no. 16 in the US and no. 8 in the UK. He then fell out of favour with the controllers of *American bandstand* and, consequently, never returned to the US Top 40. In Britain he managed one more Top Tenner *Wanderin' eyes*, but never returned to the UK listings after 1958. Gracie, whose raw live talent was never fully captured on his hits, was a victim of the cut-throat record business. After dabbling in soul music, he became a rock'n'roll revivalist in the 70's, making return visits to Britain in 1979 and '81. (Bob Macdonald, 26/9/85)
Guitarist. Born in Philadelphia in 1936 as Charles Anthony Graci, he was treated poorly by that city's star-making machinery - he was a guitar prodigy, influenced by jump blues and country boogie, but the era demanded teen idols, not real rockabillies. His only USA no.1 hit was 'Butterfly', written by Cameo owners Bernie Lowe and Kal Mann but credited to "Anthony September", pseudonym of **American Bandstand** producer Tony Mammarella (who was later implicated in the payola scandal). Pushed into a mould he didn't fit, his chart career was predictably short - his second top 20 hit was 'Fabulous', so close to 'Don't be cruel' that Elvis Presley's publishers sued successfully for publication rights. Like many others, he was more appreciated in the UK than at home. (Donald Clarke, 1989).

BUTTERFLY
Tracks: / Butterfly.
7" Single: Released Apr '57, on Parlophone, by EMI Records. Deleted '60. Catalogue no: **R 4290**

COOL BABY
Tracks: / Cool baby.
7" Single: Released Jan '58, on London-American, Deleted '61. Catalogue no: **HLU 8251**

FABULOUS
Tracks: / Fabulous.
7" Single: Released Jun '57, on Parlophone, by EMI Records. Deleted '60. Catalogue no: **R 4313**

I LOVE YOU SO MUCH IT HURTS
Tracks: / I love you so much it hurts / Wonderin' eyes.
7" Single: Released Aug '57, on London Records, by London Records. Deleted '60. Catalogue no: **HL 8467**

WANDERIN' EYES
Tracks: / Wanderin' eyes / I love you so much it hurts.
7" Single: Released Sep '57, on London Records, by London Records. Deleted '60. Catalogue no: **HL 8467**

Graduate

AMBITION
Tracks: / Ambition / Bad dreams.
7" Single: Released Nov '80, on Precision (1), Deleted Nov '83. Catalogue no: **PAR 111**

ELVIS SHOULD PLAY SKA
Tracks: / Elvis should play ska / Julie Julie.
7" Single: Released Mar '80, on Precision (USA), Deleted Mar '83. Catalogue no: **PAR 100**

EVER MET A DAY
Tracks: / Ever met a day / Shut up.
7" Single: Released May '80, on Precision (1), Deleted May '83. Catalogue no: **PAR 104**

SHUT UP
Tracks: / Shut up / Ever met a day.
7" Single: Released Mar '81, on Precision (1), Deleted Mar '84. Catalogue no: **PAR 117**

Graf, Rolf

RIGHT FROM THE START
Tracks: / Right from the start / Maxine.
7" Single: Released Jul '86, on Carrere, Catalogue no: **CAR 393**
12" Single: Released Jul '86, on Carrere, Catalogue no: **CART 393**

SHINE
Tracks: / Shine / Walk right in.
7" Single: Released Oct '86, on Broken Hill, Catalogue no: **BHP 001**
12" Single: Released Oct '86, on Broken Hill, Catalogue no: **BHPT 001**

Graffia

CYMER DI
Tracks: / Cymer di / Stop it stop.
7" Single: Released Aug '80, on Magic (1), by Submarine Records. Catalogue no: **102**

Graffiti

STAY
Tracks: / Stay.
7" Single: Released 28 Jan '89, on Revolver, by FM-Revolver Records. Deleted Jun '89. Catalogue no: **GRAFF 1**

Graham, Eileen

LAST ROAD
Tracks: / Last road / Jealous woman.
7" Single: Released Dec '80, on Diversion, by Dingle's Records. Catalogue no: **DIV 113**

Graham, Eve

YOUR LOVE
Tracks: / Your love / Falling in love again.
7" Single: Released Feb '81, on Celebrity, Deleted '84. Catalogue no: **ACS 3**

Graham, Jaki

BETTER PART OF ME, THE
Tracks: / Better part of me, The / From now own (7" remix) (12" only.) / No mercy.
Cassingle: Released Aug '89, on EMI, by EMI Records. Catalogue no: **TCJAKI 16**
CD 5": Released Aug '89, on EMI, by EMI Records. Catalogue no: **203 443 2**
CD 5": Released Aug '89, on EMI, by EMI Records. Catalogue no: **CDJAKI 16**
12" Single: Released Aug '89, on EMI, by EMI Records. Catalogue no: **12JAKI 16**
7" Single: Released Aug '89, on EMI, by EMI Records. Catalogue no: **JAKI 16**
7" Single: Released Aug '89, on EMI, by EMI Records. Catalogue no: **203 443 7**
12" Single: Released Aug '89, on EMI, by EMI Records. Catalogue no: **203 443 6**

BREAKING AWAY (SINGLE)
Tracks: / Breaking away.
12" Single: Released Jul '86, on EMI, by EMI Records. Deleted Oct '87. Catalogue no: **12JAKI 8**
7" Single: Released Jul '86, on EMI, by EMI Records. Deleted Oct '87. Catalogue no: **JAKI 8**

FROM NOW ON
Tracks: / From now on / Nobody's fool / From now on (ext. version) (12" only.) / From now on (here and now mix) (CD single & 12JAKIX only.) / From now on (doomsday dub) (12JAKIX only.) / From now on (Accadub) (12JAKIX only.).
12" Single: Released Jun '89, on EMI, by EMI Records. Deleted Oct '89. Catalogue no: **203 402 6**
CD 5": Released Jun '89, on EMI, by EMI Records. Deleted Oct '89. Catalogue no: **203 402 2**
CD 5": Released Jun '89, on EMI, by EMI Records. Deleted Oct '89. Catalogue no: **CDJAKI 15**
Cassingle: Released Jun '89, on EMI, by EMI Records. Deleted Oct '89. Catalogue no: **203 402 4**
Cassingle: Released Jun '89, on EMI, by EMI Records. Deleted Oct '89. Catalogue no: **TCJAKI 15**
7" Single: Released Jun '89, on EMI, by EMI Records. Deleted Oct '89. Catalogue no: **203 402 7**
7" Single: Released Jun '89, on EMI, by EMI Records. Deleted Oct '89. Catalogue no: **JAKI 15**
12" Single: Released Jun '89, on EMI, by EMI Records. Deleted Oct '89. Catalogue no: **12JAKI 15**
12" Single: Released Jun '89, on EMI, by EMI Records. Deleted Oct '89. Catalogue no: **12JAKIX 15**
12" Single: Released Jun '89, on EMI, by EMI Records. Deleted Oct '89. Catalogue no: **203 402 8**

HEAVEN KNOWS (FEELS SO GOOD)
Tracks: / Heaven knows / You're mine.
7" Single: Released Jun '84, on EMI, by EMI Records. Catalogue no: **JAKI 5**
12" Single: Released Aug '85, on EMI, by EMI Records. Catalogue no: **12 JAKI 5**

LET'S GET BLUE
Tracks: / Let's get blue (Duet with Derek Bramble) / Still in love / Love under moonlight / Love 2 much (too much)(12" mix) / Still in (dub).
12" Single: Released Mar '87, on EMI, by EMI Records. Deleted Oct '87. Catalogue no: **12 JAKIX 10**

MEGAMIX
Tracks: / Set me free / Closest one, The / Step right up.
12" Single: Released Nov '86, on EMI, by EMI Records. Deleted Oct '87. Catalogue no: **12 JAKIX 9**

NO MORE TEARS
Tracks: / No more tears / Have you seen him? / No more tears (Fon Force re-mix) (Only on 12".) / No more tears (Home-Bass mix) (Only on 12".) / Set me free (Only on CD single.).
7" Single: Released Jun '88, on EMI, by EMI Records. Deleted Jun '89. Catalogue no: **JAKI 12**
CD 5": Released Jun '88, on EMI, by EMI Records. Deleted Jun '89. Catalogue no: **CD AKI 12**
12" Single: Released Jun '88, on EMI, by EMI Records. Deleted Jun '89. Catalogue no: **12 AKI 12**

ROUND & ROUND
Tracks: / Round and round.
7" Single: Released Jun '85, on EMI, by EMI Records. Catalogue no: **JAKI 4**
12" Single: Released Jun '85, on EMI, by EMI Records. Catalogue no: **12 JAKI 4**

SET ME FREE
Tracks: / Set me free / Stop the world.
12" Single: Released Apr '86, on EMI, by EMI Records. Catalogue no: **12 JAKI 7**
7" Single: Released Apr '86, on EMI, by EMI Records. Deleted Oct '87. Catalogue no: **JAKI 7**

STEP RIGHT UP
Tracks: / Step right up / Closest one, The (Duet with Derek Bramble.).
7" Single: Released Nov '86, on EMI, by EMI Records. Deleted Oct '87. Catalogue no: **JAKI 9**
12" Single: Released Nov '86, on EMI, by EMI Records. Catalogue no: **12 JAKI 9**

STILL IN LOVE (LIGHTS DOWN MIX)
Tracks: / Still in love (lights down mix) / Love too much (too much mix).
7" Single: Released Feb '87, on EMI, by EMI Records. Catalogue no: **JAKE 10**
12" Single: Released Feb '87, on EMI, by EMI Records. Catalogue no: **12 JAKI 10**

Graham, Larry

Biographical details: This American singer, bassist, multi-instumentalist, songwriter and producer was a founder member of Sly & The Family Stone in 1966 - he performed bass and vocals with that highly successful band, but in his desire for greater control, quit in 1972 to form his own group Graham Central Station. The funky, danceable, soulful sounds of the Station were a worthy continuation of Sly Stone's ideas, and Graham's group released a series of well-received albums during the mid seventies. They were regular visitors to the US soul charts, and their biggest pop crossover occurred in summer 1975, when *Your love* reached no. 38 on the Billboard Hot 100 and *Ain't no bout-a-doubt it* climbed to no. 22 on the US album list. Graham Central Station's final LP was released in 1978 and, the following year, Larry Graham launched a solo career with the *Star walk* album. 1980 brought him a million-seller with the beautiful ballad *One in a million you*. This single was a colossal across-the-board hit in America, reaching the high echelons of the black and MoR charts and climbing to no. 9 on the Hot 100. It was a perfect vehicle for Larry's deep resonant voice. After *One in a million you*, Graham's career slipped back somewhat. Subsequent albums were only moderate successes, although the title track of 1982's *Sooner or later* LP provided him with his only taste of a UK chart entry, reaching no. 54 in July of that year. (Bob Macdonald,26/9/85)
Bassist and singer. Born in 1946 in Beaumont, Texas, he played with Sly and the Family Stone, becoming one of the most influential bassists in the history of rock, his undulating yet hard-edged patterns practically inventing much of the dance music of the 1970s. He then formed funk band Graham Central Station for seven hit albums in the second half of the 1970s, emerging as a ballad singer for four more hit albums in the early 1980s. (Donald Clarke, 1989).

I'M SICK & TIRED
Tracks: / I'm sick and tired.
12" Single: Released Aug '83, on Warner Bros., by WEA Records. Catalogue no: **W 9510T**
7" Single: Released Aug '83, on Warner Bros., by WEA Records. Catalogue no: **W 9510**

ONE IN A MILLION
Tracks: / One in a million / Entertainer.
7" Single: Released Sep '80, on Warner Bros., by WEA Records. Deleted '83. Catalogue no: **K 17985**

SOONER OR LATER (SINGLE)
Tracks: / Sooner or later / One in a million.
7" Single: Released Jul '82, on Warner Bros., by WEA Records. Deleted '85. Catalogue no: **K 17925**

Graham, Tony

KISS THE BOYS
Tracks: / Kiss the boys.
7" Single: Released Sep '84, on Greyhound, by Greyhound Records. Catalogue no: **GRP 109**
12" Single: Released Sep '84, on Greyhound, by Greyhound Records. Catalogue no: **GRPT 109**

Grahame, Loretta

YOUNG FREE & SINGLE
Tracks: / Young free and single.
12" Single: Released Feb '83, on Intense, by Intense Records. Catalogue no: **INT 006**

Grahamophones

CHINESE LAUNDRY BLUES
Tracks: / Chinese laundry blues / I would sooner be a crooner.
7" Single: Released Jul '87, on President, by President Records. Catalogue no: **PT 563**

VO DO DO DE O DODO
Tracks: / Vo do do de o dodo / Deep secret.
7" Single: Released Jul '89, on President, by President Records. Catalogue no: **PT 581**

Grainer, Ron

Biographical details: This British composer, conductor and orchestra leader earned a very steady living in the UK music business during the sixties and seventies. He was best known for his TV themes, which twice brought him into the UK record charts: the *Maigret* music reached no. 13 on the EP listings in 1962, and *A touch of velvet, a sting of brass* reached no. 60 on the album chart in late 1978. Also during the late seventies, he was regularly heard on ITV with his themes for the drama series, *Tales of the Unexpected* and *Edward & Mrs. Simpson*. (Bob Macdonald, 26/9/85).

TALES OF THE UNEXPECTED(THEME)
Tracks: / Tales of the unexpected / Malice aforethought.
7" Single: Released May '82, on RK, by RK Records. Deleted '84. Catalogue no: **RK 1021**

TOUCH OF VELVET-A STING OF BRASS
Tracks: / Touch of velvet, a sting of brass, A.
7" Single: Released Dec '78, on Casino Classics, by RK Records. Deleted '81. Catalogue no: **CC 5**

Grainger, Al

SUSHEA
Tracks: / Sushea.
7" Single: Released Apr '84, on Ash, by Ash Records. Catalogue no: **ASH 018**

Gramm, Lou

MIDNIGHT BLUE
Tracks: / Midnight blue / Chain of love.
12" Single: Released Mar '87, on Atlantic, by WEA Records. Deleted Jul '88. Catalogue no: **A 9034 T**
7" Single: Released Mar '87, on Atlantic, by WEA Records. Deleted Jul '88. Catalogue no: **A 9034**

Grand Funk Railroad

Biographical details: This American hard rock band consisted of Don Brewer, Mark Farner and Mel Schacher. From 1973 onwards, they were simply known as Grand Funk. The band was formed early in 1969 in Flint, Michigan. From the outset, it was their extrovert entrepreneurial manager Terry Knight who masterminded the band's rapid rise to prominence. He arranged an (allegedly unpaid) appearance at the Atlanta pop festival on 4 July 1969 where they stole the show. Their acclaimed performance quickly led to the release of a debut LP entitled *On time*, which came out in late '69 - at least, they were acclaimed by the public, but not by the pundits. During the early 70's, Grand Funk Railroad became

possibly the most critically reviled act in the history of pop journalism - the group's pounding, unceasing, deafening cacophony made them the very worst of the successful heavy metal bands of the early 70's in the minds of most reviewers. Knight successfully turned this round to the band's advantage, and they revelled in the constant chorus of criticism. The more they were hated, the more loyal their fans became - the double *Live album* and *E pluribus Funk* were particularly successful LP's and they notched up three US Top 40 singles during 1970-72. Acrimonious legal wrangles between the band and Terry Knight interrupted their career at this point, and many observers thought they would be finished without his commercially-minded influence.
But instead, they chalked up their first US no. 1 single with '73's *We're an American band* - keyboards player Craig Frost had now been added, and the band's name had been shortened to Grand Funk. The single was produced by Todd Rundgren, who also did the honours on the group's second American chart-topper *The locomotion*; this was a hard rock remake of Little Eva's 1962 no. 1. Rundgren attempted to instil a semblance of musical refinement into the combo and thus broaden their following beyond the confines of the heavy metal fraternity. He succeeded for a time, but a change of producer had sent the band hurtling towards oblivion by the end of 1975.
They folded in 1976 and reformed with little success in 1981; Schacher did not rejoin, and bass duties were taken up by newcomer Dennis Bellinger. Britain remained wisely and blissfully oblivious of Grand Funk throughout their career. Railroad's only penetration of the UK charts occurred in February 1971, when the single *Inside looking out* reached no. 40. (Bob Macdonald, 26/9/88)
Heavy metal band. They began life as Terry Knight and the Pack, garage-band one-hit wonders with 'I (who have nothing)' which went top 50 in 1966. Detroit DJ turned singer Knight turned entrepreneur and took complete control, including the name change to Grand Funk Railroad and the new image of basic blues-rock - like Status Quo in the UK they stripped the music to basics and found a youth identification factor with a heavy metal/macho mix. The first few albums were written mostly by guitarist Mark Farner; they got rid of Knight but then went slightly poppish - the merest touch of added subtlety lost their dim-witted audience by 1975.
(Donald Clarke, 1989).

INSIDE LOOKING OUT
Tracks: / Inside looking out.
7" Single: Released Feb '71, on Capitol, by EMI Records. Deleted '74. Catalogue no: **CL 15668**

Grand Groove

LET'S DANCE
Tracks: / Let's dance.
12" Single: Released Aug '88, on Rham, by Rham Records. Catalogue no: **RS 8802**
7" Single: Released Aug '88, on Rham, by Rham Records. Catalogue no: **RS 802**

Grand Mixer

Biographical details: Known as both Grandmixer and Grandmixer D Street, this American disc jockey was one of a host of 'scratchers' who came to the attention of clubgoers on the electro/hip hop scene of the eighties. Instead of merely playing records, these DJ's segued them together, slowed them down, sppeded them up and, more often than not, switched the turntables off and manhandled the decks so as to let the styli wreak havoc with the discs and create their own rhythmic excitement. Grandmixer released a spliced up single entitled *Grandmixer cuts it up* in May 1983. Then in January 1984, he reached no. 71 on the UK national chart with his crazy cuts single. In between the two offerings, Herbie Hancock issued the seminal scratch single *Rockit* - and its influence certainly displayed itself on *Crazy cuts*. (Bob Macdonald, 26/9/85).

CRAZY CUTS
Tracks: / Crazy cuts.
7" Single: Released Dec '83, on Celluloid (Island), by Island Records. Deleted '86. Catalogue no: **IS 146**

Grand Prix

Biographical details: This British band consisted of Andy Beirne, Ralph Hood, Phil Lanzon and Michael O'Donaghue. On 27 February 1982 *Keep on believing* entered the UK Top 75 singles chart at no. 75 and *Don't stop believin'* came on at no. 72; the former was by British rock group Grand Prix, the latter by American rock band Journey. Whereas the US band climbed higher and had other chart success, the UK combo disappeared the following week and were never seen in chartdom again. According to the *Guinness book of British hit singles*, Grand Prix are one of only four acts whose total chart career consists of just one week on the Top 75 singles at no. 75.
Come to think of it, Grand Prix sounded pretty much like Journey and a host of other American rock outfits. During the early eighties, UK record buyers were more interested in the waves of technopop and New Romantic bands, and US punters already had 1001 homegrown acts of the Grand Prix type to choose from; so our would-be heroes failed to win the grand prize on either side of the Atlantic. *Keep on believin'* came from *There for none to see*, Grand Prix's second album. The first, a self-titled set, was issued in 1980; the third *Samurai*, came out in 1983 and emphasized the band's heavy metal leanings. (Bob Macdonald, 26/9/85).

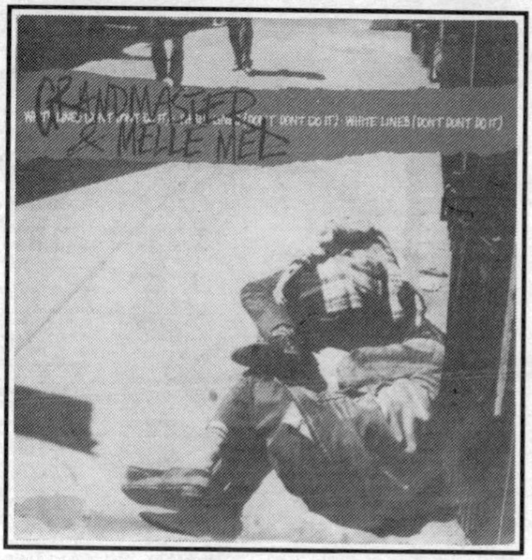

Grandmaster Flash and Melle Mel - White Lines (Don't Do It) (Sugarhill)

GIVE ME WHAT'S MINE
Tracks: / Give me what's mine / One five five.
7" Single: Released May '83, on Chrysalis, by Chrysalis Records. Catalogue no: **PRIX 1**

KEEP ON BELIEVING
Tracks: / Keep on believing / Life on the line.
7" Single: Released Feb '82, on RCA, by BMG Records (UK). Deleted '85. Catalogue no: **RCA 162**

SHOUT
Tracks: / Shout / Keep on believing.
7" Single: Released '83, on Chrysalis, by Chrysalis Records. Deleted '87. Catalogue no: **PRIX 2**

THINKING OF YOU
Tracks: / Thinking of you / Feels good.
7" Single: Released Oct '80, on RCA, by BMG Records (UK). Deleted Oct '83. Catalogue no: **RCA 7**

WHICH WAY DID THE WIND BLOW
Tracks: / Which way did the wind blow / Feels good.
7" Single: Released Jan '81, on RCA, by BMG Records (UK). Deleted Jan '84. Catalogue no: **RCA 18**

Grandad & Adam

TALL STORY
Tracks: / Tall story.
7" Single: Released Mar '82, on Look, by Look Records. Catalogue no: **LKSP 6700**

Grandmaster Caz

WILD STYLE THEME RAP 1
Tracks: / Wild style theme, rap 1 / Wild style theme rap 2.
12" Single: Released Sep '83, on Animal, by Chrysalis Records. Catalogue no: **CHS 122 737**

Grandmaster Chilly T

ROCK THE MESSAGE RAP
Tracks: / Rock the message rap.
12" Single: Released May '83, on Eclipse, Catalogue no: **SG 026T**

Grandmaster Flash

ADVENTURES OF GRANDMASTER FLASH
Tracks: / Message, The / It's nasty (genius of love).
CD 3": Released '88, on Special Edition, by Castle Communications Records. Catalogue no: **CD3-2**

ADVENTURES OF GRANDMASTER FLASH ON THE WHEELS OF
Tracks: / Adventures of Grandmaster Flash on the wheels of steel / Birthday party (instrumental) (Writers: S.Robinson/J.Chase/The Furious Five).
Note: Special thanks to: **Chic** (Good times); **Blondie** (Rapture); **Queen** (Another one bites the dust); **Sugarhill Gang** (8th Wonder); **Furious Five** (Birthday party); **Spoonie Gee** (Monster Jam). A Sylvia & Joey Robinson Jr Production.
12" Single: Released '81, on Sugarhill (USA), Deleted '85. Catalogue no: **SHL 557**
12" Single: Released May '88, on Blatant, Deleted Sep '89. Catalogue no: **BLAT 12 3**

BEAT STREET
(GRANDMASTER FLASH & MELLE MEL)
Tracks: / Beat Street.
12" Single: Released Jun '84, on Sugarhill (USA), Catalogue no: **SHL 9659**

BEAT STREET BREAKDOWN
(GRANDMASTER FLASH & MELLE MEL)
Tracks: / Beat Street breakdown.
7" Single: Released Jun '84, on Atlantic, by WEA Records. Deleted '86. Catalogue no: **A 9659**
12" Single: Released Jun '84, on Atlantic, by WEA Records. Catalogue no: **A 9659 T**

BIRTHDAY PARTY
Tracks: / Birthday party.
7" Single: Released Apr '81, on Sugarhill (USA), Deleted '85. Catalogue no: **SH 555**

CONTINUOUS WHITE LINES
(GRANDMASTER FLASH & MELLE MEL)
Tracks: / Continuous white lines.
12" Single: Released Oct '84, on Sugarhill (USA), Catalogue no: **SHLM 130**

GOLD
Tracks: / Gold.
12" Single: Released Feb '88, on Elektra, by Elektra Records (UK). Catalogue no: **EKR 70T**
7" Single: Released Feb '88, on Elektra, by Elektra Records (UK). Catalogue no: **EKR 70**

IT'S NASTY
Tracks: / It's nasty / Birthday party.
12" Single: Released Apr '82, on Sugarhill (USA), Deleted Apr '85. Catalogue no: **SHL 111**
7" Single: Released Apr '82, on Sugarhill (USA), Deleted Apr '85. Catalogue no: **SH 111**

JESSE
(GRANDMASTER FLASH & MELLE MEL)
Tracks: / Jesse.
7" Single: Released '83, on Sugarhill (USA), Catalogue no: **SH 133**
12" Single: Released '83, on Sugarhill (USA), Catalogue no: **SHL 133**

MESSAGE, THE (SINGLE)
Tracks: / Message, The.
7" Single: Released Aug '82, on Sugarhill (USA), Deleted '85. Catalogue no: **SHL 117**
12" Single: Released Aug '82, on Sugarhill (USA), Catalogue no: **SHL 117T**

NEW YORK, NEW YORK
Tracks: / New York, New York.
7" Single: Released May '83, on Sugarhill (USA), Catalogue no: **SH 125**
12" Single: Released May '83, on Sugarhill (USA), Catalogue no: **SHL 125**

PUMP ME UP
(GRANDMASTER FLASH & MELLE MEL)
Tracks: / Pump me up.
7" Single: Released Mar '85, on Sugarhill (USA), Catalogue no: **SH 141**
12" Single: Released Mar '85, on Sugarhill (USA), Catalogue no: **SHL 141**
12" Pic: Released Mar '85, on Sugarhill (USA), Catalogue no: **SHLX 141**

SCORPIO
Tracks: / Scorpio / It's a shame.
12" Single: Released Dec '82, on Sugarhill (USA), Catalogue no: **SHL 118**
7" Single: Released Dec '82, on Sugarhill (USA), Deleted '88. Catalogue no: **SH 118**

SIGN OF THE TIMES
Tracks: / Sign of the times.
7" Single: Released Jan '85, on Elektra, by Elektra Records (UK). Catalogue no: **E 9677**
12" Single: Released Jan '85, on Elektra, by Elektra Records (UK). Deleted '86. Catalogue no: **E 9677T**

STEP OFF
(GRANDMASTER FLASH & MELLE MEL)
Tracks: / Step off / Message.
12" Single: Released Dec '84, on Sugarhill (USA), Catalogue no: **SHL 139**
7" Single: Released Dec '84, on Sugarhill (USA), Catalogue no: **SH 139**

STYLE (PETER GUNN THEME)
Tracks: / Style (Peter Gunn theme) / Style (Peter Gunn theme)instrumental / Style (Peter Gunn theme)remix (On 12" version only.).
12" Single: Released May '86, on Elektra (USA), by Elektra Records (USA). Deleted Jun '87. Catalogue no: **EKR 39 T**
7" Single: Released May '86, on Elektra (USA), by Elektra Records (USA). Deleted Jun '87. Catalogue no: **EKR 39**

U KNOW WHAT TIME IT IS?
Tracks: / U know what time it is? / Bus dis (woo).
7" Single: Released Mar '87, on Elektra (USA), by Elektra Records (USA). Deleted Jan '88. Catalogue no: **EKR 54**
12" Single: Released Mar '87, on Elektra (USA), by Elektra Records (USA). Deleted Jan '88. Catalogue no: **EKR 54 T**

VICE
(GRANDMASTER FLASH & MELLE MEL)
Tracks: / Vice.
7" Single: Released Nov '85, on Sugarhill (USA), Catalogue no: **SH 146**

WE DON'T WORK FOR FREE
(GRANDMASTER FLASH & MELLE MEL)
Tracks: / We don't work for free.
12" Single: Released Sep '84, on Sugarhill (USA), Catalogue no: **SHL 136**
7" Single: Released Sep '84, on Sugarhill (USA), Catalogue no: **SH 136**

WHITE LINES (DON'T DO IT)
Tracks: / White lines (don't don't do it).
12" Single: Released Nov '83, on Sugarhill (USA), Catalogue no: **SHL 130**
12" Single: Released Jun '87, on Blatant, Catalogue no: **BLAT 121**
7" Single: Released Nov '83, on Sugarhill (USA), Catalogue no: **SH 130**
12" Pic: Released Jul '84, on Sugarhill (USA), Catalogue no: **SHPX 130**
7" Single: Released Aug '87, on Blatant, Deleted Aug '89. Catalogue no: **BLAT 71**

WHITE LINES (EP)
Tracks: / White lines (don't don't do it) / Jesse / Message II (survival).
CD 3": Released '88, on Special Edition, by Castle Communications Records. Catalogue no: **CD3-1**

WORLD WAR THREE
(GRANDMASTER FLASH & MELLE MEL)
Tracks: / World war three.
7" Single: Released Jul '85, on Sugarhill (USA), Catalogue no: **SH 143**
12" Single: Released Jul '85, on Sugarhill (USA), Catalogue no: **SHL 143**

Grandmaster Julius

LONDON JACK
Tracks: / London Jack.
12" Single: Released Dec '88, on Knock Out, Catalogue no: **KOR 12001**

Grandmaster Richie

DON'T BE FLASH
Tracks: / Don't be flash / Flash scratch / Bonus beats.
12" Single: Released Nov '86, on Spin-Off's, Deleted Nov '87. Catalogue no: **12 OFF 2**

Grandpa Neil

LITTLE BOY THAT SANTA CLAUS FORGOT
Tracks: / Little boy that Santa Claus forgot / Rosie.
7" Single: Released Nov '82, on Chick, Catalogue no: **CHRS 002**

Graney, Dave

WITH THE CORAL SNAKES AT HIS STONE BEACH
Tracks: / With the coral snakes at his stone beach.
7" Single: Released Nov '88, on Fire, by Fire Records. Catalogue no: **BLAZE 32**
12" Single: Released Nov '88, on Fire, by Fire Records. Catalogue no: **BLAZE 32T**

Grange Hill Cast

JUST SAY NO
Tracks: / Just say no.
7" Single: Released Apr '86, on BBC, by BBC Records & Tapes. Deleted '89. Catalogue no: **RESL 183**

YOU KNOW THE TEACHER (SMASH HEAD)
Tracks: / You know the teacher (smash head) / Don't stop.
7" Single: Released Nov '86, on BBC, by BBC Records & Tapes. Deleted Sep '87. Catalogue no: **RESL 205**
12" Single: Released Nov '86, on BBC, by BBC Records & Tapes. Deleted Sep '87. Catalogue no: **12 RSL 205**

Granger, Gerri

Biographical details: This American singer achieved a one-off UK chart entry in 1978, when her version of *I go to pieces (everytime)* (a US top 10 hit for Peter & Gordon in 1965) reached no. 50 on the British singles chart. She was part of the Casino Classics series of re-issues which, in the same year, provided a minor UK hit for the Ron Grainer Orchestra. (Bob Macdonald, 27/9/85).

I GO TO PIECES
Tracks: / I go to pieces / Panic / Shake a tail feather.
7" Single: Released Sep '78, on Casino Classics, by RK Records. Deleted '81. Catalogue no: **CC 3**

Granlan, Tom

STARSTRUCK
Tracks: / Starstruck.
7" Single: Released Mar '82, on Peach River, Deleted '83. Catalogue no: **PRIVY 503**

Grant, Amy

LEAD ME ON (SINGLE)
Tracks: / Lead me on / Love will find away.
CD 5": Released Aug '88, on A&M, by A&M Records. Catalogue no: **AMCD 453**
7" Single: Released Aug '88, on A&M, by A&M Records. Catalogue no: **AM 453**
12" Single: Released Aug '88, on A&M, by A&M Records. Catalogue no: **AMY 453**

SAVED BY LOVE
Tracks: / Saved by love / Shadows / Who to listen to (Only on 12").
7" Single: Released Sep '88, on A&M, by A&M Records. Catalogue no: **AM 473**
12" Single: Released Sep '88, on A&M, by A&M Records. Catalogue no: **AMY 473**

Grant, Andy

STRIKE OUT
Tracks: / Strike out / Strike out (version).
12" Single: Released Mar '88, on Bolts, by Bolts Records. Catalogue no: **BOLTS 12/12**

Grant, Carrie

TO THE BEAT
Tracks: / To the beat.
7" Single: Released Apr '82, on Magnet, by WEA Records. Deleted Apr '85. Catalogue no: **MAG 220**

Grant, David

Biographical details: British singer, percussionist and songwriter Grant came to fame in 1980 as half of the Linx duo. When he and his partner Sketch split up in October 1982 Grant quickly launched a solo career with a dire revamp of a Christmas standard. The public were not impressed by that offering, but he enjoyed a hot 1983, chalking up four UK hit singles from his eponymous debut solo LP. *Stop and go* got to no 19, *Watching you watching me* climbed to no 10, *Love will find a way* reached the no 24 spot and *Rock the midnight* peaked at no 46. These were carefully crafted slices of British black pop, intended to sound equally strong on the dancefloor and the studio. They were produced by the then red-hot Steve Levine, whose use of computer technology gave the records a trendy electronic flavour. Grant had undergone an image change at the beginning of 1983: the spectacles were changed for contact lenses, the jacket, white shirt and tie replaced by sports gear and sweatbands; he also learnt to body-pop. In early '84 Grant disappeared from the limelight and decided to stay away from the public eye for a year. He returned in spring 1985 in duet with Birmingham soul singer Jaki Graham: their remake of *Could it be I'm falling in love?* got to No 5 on the UK chart, six places higher than the Detroit Spinners had managed with the same song in 1973. He seemed to be back with a vengeance, but although the disc advanced Graham's career - she rapidly released another British Top Tenner - his new album, *Hopes and dreams* (produced and co-penned by regular writing partner Derek Bramble) proved a relative failure. It was a little too slick and did not give full expression to Grant's soulful voice. (Bob MacDonald, September 1985.).

BEFORE TOO LONG
Tracks: / Before too long / Before too longsooncome mix / Tonight.
7" Single: Released Oct '87, on Polydor, by Polydor Ltd. Catalogue no: **POSP 889**
12" Single: Released Oct '87, on Polydor, by Polydor Ltd. Catalogue no: **POSPX 889**

CHANGE
Tracks: / Change / Change (Alternate Mix) (On 12" version only.) / Change (Dub version) (On 12" version only.) / Fire me up.
7" Single: Released Jul '87, on Polydor, by Polydor Ltd. Deleted Mar '88. Catalogue no: **POSP 871**
12" Single: Released Jul '87, on Polydor, by Polydor Ltd. Deleted Mar '88. Catalogue no: **POSPX 871**

CLOSE TO YOU
Tracks: / Goodbye love / Close to you.
12" Single: Released Mar '86, on Chrysalis, by Chrysalis Records. Catalogue no: **GRANX 8**
7" Single: Released Mar '86, on Chrysalis, by Chrysalis Records. Catalogue no: **GRAN 8**

COULD IT BE I'M FALLING IN LOVE
Tracks: / Could it be i'm falling in love / Turn around.
12" Single: Released Mar '85, on Chrysalis, by Chrysalis Records. Catalogue no: **GRANX 6**
7" Single: Released Mar '85, on Chrysalis, by Chrysalis Records. Catalogue no: **GRAN 6**

HAVE YOURSELF A MERRY CHRISTMAS
Tracks: / Have yourself a merry Christmas / It's my life.
7" Single: Released Dec '82, on Chrysalis, by Chrysalis Records. Deleted Dec '85. Catalogue no: **CHS 2659**

INTUITION '88'
Tracks: / Intuition '88' / Intuition '88' (version).
7" Single: Released Nov '88, on Fresh, by Jetstar Records. Catalogue no: **FRESTR 001**
12" Single: Released Nov '88, on Fresher, by Fresher Records. Catalogue no: **FRES T1**
7" Single: Released Nov '88, on Fresher, by Fresher Records. Catalogue no: **FRES 1**
7" Single: Released Nov '88, on Fresher, by Fresher Records. Catalogue no: **FRES TX 1**

LIFE
Tracks: / Life / Life (inst) / Life (eternal mix) (On 12" and CD only) / Life (acapella) (On 12" and CD only).
7" Single: Released Sep '89, on 4th & Broadway, by Island Records. Catalogue no: **BRW 145**
CD 5": Released Sep '89, on 4th & Broadway, by Island Records. Catalogue no: **BRCD 145**
12" Single: Released Sep '89, on 4th & Broadway, by Island Records. Catalogue no: **12 BRW 145**

LOVE WILL FIND A WAY
Tracks: / Love will find a way / Klix trax.
12" Single: Released Oct '83, on Chrysalis, by Chrysalis Records. Catalogue no: **GRANX 3**
7" Single: Released Oct '83, on Chrysalis, by Chrysalis Records. Catalogue no: **GRAN 3**

MATED
Tracks: / Mated / Facts of love / Have yourself a merry little Christmas.
12" Single: Released Nov '85, on EMI, by EMI Records. Catalogue no: **12 JAKI 6**
7" Single: Released Nov '85, on EMI, by EMI Records. Catalogue no: **JAKI 6**

ORGANISE
Tracks: / Organise / Wrap yourself around me / Kiss away the blues (on 12" only).
12" Single: Released Feb '84, on Chrysalis, by Chrysalis Records. Catalogue no: **GRANX 5**
7" Single: Released Feb '84, on Chrysalis, by Chrysalis Records. Catalogue no: **GRAN 5**

ROCK THE MIDNIGHT
Tracks: / Rock the midnight.
7" Single: Released Nov '83, on Chrysalis, by Chrysalis Records. Deleted '86. Catalogue no: **GRAN 4**

STOP & GO
Tracks: / Stop and go / Stop and go (instrumental).
7" Single: Released Apr '83, on Chrysalis, by Chrysalis Records. Catalogue no: **GRAN 1**
12" Single: Released Apr '83, on Chrysalis, by Chrysalis Records. Deleted '85. Catalogue no: **GRANX 1**

TAKE US BACK
Tracks: / Take us back / Tell me.
12" Single: Released Mar '87, on Polydor, by Polydor Ltd. Deleted Jan '88. Catalogue no: **POSPX 854**
7" Single: Released Mar '87, on Polydor, by Polydor Ltd. Deleted Jan '88. Catalogue no: **POSP 854**

VAIN
Tracks: / Vain / Life.
CD 5": Released Sep '89, on 4th & Broadway, by Island Records. Catalogue no: **BRCD 145**

WATCHING YOU WATCHING ME
Tracks: / Watching you watching me / In the flow of love.
7" Single: Released '83, on Chrysalis, by Chrysalis Records. Deleted '87. Catalogue no: **GRAN 2**

WATCHING YOU WATCHING ME (OLD GOLD)
Tracks: / Watching you watching me / Could it be I'm falling in love.
12" Single: Released 28 Aug '89, on Old Gold, by Old Gold Records. Catalogue no: **OG 4135**

Grant, Earl

HOUSE OF BAMBOO
Tracks: / House of Bamboo / Fever / Mission impossible / Crickets sing for Anna Maria,The.
12" Single: Released Sep '86, on London Records, by London Records. Deleted Feb '89. Catalogue no: **LONX 111**

Grant, Eddy

Biographical details: This singer, multi-instrumentalist, songwriter and producer was born in Guyana in 1948, moved to London with his parents in 1960 and relocated to Barbados in 1982. He helped to form the Equals in 1965 and the fact that they were racially mixed, a novelty at the time, brought them attention. Grant was their key songwriter, main creative source and lead guitarist. He quit the Equals in 1971 to pursue a solo career as producer and artist. After years out of the public eye, during which he formed his own Ice Records and built his Coach House Studios in Lndon, Grant found a commercial formula once again and began a UK chart career in 1979. *His walking on sunshine* album yielded a British No 11 single with the compelling reggae anthem *Living on the front line*. Despite his dreadlocks and image he has always been a peripheral reggae artist; from his Equals days in the 60's to his solo stardom in the 80's bouncy pop and dance music have been his real stock-in-trade, with reggae themes and rhythms included in a comparatively minor degree. During the first half of the 80's, Grant's two biggest British singles ranged lyrically from the nursery rhyme triteness of 1982's *I don't wanna dance (which returned him to the no 1 spot 14 years after the Equals' Baby come back)* to the urban social consciousness of 1983's *Electric Avenue*, which hit No 2 on both sides of the Atlantic - it was his only major US single. The melodies were generally kept simple and his singalong style often erred on the side of blandness. He was the ultimate solo artist: he wrote and produced his own material in his own studios (latterly Blue Wave, in Barbados), performed all vocals, played all instruments, and released the discs on his own record label. Rocker's Revenge covered the title track from *Walking on sunshine* in 1982, achieving an international disco hit and a UK Top Five pop success. (Bob MacDonald, September 1985.).

BABY COME BACK
Tracks: / Baby come back / Political bassa-bassa.
CD 5": Released Jul '89, on Blue Wave, Catalogue no: **203 418 2**
7" Single: Released Jul '89, on Blue Wave, Catalogue no: **203 418 7**
7" Single: Released Feb '85, on Ice, by Ice Records. Catalogue no: **ICE 63**
7" Single: Released Jul '89, on Blue Wave, Catalogue no: **R 6224**
12" Single: Released Jul '89, on Blue Wave, Catalogue no: **203 418 6**
CD 5": Released Jul '89, on Blue Wave, Catalogue no: **CDR 6224**
12" Single: Released Jul '89, on Blue Wave, Catalogue no: **12R 6224**
12" Single: Released Feb '85, on Ice, by Ice Records. Catalogue no: **ICET 63**

BOYS IN THE STREET
Tracks: / Boys in the street.
12" Single: Released Oct '84, on Ice, by Ice Records. Catalogue no: **ICET 62**
7" Single: Released Oct '84, on Ice, by Ice Records. Catalogue no: **ICE 62**

CAN'T GET ENOUGH OF YOU
Tracks: / Can't get enough of you.
7" Single: Released Mar '81, on Ensign, by Ensign Records. Deleted '81. Catalogue no: **ENY 207**
12" Single: Released Mar '81, on Ensign, by Ensign Records. Deleted '82. Catalogue no: **ENYT 207**

DANCE PARTY
Tracks: / Dance party / Rock you good.
7" Single: Released Jul '86, on Ice, by Ice Records. Catalogue no: **ICE 64**
12" Single: Released Jul '86, on Ice, by Ice Records. Catalogue no: **ICET 64**

EDDY GRANT - I DON'T WANNA DANCE (Released on Ice)

DO YOU FEEL MY LOVE
Tracks: / Do you feel my love.
7" Single: Released Nov '80, on Ensign, by Ensign Records. Deleted '83. Catalogue no: **ENY 45**

ELECTRIC AVENUE
Tracks: / Electric Avenue / Walking on sunshine.
7" Single: Released Jan '83, on Ice, by Ice Records. Catalogue no: **ICE 57**
12" Single: Released Jan '83, on Ice, by Ice Records. Catalogue no: **ICET 57**

GIMME HOPE JO'ANNA
Tracks: / Gimme hope Jo'anna / Say hello to Fidel / Living on the frontline (live) (Available on 12" only).
7" Single: Released Jan '88, on Ice, by Ice Records. Catalogue no: **ICE 78701**
12" Single: Released Jan '88, on Ice, by Ice Records. Catalogue no: **ICE 12 8701**
CD 5": Released May '88, on EMI (Holland), by EMI Records. Catalogue no: **2025142**

HARMLESS PIECE OF FUN
Tracks: / Harmless piece of fun / Blood money / Born tuff / Electric Avenue* / Who's leaving who?.
Note: * extra track on CD single.
7" Single: Released Apr '88, on Blue Wave, Deleted Nov '88. Catalogue no: **R 6180**
12" Single: Released Apr '88, on Blue Wave, Deleted Nov '88. Catalogue no: **12R 6180**
CD 5": Released May '88, on Blue Wave, Deleted Jun '89. Catalogue no: **CDR 6180**

I DON'T WANNA DANCE (see panel on previous page)
Tracks: / I don't wanna dance / I don't wanna dance (Accapella).
7" Single: Released Sep '82, on Ice, by Ice Records. Catalogue no: **ICE 56**
12" Single: Released Sep '82, on Ice, by Ice Records. Catalogue no: **ICET 56**

I LOVE YOU YES I LOVE YOU
Tracks: / I love you yes I love you / It's our time.
12" Single: Released Aug '81, on Ensign, by Ensign Records. Deleted '83. Catalogue no: **ENYT 216**
7" Single: Released Jul '81, on Ensign, by Ensign Records. Deleted '82. Catalogue no: **ENY 216**

LIVING ON THE FRONT LINE
Tracks: / Living on the frontline.
7" Single: Released Jun '79, on Ensign, by Ensign Records. Deleted '82. Catalogue no: **ENY 26**
7" Single: Released Mar '83, on Mercury, by Phonogram Ltd. Deleted '86. Catalogue no: **MER 135**

MY TURN TO LOVE YOU
Tracks: / My turn to love you / Use it or lose it.
7" Single: Released May '80, on Ice, by Ice Records. Deleted May '83. Catalogue no: **GUY 37**

PUT A HOLD ON IT
Tracks: / Put a hold on it / Put a hold on it (New York mix 7" edit) / Put a hold on it (New York club mix) (12" only.) / Gimme hope Jo'Anna (Spanish version) (12" only.).
Note: Produced and arranged by Eddy Grant.
CD 5": Released Oct '88, on Blue Wave, Deleted Jun '89. Catalogue no: **CDR 6191**
12" Single: Released Oct '88, on Blue Wave, Deleted Aug '89. Catalogue no: **12R 6191**
7" Single: Released Oct '88, on Blue Wave, Deleted Aug '89. Catalogue no: **R 6191**

ROMANCING THE STONE
Tracks: / Romancing the stone / My turn to love you.
7" Single: Released May '84, on Ice, by Ice Records. Catalogue no: **ICE 61**
12" Single: Released May '84, on Ice, by Ice Records. Catalogue no: **ICET 61**

TILL I CAN'T TAKE LOVE NO MORE
Tracks: / Till I can't take love no more.
12" Single: Released Oct '83, on Ice, by Ice Records. Catalogue no: **ICET 60**
7" Single: Released Oct '83, on Ice, by Ice Records. Catalogue no: **ICE 60**

TIME TO LET GO
Tracks: / Time to let go.
7" Single: Released Nov '81, on Ice, by Ice Records. Catalogue no: **ICE 52**
12" Single: Released Nov '81, on Ice, by Ice Records. Catalogue no: **ICET 52**

WALKING ON SUNSHINE (SINGLE)
Tracks: / Walking on sunshine / Walking on sunshine (7" mix) (not on 7".) / Walking on sunshine (original mix) (not on 7".) / California style.
CD 5": Released Apr '89, on Blue Wave, Deleted Oct '89. Catalogue no: **CDR 6217**
CD 5": Released Apr '89, on Blue Wave, Deleted Oct '89. Catalogue no: **203 350 2**
7" Single: Released Apr '89, on Blue Wave, Deleted Oct '89. Catalogue no: **203 350 7**
12" Single: Released Apr '89, on Blue Wave, Deleted Oct '89. Catalogue no: **12R 6217**
12" Single: Released Apr '89, on Blue Wave, Deleted Oct '89. Catalogue no: **203 3506**
7" Single: Released Apr '89, on Blue Wave, Deleted Oct '89. Catalogue no: **R 6217**

WAR PARTY
Tracks: / War party (Bajan mix).
7" Single: Released Apr '83, on Ice, by Ice Records. Catalogue no: **ICE 58**
12" Single: Released Apr '83, on Ice, by Ice Records. Catalogue no: **ICET 58**

Grant & Forsyth

SUN AIN'T GONNA SHINE ANYMORE, THE
Tracks: / Sun ain't gonna shine anymore, The / Be my baby / Ditty.
7" Single: Released Oct '88, on Double 8, Catalogue no: **GF 881**

Grant, Gogi

Biographical details: This American singer, whose real name was Audrey Brown, was 18 years old when she achieved her first UK smash hit in 1955. *Suddenly there's a valley* reached no. 9 for the Los Angeles lass, beating rival renditions by Jo Stafford and Julius La Ross; in Britain, Petula Clark had the biggest hit with the song. 1956 brought Gogi a long-running US no. 1 smash with *Wayward wind*. This giant hit reached no. 9 in the UK, where she had to share the sales with the no. 8 version by Tex Ritter. The memorable song became a British no. 1 for Frank Ifield in 1963, who retained its country flavour. Though young in years, Gogi Grant belonged to the old school of safe MoR vocalists and was quickly torpedoed out of the charts by the rock'n'roll revolution. (Bob Macdonald, 27/9/85)
Singer. Born in Philadelphia in 1924 (as Audrey Brown), she was a superior pop singer, influenced by Russ Columbo and torch singer Ruth Etting. On her hits in the mid 1950s she was backed by the Buddy Bregman band. 'Suddenly there's a valley' went top ten in the USA, 'Wayward wind' was no.1 1955-6. She dubbed vocals for actress Anne Blyth in a film biography of another famous torch singer, Helen Morgan, in 1957. (Donald Clarke, 1989).

WAYWARD WIND
Tracks: / Wayward wind.
7" Single: Released Jun '56, on London-American, Deleted '59. Catalogue no: **HLB 8262**
7" Single: Released Jul '82, on Old Gold, by Old Gold Records. Catalogue no: **OG 9051**

Grant, Julie

COME TO ME
Tracks: / Come to me.
7" Single: Released Sep '64, on Pye, Deleted '67. Catalogue no: **7N 15684**

COUNT ON ME
Tracks: / Count on me.
7" Single: Released Mar '63, on Pye, Deleted '66. Catalogue no: **7N 15508**

UP ON THE ROOF
Tracks: / Up on the roof.
7" Single: Released Jan '63, on Pye, Deleted '66. Catalogue no: **7N 15483**

Grant, Kitty

GLAD TO KNOW YOU
Tracks: / Glad to know you.
7" Single: Released Jun '83, on Leo Records, by Leo Records. Catalogue no: **LOS 2**

Grant, Manson

I WON'T GO HUNTIN' WITH YOU JAKE
Tracks: / I won't go huntin' with you Jake / What can I tell the folks?.
7" Single: Released Dec '85, on Ross, by Ross Records. Catalogue no: **SWGR 011**

PICTURES FROM THE PAST
Tracks: / Pictures from the past / Bricklayer's song.
7" Single: Released Dec '84, on Ross, by Ross Records. Catalogue no: **SWGR 010**

Grant, Michael

DON'T TURN YOUR BACK
Tracks: / Don't turn your back / Don't turn your back (instrumental) / Don't turn your back (dub) (Available on 12" only.).
12" Single: Released 24 May '88, on Legend (1), by Legend Records (UK). Catalogue no: **LM 12 014**
7" Single: Released 24 May '88, on Legend (1), by Legend Records (UK). Catalogue no: **LM 014**

Grant, Norman

MISS WORLD (PART 1)
Tracks: / Miss World (part 1) / Miss World (part 2).
7" Single: Released 20 Jul '80, on Virgin, by Virgin Records. Deleted '83. Catalogue no: **VS 345**

Grant, Rudy

Biographical details: This singer was born in Guyana but moved to London with his parents during childhood. He is the younger brother of Eddy Grant. Rudy does not share his brother's all-round musical skills, and his only taste of UK chart success was with a cover version of a Stevie Wonder song. When Stevie released his *Hotter than July* LP in November 1980, many people thought that the mellow ballad *Lately* would make a strong single. As there were no immediate plans for the track to be issued on 45, the reggae-influenced Rudy recorded a lovers' rock rendition. It reached no. 58 on the British chart in February 1981, but then the Wonder original was finally released. The week that Stevie entered the UK Top 75 (ultimately peaking at no. 3), Rudy dropped off the list. Subsequent Rudy Grant singles, which included a revamp of John Lennon's *Women* plus some efforts for Mickie Most's RAK label, failed to make much impact. (Bob Macdonald, 27/9/85).

FUNNY GIRL
Tracks: / Funny girl / Every step i made.
7" Single: Released Mar '82, on Ice, by Ice Records. Catalogue no: **ICE 54**
12" Single: Released Feb '82, on Ice, by Ice Records. Catalogue no: **ICET 54**

HIT OF THE CITY
Tracks: / Hit of the city.
12" Single: Released Jun '88, on Seara, Catalogue no: **SEA 16 T**

LATELY
Tracks: / Lately / Your loving is something else.
7" Single: Released Feb '81, on Ensign, by Ensign Records. Deleted '84. Catalogue no: **ENY 202**
12" Single: Released Feb '81, on Ensign, by Ensign Records. Deleted '84. Catalogue no: **ENYT 202**

LITTLE CHRISTMAS TREE
Tracks: / Little Christmas tree.
12" Single: Released Dec '88, on Seara, Catalogue no: **SE 20T**

MASH IN GUYANA
Tracks: / Mash in Guyana / Mash in Guyana (version).
12" Single: Released Jul '87, on Seara, Catalogue no: **SCA T14**

WOMAN
Tracks: / Woman / Treasure the moments.
7" Single: Released Nov '81, on Ice, by Ice Records. Catalogue no: **ICE 51**
12" Single: Released Nov '81, on Ice, by Ice Records. Catalogue no: **ICET 51**

Grant, Steve

CONVICTION
Tracks: / Conviction.
7" Single: Released Jun '85, on Record Shack, by Record Shack Records. Catalogue no: **SOHO 46**
12" Single: Released Jun '85, on Record Shack, by Record Shack Records. Catalogue no: **SOHOT 46**

RUN FOR COVER
Tracks: / Run for cover.
7" Single: Released Aug '84, on Record Shack, by Record Shack Records. Catalogue no: **SOHO 26**
12" Single: Released Aug '84, on Record Shack, by Record Shack Records. Catalogue no: **SOHOT 26**

Grantham, Leslie

WINNERS AND LOSERS
Tracks: / Winners and losers.
12" Single: Released Mar '89, on Lismor, by Lismor Records. Catalogue no: **LINI 001T**
7" Single: Released Mar '89, on Lismor, by Lismor Records. Catalogue no: **LINI 001**

Grants

SLANGEVA
Tracks: / Slangeva.
7" Single: Released '79, on Rel, by REL Records. Catalogue no: **RES 007**

Grapefruit

C'MON MARIANNE
Tracks: / C'mon Marianne.
7" Single: Released Aug '68, on RCA, by BMG Records (UK). Deleted '71. Catalogue no: **RCA 1716**

DEAR DELILAH
Tracks: / Dear Delilah.
7" Single: Released Feb '68, on RCA, by BMG Records (UK). Deleted '71. Catalogue no: **RCA 1656**

Grapes Of Wrath

DEBUT E.P.
12" Single: Released 17 Jul '87, on Nettwerk, by Nettwerk Records. Catalogue no: **33 NTWK 012**

Grasshoppers

TEARDROPS FALL LIKE RAIN
Tracks: / Teardrops fall like rain / Teen queen.
7" Single: Released May '81, on Polydor, by Polydor Ltd. Deleted May '84. Catalogue no: **POSP 278**

Grateful Dead

Biographical details: The classic line-up of this American rock band featured Jerry Garcia, Robert Hunter, Bill Kreutzmann, Phil Lesh, Ron "Pigpen" McKernan and Bob Weir. Hunter's contribution was in a lyric-writing rather than performing capacity, but he was generally considered a member of the group. The Grateful Dead were the epitome of the San Francisco hippie scene of the late sixties. Although they were still playing in the seventies and eighties, their name will always be associated with one particular era. The esoteric aura that surrounded the band is a result of the fact that their live reputation has never been truly transferred to vinyl - rarely have their studio albums lived up to the "vibes" created by a Grateful Dead concert. Although some of the members had been playing together under different names since 1963, the above line-up and name were finalised in 1966. They quickly established themselves at the forefront of San Francisco's druggy rock scene. The band's use of acid, which became a part of their everyday lives, influenced their songs to such an extent that the Dead's songs became extended pieces of self-indulgent psychedelia. The heady meanderings of the group's songs, and the loose format of their shows, would have seemed excessively lengthy to an audience of abstainers; but with many of the fans being as high on drugs as the performers on stage, time was no object. The band's bluesy rock music was spearheaded by the guitar work of leader Gerry Garcia, who also took the group into areas of jazz and what came to be termed "progressive rock". During their early heyday, the Dead and their entourage lived together in a communal house in the Haight Street, Ashbury area of Frisco; they gave numerous concerts for free. Having issued their eponymous debut LP in 1967 plus a couple of follow-ups in ensuing years, the Grateful Dead finally found their recording feet with the album *Workingman's dead* (1970) and *American beauty* (1971). These records were more structured and commercial than earlier efforts, and saw the Dead moving in a classy country-rock direction. This did not last for long, however. The jam sessions returned, and as the sixties grew further away and the world became enmeshed in the 70's, their music seemed increasingly dated. But their fans, known as Dead Heads, remained loyal during these later years - years which saw the death of keyboards Pigpen from liver disease in March 1973 at the age of 27, and the death of his replacement Keith Godchaux in 1979. During the 80's Garcia and many of his original cohorts continued to be a major concert attraction in the States - as usual, the Grateful Dead's name was featured far more prominently on box office attendance lists than on record charts. Throughout their career, they never achieved a Top 40 single on either side of the Atlantic. In Britain none of their LP's stayed on the charts for longer than two weeks - the highest placed was 1977's *Terrapin station*, which reached the UK no. 30 position. Their best moment was probably *Dark star*, the opening track on 1970's *Live dead* LP. (Bob Macdonald, 30/9/85)
When Grace Slick left Jefferson Starship in 1988, that band no longer had any original members, and the Grateful Dead became the sole survivor of the San Francisco hippy era. Beginning in psychedelic/acid rock, they remained one of the most improvisatory of all rock bands: they never had a hit single in their heyday, but year after year they are the largest grossing live act in the USA, thanks to their nationwide group of fans, called Deadheads, nowadays linked by computer.Jerry Garcia was born in 1942 and took up the guitar at 15, he also played banjo in folk groups (Incidentally a chain of USA ice-cream parlours offers a flavour called 'Cherry Garcia'). He met Robert Hunter, who later became the

Dead's lyricist - one of the most successful yet least well-known of rock writers. By 1964 they were called Mother McCree's Uptown Jug Champions, with 'Pigpen' McKernan (1945-73) on keyboards and Bob Weir on guitar; they became the Warlocks in 1965 with Phil Lesh on bass, then found their permanent name from the folk-song genre, typically about a good samaritan who settles a debt so that a dead man can be properly buried, then finds himself helped by the benevolent spirit. Meanwhile they adopted electric instruments and took part in public LSD parties before the drug was outlawed, later chronicled in Ken Kersey's **Electric Kool-Aid Acid Test**. They signed with Warner Brothers in 1967; that year's 'Grateful Dead' was a conventional rock album, Anthem of the Sun and Aoxomoxoa were experimental and patched together, 1970's double Live Dead being more highly regarded. They allegedly performed while stoned on LSD, and took rather a long time to tune up; theyused lots of studio time, which left them in debt to the record label. The next albums were country-rock style, with Hunter's songs; Garcia being one of the first rock artists to take up pedal steel. Workingman's Dead and American Beauty in 1970 were their best-sellers and are still their best albums for non-aficionados. Garcia, Lesh and percussionist Mickey Hart took part initially in the country-rock group New Riders of the Purple Sage in 1970, first of many Dead spin-offs - part of their success has been their willingness to experiment. Garcia's other projects include the neo-bluegrass group Old And In The Way. (Donald Clarke, 1989).

TOUCH OF GREY
Tracks: / Touch of grey / My brother Esau.
7" Single: Released Aug '87, on Arista, by BMG Records (UK). Deleted May '89. Catalogue no: **RIS 35**
12" Single: Released Aug '87, on Arista, by BMG Records (UK). Deleted May '89. Catalogue no: **RIST 35**

Grauzone

EISBEAR
Tracks: / Eisbear.
12" Single: Released 26 Jan '87, on Licensed, Catalogue no: **LD 873**
CD 5": Released Aug '88, on Licensed, Catalogue no: **LD 873CD**

Gray, Barry

JOE 90
Tracks: / Joe 90 (86 Dance mix) / Captain Scarlet / Joe 90 (original version) (On 12" version only.).
7" Single: Released May '86, on PRT, by Castle Communications Records. Catalogue no: **7PX 345**
12" Single: Released May '86, on PRT, by Castle Communications Records. Catalogue no: **12 PX 345**

THUNDERBIRDS
Tracks: / Thunderbirds / Joe 90 / Parker well done.
7" Single: Released Jun '81, on PRT, by Castle Communications Records. Catalogue no: **7P 216**

Gray Bunnies

GRAY BUNNIES
Tracks: / Gray bunnies.
12" Single: on Clone, Catalogue no: **CSX 15**

Gray, Dobie

Biographical details: This American singer was born Leonard Victor Ainsworth in Brookshire, Texas, and was one of eight children of sharecropping parents. He travelled to California in the early sixties as a young man in search of a musical career. After impressing Sonny Bono (later to become famous as 50% of the Sonny & Cher duo), Gray first cracked the Billboard Hot 100 with 1963's *Look at me*. His big breakthrough came in early '65, when his pulsating dance single *The "In" crowd* reached no. 13 in the US and no. 25 in the UK. Later that year, it became a bigger American hit for pianist Ramsey Lewis; in 1974 it was a British hit for Bryan Ferry. Dobie Gray failed to consolidate upon the success of *The "In" crowd*. For the next eight years, apart from a brief spell in an insignificant group called Pollution, he dropped out of recording: he spent his time studying law at a Los Angeles college and pursuing a stage career, including a two-year period in *Hair*. Gray suddenly returned to chart action in 1973 with a song written and produced by the appropriately named Mentor Williams. *Drift away* combined Dobie's soulful voice with a country-rock arrangement; thus, a memorable song was given an unusual, relaxing and distinctive feel. *Drift away* was a million-selling no. 5 pop hit in the States and became a classic; in Britain, where glitter pop and heavy rock were the order of the day, the single was a complete flop. The *Drift away* and *Loving arms* albums were hailed by the critics in America. Britain, which ignored them, did manage to give Gray a minor hit single in autumn 1975 with *Out on the floor* plus a turntable hit in 1979 with the infectious disco cash-in *You can do it*. But apart from these, the spasmodic Gray has drifted away from the charts on both sides of the Atlantic - he has never really known in which direction to channel his musical talents. (Bob Macdonald, 30/9/85).

DRIFT AWAY
Tracks: / Drift away / In crowd, The.
7" Single: Released 20 Jun '87, on MCA, by MCA Records. Catalogue no: **MCA 1154**
7" Single: Released Jul '84, on Old Gold, by Old Gold Records. Catalogue no: **OG 9428**

IN CROWD, THE
Tracks: / In crowd, The / Be a man.
7" Single: Released Feb '65, on London Records, by London Records. Deleted '68. Catalogue no: **HL 9953**
7" Single: Released Mar '82, on Decca, by Decca Records. Deleted '88. Catalogue no: **F 13918**

OUT ON THE FLOOR
Tracks: / Out on the floor / Funky funky feeling.
7" Single: Released Sep '75, on Black Magic, by Topic Records. Deleted '78. Catalogue no: **BM 107**
7" Single: Released Oct '83, on Inferno (1), by Inferno Records. Catalogue no: **UKBURN 2**
12" Single: Released Oct '83, on Inferno (1), by Inferno Records. Catalogue no: **12 UKBURN 2**

Gray, Dorian

I'VE GOT YOU ON MY MIND
Tracks: / I've got you on my mind.
7" Single: Released Mar '68, on Parlophone, by EMI Records. Deleted '71. Catalogue no: **R 5667**

PROMISE OF LOVE
Tracks: / Promise of love.
7" Single: Released Sep '85, on Leeds Independent (LIL), by Revolver Records. Catalogue no: **LIL 7051**

Gray, Gregory

STRAWBERRIES
Tracks: / Strawberries / Meanwhile.
12" Single: Released Jan '86, on CBS, by CBS Records. Catalogue no: **TA 6782**
7" Single: Released Jan '86, on CBS, by CBS Records. Catalogue no: **A 6782**

Gray, Jimmie

KOOL PEOPLE
Tracks: / Kool people.
12" Single: Released Oct '82, on JKO, Catalogue no: **12 JKO 100**

Gray, Les

Biographical details: Gray, from Carshalton in Surrey, was lead singer with Mud, one of Britain's most successful mid-70's groups. Some of Mud's hits made clever use of Gray's Elvis Presley impersonations. In early 1977, just after Mud had achieved their final UK hit, Gray chalked up a one-off British entry with a solo remake of the Mindbenders' 1966 smash *A groovy kind of love* - but whereas the earlier record reached no 2, Les could only manage no 32 with his low-key, thin-sounding version. Since then he has attempted the occasional solo offering, such as 1982's *Don't you say it*, but neither these nor later Mud records have been successful. (Bob MacDonald, September 1985.).

DON'T YOU SAY IT
Tracks: / Don't you say it / Street fighter.
7" Single: Released Jun '82, on Runaway, Deleted '85. Catalogue no: **RUN 503**

GROOVY KIND OF LOVE, A
Tracks: / Groovy kind of love.
7" Single: Released Feb '77, on Warner Bros., by WEA Records. Deleted '80. Catalogue no: **K 16883**

Gray, Mel

SCHOOL'S OUT
Tracks: / School's out.
7" Single: Released Aug '81, on Cool King, Deleted '83. Catalogue no: **CK 004**

Gray, Owen

DON'T TURN AROUND
Tracks: / Don't turn around.
12" Single: Released Jul '88, on Moodies, Catalogue no: **L 001**

ETHIOPIA
Tracks: / Ethiopia.
12" Single: Released Sep '85, on King Jam, Catalogue no: **KJ 086**

GREEN GRASS OF JAMAICA
Tracks: / Green grass of Jamaica.
12" Single: Released Feb '83, on Sapphire, Catalogue no: **SR 100**

HE'LL HAVE TO GO TO HELL
Tracks: / He'll have to go to hell.
12" Single: Released May '84, on Face Int, Catalogue no: **FTF 1008**

I'M STANDING IN HIS WAY
Tracks: / I'm standing in his way.
12" Single: Released Nov '85, on Revolutionary Sounds, Catalogue no: **DG 7**

LAST NIGHT
Tracks: / Last night.
12" Single: Released Dec '86, on Barry U, Catalogue no: **BUDIS 002**

LET'S DO IT AGAIN
Tracks: / Let's do it again.
12" Single: Released Feb '89, on Park Heights, Catalogue no: **PHD 0065**

MY BEST FRIEND
Tracks: / My best friend.
12" Single: Released Nov '82, on Sapphire, Catalogue no: **SR 002**

RED RED WINE
Tracks: / Red red wine.
7" Single: Released '88, on Gold Disc, Catalogue no: **VPRD 370**

ROLLING STONE
Tracks: / Rolling stone / Rolling dub.
7" Single: Released Nov '81, on Pama, by Pama Records. Catalogue no: **PMD 3210**

SEXUAL HEALING
Tracks: / Sexual healing.
12" Single: Released Nov '82, on Pama, by Pama Records. Catalogue no: **PMD 3226**

SHAKE YOU DOWN
Tracks: / Shake you down.
12" Single: Released Dec '86, on Barry U, Catalogue no: **BUDIS 001**

SOMETHING TO REMIND ME
Tracks: / Something to remind me / Girl what.
12" Single: Released Oct '82, on Pama, by Pama Records. Catalogue no: **PMD 3221**

SWING HIGH WITH OWEN
Tracks: / Swing high with Owen / Put your money where your mouth is.
12" Single: Released Nov '83, on Speciality (reggae), Catalogue no: **SP 02**

Grayson, Larry

TERRY WOGAN
Tracks: / Terry Wogan.
7" Single: Released Jul '83, on Monarch, by Monarch Records. Catalogue no: **MON 045**

Graystoke

EVERY BEAT OF MY HEART
Tracks: / Every beat of my heart.
CD 5": Released Sep '89, on Union, Catalogue no: **X UNION 3**
12" Single: Released Sep '89, on Union, Catalogue no: **12 UNION 3**
7" Single: Released Sep '89, on Union, Catalogue no: **UNION 3**

UP ON THE ROOF
Tracks: / Up on the roof / Perfect is the girl.
7" Single: Released Oct '88, on Indi-go, by Indi-go Records. Catalogue no: **INDS 1**
12" Single: Released Oct '88, on Indi-go, by Indi-go Records. Catalogue no: **INDX 1**

Great British DJ's

GREAT BRITISH DJ'S ROLL CALL 89
12" Single: Released Jun '89, on GT's Records, by GT'S Records. Catalogue no: **GTLP 2**

Great Divide

GOT TO BE LOVE
Tracks: / Got to be love.
12" Single: Released Oct '84, on Blue Murder, by Blue Murder Records. Catalogue no: **BLUE 701**

WHO BROKE THE LOVE BANK
Tracks: / Who broke the love bank / Bless my soul.
7" Single: Released Dec '82, on Wimp, by Wimp Records. Catalogue no: **WIMP 004**

Great & Lady Soul

I WON'T HOLD MY BREATH
Tracks: / I won't hold my breath / Stretch / I won't hold my breath (version) (Only on 12" version.).
12" Single: Released 22 May '89, on Virgin, by Virgin Records. Catalogue no: **VST 1185**
7" Single: Released 22 May '89, on Virgin, by Virgin Records. Catalogue no: **VS 1185**

TRACE THE LINE (TO MY HEART)
Tracks: / Trace the line (to my heart) / Harriet walk.
7" Single: Released 27 Feb '89, on Virgin, by Virgin Records. Catalogue no: **VS 1169**
12" Single: Released 27 Feb '89, on Virgin, by Virgin Records. Catalogue no: **VST 1169**

Great Leap Forward

CONTROLLING THE EDGES OF TONE
Tracks: / Controlling the edges of tone.
12" Single: Released Feb '87, on Ron Johnson, by Ron Johnson Records. Catalogue no: **ZRON 19**

PECK ON THE CHEEK, A
Tracks: / Peck on the cheek, A.
12" Single: Released Dec '87, on Ron Johnson, by Ron Johnson Records. Catalogue no: **ZRON 27**

WHO WORKS THE WEATHER?
Tracks: / Who works the weather?.
12" Single: Released May '88, on Ron Johnson, by Ron Johnson Records. Catalogue no: **ZRON 34**

Great Outdoors

WORLD AT MY SHOES
Tracks: / World at my shoes.
7" Single: Released Sep '85, on Upright, by Upright Records. Catalogue no: **GOD 1**

Great Plains

BEFORE WE STOPPED TO THINK (SINGLE)
Tracks: / Before we stopped to think.
12" Single: Released Feb '88, on Shadowline, Catalogue no: **SR 0588**

DICK CLARKE
Tracks: / Dick Clarke.
7" Single: Released Feb '88, on Shadowline, Catalogue no: **SR 0386**

EXERCISE
Tracks: / Exercise.
7" Single: Released Apr '89, on Homestead, Catalogue no: **HMS 129 7**

Great Rap Hits

GREAT RAP HITS
Tracks: / Rapper's delight: *Various artists* / Freedom: *Various artists* / Sequence: *Various artists*.
7" Single: Released Feb '81, on Sugarhill (USA), Deleted '84. Catalogue no: **SHL 105**

Great Unwashed

YELLOW RAIN
Tracks: / Yellow rain / Fire burns.
7" Single: Released Sep '86, on Lambs To The Slaughter, by Prism Records. Catalogue no: **LTS 3**

Great White

FACE THE DAY
Tracks: / Face the day.
12" Single: Released Jan '87, on Capitol, by EMI Records. Catalogue no: **12CL 424**
7" Single: Released Jan '87, on Capitol, by EMI Records. Catalogue no: **CL 424**

ONCE BITTEN, TWICE SHY
Tracks: / Once bitten, twice shy / Wasted rock ranger / Slow ride.
CD 5": Released Jul '89, on Capitol, by EMI Records. Catalogue no: **203 425 2**
12" Pic: Released Jul '89, on Capitol, by EMI Records. Catalogue no: **203 425 0**
12" Pic: Released Jul '89, on Capitol, by EMI Records. Catalogue no: **12CLPD 532**
CD 5": Released Jul '89, on Capitol, by EMI Records. Catalogue no: **CDCL 532**
12" Single: Released Jul '89, on Capitol, by EMI Records. Catalogue no: **12CL 532**
7" Single: Released Jul '89, on Capitol, by EMI Records. Catalogue no: **CL 532**

ROCK ME
Tracks: / Rock me / Fast road / Immigrant / Rock and roll (This track is only on 12" format).
7" Single: Released Aug '87, on Capitol, by EMI Records. Deleted Apr '88. Catalogue no: **CL 455**
12" Single: Released Aug '87, on Capitol, by EMI Records. Deleted Apr '88. Catalogue no: **12CL 455**

Greater Than One

EVERYBODY'S CRAZY
Tracks: / Everybody's crazy.
12" Single: Released 20 Nov '87, on K = K (Kunst Equals Kapital), by Kunst Kapital. Catalogue no: **KGK 001**

I DON'T NEED GOD
Tracks: / I don't need God / Ignorance is the agent of fear.
12" Single: Released Jul '89, on Kunst = Kapital (see K=K), Catalogue no: **KGK 4**

IGNORANCE IS THE AGENT

Tracks: / Ignorance is the agent / I don't need God.
12" Single: Released 30 May '89, on K = K (Kunst Equals Kapital), by Kunst Kapital. Catalogue no: **KGK 004**

NOW IS THE TIME
Tracks: / Now is the time.
12" Single: Released Apr '88, on K = K (Kunst Equals Kapital), by Kunst Kapital. Catalogue no: **KGK 002**

PEACE
Tracks: / Peace.
7" Single: Released Aug '88, on K = K (Kunst Equals Kapital), by Kunst Kapital. Catalogue no: **KGK 003A**
12" Single: Released Aug '88, on K = K (Kunst Equals Kapital), by Kunst Kapital. Catalogue no: **KGK 003**

Greatest Conman

TOUGHEST
Tracks: / Toughest.
12" Single: Released 24 Jul '89, on Live & Love, Catalogue no: **LLD 124**

Greatest Show On Legs

BALLOON CHA-CHA
Tracks: / Balloon cha-cha.
7" Single: Released Mar '82, on Index, Catalogue no: **IND 4**

Greaves, Dennis

GOD GAVE ROCK 'N' ROLL TO YOU
Tracks: / God gave rock'n'roll to you.
7" Single: Released Jul '89, on I.R.S, Catalogue no: **EIRS 119**
7" Single: Released Jul '88, on I.R.S, Catalogue no: **IRM 167**
12" Single: Released Jul '89, on I.R.S, Catalogue no: **EIRST 119**
12" Single: Released Jul '88, on I.R.S, Catalogue no: **IRMT 167**
CD 5": Released Jul '89, on I.R.S, Catalogue no: **EIRCD 119**

JEALOUS MAN
Tracks: / Jealous man / Wings of a prayer / Edge of town, The (Only on 12" version.).
CD 5": Released May '89, on I.R.S, Catalogue no: **EIRSCD 113**
7" Single: Released May '89, on I.R.S, Catalogue no: **EIRS 113**
12" Single: Released May '89, on I.R.S, Catalogue no: **EIRST 113**

THROWING IT ALL AWAY
Tracks: / Throwing it all away / It's hidden (Theme from film 'The Hidden'.) / Weapons of love (12" only.).
7" Single: Released Mar '89, on I.R.S, Catalogue no: **EIRS 102**
12" Single: Released Mar '89, on I.R.S, Catalogue no: **EIRST 102**

Grebenshikov, Boris

POSTCARD, THE
Tracks: / Postcard, The / That voice again / Winter (Only on 12" and CD single.) / Postcard, The (LP version) (Only on 12" and CD single.).
7" Single: Released Sep '89, on CBS, by CBS Records. Catalogue no: **655183 7**
12" Single: Released Sep '89, on CBS, by CBS Records. Catalogue no: **655183 6**

RADIO SILENCE
Tracks: / Radio silence / That voice again / Young lions (12" only).
CD 5": Released May '89, on CBS, by CBS Records. Deleted Oct '89. Catalogue no: **654 956 2**
7" Single: Released May '89, on CBS, by CBS Records. Deleted Oct '89. Catalogue no: **654 956 7**
12" Single: Released May '89, on CBS, by CBS Records. Deleted Oct '89. Catalogue no: **654 956 6**

Greco, Buddy

Biographical details: Born in Philadelphia, this American singer and pianist made his radio debut at the age of four (1931). He came to prominence with his 1948 recording of a 1933 song, *Ooh look-a there, ain't she pretty*. In 1949 he began a two-year spell at the forefront of Benny Goodman's band. After building up a cabaret career, Greco achieved a one-off UK chart entry in 1960 - he reached no. 26 with his version of Rodgers & Hart's 1937 standard *The lady is a tramp*. With a piano style heavily influenced by jazz great Art Tatum, Greco continued to earn a steady living as a live performer without ever becoming a major star. (Bob Macdonald, 30/9/85).

LADY IS A TRAMP
Tracks: / Lady is a tramp, The.
7" Single: Released Jul '60, on Fontana, by Phonogram Ltd. Deleted '63. Catalogue no: **H 225**

Greedies

MERRY JINGLE, A
Tracks: / Merry jingle, A / Merry jingle, A (part 2).
7" Single: Released Dec '79, on Vertigo, by Phonogram Ltd. Deleted '82. Catalogue no: **GREED 1**

Greedy Beat Syndicate

ENERGY
Tracks: / Energy.
12" Single: Released May '89, on Greedy Beat, Catalogue no: **12GREED 8**

THIS IS LONDON
Tracks: / This is London.
12" Single: Released May '89, on Greedy Beat, Catalogue no: **12 GREED 8**

Green, Al

Biographical details: Born in Ferrat City, Arkansas, this American singer and songwriter grew up singing gospel music with his family, who moved to Michigan when Al was 13 years old (1959). After several years in a local group called the Creations, Green's first taste of success occurred with the 1968 soul ballad *Back up train*. The following year, he met the Memphis-based producer Willie Mitchell - which proved to be a crucial event in Al's career. After trying out various styles, the Green/Mitchell alliance found its feet with a 1970 cover version of the Temptations' *I can't get next to you*. In autumn of the following year, Al achieved his big breakthrough with the self-penned *Tired of being alone* - this laid back offering reached no. 11 in the US and no. 4 in the UK. Between 1971 and 1974, Green chalked up eight million-selling smash singles in the States. With Mitchell remaining at the production desk, most of the hits were written by Green in conjunction with Mitchell and Al Jackson (who had come to prominence as a drummer with Booker T. & the MG's, and who was killed by an intruder at his home in 1975). The biggest was 1972's *Let's stay together*, which hit the American no. 1 slot and peaked at no. 7 in Britain. Green became one of the most successful black artists of the seventies, thanks to his highly distinctive vocal delivery - he was emotional yet simultameously restrained, making full use of his wide vocal range yet simultaneously restrained, making full use of his wide vocal range yet remaining so understated that one sometimes had difficulty in hearing him. By 1975 the Al Green formula was wearinfg thin. By the end of that year, he had made his last appearance on the British charts and was soon to say goodbye to the American Top 40. Having always emphasized the romantic and sexy elements of his appeal, Green's career decline was accelerated by the stupid antica of an envious female fan, who broke into his apartment and proceeded to enter the bathroom and severely scald his back. A period of incapacitation followed, during which time Green became a born-again Christian. During the early 80's the Rev. Al Green established himself as a substantial force in gospel music with albums like *Higher plane Precious lord* and *I'll rise again*; his name appeared regularly on the US gospel LP charts. At the end of '83 a strikingly different and imaginative remake of *Let's stay together* was used by Tina Turner to launch her spectacular comeback. (Bob Macdonald, 30/9/85).

AS LONG AS WE'RE TOGETHER
Tracks: / As long as we're together / As long as we're together (version).
7" Single: Released Jun '89, on Breakout, by A&M Records. Catalogue no: **USA 654**
12" Single: Released Jun '89, on Breakout, by A&M Records. Catalogue no: **USAT 654**

I'M STILL IN LOVE WITH YOU (SINGLE)
Tracks: / I'm still in love with you.
7" Single: Released Aug '72, on London-American, Deleted '75. Catalogue no: **HL 10382**

LET'S STAY TOGETHER
Tracks: / Let's stay together
7" Single: Released Jan '72, on London-American, Deleted '75. Catalogue no: **HL 10348**
7" Single: Released Oct '88, on Hi, by Demon Records. Catalogue no: **HI 001**
7" Single: Released Sep '85, on Hi, by Demon Records. Catalogue no: **HIUK 45 7001**
12" Single: Released Sep '85, on Hi, by Demon Records. Catalogue no: **HIUK 45 7001T**

LOOK WHAT YOU DONE FOR ME
Tracks: / Look what you done for me.
7" Single: Released May '72, on London-American, Deleted '75. Catalogue no: **HL 10369**

L.O.V.E. (LOVE)
Tracks: / L.O.V.E. (love).
7" Single: Released Mar '75, on London-American, Deleted '78. Catalogue no: **HL 10482**

NEVER MET NOBODY LIKE YOU
Tracks: / Never met nobody like you.
7" Single: Released Feb '85, on Hi, by Demon Records. Catalogue no: **HIUK 45 7003**

SHA-LA-LA (MAKE ME HAPPY)
Tracks: / Sha-la-la.
7" Single: Released Nov '74, on London-American, Deleted '77. Catalogue no: **HL 10470**

TIRED OF BEING ALONE
Tracks: / Tired of being alone / How can you mend a broken heart.
7" Single: Released Jan '83, on Flashback, by Mainline Records. Catalogue no: **FBS 14**
7" Single: Released Jan '80, on Hi-Cream, by Demon Records. Deleted '86. Catalogue no: **HCS 107**
12" Single: Released Jan '80, on Hi-Cream, by Demon Records. Deleted '86. Catalogue no: **12 HCS 107**
7" Single: Released Oct '71, on London-American, Deleted '74. Catalogue no: **HL 10337**

TRUE LOVE
Tracks: / True love / You brought the sunshine / Going away (On 12"version only.).
7" Single: Released Jan '86, on A&M, by A&M Records. Deleted '88. Catalogue no: **AM 302**
12" Single: Released Jan '86, on A&M, by A&M Records. Deleted '88. Catalogue no: **AMY 302**

Green, Carl

WAM
Tracks: / Wam / Girl from Barongarth House.
7" Single: Released Mar '81, on RCA, by BMG Records (UK). Deleted Mar '84. Catalogue no: **RCA 52**

Green, Dotty

I CAUGHT YOU OUT
Tracks: / I caught you out.
7" Single: Released Nov '85, on Hot Melt, by Hot Melt Records. Catalogue no: **TC 004**
12" Single: Released Nov '85, on Hot Melt, by Hot Melt Records. Catalogue no: **12 TC 4**

I WANT YOU
Tracks: / I want you / Melt down dub mix / I want you.
7" Single: Released Nov '86, on Hot Melt, by Hot Melt Records. Catalogue no: **7 TC 008**
12" Single: Released Nov '86, on Hot Melt, by Hot Melt Records. Catalogue no: **12 TC 008**

Green Fields Of Tong

POLAND
Tracks: / Poland.
7" Single: Released Nov '82, on Speed, Catalogue no: **FIRED 2**

Green, Jack

ONE BY ONE
Tracks: / One by one / Brave madonna.
7" Single: Released Feb '82, on RCA, by BMG Records (UK). Deleted Feb '87. Catalogue no: **RCA 194**

THIS IS JAPAN
Tracks: / This is Japan / Can't stand it.
7" Single: Released Jan '81, on RCA, by BMG Records (UK). Deleted Jan '84. Catalogue no: **RCA 26**

Green, Jesse

COME WITH ME
Tracks: / Come with me.
7" Single: Released Jun '77, on EMI, by EMI Records. Deleted '80. Catalogue no: **EMI 2615**

FLIP
Tracks: / Flip.
7" Single: Released Dec '76, on EMI, by EMI Records. Deleted '79. Catalogue no: **EMI 2564**

NICE AND SLOW
Tracks: / Nice and slow / Come with me.
7" Single: Released Aug '76, on EMI, by EMI Records. Deleted '79. Catalogue no: **EMI 2492**
12" Single: Released Jun '82, on Excaliber, by Red Bus Records. Deleted Jun '85. Catalogue no: **EXCL 520**
7" Single: Released Jul '87, on Atlas, by Atlas Records. Catalogue no: **JESSE 2**
12" Single: Released Aug '87, on Red Bus, by Red Bus Records. Catalogue no: **RBL 01**
12" Single: Released Jul '87, on Atlas, by Atlas Records. Catalogue no: **JESSE T2**

YOUR LOVE
Tracks: / Your love / Your love(Instrumental).
7" Single: Released Oct '86, on BMW, by BMW Records. Catalogue no: **JESSE 1**
12" Single: Released Oct '86, on BMW, by BMW Records. Catalogue no: **JESSET 1**

Green, Leroy

ONLY YOU
Tracks: / Only you.
12" Single: Released Dec '85, on MK, Catalogue no: **MKRD 0032**

Green On Red

BORN TO FIGHT
Tracks: / Born to fight / Don't shine your light on me / While the widow weeps (extra track on 12").
12" Single: Released Jun '87, on Mercury, by Phonogram Ltd. Deleted Dec '87. Catalogue no: **GOR 212**
7" Single: Released Jun '87, on Mercury, by Phonogram Ltd. Deleted Dec '87. Catalogue no: **GOR 2**

CLARKSVILLE
Tracks: / Clarksville / No drinkin' / Broken (Available on 12" version only.).
Note: 'Broken'-extra track available on 12" version only.
7" Single: Released Feb '87, on Mercury, by Phonogram Ltd. Deleted Dec '87. Catalogue no: **GOR 1**
12" Single: Released Feb '87, on Mercury, by Phonogram Ltd. Deleted Jul '87. Catalogue no: **GOR 112**

GAS FOOD LODGING
Tracks: / That's what dreams / Black river / Hair of the dog / This I know / Fading away / Easy way out / Sixteen ways / Drifter, The / Sea of Cortez / We shall overcome.
7" Single: Released Nov '85, on Torso, by Torso Records. Catalogue no: **TORSO 70004**

KEITH CAN'T READ
Tracks: / Keith can't read.
7" Single: Released Apr '89, on China, by Polydor Ltd. Catalogue no: **CHINA 16**
12" Single: Released Apr '89, on China, by Polydor Ltd. Catalogue no: **CHINX 16**

THIS TIME AROUND (SINGLE)
Tracks: / This time around / Fading away.
CD 5": Released Oct '89, on Polydor, by Polydor Ltd. Catalogue no: **CHICD 21**
7" Single: Released Oct '89, on Polydor, by Polydor Ltd. Catalogue no: **CHINA 21**
12" Single: Released Oct '89, on Polydor, by Polydor Ltd. Catalogue no: **CHINX 21**

Green Onions

GREEN ONIONS
Tracks: / Green onions: *Various artists* / Chinese checkers: *Various artists* / Memphis soul stew: *Various artists* / Sock it to them JB: *Various artists*.
Note: With Booker T & MG's, King Curtis & Rex Garvin.
7" Single: Released Apr '80, on Atlantic, by WEA Records. Deleted Apr '83. Catalogue no: **ATM 10**

Green, Peter

Biographical details: This British guitarist, vocalist and songwriter was born in Bethnal Green and began his career in two short-lived 1966 groups, the Peter Bees and Shotgun Express, before joining John Mayall's Bluesbreakers. After a year with that seminal blues combo, he formed Fleetwood Mac in July 1967. The first incarnation of Fleetwood Mac was at the forefront of Britain's late sixties blues boom. Green wrote their three monster UK singles, *Albatross* (no. 1), *Man of the world* (no. 2) and *Oh well* (no. 2). Green's departure from Mac in May 1970 left a major hole in the band, from which it took them several years to recover. Peter was in a confused state of mind at the time, immersed in self doubt and becoming obsessed with religion. After one mainly instrumental solo album *The end of the game* plus a brief 1971 return to Fleetwood Mac as a temporary substitute on a US tour, Green retired from the music business and donated his royalties to charity. He re-emerged in 1979 with a series of low-key solo albums. The intervening 8 years were shrouded in mystery and rumour. According to various reports and tales, he joined a religious sect, worked as a grave-digger and a barman and gave away all his guitars. It is certainly true that he appeared in court in February 1977 after visiting his accountant's home armed with a rifle and vehemently returning an unwanted royalty cheque; he was consigned to a mental hospital. Green's comeback *In the skies* reached no. 32 on the UK album chart in 1979, logging 32 weeks on the survey. The follow-up, 1980's *Little dreamer*, reached no. 34. He continued releasing albums during the early 80's, while being careful to keep away from the glare of publicity. None of the comeback records matched the quality of his late 60's work, and they were regarded by most pundits as moderately interesting curiosities. All retained his bluesy approach. (Bob Macdonald, 1/10/85).

CLOWN, THE
Tracks: / Clown, The / Time for me to go.
7" Single: Released Jun '82, on Headline, by Creole Records. Deleted '85. Catalogue no: **LIN 2**

GIVE ME BACK MY FREEDOM
Tracks: / Give me back my freedom / Lost my love.
7" Single: Released Mar '81, on PVK, by PVK Records. Catalogue no: **PV 103**

LOSER TWO TIMES
Tracks: / Loser two times / Mama don'tcha cry.
7" Single: Released Jun '80, on PVK, by PVK Records. Deleted Jun '83. Catalogue no: **PV 41**

PROMISED LAND
Tracks: / Promised land.
7" Single: Released Jul '81, on PVK, by PVK Records. Catalogue no: **PVK 112**

WALKIN' THE ROAD
Tracks: / Walkin' the road / Woman don't.
7" Single: Released Mar '80, on PVK, by PVK Records. Deleted Mar '83. Catalogue no: **PV 36**

Green Telescope

FACE IN A CROWD
Tracks: / Face in the crowd / Thoughts of a madman.
7" Single: Released Aug '86, on Wump, by Wump Records. Catalogue no: **BIF 4811**

Green, Tim

WHO CAN TELL?
Tracks: / Who can tell?.
7" Single: Released Sep '82, on Rabid, by Rabid Records. Catalogue no: **TOSH 110**

Greenbaum, Norman

Biographical details: This American singer, guitarist, keyboardist and songwriter came from Boston, Massachusetts. He first came to public attention in 1966 as a lead singer with Dr. West's Medicine Show & Junk Band, who achieved an unlikely US Top 50 hit with the novelty single *The eggplant that ate Chicago*. Their jug band musical style and painted faces caused brief ripples of excitement, but the group broke up in '67. After meeting producer Eric Jacobson, Greenbaum re-emerged in 1970 with one of the greatest One Hit Wonder classics of all time. The pulsating religious anthem *Spirit in the sky* was a wholly distinctive and original single - sung in praise of the afterlife, it preceded such epic religion/rock fusions such as *Godspell* and *Jesus Christ superstar*; its persistent fuzz-tone guitar riff was thoroughly infectious; and it was accompanied by a memorable film clip, a mini-video that predated the promo video boom by a decade. After failing to achieve success with his follow-ups to *Spirit*, Greenbaum retired from the music business. His 1972 album *Petaluma*, which failed to make any impact, was named after the place in California where he chose to make his home. He spent the mid-seventies, breeding goats. (Bob Macdonald, 1/10/85).

SPIRIT IN THE SKY
Tracks: / Spirit in the sky / Milk cow.
7" Single: Released Mar '70, on Reprise, by WEA Records. Deleted '73. Catalogue no: **RS 20885**
7" Single: Released Jul '81, on Reprise (USA). Deleted Jun '87. Catalogue no: **K 14025**

SPIRIT IN THE SKY (OLD GOLD)
Tracks: / Spirit in the sky.
7" Single: Released Sep '85, on Old Gold, by Old Gold Records. Catalogue no: **OG 9550**

Greene, Lorne

RINGO
Tracks: / Ringo.
7" Single: Released Dec '64, on RCA, by BMG Records (UK). Deleted '67. Catalogue no: **RCA 1428**

Greene, Sarah

EENY MEENIE
Tracks: / Eeny meeny.
7" Single: Released Nov '83, on Lamborghini, by Lamborghini Records. Catalogue no: **LMG 5**

Greenfield, Dave

RAIN, DOLE & TEA
Tracks: / Rain, dole & tea / Consequences.
7" Single: Released Feb '84, on Epic, by CBS Records. Catalogue no: **A 4076**

Greenfield Leisure

THOSE FAR-OFF SUMMERS (EP)
Tracks: / Those far-off summers.
12" Single: Released Feb '82, on Strange Orchestra, Catalogue no: **CAMP 2**

Greenhill Singers

CHRISTMAS LIGHT
Tracks: / Christmas light.
7" Single: Released Nov '85, on Greenhill, by Greenhill Records. Catalogue no: **GMI 1003**

Greenhouse

TIGERS
Tracks: / Tigers / Risking your life for your accent.
7" Single: Released Sep '89, on Fro, Catalogue no: **FR 001**

Greenhouse Of Terror

COMPULSION
Tracks: / Compulsion.
12" Single: Released Feb '86, on Racket Manufacture, Catalogue no: **GREEN 1**

Greenslade, Dave

PENTATEUCH OVERTURE
Tracks: / Pentateuch overture / Mischief and war.
7" Single: Released Feb '80, on EMI, by EMI Records. Deleted '83. Catalogue no: **EMI 5034**

Greenwood, Lee

Biographical details: This American country singer released his debut album *Inside and out* in 1982. The following year, he issued the LP *Somebody's gonna love you*. These platters showed that, when given the right song, Greenwood's powerful and evocative voice could really deliver the goods. One of these songs was *The wind beneath my wings*, a memorable ballad that gave him a sizeable entry on the US country charts plus his first UK chart entry - the single reached the UK no. 49 position in the summer of 1984. By the mid 80's, Greenwood was a substantial star in the American country and MoR markets; his 1985 *Greatest hits* collection logged more than half a year on Billboard's country Albums List. The patriotic nature of some of his work made him a big mate of Ronald and Nancy Reagan, who even sat next to him at one black tie banquet. (Bob Macdonald, 1/10/85).

WIND BENEATH MY WINGS (SINGLE)
Tracks: / Wind beneath my wings / Barely holding on.
7" Single: Released May '84, on MCA, by MCA Records. Deleted '87. Catalogue no: **MCA 877**

Greer, Gail

IN HEAT
Tracks: / In heat.
7" Single: Released Oct '82, on Identity, by Identity Records. Catalogue no: **ID 001**

INSEPARABLE
Tracks: / Inseparable / We'll carry on.
7" Single: Released Jan '83, on Identity, by Identity Records. Catalogue no: **IDS 003**

Greer, John

ROSES FOR MAMA (SINGLE)
Tracks: / Roses for mama / D.J. cried.
7" Single: Released Nov '83, on Homespun (Ireland), by Outlet Records. Catalogue no: **HS 038**

TEDDY BEAR
Tracks: / Teddy bear / Marriage C.B. way.
7" Single: Released Feb '81, on Homespun (Ireland), by Outlet Records. Catalogue no: **HS 042**

Greeting Number Four

CIVILISED TO DEATH
Tracks: / Civilised to death.
12" Single: Released Aug '85, on Very Mouth, Catalogue no: **EAT 7**

CONDITION
Tracks: / Condition.
7" Single: Released Feb '83, on Very Mouth, Catalogue no: **EAT 2**

Gregg, John

COME BACK MARIANNE
Tracks: / Come back Marianne / I get high.
7" Single: Released Sep '80, on Magic Moon, Catalogue no: **MACH 2**

Gregg, Jonathan

I DON'T WANT TO BE ALONE TONIGHT
Tracks: / I don't want to be alone tonight / Is this love that I'm feeling.
7" Single: Released Aug '86, on Tembo, by Tembo Records. Catalogue no: **TML 118**

YOUNG HEARTS
Tracks: / Young hearts.
7" Single: Released May '86, on Tembo, by Tembo Records. Catalogue no: **TML 115**
12" Single: Released May '86, on Tembo, by Tembo Records. Catalogue no: **TMLX 115**

Gregory, Dennis

LOVE'S GONNA LOVE
Tracks: / Love's gonna love.
12" Single: Released Nov '85, on Sound City, by Sound City Records. Catalogue no: **SCD 016**

OH YOUNG LADY
Tracks: / Oh young lady / Young lady (Dub).
12" Single: Released Jul '86, on Sound City, by Sound City Records. Catalogue no: **SCD 017**

TONIGHT I'M STAYING HERE WITH YOU
Tracks: / Tonight i'm staying here with you.
7" Single: Released Apr '85, on Sound City, by Sound City Records. Catalogue no: **SCD 014**

Gregory, Glen

WHEN YOUR HEART RUNS OUT OF TIME
Tracks: / When your heart runs out of time.
12" Single: Released '85, on ZTT, by ZTT Records. Deleted Jun '88. Catalogue no: **12 ZTS 21**
12" Single: Released Aug '85, on ZTT, by ZTT Records. Deleted '87. Catalogue no: **12 ZTAS 15**
7" Single: Released Aug '85, on ZTT, by ZTT Records. Catalogue no: **ZTAS 15**
12" Single: Released '85, on ZTT, by ZTT Records. Deleted Jun '88. Catalogue no: **12 ZTS 15**

Gregory, Iain

CAN'T YOU HEAR THE BEAT OF A BROKEN HEART
Tracks: / Can't you hear the beat of a broken heart.
7" Single: Released Jan '62, on Pye, Deleted '65. Catalogue no: **7N 15397**

Gregory, Leigh

START
Tracks: / Start.
12" Single: Released 5 Mar '88, on Explicit, by Explicit Records. Catalogue no: **XPL 2**
7" Single: Released 5 Mar '88, on Explicit, by Explicit Records. Catalogue no: **7 XPL 2**

Gregory, Michael

JUBILEE
Tracks: / Jubilee / Jubilee (dub).
7" Single: Released 23 Jan '89, on Novus, by BMG Records (UK). Deleted Aug '89. Catalogue no: **PB 49517**
12" Single: Released 23 Jan '89, on Novus, by BMG Records (UK). Catalogue no: **PT 49518**

Gregory, Tony

I DON'T WANNA BE LONELY
Tracks: / I don't wanna be lonely.
12" Single: Released Sep '84, on TGM, Catalogue no: **Unknown**

Gregson, Clive

HOME IS WHERE THE HEART IS
Tracks: / Home is where the heart is.
7" Single: Released Apr '85, on Demon, by Demon Records. Catalogue no: **D 1036**

I WOULDN'T TREAT A DOG
Tracks: / I wouldn't treat a dog / I wonder what went wrong / Tender trap, The / Everybody cheats on you.
12" Single: Released 20 Feb '88, on Special Delivery, by Topic Records. Catalogue no: **SPET 12003**

Grey, Gregory

SENSUAL
Tracks: / Sensual / Johnny Purify.
7" Single: Released Apr '86, on CBS, by CBS Records. Deleted '86. Catalogue no: **A 7085**

Grey & Hanks

NOW I'M FINE
Tracks: / Now I'm fine / Love's in command.
12" Single: Released Mar '80, on RCA, by BMG Records (UK). Deleted Mar '83. Catalogue no: **PC 1922**

Grey Parade

ASLEEP
Tracks: / Asleep / House of steel.
12" Single: Released Jan '86, on Numa, by Numa Records. Catalogue no: **NUM 10**
7" Single: Released Jan '86, on Numa, by Numa Records. Catalogue no: **NU 10**

EXTERIORS
Tracks: / Exteriors.
12" Single: Released Jun '83, on Rialto (1), by Rialto Records. Catalogue no: **12 RIA 18**

Grey Roman

SHAKEDOWN
Tracks: / Shakedown.
12" Single: Released May '84, on FFT, Catalogue no: **YUMT 106**

Greyhound

Biographical details: After being Freddie Notes & The Rudies, and before being Dhanzak, this group were called Greyhound. They were certain;y more successful as Greyhound, enjoying three UK Top 20 singles during 1971-2. The Band were of Jamaican nationality but were based in Britain. The three hits were on the Trojan label, which was adept at supplying the UK market with pop-oriented reggae records in the early 70's. Greyhound's style was a catchy, sub Johnny Nash brand of the reggae genre. Their first hit was a tuneful plea for racial harmony entitled *Black and white* - it reached no. 6 in Britain, and was covered for the American market by Three Dog Night who took it to no. 1 there. Then came *Moon river*, a Greyhounf revival of Henry Mancini & Johnny Mercer's standard; it reached the UK no. 12 position. Greyhound's final success was *I am what I am*, a no. 20 hit from the songbook of Scott English (of *Brandy* fame). The lads then faded into obscurity. (Bob Macdonald, 1/10/85).

BLACK AND WHITE
Tracks: / Black and white / Moon River.
7" Single: Released Jun '71, on Trojan, by Trojan Records. Deleted '74. Catalogue no: **TR 7820**

BLACK AND WHITE (OLD GOLD)
Tracks: / Black and white.
7" Single: Released Apr '79, on Old Gold, by Old Gold Records. Catalogue no: **OG 9274**

CLASSIC TRACKS
CD 5": Released Nov '88, on Classic Tracks, Catalogue no: **CDEP 7**

DANDY LIVINGSTONE/GREYHOUND
CD 5": Released Nov '88, on Counterpoint, Catalogue no: **CDEP 7 C**

I AM WHAT I AM
Tracks: / I am what I am.
7" Single: Released Mar '72, on Trojan, by Trojan Records. Deleted '75. Catalogue no: **TR 7853**

MOON RIVER
Tracks: / Moon River.
Note: 4 track EP with other artists.
7" Single: Released Jan '72, on Trojan, by Trojan Records. Deleted '75. Catalogue no: **TR 7848**
7" Single: Released Aug '81, on Trojan, by Trojan Records. Deleted May '88. Catalogue no: **TMX 4014**

Gribbin, Tom

GUNS OF BRIXTON
Tracks: / Guns of Brixton.
7" Single: Released Jun '81, on Country Roads Records, Deleted '87. Catalogue no: **CRE 002**

Gridley, Andrew

LOST IN TIME REFLECTIONS
Tracks: / Lost in time reflections.
7" Single: Released Jul '83, on ADG, by ADG Records. Catalogue no: **ADG 001**

Grief

FEAR & DESIRE
Tracks: / Fear and desire.
12" Single: Released May '88, on Danceteria, Catalogue no: **12 DAN 006**

KYN
Tracks: / Kyn.
12" Single: Released May '88, on Danceteria, Catalogue no: **12 DAN 004**

KYN (REMIX)
Tracks: / Kyn (remix).
12" Single: Released May '89, on Danceteria, Catalogue no: **12 DAN 004R**
CD 5": Released May '89, on Danceteria, Catalogue no: **DANCD 004**

Grier, Gale

WORK IT OUT
Tracks: / Work it out / Do what you want.
7" Single: Released Dec '81, on Ariola, by BMG Records (UK). Deleted Dec '84. Catalogue no: **ARO 270**

Grier, Sonja

LOVE FLIGHT 109
Tracks: / Love flight 109 / Love flight 109 (dub).
12" Single: Released Jul '87, on RCA, by BMG Records (UK). Catalogue no: **PB 49732**
7" Single: Released Jul '87, on RCA, by BMG Records (UK). Catalogue no: **PB 49731**

Grierson, Jimmy

THIS WAY UP
Tracks: / This way up / Galactic tat.
7" Single: Released Jun '82, on Jet, by Jet Records. Deleted Jun '85. Catalogue no: **JET 164**

Griff, Zaine

Biographical details: Hailing from New Zealand, this singer, bassist and synthesiser player chalked up a pair of minor UK hits singles in 1980. Griff was a David Bowie lookalike and was teamed in the studio with Bowie's long-time producer Tony Visconti, who tried to ensure that Griff did not sound too much like a Bowie clone. In BBC Radio 1's series *The record producers?. Visconti recalled an occasion when Griff and Bowie met each other - they looked at each other and both did a double take. Griff's first chart single was Tonight,* which reached the UK no. 54 position; it was followed by *Ashes and diamonds,* which peaked at no. 68. The *Ashes & diamonds* LP failed to make any impact, as did his 1982 set *Figures.* (Bob Macdonald, 1/10/85).

ASHES AND DIAMONDS
Tracks: / Ashes and diamonds / Haunt.
7" Single: Released May '80, on Automatic, by Automatic Records. Deleted May '85. Catalogue no: **K 17610**

FIGURES (SINGLE)
Tracks: / Figures / Mental pictures.
7" Single: Released Jul '82, on Polydor, by Polydor Ltd. Deleted Jul '85. Catalogue no: **POSP 458**
12" Single: Released Jul '82, on Polydor, by Polydor Ltd. Deleted Jul '85. Catalogue no: **POSPX 458**

FLOWERS
Tracks: / Flowers / Turn out the light.
7" Single: Released Sep '82, on Polydor, by Polydor Ltd. Deleted Sep '85. Catalogue no: **POSP 506**

TONIGHT
Tracks: / Tonight / This could be everything.
7" Single: Released Feb '80, on Automatic, by Automatic Records. Deleted '83. Catalogue no: **K 17547**

Griffin, Billy

Biographical details: This American singer and songwriter came to public attention in 1972, when he performed the formidable task of replacing Smokey Robinson as leader of the Miracles. Griffin's name was unfamiliar to fans, as he had not been a member of the group up until that point. The Miracles struggled somewhat without Smokey, except for an international smash with 1976's *Love machine.* Griffin launched a solo career in early 1983 with the classy, romantic, midtempo soul single *Hold me tighter in the rain* - this scored well on the US black charts and became a UK Top 20 pop hit. This was taken from his debut solo album *Be with me.* His next LP *Respect* yielded another sensual single *Serious,* which peaked at no. 64 on the UK chart in January 1984. Griffin's silky soul voice continued to maintain its owner's status as a moderate though not major star in black music. (Bob Macdonald, 1/10/85).

BE WITH ME (SINGLE)
Tracks: / Be with me.
12" Single: Released Mar '83, on CBS, by CBS Records. Catalogue no: **A 13 3209**
7" Single: Released Mar '83, on CBS, by CBS Records. Catalogue no: **A 3209**

BELIEVE IT OR NOT
Tracks: / Believe it or not / E.S.P.
12" Single: Released Nov '86, on Atlantic, by WEA Records. Deleted Jan '88. Catalogue no: **A 9374 T**
7" Single: Released Nov '86, on Atlantic, by WEA Records. Deleted Jun '87. Catalogue no: **A 9374**

GIRL IS FINE, THE
Tracks: / Girl is fine / E.S.P..
7" Single: Released Apr '87, on Atlantic, by WEA Records. Deleted Jan '88. Catalogue no: **A 9275**
12" Single: Released Apr '87, on Atlantic, by WEA Records. Deleted Jan '88. Catalogue no: **A 9275 T**

HOLD ME TIGHTER IN THE RAIN
Tracks: / Hold me tighter in the rain / Understand.
7" Single: Released Jan '83, on CBS, by CBS Records. Deleted '86. Catalogue no: **A 2935**
12" Single: Released Jan '83, on CBS, by CBS Records. Deleted '86. Catalogue no: **A 132935**

HOLD ME TIGHTER IN THE RAIN (OLD GOLD)
Tracks: / Hold me tighter in the rain.
12" Single: Released Aug '88, on Old Gold, by Old Gold Records. Catalogue no: **OG 4077**
7" Single: Released Sep '85, on Old Gold, by Old Gold Records. Deleted Jul '88. Catalogue no: **OG 9563**

SERIOUS
Tracks: / Serious / Hit me with the beat.
7" Single: Released Jan '84, on CBS, by CBS Records. Deleted '87. Catalogue no: **A 4053**

Griffin, Clive

BE THERE
Tracks: / Be there / Try to be happy.
CD 5": Released 13 Feb '89, on Phonogram, by Phonogram Ltd. Catalogue no: **STECD 3**
7" Single: Released 13 Feb '89, on Phonogram, by Phonogram Ltd. Deleted 31 Jul '89. Catalogue no: **STEPP 3**
7" Single: Released 13 Feb '89, on Phonogram, by Phonogram Ltd. Deleted 31 Jul '89. Catalogue no: **STEP 3**
12" Single: Released 13 Feb '89, on Phonogram, by Phonogram Ltd. Deleted 31 Jul '89. Catalogue no: **STEP 312**
10" single: Released 13 Feb '89, on Phonogram, by Phonogram Ltd. Deleted 31 Jul '89. Catalogue no: **STEP 310**

DON'T MAKE ME WAIT
Tracks: / Don't make me wait.
7" Single: Released 28 Jul '88, on Phonogram, by Phonogram Ltd. Deleted Feb '89. Catalogue no: **STEP 2**
12" Single: Released 28 Jul '88, on Phonogram, by Phonogram Ltd. Deleted Feb '89. Catalogue no: **STEP 212**
CD 5": Released 28 Jul '88, on Phonogram, by Phonogram Ltd. Deleted Feb '89. Catalogue no: **STECD 2**

HEAD ABOVE WATER
Tracks: / Head above water / By heart / Love street (Only on 12" and CD single.) / Head above water (remix) (Only on 12".) / Head above water (full length version) (Only on CD single.).
7" Single: Released May '89, on Mercury, by Phonogram Ltd. Deleted Oct '89. Catalogue no: **STEP 4**
12" Single: Released May '89, on Mercury, by Phonogram Ltd. Deleted Oct '89. Catalogue no: **STEP 412**
CD 5": Released May '89, on Mercury, by Phonogram Ltd. Catalogue no: **STECD 4**

WAY WE TOUCH, THE
Tracks: / Way we touch, The.
Note: Debut single from Clive Griffin one of Phonogram's latest signings, and biggest hopes for major success in '88. Co-written and produced by Clive offers a soul/pop blend, utilising the power and range of his distinctive vocal style. Upfront support from the specialist radio areas which should spread across the board to mainstream media coverage upon its commercial release. Full effort from Phonogram through marketing and media promotion - our aim is to establish Clive Griffin as a major U.K. artist, whcih on the strngth of his songwriting, his natural talent and all round charisma shouldn't be a masive problem. This debut single is 'Step One' in our long term plan. (Phonogram 5/88).
7" Single: Released May '88, on Phonogram, by Phonogram Ltd. Deleted Feb '89. Catalogue no: **STEP 1**
12" Single: Released May '88, on Phonogram, by Phonogram Ltd. Deleted Feb '89. Catalogue no: **STEP 112**
CD 5": Released May '88, on Phonogram, by Phonogram Ltd. Deleted Feb '89. Catalogue no: **STECD 1**

Griffin, Reggie

MIRADA ROCK
Tracks: / Mirada rock.
12" Single: Released Jan '83, on Sugarhill (USA), Catalogue no: **SHL 121**

Griffin & Sylvester

PLEASE COME INTO MY LIFE
Tracks: / Please come into my life / If you give your love to me.
7" Single: Released Jun '82, on Polydor, by Polydor Ltd. Deleted Jun '85. Catalogue no: **POSP 466**

Griffin, Sylvia

LOVE'S A STATE OF MIND
Tracks: / Loves a state of mind / Lonely heart (Extra track on 12" and CD single, featuring George Harrison) / Forgive the girl.
CD 5": Released 16 May '88, on Phonogram, by Phonogram Ltd. Deleted Feb '89. Catalogue no: **BLASTCD 7**
12" Single: Released 16 May '88, on Phonogram, by Phonogram Ltd. Deleted Feb '89. Catalogue no: **BLAST 712**
7" Single: Released 16 May '88, on Phonogram, by Phonogram Ltd. Deleted Feb '89. Catalogue no: **BLAST 7**

WHITE HUNTER
Tracks: / White hunter.
7" Single: Released Jan '84, on Magnet, by WEA Records. Catalogue no: **MAG 253**
12" Single: Released Jan '84, on Magnet, by WEA Records. Catalogue no: **12 MAG 253**

Griffith, Nanci

COLD HEARTS
Tracks: / Cold hearts, closed minds / Cold minds / Ford econoline / Lonestar state of mind.
7" Single: Released 21 Nov '87, on MCA, by MCA Records. Catalogue no: **MCA 1221**

FROM A DISTANCE
Tracks: / From a distance / Sing one for sister.
CD 5": Released Sep '88, on MCA, by MCA Records. Catalogue no: **DMCA 1282**
7" Single: Released Jul '87, on MCA, by MCA Records. Catalogue no: **MCA 1169**
7" Single: Released Sep '88, on MCA, by MCA Records. Deleted 1 Jul '89. Catalogue no: **MCA 1282**

I KNEW LOVE
Tracks: / I knew love / Never mind / Lone star state of mind.
7" Single: Released Apr '88, on MCA, by MCA Records. Catalogue no: **MCA 1240**
12" Single: Released Apr '88, on MCA, by MCA Records. Catalogue no: **MCAT 1240**

IT'S A HARD LIFE
Tracks: / It's a hard life.
CD 5": Released Jul '89, on MCA, by MCA Records. Catalogue no: **DMCAT 1358**
7" Single: Released Jul '89, on MCA, by MCA Records. Catalogue no: **MCA 1358**
12" Single: Released Jul '89, on MCA, by MCA Records. Catalogue no: **MCAT 1358**

OUTBOUND PLANE
Tracks: / Outbound plane / So long ago / Trouble in the fields.
7" Single: Released Feb '88, on MCA, by MCA Records. Catalogue no: **MCA 1230**
12" Single: Released Feb '88, on MCA, by MCA Records. Catalogue no: **MCAT 1230**

Griffith, Roni

MONDO MAN
Tracks: / Mondo man / Desire.
12" Single: Released Nov '81, on Virgin, by Virgin Records. Deleted '84. Catalogue no: **VSL 5021**
7" Single: Released Nov '81, on Virgin, by Virgin Records. Deleted '84. Catalogue no: **VS 5021**

Griffiths, Hugh

BE HAPPY
Tracks: / Be happy.
7" Single: Released May '89, on Scorpion, Catalogue no: **UNKNOWN**

BIG, WE BIG
Tracks: / Big we big.
12" Single: Released Oct '84, on Scorpio, by Scorpio Records. Catalogue no: **Unknown**

DON'T YOU EVER LEAVE
Tracks: / Don't you ever leave me / Marigoine.
12" Single: Released Dec '84, on Gamble, Catalogue no: **GAD 07**

SEXY LADY
Tracks: / Sexy lady / Now I know.
12" Single: Released Sep '83, on Greensleeves, by Greensleeves Records. Catalogue no: **GRED 128**

SPLENDID THINGS
Tracks: / Splendid things / All because of you.
12" Single: Released Nov '83, on Uptempo, Catalogue no: **UT 002**

STUCK ON YOU
Tracks: / Stuck on you.
12" Single: Released Oct '84, on Jedi, Catalogue no: **JJ 207**

THEM R A TEASE
Tracks: / Them r a tease / Them nah please.
12" Single: Released Dec '86, on Pioneer International, Catalogue no: **PI 8**

Griffiths, Joe

BREAKAWAY, THEME FROM
Tracks: / Breakaway, Theme from / Red ice.
7" Single: Released Jan '80, on BBC, by BBC Records & Tapes. Deleted Jan '83. Catalogue no: **RESL 74**

Griffiths, Marcia

DEEP IN MY HEART
Tracks: / Deep in my heart.
7" Single: Released '88, on Germaine, Catalogue no: **DGT 40**

DON'T EVER LEAVE
Tracks: / Don't ever leave.
12" Single: Released Sep '81, on Sheba, Catalogue no: **MG 713**

EVERYWHERE
Tracks: / Everywhere.
12" Single: Released Jan '88, on Germaine, Catalogue no: **DGT 27**

FEVER
Tracks: / Fever.
7" Single: on Island, by Island Records. Deleted Jun '88. Catalogue no: **IS 361**
12" Single: on Island, by Island Records. Deleted Jun '88. Catalogue no: **12IS 361**

IT HURTS TO BE ALONE
Tracks: / It hurts to be alone / Solomonic serenade.
12" Single: Released Jan '84, on Solomonic (1), by Solomonic Records. Catalogue no: **SM 12019**
7" Single: Released Jan '84, on Solomonic (1), by Solomonic Records. Catalogue no: **SM 7019**

SOMETHING INSIDE SO STRONG
Tracks: / Something inside so strong.
12" Single: Released Jan '89, on Body Music, by Nuclear Records. Catalogue no: **BZT 23**

Griffiths, Roni

Biographical details: Originally a member of Kid Creole & The Coconuts, this American singer issued her self-titled debut LP in July 1982. One of the tracks was *(The best part of) breaking up,* which flopped when released as a single in March 1983. However, the track finally enjoyed a taste of success in summer 1984 - it reached no. 63 on the UK chart; at the same time, another Kid Creole-associated single, Daisy Chain's *No time to stop believing in love,* was being woefully and undeservedly ignored. Roni Griffiths failed to consolidate on her chart threshold. (Bob Macdonald, 2/10/85).

BEST PART OF BREAKING UP
Tracks: / Best part of breaking up / Love is the drug.
7" Single: Released Mar '83, on Vanguard, by Start Records Ltd.. Catalogue no: **VS 5022**
12" Single: Released Apr '86, on Making Waves, by Celtic Music. Catalogue no: **SURFT 101**
12" Single: Released Mar '83, on Vanguard, by Start Records Ltd.. Catalogue no: **VSL 5022**
7" Single: Released Apr '86, on Making Waves, by Celtic Music. Catalogue no: **SURF 101**

BREAKING MY HEART
Tracks: / Breaking my heart.
7" Single: Released Apr '83, on Vanguard, by Start Records Ltd.. Catalogue no: **VS 5025**
12" Single: Released Apr '83, on Vanguard, by Start Records Ltd.. Catalogue no: **VSL 5025**

Grill, Rob

ROCK SUGAR
Tracks: / Rock sugar / Have mercy.
7" Single: Released Feb '80, on Mercury, by Phonogram Ltd. Deleted '83. Catalogue no: **6167836**

Grimes, Carol

AIN'T THAT PECULIAR
Tracks: / Ain't that peculiar / Fashion passion.
7" Single: Released Nov '82, on Polydor, by Polydor Ltd. Deleted Nov '85. Catalogue no: **POSP 417**

Grimethorpe Colliery

RAISE YOUR BANNERS HIGH
Tracks: / Raise your banners high.
7" Single: Released Oct '85, on Rough Trade, by Rough Trade Records. Catalogue no: **TUC 784**

Grimm Death

TOO TUFF TO RIP
Tracks: / Too tuff to rip.
12" Single: Released Jan '88, on Vinyl Solution, by Vinyl Solution Records. Catalogue no: **VS 8**

Grimm, Roland

SELFISH AMERICAN BITCH

Tracks: / Selfish American bitch / Demolition.
7" Single: Released Jul '87, on U-Turn, by U-Turn Records. Catalogue no: **U-TURN**

Grinder

SPIDERMAN
Tracks: / Spiderman / Furry dice / Other people.
7" Single: Catalogue no: **EAR 2**

Grine,Joe

LIFE
Tracks: / Life / Well pleased & satisfied.
12" Single: Released Aug '82, on Exclusive, Catalogue no: **EXC 601128**

Grip

ENGLAND YOUR DEAD
Tracks: / England your dead.
12" Single: Released Oct '87, on Grip, Catalogue no: **RPG 001**

KEEPING THE PEACE
Tracks: / Keeping the peace / Musicland.
7" Single: Released Aug '82, on Gripping Youth, Catalogue no: **GRIP 1**

LOOK AT WHAT YOU'VE DONE
Tracks: / Look at what you've done.
12" Single: Released Sep '89, on Survival (1), by Survival Records. Catalogue no: **SUR 12049**
7" Single: Released Sep '89, on Survival (1), by Survival Records. Catalogue no: **SUR 049**

TEENAGE BRIDE
Tracks: / Teenage bride / Silicon and wire / England you're dead.
7" Single: Released Apr '89, on Survival (1), by Survival Records. Catalogue no: **SUR 048**
12" Single: Released Apr '89, on Survival (1), by Survival Records. Catalogue no: **SUR 12048**

Griswalds

DO THE HUCKLEBUCK
Tracks: / Do the hucklebuck.
12" Single: Released Jul '88, on Raucous, Catalogue no: **RAUC 005**

Grogan, Claire

LOVE BOMB
Tracks: / Love bomb / I love the way you beg.
7" Single: Released 23 May '87, on London Records, by London Records. Deleted Sep '87. Catalogue no: **LON 134**
12" Single: Released 23 May '87, on London Records, by London Records. Catalogue no: **LONX 134**

Groove

DANCING & MUSIC
Tracks: / Dancing and music.
12" Single: Released Jan '88, on Submission, by Submission Records. Catalogue no: **SUBX 04**

HIJACK THE BEAT
Tracks: / Hijack the beat.
7" Single: Released Aug '88, on Submission, by Submission Records. Catalogue no: **SUB 05**
12" Single: Released Jul '88, on Submission, by Submission Records. Catalogue no: **SUBX 05**

Groove Control

DO IT ANYWAY
Tracks: / Do it anyway.
12" Single: Released Nov '84, on Nunk, Catalogue no: **NUNK 1009**

Groove Farm

BIG BLACK PLASTIC EXPLOSION
Tracks: / Big black plastic explosion / Nancy Sinatra / Red dress / Baby blue marine / Riot on sunset strip.
12" Single: Released 14 May '88, on Subway, by Subway Records. Catalogue no: **SUBWAY 19T**

DRIVING IN YOUR NEW CAR
Tracks: / Driving in your new car / I can't dance with you.
10" single: Released Oct '88, on Subway, by Subway Records. Catalogue no: **SUBWAY 022N**

HATE US & WE'LL LOVE YOU TO DEATH EP
Tracks: / Hate us & we'll love you to death.
12" Single: Released Apr '89, on Raving Pop Blast, Catalogue no: **RAVE 001T**

SECOND EP
7" Single: Released Feb '89, on Raving Pop Blast, Catalogue no: **RPBGF 002**

SORE HEADS & HAPPY HEARTS (EP)
7" Single: Released Mar '87, on Raving Pop Blast, Catalogue no: **RPBGF 001**

SURFIN' INTO YOUR HEART
Tracks: / Surfin' into your heart.
7" Single: Released Jul '87, on Subway, by Subway Records. Catalogue no: **SUBWAY 15**
12" Single: Released Jul '87, on Subway, by Subway Records. Catalogue no: **SUBWAY 15T**

Groove Gangsters

JUMP TO THE BEAT (REMIX)
Tracks: / Jump to the beat (remix).
12" Single: Released '88, on Groove Gangster, Catalogue no: **THGG 12/2**
7" Single: Released '88, on Groove Gangster, Catalogue no: **THGG 12/1**

Groove Harmony

REASONS
Tracks: / Reasons.
12" Single: Released Aug '88, on Grooveatron, Catalogue no: **GAT 03**

Groove Masters

JUMP TO THE BEAT
Tracks: / Jump to the beat.
12" Single: Released '88, on Groove Gangster, Catalogue no: **THGG 12/1**

SUNSHINE ON A BLUE DAY
Tracks: / Sunshine on a blue day.
7" Single: Released Jun '84, on Electricity, by Electricity Records. Deleted '88. Catalogue no: **TRIC 1001**
12" Single: Released Jun '84, on Electricity, by Electricity Records. Deleted '88. Catalogue no: **TRICT 1001**

Groove Robbers

HOW FAR CAN WE GO?
Tracks: / How far can we go ?.
12" Single: Released Aug '88, on Cat, by Cat Records. Catalogue no: **ABB 99**

WORK IT OUT (WE CAN MAKE IT BETTER)
Tracks: / Work it out (we can make it better).
7" Single: Released Aug '89, on Cheque This, by Cheque This Records. Catalogue no: **CTT 3**
12" Single: Released Aug '89, on Cheque This, by Cheque This Records. Catalogue no: **7CCT 3**

Groove Train

WHY DID YOU DO IT
Tracks: / Why did you do it / All aboard.
12" Single: Released Jul '88, on Urban, by Polydor Ltd. Catalogue no: **URBX 21**
7" Single: Released Jul '88, on Urban, by Polydor Ltd. Catalogue no: **URB 21**

Groovin' with Lucy

THAT'S ROCK'N'ROLL
Tracks: / That's rock'n'roll / Lenny's lament / Wired in Wonderland (Only on 12").
7" Single: Released Sep '88, on Karbon, by Karbon Records. Catalogue no: **KAR 610**
12" Single: Released Sep '88, on Karbon, by Karbon Records. Catalogue no: **KAR 610 T**

Groovy Chainsaw

CHAINSAW
Tracks: / Chainsaw / Rock hard / Human meat / Voodoo head.
7" Single: Released Nov '88, on Flicknife, by Flicknife Records. Catalogue no: **FLEP 107**

GROOVY CHAINSAWS EP
Tracks: / Groovy chainsaws.
7" Single: Released Feb '89, on Flicknife, by Flicknife Records. Catalogue no: **FLEP 107**

Groovy Little Numbers

HAPPY LIKE YESTERDAY
Tracks: / Happy like yesterday.
12" Single: Released Aug '88, on 53rd & 3rd, by 53rd & 3rd Records. Catalogue no: **AGARR 21T**
7" Single: Released Dec '88, on 53rd & 3rd, by 53rd & 3rd Records. Catalogue no: **AGARR 21**

YOU MAKE MY HEAD EXPLODE
Tracks: / You make my head explode.
12" Single: Released Jan '88, on 53rd & 3rd, by 53rd & 3rd Records. Catalogue no: **AGARR 13T**

Groovy, Paul

ANDY WATCHOUT
Tracks: / Andy watchout.
Note: See also under Pop Art Experience,& Paul Groovy
7" Single: Released Mar '87, on Bite Back, Catalogue no: **BB 012**

Groovy, Winston

ADAM AND EVE
Tracks: / Adam and eve / Girl next door.
12" Single: Released Jan '82, on PRT, by Castle Communications Records. Deleted Jan '85. Catalogue no: **12P 230**
7" Single: Released Jan '82, on PRT, by Castle Communications Records. Deleted Jan '85. Catalogue no: **7P 230**

BLANKET ON THE GROUND
Tracks: / Blanket on the ground.
12" Single: Released Jul '89, on A.1, by A.1 Records. Catalogue no: **12A 1297**

DON'T BLAME ME
Tracks: / Don't blame me / Second chance.
12" Single: Released Oct '80, on Time, Catalogue no: **EBY 008**

FROM WE MET
Tracks: / From we met.
12" Single: Released Nov '83, on Three Kings, Catalogue no: **TK 006**

HELLO ROBIN REDBREAST
Tracks: / Hello robin redbreast / Wendy.
7" Single: Released Jan '81, on Laser, Deleted Jan '94. Catalogue no: **LAS 19**

I REALLY LOVE YOU
Tracks: / I really love you.
12" Single: Released Jan '84, on Dancebeat, Catalogue no: **DBD 1318**

LIVING IN A DREAM
Tracks: / Living in a dream.
12" Single: Released Nov '84, on Sound City, by Sound City Records. Catalogue no: **SCD 012**

NIGHTSHIFT
Tracks: / Nightshift / What will I do.
7" Single: Released Apr '85, on Jive, by Zomba Records. Catalogue no: **JIVE 93**
12" Single: Released Apr '85, on Jive, by Zomba Records. Catalogue no: **JIVET 93**
12" Single: Released Mar '85, on Sound City, by Sound City Records. Catalogue no: **SCD 015**

PARADISE IN YOUR EYES
Tracks: / Paradise in your eyes.
12" Single: Released Nov '83, on Dafala, Catalogue no: **DAF 001**

PLEASE DON'T MAKE ME CRY
Tracks: / Please don't make me cry / All because of you / Give me time.
12" Single: Released Nov '83, on Sound City, by Sound City Records. Catalogue no: **SCT 7009**
7" Single: Released Nov '83, on Sound City, by Sound City Records. Catalogue no: **SC 7009**

PLEASE DON'T MAKE ME CRY (EP)
7" Single: Released Nov '83, on Trojan, by Trojan Records. Catalogue no: **TRO 9075**
12" Single: Released Nov '83, on Trojan, by Trojan Records. Catalogue no: **TROT 9075**

ROCK ME TONIGHT
Tracks: / Rock me tonight (for old time's sake).
7" Single: Released Sep '85, on Jive, by Zomba Records. Catalogue no: **JIVE 103**
12" Single: Released Sep '85, on Jive, by Zomba Records. Catalogue no: **JIVET 103**

SO IN LOVE WITH YOU
Tracks: / So in love with you.
7" Single: Released Nov '82, on Top Ranking (1), Catalogue no: **TRY 6**

SOMETHING ON THE SIDE
Tracks: / Something on the side / I don't mind.
7" Single: Released 21 Nov '87, on DJM, Catalogue no: **DJM 10975**
12" Single: Released 21 Nov '87, on Creole, by Creole Records. Catalogue no: **DJM 10975T**
12" Single: Released Feb '84, on Sound City, by Sound City Records. Catalogue no: **SCD 010**

SOMETHING ON THE SIDE (SINGLE)
Tracks: / Something on the side / Don't call on me / I don't mind (12" only).
7" Single: Released '88, on DJM, Catalogue no: **DJS 10970**
12" Single: Released '88, on DJM, Catalogue no: **DJR 10970**

SOUTH OF THE BORDER
Tracks: / South of the border.
7" Single: Released Oct '88, on WG, Catalogue no: **WG 03**

YOU MADE LOOK IT SO EASY
Tracks: / You made it look so easy / Easy(Version).
12" Single: Released Jun '86, on WG, Catalogue no: **WG 01**

Gross, Henry

SHANNON
Tracks: / Shannon.
7" Single: Released Aug '76, on Lifesong, Deleted '79. Catalogue no: **ELS 45002**

Groucutt, Kelly

LET THE KIDS DO IT
Tracks: / Let the kids do it / You didn't need to hold me tight.
7" Single: Released Jan '83, on Riva, by Riva Records. Catalogue no: **RIVA 39**

OH LITTLE DARLIN'
Tracks: / Oh little darlin' / I can't stand the morning.
7" Single: Released Jul '82, on RCA, by BMG Records (UK). Deleted Jul '85. Catalogue no: **RCA 245**

WE LOVE ANIMALS
Tracks: / We love animals.
7" Single: Released May '85, on Premier, by Premier Records. Catalogue no: **RSPCA 1**

Ground Zero

GROUND ZERO
7" EP: Released Mar '84, on Azra (USA), by Azra International (USA). Catalogue no: **A 64**

Group

AMERICAN
Tracks: / American / White hammer.
7" Single: Released Apr '84, on Jive, by Zomba Records. Catalogue no: **JIVE 63**
12" Single: Released Apr '84, on Jive, by Zomba Records. Catalogue no: **JIVET 63**

I DON'T LIKE TO LOSE
Tracks: / I don't like to lose.
7" Single: Released Dec '84, on Soul Supply, by Soul Supply Records. Catalogue no: **7SS 105**

IRON CHAIN
Tracks: / Iron chain.
12" Single: Released Sep '84, on Jive, by Zomba Records. Catalogue no: **JIVET 72**
7" Single: Released Sep '84, on Jive, by Zomba Records. Catalogue no: **JIVE 72**

TECHNOLOGY
Tracks: / Technology / You're my flag.
7" Single: Released Sep '83, on Jive, by Zomba Records. Catalogue no: **JIVE 42**
12" Single: Released Sep '83, on Jive, by Zomba Records. Catalogue no: **JIVET 42**

VICTIMS OF CIRCUMSTANCE
Tracks: / Victims of circumstance.
7" Single: Released Jun '84, on Jive, by Zomba Records. Catalogue no: **JIVE 68**
12" Single: Released Jun '84, on Jive, by Zomba Records. Catalogue no: **JIVET 68**

Group Therapy

ARTY-FACT
Tracks: / Arty fact / Drug chic.
7" Single: Released Jul '82, on Kamera, Deleted '88. Catalogue no: **ERA 011**

Groves, Edgel

FOOTPRINTS IN THE SAND
Tracks: / Footprints in the sand.
7" Single: Released Aug '81, on Chips, Deleted '83. Catalogue no: **CHI 106**

Grown Up Strange

WING AND A PRAYER
Tracks: / Wing and a prayer.
12" Single: Released 17 Oct '86, on Ugly Man, by Ugly Man Records. Catalogue no: **UGLY 001T**

Gruesome Twosome

HALLUCINATION GENERATION
Tracks: / Hallucination generation / Hallucination generation (version).
12" Single: Released Jul '89, on SSR, Catalogue no: **12SSR 96**

Grumbleweeds

COME ON DOWN T'BREAD SHOP
Tracks: / Come on down t'bread shop / Come on baby.
7" Single: Released Mar '81, on MFP, by EMI Records. Catalogue no: **FP 901**

SHALL I GIVE YOU A NUDGE
Tracks: / Shall I give you a nudge / We are the grumbleweeds.
7" Single: Released May '81, on MFP, by EMI Records. Catalogue no: **FP 902**

WOMEN'S INTUITION
Tracks: / Women's intuition / That's all I have to say.
7" Single: Released Jul '86, on Spirit (1), by Spirit Records. Catalogue no: **FIRE 13**

Grundy, Eddie

CLARRIE
Tracks: / Clarrie.
7" Single: Released Sep '85, on Foxy, by Foxy Records. Catalogue no: **CUB 4**

LAMBS TO THE SLAUGHTER
Tracks: / Lambs to the slaughter.
7" Single: Released Jul '81, on Dingle's, by Dingle's Records. Catalogue no: **SID 230**

POOR PIG
Tracks: / Poor pig / Clarries song / Poor pater.
7" Single: Released Nov '82, on Foxy, by Foxy Records. Catalogue no: **CUB 1**

G-Squad

IN MY MIND
Tracks: / In my mind / Room full of paper.
7" Single: Released Sep '81, on SMT, Deleted '82. Catalogue no: **SMT 007**

GTR

WHEN THE HEART RULES THE MIND
Tracks: / When the heart rules the mind / Reach out (never say no) / Sketches in the sun (Extra track on 12" version only.) / Hackett to bits (Extra track on 12" version only.).
7" Single: Released May '86, on Arista, by BMG Records (UK). Catalogue no: **GTR 1**
7" Pic: Released Sep '86, on Arista, by BMG Records (UK). Catalogue no: **GTR SD 1**
12" Single: Released May '86, on Arista, by BMG Records (UK). Catalogue no: **GTR 121**

GT'S

BOYS HAVE FEELINGS TOO
Tracks: / Boys have feelings too.
7" Single: Released Feb '80, on Stiff, by Stiff Records. Catalogue no: **BUY 60**

Guadalcanal Diary

WATUSI RADIO
Tracks: / Watusi radio.
7" Single: Released Aug '85, on Elektra, by Elektra Records (UK). Catalogue no: **EKR 23**

Guamary

FLOREO DE LLAMAS
Tracks: / Floreo de llamas / A vos te h'ai pesar.
7" Single: Released Dec '82, on BBC, by BBC Records & Tapes. Deleted Dec '87. Catalogue no: **RESL 125**

Guana Batz

CAVE
Tracks: / Cave, The / Werewolf blues.
7" Single: Released Apr '84, on Big Beat, by Ace Records. Catalogue no: **NS 96**

I'M ON FIRE
Tracks: / I'm on fire.
7" Single: Released Jun '86, on I.D., by I.D. Records. Catalogue no: **EYE 9**
12" Single: Released Jun '86, on I.D., by I.D. Records. Catalogue no: **EYET 9**

LOAN SHARKS
Tracks: / Loan shark / Radio sweetheart.
7" Single: Released Dec '86, on I.D., by I.D. Records. Catalogue no: **EYE 12**

ROCK THIS TOWN
Tracks: / Rock this town / Just love me.
7" Single: Released 23 May '87, on I.D., by I.D. Records. Catalogue no: **EYE 13**

SEETHROUGH
Tracks: / Seethrough / Batman (live) / Side blues.
12" Single: Released Feb '86, on I.D., by I.D. Records. Catalogue no: **EYET 6**

YOU'RE SO FINE
Tracks: / You're so fine / Rockin' in my coffin / Jungle rumble / Guana rock.
7" Single: Released Nov '83, on Big Beat, by Ace Records. Catalogue no: **SW 89**

Guardian Angel

CRUCIAL LOVING
Tracks: / Crucial loving / Spirit.
7" Single: Released Jul '82, on Solid Groove, Catalogue no: **SGS 012**
12" Single: Released Jul '82, on Solid Groove, Catalogue no: **SG 012**

LOVES ALIVE AND KICKING
Tracks: / Love's alive and kicking / Woman at.
12" Single: Released Oct '80, on Cavalis, Deleted '87. Catalogue no: **CAV 002**

SELF SERVICE LOVE
Tracks: / Self service love / Jim Screechie.
7" Single: Released Jan '80, on EMI, by EMI Records. Deleted Jan '83. Catalogue no: **RIC 106**
12" Single: Released Jan '80, on EMI, by EMI Records. Deleted Jan '83. Catalogue no: **12RIC 106**

Gubal

MY LIFE
Tracks: / My life / Live dub.
12" Single: Released Aug '82, on Vision, by Vision Records. Catalogue no: **VIS 002**

Guduil

POOT
Tracks: / Poot.
12" Single: Released Jul '85, on Backs, by Backs Recording Co.. Catalogue no: **12 NCH 104**

Guernica

GUERNICA
Tracks: / Guernica.
12" Single: Released Mar '87, on Idol, Catalogue no: **12ID 2**

HUMMING OF THE ENGINE
Tracks: / Humming of the engine.
12" Single: Released May '88, on Miss Pedestal, Catalogue no: **MP 001**

Guess Who

AMERICAN WOMAN
Tracks: / American woman.
7" Single: Released May '70, on RCA, by BMG Records (UK). Deleted '73. Catalogue no: **RCA 1943**

HIS GIRL
Tracks: / His girl.
7" Single: Released Feb '67, on King (2), by R & B Discs Ltd. Deleted '70. Catalogue no: **KG 1044**

Guided Muscle

PRETTY ONES
Tracks: / Pretty ones / Autotheft.
7" Single: Released Nov '80, on Rocket, by Rocket Records. Deleted Nov '83. Catalogue no: **XPRES 38**

Guiding Star

COME SING WITH US
Tracks: / Come sing with us.
7" Single: Released Dec '81, on Eagle (West Germany), by Bear Family Records (Germany). Catalogue no: **ERS 015**

Guido

I'M ALONE
Tracks: / I'm alone.
7" Single: Released Mar '87, on Recoil, by Prism Records. Catalogue no: **RCLG 6**

Guidry, Greg

GOIN' DOWN
Tracks: / Goin' down / Darlin' it's yours.
7" Single: Released May '82, on CBS, by CBS Records. Deleted May '85. Catalogue no: **CBSA 2051**

Guinn

OPEN YOUR DOOR
Tracks: / Open your door / Sincerely.
7" Single: Released Apr '86, on Motown, by BMG Records (UK). Catalogue no: **GUINN 1**
12" Single: Released Apr '86, on Motown, by BMG Records (UK). Deleted '87. Catalogue no: **GUINN 1T**

PEOPLE WILL BE PEOPLE
Tracks: / People will be people / Dreamin'.
12" Single: Released Jul '86, on Motown, by BMG Records (UK). Catalogue no: **GUNNT 2**
7" Single: Released Jul '86, on Motown, by BMG Records (UK). Catalogue no: **GUNN 2**

Guinness, Valentine

(HEY, HEY) C.J.T.
Tracks: / (Hey, hey) C.J.T. / When Mandy calls.
7" Single: Released Apr '80, on RAK, by EMI Records. Deleted Apr '83. Catalogue no: **RAK 308**

Guitar George

WHO IS INNOCENT
Tracks: / Who is innocent / Death in the Nile / Manchester boys.
12" Single: Released May '88, on Graduate, by Graduate Records. Deleted Dec '88. Catalogue no: **12 GRAD 17**

Guitars & Drums

BELIEVE IT OR NOT
Tracks: / Believe it or not.
12" Single: Released '84, on Guitar Masters, Catalogue no: **EARLEP 184**

Gun

Biographical details: This British rock band consisted of brothers Adrian and Paul Gurvitz plus Louis Farrell. Gun was a frenetic hard rock combo who shot to fame at the end of 1968 with their one-off UK hit *Race with the devil*;penned by Adrian, this single bulleted to no. 8. They tried to capitalize with further singles plus a pair of albums, but none were successful. Gun quickly folded, and the Gurvitz brothers re-emerged in 1971 with Three Man Army. The latter group achieved no success so, in 1975, they joined forces with ex-Graham Bond Organisation/Cream/Blind Faith drummer Ginger Baker to form the Baker-Gurvitz Army. Although the new band's eponymous debut LP reached the UK Top 30, their two follow-up albums were failures on account of their increasingly dated sub-Cream sound. Both the brothers and Baker then drifted into obscurity, although Adrian made a brief comeback in 1982 with the UK Top 10 single *Classic*. (Bob Macdonald, 2/10/85).

BETTER DAYS
Tracks: / Better days / When you love somebody / Coming home (12" & CD only).
12" Single: Released 5 Jun '89, on A&M, by A&M Records. Catalogue no: **AMY 505**
CD 5": Released 5 Jun '89, on A&M, by A&M Records. Catalogue no: **CDEE 505**
7" Single: Released 5 Jun '89, on A&M, by A&M Records. Catalogue no: **AM 505**

MONEY
Tracks: / Money.
7" Single: Released Oct '89, on A&M, by A&M Records. Catalogue no: **AMP**

MONEY (EVERYBODY LOVES HER)
Tracks: / Money (everybody loves her) / Prime time.
7" Single: Released Sep '89, on A&M, by A&M Records. Catalogue no: **AM 520**
CD 5": Released Sep '89, on A&M, by A&M Records. Catalogue no: **CDEE 520**
12" Pic: Released Sep '89, on A&M, by A&M Records. Catalogue no: **AMP 520**
12" Single: Released Sep '89, on A&M, by A&M Records. Catalogue no: **AMY 520**

RACE WITH THE DEVIL
Tracks: / Race with the devil.
7" Single: Released Nov '68, on CBS, by CBS Records. Deleted '71. Catalogue no: **CBS 3764**

RACE WITH THE DEVIL (OLD GOLD)
Tracks: / Race with the devil.
7" Single: Released '82, on Old Gold, by Old Gold Records. Catalogue no: **OG 9193**

Gun Club

BREAKING HANDS
Tracks: / Breaking hands.
7" Single: Released 25 Mar '88, on Red Rhino, by Red Rhino Records. Catalogue no: **RED 089**
12" Single: Released Apr '88, on Red Rhino, by Red Rhino Records. Catalogue no: **REDT 089**

FIRE OF LOVE (SINGLE)
Tracks: / Fire of love / Walking with the beast.
7" Single: Released '82, on Animal, by Chrysalis Records. Catalogue no: **CHCAT 2635**

GHOST ON THE HIGHWAY
Tracks: / Ghost on the highway / Sex beat.
7" Single: Released '82, on Beggars Banquet, by Beggars Banquet Records. Deleted Jan '88. Catalogue no: **BEG 80**

HOUSE OF HIGHLAND AVENUE
Tracks: / House of highland avenue.
12" Single: Released '83, on Animal, by Chrysalis Records. Catalogue no: **GUN 12-1**
7" Single: Released '83, on Animal, by Chrysalis Records. Catalogue no: **GUN 1**

SEX BEAT
Tracks: / Sex beat / For the love of ivy / Black train.
CD 5": Released May '89, on New Rose (1), by New Rose Records. Catalogue no: **NEAT 1 CD**

Gun Shy

JUST TO BE YOUR SECRET
Tracks: / Just to be your secret / Jumping off the train.
12" Single: Released Jul '87, on MCA, by MCA Records. Catalogue no: **JEZT 1**
7" Single: Released Jul '87, on MCA, by MCA Records. Catalogue no: **JEZ 1**

Gung Ho

PLAY TO WIN (ENGLISH VERSION)
Tracks: / Play to win / Ike Gung-ho.
7" Single: Released May '87, on Magnet, by WEA Records. Deleted Jan '88. Catalogue no: **GUN 1**
12" Single: Released May '87, on Magnet, by WEA Records. Deleted Jan '88. Catalogue no: **GUNG 1**

REMEMBER
Tracks: / Remember / Occupation of my heart.
7" Single: Released Oct '87, on Magnet, by WEA Records. Deleted Jan '88. Catalogue no: **GUN 2**
12" Single: Released Oct '87, on Magnet, by WEA Records. Deleted Jun '88. Catalogue no: **GUNG 2**

Gunn, Ben

FERGIE'S FUSILIERS
Tracks: / Fergie's fusiliers / Jock Stein tartan, The.
7" Single: Released Mar '86, on Klub, by Klub Records. Catalogue no: **KLUB 52**

VIVA SCOTLAND
Tracks: / Viva Scotland.
7" Single: Released '82, on Lismor, by Lismor Records. Deleted '88. Catalogue no: **LISP 2006**

Guns for hire

MY GIRLFRIEND'S BOYFRIEND
Tracks: / My girlfriend's boyfriend / I'm famous now.
7" Single: Released May '80, on Korova, by WEA Records. Deleted May '83. Catalogue no: **KOW 6**

Guns 'n' Roses

GUNS N ROSES: INTERVIEW PICTURE DISC COLLECTION
7" Set: Released '88, on Baktabak, by Baktabak Records. Catalogue no: **BAKPAK 1011**

IT'S SO EASY
Tracks: / It's so easy / Mr. Brownstone.
7" Single: Released 20 Jun '87, on Geffen, by Geffen Records (USA). Catalogue no: **GEF 22**

IT'S SO EASY (IMPORT)
Tracks: / It's so easy / Mr. Brownstone / Shadow of your love / Move to the city (live).
12" Single: Released Oct '88, on Geffen (USA), by Geffen Records (USA). Catalogue no: **920710 0**

NIGHT TRAIN
Tracks: / Night train / Reckless life.
7" Single: Released Aug '89, on Geffen, by Geffen Records (USA). Catalogue no: **GEF 60**
CD 5": Released Aug '89, on Geffen, by Geffen Records (USA). Catalogue no: **GEF 60CD**
Cassingle: Released Aug '89, on Geffen, by Geffen Records (USA). Catalogue no: **GEF 60C**
12" Single: Released Aug '89, on Geffen, by Geffen Records (USA). Catalogue no: **GEF 60T**

PARADISE CITY
Tracks: / Paradise city / Used to love her / Anything goes (Only on the 12" version.) / Sweet child o mine (Only on CD single.).
12" Single: Released Mar '89, on Geffen, by Geffen Records (USA). Catalogue no: **GEF 50 T**
Cassingle: Released Apr '89, on Geffen, by Geffen Records (USA). Catalogue no: **927 5704**
7" Single: Released Apr '89, on Geffen, by Geffen Records (USA). Catalogue no: **GEF 50 X**
7" Single: Released Mar '89, on Geffen, by Geffen Records (USA). Catalogue no: **GEF 50**
7" Single: Released Apr '89, on Geffen, by Geffen Records (USA). Catalogue no: **GEF 50 P**

PATIENCE
Tracks: / Patience / Rocket queen / Axl Rose Interview.
CD 5": Released Jun '89, on Geffen, by Geffen Records (USA). Catalogue no: **GEF 56CD**
12" Single: Released Jun '89, on Geffen, by Geffen Records (USA). Catalogue no: **GEF 56T**
Cassingle: Released Jun '89, on Geffen, by Geffen Records (USA). Catalogue no: **GEF 56C**
7" Single: Released Jun '89, on Geffen, by Geffen Records (USA). Catalogue no: **GEF 56**

SWEET CHILD O' MINE
Tracks: / Sweet child o' mine / Out to get me / Rocket queen (Only on 12".).
7" Single: Released Aug '88, on Geffen, by Geffen Records (USA). Catalogue no: **GEF 43**
12" Single: Released Aug '88, on Geffen, by Geffen Records (USA). Catalogue no: **GEF 43T**

SWEET CHILD O' MINE (RE-RELEASE)
Tracks: / Sweet child o' mine / Out to get me / Move to the city (Only on CD single.) / It's so easy (Only on CD single.) / Whole lotta Rosie (Only on CD single.).
CD 5": Released May '89, on Geffen, by Geffen Records (USA). Catalogue no: **GEF 55 CD**
12" Single: Released May '89, on Geffen, by Geffen Records (USA). Catalogue no: **GEF 55 T**
7" Single: Released Jun '89, on Geffen, by Geffen Records (USA). Catalogue no: **GEF 55 X**
7" Single: Released May '89, on Geffen, by Geffen Records (USA). Catalogue no: **GEF 55**

WELCOME TO THE JUNGLE
Tracks: / Welcome to the jungle / Whole

lotta Rosie / It's so easy (12" only) / Knockin' on heavens door.
7" Single: Released Sep '87, on Geffen, by Geffen Records (USA). Catalogue no: **GEF 30**
12" Single: Released Sep '87, on Geffen, by Geffen Records (USA). Deleted Jul '88. Catalogue no: **GEF 30 T**

WELCOME TO THE JUNGLE (RE-RELEASE)
Tracks: / Welcome to the jungle / Nightrain.
12" Single: Released Oct '88, on Geffen, by Geffen Records (USA). Catalogue no: **GEF 47T**
CD 5": Released Oct '88, on Geffen, by Geffen Records (USA). Catalogue no: **GEF 47CD**
7" Single: Released Oct '88, on Geffen, by Geffen Records (USA). Catalogue no: **GEF 47**

Gunter, Hardrock

JUKEBOX HELP ME FIND MY BABY
Tracks: / Jukebox help me find my baby / Fiddle bop.
7" Single: Released '80, on Rollercoaster, by Rollercoaster Records. Catalogue no: **RRC 2006**

Gurl, Fletcher

I'VE BEEN IN LOVE
Tracks: / I've been in love / I ain't getting right.
7" Single: Released Feb '80, on Logo, by Logo Records. Deleted Feb '85. Catalogue no: **GO 381**

Gurney Slade

GURNEY SLADE
Tracks: / Gurney slade.
7" Single: Released '83, on PRT, by Castle Communications Records. Catalogue no: **TVR 1**

Gurvitz, Adrian

Biographical details: This British singer, guitarist and songwriter came to brief fame at the end of 1968 as leader of Gun. Another member of that rock trio was his bass-playing brother Paul, who also figured in Adrian's second briefly successful project, 1975's Baker-Gurvitz Army. This was a celebration with ex-Graham Bond Organisation/Cream/Blind Faith drummer Ginger Baker. It seems that success comes round every seven years for Adrian Gurvitz. In 1982 he reached no 8 on the British chart with *Classic* (exactly the same position attained by Gun's *Race with the devil*, which was his only other UK Top 10 single). Produced by the two brothers, *Classic* was the title track of Adrian's third solo album. It was a straightforward but classy pop song, quite unlike his earlier rock material; it did not give great prominence to the showy guitar style for which he had been well known. What was even more remarkable about *Classic* was that it was released on Mickie Most's pop-oriented RAK label. It seemed that history was repeating itself - fifteen years earlier, Mickie had masterminded *Hi-ho silver lining*, another equally out of character offering by guitar wizard Jeff Beck. In June 82 Gurvitz chalked up a minor follow-up hit single with *Your dream*, a wimpy ballad that peaked at no. 61. Subsequent platters failed to matter - but who knows what Gurvitz may come up with in 1979? (Bob Macdonald, 2/10/85).

CLASSIC (SINGLE)
Tracks: / Classic / Runaway.
7" Single: Released Nov '89, on RAK, by EMI Records. Catalogue no: **RAK 339**

CORNER OF LOVE
Tracks: / Corner of love.
7" Single: Released '83, on RAK, by EMI Records. Catalogue no: **RAK 358**

NEW WORLD
Tracks: / New world / Time is endless.
7" Single: Released Apr '80, on Jet, by Jet Records. Deleted Apr '83. Catalogue no: **JET 172**

PALACE SIGN
Tracks: / Palace sign / Clown.
7" Single: Released '82, on RAK, by EMI Records. Catalogue no: **RAK 347**

YOUR DREAM
Tracks: / Your dream / Slow dive.

7" Single: Released '82, on RAK, by EMI Records. Catalogue no: **RAK 343**

Gusto

MATERIALISTIC GIRL
Tracks: / Materialistic girl / Materialistic girl (version).
12" Single: Released Feb '88, on 4th & Broadway, by Island Records. Deleted Jun '88. Catalogue no: **12 BRW 89**

Gutbucket, Arnold

MARY ROSE
Tracks: / Mary rose.
7" Single: Released Oct '82, on Bucket, by Bucket Records. Catalogue no: **BUCK 005**

Guthrie, Gwen

Biographical details: A native of Newark, New Jersey, Gwen Guthrie received her formal music training from her father who began teaching her piano at the age of eight. After a two-year study the music took a backseat to other interests only to be rekindled in the mid 70's. In 1974 Gwen decided on a career as a studio singer and has appeared in concert halls and on albums with a wide variety of artists. Gwen's songwriting ability first became evident in 1975 when she penned the hit single *Supernatural Thing* for Ben E King. Later that same year she wrote a second hit single *Love Don't You Go Through No Changes On Me* this time for Sister Sledge. Gwen wrote five tunes for Sister Sledge's *Circle Of Love* album. It was during a stint singing backing vocals with Peter Tosh that Gwen met Sly Dunbar and Robbie Shakespeare, arguably Jamaica's no.1 rhythm section. Their rapport was immediate and when Sly and Robbie became the resident wizards at Compass Point Studios in Nassau they invited Gwen down to work. The sessions turned out so well it was decided that Gwen should cut an album in her own right. The result was Gwen's debut album, released to an enthusiastic critical response in the summer of '82; the hit single *It Should Have Been You* hit no.1 in the British club chart and went top five in the American dance listings. The Gwen Guthrie/Sly & Robbie combination proved an enduring partnership and the next album recorded was *Portrait* (Island Records, February 1984).

AIN'T NOTHIN' GOIN' ON BUT THE RENT (OLD GOLD)
Tracks: / Ain't nothin' goin' on but the rent / (They long to be) close to you.
12" Single: Released Nov '88, on Old Gold, by Old Gold Records. Catalogue no: **OG 4084**

AIN'T NOTHING GOIN' ON BUT THE RENT
Tracks: / Ain't nothing goin' on but the rent / Passions eyes.
12" Single: Released Jul '86, on Boiling Point, by Polydor Ltd. Deleted Jan '88. Catalogue no: **POSPX 807**
7" Single: Released Jul '86, on Boiling Point, by Polydor Ltd. Deleted Jan '88. Catalogue no: **POSP 807**

CAN'T LOVE YOU TONIGHT
Tracks: / Can't love you tonight / Surgeon General's funky 4-4 beat, The.
7" Single: Released Apr '88, on Warner Bros., by WEA Records. Catalogue no: **W 7990**
12" Single: Released Apr '88, on Warner Bros., by WEA Records. Catalogue no: **W 7990T**

CLOSE TO YOU
Tracks: / Close to you / You touch my life / Save your love for me (Extra track available on 12" version only).
7" Single: Released Sep '86, on Polydor, by Polydor Ltd. Deleted Mar '87. Catalogue no: **POSP 822**
12" Single: Released Sep '86, on Polydor, by Polydor Ltd. Deleted Mar '88. Catalogue no: **POSPX 822**

FAMILY AFFAIR
Tracks: / Family affair / Peek-a-boo / It should have been you.
12" Single: Released Jan '88, on 4th & Broadway, by Island Records. Deleted Jun '88. Catalogue no: **12 BRW 86**
7" Single: Released Jan '88, on 4th & Broadway, by Island Records. Deleted Jun '88. Catalogue no: **BRW 86**

FOR YOU
Tracks: / For you / Peek-a-boo.
7" Single: Released Oct '82, on Island, by Island Records. Deleted Oct '85. Catalogue no: **WIP 6827**
12" Single: Released Oct '82, on Island, by Island Records. Deleted Oct '85. Catalogue no: **12WIP 6827**

FRIENDS & LOVERS
Tracks: / Friends & lovers.
12" Single: Released Aug '87, on Creole, by Creole Records. Catalogue no: **CRT 1**
7" Single: Released Aug '87, on Creole, by Creole Records. Catalogue no: **CR 1**

GOOD TO GO LOVER (SINGLE)
Tracks: / Good to go lover / Outside in the rain (US remix).
12" Single: Released Feb '87, on Boiling Point, by Polydor Ltd. Deleted Aug '87. Catalogue no: **POSPX 841**
7" Single: Released Feb '87, on Boiling Point, by Polydor Ltd. Deleted Jan '88. Catalogue no: **POSP 841**
7" Set: on Boiling Point, by Polydor Ltd. Deleted Aug '87. Catalogue no: **POSPD 841**

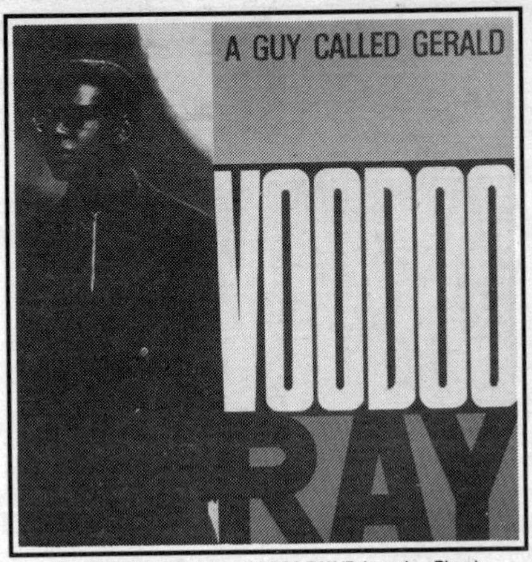

GUY CALLED GERALD - VOODOO RAY (Released on Rham)

IT SHOULD HAVE BEEN YOU
Tracks: / It should have been you / God don't like ugly.
7" Single: Released Apr '82, on Island, by Island Records. Deleted Apr '85. Catalogue no: **WIP 6757**
12" Single: Released Apr '82, on Island, by Island Records. Deleted Apr '85. Catalogue no: **12WIP 6757**

LOVE IN MODERATION
Tracks: / Love in moderation.
7" Single: Released Jan '85, on 4th & Broadway, by Island Records. Catalogue no: **BRW 17**
12" Single: Released Jan '85, on 4th & Broadway, by Island Records. Deleted '87. Catalogue no: **12 BRW 17**

OUTSIDE IN THE RAIN
Tracks: / Outside in the rain / I still want you.
7" Single: Released Nov '86, on Boiling Point, by Polydor Ltd. Catalogue no: **POSB 841**
12" Single: Released Nov '86, on Boiling Point, by Polydor Ltd. Catalogue no: **POSBX 841**

SEVENTH HEAVEN
Tracks: / Seventh heaven / It should have been you / Getting hot (Extra track available on 12").
Note: Extra track included
12" Single: Released Sep '86, on 4th & Broadway, by Island Records. Deleted Jul '87. Catalogue no: **12 BRW 52**
7" Single: Released Sep '86, on 4th & Broadway, by Island Records. Catalogue no: **BRW 52**

THEY LONG TO BE CLOSE TO YOU
Tracks: / (They long to be) close to you.
7" Single: Released Oct '86, on Boiling Point, by Polydor Ltd. Deleted '89. Catalogue no: **POSP 822**

Guttersnipes

ADDICTED TO LOVE
Tracks: / Addicted to love.
7" Single: Released Jul '88, on Razor, by Razor Records. Catalogue no: **GUTT 1**

Guy

GROOVE ME
Tracks: / Groove me.

7" Single: Released Apr '89, on MCA, by MCA Records. Catalogue no: **MCA 1331**
12" Single: Released Apr '89, on MCA, by MCA Records. Catalogue no: **MCAT 1331**

MY FANTASY
Tracks: / My fantasy.

7" Single: Released Jul '89, on MCA, by MCA Records. Catalogue no: **MCA 1353**
CD 5": Released Jul '89, on MCA, by MCA Records. Catalogue no: **DMCAT 1353**
12" Single: Released Jul '89, on MCA, by MCA Records. Catalogue no: **MCAT 1353**

Guy Called Gerald

PEEL SESSIONS:GUY CALLED GERALD
12" Single: Released Jul '89, on Strange Fruit, by Strange Fruit Records. Catalogue no: **SFPS 071**

VOODOO RAY (see panel above)
Tracks: / Voodoo ray / Arcade fantasy.
CD 5": Released Dec '88, on Rham, by Rham Records. Catalogue no: **RCD 8804**
12" Single: Released Oct '88, on Rham, by Rham Records. Catalogue no: **RS 8804**
7" Single: Released Oct '88, on Rham, by Rham Records. Catalogue no: **RS 804**

Guys & Dolls

Biographical details: At the time of their greatest success, this British pop vocal group consisted of Dominic Grant, Paul Griggs, David Van Day, Thereza Bazar, Julie Forsyth (daughter of Bruce Forsyth) and Martine Howard. The three guys and three dolls were brought together in November 1974 by producers David Martin and Geoff Morrow, who auditioned over 300 singers to find the final six. The calculated thinking behind the creation of Guys & Dolls brought immediate dividends - the sextet's debut single *There's a whole lot of loving* cruised to no. 2 on the UK chart in the spring of 1975. The whole package looked as if it was tailor-made for the Eurovision song contest, and would probably have fared a lot better than that year's real UK entry *Let me be the one*. After the bright singalong catchiness of *There's a whole lot of loving*, Guys & Dolls' follow-up single was the surprisingly downbeat and dreary *Here I go again* which peaked at no. 33 on the British chart. They returned to the Top 5 in Spring 76 with a revival of the Dusty Springfield/Elvis Presley standard *You don't have to say you love me*. Apart from a couple of of minor successes, the group then faded from chart action in Britain but proceeded to enjoy success in Europe and Japan. Holland was particularly receptive in 1977, giving the group big hits with *You're my world* and *Mamacita*. By this time, the MoR sound of Guys & Dolls was already well established on the international cabaret circuit. However, David Van Day and Theresa Bazar wanted to remain within the world of chart-oriented pop music; they broke away from the group in July 1977, and formed the highly successful Dollar duo. Dollar were husband and wife when they achieved their first UK hit in 1978, but by 1983 they had split up in both professional and personal terms. (Bob Macdonald, 3/10/85).

BREAKOUT
Tracks: / Breakout.
7" Single: Released Jul '83, on Moon, by Moon Records (UK). Catalogue no: **LUNA 7**

FREEZE
Tracks: / Freeze.
7" Single: Released Nov '83, on Moon, by Moon Records (UK). Catalogue no: **LUNA 8**

HERE I GO AGAIN

GUYS & DOLLS - ONLY LOVIN' DOES IT (Released on Magnet)

Tracks: / Here I go again.
7" Single: Released May '75, on Magnet, by WEA Records. Deleted '78. Catalogue no: **MAG 30**

ONLY LOVIN' DOES IT (see panel above)
Tracks: / Only loving does it / Starlight, starbright.
7" Single: Released May '78, on Magnet, by WEA Records. Deleted '81. Catalogue no: **MAG 115**

STONEY GROUND
Tracks: / Stoney ground.
7" Single: Released Nov '76, on Magnet, by WEA Records. Deleted '79. Catalogue no: **MAG 76**

THERE'S A WHOLE LOT OF LOVING
Tracks: / There's a whole lot of loving / You don't have to say you love me.
7" Single: Released Mar '75, on Magnet, by WEA Records. Deleted '78. Catalogue no: **MAG 20**
7" Single: Released Sep '81, on Magnet, by WEA Records. Catalogue no: **MAG 303**

YOU DON'T HAVE TO SAY YOU LOVE ME
Tracks: / You don't have to say you love me.
7" Single: Released Feb '76, on Magnet, by WEA Records. Deleted '79. Catalogue no: **MAG 50**

Gwenno

DOWNTOWN
Tracks: / Downtown.
7" Single: Released Jun '88, on Antler, by Antler Records (Belgium). Catalogue no: **ANT 016**

Gymslips

48 CRASH
Tracks: / 48 crash.
7" Single: Released Oct '82, on Abstract, by Abstract Sounds. Catalogue no: **ABS 011**

BIG SISTER
Tracks: / Big sister / Yo-yo / Pie and mash.
7" Single: Released Jan '83, on Abstract, by Abstract Sounds. Catalogue no: **ABS 014**

EVIL EYE
Tracks: / Evil eye.
7" Single: Released Apr '85, on Abstract, by Abstract Sounds. Catalogue no: **ABS 033**
12" Single: Released Apr '85, on Abstract, by Abstract Sounds. Catalogue no: **ABS 03312**

ROBOT MAN
Tracks: / Robot man.
7" Single: Released Jul '83, on Abstract, by Abstract Sounds. Catalogue no: **ABS 016**

Gynaecologists

RED PULLOVER
Tracks: / Red pullover, The.
7" Single: Released Sep '81, on Teesbeat, by Teesbeat Records. Catalogue no: **TB 2**

Gyngell, Denise

YOU BROKE MY HEART IN 17 PLACES
Tracks: / You broke my heart in 17 places / Why don't you call me.
7" Single: Released Jun '84, on Loose End, by MCA Records. Catalogue no: **LE 112**
12" Single: Released Jun '84, on Loose End, by MCA Records. Catalogue no: **LEX 112**

Gypsy (Group)

I'M A WINNER
Tracks: / I'm a winner.
12" Single: Released Mar '85, on Personal, by Personal Records. Catalogue no: **12 PER 3900**

SINKING SHIP, THE
Tracks: / Sinking ship, The / On the park way.
12" Single: Released Aug '86, on Hot Vinyl, Catalogue no: **HVT 25**

Gypsy Kings

MY WAY
12" Single: Released Sep '89, on A.1, by A.1 Records. Catalogue no: **12A 1310**
7" Single: Released Sep '89, on A.1, by A.1 Records. Catalogue no: **A 1310**

Gypsy Queen

SNARL 'N STRIPES EP
Tracks: / Radio (remix EP) / Doctor needs a doctor (ext. version) / War and peace / Where does our love go.
Note: 3 track EP/4 track 12". Produced by Jack Douglas
7" EP: Released Jan '88, on Loop, by Loop Records. Catalogue no: **LOOP 100**
12" Single: Released Jan '88, on Loop, by Loop Records. Catalogue no: **12 LOOP 100**

TAKE CARE OF YOURSELF
Tracks: / Take care of yourself.
7" Single: Released 6 Mar '89, on Loop, by Loop Records. Catalogue no: **LOOP 102**
12" Single: Released 6 Mar '89, on Loop, by Loop Records. Catalogue no: **12 LOOP 102**

Gyro

CENTRAL DETENTION CENTRE
Tracks: / Central detention centre.
7" Single: Released Sep '82, on Rabid, by Rabid Records. Catalogue no: **TOSH 104**

H

The following information was taken from the Music Master database on October 20th, 1989.

H2O

Biographical details: *I Dream To Sleep* gave this British pop sextet their breakthrough hit in the summer of 1983. A well-crafted, moody single, co-written by all six guys in the band, it was a beautifully understated slowie and an excellent accompaniment to that year's scorching weather, reaching the UK No 17 position. But nothing else in the group's repertoire was as strong. The follow-up, *Just outside of heaven*, was a run-of-the-mill offering which peaked at No 38 and other singles, such as *Who'll Stop The Rain?*, were competent but failed to see chart action. (Bob MacDonald, October 1985.)
H20 was formed in Glasgow, back in 1978 after lead singer, Ian Donaldson, parted company with punk band Skroo. First recruit was drummer Kenny Dorman - a one time Boy's Brigade Pipe Band member - who also turned to punk in the 70's. Next came keyboard man Ross Alcock, known to his friends as Pythagoras, after becoming a physics graduate. Ross started his musical career as a choir boy and after some serious classical training became a church organist. He is the only Englishman in the band having been born and bred in Crewe. After being bored with his stint as a string bass player in a Glenn Miller style band, Colin Ferguson joined H20 adapting rapidly to the electric version of the instrument. Lead guitarist Pete Keane also adapted quickly to the H20 way having joined in 1981 from heavy metal band Heavy Pettin. In the tradition of many great guitarists Pete dedicated himself to his instrument at a very early age, leaving school prematurely to find the money to buy equipment. After a year's hard work, he became one of the most sought after guitarists in Glasgow. Sax player Colin Gavigan (Biggles) originally joined the band as a session man in 1981 - so after two years he might now consider himself a permanent fixture. Biggles, a former child actor (although he's the oldest in the band) left drama college to play in tamla and rock 'n' roll groups, before meeting the rest of H20. (Sheila Sedgwick, Press Office RCA Records, February 1984).

ALL THAT GLITTERS
Tracks: / All that glitters.
7" Single: Released Oct '83, on RCA, by BMG Records (UK). Catalogue no: **RCA 367**
12" Single: Released Oct '83, on RCA, by BMG Records (UK). Catalogue no: **RCAT 367**

BLUE DIAMOND
Tracks: / Hip corporation (On CD only) / Blue diamond / Go on / I fought the law (Available on 12" and CD versions only.).
7" Single: Released Feb '87, on Legend (1), by Legend Records (UK). Catalogue no: **LM 07**
CD 5": Released May '87, on Island, by Island Records. Deleted Jun '88. Catalogue no: **CDLM 7**
12" Single: Released Feb '87, on Legend (1), by Legend Records (UK). Catalogue no: **12LM 07**

I DREAM TO SLEEP
Tracks: / I dream to sleep.
12" Single: Released Apr '83, on RCA, by BMG Records (UK). Catalogue no: **RCAT 330**
7" Single: Released Apr '83, on RCA, by BMG Records (UK). Catalogue no: **RCA 330**

JUST OUTSIDE OF HEAVEN
Tracks: / Just outside of heaven / Stranger to stranger.
12" Single: Released Jul '83, on RCA, by BMG Records (UK). Catalogue no: **RCAT 349**
7" Pic: Released Aug '83, on RCA, by BMG Records (UK). Catalogue no: **RCAP 349**
7" Single: Released Jul '83, on RCA, by BMG Records (UK). Catalogue no: **RCA 349**

WHO'LL STOP THE RAIN?
Tracks: / Who'll stop the rain / Telling lies.
7" Single: Released May '84, on RCA, by BMG Records (UK). Catalogue no: **RCA 406**
12" Single: Released May '84, on RCA, by BMG Records (UK). Catalogue no: **RCAT 406**

YOU TAKE MY BREATH AWAY
Tracks: / You take my breath away / Leonard / Hollywood dream.
7" Single: Released Dec '84, on RCA, by BMG Records (UK). Catalogue no: **RCA 468**
12" Single: Released Dec '84, on RCA, by BMG Records (UK). Catalogue no: **RCAT 468**

Ha Ha Ha

UP & DOWN (SINGLE)
7" Single: Released Jan '86, on Hobby Horse. Catalogue no: **H 001**

Habit

GET BACK
Tracks: / Get back / Funky train / Get back (extended mix) (12" only).
7" Single: Released Oct '88, on Virgin, by Virgin Records. Catalogue no: **VS 1132**
12" Single: Released Oct '88, on Virgin, by Virgin Records. Catalogue no: **VST 1132**

LUCY
Tracks: / Lucy (7" only) / Lucy (TFZ mix) (Not on 7" version) / Rise.
12" Single: Released 16 Jan '89, on Virgin, by Virgin Records. Catalogue no: **VSTR 1063**
10" single: Released '88, on Virgin, by Virgin Records. Catalogue no: **VSA 1063**
7" Single: Released 16 Jan '89, on Virgin, by Virgin Records. Catalogue no: **VSR 1063**
7" Single: Released Mar '88, on Virgin, by Virgin Records. Catalogue no: **VS 1063**
12" Single: Released Mar '88, on Virgin, by Virgin Records. Catalogue no: **VST 1063**
CD 3": Released 30 Jan '89, on Virgin, by Virgin Records. Catalogue no: **VSRCD 1063**

SHOTGUN CITY
Tracks: / Shotgun city (On 7" & CD only) / Habit / Shotgun city (12 bore mix) (On 12" & CD only) / Shotgun city (Bobby Z mix) (On 10" only).
CD 3": Released '88, on Virgin, by Virgin Records. Catalogue no: **VSCJ 1083**
10" single: Released '88, on Virgin, by Virgin Records. Catalogue no: **VSA 1083**
7" Single: Released Aug '88, on Virgin, by Virgin Records. Catalogue no: **VS 1083**
7" Single: Released 8 Aug '88, on Virgin, by Virgin Records. Deleted '88. Catalogue no: **VSG 1083**
12" Single: Released 8 Aug '88, on Virgin, by Virgin Records. Catalogue no: **VST 1083**

STARLIGHT
Tracks: / Starlight / Funky train.
12" Single: Released 13 Mar '89, on Virgin, by Virgin Records. Catalogue no: **VST 1171**
7" Single: Released 13 Mar '89, on Virgin, by Virgin Records. Catalogue no: **VS 1171**
CD 3": Released 13 Mar '89, on Virgin, by Virgin Records. Catalogue no: **VSCD 1171**

Hackett, Steve

Biographical details: This British guitarist, singer, composer and keyboards player became famous as a member of Genesis. He was part of the classic line-up of that internationally successful rock band from late 1970 onwards. His guitar skills remained with the group until 1977. However, his debut solo LP was actually released in october 1975, during the interruption to Genesis activities following the departure of leader Peter Gabriel: while hundreds of hopefuls were being auditioned (none of them making the grade, thus causing the internal promotion of drummer Phil Collins), Hackett recorded *Voyage of the acolyte*. The album, which featured guest appearances from two Genesis mates, reached no. 26 on the British chart. When Hackett finally quit the band in 1977, he reduced them to a threesome; but this in no way reduced their huge success. Steve had enjoyed making his first solo album, and wanted to be free to indulge his own musical leanings outside the pressures and compromises of a superstar group framework. His subsequen albums *Please don't touch, Spectral mornings, Defector, Cured, Highly strung, Bay of kings* and *Till we have faces* - usually achieved respectable though not spectacular UK chart success, and generally contained classically inclined extensions of seventies art-rock themes. All were superbly performed, though they were ofthn cricised for being aimless in content. Steve's only UK chart single was *Cell 151* from 1983's *Highly strung* LP - the track reached no. 66 in April of that year. (Bob Macdonald, 4/10/85).

CELL 151
Tracks: / Cell 151.
7" Single: Released Apr '83, on Charisma, by Virgin Records. Deleted '86. Catalogue no: **CELL 1**

DOLL THAT'S MADE IN JAPAN
Tracks: / Doll that's made in Japan.
12" Single: Released Aug '84, on Lamborghini, by Lamborghini Records. Catalogue no: **12LMG 16**
7" Single: Released Aug '84, on Lamborghini, by Lamborghini Records. Catalogue no: **LMG 16**

SENTIMENTAL INSTITUTION
Tracks: / Sentimental institution / Toast.
7" Single: Released Aug '80, on Charisma, by Virgin Records. Deleted '83. Catalogue no: **CB 368**

SHOW
Tracks: / Show / Hercules unchained.
7" Single: Released Apr '80, on Charisma, by Virgin Records. Deleted '83. Catalogue no: **CB 357**

Hackney Five-0

CATALOGUE (OF TROUBLE AND THE BLUES)
Tracks: / Catalogue (of trouble and the blues) / Gorilla / Dalston (express version) / I'm so lonesome I could cry.
12" Single: Released Feb '86, on Midnight Music, by Midnight Music Records. Catalogue no: **DONG 21**

Hades

PITTER PATTER BISCUIT
Tracks: / Pitter patter biscuit.
12" Single: Released Jun '89, on Vinyl Solution, by Vinyl Solution Records. Catalogue no: **STORM 6**

Haeffner, Nick

BACK IN TIME FOR TEA
Tracks: / Mean guitar / Every time you say goodbye.
12" Single: Released Jan '87, on Bam Caruso, by Demon Records. Catalogue no: **PABL 073**

MASTER, THE
Tracks: / Master, The.
12" Single: Released Jun '88, on Bam Caruso, by Demon Records. Catalogue no: **PABL 072**

Hafler Trio

ALTERNATION, PERCEPTION
Tracks: / Alternation, perception.
12" Single: Released Nov '88, on Laylah, by Laylah Records. Catalogue no: **LAY 013**

SEA ORGANISATION, THE
Tracks: / Sea organisation, The.
10" single: Released Nov '86, on Touch, by Touch Records. Catalogue no: **TO.5**

Hagar, Sammy

Biographical details: American singer, guitarist and composer Hagar was a founder member and lead singer of the hard rock band Montrose from 1973-75 but quit to start a solo career: his debut album, *Nine on a ten scale*, was issued in 1976. Staying in the heavy metal field, Hagar struggled to establish himself, but his luck changed with the release, in September '79, of the *Street machine* album which gave him his first UK chart success. The following year brought his only British Top forty single with the catchy *I've done everything for you*, to be a US Top Ten hit a year later for Rick Springfield. Hagar's biggest US hit has been 1983's *Your love is driving me crazy*, which climbed to No 13, and 1984's *VOA* album yielded a pair of smaller American Top forty singles, *Two sides of love* and *I can't drive 55*. His brand of heavy metal has been predictable but enjoyable, displaying an ear for a melody as well as a head for a bang. (Bob MacDonald, October 1985.).

GIVE TO LIVE
Tracks: / Give to live / When the hammer falls.
7" Single: Released Aug '87, on Geffen, by Geffen Records (USA). Deleted Jul '88. Catalogue no: **GEF 23**
12" Single: Released Aug '87, on Geffen, by Geffen Records (USA). Deleted Jul '88. Catalogue no: **GEF 23T**

HEARTBEAT
Tracks: / Heartbeat / Love or money.
7" Single: Released May '80, on Capitol, by EMI Records. Deleted May '83. Catalogue no: **RED 1**

HEARTBEAT/LOVE OR MONEY
Tracks: / Heartbeat / Love or money.
7" Single: Released May '80, on Capitol, by EMI Records. Deleted '83. Catalogue no: **RED 1**

HEAVY METAL
Tracks: / Heavy metal / Satisfied.
12" Single: Released Oct '81, on Epic, by CBS Records. Deleted Oct '94. Catalogue no: **EPCA 131600**
7" Single: Released Oct '81, on Epic, by CBS Records. Deleted Oct '94. Catalogue no: **EPCA 1600**

I'VE DONE EVERYTHING FOR YOU
Tracks: / I've done everything for you / Red.
7" Single: Released Feb '80, on Capitol, by EMI Records. Deleted '83. Catalogue no: **16120**

PIECE OF MY HEART
Tracks: / Piece of my heart / Baby's on fire.
7" Single: Released Jan '82, on Geffen, by Geffen Records (USA). Deleted '85. Catalogue no: **GEFA 1884**

THIS PLANET'S ON FIRE
Tracks: / This planet's on fire / Space station No. 5.
7" Single: Released Dec '79, on Capitol, by EMI Records. Deleted '82. Catalogue no: **16114**

TWO SIDES OF LOVE
Tracks: / Two sides of love / Burnin' down the city.
7" Single: Released Aug '84, on Geffen, by Geffen Records (USA). Catalogue no: **A 4696**

WINNER TAKES IT ALL
Tracks: / Winner takes it all, The / Fight, The.
7" Single: Released Apr '87, on CBS, by CBS Records. Deleted Nov '87. Catalogue no: **650 407 7**

YOUR LOVE IS DRIVING ME MAD
Tracks: / Your love is driving me mad / I don't need love.
7" Single: Released Jan '83, on Geffen, by Geffen Records (USA). Catalogue no: **GEF A 3043**

Hagar The Womb

FUNNERY IN A NUNNERY
Tracks: / Funnery in a nunnery.
12" Single: Released Feb '85, on Abstract, by Abstract Sounds. Catalogue no: **12 ABS 029**

WORD OF THE WOMB
12" Single: Released Jan '84, on Mortarhate, by Mortarhate Records. Deleted '88. Catalogue no: **MORT 2**

Hagen, Nina

AFRICAN REGGAE
Tracks: / African reggae / Wau wau.
7" Single: Released Mar '80, on CBS, by CBS Records. Deleted '83. Catalogue no:

CBS 8304

DON'T KILL THE ANIMALS
Tracks:
7" Single: Released Jan '87, on Arista, by BMG Records (UK). Catalogue no: **RIS 3**
12" Single: Released Jan '87, on Arista, by BMG Records (UK). Catalogue no: **RIST 3**

ZARAH
Tracks: / Zarah.
7" Single: Released Feb '84, on CBS, by CBS Records. Catalogue no: **A 4216**

Hagman, Larry

BALLAD OF THE GOOD LUCK CHARM
Tracks: / Ballad of the good luck charm / My favourite sins.
7" Single: Released Dec '80, on Epic, by CBS Records. Deleted Dec '85. Catalogue no: **EPC 9336**

Ha-Ha-Mono

RUN FOR MILES
Tracks: / Run for miles.
7" Single: Released Jul '83, on Northeast Music, by Northeast Music Records. Catalogue no: **CIS 1481**

Hahn, Carol

DO YOUR BEST
Tracks: / Do your best.
12" Single: Released May '83, on Malaco, by Malaco Records (UK). Deleted '88. Catalogue no: **MAL 12 007**
7" Single: Released May '83, on Malaco, by Malaco Records (UK). Deleted '88. Catalogue no: **MAL 007**

Hahn, Justice

DOWN BY LOVE
Tracks: / Down by love.
10" single: Released 16 Sep '88, on Exile, Catalogue no: **EX 10EP 05**

Haig, Paul

Biographical details: This British singer first attracted the attention of the music press in 1980, when he was leader of a band called Josef K. Together with the more successful Aztec Camera and Orange Juice, they were one of the first groups signed to Glasgow's critically acclaimed independent Postcard label. Together with guitarist Malcolm Ross (who later joined Orange Juice), Haig led Josef K on such cult singles as *Radio drill time*, *It's kinda funny* and *Chance meeting*; the only LP was entitled *The only fun in town*. After the band's termination, Paul Haig continued his exploration of synthesised, danceable pop music by pursuing a solo career. His first single, *Running away* was issued in June 1982. One year later, now signed to Island Records, he made his first, albeit minor, impression on the UK charts - the well-crafted single *Heaven sent* spent 3 weeks on the Top 75 singles chart, but never climbed higher than no. 74. The track later appeared on his debut album *Rhythm of life*, on which he worked with noted producer Alex Sadkin, who was also heavily involved with the Thompson Twins; indeed the Twins' leader Tom Bailey gave much musical assistance on the LP. Despite the journalistic support, Haig was somehow unable to build upon the chart toehold of *Heaven sent*. He could not make himself stand out from the plethora of other acts performing a similar type of material. (Bob Macdonald, 4/10/85).

BIG BLUE WORLD
Tracks: / Big blue world.
7" Single: Released Jun '84, on Factory Benelux, by Rough Trade Records. Catalogue no: **TWI 230**
12" Single: Released Jun '84, on Factory Benelux, by Rough Trade Records. Catalogue no: **TWI 231**

BLUE FOR YOU
Tracks: / Blue for you.
7" Single: Released Dec '82, on Operation Twilight, Catalogue no: **TWI 106**

HEAVEN HELP YOU NOW
Tracks: / Heaven help you now.
12" Single: Released Sep '85, on Operation Afterglow, Catalogue no: **12 OPA 002**
7" Single: Released Sep '85, on Operation Afterglow, Catalogue no: **OPA 002**
12" Single: Released 22 Aug '88, on Crepescule, by Island Records. Catalogue no: **TWI 624**

HEAVEN SENT
Tracks: / Heaven sent.
7" Single: Released Sep '84, on Les Disques Du Crepuscule(Belgium), by Les Disques Du Crepuscule(Belgium). Catalogue no: **7TWI 240**

JUSTICE
Tracks: / Justice.
7" Single: Released Aug '82, on Operation Twilight, Catalogue no: **OPT 001**

LOVE ETERNAL
Tracks: / Love eternal.
7" Single: Released Feb '86, on Operation Afterglow, Catalogue no: **OPA 006**
12" Single: Released Sep '88, on Les Disques Du Crepuscule(Belgium), by Les Disques Du Crepuscule(Belgium). Catalogue no: **TWI 660**
12" Single: Released Feb '86, on Operation Afterglow, Catalogue no: **12 OPA 006**

ONLY TRUTH, THE
Tracks: / Only truth, The.
12" Single: Released Sep '84, on Les Disques Du Crepuscule(Belgium), by Les Disques Du Crepuscule(Belgium). Deleted '85. Catalogue no: **12IS 198**
Cassingle: Released Oct '84, on Les Disques Du Crepuscule(Belgium), by Les Disques Du Crepuscule(Belgium). Catalogue no: **CIS 198**
7" Single: Released Sep '84, on Les Disques Du Crepuscule(Belgium), by Les Disques Du Crepuscule(Belgium). Catalogue no: **IS 198**
12" Single: Released '88, on Crepescule, by Island Records. Catalogue no: **TWI 390**

ONLY TRUTH(US REMIX), THE
Tracks: / Only truth (US remix).
12" Single: Released Oct '84, on Les Disques Du Crepuscule(Belgium), by Les Disques Du Crepuscule(Belgium). Catalogue no: **ISX 198**

RUNNING AWAY
Tracks: / Running away.
7" Single: Released Jun '82, on Operation Twilight, Catalogue no: **OPT 003**

SOMETHING GOOD
Tracks: / Something good / Over you / Free to go (12" only) / Something good (version) (12" only).
CD 3": Released Jun '89, on Circa, by Virgin Records. Catalogue no: **YRCD 25**
7" Single: Released Jun '89, on Circa, by Virgin Records. Catalogue no: **YR 25**
12" Single: Released Jun '89, on Circa, by Virgin Records. Catalogue no: **YRT 25**
Special: Released Jun '89, on Circa, by Virgin Records. Catalogue no: **YRTX 25**

TORCHOMATIC
Tracks: / Torchomatic.
12" Single: Released Mar '88, on For A Song, Catalogue no: **TW 1832**

Haigh, Robert

VALENTINE
Tracks: / Valentine.
12" Single: Released Oct '88, on Laylah, by Laylah Records. Catalogue no: **LAY 021**

Hails, Gary

LONELY BOY
Tracks: / Lonely boy.
7" Single: Released May '88, on Arm, Catalogue no: **HAILS 1**

Hain, Kit

DANNY
Tracks: / Danny / Inner ring.
7" Single: Released Apr '81, on Decca, by Decca Records. Deleted '85. Catalogue no: **F 13903**

LOOKING FOR YOU
Tracks: / Looking for you / Hundreds and thousands.
7" Single: Released Nov '81, on Deram, by London Records. Deleted '84. Catalogue no: **DM 445**
7" Single: Released Oct '82, on Mercury, by Phonogram Ltd. Deleted Oct '85. Catalogue no: **KH 1**

PERFECT TIMING
Tracks: / Perfect timing / Fly by night.
7" Single: Released Oct '83, on Mercury, by Phonogram Ltd. Catalogue no: **KH 3**

SLOW MOVES
Tracks: / Slow moves / Fallen angel.
10" single: Released Mar '84, on Mercury, by Phonogram Ltd. Catalogue no: **MER 15310**

UNINVITED GUESTS
Tracks: / Uninvited guests / Talk to me.
7" Single: Released Feb '81, on Decca, by Decca Records. Deleted '84. Catalogue no: **F 13900**

Haines Gang

SO HOT
Tracks: / So hot / Close shave (extended mix).
7" Single: Released Oct '83, on London Records, by London Records. Catalogue no: **LON 34**
12" Single: Released Oct '83, on London Records, by London Records. Catalogue no: **LONX 34**

Haines, Perry

WHAT'S WHAT
Tracks: / What's what / What's funk.
7" Single: Released Nov '81, on Fetish, Catalogue no: **FE 14**
12" Single: Released Dec '81, on Fetish, Deleted Dec '84. Catalogue no: **FE 14 12**

Haircut 100

Biographical details: This British pop band consisted of Blair Cunningham, Mark Fox, Nick Heyward, Graham Jones, Les Nemes and Phil Smith. Haircut 100 had their beginnings in the Beckenham area of Kent, where the nucleus of Heyward, Jones and Nemes had all been in the same year at school. The three lads formed Haircut 100 in 1980 - legend has it that their three girlfriends all decided to dispense with them in the same week, and that the three 19 year old guys formed the group as a method of filling in their suddenly expanded three time. During 1981 the trio was augmented by new recruits until the Haircuts were a sextet. The most experienced member was the American-raised drummer Blair Cunningham, who had done session work and live back-ups for a host of major US soul acts. But the fresh-faced leader was Heyward, whose lead vocals, songwriting and youthful exuberance were the centrepiece of the combo; his was a precocious and refreshing talent. Between autumn 1981 (the band's breakthrough period) and autumn 1982, Haircut 100 chalked up four UK Top 10 singles plus a smash debut album *Pelican west*. All were in a pure pop vein, and highly danceable. The group's image was fashionable and trendy yet also homely. This stunning 12-month period of success was abruptly ended as the Haircuts entered their second year in the limelight. In January 1983, the long-running friction between Heyward and percussionist Mark Fox caused Nick to part company with the recording of the second LP. In the event, no second Haircut album appeared until 1984, by which time Heyward had established himself as a solo hit-maker. But after one minor success with the *Prime time* single, the 5-piece Haircut 100 plunged headlong into the land of obscurity. Without the songs and charisma of their leader, the new Fox-led band did not have what it takes. By late '84 most of the Haircuts (not Fox) were playing with Nick again. (Bob Macdonald, 4/10/85).

FANTASTIC DAY (see panel below)
Tracks: / Fantastic day / Ski club.
7" Single: Released Apr '82, on Arista, by BMG Records (UK). Deleted '87. Catalogue no: **CLIP 3**
12" Single: Released Apr '82, on Arista, by BMG Records (UK). Deleted '86. Catalogue no: **CLIP 123**

FAVORITE SHIRTS (BOY MEETS GIRL)
Tracks: / Favorite shirts (boy meets girl).
12" Single: Released Oct '81, on Arista, by BMG Records (UK). Deleted '85. Catalogue no: **CLIP 121**
7" Single: Released Oct '81, on Arista, by BMG Records (UK). Deleted '85. Catalogue no: **CLIP 1**

FAVOURITE SHIRTS(BOY MEETS GIRL) (OLD GOLD)
Tracks: / Favourite shirts (Boy meets girl) / Love plus one.
7" Single: Released Jul '84, on Old Gold, by Old Gold Records. Deleted Jul '88. Catalogue no: **OG 9456**

LOVE PLUS ONE
Tracks: / Love plus one / Marine boy.
12" Single: Released Jan '82, on Arista, by BMG Records (UK). Deleted '86. Catalogue no: **CLIP 122**
7" Single: Released Jan '82, on Arista, by BMG Records (UK). Deleted '86. Catalogue no: **CLIP 2**

NOBODY'S FOOL
Tracks: / Nobody's fool / October is orange.
7" Single: Released Aug '82, on Arista, by BMG Records (UK). Deleted '87. Catalogue no: **CLIP 4**
12" Single: Released Aug '82, on Arista, by BMG Records (UK). Deleted '86. Catalogue no: **CLIP 124**

PRIME TIME
Tracks: / Prime time.
7" Single: Released Aug '83, on Polydor, by Polydor Ltd. Deleted '86. Catalogue no: **HC 1**

TOO UP TWO DOWN
Tracks: / Too up two down.
7" Single: Released Jun '84, on Polydor, by Polydor Ltd. Catalogue no: **HC 3**
12" Single: Released Jun '84, on Polydor, by Polydor Ltd. Catalogue no: **HCX 3**

Hairman, Robit

AFRICA'S ON FIRE
Tracks: / Africa's on fire.
7" Single: Released Jul '84, on MCA, by MCA Records. Catalogue no: **MCA 903**
12" Single: Released Jul '84, on MCA, by MCA Records. Catalogue no: **MCAT 903**

Hairston, Curtis

Biographical details: This American singer works in the field of black soul and dance music, but has achieved a fair degree of pop crossover success in Britain. He first cracked the UK national charts in the autumn of 1983 with *I want you (all tonight)*, a classy funk single that reached no. 44. He then faded from view for eighteen months, but re-emerged with two successes in the summer of 1985 - the unadventurous but ultra-danceable *I want your lovin'* zoomed to the UK no. 13 position, and he reached no. 40 as guest lead vocalist on B B & Q's slow soul swayer *Genie*. Hairston's fine voice stood him in good stead to compete in the ever-growing soul marketplace. (Bob Macdonald, 5/10/85).

CHILLIN' OUT
Tracks: / Hold on (for me) / Chillin' out.
12" Single: Released Nov '86, on Atlantic, by WEA Records. Deleted Jan '88. Catalogue no: **A 9335 T**
7" Single: Released Nov '86, on Atlantic, by WEA Records. Deleted Jan '88. Catalogue no: **A 9335**

I WANT YOU (ALL TONIGHT)
Tracks: / I want you(all tonight).

HAIRCUT 100 - FANTASTIC DAY (Released on Arista)

12" Single: Released Oct '83, on RCA, by BMG Records (UK). Catalogue no: **RCAT 368**
7" Single: Released Jun '85, on RCA, by BMG Records (UK). Catalogue no: **PB 40169**
7" Single: Released Oct '83, on RCA, by BMG Records (UK). Catalogue no: **RCA 368**
12" Single: Released Jun '85, on RCA, by BMG Records (UK). Catalogue no: **PT 40170**

I WANT YOUR LOVIN' (JUST A LITTLE BIT)
Tracks: / I want your lovin' (just a little bit).
7" Single: Released Apr '85, on London (Decca), by Decca International. Deleted '88. Catalogue no: **LON 66**

MORNING AFTER, THE
Tracks: / Morning after, The.
7" Single: Released Feb '87, on Atlantic, by WEA Records. Deleted Jan '88. Catalogue no: **A 9280**
12" Single: Released Feb '87, on Atlantic, by WEA Records. Deleted Jan '88. Catalogue no: **A 9280 T**

Haldra & Woody

UP WHERE WE BELONG
Tracks: / Up where we belong / Poem, The.
7" Single: Released Oct '73, on WKS, Catalogue no: **BFR 0595**

Hale, Barry

CHRISTMAS STORY
Tracks: / Christmas story / Tell me where.
7" Single: Released Dec '83, on Scarecrow, Catalogue no: **BH 105**

COME ON BABY
Tracks: / Come on baby / California.
7" Single: Released Apr '84, on Scarecrow, Catalogue no: **BH 104**

HEY GIRL
Tracks: / Be my guest / Hey girl.
7" Single: Released Sep '81, on Revolver, by FM-Revolver Records. Catalogue no: **REV 7**

KEEP YOUR CB RADIO SWITCHED ON
Tracks: / Keep your CB radio switched on.
7" Single: Released Oct '82, on Scarecrow, Catalogue no: **BH 102**

Hale, Corky

SO MUCH IN LOVE Roof garden
Tracks: / So much in love / Roof garden.
Note: Double A Side
12" Single: Released Mar '86, on Celluloid (Island), by Island Records. Deleted '88. Catalogue no: **CYZ 115**

Hale, Ritchie &

DUNKSKI
Tracks: / Dunkski / I never can find you.
7" Single: Released Jan '80, on Velvet, Deleted Jan '85. Catalogue no: **FP 151**

Hale, Willie Beaver

GROOVE ON
Tracks: / Groove on / Party times.
7" Single: Released Nov '80, on TK, Deleted Nov '83. Catalogue no: **TKR 7587**
12" Single: Released Nov '80, on TK, Deleted Nov '83. Catalogue no: **TKR 137587**

Haley, Bill

Biographical details: When *Rock around the clock* hit no. 1 on the American charts in the summer of 1955 (and in Britain in November of that year), most historians say it was the start of the rock'n'roll era and the beginning of the whole pop music revolution. *Rock around the clock* by Bill Haley & The Comets was one of the biggest-selling singles in history, returning to record charts on repeated occasions and clocking up an eventual worldwide total in excess of 20 million copies. Not bad, considering that Haley only recorded the song as a favour to his manager, who had co-written and published it a couple of years earlier without success. Bill Haley was born in Detroit in 1925, and moved to Pennsylvania at the age of four. He grew up with C&W and hillbilly music, and turned professional during the early forties. Haley spent the rest of the decade playing in those styles with various small-time bands. In the early fifties, he took the bold decision to record some black rhythm and blues songs and adapt them for the white market - these included, most notably, *Rocket 88* and *Rock the joint.* This fusion of white C&W with black R&B became known as rock'n'roll - Haley was one of the forst to do it, and the first to succeed with it. In 1953 Bill Haley & his Comets (as they had just been christened) reached the US national charts with Bill's own compilation *Crazy man crazy.* During 1954-5 he recorded songs from a variety of sources, and when *Shake rattle and roll, Dim dim the lights* and *Mambo rock* began appearing in national Top 20's on both sides of the Atlantic alongside names like Doris Day and Frankie Laine, the music business smelt the whiff of a new musical revolution. This was confirmed by the arrival of *Rock around the clock,* which had actually been recorded in April 1954 but did not make its impact till the second half of 1955. Its elevation to legendary status was fuelled by its use as the theme for the seminal '55 youth movie *Blackboard jungle.* During the remainder of 55 and 56, Haley's Comets chalked up a prolific string of hits, often featuring the word "rock" somewhere in the title. They were especially popular in Britain, where *Rock around the clock, Rock a-beatin' boogie, See you later alligator, The saints rock'n'roll, Rockin' through the rye, Razzle dazzle, Rip it up* and *Rudy's rock* combined to give Haley a golden 1956 and, according to the Guinness book of Hit Singles, the best year for any act in UK chart history. When Bill arrived in Britain in February 1957, he was given an overwhelming reception. Paradoxically, the tour also helped to kill his short career stone dead - fans suddenly realised that he was a somewhat podgy married man in his early 30's. British youngsters quickly followed the leads of their American counterparts by crowning the frenetic 22-year-old Elvis Presley as king of rock'n'roll. During the 60's and 70's Haley remained an active international touring performer, although these tours were latterly interrupted by sporadic periods of semi-retirement. Successful re-issued of *Rock around the clock* also helped keep him in the publiceye. Another European tour was being planned when Haley died of a heart attack in February 1981 in Harlingen, Texas; he was 55, and had recently celebrated the 25th anniversary of *Rock around the clock.* (Bob Macdonald, 5/10/85).

6 TRACK HITS
Tracks: / Whole lotta shakin' goin' on / Rock around the clock / Shake, rattle and roll / Kansas city / Me and Bobby McGee / Rip it up.
7" EP: Released Aug '83, on Scoop 33, by Pickwick Records. Catalogue no: **7SR 5012**

CRAZY MAN CRAZY
Tracks: / Crazy man crazy.
7" Single: Released Jun '74, on Sonet, by Sonet Records. Catalogue no: **SON 2043**

DON'T KNOCK THE ROCK
Tracks: / Don't knock the rock.
7" Single: Released Feb '57, on Brunswick, by Decca Records. Deleted '60. Catalogue no: **05640**

EVERYONE CAN ROCK AND ROLL
Tracks: / Everyone can rock and roll.
7" Single: Released Feb '81, on Sonet, by Sonet Records. Catalogue no: **SON 2194**

GOD BLESS ROCK AND ROLL
Tracks: / God bless rock and roll.
7" Single: Released Feb '82, on Sonet, by Sonet Records. Catalogue no: **SON 2202**

HAIL HAIL ROCK AND ROLL (SINGLE)
Tracks: / Hail, hail rock'n'roll.
7" Single: Released Feb '81, on Sonet, by Sonet Records. Catalogue no: **SON 2188**

HALEY'S GOLDEN MEDLEY
Tracks: / Haley's golden medley.
7" Single: Released Apr '81, on MCA, by MCA Records. Deleted '84. Catalogue no: **MCA 694**

MAMBO ROCK
Tracks: / Mambo rock.
7" Single: Released Apr '55, on Brunswick, by Decca Records. Deleted '58. Catalogue no: **05405**

RAZZLE DAZZLE
Tracks: / Razzle dazzle.
7" Single: Released Aug '56, on Brunswick, by Decca Records. Deleted '59. Catalogue no: **05453**

REAL ROCK DRIVE
Tracks: / Real rock drive / Live it up / Dance with a dolly / Rockin' chair on the moon.
7" EP: Released Jan '80, on Rollercoaster, by Rollercoaster Records. Deleted Jan '88. Catalogue no: **RCEP 102**

RIP IT UP
Tracks: / Rip it up.
7" Single: Released Nov '56, on Brunswick, by Decca Records. Deleted '59. Catalogue no: **05615**

ROCK A BEATIN BOOGIE
Tracks: / Rock-a-beatin' boogie.
7" Single: Released Dec '55, on Brunswick, by Decca Records. Deleted '58. Catalogue no: **05509**

ROCK AROUND THE CLOCK (OLD GOLD)
Tracks: / Rock around the clock / Thirteen women.
7" Single: Released Jun '88, on Old Gold, by Old Gold Records. Catalogue no: **OG 9920**

ROCK AROUND THE CLOCK (SINGLE)
Tracks: / Rock around the clock.
7" Single: Released Jan '55, on Brunswick, by Decca Records. Deleted '58. Catalogue no: **05317**
7" Single: Released Feb '81, on MCA, by MCA Records. Catalogue no: **MCA 128**
7" Single: Released '68, on MCA, by MCA Records. Deleted '71. Catalogue no: **MU 1013**

ROCK THE JOINT (SINGLE)
Tracks: / Rock the joint / Fractured.
7" Single: Released Sep '80, on Rollercoaster, by Rollercoaster Records. Catalogue no: **RRC 2004**

ROCK THE JOINT (SINGLE - ORIGINAL RELEASE)
Tracks: / Rock the joint.
7" Single: Released Feb '57, on London-American, Deleted '60. Catalogue no: **HLF 8371**

ROCKET 88
Tracks: / Rocket 88.
7" Single: Released Feb '81, on Thumbs Up, Catalogue no: **TU 103**

ROCKIN' THROUGH THE RYE
Tracks: / Rockin' through the rye.
7" Single: Released Aug '56, on Brunswick, by Decca Records. Deleted '59. Catalogue no: **05582**

RUDY'S ROCK
Tracks: / Rudy's rock.
7" Single: Released Jul '82, on Revival, Catalogue no: **REV 6016**
7" Single: Released Nov '56, on Brunswick, by Decca Records. Deleted '59. Catalogue no: **05616**

SAINTS ROCK 'N' ROLL, THE
Tracks: / Saints rock 'n' roll.
7" Single: Released May '56, on Brunswick, by Decca Records. Deleted '59. Catalogue no: **05565**

SEE YOU LATER ALLIGATOR
Tracks: / See you later alligator.
7" Single: Released Mar '56, on Brunswick, by Decca Records. Deleted '59. Catalogue no: **05530**

SEE YOU LATER ALLIGATOR (OLD GOLD)
Tracks: / See you later alligator / Shake, rattle and roll.
7" Single: Released Jul '82, on Old Gold, by Old Gold Records. Catalogue no: **OG 9221**

SHAKE RATTLE AND ROLL
Tracks: / Shake, rattle and roll.
7" Single: Released Dec '54, on Brunswick, by Decca Records. Deleted '58. Catalogue no: **05338**

WHY DO I CRY OVER YOU
Tracks: / Why do I cry over you?.
7" Single: Released '79, on Rollercoaster, by Rollercoaster Records. Deleted Dec '88. Catalogue no: **RZ 137**

Haley Brothers

WHAT DO YOU WANT TO MAKE THOSE EYES...
Tracks: / What do you want to make those eyes at me for.
7" Single: Released Aug '83, on Weasel, by Weasel Records. Catalogue no: **WR 4006**

Haley, Mark

WHY CAN'T THEY LEAVE HIM ALONE
Tracks: / Why can't they leave him alone / I'm just hearing you out.
7" Single: Released Jul '87, on RCA, by BMG Records (UK). Deleted May '89. Catalogue no: **PB 41459**

Half Japanese

SILVER AND KATHERINE
Tracks: / Silver and Katherine.
7" Single: Released Feb '88, on Shadowline, Catalogue no: **SR 0188**

SPY
Tracks: / Spy / My knowledge was wrong.
7" Single: Released May '81, on Armageddon, by Armageddon Records. Catalogue no: **AS 008**
12" Single: Released May '81, on Armageddon, by Armageddon Records. Catalogue no: **AS 009**

Half Man Half Biscuit

DICKIE DAVIES EYES
Tracks: / Dickie Davies eyes / I left my heart (in Papworth General) / Bastard son of Dean Friedman, The.
Note: with extra track on 12": version only
12" Single: Released Oct '86, on Probe Plus, by Probe Plus Records. Catalogue no: **PP 21T**
7" Single: Released Oct '86, on Probe Plus, by Probe Plus Records. Catalogue no: **PP 21**

PEEL SESSIONS:HALF MAN HALF BISCUIT
Tracks: / D'ye kn Ted Moult / Arthur's farm / All I want for xmas is a Dukla Prague away kit / Trumpton riots / Old Tige.
CD 5": Released Oct '88, on Strange Fruit, by Strange Fruit Records. Catalogue no: **SFPSCD 057**
12" Single: Released Oct '88, on Strange Fruit, by Strange Fruit Records. Catalogue no: **SFPS 057**

TRUMPTON RIOTS
Tracks: / Trumpton riots / Ducla Prague away kit / Architecture morality (Extra track on 12" version only.) / Ted and Alice (Extra track on 12" version only.) / 1966 and all that (Extra track on 12" version only.) / Albert Hammond bootleg (Extra track on 12" version only.).
7" Single: Released Mar '86, on Probe Plus, by Probe Plus Records. Catalogue no: **TRUM 17**
12" Single: Released Mar '86, on Probe Plus, by Probe Plus Records. Catalogue no: **TRUMP 1**

Half Pint

FREEDOM FIGHTER
Tracks: / Freedom fighter / Hold on.
12" Single: Released Jul '85, on Greensleeves, by Greensleeves Records. Catalogue no: **GRED 178**

GO BACK HOME
Tracks: / Go back home.
12" Single: Released Jun '85, on Hawkeye, by Hawkeye Records. Catalogue no: **HD 60**

GREETINGS (SINGLE)
Tracks: / Greetins.
12" Single: Released Jul '86, on Power House, Catalogue no: **PHT 12**

HOLD ON
Tracks: / Hold on.
12" Single: Released Apr '85, on Jedi Catalogue no: **Unknown**

MR LANDLORD
Tracks: / Mr. Landlord.
12" Single: Released Sep '84, or Jammy's, Catalogue no: **AA 1001**

NIGHT LIFE LADY
Tracks: / Night life lady.
12" Single: Released Mar '86, on Island by Island Records. Catalogue no: **12IS 277**

ONE IN A MILLION (SINGLE)
Tracks: / One in a million.
12" Single: Released Oct '84, on Greensleeves, by Greensleeves Records. Catalogue no: **GRED 159**

POLITICAL FICTION
Tracks: / Political fiction.
12" Single: Released Sep '84, on Sun Se (reggae), Catalogue no: **Unknown**

SALLY
Tracks: / Sally.
12" Single: Released Oct '84, on Jed Catalogue no: **JJ 209**

Halkett, Rene

ARMOUR
Tracks: / Armour.
7" Single: Released Dec '81, on 4AD, b 4AD Records. Catalogue no: **AD 112**

Hall, Audrey

ANGEL IN THE MORNING
Tracks: / Angel in the morning.
12" Single: Released Mar '83, on Regga Catalogue no: **REG 14**

ANYONE WHO HAD A HEART
Tracks: / Anyone who had a heart.
12" Single: Released Dec '85, on Ge maine, Catalogue no: **DG 131985**

BEST THING FOR ME, THE
Tracks: / Best thing for me, The.
7" Single: Released Oct '86, on Germair Catalogue no: **DG 20**
12" Single: Released Oct '86, on Ge maine, Catalogue no: **DGT 20**

HEART MADE OF STONE
Tracks: / Heart made of stone / Hea made of stone (alternative version) / hard to believe.
12" Single: Released Sep '86, on Troja by Trojan Records. Deleted May '88. Ca logue no: **TROT 9091**
7" Single: Released Sep '86, on Trojan, Trojan Records. Deleted May '88. Ca logue no: **TRO 9091**

I WANT TO KNOW WHAT LOVE IS

Tracks: / I want to know what love is.
12" Single: Released Mar '85, on Germaine, Catalogue no: **Unknown**

NOBODY ELSE BUT ME
Tracks: / Nobody else but me.
7" Single: Released Aug '89, on Germaine, Catalogue no: **DGT 55**

ONE DANCE WON'T DO
Tracks: / One dance won't do.
7" Single: Released Jan '86, on Germaine, Catalogue no: **DG7-1985**

SMILE
Tracks: / Smile.
12" Single: Released Jun '86, on Germaine, Catalogue no: **DGT 15**
7" Single: Released Jun '86, on Germaine, Catalogue no: **DG 15**

Hall, Daryl

DREAMTIME
Tracks: / Dreamtime.
7" Single: Released Jul '86, on RCA, by BMG Records (UK). Catalogue no: **HALL 1**
12" Single: Released Jul '86, on RCA, by BMG Records (UK). Catalogue no: **HALLT 1**

I WASN'T BORN YESTERDAY
Tracks: / I wasn't born yesterday / What's gonna happen to us / Dreamtime* (*Extra track on 12" version only.).
7" Single: Released Nov '86, on RCA, by BMG Records (UK). Catalogue no: **HALL 2**
12" Single: Released Nov '86, on RCA, by BMG Records (UK). Catalogue no: **HALLT 2**

Hall, Henry

LA DI DA DI DA
Tracks: / La di da di da.
12" Single: Released Nov '82, on Music For Living, by Music For Living Records. Catalogue no: **AA 1**
7" Single: Released Nov '82, on Music For Living, by Music For Living Records. Catalogue no: **A 1**

Hall, Jennifer

DANGER MEN AT WORK
Tracks: / Danger men at work / Mastery.
12" Single: Released Oct '87, on Warner Bros., by WEA Records. Deleted Jul '88. Catalogue no: **W 8162T**
7" Single: Released Oct '87, on Warner Bros., by WEA Records. Deleted Jul '88. Catalogue no: **W 8162**

ICE CREAM DAYS
Tracks: / Ice cream days / Mastery.
7" Single: Released May '88, on Warner Bros., by WEA Records. Catalogue no: **W 7965**
12" Single: Released May '88, on Warner Bros., by WEA Records. Catalogue no: **W 7965T**

Hall, Jim

Biographical details: See also under Carter, Ron..

I'M HAPPY THAT LOVE HAS FOUND YOU
Tracks: / I'm happy that love has found you / Touch you.
7" Single: Released Jan '81, on Epic, by CBS Records. Deleted Jan '84. Catalogue no: **EPC 9397**

Hall & Oates

A NIGHT AT THE APOLLO LIVE!
Tracks: / Night at the apollo live, A.
7" Single: Released Sep '85, on RCA, by BMG Records (UK). Catalogue no: **PB 49935**

ADULT EDUCATION
Tracks: / Adult education / Say it isn't so.
7" Single: Released Mar '84, on RCA, by BMG Records (UK). Catalogue no: **RCA 396**
12" Single: Released Mar '84, on RCA, by BMG Records (UK). Catalogue no: **RCAT 396**

DOWNTOWN LIFE
Tracks: / Downtown life.
CD 5": Released 16 Sep '88, on Arista, by BMG Records (UK). Catalogue no: **661730**
7" Single: Released 16 Sep '88, on Arista, by BMG Records (UK). Catalogue no: **111730**
12" Single: Released 16 Sep '88, on Arista, by BMG Records (UK). Catalogue no: **611730**

EVERYTHING YOUR HEART DESIRES
Tracks: / Everything your heart desires / Real love.
CD 5": Released Jun '89, on Arista, by BMG Records (UK). Catalogue no: **659869**
7" Single: Released Apr '88, on Arista, by BMG Records (UK). Catalogue no: **109869**
12" Single: Released Apr '88, on Arista, by BMG Records (UK). Catalogue no: **609869**

HALL & OATES - FAMILY MAN (Released on RCA)

FAMILY MAN (see apnel above)
Tracks: / Family man / Open all night.
12" Single: Released Apr '83, on RCA, by BMG Records (UK). Catalogue no: **RCAT 323**
7" Single: Released Apr '83, on RCA, by BMG Records (UK). Catalogue no: **RCA 323**

I CAN'T GO FOR THAT
Tracks: / I can't go for that / Unguarded minute.
7" Single: Released Jan '82, on RCA, by BMG Records (UK). Catalogue no: **RCA 172**
12" Single: Released Jan '82, on RCA, by BMG Records (UK). Deleted '85. Catalogue no: **RCAT 172**

KISS ON MY LIST
Tracks: / Kiss on my list / Africa.
7" Single: Released Nov '80, on RCA, by BMG Records (UK). Deleted '83. Catalogue no: **RCA 15**
7" Single: Released May '82, on RCA, by BMG Records (UK). Catalogue no: **GOLD 547**

MANEATER
Tracks: / Maneater / Delayed reaction.
CD 5": Released Jun '89, on RCA, by BMG Records (UK). Catalogue no: **PD 49465**
7" Single: Released Oct '82, on RCA, by BMG Records (UK). Deleted '85. Catalogue no: **RCA 290**
12" Single: Released Oct '82, on RCA, by BMG Records (UK). Deleted '85. Catalogue no: **RCAT 290**

MANEATER (OLD GOLD)
Tracks: / Maneater / I can't go for that.
7" Single: Released Nov '86, on Old Gold, by Old Gold Records. Catalogue no: **OG 9658**

METHOD OF MODERN LOVE
Tracks: / Method of modern love.
7" Single: Released Jan '85, on RCA, by BMG Records (UK). Catalogue no: **RCA 472**
12" Single: Released Jan '85, on RCA, by BMG Records (UK). Catalogue no: **RCAT 472**

NITE AT THE APOLLO LIVE, A
12" Single: Released Sep '85, on RCA, by BMG Records (UK). Catalogue no: **PT 49936**
7" Single: Released Sep '85, on RCA, by BMG Records (UK). Catalogue no: **PB 49935**

ONE ON ONE
Tracks: / One on one / Art of heartbreaker.
7" Single: Released Jan '83, on RCA, by BMG Records (UK). Catalogue no: **RCA 305**
12" Single: Released Jan '83, on RCA, by BMG Records (UK). Catalogue no: **RCAT 305**

OUT OF TOUCH
Tracks: / Out of touch / Dance on your knees.
7" Single: Released Sep '84, on RCA, by BMG Records (UK). Catalogue no: **RCA 449**
7" Single: Released Jun '85, on RCA, by BMG Records (UK). Catalogue no: **PB 49967**
12" Single: Released Sep '84, on RCA, by BMG Records (UK). Catalogue no: **RCAT 449**

PRIVATE EYES (SINGLE)
Tracks: / Private eyes / Tell me what you want.
12" Single: Released Apr '82, on RCA, by BMG Records (UK). Deleted '85. Catalogue no: **RCAT 134**
7" Single: Released Apr '82, on RCA, by BMG Records (UK). Deleted '85. Catalogue no: **RCA 134**

RUNNING FROM PARADISE (see panel below)
Tracks: / Running from paradise / Bebop/Drop.
7" Single: Released Jun '80, on RCA, by BMG Records (UK). Deleted '83. Catalogue no: **RUN 1**

SAY IT ISN'T SO
Tracks: / Say it isn't so.
7" Single: Released Oct '83, on RCA, by BMG Records (UK). Catalogue no: **RCA 375**

SHE'S GONE
Tracks: / She's gone.
7" Single: Released Oct '76, on Atlantic, by WEA Records. Deleted '79. Catalogue no: **K 10828**
7" Single: Released Jul '81, on Atlantic, by WEA Records. Catalogue no: **K 11597**

YOU MAKE MY DREAMS
Tracks: / You make my dreams / Gotta lotta nerve.
7" Single: Released Jun '81, on RCA, by BMG Records (UK). Deleted Jun '84. Catalogue no: **RCA 68**

YOUR IMAGINATION
Tracks: / Your imagination / Sarah smiles.
7" Single: Released Jun '82, on RCA, by BMG Records (UK). Catalogue no: **RCA 239**
12" Single: Released Jun '82, on RCA, by BMG Records (UK). Catalogue no: **RCAT 239**

YOU'VE LOST THAT LOVIN' FEELIN'
Tracks: / You've lost that lovin' feeling / United State.
7" Single: Released Sep '80, on RCA, by BMG Records (UK). Deleted '83. Catalogue no: **RCA 1**

Hall, Pam

BET YOU DON'T KNOW
Tracks: / Bet you don't know.
12" Single: Released Oct '88, on Blue Trac, by Blue Trac Records. Catalogue no: **BTRD 028**

DEAR BOOPSIE
Tracks: / Dear Boopsie.
Cassingle: Released Aug '86, on Blue Mountain, Catalogue no: **BMD 027**
7" Single: Released Aug '86, on Blue Mountain, Catalogue no: **BM 027**

DON'T LET HER TAKE YOU AWAY
Tracks: / Don't let her take you away.
12" Single: Released Sep '89, on Blue Mountain, Catalogue no: **BMD 068**

HOW GLAD I AM
Tracks: / How glad I am / Hot hot loving.
12" Single: Released Aug '87, on Blue Trac, by Blue Trac Records. Catalogue no: **BTRD 010**

LATE AT NIGHT
Tracks: / Late at night.
12" Single: Released Jan '84, on Malaco, by Malaco Records (UK). Deleted '88. Catalogue no: **MAL 12 016**
7" Single: Released Jan '84, on Malaco, by Malaco Records (UK). Deleted '88. Catalogue no: **MAL 016**

LET ME TELL YOU BOY
Tracks: / Let me tell you boy.
12" Single: Released Sep '89, on Steely & Cleevie, Catalogue no: **VPRD 458**

NOT ONLY MY WIFE
Tracks: / Not only my wife.
12" Single: Released Mar '86, on Mobiliser, by Jetstar Records. Catalogue no: **Unknown**

PERFIDIA Instrumental version
Tracks: / Perfidia.
12" Single: Released Feb '84, on Mobiliser, by Jetstar Records. Catalogue no: **MM 75**

HALL & OATES - RUNNING FROM PARADISE (Released on RCA)

PERFIDIA, THE
Tracks: / Perfidia / Come in a dis.
12" Single: Released Nov '86, on World Enterprise, Catalogue no: **WENDIS 3034**

Hall, Patrick

WITHOUT YOU
Tracks: / Without you.
12" Single: Released Mar '83, on A.Small, Catalogue no: **SMA 001**

Hall, Terry

MISSING
Tracks: / Missing / Happy families.
CD 5": Released Oct '89, on Chrysalis, by Chrysalis Records. Catalogue no: **CHSCD 3381**
12" Single: Released Jul '89, on Chrysalis, by Chrysalis Records. Catalogue no: **CHS 12 3381**
7" Single: Released Jul '89, on Chrysalis, by Chrysalis Records. Catalogue no: **CHS 3381**
Cassingle: Released Oct '89, on Chrysalis, by Chrysalis Records. Catalogue no: **CHSMC 3381**

Hall, Tom T.

LOVE LETTERS IN THE SAND
Tracks: / Love letters in the sand / Song in a sea shell.
7" Single: Released Oct '86, on Mercury, by Phonogram Ltd. Deleted '87. Catalogue no: **TOM 102**

P.S I LOVE YOU
Tracks: / P.S. I love you.
7" Single: Released Oct '84, on Phonogram, by Phonogram Ltd. Catalogue no: **TOM 1**

WHO DO YOU PRAY FOR
Tracks: / Who do you pray for.
7" Single: Released Oct '83, on Range, by Range Records. Catalogue no: **RANS 71**

Halleymites

WE ARE THE HALLEYMITES
Tracks: / We are the Halleymites.
7" Single: Released Nov '85, on Red Bus, by Red Bus Records. Catalogue no: **RBUS 2206**

Halliday, Toni

LOVE ATTRACTION
Tracks: / Love attraction / Child.
12" Single: Released Jul '88, on Anxious, by Anxious Records. Deleted May '89. Catalogue no: **ANXT 005**
CD 5": Released Jul '88, on Anxious, by Anxious Records. Catalogue no: **ANX 005 CD**
7" Single: Released Jul '88, on Anxious, by Anxious Records. Deleted May '89. Catalogue no: **ANX 005**

TIME TURNS AROUND
Tracks: / Time turns around / Dullman / Time turns around (euro tech version).
CD 5": Released Mar '89, on Anxious, by Anxious Records. Catalogue no: **ANXCD 010**
7" Single: Released Mar '89, on Anxious, by Anxious Records. Catalogue no: **ANX 010**
12" Single: Released Mar '89, on Anxious, by Anxious Records. Catalogue no: **ANXT 010**

WEEK DAY
Tracks: / Week day / Top of the tree.
7" Single: Released Apr '88, on Anxious, by Anxious Records. Deleted May '89. Catalogue no: **ANX 003**
CD 5": Released Apr '88, on Anxious, by Anxious Records. Catalogue no: **ANX 003 CD**
12" Single: Released Apr '88, on Anxious, by Anxious Records. Deleted May '89. Catalogue no: **ANXT 003**

WOMAN IN MIND
Tracks: / Woman in mind / Chemical come-down / Woman in mind (thinker version) (Available on 12" and CD only) / Woman in mind (live) (Available on 12" only).
7" Single: Released Jun '89, on RCA, by BMG Records (UK). Catalogue no: **ANX 013**
CD 5": Released Jun '89, on RCA, by BMG Records (UK). Catalogue no: **ANXCD 013**
12" Single: Released Jun '89, on RCA, by BMG Records (UK). Catalogue no: **ANXT 013**

Halliwell, Nick

IT'LL END IN TEARS
Tracks: / It'll end in tears / Crashing down.
7" Single: Released Aug '84, on Office Box, Catalogue no: **OCS 1**

Hallyday, David

HE'S MY GIRL
Tracks: / He's my girl / He's my girl (ext. remix) (track on 12" only.) / Church of the poison spider.
7" Single: Released Feb '88, on Polydor, by Polydor Ltd. Catalogue no: **888 824 7**
12" Single: Released Feb '88, on Polydor, by Polydor Ltd. Deleted 31 May '89. Catalogue no: **888 824 1**

HIGH
Tracks: / High.
7" Single: Released Feb '89, on Polydor, by Polydor Ltd. Deleted Aug '89. Catalogue no: **PO 37**
12" Single: Released Feb '89, on Polydor, by Polydor Ltd. Deleted Aug '89. Catalogue no: **PZ 37**

MOVE
Tracks: / Move / Ya seen one, ya seen 'em all.
7" Single: Released Aug '88, on Scotti Bros (Germany), Catalogue no: **PO 2**

Halpin, Kieran

BELIEVING
Tracks: / Believing / Too long away.
7" Single: Released Dec '84, on CMS, Catalogue no: **CMS 400**

Ham

VOULEZ VOUS
Tracks: / Voulez vous.
12" Single: Released Jul '89, on One Little Indian, by One Little Indian Records. Catalogue no: **27 TP 12**

Hambi ....

25 TEARS A DAY
(HAMBI & THE DANCE)
Tracks: / 25 tears a day.
7" Single: Released Sep '84, on MCA, by MCA Records. Catalogue no: **MCA 900**
12" Single: Released Sep '84, on MCA, by MCA Records. Deleted '85. Catalogue no: **MCAT 900**

I DON'T WANT TO LOSE YOU
Tracks: / I don't want to lose you / Julie.
12" Single: Released Jan '86, on Harry Barter Productions, Deleted '87. Catalogue no: **HAMB 121**
7" Single: Released Jan '86, on Harry Barter Productions, Deleted '87. Catalogue no: **HAMB 1**

L'IMAGE CRAQUE
Tracks: / L'image craque.
7" Single: Released Sep '81, on Virgin, by Virgin Records. Deleted Sep '84. Catalogue no: **VS 437**

LIVING IN A HEARTACHE
(HAMBI & THE DANCE)
Tracks: / Living in a heartache.
7" Single: Released Nov '82, on Virgin, by Virgin Records. Deleted Nov '85. Catalogue no: **VS 474**

MADELAINE
Tracks: / Madelaine.
7" Single: Released Apr '82, on Virgin, by Virgin Records. Deleted Apr '85. Catalogue no: **VS 474**

TOO LATE TO FLY THE FLAG
(HAMBI & THE DANCE)
Tracks: / Too late to fly the flag.
7" Single: Released May '81, on Virgin, by Virgin Records. Deleted May '84. Catalogue no: **VS 414**

Hamill, Chris

ANGIE
Tracks: / Angie.
7" Single: Released Apr '81, on Random, Catalogue no: **RAMDOM 2**
7" Single: Released Feb '83, on Solid Rock, by Word Records (UK). Catalogue no: **SR 473633**

Hamill, Claire

24 HOURS FROM TULSA
Tracks: / 24 hours from Tulsa.
7" Single: Released Apr '83, on Beggars Banquet, by Beggars Banquet Records. Deleted Jan '88. Catalogue no: **BEG 90**
12" Single: Released Apr '83, on Beggars Banquet, by Beggars Banquet Records. Deleted Jan '88. Catalogue no: **BEG 90T**

DENMARK
Tracks: / Denmark.
12" Single: Released Jul '84, on Coda, by Coda Records. Catalogue no: **CODS 8T**
7" Single: Released Jul '84, on Coda, by Coda Records. Catalogue no: **CODS 8**

DOOMSDAY, THE (EP)
Tracks: / Doomsday, The / Glastonbury / Tides / Spring awaken, lark rise / Stars.
7" Single: Released Nov '86, on Coda, by Coda Records. Catalogue no: **CODS 21**

FIRST NIGHT IN NEW YORK
Tracks: / First night in New York / Ultraviolet light.
7" Single: Released Feb '81, on WEA, by WEA Records. Deleted Feb '84. Catalogue no: **K 18440**

GLASTONBURY
Tracks: / Glastonbury / Crossing, The.
7" Single: Released 23 Apr '88, on Coda, by Coda Records. Catalogue no: **CODS 24**

IF YOU'D ONLY TALK TO ME
Tracks: / If you'd only talk to me / Don't prolong the agony.
12" Single: Released May '85, on Coda, by Coda Records. Catalogue no: **CODS 14T**
7" Single: Released May '85, on Coda, by Coda Records. Catalogue no: **CODS 14**

MOON IS A POWERFUL LOVER, A
Tracks: / Moon is a powerful lover / Once is not enough.
7" Single: Released Jun '84, on Coda, by Coda Records. Catalogue no: **CODS 5**
12" Single: Released Jun '84, on Coda, by Coda Records. Catalogue no: **CODS 5T**

PALM OF MY HAND
Tracks: / Palm of my hand.
7" Single: Released Nov '83, on Coda, by Coda Records. Catalogue no: **CODS 2**
12" Single: Released Nov '83, on Coda, by Coda Records. Catalogue no: **CODS 2T**

Hamill, Peter

MY EXPERIENCE
Tracks: / My experience.
7" Single: Released May '81, on Virgin, by Virgin Records. Deleted May '84. Catalogue no: **VS 424**

Hamilton, Colbert

LONG BLACK SHINY CAR
Tracks: / Long black shiny car.
7" Single: Released Aug '84, on Rewind, Catalogue no: **FEAR 3**

Hamilton, Dirk

IN A MIRACLE
Tracks: / In a miracle / Change in a child's hands.
7" Single: Released May '80, on Electra, Deleted May '83. Catalogue no: **K 12438**

MAIN ATTRACTION
Tracks: / Main attraction / I will acquiesce.
7" Single: Released Feb '80, on Elektra, by Elektra Records (UK). Deleted Feb '83. Catalogue no: **K 12422**

Hamilton, Edward

BABY DON'T YOU WEEP
Tracks: / Baby don't you weep / I'm gonna love you.
7" Single: Released Feb '80, on Grapevine (Northern Soul), by BMG Records (UK). Deleted Feb '83. Catalogue no: **GRP 134**

Hamilton, George IV

ENGLAND
Tracks: / England.
7" Single: Released Sep '82, on MRE, Catalogue no: **MRE 001**

I KNOW WHERE I'M GOING
Tracks: / I know where i'm going.
7" Single: Released Jul '58, on H.M.V., by EMI Records. Deleted '61. Catalogue no: **POP 505**

NATIVIDAD
Tracks: / Natividad / I love music.
7" Single: Released Dec '80, on Mervyn Conn Presents, Catalogue no: **DSM 7003**

WAY OLD FRIENDS DO
Tracks: / Way old friends do / Songs for a winter's night.
7" Single: Released Dec '82, on Mervyn Conn Presents, Catalogue no: **MRE 002**

WHY DON'T THEY UNDERSTAND
Tracks: / Why don't they understand.
7" Single: Released Mar '58, on H.M.V., by EMI Records. Deleted '61. Catalogue no: **POP 429**

WILD MOUNTAIN THYME
Tracks: / Wild mountain thyme / I'll be here in the morning.
7" Single: Released Feb '80, on MCA, by MCA Records. Deleted Feb '83. Catalogue no: **MCA 558**

Hamilton, John

THEM CHANGES
Tracks: / Them changes.
7" Single: Released Mar '81, on Charly, by Charly Records. Deleted '87. Catalogue no: **CTD 128**

Hamilton, Lynne

ON THE INSIDE
Tracks: / On the inside / Prisoner cell block H love theme.
7" Single: Released Apr '89, on A.1, by A.1 Records. Catalogue no: **A1 311**

Hamilton, Roy

HOLD ONTO THIS MOOD
Tracks: / Hold onto this mood / Hold onto this mood (inst).
7" Single: Released 23 May '87, on 4th & Broadway, by Island Records. Catalogue no: **BRW 67**
12" Single: Released 23 May '87, on 4th & Broadway, by Island Records. Deleted Apr '88. Catalogue no: **12 BRW 67**

HOLD ONTO THIS MOOD (REMIX)
Tracks: / Hold onto this mood (remix) / Hold onto this mood (inst).
12" Single: Released Jun '87, on 4th & Broadway, by Island Records. Catalogue no: **BRWX 67**

HOLD TIGHT
Tracks: / Hold tight.
7" Single: Released Apr '84, on PRT, by Castle Communications Records. Catalogue no: **EXC 535**

HOW DO YOU DO
Tracks: / How do you do / How do you do(instrumental mix).
7" Single: Released Jul '83, on PRT, by Castle Communications Records. Catalogue no: **EXC 534**

TAKE YOUR TIME
Tracks: / Take your time.
12" Single: Released Oct '82, on PRT, by Castle Communications Records. Deleted '85. Catalogue no: **EXCL 522**
7" Single: Released Oct '82, on PRT, by Castle Communications Records. Deleted '85. Catalogue no: **EXC 522**

Hamilton, Russ

Biographical details:
This British singer and songwriter hailed from Everton, Liverpool. Before becoming a music business professional, he had jobs as a Butlin's holiday camp redcoat and as a costing clerk. It was while in the latter occupation that he wrote *We will make love*. This song became a British no. 2 smash for the previously unknown Hamilton in 1957.

Amazingly, the B-side, another self penned song called *Rainbow* - cruised to no. 4 in America. In those days it was rare for a UK singer to reach the American Top 5, rarer still for a UK singer to write his own material and even more rare for an artists to hit the Top 5 on both sides of the Atlantic with different sides of the same single.
However, despite these achievemants, Hamilton was unable to sustain his chart career. His ballads were not particularly fashionable in the rock'n'roll era, and he was not helped by the fact that he had a lisp and was not as good-looking as some of his rivals.
After one further UK hit *Wedding ring* (no. 20), he drifted into obscurity. His real name was Ron Hulme.
(Bob Macdonald, 7/10/85).

WE WILL MAKE LOVE
Tracks: / We will make love.
7" Single: Released May '57, on Oriole, Deleted '60. Catalogue no: **CB 1359**
7" Single: Released Jul '82, on Old Gold, by Old Gold Records. Deleted Jul '88. Catalogue no: **OG 9053**

WEDDING RING
Tracks: / Wedding ring.
7" Single: Released Sep '57, on Oriole, Deleted '60. Catalogue no: **CB 1388**

Hamilton/Joe/Frank..

FALLIN' IN LOVE
Tracks: / Falling in love.
7" Single: Released Sep '75, on Pye International, Deleted '78. Catalogue no: **7N 25690**

Hamlisch, Marvin

Biographical details:
Born in New York, this American pianist composer and conductor came to fame in the seventies as a composer of movie scores.
His first major success in that capacity came with the 1973 film *The way we were*; the movie's title theme, which he co-wrote with Alan & Marilyn Bergman, became a US no 1 single for Barbra Streisand in 1974 and a UK Top 5 for Gladys Knight & The Pips in 1975. 1974 also brought Hamlisch his other most important success.
Both he and movie director George Roy Hill were admirers of the work of the late 19th century ragtime pianist and composer Scott Joplin.
Hill decided to use some of Joplin's many compositions as the basis for the score of his movie *The sting*.
He commissioned fellow Joplin fan Hamlisch to carry out the idea, and the result was a huge-selling soundtrack LP on both sides of the Atlantic.
The album of *The sting* was almost as big a success as the film itself, and created a considerable revival of interest in the long neglected Joplin. Hamlisch's rendition of the 1902 song *The entertainer* was the film's theme, and reached no. 3 on the US chart when released as a single, in Britain, it climbed to number 25 and logged 13 weeks on the Top 50. Hamlisch has continued to compose, and record, numerous sound tracks. One of his best songs was *If he re-*

ally knew me, co-written with lyricist Carole Bayer Sager. (Bob Macdonald, 7/10/85).

ENTERTAINER
Tracks: / Entertainer, The.
7" Single: Released Jun '83, on MCA, by MCA Records. Catalogue no: **MCA 812**

ORDINARY PEOPLE THEME
Tracks: / Ordinary people / Cannon in D.
7" Single: Released Apr '81, on Planet, Catalogue no: **K 12497**

Hammatan

NITE OF BLISS
Tracks: / Nite of bliss / Don't turn away.
7" Single: Released Oct '80, on Lagos International, by L.A. international Records Ltd.. Catalogue no: **LIS 01**
12" Single: Released Oct '80, on Lagos International, by L.A. International Records Ltd.. Deleted '83. Catalogue no: **LIS 1201**

Hammer, Jan

CROCKETT'S THEME
Tracks: / Crockett's theme.
12" Single: Released Aug '87, on MCA, by MCA Records. Catalogue no: **MCAT 1193**
7" Single: Released Aug '87, on MCA, by MCA Records. Deleted 1 Jul '89. Catalogue no: **MCA 1193**
12" Single: Released Oct '87, on MCA, by MCA Records. Catalogue no: **MCAX 1193**

MIAMI VICE THEME
Tracks: / Miami Vice theme.
7" Single: Released Sep '85, on MCA, by MCA Records. Catalogue no: **MCA 1000**

RUNNER, THE
Tracks: / Runner, The.
7" Single: Released Dec '88, on MCA, by MCA Records. Deleted 1 Jul '89. Catalogue no: **MCA 1305**
CD 5": Released Dec '88, on MCA, by MCA Records. Catalogue no: **DMCA 1305**
12" Single: Released Dec '88, on MCA, by MCA Records. Catalogue no: **MCAT 1305**

TUBBS & VALERIE
Tracks: / Tubbs & Valerie / Rico's blues / Tubbs & Valerie (extended) (Available on 12" only) / Crockett's theme**.
Note: * extra track on 12" version. ** track on CD single only.
CD 5": Released Nov '87, on MCA, by MCA Records. Catalogue no: **DMCA 1200**
12" Single: Released Oct '87, on MCA, by MCA Records. Catalogue no: **MCAT 1200**
Cassingle: Released Nov '87, on MCA, by MCA Records. Catalogue no: **MCAA 1200**
7" Single: Released Oct '87, on MCA, by MCA Records. Deleted 1 Jul '89. Catalogue no: **MCA 1200**

Hammer, MC

THEY PUT ME IN THE MIX
Tracks: / They put me in the mix.
12" Single: Released Jul '89, on Jetstar, by Jetstar Records. Catalogue no: **V 15460**

Hammer, Mike

DIVINE
Tracks: / Divine.
7" Single: Released May '89, on Loading Bay, Catalogue no: **LBAY 3**

Hammill, Peter

FILM NOIR
Tracks: / Film noir / Seven wonders.
7" Single: Released Sep '83, on Naive, by Naive Records. Catalogue no: **NAV 8**

JUST GOOD FRIENDS
Tracks: / Just good friends.
7" Single: Released May '85, on Charisma, by Virgin Records. Deleted May '88. Catalogue no: **CB 414**

PAINTING BY NUMBERS
Tracks: / Painting by numbers / Hit me where you live / Painting by numbers.
7" Single: Released Mar '86, on Foundry, Catalogue no: **FOUND 3**

PARADOX DRIVE
Tracks: / Paradox drive / Now more than ever.
7" Single: Released Oct '82, on Naive, by Naive Records. Catalogue no: **NAV 3**

Hammond, Albert

Biographical details: Born in London, this British singer/songwriter/guitarist was raised in Gibraltar. By the time he reached his 21st birthday in 1965, he had already been performing professionally (mainly in a Spanish language capacity) for eight years. In 1966 he forged a songwriting partnership with Mike Hazelwood and returned to Britain. Two years later, the pair scored a smash hit by writing *Little arrows* for Leapy Lee, which reached no. 2 in Britain and no. 16 in the States. 1970 brought them a top 10 hit on both sides of the Atlantic as writers of the Pipkins' *Gimme dat ding*. Among H&H's other UK hits were three Top 20 successes for Joe Dolan, including his 1969 Top 3 smash *Make me an island*. In 1972 Hammond moved to the west coast of America and launched a fresh career as a performer (still working with Hazelwood). At the end of the year, the pair were rewarded with an American million-selling no. 5 hit with Hammond's rendition of *It never rains in southern California*. 1973 brought him his only UK hit as a performer - *Free electric band*, a catchy album concerning a young man who rebels against the business life that has been prepared for him and opts for a career in the music business, climbed to no. 19 and logged 11 weeks on the British Top 50. 1974 saw him reach no. 31 on the US chart with *I'm a train*. There was no further recording success for Hammond, although he continued releasing albums into the eighties. But he still provided hits for other artists - the Hollies took *The air that I breathe* into the Top 10 on both sides of the Atlantic in 1974; and in 1977, Leo Sayer hit no. 1 in UK and US with *When I need you*, written by Hammond in conjunction with Carole Bayer Sager. The bulk of Albert's work has been in a light pop MoR vein. (Bob Macdonald, 7/10/85).

FREE ELECTRIC BAND
Tracks: / Free electric band.
7" Single: Released Jun '73, on Mums, Deleted '76. Catalogue no: **1494**

IT NEVER RAINS IN SOUTHERN CALIFORNIA
Tracks: / It never rains in Southern California.
7" Single: Released Jul '82, on Old Gold, by Old Gold Records. Catalogue no: **OG 9183**

WHEN I'M GONE
Tracks: / When I'm gone / World of love.
7" Single: Released May '81, on CBS, by CBS Records. Deleted May '84. Catalogue no: **CBS A 1064**

Hammond, Beres

ALL BECAUSE I'M LONELY
Tracks: / All because I'm lonely.
12" Single: Released May '87, on Charm, by Charm Records. Catalogue no: **CRT 5**

CALL ME
Tracks: / Call me.
12" Single: Released Dec '88, on Greensleeves, by Greensleeves Records. Catalogue no: **GRED 233**

GROOVY LITTLE THING
Tracks: / Groovy little thing.
12" Single: Released Jun '85, on Harmony House, Catalogue no: **Unknown**

IRE & MELLO
Tracks: / Ire and mello / Ire (version).
12" Single: Released Jan '84, on Londisc, by Londisc Records. Catalogue no: **LD 008**

LET HELP YOU SMILE AGAIN
Tracks: / Let me help you smile again.
12" Single: Released May '89, on Charm, by Charm Records. Catalogue no: **CRT 31**

LET ME LOVE YOU
Tracks: / Let me love you / Love sound.
7" Single: Released Aug '83, on Nighthawk, by Nighthawk Records (USA). Catalogue no: **NHS 26**

LONG VACATION
Tracks: / Long vacation.
12" Single: Released Sep '89, on WKS, Catalogue no: **VPRD 493**

SEND FOR ME
Tracks: / Send for me.
12" Single: Released Feb '89, on Exterminator, Catalogue no: **VPRD 389**

SHE LOVES ME NOW
Tracks: / She loves me now.
12" Single: Released Mar '86, on Greensleeves, by Greensleeves Records. Catalogue no: **GRED 196**

STUCK ON YOU
Tracks: / Stuck on you.
12" Single: Released Jan '85, on Revue, by Creole Records. Catalogue no: **REV 015T**

SUNSHINE PEOPLE
Tracks: / Sunshine people / Holy mountain lion.
12" Single: Released Jun '86, on Hawkeye, by Hawkeye Records. Catalogue no: **HD 72**

TENDER LIE, A
Tracks: / Tender lie, A / You don't have to cry.
7" Single: Released Sep '89, on Chrysalis, by Chrysalis Records. Catalogue no: **CHS 3422**
12" Single: Released Sep '89, on Chrysalis, by Chrysalis Records. Catalogue no: **CHS 123422**

WHAT ONE DANCE CAN DO
Tracks: / What one dance can do.
12" Single: Released Oct '85, on Revue, by Creole Records. Catalogue no: **REV 029T**
7" Single: Released Apr '86, on Revue, by Creole Records. Catalogue no: **REV 029**

WHEN
Tracks: / When.
12" Single: Released Apr '88, on Charm, by Charm Records. Catalogue no: **CRT 15**

WHO'A LOVING NOW
Tracks: / Who'a loving now.
12" Single: Released Oct '87, on Charm, by Charm Records. Catalogue no: **CRT 7**

Hammond, Johnny

SHIFTING GEARS
Tracks: / Shifting gears / Tell me what.
12" Single: Released Feb '88, on BGP, by Ace Records. Catalogue no: **BGPT 001**

Hampshire Primary

SING A NEW SONG
Tracks: / Sing a new song / Sing a new song (playback).
7" Single: Released Dec '87, on Plankton, by Plankton Records. Catalogue no: **PLANK 004**

Hancock, Herbie

Biographical details: This American keyboard player, composer and vocalist was born in Chicago and received classical training as a child. He studied to become an engineer, but quit his course before graduation in order to pursue a musical career. During the early sixties, he was a member of jazz trumpeter Donald Byrd's band. Hancock's debut LP *Takin' off* was released in 1963 - in that same year, just as he was celebrating his 23rd birthday, the opening track *Watermelon man* became a surprise US Top 10 hit in a cover version by Mongo Santamaria. Herbie himself did not flirt with the pop market until the mid-seventies, for the intervening years were spent playing jazz. From 1963-68 Hancock led a double life. He released acclaimed solo albums like *Empyrean Isles* and *Maiden voyage*, and played in one of the best line-ups of trumpeter Miles Davis' band. The group's 1968 album, *Miles in the sky* saw Davis moving into the rock sphere, and for the first time, adding electric instruments to his band. Tracks such as *Big stuff* brought him a crossover audience from the realms of the drug-influenced hippie rock fraternity of the late 60's. Herbie was inspired by this, and decided to quit Davis in order to pursue similar themes with his own band. His 1969 album *The prisoner* was the first solo Hancock record to include electric piano. During the early seventies, Hancock continued to explore the possibilities of electronic keyboards and the new synthesiser technology, and continued to garnish his jazz with rock influences; and he also began to dabble in an even more durable and important fusion, jazz-funk. Such experiments did not please jazz purists, but they enhanced his reputation as an innovative and talented artist. As the disco scene began to get off the ground in 1974, he registered his first major commercial success with the funky album *Head hunters*. Many more in similar vein followed. After a brief return to his jazz roots, Herbie emerged in 1978 with a record that was aimed at the disco and pop markets; from this point onwards, he forsook the jazz audiences altogether. *I thought it was you* reached no. 15 on the UK singles chart, and introduced the world to another piece of Herbie experimentation, the vocoder. This synthesiser-cum-voicebox made his inexperienced voice sound like a robot, which was handy for someone who couldn't sing. He repeated the trick on his 1979 disco single *You bet your love*, which also reached the Top 20. 1983 brought Hancock into the UK Top 10 and onto dancefloors all over the world with his biggest disco success yet. Teaming with Material, the New York electro-jazz-funk experimentalists, he came up with the dynamic single *Rockit*. This showed that veteran Herbie was thoroughly in tune with contemporary electro/hip hop/scratching trends, and was accompanied by an equally innovative and upfront video clip. (Bob Macdonald, 7/10/85).

AUTO DRIVE
Tracks: / Autodrive.
7" Single: Released Oct '83, on CBS, by CBS Records. Deleted '86. Catalogue no: **3802**

BY ALL MEANS (SINGLE)
Tracks: / By all means / Do I have to.
12" Single: Released Jul '87, on Excaliber, by Red Bus Records. Deleted '88. Catalogue no: **EXCL 509**
7" Single: Released Jul '87, on Excaliber, by Red Bus Records. Deleted '88. Catalogue no: **EXC 509**

FUTURE SHOCK
Tracks: / Future shock.
7" Single: Released Jan '84, on CBS, by CBS Records. Deleted '87. Catalogue no: **A 4075**

GO FOR IT
Tracks: / Go for it / Making love.
7" Single: Released Apr '80, on CBS, by CBS Records. Deleted Apr '83. Catalogue no: **CBS 8529**

HARDROCK
Tracks: / Hardrock.
7" Single: Released Aug '84, on CBS, by CBS Records. Catalogue no: **A 4616**
12" Single: Released Aug '84, on CBS, by CBS Records. Catalogue no: **TA 4616**

I THOUGHT IT WAS YOU
Tracks: / I thought it was you.
7" Single: Released May '82, on CBS, by CBS Records. Catalogue no: **CBS 6530**
7" Single: Released Aug '78, on CBS, by CBS Records. Deleted '81. Catalogue no: **CBS6530**

I THOUGHT IT WAS YOU (OLD GOLD)
Tracks: / I thought it was you.
7" Single: Released Sep '85, on Old Gold, by Old Gold Records. Deleted Jul '88. Catalogue no: **OG 9561**

LITE ME UP (SINGLE)

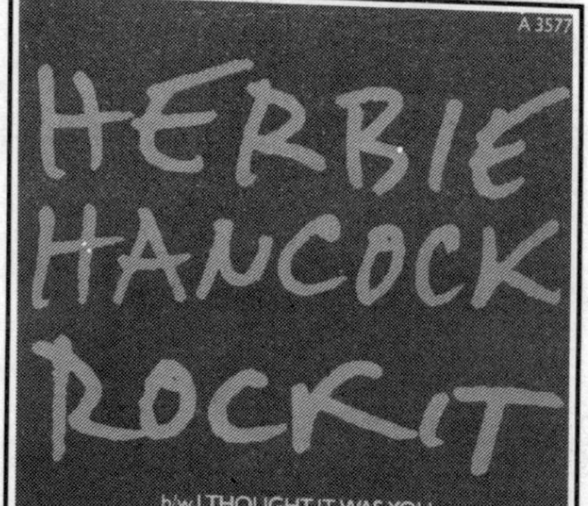

HERBIE HANCOCK - ROCK IT (Released on CBS)

Tracks: / Lite me up / Satisfied with love.
7" Single: Released Nov '82, on CBS, by CBS Records. Deleted Nov '85. Catalogue no: **A 2222**

ROCK IT (see panel on previous page)
Tracks: / Rock it.
7" Single: Released '83, on CBS, by CBS Records. Catalogue no: **A 3577**
7" Single: Released Jul '83, on CBS, by CBS Records. Deleted '86. Catalogue no: **3577**

ROCK IT (OLD GOLD)
Tracks: / Rock it / You bet your love / I thought it was you.
12" Single: Released Feb '86, on Old Gold, by Old Gold Records. Catalogue no: **OG 4001**

VIBE ALIVE
Tracks: / Vibe alive / Vibe alive (ext. dance remix) (Available on 12" version only.) / Vibe alive (bonus beats) (Track on 12" version only.) / Maiden voyage P. bop.
CD 5": Released 14 May '88, on CBS, by CBS Records. Deleted Jan '89. Catalogue no: **651 432 9**
7" Single: Released May '88, on CBS, by CBS Records. Deleted Jan '89. Catalogue no: **651 432 7**
12" Single: Released May '88, on CBS, by CBS Records. Deleted Jan '89. Catalogue no: **651 432 8**

YOU BET YOUR LOVE
Tracks: / You bet your love.
7" Single: Released Feb '79, on CBS, by CBS Records. Deleted '81. Catalogue no: **7010**

Handley Family

WAM BAM
Tracks: / Wam Bam.
7" Single: Released Apr '73, on GL. Deleted '76. Catalogue no: **GL 100**

Handley, Guthrie

WHERE WAS
Tracks: / Where was / Ha ha world / Four boats still negative (Extra track on 12").
12" Single: Released Jun '87, on Lambs To The Slaughter, by Prism Records. Catalogue no: **LTS 21T**
7" Single: Released Jun '87, on Lambs To The Slaughter, by Prism Records. Catalogue no: **LTS 21**

Handsome Beasts

ALL RIOT NOW
Tracks: / All riot now / Mark of the beast.
7" Single: Released May '80, on Heavy Metal, by FM-Revolver Records. Deleted '83. Catalogue no: **HEAVY 1**

BREAKER
Tracks: / Breaker / Crazy / One in a crowd.
7" EP: Released Mar '81, on Heavy Metal, by FM-Revolver Records. Deleted Mar '84. Catalogue no: **HEAVY 2**

SWEETIES
Tracks: / Sweeties / You're on your own.
7" Single: Released Feb '82, on Heavy Metal, by FM-Revolver Records. Deleted Feb '87. Catalogue no: **HEAVY 11**

Handson & Davis

TONIGHT Love will make it right
12" Single: Released Nov '85, on ZYX (Germany), Catalogue no: **ZYX 5289**

Handy, John

HARD WORK (SINGLE)
Tracks: / Hard work / Young enough to dream.
12" Single: Released May '82, on MCA, by MCA Records. Deleted '85. Catalogue no: **MCAT 626**
7" Single: Released May '82, on MCA, by MCA Records. Deleted '85. Catalogue no: **MCA 626**

Hang The Dance

BREAK ON THROUGH
Tracks: / Break On Through.
7" Single: Released Jun '87, on Black Map, by Black Map Records. Deleted '88. Catalogue no: **BMM 001**

HORSE FLESH
Tracks: / Horse flesh.
12" Single: Released Jul '86, on Leeds Independent (LIL), by Revolver Records. Catalogue no: **LIL 12006**

LAUGHING JACK SAID
Tracks: / Laughing Jack said.
7" Single: Released Apr '85, on Well Hung, Catalogue no: **WELL HUNG 1**

Hangman's Beautiful

LOVE IS BLUE
Tracks: / Love is blue / Popular trend / Jonathan / Don't ask my name.
12" Single: Released Mar '87, on Dreamworld, by Dreamworld Records. Catalogue no: **DREAM 011T**

THEY FELL FOR WORDS LIKE LOVE
Tracks: / They fell for words like love.
7" Single: Released 21 Nov '87, on Dreamworld, by Dreamworld Records. Catalogue no: **DREAM 015**

Hanoi Rocks

Biographical details: Hailing from Scandinavia, this heavy metal band are somewhat influenced by the Sweet/Slade school of seventies glam rock. Hanoi Rocks released several albums during the early eighties and first penetrated the UK charts with their 1984 single *Up around the bend* - this remake of Creedence Clearwater Revival's 1970 smash was merely a minor hit, peaking at no. 61 in July 1984. Hanoi Rocks have established themselves as a hard-working live act, thanks to their powerful but melodic brand of HM. *Bob Macdonald, 7/10/85).*

MALIBU BEACH
Tracks: / Malibu beach / Rebel on the run.
12" Single: Released Oct '86, on Lick, by Lick Records. Catalogue no: **LIXT 1**
7" Pic: Released Oct '86, on Lick, by Lick Records. Catalogue no: **LIXPD 1**
7" Single: Released May '83, on Licks, Catalogue no: **LIX 1**

UNTIL I GET YOU
Tracks: / Until I get you / Tragedy / Oriental beat.
7" Single: Released Aug '83, on Licks, Catalogue no: **LIX 2**
12" Single: Released Aug '82, on Licks, Catalogue no: **LIXT 2**

UP AROUND THE BEND
Tracks: / Up around the bend.
7" Set: Released Jun '84, on CBS, by CBS Records. Catalogue no: **DA 4513**
7" Single: Released Jun '84, on CBS, by CBS Records. Catalogue no: **A 4513**
12" Single: Released Jun '84, on CBS, by CBS Records. Catalogue no: **TA 45 13**

Hanson & Davis

COME TOGETHER
Tracks: / Come together.
12" Single: Released Aug '87, on Fresh (USA), Deleted Oct '87. Catalogue no: **FRE 12**

I CAN'T STOP
Tracks: / I can't stop.
12" Single: Released Jan '89, on Sleeping Bag, by Sleeping Bag Records. Catalogue no: **SBUK 3T**
7" Single: Released Jan '89, on Sleeping Bag, by Sleeping Bag Records. Catalogue no: **SBUK 3**

I'LL TAKE YOU ON
Tracks: / I'll take you on.
12" Single: Released Sep '87, on Fresh (USA), Catalogue no: **FRE 5EP**

Hanvey, Bobbie

BALLAD OF HURRICANE HIGGINS
Tracks: / Ballad of Hurricane Higgins / Master McGrath.
7" Single: Released Jun '82, on Mint, by Emerald Records. Deleted '88. Catalogue no: **CHEW 67**

Happenings

I GOT RHYTHM
Tracks: / I got rhythm.
7" Single: Released May '67, on Stateside, by EMI Records. Deleted '70. Catalogue no: **SS 2013**

MY MAMMY
Tracks: / My mammy.
7" Single: Released Aug '67, on Pye International, Deleted '70. Catalogue no: **7N 25501**

Happiness Ad

GEBURAH
Tracks: / Geburah / Alone inside.
7" Single: Released Oct '86, on Flexible Response, Deleted '88. Catalogue no: **FR 001**

LOVE CAN BE CRUEL
Tracks: / Love can be cruel.
7" Single: Released Jun '85, on Off-Beat (1), Catalogue no: **OB SH 1**

Happy Family

PURITANS(EP)
7" Single: Released Apr '82, on 4AD, by 4AD Records. Catalogue no: **AD 204**

THINGS ARE FINE
Tracks: / Things are fine.
7" Single: Released Jan '88, on Au-Go-Go (Australia), by Au-Go-Go Records (Australia). Catalogue no: **ANDA 59**

Happy Few

HUNTER
Tracks: / Hunter, The / Heaven is so difficult.
7" Single: Released Jun '82, on Smug, Deleted '83. Catalogue no: **SMUG 1**

Happy Flowers

BB GUN
Tracks: / BB gun.
7" Single: Released Apr '89, on Homestead, Catalogue no: **HMS 135**

THEY CLEANED MY CUT OUT WITH A WIRE BRUSH
Tracks: / They cleaned my cut out with a wire brush.
7" Single: Released Jun '88, on Homestead, Catalogue no: **HMS 105**

Happy Mondays

24HR PARTY PEOPLE
Tracks: / 24hr party people.
12" Single: Released Oct '87, on Factory (1), by Factory Records. Catalogue no: **FAC 192**

FORTY FIVE (EP)
7" Single: Released Sep '85, on Factory (1), by Factory Records. Catalogue no: **FAC 129**

FREAKY DANCING
Tracks: / Freaky dancing.
7" Single: Released Jun '86, on Factory (1), by Factory Records. Catalogue no: **FAC 142**
12" Single: Released Jun '86, on Factory (1), by Factory Records. Catalogue no: **FAC 142T**

LAZYITIS
Tracks: / Lazyitis.
12" Single: Released Apr '89, on Factory (1), by Factory Records. Catalogue no: **FAC 222**
7" Single: Released Apr '89, on Factory (1), by Factory Records. Catalogue no: **FAC 2227**

TART TART
Tracks: / Tart, Tart.
12" Single: Released Mar '87, on Factory (1), by Factory Records. Catalogue no: **FAC 176**

THINK ABOUT THE FUTURE
Tracks: / Think about the future.
7" Single: Released Sep '89, on Factory (1), by Factory Records. Catalogue no: **FAC 232**

WFL (WROTE FOR LUCK)
Tracks: / WFL (Wrote for luck).
CD 5": Released Sep '89, on Factory (1), by Factory Records. Catalogue no: **FACD 232**
7" Single: Released Sep '89, on Factory (1), by Factory Records. Catalogue no: **FAC 2327**
12" Single: Released Sep '89, on Factory (1), by Factory Records. Catalogue no: **FAC 232**
7" Single: Released Nov '88, on Factory (1), by Factory Records. Catalogue no: **FAC 212**
12" Single: Released Nov '88, on Factory (1), by Factory Records. Catalogue no: **FAC 2127**

Happy People

LOVE POTION
Tracks: / Love potion / Don't stop me.
7" Single: Released Oct '81, on Solid Gold (1), by Creole Records. Deleted '86. Catalogue no: **SGR 108**

Happy Traum Band

BRIGHT MORNING STARS
Tracks: / Bright morning stars.
7" Single: Released Mar '84, on Waterfront, by Waterfront Music. Catalogue no: **WF 005**

Happy-Hate-Me-Nots

SALT, SOUR
Tracks: / Salt, sour.
7" Single: Released Jan '88, on Waterfront, by Waterfront Music. Catalogue no: **DAMP 051**

Happy's

HAPPY MEXICO
Tracks: / Happy Mexico / Flower of Scotland.
Note: Distributed by Gordon Duncan Tele:- 0647 21517.
7" Single: Released May '86, on August (USA), by Rounder Records (USA). Catalogue no: **GBH 7S 413**

Harbour Lights

RUB A DUB FEELING
Tracks: / Rub-a-dub feeling.
12" Single: Released Oct '84, on Jaguar, Catalogue no: **UNKNOWN**

Harbour, Pearl

COWBOYS AND INDIANS
Tracks: / Cowboys and indians / You've got me all wrong.
7" Single: Released Apr '81, on Warner Bros., by WEA Records. Deleted '85. Catalogue no: **K 17781**

FUJIYAMA MAMA
Tracks: / Fujiyama mama / Nerves.
7" Single: Released Jan '81, on Warner Bros., by WEA Records. Deleted Jan '84. Catalogue no: **K 17741**

HULA LOVE
Tracks: / Hula love.
7" Single: Released Jul '84, on Island, by Island Records. Catalogue no: **IS 191**
12" Single: Released Jul '84, on Island, by Island Records. Deleted '85. Catalogue no: **10IS 191**

UP AND OVER
Tracks: / Up and over / Up and over part 2.
7" Single: Released Apr '80, on Warner Bros., by WEA Records. Deleted '82. Catalogue no: **K 17554**

YOU GOT IT
Tracks: / You got it / Busy little B-side.
7" Single: Released Mar '80, on Warner Bros., by WEA Records. Deleted '83. Catalogue no: **K 17572**

Harbour, Sydney

KILL THE WEATHER MAN
Tracks: / Kill the weather man / Weather report.
7" Single: Released Apr '84, on Reject, Catalogue no: **RET 2001**

Hard Corps

DIRTY
Tracks: / Dirty / Respirer.
12" Single: Released Aug '84, on Survival (1), by Survival Records. Catalogue no: **SUR 12 026**

JE SUIS PASSEE
Tracks: / Je suis passee.
7" Single: Released May '85, on Polydor, by Polydor Ltd. Catalogue no: **HARD 1**
12" Single: Released May '85, on Immaculate, by Immaculate Records. Catalogue no: **12IMMAC 2**
12" Single: Released May '85, on Polydor, by Polydor Ltd. Catalogue no: **HARDX 1**

LUCKY CHARM
Tracks: / Lucky charm.
7" Single: Released 30 May '87, on Transglobal/Rhythm King, by Mute Records. Catalogue no: **TYPE 3**
12" Single: Released 30 May '87, on Transglobal/Rhythm King, by Mute Records. Catalogue no: **TYPE 3T**

TO BREATHE
Tracks: / To breathe.
12" Single: Released Oct '85, on Polydor, by Polydor Ltd. Catalogue no: **HARDX 2**
7" Single: Released Oct '85, on Polydor, by Polydor Ltd. Catalogue no: **HARD 2**

Hard Options

BLIND FAITH
Tracks: / Blind faith / Homeland.
7" Single: Released Oct '88, on Mosa, by Mosa Records. Catalogue no: **MOSA 110**

Hard Rain

DIAMONDS
Tracks: / Diamonds / Monkey House.
7" Single: Released Jun '88, on London Records, by London Records. Deleted Feb '89. Catalogue no: **LON 185**
12" Single: Released Jun '88, on London Records, by London Records. Deleted Feb '89. Catalogue no: **LONX 185**
10" single: Released Jul '88, on London Records, by London Records. Deleted Feb '89. Catalogue no: **LONT 185**

I WILL REMEMBER
Tracks: / I will remember / Carry on / Dreaming.
12" Single: Released Dec '87, on London Records, by London Records. Deleted Oct '88. Catalogue no: **LONX 160**
7" Single: Released Jan '88, on London Records, by London Records. Deleted Oct '88. Catalogue no: **LON 160**

Hard Rock

FEEL NO WAY
Tracks: / Feel no way.
12" Single: Released May '84, on Inner Light, Catalogue no: **DLT 103**

YOU'RE DRIVING ME CRAZY
Tracks: / You're driving me crazy.
12" Single: Released Oct '85, on Omega, Deleted Jun '89. Catalogue no: **OMS 4**

Hard Rock Soul

BEAT IS MINE
Tracks: / Beat is mine, The / Double de-

fresh (the get stupid fresh mix).
12" Single: Released Jul '86, on Elite Records, by Elite Records. Deleted '88. Catalogue no: **DAZ 56**

DO IT ANYWAY YOU WANNA
Tracks: / Do it anyway you wanna.
12" Single: Released Oct '85, on Elite Records, by Elite Records. Deleted '86. Catalogue no: **DAZZ 43**

DOUBLE DEFRESH
Tracks: / Double defresh / Def Hypnosis.
12" Single: Released Feb '86, on Elite Records, by Elite Records. Deleted '88. Catalogue no: **DAZZ 46**

ELAWEAZER JUST A SKEEZER
Tracks: / Elaweazer just a skeezer / Elaweazer just a skeezer (dub mix).
7" Single: Released Jun '87, on Serious, by Serious Records. Catalogue no: **7OUS 2**
12" Single: Released Jun '87, on Serious, by Serious Records. Catalogue no: **OUS 2**

FUNKY GROOVE
Tracks: / Funky groove / Funky groove(Alternative mix).
12" Single: Released Oct '86, on Streetwave, Catalogue no: **UKHAN 2**
7" Single: Released Oct '86, on Streetwave, Catalogue no: **UKN 2**

Hard Sonic ...

DO IT ANY WAY YOU WANNA
Tracks: / Do it anyway you wanna.
12" Single: Released Nov '88, on Contempo, Catalogue no: **BBAT 001T**

DISCO INFERNO
Tracks: / Disco inferno.
12" Single: Released Aug '89, on Bbat, Catalogue no: **BBAT 006T**

Hard Times

NEVER GIVE IN
Tracks: / Never give in.
7" Single: Released 30 May '87, on E & F, by Supreme Records. Deleted '88. Catalogue no: **EF 3**
12" Single: Released 30 May '87, on E & F, by Supreme Records. Deleted '88. Catalogue no: **EFT 3**

OCTOBER DAWN
Tracks: / October dawn / Nostradamus.
7" Single: Released Jul '83, on Edit, Deleted '87. Catalogue no: **ED 001**

Hardcastle, Paul

19
Tracks: / 19 / Fly by night.
12" Single: Released Apr '85, on Chrysalis, by Chrysalis Records. Catalogue no: **CHS 122860**
7" Single: Released Apr '85, on Chrysalis, by Chrysalis Records. Catalogue no: **CHS 2860**

ARE YOU READY
Tracks: / Are you ready / Dark star.
7" Single: Released May '89, on K-Tel, by K-Tel Records. Catalogue no: **ONE 6105**
CD 5": Released May '89, on K-Tel, by K-Tel Records. Catalogue no: **ONE 6905**
12" Single: Released May '89, on K-Tel, by K-Tel Records. Catalogue no: **ONE 6605**

DON'T WASTE MY TIME
Tracks: / Don't waste my time / Moonhopper / Loitering with intent (On 12" version only.).
7" Single: Released Jan '86, on Chrysalis, by Chrysalis Records. Catalogue no: **PAUL 1**
12" Single: Released Jan '86, on Chrysalis, by Chrysalis Records. Catalogue no: **PAULX 1**

EAT YOUR HEART OUT
Tracks: / Eat your heart out.
12" Single: Released '86, on Cool Tempo, by Chrysalis Records. Catalogue no: **COOLX 102**

FOOLIN' YOURSELF
Tracks: / Foolin' yourself / King Tut / Strollin (On 12" version only.).
7" Single: Released Jun '86, on Chrysalis, by Chrysalis Records. Catalogue no: **PAUL 2**
12" Single: Released Jun '86, on Chrysalis, by Chrysalis Records. Catalogue no: **PAULX 2**

FORTY YEARS
Tracks: / Forty years / Movin' sound / Nineteen (on CD version only.) / Nineteen (the final story) (on CD version only.).
7" Single: Released May '88, on Chrysalis, by Chrysalis Records. Catalogue no: **PAUL 5**
CD 5": Released May '88, on Chrysalis, by Chrysalis Records. Catalogue no: **PAULCD 5**
12" Single: Released May '88, on Chrysalis, by Chrysalis Records. Catalogue no: **PAULX 5**

GUILTY
Tracks: / Guilty.
7" Single: Released Jul '84, on Total Control, by Total Control Records. Deleted '87. Catalogue no: **TOCO 2**

JUST FOR MONEY
Tracks: / Just for money.
12" Single: Released Nov '85, on Chrysalis, by Chrysalis Records. Catalogue no: **CASHX 1**
7" Single: Released Nov '85, on Chrysalis, by Chrysalis Records. Catalogue no: **CASH 1**

PAPA'S GOT A BRAND NEW PIGBAG
Tracks: / Papa's got a brand new pig bag.
7" Single: Released Jul '85, on Kaz, by Kaz Records. Catalogue no: **KAZ 50**
12" Single: Released Jul '85, on Kaz, by Kaz Records. Catalogue no: **KAZ 50T**

RAIN FOREST
Tracks: / Rain forest.
7" Single: Released Jun '85, on Bluebird (2), by BMG Records (UK). Catalogue no: **BR 15**
12" Single: Released Jun '85, on Bluebird (2), by BMG Records (UK). Catalogue no: **BRT 15**
12" Single: Released Aug '84, on Bluebird (2), by BMG Records (UK). Catalogue no: **BRT 8**

WALK IN THE NIGHT
Tracks: / Walk in the night / Star wars / Just passin' through (Extra track on 12" version.).
7" Single: Released 21 Mar '88, on Chrysalis, by Chrysalis Records. Catalogue no: **PAUL 4**
12" Single: Released 21 Mar '88, on Chrysalis, by Chrysalis Records. Catalogue no: **PAULX 4**

WIZARD,THE
Tracks: / Wizard, The (part 1) / Wizard, The (part 2).
7" Single: Released Sep '86, on Chrysalis, by Chrysalis Records. Catalogue no: **PAUL 3**
12" Single: Released Sep '86, on Chrysalis, by Chrysalis Records. Catalogue no: **PAULX 3**

YOU'RE THE ONE FOR ME
Tracks: / You're the one for me.
12" Single: Released Mar '84, on Total Control, by Total Control Records. Catalogue no: **TOCO 1**

Hardhats

TEAR DOWN THE HOUSE Wrecking crew mix
Tracks: / Tear down the house.
12" Single: Released Aug '87, on Groove & Move, by Groove & Move Records. Catalogue no: **GMT 12003**

Hardhouse

CHECK THIS OUT
Tracks: / Check this out / 11.55 (B Boy dub).
7" Single: Released Nov '88, on Easy Street, Catalogue no: **EZS 7542**

Hardin, Eddie

GOOD MORNING TO YOU
Tracks: / Good morning to you.
7" Single: Released Sep '85, on President, by President Records. Catalogue no: **PT 538**

RED NOSE CITY
Tracks: / Red nose city / Caribbean nights.
7" Single: Released Jul '87, on President, by President Records. Catalogue no: **PT 561**

Hardin, Tim

Biographical details: Hardin, Tim. This American singer, songwriter and guitarist only ever managed to achieve one hit single on either side of the Atlantic: he reached the US Hot 100 in 1969 with *Simple Song of Freedom* and scraped the UK Top 50 in 1967 with *Hang On To A Dream.* But this meagre track record belied his songwriting prowess; and he would probably have achieved much more, had his personal life not been so tragic.
Tim Hardin was born in Eugene, Oregon in 1940 and had a spell as a US marine before entering the music business in the early Sixties. He was lured into music by the era's burgeoning folk boom and gradually built up a cult following. His debut LP was issued in 1966 and one of its best tracks, *If I Were A Carpenter*, was rapidly covered by Bobby Darin who took it over again for The Four Tops; two years later, it was successfully recorded by Johnny Cash & June Carter. Thus, an impressively broad spread of major acts had found success with the song within five years of its first appearance.
1971 brought Hardin success with another of his early recordings - Rod Stewart recorded the moving *Reason to Believe* in '71, placing it on the B side of his monster hit *Maggie May* and including it on the smash LP *Every Picture Tells A Story.* Meanwhile, Hardin's own highly emotional voice continued to record new material with limited success. From the mid-Sseventies onwards, the oft-troubled Tim virtually abandoned his recording career, as his drugs problems grew worse. These problems finally killed him in December 1980 at the age of 40. (Bob MacDonald 8 October 1985).

HANG ON TO A DREAM
Tracks: / Hang on to a dream.
7" Single: Released Jan '67, on Verve, Deleted '70. Catalogue no: **VS 1504**

Harding, Carolyn

MOVIN' ON
Tracks: / Movin' on / Memories.
7" Single: Released Jul '87, on Magnetic Dance, by Magnet Records. Deleted Jan '88. Catalogue no: **MAGD 6**
12" Single: Released Jul '87, on Magnetic Dance, by Magnet Records. Deleted Jun '88. Catalogue no: **MAGDT 6**

Harding, Mike

Biographical details: Harding, Mike. This British comedian enjoyed his only UK hit single in 1975 when *The Rochdale Cowboy* reached no.22. This record became his theme tune and nickname, Rochdale being his native twon (situated just to the north of Manchester). During 1965-78 he placed one comedy LP per year onto the British album charts; the most successful was *One Man Show* which reached no.19 in 1976 and logged ten weeks on the listings. His 1977 LP was entitled *Old Four Eyes Is Back*, in imitation of Frank Sinatra's *Ol' Blue Eyes Is Back*.
During the late seventies and early eighties, Hardin'gs one-man show continued to be a major attraction in theatres across Britain and on Tv. His ability to make a three-hour stage show seem like 60 minutes bore out the adage that 'time flows when you're enjoying yourself'. His anecdotal style of humour was leavened with the occasional serious song featuring just his voice and guitar. Despite the odd mishap, such as his 1985 drunk driving conviction, Mike Harding's place in British comedy remains secure. He has not fallen into the trap of becoming 'showbizzy' and has retained a folk-club type appeal. (Bob Macdonald 8 October 1985).

ROCHDALE COWBOY
Tracks: / Rochdale cowboy.
7" Single: Released Jun '75, on Rubber, by Mawson & Wareham Music. Catalogue no: **ADUB 3**

Hardman, John

LITTLE COMFORT IN THE NIGHT
Tracks: / Little comfort in the night / She's leaving you.
7" Single: Released Mar '80, on Gallery, Deleted '83. Catalogue no: **GA 2**

Hardware

DANCE
Tracks: / Dance.
7" Single: Released Jul '85, on Reset, Catalogue no: **7REST 7**
12" Single: Released Jul '85, on Reset, Catalogue no: **12REST 7**

Hardy, Francoise

ALL OVER THE WORLD
Tracks: / All over the world.
7" Single: Released Mar '65, on Pye, Deleted '68. Catalogue no: **7N 15802**

ET MEME
Tracks: / Et meme.
7" Single: Released Jan '65, on Pye, Deleted '68. Catalogue no: **7N 15740**

TOUS LES GARCONS ET LES FILLES
Tracks: / Tous les garcons et les filles.
7" Single: Released Jun '64, on Pye, Deleted '67. Catalogue no: **7N 15653**

Harewood, Dorian

SHOW ME (ONE MORE TIME)
Tracks: / Show me (one more time) / No excuses.
12" Single: Released Nov '88, on Ichiban, by Ichiban Records (UK). Catalogue no: **12PO 17**

Hargrave, Ron

LATCH ON
Tracks: / Latch on / Bop-a-rock / Do that thing.

7" EP: Released May '81, on MGM, by Polydor Ltd. Deleted May '84. Catalogue no: **POSP 265**

Hargreaves, Dale

EASTERN SIDE
Tracks: / Eastern side.
7" Single: Released Oct '83, on Zap International, by Zap International Records. Catalogue no: **FIRE 1**

SCARED TO DEATH EP
Tracks: / Scared to death
7" Single: Released May '82, on Lightbeat, Catalogue no: **LIGHT 001**
7" Single: Released Aug '82, on Safari, by Safari Records. Catalogue no: **SAFE 47**

Harlem Shuffle

HARLEM SHUFFLE
Tracks: / Harlem shuffle: *Various artists* / You don't know like I know: *Various artists* (On 10" only) / Let's go baby: *Various artists* / Little piece of leather: *Various artists* / Billy's bag: *Various artists* (On 10" only) / Justine: *Various artists* (On 10" only).
7" Single: Released Apr '80, on Island, by Island Records. Deleted Apr '83. Catalogue no: **WIP 6599**
10" single: Released Apr '80, on Island, by Island Records. Deleted Apr '83. Catalogue no: **10WIP 6599**

Harlem Spirit

DANCING CHEEK TO CHEEK
Tracks: / Dancing cheek to cheek.
7" Single: Released Apr '84, on Fusion, by Fusion Records. Catalogue no: **FU 005**

DEM A SUS
Tracks: / Dem a sus / Make you mine.
7" Single: Released Nov '80, on EMI, by EMI Records. Deleted '83. Catalogue no: **EMI 5125**

HAVE A GOOD TIME TONIGHT
Tracks: / Have a good time tonight.
12" Single: Released Jan '88, on Fusion, by Fusion Records. Catalogue no: **FU 006**

HOW SWEET IT IS
Tracks: / How sweet it is to be loved by you.
7" Single: Released Oct '83, on Fusion, by Fusion Records. Catalogue no: **FU 004**

UNIVERSAL MAN
Tracks: / Universal man / Money maker.
7" Single: Released Mar '82, on Limo, Deleted '85. Catalogue no: **LIMO 7**
12" Single: Released May '82, on Limo, Deleted '85. Catalogue no: **LIMO 137**

WHY CAN'T WE BE LOVERS
Tracks: / Why can't we be lovers
7" Single: Released Feb '83, on MVM, by MVM Records. Deleted '84. Catalogue no: **MVM 8**

Harlequin Four's

SET IT OFF
Tracks: / Set it off / Mastermind Remix.
7" Single: Released Jul '86, on Champion, by Champion Records. Deleted Jul '89. Catalogue no: **CHAMP 16**
12" Single: Released Jul '86, on Champion, by Champion Records. Catalogue no: **CHAMP 1216**

Harleqyn

BURN
Tracks: / Burn.
7" Single: Released Nov '86, on Starlight, Catalogue no: **ST 001**

Harley Quinne

NEW ORLEANS
Tracks: / new orleans.
7" Single: Released Oct '72, on Bell, Deleted '75. Catalogue no: **1255**

Harley, Steve

Biographical details: This British singer, songwriter and producer formed the band Cockney Rebel in 1973. He advertised for musicians and obtained a five-piece line-up. With a background in journalism, Harley was an adept self-publicist and quickly built up a buzz in the UK music press about his group. Their first album was entitled *The human menagerie*, but it was their second LP - 1974's *The psychomodo* - that broke them big, reaching no. 8 on the British album chart and staying on the list for 20 weeks. That same year the group achieved two top 10 singles *Judy teen* and *Mr Soft* were quirky and highly original pop songs. Just when it seemed the world was their oyster, Cockney Rebel suffered an acrimonious break-up. Three members left, but Harley told the press that he would soon be back with the biggest band in the world. With three new recruits, the group returned under the billing Steve Harley and Cockney Rebel in early '75. They immediately scored a British no. 1 single with *Make me smile (come up and see me)*, one of the most magical and brilliantly crafted pop records of the era. But despite the success of this single and their new LP *The*

best years of our lives (no. 4), they once again failed to live up to their original promise - Harley's only subsequent UK Top 10 single was an idiosyncratic rendition of George Harrison's *Here comes the sun*, and the hits tailed off at the end of 1976. Harley has attempted several comebacks, but has never really found the right formula. 1979 brought him a UK no.. 58 hit with *Freedom's prisoner*, and 1983 saw him reach no. 51 with *Ballerina (prima donna)*. His 1985 single *Irresistible* was a pop singalong effort that sounded so dated that it would have been old-fashioned in his 1975 heyday. Harley's not inconsiderable talents were never able to find their focus after '75. (Bob Macdonald, 9/10/85)
Born Steven Nice in London in 1951, he formed Cockney Rebel in 1973; the band had top ten hits, split up and re-formed with three new members now billed as 'Steve Harley and Cockney Rebel'. The former journalist's large ego and smaller talent had led to feuding with pop music press; he was given a constant critical drubbing and was anyway caught beween the prevalent glam rock and his desire to be seen as serious. The albums were patchy; with the rise of punk the group split, embarrased by Harley, who settled in the USA for a while, made solo albums in 1978-79 and came back in 1985 with a band and the catchy *Irresistable*. (Donald Clarke, April 1989)5.

BALLERINA
Tracks: / Ballerina.
7" Single: Released Jul '83, on Stiletto, by Fast Forward Distribution. Catalogue no: **STL 14**

(COME UP AND SEE ME) MAKE ME SMILE
Tracks: / (Come up and see me) make me smile / Judy teen.
7" Single: Released Oct '80, on EMI, by EMI Records. Deleted Oct '87. Catalogue no: **EMI 2263**
7" Single: Released '85, on Old Gold, by Old Gold Records. Deleted Sep '89. Catalogue no: **OG 9375**
7" Single: Released Feb '75, on EMI, by EMI Records. Deleted '78. Catalogue no: **2263**

FREEDOM'S PRISONER (see panel below)
Tracks: / Freedom's prisoner / One more time.
7" Single: Released Oct '79, on EMI, by EMI Records. Deleted '82. Catalogue no: **EMI 2994**

HEARTBEAT LIKE THUNDER
Tracks: / Heartbeat like thunder / Warm my cold heart.
12" Single: Released Apr '86, on RAK, by EMI Records. Catalogue no: **12RAK 387**
7" Single: Released Apr '86, on RAK, by EMI Records. Catalogue no: **RAK 387**

HERE COMES THE SUN
Tracks: / Here comes the sun.
7" Single: Released Jul '76, on EMI, by EMI Records. Deleted '79. Catalogue no: **2505**

IRRESISTIBLE
Tracks: / Irresistible / Lucky man.
12" Single: Released Jul '86, on RAK, by EMI Records. Catalogue no: **12RAK 389**
7" Single: Released Jun '86, on RAK, by EMI Records. Catalogue no: **RAK 389**

JUDY TEEN
Tracks: / Judy teen.
7" Single: Released May '74, on EMI, by EMI Records. Deleted '77. Catalogue no: **2128**

LOVE'S A PRIMA DONNA
Tracks: / Love's a prima donna.
7" Single: Released Nov '76, on EMI, by EMI Records. Deleted '79. Catalogue no: **2539**

MAKE ME SMILE
Tracks: / Make me smile / Sebastian.
7" Single: Released Oct '80, on EMI, by EMI Records. Deleted Oct '83. Catalogue no: **EMI 5122**

MR RAFFLES (MAN IT WAS MEAN)
Tracks: / Mr. Raffles (man it was mean).
7" Single: Released Jun '75, on EMI, by EMI Records. Deleted '78. Catalogue no: **2299**

MR. SOFT
Tracks: / Mr. Soft.
7" Single: Released Mar '88, on EMI, by EMI Records. Deleted Jun '89. Catalogue no: **EM 50**
7" Single: Released Aug '74, on EMI, by EMI Records. Deleted '77. Catalogue no: **2191**

WHEN I'M WITH YOU
Tracks: / When I'm with you / Babbacombe Lee.
7" Single: Released Jun '89, on Vital Vinyl, Catalogue no: **VIT 003**

Harlow

TAKE OFF
Tracks: / Take off / Movie Queen.
7" Single: Released Aug '81, on Champagne Records, Deleted Aug '84. Catalogue no: **FIZZ 103**

Harmonica Fats

TORE UP
Tracks: / Tore up / I get so tired.
7" Single: Released Jun '88, on Fleetville, Catalogue no: **FV 304**

Harmony Grass

MOVE IN A LITTLE CLOSER
Tracks: / Move in a little closer.
7" Single: Released Jan '69, on RCA, by BMG Records (UK). Deleted '72. Catalogue no: **1772**

Harnen, Jimmy

WHERE ARE YOU NOW?
Tracks: / Where are you now / Only for the night / Little Nikki.
7" Single: Released Jun '89, on Epic, by CBS Records. Catalogue no: **655026 7**
12" Single: Released Jun '89, on Epic, by CBS Records. Catalogue no: **6550266**

Harper, Billy

SORAN BUSHI
Tracks: / Trying to get ready/Loverhood.
CD 5": Released Nov '84, on Denon, Deleted '88. Catalogue no: **C38-7007**

FREEDOM'S PRISONER (Released on EMI)

Harper, Charlie

Biographical details: This British singer and songwriter became leader and founder member of the UK Subs in 1977. This furious punk band enjoyed a string of medium sized hits on the British singles and albums charts during the late seventies and early eighties, all featuring curly-haired Charlie's vehement vocals. In the midst of this success, he launched a subsidiary solo career in 1980. This only produced one UK chart entry - *Barmy London army* reached no. 68 on the British singles chart in July 1980 - although he released a throwaway LP of rock remakes *Stolen property* in 1982. He was no lover of showbiz stardom, and always preferred to perform in small pubs and clubs in order to be as close to his audiences as possible. (Bob Macdonald, 9/10/88).

BARMY LONDON ARMY
Tracks: / Barmy London Army / Talk is cheap.
7" Single: Released Jul '80, on Gem, Deleted '83. Catalogue no: **GEMS 35**

FREAKED
Tracks: / Freaked / Jo.
7" Single: Released Jul '81, on Ramkup, Catalogue no: **CAC 005**

NEW BARBARIANS
Tracks: / New barbarians.
7" Single: Released Nov '82, on Fall Out, Catalogue no: **FALL 008**

Harper, Jeanette

PICK ME UP & PUT ME IN YOUR POCKET
Tracks: / Pick me up & put me in your pocket / Falling.
7" Single: Released Jul '83, on Soul Stop, by Dawn Promotions. Catalogue no: **SS 3004**

Harper, Roy

Biographical details: This British singer, songwriter and guitarist was born in Manchester and joined the RAF at the age of 15 (1956). During the following ten years, his erratic life included periods in mental institutions and prisons, but he also found time to begin a musical career. By thr time he released his debut album *The sophisticated beggar* in 1966, he had built up a cult following on the London folk scene. From then onwards, the Roy Harper story is one of huge critical acclaim but minimal commercial success. Blending folk and rock styles, he has written and recorded numerous songs that are powerful, emotional and austere. His concert reputation has ranged from ecstatic (he attracted much praise during the hippie era for his numerous free concerts) to derisory (he often attacked audiences with torrents of unwanted diatribes.) The high quality of his songwriting and poetry has attracted frequent bouquets from famous fellow musicians: among the people who have played sessions for his albums are Led Zeppelin's Jimmy Page, Ronnie Lane, Jethro Tull's Ian Anderson, Keith Emerson, Kate Bush and Pete Wingfield. The closing track on 1970's *Led Zeppelin 3"* album was *Hats off to Harper*, and in 1975 Harper performed guest lead vocals on *Have a cigar*, a track on Pink Floyd's *Wish you were here*. Harper's only glimmer of commercial success (apart from the Floyd song) occurred during the mid-seventies, where he achieved three entries on the UK album charts: *Valentine* reached no 27 in 1974, *HQ* got to no 31 in 1975 and *Bullinamingvase* climbed to no 25 in 1977. Although overly concerned with his own condition, Harper's best songs have been moving and inspiring; his work has always been very English, and is rooted in the sixties. Among the best examples are *One of these days in England* and *When an old cricketer leaves the crease*. He has continued to release albums on an occaisional basis during the eighties. All in all, he would probably have received far greater public recognition if he had not been hindered by his eccentric temperament and frequent ill-health. (Bob Macdonald, 9/10/88).

ELIZABETH
Tracks: / Elizabeth.
7" Single: Released Mar '85, on Beggars Banquet, by Beggars Banquet Records. Catalogue no: **BEG 131**

I STILL CARE
Tracks: / I still care / Goodbye ladybird.
7" Single: Released Feb '83, on Public, Deleted '87. Catalogue no: **PUBS 1002**

NO ONE EVER GETS OUT ALIVE
Tracks: / No one ever gets out alive.
7" Single: Released Oct '82, on Public, Catalogue no: **PUBS 1001**

PLAYING GAMES
Tracks: / Playing games / First thing in the morning.
7" Single: Released Mar '80, on Harvest (1), by EMI Records. Deleted '83. Catalogue no: **HAR 5203**

SHORT AND SWEET
Tracks: / Short and sweet / Unknown soldier / Water sports.
7" Single: Released 20 Jul '80, on Harvest (1), by EMI Records. Deleted '83. Catalogue no: **HAR 5207**

Harpers Bizarre

Biographical details: This American group consisted of Eddie James, John Peterson, Dick Scoppettone, Ted Templman and Dick Yount. Hailing from Santa Cruz, California, Harper's Bizarre originally formed in 1963 as the Tikis. They were an imitation of the Beach Boys, and had not changed much by the time they came to fame as Harper's Bizarre in 1967. Their classy 5-part harmony reached the US no 13 position in that year with their rendition of Simon and Garfunkel's *59th Street Bridge song (Feelin' groovy)*. Although Harper's Bizarre was an instrumental as well as a vocal group, the band's sophisticated singing was definitely yheir main strength. However, their choice of cover versions was often bizarre indeed - for example, their only other UK Top 40 hit was Cole Porter's *Anything goes*; this was hardly the stuff of the psychedelic era, and the quintet quickly faded into obscurity on both sides of the Atlantic. They broke up in 1970, although three of the members staged a comeback in 1976. By this time Ted Templeman had switched from being a Warner Bros. performer to a Warner Bros. in-house producer - during the seventies and eighties, he built up an impressive track record of hit credits. He produced all the Doobie Brothers and Van Halen albums, and he also chalked up success with Nicolette Larson, Little Feat and Van Morrison. (Bob Macdonald, 9/10/85).

59TH STREET BRIDGE SONG (FEELING GROOVY)
Tracks: / 59th Street bridge song.
7" Single: Released Mar '67, on Warner Bros., by WEA Records. Deleted '70. Catalogue no: **WB 5890**

ANYTHING GOES
Tracks: / Anything goes.
7" Single: Released Oct '67, on Warner Bros., by WEA Records. Deleted '70. Catalogue no: **WB 7063**

FEELING GROOVY (OLD GOLD)
Tracks: / Feeling groovy / Anything goes.
7" Single: Released May '81, on Old Gold, by Old Gold Records. Deleted May '84. Catalogue no: **OG 9094**

Harpo

MOVIE STAR
Tracks: / Movie star.
7" Single: Released Apr '76, on DJM, Deleted '79. Catalogue no: **DJS 400**

Harrier

OUT ON THE STREET
Tracks: / Out on the street / Nickels and dimes / Shine on.
12" Single: Released Mar '84, on Neon, by Neon Records. Catalogue no: **HARR 1T**

Harriott, Derrick

BABY HANG UP THE PHONE
Tracks: / Baby hang up the phone / 18 with the bullet.
7" Single: Released Apr '86, on Classy, Catalogue no: **CSY 1**

CARIBBEAN STYLE
Tracks: / Caribbean style.
12" Single: Released Jul '84, on Sarge, Catalogue no: **SRLDD 2**

CHECKING OUT
Tracks: / Checking out.
12" Single: Released Jul '85, on Hawkeye, by Hawkeye Records. Catalogue no: **HD 62**

EIGHTEEN WITH A BULLET
Tracks: / Eighteen with a bullet (version) / Eighteen with a bullet.
12" Single: Released Sep '86, on Trojan, by Trojan Records. Deleted May '88. Catalogue no: **CLASSY 1**
7" Single: Released Sep '86, on Trojan, by Trojan Records. Deleted May '88. Catalogue no: **7 CLASSY 1**

HOMELY GIRL
Tracks: / Homely girl.
12" Single: Released Oct '83, on Crystal, by President Records. Catalogue no: **A 2029**

I'M YOUR PUPPET
Tracks: / I'm your puppet / Birthday song.

12" Single: Released Dec '81, on Hawkeye, by Hawkeye Records. Catalogue no: **HD 39**

START ALL OVER AGAIN
Tracks: / Start all over again.
12" Single: Released Nov '88, on Black Scorpio, Catalogue no: **BSCD 11**

SWEETHEART
Tracks: / Sweetheart.
12" Single: Released Jul '82, on Crystal, by President Records. Catalogue no: **A 523**

Harris, Anita

Biographical details: This British singer, born in Somerset, harboured showbusiness ambitions as a young child. As she grew older, she became a keen ice-skater; legend has it that the manager of a London icerink engineered her initial opening into the entertainment business. She became a solo singer at the age of 17 (1961) and spent the next six years establishing herself in cabaret, song festivals and the like. Harris surged to fame in 1967 with *Just loving you* a single written by Tom Springfield (ex-Springfields, and writer of many of the Seekers' hits). Adapted from a Chopin piece, *Just loving you* gave Anita a UK no. 6 hit and logged a most impressive total of 30 weeks on the Top 50. Subsequent singles were a similar light, MoR vein, but were not as successful. *Playground, Anniversary waltz* and *Dream a little dream of me* all peaked between nos 21-50 on the UK Top 50. Her chart career was over by the end of 1968, but she has remained a popular showbusiness figure ever since. (Bob Macdonald, 9/10/88).

ANNIVERSARY WALTZ
Tracks: / Anniversary waltz / Just loving you.
7" Single: Released Jun '88, on Old Gold, by Old Gold Records. Catalogue no: **OG 9314**
7" Single: Released Jan '68, on CBS, by CBS Records. Deleted '71. Catalogue no: **3211**

DREAM A LITTLE DREAM OF ME
Tracks: / Dream a little dream of me.
7" Single: Released Aug '68, on CBS, by CBS Records. Deleted '71. Catalogue no: **3637**

JUST LOVING YOU
Tracks: / Just loving You.
7" Single: Released Jun '67, on CBS, by CBS Records. Deleted '70. Catalogue no: **2724**

PLAYGROUND
Tracks: / Playground.
7" Single: Released Oct '67, on CBS, by CBS Records. Deleted '70. Catalogue no: **2991**

Harris, Betty

RIDE YOUR PONY
Tracks: / Ride your pony.
7" Single: Released Jul '80, on Charly, by Charly Records. Deleted '87. Catalogue no: **CTD 102**

Harris, Chopper

ESCARGOT A LA BONGO
Tracks: / Escargot a la bongo.
7" Single: Released Aug '83, on Utopia, by Utopia Records. Catalogue no: **UTO 4**
12" Single: Released Aug '83, on Utopia, by Utopia Records. Catalogue no: **UTOL 4**

Harris, Dana

BEASTY MAN
Tracks: / Beasty man.
7" Single: Released Feb '86, on Aura Records, by Aura Records. Deleted '88. Catalogue no: **AUS 148**

FAME LOVE
Tracks: / Fame love.
7" Single: Released Apr '85, on Aura Records, by Aura Records. Deleted '88. Catalogue no: **AUS 146**

Harris, Dee

LOVE SHADOW
Tracks: / Love shadow / Love shadow.
12" Single: Released Sep '87, on Arista, by BMG Records (UK). Catalogue no: **RIST 32**
7" Single: Released Sep '87, on Arista, by BMG Records (UK). Catalogue no: **RIS 32**

Harris, Elena

IMAGINATION (Come on rescue me)...
Tracks: / Imagination.
7" Single: Released Oct '85, on Rhythmic, by Rhythmic Records. Catalogue no: **7RMIC 6**

Harris, Emmylou

Biographical details: This American singer, guitarist and songwriter was born in Birmingham, Alabama but had moved with her family to Washington DC by the time her musical career began in earnest. Having been interested in country music since an early age, she spent the late 60's playing country and folk material in clubs and bars along the East Coast. Her debut LP *Gliding bird* was issued in 1969 but made no impact, and her second offering *Pieces of the sky* did not appear till 1975. In the intervening years, she teamed with fellow country-influenced vocalist,guitarist Gram Parsons (ex-Byrds, ex-Flying Burrito Brothers) - she harmonised with him on his records and became a member of the Hot Band. After his tragic death from a drug overdose in Sept. 73, Harris retained the Hot Band (which included such highly respected musicians as James Burton and Rodney Crowell) and started her own career afresh. *Pieces of the sky* was a fine country rock album which earned her wide acclaim. Her superb backing group complemented her lovely, slightly sad voice and her inspired choice of material. She has continued in similar vein ever since; she has not been able to improve upon *Pieces of the sky*, but has nonetheless released quality albums full of polish and good playing. 1976's *Elite hotel* LP yielded Harris' only British chart single - her rendition of Lennon and McCartney's *Here there and everywhere* reached no 30 in March of that year. The LP reached the UK no 17 position, as did 1977's *Luxury liner* LP. In America, her albums made regular appearences on the pop and country charts. The one thing that Emmylou has lacked has been a major pop single - 1981's *Mr. Sandman*, a remake of the mid-fifties standard, reached no 37 in the States, but remains her only Top 40 entry. (Bob Macdonald, 9/10/85).

BAD MOON RISING
Tracks: / Bad moon rising / I don't have to crawl.
7" Single: Released Jun '81, on Warner Bros., by WEA Records. Deleted Jun '84. Catalogue no: **K 17804**

BORN TO RUN
Tracks: / Born to run / Ashes by now.
7" Single: Released Feb '82, on Warner Bros., by WEA Records. Deleted Feb '87. Catalogue no: **K 17896**

HERE THERE AND EVERYWHERE
Tracks: / Here there and everywhere.
7" Single: Released Mar '76, on Reprise, by WEA Records. Deleted '79. Catalogue no: **K 14415**

MR. SANDMAN
Tracks: / Mr. Sandman / Ashes by now.
7" Single: Released Feb '81, on Warner Bros., by WEA Records. Catalogue no: **K 17758**

ON THE RADIO
Tracks: / On the radio / Good news.
7" Single: Released May '84, on Warner Bros., by WEA Records. Catalogue no: **W 9364**

THAT LOVIN' YOU FEELIN' AGAIN
Tracks: / That lovin' you feelin' again / Lola.
7" Single: Released Oct '80, on Warner Bros., by WEA Records. Deleted Oct '83. Catalogue no: **K 17649**

YOU NEVER CAN TELL
Tracks: / You never can tell / Boulder to Birmingham.
7" Single: Released Mar '80, on Warner Bros., by WEA Records. Deleted '83. Catalogue no: **K 17580**

Harris, Hugh

ALICE
Tracks: / Alice (The Wonderland mix) (Not on 7".) / Train, The (12" only.) / Let it rain (Not on 7") / Alice (could've been anything) (7" & CD single only.).
CD 5": Released Aug '89, on Capitol, by EMI Records. Catalogue no: **CDCL 541**
12" Single: Released Aug '89, on Capitol, by EMI Records. Catalogue no: **12CL 541**
7" Single: Released Aug '89, on Capitol, by EMI Records. Catalogue no: **203 453 7**
7" Single: Released Aug '89, on Capitol, by EMI Records. Catalogue no: **CL 541**
12" Single: Released Aug '89, on Capitol, by EMI Records. Catalogue no: **203 453 6**

Harris, James

ALL THE LOVERS
Tracks: / All the lovers / All the lovers (version).
12" Single: Released Feb '89, on Warriors Dance, by Warriors Dance Records. Catalogue no: **WAST 8**

STILL IN LOVE WITH YOU
Tracks: / Still in love with you / Still in love with you (version).
7" Single: Released Apr '88, on Kalli, Catalogue no: **KG 2**
12" Single: Released Apr '88, on Kalli, Catalogue no: **12KG 2**

Harris, Jerry

I'M SO GLAD
Tracks: / I'm so glad.
12" Single: Released Nov '85, on Procedure, Catalogue no: **JAH 185**

Harris, Jet

Biographical details: This British bass guitarist, who was born Terence Harris in Kingsbury, Middlesex, was faous in the early sixties as a member of the Shadows. In 1962, while their biggest smash *Wonderful land* was topping the UK charts, Harris quit the combo to pursue a solo career. This brave decision followed hard on the heels of a similar choice by Shadows' drummer Tony Meehan, who had left in Oct 61. Harris quickly chalked up a pair of UK hit singles - his version of the Mexican tune *Besame mucho* reached no 22, and his revival of the main title theme from *The man with the golden arm* climbed to no. 12. But he really got into his Shadows-like hit stride in 1963, when he formed a duo with Meehan. Because their bass/drum sound gave prominence to two instruments that are normally in the background, the duo's records were unusual and ear-catching. *Diamonds* and *Scarlett O'Hara* (both penned by composer Jerry Lordan) reached no1 and no2 respectively on the British chart, and were followed in late '63 by a third smash *Applejack* (which got to no4). It would have been interesting to see whether Jet Harris and Tony Meehan would have maintained their huge popularity as the Beatles-led Merseybeat revolution gathered momentum. But in the event, fate caused the pair to split up at the end of '63 - Jet was seriously injured in a car crash, the effects of which never quite went away. Meehan achieved his own minor hit single in early '64 with *Song of Mexico*, while Harris enjoyed or endured a traumatic relationship with singer Billie Davis and filled many inches of newspaper column in the process. He had an ultra-brief spell in the Jeff Beck group in 1967, but remained in obscurity from then on. (Bob Macdonald, 9/10/85).

APPLEJACK
Tracks: / Applejack.
7" Single: Released Sep '63, on Decca, by Decca Records. Deleted '66. Catalogue no: **F 11710**

BESAME MUCHO
Tracks: / Besame mucho.
7" Single: Released May '62, on Decca, by Decca Records. Deleted '65. Catalogue no: **F 11466**

DIAMONDS (OLD GOLD)
Tracks: / Diamonds.
7" Single: Released Oct '83, on Old Gold, by Old Gold Records. Deleted Jul '88. Catalogue no: **OG 9332**

DIAMONDS (SINGLE)
Tracks: / Diamonds.
7" Single: Released Oct '80, on Decca, by Decca Records. Deleted '88. Catalogue no: **F 13892**
7" Single: Released Jan '63, on Decca, by Decca Records. Deleted '66. Catalogue no: **F 11563**
7" Single: Released '88, on Q Records, by Standard Sound Productions. Catalogue no: **Q 101**

MAIN TITLE THEME FROM MAN WITH THE GOLDEN ARM
Tracks: / Man with the golden arm, Theme from.
7" Single: Released Aug '62, on Decca, by Decca Records. Deleted '65. Catalogue no: **F 11488**

SCARLETT O'HARA
Tracks: / Scarlett O'Hara.
7" Single: Released Apr '63, on Decca, by Decca Records. Deleted '66. Catalogue no: **F 11644**

Harris, Keith

Biographical details: This British ventriloquist and comedian came to fame as the companion of the kiddies' duck character Orville, the natural successor to the equally excruciating Rod Hull & Emu. During the early eighties, Keith and his feathered friend were never off childrens' TV screens. At the beginning of 1983, Keith Harris & Orville shot to no 4 on the UK chart with their novelty single *Orville's song*; this downtempo, schmaltzy number was written by pianist Bobby Crush. The following year's offering was not quite so successful - *Come to my party*, credited to Keith Harris, Orville and Dippy (another friend from the animal kingdom) peaked at no. 44. Other releases failed to darken the doors of the UK charts, although Harris and friends were a staple diet for audiences at seaside summer seasons and Christmas shows. (Bob Macdonald, 9/10/85).

BEIN' GREEN
Tracks: / Bein' green / Captain Cuddles.
7" Single: Released May '84, on BBC, by BBC Records & Tapes. Deleted '87. Catalogue no: **RESL 145**

COME TO MY PARTY
Tracks: / Come to my party.
7" Single: Released Nov '83, on BBC, by BBC Records & Tapes. Deleted Sep '87. Catalogue no: **RESL 138**

ORVILLE'S SONG
Tracks: / Orville's song / I didn't.
7" Single: Released Nov '82, on BBC, by BBC Records & Tapes. Deleted '87. Catalogue no: **RESL 124**

SUPERDUCK
Tracks: / Superduck.
7" Single: Released Nov '84, on BBC, by BBC Records & Tapes. Deleted '87. Catalogue no: **RESL 154**

WHITE CHRISTMAS
Tracks: / White christmas.
7" Pic: Released Dec '85, on Columbia, by EMI Records. Catalogue no: **DBP 9121**
7" Single: Released Nov '85, on Columbia, by EMI Records. Catalogue no: **DB 9121**

WILL YOU STILL LOVE ME IN THE MORNING
Tracks: / Will you still love me in the morning.
7" Single: Released Apr '83, on BBC, by BBC Records & Tapes. Deleted '87. Catalogue no: **RESL 130**

Harris, Lenny

LONG AFTER TONIGHT IS ALL OVER
Tracks: / Long after tonight is all over / Impressions.
7" Single: Released Feb '84, on Soul Stop, by Dawn Promotions. Catalogue no: **SS 3008**

Harris, Major

Biographical details: This American soul singer was a member of the Delfonics from 1971 to 1973. He joined that sweet soul vocal group after their hitmaking days were over, so he had to wait until he became a solo artists before enjoying real success. Harris' big solo smash was *Love won't let me wait*, a million-selling ballad that reached no 5 on the US pop chart in 1975; in Britain, the single peaked at no. 37. "Solo" was perhaps a slight misnomer, because the single featured the vocal accompaniment of an uncredited female partner whose moaning made it quite obvious what she was waiting for. After this one-off smash, Major Harris became minor in terms ofsuccess. His records grew increasingly pedestrian, although he made a brief appearance on the UK pop chart in november 1983 with *All my life*. (Bob Macdonald, 10/10/88_.

ALL MY LIFE
Tracks: / All my life.
7" Single: Released Nov '83, on London Records, by London Records. Catalogue no: **LON 37**
12" Single: Released Nov '83, on London Records, by London Records. Catalogue no: **LONX 37**

I WANT YOUR LOVE
Tracks: / I want your love.
7" Single: Released Feb '84, on Buzz Int., Catalogue no: **VIBE 1**
12" Single: Released Feb '84, on Buzz Int., Catalogue no: **VIBE 1T**

LOVE WON'T LET ME WAIT
Tracks: / Love won't let me wait / After loving you.
7" Single: Released Aug '75, on Atlantic, by WEA Records. Deleted '78. Catalogue no: **K 10585**

Harris, Rahni And

SIX MILLION STEPS(WEST RUNS SOUTH)
Tracks: / Six million steps (west runs south).
7" Single: Released Dec '78, on Mercury, by Phonogram Ltd. Deleted '81. Catalogue no: **6007 198**

Harris, Richard

Biographical details: This Irish singer, actor and film star had a giant one-off pop hit in 1968 with *MacArthur Park*. This single helped to break the time barrier for singles by extending to more than 7 minutes (three months in advance of the Beatles *Hey Jude*), and was a true orchestral epic. The who thing was written and produced by the brilliant 21 year old American Jim Webb, who was some 13 years younger than Harris. *MacArthur Park* (inspired by the park of that name in LA) surged to no.2 in America and no.4 in Britain. Although dismissed as overblown schmaltz in some quarters, the record is widely acknowledged as a classic. It was reviveda decade later by Donna Summer and her disco-orientated producer Giordio Moroder. Unfortunately for Harris' musical aspirations, the success of *MacArthur Park* owed much more to Webb than his own breathless vocals. Fortunately Richard was already established in the cinema world - in 1967 the Limerick-born ex-RADA student had landed his first starring role as King Arthur in the movie version of Camelot. (Bob Macdonald, 10/10/85).

MACARTHUR PARK
Tracks: / Macarthur Park.
7" Single: Released Jun '68, on RCA, by BMG Records (UK). Deleted '71. Catalogue no: **RCA 1699**

MACARTHUR PARK (OLD GOLD)
Tracks: / MacArthur Park.
7" Single: Released Jul '82, on Old Gold, by Old Gold Records. Catalogue no: **OG 9216**

Harris, Rolf

Biographical details: This Australian singer, songwriter and all-round showbiz entertainer was born in Perth in 1930. He took up the piano at the age of nine, and grew up with showbusiness ambitions. While working as a music teacher, he built up a promising entertainment career in his native country before sailing to Britain during the fifties. He achieved major fame in 1960 with his self-penned novelty ditty *Tie me kangaroo down, sport*, which reached no. 9 in Britain. It was, of course, also a smash whose traditions it parodied, Australia. Like Men At Work's *Down under* many years later, the song pandered to peoples' most superficial perceptions of Aussies but was nonetheless an enjoyable record. It introduced the world to the semi-legendary wobble board, a novelty instrument that Rolf had recently invented. The bongo drum sound of the wobble board stemmed from another of Harris' talents- painting. Legend has it that he placed an oil painting on a heater to dry, and then discovered the wobble board while shaking the board to cool it down. During the sixties, he became a household name on British television with his cartoon characters and lightning speed impromptu drawings. He became a showbusiness institution in the UK, hosting such programmes as *We want to sing* and *Rolf on Saturday OK*. His bearded face and amiable personality made him particularly appealing to kiddie audiences, who saw him as a friendly father figure. He was awarded the MBE in 1968 and the OBE in 1977. Harris' recordings have merely been a subsidiary strand of his career, and he is generally regarded as a novelty artist. *Tie me kangaroo down, sport*, which became a US Top 3 smash in 1963, *Jake the peg* (which was never actually a hit record) and *Two little boys* (a sentimental 1903 song that gave Rolf a massive six-week chart topper in Jan. 70) have made people overlook the fact that he also made two important pop records. 1962's *Sun arise*, a UK no. 3 hit that was adapted by Harris from an Aboriginal chant, helped to enliven one of Britain's less illustrious chart years; and 1963's *Fijian girl*, although an obscure flop, was virtually the Siamese twin of Adam & The Ants' 1981 chart topper *Prince Charming*. Still going strong in the 80's, Rolf played the digeridoo on Kate Bush's 1982 single *The dreaming*, and he was a member of The Crowd, an all-star impromptu gathering of singers who reached no. 1 in 1985 with their disaster relief single *You'll never walk alone*.
(Bob Macdonald, 10/10/88).

BLUER THAN BLUE
Tracks: / Bluer than blue.
7" Single: Released Apr '69, on Columbia, by EMI Records. Deleted '72. Catalogue no: **DB 8553**

HEY JIMMY JOHNSON
Tracks: / Hey Jimmy Johnson / Ginger Tom.
7" Single: Released Nov '81, on R.H.E., Catalogue no: **RHE 1**

JOHNNY DAY
Tracks: / Johnny Day.
7" Single: Released Feb '63, on Columbia, by EMI Records. Deleted '66. Catalogue no: **DB 4979**

SUN ARISE
Tracks: / Sun arise.
7" Single: Released Oct '62, on Columbia, by EMI Records. Deleted '65. Catalogue no: **DB 4888**

TIE ME KANGAROO DOWN SPORT
Tracks: / Tie me kangaroo down sport.
7" Single: Released Jul '60, on Columbia, by EMI Records. Deleted '63. Catalogue no: **DB 4483**

TOMMY (FROM '88 PINE')
Tracks: / Tommy.
7" Single: Released Nov '86, on Tembo, by Tembo Records. Catalogue no: **TML 111**

TWO LITTLE BOYS
Tracks: / Two little boys.
7" Single: Released Nov '69, on Columbia, by EMI Records. Deleted '72. Catalogue no: **DB 8630**

TWO LITTLE BOYS (2)
Tracks: / Two little boys / Sun arise.
7" Single: Released Sep '80, on EMI, by EMI Records. Deleted Sep '83. Catalogue no: **POP 2011**

Harris Ronnie

STORY OF TINA
Tracks: / Story of Tina.
7" Single: Released Sep '54, on Columbia, by EMI Records. Deleted '57. Catalogue no: **DB 3499**

Harris, Sam

HEARTS ON FIRE
Tracks: / Hearts on fire.
7" Single: Released Feb '85, on Motown, by BMG Records (UK). Deleted '88. Catalogue no: **TMG 1370**

I'D DO IT ALL AGAIN
Tracks: / I'd do it all again / Rescue, The.
7" Single: Released May '86, on Motown, by BMG Records (UK). Catalogue no: **SAMMY 1**
12" Single: Released May '86, on Motown, by BMG Records (UK). Catalogue no: **SAMMYT 1**

OVER THE RAINBOW
Tracks: / Over the rainbow / Hearts on fire.
12" Single: Released Mar '85, on Motown, by BMG Records (UK). Deleted '87. Catalogue no: **TMGT 1370**
7" Single: Released Mar '85, on Motown, by BMG Records (UK). Deleted '87. Catalogue no: **TMG 1370**

SUGAR DON'T BITE
Tracks: / Sugar don't bite.
12" Single: Released Oct '84, on Motown, by BMG Records (UK). Catalogue no: **TMGT 1354**
12" Single: Released Oct '84, on Motown, by BMG Records (UK). Catalogue no: **TMG 1354**

Harris, Simon

BAD ON THE MIKE
Tracks: / Bad on the mike / Drumapella / Sample breakdown / Bad beats.
12" Single: Released Oct '87, on London Records, by London Records. Deleted Feb '89. Catalogue no: **LONX 162**

BASS (HOW LOW CAN YOU GO)
Tracks: / Bass (how low can you go) / Playback, The (edit) (Track on 7".) / Bass (how low can you go)(Bomb the house mix) (Track on 12".) / Bass (how low can you go)(Inst.) (Track on 12".).
Note: Simon Harris is the UK's leading 'rap' producer & this single is re-mixed by Professor Griff of Public Enemy & features the voice of Public Enemy's Chuck Dee.
12" Single: Released '88, on ffrr, by London Records. Deleted Feb '89. Catalogue no: **FFRXR 4**
7" Single: Released Mar '88, on ffrr, by London Records. Deleted Oct '88. Catalogue no: **FFR 4**
CD 5": Released May '88, on Metronome (Germany), Catalogue no: **unknown**
12" Single: Released Mar '88, on ffrr, by London Records. Deleted Oct '88. Catalogue no: **FFRX 4**

HERE COMES THAT SOUND
Tracks: / Here comes that sound / Only a demo / Perfect beat (Only on the 12" version.) / Acid fingers breakdown (Only on the 12" version.).

7" Single: Released 16 Sep '88, on ffrr, by London Records. Deleted May '89. Catalogue no: **FFR 12**
12" Single: Released Oct '88, on ffrr, by London Records. Deleted May '89. Catalogue no: **FFRXR 12**
12" Single: Released 16 Sep '88, on ffrr, by London Records. Deleted May '89. Catalogue no: **FFRX 12**

(I'VE GOT YOUR) PLEASURE CONTROL
Tracks: / (I've got your) pleasure control.
CD 5": Released Jun '89, on A&M, by A&M Records. Catalogue no: **FCD 106**
Cassingle: Released Jun '89, on A&M, by A&M Records. Catalogue no: **FCS 106**
12" Single: Released Jun '89, on A&M, by A&M Records. Catalogue no: **FX 106**
7" Single: Released Jun '89, on A&M, by A&M Records. Catalogue no: **F 106**

Harris, Stewart

LOVIN' OR LEAVIN'
Tracks: / Lovin' or leavin'.
7" Single: Released Oct '86, on Network, by CBS Records. Catalogue no: **PLOT 7002**

Harrison

NO REFRAIN
Tracks: / No refrain.
7" Single: Released Dec '84, on Skipping Rope, Catalogue no: **SKIP 1**

Harrison, Geoff

EVE OF DESTRUCTION
Tracks: / Eve of destruction / How do you sleep.
7" Single: Released Apr '84, on Banana, Catalogue no: **FRUIT 8**

Harrison, George

Biographical details: This British artist was the first member of the Beatles to release a solo album, and the first to achieve a solo no. 1 single in either Britain or America. Born in Liverpool in 1943, Harrison was the youngest member of the group. Although he was their lead guitarist from the outset, his songwriting and singing abilities were overshadowed by those of Lennon & McCartney for several years - he began to establish himself as a third creative force in the mid-sixties with tracks like *Norwegian wood*, where he introduced the sitar to the group's work, and *Taxman*. He was the driving force behind the Beatles' dabbling in Eastern religion and transcendental meditation. By the time they broke up in 1970, he had written and sung such Beatle classics as *While my guitar gently weeps*, *Something* and *Here comes the sun*. He had also written Cream's *Badge* with Eric Clapton (who later poached George's wife Patti Boyd after singing about her in *Layla*) and produced UK Top 20 hits for Billy Preston (*That's the way God planned it*) and the Radha Krishna Temple (*Hare Krishna mantra*). Harrisin's first two solo albums *Wonderwall* (1968) and *Electronic sounds* (1969) were weird in the extreme. They did not achieve commercial success, and were simply an experimental and self indulgent diversion from the Beatles' activities. But in December 1970, following the group's disintegration, he issued the mind-boggling triple LP *All things must pass*. Assisted by an all-star cast of guest musicians and co-produced by the legendary Phil Spector, the record was a major musical, philosophical and spiritual work; it was George's crowning achievement. The triple set was launched by the smash single *My sweet lord*, a multi-denominational worship that shot to no. 1 on both sides of the Atlantic. August 1971 saw Harrison organise the massive *Concert for Bangladesh* at New York's Madison Square Garden. The star-studdes show and the resulting triple album were excellent musical events, although they were followed by endless contractual and logistical problems regarding the transfer of proceeds to the disaster-stricken recipients. A substantial sum was finally donated, but Bob Geldof was careful to take note of Harrision's experiences when organising the Band Aid and Live Aid projects. From 1973 onwards, George's life was a mixture of ups and downs. The 1973 album *Living in the material world* yielded the US no. 1 and UK Top 10 single *Give me love (Give me peace on earth)*, but he never again reached his previously familiar heights of critical acclaim or commercial success. In 1976 he fell victim to pop music's most famous plagiarism case, when *My sweet Lord* was ruled in court to be musically identical to the Chiffons' 1963 US no. 1 *He's so fine*. The composer of this song, Ronald Mack, won $500,000 in damages. In the summer of 1981, soon after the murder of John Lennon, George reached no. 2 in the US and no. 13 in the UK with *All those years ago* single, on which he received back-up from the two other surviving ex-Beatles. Despite the worthy sentiment, this tribute to his slain friend was hardly a musical masterpiece. It showed why most of Harrison's late Seventies and eighties releases have been low key affairs. He has latterly kept a low profile, devoting much time to motor racing, film production and a happy second marriage. (Bob Macdonald, 11/10/85).

ALL THOSE YEARS AGO
Tracks: / All those years ago / Writing's on the wall, The.
7" Single: Released May '81, on Dark Horse, by Dark Horse Records. Catalogue no: **K 17807**

BANGLA DESH
Tracks: / Bangla Desh.
7" Single: Released Aug '71, on Apple, by Apple Records. Deleted '74. Catalogue no: **R 5912**

BLOW AWAY
Tracks: / Blow away.
7" Single: Released Mar '79, on Apple, by Apple Records. Deleted '82. Catalogue no: **K 17327**

DING DONG
Tracks: / Ding dong.
7" Single: Released Dec '74, on Apple, by Apple Records. Deleted '77. Catalogue no: **R 6002**

GIVE ME LOVE (GIVE ME PEACE ON EARTH)
Tracks: / Give me love (give me peace on earth).
7" Single: Released Jun '73, on Apple, by Apple Records. Deleted '76. Catalogue no: **R 5988**

GOT MY MIND SET ON YOU
Tracks: / Got my mind set on you / Lay his head.
7" Single: Released Oct '87, on Dark Horse, by Dark Horse Records. Deleted Jul '88. Catalogue no: **W 8178**

IS THIS LOVE?
Tracks: / Is this love? / Breath away from Heaven / All those wasted years ago* (Only on 12" version.) / Hong Kong blues**.
Note: **track on CD single.l
CD 5": Released May '88, on Dark Horse, by Dark Horse Records. Catalogue no: **W 7913CD**
12" Single: Released May '88, on Dark Horse, by Dark Horse Records. Catalogue no: **W 7913T**
7" Single: Released May '88, on Dark Horse, by Dark Horse Records. Catalogue no: **W 7913**

MY SWEET LORD
Tracks: / My sweet Lord / What is life.
7" Single: Released Apr '83, on EMI (Germany), by EMI Records. Catalogue no: **2C 008 04692**
7" Single: Released Nov '76, on Apple, by Apple Records. Catalogue no: **R 5884**

TEARDROPS
Tracks: / Teardrops.
7" Single: Released Jul '81, on Dark Horse, by Dark Horse Records. Catalogue no: **K 17837**

WAKE UP MY LOVE
Tracks: / Wake up my love / Greece.
7" Single: Released Nov '82, on Dark Horse, by Dark Horse Records. Catalogue no: **K 929864 7**

WHEN WE WAS FAB
Tracks: / When we was fab / Zig zag / That's the way it goes (track on 12").
7" Single: Released Feb '88, on Warner Bros., by WEA Records. Catalogue no: **W 8131**
12" Single: Released Feb '88, on Warner Bros., by WEA Records. Catalogue no: **W 8131T**

YOU
Tracks: / You.
7" Single: Released Oct '75, on Apple, by Apple Records. Deleted '78. Catalogue no: **R 6007**

Harrison, Jane

AVE MARIA
Tracks: / Ave Maria / One fine day / Oh my beloved Father (12" only) / Lord's prayer, The (12" only).
12" Single: Released 22 Aug '88, on BBC, by BBC Records & Tapes. Catalogue no: **12RSL 227**
CD 5": Released 22 Aug '88, on BBC, by BBC Records & Tapes. Catalogue no: **BBCDS 227**
7" Single: Released 22 Aug '88, on BBC, by BBC Records & Tapes. Catalogue no: **RESL 227**

I WILL PROTECT YOU
Tracks: / I will protect you.
CD 5": Released Mar '89, on Tribute, Catalogue no: **TRIBCD 3**
7" Single: Released Mar '89, on Tribute, Catalogue no: **TRIB 3**

NEW DAY
Tracks: / New day.
7" Single: Released Dec '88, on Tribute, Catalogue no: **TRIB 2**

Harrison, Jerry

MAN WITH A GUN
Tracks: / Man with a gun / Man with a gun (radio edit) / Breakdown on the passing lane (On 12" and CD single only) / We're always talking (On 12" and CD single only).
Note: "Man with a gun" on 7", 4 track 12" and 4 track CD single with a guitar version featuring Chris Spedding. (Phonogram Records, May 1988).
7" Single: Released 23 May '88, on Fontana, by Phonogram Ltd. Deleted Oct '88. Catalogue no: **JERRY 2**

12" Single: Released 23 May '88, on Fontana, by Phonogram Ltd. Deleted Oct '88. Catalogue no: **JERRY 212**
CD 5": Released 23 May '88, on Fontana, by Phonogram Ltd. Deleted Oct '88. Catalogue no: **JERCD 2**

REV IT UP
Tracks: / Bobby / Rev it up.
Note: "Due to media demand Fontana Records announces the re-release of 'Rev it up' the single taken from the second acclaimed album 'Jerry Harrison: Casual Gods'." (Phonogram Records, July 1988).
12" Pic: Released Sep '88, on Fontana, by Phonogram Ltd. Catalogue no: **JERYP 112**
CD 5": Released 11 Jul '88, on Fontana, by Phonogram Ltd. Catalogue no: **JERCD 1**
7" Single: Released 11 Jul '88, on Fontana, by Phonogram Ltd. Deleted Feb '89. Catalogue no: **JERRY 1**
12" Single: Released 11 Jul '88, on Fontana, by Phonogram Ltd. Deleted Feb '89. Catalogue no: **JERRY 112**

THINGS FALL APART
Tracks: / Things fall apart / Worlds in collision.
7" Single: Released Nov '81, on Sire, by Sire Records. Deleted Nov '84. Catalogue no: **SIR 4053**

Harrison, John

LIGHTS OF LONDON
Tracks: / Lights of London / Lights of London (version).
7" Single: Released Jul '88, on SE 1, by Hard Times Productions. Catalogue no: **7 SDE 1**
12" Single: Released Jul '88, on SE 1, by Hard Times Productions. Catalogue no: **12 SDE 1**

Harrison, Kevin

FLY
Tracks: / Fly / Inkman.
7" Single: Released Jun '82, on Glass, by Glass Records. Deleted '83. Catalogue no: **GLASS 017**

Harrison, Michelle

BEING IN LOVE
Tracks: / Being in love.
12" Single: Released Jun '84, on Lion Kingdom, Catalogue no: **K 06**

DON'T TAKE LOVE SO EASY
Tracks: / Don't take love so easy.
12" Single: Released May '83, on Lion Kingdom, Catalogue no: **LK 004**

Harrison, Noel

Biographical details: This British singer and actor is the son of the far more famous actor Rex Harrison. Noel made his recording debut with a self-titled LP in 1966, and followed it with the similarly unsuccessful offerings, *Collage* (1967) and *Santa Monica pier* (1968). Then, in early 1969, Noel achieved his only success with the single *Windmills of your mind*; this reached no. 8 in Britain. This beautiful, evocative and slightly eerie song was written by Alan and Marilyn Bergman (words) and Michel Legrand (music) for the movie *The Thomas Crown affair*. It won an Oscar for Best Song Of The Year. (Bob Macdonald, 11/10/85).

WINDMILLS OF YOUR MIND
Tracks: / Windmills of your mind / Leitch on the beach.
7" Single: Released Jul '81, on Reprise (USA), Catalogue no: **K 14004**
7" Single: Released Feb '69, on Reprise, by WEA Records. Deleted '72. Catalogue no: **RS 20758**
7" Single: Released Jul '82, on Old Gold, by Old Gold Records. Catalogue no: **OG 9090**

Harrison, Russ

PLAYING AT TRAINS
Tracks: / Playing at trains.
12" Single: Released May '87, on Sincere Sounds, Catalogue no: **IDT 001**

Harrison, Valerie

FOOL'S PARADISE
Tracks: / Fool's paradise / Let's get funky.
12" Single: Released Aug '86, on Blackbeat, Catalogue no: **BBD 179**

LITTLE BIT MORE, A
Tracks: / Little bit more, A / You're so good.
12" Single: Released Nov '86, on Blackbeat, Catalogue no: **BBD 183**

Harrow, David

NO EASY TARGETS
Tracks: / No easy targets.
12" Single: Released Oct '84, on Ink, by Red Flame Records. Catalogue no: **INK 128**

OUR LITTLE GIRL
Tracks: / Our little girl.
7" Single: Released Nov '83, on Red Flame 10, by Virgin Records. Catalogue no: **RFB 27**
12" Single: Released Nov '83, on Red Flame 10, by Virgin Records. Catalogue no: **RFB 2712**

Harry, Debbie

Biographical details: This American singer achieved huge international fame in the late 70's and early 80's as lead vocalist with Blondie. The good looking Debbie Harry was projected as the band's main selling point. Her artificial blonde hair gave the group its name and, indeed, many people believed that she was "Blondie" and the five men were her backing group. Harry possessed a fine, distinctive voice that was equally effective when raucously belting out raw rock material or calmly singing mid-tempo pop. She was idolised as a photogenic sex symbol, despite being in her mid thirties when the group were at their peak. Debbie entered the music business in 1966 with two obscure groups, the second of which (Wind In The Willows) released a flop album and undertook a US national tour. From 1968 till 1973, Harry left music and worked as a waitress, a bunny girl and various other occupations. Upon returning to the music business, she worked in a group called The Stilettos before forming Blondie in 1974. In 1981 she took a break from Blondie activities in order to make her debut solo LP. Teaming with Chic maestros Bernard Edwards and Nile Rodgers, who had just produced a smash album for Diana Ross, she released the album *Koo koo*. Unfortunately, the result was disappointing in both commercial and artistic terms. *Koo koo* must rank as one of the most boring albums of all time, mainly due to the dreariness of the material; the fact that it reached the Top 10 in Britain and the Top 30 in the US, was due to the prior reputation of the singer and the producers. Blondie folded in 1983, whereupon Debbie continued an acting career which had commenced at the beginning of the decade with the films *Union city* and *Roadie*. Her 1984 single *Rush rush* flopped, although she aroused controversy with her *Videodrome* project which was condemned as a video nasty in some quarters. (Bob Macdonald, 11/10/85).

BACKFIRED (see panel below)
Tracks: / Backfired / Military rap.
7" Single: Released Aug '81, on Chrysalis, by Chrysalis Records. Deleted '84. Catalogue no: **CHS 2526**

FREE TO FALL
Tracks: / Free to fall / Secret life.
7" Single: Released Feb '87, on Chrysalis, by Chrysalis Records. Catalogue no: **CHS 3093**
12" Single: Released Feb '87, on Chrysalis, by Chrysalis Records. Catalogue no: **CHS 123093**

FRENCH KISSING IN THE USA
Tracks: / French kissin' in the USA / Rockbird.
12" Single: Released Nov '86, on Chrysalis, by Chrysalis Records. Catalogue no: **CHS 123066**
7" Single: Released Nov '86, on Chrysalis, by Chrysalis Records. Catalogue no: **CHS 3066**

I WANT THAT MAN
Tracks: / I want that man / Bike boy.
7" Single: Released Sep '89, on Chrysalis, by Chrysalis Records. Catalogue no: **CHS 3369**
12" Single: Released Sep '89, on Chrysalis, by Chrysalis Records. Catalogue no: **CHS 12 3369**

IN LOVE WITH LOVE
Tracks: / In love with love / French kissin' (French).
7" Single: Released Apr '87, on Chrysalis, by Chrysalis Records. Catalogue no: **CHS 3128**
12" Single: Released Apr '87, on Chrysalis, by Chrysalis Records. Catalogue no: **CHS 123128**

JAM WAS MOVING
Tracks: / Jam was moving / Chrome / Inner city spillover (Available on 12" only.).
7" Single: Released Sep '81, on Chrysalis, by Chrysalis Records. Deleted Sep '84. Catalogue no: **CHS 2554**
12" Single: Released Sep '81, on Chrysalis, by Chrysalis Records. Deleted Sep '84. Catalogue no: **CHS 12 2554**

Hart, Corey

ANGRY YOUNG MAN
Tracks: / Angry young man / Angry young men (Dub version).
12" Single: Released Nov '86, on EMI-America, by EMI Records. Deleted Jul '87. Catalogue no: **12EA 223**
7" Single: Released Nov '86, on EMI-America, by EMI Records. Deleted Jul '87. Catalogue no: **EA 223**

CAN'T HELP FALLING IN LOVE
Tracks: / Can't help falling in love / Broken arrow / My brothers leaving today (Available on 12" version only.).
7" Single: Released Feb '87, on EMI-America, by EMI Records. Deleted Jul '87. Catalogue no: **EAX 227**
12" Single: Released Feb '87, on EMI-America, by EMI Records. Catalogue no: **12EAX 227**

NEVER SURRENDER
Tracks: / Never surrender.
7" Single: Released '85, on EMI-America, by EMI Records. Catalogue no: **EA 202**
12" Single: Released '85, on EMI-America, by EMI Records. Catalogue no: **12EA 202**

SUNGLASSES AT NIGHT
Tracks: / Sunglasses at night.
7" Single: Released '84, on EMI-America, by EMI Records. Catalogue no: **EA 176**

Hart, Dicky

HUNGRY FOR YOU
Tracks: / Hungry for you / Closer to you.
7" Single: Released '84, on Medikal, Catalogue no: **DOC 1**

DEBBIE HARRY - BACKFIRED (Released on Chrysalis)

Hart, Grant

2541
Tracks: / 2541.
12" Single: Released Oct '88, on SST (USA), by SST Records (USA). Catalogue no: **SST 219**
CD 5": Released Jan '89, on SST (USA), by SST Records (USA). Catalogue no: **SSTCD 219**

Hart, Jon

TOYTOWN
Tracks: / Toytown / Recollections.
7" Single: Released Sep '80, on WEA, by WEA Records. Deleted '83. Catalogue no: **K 18317**

Hart, Lea

IT'S NEW TO ME
Tracks: / It's new to me / Your love affair's over now.
7" Single: Released Jan '82, on RCA, by BMG Records (UK). Deleted '85. Catalogue no: **RCA 170**

NO ONE LEFT TO BLAME
Tracks: / No one left to blame / Hideaway.
7" Single: Released Aug '82, on RCA, by BMG Records (UK). Deleted Aug '85. Catalogue no: **RCA 257**

Hart, Maureen

HEY LORD, IT'S ME (SINGLE)
Tracks: / Hey Lord, it's me / Sweet dreams.
7" Single: Released Dec '85, on Mint, by Emerald Records. Deleted '88. Catalogue no: **CHEW 103**

Hart, Paul

HALLEY'S COMET
Tracks: / Halley's comet.
7" Single: Released '85, on Columbia, by EMI Records. Catalogue no: **DB 9117**

Hart, Philip

ANGEL
Tracks: / Angel.
12" Single: Released Nov '83, on Simba, Catalogue no: **SM 006**
7" Single: Released Jan '86, on Sonet, by Sonet Records. Catalogue no: **SON 2291**

EVERYTHING TO ME
Tracks: / Everything to me / Take me away.
7" Single: Released '84, on Sonet, by Sonet Records. Catalogue no: **SON 2273**

Hart, Rod

CHICKEN OF THE COUNTY
Tracks: / Chicken of the county / Do you know why?.
7" Single: Released Aug '80, on RCA, by BMG Records (UK). Deleted '83. Catalogue no: **PB 5268**

Hart, Tim

DRUNKEN SAILOR, THE
Tracks: / Drunken sailor, The / Froggy's courting.
7" Single: Released '83, on MFP, by EMI Records. Catalogue no: **FP 910**

Harte, Ciaran

LOVE IS STRANGE
Tracks: / Love is strange.
7" Single: Released '82, on Glass, by Glass Records. Deleted '83. Catalogue no: **GLASS 003**

Hartford, John

ANNUAL WALTZ (SINGLE)
Tracks: / Annual waltz.
7" Single: Released May '87, on MCA, by MCA Records. Catalogue no: **MCA 1147**

Hartley, Trevor

CALL ON ME
Tracks: / Call on me.
7" Single: Released Oct '86, on Virgin, by Virgin Records. Deleted May '88. Catalogue no: **VS 905**
12" Single: Released Oct '86, on Virgin, by Virgin Records. Deleted May '88. Catalogue no: **VS 905-12**

CAN YOU FEEL THE LOVE
Tracks: / Can you feel the love / Can you feel the love (Instrumental).
12" Single: Released Apr '86, on Sir George, Catalogue no: **SG 003T**

IT MUST BE LOVE
Tracks: / It must be love / It must be love (version).
12" Single: Released Apr '87, on Unity Sound, Catalogue no: **UN 001**

NINE TILL FIVE (NO MORE)
Tracks: / (No more) Nine till five / Hooked on you / Amanda / (No more) Nine till five (instrumental).
12" Single: Released Apr '89, on London Records, by London Records. Catalogue

no: **LONX 216**
CD 5": Released Apr '89, on London Records, by London Records. Catalogue no: **LONCD 216**
7" Single: Released Apr '89, on London Records, by London Records. Catalogue no: **LON 216**

OPEN THE DOOR
Tracks: / Open the door.
12" Single: Released Jun '88, on Massive, by Massive Records. Catalogue no: **MASS2T**

PACK YOUR THINGS AND GO
Tracks: / Pack your things and go.
12" Single: Released Dec '82, on Tanga Music, Catalogue no: **LAC 001**

WARM LOVE
Tracks: / Warm love / Honey.
7" Single: Released Feb '83, on Top Ranking (1), Catalogue no: **TRY 7**
12" Single: Released Feb '83, on Top Ranking (1), Catalogue no: **12 TRY 7**

Hartman, Billy 'GBH'

RETURN TO SENDER
Tracks: / Return to sender / Rich girls.
7" Single: Released Jan '80, on EMI, by EMI Records. Deleted Jan '85. Catalogue no: **EMI 5019**

Hartman, Dan

FREE RIDE
Tracks: / Free ride / Love strong.
7" Single: Released Jun '80, on Blue Sky, Deleted '83. Catalogue no: **SKY 8562**

I CAN DREAM ABOUT YOU (SINGLE)
Tracks: / I can dream about you.
7" Single: Released Sep '85, on MCA, by MCA Records. Catalogue no: **MCA 988**
12" Single: Released Sep '85, on MCA, by MCA Records. Catalogue no: **MCAX 988**
12" Single: Released Sep '85, on MCA, by MCA Records. Catalogue no: **MCAT 988**

INSTANT REPLAY (SINGLE)
Tracks: / Instant Replay.
7" Single: Released Oct '78, on Sky, by President Records. Deleted '81. Catalogue no: **SKY 6706**

RELIGHT MY FIRE
Tracks: / Relight my fire / Vertigo.
12" Single: Released Jan '80, on Blue Sky, Deleted Jan '85. Catalogue no: **138104**
7" Single: Released Jan '80, on Blue Sky, Deleted Jan '85. Catalogue no: **SKY 8104**

SECOND NATURE
Tracks: / Second Nature.
7" Single: Released May '85, on MCA, by MCA Records. Deleted '88. Catalogue no: **MCA 957**

THIS IS IT
Tracks: / This is it.
7" Single: Released Jan '79, on Blue Sky, Deleted '82. Catalogue no: **SKY 6999**

WAITING TO SEE YOU
Tracks: / Waiting to see you.
12" Single: Released Aug '86, on Epic, by CBS Records. Deleted '87. Catalogue no: **TA 7186**

Hartman, Lisa

WHERE THE BOYS ARE
Tracks: / Where the boys are.
7" Single: Released Jul '84, on RCA, by BMG Records (UK). Catalogue no: **RCA 435**

Harvest Moon

TALES OF WONDER
Tracks: / Tales of wonder / Take a dream.
7" Single: Released Jun '81, on Charisma, by Virgin Records. Deleted '84. Catalogue no: **CB 386**

Harvey, Alex

Biographical details: This British singer and guitarist was born in Glasgow in 1935. He left school at 15 and tried his hand at a whole host of diverse jobs. He played trumpet in a jazz combo for a while, but switched to guitar in 1956. At the end of that year, his skiffle group won a talent contest and Harvey was temporarily hailed as Scotland's answer to Tommy Steele. That excitement quickly evaporated, but in 1958 he formed the highly original Alex Harvey Soul Band. Dabbling in rhythm and blues, rock'n'roll and pop styles, they became a hard-working live group and built up strong reputations in Scotland, England and West Germany. Their graft never paid off in commercial terms, and they folded in 1966. For the following half-dozen years, Harvey scratched a living in a variety of musical capacities, most noticeably as a guitarist in the pit orchestra of the London production of *Hair*. In 1972 the Sensational Alex Harvey Band came into being, and he was at last on the road to substantial success. Formed in the glam rock era, SAHB mixed theatrics with their hybrid rock styles to the extent that the visuals became as important as the music. The band became one of the top concertattractions of the mid-seventies, both in Britain and internationally, and reached their commercial peak shortly after Alex's 40th birthday. Inevitably they were bigger live than on record, and their only UK Top 10 single was a live 1975 recording of the Tom Jones hit *Delilah* - this frenetic and irreverent single summed up the band's sense of humour. SAHB scored a UK no. 13 hit in 1976 with *The Boston tea party*; their Top 20 albums included *The impossible dream* (1974), *Tomorrow belongs to me*, and *Live* (1975), *Penthouse tapes* and *SAHB stories* (1976). In 1977 the punk revolution, coinciding with health problems for the workaholic Harvey, knocked SAHB's career on the head. They split in late 77, whereupon Alex took life at a slightly less frenetic pace and slipped from the public eye. He suffered from recurring back trouble, which impaired his attempts to revive his career. Alex Harvey's years of hard work and touring caught up with him in Feb. 1982 in Belgium, on the eve of his 47th birthday, he died of a heart attack. (Bob Macdonald, 11/10/85).

BOSTON TEA PARTY, THE
Tracks: / Boston tea party, The.
7" Single: Released Jun '76, on Mountain, Deleted '79. Catalogue no: **TOP 12**

DELILAH
Tracks: / Delilah.
7" Single: Released Jul '75, on Vertigo, by Phonogram Ltd. Deleted '78. Catalogue no: **ALEX 002**
7" Single: Released Jul '80, on Mountain, Deleted Jul '83. Catalogue no: **HOT 2**

GAMBLIN' BAR ROOM BLUES
Tracks: / Gamblin' bar room blues.
7" Single: Released Nov '75, on Vertigo, by Phonogram Ltd. Deleted '78. Catalogue no: **ALEX 002**

POET AND I
Tracks: / Poet and I.
7" Single: Released Nov '83, on Powerstation, by Powerstation Records. Catalogue no: **OHM 3**

SMALL AXE
Tracks: / Small axe / Whalers.
7" Single: Released May '80, on RCA, by BMG Records (UK). Deleted May '83. Catalogue no: **PB 5252**

Harvey, Connie

LOVE CAME RIGHT ON TIME
Tracks: / Love came right on time / Love came right on time (inst).
7" Single: Released Feb '88, on New York 42, by Satril Records. Catalogue no: **NY 102**
12" Single: Released Feb '88, on New York 42, by Satril Records. Catalogue no: **NYT 102**

Harvey, Richard

ELEGY
Tracks: / Elegy / Fenlands.
7" Single: Released Nov '85, on ASV (Academy Sound & Vision), by Academy Sound & Vision Records. Deleted Jul '87. Catalogue no: **ASV 104**

GAME SET AND MATCH
Tracks: / Game set and match / Goodbye codes.
7" Single: Released Nov '88, on Chrysalis, by Chrysalis Records. Catalogue no: **CHS 3324**

Harvey, Steve

Biographical details: This British singer, multi-instumentalist, songwriter and producer reached the lower regions of the UK Top 75 singles chart on two occasions in 1983: *Something special* climbed to no 46 and *Tonight* reached no 63. In 1985 he produced and co-wrote the whole of the debut LP by London soul duo Total Contrast, which was preceded by their UK no 17 single *Takes a little time*. In the same year, Harvey was responsible for producing three tracks on Five Star's UK Top 30 album *Luxury of life*; and away from soul music, he produced six tracks on the Adventures' first LP and also worked with a new band called Flesh. (Bob Macdonald, 11/10/85).

SOMETHING SPECIAL
Tracks: / Something special.
7" Single: Released May '83, on London Records, by London Records. Catalogue no: **LON 25**
12" Single: Released May '83, on London Records, by London Records. Catalogue no: **LONX 25**

TONIGHT
Tracks: / Tonight.
7" Single: Released Oct '83, on London Records, by London Records. Catalogue no: **LON 36**
12" Single: Released Oct '83, on London Records, by London Records. Catalogue no: **LONX 36**

Harvey & The...

PARK THE TIGER (EP)
Tracks: / I ain't got you / Tons & tons of sunshine / Dancing in the backroom / Devil went down to Georgia, The / Like I should.
7" Single: Released May '86, on Hubba Discs, Catalogue no: **HUBEP 1**

Harwoods

IT'S A MODERN ROMANCE
Tracks: / It's a modern romance.
12" Single: Released Jul '85, on Tembo, by Tembo Records. Catalogue no: **TMLX 108**
7" Single: Released Jul '85, on Tembo, by Tembo Records. Catalogue no: **TML 108**

Hashim

UK FRESH '86 - THE ANTHEM
Tracks: / UK fresh '86 - the anthem / UK fresh '86 - the anthem (remix).
12" Single: Released Jul '86, on Streetwave, Catalogue no: **MKHAN 72**

WE'RE ROCKIN' THE PLANET
Tracks: / We're rockin' the planet / We're rockin' the planet (Inst) / Bonus beats.
12" Single: Released Feb '86, on ZYX (Germany), Catalogue no: **ZYX 5161**

Haskell, Gordon

5-10-15
Tracks: / 1-10-15 / Whisky.
7" Single: Released Jan '81, on RCA, by BMG Records (UK). Deleted Jan '84. Catalogue no: **RCA 30**

I NEED YOUR LOVE SO MUCH
Tracks: / I need your love so much / Living in the attic.
7" Single: Released Apr '80, on RCA, by BMG Records (UK). Deleted Apr '83. Catalogue no: **PB 5249**

Haslam, Annie

GOING HOME
Tracks: / Going home / Inside my life.
7" Single: Released Feb '80, on Warner Bros., by WEA Records. Deleted Feb '83. Catalogue no: **K 17663**

Hassans

OUR LOVE WILL LAST FOREVER
Tracks: / Our love will last forever / It's time.
7" Single: Released Sep '81, on EMI, by EMI Records. Deleted Sep '84. Catalogue no: **EMI 5230**

Hasselhoff, David

LOOKING FOR FREEDOM
Tracks: / Looking for freedom.
7" Single: Released Jul '89, on Arista, by BMG Records (UK). Catalogue no: **111936**
12" Single: Released Jul '89, on Arista, by BMG Records (UK). Catalogue no: **611936**

Hasson, Gemma

LOVE IS THE ONLY WAY
Tracks: / Love is the only way / Penny lover.
7" Single: Released Dec '84, on Ritz, by Ritz Records. Catalogue no: **RITZ 089**

Hatch, Tony

AIRLINE
Tracks: / Airline / Hiffa.
7" Single: Released Jan '82, on Tube, Deleted Jan '85. Catalogue no: **TUBE 003**

OUT OF THIS WORLD
Tracks: / Out of this world.
7" Single: Released Oct '62, on Pye, Deleted '65. Catalogue no: **7N 15460**

Hatchett, Molly

BOUNTY HUNTER
Tracks: / Bountry hunter / Boogie no more / Flirtin' with disaster.
7" Single: Released Jun '80, on Epic, by CBS Records. Deleted '83. Catalogue no: **EPC 8636**
12" Single: Released Jun '80, on Epic, by CBS Records. Deleted '83. Catalogue no: **EPC 12 8636**

FLIRTIN' WITH DISASTER
Tracks: / Flirtin' with disaster / Gunsmoke.
7" Single: Released Feb '80, on Epic, by CBS Records. Deleted '83. Catalogue no: **EPC 8221**

Haunted Staircase

FLUTTERS
Tracks: / Flutters.
7" Single: Released Sep '84, on Rabbit, by Rabbit Records. Catalogue no: **STEW 101**

Hausen, Ana

PROFESSIONALS
Tracks: / Professionals, The.
7" Single: Released Jul '81, on Human (2), Catalogue no: **HUM 12**

Havana Let's Go

SPANISH CABARET
Tracks: / Spanish cabaret / Continental shelf.
7" Single: Released Nov '81, on Polydor, by Polydor Ltd. Deleted '84. Catalogue no: **POSP 364**

TORPEDO
Tracks: / Torpedo / Rio.
7" Single: Released Aug '81, on Polydor, by Polydor Ltd. Deleted Aug '84. Catalogue no: **POSP 313**

Have A Nice Day

ANOTHER DAY, ANOTHER DOLLAR
Tracks: / Another day, another dollar.
7" Single: Released Aug '86, on Temple Records, by Temple Records (2). Catalogue no: **OTHER 1**
12" Single: Released Aug '86, on Temple Records, by Temple Records (2). Catalogue no: **OTHER 12**

Have No Fury

WRITE YOUR NAME IN SAND
Tracks: / Write your name in sand / Thank you.
7" Single: Released Aug '89, on Sierra, by Sierra Records. Catalogue no: **FED 60**

Havens, Richie

DEATH AT AN EARLY AGE
Tracks: / Death at an early age.
7" Single: Released Jun '83, on Connexion, Deleted '85. Catalogue no: **CX 5381**

Hawk & Co

NIGHT LIFE TURNS ME ON
Tracks: / Night life turns me on.
7" Single: Released Nov '81, on Epic, by CBS Records. Deleted Nov '84. Catalogue no: **EPCA 1735**

Hawk, Robert

WHOSE LAND IS THIS
Tracks: / Whose land is this.
7" Single: Released Apr '82, on Raw, Catalogue no: **GTSO 1**

Hawke, Elmer

CHEERS
Tracks: / Cheers.
7" Single: Released Nov '85, on Wye, by Wye Records. Deleted '88. Catalogue no: **DC 006**

LITTLE LOVE, A
Tracks: / Little love, A.
7" Single: Released Jan '89, on Stether Music, Catalogue no: **SKB 2**

TELL ME
Tracks: / Tell me.
7" Single: Released Sep '84, on Hollywood, by Hollywood Records. Catalogue no: **HWD 014**

Hawkey, Andrew

AND THIS....
Tracks: / And this....
12" Single: Released Sep '83, on Solar Sound, Catalogue no: **SOSO 021**

Hawkins, Buzz

DANCER
Tracks: / Dancer.
7" Single: Released Jul '81, on Smile, Catalogue no: **SRO 33**

Hawkins, Coleman

Biographical details: Coleman Hawkins (1904-69) single-handedly brought the saxophone into prominence as a jazz instrument becoming undisputed master of the tenor sax. He spent a fruitful period in Europe in the mid-thirties. (condensed from ASV newssheet 7/88)..

BODY AND SOUL
Tracks: / Body and soul / Meet Doctor Foo / She's funny that way / Fine dinner.
CD 5": Released Oct '89, on Bluebird (2), by BMG Records (UK). Catalogue no: **ZD 43188**

Hawkins, Edwin

Biographical details: This American singer, arranger, choir leader and pianist was born in Oakland, California. In April 1967 the 23 year old Hawkins co-founded the North California State Youth Choir, by recruiting the most able 17-25 year old vocalists from other church ensembles in the San Francisco area. To raise funds for the choir, they recorded an LP on a 2-track tape recorder and sold copies at the Annual Youth Congress in Cleveland, Ohio in

June 1968. The choir won the singing contest at that event, and sold about 60% of the 1000 copies of their album. Suddenly in early 1969, a Cisco disc jockey began giving heavy airplay to the track *Oh happy day* from the album. It was picked up by a major record company and released under the billing of the Edwin Hawkins Singers. During the summer of '69 it became a surprise smash, reaching no 4 on the US chart and climbing to no 2 in the UK. The uplifting *Oh happy day* was thus the only black gospel record ever to become a major international pop hit. It was an exuberant and thoroughly inspirational performance by the 46 strong choir of a traditional song that originally dated from 1755. The featured soloist on *Oh happy day*, Dorothy Combs Morrison, soon left to pursue a solo career. Hawkins never achieved another pop hit, except in a one-off collaboration with Melanie, but his name was now established in the gospel field and he became something of an institution on the genre's international touring circuit, albeit with an increasingly MoR sounf. (Bob Macdonald, 12/10/85).

OH HAPPY DAY (OLD GOLD)
Tracks: / Oh happy day / Brand new key.
7" Single: Released Oct '88, on Old Gold, by Old Gold Records. Catalogue no: **OG 9802**

OH HAPPY DAY (SINGLE)
Tracks: / Oh happy day.
7" Single: Released May '69, on Buddah, by Buddah Records Inc.(USA). Deleted '72. Catalogue no: **201 048**

Hawkins, Screamin' Jay

I PUT A SPELL ON YOU (SINGLE)
Tracks: / I put a speel on you / Armpit no.6.
7" Single: Released Oct '82, on Polydor, by Polydor Ltd. Deleted Oct '85. Catalogue no: **POSP 183**

Hawkins, Ted

BAD DOG
Tracks: / Bad dog.
12" Single: Released Jan '87, on Gull, by Gull Records. Deleted '88. Catalogue no: **WOW 5812**

GOLDEN SUN
Tracks: / Golden sun / You spoiled my Christmas.
7" Single: Released Dec '88, on PT, Catalogue no: **PTL 002**

WATCH YOUR STEP (SINGLE)
Tracks: / Watch your step / Sweet baby / Bring it home Daddy.
12" Single: Released Feb '86, on Gull, by Gull Records. Deleted '88. Catalogue no: **WOW 5712**
12" Single: Released Feb '85, on Windows On The World, Catalogue no: **WOW 112**

Hawklords

WHO'S GONNA WIN THE WAR
Tracks: / Who's gonna win the war / Time off.
7" Single: Released Jun '82, on Flicknife, by Flicknife Records. Catalogue no: **FLS 209**

Hawks, Tony

TOGETHER
Tracks: / Together.
7" Single: Released Feb '85, on Hobo, Catalogue no: **HOS 026**

Hawkwind

Biographical details: At the time of their greatest success, this British heavy metal band consisted of Dave Brock, Bob Calvert, Del Dettmar, Simon King, Lemmy, Dik Mik, Stacia and Nik Turner. Hawkwind were formed in 1969 by guitarist/vocalist Brock (the only lifelong member - he was still there in the Eighties), electronic wizard Dik Mik and saxophonist/vocalist Turner plus three other short-lived members. Hailing from Ladbroke Grove in London, they released their eponymous debut LP in 1970. Following many strong live appearances - including the 1970 Isle of Wight Festival, where they played a free gig outside the fence - their second album *In search of space* gave Hawkwind their first UK chart entry, reaching No.18 and logging 19 weeks on the LP chart.
For the next few years, Hawkwind enjoyed a large cult following and became 'underground' heroes. The group's hippie philosophy resulted in numerous benefit concerts and community gigs. The summer of 1972 brought them a surprise smash single with *Silver machine*, an atmospheric and hard-driving rock track which cruised to No.3 in Britain. Their Lps *Doremi fasol latido* (1972), *Space ritual alive*(1973), *Hall of the mountain grill*(1974) and *Warrior on the edge of time*(1975) *all reached the UK Top 20. The band were known for their space rock concepts and sci-fi explorations, as well as their drug habits and frequent line-up changes.*
The arrival of punk rock in 1976 (by which time bassist/vocalist Lemmy had left to form another notorious heavy metal band, Motorhead) dampened Hawkwind's album sales and live following. But despite the fact that they were becoming more and more of an anachronism, with every new song sounding like a rehash of Silver machine, Hawkwind refused to die. In 1978 they released the *25 years on* album under the name of the Hawklords, but soon reverted to the familiar billing. *Live 1979* and *Sonic attack* (1981) put the band back in the Top 20 of the British album charts, thanks to a general revival of interest in HM music, and dave Brock and his cohorts were still going strong in the mid Eighties. (Bob MacDonald 14th October 1985).

ANGELS OF DEATH (SINGLE)
Tracks: / Angels of death / Trans-dimensional man.
7" Single: Released Oct '81, on RCA, by BMG Records (UK). Deleted Oct '84. Catalogue no: **RCA 137**

MOTORHEAD
Tracks: / Motorhead / Valium ten.
7" Single: Released Jul '86, on Flicknife, by Flicknife Records. Catalogue no: **FLS 034**

MOTORHEAD (KILL MISTER)
Tracks: / Motorhead (kill mister) / Valium 10.
12" Single: Released '82, on Flicknife, by Flicknife Records. Catalogue no: **FLSEP 205**
7" Single: Released Sep '81, on Flicknife, by Flicknife Records. Deleted '84. Catalogue no: **FLS 205**

MOTORWAY CITY
Tracks: / Motorway city / Master of the universe.
7" Single: Released '83, on Flicknife, by Flicknife Records. Catalogue no: **FLS 025**

NEEDLE GUN
Tracks: / Needle gun / Arioch.
7" Single: Released '85, on Flicknife, by Flicknife Records. Catalogue no: **FLS 032**
12" Single: Released '85, on Flicknife, by Flicknife Records. Catalogue no: **FLST 032**

NIGHT OF THE HAWKS (EP) The earth ritual preview
Tracks: / Night of the hawks / Green finned demon / Dream dancers / Dragons & fables.
7" Single: Released Jan '84, on Flicknife, by Flicknife Records. Catalogue no: **FLEP 104**

OVER THE TOP
Tracks: / Over the top / Free fall / Death trap.
12" Single: Released Nov '81, on Flicknife, by Flicknife Records. Catalogue no: **FLEP 101**

SHOT DOWN IN THE NIGHT
Tracks: / Shot down in the night.
7" Single: Released Jul '80, on Bronze, by Bronze Records. Deleted '83. Catalogue no: **BRO 98**

SILVER MACHINE
Tracks: / Silver machine.
12" Single: Released May '86, on Samurai, Catalogue no: **HW 12001**
7" Pic: Released Jan '83, on United Artists, by EMI Records. Deleted '86. Catalogue no: **UPP 35381**
7" Single: Released Jan '83, on United Artists, by EMI Records. Catalogue no: **UP 35381**
7" Pic: Released May '86, on Samurai, Catalogue no: **HW 001**
7" Single: Released Sep '82, on RCA, by BMG Records (UK). Deleted Sep '85. Catalogue no: **RCA 276**
7" Single: Released May '86, on Samurai, Catalogue no: **HW 7001**
12" Single: Released Jan '83, on United Artists, by EMI Records. Deleted '86. Catalogue no: **12 UP 35381**

URBAN GUERILLA
Tracks: / Urban Guerilla.
7" Single: Released Aug '73, on United Artists, by EMI Records. Deleted '76. Catalogue no: **UP 35566**

WHO'S GONNA WIN THE WAR
Tracks: / Who's gonna win the war / Nuclear toy.
7" Single: Released Oct '82, on Bronze, by Bronze Records. Deleted Oct '85. Catalogue no: **BRO 109**

ZAROZINIA
Tracks: / Zarozinia / Assault and battery / Sleep of a thousand tears (This track on 12" version only.).
7" Single: Released Mar '86, on Flicknife, by Flicknife Records. Catalogue no: **FLS 033**
12" Single: Released Mar '86, on Flicknife, by Flicknife Records. Catalogue no: **FLST 033**

ZOO
Tracks: / Zoo / Hurry on sundown / Kings of speed / Sweet mistress of Paris.
12" Single: Released Dec '83, on Flicknife, by Flicknife Records. Catalogue no: **FLEP 100**

Haxby, Strensall

MACK THE KNIFE
Tracks: / Mack the knife / Here I am.
7" Single: Released Jul '86, on Mr.Sam, by Mr.Sam Music. Catalogue no: **SAS 106**

Hay, Colin James

CAN I HOLD YOU?
Tracks: / Can I hold you / Nature of the beast.
7" Single: Released May '87, on Epic, by CBS Records. Deleted Nov '87. Catalogue no: **650781 7**
12" Single: Released May '87, on Epic, by CBS Records. Deleted Nov '87. Catalogue no: **650781 6**

HOLD ME
Tracks: / Home sweet home / Hold me.
7" Single: Released Feb '87, on Epic, by CBS Records. Deleted Nov '87. Catalogue no: **650297 0**
7" Single: Released Jan '87, on Epic, by CBS Records. Deleted Nov '87. Catalogue no: **650297 7**
12" Single: Released Jan '87, on Epic, by CBS Records. Deleted Nov '87. Catalogue no: **650297 6**

Haycock, Pete

LUCIENNE
Tracks: / Lucienne.
7" Single: Released May '88, on I.R.S, Catalogue no: **IRM 163**

Haycock's Climax, Pete

SUNBIRD
Tracks: / Sunbird.
7" Single: Released Jun '85, on Nu-Disk, by Pan Polychord Records. Catalogue no: **HAY 1**

YOUNG EXECUTIVE
Tracks: / Young executive.
7" Single: Released Oct '85, on Nu-Disk, by Pan Polychord Records. Catalogue no: **HAY 2**

Hayes, Billy

BALLAD OF DAVY CROCKETT
Tracks: / Ballad of Davy Crockett, The.
7" Single: Released Jan '56, on London-American, Deleted '59. Catalogue no: **HLA 8220**

Hayes, Isaac

Biographical details: This American singer, composer, multi-instrumentalist, producer and actor was born and raised in Tennessee in relative poverty. He released his first single in 1962, and spent the early Sixties trying to break into the music business while holding down a series of dreary dayjobs. Settling in Memphis, he managed to join the in-house creative team of the city's Stax/Volt labels, who were second only to Detroit's Tamla Motown in the field of Sixties soul music. After working as a studio musician for such Stax/Volt stars as Otis Redding, Hayes began a fruitful songwriting partnership with an unknown ex-insurance salesman called David Porter. The pair's breakthrough hit was *Hold on I'm comin'*, which they wrote and produced for Sam & Dave; it reached No.1 on the US rhythm-and-blues chart in the summer of 1966, and hit No.21 on the pop list. It was the first of a string of great soul/dance/pop records that the Hayes-Porter alliance provided for the vocal duo. The biggest and best was 1967's *Soul man*, an exuberant anthem that was not only an R&B chart-topper but also a US No.2 pop smash; but there were also beautiful ballads like *When something is wrong with my baby*, plus a one-off UK Top.20 hit with 1969's *Soul sister brown sugar*. Hayes & Porter's other highly successful act was Carla Thomas, for whom they wrote a number of R&B hits including the 1966 US Top.20 pop success *B-A-B-Y*.
In 1969, with Sam & Dave on the verge of breaking up, the partnership with Porter was ended and Hayes became a successful performer in his own right. No-one expected big things of Isaac's *Hot buttered soul* album when it was issued, but it became one of the all time classic Lps in black soul music. The album contained just four tracks, all of which were extended pieces of half-sung/half spoken ultra-moody ultra-sexy soul. The key track was an extraordinary 18-minute rendition of Glen Cambell's 3 minute hit *By the time I get to Phoenix*, which provided listeners with one of the most sophisticated and intense experiences in modern music. A few years later, the equally butch-voiced Barry White borrowed the Isaac Hayes sound and condensed it into a shorter singles-oriented format.
With *Hot buttered soul* establishing Hayes as a major star in the American soul market (where he was dubbed Black Moses), he then became known to pop and rock audiences with the *Theme from Shaft*. This stunning single, a multi-genre fusion with an instantly memorable guitar riff, reached No.1 in America and No.4 in Britain at the end of 1971. The whole double soundtrack LP for the pioneering black movie was written and performed by Hayes, and reached the Top 20 on both sides of the Atlantic; it won him four Grammies and an Oscar. After this, however, the career of the widely idolised Black Moses was a mixed up bag of ups and downs. His music became a weak self-parody of earlier glories, and the quality of his mid-Seventies output was barren except a UK Top 10 single in 1976 with the catchy instrumental *Disco connection*. His profligate spending (a combination of excessive personal materialism, generous donations to charity work for the need, and bad advice) caught up with him in 1978, when he was declared bankrupt. His career was rescued in 1979 by a sudden flurry of successful cover versions of his material - by Rachel Sweet, Dionne Warwick and the Blues Brothers - plus a US Top 20 hit in his own right with *Don't let go*. In 1981 he landed an important acting role in the hit movie *Escape from New York*. Hayes has not re-established himself as a major star but his influence on soul music, and popular music in general, lives on. (Bob MacDonald, 14th October 1985).

DISCO CONNECTION
Tracks: / Disco connection.
7" Single: Released Apr '76, on ABC Records, by MCA Records. Deleted '79. Catalogue no: **ABC 4100**

HEY GIRL
Tracks: / Ike's rap / Hey Fred / Hey girl.
7" Single: Released Nov '86, on CBS, by CBS Records. Catalogue no: **650236 7**
12" Single: Released Nov '86, on CBS, by CBS Records. Catalogue no: **650236 6**

I AIN'T NEVER
Tracks: / I ain't never / Shaft / Love has been good to us.
7" Single: Released Jun '80, on Polydor, by Polydor Ltd. Deleted '83. Catalogue no: **2141262**

SHAFT, THEME FROM
Tracks: / Shaft, Theme from / Men, The (theme from) / Walk on by (Only on CD single.) / Type thang (Only on CD single.).
7" Single: Released Mar '82, on Stax, by Fantasy Inc (USA). Catalogue no: **STAX 1009**
7" Single: Released Sep '85, on Old Gold, by Old Gold Records. Catalogue no: **OG 9528**
CD 5": Released May '89, on South Bound, Catalogue no: **CDSEWT 701**
7" Single: Released May '89, on South Bound, Catalogue no: **SEWS 701**
7" Single: Released Dec '71, on Stax, by Fantasy Inc (USA). Deleted '74. Catalogue no: **2025 069**
7" Single: Released Aug '87, on Stax, by Fantasy Inc (USA). Catalogue no: **STAX 810**
12" Single: Released May '89, on South Bound, Catalogue no: **SEWT 701**

Hayes, Lynda

DON'T YOU LOVE ME ANYMORE
Tracks: / Don't you love me anymore.
7" Single: Released Jul '84, on Safari, by Safari Records. Catalogue no: **LYNDA 1**
12" Single: Released Sep '84, on Safari, by Safari Records. Catalogue no: **LYNDA L1**
12" Single: Released Jul '84, on Safari, by Safari Records. Catalogue no: **LYNDA 121**

HEARTBEAT
Tracks: / Heartbeat / You're the one.
7" Single: Released Jan '81, on Precision (1). Deleted Jan '84. Catalogue no: **PAR 113**

Haynes, Jimmy

FUNK ON THE ROCKS
Tracks: / Funk on the rocks / Charge it up.
7" Single: Released Nov '81, on RCA, by BMG Records (UK). Deleted '84. Catalogue no: **RCA 141**
12" Single: Released Nov '81, on RCA, by BMG Records (UK). Deleted '84. Catalogue no: **RCAT 141**

Haynes, Steve

PICTURE PUZZLE
Tracks: / Picture puzzle / I get so lonely.
7" Single: Released Jan '80, on Harbour, by Harbour Records. Catalogue no: **HRB 7**

Haysi Fantayzee - Shiny Shiny (Released on Regard)

Haysi Fantayzee

Biographical details: Kate Garner and Jeremiah Healy were friends of Culture Club leader Boy George, and beat him into the UK charts by a mere two months. Haysi Fantayzee's *John Wayne is a big leggy*, produced by veteran studio maestro Tony Visconti, reached No.11 in the summer of 1982. It was one of Britains catchiest novelty hits of the year, and the perfomers had a suitably freaky appearance - their rasta dreadlocks (most unusual for white people) clashed amusingly with their kitsch style of jumble-sale dress. It seemed somehow appropriate that Kate and manager Paul Caplin lived above a disused underwear factory.

The three of them wrote *Shiny shiny*, which gave Haysi Fantayzee their second UK Top 20 hit in '83. However, their brand of gimmicky pop music was very lightweight, and they split up to pursue solo careers after just on LP (*Battle hymns for children singing*). They were one of Britain's most bizarre duos, but there was no music of any substances behind the freaky image to sutain either member as a solo artist.
(Bob MacDonald, 14th October 1985).

HOLY JOE
Tracks: / Holy Joe.
7" Pic: Released Nov '82, on Regard, Catalogue no: **RGP 104**
12" Single: Released Oct '82, on Regard, Catalogue no: **RGT 104**
7" Single: Released Oct '82, on Regard, Catalogue no: **RG 104**

JOHN WAYNE IS BIG LEGGY
Tracks: / John Wayne is big leggy / Sabres of paradise.
7" Pic: Released Jun '82, on Regard, Catalogue no: **RG 10**
12" Single: Released Jun '82, on Regard, Catalogue no: **RGT 100**
7" Single: Released Jun '82, on Regard, Catalogue no: **RG 100**

SHINY SHINY (see panel above)
Tracks: / Shiny shiny / Shiny shiny bon temps.
Note: Haysi fan club: PO box 40R London W1A 4OR
7" Single: Released Jan '83, on Regard, Catalogue no: **RG 106**
7" Pic: Released Jan '83, on Regard, Catalogue no: **RGP 106**
12" Single: Released Jan '83, on Regard, Catalogue no: **RGT 106**

SISTER FRICTION
Tracks: / Sister friction.
7" Pic: Released Jul '83, on Regard, Catalogue no: **RGP 108**
7" Single: Released May '83, on Regard, Catalogue no: **RG 108**
12" Single: Released May '83, on Regard, Catalogue no: **RGT 108**

Hayward, Andrew

TELEPHONE BOX (EP)
Tracks: / Telephone box / News after day / New suit.
7" EP: Released Jul '80, on Twist & Shout, Catalogue no: **T&S 1**

Hayward, Justin

Biographical details: British singer-songwriter-guitarist Hayward, born in Swindon, was 21 when he composed the Moody Blues classic *Nights In White Satin* in 1967. Having initially failed as a solo artist he had joined the group in 1966, replacing founder member Denny Laine.

Hayward went on to write such Moodies classics as *Question*. The Moody Blues were in abeyance during the mid-70's and Hayward and bassist/vocalist John Lodge decided to release an album as a duo.

Blue Jays ('75) was very much in the Moodies vein and offered few surprises, but it was what their public wanted and reached No 4, with 18 weeks on the UK chart.

Towards the end of '75 the pair scored a British Top Ten single with the atmospheric *Blue Guitar*. Hayward's debut solo album, *Songwriter*, was issued in 1977 and peaked at a disappointing No 28 on the British LP list, but in the summer of '78 he achieved a UK Top Five single with *Forever Autumn*, the big hit from Jeff Wayne's phenominally successful vinyl adaptation of H.G. Wells' *War Of The Worlds*. The Moodies reformed in 1978 but Hayward found time in 1980 to release a second solo album, *Night Flight*, which peaked at No 41 on the British chart.
(Bob MacDonald, October 1985.).

BEST IS YET TO COME
Tracks: / Best is yet to come, The.
7" Single: Released Nov '85, on Towerbell, Catalogue no: **TOW 79**

BLUE GUITAR
(JUSTIN HAYWARD & JOHN LODGE)
Tracks: / Blue Guitar.
7" Single: Released Oct '75, on Threshold (1), by Threshold Records. Deleted '78. Catalogue no: **TH 21**

FOREVER AUTUMN
Tracks: / Forever Autumn.
7" Single: Released Jul '78, on CBS, by CBS Records. Deleted '81. Catalogue no: **CBS 6368**
7" Single: Released Jan '87, on Old Gold, by Old Gold Records. Catalogue no: **OG 9401**

NEARER TO YOU
Tracks: / Nearer to you / It's not on.
7" Single: Released Sep '80, on Decca, by Decca Records. Deleted '83. Catalogue no: **F 13895**

SILVERBIRD
Tracks: / Silver bird.
7" Single: Released Aug '85, on Towerbell, Catalogue no: **TOW 71**

STAR COPS(It won't be easy)
Tracks: / Star cops / Outer space.
7" Single: Released Jul '87, on BBC, by BBC Records & Tapes. Deleted Apr '89. Catalogue no: **RESL 208**
12" Single: Released Jul '87, on BBC, by BBC Records & Tapes. Deleted Apr '89. Catalogue no: **12RSL 208**

Haywood, Leon

DON'T PUSH IT DON'T FORCE IT
Tracks: / Don't push it Don't force it / Who you been giving it up to?.
7" Single: Released Mar '80, on 20th Century, by 20th Century Records. Deleted '83. Catalogue no: **TC 2443**
12" Single: Released Mar '80, on 20th Century, by 20th Century Records. Deleted '83. Catalogue no: **TCB 2443**

Haywoode

Biographical details: This British singer broke through into her native London's thriving black soul scene in 1983 with *A time like this*.

It was a classy, catchy danceable single; it reached No.48 on the UK national pop chart, and might have fared better if it had received more radio airplay instead of just being a club favourite. Haywoode's star seemed to be in the ascendant, but her next few singles were not as good or as successful as *A time like this* although they were in a similar vein. In 1984's *I can't let you go* peaked at No.63, and the Leeson & Vale penned *Roses* was also only a minor hit.

Later in '85, she charted with *Getting closer* -this was written and produced by the hot hitmaking team of Matt Aitken, Mike Stock and Pete Waterman.

Meanwhile, similar sounding girl vocalists on the UK soul scene -Jaki Graham and Princess - had already enjoyed UK Top 10 success.
(Bob MacDonald, 14th October 1985).

A TIME LIKE THIS
Tracks: / Time like this, A.
7" Single: Released Sep '83, on CBS, by CBS Records. Deleted '86. Catalogue no: **A 3651**

GETTING CLOSER
Tracks: / Getting closer.
7" Single: Released Oct '85, on CBS, by CBS Records. Deleted '88. Catalogue no: **A 6582**

I CAN'T LET YOU GO
Tracks: / My kind of hero / I can't let you go.
12" Single: Released Aug '86, on CBS, by CBS Records. Deleted '87. Catalogue no: **650076 6**
12" Single: Released Sep '84, on CBS, by CBS Records. Catalogue no: **QTX4664**
7" Single: Released Sep '84, on CBS, by CBS Records. Catalogue no: **A 4664**
7" Single: Released Aug '86, on CBS, by CBS Records. Deleted '87. Catalogue no: **650076 7**

I'M YOUR PUPPET
Tracks: / I'm your puppet / Take me up to heaven.
12" Single: Released Feb '87, on CBS, by CBS Records. Deleted Aug '87. Catalogue no: **SYDT 1**
7" Single: Released Feb '87, on CBS, by CBS Records. Deleted Aug '87. Catalogue no: **SYD 1**

ROSES
Tracks: / Tease me / Roses.
12" Single: Released May '86, on CBS, by CBS Records. Catalogue no: **TA 7224**
7" Single: Released May '86, on CBS, by CBS Records. Deleted '86. Catalogue no: **A 7224**

YOU'D BETTER NOT FOOL AROUND
Tracks: / Missing you / You'd better not fool around.
7" Single: Released Mar '86, on CBS, by CBS Records. Deleted '86. Catalogue no: **A 6743**
12" Single: Released Mar '86, on CBS, by CBS Records. Catalogue no: **TX 6743**

Haywoode, Syd

BOOGIE OOGIE OOGIE
Tracks: / Boogie oogie oogie.
12" Single: Released Apr '88, on Fresher by Fresher Records. Catalogue no: **12 SID 001**
7" Single: Released Apr '88, on Fresher, by Fresher Records. Catalogue no: **SID 001**

MAGIC
Tracks: / Magic.
12" Single: Released Jan '89, on Fresher by Fresher Records. Catalogue no: **SID 12**
Special: Released 3 Jan '89, on Fresher, b Fresher Records. Catalogue no: **SID 2 P**
7" Single: Released Jan '89, on Fresher, b Fresher Records. Catalogue no: **SID 2**

Haza, Ofra

GALBI
Tracks: / I'm nin' alu / Galbi / Love song Galbi(remix).
12" Single: Released Jun '86, on Ace, b Ace Records. Catalogue no: **NST 117**
7" Single: Released Jul '88, on WEA, b WEA Records. Catalogue no: **YZ 301**
12" Single: Released Jul '88, on WEA, b WEA Records. Catalogue no: **YZ 301T**

HIGH
Tracks: / High.
7" Single: Released May '83, on CBS, b CBS Records. Catalogue no: **A 3415**

IM NIN' ALU
Tracks: / Im nin'alu.
12" Single: Released May '88, on WEA, b WEA Records. Catalogue no: **YZ 190T**
12" Single: Released Mar '88, on Glo estyle, by Ace Records. Catalogue no: **NS 122**
7" Single: Released May '88, on WEA, b WEA Records. Catalogue no: **YZ 190**

SHADAY (SINGLE)
Tracks: / Shaday.
12" Single: Released Dec '88, on WEA, WEA Records. Catalogue no: **WZ 326T**
CD 5": Released Dec '88, on WEA, by WE Records. Catalogue no: **WZ 326CD**
7" Single: Released Dec '88, on WEA, WEA Records. Catalogue no: **WZ 326**

DREAMER DEVANE
Tracks: / Dreamer devane.
7" Single: Released May '83, on EMI, EMI Records. Catalogue no: **EMI 5374**
12" Single: Released May '83, on EMI, EMI Records. Catalogue no: **12 EMI 537**

Haze

EMBER, THE

Haze - Tunnel Vision (Released on Gabadon)

Tracks: / Ember / Ceiling's coming down / Freedom road / Mountain.
Note: Paul Chisnell - Percussion, vocals / Chris McMahon - Basses, keyboards, vocals / Paul McMahon - Lead vocals, guitars, bass on ceilling. All songs by Haze. Produced by PaulMcMahon. Engineered by Haze. C&P 1985.
Cassingle: Released Oct '85, on Gabadon, by Gabadon Musical Services. Catalogue no: **GABC 3**
12" Single: Released Oct '85, on Gabadon, by Gabadon Musical Services. Catalogue no: **GABS 3**

TUNNEL VISION (see panel on previous page)
Tracks: / Tunnel vision / Shadows.
7" Single: Released Oct '86, on Gabadon, by Gabadon Musical Services. Catalogue no: **GABS 5**

H.D.Q.

BELIEVE
Tracks: / Believe.
7" Single: Released May '89, on Loony Tunes, by Loony Tunes Records. Catalogue no: **TUNE 13**

He Said

COULD YOU?
Tracks: / Could you?.
7" Single: Released Feb '89, on Mute, by Mute Records. Catalogue no: **MUTE 73**
12" Single: Released Feb '89, on Mute, by Mute Records. Catalogue no: **12MUTE 73**

ONLY ONE 1
Tracks: / Only one 1.
7" Single: Released Oct '85, on Mute, by Mute Records. Catalogue no: **7 MUTE 41**
12" Single: Released Oct '85, on Mute, by Mute Records. Catalogue no: **12 MUTE 41**

PALE FEET
Tracks: / Pulling three G's / Pale feet.
7" Single: Released Aug '86, on Mute, by Mute Records. Catalogue no: **MUTE 48**
12" Single: Released Aug '86, on Mute, by Mute Records. Catalogue no: **12 MUTE 48**

PUMP
Tracks: / Pump (inst) / To and fro (Track on 12" version only) / Pump.
7" Single: Released Apr '86, on Mute, by Mute Records. Catalogue no: **7 MUTE 43**
12" Single: Released Apr '86, on Mute, by Mute Records. Catalogue no: **12 MUTE 43**

He She Him

TRY A LITTLE TENDERNESS
Tracks: / Try a little tenderness.
7" Single: Released Jul '83, on Loose End, by MCA Records. Catalogue no: **LE 105**

Head

ALL THE BOYZ
Tracks: / All the boyz / Heaven is only six miles away / You're so vain (12" Only.).
7" Single: Released 30 May '89, on Virgin, by Virgin Records. Catalogue no: **VS 1190**
12" Single: Released 30 May '89, on Virgin, by Virgin Records. Catalogue no: **VST 1190**
CD 3": Released 30 May '89, on Virgin, by Virgin Records. Catalogue no: **VSCD 1190**

CAR'S OUTSIDE
Tracks: / Car's outside (7" only) / This face (is a lonely place) / Jesus ain't got a daddy (12' only) / Car's outside (joy-ride mix) (12" only).
7" Single: Released Jun '88, on Virgin, by Virgin Records. Catalogue no: **VS 1097**
12" Single: Released Jun '88, on Virgin, by Virgin Records. Catalogue no: **VST 1097**

I AM THE KING
Tracks: / I am the king / Killing time.
7" Single: Released May '87, on Demon, by Demon Records. Catalogue no: **D 1053**
12" Single: Released May '87, on Demon, by Demon Records. Catalogue no: **D 1053T**

I CAN'T STOP
Tracks: / I can't stop / Me & Mrs Jones / Ditchin' ma babee (Extra track on 12").
7" Single: Released Jul '87, on Demon, by Demon Records. Catalogue no: **D 1054**
12" Single: Released Jul '87, on Demon, by Demon Records. Catalogue no: **D 1054 T**

SINBIN
Tracks: / Sinbin (7" version also on CD) / Heads go up, The / 32A (12" extended mix) (CD & 12" only) / Sinbin (the stadium mix) (12" only).
CD 5": Released Aug '88, on Virgin, by Virgin Records. Catalogue no: **VSCD 1073**
7" Single: Released Apr '88, on Virgin, by Virgin Records. Catalogue no: **VS 1073**
12" Single: Released Apr '88, on Virgin, by Virgin Records. Catalogue no: **VST 1073**

Head Cleaners

DISINFECTION (EP)
Tracks: / Disinfection.
7" Single: Released Feb '82, on Xcentric Noise, by Xcentric Noise Records & Tapes. Catalogue no: **HCP 1**

INFECTION GROWS (EP)
Tracks: / Infection grows.
7" Single: Released Oct '83, on Xcentric Noise, by Xcentric Noise Records & Tapes. Catalogue no: **THIRD 1**

Head, Jowe

SUDDEN SHOWER
Tracks: / Sudden shower.
7" Single: Released Oct '88, on Hollow Planet, Catalogue no: **HOP 004**

Head, Murray

Biographical details: This British singer, actor, guitarist and songwriter came to fame in 1970 by playing Judas Iscariot in Tim Rice & Andrew Lloyd Webber's phenomenal rock opera 'Jesus Christ Superstar'. He sang the title song *Superstar* (backed by the Triniday Singers), which was a flop single when initially released in 1969, but the moral was 'try try and try again' - the track reached No.74 on the US Hot 100 in 1970, climbed to No.14 on the same chart in 1971 and crept to No.47 in Britain in 1972. In addition Murray played Bob in 'Sunday bloody Sunday'. The high drama of *Superstar* established Head as a fine singer, but he found commercial success hard to come by when he released his debut solo album *Nigel lived* in 1973. The title track of the follow-up LP, 1975's *Say it ain't so*, was an intense ballas which attracted critical but not commercial acclaim. Head did, however, manage to mount a considerable penetration of the normally insular French market. France continued to appreciate his folk-influenced pop material, but there was so little UK interest in such tracks as the 1981 single *How many ways* that it had to be released in Britain by the tiny Horsham-based Music Lovers label. When Head surged back to international fame in the mid-Eighties, he again had Tim Rice to thank for his success. *One night in Bangkok* was the public's first taster of the 'Chess' project, a new musical conceived by lyricist Rice in conjunction with Benny & Bjorn of Abba; the curiously appealing single, which featured Murray speaking a set of ultra-camp verses and being interupted by an Abba type chorus, peaked at No.12 in Britain at the end of 1984. However, this was a mere foretaste of what was in store for *One night in Bangkok* in 1985 - it reached No.1 all over Europe, becoming one of the continent's biggest sellers of the year, and cruised to No.3 in the States. (14th October 1985).

HOW MANY WAYS? (SINGLE)
Tracks: / How many ways? / Hey lady.
7" Single: Released Feb '81, on Music Lovers, Deleted Feb '84. Catalogue no: **MLS 1**

IN THE HEART OF YOU
Tracks: / In the heart of you / Fear and ambition / Wanderer (on 12" only).
7" Single: Released Jan '87, on Virgin, by Virgin Records. Deleted May '88. Catalogue no: **VS 932**
12" Single: Released Jan '87, on Virgin, by Virgin Records. Deleted May '88. Catalogue no: **VS 932-12**

OLD SOHO
Tracks: / Old Soho.
7" Single: Released Sep '81, on Music Lovers, Catalogue no: **MLS 3**

ONE NIGHT IN BANGKOK
Tracks: / One night in Bangkok.
7" Single: Released Oct '84, on RCA, by BMG Records (UK). Catalogue no: **CHESS 1**
12" Single: Released Oct '84, on RCA, by BMG Records (UK). Deleted May '89. Catalogue no: **CHESST 1**

PITY THE CHILD
Tracks: / Pity the child / Deal / One night in Bangkok (Extra track on 12" version only).
7" Single: Released Jun '86, on RCA, by BMG Records (UK). Catalogue no: **CHESS 6**
12" Single: Released Jun '86, on RCA, by BMG Records (UK). Catalogue no: **CHESST 6**

SOME PEOPLE
Tracks: / Maybe tomorrow / Some people.
7" Single: Released Mar '86, on Virgin, by Virgin Records. Deleted '89. Catalogue no: **VS 857**

SUPERSTAR
Tracks: / Superstar.
7" Single: Released Jan '72, on MCA, by MCA Records. Deleted '75. Catalogue no: **MMKS 5077**

Head Of David

SAVEANNA MIXES
Tracks: / Saveanna mixes.
12" Single: Released Feb '89, on Blast First, by Blast First Records. Catalogue no: **BFFP 027**
12" Single: Released 6 Feb '89, on Blast First, by Blast First Records. Catalogue no: **BFFP 37**

Head, Roy

TREAT HER RIGHT
Tracks: / Treat her right.
7" Single: Released Nov '65, on Vocalion, by Vocalion Records. Deleted '68. Catalogue no: **V-P 9248**

Head to Head

SHANTY SHANTY
Tracks: / Shanty shanty.
7" Single: Released Oct '85, on Hollywood, by Hollywood Records. Catalogue no: **HWD 017**

Headbangers

STATUS ROCK
Tracks: / Status rock.
7" Single: Released Oct '81, on Magnet, by WEA Records. Deleted '84. Catalogue no: **MAG 206**

Headboys

KICKING THE KANS
Tracks: / Kicking the kans / Double vision / My favourite DJ.
7" EP: Released Mar '80, on RSO, by Polydor Ltd. Deleted Mar '83. Catalogue no: **RSO 56**

MY FAVOURITE DJ
Tracks: / My favourite DJ / Kicking.
7" Single: Released Feb '80, on RSO, by Polydor Ltd. Deleted '83. Catalogue no: **RSO 56**

SHAPE OF THINGS TO COME, THE
Tracks: / Shape of things to come.
7" Single: Released Sep '79, on RSO, by Polydor Ltd. Deleted '82. Catalogue no: **RSO 40**

Headhunters

IMPOSSIBLE
Tracks: / Impossible / Strait-jacket.
7" Single: Released Dec '83, on Shout, by Shout Records. Catalogue no: **XS 005**

WAY OF THE SOUTH
Tracks: / Way of the south.
12" Single: Released Jun '86, on Quiet, by Quiet Records. Catalogue no: **QST 009**

WIPE OUT THE FUNK
Tracks: / Wipe out the funk.
12" Single: Released Oct '82, on Shout, by Shout Records. Catalogue no: **XW 1201**

Headless Horsemen

GOTTA BE COOL
Tracks: / Gotta be cool.
12" Single: Released Feb '89, on NYC, Catalogue no: **R 458820**

Headline

DON'T KNOCK THE BALDHEAD
Tracks: / Don't knock the baldhead / Highway hassie.
7" Single: Released 20 Jun '80, on Virgin, by Virgin Records. Deleted '83. Catalogue no: **VS 356**

Headon, Topper

DRUMMIN' MAN
Tracks: / Drummin' man.
7" Single: Released Jun '85, on Mercury, by Phonogram Ltd. Catalogue no: **MER 194**
12" Single: Released Jun '85, on Mercury, by Phonogram Ltd. Catalogue no: **MERX 194**

I'LL GIVE YOU EVERYTHING
Tracks: / You're so cheeky / I'll give you everything.
7" Single: Released Feb '86, on Mercury, by Phonogram Ltd. Catalogue no: **MER 213**
12" Single: Released Feb '86, on Mercury, by Phonogram Ltd. Catalogue no: **MERX 213**

Headquarters

IN MY ENGLAND
Tracks: / In my England / Beauty and the blind / All fall down.
Note: 33 rpm
7" Single: Released Mar '87, on Cottage Pie, Catalogue no: **CTP 001**

NEW YORK RUNAROUND
Tracks: / New York runaround.
7" Single: Released Apr '80, on Skeleton, by Skeleton Records. Catalogue no: **SKL 004**

Headroom, Max

CHRISTMAS SANTA CLAUS (YOU'RE A LOVELY GUY)
Tracks: / Christmas Santa Claus (you're a lovely guy) / Gimme shades.
7" Single: Released Dec '86, on Chrysalis, by Chrysalis Records. Catalogue no: **CLAUS 1**

DON'T PANIC
Tracks: / Don't panic / Rhythm and blue beat.
7" Single: Released Apr '80, on Parlophone, by EMI Records. Deleted Apr '83. Catalogue no: **R 6034**

Heads

AZTEC LIGHTNING
Tracks: / Mayan interlude / Aztec lightning.
7" Single: Released Jun '86, on BBC, by BBC Records & Tapes. Deleted Sep '87. Catalogue no: **RESL 184**

Heads of Agreement

LOOSE TALK
Tracks: / Loose talk / Thunderbirds.
7" Single: Released Oct '82, on Admin B., by Admin B. Records. Catalogue no: **AD 1**

Headstones

LOVE STORY
Tracks: / Love story.
7" Single: Released Mar '88, on Waterfront, by Waterfront Music. Catalogue no: **DAMP 056**

Healey, Jeff

ANGEL EYES
Tracks: / Angel eyes / Don't let your chance go by / See the light (Live at the marquee) / That's what they say.
CD 5": Released Apr '89, on Arista, by BMG Records (UK). Catalogue no: **662210**
10" single: Released Apr '89, on Arista, by BMG Records (UK). Catalogue no: **612290**
7" Single: Released Apr '89, on Arista, by BMG Records (UK). Catalogue no: **112210**
12" Single: Released Apr '89, on Arista, by BMG Records (UK). Catalogue no: **612210**

CONFIDENCE MAN
Tracks: / Confidence man / That's what they say.
CD 5": Released Jan '89, on Arista, by BMG Records (UK). Catalogue no: **661 872**
7" Single: Released Nov '88, on Arista, by BMG Records (UK). Catalogue no: **111872**
12" Single: Released Nov '88, on Arista, by BMG Records (UK). Catalogue no: **611 872**

Healy, Tim

IF YOU COULD READ MY MIND
Tracks: / Take your last chance on me / If you could read my mind.
7" Single: Released Mar '86, on Columbia, by EMI Records. Catalogue no: **DB 9127**

STICK YA JOB
Tracks: / Stick ya job.
7" Single: Released Mar '85, on Spartan, Catalogue no: **SP 20**

Hear No Evil

MANEATER
Tracks: / Maneater / Maneater (inst).
7" Single: Released Jan '88, on Unique, by Unique Records. Catalogue no: **NIQ 01**
12" Single: Released Jan '88, on Unique, by Unique Records. Catalogue no: **12NIQ 01**

TAKING OVER
Tracks: / Taking over / Taking over (version).
7" Single: Released Sep '88, on Unique, by Unique Records. Catalogue no: **NIQ 05**
12" Single: Released Sep '88, on Unique, by Unique Records. Catalogue no: **12NIQ 05**

Heard, Jack

SEX MACHINE
Tracks: / Sex machine.
7" Single: Released Jul '86, on DB, by DB Records. Catalogue no: **DB 59**

Hear'N'Aid

STARS
Tracks: / Stars.
7" Single: Released Apr '86, on Vertigo, by Phonogram Ltd. Catalogue no: **HEAR 1**
7" Single: Released Apr '86, on Vertigo, by Phonogram Ltd. Catalogue no: **HEAR 1**
12" Single: Released Apr '86, on Vertigo, by Phonogram Ltd. Catalogue no: **HEAR 112**

Hearne, Tony

BROTHER & SISTER
Tracks: / Brother & sister.
7" Single: Released Oct '88, on White Label (1), Catalogue no: **FBT 6**

GOTTA GET YOU HOME TONIGHT
Tracks: / Gotta get you home tonight.
12" Single: Released Nov '84, on Neville King, by Neville King Records. Catalogue no: **NKRD 0023**

SHAKE YOU DOWN
Tracks: / Shake you down / Shake you down (instrumental).
12" Single: Released Jan '87, on Fresh, by Jetstar Records. Catalogue no: **FBT 002**

WITHOUT YOU I'D GO CRAZY
Tracks: / Without you I'd go crazy.
12" Single: Released Sep '84, on Neville King, by Neville King Records. Catalogue no: **NKRD 0020**

Heart

Biographical details: This American band consists of Michael Derosier, Steve Fossen, Howard Leese plus sisters Ann and Nancy Wilson. Until 1979 there was a sixth member, guitarist Roger Fisher. The group was formed in Seattle but moved temporarily to British Columbia just before becoming famous, to avoid some legal hassles; hence, some people mistakenly believe that Heart are a Canadian band. Heart came into being in 1973 and, for the first few years of their existence, attracted considerable publicity for the then novel situation of being a rock band fronted and masterminded by two women, with the men fulfilling an ancillary role. The Wilson's were initially dubbed 'a female Led Zeppelin.' They debut Heart album *Dreamboat Annie* was released in early 1976 and entered the US LP chart at an inauspicious No.194 in April of that year. By November it had climbed slowly but surely to No.7, boosted by the US Top 10 single *Magic man*. Heart were acclaimed as one of the year's major rock discoveries, and were applauded for their apparent ability to blend subtle ballads with out and out hard rock. They continued in similar vein for the rest musical or commercial terms; well publicised legal disputes with their first label, Mushroom Records, were partly to blame for the group failing to live up to their early promise. Heart continued in an unspectacular but respectable fashion during the early Eighties, achieving a US Top 10 single in 1981 with their remake of the 1967 Aaron Neville hit *Tell it like it is*. Their gradual sales decline was halted in the mid-Eightis, when Ann Wilson's duet with Mike Reno (from the band Loverboy) on *Almost paradise - the love theme from footloose* hit the No.7 position, and the imaginatively titled 1985 album *Heart* returned the group to platinum sales status. The LP was fuelled by the powerful singles, *What about love* and *Never*.
Britain has never really taken to Heart. The band's debut album *Dreamboat Annie* arrived just as the punk revelolution was getting underway, and was thus dismissed as an irrelevance by many observers. That LP peaked at No.36 on the UK chart, and the follow-up *Little queen* reached No.34. They did not reache the album listings again until 1982, when *Private audition* crawled to No.77. Heart have never penetrated the British singles chart. (Bob MacDonald, 15th October 1985).

ALONE
Tracks: / Alone / Barracuda / Magic man.
Cassingle: Released 30 May '87, on Capitol, by EMI Records. Catalogue no: **TCCL 448**
7" Single: Released May '87, on Capitol, by EMI Records. Deleted Nov '88. Catalogue no: **CL 448**
12" Single: Released May '87, on Capitol, by EMI Records. Deleted Aug '89. Catalogue no: **12 CL 448**

EVEN IT UP
Tracks: / Even it up / Pilot.
7" Single: Released Mar '80, on Epic, by CBS Records. Deleted '83. Catalogue no: **EPC 8270**

NEVER
Tracks: / Never (extended remix) / These dreams / Never (remix) / These dreams (7" version) / Heart of darkness (Available on CD single only) / If looks could kill.
CD 5": Released Mar '88, on Capitol, by EMI Records. Deleted Jun '89. Catalogue no: **CDCL 482**
7" Pic: Released Feb '88, on Capitol, by EMI Records. Deleted 31 Jul '88. Catalogue no: **CLP 482**
7" Single: Released Feb '88, on Capitol, by EMI Records. Deleted 31 Jul '88. Catalogue no: **CLG 482**
7" Single: Released Feb '88, on Capitol, by EMI Records. Deleted Nov '88. Catalogue no: **CL 482**
12" Single: Released Feb '88, on Capitol, by EMI Records. Deleted Nov '88. Catalogue no: **12CLE 482**
12" Single: Released Feb '88, on Capitol, by EMI Records. Deleted Nov '88. Catalogue no: **12CL 482**

NOTHIN' AT ALL (RE-ISSUE)
Tracks: / Nothin' at all (remix) (7" & CD single only.) / Nothin' at all (ext. remix) (12" only.) / I've got the music in me / I want you so bad (ext. version) (12" only.) / I want you so bad (remix) (CD single only.).
CD 5": Released Oct '88, on Capitol, by EMI Records. Catalogue no: **CDCL 507**
12" Pic: Released Oct '88, on Capitol, by EMI Records. Catalogue no: **12CLP 507**
7" Single: Released Oct '88, on Capitol, by EMI Records. Deleted Aug '89. Catalogue no: **CL 507**
12" Single: Released Oct '88, on Capitol, by EMI Records. Deleted Aug '89. Catalogue no: **12CL 507**

NOTHIN' AT ALL (REMIX)
Tracks: / Wolf / Nothin' at all.
7" Single: Released May '86, on Capitol, by EMI Records. Deleted '88. Catalogue no: **CL 406**
12" Single: Released May '86, on Capitol, by EMI Records. Deleted '88. Catalogue no: **12CL 406**

TELL IT LIKE IT IS
Tracks: / Tell it like it is / Barracuda.
7" Single: Released Jan '81, on Epic, by CBS Records. Deleted Jan '84. Catalogue no: **EPC 9436**

THERE'S THE GIRL
Tracks: / There's the girl (12" remix) / Alone / Bad animals / There's the girl (7" remix).
CD 5": Released Nov '87, on Capitol, by EMI Records. Deleted 31 Jul '88. Catalogue no: **CDCL 473**
12" Pic: on Capitol, by EMI Records. Deleted Nov '88. Catalogue no: **12CLP 473**
Cassingle: Released Dec '87, on Capitol, by EMI Records. Deleted Aug '89. Catalogue no: **TCCL 473**
7" Single: Released Nov '87, on Capitol, by EMI Records. Deleted Nov '88. Catalogue no: **CL 473**
12" Single: Released Nov '87, on Capitol, by EMI Records. Deleted Nov '88. Catalogue no: **CLP 473**
12" Single: Released Nov '87, on Capitol, by EMI Records. Deleted Nov '88. Catalogue no: **12CL 473**

THESE DREAMS
Tracks: / These dreams / If looks could kill / Live (version) / Shellshock / What about love ? (Track on double pack only) / Heart of darkness (Track on double pack only) / There's the girl (rock-a-pella-version) / These dreams (remix) (Track on special etched disc.) / These dreams (extended remix) (Track on special etched disc.) / These dreams (instrumental remix) (Track on special etched disc.) / Never (extended remix)* (*Track on special etched disc.).
CD 5": Released Feb '88, on EMI, by EMI Records. Catalogue no: **CDCL 477**
7" Set: Released Mar '86, on Capitol, by EMI Records. Catalogue no: **CLD 394**
7" Single: Released Mar '86, on Capitol, by EMI Records. Deleted '88. Catalogue no: **CL 394**
12" Single: Released Mar '86, on Capitol, by EMI Records. Deleted '88. Catalogue no: **12CL 394**
Special: Released Mar '88, on Capitol, by EMI Records. Catalogue no: **12 CLE 482**

THIS MAN IS MINE
Tracks: / This man is mine / America.
7" Single: Released Jun '82, on Epic, by CBS Records. Deleted Jun '85. Catalogue no: **EPCA 2436**

WHAT ABOUT LOVE?
Tracks: / What about love? / Shellshock / Crazy on you* / Dreamboat Annie* / What about love (extended version) (Available on 12" only).
Note: *Tracks on CD single version. +Track on 12" version.
CD 5": Released May '88, on Capitol, by EMI Records. Deleted Aug '89. Catalogue no: **CDCL 487**
7" Pic: Released May '88, on Capitol, by EMI Records. Deleted Nov '88. Catalogue no: **CLP 487**
7" Single: Released May '88, on Capitol, by EMI Records. Deleted Nov '88. Catalogue no: **CL 487**
7" Single: Released Jul '85, on Capitol, by EMI Records. Deleted '87. Catalogue no: **CL 361**
12" Single: Released May '88, on Capitol, by EMI Records. Deleted Nov '88. Catalogue no: **12CLG 487**
12" Single: Released May '88, on Capitol, by EMI Records. Deleted Nov '88. Catalogue no: **12CL 487**

WHO WILL YOU RUN TO
Tracks: / Who will you run to / Nobody home / These dreams (Extra track on 12").
7" Pic: Released Sep '87, on Capitol, by EMI Records. Deleted 31 Jul '88. Catalogue no: **CLP 457**
7" Single: Released Sep '87, on Capitol, by EMI Records. Deleted Nov '88. Catalogue no: **CL 457**
12" Single: Released Sep '87, on Capitol, by EMI Records. Deleted Nov '88. Catalogue no: **12CL 457**

Heart In Hand

WE ARE GOING TO EAT YOU
Tracks: / We are going to eat you.
7" Single: Released Nov '88, on Cat & Mouse, by Cat & Mouse Records. Catalogue no: **ABBO 7**
12" Single: Released Nov '88, on Cat & Mouse, by Cat & Mouse Records. Catalogue no: **ABBO 7 T**

Heart & Mind

TURNING TURTLE
Tracks: / Turning turtle / Change.
7" Single: Released Sep '87, on Epic, by CBS Records. Catalogue no: **TUT 1**
12" Single: Released Sep '87, on Epic, by CBS Records. Catalogue no: **TUTT 1**

Heart of Ice

DELVING AWAY
Tracks: / Delving away / Delving away (instrumental) / Delving away (extended version) (12" only).
7" Single: Released 23 Jul '88, on Virgin, by Virgin Records. Catalogue no: **VS 1120**
12" Single: Released Jul '88, on Virgin, by Virgin Records. Catalogue no: **VST 1120**

Heart On Fire

YOU PROMISED ME A CAMERA
Tracks: / Heaven / Starting line / Because you care / You promised me a camera.
12" Single: Released Jul '86, on Midnight Music, by Midnight Music Records. Catalogue no: **DONG 25**

Heart Throbs (group)

BANG
Tracks: / Bang.
12" Single: Released 17 Oct '87, on Rough Trade, by Rough Trade Records. Catalogue no: **RTT 211**

BLOOD FROM A STONE
Tracks: / Blood from a stone / Because it's beautiful / Smothered (12" only).
12" Single: Released Feb '89, on Profumo, Catalogue no: **PROST 2**
7" Single: Released Feb '89, on Profumo, Catalogue no: **PROS 2**

HERE I HIDE
Tracks: / Here I hide / Pale face.
7" Single: Released Oct '88, on Profumo, Catalogue no: **PROS 1**
12" Single: Released Oct '88, on Profumo, Catalogue no: **PROST 1**

TOO MANY SHADOWS
Tracks: / Too many shadows.
7" Single: Released Jul '88, on Rough Trade, by Rough Trade Records. Catalogue no: **RT 221**
12" Single: Released Jul '88, on Rough Trade, by Rough Trade Records. Catalogue no: **RTT 221**

TOY
Tracks: / Toy / Make my day / I, the jury.
7" Single: Released Jun '87, on In Tape, by In Tape Records. Catalogue no: **IT 043**
12" Single: Released Jun '87, on In Tape, by In Tape Records. Catalogue no: **ITTI 043**

Heart To Heart (group)

THREE CHORD TRICK
Tracks: / Three chord trick / Wake up America.
7" Single: Released May '84, on EMI, by EMI Records. Catalogue no: **EMI 5461**
12" Single: Released May '84, on EMI, by EMI Records. Catalogue no: **12 EMI 5461**

Heartbeat

TEARS FROM HEAVEN
Tracks: / Tears from heaven / Only one, The.
7" Single: Released Oct '87, on Priority, by Priority Records. Catalogue no: **P 17**
12" Single: Released Oct '87, on Priority, by Priority Records. Deleted Dec '87. Catalogue no: **PX 17**

WINNER, THE
7" Single: Released Apr '88, on Priority, by Priority Records. Catalogue no: **P 19**
12" Single: Released Apr '88, on Priority, by Priority Records. Catalogue no: **PX 19**

Heartbeats

HERE COME THE JETS
Tracks: / Here come the jets / Lies.
7" Single: Released Oct '82, on RCA, by BMG Records (UK). Catalogue no: **RCA 285**

I'LL BE TRUE
Tracks: / I'll be true.
7" Single: Released Jul '82, on RCA, by BMG Records (UK). Catalogue no: **RCA 244**

MAGIC MAN
Tracks: / Magic man.
7" Single: Released Apr '83, on RCA, by BMG Records (UK). Catalogue no: **RCA 322**

TALK TO ME
Tracks: / Talk to me / Don't want romance.
7" Single: Released Mar '80, on R.E.D., Deleted '83. Catalogue no: **REDS 002**

Heartbreakers

DESPERADO
Tracks: / Desperado.
7" Single: Released Apr '89, on Starr, by Polydor Ltd. Deleted Aug '89. Catalogue no: **ANGEL 001**

Hearty, Trevor

CLOSER TOGETHER
Tracks: / Closer together.
12" Single: Released Dec '84, on Pressure, Catalogue no: **ARKD 5**

Heat

LOVE DANCE
Tracks: / Love dance.
7" Single: Released Jan '85, on MCA, by MCA Records. Catalogue no: **GC 1003**

Heaters

CARMEN
Tracks: / Carmen.
7" Single: Released Jul '81, on Precinct, Catalogue no: **PR 1**

Heath, Ted

Biographical details: To those people who only think of the former Prime Minister when the name Ted Heath is mentioned, it may come as a surprise to learn that the first famous Ted Heath was one of Britain's top conductors and bandleaders of the Forties and Fifties. The original Mr Heath was already well established by the time the UK record charts were inaugurated in 1952. His first entry on those charts was *Vanessa*, which reached No.11 in January 1953. Most of his later hits - such as *Dragnet* (No.9 in 1953), *Skin deep* (No.9 in 1954) and *Swingin' shepherd blues* (No.3 in 1958) - also provided simultaneous successes for American jazz and dance band favourites like Ray Anthony, Duke Ellington and Ella Fitzgerald. Heath, who died in November 1969, made a bow to the younger generation in 1956 when his orchestra appeared in *It's a wonderful world*, Britain's first attempt at a rock'nroll movie. Heath's final appearance on the UK singles chart occurred in late 1961, when he reached No.36 with his rendition of *Sucu sucu*. He did however, achieve a Top 20 album in 1962 with *Big band percussion* (Bob MacDonald, 15th Oct 1985).

DRAGNET
Tracks: / Dragnet.
7" Single: Released Oct '53, on Decca, by Decca Records. Deleted '56. Catalogue no: **F 10176**

FAITHFUL HUSSAR, THE
Tracks: / Faithful Hussar, The.
7" Single: Released Jul '56, on Decca, by Decca Records. Deleted '59. Catalogue no: **F 10746**

HOT TODDY
Tracks: / Hot toddy.
7" Single: Released Jul '53, on Decca, by Decca Records. Deleted '56. Catalogue no: **F 10093**

SKIN DEEP
Tracks: / Skin Deep.
7" Single: Released Feb '54, on Decca, by Decca Records. Deleted '57. Catalogue no: **F 10246**

SUCU SUCU
Tracks: / Sucu sucu.
7" Single: Released Oct '61, on Decca, by Decca Records. Deleted '64. Catalogue no: **F 11392**

SWINGIN' SHEPHARD BLUES
Tracks: / Swingin' shepherd blues.
7" Single: Released Mar '58, on Decca, by Decca Records. Deleted '61. Catalogue no: **F 11000**

TEQUILA
Tracks: / Tequila.
7" Single: Released Apr '58, on Decca, by Decca Records. Deleted '61. Catalogue no: **F 11003**

TOM HARK
Tracks: / Tom Hark.
7" Single: Released Jul '58, on Decca, by Decca Records. Deleted '61. Catalogue no: **F 11025**

VANESSA

Tracks: / Vanessa.
7" Single: Released Jan '53, on Decca, by Decca Records. Deleted '56. Catalogue no: **F 9983**

Heathrow Flyers

M25 BLUES
Tracks: / M25 blues.
7" Single: Released Sep '88, on Red Baron, by Red Baron Records. Catalogue no: **RB 002**

SNOOPY V THE RED BARON
7" Single: Released Nov '88, on Red Baron, by Red Baron Records. Catalogue no: **RB 003**

Heatwave

Biographical details: At the time of their greatest success, this multi-national disco/soul group consisted of Ernest Berger (born in Czechoslovakia, discovered in Switzerland), Eric Johns, Jessie Whitten and brothers Johnnie and Keith Wilder (all from the USA), Mario Mantese (Spanish) and Rod Temperton (British). The band were based in London.
The Heatwave story was a tale of a successful group who struggled bravely on despite a series of misfortunes. The group were formed in 1975, just as the disco era was getting underway. They established a name for themselves on the UK club scene, and stormed to national fame in early '77 with their explosive and absolutely irresistible single *Boogie nights* - this reached No.2 on the UK charts. It was written by Temperton and produced by former teenybop singer Barry Blue, and this team soon came up with a second aptly titled UK Top 20 hit, ,Too hot to handle. In late '77, *Boogie nights* became a two-million-selling No.2 smash in the States - it was only prevented from reaching No.1 by Debby Boone's 10-week chart topper *You light up my life*. While on a home visit to Chicago, guitarist Whitten was stabbed to death. The group's transatlantic success continued, howver. *The groove line* and the ultra-smoochy, lights down ballad *Always and forever*. Both of these were million sellers in the states, and they chalked up another big British hit with the Johnnie Wilder-penned *Mind blowing decisions*. In early 1979 Johnnie was seriously injured in a car crash, paralysed from the neck downwards; displaying exemplary courage, he remained in the group with the aid of a specially built wheelchair whose controls he operated via facial gestures. However, when bassist Mantese suffered paralysis in a road accident, he was forced to quit.
These catastrophes caused Heatwave to take an 18 month break from the public eye. When they returned in early 1981, they achieved a UK Top 20 single with *Gangsters of the groove*. But by this time, their main writer Rod Temperton was establishing a reputation as one of the hottest composers in the business - his slick writing style provided hits for the likes of Michael Jackson, George Benson, Quincy Jones and the Manhattan Transfer. Without his presence, Heatwave died a natural death. After the release of their final LP, 1982's *Current*, Derek Bramble (one of the later members) follwed Temperton into the world of songwriting for other artists and eventually production. (Bob MacDonald, 15th Oct 1985).

ALWAYS AND FOREVER
Tracks: / Always and Forever.
7" Single: Released Nov '78, on GTO, Deleted '81. Catalogue no: **GT 236**

BOOGIE NIGHTS
Tracks: / Boogie Nights.
7" Single: Released Jan '77, on GTO, Deleted '80. Catalogue no: **GT 77**
7" Single: Released Nov '82, on Epic, by CBS Records. Catalogue no: **EPC A 2965**

BOOGIE NIGHTS (OLD GOLD)
Tracks: / Boogie nights / Always and forever.
7" Single: Released Jun '84, on Old Gold, by Old Gold Records. Catalogue no: **OG 9395**

GANGSTERS OF THE GROOVE
Tracks: / Gangsters of the groove / Someone like you.
7" Single: Released Jan '81, on GTO, Deleted '84. Catalogue no: **GT 285**
12" Single: Released Jan '81, on GTO, Deleted '84. Catalogue no: **GT 13 285**

GANGSTERS OF THE GROOVE (OLD GOLD)
Tracks: / Groove line / Mind blowing decisions / Too hot to handle.
12" Single: Released Feb '86, on Old Gold, by Old Gold Records. Catalogue no: **OG 4003**

GROOVE LINE, THE
Tracks: / Groove Line, The.
7" Single: Released Jan '78, on GTO, Deleted '81. Catalogue no: **GT 115**

JITTERBUGGIN'
Tracks: / Jitterbuggin' / Wack that axe (on 12" only) / Goin' crazy.
7" Single: Released Mar '81, on GTO, Deleted '84. Catalogue no: **GT 290**
12" Single: Released Mar '81, on GTO, Deleted '84. Catalogue no: **GT 13290**

LETTIN' IT LOOSE
Tracks: / Lettin' it loose / Mind what you find.
7" Single: Released Jun '82, on Epic, by CBS Records. Deleted Jun '85. Catalogue no: **EPCA 2414**
12" Single: Released Jun '82, on Epic, by CBS Records. Deleted Jun '85. Catalogue no: **EPCA 132414**

MIND BLOWING DECISIONS
Tracks: / Mind blowing decisions.
7" Single: Released Jun '78, on GTO, Deleted '81. Catalogue no: **GT 226**

POSING TILL CLOSING
Tracks: / Posing till closing / Where did I go wrong.
7" Single: Released Jun '81, on GTO, Deleted Jun '84. Catalogue no: **GT 294**

RAZZLE DAZZLE
Tracks: / Razzle dazzle.
7" Single: Released May '79, on GTO, Deleted '82. Catalogue no: **GT 285**

STRAIGHT FROM THE HEART
Tracks: / Straight from the heart / Introducing my love.
7" Single: Released 31 Oct '87, on Soul City, by Soul City Records. Catalogue no: **SITY 2**
12" Single: Released 31 Oct '87, on Soul City, by Soul City Records. Catalogue no: **SITYT 2**

TOO HOT TO HANDLE (SINGLE)
Tracks: / Too hot to handle / Slip your disc to this.
7" Single: Released May '77, on GTO, Deleted '80. Catalogue no: **GT 91**

WHO DAT?
Tracks: / Who dat? / Turn the clock back.
7" Single: Released Jul '88, on Soul City, by Soul City Records. Catalogue no: **SITY 7**
12" Single: Released Jul '88, on Soul City, by Soul City Records. Catalogue no: **SITYT 7**

Heat-X-Change

THUNDER & LIGHTNING
Tracks: / Thunder and lightning.
12" Single: Released '88, on Passion, by Skratch Records. Catalogue no: **PASH 34(12)**

Heaven

IN THE BEGINNING
Tracks: / In the beginning / Storm.
7" Single: Released Aug '82, on RCA, by BMG Records (UK). Catalogue no: **RCA 258**

ROCK SCHOOL
Tracks: / Rock school / Madness.
7" Single: Released Apr '84, on CBS, by CBS Records. Catalogue no: **A 4273**
12" Single: Released Apr '84, on CBS, by CBS Records. Catalogue no: **TA 4273**

Heaven 17

Biographical details: This British band consists of Glenn Gregory, Ian Craig Marsh and Martyn Ware. Marsh and Ware were the founder members of both the Human League and Heaven 17. The former came into being in 1977, when the two synthesiser players decided to apply their knowledge as computer operators to the challenging new world of electronic pop music. Despite having no musical training, the League had won a strong cult following and a toehold on the UK national charts by 1980. In October of that year, Marsh and Ware shocked obsevers by quitting the group just as they seemed on the verge of a major breakthrough. The Human League did indeed storm to superstardom in 1981 with a bunch of new recruits, while Ian and Martyn formed Heaven 17 (plus the group's alter-ego the British Electric Foundation). In the same way as the two guys had discovered Phil Oakey as the frontman and vocalist for the League, they found a former photographer and stagehand called Glenn Gregory to be the affable, strong voiced singer for Heaven 17. Unlike the revamped Human League, Heaven 17 (named after a group in the novel and movie 'A clockwork orange') aimed principally for critcal acclaim and 'credibility' rather than major commercial success. During 1981-2 they chalked up a series of minor UK hit singles with *(We don't need this) Fascist groove thang*, *Play to win*, *Penthouse and pavement* and *Let me go*. Their debut LP *Penthouse and pavement* was a very steady seller, logging nearly a year on the British Top 100 Albums list. Achieving a perfect fusion of new technorock and conventional pop, the trio enjoyed major success in 1983 with the singles *Temptation* (which featured a soaring guest vocal performance by Carol Kenyon and reached the UK No.2 position), *Come live with me* (N0.5) and *Crushed by the wheels of industry* (No.17). The hits continued in 1984, though on a slightly more modest scale. The first project by the BEF alter-ego was released in April 1982 - *Music of quality and distinction* was an album of remakes of pop classics by a series of guest singers, under the production of Marsh and Ware. Several big names from the past contributed vocal performances, including Tina Turner. This liaison proved particularly important for Tina, for it was the BEF team who, at the end of 1983, launched her dramatic international comeback by producing her remake of *Let's stay together*. (Bob MacDonald, 15th Oct 1985).

HEAVEN 17 - PLAY TO WIN (Released on Virgin)

AND THAT'S NO LIE
Tracks: / And that's no lie.
7" Single: Released Jan '85, on Virgin, by Virgin Records. Deleted '85. Catalogue no: **VS 740**
12" Single: Released Jan '85, on Virgin, by Virgin Records. Deleted May '88. Catalogue no: **VS 740-12**

BALLAD OF GO GO BROWN, THE
Tracks: / Ballad of Go Go Brown, The (7" mix on all versions) / I set you free (On all versions) / Ballad of Go Go Brown, The (extended version) (On CD & 12" only) / Ballad of Go Go Brown (version) (On 12" only) / Slow all over (On CD only).
CD 5": Released '88, on Virgin, by Virgin Records. Catalogue no: **VSCD 1113**
7" Single: Released Aug '88, on Virgin, by Virgin Records. Catalogue no: **VS 1113**
12" Single: Released Aug '88, on Virgin, by Virgin Records. Catalogue no: **VST 1113**

COME LIVE WITH ME
Tracks: / Come live with me / Let's all make a bomb (new version) / Song with no name (new version) (12" only).
7" Single: Released Jun '83, on B.E.F., by Virgin Records. Catalogue no: **VS 607**
12" Single: Released Jun '83, on B.E.F., by Virgin Records. Catalogue no: **VS 607-12**

CONTENDERS
Tracks: / 'Diary of a contender' (excerpts from) / Contenders (7" only) / Contenders (dance version) (12" only) / Contenders (full length version) (12" only).
7" Single: Released Oct '86, on Virgin, by Virgin Records. Deleted May '88. Catalogue no: **VS 881**
12" Single: Released Oct '86, on Virgin, by Virgin Records. Catalogue no: **VS 881-12**

CRUSHED BY THE WHEEL OF INDUSTRY
Tracks: / Crushed by the wheels of industry (7" only) / Crushed by the wheels of industry (part 1 & 2-uninterupted) (12" only) / Crushed by the wheels of industry (album version) (12" only) / Crushed by the wheels of industry (extended dance version) (12" only).
7" Single: Released Aug '83, on Virgin, by Virgin Records. Deleted '86. Catalogue no: **VS 628**
12" Single: Released Aug '83, on Virgin, by Virgin Records. Catalogue no: **VS 628-12**

FOOLISH THING TO DO
Tracks: / My sensitivity / Foolish thing to do.
7" Single: Released Apr '86, on Virgin, by Virgin Records. Deleted '89. Catalogue no: **VS 859**
12" Single: Released Apr '86, on Virgin, by Virgin Records. Deleted May '88. Catalogue no: **VS 859-12**

HEIGHT OF THE FIGHTING
Tracks: / Height of the fighting (he-la-hu) / He-la-hu / Honeymoon in New York.
12" Single: Released Feb '82, on Virgin, by Virgin Records. Catalogue no: **VS 483-12**

I'M YOUR MONEY
Tracks: / I'm your money / Are everything.
12" Single: Released May '81, on Virgin, by Virgin Records. Deleted May '84. Catalogue no: **VS 417**
12" Single: Released '81, on Virgin, by Virgin Records. Catalogue no: **VS 417-12**

LET ME GO
Tracks: / Let me go / Let me go (instrumental).
7" Single: Released Oct '82, on Virgin, by Virgin Records. Catalogue no: **VS 532**
12" Single: Released Oct '82, on Virgin, by Virgin Records. Catalogue no: **VS 532-12**

LET ME GO (OLD GOLD)
Tracks: / Let me go / Play to win.
12" Single: Released 27 Feb '89, on Old Gold, by Old Gold Records. Catalogue no: **OG 4105**

PENTHOUSE & PAVEMENT (SINGLE)
Tracks: / Penthouse and pavement / Penthouse and pavement (instrumental).
7" Single: Released Oct '81, on Virgin, by Virgin Records. Deleted '86. Catalogue no: **VS 455**
12" Single: Released Oct '81, on Virgin, by Virgin Records. Catalogue no: **VS 455-12**

PLAY TO WIN (see panel above)
Tracks: / Play to win / Play.
7" Single: Released Jul '81, on Virgin, by Virgin Records. Deleted '89. Catalogue no: **VS 433**
12" Single: Released Jul '81, on Virgin, by Virgin Records. Catalogue no: **VS 433-12**

SUNSET NOW
Tracks: / Sunset now / Sunset now (extended version) / Flame down / Counterforce / Sunset now (album version) / Counterforce 2.
7" Single: Released Aug '84, on Virgin, by Virgin Records. Deleted '85. Catalogue no: **VS 708**
12" Single: Released Aug '84, on Virgin, by Virgin Records. Catalogue no: **VS 708-12**

TEMPTATION (OLD GOLD)

Tracks: / Temptation / Come live with me.
7" Single: Released Nov '88, on Old Gold, by Old Gold Records. Catalogue no: **OG 9820**

TEMPTATION (SINGLE)
Tracks: / Temptation / Who'll stop the rain / We live so fast.
CD 3": Released Jun '88, on Virgin, by Virgin Records. Catalogue no: **CDT 19**
7" Single: Released '83, on Virgin, by Virgin Records. Catalogue no: **VS 570**
12" Single: Released '83, on Virgin, by Virgin Records. Catalogue no: **VS 570-12**

THIS IS MINE
Tracks: / This is mine (7" only) / This is mine (filmix) (12' only) / This is mine (cinemix) (12" only).
7" Single: Released Oct '84, on Virgin, by Virgin Records. Deleted '86. Catalogue no: **VS 722**
12" Single: Released Oct '84, on Virgin, by Virgin Records. Catalogue no: **VS 722-12**

TRAIN OF LOVE IN MOTION
Tracks: / Train of love in motion / Work / Train of love in motion (extended version) (On CD & 12" only) / Giving up (on CD & 12" only).
7" Single: Released Oct '88, on Virgin, by Virgin Records. Catalogue no: **VS 1134**
12" Single: Released Oct '88, on Virgin, by Virgin Records. Catalogue no: **VST 1134**
CD 3": Released '88, on Virgin, by Virgin Records. Catalogue no: **VSCD 1134**

TROUBLE
Tracks: / Trouble / (Big) trouble / Move out (album mix) / Trouble (UK club mix) / Contenders (US club mix).
7" Set: Released Jan '87, on Virgin, by Virgin Records. Catalogue no: **VSD 920-12**
7" Single: Released Jan '87, on Virgin, by Virgin Records. Deleted May '88. Catalogue no: **VS 920**
12" Single: Released Jan '87, on Virgin, by Virgin Records. Deleted May '88. Catalogue no: **VS 920-12**

(WE DON'T NEED THIS) FASCIST GROOVE THANG
Tracks: / (We don't need this) fascist groove thang / I'm your money (On CD only) / Height of the fighting (he-la-hu) (On CD only) / Decline of the west (NOT on CD).
7" Single: Released Mar '81, on Virgin, by Virgin Records. Catalogue no: **VS 400**
12" Single: Released '81, on Virgin, by Virgin Records. Catalogue no: **VS 400-12**
CD 3": Released '88, on Virgin, by Virgin Records. Catalogue no: **CDT 21**

Heaven, Ken

YOU MAKE ME FEEL (MIGHTY REAL)
Tracks: / You make me feel (mighty real) (version) / You make me feel (mighty real).
12" Single: Released Jun '89, on Savage, by Savage Records. Catalogue no: **12SAV 001**

Heaven On Earth

ON AN ANGEL'S WING
Tracks: / On an angel's wing / Time for a change.
7" Single: Released Sep '88, on Atlantic, by WEA Records. Catalogue no: **A 9025**
12" Single: Released Sep '88, on Atlantic, by WEA Records. Catalogue no: **A 9025 T**

Heavenly Bodies

RAINS ON ME
Tracks: / Rains on me.
12" Single: Released Nov '88, on Third Mind, by Third Mind Records. Catalogue no: **TMS 10**

Heaven's Gate

SLOW WATER
Tracks: / Slow water / Sweet breeze.
7" Single: Released Jul '81, on United Artists, by EMI Records. Deleted Jul '84. Catalogue no: **UP 641**

Heavy D. & The Boyz

MR.BIG STUFF
Tracks: / Mr. Big Stuff / Mr. Big Stuff (instrumental) / Mr. Big Stuff (7" mix).
7" Single: Released Nov '86, on MCA, by MCA Records. Catalogue no: **MCA 1106**
12" Single: Released Nov '86, on MCA, by MCA Records. Catalogue no: **MCAT 1106**

OVERWEIGHT LOVERS IN THE HOUSE, THE
Tracks: / Overweight lovers in the house, The / Money earnin Mount Vernon / Nike / Derek B meets heavy D and the Uptown Crew.
7" Single: Released Oct '87, on MCA, by MCA Records. Catalogue no: **MCA 1206**
12" Single: Released Jul '87, on MCA, by MCA Records. Catalogue no: **MCAX 1206**
12" Single: Released Oct '87, on MCA, by MCA Records. Catalogue no: **MCAT 1206**

OVERWEIGHTER, THE
Tracks: / Overweighter, The / Mr. Big Stuff / Final slamdown, The (on 12" only.).
7" Single: Released Jan '88, on MCA, by MCA Records. Catalogue no: **MCA 1229**
12" Single: Released Jan '88, on MCA, by MCA Records. Catalogue no: **MCAT 1229**

SOMEBODY FOR ME
Tracks: / Somebody for me.
12" Single: Released Oct '89, on MCA, by MCA Records. Catalogue no: **MCA 23982**

WE'VE GOT OUR OWN THANG
Tracks: / We've got our own thang.
CD 5": Released Jul '89, on MCA, by MCA Records. Catalogue no: **DMCAT 1344**
7" Single: Released Jun '89, on MCA, by MCA Records. Catalogue no: **MCA 23942**
7" Single: Released Jul '89, on MCA, by MCA Records. Catalogue no: **MCA 1344**
12" Single: Released Jul '89, on MCA, by MCA Records. Catalogue no: **MCAT 1344**

Heavy Discipline

LIBERATION OF ECONOMICS
Tracks: / Liberation of economics.
7" Single: Released 20 Feb '88, on Real World, Catalogue no: **RWR 001**

Heavy Duty Breaks

HEAVY DUTY BREAKS (SINGLE)
Tracks: / Heavy duty breaks.
12" Single: Released Feb '85, on Illuminated, Catalogue no: **ILL 5512**

Heavy Pettin'

Biographical details: Two good things were going for Glasgow's Heavy Pettin' when they launched themselves on the heavy metal scene with their debut album in October 1983 - firstly, they were one of the more proficient and genuinely powerful headbanging bands; secondly, the LP was produced by Brian May and Mack of Queen fame. The album entitled *Lettin' loose* and it yielded Heavy Pettin's first chart single - *Love times love* reached No.69 in their native Britain in March 1984. The song had originally appeared on the B side of the group's independently released 1982 single *Roll the disc*. (Bob MacDonald, 16th Oct 1985).

LOVE TIMES LOVE
Tracks: / Love times love / Shout it out.
7" Pic: Released Mar '84, on Polydor, by Polydor Ltd. Catalogue no: **HEPP 3**
7" Single: Released Mar '84, on Polydor, by Polydor Ltd. Deleted '84. Catalogue no: **HEP 3**
12" Single: Released Mar '84, on Polydor, by Polydor Ltd. Deleted '84. Catalogue no: **HEPX 3**

ROLL THE DICE
Tracks: / Roll the dice (on 12" only) / Love x love.
7" Single: Released Aug '82, on Neat, by Neat Records. Catalogue no: **NEAT 17**

ROMEO
Tracks: / Romeo / Don't call it love / City girl*.
Note: * = Extra track on 12" only.
7" Single: Released Apr '87, on Polydor, by Polydor Ltd. Deleted Jan '88. Catalogue no: **POSP 849**
12" Single: Released Apr '87, on Polydor, by Polydor Ltd. Deleted Jan '88. Catalogue no: **POSPX 849**

SOLE SURVIVOR
Tracks: / Sole survivor.
7" Single: Released Jun '85, on Polydor, by Polydor Ltd. Catalogue no: **HEP 4**
12" Single: Released Jun '85, on Polydor, by Polydor Ltd. Catalogue no: **HEPX 4**

Heavy Shift

SUMMERTIME
Tracks: / Summertime.
12" Single: Released Jul '89, on Blueback, Catalogue no: **12 BBBK 5**

Hebb, Bobby

LOVE LOVE LOVE
Tracks: / Love love love.
7" Single: Released Aug '72, on Philips, by Phonogram Ltd. Deleted '75. Catalogue no: **6051 023**

SUNNY
Tracks: / Sunny.
7" Single: Released Sep '66, on Philips, by Phonogram Ltd. Deleted '69. Catalogue no: **BF 1503**
7" Single: Released Jan '85, on Old Gold, by Old Gold Records. Catalogue no: **OG 9491**

Hedgehoppers Anonymous

Biographical details: In the summer of 1965 a young Cambridge University undergraduate called Jonathon King zoomed to No.4 on the British charts with his nonsensical protest song *Everyone's gone to the moon*. Instead of going into the music business on a full-time basis, he resolved to complete his degree course, and just embark on one-off projects as an independent writer and producer. The first of these was *It's good news week* by Hedgehoppers Anonymous, which reached the UK No.5 position in the autumn of '65. Once again, it displayed King's ability to parody the then fashionable anti-war protest movement.
The group consisted of Leslie Dash, Ray Honeyball, John Stewart and Mick Tinsley. They were all working as RAF ground staff at Leighton Buzzard when they originally formed a combo called the Trendsetters in 1963. They became the Hedgehoppers and established a name for themselves on the gigging circuit and lack of subtlety, the self-styled King changed their name to Hedgehoppers Anonymous when he became their manager in 1965 because 'nobody wants to know who you are or ever will want to know who you are'. Only the lead singer actually performed on *It's good news week*, and Jonathon told the other member that they were not allowed to play on their own record. After *It's good news week*, the group did indeed fade into instant obscurity and King continued with his studies. He was later to be responsible for masterminding many similar one-off pop hits. (Bob MacDonald, 16th Oct 1985).

IT'S GOOD NEWS WEEK
Tracks: / It's good news week / Afraid of love.
7" Single: Released Feb '82, on EMI, by EMI Records. Deleted Feb '87. Catalogue no: **EMI 5271**
7" Single: Released Sep '65, on Decca, by Decca Records. Deleted '68. Catalogue no: **F 12241**
7" Single: Released Apr '83, on Old Gold, by Old Gold Records. Catalogue no: **OG 9262**

Hedger, Alison

MARY ROSE SONG
Tracks: / Mary Rose song.
7" Single: Released Oct '82, on Golden Apple, by Golden Apple Records. Deleted '87. Catalogue no: **GA 100**

Hedges, Michael

ALL ALONG THE WATCHTOWER
Tracks: / All along the watchtower / Aerial boundaries.
7" Single: Released Apr '88, on Windham Hill, by Windham Hill Records (USA). Catalogue no: **WY 001**
12" Single: Released Apr '88, on Windham Hill, by Windham Hill Records (USA). Catalogue no: **WZ 001**

Hedone

SENSIBLE
Tracks: / Sensible.
7" Single: Released Jun '84, on On Gowa Power, Catalogue no: **HEAD 001**

Hee Bee Gee Bees

BORING SONGS
Tracks: / Boring songs / Dead cicada.
Note: The Hee Bee Gee Bees under pseudonyms of Status Quid & The Beagles doing more send-ups of well-known groups.
7" Single: Released Nov '81, on Heebeegeebees, Catalogue no: **HBGB 2**

MEANINGLESS SONGS
Tracks: / Meaningless songs / Posing in the moonlight.
7" Single: Released Aug '80, on Original, Deleted '83. Catalogue no: **AB 02**

PURPLE PAINTS
Tracks: / Purple paints.
7" Single: Released Sep '85, on 10 Records, by Virgin Records. Deleted '89. Catalogue no: **TEN 61**

TOO DEPRESSED TO COMMIT SUICIDE
Tracks: / Too depressed to commit suicide / Up the wall / Meaningless songs.
7" Single: Released Jan '83, on Heebeegeebees, Catalogue no: **HGBG 1**

Hee Haw

WRIGGLEP
Tracks: / Ice age / Beaverdamn man / In the shit / Speedbumps / Fog.
12" Single: Released Sep '89, on bosque, Catalogue no: **BOSC 006**

Heera

BEAT THE RHYTHM BALLE BALLE
Tracks: / Beat the rhythm balle balle / Beat the rhythm balle balle (version).
12" Single: Released '88, on Arishma, by Arishma Records. Catalogue no: **ARIS 2002**

Heffner, Nick

SNEAKY MOTHERS, THE
Tracks: / Sneaky mothers, The / Parking lot, The / World spinning sadly.
Note: Double 'A' side
7" Single: Released Apr '87, on Bam Caruso, by Demon Records. Catalogue no: **OPRA 060**

Hefti, Neal

BATMAN THEME (1966 version)
Tracks: / Batman theme.
7" Pic: Released Jul '89, on RCA, by BMG Records (UK). Catalogue no: **PB 49571 PD**

Hegarty, Big Dan

BIG COUNTRY
Tracks: / Big country / Papa-oom-mow-mow.
7" Single: Released Jan '82, on Bronze, by Bronze Records. Deleted Jan '85. Catalogue no: **BRO 139**

Hegarty Den

VOODOO VOODOO
Tracks: / Voodoo voodoo.
7" Single: Released Mar '79, on Magnet, by WEA Records. Deleted '81. Catalogue no: **MAG 143**

Hegarty, Dermot

21 YEARS
Tracks: / 21 years.
7" Single: Released '88, on Homespun (Ireland), by Outlet Records. Catalogue no: **HIS 17**

Hegley, John

I SAW MY DINNER ON TV
Tracks: / I saw my dinner on TV / Grandads glasses / Amoeba.
12" Single: Released 20 Feb '88, on Glass Fish, Catalogue no: **OOZE 2T**

Heidi

RELATIONSHIPS
Tracks: / Lizzie Anne / Relationships / Relationships.
7" Single: Released Mar '86, on Splinter, Catalogue no: **SPNT 1**

Heights, Dizzi

GET INTO IT
Tracks: / Get into it / Would I find love / Cash money (boogie mix).
7" Single: Released Nov '86, on Parlophone, by EMI Records. Deleted Apr '88. Catalogue no: **R 6162**

GET INTO IT (MONSTER MIX)
Tracks: / Get into it (monster mix) / Cash money (boogie mix) / Would I find love.
12" Single: Released Nov '86, on Parlophone, by EMI Records. Deleted 31 Jul '88. Catalogue no: **12 R 6162**

Heild, Hehemiah

YOUR BODY'S HERE WITH ME
Tracks: / Your body's here with me.
12" Single: Released Sep '83, on Joe Gibbs, Catalogue no: **JGM 8183**

Heiloo, Ronald

IN TIMES OF PANIC
Tracks: / In times of panic.
7" Single: Released Jun '82, on Amphibious, Catalogue no: **A 002**

Heinz

Biographical details: There were 5 varieties of this particular Heinz, rather than 57: they were *Just like Eddie, Country boy, You were there, Questions I can't answer* and *Diggin' my potatoes*, all of which reached the UK singles chart during 1963-65. The blond-haired vocalist/bassist Heinz Burt was obviously the main attraction on this menu, but another key ingredient was producer/menter Joe Meek who had formed Heinz's two previous groups, the Outlaws and the Tornadoes. Hailing from Southampton, Heinz had played on John Leyton records and been a member of Billy Fury's touring group, in addition to performing on the Tornadoes instrumental 1962 smash *Telstar*. Meek decided to launch Heinz as a solo singer despite the fact that Burt was hardly Britain's greatest vocal virtuose. The first record flopped, but heinz's second attempt *Just like Eddie* (a sincere but simultaneously silly tribute to the late Eddie Cochran) surged to No.5 on the UK chart in the late summer of 1963. It was followed by four smaller successes plus a few more flops. After doing some cabaret work, Heinz retired from the music business in the late Sixtgies, but made several low-key comebacks including a 1976 acting role in a television play. (Bob MacDonald, 16th Oct 1985).

COUNTRY BOY
Tracks: / Country boy.
7" Single: Released Nov '63, on Decca, by Decca Records. Deleted '66. Catalogue no: **F 11768**

DIGGIN' MY POTATOES
Tracks: / Diggin' my potatoes.
7" Single: Released Mar '65, on Columbia, by EMI Records. Deleted '68. Catalogue no: **DB 7482**

JUST LIKE EDDIE
Tracks: / Just like eddie / Don't you knock at my door.
7" Single: Released Oct '83, on Old Gold, by Old Gold Records. Catalogue no: **OG 9353**
7" Single: Released Mar '82, on Decca, by Decca Records. Deleted '88. Catalogue no: **F 11693**

JUST LIKE EDDIE (OLD GOLD)
Tracks: / Just like Eddie.
7" Single: Released Oct '83, on Old Gold, by Old Gold Records. Catalogue no: **OG 9353**

QUESTIONS I CAN'T ANSWER
Tracks: / Questions I can't answer.
7" Single: Released Oct '64, on Columbia, by EMI Records. Deleted '67. Catalogue no: **DB 7374**

YOU WERE THERE
Tracks: / You were there.
7" Single: Released Feb '64, on Decca, by Decca Records. Deleted '67. Catalogue no: **F 11831**

Heist

HEIST
Tracks: / Heist.
12" Single: Released Feb '86, on NV, Deleted '87. Catalogue no: **NV 001**

Heist, Marco Van

SONG FOR THE FALKLANDS
Tracks: / Song for the Falklands.
7" Single: Released Jun '82, on Disques Markel, Catalogue no: **AA 705**

Helden

HOLDING ON
Tracks: / Holding on.
7" Single: Released Nov '83, on Zica, Catalogue no: **ZICA 01**
12" Single: Released Nov '83, on Zica, Catalogue no: **12ZICA 01**

Helen & The Horns

FREIGHT TRAIN
Tracks: / Freight train / Pioneer town.
7" Single: Released Feb '84, on Thin Sliced, by Thin Sliced Records. Catalogue no: **TSR 3**

Helena

BE SOFT WITH ME TONIGHT
Tracks: / Be soft with me tonight / Love that's real.
7" Single: Released Feb '87, on Arista, by BMG Records (UK). Deleted May '89. Catalogue no: **RIS 5**
12" Single: Released Feb '87, on Arista, by BMG Records (UK). Deleted May '89. Catalogue no: **RIST 5**

CALL ME
Tracks: / Call me / Call me (version).
7" Single: Released Sep '89, on Total, Catalogue no: **DETAIL 4**
12" Single: Released Sep '89, on Total, Catalogue no: **12DETAIL 4**

I WANT YOU
Tracks: / Love that's real / I want you.
7" Single: Released Sep '86, on Arista, by BMG Records (UK). Catalogue no: **ARIST 675**
12" Single: Released Sep '86, on Arista, by BMG Records (UK). Catalogue no: **ARIST 12675**

Helgason, Johann

TAKE YOUR TIME
Tracks: / Take your time.
7" Single: Released Nov '84, on Steinar, by Steinar Records (UK). Catalogue no: **LAT 1511**

Helix

GIMME GOOD LOVIN'
Tracks: / Gimme good loving.
7" Pic: Released Jan '85, on Capitol, by EMI Records. Catalogue no: **12CLP 349**

WILD IN THE STREETS (SINGLE)
Tracks: / Wild in the streets.
7" Single: Released '87, on Capitol, by EMI Records. Deleted 31 Jul '88. Catalogue no: **CL 468**
12" Single: Released Oct '87, on Capitol, by EMI Records. Deleted 31 Jul '88. Catalogue no: **12CL 468**

Hell

SAVE US (FROM THOSE WHO WOULD SAVE US)
Tracks: / Save us (from those who would save us) / Deathsquad.
Single: on Deadly Weapon, Catalogue no: **DWS 666**

Hellfire Club

HEAVEN CAN WAIT
Tracks: / Heaven can wait / Confession time.
12" Single: Released Sep '88, on Wizz, by Sierra Records. Catalogue no: **WF 1 001 T**

Hello

NEW YORK GROOVE
Tracks: / New York groove.
7" Single: Released Oct '75, on Bell, Deleted '78. Catalogue no: **1438**

NEW YORK GROOVE (SINGLE)
Tracks: / New York groove.
7" Single: Released Jan '85, on Old Gold, by Old Gold Records. Catalogue no: **OG 9463**

TELL HIM
Tracks: / Tell him.
7" Single: Released Nov '74, on Bell, Deleted '77. Catalogue no: **1377**

Helloween

DOCTOR STEIN
Tracks: / Doctor Stein / Savage / Livin' ain't no crime (Only on 3"CD single.) / Victim of fate (Only on 3"CD single.).
12" Pic: Released Sep '88, on Noise (Germany), Catalogue no: **N 01168**
12" Pic: Released Aug '88, on Noise, by Dorane Records. Catalogue no: **PHELLO 1**
7" Single: Released Aug '88, on Noise, by Dorane Records. Catalogue no: **7HELLO 1**
12" Single: Released Sep '88, on Noise (Germany), Catalogue no: **N 01165G**
12" Single: Released Aug '88, on Noise, by Dorane Records. Catalogue no: **12HELLO 1**
12" Single: Released Sep '88, on Noise (Germany), Catalogue no: **N 01165**
12" Single: Released Sep '88, on Noise (Germany), Catalogue no: **N 01165W**
CD 3": Released Sep '88, on Noise (Germany), Catalogue no: **N 01163**
CD 3": Released Aug '88, on Noise, by Dorane Records. Catalogue no: **3HELLO 1**

I WANT OUT
Tracks: / I want out.
7" Single: Released Oct '88, on Noise, by Dorane Records. Catalogue no: **7 HELLO 2**
12" Single: Released Oct '88, on Noise, by Dorane Records. Catalogue no: **12HELLO 2**

JUDAS
12" Single: Released 23 Sep '89, on Noise, by Dorane Records. Catalogue no: **12NUK 022**

Hell's Belles

BARRICADES
Tracks: / Barricades.
7" Single: Released Feb '86, on Raw Power, by Castle Communications Records. Catalogue no: **RAWS 001**
12" Single: Released Feb '86, on Raw Power, by Castle Communications Records. Catalogue no: **RAWT 001**

Helmer, John

DEEP
Tracks: / Deep.
7" Single: Released Aug '89, on Kool Kat, by Kool Kat Records. Catalogue no: **KOOL 508**
12" Single: Released Aug '89, on Kool Kat, by Kool Kat Records. Catalogue no: **KOOLT 508**

Helmet Boys

HURTS LIKE LOVE
Tracks: / Hurts like love / I'm not so sure.
7" Single: Released Sep '80, on Elektra, by Elektra Records (UK). Deleted '83. Catalogue no: **K 12475**

Helms, Bobby

JACQUELINE
Tracks: / Jacqueline.
7" Single: Released Aug '58, on Brunswick, by Decca Records. Deleted '61. Catalogue no: **05748**

MY SPECIAL ANGEL
Tracks: / My special angel.
7" Single: Released Nov '57, on Brunswick, by Decca Records. Deleted '60. Catalogue no: **05721**

NO OTHER BABY
Tracks: / No other baby.
7" Single: Released Feb '58, on Brunswick, by Decca Records. Deleted '61. Catalogue no: **05730**

Helms, Jimmy

Biographical details: British session singer Helms popped up from time to time on album sleeve credits during the 70's and 80's but only had one hit in his own right. *Gonna Make You An Offer You Can't Refuse*, written and produced by John Worth, reached No 8 on the UK singles chart in 1973. It was a memorable soul/pop record on which Helms gave us a sample of his high-pitched Eddie Holman-type vocals. (Bob MacDonald, October 1985.).

GONNA MAKE YOU AN OFFER YOU CAN'T REFUSE
Tracks: / Gonna make you an offer you can't refuse.
7" Single: Released Feb '73, on Cube, Deleted '76. Catalogue no: **BUG 27**
7" Single: Released Jan '84, on Cube, Catalogue no: **BUG 98**
12" Single: Released Jan '84, on Cube, Catalogue no: **HBUG 98**

Helter Skelter

LAST TRAIN
Tracks: / Last train.
7" Single: Released Sep '89, on Rough Trade, by Rough Trade Records. Catalogue no: **RT 236**
12" Single: Released Sep '89, on Rough Trade, by Rough Trade Records. Catalogue no: **RTT 236**

Hemmings, Lloyd

YOU'RE MY LOVING BABY
Tracks: / You're my loving baby.
7" Single: Released Apr '89, on C & E, Catalogue no: **KCKM 4106**

Henderson, Eddie

PRANCE ON
Tracks: / Prance on.
7" Single: Released Oct '78, on Capitol, by EMI Records. Deleted '81. Catalogue no: **CL 16015**

Henderson, Finis

SKIP TO MY LOU
Tracks: / Skip to my Lou.
7" Single: Released Jul '83, on Motown, by BMG Records (UK). Catalogue no: **TMG 1304**
12" Single: Released Jun '83, on Gordy (USA), by Motown Records (UK). Catalogue no: **TMGT 1304**

Henderson, Greg

DREAMIN'
Tracks: / Dreamin' / Dreamin' (instrumental).
7" Single: Released Sep '84, on Greyhound, by Greyhound Records. Catalogue no: **GRP 101**
12" Single: Released Nov '82, on Greyhound, by Greyhound Records. Catalogue no: **GRPT 101**

Henderson, Joe 'Mr

OOH LA LA
Tracks: / Ooh la la.
7" Single: Released Mar '60, on Pye, Deleted '63. Catalogue no: **7N 15257**

SING IT AGAIN WITH JOE
Tracks: / Sing it again with Joe.
7" Single: Released Sep '55, on Polygon, Deleted '58. Catalogue no: **P 1184**

SING IT WITH JOE
Tracks: / Sing it with Joe.
7" Single: Released Jun '55, on Polygon, Deleted '58. Catalogue no: **P 1167**

TREBLE CHANCE
Tracks: / Treble chance.
7" Single: Released Oct '53, on Pye, Deleted '56. Catalogue no: **7N 15224**

TRUDIE
Tracks: / Trudie.
7" Single: Released Jul '58, on Pye, Deleted '61. Catalogue no: **N 15147**

Henderson, Kelvin

DOOR IS ALWAYS OPEN, THE
Tracks: / Door is always open, The.
7" Single: Released Mar '79, on Buffalo (UK), by M.I.S.Records. Catalogue no: **BUFF 1001**

FROM A JACK TO A KING
Tracks: / From a Jack to a King.
7" Single: Released Jun '81, on Country Roads Records. Deleted '87. Catalogue no: **CRE 003**

Henderson, Michael

FICKLE (SINGLE)
7" Single: Released May '83, on Buddah, by Buddah Records Inc.(USA). Catalogue no: **BDS 501**
12" Single: Released May '83, on Buddah, by Buddah Records Inc.(USA). Catalogue no: **BDSL 501**

WIDE RECEIVER(SINGLE)
Tracks: / Wide receiver / I can't help it.
7" Single: Released Sep '80, on Buddah, by Buddah Records Inc.(USA). Catalogue no: **BDS 494**
12" Single: Released Sep '80, on Buddah, by Buddah Records Inc.(USA). Catalogue no: **BDSL 494**

Henderson, Phil

SECRET PICTURES
Tracks: / Secret pictures / Deckchairs in the rain.
7" Single: Released Oct '86, on Splash, by Splash Records. Catalogue no: **CPS 1007**

Hendrix, Jimi

Biographical details: This American guitarist, vocalist and songwriter was one of the all-time greats of rock music. His tragically early death was caused by the fact that he could cope with neither the personal and business pressures of fame nor with the socio-political pressure attached to being the first black rock star of the Sixties. Born in Seattle, Washington in 1942, Hendrix taught himself to play the guitar at the age of eleven and spent his teenage years listening attentively to blues and rock'n'roll records and playing in local groups. During 1961-63 he carried out his military service as a member of the US Paratroopers. After that, the following couple of years were spent as a backing musician for a host of top black rhthm-and-blues stars. With Britian leading the world in the pop music scene of the mid-Sixties, it was perhaps appopriate that this supremely talented musician should have to travel to the UK to find superstardom. He had been playing with his own new band at the New York club when, in 1966, he was discovered by ex-Animals bassist Chas Chandler. The Brit brought Hendrix to London and became his manager, embarking upon a big publicity drive for his young charge. Chandler arranged for the guitarist to play at some of the most fashionable clubs in the capital, where Jimi's stunningly flashy performances won the acclaim of such guitar stars as Eric Clapton, George Harrison and Pete Townshend. In the first six months of 1967, Hendrix burst into the British charts with three consecutive Top 10 singles - *Hey Joe* plus two self-penned numbers, *Purple haze* and *The wind cries Mary*.
The Jimi Hendrix success story rebounded in America via his outrageous concert at the 1967 Monterey Pop Festival. From then onwards, his reputation was established around the world, not only as a thoroughly innovative musician but also as a master showman. He would play his guitar with his teeth or behind his neck, make love to it and ultimately burn it. His performances were obscene and destructive yet musically and visually exhilarating. The albums *Are you experienced?* (1967), *Axis: Bold as love* (1967) and *Electric ladyland* (1968) were commercial and artistic triumphs. Hendrix became the epitome of the permissive, progresseve, drug oriented heavy psychedelic rock era of the late Sixties. From late 1968 onwards, despite continuing international success with such classic tracks as the Bob Dylan-penned *All along the watchtower*, Hendrix's world was starting to collapse around him. The hectic work schedule, combined with drug and drink abuse, was impairing his physical and mental health; his vast earnings were being mishandled; he was landing himself in legal trouble with drug enforcement squads; his band was breaking up; and the US Black Power movement was prodding him to form an all-black band and aim at black audiences, instead of catering for the needs of the predominantly white rock market. When he yielded to the latter pressure, the result was a shambles.
In September 1970, a few weeks after appearing at the Isle of Wight Festival, Hendrix died in his London flat at the age of 27. The cause of death was officially described as 'suffocation from inhalation of vomit due to barbiturate intoxication'. Two months later, fans gave him a posthumous UK No.1 single with *Voodoo chile*. Unfortunately, during the ensuing years, a massive exploitation has done little justice to his legendary status or to his enormous influence upon rock music in general and guitar-playing in particular. (Bob MacDonald, 16th Oct 1985).

ALL ALONG THE WATCH TOWER
Tracks: / All along the watchtower / Foxy lady / Purple haze / Manic depression.
12" Single: Released Dec '81, on Polydor, by Polydor Ltd. Deleted Dec '84. Catalogue no: **POSPX 401**
7" Single: Released Jul '84, on Old Gold, by Old Gold Records. Catalogue no: **OG 9429**
7" Single: Released Oct '80, on Polydor, by Polydor Ltd. Deleted Oct '83. Catalogue no: **2141 279**
7" Single: Released Oct '68, on Track, by Polydor Ltd. Deleted '71. Catalogue no: **604 025**
7" Single: Released Jul '84, on Old Gold, by Old Gold Records. Catalogue no: **OG 9432**

BURNING OF THE MIDNIGHT LAMP
Tracks: / Burning of the midnight lamp.
7" Single: Released Aug '67, on Track, by Polydor Ltd. Deleted '70. Catalogue no: **604 007**

CROSSTOWN TRAFFIC
Tracks: / Crosstown traffic.
7" Single: Released Apr '69, on Track, by Polydor Ltd. Deleted '72. Catalogue no: **604 029**

GYPSY EYES/REMEMBER
Tracks: / Gypsy eyes.
7" Single: Released Oct '71, on Track, by Polydor Ltd. Deleted '74. Catalogue no: **2094 010**

HEY JOE
Tracks: / Hey Joe.
7" Single: Released Jan '67, on Polydor, by Polydor Ltd. Deleted '70. Catalogue no: **56 139**
7" Single: Released Sep '80, on Polydor/Dreyfus (USA), by Polydor Ltd. Catalogue no: **2608 001**

JOHNNY B.GOODE
Tracks: / Johnny B. Goode.
7" Single: Released Feb '72, Deleted '75. Catalogue no: **2001 277**

PEEL SESSIONS:JIMI HENDRIX
12" Single: Released Dec '88, on Strange Fruit, by Strange Fruit Records. Catalogue no: **SFPS 065**
CD 5": Released Dec '88, on Strange Fruit, by Strange Fruit Records. Catalogue no: **SFPSCD 065**

PURPLE HAZE
Tracks: / Purple haze / 51st anniversary / All along the watchtower* (*Extra track on 12" & CD singles only) / Hey Joe** (**Extra track on CD single only).
Note: (Purple haze reached No.3 in 1967 and is now featured in the film 'Blue Jean Cap')
CD 5": Released 16 Jan '89, on Polydor, by Polydor Ltd. Catalogue no: **PZCD 33**
7" Single: Released 16 Jan '89, on Polydor, by Polydor Ltd. Deleted Aug '89. Catalogue no: **PO 33**
12" Single: Released 16 Jan '89, on Polydor, by Polydor Ltd. Deleted Aug '89. Catalogue no: **PZ 33**
7" Single: Released Mar '67, on Track, by Polydor Ltd. Deleted '70. Catalogue no: **604 001**
7" Single: Released Jul '84, on Old Gold, by Old Gold Records. Catalogue no: **OG 9430**

VOODOO CHILE
Tracks: / Voodoo Chile.
7" Single: Released Sep '82, on Polydor, by Polydor Ltd. Catalogue no: **POSP 608**
12" Single: Released Sep '82, on Polydor, by Polydor Ltd. Catalogue no: **POSPX 608**
7" Single: Released Nov '70, on Track, by Polydor Ltd. Deleted '73. Catalogue no: **2095 001**

VOODOO CHILE (OLD GOLD)
Tracks: / Voodoo Chile.
7" Single: Released Jul '84, on Old Gold, by Old Gold Records. Catalogue no: **OG 9431**

WIND CRIES MARY, THE
Tracks: / Wind cries Mary, The.
7" Single: Released May '67, on Track, by Polydor Ltd. Deleted '70. Catalogue no: **604 004**

Hendrix, Karen

SAY IT AIN'T TRUE
Tracks: / Say it ain't true / Say it ain't true (Instrumental).
7" Single: Released Jun '86, on Carrere, Catalogue no: **CAR 392**
12" Single: Released Jun '86, on Carrere, Catalogue no: **CART 392**

Hendryx, Nona

Biographical details: The one-time lyric force behind the seminal, pop-soul trio Labelle, Nona has emerged as a thoughtful and compelling explorer along the front lines of new rock, melding funk and new wave, soul and techno-pop into an accessible, highly individual style. *Nona* her first solo album for RCA Records, blends these elements into a compassionate, erotically intriguing statement by one of pop music's most outspoken free spirits. Coproduced by Nona with the progressive funk-jazz unit Material (bassist Bill Laswell, synthesizer player Michael Beinhorn and soundman Martin Bisi), the album combines propulsive funk grooves with strong pop tunes, lusty vocals and evocative guitar and synthesizer textures. One cut *Design for living* brings together an unprecedented all-star, all-female lineup that includes Gina Schock, Tina Weymouth, Valerie Simpson, Nancy Wilson of Heart, Patti LaBelle and Laurie Anderson. Raised in the South Trenton, NJ ghetto, Nona developed a politicized consciousness while still in her teens, a consciousness she was to bring to bear when she joined Patti LaBelle and the Bluebelles. Regulars on the East Coast "chitlin circuit", the group scored a top ten hit with the girl-group classic *I sold my heart to the junkman* but never enjoyed a success commensurate with their talents. It remained for a new English manager, Vicki Wickham, who re-christened the trio Labelle, to help the group realise its full artistic potential in the seventies. They were the first black pop group to perform at New York's Metropolitan Opera House and on the wings of the hit *Lady Marmalade*, they scored a gold album with *Nightbirds*. Labelle dissolved in 1977.
Keeping New York City as her home base, Nona toured and wrote and recorded in Europe and the States. Hooking herself into the New York club scene, Nona began performing, writing and recording with acts as diverse as Defunkt, David Johansen, Garland Jeffries, Rough Trade and Cameo. With the Indian-Hispanic guitarist Naux, Nona also put together the experimental rock band Zero Cool, who played everything from atonal jazz to electronic motown. Her friendship with Talking Heads' keyboardist, Jerry Harrison, led to some landmark performances with the group and appearances on the albums *Remain in light* and *The name of this band is Talking Heads*. With Busta Jones, Jerry Harrison also produced Nona's European hit single, a remake of the Supremes' *Itching in my heart*. Other successes included the dance-rock hit *Do what you wanna do* recorded with the Cage, an English group featuring Visage drummer Rusty Egan and *Busting out*, her first studio collaboration with Material. Her current group, the funkier more accessible Propoganda, has a flexible lineup and a more casual approach to performing..

BABY GO GO
Tracks: / Baby go go / Drive me wild.
7" Single: Released Sep '87, on EMI-America, by EMI Records. Deleted Jan '88. Catalogue no: **EA 238**
12" Single: Released Sep '87, on EMI-America, by EMI Records. Deleted Jan '88. Catalogue no: **12 EA 238**

HEAT, THE (SINGLE)
Tracks: / Heat, The.
12" Single: Released Sep '85, on RCA, by BMG Records (UK). Deleted '87. Catalogue no: **PK 85465**

I SWEAT
Tracks: / I sweat.
7" Single: Released Jul '85, on Arista, by BMG Records (UK). Catalogue no: **ARIST 628**
12" Single: Released Jul '85, on Arista, by BMG Records (UK). Catalogue no: **ARIST 12628**

I SWEAT (GOING THROUGH THE MOTIONS)
Tracks: / I sweat (going through the motions) / Living on the border.
7" Single: on RCA, by BMG Records (UK). Catalogue no: **RCA 400**
12" Single: on RCA, by BMG Records (UK). Deleted '85. Catalogue no: **RCAT 400**

IF LOOKS COULD KILL (D.O.A.)
Tracks: / If looks could kill (D.O.A) / Het - part 2.
7" Single: Released Sep '85, on RCA, by BMG Records (UK). Catalogue no: **PB 49939**
12" Single: Released Sep '85, on RCA, by BMG Records (UK). Catalogue no: **PT 49940**

KEEP IT CONFIDENTIAL
Tracks: / Keep it confidential.
7" Single: Released Aug '83, on RCA, by BMG Records (UK). Catalogue no: **RCA 356**
12" Single: Released Aug '83, on RCA, by BMG Records (UK). Catalogue no: **RCAT 356**

WHY SHOULD I CRY
Tracks: / Why should I cry / Funkyland / Why should I cry (boo-hoo mix) (extra track on extended 12" only) / Why should I cry (dub boo-hoo mix) (extra track on extended 12" only).
7" Single: Released May '87, on EMI-America, by EMI Records. Deleted Oct '87. Catalogue no: **EA 234**
12" Single: Released 23 May '87, on EMI-America, by EMI Records. Deleted Jan '88. Catalogue no: **12 EAX 234**
12" Single: Released May '87, on EMI-America, by EMI Records. Deleted Apr '88. Catalogue no: **12EA 234**

WINDS OF CHANGE (Mandela to Mandela)
Tracks: / Winds of change / Too hot too handle / Female trouble.
7" Single: Released 7 Mar '88, on EMI-Manhattan, by EMI Records. Deleted 31 Jul '88. Catalogue no: **MT 34**
12" Single: Released 7 Mar '88, on EMI-Manhattan, by EMI Records. Deleted 31 Jul '88. Catalogue no: **12MT 34**

WOMEN WHO FLY
Tracks: / Women who fly / Interior voices.
CD 5": Released Sep '89, on Private Music (USA), by Private Music Records (USA). Catalogue no: **662645**
7" Single: Released Sep '89, on Private Music (USA), by Private Music Records (USA). Catalogue no: **112645**
12" Single: Released Sep '89, on Private Music (USA), by Private Music Records (USA). Catalogue no: **612645**

Hendy

ALL FOR THE SAKE OF ROCK'N'ROLL
Tracks: / All for the sake of rock'n'roll / Good good feeling.
7" Single: Released Aug '80, on Bronze, by Bronze Records. Deleted '83. Catalogue no: **BRO 101**

BODY LANGUAGE
Tracks: / Body language / Fantasy.
7" Single: Released Apr '80, on Bronze, by Bronze Records. Deleted Apr '83. Catalogue no: **BRO 93**

Henley, Don

Biographical details: This American singer, drummer and songwriter had been a member of Linda Ronstadt's backing group prior to becoming a member of the Eagles in 1971. Henley and guitarist / keyboardist Glenn Frey were the nucleus of the Eagles, being the only two players who remained in the band from start to finish; the pair wrote the lions share of the material, and split most of the lead vocal duties between the two of them. After 1980's live album, the hugely successful group gradually drifter apart, although no official split was announced. Henley & Frey both went on to achieve substantial solo success, starting in 1982.
After reaching the US Top 10 with *Leather and lace* in duet with Fleetwood Mac's Stevie Nicks, Henley released his first solo LP *I can't stand still* in July 1982. From the outset, it was clear that his post-Eagles work was punchier and rockier that Frey's. Whereas Glenn emphasised the group's traditional soft-rock conservatism, Don had a harder musical edge and dealt with such socio-political topics as the US educations system (*Johnny can't read*) and the state of the news media (*Dirty laundry*). The latter song, a hard hitting diatribe, became a million-selling US No.3 single in early 1983 although it stopped at No.5 in Britain.
Henley's second solo set, 1985's *Building the perfect beast*, contained another smash single in the shape of *The boys of summer*. This multi-faceted track included the classic line 'I saw a Dead Head sticker on a Cadillac', which summarised modern America in one fell swoop. The song reached No.5 in the States and No.12 in Britain, his first major solo hit in the latter country. By a curious coincidence, it was only a few weeks later that Frey reached the No.12 position in the UK with his first solo British success *The heat is on*. (Bob MacDonald, 17th Oct 1985).

DON HENLY - END OF THE INNOCENCE, THE (Released on Geffen)

BOYS OF SUMMER
Tracks: / Boys of summer, The.
7" Single: Released Dec '84, on Geffen, by Geffen Records (USA). Deleted '86 Catalogue no: **A 4945**
12" Single: Released Dec '84, on Geffen by Geffen Records (USA). Deleted '86 Catalogue no: **TA 4945**

DIRTY LAUNDRY
Tracks: / Dirty laundry / Lilah / Them and us.
7" Single: Released Jan '83, on Elektra by Elektra Records (UK). Catalogue no: **E 9849**
12" Single: Released Jan '83, on Elektra by Elektra Records (UK). Catalogue no: **E 9849**

END OF THE INNOCENCE, THE (see panel above)
Tracks: / End of the innocence, The / If dir were dollars / Boys of summer, The (No available on 7" single.).
CD 5": Released Jul '89, on Geffen, by Geffen Records (USA). Catalogue no: **GE 57 CD**
Cassingle: Released Jul '89, on Geffen by Geffen Records (USA). Catalogue no **GEF 57 C**
7" Single: Released Jul '89, on Geffen, by Geffen Records (USA). Catalogue no: **GE 57**
12" Single: Released Jul '89, on Geffen by Geffen Records (USA). Catalogue no **GEF 57 T**

JOHNNY CAN'T READ
Tracks: / Johnny can't read.
7" Single: Released Sep '82, on WEA, by WEA Records. Catalogue no: **K 13200**

NOT ENOUGH LOVE IN THE WORLD
Tracks: / Not enough love in the world.
7" Single: Released Jul '85, on Geffen, by Geffen Records (USA). Deleted '86. Catalogue no: **A 6419**

UNCLOUDED DAY
Tracks: / Unclouded day, The.
7" Single: Released May '83, on Elektra by Elektra Records (UK). Catalogue no: **9876**
12" Single: Released May '83, on Elektra by Elektra Records (UK). Catalogue no: **9876T**

Henner, Mike

KISS ME DEVINE
Tracks: / Kiss me devine.
12" Single: Released Apr '89, on Loadin Bay, Catalogue no: **LBAY 3**

Henreid, Polar

TOMORROW HAS BEEN CANCELLED
Tracks: / Tomorrow has been cancelled.
7" Single: Released Dec '83, on Delux (1), Catalogue no: **POLA 1**

Paul 'Benny' Henry - Waiting at the Crossroads (Released on Pel)

Henry, Clarence

Biographical details: This American singer, born in Algiers near New Orleans, was just 19 years old when he came to fame with his 1957 novelty *Ain't got no home.* This silly rock'n'roll ditty reached No.20 on the US charts and featured Henry's impressions of frog noises, hence the nickname. He was dismissed by observers as a one-off gimmick artist, but came back stronger than before with two big 1961 hits. The first was *(I don't know why I love you) But I do,* which reached No.4 in the US and introduced him to the British charts, reaching No.3. It was quickly followed by *You always hurt the one you love,* a remake of the Mills Brothers/Connie Francis standard - Clarence took it to No.12 in the States and No.6 in Britain. Both of Clarence 'Frogman' Henry's 1961 hits were in a poppy rhythm and blues vein. He quickly faded from the national and international chart scene, but continued working in New Orleans clubs right into the Seventies, pumping out his increasingly nostalgic brand or R&B. (Bob MacDonald, 17th Oct 1985).

AIN'T GOT NO HOME (CHESS)
Tracks: / Ain't got no home.
7" Single: Released Jul '85, on Chess (PRT), Deleted '88. Catalogue no: **CHES 4003**

BUT I DO
Tracks: / But I Do.
7" Single: Released May '61, on Pye International, Deleted '64. Catalogue no: **7N 25078**
7" Single: Released Jan '83, on Flashback, by Mainline Records. Catalogue no: **FBS 19**

I DON'T KNOW WHY
Tracks: / I don't know why / You always hurt the one you love.
7" Single: Released Mar '82, on Juke Box (Re-issue), Deleted '85. Catalogue no: **JB 015**

LONELY STREET/WHY CAN'T YOU
Tracks: / Lonely street / Why can't you.
7" Single: Released Sep '61, on Pye International, Deleted '64. Catalogue no: **7N 25108**

THAT OLDE PIANO
Tracks: / That olde piano.
7" Single: Released Aug '83, on Rockney, Catalogue no: **KOR 20**

YOU ALWAYS HURT THE ONE YOU LOVE
Tracks: / You always hurt the one you love.
7" Single: Released Jul '61, on Pye International, Deleted '64. Catalogue no: **7N 25089**

Henry, Errol

GOOD LOVIN'
Tracks: / Good lovin'.
12" Single: Released Apr '88, on G.T.I. Records, by G.T.I. Music. Catalogue no: **GTI 001**

Henry, Georgie

I SEE YOU MY LOVE
Tracks: / I see you love.
12" Single: Released Jun '82, on Rudy T, Catalogue no: **RT 01**

Henry, Lenny

MOLE IN THE HOLE
Tracks: / Mole in the hole.
7" Single: Released Mar '81, on Jet, by Jet Records. Catalogue no: **JET 7006**

Henry, Paul

BENNY'S THEME
Tracks: / Benny's Theme.
7" Single: Released Jan '78, on Pye, Deleted '81. Catalogue no: **7N 46027**

WAITING AT THE CROSSROADS
Tracks: / Waiting at the crossroads / Love affair.
7" Single: Released Nov '81, on Pel, Deleted '82. Catalogue no: **POO 1**

Henry's Herd

MUH SONG, THE
Tracks: / Muh song, The / Daisy's rag.
7" Single: Released Jul '86, on Sierra, by Sierra Records. Deleted Jun '87. Catalogue no: **FED 24**
12" Single: Released Jul '86, on Sierra, by Sierra Records. Catalogue no: **FED 24 T**

Hensley, Ken

SYSTEM, THE
Tracks: / System, The / Inspiration.
7" Single: Released Apr '81, on Bronze, by Bronze Records. Deleted '81. Catalogue no: **BRO 117**

Hentschel, David

EDUCATING RITA
Tracks: / Educating Rita / I can't dance.
7" Single: Released May '83, on Mercury, by Phonogram Ltd. Catalogue no: **RITA 1**

Hepburns

ELECTRIFIED
Tracks: / Electrified.
12" Single: Released Jul '89, on Magic (2), Catalogue no: **MAGIC 1 T**

GOALMOUTH INCIDENT
Tracks: / Made up / World is, The / Pier head / Bath house, The.
12" Single: Released May '87, on Cherry Red, by Cherry Red Records. Catalogue no: **12 CHERRY 98**

Heptics

SPEND SOME TIME TOGETHER
Tracks: / Spend some time together.
12" Single: Released Aug '85, on Starlight, Catalogue no: **SLD 535**

Heptones

FATTIE FATTIE
Tracks: / Fattie fattie.
7" Single: Released May '89, on Studio One, Catalogue no: **UNKNOWN**

IN MY TIME
Tracks: / In my time.
12" Single: Released Jul '85, on MM Music, Catalogue no: **MM 0001**

ONE STEP AHEAD
Tracks: / One step ahead.
12" Single: Released Oct '85, on Move, Catalogue no: **S 4**

SEA OF LOVE
Tracks: / Sea of love / Loving you alright.
12" Single: Released May '83, on Supertone, Catalogue no: **SR 001**

SUSPICIOUS MINDS
Tracks: / Suspicious minds / Crystal blue persuasion.
12" Single: Released Mar '86, on Paradise, Catalogue no: **PD 15516**

SWEPT FOR YOU BABY
Tracks: / Swept for you baby.
12" Single: on Burning Sounds, by Burning Sounds Records. Deleted May '88. Catalogue no: **BSD 019**

YOU DECORATED MY HEART
Tracks: / You decorated my heart.
12" Single: Released Mar '83, on Art & Craft, Catalogue no: **ACD 24**

Herbert, Percy

CHRISTMAS DRINK UP SONG, THE
Tracks: / Christmas drink up song, The / Percy's theme.
7" Single: Released Dec '87, on PD, Catalogue no: **PD 001**

Herd

Biographical details: At the time of their success, this British pop group consisted of Andy Brown, Peter Frampton, Andrew Steele and Gary Taylor.
The Herd were initially formed in 1965, with the above line-up emerging the following year. After plenty of live gigs and a few flop records, the combo joined up with the songwriting and management team of Ken Howard & Alan Blaikley at the beginning of 1967.
These two gentlemen had already provided major hits for the Honeycombs and Dave Dee, Dozy, Beaky, Mick and Tich. During late '67 and early '68, they wrote three consecutive UK Top 20 hits for the Herd: the lushly orchestrated *From the underworld* reached No.6, *Paradise lost* peaked at No.15 and the instantly hummable *I don't want out loving to die* climbed to No.5. The focal point of the Herd was lead vocalist/guitarist Peter Frampton whose teen idol status was confirmed when Rave magazine voted him 'Face of '68'. This description did not really suit the singer, because he had aspirations to become accepted as a serious musician rather than just a pin-up. Although the Herd's hits were enjoyable slices of pop psychedelia, Frampton felt frustrated by the image-conscious Howard Blaikley hit machine and, after the failure of later Herd releases, quit the group in March 1969 to form the successful Humble Pie with the Small Faces leader Steve Marriott. Peter left the Pie in 1971 but 'came alive' in no uncertain terms in the American rock scent of the mid-Seventies - indeed, it was his subsequent superstardom that kept the name of the Herd alive in people's memories. Meanwhile, bassist Gary Taylor found mid-Seventies success on the British charts as a member of Fox.
(Bob MacDonald, 17th Oct 1985).

FROM THE UNDERWORLD
Tracks: / From the underworld.
7" Single: Released Sep '67, on Fontana, by Phonogram Ltd. Deleted '70. Catalogue no: **TF 856**
7" Single: Released Jul '82, on Old Gold, by Old Gold Records. Deleted Jul '88. Catalogue no: **OG 9236**

I DON'T WANT OUR LOVIN' TO DIE
Tracks: / I don't want our lovin' to die.
7" Single: Released Apr '68, on Fontana, by Phonogram Ltd. Deleted '71. Catalogue no: **TF 925**
7" Single: Released Jul '82, on Old Gold, by Old Gold Records. Deleted Jul '88. Catalogue no: **OG 9245**

PARADISE LOST
Tracks: / Paradise lost.
7" Single: Released Dec '67, Deleted '70. Catalogue no: **TF 887**

Here And Now

STANDING FOREVER
Tracks: / Standing forever.
12" Single: Released May '89, on Hancan, Catalogue no: **HANCAN 001**

Here's Johnny

HELLZ A POPPIN'
Tracks: / Hellzapoppin' / Absence of malice.
7" Single: Released May '86, on RCA, by BMG Records (UK). Catalogue no: **PB 40713**
12" Single: Released May '86, on RCA, by BMG Records (UK). Catalogue no: **PT 40714**

I FALL APART
Tracks: / I fall apart / Belief.
7" Single: Released Jul '85, on RCA, by BMG Records (UK). Catalogue no: **PB 40197**
12" Single: Released Jul '85, on RCA, by BMG Records (UK). Catalogue no: **PT 40198**

IDLE WIND
Tracks: / Idle wind.
7" Single: Released Oct '85, on RCA, by BMG Records (UK). Catalogue no: **PB 40391**
12" Single: Released Oct '85, on RCA, by BMG Records (UK). Catalogue no: **PT 40392**

LOVE YOU TO DEATH
Tracks: / Love you to death.
7" Single: Released Mar '86, on RCA, by BMG Records (UK). Catalogue no: **PB 40563**
12" Single: Released Mar '86, on RCA, by BMG Records (UK). Catalogue no: **PT 40564**

Heresy

WHO'S GENERATION EP
Tracks: / Who's generation.
7" Single: Released Mar '89, on In Your Face, Catalogue no: **FACE 4**

WHOSE GENERATION
Tracks: / Whose generation.
7" Single: Released Apr '89, on In Your Face, Catalogue no: **FACE 004**

Heretic

BURNT AT THE STAKE
Tracks: / Water of vice / Keep on telling those lies / Fever of love / Watch me grow.
Note: Outstanding young heavy rock band constantly in demand on the club circuit. (Magnum Music May, 1988).
12" Single: Released Apr '84, on Thunderbolt, by Magnum Music Group. Catalogue no: **THBE 1.004**

Herion, Trevor

KISS OF NO RETURN
Tracks: / Kiss of no return.
7" Single: Released Nov '82, on Imperial, by K-Tel Records. Deleted Nov '85. Catalogue no: **MPE 1**

Heritage

STRANGE PLACE TO BE
Tracks: / Strange place to be / Misunderstood.
7" Single: Released Apr '81, on Rondelet Music, by Rondelet Music & Records. Catalogue no: **ROUND 8**

Herman, Woody

CRAZY RHYTHM
Tracks: / Woodchoppers ball / Caldonia / Midnight sun / Bijou / Northwest passage / Lullaby of Birdland / Carioca / I cover the waterfront / Blowin' up a storm / Crazy rhythm.
7" Single: Released May '89, on Garland, Catalogue no: **GRZ 007**

Herman Ze German

WIPE OUT
Tracks: / Wipe out / Pancake.
7" Single: Released Mar '86, on Capitol, by EMI Records. Deleted '88. Catalogue no: **CL 389**

Herman's Hermits

Biographical details: This British pop group consisted of Karl Green, Keith Hopwood, Derek Leckenby, Peter Noone and Barry Whitwam.
On most of the records, however, only lead singer Noone performed; the music was usually played by session musicians, often including future Led Zeppelin stars John Paul Jones and Jimmy Page.
The group's records were produced and carefully controlled by pop svengali Mickie Most, who also conceived their name and selected their material.
The combo were originally formed as the Heartbeats in 1963 in their native Manchester, the sixteen year old Noone having previously been a successful teenage actor.
When he went to see them perform, Most was not particularly impressed by the group's playing but thought that Peter (whom he christened Herman) possessed a certain charm and bore a striking resemblence to John F Kennedy.
By the time Noone had celebrated his 17th birthday, Herman's Hermits had already enjoyed a UK No.1 smash with their first single *I'm into something good* (a Gerry Goffin/Carole King song).
Despite a run of further British hits, it was in America that Herman's Hermits really went down a storm.
Between early '65 and mid '66, they chalked up nine consecutive Top 10 singles in the United States space of fifteen months. Indeed, many of their biggest American hits - *Can't you hear my heartbeat* (No.2), *Mrs Brown, you've got a lovely daughter* (No.1), *I'm Henry VIII I am* (No.1 - originally made

famous in Britain in 1911!), *Listen people* (No.3) and *Leaning on the lamp post (N0.9) - were not even released as singles in Britain, although they did appear as EP tracks.*
Most may well have been right about the Kennedy connection - with the memory of the President's assassination still fresh in the minds of the American public, a subconscious association was a plausible explanation of the group's success. Another theory was that the horrendous cuteness of Noone, combined with the equally innocuous nature of their music, provided the perfect antidote for younger kids (and their parents) who did not appreciate or understand the aggressive stance of other UK exports like the Rolling Stones or the Who. Whatever the reasons, Herman's Hermits were, for a brief period, almost as big in America as the Beatles. The American hits dried up in 1968, but Most managed to eke them out in Britain until 1970. Noone attempted a briefly successful solo career, before sinking into obscurity. He formed an unsuccessful rock band called the Tremblers in 1979, who had folded by the time he starred in the well received 1983 version of the Pirates of Penzance musical. (Bob MacDonald, 18th Oct 1985).

A MUST TO AVOID
Tracks: / Must to avoid, A.
7" Single: Released Dec '65, on Columbia, by EMI Records. Deleted '68. Catalogue no: **DB 7791**

BET YER LIFE I DO
Tracks: / Bet yer life I do.
7" Single: Released May '70, on RAK, by EMI Records. Deleted '73. Catalogue no: **RAK 102**

EAST WEST
Tracks: / East West.
7" Single: Released Dec '66, on Columbia, by EMI Records. Deleted '69. Catalogue no: **DB 8076**

HERE COMES THE SUN
Tracks: / Here comes the star.
7" Single: Released Nov '69, on Columbia, by EMI Records. Deleted '72. Catalogue no: **DB 8626**

I CAN TAKE OR LEAVE YOUR LOVING
Tracks: / I can take or leave your loving.
7" Single: Released Jan '68, on Columbia, by EMI Records. Deleted '71. Catalogue no: **DB 8327**

I'M INTO SOMETHING GOOD
Tracks: / I'm into something good.
7" Single: Released Aug '64, on Columbia, by EMI Records. Deleted '67. Catalogue no: **DB 7338**
7" Single: Released Jul '84, on EMI Golden 45's, by EMI Records. Catalogue no: **G45 26**

JUST A LITTLE BIT BETTER
Tracks: / Just a little bit better.
7" Single: Released Sep '65, on Columbia, by EMI Records. Deleted '68. Catalogue no: **DB 7670**

LADY BARBARA
Tracks: / Lady Barbara.
7" Single: Released Nov '70, on RAK, by EMI Records. Deleted '73. Catalogue no: **RAK 106**

MY SENTIMENTAL FRIEND
Tracks: / My sentimental friend.
7" Single: Released Apr '69, on Columbia, by EMI Records. Deleted '72. Catalogue no: **DB 8563**

NO MILK TODAY
Tracks: / No milk today.
7" Single: Released Oct '66, on Columbia, by EMI Records. Deleted '69. Catalogue no: **DB 8012**
7" Single: Released Apr '83, on EMI (France), by EMI Records. Catalogue no: **2C 008 93548**

SHOW ME GIRL
Tracks: / Show me girl.
7" Single: Released Nov '64, on Columbia, by EMI Records. Deleted '67. Catalogue no: **DB 7408**

SILHOUETTES
Tracks: / Silhouettes.
7" Single: Released Feb '65, on Columbia, by EMI Records. Deleted '68. Catalogue no: **DB 7475**

SLEEPY JOE
Tracks: / Sleepy Joe.
7" Single: Released May '68, on Columbia, by EMI Records. Deleted '71. Catalogue no: **DB 8404**

SOMETHING'S HAPPENING
Tracks: / Something's happening.
7" Single: Released Dec '68, on Columbia, by EMI Records. Deleted '71. Catalogue no: **DB 8504**

SUNSHINE GIRL
Tracks: / Sunshine Girl.
7" Single: Released Jul '68, on Columbia, by EMI Records. Deleted '71. Catalogue no: **DB 8446**

THERE'S A KIND OF HUSH
Tracks: / There's a kind of hush.
7" Single: Released Feb '67, on Columbia, by EMI Records. Deleted '70. Catalogue no: **DB 8123**
7" Single: Released Nov '86, on RAK, by EMI Records. Deleted Oct '89. Catalogue no: **RR 8**

THIS DOOR SWINGS BOTH WAYS
Tracks: / This door swings both ways.
7" Single: Released Jun '66, on Columbia, by EMI Records. Deleted '69. Catalogue no: **DB 7947**

WONDERFUL WORLD
Tracks: / Wonderful world.
7" Single: Released Apr '65, on Columbia, by EMI Records. Deleted '68. Catalogue no: **DB 7546**

YEARS MAY COME, YEARS MAY GO
Tracks: / Years may come, years may go.
7" Single: Released Feb '70, on Columbia, by EMI Records. Deleted '73. Catalogue no: **DB 8656**

YOU WON'T BE LEAVING
Tracks: / You won't be leaving.
7" Single: Released Mar '66, on Columbia, by EMI Records. Deleted '69. Catalogue no: **DB 7861**

Hermans Vision

PARTY
Tracks: / Party.
7" Single: Released Mar '84, on Hermans Vision, Catalogue no: **HEVIS 1**

Hermes, Corrine

SI LA VIE EST CADEAUX
Tracks: / Si la vie est cadeaux.
7" Single: Released Apr '83, on Polydor, by Polydor Ltd. Catalogue no: **POSP 597**

WORDS OF LOVE
Tracks: / Words of love.
7" Single: Released May '83, on Polydor, by Polydor Ltd. Catalogue no: **POSPE 597**

Hermine

TORTURE
Tracks: / Torture.
7" Single: Released Jul '81, on Human (2), Catalogue no: **HUM 3**

TV LOVERS
Tracks: / T.V. lovers.
7" Single: Released Jul '81, on Human (2), Catalogue no: **HUM 11**

Hermit Crabs

YEAH
Tracks: / Yeah / Surfer girl.
12" Single: Released Nov '88, on Thunderball, Catalogue no: **12TBL 1**

Hernandez

ALL MY LOVE
Tracks: / All my love / All my love (instrumental) / All my love (extended version) (Only on CD single and 12".) / All my love (Ben Liebrand mix) (Only on 12" (HERQT 1)).
CD 5": Released 13 Mar '89, on Epic, by CBS Records. Deleted Oct '89. Catalogue no: **CDHER 1**
7" Single: Released 24 Apr '89, on Epic, by CBS Records. Deleted Oct '89. Catalogue no: **HERQ 1**
7" Single: Released 13 Mar '89, on Epic, by CBS Records. Deleted Oct '89. Catalogue no: **HER 1**
12" Single: Released 13 Mar '89, on Epic, by CBS Records. Deleted Oct '89. Catalogue no: **HERT 1**
12" Single: Released 20 Mar '89, on Epic, by CBS Records. Deleted Oct '89. Catalogue no: **HERQT 1**

I'M NOT THAT KIND OF GUY
Tracks: / I'm not that kind of guy / One day at a time.
CD 5": Released 21 Aug '89, on Epic, by CBS Records. Catalogue no: **CDHER 2**
7" Single: Released 21 Aug '89, on Epic, by CBS Records. Catalogue no: **HER 2**
12" Single: Released 21 Aug '89, on Epic, by CBS Records. Catalogue no: **HER T2**

Hernandez, Patrick

Biographical details: Of Belgian nationality but based in West Germany, land of the Eurodisco conveyor belt, this singer came to fame in 1979 with his international smash *Born to be alive.* The single had already established itself as one of the year's biggest European hits by the time it reached No.10 in Britain and became a million-seller in the States. Hernandez growled his way through the naff words of *Born to be alive*, backed by a Giorgio Moroder-type electronic disco-rock backing. Partick quickly faded into obscurity, although he continued recording into the Eighties. (Bob MacDonald, 18th Oct 1985).

BACK TO BOOGIE
Tracks: / Back to boogie / Born to be alive.
12" Single: Released Mar '80, on Gem, Deleted '83. Catalogue no: **GEM 12-26**

BORN TO BE ALIVE
Tracks: / Born to be alive.
7" Single: Released Jun '79, on Gem, Deleted '82. Catalogue no: **GEM 4**

GOODBYE
Tracks: / Goodbye / Can't keep it up.
7" Single: Released Nov '81, on Recorded Delivery, Catalogue no: **RDR 005**
12" Single: Released Nov '81, on Recorded Delivery, Catalogue no: **RDRT 005**

Hernandez, Wayne

BAD NEWS
Tracks: / Bad news / Bad news (bulletin mix) ** (CD single only.) / You got, The / Bad news (news at twelve mix) (Only on 12" version.).
CD 5": Released May '88, on Epic, by CBS Records. Deleted Jan '89. Catalogue no: **WAYNE C4**
7" Single: Released May '88, on Epic, by CBS Records. Deleted Jan '89. Catalogue no: **WAYNE 4**
12" Single: Released Jun '88, on Epic, by CBS Records. Deleted Jan '89. Catalogue no: **WAYNE Q 4**
12" Single: Released May '88, on Epic, by CBS Records. Deleted Jan '89. Catalogue no: **WAYNE T4**

CORNERS OF THE SUN
Tracks: / Corners of the sun / I am the night.
7" Single: Released Oct '87, on Epic, by CBS Records. Deleted Jun '88. Catalogue no: **WAYNE 2**
12" Single: Released Oct '87, on CBS, by CBS Records. Deleted Jun '88. Catalogue no: **WAYNE Q2**
12" Single: Released 17 Oct '87, on Epic, by CBS Records. Catalogue no: **WAYNE T2**

LET ME CALL YOU ANGEL
Tracks: / Let me call you angel / Must be dreaming.
7" Single: Released 20 Jun '87, on Epic, by CBS Records. Deleted Nov '87. Catalogue no: **WAYNE 1**
12" Single: Released Jul '87, on Epic, by CBS Records. Catalogue no: **WAYNEQ 1**
12" Single: Released 20 Jun '87, on Epic, by CBS Records. Deleted Nov '87. Catalogue no: **WAYNET 1**

LIVIN' WITHOUT YOUR LOVE
Tracks: / Livin' without your love / Livin' without your love (forest's straight 12) / Fazed out / Livin' without your love (dub mix) / Livin' without your love (change up mix).
7" Single: Released Mar '88, on Epic, by CBS Records. Catalogue no: **WAYNE 3**
12" Single: Released Mar '88, on Epic, by CBS Records. Catalogue no: **WAYNE T3**
12" Single: Released Mar '88, on Epic, by CBS Records. Catalogue no: **WAYNE Q3**

Hero, Stephen

LET'S HEAR IT FOR THE RED MAN
Tracks: / Let's hear it for the red man / Slave to the phoenix.
7" Single: Released Nov '87, on Pyramid, by Pyramid Records. Catalogue no: **PYR 1**
12" Single: Released Nov '87, on Pyramid, by Pyramid Records. Catalogue no: **12 PYR 1**

Heroes

BABY HAD A TASTE
Tracks: / Baby had a taste / Waiting for you.
7" Single: Released Jul '81, on Carrere, Deleted '84. Catalogue no: **CAR 197**

BABY'S HAD A TASTE
Tracks: / Baby's had a taste.
7" Single: Released Jul '81, on Carrere, Catalogue no: **CAR 197**

DRIFTAWAY
Tracks: / Drift away / Dreams for lovers.
7" Single: Released Oct '87, on RCA, by BMG Records (UK). Deleted May '89. Catalogue no: **PB 49633**
12" Single: Released Oct '87, on RCA, by BMG Records (UK). Deleted May '89. Catalogue no: **PT 49634**

RUSSIA AND AMERICA Why can't we be friends
Tracks: / Russia and America (why can't we be friends).
7" Single: Released Jun '84, on Calibre, Deleted '85. Catalogue no: **CAB 127**
12" Single: Released Jun '84, on Calibre, Deleted '85. Catalogue no: **CABL 127**

SOME KIND OF WOMAN
Tracks: / Some kind of woman / 10% will do.
7" Single: Released Feb '80, on Polydor, by Polydor Ltd. Deleted Feb '83. Catalogue no: **POSP 105**

Herreys

DIGGI LOO- DIGGI LEY
Tracks: / Diggi loo- diggi ley / Every song you sing.
7" Single: Released May '84, on MCA/Panther, Deleted '87. Catalogue no: **PAN 5**

Herte, Kim

DANCE WITH A STRANGER
Tracks: / Dance with a stranger (East rap mix) / Dance with a stranger (7" radio mix) / Anything lying on the floor (inst.).
7" Single: Released Nov '86, on Big Top, by Big Top Records. Deleted '87. Catalogue no: **KYM 1**

DO YOU WANNA DANCE(WITH ME)
Tracks: / Do you wanna dance (with me).
7" Single: Released Jun '85, on Londisc, by Londisc Records. Catalogue no: **7 LDR 048**
12" Single: Released May '85, on RMO, by RMO Records. Catalogue no: **12 ZAM 1**
12" Single: Released Jun '85, on Londisc, by Londisc Records. Catalogue no: **LDR 048**

IT AIN'T HEAVY
Tracks: / It ain't heavy / It ain't heavy (house mix).
7" Single: Released Jul '87, on Nine O Nine, by Creole Records. Catalogue no: **NINE 710**

IT AIN'T HEAVY (EXTENDED MIX)
Tracks: / It ain't heavy (extended mix) / It ain't heavy / It ain't heavy (house mix).
12" Single: Released Jul '87, on Nine O Nine, by Creole Records. Catalogue no: **NINE 10**

Hesernen, Honor

DANNY BOY
Tracks: / Danny boy.
7" Single: Released Mar '83, on Palace, by Virgin Records. Catalogue no: **PS 2**

Hewerdine, Boo

ALL I WANT IS EVERYTHING
Tracks: / All I want is everything / South by south west / Tell me why.
CD 5": Released Jul '89, on Ensign, by Ensign Records. Catalogue no: **ENYCD 625**
7" Single: Released Jul '89, on Ensign, by Ensign Records. Catalogue no: **ENY 625**
12" Single: Released Jul '89, on Ensign, by Ensign Records. Catalogue no: **ENY X 625**

Hewett, Colleen

DREAMING MY DREAMS WITH YOU
Tracks: / Dreaming my dreams with you / One eyed man.
7" Single: Released Aug '80, on Columbia, by EMI Records. Deleted '83. Catalogue no: **DB 9084**

Hewett, Howard

I'M FOR REAL
Tracks: / I'm for real / Eye on you.
7" Single: Released Aug '86, on Elektra (USA), by Elektra Records (USA). Catalogue no: **EKR 47**
12" Single: Released Aug '86, on Elektra (USA), by Elektra Records (USA). Deleted Jun '87. Catalogue no: **EKR 47 T**

STAY (AFTER MIDNIGHT MIX)
Tracks: / Stay (after midnight mix) / Eye on you.
7" Single: Released Feb '87, on Elektra (USA), by Elektra Records (USA). Deleted Jan '88. Catalogue no: **EKR 51**
12" Single: Released Feb '87, on Elektra (USA), by Elektra Records (USA). Deleted Jan '88. Catalogue no: **EKR 51 T**

Hewick, Kevin

FEATHERING THE NEST
Tracks: / Feathering the nest.
7" Single: Released May '83, on Cherry Red, by Cherry Red Records. Deleted '87. Catalogue no: **CHERRY 64**

OPHELIA'S DRINKING
Tracks: / Ophelia's drinking.
7" Single: Released Feb '82, on Factory (1), by Factory Records. Catalogue no: **FACT 48**

THIS COVER KEEPS REALITY UNREAL
Tracks: / This cover keeps reality unreal / Plenty / Amber / Neath dancing waves.
12" Single: Released Feb '84, on Cher

Red, by Cherry Red Records. Deleted '87. Catalogue no: **12 CHERRY 76**

Hewitt, Ben

FOR QUITE A WHILE
Tracks: / For quite a while / I saw Linda yesterday.
7" Single: Released Feb '87, on Pinner, Catalogue no: **PRM 903**

Hewitt, Chris

DELIRIOUS
Tracks: / Delirious (7" only) / Manhattan sunset / Delirious (12" extended version) (12" only) / Delirious (radio edit) (12" only).
7" Single: Released Dec '87, on Virgin, by Virgin Records. Deleted May '88. Catalogue no: **VS 1032**
12" Single: Released Dec '87, on Virgin, by Virgin Records. Catalogue no: **VST 1032**

Hewitt, Garth

HUNGRY WIND
Tracks: / Hungry wind, The / Red hot and cooking.
Note: Anti-nuclear song from Gospel favourite, Garth Hewitt.
7" Single: Released Dec '83, on Blue Moon (1), by Magnum Music Group. Catalogue no: **BMS 001**

I CAN HEAR LOVE
Tracks: / I can hear love / Come out fighting.
7" Single: Released Apr '80, on Pye, Deleted '83. Catalogue no: **7P 172**

Hewson, Pete

TAKE MY HAND
Tracks: / Take my hand / Her.
7" Single: Released Aug '83, on Reset, Catalogue no: **RES 2**
12" Single: Released Aug '83, on Reset, Catalogue no: **REST 2**

Hex

YOU ARE NOT ALONE(EP)
Note: Features Hex, Oi Polloi, Stalag 17, Symbol of Freedom.
7" Single: Released Aug '86, on Words Of Warning, Catalogue no: **WOW 1**

Hex & Feed Your Head

NOTHING VENTURED NOTHING GAINED
7" EP: Released 30 May '87, on Words Of Warning, Catalogue no: **WOW 3**

Hey Day

COME AND GO
Tracks: / Come and go / This change of yours (vocal).
7" Single: Released Feb '86, on EMI, by EMI Records. Catalogue no: **EMI 5546**
12" Single: Released Feb '86, on EMI, by EMI Records. Catalogue no: **12EMI 5546**

Hey Elastica

EAT YOUR HEART OUT
Tracks: / Eat your heart out.
7" Single: Released Oct '82, on Virgin, by Virgin Records. Deleted Oct '85. Catalogue no: **VS 547**
12" Single: Released Oct '82, on Virgin, by Virgin Records. Deleted Oct '85. Catalogue no: **VS 547 12**

SUCK A LITTLE HONEY
Tracks: / Suck a little honey.
7" Single: Released Mar '83, on Virgin, by Virgin Records. Deleted '89. Catalogue no: **VS 561**
12" Single: Released Mar '83, on Virgin, by Virgin Records. Deleted '89. Catalogue no: **VS 561-12**

Hey You

MATTHEW AND SON
Tracks: / Matthew and son / Black and white in colour.
7" Single: Released Apr '82, on Epic, by CBS Records. Deleted Apr '85. Catalogue no: **EPC A2126**

Heyward, Nick

Biographical details: Hailing from the Beckenham area of Kent, this British singer, songwriter and guitarist came to fame in late 1981 as leader of Haircut 100. The group's stunning twelve-month period of success was abruptly ended as the Haircuts entered their second year in the limelight. In January 1983, the long running friction between Heyward and percussionist Mark Fox caused Nick to part company with the band during the recording of their second LP. While his former colleagues struggled to maintain their career, Nick quickly achieved a trio of UK Top 20 singles: *Whistle down the wind* reached No.13, *Take that situation* climbed to No.11 and *Blue hat for a blue day* peaked at No.14. In October '83 he released his debut solo LP *North of a miracle*, co-produced by former Beatles engineer Geoff Emerick. It was another British Top 20 success.
The fresh faced 22 year old Heyward continued his solo career in the whimsical, pure pop vein that he had employed in his Haircut days. However, when his chart status began to decline, he came up with a harder and funkier single called *Warning sign*. This reached the UK Top 30, but his 1985 single *Laura* marked a return to his old sound and to his now dangerously familiar mino hit status. (Bob MacDonald, 18th Oct 1985).

NICK HEYWARD - WHISTLE DOWN THE WIND (Released on Arista)

BLUE HAT FOR A BLUE DAY
Tracks: / Blue hat for a blue day / Love at the door / Don't get me wrong (on 12" only).
7" Single: Released '83, on Arista, by BMG Records (UK). Deleted '86. Catalogue no: **HEY 3**
12" Single: Released '83, on Arista, by BMG Records (UK). Deleted '87. Catalogue no: **HEY 123**

GOODBYE YESTERDAY
Tracks: / Goodbye yesterday / We've all been kissed / Goodbye yesterday (instrumental) (Extra Track on 12" version only.).
12" Single: Released Jun '86, on Arista, by BMG Records (UK). Catalogue no: **HEY 1210**

LAURA
Tracks: / Laura.
7" Pic: Released May '85, on Arista, by BMG Records (UK). Catalogue no: **HEYSD 8**
7" Single: Released May '85, on Arista, by BMG Records (UK). Catalogue no: **HEY 8**
12" Single: Released May '85, on Arista, by BMG Records (UK). Catalogue no: **HEY 128**

LOVE ALL DAY
Tracks: / Love all day.
7" Single: Released May '84, on Arista, by BMG Records (UK). Catalogue no: **HEY 5**
12" Single: Released May '84, on Arista, by BMG Records (UK). Catalogue no: **HEY 125**

ON A SUNDAY
Tracks: / On a Sunday.
7" Single: Released '83, on Arista, by BMG Records (UK). Deleted '86. Catalogue no: **HEY 4**
12" Single: Released '83, on Arista, by BMG Records (UK). Deleted '87. Catalogue no: **HEY 124**

OVER THE WEEKEND
Tracks: / Over the weekend / Cry just a bit (Extra Track on 12" Version only.) / Cry just a bit (God knows I love you).
7" Single: Released Apr '86, on Arista, by BMG Records (UK). Catalogue no: **HEY 9**
12" Single: Released Apr '86, on Arista, by BMG Records (UK). Catalogue no: **HEY 129**

TAKE THAT SITUATION
Tracks: / Take that situation.
7" Single: Released '83, on Arista, by BMG Records (UK). Deleted '86. Catalogue no: **HEY 2**
12" Single: Released '83, on Arista, by BMG Records (UK). Deleted '87. Catalogue no: **HEY 122**

TELL ME WHY
Tracks: / Tell me why / Song, A (On 7" version only.) / Traffic in Fleet Street (On 12" version only.).
7" Single: Released Jan '89, on Warner Bros., by WEA Records. Catalogue no: **W 7579**
12" Single: Released Jan '89, on Warner Bros., by WEA Records. Catalogue no: **W 7579 T**

WARNING SIGN
Tracks: / Warning sign.
7" Single: Released Oct '84, on Arista, by BMG Records (UK). Catalogue no: **HEY 6**
12" Single: Released Oct '84, on Arista, by BMG Records (UK). Catalogue no: **HEY 126**

WARNING SIGN (EXT. REMIX)
Tracks: / Warning sign.
12" Single: Released Oct '84, on Arista, by BMG Records (UK). Catalogue no: **HEY 226**

WHISTLE DOWN THE WIND (see panel above)
Tracks: / Whistle down the wind / Whistle down the wind.
7" Single: Released '83, on Arista, by BMG Records (UK). Deleted '86. Catalogue no: **HEY 1**
12" Single: Released '83, on Arista, by BMG Records (UK). Deleted '87. Catalogue no: **HEY 121**

YOU'RE MY WORLD
Tracks: / You're my world / Pizza tears.
7" Single: Released 22 Aug '88, on Warner Bros., by WEA Records. Catalogue no: **W 7758**
7" Single: Released Jul '88, on WEA, by WEA Records. Catalogue no: **YZ 200**
12" Single: Released Jul '88, on WEA, by WEA Records. Catalogue no: **YZ 200 T**
12" Single: Released 22 Aug '88, on Warner Bros., by WEA Records. Catalogue no: **W 7758T**

Heywood, Colin

DREAM LOVER
Tracks: / Dream lover / In on the action.
7" Single: Released Jan '83, on Crash, by Satril Records. Deleted '85. Catalogue no: **CRA 503**

NO EASY WAY TO LOVE
Tracks: / No easy way to love / Together.
7" Single: Released Apr '86, on Spartan, Catalogue no: **SP 135**

SAFETY IN NUMBERS
Tracks: / Safety in numbers.
7" Single: Released Oct '83, on Monarch, by Monarch Records. Catalogue no: **MON 048**

H.F.M.

PEANUTS
Tracks: / Peanuts.
7" Single: Released 23 Jul '88, on Circle City, Catalogue no: **P 1**
12" Single: Released 23 Jul '88, on Circle City, Catalogue no: **PT 1**

HGB

CHASE THE NIGHT AWAY
Tracks: / Chase the night away.
7" Single: Released Nov '81, on Backshot, by Back Shot Records. Deleted '88. Catalogue no: **BS 001**

Hi Tension

Biographical details: At the time of their greatest success, this British disco band consisted of Jeffrey Guishard, David Joseph, Ken Joseph, Patrick McLean, Paul McLean, David Philips, Paul Philips, David Reid and Leroy Williams. In 1978 at the height of the disco boom, Hi-Tension zoomed into the Top 20 of the British pop charts with a brace of ultra-danceable singles. The first was the self-titled *Hi-tension* chant, which reached No.13 despite a dearth of radio airplay; it was followed by the anthem like *British hustle*, which attempted to give a UK identity to a basically American genre. The latter song reached the UK No.8 position, and was listed as a double A sided single with *Peace on earth*. However, the group's next single, which was a breezy ballad entitled *Autumn love*, flopped because its release was delayed until Christmas! Hi-Tension soon faded from view, but their frontman David Joseph emerged as a successful solo artist in 1983. In the same year, one of their later members, Phil Fearon, found fame as leader of Galaxy. (Bob MacDonald, 21st Oct 1985).

BRITISH HUSTLE/PEACE ON EARTH
Tracks: / British Hustle/Peace on earth.
7" Single: Released Aug '78, on Island, by Island Records. Deleted '81. Catalogue no: **WIP 6446**

HAPPY
Tracks: / Happy.
7" Single: Released Oct '84, on Streetwave, Catalogue no: **KHAN 30**
12" Single: Released Oct '84, on Streetwave, Catalogue no: **MKHAN 30**

HI TENSION
Tracks: / Hi Tension.
7" Single: Released May '78, on Island, by Island Records. Deleted '81. Catalogue no: **WIP 6422**

HOW D'YOU FEEL
Tracks: / How d'you feel / Lyin' low.
7" Single: Released May '82, on EMI, by EMI Records. Catalogue no: **EMI 5303**
12" Single: Released May '82, on EMI, by EMI Records. Catalogue no: **12 EMI 5303**

WE'VE GOT THE FUNK
Tracks: / We've got the funk / Objects.
7" Single: Released Sep '81, on EMI, by EMI Records. Deleted '84. Catalogue no: **EMI 5225**
12" Single: Released Sep '81, on EMI, by EMI Records. Deleted '84. Catalogue no: **12EMI 5225**

Hiatt, John

BACK TO NORMAL
Tracks: / Back to normal / String pull job.
7" Single: Released Feb '81, on MCA, by MCA Records. Catalogue no: **MCA 664**

BACK TO THE WAR
Tracks: / Back to the war.
7" Single: Released Oct '80, on MCA, by MCA Records. Catalogue no: **MCA 649**

SHE LOVES THE JERK
Tracks: / She loves the jerk / Love like blood.
7" Single: Released Feb '84, on Geffen, by Geffen Records (USA). Catalogue no: **A 4086**

SHE SAID THE SAME THINGS TO ME
Tracks: / She said the same things to me.
7" Single: Released Jan '85, on Geffen, by Geffen Records (USA). Catalogue no: **A 5033**

SLOW TURNING (SINGLE)
Tracks: / Slow turning / Is anybody there / Already love (Only on 12".).
7" Single: Released Oct '88, on A&M, by A&M Records. Catalogue no: **AM 478**
12" Single: Released Oct '88, on A&M, by A&M Records. Catalogue no: **AMY 478**

SNAKE CHARMER
Tracks: / Snake charmer / This is your day.
7" Single: Released Mar '85, on Atlantic, by WEA Records. Catalogue no: **A 9461**

TENNESSEE PLATES
Tracks: / Tennesse plates / Georgie Rae (live).
7" Single: Released 13 Feb '89, on A&M, by A&M Records. Catalogue no: **AM 499**
12" Single: Released 13 Feb '89, on A&M, by A&M Records. Catalogue no: **AMY 499**

THANK YOU GIRL
Tracks: / Thank you girl / My girl.

7" Single: Released May '87, on Demon, by Demon Records. Catalogue no: **D 1050**

Hibbert, Jimmy

MR. WONDERFUL
Tracks: / Mr. Wonderful / Tough.
7" Single: Released Apr '80, on Logo, by Logo Records. Deleted '83. Catalogue no: **GO 379**

Hibbler, Al

UNCHAINED MELODY
Tracks: / Unchained melody.
7" Single: Released May '55, on Brunswick, by Decca Records. Deleted '58. Catalogue no: **05420**

UNCHAINED MELODY (OLD GOLD)
Tracks: / Unchained melody.
7" Single: Released Jul '82, on Old Gold, by Old Gold Records. Deleted Jul '88. Catalogue no: **OG 9207**

Hickory Country

HICKORY COUNTRY
Tracks: / You win again: *Various artists* / How I love them old songs: *Various artists* / Blue eyes crying in the rain: *Various artists* / Goin' out of my head: *Various artists.*
7" EP: Released '87, on Sundown, by Magnum Music Group. Catalogue no: **SDEP 001**

Hickory Rockabilly

HICKORY ROCKABILLY
Tracks: / Hey Mae: *Various artists* / Hey you there: *Various artists* / I ain't gonna waste my time: *Various artists* / I've got a brand new baby: *Various artists.*
7" EP: Released Jan '87, on Magnum Force, by Magnum Music Group. Catalogue no: **MFEP 011**

Hicks, Claire

PUSH (IN THE BUSH)
Tracks: / Push (in the bush).
7" Single: Released Feb '85, on Epic, by CBS Records. Catalogue no: **A 6075**
12" Single: Released Feb '85, on Epic, by CBS Records. Catalogue no: **TA 6075**

Hicks, D'Atra

SWEET TALK
Tracks: / Sweet talk / Sweet talk (inst.) (7" only.) / Sweet talk (Sweet revenge mix) (12" only.) / Sweet talk (ext.) (12" only.).
CD 5": Released Oct '89, on Capitol, by EMI Records. Catalogue no: **CDCL 545**
7" Single: Released Oct '89, on Capitol, by EMI Records. Catalogue no: **203 491 7**
7" Single: Released Oct '89, on Capitol, by EMI Records. Catalogue no: **CL 545**
12" Single: Released Oct '89, on Capitol, by EMI Records. Catalogue no: **203 491 6**
12" Single: Released Oct '89, on Capitol, by EMI Records. Catalogue no: **12CL 545**

Hicky, Don

WHAT A LOVER
Tracks: / What a lover.
12" Single: Released May '89, on Taurus, Catalogue no: **TRS 009**

Hidden Charms

LOVERS ROCK
Tracks: / Lover's rock / Lover's rock (club mix).
7" Single: Released Sep '83, on PRT, by Castle Communications Records. Catalogue no: **7P 285**
12" Single: Released Sep '83, on PRT, by Castle Communications Records. Catalogue no: **12P 285**

RUN FOR YOUR MONEY
Tracks: / Run for your money / I'm fine.
7" Single: Released Mar '83, on PRT, by Castle Communications Records. Catalogue no: **7P 267**
12" Single: Released Mar '83, on PRT, by Castle Communications Records. Catalogue no: **12P 267**

Hi-Fi

DON'T BREAK THE SPELL
Tracks: / Don't break the spell / Tigers and fire.
7" Single: Released Sep '81, on Abstract, by Abstract Sounds. Deleted Sep '84. Catalogue no: **ABS 2002**

LIVE EP (demonstration record)
12" Single: Released Apr '82, on Butt, by Butt Records. Catalogue no: **FUN EP 12-3**

Higgins, Alex

ONE FOUR SEVEN
Tracks: / One four seven / Life's in the pocket.
7" Single: Released Dec '83, on Solid, by Solid Records. Catalogue no: **STOP 003**

Higgins, Baz

BINGO
Tracks: / Bingo.
12" Single: Released Feb '85, on Mordent, Catalogue no: **DMOR 2**

Higgins, Bertie

Biographical details: American singer and songwriter Higgins came to fame in 1982 with *Key Largo*, a gentle ballad inspired by the Humphrey Bogart film of the same name. The single was a sleeper smash, entering the US Hot Hundred in November 1981, reaching the Top Forty the following January and attaining its No 8 peak in April. In Britain *Key Largo* could only peak at No 60. It seemed that Higgins had a Bogart fixation, for his debut album -- which reached No 38 in America -- included a similar-sounding song called *Casablanca*. But not even the Americans really wanted to know about Higgins' second LP, another laid-back selection of ballads which began and ended with *As Time Goes By*. Somehow "Play it again, Bertie" just didn't sound right... (Bob MacDonald, October 1985.).

CASABLANCA
Tracks: / Casablanca / She's gone to live on the mountain.
7" Single: Released Aug '82, on Epic, by CBS Records. Deleted Aug '85. Catalogue no: **EPCA 2673**

KEY LARGO
Tracks: / Key Largo / White line fever.
7" Single: Released Jun '82, on Epic, by CBS Records. Deleted '85. Catalogue no: **EPC A 2168**

Higgins, Chuck

BIP BOP BOM
Tracks: / Bip bop bom / Too smart.
7" Single: Released Jun '80, on Rollin' Rock, Catalogue no: **45 001**

Higgins, Mark

O FOR THE WINGS OF A DOVE
Tracks: / O for the wings of a dove.
7" Single: Released Sep '82, on Pip, by Pip Records. Catalogue no: **PIP 8201**

Higgs, Joe

WAGE A WAR
Tracks: / Wage a war.
12" Single: Released Nov '84, on Harry, Catalogue no: **unknown**

Higgs & Twins

GLAMOUR GIRL
Tracks: / Glamour girl.
12" Single: Released May '88, Catalogue no: **HTD 001**

High 5

COLD STEEL GANG
Tracks: / Cold steel gang / Confessions / Turn this car around (Extra Track on 12" Version only.) / On the banks (Extra Track on 12" Version only.).
7" Single: Released Nov '83, on Probe Plus, by Probe Plus Records. Catalogue no: **PP 8**

High Bees

SHE'S KILLING TIME
Tracks: / She's killing time / Some indulgence.
12" Single: Released Oct '85, on Supreme Int.Editions, by Supreme Int.Records. Catalogue no: **EDITION 85-8**

High Fashion

FEELIN' LUCKY LATELY
Tracks: / Feelin' lucky lately / Brainy children.
7" Single: Released May '82, on Capitol, by EMI Records. Deleted '85. Catalogue no: **CL 250**
12" Single: Released May '82, on Capitol, by EMI Records. Deleted '85. Catalogue no: **12 CL 250**

High Five

WORKING FOR THE MAN
Tracks: / Working for the man.
7" Single: Released Oct '84, on Big Village, Deleted '87. Catalogue no: **BIGV 001**

High Inergy

FIRST IMPRESSIONS
Tracks: / First impressions / Could this be love.
7" Single: Released Jun '82, on Motown, by BMG Records (UK). Catalogue no: **TMG 1268**

HE'S A PRETENDER
Tracks: / He's a pretender (part 1) / He's a pretender (part 2).
7" Single: Released Feb '83, on Gordy (USA), by Motown Records (UK). Catalogue no: **TMG 1294**
12" Single: Released Feb '83, on Gordy (USA), by Motown Records (UK). Catalogue no: **TMGT 1294**

HOLD ON TO MY LOVE
Tracks: / Hold on to my love / If i love you tonight.
7" Single: Released Oct '81, on Motown, by BMG Records (UK). Catalogue no: **TMG 1214**

I JUST WANNA DANCE WITH YOU
Tracks: / I just wanna dance with you / Take my life.
7" Single: Released Oct '81, on Motown, by BMG Records (UK). Catalogue no: **TMG 1234**

MAKE ME YOURS
Tracks: / Make me yours / I love makin' love.
7" Single: Released Oct '81, on Motown, by BMG Records (UK). Catalogue no: **TMG 1205**

High Jinks

IF IT COULD BE LIKE THIS FOREVER
Tracks: / If it could be like this forever / If it could be like this forever (Christmas mix).
7" Single: Released Dec '86, on Arista, by BMG Records (UK). Catalogue no: **ARIST 688**

High, Judy

FRENCH NITES
Tracks: / French nites / Miss missin' you.
7" Single: Released May '85, on Spirit (1), by Spirit Records. Catalogue no: **FIRE 5**

PUSH JUST A LITTLE BIT HARDER
Tracks: / Push just a little bit harder / When you're with the one you want.
7" Single: Released Nov '83, on Spirit (1), by Spirit Records. Catalogue no: **FIRE 4**
12" Single: Released Nov '83, on Spirit (1), by Spirit Records. Catalogue no: **FIRET 4**

High Numbers

I'M THE FACE
Tracks: / I'm the face / Zoot suit.
7" Single: Released Apr '80, on Back Door (Holland), Deleted '83. Catalogue no: **DOOR 4**

High Society

Biographical details: *If I ever go out in the rain* provided this obscure British band with their only UK chart entry - the single reached No.53 in late 1980. It was an enjoyable Manhattan Transfer style pastiche of the Hollywood era. But the lads' 1981 single *Gotta get out of this rut* failed to consolidate upon their previous chart toehold. (Bob MacDonald, 21st Oct 1985).

GOTTA GET OUT OF THIS RUT
Tracks: / Gotta get out of this rut / Powder blue.
7" Single: Released Aug '81, on Eagle (London), by Eagle (London) Records. Deleted '88. Catalogue no: **ERS 008**

I NEVER GO OUT IN THE RAIN
Tracks: / I never go out in the rain / I could never live without you.
7" Single: Released Sep '80, on Eagle (London), by Eagle (London) Records. Deleted '88. Catalogue no: **ERS 002**

High Tide

DANCING IN MY MIND
Tracks: / Dancing in my mind / Electric blue.
7" Single: Released Jan '82, on WEA, by WEA Records. Catalogue no: **K 18930**

High Voltage

JUNKANOO-OO-OO
Tracks: / Junkanoo-oo-oo.
7" Single: Released Aug '85, on Audiotrax, Deleted '86. Catalogue no: **ATX 11**

LOVE IS THE MESSAGE
Tracks: / Love is the message.
12" Single: Released Dec '83, on KRP, Catalogue no: **KPRT 103**

LOVE IS THE MESSAGE (87)
12" Single: Released Jul '87, on ISR, Catalogue no: **KEVT 5**

Highlanders

CHILDREN WONDER WHY
Tracks: / Children wonder why / Back to land / Lament.
7" Single: Released Oct '89, on Virgin, by Virgin Records. Catalogue no: **VS 1217**
12" Single: Released Oct '89, on Virgin, by Virgin Records. Catalogue no: **VST 1217**

NEVER ENOUGH
Tracks: / Never enough / Hour glass.
CD 5": Released Apr '89, on Virgin, by Virgin Records. Catalogue no: **VSCD 1155**
7" Single: Released 24 Apr '89, on Virgin, by Virgin Records. Catalogue no: **VS 1155**
12" Single: Released 24 Apr '89, on Virgin, by Virgin Records. Catalogue no: **VST 1155**

TELL ME THINGS
Tracks: / Tell me things (7" only) / No mean city / Tell me things (extended version) (12" only) / No mean city (instrumental) (12" only).
7" Single: Released 3 Oct '88, on Virgin, by Virgin Records. Catalogue no: **VS 1130**
12" Single: Released 3 Oct '88, on Virgin, by Virgin Records. Catalogue no: **VST 1130**

Highliners

BENNY HILL BOOGIE
Tracks: / Benny Hill boogie.
7" Single: Released Sep '89, on Razor, Catalogue no: **RZS 115**
12" Single: Released Sep '89, on Razor, Catalogue no: **RZST 115**

DOUBLE SHOT (OF MY BABY'S LOVE)
Tracks: / Double shot (of my baby's love) / Come dancing / Henry the wasp (Only available on 12" version.).
7" Single: Released Jul '88, on ABC (indie), Catalogue no: **ABCS 017**
12" Single: Released Jul '88, on ABC (indie), Catalogue no: **ABCS 017T**

HENRY THE WASP
Tracks: / Henry the wasp.
7" Single: Released Oct '88, on ABC (indie), Catalogue no: **ABCS 017**
12" Single: Released Oct '88, on ABC (indie), Catalogue no: **ABCS 17X**

HI - GLOSS - YOU'LL NEVER KNOW (Released on Epic)

12" Single: Released Oct '88, on ABC (indie), Catalogue no: **ABCS 017T**

IF YOU WANT TO BE HAPPY
Tracks: / If you want to be happy.
12" Single: Released Jun '88, on ABC (indie), Catalogue no: **ABCS 017T**

Highly Likely

WHATEVER HAPPENED TO YOU (LIKELY LADS THEME)
Tracks: / Whatever happened to you (likely lads theme).
7" Single: Released Apr '73, on BBC, by BBC Records & Tapes. Deleted '76. Catalogue no: **RESL 10**

Highly Strung

DON'T LET IT END
Tracks: / Don't let it end / Flame's lit, The.
7" Single: Released Jul '86, on Spartan, Catalogue no: **SP 141**

Hightower, Rosetta

WE FOUND LOVE TODAY
Tracks: / We found love today / Emergency.
7" Single: Released Feb '81, on Mirage (USA), Catalogue no: **IMA 001**

Highwaymen

GYPSY ROVER
Tracks: / Gypsy Rover, The.
7" Single: Released Dec '61, on H.M.V., by EMI Records. Deleted '64. Catalogue no: **POP 948**

MICHAEL
Tracks: / Michael.
7" Single: Released Sep '61, on H.M.V., by EMI Records. Deleted '64. Catalogue no: **POP 910**

Hi-Gloss

Biographical details: *You'll never know* was the title of Hi-Gloss' one off success - it reached No.12 on the UK singles chart in 1981 without making any impression in their native America. *You'll never know* seemed an appropriate title, for most people never knew who this faceless disco conglomeration really consisted of. But Hi-Gloss were good while they existed - *You'll never know* was one of the year's most powerful soul ballads. (20th Oct 19850.

YOU'LL NEVER KNOW (see panel on previous page)
Tracks: / You'll never know / totally yours.
7" Single: Released Jul '81, on Epic, by CBS Records. Deleted '84. Catalogue no: **EPC A 1387**
12" Single: Released Jul '81, on Epic, by CBS Records. Catalogue no: **EPC A 13 1387**

Higsons

CONSPIRACY
Tracks: / Conspiracy / Touch down.
7" Single: Released Apr '82, on Waap, Catalogue no: **WAAP 2**

GOT TO LET THIS HEAT OUT
Tracks: / Got to let this heat out.
7" Single: Released Jul '83, on Waap, Catalogue no: **WAAP 1**
12" Single: Released Jul '83, on Waap, Catalogue no: **WAAP 12**

I DON'T WANT TO LIVE WITH MONKEYS
Tracks: / I don't want to live with monkeys / Insect love.
7" Single: Released Jul '81, on Romans In Britain, Deleted '83. Catalogue no: **HIG 2**

LOST AND LONELY
Tracks: / Lost and lonely.
7" Single: Released Dec '81, on Waap, Catalogue no: **WAAP 5**

MUSIC TO WATCH GIRLS BY
Tracks: / Music to watch girls by / Lying on the phone.
7" Single: Released Sep '84, on Upright, by Upright Records. Catalogue no: **UP 9**
12" Single: Released Sep '84, on Upright, by Upright Records. Catalogue no: **12 UP 9**

PUSH OUT THE BOAT
Tracks: / Push out the boat.
7" Single: Released Oct '83, on Waap, Catalogue no: **WAAP 4**

RUN ME DOWN
Tracks: / Run me down / Put the punk back into funk / Run me down (extended version) (Only on 12" version.) / Run me down (instrumental) (Only on 12" version.) / Put the punk back into funk (parts 1 & 2) (Only on 12" version.).
7" Single: Released Feb '83, on Two-Tone, by Chrysalis Records. Deleted '85. Catalogue no: **CHS TT 24**
12" Single: Released Feb '83, on Two-Tone, by Chrysalis Records. Catalogue no: **CHS TT 1224**

TAKE IT
Tracks: / Take it.
7" Single: Released Jul '85, on R4, Deleted '86. Catalogue no: **FOR 2**
12" Single: Released Jul '85, on R4, Deleted '86. Catalogue no: **12 FOR 2**

TEAR THE WHOLE THING DOWN
Tracks: / Tear the whole thing down / Ylang ylang.
7" Single: Released '83, on Chrysalis, by Chrysalis Records. Deleted '87. Catalogue no: **CHS TT 21**

Hijack

HOLD NO HOSTAGE
Tracks: / Hold no hostage / Doomsday of rap / Drummer of doom, The / Sound of the knell, The.
12" Single: Released Nov '88, on Music Of Life, by Music Of Life Records. Catalogue no: **NOTE 21**

STYLE WARS
Tracks: / Style wars.
12" Single: Released Apr '88, on Music Of Life, by Music Of Life Records. Catalogue no: **NOTE 16**

Hi-Jinx

STREAMLINING SONG, THE
Tracks: / Streamlining song, The.
7" Single: Released Jul '84, on Southbank-GLC, Catalogue no: **GLC 2**

Hi-Liters

DANCE ME TO DEATH
Tracks: / Dance me to death.
7" Single: Released Jul '84, on Pinner, Catalogue no: **PRM 902**

Hi-Lites

STYLISTIC LOVE
Tracks: / Stylistic love / If music be the food of love.
7" Single: Released Nov '81, on EMI, by EMI Records. Deleted '84. Catalogue no: **EMI 5253**

Hill Bandits

HOTROD BUCKBOARD BOOGIE
Tracks: / Hotrod buckboard boogie.
12" Single: Released Nov '87, on Ediesta, Catalogue no: **CALC 040**

NOWHERE TRAIN
Tracks: / Nowhere train, The.
12" Single: Released May '88, on Ediesta, Catalogue no: **CALC 052**

PLANNING TOMORROW'S SINS
Tracks: / Planning tomorrow's sins.
7" Single: Released Nov '88, on Ediesta, Catalogue no: **CALC 075**
12" Single: Released Nov '88, on Ediesta, Catalogue no: **CALC 075T**

Hill, Benny

Biographical details: This British comedian and songwriter, born in 1925, had been a national institution on UK television since the late Fifties. Sporting a country bumpkin image, he supplemented his TV work with a trio of British hit singles during the early Sixties: *Gather in the mushrooms* (1961), *Transistor radio* (1961) and *Harvest of love* (1963) all reached the UK Top 30, and contained the risque titillation that became a regular part of his act.
After an absence of eight years, Hill suddenly returned to the record charts with his biggest ever hit. *Ernie (The fastest milkman in the west)* rocketed to No.1 in Britain at Christmas 1971, staying there for four weeks. Penned and performed by Hill, this silly story of an unlikely love triangle was one of the few 'death discs' that was actually intended to be funny; others like Ricky Valance's *Tell Laura I love her* and the Shangri Las' *Leader of the pack*, were hilarious but were not supposed to be. Hill did not make any further chart appearances, but has continued to be a familiar figure on the small and large screen. During the late Seventies and early Eighties, he unexpectedly became a cult figure in the States. The fact that he has survived so long in showbusiness must be largely due to his own scriptwriting skills, which have set him apart from the majority of comedians who rely on behing-the-scenes writers to come up with the material. (Bob MacDonald, 21st Nov 1985).

ERNIE (THE FASTEST MILKMAN IN THE WEST)
Tracks: / Ernie (The fastest milkman in the west).
7" Single: Released Nov '71, on Columbia, by EMI Records. Deleted '74. Catalogue no: **DB 8833**

GATHER IN THE MUSHROOMS
Tracks: / Gather in the mushrooms.
7" Single: Released Feb '61, on Pye, Deleted '64. Catalogue no: **7N 15327**

HARVEST OF LOVE
Tracks: / Harvest of love.
7" Single: Released May '63, on Pye, Deleted '66. Catalogue no: **7N 15520**

TRANSISTOR RADIO
Tracks: / Transistor radio.
7" Single: Released Jun '61, on Pye, Deleted '64. Catalogue no: **7N 15359**

Hill, Chris

BIONIC SANTA
Tracks: / Bionic Santa.
7" Single: Released Dec '76, on Philips, by Phonogram Ltd. Deleted '79. Catalogue no: **6006 551**

RENTA SANTA
Tracks: / Renta Santa.
7" Single: Released Dec '75, on Philips, by Phonogram Ltd. Deleted '78. Catalogue no: **6006 491**

Hill, Dan

Biographical details: This Canadian singer, guitarist and songwriter released his eponymous debut LP in 1975. It eventually reached No.104 on the Billboard album chart in the US, fuelled by a single called *Growin' up* which obtained a US No.67 placing. Hill's second albums *Hold on* was not successful, but the third (*Longer fuse*) contained the single which really made him famous - *Sometimes when we touch*. Reaching No.3 in America and No.13 in Britain in early 1978, *Sometimes when we touch* was one of the year's most memorable love ballads, although it classed Hill firmly in the middle-of-the-road bracket. His co-writer on this song was the verteran Barry Mann. Very few of Hill's solo compositions measured up to the standard of *Sometimes when we touch*, and he did not return to the charts on either side of the Atlantic. (Bob MacDonald, 21st Oct 1985).

IT'S A LONG ROAD
Tracks: / It's a long road.
7" Single: Released Feb '83, on T. E. R., by That's Entertainment Records. Catalogue no: **STER 003**

SOMETIMES WHEN WE TOUCH
Tracks: / Sometimes when we touch.
7" Single: Released Feb '78, on 20th Century, by 20th Century Records. Deleted '81. Catalogue no: **BTC 2355**
7" Single: Released Jul '81, on 20th Century, by 20th Century Records. Catalogue no: **GOLD 505**

YOU PULLED ME THROUGH
Tracks: / You pulled me through.
7" Single: Released Jan '84, on PRT, by Castle Communications Records. Catalogue no: **7P 300**

Hill, Lonnie

COULD IT BE LOVE
Tracks: / Could it be love / Step on out.
7" Single: Released May '86, on 10 Records, by Virgin Records. Deleted '89. Catalogue no: **TEN 117**
12" Single: Released May '86, on 10 Records, by Virgin Records. Deleted May '88. Catalogue no: **TENT 117**

GALVASTON BAY
Tracks: / Galveston Bay / My sweet love.
7" Single: Released Jun '86, on 10 Records, by Virgin Records. Deleted '89. Catalogue no: **TEN 111**
12" Single: Released Jun '86, on 10 Records, by Virgin Records. Deleted May '88. Catalogue no: **TEN 111-12**

Hill, Marden

OH CONSTANCE
Tracks: / Oh Constance / Execution of Emperor Maximillion, The / Bar room fly.
10" single: Released 14 Mar '88, on El, by Cherry Red Records. Catalogue no: **GPOT 36**

ROBE
Tracks: / Robe / Hangman.
7" Single: Released Oct '87, on El, by Cherry Red Records. Catalogue no: **GPO 30**

Hill, Michael P

SHE'S MY QUEEN
Tracks: / She's my queen.
12" Single: Released Aug '87, on Big Top, by Big Top Records. Deleted '88. Catalogue no: **MBT 04**

Hill, Rocky

I WON'T BE YOUR FOOL
Tracks: / I won't be your fool (7" mix) / Take my love.
7" Single: Released Mar '88, on Virgin, by Virgin Records. Catalogue no: **VS 1042**

Hill, Roni

YOU KEEP ME HANGIN' ON
Tracks: / You keep me hangin'on / Stop in the name of love.
7" Single: Released May '77, on Creole, by Creole Records. Deleted '80. Catalogue no: **CR 138**

Hill, Tony

CUCKOO CLOCK
Tracks: / Cuckoo clock, The.
7" Single: Released Dec '82, on Blue Hat, by Blue Hat Records. Catalogue no: **BHR 8**

H.M.S. PINAFORE MEDLEY
7" Single: Released Oct '84, on Blue Hat, by Blue Hat Records. Catalogue no: **BHR 22**

I'M A PIRATE KING
Tracks: / I'm a pirate king.
7" Single: Released Apr '83, on Blue Hat, by Blue Hat Records. Catalogue no: **BHR 12**

OLD KING COLE
Tracks: / Old King Cole.
7" Single: Released Sep '83, on Blue Hat, by Blue Hat Records. Catalogue no: **BHR 18**

TERRY WOGAN'S PARTY
Tracks: / Terry Wogan's party.
7" Single: Released May '84, on Blue Hat, by Blue Hat Records. Catalogue no: **BHR 20**

Hill, Vince

BRAVO POUR LA MUSICA
Tracks: / Bravo pour la musica.
7" Single: Released Mar '83, on Everest(Premier), by Everest Records. Catalogue no: **EVB 1001**

DOESN'T ANYBODY KNOW MY NAME?
Tracks: / Doesn't anybody know my name?.
7" Single: Released Feb '69, on Columbia, by EMI Records. Deleted '72. Catalogue no: **DB 8515**

EDELWEISS
Tracks: / Edelweiss.
7" Single: Released Feb '67, on Columbia, by EMI Records. Deleted '70. Catalogue no: **DB 8127**

EDELWEISS (OLD GOLD)
Tracks: / Edelweiss.
7" Single: Released Jul '82, on Old Gold, by Old Gold Records. Deleted Jul '88. Catalogue no: **OG 9045**

HEARTACHES
Tracks: / Heartaches.
7" Single: Released Mar '66, on Columbia, by EMI Records. Deleted '69. Catalogue no: **DB 7852**

IMPORTANCE OF YOUR LOVE
Tracks: / Importance of your love, The.
7" Single: Released Jun '68, on Columbia, by EMI Records. Deleted '71. Catalogue no: **DB 8414**

LITTLE BLUE BIRD
Tracks: / Little bluebird.
7" Single: Released Oct '69, on Columbia, by EMI Records. Deleted '72. Catalogue no: **DB 8616**

LOOK AROUND
Tracks: / Look around.
7" Single: Released Sep '71, on Columbia, by EMI Records. Deleted '74. Catalogue no: **DB 8804**

LOVE LETTERS IN THE SAND
Tracks: / Love letters in the sand.
7" Single: Released Sep '67, on Columbia, by EMI Records. Deleted '70. Catalogue no: **DB 8268**

MERCI CHERI
Tracks: / Merci Cherie.
7" Single: Released Jun '66, on Columbia, by EMI Records. Deleted '69. Catalogue no: **DB 7924**

MIRACLES
Tracks: / Miracles / If you want me to want you.
7" Single: Released Nov '80, on Piccadilly, Deleted Nov '83. Catalogue no: **7P 202**

PRAY FOR LOVE
Tracks: / Pray for love.
7" Single: Released May '82, on Multi-Media, Catalogue no: **MMT 7**

RIVER'S RUN DRY, THE
Tracks: / River's run dry, The.
7" Single: Released Jun '62, on Piccadilly, Deleted '65. Catalogue no: **7N 35043**

ROSES OF PICARDY
Tracks: / Roses of Picardy.
7" Single: Released May '67, on Columbia, by EMI Records. Deleted '70. Catalogue no: **DB 8185**

TAKE ME TO YOUR HEART
Tracks: / Take me to your heart.
7" Single: Released Jan '66, on Columbia, by EMI Records. Deleted '69. Catalogue no: **DB 7781**

THIEF IN THE NIGHT
Tracks: / Thief in the night / Don't let me know.
7" Single: Released May '81, on Celebrity, Deleted May '84. Catalogue no: **ACS 7**

WHILE THE FEELING'S GOOD (SINGLE)
Tracks: / While the feeling's good / Way I am.
7" Single: Released Jul '80, on Celebrity, Deleted Jul '83. Catalogue no: **ACS 1**

Hill, Z.Z.

CHEATING IN THE NEXT ROOM
Tracks: / Cheating in the next door / Right arm for your love.
7" Single: Released Jun '82, on Malaco, by Malaco Records (UK). Deleted '88. Catalogue no: **MAL 002**

Hillage, Steve

Biographical details: This British guitarist, synthesiser player, vocalist, composer and producer first attracted attention during 1973-74 as guitarist with the avant-garde jazz-rock band Gong. That multi-national group enjoyed a loyal cult following but no major commercial success. Hillage left to pursue a solo career in 1975 (although he played on Gong's 1976 album *Shamal*) and reached the UK No.33 position with his second solo LP *Fish rising*. (The first was an obscure item called *Arzachal* issued in 1969). Hillage's biggest album, simply entitled *L*, reached the UK Top 10 in late 1976; produced by Todd Rundgren, this was a fine example of Steve's hippie-oriented progressive rock. However, times were changing, and Hillage's dreamy music sounded increasingly passe as the New Wave gathered momentum. Subsequent albums gradually became less successful and, by the end of the Seventies, his status had diminished once more to that of an esoteric cult figure. After a lengthy absence from the recording scene, Hillage returned in late 1981 as producer of Simple Minds' UK Top 20 LP *Sons and fascination/Sister feelings call*, and in 1983 with his album *For to next/And not or*. The latter record showed Steve dabbling in the world on computers and technorock, but the music was still in his improvised style and the lyrics were still steeped in ethereal hippiedom. In 1985 Hillage achieved a minor American hit single as producer of Cock Robin's *When your heart is weak*. (Bob MacDonald, 21st Oct 1985).

KAMIKAZE EYES
Tracks: / Kamikaze eyes / Before the world.
7" Single: Released Jan '83, on Virgin, by Virgin Records. Deleted '89. Catalogue no: **VS 574**
12" Single: Released Jan '83, on Virgin, by Virgin Records. Deleted '89. Catalogue no: **VS 574-12**

Hiller, Holger

JONNY
Tracks: / Jonny / Das feuer.
12" Single: Released Feb '84, on Cherry Red, by Cherry Red Records. Catalogue no: **12 CHERRY 77**

WHIPPETS
Tracks: / Whippets.
12" Single: Released Mar '87, on Mute, by Mute Records. Catalogue no: **12 MUTE 55**

Hillier, Lyn

LOVE IS BAD FOR YOUR HEALTH
Tracks: / Love is bad for your health / They said.
7" Single: Released Apr '80, on Gem, Deleted Apr '83. Catalogue no: **GEMS 28**

Hillsbrough Crew

STEEL CITY
Tracks: / Steel city / Move on up.
7" Single: Released Dec '86, on Virgin, by Virgin Records. Deleted May '88. Catalogue no: **VS 908**
12" Single: Released Dec '86, on Virgin, by Virgin Records. Deleted May '88. Catalogue no: **VS 908-12**

Hillsiders

DRIVER GET ME HOME ON TIME
Tracks: / Driver get me home on time.
7" Single: Released '80, on Live Prom, Catalogue no: **LPS 006**

SHE WAS MY ONLY ONE
Tracks: / She was my only one / Last dollar.
7" Single: Released '81, on Live Prom, Catalogue no: **LPS 007**

Hillstreet

YOU PICK ME UP
Tracks: / You pick me up.
7" Single: Released Aug '87, on K West, by Creole Records. Catalogue no: **CR 110**
12" Single: Released Aug '87, on K West, by Creole Records. Catalogue no: **CRT 110**

Hilltoppers

MARRIANNE
Tracks: / Marrianne.
7" Single: Released Apr '57, on London-American, Deleted '60. Catalogue no: **HLD 8381**

ONLY YOU
Tracks: / Only You.
7" Single: Released Jan '56, on London-American, Deleted '59. Catalogue no: **HLD 8221**

TRYIN'
Tracks: / Trying.
7" Single: Released Sep '56, on London-American, Deleted '59. Catalogue no: **HLD 8298**

Hilton, J

CHERISH THE LOVE
Tracks: / Cherish the love.
7" Single: Released May '89, on Progressive, Catalogue no: **UNKNOWN**

Hilton, Ronnie

AROUND THE WORLD
Tracks: / Around the world.
7" Single: Released May '57, on H.M.V., by EMI Records. Deleted '60. Catalogue no: **POP 338**

BLOSSOM FELL, A
Tracks: / Blossom fell, A.
7" Single: Released Mar '55, on H.M.V., by EMI Records. Deleted '58. Catalogue no: **B 10808**

DON'T LET THE RAIN COME DOWN
Tracks: / Don't let the rain come down.
7" Single: Released May '64, on H.M.V., by EMI Records. Deleted '67. Catalogue no: **POP 1291**

I MAY NEVER PASS THIS WAY AGAIN
Tracks: / I may never pass this way again.
7" Single: Released Apr '58, on H.M.V., by EMI Records. Deleted '61. Catalogue no: **POP 468**

I STILL BELIEVE
Tracks: / I still believe.
7" Single: Released Nov '54, on H.M.V., by EMI Records. Deleted '57. Catalogue no: **B 10785**

I'LL SLEEP A LITTLE EASIER TONIGHT
Tracks: / I'll sleep a little easier tonight / Lazy.
7" Single: Released Jul '89, on Redrock, by Redrock Records. Catalogue no: **REDR 8**

MAGIC MOMENTS
Tracks: / Magic moments.
7" Single: Released Feb '58, on H.M.V., by EMI Records. Deleted '61. Catalogue no: **POP 446**

NO OTHER LOVE
Tracks: / No other love.
7" Single: Released Apr '56, on H.M.V., by EMI Records. Deleted '59. Catalogue no: **POP 198**

STARS SHINE IN YOUR EYES
Tracks: / Stars shine in your eyes.
7" Single: Released Aug '55, on H.M.V., by EMI Records. Deleted '58. Catalogue no: **B 10901**

TWO DIFFERENT WORLDS
Tracks: / Two different worlds.
7" Single: Released Nov '56, on H.M.V., by EMI Records. Deleted '59. Catalogue no: **POP 274**

VENI VIDI VICI
Tracks: / Veni vidi vici.
7" Single: Released Dec '54, on H.M.V., by EMI Records. Deleted '57. Catalogue no: **B 10785**

WHO ARE WE
Tracks: / Who are we.
7" Single: Released Jun '56, on H.M.V., by EMI Records. Deleted '59. Catalogue no: **POP 221**

WINDMILL IN OLD AMSTERDAM, A
Tracks: / Windmill in old Amsterdam, A.
7" Single: Released Feb '65, on H.M.V., by EMI Records. Deleted '68. Catalogue no: **POP 1378**

WOMAN IN LOVE
Tracks: / Woman in love.
7" Single: Released Sep '56, on H.M.V., by EMI Records. Deleted '59. Catalogue no: **POP 221**

WONDER OF YOU, THE
Tracks: / Wonder of you, The.
7" Single: Released Sep '59, on H.M.V., by EMI Records. Deleted '62. Catalogue no: **POP 638**

HINDSIGHT - SMALL CHANGE (Released on Circa)

WONDERFUL WONDERFUL
Tracks: / Wonderful wonderful.
7" Single: Released Aug '57, on H.M.V., by EMI Records. Deleted '60. Catalogue no: **POP 364**

WORLD OUTSIDE, THE
Tracks: / World outside, The.
7" Single: Released Jan '59, on H.M.V., by EMI Records. Deleted '62. Catalogue no: **POP 559**

YELLOW ROSE OF TEXAS
Tracks: / Yellow rose of Texas.
7" Single: Released Nov '55, on H.M.V., by EMI Records. Deleted '58. Catalogue no: **B 10924**

YOUNG AND FOOLISH
Tracks: / Young and foolish.
7" Single: Released Feb '56, on H.M.V., by EMI Records. Deleted '59. Catalogue no: **POP 154**

Hindle Pickets And TBE

PART OF THE UNION
Tracks: / Part of the union.
7" Single: Released Aug '84, on Catch 22, Catalogue no: **CTT 1**

Hinds, Donna

SPECIAL PRAYER
Tracks: / Special prayer / From me to you.
7" Single: Released Dec '86, on Multi, Catalogue no: **MUL 001**

Hinds, Errol

HO WHAT A SATURDAY NIGHT
Tracks: / Ho what a Saturday night.
12" Single: Released May '85, on Witty, Catalogue no: **MM 039**

Hinds, Jerome

SUMMER LEAVE
Tracks: / Summer leave.
12" Single: Released Oct '87, on Hindsight, Catalogue no: **HS2XHB 001**

Hinds, Ornell

CAN'T HELP FALLING IN LOVE WITH YOU
Tracks: / Can't help falling in love with you / My favourite song.
7" Single: Released Jan '80, on Ariola, by BMG Records (UK). Deleted Jan '85. Catalogue no: **AHA 556**

Hindsight

HEAVEN'S JUST A BREATH AWAY
Tracks: / Heaven's just a breath away (7" only) / Come's the sunshine / Small change (Corn Exchange mix) (On YRD 3 only) / Heaven's just a breath away (heaven can wait) (On YRD 3 only) / Heaven's just a breath away (the bliss mix) (On 12" only).
CD 5": Released May '87, on Circa, by Virgin Records. Deleted '89. Catalogue no: **YRCD 3**
7" Single: on Circa, by Virgin Records. Deleted May '88. Catalogue no: **YR 3**
12" Single: Released May '87, on Circa, by Virgin Records. Catalogue no: **YRT 3**
Special: Released '87, on Virgin, by Virgin Records. Catalogue no: **YRD 3**

LOWDOWN
Tracks: / Lowdown (the highlife mix) / Everybody in the house / Lowdown.
12" Single: Released '87, on Circa, by Virgin Records. Catalogue no: **YRT 5**

SMALL CHANGE (see panel above)
Tracks: / Small change (7" only) / Be free / Small change (corn exchange mix) (On YRTX 1 only) / Small change (backhander dub) (On YRTX 1 only) / Small change (spare a dime mix) (On YRT 1 only) / Small change (spare a dime instumental) (On YRT 1 only) / Small change (backhander mix) (On YRT 1 only).
7" Single: Released '86, on Circa, by Virgin Records. Catalogue no: **YR 1**
12" Single: on Circa, by Virgin Records. Catalogue no: **YRTX 1**
12" Single: Released Nov '86, on Circa, by Virgin Records. Catalogue no: **YRT 1**

Hine, Eric

EXPECTATION Brave new world
Tracks: / Expectation / Not fade away.
7" Single: Released Jul '82, on Radioactive, Catalogue no: **RAD 505**

NOT FADE AWAY
Tracks: / Not fade away / After dark.
7" Single: Released Apr '81, on Radioactive, Catalogue no: **RAD 101**
12" Single: Released Apr '81, on Radioactive, Catalogue no: **RADL 101**

Hine, Rupert

CURIOUS KIND
Tracks: / Curious kind / Dark windows.
7" Single: Released Jun '82, on A&M, by A&M Records. Deleted Jun '85. Catalogue no: **AMS 8225**

LIVING IN A SIN
Tracks: / Living in a sin.
7" Single: Released Apr '83, on A&M, by A&M Records. Deleted '88. Catalogue no: **AM 111**
12" Single: Released Apr '83, on A&M, by A&M Records. Deleted '88. Catalogue no: **AMX 111**

MISPLACED LOVE
Tracks: / Misplaced love / I think a man.
7" Single: Released Feb '81, on A&M, by A&M Records. Deleted '84. Catalogue no: **AMS 8106**

SURFACE TENSION
Tracks: / Surface tension / House arrest.
7" Single: Released May '81, on A&M, by A&M Records. Deleted May '84. Catalogue no: **AMS 8126**

Hines, Carlton

SHE LOVES ME
Tracks: / She loves me / She loves me (dub) / Jah Bull / Conference table(Dub).
12" Single: Released Nov '86, on Island, by Island Records. Deleted Jul '87. Catalogue no: **12IS 307**

Hines, Gregory

THAT GIRL WANTS TO DANCE(WITH ME)
Tracks: / That girl wants to dance with me

CD 5": Released Aug '88, on Epic, by CBS Records. Deleted Jan '89. Catalogue no: **653812 2**
7" Single: Released Jul '88, on Epic, by CBS Records. Deleted Jan '89. Catalogue no: **652812 7**
12" Single: Released Jul '88, on Epic, by CBS Records. Deleted Jan '89. Catalogue no: **652812 8**

YOU NEED SOMEBODY
Tracks: / You need somebody / You need somebody (instrumental) / There's nothing better than love (Only on 12"version and CD single.) / That girl wants to dance with me (Only on 12" version & CD single.).
CD 5": Released Oct '88, on Epic, by CBS Records. Deleted 17 Apr '89. Catalogue no: **653109 2**
7" Single: Released Oct '88, on Epic, by CBS Records. Deleted 17 Apr '89. Catalogue no: **653109 7**
12" Single: Released Oct '88, on Epic, by CBS Records. Deleted 17 Apr '89. Catalogue no: **653109 6**

Hines, Justin

RUB UP, PUSH UP
Tracks: / Rub up, push up / Copasetic.
7" Single: Released Feb '80, on Island, by Island Records. Deleted '83. Catalogue no: **WIP 6580**

SITTING IN THE JUNGLE
Tracks: / Sitting in the jungle / I follow the rainbow.
12" Single: Released Jan '87, on Jay Dee, Catalogue no: **JD 018**

Hines, Marcia

LET THE MUSIC PLAY
Tracks: / Let the music play / April sun in Cuba / Save the last dance for me.
12" Single: Released Oct '80, on Logo, by Logo Records. Deleted Oct '83. Catalogue no: **GOT 392**

OOH CHILD
Tracks: / Ooh child / Dance you fool, dance.
7" Single: Released Mar '80, on Logo, by Logo Records. Deleted Mar '83. Catalogue no: **GO 377**

SAVE THE LAST DANCE FOR ME
Tracks: / Save the last dance for me / Moments.
7" Single: Released Mar '80, on Logo, by Logo Records. Deleted '83. Catalogue no: **GO 383**

TAKING IT ALL IN STRIDE
Tracks: / Taking it all in stride / Take it from the boys.
7" Single: Released Dec '81, on Logo, by Logo Records. Deleted Dec '84. Catalogue no: **GO 405**

WHAT A BITCH IS LOVE
Tracks: / What a bitch is love / I like it.
7" Single: Released Feb '82, on Logo, by Logo Records. Deleted Feb '87. Catalogue no: **GO 411**

YOUR LOVE STILL BRINGS ME TO MY KNEES
Tracks: / Your love still brings me to my knees / All the things we do when were alone.
7" Single: Released Jul '81, on Logo, by Logo Records. Deleted '85. Catalogue no: **GO 403**

Hino, Terumasa

GIVE MY HEART A BREAK
Tracks: / Give my heart a break / Give my heart a break (Ext.) (12" only.) / Light is right.
7" Single: Released Feb '89, on Syncopate, by EMI Records. Deleted Aug '89. Catalogue no: **SY 23**
12" Single: Released Feb '89, on Syncopate, by EMI Records. Deleted Aug '89. Catalogue no: **12SY 23**

Hipsway

ASK THE LORD
Tracks: / Ask the Lord / Are you ready to listen / Pain machine (Extra Track on 12" version only.).
7" Single: Released Apr '86, on Mercury, by Phonogram Ltd. Deleted '87. Catalogue no: **LORD 1**
12" Single: Released Apr '86, on Mercury, by Phonogram Ltd. Deleted '87. Catalogue no: **LORDX 1**

BROKEN YEARS
Tracks: / Broken years / Forbidden.
12" Single: Released Jun '85, on Mercury, by Phonogram Ltd. Deleted '87. Catalogue no: **MERX 193**

HONEY THIEF
Tracks: / Honey thief / Wild sorrow.
7" Single: Released Feb '86, on Mercury, by Phonogram Ltd. Deleted Jul '87. Catalogue no: **MER 212**
12" Single: Released Feb '86, on Mercury, by Phonogram Ltd. Deleted Jul '87. Catalogue no: **MERX 212**
7" Set: Released Feb '86, on Mercury, by Phonogram Ltd. Deleted Jul '87. Catalogue no: **MERXD 212**

LONG WHITE CAR
Tracks: / Ring out the bell / Tinder (Extra track on 12" version only).
7" Single: Released Aug '86, on Mercury, by Phonogram Ltd. Deleted '87. Catalogue no: **MER 230**
12" Single: Released Aug '86, on Mercury, by Phonogram Ltd. Deleted '87. Catalogue no: **MERX 230**

YOUR LOVE
Tracks: / Your love / Sweet talk / What makes a man (love a woman so bad) (Only on 12" and CD single.).
CD 5": Released 20 Mar '89, on Mercury, by Phonogram Ltd. Catalogue no: **MERCD 279**
7" Single: Released 20 Mar '89, on Mercury, by Phonogram Ltd. Deleted 31 Jul '89. Catalogue no: **MER 279**
12" Single: Released 20 Mar '89, on Mercury, by Phonogram Ltd. Deleted 31 Jul '89. Catalogue no: **MERX 279**

Hiroshima

CRUISIN' J-TOWN
Tracks: / Cruisin' J-Town / Warriors / Lion dance.
12" Single: Released Jan '81, on Arista, by BMG Records (UK). Deleted Jan '84. Catalogue no: **T 12388**

LION DANCE
Tracks: / Lion dance / Roomful of mirrors.
7" Single: Released Mar '80, on Arista, by BMG Records (UK). Deleted Mar '83. Catalogue no: **ARIST 340**
12" Single: Released Mar '80, on Arista, by BMG Records (UK). Deleted Mar '83. Catalogue no: **ARIST 12340**

SEND YOUR LOVE TO ME
Tracks: / Another place / Send your love to me.
7" Single: Released Apr '86, on Epic, by CBS Records. Deleted '86. Catalogue no: **A 7113**

His Latest Flame

LONDONDERRY ROAD
Tracks: / Londonderry road / For the sake of / What makes you (12" only) / Come on, come on (CD single only).
CD 5": Released 24 Jul '89, on London Records, by London Records. Catalogue no: **LONCD 234**
Cassingle: Released 24 Jul '89, on London Records, by London Records. Catalogue no: **LONCS 234**
7" Single: Released 24 Jul '89, on London Records, by London Records. Catalogue no: **LON 234**
12" Single: Released 24 Jul '89, on London Records, by London Records. Catalogue no: **LONX 234**

SOMEBODY'S GONNA GET HURT
Tracks: / All the same to me / Somebody's gonna get hurt (instrumental) (Extra track on 12" version only).
7" Single: Released May '86, on Go Discs, by Chrysalis Records. Catalogue no: **GOD 10**
12" Single: Released May '86, on Go Discs, by Chrysalis Records. Catalogue no: **GODX 10**

STOP THE TIDE
Tracks: / Wake up (and smell the coffee) / Stop the tide.
7" Single: Released Sep '86, on Go Discs, by Chrysalis Records. Catalogue no: **GOD 14**
12" Single: Released Sep '86, on Go Discs, by Chrysalis Records. Catalogue no: **GODX 14**

Hit Parade

BAD NEWS (EP)
Tracks: / Bad news.
12" Single: Released Jun '83, on Crass, by Crass Records. Catalogue no: **CRASS 221984/12**

FOREVER
Tracks: / Forever / Stop.
7" Single: Released Jun '84, on JSH, by JSH Records. Catalogue no: **JSH 1**

I GET SO SENTIMENTAL
Tracks: / I get so sentimental / Sue.
7" Single: Released Apr '87, on JSH, by JSH Records. Catalogue no: **JSH 6**

MY FAVOURITE GIRL
Tracks: / My favourite girl / It rained on Monday afternoon.
7" Single: Released Oct '84, on JSH, by JSH Records. Catalogue no: **JSH 2**

SEE YOU IN HAVANA
Tracks: / See you in Havana / Wipe away the tears.
7" Single: Released Jul '86, on JSH, by JSH Records. Catalogue no: **JSH 5**

SUN SHINES IN GERRARDS CROSS, THE
Tracks: / Sun shines in Gerrards Cross, The / You hurt me too.
7" Single: Released Mar '85, on JSH, by JSH Records. Catalogue no: **JSH 3**

YOU DIDN'T LOVE ME THEN
Tracks: / You didn't love me then.
7" Single: Released Oct '85, on JSH, by JSH Records. Catalogue no: **JSH 4**

Hit & Run

HOW LONG
Tracks: / How long / How long (piece of string remix) (Only on special remix.).
7" Single: Released Oct '88, on Danceyard, by Danceyard Records. Catalogue no: **DOPE 2**
12" Single: Released Nov '88, on Danceyard, by Danceyard Records. Catalogue no: **DOPETR 2**
12" Single: Released Oct '88, on Danceyard, by Danceyard Records. Catalogue no: **DOPE T2**

Hit Squad M.C.B

WAX ON THE MELT
Tracks: / Wax on the melt.
12" Single: Released Apr '88, on Eastern Bloc, Catalogue no: **EASTERN 001**

Hit The Roof

CONTACT
Tracks: / Contact.
7" Single: Released 16 Jan '89, on One Little Indian, by One Little Indian Records. Catalogue no: **7 TP 15**
12" Single: Released 16 Jan '89, on One Little Indian, by One Little Indian Records. Catalogue no: **12 TP 15**

Hitback EP

HITBACK EP
Tracks: / Pig in a suit: *Laverne & Shirlie* / Rich rewards: *Skiptracers* / How to smile: *Said Liquidator* / Thai holiday: *Movietone.*
7" EP: Released Mar '88, on Hitback, by Hitback Records. Catalogue no: **HITBACK 1**

Hitchcock, Carol

GET READY (THE EXTRATERRESTRIAL MIX)
Tracks: / Get ready / More than words can say.
7" Single: Released Apr '87, on A&M, by A&M Records. Deleted Mar '88. Catalogue no: **AM 391**
12" Single: Released Apr '87, on A&M, by A&M Records. Deleted Mar '88. Catalogue no: **AMY 391**

Hitchcock, Robyn

AMERICA
Tracks: / America / It was the night / How do you work this thing?.
7" Single: Released Mar '82, on Albion, by Albion Records. Catalogue no: **ION 1031**

BELLS OF RHYMNEY
Tracks: / Bells of Rhymney.
12" Single: Released Dec '84, on Midnight Music, by Midnight Music Records. Catalogue no: **DONG 8**

BRENDA'S IRON SLEDGE
Tracks: / Only the stones remain / Pit of souls (parts 1-4) / Brenda's iron sledge.
12" Single: Released Feb '86, on Midnight Music, by Midnight Music Records. Catalogue no: **DONG 17**

EATEN BY HER OWN DINNER
Tracks: / Eaten by her own dinner / Grooving on an inner plane / Messages of dark / Bandoned brain, The / Happy the golden prince
7" Single: Released Nov '82, on Midnight Music, by Midnight Music Records. Catalogue no: **DING 2**
12" Single: Released Oct '86, on Midnight Music, by Midnight Music Records. Catalogue no: **DONG 2**

HEAVEN
Tracks: / Heaven.
12" Single: Released May '85, on Midnight Music, by Midnight Music Records. Catalogue no: **DONG 12**

IF YOU WERE A PRIEST
Tracks: / Crawling glass fish, The / If you were a priest.
12" Single: Released Jan '87, on Glass Fish, Catalogue no: **OOZE 1**
7" Single: Released Jan '87, on Glass Fish, Catalogue no: **OOZE 1**

MAN WHO INVENTED HIMSELF
Tracks: / Man who invented himself / Dancing on God's thumb.
7" Single: Released Apr '81, on Armageddon, by Armageddon Records. Catalogue no: **AS 008**

NIGHTRIDE TO TRINIDAD
Tracks: / Nightride to Trinidad / Kingdom of....
12" Single: Released May '83, on Albion, by Albion Records. Catalogue no: **12ION 1036**

Hi-Tek

CAR TUNE
Tracks: / Car tune / Take the A side.
12" Single: Released Jun '81, on Original, Deleted Jun '84. Catalogue no: **TAB 006**

Hithouse

JACK TO THE SOUND OF THE UNDERGROUND
Tracks: / Jack to the sound of the underground / Jack to the sound of the underground (version).
7" Single: Released Nov '88, on Supreme, by Supreme Records. Catalogue no: **SUPE 137**
12" Single: Released Nov '88, on Supreme, by Supreme Records. Catalogue no: **SUPTEZ 137**
12" Single: Released Nov '88, on Supreme, by Supreme Records. Catalogue no: **SUPETX 137**

MOVE YOUR FEET TO THE RHYTHM OF THE BEAT
Tracks: / Move your feet to the rhythm of the beat / Deep piano, The.
7" Single: Released Jul '89, on Supreme, by Supreme Records. Catalogue no: **SUPE 149**
12" Single: Released Jul '89, on Supreme, by Supreme Records. Catalogue no: **SUPT 149**
12" Single: Released Mar '89, on ARS, Catalogue no: **ARS 3735**

Hitlist (group)

INTO THE FIRE
Tracks: / Total isolation / Into the fire.
7" Single: Released Mar '86, on Virgin, by Virgin Records. Deleted '86. Catalogue no: **VS 756**
12" Single: Released Mar '86, on Virgin, by Virgin Records. Deleted '86. Catalogue no: **VS 756-12**

OKAY FOR YOU
Tracks: / High treason / Okay for you.
7" Single: Released Apr '86, on Virgin, by Virgin Records. Deleted '86. Catalogue no: **VS 812**
12" Single: Released Apr '86, on Virgin, by Virgin Records. Deleted '86. Catalogue no: **VS 812-12**

Hitmasters

SAWMIX 1
Tracks: / Sawmix 1.
7" Single: Released Jan '88, on Quazar, Catalogue no: **QUA 5**
12" Single: Released Jan '88, on Quazar, Catalogue no: **QUAT 5**

Hitmen

BATES MOTEL
Tracks: / Bates motel / Don't speak with the enemy.
7" Single: Released Apr '81, on CBS, by CBS Records. Deleted '85. Catalogue no: **A 1088**

HOLD ON TO HER
Tracks: / Hold on to her / Slay me with your 45.
7" Single: Released Nov '80, on Urgent, Deleted Nov '83. Catalogue no: **PRONTO 4**

I STILL REMEMBER IT
Tracks: / I still remember it / Bad timing.
7" Single: Released Aug '80, on CBS, by CBS Records. Deleted '83. Catalogue no: **PRONTO 3**

OUIJA
Tracks: / Ouija / Shade in fade out.
12" Single: Released Oct '81, on CBS, by CBS Records. Deleted Oct '84. Catalogue no: **CBSA 131591**

Hive

KINGDOM RISE,KINGDOM FALL
Tracks: / Kingdom rise, kingdom fall.
12" Single: Released Apr '85, on Hum Music, Catalogue no: **HUM 1**

Hizer,Mike

COME OUTSIDE
Tracks: / Come outside.
7" Single: Released Aug '85, on Sierra, by Sierra Records. Deleted '86. Catalogue no: **FED 16**

H-Men

SCREAM
Tracks: / Scream.
12" Single: Released Nov '88, on Rocking, Catalogue no: **RH 011**

H.M.S Ark Royal

SAILING
Tracks: / Sailing.
7" Single: Released Jul '82, on BBC, by BBC Records & Tapes. Deleted '87. Catalogue no: **RESL 118**

H.M.S Bounty

GIRL
Tracks: / Girl.
7" Single: Released Jun '85, on Cherry Red, by Cherry Red Records. Catalogue no: **CHERRY 88**

Ho Ho Kam

DON'T YOU KNOW
Tracks: / Envy your innocence / Don't you know.
7" Single: Released Aug '86, on Numa, by Numa Records. Catalogue no: **NU 18**
12" Single: Released Aug '86, on Numa, by Numa Records. Catalogue no: **NUM 18**

HARLEQUIN TEARS
Tracks: / To sleep / Harlequin tears.
7" Single: Released Jun '86, on Numa, by Numa Records. Catalogue no: **NU 8**
12" Single: Released Jun '86, on Numa, by Numa Records. Catalogue no: **NUM 8**

Hoax

BLIND PANIC
Tracks: / Blind panic.
7" EP: Released Mar '82, on Hologram, by Aardvark Records. Catalogue no: **HOAX 6**

Hobbies Of Today

IN MY MINDS EYE
Tracks: / You / In my minds eye.
7" Single: Released Jan '86, on Rune, Catalogue no: **CAST 02**

Hobo Radio...

OH OH WHAT A DRAG
Tracks: / Oh oh what a drag / It's always rubbish on the B side.
7" Single: Released Nov '81, on Red Bus, by Red Bus Records. Deleted Nov '84. Catalogue no: **RBUS 63**

Hockridge, Edmund

BY THE FOUNTAINS OF ROME
Tracks: / By the fountains of Rome.
7" Single: Released Aug '56, on Nixa, by Pye Records. Deleted '59. Catalogue no: **N 15063**

NO OTHER LOVE
Tracks: / No other love.
7" Single: Released May '56, on Nixa, by Pye Records. Deleted '59. Catalogue no: **N 15046**

YOUNG AND FOOLISH
Tracks: / Young and foolish.
7" Single: Released Feb '56, on Nixa, by Pye Records. Deleted '59. Catalogue no: **N 15039**

Hodges, Eddie

I'M GONNA KNOCK ON YOUR DOOR
Tracks: / I'm gonna knock on your door.
7" Single: Released Sep '61, on London-American, Deleted '64. Catalogue no: **HLA 9369**

MADE TO LOVE (GIRLS,GIRLS,GIRLS)
Tracks: / Made to love (girls,girls,girls).
7" Single: Released Aug '62, on London-American, Deleted '65. Catalogue no: **HLA 9576**

Hodges, Jack

EVERYTHING IS FRESH TODAY (THE RASPBERRY SONG)
Tracks: / Everything is fresh today (The raspberry song) / Song of the prune.
Note: From the album "The Classic Years in Digital Stereo - 'Silly Songs' (1922-1934)".
7" Single: Released Jan '88, on BBC, by BBC Records & Tapes. Catalogue no: **RESL 223**

Hodgson, Roger

HAD A DREAM
Tracks: / Had a dream.
7" Single: Released Oct '84, on A&M, by A&M Records. Deleted '88. Catalogue no: **AM 221**

IN JEOPARDY
Tracks: / In jeopardy.
7" Single: Released Jan '85, on A&M, by A&M Records. Deleted '88. Catalogue no: **AM 232**

LONDON
Tracks: / London / In jeopardy.
7" Single: Released Sep '87, on A&M, by A&M Records. Deleted Mar '88. Catalogue no: **AM 405**
12" Single: Released Sep '87, on A&M, by A&M Records. Deleted Mar '88. Catalogue no: **AMY 405**

YOU MAKE ME LOVE YOU
Tracks: / You make me love you / Lovers in the wind / You make me love you (version) (Available on 12" only).
Note: *Available on 12" verion only.
12" Single: Released Nov '87, on A&M, by A&M Records. Deleted 1 Aug '88. Catalogue no: **AMY 418**
7" Single: Released Nov '87, on A&M, by A&M Records. Deleted 1 Aug '88. Catalogue no: **AM 418**

Hofmann, Peter

NIGHTS IN WHITE SATIN
Tracks: / Nights in white satin / Sailing.
7" Single: Released May '83, on CBS, by CBS Records. Catalogue no: **A 3482**

SUN AINT GONNA SHINE ANY MORE
Tracks: / Sun ain't gonna shine anymore, The / Goodbye to Hollywood.
7" Single: Released Oct '83, on CBS, by CBS Records. Catalogue no: **A 3178**

Hogan, Annie

EACH DAY
Tracks: / Each day.
7" Single: Released Mar '88, on Dinamo, Catalogue no: **DIN 17**
12" Single: Released Mar '88, on Dinamo, Catalogue no: **DIN 112**

Hogay..

LAST FOOTBALL SONG, THE
Tracks: / Last football song, The.
7" Single: Released Jun '84, on Silvertown, by Silvertown Records. Catalogue no: **STS 8**

Hohokam

KING
Tracks: / King.
7" Single: Released Nov '84, on Numa, by Numa Records. Catalogue no: **NU 3**

Hokus Pokus

HOUSE IT UP
Tracks: / House it up.
12" Single: Released Sep '87, on West Madison St.(USA), Catalogue no: **WMSD 1201**

Holbrook, Robin

FRIENDLY ISLE
Tracks: / Friendly isle.
7" Single: Released Aug '84, on Solent, by Solent Records. Catalogue no: **SS 062**

Holder, Jack

NEVER LET YOU GO
Tracks: / Never let you go / I found love.
7" Single: Released Nov '80, on WEA, by WEA Records. Deleted '83. Catalogue no: **K 18361**

Hole

DYSKINESIA
Tracks: / Dyskinesia.
12" Single: Released Oct '89, on Eyas Media, by Eyas Media. Catalogue no: **EYAS 031**

Hole In The Wall

LITTLE DEVIL
Tracks: / Little devil.
12" Single: Released Jul '89, on Institute, Catalogue no: **12 INS 2**

Holiday, Billie

THAT OLE DEVIL CALLED LOVE (SINGLE)
Tracks: / That ole devil called love.
7" Single: Released Oct '85, on MCA, by MCA Records. Catalogue no: **MCA 1007**

Holiday Patrons

HOTTEST TIME OF THE YEAR
Tracks: / Hottest time of the year.
7" Single: Released Aug '85, on Rod, Catalogue no: **RATE 1**

Holidaymakers

CINCINNATI
Tracks: / Cincinnati / Seventh Valley girl.
7" Single: Released 16 Jan '89, on Woosh, by Woosh Records. Catalogue no: **WOOSH 4**

SKYRIDER
12" Single: Released Sep '89, on Gay Cowboy, Catalogue no: **MAKER 001T**

Holland, Amy

HOW DO I SURVIVE
Tracks: / How do I survive / Don't kid yourself.
7" Single: Released May '80, on Capitol, by EMI Records. Deleted May '83. Catalogue no: **CL 16150**

Holland, Fox

FOX HOLLAND
Special: Released Dec '87, on Iron Works (USA), by Azra International (USA). Catalogue no: **IW 1019**

Holland, Jools

BUMBLE BOOGIE
Tracks: / Bumble boogie / That don't matter to me.
7" Single: Released Mar '81, on A&M, by A&M Records. Deleted Mar '84. Catalogue no: **AMS 8111**

CRAZY OVER YOU
Tracks: / Crazy over you.
7" Single: Released Oct '83, on I.R.S, Catalogue no: **PFP 1020**

PINEAPPLE CHUNK
Tracks: / Pineapple chunk / Much more hope for me.
7" Single: Released Feb '82, on A&M, by A&M Records. Deleted Feb '87. Catalogue no: **AMS 8205**

Holland/Dozier

WHY CAN'T WE BE LOVERS
Tracks: / Why can't we be lovers.
7" Single: Released Feb '85, on HDH (Holland/Dozier/Holland), by Demon Records. Catalogue no: **HDH 4513**
7" Single: Released Oct '72, on Invictus, Deleted '75. Catalogue no: **INV 525**

Holliday, Jennifer

Biographical details: This rotund singer and actress was just 21 years old when she won the 1982 Tony Amard for Best Actress in the Broadway show *Dreamgirls*. Undoubtedly the standout segment of her performance was *And I'm telling you I'm not going*, a stunning song which she belted out in breathtaking fashion. This number was released as a single, reaching No.22 in the States and No.32 in Britain. The surprisingly modest chart success awarded to *And I'm telling you I'm not going* set a pattern that was to continued when Holliday launched her own solo recording career in 1983. Her first album *Feel my soul* was produced by Earth Wind & Fire leader Maurice White, but suffered on account of its lack of strong material and consequently flopped. She returned to top form in 1985 with the single *Hard times for lovers* but this exquisite and totally contempory offering could only manage a minot placing on the US Hot 100. (Bob MacDonald, 22nd October 1985).

AND I'M TELLING YOU I'M NOT GOING
Tracks: / And I'm telling you I'm not going.
7" Single: Released Aug '82, on Geffen, by Geffen Records (USA). Catalogue no: **GEF A 2644**

I AM CHANGING
Tracks: / I am changing / Cadillac car.
7" Single: Released Oct '82, on Geffen, by Geffen Records (USA). Catalogue no: **GEF A 2895**

I AM LOVE
Tracks: / I am love.
12" Single: Released Feb '84, on Geffen, by Geffen Records (USA). Catalogue no: **TA 3704**
7" Single: Released Feb '84, on Geffen, by Geffen Records (USA). Catalogue no: **A 3704**

SHINE A LIGHT
Tracks: / Shine a light.
7" Single: Released Oct '83, on Geffen, by Geffen Records (USA). Catalogue no: **A 3867**

Holliday, Michael

Biographical details: This British singer was born Michael Miller in Liverpool. He changed his name to Michael Milne by deed poll but then, strangely, decided to use his mother's maiden name Holliday when he began his showbusiness career. He first reached the UK charts in March 1956, peaking at no.20 with the Les Paul and Mary Ford oldie *Nothin' to do*. Later in 1956, he hit the Top 20 with *Hot diggity* but was outdone by the rival American version by Perry Como, the singer who most closely influenced Holliday's own vocal style. It was appropriate, therefore, that when Michael achieved his first UK No.1 single was 1958's *The story of my life*, he was dethroned by Perry Como's *Magic moments*. In an erratic chart career, Holliday reached No.3 in the summer of '58 with *Stairway of love*,then experienced a series of flops, then suddenly zoomed to No.1 in January 1960 with a cover version of a relatively unknown American hit called *Starry eyed*. The latter record proved to be only a temporary reprieve from obscurity, however, and Michael never returned to the UK charts after 1960. Despite the becalming influence of his recording manager and producer Norrie Paramor, Holliday was never quite able to withstand the pressures of an unpredictable life in showbusiness. He might have felt more at ease if he had made his name at the beginning of the Fifties, when his casual vocal style of middle-of-the-road crooning was more in vogue. But instead he took centre stage just as the rock'n'roll boom was getting underway, and was consequently always struggling to maintain his position. Holliday was only in his mid- thirties when he shot himself to death in 1963. (Bob MacDonald, 22nd Oct 1985).

GAL WITH THE YALLER SHOES
Tracks: / Gal with the yaller shoes.
7" Single: Released Jun '56, on Columbia, by EMI Records. Deleted '59. Catalogue no: **DB 3783**

HOT DIGGITY
Tracks: / Hot diggity.
7" Single: Released Jun '56, on Columbia, by EMI Records. Deleted '59. Catalogue no: **DB 3783**

I'LL ALWAYS BE IN LOVE WITH YOU
Tracks: / I'll always be in love with you.
7" Single: Released Jul '58, on Columbia, by EMI Records. Deleted '61. Catalogue no: **DB 4155**

IN LOVE
Tracks: / In love.
7" Single: Released Mar '58, on Columbia, by EMI Records. Deleted '61. Catalogue no: **DB 4087**

LITTLE BOY LOST
Tracks: / Little boy lost.
7" Single: Released Sep '60, on Columbia, by EMI Records. Deleted '63. Catalogue no: **DB 4475**

NOTHIN' TO DO
Tracks: / Nothin' to do.
7" Single: Released Mar '56, on Columbia by EMI Records. Deleted '59. Catalogue no: **DB 3746**

SKYLARK
Tracks: / Skylark.
7" Single: Released Apr '60, on Columbia, by EMI Records. Deleted '63. Catalogue no: **DB 4437**

STAIRWAY OF LOVE
Tracks: / Stairway of love.
7" Single: Released May '58, on Columbia, by EMI Records. Deleted '61. Catalogue no: **DB 4121**

STARRY EYED
Tracks: / Starry eyed.
7" Single: Released Jan '60, on Columbia, by EMI Records. Deleted '63. Catalogue no: **DB 4378**

STORY OF MY LIFE, THE
Tracks: / Story of my life.
7" Single: Released Jan '58, on Columbia, by EMI Records. Deleted '61. Catalogue no: **DB 4058**
7" Single: Released Jul '82, on Old Gold, by Old Gold Records. Deleted Jul '88. Catalogue no: **OG 9049**

TEN THOUSAND MILES
Tracks: / Ten thousand miles.
7" Single: Released Oct '56, on Columbia, by EMI Records. Deleted '59. Catalogue no: **DB 3813**

Holliday, Oliver

DO WHAT YOU DO
Tracks: / Do what you do.
7" Single: Released Jun '84, on In Records, Catalogue no: **KETCH 1**

Hollies

Biographical details: At the time of their greatest success, this British pop group comprised Allan Clarke, Bobby Elliot, Eric Haydock, Tony Hicks and Graham Nash. During their long career, their membership has also included Bernie Calvert, Terry Sylvester and Michael Rickfors. The combo's name was inspired by their idol Buddy Holly. The Hollies were formed in Manchester in 1962, just at the right time to take advantage of the Beatles-led boom in beat groups. Their first two singles *Just like me* and *Searchin'*, were both remakes of old Coasters tracks; both became UK Top 30 singles for the Hollies. Then came their first two Top Tenners, *Stay* (No.8) and *Just one look* (No.2), which were also cover versions of American songs. The band then started having original material written for them, beginning with 1964's *Here I go again* which reached the UK No.4 position. A year later, they achieved their first and only British No.1 single with *I'm alive*. Despite having only one chart topper to their credit, the Hollies chalked up big hits on the British singles chart during the Sixties with a degree of consistency that was beaten only by the Beatles and the Rolling

Stones. The group's success was based upon an excellent choice of material, and the confident lead vocals of Clarke and the polished vocal harmonies of Hicks and Nash. During the midst of this success, these three gentlemen emerged as a formidable songwriting team - such Hollies hits as *We're through* (1964), *Stop stop stop* (1966), *On a carousel* (1967), *Carrie Anne* (1967) and *King Midas in reverse* (1967) were composed by the Clarke/Hicks/Nash triumvirate.
From 1966 onwards, the Hollies enjoyed major success in the States too. In Britain their *Greatest hits* Lp spent seven weeks at No.1 on the album chart in 1968. But in spite of all this, guitarist/vocalist Nash felt restricted by the combo's singles-oriented pop image and wanted to move into the more trendy world of peace-and-love hippiedome. He thus quit the Hollies in '68 to become one-third of the Crosby, Stills & Nash supergroup; his replacement was Sylvester. After Graham's departure, the group ceased writing their own hits but relied on outside writers for such songs as *Sorry Suzanne, He ain't heavy, he's my brother* and *I can't tell the bottom from the top*.
The group's 1972 single *Long cool woman (in a black dress)* saw them briefly adopting a harder rock sound - and obtainin their biggest American hit in the process - but they were soon back in their tuneful pop mould with the international 1974 monster *The air that I breathe*. The latter record was the Hollies last major triumph. They continued to record, but without success - singles like 1976's *Wiggle that wotsit* explain why - and earned their living on the cabaret circuit. During the early Eighties they made modest returns to the charts with *Soldier's song* (No.58 in the UK), *Holliedaze* (a re-recorded medley of their old hits - No.28 in the UK and *Stop in the name of love* (a dire remake of the Supremes' classic No.29 in the US). (Bob MacDonald, 22nd Oct 1985).

AIR THAT I BREATHE, THE
Tracks: / Air that I breathe, The / We're through / King Midas in reverse / Just one look / He ain't heavy he's my brother (CD single/EMS 80 only.).
7" Single: Released Jan '89, on EMI, by EMI Records. Catalogue no: **EMS 80**
CD 5": Released Nov '88, on EMI, by EMI Records. Catalogue no: **CDEM 80**
7" Single: Released Feb '74, on Polydor, by Polydor Ltd. Deleted '77. Catalogue no: **2058 435**
7" Single: Released Nov '88, on EMI, by EMI Records. Deleted Jan '89. Catalogue no: **EM 80**
12" Single: Released Nov '88, on EMI, by EMI Records. Deleted Aug '89. Catalogue no: **12EM 80**

BABY, THE
Tracks: / Baby, The.
7" Single: Released Feb '72, on Polydor, by Polydor Ltd. Deleted '75. Catalogue no: **2058 199**

BUS STOP
Tracks: / Bus stop.
7" Single: Released Jun '66, on Parlophone, by EMI Records. Deleted '69. Catalogue no: **R 5469**
7" Single: Released Jul '84, on EMI (Holland), by EMI Records. Catalogue no: **1A 006 05556**

CARRIE-ANNE
Tracks: / Carrie Anne.
7" Single: Released Jun '67, on Parlophone, by EMI Records. Deleted '70. Catalogue no: **R 5602**

DAY THAT CURLY BILLY SHOT CRAZY SAM MCGHEE, THE
Tracks: / Day that curly Billy shot crazy Sam McGhee, The.
7" Single: Released Oct '73, on Polydor, by Polydor Ltd. Deleted '76. Catalogue no: **2058 403**

FIND ME A FAMILY
Tracks: / Find me a family / No rules.
7" Single: Released Feb '89, on EMI, by EMI Records. Deleted Oct '89. Catalogue no: **EM 86**

GASOLINE ALLEY BRED
Tracks: / Gasoline Alley bred.
7" Single: Released Oct '70, on Parlophone, by EMI Records. Deleted '73. Catalogue no: **R 5862**

HE AIN'T HEAVY HE'S MY BROTHER
Tracks: / He ain't heavy he's my brother.
7" Single: Released Oct '69, on Parlophone, by EMI Records. Deleted '72. Catalogue no: **R 5806**
7" Single: Released Aug '82, on EMI-Past Masters Series, by EMI Records. Deleted '83. Catalogue no: **PMS 1001**
CD 5": Released Aug '88, on EMI, by EMI Records. Deleted Aug '89. Catalogue no: **CDEM 74**
7" Single: Released 22 Aug '88, on EMI, by EMI Records. Catalogue no: **EM 74**
12" Single: Released Aug '88, on EMI, by EMI Records. Deleted Aug '89. Catalogue no: **12EM 74**

HE AIN'T HEAVY HE'S MY BROTHER (OLD GOLD)
Tracks: / He ain't heavy he's my brother / Bus stop.
7" Single: Released Oct '83, on Old Gold, by Old Gold Records. Catalogue no: **OG 9386**

HEARTBEAT
Tracks: / Heartbeat / Take your time.
7" Single: Released Sep '80, on Polydor, by Polydor Ltd. Deleted Sep '83. Catalogue no: **UNKNOWN**

HERE I GO AGAIN
Tracks: / Here i go again.
7" Single: Released May '64, on Parlophone, by EMI Records. Deleted '67. Catalogue no: **R 5137**

HEY WILLY
Tracks: / Hey Willy.
7" Single: Released May '71, on Parlophone, by EMI Records. Deleted '74. Catalogue no: **R 5905**

HOLLIEDAZE (MEDLEY)
Tracks: / Holliedaze (medley).
7" Single: Released Aug '81, on EMI, by EMI Records. Deleted '84. Catalogue no: **5229**

I CAN'T LET GO
Tracks: / I can't let go.
7" Single: Released Feb '66, on Parlophone, by EMI Records. Deleted '69. Catalogue no: **R 5409**

I CAN'T TELL THE BOTTOM FROM THE TOP
Tracks: / I can't tell the bottom from the top.
7" Single: Released Apr '70, on Parlophone, by EMI Records. Deleted '73. Catalogue no: **R 5837**

IF I NEEDED SOMEONE
Tracks: / If i needed someone.
7" Single: Released Dec '65, on Parlophone, by EMI Records. Deleted '68. Catalogue no: **R 5392**

I'M ALIVE
Tracks: / I'm alive.
7" Single: Released May '65, on Parlophone, by EMI Records. Deleted '68. Catalogue no: **R 5287**

JENNIFER ECCLES
Tracks: / Jennifer Eccles.
7" Single: Released Mar '68, on Parlophone, by EMI Records. Deleted '71. Catalogue no: **R 5680**

JUST LIKE ME
Tracks: / Just like me.
7" Single: Released May '63, on Parlophone, by EMI Records. Deleted '66. Catalogue no: **R 5030**

JUST ONE LOOK
7" Single: Released Mar '84, on EMI Golden 45's, by EMI Records. Catalogue no: **G45 11**
7" Single: Released Feb '64, on Parlophone, by EMI Records. Deleted '67. Catalogue no: **R 5104**

KING MIDAS IN REVERSE
Tracks: / King Midas in reverse.
7" Single: Released Sep '67, on Parlophone, by EMI Records. Deleted '70. Catalogue no: **R 5637**

LISTEN TO ME
Tracks: / Listen to me.
7" Single: Released Oct '68, on Parlophone, by EMI Records. Deleted '71. Catalogue no: **R 5733**

LONG COOL WOMAN IN A BLACK DRESS (SINGLE)
Tracks: / Long cool woman in a black dress.
7" Single: Released Sep '72, on Parlophone, by EMI Records. Deleted '75. Catalogue no: **R 5939**

LOOK THROUGH ANY WINDOW
Tracks: / Look through any window.
7" Single: Released Sep '65, on Parlophone, by EMI Records. Deleted '68. Catalogue no: **R 5322**

ON A CAROUSEL
Tracks: / On a carousel.
7" Single: Released Feb '67, on Parlophone, by EMI Records. Deleted '70. Catalogue no: **R 5562**

REUNION OF THE HEART
Tracks: / Reunion of the heart / Too many hearts get broken / Holliedaze (medley).
7" Single: Released Mar '87, on Columbia, by EMI Records. Deleted Oct '87. Catalogue no: **DB 9151**
12" Single: Released Mar '87, on Columbia, by EMI Records. Catalogue no: **12 DB 9151**

SEARCHIN'
Tracks: / Searchin'.
7" Single: Released Aug '63, on Parlophone, by EMI Records. Deleted '66. Catalogue no: **R 5052**

SOLDIER'S SONG
Tracks: / Soldier's song / Draggin' my heels.
7" Single: Released Jun '80, on Polydor, by Polydor Ltd. Deleted '83. Catalogue no: **2059 246**

SORRY SUZANNE
Tracks: / Sorry Suzanne.
7" Single: Released Mar '69, on Parlophone, by EMI Records. Deleted '72. Catalogue no: **R 5765**

STAY
Tracks: / Stay.
7" Single: Released Nov '63, on Parlophone, by EMI Records. Deleted '66. Catalogue no: **R 5077**

STOP IN THE NAME OF LOVE
Tracks: / Stop in the name of love.
7" Single: Released Jul '83, on WEA (International), by WEA Records. Catalogue no: **U 9888**

STOP STOP STOP (SINGLE)
Tracks: / Stop stop stop.
7" Single: Released Oct '66, on Parlophone, by EMI Records. Deleted '69. Catalogue no: **R 5508**

TAKE MY LOVE
Tracks: / Take my love / Run / Driver.
7" Single: Released Nov '81, on Polydor, by Polydor Ltd. Deleted Nov '84. Catalogue no: **POSP 379**

THIS IS IT
Tracks: / You gave me strength / You're all woman* (Track on 12" version only.) / This is it.
12" Single: Released Jan '87, on Columbia, by EMI Records. Deleted Oct '87. Catalogue no: **12DB 9146**
7" Single: Released Jan '87, on Columbia, by EMI Records. Deleted Oct '87. Catalogue no: **DB 9146**

TOO MANY HEARTS GET BROKEN
Tracks: / Too many hearts get broken.
7" Single: Released May '85, on Columbia, by EMI Records. Catalogue no: **DB 9110**
12" Single: Released May '85, on Columbia, by EMI Records. Catalogue no: **12DB 9110**

WE'RE THROUGH
Tracks: / We're through.
7" Single: Released Sep '64, on Parlophone, by EMI Records. Deleted '67. Catalogue no: **R 5178**

YES I WILL
Tracks: / Yes i will.
7" Single: Released Jan '65, on Parlophone, by EMI Records. Deleted '68. Catalogue no: **R 5232**

Hollow, Ken

BRING HER BACK HOME TO ME
Tracks: / Bring her back home to me.
7" Single: Released Jun '81, on Dingle's, by Dingle's Records. Catalogue no: **SID 228**

Hollow Men

DROWNING MAN, THE
Tracks: / Drowning man.
12" Single: Released 13 Feb '89, on Blind Eye, Catalogue no: **BE 007**

GOLD & IVORY
Tracks: / Gold and ivory.
12" Single: Released 8 Jun '87, on Evensong, Catalogue no: **EVE 212**

WHITE MAN
Tracks: / White man.
7" Single: Released May '88, on Gigantic, by Gigantic Records. Catalogue no: **GI 001**

WHITE TRAIN
Tracks: / White train / Thief / Loneliness (Available on 12" only.).
CD 5": Released Oct '89, on Arista, by BMG Records (UK). Catalogue no: **662 695**
7" Single: Released Oct '89, on Arista, by BMG Records (UK). Catalogue no: **112 695**
12" Single: Released Oct '89, on Arista, by BMG Records (UK). Catalogue no: **612 695**

Holloway, Brenda

GIVE ME A LITTLE INSPIRATION
Tracks: / Give me a little inspiration / Give me a little inspiration (version).
7" Single: Released Jun '88, on Nightmare, by Nightmare Records. Catalogue no: **MARES 53**
12" Single: Released Jun '88, on Nightmare, by Nightmare Records. Catalogue no: **MARE 53**

JUST LOOK WHAT YOU'VE DONE
Tracks: / Just look what you've done / When I'm gone.
7" Single: Released Apr '88, on Motown, by BMG Records (UK). Catalogue no: **ZB 41911**

Holloway, Elaine

MR. CHRISTMAS
Tracks: / Mr. Christmas.
7" Single: Released Nov '81, on State, by State Records. Catalogue no: **STAT 111**

Holloway, Lolletta

CRY TO ME
Tracks: / Cry to me.
7" Single: Released Jun '84, on RCA, by BMG Records (UK). Catalogue no: **RCA 413**
12" Single: Released Jun '84, on RCA, by BMG Records (UK). Catalogue no: **RCAT 413**

LOVE SENSATION
Tracks: / Love sensation.
7" Single: Released Sep '80, on Salsoul, Deleted Sep '83. Catalogue no: **SAL T6**
7" Single: Released Jan '84, on Salsoul, Catalogue no: **SAL 105**
12" Single: Released Jan '84, on Salsoul, Catalogue no: **SAL 105**

Hollowell, Terri

JUST STAY WITH ME
Tracks: / Just stay with me / Say what I feel tonight.
7" Single: Released Jan '81, on Amigo, Catalogue no: **AMGO 004**

Holly

I WANNA GO HOME
Tracks: / I wanna go home / Fanzine.
7" Single: Released Apr '81, on Virgin, by Virgin Records. Deleted '85. Catalogue no: **VS 411**

Holly, Buddy

Biographical details: This American singer, songwriter and guitarist was one of the all-time greats of rock 'n' roll and pop music. Born Charles Hardin Holley (the 'e' of his surname was later dropped) in Lubbock, Texas in September 1936, Buddy took up singing and guitar-playing at school. He played regularly with his drumming schoolfriend Jerry Allison, and the pair formed a professional partnership in 1957. They then formed a group called the Crickets, whose line-up was in 1957. In that year, the combo released the final version of a song Holly had been offering to various unenthusiastic record labels for several months-*That'll Be The Day* proved to be worth waiting for, eventually reaching No.1 on both the US and UK. *That'll Be The Day* was a bright , uplifting record; it made stars of the Crickets and especially leader Buddy Holly. For complicated contractual reasons, subsequent disc were separated into Buddy Holly releases and Crickets releases although the same musicians performed on the records. By the end of 1958, Holly & the Crickets had achieved success with *Peggy Sue, Oh Boy!, Listen To Me, Maybe Baby, Rave On, Think It Over and Early In The Morning; most of these were bigger in Britain than in America. The singer parted company with his group during 1958, but he continued using the old group name with some newly recurted Crickets (including the future country music superstar Waylon Jennings). In February 1959, while travelling on a private plane from concert venue in Iowa to another in North Dakota, the 22 year old Holly was killed as the small aircraft crashed into a frozen cornfield during a heavy snowstorm. The accident also claimed the lives of two other rock 'n' roll stars The Big Bopper and Ritchie Valens, as well as that of the pilot. At the time of his tragically early death, Buddy was suffering a lull of his career fortunes. It is highly probable that this loll would only have been temporary, judging by the unreleased records and unfinished demos that were posthumously embellished by producer Norman Petty and unleashed onto the marketplace. The first posthumous record was Paul Anka's song It Doesn't Matter Anymore,* which reached No.1 in Britain and No.13 in the States. Numerous other tracks appeared over the next few years, achieving considerable commercial success in the UK. Although Buddy Holly is revered by American pop historians, it is in Britain that his status has become truly legendary; for it was the fledging UK pop Sixties. Adam Faith closely imitated his distinctive vocal hiccup, the Hollies named themselves after him and countless artists recorded remakes of his hits. It could be argued that Buddy Holly was the first pop star, as opposed to rock 'n' roll star - i.e. the first to combine the raw energy of rock'n'roll with a fine melodic sensibility - and Paul McCartney has always been particularly keen to acknowledge the debt that the Beatles owed to him. McCartney purchased the publishing rights to Buddy Holly's catalogue in 1976, organised a 'Buddy Holly week' in September of that year the 40th Anniversary of the artists' birth; this became an annual event. A TV - advertised "20 Golden Greats" collection topped the British LP chart in 1978. (Bob MacDonald, 22nd Oct 1985).

BABY BABY
Tracks: / Baby baby.
7" Single: Released Aug '85, on MCA, by MCA Records. Catalogue no: **BH 4**

BABY I DON'T CARE
Tracks: / Baby I don't care / Valley of tears.
7" Single: Released Jul '61, on Coral, by MCA Records. Deleted '64. Catalogue no: **Q 72432**

BO DIDDLEY
Tracks: / Bo Diddley.
7" Single: Released Jun '63, on Coral, by MCA Records. Deleted '66. Catalogue no: **Q 72463**

BROWN EYED HANDSOME MAN
Tracks: / Brown eyed handsome man.
7" Single: Released Mar '63, on Coral, by MCA Records. Deleted '66. Catalogue no: **Q 72459**
7" Single: Released Aug '85, on MCA, by MCA Records. Catalogue no: **BH 10**

EARLY IN THE MORNING
Tracks: / Early in the morning.
7" Single: Released Aug '58, on Coral, by MCA Records. Deleted '61. Catalogue no: **Q 72333**

GOOD ROCKIN' TONIGHT
Tracks: / Good rockin' tonight / Rip it up / Ain't got no home / Holly hop.
7" EP: Released Oct '87, on Rollercoaster, by Rollercoaster Records. Catalogue no: **RCEP 104**

HEARTBEAT
Tracks: / Heartbeat.
7" Single: Released Apr '60, on Coral, by MCA Records. Deleted '63. Catalogue no: **Q 72392**
7" Single: Released Jan '59, on Coral, by MCA Records. Deleted '62. Catalogue no: **Q 72346**

IT DOESN'T MATTER ANYMORE
Tracks: / It doesn't matter anymore.
7" Single: Released Aug '85, on MCA, by MCA Records. Deleted '88. Catalogue no: **BH 7**
7" Single: Released Feb '59, on Coral, by MCA Records. Deleted '62. Catalogue no: **Q 72360**

IT DOESN'T MATTER ANYMORE (OLD GOLD)
Tracks: / It doesn't matter anymore.
7" Single: Released Apr '83, on Old Gold, by Old Gold Records. Deleted Sep '89. Catalogue no: **OG 9352**

LEARNIN' THE GAME
Tracks: / Learnin' the game.
7" Single: Released Oct '60, on Coral, by MCA Records. Deleted '63. Catalogue no: **Q 72411**

LISTEN TO ME
Tracks: / Listen to me.
7" Single: Released Mar '58, on Coral, by MCA Records. Deleted '61. Catalogue no: **Q 72288**
7" Single: Released Mar '62, on Coral, by MCA Records. Deleted '65. Catalogue no: **Q 72449**

LOVE'S MADE A FOOL OF YOU
Tracks: / Love's made a fool of you.
7" Single: Released Sep '64, on Coral, by MCA Records. Deleted '67. Catalogue no: **Q 72475**

MAYBE BABY
Tracks: / Maybe baby.
7" Single: Released Sep '84, on MCA, by MCA Records. Catalogue no: **BH 4**

MIDNIGHT SHIFT
Tracks: / Midnight shift.
7" Single: Released Jul '59, on Brunswick, by Decca Records. Deleted '62. Catalogue no: **05800**

OH BOY
Tracks: / Oh boy.
10" single: Released Sep '89, on MCA, by MCA Records. Catalogue no: **MCAV 1368**
7" Single: Released Aug '85, on MCA, by MCA Records. Catalogue no: **BH 3**
CD 5": Released Sep '89, on MCA, by MCA Records. Catalogue no: **DMCAT 1368**
7" Single: Released Sep '89, on MCA, by MCA Records. Catalogue no: **MCA 1368**

PEGGY SUE
Tracks: / Peggy Sue.
7" Single: Released Aug '85, on MCA, by MCA Records. Deleted '88. Catalogue no: **BH 2**
7" Single: Released Dec '57, on Coral, by MCA Records. Deleted '60. Catalogue no: **Q 72293**

PEGGY SUE GOT MARRIED
Tracks: / Peggy Sue got married.
7" Single: Released Sep '59, on Coral, by MCA Records. Deleted '62. Catalogue no: **Q 72376**

PEGGY SUE (OLD GOLD)
Tracks: / Peggy Sue.
7" Single: Released Jul '82, on Old Gold, by Old Gold Records. Catalogue no: **OG 9222**

PEGGY SUE/RAVE ON
Tracks: / Peggy Sue.
7" Single: Released Apr '68, on MCA, by MCA Records. Deleted '71. Catalogue no: **MU 1012**

RAVE ON
Tracks: / Rave on.
7" Single: Released Aug '85, on MCA, by MCA Records. Deleted '88. Catalogue no: **BH 5**
7" Single: Released Jun '58, on Coral, by MCA Records. Deleted '61. Catalogue no: **Q 72325**

RAVE ON (OLD GOLD)
Tracks: / Rave on / True love ways.
7" Single: Released Apr '83, on Old Gold, by Old Gold Records. Catalogue no: **OG 9319**

REMINISCING
Tracks: / Reminiscing.
7" Single: Released Sep '62, on Coral, by MCA Records. Deleted '65. Catalogue no: **Q 72455**
7" Single: Released Aug '85, on MCA, by MCA Records. Deleted '88. Catalogue no: **BH 9**

THAT'LL BE THE DAY
Tracks: / That'll be the day / I'm looking for someone to love / It doesn't matter anymore / Raining in my heart.
7" Single: Released Aug '86, on MCA, by MCA Records. Deleted 1 Jul '89. Catalogue no: **THAT 1**
12" Single: Released Aug '86, on MCA, by MCA Records. Catalogue no: **TTHAT 1**
CD 5": Released 30 May '89, on Old Gold, by Old Gold Records. Catalogue no: **OG 6147**

THAT'LL BE THE DAY (BOXED SET)
Tracks: / That'll be the day / It doesn't matter anymore / Bo Diddley / I'm looking for someone to love / Raining in my heart / That'll be the day / Rock me baby / Peggy Sue / Everyday / Oh boy / Not fade away / May be baby / Tell me how / Rave on / Ready Teddy / Think it over / It's so easy / True love ways / Word of love / Reminiscing / Baby I don't care / Brown eyed handsome man.
7" Set: Released Aug '85, on MCA, by MCA Records. Catalogue no: **BHB 1**

THINK IT OVER
Tracks: / Think it over.
7" Single: Released Aug '85, on MCA, by MCA Records. Catalogue no: **BH 6**

TRUE LOVE WAYS
Tracks: / True love ways.
7" Single: Released May '60, on Coral, by MCA Records. Deleted '63. Catalogue no: **Q 72397**

TRUE LOVE WAYS (SINGLE)
Tracks: / True love ways / Raining in my heart.
7" Single: Released Sep '81, on MCA, by MCA Records. Deleted '84. Catalogue no: **MCA 252**
7" Single: Released Nov '88, on MCA, by MCA Records. Deleted 1 Jul '89. Catalogue no: **MCA 1302**
12" Single: Released Dec '88, on MCA, by MCA Records. Catalogue no: **MCAT 1302**
CD 5": Released Nov '88, on MCA, by MCA Records. Catalogue no: **DMCA 1302**

WHAT TO DO (SINGLE)
Tracks: / What to do.
7" Single: Released Dec '63, on Coral, by MCA Records. Deleted '66. Catalogue no: **Q 72469**
7" Single: Released Jan '61, on Coral, by MCA Records. Deleted '64. Catalogue no: **Q 72419**

WISHING
Tracks: / Wishing.
7" Single: Released Sep '63, on Coral, by MCA Records. Deleted '66. Catalogue no: **Q 72466**

YOU'VE GOT LOVE
Tracks: / You've got love.
7" Single: Released May '64, on Coral, by MCA Records. Deleted '67. Catalogue no: **Q 72472**

Holly & Italians

JUST FOR THOUGHT
Tracks: / Just for tonight.
7" Single: Released Jun '81, on Virgin, by Virgin Records. Deleted Jun '84. Catalogue no: **VS 429**

MILES AWAY
Tracks: / Miles away / It's only me.
7" Single: Released Apr '80, on Virgin, by Virgin Records. Deleted Apr '83. Catalogue no: **VS 341**

Holly & Joey

I GOT YOU BABE
Tracks: / I got you babe.
7" Single: Released Jan '82, on Virgin, by Virgin Records. Deleted Jan '85. Catalogue no: **VS 478**

Holly & The Italians

TELL THAT GIRL TO SHUT UP
Tracks: / Tell that girl to shut up / Chapel of love.
7" Single: Released Feb '80, on Oval, by Oval Records. Deleted '83. Catalogue no: **OVAL 1016**
7" Single: Released Jul '82, on Oval, by Oval Records. Catalogue no: **HOLLY 16**

YOUTH COUP
Tracks: / Youth coup / Poster boy.
7" Single: Released Feb '81, on Virgin, by Virgin Records. Deleted Feb '84. Catalogue no: **VS 391**

Holly & The Ivys

CHRISTMAS ON 45
Tracks: / Christmas on 45.
7" Single: Released Dec '81, on Decca, by Decca Records. Deleted '84. Catalogue no: **SANTA 1**

Holly Twins

I WANT ELVIS FOR CHRISTMAS
Tracks: / I want Elvis for Christmas / Tender age.
7" Single: Released Dec '80, on Rockstar (1), Catalogue no: **SP 3004**

Hollywood!

FUNK ME JACK ME
Tracks: / Funk me jack me.
12" Single: Released Apr '87, on Kool Kat, by Kool Kat Records. Catalogue no: **KOOLT 2**

HOLLYWOOD MUSICALS Medley
Tracks: / Hollywood musicals.
7" Single: Released Dec '83, on RCA, by BMG Records (UK). Catalogue no: **RCA 381**

Hollywood Argyles

ALLEY OOP
Tracks: / Alley oop.
7" Single: Released Jul '60, on London-American, Deleted '63. Catalogue no: **HLU 9146**

Hollywood Beyond

AFTER MIDNIGHT
Tracks: / After midnight / Gift to the innocent.
7" Single: Released Sep '87, on WEA, by WEA Records. Deleted Jul '88. Catalogue no: **YZ 142**
12" Single: Released Sep '87, on WEA, by WEA Records. Deleted Jul '88. Catalogue no: **YZ 142T**

NO MORE TEARS
Tracks: / No more tears / No time for losers.
7" Single: Released Sep '86, on WEA, by WEA Records. Deleted Jun '87. Catalogue no: **YZ 81**
12" Single: Released Sep '86, on WEA, by WEA Records. Deleted Jan '88. Catalogue no: **YZ 81 T**

SAVE ME
Tracks: / Save me / No more tears.
12" Single: Released Apr '87, on WEA, by WEA Records. Deleted Jan '88. Catalogue no: **YZ 112T**
7" Single: Released Apr '87, on WEA, by WEA Records. Deleted Jan '88. Catalogue no: **YZ 112**

WHAT'S THE COLOUR OF MONEY?
Tracks: / What's the colour of money?.
7" Single: Released Jul '86, on WEA, by WEA Records. Catalogue no: **YZ 76**
12" Single: Released Jul '86, on WEA, by WEA Records. Catalogue no: **YZ 76T**

Hollywood Brats

THEN HE KISSED ME
Tracks: / Then he kissed me.
12" Single: Released Apr '84, on Cherry Red, by Cherry Red Records. Deleted '87. Catalogue no: **12 CHERRY 6**

Hollywood, D.J.

UM TANG UM TANG/ TO WHOEVER IT MAY CONCERN.
Tracks: / Um tang um tang / Um tang um tang (instrumental).
7" Single: Released Sep '86, on Crossover, Catalogue no: **7 CROSS 3**
12" Single: Released Sep '86, on Crossover, Catalogue no: **CROSS 3**

Hollywood Exiles

ANONYMOUS LETTERS
Tracks: / Anonymous letters / Calling.
7" Single: Released Sep '81, on RCA, by BMG Records (UK). Deleted '84. Catalogue no: **RCA 116**

Hollywood Follies

BEYOND THE BLUE HORIZON
Tracks: / Beyond the blue horizon / Gently.
7" Single: Released Sep '81, on Earlobe, by Earlobe Records. Deleted '84. Catalogue no: **ELBS 106**

Hollywood Killers

BUTTERFLY
Tracks: / Butterfly / Killer's wail.
7" Single: Released Nov '82, on Creole, by Creole Records. Catalogue no: **HK 1**

Holm, Lasse

CANNELLONI MACARONI (PIZZERIA FANTASIA)
Tracks: / Cannelloni macaroni (pizzeria fantasia) / Such a miracle.
7" Single: Released Nov '86, on Sonet, by Sonet Records. Catalogue no: **SON 3212**

Holman, Eddie

Biographical details: This American singer was born in Norfolk, Virginia, and entered the world of soul music in the early Sixties. His first taste of success came in 1965 with *This can't be true*. Although he put out other records like *I'm not gonna give up* and *Since I don't have you*, he is really only remembered for the classic *Hey there lonely girl*. Ruby & the Romantics had originally taken *Hey there lonely boy* to the US No.27 position in 1963. Holman's trademark falsetto vocals, which were an extraordinary experience for any listener's eardrums, gave this ballad a totally fresh lease of life. *Hey there lonely girl* was a US million-seller, reaching No.2 in early 1970. It failed to enter the British charts, but nonetheless gradually accrued a cult following. When BBC Radio One disc jockey Tony Blackburn broadcast his listeners Top 100 Most Requested Records in 1974 Holman's *Hey there lonely girl* found itself in the Top 20 of this special chart despite the fact that it had never been a UK hit. This resulted in the record being re-issued, and it climbed to No.4 on the British charts. *Hey there lonely girl* was still a lights down disco favourite in 1979, the year that the singer was immortalised in the Leyton Buzzards' delightfully cynical UK chart single *Saturday night (beneath the plastic palm trees)* - 'Eddie Holman slows things down, you ask a girl to dance and get turned down'. (Bob MacDonald, 23rd Oct 1985).

HEY THERE LONELY GIRL
Tracks: / (Hey there)lonely girl.
7" Single: Released Oct '74, on ABC Records, by MCA Records. Deleted '77. Catalogue no: **4012**
7" Single: Released Jul '82, on Old Gold, by Old Gold Records. Catalogue no: **OG 9218**

I SURRENDER
Tracks: / I surrender / Just one more chance.
7" Single: Released Jun '85, on Kent, by Ace Records. Catalogue no: **TOWN 109**

Holmes, Richard

FORTUNES OF WAR
Tracks: / Fortunes of war / Song of sonunion, The.
12" Single: Released Oct '87, on BBC, by BBC Records & Tapes. Deleted Apr '89. Catalogue no: **12RSL 221**
7" Single: Released Oct '87, on BBC, by BBC Records & Tapes. Deleted Apr '89. Catalogue no: **RESL 221**

Holmes, Robert

ANGEL IN THE HOUSE
Tracks: / Hurting kind, The / Queen of my world / Angel in the house.
CD 3": Released Mar '89, on Virgin, by Virgin Records. Catalogue no: **VSCD 1142**
7" Single: Released Feb '89, on Virgin, by Virgin Records. Catalogue no: **VS 1142**
12" Single: Released Feb '89, on Virgin, by Virgin Records. Catalogue no: **VST**

INTERNATIONAL SUNSHINE
Tracks: / International sunshine / Monkey song, The.
7" Single: Released Jun '87, on Virgin, by Virgin Records. Deleted May '88. Catalogue no: **VS 963**
12" Single: Released Jun '87, on Virgin, by Virgin Records. Deleted May '88. Catalogue no: **VS 963-12**

Holmes, Rupert

Biographical details: This American singer, songwriter, arranger, producer and keyboards player will always be best remembered for his 1979 US No.1 smash *Escape (The pina colada song)*. He was actually born in Britain - his father was an American G.I. who married a British woman - but his family moved to New York during his early childhood. He grew up with music, and won a scholarship to the Manhattan School of Music. During the early Seventies Holmes worked for a New York publishing house, achieving his first major success in 1971 as writer of the Buoys' US No.17 hit *Timothy*. This set the patten for the cinema-type story songs which became Holmes' forte. Rupert had scored music for TV commercials and soft porn movies by the time he released his debut album *Wide screen* in 1974. Further LP's were issued, but his recording career was far from meteoric during the mid-Seventies. Instead, he became better known as a songwriter and producer for other artists. His material was recorded by such MoR greats as Barry Manilow, Barbra Streisand and Dionne Warwick, and he produced or co-produced UK hits for Sailor (*Girls girls girls* - No.7 in 1976) and John Miles (*Slow down* - No.10 in 1977). Then, at the end of 1979, came *Escape (The pina colada song), which finally made Holmes famous as an artist. The single became America's final chart topper of the Seventies, despite the fact that his record company folded while the song was climbing the charts! Escape* also reached No.23 in the UK. It converted many people to the pineapple/coconut/rum cocktail mentioned in the title, although the drink was not central to the song's message. It told the story of a man and girlfriend whose relationship had become so stale that the woman secretly placed a personal ad in search of a new boyfriend; a man answers the ad, and when they meet at the arranged time and place, it turns out to be her original boyfriend and they realise they have much in common after all. Holmes quickly achieved another US Top 10 h and UK Top 40 with *Him* and continued in melodramatic vein with a smaller American hit called *Answering machine*. From 1981 onwards, however, his career sank like a stone. (Bob MacDonald, 23rd Nov 1985).

ADVENTURE (SINGLE)
Tracks: / Adventure / Mask.
7" Single: Released Nov '80, on MCA, by MCA Records. Deleted '83. Catalogue no: **MCA 653**

BLACK JACK
Tracks: / Black jack / Crowd pleaser.
7" Single: Released Feb '81, on MCA, by MCA Records. Deleted '84. Catalogue no: **MCA 669**

END
Tracks: / End / Loved by the one you love.
7" Single: Released '82, on WEA, by WEA Records. Deleted '85. Catalogue no: **K12593**

ESCAPE (PINA COLADA SONG)
Tracks: / Escape (Pina colada song).
7" Single: Released Jan '80, on Infinity, by MCA Records (USA). Deleted '83. Catalogue no: **INF 120**

ESCAPE (PINA COLADA SONG)(OLD GOLD)
Tracks: / Escape (pina colada song).
7" Single: Released Jan '85, on Old Gold, by Old Gold Records. Catalogue no: **OG 9462**

HIM
Tracks: / Him / Get outta yourself.
7" Single: Released Mar '80, on MCA, by MCA Records. Deleted '83. Catalogue no: **MCA 565**

I DON'T NEED YOU
Tracks: / I don't need you / Cold.
7" Single: Released May '81, on MCA, by MCA Records. Deleted May '84. Catalogue no: **MCA 722**

LOVED BY THE ONE YOU LOVE
Tracks: / Loved by the one you love / One born every minute.
7" Single: Released Nov '81, on Elektra, by Elektra Records (UK). Deleted Nov '84. Catalogue no: **K 12572**

PARTNERS IN CRIME (SINGLE)
Tracks: / Partners in crime / Lunch hour.
7" Single: Released May '80, on MCA, by MCA Records. Deleted '83. Catalogue no: **MCA 600**

Holocaust

COMING THROUGH
Tracks: / Coming through / Don't wanna be a loser / Good thing going.
12" Single: Released Apr '82, on Phoenix (1), by Phoenix Records. Catalogue no: **12 PSP 4**

HEAVY METAL MANIA
Tracks: / Heavy metal mania.
12" Single: Released Jul '80, on Phoenix (1), by Phoenix Records. Catalogue no: **12 PSP 1**

Holoway, Mike

COME GO WITH ME
Tracks: / Come go with me / Beautiful loser.
7" Single: Released Nov '81, on Bell, Deleted Nov '84. Catalogue no: **BELL 1500**

DON'T LET LIFE GET YOU DOWN
Tracks: / Don't let life get you down.
7" Single: Released Nov '83, on Smike, Catalogue no: **SMIKE 6**

HERE I AM
Tracks: / Here I am.
7" Single: Released Aug '83, on Simon, Catalogue no: **SMIKE 4**

OVERNIGHT
Tracks: / Overnight / Just another song.
7" Single: Released Jun '81, on Arista, by BMG Records (UK). Deleted '84. Catalogue no: **ARISTA 1496**

Holt, Errol

DANGER ZONE
Tracks: / Danger zone.
12" Single: Released Jun '82, on African Museum, Catalogue no: **AM 06**

Holt, John

Biographical details: This Jamaican singer and songwriter was born in Kingston and entered many local talent contests during his teens. He became lead singer of the Paragons in 1965 and, during the following three years, they established themselves as one of their nation's leading group's. Holt pursued a solo career from 1968 onwards and gradually established an international reputation as a major reggae artist. Staying away from the political and overtly sexual aspects of the genre, he specialised in sentimental romantic ballads; some British pop charts, past and present - he loved turning familiar pop songs into reggae records. The two angles of Holt's work are best summarised by his two big crossover successes in the Western pop market. In early 1975 he reached No.6 in the UK with his remake of the Kris Kristofferson song *Help me make it through the night*. At the end of 1980 Blondie recorded a faultless cover version of *The tide is high*, a Holt song that had originally been done by the Paragons. Although retaining the West Indies flavour of the original, the Blondie record was pure pop and cruised to No.1 in both Britain and America. John Holt has continued to release singles and albums through the Eighties, although he is no longer the giant reggae artist that he once was. Tracks like 1985's *Easy loving* are enough to keep him ticking over but that's all. (Bob MacDonald, 23rd Oct 1985).

A SPACEMAN CAME TRAVELLING
Tracks: / Spaceman came travelling, A.
7" Single: on Trojan, by Trojan Records. Deleted May '88. Catalogue no: **TRO 9094**

DEEP RIVER WOMAN
Tracks: / Deep river woman.
12" Single: Released Sep '88, on Moodies, Catalogue no: **RG 010**

DRESS UP YOURSELF
Tracks: / Dress up yourself.
12" Single: Released Dec '84, on Chartsounds, Catalogue no: **MPCJH 212**

EASY LOVING
Tracks: / Easy loving.
12" Single: Released Sep '85, on Uptempo, Catalogue no: **UT 011**

FAT SHE FAT
Tracks: / Fat she fat / Rat.
12" Single: Released Sep '82, on Greensleeves, by Greensleeves Records. Catalogue no: **GRED 99**

GHETTO QUEEN
Tracks: / Ghetto queen / Version.
7" Single: Released Oct '81, on Creole, by Creole Records. Catalogue no: **CR 22**
12" Single: Released Oct '81, on Creole, by Creole Records. Catalogue no: **CR 12 22**

HELP ME MAKE IT THROUGH THE NIGHT (OLD GOLD)
Tracks: / Help me make it through the night.
7" Single: Released Apr '83, on Old Gold, by Old Gold Records. Catalogue no: **OG 9271**
7" Single: Released Dec '74, on Trojan, by Trojan Records. Deleted '77. Catalogue no: **TR 7909**

I DON'T WANT TO WAKE UP EARLY
Tracks: / I don't want to wake up early.
12" Single: Released Nov '87, on Body Music, by Nuclear Records. Catalogue no: **BZT 08**

I JUST CALLED TO SAY I LOVE YOU
Tracks: / I just called to say I love you.
12" Single: Released Oct '84, on JKH, Catalogue no: **JDH 111**

I LOVE YOU BABY
Tracks: / I love you baby / I love music.
12" Single: Released Apr '86, on Natty Congo, Catalogue no: **NCDM 032**

IF YOU WERE MY LOVER
Tracks: / If you were my lover.
12" Single: Released Nov '84, on Black Joy, Catalogue no: **DH 833**

JAZZY LADY
Tracks: / Jazzy lady.
12" Single: Released Nov '84, on JKH, Catalogue no: **JKH 333**

JUST THE WAY YOU ARE
Tracks: / Just the way you are.
7" Single: on Trojan, by Trojan Records. Deleted May '88. Catalogue no: **TRO 9054**

LEAN ON ME
Tracks: / Lean on me / This old lady.
10" single: Released Dec '84, on Chartsounds, Catalogue no: **MPCJH 1**

LET'S GET IT WHILE IT'S HOT
Tracks: / Let's get it while it's hot.
7" Single: on Trojan, by Trojan Records. Deleted May '88. Catalogue no: **TRO 9018**

LOVE I CAN FEEL, A
Tracks: / Love I can feel / Tonight / Your arms reaching out for me / Nobody else / Then you can tell me goodbye.
Note: Tracks include those listed above.
7" Single: Released May '89, on Coxsone, Catalogue no: **UNKNOWN**
7" Single: Released Oct '83, on Allemande, Catalogue no: **A 015**

LOVE TO SHAVE
Tracks: / Love to shave.
12" Single: Released Mar '86, on Basket, Catalogue no: **BR 001**

LOVELY WOMAN
Tracks: / Lovely woman / If I were a carpenter.
12" Single: on Attack, Deleted '88. Catalogue no: **TACK 16**

MR BIG BOSS
Tracks: / Mr. Big Boss.
12" Single: Released May '83, on Creole, by Creole Records. Catalogue no: **CR 12 55**

NATURAL GIRL
Tracks: / Natural girl.
12" Single: Released Feb '89, on BP International, Catalogue no: **BPP 001**

NEVER GONNA GIVE YOU UP
Tracks: / Never gonna give you up / Going steady.
12" Single: Released Jun '86, on King Jam, Catalogue no: **KJ 042**

NEXT TEARDROP
Tracks: / Next teardrop.
7" Single: Released Oct '83, on Jackpot, Catalogue no: **JP 001**

POLICE IN HELICOPTER
Tracks: / Police in helicopter.
12" Single: Released May '83, on Greensleeves, by Greensleeves Records. Catalogue no: **GRED 120**

PRETTY GIRL
Tracks: / Pretty girl.
12" Single: Released Oct '85, on Three Kings, Catalogue no: **TK 028**

PRIVATE DOCTOR
Tracks: / Private doctor.
12" Single: Released Sep '83, on Greensleeves, by Greensleeves Records. Catalogue no: **GRED 127**

ROCK WITH ME BABY
12" Single: on Trojan, by Trojan Records. Deleted May '88. Catalogue no: **TRT 9051**

SHE'S A RISER
Tracks: / She's a riser / She's a riser (version).
12" Single: Released Nov '86, on Blue Trac, by Blue Trac Records. Catalogue no: **BTR 006**

SWEETIE COME BRUSH ME
Tracks: / Sweetie come brush me.
12" Single: Released Jun '82, on Creole, by Creole Records. Catalogue no: **CR 12 37**

THIS OLD HEART OF MINE
Tracks: / This old heart of mine.
12" Single: Released Nov '84, on Art & Craft, Catalogue no: **ACD 26**

TONIGHT I'M GONNA HOLD YOU
Tracks: / Tonight I'm gonna hold you.
12" Single: Released Apr '87, on Tapta, Catalogue no: **T 1012**

TOO MUCH LOVE
Tracks: / Too much love / Mr. Bojangles / You'll never find another love like mine (on 12" only) / Help me make it through the night (on 12" only).
7" Single: Released Sep '84, on Trojan, by Trojan Records. Deleted May '88. Catalogue no: **TRO 9077**
12" Single: Released Sep '84, on Trojan, by Trojan Records. Deleted May '88. Catalogue no: **TROT 9077**

WHY I CARE (SINGLE)
Tracks: / Why I care.
12" Single: Released Jul '88, on Redman International, Catalogue no: **RED 17**

WILD FIRE
Tracks: / Wild fire.
12" Single: Released Aug '85, on Yvonne's, Catalogue no: **YS 019**

YOU POUR SUGAR ON ME
Tracks: / You pour sugar on me.
12" Single: Released Jul '85, on Sure, Catalogue no: **SAL 001**

YOU'RE EVERYTHING TO ME
Tracks: / You're everything to me / I'll be everything to you.
12" Single: Released Nov '86, on Trojan, by Trojan Records. Deleted May '88. Catalogue no: **TROT 9093**

Holton, Gary

CATCH A FALLING STAR
Tracks: / Catch a falling star.
7" Single: Released Nov '84, on Magnet, by WEA Records. Catalogue no: **GARY 2**
12" Single: Released Nov '84, on Magnet, by WEA Records. Catalogue no: **12 GARY 2**

PEOPLE IN LOVE
Tracks: / People in love / Angel.
12" Single: Released Jul '86, on ACTS International, Deleted Jun '88. Catalogue no: **12 GAZA 1**
7" Single: Released Jul '86, on ACTS International, Deleted Jun '88. Catalogue no: **GAZA 1**

RUBY (DON'T TAKE YOUR LOVE TO TOWN) (see also Casino Steel)
Tracks: / Ruby (don't take your love to town).
7" Single: Released Jan '84, on Pinnacle, by Pinnacle Records. Catalogue no: **PIN 501**

Holy Toy

MEETING II (EP)
12" Single: Released Jan '84, on Uniton Records, Catalogue no: **U 022**

PERFECT DAY
Tracks: / Perfect day.
12" Single: Released Sep '84, on Uniton Records, Catalogue no: **U 007**

SOLDIER TOY
Tracks: / Soldier toy / Lada vada.
12" Single: Released Sep '84, on Uniton Records, Catalogue no: **HOLYT 1**

Home Service

DOING THE INGLISH
Tracks: / Bramsley / Doing the Inglish.
7" Single: Released Aug '81, on Luggage, by Multicord Records. Catalogue no: **LUG 01**

MYSTERIES, THE (EP) Shey Fan Yan Ley
Tracks: / Shey fan yan ley / We sing Hallelujah / Shepherds arise / Lewk up lewk up.
7" EP: Released Jan '86, on Coda, by Coda Records. Catalogue no: **CODS 15**

ONLY MEN FALL IN LOVE
Tracks: / Only men fall in love.
7" Single: Released Jul '81, on Situation 2, by Beggars Banquet Records. Catalogue no: **SIT 6**

SORROW
Tracks: / Sorrow.
7" Single: Released Jun '86, on Making Waves, by Celtic Music. Catalogue no: **SURF 114**

Home T-Four

BREAK YOU DOWN
Tracks: / Break you down.

12" Single: Released Sep '89, on Live & Love, Catalogue no: **LLD 128**

Home Wreckers

JACKIN'
Tracks: / Jackin' (base mix) / Build your own house beats / Jackin' (emu style) / Jackin'.
12" Single: Released Jan '87, on Champion, by Champion Records. Catalogue no: **CHAMP 1231**
7" Single: Released Jan '87, on Champion, by Champion Records. Catalogue no: **CHAMP 31**

Homeboyz

CAUGHT IN THE ACT (HOMEBOYZ)
Tracks: / Caught in the act.
7" Pic: Released Nov '88, on PRT, by Castle Communications Records. Catalogue no: **PYS 20**
12" Single: Released Nov '88, on PRT, by Castle Communications Records. Catalogue no: **PYT 20**

DON'T TALK
Tracks: / Don't talk / Don't talk (dub) / Don't talk (extended) (Available on 12" version only.) / Don't talk (longer dub) (Available on 12" version only.).
Note: * Only available on the 12" version.
7" Single: Released Jun '88, on 4th & Broadway, by Island Records. Deleted Apr '89. Catalogue no: **BRW 103**
12" Single: Released Jun '88, on 4th & Broadway, by Island Records. Deleted Apr '89. Catalogue no: **12 BRW 103**

Homeland

PURE
Tracks: / Pure.
7" Single: Released Apr '89, on Imaginary, by Imaginary Records. Catalogue no: **MIRAGE 008**

SNAPSHOTS OF ENGLAND
Tracks: / Snapshots of England.
7" Single: Released '88, on Imaginary, by Imaginary Records. Catalogue no: **MIRAGE 008**

Home-T

DO YOU BELIEVE
Tracks: / Land of Rydim / Do you believe.
12" Single: Released Sep '85, on Taxi (1), Catalogue no: **JATX 20**

DON'T THROW IT ALL AWAY
Tracks: / Don't throw it all away.
12" Single: Released Oct '88, on Jammy's, Catalogue no: **VPRD 335**

IF THE ROCKERS DON'T GROOVE YOU
Tracks: / If the rockers don't groove you.
12" Single: Released Feb '89, on Jammy's, Catalogue no: **VPRD 396**

MR.CONSULAR
Tracks: / Could it be I'm falling in love / What's going on / Mr. Consular.
12" Single: Released May '85, on Island, by Island Records. Deleted '87. Catalogue no: **12IS 230**

SOUL SHAKEDOWN PARTY
Tracks: / Soul shakedown party / Dub.
12" Single: Released Jul '81, on Decca, by Decca Records. Deleted '84. Catalogue no: **FX 13906**
7" Single: Released Jul '81, on Decca, by Decca Records. Deleted '84. Catalogue no: **F 13906**

STOP SPREADING RUMOURS
Tracks: / Stop spreading rumours / Stop spreading rumours (version).
12" Single: Released Aug '89, on Greensleeves, by Greensleeves Records. Catalogue no: **GRED 251**

Hometown Atrocities

HOMETOWN ATROCITIES
Tracks: / Home Town atrocities: *Various artists*.
7" Single: Released 31 Jul '89, on Hometown Atrocities, Catalogue no: **HOME 1**

Honda, Minako

GOLDEN DAYS
Tracks: / Golden days / Crazy nights.
7" Single: Released May '87, on Columbia, by EMI Records. Deleted Oct '87. Catalogue no: **DB 9153**

Hondo

FALLOUT
Tracks: / Can't turn you round / Fallout.
7" Single: Released Mar '84, on Hondo, Catalogue no: **OV 002**

Honest Doc

DOGHOUSE (JACK THE DOG)
Tracks: / Doghouse (Jack the dog) / Spell, The / Spell, The (remix).
12" Single: Released Apr '88, on Debut, by Skratch Records. Catalogue no: **DEBTX 3047**

SPELL, THE
Tracks: / Spell, The / Now spell house.
12" Single: Released 13 Jun '87, on Jaxx, Deleted '88. Catalogue no: **JAX 1**

Honest Johns

TELL ME ABOUT
Tracks: / Tell me about.
12" Single: Released 28 Jun '87, on Minehead, Catalogue no: **MHMAX 001**

Honesty 69

FRENCH KISS
Tracks: / French kiss.
7" Single: Released Aug '89, on BCM (Germany), Catalogue no: **12306**

Honey

ACID TEST, THE
Tracks: / Acid test, The.
12" Single: Released 23 Jul '88, on Audio Instant, by Audio Instant Records. Catalogue no: **INST 009**

MORE WILD THAN HONEY
Tracks: / More wild than Honey.
12" Single: Released Mar '87, on Audio Instant, by Audio Instant Records. Catalogue no: **INST 005**
7" Single: Released Mar '87, on Audio Instant, by Audio Instant Records. Catalogue no: **INS 005**

Honey Boy

LONELY
Tracks: / Gaye / Lonely.
12" Single: Released May '83, on Starline (EMI), by EMI Records. Catalogue no: **SL 7001**

MOVE CLOSER
Tracks: / Fantasy woman / Move closer.
12" Single: Released Apr '85, on Londisc, by Londisc Records. Catalogue no: **LDR 044**

SWEET CHERRIES
Tracks: / Sweet cherries (sweet honey version).
12" Single: Released Jul '84, on BB, Catalogue no: **BBD 157**

WHAT'S YOUR NAME
Tracks: / What's your name / Rock me baby.
12" Single: Released May '86, on World International, Catalogue no: **WIR 12 D 509**

Honey Cone

WANT ADS
Tracks: / Girls it ain't easy / Want ads.
7" Single: Released May '84, on HDH (Holland/Dozier/Holland), by Demon Records. Catalogue no: **DH 454**

Honey Dolly

NO SQUALL TALK
Tracks: / No squall talk.
12" Single: Released '88, on Subway, by Subway Records. Catalogue no: **SUB 026**

Honey Drippers

SEA OF LOVE
Tracks: / Rockin' at midnight / Sea of love.
7" Single: Released Feb '85, on Es Paranza (USA), Catalogue no: **YZ 33**

Honey Hush

GET AWAY GIRL
Tracks: / She's so fine / Get away girl.
7" Single: Released Jun '83, on Rockhouse, by Rockhouse Records (Holland). Catalogue no: **SP 8305**

Honeybus

Biographical details: This British pop group consisted of Ray Cane, Pete Dello, Collin Hare and Pete Kircher. Honeybus were led by vocalist/guitarist Delle, who wrote and produced their singles *Do I figure in your life* and *I can't let Maggie go*; his real name was Peter Blumson. The former record did not figure in many consumers' lives, for it flopped totally; but the latter, a bright singalong pop excursion which sounded like the Beach Boys on a lazy day, sailed to No.8 on the UK chart in 1968. Dello quit the band soon afterwards, and the other Honeybus riders quickly ground to a halt without the presence of their main creative driver. All four men faded into obscurity, although Kircher worked occasionally as a session drummer. But *I can't let Maggie go* lived on through the Seventies. Better known to many people as *She flies like a bird*, an extract from the song was used by the Nimble company in their bread commercials on TV. And any song with 'Maggie' in the title took on a greater meaning in 1979, when a certain M.Thatcher became Britain's Prime Minister. (Bob MacDonald, 23rd Oct 1985)

I CAN'T LET MAGGIE GO.
Tracks: / I can't let Maggie go.
7" Single: Released Mar '68, on Deram, by London Records. Deleted '71. Catalogue no: **DM 182**
7" Single: Released Mar '82, on Decca, by Decca Records. Deleted '88. Catalogue no: **F 13915**

I CAN'T LET MAGGIE GO (OLD GOLD)
Tracks: / Jesamine / I can't let Maggie go.
7" Single: Released Oct '83, on Old Gold, by Old Gold Records. Catalogue no: **OG 9347**

Honeycombs

Biographical details: This British pop group consisted of Dennis D'Ell (real name Dennis Dalziel), Ann 'Honey' Lantree, John Lantree, Martin Murray and Alan Ward. The Honeycombs were formed in North Longon in 1963, inspired by the explosion of beat groups that was emanating from Liverpool. They teamed up with managers Ken Howard and Alan Blaikley, who also wrote the combo's material. In the late summer of 1964, their very first single *Have I the right* surged to No.1 in Britain; and it sooned joined the British Invasion bandwagon by reaching No.5 in America. The ultra-catchy *Have I the right* was followed by *Is it because*, which failed to make a significant impact on either side of the Atlantic on account of the fact that the group were away on tour in Australia at the time. Their career was briefly revived in 1965 by the UK No.12 success of *That's the way*, but they sank into oblivion in 1966. The Honeycombs were a very mediocre combo, whose brief success was due more to Howard & Blaikley and to the novelty of the group having a female drummer (Honey Lantree) than to the Honeycombs' musical prowess. As the group faded in '66, the management/writing duo began a long run of UK hits with Dave Dee, Dozy, Beaky, Mick & Tich; and in 1967 they found success with the Herd. *Have I the right* became a UK No.6 hit in 1977 for a group whose success was even more short-lived than that of the Honeycombs, the aptly named Dead End Kids. (Bob MacDonald, 24th Oct 1985).

HAVE I THE RIGHT
Tracks: / That's the way / Have I the right.
7" Single: Released Apr '83, on Old Gold, by Old Gold Records. Catalogue no: **OG 9289**
7" Single: Released Jul '64, on Pye, Deleted '67. Catalogue no: **7N 15664**
7" Single: Released Apr '79, on Flashback, by Mainline Records. Catalogue no: **FBS 3**

HAVE I THE RIGHT (OLD GOLD)
Tracks: / Have I the right / Sugar sugar / Love grows (where my Rosemary goes).
CD 5": Released 28 Mar '89, on Old Gold, by Old Gold Records. Catalogue no: **OG 6121**

IS IT BECAUSE
Tracks: / Is it because.
7" Single: Released Oct '64, on Pye, Deleted '67. Catalogue no: **7N 15705**

SOMETHING BETTER BEGINNING
Tracks: / Something better beginning.
7" Single: Released Apr '65, on Pye, Deleted '68. Catalogue no: **7N 15827**

THAT'S THE WAY
Tracks: / That's the way.
7" Single: Released Aug '65, on Pye, Deleted '68. Catalogue no: **7N 15890**

Honeygale, Martin

FLIPPIN AWAY
Tracks: / Flippin' away.
12" Single: Released May '87, on LGR, Catalogue no: **LGR 014**

Honeygale, Peter

BE MY LADY
Tracks: / Be my lady / Be my lady (dub).
12" Single: Released Aug '86, on Streetside, Catalogue no: **SC 004**

Honeymoon Killers

ROUTE NATIONALE 7
Tracks: / Route nationale No. 7.
7" Single: Released Mar '82, on Crammed Discs, by Crammed Discs. Deleted '88. Catalogue no: **CRAM 3457**

WAIT AND SEE
Tracks: / Lady and the pig man / Wait and see.
12" Single: Released May '83, on Crammed Discs, by Crammed Discs. Catalogue no: **CRAM 024**

Honeymoon Suite

BAD ATTITUDE
Tracks: / Bad attitude / Wounded.
7" Single: Released Feb '86, on WEA, by WEA Records. Catalogue no: **X 8772**

FEEL IT AGAIN
Tracks: / Feel it again / One by one.
12" Single: Released Mar '86, on WEA, by WEA Records. Catalogue no: **U 8715 T**
7" Single: Released Mar '86, on WEA, by WEA Records. Catalogue no: **U 8715**

OTHER SIDE OF MIDNIGHT
Tracks: / Other side of midnight / Fast company / Feel it again (On 12" only.) / Stay in the light (On 12" only.).
7" Single: Released Jun '88, on WEA, by WEA Records. Catalogue no: **YZ 185**
12" Single: Released Jun '88, on WEA, by WEA Records. Catalogue no: **YZ 185 T**

WAVE BABIES
Tracks: / It's your heart / Wave babies.
7" Single: Released Jul '85, on WEA, by WEA Records. Catalogue no: **U 9028**

Honeymooners

ANOTHER FIT OF LAUGHTER
Tracks: / Another fit of laughter.
7" Single: Released Jun '87, on Mr.Ridiculous, Catalogue no: **RID 001**

Hong Kong

DANCING ON A BASSLINE
Tracks: / Dancing on a bassline.
12" Single: Released Jun '86, on Ariwa Sounds, by Ariwa Sounds. Catalogue no: **ARI 44**

Hong Kong Syndicate

BERLIN
Tracks: / Berlin (dub version) / Berlin.
12" Single: Released Apr '84, on Sire (USA), Catalogue no: **W 9300T**

TOO MUCH
Tracks: / Too much.
Note: Pic bag
7" Single: Released 23 May '87, on E & F, by Supreme Records. Deleted '88. Catalogue no: **EF 1**
12" Single: Released 23 May '87, on E & F, by Supreme Records. Deleted '88. Catalogue no: **EFT 1**

Honky

Biographical details: This British disco band consisted of Cliff Barks, Malcolm Baggott, Trevor Cummins, Clark Newton, Ray Othen, Ron Taylor and Bob White. Honky achieved a one-off success on the UK charts in 1977, reaching No.28 with their single *Join the party*. With the disco boom gathering momentum at that time, it reached its position on the strength of club exposure and received little radio support. *Join the party* was written by guitarist Cummins and produced by Ken Gold, the man who had masterminded the major 1976 success of the black Liverpool group, the Real Thing. (Bob MacDonald, 24th Oct 1985).

JOIN THE PARTY
Tracks: / Join the party.
7" Single: Released May '77, on Creole, by Creole Records. Deleted '80. Catalogue no: **CR 137**

Hood

SALVATION
Tracks: / Salvation / You can't blackmail Jesus.
12" Single: Released Sep '87, on Factory (1), by Factory Records. Catalogue no: **FAC 182**

TOUGH GUYS DON'T DANCE
Tracks: / Tough guys don't dance / Tough guys don't dance (dub).
12" Single: Released Dec '86, on Les Disques Du Crepuscule(Belgium), by Les Disques Du Crepuscule(Belgium). Catalogue no: **TWI 687**

Hood, Claire

LITTLE CHRISTMAS
Tracks: / Little Christmas.
7" Single: Released Nov '81, on Spectra, by Spectra Records. Deleted '87. Catalogue no: **SPC 3**

Hoodoo Gurus

BITTER SWEET
Tracks: / Bitter sweet.
7" Single: Released Oct '85, on Chrysalis, by Chrysalis Records. Catalogue no: **CHS 2926**

COME ANYTIME
Tracks: / Come anytime / Cajun country.
7" Single: Released Aug '89, on RCA, by BMG Records (UK). Catalogue no: **PB 49349**
CD 5": Released Aug '89, on RCA, by BMG Records (UK). Catalogue no: **PD 49350**
7" Single: Released Aug '89, on RCA, by BMG Records (UK). Catalogue no: **PA 49347**
7" Single: Released Aug '89, on RCA, by

BMG Records (UK). Catalogue no: **PB 49345**
12" Single: Released Aug '89, on RCA, by BMG Records (UK). Catalogue no: **PT 49350**

GOOD TIMES
Tracks: / Good times / On my street.
7" Single: Released Jul '87, on Chrysalis, by Chrysalis Records. Catalogue no: **CHS 3151**
12" Single: Released Jul '87, on Chrysalis, by Chrysalis Records. Catalogue no: **CHS 123151**

I WANT YOU BACK
Tracks: / I want you back.
7" Single: Released Jan '85, on Demon, by Demon Records. Catalogue no: **D 1028**

MY GIRL
Tracks: / My girl.
7" Single: Released Jun '85, on Demon, by Demon Records. Catalogue no: **D 1033**

Hooked On...

HOOKED ON NUMBER ONES
12" Single: Released Nov '84, on Record Shack, by Record Shack Records. Catalogue no: **HOC (T)8**
7" Single: Released Nov '84, on Record Shack, by Record Shack Records. Catalogue no: **HOC 8**

Hooker, Frank

ROCK ME
Tracks: / Looking for my no. 1 love.
7" Single: Released Jan '80, on DJM, Deleted Jan '85. Catalogue no: **DJS 10931**
12" Single: Released Jan '80, on DJM, Deleted Jan '85. Catalogue no: **DJR 18009**

THIS FEELIN'
Tracks: / This feelin' / I wanna know your name.
12" Single: Released '88, on DJM, Catalogue no: **DJR 18012**
7" Single: Released '88, on DJM, Catalogue no: **DJS 10947**

Hooker, John Lee

Biographical details: This American blues singer, guitarist and songwriter was one of the true masters of his genre and an important influence upon the development of rock music. He was born in Clarkesdale, Mississippi in 1917 and was taught to play guitar by his grandfather. During his late teens and early twenties, Hooker led a gypsy-like existence on the road, trekking from place to place without achieving much. He settled in Detroit in 1943 and began working with local blues performers. During the late Forties and early Fifties, Hooker's tenacity paid off: he rose to prominence amongst blues lovers throughout the United States with his smash hits, *Boogie chillun* and *I'm in the mood*.
With his gravel-voiced singing style, his throbbing guitar and thumping rhythms, John Lee was feverishly active in the recording studio during the Fifties; indeed, he had to adopt several pseudonyms in order to avoid flooding the burgeoning rhythm-and-blues market with John Lee Hooker discs! Having helped to sow the seeds of the rock'n'roll revolution, he earned new respect and acclaim in Britain during the early Sixties as the vital UK blues boom got underway. With groups like the Animals, the Rolling Stones, the Small Faces, the Who and the Yardbirds adopting his style and incorporating it into the new era of Sixties pop, he came to the UK to perform in 1964 and landed a surprise chart hit of his own with *Dimples* which reached the UK No.23 position. In 1967 he chalked up a British Top 40 album with *House of the blues*.
During the Seventies and Eighties, the ageing process failed to diminish Hooker's musical skill and prowess. Having been instrumental in inspiring white rockers to play the blues, his name continued to be revered, especially in Britain. A 1982 UK package show with Bobby 'Blue' Bland and B.B.King proved that the man had lost none of his infectious magic. (Bob MacDonald, 24th Oct 1985).

DIMPLES
Tracks: / Dimples.
7" Single: Released Jun '64, on Stateside, by EMI Records. Deleted '67. Catalogue no: **SS 297**

DIMPLES (SINGLE)
Tracks: / Dimples / Boom boom / Onions.
7" Single: Released Jul '80, on Charly, by Charly Records. Deleted '87. Catalogue no: **CTD 106**

Hooker, Steve

IT'S ALL OVER NOW
Tracks: / It's all over now.
7" Single: Released Nov '88, on Arela, Catalogue no: **ARE 002**

KEEP DANCING
Tracks: / Keep dancing / How did you know?.
7" Single: Released Jan '80, on Wax, by Wax Records. Deleted '83. Catalogue no: **EAR 3**

Hookline & Silverfish

GOOD DEEDS
Tracks: / Good deeds / Hope.
Note: Double A side single. Self - 0734 341694
7" Single: Released Feb '87, on Shrubbery, Catalogue no: **SHRUB 001**

Hook'N'Pull Gang

POUR IT DOWN YER THROAT
Tracks: / Pour it down yer throat.
7" Single: Released Mar '87, on Bitch Hog, Catalogue no: **BITCH 1**

Hooley, Terry

LAUGH AT ME
Tracks: / Laugh at me.
7" Single: Released Apr '81, on Fresh, by Jetstar Records. Catalogue no: **FRESH 4**

Hooper, Eddie

KEEP YOUR WOMAN SATISFIED
Tracks: / Keep your woman satisfied / One sided affair.
7" Single: Released Sep '82, on Half Moon, by Rondelet Music & Records. Catalogue no: **ROUND 2000**

Hooper, Neil

ONLY WHEN I'M LONELY
Tracks: / Only when I'm lonely / Only when I'm lonely (inst.).
7" Single: Released Nov '86, on Tux, Deleted '87. Catalogue no: **TUX 1**

Hoorah, Boys Hoorah.

HOW THE WEST WAS WON
Tracks: / How the west was won / You love me, I love me..
7" Single: Released Apr '86, on Pressgang, by Pressgang Records. Catalogue no: **RUM 001**

Hooray & The Henrys

ALL STUCK UP
Tracks: / All stuck up / Chap's tale, A.
7" Single: Released Dec '83, on Works, by Works Records. Deleted '84. Catalogue no: **1K 2**

Hooters

ALL YOU ZOMBIES
Tracks: / All you zombies / Where the children go.
12" Single: Released Aug '86, on CBS, by CBS Records. Deleted '87. Catalogue no: **650025 6**
7" Single: Released Jun '85, on CBS, by CBS Records. Deleted '86. Catalogue no: **A 6155**
7" Single: Released Jul '86, on CBS, by CBS Records. Deleted '87. Catalogue no: **650025 7**

AND WE DANCED
Tracks: / And we dance / She comes in colours / Blood from a stone.
12" Single: Released Jun '86, on CBS, by CBS Records. Deleted '86. Catalogue no: **TA 6487**
7" Single: Released May '86, on CBS, by CBS Records. Deleted '87. Catalogue no: **A 6487**
12" Single: Released May '86, on CBS, by CBS Records. Catalogue no: **GA 6487**

JOHNNY B
Tracks: / Lucy in the sky with diamonds / And we danced / Johnny B / Lucy in the sky with diamonds / Karla with a K.
7" Single: Released Mar '88, on CBS, by CBS Records. Deleted Aug '88. Catalogue no: **650982 7**
CD 5": Released Mar '88, on CBS, by CBS Records. Deleted Jan '89. Catalogue no: **650982 2**
7" Single: Released Mar '88, on CBS, by CBS Records. Deleted Aug '88. Catalogue no: **650982 1**
12" Single: Released Mar '88, on CBS, by CBS Records. Deleted Aug '88. Catalogue no: **650982 8**

KARLA WITH A K
Tracks: / Karla with a K / Washington's day.
Note: Shaped picture disc.
7" Single: Released Jan '88, on CBS, by CBS Records. Deleted Aug '88. Catalogue no: **651 302 9**
CD 5": Released Jan '88, on CBS, by CBS Records. Deleted Jan '89. Catalogue no: **651 302 2**
12" Pic: Released Jan '88, on CBS, by CBS Records. Deleted Aug '88. Catalogue no: **651 302 0**
7" Single: Released Jan '88, on CBS, by CBS Records. Deleted Aug '88. Catalogue no: **651 302 7**
12" Single: Released Jan '88, on CBS, by CBS Records. Deleted Aug '88. Catalogue no: **651 302 6**

SATELLITE
Tracks: / Satellite / One way home / All you zombies*.
Note: *Available on 12" only.
CD 5": Released Nov '87, on CBS, by CBS Records. Deleted Jan '89. Catalogue no: **651 168-2**
7" Single: Released Nov '87, on CBS, by CBS Records. Deleted Jun '88. Catalogue no: **651 168 7**
12" Single: Released Nov '87, on CBS, by CBS Records. Deleted Jun '88. Catalogue no: **651 168 6**

Hope, Ellie

LUCKY
Tracks: / Lucky / Shake.
7" Single: Released Jan '83, on Polo, by Polo Records. Deleted '88. Catalogue no: **POLO 25**
12" Single: Released Jan '83, on Polo, by Polo Records. Deleted '88. Catalogue no: **POLO 1225**

Hope, Johnny

WEEKEND SERENADE
Tracks: / Weekend serenade / Confidential.
12" Single: Released May '82, on Orbitone, by Orbitone Records. Catalogue no: **ORB 5**

Hope, Marie

FREE PEOPLE
Tracks: / Free people / Free people.
12" Single: Released May '87, on UNKNOWN, Catalogue no: **12 FBT3 A**

Hope, Peter

KITCHENETTE
Tracks: / Industrial fatality / Kitchenette (version) / Kitchenette.
12" Single: Released Feb '87, on Native (1), by Native Records. Catalogue no: **NTV 12013**
7" Single: Released Feb '87, on Native (1), by Native Records. Catalogue no: **NTV 13**

SURGEONS
Tracks: / Surgeons / Beats / Resurgency / N.O..
12" Single: Released Oct '88, on Native (1), by Native Records. Catalogue no: **NTV 36**

TOO HOT
Tracks: / Too hot.
12" Single: Released Jun '85, on Ink, by Red Flame Records. Catalogue no: **INK 1211**

Hopeton Junior

COUNTRY MAN
Tracks: / Country man.
12" Single: Released Sep '84, on Look To Afrika, Catalogue no: **LTAF 1A**

Hopkin, Mary

GOODBYE
Tracks: / Goodbye.
7" Single: Released Apr '69, on Apple, by Apple Records. Deleted '72. Catalogue no: **APPLE 10**

KNOCK KNOCK WHO'S THERE
Tracks: / Knock knock who's there.
7" Single: Released Mar '70, on Apple, by Apple Records. Deleted '73. Catalogue no: **APPLE 26**

TEMMA HARBOUR
Tracks: / Temma Harbour.
7" Single: Released Jan '70, on Apple, by Apple Records. Deleted '73. Catalogue no: **APPLE 22**

THINK ABOUT YOUR CHILREN
Tracks: / Think about your children.
7" Single: Released Oct '70, on Apple, by Apple Records. Deleted '73. Catalogue no: **APPLE 30**

THOSE WERE THE DAYS
Tracks: / Those were the days.
7" Single: Released Sep '68, on Apple, by Apple Records. Deleted '71. Catalogue no: **APPLE 2**

Hopkins, Anthony

DISTANT STAR
Tracks: / Distant star / Ordinary man.
7" Single: Released Dec '86, on Juice, by Juice Records. Deleted '88. Catalogue no: **AA 5**

Hopkins, Barry

ANYTIME YOU WANT ME
Tracks: / Anytime you want me / If I could live on your street.
7" Single: Released Oct '85, on Good, Catalogue no: **MGL 100**
7" Single: Released Mar '86, on Good, Catalogue no: **MSGL 100**

Hopkins, Pickford Gary

WHY
Tracks: / Why / Why (the story).
12" Single: Released Apr '87, on Spartan, Catalogue no: **12SP 143**
7" Single: Released Apr '87, on Spartan, Catalogue no: **SP 143**

Hopscotch

LITTLE BOY WHO..., THE
7" Single: Released Dec '87, on Funkin' Marvellous, by Steinar Records (UK). Catalogue no: **MARV 11**

Horizon

STAGE STRUCK
Tracks: / Stage struck / Remember the bad boys.
7" Single: Released Jul '81, on SRT, by SRT Records. Deleted Jul '84. Catalogue no: **STRS 81432**

SUNSHINE REGGAE
Tracks: / Sunshine reggae.
7" Single: Released Jun '84, on Orbit, by Orbit Records. Catalogue no: **TRIP 4**

Horizons

STAGE STRUCK
Tracks: / Stage struck.
7" Single: Released Jun '81, on SRT, by SRT Records. Catalogue no: **SRTS 81432**

Horn Section

LADY SHINE
Tracks: / Lady shine.
12" Single: Released Aug '84, on 4th & Broadway, by Island Records. Catalogue no: **12 BRW 10**
7" Single: Released Aug '84, on 4th & Broadway, by Island Records. Catalogue no: **BRW 10**

Horne, Jimmy 'Bo'

IS IT IN
Tracks: / Is it in / Spank.
7" Single: Released Nov '80, on TK, Deleted Nov '83. Catalogue no: **TKR 7586**
12" Single: Released Nov '80, on TK, Deleted Nov '83. Catalogue no: **TKR 137586**

WITHOUT YOU
Tracks: / Without you / Goin' home for love.
7" Single: Released Apr '80, on TK, Deleted Apr '83. Catalogue no: **TKR 7575**

YOU'RE SO GOOD TO ME
Tracks: / You're so good to me.
12" Single: Released Jan '84, on Sunny View (USA), by Sunnyview Records (USA). Catalogue no: **SUNYL 102**

Hornsby, Bruce

DEFENDERS OF THE FLAG
Tracks: / Defenders of the flag / Look out of any window / Look out any window (live) (not on 7" single.) / Defenders of the flag (live) (On CD single only.).
7" Single: Released Nov '88, on RCA, by BMG Records (UK). Deleted Aug '89. Catalogue no: **PB 49511**
12" Single: Released Nov '88, on RCA, by BMG Records (UK). Catalogue no: **PT 49512**
CD 5": Released Nov '88, on RCA, by BMG Records (UK). Deleted Jul '89. Catalogue no: **PD 49512**

EVERY LITLE KISS
Tracks: / Every little kiss / River runs low, The / Way it is,The (instrumental) (On 12" version only.).
7" Single: Released Sep '86, on RCA, by BMG Records (UK). Deleted '87. Catalogue no: **PB 49797**
12" Single: Released Sep '86, on RCA, by BMG Records (UK). Catalogue no: **PT 49798**

LOOK OUT ANY WINDOW
Tracks: / Look out any window / On the western skyline / Mandolin rain *.
Note: * 12" and C.D. versions only.
7" Single: Released 8 Aug '88, on RCA, by BMG Records (UK). Deleted May '89. Catalogue no: **PB 49533**
12" Single: Released 8 Aug '88, on RCA, by BMG Records (UK). Deleted May '89. Catalogue no: **PT 49534**
CD 5": Released 8 Aug '88, on RCA, by BMG Records (UK). Deleted Jul '89. Catalogue no: **PD 49534**

MANDOLIN RAIN
Tracks: / Mandolin rain / Red plains, the / Way it is, The (Only available on 12" version) / Every little kiss (Only available on 12" version.).
Note: The way it is/Every little kiss - these two extra tracks are only available on the 12" version.
12" Single: Released Feb '87, on RCA, by

BMG Records (UK). Catalogue no: **PT 49770**
7" Single: Released Feb '87, on RCA, by BMG Records (UK). Deleted May '89. Catalogue no: **PB 49769**

VALLEY ROAD, THE
Tracks: / Valley Road / Long race, The / Mandolin rain (live) (Track on 12" and CD versions only.).
12" Single: Released May '88, on RCA, by BMG Records (UK). Deleted May '89. Catalogue no: **PT 49562**
CD 5": Released May '88, on RCA, by BMG Records (UK). Deleted Jul '89. Catalogue no: **PD 49562**
7" Single: Released May '88, on RCA, by BMG Records (UK). Deleted May '89. Catalogue no: **PB 49561**

WAY IT IS, THE (SINGLE)
Tracks: / Way it is, The.
12" Single: Released Jul '86, on Juice, by Juice Records. Catalogue no: **PT 49806**
7" Single: Released Jul '86, on Juice, by Juice Records. Catalogue no: **PB 49805**

Horovitz, Joseph

RUMPOLE OF THE BAILEY
Tracks: / Rumpole of the Bailey / Soft-shoe shuffle / Les girls.
7" Single: Released Jan '87, on Columbia, by EMI Records. Deleted Oct '87. Catalogue no: **DB 9143**

Horse

YOU COULD BE FORGIVEN
Tracks: / You could be forgiven / Somebody / Down to the dizzy heights (12" & CD single only.) / I close my eyes and count to ten (CD single only.).
CD 5": Released Jul '89, on Capitol, by EMI Records. Catalogue no: **CDCL 514**
7" Single: Released Jul '89, on Capitol, by EMI Records. Catalogue no: **CL 514**
12" Single: Released Jul '89, on Capitol, by EMI Records. Catalogue no: **12CL 514**

Horseflies

HUSH LITTLE BABY
Tracks: / Hush little baby / Human fly / I live where it's gray (12" only.).
7" Single: Released Oct '88, on Cooking Vinyl, by Cooking Vinyl Records. Catalogue no: **FRY 004**
12" Single: Released Nov '88, on Cooking Vinyl, by Cooking Vinyl Records. Catalogue no: **FRY 004T**

Horseland

LOVE DIES AGAIN
Tracks: / Love dies again.
12" Single: Released Apr '88, on Red Rhino, by Red Rhino Records. Catalogue no: **REDT 090**
7" Single: Released Apr '88, on Red Rhino, by Red Rhino Records. Catalogue no: **RED 090**

Horseman

EASY COUNTRY GAL
Tracks: / Easy country gal.
12" Single: Released Nov '88, on Jammy's, Catalogue no: **VPRD 369**

FOLLOW ME
Tracks: / Follow me.
12" Single: Released Mar '88, on Digitec, Catalogue no: **DT 001**

HORSE MOVE
Tracks: / Horse move.
12" Single: Released May '85, on Raiders, Catalogue no: **LGR 009**

RAGGAMUFFIN DJ OF THE YEAR
Tracks: / Raggamuffin DJ of the year.
7" Single: Released Jan '89, on Jammy's, Catalogue no: **Unknown**

Horseman, Daddy

CHICKEN FLAP
Tracks: / Chicken flap.
12" Single: Released Sep '85, on Magic Shoot, Catalogue no: **MS 001**

WARM UP
Tracks: / Warm up / Shake your shoulder.
12" Single: Released May '85, on Rusty International, Catalogue no: **RI 017**

Horsemouth

REGGAE MUSIC
Tracks: / Reggae music / I want to be with you.
12" Single: Released Apr '82, on Horsemouth, Catalogue no: **HM 001**

Horton, Johnny

Biographical details: This American singer, guitarist and songwriter was initially dubbed 'the singing fisherman' because of his original career. He spent the Fifties working his way up the country and western ladder via such shows as *Louisiana hayride*, and eventually establishing himself on the US country charts with a series of rock-influenced singles like *Honky tonk hardwood floor* and *Honky tonk man*. Horton suddenly surged to major pop stardom in 1959 with *Battle of New Orleans*, which logged six weeks on top of the American Hot 100. It was the biggest novelty hit of that year. The tune originally dated from 1815, and was composed in celebration of the victory of Andrew Jackson's men against the British forces of Commander Pakenham at New Orleans during the final battle of a bloody war. Lyrics were written by Jimmy Driftwood in 1955. One would have thought that Horton's *Battle of New Orleans* might have caused some transatlantic offence, by cockily crowing about past conflicts during out modern era of Anglo-American harmony. But the song reached No.2 on the British chart, in a cover version by UK singer Lonnie Donegan! Johnny's rendition had to be content with a UK No.16 placing. In 1960 Horton achieved two further big hits in America with more examples of the then fashionable 'saga song' genre. He reached No.3 with *Sink the Bismarch* (inspired by the movie of the same name) and No.4 with the theme from the John Wayne film *North to Alaska* was climbing the US chart, Johnny Horton was killed in a car crash in November 1960 at the age of 33. It is said that during the last few weeks of his life, he had premonitions of his own death and consequently cancelled potentially risky activities such as aeroplane flights. At the time of his death, Horton's LP material was showing signs of veering towards a more conventional country style; had he lived, he might have been a major C&W artist for several years more. (24th Oct 1985).

BATTLE OF NEW ORLEANS
Tracks: / Battle of New Orleans.
7" Single: Released May '59, on Philips, by Phonogram Ltd. Catalogue no: **PB 932**

BATTLE OF NEW ORLEANS (OLD GOLD)
Tracks: / Battle of New Orleans / Waterloo.
7" Single: Released Nov '80, on Old Gold, by Old Gold Records. Deleted '83. Catalogue no: **OG 9074**

NORTH TO ALASKA
Tracks: / North to Alaska.
7" Single: Released Dec '60, on Philips, by Phonogram Ltd. Deleted '63. Catalogue no: **PB 1062**

Host

WALK ON LOVE
Tracks: / Walk on love.
7" Single: Released Jan '85, on Aura Records, by Aura Records. Deleted '88. Catalogue no: **AUS 144**

Hostages

GOING UP IN THE WORLD
Tracks: / Going up in the world.
7" Single: Released Aug '84, on EMI, by EMI Records. Catalogue no: **EMI 5487**
12" Single: Released Aug '84, on EMI, by EMI Records. Deleted '86. Catalogue no: **12 EMI 5487**

HERE'S THE PEOPLE
Tracks: / Here's the people / In a minute.
7" Single: Released Mar '82, on This, Catalogue no: **THIS 1**

Hot 40's

THEME FROM FIREPOWER
Tracks: / Theme from firepower / Smack in the middle of love.
7" Single: Released '88, on DJM, Catalogue no: **DJS 10934**

Hot Blood

SOUL DRACULA
Tracks: / Soul Dracula.
7" Single: Released Sep '76, on Creole, by Creole Records. Catalogue no: **CR 132**

Hot Butter

POPCORN
Tracks: / Popcorn.
7" Single: Released Jun '72, on Pye International, Deleted '75. Catalogue no: **7N 25583**
7" Single: Released Jan '85, on Old Gold, by Old Gold Records. Catalogue no: **OG 9394**

Hot Chocolate

Biographical details: This British pop band consists of Errol Brown, Tony Connor, Larry Ferguson, Harvey Hinsley and Patrick Olive. Until 1975 there was a sixth member, Tony Wilson. Hot Chocolate were formed at the beginning of 1970 by the songwriting duo of Brown and Wilson. They were initially signed to the Beatles' Apple label for whom the two guys wrote Mary Hopkin's UK Top 20 single *Think about your children*. But after another of their songs, *Bet yer life I do*, became a chart success for Herman's Hermits, Brown and his colleagues quickly switched their affiliations to RAK Records, the newly formed company owned by Herman's producer Mickie Most. Hot Chocolate's first Most-produced record was *Love is life*, only the third single to be released by RAK. It reached No.6 on the British chart in the autumn of 1970. Thus began the chart career of the most consistently successful British group of the Seventies, in terms of hit singles. Between 1970 and 1984 they chalked up at least one UK hit per year - something no other group could match - and achieved 30 chart singles in all. All were produced by the ever astute Most and the majority were written by lead singer Brown (in association with Wilson until 1975), although their only UK No.1 single - 1977's *So you win again* was penned by Russ Ballard. The extraordinary consistency of Hot Chocolate/Mickie Most alliance owed its success to a good selection of material, a highly professional working relationship, plus a readily identifiable yet always flexible sound. Like the Equals and the Foundations in the Sixties, Hot Chocolate were a multi-racial combo who purveyed pure pop platters that possessed an across-the-board soul/dance/teenybop appeal. They always relied primarily on singles - the group's debut LP *Cicero Park* did not appear until 1974, and their only two UK Top 20 albums were compilations of old hits. The band's visual image centred on Errol, whose shaven head was familiar to the British public long before that of Telly Savalas. Hot Chocolate's material was introduced to the American market in 1973 via a No.1 cover version of *Brother Louie* by the Stories. In later years, Hot Chocolate themselves enjoyed US Top 10 hits with the dramatic suicide song *Emma* (No.8 in US, No.3 in UK), the ultra-catchy *You sexy thing* (No.3 in US, No.2 in UK) and the insidiously infectious disco-rock number *Every 1's a winner* (N0.6 in US, No.12 in UK). In the Eighties, America chose to overlook such major British hits as *No doubt about it* (No.2) and the schoolkid romance saga (It started with a kiss) (No.5). (Bob MacDonald, 25th Oct 1985).

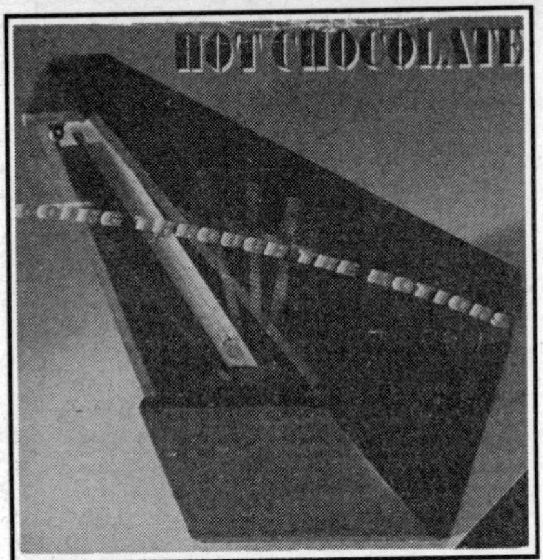

HOT CHOCOLATE - GOING THROU GH THE MOTIONS (Released on RAK)

ARE YOU GETTING ENOUGH (of what makes you happy)?
Tracks: / Are you getting enough (of what makes you happy) / I've got you on my mind.
7" Single: Released Jun '80, on RAK, by EMI Records. Deleted '83. Catalogue no: **RAK 318**
12" Single: Released Jun '80, on RAK, by EMI Records. Deleted '83. Catalogue no: **12RAK 318**

BROTHER LOUIE
Tracks: / Brother Louie.
7" Single: Released Mar '73, on RAK, by EMI Records. Deleted '76. Catalogue no: **RAK 149**

CHANCES
Tracks: / Chances / Nights to remember.
7" Single: Released Sep '82, on RAK, by EMI Records. Deleted '85. Catalogue no: **RAK 350**

CHERI BABE
Tracks: / Cheri babe.
7" Single: Released Oct '74, on RAK, by EMI Records. Deleted '77. Catalogue no: **RAK 188**

CHILD'S PRAYER, A
Tracks: / Child's prayer, A.
7" Single: Released Aug '75, on RAK, by EMI Records. Deleted '78. Catalogue no: **RAK 212**

DISCO QUEEN
Tracks: / Disco queen.
7" Single: Released Aug '75, on RAK, by EMI Records. Deleted '78. Catalogue no: **RAK 202**

DON'T STOP IT NOW
Tracks: / Don't stop it now.
7" Single: Released Mar '76, on RAK, by EMI Records. Deleted '79. Catalogue no: **RAK 230**

EMMA
Tracks: / Emma.
7" Single: Released Mar '74, on RAK, by EMI Records. Deleted '77. Catalogue no: **RAK 168**

EVERY 1'S A WINNER
Tracks: / Every 1's a winner (groove mix) / So you win again.
12" Single: Released Mar '87, on EMI, by EMI Records. Catalogue no: **12 MI 5607**
7" Single: Released Mar '87, on EMI, by EMI Records. Catalogue no: **EMI 5607**

EVERY 1'S A WINNER (ORIGINAL)
Tracks: / Every 1's a winner.
7" Single: Released Feb '78, on RAK, by EMI Records. Deleted '81. Catalogue no: **RAK 270**

GIRL CRAZY
Tracks: / Girl crazy / Bed games.
7" Single: Released Apr '82, on RAK, by EMI Records. Deleted '85. Catalogue no: **RAK 341**

GOING THROUGH THE MOTIONS (ORIGINAL) (see panle above)
Tracks: / Going through the motions.
7" Single: Released Jun '78, on RAK, by EMI Records. Deleted '81. Catalogue no: **RAK 296**

HEARTACHE NO.9
Tracks: / Heartache no.9 / One life / Extended mix (On 12' version only.) / Heartache no.9 (Dub) (On 12'version only.).
7" Single: Released Mar '86, on RAK, by EMI Records. Catalogue no: **RAK 386**
12" Single: Released Mar '86, on RAK, by EMI Records. Catalogue no: **12RAK 386**

HEAVEN IS IN THE BACK SEAT OF MY CADILLAC
Tracks: / Heaven is in the back seat of my Cadillac.
7" Single: Released Jul '76, on RAK, by EMI Records. Deleted '79. Catalogue no: **RAK 240**

I BELIEVE (IN LOVE)
Tracks: / I believe (in love).
7" Single: Released Jul '71, on RAK, by EMI Records. Deleted '74. Catalogue no: **RAK 118**

I GAVE YOU MY HEART (DIDN'T I)

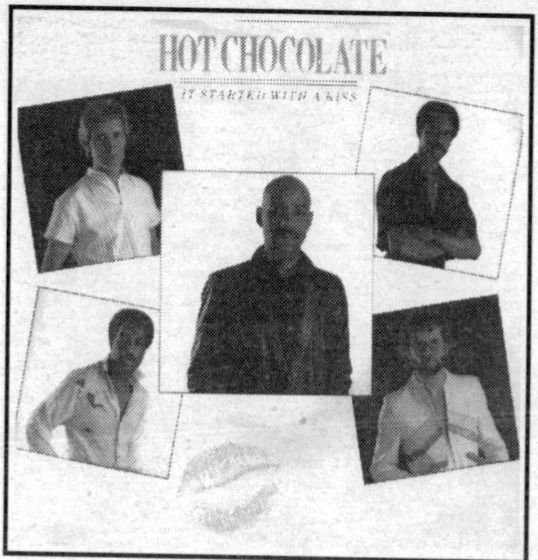

HOT CHOCOLATE - IT STARTED WITH A KISS (Released on RAK)

Tracks: / I gave you my heart (didn't I).
7" Single: Released Feb '84, on RAK, by EMI Records. Deleted '87. Catalogue no: **RAK 369**

I'LL PUT YOU TOGETHER AGAIN
Tracks: / I'll put you together again.
7" Single: Released Nov '78, on RAK, by EMI Records. Deleted '81. Catalogue no: **RAK 286**

I'M SORRY
Tracks: / I'm sorry.
7" Single: Released Nov '83, on RAK, by EMI Records. Catalogue no: **RAK 366**

IT STARTED WITH A KISS
Tracks: / It started with a kiss / Emotion explosion.
7" Single: Released Jun '82, on RAK, by EMI Records. Deleted '85. Catalogue no: **RAK 344**

LOSING YOU
Tracks: / Losing you / Children of spacemen.
7" Single: Released Feb '81, on RAK, by EMI Records. Deleted '84. Catalogue no: **RAK 328**

LOVE IS LIFE
Tracks: / Love is life.
7" Single: Released Jul '70, on RAK, by EMI Records. Deleted '73. Catalogue no: **RAK 103**

LOVE ME TO SLEEP
Tracks: / Love me to sleep / Girl is a fox.
7" Single: Released Nov '80, on RAK, by EMI Records. Deleted '83. Catalogue no: **RAK 324**

MAN TO MAN (ORIGINAL)
Tracks: / Man to man.
7" Single: Released Jun '76, on RAK, by EMI Records. Deleted '79. Catalogue no: **RAK 238**

MINDLESS BOOGIE
Tracks: / Mindless boogie.
7" Single: Released Apr '79, on RAK, by EMI Records. Deleted '82. Catalogue no: **RAK 292**

NO DOUBT ABOUT IT
Tracks: / No doubt about it / Gimme some of your loving.
7" Single: Released Apr '80, on RAK, by EMI Records. Deleted '83. Catalogue no: **RAK 310**
12" Single: Released Apr '80, on RAK, by EMI Records. Deleted Apr '83. Catalogue no: **12RAK 310**

PUT YOUR LOVE IN ME
Tracks: / Put your love in me.
7" Single: Released Nov '77, on RAK, by EMI Records. Deleted '80. Catalogue no: **RAK 266**

RUMOURS
Tracks: / Rumours.
7" Single: Released Jul '73, on RAK, by EMI Records. Deleted '76. Catalogue no: **RAK 157**

SO YOU WIN AGAIN
Tracks: / So you win again.
7" Single: Released May '77, on RAK, by EMI Records. Deleted '80. Catalogue no: **RAK 259**

TEARS ON THE TELEPHONE
Tracks: / Tears on the telephone / It's my birthday.
7" Single: Released Sep '83, on RAK, by EMI Records. Catalogue no: **RAK 363**

WHAT KINDA BOY YOU LOOKING FOR (GIRL)
Tracks: / What kinda boy you looking for (girl).
7" Single: Released Apr '83, on RAK, by EMI Records. Deleted '86. Catalogue no: **RAK 357**

YOU COULD'VE BEEN A LADY
Tracks: / You could've been a lady.
7" Single: Released Feb '71, on RAK, by EMI Records. Deleted '74. Catalogue no: **RAK 110**

YOU SEXY THING
Tracks: / You sexy thing / No doubt about it.
7" Single: Released Mar '84, on EMI Golden 45's, by EMI Records. Deleted Aug '89. Catalogue no: **G45 12**
7" Single: Released Jan '87, on EMI, by EMI Records. Deleted '88. Catalogue no: **EMI 5592**
12" Single: Released Jan '87, on EMI, by EMI Records. Deleted Apr '88. Catalogue no: **12EMI 5592**

YOU SEXY THING (EXT REPLAY MIX)
Tracks: / You sexy thing (ext replay mix) / Megamix-Emma / So you win again / You sexy thing / Every 1's a winner / You could've been a lady / Heaven is in the back seat of my Cadillac / Every 1's a winner.
12" Single: Released Jan '87, on EMI, by EMI Records. Catalogue no: **EMIX 5592**

YOU SEXY THING (ORIGINAL)
Tracks: / You sexy thing.
7" Single: Released Oct '75, on RAK, by EMI Records. Deleted '78. Catalogue no: **RAK 221**

YOU'LL ALWAYS BE A FRIEND
Tracks: / You'll always be a friend.
7" Single: Released Sep '72, on RAK, by EMI Records. Deleted '75. Catalogue no: **RAK 139**

YOU'LL NEVER BE SO WRONG
Tracks: / You'll never be so wrong / Robot love.
7" Single: Released Apr '81, on RAK, by EMI Records. Deleted '84. Catalogue no: **RAK 331**
12" Single: Released Apr '81, on RAK, by EMI Records. Deleted '84. Catalogue no: **12RAK 331**

Hot Club

DIRT THAT SHE WALKS IN IS SACRED GROUND
Tracks: / Dirt that she walks in is sacred ground / Heat.
7" Single: Released Aug '82, on RAK, by EMI Records. Catalogue no: **RAK 346**

IT AIN'T ME GIRL
Tracks: / It ain't me girl.
7" Single: Released Jul '83, on RAK, by EMI Records. Catalogue no: **RAK 361**
12" Single: Released Jul '83, on RAK, by EMI Records. Catalogue no: **12 RAK 361**

Hot Cuisine

DANCIN' ME TO ECSTACY
Tracks: / Dancin' me to ecstacy / All fired up.
7" Single: Released Jan '81, on Kaleidoscope Sound, by Kaleidoscope Sound Records. Deleted Jan '84. Catalogue no: **KRL 9461**
12" Single: Released Jan '81, on Kaleidoscope Sound, by Kaleidoscope Sound Records. Deleted Jan '84. Catalogue no: **KRL 13 9461**

KEEP THAT SAME OLD FEELING
Tracks: / Keep that same old feeling / You and me.
12" Single: Released Oct '82, on Kaleidoscope Sound, by Kaleidoscope Sound Records. Deleted Oct '85. Catalogue no: **KRLA 132560**
7" Single: Released Oct '82, on Kaleidoscope Sound, by Kaleidoscope Sound Records. Deleted Oct '85. Catalogue no: **KRLA 2560**

ONE NIGHT STAND
Tracks: / One night stand.
12" Single: Released Apr '86, on Soul Supply, by Soul Supply Records. Catalogue no: **HQ 1**

RIDE A RHYTHM
Tracks: / Ride a rhythm / Live my life.
7" Single: Released Mar '82, on KRL, by Kaleidoscope Records (UK). Deleted '85. Catalogue no: **A 2107**
12" Single: Released Mar '82, on KRL, by Kaleidoscope Records (UK). Deleted '85. Catalogue no: **A 13-2107**

SKANKIN'
Tracks: / Skankin' / Disco calypso.
7" Single: Released Oct '81, on Kaleidoscope Sound, by Kaleidoscope Sound Records. Deleted Oct '84. Catalogue no: **KRLA 1661**

WHO'S BEEN KISSING YOU
Tracks: / Who's been kissing you / Live my life.
12" Single: Released May '87, on ISR, Catalogue no: **KEV 4T**
7" Single: Released Apr '81, on Kaleidoscope Sound, by Kaleidoscope Sound Records. Deleted Apr '84. Catalogue no: **KRLA 1105**

Hot Gossip

BREAK ME INTO LITTLE PIECES
Tracks: / Break me into little pieces.
7" Single: Released Jun '84, on Fanfare, by Captain Billy's Music. Catalogue no: **HG 1**
12" Single: Released Jun '84, on Fanfare, by Captain Billy's Music. Catalogue no: **HGT 1**

CRIMINAL WORLD
Tracks: / Criminal world / Criminal world (part 2).
7" Single: Released Sep '81, on Dindisc, by Virgin Records. Deleted '84. Catalogue no: **DIN 37**
12" Single: Released Sep '81, on Dindisc, by Virgin Records. Deleted '84. Catalogue no: **DIN 3712**

DON'T BEAT AROUND THE BUSH
Tracks: / Don't beat around the bush.
7" Single: Released Nov '84, on Fanfare, by Captain Billy's Music. Catalogue no: **FAN 1**
12" Single: Released Nov '84, on Fanfare, by Captain Billy's Music. Catalogue no: **12 FAN 1**

SOUL WARFARE
Tracks: / Soul warfare.
7" Single: Released Nov '81, on Dindisc, by Virgin Records. Deleted Nov '84. Catalogue no: **DIN 38**

SPACE INVADERS (see panel below)
Tracks: / Space Invaders / Space Invaders (inst.).
7" Single: Released '80, on This Record Co. Ltd., Catalogue no: **DJS 10939**

Hot Hot Hot

ARROW
Tracks: / Arrow.
Note: One of those classic party tracks that everybody knows.. Deleted in the U.K..
12" Single: Released Nov '87, on Chrysalis (USA), by CBS Records. Catalogue no: **4 V 942701**

Hot House

CRAZY
Tracks: / Crazy / My boys arms / Pull over (on 12" only.) / Way that we walk, The (Available on CD only).
Note: **Only on CD version. "Hot House's return after a year's absence with a moody blue cover version of the Willie Nelson track." (Music Week, July 1988)M
CD 5": Released Jun '88, on RCA, by BMG Records (UK). Deleted Jul '89. Catalogue no: **PD 42114**
7" Single: Released Jun '88, on RCA, by BMG Records (UK). Deleted May '89. Catalogue no: **PB 42113**
12" Single: Released Jun '88, on RCA, by BMG Records (UK). Deleted May '89. Catalogue no: **PT 42114**

DON'T COME TO STAY
Tracks: / Me and you.
7" Single: on RCA, by BMG Records (UK). Catalogue no: **CHEZ 1**
CD 5": Released Jun '89, on RCA, by BMG Records (UK). Deleted Jul '89. Catalogue no: **PD 42234**
7" Single: Released Nov '86, on Construction, Catalogue no: **M 621**
7" Single: Released Sep '88, on RCA, by BMG Records (UK). Deleted May '89. Catalogue no: **PB 42233**
12" Single: Released Nov '86, on Construction, Catalogue no: **M 6212**
12" Single: Released Sep '88, on RCA, by BMG Records (UK). Deleted May '89. Catalogue no: **PT 42234**

EVERYTHING YOU SAID
Tracks: / Everything you said / All comes down.

HOT GOSSIP - SPACE INVADERS (Released on This Record Co.)

CD 5": Released May '89, on De Construction, by BMG Records (UK). Catalogue no: **PD 42846**
12" Single: Released May '89, on De Construction, by BMG Records (UK). Catalogue no: **PT 42846**
7" Single: Released May '89, on De Construction, by BMG Records (UK). Catalogue no: **PB 42845**

HARD AS I TRY
Tracks: / Hard as I try / Person who's taking you home, The / Home boy (Only on CD single and 12") / Don't come to stay (Only on CD single.).
CD 5": Released Jun '89, on De Construction, by BMG Records (UK). Deleted Jul '89. Catalogue no: **PD 42658**
7" Single: Released Mar '89, on De Construction, by BMG Records (UK). Deleted Aug '89. Catalogue no: **PB 42657**
12" Single: Released Mar '89, on De Construction, by BMG Records (UK). Deleted Aug '89. Catalogue no: **PT 42658**

WAY WE TALK, THE
Tracks: / Way we talk, The.
7" Single: Released Aug '87, on Construction, Catalogue no: **CHEZ 2**
12" Single: Released Aug '87, on Construction, Deleted May '89. Catalogue no: **CHEZT 2**

Hot Ice

A VERY MEDLEY CHRISTMAS
Tracks: / A very medley Christmas / Christmas in the air.
7" Single: Released Nov '81, on Kaleidoscope Sound, by Kaleidoscope Sound Records. Deleted Nov '84. Catalogue no: **A 1763**

Hot Licks

D.A.N.C.E.
Tracks: / D.A.N.C.E. / Sweet pain.
7" Single: Released Mar '82, on Eagle (London), by Eagle (London) Records. Deleted '88. Catalogue no: **BSB 016**
12" Single: Released Mar '82, on Eagle (London), by Eagle (London) Records. Deleted '88. Catalogue no: **BSB 016 12**

Hot 'N' Horrid

TOURISTS MAKE THE TREES GROW
Tracks: / Tourists make the trees grow.
12" Single: Released Jul '87, on Tim, by Tim Records. Catalogue no: **12 MOT 8**

Hot Pursuit

VICTIM OF THE BEAT
Tracks: / Victim of the beat / Victim of the beat (Dub mix).
12" Single: Released Sep '86, on Genie, Catalogue no: **12 GEN 6**

Hot Rain

IT'S A LIE
Tracks: / It's a lie / Brainwash.
7" Single: Released Sep '89, on Pantry, Catalogue no: **TWIG 001**

Hot Rox

SUMMER FEVER (PUTS YOUR EMOTIONS IN MOTION)
Tracks: / Summer fever (puts your emotions in motion).
12" Single: Released Jun '84, on CBS, by CBS Records. Catalogue no: **TA4563**
7" Single: Released Jun '84, on CBS, by CBS Records. Catalogue no: **A 4563**

Hot R.S.

HOUSE OF THE RISING SUN
Tracks: / House of the rising sun / House of the rising sun (version).
12" Single: Released '83, on Chrysalis, by Chrysalis Records. Deleted '87. Catalogue no: **CHS 12 2228**

Hot Shot

I FOUND MORE LOVE
Tracks: / I found more love.
7" Single: Released Feb '85, on Justice, Catalogue no: **JUS 005**
12" Single: Released Feb '85, on Justice, Catalogue no: **12JUS 005**

SEXY TOUCH (MEDLEY)
Tracks: / Sexy touch (medley).
12" Single: Released Nov '84, on Inferno (1), by Inferno Records. Catalogue no: **Unknown**

Hot Shots

SNOOPY V THE RED BARON (SINGLE)
Tracks: / Snoopy v the Red Baron.
7" Single: Released May '73, on Mooncrest, by Trojan Records. Deleted '76. Catalogue no: **MOON 5**

Hot Streak

Biographical details: *Body work* was the title of this faceless New York band's one-off UK release - it reached No.19 on the singles chart in the autumn of 1983 after receiving heavy exposure in the clubs but little radio airplay. After motivating many dancing feet with the ultra-funky but ultimately forgettable *Body work*, the five of six black guys who comprised Hot Streak moved on to other projects. (Bob MacDonald, 25th Oct 1985).

BODY WORK
Tracks: / Body work / Body work (inst).
7" Single: Released Aug '83, on Polydor, by Polydor Ltd. Deleted '85. Catalogue no: **POSP 642**
7" Single: Released Sep '86, on Boiling Point, by Polydor Ltd. Deleted Mar '87. Catalogue no: **POSP 821**
12" Single: Released Sep '86, on Boiling Point, by Polydor Ltd. Catalogue no: **POSPX 821**

BODY WORK (OLD GOLD)
Tracks: / Body work / Go deh yaka (Go to the top).
Note: B-side features 'Go deh yaka (Go to the top)' by Monyaka
12" Single: Released Feb '88, on Old Gold, by Old Gold Records. Catalogue no: **OG 4045**

Hot Stuff

JACK IN THE BOX Featuring Lee Vanderbilt
Tracks: / Jack in the box.
7" Single: Released Oct '85, on Sharpville, Deleted '86. Catalogue no: **7PG 20**
12" Single: Released Oct '85, on Sharpville, Deleted '86. Catalogue no: **12PG 20**

Hot Syndicate

TAKE ME BACK
Tracks: / Take me back.
12" Single: Released Jan '84, on Sunburn, by Orbitone Records. Catalogue no: **SBD 45**

Hotel

DANCING WITH THE MOONLIGHT
Tracks: / Dancing with the moonlight / C'mon everybody (7" only.) / Legend of future (12" only.) / Power: live version (12" only.) / C'mon everybody (live) (12" only.).
7" Single: Released Mar '89, on Parlophone, by EMI Records. Deleted Aug '89. Catalogue no: **HOTE 1**
7" Single: Released Mar '89, on Parlophone, by EMI Records. Deleted Aug '89. Catalogue no: **203 305 7**
12" Single: Released Mar '89, on Parlophone, by EMI Records. Deleted Aug '89. Catalogue no: **12HOTE 1**
12" Single: Released Mar '89, on Parlophone, by EMI Records. Deleted Aug '89. Catalogue no: **203 305 6**

Hotel UK

DREAM STREET
Tracks: / Dream Street / Silver boy.
7" Single: Released Aug '81, on Logo, by Logo Records. Deleted '84. Catalogue no: **GO 404**

Hotfoot Gale

MACHINE GUN BOOGIE
Tracks: / Machine gun boogie / I want you, I need you, I love you.
7" Single: Released Dec '82, on JJ, by JJ Records. Catalogue no: **JJ 625**

Hothouse Flowers

DON'T GO
Tracks: / Don't go / Saved / Hydroman (Only 12" only).
12" Single: Released Apr '88, on London Records, by London Records. Deleted Feb '89. Catalogue no: **LONX 174**
12" Single: Released 31 Oct '87, on London Records, by London Records. Deleted Feb '89. Catalogue no: **LONX 159**
7" Single: Released 31 Oct '87, on London Records, by London Records. Deleted Feb '89. Catalogue no: **LON 159**
10" single: Released '88, on London Records, by London Records. Deleted Feb '89. Catalogue no: **LONT 159**
7" Single: Released Apr '88, on London Records, by London Records. Deleted Feb '89. Catalogue no: **LON 174**

EASIER IN THE MORNING
Tracks: / Easier in the morning / Carrickfergus (Previously unissued.) / Feet on the ground (live) (On 12" only) / Better and better (Only on the CD single.).
CD 5": Released Aug '88, on London Records, by London Records. Catalogue no: **LONCD 186**
7" Single: Released Aug '88, on London Records, by London Records. Deleted Feb '89. Catalogue no: **LON 186**
7" Single: Released Sep '88, on London Records, by London Records. Deleted May '89. Catalogue no: **LONB 186**
12" Single: Released Aug '88, on London Records, by London Records. Deleted Feb '89. Catalogue no: **LONX 186**

FEET ON THE GROUND
Tracks: / Feet on the ground / Hard rain / Strange feeling (Extra track on 12".).
Note: A single from one of Ireland's most successful new bands.
7" Single: Released Mar '88, on London Records, by London Records. Deleted Feb '89. Catalogue no: **LON 172**
12" Single: Released Mar '88, on London Records, by London Records. Deleted Feb '89. Catalogue no: **LONX 172**

I'M SORRY
Tracks: / I'm sorry / Mountains / Seeline woman (On 12" only) / Don't go (live acoustic version) (On CD single only).
CD 5": Released Jul '88, on London Records, by London Records. Catalogue no: **LONCD 187**
7" Pic: Released Jul '88, on London Records, by London Records. Deleted May '89. Catalogue no: **LONXP 187**
7" Single: Released Jul '88, on London Records, by London Records. Deleted May '89. Catalogue no: **LON 187**
12" Single: Released Jul '88, on London Records, by London Records. Deleted Feb '89. Catalogue no: **LONX 187**

LOVE DON'T WORK THIS WAY (see panel below)
Tracks: / Love don't work this way / Freedom.
7" Single: Released May '87, on Mother, by Mother Records. Catalogue no: **MUM 7**
12" Single: Released May '87, on Mother, by Mother Records. Catalogue no: **12 MUM 7**

HOTHOUSE FLOWERS - LOVE DON'T WORK THIS WAY (Released on Mother)

Hothouse Species

TRUST
Tracks: / Trust.
7" Single: Released Apr '82, on Compulsive, Deleted '83. Catalogue no: **CFE 1**

Hotlegs

Biographical details: This British band consisted of Lol Creme, Kevin Godley and Eric Stewart. For pop historians, Hotlegs are of greater interest for being a forerunner of 10 CC than for their one off 1970 hit *Neanderthal man*. Kevin and Lol had been art school friends before teaming up with Eric for this UK No.2 smash. Stewart had achieved Sixties pop success as a member of the Mindbenders (before and after the departure of Wayne Fontana). All three guys hailed from Manchester. The heavy-handed *Neanderthal man* was written and produced by the trio and, in addition to its British success, reached No.22 in the States and became a worldwide hit. Afterwards, the threesome spent much time experimenting at Stewart's Strawberry Studios in Stockport, Cheshire. With the addition of Graham Gouldman, Hotlegs evolved into 10 CC in 1972 and signed to the irrespressible Jonathan King's UK label. *Neanderthal man* had given little hint of the supremely creative work that was to follow. (Bob MacDonald, 25th October 1985).

NEANDERTHAL MAN
Tracks: / Neanderthal man.
7" Single: Released Jun '70, on Fontana, by Phonogram Ltd. Deleted '73. Catalogue no: **6007 019**

NEANDERTHAL MAN (OLD GOLD)
Tracks: / Neanderthal man.
7" Single: Released Jul '82, on Old Gold, by Old Gold Records. Deleted Jul '88. Catalogue no: **OG 9245**

Hotline

FEEL SO STRONG
Tracks: / Feel so strong.
7" Single: Released May '83, on Red Bus, by Red Bus Records. Catalogue no: **RBUS 80**
12" Single: Released May '83, on Red Bus, by Red Bus Records. Catalogue no: **RBUSL 80**

HANG UP
Tracks: / Hang up.
7" Single: Released Sep '83, on President, by President Records. Catalogue no: **PT 518**

HELP
Tracks: / Help / Burn out.
7" Single: Released Mar '84, on Red Bus, by Red Bus Records. Catalogue no: **RBUS 89**

HOUSE OF HELL
Tracks: / House of hell / Rock this house.
12" Single: Released Jul '87, on Mute, by Mute Records. Catalogue no: **LEFT 17R**

ROCK THIS HOUSE
Tracks: / Rock this house.
12" Single: Released 30 May '87, on Rhythm King, by Mute Records. Catalogue no: **LEFT 10**

STAY AWAY
Tracks: / Stay away.
7" Single: Released Jul '88, on Rhythm King, by Mute Records. Catalogue no: **LEFT 24**
12" Single: Released Jul '88, on Rhythm King, by Mute Records. Catalogue no: **LEFT 24 T**

Hotstyle

ROB YOU
Tracks: / Rob you.
7" Single: Released Jun '88, on Madcap, Catalogue no: **MAD 2**

TOO GOOD TO TALK
Tracks: / Too good to talk.
7" Single: Released Jun '88, on Madcap, Catalogue no: **MAD 3**

HOTT

SPACE CIRCUS
Tracks: / Space circus.
12" Single: Released Aug '84, on Hippodrome, by Hippodrome Records. Catalogue no: **HIPPO 101**

Hotta Clapps Band

KNOWING IT ALL
Tracks: / Knowing it all / Really want to know.
12" Single: Released Mar '84, on Spy, Catalogue no: **SPY 001**

Houghton Weavers

BLACKPOOL BELLE
Tracks: / Blackpool belle / That stranger is a friend.
Note: Grasmere Music-59 Marlpit Lane, Coulsdon, Surrey, CR3 2HF
7" Single: Released Mar '87, on Langdale, by Grasmere Records. Catalogue no: **BEL1**

WE WANT WORK
Tracks: / We want work / Maggie.
7" Single: Released Apr '81, on EMI, by EMI Records. Deleted '85. Catalogue no: **EMI 5161**

WHERE DO YOU GO FROM HERE
Tracks: / Where do you go from here / Blackpool Belle.
7" Single: Released Jan '81, on Columbia, by EMI Records. Deleted Jan '84. Catalogue no: **DB 9090**

Hounds

UNDER MY THUMB
Tracks: / Under my thumb / Moth and the fire.
7" Single: Released Feb '80, on CBS, by CBS Records. Deleted '83. Catalogue no: **CBS 8204**

Hour In The Shower

WE ARE THE WORLD
Tracks: / We are the world / We are the world (Orchestra version) / We are the world (Global Mix) (Extra track on 12" version only.).
12" Single: Released Jan '86, on Absolute, by Absolute Records. Catalogue no: **LOOTX 1**
7" Single: Released Jan '86, on Absolute, by Absolute Records. Catalogue no: **LOOT 1**

House...

CHICAGO HOUSE MIX
Tracks: / Chicago house mix.
12" Single: Released Nov '87, on Chicago House (USA), Catalogue no: **CHR 1011**

HOUSE SOUND OF CHICAGO MEGAMIX
7" EP: Released Nov '87, on DJ Int.(Germany), Catalogue no: **DJ 33100645**

House Boys

CHRISTMAS IN THE HOUSE
Tracks: / Christmas in the house / Christmas in the house (instrumental mix).
7" Single: Released Dec '87, on Flair, by Flair Records. Catalogue no: **FLA 109**
12" Single: Released Dec '87, on Flair, by Flair Records. Catalogue no: **12 FLA 109**

House Doctors

GOTTA GET DOWN
Tracks: / Gotta get down.
12" Single: Released Mar '88, on VV Big, Catalogue no: **VVBIG 8R**

House Engineers

GHOST HOUSE
Tracks: / Ghost house (haunted house mix) / Ghost House (Jack The Ripper mix) / Ghost house (the haunted house edit) (Extra track available on 12". Also includes various remixes.) / Ghost house (jackappella) (Extra track available on 12". Also includes various remixes.).
12" Single: Released Nov '87, on Syncopate, by EMI Records. Deleted 31 Jul '88. Catalogue no: **12SY 8**
12" Single: Released 30 Nov '87, on Syncopate, by EMI Records. Deleted Apr '88. Catalogue no: **12 SYG 8**
7" Single: Released Nov '87, on Syncopate, by EMI Records. Deleted Nov '88. Catalogue no: **SY 8**
12" Single: Released Dec '87, on Syncopate, by EMI Records. Deleted Nov '88. Catalogue no: **12SYX 8**

HIT THE HOUSE
Tracks: / Hit the house (royal beat box mix) (on 12" only.) / Hit the house (back side mix) (on 12" only.) / Hit the house (beataboxapella mix) (on 12" only.) / Hit the house (royal beatbox edit) (on 7" only.) / Hit the house (back side edit) (on 7" only.).
7" Single: Released Aug '88, on Syncopate, by EMI Records. Deleted Nov '88. Catalogue no: **SY 14**
12" Single: Released Aug '88, on Syncopate, by EMI Records. Deleted Oct '89. Catalogue no: **12SY 14**

House Factors

PLAY IT LOUD
Tracks: / Play it loud / Go crazy, freesyle.
12" Single: Released Aug '88, on Black Market, Catalogue no: **BLMK 3**

House Gang

COOL J TRAX
Tracks: / Cool J trax.
7" Single: Released Jun '88, on Kool Kat, by Kool Kat Records. Catalogue no: **KOOLT 19**

HITTRAX
Tracks: / Hittrax.
Note: On the high-profiled underground label...crucial house.
12" Single: Released Nov '87, on Underground (USA), Catalogue no: **UN 130**

House Girl

BESSIE SMITH (SINGLE)
Tracks: / Bessie Smith.
12" Single: Released Oct '87, on House (USA), Catalogue no: **HU 40**

House Grinder

HIT ME
Tracks: / Hit me / Heavy beat.
12" Single: Released 23 Jul '88, on Prods In The Dark, Catalogue no: **GRIND 2**

RAPDOWN
Tracks: / Rapdown / Hard evidence / Shockwaves (Extra track on 12" version only.).
12" Single: Released 20 Feb '88, on Prods In The Dark, Catalogue no: **GRIND 1**

House Master General

HOUSEMASTER GENERAL
Tracks: / Housemaster General.
12" Single: Released Oct '87, on Flick & Romero, Deleted '88. Catalogue no: **FR 0001**

WE'LL SET YOU FREE
Tracks: / We'll set you free (acid attack mix-edit) (On 7" only) / We'll set you free (acid attack instrumental) (On 7" only) / We'll set you free (acid attack) (On 12" only) / We'll set you free (original bonus beat) (On 12" only) / We'll set you free (electro house mix) (On 12" only) / We'll set you free (acid attack mix) (On 12" only).
7" Single: Released Oct '88, on 10 Records, by Virgin Records. Catalogue no: **TEN 247**
12" Single: Released '88, on 10 Records, by Virgin Records. Catalogue no: **TENX 247**

House Of Chaos

WAVE SAMPLER, THE
CD 5": Released Jul '89, on House of Chaos, Catalogue no: **CHAOS CDS 2**

WONGO SAMPLER, THE
CD 5": Released Jul '89, on House of Chaos, Catalogue no: **CHAOS CDS 1**

House Of Dolls

HOUSE OF DOLLS
Tracks: / House of dolls: *Various artists.*
7" Single: Released May '88, on House Of Dolls, Catalogue no: **HOD 017**

House Of Lords

I WANNA BE LOVED (SINGLE)
Tracks: / I wanna be loved / Call my name / Slip of the tongue (Only on 12" version.).
12" Single: Released 6 Mar '89, on RCA, by BMG Records (UK). Catalogue no: **PT 49486**

House Of Love

CHRISTINE
Tracks: / Christine.
12" Single: Released Apr '88, on Creation, by Creation Records. Catalogue no: **CRE 053T**
7" Single: Released Apr '88, on Creation, by Creation Records. Catalogue no: **CRE 053**

DESTROY THE HEART
Tracks: / Destroy the heart.
7" Single: Released Aug '88, on Creation, by Creation Records. Catalogue no: **CRE 057**
12" Single: Released Aug '88, on Creation, by Creation Records. Catalogue no: **CRE 057 T**

NEVER
Tracks: / Never.
12" Single: Released Apr '89, on Fontana, by Phonogram Ltd. Deleted 31 Jul '89. Catalogue no: **HOL 112**
7" Single: Released Apr '89, on Fontana, by Phonogram Ltd. Deleted 31 Jul '89. Catalogue no: **HOL 1**
CD 5": Released Apr '89, on Fontana, by Phonogram Ltd. Catalogue no: **HOLCD 1**

REAL ANIMAL
Tracks: / Real animal.
12" Single: Released '87, on Creation, by Creation Records. Catalogue no: **CRE 044T**
7" Single: Released '87, on Creation, by Creation Records. Catalogue no: **CRE 044**

SAFE
Tracks: / Safe.
12" Single: Released Oct '88, on Creation, by Creation Records. Catalogue no: **UNKNOWN**

SHINE ON
Tracks: / Shine on.
7" Single: Released 23 May '87, on Creation, by Creation Records. Catalogue no: **CRE 043T**
7" Single: Released 23 May '87, on Creation, by Creation Records. Catalogue no: **CRE 043**

House Sound Of Chicago

HOUSE SOUND OF CHICAGO
Tracks: / Jack your body: *Hurley, Steve 'Silk'* / Mystery of love: *Fingers Inc'* / Shadows of your love: *Silk, Jim* / Love can't turn around: *Farley 'Jackmaster' Funk* / Music is the key: *Silk, Jim* / Move your body: *House Music* / Anthem: *Jefferson, Marshall.*
Note: The first album compilation to feature 'House Music'- The modern club sound of Chicago which has been the subject of much coverage in the UK Music press.
CD 5": Released Nov '87, on DJ Int.(Germany), Catalogue no: **DJ 50100744**

Househunters

COOLER THAN THOU
Tracks: / Cooler than thou / Mole in a hole.
12" Single: Released Jan '88, on 53rd & 3rd, by 53rd & 3rd Records. Catalogue no: **AGARR 11T**

CUTICLES
Tracks: / Cuticles / Shopping city.
12" Single: Released Jul '86, on 53rd & 3rd, by 53rd & 3rd Records. Catalogue no: **AGARR 2**

WARP FACTOR 13
Tracks: / Warp factor 13.
7" Single: Released Oct '88, on Hollow Planet, Catalogue no: **HOP 003**

Housemartins

BUILD
Tracks: / Build / Paris in flares / Forwards and backwards (On 12" single only.) / Light is always green, The (On 12" single only.).
Cassingle: Released Nov '87, on Go Discs, by Chrysalis Records. Catalogue no: **ZGOD 21**
7" Single: Released Nov '87, on Go Discs, by Chrysalis Records. Catalogue no: **GOD 21**
10" single: Released May '88, on Go Discs, by Chrysalis Records. Catalogue no: **X14576**
12" Single: Released Nov '87, on Go Discs, by Chrysalis Records. Catalogue no: **GODX 21**

CARAVAN OF LOVE
Tracks: / Caravan of love / When I first met Jesus / We shall not be moved (Available on 12" only) / So much in love* / Heaven help us all* (*Tracks on 12" version only.).
7" Single: Released Nov '86, on Go Discs, by Chrysalis Records. Catalogue no: **GOD 16**
12" Single: Released Nov '86, on Go Discs, by Chrysalis Records. Catalogue no: **GODX 16**

FIVE GET OVER EXCITED
Tracks: / Five get over excited / Rebel without the airplay / So glad (On 12" only) / Hopelessly devoted to them (On 12" only).
12" Single: Released May '87, on Go Discs, by Chrysalis Records. Catalogue no: **GODX 18**
7" Single: Released May '87, on Go Discs, by Chrysalis Records. Catalogue no: **GOD 18**

FLAG DAY
Tracks: / Flag day.
7" Single: Released Oct '85, on Go Discs, by Chrysalis Records. Catalogue no: **GOD 7**
12" Single: Released Oct '85, on Go Discs, by Chrysalis Records. Catalogue no: **GODX 7**

HAPPY HOUR
Tracks: / Happy hour / Mighty ship, The / Sitting on a fence (Extra track on 12' version only.) / He ain't heavy, he's my brother (Extra track on 12' version only.).
12" Single: Released May '86, on Go Discs, by Chrysalis Records. Catalogue no: **GODX 11**
7" Single: Released May '86, on Go Discs, by Chrysalis Records. Catalogue no: **GOD 11**

ME AND THE FARMER
Tracks: / Me and the farmer.
7" Single: Released Aug '87, on Go Discs, by Chrysalis Records. Catalogue no: **GOD 19**
12" Single: Released Aug '87, on Go Discs, by Chrysalis Records. Catalogue no: **GODX 19**

SHEEP
Tracks: / Sheep / Drop down dead.
7" Single: Released Feb '86, on Go Discs, by Chrysalis Records. Catalogue no: **GOD 9**
12" Single: Released Feb '86, on Go Discs, by Chrysalis Records. Catalogue no: **GODX 9**

THERE IS ALWAYS SOMETHING THERE TO REMIND ME
Tracks: / There is always something there to remind me / Get up off our knees / Get up off our knees (live) (Extra track on 12" version and CD.) / Five get over excited (live) (on 12" only.) / Johannesburg*.
CD 5": Released Apr '88, on Go Discs, by Chrysalis Records. Catalogue no: **GODCD 22**
12" Single: Released Apr '88, on Go Discs, by Chrysalis Records. Catalogue no: **GODX 22**
7" Single: Released Apr '88, on Go Discs, by Chrysalis Records. Catalogue no: **GOD 22**

THINK FOR A MINUTE
Tracks: / Think for a minute / Who needs the limelight / I smell winter / Joy, joy ,joy (Extra track on 12" version only.) / Rap around the clock (Extra track on 12" version only.).
7" Single: Released Sep '86, on Go Discs, by Chrysalis Records. Catalogue no: **COD 13**
12" Single: Released Sep '86, on Go Discs, by Chrysalis Records. Catalogue no: **GODX 13**

Housemaster Baldwin

DELTA HOUSE
Tracks: / Delta house.
12" Single: Released Jul '88, on Kool Kat, by Kool Kat Records. Catalogue no: **KOOLT 21**

DON'T LEAD ME Featuring Paris Grey
Tracks: / Don't lead me / Delta house rap.
12" Single: Released Dec '88, on Kool Kat, by Kool Kat Records. Catalogue no: **KOOLT 24**

DON'T LEAVE ME
Tracks: / Don't leave me / Delta house rap / Don't leave me (version).
12" Single: Released Dec '88, on Kool Kat, by Kool Kat Records. Catalogue no: **KOOLT 22**

Housemaster Boyz

HOUSE NATION
Tracks: / House nation / Track'n the house / Accahouse.
7" Single: Released Apr '87, on Magnet, by WEA Records. Deleted Jun '88. Catalogue no: **MAGD 1**
12" Single: Released Aug '87, on Magnetic Dance, by Magnet Records. Deleted Jun '88. Catalogue no: **MAGDT 1R**
12" Single: Released Apr '87, on Magnet, by WEA Records. Catalogue no: **MAGDT 1**

Houston, Cissy

BREAK IT TO ME GENTLY
Tracks: / Break it to me gently / Gonna take the easy way out.
7" Single: Released Mar '80, on EMI, by EMI Records. Deleted Mar '83. Catalogue no: **EMI 5049**

IT DOESN'T ONLY HAPPEN AT NIGHT
Tracks: / It doesn't only happen at night.
7" Single: Released May '80, on EMI, by EMI Records. Deleted May '83. Catalogue no: **EMI 5057**

WITH YOU I COULD HAVE IT ALL
Tracks: / With you I could have it all / What you gonna do / (Dance Mix) / Ballad (Extra track on 12" version only.).
12" Single: Released Feb '86, on Creole, by Creole Records. Catalogue no: **CRT 86**
7" Single: Released Feb '86, on Creole, by Creole Records. Catalogue no: **CR 86**

Houston, D

I WANT TO BE WITH YOU
Tracks: / I want to be with you.
12" Single: Released Jul '88, on Londisc, by Londisc Records. Catalogue no: **12 LDR 061**

Houston, David

MY WOMAN'S GOOD TO ME
Tracks: / My woman's good to me.
7" Single: Released Mar '85, on First Base, Catalogue no: **LWS 001**

Houston, Larry

LET'S SPEND SOME TIME TOGETHER
Tracks: / Let's spend some time together.
7" Single: Released Apr '83, on Inferno (1), by Inferno Records. Catalogue no: **HFM 001**

PROMISE
Tracks: / Promise

12" Single: Released Apr '83, on Inferno (1), by Inferno Records. Catalogue no: **HFMP 1001**

Houston, Thelma

Biographical details: This American soul singer was raised in Mississippi and then California. Her childhood ambition was to become a Hollywood film star, but an early marriage ended in divorce and left her with sole custody of two children. A stint with a gospel group called the Art Reynolds Singers, with whom she toured the US and recorded and LP, inspired her to attempt a solo career in music. After some hesitation, she took the plunge and released her debut solo music *Sunshower* in 1969. Despite being written and produced by the then red-hot Jim Webb, the LP was a stiff. Houston spent the first seven years of the Seventies struggling to establish herself, but the hits were not forthcoming. She won considerable critical acclaim and there was no doubting the strength of her superb voice, which some journalists compared to that of Aretha Franklin. In early 1977 Thelma finally achieved her breakthrough with the explosive disco single *Don't leave me this way*, which reached No.1 in America. The song had been originally recorded by Harold Melvin & The Bluenotes; the new Houston version combined the power of the original with her own gospel-influenced vocal style, and added a contemporary dancefloor feel. In Britain the Bluenotes' rendition stole a march on Thelma - it was promptly released as a single by a shrewd record company and cruised to the UK No.5 position while Houston had to be content with No.13. The singer failed to consolidate upon the success of *Don't leave me this way*, although an LP of duets with Jerry Butler fared moderately well. Subsequent success was sporadic and modest - she reached the US No.34 position in 1979 with *Saturday night, Sunday morning* and scored a minor UK hit in 1981 with *If you feel it*. *You used to hold me so tight* was an infectious club hit at the end of 1984, but the smashing pop-orientated follow-up *I guess it must be love* was an inexplicable flop. (Bob MacDonald, 25th Oct 1985).

96 TEARS
Tracks: / 96 tears / There's no runnin' away from love.
12" Single: Released Sep '81, on RCA, by BMG Records (UK). Catalogue no: **RCAT 120**
7" Single: Released Sep '81, on RCA, by BMG Records (UK). Catalogue no: **RCA 120**

DON'T LEAVE ME THIS WAY
Tracks: / Don't leave me this way.
7" Single: Released Apr '85, on Motown, by BMG Records (UK). Catalogue no: **TMG 1382**
12" Single: Released Apr '85, on Motown, by BMG Records (UK). Catalogue no: **TMGT 1382**
7" Single: Released Oct '81, on Motown, by BMG Records (UK). Deleted '83. Catalogue no: **TMG 1060**

I GUESS IT MUST BE LOVE
Tracks: / I guess it must be love.
7" Single: Released Feb '85, on MCA, by MCA Records. Catalogue no: **MCA 940**
12" Single: Released Feb '85, on MCA, by MCA Records. Catalogue no: **MCAT 940**

IF YOU FEEL IT
Tracks: / If you feel it / Hollywood.
7" Single: Released May '81, on RCA, by BMG Records (UK). Deleted '83. Catalogue no: **RCA 77**
12" Single: Released May '81, on RCA, by BMG Records (UK). Deleted '83. Catalogue no: **RCAT 77**

SUSPICIOUS MIND
Tracks: / Suspicious mind / Gone.
7" Single: Released Mar '80, on RCA, by BMG Records (UK). Deleted Mar '83. Catalogue no: **PB 1913**

YOU USED TO HOLD ME SO TIGHT
Tracks: / You used to hold me so tight.
7" Single: Released Nov '84, on MCA, by MCA Records. Catalogue no: **MCA 932**
12" Single: Released Nov '84, on MCA, by MCA Records. Catalogue no: **MCAT 932**

Houston We Have ...

ANOTHER BOTTLE OF WINE
Tracks: / Another bottle of wine / 2-25.
12" Single: Released Jul '82, on PRT, by Castle Communications Records. Deleted '85. Catalogue no: **12P 242**
7" Single: Released Jul '82, on PRT, by Castle Communications Records. Deleted '85. Catalogue no: **7P 242**

Houston, Whitney

DIDN'T WE ALMOST HAVE IT ALL
Tracks: / Didn't we almost have it all.
12" Single: Released Aug '87, on Arista, by BMG Records (UK). Catalogue no: **RIST 31**
7" Single: Released Aug '87, on Arista, by BMG Records (UK). Catalogue no: **RIS 31**

GREATEST LOVE OF ALL
Tracks: / Greatest love of all, The / Thinking about you / Shock me (On 12" version only.).
7" Single: Released Mar '86, on Arista, by BMG Records (UK). Catalogue no: **ARIST 658**
12" Single: Released Mar '86, on Arista, by BMG Records (UK). Catalogue no: **ARIST 12658**

HOLD ME
Tracks: / Hold me / Love.
7" Single: Released Jan '86, on Elektra (USA), by Elektra Records (USA). Deleted Sep '87. Catalogue no: **EKR 32**

HOW WILL I KNOW
Tracks: / How will I know / Someone for me.
7" Single: Released Jan '86, on Arista, by BMG Records (UK). Catalogue no: **ARIST 656**
12" Single: Released Jan '86, on Arista, by BMG Records (UK). Catalogue no: **ARIST 12656**

I WANNA DANCE WITH SOMEBODY
Tracks: / I wanna dance with somebody / I wanna dance with somebody (remix) / I wanna dance with somebody (dub) / Moment of truth.
12" Single: Released 23 May '87, on Arista, by BMG Records (UK). Catalogue no: **RIST 1**
CD 5": Released May '87, on Arista, by BMG Records (UK). Catalogue no: **RISCD 1**
7" Single: Released 23 May '87, on Arista, by BMG Records (UK). Catalogue no: **RIS 1**

LOVE WILL SAVE THE DAY
Tracks: / Love will save the day / Hold me / Love will save the day (dub).
12" Single: Released May '88, on Arista, by BMG Records (UK). Catalogue no: **611 516**
7" Single: Released May '88, on Arista, by BMG Records (UK). Catalogue no: **111 516**
7" Single: Released May '88, on Arista, by BMG Records (UK). Catalogue no: **111 576B**
CD 5": Released May '88, on Arista, by BMG Records (UK). Deleted Jul '89. Catalogue no: **661 516**

LOVE WILL SAVE THE DAY (IMPORT)
Tracks: / Love will save the day (extended remix) / Love will save the day (acapella mix) / Love will save the day (single mix) / Love will save the day (dub mix).
Note: Four versions of'Love...' of which 2 have never been released in the UK.
12" Single: Released Oct '88, on Arista (USA), Catalogue no: **AD 19721**

ONE MOMENT IN TIME
Tracks: / One moment in time.
CD 5": Released Sep '88, on Arista, by BMG Records (UK). Catalogue no: **661548**
7" Single: Released 16 Sep '88, on Arista, by BMG Records (UK). Catalogue no: **111613**
12" Single: Released 16 Sep '88, on Arista, by BMG Records (UK). Catalogue no: **611613**

SAVING ALL MY LOVE FOR YOU
Tracks: / Saving all my love for you.
7" Single: Released Oct '85, on Arista, by BMG Records (UK). Catalogue no: **ARIST 640**
12" Single: Released Oct '85, on Arista, by BMG Records (UK). Catalogue no: **ARIST 12640**

SO EMOTIONAL
Tracks: / So emotional / For the love of you / So emotional (extended) / So emotional (dub) / Didn't we almost have it all (live).
7" Pic: Released Nov '87, on Arista, by BMG Records (UK). Catalogue no: **RISP 43**
7" Single: Released Nov '87, on Arista, by BMG Records (UK). Catalogue no: **RIS 43**
12" Single: Released Nov '87, on Arista, by BMG Records (UK). Catalogue no: **RIST 43**
CD 5": Released Nov '87, on Arista, by BMG Records (UK). Catalogue no: **RISCD 43**

SOMEONE FOR ME
Tracks: / Someone for me.
12" Single: Released Apr '85, on Arista, by BMG Records (UK). Catalogue no: **ARIST 12614**
7" Single: Released Apr '85, on Arista, by BMG Records (UK). Catalogue no: **ARIST 614**

WHERE DO BROKEN HEARTS GO
Tracks: / Where do broken hearts go / Where you are / If you say my eyes are beautiful (Extra track on 12". Duet with Jermaine Jackson.).
7" Single: Released Feb '88, on Arista, by BMG Records (UK). Catalogue no: **109 793**
12" Single: Released Feb '88, on Arista, by BMG Records (UK). Catalogue no: **609 793**

YOU GIVE GOOD LOVE
Tracks: / You give good love.
12" Single: Released Jul '85, on Arista, by BMG Records (UK). Catalogue no: **ARIST 12625**
7" Single: Released Jul '85, on Arista, by BMG Records (UK). Catalogue no: **ARIST 625**

Hoverchairs

HIDE AND SEEK
Tracks: / Hide and seek.
7" Single: Released Jul '89, on Tempest, Catalogue no: **TROY 007**

How We Live

ALL THE TIME IN THE WORLD
Tracks: / All the time in the world / Lost at sea.
7" Single: Released May '87, on Portrait, by CBS Records. Deleted Nov '87. Catalogue no: **650088 0**
7" Single: Released Apr '87, on Portrait, by CBS Records. Deleted Nov '87. Catalogue no: **650088 7**
12" Single: Released Apr '87, on Portrait, by CBS Records. Deleted Nov '87. Catalogue no: **650088 6**

WORKING GIRL
Tracks: / Working girl / In the city.
7" Single: Released Jul '87, on Portrait, by CBS Records. Catalogue no: **HWL 1**
12" Single: Released Jul '87, on Portrait, by CBS Records. Catalogue no: **HWLT 1**

Howard, Austin

I'M THE ONE WHO REALLY LOVES YOU
Tracks: / I'm the one who really loves you / I'm the one who really loves you (instrumental.
12" Single: Released Aug '86, on 10 Records, by Virgin Records. Deleted May '88. Catalogue no: **TEN 97-12**
7" Single: Released Aug '86, on 10 Records, by Virgin Records. Deleted May '88. Catalogue no: **TEN 97**

I'M THE ONE WHO REALLY LOVES YOU (REMIX)
Tracks: / I'm the one who really loves you (remix) (On 7" only) / I'm the one who really loves you (On 7" only) / I'm the one who really loves you (extended mix) (On 12" only) / I'm the one who really loves you (extended) (On 12" only).
7" Single: on 10 Records, by Virgin Records. Catalogue no: **TEN 205**
12" Single: on 10 Records, by Virgin Records. Catalogue no: **TENT 205**

Howard, Billy

Biographical details: This British comedian and impersonator achieved a one-off UK chart entry in early 1976 with *King of the cops*, which reached No.6. Based musically upon Roger Miller's 1965 No.1 smash *King of the road*, Howard's single personified the top TV police characters of the Seventies (Kojak, Frank Cannon, etc.) in a mock arguement about who was champ. Like most comedy records, it grew stale after a few hearings but at least it was more palatable than Telly 'Kojack' Savalas' UK No.1 of the previous year, *If*. Subsequent Howard records, such as 1982's *Truckin' with Santa*, failed to get Billy laughing all the way to the bank. (Bob MacDonald, 25th Oct 1985).

KING OF THE COPS
Tracks: / King of the cops.
7" Single: Released Nov '75, on Penny Farthing, by Penny Farthing Records. Deleted '78. Catalogue no: **PEN 892**

TRUCKIN' WITH SANTA
Tracks: / Truckin' with Santa.
7" Single: Released Dec '82, on Hat Factory, Catalogue no: **HF 001**

Howard Brothers

PLEASURE OF PAIN
Tracks: / Pleasure of pain / Shakin' All over / How was I to know / Road Warrior.
12" Single: Released May '86, on Hallelujah Sounds, Catalogue no: **HAL 92T**

Howard, D

RAGGIE ROCK
Tracks: / Raggie rock.
7" Single: Released May '89, on Progressive, Catalogue no: **UNKNOWN**

Howard, Dave Singers

CHANCES
Tracks: / Chances.
7" Single: Released Oct '88, on Hallelujah Sounds, Catalogue no: **HAL 005**
12" Single: Released Oct '88, on Hallelujah Sounds, Catalogue no: **HAL 05T**

GOODNIGHT KARL MALDEN
Tracks: / Goodnight Karl Malden.
12" Single: Released 14 Oct '87, on Old Hallelujah, Catalogue no: **HAL 002T**

ROCK ON
Tracks: / Rock On.
7" Single: Released Oct '86, on Fun After All, by Music For Nations Records. Catalogue no: **FAA 106**
12" Single: Released Oct '86, on Fun After All, by Music For Nations Records. Catalogue no: **12 FAA 106**

WHAT DO YOU SAY TO AN ANGEL
Tracks: / What do you say to an angel / Sabata 88.
CD 5": Released Mar '89, on Pinpoint, Catalogue no: **572 911 36 CZ**
7" Single: Released Feb '89, on Pinpoint, Catalogue no: **572 911 31**
12" Single: Released Feb '89, on Pinpoint, Catalogue no: **572 911 36**

WHO IS SHE
Tracks: / Who is she.
12" Single: Released Nov '85, on Hallelujah Sounds, Catalogue no: **HAL Q1 T**

YON YONSON
Tracks: / Yon yonson.
12" Single: Released 20 Jun '87, on Hallelujah Sounds, Catalogue no: **HAL 04T**

Howard, John

I TUNE INTO YOU
Tracks: / I tune into you / Got a new toy.
7" Single: Released Mar '80, on CBS, by CBS Records. Deleted Mar '83. Catalogue no: **CBS 8313**

IN AT THE DEEP END
Tracks: / In at the deep end.
7" Single: Released Oct '84, on Loose, by Loose Records. Catalogue no: **LSE 17**

LONELY LONELY ME
Tracks: / Lonely lonely me / Gotta new toy.
7" Single: Released Sep '80, on CBS, by CBS Records. Deleted '83. Catalogue no: **CBS 8902**

NOTHING MORE TO SAY (BUT GOODBYE)
Tracks: / Nothing more to say (but goodbye) / You keep me steady.
7" Single: Released Mar '84, on Loose, by Loose Records. Catalogue no: **LSE 7**

Howard, Maxine

LOVE ME NOW
Tracks: / Love me now.
12" Single: Released Sep '85, on Streetwave, Catalogue no: **MKHAN 4**

Howard, Miki

COME SHARE MY LOVE (SINGLE)
Tracks: / Come share my love.
7" Single: on WEA, by WEA Records. Deleted Jan '88. Catalogue no: **A 9351**
12" Single: on WEA, by WEA Records. Deleted Jan '88. Catalogue no: **A 9351 T**

IMAGINATION
Tracks: / Imagination / You better be ready to love me.
7" Single: Released Apr '87, on Atlantic, by WEA Records. Deleted Jan '88. Catalogue no: **A 9284**
12" Single: Released Apr '87, on Atlantic, by WEA Records. Deleted Jan '88. Catalogue no: **A 9284 T**

Howard, Paul

UNIFICATION
Tracks: / Unification.
12" Single: Released 20 Jun '87, on Davy Lamp, Catalogue no: **DLEP 6**

Howard, Robert

WAIT
Tracks: / Wait / Wait (version) / Wait (short version) (On 12" remix.) / Wait (beats & pieces) (On 12" remix.).
7" Single: Released Jan '89, on RCA, by BMG Records (UK). Catalogue no: **PB 42595**
CD 5": Released Jan '89, on RCA, by BMG Records (UK). Catalogue no: **PD 42596**
12" Single: Released Jan '89, on RCA, by BMG Records (UK). Catalogue no: **PT 42596**

WAIT (REMIX)
Tracks: / Wait.
12" Single: Released Jan '89, on RCA, by BMG Records (UK). Catalogue no: **PT**

42598

Howard, Roland

SOME VELVET MORNING
Tracks: / Some velvet morning / I fell in love with a ghost.
Note: Originally a hit for Lee Hazlewood & Nancy Sinatra.
12" Single: Released Jan '86, on 4AD, by 4AD Records. Catalogue no: **BAD 210**

Howard, Sanders

FEEL THE MUSIC
Tracks: / Feel the music / Feel the music (version).
12" Single: Released Jun '88, on Kool Kat, by Kool Kat Records. Catalogue no: **KOOLT 20**

Howard The Duck

HOWARD THE DUCK
Tracks: / Howard the duck: *Dolby's Cube* / Don't turn away: *Dolby's Cube*.
7" Single: Released Nov '86, on MCA, by MCA Records. Catalogue no: **MCA 1092**
12" Single: Released Nov '86, on MCA, by MCA Records. Catalogue no: **MCAT 1092**

Howdy Boys

SUNDAY
7" EP: Released Sep '82, on Despatch, Catalogue no: **PATCH 002 S**

Howe, Catherine

GOING BACK
Tracks: / Going back / How does love feel.
7" Single: Released 20 Jul '80, on Ariola, by BMG Records (UK). Deleted '83. Catalogue no: **ARO 232**

HARRY (SINGLE)
Tracks: / Harry.
7" Single: Released Oct '84, on RCA, by BMG Records (UK). Catalogue no: **2RCA 458**

WHEN THE NIGHT COMES
Tracks: / When the night comes / How does love feel.
7" Single: Released Mar '80, on Ariola, by BMG Records (UK). Deleted Mar '83. Catalogue no: **ARO 223**

Howell, Eddie

HATCHECK GIRL
Tracks: / Hatcheck girl / Strong is the love.
7" Single: Released Apr '80, on Gem, Deleted '83. Catalogue no: **GEMS 27**

SITTING IN THE CAFE
Tracks: / Sitting in the cafe / Hold on.
7" Single: Released Sep '80, on Gem, Deleted Sep '83. Catalogue no: **GEMS 40**

Howell, Peter

GREENWICH CHORUS
Tracks: / Greenwhich chorus / Mesmer.
7" Single: Released Aug '81, on BBC, by BBC Records & Tapes. Deleted Aug '84. Catalogue no: **RESL 98**

Howlin' Wilf

SHAKE YOUR HIPS
Tracks: / Shake your hips.
12" Single: Released Jul '88, on Waterfront, by Waterfront Music. Catalogue no: **WFT 43**

Howlin' Wolf

Biographical details: Born Chester Arthur Burnett in Mississippi in 1910, Howlin' Wolf was, by the time he died in Illinois in 1976, a potent rival to Muddy Waters as the most influential of black country bluesmen. As a singer, guitarist and harmonica player he became a legend with his compulsively powerful performance, named after a howl of frustration and bitterness. He worked as a farmer until 1948, performing at juke joints and learning the harmonica from Sonny Boy Williamson (Rice Miller). His first records were made for Sun in Memphis, leased to Chess and RPM; he moved to Chicago in 1952 and stayed with Chess. He had several heart attacks but would not stop working. Like Waters he had relatively few hits: his stuff was too powerful for the charts. (Donald Clarke, March 1988.)
This American blues singer, guitarist, harmonica player and songwriter was born Chester Arthur Burnett in Aberdeen, Mississippi in 1910. His original occupation was in farming, and he did not learn to play the guitar until the age of 18. Burnett spent many years as a touring performer, gradually making a name for himself as an earthy and intense artist. Burnett finally began to make records in the late Forties and early Fifties, and it was at this point that the Howlin' Wolf nickname was established - he earned this distinctive monicker for his extraordinary moaning vocals, which careered recklessly from a gruff growl to a fiery falsetto. Tracks like *How many more years* - his first real taste of disc success, a US Top 10 R&B hit in 1952 - established Howlin' Wolf as one of the most dynamic and uncompromising artists in the blues genre. His physical presence was both tall and stout; his musical prowess was equally overpowering. He was crude and emotional, and many of his songs contained abrasive sexual references.
Like several of the blues peers, Wolf earned new respect and acclaim amongst British musicians in the early Sixties. As the UK's seminal R&B boom got underway, such vital new groups as the Rolling Stones, the Who and the Yardbirds acknowledged him as a major influence. In December 1964 the Stones reached the UK No.1 slot with *Little red rooster*, a Willie Dixon song that Wolf had made famous. Wolf himself made a one-off appearance on the British charts in '64, reaching No.42 with his eight year old recording of the infectious *Smokestack lightnin'*; he also reached No.16 on the special EP chart with *Tell me*. His career went through a duff period in the late Sixties but, in 1971, the 61 year-old Wolf travelled to London at the behest of the Rolling Stones and recorded an acclaimed album with an impressive array of admiring rock stars including Eric Clapton, Ringo Starr and Steve Winwood. Ill health then began to dog the singer's life. After suffering a heart attack, his problems were unfortunately compounded by a 1973 car accident in which he suffered kidney damage. He made a partial recovery and resumed his career on a part time basis; but he died from kidney failure in January 1976 at the age of 65. The Wolf was silenced, but his howl continued to be echoed in much of rock's output. (Bob MacDonald, 26th Oct 1985)
Howlin' Wolf was born Chester Arthur Burnett in 1910 in Mississippi; by the time he died in Hines, Illinois in 1976 he was a potent rival of muddy Waters as the most influential of black bluesmen. As a singer, guitarist and harmonica player he became a legend with his compulsively powerful performance and was named after his howls of frustration and bitterness. He worked as a farmer until 1948, but performed at juke joints etc, learning harmonica from Sonny Boy Williamson (Rice Miller). His first records were made for sun in Memphis, leased to Chess and RPM; he moved to Chicago in 1952 and stayed with Chess. He had several heart attacks but would not stop working; like waters he had relatively few hits; his stuff was too powerful for the charts. (Donald Clarke, May 1988)..

SMOKESTACK LIGHTNIN' (SINGLE)
Tracks: / Smokestack lightning.
7" Single: Released May '64, on Pye International, Deleted '67. Catalogue no: **7N 25244**

Hoy, Steve

WHERE I COME FROM
Tracks: / Where I come from.
7" Single: Released Nov '88, on Mighty Boy, by Mighty Boy Records. Catalogue no: **MB 20107**

Hoyte, Janice

LIVE IT UP (2 parts)
12" Single: Released Sep '83, on PRT, by Castle Communications Records. Catalogue no: **12P 280**
7" Single: Released Sep '83, on PRT, by Castle Communications Records. Catalogue no: **7P 280**

HR

IT'S ABOUT LOVE
Tracks: / It's about love.
12" Single: Released Jun '88, on SST (USA), by SST Records (USA). Catalogue no: **SST 179**

KEEP OUT OF REACH
Tracks: / Keep out of reach.
12" Single: Released Jun '88, on SST (USA), by SST Records (USA). Catalogue no: **SST 177**
CD 5": Released Mar '89, on SST (USA), by SST Records (USA). Catalogue no: **SSTCD 177**

Huang Chung

CHINA
Tracks: / China.
7" Single: Released '82, on Arista, by BMG Records (UK). Deleted '87. Catalogue no: **ARIST 447**

HOLD BACK THE TEARS
Tracks: / Hold back the tears / Journey without maps.
7" Single: Released '82, on Arista, by BMG Records (UK). Deleted '87. Catalogue no: **ARIST 420**

ISN'T IT ABOUT TIME WE WERE ON T.V.
Tracks: / Isn't it about time we were on T.V..
7" Single: Released Apr '80, on Rewind, Catalogue no: **REWIND 1**

TI NA NA
Tracks: / Ti na na / I can't sleep.
7" Single: Released Apr '82, on Arista, by BMG Records (UK). Deleted Apr '85. Catalogue no: **ARIST 461**

Hubbard, Freddie

YOU'RE GONNA LOSE ME
Tracks: / You're gonna lose me / Listen.
7" Single: Released Sep '81, on Fantasy (1), by BMG Records (UK). Deleted '84. Catalogue no: **FTC 199**

Hubbards Cubbard

SHRINK RAP (SINGLE)
Tracks: / Shrink rap / Drivin' the porcelain bus.
12" Single: Released Apr '85, on Landscape, by Coda Records. Catalogue no: **CODS 13T**

Hubert The Tree

DIG ME UP
Tracks: / Dig me up / Let's go bonkers for Christmas.
7" Single: Released Nov '85, on Lambs To The Slaughter, by Prism Records. Catalogue no: **ODD 3**

Hucksters

WAY OF THE FEELING
Tracks: / Way of the feeling.
7" Single: Released Feb '88, on Rocket 5, Catalogue no: **HUCS 101**

Hudson, Al

DANCE, GET DOWN
Tracks: / Dance, get down / How do you do.
7" Single: Released Aug '78, on ABC Records, by MCA Records. Deleted '81. Catalogue no: **ABC 4229**

DON'T THINK ABOUT IT
Tracks: / Don't think about it / Don't think about it (bass appella).
12" Single: Released Jun '87, on MCA, by MCA Records. Catalogue no: **MCAT 1097**
7" Single: Released Jun '87, on MCA, by MCA Records. Catalogue no: **MCA 1097**

LADY YOU ARE
Tracks: / Lady you are / Can't get enough of your love.
12" Single: Released Apr '84, on MCA, by MCA Records. Catalogue no: **MCAT 883**
7" Single: Released Apr '84, on MCA, by MCA Records. Catalogue no: **MCA 883**

LET'S TALK
Tracks: / Let's talk.
7" Single: Released Jun '85, on MCA, by MCA Records. Catalogue no: **MCA 972**
12" Single: Released Jun '85, on MCA, by MCA Records. Catalogue no: **MCAT 972**

MR GROOVE
Tracks: / Mr. Groove.
7" Single: Released Jun '84, on MCA, by MCA Records. Catalogue no: **MCA 890**
12" Single: Released Jun '84, on MCA, by MCA Records. Deleted '87. Catalogue no: **MCAT 890**

NOW THAT I FOUND YOU
Tracks: / Now that I found you / Rock.
12" Single: Released Mar '80, on MCA, by MCA Records. Deleted '83. Catalogue no: **MCAT 553**
7" Single: Released Mar '80, on MCA, by MCA Records. Deleted '83. Catalogue no: **MCA 553**

ONE WAY (SINGLE)
Tracks: / One way.
7" Single: Released Feb '82, on MCA, by MCA Records. Catalogue no: **MCA 768**
12" Single: Released Feb '82, on MCA, by MCA Records. Catalogue no: **MCAT 768**

YOU BETTER QUIT
Tracks: / You better quit / Oh girl.
7" Single: Released Apr '87, on MCA, by MCA Records. Catalogue no: **MCA 1142**
12" Single: Released Apr '87, on MCA, by MCA Records. Catalogue no: **MCAT 1142**

YOU CAN DO IT
Tracks: / You can do it.
7" Single: Released Aug '79, on MCA, by MCA Records. Deleted '81. Catalogue no: **MCA 511**

Hudson, Dave

WHO BABY
Tracks: / Who baby.
12" Single: Released May '84, on Redman International, Catalogue no: **RED 006**

Hudson, David

HONEY HONEY
Tracks: / Honey honey / Come back baby.
7" Single: Released Sep '80, on TK, Deleted Sep '83. Catalogue no: **TKR 7583**

Hudson - Ford

BURN BABY BURN
Tracks: / Bum baby bum.
7" Single: Released Feb '74, on A&M, by A&M Records. Deleted '77. Catalogue no: **AMS 7096**

FLOATING IN THE WIND
Tracks: / Floating in the wind.
7" Single: Released May '74, on A&M, by A&M Records. Deleted '77. Catalogue no: **AMS 7116**

PICK UP THE PIECES
Tracks: / Pick up the pieces.
7" Single: Released Aug '73, on A&M, by A&M Records. Deleted '75. Catalogue no: **AMS 7078**

Hudson Giants

TELL ME WHY
Tracks: / Tell me why (7" only) / Close your eyes (7" only) / Tell me why (extended version) (Available on 12" only) / Tell me why (instrumental) (Available on 12" only) / Tell me why (edit) (Available on 12" only).
7" Single: Released Jun '88, on Regal Zonophone, by EMI Records. Deleted Nov '88. Catalogue no: **Z 42**
12" Single: Released Jun '88, on Regal Zonophone, by EMI Records. Catalogue no: **12Z 42**

Hudson, Keith

ACTION WORLD
Tracks: / Action world.
12" Single: Released 14 May '88, on Atra, Catalogue no: **D 001**

Hudson, Laurice

AUTOMATIC LOVER
Tracks: / Automatic lover.
12" Single: Released Apr '84, on Carrere, Catalogue no: **CART 325**
7" Single: Released Apr '84, on Carrere, Catalogue no: **CAR 325**

Hudson, Lavine

FLESH OF MY FLESH (WHAT I WANT THE WORLD TO KNOW
Tracks: / Flesh of my flesh (Not on CD) / Testimony (On all versions) / Intervention (sanctified remix) (On CD only).
CD 5": Released '88, on Virgin, by Virgin Records. Catalogue no: **VSCD 1096**
7" Single: Released Jul '88, on Virgin, by Virgin Records. Catalogue no: **VS 1096**
12" Single: Released Jul '88, on Virgin, by Virgin Records. Catalogue no: **VST 1096**

INTERVENTION (SINGLE)
Tracks: / Intervention (7" version) (On all versions except VSTR/VCDR 1067) / It's me (On all versions except VSTR/VSCDR 1067) / Intervention (extended mix) (On VSCD/VST 1067 only) / Intervention (sanctified mix) (On VSR 1067 only) / Intervention (bootleg mix) (On VSTR 1067 only) / Intervention (7" remix) (On VSTR/VSCDR 1067 only) / Home (On VSCDR 1067 only) / Testimony (On VSCDR 1067 only) / Intervention (acapella) (On VSTR/VSCDR 1067 only).
CD 5": Released Dec '88, on Virgin, by Virgin Records. Catalogue no: **VSCD 1067**
7" Single: Released Dec '88, on Virgin, by Virgin Records. Catalogue no: **VSE 1067**
12" Single: Released '88, on Virgin, by Virgin Records. Catalogue no: **VSR 1067**
12" Single: Released Dec '88, on Virgin, by Virgin Records. Catalogue no: **VSTR 1067**
12" Single: Released Dec '88, on Virgin, by Virgin Records. Catalogue no: **VST 1067**
CD 3": Released '88, on Virgin, by Virgin Records. Catalogue no: **VSCDR 1067**
7" Single: Released Dec '88, on Virgin, by Virgin Records. Catalogue no: **VS 1067**

Hudson, Paul

SOMEBODY STOLE MY GAL
Tracks: / Somebody stole my gal / Marianne.
7" Single: Released Nov '81, on Solid Gold (1), by Creole Records. Deleted Nov '84. Catalogue no: **SGR 110**

Hudson People

BOY SCOUT
Tracks: / Boy scout / Hudson's funked it again.
7" Single: Released May '80, on Liberty (USA), by EMI Records. Deleted May '83. Catalogue no: **BP 350**

Hudsons

ONE'S MAN MEAT
Tracks: / One man's meat / Heat got you down.
7" Single: Released Jan '86, on Wheelchair, Deleted '87. Catalogue no: **WCH 1**
12" Single: Released Jan '86, on Wheelchair, Deleted '87. Catalogue no: **12 WCH 1**

Hue & Cry

HERE COMES EVERYBODY
Tracks: / Here comes everybody.
12" Single: Released Feb '86, on Stampede, Deleted '87. Catalogue no: **STAMP 2**

I REFUSE
Tracks: / I refuse (7" only) / Indifference (On YRCD & YRC 8 only) / I refuse (route 88) (On YRCD & YRC 8 only) / History city (live) (On CD only) / Labour of love (version superbad) (On CD only) / Joe and Josephine (On 7" & 12" only) / I refuse (extended version) (On 12" & YRC 2 only) / I refuse (bitter suite) (On 12" only) / Tempted (On YRC 2 only) / Dangerous wreck (On YRC 2 only) / Shipbuilding (On YRC 2 only) / Just one word (live) (On YRC 8 only).
CD 5": Released Apr '88, on Circa, by Virgin Records. Catalogue no: **YRCD 8**
Cassingle: Released '88, on Circa, by Virgin Records. Catalogue no: **YRC 8**
7" Single: Released Jan '88, on Circa, by Virgin Records. Catalogue no: **YR 8**
12" Single: Released '87, on Circa, by Virgin Records. Catalogue no: **YRT 2**
12" Single: Released Jan '88, on Circa, by Virgin Records. Catalogue no: **YRT 8**
Cassingle: Released Feb '87, on Circa, by Virgin Records. Catalogue no: **YRC 2**

LABOUR OF LOVE
Tracks: / Labour of love (On 7" & 12" only) / Wide screen (On all versions) / Goodbye to me (On 12" & cassette only) / Labour of love (super-bad) (On 10" & cassette only)) / I refuse (On cassette only) / I refuse (bitter suite) (On 10" only).
10" single: Released '87, on Circa, by Virgin Records. Catalogue no: **YRTX 4**
Cassingle: Released '87, on Circa, by Virgin Records. Catalogue no: **YRC 4**
12" Single: Released Jun '87, on Circa, by Virgin Records. Catalogue no: **YRT 4**
7" Single: Released Jun '87, on Circa, by Virgin Records. Catalogue no: **YR 4**

LOOKING FOR LINDA
Tracks: / Looking for Linda / He won't smile / Under neon (12" only) / Remote.
12" Single: Released Jan '89, on Circa, by Virgin Records. Catalogue no: **YRTX 24**
12" Single: Released Jan '89, on Circa, by Virgin Records. Catalogue no: **YRT 24**
7" Single: Released Jan '89, on Circa, by Virgin Records. Catalogue no: **YR 24**

ORDINARY ANGEL (SINGLE)
Tracks: / Ordinary angel (On 7" only) / I am John's heart (On all versions) / Hymn to hands (ON CD & 12" only) / Ordinary angel (extended version) (On 12" only) / Ordinary angel (hoedown mix) (On CD & 10" only) / Spending you (On CD only) / He won't smile (On 10" only) / Remote (On 10" only).
10" single: Released '88, on Circa, by Virgin Records. Catalogue no: **YRTX 18**
7" Single: Released 3 Oct '88, on Circa, by Virgin Records. Catalogue no: **YRG 18**
7" Single: Released 3 Oct '88, on Circa, by Virgin Records. Catalogue no: **YR 18**
12" Single: Released 3 Oct '88, on Circa, by Virgin Records. Catalogue no: **YRTG 18**
12" Single: Released 3 Oct '88, on Circa, by Virgin Records. Catalogue no: **YRT 18**
CD 5": Released '88, on Circa, by Virgin Records. Catalogue no: **YRCD 18**

STRENGTH TO STRENGTH
Tracks: / Strength to strength (7" only) / Dangerous wreck (On all versions) / Seen it all (On cassette & 12" only) / Strength to strength (extended version) (On cassette & 12" only).
7" Single: Released Sep '87, on Circa, by Virgin Records. Catalogue no: **YR 6**
12" Single: Released Sep '87, on Circa, by Virgin Records. Catalogue no: **YRT 6**
Special: Released '87, on Circa, by Virgin Records. Catalogue no: **YRX 6**
Cassingle: Released Sep '87, on Circa, by Virgin Records. Catalogue no: **YRC 6**

SWEET INVISIBILITY
Tracks: / Sweet invisibility.
7" Single: Released Sep '89, on Circa, by Virgin Records. Catalogue no: **YR 37**
12" Single: Released Sep '89, on Circa, by Virgin Records. Catalogue no: **YRT 37**
CD 5": Released Sep '89, on Circa, by Virgin Records. Catalogue no: **YRCD 37**

VIOLENTLY
Tracks: / Violently / Man with the child in his eyes, The / Calamity John / Rollin' home (12"s only).
CD 5": Released Apr '89, on Virgin, by Virgin Records. Catalogue no: **YRCD 29**
Cassingle: Released May '89, on Virgin, by Virgin Records. Catalogue no: **YRC 29**
7" Single: Released 24 Apr '89, on Virgin, by Virgin Records. Catalogue no: **YR 29**
12" Single: Released 24 Apr '89, on Virgin, by Virgin Records. Catalogue no: **YRET 29**
12" Single: Released 24 Apr '89, on Virgin, by Virgin Records. Catalogue no: **YRT 29**
7" EP: Released 24 Apr '89, on Virgin, by Virgin Records. Catalogue no: **YRE 29**

Hues Corporation

Biographical details: At the time of their greatest success, this American soul vocal group consisted of H.Ann.Kelly, Bernard St Clair Lee and Fleming Williams. Formed in Los Angeles, the Hues Corporation issued their debut LP *Freedom for the stallion* in 1973. Although the title track reached No.63 on the US Hot 100, a very respectable position for a new group, the most remarkable thing about the LP was that it contained a smash single which was overlooked by everyone and left sitting on the album for many months. When *Rock the boat* was eventually released as a single in 1974, it evoked an ecstatic response from club disc jockeys and, after crossing over to radio, cruised effortlessly to No.1 on the American charts. It reached No.6 in the UK. Written by the trio's mentor Wally Holmes, *Rock the boat* was one of the brightest records of the decade - it jumped out of the radio at you, engulfing you in it's ludicrously catchy chorus. The group's vocal performance was superb. It was knocked off the top of the US chart by the equally danceable and infectious *Rock your baby* by George McCrae. Disco music had well and truely arrived. With their leaning towards the Las Vegas end of the soul market, the Hues Corporation were unable to truely capitalise upon the disco boom. They managed one similar sounding follow-up hit, *Rockin' soul* (No.18 in US, No24 in UK), before drifting into minor hit status and then obscurity. Williams, who had sung lead on *Rock the boat* had already left the Corporation by the time *Rockin' soul* came out, and was replaced on the sinking ship by Tommy Brown. *Rock the boat* was revived by Forrest in 1983, who impressively climbed to the UK No.4 position, thereby outdoing the original version by two places. (Bob MacDonald, 26th Oct 1985).

ROCK THE BOAT
Tracks: / Rock the boat.
7" Single: Released Jul '81, on Soul Train, Deleted '83. Catalogue no: **GOLD 504**
7" Single: Released Nov '84, on RCA, by BMG Records (UK). Catalogue no: **RCA 464**
7" Single: Released Jun '74, on RCA, by BMG Records (UK). Deleted '77. Catalogue no: **APBO 0232**

ROCK THE BOAT (OLD GOLD SERIES)
Tracks: / Rock the boat / Turn the beat around / Rockin' soul (Available on 12" only) / Ms. Grace (on 12" only) / You little trust maker (on 12" only).
Note: 12" B side features Tymes with Ms Grace and Quiet life.
12" Single: Released Dec '87, on Old Gold, by Old Gold Records. Catalogue no: **OG 4030**
7" Single: Released Nov '86, on Old Gold, by Old Gold Records. Catalogue no: **OG 9657**

ROCKIN' SOUL
Tracks: / Rockin' soul.
7" Single: Released Sep '74, on RCA, by BMG Records (UK). Deleted '77. Catalogue no: **PB 10066**

Huffey, Winston

YOU FACE LOOK GOOD
Tracks: / You face look good.
12" Single: Released Mar '85, on Power House, Catalogue no: **Unknown**

Huge Corporation

HUGE CORPORATION PRESENTS
Various artists
Tracks: / Sun in splendour: *Sister Crow* / Warm is my farm: *This Yabis* / Throwing Stones: *Ten days that shook the world* / Warts: *Land of the giants*.
Note: Self-143 Station road,Wigston,Leceister.Tel:(0533) 880686.
10" single: Released Jun '86, on Huge Corporation, by Huge Corporation Records. Catalogue no: **HCP 1**

Hugh, Grayson

TALK IT OVER
Tracks: / Talk it over / Empty as the wind.
CD 5": Released Jul '89, on RCA, by BMG Records (UK). Catalogue no: **PD 49484**
12" Single: Released Jul '89, on RCA, by BMG Records (UK). Catalogue no: **PT 49484**
7" Single: Released Jul '89, on RCA, by BMG Records (UK). Catalogue no: **PB 49483**

Hughes, David

BY THE FOUNTAINS OF ROME
Tracks: / By the fountains of Rome.
7" Single: Released Aug '56, on Philips, by Phonogram Ltd. Deleted '59. Catalogue no: **PB 606**

Hughes, Emlyn

AT CHRISTMAS TIME
Tracks: / At Christmas time.
7" Single: Released Nov '85, on Sub-Zero Music, by Sub-Zero Music. Catalogue no: **SZM 5**

Hughes, Howard

BUFFALO BILL PART 1
Tracks: / Buffalo Bill Part 1.
7" Single: Released Jul '86, on Abstract, by Abstract Sounds. Catalogue no: **ABS 041**
12" Single: Released Jul '86, on Abstract, by Abstract Sounds. Catalogue no: **12 ABS 041**

PALEFACE
Tracks: / Paleface (7" only) / Paleface (extended version) (12" only) / Paleface (MS 45 Dub) (12" only) / Big badge on / Beat girl (12" only).
7" Single: Released Feb '88, on E.G., by E.G. Records. Catalogue no: **EGO 38**
12" Single: Released Feb '88, on E.G., by E.G. Records. Catalogue no: **EGOX 38**

SAY WESTERN
Tracks: / Say western (Extended Ranch House Mix on 12" only) / Country wedding / Buffalo Bill Pt.2 (12" only).
Note: Howard Hughes's second single . Speaking from a Barnsbury rodeo, Hughes describes the single as "an arm-on-the-window cadillac cruise through the mangled metropolis to the plains beyond, a jaunty wave to the new consumers over the wall to"come on in, the water's lovely!" EH? (Virgin 10/88)
12" Single: Released 17 Oct '88, on E.G., by E.G. Records. Catalogue no: **EGOX 45**
7" Single: Released 17 Oct '88, on E.G., by E.G. Records. Catalogue no: **EGO 45**

WEST OF PECO'S
Tracks: / West of Peco's.
7" Single: Released Mar '86, on Abstract, by Abstract Sounds. Catalogue no: **ABS 039**
12" Single: Released Mar '86, on Abstract, by Abstract Sounds. Catalogue no: **12 ABS 039**

Hughes, Jimmy

SHOT OF RHYTHM AND BLUES, A
Tracks: / Shot of rhythm and blues, A.
7" Single: Released Jul '80, on Charly, by Charly Records. Deleted '87. Catalogue no: **CTD 103**

Hughes, Ken

WE ARE HERE TO MANDELA'S FREE
Tracks: / We are here to Mandela's free / Auta.
7" Single: Released Jul '86, on TFI, Catalogue no: **TFI 2582**

Hugo & Luigi

LA PLUME DE MA TANTE
Tracks: / La plume de ma tante.
7" Single: Released Jun '59, on RCA, by BMG Records (UK). Deleted '61. Catalogue no: **RCA 1127**

Hula

BLACK POP WORKOUT
Tracks: / Black pop workout.
12" Single: Released 27 Jun '85, on Red Rhino, by Red Rhino Records. Catalogue no: **REDT 018**

BLACK WALL BLUE
Tracks: / Black wall blue.
12" Single: Released Sep '86, on Red Rhino, by Red Rhino Records. Catalogue no: **REDT 72**

CUT ME LOOSE
Tracks: / Cut me loose.
12" Single: Released Aug '87, on Red Rhino, by Red Rhino Records. Catalogue no: **REDT 80**

FEVER CAR
Tracks: / Fever car.
12" Single: Released Sep '84, on Red Rhino, by Red Rhino Records. Deleted '88. Catalogue no: **REDT 047**

FREEZE OUT
Tracks: / Freeze out.
12" Single: Released Mar '86, on Red Rhino, by Red Rhino Records. Catalogue no: **REDT 64**

GET THE HABIT
Tracks: / Get the habit.
12" Single: Released Jun '85, on Red Rhino, by Red Rhino Records. Catalogue no: **REDT 56**

GIN GAN GOOLIE
Tracks: / Gin gan goolie.
7" Single: Released Oct '82, on Crash, by Satril Records. Deleted '84. Catalogue no: **CRA 500**

NO ONE LEAVES THE FEVER CAR
Tracks: / No one leaves the fever car.
12" Single: Released Nov '84, on Red Rhino, by Red Rhino Records. Catalogue no: **REDT 47**

POISON
Tracks: / Poison.
12" Single: Released Mar '87, on Red Rhino, by Red Rhino Records. Catalogue no: **REDT 074**
7" Single: Released Mar '87, on Red Rhino, by Red Rhino Records. Catalogue no: **RED 074**

WALK ON STALKS OF SHATTERED GLASS
Tracks: / Walk on stalks of shattered glass.
12" Single: Released Oct '85, on Red Rhino, by Red Rhino Records. Catalogue no: **REDT 62**

Hull, Alan

Biographical details: This British singer, songwriter and guitarist was a member of a local Newcastle combo called the Chosen Few, before becoming a founder member and leader of Lindisfarne in 1967. The latter band achieved huge but short lived success with their brand of folk-rock in the early Seventies, and suffered an unexpectedly early rupture in 1973. Hull released his debut solo album *Pipedream* in that same year, but it peaked at a disappointing No.29 on the UK LP chart and stayed on the Top 50 for just three weeks. Hull's second solo set, 1975's *Squire*, was a complete flop; and the projects of the other ex-Lindisfarne members were equally disastrous. The original line-up thrus reformed in 1978. The band have remained in existence through the early and mid-Eighties, although Hull has continued to issue his own records on an occasional basis. Tracks like *Malvinas melody* (1983) have strayed little from his usual folk-rock style. (Bob MacDonald, 26th Oct 1985).

MALVINAS MELODY
Tracks: / Malvinas melody.
7" Single: Released Oct '83, on Black Crow, by Mawson & Wareham Music. Catalogue no: **CROS 2**

Human League

Biographical details: This British pop band consists of Ian Burden, Jo Callis, Joanne Cathedral, Philip Oakey, Susanne Sulley and Philip Adrian Wright. The Human League came into existence in 1977 when two quite inexperienced synthesiser players called Ian Craig Marsh and Martyn Ware decided to apply their knowledge as computer operators to the challenging new world of electronic pop music. They recruited vocalist Philip Oakey and, in 1978, were joined by 'visual director' and occasional synth player Philip Adrian Wright. During the next few years, they built up a strong cult following with their experimental music accompanied by Wright's multitude of projected slides. The group's debut single *Being boiled* appeared in 1978, and it was followed in 1979 by the first album *Reproduction*. By 1980 the League were starting to make appearances in the lower regions of the British singles chart and were sufficiently well known to be namechecked in the Undertones' UK Top 10 single *My perfect cousin*. In October of that year, however, Marsh and Ware shocked obsevers by quitting the band just as they seemed on the verge of a major breakthrough. Ian and Martyn formed the successful Heaven 17 plus an alter-ego project called the British Electric Foundation, but their success was not as rapid or as major as that awaiting the remaining members of the Human League. With a mere week to go before the beginning of a European tour, the stunned Oakey and Wright quickly replenished the group's membership by virtually grabbing the nearest musicians they could find. These turned out to be Burden, a synth player and bassist who was an old friend of Oakey's, plus, Catherall and Sulley, who were two attractive but musically inexperienced 17 year old schoolgirls whom Phil found in a Sheffield disco and invited to become singers/dancers. Another synth in a player, Jo Callis (the Rezillos' former guitarist), was later added. Such a hastily assembled collection of motley individuals had all the makings of a disaster. But by sheer good fortune, the combination was a stroke of unintentional musical genius. With the help of astute producer Martin Rushent, the Human League became a sensation in 1981. A run of three consecutive UK Top 20 singles - *The sound of the crowd, Love action (I believe in love)* and *Open your heart* - was followed by a simultaneous No.1 single and LP with the classic song *Don't you want me* proceeded to top charts all over the world, including the United States. *Dare* was a totally synthesised ef-

HUMAN LEAGUE - MIRROR MAN (Released on Virgin)

fort - no conventional instruments were used, and all the sounds were clinically programmed in computer fashions. It showed that great, commercial pop songs, no matter what they were played on. Although the Human League achieved follow-up hits with *Mirror man* (No.2 in UK in 1982) and *(Keep feeling) Fascination* (No.2 in UK in 1983), they did not release their next LP *Hysteria* until mid-84. The album yielded three British Top 20 singles, including the political song *The Lebanon*, but the group had now lost some of their commercial and musical impetus. In late '84 Oakey took time off from League activities to embark upon a successful collaboration with disco producer/composer Giorgio Moroder. (Bob MacDonald, 26th Oct 1985).

BEING BOILED
Tracks: / Being boiled / Rock 'n' roll (On Virgin version).
7" Single: Released Apr '80, on Virgin, by Virgin Records. Deleted Apr '83. Catalogue no: **SV 105**

BEING BOILED (ORIGINAL VERSION)
Tracks: / Being boiled / Circus of death.
7" Single: Released Aug '80, on EMI, by EMI Records. Deleted '83. Catalogue no: **FAST 4**

BOYS AND GIRLS
Tracks: / Boys and girls / Tom Baker.
7" Single: Released Feb '81, on Virgin, by Virgin Records. Catalogue no: **VS 395**

DON'T YOU WANT ME (see panel below)
Tracks: / Don't you want me / Seconds / Don't you want me (extended dance mix) (12" only).
12" Single: Released Nov '81, on Virgin, by Virgin Records. Deleted '83. Catalogue no: **VS 466-12**
7" Single: Released Nov '81, on Virgin, by Virgin Records. Deleted '83. Catalogue no: **VS 466**

EMPIRE STATE HUMAN
Tracks: / Empire state human / Introducing.
7" Single: Released May '80, on Virgin, by Virgin Records. Deleted '83. Catalogue no: **VS 351**

HARD TIMES/LOVE ACTION (I BELIEVE IN LOVE)
Tracks: / Hard times / Love action (I believe in love) / Hard times (instrumental) / Love action (instrumental).
CD 3": Released Jun '88, on Virgin, by Virgin Records. Catalogue no: **CDT 6**

HOLIDAY 80
Tracks: / Holiday 80.
7" Set: Released Apr '80, on Virgin, by Virgin Records. Deleted '83. Catalogue no: **SV 105**

HUMAN
Tracks: / Human (7" only) / Human (instrumental version) / Human (extended version) (12" only) / Human (accapella version) (12" only).
7" Single: Released Aug '86, on Virgin, by Virgin Records. Catalogue no: **VS 880**

HUMAN LEAGUE - DON'T YOU WANT ME (Released on Virgin)

12" Single: Released Aug '86, on Virgin, by Virgin Records. Catalogue no: **VS 880-12**

I NEED YOUR LOVING
Tracks: / I need your lovin' (7" only) / I need your lovin' (extended version) (12" only) / I need your lovin' (acapella version) (12" only) / I need your lovin' (dub version) (12" only) / I need your lovin' (instrumental) (12" only).
7" Single: Released Nov '86, on Virgin, by Virgin Records. Deleted May '88. Catalogue no: **VS 900**
12" Single: Released Nov '86, on Virgin, by Virgin Records. Catalogue no: **VS 900-12**

(KEEP FEELING) FASCINATION
Tracks: / (Keep feeling) fascination.
12" Single: Released May '83, on John Webster, Deleted '85. Catalogue no: **HL 1**
7" Single: Released Apr '83, on Virgin, by Virgin Records. Deleted '85. Catalogue no: **VS 569**

(KEEP FEELING) FASCINATION (CD)
Tracks: / (Keep feeling) fascination (extended version) / (Keep feeling) fascination (improvisation) / Total panic.
CD 3": Released '88, on Virgin, by Virgin Records. Catalogue no: **CDT 24**

(KEEP FEELING) FASCINATION (EXTENDED VERSION)
Tracks: / Fascination (extended version) / Fascination (dub).
12" Single: Released '83, on Virgin, by Virgin Records. Catalogue no: **VS 569-12**

LEBANON, THE
Tracks: / Lebanon, The / Thirteen / Lebanon, The (instrumental) (12" only).
7" Single: Released Apr '84, on Virgin, by Virgin Records. Catalogue no: **VS 672**
12" Single: Released Apr '84, on Virgin, by Virgin Records. Catalogue no: **VS 672-12**

LIFE ON YOUR OWN
Tracks: / Life on your own.
12" Single: Released Jun '84, on Virgin, by Virgin Records. Deleted May '88. Catalogue no: **VS 688-12**
7" Single: Released Jun '84, on Virgin, by Virgin Records. Deleted '85. Catalogue no: **VS 688**

LOUISE
Tracks: / Louise / Sign, The (extended remix).
7" Single: Released Oct '84, on Virgin, by Virgin Records. Catalogue no: **VS 723**
12" Single: Released Oct '84, on Virgin, by Virgin Records. Catalogue no: **VS 723-12**

LOVE ACTION (I BELIEVE IN LOVE)
Tracks: / Love action (I believe in love) / Hard times.
12" Single: Released Jul '81, on Virgin, by Virgin Records. Deleted '83. Catalogue no: **VS 435-12**
7" Single: Released Jul '81, on Virgin, by Virgin Records. Deleted '83. Catalogue no: **VS 435**

LOVE IS ALL THAT MATTERS
Tracks: / Love is all that matters (edit) (On all versions) / I love you too much (7" only) / Love is all that matters (extended version) (On CD & 12" only) / I love you too much (dub version) (Not on 7").
CD 5": Released '88, on Virgin, by Virgin Records. Catalogue no: **VSCD 1025**
12" Single: Released 26 Sep '88, on Virgin, by Virgin Records. Catalogue no: **VST 1025**
7" Single: Released 26 Sep '88, on Virgin, by Virgin Records. Catalogue no: **VS 1025**

MIRROR MAN (see panel above)
Tracks: / Mirror man / You remind me of gold.
7" Pic: Released '82, on Virgin, by Virgin Records. Catalogue no: **VSY 522**
12" Single: Released '82, on Virgin, by Virgin Records. Catalogue no: **VS 522-12**

ONLY AFTER DARK
Tracks: / Only after dark / Empire state human.
7" Single: Released 20 Jul '80, on Virgin, by Virgin Records. Deleted '83. Catalogue no: **VS 351**

OPEN YOUR HEART
Tracks: / Open your heart / Non-stop / Open your heart (extended) (12" only) / Non-stop (instrumental) (12" only).
7" Single: Released Oct '81, on Virgin, by Virgin Records. Deleted '83. Catalogue no: **VS 453**
12" Single: Released Oct '81, on Virgin, by Virgin Records. Deleted '83. Catalogue no: **VS 453-12**

SOUND OF THE CROWD, THE
Tracks: / Sound of the crowd, The (7" only) / Sound of the crowd, The (add your voice) (7" only) / Sound of the crowd, The (complete) (12" only) / Sound of the crowd, The (instrumental) (12" only).
7" Single: Released Apr '81, on Virgin, by Virgin Records. Catalogue no: **VS 416**
12" Single: Released May '81, on Virgin, by Virgin Records. Catalogue no: **VS 416-12**

Human Sexual Response

ANDY FELL
Tracks: / Andy fell.
7" Single: Released Oct '81, on Don't Fall Off The Mountain, by Don't Fall Off The Mountain Records. Catalogue no: **Z 12**

GUARDIAN ANGEL
Tracks: / Guardian angel / Jackie Onassis.
7" Single: Released Mar '81, on Don't Fall Off The Mountain, by Don't Fall Off The Mountain Records. Catalogue no: **Z 5**

WHAT DOES SEX MEAN TO ME
Tracks: / What does sex mean to me / Cool jerk.
7" Single: Released Jan '81, on Don't Fall Off The Mountain, by Don't Fall Off The Mountain Records. Catalogue no: **Z 2**

Humanoid

SLAM
Tracks: / Slam.
7" Single: Released Apr '89, on Westside, by Westside Records. Catalogue no: **WSR 14**
12" Single: Released Apr '89, on Westside, by Westside Records. Catalogue no: **WSRT 14**
CD 5": Released Apr '89, on Westside, by Westside Records. Catalogue no: **CDSWR 14**

TONIGHT
Tracks: / Tonight.
7" Single: Released Aug '89, on Radical, by Radical Records. Catalogue no: **HUM 1**
12" Single: Released Aug '89, on Radical, by Radical Records. Catalogue no: **HUM 112**
CD 5": Released Aug '89, on Radical, by Radical Records. Catalogue no: **HUM 1CD**

Humble I

CATERING FOR HITS
Tracks: / Catering for hits.
12" Single: Released Sep '89, on Flying High, Catalogue no: **FH 002**

Humble Pie

Biographical details: At the time of their greatest success, this British rock band consisted of Dave Clempson, Steve Marriot, Greg Ridley and Jerry Shirley. Humble Pie were one of a wave of 'supergroups' that emerged in the late Sixties, as top musicians went from band to band looking for their niche in the burgeoning heavy rock field. The group came together in April 1969, led by guitarists/vocalists Peter Frampton and Steve Marriott - the former had been the 'Face of '68' in the Herd while the latter had been the leader of the Small Faces. Bassist Ridley had come from the much talked about underground group Spooky Tooth, and drummer Shirley had played in various small-time combos. Amidst a blaze of promotion and publicity, Humble Pie's career was launched with a hard driving UK No.4 single, *Natural born bugie*. However, their debut LP *As safe as yesterday is* peaked at No.32 and it seemed that the quartet could not live up to the hyperbole and expectations that had been thrust upon them. After months of struggles, the 'supergroup' decided to remove all the acoustic pop elements from their repertoire and concentrate solely on the out-and-out rock material. The band to build a solid following in the USA through endless touring, but their uncompromising rock policy predictably led to Frampton's departure. He was replaced in October 1971 by ex-Colosseum guitarist Dave Clempson. The new line-up's first album *Smokin'* reached No.28 in Britain and more importantly, consolidated the band's position in the States. By the time Humble Pie broke up in 1975, they had undertaken 22 American tours; but they eventually realised that they could take this blistering hard rock no further. Shortly after the demise of the band, their former colleague Peter Frampton enjoyed massive success as a solo artist. A revamped Humble Pie, featuring Marriott and Shirley, released a couple of albums in the early Eighties without success. (27th Oct 1985).

FOOL FOR A PRETTY FACE
Tracks: / Fool for a pretty face / You soppy pratt.
7" Single: Released Apr '80, on Jet, by Jet

Records. Deleted Apr '83. Catalogue no: **JET 180**

NATURAL BORN BOOGIE
Tracks: / Natural born boogie.
7" Single: Released Aug '69, on Immediate, Deleted '72. Catalogue no: **IM 082**

NATURAL BORN BOOGIE (OLD GOLD)
Tracks: / Natural born boogie.
7" Single: Released Sep '85, on Old Gold, by Old Gold Records. Catalogue no: **OG 9529**

Humbug

WEARING SUSPENDERS
Tracks: / Wearing suspenders.
7" Single: Released Aug '81, on Castle, by Castle Communications Records. Catalogue no: **CAS 007**

Humdingers

LITTLE LOVE
Tracks: / Little love, A.
7" Single: Released Jan '88, on Waterfront, by Waterfront Music. Catalogue no: **DAMP 055**

Humpe Humpe

3 OF US
Tracks: / 3 of us / You didn't want me.
7" Single: Released Jun '85, on WEA (International), by WEA Records. Catalogue no: **X 9111**

Humperdinck, Engelbert

Biographical details: When *Release me* took this British singer to the UK No.1 slot for six weeks in early 1967, he prevented the Beatles' double A sided classic *Penny Lane/Strawberry fields forever* from reaching the top and therefore deprived the Fab Four of a No.1 single for the first time since their 1963 breakthrough. *Release me* remained on the UK charts for 56 weeks, the longest unbroken run in history. This dramatic success seemed to suggest that Engelbert Humperdinck was an overnight sensation, but in fact *Release me* was the culmination of a ten-year struggle in showbusiness. The singer was born Arnold George Dorsey in Madras, India in 1936. He was one of eight children and was known by the nickname Gerry. The family moved to Britain in 1947. After leaving school, Gerry made tentative steps to follow his father into the engineering profession but also began singing in local clubs by night. Upon completing his National Service in 1956, he spent the next nine years working as a vocalist under the name of Gerry Dorsey. His first five years of the Sixties were barren for Dorsey, with little work and little money coming in. His luck changed in 1965 when he renewed the acquaintance of an old friend called Gordon Mills, who was managing the newly successful singer Tom Jones. Mills persuaded Gerry to change his name to Engelbert Humperdinck, borrowed from the noted German composer. The new Engelbert proceeded to achieve some success in continental Europe during the mid-Sixties.
At the beginning of 1967 Jones and Humperdinck (both signed to Decca Records) cornered the middle-of-the-road ballad market between them, Tom with *Green green grass of home* and Engelbert with *Release me.* Their crooning attracted housewives in their hordes. By the end of '67, the Hump had reached No.2 with *There goes my everything* and No.1 with his all-time classic lights-down party closer *The last waltz* - both smashes logged more than half a year on the British charts. Success continued in 1968 with *Am I that easy to forget, A man without love* and *Les bicyclettes de Belsize.* Some of his hits were remakes of American country-and-western standards; others were penned by the British songwriting team, Les Reed and Barry Mason.
By the end of the Sixties, Humperdinck was also an established star in America. Although he gradually faded from the pop charts on both sides of the Atlantic during the early Seventies, his career in television and cabaret was assured forever. He has remained a showbusiness institution ever since, and has always possessed the ability to take the mickey out of himself. His occasional latterday chart successes have included a UK No.1 album in 1975 with *His greatest hits* and a surprise return to the US Top 10 in 1977 with his single *After the lovin'.* (Bob MacDonald, 28th Oct 1985).

A MAN WITHOUT LOVE
Tracks: / Man without love, A.
7" Single: Released Apr '68, on Decca, by Decca Records. Deleted '71. Catalogue no: **F 12770**

AFTER THE LOVING
Tracks: / After the loving / Just the way you are.
7" Single: Released Mar '81, on Epic, by CBS Records. Deleted Mar '84. Catalogue no: **EPC 1082**

AM I THAT EASY TO FORGET?
Tracks: / Am I that easy to forget?.
7" Single: Released Jan '68, on Decca, by Decca Records. Deleted '71. Catalogue no: **F 12722**

ANOTHER TIME, ANOTHER PLACE
Tracks: / Another time, another place.
7" Single: Released Aug '71, on Decca, by Decca Records. Deleted '74. Catalogue no: **F 1312**

HOW DO I STOP LOVING YOU
Tracks: / How do I stop loving you / On the wings of a silverbird.
7" Single: Released Jul '88, on RCA, by BMG Records (UK). Deleted May '89. Catalogue no: **PB 42129**

I'M A BETTER MAN
Tracks: / I'm a better man (for having loved you).
7" Single: Released Jul '69, on Decca, by Decca Records. Deleted '72. Catalogue no: **F 12957**

LAST WALTZ (SINGLE)
Tracks: / Last waltz, The.
7" Single: Released Aug '67, on Decca, by Decca Records. Deleted '70. Catalogue no: **F 12655**
7" Single: Released Oct '83, on Old Gold, by Old Gold Records. Catalogue no: **OG 9351**
7" Single: Released Aug '67, on Decca, by Decca Records. Deleted '88. Catalogue no: **F 12655**

LES BICYCLETTES DE BELSIZE
Tracks: / Les bicyclettes de Belsize.
7" Single: Released Aug '68, on Decca, by Decca Records. Deleted '71. Catalogue no: **F 12834**

LOVE IS ALL
Tracks: / Love is all.
7" Single: Released Oct '73, on Decca, by Decca Records. Deleted '76. Catalogue no: **F 13443**

LOVE IS THE REASON
Tracks: / Love is the reason / You made a believer out of me / Love is all (12" only).
7" Single: Released Jul '87, on RCA, by BMG Records (UK). Deleted May '89. Catalogue no: **PB 41617**
12" Single: Released Jul '87, on RCA, by BMG Records (UK). Deleted May '89. Catalogue no: **PT 41618**

MY MARIE
Tracks: / My Marie.
7" Single: Released Apr '70, on Decca, by Decca Records. Deleted '73. Catalogue no: **F 13032**

NOTHING'S GONNA CHANGE MY LOVE FOR YOU
Tracks: / Nothing's gonna change my love for you / Under the man in the moon / Love is all (Extra track on 12".).
7" Single: Released Feb '88, on RCA, by BMG Records (UK). Deleted May '89. Catalogue no: **PB 41847**
12" Single: Released Feb '88, on RCA, by BMG Records (UK). Deleted May '89. Catalogue no: **PT 41848**

RELEASE ME (OLD GOLD)
Tracks: / Release me.
7" Single: Released Oct '83, on Old Gold, by Old Gold Records. Catalogue no: **OG 9338**

RELEASE ME (SINGLE)
Tracks: / Release me.
7" Single: Released Jan '67, on Decca, by Decca Records. Deleted '70. Catalogue no: **F 12541**

SWEETHEART
Tracks: / Sweetheart.
7" Single: Released Aug '70, on Decca, by Decca Records. Deleted '73. Catalogue no: **F 13068**

THERE GOES MY EVERYTHING
Tracks: / There goes my everything.
7" Single: Released May '67, on Decca, by Decca Records. Deleted '70. Catalogue no: **F 12610**

TO ALL THE GIRLS I LOVED BEFORE
Tracks: / To all the girls I've loved before.
7" Single: Released Jun '84, on Warwick, by Warwick Records. Catalogue no: **SW 7001**

TOO BEAUTIFUL TO LAST
Tracks: / Too beautiful to last.
7" Single: Released Feb '72, on Decca, by Decca Records. Deleted '75. Catalogue no: **F 13281**

WAY IT USED TO BE, THE
Tracks: / Way it used to be, The.
7" Single: Released Jan '69, on Decca, by Decca Records. Deleted '72. Catalogue no: **F 12879**

WINTER WORLD OF LOVE
Tracks: / Winter world of love.
7" Single: Released Oct '69, on Decca, by Decca Records. Deleted '72. Catalogue no: **F 12980**

Humphrey, Bobbi

NOW WAY
Tracks: / Now way / Now way (Instrumental).

7" Single: Released Sep '86, on Club, by Phonogram Ltd. Deleted '86. Catalogue no: **JAB 39**
12" Single: Released Sep '86, on Club, by Phonogram Ltd. Deleted '86. Catalogue no: **JABX 39**

Hunger Project

SAME INSIDE
Tracks: / Same inside.

7" Single: Released Nov '84, on Latent, Catalogue no: **LATEX 3**

Hunniford, Gloria

GIVE THE CHILDREN BACK THEIR CHILDHOOD
Tracks: / Give the children back their childhood.
CD 5": Released Oct '88, on Ocean (2), Catalogue no: **OCN 6CD**
12" Single: Released Oct '88, on Ocean (2), Catalogue no: **OCN 6T**
7" Single: Released Oct '88, on Ocean (2), Catalogue no: **OCN 6**

Hunningale, Peter

FOOL FOR YOU
Tracks: / Fool for you, A / Let's get it together.
12" Single: Released Dec '86, on Street Vibes, Catalogue no: **SV 005**

GIVING MYSELF AWAY
Tracks: / Giving myself away.
12" Single: Released Jun '85, on Street Vibes, Catalogue no: **SV 1002**

GOT TO KNOW YOU
Tracks: / Got to know you / Extraordinary.
12" Single: Released Aug '84, on Street Vibes, Catalogue no: **ST 1001**

HEART OF STEEL
Tracks: / Heart of steel.
12" Single: Released Apr '88, on Street Vibes, Catalogue no: **SV 008**

IT'S MY TURN
Tracks: / It's my turn.
12" Single: Released Feb '89, on Street Vibes, Catalogue no: **SV 009**

RAGAMUFFIN GIRL
Tracks: / Ragamuffin girl / Ickie fashion.
12" Single: Released May '89, on Clarkey & Blakey, Deleted Sep '89. Catalogue no: **CB 001**
12" Single: Released Sep '89, on ffrr, by London Records. Catalogue no: **FX 120**
7" Single: Released Sep '89, on ffrr, by London Records. Catalogue no: **F 120**

UNTAMED LOVE
Tracks: / Untamed love / Untamed love (dub).
12" Single: Released Sep '86, on Cosmic, Catalogue no: **Cosmic 001**
7" Single: Released Sep '86, on Cosmic, Catalogue no: **COS 001**

Hunny Yum

DIDDUMS
Tracks: / Diddums / Tweet.
7" Single: Released Nov '81, on Cat Tracks, Catalogue no: **PURR 1**

Hunt

IT'S ALL TOO MUCH
Tracks: / It's all too much / Heart bender.
7" Single: Released May '81, on Logo, by Logo Records. Deleted May '84. Catalogue no: **GO 400**

Hunt, Clive

MIKY TYSON
Tracks: / Miky Tyson.
7" Single: Released May '89, on Tappa, Catalogue no: **UNKNOWN**

SLOW ROCKINT
Tracks: / Slow rockint.
7" Single: Released May '89, on Tappa, Catalogue no: **UNKNOWN**

Hunt, Geraldine

CAN'T FAKE THE FEELING
Tracks: / Can't fake the feeling.
7" Single: Released Sep '80, on Champagne Records, Deleted '83. Catalogue no: **FIZZ 501**
12" Single: Released Oct '80, on Champagne Records, Deleted Oct '83. Catalogue no: **FIZY 501**

Hunt, Marsha

KEEP THE CUSTOMER SATISFIED
Tracks: / Keep the customer satisfied.
7" Single: Released Apr '70, on Track, by Polydor Ltd. Deleted '73. Catalogue no: **604 037**

WALK ON GUILDED SPLINTERS (SINGLE)
Tracks: / Walk on guilded splinters.
7" Single: Released May '69, on Track, by Polydor Ltd. Deleted '72. Catalogue no: **604 030**

Hunt, Tommy

CRACKIN' UP
Tracks: / Crackin' up.
7" Single: Released Oct '75, on Spark, by Spark Records. Deleted '78. Catalogue no: **SRL 1132**

LOVIN' ON THE LOSING SIDE
Tracks: / Lovin' on the losing side.
7" Single: Released Aug '76, on Spark, by Spark Records. Deleted '79. Catalogue no: **SRL 1146**

ONE FINE MORNING
Tracks: / One fine morning.
7" Single: Released Nov '76, on Spark, by Spark Records. Deleted '79. Catalogue no: **SRL 1148**

WORK SONG, THE
Tracks: / Work song.
7" Single: Released Jun '85, on Kent, by Ace Records. Catalogue no: **TOWN 103**

Hunter

DREAMS OF ORDINARY MEN (SINGLE)
Tracks: / Dreams of ordinary men / Start it up.
12" Single: Released 23 May '87, on Polydor, by Polydor Ltd. Deleted Jan '88. Catalogue no: **POSPX 867**
7" Single: Released 23 May '87, on Polydor, by Polydor Ltd. Deleted Jan '88. Catalogue no: **POSP 867**

Hunter, Chris

KEEP THIS ONE IN TUNE
Tracks: / Keep this one in tune / Moody.
7" Single: Released Jul '82, on Polydor, by Polydor Ltd. Deleted Jul '85. Catalogue no: **POSP 472**
12" Single: Released Jul '82, on Polydor, by Polydor Ltd. Deleted Jul '85. Catalogue no: **POSPX 472**

Hunter, George

BOASTING
Tracks: / Boasting.
12" Single: Released Dec '82, on Dread At The Controls, Catalogue no: **DATC 016**

Hunter, Ian

Biographical details: This British singer, songwriter, guitarist, pianist and producer launched his solo career in early 1975 after five years as leader of the successful Mott the Hoople. With the assistance of David Bowie's former masterly guitarist Mick Ronson, Ian reached the UK No.21 position with the *Ian Hunter* LP and No.14 with the boogie rock single *Once bitten twice shy.* To the disappointment of his many fans, he failed to capitalise upon this promising start. His newly formed backing band quickly faded and he moved to New York. During the remainder of the Seventies, Hunter's albums attracted his customary critical acclaim but sales dropped off. His name, however, received high praise from the New Wave of British punk musicians, who citied Ian's Mott heyday as a major influence. In response to this, Ian became the temporary producer for the UK Top 30 singles, *King rocker* and *Valley of the dolls.* He simultaneously adopted a more contemporary style with his own LP *You're never alone with a schizophrenic,* but could not climb no higher than No.49 on the British LP chart despite favourable reviews. During the early Eighties, with Ronson still at his side, Hunter kept soldiering on but with little commercial success. His associations with such critics' favourites as the Clash, Ellen Foley and Todd Rundgren have kept his name in the music press but not the record charts. (Bob MacDonald, 28th Oct 1985).

ONCE BITTEN, TWICE SHY
Tracks: / Once bitten, twice shy.
7" Single: Released May '75, on CBS, by CBS Records. Deleted '78. Catalogue no: **CBS 3194**

WE GOTTA GET OUTTA HERE
Tracks: / We gotts get outta here / Once bitten twice shy / Bastard / Cleveland rocks / Sons & daughters / One of the boys.
7" Single: Released May '80, on Chrysalis, by Chrysalis Records. Deleted May '83. Catalogue no: **CHS 2434**

Hunter, John

TRAGEDY
Tracks: / Tragedy / Aphrodisiac here.
7" Single: Released Jan '85, on Epic, by CBS Records. Catalogue no: **A 5006**

Hunter, Leeford

SU SU SU
Tracks: / Su su su.
12" Single: Released Oct '84, on Small Acts, Catalogue no: **UNKNOWN**

Hunter, Tab

Biographical details: This American singer and actor (the former description should perhaps appear in inverted commas) is remembered by the record world solely for his 1957 smash *Young love*, which hit No.1 on both sides of the Atlantic. Although he did achieve a follow-up hit with *99 ways*, the good looking Hunter's disc career was basicallyno more than an opportunisticf offshoot of his film fame. Born Arthur Andrew Kelm in New York City, and later using his mother's maiden name Gelien, he was working at a horse stable when he was discovered by a talent agent. He was rechristened Tab Hunter and, by 1957, had established himself as a handsome if mediocre actor in a series of films including *The lawless*, *Island of desire* and *The spirit of St Louis*. *Young love* was a pleasant and catchy ballad which was originally recorded in 1956 by its co-writer Ric Cartey. That version flopped but, in early '57, it became a simultaneous smash on the American charts for bothe Hunter and country-and-western singer Sonny James. Sonny peaked at No.2 on Billboard's Top 100 and Tab cruised to No.1. In Britain James had to be content with No.11 while Hunter logged seven weeks at the summit. The fact that the James rendition was musically superior but the Hunter recording was more successful testified to the widely held assumption that the latter sold mainly on the strength of the singer's face. The now forgotton follow-up *99 ways* reached No.11 in the States and No.5 in Britain; it was written and originally recorded by rock'n'roll singer Charlie Gracie. Although Hunter made a brief returned to the US Top 40 with 1959's *Apple blossom time*, he quickly returned to acting in movies and also began to build a career in television. His face has continued to appear from time to time even in the Eighties, although his latterday projects such as *Polyester* (with Divine) and *Grease 2* (a dire attempt at a sequel to the original blockbuster), have rarely risen above the level of trash. *Young love* was revived by Donny Osmond in 1973, who took it to No.1 in Britain. (28th Oct 1985).

99 WAYS
Tracks: / 99 Ways.
7" Single: Released Mar '57, on London-American, Deleted '60. Catalogue no: **HLD 8410**

YOUNG LOVE
Tracks: / Young love.
7" Single: Released Jan '57, on London-American, Deleted '60. Catalogue no: **HLD 8380**

YOUNG LOVE (OLD GOLD)
Tracks: / Young love / Red sails in the sunset.
7" Single: Released Jul '82, on Old Gold, by Old Gold Records. Catalogue no: **OG 9107**

Hunter, Tad

MENTAL HOSPITAL
Tracks: / Mental hospital / Good lovin'.
12" Single: Released Nov '88, on Dance Vibes, Catalogue no: **DV 001**

Hunters Club

GIMME YOUR SOUL
Tracks: / Gimme your soul.
12" Single: Released Sep '88, on Trashcan, by Trashcan Records. Catalogue no: **THC 12002**

YOU AIN'T SEEN NOTHING YET
Tracks: / You ain't seen nothing yet / Trashcan.
7" Single: Released Apr '87, on Trashcan, by Trashcan Records. Catalogue no: **DTO 956**

Hunters & Collectors

BREADLINE
Tracks: / Breadline / Breadline (version) / Under the sun (12" & CD single only.).
CD 5": Released Nov '88, on I.R.S. Catalogue no: **DIRM 177**
12" Single: Released Nov '88, on I.R.S. Catalogue no: **IRMT 177**
7" Single: Released Nov '88, on I.R.S. Deleted 1 Jul '89. Catalogue no: **IRM 177**

CARRY ME
Tracks: / Carry me / Unbeliever / Follow me no more (on 12" only).
7" Single: Released Aug '84, on Epic, by CBS Records. Catalogue no: **A 4648**
12" Single: Released Aug '84, on Epic, by CBS Records. Catalogue no: **TA 4648**

DO YOU SEE WHAT I SEE
Tracks: / Do you see what I see.
7" Single: Released 22 Aug '88, on MCA, by MCA Records. Catalogue no: **IRM 171**
12" Single: Released 22 Aug '88, on MCA, by MCA Records. Catalogue no: **IRMT 171**

Hunting Party

HUNTING PARTY (EP)
7" EP: Released Sep '85, on Movement, by Movement Records. Deleted '87. Catalogue no: **MOVEMENT 007**

Huntington, Eddie

MEET MY FRIEND
Tracks: / Meet my friend (instrumental friend) / Meet my friend / Meet my friend (version).
7" Single: Released Jul '87, on Passion, by Skratch Records. Catalogue no: **PASH 75**
12" Single: Released Jul '87, on Passion, by Skratch Records. Catalogue no: **PASH 75(12)**

Huntsberry, Howard

LONELY TEARDROPS
Tracks: / Lonely teardrops / Goodnight my love.
12" Single: Released Oct '87, on London Records, by London Records. Deleted Oct '88. Catalogue no: **LONX 152**
7" Single: Released Sep '87, on London Records, by London Records. Deleted Oct '88. Catalogue no: **LON 152**

Hurley, Armando

MUSIC CHANGE THE WORLD
Tracks: / Music change the world / Circus world.
Note: Proceeds to YMCA anti-drugs campaign.
7" Single: Released Jan '86, on Priority, by Priority Records. Deleted Jun '87. Catalogue no: **P 13**
7" Single: Released Aug '86, on YMCA, Deleted Nov '87. Catalogue no: **YMCA 1**

Hurley, Bill

RECONSIDER ME
Tracks: / Reconsider me.
7" Single: Released Jul '85, on Demon, by Demon Records. Catalogue no: **D 1034**

Hurley, Red

HEY
Tracks: / Hey.
7" Single: Released Apr '83, on Mint, by Emerald Records. Deleted '88. Catalogue no: **CHEW 80**

Hurley, Steve 'Silk'

JACK YOUR BODY
Tracks: / Jack your body / Dub your body.
12" Single: Released Jan '87, on London Records, by London Records. Catalogue no: **LONX 117**
7" Single: Released Jan '87, on London Records, by London Records. Catalogue no: **LON 117**

WORK IT OUT (SINGLE)
Tracks: / Work it out / Work it out (version).
7" Single: Released Aug '89, on Atlantic, by WEA Records. Catalogue no: **A8856**

Hurrah

BIG SKY
Tracks: / Big sky / Saturdays train / Secret of life, The / Walk in the park, A.
10" single: Released Apr '89, on Arista, by BMG Records (UK). Catalogue no: **612 207**
10" single: Released Apr '89, on Kitchenware, by Kitchenware Records. Catalogue no: **SKPD 42**
CD 5": Released Apr '89, on Kitchenware, by Kitchenware Records. Catalogue no: **SKCD 42**
7" Single: Released Apr '89, on Arista, by BMG Records (UK). Catalogue no: **111 770**
12" Single: Released Apr '89, on Kitchenware, by Kitchenware Records. Catalogue no: **SKX 42**
12" Single: Released Apr '89, on Arista, by BMG Records (UK). Catalogue no: **611 770**
CD 3": Released Apr '89, on Arista, by BMG Records (UK). Catalogue no: **161 770**
7" Single: Released Mar '89, on Kitchenware, by Kitchenware Records. Catalogue no: **SK 42**

GLORIA
Tracks: / Gloria.
12" Single: Released Feb '85, on Kitchenware, by Kitchenware Records. Catalogue no: **SKX 18**
7" Single: Released Feb '85, on Kitchenware, by Kitchenware Records. Catalogue no: **SK 18**

HIP-HIP
Tracks: / Hip hip.
7" Single: Released Nov '84, on Kitchenware, by Kitchenware Records. Deleted '86. Catalogue no: **SK 6**

HOW MANY RIVERS
Tracks: / How many rivers / Three wishes / If it rains (12" only).
12" Single: Released 23 May '87, on Kitchenware, by Kitchenware Records. Catalogue no: **SKX 31**
7" Single: Released 23 May '87, on Kitchenware, by Kitchenware Records. Catalogue no: **SK 31**

IF I COULD KILL
Tracks: / If I could kill / Tell me about your problems / Girl of my dreams (12" only).
7" Single: Released Dec '86, on Kitchenware, by Kitchenware Records. Catalogue no: **SK 29**
12" Single: Released May '87, on Kitchenware, by Kitchenware Records. Catalogue no: **SKX 29**

SUN SHINES HERE
Tracks: / Sun shines here, The / I'll be your suprise.
7" Single: Released Dec '83, on Kitchenware, by Kitchenware Records. Deleted '86. Catalogue no: **SK 2**

SWEET SANITY
Tracks: / Sweet sanity / Heart and hand / Don't need food.
CD 5": Released Jun '89, on Kitchenware, by Kitchenware Records. Catalogue no: **SKCD 40**
7" Single: Released Feb '87, on Kitchenware, by Kitchenware Records. Catalogue no: **SK 28**
12" Single: Released Feb '87, on Kitchenware, by Kitchenware Records. Catalogue no: **SKX 28**

SWEET SANITY (ARISTA)
Tracks: / Sweet sanity / Heart and hand / Gloria / How many rivers (Available on 12" and CD single format.).
CD 5": Released Dec '88, on Arista, by BMG Records (UK). Catalogue no: **661 911**
7" Single: Released Nov '88, on Arista, by BMG Records (UK). Deleted May '89. Catalogue no: **111911**
12" Single: Released Nov '88, on Arista, by BMG Records (UK). Deleted May '89. Catalogue no: **611911**

WHO'D OF THOUGHT
Tracks: / Who'd of thought.
7" Single: Released Oct '84, on Kitchenware, by Kitchenware Records. Deleted May '89. Catalogue no: **SK 14**
12" Single: Released Oct '84, on Kitchenware, by Kitchenware Records. Catalogue no: **SKX 14**

Hurricane

I'M ON TO YOU
Tracks: / I'm on to you / Baby snakes / Girls are out tonight, The.
12" Single: Released Feb '89, on Enigma, by Enigma Records (USA). Catalogue no: **ENV T7**
7" Single: Released Feb '89, on Enigma, by Enigma Records (USA). Catalogue no: **ENV 7**

Hurt & Husband

HOLY COW
Tracks: / Holy cow / Dirty lies.
7" Single: Released Nov '81, on Mosa, by Mosa Records. Catalogue no: **MOSA 3**

Hurt, John

I LOVE WOMEN
Tracks: / I love women / Someone to put out the fire.
7" Single: Released Dec '80, on Scotti Bros (Germany), Deleted Dec '85. Catalogue no: **K 11629**

Hurtt, Phil

GIVING IT BACK
Tracks: / Giving it back.
7" Single: Released Oct '78, on Fantasy (2), by Ace Records. Deleted '81. Catalogue no: **FTC 161**

Hush

HEARTS ON FIRE
Tracks: / Hearts on fire.
12" Single: Released Oct '83, on Spirit (1), by Spirit Records. Catalogue no: **FIRET 1**
7" Single: Released Oct '83, on Spirit (1), by Spirit Records. Catalogue no: **FIRE 1**

SINGIN' THE BLUES
Tracks: / Singing the blues / Don't say goodbye / Singing the blues / Don't say goodbye.
7" Single: Released Jan '86, on PVK, by PVK Records. Catalogue no: **PV 123**

SON OF AN OLD ROCK AND ROLLER
Tracks: / Son of an old rock and roller.
7" Single: Released Dec '81, on Brilliant, by Brilliant Records. Catalogue no: **HIT 2**

Husker Du

COULD YOU BE THE ONE
Tracks: / Could you be the one / Every time.
7" Single: Released Jan '87, on Warner Bros., by WEA Records. Deleted Jan '88. Catalogue no: **W 8456**
12" Single: Released Jan '87, on Warner Bros., by WEA Records. Deleted Jan '88. Catalogue no: **W 8456T**

DON'T WANT TO KNOW IF YOUR LONELY
Tracks: / Don't want to know if your lonely / All work no play / Helter skelter (Live. Extra track avaliable on 12" version only.).
12" Single: Released Feb '86, on Warner Bros., by WEA Records. Catalogue no: **W 8746 T**
7" Single: Released Feb '86, on Warner Bros., by WEA Records. Catalogue no: **W 8746**

EIGHT MILES HIGH
Tracks: / Eight miles high / Masochism world.
Note: Single is on limited edition coloured vinyl.
CD 5": Released Dec '88, on SST (USA), by SST Records (USA). Catalogue no: **SSTCD 025**
7" Single: Released Apr '84, on SST (USA), by SST Records (USA). Catalogue no: **SST 025**

ICE COLD ICE
Tracks: / Ice cold ice / Gotta lotta.
7" Single: Released 20 Jun '87, on Warner Bros., by WEA Records. Deleted Jul '88. Catalogue no: **W 8276**
12" Single: Released 20 Jun '87, on Warner Bros., by WEA Records. Deleted Jul '88. Catalogue no: **W 8276T**

MAKES NO SENSE AT ALL
Tracks: / Makes no sense at all.
7" Single: Released Sep '85, on SST (USA), by SST Records (USA). Catalogue no: **SST 051**
CD 5": Released Dec '88, on SST (USA), by SST Records (USA). Catalogue no: **SSTCD 051**

METAL CIRCUS
Tracks: / Metal circus.
12" Single: Released Dec '83, on SST (USA), by SST Records (USA). Catalogue no: **SST 020**
Cassingle: Released Mar '86, on SST (USA), by SST Records (USA). Catalogue no: **SST 020 C**

SORRY SOMEHOW
Tracks: / Sorry somehow / All this I've done for you / Flexible flyer (Extra track available on 12" version only.) / Celibated summer (Extra track available on 12" version only.).
7" Pic: Released Sep '86, on WEA (International), by WEA Records. Deleted Jun '87. Catalogue no: **W 8612 P**
12" Single: Released Sep '86, on WEA (International), by WEA Records. Deleted Jun '87. Catalogue no: **W 8612 T**
7" Single: Released Sep '86, on WEA (International), by WEA Records. Deleted Jun '87. Catalogue no: **W 8612**

WAREHOUSE SONGS AND STORIES
Tracks: / These important years / Charity, charity, prudence and hope / Standing in the rain / Back from somewhere / Ice cold ice / You're a soldier / Could you be the one / Too much spice / Friend, you've got to fall / She floated away / Bed of nails / Tell you why tomorrow / It's not peculiar / Actual condition / No reservations / Turn it around / She's a woman / Up in the air / You can live at home.

Special: Released Jan '87, on Warner Bros., by WEA Records. Catalogue no: **925544 4**

Hussars

CHARGE OF THE LIGHT BRIGADE
Tracks: / Charge of the light brigade.
7" Single: Released Sep '82, on RK, by RK Records. Deleted '84. Catalogue no: **EON 103**

Hussey, Winston

JOE GRINE LAST NIGHT
Tracks: / Joe Grine last night.
12" Single: Released Jun '83, on Greensleeves, by Greensleeves Records. Catalogue no: **GRED 123**

Huston, Dudley

WANNA BE WITH YOU
Tracks: / Wanna be with you.
12" Single: Released Jul '88, on Londisc, by Londisc Records. Catalogue no: **LDR 061**

Hutch, Willie

Biographical details: This American singer, guitarist, songwriter and producer was on the Motown roster for most of the Seventies and made frequent appearances on the US soul charts without ever crossing over to the pop market. He first established himself with the soundtrack to *The Mack* and followed through with a series of competent but unadventurous albums. Hutch's first taste of UK chart success occurred at the end of 1982, when he reached No.51 on the singles list with a classy slice of funk entitled *In and out*. By this time he was back with Motown after a brief sojourn elsewhere. (Bob MacDonald, 28th Oct 1985).

IN & OUT (SINGLE)
Tracks: / In and out / Brothers gonna work it out.
7" Single: Released Nov '82, on Motown, by BMG Records (UK). Deleted '86. Catalogue no: **TMG 1285**
12" Single: Released Nov '82, on Motown, by BMG Records (UK). Deleted '86. Catalogue no: **TMGT 1285**

KEEP ON JAMMIN
Tracks: / Keep on jammin'.
7" Single: Released Jun '85, on Motown, by BMG Records (UK). Catalogue no: **ZB 40173**
12" Single: Released Jun '85, on Motown, by BMG Records (UK). Catalogue no: **ZT 40174**

PARTY DOWN
Tracks: / Party down / Slick.
7" Single: Released Feb '83, on Motown, by BMG Records (UK). Catalogue no: **TMG 1293**
12" Single: Released Feb '83, on Motown, by BMG Records (UK). Catalogue no: **TMGT 1293**

Hutton, June

SAY YOU'RE MINE AGAIN
Tracks: / Say you're mine again.
7" Single: Released Jul '53, on Capitol, by EMI Records. Deleted '57. Catalogue no: **CL 13918**

Hybrid Kids

DO YOU THINK I'M SEXY?
Tracks: / Do you think I'm sexy.
7" Single: Released Mar '82, on Cherry Red, by Cherry Red Records. Deleted '87. Catalogue no: **CHERRY 12**

HAPPY XMAS WAR IS OVER
Tracks: / Happy xmas war is over.
7" Single: Released Dec '80, on Cherry Red, by Cherry Red Records. Deleted '87. Catalogue no: **CHERRY 17**

Hyde, Pat

MELANCHOLY BABY
Tracks: / Melancholy baby / Someday you'll want me to want you.
7" Single: Released Feb '81, on Zodiac, by Zodiac-Wilcox Records. Catalogue no: **ZR 1010-45**

Hyde, Paul

HERE'S THE WORLD FOR YA
Tracks: / Here's the world for ya.
7" Single: Released May '85, on A&M, by A&M Records. Deleted '88. Catalogue no: **AM 253**

Hyks, Veronika

VICTORIA PLUM (Four stories)
Special: Released May '84, on Tempo Storytime, by Warwick Records. Catalogue no: **TBC 9512**

VICTORIA PLUM GIVES BEN A SURPRISE
Special: Released Aug '84, on Tempo, by Warwick Records. Catalogue no: **TTS 9826**

VICTORIA PLUM HAS A TREASURE HUNT
Special: Released Aug '84, on Tempo, by Warwick Records. Catalogue no: **TTS 9828**

VICTORIA PLUM HELPS THE BADGERS
Special: Released Aug '84, on Tempo, by Warwick Records. Catalogue no: **TTS 9825**

VICTORIA PLUM & THE....
Special: Released Aug '84, on Tempo, by Warwick Records. Catalogue no: **TTS 9827**

Hyland, Brian

Biographical details: This American singer, born in New York, was just 16 years old when he shot from nowhere to stardom in August 1960 with his US No.1 novelty smash *Itsy bitsy teeny weeny yellow polka dot bikini*. Like all the best gimmick records, it was extremely nauseating and infuriatingly catchy; the single reached No.8 in Britain. Hyland struggled to follow up this smash, and he did not return to the US Top 40 for over a year - in late 1961 he finally reached No.20 with a song called *Let me belong to you*. By the time Brian became famous in 1960, there was already an established tradition in American pop music of young lads shooting to prominence from nowhere - over the preceding three years, Paul Anka, Ricky Nelson, Frankie Avalon and Fabian had all stormed into the US Top 10 while still in their mid-teens. Some (like Fabian) were talentless non-entities who were manipulated to the top because they looked good; others (like Anka) made it on genuine ability. Hyland possessed a pleasant voice, and had had several years of singing experience in small-time choirs and groups, but he could only shine when given the right material to sing. Hence, his subsequent career was sporadic. 1962 brought Hyland his second monster with the classic teen angst ballad *Sealed with a kiss*, which hit No.3 in both the US and UK. He also reached No.21 in the US and No.5 in the UK with *Ginny come lately*. After four years in the wilderness, he returned to the US Top 40 in 1966 with *The joker went wild* and *Run, run look and see*. After a further four years in obscurity, Brian stormed back with a one-off US million seller, climbing to No.3 in America in 1970 with an acclaimed remake of Curtis Mayfield's soul standard *Gypsy woman*. Five years later, in the summer of ,75, Hyland made a surprise return to the British Top 10 with a re-issue of *Sealed with a kiss* and actually appeared personally on *Top of the Pops* to promote his 13 year-old hit. However, there was nothing in store for him during 1979-80. (Bob MacDonald, 28th Oct 1985)
The early 60's have become characterised as the period of novelty hits delivered by cute singers who could'nt really sing. Despite the fact that Hyland really could sing, he has become indelibly associated with the novelty hit - *Itsy bitsy teeny weenie yellow polka dot bikini* the summer hit of 1960. However, his later recordings showed that he could handle more than just trite novelties. In 1962 Hyland recaptured his momentum with *Ginny come lately* and *Sealed with a kiss*. Someone in the management decided that *Ginny come lately* bore a similarity to some of the songs that were selling well in Germany, so they brought in a translator to rewrite the lyrics. Hyland went back into the Bell Sound Studio in New York and overdubbed the German vocal tracks on the original playbacks. (Bear Family, Nov 1988).

FOUR LITTLE HEELS
Tracks: / Four little heels.
7" Single: Released Oct '60, on London-American, Deleted '63. Catalogue no: **HLR 9203**

GINNY COME LATELY
Tracks: / Ginny come lately.
7" Single: Released Apr '62, on H.M.V., by EMI Records. Deleted '65. Catalogue no: **POP 1013**

GYPSY WOMAN
Tracks: / Gypsy woman.
7" Single: Released Mar '71, on UNI, by MCA Records. Deleted '74. Catalogue no: **UN 530**

ITSY BITSY TEENY WEENY ...(OLD GOLD)
Tracks: / Itsy bitsy teeny weeny yellow polka dot bikini / Susie darlin'.
7" Single: Released Apr '86, on Old Gold, by Old Gold Records. Catalogue no: **OG 9598**

ITSY BITSY TEENY WEENY... (SINGLE)
Tracks: / Itsy bitsy teeny weeny yellow polka dot bikini.
7" Single: Released Jun '60, on London-American, Deleted '63. Catalogue no: **HLR 9161**

JOKER WENT WILD
Tracks: / Joker went wild.
7" Single: Released Mar '83, on Neil Rushton, Catalogue no: **44028**

SEALED WITH A KISS
Tracks: / Sealed with a kiss.
7" Single: Released Aug '62, on H.M.V., by EMI Records. Deleted '65. Catalogue no: **POP 1051**

SEALED WITH A KISS (OLD GOLD)
Tracks: / Sealed with a kiss / Ginny come lately / Itsy bitsy teeny weeny yellow polka dot bikini.
7" Single: Released Jul '82, on Old Gold, by Old Gold Records. Catalogue no: **OG 9174**
CD 5": Released 30 May '89, on Old Gold, by Old Gold Records. Catalogue no: **OG 6150**

WARMED OVER KISSES
Tracks: / Warmed over kisses.
7" Single: Released Oct '62, on H.M.V., by EMI Records. Deleted '65. Catalogue no: **POP 1079**

Hylton, Sheila

Biographical details: This Jamaican singer first cracked the British charts in 1979, reaching No.57 with her single *Breakfast in bed*. In the Eighties, she has concentrated on reggae remakes of familiar pop hits. One of these, her version of the Police's *The bed's too big without you*, climbed to the UK No.35 slot in 1981. She has subsequently released renditions of the Rose Royce hit *Love don't live here anymore* and David Bowie's *Let's dance*. (Bob MacDonald, 29th Oct 1985).

BED'S TO BIG WITHOUT YOU
Tracks: / Bed's too big without you, The / Give me your love.
7" Single: Released Jan '81, on Island, by Island Records. Deleted '84. Catalogue no: **WIP 6671**

BREAKFAST IN BED
Tracks: / Breakfast in bed.
7" Single: Released Aug '79, on United Artists, by EMI Records. Deleted '82. Catalogue no: **BP 304**

FALLING IN LOVE
Tracks: / Falling in love.
7" Single: Released Dec '83, on Sun Set (reggae), Catalogue no: **DSR 0914**

LET'S DANCE
Tracks: / Let's dance.
12" Single: Released Jul '83, on Sun Set (reggae), Catalogue no: **SSRD 005**

LOVE DON'T LIVE HERE ANYMORE
Tracks: / Love don't live here anymore.
12" Single: Released Mar '82, on Kerry Blue, Catalogue no: **CB 01**

Hyman, Dick

THEME FROM THE 'THREEPENNY OPERA'
Tracks: / Theme from 'The Threepenny Opera'.
7" Single: Released Mar '56, on MGM, by Polydor Ltd. Deleted '59. Catalogue no: **MGM 890**

Hyman, Phyllis

Biographical details: This American singer and songwriter released her eponymous debut album in 1977. It made a good showing on the US soul charts and reached a respectable No.107 placing on Billboard's Top 200 Albums list. The LP established Hyman as a classy jazz-soul artist, but she has somehow never quite consolidated this initial breakthrough. In the early Eighties Phyllis scored a pair of UK chart singles, thanks to heavy club exposure - the infectious disco single *You know how to love me* reached No.47 in early 1980, and *You sure look good to me* peaked at No.56 in late 1981. Despite the production talents of Thom Bell and Narada Michael Walden, 1983's *Goddess of love* LP was not a substantial success. (Bob MacDonald, 29th Oct 1985).

LOVING YOU, LOSING YOU
Tracks: / Loving you, losing you / Betcha by golly wow.
7" Single: Released Mar '80, on Buddah, by Buddah Records Inc.(USA). Deleted '83. Catalogue no: **BDS 493**
12" Single: Released Mar '80, on Buddah, by Buddah Records Inc.(USA). Deleted '83. Catalogue no: **BDSL 493**

SCREAMING AT THE MOON (EXT REMIX)
Tracks: / Screaming at the moon (ext remix) / Screaming at the moon / Ain't you had enough love / Ain't you had enough love (ext) / Ain't you had enough love (percussapella version).
Special: Released Apr '87, on Philadelphia Int., by EMI Records. Deleted Oct '87. Catalogue no: **12 PIRD 4**

SCREAMING AT THE MOON (SINGLE)
Tracks: / Screaming at the moon / Ain't you had enough love.
7" Single: Released Mar '87, on Philadelphia Int., by EMI Records. Deleted Oct '87. Catalogue no: **PIR 4**
12" Single: Released Mar '87, on Philadelphia Int., by EMI Records. Deleted Oct '87. Catalogue no: **12 PIR 4**

TONIGHT YOU AND ME
Tracks: / Tonight you and me.
7" Single: Released Nov '81, on Arista, by BMG Records (UK). Deleted Nov '84. Catalogue no: **ARIST 444**

UNDER YOUR SPELL (OLD GOLD)
Tracks: / Under your spell / Rainbow.
12" Single: Released 24 Apr '89, on Old Gold, by Old Gold Records. Catalogue no: **OG 4510**

UNDER YOUR SPELL (SINGLE)
Tracks: / Under your spell / Kiss you all over / Hold on (Only on 12" single.).
7" Single: Released May '80, on Arista, by BMG Records (UK). Deleted May '83. Catalogue no: **ARIST 343**
12" Single: Released May '80, on Arista, by BMG Records (UK). Deleted May '83. Catalogue no: **ARIST 12343**

YOU KNOW HOW TO LOVE ME
Tracks: / You know how to love me / We should be lovers / Riding the tiger (Extra track on 12" version only.) / Don't tell me tell her (Only on the 12" version released by Old Gold.) / Give a little more.
Note: * Only on the 12" version released by Old Gold.
7" Single: Released Aug '86, on Arista, by BMG Records (UK). Catalogue no: **ARIST 669**
12" Single: Released Jul '88, on Old Gold, by Old Gold Records. Catalogue no: **OG 4067**
12" Single: Released Aug '86, on Arista, by BMG Records (UK). Catalogue no: **ARIST 12669**
7" Single: Released Jan '80, on Arista, by BMG Records (UK). Deleted Jan '85. Catalogue no: **ARIST 323**
12" Single: Released Jan '80, on Arista, by BMG Records (UK). Deleted Jan '85. Catalogue no: **ARIST 12323**

YOU SURE LOOK GOOD TO ME
Tracks: / You sure look good to me.
7" Single: Released '82, on Arista, by BMG Records (UK). Deleted '87. Catalogue no: **ARIST 424**

Hypertension

CAN YOU FEEL IT?
Tracks: / Can you feel it.
7" Single: Released Oct '82, on ERC, Catalogue no: **ERC 103**
12" Single: Released Oct '82, on ERC, Catalogue no: **ERCL 103**

Hypnomatics

PERFECT STRANGER
Tracks: / Perfect stranger.
7" Single: Released Jul '85, on Cryptic, by Cryptic Records. Catalogue no: **SPYRO 99**
12" Single: Released Jul '85, on Cryptic, by Cryptic Records. Catalogue no: **RULER 99**

Hypnosis

DROID
Tracks: / Droid / Droid (version).
12" Single: Released Oct '89, on Debut, by Skratch Records. Catalogue no: **DEBTXR 3083**

Hypnotics

JUSTICE IN FREEDOM
Tracks: / Justice in freedom.
12" Single: Released 27 Feb '89, on Situation 2, by Beggars Banquet Records. Catalogue no: **SIT 056 T**

Hypothetical Prophets

PERSON TO PERSON
Tracks: / Person to person.
7" Single: Released Apr '83, on Epic, by CBS Records. Catalogue no: **A 3257**
12" Single: Released Apr '83, on Epic, by CBS Records. Catalogue no: **AT 3257**

WALLENBERG
Tracks: / Wallenberg / Budapest 45.
7" Single: Released Mar '82, on Dining Out, by Dining Out Records. Deleted '85. Catalogue no: **TUX 19**
12" Single: Released Apr '82, on Hypothetical, Catalogue no: **ZUG 2**

Hysteria

BEHIND THE VEIL
12" Single: Released Oct '84, on Sculpture, Catalogue no: **SCT 4-1**

PURPLE HAZE
Tracks: / Purple haze / Cheap thrills.
7" Single: Released 21 Nov '87, on Urban, by Polydor Ltd. Catalogue no: **URB 11**
12" Single: Released 21 Nov '87, on Urban, by Polydor Ltd. Catalogue no: **URBX 11**

Hysterics

FIVE TRACKS OF LAUGHTER
Tracks: / Five tracks of laughter.
7" Single: Released Nov '82, on KA, Catalogue no: **KA 5**

JINGLE BELLS LAUGHING ALL THE WAY
Tracks: / Jingle bells laughing all the way.
7" Single: Released Nov '81, on Recorded Delivery, Deleted '83. Catalogue no: **KA 5**

I

The following information was taken from the Music Master database on October 20th, 1989.

I Am Siam

TALK TO ME (I CAN HEAR YOU KNOW)
Tracks: / Talk to me (I can hear you know) / Escape to Lamoria.
7" Single: Released Jan '85, on CBS, by CBS Records. Catalogue no: **A 4795**
12" Single: Released Jan '85, on CBS, by CBS Records. Catalogue no: **TA 4795**

I Benjahman

GIVE LOVE A TRY
Tracks: / Give love a try / Mind blowing dub.
12" Single: Released Jul '82, on Lion Kingdom, Catalogue no: **LK 002**

JAH WORLD WILL KEEP ON TURNING
Tracks: / Jah world will keep on turning / Prosperous dub.
12" Single: Released Jan '83, on Lion Kingdom, Catalogue no: **LK 003**

I Can Crawl

HIT THE MISTY MOUNTAIN
Tracks: / Hit the misty mountain.
12" Single: Released Jul '87, on Zinger, Catalogue no: **ZINGIT 3**

I Catch

MY DARLIN, I
Tracks: / My darlin', I.
7" Single: Released Jun '85, on Excellent, by Survival Records. Catalogue no: **EXC 1401**
12" Single: Released Jun '85, on Excellent, by Survival Records. Catalogue no: **EXCL 1401**

I Jahman Levi

CLOSER TO YOU
Tracks: / Closer to you / Lend a hand.
12" Single: Released Jun '82, on Tree Roots, Deleted Jun '85. Catalogue no: **JMI 12266**
7" Single: Released Jun '82, on Tree Roots, Deleted Jun '85. Catalogue no: **JMI 7266**

I Know A Gondola

DO BANG JINGLY JANG
Tracks: / Do bang jingly jang.
10" single: Released Nov '88, on Plop, Catalogue no: **PLOP 001**

I Know How

I KNOW HOW
Tracks: / I know how: *Various artists*.
7" Single: Released Jun '87, on First Night, by First Night Records. Catalogue no: **SCORE 10**

I Plee

ALL NIGHT LONG
Tracks: / All night long.
12" Single: Released Jun '84, on Daybreak, Catalogue no: **KA 002**

I Q Decides

CHEEK TO CHEEK
Tracks: / Cheek to cheek / Won't you come home.
CD 5": Released Apr '89, on Inter-Melody, by Inter Melody Music. Catalogue no: **IQDT 1**
7" Single: Released Apr '89, on Inter-Melody, by Inter Melody Music. Catalogue no: **IQD 7**

I Refuse It

WE HATE YOU
Tracks: / We hate you.
7" Single: Released May '86, on Toto, Catalogue no: **TOTO 02.39**

I Said Bleep

IN YOUR SYSTEM
Tracks: / In your system.
12" Single: Released 27 Feb '89, on SSR, Catalogue no: **12 SSR 94**

SIR, BE GLAD WHEN YOU'RE DEAD
Tracks: / Sir, be glad when your dead.
12" Single: Released Feb '89, on SSR, Catalogue no: **12SSR 91**

I Shinko

SHINING
Tracks: / Shining / Daze of pleasure.
7" Single: Released Oct '80, on Gem, Deleted Oct '83. Catalogue no: **GEMS 44**

I Spit On Your Gravy

PIRANHA
Tracks: / Piranha / Man's not a camel.
7" Single: Released Jul '87, on Virgin, by Virgin Records. Catalogue no: **VOZ 015**

I Start Counting

CATCH THAT LOOK
Tracks: / Catch that look / Cooler than Calcutta.
7" Single: Released Aug '86, on Mute, by Mute Records. Catalogue no: **MUTE 49**
12" Single: Released Aug '86, on Mute, by Mute Records. Catalogue no: **12 MUTE 49**

LETTERS TO A FRIEND
Tracks: / Letters to a friend.
7" Single: Released Jun '84, on Mute, by Mute Records. Catalogue no: **MUTE 034**

LOSE HIM
Tracks: / Lose him / See how it cuts / Tie me tight.
7" Single: Released Dec '87, on Mute, by Mute Records. Catalogue no: **MUTE 69**
12" Single: Released Dec '87, on Mute, by Mute Records. Catalogue no: **12 MUTE 69**

MILLION HEADED MONSTER
Tracks: / Million headed monster.
CD 5": Released Apr '89, on Mute, by Mute Records. Catalogue no: **CD MUTE 95**
7" Single: Released Apr '89, on Mute, by Mute Records. Catalogue no: **MUTE 95**
12" Single: Released Apr '89, on Mute, by Mute Records. Catalogue no: **12 MUTE 95**

MY TRANSLUCENT HANDS (SINGLE)
Tracks: / My translucent hands.
7" Single: on Mute, by Mute Records. Catalogue no: **MUTE 54**

RA RA RAWHIDE
Tracks: / Ra ra rawhide.
12" Single: Released '88, on Mute, by Mute Records. Catalogue no: **12 MUTE 81**

STILL SMILING
Tracks: / Still smiling.
7" Single: Released Apr '85, on Mute, by Mute Records. Catalogue no: **7MUTE 35**
12" Single: Released Apr '85, on Mute, by Mute Records. Catalogue no: **12 MUTE 35**

Ian, Janis

Biographical details: Ian, Janis This American singer, songwriter, guitarist and pianist was born Janis Fink in New York City in 1951. After having work published in the Broadside folk magazine and making acclaimed appearances in the New York area, Janis Ian shot to fame as a 16 year old sensation in the summer of 1967 with *Society's Child (Baby I've been thinking)*. This extraordinary single took an interracial romance as its theme and attacked discrimination, hypocrisy and the attitudes of parental and educational authority. Despite being released too late for the folk protest movement and too early for the singer-songwriter era, *Society's Child* reached no.14 on the US charts. Her eponymous debut album was issued in the same year and featured a whole batch of incisive sociological observations.
Several more Janis Ian LPs were released during the late Sixties and early Seventies, but none met with the same degree of commercial or critical acceptance and it seemed that her 1967 success was a flash in the pan. She even quit recording for a time. In 1975, however, the 24 year old Ian suddenly came up with *At Seventeen*, an American Top 3 smash - on this record her detached and brooding voice recounted the trials and tribulationss of undergoing the transformation from adolescence to adulthood. The song's parent album *Between The Lines* reached no.1 on the US LP chart.
Once again Janis failed to follow up this success and her career slipped back into the realms of minor hit status - 1976's *Aftertones* LP reached a respectable no.12 placing, but 1877's *Miracle Row* peaked at no.45.
Despite a cult following, the British charts remained totally impervious to Janis Ian until 1979 and 1980 when she reached no. 44 with the catchy *Fly too High* and no.44 again with *The other side of the sun*. Those singles were followed in 1981 by a minor American hit called *Under The Covers*. These later records were often of a high quality, but *Society's Child* and *At Seventeen* remain her two best songs and her only major successes. Bob Macdonald 4/11/85.

DON'T SLOW DOWN
Tracks: / Don't slow down / Love love love.
7" Single: Released Apr '80, on Evolution, by Evolution Records. Deleted Apr '81. Catalogue no: **EV 6**

FLY TOO HIGH
Tracks: / Fly too high.
7" Single: Released Oct '79, on CBS, by CBS Records. Deleted '82. Catalogue no: **CBS 7936**

HAVE MERCY LOVE
Tracks: / Have mercy love / Jenny.
7" Single: Released Jan '80, on CBS, by CBS Records. Deleted Dec '80. Catalogue no: **CBS 8136**

HERE COMES THE NIGHT
Tracks: / Here comes the night / Memories.
7" Single: Released Nov '80, on CBS, by CBS Records. Deleted Nov '81. Catalogue no: **CBS 9324**

I REMEMBER YESTERDAY
Tracks: / I remember yesterday / Restless eyes.
7" Single: Released Oct '81, on CBS, by CBS Records. Deleted Oct '83. Catalogue no: **A 1603**

OTHER SIDE OF THE SUN
Tracks: / Other side of the sun, The / Photographs.
7" Single: Released May '80, on CBS, by CBS Records. Deleted '83. Catalogue no: **CBS 8611**

UNDER THE COVERS
Tracks: / Under the covers / Passion play.
7" Single: Released Jun '81, on CBS, by CBS Records. Deleted Dec '82. Catalogue no: **A 1324**

Ian's Blue Van

PASS THE PEAS
Tracks: / Pass the peas / Pass the peas (part 2).
7" Single: Released Sep '84, on Buypheu, by Fast Forward Records. Catalogue no: **BUYPHEU 001**

Icarus

IN ZAIRE
Tracks: / In Zaire.
12" Single: Released Oct '87, on Ultraprime, Catalogue no: **121803**

Ice Babies

SOME DAY REMEMBER
Tracks: / Some day remember / Emma sez / Madeleine's reign.
12" Single: Released Feb '89, on La Stillette, by La Stillette Records. Catalogue no: **LAO 12X**

Ice Club

DANCE
Tracks: / Dance.
7" Single: Released Mar '85, on Lost Moments, Catalogue no: **LM 022**
12" Single: Released Mar '85, on Lost Moments, Catalogue no: **LM 12 022**

Ice Cold In Alice

CAUSING A COMMOTION
Tracks: / Causing a commotion / Tears in the rain.
7" Single: Released Oct '88, on Revelation, by Revelation Records. Catalogue no: **REVA 3**
12" Single: Released Dec '88, on Revelation, by Revelation Records. Catalogue no: **REVA T3**

FADE AWAY
Tracks: / Fade away.
7" Single: Released May '88, on Revelation, by Revelation Records. Catalogue no: **REVA 1**

THROW YOUR LOVE AWAY
Tracks: / Throw your love away.
7" Single: Released May '89, on Revelation, by Revelation Records. Catalogue no: **REVA 4**
12" Single: Released May '89, on Revelation, by Revelation Records. Catalogue no: **REVAT 4**

WHEN THE RAIN COMES DOWN
Tracks: / When the rain comes down.
7" Single: Released Jul '88, on Revelation, by Revelation Records. Catalogue no: **REVA 2**

Ice Crush II

SACKCHASER
Tracks: / Sackchaser.
12" Single: Released Nov '87, on A&G (USA), Catalogue no: **AG 1229**

Ice Nine

ANOTHER LOVE AFFAIR
Tracks: / Another love affair.
7" Single: Released Jan '84, on Clockwork, by Clockwork Records. Catalogue no: **TIK 01**

Ice The Falling Rain

LIFE'S ILLUSION 2 parts
Tracks: / Life's illusion.
7" Single: Released Nov '83, on Future, Catalogue no: **FS 7**

Icehouse

Biographical details: Icehouse Iva Davies is the key member of this Australian band - although many other (mainly Aussie) musicians have often been recruited for touring purposes, much of the recording work has been done solely by Davies and his producer. Davies, a guitarist and sub Bryan Ferry vocalist, formed his first serious group, the Flowers in 1977. They initially played cover versions of material by the likes of Roxy Music and David Bowie, but graduated to considerable Australian success with their own material in 1980. To avoid confusion with another group of the same name, they became Icehouse in 1981 (This had been the title of their debut album)
Despite making promising ripples on the American album chart, Icehouse soon disbanded but Davies retained the group name. The expert assistance of producer Keith Forsey (a lieutenant of the famous Giorgio Moroder) failed to build upon American interest, to the suprise of some observers. *Hey Little Girl*, an infectious single which derived much from Roxy Music and Japan, gave Icehouse a UK Top 20 single in early 1983; but Davies was no more capable of expanding his British success than he was of consolidating upon his US toehold. The 1984 LP *Sidewalk* failed to arouse much interest on either side of the Atlantic. Bob Macdonald 4.11.85.

CAN'T HELP MYSELF
Tracks: / Can't help myself / Can't help myself (club mix 2) / Fat man.
7" Single: Released '82, on Chrysalis, by Chrysalis Records. Deleted '85. Catalogue no: **CHS 2550**
12" Single: Released '82, on Chrysalis, by Chrysalis Records. Deleted '87. Catalogue no: **CHS 12 2550**

CRAZY
Tracks: / Crazy / Completely gone.
7" Single: Released Jul '87, on Chrysalis, by Chrysalis Records. Catalogue no: **CHS 3156**
12" Single: Released Jul '87, on Chrysalis, by Chrysalis Records. Catalogue no: **CHS 123156**

DON'T BELIEVE ANY MORE
Tracks: / Don't believe any more / Dance on / Mountain.
7" Single: Released Jun '84, on Chrysalis, by Chrysalis Records. Catalogue no: **COOL 4**

ICEHOUSE - HEY LITTLE GIRL (Released on Chrysalis)

ELECTRIC BLUE
Tracks: / Electric blue / Over my head / Electric blue (dub mix) (on 12" only.) / Electric blue (ST edit) (on 12" only.) / Electric blue (inst) (on 12" only.) / Crazy (Manic mix) (Extra track on CD single only.).
CD 5": Released Apr '88, on Chrysalis, by Chrysalis Records. Catalogue no: **CHS CD 3239**
7" Single: Released Apr '88, on Chrysalis, by Chrysalis Records. Catalogue no: **CHS 3239**
12" Single: Released Apr '88, on Chrysalis, by Chrysalis Records. Catalogue no: **CHS 12 3239**

HEY LITTLE GIRL (see panel above)
Tracks: / Hey little girl / Mysterious thing / Hey little girl (disco edit mix) (Only on 12" version.) / Can't help myself (US Club mix).
7" Single: Released Jan '83, on Chrysalis, by Chrysalis Records. Catalogue no: **CHS 2670**
12" Single: Released Jan '83, on Chrysalis, by Chrysalis Records. Catalogue no: **CHS 12 2670**

ICEHOUSE (SINGLE)
Tracks: / Icehouse / All the way / Cold turkey.
7" Single: Released Jan '82, on Chrysalis, by Chrysalis Records. Deleted '83. Catalogue no: **CHS 2577**
12" Single: Released Feb '82, on Chrysalis, by Chrysalis Records. Deleted '83. Catalogue no: **CHS 12 2577**

NO PROMISES
Tracks: / No promises / Perfect crime, The.
7" Single: Released Feb '86, on Chrysalis, by Chrysalis Records. Deleted '87. Catalogue no: **CHS 2978**
12" Single: Released Feb '86, on Chrysalis, by Chrysalis Records. Deleted '87. Catalogue no: **CHS 122978**

PARADISE
Tracks: / Paradise / Baby you're so strange / Hey little girl (Extra track available on 12" version only.).
7" Single: Released Aug '86, on Chrysalis, by Chrysalis Records. Catalogue no: **CHS 3206**
12" Single: Released Aug '86, on Chrysalis, by Chrysalis Records. Catalogue no: **CHS 123206**

STREET CAFE
Tracks: / Street cafe / Walls.
7" Single: Released Apr '83, on Chrysalis, by Chrysalis Records. Deleted '84. Catalogue no: **COOL 1**

TAKING THE TOWN
Tracks: / Taking the town.
7" Single: Released Apr '84, on Chrysalis, by Chrysalis Records. Catalogue no: **COOL 3**

UNIFORM
Tracks: / Uniform / Great southern land.
7" Single: Released '83, on Chrysalis, by Chrysalis Records. Deleted '87. Catalogue no: **COOL 2**

WE CAN GET TOGETHER
Tracks: / We can together / Send somebody / Paradise lost.
10" single: Released '83, on Chrysalis, by Chrysalis Records. Deleted '87. Catalogue no: **CXP 2527**
7" Single: Released Jul '81, on Chrysalis, by Chrysalis Records. Deleted '85. Catalogue no: **CHS 2527**

I'cess

LOOK PON SHE
Tracks: / Look pon she.
7" Single: Released Nov '84, on Uptempo, Catalogue no: **UT 005**

Ice-T

HIGH ROLLERS
Tracks: / High rollers / Hunted child, The / Power (Only on 12" version.).
7" Single: Released Mar '89, on Sire, by Sire Records. Catalogue no: **W 7574**
12" Single: Released Mar '89, on Sire, by Sire Records. Catalogue no: **W 7574 TW**
12" Single: Released Mar '89, on Sire, by Sire Records. Catalogue no: **W 7574 T**

LETHAL WEAPON
Tracks: / Lethal weapon / Heartbeat.
7" Single: Released Sep '89, on Warner Bros., by WEA Records. Catalogue no: **W 2802**
12" Single: Released Sep '89, on Warner Bros., by WEA Records. Catalogue no: **W 2802T**

MAKE IT FUNKY
Tracks: / Make it funky / Sex.
7" Single: Released Jul '87, on Sire (USA), Catalogue no: **YZ 145**
12" Single: Released Jul '87, on Sire (USA), Deleted Jan '88. Catalogue no: **YZ 145T**

SOMEBODY GOTTA DO IT
Tracks: / Somebody gotta do it.
12" Single: Released Nov '87, on Sire (USA), Catalogue no: **020805**

Icicle Works

Biographical details: Icicle Works This British band consists of Chris Layhe, Ian McNabb and Chris Sharrock. Formed in 1980, the Icicle Works were of many groups to emerge from the new Liverpool explosion of the early Eighties. After creating ripples of interest on the indie label scene, they came to fame in early 1984 with their UK Top 20 single *Love is a Wonderful Colour.* Written and powerfully sung by leader Ian McNabb, this record contained a dramatic Sixties flavour and was particularly reminiscent of Simon Dupree & The Big Sounds 1967 hit *Kites.*
A previously released track called *Birds Fly (Whisper to a scream)* was reactivated as the follow up to *Love Is a Wonderful Colour,* it reached no.53 in Britain and, more impressively no.37 in America. Yet the band were unable to consolidate upon their position in either country - subsequent singles, such as *Hollow Horse* and *When It All Comes Down,* were lushly arranged showcases for McNabb's sub Scott Walker vocals; but the group's sound got into a rut. Their albums *The Icicle Works* (1984) and *The Small Price of a Bicycle* (1985) were well crafted but did not achieve significant commercial success. Bob Macdonald 4/11/85.

ALL THE DAUGHTERS
Tracks: / All the daughters.
7" Single: Released May '85, on Beggars Banquet, by Beggars Banquet Records. Deleted Jun '87. Catalogue no: **BEG 133**
12" Single: Released May '85, on Beggars Banquet, by Beggars Banquet Records. Deleted Jan '88. Catalogue no: **BEG 133T**

BIRDS FLY
Tracks: / Birds fly / Whisper to a scream / Cauldron of love, The.
7" Single: Released Mar '84, on Beggars Banquet, by Beggars Banquet Records. Catalogue no: **BEG 108**
7" Single: Released Jun '83, on Situation 2, by Beggars Banquet Records. Deleted '87. Catalogue no: **SIT 22**
12" Single: Released Jun '83, on Situation 2, by Beggars Banquet Records. Deleted '87. Catalogue no: **SIT 22T**
12" Single: Released Mar '84, on Beggars Banquet, by Beggars Banquet Records. Catalogue no: **BEG 108T**

EVANGELINE
Tracks: / Evangeline / Everybody loves to play the fool / Waiting in the wings (Track on 12 inch version only.).
7" Single: Released Jan '87, on Beggars Banquet, by Beggars Banquet Records. Deleted Jan '88. Catalogue no: **BEG 181**
12" Single: Released Jan '87, on Beggars Banquet, by Beggars Banquet Records. Catalogue no: **BEG 181T**

HERE COMES TROUBLE
Tracks: / Here comes trouble / Starry blue-eyed wonder (live) / Rock 'n' roll (live) (Picture bag edition only.) / For what it's worth (live) (Picture bag edition only.).
7" Single: Released Jun '88, on Beggars Banquet, by Beggars Banquet Records. Catalogue no: **BEG 220**
12" Single: Released 23 Jul '88, on Beggars Banquet, by Beggars Banquet Records. Catalogue no: **IW 3**
12" Single: Released Jul '88, on Beggars Banquet, by Beggars Banquet Records. Catalogue no: **BEG 220 T**

HIGH TIME
Tracks: / High time / Broken hearted fool / Travelling chest (live) (Only on 12" single.) / Private revolution (live) (On 12" only.).
7" Single: Released Nov '87, on Beggars Banquet, by Beggars Banquet Records. Catalogue no: **BEG 203**
12" Single: Released Nov '87, on Beggars Banquet, by Beggars Banquet Records. Catalogue no: **BEG 203T**

HOLLOW HORSE
Tracks: / Hollow horse.
7" Single: Released Sep '84, on Beggars Banquet, by Beggars Banquet Records. Catalogue no: **BEG 119**
12" Single: Released Sep '84, on Beggars Banquet, by Beggars Banquet Records. Catalogue no: **BEG 119T**

KISS OFF, THE
Tracks: / Kiss off, The / Sure thing / High time / Whipping boy.
CD 5": Released 20 Feb '88, on Beggars Banquet, by Beggars Banquet Records. Catalogue no: **IW1 CD**
Cassingle: Released 20 Feb '88, on Beggars Banquet, by Beggars Banquet Records. Catalogue no: **IW1 C**
7" Single: Released 20 Feb '88, on Beggars Banquet, by Beggars Banquet Records. Catalogue no: **BEG 208**
12" Single: Released 20 Feb '88, on Beggars Banquet, by Beggars Banquet Records. Catalogue no: **BEG 208T**

LITTLE GIRL LOST
Tracks: / Little girl lost / Tin can / Hot prophet gospel (Available on 12" only) / One time (Only on 12" version.) / Evangeline (Only on CD single.) / Understanding Jane (On CD single only.).
CD 5": Released May '88, on Beggars Banquet, by Beggars Banquet Records. Catalogue no: **BEG 215CD**
7" Single: Released Apr '88, on Beggars Banquet, by Beggars Banquet Records. Catalogue no: **BEG 215**
12" Single: Released Apr '88, on Beggars Banquet, by Beggars Banquet Records. Catalogue no: **BEG 215T**

LOVE IS A WONDERFUL COLOUR
Tracks: / Love is a wonderful colour.
7" Pic: Released Aug '84, on Beggars Banquet, by Beggars Banquet Records. Deleted Jan '88. Catalogue no: **BEG 99P**
7" Single: Released Nov '83, on Beggars Banquet, by Beggars Banquet Records. Deleted Jan '88. Catalogue no: **BEG 99**
12" Single: Released Nov '83, on Beggars Banquet, by Beggars Banquet Records. Catalogue no: **BEG 99T**

NIGHT TRACKS EP
Tracks: / Night tracks.
12" Single: Released Oct '88, on Night Tracks, by Pinnacle Records. Catalogue no: **SFNT 015**

NIRVANA
Tracks: / Nirvana.
7" Single: Released Oct '82, on Troll Kitchen, by Troll Kitchen Records. Catalogue no: **WORKS 001**

SEVEN HORSES
Tracks: / Seven horses.
7" Set: Released Jun '85, on Beggars Banquet, by Beggars Banquet Records. Deleted Jan '88. Catalogue no: **BEG 142 D**
7" Single: Released Jun '85, on Beggars Banquet, by Beggars Banquet Records. Deleted Jun '87. Catalogue no: **BEG 142**
12" Single: Released Jun '85, on Beggars Banquet, by Beggars Banquet Records. Catalogue no: **BEG 142 T**

UNDERSTANDING JANE
Tracks: / Understanding Jane / I never saw my hometown 'till I went around the world / Seven horses - live / Perambulator - live / Rapids - live.
7" Single: Released Jul '86, on Beggars Banquet, by Beggars Banquet Records. Catalogue no: **BEG 160**
12" Single: Released Jul '86, on Beggars Banquet, by Beggars Banquet Records. Catalogue no: **BEG 160T**

UP HERE IN THE NORTH OF ENGLAND
Tracks: / Up here in the North of England / Sea songs / Nature's way / It makes no difference / Way laid.
12" Single: Released Dec '86, on Situation 2, by Beggars Banquet Records. Catalogue no: **SIT 45T**

WHEN IT ALL COMES DOWN
Tracks: / When it all comes down.
7" Single: Released Oct '85, on Beggars Banquet, by Beggars Banquet Records. Deleted Jun '87. Catalogue no: **BEG 151**
12" Single: Released Oct '85, on Beggars Banquet, by Beggars Banquet Records. Catalogue no: **BEG 151T**

WHO DO YOU WANT FOR YOUR LOVE
Tracks: / Who do you want for your love / Understanding Jane - live / Should I stay or should I go / Roadhouse blues (Extra track available on 12" version only.).
7" Single: Released Sep '86, on Beggars Banquet, by Beggars Banquet Records. Deleted Jan '88. Catalogue no: **BEG 172**
12" Single: Released Sep '86, on Beggars Banquet, by Beggars Banquet Records. Catalogue no: **BEG 172 T**

Icons

LOTS OF MONEY
Tracks: / Walk / Nothin' left to save / Lots of money / Privilege and easy.
12" Single: Released Jul '86, on Press, by Compendium Int.Records. Catalogue no: **P 1208**

Icons of Filth

BRAIN DEATH
Tracks: / Brain death.
7" Single: Released Mar '85, on Mortarhate, by Mortarhate Records. Deleted '88. Catalogue no: **MORT 10**

FILTH AND THE FURY, THE
Tracks: / Filth and fury, The.
7" Single: Released Feb '86, on Mortarhate, by Mortarhate Records. Catalogue no: **MORT 18**

ICQ

FLIGHT OF VENDOHAIR
Tracks: / Flight of Vendohair.
12" Single: Released Jul '84, on Unsquare, Catalogue no: **ICQ 1203**

Idaho

UNION MARE & CONFEDERATE GREY
Tracks: / Union mare and Confederate grey / Making believe / Farewell party / Promise me.
7" Single: Released Apr '80, on Phoenix (1), by Phoenix Records. Deleted '82. Catalogue no: **PH 3**

Ideal

MONOTONY
Tracks: / Monotony / Downtown mystery.
7" Single: Released Jun '82, on WEA, by WEA Records. Deleted Jun '85. Catalogue no: **K 19192**

Ideal Giants

AMPHIBIAN CULT E.P.
Tracks: / Civilian.
7" Single: Released Sep '86, on Amphibian, by Red Rhino Records. Deleted Aug '87. Catalogue no: **HAM 1**
7" Single: Released Mar '86, on UN-

KNOWN, Catalogue no: **RSA 3**

Idee Fixe

EASY MADONNA
Tracks: / Easy madonna.
7" Single: Released Jul '84, on Button, by Musical Characters Records. Catalogue no: **BTN 116**

Identity Crisis

ELOISE
Tracks: / Eloise.
7" Single: Released Sep '82, on FMR, Deleted '84. Catalogue no: **FMR 1**

Ides Of March

Biographical details: This American group consists of James Peterik (lead vocals/guitar/keyboards/saxophone), Ray Herr (vocals/guitar/bass), Larry Millas (guitar/organ/vocals), Bob Bergland (Bass/Saxophone), John Larson (trumpet), Chuck Somar (horn) and Michael Borch (drums). They were formed in Illinois, Chicago in 1964. The Ides of March had a very similar musical style to Blood Sweat & Tears, who appeared four years later and achieved greater commercial success. The Ides had only one major hit in the States with the single *Vehicle* in 1970 when it reached number 2. In the UK it only rose to No.31. The band's subsequent releases (such as the album *Midnight oil in 1973) were comparative failures. A change of record company to RCA did little to improve their chart performance and the Ides eventually disbanded. James Peterik later joined Survivor. (Ian Wilkins).*

ON THE FACE
Tracks: / On the face.
12" Single: Released Dec '86, on RS, Catalogue no: **RSAT 2**

VEHICLE
Tracks: / Vehicle.
7" Single: Released May '70, on Warner Bros., by WEA Records. Deleted '73. Catalogue no: **WB 7378**

Idlewiles

ROOM AS HIGH, A
Tracks: / Room as high, A.
7" Single: Released Feb '88, on Shadowline, Catalogue no: **SR 0687**

Idol, Billy

Biographical details: Idol, Billy This British singer and songwriter, whose real name is William Broad, came to fame in the late Seventies as the photogenic leader of Generation X. They were amongst the original wave of UK pubk groups, but had became an anachronism by the time they folded in 1981. Retaining the services of producer Keith Forsey (a lieutenant of the famous Giorgio Moroder) and hiring Kiss' manager William Aucoin, the peroxidised Mr Idol then proceeded to embark upon a successful solo career in America, where Generation X had only been known in cult circles.
Continuing to cultivate his studidly surly demeanour, Billy won US acceptance by combining his punk roots with a more commercially viable American rock sound. The hackneyed but catchy *Hot In The City* took him to no.23 on the billboard Hot 100 in late 1982, and he followed it with the sleepet hit *White Wedding* (no.36 in 1983). The uncharacteristic ballad *Eyes Withour a Face*, which included an ear-catching female vocal accompaniment, became his biggest US success, reaching no.4 in the summer of '84. It also re-introduced Idol to the higher echelons of the British charts, reaching the UK no.18 position.
1985 saw Billy achieve his first ever British Top 10 success - the reactivated singles *White Wedding* and *Rebel Yell* reached no. 6, thus becoming bigger than anything he had previously obtained in the UK, either as a solo artist or as a member of Generation X. The *Vital Idol* compilation Lp was also a Top 10 item. Though regarded as something of a joke by the British music press, there was no doubt that the solo Billy was finally living up to his assumed surname. Bob Macdonald 4/11/85.

CATCH MY FALL
Tracks: / Catch my fall.
7" Single: Released Aug '88, on Chrysalis, by Chrysalis Records. Catalogue no: **IDOL 13**
12" Single: Released Aug '88, on Chrysalis, by Chrysalis Records. Catalogue no: **IDOLX 13**

DANCING WITH MYSELF
Tracks: / Dancing with myself.
12" Single: Released Oct '83, on Chrysalis, by Chrysalis Records. Catalogue no: **IDOLX 1**

DON'T NEED A GUN
Tracks: / Don't need a gun / Fatal charm.
7" Single: Released Feb '87, on Chrysalis, by Chrysalis Records. Catalogue no: **IDOL 9**
12" Single: Released Feb '87, on Chrysalis, by Chrysalis Records. Catalogue no: **IDOLX 9**

EYES WITHOUT A FACE
Tracks: / Eyes without a face.
7" Single: Released Aug '84, on Chrysalis, by Chrysalis Records. Catalogue no: **IDOLP 3**
7" Single: Released May '84, on Chrysalis, by Chrysalis Records. Catalogue no: **IDOL 3**
12" Single: Released May '84, on Chrysalis, by Chrysalis Records. Catalogue no: **IDOLX 3**

FLESH FOR FANTASY
Tracks: / Flesh for fantasy.
7" Single: Released '86, on Chrysalis, by Chrysalis Records. Catalogue no: **IDOL 4**
12" Single: Released '86, on Chrysalis, by Chrysalis Records. Catalogue no: **IDOLX 4**

HOT IN THE CITY
Tracks: / Hot in the city / Catch my fall (remix 6) / Soul standing by (Only on 12" version.) / Dead on arrival (Only on the 12" version.).
7" Single: Released Jul '83, on Chrysalis, by Chrysalis Records. Deleted Jan '84. Catalogue no: **CHS 2625**
7" Single: Released Dec '87, on Chrysalis, by Chrysalis Records. Catalogue no: **IDOL 12**
12" Single: Released '86, on Chrysalis, by Chrysalis Records. Catalogue no: **CHS 12 2625**
12" Single: Released Dec '87, on Chrysalis, by Chrysalis Records. Catalogue no: **IDOLX 12**

MONY MONY
Tracks: / Mony Mony (live) / Mony Mony (hung like a pony mix) / Shakin all over / Shakin all over / Baby talk / Untouchables / Dancing with myself / Mony mony.
7" Single: Released Sep '87, on Chrysalis, by Chrysalis Records. Catalogue no: **IDOL 11**
7" Single: Released Sep '81, on Chrysalis, by Chrysalis Records. Deleted '85. Catalogue no: **CHS 2543**
12" Single: Released Sep '87, on Chrysalis, by Chrysalis Records. Catalogue no: **IDOLX 11**
12" Single: Released Sep '81, on Chrysalis, by Chrysalis Records. Catalogue no: **CHS 12 2543**

REBEL YELL
Tracks: / Rebel yell / White wedding.
7" Single: Released Aug '85, on Chrysalis, by Chrysalis Records. Catalogue no: **IDOL 6**
12" Single: Released Aug '85, on Chrysalis, by Chrysalis Records. Catalogue no: **IDOLX 6**

SWEET 16
Tracks: / Sweet 16 / Beyond belief.
7" Single: Released 30 May '87, on Chrysalis, by Chrysalis Records. Catalogue no: **IDOL 10**
12" Single: Released 30 May '87, on Chrysalis, by Chrysalis Records. Catalogue no: **IDOLX 10**

TO BE A LOVER
Tracks: / All summer single / To be a lover.
7" Single: Released Sep '86, on Chrysalis, by Chrysalis Records. Catalogue no: **IDOL 8**
12" Single: Released Sep '86, on Chrysalis, by Chrysalis Records. Catalogue no: **IDOLX 8**

WHITE WEDDING
Tracks: / White wedding / Dead next door, The / Mega-Idol mix / Flesh for fantasy / Hot in the city.
7" Single: Released Jun '85, on Chrysalis, by Chrysalis Records. Catalogue no: **IDOL 5**
12" Single: Released Jun '85, on Chrysalis, by Chrysalis Records. Catalogue no: **IDOLX 5**
12" Single: Released Sep '83, on Chrysalis, by Chrysalis Records. Catalogue no: **IDOL 1**

WHITE WEDDING (ORIGINAL)
Tracks: / White wedding / Hole in the wall.
7" Single: Released '83, on Chrysalis, by Chrysalis Records. Deleted '83. Catalogue no: **CHS 2656**

Idol Eyes

TOKYO ROSE
Tracks: / Unform / Tokyo rose.
7" Single: Released Jan '86, on WEA, by WEA Records. Deleted Sep '87. Catalogue no: **X 9094**

Idol Flowers

ALL I WANT IS YOU
Tracks: / All I want is you.
7" Single: Released Jan '84, on Miles Ahead, Catalogue no: **AHEAD 1**

Idol Rich

BLAZE OF LOVE
Tracks: / Blaze of love.
7" Single: Released Nov '84, on Dork, by Dork Records. Catalogue no: **IDOL 3**

PESO TRAIL
Tracks: / Peso trail.
7" Single: Released Sep '84, on Dork, by Dork Records. Catalogue no: **UR IDOL 3**

Idrah

GOING DOWN
Tracks: / Going down / Things didn't work out fine.
12" Single: Released Sep '82, on Idrah, Catalogue no: **ID 1**

If All Else Fails

DISTINCT
Tracks: / Distinct.
7" Single: Released Jan '82, on Fail, Catalogue no: **FAIL 1**

If It Moves

MEAT CATHEDRAL
Tracks: / Meat cathedral.
12" Single: Released Sep '88, on Play It Again Sam(Belgium), by Play It Again Sam (Belgium). Catalogue no: **BIAS 110**

If It Sells ...

IF IT SELLS IT SMELLS
Tracks: / If it sells it smells: *Various artists.*
12" Single: Released Oct '86, on Pink Label, by Pink Label Records. Catalogue no: **PINKY 11**

Ifield, Frank

Biographical details: Ifield Frank This British singer was born in Coventry, brought up in Australia and became a major UK star in the early Sixties. He began his career at the age of 15, and spent the fifties building a substantial career on Aussie television and radio. Because Australia was a showbusiness backwater in those days, he followed the example of Rolf Harris and decided to travel to the UK to advance his career. Teaming with Columbia Records' key producer Norrie Paramor he started promisinly enough with the 1960 no.22 hit *Lucky Devil.* But for the next two years, Ifield's luck collapsed.
The turning point came in mid-1962, when Ifield and Paramor chose to record a 1942 song called *I remember you.* Making maximum use of his distinctive falsetto sound, which often broke into a yodel. Frank's rendition stormed to the UK no.1 slot and stayed there for seven weeks. This disc introduced millions of record buyers to Ifield's style and the sub Slim Whitman yodel thus became his trademark. *I Remember You* reached no.5 in the States, a notable achievement in pre-Beatle days.
Realising that they were onto a good thing, the singer and his producer continued to raid the vaults and scored a lucrative run of UK hits with revivals of ancient songs, many of which had been previously recorded by country and western artists. Ifield's approximation of country music brought him further British chart-toppers with *Lovesick Blues* (No.1 for five weeks in late '62), *Wayward Wind,* (three weeks in early '63) and *Confessin'*(two weeks in July '63). He was the first British born act to reach the UK no.1 position with three consecutive singles and he also hit big with *Nobody's darlin' but Mine* (No.4 in '63) and *Don't Blame Me* (No.8 in '64).
Ifield also achieved a No 1 success on the British EP charts in 1963 and enjoyed several big selling albums. However, he could not hold out against the unstoppable Liverpool pop revolution for very long and his chart career tailed off during the mid-sixties. He maintained a steady income via the well-trodden cabaret circuit, but suffered a severe embarrassment in 1976 when he attempted a pop comeback through the medium of the Eurovision Song Contest - despite being the best-known of the dozen acts taking part in the UK's *Song For Europe* heats, he finished bottom of the pile! Bob Macdonald 4.11.85.

ANGRY AT THE BIG OAK TREE
Tracks: / Angry at the Big Oak Tree.
7" Single: Released Mar '64, on Columbia, by EMI Records. Deleted '67. Catalogue no: **DB 7263**

CALL HER YOUR SWEETHEART
Tracks: / Call her your sweetheart.
7" Single: Released Nov '66, on Columbia, by EMI Records. Deleted '69. Catalogue no: **DB 8078**

CONFESSIN'
Tracks: / Confessin'.
7" Single: Released Jun '63, on Columbia, by EMI Records. Deleted '66. Catalogue no: **DB 7062**

CRAWLING BACK
Tracks: / Crawling back / So sad.
7" Single: Released Jan '82, on PRT, by Castle Communications Records. Catalogue no: **7P 229**

DON'T BLAME ME
Tracks: / Don't blame me.
7" Single: Released Jan '64, on Columbia, by EMI Records. Deleted '67. Catalogue no: **DB 7184**

GOTTA GET A DATE
Tracks: / Gotta get a date.
7" Single: Released Jul '60, on Columbia, by EMI Records. Deleted '63. Catalogue no: **DB 4496**

I REMEMBER YOU (OLD GOLD)
Tracks: / I remember you.
7" Single: Released Jul '82, on Old Gold, by Old Gold Records. Deleted Jul '88. Catalogue no: **OG 9043**

I REMEMBER YOU (SINGLE)
Tracks: / I remember you.
7" Single: Released Jun '62, on Columbia, by EMI Records. Deleted '65. Catalogue no: **DB 4856**

I SHOULD CARE
Tracks: / I should care.
7" Single: Released Jun '64, on Columbia, by EMI Records. Deleted '67. Catalogue no: **DB 7319**

LOVESICK BLUES
Tracks: / Lovesick blues.
7" Single: Released Sep '62, on Columbia, by EMI Records. Deleted '65. Catalogue no: **DB 4913**

LUCKY DEVIL
Tracks: / Lucky devil.
7" Single: Released Jan '60, on Columbia, by EMI Records. Deleted '63. Catalogue no: **DB 4399**

MULE TRAIN
Tracks: / Mule train.
7" Single: Released Sep '63, on Columbia, by EMI Records. Deleted '66. Catalogue no: **DB 7131**

NO ONE WILL EVER KNOW
Tracks: / No one will ever know.
7" Single: Released May '66, on Columbia, by EMI Records. Deleted '68. Catalogue no: **DB 7940**

NOBODY'S DARLING BUT MINE
Tracks: / Nobody's darlin' but mine.
7" Single: Released Mar '63, on Columbia, by EMI Records. Deleted '65. Catalogue no: **DB 7007**

PARADISE
Tracks: / Paradise.
7" Single: Released Jul '65, on Columbia, by EMI Records. Deleted '68. Catalogue no: **DB 7655**

SUMMER IS OVER
Tracks: / Summer is over.
7" Single: Released Sep '64, on Columbia, by EMI Records. Deleted '67. Catalogue no: **DB 7355**

TOUCH THE MORNING
Tracks: / Touch the morning.
7" Single: Released Mar '83, on PRT, by Castle Communications Records. Catalogue no: **7P 265**

WAYWARD WIND
Tracks: / Wayward wind / I'm confessin'.
7" Single: Released Nov '80, on H.M.V., by EMI Records. Deleted '83. Catalogue no: **POP 2014**
7" Single: Released Jan '63, on Columbia, by EMI Records. Deleted '65. Catalogue no: **DB 4960**

Ifill, Gloria

ALL NIGHT LONG
Tracks: / All night long.
12" Single: Released Mar '84, on Trindisc, by Trindisc Records. Catalogue no: **TRIN 011**

Iggins Lot

MONDAY MORNING BLUES
Tracks: / Monday morning blues / One day.
7" Single: Released Nov '80, on JM, by JM Records. Deleted '83. Catalogue no: **JM 1006**

Iggy & The Stooges

Biographical details: This rock group consisted of James Jewel Osterberg (known as Iggy Pop on guitar and vocals), Ron Asheton (guitar), Dave Alexander (bass) and Scott Asheton (drums). They were formed in 1967..

GIMME DANGER
Tracks: / Gimme danger.
12" Single: Released May '88, on

JULIO IGLESIAS
BEGIN THE BEGUINE

JULIO IGLESIAS - BEGIN THE BEGUINE (Released on CBS)

Revenge (France), Catalogue no: **CAX 3**

SHE CREATURES OF HOLLYWOOD HILLS
Tracks: / She creatures of Hollywood Hills.
12" Single: Released Dec '88, on Revenge (France), Catalogue no: **CAX 4**

Iglesias, Julio

Biographical details: Iglesias, Julio This Spanish singer, born in 1943 was a reserve goalkeeper for the Real Madrid football team before becoming a professional vocalist. The latter occupation proved to be somewhat more successful - for, by 1981, he had managed to sell 70 million albums around the world without being a star in the United States or Britain.

Having built himself up, through the Seventies, into the top male vocalist of Spanish and Latin markets, the charismatic Iglesias stormed to success in the UK in December 1981 with his No.1 smash *Begin the Beguine*. This Spanish language rendition of Cole Porter's 1935 standard was an unlikely chart-topper, sandwiched between Queen & David Bowie's *Under Pressure* and the Juman League's *Don't You Want Me*. The power of housewives' wallets was also demonstrated on the British album chart, where the *Begin The Beguine* Lp reached no.5 and logged 28 weeks on the list. In early 1982 the smiling Spaniard enjoyed another UK Top 3 single with *Quiereme mucho (Yours)*. Further British LP success was achieved with *Amor* and *Julio*.

Iglesias' assault on the USA market took place in 1984 when he cruised into the Top 10 of the Billboard album chart with *1100 Bel Air Place*. This Yankee success was calculated and planned to the most minute detail. The campaign was craftily spearheaded by a pair of duets with top American singers: *To All The Girls I've Loved Before*, with Willie Nelson, reached no.5 (and no.17 in Briain); *All of You*, with Diana Ross got to no.19.

By 1985 the ever- romantic Julio was a superstar all over the globe and was singing in Spanish, English, Italian, French and Portuguese. Despite his new found American status, he was careful not to neglect his Latin Base - the 1985 album *Libra* sprinted to no.1 on the Billboard Latin charts. Bob Macdonald 4.11.85.

AE, AO
Tracks: / Ae, ao / Everytime we fall in love / Ae, ao (ext.) (12" & CD single only.) / Ae, ao (dub) (12" & CD single only.) / Amor (Pic. bag with poster only.) / Quiereme mucho (Pic. bag with poster only.).
CD 5": Released Sep '88, on CBS, by CBS Records. Deleted 17 Apr '89. Catalogue no: **JULIO C3**
7" Single: Released Sep '88, on CBS, by CBS Records. Deleted 17 Apr '89. Catalogue no: **JULIO 3**
12" Single: Released Oct '88, on CBS, by CBS Records. Deleted 17 Apr '89. Catalogue no: **JULIO Q3**
12" Single: Released Sep '88, on CBS, by CBS Records. Deleted 17 Apr '89. Catalogue no: **JULIO T3**

AMOR (SINGLE)
Tracks: / Amor.
7" Single: Released Sep '82, on CBS, by CBS Records. Deleted '85. Catalogue no: **A 2801**

BEGIN THE BEGUINE (see panel above)
Tracks: / Begin the beguine / De nina a mujer.
7" Single: Released '81, on CBS, by CBS Records. Catalogue no: **A 1612**

BRASILIA
Tracks: / Brasilia (part 1) / Brasilia (part 2) / Brasilia (medley) / Ae ao / Begin the beguine.
CD 5": Released 12 Jun '89, on CBS, by CBS Records. Deleted Oct '89. Catalogue no: **JULIO C6**
7" Single: Released 12 Jun '89, on CBS, by CBS Records. Deleted Oct '89. Catalogue no: **JULIO 6**
12" Single: Released 12 Jun '89, on CBS, by CBS Records. Deleted Oct '89. Catalogue no: **JULIO T6**

CABALLO VIEJO
Tracks: / Caballo viejo / Bamboleo / Francia (edit).
CD 5": Released Sep '89, on CBS, by CBS Records. Catalogue no: **JULIO C7**
7" Pic: Released Sep '89, on CBS, by CBS Records. Catalogue no: **JULIO 7**
7" Single: Released 18 Sep '89, on CBS, by CBS Records. Catalogue no: **JULIO S7**
12" Single: Released Sep '89, on CBS, by CBS Records. Catalogue no: **JULIO T7**

FOREVER AND EVER
Tracks: / Forever and ever.
7" Single: Released Jun '83, on CBS, by CBS Records. Catalogue no: **A 3535**

HEY (SINGLE)
Tracks: / Hey.
7" Single: Released Mar '83, on CBS, by CBS Records. Catalogue no: **JULIO 1**

IF I EVER NEEDED YOU
Tracks: / If I ever needed you (I need you now) / Too many women / Isla en el sol (On 12" & CD only.) / Me olvide de vivir (On 12" & CD only.).
CD 5": Released 6 Feb '89, on CBS, by CBS Records. Deleted 10 Jul '89. Catalogue no: **JULIO C5**
7" Pic: Released 6 Feb '89, on CBS, by CBS Records. Deleted 10 Jul '89. Catalogue no: **JULIO P5**
7" Single: Released 20 Feb '89, on CBS, by CBS Records. Deleted 10 Jul '89. Catalogue no: **JULIO Q5**
7" Single: Released 6 Feb '89, on CBS, by CBS Records. Deleted 10 Jul '89. Catalogue no: **JULIO 5**
12" Single: Released 6 Feb '89, on CBS, by CBS Records. Deleted 10 Jul '89. Catalogue no: **JULIO T5**

I'VE GOT YOU UNDER MY SKIN
Tracks: / I've got you under my skin.
7" Single: Released Sep '85, on CBS, by CBS Records. Catalogue no: **A 6516**

LO MEJOR DE TU VIDA
Tracks: / Lo mejor de tu vida / America.
7" Single: Released Nov '87, on CBS, by CBS Records. Deleted Jun '88. Catalogue no: **651 244 7**

LOVE Featuring Stevie Wonder
Tracks: / Love.
7" Single: Released Aug '88, on CBS, by CBS Records. Deleted 17 Apr '89. Catalogue no: **JULIO 2**
12" Single: Released Aug '88, on CBS, by CBS Records. Catalogue no: **JULIOC 2**

LOVE IS ON OUR SIDE AGAIN
Tracks: / Love is on our side again / Never never never / To all the girls I've loved before (Only on 12" version & CD single.) / Nathalie (Only on 12" version & CD single.).
CD 5": Released 28 Nov '88, on CBS, by CBS Records. Deleted 17 Apr '89. Catalogue no: **JULIO D4**
CD 5": Released Nov '88, on CBS, by CBS Records. Deleted 17 Apr '89. Catalogue no: **JULIO C4**
7" Single: Released Nov '88, on CBS, by CBS Records. Deleted 17 Apr '89. Catalogue no: **JULIO 4**
12" Single: Released 21 Nov '88, on CBS, by CBS Records. Deleted 17 Apr '89. Catalogue no: **JULIO Q4**
12" Single: Released Nov '88, on CBS, by CBS Records. Deleted 17 Apr '89. Catalogue no: **JULIO T4**

MY LOVE
Tracks: / My love / Words and music / To all the girls I've loved before* / All of you*.
Note: * track on CD single.
7" Single: Released May '88, on CBS, by CBS Records. Deleted Jan '89. Catalogue no: **JULIO E2**
12" Single: Released May '88, on CBS, by CBS Records. Deleted Jan '89. Catalogue no: **JULIO T2**
CD 5": Released May '88, on CBS, by CBS Records. Deleted 17 Apr '89. Catalogue no: **JULIO C2**

QUIEREME MUCHO
Tracks: / Quiereme mucho.
7" Single: Released Feb '83, on CBS, by CBS Records. Deleted '86. Catalogue no: **A 1939**

SO CLOSE TO ME
Tracks: / So close to me / Quijote.
7" Single: Released Nov '82, on CBS, by CBS Records. Deleted Nov '85. Catalogue no: **A 2932**

Igloos

WOLF
Tracks: / Wolf.
7" Single: Released Apr '81, on Fresh, by Jetstar Records. Catalogue no: **FRESH 23**

Ignerents

RADIO INTERFERENCE
Tracks: / Radio interference.
7" Single: Released Dec '79, on Rundown, by Rundown Records. Catalogue no: **RUNS 001**
7" Single: Released Feb '80, on Ace, by Ace Records. Deleted Jun '88. Catalogue no: **ACE 008**

Igors Night Off

WE'RE HAVING A PARTY
Tracks: / We're having a party.
7" Single: Released Apr '85, on Make A Way, Catalogue no: **TAKE 100**

Ijahman & Madge

HOLD ON HONEY
Tracks: / Hold on honey.
12" Single: Released Nov '85, on Jahmani, Catalogue no: **JMI 602**

I DO
Tracks: / I do.
12" Single: Released May '85, on Jahmani, Catalogue no: **JMI 601**

IN THE NIGHT
Tracks: / In the night.
12" Single: Released Aug '87, on Tree Roots, Catalogue no: **JMI 605**

MY LOVE
Tracks: / Chariot of love (Ijahman) / My love.
12" Single: Released Nov '86, on Jah Man, Catalogue no: **JMI 604**

Ijog & The Tracksuits

BEDROOM TUNE
Tracks: / Bedroom tune.
7" Single: Released Feb '82, on Tyger, Deleted '83. Catalogue no: **TYG 6**

Ik

WHEN THE RIVER BREAKS
Tracks: / When the river breaks.
7" Single: Released Jul '85, on Off-Beat (1), Catalogue no: **OB1 IK1**
12" Single: Released Jul '85, on Off-Beat (1), Catalogue no: **OB1 IK2**

Ikafa Leiah

DISCO 2000
Tracks: / Disco 2000 / Together in love.
7" Single: Released May '79, on Hobo, Catalogue no: **HOS 002**

Ikon Ad

DON'T FEED US SHIT
Tracks: / Don't feed us shit.
7" EP: Released Aug '82, on Radical Change, by Backs Recording Co.. Catalogue no: **RC 3**

LET THE VULTURES FLY
Tracks: / Let the vultures fly.
7" EP: Released Jun '83, on Radical Change, by Backs Recording Co.. Catalogue no: **RC 4**

Il Y A Volkswagens

KILL MYSELF
Tracks: / Kill myself / American dream.
7" Single: Released Aug '81, on Mechanical Reproductions, Deleted '83. Catalogue no: **MR 001**

Ilana

PAPER CHASE
Tracks: / Paper chase / We'll love again.
7" Single: Released May '82, on Stagecoach, Catalogue no: **MAIL 39**

I-Lands

IN THE RAIN
Tracks: / In the rain / Velvet glove / Summertime No. 1.
7" Single: Released Nov '85, on Little Prince, by Little Prince Records. Catalogue no: **LIPS 2**

I-Level

Biographical details: Minefield and Teacher gave this British disco trio a brace of minor hit singles in the UK during 1983. The multi-racial threesome's eponymous debut album, the same year, featured a blend of danceable soul and reggae-inflected styles. And I-Level's 1984 singles, In The River and Our Song, kept the band's music on the turntables of club DJs but failed to build upon the group's 1983 success. (Bob MacDonald, November 1985.)

Minefield and *Teacher* gave this British disco trio a brace of minor UK hit singles during 1983. The multi-racial threesome's eponymous debut album was released in the same year, and featured a blend of danceable soul and reggae-inflected styles. I-Level's 1984 singles, *In The River* and *Our Song*, kept the band's music on the turntables of some club disc jockeys but did not build upon the lads' 1983 success. Bob Macdonald 4/11/85.

GIVE ME
Tracks: / Give me.
7" Single: Released Aug '82, on Virgin, by Virgin Records. Deleted '89. Catalogue no: **VS 523**
12" Single: Released Aug '82, on Virgin, by Virgin Records. Deleted '85. Catalogue no: **VS 523-12**

IN THE RIVER
Tracks: / In the river.
7" Single: Released Jun '84, on Virgin, by Virgin Records. Deleted '89. Catalogue no: **VS 681**

IN THE SAND
Tracks: / In the sand / Latin antics.
7" Single: Released Feb '85, on Virgin, by Virgin Records. Deleted '89. Catalogue no: **VS 718**

MINEFIELD
Tracks: / Minefield / Number 4 / Give me.
7" Single: Released Apr '83, on Virgin, by Virgin Records. Deleted '89. Catalogue no: **VS 563**

MINEFIELD (OLD GOLD)
Tracks: / Minefield / River, The.
12" Single: Released 28 Mar '89, on Old Gold, by Old Gold Records. Catalogue no: **OG 4112**

OUR SONG
Tracks: / Our song.
7" Single: Released Jul '84, on Virgin, by Virgin Records. Deleted '89. Catalogue no: **VS 699**

STONE HEART
Tracks: / Stone heart / Historical nights / Wagon (on 12" only).

7" Single: Released Aug '83, on Virgin, by Virgin Records. Deleted Aug '86. Catalogue no: **VS 626**

TEACHER
Tracks: / Teacher / All my love.
7" Single: Released Jun '83, on Virgin, by Virgin Records. Deleted '89. Catalogue no: **VS 595**

Illsley, John

I WANT TO SEE THE MOON
Tracks: / I want to see the moon.
Note: John Illsley, bass player and one half of Dire Straits comes up with a great new solo single. Taken from his forthcoming album 'Glass'. (Phonogram 1988).
CD 5": Released May '88, on Vertigo, by Phonogram Ltd. Deleted Oct '88. Catalogue no: **VERCD 39**
7" Single: Released May '88, on Vertigo, by Phonogram Ltd. Deleted Oct '88. Catalogue no: **VER 39**
12" Single: Released May '88, on Vertigo, by Phonogram Ltd. Deleted Oct '88. Catalogue no: **VERX 39**

NEVER TOLD A SOUL (SINGLE)
Tracks: / Never told a soul / Hypnotised.
7" Single: Released May '84, on Vertigo, by Phonogram Ltd. Catalogue no: **PH 6**
12" Single: Released May '84, on Vertigo, by Phonogram Ltd. Catalogue no: **PH 612**

Illusion

Biographical details: This group consists of Jane Relf (vocals), Jim McCarty (guitar/vocals), John Hawken (keyboards), Eddie McNeil (drums) and Louis Cennamo (bass)..

WHY CAN'T WE LIVE TOGETHER?
Tracks: / Why can't we live together / Why can't we live together (part 2).
7" Single: Released Apr '89, on Rumour, Catalogue no: **RUMA 1**
7" Single: Released Jun '82, on PRT, by Castle Communications Records. Catalogue no: **7P 238**
12" Single: Released Apr '89, on Rumour, Catalogue no: **RUMAT 1**
12" Single: Released Jun '82, on PRT, by Castle Communications Records. Deleted '85. Catalogue no: **12P 238**

Illusion Orchestra

AUTUMN LEAVES
Tracks: / Autumn leaves.
7" Single: Released Nov '82, on R & B, by Red Bus Records. Catalogue no: **RBS 212**
12" Single: Released Nov '82, on R & B, by Red Bus Records. Catalogue no: **RBL 212**

Illustrated Man

JUST ENOUGH
Tracks: / Just enough / Sensation.
7" Single: Released Jun '84, on Parlophone, by EMI Records. Catalogue no: **R 6070**
12" Single: Released Jun '84, on Parlophone, by EMI Records. Deleted '87. Catalogue no: **12R 6070**

Illustrious Cutlery

SCARECROW
Tracks: / Scarecrow.
7" Single: Released Aug '87, on North West, Catalogue no: **NW 003**
12" Single: Released Aug '87, on North West, Catalogue no: **NW 003T**

Iludicrous

QUITE EXTRAORDINARY
Tracks: / Quite extraordinary.
7" Single: Released May '88, on Kaleidoscope Sound, by Kaleidoscope Sound Records. Catalogue no: **KS 707**
12" Single: Released May '88, on Kaleidoscope Sound, by Kaleidoscope Sound Records. Catalogue no: **KS 107**

Iluwata

YESTERME YESTERYOU YESTERDAY
Tracks: / Yester-me, yester-you, yesterday.
12" Single: Released Dec '83, on Natty Congo, Catalogue no: **NCDM 021**

I'm Dead

SECOND IDENTITY
Tracks: / Second identity.
7" Single: Released Jun '83, on Goldhanger, by Goldhanger Records. Catalogue no: **GLUM 001**

I'm Just A Lucky

I'M JUST A LUCKY SO-AND-SO Original London cast
Tracks: / I'm just a lucky so and so: *Various artists* / Take it right back: *I'm Just A Lucky So-And-So.*
Note: From "Blues In The Night".
7" Single: Released Jan '88, on First Night, by First Night Records. Catalogue no: **SCORE 15**

I'm Talking

DO YOU WANNA BE
Tracks: / Do you wanna be.
7" Single: Released Oct '86, on London Records, by London Records. Deleted Sep '87. Catalogue no: **LON 114**
12" Single: Released Oct '86, on London Records, by London Records. Catalogue no: **LONX 114**

Image

YOU MAKE ME FEEL
Tracks: / You make me feel.
7" Single: Released Feb '82, on Bowler Music, Catalogue no: **BOW 151**

Imagination

Biographical details: Imagination This British soul band consists of Ashely Ingram, Lee John and Errol Kennedy. The group's name was chosen shortly after John Lennon's murder and was intended as a tribute to him and and his song *Imagine.*
Having gained individual experience during the Seventies by peforming in the touring groups of various American soul acts, the three members came together in 1980. The trio's masterstroke was to team up with the up and coming production team of Tony Swain and Steve Jolley, who also collaborated with Ingram and John on the writing of the material. Iamgination's first single *Body Talk* was released in 1981 and became a sleeper summer smash. This slinky, sexy slowie took its time in climbing the British charts but evantually reached No.4 and logged 18 weeks on the Top 75. It was the start of something big.
During the rest of 1981 and '82, Imagination became Britain's top black act. Their string of superbly crafted dance/soul hits included *In and out of love* (which reached no.16 on the Uk chart), *Flashback* (also no.16), *Just an Illusion* (no.2), *Music And Lights*, (no.5), *In The Heat of the Night* (no.22) and *Changes* (no.31). Their albums were also strong sellers and they built up a large concert following with their notoriously risque stage shows/
From 1983 onwards, however, the Imagination alliance with Swain and Jolley grew increasinly stale and the sound became more and more predictable. The hits kept on coming, but all fell short of the Uk Top 20. By late 1984 the trio had been dropped by Swain & Jolley, whose distinctive sound was now enjoying huge success with Banarama, Spandua Ballet and Alison Moyet - Tony and Steve certainly owed Imagination a debt for giving early exposure to the duo's studio talents. Bob Macdonald 4/11/85.

IMAGINATION - IN AND OUT OF LOVE (Released on R & B)

BODY TALK (SINGLE)
Tracks: / Body talk.
7" Single: Released May '81, on R & B, by Red Bus Records. Catalogue no: **RBS 201**
12" Single: Released May '81, on R & B, by Red Bus Records. Catalogue no: **RBL 201**

CHANGES
Tracks: / Changes / So good, so right.
7" Pic: Released Dec '82, on R & B, by Red Bus Records. Deleted '85. Catalogue no: **RBP 213**
7" Single: Released Nov '82, on R & B, by Red Bus Records. Deleted '85. Catalogue no: **RBS 213**
12" Single: Released Nov '82, on R & B, by Red Bus Records. Deleted '85. Catalogue no: **RBSL 213**

FLASHBACK
Tracks: / Flashback.
7" Single: Released Nov '81, on R & B, by Red Bus Records. Catalogue no: **RBS 206**
12" Single: Released Nov '81, on R & B, by Red Bus Records. Catalogue no: **RBL 206**

FOUND MY GIRL
Tracks: / Found my girl.
7" Single: Released Apr '85, on R & B, by Red Bus Records. Catalogue no: **RBS 1800**
12" Single: Released Apr '85, on R & B, by Red Bus Records. Catalogue no: **RBL 1800**

HOLD ME IN YOUR ARMS
Tracks: / Hold me in your arms / Instinctual (US remix) / Operator (Only on 12" version.).
7" Single: Released May '88, on RCA, by BMG Records (UK). Deleted May '89. Catalogue no: **PB 42057**
12" Single: Released May '88, on RCA, by BMG Records (UK). Deleted May '89. Catalogue no: **PT 42058**

I KNOW WHAT LOVE IS
Tracks: / I know what love is / One day I found me.
7" Single: Released Sep '87, on RCA, by BMG Records (UK). Deleted May '89. Catalogue no: **PB 41563**
12" Single: Released Sep '87, on RCA, by BMG Records (UK). Deleted May '89. Catalogue no: **PT 41564**

I'LL ALWAYS LOVE YOU
Tracks: / I'll always love you / Burnin' up.
7" Single: Released Nov '81, on R & B, by Red Bus Records. Catalogue no: **RBS 205**

IN AND OUT OF LOVE (see panel above)
Tracks: / In and out of love / In and out of love (instrumental).
7" Single: Released Sep '81, on R & B, by Red Bus Records. Catalogue no: **RBS 202**
12" Single: Released Sep '81, on R & B, by Red Bus Records. Catalogue no: **RBSL 202**

IN THE HEAT OF THE NIGHT (SINGLE)
Tracks: / In the heat of the night.
7" Single: Released Aug '82, on R & B, by Red Bus Records. Deleted '85. Catalogue no: **RBS 211**
12" Single: Released Aug '82, on R & B, by Red Bus Records. Deleted '85. Catalogue no: **RBSL 211**

INSTINCTUAL
Tracks: / Instinctual / Touch / Instinctual (freak mix) (Only on 12" single.) / Instinctual (dub) (Only on 12" single.).
7" Single: Released Dec '87, on RCA, by BMG Records (UK). Deleted May '89. Catalogue no: **PB 41697**
12" Single: Released Dec '87, on RCA, by BMG Records (UK). Deleted May '89. Catalogue no: **PT 41698**

JUST AN ILLUSION
Tracks: / Just an illusion.
7" Single: Released Feb '82, on R & B, by Red Bus Records. Catalogue no: **RBS 208**
12" Single: Released Feb '82, on R & B, by Red Bus Records. Catalogue no: **RBL 208**

LAST DAYS OF SUMMER
Tracks: / Last days of summer.
7" Single: Released Aug '85, on R & B, by Red Bus Records. Catalogue no: **RBS 1802**
12" Single: Released Aug '85, on R & B, by Red Bus Records. Catalogue no: **RBL 1802**

LAST TIME, THE
Tracks: / Touch / Last time, The.
7" Single: Released Aug '87, on RCA, by BMG Records (UK). Catalogue no: **PB 41471**
12" Single: Released Aug '87, on RCA, by BMG Records (UK). Catalogue no: **PT 41472**

LOOKING AT MIDNIGHT
Tracks: / Looking at midnight.
7" Single: Released May '83, on R & B, by Red Bus Records. Deleted '86. Catalogue no: **RBS 214**
12" Single: Released May '83, on R & B, by Red Bus Records. Deleted '86. Catalogue no: **RBL 214**

LOVE'S TAKING OVER
Tracks: / Love's taking over / Love's taking over (sensitive mix) (Available on 12" and CD only) / Love's taking over (club mix) (Available on 12" and CD only) / Instinctual (Available on CD only).
CD 5": Released Jun '89, on RCA, by BMG Records (UK). Catalogue no: **PD 42660**
7" Single: Released Jun '89, on RCA, by BMG Records (UK). Catalogue no: **PB 42659**
12" Single: Released Jun '89, on RCA, by BMG Records (UK). Catalogue no: **PT 42660**

MUSIC & LIGHTS
Tracks: / Music & lights.
7" Single: Released Jun '82, on R & B, by Red Bus Records. Deleted '85. Catalogue no: **RBS 210**
12" Single: Released Jun '82, on R & B, by Red Bus Records. Deleted '85. Catalogue no: **RBSL 210**

NEW DIMENSIONS
Tracks: / New dimension.
7" Single: Released Oct '83, on R & B, by Red Bus Records. Deleted '86. Catalogue no: **RBS 216**
12" Single: Released Oct '83, on R & B, by Red Bus Records. Deleted '86. Catalogue no: **RBL 216**

STATE OF LOVE
Tracks: / State of love / Wrong in love.
7" Pic: Released May '84, on R & B, by Red Bus Records. Deleted '87. Catalogue no: **RBP 218**
7" Single: Released May '84, on R & B, by Red Bus Records. Deleted '87. Catalogue no: **RBS 218**
12" Single: Released May '84, on R & B, by Red Bus Records. Deleted '87. Catalogue no: **RBL 218**

SUNSHINE
Tracks: / Sunshine / Triology / Streetmix (medley) (Extra track on double 12" single only) / Body talk (live version) (Extra track on double 12" single only).
7" Set: Released Apr '86, on R & B, by Red Bus Records. Catalogue no: **RBLX 1804**
7" Single: Released Apr '86, on R & B, by Red Bus Records. Catalogue no: **RBS 1804**
12" Single: Released Apr '86, on R & B, by Red Bus Records. Catalogue no: **RBL 1804**

THANK YOU MY LOVE
Tracks: / Thank you my love.
12" Pic: Released Feb '85, on R & B, by Red Bus Records. Deleted '86. Catalogue no: **RBX 219**
7" Single: Released Oct '84, on R & B, by Red Bus Records. Deleted '87. Catalogue no: **RBS 219**
12" Single: Released Oct '84, on R & B, by Red Bus Records. Deleted '87. Catalogue no: **RBL 219**

Imagination Brass

ZOOM ZOOM
Tracks: / Zoom zoom / Zoom zoom (inst).
7" Single: Released Jul '87, on Bumble Bee, Catalogue no: **7 BUMB 107**
12" Single: Released Jul '87, on Bumble Bee, Catalogue no: **BUMB 107**

Imajinca

VERY FIRST VIDEO KISS, THE
Tracks: / Very first video kiss, The.
7" Single: Released Jun '84, on A Record Company, Deleted '88. Catalogue no: **ARC**

003

Imanuel, Eli

EASY LOVER
Tracks: / Easy lover.
12" Single: Released Jan '82, on Silver Camel, Catalogue no: **SC 008**

Im - mac Logic

BOLERO
Tracks: / Bolero / Logics of emotion.
12" Single: Released May '84, on Assorted Images, by Graduate Records. Deleted Jan '87. Catalogue no: **AI 001**

Immaculate Fools

HEARTS OF FORTUNE (SINGLE)
Tracks: / Hearts of fortune.
7" Single: Released May '85, on A&M, by A&M Records. Deleted '88. Catalogue no: **AM 257**
12" Single: Released May '85, on A&M, by A&M Records. Deleted '88. Catalogue no: **AMY 257**

IMMACULATE FOOLS
Tracks: / Immaculate Fools.
7" Single: Released Jan '85, on A&M, by A&M Records. Deleted '88. Catalogue no: **AM 227**
12" Single: Released Jan '85, on A&M, by A&M Records. Deleted '88. Catalogue no: **AMY 227**

NEVER GIVE LESS THAN EVERYTHING
Tracks: / Never give less than everything / She fools everyone / Love bites (On 12" only).
7" Single: Released May '87, on A&M, by A&M Records. Deleted Mar '88. Catalogue no: **AM 393**
12" Single: Released May '87, on A&M, by A&M Records. Deleted Mar '88. Catalogue no: **AMY 393**

NOTHING MEANS NOTHING (see panel below)
Tracks: / Nothing means nothing / Little tickets.
7" Single: Released Sep '84, on A&M, by A&M Records. Deleted '88. Catalogue no: **AM 214**
12" Single: Released Sep '84, on A&M, by A&M Records. Deleted '88. Catalogue no: **AMX 214**

SAVE IT (re-recorded version)
Tracks: / Save it.
7" Single: Released Oct '85, on A&M, by A&M Records. Catalogue no: **AM 289**
12" Single: Released Oct '85, on A&M, by A&M Records. Deleted '88. Catalogue no: **AMY 289**

TRAGIC COMEDY
Tracks: / Tragic comedy / Dub poets (live) / All fall down (Available on 12" version only.).
Note: All fall down is an extra track available on 12" version only.
7" Single: Released Feb '87, on A&M, by A&M Records. Deleted Mar '88. Catalogue no: **AM 377**
12" Single: Released Feb '87, on A&M, by A&M Records. Deleted Mar '88. Catalogue no: **AMY 377**

WISH YOU WERE HERE
Tracks: / Pretty prize now / Wish you were here.
7" Single: Released Aug '87, on A&M, by A&M Records. Deleted Mar '88. Catalogue no: **AM 399**
12" Single: Released Aug '87, on A&M, by A&M Records. Deleted Mar '88. Catalogue no: **AMY 399**

Immortals

NO TURNING BACK
Tracks: / No turning back (Chocks away mix).
7" Single: Released May '86, on MCA, by MCA Records. Catalogue no: **MCA 1057**
12" Single: Released May '86, on MCA, by MCA Records. Catalogue no: **MCAT 1057**

ULTIMATE WARLORD
Tracks: / Ultimate warlord / Warlords pt 2.
7" Single: Released Feb '82, on Excaliber, by Red Bus Records. Deleted Feb '87. Catalogue no: **EXC 517**
12" Single: Released Feb '82, on Excaliber, by Red Bus Records. Deleted Feb '87. Catalogue no: **EXCL 517**

Impact

PARADISE
Tracks: / Paradise / One more step to take.
7" Single: Released Apr '88, on Angel (2), by Nine Mile. Catalogue no: **ABP 002**

PUNK CHRISTMAS
Tracks: / Punk Christmas.
7" Single: Released Nov '83, on Cyanide, Catalogue no: **CN 01**

Impact Auto Edit

IMPACT AUTO EDIT
Tracks: / Impact auto edit: *Various artists* / Inc hula: *Various artists* / Sonic youth: *Various artists* / Portion control: *Various artists.*
12" Single: Released Jan '86, on Impact, by Ace Records. Catalogue no: **INST 2**

Impalas

Biographical details: This rock'n'roll group consists of Joe Frazier, Tony Carlucci, Lenny Renda and Richie Wagner. Originating from Brooklyn, New York, this rock'n'roll quartet had their only million selling hit in the US with *Sorry (I ran all the way home)* in 1959. It reached No.2 in the American charts, but only No.28 in Britain. The song was written by Harry Giosasi and Artie Zwirn and it was Giosasi who first discovered the band. The single was re-released in Britain in 1975. (Ian Wilkins, Sept 1986).

SORRY (I RAN ALL THE WAY HOME)
Tracks: / Sorry (I ran all the way).
7" Single: Released Jul '59, on MGM, by Polydor Ltd. Deleted '62. Catalogue no: **MGM 1015**

Impatience

SLICE ME NICE
Tracks: / Slice me nice.
12" Single: Released Sep '84, on Proto, by Proto Records. Catalogue no: **ENAT 120**

Imperial, Mark

I CAN FEEL THE MUSIC
Tracks: / I can feel the music.
12" Single: Released Nov '87, on House Nation (USA), Catalogue no: **HN 87091**

Imperials

Biographical details: Imperials Not to be confused with Little Anthony & The Imperials, this all male American soul vocal group scored a one off UK hit in early 1978 with their single *Who's Gonna Love Me*, which reached no.17. Subsequent singles, such as *Do What I Gotta Do*, flopped, and the group switched to gospel music. Bob Macdonald 5/11/85.

WHO'S GONNA LOVE ME
Tracks: / Who's gonna love me.
7" Single: Released Nov '77, on Power Exchange, Deleted '80. Catalogue no: **PX 266**

Imperiet

PEACE
Tracks: / Wild world / Blue heaven blues (Track on 12" version only) / Peace.
7" Single: Released Mar '86, on Mistlur, by Mistlur Records. Catalogue no: **MLRS 49**
12" Single: Released Mar '86, on Mistlur, by Mistlur Records. Catalogue no: **MLRSMZ 49**

Impi

IMPI
Tracks: / Impi.
7" Single: Released Sep '82, on Jive, by Zomba Records. Catalogue no: **JIVE 24**
12" Single: Released Sep '82, on Jive, by Zomba Records. Catalogue no: **JIVET 24**

Implied Consent

NOBODY IN PARTICULAR
Tracks: / Nobody in particular.
7" Single: Released Feb '84, on In Tape, by In Tape Records. Catalogue no: **IT 003**

Impossible Dreamers

AUGUST AVENUE
Tracks: / August avenue.
7" Single: Released Sep '85, on RCA, by BMG Records (UK). Catalogue no: **PB 40349**
12" Single: Released Sep '85, on RCA, by BMG Records (UK). Catalogue no: **PT 40350**

HOUSE BUILT ON SAND
Tracks: / House built on sand.
7" Single: Released Oct '84, on Arcadia, Catalogue no: **7ID 001**
12" Single: Released Oct '84, on Arcadia, Catalogue no: **12ID 001**

I HAVE LOVE IN MY HANDS
Tracks: / I have love in my hands.
7" Single: Released Mar '87, on RCA, by BMG Records (UK). Deleted '87. Catalogue no: **LOVE 1**
12" Single: Released Mar '87, on RCA, by BMG Records (UK). Deleted '87. Catalogue no: **HOVE T1**

LIFE ON EARTH
Tracks: / Life on earth.
7" Single: Released Mar '82, on 1982, Deleted '86. Catalogue no: **MR 5**

RUNNING FOR COVER
Tracks: / Running for cover / Wayfaring stranger / This land of woe (Track on 12" version only).
7" Single: Released Oct '86, on RCA, by BMG Records (UK). Deleted '87. Catalogue no: **CARO 1**
12" Single: Released Oct '86, on RCA, by BMG Records (UK). Catalogue no: **CAROT 1**

SAY GOODBYE TO NO-ONE
Tracks: / Say goodbye to no-one / Twisted shapes of all my mistakes / Rainbow warrior (Track on 12" version only).
7" Single: Released May '86, on RCA, by BMG Records (UK). Catalogue no: **RCA 500**
12" Single: Released May '86, on RCA, by BMG Records (UK). Catalogue no: **RCAT 500**

Imposter

Biographical details: Imposter This alter ego of Elvis Costello was launched in 1983 for reasons of convenience. He had a song called *Pills and Soap* whose lyrics were pertinent to Britain's imminent General Election and he wanted to issue it as quickly as possible. Because there was a new Elvis Costello single called *Everyday I Write the Book* due soon and because his regular backing band, The Attractions, were not playing on *Pills and Soap*, it seemed more suitable to release the record under a pseudonym. It was also convenient in legal and business terms, because Costello's record label was in the midst of changing its distribution deal - the single was issued on the special Imp label. *Pills and Soap* did indeed enter the British chart in the week of the election. It peaked at no.16 but only remained on the Top 75 for four weeks because Elvis decreed that the song should only be available for a limited period. This ploy not only maximised the song's impact at that particular time, it also assured him of a higher chart position than he had been accustomed to during the preceeding 18 months.
A second Imposter single, *Peace In Our Time*, was released in 1984 - this was another brilliantly perceptive political piece, although it peaked at No. 48 on the Uk chart. This was the last we heard from the Imposter for a while, though Elvis Costello remained as prolific as ever. On *Pills and Soap* and *Peace In Our Time*, he was certainly the most instantly recognisable imposter in history! Bob Macdonald 5/1185.

PEACE IN OUR TIME
Tracks: / Peace in our time / Withered and died.
7" Single: Released May '84, on Imposter, Deleted '86. Catalogue no: **TRUCE 1**

PILLS & SOAP
Tracks: / Pills & soap.
7" Single: Released Aug '83, on Imp, by Demon Records. Deleted '85. Catalogue no: **IMP 002**
7" Single: Released Jun '83, on Imp, by Demon Records. Deleted '85. Catalogue no: **IMP 001**

Impression

MIGHTY REAL
Tracks: / Mighty real.
7" Single: Released Nov '85, on New Language, Deleted '87. Catalogue no: **LANG 001**
12" Single: Released Nov '85, on New Language, Deleted '87. Catalogue no: **12LANG 001**

Impressions (Group)

Biographical details: Impressions The classic line up of this American soul vocal group was Fred Cash, Sam Gooden and Curtis Mayfield.
The Impressions were formed in 1958 by the 15 year old Mayfield and an 18 year old singer called Jerry Butler. The group quickly achieved a No.11 hit on the US pop charts with the beautiful R&B ballad *For Your Precious Love*. Because the record was credited to Jerry Butler & The Impressions. Butler suddenly found himself with a high public profile while Mayfield was still a relatively unknown name. In the event, Jerry decided to launch a solo career while Curtis became the undisputed leader of the Impressions - both acts gave the soul world some of the greatest music of the Sixties.
Cash, Gooden and Mayfield began their run of hits at the end of 1961 with Curtis' song *Gypsy Woman*, which became a soul and pop standard and was later recorded by artists as diverse as Brian Hyland, Ry Cooder and Bobby Womack. Between 1963 and 1965 Mayfield's compositions for the Impressions managed to satisfy both black and white audiences in America, and they hit the US Top 20 with a consistently fine string of superb singles - these included *It's All Right*, *Talking about My Baby*, *I'm So Proud*, *Keep On Pushing*, *You Must Believe Me* pluss two great gospel pop offerings, *Amen*, and *People Get Ready*.
During the middle part of the Sixties, the Chicago based Impressions found it difficult to compete with the soul competition coming from Detroit (Tamla Motown) and Memphis (the Stax/Volt labels), and they lost their way a little. They returned to form in 1968 by addressing themselves to the black consciousness issues of the era - this resulted in a series of moving US hits (*We're a Winner*, *This Is My Country*, and *Choice of Colors*), which managed to convey the message of the civil rights movement while avoiding the biting sharpness of the Black Power spokesmen.
Mayfield quit the Impressions in 1970 and launched a successful solo career; he also had the endless satisfaction of seeing other artists continually achieving hits with his songs. Meanwhile the depleted Impressions struggled without their leader - Cash and Gooden were joined by Leroy Hutson, who was himself replaced in 1972 by Ralph Johnson and Reggie Torian. They eventually came up with a new hit in 1974, reaching the US no.17 with the aptly titled *Finally Got Myself Together*.
Incredibly, none of the classic Impressions tracks of the Sixties reached the British charts. This almost criminal lack of awareness by the UK public was finally rectified at the end of 1975, when the mediocre

IMMACULATE FOOLS - NOTHING MEANS NOTHING (Released on A & M)

First Impressions gave them a British No.16 single. During the late Seventies, however, they faded into obscurity on both sides of the Atlantic as the word 'soul' was temporarily replaced by the term 'disco' with which the Impressions had little affinity. Bob Macdonald 5/11/85.

FAN THE FIRE (SINGLE)
Tracks: / Fan the flame / For your precious love.
7" Single: Released Aug '81, on 20th Century, by 20th Century Records. Catalogue no: **TC 2500**
12" Single: Released Aug '81, on 20th Century, by 20th Century Records. Catalogue no: **TCD 2500**

FIRST IMPRESSIONS
Tracks: / First impressions.
7" Single: Released Nov '75, on Curtom, Deleted '78. Catalogue no: **K 16638**

Imprints

IT'S OVER
Tracks: / It's over / Free ourselves.
7" Single: Released Jun '82, on Jammy, by Jammy Records. Catalogue no: **JRS 821**

Impulse

ACT ON IMPULSE
Tracks: / Act on impulse / World in flames.
7" Single: Released Jan '83, on Polydor, by Polydor Ltd. Catalogue no: **POSP 552**
12" Single: Released Jan '83, on Polydor, by Polydor Ltd. Catalogue no: **POSPX 552**

PRIZE, THE
Tracks: / Prize, The.
7" Single: Released May '83, on Polydor, by Polydor Ltd. Catalogue no: **POSP 583**
12" Single: Released May '83, on Polydor, by Polydor Ltd. Catalogue no: **POSPX 583**

WILL YOU LOVE
Tracks: / Will you love (instrumental).
7" Single: Released Aug '86, on Willowdene, Deleted '87. Catalogue no: **WDR 1002**
12" Single: Released Aug '86, on Willowdene, Deleted '87. Catalogue no: **WDR 1002X**

IN2XS

LOVE WILL COME
Tracks: / Love will come.
7" Single: Released Aug '82, on Lightbeat, Catalogue no: **LIGHT 007**

MAMA DON'T DANCE
Tracks: / Mama don't dance / In the beginning.
7" Single: Released Apr '83, on Lightbeat, Catalogue no: **LIGHT 008**

In And Out

SPINE COCK
Tracks: / Spine cock.
7" Single: Released '88, on Constrictor, by Constrictor Records (Germany). Catalogue no: **COLL 010**

In Camera

Biographical details: This group consists of Dave Steiner on vocals, Andy Gray on guitar, Pete Moore on Bass and Jeff Willmott on drums..

FIN
Tracks: / Fin.
12" Single: Released Apr '82, on 4AD, by 4AD Records. Catalogue no: **BAD 205**

In Crowd (Group)

ADD A LITTLE LIGHT
Tracks: / Add a little light / Honey bee.
12" Single: Released Dec '82, on Smokey, Catalogue no: **SMJD 009**

BACK A YARD
Tracks: / Back a yard.
12" Single: Released May '83, on Revue, by Creole Records. Catalogue no: **REVD 001**

THAT'S HOW STRONG MY LOVE IS
Tracks: / That's how strong my love is.
7" Single: Released Apr '65, on Parlophone, by EMI Records. Deleted '67. Catalogue no: **R 5276**

In Embrace

INITIAL CARESS
Tracks: / Initial caress.
12" Single: Released May '82, on Glass, by Glass Records. Deleted '83. Catalogue no: **GLASS 019**

LIVING DAYLIGHTS
Tracks: / Living daylights, The / Blue beach.
7" Single: Released Sep '83, on Glass, by Glass Records. Deleted '83. Catalogue no: **GLASS 030**

PLAY IN LIGHT
Tracks: / Play in light / Sun brings smiles.

IN SWING - DON'T CALL MY NAME (Released on Inasense)

7" Single: Released Dec '82, on Glass, by Glass Records. Deleted Dec '85. Catalogue no: **GLASS 024**

ROOM UPSTAIRS, A
Tracks: / Room upstairs, A.
7" Single: Released Dec '86, on Glass, by Glass Records. Catalogue no: **GLASS 051**
12" Single: Released Dec '86, on Glass, by Glass Records. Catalogue no: **GLASS 12051**

SHOUTING IN CAFES
Tracks: / Shouting in cafes.
7" Single: Released Feb '85, on Cherry Red, by Cherry Red Records. Deleted '87. Catalogue no: **CHERRY 84**
12" Single: Released Feb '85, on Cherry Red, by Cherry Red Records. Deleted '87. Catalogue no: **12 CHERRY 84**

SUN BRINGS SMILES
Tracks: / Sun brings smiles.
7" Single: Released Feb '83, on Glass, by Glass Records. Deleted '83. Catalogue no: **GLASS 024**

THIS BRILLIANT EVENING
Tracks: / This brilliant evening.
7" Single: Released Oct '85, on Cherry Red, by Cherry Red Records. Catalogue no: **CHERRY 90**
12" Single: Released Oct '85, on Cherry Red, by Cherry Red Records. Catalogue no: **12 CHERRY 90**

WHAT'S GOT INTO ME
Tracks: / What's got into me.
7" Single: Released Jul '87, on Glass, by Glass Records. Catalogue no: **GLAEP 106**

YOU'RE HEAVEN SCENT
Tracks: / You're heaven scent / Fluid.
7" Single: Released Mar '84, on Glass, by Glass Records. Deleted Jan '89. Catalogue no: **GLASS 034**
12" Single: Released Mar '84, on Glass, by Glass Records. Catalogue no: **GLASS 12034**

In Excelsis

CARNIVAL OF DAMOCLES
Tracks: / Carnival of the gullible / Sword, The / Vowels (initiation) / One man's heaven / Carnival of Damocles.
12" Single: Released Nov '83, on Jungle, by Jungle Records. Catalogue no: **JUNG 9**

CREEPS IN THE TREES
Tracks: / Creeps in the trees.
12" Single: Released 13 Jun '85, on In Ex, Catalogue no: **INEX 001/12**

LADDER OF LUST
Tracks: / Ladder of lust.
12" Single: Released Jun '84, on Jungle, by Jungle Records. Catalogue no: **JUNG 13**

ONE DAY
Tracks: / One day.
7" Single: Released Oct '84, on In Ex, Catalogue no: **INEX 1**
12" Single: Released Oct '84, on In Ex, Catalogue no: **INEX 1/12**

In Hill House

SANCTUARY
Tracks: / Sanctuary / Never again.
7" Single: Released Sep '84, on EMI, by EMI Records. Catalogue no: **EMI 5494**
7" Single: Released Mar '85, on Seyscan, Catalogue no: **IHH 001**
12" Single: Released Sep '84, on EMI, by EMI Records. Catalogue no: **12EMI 5494**

In Motion (Group)

AINT NOBODY
Tracks: / Aint nobody.
12" Single: Released Apr '89, on Blue Chip, by Blue Chip Records. Catalogue no: **BLUECHIP 15T**

In Pursuit Of

I'M AN ADULT NOW
Tracks: / I'm an adult now / Ten fingers.
7" Single: Released Mar '89, on Chrysalis, by Chrysalis Records. Catalogue no: **CHS 3316**
12" Single: Released Mar '89, on Chrysalis, by Chrysalis Records. Catalogue no: **12 CHS 3316**

In Sotto Voce

IN SOTTO VOCE
CD 5": Released Apr '89, on Antler, by Antler Records (Belgium). Catalogue no: **ANT 102CD**
12" Single: Released Jun '88, on Antler, by Antler Records (Belgium). Catalogue no: **ANT 084**

In Swing

DON'T YOU CALL MY NAME (see panel above)
Tracks: / Reason why / Come on / Don't you call my name.
7" Single: Released Mar '86, on Inasense, by Inasense Records. Catalogue no: **ISWG 1**

In The Key Of E...

IN THE KEY OF E
CD 5": Released Jan '89, on Desire, by Desire Records. Catalogue no: **LUVCD 1**

In The Nursery

COMPULSION
Tracks: / Compulsion.
12" Single: Released Jul '87, on Sweatbox, by Sweatbox Records. Catalogue no: **SOX 27**

DEUS EX MACHINA
Tracks: / Deus ex machina.
12" Single: Released Mar '85, on New European, Catalogue no: **BADVC 55**

TEMPER
Tracks: / Temper.
12" Single: Released Nov '85, on Sweatbox, by Sweatbox Records. Catalogue no: **SOX 008**

TRINITY
Tracks: / Trinity.
12" Single: Released Jun '87, on Sweatbox, by Sweatbox Records. Catalogue no: **SOX 19**

WITNESS TO A SCREAM
Tracks: / Witness to a scream.
7" Single: Released Mar '84, on Paragon, Catalogue no: **VIRTUE 5**

In Tua Nua

ALL I WANTED
Tracks: / All I wanted (On all versions) / Word punishment, The (On all versions) / (Holy hour) at the beggar's bush (CD & 12" only) / Inch of an acre, An (CD only).
CD 5": Released Aug '88, on Virgin, by Virgin Records. Catalogue no: **VSCD 1072**
7" Single: Released Apr '88, on Virgin, by Virgin Records. Catalogue no: **VS 1072**
12" Single: Released Apr '88, on Virgin, by Virgin Records. Catalogue no: **VST 1072**

DON'T FEAR ME NOW (KISS YOU ONCE MORE)
Tracks: / Don't fear me now (kiss you once more) (On all versions) / Everybody's darling (On all versions) / See no evil (On 12" only) / Burning of the midnight lamp (On 12" only) / Boys keep swinging (On CD only) / All I wanted (On CD only).
CD 5": Released '88, on Virgin, by Virgin Records. Catalogue no: **VSCD 1091**
7" Single: Released Jun '88, on Virgin, by Virgin Records. Catalogue no: **VS 1091**
12" Single: Released Jun '88, on Virgin, by Virgin Records. Catalogue no: **VST 1091**

HEAVEN CAN WAIT
Tracks: / Heaven can wait / Belt me / Man, The (12" only).
7" Single: Released Mar '87, on Virgin, by Virgin Records. Deleted May '88. Catalogue no: **VS 939**
12" Single: Released Mar '87, on Virgin, by Virgin Records. Catalogue no: **VS 939-12**

SEVEN INTO THE SEA
Tracks: / Ballad of Irish love / Seven into the sea.
7" Single: Released Jun '86, on Virgin, by Virgin Records. Deleted '89. Catalogue no: **VS 855**
12" Single: Released Jun '86, on Virgin, by Virgin Records. Deleted '89. Catalogue no: **VS 855-12**

SOMEBODY TO LOVE
Tracks: / Somebody to love.
7" Single: Released Apr '85, on Island, by Island Records. Catalogue no: **IS 223**
12" Single: Released Apr '85, on Island, by Island Records. Catalogue no: **12IS 223**

TAKE MY HAND
Tracks: / Take my hand.
7" Single: Released Jan '85, on Island, by Island Records. Catalogue no: **IS 211**
12" Single: Released Nov '84, on Island, by Island Records. Deleted Jul '87. Catalogue no: **12IS 211**

WHEEL OF EVIL
Tracks: / Wheel of evil / Innocent and the honest ones, The (live) / Heaven can wait (live) (on 12" & CD only) / Molloy (on CD only).
Note: Wheel of Evil is the single from this young Irish band who are poised for chart success. The b-side is a live version of a popular album track"The Innocent & The Honest Ones", & the 12" b-side has another live recording of one of their earliest Virgin singles "Heaven Can Wait".
7" Single: Released 17 Oct '88, on Virgin, by Virgin Records. Catalogue no: **VS 1118**
12" Single: Released 17 Oct '88, on Virgin, by Virgin Records. Catalogue no: **VST 1118**
CD 3": Released '88, on Virgin, by Virgin Records. Catalogue no: **VSCD 1118**

In Two A Circle

RISE
Tracks: / Rise.
12" Single: Released Aug '86, on Temple Records, by Temple Records (2). Catalogue no: **ARC 001**

In Vogue

SPIES ON THE WIRE
Tracks: / Spies on the wire.
7" Single: Released Sep '84, on Unit, Catalogue no: **TRANS 100**

Inane

MORE MUSIC
Special: Released Oct '83, on Subway Organisation, Deleted '89. Catalogue no: **WANT 7**

Inca Babies

BIG JUGULAR
Tracks: / Big jugular.
12" Single: Released May '84, on Black Lagoon, by Black Lagoon Records. Deleted '88. Catalogue no: **INC 003**

BUSTERS ON FIRE
Tracks: / Busters on fire.
7" Single: Released 19 Oct '87, on Constrictor, by Constrictor Records (Germany). Catalogue no: **CON 00027**

GRUNT CADILLAC HOTEL
Tracks: / Grunt cadillac hotel.
7" Single: Released Mar '84, on Black Lagoon, by Black Lagoon Records. Deleted '88. Catalogue no: **INC 002**

INTERIOR, THE
Tracks: / Interior, The.
7" Single: Released Nov '83, on Black Lagoon, by Black Lagoon Records. Catalogue no: **ISC 001**

JUDGE, THE
Tracks: / Judge, The.
7" Single: Released Aug '84, on Black Lagoon, by Black Lagoon Records. Deleted '88. Catalogue no: **INC 004**
12" Single: Released Jun '85, on Black Lagoon, by Black Lagoon Records. Deleted '88. Catalogue no: **INCT 004**

SPLATTER BALLISTICS COP
Tracks: / Splatter Ballistics Cop / Splatter Ballistics Cop (version).
7" Single: Released Mar '86, on Black Lagoon, by Black Lagoon Records. Deleted '88. Catalogue no: **INC 009**
12" Single: Released Mar '86, on Black Lagoon, by Black Lagoon Records. Deleted '88. Catalogue no: **INC 009T**

SURFIN' IN LOCUST LAND
Tracks: / Surfin' in locust land.
12" Single: Released Sep '85, on Black Lagoon, by Black Lagoon Records. Catalogue no: **INC 007**

Inca Rhodes

HIDE AWAY
Tracks: / Hide away.
7" Single: Released '88, on Silk, Catalogue no: **SK 001**

Incantation

Biographical details: Incantation This British instrumental group consists of Forbes Henderson, Tony Hinnigan, Simon Rogers, Chris Swithinbank and Mike Taylor. Formed in 1982, Incantation enjoyed some left field pop success in early '83 with their single and album *Cacharpaya*. The LP, sub-titled *Panpipes of the Andes*, reached the Uk Top 10 while the irresistebly catchy single peaked at No.12. The latter featured a striking climax, in which the same tune was repeated over and over again with a faster and faster temp, leaving the listener almost breathless. Such a record was normally the fodder of folk clubs rather than pop charts, and its suprise success recalled the hitmaking achievements of East of Eden's *Jig A Jig* (1971) and Gheorghe Zamfir's panpipe offering *Doina De Jale* (1976).
In late 1983 Incantation released the LP *Dance of the Flames*, which did not repeat the success of its predecessor, but the band was sufficiently established to earn a good living via live performances. They were certainly the highlight of the 1983 Goodwood Folk Festival. Bob Macdonald 5/11/85.

CACHARPAYA (ANDES PUMPSA DAESI)
Tracks: / Cacharpaya / On the wing of a condor / On the wing of the condor.
7" Single: Released Sep '82, on Beggars Banquet, by Beggars Banquet Records. Deleted Jun '87. Catalogue no: **BEG 84**
12" Single: Released Sep '82, on Beggars Banquet, by Beggars Banquet Records. Deleted Jan '88. Catalogue no: **BEG 84T**

CANARIOUS
Tracks: / Canarious.
7" Single: Released Dec '83, on Beggars Banquet, by Beggars Banquet Records. Deleted '85. Catalogue no: **BEG 102**
7" Single: Released Nov '84, on Coda, by Coda Records. Catalogue no: **CODS 9**
12" Single: Released Dec '83, on Beggars Banquet, by Beggars Banquet Records. Deleted '87. Catalogue no: **BEG 102T**

ON EARTH AS IT IS IN HEAVEN
Tracks: / On earth as it is in heaven (Theme from the mission) / Canto del agua.
7" Single: Released Nov '86, on Filmtrax, by Filmtrax Records. Catalogue no: **FRAME 103**

PIPE DANCE
Tracks: / Pipe dance.
7" Single: Released Dec '84, on Beggars Banquet, by Beggars Banquet Records. Deleted '88. Catalogue no: **CODS 9**

SCARBOROUGH FAIR
Tracks: / Scarborough Fair.
7" Single: Released Oct '87, on Hiam, by Hiam Records. Catalogue no: **HIAM 106**

SIKURIADES
Tracks: / Sikuriades / Italique.
7" Single: Released Mar '83, on Beggars Banquet, by Beggars Banquet Records. Deleted Jan '88. Catalogue no: **BEG 89**
12" Single: Released Mar '83, on Beggars Banquet, by Beggars Banquet Records. Deleted '88. Catalogue no: **BEGT 89**

Ince, Jan

CATCHEE MONKEY
Tracks: / Catchee monkey / Room in your heart.
7" Single: Released Apr '87, on Zapu, by Priority Records. Deleted Nov '87. Catalogue no: **ZAPU 1**
12" Single: Released Apr '87, on Zapu, by Priority Records. Deleted Nov '87. Catalogue no: **12 ZAPU 1**

Inchequin

CITY ON THE LAGAN
Tracks: / Clove rock / City on the Lagan.
7" Single: Released Jul '87, on Mint, by Emerald Records. Deleted '88. Catalogue no: **CHEW 112**

Incognito

Biographical details: Incognito This British band consisted of Jean Paul 'Bluey' Maunick and Paul 'Tubs' Williams plus a loose assemblage of flexible friends including Ganiyu 'Gee' Bello, Ray Carless, Jeff Dunn, Vin Gordon and Peter Hinds.
Incognito were a short lived spinoff of the successful London based disco/soul/jazz band Light Of The World. Having illuminated many a dance floor with such hits as *Swingin'* and *London Town* during 1979-80, Light Of The World spawned two subsidiary combos, the other being Beggar & Co. The first Incognito single was in fact a demo, but it was released commercially after receiving strong club support - *Parisienne Girl* managed to reach No.73 on the UK pop chart. Their subsequent singles did not make the charts, but the band reached the UK No.28 position with their only LP *Jazz Funk* (April 1981). This title summed up their music at a time when this fusion of styles was steadily gaining in popularity.
After the end of Incognito, Maunick and Williams formed a jazzier and less successful outfit called The Warriors. In 1985 Williams became a member of The Team, a new funk conglomeration assembled by Gee Bello. Bob Macdonald 5/11/85.

INCOGNITO
Tracks: / Incognito / Shine on.
7" Single: Released Jun '81, on Ensign, by Ensign Records. Deleted '82. Catalogue no: **ENY 211**
12" Single: Released Jun '81, on Ensign, by Ensign Records. Deleted '83. Catalogue no: **ENYT 211**

NORTH LONDON BOY
Tracks: / North London boy / Second chance.
7" Single: Released Nov '81, on Ensign, by Ensign Records. Deleted '82. Catalogue no: **ENY 221**
12" Single: Released Nov '81, on Ensign, by Ensign Records. Deleted '83. Catalogue no: **ENYT 221**

PARISIENNE GIRL
Tracks: / Parisienne girl.
7" Single: Released Nov '80, on Ensign, by Ensign Records. Deleted '83. Catalogue no: **ENY 44**

Incredible Blondes

WHERE DO I STAND
Tracks: / Where do I stand.
7" Single: Released Feb '87, on No Strings, Catalogue no: **NOSP 3**

Incredible Mr.Freeze

BACK TO THE SCENE OF THE CRIME
Tracks: / Frozen theme / Back to the scene of the crime.
7" Single: Released Aug '86, on London Records, by London Records. Catalogue no: **LON 112**
12" Single: Released Aug '86, on London Records, by London Records. Catalogue no: **LONX 112**

Incredible O'Reilly

BIRTH OF MAUDIE
Tracks: / Birth of Maudie, The / An Chuileann'.
7" Single: Released Sep '89, on CBS, by CBS Records. Catalogue no: **EGOR 1**

Incredible Zombie

MACHINE STOPS
Tracks: / Machine stops.
7" Single: Released Oct '87, on Abstract, by Abstract Sounds. Catalogue no: **ABS 046**
12" Single: Released Oct '87, on Abstract, by Abstract Sounds. Catalogue no: **12 BS 046**

In-D

BASTION IN-D STRESS
Tracks: / Bastion In-D stress.
12" Single: Released Jun '88, on Subway, by Subway Records. Catalogue no: **SUB 028**

BEAT IN-D DREAM
Tracks: / Beat IN-D dream.
CD 5": Released '89, on Subway, by Subway Records. Catalogue no: **SUB 042CD**
12" Single: Released '88, on Subway, by Subway Records. Catalogue no: **SUB 042**

VIRGIN IN-D SKY'S
Tracks: / Virgin In-D sky's.
12" Single: Released Apr '88, on Subway, by Subway Records. Catalogue no: **SUB 014**

Indeep

Biographical details: Indeep *Last Night A DJ Saved My Life*, was one of the most ludicrous but irritatingly infectious disco records ever made. It scorched the dancefloors on both sides of the Atlantic in early 1983, and gave this New York vocal duo (one guy, one girl) a No.13 hit on the UK pop chart. The whole silly shebang was written and co-produced by Michael Cleveland, who was shrewd enough to realise that a single which eulogised disc jockeys was sure to receive many plays! Subsequent records, however, torpedoed Indeep into the realms of obscurity and no DJ seemed to be willing to save them. Bob Macdonald 5/11/85.

GIRL'S GOT SOUL
Tracks: / Girl's got soul / Night the boy learned to dance.
7" Single: Released Jun '84, on Beckett, Deleted '86. Catalogue no: **BKS 12**
12" Single: Released Jun '84, on Beckett, Deleted '86. Catalogue no: **BKSL 12**

LAST NIGHT A DJ SAVED MY LIFE
Tracks: / Last night a DJ saved my life / D.J. delight.
7" Single: Released Jan '83, on Sound Of New York (USA), by Sound Of New York Records(USA). Deleted '85. Catalogue no: **SNY 1**
12" Single: Released Nov '87, on Deejay (USA), Catalogue no: **BLUE 008**
12" Single: Released Sep '87, on RCA (Australia), Catalogue no: **TDS 124**
12" Single: Released Jan '83, on Sound Of New York (USA), by Sound Of New York Records(USA). Deleted '85. Catalogue no: **SNYL 1**

RECORD KEEPS SPINNING
Tracks: / Record keeps spinning.
7" Single: Released Jan '84, on Beckett, Deleted '86. Catalogue no: **BKS 11**
12" Single: Released Jan '84, on Beckett, Deleted '86. Catalogue no: **BKSL 11**

WHEN BOY'S TALK
Tracks: / When boy's talk.
7" Single: Released Apr '83, on Sound Of New York (USA), by Sound Of New York Records(USA). Deleted '85. Catalogue no: **SNY 3**
12" Single: Released Apr '83, on Sound Of New York (USA), by Sound Of New York Records(USA). Deleted '85. Catalogue no: **SNYL 3**

Inder, Paul

CHELSEA GIRL
Tracks: / Chelsea girl / Hell's angels.
7" Single: Released Nov '83, on Hippodrome, by Hippodrome Records. Catalogue no: **HIP 1**
12" Single: Released Nov '83, on Hippodrome, by Hippodrome Records. Catalogue no: **12 HIP 1**

DON'T SAY GOODNIGHT
Tracks: / Don't say goodnight / Twisted roots.
7" Single: Released Apr '84, on Hippodrome, by Hippodrome Records. Catalogue no: **HIPPO 7**

EDIT
Tracks: / Edit.
7" Single: Released Feb '82, on Electro, Catalogue no: **ES 3**

Index

GIVE ME A SIGN
Tracks: / Give me a sign.
7" Single: Released Aug '89, on Exit, Catalogue no: **LIN 030765**

I'M GONNA GET YOU
Tracks: / I'm gonna get you / Computer love.
7" Single: Released Feb '80, on DJM, Deleted Feb '83. Catalogue no: **DJS 10933**

LOVE YOU'VE BEEN FAKIN'
Tracks: / Love you've been fakin'.
7" Single: Released Aug '82, on Excaliber, by Red Bus Records. Deleted '88. Catalogue no: **EXC 521**
12" Single: Released Aug '82, on Excaliber, by Red Bus Records. Deleted '88. Catalogue no: **EXCL 521**

STARLIGHT
Tracks: / Starlight / Virgin.
7" Single: Released Sep '81, on Record Shack, by Record Shack Records. Catalogue no: **SHACK 8**

Indian Givers

FAKE I.D.
Tracks: / Fake I.D. / It's a wonderful life / Suffocate yourself (12" only).
10" single: Released 24 Jul '89, on Virgin, by Virgin Records. Catalogue no: **VSA 1199**
Cassingle: Released 24 Jul '89, on Virgin, by Virgin Records. Catalogue no: **VSC 1199**
7" Single: Released 24 Jul '89, on Virgin, by Virgin Records. Catalogue no: **VS 1199**
12" Single: Released 24 Jul '89, on Virgin, by Virgin Records. Catalogue no: **VST 1199**
CD 3": Released 24 Jul '89, on Virgin, by Virgin Records. Catalogue no: **VSCD 1199**

HATCHECK GIRL
Tracks: / Hatcheck girl / Some kind of mover / Hate song, The.
7" Single: Released 5 Jun '89, on Virgin, by Virgin Records. Catalogue no: **VS 1187**
12" Single: Released 5 Jun '89, on Virgin, by Virgin Records. Catalogue no: **VST 1187**
CD 3": Released 5 Jun '89, on Virgin, by Virgin Records. Catalogue no: **VSCD 1187**

Indian Monks

PAPPADUM PAPPADUM
Tracks: / Pappadum pappadum.
7" Single: Released Jul '83, on Battersea, Catalogue no: **BATT 4**
12" Single: Released Jul '83, on Battersea, Catalogue no: **BATTL 4**

Indian Summer

JUST LIKE LOVERS
Tracks: / Just like lovers / Shattered and died.
CD 5": Released Aug '89, on Total, Catalogue no: **CDSTRAD 1**
7" Single: Released Aug '89, on Total, Catalogue no: **STRAD 1**
12" Single: Released Aug '89, on Total, Catalogue no: **12STRAD 1**

Indians In Moscow

BIG WHEEL
Tracks: / Big wheel.
7" Single: Released 13 Jun '85, on Kennick, by Kennick Records. Deleted '87. Catalogue no: **KNK 1005**
12" Single: Released 13 Jun '85, on Kennick, by Kennick Records. Deleted '87. Catalogue no: **KENK 001**

I WISH I HAD
Tracks: / I wish I had / Slide.
7" Single: Released Mar '84, on Kennick, by Kennick Records. Deleted '87. Catalogue no: **KNK 1003**
12" Single: Released 14 Jun '85, on Kennick, by Kennick Records. Deleted '87. Catalogue no: **KNK 1003T**

JACK PELTER & HIS SEX-CHANGE CHICKEN
Tracks: / Jack Pelter & his sex-change chicken / Salt.
7" Single: Released Jun '84, on Kennick, by Kennick Records. Deleted '87. Catalogue no: **KNK 1004**
12" Single: Released Jun '84, on Kennick, by Kennick Records. Deleted '87. Catalogue no: **KNK 1004T**

NAUGHTY MIRANDA
Tracks: / Naughty Miranda.
7" Single: Released 14 Jun '85, on Kennick, by Kennick Records. Deleted '87. Catalogue no: **KNK 1002**
12" Single: Released 14 Jun '85, on Kennick, by Kennick Records. Deleted '87. Catalogue no: **KNK 1002T**

Indicators

MODERN LOVE
Tracks: / Modern love / Strange kind of lady.
7" Single: Released May '80, on Gem, Deleted May '85. Catalogue no: **GEMS 31**

Indifferent Dance

FLIGHT OF PURSUIT
Tracks: / Flight of pursuit.
7" Single: Released Oct '81, on Centre, Catalogue no: **CENTRE 1**

Indigo Girls

CLOSER TO FINE
Tracks: / Closer to fine / History of us / Center stage (Only on 12" and CD single.) / Mona Lisas & mad hatters (Only on 12" (654907 8)) / American tune (Only on 12" (654907 8)).
CD 5": Released Jul '89, on Epic, by CBS Records. Catalogue no: **655135 2**

CD 5": Released Jun '89, on Epic, by CBS Records. Catalogue no: **654907 2**
7" Single: Released Jun '89, on Epic, by CBS Records. Catalogue no: **654907 7**
12" Single: Released Jul '89, on Epic, by CBS Records. Catalogue no: **654907 8**
12" Single: Released Jun '89, on Epic, by CBS Records. Catalogue no: **654907 6**

Indio

HARD SUN
Tracks: / Hard sun / Hard sun (Acoustic version).
CD 5": Released 18 Sep '89, on A&M, by A&M Records. Catalogue no: **CDEE 521**
7" Single: Released 18 Sep '89, on A&M, by A&M Records. Catalogue no: **AM 521**

Indoor Games

ALL OF YOUR LIES
Tracks: / All of your lies / Take the party down.
7" Single: Released May '83, on Holyrood, by REL Records. Deleted '87. Catalogue no: **HOLLY 003**

Industry

STATE OF THE NATION
Tracks: / State of the nation.
7" Single: Released Mar '84, on Capitol, by EMI Records. Deleted '88. Catalogue no: **CL 321**

Infa Riot

Biographical details: Infa Riot *Still Out of Order* gave these raucous rockers a one off entry on the UK album chart, reaching No.42 in 1982. The lads had risen to infamy during th preceding year via the British Oi! Movement, a post-punk wave of riotous rock bands whose publicity outweighed their commercial success. The singles *Kids of the 80's* and *The Winner*, were released before Infa Riot transmogrified themselves into The Infas and gave us *Sound and Fury*. Bob Macdonald 5/11/85.

KIDS OF THE 80'S
Tracks: / Kids of the 80's.
7" Single: Released Jul '82, on Secret, by Secret Records. Catalogue no: **SHH 117**

WINNER, THE
Tracks: / Winner, The / Schools out.
7" Single: Released Jul '82, on Secret, by Secret Records. Deleted May '88. Catalogue no: **SHH 133**

Infaction

LISTEN TO THE WISE MEN
Tracks: / Listen to the wise men.
7" Single: Released Jun '85, on Lambs To The Slaughter, by Prism Records. Catalogue no: **WISE 22**

Infas

SOUND AND FURY
7" Single: Released Mar '84, on Island, by Island Records. Catalogue no: **PAN 101**

Infinity

GRAND MIXER CUTS IT UP
Tracks: / Grand mixer cuts it up.
12" Single: Released Jul '83, on Celluloid (USA), by Celluloid Records (USA). Catalogue no: **CYZ 105**

Influence

NO SURVIVORS
Tracks: / No survivors.
7" Single: Released May '83, on Influence, Catalogue no: **INF 1**

Information Society

WHAT'S ON YOUR MIND (PURE ENERGY)
Tracks: / What's on your mind (radio edit) (7' only) / What's on your mind (club radio edit) (7" only) / What's on your mind (club mix) (12" only) / What's on your mind (dub mix) (12" only).
CD 5": Released Oct '88, on London Records, by London Records. Deleted May '89. Catalogue no: **LONCD 211**
7" Single: Released Oct '88, on London Records, by London Records. Deleted May '89. Catalogue no: **LON 211**
12" Single: Released Oct '88, on London Records, by London Records. Deleted May '89. Catalogue no: **LONX 211**

Ingram

Biographical details: Ingram The seductive single *Smoothin' Groovin'* gave this all male American soul band a one-off Uk chart entry in June 1983, reaching No.56. The track received its exposure via the clubs and garnered little radio airplay. Subsequent Ingram singles, such as *We Like To Do It* and *When You're Hot You're Hot*, were equally sexy but not so successful. Bob Macdonald 5/11/85.

SMOOTHIN' GROOVIN'
Tracks: / Smoothin' groovin'.
7" Single: Released Jun '83, on Streetwave, Deleted '85. Catalogue no: **WAVE 3**

WHEN YOU'RE HOT YOU'RE HOT
Tracks: / When you're hot you're hot.
7" Single: Released May '84, on Other End, Catalogue no: **OET 1**

WITH YOU
Tracks: / With you.
7" Single: Released Jun '84, on Other End, Catalogue no: **7 OET 2**
12" Single: Released Jun '84, on Other End, Catalogue no: **12 OET 2**

Ingram Inc

HOUSE
Tracks: / House.
7" Single: Released Jun '88, on Champion, by Champion Records. Catalogue no: **CHAMP 71**
12" Single: Released Jun '88, on Champion, by Champion Records. Catalogue no: **CHAMP 1271**

Ingram, James

ALWAYS
Tracks: / Always (Instrumental).
7" Single: Released Jul '86, on Qwest (USA), by Qwest Records (USA). Deleted Jun '87. Catalogue no: **W 8669**
12" Single: Released Jul '86, on Qwest (USA), by Qwest Records (USA). Deleted Jun '87. Catalogue no: **W 8669T**

BETTER WAY'
Tracks: / Better way.
7" Single: Released Aug '87, on MCA, by MCA Records. Catalogue no: **MCA 1182**
12" Single: Released Aug '87, on MCA, by MCA Records. Catalogue no: **MCAT 1182**

IT'S REAL (SINGLE)
Tracks: / It's real / Aren't you tired.
CD 5": Released Jun '89, on Warner Bros., by WEA Records. Catalogue no: **W 2975CD**
Cassingle: Released Jun '89, on Warner Bros., by WEA Records. Catalogue no: **W 2975C**
7" Single: Released Jun '89, on Warner Bros., by WEA Records. Catalogue no: **W 2975**
12" Single: Released Jun '89, on Warner Bros., by WEA Records. Catalogue no: **W 2975T**

IT'S YOUR NIGHT (SINGLE)
Tracks: / It's your night / She loves me.
7" Single: Released Mar '85, on Warner Bros., by WEA Records. Catalogue no: **W 9026**
12" Single: Released Mar '85, on Warner Bros., by WEA Records. Catalogue no: **W 9026T**

PARTY ANIMAL
Tracks: / Party animal.
7" Single: Released Oct '83, on Qwest (USA), by Qwest Records (USA). Catalogue no: **W 9493**
12" Single: Released Oct '83, on Qwest (USA), by Qwest Records (USA). Catalogue no: **W 9493T**

YAH MO BE THERE
Tracks: / Yah mo B there.
7" Single: Released Jan '85, on Qwest (USA), by Qwest Records (USA). Catalogue no: **W 9394**

Ingram, Johnny

CAN I TAKE YOU HOME TONIGHT?
Tracks: / Can I take you home tonight.
7" Single: Released Sep '85, on Mirror (USA), by Mirror Records Inc.(USA). Catalogue no: **BUTCH 2**
12" Single: Released Sep '85, on Mirror (USA), by Mirror Records Inc.(USA). Catalogue no: **12BUTCH 2**

Ingrid

EASTER PARADE
Tracks: / Easter parade / Boy.
7" Single: Released Apr '82, on Polydor, by Polydor Ltd. Deleted Apr '85. Catalogue no: **POSP 429**
12" Single: Released Apr '82, on Polydor, by Polydor Ltd. Deleted Apr '85. Catalogue no: **POSPX 429**

Inheritance

I STILL LOVE YOU
Tracks: / I still love you.
7" Single: Released Nov '83, on Mynah, Catalogue no: **SCS 831**

Ink Spots

Biographical details: Ink Spots The classic line up of this American vocal group was Charles Fuqua, Orville 'Hoppy' Jones, Billy Kenny and Ivory 'Deek' Watson.
The Ink Spots were originally formed in New York in 1935. They started life as a street corner group called The Percolating Puppies, but soon ralsed that such a silly name would be a handicap if their career was to progress. As The Ink Spots their career cruised into top gear in 1939 when they achieved their first major disc success with *I I Didn't Care*. This introduced the world to sthe group's pioneering vocal style which would evantually become known as doo-wop. The Ink Spots laid down a formula - tenor, baritone and bass voices singing in polished harmony behind the lead - that was imitated by black vocal groups throughout the Forties and Fifties. ill Kenny and Co. thus helped to lay the foundations of rhythm and blues and soul music. One of the best known numbers in their repertoire was *My Prayer* - this became a smash hit in 1956 for The Platters, who were directly influenced by the Spots. Hoppy Jones' bass lines were the prototype used by such acts as The Coasters and The Drifters and parodied in Johnny Cymbal's 1963 hit *Mr Bass Man*.
The Ink Spots teamed up with the great Ella Fitzgerald in 1944 to record *Into Ech Life Some Rain Must Fall*, which proved to be a million-selling combination. Jones' death in November 1944 robbed the quartet of their most distinctive voice; but they managed to continue scoring hits for many years, including *To Each His Own* (1946), *The Gypsy* (1946) and *Melody of Love* (a UK No.10 hit in 1955). The subsequent deaths of Fequa and Watson meant that the Ink Spots' name passed gracefully into the past tense, but their influence lived on. Via their worldwide concerts and their cameo appearance in Hollywood movies, they had introduced black music to a whole new mass white audience. Bob MacDonald 5/11/85.

BEAUTIFUL EXPERIENCE
Tracks: / Beautiful experience / Love's got a hold on you.
7" Single: Released Nov '80, on Splash, by Splash Records. Deleted '83. Catalogue no: **SP 18**

MELODY OF LOVE
Tracks: / Melody of love.
7" Single: Released Mar '55, on Parlophone, by EMI Records. Deleted '58. Catalogue no: **MSP 6152**

Inman, John

Biographical details: Inman, John This British actor came to fame as Mr Humphries the gay shop assistant in Are You Being Served, one of the UK's most popular TV sitcoms of the Seventies. He achieved a one off UK chart entry in late 1975 with his cash in single *Are You Being Served Sir*, which reached No.39. This record made maximum use of his catchphrase 'I'm Free', a thinly veiled reference to the character's homosexual availability. Inman's follow up single did not reach the British charts, but became a favourite comedy item on radio shows over the following years - *Teddy Bears' Picnic* was a saucy revival of the favourite children's song. Bob MacDonald 5/11/85.

ARE YOU BEING SERVED SIR?
Tracks: / Are you being served sir?.
7" Single: Released Oct '75, on DJM, Deleted '78. Catalogue no: **DJS 602**

TEDDY BEAR'S PICNIC
Tracks: / Teddy bear's picnic / Sun signs.
7" Single: Released '88, on DJM, Catalogue no: **DJS 10645**

Inmates

Biographical details: Inmates This British rock band conisted of Ben Donnelly, Peter Gunn, Bill Hurley, Tony Oliver and Jim Russell.
The Inmates' debut album *First Offence* was released in January 1980, and contained two tracks that had previously received substantial airplay as singles *Dirty Water* was a remake of The Standells' 1966 US hit but with the lyrics ammended to apply to London; *The Walk* gave th Inmates their only UK chart entry, reaching No.36 at the end of '79.
The group's raw rhythm and blues sound was reminiscent of Doctor Feelgood and the other pub rock bands which had emerged during the preceding few years. The Inmates' success might have lasted longer if it had happened a little earlier but, in the event, they faded from view soon after the release of their second LP *Shot In The Dark*. Despite his success with Shakin' Stevens, producer Stuart Colman was unable to rescue their third album *Heatwave In Alaska* from oblivion. Bob Macdonald 6/11/85.

HEARTBEAT
Tracks: / Heartbeat / Tallahassie lassie.
7" Single: Released Apr '81, on Radar, Catalogue no: **ADA 63**

LOVE GOT ME
Tracks: / Love got me / If time would turn backwards.
7" Single: Released Feb '80, on Radar, Deleted Feb '85. Catalogue no: **ADA 50**

ME AND THE BOYS
Tracks: / Me and the boys.
7" Single: Released Sep '81, on WEA, by WEA Records. Catalogue no: **K 18850**

SHE'S GONE ROCKIN'
Tracks: / She's gone rockin' / Long distance man.
7" Single: Released Apr '82, on WEA, by WEA Records. Deleted Apr '85. Catalogue no: **K 19131**

SO MUCH IN LOVE
Tracks: / So much in love / Tell me what's wrong.
7" Single: Released Sep '80, on Radar, Deleted Sep '83. Catalogue no: **ADA 59**

STOP IT BABY
Tracks: / Stop it baby / Sweet rain.
7" Single: Released Nov '80, on Radar, Deleted '83. Catalogue no: **ADA 61**

THREE TIMES LOSER
Tracks: / Three times loser / If time could turn backwards.
7" Single: Released Apr '80, on Radar, Deleted Apr '83. Catalogue no: **ADA 53**

WALK, THE
Tracks: / Walk, The.

7" Single: Released Dec '79, on Radar, Deleted '82. Catalogue no: **ADA 47**

INNER CITY - DO YOU LOVE WHAT YOU FEEL (Released on 10 Records)

INNER CITY - GOOD LIFE (Released on 10 Records)

Inna Feelings

BOYFRIEND
Tracks: / Boyfriend.
12" Single: Released May '85, on Paradise, Catalogue no: **PDIS 511**

Inner Circle

Biographical details: Inner Circle Had it not been for Jacob Miller's tragic death in a car crash in March 1980, this Jamaican reggae band might have followed fellow countryman Bob Marley into the realms of international stardom. The lads issued their debut LP *Rock The Boat*, in 1974, and consolidated their position in their homeland with a series of well-received albums during the rest of the Seventies. In 1979 they began to break through in Britain with a pair of modest chart singles, *Everything Is Great* (No.37) and *Stop Breaking My Heart* (No.50).
When Miller passed away, the Jamaican government declared 24 hours' national mourning. The restof the band struggled bravely on without their leader, issuing a couple of albums in the early Eighties. Bob MacDonald 6/11/85.

EVERYTHING IS GREAT
Tracks: / Everything is great.
7" Single: Released Feb '79, on Island, by Island Records. Deleted '82. Catalogue no: **WIP 6472**

GROOVIN' IN LOVE
Tracks: / One way / Groovin' in love.
12" Single: Released Jul '86, on Charm, by Charm Records. Catalogue no: **CRT 3**

STOP BREAKING MY HEART
Tracks: / Stop breaking my heart.
7" Single: Released May '79, on Island, by Island Records. Deleted '82. Catalogue no: **WIP 6488**

Inner City

AIN'T NOBODY BETTER
Tracks: / Ain't nobody better / Ain't nobody better (version).
CD 5": Released Apr '89, on 10 Records, by Virgin Records. Catalogue no: **TENCD 252**
7" Single: Released 10 Apr '89, on Virgin, by Virgin Records. Catalogue no: **TEN 252**
12" Single: Released Apr '89, on 10 Records, by Virgin Records. Catalogue no: **TENR 252**
12" Single: Released 10 Apr '89, on Virgin, by Virgin Records. Catalogue no: **TENX 252**

BIG FUN (featuring Kevin Saunderson)
Tracks: / Big fun (On TENX 240 only) / Big fun (Juan's magic remix) (On all versions) / Big fun (club remix) (On TENR 240 only) / Big fun (techno frisbee-megamix) (On TENR 240) / Big fun (radio fun) (7" only).
7" Single: Released 22 Aug '88, on 10 Records, by Virgin Records. Catalogue no: **TEN 240**
12" Single: on 10 Records, by Virgin Records. Catalogue no: **TENR 240**
12" Single: Released 22 Aug '88, on 10 Records, by Virgin Records. Catalogue no: **TENX 240**

DO YOU LOVE WHAT YOU FEEL (see panle on previous page)
Tracks: / Do you love what you feel / And I do.
Cassingle: Released 3 Jul '89, on 10 Records, by Virgin Records. Catalogue no: **TENC 273**
7" Single: Released 3 Jul '89, on 10 Records, by Virgin Records. Catalogue no: **TEN 273**
12" Single: Released 3 Jul '89, on 10 Records, by Virgin Records. Catalogue no: **TENZ 273**
12" Single: Released 3 Jul '89, on 10 Records, by Virgin Records. Catalogue no: **TENX 273**
CD 3": Released 3 Jul '89, on 10 Records, by Virgin Records. Catalogue no: **TENCD 273**

DO YOU LOVE WHAT YOU FEEL (SMOKING REMIX)
Tracks: / Do you love what you feel(magic Juan's smoking / Do you love what you feel (power 41 remix) / Do you love what you feel (dark dub, bright.
12" Single: Released '89, on 10 Records, by Virgin Records. Catalogue no: **TENR 273**

GOOD LIFE (see panel above)
Tracks: / Good life / Good life (instrumental) / Good life (magic juans mix) (Only on 12" & CD) / Good life (may day club mix) (Only on 12" version.) / Big fun (LA big big fun mix) (Only on 12" version.) / Good life (master reese edit) (On CD only).
7" Single: Released Nov '88, on 10 Records, by Virgin Records. Catalogue no: **TEN 249**
12" Single: Released '88, on 10 Records, by Virgin Records. Catalogue no: **TENR 249**
12" Single: Released Nov '88, on 10 Records, by Virgin Records. Catalogue no: **TENX 249**
CD 3": Released '88, on 10 Records, by Virgin Records. Catalogue no: **TENCD 249**

Inner City Express

SHOW ME WHERE YOUR FUNK IS
Tracks: / Show me where your funk is.
7" Single: Released Aug '81, on Earlobe, by Earlobe Records. Deleted '87. Catalogue no: **ELBS 104**

Inner City Unit

Biographical details: This group consisted of Nik Turner (vocals/sax), Tren Thoms (guitar/vocals), Dead Fred (vocals/keyboards), Baz Magneto (Bass/vocals) and Mick Stupp (drums)..

BEER BACCY BINGO BENIDORM
Tracks: / Beer baccy bingo Benidorm.
7" Single: Released Sep '81, on Avatar, by Avatar Record Corporation. Catalogue no: **AAA 113**

PARADISE BEACH
Tracks: / Paradise beach.
7" Single: Released Jul '80, on Riddle, by Riddle Records. Catalogue no: **RID 003**

SOLITARY ASHTRAY
Tracks: / Solitary ashtray.
7" Single: Released Oct '79, on Riddle, by Riddle Records. Catalogue no: **RID 001**

Inner Force

CARNIVAL TIME
Tracks: / Carnival time.
7" Single: Released Sep '84, on Voida, Catalogue no: **VDA 1A**

DON'T STOP I LIKE IT
Tracks: / Don't stop I like it.
12" Single: Released Oct '84, on Voida, Catalogue no: **VDA 2**

HOLIDAY
Tracks: / Holiday / Am I wasting my time.
7" Single: Released Aug '82, on Music International, by Music International Records. Catalogue no: **M 10014**

Inner Life

LET'S CHARGE IT UP
Tracks: / Let's charge it up.
7" Single: Released Apr '85, on Personal, by Personal Records. Catalogue no: **PERS 3901**
12" Single: Released Apr '85, on Personal, by Personal Records. Catalogue no: **12 PER 3901**

NO WAY
Tracks: / No way.
7" Single: Released Jun '84, on Personal, by Personal Records. Catalogue no: **PERS 101**
12" Single: Released Apr '84, on Personal, by Personal Records. Catalogue no: **12PER 101**

Inner Vibes

TRAIL AND CROSSES
Tracks: / Me no respond / Trail and crosses.
12" Single: Released May '86, on Firehouse, Catalogue no: **FH 005**

Innes, Neil

AMOEBA BOOGIE
Tracks: / Amoeba boogie / Theme.
7" Single: Released Feb '80, on Polydor, by Polydor Ltd. Deleted '83. Catalogue no: **POSP 107**

DEAR FATHER CHRISTMAS
Tracks: / Dear Father Christmas / City of angels.
7" Single: Released Nov '85, on Making Waves, by Celtic Music. Catalogue no: **SURF 104**

HUMANOID BOOGIE
Tracks: / Humanoid boogie.
7" Single: Released Jan '84, on PRT, by Castle Communications Records. Catalogue no: **7P 298**
12" Single: Released Jan '84, on PRT, by Castle Communications Records. Catalogue no: **12P 298**

KENNY AND LISA
Tracks: / Kenny and Lisa / Human race.
7" Single: Released 20 Jun '80, on Polydor, by Polydor Ltd. Deleted '83. Catalogue no: **205924 7**

THEM
Tracks: / Them / Rock of the ages.
7" Single: Released Mar '84, on MMC, by MMC Records. Catalogue no: **MMC 100**

Innocents

ONE WAY LOVE
Tracks: / One way love.
7" Single: Released Oct '80, on Kingdom, by Kingdom Records. Deleted '82. Catalogue no: **KV 8010**

Insane

EL SALVADOR
Tracks: / El Salvador.
7" Single: Released Jul '82, on No Future, Deleted '87. Catalogue no: **01 10**

POLITICS
Tracks: / Politics.
7" Single: Released Oct '82, on Riot City, by Riot City Records. Catalogue no: **RIOT 3**

WHY DIE
Tracks: / Why die.
7" Single: Released Oct '82, on Insane, Catalogue no: **INSANE 1**

Insane Picnic

MAGISTRATES & SAINTS
Tracks: / Village boys / Ruin moon / Summer rain / Magistrates & saints.
12" Single: Released Oct '86, on Waterfall, by Waterfall Records. Catalogue no: **WFL 12002**

ROMANCE
Tracks: / Romance.
7" Single: Released Oct '84, on Falling A, Catalogue no: **EBS 5**

Insex

INNER SANCTION
Tracks: / Inner sanction.
7" Single: Released Jun '81, on Dining Out, by Dining Out Records. Catalogue no: **TUX 3**

LIFESPAN
Tracks: / Lifespan.
7" Single: Released Jun '81, on Dining Out, by Dining Out Records. Catalogue no: **TUX 10**

Inside Storey

WHO I AM
Tracks: / Who I am / Walking away / Waking.
12" Single: Released Feb '89, on Revolution, by Revolution Records. Catalogue no: **RR 0101**

Inspiral Carpets

FIND OUT WHY
Tracks: / Find out why.
CD 5": Released Jul '89, on Cow, Catalogue no: **DUNG 5 CD**
7" Single: Released Jul '89, on Cow, Catalogue no: **DUNG 5**
12" Single: Released Jul '89, on Cow, Catalogue no: **DUNG 5 T**

JOE
Tracks: / Joe.
12" Single: Released 2 May '89, on Uni-

INSPIRATIONAL CHOIR - PICK ME UP (Released on Stiff)

corn Records, by Unicorn Records. Catalogue no: **MOO 3**

KEEP THE CIRCLE AROUND
Tracks: / Keep the circle around / Cow, Theme from.
7" Single: Released Jul '88, on Playtime, by Playtime Records. Catalogue no: **AMUSE 2**

PEEL SESSIONS:INSPIRAL CARPETS
CD 5": Released Jul '89, on Strange Fruit, by Strange Fruit Records. Catalogue no: **SFPSCD 072**
12" Single: Released Jul '89, on Strange Fruit, by Strange Fruit Records. Catalogue no: **SFPS 072**

PLANE CRASH
Tracks: / Plane crash.
7" Single: Released Jul '88, on Playtime, by Playtime Records. Catalogue no: **AMUSE 002**
12" Single: Released Apr '89, on Cow, Catalogue no: **MOO 1**
12" Single: Released Jul '88, on Playtime, by Playtime Records. Catalogue no: **AMUSE 002T**

TRAIN SURFING
Tracks: / Train surfing.
12" Single: Released Feb '89, on Cow, Catalogue no: **MOO 2**

Inspirational Choir

Biographical details: The Inspirational Choir Of Th Pentecostal First Born Church Of The Living God gave a boost to Britain's burgeoning black gospel music scen, when they took Andrew Pryce Jackman's arrangement of the classic hymn *Abide With Me* to No.44 on the UK singles chart at Christmas 1984. Bob MacDonald 6/11/85.

ABIDE WITH ME
Tracks: / Sweet Holy Spirit / Abide with me.
7" Single: Released Nov '85, on Epic, by CBS Records. Catalogue no: **A 4997**
7" Single: Released Dec '85, on Portrait, by CBS Records. Catalogue no: **QA 4997**

IVE GOT A FEELING
Tracks: / I've got a feeling.
7" Single: Released Sep '85, on Portrait, by CBS Records. Catalogue no: **A 6611**
12" Single: Released Sep '85, on Portrait, by CBS Records. Catalogue no: **TX 6611**

ONE LOVE
Tracks: / Right there / One love.
7" Single: Released Feb '86, on Portrait, by CBS Records. Catalogue no: **A 6902**
12" Single: Released Feb '86, on Portrait, by CBS Records. Catalogue no: **TA 6902**

PICK ME UP
Tracks: / Pick me up / Do not pass me by / Love lifted me (on 12" only) / Give me a clean heart (on 12" only) / Sign me up (on 12" only).
7" Single: Released Nov '83, on Stiff, by Stiff Records. Catalogue no: **BUY 193**
12" Single: Released Nov '83, on Stiff, by Stiff Records. Catalogue no: **BUYIT 193**

(YOUR LOVE HAS LIFTED ME) HIGHER AND HIGHER
Tracks: / (your love has lifted me) Higher and higher / Amazing grace.
7" Single: Released Nov '86, on Portrait, by CBS Records. Catalogue no: **CHOIR 1**
12" Single: Released Nov '86, on Portrait, by CBS Records. Catalogue no: **CHOIRT 1**

Instant Agony

FASHION PARADE
Tracks: / Fashion parade.
7" Single: Released Feb '83, on Half Man-Half Biscuit, by Skeleton Records. Catalogue no: **DUNK 2**

NICELY DOES IT
Tracks: / Nicely does it / We don't need you.
7" Single: Released Apr '84, on Flicknife, by Flicknife Records. Catalogue no: **FLS 028**

NO SIGN OF LIFE
Tracks: / No sign of life.
7" Single: Released Jul '83, on Flicknife, by Flicknife Records. Catalogue no: **FLS 022**

THINK OF ENGLAND
Tracks: / Think of England.
7" Single: Released Aug '82, on Half Man-Half Biscuit, by Skeleton Records. Catalogue no: **DUNK 1**

Instant Funk

Biographical details: Instant Funk. James Carmichael led this faceless nine-piece disco band to brief glory in their native America in 1979 with the million-selling single *I Got My Mind Made Up*. As well as being a smash on the soul charts, it also reached No.20 on the US pop list. In Britain *I Got My Mind Made Up* reached No.46. The record was released at the height of the disco boom and its infectious tribal feel and catchy 'Say What?' vocal hook made it ideal dancefloor fooder. Subsequent records, produced by veteran soul mogul Bunny Sigler, contained competent but unexciting disco material which lived up to the mechanical inference of the group's name. Bob Macdonald 6/11/85.

EVERYBODY
Tracks: / Everybody / You want my love.
7" Single: Released Nov '80, on Salsoul, Deleted '83. Catalogue no: **SAL 8**
12" Single: Released Nov '80, on Salsoul, Deleted '83. Catalogue no: **SALT 8**

GOT MY MIND MADE UP
Tracks: / Got my mind made.
7" Single: Released Jan '79, on Salsoul, Deleted '82. Catalogue no: **SSOL 114**

WHY DON'T YOU THINK ABOUT ME
Tracks: / Why don't you think about me / Slam dunk the funk / I got my mind made up.
12" Single: Released Jun '82, on Battersea, Catalogue no: **BATTL 2**

Instigators

BOOM
Tracks: / Boom / Pretty girl.
12" Single: Released Aug '83, on Shuttle, Catalogue no: **SH 007**

FULL CIRCLE
Tracks: / Full circle / Sleeper, The.
7" Single: Released 20 Feb '88, on Double A, Catalogue no: **AA 010**

HAWAII 5-0 THEME
Tracks: / Hawaii five-O (Theme from Hawaii five-O).
7" Single: Released Apr '85, on Shuttle, Catalogue no: **SHO 15**
12" Single: Released Apr '85, on Shuttle, Catalogue no: **SHO 1512**

INVASION
Tracks: / Invasion.
7" Single: Released Apr '88, on Positive, by Positive Records. Catalogue no: **SSEP 220**

KEEP TRYING
Tracks: / Keep trying.
12" Single: Released 20 Feb '88, on Ins-Ting, Catalogue no: **INS 001**

THICK AND THIN
Tracks: / Thick and thin.
12" Single: Released Oct '89, on Mafia/Fluxy, Catalogue no: **MF 012**

WE AIN'T GETTING ALONG
Tracks: / We ain't getting along.
12" Single: Released Mar '89, on Mafia/Fluxy, Catalogue no: **M&F 009**

Instrumental Reggae

INSTRUMENTAL REGGAE HITS
Tracks: / Tchaikovsky piano concerto: *Various artists* / Take five: *Various artists* / Liquidator: *Various artists* / Return of Django: *Various artists*.
7" EP: Released May '83, on Trojan, by Trojan Records. Deleted May '88. Catalogue no: **TMX 4012**

Insync

SAD SWEET DREAMER
Tracks: / Sad sweet dreamer.
12" Single: Released 31 Jul '89, on White Label (1), Catalogue no: **GAYM 001**

Intaferon

Biographical details: The duo consist of Simon X and Simon G..

GET OUT OF LONDON
Tracks: / Get out of London / Elvis / Get out of London (intacontinentalballisticmix) (Only on 12" version.).
7" Single: Released '83, on Chrysalis, by Chrysalis Records. Deleted '87. Catalogue no: **CHS 2715**
12" Single: Released Aug '83, on Chrysalis, by Chrysalis Records. Catalogue no: **CHS 12 2715**

Intense

MELLOW
Tracks: / Mellow / Mellow (version).
12" Single: Released Aug '88, on Ariwa Sounds, by Ariwa Sounds. Catalogue no: **ARI 077**

ON MY MIND
Tracks: / On my mind.
12" Single: Released May '89, on Ariwa Sounds, by Ariwa Sounds. Catalogue no: **ARI 91**

VERY BEST, THE
Tracks: / Very best, The.
12" Single: Released Jan '89, on Ariwa Sounds, by Ariwa Sounds. Catalogue no: **ARI 80**

Intense Degree

PEEL SESSIONS:INTENSE DEGREE
12" Single: Released Aug '88, on Strange Fruit, by Strange Fruit Records. Catalogue no: **SFPS 053**

Intense Heat

SWEET TINA
Tracks: / Sweet Tina.
12" Single: Released Oct '89, on Soca, Catalogue no: **SOT 010**

Intensive Care

REBELS, ROCKETS AND RUBBERMEN
Tracks: / Rebels / Exocet UK / Rubber man / Hypocrite / Sober as a judge / Point of view.
12" Single: Released Sep '87, on Back To Back Records, Catalogue no: **BTB 001**

Interface

AUTOMATION
Tracks: / Automation.
7" Single: Released May '82, on Blue Beat, Catalogue no: **HIT 001**

LOUDER THAN WORDS
Tracks: / Louder than words.
7" Single: Released Mar '82, on Clone, Catalogue no: **SAME 1**
12" Single: Released Mar '82, on Clone, Catalogue no: **SAME 1 12**

MEMORIES
Tracks: / Memories.
7" Single: Released Dec '84, on Embryo Arts (Belgium), Catalogue no: **EAS 001**

Interloerator 3

HARRY'S HOUSE
Tracks: / Harry's house.
12" Single: Released Nov '88, on Big One Records, by Big One Records. Catalogue no: **VVBIG 12**

International

POWER FROM WITHIN
Tracks: / Power within (inst version).
7" Single: Released Aug '86, on BBC, by BBC Records & Tapes. Deleted Sep '87. Catalogue no: **RESL 198**
12" Single: Released Aug '86, on BBC, by BBC Records & Tapes. Deleted Sep '87. Catalogue no: **12 RSL 198**

International Rescue

LEATHER JACKET (SINGLE)
Tracks: / Leather jacket.
7" Single: Released 4 Apr '86, on Cowboy City, Catalogue no: **SHOE 004**

LIFE IN AN ELEVATOR
Tracks: / Life in an elevator.
7" Single: Released Sep '84, on Cowboy City, Catalogue no: **SHOE 2**

LOVE IN THE RIGHT DIRECTION
Tracks: / Love in the right direction.
Note: "A new band with tremendous live following, particulary in the Reading area. An uptempo sophisticated punk in the Madness mould with terrific sax breaks by ex Dexy's Midnight Runners saxophonist Alan Wheeton." (Supertrack, June 1988)
7" Single: Released Jun '88, on Supertrack, Catalogue no: **ACOR 2**

YOU NEED SHOES
Tracks: / You need shoes / Balance.
7" Single: Released Mar '84, on Cowboy City, Catalogue no: **FMR 078**

Internationals

HOOTS MON
Tracks: / Hoots mon / Never gonna give you up.
7" Single: Released Nov '83, on Alan Wood, Catalogue no: **SAW 007**

IT'S NOT UNUSUAL
Tracks: / It's not unusual / Headline news.
7" Single: Released May '84, on AWA, Catalogue no: **SAW 008**

Interplay

PRETTY FACE
Tracks: / Pretty face / Terminal vision.
7" Single: Released Jan '82, on RCA, by BMG Records (UK). Deleted '84. Catalogue no: **RCA 211**

PRETTY FACE (ZIZI JEANMARIE)
Tracks: / Pretty face.
7" Single: Released Jan '82, on Carrere America (USA), by PolyGram Rec.Inc.(USA). Catalogue no: **CAR 211**
12" Single: Released Jan '82, on Carrere America (USA), by PolyGram Rec.Inc.(USA). Catalogue no: **CART 211**

Interview

Biographical details: This group consisted of Jeff Stars (vocals), Pete Allerhand (guitar/vocals/keyboards), Alan Brian (guitar/vocals), Phil Crowther (bass) and Manny Elias (drums)..

HIDE AND SEEK
Tracks: / Hide and seek / Yes, man.
7" Single: Released Apr '80, on Virgin, by Virgin Records. Deleted '83. Catalogue no: **VS 331**

Intestines

LIFE IN A CARDBOARD BOX
Tracks: / Life in a cardboard box.
7" Single: Released Jan '81, on Alternative, Deleted '88. Catalogue no: **ACS 001**

Intimate Obsessions

ASSASSIN
Tracks: / Assassin.
12" Single: Released Oct '85, on Third Mind, by Third Mind Records. Catalogue no: **TMS 06**

Intimate Strangers

BLUE HOUR
Tracks: / Into the wilderness / Blue hour.
7" Single: Released Nov '86, on I.R.S, Catalogue no: **IRM 124**
12" Single: Released Nov '86, on I.R.S, Catalogue no: **IRMT 124**

IN THE WILDERNESS
Tracks: / In the wilderness / Religion or pleasure / Death letter / Party till noon / On the river in 59 / Tell me (that you don't) / Destry rides again / John the revelator / If this is love can I get my money back / Four wise men.
7" Single: Released Oct '85, on I.R.S, Catalogue no: **IRM 108**
12" Single: Released Oct '85, on I.R.S, Catalogue no: **IRT 108**

LET GO
Tracks: / My brilliant career / Set me free (Extra track on 12" version only) / Let go.
7" Single: Released May '86, on I.R.S, Catalogue no: **IRM 115**
12" Single: Released May '86, on I.R.S, Catalogue no: **IRMT 115**

RAISE THE DRAGON
Tracks: / Worlds apart / Raise the dragon.
12" Single: Released Mar '86, on I.R.S, Catalogue no: **IRM 110**
12" Single: Released Mar '86, on I.R.S, Catalogue no: **IRT 110**

Into A Circle

EVERGREEN
Tracks: / Evergreen.
7" Single: Released Mar '88, on Abstract, by Abstract Sounds. Catalogue no: **ABS 050**
12" Single: Released Mar '88, on Abstract, by Abstract Sounds. Catalogue no: **12 ABS 050**

FOREVER
Tracks: / Forever.
7" Single: Released Aug '87, on Abstract, by Abstract Sounds. Catalogue no: **ABS 044**
12" Single: Released Jul '87, on Abstract, by Abstract Sounds. Catalogue no: **12 ABS 044**

INSIDE OUT
Tracks: / Inside out / Reward / Flow / Field of sleep.
12" Single: Released Nov '86, on Abstract, by Abstract Sounds. Catalogue no: **12 ABS 042**

Intolerance

CHOKING ON DUST
Tracks: / Choking on dust.
7" Single: Released Jul '88, on Soft Cushion, by Soft Cushion Records. Catalogue no: **INTOL S 286**

Intransit

MICRO ON THE MOVE
Tracks: / Micro on the move.
7" Single: Released Aug '85, on Embryo Arts (Belgium), Catalogue no: **EAS 5**

OUT OF THE DARK
Tracks: / Divided, The / Visions of blue / I want / News, not history / In transit.
7" Single: Released Dec '84, on Plankton, by Plankton Records. Catalogue no: **PCN 108**

Intrigue

HEAVEN MADE
Tracks: / Heaven made.
7" Single: Released Jun '85, on Project, Catalogue no: **PRO 1**
12" Single: Released Jun '85, on Project,

Catalogue no: **12PRO 1**

I LIKE IT
Tracks: / I like it.
12" Single: Released Feb '83, on Pressure, Catalogue no: **PRESSD 1003**

LET SLEEPING DOGS LIE
Tracks: / Let sleeping dogs lie.
7" Single: Released Sep '84, on Music Power, Catalogue no: **MPR 2**
12" Single: Released Sep '84, on Music Power, Catalogue no: **MPRT 2**

NO TURNING BACK
Tracks: / No turning back / Call of the heart.
7" Single: Released Jun '84, on Music Power, Catalogue no: **MPR 1**
12" Single: Released Apr '84, on Music Power, Catalogue no: **MPRT 1**

TOGETHER FOREVER
Tracks: / Fly girl / Fly girl (dance mix) / Together forever.
7" Single: Released Sep '87, on Cool Tempo, by Chrysalis Records. Catalogue no: **COOL 153**
12" Single: Released Sep '87, on Cool Tempo, by Chrysalis Records. Catalogue no: **COOLX 153**

Intro

HAUNTED COCKTAILS
Tracks: / Haunted cocktails / Departures.
7" Single: Released Jan '83, on MCA, by MCA Records. Catalogue no: **MCA 794**

LOST WITHOUT YOUR LOVE
Tracks: / Lost without your love.
7" Single: Released Jun '83, on MCA, by MCA Records. Catalogue no: **MCA 819**
12" Single: Released Jun '83, on MCA, by MCA Records. Catalogue no: **MCAT 819**

Introze

LAMBETH WALK
Tracks: / Lambeth walk / Kids in uniform.
7" Single: Released Nov '82, on Monarch, by Monarch Records. Catalogue no: **MON 037**

Intruder

INTRUDER
Special: Released Oct '87, on Iron Works (USA), by Azra International (USA). Catalogue no: **IW 1024**

Intruders

Biographical details: This American R & B group consisted of Samuel 'Little Sonny' Brown (vocals), Phil Terry (vocals), Eugene 'Bird' Dautrey, Robert 'Big Sonny' Brown (vocals). Formed in Philadelphia, this quartet's first US charts single was *(We'll be) united* in 1966. Various other hits followed, and the band's greatest success came in 1968 with the single *Cowboys to girls* which was a million seller. The Intruders were signed to Gamble Records, owned by Kenny Gamble and Leon Huff, who produced all their chart hits. Later, minot hits included *Win, place or show (She's a winner)* which reached No.14 in the British charts in 1974, and *I'll always love my mama* reaching only No.32, (1974) but No.6 (1975) in the Billboard R&B charts. The band were also popular on local Philadelphia TV shows in the early Seventies, which boosted their following further. (Ian Wilkins, Sept 1986).

I'LL ALWAYS LOVE MY MAMA
Tracks: / I'll always love my mama.
7" Single: Released Apr '74, on Philadelphia Int., by EMI Records. Deleted '77. Catalogue no: **PIR 2147**

WHO DO YOU LOVE (SINGLE)
Tracks: / Who do you love?.
7" Single: Released Dec '84, on Streetwave, Deleted '86. Catalogue no: **KHAN 34**

(WIN SHOW OR PLACE) SHE'S A WINNER
Tracks: / (Win show or place) She's a winner.
7" Single: Released Jun '74, on Philadelphia Int., by EMI Records. Deleted '77. Catalogue no: **PIR 2212**

Invaders

BACK STREET ROMEO
Tracks: / Back street romeo / Rock methodology / Invasion of privacy.

7" Single: Released Oct '82, on Polydor, by Polydor Ltd. Deleted Oct '85. Catalogue no: **POSP 180**

MAGIC MIRROR
Tracks: / Magic mirror / Shirley you're wrong.

7" Single: Released Aug '80, on Polydor, by Polydor Ltd. Deleted '83. Catalogue no: **2059263**

Inversions

LOCO-MOTO
Tracks: / Loco-moto.
7" Single: Released Oct '81, on Groove PR, by Beggars Banquet Records. Catalogue no: **GP 108**
12" Single: Released Oct '81, on Groove PR, by Beggars Banquet Records. Catalogue no: **GP 108 T**

MR. MACK
Tracks: / Mr. Mack / Passport / In the mean time.
12" Single: Released Feb '81, on Groove PR, by Beggars Banquet Records. Catalogue no: **GP 106T**

Investigators

BABY IT'S YOURS
Tracks: / Baby it's yours.
12" Single: Released Jun '85, on Private Eye, Catalogue no: **VEST 02**

DOUBTS TO THE WIND
Tracks: / Doubts to the wind.
12" Single: Released Dec '84, on Private Eye, Catalogue no: **VEST 1**

HOW COULD I LET YOU GET AWAY
Tracks: / How could I let you get away.
12" Single: Released '79, on Plastic, Deleted '80. Catalogue no: **PFUL 1008**

LIVING IN A WORLD OF MAGIC
Tracks: / Living in a world of magic.
12" Single: Released Jul '83, on Private Eye, Catalogue no: **PE 103**

LOVING FEELING
Tracks: / Loving feeling / Where do we go.
10" single: Released Dec '82, on Private Eye, Catalogue no: **PE 01**

WHERE DO WE GO FROM HERE
Tracks: / Where do we go from here.
12" Single: Released 20 Mar '89, on Private Eye, Catalogue no: **PE 101**

WOMAN I NEED YOUR LOVING
Tracks: / Woman I need your loving.
12" Single: Released Jun '84, on Private Eye, Catalogue no: **PE 104**

Invisible

LOVE STREET
Tracks: / Sunday / Twilight zone / Love street.
12" Single: Released Oct '86, on Midnight Music, by Midnight Music Records. Catalogue no: **DONG 28**

Invisible Limits

GOLDEN DREAMS
Tracks: / Golden dreams.
CD 5": Released Sep '89, on Fun Factory, Catalogue no: **FUNFACMCD 3917**
12" Single: Released Sep '89, on Fun Factory, Catalogue no: **FUNFACM 3917**

Invisible Man's Band

ALL NIGHT THING
Tracks: / All night thing.
7" Single: Released Jun '80, on Island, by Island Records. Deleted '81. Catalogue no: **WIP 6571**
12" Single: Released Jun '80, on Island, by Island Records. Deleted '81. Catalogue no: **12WIP 6571**

LOVE CAN'T COME (PART 1)
Tracks: / Love can't come (part 1) / Love can't come (part 2) / 9 X's out of ten.
12" Single: Released Aug '80, on Island, by Island Records. Deleted '83. Catalogue no: **12WIP 6642**

Invision

GOTTA GIVE AS GOOD AS YOU GET
Tracks: / Gotta give as good as you get.
7" Single: Released '88, on Champion, by Champion Records. Catalogue no: **CHAMP 62**
12" Single: Released '88, on Champion, by Champion Records. Catalogue no: **CHAMP 1262**

Invivo

DON'T LET ME DOWN
Tracks: / Don't let me down / Gemini / Sheet of ice / Silent scream.
12" Single: Released Nov '87, on Crook Cassettes, by Crook Cassettes. Catalogue no: **IV 1**

INXS

BURN FOR YOU (EXTENDED REMIX)
Tracks: / Burn for you (extended remix).
12" Single: Released '88, on WEA (Australia), by WEA Records. Catalogue no: **0259442**

DEVIL INSIDE
Tracks: / Devil inside / On the rocks / Devil inside (12" ext. version) / Devil inside (LP version) / What you need.
CD 5": Released Feb '88, on Mercury, by Phonogram Ltd. Deleted Oct '88. Catalogue no: **INXCD 10**
10" single: Released Mar '88, on Mercury, by Phonogram Ltd. Deleted 31 May '89. Catalogue no: **INXS 1010**
7" Single: Released Feb '88, on Mercury, by Phonogram Ltd. Deleted Oct '88. Catalogue no: **INXS 10**
12" Single: Released Feb '88, on Mercury, by Phonogram Ltd. Deleted Oct '88. Catalogue no: **INXS 1012**
Special: Released 20 Feb '88, on Mercury, by Phonogram Ltd. Deleted Oct '88. Catalogue no: **INXS P10**
CD 3": Released Aug '88, on WEA (Japan), by WEA Records. Catalogue no: **10 SW 33**

DON'T CHANGE
Tracks: / Don't change / You never used to cry.
7" Single: Released Jun '83, on Mercury, by Phonogram Ltd. Catalogue no: **INXS 1**
12" Single: Released Jun '83, on Mercury, by Phonogram Ltd. Catalogue no: **INXS 12**

I SEND A MESSAGE
Tracks: / I send a message / Mechanical.
7" Single: Released May '84, on Mercury, by Phonogram Ltd. Catalogue no: **PH 2**

JUST KEEP WALKING
Tracks: / Just keep walking.
7" Single: on RCA, by BMG Records (UK). Deleted Sep '81. Catalogue no: **RCA 89**

KISS THE DIRT (FALLING DOWN THE MOUNTAIN)
Tracks: / Six knots / One thing, The (Track on 12" version only) / Spy of love (Track on 12" version only).
7" Single: Released Aug '86, on Mercury, by Phonogram Ltd. Deleted '87. Catalogue no: **INXS 7**
12" Single: Released Aug '86, on Mercury, by Phonogram Ltd. Deleted '87. Catalogue no: **INXS 7 12**

LISTEN LIKE THIEVES (SINGLE)
Tracks: / Begotten / Listen like thieves / Listen like thieves (ext remix) / Listen like thieves (instrumental) / Listen like thieves (live version).
7" Single: Released Jun '86, on Mercury, by Phonogram Ltd. Deleted '87. Catalogue no: **INXS 6**
12" Single: Released Jul '88, on Atlantic (USA), by WEA Records. Catalogue no: **086818**
12" Single: Released Jun '86, on Mercury, by Phonogram Ltd. Deleted '87. Catalogue no: **INXS 612**

MYSTIFY
Tracks: / Mystify / Devil inside / Need you tonight (Ben Liebrand mix) (Only on 12".) / What you need (extended version) (Only on CD single.) / Listen like thieves (Only on CD single.) / Devil inside (extended remix) (Only on CD single.).
CD 5": Released 27 Mar '89, on Mercury, by Phonogram Ltd. Deleted Oct '89. Catalogue no: **INXSCD 13**
7" Single: Released 27 Mar '89, on Mercury, by Phonogram Ltd. Deleted 31 Jul '89. Catalogue no: **INXS 13**
12" Single: Released 27 Mar '89, on Mercury, by Phonogram Ltd. Deleted 31 Jul '89. Catalogue no: **INXS 1322**
12" Single: Released 27 Mar '89, on Mercury, by Phonogram Ltd. Deleted 31 Jul '89. Catalogue no: **INXS 1312**
Special: Released 27 Mar '89, on Mercury, by Phonogram Ltd. Deleted Oct '89. Catalogue no: **INXSG 13**

NEED YOU TONIGHT
Tracks: / Need you tonight / I'm coming (home) / Mediate (On 12" only).
Note: Produced by Chris Thomas. (Cat No. 981884) cassette single is an Import.
Cassingle: Released Nov '87, on Atlantic (USA), by WEA Records. Catalogue no: **98184**
7" Single: Released Oct '87, on Mercury, by Phonogram Ltd. Deleted 31 May '89. Catalogue no: **INXS 8**
12" Single: Released Oct '87, on Mercury, by Phonogram Ltd. Deleted 31 May '89. Catalogue no: **INXS 1222**
12" Single: Released Oct '87, on Mercury, by Phonogram Ltd. Deleted 31 May '89. Catalogue no: **INXS 812**

NEED YOU TONIGHT (RE-RELEASE)
Tracks: / Need you tonight / Move on / Kiss the dirt (falling down the mountain) (Only on 12" version.) / Need you tonight (album version) (Only on 12" version.) / Need you tonight (Julian Mendelsohn version) (Only on CD single.) / Original sin (Only on CD single.) / Don't change (Only on CD single.).
CD 5": Released Oct '88, on Mercury, by Phonogram Ltd. Catalogue no: **INXCD 12**
7" Single: Released Oct '88, on Mercury, by Phonogram Ltd. Deleted 31 Jul '89. Catalogue no: **INXS 12**
7" Single: Released Oct '88, on Mercury, by Phonogram Ltd. Deleted 31 May '89. Catalogue no: **INXSG 12**
12" Single: Released Oct '88, on Mercury, by Phonogram Ltd. Catalogue no: **INXS 1212**

NEVER TEAR US APART
Tracks: / Never tear us apart / Guns in the sky (Kick Ass remix) / Burn for you (Only available on 12" limited edition.) / Old world, new world (Only available on 12" limited edition.) / This time (Only on CD single.) / Different world (Only on 12" and CD single.).
CD 5": Released Jun '88, on Mercury, by Phonogram Ltd. Catalogue no: **INXCD 11**
10" single: Released Jun '88, on Mercury, by Phonogram Ltd. Deleted 31 May '89. Catalogue no: **INXS 1110**
7" Single: Released Jun '88, on Mercury, by Phonogram Ltd. Deleted 31 May '89. Catalogue no: **INXS 1100**
7" Single: Released Jun '88, on Mercury, by Phonogram Ltd. Deleted 31 May '89. Catalogue no: **INXS 11**
7" Single: Released Jun '88, on Mercury, by Phonogram Ltd. Deleted 31 May '89. Catalogue no: **INXSP 11**
12" Single: Released Jun '88, on Mercury, by Phonogram Ltd. Deleted 31 Jul '89. Catalogue no: **INXS 1112**
12" Single: Released Jun '88, on Mercury, by Phonogram Ltd. Deleted 31 May '89. Catalogue no: **INXSG 1112**

NEVER TEAR US APART (IMPORT)
Tracks: / Never tear us apart / Different world (12" mix) (From the film 'Crocodile Dundee') / Move on (Previously unissued).
Note: Two different tracks from the UK release- this has the 12" mix of 'Different World' (from Crocodile Dundee) plus 'Move On' (previously unissued). Picture sleeve.
12" Single: Released Oct '88, on Atlantic (USA), by WEA Records. Catalogue no: **086538**
CD 3": Released '88, on WEA (Japan), by WEA Records. Catalogue no: **10 P 36019**

NEW SENSATION
Tracks: / New sensation / Love is (what I say) (Track available on 12" version only.) / Same direction (Track available on 12" version only.) / Do wot you do / Guns in the sky.
CD 5": on Mercury, by Phonogram Ltd. Deleted Oct '88. Catalogue no: **INXCD 9**
12" Pic: Released Jul '88, on Atlantic (USA), by WEA Records. Catalogue no: **086563**
7" Pic: Released Jan '88, on Phonogram, by Phonogram Ltd. Deleted Oct '88. Catalogue no: **INXSR 9**
7" Single: Released Dec '87, on Mercury, by Phonogram Ltd. Deleted Oct '88. Catalogue no: **INXSP 9**
7" Single: Released Dec '87, on Mercury, by Phonogram Ltd. Deleted Oct '88. Catalogue no: **INXS 9**
12" Single: Released May '88, on Atlantic (USA), by WEA Records. Catalogue no: **086572**
12" Single: Released Dec '87, on Mercury, by Phonogram Ltd. Deleted 31 May '89. Catalogue no: **INXSP 912**
12" Single: Released Dec '87, on Mercury, by Phonogram Ltd. Deleted Oct '88. Catalogue no: **INXS 912**

ONE THING, THE
Tracks: / One thing, The / Sax thing / Black and white.
7" Single: Released Sep '83, on Mercury, by Phonogram Ltd. Catalogue no: **INXS 2**
12" Single: Released Sep '83, on Mercury, by Phonogram Ltd. Catalogue no: **INXS 212**

ORIGINAL SIN
Tracks: / Original sin / Ian's song / To look at you.
7" Single: Released Feb '84, on Mercury, by Phonogram Ltd. Catalogue no: **INXS 3**
12" Single: Released '88, on WEA (Australia), by WEA Records. Catalogue no: **0259717**
12" Single: Released Feb '84, on Mercury, by Phonogram Ltd. Catalogue no: **INXS 312**

THIS TIME
Tracks: / Original sin / Burn for you (Extra track on 12" & double pack only) / Dancing on the jetty (live) (Extra track on 12" & double pack only).
7" Set: Released Feb '86, on Mercury, by Phonogram Ltd. Deleted '87. Catalogue no: **INXSD 4**
7" Single: Released Feb '86, on Mercury, by Phonogram Ltd. Deleted '87. Catalogue no: **INXS 4**
12" Single: Released Feb '86, on Mercury, by Phonogram Ltd. Deleted '87. Catalogue no: **INXSD 124**

WHAT YOU NEED
Tracks: / Sweet as sin / What you need (remix) (Extra track on 12" version only) /

What you need (live) (Extra track on 12" version only) / One thing, The (live) (Extra track on 12" version only).
7" Single: Released Apr '86, on Mercury, by Phonogram Ltd. Catalogue no: **INXS 5**
12" Single: Released Apr '86, on Mercury, by Phonogram Ltd. Deleted '87. Catalogue no: **INX 512**

WHAT YOU NEED (REMIX)
Tracks: / What you need (remix).
12" Single: Released '88, on WEA (Australia), by WEA Records. Catalogue no: **0258868**

Iona & Andy

GOING GONE
Tracks: / Going gone (re-mix) / Lion in the winter.
7" Single: Released '88, on Barge, by Barge Records. Catalogue no: **BGE 7 1004**

I.O.U.

NO ENTRY
Tracks: / No entry / Hot blood.
7" Single: Released Aug '79, on DJM, Deleted '80. Catalogue no: **DJS 10922**

Ipanima Kaz

NIGHT KIXX
Tracks: / Night kixx.
7" Single: Released Jul '85, on Official, by Official Records. Catalogue no: **OFFA 3**

Ippu Do

TIME OF THE SEASON
Tracks: / Time of the season / Radio Japan / Listen to me.
7" Single: Released Jan '82, on Epic, by CBS Records. Deleted Jan '85. Catalogue no: **EPC A 1926**
12" Single: Released Jan '82, on Epic, by CBS Records. Deleted Jan '85. Catalogue no: **13-1926**

Ipso Facto

GIVE IT TO HER
Tracks: / Give it to her.
12" Single: Released Sep '84, on Zodiak, Catalogue no: **IF 884**

GLASS TIGERS
Tracks: / Glass tigers.
7" Single: Released May '85, on Zodiac, by Zodiac-Wilcox Records. Catalogue no: **IF 985**

MANNEQUIN
Tracks: / Mannequin.
7" Single: Released Sep '84, on If, by Zodiac Records. Catalogue no: **IFV 83**

NOIR DIOR
Tracks: / Noir dior.
7" Single: Released Sep '84, on If, by Zodiac Records. Catalogue no: **IF 784**

I.Q.

BABEL IS NOW
Tracks: / Babel is now.
7" Single: Released Oct '84, on Jim White, Catalogue no: **IQ 1002**
12" Single: Released Oct '84, on Jim White, Catalogue no: **12 IQ 1002**

BARBELL IS IN
Tracks: / Barbell is in.
12" Single: Released Oct '84, on Sahara, Catalogue no: **IQ 12 1002**

CORNERS
Tracks: / Corners / Thousand days, The.
7" Single: Released Oct '85, on Sahara, Catalogue no: **IQ 1003**
12" Single: Released Oct '85, on Sahara, Catalogue no: **IQ 12 1003**

IT ALL STOPS HERE
Tracks: / It all stops here.
7" Single: Released May '86, on Samurai, Catalogue no: **IQSD 1**

PASSING STRANGERS
Tracks: / Passing strangers / Nomzamo / No love lost.
7" Single: Released May '87, on Vertigo, by Phonogram Ltd. Deleted Dec '87. Catalogue no: **VER 30**
12" Single: Released May '87, on Vertigo, by Phonogram Ltd. Deleted Dec '87. Catalogue no: **VERX 30**

PROMISES (AS THE YEARS GO BY)
Tracks: / Promises (as the years go by).
7" Single: Released Aug '87, on Squawk (USA), by PolyGram Rec.Inc.(USA). Catalogue no: **VER 34**
12" Single: Released Aug '87, on Squawk (USA), by PolyGram Rec.Inc.(USA). Catalogue no: **VERX 34**

SOLD ON YOU
Tracks: / Sold on you / Through my fingers.
CD 5": Released Jan '89, on Vertigo, by Phonogram Ltd. Catalogue no: **VERCD 42**
7" Single: Released Jan '89, on Vertigo, by Phonogram Ltd. Deleted 31 Jul '89. Catalogue no: **VER 42**
12" Single: Released Jan '89, on Vertigo, by Phonogram Ltd. Deleted 31 Jul '89. Catalogue no: **VERX 42**

IQ Zero

SHE'S SO RARE
Tracks: / She's so rare / Candy dolls.
7" Single: Released Jun '80, on Logo, by Logo Records. Deleted '80. Catalogue no: **GO 324**

Ire, Clifton

THINKING OF JUNE
Tracks: / Thinking of June.
12" Single: Released Dec '88, on Clique, by Clique Records. Catalogue no: **ML 001**

Irie, Clement

BUN AND CHEESE
Tracks: / Bun and cheese.
12" Single: Released Mar '89, on Blue Mountain, Catalogue no: **BMD 055**

FOLLOW ME
Tracks: / Follow me.
7" Single: Released 21 Apr '89, on Blue Mountain, Catalogue no: **BMD 039**

KOLO KO (REMIX)
Tracks: / Kolo ko.
12" Single: Released May '89, on Greensleeves, by Greensleeves Records. Catalogue no: **GRED 246**

NICE EVERY TIME
Tracks: / Nice every time.
12" Single: Released 12 May '89, on Sir George, Catalogue no: **SG 058**

Irie, Culture

GOD A COME
Tracks: / God a come.
12" Single: Released Nov '88, on Parish, Catalogue no: **UNKNOWN**

Irie, David

TRASH 'N' READY
Tracks: / Didn't you say you love me / Trash 'n' ready.
12" Single: Released May '86, on Ace, by Ace Records. Catalogue no: **M 0002**

Irie, Derek

CRY FE DE COLD
Tracks: / Cry fe de cold.
7" Single: Released Oct '88, on Pioneer Muzik, Catalogue no: **PM 015**

Irie, Henkel

DON'T WORRY
Tracks: / Don't worry.
12" Single: Released Mar '89, on Penthouse, by Penthouse Records. Catalogue no: **PH 009**

Irie, Jim

NEW YORK DEM WANT TO GO
Tracks: / New York dem want to go.
12" Single: Released May '89, on Blue Mountain, Catalogue no: **BMD 060**

WILD AFRICAN
Tracks: / Wild African.
12" Single: Released '88, on Don Sebastian, Catalogue no: **DSR 003**

Irie, Tippa

BILLY BRONCO
Tracks: / Billy Bronco.
12" Single: Released Mar '89, on GT's Records, by GT'S Records. Catalogue no: **GT 005**

COMPLAIN NEIGHBOUR
Tracks: / Complain neighbour.
7" Single: Released Jul '85, on UK Bubblers, by Greensleeves Records. Catalogue no: **TIPPA 2**
12" Single: Released Jul '85, on UK Bubblers, by Greensleeves Records. Deleted Nov '87. Catalogue no: **TIPPAT 2**

DANCE DOWN A YARD
Tracks: / Dance down a yard / Dance up a lead.
12" Single: Released Feb '87, on UK Bubblers, by Greensleeves Records. Deleted '88. Catalogue no: **UKMC 22**

DANCE MOVES
Tracks: / Dance moves.
12" Single: Released Feb '86, on UK Bubblers, by Greensleeves Records. Catalogue no: **UKEP 101**

HEARTBEAT
Tracks: / Live as one / Heartbeat.
7" Single: Released Jun '86, on UK Bubblers, by Greensleeves Records. Catalogue no: **TIPPA 5**
12" Single: Released Jun '86, on UK Bubblers, by Greensleeves Records. Catalogue no: **TIPPAT 5**

HELLO DARLING
Tracks: / Hello darling (Insrumental) / Hello darling (Jazz version) (Track on 12" version only) / Hello darling.
12" Single: Released Mar '86, on UK Bubblers, by Greensleeves Records. Deleted Nov '87. Catalogue no: **TIPPAT 4**
7" Single: Released Mar '86, on UK Bubblers, by Greensleeves Records. Deleted Nov '87. Catalogue no: **TIPPA 4**

IT'S GOOD TO HAVE THE FEELING YOU'RE THE BEST
Tracks: / It's good to have the feeling you're the best / All the time the lyric a rhyme.
7" Single: Released Mar '85, on UK Bubblers, by Greensleeves Records. Catalogue no: **7 UKMC 4**
12" Single: Released Mar '85, on UK Bubblers, by Greensleeves Records. Deleted Jun '87. Catalogue no: **UKMC 4**

JUST A SPEAK
Tracks: / Just a speak / 769 1230.
12" Single: Released Aug '84, on UK Bubblers, by Greensleeves Records. Catalogue no: **UKMC 1**

PANIC PANIC
Tracks: / Panic panic (Instrumental).
7" Single: Released Nov '86, on UK Bubblers, by Greensleeves Records. Catalogue no: **TIPPA 6**
12" Single: Released Nov '86, on UK Bubblers, by Greensleeves Records. Catalogue no: **TIPPAT 6**

TELEPHONE, THE
Tracks: / Telephone, The.
7" Single: Released Oct '85, on UK Bubblers, by Greensleeves Records. Catalogue no: **TIPPA 3**
12" Single: Released Oct '85, on UK Bubblers, by Greensleeves Records. Catalogue no: **TIPPAT 3**

Irie, Tipper

ACID
Tracks: / Acid.
12" Single: Released Jan '89, on GT's Records, by GT'S Records. Catalogue no: **GT 003**

Irie, Tonto

GENERAL A GENERAL
Tracks: / General a general.
12" Single: Released Sep '84, on Jammy's, Catalogue no: **Unknown**

NA GET NOTHING
Tracks: / Two foot walk / Na get nothing.
12" Single: Released Oct '86, on Jammy's, Catalogue no: **PJAPIS 002**

NEW YORK LIFE (see panel below)
Tracks: / New York life (vocal) / New York life (instrumental) / New York life (version) (Track on 12" only.) / Slim belly man (Track on 12" only.) / Slim belly man (Version) (Track on 12" only.).
7" Single: Released Jul '87, on Mango, by Island Records. Deleted Apr '88. Catalogue no: **IS 334**
12" Single: Released Jul '87, on Mango, by Island Records. Deleted Apr '88. Catalogue no: **12IS 334**

PROBLEM
Tracks: / Problem.
7" Single: Released 21 Apr '89, on Blue Trac, by Blue Trac Records. Catalogue no: **BTRD 032**

Irie, Welton

IT FEELS SO GOOD
Tracks: / It feels so good.
12" Single: Released '87, on Joe Gibbs, Deleted Jun '89. Catalogue no: **JG 6043**

JAILHOUSE AFFAIR
Tracks: / Jailhouse affair / Captain of the ship.
12" Single: Released Nov '82, on Black Roots, Catalogue no: **BRD 05**

Iris, Donnie

AH LEAH
Tracks: / Ah Leah / Joking.
7" Single: Released Feb '81, on MCA, by MCA Records. Deleted Feb '84. Catalogue no: **MCA 662**

MY GIRL
Tracks: / My girl / Last to know.
7" Single: Released Jun '82, on MCA, by MCA Records. Deleted Jun '85. Catalogue no: **MCA 776**

Irish Mist

ROCKY ROAD TO DUBLIN
7" Single: Released 14 May '88, on Etude, by Etude Records. Catalogue no: **ET 2**

Irish Mists

MOUNTAINS OF MOURNE, THE
Tracks: / Mountains of Mourne.
7" Single: Released Jul '85, on Ritz, by Ritz Records. Catalogue no: **RITZ 104**

Irish Rovers

WASN'T THAT A PARTY (SINGLE)
Tracks: / Wasn't that a party / Valparaiso.
7" Single: Released Sep '87, on Scotdisc, by Scotdisc Records. Catalogue no: **ITV 7S 437**

Iron City Houserockers

Biographical details: This group consists of Joe Grusheckly (guitar/vocals), Rodney Psyka (vocals), Ned E Rankin (drums) and Gary Scalese (guitar). Also on *Love so tough* album Billy Cross (guitar), Marc Reisman (harmonica), Denny Martin (accordian), Richard Reising (vocals), Paul Glanz (piano), Tampa Lann (vocals), Susan Lynch (vocals) and Art Nadini (bass)..

HYPNOTISED
Tracks: / Hypnotised / Old man bar.
7" Single: Released Nov '80, on MCA, by MCA Records. Deleted '83. Catalogue no: **MCA 651**

Iron Heart

RUNNING AWAY
Tracks: / Running away / How do you feel / Last chance.
12" Single: Released Jan '88, on Listen, Catalogue no: **LIST 112**

TONTO IRIE - NEW YORK LIFE (Released on Mango)

Iron Horse

Biographical details: Ironhorse At the time of their only hit single, this Canadian rock band consisted of Randy Bachman, Mike Baird, John Pierce and Tom Sparks. After enjoying major success with Guess Who and Bachman Turner Overdrive (whom he quit in 1977), guitarist/vocalist/songwriter Randy Bachman launched Ironhorse in 1979 with an eponymous debut album. It contained the single *Sweet Lui-Louise* which was nothing more than a tired rehash of BTO's classic single *You Ain't Seen Nothing Yet. Sweet Lui Louise peaked at No.36 in the States and No. 60 in Britain.*
For the second LO Everything Is Grey, Bachman revamped the group's line-up; but it was quite clear that they had nothing original to offer and Ironhorse soon disintegrated. Bachman, who is the father of eight children then disappeared from the music scene for a while but reformed BTO in 1984. Bob Macdonald 6/11/85.

SWEET LUI-LOUISE
Tracks: / Sweet Lui-Louise.
7" Single: Released Apr '79, on Scotti Bros (USA), Deleted '82. Catalogue no: **K 11271**

WHAT'S YOUR HURRY DARLIN'
Tracks: / What's your hurry darlin' / Try a little harder.
7" Single: Released Nov '80, on Scotti Bros (USA), Deleted '83. Catalogue no: **K 11497**

Iron Maiden

Biographical details: Irom Maiden At the time of their greatest success, this British heavy metal band comprised Clive Burr, Bruce Dickinson, Steve Harris, Dave Murray and Adrian Smith. The group took its name from a medieval torture cage with spikes inside its lid, which closed in on its victim - the band's music was intended to contain equally incisive characteristics.
Iron Maiden was formed by bassist Harris in 1976, who became the group's key songwriter. His story was one of dogged determination to succeed on his own terms despite all the odds being against him; he could claim to be one of rock's true grafters. The band was formed at the start of Britain's punk explosion and for the following three years, the heavy metal genre was dismissed as passe by almost everyone except for a small hard-core of musicians and fans.
The tenacity of those loyal headbangers was rewarded in 1980, when HM made a major comeback on the British charts. In that year Iron Maiden's self-titled debut LP cruised to No.4 on the UK album chart; and they achieved a trio of Top 40 singles - *Running Free, Sanctuary,* and *Women In Uniform,* - despite the fact that heavy metal was almost totally ignored by the British Radio establishment.
A succession of personnel changes culminated in the replacement of lead vocalist Paul Di'anno by former Samson singer Bruce Dicksinson. In commercial terms, the bands hit its UK peak in 1982 with the No.1 album *The Number of the Beast* and the Top 10 single *Run To The Hills.* The LP also enjoyed a healthy forefront of the international hard rock scene. In keeping with Harris's 'success the hard way' life story, they gained the reputation of being one of the world's most feverishly workaholic touring groups. Their record sleeves were instantly recognisable because of Derek Riggs' revolting horror comic artwork which depicted the band's demonic mascot, Eddie the Head, in a never ending variety of gory guises.
Iron Maiden continued to combine melodic class and dynamic musicianship with their uncompromisingly frantic energy. The albums *Piece of Mind* (1983) and *Powerslave* (1984) were both UK Top 5 items, and they each spawned a pair of Top 20 singles despite a continued dearth of airplay. In the autumn of 1984, the band embarked on a 13 month world tour in which they played 287 concerts in 28 countries. As it reached its climax in 1985, the *Live After Death* LP was released; and all royalties from their UK Top 20 single *Running Free* (a live revival of their very first hit) were donated to the fight against drug abuse. Bob Macdonald 6/11/85.

2 MINUTES TO MIDNIGHT
Tracks: / 2 minutes to midnight.
7" Single: Released Aug '84, on EMI, by EMI Records. Catalogue no: **EMI 5489**
12" Single: Released Nov '87, on EMI (Germany), by EMI Records. Catalogue no: **2002896**
12" Single: Released Aug '84, on EMI, by EMI Records. Catalogue no: **12 EMI 5489**

ACES HIGH (SINGLE)
Tracks: / Aces high.
Note: (Cat. No. 2003856)-12" Import Single.
12" Pic: Released Oct '84, on EMI, by EMI Records. Deleted '88. Catalogue no: **12EMIP 5502**
7" Single: Released Oct '84, on EMI, by EMI Records. Catalogue no: **EMI 5502**
12" Single: Released Nov '87, on EMI (Germany), by EMI Records. Catalogue no: **2003856**
12" Single: Released Oct '84, on EMI, by EMI Records. Catalogue no: **12 EMI 5502**

CAN I PLAY WITH MADNESS
Tracks: / Can I play with madness / Black Bart blues / Massacre* (*Extra track on 12" and CD only.).
CD 5": Released May '88, on EMI (Holland), by EMI Records. Catalogue no: **2024602**
CD 5": Released 21 Mar '88, on EMI, by EMI Records. Deleted Jun '89. Catalogue no: **CDEM 49**
7" Pic: Released Oct '88, on Capitol (USA), by Capitol (USA) Records. Catalogue no: **V 15375**
7" Pic: Released 21 Mar '88, on EMI, by EMI Records. Deleted Jun '89. Catalogue no: **EMP 49**
7" Single: Released 14 Mar '88, on EMI, by EMI Records. Deleted Aug '89. Catalogue no: **EM 49**
7" Single: Released 14 Mar '88, on EMI, by EMI Records. Deleted 31 Jul '88. Catalogue no: **EMS 49**
12" Single: Released 21 Mar '88, on EMI, by EMI Records. Catalogue no: **12EM 49**

CLAIRVOYANT, THE
Tracks: / Clairvoyant, The / Prisoner, The (live) / Heaven can wait (live) (Not on 7".).
Note: Recorded live at Monsters Of Rock, Donington Park, 20th August 1988.
CD 5": Released Nov '88, on EMI, by EMI Records. Deleted Jun '89. Catalogue no: **CDEM 79**
7" Pic: Released Nov '88, on EMI, by EMI Records. Deleted Oct '89. Catalogue no: **EMP 79**
7" Single: Released Nov '88, on EMI, by EMI Records. Catalogue no: **EM 79**
7" Single: Released Nov '88, on EMI, by EMI Records. Catalogue no: **EMS 79**
12" Single: Released Nov '88, on EMI, by EMI Records. Deleted Aug '89. Catalogue no: **12EMG 79**
12" Single: Released Nov '88, on EMI, by EMI Records. Catalogue no: **12EM 79**

EVIL THAT MEN DO, THE
Tracks: / Evil that men do, The / Prowler '88 / Charlotte the harlot '88.
Note: All tracks engineered and mixed by Martin Birch. (P) 1988 Original Sound Recordings made by EMI Records Ltd.
CD 5": Released Aug '88, on EMI, by EMI Records. Deleted Oct '89. Catalogue no: **CDEM 64**
7" Pic: Released Aug '88, on EMI, by EMI Records. Deleted Jun '89. Catalogue no: **EMP 64**
7" Single: Released Aug '88, on EMI, by EMI Records. Deleted Aug '89. Catalogue no: **EM 64**
7" Single: Released Aug '88, on EMI, by EMI Records. Deleted Aug '89. Catalogue no: **EMG 64**
12" Single: Released Aug '88, on EMI, by EMI Records. Deleted Jun '89. Catalogue no: **12EMS 64**
12" Single: Released Aug '88, on EMI, by EMI Records. Catalogue no: **12EM 64**

FLIGHT OF ICARUS
Tracks: / Flight of Icarus.
7" Single: Released May '82, on EMI, by EMI Records. Deleted '85. Catalogue no: **EMI 5378**
12" Single: Released Nov '87, on EMI (Germany), by EMI Records. Catalogue no: **05207721**

IRON MAIDEN EP
Tracks: / Running free / Remember tomorrow / Killers / Innocent exile.
12" Single: Released Aug '81, on EMI, by EMI Records. Deleted '84. Catalogue no: **12EMI 5219**

LIVE + ONE (EP)
Tracks: / Sanctuary (live) / Phantom of the opera (live) / Women in uniform (live) / Drifter (live).
12" Single: Released Jul '88, on EMI (Japan), by EMI Records. Catalogue no: **EMS 41001**

MAIDEN JAPAN
Tracks: / Maiden Japan / Running free / Remember tomorrow / Killers / Innocent excile.
7" Single: Released Sep '81, on EMI, by EMI Records. Deleted '83. Catalogue no: **EMI 5219**
12" Single: Released Sep '81, on EMI, by EMI Records. Deleted '83. Catalogue no: **EMI 125219**
12" Single: Released Nov '87, on EMI (Germany), by EMI Records. Catalogue no: **06207534**

NUMBER OF THE BEAST (SINGLE)
Tracks: / Number of the beast, The / Remember tomorrow.
7" Single: Released May '82, on EMI, by EMI Records. Catalogue no: **EMI 5287**
12" Single: Released Jul '88, on EMI (Holland), by EMI Records. Catalogue no: **0521076386**

PURGATORY
Tracks: / Purgatory / Genghis Khan.
7" Single: Released Jun '81, on EMI, by EMI Records. Deleted '84. Catalogue no: **EMI 5184**

RUN TO THE HILLS (LIVE)
Tracks: / Run to the hills (live).
12" Pic: Released Dec '85, on EMI, by EMI Records. Deleted '86. Catalogue no: **12EMIP 5542**
7" Single: Released Dec '85, on EMI, by EMI Records. Catalogue no: **EMI 5542**
12" Single: Released Dec '85, on EMI, by EMI Records. Catalogue no: **12EMI 5542**

RUN TO THE HILLS (SINGLE)
Tracks: / Run to the hills / Total eclipse.
Note: (Cat.No. 2009826 - 12" Import single).
7" Pic: Released Jan '82, on EMI, by EMI Records. Deleted '84. Catalogue no: **EMIP 5263**
7" Single: Released Jan '82, on EMI, by EMI Records. Catalogue no: **EMI 5263**
12" Single: Released Nov '87, on EMI (Germany), by EMI Records. Catalogue no: **2009826**

RUNNING FREE
Tracks: / Running free / Burning ambition.
Note: (Cat. No. 200819. 12" Import Single).
7" Single: Released Feb '80, on EMI, by EMI Records. Deleted '83. Catalogue no: **EMI 5032**
12" Single: Released Nov '87, on EMI (Germany), by EMI Records. Catalogue no: **2008196**

RUNNING FREE (LIVE)
Tracks: / Running free (live).
7" Single: Released Sep '85, on EMI, by EMI Records. Catalogue no: **EMI 5532**
12" Single: Released Sep '85, on EMI, by EMI Records. Catalogue no: **12 EMI 5532**

SANCTUARY
Tracks: / Sanctuary / Drifter.
7" Single: Released Jun '80, on EMI, by EMI Records. Deleted '83. Catalogue no: **EMI 5065**

STRANGER IN A STRANGE LAND
Tracks: / Stranger in a strange land / That girl / Juanita.
12" Pic: Released Nov '86, on EMI, by EMI Records. Deleted Jan '88. Catalogue no: **12EMIP 5589**
7" Single: Released Nov '86, on EMI, by EMI Records. Catalogue no: **EMI 5589**

TROOPER, THE
Tracks: / Trooper, The.
7" Pic: Released Jun '83, on EMI, by EMI Records. Catalogue no: **EMIP 5397**
7" Single: Released Jun '83, on EMI, by EMI Records. Catalogue no: **EMI 5397**
12" Single: Released Nov '87, on EMI (Germany), by EMI Records. Catalogue no: **1077646**

TWILIGHT ZONE
Tracks: / Twilight zone / Wrathchild.
7" Single: Released Mar '81, on EMI, by EMI Records. Deleted '84. Catalogue no: **EMI 5145**
12" Single: Released Mar '81, on EMI, by EMI Records. Deleted '84. Catalogue no: **TC EMI 5145**

WASTED YEARS
Tracks: / Wasted years / Reach out / Sheriff of Huddersfield, The (Extra track available on 12" version only.).
7" Pic: Released Aug '86, on EMI, by EMI Records. Deleted Oct '87. Catalogue no: **EMIP 5583**
7" Single: Released Aug '86, on EMI, by EMI Records. Deleted '88. Catalogue no: **EMI 5583**
12" Single: Released Aug '86, on EMI, by EMI Records. Catalogue no: **12 EMI 5583**

WOMEN IN UNIFORM
Tracks: / Women in uniform / Invasion / Phantom of the opera (Only on 12" single.).
Note: (Cat.No. 06207418) Seven Iron Maiden 12" singles, all in original picture bags. (Long unavailable in the U.K.).
7" Single: Released Oct '80, on EMI, by EMI Records. Catalogue no: **EMI 5105**
12" Single: Released Nov '87, on EMI (Germany), by EMI Records. Catalogue no: **06207418**
12" Single: Released Oct '80 on EMI, by EMI Records. Catalogue no: **12 EMI 5105**

I-Royals

CORONATION STREET
Tracks: / Coronation Street.
7" Single: Released May '83, on Media Marvels, Catalogue no: **MM 7004**
12" Single: Released May '83, on Media Marvels, Catalogue no: **MM 7004T**

Irrelevant Time

IF YOU WERE HERE
Tracks: / If you were here tonight.
7" Single: Released Aug '83, on Rhythmic, by Rhythmic Records. Catalogue no: **RMNS 4**

Irresistable Force

FREESTYLE
Tracks: / Freestyle.
12" Single: Released Jul '89, on Blueback, Catalogue no: **12 BBBK 7**

I WANT YOU
Tracks: / I want you.
12" Single: Released May '88, on Red Megaphone, Catalogue no: **DMT 001**

Irving, Bobby

MISS MALIBU
Tracks: / Miss Malibu.
12" Single: Released Oct '84, on Jaguar, Catalogue no: **Unknown**

Irving, Kevin

CHILDREN OF THE NIGHT
Tracks: / Children of the night.
12" Single: Released Oct '87, on Trax (USA), Catalogue no: **TX 145**

Irwin, Big Dee

SWINGING ON A STAR
Tracks: / Swinging on a star.
7" Single: Released Nov '63, on Colpix, by Columbia Pictures. Deleted '66. Catalogue no: **PX 11010**

Isaac, Chris

GONE RIDIN'
Tracks: / Gone ridin' / Talk to me.
7" Single: Released Jan '86, on Warner Bros., by WEA Records. Catalogue no: **W 8799**

Isaac, Tony

SQUADRON
Tracks: / Squadron.
7" Single: Released Oct '82, on BBC, by BBC Records & Tapes. Deleted '87. Catalogue no: **RESL 120**

Isaacs, Barry

SHE IS READY
Tracks: / She is ready / She is ready (version).
12" Single: Released Feb '86, on ADA, Catalogue no: **DAD 004**

THIS TIME BABY
Tracks: / This time baby / We're all in the rhythm.
12" Single: Released Jul '86, on Must Dance, Catalogue no: **MD 010**

Isaacs, David

JUST LIKE A SEA
Tracks: / Just like a sea.
12" Single: on Attack, Deleted '88. Catalogue no: **TACK 13**

MORE LOVE
Tracks: / More love.
12" Single: Released May '82, on Cartridge, Catalogue no: **CRD 102**

Isaacs, Dennis

SHE LOVES ME NOW
Tracks: / She loves me now / Come dub me now.
12" Single: Released Mar '86, on Striker Lee, Catalogue no: **SSLD 001**

Isaacs, Gregory

Biographical details: Isaacs, Gregory This Jamaican singer and songwriter was raised in the shanty towns of the nation's capital Kingston. He began his recording career in the late Sixties, just as the established ska and rock steady genres were evolving into the new 'reggae' music. He released a series of well-received singles during the early Seventies, culminating in the appearance of his debut LP *In Person* in 1975. The latter part of the decade saw Isaacs' work gaining greater and greater recognition, not only in Jamaica but also amongst the reggae fraternity in Britain. His work, often of a political and sociological nature, was somehow given an added ingredient of integrity by the simmering clarity and quality of high high but not delicate voice.
Paying increasing attention to the British market, Isaaces (now nicknamed the Cool Ruler) established himself in the early Eighties as arguably the top reggae performer in the world, following the tragically early death of Bob Marley. Turning his attention more and more towards the triumphs, ten-

derness and tribulations of love, he scored his first two entries on the UK national LP charts with *More Gregory* (1981) and the classic *Night Nurse* (1982). The latter set included the beautiful single *Cool Down The Pace*. He continued in fine form in late 1983 with the *Out Deh!* album, which ranged from the infectious riff-laden snappiness of *Good Morning* to the dignified passion of *Love Me With Feeling*.
The suave, dapper image of the Cool Ruler projected on the cover of *Out Deh!* belied the fact that he had recently endured a brief prison spell for possession of firearms, the latest of many altercations with the law. Like many of his fellow countrymen, his road to success had been a long and hazardous one. (Bob Macdonald 6/11/85).

BABY I LIED TO YOU
Tracks: / Baby I lied to you.
12" Single: Released Sep '84, on Dynamite, Catalogue no: **Not known**

BANG BALLET
Tracks: / Bang ballet.
12" Single: Released Jun '86, on Tads, Catalogue no: **TRD 15586**

CHUNNIE YOU ARE NO.1
Tracks: / Chunnie you are no.1.
12" Single: Released '79, on GG'S, Deleted '80. Catalogue no: **GG 037 80**

COOL DOWN THE PACE
Tracks: / Cool down the pace / Stranger.
10" single: Released Oct '82, on Island, by Island Records. Catalogue no: **10WIP 6828**
7" Single: Released Oct '84, on Island, by Island Records. Deleted '84. Catalogue no: **WIP 6828**
12" Single: Released Dec '82, on Island, by Island Records. Catalogue no: **12WIP 6828**

CORONATION MARKET
Tracks: / Coronation market.
12" Single: Released Sep '88, on Tads, Catalogue no: **TRD 1187**

DANCING TIME
Tracks: / Dancing time.
12" Single: Released Nov '88, on Live & Love, Catalogue no: **LLD 96**

DISRESPECTFUL WOMAN
Tracks: / Disrespectful woman.
12" Single: Released Nov '85, on Fidel, Catalogue no: **FOO 1**

DON'T BELIEVE IN HIM
Tracks: / Don't believe in him / Who cares.
12" Single: Released Apr '83, on Silver Camel, Catalogue no: **SC 009**

DON'T DISTRESS
Tracks: / Don't distress.
12" Single: Released Oct '88, on Bun Gem, Catalogue no: **BG 0023**

DREAM MY LIFE OVER
Tracks: / Dream my life over.
12" Single: Released Sep '86, on African Museum, Catalogue no: **Unknown**

DRIFTING AWAY
Tracks: / Drifting away.
12" Single: Released Oct '84, on African Museum, Catalogue no: **BTR 006**

GP
Tracks: / GP.
12" Single: Released Mar '85, on African Museum, Catalogue no: **AF 0050**

HARD DRUGS
Tracks: / Hard drugs.
12" Single: Released Aug '86, on Tappa Zukie, Catalogue no: **TZ 002**

HOLD ON
Tracks: / Hold on.
12" Single: Released Feb '89, on Manzie, Catalogue no: **MAN 001**

HOW I FEEL
Tracks: / How I feel.
12" Single: Released Jul '88, on Moodies, Catalogue no: **RG 14**

I DO
Tracks: / I do.
12" Single: Released Jan '89, on Redman International, Catalogue no: **VPRED 124**

I DO LOVE YOU
Tracks: / I do love you.
12" Single: Released Dec '88, on Phaze 1, Catalogue no: **PRF 2**

INSECURE
Tracks: / Insecure.
12" Single: Released Nov '88, on Supreme, by Supreme Records. Catalogue no: **UNKNOWN**

JUST HAVIN' FUN
Tracks: / Just having fun / Village, The.
12" Single: Released Oct '86, on Third World, Catalogue no: **TWDIS 3032**

JUST INFATUATION
Tracks: / Just infatuation.
7" Single: Released May '89, on African Museum, Catalogue no: **UNKNOWN**
12" Single: Released 10 Jul '89, on Jah Shaka, Catalogue no: **SHAKA 874**

KOOL RULER COME AGAIN
Tracks: / Kool ruler come again.
12" Single: Released Dec '84, on Tads, Catalogue no: **TRD 131184**

LET OFF SUPM
12" Single: Released May '85, on Greensleeves, by Greensleeves Records. Catalogue no: **GRED 181**

LOOKING FOR A LOVE
Tracks: / Looking for a love.
12" Single: Released Mar '89, on Bun Gem, Catalogue no: **BG 0035**

LOSING WAIT
Tracks: / Losing weight.
12" Single: Released May '86, on Blue Mountain, Catalogue no: **BM 019**

LOVE IS OVERDUE
Tracks: / Love is overdue / Why did you leave me.
7" Single: Released Mar '80, on GG, Deleted '83. Catalogue no: **GG 070**

LOVER'S MAGIC
Tracks: / Lover's magic / Magically yours.
12" Single: Released Apr '84, on Diamond C, Catalogue no: **DCD 003**

ME CAME AGAIN
Tracks: / Me came again.
12" Single: Released Nov '84, on African Museum, Catalogue no: **Not Known**

MIND YU DIS
Tracks: / Mind yu dis.
12" Single: Released Oct '88, on Greensleeves, by Greensleeves Records. Catalogue no: **GRED 230**

MUSICAL MURDER
Tracks: / Musical murder.
12" Single: Released Jul '85, on Blue Mountain, Catalogue no: **AM 010**

MUSICAL REVENGE
Tracks: / Musical revenge / Musical revenge (version).
12" Single: Released 23 May '87, on Tads, Catalogue no: **TRD 27287**

MY HEART IS BLEEDING
Tracks: / My heart is bleeding.
12" Single: Released Jun '89, on Super Power, Catalogue no: **SPD 44**

MY LOVE IS OVERDUE
Tracks: / My love is overdue.
12" Single: Released Jul '84, on GG'S, Catalogue no: **GG 070**

NIGHT NURSE (SINGLE)
Tracks: / Night nurse / Material man.
10" single: Released Aug '82, on Island, by Island Records. Deleted Aug '85. Catalogue no: **10WIP 6800**

NO GOOD GIRL
Tracks: / No good girl / Rockers non stop.
12" Single: Released Jun '86, on Greensleeves, by Greensleeves Records. Catalogue no: **GRED 202**

NO ONE BUT ME
Tracks: / No one but me.
12" Single: Released Jun '84, on Fu-Manchu, Catalogue no: **TC 15484**

ONE MAN AGAINST THE WORLD
Tracks: / One man against the world.
12" Single: Released Sep '88, on Tappa Zukie, Catalogue no: **TZ 2**

PERMANENT LOVER
Tracks: / Permanent lover / Version.
7" Single: Released Nov '81, on Pre, by Charisma Records. Deleted Nov '84. Catalogue no: **PRE 20**
12" Single: Released Nov '81, on Pre, by Charisma Records. Deleted Nov '84. Catalogue no: **PRE 20 12**

PRIVATE BEACH PARTY (SINGLE)
Tracks: / Private beach party.
12" Single: Released Jun '85, on Greensleeves, by Greensleeves Records. Catalogue no: **GRED 185**

REPORT TO ME
Tracks: / Report to me.
12" Single: Released Oct '89, on Greensleeves, by Greensleeves Records. Catalogue no: **GRED 256**
12" Single: Released Oct '89, on Greensleeves, by Greensleeves Records. Catalogue no: **GRED 256**

ROUGH NECK
Tracks: / Rough neck / Rough neck (instrumental).
12" Single: Released Aug '88, on Greensleeves, by Greensleeves Records. Catalogue no: **GRED 225**

RUMOURS
Tracks: / Rumours / Midnight / You'll never go to heaven (live).
12" Single: Released Apr '88, on Greensleeves, by Greensleeves Records. Catalogue no: **GRED 221**

TAKE A LOOK
Tracks: / Take a look.
12" Single: Released 5 Mar '88, on Live & Love, Catalogue no: **LLD 71**

TICKLE ME
Tracks: / Tickle me / Tickle me (version).
12" Single: Released Nov '86, on Tappa Zukie, Catalogue no: **TZ 101**

TOO GOOD TO BE TRUE
Tracks: / Too good to be true / Too good to be true (version).
7" Single: Released Jul '89, on Greensleeves, by Greensleeves Records. Catalogue no: **GRE 250**
12" Single: Released Jul '89, on Greensleeves, by Greensleeves Records. Catalogue no: **GRED 250**

TOO LATE
Tracks: / Too late / Lonely man.
7" Single: Released Mar '80, on Success (2), Deleted '83. Catalogue no: **SRLD 008**
12" Single: Released Aug '84, on Londisc, by Londisc Records. Catalogue no: **LDR 026**

UNFORGETTABLE
Tracks: / Unforgettable.
12" Single: Released Jan '89, on Pickout, Catalogue no: **PICK 20**

WHAT A DISASTER
Tracks: / What a disaster.
12" Single: Released Jan '89, on BP International, Catalogue no: **BPKT 1**

WHEN WILL I SEE YOU AGAIN?
Tracks: / When will I see you again?.
12" Single: Released May '88, on Now Generation, Catalogue no: **NG 018**

WHO HAVE EYES
Tracks: / Who have eyes.
12" Single: Released Oct '88, on Bun Gem, Catalogue no: **BG 0026**

WORKING HARD
Tracks: / Working hard.
7" Single: Released May '89, on Power House, Catalogue no: **PHT 22**

Isaacs, Owen

HEAVY LOAD
Tracks: / Heavy load / Heavy pressure.
12" Single: Released Aug '82, on Exclusive, Catalogue no: **EXC 601127**

MY STYLE
Tracks: / My style / Come on.
12" Single: Released Jan '86, on Natami Music, Catalogue no: **O.1.003**

Isaak, Chris

BLUE HOTEL
Tracks: / Blue hotel / Waiting for the rain to fall.
12" Pic: Released Jul '87, on Warner Bros., by WEA Records. Deleted Jul '88. Catalogue no: **W 8374TP**
7" Single: Released Jul '87, on Warner Bros., by WEA Records. Deleted Jul '88. Catalogue no: **W 8374**
12" Single: Released Jul '87, on Warner Bros., by WEA Records. Catalogue no: **W 8374T**

YOU OWE ME SOME KIND OF LOVE
Tracks: / You owe me some kind of love / Waiting for the train to fall.
7" Single: Released Apr '87, on Warner Bros., by WEA Records. Deleted Jan '88. Catalogue no: **W 8467**
12" Single: Released Apr '87, on Warner Bros., by WEA Records. Deleted Jan '88. Catalogue no: **W 8467T**

Ish

YOU'RE MY ONLY LOVER
Tracks: / You're my only lover / It ain't necessarily so.
7" Single: Released Apr '86, on Geffen, by Geffen Records (USA). Deleted '86. Catalogue no: **A 7029**

Isley Brothers

Biographical details: Isley Brothers This American family soul group consists of three singing siblings: O'Kelly Isley, Ronald Isley and Rudolph Isley. For much of their career, they have been augmented by a younger instrumental trio comprising two further brothers, Ernie Isley and Marvin Isley, plus cousin Chris Jasper.
The Isley Brothers hailed originally from Cincinnati and started out as gospel sisngers. They moved to New York in 1957 and soon followed the lead of such gospel greats as Sam Cooke in switching to a secular style. Despite the fact that the Isleys did not get into their commercial stride until the late Sixties, their early career contained three landmarks that had a bearing upon future pop music - their wild and exuberant 1959 single *Shout* became a US Top 10 hit for Joey Dee & The Starliters in 1962 and a British smash for Lulu & The Luvvers in 1964; their 1962 single *Twist and Shout* was made even more famous by The Beatles and Brian Poole & The Tremeloes; and they nurtured the career of the up and comming Jimmi Hendrix by employing him as a session guitarist.
The erratic career of the Isleys received a boost in 1966, when they reached the US No.12 position with *This Old Heart of Mine*, written by Tamla Motown's golden Holland/Dozier/Holland team. This single was a belated UK Top 3 smash in late 1968, and came to be regarded as a classic by the British public. During 1969 there were several more Tamla hits for the Brothers in the UK, including a No.5 success with *Behind A Painted Smile*. However, the Isleys were dissatisfield with Motown and quit the company in 1969 in order to excercise greater control over their output via their own T-Neck label. Tis move quickly resulted in a US No.2 hit with the self-penned *It's Your Thing*.
Many observers would cite 1973-76 as the Isley Brothers' most creative period. During these years, their hits ranged from the mesmerising soul-rock fusion of *That Lady* to the evocative relaxed bliss of *Summer Breeze*, from the raw earthiness of *Fight The Power* to the humanitarian concern of *Harvest For The World*. The latter song raised the subject of Third World hunger, many years before projects like Band Aid and USA for Africa made it a fashionable cause in pop music.
Take Me To The Next Phase (1978) and *It's A Disco Night* (1979) were worthy attempts to jump on the disco bandwagon, but the Brothers were never quite at home in the beats-per-minute era of the late Seventies. The ultra-soulful *Between The Sheets* (1983) was their best song of the early Eighties but, by this time, their chart success on both sides of the Atlantic was less than spectacular. Wishing to break free from their junior status in the sextet, the three younger members formed a new trio in 1984 - billed as Isley, Jasper & Isley, they proved they could make it on their own with their beautiful 1985 song *Caravan of Love*. Meanwhile the remaining Isley Brothers were left as a trio, just as they had been in the early days. They could look back on a career, spanning from the Fifties to the Eighties, which had been inconsistent but had yielded much great soul music. (Bob MacDonald 6/11/85).
Over the past thirty years the Isley Brothers have become one of the most enduring and original acts in black music. Starting as a gospel quartet in their hometown of Cincinnati, Ohio, with their mother backing them on piano, they have since travelled a long and winding road to become black music's first self contained band. Unlike many groups calling themselves brothers, the Isleys really were brothers, Ronnie, Rudolph, O'Kelly and Vernon first started singing together in the fifties. After Vernon's tragic death, the group disbanded, but returned to singing a year later. The recordings made between April 1959 and July 1960, were recorded for their first affiliation with a major label, RCA Victor. By the time their first session for RCA in 1959, The Isley Brothers had already been recording for a couple of years (Teenage, Cindy, Gone and Mark X labels). RCA producers Hugo Peretti and Luigi Creatore tried some titles with the Isleys in the '50's vocal group tradition (*Not one minute more* and *Turn to me*). By contrast, *I'm gonna knock on your door* was a flamboyant and gritty performance that was obviously a gesture toward the rock & roll market. A year later *Shout! (Parts 1 & 2)* appeared back-to-back on a new single - and a rock 'n' roll standard was born! It was during the RCA sessions that the Isley Brothers first established their unique and justly renowned style that would, of course, influence the Beatles and a host of lesser lights. And after the passage of almost 30 years, many of these sides still sound as explosive as ever. (Bear Family, 1988)..

6 TRACK HITS: ISLEY BROTHERS
Tracks: / Listen to the music / Brown eyed girl / Harvest for the world / Under the influence of love / You still feel the need / Don't let me be lonely tonight.
7" EP: Released Sep '83, on Scoop 33, by Pickwick Records. Catalogue no: **7SR 5026**

BEHIND A PAINTED SMILE
Tracks: / Behind a painted smile.
7" Single: Released May '69, on Motown, by BMG Records (UK). Deleted '72. Catalogue no: **TMG 693**

BETWEEN THE SHEETS (SINGLE)
Tracks: / Between the sheets.
7" Single: Released Jun '83, on Epic, by CBS Records. Catalogue no: **A 3513**
12" Single: Released Jun '83, on Epic, by

CBS Records. Deleted '84. Catalogue no: **TA 3513**

COLDER ARE MY NIGHTS
Tracks: / Colder are my nights / Colder are my nights (Instrumental).
7" Single: Released Jan '86, on Warner Bros., by WEA Records. Catalogue no: **W 8860**
12" Single: Released Jan '86, on Warner Bros., by WEA Records. Catalogue no: **W 8860T**

DON'T SAY GOODNIGHT, IT'S TIME FOR LOVE
Tracks: / Don't say goodnight it's time for love / Don't say goodnight it's time for love (part 2.
7" Single: Released 20 Jun '80, on Epic, by CBS Records. Deleted '83. Catalogue no: **EPC 8664**

HARVEST FOR THE WORLD (OLD GOLD)
12" Single: Released Jul '88, on Old Gold, by Old Gold Records. Catalogue no: **OG 4069**

HARVEST FOR THE WORLD (SINGLE)
Tracks: / Harvest for the world / Who loves you better (parts 1 & 2) (on 12" only) / Summer breeze (Only on (6531547) 7".).
7" Single: Released Jul '76, on Epic, by CBS Records. Deleted '79. Catalogue no: **EPC 4369**
7" Single: Released Oct '88, on Epic, by CBS Records. Deleted 17 Apr '89. Catalogue no: **653154 7**
7" Single: Released May '82, on Epic, by CBS Records. Catalogue no: **CBS 8862**
7" Single: Released Jun '86, on Epic, by CBS Records. Deleted '86. Catalogue no: **A 7234**

HIGHWAY OF MY LIFE
Tracks: / Highway of my life.
7" Single: Released Jan '74, on Epic, by CBS Records. Deleted '77. Catalogue no: **EPC 1980**

HIGHWAY OF MY LIFE(OLD GOLD)
Tracks: / Highway of my life.
7" Single: Released Apr '83, on Old Gold, by Old Gold Records. Catalogue no: **OG 9311**

I GUESS I'LL ALWAYS LOVE YOU
Tracks: / I guess I'll always love you.
7" Single: Released Sep '66, on Motown, by BMG Records (UK). Deleted '69. Catalogue no: **TMG 572**
7" Single: Released Mar '83, on Motown, by BMG Records (UK). Catalogue no: **TMG 979**

INSIDE YOU (SINGLE)
Tracks: / Inside you / Love zone.
7" Single: Released Jan '80, on Epic, by CBS Records. Deleted Jan '83. Catalogue no: **EPC A 131741**
7" Single: Released Oct '81, on Epic, by CBS Records. Deleted '85. Catalogue no: **EPC A 1741**

ITS A DISCO NIGHT (OLD GOLD)
Tracks: / It's a disco night (rock don't stop) / That lady / Summer breeze / It's your thing.
12" Single: Released Feb '86, on Old Gold, by Old Gold Records. Catalogue no: **OG 4006**

ITS A DISCO NIGHT (ROCK DON'T STOP)
Tracks: / It's a disco night (Rock don't stop).
7" Single: Released Nov '79, on Epic, by CBS Records. Deleted '82. Catalogue no: **EPC 7911**

IT'S YOUR THING
Tracks: / It's your thing.
7" Single: Released Jun '69, on Major Minor, Deleted '72. Catalogue no: **MM 621**

PUT YOURSELF IN MY PLACE
Tracks: / Put yourself in my place.
7" Single: Released Jul '69, on Motown, by BMG Records (UK). Deleted '72. Catalogue no: **TMG 708**

SUMMER BREEZE
Tracks: / Summer breeze.
7" Single: Released May '74, on Epic, by CBS Records. Deleted '77. Catalogue no: **EPC 2244**

TAKE ME TO THE NEXT PHASE
Tracks: / Take me to the next phase.
7" Single: Released May '78, on Epic, by CBS Records. Deleted '80. Catalogue no: **EPC 6292**

THAT LADY
Tracks: / That lady.
7" Single: Released Sep '73, on Epic, by CBS Records. Deleted '76. Catalogue no: **EPC 1704**

THAT LADY (OLD GOLD)
Tracks: / That lady.
7" Single: Released Apr '83, on Old Gold, by Old Gold Records. Catalogue no: **OG 9317**

THIS OLD HEART OF MINE (SINGLE)
Tracks: / This old heart of mine / Behind a painted smile.
7" Single: Released Apr '66, on Motown, by BMG Records (UK). Deleted '69. Catalogue no: **TMG 555**
7" Single: Released Oct '81, on Motown, by BMG Records (UK). Catalogue no: **TMG 937**
7" Single: Released Jun '83, on Motown, by BMG Records (UK). Catalogue no: **TMG 1050**

TONIGHT IS THE NIGHT
Tracks: / Tonight is the night / Who said.
7" Single: Released Apr '81, on Epic, by CBS Records. Deleted '85. Catalogue no: **EPC A 1122**

TWIST & SHOUT (SINGLE)
Tracks: / Twist and shout.
7" Single: Released Jul '63, on Stateside, by EMI Records. Deleted '66. Catalogue no: **SS 112**

WINNER TAKES ALL (SINGLE)
Tracks: / Winner takes all / Fun and games.
7" Single: Released Jan '80, on Epic, by CBS Records. Deleted '83. Catalogue no: **EPC 7795**

Isley Jasper Isley

CARAVAN OF LOVE (OLD GOLD)
Tracks: / Caravan of love / Voyage to Atlantis.
12" Single: Released Aug '88, on Old Gold, by Old Gold Records. Catalogue no: **OG 4076**

CARAVAN OF LOVE (SINGLE)
Tracks: / Caravan of love.
7" Single: Released Nov '85, on Epic, by CBS Records. Catalogue no: **A 6612**
12" Single: Released Nov '85, on Epic, by CBS Records. Catalogue no: **TA 6612**

EIGHTH WONDER OF THE WORLD
Tracks: / Eighth wonder of the world / Broadway's closer to Sunset Boulevard.
7" Single: Released Apr '87, on Epic, by CBS Records. Deleted Nov '87. Catalogue no: **650750 7**
12" Single: Released Jun '87, on Epic, by CBS Records. Deleted Nov '87. Catalogue no: **650750 8**
12" Single: Released Apr '87, on Epic, by CBS Records. Deleted Nov '87. Catalogue no: **650750 6**

INSATIABLE WOMAN
Tracks: / Insatiable woman / Break this chain / Caravan of love / I can't get over losing you.
7" Set: Released Feb '86, on Epic, by CBS Records. Catalogue no: **DTA 6861**
7" Single: Released Feb '86, on Epic, by CBS Records. Catalogue no: **A 6861**
12" Single: Released Feb '86, on Epic, by CBS Records. Catalogue no: **TA 6861**

Isley, Rem

WHEN ARE WE FATED IN ME YARD
Tracks: / When are we fated in me yard.
12" Single: Released Jul '85, on Dubplate, Catalogue no: **DUB 02**

Isol

WEATHERED STATUES
Tracks: / Weathered statues.
7" Single: Released Sep '82, on Alternative Tentacles, by Alternative Tentacles Records. Catalogue no: **VIRUS 10**

Isolation

MARIANNA
Tracks: / Marianna.
7" Single: Released Aug '85, on What Records, Catalogue no: **WR 72**

I.S.P.

I'M ON A ROLL
Tracks: / I'm on a roll / Making a killing.
7" Single: Released Aug '88, on Champion, by Champion Records. Catalogue no: **CHAMP 87**
12" Single: Released Aug '88, on Champion, by Champion Records. Deleted Aug '89. Catalogue no: **CHAMP 12 87**

I-Spy Club

MEMORIES ARE MADE OF THIS
Tracks: / Memories are made of this.
7" Single: Released Nov '82, on State, by State Records. Catalogue no: **STAT 116**

ROSETTA BLUE
Tracks: / Rosetta blue / I-spy.
7" Single: Released Sep '82, on State, by State Records. Catalogue no: **STAT 114**
12" Single: Released Oct '82, on State, by State Records. Catalogue no: **STAT 114T**

Israelites

ISRAELITES
Tracks: / Israelites: *Various artists* / Monkey spanner: *Various artists* / It Mek: *Various artists* / Side show: *Various artists*.
7" EP: Released Mar '80, on Trojan, by Trojan Records. Deleted Mar '83. Catalogue no: **TMX 4010**

Issachar, Barry

TURN ME ON
Tracks: / Turn me on.
12" Single: Released Jun '82, on Black Music, Catalogue no: **BM 701**

Issachar, Hudhie

COVER LOVER
Tracks: / Cover lover.
12" Single: Released Aug '83, on Negus Roots, Catalogue no: **NERT 020**

GHOSTBUSTERS
Tracks: / Ghostbusters.
12" Single: Released Mar '85, on Macabeen, Catalogue no: **MPCH 1**

It

GALLUMAUFRY GALLERY
Tracks: / Gallimaufry gallery / Larry Heard and Harry Dennis.
12" Single: Released Jul '88, on Anxious, by Anxious Records. Catalogue no: **BLMK 1**

It Bites

CALLING ALL THE HEROES
Tracks: / Calling all the heroes / Strange but true (7" only) / Calling all the heroes (full length version) (12" only) / Strange but true (full length version) (12" only).
7" Single: Released Jun '86, on Virgin, by Virgin Records. Catalogue no: **VS 872**
12" Single: Released Jun '86, on Virgin, by Virgin Records. Catalogue no: **VS 872-12**

KISS LIKE JUDAS
Tracks: / Kiss like Judas / Staring at the whitewash / Kiss like Judas (extended mix) (On CD & cassette only).
CD 5": Released Apr '88, on Virgin, by Virgin Records. Catalogue no: **CDEP 21**
7" Single: Released Feb '88, on Virgin, by Virgin Records. Catalogue no: **VS 983**
12" Single: Released Feb '88, on Virgin, by Virgin Records. Catalogue no: **VS 983-12**

MIDNIGHT
Tracks: / Midnight / You'll never go to heaven (live) (7 & 12" only) / You'll never go to heaven (CD only) / Midnight (extended version) (CD & 12" only).
CD 5": Released Aug '88, on Virgin, by Virgin Records. Catalogue no: **VSCD 1065**
7" Single: Released Apr '88, on Virgin, by Virgin Records. Catalogue no: **VS 1065**
12" Single: Released Apr '88, on Virgin, by Virgin Records. Catalogue no: **VST 1065**

OLD MAN AND THE ANGEL, THE
Tracks: / Old man and the angel, The (On all versions) / Castles (7" only) / Old man and the angel, The (CD & 12' only) / Castles (full-length version) (CD & 12" only) / Calling all the heroes (full length version) (CD only).
CD 5": Released '88, on Virgin, by Virgin Records. Catalogue no: **MIKE 94112**
7" Single: Released Apr '87, on Virgin, by Virgin Records. Deleted '89. Catalogue no: **VS 941**
12" Single: Released Apr '87, on Virgin, by Virgin Records. Catalogue no: **VS 941-12**
12" Single: Released Apr '87, on Virgin, by Virgin Records. Deleted May '88. Catalogue no: **VSG 941-12**

SISTER SARAH
Tracks: / Sister Sarah / Bullet in the barrel / Woman is an addict, The.
7" Single: Released Jul '89, on Virgin, by Virgin Records. Catalogue no: **VS 1202**
12" Single: Released Jul '89, on Virgin, by Virgin Records. Catalogue no: **VST 1202**
CD 3": Released Jul '89, on Virgin, by Virgin Records. Catalogue no: **VSCD 1202**

STILL TOO YOUNG TO REMEMBER
Tracks: / Still too young to remember / Vampires / Still too young to remember (extended version).
CD 5": Released 2 May '89, on Virgin, by Virgin Records. Catalogue no: **VSCDT 1184**
CD 5": Released 2 May '89, on Virgin, by Virgin Records. Catalogue no: **VSCDX 1184**
CD 5": Released 2 May '89, on Virgin, by Virgin Records. Catalogue no: **VSCD 1184**
7" Single: Released 2 May '89, on Virgin, by Virgin Records. Catalogue no: **VS 1184**
12" Single: Released 2 May '89, on Virgin, by Virgin Records. Catalogue no: **VST 1184**

UNDERNEATH YOUR PILLOW
Tracks: / Underneath your pillow / Still too young to remember (live).
7" Single: Released Sep '89, on Virgin, by Virgin Records. Catalogue no: **VS 1215**
12" Single: Released Sep '89, on Virgin, by Virgin Records. Catalogue no: **VST 1215**

WHOLE NEW WORLD
Tracks: / Whole new world / Black December / Calling all the heroes (live version) (12" only) / Whole new world (full length version) (12" only).
7" Single: Released Oct '86, on Virgin, by Virgin Records. Deleted May '88. Catalogue no: **VS 896**
12" Single: Released Oct '86, on Virgin, by Virgin Records. Catalogue no: **VS 896-12**

Italian Heroes

ALL FOR NOTHING
Tracks: / All for nothing.
7" Single: Released Jun '85, on Successful, Deleted '86. Catalogue no: **SR 304**

IT MUST BE THE LOVE
Tracks: / It must be the love.
7" Single: Released Oct '83, on Successful, Deleted '84. Catalogue no: **SR 303**

Italo Boot Mix

ITALO BOOT MIX VOLUME 4 Various artists
12" Single: Released Jan '86, on ZYX (Germany), Catalogue no: **ZYX 5338**

ITALO BOOT MIX VOLUME 5 Various artists
12" Single: Released Mar '86, on ZYX (Germany), Catalogue no: **ZYX 5397**

Itals

WHAT ABOUT ME?
Tracks: / What about me / Settle fe me.
12" Single: Released Aug '84, on Blues-ville International, Catalogue no: **BI 003**

Itch

TAKE ME TO YOUR LEADER
Tracks: / Take me to your leader.
12" Single: Released Sep '84, on Cafe Associates, Catalogue no: **OBCT 2**

Itopia

SUNSHINE LOVE
Tracks: / Sunshine love.
12" Single: Released Apr '85, on Wackies, Catalogue no: **W 999**

YOU'VE LOST THAT LOVING FEELING
Tracks: / You've lost that lovin' feeling.
12" Single: Released Nov '84, on Wackies, Catalogue no: **W 975**

It's A Secret

I CAN'T DANCE
Tracks: / I can't dance / This goes anywhere.
7" Single: Released Nov '86, on GC, Catalogue no: **GC 04**
12" Single: Released Nov '86, on GC, Catalogue no: **GCT 04**

It's Bigger...

IT'S BIGGER THAN BOTH OF US
Tracks: / It's bigger than both of us: *Various artists*.
7" Single: Released Feb '89, on Festival, by Musidisc Records (France). Catalogue no: **REV 210**

It's Immaterial

BETTER IDEA
Tracks: / Better idea, The.
12" Single: Released Mar '85, on Ark, by Ark Records (UK). Catalogue no: **DOVE 3**

DRIVING AWAY FROM HOME (JIM'S TUNE)
Tracks: / Driving away from home (Jim's tune) (On 7" only) / Trains,boats,planes / Driving away from home (wicked weather for walking) (on 12" only) / Crooked tune, A (On 12" only).
7" Single: Released May '86, on Siren, by Virgin Records. Catalogue no: **SIREN 15**
12" Single: Released May '86, on Siren, by Virgin Records. Catalogue no: **SIREN 1512**

DRIVING AWAY FROM HOME(CD SINGLE)
Tracks: / Driving away from home (Jim's tune) / Ed's funky diner / Driving away from home(after all its only "Dead man's curve).
CD 3": Released '88, on Virgin, by Virgin Records. Catalogue no: **CDT 26**

ED'S FUNKY DINER
Tracks: / Ed's funky diner / Friday night Saturday morning / I mean after all it's only dead man's curve (12" only).
7" Single: Released Oct '85, on Siren, by Virgin Records. Deleted May '88. Catalogue no: **SIREN 8**
12" Single: Released Oct '85, on Siren, by

Virgin Records. Deleted '89. Catalogue no: **SIREN 8-12**

ED'S FUNKY DINER (RE-ISSUE)
Tracks: / Ed's funky diner / Only the lonely / Driving away from home (I mean after all...) (12" only).
7" Single: Released Jul '86, on Siren, by Virgin Records. Catalogue no: **SIREN 24**
12" Single: Released Jul '86, on Siren, by Virgin Records. Catalogue no: **SIREN 24-12**

GIANT RAFT
Tracks: / Giant raft.
7" Single: Released Oct '82, on Wonderful World Of, by Wonderful World Of Records. Catalogue no: **WW 4**

GIGANTIC RAFT
7" Single: Released Feb '84, on Eternal, by Eternal Records. Catalogue no: **JF 4**
12" Single: Released Feb '84, on Eternal, by Eternal Records. Catalogue no: **JF 4T**

HE CALLED FROM THE KITCHEN...SPACE
Tracks: / Space, he called from the kitchen / Hereby hangs a tale / Space (version) (12" only).
7" Single: Released Nov '86, on Siren, by Virgin Records. Deleted May '88. Catalogue no: **SIREN 34**
12" Single: Released Nov '86, on Siren, by Virgin Records. Catalogue no: **SIREN 34-12**

ROPE
Tracks: / Rope / Festival time.
7" Single: Released Feb '87, on Siren, by Virgin Records. Deleted May '88. Catalogue no: **SIREN 38**
12" Single: Released Feb '87, on Siren, by Virgin Records. Deleted '89. Catalogue no: **SIREN 38-12**

It's Official

SPIES
Tracks: / Spies / No words.
12" Single: Released 31 Jul '89, on Subway dance, Catalogue no: **SD 4007**

WE ARE RESPONSIBLE
Tracks: / We are responsible.
12" Single: Released '88, on Subway, by Subway Records. Catalogue no: **SUB 049**

Ivan, Ranking

EDUCATION
Tracks: / Education / Guess who's a sucker for you.
12" Single: Released Sep '84, on Disco Tex, Catalogue no: **DT 10**

I've Got The Bullets

IT SHOULD HAVE BEEN ME
Tracks: / It should have been me / Special one.
7" Single: Released Feb '87, on Epic, by CBS Records. Deleted Aug '87. Catalogue no: **650091 7**

Ives, Burl

Biographical details:
Ives, Burl This American singer and actor began his career in folk music during the Thirties, trekking round the States as a solo performer.
During the late Forties and Fifties he did much to increase public awareness of folk and had a considerable influence on several of the genre's later artists.
In 1962 Ives suddenly achieved a run of hit singles on the pop charts.
A Little Bitty Tear reached No.9 on both sides of the Atlantic. *Funny Way of Laughin'* got to No.10 in the US and No.29 in UK, *Call Me Mr. In-Between* reached No.19 in the US and *Mary Ann regrets* peaked at No.39 in the US. Ives deep voice graced many novelty and children's records during his career and he later concentrated on religious material.
(Bob Macdonald 6/11/85).

FUNNY WAY OF LAUGHING
Tracks: / Funny way of laughing.
7" Single: Released May '62, on Brunswick, by Decca Records. Deleted '65. Catalogue no: **05868**

LITTLE BITTY TEAR, A
Tracks: / Little bitty tear, A.
7" Single: Released Jan '62, on Brunswick, by Decca Records. Deleted '65. Catalogue no: **05863**

Ivey, Lee

OLDER WOMEN
Tracks: / Older women.
7" Single: Released Jun '84, on Dingle's, by Dingle's Records. Catalogue no: **SID 237**

Ivory

LADY (IVORY)
Tracks: / Lady.
7" Single: Released May '85, on Gomez, Catalogue no: **JGM 7002**

YOU CAN'T FOOL EVERYBODY
Tracks: / You can't fool everybody / Every Friday.
7" Single: Released Sep '83, on Gomez, Catalogue no: **GM 7001**

Ivory Coasters

MAKOSSA MUNGAKA
Tracks: / Makossa mungaka.
7" Single: Released May '82, on Recreational, by Revolver Records. Catalogue no: **SPORT 6**
12" Single: Released May '82, on Recreational, by Revolver Records. Catalogue no: **SPORT 62**

Ivy League

Biographical details: Ivy League At the time of their greatest success, this British pop vocal group consisted of John Carter (real name John Shakespeare), Perry Ford (real name Bryan Pugh) and Ken Lewis (real name Kenneth Hawker).
The Ivy League came into being at the beginning of 1965. Prior to this, John and Ken had fronted a partially successful combo called Carter Lewis & The Southerners and had also worked as session singers. The three members of the Ivy League were basically lightweight songwriters with an excellent ear for compositions. The first hit was *Funny How Love Can Be*, which cruised to No.8 on the UK chart in early '65. It was followed by *That's Why I'm Crying* (No.22) and the real biggie *Tossing and Turning* (no.3). They sang the songs in a high-pitched harmony style reminiscent of the early Four Seasons and Beach Boys hits.
Carter quit the group in January 1966 and was replaced by another session singer, Tony Burrows. They had one minor Uk hit with *Willow Tree* by which time Neil Landon had reached Lewis' place. In 1967 the Ivy League became The Flowerpot Men and reached the Uk No.4 position with their blatantly opportunistic flower power cash-in *Let's Go To San Fransisco*.
The ubiquitous Burrows proceeded to sing on hits by Edison Lighthouse, White Plains, Brotherhood of Man, The Pipkins and First Class. The latter group's sole hit 1974's *Beach Baby* also featured the voice of John Carter who has subsequently made a living by doing music for commercials and jingles. Lewis had followed a similar road.

FUNNY HOW LOVE CAN BE
Tracks: / Funny how love can be.
7" Single: Released Feb '65, on Piccadilly, Deleted '68. Catalogue no: **7N 35222**

THAT'S WHY I'M CRYING
Tracks: / That's why I'm crying.
7" Single: Released May '65, on Piccadilly, Deleted '68. Catalogue no: **7N 35228**

TOSSIN' AND TURNIN' (OLD GOLD)
Tracks: / Tossin' and turnin' / Funny how love can be.
7" Single: Released Jan '89, on Old Gold, by Old Gold Records. Catalogue no: **OG 9838**

TOSSIN' AND TURNIN'
Tracks: / Tossin' and turnin'.
7" Single: Released Feb '65, on Piccadilly, Deleted '68. Catalogue no: **7N 35251**
7" Single: Released Apr '79, on Flashback, by Mainline Records. Catalogue no: **FBS 5**

WILLOW TREE
Tracks: / Willow tree.
7" Single: Released Jul '66, on Piccadilly, Deleted '69. Catalogue no: **7N 35326**

Ivy's

LONELY NIGHTS
Tracks: / Lonely nights.
7" Single: Released Jan '81, on Images, by Images Records. Deleted Jan '84. Catalogue no: **IMG 001**

J

The following information was taken from the Music Master database on October 20th, 1989

J, David

BLUE MOODS
Tracks: / Blue moods.
7" Single: Released Jul '85, on Glass, by Glass Records. Deleted Jan '87. Catalogue no: **GLAEP 101**

CROCODILE TEARS AND THE VELVET COSH (SINGLE)
Tracks: / Crocodile tears and the velvet cosh.
7" Single: Released Apr '85, on Glass, by Glass Records. Catalogue no: **GLASS 042**
12" Single: Released Apr '85, on Glass, by Glass Records. Catalogue no: **GLASS 12042**

I CAN'T SHAKE THIS SHADOW OF FEAR
Tracks: / I can't shake this shadow of fear / War game.
12" Single: Released Sep '84, on Glass, by Glass Records. Catalogue no: **GLASS 12039**
7" Single: Released Sep '84, on Glass, by Glass Records. Catalogue no: **GLASS 039**

JOE ORTON'S WEDDING
Tracks: / Joe Orton's wedding / Requiem for Joe / Gospel according to fear / Point of departure.
7" Single: Released Aug '83, on Situation 2, by Beggars Banquet Records. Catalogue no: **SIT 26**
12" Single: Released Aug '83, on Situation 2, by Beggars Banquet Records. Catalogue no: **SIT 26T**

PROMISED LAND
Tracks: / Promised / Saint Jackie / Seducer, a doctor, a card you cannot trust (on 12" only).
7" Single: Released Dec '83, on Glass, by Glass Records. Catalogue no: **GLASS 031**
12" Single: Released Dec '83, on Glass, by Glass Records. Catalogue no: **GLASS 12031**

V FOR VENDETTA
Tracks: / V for vendetta / This vicious cabaret.
12" Single: Released Jun '84, on Glass, by Glass Records. Deleted Jan '86. Catalogue no: **12GLASS 032**

J, Harry

LIQUIDATOR
Tracks: / Liquidator / Return of Django / Elizabethan reggae / It mek.
7" Single: Released May '82, on Trojan, by Trojan Records. Deleted '85. Catalogue no: **TMX 4005**

J, Polly

WHY DON'T THEY UNDERSTAND
Tracks: / Why don't they understand / Sailaway.
7" Single: Released Jul '82, on Regard, Deleted Jul '85. Catalogue no: **RG 101**

J, Sammy

ONE AND ONLY
Tracks: / One and only.
12" Single: Released Sep '89, on Flick, Catalogue no: **FLK 0029R**

J, Teresa

BUBBLING
Tracks: / Bubbling.
12" Single: Released Jun '89, on Rock'n'Groove, Catalogue no: **RNG 005**

J, Tommy

LOW PROFILE
Tracks: / Low profile / Take one.
7" Single: Released Apr '87, on Silent (1), by Silent Records. Deleted Jan '88. Catalogue no: **SIL 1**
12" Single: Released Apr '87, on Silent (1), by Silent Records. Deleted Jan '88. Catalogue no: **12 SIL 1**

Ja Ja Ja

KATZ RAP
Tracks: / Katz rap.
7" Single: Released Aug '83, on Atatak, Catalogue no: **6274**

Jab

PRETTY POLLY
Tracks: / Pretty Polly.
12" Single: Released Mar '89, on Jab, Catalogue no: **JAB 12001**

Jab Jab

KEEP ON SMILING
12" Single: Released Aug '85, on Rip Off (1), Catalogue no: **RPFF 1**

Jab Jab Music

LONELINESS IS NOT HAPPINESS
Tracks: / Loneliness is not happiness.
7" Single: Released Aug '81, on Shades, Catalogue no: **SH 3**

Jacas, Jake

HOLD ME (see panel below)
Tracks: / Hold me / Hold me (instr.).
7" Single: Released Jun '85, on Motown, by BMG Records (UK). Catalogue no: **ZB 40201**
12" Single: Released Jun '85, on Motown, by BMG Records (UK). Catalogue no: **ZT 40201**

Jacetti, Roberto

I SAVE THE DAY
Tracks: / I save the day.
7" Single: Released Jun '84, on Carrere, Catalogue no: **CAR 333**
12" Single: Released Jun '84, on Carrere, Catalogue no: **CART 333**

Jacinth, Joy

BABY BOY
Tracks: / Baby boy / Red lights.
7" Single: Released Mar '84, on Zebratone, by Zebratone Records. Catalogue no: **ZT 98**

Jack

SSSENSATIONAL
Tracks: / Sssensational.
7" Single: Released May '89, on Tosh, Catalogue no: **TOSH 001**
12" Single: Released May '89, on Tosh, Catalogue no: **12TOSH 001**

Jack E. Makossa

OPERA HOUSE, THE
Tracks: / Opera house, The / Opera house, The (African mix).
12" Single: Released Oct '88, on Champion, by Champion Records. Catalogue no: **CHAMPZ 1250**
7" Single: Released Sep '87, on Champion, by Champion Records. Catalogue no: **CHAMP 50**
12" Single: Released Oct '88, on Champion, by Champion Records. Catalogue no: **CHAMPX 1250**
12" Single: Released Sep '87, on Champion, by Champion Records. Catalogue no: **CHAMP 1250**
12" Single: Released Oct '88, on Champion, by Champion Records. Catalogue no: **CHAMP K1250**

Jack Factory

JACKIN JAMES
Tracks: / Jackin James / Bouncy house - Adrenalin.
12" Single: Released Jan '88, on Warrior, by Warrior Records. Catalogue no: **WR 12 002**

Jack & Jill

YOU
Tracks: / You.
7" Single: Released Jan '85, on Splash, by Splash Records. Catalogue no: **SP 28**

Jack 'n' Chill

BEATIN' THE HEAT
Tracks: / Beatin' the heat (7" only) / Dub that tune (NOT on 12") / Beatin' the heat (122 BPM in the shade) (On 12"& CD only) / Jack 'n' Chill (12" only) / Jack that house built, The (CD only).
CD 5": Released Jun '88, on 10 Records, by Virgin Records. Catalogue no: **TENCD 234**
7" Single: Released Jun '88, on 10 Records, by Virgin Records. Catalogue no: **TEN 234**
12" Single: Released Jun '88, on 10 Records, by Virgin Records. Catalogue no: **TENX 234**
12" Single: Released Jun '88, on 10 Records, by Virgin Records. Catalogue no: **TENR 234**

JACK THAT HOUSE BUILT, THE
Tracks: / Jack that house built, The / Jack that house dubbed, The (On all versions) / Jack that house built, The (demolition mix) (On TENR only).
12" Single: Released May '87, on 10 Records, by Virgin Records. Catalogue no: **TENT 174**
7" Single: Released May '87, on 10 Records, by Virgin Records. Catalogue no: **TEN 174**
12" Single: Released May '87, on 10 Records, by Virgin Records. Catalogue no: **TENR 174**

JAKE JACAS - HOLD ME (Released on Motown)

Jack Pack

SOUL IN THE BOX
Tracks: / Soul in the box / Star struck.
7" Single: Released Jan '81, on Dart, by President Records. Catalogue no: **ART 2063**

Jack, Ronnie

GOING FOR THE BIG ONE (SINGLE)
Tracks: / Going for the big one / Friends & lovers.
7" Single: Released Mar '81, on Ritz, by Ritz Records. Deleted Mar '84. Catalogue no: **RITZ 5**

HEY MARY ANN
Tracks: / Hey Mary Ann.
7" Single: Released Oct '83, on Plaza, by Plaza Records. Catalogue no: **PLAZA 005**

MOTOR RIDING
Tracks: / Motor riding / Friends and lovers.
7" Single: Released Apr '82, on Plaza, by Plaza Records. Catalogue no: **PLAZA 001**

Jack Rubies

BE WITH YOU
Tracks: / Be with you.
12" Single: Released 30 May '87, on Idea, by Idea Records. Catalogue no: **IDT 004**

FOOLISH BOY
Tracks: / Foolish boy.
12" Single: Released May '88, on Lush, by Lush Records. Catalogue no: **LUSH 001T**
7" Single: Released May '88, on Lush, by Lush Records. Catalogue no: **LUSH 001**

LOBSTER
Tracks: / Lobster, The.
7" Single: Released Oct '87, on Idea, by Idea Records. Catalogue no: **IDEA 008**
12" Single: Released Oct '87, on Idea, by Idea Records. Catalogue no: **IDEAT 008**

WRECKERS OF ENGINES
Tracks: / Wreckers of engines.
12" Single: Released Sep '88, on Lush, by Lush Records. Catalogue no: **LUSH 002 T**
7" Single: Released Sep '88, on Lush, by Lush Records. Catalogue no: **LUSH 002**

Jack The Bear

SKIN & BONE
Tracks: / Skin and bone / Carshunting / Cadillac.
7" Single: Released 13 Jun '87, on Backs, by Backs Recording Co.. Catalogue no **NCH 113**

Jack the Lad

REGGAE MUSIC
Tracks: / Reggae music.
7" Single: Released Apr '83, on Outlook Deleted '85. Catalogue no: **OUT 002**
12" Single: Released Jul '83, on Outlook, Deleted '85. Catalogue no: **OUTX 002**

Jackals

ALL IN A DAY
Tracks: / All in a day / Ringing in my ear / She just flies in / Baby let me follow you down.
12" Single: Released Jun '86, on Constitution, Catalogue no: **CON 1T**

UNDERNEATH THE ARCHES
Tracks: / Underneath the arches / Thunde machine.
12" Single: Released Jun '86, on Crimina Damage, Catalogue no: **CRI 12134**

WE ALL SIGN ON
Tracks: / We all sign on.
7" Single: Released Jul '87, on Constitu tion, Catalogue no: **CON 5**

Jackdaw With Crowbar

ICEBERG
Tracks: / Iceberg.
12" Single: Released Aug '87, on Ro Johnson, by Ron Johnson Records. Catalogue no: **ZRON 32**

Jackhammer 5

ST.PETER'S EGG
Tracks: / St. Peter's Egg.
12" Single: Released Oct '86, on Cathexis, by Cathexis Records. Deleted '88. Catalogue no: **CRJ 651**

Jackie

LIKE I AM
Tracks: / Like I am.
7" Single: Released Sep '82, on Hobbs, by Hobbs Music. Catalogue no: **HMO 1**

Jackmaster Black

DJ MEGATRACK
Tracks: / D.J. megatrack / Westside jacks.
7" Single: Released 27 Feb '88, on DJ International, by Westside Records. Catalogue no: **DJIN 2**
12" Single: Released 27 Feb '88, on DJ International, by Westside Records. Catalogue no: **DJINT 2**

Jacko

T. JAM (CLUB MIX)
Tracks: / T. Jam (club mix).
12" Single: Released Apr '87, on Hot Melt, by Hot Melt Records. Catalogue no: **12 TC 009**

Jacks, Terry

Biographical details: Raised in Vancouver, singer and guitarist Jacks spent most of the 60's leading a moderately-successful Canadian group, the Chessmen. In 1969 he married a fellow Canadian, Susan Pesklevits, and as the Poppy Family they achieved an international Top Ten hit in 1970 with Pesklevits' song *Which Way You Goin', Billy?* The couple's relationship -- both personally and professionally -- ended in '73 and Jacks found himself working briefly with the Beach Boys. He recommended that they record a Jacques Brel song which had been translated into English by Rod McKuen, but the group turned this down so Jacks himself recorded *Seasons In The Sun...* When eventually released it was a worldwide monster, three weeks at No 1 in the States in '74, four weeks at the top in Britain, with global sales of six million. Sung from the point of view of a young man on his death bed saying goodbye to members of his family, it was a moving and unusual record. Jacks followed Seasons with another Brel song, *If You Go Away*, a highly-charged piece about a man pleading with his lover not to walk out. Sung in the same midtempo manner as the previous hit, it reached No 8 in the UK but peaked at 68 in the States. Jacks tried to sustain his career with *Rock 'n' Roll I Gave You All The Best Years Of My Life*, but was beaten to the charts by Mac Davis in America and Kevin Johnson in Britain. He then slipped quietly into obscurity. (Bob MacDonald, November 1985.).

IF YOU GO AWAY
Tracks: / If you go away.
7" Single: Released Jun '74, on Bell, Deleted '77. Catalogue no: **BELL 1362**

SEASONS IN THE SUN
Tracks: / Seasons in the sun.
7" Single: Released Mar '74, on Bell, Deleted '77. Catalogue no: **BELL 1344**

SEASONS IN THE SUN (OLD GOLD)
Tracks: / Seasons in the sun / If you go away.
7" Single: Released Jun '88, on Old Gold, by Old Gold Records. Catalogue no: **OG 9119**

Jacks, Tony

I HEAR A HEARTBEAT
Tracks: / I hear a heartbeat.
7" Single: Released Nov '81, on Strike (1), by Strike Records. Catalogue no: **KIK 6**

Jackson, Amy

LET IT LOOSE
Tracks: / Let it loose / Let it loose(dub).
7" Single: Released Jun '89, on BSBI, by BSB Records. Catalogue no: **BENN 6**
12" Single: Released Jun '89, on BSBI, by BSB Records. Catalogue no: **BENN 6T**

Jackson, Billy

HAVE A HAPPY CHRISTMAS
Tracks: / Have a happy Christmas.
7" Single: Released Nov '83, on London Records, by London Records. Catalogue no: **LON 42**
12" Single: Released Nov '83, on London Records, by London Records. Catalogue no: **LONX 42**

Jackson, Chuck

ALL OVER THE WORLD
Tracks: / All over the world.
7" Single: Released Jul '89, on Nightmare, by Nightmare Records. Catalogue no: **MARES 103**

Jackson, Dee D

AUTOMATIC LOVER
Tracks: / Automatic lover.
7" Single: Released Apr '78, on Mercury, by Phonogram Ltd. Deleted '81. Catalogue no: **6007 171**

METEOR MAN
Tracks: / Meteor man.
7" Single: Released Sep '78, on Mercury, by Phonogram Ltd. Deleted '81. Catalogue no: **6007 182**

Jackson Five

Biographical details: Jackson 5 This American family soul vocal group consisted of brothers Jackie, Tito, Jermaine, Marlon and Michael Jackson (in descending age order).
On the British charts, Gerry & The Pacemakers (1963) and Frankie Goes To Hollywood (1984) made history by being the only two acts to hit No.1 with their first three single releases. On the American charts, the Jackson 5 did something even more spectacular - their 1970 smashes, *I Want You Back, ABC, The Love You Save*, and *I'll Be There*, made them the only act ever to reach the US No.1 slot with their first FOUR singles. Not a bad achievement, considering the oldest member of the quinter was only 19 and youngest and most talented Jackson (Michael) was only eleven, going on twelve. Both of the Beatles' final two American chart-toppers were knocked off the summit by this bunch of kids!
Hailing from Gary, Indiana, the Jackson 5 were born into a musical enviroment - their father Joe Jackson was a member of a partially successful rhythm and blues outfit called The Falcons and their mother Katherine was a keen clarinettist. Encouraged by parents and friends, the five prodigies established themselves as a hot local act and were discovered in the late Sixties by Berry Gordy's legendary Tamla Motown company. After a year's intense rehearsal and grooming, Motown launched the sibling singers onto an unsuspecting world with overwhelming results.
With the help of a slsick Tamla writing and production team known as The Corporation, The Jackson 5 lived and breathed energy and exuberance. Those first four historic hits (three dynamic dance discs plus one scorching ballad) all reached the British Top 10 as well as the US No.1 position. Their fifth and sixth singles, *Mama's Pearl*, and *Never Can Say Goodbye*, both peaked at No.2 on the American Hot 100.
From then onwards, however, the Jackson 5's Motown career coasted along in a lower gear. Michael and Jermaine began subsidiary solo careers, but these tended to distract from the group's regular work. Gordy and his colleagues seemed unsure how to develop their career at a time when they were being rivalled in the teenybopper stakes by abother group of singing brothers - The Osmonds. The Jackson 5 still had occasional smashes - *Lookin' Through The Windows* (1972) and Jackson Browne's *Doctor My Eyes* (1973) both reached the British Top 10 and the funky workout *Dancing Machine* (1974) hit No.2 in America - but their chart career was becoming increasinly erratic.
Realising that their career needed a breath of fresh air, the family elected to leave Motown in 1975. By this time Jermaine was married to Berry Gordy's daughter Hazel, and he decided to stay. The others replaced him with Randy Jackson, a sixth brother who had been to young to join the group in the early days. They could not continue to call themselves the Jackson 5, however, because Tamla retained the rights to that name. As The Jacksons, they began a new series of hits with Epic Records in 1977. And for Michael, all of this was only just the beginning. (Bob Macdonald 7/11/85).

ABC (SINGLE)
Tracks: / ABC.
7" Single: Released May '70, on Tamla Motown, by Motown Records (UK). Deleted '73. Catalogue no: **TMG 724**

DOCTOR MY EYES
Tracks: / Doctor my eyes.
7" Single: Released Feb '73, on Tamla Motown, by Motown Records (UK). Deleted '76. Catalogue no: **TMG 842**

HALLELUJAH DAY
Tracks: / Hallelujah day.
7" Single: Released Jun '73, on Tamla Motown, by Motown Records (UK). Deleted '76. Catalogue no: **TMG 856**

I WANT YOU BACK
Tracks: / I want you back / Love you safe.
7" Single: Released Jan '70, on Tamla Motown, by Motown Records (UK). Deleted '73. Catalogue no: **TMG 724**
CD 5": Released Jun '89, on Motown, by BMG Records (UK). Catalogue no: **ZD 41949**
7" Single: Released Oct '81, on Motown, by BMG Records (UK). Catalogue no: **TMG 963**

I'LL BE THERE
Tracks: / I'll be there / ABC.
7" Single: Released Jun '83, on Motown, by BMG Records (UK). Deleted '85. Catalogue no: **TMG 969**
7" Single: Released Nov '70, on Tamla Motown, by Motown Records (UK). Deleted '73. Catalogue no: **TMG 758**

LOOKIN' THROUGH THE WINDOWS
Tracks: / Lookin' through the windows / Doctor my eyes.
7" Single: Released Oct '80, on Motown, by BMG Records (UK). Deleted Oct '83. Catalogue no: **TMG 975**
7" Single: Released Nov '72, on Tamla Motown, by Motown Records (UK). Deleted '75. Catalogue no: **TMG 833**

LOVE YOU SAVE, THE
Tracks: / Love you save, The.
7" Single: Released Aug '70, on Tamla Motown, by Motown Records (UK). Deleted '73. Catalogue no: **TMG 746**

MAMA'S PEARL
Tracks: / Mama's pearl.
7" Single: Released Apr '71, on Tamla Motown, by Motown Records (UK). Deleted '74. Catalogue no: **TMG 769**

NEVER CAN SAY GOODBYE
Tracks: / Never can say goodbye.
7" Single: Released Jul '71, on Tamla Motown, by Motown Records (UK). Deleted '74. Catalogue no: **TMG 778**

SANTA CLAUS IS COMING TO TOWN
Tracks: / Santa Claus is coming to town.
7" Single: Released Dec '72, on Tamla Motown, by Motown Records (UK). Deleted '75. Catalogue no: **TMG 833**

SKYWRITER (SINGLE)
Tracks: / Skywriter.
7" Single: Released Sep '73, on Tamla Motown, by Motown Records (UK). Deleted '76. Catalogue no: **TMG 842**

Jackson, Freddie

CRAZY (FOR ME)
Tracks: / Crazy (for me)- Radio edit / Crazy (for me) - The done properly dub / Crazy (for me) - The done properly mix (12" & CD single only.).
Note: Executive producers Beau Huggins, Freddie Jackson and Wayne Edwards.
7" Single: Released Sep '88, on Capitol, by EMI Records. Deleted Aug '89. Catalogue no: **CL 510**
CD 5": Released Sep '88, on Capitol, by EMI Records. Deleted Oct '89. Catalogue no: **CDCL 510**
12" Single: Released Sep '88, on Capitol, by EMI Records. Deleted Aug '89. Catalogue no: **12CL 510**

HAVE YOU EVER LOVED SOMEBODY
Tracks: / Have you ever loved somebody (Double pack.) / Tasty love (inst) (Double pack.) / Rock me tonight (for old time's sake) (Double pack.) / Have you ever loved somebody (inst mix) (Double pack.).
7" Single: Released Jan '87, on Capitol, by EMI Records. Deleted '88. Catalogue no: **CL 437**
7" Set: Released Jan '87, on Capitol, by EMI Records. Catalogue no: **CLD 437**
12" Single: Released Jan '87, on Capitol, by EMI Records. Deleted '88. Catalogue no: **12 CL 437**

HE'LL NEVER LOVE YOU LIKE I DO
Tracks: / He'll never love you (like I do)(maserati mix) (Extra track on 12" version only) / I wanna say I love you / He'll never love you (like I do) / Tasty love / Have you ever loved someobody / Look around / Jam tonight / Just like the first time / I can't let you go / I don't want to lose your love.
12" Single: Released Apr '86, on Capitol, by EMI Records. Deleted '88. Catalogue no: **12 CL 387**
7" Single: Released Apr '86, on Capitol, by EMI Records. Deleted '88. Catalogue no: **CL 387**

JAM TONIGHT
Tracks: / Jam tonight.
7" Single: Released Sep '87, on Capitol, by EMI Records. Deleted Apr '88. Catalogue no: **CL 461**
12" Single: Released Sep '87, on Capitol, by EMI Records. Deleted Apr '88. Catalogue no: **12 CL 461**

LITTLE BIT MORE, A (See under Moore, Melba)
Tracks: / Little bit more, A / It's been so long / Calling.
12" Single: Released 30 May '87, on Capitol, by EMI Records. Deleted Apr '88. Catalogue no: **12 CL 446**
7" Single: Released 30 May '87, on Capitol, by EMI Records. Deleted '88. Catalogue no: **CL 446**

NICE 'N' SLOW
Tracks: / Nice 'n' slow / You are my love / Nice 'n' slow (ext. version)* / Nice 'n' slow (radio remix)*.
Note: Producer Barry Eastmond for Orpheus Productions. (P) 1988 Original sound recording (s) made by Capitol Records Inc.
7" Single: Released Jun '88, on Capitol, by EMI Records. Deleted Jun '89. Catalogue no: **CL 502**
12" Single: Released Jun '88, on Capitol, by EMI Records. Deleted Jun '89. Catalogue no: **12CL 502**
CD 5": Released Jun '88, on Capitol, by EMI Records. Deleted Jun '89. Catalogue no: **CDCL 502**

ROCK ME TONIGHT (FOR OLD TIMES SAKE)
Tracks: / Rock me tonight (for old times sake) / Rock me tonight (for old times sake)(groove version).
7" Set: Released Nov '85, on Capitol, by EMI Records. Catalogue no: **CLD 379**
12" Single: Released Feb '86, on Capitol, by EMI Records. Deleted Jan '88. Catalogue no: **12CL 358**
7" Single: Released Feb '86, on Capitol, by EMI Records. Deleted Jul '87. Catalogue no: **CL 358**

TASTY LOVE
Tracks: / Tasty love / I wanna say I love you.
7" Single: Released Sep '86, on Capitol, by EMI Records. Catalogue no: **CL 428**
12" Single: Released Sep '86, on Capitol, by EMI Records. Deleted Jan '88. Catalogue no: **12CL 428**

YOU ARE MY LADY
Tracks: / You are my lady.
7" Single: Released Oct '85, on Capitol, by EMI Records. Deleted '88. Catalogue no: **CL 379**
12" Single: Released Oct '85, on Capitol, by EMI Records. Deleted '88. Catalogue no: **12CL 379**

Jackson, Guy

RADIO ONE
Tracks: / Radio one / Metal fatigue.
7" Single: Released Oct '81, on Rondelet Music, by Rondelet Music & Records. Catalogue no: **ROUND 11**

Jackson, Janet

COME GIVE YOUR LOVE TO ME
Tracks: / Come give your love to me / Magic is working.
7" Single: Released Jan '83, on A&M, by A&M Records. Deleted '88. Catalogue no: **AMS 8303**
12" Single: Released Jan '83, on A&M, by A&M Records. Deleted '88. Catalogue no: **AMSX 8303**

CONTROL(SINGLE)
Tracks: / Control.
7" Single: Released Oct '86, on A&M, by A&M Records. Deleted '87. Catalogue no: **AM 359**
12" Single: Released Oct '86, on A&M, by A&M Records. Deleted '87. Catalogue no: **AMY 359**

DON'T MESS UP THIS GOOD THING
Tracks: / Don't mess up a good thing.
12" Single: Released May '83, on A&M, by A&M Records. Deleted '88. Catalogue no: **AMX 112**
7" Single: Released May '83, on A&M, by A&M Records. Deleted '88. Catalogue no: **AM 112**

FUNNY HOW TIME FLIES (WHEN YOU'RE HAVING FUN)
Tracks: / Funny how time flies / When I think of you / Nasty (cool summer mix part one).
Note: Nasty (cool summer part 1) on USA 613 version only
12" Single: Released 31 Oct '87, on Breakout, by A&M Records. Catalogue no: **AMY 419**
7" Single: Released '87, on Breakout, by A&M Records. Catalogue no: **USA 613**
7" Single: Released 31 Oct '87, on Breakout, by A&M Records. Catalogue no: **AM 419**

LET'S WAIT AWHILE
Tracks: / Let's wait awhile / Nasty (cool summer mix part one) / Nasty (original mix) / Control / Let's wait awhile (remix) / Nasty (cool summer mix part one).
7" Set: Released Mar '87, on Breakout, by A&M Records. Deleted Mar '88. Catalogue no: **USAD 601**

7" Single: Released Mar '87, on Breakout, by A&M Records. Catalogue no: **USA 601**

MISS YOU MUCH
Tracks: / Miss you much / You need me.
CD 5": Released Aug '89, on A&M, by A&M Records. Catalogue no: **USACD 663**
7" Single: Released Aug '89, on A&M, by A&M Records. Catalogue no: **USA 663**
Cassingle: Released Aug '89, on A&M, by A&M Records. Catalogue no: **USATC 663**
7" Single: Released Aug '89, on A&M, by A&M Records. Catalogue no: **USAS 663**
12" Single: Released Aug '89, on A&M, by A&M Records. Catalogue no: **USAT 663**

NASTY
Tracks: / Nasty / You'll never find (a love like mine).
7" Single: Released May '86, on A&M, by A&M Records. Deleted '87. Catalogue no: **AM 316**

PLEASURE PRINCIPLE, THE
Tracks: / Pleasure principle, The / Pleasure principle, The (remix edit) / Pleasure principle, The (edit).
Cassingle: Released 30 May '87, on Breakout, by A&M Records. Deleted Mar '88. Catalogue no: **USATC 604**
7" Single: Released 30 May '87, on Breakout, by A&M Records. Catalogue no: **USA 604**
12" Single: Released 30 May '87, on Breakout, by A&M Records. Catalogue no: **USAT 604**

WHAT HAVE YOU DONE FOR ME LATELY
Tracks: / What have you done for me lately / Young love.
7" Single: Released Mar '86, on A&M, by A&M Records. Deleted '87. Catalogue no: **AM 308**
12" Single: Released Mar '86, on A&M, by A&M Records. Deleted '87. Catalogue no: **AMY 308**

WHEN I THINK OF YOU
Tracks: / When I think of you / Come give your love to me.
12" Single: Released Jul '86, on A&M, by A&M Records. Deleted '87. Catalogue no: **AMY 337**
7" Single: Released Jul '86, on A&M, by A&M Records. Deleted '87. Catalogue no: **AM 337**

Jackson, Jermaine

Biographical details: Jackson, Jermaine This American singer, born in Gary, Indiana in 1954 came to fame in 1970 as the third oldest member of the Jackson 5. At the end of 1972 with the group's chart career beginning to decline, he followed in younger brother Michael's footsteps by launching a subsidiary solo career. His remake of *Shep & The Limelites* 1961 smash *Daddy's Home* took him to No.9 on the US chart but flopped in the UK.
By the time the Jackson family decided to quit Tamla Motown in 1975, Jermaine was married to Hazel, the daughter of the company's boss Berry Gordy. He understandably chose to remain loyal to Motown and his place in the brothers' group was taken by Randy Jackson, a sixth brother who had been too young to join the group in the early days.
Because of mediocre material and lack of inspiration, Jermaine's fortunes went through the floor during the remainder of the Seventies. His flagging career was revived by Stevie Wonder and Lee Garrett who wrote him a funky smash in 1980 called *Let's Get Serious*; this single cruised to No.9 in the States and No.8 in Britain. From then onwards, Jermaine pursued an eclectic recording path, never content to stay within the confines of soul music. His work ranging from the delicate single *You Like Me Don't You* (which reached No.41 in Britain in 1981) to an unexpected collaboration with the quirky rock band Devo on *Let Me Tickle Your Fancy* (which reached No.18 in the US in 1982).
Jermaine finally left Motown in 1984 and joined Arista Records. He also rejoined his brothers for their massively publicised Victory tour an album. And just when he needed a substantial international hit to boost his personal status, he got one in early 1985 with the beautiful ballad *Do What You Do*. (Bob Macdonald 7/11/85).

BURNIN' HOT
Tracks: / Burnin' hot / Castles of sand.
7" Single: Released Oct '81, on Motown, by BMG Records (UK). Catalogue no: **TMG 1194**
12" Single: Released Oct '81, on Motown, by BMG Records (UK). Catalogue no: **12TMG 194**

DO WHAT YOU DO
Tracks: / Do what you do.
7" Single: Released Jan '85, on Arista, by BMG Records (UK). Catalogue no: **ARIST 609**
12" Single: Released Jan '85, on Arista, by BMG Records (UK). Catalogue no: **ARIST 12609**

DO YOU REMEMBER ME
Tracks: / Do you remember me (USA mix) (12" version also includes "Bonus Beats" mix and "Dub Mix" of title.) / Voices in the dark.
12" Single: Released Jul '86, on Arista, by BMG Records (UK). Catalogue no: **ARIST 22664**
7" Single: Released May '86, on Arista, by BMG Records (UK). Catalogue no: **ARIST 664**
12" Single: Released May '86, on Arista, by BMG Records (UK). Catalogue no: **ARIST 12664**

DON'T TAKE IT PERSONAL
Tracks: / Don't take it personal / Clean up your act.
Cassingle: Released Oct '89, on Arista, by BMG Records (UK). Catalogue no: **410 634**
CD 5": Released Sep '89, on Arista, by BMG Records (UK). Catalogue no: **662 634**
7" Single: Released Sep '89, on Arista, by BMG Records (UK). Catalogue no: **112 634**
12" Single: Released Sep '89, on Arista, by BMG Records (UK). Catalogue no: **612 634**

DYNAMITE (JELLY BEAN REMIX)
Tracks: / Dynamite (jelly bean remix) / Take good care of my heart.
7" Single: Released May '85, on Arista, by BMG Records (UK). Catalogue no: **ARIST 616**
12" Single: Released May '85, on Arista, by BMG Records (UK). Catalogue no: **ARIST 12616**

DYNAMITE (SINGLE)
Tracks: / Dynamite.
12" Single: Released Jul '84, on Arista, by BMG Records (UK). Catalogue no: **JJK 122**
7" Single: Released Jul '84, on Arista, by BMG Records (UK). Catalogue no: **JJK 2**

I THINK IT'S LOVE
Tracks: / I think it's love / Voices in the dark.
7" Single: Released Feb '86, on Arista, by BMG Records (UK). Catalogue no: **ARIST 655**
12" Single: Released Feb '86, on Arista, by BMG Records (UK). Catalogue no: **ARIST 12655**

I'M JUST TOO SHY
Tracks: / I'm just too shy / All because of you.
7" Single: Released Nov '81, on Motown, by BMG Records (UK). Catalogue no: **TMG 1242**

LET ME TICKLE YOUR FANCY (SINGLE)
Tracks: / Let me tickle your fancy / Maybe next time.
7" Single: Released Aug '82, on Motown, by BMG Records (UK). Catalogue no: **TMG 1276**
12" Single: Released Aug '82, on Motown, by BMG Records (UK). Catalogue no: **TMGT 1276**

LET'S GET SERIOUS (SINGLE)
Tracks: / Let's get serious / Je vous aime beaucoup.
7" Single: Released May '80, on Motown, by BMG Records (UK). Deleted '83. Catalogue no: **TMG 1183**
12" Single: Released May '80, on Motown, by BMG Records (UK). Deleted '83. Catalogue no: **12TMG 1183**

LITTLE GIRL DON'T YOU WORRY
Tracks: / Little girl don't you worry / We can put it back together.
12" Single: Released Oct '81, on Motown, by BMG Records (UK). Catalogue no: **TMGT 1212**
7" Single: Released Oct '81, on Motown, by BMG Records (UK). Catalogue no: **TMG 1212**

PARADISE IN YOUR EYES
Tracks: / Paradise in your eyes / I'm my brother's keeper.
7" Single: Released Feb '82, on Motown, by BMG Records (UK). Catalogue no: **TMG 1253**

PERFECT
Tracks: / Perfect.
12" Single: Released Aug '85, on Arista, by BMG Records (UK). Catalogue no: **ARIST 12619**
7" Single: Released Aug '85, on Arista, by BMG Records (UK). Catalogue no: **ARIST 619**

SWEETEST SWEETEST
Tracks: / Sweetest sweetest / Come to me.
7" Single: Released Apr '84, on Arista, by BMG Records (UK). Catalogue no: **JJK 1**
7" Pic: Released Jun '84, on Arista, by BMG Records (UK). Catalogue no: **JJKPD 1**
12" Single: Released Apr '84, on Arista, by BMG Records (UK). Catalogue no: **JJK 121**

VERY SPECIAL PART
Tracks: / Very special part / You're giving me the runaround.
12" Single: Released Nov '82, on Motown, by BMG Records (UK). Catalogue no: **TMGT 1286**
7" Single: Released Nov '82, on Motown, by BMG Records (UK). Catalogue no: **TMG 1286**

WHEN THE RAIN BEGINS TO FALL
Tracks: / When the rain begins to fall.
12" Single: Released Sep '84, on Arista, by BMG Records (UK). Catalogue no: **ARIST 12584**
7" Single: Released Sep '84, on Arista, by BMG Records (UK). Catalogue no: **ARIST 584**

YOU LIKE ME DON'T YOU
Tracks: / You like me don't you.
7" Single: Released Oct '81, on Motown, by BMG Records (UK). Catalogue no: **TMG 1222**
12" Single: Released Oct '81, on Motown, by BMG Records (UK). Catalogue no: **TMGT 1222**

YOU MOVED A MOUNTAIN
Tracks: / You moved a mountain.
7" Single: Released Apr '83, on Motown, by BMG Records (UK). Catalogue no: **TMG 1303**

YOU'RE SUPPOSED TO KEEP YOUR LOVE...
Tracks: / You're supposed to keep your love.....
7" Single: Released Oct '81, on Motown, by BMG Records (UK). Catalogue no: **TMG 1201**

Jackson, Joe

Biographical details: Jackson, Joe This British singer, songwriter, keyboardist and saxophonist has established himself as one of the most unpredictable and eclectic artists in modern pop music. His restless habit of jumping around from one style to another may have cost him considerably in commercial terms, but almost every move has been musically fascinating.
Born in Burton-on-Trent and raised in Portsmouth, Joe Jackson studied for three years at the Royal Academy of Music and played for a while in The National Youth Jazz Orchestra. During the mid-Seventies he played with a variety of small-time bands before forming his own group and signing with A&M Records in 1978. He has remained with that label ever since, usually working with sympathetic producer David Kershenbaum.
1979 saw the release of Jackson's first two albums, *Look Sharp* and *I'm The Man*. Both charted respectably in Britain although, strangely, it was the American Top 40 success of the single *Is She Really Going Out With Him?* that gave him his breakthrough. That memorable song eventually scored in the UK, reaching No.13 Jackson's early output placed him in the New Wave bracket, although his caustic social commentary was more akin to Elvis Costello than to the chaotic fury of the punk groups, as was his vocal style.
It's Different For Girls gave Jackson his biggest British single, reaching No.5 in early 1980. That year's *Beat Crazy* album, however, was a stiff. The unpredictable performer revived his career in 1981 by declaring of all things, a Louis Jordan revival - the album *Joe Jackson's Jumpin' Jive* became a UK Top 20 success and was accompanied by a successful, exuberant tour on both sides of the Atlantic. Joe thus brought back memories of a seminal Forties jazz and blues artist whom many Eighties rock fans had never heard of, but whose influence upon the development of rock 'n' roll had been undeniable.
Changing his style again, Jckson hit his commercial peak with the slow burning 1982 album *Night and Day*. This was the result of his residence in New York City, where he lovingly soaked up the Big Apple's incredibly diverse musical menu. *Night and Day* was a craftily coherent concoction of jazz, rock, salsa, blues, disco, pop and easy listening genres. The infectious *Steppin' Out* single reached No.6 in both the US and UK, and the powerful ballad *Breaking Us In Two* gave him another American Top 20 hit. *Real Men* a careful examination of sexual stereotyping was an equally outstanding track. The *Night And Day* album reached No.4 in the States.
Jackson took yet another change of direction with his 1983 soundtrack to the critically lambasted film 'Mike's Murder', and captured an atmospheric 'live' feel on his underrated 1984 album *Body and Soul*. This yielded the US Top 20 single *You Can't Get What You Want (Till You Know What You Want)* - while that song was climbing the American charts, Jackson publicly derided the boom in promotional videos and similar modern marketing techniques, an regused to make an accompanying clip for his hit single. (Bob Macdonald 7/11/85).

BE MY NUMBER TWO
Tracks: / Be my number two / Is she really going out with him.
7" Single: Released Jul '84, on A&M, by A&M Records. Deleted '87. Catalogue no: **AM 200**

BEAT CRAZY (SINGLE)
Tracks: / Beat crazy / Enough is enough.
7" Single: Released Oct '80, on A&M, by A&M Records. Deleted Oct '83. Catalogue no: **AMS 7563**

BREAKING US IN TWO
Tracks: / Breaking us in two.
12" Single: Released Feb '83, on A&M, by A&M Records. Deleted '88. Catalogue no: **AMX 101**
7" Single: Released Feb '83, on A&M, by A&M Records. Deleted '86. Catalogue no: **AM 101**

COSMOPOLITAN
Tracks: / Cosmopolitan.
7" Single: Released Aug '83, on A&M, by A&M Records. Deleted '88. Catalogue no: **AM 134**

DOWN TO LONDON
Tracks: / Down to London / You can't get what you want.
7" Single: Released Sep '89, on A&M, by A&M Records. Catalogue no: **AM 512**
CD 5": Released Sep '89, on A&M, by A&M Records. Catalogue no: **CDEE 512**

HAPPY ENDING
Tracks: / Happy ending.
7" Single: Released Apr '84, on A&M, by A&M Records. Deleted '87. Catalogue no: **AM 186**

HARDER THEY COME
Tracks: / Harder they come / Out of style / Tilt.
12" Single: Released 20 Jun '80, on A&M, by A&M Records. Deleted '83. Catalogue no: **AMSP 7536**
7" Single: Released 20 Jun '80, on A&M, by A&M Records. Deleted '83. Catalogue no: **AMS 7536**

(HE'S A SHAPE) IN A DRAPE
Tracks: / (He's a shape) in a drape / Speedway.
7" Single: Released Nov '88, on A&M, by A&M Records. Catalogue no: **AM 481**

HOME TOWN
Tracks: / Home town / Tango Atlantico.
7" Single: Released May '86, on A&M, by A&M Records. Deleted '88. Catalogue no: **AM 324**
12" Single: Released May '86, on A&M, by A&M Records. Deleted '88. Catalogue no: **AMY 324**

IS SHE REALLY GOING OUT WITH HIM?
Tracks: / Is she really going out with him / Is she really going out with him (Acapella) (On CD single only) / Slow song (On CD single only).
CD 5": Released Aug '88, on A&M(Holland), by A&M Records. Catalogue no: **3903312**
7" Single: Released Aug '79, on A&M, by A&M Records. Deleted '82. Catalogue no: **AMS 7459**

IT'S DIFFERENT FOR GIRLS
Tracks: / It's different for girls / Friday.
7" Single: Released Jan '80, on A&M, by A&M Records. Deleted '83. Catalogue no: **AMS 7493**

JUMPIN' JIVE (LIVE)
Tracks: / Jumpin' jive (live) / Memphis (live).
7" Single: Released Apr '88, on A&M, by A&M Records. Deleted Feb '89. Catalogue no: **AM 441**
12" Single: Released Apr '88, on A&M, by A&M Records. Deleted Feb '89. Catalogue no: **AMY 441**

JUMPIN' JIVE (SINGLE)
Tracks: / Jumpin' jive / Knock me a kiss.
7" Single: Released Jul '81, on A&M, by A&M Records. Deleted '84. Catalogue no **AMS 8145**

NINETEEN FOREVER
Tracks: / Nineteen forever / Acropolis now (Instr.).
CD 5": Released May '89, on A&M, by A&M Records. Catalogue no: **CDEE 506**
7" Single: Released May '89, on A&M, by A&M Records. Catalogue no: **AM 506**

ONE TO ONE

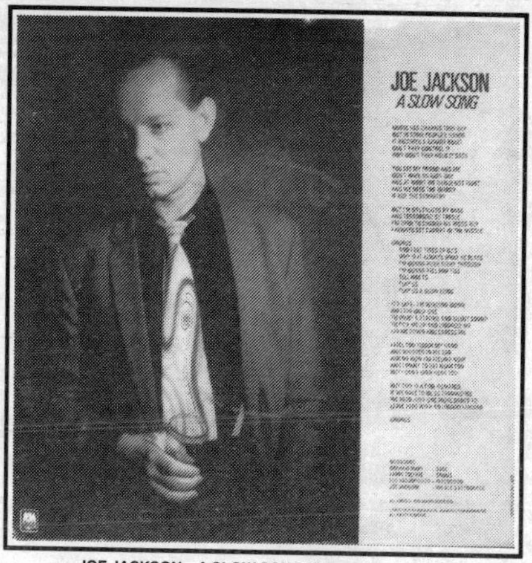

JOE JACKSON - A SLOW SONG (Released on A & M)

Tracks: / One to one.
7" Single: Released Mar '81, on A&M, by A&M Records. Deleted '82. Catalogue no: **AMS 8116**

REAL MEN
Tracks: / Real men / Chinatown.
7" Single: Released Jun '82, on A&M, by A&M Records. Deleted Jun '85. Catalogue no: **AMS 8231**

RIGHT AND WRONG
Tracks: / Right and wrong / Breaking us in two (live) / I'm the man (live) (Extra track on 12" version only).
7" Single: Released Apr '86, on A&M, by A&M Records. Deleted '88. Catalogue no: **AM 312**
12" Single: Released Apr '86, on A&M, by A&M Records. Deleted '88. Catalogue no: **AMY 312**

SLOW SONG, A (see panel above)
Tracks: / Slow song, A / Real men.
7" Single: Released '82, on A&M, by A&M Records. Catalogue no: **AM 114**

STEPPIN' OUT
Tracks: / Steppin' out.
7" Single: Released Jan '83, on A&M, by A&M Records. Deleted '86. Catalogue no: **AMS 8262**

Jackson, Latoya

HEART DON'T LIE
Tracks: / Heart don't lie / Without you.
7" Single: Released May '84, on Epic, by CBS Records. Catalogue no: **A 4369**
12" Single: Released May '84, on Epic, by CBS Records. Catalogue no: **TA 4369**

IF YOU FEEL THE FUNK
Tracks: / If you feel the funk / Lovely is she.
7" Single: Released Nov '80, on Polydor, by Polydor Ltd. Deleted Nov '83. Catalogue no: **POSP 147**
12" Single: Released Nov '80, on Polydor, by Polydor Ltd. Deleted Nov '83. Catalogue no: **POSPX 147**

OOPS OH NO CLUB MIX
Tracks: / Oops oh no club mix.
7" Single: Released Oct '86, on Music Of Life, by Music Of Life Records. Catalogue no: **MOL 7**
12" Single: Released Oct '86, on Music Of Life, by Music Of Life Records. Catalogue no: **MOLIF 7**

STAY THE NIGHT
Tracks: / Stay the night / Camp Kuchi Kaiai.
7" Single: Released Oct '81, on Polydor, by Polydor Ltd. Deleted Oct '84. Catalogue no: **POSP 332**

YOU'RE GONNA GET ROCKED
Tracks: / You're gonna get rocked / Does it really matter.
7" Single: Released Sep '88, on RCA, by BMG Records (UK). Deleted May '89. Catalogue no: **PB 49527**
12" Single: Released Sep '88, on RCA, by BMG Records (UK). Deleted Aug '89. Catalogue no: **PT 49528**

Jackson, Michael

Biographical details: Jackson, Michael This American singer, songwriter and dancer confirmed his place against the true legends of the 20th century in March 1984 when his *Thriller* LP sailed past Bing Crosbys' *White Christmas* to become the world's top selling recording of all time. By mid-1985 global sales of the blockbusing album were estimated at 40 million. And Michael was still only in his mid twenties, having already been a superstar for fifteen years.
Thriller was the culmination of a n exceptional career that had been dotted with some striking landmarks. Born in Gary, Indiana in 1958, Michael was five years old when he became a member of his four elder brotheers' singing group. At the age of six, they gave him the role of lead vocalist. The young siblings won several local talent contests before being snapped up by Berry Gordy's Tamla Motown company and groomed for stardom. In 1970 The Jackson 5 made chart history by becoming the only act ever to reach No.1 on the US Hot 100 with their first four single releases.
After the initial excitement surrounding the quintet had wanted, Motown maintained the momentum by launching Michael as a solo artist. The first offering was a ballad called *Got To Be There* released at the end of 1971. It reached No.4 in the US and No.5 in the UK, and was followed by the frantic *Rockin' Robin* (No.2 in US, No.3 in UK) which had originally been an American No.2 hit for Bobby Day in the year that Michael was born. In late 1972 the youngster achieved his first solo US No.1 hit with the sentimental *Ben*, an unlikely tribute to a rat featured in a film of the same name. By handling uptempo dance discs and sad slowies with equal skill and intensity, he proved himself to be a great soul singer in the best traditions of the genre. During his childhood, he had grown up listening to the great gospel singers and rhythm and blues vocalist of previous eras as well as the participants of the Sixties soul explosion - he had absorbed all these influences with consummate ease.
From 1973 onwards, the Jacksons family's career at Motown coasted along in less spectacular fashion and they seemed to lose their way somewhat. In response to this, they quit the company in 1975 (leaving brother Jermaine behind) and moved to Epic Records. Now known simply as The Jacksons they returned to form in '77 with a new series of hits. In 1978 Michael appeared in an abysmal Hollywood remake of the Wizard of Oz - although *The Wiz* was a disaster, it was an important chapter in his career because, during its making he struck up a friendship with the film's musical director, the veteran Quincy Jones.
Jones became the producer for Jackson's reactivated solo recording career and this dynamic combination of talent yielded the monster-selling albums *Off The Wall* (released August 1979) and *Thriller* (December 1982). With the songs being written mainly by Jackson himself and Britain's Rod Temperton (of Heatwave fame), Michael Jackson fused soul, rock, pop styles in a manner that was irrestistible to millions. (Bob Macdonald 7/11/85).

ABC
Tracks: / ABC.
7" Single: Released Apr '88, on Motown, by BMG Records (UK). Catalogue no: **ZB 41941**

AIN'T NO SUNSHINE (SINGLE)
Tracks: / Ain't no sunshine / I wanna be.
Note: Originally released in August 1972 on the Tamla Motown label.
7" Single: Released Oct '81, on Motown, by BMG Records (UK). Deleted '83. Catalogue no: **TMG 826**

ANOTHER PART OF ME
Tracks: / Another part of me / Another part of me (inst.).
7" Single: Released Aug '88, on Epic, by CBS Records. Deleted 17 Apr '89. Catalogue no: **652844 0**
CD 5": Released Sep '88, on Epic, by CBS Records. Deleted 17 Apr '89. Catalogue no: **653004 2**
7" Single: Released '88, on Epic, by CBS Records. Deleted 17 Apr '89. Catalogue no: **652844 9**

ANOTHER PART OF ME (EXT. DANCE MIX)
Tracks: / Another part of me (extended dance mix) / Another part of me (radio edit) / Another part of me (dub mix) / Another part of me (a cappella).
12" Single: Released Aug '88, on Epic, by CBS Records. Deleted 17 Apr '89. Catalogue no: **652844 6**
7" Single: Released Aug '88, on Epic, by CBS Records. Deleted 17 Apr '89. Catalogue no: **652844 7**
CD 5": Released Aug '88, on Epic, by CBS Records. Deleted 17 Apr '89. Catalogue no: **652844 2**

ANOTHER PART OF ME (IMPORT)
Tracks: / Another part of me(Ext. dance mix) / Another part of me(radio edit.) / Another part of me(dub mix) / Another part of me(acappella) (Only on 12") / Another part of me (inst) (Only on 3"CD single).
CD 3": Released Aug '88, on Epic (Holland), by CBS Records. Catalogue no: **6528443**
12" Single: Released Oct '88, on Epic (USA), by CBS Records (USA). Catalogue no: **4907855**

BAD
Tracks: / Bad / Way you make me feel, The / Speed demon / Liberian girl / Just good friends / Another part of me / Man in the mirror / I just can't stop loving you / Dirty Diana / Smooth criminal.
Special: Released Nov '87, on Epic, by CBS Records. Deleted 10 Jul '89. Catalogue no: **450 290-9**

BAD (DANCE EXTENDED REMIX)
Tracks: / Bad (dance extended remix) / Bad (dub version) / Bad (acapella).
Cassingle: Released Sep '87, on Epic, by CBS Records. Catalogue no: **651155 4**

BAD (SINGLE)
Tracks: / Bad.
7" Single: Released Sep '87, on CBS, by CBS Records. Deleted 10 Jul '89. Catalogue no: **651 155-7**
Cassingle: Released Sep '87, on CBS, by CBS Records. Catalogue no: **651155 4**
12" Single: on CBS, by CBS Records. Deleted 10 Jul '89. Catalogue no: **651 100-6**
12" Single: Released Sep '87, on CBS, by CBS Records. Deleted 10 Jul '89. Catalogue no: **651 155-6**

BEAT IT
Tracks: / Beat it / Billie Jean.
CD 3": Released Aug '88, on Epic (USA), by CBS Records (USA). Catalogue no: **34K 06453**
7" Single: Released Apr '83, on Epic, by CBS Records. Deleted '86. Catalogue no: **EPC A 3084**

BEN (SINGLE)
Tracks: / Ben / Abraham, martin and john.
7" Single: Released Oct '81, on Motown, by BMG Records (UK). Deleted '84. Catalogue no: **TMG 1165**
7" Single: Released Nov '72, on Tamla Motown, by Motown Records (UK). Deleted '75. Catalogue no: **TMG 834**

BILLIE JEAN
Tracks: / Billie Jean / You can't win (part 1).
7" Single: Released Jan '83, on Epic, by CBS Records. Deleted '86. Catalogue no: **EPC A 3084**
12" Single: Released Jul '88, on Epic (USA), by CBS Records (USA). Catalogue no: **49H07549**

DIRTY DIANA
Tracks: / Dirty Diana / Dirty Diana (instrumental) / Bad (dance extended mix) (Features the song 'False Fade').
Note: * Only available on the CD single.
CD 5": Released Jul '88, on Epic, by CBS Records. Deleted Jan '89. Catalogue no: **651546 9**
7" Single: Released Jul '88, on Epic, by CBS Records. Deleted Jan '89. Catalogue no: **651546 7**
12" Single: Released May '88, on Epic (Germany), by CBS Records. Catalogue no: **651 546-6**
12" Single: Released Jul '88, on Epic, by CBS Records. Deleted Jan '89. Catalogue no: **652 864-6**
CD 5": Released May '88, on Epic (Germany), by CBS Records. Catalogue no: **651 546-2**
7" Single: Released Jul '88, on Epic, by CBS Records. Deleted Jan '89. Catalogue no: **651546 0**
12" Single: Released Jul '88, on Epic, by CBS Records. Deleted Jan '89. Catalogue no: **651546 8**

DON'T STOP 'TIL YOU GET ENOUGH
Tracks: / Don't stop 'til you get enough / Wanna be startin' something.
Cassingle: Released Dec '82, on Epic, by CBS Records. Deleted Dec '85. Catalogue no: **EPC A 40 2906**
12" Single: Released Jul '88, on Epic (USA), by CBS Records (USA). Catalogue no: **49H06911**
CD 3": Released '88, on Epic (Holland), by

MICHAEL JACKSON - FAREWELL MY SUMMER LOVE (Released on Motown)

CBS Records. Catalogue no: **6516573**
7" Single: Released Apr '82, on Epic, by CBS Records. Catalogue no: **CBS 8856**
7" Single: Released Sep '79, on Epic, by CBS Records. Deleted '82. Catalogue no: **EPC 7763**

DON'T STOP 'TIL YOU GET ENOUGH (IMPORT)
Tracks: / Don't stop 'till you get enough / Wanna be startin' something.
CD 3": Released Dec '88, on Epic (Holland), by CBS Records. Catalogue no: **6516573**

EASE ON DOWN THE ROAD
Tracks: / Ease on down the road / Poppy girls.
7" Single: Released Jun '84, on MCA, by MCA Records. Catalogue no: **MCA 898**
7" Single: Released Nov '78, on MCA, by MCA Records. Deleted '81. Catalogue no: **MCA 396**

FAREWELL MY SUMMER LOVE (SINGLE)
Tracks: / Farewell my summer love / Call on me.
7" Single: Released May '84, on Motown, by BMG Records (UK). Catalogue no: **TMG 1342**
12" Single: Released May '84, on Motown, by BMG Records (UK). Catalogue no: **TMGT 1342**

GIRL YOU'RE SO TOGETHER
Tracks: / Girl you're so together.
7" Single: Released Aug '84, on Motown, by BMG Records (UK). Deleted '86. Catalogue no: **TMG 1355**
12" Single: Released Aug '84, on Motown, by BMG Records (UK). Catalogue no: **TMGT 1355**

GIRLFRIEND
Tracks: / Girlfriend.
7" Single: Released Jul '80, on Epic, by CBS Records. Deleted '83. Catalogue no: **EPC 8782**

GOT TO BE THERE (SINGLE)
Tracks: / Got to be there.
7" Single: Released Apr '85, on Motown, by BMG Records (UK). Catalogue no: **TMG 994**
7" Single: Released Oct '81, on Motown, by BMG Records (UK). Catalogue no: **TMG 973**
CD 5": Released Jun '89, on Motown, by BMG Records (UK). Catalogue no: **ZD 41951**
12" Single: Released Apr '85, on Motown, by BMG Records (UK). Catalogue no: **TMGT 994**
7" Single: Released Feb '72, on Motown, by BMG Records (UK). Deleted '75. Catalogue no: **TMG 797**

GREATEST ORIGINAL HITS (4 TRACK EP)
7" Single: Released Mar '83, on Epic, by CBS Records. Catalogue no: **EPC A 2906**

HAPPY
Tracks: / Happy / We're almost there.
7" Single: Released Jul '83, on Motown, by BMG Records (UK). Deleted '85. Catalogue no: **TMG 986**
12" Single: Released Jul '83, on Motown, by BMG Records (UK). Deleted '85. Catalogue no: **TMGT 986**

I JUST CAN'T STOP LOVING YOU
Tracks: / I just can't stop loving you / Baby be mine.
7" Single: Released Jul '87, on Epic, by CBS Records. Catalogue no: **650202 7**
12" Single: Released Aug '87, on Epic, by CBS Records. Catalogue no: **650202 6**
CD 3": Released Aug '88, on Epic (USA), by CBS Records (USA). Catalogue no: **34K 07253**
7" Single: Released Aug '87, on Epic, by CBS Records. Catalogue no: **650202 0**

I SAW MOMMY KISSING SANTA CLAUS
Tracks: / I saw mommy kissing Santa Claus / Santa Claus is coming to town / Up on the house top / Frosty the Snowman.
7" Single: Released 21 Nov '87, on Motown, by BMG Records (UK). Catalogue no: **ZB 41655**

I WANT YOU BACK
Tracks: / I want you back / Never can say goodbye.
7" Single: Released 23 Apr '88, on Motown, by BMG Records (UK). Catalogue no: **ZB 41913**
12" Single: Released 23 Apr '88, on Motown, by BMG Records (UK). Catalogue no: **ZT 41914**

LEAVE ME ALONE
Tracks: / Leave me alone / Human nature / Don't stop 'til you get enough / Wanna be startin' something (extended).
7" Single: Released 27 Feb '89, on Epic, by CBS Records. Deleted 10 Jul '89. Catalogue no: **654 672-0**
Cassingle: Released 20 Feb '89, on Epic, by CBS Records. Catalogue no: **654 6724**
12" Single: Released Feb '89, on Epic, by

Michael Jackson - Liberian Girl (Released on Epic)

CBS Records. Deleted 10 Jul '89. Catalogue no: **654 672-6**
CD 5": Released Feb '89, on Epic, by CBS Records. Deleted 10 Jul '89. Catalogue no: **654 672-2**
7" Single: Released Feb '89, on Epic, by CBS Records. Deleted 10 Jul '89. Catalogue no: **654 672-7**

LIBERIAN GIRL (See panel above)
Tracks: / Liberian girl / Girlfriend / You can't win (Only on 12" single. (654947 1).).
7" Single: Released Jun '89, on Epic, by CBS Records. Catalogue no: **6549470**
7" Single: Released Jul '89, on Epic, by CBS Records. Catalogue no: **6549479**
12" Single: Released Jul '89, on Epic, by CBS Records. Catalogue no: **6549471**
12" Single: Released Jun '89, on Epic, by CBS Records. Catalogue no: **6549478**
CD 5": Released Jun '89, on Epic, by CBS Records. Catalogue no: **6549472**

MAN IN THE MIRROR
Tracks: / Man in the mirror / Man in the mirror (album mix) / Man in the mirror (instrumental)

7" Pic: Released Feb '88, on Epic, by CBS Records. Catalogue no: **651 388-9**
CD 5": Released Feb '88, on Epic, by CBS Records. Deleted 10 Jul '89. Catalogue no: **651 388-2**
7" Single: on Epic, by CBS Records. Deleted 10 Jul '89. Catalogue no: **651 388-7**
7" Single: Released Feb '88, on Epic, by CBS Records. Catalogue no: **651338 7**
12" Single: Released Feb '88, on Epic, by CBS Records. Deleted 10 Jul '89. Catalogue no: **651 388-6**

MICHAEL JACKSON SINGLES SET
Tracks: / Man in the mirror / Man in the mirror (instrumental) / Dirty Diana / Dirty Diana (instrumental) / Way you make me feel, The / Way you make me feel, The (instrumental) / I just can't stop loving you / Baby be mine / Bad / Bad (dance radio).
7" Set: Released 18 Jul '88, on Epic, by CBS Records. Catalogue no: **MJ 5**

OFF THE WALL (SINGLE)
Tracks: / Off the wall.
7" Single: Released Nov '79, on Epic, by CBS Records. Deleted '82. Catalogue no: **EPC 8046**
7" Single: Released Apr '82, on CBS, by CBS Records. Catalogue no: **CBS 8046**

ONE DAY IN YOUR LIFE (SINGLE)
Tracks: / One day in your life / Take me back.
7" Single: Released Oct '81, on Motown, by BMG Records (UK). Catalogue no: **TMG 976**

P.Y.T.
Tracks: / P.Y.T. (pretty young thing) / Heartbreak hotel.
7" Single: Released Mar '84, on CBS, by CBS Records. Catalogue no: **A 4136**

ROCK WITH YOU
Tracks: / Rock with you / Get on the floor / You can't win.
12" Single: Released Feb '80, on Epic, by CBS Records. Deleted '83. Catalogue no: **EPC 13 8206**
7" Single: Released Feb '80, on Epic, by CBS Records. Deleted '83. Catalogue no: **EPC 8206**
7" Single: Released Apr '82, on CBS, by CBS Records. Catalogue no: **CBS 8206**

ROCKIN' ROBIN
Tracks: / Rockin' robin / Love is here and now you're gone.
7" Single: Released Oct '81, on Motown, by BMG Records (UK). Deleted '83. Catalogue no: **TMG 816**
7" Single: Released May '72, on Tamla Motown, by Motown Records (UK). Deleted '75. Catalogue no: **TMG 816**

SAY SAY SAY (MICHAEL JACKSON & PAUL McCARTNEY)
Tracks: / Say say say / Ode to a koala bear

7" Single: Released Oct '83, on Parlophone, by EMI Records. Deleted Oct '87. Catalogue no: **R 6062**
12" Single: Released Oct '83, on Parlophone, by EMI Records. Catalogue no: **12R 6062**

SHE'S OUT OF MY LIFE
Tracks: / She's out of my life / Push me away.
7" Single: Released May '80, on Epic, by CBS Records. Deleted '83. Catalogue no: **EPC 8384**

SINGLES PACK
Tracks: / Don't stop till you get enough / Off the wall / Rock with you / Wanna be startin' something / Thriller / She's out of my life / Girl is mine, The / Billie Jean / Beat it.
7" Single: Released Nov '83, on Epic, by CBS Records. Deleted Jan '89. Catalogue no: **MJ 1**

SMOOTH CRIMINAL
Tracks: / Smooth criminal / Smooth criminal (instrumental) (Only on 7" single.) / Smooth criminal (extended dance mix) (Only on 12" version & CD single.) / Smooth criminal (dance mix dub) (Only on 12" version.) / Smooth criminal (a cappella) (Only on 12" version & CD single.) / Smooth criminal (Annie mix) (Only on CD single.)

CD 5": Released Nov '88, on Epic, by CBS Records. Deleted 10 Jul '89. Catalogue no: **653 026-2**
7" Single: Released 28 Nov '88, on Epic, by CBS Records. Deleted 17 Apr '89. Catalogue no: **653026 0**
12" Single: Released Nov '88, on Epic, by CBS Records. Deleted 17 Apr '89. Catalogue no: **653026 8**
12" Single: Released Dec '88, on Epic, by CBS Records. Deleted 10 Jul '89. Catalogue no: **653 026-1**
12" Single: Released '88, on Epic, by CBS Records. Deleted 17 Apr '89. Catalogue no: **653170 6**
7" Single: Released Nov '88, on Epic, by CBS Records. Deleted 17 Apr '89. Catalogue no: **653026 7**

THRILLER (SINGLE)
Tracks: / Thriller / Things I do for you / Thriller (inst)

12" Single: Released Nov '83, on Epic, by CBS Records. Catalogue no: **TA 3643**
CD 3": Released Aug '88, on Epic (USA), by CBS Records (USA). Catalogue no: **49K 04961**
12" Single: Released Jul '88, on Epic (USA), by CBS Records (USA). Catalogue no: **490 496 1**
7" Single: Released Nov '83, on Epic, by CBS Records. Deleted '86. Catalogue no: **A 3643**

WANNA BE STARTIN' SOMETHING
Tracks: / Wanna be startin' something.
7" Single: Released Jun '83, on Epic, by CBS Records. Catalogue no: **A 3427**
12" Single: Released Jun '83, on Epic, by CBS Records. Catalogue no: **TA 3427**

WAY YOU MAKE ME FEEL, THE
Tracks: / Way you make me feel, The / Way you make me feel, The (instrumental) / Way you make me feel, The (dance ext. mix) (Available on 12" only) / Way you make me feel, The (dub version) (Available on 12" only) / Way you make me feel, The (acapella) (Available on 12" only)

Note: * tracks on 12" version only. 6512753 is a special edition double groove single.

CD 5": Released Nov '87, on Epic, by CBS Records. Deleted 10 Jul '89. Catalogue no: **651 275-9**
Special: Released Dec '87, on Epic, by CBS

Michael Jackson - We're Almost There (Released on Motown)

CBS Records. Deleted 10 Jul '89. Catalogue no: **651 275-3**
7" Single: Released Nov '87, on Epic, by CBS Records. Deleted 10 Jul '89. Catalogue no: **651 275-7**
12" Single: Released Nov '87, on Epic, by CBS Records. Deleted 10 Jul '89. Catalogue no: **651 275-8**

WE'RE ALMOST THERE (see panel on previous page)
Tracks: / We're almost there / We've got a good thing going.
7" Single: Released Oct '81, on Motown, by BMG Records (UK). Deleted '83. Catalogue no: **TMG 977**
12" Single: Released Oct '81, on Motown, by BMG Records (UK). Deleted '83. Catalogue no: **TMGT 977**

YOU CAN'T WIN (PART 1)
Tracks: / You can't win (part 1) / Billie Jean.
CD 3": Released '88, on Epic (Holland), by CBS Records. Catalogue no: **6516613**

Jackson, Mick

Biographical details: Jackson, Mick On 21 October 1978 the British singles chart featured *Blame It On The Boogie* by the Jacksons (including of course, Michael Jackson) at No.14. It just so happened that the No15 record that week was *Blame It On The Boogie* by Mick Jackson. The latter gentleman was a British singer and songwriter, based in West Germany, who was in no way related to the famous American family. Having recorded the original version of this disco ditty (a sort of belated answer to *Blame It On The Bossa Nova*), Mick found himself competing against a rival rendition by a bunch of namesakes. Mick's version was undoubtedly inferior and he also had the disadvantage of being a chart newcomer fighting with a long established chart act. In the end the Jacksons cruised to the UK No.8 position while Mick Jackson peaked at No.15.
No such confusion arose when Mick's second hit *Weekend* appeared on the British chart in early 1979. It was another strong song, but had to be content with a No.38 placing. This time, there was a cover version by American rock band Wet Willie (really!) who took the song to No.29 in their native country. Mick Jackson quickly faded into obscurity, although he continued recording into the Eighties. (Bob Macdonald 7/11/85).

BLAME IT ON THE BOOGIE
Tracks: / Blame it on the boogie.
7" Single: Released Sep '78, on Atlantic, by WEA Records. Deleted '81. Catalogue no: **K 11102**

HANGOVER
Tracks: / Hangover / Brothers in the band.
7" Single: Released Apr '80, on CBS, by CBS Records. Deleted Apr '83. Catalogue no: **CBS 8353**

LET'S MAKE SUNSHINE
Tracks: / Let's make sunshine / Something to remember you by.
12" Single: Released Mar '86, on Deja Vu, Catalogue no: **12 DEJA 1**
7" Single: Released Mar '86, on Deja Vu, Catalogue no: **7 DEJA 1**

THIS IS THE REAL THING
Tracks: / This is the real thing / Good lovin'.
7" Single: Released Sep '82, on PRT, by Castle Communications Records. Catalogue no: **7P 248**
12" Single: Released Sep '82, on PRT, by Castle Communications Records. Catalogue no: **12P 248**

WEEKEND
Tracks: / Weekend.
7" Single: Released Feb '79, on Atlantic, by WEA Records. Deleted '82. Catalogue no: **K 11224**

YOU DON'T LIGHT MY FIRE
Tracks: / You don't light my fire / Step inside my rainbow.
7" Single: Released Mar '80, on CBS, by CBS Records. Deleted Mar '83. Catalogue no: **CBS 8008**

Jackson, Millie

Biographical details: Jackson, Millie This American soul singer who hails from Georgia came to fame in 1972 with the US hit single *Ask Me What You Want*. As well as reaching the high echelons of the soul charts, it crossed over to the American pop chart and climbed to No.27. In November of that year, she achieved a minor British hit with *My Man, a Sweet man* which got to No.50. 1973 brought Millie her biggest US pop success in the shape of *Hurts So Good*, a No.24 hit from the movie Cleopatra Jones.
Jackson has never returned to the US Pop Top 40 and indeed many pop and rock fans are quite unfamiliar with her music. But to soul fans she has remained a major artist ever since. Benefiting from the consistent studio supervision of one long standing producer, Brad Shapiro, her output ranged from the raunchy to the sensuous, from passionate pleading to vehement voluptuousness. Her refusal to tone down her outrageous stage act effectively precluded her from the superstardom enjoyed by such singers as Tina Turner and Chaka Khan.
Much of Jackson's repertoire contained soulful remakes of familiar pop hits, such as Bad Company's *Feel Like Makin' Love* and Exile's *Kiss You All Over*. She also received critical acclaim for her rendition of Luther Ingram's love triangle ballad *(If Loving You Is Wrong) I Don't Want To Be Right*. Millie's shows could best be scribed as unrestained celebrations of sexual temptation, laced with generous doses of gratuitous expletives. When BBC Radio London broadcast an unedited and uncensored Millie Jackson concert in 1985, transmission had to be delayed until after midnight.
In that same year, she enjoyed her first UK Top 40 pop hit with *Act of War* a raucous rock duet with Elton John. (Bob Macdonald 8/11/85).

DIDN'T I BLOW YOUR MIND
Tracks: / Didn't I blow your mind / Be a sweetheart.
7" Single: Released Mar '80, on Polydor, by Polydor Ltd. Deleted '83. Catalogue no: **POSP 126**

HOT, WILD, UNRESTRICTED CRAZY LOVE
Tracks: / Hot, wild, unrestricted carzy love / Hot, wild, unrestricted crazy love (instrumental).
7" Single: Released Sep '86, on Jive, by Zomba Records. Deleted Jul '87. Catalogue no: **JIVE 131**
12" Single: Released Sep '86, on Jive, by Zomba Records. Deleted Jul '87. Catalogue no: **JIVET 131**

HOUSE FOR SALE
Tracks: / House for sale, A / There you are.
7" Single: Released Mar '83, on Neil Rushton, Catalogue no: **2066713**

I FEEL LIKE WALKING IN THE RAIN
Tracks: / I feel like walking in the rain / Why me.
7" Single: Released Mar '85, on Warner Bros., by WEA Records. Catalogue no: **W 9348**
12" Single: Released Mar '85, on Warner Bros., by WEA Records. Deleted Sep '87. Catalogue no: **W 9348T**

I HAD TO SAY IT (SINGLE)
Tracks: / I had to say it / I ain't no glory story.
12" Single: Released Jan '81, on Spring, Deleted Jan '84. Catalogue no: **POSPX 223**
7" Single: Released Jan '81, on Spring, Deleted Jan '84. Catalogue no: **POSP 223**

I WANNA KISS YOU ALL OVER
Tracks: / I wanna kiss you all over.
7" Single: Released Mar '85, on Important, Catalogue no: **TAN 001**
12" Single: Released Mar '85, on Important, Catalogue no: **12TAN 001**

LOVE IS A DANGEROUS GAME
Tracks: / Love is a dangerous game.
CD 5": on Jive, by Zomba Records. Catalogue no: **C135**

LOVING ARMS
Tracks: / Loving arms / Leftovers.
7" Single: Released Apr '81, on Polydor, by Polydor Ltd. Deleted Apr '86. Catalogue no: **POSP 254**

MY MAN, A SWEET MAN
Tracks: / My man, a sweet man / I gotta get away (from my own self).
7" Single: Released 2 Oct '89, on South Bound, Catalogue no: **SEWS 702**
CD 5": Released Oct '89, on South Bound, Catalogue no: **CDSEWT 702**
7" Single: Released Nov '72, on Mojo, Deleted '75. Catalogue no: **2093 002**

SOMETHING YOU CAN FEEL
Tracks: / Something you can feel.
12" Single: Released May '88, on Jive, by Zomba Records. Deleted '88. Catalogue no: **JIVET 175**
7" Single: Released May '88, on Jive, by Zomba Records. Deleted '88. Catalogue no: **JIVE 175**

SPECIAL OCCASION
Tracks: / Special occaision / Blues don't get tired of me.
7" Single: Released Nov '82, on Polydor, by Polydor Ltd. Deleted Nov '85. Catalogue no: **POSP 524**

THIS IS IT
Tracks: / This is it / Not on your life.
7" Single: Released Aug '80, on Polydor, by Polydor Ltd. Deleted '83. Catalogue no: **POSP 159**

WANNA BE YOUR LOVER
Tracks: / Wanna be your lover / Mind over matter.
7" Single: Released 23 May '87, on Jive, by Zomba Records. Deleted Jul '87. Catalogue no: **JIVE 142**
12" Single: Released 23 May '87, on Jive, by Zomba Records. Deleted Jul '87. Catalogue no: **JIVET 142**

Jackson, Neale

SCREAM IN VAIN
Tracks: / Scream in vain.
7" Single: Released Feb '85, on Indiscreet, Catalogue no: **RITA 3**

Jackson, Paul

SAY YOU'LL WAIT FOR ME
Tracks: / Say you'll wait for me.
12" Single: Released Jul '89, on Orbitone, by Orbitone Records. Catalogue no: **OR 1239**

SPANISH EYES
Tracks: / Spanish eyes.
12" Single: Released Dec '88, on Orbitone, by Orbitone Records. Catalogue no: **OR 1227**

STORY OF GONE WITH THE WIND, THE
Tracks: / Story of Gone With The Wind, The.
7" Single: Released Oct '86, on Hippodrome, by Hippodrome Records. Catalogue no: **HIPPO 110**
12" Single: Released Oct '86, on Hippodrome, by Hippodrome Records. Catalogue no: **12HIPPO 110**

TIME WILL EASE
Tracks: / Time will ease / Can't stand losing you.
7" Single: Released 17 Oct '87, on Orbitone, by Orbitone Records. Catalogue no: **OR 724**
12" Single: Released 17 Oct '87, on Orbitone, by Orbitone Records. Catalogue no: **OR 1224**

YOU MADE ME A WINNER (SINGLE)
Tracks: / You made me a winner.
7" Single: Released Aug '88, on Orbitone, by Orbitone Records. Catalogue no: **OR 729**
12" Single: Released 8 Aug '88, on Orbitone, by Orbitone Records. Catalogue no: **OR 1229**

Jackson, Ray

IN THE NIGHT (SINGLE)
Tracks: / In the night / Waiting for the time.
7" Single: Released Feb '80, on Mercury, by Phonogram Ltd. Deleted '83. Catalogue no: **JACK 01**

LITTLE TOWN FLIRT
Tracks: / Little town flirt / Make it last.
7" Single: Released Apr '80, on Mercury, by Phonogram Ltd. Deleted '83. Catalogue no: **MER 8**

Jackson, Rebbie

CENTIPEDE
Tracks: / Centipede.
7" Single: Released Jan '85, on CBS, by CBS Records. Catalogue no: **A 4528**
12" Single: Released Jan '85, on CBS, by CBS Records. Catalogue no: **TA 4528**

REACTION
Tracks: / Reaction / Reaction (instrumental).
12" Single: Released Sep '86, on CBS, by CBS Records. Deleted '87. Catalogue no: **TA 7323**
7" Single: Released Sep '86, on CBS, by CBS Records. Deleted '87. Catalogue no: **A 7323**

Jackson, R.Zee

REGGAE DISCO MEDLEY
Tracks: / Reggae disco medley.
12" Single: Released Feb '82, on Echo, by Echo Records. Catalogue no: **ECHO 006**

Jackson, Shawne

LOVELINE
12" Single: Released May '83, on Loose End, by MCA Records. Catalogue no: **LET 103**
7" Single: Released May '83, on Loose End, by MCA Records. Catalogue no: **LE 103**

Jackson Sisters

I BELIEVE IN MIRACLES
Tracks: / I believe in miracles / Boy you're dynamite / Why can't we be more than friends.
7" Single: Released Jun '87, on Urban, by Polydor Ltd. Catalogue no: **URB 4**
12" Single: Released Jun '87, on Urban, by Polydor Ltd. Deleted 30 May '89. Catalogue no: **URBX 4**

Jackson, Steve 'Shade'

I ADMIRE YOU
Tracks: / I admire you.
12" Single: Released Jan '84, on M&M, by M&M Music Company. Catalogue no: **MM 001**

Jackson, Stevie

GIVE ME A ROMANCE
Tracks: / Romantic mix-up.
7" Single: Released Nov '86, on Stage Show, Catalogue no: **SSW 001**

Jackson, Stonewall

Biographical details: Jackson, Stonewall This American country singer and guitarist is named after the Confederate general Stonewall Jackson. The vocalist was born in Georgia and raised in North Carolina, but based his career in Tennessee's burgeoning country and western mecca Nashville. In 1959 Jackson came to fame with a one off pop hit called *Waterloo*, co-written by John D.Loudermilk; it reached No.4 in the US and No.24 in the UK.
Stonewall then disappeared, as fat as pop audiences were concerned. But *Waterloo* had established his reputation in Nashville forever and he became one of the country genre's everlasting institutions. His style changed little but then it didn't really need to. (Bob Macdonald 8/11/85).

I CAN'T SING A LOVE SONG
Tracks: / I can't sing a love song / My favourite sin.
7" Single: Released Oct '80, on President, by President Records. Deleted Oct '83. Catalogue no: **PT 486**

WATERLOO
Tracks: / Waterloo.
7" Single: Released Jul '59, on Philips, by Phonogram Ltd. Deleted '82. Catalogue no: **PB 941**
7" Single: Released Jul '82, on Old Gold, by Old Gold Records. Catalogue no: **OG 9074**

Jackson, Tom

GOOD MORNING AMERICA
7" Single: Released Feb '83, on Magic (1), by Submarine Records. Catalogue no: **MAGIC 3**

Jackson, Tony

BYE BYE BABY
Tracks: / Bye bye baby.
7" Single: Released Oct '64, on Pye, Deleted '67. Catalogue no: **7N 15685**

LOVE BLIND
Tracks: / Love blind.
7" Single: Released Sep '84, on Cedar, Catalogue no: **CAG 2**
12" Single: Released Sep '84, on Cedar, Catalogue no: **12CAG 2**

LOVE I LOST, THE
Tracks: / Love I lose, The / Secretary in love.
12" Single: Released Jul '88, on Opium, by Opium Records. Catalogue no: **OPINT 24**
7" Single: Released Jul '88, on Opium, by Opium Records. Catalogue no: **OPIN 24**

NEW YEAR'S RESOLUTION
Tracks: / New year's resolution.
7" Single: Released Dec '84, on Cedar, Catalogue no: **XMAS 1**
12" Single: Released Dec '84, on Cedar, Catalogue no: **12XMAS 1**

SNOWY WHITE CHRISTMAS
Tracks: / Snowy white Christmas.
7" Single: Released Oct '84, on Cedar, Catalogue no: **XMAS 1**
12" Single: Released Oct '84, on Cedar, Catalogue no: **XMAS 121**

STEPPIN' OUT OF THE GROOVE
Tracks: / Steppin' out of the groove.
7" Single: Released Aug '83, on Switch, Catalogue no: **SW 6**

SUMMER GROOVE
Tracks: / Summer groove.
7" Single: Released Jul '84, on Cedar, Catalogue no: **CAG 1**
12" Single: Released Jul '84, on Cedar, Catalogue no: **12CAG 1**

Jackson, Walter

TOUCHING IN THE DARK
Tracks: / Touching in the dark.
12" Single: Released Dec '84, on Bluebird (2), by BMG Records (UK). Catalogue no: **BRT 11**
7" Single: Released Dec '84, on Bluebird (2), by BMG Records (UK). Catalogue no: **BR 11**

Jackson, Wanda

Biographical details: Jackson, Wanda This American singer was one of the few women to have a crack at the rock 'n' roll market during the late Fifties and early Sixties. In those days, the raucousness and raw energy of rock was an almost exclusively male domain; the small number of successful girl singers were usually heard on middle of the road ballads, lightweight pop novelties or country and western songs. Jackson, who hailed from Oklahoma, had a country background but her interest in the 'rock' part of rockabilly led to her achieving a Top 40 hit on both sides of the Atlantic in 1960 with *Let's Have a Party*. The frantic *Mean, Mean Man* gave Wanda a second Uk Top 40 single in early 1961.
In late 1961 Jackson scored two further American Top 40 singles, *Right or Wrong* and *In The Middle of a Heartache* which saw her veering back towards country. The experiment has been bold and brash while it lasted. In the early Seventies Jackson began a prolific fusion of country and gospel. (Bob Macdonald 8/11/85).

LET'S HAVE A PARTY (SINGLE)
Tracks: / Let's have a party.
7" Single: Released Sep '60, on Capitol, by EMI Records. Deleted '63. Catalogue no: **CL 15147**

MEAN MEAN MAN
Tracks: / Mean mean man.
7" Single: Released Jan '61, on Capitol, by EMI Records. Deleted '64. Catalogue no: **CL 15176**

Jackson, Willis

NUTHER'N LIKE THUTH'N'
Tracks: / Nuther'n like thuth'n'.
7" Single: Released Dec '88, on BGP, by Ace Records. Catalogue no: **BGPT 004**

Jacksons

Biographical details: Jacksons This American Family soul vocal group consists of brothers Jackie, Tito, Marlon, Michael and Randy Jackson (in descending order).
The historic success that the young Jackson 5 group had enjoyed with Tamla Motown during the early Seventies, was on the wane by 1975. Realising that their career required fresh impetus, the family elected to leave Motown and accept an enticing offer from Epic Records. Jermaine Jackson, who was now married to the daughter of Tamla boss Berry Gody, chose to stay behind. To keep the numbers up to full strength, the others replaced him with Randy, a sixth brother who had been too young to join the group in the early days. Because Gordy retained the rights to the Jackson 5 name, the revamped quintet became known simply as The Jackson.
Teaming with the ace Philadelphia songwriting and production team of Kenny Gamble & Leon Huff, The Jacksons got back in stride in 1977 with the million selling US Top 10 single, *Enjoy Yousell*. The next single *Show You The Way To Go*, returned the Jackson family to the limelight on the other side of the Atlantic, becoming the clan's first ever UK No.1.
After undergoing another mediocre path with the *Goin' Places* LP, the Jacksons returned to form again in 1978-79 with the *Destiny* album and its two disco smashes, *Blame It On The Boogie* and *Shake Your Body (Down To the Ground)*. These two singles were released at the height of the international disco boom and they gratifyingly brought the Jacksons to the forefront of that explosion, a genre that was giving disproportionate success to a host of less worthy, faceless acts. *Shake Your Body* was particulary huge, reaching No.4 in Britain and selling two million copies in the States: it even spawned a belated answer record for Julia and Company declared that *Shake Your Body* was the direct inspiration for their 1984 hit *Breakin' Down (Sugar Samba)*.
Following Michael Jackson's sensational solo success with the multi-million selling *Off The Wall* LP, the Jacksons regrouped at the end of 1980 for the *Triumph* album. *Triumph* fared well on both sides of the Atlantic and yielded a series of hit singles with such dancefloor scorchers as *Lovely One* and *Can You Feel It*, but its commercial success and musical content seemed tame by comparison with Michael's globale conquest with *Off The Wall*. Despite the fact that Michael's work was carefully timed to ensure that it was not released while the Jacksons' group efforts were on the streets, his brothers could not live up to his superstardom.
This problem was further pronounced in 1984, when Michael's *Thriller* album was officially declared as the world's best selling recording of all time. The result was that the Jacksons' new projects, the *Victory* LP an tour were greeted with such publicity overkill that they could not possibly match expectations. *Victory* was a rather unsatisfactory piecemeal record with individual members taking writing and production responsibility for individual tracks; the album reached the Top 5 in both the US and UK, but moved down the charts fairly rapidly after that. *Victory* was no triumph. (Bob Macdonald 8/11/85)

JACKSONS - NOTHIN' (THAT COMPARES 2U) (Released on Epic)

2300 JACKSON STREET (SINGLE)
Tracks: / 2300 Jackson Street (edit) (On 7" only) / When I look at you / Keep her (On 12" & CD single.) / 2300 Jackson Street (album version) (On 12" & CD single.) / Please come back to me when I look at you (Only on 12" (655206)).
Cassingle: Released 14 Aug '89, on Epic, by CBS Records. Catalogue no: **655206 4**
CD 5": Released 14 Aug '89, on Epic, by CBS Records. Catalogue no: **655206 2**
12" Single: Released 14 Aug '89, on Epic, by CBS Records. Catalogue no: **655206 6**
7" Single: Released 14 Aug '89, on Epic, by CBS Records. Catalogue no: **655206 7**
12" Single: Released 14 Aug '89, on Epic, by CBS Records. Catalogue no: **655206 8**

BLAME IT ON THE BOOGIE
Tracks: / Blame it on the boogie.
7" Single: Released Sep '76, on Epic, by CBS Records. Deleted '81. Catalogue no: **EPC 6683**

CAN YOU FEEL IT
Tracks: / Can you feel it / Wondering who / Shake your body (On 12" only).
12" Single: Released Feb '81, on Epic, by CBS Records. Deleted '84. Catalogue no: **EPC 13-9554**
7" Single: Released Feb '81, on Epic, by CBS Records. Deleted '84. Catalogue no: **EPC 9554**

DESTINY
7" Single: Released Feb '79, on Epic, by CBS Records. Deleted '82. Catalogue no: **EPC 6983**

DREAMER
Tracks: / Dreamer.
7" Single: Released Aug '77, on Epic, by CBS Records. Deleted '80. Catalogue no: **EPC 5458**

ENJOY YOURSELF
Tracks: / Enjoy yourself.
7" Single: Released Apr '77, on Epic, by CBS Records. Deleted '80. Catalogue no: **EPC 5063**

EVEN THOUGH YOU'VE GONE
Tracks: / Even though you've gone.
7" Single: Released Feb '78, on Epic, by CBS Records. Deleted '81. Catalogue no: **EPC 5919**

GOIN' PLACES (SINGLE)
Tracks: / Going places.
7" Single: Released Nov '77, on Epic, by CBS Records. Deleted '80. Catalogue no: **EPC 5732**

HEARTBREAK HOTEL
Tracks: / Heartbreak hotel / Different kind of lady.
7" Single: Released Dec '80, on Epic, by CBS Records. Deleted '83. Catalogue no: **EPC 9391**

LOVELY ONE
Tracks: / Lovely one / Can you feel it.
7" Single: Released Oct '80, on Epic, by CBS Records. Deleted '83. Catalogue no: **EPC 9302**
CD 3": Released Dec '88, on Epic (Holland), by CBS Records. Catalogue no: **651 6603**

NOTHIN' (THAT COMPARES 2 U) (see panel above)
Tracks: / Nothin (that compares 2 U) (the mix) / Nothin (that compares 2 U) (extended version) / Nothin (that compares 2 U) (choice dub) / Heartbreak hotel / Alright with me.
CD 5": Released 24 Apr '89, on Epic, by CBS Records. Deleted Oct '89. Catalogue no: **654808 2**
7" Single: Released 24 Apr '89, on Epic, by CBS Records. Deleted Oct '89. Catalogue no: **654808 7**
Cassingle: Released 15 May '89, on Epic, by CBS Records. Deleted Oct '89. Catalogue no: **654808 4**
7" Single: Released 8 May '89, on Epic, by CBS Records. Deleted Oct '89. Catalogue no: **654909 8**
12" Single: Released Apr '89, on Epic, by CBS Records. Deleted Oct '89. Catalogue no: **654808 6**
12" Single: Released 24 Apr '89, on Epic, by CBS Records. Deleted Oct '89. Catalogue no: **654808 1**

SHAKE YOUR BODY DOWN (TO THE GROUND)
Tracks: / Shake your body.
7" Single: Released Mar '79, on Epic, by CBS Records. Deleted '82. Catalogue no: **EPC 7181**
7" Single: Released Apr '82, on CBS, by CBS Records. Catalogue no: **CBS 7181**

SHOW YOU THE WAY TO GO
Tracks: / Show you the way to go.
7" Single: Released Jun '77, on Epic, by CBS Records. Deleted '80. Catalogue no: **EPC 5266**

STATE OF SHOCK (see also Mick Jagger)
Tracks: / State of shock.
7" Single: Released Jun '84, on Epic, by CBS Records. Catalogue no: **A 4431**
12" Single: Released Jun '84, on Epic, by CBS Records. Catalogue no: **TA 4431**

THINGS I DO FOR YOU
Tracks: / Things I do for you / Don't stop till you get enough.
7" Single: Released Dec '81, on Epic, by CBS Records. Deleted Dec '84. Catalogue no: **EPC A 1902**

TIME OUT FOR THE BURGLAR
Tracks: / Time out for the burglar / News at 11.
12" Single: Released Feb '87, on MCA, by MCA Records. Catalogue no: **MCAS 1129**

TIME WAITS FOR NO ONE
Tracks: / Time waits for no one / Give it up.
7" Single: Released Sep '81, on Epic, by CBS Records. Deleted Sep '84. Catalogue no: **EPCA 1579**

TORTURE
Tracks: / Torture.
7" Single: Released Aug '84, on Epic, by CBS Records. Deleted '85. Catalogue no: **A 4675**
12" Single: Released Aug '84, on Epic, by CBS Records. Catalogue no: **TA 4675**

WALK RIGHT NOW
Tracks: / Walk right now / Your ways.
7" Single: Released Jul '81, on Epic, by CBS Records. Deleted '84. Catalogue no: **EPC A 1294**
7" Single: Released Jun '81, on Epic, by CBS Records. Deleted '84. Catalogue no: **EPC 13-1294**

Jacky

WHITE HORSES
Tracks: / White horses.
7" Single: Released Apr '68, on Philips, by Phonogram Ltd. Deleted '71. Catalogue no: **BF 1674**

Jacobites

PIN YOUR HEART
Tracks: / Pin your heart.
12" Single: Released Sep '85, on Glass, by Glass Records. Deleted Jan '87. Catalogue no: **GLAEP 101**

WHEN THE RAIN COMES
Tracks: / When the rain comes.
Note: Featuring Nikki Sudden, Dave Kusworth and Epic Soundtracks. Rock'n'roll troubadours, Keith Richards look-alikes, ragged romantics.
7" Single: Released Jan '86, on Glass, by Glass Records. Deleted Jan '89. Catalogue no: **GLASS 045**
12" Single: Released Jan '86, on Glass, by Glass Records. Catalogue no: **GLASS 12045**

Jacobs, Debbie

HIGH ON YOUR LOVE
Tracks: / High on your love / I can never forget a friend.
7" Single: Released Jun '80, on MCA, by MCA Records. Deleted '83. Catalogue no: **MCA 597**

Jacobs, Jo Jo

SUPERGLUE
Tracks: / Superglue / Don't treat me like a fool.
7" Single: Released Oct '80, on AMI, by AMI Records. Deleted Oct '83. Catalogue no: **AIS 108**

Jacques, Peter

COUNTING ON LOVE
Tracks: / Counting on love / Is it it ?.
12" Single: Released Feb '81, on RCA, by BMG Records (UK). Deleted '84. Catalogue no: **RCAT 36**
7" Single: Released Feb '81, on RCA, by BMG Records (UK). Deleted '84. Catalogue no: **RCA 36**

LOUDER, THE
Tracks: / Louder, The / Mighty fire.
12" Single: Released Jan '81, on RCA, by BMG Records (UK). Deleted Jan '84. Catalogue no: **RCAT 20**

Jacuzzi

HAPPENS ALL THE TIME
Tracks: / Happens all the time.
7" Single: Released Jun '84, on Freeway, Catalogue no: **FRW 2**

Jad W10

CELLAR DANCE
Tracks: / Cellar dance.
12" Single: Released Jan '85, on Invitation Au Suicide, Catalogue no: **ID 9**

Jade

BOBBY'S GIRL
Tracks: / Bobby's girl / I'm in love again.
7" Single: Released Jan '84, on Page One, by Page One Records. Catalogue no: **POR 007**

I CAN'T BELIEVE IT'S OVER
Tracks: / I can't believe it's over / Blue jade (Extra track on 12" version only).
12" Single: Released Oct '86, on Master Funk, Catalogue no: **TWD 1953**

I'M A GIRL
Tracks: / I'm a girl / Little girl.
7" Single: Released Jan '82, on Page One, by Page One Records. Catalogue no: **POR 001**

LIAR
Tracks: / Liar.
7" Single: Released Aug '83, on Page One, by Page One Records. Catalogue no: **POR 013**

POSIN'
Tracks: / Posin'.
7" Single: Released Aug '81, on Siam,

JAGS - BACK OF MY HAND (Released on Island)

Catalogue no: **SM 2**

YOUNG LOVE
Tracks: / Young love / Destiny.
7" Single: Released Feb '83, on Page One, by Page One Records. Catalogue no: **POR 009**

Jade 4 U

RAINBOWS
Tracks: / Rainbows.
12" Single: Released 27 Feb '88, on Subway, by Subway Records. Catalogue no: **SUB 009**

ROCK IT TO THE BONE
Tracks: / Rock it to the bone / Rock to the beat.
12" Single: Released Apr '89, on House, Catalogue no: **HS001 12**
12" Single: Released Jun '89, on Antler, by Antler Records (Belgium). Catalogue no: **ASB 901**
12" Single: Released Jul '89, on Subway, by Subway Records. Catalogue no: **AS 89012**

THAT BOY (Acid mix)
Tracks: / That boy.
12" Single: Released Oct '88, on Subway, by Subway Records. Catalogue no: **SUB 043**

Jaeger, Leigh

JOHNNY AND MARY
Tracks: / Johnny and Mary.
7" Single: Released Aug '89, on A&M, by A&M Records. Catalogue no: **VOGUE 2**
7" Single: Released Jun '89, on A&M, by A&M Records. Catalogue no: **VOGUE 1**
12" Single: Released Jun '89, on A&M, by A&M Records. Catalogue no: **VOGUE 12**

Jagger, Mick

JUST ANOTHER NIGHT
Tracks: / Just another night.
7" Single: Released Feb '85, on CBS, by CBS Records. Deleted '88. Catalogue no: **A 4722**

LET'S WORK
Tracks: / Let's work / Catch as catch can.
12" Single: Released Aug '87, on CBS, by CBS Records. Catalogue no: **651028-12**
7" Single: Released Sep '87, on CBS, by CBS Records. Catalogue no: **651028 0**
7" Single: Released Aug '87, on CBS, by CBS Records. Catalogue no: **651 028 7**

MEMO FROM TURNER
Tracks: / Memo from Turner.
7" Single: Released Nov '70, on Decca, by Decca Records. Deleted '73. Catalogue no: **F 13067**

THROWAWAY
Tracks: / Throwaway / Throwaway (remix) (Available on 12" single only.) / Throwaway (vocal dub) (Available on 12" single only.) / Peace for the wicked.
7" Single: Released Nov '87, on CBS, by CBS Records. Deleted Jun '88. Catalogue no: **THROW 1**
12" Single: Released Nov '87, on CBS, by CBS Records. Deleted Jun '88. Catalogue no: **THROW T1**
7" Pic: Released Dec '87, on CBS, by CBS Records. Deleted Jun '88. Catalogue no: **THROW P1**
CD 5": Released Nov '87, on CBS, by CBS Records. Deleted Jan '89. Catalogue no: **THROW C1**

Jags

Biographical details: Jags At the time of their success, this British band consisted of John Alder, Alex Baird, Steve Prudence and Nick Watkinson.
The Jags were part of a mini-boom of the late Seventies known as 'power pop' this was a fusion of punk rock and the more commercial dictates of the pop charts. The Jags came to brief fame in 1979 with their catchy single *Back Of My Hand*, which reached the UK No.17 position. Success could not be maintained because their songs were not strong enough to stand out from a plethora of similar material. The group's follow up to *Back Of My Hand* was *Woman's World* which peaked at No75. Their 1981 album *No Tie Like A Present* produced by Alex Sadkin, Failed to collar the record-buying public and the band faded into obscurity. (Bob Macdonald 8/11/85).

BACK OF MY HAND (see panel above)
Tracks: / Back of my hand / Double vision.
7" Single: Released Sep '79, on Island, by Island Records. Deleted '82. Catalogue no: **WIP 6501**

I NEVER WAS A BEACH BOY
Tracks: / I never was a beach boy / Tune into heaven.
7" Single: Released Jan '81, on Island, by Island Records. Catalogue no: **WIP 6666**

PARTY GAMES
Tracks: / Party games / She's so considerate.
7" Single: Released May '80, on Island, by Island Records. Deleted May '83. Catalogue no: **WIP 6587**

SOUND OF GOODBYE
Tracks: / Sound of goodbye / Hurt.
7" Single: Released Apr '81, on Island, by Island Records. Deleted Apr '84. Catalogue no: **WIP 6683**

WOMAN'S WORLD
Tracks: / Woman's world, A / Dumb blonde.
7" Single: Released Feb '80, on Island, by Island Records. Deleted '83. Catalogue no: **WIP 6531**

Jaguar

AXE CRAZY
Tracks: / Axe crazy / War machine.
7" Single: Released Aug '82, on Neat, by Neat Records. Catalogue no: **NEAT 16**

BACK STREET WOMAN
Tracks: / Back street woman / Chasing the dragon.
7" Single: Released Nov '81, on Heavy Metal, by FM-Revolver Records. Catalogue no: **HEAVY 10**

GET IT AND TALK
Tracks: / Get it and talk.
7" Single: Released Nov '88, on Taurus, Catalogue no: **UNKNOWN**

Jah Dave

FISHERMAN
Tracks: / Fisherman.
12" Single: Released Jul '85, on Ishence Musik, Catalogue no: **ISD 003**

HOW LONG
Tracks: / How long part 1 / How long part 2.
12" Single: Released May '83, on Ishence Musik, Catalogue no: **ISD 001**

INFORMER
Tracks: / Informer, The / Taken away.
12" Single: Released Feb '83, on Solid Groove, Catalogue no: **SG 019**

Jah Globe

MORE PEOPLE ARE WALKING
Tracks: / More people are walking / Keep it in reality.
12" Single: Released Mar '84, on Pyramid, by Pyramid Records. Catalogue no: **PAD 002**

Jah Light

PERFECT PEACE
Tracks: / Perfect peace.
12" Single: Released Mar '89, on Jah Light, Catalogue no: **JL 001**

Jah Lloyd

SHAKE AND FLICKER
Tracks: / Shake and flicker.
7" Single: Released Jul '82, on Sheet, Catalogue no: **SHEET 4**

Jah Mel

DON'T BE CRUEL
Tracks: / Don't be cruel.
12" Single: Released Oct '89, on Jetstar, by Jetstar Records. Catalogue no: **JMRF 05**

Jah Pollack

HOUSE OF JAH
Tracks: / House of Jah / Willie bang.
12" Single: Released Jul '82, on Conscious Man, Catalogue no: **CON 001**

Jah Scouse

MERGE
Tracks: / Merge.
7" Single: Released Apr '85, on Better Things, Catalogue no: **BETS 1**

Jah Screechie

SHADOW MOVE
Tracks: / Shadow move / Hopscotch.
12" Single: Released Dec '84, on Scom, Catalogue no: **BD 014**

WALK AND SKANK
Tracks: / Walk and skank.
12" Single: Released Jul '84, on Blacka Dread, Catalogue no: **BD 002**

Jah Shaka

GOT TO KNOW
Tracks: / Got to know.
12" Single: Released Mar '86, on Jah Shaka, Catalogue no: **SHAKA 852**

JAH CHILDREN
Tracks: / Jah children / Jah works.
12" Single: Released Sep '82, on Jah Shaka, Catalogue no: **JS 823**

LION YOUTH
Tracks: / Lion youth / Beyond the realms.
12" Single: Released Nov '82, on Jah Shaka, Catalogue no: **SHAKA 828**

Jah Son

SHE LOVES A RUB A DUB
Tracks: / She loves a rub a dub.
12" Single: Released Apr '82, on Negus Roots, Catalogue no: **NERT 011**

Jah Stone

PINK EYE DISEASE
Tracks: / Pink eye disease / Rhythmic rock.
12" Single: Released May '82, on Regal, Catalogue no: **RD 005**

Jah Thomas

FRIDAY NIGHT JAMBOREE
Tracks: / Friday night jamboree.
12" Single: Released Apr '83, on Silver Camel, Catalogue no: **SC 023**

HAIL LYRICS FOR SALE
Tracks: / Hail lyrics for sale / Haul and pull up.
12" Single: Released Feb '83, on Midnight Rock, Catalogue no: **MR 012**

MAKE A MOVE
Tracks: / Make a move / Dancin' move.
12" Single: Released Jan '84, on Midnight Rock, Catalogue no: **MR 021**

Jah Warriors

APARTHEID
Tracks: / Apartheid.
7" Single: Released Oct '84, on A Record Company, Deleted '88. Catalogue no: **ARC 008**

CAN'T TAKE NO MORE
Tracks: / Can't take no more / If you only knew.
12" Single: Released Oct '82, on Bushman, Catalogue no: **BUSH 1**

TROUBLED WATERS
Tracks: / Troubled waters.
12" Single: Released 20 Feb '88, on Ariwa Sounds, by Ariwa Sounds. Catalogue no: **ARI 68**

UNDER THE APPLETREE
Tracks: / Under the apple tree.
12" Single: Released Apr '88, on Ariwa Sounds, by Ariwa Sounds. Catalogue no: **ARI 068**

WHATS THIS FEELING
Tracks: / What's this feeling / Radical / African queen.
7" Single: Released Sep '84, on A Record Company, Deleted '88. Catalogue no: **ARC 007**

Jah Whoosh

DEH PON STREET AGAIN
Tracks: / Deh pon street again / Street dub.
12" Single: Released Nov '86, on Sky Juice, Catalogue no: **SJD 017**

WHIP(2 PARTS)
Tracks: / Whip (part 1) / Whip (part 2).
12" Single: Released Oct '83, on Sky Juice, Catalogue no: **SJ 001**

Jahlib & Suns Of Arda

MYSTERIES OF THE EAST
Tracks: / Mysteries of the east.
12" Single: Released Jul '82, on Virgin, by Virgin Records. Deleted '82. Catalogue no: **VS 512-12**

Jakata

GOLDEN GIRL
Tracks: / Golden girl / Light at the end of the tunnel.
7" Single: Released Apr '85, on Morocco (USA), by Motown Records (UK). Catalogue no: **TMG 1379**
12" Single: Released Apr '85, on Morocco (USA), by Motown Records (UK). Catalogue no: **TMGT 1379**

HELL IS ON THE RUN
Tracks: / Hell is on the run.
12" Single: Released Sep '84, on Morocco (USA), by Motown Records (UK). Catalogue no: **TMGT 1357**
7" Single: Released Sep '84, on Morocco (USA), by Motown Records (UK). Catalogue no: **TMG 1357**

Jake The Pilgrim

GAIA
Tracks: / Gaia.
12" Single: Released Aug '87, on Wounded Knee, by Waterfall Records. Catalogue no: **WKN 4**

Jakko

Biographical details: Jakko is a guitarist, a man who has made a career out of playing on other peoples albums that never came out, an accomplished actor, a Watford fan, an expert on the evolution of the tremelo arm, a face on an XTC poster and an eternal musical optimist. (Stiff Records, Feb 1984).

DANGEROUS DREAMS
Tracks: / Little town.
7" Single: Released Oct '86, on MDM, by MDM Communications. Deleted May '88. Catalogue no: **MDM 14**
12" Single: Released Oct '86, on MDM, by MDM Communications. Deleted May '88. Catalogue no: **MDM 14-12**
12" Single: Released May '83, on Stiff, by Stiff Records. Catalogue no: **SBUY 183**
7" Single: Released May '83, on Stiff, by Stiff Records. Catalogue no: **BUY 183**

GRAB WHAT YOU CAN
Tracks: / Grab what you can.
7" Single: Released Sep '82, on Chiswick Records, Catalogue no: **DICE 14**
12" Single: Released Sep '82, on Chiswick Records, Catalogue no: **DICE 1214**

I CAN'T STAND THIS PRESSURE
Tracks: / I can't stand this pressure.
12" Single: Released Sep '84, on Stiff, by Stiff Records. Catalogue no: **BUYIT 208**
7" Single: Released Sep '84, on Stiff, by Stiff Records. Catalogue no: **BUY 208**

JUDY GET DOWN
Tracks: / Judy get down / This old man.
7" Single: Released Jun '86, on MDM, by

MDM Communications. Deleted May '88. Catalogue no: **MDM 11**
12" Single: Released Jun '86, on MDM, by MDM Communications. Deleted May '88. Catalogue no: **MDM 11-12**

LEARNING TO CRY
Tracks: / Learning to cry / Learning to cry (georgian mix).
7" Single: Released Apr '86, on MDM, by MDM Communications. Deleted '86. Catalogue no: **MDM 4**
12" Single: Released Apr '86, on MDM, by MDM Communications. Deleted May '88. Catalogue no: **MDM 4-12**

NIGHT HAS A THOUSAND EYES
Tracks: / Night has a thousand eyes, The / Something tells me.
7" Single: Released Jan '82, on Chiswick Records, Deleted '82. Catalogue no: **DICE 1**

STRAINING OUR EYES
Tracks: / Straining our eyes / Fall to pieces.
7" Single: Released May '82, on Chiswick Records, Deleted May '85. Catalogue no: **DICE 7**

WHO'S FOOLING WHO
Tracks: / Who's foolin' who / Grown man immersed in Tin-Tin.
12" Single: Released Mar '84, on Stiff, by Stiff Records. Catalogue no: **SBUY 198**
7" Single: Released Mar '84, on Stiff, by Stiff Records. Catalogue no: **BUY 198**

Jaktrapp

SAMPLE THIS HOUSE
Tracks: / Sample this house / Sample this house (version).
12" Single: Released Jun '88, on Beat Box, by Beat Box Records. Catalogue no: **BBOX 1**

Jakuzzi

RICOCHET
Tracks: / Ricochet / Heliotrope.
12" Single: Released Oct '81, on Creole, by Creole Records. Catalogue no: **CR 1221**

J.A.L.N. Band

DISCO MUSIC
Tracks: / Disco music / I like it.
7" Single: Released Aug '76, on Magnet, by WEA Records. Deleted '79. Catalogue no: **MAG 73**

GET UP
Tracks: / Get up.
7" Single: Released Jun '78, on Magnet, by WEA Records. Deleted '81. Catalogue no: **MAG 118**

I GOT TO SING
Tracks: / I got to sing.
7" Single: Released Aug '77, on Magnet, by WEA Records. Deleted '80. Catalogue no: **MAG 97**

Jam

Biographical details: Jam This British band consisted of Rick Buckler, Bruce Foxton and Paul Weller.
The Jam were always dominated by Paul Weller, their key songwriter/singer/guitarist/public spokesman. His track record on the British charts is phenomonal - all 18 Jam singles reached The Top 40 and, after the trio's termination at the end of 1982, every single issued by Weller's new outfit, the Style Council enjoyed similar success. Paul has yet to experience a flop!
Emerging from a schoolboy band in the mid Seventies the Jam came from the Surrey and London club circuits to be signed by Polydor Records in February 1977. Weller has remained with that company ever since. The trio's first three single *In The City, All Around The World* and *The Modern World* were released during that same year. Together with the Sex Pistols, the Buzzcocks, The Clash and The Dammed, The Jam were one of the five most important groups of the 1976-77 punk rock explosion. They helped to turn the UK music business on its head, shaking it out of the complacency that had been caused by the teenybop manipulation of the preceding pop scene and the remote musicianship of the arty rock bands.
Although the Jam were more closely influenced by previous rock music - notably the Sixties sounds of The Who - than their punk peers, the New Wave was a convenient scene to cling to until the threesome's identity could be fully established. They had another three UK hits in 1978 and a further three in 1979, during which Weller advanced his reputation as a no-holds barred commentator on the state of the British nation and, in particular, the concerns of the working classes. Though musically restricted - most of the hits were variations on the same basic melody - the Jam's sheer energy and Weller's lyrics made the group a listening must. *Down In The Tube Station At Midnight* and *Strange Town* were particularly incisive statements on the problems of inner city life.
Because of the singularly British nature of their work and because of the lack of interest by foreign countries in the UK's punk revolution, the Jam never achieved major success abroad. When 1979's *The Eton Rifles* became their first UK Top 10 single, and when 1980's *Going Underground/The Dreams of Children* became the first single in six years to enter the British chart at No.1, the rest of the world did not pay any attention. Another UK No.1 the Beatle-esque *Start* was achieved before 1980 was over.
1982 was undoubtedly the hottest year of the Jam's career. *The Gift* LP entered the British chart at No.1 as did the singles *Town Called Malice/Precious* and *Beat Ssurrender.* They became the first band since Slade to have three records go straight to No.1 in the first week of release and the first group since The Beatles to have both sides of a chart-topper featured in the same edition of Top Of The Pops. The Jam had more Uk Top 10 hits in '82 than they had managed in any year since their formation; and, what's more, things at last began to happen on the international front.
At the end of 1982, however, despite this level of success, Weller disbanded the Jam, saying that they had outlived their useful life. He wanted to inject a more soulful flavour into his music and felt constrained by the format of the group. It shocked Buckler and Foxton as much as anyone else - they launched tepid individual careers, while Weller continued in his usual successful, sincere, political and loud-mouthed vein with the Style Council. (Bob Macdonald 8/11/85).

ABSOLUTE BEGINNERS
Tracks: / Absolute beginners.
7" Single: Released Oct '81, on Polydor, by Polydor Ltd. Deleted '84. Catalogue no: **POSP 350**

ALL AROUND THE WORLD
Tracks: / All around the world.
7" Single: Released Jul '77, on Polydor, by Polydor Ltd. Deleted '85. Catalogue no: **2058 903**

BEAT SURRENDER
Tracks: / Beat surrender / Shopping / Move on up / Stoned out of my mind / War.
7" Set: Released Jan '83, on Polydor, by Polydor Ltd. Catalogue no: **OSPJ 540**
7" Single: Released Jan '83, on Polydor, by Polydor Ltd. Catalogue no: **POSP 540**

BITTEREST PILL (I EVER HAD TO SWALLOW), THE
Tracks: / Bitterest pill (I ever had to swallow), The.
7" Single: Released Sep '82, on Polydor, by Polydor Ltd. Deleted '85. Catalogue no: **POSP 505**

DAVID WATTS
Tracks: / David Watts / 'A' bomb in Wardour Street.
7" Single: Released Aug '78, on Polydor, by Polydor Ltd. Deleted '85. Catalogue no: **2059 054**

DOWN IN THE TUBE STATION AT MIDNIGHT
Tracks: / Down in the tube station at midnight.
7" Single: Released Oct '78, on Polydor, by Polydor Ltd. Deleted '85. Catalogue no: **POSP 8**

ETON RIFLES
Tracks: / Eton rifles.
7" Single: Released Nov '79, on Polydor, by Polydor Ltd. Deleted '82. Catalogue no: **POSP 83**

FUNERAL PYRE
Tracks: / Funeral pyre / Disguises.
7" Single: Released Jun '81, on Polydor, by Polydor Ltd. Deleted '84. Catalogue no: **POSP 257**

GOING UNDERGROUND
Tracks: / Going underground / Dreams of children.
7" Single: Released Mar '80, on Polydor, by Polydor Ltd. Deleted '85. Catalogue no: **POSP 113**
12" Single: Released Mar '80, on Polydor, by Polydor Ltd. Deleted '85. Catalogue no: **OSPJ 113**

IN THE CITY (SINGLE)
Tracks: / In the city.
7" Single: Released May '77, on Polydor, by Polydor Ltd. Deleted '85. Catalogue no: **2058 866**

JUST WHO IS THE FIVE O'CLOCK HERO
Tracks: / Just who is the five o'clock hero / Great depression.
7" Single: Released Jul '82, on Polydor, by Polydor Ltd. Deleted '85. Catalogue no: **2059 504**
12" Single: Released Jul '82, on Polydor, by Polydor Ltd. Deleted '85. Catalogue no: **2141558**

MODERN WORLD, THE
Tracks: / Modern world, The.
7" Single: Released Nov '77, on Polydor, by Polydor Ltd. Deleted '85. Catalogue no: **2058 945**

NEWS OF THE WORLD
Tracks: / News of the world.
7" Single: Released Mar '78, on Polydor, by Polydor Ltd. Deleted '85. Catalogue no: **2059 054**

START
Tracks: / Start / Liza Radley.
7" Single: Released Aug '80, on Polydor, by Polydor Ltd. Deleted '83. Catalogue no: **2059 266**

STRANGE TOWN
Tracks: / Strange town / Butterfly collector, The.
7" Single: Released Mar '79, on Polydor, by Polydor Ltd. Deleted '85. Catalogue no: **POSP 34**

THAT'S ENTERTAINMENT
Tracks: / That's entertainment / Down in the tube station at midnight.
7" Single: Released Feb '81, on Metronome, by Magnum Music Group. Deleted '84. Catalogue no: **0030 364**

TOWN CALLED MALICE
Tracks: / Town called Malice / Precious.
7" Single: Released Feb '82, on Polydor, by Polydor Ltd. Deleted '85. Catalogue no: **POSP 400**
12" Single: Released Feb '82, on Polydor, by Polydor Ltd. Deleted '85. Catalogue no: **POSPX 400**

WHEN YOU'RE YOUNG
Tracks: / When you're young / Smithers-Jones.
7" Single: Released Aug '79, on Polydor, by Polydor Ltd. Deleted '82. Catalogue no: **POSP 69**

Jam '86

WE'VE GOT THE LOVE
Tracks: / We've got the love / Save love, save life.
12" Single: Released Jun '86, on Arista, by BMG Records (UK). Catalogue no: **JAM 221**

Jam Down

EXTRAORDINARY WOMAN
Tracks: / Extraordinary woman.
12" Single: Released Dec '83, on Jam Down, Catalogue no: **JAM 1**

Jamaica Boys

LET ME HOLD YOU CLOSER
Tracks: / Let me hold you closer.
7" Single: Released Aug '85, on Cool Tempo, by Chrysalis Records. Catalogue no: **COOL 113**
12" Single: Released Aug '85, on Cool Tempo, by Chrysalis Records. Catalogue no: **COOLX 113**

PALM OF YOUR HAND
Tracks: / Palm of your hand.
7" Single: Released May '86, on Cool Tempo, by Chrysalis Records. Catalogue no: **COOL 122**
12" Single: Released May '86, on Cool Tempo, by Chrysalis Records. Catalogue no: **COOLX 122**

Jamaica Girls

ROCK THE BEAT
Tracks: / Rock the beat.
12" Single: Released Oct '82, on Beckett, Deleted '84. Catalogue no: **BKSL 5**
7" Single: Released Oct '82, on Beckett, Deleted '84. Catalogue no: **BKS 5**

Jamaica Mean Time

ROCK TO DIS
Tracks: / Rock to dis.
7" Single: Released Sep '89, on Tam Tam, Catalogue no: **TTT 012**
12" Single: Released Sep '89, on Tam Tam, Catalogue no: **TTT 012 T**

Jamal, Ahmad

AWAKENING, THE (SINGLE)
Tracks: / Awakening, The.
7" Single: Released Aug '84, on Jim White, Catalogue no: **IQ PROMO 101**

James

CHAIN MAIL
Tracks: / Chain mail / Hup springs / Up rising.
7" Single: Released Feb '86, on Sire (USA), Catalogue no: **JIM 3**
12" Single: Released Feb '86, on Sire (USA), Deleted Jan '88. Catalogue no: **JIM 3T**

FOLKLORE Cover design by Johnny (Hedgehog) Carroll
Tracks: / Folklore / What's the world / Fire so.
7" Single: Released Sep '83, on Factory (1), by Factory Records. Catalogue no: **FAC 78**

HYMN FROM A VILLAGE Cover design by Johnny (Hedgehog) Carroll
Tracks: / Hymn from a village / If things were perfect.
12" Single: Released Jun '85, on Factory (1), by Factory Records. Catalogue no: **FAC 138**

SIT DOWN
Tracks: / Sit down.
7" Single: Released Jun '89, on Rough Trade, by Rough Trade Records. Catalogue no: **RT 225**
CD 5": Released Jun '89, on Rough Trade, by Rough Trade Records. Catalogue no: **RTT 225 CD**
12" Single: Released Jun '89, on Rough Trade, by Rough Trade Records. Catalogue no: **RTT 225**

SO MANY WAYS
Tracks: / So many ways / Withdrawn / Just hipper (Extra track available on 12" version only).
12" Single: Released Jun '86, on Sire (USA), Deleted Jun '87. Catalogue no: **JIM 4T**
7" Single: Released Jun '86, on Sire (USA), Deleted Jun '87. Catalogue no: **JIM 4**

WHAT FOR
Tracks: / What for / Island swing / Not there.
7" Single: Released Mar '88, on Blanco Y Negro, by Blanco Y Negro Records. Catalogue no: **NEG 31**
12" Single: Released Mar '88, on Blanco Y Negro, by Blanco Y Negro Records. Catalogue no: **NEG 31T**

YAHO
Tracks: / Yaho / Mosquito / New nature / Left out of her will.
12" Single: Released Sep '87, on Blanco Y Negro, by Blanco Y Negro Records. Catalogue no: **NEG 26T**
7" Single: Released Sep '87, on Blanco Y Negro, by Blanco Y Negro Records. Catalogue no: **NEG 26**

James, Allen

GOODBYE
Tracks: / Goodbye.
12" Single: Released 24 Jul '89, on Silver Heart, by Silver Heart Records. Catalogue no: **CUFF 1B**

James, Biby

IF I HAD YOU
Tracks: / If I had you.
12" Single: Released Apr '86, on Toe, Catalogue no: **TOE 006**

James, Bob

SHEPERD'S SONG
Tracks: / Sheperd's song / Taxi.
7" Single: Released Dec '82, on CBS, by CBS Records. Deleted Dec '87. Catalogue no: **A 3012**

SIGN OF THE TIMES (SINGLE)
Tracks: / Sign of the times / Tappan Zee / Westchester lady.
7" Single: Released Oct '81, on CBS, by CBS Records. Deleted Oct '84. Catalogue no: **CBSA 1608**
12" Single: Released Oct '81, on CBS, by CBS Records. Deleted Oct '84. Catalogue no: **CBSA 131608**

STAR TREK
Tracks: / Star trek / I want to thank you.
7" Single: Released Jan '80, on CBS, by CBS Records. Deleted Jan '85. Catalogue no: **CBS 8128**

STEAMIN' FEELING
Tracks: / Steamin' feeling / Enchanted forest.
7" Single: Released Dec '81, on CBS, by CBS Records. Deleted Dec '84. Catalogue no: **A 1837**

TAXI
Tracks: / Taxi / Touch down.
7" Single: Released Mar '82, on CBS, by CBS Records. Deleted '85. Catalogue no: **A 2176**

TAXI, THEME FROM
Tracks: / Taxi, Theme from / Caribbean nights.
12" Single: Released Apr '82, on CBS, by CBS Records. Deleted Apr '85. Catalogue no: **CBA A 132176**
7" Single: Released May '80, on CBS, by CBS Records. Deleted '83. Catalogue no: **CBS 8540**

James, Bob & Earl

CARI
Tracks: / Cari / Mallorca.
7" Single: Released Feb '80, on CBS, by CBS Records. Deleted Feb '85. Catalogue no: **CBS 8139**

James Boys

OVER AND OVER
Tracks: / Over and over.
7" Single: Released May '73, on Penny Farthing, by Penny Farthing Records. Deleted '76. Catalogue no: **PEN 806**

James, Brian

WHY WHY WHY
Tracks: / Why why why / Where did I find a girl like you.
7" Single: Released Jan '82, on Illegal, by Faulty Products Records. Catalogue no: **ILS 0026**

James Brothers

SO EASY
Tracks: / So easy / Whatcha gonna do.
7" Single: Released Jun '80, on Precision (1). Deleted Jun '83. Catalogue no: **PAR 103**

James, Charlie

EYE OF THE STORM
Tracks: / Eye of the storm.
12" Single: Released Aug '84, on Sour Grape, by Sour Grape Records. Deleted '87. Catalogue no: **SGR 118**
7" Single: Released Aug '84, on Sour Grape, by Sour Grape Records. Deleted '87. Catalogue no: **SG 118**

James, Danny

ROCKIN' ROBIN
Tracks: / Rockin' robin.
12" Single: Released Nov '83, on Passion, by Skratch Records. Deleted Nov '86. Catalogue no: **PASH 13(12)**

James, David

ABSOLUTELY NOTHING
Tracks: / Absolutely nothing.
7" Single: Released Jan '82, on Towerbell, Catalogue no: **TOW 18**

DRUM MACHINE
Tracks: / Drum machine.
7" Single: Released Feb '85, on Sirocco, Catalogue no: **SIR 105**

GIRL FROM IPANEMA
Tracks: / Girl from Ipanema.
12" Single: Released Aug '89, on Survival (2), Catalogue no: **12SURR 1**
7" Single: Released Aug '89, on Survival (2), Catalogue no: **SURR 1**
CD 5": Released Aug '89, on Survival (2), Catalogue no: **CDSURR 1**

ORIGINAL CUCKOO BIRD PINEAPPLE TRUCK
Tracks: / Original cuckoo bird pineapple truck / Louisiana rebel.
7" Single: Released Oct '81, on Towerbell, Catalogue no: **TOW 13**

James Dean Driving

CLEARLAKE REVISITED
Tracks: / Clearlake revisited.
12" Single: Released Sep '89, on Plastic Head, by Plastic Head Records. Catalogue no: **PLASS 013**

DEANS ELEVENTH DREAM
Tracks: / Deans eleventh dream.
7" Single: Released Jul '88, on Autumn Glow, Catalogue no: **AUT 001**

James, Deeana

TO MY HEART
Tracks: / To my heart.
12" Single: Released Dec '86, on Elite Records, by Elite Records. Deleted '88. Catalogue no: **DAZZ 61**

James, Dick

GARDEN OF EDEN
Tracks: / Garden of Eden.
7" Single: Released Jan '57, on Parlophone, by EMI Records. Deleted '60. Catalogue no: **R 4255**

ROBIN HOOD
Tracks: / Robin Hood / Ballad of Davy Crockett, The.
7" Single: Released Jan '56, on Parlophone, by EMI Records. Deleted '59. Catalogue no: **R 4117**

James, Elmore

DONE SOMEBODY WRONG
Tracks: / Done somebody wrong.
7" Single: Released Mar '81, on Charly, by Charly Records. Deleted '87. Catalogue no: **CTD 126**

James, Etta

AVENUE D

ETTA JAMES - I GOT THE WILL (Released on Island)

Tracks: / Avenue D / My head is a city / Avenue D (Kevorkian remix) / Avenue D (Avenue dub) / Avenue D (sound assassins mix).
12" Single: Released May '89, on Capitol, by EMI Records. Deleted Oct '89. Catalogue no: **12CL 533**
7" Single: Released May '89, on Capitol, by EMI Records. Deleted Oct '89. Catalogue no: **CL 533**

I GOT THE WILL (see panel above)
Tracks: / I got the will / Come to mamma / One night (Available on 10" and CD only).
CD 5": Released Jul '89, on Island, by Island Records. Catalogue no: **CID 418**
10" single: Released Jul '89, on Island, by Island Records. Catalogue no: **10 IS 418**
7" Single: Released Jul '89, on Island, by Island Records. Catalogue no: **IS 418**

TELL MAMA (SINGLE)
Tracks: / Tell mama.
7" Single: Released Jul '85, on Chess (PRT), Deleted '88. Catalogue no: **CHES 4005**

James, Freddie

Biographical details: James, Freddie This American singer was one of numerous faceless disco acts to achieve a one off chart entry during the late Seventies. *Get Up and Boogie* reached No.54 on the Top 75 singles list in 1979. Subsequent offerings such as 1982's *Don't Turn Your Back On Love* fell on deaf ears and unwilling feet. (Bob Macdonald 8/11/85).

DON'T TURN YOUR BACK ON LOVE
12" Single: Released Sep '82, on Arista, by BMG Records (UK). Catalogue no: **ARIST 12 489**
7" Single: Released Sep '82, on Arista, by BMG Records (UK). Deleted '83. Catalogue no: **ARIST 489**

GET UP AND BOOGIE (SINGLE)
Tracks: / Get up and boogie.
7" Single: Released Nov '79, on Warner Bros., by WEA Records. Deleted '82. Catalogue no: **K 17478**

James, Halo

WANTED
Tracks: / Wanted / Worlds apart / If tomorrow ever comes around (Only on 12" and CD single.).
Cassingle: Released 18 Sep '89, on Epic, by CBS Records. Catalogue no: **HALOM 1**
12" Single: Released Aug '89, on Epic, by CBS Records. Catalogue no: **HALO T1**
Special: Released 18 Sep '89, on Epic, by CBS Records. Catalogue no: **HALO P1**
7" Single: Released Aug '89, on Epic, by CBS Records. Catalogue no: **HALO 1**
CD 5": Released Aug '89, on Epic, by CBS Records. Catalogue no: **CDHALO 1**

James, Hopeton

BE HAPPY
Tracks: / Be happy.
12" Single: Released Feb '89, on Sky high, Catalogue no: **SH 1930**

James, Jimmy

Biographical details: James, Jimmy This Jamaican singer arrived in Britain in the early Sixties to pursue a musical career. His first love was soul music, and he began to perform conerts in and around those areas of London with a West Indina community. He perfected his backing band in 1965 and the combo became known as Jimmy James & The Vagabonds. During the mid Sixties they became one of the hottest live attractions in Britain and people crammed into clubs wherever they were appearing. The rotund James was supported on stage by a second vocalist. Count Prince Miller, whose job was to be a cheerleader and encourage maximum audience participation.
Jimmy James & The Vagabonds were in a similar situation to Geno Washington & The Ram Jam Band. Both acts were certainly around at the right time - the mid Sixties saw a veritable explosion of soul music in America, with such talents as Wilson Pickett, Otis Redding, Carla Thomas, Sam & Dave, Arthur Conley and the legendary James Brown all hitting the higher echelons of the pop charts; thus, there was no shortage of material for the two groups to perform, and their repertiores were full of cover versions of the latest US soul hits. Because their music and stage acts were so unashamedly derivative, and because James and Washington were both essentially live performers, neither were able to translate their club reputation into hit singles. Jimmy James & The Vagabonds were one of the few well-known acts of the era to base their reputation solely on live work, with records playing an ancillary role.
When James & Co did finally enter the UK charts in the autumn of 1968, it was, somewhat suprisingly, a soul remake of a Neil Diamond song - although the single peaked at No.36, it gave Jimmy James & The Vagabonds the distinction of being the first act to achieve a pop hit with *Red Red Wine*. It was made into a reggae standard the following year by Tony Tribe and taken to the UK No.1 spot in 1983 by UB40.
Red Red Wine proved to be a one-off success for James, for the London soul scene was starting to decline as the punters drifted away to psychedelia and other newly trendy forms of popular culture. James was, however, determined to stick to his musical guns in clubs and cabaret up and down the country. After toiling away at live shows for several more years, the group suddenly teamed up with the red hot producer Biddu and chalked up a pair of 1976 UK Top 30 singles. Biddu, who had recently twiddled the knobs on British No.1 smashes by Carl Douglas and Tina Charles not only produced but also wrote *I'll Go Where Your Music Takes Me* (No.23) and *Now Is The Time* (No.5) for Jimmy James & The Vagabonds. Both discs were bland but pleasant fusions of soul, disco and teenybopper pop music. Once again, James was unable to consolidate upon his recording success. He returned to the clubs and carried on with business as usual. (Bob Macdonald 8/11/85).

I'LL GO WHERE YOUR MUSIC TAKES ME
Tracks: / I'll go where your music takes me.
7" Single: Released Apr '76, on Pye, Deleted '79. Catalogue no: **7N 45585**
7" Single: Released Jul '82, on Old Gold, by Old Gold Records. Catalogue no: **OG 9137**

LOVE FIRE
Tracks: / Love fire / Live for the night.
7" Single: Released Apr '84, on ERC, Catalogue no: **ERC 110**

NOW IS THE TIME
Tracks: / Now is the time / I'll go where your music takes me / Missing you.
Note: Composed by Biddu. Produced and arranged by Keff McCulloch for Satril Records.
7" Single: Released May '87, on Nine O Nine, by Creole Records. Catalogue no: **NINE 75**
12" Single: Released May '87, on Nine O Nine, by Creole Records. Catalogue no: **NINE 5**
7" Single: Released Jul '76, on Pye, Deleted '79. Catalogue no: **7N 45606**

REACH OUT
Tracks: / Reach out.
7" Single: Released Aug '84, on ERC, Catalogue no: **ERC 119**

RED RED WINE
Tracks: / Red red wine.
7" Single: Released Sep '68, on Pye, Deleted '71. Catalogue no: **7N 17579**

James, Joni

THERE MUST BE A WAY
Tracks: / There must be a way.
7" Single: Released Jan '59, on MGM, by Polydor Ltd. Deleted '62. Catalogue no: **MGM 1002**

WHY DON'T YOU BELIEVE ME
Tracks: / Why don't you believe me.
7" Single: Released Mar '53, on MGM, by Polydor Ltd. Deleted '56. Catalogue no: **MGM 582**

James, Josie

CALL ME (WHEN YOU NEED MY LOVE)
Tracks: / Call me (when you need my love).
7" Single: Released Aug '85, on TPL, by Production League, The. Deleted '86. Catalogue no: **7TPL 1**

DANCE YOU UP
Tracks: / Dance you up.
7" Single: Released Aug '86, on One Little Indian, by One Little Indian Records. Catalogue no: **TPLO 2**
12" Single: Released Aug '86, on One Little Indian, by One Little Indian Records. Catalogue no: **12 TPL 2**

James, Keith

BEAUJOLAIS AND BALLERINAS
Tracks: / Beaujolais and ballerinas.
7" Single: Released Apr '82, on Keith James, Catalogue no: **KJ 5**

BOTTLE OF WINE A GUITAR BOX AND SAX
Tracks: / Bottle of wine a guitar box and sax.
7" Single: Released May '83, on Keith James, Catalogue no: **KJ 9**

KEEP IT TO YOURSELF
Tracks: / Keep it to yourself / Behind your eyes.
7" Single: Released Jan '84, on Keith James, Catalogue no: **KJ 10**

LIFE IN A WESTERN WORLD
Tracks: / Life in a western world / Screen, stage, words on a page.
7" Single: Released Feb '73, on Keith James, Catalogue no: **KJ 6**

ON THE REBOUND (SINGLE)
Tracks: / Go for it / On the rebound.
7" Single: Released Aug '82, on Paro, by Paro Records. Catalogue no: **PAROS 1**

SNEAK A LITTLE TIME
Tracks: / Sneak a little time / Don't lose the old for the new.
7" Single: Released Oct '83, on Keith James, Catalogue no: **KJ 7**

TEARS DON'T SEEM TO HURT ANYMORE
Tracks: / Tears don't seem to hurt anymore.
7" Single: Released Oct '81, on Keith James, Catalogue no: **KJ 2**

James, Kimberly

DEJA VU
Tracks: / Deja vu.
12" Single: Released Oct '87, on Criminal (1), by Criminal Records. Catalogue no:

BUST 3

James, Mavin

HE-BE HAR-BE
Tracks: / He-be har-be / He me and you.
7" Single: Released Apr '86, on Havasong, by Havasong Records. Catalogue no: **HAVA 111**

I'LL BE AROUND
Tracks: / I'll be around.
12" Single: Released Apr '87, on Hot Vinyl, Catalogue no: **HVT 38**

LET ME DOWN EASY
Tracks: / Let me down easy.
12" Single: Released Jun '86, on Hot Vinyl, Catalogue no: **HVT 24**

MY DAD
Tracks: / My Dad / Together in Iceland.
7" Single: Released Jan '87, on Havasong, by Havasong Records. Catalogue no: **HAVA 333**

SOLDIER ON HIS HORSE, THE
Tracks: / Soldier on his horse, The / Drumbeat.
7" Single: Released Feb '88, on Havasong, by Havasong Records. Catalogue no: **HAVA 444**

YOU'RE JUST LIKE A BUBBLE IN WINE
Tracks: / You're just like a bubble in wine / Nothing to do.
7" Single: Released Oct '86, on Havasong, by Havasong Records. Catalogue no: **HAVA 222**

James, Micky

MCGUIGAN
Tracks: / McGuigan.
7" Single: Released Oct '85, on Gem, Catalogue no: **GEM 101**

James, Nick

JUST LIKE A YO YO
Tracks: / Just like a yo yo.
12" Single: Released Aug '87, on Columbia, by EMI Records. Deleted Jan '88. Catalogue no: **12DB 9156**
7" Single: Released Aug '87, on Columbia, by EMI Records. Deleted Jan '88. Catalogue no: **DB 9156**

James, Oscar

CARNIVAL JAM
Tracks: / Carnival jam.
7" Single: Released Sep '87, on Flick, Deleted Jan '88. Catalogue no: **FLK 7 0013**
12" Single: Released Aug '87, on Flick, Deleted Jan '88. Catalogue no: **FLK 0013**

LOVE RIDING HIGH
Tracks: / Original fin / Love riding high.
12" Single: Released Oct '86, on 10 Records, by Virgin Records. Deleted May '88. Catalogue no: **TENT 166**

James & Percy

IF ONLY BEFORE
Tracks: / If only before / Above and beyond.
12" Single: Released Apr '84, on Code Green, Deleted Apr '87. Catalogue no: **CODE GREEN 120**

James, Phil

YOU AND I
Tracks: / You and I / Run little girl.
7" Single: Released Jun '86, on LBA, Catalogue no: **LBA 109**

James, Richard

NEVER
Tracks: / Never.
7" Single: Released Oct '87, on Record Shack, by Record Shack Records. Catalogue no: **RICK J1**
12" Single: Released Oct '87, on Record Shack, by Record Shack Records. Catalogue no: **RICK JT1**

James, Rick

Biographical details:
James, Rick This American singer, songwriter, producer and guitarist was born James Johnson in Buffalo, New York.
He joined the US Navy at the age of 15 but absconded to Canada soon afterwards.
He later worked in a behind the scenes capacity for Tamla Motown, who eventually signed him as a recording artist in 1978. James' debut LP for the company, *Come Get It*, yielded a US No.13 single *You and I*. From this point onwards, the multi-talented James not only advanced his own career but also began to show a talent for nurturing those of up and coming Motown artists.
The first was Teena Marie, with whom he duetted on the 1979 single *I'm A Sucker For Your Love*; it was not long before she was writing and producing her own hits, just like Rick, although she later had to leave Motown in order to further her career.
1981's *Street Songs* LP took James into the superstar bracket. It reached the Top 3 of Billboard's pop album chart and yielded two major US hits with *Give It To Me Baby* and *Super Freak*. The LP also contained another collaboration with Marie, the deep and intense ballad *Fire And Desire*.
After *Street Songs*, Rick James seemed to let his new found fame and status slip away. Although he continued to achieve a respectable degree of chart success, he lost out in the superstar stakes to his arch-rival Prince. Both of these eccentric, sexually risque artists (who both experienced total creative control over their own work) were classed as 'punk-funkers' - they amalgamated the New Wave rock with the modern danceable slinky soul.
Despite not being quite as successful as some pundits had predicted in the early days, James had some very famous frinds He guested on The Temptations' 1982 single *Standing On The Top* and duetted with Smokey Robinson in late 1983 on the acclaimed track *Ebony Eyes*.
Rick's next female protegees, The Mary Jane Girls, chalked up a suprise UK Top 20 hit with 1983's *All Night Long* (James' own releases were permanently confined to minor hit status in Britain) and a US Top Tenner with 1985's *In My House*. Also in '85 he wrote and produced a single called *Seduction* for his newest charge Val Young and, with his own *Glow* single, provided us with one of his most danceable and melodic offerings to date.
(Bob Macdonald 8/11/85).

17
Tracks: / 17.
12" Single: Released Jul '84, on Gordy (USA), by Motown Records (UK). Catalogue no: **TMGT 1348**
7" Single: Released Jul '84, on Gordy (USA), by Motown Records (UK). Catalogue no: **TMG 1348**

BIG TIME
Tracks: / Big time / Island lady.
7" Single: Released Oct '81, on Motown, by BMG Records (UK). Catalogue no: **TMG 1198**
12" Single: Released Aug '80, on Motown, by BMG Records (UK). Deleted '83. Catalogue no: **12TMG 1198**

CAN'T STOP
Tracks: / Can't stop / Oh what a night for luv.
7" Single: Released Mar '85, on Gordy (USA), by Motown Records (UK). Catalogue no: **TMG 1378**
12" Single: Released Mar '85, on Gordy (USA), by Motown Records (UK). Catalogue no: **TGMT 1378**

COLD BLOODED (2 PARTS)
Tracks: / Cold blooded (part 1) / Cold blooded (part 2).
12" Single: Released Aug '83, on Motown, by BMG Records (UK). Deleted '85. Catalogue no: **TMGT**
7" Single: Released Aug '83, on Motown, by BMG Records (UK). Deleted '85. Catalogue no: **TMG 1314**

DANCE WIT ME
Tracks: / Dance wit me.
7" Single: Released Jun '82, on Motown, by BMG Records (UK). Deleted '84. Catalogue no: **TMG 1266**
12" Single: Released Jun '82, on Motown, by BMG Records (UK). Deleted '84. Catalogue no: **TMGT 1266**

EBONY EYES
Tracks: / Ebony eyes / 123, you and her and me / Standing on the top.
7" Single: Released Jan '84, on Gordy (USA), by Motown Records (UK). Catalogue no: **TMG 1327**
12" Single: Released Jan '84, on Gordy (USA), by Motown Records (UK). Catalogue no: **TMGT 1327**

GHETTO LIFE
Tracks: / Ghetto life / Below the funk.
7" Single: Released Jan '82, on Motown, by BMG Records (UK). Deleted '84. Catalogue no: **TMG 1250**
12" Single: Released Jan '82, on Motown, by BMG Records (UK). Deleted '84. Catalogue no: **TMGT 1250**

GIVE IT TO ME BABY
Tracks: / Give it to me baby / Don't give up on love.
12" Single: Released Oct '81, on Motown, by BMG Records (UK). Deleted '83. Catalogue no: **TMGT 1229**
7" Single: Released Oct '81, on Motown, by BMG Records (UK). Deleted '83. Catalogue no: **TMG 1229**

GLOW
12" Single: Released Jun '85, on Gordy (USA), by Motown Records (UK). Deleted '87. Catalogue no: **ZT 40224**
7" Single: Released Jun '85, on Gordy (USA), by Motown Records (UK). Catalogue no: **ZB 40223**

HARD TO GET
Tracks: / Hard to get / My love / Give it me.
7" Single: Released Aug '82, on Motown, by BMG Records (UK). Deleted '84. Catalogue no: **TMG 1277**
12" Single: Released Aug '82, on Motown, by BMG Records (UK). Deleted '84. Catalogue no: **TGMT 1277**

LOOSEY'S RAP
Tracks: / Loosey's rap.
7" Single: Released May '88, on Warner Bros., by WEA Records. Catalogue no: **W 7885**
12" Single: Released May '88, on Warner Bros., by WEA Records. Catalogue no: **W 7885T**

LOVE GUN
Tracks: / Love gun / Stormy love.
7" Single: Released Jan '80, on Motown, by BMG Records (UK). Deleted Jan '83. Catalogue no: **TMG 1174**

SUMMER LOVE
Tracks: / Summer love / Gettin' it on.

12" Single: Released Oct '81, on Motown, by BMG Records (UK). Deleted '83. Catalogue no: **TMGT 1209**
7" Single: Released Oct '81, on Motown, by BMG Records (UK). Deleted '83. Catalogue no: **TMG 1209**

SUPER FREAK (PART 2)
Tracks: / Super freak (part 2) / Fire and desire.
7" Single: Released Nov '82, on Motown, by BMG Records (UK). Catalogue no: **TMG 1241**
12" Single: Released Nov '82, on Motown, by BMG Records (UK). Deleted '87. Catalogue no: **TMGT 1241**

SWEET AND SEXY THING
Tracks: / Sweet and sexy thing.
7" Single: Released Jun '86, on Motown, by BMG Records (UK). Deleted '88. Catalogue no: **ZB 40755**
12" Single: Released Jun '86, on Motown, by BMG Records (UK). Deleted '88. Catalogue no: **ZT 40756**

YOU AND I
Tracks: / You and I / Hollywood.
7" Single: Released Oct '81, on Motown, by BMG Records (UK). Deleted '83. Catalogue no: **TMG 1110**

YOU TURN ME ON
Tracks: / You turn me on.
7" Single: Released Oct '84, on Motown, by BMG Records (UK). Deleted '86. Catalogue no: **TMG 1359**
12" Single: Released Oct '84, on Motown, by BMG Records (UK). Deleted '86. Catalogue no: **TMGT 1359**

James, Shirley

ASK ME TO STAY
Tracks: / Ask me to stay.
7" Single: Released May '82, on Black Jack, Catalogue no: **BJ 014**

RIGHT TIME OF THE NIGHT
Tracks: / Right time of the night.
7" Single: Released Sep '81, on Black Jack, Catalogue no: **BJ 012**
12" Single: Released Sep '81, on Black Jack, Catalogue no: **BJD 012**

WHY DON'T YOU SPEND THE NIGHT?
Tracks: / Why don't you spend the night? / Night in dub / Let me love you tonight (on 12" only).

12" Single: Released May '81, on Black Jack, Deleted May '84. Catalogue no: **BJD 4509**
7" Single: Released May '81, on Black Jack, Deleted May '84. Catalogue no: **BJ 4509**

James Silk

C B CASANOVA
Tracks: / C B Casanova / Lonely trucker.
7" Single: Released Jul '81, on Ramkup, Catalogue no: **CAC 006**

James, Sonny

CAT CAME BACK, THE
Tracks: / Cat came back, The.
7" Single: Released Nov '56, on Capitol, by EMI Records. Deleted '59. Catalogue no: **CL 14635**

YOUNG LOVE
Tracks: / Young love.
7" Single: Released Feb '57, on Capitol, by EMI Records. Deleted '60. Catalogue no: **CL 14683**

James, Stephen

I NEED YOU NOW
Tracks: / I need you now.
12" Single: Released May '85, on Seven Leaves, Catalogue no: **SLD 004**

James, Stuart

ONLY WHEN I LAUGH
Tracks: / Only when I laugh / Kypros.
7" Single: Released Sep '82, on Radioactive, Catalogue no: **RAD 506**

James, Tina

SAN ANTONIO STROLL
Tracks: / San Antonio stroll / Love is a rose.
7" Single: Released Feb '81, on Mint, by Emerald Records. Deleted '88. Catalogue no: **CHEW 47**

James, Tommy

Biographical details:
James, Tommy This American singer and songwriter was born in Dayton, Ohio and moved to Michigan at the age of 11.
He formed a school group called the Sschondells, who made their first record *Long Pny Tail* when Tommy was 12 (1960)
Not suprisingly it was not a hit and neither was the group's 1964 single *Hanky Panky*. Suddenly in 1966 when it looked as though Tommy James' attempt at a pop career had been an unqualified failure, a Pittsburgh disc jockey found an obscure copy of *Hanky Panky* and began giving it heavy airplay.
The single's popularity evantually spread across America, and it knocked Frank Sinatra off the US No.1 slot in July '66.
Tommy Janes & The Shondells followed the ridiculously lightweight *Hanky Panky* with a whole series of US Top 40 hits, lasting until 1970. James himself had a hand in writing some of the singles, while others come from producer Ritchie Cordell.
They ranged from the bubblegum banality of *Mony Mony* (a British No.1 in 1968 and now a party classic, although none of the group's other records made a significant impact on the UK charts) to the subtle ballad *Crystal Blue Persuasion* (No.2 in US in 1969). *Crimson and Clover* (an American No.1 smash in '69) was successfully revived by Joan Jett & The Blackhearts in 1982.

In 1970 James parted company with the Shondells after he collapsed on stage and was hospitalised.
He took a sabbatical from performing, during which he produced a US Top 10 hit called *Tighter, Tighter* for *Alive and Kicking*.
He launched a solo recording career and quickly achieved a US No.4 hit with 1971's *Draggin' The Line.*.
However his other records were only minor successes and he was only rescued from obscurity by a 1980 US Top 20 hit with the country-flavoured *Three Tmes In Love*.
(Bob Macdonald 9/11/85).

HANKY PANKY
Tracks: / Hanky panky.
7" Single: Released Jul '66, on Roulette, by Vogue Records. Deleted '69. Catalogue no: **RK 7000**

MONY MONY
Tracks: / Mony mony / Crimson.
7" Single: Released Jul '80, on Flashback, by Mainline Records. Catalogue no: **FDBEP 101**
7" Single: Released Jun '68, on Major Minor, Deleted '71. Catalogue no: **MM 567**

MONY MONY (OLD GOLD)
Tracks: / Mony mony.
7" Single: Released Jun '84, on Old Gold, by Old Gold Records. Deleted Jul '88. Catalogue no: **OG 9410**

SAY PLEASE
Tracks: / Mony mony / Crimson / Say please / Two time lover.
7" Single: Released May '83, on 21 Records, by Polydor Ltd. Catalogue no: **POSP 564**

SHORT SHARP SHOTS
Tracks: / Mony mony / Hanky panky / Sweet cherry wine / It's only love / I think we're alone now / Crystal blue persuasion / Crimson and clover / Mirage.

Special: Released Apr '83, on PRT, by Castle Communications Records. Catalogue no: **DOW 6**

THREE TIMES IN LOVE
Tracks: / Three times in love / I just wanna play the music.

7" Single: Released Mar '80, on RCA, by BMG Records (UK). Deleted '83. Catalogue no: **FB 1785**

Jameson Raid

HYPNOTISTS
Tracks: / Hypnotists / Gettin' hotter.
7" Single: Released Nov '80, on Blackbird, Deleted '88. Catalogue no: **BRAID 001**

Jamieson, Derek

DO THEY MEAN US?
Tracks: / Do they mean us / Yes Virginia.
12" Single: Released Oct '86, on Polydor, by Polydor Ltd. Deleted Aug '87. Catalogue no: **POSPX 831**
7" Single: Released Oct '86, on Polydor, by

Polydor Ltd. Deleted Aug '87. Catalogue no: **POSP 831**

YES VIRGINIA
Tracks: / Yes Virginia / Do they mean us?.
12" Single: Released Nov '86, on Polydor, by Polydor Ltd. Deleted Mar '87. Catalogue no: **POSPA 831**
7" Single: Released Nov '86, on Polydor, by Polydor Ltd. Catalogue no: **POSA 831**

Jamil

SAVE IT FOR ME
Tracks: / Save it for me.
7" Single: Released Aug '87, on Nagla, Catalogue no: **NR 1**

Jamma, Andy

HOOKED UP ON YOUR LOVE
Tracks: / Hooked up on your love.
12" Single: Released Sep '89, on Soul Sonic, Catalogue no: **SOU 01**

Jammers

Biographical details: Jammers *Be Mine Tonight* was the title of this all male American funk band's only UK chart entry - the ultra danceable single reached No59 in early 1983. No one on either side of the Atlantic knew or cared who the Jammers were, and the music world had witnessed yet another one off hit by a faceless disco act. (Bob Macdonald 9/11/85).

BE MINE TONIGHT
Tracks: / Be mine tonight / What have you got to lose / And you know that.
7" Single: Released Dec '82, on Salsoul, Catalogue no: **SAL 101**
12" Single: Released Dec '82, on Salsoul, Catalogue no: **SALT 101**

Jan & Dean

Biographical details: Jan & Dean Jan Berry and Dean Torrance were the guys who provided the initial inspiration for The Beach Boys. In return, group leader Brian Wilson wrote and/or produced some of Jan & Dean's hit material. The two acts' careers consistently intertwined - they often guested on each others' hits and played gigs together.
Like the Beach Boys, Jan & Dean hailed from Los Angeles. Berry was born in 1941 and Torrance in 1940. They became close buddies at high school, where they realised that the acoustics of the boys' shower room gave them a perfect enviroment in which to develop their singing skills. Because tape recorders were not allowed in the shower room, they went into Jan's garage to record the song *Jennie Lee*. Several months later, in the summer of 1958 the single became a US Top 10 hit.
This fairytale success story reached its Top 10 climax while Dean was in the Army; for this reason, *Jennie Lee* was credited to Jan & Arnie - Arnie Ginsberg was another singing friend who sat in on the garage session. After Torrence's discharge Jan & Dean began a fully fledged career as a duo reaching the American Top 10 in late '59 with *Baby Talk* and hitting the Top 30 in 1961 with *Heart and Soul*.
After these sporadic one off hits, Jan & Dean clinched a much steadier chart career in 1963 by concentrating on the favourite subjects of Californian youth, surfing and drag racing. The whole surfing craze exploded onto the US charts during that period and its biggest hit of all went to Jan & Dean with the No.1 *Surf City* (July '63) - with its black influenced doo wop vocals set against a falsetto lead, this record epitomised the duo's style. The key line in the sosng - 'Two Girls for Every Boy' would be condemned as sexist in the Eighties but, in the early Sixties it was entirely acceptable.
The hits continued for a couple of years with such songs as *Honolulu Lulu*, *Drag City*, *The Little Old lady From Pasadena* and *Ride The Wild SSurf*. Another of their big singles was *Dead Man's Curve* a song about a car accident which included the line 'Well it was like this Doc, I started to swerve' - and this proved to be horribly precognitive for Jan Berry. In April 1966 he smashed his car into a parked truck and suffered severe brain damage. He was in a coma for months, during which Jan & Dean made the charts with their final American Top 40 hit *Popsicle*. He had to learn to walk and talk afresh, while Dean started a graphic art company called Kittyhawk which specialised in pop posters and record sleeves.
They tried to make a comeback in 1973, miming on stage to the old records; audiences objected to this ploy, but the duo evantually managed to resume a low key career singing live. CBS tlevision showed a well-received film in 1978 which told the pair's story - 'Dead Man's Curve' was later shown in Britain by the BBC.
Because surfing was alien to British culture, Jan & Dean were never stars in the UK. Only

Janice - Bye-Bye (Released on 4th & Broadway)

Heart and Soul (No.24 in 1961) and *Surf City* (No.26 in 1963) reached the UK Top 50.
In the mid-Eighties, however, their healthy and carefree image was revived by Wham. (Bob Macdonald 11/11/85).

HEART AND SOUL
Tracks: / Heart and soul.
7" Single: Released Aug '61, on London-American, Deleted '64. Catalogue no: **HLH 9395**

SURF CITY (SINGLE)
Tracks: / Surf city / Dead man's curve.
7" Single: Released Aug '63, on Liberty, by EMI Records. Deleted '66. Catalogue no: **LIB 55580**
7" Single: Released Jul '80, on Creole, by Creole Records. Catalogue no: **CR 204**

Jan & Kjeld

BANJO BOY
Tracks: / Banjo boy.
7" Single: Released Jul '60, on ember, Deleted '63. Catalogue no: **S 101**

Jane

I KNEW SHE WAS ABOUT TO SAY IT
Tracks: / I knew she was about to say it.
12" Single: Released Jun '88, on Wooden, by Wooden Records. Catalogue no: **WOOD 003**

IT'S A FINE DAY
Tracks: / It's a fine day.
7" Single: Released May '83, on Cherry Red, by Cherry Red Records. Catalogue no: **CHERRY 65**

Jane & Barton

I WANT TO BE WITH YOU
Tracks: / I want to be with you.
7" Single: Released Sep '83, on Cherry Red, by Cherry Red Records. Deleted '87. Catalogue no: **CHERRY 69**

Jane's Addiction

SHOCKING EP : MOUNTAIN SONG
Tracks: / Mountain song / Jane says / Had a dad (live).
12" Single: Released May '89, on Warner Bros., by WEA Records. Catalogue no: **W 7520 T**

Janette & The Planets

NINE,NINE,NINE
Tracks: / Nine, nine, nine.
7" Single: Released Oct '84, on Dig This, Deleted '87. Catalogue no: **SKEET 1**

Jani & The planets

EXTRA TERRESTRIAL SONG
Tracks: / Extra terrestial song.
7" Single: Released Jan '83, on Images, by Images Records. Catalogue no: **IMGS 0005**

Janice

BYE-BYE (see panel above)
Tracks: / Bye-bye (instrumental) / Bye-bye.
12" Single: Released Jul '86, on 4th & Broadway, by Island Records. Deleted Jul '87. Catalogue no: **12 BRW 49**
7" Single: Released Jul '86, on 4th & Broadway, by Island Records. Catalogue no: **BRW 49**

Janie

SWINGING SANTA
Tracks: / Swinging Santa / Christmas evening.
7" Single: Released Nov '82, on Mach 1, by Mach 1 Records. Catalogue no: **MAGIC 2**

Janitors

CHICKEN STOODGE
Tracks: / Chicken stoodge.
7" Single: Released Jul '85, on In Tape, by In Tape Records. Deleted '88. Catalogue no: **IT 017**

FAMILY FANTASTIC
Tracks: / Family fantastic.
7" Single: Released 13 Jun '87, on Abstract, by Abstract Sounds. Catalogue no: **ABS 045**
12" Single: Released 13 Jun '87, on Abstract, by Abstract Sounds. Catalogue no: **12 ABS 045**

GOOD TO BE KING
Tracks: / Good to be king.
7" Single: Released May '86, on In Tape, by In Tape Records. Catalogue no: **IT 031**

HALFWAY TO A HAPPENING
Tracks: / Halfway to a happening / Dead set on destruction / Hubba hubba (She's a weird animal).
7" Single: Released Dec '88, on Abstract, by Abstract Sounds. Catalogue no: **ABS 054**

MOONSHINE
Tracks: / Moonshine.
12" Single: Released Mar '88, on Abstract, by Abstract Sounds. Catalogue no: **12 ABS 047**

Jankel, Chas

109
Tracks: / 109 / Three million synths.
12" Single: Released Jan '82, on A&M, by A&M Records. Deleted Jan '85. Catalogue no: **AMSX 8173**
7" Single: Released Jan '82, on A&M, by A&M Records. Deleted Jan '85. Catalogue no: **AMS 8173**

GLAD TO KNOW YOU
Tracks: / Glad to know you / Am I honest with myself.
7" Single: Released Apr '82, on A&M, by A&M Records. Deleted Apr '85. Catalogue no: **AMS 8213**
12" Single: Released Apr '82, on A&M, by A&M Records. Deleted Apr '85. Catalogue no: **AMSX 8213**

I CAN GET OVER IT
Tracks: / I can get over it.
12" Single: Released Oct '83, on A&M, by A&M Records. Catalogue no: **AMX 143**

LOOKING AT YOU
Tracks: / Looking at you / Little Eva.
7" Single: Released Jun '85, on A&M, by A&M Records. Deleted '88. Catalogue no: **AM 252**

NUMBER 1
Tracks: / Number 1.
12" Single: Released Feb '85, on A&M, by A&M Records. Deleted '88. Catalogue no: **AMY228**
7" Single: Released Feb '85, on A&M, by A&M Records. Deleted '88. Catalogue no: **AM 228**

QUESTIONNAIRE
Tracks: / Questionnaire / Boy.
7" Single: Released Oct '81, on A&M, by A&M Records. Deleted '85. Catalogue no: **AMS 8176**
12" Single: Released Oct '81, on A&M, by A&M Records. Deleted '85. Catalogue no: **AMSP 8176**

WITHOUT YOU
Tracks: / Without you.
7" Single: Released Jul '83, on A&M, by A&M Records. Deleted '88. Catalogue no: **AMS 8239**

Jankowski, Horst

Biographical details: Jankowski, Horst This West German pianist and arranger came to fame on his country's jazz scene at the start of the Sixties. Influenced by the US arranger and orchestra leader Ray Conniff, he moved steadily closer to middle of the road music by assembling a large cast of musicians and singers and subtly integrating the choral and orchestral elements of the massed ensemble.
1965 brought Jankowski a one off hit on the pop charts with the self-composed instrumental single *A Walk In The Black Forest*. It reached No.3 in Britain, No.12 in the States and cemented his international status. An LP entitled *The Genius of Jankowski* was a big US seller during the same period. (Bob Macdonald 11/11/85).

WALK IN THE BLACK FOREST
Tracks: / Walk in the Black Forest, A.
7" Single: Released Jul '65, on Mercury, by Phonogram Ltd. Deleted '68. Catalogue no: **MF 861**
7" Single: Released Jan '85, on Old Gold, by Old Gold Records. Catalogue no: **OG 9481**

Jannot, Veronique

DESIRE DESIRE
Tracks: / Desire desire.
7" Single: Released Jun '85, on 10 Records, by Virgin Records. Deleted '89. Catalogue no: **TEN 55**

Janole

MOON SHINES TONIGHT
Tracks: / Moon shines tonight / Rodney this is it.
7" Single: Released Jan '80, on A&M, by A&M Records. Deleted Jan '83. Catalogue no: **AMS 8186**

Jansch, Bert

HEARTBREAK HOTEL
Tracks: / Heartbreak hotel / Up to the stars.
7" Single: Released Feb '82, on Logo, by Logo Records. Deleted Feb '87. Catalogue no: **GO 409**

Jap, Philip

Biographical details: This British singer and songwriter won, in summer 1982, The David Essex Showcase, a talent contest hosted by top star Essex who viewed the project as a worthwhile but temporary activity.
There was just one series, of which Jap was the overall winner. His subsequent career was hardly meteoric and runners-up such as Mari Wilson and White & Torch enjoyed brief flurries of chart success that did not measure up to expectations. Jap reached the UK No 53 position with a 1982 single, *Save Us*, and followed it with a No 41, *Total Erasure*. But his self-titled debut album, released in April '83, aroused little interest despite being supervised by three noted technopop producers, Trevor Horn, Tony Mansfield and Colin Thurston.
Although his modern music and highly-visual stage presence were totally in keeping with the fashionable trends of the day, his material was simply not strong enough and he was soon forgotten.
(Bob MacDonald, November 1985.).

BRAIN DANCE
Tracks: / Brain dance.
7" Single: Released May '83, on A&M, by A&M Records. Deleted '88. Catalogue no: **AM 110**

RED DOGS
Tracks: / Red dogs / 100 Japanese babies.
7" Single: Released Feb '83, on A&M, by A&M Records. Deleted '88. Catalogue no: **JAP 2**
12" Single: Released Feb '83, on A&M, by A&M Records. Deleted '88. Catalogue no:

JAPP 2

SAVE US
Tracks: / Save us.
7" Single: Released Jul '82, on A&M, by A&M Records. Deleted '85. Catalogue no: **AMS 8217**

TOTAL ERASURE
Tracks: / Total erasure.
7" Single: Released Sep '82, on A&M, by A&M Records. Deleted '85. Catalogue no: **JAP 1**

Japan

Biographical details: Japan This British band consisted of Steve Jansen and David Sylvian (two brothers whose real surname was Batt), plus Richard Barbieri and Mick Karn (real name Anthony Michaelides). Until 1981 there was a fifth member, guitarist Rob Dean, who quit when the group's sound became dominated by synthesisers. Japan were formed in 1974 in the London area, with Dean joining in 1977. In the latter year, they were ssigned by the German based Hansa label after being rejected by all the British record companies. Their debut album *Adolescent Sex* was released in 1978 but flopped in both commercial and critical terms, particularly in the UK where no punk rocker was interested in this bunch of glamour-conscious arty rockers. The second LP *Obscure Alternatives* also fell on deaf ears, although their namesake nation Japan took a considerable interest in the band.
By 1980 the British punk scene was starting to diminish and the New Romantic era was dawning. The group adapted their image accordingly (getting rid of their long hair) and refined their music to suit the increasingly fashionable futurist, technopop market. The group entered the lower reaches of the UK album chart during 1980 with *Quiet Life* and *Gentlement Take Polaroids*, the latter's title track also providing a minor hit single. The astute guidance of one Britain's best known managers, Simon Napier-Bell was paying off.
During 1981-82 Japan chalked up nine entries on the Uk singles chart, four from Hansa and five on the band's new label, Virgin. Hansa's *Assemblage* LP and Virgin's *Tin Drum* album spent almost 100 weeks on the British chart between them, the latter becoming one of the most critically acclaimed albums of the early Eighties. The persistent re-issuing of old material would normally enrage a group but, in Japan's case, it served them well. The band's two biggest UK singles were the subtle, reflective *Ghosts* and a revamp of Smokey Robinson's *I Second That Emotion*, both reaching the Top 10 in '83.
The main criticism levelled at Japan was the similarity between the voice of singer David Sylvian and that of Brian Ferry; it did not pass unnoticed that two of the group's producers had also worked with Ferry in the past. For their part, Japan's made-up androgynous image helped to pave the way for the breakthrough of Boy George and Culture Club.
In a move as bold as it was unexpected Japan broke up in early 1983. All the members were highly creative individuals, and were bursting to do other things without the compromises of a group format. Sylvian worked with Japanese musician and composer Riuichi Sakamoto (of Yellow Magic Orchestra fame) and then launched a solo career. Jansen worked with various Japanese musicians and also developed a photographic career. Barbieri worked with Ballet Rambert and began to explore Turkish and Spanish cultures. Karn worked as a sculptor via exhibitions in London Tokyo, worked as a session bass guitarist with some 'name' acts, achieved a Uk Top 40 single in association with Midge Ure and teamed up with ex Bauhaus leader Peter Murphy to form Dali's car. (Donald Clarke 11/1185).

ALL TOMORROW'S PARTIES
Tracks: / All tomorrow's parties.
12" Single: Released Mar '83, on Hansa, by Hansa Records. Catalogue no: **HANSA 1218**
7" Single: Released Mar '83, on Hansa, by Hansa Records. Catalogue no: **HANSA 18**

ART OF PARTIES, THE
Tracks: / Art of parties, The / Life without buildings.
7" Single: Released May '81, on Virgin, by Virgin Records. Catalogue no: **VS 409**
12" Single: Released May '81, on Virgin, by Virgin Records. Deleted '89. Catalogue no: **VS 409-12**

CANTON
Tracks: / Canton / Visions of China.
7" Single: Released '83, on Virgin, by Virgin Records. Deleted '89. Catalogue no: **VS 581**
7" Single: Released Mar '86, on CBS, by CBS Records. Catalogue no: **A 6874**
12" Single: Released May '83, on Virgin, by Virgin Records. Catalogue no: **VS 581-12**

CANTONESE BOY
Tracks: / Cantonese boy / Burning bridges (7" only) / Gentlemen take polaroids / Experience of swimming, The.
7" Set: Released May '82, on Virgin, by Virgin Records. Catalogue no: **VS 502**
12" Single: Released May '82, on Virgin, by Virgin Records. Catalogue no: **VS 502-12**

EUROPEAN SON
Tracks: / European son / Alien.
12" Single: Released Jan '82, on Hansa, by Hansa Records. Catalogue no: **HANSA 1210**
7" Single: Released Jan '82, on Hansa, by Hansa Records. Catalogue no: **HANSA 10**

GENTLEMEN TAKE POLAROIDS (CD SINGLE)
Tracks: / Gentlemen take polaroids / Cantonese boy / Methods of dance.
CD 3": Released '88, on Virgin, by Virgin Records. Catalogue no: **CDT 32**

GENTLEMEN TAKE POLAROIDS (SINGLE)
Tracks: / Gentlemen take polaroids.
7" Single: Released Oct '80, on Virgin, by Virgin Records. Deleted '83. Catalogue no: **VS 379**

GHOSTS
Tracks: / Ghosts / Art of parties, The (version) / Visions of China (CD only).
CD 3": Released '88, on Virgin, by Virgin Records. Catalogue no: **CDT 11**
7" Single: Released Mar '82, on Virgin, by Virgin Records. Catalogue no: **VS 472**
12" Single: Released Mar '82, on Virgin, by Virgin Records. Catalogue no: **VS 472-12**

GHOSTS (OLD GOLD)
Tracks: / Ghosts / Cantonese boy.
7" Single: Released Nov '88, on Old Gold, by Old Gold Records. Catalogue no: **OG 9817**

I SECOND THAT EMOTION
Tracks: / I second that emotion / Life in Tokyo / All tomorrow's parties.
7" Single: Released Sep '82, on Hansa, by Hansa Records. Catalogue no: **HANSA 12**
7" Single: Released Mar '80, on Ariola, by BMG Records (UK). Deleted Mar '83. Catalogue no: **AHA 559**
12" Single: Released Sep '82, on Hansa, by Hansa Records. Catalogue no: **HANSA 1212**
7" Single: on Old Gold, by Old Gold Records. Catalogue no: **OG 9666**
12" Single: Released Sep '87, on Old Gold, by Old Gold Records. Catalogue no: **OG 4020**

LIFE IN TOKYO
Tracks: / Life in Tokyo / European sun.
7" Single: Released May '81, on Hansa, by Hansa Records. Deleted '85. Catalogue no: **HANSA 124**
7" Single: Released Sep '82, on Hansa, by Hansa Records. Deleted May '89. Catalogue no: **HANSA 17**
12" Single: Released Sep '82, on Hansa, by Hansa Records. Catalogue no: **HANSA 1217**

LIFE IN TOKYO (OLD GOLD)
Tracks: / Life in Tokyo / Quiet life.
12" Single: Released Nov '87, on Old Gold, by Old Gold Records. Catalogue no: **OG 4031**

NIGHTPORTER
Tracks: / Nightporter / Ain't that peculiar (7" only) / Methods of dance (12" only).
7" Single: Released Nov '82, on Virgin, by Virgin Records. Catalogue no: **VS 554**
12" Single: Released Nov '82, on Virgin, by Virgin Records. Catalogue no: **VS 554-12**

QUIET LIFE (SINGLE)
Tracks: / Quiet life.
7" Single: Released Sep '82, on Hansa, by Hansa Records. Deleted May '89. Catalogue no: **HANSA 6**
12" Single: Released Sep '81, on Hansa, by Hansa Records. Deleted '85. Catalogue no: **HANSA 126**

VISIONS OF CHINA
Tracks: / Visions of China / Taking islands in Africa (7" only) / Swing (12" only).
12" Single: Released Dec '84, on Virgin, by Virgin Records. Catalogue no: **VS 436-12**
7" Single: Released Dec '84, on Virgin, by Virgin Records. Catalogue no: **VS 436**

Japes, Johnny

BAGS OF FUN WITH BUSTER GONAD
Tracks: / Bags of fun with Buster Gonad.
7" Single: Released 15 Dec '87, on Fulchester, by Fulchester Records. Catalogue no: **VIZ 001**

Jaqui

YOU MEAN EVERYTHING
Tracks: / You mean everything to me.
7" Single: Released Apr '84, on Code, by Code Records. Catalogue no: **COD 10**
12" Single: Released Apr '84, on Code, by Code Records. Catalogue no: **COD 1012**

Jar

ONLY YOU
Tracks: / Only You.
7" Single: Released 30 Aug '88, on Chrysalis, by Chrysalis Records. Catalogue no: **CHS 3302**

Jardim, Linda

ENERGY IN NORTHAMPTON
Tracks: / Energy in Northampton / Northampton.
7" Single: Released May '80, on EMI, by EMI Records. Deleted May '83. Catalogue no: **EMI 5077**

Jareba

ANOTHER STORY version
Tracks: / Another story.
7" Single: Released Aug '82, on Jade Records, Catalogue no: **JD 004**

Jarmel,Maurice

LOVE'S A MANY SPLENDOURED THING
Tracks: / Love's a many splendoured thing.
7" Single: Released Jan '85, on Spin, Catalogue no: **SPN 101**

Jarre, Jean Michel

Biographical details: Jarre, Jean Michel This French keyboardist, multi-instrumental, composer and producer was born in Lyon and began to play piano and guitar at the age of five.He was born into a musical enviroment, being the son of famous film score composer Maurice Jarre. After dropping out of his formal musical studies during his early twenties, because he felt restricted, he decided to follow his own heart and pursue his interest in synthesisers and improvised music. During the first half of the Seventies, he built up his own recording studio with its own special instruments and gadgetry and produced music for a number of diverse genres - these included commercials, jingles, films, ballet, pop singers and most strangely electronic operas!
The culmination of all this activity was the 1977 release of *Oxygene*, the first LP to be issued under his own name instead of being a musical contribution to somebody else's project. *Oxygene* was a massive success, reaching No.2 in Britain and selling a global total of six million copies. The single *Oxygene 4* reached No.4 on the UK chart. Like Mike Oldfield's debut offering *Tubular Bells*, the album transcended normal classical/pop/rock boundaries to form a mesmerising instrumental whole. There were no individually titled tracks, but all the segments were billed simply as *Oxygene 1*, *Oxygene 2* etc.
Oxygene set the pattern for a series of albums in similar vein. 1978's *Equinoxe* spent half a year on the UK charts and yielded the hit single *Equinoxe 5*; it was followed in 1981 by *Magnetic Fields*. Some people applauded Jarre's musical and technical brilliance, plus his melodic sense; others dismissed his output as muzak. Those who liked his work most of all were television and radio producers, who discovered that his albums were a rich souce of signature tunes and incidental music for programmes. Even people who have never heard of Jean Michel Jarre will have heard his music from time to time without realising it.
Jarre got into the habit of attracting publictiy for the sheet magnitude or minuteness of some of his activities. A French concert in 1979 attracted a million live spectators plus a worldwide total of 100 million TV viewers. He undertook a series of pioneering concerts in China in 1981 (predating Wham's visit by several years) and was heard by 30 million TV watchers and an estimated 500 million listeners on radio. In 1983 he became what is believed to be the only musician in history to have recorded a whole album *Music For Supermarkets*, then issued just one copy, sold it to the highest bidder and then destroyed the master tapes. Some cynics suggested that the title *Music For Supermarkets* summed up his whole attitude, and that he had done the rest of the music world a favour by only subjecting one listener to it! (Bob Macdonald 11/11/85).

EQUINOXE PART 5
Tracks: / Equinoxe part 5.
7" Single: Released Jan '79, on Polydor, by Polydor Ltd. Deleted '82. Catalogue no: **POSP 20**

EQUINOXE (PARTS 7/8)
Tracks: / Equinoxe part 7 / Equinoxe parts 7 & 8.
7" Single: Released Jul '80, on Polydor, by Polydor Ltd. Catalogue no: **2001 968**

FOURTH RENDEZ-VOUS
Tracks: / Fourth rendez-vous / First rendez-vous / Rendezvous IV (Special remix) / Rendezvous IV (Original Mix) / Moon Machine.
12" Single: Released Oct '86, on Disques Dreyfus, by Polydor Ltd. Deleted Jan '88. Catalogue no: **POSPX 788**
7" Single: Released Oct '86, on Disques Dreyfus, by Polydor Ltd. Deleted Jan '88. Catalogue no: **POSP 788**

LONDON KID
Tracks: / London kid / Industrial revolution / Revolutions (Avaliable on 12" format only.).
12" Single: Released Dec '88, on Polydor, by Polydor Ltd. Deleted 30 Jun '89. Catalogue no: **PZ 32**
CD 5": Released Dec '88, on Polydor, by Polydor Ltd. Catalogue no: **PZCD 32**
7" Single: Released Dec '88, on Polydor, by Polydor Ltd. Deleted 30 Jun '89. Catalogue no: **PO 32**

MAGNETIC FIELDS (PART 4)
Tracks: / Magnetic fields (part 4).
7" Single: Released Nov '81, on Polydor, by Polydor Ltd. Catalogue no: **POSP 363**

MAGNETIC FIELDS (PARTS 1/2)
Tracks: / Magnetic fields (part 1) / Magnetic fields (part 2).
7" Single: Released Jun '81, on Polydor, by Polydor Ltd. Catalogue no: **POSP 292**

ORIENT EXPRESS
Tracks: / Orient express / Fishing junks at sunset.
7" Single: Released May '82, on Polydor, by Polydor Ltd. Catalogue no: **POSP 430**

OXYGEN PART IV (REMIX)
Tracks: / Oxygen part IV (Remix).
12" Single: Released 25 Sep '89, on Polydor, by Polydor Ltd. Catalogue no: **PZ 55**
7" Single: Released 25 Sep '89, on Polydor, by Polydor Ltd. Catalogue no: **PO 55**
CD 5": Released 25 Sep '89, on Polydor, by Polydor Ltd. Catalogue no: **889 921-2**

OXYGENE PART IV
Tracks: / Oxygene (part IV).
7" Single: Released Aug '77, on Polydor, by Polydor Ltd. Deleted '80. Catalogue no: **2001 721**

OXYGENE PART IV (OLD GOLD)
Tracks: / Oxygene (part IV) / Equinoxe part 5.
7" Single: Released Feb '88, on Old Gold, by Old Gold Records. Catalogue no: **OG 9780**

REVOLUTIONS (SINGLE)
Tracks: / Revolutions / Industrial revolution (part 2) / Revolutions (extended mix) (On 12" and CD single only.) / Revolutions (single mix) (Only on CD single.).
7" Single: Released Oct '88, on Polydor, by Polydor Ltd. Deleted 30 May '89. Catalogue no: **PO 25**
CD 5": Released Oct '88, on Polydor, by Polydor Ltd. Catalogue no: **PZCD 25**
12" Single: Released Oct '88, on Polydor, by Polydor Ltd. Deleted 30 May '89. Catalogue no: **PZ 25**

ZOOLOOK (REMIX)
Tracks: / Zoolook (remix).
12" Single: Released Jan '85, on Polydor, by Polydor Ltd. Catalogue no: **FIAT 5**

ZOOLOOKOLOGIE (REMIX)
Tracks: / Zoolookologie (remix) / Ethnicolour II.
12" Single: Released May '85, on Dreyfus, by Polydor Ltd. Deleted May '88. Catalogue no: **POSPX 740**

Jarre, Maurice

LION OF THE DESERT (SINGLE)
Tracks: / Lion of the desert / March of freedom.
7" Single: Released Aug '81, on RK, by RK Records. Deleted '84. Catalogue no: **RK 1034**

Jarreau, Al

Biographical details: Jarreau, Al This American singer, who hails from Milwaukee, first came to prominence in the jazz field in the early Seventies. Since then he has gradually built up a larger and larger following, retaining his jazz base but also exploring areas of soul, MoR and pop. From a technical standpoint, he is certainly one of the world's finest singers; his range and precision are outstanding.
Because Jarreau's climb to fame has been steady rather than dramatic, he has never

quite become the major household name that might have been expected of a man of his calibre. He reached his commercial peak in 1981 with the US Top 20 pop success of his sisngle *We're In This Love Together* and the LP *Breakin' Away*. He followed this in 1983 with the *Jarreau* album (titled *Trouble In Paradise* in the States), which yielded the beautiful single *Mornin'* - this delicately evocative rendition reached No.21 on the US singles chart and became his biggest UK hit, climbing to No.28. His silky smooth singing has consolidated his status on both sides of the Atlantic during the mid-Eighties with regular concerts. The 1985 LP *In ondon* quickly penetrated the Top 10 of the American jazz charts, thus proving that Jarreau has lost none of his original following. After all, he has a degree in psychology, so he should be able to suss what the public wants. (Bob Macdonald 11/1185).

ALL OR NOTHING AT ALL
Tracks: / All or nothing at all.
CD 5": Released Apr '89, on WEA, by WEA Records. Catalogue no: **U 7663CD**
7" Single: Released Apr '89, on WEA, by WEA Records. Catalogue no: **U 7663**
12" Single: Released Apr '89, on WEA, by WEA Records. Catalogue no: **U 7663T**

BOOGIE DOWN
Tracks: / Boogie down / Our love.
7" Single: Released Sep '83, on WEA, by WEA Records. Deleted '86. Catalogue no: **U 9814**

CLOSER TO YOUR LOVE
Tracks: / Closer to your love / Love is real.
12" Single: Released Nov '81, on WEA, by WEA Records. Catalogue no: **K 17876T**
7" Single: Released Nov '81, on WEA, by WEA Records. Catalogue no: **K 17876**

L IS FOR LOVER (SINGLE)
Tracks: / L is for lover.
7" Single: Released Oct '86, on WEA (International), by WEA Records. Deleted Jun '87. Catalogue no: **U 8612**
12" Single: Released Oct '86, on WEA (International), by WEA Records. Deleted Jun '87. Catalogue no: **U 8612T**

LET'S PRETEND (LIVE)
Tracks: / Let's pretend (live).
7" Single: Released Sep '85, on Warner Bros., by WEA Records. Catalogue no: **U 8911**
12" Single: Released Sep '85, on Warner Bros., by WEA Records. Catalogue no: **U 8911 T**

MOONLIGHTING
Tracks: / Moonlighting / Golden girl (LP version).
12" Single: Released Feb '87, on WEA (International), by WEA Records. Deleted Jul '88. Catalogue no: **U 8407 T**
7" Single: Released Feb '87, on WEA (International), by WEA Records. Catalogue no: **U 8407**

MORNIN'
Tracks: / Mornin' / Not like this / Roof garden.
12" Single: Released Apr '83, on WEA (International), by WEA Records. Catalogue no: **U 9929 T**
7" Single: Released May '83, on WEA, by WEA Records. Catalogue no: **U 9929**

OUR LOVE
Tracks: / Our love / Roof garden.
7" Single: Released Feb '82, on Warner Bros., by WEA Records. Deleted '85. Catalogue no: **K17907**

RAGING WATERS
Tracks: / Raging waters / Too hot.
7" Single: Released Apr '85, on Warner Bros., by WEA Records. Catalogue no: **W 9145**
12" Single: Released Apr '85, on Warner Bros., by WEA Records. Catalogue no: **W 9154T**

SO GOOD
Tracks: / So good / Pleasure over pain / Mornin' (12" only).
12" Single: Released Dec '88, on WEA (International), by WEA Records. Catalogue no: **W 7664T**
7" Single: Released Dec '88, on WEA (International), by WEA Records. Catalogue no: **W 7664**

TELL ME WHAT I GOTTA DO
Tracks: / Tell me what I gotta do / Roof garden.
7" Single: Released Apr '87, on WEA (International), by WEA Records. Deleted Jan '88. Catalogue no: **U 8523**
12" Single: Released Nov '86, on WEA (International), by WEA Records. Deleted Jan '88. Catalogue no: **U 8523T**

TROUBLE IN PARADISE
Tracks: / Trouble in paradise / Save me.
7" Single: Released Jul '83, on WEA (International), by WEA Records. Catalogue no: **U 9871**
12" Single: Released Jul '83, on WEA (International), by WEA Records. Catalogue no: **U 9871 T**

WE'RE IN THIS LOVE TOGETHER
Tracks: / We're in this love together / Easy.
12" Single: Released Sep '81, on Warner Bros., by WEA Records. Deleted '84. Catalogue no: **K 17849T**
7" Single: Released Sep '81, on Warner Bros., by WEA Records. Deleted '84. Catalogue no: **K 17849**

Jarrett, Mikey

DOWN TOWN
Tracks: / Down town.
12" Single: Released Feb '89, on Gyas, Catalogue no: **GA 043**

SOMEONE LOVES YOU HONEY
Tracks: / Someone loves you honey.
7" Single: Released Apr '89, on Gyas, Catalogue no: **GA 044**

WHO MI LOVE
Tracks: / Who mi love.
7" Single: Released Apr '89, on Gyas, Catalogue no: **GA 049**

Jarrett, Wayne

BILLIE JEAN
Tracks: / Billie Jean / Summer Jean.
12" Single: Released May '84, on Kaya, Catalogue no: **KAYA 001**

HOW CAN I LOVE ONE WOMAN
Tracks: / How can I love one woman.
12" Single: Released Sep '84, on Jedi, Catalogue no: **Unknown**

SATTA DREAD
Tracks: / Satta dread.
7" Single: Released Feb '82, on Echo, by Echo Records. Catalogue no: **ECHO 011**

SATURDAY NIGHT JAMBOREE
Tracks: / Saturday night jamboree / Got to be sure.
7" Single: Released Nov '80, on Greensleeves, by Greensleeves Records. Deleted Nov '83. Catalogue no: **GRED 41**

YOUTH MAN
Tracks: / Youth man.
12" Single: Released Apr '85, on Wackies, Catalogue no: **W 181**

Jarrett, Winston

COME A ME
Tracks: / Come a me / Rub-a-dub.
12" Single: Released Sep '83, on Supertone, Catalogue no: **SR 003**

Jarvic 7

BUSH OF LOVE
Tracks: / Bush of love.
CD 5": Released Dec '88, on Who's That Beat, by Play It Again Sam (Belgium). Catalogue no: **WHOS 011CD**
12" Single: Released Dec '88, on Who's That Beat, by Play It Again Sam (Belgium). Catalogue no: **WHOS 011**

FIRE BRIGADE
Tracks: / Fire brigade.
12" Single: Released '89, on Who's That Beat, by Play It Again Sam (Belgium). Catalogue no: **WHOS 017**

Jarvis, Arnold

TAKE SOME TIME OUT
Tracks: / Take some time out (Tommy Musto remix) / Take some time out (rough & rugged remix) / Take some time out (original remix).
12" Single: Released Mar '89, on Republic, by Code Records. Catalogue no: **LICT 024**

Jarvis, Linda

I WANT TO STAY WITH YOU
Tracks: / I want to stay with you / I want to stay with you (instrumental).
7" Single: Released Mar '88, on Sagittarius, by Sagittarius Records. Catalogue no: **SAG/SRL/1**

YOU THREW A GOOD LOVE AWAY
Tracks: / You threw a good love away / You threw a good love away (instrumental).
7" Single: Released Mar '88, on Sagittarius, by Sagittarius Records. Catalogue no: **SAG/SRL/3**

Jarvis, Steve

I DON'T GIVE A DAMN
Tracks: / I don't give a damn.
7" Single: Released Jun '82, on Marco Music, Catalogue no: **MARZ 1**

Jasmine Minks

COLD HEART
Tracks: / Cold heart / World's no place / Forces network (AFM version) (Extra track on 12" version only) / You got me wrong (Available on 12" only).
12" Single: Released May '86, on Creation, by Creation Records. Deleted Jul '88. Catalogue no: **CRE 025T**
7" Single: Released May '86, on Creation, by Creation Records. Deleted Jul '88. Catalogue no: **CRE 025**

PURE JASMIN MINKS
Tracks: / Pure Jasmine Minks.
7" Single: Released Oct '87, on Esuriant, Catalogue no: **PACE 1**

THINK
Tracks: //Think.
7" Single: Released Mar '84, on Creation, by Creation Records. Deleted Jul '88. Catalogue no: **CRE 004**

WHAT'S HAPPENING
Tracks: / What's happening.
7" Single: Released Jun '85, on Creation, by Creation Records. Deleted Jul '88. Catalogue no: **CRE 018**

WHERE TRAFFIC GOES
Tracks: / Where traffic goes.
7" Single: Released Aug '84, on Creation, by Creation Records. Deleted Jul '88. Catalogue no: **CRE 008**

Jason, Kenny "Jammin"

CAN U DANCE
Tracks: / Can U dance / Can U dance (dub inst) / Can U dance (remix) (on CHAMPX 1241 only) / Can U dance (dub remix) (on CHAMPX 1241 only).
12" Single: Released 13 Jun '87, on Champion, by Champion Records. Catalogue no: **CHAMPX 1241**
7" Single: Released Mar '87, on Champion, by Champion Records. Catalogue no: **CHAMP 41**
12" Single: Released Mar '87, on Champion, by Champion Records. Catalogue no: **CHAMP 1241**

Jason & The Scorchers

19TH NERVOUS BREAKDOWN
Tracks: / 19th Nervous breakdown / Greetings from Nashville.
12" Single: Released Nov '86, on EMI-America, by EMI Records. Deleted Oct '87. Catalogue no: **12EA 224**
7" Single: Released Nov '86, on EMI-America, by EMI Records. Deleted Oct '87. Catalogue no: **EA 224**

ABSOLUTELY SWEET MARIE
Tracks: / Absolutely sweet Marie / I can't help myself.
7" Single: Released May '84, on EMI-America, by EMI Records. Catalogue no: **EA 170**
12" Single: Released May '84, on EMI-America, by EMI Records. Catalogue no: **12 EA 170**

SHOP IT AROUND
Tracks: / Shop it around.

12" Single: Released Jul '85, on EMI-America, by EMI Records. Deleted '86. Catalogue no: **12 EA 200**
7" Single: Released Jun '85, on EMI-America, by EMI Records. Deleted '86. Catalogue no: **EA 200**
Special: Released Jun '85, on EMI-America, by EMI Records. Catalogue no: **EAP200**

WHITE LIES
Tracks: / White lies / Are you ready for the country / Honky tonk blues.
12" Single: Released Mar '85, on EMI-America, by EMI Records. Deleted '86. Catalogue no: **12 EA 192**
7" Single: Released Mar '85, on EMI-America, by EMI Records. Deleted '86. Catalogue no: **EA 192**

Jasper, Chris

ONE MORE TIME
Tracks: / One more time / Givin' my all.
7" Single: Released Apr '88, on CBS, by CBS Records. Catalogue no: **651 510 7**

ONE TIME LOVE
Tracks: / One time love.
7" Single: Released '88, on CBS, by CBS Records. Deleted Jan '89. Catalogue no: **661 510-7**
12" Single: Released '88, on CBS, by CBS Records. Deleted Jan '89. Catalogue no: **661 510-6**

Jasper, Jerome

I'LL DO ANYTHING FOR YOU
Tracks: / I'll do anything for you / Treasure the moment.
7" Single: Released Nov '82, on RAK, by EMI Records. Deleted Nov '85. Catalogue no: **RAK 354**
12" Single: Released Nov '82, on RAK, by EMI Records. Deleted Nov '85. Catalogue no: **12RAK 354**

Jass

THEME (W.R)
Tracks: / Theme (W.R).
12" Single: Released Jun '88, on Wax Trax, by Wax Trax Records. Catalogue no: **WAXUK 043**

Javaroo

BREAKIN' IN
Tracks: / Breakin' in / Change it up / Bring out the woman.
12" Single: Released May '80, on Capitol, by EMI Records. Deleted '83. Catalogue no: **12CL 16142**

BRING OUT THE WOMAN
Tracks: / Bring out the woman / Problem child.
7" Single: Released Mar '80, on Capitol, by EMI Records. Deleted Mar '83. Catalogue no: **CL 16131**

JAVAROO
Tracks: / Javaroo / Buzz.
7" Single: Released Oct '80, on Capitol, by EMI Records. Deleted Oct '83. Catalogue no: **CL 16168**

Javelins

YOU'RE NO HUSTLER
Tracks: / You're no hustler / Thoughts of a frustrated songwriter.

7" Single: Released Mar '80, on Ice, by Ice Records. Deleted Mar '83. Catalogue no: **GUY 34**

JAY BEE - TIME FOR LOVE (Released on JBM)

Javells

GOODBYE NOTHING TO SAY
Tracks: / Goodbye nothing to say.
7" Single: Released Nov '74, on Pye Disco Demand, by Pye Records. Deleted '77. Catalogue no: **DDS 2003**

Jax

BITS AND PIECES
Tracks: / Bits and pieces / I can't get over losing you.
7" Single: Released Apr '80, on Creole, by Creole Records. Catalogue no: **CR 200**

LICENSED TO CHILL
Tracks: / Licensed to chill / Licensed to chill (dub mix).
7" Single: Released Jul '87, on Urban, by Polydor Ltd. Catalogue no: **URB 7**
12" Single: Released Jul '87, on Urban, by Polydor Ltd. Catalogue no: **URBX 7**

Jay Bee

TIME FOR LOVE
Tracks: / Time for love, A / Don't stop me dancing.
7" Single: Released May '85, on JBM, by Jason Black Music. Catalogue no: **JBM 1**

Jay Duck

JAY DUCK'S THEME
Tracks: / Jay duck's theme.
7" Single: Released Jul '83, on Magnet, by WEA Records. Catalogue no: **QUACK 1**

Jay, Harry Allstars

Biographical details: Composed and produced by leader Harry Johnson, *The Liquidator* by Harry Jay & The All Stars was a one off UK chart entry for the Jamaican reggae combo in late 1969, reaching No.9 on the singles chart. It was an infectious instrumental record. *The Liquidator* was part of a reggae boom in Britain, a phenomenon largely created by white skinheads who loved the genre at that time - in the same week that Harry Jay & The All Stars were No.9, The Upsetters were No.8 with their double A sided smash *Return of Django/Dollar In The Teeth* and Jimmy Cliff was No.7 with *Wonderful World, Beautiful People.* Earlier in the same year, yet another Jamaican act, Desmond Dekker & The Aces, had introduced reggae to the UK No.1 position with *The Israelites.*
Harry's band never achieved another UK hit, although a re-issue of *The Liquidator* took the lads to No.42 in 1980. On that occasion, it was again white pop fans who were mainly responsible for its sales. (Bob Macdonald 11/11/85).

LIQUIDATOR
Tracks: / Liquidator / Long shot kick de bucket.
12" Single: on Trojan, by Trojan Records. Deleted May '88. Catalogue no: **TRT 9063**
7" Single: Released Oct '69, on Trojan, by Trojan Records. Deleted '72. Catalogue no: **TR 675**
7" Single: on Trojan, by Trojan Records. Deleted May '88. Catalogue no: **TRO 9063**
7" Single: Released Mar '80, on Trojan, by Trojan Records. Deleted '83. Catalogue no: **TRO 9063**

LIQUIDATOR, THE (OLD GOLD)
Tracks: / Liquidator / Love of the common people.
7" Single: Released Jul '84, on Old Gold, by Old Gold Records. Catalogue no: **OG 9389**

LIQUIDATOR,THE
Tracks: / Liquidator / Book of rules.
12" Single: Released Jul '83, on Sun Set (reggae), Catalogue no: **SSRD 005**

Jay, Julian

SUMMER LOVE
Tracks: / Summer love / I don't think she's in love anymore.
12" Single: Released Aug '86, on Square Biz, by Square Biz Records. Catalogue no: **12SUJ 110**

WAS IT WORTH IT
Tracks: / Was it worth it.
7" Single: Released Apr '89, on Square Biz, by Square Biz Records. Catalogue no: **SUJ 116**
12" Single: Released Apr '89, on Square Biz, by Square Biz Records. Catalogue no: **12SUJ 116**

Jay, Mike

MADDER
Tracks: / Madder / She's so.
7" Single: Released Jul '80, on M.A.M, by M.A.M. Records. Deleted Jul '83. Catalogue no: **MAMS 202**

ROMANCE
Tracks: / Romance / Automatic.
7" Single: Released Mar '81, on M.A.M, by M.A.M. Records. Deleted Mar '84. Catalogue no: **MAMS 209**

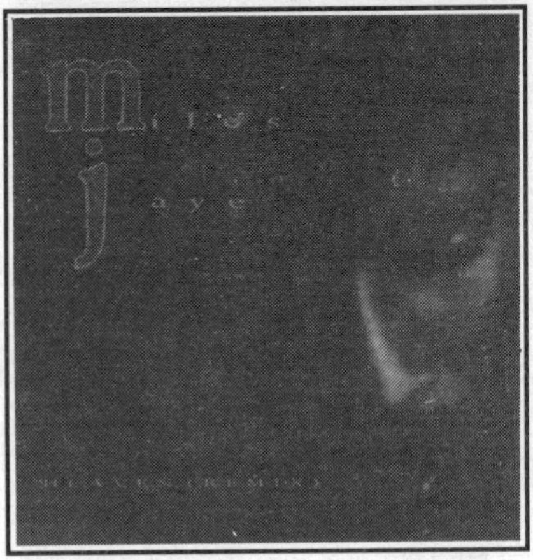

Miles Jay - Heaven (remix) - (Released on 4th & Broadway)

Jay, Miles

OBJECTIVE
Tracks: / Objective.
12" Single: Released Oct '89, on 4th & Broadway, by Island Records. Catalogue no: **12 BRW 144**

Jay, Peter

CAN CAN '62
Tracks: / Can can '62.
7" Single: Released Nov '62, on Decca, by Decca Records. Deleted '65. Catalogue no: **F 11531**

Jay, Singer

EYE WATER FE SUGAR
Tracks: / Eye water fe sugar.
12" Single: Released Nov '88, on Sonic Records, by Sonic Records. Catalogue no: **UNKNOWN**

Jaye, Miles

HEAVEN
Tracks: / Heaven (remix) / Heaven (original version - Ed's mix).
7" Single: Released '89, on 4th & Broadway, by Island Records. Catalogue no: **BRW 133**
CD 5": Released Jun '89, on Island, by Island Records. Catalogue no: **BRCD 133**
12" Single: Released May '89, on Island, by Island Records. Catalogue no: **12BRW 133**

HEAVEN (REMIX)
Tracks: / Heaven (remix) / Heaven (remix)(versions).
12" Single: Released Jun '89, on 4th & Broadway, by Island Records. Catalogue no: **12BRW 133**
7" Single: Released Jun '89, on 4th & Broadway, by Island Records. Catalogue no: **BRW 133**

I'VE BEEN A FOOL FOR YOU
Tracks: / I've been a fool for you / Happy 2 have U / Let's start over (Extra track available on 12" only).
Note: Extra track available on 12" only.
7" Single: Released Apr '88, on 4th & Broadway, by Island Records. Deleted Jun '88. Catalogue no: **BRW 92**
12" Single: Released Apr '88, on 4th & Broadway, by Island Records. Deleted Jun '88. Catalogue no: **12 BRW 92**

LET'S START OVER
Tracks: / Let's start over / Lazy love.
7" Single: Released Nov '87, on 4th & Broadway, by Island Records. Deleted Jun '88. Catalogue no: **BRW 81**
12" Single: Released Nov '87, on 4th & Broadway, by Island Records. Deleted Dec '88. Catalogue no: **12 BRW 81**

OBJECTIVE
Tracks: / Objective / Objective (sax mix) / Objective (club mix) (On 12"and CD only) / Objective (reprise) (On CD only).
7" Single: Released Jul '89, on 4th & Broadway, by Island Records. Catalogue no: **BRW 142**
CD 5": Released Jul '89, on 4th & Broadway, by Island Records. Catalogue no: **BRCD 142**
12" Single: Released Jul '89, on 4th & Broadway, by Island Records. Catalogue no: **12 BRW 142**

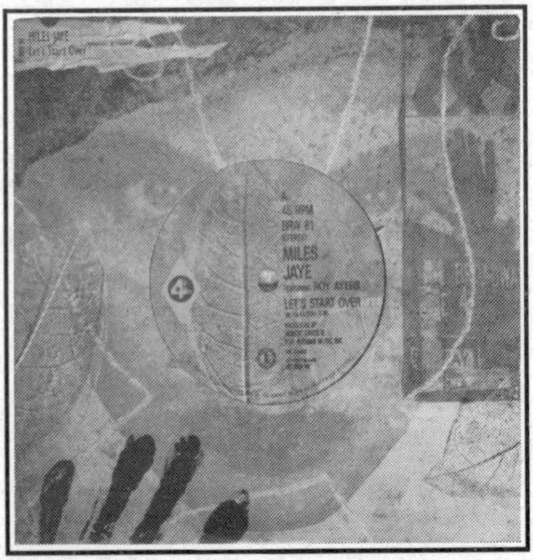

Miles Jaye - Let's Start Over (Released on 4th & Broadway)

Jaymes, David

EVERYBODY SALSA, '88
Tracks: / Everybody salsa, '88 / Best years of our lives, '88.
12" Single: Released '88, on President, by President Records. Catalogue no: **PT 12-572**
7" Single: Released Aug '88, on President, by President Records. Catalogue no: **PT 572**

Jaymes, Kimberley

SENDING
Tracks: / Sending.
12" Single: Released Oct '88, on Craze, Catalogue no: **CF 005**

Jayne,Lesley

ROCKING WITH MY RADIO
Tracks: / Rocking with my radio / Isle of Wight.
7" Single: Released Jul '82, on BK, Catalogue no: **PPC 108**

SAILING AWAY
Tracks: / Sailing away / He's always telling me lies.
7" Single: Released Jan '83, on Miracle, by Gull Records. Deleted '88. Catalogue no: **M 30**

Jays

PUT YOUR HEAD ON MY SHOULDER
Tracks: / Put your head on my shoulder.
12" Single: Released Sep '88, on Hawkeye, by Hawkeye Records. Catalogue no: **HD 89**

Jayston,Michael

HOW DO I LOVE THEE
Tracks: / How do I love thee / Classical medley.
7" Single: Released Nov '81, on Flight, Deleted '86. Catalogue no: **XJ 1**

Jayvees

RIGHT BACK WHERE WE STARTED FROM
Tracks: / Right back where we started from.
7" Single: Released Mar '81, on V-Tone, Catalogue no: **VTONE 001**

Jazawaki

DON'T PANIC
Tracks: / Don't panic / Wot / Something's cooking.
12" Single: Released Dec '85, on Abstract, by Abstract Sounds. Catalogue no: **12 ABS 037**

Jazz Butcher

ANGELS
Tracks: / Angels / Rebecca wants her bike back / Mersey (*Extra track on 12" version only).
7" Single: Released Nov '86, on Glass, by Glass Records. Catalogue no: **GLASS 049**
12" Single: Released Nov '86, on Glass, by Glass Records. Catalogue no: **GLASS 12049**

HARD
Tracks: / Hard / Grooving in the bus lane.
12" Single: Released Mar '86, on Glass, by Glass Records. Catalogue no: **GLASS 12046**
7" Single: Released Mar '86, on Glass, by Glass Records. Catalogue no: **GLASS 046**

NEW INVENTION
Tracks: / New invention.
12" Single: Released 16 Oct '89, on Creation, by Creation Records. Catalogue no: **CRE 069T**

SPOOKY
Tracks: / Spooky.
Note: Available on 12" and also as a limited edition 7"for just 0.99p.
12" Single: Released '88, on Creation, by Creation Records. Catalogue no: **CRE 059T**
7" Single: Released '88, on Creation, by Creation Records. Catalogue no: **CRE 059**

Jazz Devils

BACK IN TOWN
Tracks: / Back in town (On all versions) / Raid, The (On 7" & CD only) / Back in town (12" version) (On CD & 12" only) / Back in town (dub mix) (On CD only) / Raid, The (full length version) (On 12" only).
7" Single: Released 5 Sep '88, on Virgin, by Virgin Records. Catalogue no: **VS 1108**
CD 5": Released '88, on Virgin, by Virgin Records. Catalogue no: **VSCD 1108**

12" Single: Released 5 Sep '88, on Virgin, by Virgin Records. Catalogue no: **VST 1108**

IT'S A CRIME
Tracks: / It's a crime / Raid, The (Glove Club remix) / It's a crime (full length version) (on CD & 12" only) / Chase the blues (on CD only).
12" Single: Released 24 Oct '88, on Virgin, by Virgin Records. Catalogue no: **VST 1138**
7" Single: Released 24 Oct '88, on Virgin, by Virgin Records. Catalogue no: **VS 1138**
CD 3": Released '88, on Virgin, by Virgin Records. Catalogue no: **VSCD 1138**

IT'S A CRIME (RE-ISSUE)
Tracks: / It's a crime / Raid, The / It's a crime (version).
12" Single: Released Jul '89, on Virgin, by Virgin Records. Catalogue no: **VST 1138**
7" Single: Released Jul '89, on Virgin, by Virgin Records. Catalogue no: **VS 1138**

OUT OF THE DARK (SINGLE)
Tracks: / Out of the dark / Chase the blues / Postman song, The.
12" Single: Released Feb '89, on Virgin, by Virgin Records. Catalogue no: **VST 1164**
CD 5": Released Mar '89, on Virgin, by Virgin Records. Catalogue no: **VSDCD 1164**
7" Single: Released Feb '89, on Virgin, by Virgin Records. Catalogue no: **VS 1164**

Jazz Hipsters

TENDER TRAP, THE
Tracks: / Tender trap, The.
7" Single: Released Jan '86, on Axis, by Axis Records. Deleted '87. Catalogue no: **AXI 1**

Jazz Insects

GHOST TRAIN
Tracks: / Ghost train / Elephants.
7" Single: Released Mar '82, on Rococco, Catalogue no: **ROC 002**

Jazz Men T

PLAY THAT HOUSE
Tracks: / Play that house.
Note: "This must be the anthem of house. An excellent acid mix with all the ingredients to be a scorcher. Strong overtones of the Cult film 'Blues Brothers'" (Supertrack, June 1988)
7" Single: Released Jun '88, on Supertrack, Catalogue no: **7 HSE 001**
12" Single: Released Jun '88, on Supertrack, Catalogue no: **HSE 001**

Jazz Renegades

DO IT THE HARD WAY
Tracks: / Do the hard way / Blues on the beach / Do the hard way(version).
12" Single: Released Jun '89, on Urban, by Polydor Ltd. Catalogue no: **URBX 41**
7" Single: Released Jun '89, on Urban, by Polydor Ltd. Catalogue no: **URB 41**

Jazz Sluts

FUCHI
Tracks: / Fuchi / Maniacs of the fourth dimension.
7" Single: Released Sep '80, on Epic, by CBS Records. Deleted '83. Catalogue no: **EPC 8974**

Jazz & The Brothers

CASANOVA (PASSION HERO)
Tracks: / Casanova (passion hero) / Casanova (passion hero) (version).
12" Single: Released Jul '89, on Production House (1), Catalogue no: **PNT 008**

GET FLAT
Tracks: / Get flat / X.T.C street party / X.T.C street party (controversial mix) (Only on 12".).
7" Single: Released Oct '88, on Polydor, by Polydor Ltd. Catalogue no: **PO 21**
12" Single: Released Oct '88, on Polydor, by Polydor Ltd. Deleted 31 May '89. Catalogue no: **PZ 21**

LET'S ALL GO BACK (DISCO NIGHTS)
Tracks: / Let's all go back (disco nights).
12" Single: Released Jul '88, on Ensign, by Ensign Records. Catalogue no: **ENYX 616**
12" Single: Released Jun '88, on Ensign, by Ensign Records. Catalogue no: **JAZZX 1**
7" Single: Released Jun '88, on Ensign, by Ensign Records. Catalogue no: **JAZZ 1**
7" Single: Released Jul '88, on Ensign, by Ensign Records. Catalogue no: **ENY 616**

Jazzateers

PRESSING ON
Tracks: / Pressing on.
12" Single: Released Jun '85, on Stampede, Catalogue no: **STAMP 1**

SHOW ME THE DOOR
Tracks: / Show me the door / Sixteen reasons.

J.B.'s All Stars - Ready, Willing and Able (Released on BMG)

7" Single: Released Jul '83, on Rough Trade, by Rough Trade Records. Catalogue no: **RT 138**

Jazzy

WIDE-EYED BOY
Tracks: / Wide-eyed boy / Tuesday.
7" Single: Released Jan '87, on Our Own, Catalogue no: **TAJ 001**

Jazzy Jeff

KING HEROIN (DON'T MESS WITH HEROIN)
Tracks: / King heroin (don't mess with heroin).
7" Single: on Jive Electro, by Zomba Records. Catalogue no: **JIVE 88**
12" Single: Released Apr '85, on Jive Electro, by Zomba Records. Catalogue no: **JIVET 88**

MIX SO I CAN GO CRAZY
Tracks: / Mix so I can go crazy.
12" Single: Released Jul '85, on Jive, by Zomba Records. Catalogue no: **JIVET 95**
7" Single: Released Sep '85, on Jive, by Zomba Records. Catalogue no: **JIVE 95**

PARENTS JUST DON'T UNDERSTAND
Tracks: / Parents just don't understand.
7" Single: Released Jul '88, on Jive, by Zomba Records. Deleted '88. Catalogue no: **JIVE 181**
12" Single: Released Jul '88, on Jive, by Zomba Records. Deleted '88. Catalogue no: **JIVET 181**

J.B.'s

GRUNT, THE
Tracks: / Grunt, The (part 1) / Grunt, The (part 2).
7" Single: Released Mar '87, on King (USA), Catalogue no: **45-6317**

J.B's Allstars

Biographical details: J.B's Allstars As a part-time diverson from his activities with The Specials drummer, John Bradbury formed this spinoff band in 1983. While the Special AKA continued in their usual political and sociological vein, J.B.'s All Stars specialised in remakes of Brad's favourite rhythm and blues oldies. The only one to reach the UK chart was *Backfield In Motion*, which peaked at No.48 in early 1984; this was a revival of the 1969 US million-seller written and originally performed by Mel & Tim. Bradbury and his colleagues also had a stab at *One Minute Every Hour*, *Sign On The Dotted Line* and *Ready Willing and Able*. (Bob Macdonald 11/11/85).

ALPHABET ARMY
Tracks: / Alphabet army / Alarm.
7" Single: Released Jan '86, on Two-Tone, by Chrysalis Records. Catalogue no: **CHSTT 29**
12" Single: Released Jan '86, on Two-Tone, by Chrysalis Records. Catalogue no: **CHSTT 1229**

BACKFIELD IN MOTION
Tracks: / Backfield in motion.
7" Single: Released Jan '84, on RCA, by BMG Records (UK). Catalogue no: **RCA 384**
12" Single: Released Jan '84, on RCA, by BMG Records (UK). Catalogue no: **RCAT 384**

ONE MINUTE EVERY HOUR
Tracks: / One minute every hour / Theme from 903.
7" Single: Released Sep '83, on RCA, by BMG Records (UK). Catalogue no: **RCA 357**
12" Single: Released Sep '83, on RCA, by BMG Records (UK). Catalogue no: **RCAT 357**

READY, WILLING AND ABLE
Tracks: / Ready, willing and able / Chance meeting.
7" Single: Released '84, on RCA, by BMG Records (UK). Catalogue no: **RCA 440**

SIGN ON THE DOTTED LINE
Tracks: / Sign on the dotted line / And he was gone.
7" Single: Released May '84, on RCA, by BMG Records (UK). Catalogue no: **RCA 408**
12" Single: Released May '84, on RCA, by BMG Records (UK). Catalogue no: **RCAT 408**

JC

I DIS THEREFORE I AM
Tracks: / I dis therefore I am.
12" Single: Released Sep '88, on Furious Fish, Catalogue no: **FFJC 01**

J.C.B.

I WISH I WAS A CAMERA
Tracks: / I wish I was a camera / Walk it like you talk it.
7" Single: Released Feb '81, on Red Rat, Deleted '84. Catalogue no: **RRR 401**

Jealous

ANOTHER BROKEN HEART
Tracks: / Another broken heart.
7" Single: Released Jul '83, on KA, Catalogue no: **KA 15**

Jealous Girl

JEALOUS GIRL
Tracks: / Jealous girl / Teenage wastage.
7" Single: Released May '82, on Zilch, by Zilch Records. Catalogue no: **ZILCH 21**

THREE DAYS AND RIKKI
Tracks: / Three days and Rikki / Red.
7" Single: Released Apr '82, on Zilch, by Zilch Records. Catalogue no: **ZILCH 18**

Jean Paul Sartre Exp

JEAN PAUL SATRE EXP
Tracks: / Jean Paul Satre experience.
12" Single: Released Dec '87, on Flying Nun, Catalogue no: **FNE 4**

Jean Pierre & Vicky

LA MEME CHOSE
Tracks: / La meme chose.
12" Single: Released Aug '83, on Battersea, Catalogue no: **ETTO 121**

Jeanette

CRUSHED NICOTINE VIBRATO
Tracks: / Crushed nicotine vibrato.
7" Single: Released Jun '84, on Survival (1), by Survival Records. Catalogue no: **SUR 021**

HAPPENING, THE
Tracks: / Happening, The.
7" Single: Released Oct '84, on Artic, Catalogue no: **SART 002**

IN THE MORNING
Tracks: / In the morning.
12" Single: Released May '83, on Survival (1), by Survival Records. Catalogue no: **SUR 012**

JOHNNY (EXTENDED MIX)
Tracks: / Johnny (extended mix) / Midnight on a rusting train / Snakeyes (extended dub mix) (Only on 12" single.).
7" Single: Released Mar '89, on Survival (1), by Survival Records. Catalogue no: **SUR 047**
12" Single: Released Mar '89, on Survival (1), by Survival Records. Catalogue no: **SUR 12047**

LADY BLUE
Tracks: / Lady blue.
12" Single: Released Jul '85, on Premonition, by Survival Records. Catalogue no: **PREM 4**

LEO
Tracks: / Leo / Dawn arises / Leo (ext).
12" Single: Released Sep '87, on Survival (1), by Survival Records. Catalogue no: **SUR 12 038**

PREFAB IN THE SUN
Tracks: / Prefab in the sun / Woman's love.
7" Single: Released Aug '88, on Survival (1), by Survival Records. Catalogue no: **SUR 044**

WOMAN'S LOVE
Tracks: / Woman's love.
7" Single: Released Aug '88, on Survival (1), by Survival Records. Catalogue no: **SUR 004**

Jeannie's Beau

HAUNTING MY HOUSE
Tracks: / Haunting my house / Love is the only way.
7" Single: Released Oct '86, on Sedition, by Sedition Records. Catalogue no: **EDIT 3316**
12" Single: Released Oct '86, on Sedition, by Sedition Records. Catalogue no: **EDITL 3316**

Jeddah

ELEANOR RIGBY
Tracks: / Eleanor Rigby.
7" Single: Released Nov '83, on Death (1), by Death Records. Catalogue no: **RIP 2001**

Jedson,Jon

CITY GIRL
Tracks: / City girl / Life's journey.
7" Single: Released Feb '80, on President, by President Records. Deleted Feb '83. Catalogue no: **PT 482**

Jeep

FACTORY
Tracks: / Factory / Factory revisited (discomix).
7" Single: Released Jul '83, on Airport, Catalogue no: **AIRPORT 006**

HAPPY WANDERER
Tracks: / Happy wanderer, The / Do it right.
7" Single: Released May '82, on Rough Trade, by Rough Trade Records. Catalogue no: **AIRPORT 005**

I CAN'T REMEMBER YOUR NAME
Tracks: / I can't remember your name / Just one look.
7" Single: Released Sep '81, on Bronze, by Bronze Records. Deleted '84. Catalogue no: **BRO 128**

TRYING TO FORGET
Tracks: / Trying to forget / Roger the jogger.
7" Single: Released Oct '81, on Airport, Deleted Oct '84. Catalogue no: **AIRP 003**

WILD ROVER
Tracks: / Wild rover / Lark in the dark.
7" Single: Released Jan '80, on Cobra, Deleted Jan '85. Catalogue no: **COB 9**

Jeep Style

IF THERE'S A CURE
Tracks: / If there's a cure.
12" Single: Released Oct '89, on UNKNOWN, Catalogue no: **KV 729**

Jeff & Co.

SCRUFFY'S SONG
Tracks: / Scruffy's song / Knocking at the door.

7" Single: Released Nov '82, on Sherpa. Deleted '83. Catalogue no: **SPA 001**

Jefferson

COLOUR OF MY LOVE
Tracks: / Colour of my love.
7" Single: Released Mar '69, on Pye. Deleted '72. Catalogue no: **7N 17706**

Jefferson Airplane

Biographical details: The classic line-up of this American rock band comprised Grace Slick, Marty Balin, Jack Casady, Spencer Dryden, Paul Kantner and Jorma Kaukonen. Formed in 1965 they were the first of the wave of San Francisco bands to sign a recording contract and their debut LP, Jefferson Airplane Taking Off, was released in '66. But it was in '67 -- the year of peace, love and acid-rock -- that they shot to fame. Together with the Grateful Dead and Big Brother & The Holding Company, Jefferson Airplane helped to make San Francisco the Mecca of hippiedom. Their second album, Surrealistic Pillow, plus US Top Ten singles Somebody to Love and White Rabbit -- both written by lead singer Slick -- were also released in '67. As the band's career progressed during the rest of the 60's their music came to be dominated more and more by the distinctive Slick and her guitarist/singer boyfriend Kantner, to the displeasure of founding guitarist/vocalist Balin. For many rock fans Jefferson Aisplane epitomised the late 60's: albums like Bless Its Pointed Little Head (a live set released in '69) and Volunteers (a late '69 studio LP) ran the gamut from drug-dominated psychedilic tripping to anti-Vietam War political preaching. On the British chart the albums peaked respectively at 38 and 34 -- like the Grateful Dead they never really caught on in Britain despite the efforts of top DJ John Peel. The pressures of their US status eventually proved too much and the group gradually disintegrated during the early 70's amid a host of line-up changes. Although the band still existed all the members became more interested in outside projects. In 1974 Slick, Kantner and Balin pulled themselves together again and launched the band afresh with the name Jefferson Starship. (Bob MacDonald, November 1985.).

WHITE RABBIT (OLD GOLD)
Tracks: / White rabbit / Somebody to love.
7" Single: Released Nov '86, on Old Gold, by Old Gold Records. Catalogue no: **OG 9631**

WHITE RABBIT (RE-ISSUE) (see panel below)
Tracks: / White rabbit / Somebody to love / She has funny cars* / Third week in the Chelsea.
7" Single: Released 30 May '87, on Ariola, by BMG Records (UK). Catalogue no: **JEFF 1**
12" Single: Released 30 May '87, on Ariola, by BMG Records (UK). Catalogue no: **JEFFT 1**

Jefferson, Marshall

DO THE DO
Tracks: / Do the do.
12" Single: Released Apr '89, on DJ International, by Westside Records. Catalogue no: **DJINT 10**

HOUSE MUSIC ANTHEM, THE
Tracks: / House music anthem, The / Move your body.
7" Single: Released Oct '86, on Affair, Catalogue no: **TARTS 3**

OPEN YOUR EYES
Tracks: / Open your eyes / Open your eyes (version).
12" Single: Released Dec '88, on ffrr, by London Records. Deleted 26 Jun '89. Catalogue no: **FFRX 18**
7" Single: Released Dec '88, on ffrr, by London Records. Catalogue no: **FFRR 18**

Jefferson Starship

Biographical details: Jefferson Starship At the time of their biggest mid-Seventies success, this American rock band consisted of Marty Balin, John Barbata, Craig Chaquico, Papa John Creach, David Freiberg, Paul Kantner, Pete Sears and Grace Slick.
Having been one one the most significant of the San Fransisco rock acts of the late Sixties, Jefferson Airplane gradually fell apart during the early Seventies while all the members became more interested in outside projects. One such activity was founder member Paul Kantner's 1970 album *Blow Against The Empire*, which he credited to Jefferson Starship. After the Airplane had foundered, the legendary Balin/Kantner/Slsick nucleus decided to use this name when they regrouped in 1974. Gathering together a collection of old and new friends, they officially launched the new band with the *Dragonfly* album. Like the later Airplane records, and like all the subsequent Starship recordings, it was released on their own Grunt label.
It was the 1975 LP *Red Octopus* that really put Jefferson back on the map. The album cruised to the US No.1 position in September of that year, spearheaded by the smash hit ballad *Miracles*. That single represented a sweet triumph for its writer, Balin - he has helped to form the original Airplane in 1965 but had gradually lost creative control during the late sixties, evantually causing him to quit in 1971.
Jefferson Starship's 1976 album *Spitfire* reached No.3 in the US and their success continued on a lesser but nonetheless impressive scale for the rest of the Seventies and early Eighties. Their hit singles included *Count On Me* (No.8 in US in 1978) and *Jane* (No.14 in US, No.21 in UK in 1980). There was less harmoney, however, behind the scenes - Balin and Slick drifted away from the group to launch solo careers, the latter experiencing alcohol problems for a while. Kantner soldiered on with the group through the early Eighties, but suffered an acrimonious break up with the rest of the band in 1984. He sued the group, with the result that they paid him $250,000 not to play with them anymore; this included $80,000 for the band's right to continue using the old name, but shortened to Starship.
In 1985 Kantner rejoined two old Jefferson cronies, Marty Balin and Jack Casady to rehearse and launch a new combo. Meanwhile Grace Slick was back in the Starship fold and was now the only survivor from Jefferson Airplane days. In a manner that amazed the entire music world but which was, in fact, entirely typical of the band's extraordinarly turbulent and unpredictable career, the revamped Starship immediately rocketed to the US No.1 slot with their first ever chart-topping single and their first ever British smash *We Built This City*. With lyrics by Bernie Taupin (of Elton John fame) and much musical help from new associate Peter Wolf (the former frontman with the J.Geils Band), *We Built This City* protested at a San Fransisco government decision to restrict the playing of rock music in some of the city's public areas.
As Jefferson Airplane, they were one of the leading acid-rock bands of the Sixties. As Jefferson Starship, they were a successful mainstream melodic rock group of the Seventies. As Starship, they addressed th new technopop generation but nonetheless remembered that they themselves had *Built This City on Rock'n'Roll*. (Bob Macdonald 12/11/85).

GIRL WITH THE HUNGRY EYES
Tracks: / Girl with the hungry eyes / Just the same.
7" Single: Released Apr '80, on Grunt, by BMG Records (UK). Deleted '83. Catalogue no: **GB 1921**

JANE
Tracks: / Jane / Freedom at point zero.
7" Single: Released Jan '80, on Grunt, by BMG Records (UK). Deleted '83. Catalogue no: **FB 1750**

Jeffrey, Billy

SCOTLAND AGAIN
Tracks: / Scotland again / Music of the Spey.
7" Single: Released Sep '80, on Klub, by Klub Records. Deleted Sep '83. Catalogue no: **KLUS 28**

Jeffreys

IT'S CHRISTMAS
Tracks: / It's Christmas.
7" Single: Released Nov '83, on Go For It, Catalogue no: **GFI 001**

Jeffreys, Garland

CHRISTINE
Tracks: / Christine / Scapegoat club.
7" Single: Released Feb '81, on Epic, by CBS Records. Deleted Feb '84. Catalogue no: **EPC 9577**

NINETY SIX TEARS
Tracks: / Ninety six tears / Escape goat dub.
7" Single: Released Mar '81, on Epic, by CBS Records. Deleted Mar '84. Catalogue no: **EPC A 1045**

Jeffries, Michael

RAZZLE DAZZLE
Tracks: / Razzle dazzle / Half time / Razzle dazzle (Instrumental).
7" Single: Released May '86, on Warner Bros., by WEA Records. Catalogue no: **W 8681**
12" Single: Released May '86, on Warner Bros., by WEA Records. Deleted Jun '87. Catalogue no: **W 8681T**

Jelly Beans

YOU DON'T MEAN ME NO GOOD
Tracks: / You don't mean me no good.
7" Single: Released Jul '80, on Inferno (1), by Inferno Records. Catalogue no: **HEAT 14**

Jellybean

COMING BACK FOR MORE PART 1
Tracks: / Coming back for more(Part 1).
7" Single: Released Aug '88, on Chrysalis, by Chrysalis Records. Catalogue no: **JELL 4**
12" Single: Released Aug '88, on Chrysalis, by Chrysalis Records. Catalogue no: **JELX 4**

JINGO
Tracks: / Jingo.
Note: Contains various remixes.
7" Single: Released Oct '87, on Chrysalis, by Chrysalis Records. Catalogue no: **JEL 2**
12" Single: Released Oct '87, on Chrysalis, by Chrysalis Records. Catalogue no: **JELX 2**

JUST A MIRAGE
Tracks: / Just a mirage / Just a mirage (dub) / Who found who? (UK house mix) (extra track on 12" version only.).
7" Single: Released 20 Feb '88, on Chrysalis, by Chrysalis Records. Catalogue no: **JEL 3**
12" Single: Released 20 Feb '88, on Chrysalis, by Chrysalis Records. Catalogue no: **JELX 3**

REAL THING, THE
Tracks: / Real thing, The / Real thing, The (inst).
Note: featuring Steve Dante
7" Single: Released Sep '87, on Chrysalis, by Chrysalis Records. Catalogue no: **CHS 3167**
12" Single: Released Sep '87, on Chrysalis, by Chrysalis Records. Catalogue no: **CHS 123167**

SIDEWALK TALK
Tracks: / Sidewalk talk / Was dog a doughnut / Sidewalk talk (Funhouse remix) (Extra track on 12" Remix version only) / Was dog a doughnut (remix) (Extra track on 12" Remix version only.).
7" Single: Released Jan '86, on EMI-America, by EMI Records. Catalogue no: **EA 210**
12" Single: Released Jan '86, on EMI-America, by EMI Records. Deleted Oct '87. Catalogue no: **12 EA 210**
12" Single: Released Jan '86, on EMI-America, by EMI Records. Catalogue no: **12 EAX 310**

WHO FOUND WHO?
Tracks: / Who found who? (7" edit) (On 7" single only.) / Who found who? (uptown dub) (On 7" single only.) / Who found who? (club mix) (On 12" single only.) / Real thing, The (El Barrio mix) (On 12" single only.) / Real thing, The (Hot Salsa piano dub) (On 12" single only.).
7" Single: Released Nov '87, on Chrysalis, by Chrysalis Records. Catalogue no: **JEL 1**
12" Single: Released Nov '87, on Chrysalis, by Chrysalis Records. Catalogue no: **JELX 1**

Jenkins, Kechia

I NEED SOMEBODY
Tracks: / I need somebody / I need somebody (version).
7" Single: Released Apr '88, on Citybeat, by Beggars Banquet Records. Catalogue no: **CBE 722**
12" Single: Released Apr '88, on Citybeat, by Beggars Banquet Records. Catalogue no: **CBE 1222**

STILL WAITING
Tracks: / Still waiting.
7" Single: Released 15 May '89, on Profile (USA), by Profile Records (USA). Catalogue no: **PROF 250**
12" Single: Released 15 May '89, on Profile (USA), by Profile Records (USA). Catalogue no: **PROFT 250**

Jennings, Waylon

DUKES OF HAZZARD
Tracks: / Dukes of Hazzard / Chips Corniche.
7" Single: Released May '82, on RCA, by BMG Records (UK). Catalogue no: **GOLD 550**

GOOD OL' BOYS
Tracks: / Good ol' boys / Storms never last.
7" Single: Released Jan '81, on RCA, by BMG Records (UK). Deleted Jan '84. Catalogue no: **PB 9561**

JUST TO SATISFY YOU
Tracks: / Just to satisfy you / Get naked with me.
7" Single: Released Oct '83, on RCA, by BMG Records (UK). Catalogue no: **RCA 366**
7" Single: Released May '82, on RCA, by BMG Records (UK). Catalogue no: **RCA 224**

Jenny

UPTOWN DOWNTOWN
Tracks: / Uptown downtown.
7" Single: Released Dec '81, on People Unite, by People Unite Records. Catalogue no: **PU 001 S**

Jenny & The Joystix

TALKIN' TO MY TOYS
Tracks: / Talkin' to my toys / Sell sky.
7" Single: Released Sep '81, on Epic, by CBS Records. Deleted '84. Catalogue no: **EPCA 1516**

Jensen, Carl

DIFFERENT CORNER
Tracks: / Different corner, A.
7" Single: Released Jun '88, on Hapnin, Catalogue no: **HAP 005**
12" Single: Released Jun '88, on Hapnin, Catalogue no: **HAP 006**

Jeopardie, Jeff

2468 DOUBLE 9
Tracks: / 2468 double 9.
7" Single: Released Feb '86, on Gull, by Gull Records. Deleted '88. Catalogue no: **GULS 85**

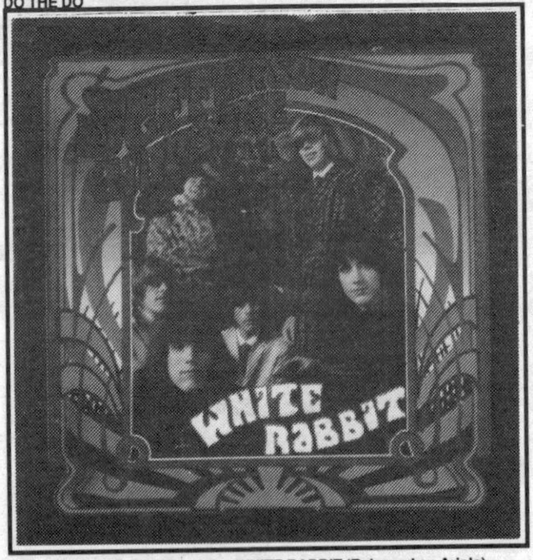

JEFFERSON AIRPLANE - WHITE RABBIT (Released on Ariola)

Jeremiahs

DRIVING INTO THE SUN
Tracks: / Driving into the sun.
7" Single: Released Jun '88, on Abstract, by Abstract Sounds. Catalogue no: **ABS 053**
12" Single: Released Jun '88, on Abstract, by Abstract Sounds. Catalogue no: **12 ABS 053**

Jeremy Days

BRAND NEW TOY
Tracks: / Brand new toy.
7" Single: Released 22 May '89, on Polydor, by Polydor Ltd. Catalogue no: **PO 45**
12" Single: Released 22 May '89, on Polydor, by Polydor Ltd. Catalogue no: **PZ 45**

BRAND NEW TOY, THE
Tracks: / Brand new toy, The / Raintree country (live version).
7" Single: Released Jun '89, on Polydor, by Polydor Ltd. Catalogue no: **PO 45**

JULIE THRU THE BLINDS
Tracks: / Julie thru the blinds.
7" Single: Released Aug '89, on Polydor, by Polydor Ltd. Catalogue no: **889 478 7**
12" Single: Released Aug '89, on Polydor, by Polydor Ltd. Catalogue no: **889 479 1**

ROME WASN'T BUILT IN A DAY
Tracks: / Rome wasn't built in a day / Trust (the poison man).
CD 5": Released Sep '89, on Polydor, by Polydor Ltd. Catalogue no: **873 040-3**
7" Single: Released Sep '89, on Polydor, by Polydor Ltd. Catalogue no: **PO 59**
12" Single: Released Sep '89, on Polydor, by Polydor Ltd. Catalogue no: **PZ 59**

Jeremy's Secret

KEY TO JEREMY'S SECRET
Tracks: / Key to Jeremy's Secret.
7" Single: Released Jun '83, on Papier Mache, by Papier Mache Records. Catalogue no: **PULP TT 12**

Jerks

COME BACK BOGART
Tracks: / Come back Bogart / Are you strong enough / Strangest man.
7" Single: Released Apr '80, on Laser, Deleted '82. Catalogue no: **LAS 25**

Jerome

BETCHA
Tracks: / Betcha.
12" Single: Released May '85, on Calibre, Deleted '86. Catalogue no: **CABL 202**

EXTRA SPECIAL
Tracks: / Extra special / Extra special (instrumental).
7" Single: Released Sep '85, on Calibre, Deleted '86. Catalogue no: **CAB 206**
7" Single: Released Jan '86, on Calibre, Deleted '87. Catalogue no: **CABS 206**
12" Single: Released Sep '85, on Calibre, Deleted '86. Catalogue no: **CABL 206**
12" Single: Released Jan '86, on Calibre, Deleted '87. Catalogue no: **CABLS 206**

IF YOU WALK OUT THAT DOOR
Tracks: / If you walk out that door / Token.
7" Single: Released '88, on DJM, Catalogue no: **DJS 10956**
12" Single: Released '88, on DJM, Catalogue no: **DJR 18015**

I'M INTO YOUR LOVE
Tracks: / I'm into your love / I'm into your love (part 2).
7" Single: Released Jun '82, on RCA, by BMG Records (UK). Catalogue no: **RCA 225**
12" Single: Released Jun '82, on RCA, by BMG Records (UK). Catalogue no: **RCAT 225**

IN THE RIGHT DIRECTION
Tracks: / In the right direction.
7" Single: Released Jan '82, on Soto Sound, by Soto Sound Records. Catalogue no: **STD 1**
12" Single: Released Jan '82, on Soto Sound, by Soto Sound Records. Catalogue no: **STD 1 12**

IT'S MINE AND YOU DON'T OWN IT
Tracks: / It's mine and you don't own it / Home grown blue eyed soul.
7" Single: Released '88, on DJM, Catalogue no: **DJS 10966**
12" Single: Released '88, on DJM, Catalogue no: **DJR 10966**

LIVING A GOOD THING
Tracks: / Living a good thing.
7" Single: Released Jun '84, on Calibre, Deleted '86. Catalogue no: **CAB 126**
12" Single: Released Jun '84, on Calibre, Deleted '86. Catalogue no: **CABL 126**

SOMETHING TO SAY ABOUT LOVE
Tracks: / Something to say about love.
7" Single: Released Jan '85, on Calibre, Deleted '86. Catalogue no: **CAB 128**
12" Single: Released Jan '85, on Calibre, Deleted '86. Catalogue no: **CABL 128**

YOU'RE SUPPOSED TO BE MY FRIEND
Tracks: / You're supposed to be my friend / Anytime you're ready.
7" Single: Released '88, on DJM, Catalogue no: **DJS 10976**
12" Single: Released '88, on DJM, Catalogue no: **DJR 10976**

Jerome, Mike

I WANNA BE A TOYBOY
Tracks: / I wanna be a toyboy / Wonderful Anneka Rice.
7" Single: Released May '89, on Dingle's, by Dingle's Records. Catalogue no: **SID 242**

Jerome, Steve

DON'T KEEP HAUNTING ME
Tracks: / Don't keep haunting me / Kiss and tell.
7" Single: Released Aug '87, on Needle, by Needle Records. Catalogue no: **7 NEED 1**
12" Single: Released Aug '87, on Needle, by Needle Records. Catalogue no: **NEED 1**

SONG THAT NEVER DIES
Tracks: / Song that never dies / Token.
7" Single: Released 20 Jun '80, on DJM, Deleted '83. Catalogue no: **DJS 10941**

Jerry The Ferret

MUSIC GOES ON AND ON, THE
Tracks: / Music goes on and on / Ginny / Ring road / Your head in the clouds.
7" Single: Released May '87, on Dead Horse, by Dead Horse Records. Catalogue no: **DH 2001**

ONE STEP FORWARD
Tracks: / One step forward / I think you're lying.
7" Single: Released Jan '87, on Jerry The Ferret, by Dead Horse Records. Catalogue no: **EGH 919**

Jersey Artists

WE GOT THE LOVE
Tracks: / We got the love / Save love save life.
7" Single: Released May '86, on Arista, by BMG Records (UK). Catalogue no: **JAM 1**
12" Single: Released May '86, on Arista, by BMG Records (UK). Catalogue no: **JAM 121**

Jersey Hitchikers

YOU MAKE IT COME ALIVE
Tracks: / You make it come alive.
7" Single: Released May '83, on Monarch, by Monarch Records. Catalogue no: **MON 040**

Jesrael

LET ME IN
Tracks: / Let me in.
7" Single: Released Feb '82, on Solid Groove, Catalogue no: **SG 5**
12" Single: Released Feb '82, on Solid Groove, Deleted Feb '87. Catalogue no: **SG 005**

Jesse, Steve

SHIFTING SANDS
Tracks: / Shifting sands / Post hal life.
7" Single: Released May '82, on President, by President Records. Catalogue no: **PT 502**

SHUFFLE THE PACK
Tracks: / Shuffle the pack.
7" Single: Released Jul '81, on President, by President Records. Catalogue no: **PT 495**

SLEEPLESS NIGHTS
Tracks: / Sleepless nights / Shuffle the pack.
7" Single: Released Jan '82, on President, by President Records. Catalogue no: **PT 498**

Jesse's Gang

REAL LOVE
Tracks: / Real love / My ride.
7" Single: Released Oct '86, on Geffen, by Geffen Records (USA). Deleted Jun '87. Catalogue no: **GEF 15**
12" Single: Released Oct '86, on Geffen, by Geffen Records (USA). Deleted Jun '87. Catalogue no: **GEF 15T**

Jessica's Tee Shirt

ETHIOPIA
Tracks: / Ethiopia.
7" Single: Released Mar '85, on Rock Star (2), Deleted '87. Catalogue no: **STAR 101**

Jesus Couldn't Drum

AUTUMN LEAVES
Tracks: / Autumn leaves.
7" Single: Released Aug '85, on Lost Moments, Catalogue no: **LM 044**
7" Single: Released Nov '85, on Lost Moments, Catalogue no: **LM 044**
12" Single: Released Aug '85, on Lost Moments, Catalogue no: **LM 12 044**

EVEN ROSES HAVE THORNS
Tracks: / Even roses have thorns.
7" Single: Released Jul '84, on Lost Moments, Catalogue no: **LM 004**
12" Single: Released Jul '84, on Lost Moments, Catalogue no: **LM 12004**

I'M A TRAIN
Tracks: / I'm a train.
7" Single: Released Nov '85, on Lost Moments, Catalogue no: **LM 444**
12" Single: Released Nov '85, on Lost Moments, Catalogue no: **LM 12 444**

Jesus Jones

BRING IT ON DOWN
Tracks: / Bring it on down (B.P.M. 125) / None of the answers / Cut and dried / Beat it down (B.P.M. 110) / Bring it on down (Liquidizer mix) / Cut and dried / Info-sicko.
CD 5": Released Sep '89, on Food, by Food Records. Catalogue no: **CDFOOD 22**
Cassingle: Released Sep '89, on Food, by Food Records. Catalogue no: **TCFOOD 22**
7" Single: Released Sep '89, on Food, by Food Records. Catalogue no: **FOOD 22**
12" Single: Released Sep '89, on Food, by Food Records. Catalogue no: **12FOOD 22**
12" Single: Released Sep '89, on Food, by Food Records. Catalogue no: **203 516 8**
12" Single: Released Sep '89, on Food, by Food Records. Catalogue no: **203 516 0**
12" Single: Released Sep '89, on Food, by Food Records. Catalogue no: **12FOODP 22**
12" Single: Released Sep '89, on Food, by Food Records. Catalogue no: **12FOODX 22**

INFO-FREAKO
Tracks: / Info-freako / Broken bones / Info-sicko (12" only.).
CD 5": Released Feb '89, on Food, by Food Records. Deleted Oct '89. Catalogue no: **CDFOOD 18**
7" Single: Released Feb '89, on Food, by Food Records. Deleted Oct '89. Catalogue no: **FOOD 18**
12" Single: Released Feb '89, on Food, by Food Records. Deleted Oct '89. Catalogue no: **12FOODX 18**
12" Single: Released Feb '89, on Food, by Food Records. Deleted Oct '89. Catalogue no: **12FOOD 18**

INFO-PSYCHO
Tracks: / Info-psycho / Info-sicko / Info-freako.
Note: Producer/arranger:- Jesus H Jones. Engineered by L Fenlon.
12" Single: Released Feb '89, on Food, by Food Records. Catalogue no: **12FOODX 18**

NEVER ENOUGH
Tracks: / Never enough / What's going on (Not on 12".) / Enough - never enough (Not on 7".) / It's the winning that counts.
CD 5": Released Jun '89, on Food, by Food Records. Catalogue no: **CDFOOD 21**
CD 5": Released Jun '89, on Food, by Food Records. Catalogue no: **203 409 2**
Cassingle: Released Jun '89, on Food, by Food Records. Catalogue no: **203 409 4**
Cassingle: Released Jun '89, on Food, by Food Records. Catalogue no: **TCFOOD 21**
7" Single: Released Jun '89, on Food, by Food Records. Catalogue no: **FOODS 21**
7" Single: Released Jun '89, on Food, by Food Records. Catalogue no: **FOOD 21**
7" Single: Released Jun '89, on Food, by Food Records. Catalogue no: **203 409 8**
7" Single: Released Jun '89, on Food, by Food Records. Catalogue no: **203 409 7**
12" Single: Released Jun '89, on Food, by Food Records. Catalogue no: **203 409 6**
12" Single: Released Jun '89, on Food, by Food Records. Catalogue no: **12FOOD 21**

Jesus & Mary Chain

APRIL SKIES
Tracks: / April skies / Kill Surf City / Who do you love (on 12" only) / Mushroom / Bo Diddley is Jesus.
7" Set: Released Apr '87, on Blanco Y Negro, by Blanco Y Negro Records. Catalogue no: **NEG 24F**
7" Single: Released Apr '87, on Blanco Y Negro, by Blanco Y Negro Records. Deleted Jul '88. Catalogue no: **NEG 24**
12" Single: Released Apr '87, on Blanco Y Negro, by Blanco Y Negro Records. Catalogue no: **NEG 24T**

BLUES FROM A GUN
Tracks: / Blues from a gun / Shimmer.
CD 5": Released Sep '89, on Blanco Y Negro, by Blanco Y Negro Records. Catalogue no: **NEGCD 41**
10" single: Released Sep '89, on Blanco Y Negro, by Blanco Y Negro Records. Catalogue no: **NEG 10E 41**
Cassingle: Released Sep '89, on Blanco Y Negro, by Blanco Y Negro Records. Catalogue no: **NEGC 41**
7" Single: Released Sep '89, on Blanco Y Negro, by Blanco Y Negro Records. Catalogue no: **NEG 41**
12" Single: Released Sep '89, on Blanco Y Negro, by Blanco Y Negro Records. Catalogue no: **NEGT 41**

DARKLANDS (SINGLE)
Tracks: / Darklands / Rider on the wall / Surfin' USA (on 12" only).
CD 5": Released Oct '87, on Blanco Y Negro, by Blanco Y Negro Records. Deleted Jul '88. Catalogue no: **NEG 29CD**
7" Single: Released Oct '87, on Blanco Y Negro, by Blanco Y Negro Records. Deleted Jul '88. Catalogue no: **NEG 29**
12" Single: Released Oct '87, on Blanco Y Negro, by Blanco Y Negro Records. Catalogue no: **NEG 29T**

HAPPY WHEN IT RAINS
Tracks: / Happy when it rains.
7" Single: Released Aug '87, on Blanco Y Negro, by Blanco Y Negro Records. Deleted Jul '88. Catalogue no: **NEG 25**
12" Single: Released Aug '87, on Blanco Y Negro, by Blanco Y Negro Records. Catalogue no: **NEG 25T**

JUST LIKE HONEY
Tracks: / Just like honey.
7" Single: Released Sep '85, on Blanco Y Negro, by Blanco Y Negro Records. Deleted Jun '87. Catalogue no: **NEG 17**
12" Single: Released Sep '85, on Blanco Y Negro, by Blanco Y Negro Records. Catalogue no: **NEG 17T**

NEVER UNDERSTAND
Tracks: / Never understand / Suck / Ambition.
7" Single: Released Feb '85, on Blanco Y Negro, by Blanco Y Negro Records. Deleted Jun '87. Catalogue no: **NEG 8**
12" Single: Released Feb '85, on Blanco Y Negro, by Blanco Y Negro Records. Catalogue no: **NEG 8T**

SIDEWALKING
Tracks: / Sidewalking / Taste of Cindy / April skies (on 12" only).
7" Single: Released Mar '88, on Blanco Y Negro, by Blanco Y Negro Records. Catalogue no: **NEG 32**
12" Single: Released Mar '88, on Blanco Y Negro, by Blanco Y Negro Records. Catalogue no: **NEG 32T**

SOME CANDY TALKING
Tracks: / Some candy talking / Hit / Psycho candy / Taste of Cindy (Acoustic Version) (Extra track on 12" version only.).
7" Single: Released Jul '86, on Blanco Y Negro, by Blanco Y Negro Records. Deleted Jan '88. Catalogue no: **NEG 19**
12" Single: Released Jul '86, on Blanco Y Negro, by Blanco Y Negro Records. Catalogue no: **NEG 19 T**

UPSIDE DOWN
Tracks: / Upside down / Vegetable man.
7" Single: Released Mar '86, on Creation, by Creation Records. Deleted Jul '88. Catalogue no: **CRE 012**

YOU TRIP ME UP
Tracks: / You trip me up / You're boyfriends dead.
7" Single: Released May '85, on Blanco Y Negro, by Blanco Y Negro Records. Deleted Jun '87. Catalogue no: **NEG 13**
12" Single: Released May '85, on Blanco Y Negro, by Blanco Y Negro Records. Catalogue no: **NER 13T**

Jet Set

BEST OF THE JET SET EP
7" Single: Released Oct '83, on Dance Network, by Dance Network Records. Catalogue no: **NET 1**

Jet Vegas

LONDON
Tracks: / London / Paris / London (version) (Available on 12" only).
Note: * Denotes extra track on 12" format only.
7" Single: Released Jul '88, on MCA, by MCA Records. Catalogue no: **MCA 1266**
12" Single: Released Jul '88, on MCA, by MCA Records. Catalogue no: **MCAT 1266**

SEX POWER & FUN
Tracks: / Sex power & fun / Sex power & fun (fatally attractive mix) / Sexe controle amour / Sexe controle amour (extended).
12" Single: Released 23 May '88, on MCA, by MCA Records. Catalogue no: **MCAT 1238**
7" Single: Released 23 May '88, on MCA, by MCA Records. Catalogue no: **MCA 1238**

Jethro Tull

BROADSWORD

JETHRO TULL - LAP OF LUXURY (Released on Chrysalis)

Tracks: / Broadsword / Fallen on hard times.
7" Pic: Released May '82, on Chrysalis, by Chrysalis Records. Deleted May '85. Catalogue no: **CHSP 2619**
7" Single: Released May '82, on Chrysalis, by Chrysalis Records. Deleted May '85. Catalogue no: **CHS 2619**
7" Single: Released '82, on Chrysalis, by Chrysalis Records. Deleted '87. Catalogue no: **CHS 2624**

CORONACH
Tracks: / Coronach / Jack Frost and the hooded crow.
7" Single: Released Jun '86, on Chrysalis, by Chrysalis Records. Catalogue no: **TULL 2**
Cassingle: Released Jun '86, on Chrysalis, by Chrysalis Records. Catalogue no: **ZTULL 2**

LAP OF LUXURY (see panel above)
Tracks: / Lap of luxury / Astronomy / Automotive engineering (on 12" only) / Tundra (on 12" only).
7" EP: Released Sep '84, on Chrysalis, by Chrysalis Records. Deleted '86. Catalogue no: **TULL 1**

LIFE IS A LONG SONG
Tracks: / Life is a long song / Up the pool.
7" Single: Released Sep '71, on Island, by Island Records. Deleted '74. Catalogue no: **WIP 6106**

LIVING IN THE PAST (OLD GOLD)
Tracks: / Living in the past.
7" Single: Released Aug '87, on Old Gold, by Old Gold Records. Catalogue no: **OG 9673**

LIVING IN THE PAST (ORIGINAL)
Tracks: / Living in the past.
7" Single: Released May '69, on Island, by Island Records. Deleted '72. Catalogue no: **WIP 6056**
7" Single: Released May '69, on Chrysalis, by Chrysalis Records. Deleted '74. Catalogue no: **CHS 2081**

LOVE STORY
Tracks: / Love story.
7" Single: Released Jan '69, on Island, by Island Records. Deleted '72. Catalogue no: **WIP 6048**

PART OF THE MACHINE
Tracks: / Part of the machine.
Note: Promo for the recent '25 years' box set.
CD 5": Released Aug '88, on Chrysalis (Germany), by Chrysalis Records. Catalogue no: **TULPCD 1**

RING OUT SOLSTICE BELLS (EP)
Tracks: / Ring out solstice bells / March the mad scientist / Christmas song, The / Pan dance.
7" EP: Released Dec '76, on Chrysalis, by Chrysalis Records. Deleted '81. Catalogue no: **CXP 2**

SAID SHE WAS A DANCER
Tracks: / Said she was a dancer / Dogs in the midwinter / Down at the end of your road (Extra track on CD only) / Too many too (Extra track on CD only).
7" Single: Released Dec '87, on Chrysalis, by Chrysalis Records. Catalogue no: **TULL 4**
CD 5": Released Dec '87, on Chrysalis, by Chrysalis Records. Catalogue no: **TULLCD 4**
12" Single: Released Dec '87, on Chrysalis, by Chrysalis Records. Catalogue no: **TULLX 4**

STEEL MONKEY
Tracks: / Steel monkey / At the end of the road / Too many too (Extra track on 12") / I'm your gun (extra track on 12".).
Note: * Extra tracks avaliable on 12" format
7" Single: Released Oct '87, on Chrysalis, by Chrysalis Records. Catalogue no: **TULL 3**
7" Single: Released Oct '87, on Chrysalis, by Chrysalis Records. Catalogue no: **CHS 3172**
12" Single: Released Oct '87, on Chrysalis, by Chrysalis Records. Catalogue no: **TULLX 3**
12" Single: Released Oct '87, on Chrysalis, by Chrysalis Records. Catalogue no: **CHS12 3172**

SWEET DREAM
Tracks: / Sweet dream.
7" Single: Released Nov '69, on Island, by Island Records. Deleted '72. Catalogue no: **WIP 6070**

TOO OLD TO ROCK'N'ROLL
Tracks: / Too old to rock 'n' roll / Rainbow blues.
7" Single: Released '83, on Chrysalis, by Chrysalis Records. Deleted '87. Catalogue no: **CHS 2086**

WITCHES PROMISE
Tracks: / Witches promise / Teacher.
7" Single: Released Jan '70, on Island, by Island Records. Deleted '73. Catalogue no: **WIP 6077**

WORKING JOHN WORKING JOE
Tracks: / Working John working Joe.
7" Single: Released Oct '80, on Chrysalis, by Chrysalis Records. Catalogue no: **CHS 2468**

Jets

Biographical details: Jets This British rock'n'roll band consists of three brothers, Bobby, Ray and Tony Cotton.
In August 1981, while Shakin' Stevens was No.1 in the UK with his revival of *Green Door*, a similar sounding act called The Jets entered the British chart with *Sugar Doll*. It had not taken the family trio as long to achieve success as Stevens, but they did not manage to corner the market quite as well as he evantually did. While Shaky continued to fly high, the Jets' rock revivals had to be content with lower chart placings. Using Shakin' Stevens' producer Stuart Colman, the Jets' most successful remakes were *Yes Tonight Josephine* (No.25 in UK in 1981) and *Love Makes The World Go Round* (No.21 in 1982). The former was originally made famous in the Fifties by Johnnie Ray, the latter by Perry Como. It was interesting to note that with both Shakin' Stevens and the Jets, Colman did not revive the classic rock'n'roll hits of the Fifties but instead chose to make rockabilly cover versions of the middle-of-the-road crooning music that the original rock'n'rollers had been fighting against!
Despite their musical talent and undoubted stage presence - they almost blew Shaky off stage while supporting him on a tour, much to the annoyance of his manager Freya Miller - the Jets' subsequent singles were only minor hits. Their album *100% Cotton* reached the UK No.30 position. (Bob Macdonald 12/11/85).

ALLIGATOR EP
Tracks: / Alligator EP.
7" Single: Released Mar '86, on Jetset, Catalogue no: **JETSET EP 1**

BLUE SKIES
Tracks: / Blue skies.
7" Single: Released Jul '83, on EMI, by EMI Records. Deleted '85. Catalogue no: **EMI 5405**

CROSS MY BROKEN HEART
Tracks: / Cross my broken heart / Cross my broken heart (extended) / Cross my broken heart (dub) / Cross my broken heart (acappella).
7" Single: Released Oct '87, on MCA, by MCA Records. Deleted 1 Jul '89. Catalogue no: **MCA 1194**
12" Single: Released Oct '87, on MCA, by MCA Records. Catalogue no: **MCAT 1194**

CRUSH ON YOU
Tracks: / Curiosity / Crush on you / You got it all / Love umbrella / Private number / Heart on the line / Right before my eyes / La la means I love you / Mesmerized / Right before my eyes / Crush on you (Instrumental) (Extra track on 12" version only.) / Acapella (Extra track on 12" version only.).
Note: Features their Top 5 smash "Crush On You". "Crush On You" features 4 U.S. Top 5singles. LP, Cassette and CD booklet contains full colour, fold out portraits of The Jets.
12" Single: Released Apr '86, on MCA, by MCA Records. Catalogue no: **MCAT 1048**
7" Single: Released Apr '86, on MCA, by MCA Records. Catalogue no: **MCA 1048**

CURIOSITY
Tracks: / Crush on you (crush mix) (On 12" only) / Curiosity / Love umbrella.
7" Pic: Released Apr '87, on MCA, by MCA Records. Catalogue no: **MCAP 1119**
7" Single: Released Apr '87, on MCA, by MCA Records. Catalogue no: **MCA 1119**
12" Single: Released Feb '86, on MCA, by MCA Records. Catalogue no: **MCAT 1027**
12" Single: Released Apr '87, on MCA, by MCA Records. Catalogue no: **MCAT 1119**
7" Single: Released Feb '86, on MCA, by MCA Records. Catalogue no: **MCA 1027**

HEATWAVE
Tracks: / Heatwave / King and ring.
7" Single: Released Mar '84, on PRT, by Castle Communications Records. Catalogue no: **JETS 1**

HEY BABY
Tracks: / Hey baby.
7" Single: Released Jul '86, on Soho (1), by Soho Records. Catalogue no: **SH 7**

HONEYDRIPPER, THE
Tracks: / Honeydripper / Tonight tonight.
7" Single: Released Apr '82, on EMI, by EMI Records. Deleted '85. Catalogue no: **EMI 5289**

JAMES DEAN
Tracks: / James Dean.
7" Single: Released Jul '79, on Soho (1), by Soho Records. Catalogue no: **SH 3**

LET'S GET IT ON
Tracks: / Let's get it on / Hit it on.
7" Single: Released Apr '81, on EMI, by EMI Records. Deleted Apr '86. Catalogue no: **EMI 5167**

LOVE MAKES THE WORLD GO ROUND
Tracks: / Love makes the world go round / I'm just a score.
7" Single: Released Feb '82, on EMI, by EMI Records. Deleted '85. Catalogue no: **EMI 5262**

ORIGINAL TERMINAL BLOCK 4
Tracks: / Original terminal block 4.
7" Single: Released '79, on Good Vibration, by Good Vibrations Records. Catalogue no: **GV 1002**

PARTY DOLL
Tracks: / Party doll.
12" Single: Released Sep '84, on PRT, by Castle Communications Records. Catalogue no: **JET 122**
7" Single: Released Sep '84, on PRT, by Castle Communications Records. Catalogue no: **JET S2**

ROCKET 2 U
Tracks: / Our only chance / Rocket 2 U / Rocket 2 U (inst).
7" Single: Released Mar '88, on MCA, by MCA Records. Catalogue no: **MCA 1226**
12" Single: Released Mar '88, on MCA, by MCA Records. Catalogue no: **MCAT 1226**

ROCKIN' AROUND THE CHRISTMAS TREE
Tracks: / Rockin' around the Christmas tree.
7" Single: Released Nov '85, on PRT, by Castle Communications Records. Catalogue no: **7P 297**

SENDING ALL MY LOVE
7" Single: on MCA, by MCA Records. Deleted 1 Jul '89. Catalogue no: **MCA 1285**

SOMEBODY TO LOVE
Tracks: / Somebody to love.
7" Single: Released Oct '82, on EMI, by EMI Records. Deleted '85. Catalogue no: **EMI 5342**

SUGAR DOLL
Tracks: / Sugar doll / Love bug.
7" Single: Released Jul '81, on EMI, by EMI Records. Deleted '83. Catalogue no: **EMI 5211**

WHO'S THAT KNOCKING
Tracks: / Who's that knocking / I seen ya.
7" Single: Released Jan '81, on EMI, by EMI Records. Deleted Jan '84. Catalogue no: **EMI 5134**

JETS - YES TONIGHT JOSEPHINE (Released on EMI)

YES TONIGHT JOSEPHINE (see panel on previous page)
Tracks: / Yes tonight Josephine / Hideaway.
7" Single: Released Oct '81, on EMI, by EMI Records. Deleted '84. Catalogue no: **EMI 5247**

YOU GOT IT ALL
Tracks: / You got it all / Heart on the line / Mixdoctor mix (This mix contains: feat Crush on you/ Curiosity/ Love umbrella.).
7" Single: Released 23 May '87, on MCA, by MCA Records. Catalogue no: **MCA 1157**
12" Single: Released 23 May '87, on MCA, by MCA Records. Catalogue no: **MCAT 1157**

Jetset

APRIL, MAY, JUNE AND THE JETSETS
Tracks: / Story of the world, The / Does it look like rain? / What a way to go! / You won't believe your eyes / Dreaming of Jeannie / Judy's toy box / Can you hear my heartbeat ? / Late great Frank Lewis, The / Watch yourself.
12" Single: Released Aug '85, on Dance Network, by Dance Network Records. Catalogue no: **NET 3**

JUDY'S TOY BOX
Tracks: / Judy's toy box / Jetset theme / Good news / Wednesday girl.
7" EP: Released Feb '84, on Dance Network, by Dance Network Records. Catalogue no: **NET 1**

Jetstone

JU JU
Tracks: / Ju Ju / Ju Ju (Remix) / Ju Ju (Inst Mix) (Extra track on 12" version only.).
7" Single: Released Apr '86, on Carrere, Catalogue no: **CAR 386**
12" Single: Released Apr '86, on Carrere, Catalogue no: **CART 386**

Jett, Joan

Biographical details: Jett, Joan This American singer and guitarist was leader of The Runaways during 1975-79. She formed that band with the help of producer/entrepreneur Kim Fowley. The Runaways were an all-girl quintet, a novelty for a rock combo; they were given heavy promotion, particularly in the UK where they were marketed at the start of the punk era as a 'credible' new group, but the band failed to achieve success on either side of the Atlantic. While touring Britain with the group, Jetts saw the band Arrows on TV performing a song called *I Love Rock'n'Roll. It had been the B side of one of the Arrows' singles. Joan loved the song, but the rest of The Runaways were not interested in recording it.*
After the termination of the group, Jett worked briefly with former Sex Pistols, Paul Cook and Steve Jones. She formed Joan Jett & The Blackhearts in 1980 and released the LP Bad Reputation, the first of several collaborations with veteran producers Ritchie Cordell & Kenny Laguna.
Suddenly in early 1982, Joan Jett & The Blackhearts burst into the US Hot 100 with their rendition of *I Love Rock'n'Roll*. Jett's original hunch about that song had been correct - it was No.1 in America for a seven solid weeks and reached No.4 in Britain. *I Love Rock'n'Roll was a rallying anthem and, although very basic, proved a perfect vehicle for Joan's raunchy persona. Its success was a great personal triumph for her - it had taken years to convince anyone else of the potential of that song and of her own talent, but she had stuck to her guns and slogged away till she made it. Ironically, the record she held to No.2 was We Got The Beat* by the Go-Gos, a mould breaking all-girl band who had succeeded where the Runaways had failed.
Jett and her male Blackhearts followed their No.1 smash with a Top 10 remake of Tommy James & The Shondells' 1969 chart-topper *Crimson and Clover*. A series of smaller American hits followed, but she was unable to come up with another blockbuster. Her albums displayed a fixation for old Gary Glitter songs, but the public clearly wanted some strong new material. (Bob Macdonald 12/11/85).

CRIMSON & CLOVER
Tracks: / Crimson and clover / Oh woe is me.
7" Single: Released Jul '82, on Epic, by CBS Records. Deleted '85. Catalogue no: **EPC A 2485**

DO YA WANNA TOUCH ME
Tracks: / Do ya wanna touch me / Jezabel.
7" Single: Released Sep '82, on Epic, by CBS Records. Deleted '85. Catalogue no: **EPCA 2674**

GOOD MUSIC
Tracks: / Good music.
12" Single: Released Aug '87, on Polydor, by Polydor Ltd. Deleted Mar '88. Catalogue no: **POSPX 877**
7" Single: Released Aug '87, on Polydor, by Polydor Ltd. Deleted Mar '88. Catalogue no: **POSP 877**

I HATE MYSELF FOR LOVING YOU
Tracks: / I hate myself for loving you / Love is pain (live) / I can't control myself (12" and CD single only.) / I hate myself for loving you (live) (Only on CD single.).
CD 5": Released Aug '88, on London Records, by London Records. Catalogue no: **LONCD 195**
CD 5": Released Aug '88, on London Records, by London Records. Catalogue no: **887 644 2**
7" Single: Released Aug '88, on London Records, by London Records. Deleted May '89. Catalogue no: **LONP 195**
7" Single: Released Aug '88, on London Records, by London Records. Deleted May '89. Catalogue no: **LON 195**
12" Single: Released Aug '88, on London Records, by London Records. Deleted May '89. Catalogue no: **LONX 195**

I LOVE ROCK 'N' ROLL (SINGLE)
Tracks: / I love rock 'n' roll / Love is pain.
7" Single: Released Jul '82, on Epic, by CBS Records. Deleted '85. Catalogue no: **EPC A 2087**

I LOVE YOU LOVE ME LOVED
Tracks: / I love you love me loved.
7" Single: Released Oct '84, on Epic, by CBS Records. Catalogue no: **A 4851**

I NEED SOMEONE
Tracks: / I need someone / Talkin' bout my baby.
12" Single: Released Apr '85, on Epic, by CBS Records. Catalogue no: **TA 4392**
7" Single: Released Apr '85, on Epic, by CBS Records. Catalogue no: **A 4391**

JEZEBEL
Tracks: / Jezebel / Bad reputation.
7" Single: Released Sep '80, on Ariola, by BMG Records (UK). Deleted '83. Catalogue no: **ARO 242**

MAKE BELIEVE
Tracks: / Make believe / Call me lightning.
7" Single: Released May '80, on Ariola, by BMG Records (UK). Deleted May '83. Catalogue no: **ARO 227**

YOU DON'T KNOW WHAT YOU'VE GOT
Tracks: / You don't know what you've got / Don't abuse me.
7" Single: Released Jun '80, on Ariola, by BMG Records (UK). Deleted Jun '83. Catalogue no: **ARO 235**
7" Single: Released Oct '82, on Epic, by CBS Records. Deleted Oct '85. Catalogue no: **EPC A2880**

Jeunesse

I GET SO EXCITED
Tracks: / I get so excited / Love attack.
7" Single: Released Sep '86, on Jive, by Zomba Records. Deleted '87. Catalogue no: **JIVE 128**
12" Single: Released Sep '86, on Jive, by Zomba Records. Deleted '87. Catalogue no: **JIVET 128**

MY LOVE CAN ONLY GET STRONGER
Tracks: / My love can only get stronger.
7" Single: Released Mar '84, on R.E.D., Catalogue no: **RED 001**

Jewel, T. & L.T.C.

BELIEVE IT OR NOT
Tracks: / Believe it or not / Believe it or not (Inst) Club mix.
12" Single: Released Oct '86, on Malaco Dance, by Malaco Records (UK). Catalogue no: **MALD 123**

Jezzrell

ALL DEPENDS ON YOU
Tracks: / All depends on you.
12" Single: Released Apr '85, on Wackies, Catalogue no: **W 710**

STOP PLAYING TRICKS
Tracks: / Stop playing tricks / Cheating girl.
12" Single: Released Nov '83, on Wackies, Catalogue no: **WACKIES 672**

J.Geils Band

ANGEL IN BLUE
Tracks: / Angel in blue / River blindness.
7" Single: Released Jun '82, on EMI-America, by EMI Records. Deleted '85. Catalogue no: **EA 138**

CENTERFOLD
Tracks: / Centerfold.
7" Single: Released Feb '82, on EMI-America, by EMI Records. Deleted '85. Catalogue no: **EA 135**

COME BACK
Tracks: / Come back / Takin' you down.
7" Single: Released Feb '80, on EMI, by EMI Records. Deleted Feb '85. Catalogue no: **EA 105**

FREEZE FRAME (SINGLE)
Tracks: / Freeze frame / Rage in the cage.
7" Pic: Released Apr '82, on EMI-America, by EMI Records. Deleted '85. Catalogue no: **EAP 134**
7" Single: Released Apr '82, on EMI-America, by EMI Records. Deleted '85. Catalogue no: **EA 134**

LOVE STINKS
Tracks: / Love stinks / Till the walls come tumbling down.
7" Single: Released May '80, on EMI-America, by EMI Records. Deleted May '85. Catalogue no: **EA 111**

ONE LAST KISS
Tracks: / One last kiss.
7" Single: Released Jun '79, on EMI-America, by EMI Records. Deleted '82. Catalogue no: **AM 507**

Jiani, Carol

ASK ME
Tracks: / Ask me.
12" Single: Released Sep '82, on Excaliber, by Red Bus Records. Deleted '88. Catalogue no: **EXCL 523**

HIT'N'RUN LOVER
Tracks: / Hit and run lover / Hit and run lover (instrumental) / Hit and run lover (version) / All the people of the world.
7" Single: Released Apr '81, on Champagne Records, Deleted Apr '84. Catalogue no: **FIZZ 506**
12" Single: Released Apr '81, on Champagne Records, Deleted Apr '84. Catalogue no: **FIZY 506**
12" Single: Released Sep '88, on Passion, by Skratch Records. Catalogue no: **PASH 85(12)**

SUCH A JOY HONEY
Tracks: / Such a joy honey / Such a joy honey (instrumental).
7" Single: Released Mar '87, on MCA, by MCA Records. Catalogue no: **MCA 1130**

Jigsaw

Biographical details: Jigsaw This British band consisted of Barrie Bernard, Tony Campbell, Des Dyer and Clive Scott. Jigsaw were formed in Coventry in 1969. Together with their producer Chas Peate, they formed the Splash record label in 1974 as an outlet for their recordings. They came to fame in late 1975 with *Sky High* which was written by Dyer and Scott for the movie 'The Dragon Flies'. This evocative, somewhat melancholy pop single reached No.9 in Britain and No.3 in America; it was also a success in Japan and several other territories.
Sky High promised much for the future, but it was not delivered. The group reached the US Top 40 with *Love Fire* (No.30 in 1976) and the Uk Top 40 with *If I Have To Go Away* (No.36 in 1977), but other releases as a team until 1983; as a touring and recording unit, they were able to tick over during these years without achieving spectacular success.
When Jigsaw ended, bassist Bernard and guitarist Campbell quit the music business to work as a disc jockey and hairdresser, respectively. Dyer and Scott (the two singers and main writers) remained as directors of Splash. Dyer started a solo career with Peate as producer, while Scott concentrated on writing and producing for the label. (Bob Macdonald 12/11/85).

I
Tracks: / I / Inside out.
7" Single: Released Aug '80, on Splash, by Splash Records. Deleted '83. Catalogue no: **SP 015**

IF I HAVE TO GO AWAY
Tracks: / If I have to go away.
7" Single: Released Jul '77, on Splash, by Splash Records. Deleted '79. Catalogue no: **CP 11**

LET'S NOT SAY GOODBYE
Tracks: / Let's not say goodbye / Let's not say goodbye (inst).
7" Single: Released Sep '88, on Nightmare, by Nightmare Records. Catalogue no: **MARES 63**
12" Single: Released Sep '88, on Nightmare, by Nightmare Records. Catalogue no: **MARE 63**

LOVE ISN'T A HOME
Tracks: / Love isn't a home / We are not alone.
7" Single: Released Jan '83, on Splash, by Splash Records. Catalogue no: **SP 25**

NO LONG SONGS
Tracks: / No long songs / Rock'n'roll me.
7" Single: Released May '80, on Splash, by Splash Records. Deleted '83. Catalogue no: **SPO 12**

PRIZEFIGHTER
Tracks: / Prizefighter / Winter in L.A..
7" Single: Released Sep '80, on Splash, by Splash Records. Deleted '83. Catalogue no: **SP 017**

SKY HIGH
Tracks: / Sky high / Fly away / Brand new love affair.
7" Single: Released Apr '89, on Libido, Catalogue no: **URGE 2**
7" Single: Released Nov '75, on Splash, by Splash Records. Deleted '78. Catalogue no: **CP 1**
7" Single: Released Jul '86, on Splash, by Splash Records. Catalogue no: **CPS 1006**
12" Single: Released Apr '89, on Libido, Catalogue no: **URGET 2**
12" Single: Released Jul '86, on Splash, by Splash Records. Catalogue no: **CPST 1006**

YOU BRING OUT THE BEST IN ME
Tracks: / You bring out the best in me / Ripples on the water.
7" Single: Released Apr '81, on Splash, by Splash Records. Deleted Apr '86. Catalogue no: **SP 22**

JIH

BIG BLUE OCEAN
Tracks: / Big blue ocean / Closer now / As you fall* (*Extra track on 12" version only).
7" Single: Released Jan '87, on Breadth Of Vision, Catalogue no: **JIH 001**
12" Single: Released Jan '87, on Breadth Of Vision, Catalogue no: **JIH 001/12**

TAKE ME TO THE GIRL
Tracks: / Take me to the girl / Come summer, come winter / Wake up.
12" Single: Released 27 Feb '88, on Jungle, by Jungle Records. Catalogue no: **JUNG 32T**

THIS GIFT
Tracks: / This gift / Shadow to fall.
12" Single: Released Apr '86, on Breadth Of Vision, Catalogue no: **JIH 002/12**

Jilted Brides

BAD VIBES
Tracks: / Bad vibes / Greed, it's a good thing to have a good friend, preacher man.
7" Single: Released Oct '87, on Trashcan, by Trashcan Records. Catalogue no: **DTO 958**

Jilted John

JILTED JOHN
Tracks: / Jilted John.
7" Single: Released Aug '78, on EMI International, by EMI Records. Deleted '81. Catalogue no: **INT 567**

Jim Jiminee

DO IT ON THURSDAY
Tracks: / Do it on Thursday / Pulled a string in my heart / Housewife / Best of both girls.
7" Single: Released 20 Feb '88, on Cat & Mouse, by Cat & Mouse Records. Catalogue no: **ABB 01**
12" Single: Released '87, on Cat & Mouse, by Cat & Mouse Records. Catalogue no: **ABB 01 T**

I WANNA WORK
Tracks: / I wanna work / Habit of you.
7" Single: Released May '88, on Cat & Mouse, by Cat & Mouse Records. Catalogue no: **ABB 04**
12" Single: Released Jul '88, on Cat & Mouse, by Cat & Mouse Records. Catalogue no: **ABB 04T**

TOWN & COUNTRY BLUES
Tracks: / Town & country blues / Hunting out of season / Hottest truth, The / Do it on Thursday.
7" Single: Released Apr '89, on DJ International, by Westside Records. Catalogue no: **BEATWAX 01**
12" Single: Released Apr '89, on DJ International, by Westside Records. Catalogue no: **BEATWAX 01T**

Jimenez, Flaco

OPEN UP YOUR HEART
Tracks: / Open up your heart.
7" Single: Released Apr '85, on Waterfront, by Waterfront Music. Catalogue no: **WFS 10**

SON OF SANTIAGO
Tracks: / Son of Santiago.
12" Single: Released Oct '85, on Waterfront, by Waterfront Music. Catalogue no: **WFT 15**

Jimmy, Bobby

ROACHES
Tracks: / Roaches / Roaches (Instrumental).
12" Single: Released Aug '86, on Spartan, Catalogue no: **12SP 142**

Jimmy Jimmy

I MET HER IN PARIS
Tracks: / I met her in Paris.
7" Single: Released Jun '85, on Epic, by CBS Records. Catalogue no: **A 6368**

SILENCE
Tracks: / Silence / Songs from the street / Suddenly.
7" Single: Released Feb '86, on Epic, by CBS Records. Catalogue no: **A 6839**
12" Single: Released Feb '86, on Epic, by CBS Records. Catalogue no: **TX 6839**

Jimmy The Hoover

Biographical details:
Jimmy The Hoover Initially nurtured by the irrepressible entrepeneur Malcolm McLaren, this British pop band hit No.18 on the UK singles chart during the scorching summer o 1983 with their one off success *Tantalise (Wo Wo Ee Yeh Yeh).* It was a singalong, carefree,oddball item - just right for a heatwave. Subsequent singles failed to make any impression on the charts, and it appeared that Jimmy The Hoover were working in a vacuum. They refused to be swept under the carpet, however, and they may yet re-enter the chart scene and clean up.
(Bob Macdonald 12/11/85).

TANTALISE (WO WO EE YEH YEH) (see adjacent panel)
Tracks: / Tantalise (Wo wo ee yeh yeh) / Sing sing.
7" Single: Released Jun '83, on Inner Vision, Catalogue no: **A 3406**
12" Single: Released Jun '83, on Inner Vision, Catalogue no: **TA 3406**

Jim's Twenty-One

THROWAWAY FRIEND
Tracks: / Throwaway friend.
7" Single: Released Sep '87, on Tulip, Catalogue no: **TULIP 1**

Jingle Belles

Biographical details:
Jingle Belles A legendary aura has always surrounded *Phil Spector's Christmas Album.* For the 1983 festive season, the British record producer Nigel Wright came up with the idea of releasing a medley single featuring imitation extracts from the famous LP. Wright, the man responsible for producing the bland disco pop fodder of Shakatak, thus assembled a group of girl singers and made them sound as much as possible like The Crystals, The Ronetts and Darlene Love.

The result was *Christmas Spectre,* which reached No.37 on the British singles chart. Wright was something out of a medley maniac. In the week that the Jingle Belles dropped out of the UK chart in January '84, Mirage's *Give Me The Night (Medley)* entered; this was a clone collection of George Benson snippets.
(Bob Macdonald 13/11/85).

CHRISTMAS SPECTRE
Tracks: / Christmas spectre / This time next year.
7" Single: Released Nov '86, on Passion, by Skratch Records. Catalogue no: **PASH 14**
12" Single: Released Nov '86, on Passion, by Skratch Records. Catalogue no: **PASH 14(12)**

Jitters

CLOSER EVERY DAY
Tracks: / Closer every day / Almost convinced / Take me as I am (On 12" only) / Closer every day (remix) (On 12" only).
7" Single: Released May '88, on Capitol, by EMI Records. Deleted Nov '88. Catalogue no: **CL 488**
12" Single: Released May '88, on Capitol, by EMI Records. Deleted Nov '88. Catalogue no: **12CL 488**

LAST OF THE RED HOT FOOLS
Tracks: / Last of the red hot fools / Hard as nails / There goes love (extra track on 12" version).
7" Single: Released Feb '88, on Capitol, by EMI Records. Deleted 31 Jul '88. Catalogue no: **CL 481**
12" Single: Released Feb '88, on Capitol, by EMI Records. Deleted 31 Jul '88. Catalogue no: **12CL 481**

Jive

ANYWAY
Tracks: / Anyway / Poor little Geno.
7" Single: Released Sep '82, on Epic, by CBS Records. Deleted '85. Catalogue no: **EPCA 2735**

Jive Alive

CHOO CHOO CH' BOOGIE
Tracks: / Choo choo ch' boogie.
7" Single: Released Jun '84, on Juke Box (Re-issue), Catalogue no: **JUKE 101**

Jive Bombers

Jimmy the Hoover - Tantalise (Wo Wo Ee Yeh Yeh) (Inner Vision)

THOSE BLOODSHOT EYES
Tracks: / Those bloodshot eyes / You don't feel that good.
7" Single: Released Aug '81, on Meantime, by Meantime Records. Catalogue no: **MEAN 3**

Jive Bunny

SWING THE MOOD (SINGLE)
CD 5": Released Jun '89, on Music Factory Dance, Catalogue no: **MFDCD 001**
Cassingle: Released Aug '89, on Music Factory Dance, Catalogue no: **MFDC 001**
7" Single: Released Jun '89, on Music Factory Dance, Catalogue no: **MFD 001**
12" Single: Released Jun '89, on Music Factory Dance, Catalogue no: **MFDT 001**

Jive Bunny & The

THAT'S WHAT I LIKE
Tracks: / That's what I like / Pretty blue eyes.
CD 5": Released Sep '89, on Music Factory Dance, Catalogue no: **MFDCD 002**
12" Pic: Released Sep '89, on Music Factory Dance, Catalogue no: **MFDPT 002**
Cassingle: Released Sep '89, on Music Factory Dance, Catalogue no: **MFDC 002**
7" Single: Released Sep '89, on Music Factory Dance, Catalogue no: **MFD 002**
12" Single: Released Sep '89, on Music Factory Dance, Catalogue no: **MFDT 002**

Jive Jazz ...

JIVE JAZZ SAMPLER
Tracks: / Jive jazz sampler.
12" Single: Released Aug '89, on Jive, by Zomba Records. Catalogue no: **JIVE T218**

Jive Marines

HOLIDAY SONG
Tracks: / Holiday song / Living in the city.
7" Single: Released Aug '82, on Rewind, Catalogue no: **REWIND 12**

Jive Turkey

GOODBYE JOHNNY RAY
Tracks: / Goodbye Johnny Ray.
7" Single: Released Apr '88, on Turk, Catalogue no: **TUR 001**

RETROHEAD FLUX
Tracks: / Retrohead flux.
12" Single: Released 25 Sep '89, on Swordfish, by Swordfish Records. Catalogue no: **SWF12 013**

ROTATE
Tracks: / Rotate.
12" Single: Released Mar '89, on Chapter 22, by Chapter 22 Records. Catalogue no: **12CHAP 39**

Jive, Willie

MESSAGE IS CLEAR
Tracks: / Message is clear / Schizo kid.
7" Single: Released Jan '82, on Cheapskate, Catalogue no: **CHEAP 38**

J.J

BREAKDANCE HOLIDAY
Tracks: / Breakdance holiday.
7" Single: Released Apr '85, on Weasel, by Weasel Records. Catalogue no: **WR 4010**

FEELS LIKE I'M IN HEAVEN
Tracks: / Feels like I'm in heaven.
7" Single: Released Sep '84, on R.E.D., Catalogue no: **TWH 001**

IF I NEVER SEE SUNDAY AGAIN
Tracks: / If I never see Sunday again / Moving away.
7" Single: Released Jun '88, on Square One, Catalogue no: **SQR 3**
12" Single: Released Jun '88, on Square One, Catalogue no: **12 SQR 3**

NO PARTICULAR PLACE TO GO
Tracks: / No particular place to go / Truck stop.
7" Single: Released Aug '82, on Creepy, Deleted Aug '85. Catalogue no: **CREEP 101**

JKD Band

DRAGON POWER
Tracks: / Dragon power.
7" Single: Released Jul '78, on Satril, by Satril Records. Deleted '81. Catalogue no: **SAT 132**

Jo Jo

DIAMONDS ARE A GIRLS BEST FRIEND
Tracks: / Diamonds are a girl's best friend / It takes two.
7" Single: Released Jul '88, on Zebra Int., by Zebra International Records. Catalogue no: **ZBR 3**

LADY MARMALADE
Tracks: / Lady Marmalade / Seven times over.
7" Single: Released 13 Jun '87, on Polydor, by Polydor Ltd. Deleted Mar '88. Catalogue no: **POSP 870**
12" Single: Released 13 Jun '87, on Polydor, by Polydor Ltd. Deleted Mar '88. Catalogue no: **POSPX 870**

ONE BY ONE
Tracks: / One by one / Hurricane / All dried up (Only on 12" version.).
12" Single: Released Sep '87, on Polydor, by Polydor Ltd. Deleted Mar '88. Catalogue no: **POSPX 882**
7" Single: Released Sep '87, on Polydor, by Polydor Ltd. Deleted Mar '88. Catalogue no: **POSP 882**

PINKMOUSE (ALLEZ)
Tracks: / Pinkmouse (allez).
7" Single: Released Aug '84, on Iguana (1), by Iguana Records. Catalogue no: **HRSL 002**

WOMAN'S TOUCH
Tracks: / Woman's touch, A / Hold back the night.
7" Single: Released Oct '88, on Arista, by BMG Records (UK). Catalogue no: **111803**
12" Single: Released Oct '88, on Arista, by BMG Records (UK). Catalogue no: **611803**

Jo Jo Gunne

Biographical details:
This American rock band consisted of the following line-up at the time of their greatest success: Mark Andes, Matt Andes, Jay Ferguson and Curly Smith. Mark and Jay spent the late 60s and early 70s in the band Spirit. They quit that critically accalimed but commercially luke-warm group at the beginning of 1971 to form Jo Jo Gunne.
Their hard-driving rock style was given an early boost by the success of the spring '72 single *Run run run* -this tuneful and infectious hit sounded like a cross between Canned Heat and The Eagles, and reached no 27 in the US and in impressive no 6 in the UK.
For some reason Jo Jo Gunne failed to consolidate upon the success of *Run run run*.

As with Spirit, the band could not translate press enthusiasm into public acceptance. The LA-based group's LPs were not major sellers, and they broke up after the release of 1974's *So where's the show* album. Singer/songwriter/keyboards player Jay Ferguson launched a solo career in 1976. The title track of his second LP *Thunder Island* provided him with a UK Top 10 single in early 1978, the first on of his entire career.

Pursuing a more pop-oriented than in his band days, Ferguson has issued several subsequent solo albums without major success. Mark (who left Jo Jo Gunne after their first album) and Matt were involved in a revived Spirit during the mid-seventies; Jay abstained, apart from a one-off gig in Santa Monica.
(Bob Macdonald, 2/10/85).

Jive Bunny - Swing the Mood (Released on Music Factory)

RUN RUN RUN
Tracks: / Run run run.
7" Single: Released '76, on Asylum, by WEA Records. Deleted '79. Catalogue no: **K 13047**

Jo Manu

HOT LIKE WE
Tracks: / Hot like we / Hot like we (version).
12" Single: Released Oct '86, on Java, Catalogue no: **JR 004**

Jo, P.C.

NO PARKING
Tracks: / No parking / Madly in love.
7" Single: Released Dec '87, on Clamp, Catalogue no: **CLAMP 1**

Joan Collins Fan Club

LEADER OF THE PACK
Tracks: / Leader of the pack / Jacques.
Note: Hilarious debut single from the band which shot to fame on the cabaret circuit and on television's Friday Night Live.
7" Single: Released May '88, on 10 Records, by Virgin Records. Catalogue no: **TEN 227**
12" Single: Released May '88, on 10 Records, by Virgin Records. Catalogue no: **TENX 227**

Joanna

I'VE FOUND THE LOVE
Tracks: / I've found the love.
12" Single: Released Jul '89, on Supremedon, Catalogue no: **SDR 001**

MY MAN
Tracks: / My man.
7" Single: Released Sep '89, on Plaza, by Plaza Records. Catalogue no: **PZA 047**
12" Single: Released Sep '89, on Plaza, by Plaza Records. Catalogue no: **PZA 047T**

Joans, John Paul

MAN FRONM NAZARETH
Tracks: / Man from Nazareth.
7" Single: Released Dec '70, on RAK, by EMI Records. Deleted '73. Catalogue no: **RAK 107**

Joboxers

Biographical details: Joboxers were one one of the most successful new acts to hit the British charts in 1983, then they seemed to let it all slip away. The group evolved from Subway Sect, one of the original 1976 punk bands. Led by Vic Godard, the Sect never achieved chart success but they were heavily featured on the BBC's John Peel Show and in the UK music press. The rest of the group parted company with Godard in 1982 and recruited American singer Dig Wayne to form the Joboxers quintet. Fusing soul and rock to create a punchy sound, Joboxers reached No 3 with the vibrant Boxer Beat in early '83 and to follow they chalked up three further UK hit singles, Just Got Lucky, Johnny Friendly and Jealous Love, each peaking at a lower position that its predecessor. Just Got Lucky reached the American Top Forty. Their debut album, Like Gangbusters, was released in September of the same year and showed them to be a lively but limited combo. Nothing was heard from Joboxers during 1984, partly because of business hassles. When they returned in 1985 with some new recordings, produced by ex-Rolling Stones producer Chris Kimsey, the material proved too weak to be of interest to the public. (Bob MacDonald, November 1985.)
Joboxers were one of the most successful new acts to hit the British charts in 1983, although they seemed to let it all slip away after that. The group evolved from Subway Sect, one of the original 1976 punk bands. Led by Vic Godard, Th Sect never achieved chart success, but they were heavily featured on the BBC's John Peel show and in the UK music press. The rest of the guys parted company with Godard in 1982, and recruited American singer Dig Wayne to form the Joboxers quintet.
Nothing was heared from Joboxers during 1984, partly because of business hassles. When they returned in 1985 with some new recordings, produced by ex Rolling Stones producer Chris Kimsey, the material was too weak to be of interest to the public. (Bob Macdonald 13/11/85).

BOXERBEAT
Tracks: / Boxerbeat.
7" Single: Released Feb '83, on RCA, by BMG Records (UK). Catalogue no: **BOX 1**
12" Single: Released Feb '83, on RCA, by BMG Records (UK). Catalogue no: **BOXT 1**

IS THIS REALLY THE FIRST TIME
Tracks: / Is this really the first time / Two weeks notice / Strictly business (on 12" only).
12" Single: Released Mar '85, on RCA, by BMG Records (UK). Catalogue no: **BOXXT 5**
7" Single: Released Mar '85, on RCA, by BMG Records (UK). Catalogue no: **BOXX 5**

JEALOUS LOVE
Tracks: / Jealous love.
7" Single: Released Oct '83, on RCA, by BMG Records (UK). Deleted '85. Catalogue no: **BOXX 4**
12" Single: Released Oct '83, on RCA, by BMG Records (UK). Deleted '85. Catalogue no: **BOXXT 4**

JOHNNY FRIENDLY
Tracks: / Johnny Friendly / Why don't you do it right.
7" Single: Released Aug '83, on RCA, by BMG Records (UK). Deleted '85. Catalogue no: **BOXX 3**
12" Single: Released Aug '83, on RCA, by BMG Records (UK). Deleted '85. Catalogue no: **BOXXT 3**

JUST GOT LUCKY (see panel belpw)
Tracks: / Just got lucky / Forget me love.
7" Single: Released May '83, on RCA, by BMG Records (UK). Deleted '86. Catalogue no: **BOXX 2**
7" Pic: Released Jun '83, on RCA, by BMG Records (UK). Deleted '86. Catalogue no: **BOXXP 2**

JOBOXERS - JUST GOT LUCKY (Relased on RCA)

Jobson, Richard

BAD MAN
Tracks: / Bad man / Heat is on, The / Big fat city (On CD only).
12" Single: Released Aug '88, on Parlophone, by EMI Records. Deleted Jun '81. Catalogue no: **12R 6181**
CD 5": Released Jul '88, on Parlophone, by EMI Records. Deleted Jun '81. Catalogue no: **CDR 6181**
7" Single: Released Aug '88, on Parlophone, by EMI Records. Deleted Jun '81. Catalogue no: **R6181**

Jo'burg City Stars

GROOVIN' JIVE NO 1
Tracks: / Groovin' jive no.1 / Soweto bump / London drive.
12" Single: Released Jun '88, on Globestyle, by Ace Records. Catalogue no: **NST 123**

Jocko

RHYTHM TALK
Tracks: / Rhythm talk / Ain't no stopping us now.
12" Single: Released Feb '80, on Philadelphia Int., by EMI Records. Deleted '83. Catalogue no: **PIR 13 8222**
7" Single: Released Feb '80, on Philadelphia Int., by EMI Records. Deleted '83. Catalogue no: **PIR 8222**

Jodie & Sherri

GYPSY BOY
Tracks: / Gypsy boy.
12" Single: Released Jan '85, on Splendid, by Orbitone Records. Catalogue no: **SPD 01**

Jodimars

WELL NOW DIG THIS (SINGLE)
Tracks: / Well now dig this.
7" Single: Released Nov '79, on President, by President Records. Catalogue no: **BD 16**

Jody

ACCIDENT
Tracks: / Accident.
7" Single: Released Apr '83, on Thunderbay, Catalogue no: **TBR 019/022**

YOU AND YOUR LOVE (ONE SIDED DISC)
Tracks: / You and your love.
7" Single: Released Apr '83, on Thunderbay, Catalogue no: **TBR 018**

Joel, Billy

Biographical details: Joel, Billy This American singer, songwriter and pianist was born in Long Island, New York and took up the piano at the age of four. When he was seven the rock'n'roll explosion happened,and he became addicted to the new music. He grew up in poverty and tried to better his lot by becoming a boxer, he is reputed to have 22 out of 28 fights, but broke his nose in the final confrontation and did not rise above amateur status - his musical career won out.
In 1970 the 21 year old Joel recorded an album as 50% of a duo called Atilla. 1972 saw the release of his first solo album *Cold Spring Harbor* which aroused moderate interest. A series of business and financial problems forced him to flee from New York to California, where he worked as a cocktail bar performer under the name Bill Martin. Meanwhile Columbia Records got to hear a tape of his song *Captain Jack* (a sharp wrning about the nightmarish effects of drugs) they tracked him down in California and signed him to a recording deal. He has remained with the company ever since. Joel's second album *Piano Man*, spearheaded by its hit title track, became his first major success. His first two sets *Streetlife Serenade* (1975) and *Turnstiles* (1976) were not so well received in commercial terms but gave the artist time to perfect his songwriting techniques.
At the end of 1977 a number of factors came together to make *The Stranger* the big breakthrough LP of Joel's career, transforming him into a major international artist. It was the strongest collection of songs to date, particularly *Just The Way You Are* which became an across the board standard; it was the first album to be produced by Phil Ramone, who became his regular studio associate; it was the first time to use Joel's familiar touring band instead of session players; and it was issued whilst Elton John, the artist to whom Joel is most commonly compared, was undergoing a period of semi-reirement. *The Stranger* sold over five million copies and *Just The Way You Are* was recorded by numerous middle of the road balladeers.
With subsequent albums Joel continued to carve out his own niche within Elton John/Paul McCartney territory. He was often at pains to stress the rockier side of his musical personality in order to offset the MoR image which *Just The Way You Are* had given him. All the singer's later LPs have been strong sellers, particularly in the States and some have matched the mega success of *The Stranger* 1980's *Glass Huses* logged six weeks at No.1 in America and yielded his first US No.1 single *It's Still Rock'n'Roll To Me*. After seeing his status diminish a little on account of a motorbike accident followed by a sombre LP *The Nylon Curtain*, he bounced back bigger than ever with the 1983 album *An Innocent Man*. The latter set harked back to the music of the Fifties and Sixties, and ran through all the passions and joys and angst of being in love. It yielded Joel's second US No.1 single *Tell Her About It*; in the UK, where no previous 45 had even penetrated the Top 10, Billy spent five weeks at No.1 with the brilliant Four Seasons pastiche *Uptown Girl*. (Bob Macdonald 13/11/85).

ALL FOR LEYNA
Tracks: / All for Leyna / Close to the borderline.
7" Single: Released Apr '80, on CBS, by CBS Records. Deleted '83. Catalogue no: **8325**

ALLENTOWN
Tracks: / Allentown / Elvis Presley boulveard.
7" Single: Released Dec '82, on CBS, by CBS Records. Deleted Dec '87. Catalogue no: **A 2981**

AN INNOCENT MAN (SINGLE)
Tracks: / Innocent man, An.
7" Single: Released Feb '84, on CBS, by CBS Records. Catalogue no: **A 4142**

BACK IN THE USSR
Tracks: / Back in the USSR / Big shot / Matter of trust (live) / Times they are a-changin'(live).
12" Single: Released Nov '87, on CBS, by CBS Records. Deleted Jun '88. Catalogue no: **651 206 6**
CD 5": Released Nov '87, on CBS, by CBS Records. Catalogue no: **CDEWF 1**
7" Single: Released Nov '87, on CBS, by CBS Records. Deleted Jun '88. Catalogue no: **651 206 7**

DON'T ASK WHY
Tracks: / Don't ask why / C'etait toi.
7" Single: Released Oct '82, on CBS, by CBS Records. Deleted Oct '85. Catalogue no: **CBS 9031**

FOR THE LONGEST TIME
Tracks: / For the longest time / Christie Lee.
12" Single: Released Apr '84, on CBS, by CBS Records. Catalogue no: **TA 4280**
7" Single: Released Apr '84, on CBS, by CBS Records. Catalogue no: **A 4280**

GOODNIGHT SAIGON
Tracks: / Goodnight Saigon / Where's the orchestra.
7" Single: Released Feb '83, on CBS, by CBS Records. Catalogue no: **A 3029**

GREATEST ORIGINAL HITS (4 TRACK EP)
Tracks: / Just the way you are / My life / She's always a woman to me / Stay out of my life.
7" Single: Released Mar '83, on CBS, by CBS Records. Catalogue no: **A 2619**

INNOCENT MAN
Tracks: / Innocent man, An.
12" Single: Released Jan '84, on CBS, by CBS Records. Catalogue no: **TA 4142**

IT'S STILL ROCK & ROLL TO ME
Tracks: / It's still rock and roll to me / Just the way you are.
7" Single: Released Aug '80, on CBS, by CBS Records. Deleted '83. Catalogue no: **8753**
CD 3": Released Aug '88, on Columbia (USA), by CBS Records (USA). Catalogue no: **38 K 07950**

JUST THE WAY YOU ARE
Tracks: / Just the way you are / Get it right the first time.
7" Single: Released Feb '78, on CBS, by CBS Records. Deleted '81. Catalogue no: **CBS 5872**

LEAVE A TENDER MOMENT ALONE
Tracks: / Leave a tender moment alone / Goodnight Saigon.
7" Single: Released Jun '84, on CBS, by CBS Records. Catalogue no: **A 4521**
12" Single: Released Jun '84, on CBS, by CBS Records. Catalogue no: **TA 4521**

LONGEST TIME, THE
Tracks: / Longest time, The / Christie Lee.
7" Single: Released Apr '84, on CBS, by CBS Records. Catalogue no: **A 4280**

THIS NIGHT
This night is mine
It's only you and I
Tomorrow
Is a long time away
This night can last forever
–Billy Joel
GA 4884

BILLY JOEL - THIS NIGHT (Released on CBS)

MATTER OF TRUST, A
Tracks: / Matter of trust, A / Getting closer / Tell her about it (Extra track on 12" version only.) / Innocent man, An (Extra track on 12" version only.).
12" Single: Released Sep '86, on CBS, by CBS Records. Deleted Nov '87. Catalogue no: **650057 6**
7" Single: Released Aug '86, on CBS, by CBS Records. Deleted Nov '87. Catalogue no: **650057 7**

MODERN WOMAN
Tracks: / Modern woman / Sleeps with the television on / Night is still young, The (Extra track on 12"version only.) / You're only human (Extra track on 12"version only.) / Uptown girl (Extra track in doublepack only.) / All for love (Extra track in doublepack only.).
12" Single: Released Jul '86, on CBS, by CBS Records. Deleted '87. Catalogue no: **TA 7247**
7" Set: Released Jul '86, on CBS, by CBS Records. Deleted '87. Catalogue no: **DA 7247**
7" Single: Released Jun '86, on CBS, by CBS Records. Deleted '86. Catalogue no: **A 7247**

MOVIN' OUT (ANTHONY'S SONG)
Tracks: / Movin' out (Anthony's song).
7" Single: Released Jun '78, on CBS, by CBS Records. Deleted '82. Catalogue no: **6412**

MY LIFE
Tracks: / My life.
7" Single: Released Dec '78, on CBS, by CBS Records. Deleted '82. Catalogue no: **6821**

PRESSURE
Tracks: / Pressure / Laura.
7" Single: Released Oct '82, on CBS, by CBS Records. Deleted Oct '85. Catalogue no: **A 2730**

SAY GOODBYE TO HOLLYWOOD
Tracks: / Say goodbye to Hollywood / Summer, highland falls.
7" Single: Released Oct '81, on CBS, by CBS Records. Deleted Oct '84. Catalogue no: **CBSA 1642**

SHE'S ALWAYS A WOMAN TO ME
Tracks: / She's always a woman / Just the way you are.
7" Single: Released Feb '86, on CBS, by CBS Records. Catalogue no: **A 6862**

SHE'S GOT AWAY
Tracks: / She's got away / Ballad of billy the kid.
7" Single: Released Feb '82, on CBS, by CBS Records. Deleted Feb '87. Catalogue no: **A 2002**

SOMETIMES A FANTASY
Tracks: / Sometimes a fantasy / Sleeping with the TV on.
7" Single: Released Jan '81, on CBS, by CBS Records. Deleted Jan '84. Catalogue no: **CBS 9419**

STARING AT ME GIRL
Tracks: / Staring at me girl.
12" Single: Released Jul '82, on Leggo, Catalogue no: **LG 101**

TELL HER ABOUT IT
Tracks: / Tell her about it / Easy money / You got me hummin' (on 12" only).
12" Single: Released Aug '83, on CBS, by CBS Records. Catalogue no: **TA 3655**
7" Single: Released Aug '83, on CBS, by CBS Records. Catalogue no: **A 3655**

THIS IS THE TIME
Tracks: / This is the time.
7" Single: Released Nov '86, on CBS, by CBS Records. Catalogue no: **650204 7**

THIS NIGHT (see panel above)
Tracks: / This night / I'll cry instead.
7" Single: Released '83, on CBS, by CBS Records. Catalogue no: **GA 4884**

UNTIL THE NIGHT
Tracks: / Until the night.
7" Single: Released Apr '79, on CBS, by CBS Records. Deleted '82. Catalogue no: **7242**

UPTOWN GIRL
Tracks: / Uptown girl.
7" Single: Released Sep '83, on CBS, by CBS Records. Catalogue no: **A 3775**
12" Single: Released Sep '83, on CBS, by CBS Records. Catalogue no: **TA 3775**

WE DIDN'T START THE FIRE
Tracks: / We didn't start the fire / House of blue light / Just the way you are.
12" Single: Released Sep '89, on CBS, by CBS Records. Catalogue no: **JOEL T1**
CD 5": Released 18 Sep '89, on CBS, by CBS Records. Catalogue no: **655300 6**
CD 5": Released Sep '89, on CBS, by CBS Records. Catalogue no: **JOEL C1**
Cassingle: Released Sep '89, on CBS, by CBS Records. Catalogue no: **JOEL M1**
7" Single: Released Sep '89, on CBS, by CBS Records. Catalogue no: **JOEL 1**
7" Single: Released 18 Sep '89, on CBS, by CBS Records. Catalogue no: **655300 7**

YOU MAY BE RIGHT
Tracks: / You may be right / Through the long night.
7" Single: Released Jun '80, on CBS, by CBS Records. Deleted '83. Catalogue no: **CBS 8643**

YOU'RE MY HOME
Tracks: / You're my home / Ballad of Billy The Kid.
7" Single: Released Nov '81, on CBS, by CBS Records. Deleted Nov '84. Catalogue no: **CBS A 1808**

Johansen

WALKIN' A FINE LINE
Tracks: / Walkin' a fine line.
7" Single: Released Sep '87, on WEA, by WEA Records. Deleted Jul '88. Catalogue no: **YZ 148**
12" Single: Released Sep '87, on WEA, by WEA Records. Deleted Jul '88. Catalogue no: **YZ 148T**

Johansen, David

SWAHETO WOMAN
Tracks: / Swaheto woman / She knew she was falling in love.
7" Single: Released Mar '80, on Blue Sky, Deleted '83. Catalogue no: **SKY 8125**

Johansen, Glen

KILLER ON THE RAMPAGE
Tracks: / Killer on the rampage.
7" Single: Released Oct '83, on Silvertown, by Silvertown Records. Catalogue no: **STS 5**
12" Single: Released Oct '83, on Silvertown, by Silvertown Records. Catalogue no: **STST 5**

John

HELLO ALEXEI
Tracks: / Hello Alexei / Nobody ever listens to the B side.
7" Single: Released Dec '84, on Red Door, by Red Door Records. Catalogue no: **RD 01**

John, Chris

I NEED YOUR LOVE
Tracks: / I need your love / So in love with you.
7" Single: Released 14 May '88, on Box, Catalogue no: **BX 71004**
12" Single: Released 14 May '88, on Box, Catalogue no: **BX 1004**

John, Elton

Biographical details: John, Elton This British singer, composer and pianist was born Reginald Kenneth Dwight in Pinner, Middlesex. When he reached his 10th birthday in 1957, he began to be fascinated by the all-conquering rock'n'roll explosion; at about the same time, his parents divorced and the youngster was freed from the grip of his martinet father, who had frowned upon his obsession with music. He won a scholarship to the Royal Academy of Music at the age of 11 and joined his first rock'n'roll group three years later. In 1965 Reg joined Bluesology, his first full time combo; during the mid-Sixties, he dreamed up his own stage name by combining the Christian names of two of the people he was working with - saxophonist Elton Dean and singer Long John Baldry.
In 1967 Elton John who liked composing tunes but could not write words, met up with lyricist Bernie Taupin. They forged a strong songwriting bond and were signed up by music publisher Dick James. John's debut single *I've Been Loving You* was released in March 1968; the first LP *Empty Sky* appeared on the DJM (Dick James Music) label in June 1969. In 1970 while on tour in the US, he began to develop a flamboyant stage act and won a growing reputation as a purveyor of sensitive songs and raucous rockers. The moving ballad *Your Song* provided him with his first Top 10 single on both sides of the Atlantic in early 1971.
During the early to mid-Seventies Elton John became one of the world's leading superstars and THE hottest act in America. The combination of John's melodies, Taupin's lyrics and the steady supervision of producer Gus Dudgeon sent songs as diverse as *Rocket Man* and *Daniel* into the Top Tens of countries around th globe. Elton John albums were released at a fast and furious pace - *Honky Chateau, Don't Shoot Me I'm Only The Piano Player, Goodbye Yellow Brick Road* (a double set), *Caribou,Elton John's greatest hits* and *Captain Fantastic and the Brown Dirt Cowboy* were all isssued between May 1972 and May 1975. With his over the top dress sense and sensational stadium concerts, he was one of the few artists of the era who satisfied both the hard-rock audiences and the glitter pop lovers. Much credit for the level of his fame was attributed to his amiable manager John Reid.
Elton reached a stunning career peak in America in 1975, when *Captain Fantastic* became the first album ever to enter the Billboard chart at No.1; before the year was over, he achieved the feat again with *Rock of the Westies.* His American No.1 singles included *Crocodile Rock* (1973), *Bennie and the Jets* (1974) *Lucy In The Sky With Diamonds, Philadelphia Freedom* and *Island Girl* (all 1975) plus his monster 1976 duet with Kiki Dee on *Don't Go Breaking My Heart.* Amazingly the latter song was John's only experience of a chart-topping 45 in his native country - he has won virtually every honour that the music world can bestow, except for a solo British No.1 single.
Settling down to a less spectacular and less wildly extrovert but still prolific career in the late Seventies and early Eighties, he continued to chalk up hits in America with tracks like *Mama Can't Buy You Love* (No.9) and *Little Jeannie* (No.3) and in Britain with such singles as *Song For Guy* (No.4) - dedicated to Guy Burchett, a messenger for Elton's Rocket label who was killed in a motorbike accident), *I Guess That's Why They Call It The Blues* (No.5), *I'm Still Standing* (No.4) and *Passengers* (No.5). When he reached the UK No.3 position in November 1985 with *Nikita,* the hopes of chart-watchers were high - but, as it turned out, there was still no UK No.1 single. (Bob Macdonald 13/11/85).

ACT OF WAR
Tracks: / Act of war.
7" Single: Released Jun '85, on Rocket, by Rocket Records. Catalogue no: **EJS 8**
12" Single: Released Jun '85, on Rocket, by Rocket Records. Catalogue no: **EJSR 8**

ACT OF WAR (PART 5)
Tracks: / Act of war (part 5).
12" Single: Released Jun '85, on Rocket, by Rocket Records. Catalogue no: **EJSR 812**

ALL QUIET ON THE WESTERN FRONT
Tracks: / All quiet on the western front / Where have all the good times gone.
7" Single: Released Nov '82, on Rocket, by Rocket Records. Deleted Nov '85. Catalogue no: **XPRES 88**

ARE YOU READY FOR LOVE
Tracks: / Are you ready for love.
7" Single: Released May '79, on Rocket, by Rocket Records. Deleted '83. Catalogue no: **XPRES 13**

BENNY AND THE JETS

elton john
blue eyes

ELTON JOHN - BLUE EYES (Released on Rocket)

Elton John - Cold As Christmas (Released on Rocket)

Elton John - Loving You is Sweeter Than Ever (Released on Ariola)

Tracks: / Benny & the Jets.
7" Single: Released Sep '76, on DJM, Deleted '78. Catalogue no: **DJS 10705**

BITCH IS BACK, THE
Tracks: / Bitch is back, The / Cold highway / Grow some funk of your own.
Note: * DJS 10909 only.
7" Single: Released '88, on DJM, Catalogue no: **DJS 10322**
7" Single: Released Sep '74, on DJM, Deleted '76. Catalogue no: **DJS 322**
7" Single: Released Sep '78, on DJM, Deleted '82. Catalogue no: **DJS 10909**

BITE YOUR LIP (GET UP AND DANCE)
Tracks: / Bite your lip (Get up and dance) / Chicago.
7" Single: Released Jun '77, on DJM, Deleted '80. Catalogue no: **ROKN 526**

BLUE EYES
Tracks: / Blue eyes / Hey papa legba.
7" Single: Released Mar '82, on Rocket, by Rocket Records. Deleted Feb '89. Catalogue no: **XPRES 71**

BORDER SONG
Tracks: / Border song.
7" Single: Released Sep '78, on DJM, Catalogue no: **DJS 10902**

BREAKING HEARTS (AIN'T WHAT IT USED TO BE)
Tracks: / Breaking hearts (ain't what it used to be).
7" Single: Released Mar '85, on Rocket, by Rocket Records. Deleted '87. Catalogue no: **EJS 7**

CANDLE IN THE WIND
Tracks: / Candle in the wind / Sorry seems to be the hardest word / Your song* / Don't let the sun go down on me*.
Note: *=extra track on 12"
Cassingle: Released Dec '87, on Rocket, by Rocket Records. Deleted Feb '89. Catalogue no: **EJSM 15**
CD 5": Released Dec '87, on Rocket, by Rocket Records. Deleted Oct '88. Catalogue no: **EJSCD 15**
7" Single: Released Dec '87, on Rocket, by Rocket Records. Deleted Oct '88. Catalogue no: **EJS 15**
12" Single: Released Dec '87, on Rocket, by Rocket Records. Deleted Oct '88. Catalogue no: **EJS 1512**

CANDLE IN THE WIND (DJM)
Tracks: / Candle in the wind / I feel like a bullet (in the gun of Robert Ford).
7" Single: Released Mar '74, on DJM, Deleted '77. Catalogue no: **DJS 297**
7" Single: Released '82, on DJM, Deleted '85. Catalogue no: **DJS 10908**

CANDLE IN THE WIND (RE-RELEASE)
Tracks: / Candle in the wind / Benny and the Jets.
7" Single: Released '88, on DJM, Catalogue no: **DJS 10297**

COLD AS CHRISTMAS (see panel above)
Tracks: / Cold as Christmas / Crystal.
7" Single: Released Dec '83, on Rocket, by Rocket Records. Deleted '87. Catalogue no: **EJS 3**

CRAZY WATER
Tracks: / Crazy water.
7" Single: Released Feb '77, on Rocket, by Rocket Records. Deleted '81. Catalogue no: **ROKN 521**

CROCODILE ROCK (SINGLE)
Tracks: / Crocodile Rock / Elderberry wine / Country comfort (DJS 10904 single only).
7" Single: Released Sep '78, on DJM, Catalogue no: **DJS 10904**
7" Single: Released Nov '72, on DJM, Deleted '75. Catalogue no: **DJS 271**
7" Single: Released '88, on DJM, Catalogue no: **DJS 10271**

CRY TO HEAVEN
Tracks: / Cry to heaven / Candy by the pound / Rock and roll medley (live) (Extra track on 12" version only).
12" Single: Released Feb '86, on Rocket, by Rocket Records. Deleted '87. Catalogue no: **EJS 1112**
7" Single: Released Feb '86, on Rocket, by Rocket Records. Deleted '87. Catalogue no: **EJS 11**

DANIEL
Tracks: / Daniel / Skyline pigeon.
7" Single: Released May '78, on DJM, Catalogue no: **DJS 10275**

DANIEL (ORIGINAL)
Tracks: / Daniel.
7" Single: Released Jan '73, on DJM, Deleted '75. Catalogue no: **DJS 275**

DEAR GOD
Tracks: / Dear God.
7" Single: Released Nov '80, on Rocket, by Rocket Records. Deleted May '81. Catalogue no: **ELTON 1**

DON'T GO BREAKING MY HEART (OLD GOLD)
(ELTON JOHN & KIKI DEE)
Tracks: / Don't go breaking my heart / I got the music in me.
7" Single: Released Jun '88, on Old Gold, by Old Gold Records. Catalogue no: **OG 9789**

DON'T GO BREAKING MY HEART (ORIGINAL)
(ELTON JOHN & KIKI DEE)
Tracks: / Don't go breaking my heart / Snow queen.
7" Single: Released Jul '76, on Rocket, by Rocket Records. Deleted '80. Catalogue no: **ROKN 512**
7" Single: Released '83, on Rocket, by Rocket Records. Catalogue no: **XPRES 49**

DON'T LET THE SUN GO DOWN ON ME
Tracks: / Don't let the sun go down on me / Sick city / Someone saved my life tonight (On DJS 10907 only).
7" Single: Released Sep '78, on DJM, Deleted '82. Catalogue no: **DJS 10907**
7" Single: Released Jun '74, on DJM, Deleted '77. Catalogue no: **DJS 302**
7" Single: Released '88, on DJM, Catalogue no: **DJS 10302**

EGO
Tracks: / Ego.
7" Single: Released Apr '78, on Rocket, by Rocket Records. Deleted '82. Catalogue no: **ROKN 539**

EMPTY GARDEN
Tracks: / Empty garden / Take me down to the ocean.
7" Single: Released May '82, on Rocket, by Rocket Records. Catalogue no: **XPRES 77**

FLAMES OF PARADISE(See under Rush, Jennifer)
Tracks: / Flames of paradise / Call my name.
12" Single: Released 30 May '87, on CBS, by CBS Records. Catalogue no: **650865 6**
7" Single: Released 30 May '87, on CBS, by CBS Records. Deleted Nov '87. Catalogue no: **650865 7**

FOUR FROM FOUR EYES
Tracks: / Your song / Rocket man / Saturday night's alright (for fighting) / Whenever you're ready.
7" EP: Released '86, on DJM, Catalogue no: **DJR 18001**

FUNERAL FOR A FRIEND
Tracks: / Funeral for a friend / Love lies bleeding / We all fall in love sometimes / Curtains.
12" Single: Released '88, on DJM, Catalogue no: **DJT 15000**

GOODBYE YELLOW BRICK ROAD (SINGLE)
Tracks: / Goodbye yellow brick road / Screw you.
7" Single: Released Sep '78, on DJM, Deleted '82. Catalogue no: **DJS 10906**
7" Single: Released Sep '73, on DJM, Deleted '76. Catalogue no: **DJS 290**
7" Single: Released '88, on DJM, Catalogue no: **DJS 10285**

GROW SOME FUNK OF YOUR OWN
Tracks: / Grow some funk of your own / I feel like a bullet (in the gun of Robert Ford).
7" Single: Released '78, on DJM, Catalogue no: **DJS 10629**

HARMONY
Tracks: / Harmony / Mona Lisas and Mad Hatters.
7" Single: Released Oct '80, on DJM, Catalogue no: **DJS 10961**

HEALING HANDS
Tracks: / Healing hands / Dancing in the end zone / Sad songs.
12" Single: Released Jul '89, on Rocket, by Rocket Records. Catalogue no: **EJS 1912**
CD 5": Released Jul '89, on Rocket, by Rocket Records. Catalogue no: **EJCD 19**
Cassingle: Released Jul '89, on Rocket, by Rocket Records. Catalogue no: **EJMC 19**
7" Single: Released Jul '89, on Rocket, by Rocket Records. Catalogue no: **EJS 19**

HEARTACHE ALL OVER THE WORLD
Tracks: / Heartache all over the world /

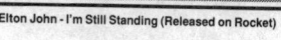

Elton John - I'm Still Standing (Released on Rocket)

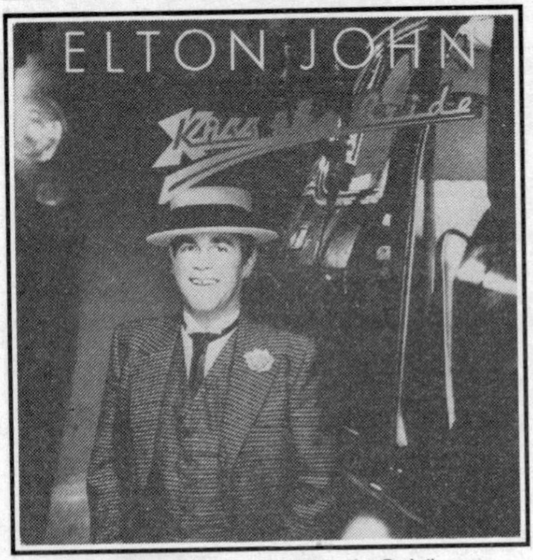

Elton John - Kiss the Bride (Released on Rocket)

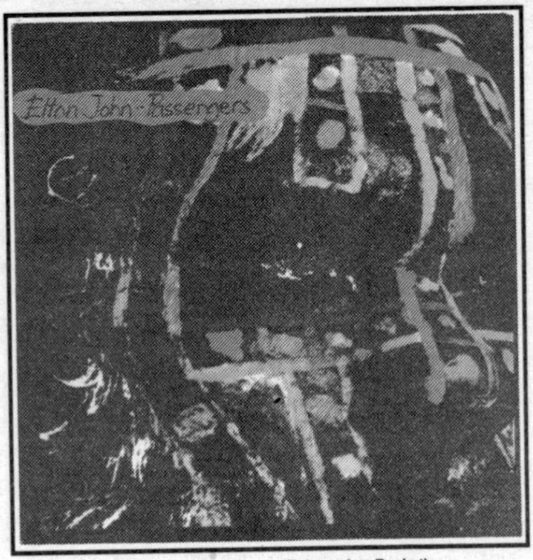

Elton John - Passengers (Released on Rocket)

Highlander.
7" Single: Released Sep '86, on Rocket, by Rocket Records. Deleted '87. Catalogue no: **EJS 12**
12" Single: Released Sep '86, on Rocket, by Rocket Records. Deleted '87. Catalogue no: **EJS 12 12**

HONKY CAT
Tracks: / Honky cat / Sixty years on.
7" Single: Released Sep '78, on DJM, Catalogue no: **DJS 10903**
7" Single: Released Sep '72, on DJM, Deleted '74. Catalogue no: **DJS 269**

I DON'T WANT TO GO ON WITH YOU LIKE THAT
Tracks: / I don't want to go on with you like that / I don't want to go on with you like that(Shep Pettibone mix).
Note: Both CD and 12" versions feature a great Shep Pettibone Mix lasting over 7 minutes. (Phonogram records, May 1988).
7" Pic: Released 23 May '88, on Phonogram, by Phonogram Ltd. Deleted Feb '89. Catalogue no: **EJSIP 16**
CD 5": Released 23 May '88, on Phonogram, by Phonogram Ltd. Deleted Feb '89. Catalogue no: **EJSCD 16**
7" Single: Released 23 May '88, on Phonogram, by Phonogram Ltd. Deleted Feb '89. Catalogue no: **EJS 16**
12" Single: Released 23 May '88, on Phonogram, by Phonogram Ltd. Deleted Feb '89. Catalogue no: **EJS 1612**

I GUESS THAT'S WHY THEY CALL IT THE BLUES
Tracks: / I guess that's why they call it the blues.
7" Single: Released Apr '83, on Rocket, by Rocket Records. Deleted '87. Catalogue no: **XPRES 91**

I SAW HER STANDING THERE
Tracks: / I saw her standing there / Whatever gets you through the night / Lucy in the sky with diamonds.
Note: Featuring The Muscle Shoals Horns.
7" Single: Released Mar '81, on DJM, Deleted '85. Catalogue no: **DJS 10965**

I'M STILL STANDING
Tracks: / I'm still standing / Earn while you learn.
12" Single: Released Jul '83, on Rocket, by Rocket Records. Deleted Mar '88. Catalogue no: **EJS 112**
7" Pic: Released Jul '83, on Rocket, by Rocket Records. Deleted Mar '88. Catalogue no: **EJPIC 1**
7" Single: Released Jul '83, on Rocket, by Rocket Records. Deleted Mar '88. Catalogue no: **EJS 1**

ISLAND GIRL
Tracks: / Island girl / Sugar on the floor (Available only on DJS 10610.) / Saturday night's alright (for fighting) *.
Note: * DJS 10910 only.h
7" Single: Released Oct '75, on DJM, Deleted '77. Catalogue no: **DJS 610**
7" Single: Released Sep '78, on DJM, Deleted '81. Catalogue no: **DJS 10910**
7" Single: Released '82, on DJM, Catalogue no: **DJS 10610**

JUST LIKE BELGIUM
Tracks: / Just like Belgium / Can't get over losing you.
7" Single: Released Jul '81, on Rocket, by Rocket Records. Deleted Jul '84. Catalogue no: **XPRES 59**

KISS THE BRIDE (see panel above)
Tracks: / Kiss the bride / Dreamboat.
7" Single: Released Oct '83, on Rocket, by Rocket Records. Deleted '87. Catalogue no: **EJS 2**

KISS THE BRIDE (BOX SET)
Tracks: / Kiss the bride / Dreamboat / Ego / Song for Guy.
7" Set: Released Oct '83, on Rocket, by Rocket Records. Deleted '86. Catalogue no: **EJS 22**

LADY SAMANTHA (SINGLE)
Tracks: / Lady Samantha / Skyline pigeon.
7" Single: Released Sep '78, on DJM, Catalogue no: **DJS 10901**

LITTLE JEANNIE
Tracks: / Little Jeannie / Conquer.
7" Single: Released May '80, on Rocket, by Rocket Records. Deleted '83. Catalogue no: **XPRES 32**

LOVING YOU IS SWEETER THAN EVER (see panel on previous page)
Tracks: / Loving you is sweeter than ever / Twenty four hours.
7" Single: Released Nov '81, on Ariola, by BMG Records (UK). Catalogue no: **ARO 269**

LUCY IN THE SKY WITH DIAMONDS (SINGLE)
Tracks: / Lucy in the sky with diamonds / One day at a time.
7" Single: Released '88, on DJM, Catalogue no: **DJS 10340**
7" Single: Released Nov '74, on DJM, Deleted '77. Catalogue no: **DJS 340**

NIKITA
Tracks: / Nikita.
7" Single: Released Sep '85, on Rocket, by Rocket Records. Deleted Mar '88. Catalogue no: **EJS 9**
12" Single: Released Sep '85, on Rocket, by Rocket Records. Deleted '87. Catalogue no: **EJS 912**

NIKITA (OLD GOLD)
Tracks: / Nikita / I'm still standing.
7" Single: Released Feb '88, on Old Gold, by Old Gold Records. Catalogue no: **OG 9776**

NOBODY WINS
Tracks: / Nobody wins / Fools in fashion.
7" Single: Released May '81, on Rocket, by Rocket Records. Deleted '84. Catalogue no: **XPRES 54**

PART-TIME LOVE
Tracks: / Part-time love.
7" Single: Released Oct '78, on Rocket, by Rocket Records. Deleted '82. Catalogue no: **XPRES 1**

PASSENGERS (see panel below)
Tracks: / Passengers / Lonely boy.
7" Single: Released Aug '84, on Rocket, by Rocket Records. Deleted '87. Catalogue no: **EJS 5**

PHILADELPHIA FREEDOM
Tracks: / Philadelphia freedom / I saw her standing there.
7" Single: Released '82, on DJM, Catalogue no: **DJS 10354**
7" Single: Released Mar '75, on DJM, Deleted '77. Catalogue no: **DJS 354**
7" Single: Released Sep '78, on DJM, Catalogue no: **DJS 10911**

PINBALL WIZARD
Tracks: / Pinball wizard / Harmony.
7" Single: Released Mar '76, on DJM, Deleted '77. Catalogue no: **DJS 652**
7" Single: Released '82, on DJM, Catalogue no: **DJS 10652**
7" Single: Released Sep '78, on DJM, Deleted '81. Catalogue no: **DJS 10912**

PRINCESS
Tracks: / Princess / Retreat.
7" Single: Released Sep '82, on Rocket, by Rocket Records. Deleted Sep '85. Catalogue no: **XPRES 85**

ROCKET MAN (ORIGINAL)
Tracks: / Rocket man.
7" Single: Released Apr '72, on DJM, Deleted '75. Catalogue no: **DJX 501**

ROCKET MAN (SINGLE)
Tracks: / Rocket man / Daniel.
7" Single: Released '82, on DJM, Catalogue no: **DJS 10905**

SAD SONGS (SAY SO MUCH)
Tracks: / Sad songs / Simple man.
7" Single: Released May '84, on Rocket, by Rocket Records. Deleted '87. Catalogue no: **PH 7**

SARTORIAL ELOQUENCE
Tracks: / Sartorial eloquence.
7" Single: Released Aug '80, on Rocket, by Rocket Records. Deleted '83. Catalogue no: **XPRES 41**

SATURDAY NIGHT'S ALRIGHT FOR FIGHTING
Tracks: / Saturday night's alright for fighting.
7" Single: Released Jul '73, on DJM, Deleted '76. Catalogue no: **DJX 502**
7" Single: Released Sep '78, on DJM, Catalogue no: **DJS 10910**

SLOW RIVERS
Tracks: / Slow rivers / Lord of the flies (Extra track on 12" versions).
12" Single: Released Nov '86, on Rocket, by Rocket Records. Deleted Jul '87. Catalogue no: **EJSD 12**
12" Single: Released Nov '86, on Rocket, by Rocket Records. Deleted Jul '87. Catalogue no: **EJS 1312**
7" Single: Released Nov '86, on Rocket, by Rocket Records. Deleted Jul '87. Catalogue no: **EJS 13**

SOMEONE SAVED MY LIFE TONIGHT
Tracks: / Someone saved my life tonight / House of cards.
7" Single: Released '82, on DJM, Catalogue no: **DJS 10385**
7" Single: Released Sep '78, on DJM, Deleted '81. Catalogue no: **DJS 10907**
7" Single: Released Jun '75, on DJM, Deleted '77. Catalogue no: **DJS 385**

SONG FOR GUY
Tracks: / Song for Guy.
7" Single: Released Dec '78, on Rocket, by Rocket Records. Deleted '83. Catalogue no: **XPRES 5**

SONG FOR GUY (OLD GOLD)
Tracks: / Song for Guy / Blue eyes.
7" Single: Released Jun '88, on Old Gold, by Old Gold Records. Catalogue no: **OG 9791**

SORRY SEEMS TO BE THE HARDEST WORD
Tracks: / Sorry seems to be the hardest word.
7" Single: Released Oct '76, on Rocket, by Rocket Records. Deleted '80. Catalogue no: **ROKN 517**

STEP INTO CHRISTMAS
Tracks: / Step into christmas / Ho, ho, ho, who'd be a turkey at Christmas?.
7" Single: Released Sep '78, on DJM, Deleted '82. Catalogue no: **DJS 10290**
7" Single: Released Dec '73, on DJM, Deleted '76. Catalogue no: **DJS 290**

SWEET PAINTED LADY
Tracks: / Sweet painted lady / Goodbye yellow brick road.

7" Single: Released '82, on DJM, Catalogue no: **DJS 10906**

THAT'S WHY THEY CALL IT THE BLUES
Tracks: / That's why they call it the blues.
7" Single: Released Apr '83, on Rocket, by Rocket Records. Deleted Feb '89. Catalogue no: **XPRES 91**

TOWN OF PLENTY
Tracks: / Town of plenty / Whipping boy / My baby's a saint (12" and CD only) / I guess that's why they call it the blues (CD only).

7" Single: Released 8 Aug '88, on Phonogram, by Phonogram Ltd. Deleted Feb '89. Catalogue no: **EJSLB 17**
CD 5": Released 8 Aug '88, on Phonogram, by Phonogram Ltd. Deleted Feb '89.

Catalogue no: **EJSCD 17**
7" Single: Released 8 Aug '88, on Phonogram, by Phonogram Ltd. Deleted Feb '89. Catalogue no: **EJS 17**
12" Single: Released 8 Aug '88, on Phonogram, by Phonogram Ltd. Deleted Feb '89. Catalogue no: **EJS 1712**

WHO WEARS THESE SHOES
Tracks: / Who wears these shoes.
7" Single: Released Oct '84, on Rocket, by Rocket Records. Deleted '87. Catalogue no: **EJS 6**

WORD IN SPANISH, A
Tracks: / Word in Spanish, A / Heavy traffic / Live in Australia medley (Only on CD single and 12". Medley includes Song for you, Blue eyes and I) / Daniel (live) (Only on CD single & gatefold sleeve.).
7" Single: Released Dec '88, on Rocket, by Rocket Records. Catalogue no: **EJSP 18**
CD 5": Released Nov '88, on Rocket, by Rocket Records. Catalogue no: **EJSCD 18**
7" Single: Released Nov '88, on Rocket, by Rocket Records. Deleted 31 May '89. Catalogue no: **EJS 18**
12" Single: Released Nov '88, on Rocket, by Rocket Records. Deleted 31 May '89. Catalogue no: **EJS 1812**

WRAP HER UP
Tracks: / Wrap her up / Restless.
7" Single: Released Dec '85, on Rocket, by Rocket Records. Catalogue no: **EJSC 10**

YOUR SONG (1)
Tracks: / Your song / Border song.
7" Single: Released Sep '78, on DJM, Catalogue no: **DJS 10902**

YOUR SONG (2)
Tracks: / Your song / Into the old man's shoes.
7" Single: Released '88, on DJM, Catalogue no: **DJS 10233**

YOUR SONG (LIVE)
Tracks: / Your song (live) / Don't let the sun go down on me / I need you to turn to* (*Extra track on 12") / Greatest discovery ('Greatest discovery' extra track on 12" only.).
12" Single: Released Jun '87, on Rocket, by Rocket Records. Deleted Dec '87. Catalogue no: **EJS1412**
7" Single: Released Jun '87, on Rocket, by Rocket Records. Deleted Dec '87. Catalogue no: **EJS14**

YOUR SONG (ORIGINAL)
Tracks: / Your song.
7" Single: Released Jan '71, on DJM, Deleted '73. Catalogue no: **DJS 233**

John, Leee

ROCK ME SLOW
Tracks: / Rock me slow / Rock me slow (instrumental) / Honey I'm yours (Extra track on 12" version only).
7" Single: Released Aug '86, on R & B, by Red Bus Records. Catalogue no: **RBL 1805**
12" Single: Released Aug '86, on R & B, by Red Bus Records. Catalogue no: **RBS 1805**

John, Mavis

HOW CAN I LOVE AGAIN
Tracks: / How can I love again / Gotta have you.
7" Single: Released Jun '81, on Sonet, by Sonet Records. Catalogue no: **SON 2222**

John, Michael

LOVE WILL TEAR US APART
Tracks: / Love will tear us apart / We're together.
7" Single: Released Sep '83, on Loose, by Loose Records. Catalogue no: **LSE 4**
12" Single: Released Sep '83, on Loose, by Loose Records. Catalogue no: **LSE 4T**

John, Paul...

JOHN, PAUL, GEORGE, RINGO & BERT London cast
Cassingle: Released '74, on RSO (USA), by Polydor Ltd. Catalogue no: **2394 141**

John, Robert

Biographical details: John, Robert This American singer and songwriter was born Robert John Pedrick Jr. in Brooklyn, New York. He began his musical career by singing in doo-wop groups on street corners and the youngster made an early appearance on the US Hot 100 in late 1958 with *White Bucks and Saddle Shoes* under the name Bobby Pedrick Jr. He failed in his attempts to consolidate on this toehold and did not find his chart feet again until 1968 when he re-emerged as Robert John.
If You Don't Want My Love took John to No.49 in America and No.42 in Britain in 1968; the song was co-written by him and featured his falsetto vocals. Once again, however, his follow up flopped. In early 1972 he suddenly surged to fame with a remake of that old evergreen *The Lion Sleeps Tonight* which turned out to be a perfect vehicle for John's high pitched singing. The single reached No.3 in the States, selling a million copies in the process; it was produced by Hank Medress, a member of the Tokens who had reached the US No.1 spot with the song a decade earlier. Inexplicably, John's record company would not allow him to make an LP to capitalise on the success of *The Lion Sleeps Tonight*. The singer retired from the music business, disillusioned.
After a stint as a construction worker in New Jersey, Robert returned to prominence in 1979 with yet another one-off hit, the self-penned *Sad Eyes*. This light, middle of the road soul single reached No.1 in the US and No.31 in the UK. It spent 21 weeks climbing the Billboard Hot 100 in order to reach the very top thus becoming one of the slowest rising chart toppers in history. What's more it had taken him 21 years from his first ever chart appearance to reach No.1 - this set a new record, which had subsequently been beaten only once.
After four one off hits, Robert achieved a fifth one in late 1980 reaching the US No.31 position with an obvious revival of Eddie Holman's *Hey There Lonely Girl*. The ever erratic Mr John then disappeared once more into the land of obscurity; but, as he has proved so many times, he can never be written off. (Bob Macdonald 14/11/85).

BREAD AND BUTTER
Tracks: / Bread and butter / If you don't want my love.
7" Single: Released Mar '83, on Motown, by BMG Records (UK). Catalogue no: **TMG 1298**

GREASED LIGHTNING
Tracks: / Greased lightning (dance mix) / Greased lightning (7" edit) / Greased lightning (inst.).
12" Single: Released Feb '88, on Domino, by Domino Records. Catalogue no: **DOM T9**

(HEY THERE) LONELY GIRL
Tracks: / (Hey there) lonely girl / You could have told me.
7" Single: Released Aug '80, on EMI-America, by EMI Records. Deleted '82. Catalogue no: **EA 116**

IF YOU DON'T WANT MY LOVE
Tracks: / If you don't want my love.
7" Single: Released Jul '68, on CBS, by CBS Records. Deleted '71. Catalogue no: **3436**

LONELY EYES
Tracks: / Lonely eyes / Dance the night away.
7" Single: Released Mar '80, on EMI-America, by EMI Records. Deleted Mar '83. Catalogue no: **EA 106**

SHAKE IT UP
Tracks: / Shake it up / Only love.
12" Single: Released Jan '81, on Motown, by BMG Records (UK). Deleted Jan '84. Catalogue no: **12 TMG 1213**

SHERRY
Tracks: / Sherry / On my own.
7" Single: Released Jan '81, on EMI-America, by EMI Records. Deleted Jan '84. Catalogue no: **EA 119**

Johnny 7

PRESSURE'S TOO HOT
Tracks: / Pressure's too hot.
7" Single: Released Dec '84, on Lost Moments, Catalogue no: **LM 009**

Johnny B

TIME IS NOW
Tracks: / Time is now.
12" Single: Released Sep '82, on MPD, Catalogue no: **MOL 2**

WHEN A MAN LOVES A WOMAN
Tracks: / When a man loves a woman.
12" Single: Released Jan '89, on New Talents, Catalogue no: **NT 008**

Johnny & Charley

LA YENKA
Tracks: / La yenka.
7" Single: Released Oct '65, on Pye International, Deleted '68. Catalogue no: **7N 25326**

Johnny, G

ALONE WITH HER TONIGHT
Tracks: / Alone with her tonight.
7" Single: Released Jan '82, on Beggars Banquet, by Beggars Banquet Records. Deleted Jan '85. Catalogue no: **BEG 65**

G BEAT (SINGLE)
Tracks: / G beat / Leave me alone.
7" Single: Released Oct '81, on Beggars Banquet, by Beggars Banquet Records. Deleted Oct '84. Catalogue no: **BEG 67**

NIGHT AFTER NIGHT
Tracks: / Night after night / Old soldiers.
7" Single: Released May '80, on Beggars Banquet, by Beggars Banquet Records. Deleted May '83. Catalogue no: **BEG 40**

Johnny Hates Jazz

DON'T SAY IT'S LOVE
Tracks: / Don't say it's love (7" remix on all versions) / Living in the past (On all versions) / Don't say its love (extended remix) (On CD & 12" only) / I don't want to be a hero (12" mix) (CD only).
Note: "'DON'T SAY IT'S LOVE' is a radically remixed version of the track that appears on the band's platinum album "TURN BACK THE CLOCK"". (Virgin Records, July 1988).
12" Single: Released Jun '88, on Virgin, by Virgin Records. Catalogue no: **VST 1081**
CD 5": Released '88, on Virgin, by Virgin Records. Catalogue no: **VSCD 1081**
7" Single: Released Jun '88, on Virgin, by Virgin Records. Catalogue no: **VS 1081**

HEART OF GOLD
Tracks: / Heart of gold (Not on 12") / Heart of gold (extended remix version) (12" only) / Heart of gold (extended mix) (CD & cassette only) / Leave it up to me (On all versions) / Cage, The (CD & cassette only) / Heart of gold (remix) (12" only).
7" Single: Released Feb '88, on Virgin, by Virgin Records. Catalogue no: **VS 1045**
CD 5": Released Aug '88, on Virgin, by Virgin Records. Catalogue no: **VSCD 1045**
Cassingle: Released '88, on Virgin, by Virgin Records. Catalogue no: **VSTC 1045**
12" Single: Released Feb '88, on Virgin, by Virgin Records. Catalogue no: **VST 1045**

I DON'T WANT TO BE A HERO
Tracks: / I don't want to be a hero / Cage, The / I don't want to be a hero (12" mix) (12" only).
7" Single: Released Aug '87, on Virgin, by Virgin Records. Catalogue no: **VS 1000**
Cassingle: Released Aug '87, on Virgin, by Virgin Records. Deleted May '88. Catalogue no: **VSTC 1000**
12" Single: Released Aug '87, on Virgin, by Virgin Records. Catalogue no: **VST 1000**

ME AND MY FOOLISH HEART
Tracks: / Me and my foolish heart / Living in the past.
12" Single: Released Mar '86, on EMI, by EMI Records. Catalogue no: **12RAK 388**
7" Single: Released Mar '86, on EMI, by EMI Records. Catalogue no: **RAK 388**

SHATTERED DREAMS
Tracks: / Shattered dreams (7" version not on cassette) / My secret garden (On all versions) / Shattered dreams (12" extended mix) (12" & cassette) / Me and my foolish heart (Cassette only) / Living in the past (Cassette only).
12" Single: Released Mar '87, on Virgin, by Virgin Records. Catalogue no: **VS 948-12**
Cassingle: Released '87, on Virgin, by Virgin Records. Catalogue no: **VSC 948**
7" Single: Released Mar '87, on Virgin, by Virgin Records. Catalogue no: **VS 948**

TURN BACK THE CLOCK (SINGLE)
Tracks: / Turn back the clock / Cracking up / Turn back the clock (extended mix) (CD & 12" only) / Shattered dreams (12" extended mix) (CD only).
12" Single: Released Nov '87, on Virgin, by Virgin Records. Catalogue no: **VST 1017**
CD 5": Released Aug '88, on Virgin, by Virgin Records. Catalogue no: **CDEP 14**
7" Single: Released Nov '87, on Virgin, by Virgin Records. Catalogue no: **VS 1017**

TURN THE TIDE
Tracks: / Turn the tide / Breaking point.
12" Single: Released '89, on Virgin, by Virgin Records. Catalogue no: **VST 1205**
Cassingle: Released '89, on Virgin, by Virgin Records. Catalogue no: **VSC 1205**
7" Single: Released '89, on Virgin, by Virgin Records. Catalogue no: **VS 1205**
CD 3": Released '89, on Virgin, by Virgin Records. Catalogue no: **VSCD 1205**

Johnny P

ITAL JOCKEY
Tracks: / Ital jockey.
12" Single: Released Jul '89, on Techniques, Catalogue no: **WRT 49**

MOUTH A BODDA
Tracks: / Mouth a bodda.
12" Single: Released Apr '88, on Techniques, Catalogue no: **WRT 29**

Johnny Says Yeah

I WON'T LET YOU GO
Tracks: / I won't let you go / Some things are more simple.
7" Single: Released Oct '87, on The Day I Eat The World, Catalogue no: **JSY 3**

Johnny & The Hurricanes

BEATNIK FLY
Tracks: / Beatnik fly / Down yonder / Rockin' goose.
7" Single: Released Mar '82, on Decca, by Decca Records. Deleted '88. Catalogue no: **F 13908**
7" Single: Released Oct '80, on London (Decca), by Decca International. Deleted Oct '82. Catalogue no: **HL 10578**
7" Single: Released Mar '60, on London (Decca), by Decca International. Deleted '63. Catalogue no: **HL 9072**

DOWN YONDER
Tracks: / Down yonder.
7" Single: Released Jun '60, on London-American, Deleted '63. Catalogue no: **HLX 9134**

JA-DA
Tracks: / Ja da.
7" Single: Released Feb '61, on London-American, Deleted '64. Catalogue no: **HLX 9289**

OLD SMOKEY
Tracks: / Old smokey / High voltage.
7" Single: Released Jun '61, on London-American, Deleted '64. Catalogue no: **HLX 9378**

RED RIVER ROCK (OLD GOLD)
Tracks: / Red river rock.
7" Single: Released Jan '85, on Old Gold, by Old Gold Records. Catalogue no: **OG 9459**

RED RIVER ROCK (SINGLE)
Tracks: / Red River Rock.
7" Single: Released Oct '59, on London (Decca), by Decca International. Deleted '62. Catalogue no: **HL 8948**
7" Single: Released Aug '82, on Dakota, Deleted '85. Catalogue no: **BAK 15**
7" Single: Released Jul '84, on Liberty, by EMI Records. Catalogue no: **1A 006 99380**

REVEILLE ROCK
Tracks: / Reveille rock / Rinky dink / Bumble boogie.
7" Single: Released Aug '82, on Blast From The Past, by Creole Records. Catalogue no: **CR 184**

REVEILLE ROCK (ORIGINAL)
Tracks: / Reveille rock.
7" Single: Released Dec '59, on London (Decca), by Decca International. Deleted '62. Catalogue no: **HL 9017**

ROCKING GOOSE
Tracks: / Rockin' goose.
7" Single: Released Aug '82, on Dakota, Catalogue no: **BAK 15**
7" Single: Released Sep '60, on London-American, Deleted '63. Catalogue no: **HLX 9190**

ROCKING GOOSE (OLD GOLD)
7" Single: Released Jan '85, on Old Gold, by Old Gold Records. Catalogue no: **OG 9460**

Johnny/Ansaphones

DOG AND BONE
Tracks: / Dog and bone.
Cassingle: Released Nov '87, on Crook Cassettes, by Crook Cassettes. Catalogue no: **JA 1**

Johnny/Jailbirds

STAY AWAY
Tracks: / Stay away / Jennie Lee.
7" Single: Released Oct '80, on Charly, by Charly Records. Deleted Oct '83. Catalogue no: **CYS 1071**

Johnny/Roccos

I HATE THE DISCO
Tracks: / I hate the disco / Drip dry.
7" Single: Released Feb '86, on Off-Beat (1), Catalogue no: **NS 113**

Johnny/Strollers

CITY OF A THOUSAND DREAMS
Tracks: / City of a thousand dreams / Best is yet to come, The.
7" Single: Released Jun '88, on ESR, by ESR Records. Catalogue no: **ESR 0021**

Johns Children

MIDSUMMER'S NIGHT SCENE
Tracks: / Midsummer's night scene.
12" Single: Released Jan '88, on Bam Caruso, by Demon Records. Catalogue no: **PABL 059**

Johnson

CHAIN REACTION
Tracks: / Chain reaction / Afraid to be real.
7" Single: Released Jun '86, on Total Control, by Total Control Records. Catalogue no: **TOCO 11**
12" Single: Released Jun '86, on Total Control, by Total Control Records. Catalogue no: **12TOCO 11**

Johnson, Al

I'M BACK FOR MORE
Tracks: / I'm back for more / You are my personal angel.
7" Single: Released May '80, on CBS, by CBS Records. Deleted '83. Catalogue no: **CBS 8545**

Johnson, Anthony

A YA WE DEH (SINGLE)
Tracks: / A ya we deh.
12" Single: Released Jul '84, on Fu-Manchu, Catalogue no: **TC 8784**

BABY WHY
Tracks: / Baby why.
12" Single: Released Dec '83, on Midnight Rock, Catalogue no: **MR 19**
7" Single: Released May '89, on Coxsone, Catalogue no: **UNKNOWN**

DANCE HALL VIBES
Tracks: / Dance hall vibes / Rap up, mix up.
12" Single: Released Apr '86, on Unity, Catalogue no: **UN 017**

DON'T LET ME DOWN
Tracks: / Don't let me down.
12" Single: Released May '82, on Music Lovers, Catalogue no: **ML 002**

DREADLOCKS FIGHT
Tracks: / Dreadlocks fight / Baby loving.
12" Single: Released Feb '83, on Rusty International, Catalogue no: **RI 005**

I LOVE YOU GIRL
Tracks: / I love you girl / Nah give up.
12" Single: Released Feb '86, on Look To Afrika, Catalogue no: **LTAS 02**

I'LL NEVER FALL IN LOVE AGAIN
Tracks: / I'll never fall in love again.
12" Single: Released Oct '83, on Greensleeves, by Greensleeves Records. Catalogue no: **12 OINKS 5**

JUST CALL ME
Tracks: / Just call me / You I love.
12" Single: Released Sep '81, on Freedom Sounds, Catalogue no: **FSD 023**

JUST TO BE CLOSE TO YOU
Tracks: / Just to be close to you.
12" Single: Released Oct '89, on Clarendon Sounds, Catalogue no: **CS 010**

LET GO THIS ONE
Tracks: / Let go this one / One split a day.
12" Single: Released Jan '82, on Greensleeves, by Greensleeves Records. Catalogue no: **GRED 76**

LOVE LOST
Tracks: / Love lost.
12" Single: Released Feb '82, on Black Symbol, Catalogue no: **BS 101**

MEK WE GO A DANCE
Tracks: / Mek we go a dance.
12" Single: Released Jan '84, on Black Roots, Catalogue no: **LML 181260**

NO MEN, NO GUY, NO BOY
Tracks: / No men, no guy, no boy / Watch it.
12" Single: Released Aug '86, on Now Generation, Catalogue no: **NG 009**

SINCE I MET YOU BABY
Tracks: / Since I met you baby / Cassandra.
12" Single: Released Jan '86, on Shabrock, Catalogue no: **SR 001**

SITTING IN THE DARK
Tracks: / Sitting in the dark.
12" Single: Released Sep '84, on Midnight Rock, Catalogue no: **Unknown**

STOP MY LOVING
Tracks: / Stop my loving.
12" Single: Released Aug '83, on Rusty International, Catalogue no: **RI 014**

STRICTLY RUB-A-DUB
Tracks: / Strictly rub-a-dub / Poffe.
12" Single: Released Sep '83, on Midnight Rock, Catalogue no: **MRE 16**

TAKE YOU TO THE SHOW
Tracks: / Take you to the show.
12" Single: Released Feb '83, on Midnight Rock, Catalogue no: **MR 013**

TOO MUCH
Tracks: / Too much / How you keep a dance.
12" Single: Released Jul '82, on Oak Sound, Catalogue no: **OSD 005**

TRUE TRUE LOVE
Tracks: / True true love.
12" Single: Released Sep '89, on Jamaica Vices, Catalogue no: **JV 001**

Johnson, Anton

HEY BABY
Tracks: / Hey baby / Ice cream.
7" Single: Released Apr '80, on Laser, Deleted '83. Catalogue no: **LAS 28**

Johnson, Bertie

NO WAY LOSE SIGHT OF JAH
Tracks: / No way lose sight of jah.
12" Single: Released Jan '83, on S & G (2), Catalogue no: **SG 25**

Johnson, Bros

TREASURE
Tracks: / Treasure / Smilin' on ya.
7" Single: Released Oct '80, on A&M, by A&M Records. Deleted '83. Catalogue no: **AMS 7561**

Johnson, Bryan

LOOKING HIGH HIGH HIGH
Tracks: / Looking high high high.
7" Single: Released Mar '60, on Decca, by Decca Records. Deleted '63. Catalogue no: **F 11213**

Johnson, Carey

REAL FASHION REGGAE STYLE
Tracks: / Real fashion reggae style (On 7" only) / Real fashion reggae style (version) / Real fashion reggae style (extended version) (On 12" only).
7" Single: Released May '86, on 10 Records, by Virgin Records. Catalogue no: **TEN 170**
12" Single: Released May '86, on 10 Records, by Virgin Records. Catalogue no: **TENT 170**

TYPICAL JAMAICAN
Tracks: / Typical Jamaican / Typical Jamaican.
12" Single: Released Sep '87, on 10 Records, by Virgin Records. Deleted May '88. Catalogue no: **TENT 197**
7" Single: Released Sep '87, on 10 Records, by Virgin Records. Deleted May '88. Catalogue no: **TEN 197**

Johnson, Carl

DON'T WANT TO BE ALONE
Tracks: / Don't want to be alone.
12" Single: Released Mar '85, on B.B. Music, Catalogue no: **BBD 162**

FATTY FATTY
Tracks: / Fatty fatty / Fatty fatty.
12" Single: Released Feb '87, on Jumbo, Catalogue no: **JMD 1010**

I WISH HE DIDN'T TRUST ME SO MUCH
Tracks: / I wish he didn't trust me so much.
12" Single: Released Nov '85, on B.B. Music, Catalogue no: **BBD 171**

Johnson, Chico

HULA HOOP
Tracks: / Hula hoop.
7" Single: Released Jun '84, on Panther, by MCA Records. Catalogue no: **PAN 2**
12" Single: Released Jun '84, on Panther, by MCA Records. Catalogue no: **PANT 2**

LOOP DE LOOP WITH THE PEPPERMINT HOOP
Tracks: / Loop de loop with the peppermint hoop.
7" Single: Released Oct '83, on Tivoli, by Tivoli Records. Catalogue no: **TIV 3**
12" Single: Released Oct '83, on Tivoli, by Tivoli Records. Catalogue no: **TVT 3**

MISS THING
Tracks: / Miss thing.
12" Single: Released Jan '85, on Splash, by Splash Records. Catalogue no: **12SP 27**

Johnson, Don

HEARTACHE AWAY
Tracks: / Heartache away / Love roulette.
12" Single: Released Nov '86, on Epic, by CBS Records. Catalogue no: **650203 6**
7" Single: Released Nov '86, on Epic, by CBS Records. Catalogue no: **650203 7**

HEARTBEAT (SINGLE)
Tracks: / Heartbeat.
12" Single: Released Aug '87, on Epic, by CBS Records. Catalogue no: **650064 6**
7" Single: Released Aug '87, on Epic, by CBS Records. Catalogue no: **650064 7**

TELL IT LIKE IT IS
Tracks: / Tell it like it is / Heartbeat / Heartache away.
CD 5": Released 12 Jun '89, on Epic, by CBS Records. Catalogue no: **654976 2**
7" Single: Released 12 Jun '89, on Epic, by CBS Records. Catalogue no: **654976 7**
12" Single: Released 12 Jun '89, on Epic, by CBS Records. Catalogue no: **654976 8**

Johnson Engineering

THUG
Tracks: / Thug.
7" Single: Released 14 Aug '88, on Gigantic, by Gigantic Records. Catalogue no: **GI 003**

Johnson, Frankie

BACK IN THE GROOVE
Tracks: / Back in the groove / Maybe tonight.
7" Single: Released Apr '89, on Polydor, by Polydor Ltd. Catalogue no: **FJ 2**
12" Single: Released Apr '89, on Polydor, by Polydor Ltd. Catalogue no: **FJX 2**

T.R.O.U.B.L.E.
Tracks: / T.R.O.U.B.L.E. / Why is it? / T.R.O.U.B.L.E. (dub mix) (Available on 12" only).
7" Single: Released May '88, on Polydor, by Polydor Ltd. Catalogue no: **FJ 1**
12" Single: Released May '88, on Polydor, by Polydor Ltd. Catalogue no: **FJX 1**

Johnson, Frankie Jr.

WHENEVER YOU CALL ME
Tracks: / Whenever you call me / Whenever you call me (remix) / Whenever you call me (Instrumental remix).
7" Single: Released Feb '86, on Debut, by Skratch Records. Catalogue no: **DEBT 3003**
12" Single: Released Feb '86, on Debut, by Skratch Records. Catalogue no: **DEBTX 3003**
12" Single: Released Feb '86, on Debut, by Skratch Records. Catalogue no: **DEBTXR 3003**

Johnson, Holly

AMERICANOS
Tracks: / Americanos.
CD 5": Released 20 Mar '89, on MCA, by MCA Records. Catalogue no: **DMCAT 1323**
Cassingle: Released 20 Mar '89, on MCA, by MCA Records. Catalogue no: **MCAC 1323**
7" Single: Released 20 Mar '89, on MCA, by MCA Records. Catalogue no: **MCA 1323**
12" Single: Released Apr '89, on MCA, by MCA Records. Catalogue no: **MCAX 1323**
12" Single: Released 20 Mar '89, on MCA, by MCA Records. Catalogue no: **MCAT 1323**

ATOMIC CITY (SINGLE)
Tracks: / Atomic city.
CD 5": Released May '89, on MCA, by MCA Records. Catalogue no: **DMCAT 1342**
Cassingle: Released May '89, on MCA, by MCA Records. Catalogue no: **MCAC 1342**
12" Single: Released Jul '89, on MCA, by MCA Records. Catalogue no: **MCAX 1342**
12" Single: Released May '89, on MCA, by MCA Records. Catalogue no: **MCAT 1342**

HEAVEN'S HERE
Tracks: / Heaven's here.
CD 5": Released Sep '89, on MCA, by MCA Records. Catalogue no: **DMCAT 1365**
7" Pic: Released Sep '89, on MCA, by MCA Records. Catalogue no: **MCAP 1365**
Cassingle: Released Sep '89, on MCA, by MCA Records. Catalogue no: **MCAC 1365**
7" Single: Released Sep '89, on MCA, by MCA Records. Catalogue no: **MCA 1365**
12" Single: Released Sep '89, on MCA, by MCA Records. Catalogue no: **MCAT 1365**

LOVE TRAIN
Tracks: / Love train.
7" Single: Released Jan '89, on MCA, by MCA Records. Catalogue no: **MCA 1306**
12" Single: Released Jan '89, on MCA, by MCA Records. Catalogue no: **MCAT 1306**
CD 3": Released Jan '89, on MCA, by MCA Records. Catalogue no: **DMCA 1306**

Johnson, Howard

Biographical details: Johnson, Howard This American singer scored a one-off UK chart entry in 1982 with his double A sided single *Keepin' Love New/So Fine*, which reached No.45. Initially the record company tried to market *Keepin. Love New* as the major side; but British clubs had already established the exuberant and infectious *So Fine* as a firm dancefloor import favourite, and it was this track which got the upper hand. Both songs were written by Johnson's mentor Kashif, who enjoyed simulataneous success as writer of Evelyn King's UK Top 10 hit *Love Come Down*. For his next LP Johnson turned to the production talents of David Frank and Mic Murphy who were better knwon to club dancers as the System - the *Doin' It My Way* album was another well made set of disco shufflers, although this fun funk concoction did not give Johnson another pop chart entry. And no. Frank Sinatra was not involved in *Doin' It My Way*. (Bob Macdonald 14/11/85).

KEEPIN' LOVE NEW
Tracks: / Keepin' love new / So fine.
7" Single: Released Aug '82, on A&M, by A&M Records. Deleted Aug '85. Catalogue no: **USAF 1221**

SAY YOU WANNA
Tracks: / Say you wanna / Jam song.
12" Single: Released Jan '83, on Funk America, by A&M Records. Catalogue no: **USAF 1226**

SO FINE
Tracks: / So fine / Keepin' love new.
Note: Full details see under BROTHERS JOHNSON "Stomp"
7" Single: Released Sep '82, on A&M, by A&M Records. Deleted '85. Catalogue no: **USA 1221**

Johnson, J.C.

WE CALL IT CHRISTMAS
Tracks: / We call it Christmas / We call it Christmas.
7" Single: Released Nov '84, on Open Space, Catalogue no: **OS 90**

Johnson, Jesse

BE YOUR MAN
Tracks: / Be your man / Special love.
7" Single: Released Apr '85, on A&M, by A&M Records. Deleted '88. Catalogue no: **AM 244**
12" Single: Released Apr '85, on A&M, by A&M Records. Deleted '88. Catalogue no: **AMY 244**

CAN YOU HELP ME
Tracks: / Can you help me.
7" Single: Released Jun '85, on A&M, by A&M Records. Deleted '88. Catalogue no: **AM 259**
12" Single: Released Jun '85, on A&M, by A&M Records. Deleted '88. Catalogue no: **AMY 259**

CRAZAY
Tracks: / Crazay / I'm your man.
7" Single: Released Nov '86, on A&M, by A&M Records. Deleted Mar '88. Catalogue no: **AM 360**
12" Single: Released Nov '86, on A&M, by A&M Records. Deleted Mar '88. Catalogue no: **AMY 360**

EVERY SHADE OF LOVE (SINGLE)
Tracks: / Every shade of love / Lovestruck.
7" Single: Released 5 Sep '88, on Breakout, by A&M Records. Deleted Feb '89. Catalogue no: **USA 637**
12" Single: Released 5 Sep '88, on Breakout, by A&M Records. Deleted Feb '89. Catalogue no: **USAT 637**

LOVESTRUCK
Tracks: / Lovestruck / Do yourself a favour.
Note: Anyone remotely familiar with the musical outpourings from the twin cities of Minneapolis over the last decade will already be well attuned to the talents of singer/songwriter/producer Jesse Johnson. As a member of funk outfit The Time, Johnson, alongside the likes of Morris Day, was one of the major figures on America's dance scene. Since the band's demise in the early 80's, Johnson has embarked on a production, songwriting and recording career, working a host of top names, including Janet Jackson. (A & M Records, May 88.)
7" Single: Released May '88, on Breakout, by A&M Records. Deleted Feb '89. Catalogue no: **USA 628**
12" Single: Released May '88, on Breakout, by A&M Records. Deleted Feb '89. Catalogue no: **USAT 628**

SHE (I CAN'T RESIST)
Tracks: / She (I can't resist) / She (I can't resist) (Version) / Crazay (Only available on 12" version.).

Note: Crazay is an extra track which is only available on the 12" version.
7" Single: Released Feb '87, on A&M, by A&M Records. Deleted Mar '88. Catalogue no: **AM 382**
12" Single: Released Feb '87, on A&M, by A&M Records. Deleted Mar '88. Catalogue no: **AMY 382**

Johnson, Joe

BRADFORD
Tracks: / Bradford / Bradford.
7" Single: Released Jun '87, on Hit The Deck, Deleted '88. Catalogue no: **CRUISE 2**

Johnson, Johnny

BLAME IT ON THE PONY EXPRESS
Tracks: / Blame it on the pony express.
7" Single: Released Nov '70, on Bell, Deleted '73. Catalogue no: **BELL 1128**

BREAKIN' DOWN THE WALLS OF HEARTACHE
Tracks: / Breakin' down the walls of heartache / Dancing master.
7" Single: Released Mar '80, on Epic, by CBS Records. Deleted Mar '83. Catalogue no: **EPC 8315**
7" Single: Released Oct '68, on Direction, Deleted '71. Catalogue no: **58-3670**

LET'S HANG ON
Tracks: / Let's hang on.
7" Single: Released May '69, on Direction, Deleted '72. Catalogue no: **58-4180**

SWEET INSPIRATION
Tracks: / Sweet inspiration.
7" Single: Released Jul '70, on Bell, Deleted '73. Catalogue no: **BELL 1111**

YOU
Tracks: / You.
7" Single: Released Feb '69, on Direction, Deleted '72. Catalogue no: **58-3923**

Johnson, Kenny

ALL THE KINGS HORSES
Tracks: / All the kings horses.
7" Single: Released Dec '82, on OBM, by RK Records. Deleted '83. Catalogue no: **OBM 7010**

CITY LIGHTS
Tracks: / City lights / Paris and Amsterdam nights.
7" Single: Released Mar '80, on OBM, by RK Records. Deleted '83. Catalogue no: **OBM 1004**

ONE KISS
Tracks: / One kiss / Rock steady.
7" Single: Released Nov '80, on OBM, by RK Records. Deleted '83. Catalogue no: **OBM 1006**

TREE IN THE MEADOW
Tracks: / Tree in the meadow / Today.
7" Single: Released May '81, on OBM, by RK Records. Deleted May '86. Catalogue no: **OBM 1008**

Johnson, Kevin

Biographical details: Johnson, Kevin This Australian singer achieved a one off UK chart entry in 1975, reaching No.23 with his single *Rock'n'Roll (I Gave You The Best Years Of My Life)*. It was a moving folk/pop/rock song telling the story of an also ran musician who had struggled through the Sixties and Seventies seeking his fame and fortune as a rock star, but who finally realised that he was always one step behind the times and was destined never to make it. Johnson, who also produced the record gave it an emotional but controlled treatment. In the States, the song was a No,15 hit for Mac Davis. There was a third version in circulation at the time by Terry Jacks, but this flopped.
Johnson's single came to the British charts cia Jonathan King's UK record label. (Bob Macdonald 14/11/85).

ROCK'N'ROLL (I GAVE YOU THE BEST YEARS)
Tracks: / Rock 'n' roll (I gave you the best years).
7" Single: Released Jan '75, on UK, by UK Records. Deleted '78. Catalogue no: **UKR 84**

Johnson, Laurie

Biographical details: Johnson, Laurie This British orchestra leader and composer enjoyed a one off Uk chart entry in 1961, reaching No.9 with his ensemble's rendition of *Sucu Sucu*. By getting this high up the chart, Johnson emerged as the runaway winner amongst no less than five simulataneous charted versions of the tune; among the people he beat were two far more famous bandleaders, Ted Heath and Joe Loss.
Johnson subsequently became in demand for television themes, incidental music and similar assignments - he provided the music for such series as 'The Avengers', 'The New Avengers' and 'The Professionals'. (Bob Macdonald 14/11/85).

PROFESSIONALS MAIN THEME
Tracks: / Professionals (main theme) / New Avengers.
7" Single: Released Mar '85, on Unicorn-Kanchana, by Unicorn - Kanchana Records. Catalogue no: **C15**

SUCU SUCU
Tracks: / Sucu sucu.
7" Single: Released Sep '61, on Pye, Deleted '64. Catalogue no: **7N 15383**

Johnson, Linton Kwesi

Biographical details: Johnson, Linton Kwesi This Jamaican poet moved to Britain in 1963, at the age of 11, with his mother. Linton has lived in the Brixton area of South London ever since. He achieved an honours degree in sociology at London University, which proved to be a vital asset in his later career. He began writing poetry on a serious basis in 1971 and had two books of verse published in the mid-seventies, 'Voices of the Living And The Dead' and 'Dread Beat and Blood'. The latter title was also used as the name for his recording debut, a 12-inch EP released in 1977. The disc was credited to Poet & The Roots - a pseudonym for Johnson and a reggae backing band which included Dennis Bovell, leader of the group Matumbi.
When th punk explosion happened in Britain in the late Seventies, it spawned the punk poet John Cooper Clarke. That whole scene was said to have a great affinity with reggae music and Linton Kwesi Johnson emerged as the reggae equivalent of Clarke. Setting his words against an infectious musical backing, Johnson began to attract a larger and larger cult following for his keenly political work. In 1979 he singed with Island Records, a label who were famous for their long standing support of reggae music.
Johnson's first Island LP *Forces of Victory* reached No.66 on the British album chart in June 1979. The follow up set *Bass Culture* reached No.46 in late 1980. His subsequent career has been steady, his status having neither increased nor diminished.
Johnson's most common concerns have been th role and aspirations of Britain's ethnic minorities vis-a-vis such predominantly white institutions as the police, the government and society at large. His work has often been biting and bitter, reflecting the anger surrounding such events as th Southall riots and the New Cross massacre. Linton's best known track is probably *Want Fi Goh Rave*, the opening piece of *Forces of Victory*. (Bob Macdonald 14/11/85).

DI BLACK PETTY BOOSHWAH
Tracks: / Di black petty booshwah / Straight to Madray's head / Action line (Only on 12" single.) / Action dub (Only on 12" single.).
7" Single: Released Feb '80, on Island, by Island Records. Deleted '83. Catalogue no: **WIP 6554**
12" Single: Released Feb '80, on Island, by Island Records. Deleted '83. Catalogue no: **12WIP 6554**

Johnson, L.J.

YOUR MAGIC PUT A SPELL ON ME
Tracks: / Your magic put a spell on me / Spellbound.
7" Single: Released Feb '76, on Philips, by Phonogram Ltd. Deleted '79. Catalogue no: **6006 492**

Johnson, Lorenza

LOVE PAINS
Tracks: / Love pains.
12" Single: Released Jun '86, on Long Island Sound, Catalogue no: **MTDX 101**

SPARE A THOUGHT FOR SANTA
Tracks: / Spare a thought for Santa / Come back home my love.
7" Single: Released Jan '81, on Eagle (London), by Eagle (London) Records. Deleted Jan '84. Catalogue no: **ERS 005**

Johnson, Lou

AIN'T GONNA BE THAT WAY
Tracks: / Ain't gonna be that way.
7" Single: Released Aug '60, on London-American, Deleted '63. Catalogue no: **HLT 9156**

I LOVE THE WAY YOU LOVE
Tracks: / I love the way you love.
7" Single: Released May '60, on London-American, Deleted '63. Catalogue no: **HLT 9109**

I MISS YOU BABY
Tracks: / I miss you baby.
7" Single: Released Oct '69, on Motown, by BMG Records (UK). Deleted '72. Catalogue no: **TMG 713**

MESSAGE TO MARTHA
Tracks: / Message to Martha.
7" Single: Released Nov '64, on London-American, Deleted '67. Catalogue no: **HL 9929**

Johnson, Marv

Biographical details: Johnson, Marv This American singer was born in Detroit in 1938, just the right time and place to get involved with Betty Gordy at the end of the Fifties. Johnson's first single *Come To Me* was the debut disc of the Tamla Motown organisation, although at that time Gordy had not actually made Tamla into a fully fledged label.
Marv was just 13 years old when he formed his first vocal group called The Serenaders; during his teenage years, he was also involved in amateur dramatics, in acting and production capacities. *Come To Me* reached No.30 on the US chart in 1959, and was followed in 1960 by three Top 20 singles - *You Got What It Takes*, *I Love The Way You Love* and *(You've Got To) Move Two Mountains*. Produced and mainly written by Gordy these were early incarnations of the 'Motown sound' that became so famous later in the Sixties. In Britain *You Got What It Takes* reached No.5 (and was taken to No.2 many years later in a revival by Showaddywaddy).
Johnson failed to consolidate upon his 1960 breakthrough and faded from the public eye until 1966's *I' Miss You Baby*. 1969 brought him his second UK Top 10 hit with *I'll Pick A Rose For My Rose*, but this was not a hit in America. Considering he had been associated with Motown's formative years, it was strange that Johnson could not compete more effectively with his Tamla colleagues after the 'sound' had become successful. But if the Sixties were erratic for Marc, the Seventies were barren. (Bob Macdonald 14/11/85).

I'LL PICK A ROSE FOR MY ROSE
Tracks: / I'll pick a rose for my rose.
7" Single: Released Jan '69, on Motown, by BMG Records (UK). Deleted '72. Catalogue no: **TMG 680**
7" Single: Released Oct '81, on Motown, by BMG Records (UK). Catalogue no: **TMG 1052**

YOU GOT WHAT IT TAKES
Tracks: / You got what it takes.
7" Single: Released Feb '60, on London-American, Deleted '63. Catalogue no: **HLT 9013**

Johnson, Orlando

JUST A KISS
Tracks: / Just a kiss.
7" Single: Released Mar '85, on Eden, Catalogue no: **XTC 12**
12" Single: Released Mar '85, on Eden, Catalogue no: **XTCT 12**

TURN THE MUSIC ON
Tracks: / Turn the music on.
7" Single: Released Jul '83, on Magnet, by WEA Records. Catalogue no: **MAG 246**
12" Single: Released Jul '83, on Magnet, by WEA Records. Catalogue no: **12 MAG 246**

Johnson, Paul

ARE WE STRONG ENOUGH
Tracks: / Are we strong enough / Intimate friends / Where can you be.
7" EP: Released Aug '87, on CBS, by CBS Records. Catalogue no: **PJOHN E3**
7" Single: Released Jul '87, on CBS, by CBS Records. Catalogue no: **PJOHN 3**
12" Single: Released Jul '87, on CBS, by CBS Records. Catalogue no: **PJOHNQ 3**
12" Single: Released Jul '87, on CBS, by CBS Records. Catalogue no: **PJOHNT 3**

BURNIN'
Tracks: / Burnin' / Wonder of you, The.
7" EP: Released Jan '88, on CBS, by CBS Records. Deleted Aug '88. Catalogue no: **PJOHN E5**
CD 5": Released Dec '87, on CBS, by CBS Records. Deleted Jan '89. Catalogue no: **PJOHNC 5**
7" Single: Released Dec '87, on CBS, by CBS Records. Deleted Aug '88. Catalogue no: **PJOHN 5**
12" Single: Released Jan '88, on CBS, by CBS Records. Deleted Aug '88. Catalogue no: **P JOHN T5**

EVERY KINDA PEOPLE
Tracks: / Burnin' / Every kinda people / Believer / Burnin' (extended mix).
CD 5": Released Mar '88, on CBS, by CBS Records. Deleted Jan '89. Catalogue no: **PJOHN C6**
12" Pic: Released Mar '88, on CBS, by CBS Records. Deleted Aug '88. Catalogue no: **PJOHNT 6**
7" Pic: Released Mar '88, on CBS, by CBS Records. Deleted Aug '88. Catalogue no: **PJOHN 6**

FEAR OF FALLING
Tracks: / Fear of falling / That was yesterday / Fear of falling (live) / Tell me something good (live).
7" Single: Released Oct '87, on CBS, by CBS Records. Catalogue no: **PJOHN 4**
12" Single: Released Oct '87, on CBS, by CBS Records. Deleted Jun '88. Catalogue no: **PJOHN Q4**
12" Single: Released Oct '87, on CBS, by CBS Records. Catalogue no: **PJOHN T4**

HALF A WORLD AWAY
Tracks: / Half a world away / Where can you be (Not on CBS PJON 52) / When love comes calling* (* On PJON 52 only).
7" Single: Released May '87, on CBS, by CBS Records. Deleted Nov '87. Catalogue no: **PJOHN 2**
12" Single: Released 23 May '87, on CBS, by CBS Records. Catalogue no: **PJON 52**
12" Single: Released May '87, on CBS, by CBS Records. Deleted Nov '87. Catalogue no: **PJOHNT 2**

MASQUERADE
Tracks: / Masquerade (Only on 7" and CD single.) / Personal (Only on 7" and CD single.) / Masquerade (extended version) (Only on 12" and CD single.) / You're no good (deep house mix) (Only on 12" single.) / You're no good (Only on CD single.) / New love (Only on EP) / Where can you be (Only on EP).
7" EP: Released 14 Aug '89, on CBS, by CBS Records. Catalogue no: **PJOHNE 8**
CD 5": Released Jul '89, on CBS, by CBS Records. Catalogue no: **PJOHNC 8**
7" Single: Released Jul '89, on CBS, by CBS Records. Catalogue no: **PJOHN 8**
12" Single: Released Jul '89, on CBS, by CBS Records. Catalogue no: **PJOHNT 8**

NO MORE TOMORROWS
Tracks: / No more tomorrows / I don't care / No more tomorrows (extended) (On CD & 12" only.) / Hold on I'm coming (On CD & 12" only.) / That was yesterday (On CD only.).
7" EP: Released Feb '89, on CBS, by CBS Records. Deleted 10 Jul '89. Catalogue no: **PJOHN E7**
CD 5": Released 6 Feb '89, on CBS, by CBS Records. Deleted 10 Jul '89. Catalogue no: **PJOHN C7**
7" Single: Released 6 Feb '89, on CBS, by CBS Records. Deleted 10 Jul '89. Catalogue no: **PJOHN 7**
12" Single: Released 20 Feb '89, on CBS, by CBS Records. Deleted 10 Jul '89. Catalogue no: **PJOHN Q7**
12" Single: Released 6 Feb '89, on CBS, by CBS Records. Deleted 10 Jul '89. Catalogue no: **PJOHN T7**

WHEN LOVE COMES CALLING
Tracks: / When love comes calling / Don't pass me by.
7" Single: Released Jan '87, on CBS, by CBS Records. Deleted Aug '87. Catalogue no: **PJOHN 1**
12" Single: Released Jan '87, on CBS, by CBS Records. Deleted Aug '87. Catalogue no: **PJOHNT 1**

Johnson, Robb

ANIMAL SONG, THE
Tracks: / Animal song, The.
7" Single: Released Jan '89, on Arfa, Catalogue no: **AFA 005**

Johnson, Sly

MS FINE BROWN FRAME
Tracks: / Ms. Fine brown frame / You don't have to go.
7" Single: Released Jan '73, on Epic, by CBS Records. Catalogue no: **EPC A 3016**
12" Single: Released Jan '73, on Epic, by CBS Records. Catalogue no: **EPC A 13 3016**

Johnson, Tex

BABY MY LOVE
Tracks: / Baby my love.
12" Single: Released Feb '89, on Disco Tex, Catalogue no: **DT 26**

BODY SNATCH
Tracks: / Body snatch.
12" Single: Released Nov '83, on Lovely, Catalogue no: **LL 001**

CAN'T GET BY WITHOUT YOU
Tracks: / Can't get by without you.
12" Single: Released Jun '83, on Disco Tex, Catalogue no: **DT 6**

CROWD OF PEOPLE
Tracks: / Crowd of people / Road block.
12" Single: Released Sep '84, on Disco Tex, Catalogue no: **DT 9**

EVER SO HAPPY
Tracks: / Ever so happy / Feeling happy.
12" Single: Released Mar '87, on Robin Hood, Catalogue no: **RH 001**

EYE TO EYE
Tracks: / Eye to eye.
7" Single: Released 21 Apr '89, on Disco Tex, Catalogue no: **DT 29**

FAITHFULLY YOURS
Tracks: / Faithfully yours.
12" Single: Released Mar '85, Catalogue no: **UNKNOWN**

GIRL NEXT DOOR, THE
Tracks: / Girl next door, The.
12" Single: Released Oct '88, on Uptempo, Catalogue no: **TEMP 027**

GIVE US A CHANCE
Tracks: / Give us a chance / Hard road.
12" Single: Released Nov '86, on Sky

Juice, Catalogue no: **SJD 018**

KEEP ON LOVING ME
Tracks: / Keep on loving me / Ecstasy.
12" Single: Released Nov '85, on Disco Tex, Catalogue no: **DT 16**

KNOCK A DANCE STYLE
Tracks: / Knock a dance style.
12" Single: Released Jun '82, on S & D, Catalogue no: **SD 003**

LOVE TO LOVE YOU
Tracks: / Love to love you.
12" Single: Released Jun '82, on Disco Tex, Catalogue no: **DT 2**

PILLOW TALK
Tracks: / Pillow talk.
12" Single: Released Apr '82, on Disco Tex, Catalogue no: **DT 1**

SONG BOOK OF LOVE
Tracks: / Song book of love.
12" Single: Released May '89, on Disco Tex, Catalogue no: **DT 30**

STILL IN LOVE WITH YOU
Tracks: / Still in love with you.
12" Single: Released Oct '85, on Disco Tex, Catalogue no: **DT 14**

WOMANISER
Tracks: / Womaniser.
12" Single: Released Dec '83, on Disco Tex, Catalogue no: **DT 7**

Johnson, T.J.

FIRE FLY
Tracks: / Fire fly / Fire fly (instrumental).
7" Single: Released Nov '88, on Slick, by Slick Records. Catalogue no: **D SLK 01**
12" Single: Released Nov '88, on Slick, by Slick Records. Catalogue no: **12SLK 01**

I CAN MAKE IT GOOD FOR YOU
Tracks: / I can make it good for you.
7" Single: Released Jul '83, on Switch, Catalogue no: **SW 5**
12" Single: Released Jul '83, on Switch, Catalogue no: **DSW 005**

PRETTY LADY
Tracks: / Pretty lady.
7" Single: Released May '82, on Switch, Catalogue no: **SW 1**

Johnson, Wilko

BOTTLE UP AND GO
Tracks: / Bottle up and go.
Note: Two top league pub rockers team up with four great original titles. (Magnum Music Msy, 1988).
7" EP: Released Jul '83, on Thunderbolt, by Magnum Music Group. Catalogue no: **THBE 001**

CASTING MY SPELL ON YOU
Tracks: / Casting my spell on you / Looked out of my window.
7" Single: Released Sep '81, on Fresh, by Jetstar Records. Deleted '84. Catalogue no: **FRESH 31**

DOWN BY THE WATERSIDE
Tracks: / Down by the waterside.
7" Single: Released Mar '80, on Rockburgh, Deleted '82. Catalogue no: **ROCS 220**

Johnston Brothers

GIVE HER MY LOVE
Tracks: / Give her my love.
7" Single: Released Feb '57, on Decca, by Decca Records. Deleted '60. Catalogue no: **F 10828**

HEART
Tracks: / Heart.
7" Single: Released May '57, on Decca, by Decca Records. Deleted '60. Catalogue no: **F 10860**

HERNANDO'S HIDEAWAY
Tracks: / Hernando's hideaway.
7" Single: Released Oct '55, on Decca, by Decca Records. Deleted '58. Catalogue no: **F 10608**

IN THE MIDDLE OF THE HOUSE
Tracks: / In the middle of the house.
7" Single: Released Nov '56, on Decca, by Decca Records. Deleted '59. Catalogue no: **F 10781**

JOIN IN & SING AGAIN
Tracks: / Join in & sing again (medley).
7" Single: Released Dec '56, on Decca, by Decca Records. Deleted '59. Catalogue no: **F 10814**
7" Single: Released Dec '55, on Decca, by Decca Records. Deleted '58. Catalogue no: **F 10636**

NO OTHER LOVE
Tracks: / No other love.
7" Single: Released Dec '55, on Decca, by Decca Records. Deleted '58. Catalogue no: **F 10721**

OH HAPPY DAY
Tracks: / Oh happy day.
7" Single: Released Apr '53, on Decca, by Decca Records. Deleted '57. Catalogue no: **F 10071**

Johnston, Bruce

PIPELINE
Tracks: / Pipeline.
7" Single: Released Aug '77, on CBS, by CBS Records. Deleted '80. Catalogue no: **CBS 5514**

Johnston, Kenny

ALL THE KING'S HORSES
Tracks: / All the king's horses / Total strangers.
7" Single: Released Dec '82, on OBM, by RK Records. Deleted Dec '85. Catalogue no: **OBM 7010**

Johnston, Sophie &

HAPPY TOGETHER
Tracks: / Happy together / Sold on you / Losing you (Extra track on 12" version only).
7" Single: Released Aug '86, on I Major, by I Major Records. Catalogue no: **YZ 78**
12" Single: Released Aug '86, on I Major, by I Major Records. Deleted Jun '87. Catalogue no: **YZ 78T**

LOSING YOU
Tracks: / Losing you.
7" Single: Released Oct '85, on Smash The Majors, Catalogue no: **SPJ 1**

TORN OPEN
Tracks: / Torn open / Getting on.
7" Single: Released 23 May '87, on I Major, by I Major Records. Deleted Jul '88. Catalogue no: **YZ 128**
12" Single: Released 23 May '87, on I Major, by I Major Records. Deleted Jul '88. Catalogue no: **YZ 128T**

TV SATELLITE
Tracks: / T.V. satellite / Take that jerkin' off / TX 45 (On 12" only).
7" Single: Released Sep '87, on I Major, by I Major Records. Deleted Jul '88. Catalogue no: **YZ 143**
12" Single: Released Sep '87, on I Major, by I Major Records. Deleted Jul '88. Catalogue no: **YZ 143T**

Johnstone, Jim

HOP SCOTCH CHRISTMAS
Tracks: / Hop scotch Christmas.
7" Single: Released Dec '83, on Ross, by Ross Records. Catalogue no: **SWGR 009**

Jo-Joanne

I'M IN LOVE WITH A ROCK 'N' ROLL STAR
Tracks: / I'm in love with a rock 'n' roll star / Wet T-shirt.
7" Single: Released Aug '82, on RCA, by BMG Records (UK). Deleted Aug '85. Catalogue no: **RCA 231**

Joker

BACK ON THE ROAD
Tracks: / Back on the road / Pusher.
7" Single: Released Feb '85, on Lost Moments, Catalogue no: **LM 018**

Jokers Wild

DON'T FALL IN LOVE
Tracks: / Don't fall in love.
7" Single: Released Sep '87, on Bold Reprieve (1), Catalogue no: **BRM 005**

Joli, France

FEEL LIKE DANCING
Tracks: / Feel like dancing / Tough luck.
7" Single: Released Aug '80, on Ariola, by BMG Records (UK). Deleted '83. Catalogue no: **ARO 240**

Joliffe, John

ALAMEIN
Tracks: / Alamein / Ships in the night.
7" Single: Released Oct '86, on Carrere, Catalogue no: **CAR 405**
12" Single: Released Oct '86, on Carrere, Catalogue no: **CART 405**

PLAYING WITH FIRE
Tracks: / Playing with fire / Dancing with myself.
7" Single: Released Jun '86, on Carrere, Catalogue no: **CAR 390**
12" Single: Released Jun '86, on Carrere, Catalogue no: **CART 390**

Joling, Gerard

LOVE IS IN YOUR EYES
Tracks: / Love is in your eyes.
7" Single: Released Aug '85, on WEA, by WEA Records. Catalogue no: **X 9085**

TICKET TO THE TROPICS
Tracks: / Ticket to the tropics / Communications.
7" Single: Released Feb '86, on WEA, by WEA Records. Catalogue no: **X 8954**

JOLLY BROTHERS - CONSCIOUS MAN (Released on Decca)

Jolling, Gerard

NO MORE BOLLEROS
Tracks: / No more bolleros.
7" Single: Released Sep '89, on Mercury, by Phonogram Ltd. Catalogue no: **MER 307**

Jolly Brothers

CONSCIOUS MAN (see panel above)
Tracks: / Conscious man / Conscious dub.
7" Single: Released Jul '79, on Decca, by Decca Records. Deleted '83. Catalogue no: **UP 36415**

Jolly Roger

ACID MAN
Tracks: / Acid man (original mix) (On all versions) / Acid man (happy mix) (On all versions) / Acid man (techno mix) (On TENR 236).
7" Single: Released Aug '88, on 10 Records, by Virgin Records. Catalogue no: **TEN 236**
12" Single: Released Aug '88, on 10 Records, by Virgin Records. Catalogue no: **TENR 236**
12" Single: Released Aug '88, on 10 Records, by Virgin Records. Catalogue no: **TENX 236**

WHY CAN'T WE LIVE TOGETHER
Tracks: / Why can't we live together.
7" Single: Released Aug '89, on Desire, by Desire Records. Catalogue no: **WANT 17**
12" Single: Released Aug '89, on Desire, by Desire Records. Catalogue no: **WANTX 17**

Jolo

SOUL
Tracks: / Soul (club mix) / Soul (instrumental) / Last call.
12" Single: Released Jan '87, on Greyhound, by Greyhound Records. Catalogue no: **GRY 008**

Jolson, Al

Biographical details: Al Jolson (real name Asa Yoelson) was born in St.Petersburg, Russia on March 26th 1886. After emigrating to the United States (they settled in Washington, D.C.), his family tried to make him follow a religious career (his father was a rabbi) but Joley, as he was known, decided to leave home and began singing with a minstrel troupe in vaudeville. He made his Broadway debut in 1911 in "La Belle Paree" - which led to starring roles in a string of musicals such as "Vera Violetta" , "The Whirl Of Society, "The Honeymoon Express", "Sinbad", and "Robinson Crusoe Jnr". Songs such as "Swanee" and "April Showers" became worldwide hits. His first talkie was the 1926 short "April Showers" but it was his 1927 appearance in "The Jazz Singer" which made him really popular. A second film "The Singing Fool", with "Sonny Boy" and "There's a rainbow round my shoulder" was a massive box-office success - Al Jolson was a celebrity. But the crash on Wall Street and the depression signalled a downward trend in his career - Bing Crosby was the nation's favourite at this time - and even his wife, Ruby Keeler, was more successful. The thirties were frustrating times for Al Jolson but things began to look up again with appearances in minor hits such as "Rose of Washington Square" in 1939 and "Swanee River" in 1940. The United States was however at war and the nation preferred the swing bands of Glenn Miller, Benny Goodman and Artie Shaw - and the voices of Frank Sinatra and Perry Como. But he was rediscovered by the masses in the Columbia picture "The Jolson Story" - a biographical film - based around his best songs, with Larry Parkes playing Jolson, and Jolson singing the songs. Al Jolson died in San Francisco in 1950.
This American singer and entertainter was the first great popular vocalist of the 20th century. He was born Asa Joelson in 1886 and was raised in Washington DC. His father, an orthodox rabbi, gave him singing tuition as he grew up and he made his debut stage appearance at the age of 13. At about the same time, he took up a role as a cantor in his father's Jewish synagogue in Washington. The ambition to become a popular singer evantually proved too strong and he went onto the road with travelling circuses and minstrel shows. He was working in New York in 1909 when a member of the entourage suggested that he should adopt a blackface routine as his permanent stage trademark.
According to Joseph Murrels' book 'The records that sold a million', Jolson's first major disc success occured in 1912 with *Ragging The Baby To Sleep* and he scored another winner in 1913 with *The Spaniard that Blighted My Life*. This was the height of the ragtime era, and Jolson proved himself adept at capitalising on a genre that was principally tailored for the piano rather than the human voice.
By the early Twenties, ragtime was out of favour and had been supplanted by jazz. Jolson adapted accordingly. He made history in the cinematic world in 1927 when he starred in 'The Jazz Singer', the first ever 'talkie'. This made him a major international star, a position he consolidated the following year with his next musical move 'The Singing Fool'. As the Twenties ended, his status began to diminish. He remained active during the Thirties and early Forties with further films, plus stage shows like 'Wonder Bar' and 'Hold On To Your Hars', but it was definitely the mediocre period of his career.
During the years of America's involvement in the Second World War, the singer spent his time entertaining the troops overseas. He made a major showbusiness comeback in 1946 with the movie 'The Jolson Story', in which Al sang the songs on the soundtrack but was portrayed in the film by Larry parks. A series of hit records occured during this time, as if Jolson had never been away from the limelight - these included *April Showers, Rockabye Your Baby With A Dixie Melody, Anniversary Song* and several others. A second retrospective movie 'Jolson sings again' appeared in 1950, the same year that the singer died. He has just returned from entertaining the US forces in

Korea, when he suffered a heart attack in San Fransisco in October '50 at the age of 64. During the rock era many music fans grew up with little or no knowledge of Al Jolson ; in an era when the western world was moving towards greater equality and developing more sophisticated attitudes towards racial matters, few people were interested in reviving the memory of a non-black who wore a painted negro face, even though he was a great artist. There was, however, a resurgence of interest in 1980 thanks to Neil Diamond and Sir Laurence Olivier's remake of 'The Jazz Singer'. Diamond's soundtrack LP was an international smash. This led to MCA UK releasing a TV advertised *20 Golden Greats* LP which gave Jolson a No.18 placing on the British album chart more than 30 years after his death. (Bob Macdonald 15/11/85).

MY MAMMY
Tracks: / My mammy / Carolina in morning / Pretty baby.
7" Single: Released Mar '81, on MCA, by MCA Records. Deleted Mar '84. Catalogue no: **MCA 677**

Jomanda

MAKE MY BODY ROCK
Tracks: / Make my body rock / Make my body rock (The stomp version) / Make my body rock (club mix sweet) (on 12" and CD single only.) / Make my body rock (sweet 7" mix) (on 12" and CD single only.) / Make my body rock (Supremely clubbed) / Make my body rock (Salsa rhythem mix).
CD 5": Released Apr '89, on RCA, by BMG Records (UK). Catalogue no: **PD 42750**
7" Single: Released Apr '89, on RCA, by BMG Records (UK). Catalogue no: **PB 42749**
7" Single: Released Jan '89, on Big Beat, by Ace Records. Catalogue no: **BB 0004**
12" Single: Released Apr '89, on RCA, by BMG Records (UK). Catalogue no: **PT 42750R**
12" Single: Released Apr '89, on RCA, by BMG Records (UK). Catalogue no: **PT 42750**

Jon, Andrew

INSPIRATION
Tracks: / Inspiration / This is love.
7" Single: Released Nov '88, on Escape, by Escape Records. Catalogue no: **AWOL 3**
12" Single: Released Nov '88, on Escape, by Escape Records. Catalogue no: **AWOLT 3**

Jon & The Nightriders

SPLASHBACK (EP)
12" Single: Released Oct '88, on Rockhouse, by Rockhouse Records (Holland). Catalogue no: **12 EP 8205**

Jon & Vangelis

Biographical details: Jon & Vangelis Jon Anderson and Vangelis (real name Evangelos Papathanassiou) were both well known individually before they teamed up as a temporary duo in 1980. Jon was famous during the Seventies as singer with leading British rock band Yes, to whom he returned in 1983; he has released several solo albums through the years but his solo career has not been as successful as his other activities. Vangelis, a Greek keyboard player/synthesiser player/multi-instrumentalist/composer/producer, was a member of Aphrodite's Child in the late Sixties and early Seventies before releasing his own series of albums throughout the rest of the decade. He won the Oscar for Best Original Score in 1982 with his famous *Chariots of Fire* soundtrack.
The Jon & Vangelis alliance quickly earned a favourable reputation in early 1980 with the mesmerising single *I Hear You Now* which reached No.8 on the British chart; its parent album *Short Stories* obtained a No.4 placing. Their second LP *The Friends of Mr Cairo* was less warmly received at first, but evantually achieved major success when the single *I'll Find My Way Home* reached the UK No.6 position in early 1982. At the end of that year Donna Summer scored a memorable hit with a cover version of another Jon & Vangelis track *State of Independence*, for which she recruited an all star cast of backing singers to achieve a choral climax.
Private Collection, the third LP by the high pitched vocalist and the kinetic keyboardist was not a great success. Like their previous efforts, it was rooted in the progressive rock era of the Seventies but, unlike the other albums, it emphasied the genre's pompous and bombastic aspects. (Bob Macdonald 15/11/85).

FRIENDS OF MR.CAIRO (SINGLE)
Tracks: / Friends of Mr.Cairo / Beside.
7" Single: Released May '81, on Polydor, by Polydor Ltd. Deleted May '84. Catalogue no: **POSP 258**

HE IS SAILING
Tracks: / He is sailing / Polonaise.
7" Single: Released Jul '83, on Polydor, by Polydor Ltd. Deleted '86. Catalogue no: **JV 4**

I HEAR YOU NOW
Tracks: / I hear you now / Thunder.
7" Single: Released Jan '80, on Polydor, by Polydor Ltd. Deleted '83. Catalogue no: **POSP 96**

I HEAR YOU NOW (OLD GOLD)
Tracks: / I hear you now / I'll find my way home.
7" Single: Released Jun '88, on Old Gold, by Old Gold Records. Catalogue no: **OG 9785**

I'LL FIND MY WAY HOME
Tracks: / I'll find my way home / Back to school.
7" Single: Released Dec '81, on Polydor, by Polydor Ltd. Deleted '84. Catalogue no: **JV 1**

STATE OF INDEPENDENCE
Tracks: / State of independence / Beside.
7" Single: Released Aug '81, on Polydor, by Polydor Ltd. Deleted '84. Catalogue no: **POSP 232**
7" Single: Released Aug '84, on Polydor, by Polydor Ltd. Catalogue no: **JV 5**

Jonae,Gwen

RED LIGHT LOVER
Tracks: / Red light lover.
7" Single: Released Apr '83, on Carrere America (USA), by PolyGram Rec.Inc.(USA). Catalogue no: **CAR272**
12" Single: Released Apr '83, on Carrere America (USA), by PolyGram Rec.Inc.(USA). Catalogue no: **CART 272**

Jonah, Julian

HOT TO TOUCH
Tracks: / Hot to the touch / Dreaming.
7" Single: Released Jun '86, on Total Control, by Total Control Records. Catalogue no: **TOCO 8**
12" Single: Released Jun '86, on Total Control, by Total Control Records. Catalogue no: **12 TOCO 8**

JEALOUSY AND LIES
Tracks: / Jealousy and lies / Jealousy and lies (instrumental).
7" Single: Released Apr '88, on Cool Tempo, by Chrysalis Records. Catalogue no: **COOL 157**
12" Single: Released Apr '88, on Cool Tempo, by Chrysalis Records. Catalogue no: **COOLX 157**

Jonah & The Wail

FLATTEN MANHATTAN
Tracks: / Flatten Manhattan.
12" Single: Released Apr '88, on Luna Da Luna, Catalogue no: **LUNA 75**

Jonas

BANG THE DRUM ALL DAY+
Tracks: / Bang the drum all day / Rockin' little rebel.
7" Single: Released Mar '85, on Lamborghini, by Lamborghini Records. Catalogue no: **LMG 19**

DEDICATION SONG
Tracks: / Dedication song, The / Oh Bonnie.
7" Single: Released Nov '83, on Lamborghini, by Lamborghini Records. Catalogue no: **LMG 6**

LIPSTICK AND CANDY AND RUBBER SOLE SHOES
Tracks: / Lipstick and candy and rubber sole shoes / Rock & roll school.
7" Single: Released Aug '86, on Genie, Catalogue no: **GEN 5**

LITTLE QUEENIE
Tracks: / Baby can you rock / Little Queenie.
7" Single: Released Feb '83, on Sundance, by Sundance Records. Catalogue no: **SUND 003**

ROCK'N'ROLL SCHOOL
Tracks: / Rock 'n' roll school.
7" Single: Released Aug '85, on Genie, Catalogue no: **GEN 1**

Jones, Aled

AVA MARIA(SINGLE)
7" Single: Released May '85, on BBC, by BBC Records & Tapes. Deleted 31 Aug '88. Catalogue no: **RESL 171**

MEMORY
Tracks: / Memory.
7" Single: Released Jul '85, on BBC, by BBC Records & Tapes. Deleted 31 Aug '88. Catalogue no: **RESL 175**

MORNING HAS BROKEN
Tracks: / Morning has broken / How great thou art.
7" Single: Released Nov '86, on RCA, by BMG Records (UK). Catalogue no: **PB 41043**

PIE JESU
Tracks: / Pie Jesu.
7" Single: on 10 Records, by Virgin Records. Deleted '88. Catalogue no: **TEN 125**

SAILING (SINGLE)
Tracks: / Sailing / Scarborough fair.
7" Single: Released Jul '87, on 10 Records, by Virgin Records. Deleted May '88. Catalogue no: **TEN 184**

TOO YOUNG TO KNOW
Tracks: / Too young to know.
7" Single: Released Jun '85, on Sain, by Sain (Recordiau) Cyf. Catalogue no: **SAIN 116**

WALKING IN THE AIR
Tracks: / Walking in the air.
7" Single: Released Oct '85, on H.M.V., by EMI Records. Deleted Jul '87. Catalogue no: **ALED 1**
12" Single: Released Oct '85, on H.M.V., by EMI Records. Deleted Jul '87. Catalogue no: **12ALED 1**

WINTER STORY, A
Tracks: / Winter story, A / Sion blewych coch.
7" Single: Released Nov '86, on H.M.V., by EMI Records. Deleted Oct '87. Catalogue no: **ALED 2**
12" Single: Released Nov '86, on H.M.V., by EMI Records. Deleted Jul '87. Catalogue no: **12 ALED 2**

Jones, Allan

HEARTACHES
Tracks: / Heartaches / I'm on fire.
7" Single: Released Feb '80, on Active, by Active Records. Deleted Feb '83. Catalogue no: **ACT 2**

Jones, Annie

MY FRIEND OLIVER
Tracks: / My friend Oliver / Country girl.
7" Single: Released Nov '80, on Creole, by Creole Records. Deleted '83. Catalogue no: **CR 209**

Jones, Barbara

Biographical details: Jones, Barbara This Jamaican reggae singer achieved a one off UK chart entry in early 1981 when her lovers' rock rendition of *Just When I Needed You Most* reached No.31 on the singles list. The original pop version of this song had been by Randy Vanwarmer, who scored a Top 10 hit on both sides of the Atlantic in 1979
The Barbara Jones single was listed on the Uk Top 40 at the same time as Sheila Hylton's *The Bed's Too Big Without You*, another 1979 pop song given a reggae revamp by a Jamaican female vocalist. Barbara's track epitomised the lovers' rock genre - a mellow merger of reggae and soul. Her other singles released during the early Eighties included *For You Eyes Only*, *I Can't Say Goodbye to You* and *Single Girl*. (Bob Macdonald 15/11/85).

BLUE SIDE OF LONESOME
Tracks: / Blue side of lonesome.
12" Single: Released Oct '88, on EAD, Catalogue no: **BG 001**

BORROWED TIME
Tracks: / Borrowed time.
12" Single: Released Jun '85, on UNKNOWN, Catalogue no: **Unknown**

DON'T STAY AWAY
Tracks: / Don't stay away.
12" Single: Released Dec '84, on Dynamic, Catalogue no: **Unknown**

DREAM LOVER
Tracks: / Dream lover.
12" Single: Released Apr '85, on Self Survivor, Catalogue no: **Unknown**

FOR YOUR EYES ONLY
Tracks: / For your eyes only.
12" Single: Released Jul '82, on GG'S, Catalogue no: **GG 112**

HAVE A GOOD TIME
Tracks: / Have a good time.
7" Single: Released '79, on GG'S, Catalogue no: **GG 020**

I CAN'T SAY GOODBYE TO YOU
Tracks: / I can't say goodbye to you.
12" Single: Released Jul '82, on GG'S, Catalogue no: **GG 111**

JUST WHEN I NEEDED YOU MOST
Tracks: / Just when I needed you most.
7" Single: Released Jan '81, on Sonet, by Sonet Records. Deleted '84. Catalogue no: **SON 2221**

PLEASE MISTER, PLEASE
Tracks: / Please Mr., please / Mister (dub).
12" Single: Released Nov '86, on Charm, by Charm Records. Catalogue no: **CRT 3**

SATIN SHEETS
Tracks: / Satin sheets.
12" Single: Released Oct '80, on EAD, Catalogue no: **BG 002**

SINGLE GIRL
Tracks: / Single girl / Hot flute.
7" Single: Released Jun '83, on Creole, by Creole Records. Catalogue no: **CR 56**
12" Single: Released Jun '83, on Creole, by Creole Records. Catalogue no: **CR 1256**

TOMORROW IS FOREVER
Tracks: / Tomorrow is forever.
12" Single: Released Jun '82, on GG'S, Catalogue no: **GG 82**

WHY DID YOU LEAVE ME?
Tracks: / Why did you leave me?.
7" Single: Released Feb '80, on GG'S, Catalogue no: **GG 070**

Jones, Billy

RADIO PARTY
Tracks: / Radio party / Shine bright.
7" Single: Released Nov '87, on Beejayzus, Catalogue no: **BJ 105**

Jones, Brenda

YOUR MY OCCUPATION
Tracks: / Your my occupation (Side B:dub mix).
7" Single: Released Aug '86, on A&M, by A&M Records. Deleted '88. Catalogue no: **AM 344**
12" Single: Released Aug '86, on A&M, by A&M Records. Deleted '88. Catalogue no: **AMY 344**

Jones, Busta

MY HANDS ARE SHAKIN'
Tracks: / My hands are shakin' / My hands are shakin' (version).
12" Single: Released Sep '88, on Sierra, by Sierra Records. Catalogue no: **12 BJ 188**

Jones, Cleopatra

HOT PANTS
Tracks: / Hot pants (7" only) / Hot pants (global village 1990) (7" only) / Hot pants (stone groove) (12" only) / Hot pants (blaxploitation) (12" only).
7" Single: Released 16 May '88, on Virgin, by Virgin Records. Catalogue no: **HEDD 2**
12" Single: Released 16 May '88, on Virgin, by Virgin Records. Catalogue no: **HEDD 212**

Jones, Davy

YOU'VE GOT A HABIT OF LEAVING
10" single: Released Nov '82, on Charly, by Charly Records. Deleted '88. Catalogue no: **CYM 1**

Jones Elliot, Bryan

BALLAD OF SANTA CLAUS
Tracks: / Ballad of Santa Claus.
7" Single: Released Nov '85, on BBC, by BBC Records & Tapes. Deleted Sep '87. Catalogue no: **RESL 179**

Jones, Eroll

DON'T YOU LOOSE THE GROOVE
Tracks: / Don't you loose the groove.
7" Single: Released Jul '89, on B-Ware, by B/Ware Records. Catalogue no: **UM 7008**
12" Single: Released Jul '89, on B-Ware, by B/Ware Records. Catalogue no: **UM 008**

Jones, Frankie

BACK OFF
Tracks: / Back off.
12" Single: Released Oct '84, on Route, Catalogue no: **Unknown**

GET OUT OF MY LIFE
Tracks: / Get out of my life.
12" Single: Released May '85, on Greensleeves, by Greensleeves Records. Catalogue no: **GRED 176**

JAILHOUSE NO NICE
Tracks: / Jailhouse no nice.
12" Single: Released Nov '85, on Top Rank (2), Catalogue no: **TR 011**

LOVING ARMS
Tracks: / Loving arms / Fight it out there.
12" Single: Released Feb '85, on Real Wax, Catalogue no: **RW 1014**

MIX UP
Tracks: / Mix up.
12" Single: Released Sep '85, on Village Roots, Catalogue no: **VRR 001**

NO TOUCH THE RIDDUM
Tracks: / No touch the riddum.
12" Single: Released Nov '85, on Greensleeves, by Greensleeves Records. Catalogue no: **GRED 186**

PROBLEM

Tracks: / Problem.
12" Single: Released May '85, on Top Rank (2), Catalogue no: **TR 005**

RAM 17
Tracks: / Ram 17 / Ram 17 instrumental.
12" Single: Released Sep '86, on Chart Hopper, Catalogue no: **TZ 102**

SETTLEMENT
Tracks: / Settlement.
12" Single: Released Oct '84, on Thunderbolt, by Magnum Music Group. Deleted '89. Catalogue no: **Unknown**

WAR AND CRIME
Tracks: / War and crime.
12" Single: Released Oct '84, on Gorgon, Catalogue no: **Unknown**

Jones, George

Biographical details: See also under **Wynette, Tammy.**

STRANGER IN THE HOUSE
Tracks: / Stranger in the house / Drunk can't be a man.
7" Single: Released May '80, on Epic, by CBS Records. Deleted May '85. Catalogue no: **EPC 8560**

Jones Girls

AT PEACE WITH WOMAN
Tracks: / At peace with woman / When I'm gone.
7" Single: Released Mar '81, on Portrait, by CBS Records. Deleted Mar '84. Catalogue no: **PIRA 1030**

NIGHTS OVER EGYPT (OLD GOLD)
Tracks: / Nights over Egypt / You can't my love / Love don't ever say goodbye.
7" Single: Released Feb '82, on Philadelphia Int., by EMI Records. Deleted Feb '87. Catalogue no: **PIR A2031**
12" Single: Released Feb '82, on Philadelphia Int., by EMI Records. Deleted Feb '87. Catalogue no: **PIR A13 2031**
12" Single: Released Jul '88, on Old Gold, by Old Gold Records. Catalogue no: **OG 4071**

ON TARGET
Tracks: / Let's hit it (dialogue) / On target / Win U back / Baby, I'm yours / Knockin' / I can make a difference / What a fool / Curious / I'm a woman here.
7" Single: Released Oct '83, on RCA, by BMG Records (UK). Catalogue no: **RCA 364**
12" Single: Released Oct '83, on RCA, by BMG Records (UK). Catalogue no: **RCAT 364**

Jones, Glenn

I AM SOMEBODY
Tracks: / I am somebody.
7" Single: Released Feb '83, on RCA, by BMG Records (UK). Catalogue no: **RCA 318**
12" Single: Released Feb '83, on RCA, by BMG Records (UK). Catalogue no: **RCAT 318**

I AM SOMEBODY (OLD GOLD)
Tracks: / I am somebody / Keep on doin' (what you're doin').
12" Single: Released 30 Jan '89, on Old Gold, by Old Gold Records. Catalogue no: **OG 4096**

LIVING IN THE LIMELIGHT
Tracks: / Living in the limelight / Love me through the night.
7" Single: Released 23 Apr '88, on Jive, by Zomba Records. Catalogue no: **JIVE 160**
12" Single: Released 23 Apr '88, on Jive, by Zomba Records. Catalogue no: **JIVET 160**

WE'VE ONLY JUST BEGUN (The romance is not over)
Tracks: / We've only just begun / We've only just begun (version).
7" Single: Released Sep '87, on Jive, by Zomba Records. Catalogue no: **JIVE 151**
12" Single: Released Sep '87, on Jive, by Zomba Records. Catalogue no: **JIVET 151**

Jones, Gloria

LISTEN TO ME
Tracks: / Listen to me.
7" Single: Released Nov '80, on Liberty (USA), by EMI Records. Deleted '83. Catalogue no: **BP 380**

TAINTED LOVE
Tracks: / Tainted love / Torch of venus.
7" Single: Released Feb '83, on Rockhouse, by Rockhouse Records (Holland). Catalogue no: **SP 8303**
7" Single: Released Oct '84, on Soul Stop, by Dawn Promotions. Catalogue no: **SS 3010**
7" Single: Released Jan '82, on Inferno (1), by Inferno Records. Catalogue no: **HEAT 6**
12" Single: Released Jan '82, on Inferno (1), by Inferno Records. Catalogue no: **12 HEAT 6**

Jones, Grace

Biographical details: One of the most bizarre stars of the 80's, American singer, actress, model and lyricist Grace Jones was born in Jamaica but moved to Syracuse at the age of 12. The family background was religious -- father a preacher, uncle a bishop -- but she rebelled against her upbringing at the earliest opportunity and has continued to defy every convention and preconception in the book throughout her career. She left home at 17, became a model and made her acting debut in the 1973 film Gordon's War. Her androgynous weirdness delighted the European fashion scene and she appeared on the covers of such magazines as Elle, Stern and Vogue. Jones launched her singing career in France in the mid-70's but soon switched to Chris Blackwell's Island label. With her Jamaican background and her association with Island it was natural that reggae should become the bedrock of her music. Although not a great singer in technical terms, she compensated by emphasising the biting and acidic qualities of her voice. Her first three Island albums, released 1977-79, built her a base in gay clubs and were early examples of the gloriously trashy camp-disco style later to be known as "boystown" or "hi-NRG". Jones' commercial breakthrough came in 1980, when she enlisted the production talents of Blackwell and Alex Sadkin plus the instrumental skills of the best reggae rhythm section in the business, Sly Dunbar and Robbie Shakespeare, and reached No 17 on the UK singles chart with Private Life, a half-spoken, half-sung rendition of a moody Pretenders album track, and No 45 on the albums list with Warm Leatherette. At the end of 1980 the newly-famous Jones made national headlines in Britain by hitting TV interviewer Russell Harty during his live show. Such incidents ensured that she was a household name even when she wasn't having hit records -- and she didn't score a real follow-up to Private Life until 1985. Songs like Pull Up To The Bumper, The Apple Stretching, Nipple To The Bottle and My Jamaican Guy were punchy dance-rock tracks which kept "Ms Square Hair" in the disco charts on both sides of the Atlantic, but her major return to the higher echelons of the UK pop charts came about via the production genius of Trevor Horn on Jones' autobiographical 1985 single and LP, Slave To The Rhythm. In that same year she appeared with Roger Moore in the James Bond film A View To A Kill. (Bob MacDonald, November 1985).

APPLE STRETCHING, THE
Tracks: / Apple stretching, The / Nipple to the bottle.
7" Single: Released Oct '82, on Island, by Island Records. Deleted '85. Catalogue no: **WIP 6779**
12" Single: Released Oct '82, on Island, by Island Records. Deleted '85. Catalogue no: **12WIP 6779**

DEMOLITION MAN
Tracks: / Demoliton man / Bull shit / Warm leatherette.
7" Single: Released Feb '81, on Island, by Island Records. Deleted '84. Catalogue no: **WIP 6673**
12" Single: Released Feb '81, on Island, by Island Records. Deleted '84. Catalogue no: **12WIP 6673**

HUNTER GETS CAPTURED BY THE GAME
Tracks: / Hunter gets captured by the game / Hunter gets captured by the game (part 2) / Warm leatherette (Only on 12" single.).
7" Single: Released Sep '80, on Island, by Island Records. Deleted '83. Catalogue no: **WIP 6645**
12" Single: Released Sep '80, on Island, by Island Records. Deleted '83. Catalogue no: **12 WIP 6645**

I'M NOT PERFECT (BUT I'M PERFECT FOR YOU)
Tracks: / I'm not perfect (but I'm perfect for you) / I'm not perfect (perfectly extended remix) (Track on 12" single only.) / I'm not perfect (Instrumental version) (Track on 12" single only.) / Scary but fun.
Note: All tracks by Grace Jones and Bruce Woolley, and published by Bruce Woolley Music Ltd./CBS Songs Ltd.-Sonet Publications Ltd.
7" Pic: Released Nov '86, on EMI-Manhattan, by EMI Records. Deleted Oct '87. Catalogue no: **72 MTP 15**
7" Single: Released Nov '86, on EMI-Manhattan, by EMI Records. Deleted Oct '87. Catalogue no: **MT 15**
12" Single: Released Nov '86, on EMI-Manhattan, by EMI Records. Deleted Oct '87. Catalogue no: **12 MT 15**

LOVE IS THE DRUG
Tracks: / Love is the drug (remix) / Living my life / Apple stretching, The (Track on 12" version only.).
12" Pic: Released Feb '86, on Island, by Island Records. Deleted '87. Catalogue no: **12IS 266**
7" Pic: Released Feb '86, on Island, by Island Records. Catalogue no: **ISP 266**
7" Single: Released Feb '86, on Island, by Island Records. Deleted '87. Catalogue no: **IS 266**
12" Single: Released Feb '86, on Island, by Island Records. Deleted '87. Catalogue no: **ISG 266**

MY JAMAICAN GUY
Tracks: / My Jamaican guy.
7" Single: Released Apr '83, on Island, by Island Records. Deleted '86. Catalogue no: **IS 103**

PARTY GIRL Special remix
Tracks: / Party girl (special remix) / White collar crime.
7" Pic: on EMI-Manhattan, by EMI Records. Catalogue no: **MTB 20 B**
7" Single: Released Mar '87, on EMI-Manhattan, by EMI Records. Deleted Oct '87. Catalogue no: **MT 20**
12" Single: Released Mar '87, on EMI-Manhattan, by EMI Records. Catalogue no: **12 MT 20**

PRIVATE LIFE
Tracks: / Private life (new "Groucho" remix) / My Jamaican guy / Feel up (vocal) (Track available on 12" single only.) / She's lost control (Track available on 12" single only.).
7" Single: Released Jul '80, on Island, by Island Records. Deleted '83. Catalogue no: **WIP 6629**
7" Single: Released May '86, on Island, by Island Records. Deleted '87. Catalogue no: **IS 273**
12" Single: Released May '86, on Island, by Island Records. Deleted '87. Catalogue no: **12IS 273**

PULL UP TO THE BUMPER
Tracks: / Pull up to the Bumper / La vie en rose / Feel up.
7" Pic: Released Jan '86, on Island, by Island Records. Catalogue no: **ISP 240**
7" Single: Released Jun '81, on Island, by Island Records. Deleted '83. Catalogue no: **WIP 6696**
7" Single: Released Jan '86, on Island, by Island Records. Deleted Jul '87. Catalogue no: **IS 240**
12" Single: Released Jan '86, on Island, by Island Records. Deleted '87. Catalogue no: **12IS 240**

ROLLING STONE
Tracks: / Rolling stone / Sinning.
7" Single: Released Apr '80, on Island, by Island Records. Deleted '83. Catalogue no: **WIP 6591**
12" Single: Released Apr '80, on Island, by Island Records. Deleted '83. Catalogue no: **12WIP 6591**

SLAVE TO THE RHYTHM (SINGLE)
Tracks: / Slave to the rhythm.
7" Pic: Released Oct '85, on ZTT, by ZTT Records. Deleted Jul '87. Catalogue no: **12ISP 206**
7" Single: Released Sep '85, on ZTT, by ZTT Records. Deleted Jul '87. Catalogue no: **IS 206**
12" Single: Released Sep '85, on ZTT, by ZTT Records. Deleted Apr '88. Catalogue no: **12IS 206**

WALKING IN THE RAIN
Tracks: / Walking in the rain / Peanut butter / Pull up to the bumper.
7" Single: Released Oct '81, on Island, by Island Records. Deleted '85. Catalogue no: **WIP 6739**
12" Single: Released Oct '81, on Island, by Island Records. Deleted '85. Catalogue no: **12WIP 6739**

Jones, Howard

Biographical details: This British singer, songwriter and synthesiser player, who hails from High Wycombe, knows the meaning of the term 'blessing in disguise'. After being involved in a road accident, he won sufficient damages to pay for his first synthesisers. Prior to this, he had studied classical piano throughout his school years and had impressed all his mates with his prowess.
After three years of hard giggling, things started happening in early 1983 when he attracted the interest of BBC Radio One and WEA Records. After playing sessions for DJ David Jensen and signing a recording contract, he reached No.3 in the autumn of that year with the ultra-catchy single *New Song*. The title was perhaps a misnomer, because some observers noticed how similar the tune was to Peter Gabriel's 1977 hit *Solsbury Hill*. While *New Song* was climbing the UK chart, Jones supported Gabriel in concert in Belgium, so there were obviously no hard feelings!
In 1984 Howard consolidated on his breakthrough in no uncertain terms. *What Is Love?* cruised to the UK No.2 position and was followed by further Top 20 singles with *Hide and Seek, Pearl In The Shell* and *Like To Get To Know You Well*. Jones' debut album *Human's Lib* entered the British LP chart at No.1. *New Song* and *What Is Love?* both penetrated the American Top 40.
1985 saw Jones breaking through into the US Top 5 with *Things Can Only Get Better* and reaching No.2 in Britain with his second regular LP *Dream Into Action*. He had established himself as a purveyor of pure pop for the mid-Eighties and a master of melody; he used his synths wisely, incorporating them into the overall sound without over emphasing them, thus avoiding being stuck with the 'technopop' tag. He was an amiable teen idol, whose female fans did not seem to mind that he was already happily married by the time he became famous. His wife Jan was part of a close knit back up team which also included manager David Stopps and Howard's unique mime artist Jed Hoile. (Bob Macdonald 15/11/85).

ALL I WANT
Tracks: / All I want / Roll up, right / Roll right up (Extra track on 12" version only.) /

HOWARD JONES - HIDE & SEEK (Released on WEA)

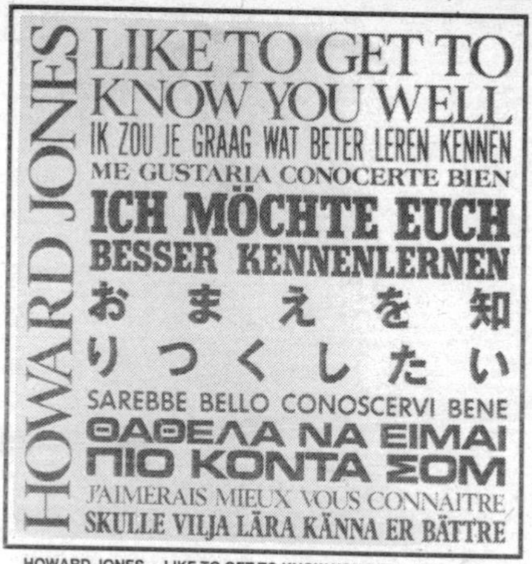
HOWARD JONES
LIKE TO GET TO KNOW YOU WELL
IK ZOU JE GRAAG WAT BETER LEREN KENNEN
ME GUSTARIA CONOCERTE BIEN
ICH MÖCHTE EUCH BESSER KENNENLERNEN
おまえを知りつくしたい
SAREBBE BELLO CONOSCERVI BENE
ΘΑΘΕΛΑ ΝΑ ΕΙΜΑΙ ΠΙΟ ΚΟΝΤΑ ΣΟΜ
J'AIMERAIS MIEUX VOUS CONNAITRE
SKULLE VILJA LÄRA KÄNNA ER BÄTTRE

HOWARD JONES - LIKE TO GET TO KNOW YOU WELL (Released on WEA)

Don't want to fight anymore (Extra track on 12" version only.).
7" Single: Released Sep '86, on WEA, by WEA Records. Deleted Jun '87. Catalogue no: **HOW 10**
12" Single: Released Sep '86, on WEA, by WEA Records. Deleted Jun '87. Catalogue no: **HOW 10T**

EVERLASTING LOVE
Tracks: / Everlasting love / Brutality of fact, The.
CD 5": Released Feb '89, on WEA, by WEA Records. Catalogue no: **HOW 13CD**
7" Single: Released Feb '89, on WEA, by WEA Records. Catalogue no: **HOW 13**
12" Single: Released Feb '89, on WEA, by WEA Records. Catalogue no: **HOW 13T**

HIDE & SEEK (see panel on previous page)
Tracks: / Hide and seek / Tao te Ching.
7" Single: Released Feb '84, on WEA, by WEA Records. Deleted Jun '87. Catalogue no: **HOW 3**
12" Single: Released Feb '84, on WEA, by WEA Records. Deleted Jun '87. Catalogue no: **HOW 3T**

LIFE IN ONE DAY
Tracks: / Life in one day.
7" Single: Released Jun '85, on WEA, by WEA Records. Catalogue no: **HOW 8**
12" Single: Released Jun '85, on WEA, by WEA Records. Catalogue no: **HOW 8T**

LIKE TO GET TO KNOW YOU WELL (see panel above)
Tracks: / Like to get to know you well / Bounce right back.
7" Single: Released Jul '84, on WEA, by WEA Records. Deleted Jun '87. Catalogue no: **HOW 5**
12" Single: Released Jul '84, on WEA, by WEA Records. Catalogue no: **HOW 5T**

LITTLE BIT OF SNOW
Tracks: / Little bit of snow / Let it flow / Will you still be there (Available on 12" only) / Hunger for flesh (orchestral) (Available on 12" only) / Hide and seek (orchestral) (Available on 12" only).
Cassingle: on WEA, by WEA Records. Deleted Jan '88. Catalogue no: **HOW 12C**
7" Single: Released Feb '87, on WEA, by WEA Records. Deleted Jan '88. Catalogue no: **HOW 12**
12" Single: Released Feb '87, on WEA, by WEA Records. Deleted Jan '88. Catalogue no: **HOW 12T**

LOOK MAMA
Tracks: / Look mama / Learning how to live / Dream into action (on 12" only).
7" Single: Released Apr '85, on WEA, by WEA Records. Catalogue no: **HOW 7**
12" Single: Released Apr '85, on WEA, by WEA Records. Catalogue no: **HOW 7T**

NEW SONG (see panel below)

HOWARD JONES - NEW SONG (Released on WEA)

Tracks: / New song / Change the man.
7" Single: Released Aug '83, on WEA, by WEA Records. Deleted Jun '87. Catalogue no: **HOW 1**
12" Single: Released Aug '83, on WEA, by WEA Records. Catalogue no: **HOW 1T**

NO ONE IS TO BLAME
Tracks: / No one is to blame / Chase, The.
7" Single: Released Feb '86, on WEA, by WEA Records. Deleted Jun '87. Catalogue no: **HOW 9**
12" Single: Released Feb '86, on WEA, by WEA Records. Deleted Jan '88. Catalogue no: **HOW 9T**

PEARL IN THE SHELL
Tracks: / Pearl in the shell / Law of the jungle / Total conditioning (on 12" only).
12" Single: Released Apr '84, on WEA, by WEA Records. Catalogue no: **HOW 4T**

PRISONER, THE
Tracks: / Prisoner, The / Rubber morals.
7" Single: Released May '89, on WEA, by WEA Records. Catalogue no: **HOW 14**
12" Single: Released May '89, on WEA, by WEA Records. Catalogue no: **HOW T14**

THINGS CAN ONLY GET BETTER
Tracks: / Things can only get better / Why look for the key.
7" Pic: Released Mar '85, on WEA, by WEA Records. Catalogue no: **HOW 6P**
7" Single: Released Jan '85, on WEA, by WEA Records. Catalogue no: **HOW 6**
12" Single: Released Jan '85, on WEA, by WEA Records. Catalogue no: **HOW 6T**

WHAT IS LOVE
Tracks: / What is love.
7" Single: Released Nov '83, on WEA, by WEA Records. Deleted Jun '87. Catalogue no: **HOW 2**
12" Single: Released Nov '83, on WEA, by WEA Records. Catalogue no: **HOW 2T**

YOU KNOW I LOVE YOU DON'T YOU?
Tracks: / You know I love you don't you / Dig this world deep / Dance in the field (mix).
7" Single: Released Nov '86, on WEA, by WEA Records. Deleted Jan '88. Catalogue no: **HOW 11**
12" Single: on WEA, by WEA Records. Deleted Jan '88. Catalogue no: **HOW 11T**

Jones, Ignatius

LIKE A GHOST
Tracks: / Like a ghost / Seductive ways.
7" Single: Released Apr '82, on Ensign, by Ensign Records. Deleted Apr '85. Catalogue no: **ENY 224**

Jones, Ira

JUNGLE JACK DASH
Tracks: / Jungle Jack dash / Get mad / Jungle Jack dash (extended mix) (12" only).
7" Single: Released 14 Aug '88, on Ghetto Recordings, by Ghetto Recording Company. Catalogue no: **WALT 1**
12" Single: Released 14 Aug '88, on Ghetto Recordings, by Ghetto Recording Company. Catalogue no: **WALT T1**

Jones, Jack

Biographical details: This American singer is the son of actor Allan Jones and actress Irene Hervey. Jack came to fame in 1964, reaching No.14 on the US chart with the Burt Bacharach/Hal David song *Wives and Lovers*. His success might have been greater had it not begun at the very start of the British Invasion - in the event, Jones had to be content with a series of four more modest US Top 40 singles: *Dear Heart*, *The Race Is On*, *The Impossible Dream* and *Lady*.
After 1967 Jones never returned to the American Top 40. In Britain where none of his sixties singles dented the charts at all, he became a major LP seller during the Seventies. In a period from 1972 until 1974, he reached the UK Top 10 with four albums *A song For You*, *Bread Winners*, *Together* and *Harbour*. As his namesake Tom Jones became more interested in the world of Las Vegas, Jack stepped into the British breach and cornered the housewife middle of the road crooning market. Having exactly the same name as one of the UK's most vociferous trade union leaders of the day proved to be no hinderance for the singer.
1977 brought Jones his final two UK hit albums, *The Full Life* and the TV advertised *All To Yourself*, before he disappeared into the land of cabaret forever. (Bob Macdonald 15/11/85)t.

DON'T STOP NOW
Tracks: / Don't stop now / I've been here all the time.
7" Single: Released Apr '80, on Polydor, by Polydor Ltd. Deleted '83. Catalogue no: **POSP 141**

LYIN' EYES
Tracks: / Lyin' eyes / Breaking up is hard to do.
7" Single: Released Mar '82, on Applause, by Riva Records. Catalogue no: **APK 202**

Jones, Jackie

I WILL ALWAYS LOVE YOU
Tracks: / I will always love you.
12" Single: Released Aug '83, on Ruff Cut, Catalogue no: **CUTT 002**

LOVE LIGHT
Tracks: / Love light / Love dub.
12" Single: Released Nov '82, on Ital, by Ital Records. Catalogue no: **STU 0011**

Jones, Jacqui

WHY SHOULD I LOVE YOU ?
Tracks: / Why should I love you ? / Why should I love you ? (inst).
7" Single: Released 25 Jul '88, on G.T.I. Records, by G.T.I. Music. Catalogue no: **JJ 001**
12" Single: Released 25 Jul '88, on G.T.I. Records, by G.T.I. Music. Catalogue no: **JJ 001T**
12" Single: Released 25 Jul '88, on Rough Trade, by Rough Trade Records. Catalogue no: **JJ 001 TX**

Jones, Janie

HOUSE OF THE JU-JU QUEEN
Tracks: / House of the ju-ju queen / Sex machine.
7" Single: Released Dec '83, on Beat Beat, by Ace Records. Catalogue no: **NS 91**

WITCHES BREW
Tracks: / Witches brew.
7" Single: Released Jan '66, on H.M.V., by EMI Records. Deleted '69. Catalogue no: **POP 1495**

Jones, Jill

MIA BOCA
Tracks: / Mia boca / Bleaker Street.
7" Single: Released Jun '87, on Paisley Park (USA), by WEA Records. Deleted Jul '88. Catalogue no: **W 8438**
12" Single: Released Jun '87, on Paisley Park (USA), by WEA Records. Deleted Jul '88. Catalogue no: **W 8438T**

Jones, Jimmy

GOOD TIMIN'
Tracks: / Good timin' / Handy man.
7" Single: Released Jul '84, on Old Gold, by Old Gold Records. Catalogue no: **OG 9445**

HANDY MAN
Tracks: / Handyman.
7" Single: Released Mar '60, on MGM, by Polydor Ltd. Deleted '63. Catalogue no: **MGM 1051**

I JUST GO FOR YOU
Tracks: / I just go for you.
7" Single: Released Aug '60, on MGM, by Polydor Ltd. Deleted '63. Catalogue no: **MGM 1091**

I TOLD YOU SO
Tracks: / I told you so.
7" Single: Released Mar '61, on MGM, by Polydor Ltd. Deleted '64. Catalogue no: **MGM 1123**

READY FOR LOVE
Tracks: / Ready for love.
7" Single: Released Nov '60, on MGM, by Polydor Ltd. Deleted '63. Catalogue no: **MGM 1103**

STRANDED
Tracks: / Stranded.
7" Single: Released Feb '83, on Lark, Deleted '87. Catalogue no: **LARK 1**

THAT'S THE NICEST THING
Tracks: / That's the nicest thing.
7" Single: Released Nov '82, on Kin'ell, Catalogue no: **KINS 1**

Jones, JJ

JOHNNY REMEMBER ME
Tracks: / Johnny remember me.
7" Single: Released May '83, on Rutland, by Rutland Records. Catalogue no: **RX 105**

Jones, Jo Ann

ELECTRIC BLANKET
Tracks: / Electric blanket.
7" Single: Released '88, on Champion, by Champion Records. Catalogue no: **CHAMP 77**
12" Single: Released '88, on Champion, by Champion Records. Catalogue no: **CHAMP 1277**

I DON'T NEED YOUR LOVE
Tracks: / I don't need your love.
7" Single: Released Oct '89, on Champion, by Champion Records. Catalogue no: **CHAMP 220**

12" Single: Released Oct '89, on Champion, by Champion Records. Catalogue no: **CHAMP 12220**

SHARE MY JOY
Tracks: / Share my joy.
CD 5": Released 22 Aug '88, on Champion, by Champion Records. Catalogue no: **CHAMP CD 81**
7" Single: Released Jun '88, on Champion, by Champion Records. Catalogue no: **CHAMP 81**
12" Single: Released Jun '88, on Champion, by Champion Records. Catalogue no: **CHAMP 12-81**

Jones, Johnny

PURPLE HAZE
Tracks: / Purple haze / Horsing around.
7" Single: Released Mar '87, on Cream. Catalogue no: **CRM 5004**

Jones, Juggy

INSIDE AMERICA
Tracks: / Inside America.
7" Single: Released Feb '76, on Contempo. Deleted '79. Catalogue no: **CS 2080**

Jones, Klinte

IN THE HEAT OF THE NIGHT
Tracks: / In the heat of the night.
12" Single: Released Aug '84, on Personal, by Personal Records. Catalogue no: **12PER 104**

Jones, Leath

BAD BOYS
Tracks: / Bad boys.
7" Single: Released Nov '81, on All That. Catalogue no: **DAT 1**

Jones, Mac

TRIBUTE TO BOB MARLEY
Tracks: / Tribute to Bob Marley / Jah jah Woman.
7" Single: Released Feb '86, on Instant (1), by Instant Records. Catalogue no: **INS RE 001**
12" Single: Released Oct '86, on Zodiac, by Zodiac-Wilcox Records. Catalogue no: **INS 001**

Jones, Matthew

MADE UP THE WORLD
Tracks: / Made up the world / Pier head / Bath house, The.
12" Single: Released May '87, on UNKNOWN. Catalogue no: **UNKNOWN**

Jones, Mick

EVERYTHING THAT COMES AROUND
Tracks: / Everything that comes around.
7" Single: Released Feb '89, on WEA, by WEA Records. Catalogue no: **A 8954**
12" Single: Released Feb '89, on WEA, by WEA Records. Catalogue no: **A 8954 T**

Jones, Nick

BALLAD OF LADY DI
Tracks: / Ballad of Lady Di / Three minutes of silence.
7" Single: Released Jun '81, on Stiff, by Stiff Records. Deleted Jun '84. Catalogue no: **WED 1**

Jones, Oran 'Juice'

1.2.1.
Tracks: / 1.2.1. / Here I go again / Curiosity.
7" Single: Released Apr '87, on Def Jam. Deleted Nov '87. Catalogue no: **650780 7**
12" Single: Released Apr '87, on Def Jam. Deleted Nov '87. Catalogue no: **650780 6**

COLD SPENDING MY MONEY
Tracks: / Cold spending my money / Cold spending my money (version).
12" Single: Released Sep '87, on Def Jam. Deleted Oct '87. Catalogue no: **440696 0**
12" Single: Released Sep '87, on Def Jam. Catalogue no: **651121 6**

CURIOSITY
Tracks: / Curiosity / Here I go again.
7" Single: Released Jan '87, on Def Jam. Deleted Aug '87. Catalogue no: **OJJ 2**
12" Single: Released Jan '87, on Def Jam. Catalogue no: **12 OJJ 2**

Jones, Paul

Biographical details: Jones, Paul This British singer and actor was born Paul Pond, but later decided that Jones was a more marketable surname. While studying at Oxford, he grew increasinly interested in rhythm and blues; at the end of 1962 he became actively involved in the UK's fast growing R&B scene by joining a combo called the Mann Hugg Blues Brothers. The group took their name from two of the constituent members, Manfred Mann and Mike Hugg; the band soon became known simply as Manfred Mann and Jones became a star. He sang lead on all their hits until mid 1966 at which time he quit to launch a solo career.
Sticking to the commercial pop formula of his old group, Jones started promisingly with *High Time* and *I've Been A Bad Bad Boy*, two songs written or co written by Mike Leander (later of Gary Glitter songwriting/production fame) which both cracked the UK Top 5. However, Paul's chart career then disintegrated because he grew far more interested in acting. In 1967 he starred in 'Privelege' a movie directed by Peter Watkins, which also provided Paul with a No.1 on the British EP charts. He then did another film, 'The Committee' followed shortly afterwards by a two year stage stint in the play 'Conduct Unbecoming'. His seventies exploits included a horror movie, much more theatre work (including the West End), a delightful cover version of The Ramones' *Sheena Is a Punk Rocker', plus numerous appearances on British television and radio where his affable charm and good looks were always welcomed.*
At the end of the Seventies Paul decided to have some real fun and formed The Blues Band with a group of mates. Initially intended as a hobby, the Blues Band went down so well that they stayed together until 1983. Also during the early Eighties, Jones took part in the London stage productions 'Cats', 'Guys and Dolls', 'Beggar's Opera' and 'Pump Boys and Dinettes'. (Bob Macdonald 15/11/85).

AQUARIUS
Tracks: / Aquarius.
7" Single: Released Feb '69, on Columbia, by EMI Records. Deleted '72. Catalogue no: **DB 8534**

HIGH TIME
Tracks: / High time.
7" Single: Released Oct '66, on H.M.V., by EMI Records. Deleted '69. Catalogue no: **POP 1554**
7" Single: Released Aug '82, on Creole (Replay), by Creole Records. Catalogue no: **CR 181**

I'VE BEEN A BAD BAD BOY
Tracks: / I've been a bad bad boy / High time.
7" Single: Released Jun '80, on H.M.V., by EMI Records. Deleted '83. Catalogue no: **POP 2004**
7" Single: Released Jan '67, on H.M.V., by EMI Records. Deleted '70. Catalogue no: **POP 1576**

THINKIN' AIN'T FOR ME
Tracks: / Thinkin' ain't for me.
7" Single: Released Aug '67, on H.M.V., by EMI Records. Deleted '70. Catalogue no: **POP 1602**

Jones, Quincy

Biographical details: Jones, Quincy This American producer, composer, keyboarist, arranger and conductor is arguably the most successful 'behind the scenes' musician in the history of the US industry.
Born in Chicago in 1933, Jones was an early friend of Ray Charles and gave encouragement to the blind multi-talented singer, who was of similar age to himself. After attending the Berkley School of Music in Boston, he became a trumpeter for Lionel Hampton's Big Band and then spent several years in Paris perfecting his composing, arranging and conducting skills. He returned to the States in the early Sixties and began working on records by a host of big names including the now famous Ray Charles. Jones was also associated with Frank Sinatra, Johnny Mathis, Tony Bennett, Count Basie, Brook Benton and Billy Eckstine. In 1963 Lesley Gore's sugary schoolgirl smash *It's My Party* gave Quincy Jones his first US No.1 single as a producer.
During the late sixties and early seventies, Jones concentrated his energies on scoring music for films and television. His output at this time was feverish, including some forty cinema soundtracks and 250 episodes of TV programmes, most of the latter being for 'Ironside'. Anyone requiring further evidence of the fact that he is a workaholic might like to know that during his career, he has recorded approximately forty albums under his own name.
During the Seventies Jones used his own LPs to achieve a fusion of his two favourite forms of music, jazz and soul. He became one of the prime protagonists of the new jazz funk genre and, in 1976 successfully launched the recording career of his proteges, The Brothers Johnson.
In the late Seventies Jones forged the most important link of his showbusiness career when he teamed up with Michael Jackson for the *Off The Wall* album. Brilliantly talented though they were individually, the combination of Jones and Jackson produced a magic that captured the imagination - and the money - of millions of record buyers around the world. *Off The All* released in August 1979 sold over eight million copies and made the 21 year old Jackson (already a veteran star) one of the hottest singers in the history of black music. The production was typical of Jones' slickness, sounding equally great on the radio and the dancefloor - his distinctive sound transcended barriers of pop, soul, disco, jazz and easy listening. But *Off The Wall* was a mere dress rehearsal for Michael Jackson's second Quincy produced LP *Thriller* which was issued in December 1982. Fifteen months after release, *Thriller* became the world's top selling recording of all time. By mid 1985 global sales of the blockbusting album were estimated at 40 million.
In between *Off The Wall* and *Thriller* Jones produced George Benson's blockbusting *Give Me The Night* album and released the most acclaimed album of his own career, *The Dude*. The latter reached th Top 20 on both sides of the Atlantic during 1981 and featured the vocal talents of his favourite singer Patti Austin. Jones' other main vocal protege was James Ingram - Quincy himself has always realised that his own vocal talents are limited and has always therefore used guest singers on his own records, including such respected names as Ashfrod and Simpson, Chaka Khan and Luther Vandross.
Jones, who runs his own Qwest label, was the producer of USA For Africa's 1985 charity sisngle *We Are The World*. When it hit No.1 in the States, Billboard magazine reported that it was his seventh chart-topper and the 22 years from Lesley Gore to USA For Africa gave him the longest span of No.1 productions in US chart history. Before the galaxy of stars entered A&M Studios in Hollywood to record *We Are The World*, Jones gave them each a letter, requesting them to 'check their egos at the door' - this demand summarised the status and respect he commands in the music industry. (Bob Macdonald 17/11/85).

AI NO CORRIDA
Tracks: / Ai no corrida.
Note: Vocals by Dune
7" Single: Released Apr '81, on A&M, by A&M Records. Deleted '83. Catalogue no: **AMS 8109**
12" Single: Released Mar '81, on A&M, by A&M Records. Deleted Mar '84. Catalogue no: **AMSX 8109**

BETCHA WOULDN'T HURT ME
Tracks: / Betcha wouldn't hurt me.
7" Single: Released Aug '81, on A&M, by A&M Records. Deleted '83. Catalogue no: **AMS 8157**

COMPACT HITS: QUINCY JONES
Tracks: / Razzamatazz / Stuff like that / Ai no corrida / Dude, The.
CD 5": Released Apr '88, on A&M, by A&M Records. Deleted Apr '88. Catalogue no: **AMCD 908**

JUST ONCE
Tracks: / Just once / Turn on the action.
7" Single: Released Oct '81, on A&M, by A&M Records. Catalogue no: **AMS 8178**

ONE HUNDRED WAYS
Tracks: / One hundred ways / Dude.
7" Single: Released Feb '82, on A&M, by A&M Records. Deleted Feb '87. Catalogue no: **AMS 8207**

RAZZAMATAZZ
Tracks: / Razzamatazz / Velas.
Note: Vocals by Patti Austin
7" Single: Released Jun '81, on A&M, by A&M Records. Deleted '83. Catalogue no: **AMS 8140**
12" Single: Released Jun '81, on A&M, by A&M Records. Deleted '83. Catalogue no: **AMSP 8140**

STUFF LIKE THAT
Tracks: / Stuff like that.
Note: Vocals by Ashford & Simpson & Chaka Khan.,
7" Single: Released Jul '78, on A&M, by A&M Records. Deleted '82. Catalogue no: **AMS 7367**

STUFF LIKE THAT (OLD GOLD)
Tracks: / Stuff like that / Ai no corrida / Rise / Feel so good.
12" Single: Released Jan '87, on Old Gold, by Old Gold Records. Catalogue no: **OG 4012**

Jones, Rickie Lee

Biographical details: Jones, Rickie Lee- This American singer, songwriter, keyboard player and guitarist was born in Chicago but wandered all over the States with her parents as she grew up, finally settling in Los Angeles in 1973. She spent the mid-Seventies performing in Californian bars and clubs and had a romantic affair with an equally idiosyncratic singer/songwriter/pianist, Tom Waits; he had a strong influence upon her music. When Little Feat leader Lowell Geroge included her song *Easy Money* on his 1979 solo LP *Thanks, I'll Eat It Here*, his record company Warner Brothers decided to sign Jones.
Warners teamed Rickie Lee with two of the company's best-known in house producers, Russ Titelman & Lenny Waronker, and enlisted the talents of many of the top session musicians in LA. The resuslt of this treatment was that her eponymous debut album, released in 1979, was a substantial success in the States and yielded the ultra-catchy No.4 single *Chuck E's In Love*. Inspired by a friend of hers called Chuck E Weiss, this song was filled with the quirky jazzy flavour that permeated much of her music. in Britain, both single and album reached No.18.
Jones' second LP *Pirates* was issued in 1981 and again featured the same producers and an all star cast of backing musicians. It reached the US Top 10 without the benefit of a chart single and peaked at No.37 in the UK. *Pirates* was not an overtly commercial work, containing highly original lyircal ideas and complex song structures. Showing herself to be as unpredictable as ever, Jones' third album was merely a 10 inch disc containing just one new song plus six cover versions. It was entitled *Girl At Her Volcano* and was no great commercial triumph. Now based in Paris, Rickie Lee proved that she was far more interested in following her own heart than in keeping an eye on the charts. (Bob Macdonald 18/11/85).

CHUCK E'S IN LOVE
Tracks: / Chuck E's in love.
7" Single: Released Jun '79, on Warner Bros., by WEA Records. Catalogue no: **K 17390**

EASY MONEY
Tracks: / Easy money / Company.
7" Single: Released Feb '80, on Warner Bros., by WEA Records. Deleted Feb '83. Catalogue no: **K 17556**

SATELLITE
Tracks: / Satellite / Ghost train.
CD 5": Released Sep '89, on Geffen, by Geffen Records (USA). Catalogue no: **GEF 64CD**
7" Single: Released Sep '89, on Geffen, by Geffen Records (USA). Catalogue no: **GEF 64**
12" Single: Released Sep '89, on Geffen, by Geffen Records (USA). Catalogue no: **GEF 64T**

UNDER THE BOARDWALK
Tracks: / Under the boardwalk.
7" Single: Released Aug '83, on Warner Bros., by WEA Records. Catalogue no: **W 9559**

WOODY & DUTCH
Tracks: / Woody & Dutch / Skeletons.
7" Single: Released Sep '81, on Warner Bros., by WEA Records. Deleted Sep '84. Catalogue no: **K 17851**

Jones, Ronnie

CAPTAIN OF HER HEART, THE
Tracks: / Captain of her heart, The / Captain of her heart, The (1st dance mix) / Loving you (extra track on 12").
7" Single: Released Mar '86, on Sublime. Catalogue no: **LIME 102**
12" Single: Released Mar '86, on Sublime. Catalogue no: **LIMET 102**

VIDEO GAMES
Tracks: / Video games / We make the music.
7" Single: Released Jan '81, on Carrere. Deleted Jan '84. Catalogue no: **CAR 173**

Jones, Sherry

HANG ON SLOOPY
Tracks: / Hang on Sloopy / Kill me, thrill me.
7" Single: Released Mar '82, on Polo, by Polo Records. Deleted '88. Catalogue no: **POLO 19**
12" Single: Released Mar '82, on Polo, by Polo Records. Deleted '88. Catalogue no: **POLO 12-19**

Jones, Shirley

DO YOU GET ENOUGH LOVE
Tracks: / Do you get enough love / We can work it out.
7" Single: Released Jul '86, on Philadelphia Int., by EMI Records. Catalogue no: **PIR 2**
12" Single: Released Jul '86, on Philadelphia Int., by EMI Records. Catalogue no: **12 PIR 2**

Jones, Sonia

HERE WE'LL STAY
Tracks: / Here we'll stay / Head over heels.
7" Single: Released Mar '80, on Magnet, by WEA Records. Deleted Mar '83. Cata-

logue no: **MAG 165**

Jones, Spencer

HEAD OVER HEELS
Tracks: / Head over heels.
7" Single: Released Mar '84, on Polo, by Polo Records. Deleted '88. Catalogue no: **POLO 31**
12" Single: Released Mar '84, on Polo, by Polo Records. Deleted '88. Catalogue no: **POLO 12-31**

HOW HIGH
Tracks: / How high.
12" Single: Released May '89, on Jam Today, by Jam Today Records. Catalogue no: **12CHIL 12**
12" Single: Released Nov '82, on Elite Records, by Elite Records. Deleted '84. Catalogue no: **DAZZ 16**

HOW TO WIN YOUR LOVE
Tracks: / How to win your love.
7" Single: Released Jan '86, on Champion, by Champion Records. Deleted Jul '89. Catalogue no: **CHAMP 10**
12" Single: Released Jan '86, on Champion, by Champion Records. Catalogue no: **CHAMP 1210**

I WANT YOU
Tracks: / I want you.
12" Single: Released Dec '83, on Elite Records, by Elite Records. Deleted '84. Catalogue no: **DAZZ 29**

MISS FRIDAY
Tracks: / Miss Friday.
7" Single: Released Oct '86, on Rise. Catalogue no: **RISE 3**
12" Single: Released Oct '86, on Rise. Catalogue no: **RISET 3**

Jones, Steve

I NEED YOU
Tracks: / I need you.
7" Single: Released Dec '84, on P Flight. Deleted '86. Catalogue no: **PFD 001**

MERCY (SINGLE)
Tracks: / Mercy.
7" Single: Released Aug '87, on I.R.S. Catalogue no: **IRM 1184**
12" Single: Released Aug '87, on I.R.S. Catalogue no: **IRMT 1184**

Jones, Tamiko

I WANT YOU
Tracks: / I want you.
12" Single: Released Dec '86, on Hot Melt, by Hot Melt Records. Catalogue no: **12 DETAIL 2**

Jones, Tammy

Biographical details: Jones, Tammy This British singer enjoyed brief fame in 1975 with her middle of the road single and album *Let Me Try Again*. The former cruised to No.5 in Britain and the latter peaked at No.38. She tried to operate in Shirley Bassey/Tom Jones big ballad territory and, although cabaret audiences warmed to this type of vocalist, record buyers would not let her try again. (Bob Macdonald 18/11/85).

DON'T BREAK THE HEART THAT LOVES YOU
Tracks: / Don't break the heart that loves you / Make love tonight.
7" Single: Released Nov '80, on Monarch, by Monarch Records. Deleted '83. Catalogue no: **MON 19**

LET ME TRY AGAIN (SINGLE)
Tracks: / Let me try again.
7" Single: Released Apr '75, on Epic, by CBS Records. Deleted '78. Catalogue no: **EPC 3211**

Jones, Tom

Biographical details: Jones, Tom This British singer was born Thomas Jones Woodward in Glamorgan, Wales. He began his career as a teenage rock'n'roller in the late Fifties, but struggled for several years looking for his break. He eventually teamed up with manager Gordon Mills, who co-wrote his first hit *It's Not Unusual*. The years of waiting proved worthwhile for *It's Not Unusual* reached No.1 in Britain and No.10 in America in 1965. A series of smaller successes followed during the next 18 months, the biggest being Bacharach & David's *What's New Pussycat ?* which climbed to No.11 in the UK and No.3 in the US.
The 1965-66 period of Jones' career saw him operating as a kind of sub Presley cabaret rocker, unsure whether to pitch for the younger pop market or the older middle of the road audience. At the end of 1966, however, he secured his long term future by aiming straight for the latter. His dramatic rendition of the country standard *Green Green Grass of Home* was a million-seller in Britain alone, logging seven weeks at No.1 and marking the first time in four years that The Beatles were not at the top of the charts at Christmas. *Green Green Grass of Home* a big ballad about a condemned prisosner who was destined never to return to his home and loved ones, was an absolutely ideal vechile for Jones' soulful and sometimes excessively strong vocal style. During the last three years of the Sixties, he was never far from the British Top 10; his run of hits included three consecutive UK No.2 singles with *I'll Never Fall In Love Again* (co-written by Lonnie Donegan), *I'm Coming Home* and *Delilah* (later revived by the Sensational Alex Harvey Band). The latter song also proved the title of one of the biggest of his many big selling albums, reaching No.1 on the British LP chart in the late summer of '68. At about the same time, he became the UK's highest paid TV entertainer.
The career of Tom Jones was almost identical to that of fellow MoR vocalist Englebert Humperdinck. Both singers began their careers as rock'n'roll hopefuls in the late fifties, and struggled until being guided to stardom in the mid-sixties by their mutual manager Gordon Mills. Both performers launched their long term MoR futures with revamps of country songs, Jones with *Grass* in late '66 and Hump with *Release Me* in early '67. They were the two top selling UK singles artists in 1967 and 1968, years which are more commonly associated with flower power, psychedelia nad LSD. Both were ssigned to Decca Records, both made regular use of songwriters Les Reed & Barry Mason and producer Peter Sullivan. Both were adored by housewives and both gradually faded from the record charts during the early Seventies in favour of the lucrative Las Vegas world of cabaret, televisionand all round showbiz superstardom; although both reached No.1 on the UK LP chart in early 1975 with TV advertised *Greatest Hits* collections. Both tried their hand at the Nashville country market during the late Seventies and early Eighties with moderate success. Both admitted feeling homesick in the mid Eighties and made moves to return from America to Britain - don't we all feel sorry for them! (Bob Macdonald 18/11/85)d.

6 TRACK HITS
Tracks: / Daughter of darkness / My way / What becomes of the broken hearted? / Raining in my heart / Till / Say you'll stay until tomorrow.
7" EP: Released Sep '83, on Scoop 33, by Pickwick Records. Catalogue no: **7SR 5004**

BORN TO BE ME
Tracks: / Born to be me / Boy from nowhere, A / Panama hat, A.
Note: * track on 12" version only.
12" Single: Released Nov '87, on Epic, by CBS Records. Deleted Jun '88. Catalogue no: **OLE T4**
7" Single: Released Nov '87, on Epic, by CBS Records. Deleted Jun '88. Catalogue no: **OLE 4**

BOY FROM NOWHERE, A
Tracks: / Boy from nowhere, A / I'll dress you in mourning / To be a matador / Dance with death.
7" Single: Released Apr '87, on Epic, by CBS Records. Deleted Nov '87. Catalogue no: **OLEQ 1**
12" Single: Released Mar '87, on Epic, by CBS Records. Deleted Aug '87. Catalogue no: **OLE T1**

BUT I DO
Tracks: / But i do / One night with you.
7" Single: Released Feb '82, on Polydor, by Polydor Ltd. Deleted Feb '87. Catalogue no: **POSP 410**

COME HOME RHONDDA BOY
Tracks: / Come home Rhondda boy / What in the world's come over you.
7" Single: Released Nov '81, on Polydor, by Polydor Ltd. Deleted Nov '84. Catalogue no: **POSP 371**

DAUGHTER OF DARKNESS
Tracks: / Daughter of darkness.
7" Single: Released Apr '70, on Decca, by Decca Records. Deleted '73. Catalogue no: **F 13013**

DELILAH (OLD GOLD)
Tracks: / Delilah.
7" Single: Released Oct '83, on Old Gold, by Old Gold Records. Deleted Sep '89. Catalogue no: **OG 9352**

DELILAH (SINGLE)
Tracks: / Delilah.
7" Single: Released Feb '68, on Decca, by Decca Records. Deleted '88. Catalogue no: **F 12747**

DETROIT CITY
Tracks: / Detroit City.
7" Single: Released Feb '67, on Decca, by Decca Records. Deleted '70. Catalogue no: **F 22555**

FROM THE HEART
7" Single: Released Jun '87, on Chapter 22, by Chapter 22 Records. Catalogue no: **LCHAP 14**

FUNNY FAMILIAR FORGOTTEN FEELINGS
Tracks: / Funny, familiar forgotten feelings.
7" Single: Released Apr '67, on Decca, by Decca Records. Deleted '70. Catalogue no: **F 12639**

GREEN GREEN GRASS OF HOME (OLD GOLD)
Tracks: / Green green grass of home.
7" Single: Released Oct '83, on Old Gold, by Old Gold Records. Catalogue no: **OG 9337**

GREEN GREEN GRASS OF HOME (SINGLE)
Tracks: / Green green grass of home.
7" Single: Released Nov '66, on Decca, by Decca Records. Deleted '69. Catalogue no: **F 22511**

HELP YOURSELF (SINGLE)
Tracks: / Help yourself.
7" Single: Released Jul '68, on Decca, by Decca Records. Deleted '71. Catalogue no: **F 12812**

I (WHO HAVE NOTHING) (SINGLE)
Tracks: / I (Who have nothing).
7" Single: Released Aug '70, on Decca, by Decca Records. Deleted '73. Catalogue no: **F 13061**

I'LL BE WHERE THE HEART IS
Tracks: / I'll be where the heart is / My last goodbye.
7" Single: Released Sep '83, on Decca, by Decca Records. Deleted '88. Catalogue no: **JONES 1**

I'LL DRESS YOU IN MOURNING
Tracks: / I'll dress you in mourning.
7" Single: Released Jul '87, on Epic, by CBS Records. Catalogue no: **OLE 3**

I'LL NEVER FALL IN LOVE AGAIN
Tracks: / I'll never fall in love again.
7" Single: Released Jul '67, on Decca, by Decca Records. Deleted '70. Catalogue no: **F 12639**

I'M COMING HOME (SINGLE)
Tracks: / I'm coming home.
7" Single: Released Nov '67, on Decca, by Decca Records. Deleted '70. Catalogue no: **F 12693**

IT'S NOT UNUSUAL (SINGLE)
Tracks: / It's not unusual.
7" Single: Released Jan '65, on Decca, by Decca Records. Deleted '68. Catalogue no: **F 12062**
7" Single: Released May '87, on London Records, by London Records. Deleted Oct '88. Catalogue no: **F 103**
12" Single: Released May '87, on London Records, by London Records. Catalogue no: **FX 103**

LETTER TO LUCILLE
Tracks: / Letter to Lucille.
7" Single: Released Apr '73, on Decca, by Decca Records. Deleted '76. Catalogue no: **F 13393**

LOVE ME TONIGHT
Tracks: / Love me tonight.
7" Single: Released May '69, on Decca, by Decca Records. Deleted '72. Catalogue no: **F 12924**

MINUTE OF YOUR TIME, A
Tracks: / Minute of your time, A.
7" Single: Released Nov '68, on Decca, by Decca Records. Deleted '71. Catalogue no: **F 12854**

MOVE CLOSER
Tracks: / Move closer.
CD 5": Released Apr '89, on Jive, by Zomba Records. Catalogue no: **JIVECD 203**
7" Single: Released Apr '89, on Jive, by Zomba Records. Catalogue no: **JIVE 203**
12" Single: Released Apr '89, on Jive, by Zomba Records. Catalogue no: **JIVET 203**

ONCE THERE WAS A TIME
Tracks: / Once there was a time / Not responsible.
7" Single: Released May '66, on Decca, by Decca Records. Deleted '69. Catalogue no: **F 12390**

ONCE UPON A TIME
Tracks: / Once upon a time.
7" Single: Released Apr '65, on Decca, by Decca Records. Deleted '68. Catalogue no: **F 12121**

PUPPET MAN
Tracks: / Puppet man.
7" Single: Released Jun '71, on Decca, by Decca Records. Deleted '74. Catalogue no: **F 13183**

SAY YOU'LL STAY UNTIL TOMORROW
Tracks: / Say you'll stay until tomorrow.
7" Single: Released Apr '77, on EMI, by EMI Records. Deleted '80. Catalogue no: **EMI 2583**

SHE'S A LADY (SINGLE)
Tracks: / She's a lady.
7" Single: Released Jan '71, on Decca, by Decca Records. Deleted '74. Catalogue no: **F 13113**

SOMETHING ABOUT YOU BABY I LIKE
Tracks: / Something about you baby I like.
7" Single: Released Sep '74, on Decca, by Decca Records. Deleted '77. Catalogue no: **F 13550**

SONNY BOY
Tracks: / Sonny boy / Words I would have liked to say.
7" Single: Released Dec '81, on Recorded Delivery. Deleted Dec '84. Catalogue no: **RDR 007**

THIS & THAT
Tracks: / This & that.
7" Single: Released Aug '66, on Decca, by Decca Records. Deleted '69. Catalogue no: **F 12461**

THUNDERBALL
Tracks: / Thunderball.
7" Single: Released Jan '66, on Decca, by Decca Records. Deleted '69. Catalogue no: **F 12292**

TILL
Tracks: / Till.
7" Single: Released Oct '71, on Decca, by Decca Records. Deleted '74. Catalogue no: **F 13236**

WHAT'S NEW PUSSYCAT
Tracks: / What's new pussycat.
7" Single: Released Aug '65, on Decca, by Decca Records. Deleted '68. Catalogue no: **F 12203**
7" Single: Released Aug '87, on Decca, by Decca Records. Deleted Oct '88. Catalogue no: **F 104**

WITH THESE HANDS
Tracks: / With these hands.
7" Single: Released Jul '65, on Decca, by Decca Records. Deleted '68. Catalogue no: **F 12191**

WITHOUT LOVE
Tracks: / Without love.
7" Single: Released Dec '69, on Decca, by Decca Records. Deleted '72. Catalogue no: **F 12990**

YOUNG NEW MEXICAN PUPPETEER, THE
Tracks: / Young New Mexican Puppeteer, The.
7" Single: Released Apr '72, on Decca, by Decca Records. Deleted '75. Catalogue no: **F 13298**

Jones, Trevor

LAST PLACE ON EARTH
Tracks: / Last place on earth.
7" Single: Released Mar '85, on Island, by Island Records. Catalogue no: **IS 225**

Jones, Val

LOVE NEVER COMES EASY
Tracks: / Love never comes easy / Tell it to me softly.
7" Single: Released Mar '80, on Piccadilly. Deleted Mar '83. Catalogue no: **7P5014**

Jones, Vivian

COULD IT BE YOU
Tracks: / Could it be you.
12" Single: Released Jan '84, on Ironside. Catalogue no: **IS 001**

EXTRA CLASSIC SUPER FANTASTIC LOVER
Tracks: / Extra classic super fantastic lover.
12" Single: Released Sep '89, on Living Room. Catalogue no: **LM 027**

JAH WORKS
Tracks: / Jah works.
12" Single: Released Aug '87, on Jah Shaka. Catalogue no: **SHAKA 863**

LOAFING
Tracks: / Loafing.
7" Single: Released Nov '82, on Rosie, by Rosie Records. Catalogue no: **RR 009**

MASH IT UP
Tracks: / Mash it up / I love.
12" Single: Released Nov '83, on Ruff Cut. Catalogue no: **RC 005**

MY BABY DON'T CARE
Tracks: / My baby don't care.
12" Single: Released May '82, on Rosie, by Rosie Records. Catalogue no: **RR 003**

PHYSICAL
Tracks: / Physical.
12" Single: Released Jun '85, on Leo Records, by Leo Records. Catalogue no: **LEO**

008

RED EYES
Tracks: / Red eyes.
12" Single: Released Dec '86, on Shaka, Catalogue no: **SHAKA 859**

SUGAR LOVE
Tracks: / Sugar love.
12" Single: Released Dec '88, on Groove & A Quarter, Catalogue no: **GRD 005**

WHAT YOU GONNA DO
Tracks: / What you gonna do.
12" Single: Released Aug '82, on Virgo, Catalogue no: **VG 106**

Joneses

SUGAR PIE GUY
Tracks: / Sugar pie guy.
7" Single: Released Mar '83, on Mercury, by Phonogram Ltd. Catalogue no: **MER 138**
12" Single: Released Mar '83, on Mercury, by Phonogram Ltd. Catalogue no: **MERX 138**

SUMMER GROOVE
Tracks: / Summer groove.
7" Single: Released Oct '81, on Champagne Records, Deleted Oct '84. Catalogue no: **FIZZ 507**
12" Single: Released Oct '81, on Champagne Records, Deleted Oct '84. Catalogue no: **FIZY 507**

Jonid & The Ids

FALSE PROMISES
Tracks: / False promises.
7" Single: Released May '82, on Prelude Club, Catalogue no: **PLAY 001**

Jonuz

BEST BOOGIE
Tracks: / Best boogie.
12" Single: Released Dec '88, on Criminal (1), by Criminal Records. Catalogue no: **BUST 12**

Jonzun Crew

LOVIN'
Tracks: / Lovin'.
7" Single: Released Feb '85, on Tommy Boy, by Polydor Ltd. Catalogue no: **POSP 725**
12" Single: Released Feb '85, on Tommy Boy, by Polydor Ltd. Catalogue no: **POSPX 725**

SPACE COWBOY
Tracks: / Space cowboy.
7" Single: Released Jul '83, on 21 Records, by Polydor Ltd. Catalogue no: **POSP 623**
12" Single: Released Jul '83, on 21 Records, by Polydor Ltd. Catalogue no: **POSPX 623**

Jonzun, Michael

BURNIN' UP
Tracks: / Burnin' up / World is a battlefield, The / World is a battlefield, The (piano dub) / World is a battlefield, The (inst dub).
7" Single: Released Aug '86, on A&M, by A&M Records. Deleted '87. Catalogue no: **AM 340**
12" Single: Released Aug '86, on A&M, by A&M Records. Deleted '87. Catalogue no: **AMY 340**

TIME IS RUNNING OUT
Tracks: / Time is running out.
7" Single: Released Aug '84, on Tommy Boy, by Polydor Ltd. Catalogue no: **POSP 698**

Jookes

I JUST WANNA STAY HERE (and love you)
Tracks: / I just wanna stay here.
7" Single: Released Jun '84, on Hollywood, by Hollywood Records. Catalogue no: **HWD 005**

Jools

SINGING IN THE RAIN
Tracks: / Singing in the rain.
7" Single: Released Jan '83, on PRT, by Castle Communications Records. Catalogue no: **7P 255**

Joolz

DENISE
Tracks: / Denise.
12" Single: Released Oct '83, on Abstract, by Abstract Sounds. Catalogue no: **12 ABS 018**

KISS, THE
Tracks: / Kiss, The.
12" Single: Released Jul '84, on Abstract, by Abstract Sounds. Catalogue no: **12 ABS 025**

LOVE IS (sweet romance)
Tracks: / Love is.
7" Single: Released Nov '85, on EMI, by EMI Records. Catalogue no: **12JLZ 1**
7" Single: Released Nov '85, on EMI, by EMI Records. Catalogue no: **JLZ 1**

MAD, BAD AND DANGEROUS TO KNOW
Tracks: / Mad, bad and dangerous to know / Legend / Babies (Extra track on 12" version).
7" Single: Released Aug '86, on EMI, by EMI Records. Catalogue no: **EMI 5582**
12" Single: Released Aug '86, on EMI, by EMI Records. Catalogue no: **12EMI 5582**

PROTECTION
Tracks: / Protection / Day in the life, A.
7" Single: Released Oct '87, on EMI, by EMI Records. Deleted Apr '88. Catalogue no: **JLZ 3**
12" Single: Released Oct '87, on EMI, by EMI Records. Deleted Apr '88. Catalogue no: **12JLZ 3**

Jordan, Danny

LADY IN MY LIFE
Tracks: / Lady in my life, The / New love.
7" Single: Released Jun '85, on Blue Note, by EMI Records. Catalogue no: **BLUE 2**
12" Single: Released Jun '85, on Blue Note, by EMI Records. Catalogue no: **12 BLUE 2**

Jordan, Dick

HALLELUJAH I LOVE HER SO
Tracks: / Hallelujah I love her so.
7" Single: Released Mar '60, on Oriole, Deleted '63. Catalogue no: **CB 1534**

LITTLE CHRISTINE
Tracks: / Little Christine.
7" Single: Released Jan '60, on Oriole, Deleted '63. Catalogue no: **CB 1548**

Jordan, Earl

I BELIEVE
Tracks: / I believe / Super man.
7" Single: Released Mar '80, on Liberty, by EMI Records. Deleted Mar '83. Catalogue no: **UP 624**

Jordan, Louis

CHOO CHOO CH' BOOGIE
Tracks: / Fifty cents / Man ain't a man, A / No chance blues / I'm going to move to the outskirts of town / Jazz lips / Don't worry / 'Bout the mule / Choo choo ch' boogie / I'm gonna shimmy like my sister Kate / Is you is or is you ain't my baby / Black and tan fantasy / Back home again in Indiana.
7" Single: Released Jul '82, on Revival, Catalogue no: **REV 6019**

Jordan, Marc

CATCH THE MOON
Tracks: / Catch the moon / Talking through pictures / Inside the glass bead (Extra track available on 12" only).
7" Single: Released Mar '88, on RCA, by BMG Records (UK). Deleted May '89. Catalogue no: **PB 49569**
12" Single: Released Mar '88, on RCA, by BMG Records (UK). Deleted May '89. Catalogue no: **PT 49570**

Jordan, Stanley

ELEANOR RIGBY
Tracks: / Eleanor Rigby.
7" Single: Released Oct '85, on Blue Note, by EMI Records. Catalogue no: **BLUE 3**

Jose & Kazoo Band

KAZOO KAZOO
Tracks: / Kazoo kazoo.
7" Single: Released Aug '82, on Baby, by New Rose Records. Catalogue no: **KAZOO 1**
12" Single: Released Aug '82, on Baby, by New Rose Records. Catalogue no: **KAZOO 112**

Josef K

ANGLE
Tracks: / Angle.
7" Single: Released Feb '82, on Les Disques Du Crepuscule(Belgium), by Les Disques Du Crepuscule(Belgium). Catalogue no: **7TWI 053**

CHANCE MEETING
Tracks: / Chance meeting.
7" Single: Released May '81, on Postcard, Deleted '82. Catalogue no: **POSTCARD 81/5**

HEAVEN SENT
Tracks: / Heaven sent.
7" Single: Released Mar '87, on Supreme Int.Editions, by Supreme Int.Records. Catalogue no: **EDITION 87-7**

IT'S KINDA FUNNY
Tracks: / It's kinda funny.
7" Single: Released Dec '80, on Postcard, Deleted '82. Catalogue no: **POSTCARD 80/5**

RADIO DRILL TIME
Tracks: / Radio drill time.
7" Single: Released Aug '80, on Postcard, Deleted '82. Catalogue no: **POSTCARD 80/3**

Joseph, David

Biographical details: Joseph, David This British singer first found fame as frontman with Hi-Tension, a successful UK disco band of the late Seventies. He emerged as a solo artist in 1983 with the funky dance-floor sizzler *You Can't Hide (Your Love From Me)*, which reached No.13 on the UK national singles chart. He soon followed it with a second pop crossover hit *Let's Let It Up (Nite People)*, which reached No.26. His classy LP *The Joys O Life* was issued in November 1983 and the title track became a minor UK hit single in February 1984. (Bob Macdonald 18/11/85).

DEAR STAR
Tracks: / Dear star.
7" Single: Released Oct '83, on Island, by Island Records. Catalogue no: **IS 128**
12" Single: Released Oct '83, on Island, by Island Records. Catalogue no: **12IS 128**

JOYS OF LIFE
Tracks: / Joys of life.
7" Single: Released Jan '84, on Island, by Island Records. Catalogue no: **IS 135**
12" Single: Released Jan '84, on Island, by Island Records. Catalogue no: **12IS 135**

LET'S LIVE IT UP (NITE PEOPLE)
Tracks: / Let's live it up (Nite people).
7" Single: Released May '83, on Island, by Island Records. Deleted '86. Catalogue no: **IS 116**

NO TURNING BACK
Tracks: / No turning back.
7" Single: Released Aug '87, on 4th & Broadway, by Island Records. Deleted Apr '88. Catalogue no: **BRW 66**
12" Single: Released Aug '87, on 4th & Broadway, by Island Records. Deleted Apr '88. Catalogue no: **12 BRW 66**

YOU CAN'T HIDE (YOUR LOVE FROM ME)
Tracks: / You can't hide (your love from me).
7" Single: Released Feb '83, on Island, by Island Records. Deleted '86. Catalogue no: **IS 101**

Joseph & Giselle

BUT YOU LOVE ME DADDY
Tracks: / But you love me daddy / Rodeo special.
7" Single: Released Dec '82, on Button, by Musical Characters Records. Catalogue no: **BTN 103**

Joseph, Jeff

BIG BEAT
Tracks: / Big beat / Side by side.
7" Single: Released Jul '89, on Polydor, by Polydor Ltd. Catalogue no: **PO 51**
12" Single: Released Jul '89, on Polydor, by Polydor Ltd. Catalogue no: **PZ 51**

Joseph, Margie

I'VE GOT TO HAVE YOUR LOVE
Tracks: / I've got to have your love / I've got to have your love (version).
12" Single: Released Sep '88, on Ichiban, by Ichiban Records (UK). Catalogue no: **12 PO 12**

KNOCKOUT
Tracks: / Knockout.
7" Single: Released Apr '83, on Jive, by Zomba Records. Catalogue no: **JIVE 32**
12" Single: Released Apr '83, on Jive, by Zomba Records. Catalogue no: **JIVET 32**

MIDNIGHT LOVER
Tracks: / Midnight lover / Big strong man / I want mo' stuff.
7" Single: Released Aug '84, on Atlantic, by WEA Records. Deleted '85. Catalogue no: **B 9713**
12" Single: Released Aug '84, on Atlantic, by WEA Records. Catalogue no: **B 9713 T**

Joseph, Nerious

NO ONE NIGHT STAND
Tracks: / No one night stand / Jealously.
12" Single: Released Mar '87, on Fine Style, by Fashion Records. Catalogue no: **FS 009**

YOU'RE MY SPECIAL LADY
Tracks: / You're my special lady.
12" Single: Released Dec '85, on Fashion, by Fashion Records. Catalogue no: **FAD 042**

Joseph, Steve

MY LIFE IS A SONG
Tracks: / My life is a song / Let me love you.
7" Single: Released Feb '81, on Songwriters Workshop, by Songwriters Workshop Publishing. Deleted '87. Catalogue no: **SW 14**

Jossiah

MAKE MY GOLD
Tracks: / Make my gold / Golden guitar.
7" Single: Released Apr '85, on RPM, Catalogue no: **RPM 3**

Joubert Singers

STAND ON THE WORD
Tracks: / Stand on the word.
7" Single: Released May '85, on 10 Records, by Virgin Records. Deleted '87. Catalogue no: **TEN 48**
12" Single: Released May '85, on 10 Records, by Virgin Records. Deleted May '88. Catalogue no: **TEN 48-12**

Journey (group)

Biographical details: Journey The most successful line up of this American rock band has been:Jonathan Cain, Steve Perry, Neal Schon, Steve Smith and Ross Valory.
Formed in San Francisco in 1973, Journey spent five years and took six line ups to make it big. Their main driving force was guitarist Schon, a former member of Santana; keyboardist/vocalist Gregg Rolie, who was a Journey member from 1973 until 1981, had also played with Santana. The first album *Journey* was issued in 1975 and made a modest impression on the US Top 200 Albums chart. After further LPs and much hard touring, they achieved their commercial and musical breakthrough with the 1978 album *Infinity* - this was produced by the famous Roy Thomas Baker and was the first Journey LP to feature the talents of the distinctive singer and frontman Steve Perry.
During the early Eighties Journey were one of America's biggest rock bands. *Escape* released in the summer of 1981, reached No.1 in the US and was still listed on the Billboard chart at the end of 1982. This album yielded a hat trick of Top 10 singles *Who's Crying Now* (no.4), *Don't Stop Believin'* (No.9) nad *Open Arms* (No.2 for six weeks). 1983's *Frontiers* LP was another big American seller and spawned the US Top 10 single *Separate Ways (Worlds Apart)*. Perry's 1984 solo album *Street Talk* produced the US No.3 hit *Oh Sherrie*. The following year, the band were back in business with the Top 10 single *Only The Young* (from the movie 'Vision Quest').
In common with Styx, Foreigner, REO Speedwagon, Journey represented the typical face of American rock during the late Seventies and early Eighties. They operated halfway between pop and rock, combining catchy melodies and harmonies with a traditional rock instrumentation, rhythm and image. They were guaranteed to sell many millions of records, filled stadiums across America - and were condemned by critics as bland, safe and repetitive. In Britain such predictable music was regarded as an irrelevance to the ever changing UK scene; but whereas the other AOR rock groups managed to achieve at least one British Top 10 single, Journey's best showing was No.46 with *Who's Crying Now*. They finally made a brief Top 10 appearance on the LP chart with 1983's *Frontiers*. (Bob Macdonald 19/11/85).

ANYWAY YOU WANT IT
Tracks: / Anyway you want it / Do you recall.
7" Single: Released May '80, on CBS, by CBS Records. Deleted '83. Catalogue no: **CBS 8558**
12" Single: Released May '80, on CBS, by CBS Records. Deleted '83. Catalogue no: **12-8558**

BE GOOD TO YOURSELF
Tracks: / Be good to yourself / Only the young / Anyway you want it* / Stone in love* / Separate ways / After the fall+ / Rubicon+.
Note: *=Extra track on 12" version only += tracks in double pack limited edition only
7" Pic: Released Apr '86, on CBS, by CBS Records. Deleted '86. Catalogue no: **DA 7095**
7" Single: Released Apr '86, on CBS, by CBS Records. Deleted '86. Catalogue no: **A 7095**
12" Single: Released Apr '86, on CBS, by CBS Records. Deleted '86. Catalogue no: **TA 7095**

DON'T STOP BELIEVIN'
Tracks: / Don't stop believin' / Open arms / Who's crying now / Lovin', touchin', squeezin'.
Cassingle: Released Dec '82, on CBS, by CBS Records. Deleted Dec '85. Catalogue no: **A 40 2908**
7" Single: Released Feb '82, on CBS, by CBS Records. Deleted '85. Catalogue no: **A 1728**
CD 3": Released Aug '88, on Columbia

(USA), by CBS Records (USA). Catalogue no: **38 K07951**

FAITHFULLY
Tracks: / Faithfully.
7" Single: Released Apr '83, on CBS, by CBS Records. Catalogue no: **A 3358**

GIRL CAN'T HELP IT
Tracks: / Girl can't help it, The / It could have been.
7" Single: Released Nov '86, on CBS, by CBS Records. Catalogue no: **650116 7**

PARTY'S OVER
Tracks: / Party's over / Wheel in the sky.
7" Single: Released Mar '81, on CBS, by CBS Records. Deleted Mar '84. Catalogue no: **CBS 9578**

SEPARATE WAYS
Tracks: / Separate ways / Frontiers.
7" Single: Released Feb '83, on CBS, by CBS Records. Catalogue no: **A 3077**
12" Single: Released Feb '83, on CBS, by CBS Records. Catalogue no: **A 13 3077**

STONE IN LOVE
Tracks: / Stone in love / Only solutions.
7" Single: Released Oct '82, on CBS, by CBS Records. Deleted Oct '85. Catalogue no: **A 2890**

SUZANNE
Tracks: / Suzanne / Ask the lonely (on 12" only.) / Raised on radio (on 12" only.).
7" Single: Released Jul '86, on CBS, by CBS Records. Catalogue no: **CBS 7265**
12" Single: Released Jul '86, on CBS, by CBS Records. Deleted '86. Catalogue no: **TA 7265**

WHO'S CRYING NOW
Tracks: / Who's crying now / Open arms / Suzanne+ / Don't stop believin(12" only).
CD 5": Released 16 Jan '89, on CBS, by CBS Records. Deleted 10 Jul '89. Catalogue no: **654 541-2**
7" Single: Released Sep '82, on CBS, by CBS Records. Deleted '85. Catalogue no: **A 2725**
7" Single: Released 16 Jan '89, on CBS, by CBS Records. Deleted 10 Jul '89. Catalogue no: **654 541-7**
12" Single: Released 16 Jan '89, on CBS, by CBS Records. Deleted 10 Jul '89. Catalogue no: **654 541-6**

Jovanotti

GIMME FIVE
Tracks: / Gimme five / Gimme five (version).
CD 5": Released Nov '88, on WEA, by WEA Records. Catalogue no: **YZ 323 CD**
7" Single: Released Nov '88, on WEA, by WEA Records. Catalogue no: **YZ 323**
12" Single: Released Nov '88, on WEA, by WEA Records. Catalogue no: **YZ 323T**

Joy

BLOODY MURDER ON THAT DANCEFLOOR
Tracks: / Bloody murder on that dancefloor.
12" Single: Released Oct '88, on Submission, by Submission Records. Catalogue no: **SUBX 07**

LOST IN HONG KONG
Tracks: / Lost in Hong Kong / Lucky star.
7" Single: Released Sep '85, on Conifer, Catalogue no: **6 20445**
12" Single: Released Mar '86, on Teldec (1), by ASV (Academy Sound & Vision). Catalogue no: **6.2045**

PARADISE ROAD
Tracks: / Paradise road / Iza nezembe.
7" Single: Released Jan '81, on Blue Chip, by Blue Chip Records. Deleted '81. Catalogue no: **BC 101**

STATE OF INDEPENDENCE
Tracks: / State of independence.
7" Single: Released Aug '82, on Island, by Island Records. Deleted '84. Catalogue no: **WIP 6819**
12" Single: Released Aug '82, on Island, by Island Records. Deleted '84. Catalogue no: **12WIP 6819**

TOUCH BY TOUCH
Tracks: / Touch by touch / Fire in the night.
7" Single: Released Mar '87, on Greyhound, by Greyhound Records. Catalogue no: **GRY 006**

Joy Circuit

DON'T TOUCH
Tracks: / Don't touch.
7" Single: Released Oct '85, on Pink Noise Product, Catalogue no: **PNP 1017**

Joy Division

Biographical details: Joy Division This British rock band consisted of Ian Curtis, Bernard Dickin (aka Bernard Albrecht) Peter Hook and Stephen Morris.
The group came into existence in 1977 under the name Warsaw. After gigging in their local Manchester area, they became Joy Division in early '78. Their debut record, an EP entitled *An Ideal for Living*, appeared in the middle of that year on the independent Enigma label. They were then taken aboard by Factory Records, a new indie company that had just been started in Manchester as an alternative to the London oriented 'ivory tower' record corporations.
Joy Division happened at just the right time. In 1979 the initial energy and raw power of the punk explosion had largely dissipated, with most of the key groups having split up or moved closer to the rock mainstream. However, the one aspect of the New Wave which was still thriving and growing, was the independent label scen. What was now needed was a new indie band who explored new and dangerous musical territories, but whose sound was still rooted in the punk philopophy - Joy Division were that band.
Fronted by the flat frim vocals and despairing lyrics of Ian Curtis, the stark sounds of Joy Division were heard to eerie effect on theri 1979 debut LP *Unknown Pleasures*. It received huge support from the UK music press and heavy airplay from BBC Radio One's ever pioneering John Peel - but the bulk of the radio establishment was not interested in such dark, depressing music. Thus, tracks like *Transmission* (a single released in October 1979) attracted a near legendary cult following throughout Britain but failed to penetrate the national charts.
Sadly Joy Division did not achieve chart success until after the group's termination. Ian Curtis committed suicide in May 1980, the result of an acute depression caused by epilepsy and a broken marriage. The band had just completed their second album *Closer* which was issued in July and sped into the UK Top 10. At the same time, the classic single *Love Will Tear Us Apart* reached No.13 position in UK.
The three surviving members of Joy Division decided that it would be inappropriate to continue to use the old name. They recruited keyboard player Gillian Gilbert and evolved into New Order, who enjoyed greater commercial success while remaining rigidly independent. As an epitaph for Joy Division, Factory released the double half studio/half live LP *Still* in late 1981 and it reached No.5 on the British chart. *Love Will Tear Us Apart* re-entered the UK Top 20 in 1983 and at the same time, Paul Young covered the song on his mega-selling *No Parlez* album.(Bob Macdonald 19/11/85).

JOY DIVISION - LOVE WILL TEAR US APART (Released on Factory(1))

ATMOSPHERE
Tracks: / Atmosphere / Only mistake, The / Sound of music, The / Love will tear us apart** / Transmission**.
Note: *Track on 12in; **tracks on CD single.
CD 5": Released Jun '88, on Factory (1), by Factory Records. Catalogue no: **FACD 213**
7" Single: Released Jun '88, on Factory (1), by Factory Records. Catalogue no: **FAC 2137**
12" Single: Released Jun '88, on Factory (1), by Factory Records. Catalogue no: **FAC 213**

JOY DIVISION - STAMPA ALTERNATIVA Lyric book & flexi
Special: Released 23 Apr '87, on Stampa Alternative (Italy), Catalogue no: **JD 001**

LOVE WILL TEAR US APART (see panel above)
Tracks: / Love will tear us apart / These days.
7" Single: Released Jun '80, on Factory (1), by Factory Records. Catalogue no: **FAC 23**

PEEL SESSIONS:JOY DIVISION I
CD 5": Released Aug '88, on Strange Fruit, by Strange Fruit Records. Catalogue no: **SFPSCD 013**
12" Single: Released Nov '86, on Strange Fruit, by Strange Fruit Records. Catalogue no: **SFPS 013**

PEEL SESSIONS:JOY DIVISION II
Tracks: / Love will tear us apart / Twenty four hours / Colony / Sound of music, The.
CD 5": Released Jul '88, on Strange Fruit, by Strange Fruit Records. Catalogue no: **SFPSCD 033**
12" Single: Released Sep '87, on Strange Fruit, by Strange Fruit Records. Catalogue no: **SFPS 033**

TRANSMISSION
Tracks: / Transmission / Novelty.
7" Single: Released '80, on Factory (1), by Factory Records. Catalogue no: **FAC 13**
12" Single: Released '80, on Factory (1), by Factory Records. Catalogue no: **FAC 13-12**

YOU'RE NO GOOD FOR ME (BOOK/7"EP)
Tracks: / You're no good for me.
Note: 100 page lyric/biography book (in English & Italian!), shrink-wrapped with a 7" 4-track EP featuring 'You're no good for me', 'Komakino' & two versions of 'Incubation'.
Special: Released Nov '87, on Stampa Alternative (Italy), Catalogue no: **SCONC 001**

Joy & Gladness

HALF PAST MIDNIGHT
Tracks: / Half past midnight / Half past midnight (version) / One hour later.
7" Single: Released Sep '89, on Subway, by Subway Records. Catalogue no: **SUBX 012**

Joy, Lucia

I'M GONNA LEAVE YOU NOW
Tracks: / I'm gonna leave you now.
12" Single: Released Jun '83, on ABL, by ABL Records. Catalogue no: **ABL 001**

Joy Strings

IT'S AN OPEN SECRET
Tracks: / It's an open secret.
7" Single: Released Feb '64, on Regal Zonophone, by EMI Records. Deleted '67. Catalogue no: **RZ 501**

STARRY NIGHT, A
Tracks: / Starry night, A.
7" Single: Released Dec '64, on Regal Zonophone, by EMI Records. Deleted '67. Catalogue no: **RZ 504**

Joyce McKinney

BORING ROCK
Tracks: / Boring rock.
7" Single: Released 31 Jul '89, on Heath Robinson, Catalogue no: **THROB 1**

Joyce, Rosaline

ARE YOU REALLY GOING
Tracks: / Are you really going.
12" Single: Released Aug '85, on Hartone, Catalogue no: **HAR 01**

FALLING IN LOVE AGAIN
Tracks: / Falling in love again / I need all your loving.
12" Single: Released 5 Mar '88, on Jam Today, by Jam Today Records. Catalogue no: **12ROS 3**

FRIENDS NOT LOVERS
Tracks: / Friends not lovers / Friends not lovers (doin' fine mix).
7" Single: Released Sep '86, on Elite Records, by Elite Records. Deleted '88. Catalogue no: **DAZZ 57**
12" Single: Released Jan '87, on Elite Records, by Elite Records. Deleted '88. Catalogue no: **DAZZ 57 R**

NO QUESTIONS, NO ANSWERS
Tracks: / No questions, no answers / Yankee / Yankee (The London mix) / B-boy mix, The.
12" Single: Released Nov '87, on Jam Today, by Jam Today Records. Catalogue no: **12ROS 1**

J.R.

WHAT CAN I SAY?
Tracks: / What can I say?.
12" Single: Released Sep '89, on Must Dance, Catalogue no: **MD 014**

Judas Priest

Biographical details: Judas Priest The nucleus of this British heavy metal band has always been Ken 'KK' Downing, Rob Halford, Ian Hill and Glen Tipton. Dave Holland has been the most successful of their many drummers.
Formed in 1972 in the heavy metal hotbed of Birmingham, Judas Priest released their debut album *Rocka Rolla* in 1974. After building up their live following, they issued their second set *Sad Wings of Destinyin* '76 and cracked the UK charts for the first time with the third LP *Sin After Sin* (1977). The loyalty of their fans meant that the Priest were one of the few HM groups to sustain their chart success during the punk era of the late Seventies, when the heavy bands were dismissed in many quarters as passe. In 1979 the rallying single *Take On The World* and the live Lp *Unleashed In the East* both reached the British Top 20.
1980 was the year when HM made a major comeback on the UK charts; sthis resurgence was led by Judas Priest together with Saxon, Iron Maiden, Gillan, Motorhead, and Black Sabbath. Priest's 1980 album *British Steel* climbed to No.4 and logged 17 weeks on the UK chart. It spawned three Top 30 singles:'*Living After Midnight*, *Breaking The Law* and *United*. The core of the band's sound was the twin lead guitar set up of Downing and Tipton, fronted by the histrionic Halford's lead vocals.
From 1981 onwards Judas Priest continued to be a subsantial LP and concert attraction although 1980 remained their peak chart year in Britain. (Bob Macdonald 19/11/85).

6 TRACK HITS
Tracks: / Sinner / Exciter / Hell bent for leather / Ripper / Hot rockin' / Green manalishi.
7" EP: Released Sep '83, on Scoop 33, by Pickwick Records. Catalogue no: **7SR 5018**

BREAKING THE LAW
Tracks: / Breaking the law / Metal gods / Living after midnight / Take on the world (Available on cassingle only.) / United (Available on cassingle only.).
7" Single: Released Jun '80, on CBS, by CBS Records. Deleted '84. Catalogue no: **8644**

CHAINS
Tracks: / Chains / Judas Priest audio file.
7" Single: Released Oct '82, on CBS, by CBS Records. Deleted '85. Catalogue no: **A 2822**

DON'T GO
Tracks: / Don't go.
7" Single: Released Feb '81, on CBS, by CBS Records. Deleted '84. Catalogue no: **9520**

EVENING STAR
Tracks: / Evening star.
7" Single: Released May '79, on Epic, by CBS Records. Catalogue no: **CBS 7312**

FREEWHEEL BURNING
Tracks: / Freewheel burning.
7" Single: Released Jan '84, on CBS, by CBS Records. Catalogue no: **A 4054**
12" Single: Released Jan '84, on CBS, by CBS Records. Catalogue no: **TA 5054**

HOT ROCKIN'
Tracks: / Hot rockin' / Trouble shooter / Breakin' the law.
7" Single: Released Feb '81, on CBS, by CBS Records. Deleted '84. Catalogue no: **CBS 9520**
7" Single: Released Apr '81, on CBS, by CBS Records. Deleted '85. Catalogue no: **1153**
12" Single: Released Apr '81, on CBS, by CBS Records. Deleted '85. Catalogue no: **A121153**

JOHNNY B. GOODE
Tracks: / Rock you all around the world / Turbo lover* (Available on 12" only) / Johnny B. Goode.
Note: *Extra track on 12in only.
7" Single: Released May '88, on Atlantic, by WEA Records. Catalogue no: **A 9114**
12" Single: Released May '88, on Atlantic, by WEA Records. Catalogue no: **A 9114 T**

LIVING AFTER MIDNIGHT
Tracks: / Living after midnight / Delivering the goods.
7" Single: Released Mar '80, on CBS, by CBS Records. Deleted '84. Catalogue no: **CBS 8379**

LIVING AFTER MIDNIGHT (OLD GOLD)
Tracks: / Living after midnight / Breaking the law.
7" Single: Released 27 Feb '89, on Old Gold, by Old Gold Records. Catalogue no: **OG 9864**

LOCKED IN
Tracks: / Locked in / Reckless.
7" Single: Released May '86, on CBS, by CBS Records. Deleted '86. Catalogue no: **QTA 7144**
12" Single: Released May '86, on CBS, by CBS Records. Deleted '86. Catalogue no: **TA 7144**

SOME HEADS ARE GONNA ROLL
Tracks: / Some heads are gonna roll / Green Manalishi.
7" Single: Released Mar '84, on CBS, by CBS Records. Catalogue no: **A 4289**
12" Single: Released Mar '84, on CBS, by CBS Records. Catalogue no: **TA 4298**

TAKE ON THE WORLD
Tracks: / Take on the world / Star breaker.
7" Single: Released Jan '79, on CBS, by CBS Records. Catalogue no: **CBS 6915**

TURBO LOVER
Tracks: / Turbo lover / Hot for love.
7" Single: Released Apr '86, on CBS, by CBS Records. Deleted '86. Catalogue no: **A 7048**

TYRANT
Tracks: / Tyrant.
12" Single: Released Jun '83, on Gull, by Gull Records. Deleted '88. Catalogue no: **GULS 7612**

UNITED
Tracks: / United / Grinder, The.
7" Single: Released Jul '80, on CBS, by CBS Records. Deleted '84. Catalogue no: **8897**

YOU'VE GOT ANOTHER THING COMIN'
Tracks: / You've got another thing comin' / Exciter.
7" Pic: Released Aug '82, on CBS, by CBS Records. Deleted '85. Catalogue no: **112611**
7" Single: Released Aug '82, on CBS, by CBS Records. Deleted '85. Catalogue no: **A 2611**

Judd, Martin

DA DA DA I DON'T LOVE YOU, YOU DON'T
Tracks: / Da da da I don't love you, you don't.
7" Single: Released Jul '82, on After Hours. Deleted '88. Catalogue no: **AFT 04**

Judds

DON'T BE CRUEL
Tracks: / Don't be cruel / Sweetest gift, The.
7" Single: Released Jan '87, on RCA, by BMG Records (UK). Catalogue no: **PB 49763**

HAVE MERCY
Tracks: / Have mercy / Mama he's crazy.
7" Single: Released 30 Jan '89, on Curb, by BMG Records (UK). Deleted Aug '89. Catalogue no: **ZB 49471**
12" Single: Released 30 Jan '89, on Curb, by BMG Records (UK). Catalogue no: **ZT 49472**

I'M FALLING IN LOVE TONIGHT
Tracks: / I'm falling in love tonight.
7" Single: Released Apr '87, on RCA, by BMG Records (UK). Deleted May '89. Catalogue no: **PB 49717**

MAMA HE'S CRAZY
Tracks: / Mama he's crazy.
7" Single: Released Oct '85, on RCA, by BMG Records (UK). Catalogue no: **PB 49917**

Jude, Teresa

THIS DREAD IS MINE
Tracks: / This dread is mine.
12" Single: Released Oct '88, on Magic Shoot. Catalogue no: **MS 002**

Judge Dread

Biographical details: This British comedian and singer, whose real name is Alex Hughes, was a disc jockey before coming to fame as a recording artist in 1972. The record that brought him success was *Big six*, which reached the UK No.11 slot and stayed on the singles chart for half a year. This disc was extraordinary, because both the song and the artist's name were inspired by another act - Prince Buster, the Jamaica ska star of the Sixties, had once recorded a lewd song entitled *Big five*; Hughes adapted it and transformed it into *Big Six* and, at the same time, decided to adopt the name of another Buster track *Judge Dread*. In 1972, with ska having evolved into reggae, the new Judge Dread recorded the song in a pseudo-reggae style. Like all his subsequent waxings, it was banned from airplay on British radio and television. Becoming known as the king of rude reggae, Judge Dread enjoyed a further ten UK chart singles between late 1972 and early 1979. These included *Big seven* (which actually peaked at No.8) plus *Big eight* and *Big ten* (both of which reached Big Fourteen on the British charts); somehow, *Big nine* failed to attract customers to the record shops. In 1975 he reached No.9 with his rendition of *Je t'aime...moi non plus*, the notorious 1969 No.1 smash originally recorded by Jane Birkin and Serge Gainsbourg. In terms of composing and producing most of the Judge Dread hits were masterminded by the artist himself in conjunction with his manager Ted Lemon. By the late Seventies, the formula was wearing very thin and the hits were getting smaller. However, by this time, the Judge was moving into the steady, lucrative cabaret circuit, where his working class club appeal found an ideal home. During the Eighties, his only foray into the charts was in 1981 when he scored briefly with his *40 big ones* LP. A 1984 version of Frankie Goes To Hollywood's *Relax* single was not a success, because people were still buying the original version, which remained on the chart for most of that year. When it comes to having records banned by the BBC and other broadcasting organisations, no other act in UK chart history comes close to Judge Dread's tally of eleven blacked hit singles. (Bob MacDonald, 5th July 1985).

5TH ANNIVERSARY EP
Tracks: / Jamaica jerk (off) / Bring back the skins / End of the world / Big everything.
7" Single: Released Apr '77, on Cactus, by Creole Records. Deleted '80. Catalogue no: **CT 98**

BIG 6
Tracks: / Big 6.
7" Single: Released Aug '72, on Big Shot. Deleted '75. Catalogue no: **BI 608**

BIG 7
Tracks: / Big 7.
7" Single: Released Dec '72, on Big Shot. Deleted '75. Catalogue no: **BI 613**

BIG 8
Tracks: / Big 8.
7" Single: Released Apr '73, on Big Shot. Deleted '76. Catalogue no: **BI 619**

BIG 10
Tracks: / Big 10.
7" Single: Released Jul '75, on Cactus, by Creole Records. Deleted '78. Catalogue no: **CT 77**

BIG ONE, THE
Tracks: / Big one, The / Big six / Big seven / Big eight.
7" EP: Released '83, on Trojan, by Trojan Records. Deleted May '88. Catalogue no: **TMX 4011**

BIG SEVEN
Tracks: / Big seven / Big eight.
7" Single: Released Oct '88, on Old Gold, by Old Gold Records. Catalogue no: **OG 9804**

BIG SEVEN '85
Tracks: / Big seven '85.
7" Single: Released Sep '85, on Creole, by Creole Records. Catalogue no: **CR 85**
12" Single: Released Sep '85, on Creole, by Creole Records. Catalogue no: **CRT 85**

CHRISTMAS IN DREADLAND
Tracks: / Christmas in Dreadland / Come outside.
7" Single: Released Dec '75, on Cactus, by Creole Records. Deleted '78. Catalogue no: **CT 80**

HELLO BABY
Tracks: / Hello baby / One eyed lodger.
7" Single: Released May '81, on Creole, by Creole Records. Catalogue no: **CR 6**
12" Single: Released May '81, on Creole, by Creole Records. Catalogue no: **CR 126**

HOKEY COKEY
Tracks: / Hokey cokey / Jingle bells.
7" Single: Released Dec '78, on EMI, by EMI Records. Deleted '81. Catalogue no: **EMI 2881**

JE T'AIME (MOI NON PLUS)
7" Single: Released Jul '75, on Cactus, by Creole Records. Deleted '78. Catalogue no: **CT 65**

JE T'AIME (MOI NON PLUS)(OLD GOLD)
Tracks: / Je t'aime (moi non plus) / Big six.
7" Single: Released Oct '88, on Old Gold, by Old Gold Records. Catalogue no: **OG 9806**

JERK YOUR BODY
Tracks: / Bring back the skins / Jerk your body.
7" Single: Released Jul '87, on Rhino, by Creole Records. Catalogue no: **RNO 78**
12" Single: Released Jul '87, on Rhino, by Creole Records. Catalogue no: **RNO 8**

JINGLE BELLS
Tracks: / Jingle bells / Hokey pokey / Christmas in Dreadland.
7" Single: Released 28 Nov '88, on Creole, by Creole Records. Catalogue no: **CR 5**
12" Single: Released 28 Nov '88, on Creole, by Creole Records. Catalogue no: **CRT 5**

LOST IN RUDENESS
Tracks: / Lost in rudeness.
7" Single: Released Dec '84, on Creole, by Creole Records. Catalogue no: **CR 72**
12" Single: Released Dec '84, on Creole, by Creole Records. Catalogue no: **CRT 72**

MY NAME'S DICK
Tracks: / My name's Dick / Worl is burning.
7" Single: Released Nov '82, on Dreamworks. Deleted '87. Catalogue no: **DW 001**

NOT GUILTY
Tracks: / Not guilty
12" Single: Released Nov '84, on Creole, by Creole Records. Catalogue no: **CRXC 8**
7" Single: Released Dec '83, on Kingdom, by Kingdom Records. Catalogue no: **KV 8027**

RELAX
Tracks: / Relax / It's a foolish way.
7" Single: Released Sep '84, on Creole, by Creole Records. Catalogue no: **CR 66**
12" Single: Released Sep '84, on Creole, by Creole Records. Catalogue no: **CRT 66**

RUB-A-DUB (SINGLE)
Tracks: / Rub-a-dub.
7" Single: Released Oct '81, on Creole, by Creole Records. Catalogue no: **CR 25**
12" Single: Released Oct '81, on Creole, by Creole Records. Catalogue no: **CR 12 25**

TEN COMMANDMENTS, THE
Tracks: / Ten commandments / Give it up Michael.
7" Single: on Trojan, by Trojan Records. Deleted May '88. Catalogue no: **TRO 9073**

UP WITH THE COCK
Tracks: / Up with the cock / Big punk.
7" Single: Released Jan '78, on Cactus, by Creole Records. Deleted '81. Catalogue no: **CT 110**

WILL I WHAT
Tracks: / Will I what / Last tango in Snodland.
7" Single: Released Nov '80, on Creole, by Creole Records. Catalogue no: **CR 208**

WINKLE MAN, THE
Tracks: / Winkle man, The / Rudeness train.
7" Single: Released May '76, on Cactus, by Creole Records. Deleted '79. Catalogue no: **CT 90**

Y VIVA SUSPENDERS
Tracks: / Y viva suspenders.
7" Single: Released Aug '76, on Cactus, by Creole Records. Deleted '79. Catalogue no: **CT 99**

Jugg

GOING OUT
Tracks: / Going out.
7" Single: Released Dec '82, on Stick It In Your Ear, by Stick It In Your Ear Records. Catalogue no: **PLUG 17**

NOAH'S CASTLE
Tracks: / Noah's castle / Runaround.
7" Single: Released May '80, on Carrere America (USA), by PolyGram Rec.Inc.(USA). Catalogue no: **CAR 145**

Juggernauts

COME THROW YOURSELF UNDER THE...
Tracks: / Come throw yourself under.....
7" Single: Released Nov '84, on Supreme Int.Editions, by Supreme Int.Records. Catalogue no: **EDITION 84-2**

Juice

ANYTHING BUT LOVE
Tracks: / Anything but love.
7" Single: Released Mar '86, on Spartan, Catalogue no: **SP 134**
12" Single: Released Mar '86, on Spartan, Catalogue no: **12SP 134**

SPOTLITE OF LOVE
Tracks: / Spotlite of love.
7" Single: Released Aug '85, on Ecstasy, by Creole Records. Catalogue no: **XTC 19**
12" Single: Released Aug '85, on Ecstasy, by Creole Records. Catalogue no: **XTCT 19**

YOU CAN'T HIDE FROM LOVE
Tracks: / You can't hide from love / Curiosity.
7" Single: Released May '86, on Def Jam, Catalogue no: **A 7056**
12" Single: Released May '86, on Def Jam, Catalogue no: **TA 7056**

Juice on the loose

ANY WAY THE WIND BLOWS
Tracks: / Any way the wind blows.
7" Single: Released Apr '80, on Songwriters Workshop, by Songwriters Workshop Publishing. Deleted '87. Catalogue no: **SW 4**

COWBOYS AND INDIANS
Tracks: / Cowboys and indians / Sweet love in the valley.
7" Single: Released Feb '81, on Songwriters Workshop, by Songwriters Workshop Publishing. Catalogue no: **SW 15**

Juicy

AFTER LOVING YOU
Tracks: / After loving you / Private party / Sugar free.
7" Single: Released Mar '87, on Epic, by CBS Records. Deleted Aug '87. Catalogue no: **650431 7**
12" Single: Released Mar '87, on Epic, by CBS Records. Deleted Aug '87. Catalogue no: **650431 6**

ALL WORK NO PLAY
Tracks: / All work no play / Serious.
7" Single: Released 23 May '87, on Private I (USA), by CBS Records (USA). Catalogue no: **650888**
12" Single: Released 23 May '87, on Private I (USA), by CBS Records (USA). Deleted Nov '87. Catalogue no: **650888 6**

BAD BOY
Tracks: / Bad boy / Bad boy (dub mix).
7" Single: Released Apr '86, on Private Eye. Deleted '87. Catalogue no: **A 6470**

SUGAR FREE
Tracks: / Sugar free / Forever and ever / Bad boy* (*Extra track available on 12" version only).
7" Single: Released Feb '86, on Private I (USA), by CBS Records (USA). Deleted '87. Catalogue no: **A 6917**
12" Single: Released Feb '86, on Private I (USA), by CBS Records (USA). Deleted '87. Catalogue no: **TA 6917**

Juicy Lucy

Biographical details: At the time of their greatest success this British rock band comprised Glenn Campbell, Pete Dobson, Keith Ellis, Neil Hubbard, Chris Mercer and Ray Owen. Juicy Lucy were formed in 1969 by American-born steel guitarist Campbell. Working in a bluesy, heavy rock vein, they reached the UK Top Twenty in 1970 with their first single, *Who Do You Love?*, a song written and originally recorded in 1956 by the great Bo Diddley. The groups self-titled debut LP reached the UK No 41 position. At the end of '70 they got to No 44 with the single *Pretty Woman* and No 53 with the album *Lie Back And Enjoy It*, but after that they never returned to the charts and, with their line-up in a state of never-ending instability, they disintegrated during 1972. One of the players who came and went was Micky Moody, who later became a Whitesnake guitarist. (Bob MacDonald, November 1985.).

PRETTY WOMAN

Tracks: / Pretty woman.
7" Single: Released Oct '70, on Vertigo, by Phonogram Ltd. Deleted '73. Catalogue no: **6059 015**

WHO DO YOU LOVE?
Tracks: / Who do you love? / Chicago Northwestern.
7" Single: Released Mar '70, on Vertigo, by Phonogram Ltd. Deleted '73. Catalogue no: **V 1**
7" Single: Released Mar '81, on Bronze, by Bronze Records. Catalogue no: **BRO 72**

Juju Message

SEASONS
Tracks: / Seasons / Spring.
12" Single: Released Nov '82, on Treacle, Catalogue no: **TRE 001**

Jules

FRIENDS
Tracks: / Friends.
7" Single: Released Oct '83, on Tastey, by Jet Records. Catalogue no: **JET 7040**

NOTHING TO ME
Tracks: / Nothing to me / Nothing to me (dub mix).
7" Single: Released Feb '87, on Fifth Avenue, Deleted '88. Catalogue no: **FIF 121**

Jules & The Polar

GOOD REASONS
Tracks: / Good reasons / All caked up.
7" Single: Released Feb '80, on CBS, by CBS Records. Deleted '83. Catalogue no: **CBS 8178**

SMELL OF HOME
Tracks: / Smell of home / Alive alone / Love played a game.
7" Single: Released Sep '80, on CBS, by CBS Records. Deleted '83. Catalogue no: **CBS 8800**

Julia & Company

BREAKIN' DOWN
Tracks: / Breakin' down.
7" Single: Released Mar '84, on London Records, by London Records. Catalogue no: **LON 46**
12" Single: Released Mar '84, on London Records, by London Records. Catalogue no: **LONX 46**

I'M SO HAPPY
Tracks: / I'm so happy.
7" Single: Released Feb '85, on London Records, by London Records. Catalogue no: **LON 61**
12" Single: Released Feb '85, on London Records, by London Records. Catalogue no: **LONX 61**

Julie

I CAN'T STAND THE PAIN
Tracks: / I can't stand the pain.
7" Single: Released Mar '85, on Calibre, Deleted '86. Catalogue no: **CAB 201**
12" Single: Released Mar '85, on Calibre, Deleted '86. Catalogue no: **CABL 201**

I'M IN LOVE WITH MICHAEL JACKSON'S ANSWERPHONE
Tracks: / I'm in love with Michael Jackson's answerphone.
7" Single: Released Oct '84, on Calibre, Deleted '86. Catalogue no: **CAB 129**
12" Single: Released Oct '84, on Calibre, Deleted '86. Catalogue no: **CABL 129**

Julie & The Jems

1-2-3
Tracks: / 1-2-3 / I wear his ring.
7" Single: Released Nov '82, on Utopia, by Utopia Records. Catalogue no: **UTO 1**
12" Single: Released Nov '82, on Utopia, by Utopia Records. Catalogue no: **UTOX 1**

Juluka

Biographical details: A multi-racial South African band was a proposition that presented problems for the UK Musicians' Union in 1983: should they be barred from playing in Britain because of their nationality, in accordance with union policy, or should they be welcomed because of their opposition to apartheid? Juluka did, in fact, get to play in Britain. Their music was not political in content but dealt with anthropological, geographical and tribal themes, combining a Zulu rhythmical feel with a more Western-orientated pop flavour. The group, led by Johnny Clegg, was sexually as well as racially integrated. *Scatterlings Of Africa* provided Juluka with a one-off taste of UK chart success, reaching No 44 in February '83. It was a memorable single but unfortunately nothing else in their repertoire was as strong and they could not consolidate on this toehold. (Bob MacDonald, November 1985.).

IMPI
Tracks: / Impi.
7" Pic: Released Jul '83, on Safari, by Safari Records. Catalogue no: **ZULU A3**
7" Single: Released Jul '83, on Safari, by Safari Records. Catalogue no: **ZULU 3**
12" Single: Released Jul '83, on Safari, by Safari Records. Catalogue no: **ZULU LS3**

SCATTERLINGS OF AFRICA
Tracks: / Scatterlings of Africa.
7" Single: Released May '87, on Safari, by Safari Records. Catalogue no: **ZULU 1**
12" Single: Released May '87, on Safari, by Safari Records. Catalogue no: **ZULU LS1**

UMBAGANGA MUSIC
Tracks: / Umbaganga music.
7" Pic: Released Apr '83, on Safari, by Safari Records. Catalogue no: **ZULU P2**
7" Single: Released Apr '83, on Safari, by Safari Records. Catalogue no: **ZULU 2**
12" Single: Released Apr '83, on Safari, by Safari Records. Catalogue no: **ZULU LS2**

Jump

SHAKE UP
Tracks: / Shake up / All in vain.
7" Single: Released Jul '80, on Caveman, Deleted Jul '83. Catalogue no: **CLUB 1**

TOMORROW'S MINE
Tracks: / Tomorrow's mine / Love in the park.
7" Single: Released Sep '80, on Rewind, Deleted '83. Catalogue no: **REWIND 4**

Jump Leads

FALSE KNIGHT
Tracks: / False Knight / Poor old horse.
7" Single: Released Feb '83, on Rogue, by Rogue Records. Catalogue no: **FMSS 103**

Jump Squad

LORD OF THE DANCE
Tracks: / Lord of the dance.
7" Single: Released Aug '81, on 101, Catalogue no: **UR 2**

Jump The Nile

LIKE THE CRUEL SEA (see panel below)
Tracks: / Like the cruel sea / Wire.
7" Single: Released Aug '84, on Music In Motion, Catalogue no: **MM 001**

Jump, Wally Jnr.

JUMP BACK
Tracks: / Jump back / Emu dub back, The.
12" Single: Released Aug '86, on Club, by Phonogram Ltd. Catalogue no: **JABX 35**
7" Single: Released Aug '86, on Club, by Phonogram Ltd. Catalogue no: **JAB 35**

PRIVATE PARTY
Tracks: / Private party / Private party (dub edit).
7" Single: Released Mar '88, on Breakout, by A&M Records. Deleted Feb '89. Catalogue no: **USA 624**
12" Single: Released Nov '87, on Criminal (USA), by Criminal Records (USA). Catalogue no: **CR 12016**
12" Single: Released Mar '88, on Breakout, by A&M Records. Deleted Feb '89. Catalogue no: **USAT 624**

WALLY JUMP JNR. - TIGHTEN UP (I JUST CAN'T STOP DANCING) (Released on Breakout)

THIEVES (VOCAL)
Tracks: / Thieves (vocal) / Thieves (vocal) (jazz in the house mix).
12" Single: Released Oct '88, on Breakout, by A&M Records. Catalogue no: **USAT 648**
7" Single: Released Oct '88, on Breakout, by A&M Records. Catalogue no: **USA 648**

TIGHTEN UP (I JUST CAN'T STOP DANCING) (see panel above)
Tracks: / Tighten up (I just can't stop dancing) / Lighten up (I just can't stop scratchin') / Lighten up (I just can't stop scratchin')(dub mix).
Note: Breakout have release one of the most eagerly awaited dance records of the year. Although previously only available on an import album, "Tighten up" has been in the dance chart for the last 13 weeks. Arthur Baker's version of the archie Bell classic is released in the U.K. on 7" and 3-track 12". The 12" features two new remixes and includes the original album track.
7" Single: Released 4 Dec '87, on Breakout, by A&M Records. Catalogue no: **USA 621**
12" Single: Released 4 Dec '87, on Breakout, by A&M Records. Catalogue no: **USAT 621**

TURN ME LOOSE
Tracks: / Turn me loose / Cut me loose.
7" Single: Released Feb '87, on London Records, by London Records. Deleted Sep '87. Catalogue no: **LON 126**
12" Single: Released Feb '87, on London Records, by London Records. Deleted Feb '89. Catalogue no: **LONX 126**

JUMP THE NILE - LIKE THE CRUEL SEA (Released on Music In Motion)

Jumpp

BOUNCY BOUNCY
Tracks: / Bouncy bouncy / bounce.
12" Single: Released Oct '81, on RCA, by BMG Records (UK). Deleted '85. Catalogue no: **RCAT 160**
7" Single: Released Oct '81, on RCA, by BMG Records (UK). Deleted '85. Catalogue no: **RCA 160**

TAKE IT EASY
Tracks: / Take it easy / Over easy.
12" Single: Released Jan '82, on RCA, by BMG Records (UK). Deleted Jan '85. Catalogue no: **RCAT 178**
7" Single: Released Jan '82, on RCA, by BMG Records (UK). Deleted Jan '85. Catalogue no: **RCA 178**

Junco Partners

TALL WINDOWS
Tracks: / Tall windows / Noizez in my head.
7" Single: Released Mar '81, on Energy (USA), by Bulldog Records (USA). Deleted Mar '84. Catalogue no: **NRG 4**

Junction Eleven

WICKED DAY
Tracks: / Wicked day.
7" Single: Released Jun '84, on LBA, Catalogue no: **LBA 105**

June Brides

EVERY CONVERSTION
Tracks: / Every conversation.
7" Single: Released Sep '84, on Pink Label, by Pink Label Records. Catalogue no: **PINKY 2**

IN THE RAIN
Tracks: / In the rain / Every Conversation.
12" Single: Released Apr '86, on Pink Label, by Pink Label Records. Catalogue no: **PINKY 9**

NO PLACE CALLED HOME
Tracks: / No place called home.
7" Single: Released Oct '85, on In Tape, by In Tape Records. Catalogue no: **IT 024**
12" Single: Released Oct '85, on In Tape, by In Tape Records. Catalogue no: **ITT 024**

PEEL SESSIONS:JUNE BRIDES
12" Single: Released Apr '87, on Strange Fruit, by Strange Fruit Records. Catalogue no: **SFPS 023**

THIS TOWN
Tracks: / This Town / This tape.
12" Single: Released Apr '86, on In Tape, by In Tape Records. Catalogue no: **ITT 030**
7" Single: Released Apr '86, on In Tape, by In Tape Records. Catalogue no: **IT 30**

June, Rosemary

APPLE BLOSSOM TIME
Tracks: / Apple blossom time.
7" Single: Released Jan '59, on Pye Inter-

national, Deleted '62. Catalogue no: **7N 25005**

Jung

REAL THING
Tracks: / Real thing / Thinking tanker / Avengers.
7" Single: Released Feb '82, on Sandwich, Deleted '84. Catalogue no: **SR 17**

Jungle Band

MARVELLOUS featuring Mickey Murray
Tracks: / Marvellous / Marvellous (ray clay mix) / Love makes the world go round*.
Note: *marvellous (red clay mix)* on 12" only.
7" Single: Released Jun '88, on Charly Groove, by Charly Records. Catalogue no: **CYZ 7 125**
12" Single: Released Jun '88, on Charly Groove, by Charly Records. Catalogue no: **CYZ 125**

MARVELLOUS (RADIO MIX)
Tracks: / Marvellous (radio mix) / Love makes the world go round*.
Note: * Featuring Carissa & Jungle Men
12" Single: Released Jun '88, on Charly Groove, by Charly Records. Catalogue no: **CYZ 125**

Jungle Brothers

BLACK IS BLACK
Tracks: / Black is black / Straight out of the jungle.
7" Single: Released 27 Feb '89, on Gee Street, by Gee Street Records. Catalogue no: **GEE 015**
12" Single: Released 27 Feb '89, on Gee Street, by Gee Street Records. Catalogue no: **GEET 015**

GIRL I'LL HOUSE YOU
Tracks: / Girl I'll house you.
7" Single: Released Aug '88, on Warlock, Catalogue no: **WAR 022**
12" Single: Released Sep '88, on Warlock, Catalogue no: **WAR 022 12**

I'LL HOUSE YOU
Tracks: / I'll house you.
12" Single: Released Oct '88, on Gee Street, by Gee Street Records. Catalogue no: **GEE 12003**
7" Single: Released Oct '88, on Gee Street, by Gee Street Records. Catalogue no: **GEE 003**

JIMBROWSKI
Tracks: / Jimbrowski.
12" Single: Released Oct '87, on Idlers (USA), Catalogue no: **WAR 014**

Jungle Juice

ALLEYOOP
Tracks: / Alleyoop.
7" Single: Released Sep '82, on Radar, Catalogue no: **CKS 1008**

Jungle Wonz

AS TIME MARCHES ON
Tracks: / As time marches on (straight up mix) / As time marches on (just right mix).
7" Single: Released Apr '89, on Breakout, by A&M Records. Catalogue no: **USA 653**
12" Single: Released Apr '89, on Breakout, by A&M Records. Catalogue no: **USAT 653**

Junglemania

ALPHABET ZOO
Tracks: / Alphabet zoo / Please yourself.
7" Single: on RK, by RK Records. Deleted '85. Catalogue no: **RK 1039**

Junior

Biographical details: Junior This British soul singer and songwriter, whose real name is Norman Giscombe, came to fame in 1982 with his sleep smash *Mama Used To Say*. Having initially flopped in the UK in 1981, it became a Top 3 success on the US soul chart in early '82, then reached No.30 on the US pop list and then proceed to reach No.7 in Britain. It was an ultra-exuberant punchy funk single of the kind which Earth Wind & Fire or Kool & The Gang would be proud of. Junior followed *Mama Used To Say* with a calmer single entiled *Too Late* which reached the UK No.20 position. His album *Ji* got to No.28 and logged 14 weeks on the British listings. For some reason, Junior failed to capitalise on his 1982 breakthrough on either side of the Atlantic. He remained a chirpy personality and an active figure on the soul scene but later singles, such as 1984's *Somebody* were simply not strong enough to rise above minor hit status. (Bob Macdonald 19/11/85).

COME ON OVER
Tracks: / Mama used To Say / Come on over.
7" Single: Released Jan '86, on London Records, by London Records. Catalogue no: **LON 84**
12" Single: Released Jan '86, on London Records, by London Records. Catalogue no: **LONX 84**

COMMUNICATION BREAKDOWN
Tracks: / Communication breakdown.
12" Single: Released Apr '83, on Mercury, by Phonogram Ltd. Catalogue no: **MERX 134**
7" Single: Released Apr '83, on Mercury, by Phonogram Ltd. Catalogue no: **MER 134**

DO YOU REALLY WANT MY LOVE
Tracks: / Do you really want my love.
7" Single: Released Jan '85, on London Records, by London Records. Catalogue no: **LON 60**
12" Single: Released Jan '85, on London Records, by London Records. Catalogue no: **LONX 60**

HIGH LIFE
Tracks: / High life / Right back at the start / High life (full length version) (12" version only.).
7" Single: Released Aug '8, on London Records, by London Records. Deleted Feb '89. Catalogue no: **LON 194**
12" Single: Released Aug '8, on London Records, by London Records. Deleted Feb '89. Catalogue no: **LONX 194**

LET ME KNOW
Tracks: / Let me know / I can't help it.
7" Single: Released Sep '82, on Mercury, by Phonogram Ltd. Deleted '85. Catalogue no: **MER 116**

MAMA USED TO SAY
Tracks: / Mama used to say / Mama used to say (part 2).
7" Single: Released Sep '81, on Mercury, by Phonogram Ltd. Deleted '84. Catalogue no: **MER 80**
12" Single: Released Oct '84, on Mercury, by Phonogram Ltd. Catalogue no: **MERX 98**
7" Single: Released Oct '84, on Mercury, by Phonogram Ltd. Deleted '86. Catalogue no: **MER 98**
12" Single: Released Sep '81, on Mercury, by Phonogram Ltd. Deleted '84. Catalogue no: **MERX 80**

OH LOUISE
Tracks: / Oh louise.
7" Single: Released Nov '85, on London Records, by London Records. Catalogue no: **LON 75**
12" Single: Released Nov '85, on London Records, by London Records. Catalogue no: **LONX 75**

RUNNIN'
Tracks: / Runnin'.
12" Single: Released Aug '83, on Mercury, by Phonogram Ltd. Deleted '84. Catalogue no: **MERX 145**
7" Single: Released Aug '83, on Mercury, by Phonogram Ltd. Catalogue no: **MER 145**

SOMEBODY
Tracks: / Somebody.
7" Single: Released Jul '84, on London Records, by London Records. Catalogue no: **LON 50**
12" Single: Released Jul '84, on London Records, by London Records. Catalogue no: **LONX 50**

TOO LATE
Tracks: / Too late / In words.
7" Single: Released Jun '82, on Mercury, by Phonogram Ltd. Deleted '85. Catalogue no: **MER 112**
12" Single: Released Jun '82, on Mercury, by Phonogram Ltd. Deleted '85. Catalogue no: **MERX 112**

YES (IF YOU WANT ME)
Tracks: / Yes (if you want me) / Not tonight.
12" Single: Released Jul '87, on London Records, by London Records. Catalogue no: **LONX 149**
7" Single: Released Jul '87, on London Records, by London Records. Catalogue no: **LON 149**

Junior Aces Football

FOOTBALL IS THE GAME FOR ME
Tracks: / Football is the game for me / Football is the game for me (part 2).
7" Single: Released Feb '80, on Feelgood, by Carlin Music Corp.. Deleted '83. Catalogue no: **FLG 112**

Junior Manson Slags

HUMAN SKIN SUIT
Tracks: / Human skin suit.
12" Single: Released Oct '89, on Blipvert, Catalogue no: **VERT 4T**

PLASTIC SMILE (EP)
12" Single: Released Dec '88, on Blipvert, Catalogue no: **VERT 001T**

SILVER TRAIN
Tracks: / Silver train.
12" Single: Released 5 Jun '89, on Blipvert, Catalogue no: **VERT 002 T**

Junior Soul

CHRISTMAS PARTY
Tracks: / Christmas party.
12" Single: Released Dec '88, on 2M, Catalogue no: **JS 113**

Junior, Trevor

GHETTO LIVING
Tracks: / Ghetto living.
12" Single: Released Jul '84, on Tonos, Catalogue no: **TON 002**

TIDAL WAVE
Tracks: / Tidal wave.
12" Single: Released May '85, on Kings Of Jazz, Catalogue no: **KLTJ 003**

Junior Vibes

WHEN WILL I SEE YOU AGAIN
Tracks: / When will I see you again.
12" Single: Released Apr '88, on Techniques, Catalogue no: **WRT 31**

Junior Wilson

SPEAK SOFTLY
Tracks: / Speak softy.
12" Single: Released 20 Mar '89, on Blue Moon (1), by Magnum Music Group. Catalogue no: **BTRD 035**

Juniors

DO YOU LOVE ME
Tracks: / Do you love me / Babylon.
7" Single: Released Aug '80, on Charisma, by Virgin Records. Deleted '83. Catalogue no: **CB 372**

Junk

CUCKOOLAND
7" Single: Released Oct '86, on Native (1), by Native Records. Catalogue no: **NTV 11**

JUNK TOWN SLAM
Tracks: / Junk town slam / Believe me / Let me live my life.
7" Single: Released 1 Feb '88, on Native (1), by Native Records. Catalogue no: **NTV 026**
7" Single: Released 23 Apr '88, on Native (1), by Native Records. Catalogue no: **JUNK 001**
12" Single: Released 1 Feb '88, on Native (1), by Native Records. Catalogue no: **12 NTV 026**
12" Single: Released Jul '88, on Native (1), by Native Records. Catalogue no: **12 JUNK 001**

MESSIAHS OF THE POP RAUNCH
Tracks: / Messiahs of the pop raunch / Your last breath was my first kiss / Cuckoo land.
12" Single: Released Jul '87, on Native (1), by Native Records. Catalogue no: **NTV 12022**

WORLD DOESN'T TURN
Tracks: / World doesn't turn, The.
7" Single: Released 1 Oct '86, on Native (1), by Native Records. Catalogue no: **NTV 012**
12" Single: Released 1 Oct '86, on Native (1), by Native Records. Catalogue no: **NTV 12012**

Junkyard Band

WORD, THE
Tracks: / Word, The.
7" Single: Released Aug '86, on Def Jam, Deleted '87. Catalogue no: **A 7296**
12" Single: Released Aug '86, on Def Jam, Deleted '87. Catalogue no: **TA 7296**

Juno the Reaper

AS SEEN ON TV
Tracks: / As seen on TV / Reaper.
7" Single: Released Apr '82, on Sunny, by Sunny Records. Catalogue no: **EON 101**

Jupiter 4

PEPPERBOX
Tracks: / Pepperbox / Beyond the universe.
7" Single: Released Jun '80, on Harbour, by Harbour Records. Deleted '83. Catalogue no: **HRB 9**

Jupiter 8

ET PHONE HOME
Tracks: / ET phone home.
7" Single: Released Dec '82, on Polydor, by Polydor Ltd. Deleted Dec '85. Catalogue no: **POSP 543**

Jupiter, Duke

LITTLE LADY
Tracks: / Little lady.
7" Single: Released Jun '84, on Morocco (USA), by Motown Records (UK). Catalogue no: **TMG 1342**
12" Single: Released Jun '84, on Morocco (USA), by Motown Records (UK). Catalogue no: **TMGT 1342**

Jupiter Red

SECRET AFFAIR
Tracks: / Secret affair.
7" Single: Released Oct '83, on Arrival, by Blaylock Management Ltd.. Deleted '86. Catalogue no: **PIK 12**

Jupp, Mickey

CLAGGIN' ON
Tracks: / Claggin' on / Driving on your lights.
Note: Produced by Mickey Jupp, Mo Witham & Chris East
7" Single: Released Mar '88, on Waterfront, by Waterfront Music. Catalogue no: **WFS 40**

DON'T TALK TO ME
Tracks: / Don't talk to me / Junk in my trunk.
7" Single: Released Mar '81, on Good Foot, by Good Foot Records (USA). Catalogue no: **GFR 001**

JOGGING
Tracks: / Jogging / Feel free.
7" Single: Released May '82, on A&M, by A&M Records. Deleted '85. Catalogue no: **AMS 8222**

ONLY FOR LIFE

JUST WATER - SINGIN' IN THE RAIN (Released on Stiff)

Tracks: / Only for life.
7" Single: Released Aug '84, on Towerbell, Catalogue no: **TOW 55**
12" Single: Released Aug '84, on Towerbell, Catalogue no: **12 TOW 55**

ROOMS IN YOUR ROOF
Tracks: / Rooms in your roof / So long.
7" Single: Released Apr '80, on Chrysalis, by Chrysalis Records. Deleted '82. Catalogue no: **CHS 2388**

Jury

JUST LIKE LOVERS
Tracks: / Just like lovers / Ride your bike / Sardines.
7" Single: Released Aug '86, on Chrysalis, by Chrysalis Records. Deleted '87. Catalogue no: **CHS 3045**

Just A Ha Ha

LUCKY DAY
Tracks: / Lucky day / Takes time.
7" Single: Released Feb '84, on PRT, by Castle Communications Records. Catalogue no: **JH 1**
12" Single: Released Feb '84, on PRT, by Castle Communications Records. Catalogue no: **JH 121**

Just Add Water

HOLD ONTO YOUR HEART
Tracks: / Hold onto your heart.
7" Single: Released Jul '88, on Different Class, Catalogue no: **HNC 2**

Just, Barry

JUST BARRY
Tracks: / Just Barry.
7" Single: Released Aug '83, on Monarch, by Monarch Records. Catalogue no: **MON 046**

Just Good Friends

ONE NIGHT
Tracks: / One night / In triplicate.
7" Single: Released Mar '84, on Magnet, by WEA Records. Catalogue no: **JUST 1**
12" Single: Released Mar '84, on Magnet, by WEA Records. Catalogue no: **12 JUST 1**

Just Ice

GOING WAY BACK
Tracks: / Going way back.
12" Single: Released Nov '87, on Fresh (USA), Catalogue no: **FRE 15**

Just Us

JUSTICE
Tracks: / Justice.

12" Single: Released Oct '87, on Pana, Catalogue no: **PRI 2009**

PATRICK JUVET - I LOVE AMERICA (Released on Casablanca)

Just Water

SINGIN' IN THE RAIN (see panel on previous page)
Tracks: / Singin' in the rain / Witness to the crime.
7" Single: Released '78, on Stiff, by Stiff Records. Catalogue no: **BUY 31**

Justice, Jimmy

AIN'T THAT FUNNY
Tracks: / Ain't that funny.
7" Single: Released Jun '62, on Pye, Deleted '65. Catalogue no: **7N 15443**

SPANISH HARLEM
Tracks: / Spanish harlem.
7" Single: Released Aug '62, on Pye, Deleted '65. Catalogue no: **7N 15457**

WHEN MY LITTLE GIRL IS SMILING
Tracks: / When my little girl is smiling.
7" Single: Released Mar '62, on Pye, Deleted '65. Catalogue no: **7N 15421**

Justice League Of ...

BLACK OUT, THE
Tracks: / Black out, The.
12" Single: Released 27 Feb '88, on Plastic Head, by Plastic Head Records. Catalogue no: **PLASS 006**

Justified Ancients

1987-THE EDITS
Tracks: / 1987-the edits.
12" Single: Released Jul '87, on KLF, by KLF Communications. Catalogue no: **JAMS 25T**

ALL YOU NEED IS LOVE
Tracks: / All you need is love.
7" Single: Released 30 May '87, on Jams, Catalogue no: **JAMS 23**
12" Single: Released 30 May '87, on Jams, Catalogue no: **JAMS 23T**

DOWNTOWN
Tracks: / Downtown.
7" Single: Released Dec '87, on KLF, by KLF Communications. Catalogue no: **JAMS 27**
12" Single: Released Dec '87, on KLF, by KLF Communications. Catalogue no: **JAM 27T**

WHITNEY JOINS THE JAMS
Tracks: / Whitney joins the jams.
12" Single: Released Sep '87, on KLF, by KLF Communications. Catalogue no: **JAMS 24T**

Just-in-Case

MAGAZINE GIRL
Tracks: / Magazine girl.
7" Single: Released Jul '83, on Thunderbay, Catalogue no: **TBR 025**

Justis, Bill

RAUNCHY
Tracks: / Raunchy.
7" Single: Released Jan '58, on London-American, Deleted '61. Catalogue no: **HLS 8517**

Juvet, Patrick

Biographical details: Jevet, Patrick This French singer, keyboards player and songwriter jumped on the disco bandwagon in the late seventies, with a little help from Jacques Morali (who was also associated with the Village People). His lightweight records attempted to sound like The Bee Gees and Boney M rolled into one! Having issued his debut album *Paris By Night* in 1977, Juvet penetrated the British singles chart twice in late 1978: *Got A Feeling* reached No.34 and the insipidly bland *I Love America* climbed to No.12. 1979's *Another Lonely Man* flopped in the UK, but he continued working through the early Eighties. (Bob Macdonald 19/11/85).

GOT A FEELING
Tracks: / Got a feelin'.
7" Single: Released Sep '78, on Casablanca, by PolyGram UK Ltd. Deleted '81. Catalogue no: **CAN 127**

I LOVE AMERICA (OLD GOLD)
Tracks: / I love America / Got a feelin'.
12" Single: Released Oct '88, on Old Gold, by Old Gold Records. Catalogue no: **OG 4083**

I LOVE AMERICA (See panel above)
Tracks: / I love America.
7" Single: Released Nov '78, on Casablanca, by PolyGram UK Ltd. Deleted '81. Catalogue no: **CAN 132**

J.V.C.F.O.R.C.E.

STRONG ISLAND
Tracks: / Strong island
12" Single: Released Apr '88, on Hardcore, Catalogue no: **HAKT 11**

K

The following information was taken from the Music Master database on October 20th, 1989.

K-9 Corporation

DOG TALK
Tracks: / Dog talk.
7" Single: Released Sep '83, on Capitol, by EMI Records. Deleted Jan '88. Catalogue no: **CL 307**
12" Single: Released Sep '83, on Capitol, by EMI Records. Deleted '88. Catalogue no: **12CL 307**

K-9 Posse

AIN'T NOTHING TO IT
Tracks: / Ain't nothing to it / Ain't nothing to it (12" version) (Only on 12" and cassette single.) / This beat is military (On cassette single.) / Turn that down (On cassette single.).
Cassingle: Released 22 May '89, on Arista, by BMG Records (UK). Catalogue no: **409975**
7" Single: Released Apr '89, on Arista, by BMG Records (UK). Catalogue no: **112256**
12" Single: Released Apr '89, on Arista, by BMG Records (UK). Catalogue no: **612256**
12" Single: Released Nov '88, on Arista, by BMG Records (UK). Catalogue no: **AD1 9763**

K Creation

CHARIOTS OF FIRE
Tracks: / Chariots of fire / Charmer's mood samba.
7" Single: Released Oct '82, on KR, Catalogue no: **KR 11**
12" Single: Released Oct '82, on KR, Catalogue no: **KRT 11**

K Wallis B

DIAMONDS
Tracks: / Diamonds / Man with the golden arm, Theme from / Diamonds (Ext. dance mix).
7" Single: Released Jun '87, on Vertigo, by Phonogram Ltd. Catalogue no: **VER 33**
12" Single: Released Jun '87, on Vertigo, by Phonogram Ltd. Catalogue no: **VERX 33**

KAA Antelope

INDIAN TRILOGY (EP)
Tracks: / Indian trilogy.
7" Single: Released May '82, on Sandwich, Deleted '84. Catalogue no: **SR 18**

Kabbala

ASHE WO ARO
Tracks: / Ashewo ara / Voltan dance.
7" Single: Released Jun '87, on Ink, by Red Flame Records. Catalogue no: **INK 728**
12" Single: Released Oct '82, on Red Flame (1), by Red Flame Records. Catalogue no: **RF 1211**
12" Single: Released 23 May '87, on Ink, by Red Flame Records. Catalogue no: **INK 1228**

GET BACK TO SUMMER
Tracks: / Get back to summer.
7" Single: Released Aug '85, on Cabal, by Cabal Records. Catalogue no: **CBL 001**
12" Single: Released Aug '85, on Cabal, by Cabal Records. Catalogue no: **12CBL 001**

WHAT LOVE IS
Tracks: / What love is / Yo - yo dance.
7" Single: Released Mar '86, on Cabal, by Cabal Records. Catalogue no: **CBL 002**
12" Single: Released Mar '86, on Cabal, by Cabal Records. Catalogue no: **12 CBL 002**

YEN NBO OSE
Tracks: / Yen nbo ose / Yo yo dance.
7" Single: Released Nov '83, on Red Flame (1), by Red Flame Records. Catalogue no: **RFB 37**
12" Single: Released Nov '83, on Red Flame (1), by Red Flame Records. Catalogue no: **RFB 3712**

YO YO DANCE
Tracks: / Yo yo dance.
12" Single: Released Aug '87, on Ink, by Red Flame Records. Catalogue no: **INK 1230**

Kabuki

I AM A HORSE
Tracks: / I am a horse / My hair.
7" Single: Released Sep '82, on Kabaret Noir, Catalogue no: **KAB 1**

KAD

SHAKIN' ALL OVER
7" Single: Released Mar '83, on Shooting Star, Catalogue no: **STAR 007**

Kadenza

LET'S DO IT
Tracks: / Let's do it.
7" Single: Released Mar '83, on PRT, by Castle Communications Records. Catalogue no: **7P 261**
12" Single: Released Mar '83, on PRT, by Castle Communications Records. Catalogue no: **12P 261**

LET'S STAY TOGETHER
Tracks: / Let's stay together.
7" Single: Released Sep '82, on PRT, by Castle Communications Records. Catalogue no: **7P 247**
12" Single: Released Sep '82, on PRT, by Castle Communications Records. Catalogue no: **12P 247**

LIVING IN A BACK STREET
Tracks: / Living in a backstreet / Back street pressure.
7" Single: Released Jan '84, on Calibre, Deleted '86. Catalogue no: **CAB 120**
12" Single: Released Jan '84, on Calibre, Deleted '86. Catalogue no: **CABL 120**

Kader, Cheb

YA GALBI
Tracks: / Ya galbi.
12" Single: Released Apr '89, on World Music (Holland), Catalogue no: **EFA 6128**

Kadettes

FIREBALL XL5
Tracks: / Fireball XL5 / Mission impossible.
7" Single: Released Apr '82, on Blank, Deleted '88. Catalogue no: **GET1**

Kadger Jacks

BILLS, BILLS, BILLS
Tracks: / Bills, bills, bills / 32 floors.
7" Single: Released Feb '81, on Cheapskate, Deleted Feb '84. Catalogue no: **CHEAP 15**

Kaempfert, Bert

Biographical details: Kaempfert, Bert This West German orchestra leader, conducot, composer, arranger, producer and multi-instrumentalist was one of the few people who could claim to have been associated with the careers of Frank Sinatra, Elvis Presley and The Beatles.
Kaempfert was born in Hamburg in 1923 and formed his own band soon after the end of World War II. His distinctive orchestral style made him a popular figure in his native country and began to garner a reputation in America and Britain with the 1959 success of Ivo Robic's *Morgen* which Bert arranged an produced - this was a Top 30 hit on both sides of the Atlantic.
In January 1961 Kaempfert surged to No.1 in America in his own right with his ensemble's rendition of *Wonderland By Night*, instrumentals were a major force on the US charts at that time and Kaempfert's hit was at the forefront of that trend. In that same year his co-adaptation of the song *Wooden Song* (originally a German folk tune) went to No.1 in Britain for Elvis Presley and No.1 in the States for Joe Dowell (RCA Records were slow to release Elvis' version in America). Also in 1961 Kaempfert became the first person to record the Beatles - they were based in Hamburg at the time and Bert supervised the recording of a couple of their own tracks, plus a couple of songs with the groups backing the singer/guitarist Tony Sheridan.
Kaempfert's next hot period was the mid-Sixties. In early 1965 he reached the US No.11 positon with *Red Roses For a Blue Lady* and at the end of that year, scored his only UK hit single as a performer with *Bye Bye Blues* (No.24). In maid 1966 he hit No.1 on both sides of the Atlantic as composer of Frank Sinatra's *Strangers In The Night*. During 1966-67 Kaempfert notched up a string of big selling orchestral albums, which occupied the same musical territory as those of Burt Bacharach and Roy Conniff; in the space of 18 months, Bert placed no less than eight LPs on the UK charts.
Kaempfert's tune *Spanish Eyes* became a US No.15 hit for Al Martino in 1966 and a belated No.5 hit in Britain in 1973. Kaempfert died in Zug, Switzerland in June 1980 at the age of 56. (Bob Macdonald 20/11/85).

BYE BYE BLUES (SINGLE)
Tracks: / Bye bye blues.
7" Single: Released Dec '65, on Polydor, by Polydor Ltd. Deleted '68. Catalogue no: **BM 56504**

Kaftan Kake

NICE VERY NICE
Tracks: / Nice very nice / Jag ur.
7" Single: Released Apr '82, on Creole, by Creole Records. Catalogue no: **CR 31**

Kah, Hubert

LIMOUSINE
Tracks: / Limousine / Drowning.
7" Single: Released Jan '87, on MCA, by MCA Records. Catalogue no: **MCA 1102**
12" Single: Released Jan '87, on MCA, by MCA Records. Catalogue no: **MCAT 1102**

Kairson, Ursuline

BUFFALO BILL
Tracks: / Buffalo Bill / Moving in the right direction.
7" Single: Released Oct '80, on WEA, by WEA Records. Deleted Oct '83. Catalogue no: **AH 2**

Kaiser, Roland

SANTA MARIA
Tracks: / Santa Maria.
7" Single: Released May '83, on Proto, by Proto Records. Catalogue no: **ENA 106**

Kaja

SHOULDN'T DO THAT
Tracks: / Shouldn't do that.
7" Single: Released Aug '85, on Parlophone, by EMI Records. Deleted '86. Catalogue no: **R 6106**
12" Single: Released Aug '85, on Parlophone, by EMI Records. Deleted '86. Catalogue no: **12R 6106**
Special: Released Aug '85, on Parlophone, by EMI Records. Catalogue no: **RD 6106**

Kajagoogoo

Biographical details: At the time of their greatest success, this British pop band consisted of Steve Askew, Nick Beggs, Limahl, Stuart Neale and Jex Strode. Kajagoogoo emerged from the Bedfordshire town of Leighton Buzzard in early 1983 with apparent overnight success. A few television appearances, plus the guiding hands of Duran Duran keyboardist Nick Rhodes and producer Colin Thurston, were enough to send the previously unknown teenyboppers to the UK No.1 spot with *Too shy*. This ultra-lightweight single reached No.5 in the States, as part of the new British Invasion, and Kajagoogoo were hailed as one of 1983's big new sensations. Their next two singles, *Ooh to be ah* and *Hang on now*, both followed *Too shy* into the UK Top 20.
The group successfully exploited the new glamour-conscious technopop market, which Duran Duran had helped to open up during 1981-82. Kajagoogoo satisfied the same juvenile audienced that had been served by Herman's Hermits in the mid-Sixties and the Bay City Rollers in the mid Seventies. In the summer of '83, a mere six months after they had first come to fame, their was an acrimnonious split between singer and frontman Limahl (real name Chris Hamill - his stage name is an anagram of his surname) and the rest of the band. Success had obviously happened too quickly for the group, and the four instrumentalists resented the fact that the singer was snatching all the limelight - he had been the last to join. He soon became the first to leave, and Kajagoogoo continued as a quartet with pretty blond bassist Nick Beggs as leader. The depleted group quickly scored a UK Top Tenner with *Big apple*, reaching No.8 in the autumn of '83. But they could not sustain their success, and stumbled through 1984 with a series of mediocre chart placings. They re-emerged in 1985 as a trio under the shortened name of Kaja and notched up a major US disco hit with *Turn your back on me* (a danceable remix of one of their old singles) plus a minor UK hit with *Shouldn't do that*. For his part Limahl enjoyed spasmodic solo success, achieving a notable worldwide hit in late 1984 with *Neverending story*. (Bob MacDonald, 20th Nov 1985).

BIG APPLE
Tracks: / Big apple / Monochromatic / Big apple (metromix).
7" Single: Released Sep '83, on EMI, by EMI Records. Catalogue no: **EMI 5423**
12" Single: Released Sep '83, on EMI, by EMI Records. Catalogue no: **12EMI 5423**

HANG ON NOW
Tracks: / Hang on now.
7" Single: Released Jun '83, on EMI, by EMI Records. Deleted '86. Catalogue no: **EMI 5394**

LIONS MOUTH, THE
Tracks: / Lions mouth, The / Garden.
7" Single: Released Mar '84, on EMI, by EMI Records. Deleted '87. Catalogue no: **EMI 5449**

OOH TO BE AH
Tracks: / Ooh to be ah.
7" Single: Released Apr '83, on EMI, by EMI Records. Deleted '86. Catalogue no: **EMI 5383**

TOO SHY
Tracks: / Too shy.
7" Single: Released Jan '83, on EMI, by EMI Records. Catalogue no: **EMI 5359**
12" Single: Released Jan '83, on EMI, by EMI Records. Deleted '87. Catalogue no: **12 EMI 5359**

TURN YOUR BACK ON ME
Tracks: / Turn your back on me / Pump rooms of Bath.
12" Pic: Released May '84, on EMI, by EMI Records. Catalogue no: **12EMIP 5465**
7" Single: Released Apr '84, on EMI, by EMI Records. Catalogue no: **EMI 5465**
12" Single: Released Apr '84, on EMI, by EMI Records. Deleted '87. Catalogue no: **12EMI 5465**

Kakoulli, Harry

BABY DON'T LIKE
Tracks: / Baby don't like / Jealous mind.
7" Single: Released Apr '83, on Strut, Catalogue no: **STRUT 1**

I'M ON A ROCKET
Tracks: / I'm on a rocket / I wanna stay / Lonely boy / I don't need you anymore.
7" Single: Released May '82, on Oval, by Oval Records. Catalogue no: **HARRY 18**

LONELY BOY
Tracks: / Lonely boy.
7" Single: Released Jul '83, on Strut, Catalogue no: **STRUT 2**

SHE'S MINE
Tracks: / She's mine / In dub.
7" Single: Released Nov '83, on Connexion, Deleted '85. Catalogue no: **NYC 103**
12" Single: Released Nov '83, on Connexion, Deleted '85. Catalogue no: **NYCX 103**

SUGAR DADDY
Tracks: / Sugar daddy.
7" Single: Released Aug '84, on Strut, Catalogue no: **STRUT 3**
12" Single: Released Aug '84, on Strut, Catalogue no: **STRUT X3**

WHY DON'T YOU COME BACK
Tracks: / Why don't you come back.
7" Single: Released Jul '85, on Ecstasy, by Creole Records. Catalogue no: **XTC 16**
12" Single: Released Jul '85, on Ecstasy, by Creole Records. Catalogue no: **XTCT 15**

Kalabash

BETRAYED
Tracks: / Betrayed.
12" Single: Released Dec '83, on Kalabash, Catalogue no: **KBH 001**

Kalambya Sisters

KATELINA
Tracks: / Katelina / Mbie nuke.
12" Single: Released Dec '83, on Zensor (Germany), Catalogue no: **ZS 07**

Kaldor, Connie

WANDERLUST
Tracks: / Wanderlust / Bird on a wing / Wood river (Only on 12" version.).
7" Single: Released Mar '89, on Nowyertalkin', by Nowyertalkin' Records. Catalogue no: **7 TALK 7**
12" Single: Released Mar '89, on Nowyertalkin', by Nowyertalkin' Records. Catalogue no: **12TALK 7**

Kalima

FLYAWAY
Tracks: / Flyaway.
CD 5": Released May '89, on Factory (1), by Factory Records. Catalogue no: **FACD 216 9**

FOUR SONGS EP - SPARKLE
12" Single: Released Jul '85, on Factory (1), by Factory Records. Catalogue no: **FAC 127**

SMILING HOUR
Tracks: / Smiling hour / Fly away.
7" Single: Released Nov '83, on Factory (1), by Factory Records. Catalogue no: **FAC 87**
12" Single: Released Nov '83, on Factory (1), by Factory Records. Catalogue no: **FAC 8712**

WEIRD FEELINGS
Tracks: / Weird feelings.
7" Single: Released May '87, on Factory (1), by Factory Records. Catalogue no: **FAC 187**
12" Single: Released 30 May '87, on Factory (1), by Factory Records. Catalogue no: **FAC 187T**

WHISPERED WORDS
Tracks: / Whispered words.
12" Single: Released Mar '86, on Factory (1), by Factory Records. Catalogue no: **FAC 147**

Kalimba

SUMMERTIME LOVERS
Tracks: / Summertime lovers / Summertime lovers (version).
7" Single: Released 8 May '89, on Kunzel, by Gemini Enterprises. Catalogue no: **KUN 4**

Kalin Twins

Biographical details: Hal and Herbie Kalin were One Hit Wonders of the highest order - an international one-off smash with a wonderful state-of-the-chart pop ditty, followed by instant obscurity. To be fair, they did achieve a second smaller hit in their native America, but it had one of the least appropriate titles in pop history - *Forget me not*. The Kalins, who were genuine twins, came to fame with *When*. It reached No.5 in the States and logged five weeks at No.1 in Britain during the summer of 1958. The singing brothers performed the number in a high-pitched harmony style, backed by a strong arrangement. Its spectacular UK success let to a British tour, on which they were supported by a young upstart called Cliff Richard who was just enjoying his first hit. Cliff had a few more hits; the Kalin Twins didn't. *When* was revived in 1977 by British fun-rockers Showaddywaddy, who took it to the UK No.3 position. Its co-writer Paul Evans has achieved sporadic success on both sides of the Atlantic down the years, both as a singer and as a writer. The 1958 success of *When* gave him his breakthrough. (Bob MacDonald, 20th Nov 1985).

WHEN (OLD GOLD)
Tracks: / When.
7" Single: Released Jul '82, on Old Gold, by Old Gold Records. Catalogue no: **OG 9164**

WHEN (ORIGINAL)
Tracks: / When.
7" Single: Released Jul '51, on Brunswick, by Decca Records. Deleted '61. Catalogue no: **05751**

Kallen, Kitty

Biographical details: This American singer, who hailed from South Philadelphia, began performing professionally while still a child. She was in her mid-teens when she became a resident vocalist with the red-hot Jimmy Dorsey Orchestra in the early Forties. She sang on the band's 1943 hit rendition of *Besame mucho*. Her career also included a stint with the equally popular Harry James Orchestra. As a solo artist Kallen came to fame in 1954 with the twee but gimmicky *Little things mean a lot*, which enjoyed a mammoth run at No.1 in America and one week at the top in Britain. She was a One Hit Wonder as far as the UK charts were concerned, but chalked up further US Top 40 successes with *Go on with the wedding* (a 1956 duet with Georgie Shaw), *If I give my heart to you* (1950) and *My colouring book* (1963). (Bob MacDonald, 20th Nov 1985).

LITTLE THINGS MEAN A LOT
Tracks: / Little things mean a lot.
7" Single: Released Jul '54, on Brunswick, by Decca Records. Deleted '57. Catalogue no: **05287**

LITTLE THINGS MEAN A LOT (OLD GOLD)
Tracks: / Little things mean a lot.
7" Single: Released Aug '82, on Old Gold, by Old Gold Records. Deleted Jul '88. Catalogue no: **OG 9207**

Kallmann, Gunter

ELISABETH SERENADE
Tracks: / Elizabethan serenade.
7" Single: Released Dec '64, on Polydor, by Polydor Ltd. Deleted '67. Catalogue no: **NH 24678**

Kalvic, Finn

HERE IN MY HEART
Tracks: / Here in my heart / Dance of the blues.
7" Single: Released Apr '81, on Epic, by CBS Records. Deleted Apr '86. Catalogue no: **EPC A1163**

ON THE RUN
Tracks: / On the run / Wake up to love.
7" Single: Released Sep '80, on Epic, by CBS Records. Deleted '83. Catalogue no: **EPC 8839**

Kalyan

HOT TEA
Tracks: / Hot tea / Rockdance.
12" Single: Released Jul '80, on RCA, by BMG Records (UK). Deleted Jul '83. Catalogue no: **PC 1955**

Kamahl

FIRST LOVE, BEST LOVE
Tracks: / First love, best love / To a son.
7" Single: Released Jan '81, on Philips, by Phonogram Ltd. Deleted Jan '84. Catalogue no: **6038013**

Kameleon

DANGER ZONE STRANGER ZONE
Tracks: / Danger zone stranger zone.
7" Single: Released Oct '81, on Elite Records, by Elite Records. Deleted '83. Catalogue no: **DAZZ 9**

Kamen, Michael

RITA, SUE & BOB TOO
Tracks: / Rita, Sue & Bob too / Silly tune / Gang bang*.
Note: * extra track on 12" version
7" Single: Released Sep '87, on RCA, by BMG Records (UK). Catalogue no: **109377**
12" Single: Released Sep '87, on RCA, by BMG Records (UK). Catalogue no: **609377**

WATCHING YOU (DUTY MEN)
Tracks: / Watching you duty men.
7" Single: Released Oct '87, on BBC, by BBC Records & Tapes. Deleted Apr '89. Catalogue no: **RESL 215**
12" Single: Released Oct '87, on BBC, by BBC Records & Tapes. Deleted Apr '89. Catalogue no: **12RSL 215**

Kamen, Nick

BRING ME YOUR LOVE
Tracks: / Bring me your love / Guilty.
CD 5": Released Jul '88, on WEA, by WEA Records. Catalogue no: **YZ 202CD**
7" Single: Released Jul '88, on WEA, by WEA Records. Catalogue no: **YZ 202**
12" Single: Released Jul '88, on WEA, by WEA Records. Catalogue no: **YZ 202T**

COME SOFTLY TO ME
Tracks: / Miss you / Come softly to me.
Note: * extra track on 12" version.
7" Single: Released Aug '87, on WEA, by WEA Records. Deleted Jul '88. Catalogue no: **YZ 133**
12" Single: Released Aug '87, on WEA, by WEA Records. Deleted Jul '88. Catalogue no: **YZ 133 T**

EACH TIME YOU BREAK MY HEART
Tracks: / Each time you break my heart.
7" Single: Released Oct '86, on WEA, by WEA Records. Deleted Jan '88. Catalogue no: **YZ 90**
12" Single: on WEA, by WEA Records. Deleted Jan '88. Catalogue no: **YZ 90T**

LOVING YOU IS SWEETER THAN EVER
Tracks: / Loving you is sweeter than ever / Baby after tonight.
7" Single: Released Feb '87, on WEA, by WEA Records. Deleted Jan '88. Catalogue no: **YZ 106**
12" Single: Released Feb '87, on WEA, by WEA Records. Deleted Jan '88. Catalogue no: **YZ 106T**

NOBODY ELSE
Tracks: / Nobody else / Any day now.
7" Single: Released May '87, on WEA, by WEA Records. Catalogue no: **YZ 122**
12" Single: Released May '87, on WEA, by WEA Records. Catalogue no: **YZ 122T**

TELL ME
Tracks: / Tell me / Better be good tonight / Loving you is sweeter than ever* / Each time you break my heart*.
CD 5": Released 14 May '88, on WEA, by WEA Records. Catalogue no: **YZ 184 CD**
7" Single: Released 14 May '88, on WEA, by WEA Records. Catalogue no: **YZ 184**
12" Single: Released 14 May '88, on WEA, by WEA Records. Catalogue no: **YZ 184 T**

Kamikaze Sex Pilots

DARK NIGHT OF THE SOUL
Tracks: / Dark night of the soul / Red Indian.
7" Single: Released Jun '83, on Lowther, Catalogue no: **HCN 002**

SHARON SIGNS TO CHERRY RED
Tracks: / Sharon signs to cherry red.
7" Single: Released Apr '85, on Lowther, Catalogue no: **HCN 003**

Kamilla

I WANNA BE THAT WOMAN
Tracks: / I wanna be that woman.
7" Single: Released Jun '88, on T.J. (USA), Catalogue no: **TJT 001**

Kamon, Karen

GIVE A LITTLE LOVE
Tracks: / Give a little love / Heart over mind.
7" Single: Released Jun '87, on Atco, by Atlantic Recording Corp.(USA). Deleted Jul '88. Catalogue no: **B 9483**
12" Single: Released Jun '87, on Atco, by Atlantic Recording Corp.(USA). Deleted Jul '88. Catalogue no: **B 9483T**

LOVERBOY
Tracks: / Loverboy.
7" Single: Released Aug '84, on CBS, by CBS Records. Catalogue no: **A 4526**

Kamoze, Ini

CALL THE POLICE (see panel below)
Tracks: / Call the police / Maxi taxi.
12" Single: Released Aug '85, on Island, by Island Records. Deleted '87. Catalogue no: **12IS 239**

PIRATE (SINGLE)
Tracks: / Pirate.
12" Single: Released Aug '86, on Island, by Island Records. Deleted Jul '87. Catalogue no: **12IS 289**

STRESS
Tracks: / Stress / Stress (version).
12" Single: Released May '89, on Greensleeves, by Greensleeves Records. Catalogue no: **GRED 127**

STRESS (RE-MIX)
Tracks: / Stress.
12" Single: Released May '89, on Greensleeves, by Greensleeves Records. Catalogue no: **GRED 247**

Kan Kan

CHANGING TRAINS (EP)
Tracks: / Changing trains.
12" Single: Released Feb '82, on Dining Out, by Dining Out Records. Catalogue no: **TUX 17**

INFORMER, THE (EP)
Tracks: / Informer, The.
12" Single: Released Oct '82, on Illuminated, Catalogue no: **ILL 1612**

Kanawa, Kiri Te

Biographical details: 'The singer from down under who performed at the Royal Wedding' was already very successful before July 1981, but her magnificent display of vocal talent at the marriage of Prince Charles and Lady Diana Spencer brought her to major international stardom. By the mid-Eighties, the New Zealand singer was regularly at No.1 on specialist classical album charts onboth sides of the Atlantic. In late 1985 she held the top two positions on the Billboard classical listing with *Blue skies* (her collaboration with Nelson Riddle & his Orchestra, one of the last assignments before his death) and Leonard Barnstein's *West side story* revamp. The latter was also a major success on the UK Top 20, while *Blue skies* was hovering in the lower regions of the Top 100. (Bob MacDonald, 20th Nov 1985).

BLUE SKIES
Tracks: / Blue skies / Folks who live on the hill, The.
7" Single: Released May '86, on Decca, by Decca Records. Deleted '88. Catalogue no: **KANA 2**

I GOT RHYTHM
Tracks: / I got rhythm / Summertime.
7" Single: Released Jul '87, on EMI, by EMI Records. Deleted Oct '88. Catalogue no: **GERSH 1**

I'M IN LOVE WITH A WONDERFUL GUY
Tracks: / I'm in love with a wonderful guy / Honey bun.
7" Single: Released Nov '86, on CBS, by CBS Records. Catalogue no: **650207 7**

SHEPHERDS SONG (BAILERO)
Tracks: / Shepherds song (bailero).
7" Single: Released May '83, on Decca, by Decca Records. Deleted '88. Catalogue no: **KANA 1**

WHITE CHRISTMAS
Tracks: / Mary's boy child.
7" Single: Released Jan '87, on Decca, by

INI KAMOZE - CALL THE POLICE (Released on island)

Decca Records. Deleted '88. Catalogue no: **KANA 4**

Kanchan

KUCHH GABDAD HAI
Tracks: / Kuchh gabdad hai / Chuk chuk gadi chali.
12" Single: Released Mar '86, on Sunburn, by Orbitone Records. Catalogue no: **SBD 52**

Kandidate

CAN'T SAY 'BYE
Tracks: / Can't say 'bye / Never say 'bye.
7" Single: Released May '82, on Polydor, by Polydor Ltd. Deleted '85. Catalogue no: **POSP 443**
7" Single: Released May '82, on Polydor, by Polydor Ltd. Deleted '85. Catalogue no: **POSPX 443**

DON'T WANNA SAY GOODNIGHT
Tracks: / Don't wanna say goodnight.
7" Single: Released Aug '78, on RAK, by EMI Records. Deleted '81. Catalogue no: **RAK 280**

GIRLS GIRLS GIRLS
Tracks: / Girls girls girls.
7" Single: Released Aug '79, on RAK, by EMI Records. Deleted '82. Catalogue no: **RAK 295**

I DON'T WANNA LOSE YOU
Tracks: / I don't wanna lose you.
7" Single: Released Mar '79, on RAK, by EMI Records. Deleted '82. Catalogue no: **RAK 289**

I DON'T WANNA LOSE YOU (OLD GOLD)
Tracks: / I don't wanna lose you / We do it.
7" Single: Released Mar '87, on Old Gold, by Old Gold Records. Deleted Sep '89. Catalogue no: **OG 9684**

I'M YOUNG
Tracks: / I'm young / Go to work on you.
7" Single: Released May '80, on RAK, by EMI Records. Deleted '83. Catalogue no: **RAK 316**
12" Single: Released May '80, on RAK, by EMI Records. Deleted '83. Catalogue no: **12RAK 316**

LET ME ROCK YOU
Tracks: / Let me rock you / Mr magic.
7" Single: Released Mar '80, on RAK, by EMI Records. Deleted '83. Catalogue no: **RAK 306**

Kane, A.R.

GREEN HAZED DAZE
Tracks: / Green hazed daze / Is this is? / Sperm travels like juggernaut (Only available on 12" format) / Is this dub? (Only available on 12" format).
7" Single: Released Nov '88, on Rough Trade, by Rough Trade Records. Catalogue no: **RT 231**
12" Single: Released Nov '88, on Rough Trade, by Rough Trade Records. Catalogue no: **RTT 231**

LOLITA
Tracks: / Lolita / Sado-masochism is a must / Butterfly collector.
7" Single: Released Jul '87, on 4AD, by 4AD Records. Catalogue no: **BAD 704**
12" Single: Released 23 May '87, on One Little Indian, by One Little Indian Records. Catalogue no: **12TP 8**

LOVESICK
Tracks: / Green hazed daze / Is this is? / Sperm travels like juggernaut (Only available on 12" format) / Is this dub? (Only available on 12" format).
7" Single: Released 24 Oct '88, on Rough Trade, by Rough Trade Records. Catalogue no: **RT 231**
12" Single: Released 24 Oct '88, on Rough Trade, by Rough Trade Records. Catalogue no: **RTT 231**

POP
Tracks: / Pop / What's all this then / Snow joke (CD single only).
CD 5": Released Jul '89, on Rough Trade, by Rough Trade Records. Catalogue no: **RT 239 CD**
7" Single: Released Jul '89, on Rough Trade, by Rough Trade Records. Catalogue no: **RT 239**
12" Single: Released Jul '89, on Rough Trade, by Rough Trade Records. Catalogue no: **RTT 239**

UP HOME
Tracks: / Up home / When you're sad.
12" Single: Released Mar '88, on Rough Trade, by Rough Trade Records. Catalogue no: **RTT 201**

WHEN YOU'RE SAD
Tracks: / When you're sad.
12" Single: Released Aug '87, on One Little Indian, by One Little Indian Records. Catalogue no: **12TP 2**

Kane, Big Daddy

SET IT OFF
Tracks: / Set it off / Get into it.
7" Single: Released Oct '88, on Cold Chillin', by Cold Chillin' Records. Catalogue no: **W 7676**
12" Single: Released Oct '88, on Cold Chillin', by Cold Chillin' Records. Catalogue no: **W 7676T**

Kane, D.J.

LATELY THINGS GET SCREWED UP ALL THE TIME
Tracks: / Lately things get screwed up all the time / Wrong condition.
7" Single: Released Jan '81, on Radar, Deleted Jan '84. Catalogue no: **ADA 62**

Kane, Eden

Biographical details: This British singer was born in Delhi, but returned with his family from India to Britain as a child. His real name was Richard Sarstedt, and his stage monicker was apparently inspired by the Orson Welles movie Citizen Kane. The 18 year old Kane got his first break by appearing in the 1960 film *Drinks all round.* His first single *Hot chocolate crazy* began life as a Cadbury's commercial on Radio Luxembourg. Then came *Well I ask you,* which was not only his first UK hit but a No.1 smash to boot - it topped the British chart in August 1961 and was followed by *Get lost* (No.10) and *Forget me not* (No.3). The three aforementioned Eden Kane hits were all penned by leading UK songwriter Les Vandyke. For his fourth success, however, he recorded a 1934 song entitled *I don't know why* and took it to the UK No.7 position. Eden growled his way through these thumping pop ditties as if they were going out of fashion. And, in fact, they did - like so many solo singers of his era, his career wan blown sky high in 1963 by the onslaught of the Beatles and the beat group revolution. Kane was forced into the wilderness by the suddenly dated nature of his music, compounded by financial difficulties. He made a one-off comback in 1964 with the UK Top 10 single *Boys cry,* and had plenty to cry about after that. In later years Eden Kane's early Sixties hits seemed to be largely forgotten by radio programmers, even in oldies shows. He is better remembered for being the first and most successful of the three Sarstedt hitmakers - Peter Sarstedt and Robin Sarstedt (who both chose to use the real family surname) enjoyed brief UK chart success in 1969 and 1976 respectively. It seemed that a singing Sarstedt came round every seven years - but the clan failed to deliver the goods in 1983. (Bob MacDonald, 20th Nov 1985).

BOYS CRY
Tracks: / Boys cry.
7" Single: Released Jan '64, on Fontana, by Phonogram Ltd. Deleted '67. Catalogue no: **TF 438**

BOYS CRY (OLD GOLD)
Tracks: / Boys cry / Well I ask you.
7" Single: Released Jan '85, on Old Gold, by Old Gold Records. Catalogue no: **OG 9473**

DIED AND WENT TO HEAVEN
Tracks: / Died and went to heaven / Pulling me thru' the bad times.
7" Single: Released Mar '80, on Monarch, by Monarch Records. Deleted Mar '83. Catalogue no: **MON 07**

FORGET ME NOT
Tracks: / Forget me not.
7" Single: Released Jan '62, on Decca, by Decca Records. Deleted '65. Catalogue no: **F 11418**

GET LOST
Tracks: / Get lost.
7" Single: Released Sep '61, on Decca, by Decca Records. Deleted '64. Catalogue no: **F 11381**

I DON'T KNOW WHY
Tracks: / I don't know why.
7" Single: Released May '62, on Decca, by Decca Records. Deleted '65. Catalogue no: **F 11460**

WELL I ASK YOU
Tracks: / Well I ask you / Forget me not.

7" Single: Released Jun '61, on Decca, by Decca Records. Deleted '64. Catalogue no: **F 11353**
7" Single: Released Mar '82, on Decca, by Decca Records. Deleted '88. Catalogue no: **F 13765**

WELL I ASK YOU (OLD GOLD)
Tracks: / Well I ask you.
7" Single: Released Oct '83, on Old Gold, by Old Gold Records. Deleted '88. Catalogue no: **OG 9359**

Kane Gang

Biographical details: This British band consists of Martin Bramer, Dave Brewis and Paul Woods. Hailing from Newcastle-upon-Tyne, the Kane Gang released their debut single *Brother brother* in 1983. A year later, with the help of the experienced producer and musician Pete Wingfield, the Gang chalked up their first minor UK hit single with the infectious chugger *Small town creed* - this song looked at the north/south divide in British society. By the end of 1984 the trio had gained two memorable UK Top 30 hits with the summery soulful ballad *Closest thing to heaven* (No.12) and *Respect yourself* (No.21), the latter being a remake of a 1971 American hit by the Staple Singers. The Kane Gang's music was just the style that Wingfield loved to get involved with - a soul pop fusion with a cutting edge. The threesome's debut LP *The bad and lowdown world of the Kane Gang* was a respectable success, although the group showed no signs of becoming major superstars. (Bob MacDonald, 20th Nov 1985).

CLOSEST THING TO HEAVEN
Tracks: / Closest thing to heaven.
7" Single: Released Jun '84, on Kitchenware, by Kitchenware Records. Catalogue no: **SK 15**
12" Single: Released Jun '84, on Kitchenware, by Kitchenware Records. Catalogue no: **SKX 15**

CLOSEST THING TO HEAVEN (OLD GOLD)
Tracks: / Closest thing to heaven / Respect yourself.
12" Single: Released Nov '88, on Old Gold, by Old Gold Records. Catalogue no: **OG 4085**

DON'T LOOK ANY FURTHER
Tracks: / Don't look any further (mantronik remix) / Don't look any further (mantronik B-Boy dub) / King Street rain.
7" Single: Released '87, on Kitchenware, by Kitchenware Records. Deleted Feb '89. Catalogue no: **SKS 33**
7" Single: Released Apr '88, on Kitchenware, by Kitchenware Records. Catalogue no: **SK 33**
12" Single: Released Jul '88, on Kitchenware, by Kitchenware Records. Deleted Feb '89. Catalogue no: **SKXR 33**
12" Single: Released Apr '88, on Kitchenware, by Kitchenware Records. Catalogue no: **SKX 33**

GUN LAW
Tracks: / Gun law / Giving up / Brother brother (on 12" only).
7" Single: Released Feb '85, on Kitchenware, by Kitchenware Records. Catalogue no: **SK 20**
12" Single: Released Feb '85, on Kitchenware, by Kitchenware Records. Catalogue no: **SKX 20**

MOTORTOWN
Tracks: / Motortown / Spend.
7" Single: Released 30 May '87, on Kitchenware, by Kitchenware Records. Deleted Oct '88. Catalogue no: **SK 30**
12" Single: Released 30 May '87, on Kitchenware, by Kitchenware Records. Deleted Oct '88. Catalogue no: **SKX 30**

RESPECT YOURSELF
Tracks: / Respect yourself.
7" Single: Released Oct '84, on Kitchenware, by Kitchenware Records. Catalogue no: **SK 16**
12" Single: Released Oct '84, on Kitchenware, by Kitchenware Records. Catalogue no: **SKX 16**

SMALL TOWN CREED
Tracks: / Small town creed / Brother brother.
7" Single: Released Mar '84, on Kitchenware, by Kitchenware Records. Catalogue no: **SK 5**
12" Single: Released Mar '84, on Kitchenware, by Kitchenware Records. Catalogue no: **SKK 5**

WHAT TIME IS IT
Tracks: / What time is it.

7" Single: Released Aug '87, on Kitchenware, by Kitchenware Records. Catalogue no: **SK 32**
12" Single: Released Aug '87, on Kitchenware, by Kitchenware Records. Deleted Oct '88. Catalogue no: **SKX 32**

Kane, General

GIRL PULLED THE DOG
Tracks: / Girl pulled the dog.
7" Single: Released Aug '87, on Motown, by BMG Records (UK). Catalogue no: **ZB 41433**
12" Single: Released Aug '87, on Motown, by BMG Records (UK). Catalogue no: **ZT 41434**

Kane, Madleen

PLAYING FOR TIME
Tracks: / Playing for time.
7" Single: Released Sep '83, on A.M.I.(USA), by American Music Corp.(USA). Catalogue no: **CF 001**

Kansas

Biographical details: At the time of their greatest success, this American rock band consisted of Phil Ehart, Dave Hope, Kerry Livgren, Robbie Steinhardt, Steve Walsh and Rich Williams. In common with another place-named group Boston, Kansas were one of a wave of unchallenging US rock bands who arrived on the American FM airwaves during the mid to late Seventies. While Britain was experiencing the upheavals of the NewWave/punk explosion, America was serving up a carefully crafted genre that combined Old Wave rock instrumentalation and rhythm with pop harmonies and melodies. Acts like Foreigner, Styx and Journey fell into this category also. Kansas were formed in 1972 and released their eponymous debut LP in 1974. The album that brought them to major prominence was *Leftoverture,* which reached No.5 on the US chart in April 1977; it was boosted by its dynamic opening track *Carry on wayward son,* which climbed to No.11 on the singles list. The next album *Point of no return* was another US Top 10 item and yielded the band's biggest and finest single, the million-selling melancholy philosophising ballad *Dust in the wind.* During the early Eighties, Kansas' career went through a long period of stagnation - they simply kept on repeating themselves, with reasonable but not spectacular success. The predictability of their music was summed up by their stale 1982 single *Play the game tonight,* which reached the US No.17 position. In Britain Kansas were ignored by press and public, and were dismissed as being totally irrelevant to the ever-changing and always inventive UK music scene. *Carry on wayward son* reached No.51 on the British singles chart - that constituted their entire UK chart track record. (Bob MacDonald, 20th Nov 1985).

ALL I WANTED
Tracks: / All I wanted / We're not alone anymore.
7" Single: Released Jan '87, on MCA, by MCA Records. Catalogue no: **MCA 1116**
12" Single: Released Jan '87, on MCA, by MCA Records. Catalogue no: **MCAS 1116**

CARRY ON WAYWARD SON
Tracks: / Carry on wayward son.
7" Single: Released Jul '78, on Kirshner (USA), by CBS Records (USA). Deleted '81. Catalogue no: **KIR 4932**

Kante, Mory

TAMA
Tracks: / Tama / Inch allah.
7" Single: Released Dec '88, on London Records, by London Records. Deleted May '89. Catalogue no: **LON 208**
12" Single: Released Dec '88, on London Records, by London Records. Deleted 26 Jun '89. Catalogue no: **LONXR 208**
12" Single: Released Dec '88, on London Records, by London Records. Deleted 26 Jun '89. Catalogue no: **LONX 208**

YE KE YE KE
Tracks: / Ye ke ye ke / Akwaba beach / Ye ke ye ke(afro acid remix) (Available on 12" only) / Ye ke ye ke(French mix) (Available on 12" only).
Note: "on 12" single only. "Remixed by Martin Young of Colourbox and Marrs fame"
CD 5": Released Aug '88, on London Records, by London Records. Catalogue no: **887 048-2**
7" Single: Released 11 Jul '88, on London Records, by London Records. Catalogue no: **LON 171**
12" Single: Released Aug '88, on London Records, by London Records. Catalogue no: **LONXR 171**
12" Single: Released 11 Jul '88, on London Records, by London Records. Catalogue no: **LONX 171**

Kanute

AMAZING MIND
Tracks: / Amazing mind.
7" Single: Released Jan '85, on EMI, by EMI Records. Catalogue no: **TAKE 1**
12" Single: Released Jan '85, on EMI, by EMI Records. Catalogue no: **12 TAKE 1**

Kaoma

LAMBADA
Tracks: / Lambada.
CD 5": Released Sep '89, on CBS, by CBS Records. Catalogue no: **655 011 2**
Cassingle: Released Sep '89, on CBS, by CBS Records. Catalogue no: **655 011 4**
7" Single: Released Sep '89, on CBS, by

CBS Records. Catalogue no: **655 011 7**
12" Single: Released Sep '89, on CBS, by CBS Records. Catalogue no: **655 011 8**

Kaos

DEFINITION OF LOVE
Tracks: / Definition of love / Definition of love (version).
CD 5": Released Jun '89, on Kool Kat, by Kool Kat Records. Catalogue no: **KOOL 504CD**
7" Single: Released 19 Jun '89, on Kool Kat, by Kool Kat Records. Catalogue no: **KOOL 504**
12" Single: Released Jul '89, on Kool Kat, by Kool Kat Records. Catalogue no: **KOOLT 504R**
12" Single: Released 19 Jun '89, on Kool Kat, by Kool Kat Records. Catalogue no: **KOOLR 504**
12" Single: Released 19 Jun '89, on Kool Kat, by Kool Kat Records. Catalogue no: **KOOLT 504**

Kaos 7

F..K ON ACID
Tracks: / F..k on acid.
12" Single: Released Nov '88, on Kaos, Catalogue no: **KAOS 007**

Kapil, Sanjay

I WISH I COULD SEE MY EARTH
Tracks: / I wish I could see my earth.
7" Single: Released Jul '81, on JSO, Deleted '87. Catalogue no: **EAT 10**

Karajova, Nadka

LAMBKIN HAS COMMENCED BLEATING
Tracks: / Lambkin has commenced bleating.
7" Single: Released Mar '82, on Folk Music Service, Catalogue no: **FMSS 1**

Karamel

IT'S OVER
Tracks: / It's over / Over dub.
12" Single: Released Sep '83, on Redman International, Catalogue no: **RED 005**

Karess

I FEEL LOVE COMIN' ON
Tracks: / I feel love comin' on / Love comes slowly.
7" Single: Released Sep '89, on Blue Beat, Catalogue no: **BBSP 07**
12" Single: Released Sep '89, on Blue Beat, Catalogue no: **BBLS 07**

Karia

LET ME LOVE YOU FOR TONIGHT
Tracks: / Let me love you tonight.
CD 5": Released Jul '89, on Sleeping Bag, by Sleeping Bag Records. Catalogue no: **SBUK CD4**
7" Single: Released 16 Jan '89, on Sleeping Bag, by Sleeping Bag Records. Catalogue no: **SBUK 4**
7" Single: Released 16 Jan '89, on Sleeping Bag, by Sleeping Bag Records. Catalogue no: **SBUK R4**
12" Single: Released 16 Jan '89, on Sleeping Bag, by Sleeping Bag Records. Catalogue no: **SBUK 4T**

Karloff, Billy

HEAD BANGER
Tracks: / Head banger / Don't keep me down.
7" Single: Released Mar '81, on Warner Bros., by WEA Records. Deleted Mar '84. Catalogue no: **K 17753**

Karn, Mick

Biographical details: This British bassist, saxophonist, bassoonist, singer, songwritor came to fame as a member of Japan. He was a founder member in 1974 and stayed with them until their termination in early 1983. The band did not really become a major commercial act until 1981, by which time all the highly creative individuals in the group were bursting to do other things without the compromises of a group format. Karn (real name Anthony Michaelides) gained a reputation as a sculptor, with exhibitions in London and Tokyo. He also became a part-time session musician, lending his highly proficient bass guitar style to such artists as Robert Palmer and Gary Numan. Karn's solo album *Titles* was released in November 1982 and reached No.74 on the UK chart. It contained the classy single *Sensitive*, which failed to chart. In 1983, after the final break-up of Japan, Mick teamed up with Midge Ure for the UK No.39 single *After a fashion*. In 1984 Karn joined forces with ex-Bauhaus leader Peter Murphy to form Dali's Car - this alliance spawned a minor UK hit single entitled *The judgement is the mirro*, but the duo soon folded. In Japan days Karn was the secon best-known member, after singer David Sylvian; so the lukewarm success of Mick's recordings outside the band was surprising and disappointing. (20th Nov 1985).

AFTER A FASHION
Tracks: / After a fashion / Textures.
7" Single: Released Jul '83, on Chrysalis, by Chrysalis Records. Catalogue no: **FEST 1**
12" Single: on Chrysalis, by Chrysalis Records. Catalogue no: **FESTX 1**

BUOY
Tracks: / Buoy / Dreams of reason / Language of ritual (12" only).
12" Single: Released Jan '87, on Virgin, by Virgin Records. Catalogue no: **VS 910-12**
7" Single: Released Jan '87, on Virgin, by Virgin Records. Deleted May '88. Catalogue no: **VS 910**

SENSITIVE
Tracks: / Sensitive / Sound of waves.
7" Single: Released Jun '82, on Virgin, by Virgin Records. Deleted Jun '85. Catalogue no: **VS 508**

Karrier

I'M BACK
Tracks: / I'm back.
7" Single: Released Sep '84, on Unit, Catalogue no: **TRANS 101**
12" Single: Released Oct '84, on Unit, Catalogue no: **12TRA 101**

Kartoon

AGE OF DANCING, THE
Tracks: / Age of dancing, The.
7" Single: Released Jul '85, on Bronze, by Bronze Records. Catalogue no: **BRO 194**
12" Single: Released Jul '85, on Bronze, by Bronze Records. Catalogue no: **BROX 194**

OVERNIGHT SENSATION
Tracks: / Overnight sensation / We get along.
7" Single: Released Feb '85, on Bronze, by Bronze Records. Catalogue no: **BRO 190**
12" Single: Released Feb '85, on Bronze, by Bronze Records. Catalogue no: **BROX 190**

Kartoon Krew

BATMAN
Tracks: / Batman.
7" Single: Released Oct '86, on Champion, by Champion Records. Catalogue no: **CHAMP 21**
12" Single: Released Oct '86, on Champion, by Champion Records. Deleted Aug '89. Catalogue no: **CHAMP 1221**

INSPECTOR GADGET
Tracks: / Inspector gadget.
7" Single: Released Nov '85, on Champion, by Champion Records. Deleted Aug '89. Catalogue no: **CHAMP 6**
12" Single: Released Nov '85, on Champion, by Champion Records. Deleted Aug '89. Catalogue no: **CHAMP 126**

Kasenetz-Katz

Biographical details: *Quick Joey Small* was a 1968 hit for the Kasenetz-Katz singing Orchestral Circus, reaching No.25 in the US and No.19 in the UK. It was written by Joey Levine and Archie Resnick and produced by Jerry Kasenetz and Jeff Katz. This single appeared to be a one-off hit, but in fact there was much more to this crew than met the eye. Jerry and Jeff were the creators of the 'bubblegum' genre, an extraordinarily successful form of pop music which yielded a string of hits in the late Sixties. The style's trademarks were a pounding, simple dance beat, a repetitive singalong chorus, nasal lead vocals and semi-moronic lyrics. Bubblegum music was designed to appeal to children and pre-adolescent teenagers, and the rowds were written accordingly - cartoons, games, comics, sweets and even bubblegum itself were the standard subjects. Super K, the production company of Kasenetz & Katz, were responsible for successful offerings by the Music Explosion, the Ohio Express and the 1910 Fruitgum Co. At a time when hippies and 'progressive' rockers were taking music more and more seriously, bubblegum and represented the opposite end of the popular music spectum. The 'Joey' in *Quick Joey Small* referred to studio vocalist Joey Levine, who was usually backed on the bubblegum discs by a team of session musicians. The Super K organisation was based in New York. When bubblegum (in its strict musical definition) died in 1970, Keasenetz and Katz virtually died with it; however, they achieved a one-off hit on both sides of the Atlantic in 1977 with Ram Jam's *Black Betty*. (Bob MacDonald, 20th Nov 1985).

QUICK JOEY SMALL
Tracks: / Quick Joey small.
7" Single: Released Nov '68, on Buddah, by Buddah Records Inc.(USA). Deleted '71. Catalogue no: **201 022**
7" Single: Released Jan '83, on Flashback, by Mainline Records. Catalogue no: **FBS 25**

Kash

QUIT HOLDIN BACK
Tracks: / Quit holdin back.
12" Single: Released 11 Sep '89, on Big One Records, by Big One Records. Catalogue no: **VVBIG 017**

ROCK DA BASS
Tracks: / Rock da bass.
12" Single: Released Jul '88, on 1st Bass, Catalogue no: **RUFF 1**

Kash Da Masta

QUIT HOLDING BACK
Tracks: / Quit holding back.
12" Single: Released Oct '89, on Big One Records, by Big One Records. Catalogue no: **VVBIG 17**

Kashif

Biographical details: Kashif was born in the legendary Harlem district of uptown Manhatten, New York, but his family moved to Brooklyn, New York. Aged nine, he started playing trumpet in the school band, but as his school was in the black part of Brooklyn, music lessons were the history of R&B. Moving from junior high school, Kashif was still playing the trumpet but didn't like the limitation of only being able to play one note at a time, so at age 13, he began playing the piano. Not only did Kashif show a gift for music, but he graduated high school aged 13, two years early. The manager of New York funk group B.T. Express recognised his talent and whisked him off on a world tour. To his credit, Kashif used much of his time on the road talking to the many music business personalities he'd come across. Whenever they'd hit a new town, Kashif would find our where the best studio was and hang out there. Kashif got a chance to learn much about the pitfalls of the business and how to work the equipment of a recording studio, thus, after leaving the group, although he was only 19, was able to start his own career. After B.T.Express, Kashif got a publishing deal with MCA, formed a group called Stepping Stone, and started recording and producing his own songs at Manhattan's Opal Studios. He formed a production company with Morrie Brown and Paul Lawrence Jones III called Mighty M and began writing, producing and playing on projects both collectively and individually. Mighty M developed a keyboard centred sound which became their trademark, and it bought success to Howard Johnson (*Keepin' love new*), Evelyn King (*Get loose*) and Melba Moore (*The other side of the rainbow*). The producers Jacques Fred Petrus and Mauro Malavasi asked Kashif to write three songs for High Fashion's *Feelin' lucky lately* album and to play keyboards on Change's *Sharing your love* album. In 1983 Kashif's solo career began, and the single that blazed the trail was entitled *I've just gotta have you. Kashif* was his debut album in 1983, followed by *Send me your love* in 1984. (Arista, June 1984).

ARE YOU THE WOMAN
Tracks: / Are you the woman.
7" Single: Released Aug '84, on Arista, by BMG Records (UK). Catalogue no: **ARIST 575**
12" Single: Released Aug '84, on Arista, by BMG Records (UK). Catalogue no: **ARIST 12575**

BABY DON'T BREAK YOUR BABY'S HEART
Tracks: / Baby don't break your baby's heart.
7" Single: Released May '84, on Arista, by BMG Records (UK). Catalogue no: **ARIST 568**
12" Single: Released May '84, on Arista, by BMG Records (UK). Catalogue no: **ARIST 12568**

I JUST GOTTA HAVE YOU
Tracks: / I just gotta have you.
12" Single: Released Feb '83, on Arista, by BMG Records (UK). Catalogue no: **ARIST 12521**

Ka-Spel, Edward

DANCE, CHINA DOLL
Tracks: / Dance, china doll.
12" Single: Released Jun '84, on In Phaze, by In Phaze Records. Catalogue no: **HAZ 6**

Kassav

SOLEIL
Tracks: / Soleil / Zoo.
7" Single: Released 14 Aug '88, on Epic, by CBS Records. Catalogue no: **KSV 1**
12" Single: Released 14 Aug '88, on Epic, by CBS Records. Catalogue no: **KSV T1**

ZOUK IS THE ONLY MEDICINE WE HAVE (SINGLE)
Tracks: / Zouk is the only medicine we have.
7" Single: Released Aug '88, on Greensleeves, by Greensleeves Records. Catalogue no: **GRE 701**
12" Single: Released Aug '88, on Greensleeves, by Greensleeves Records. Catalogue no: **GRED 701**

Kasseya, Souzy

LE TELEPHONE SONNE
Tracks: / Le telephone sonne.
12" Single: Released Nov '84, on Earthworks, by Earthworks Records. Deleted '88. Catalogue no: **DIG 12004**

Kasso

I LOVE THE PIANO
Tracks: / I love the piano / Dancing on the beach.
7" Single: Released Feb '84, on Banana, Catalogue no: **FRUIT 9**
12" Single: Released Feb '84, on Banana, Catalogue no: **FRUIT 9T**

NEW LIFE
Tracks: / New life.
7" Single: Released Jul '84, on Banana, Catalogue no: **FRUIT 12**

Katch 22

WORKSHOP LIFE
Tracks: / Workshop life / Visions of freedom.
7" Single: Released Dec '84, on Mynah, Catalogue no: **BBM 841**

Katinka

I AM A TWINKLING STAR
Tracks: / I am a twinkling star / Watching telly.
7" Single: Released Jan '81, on Carrere, Deleted Jan '84. Catalogue no: **CAR 172**

Katmandu

DYNASTY, THEME FROM
Tracks: / Dynasty (theme from).
7" Single: Released Mar '86, on Lovebeat Int., Catalogue no: **COLBY 1**
12" Single: Released Mar '86, on Lovebeat Int., Catalogue no: **COLBY 121**

Kato, Bruce

YOU CAN'T KEEP A GOOD CURRY DOWN
Tracks: / You can't keep a good curry down / Indian tea.
7" Single: Released Aug '80, on Alien, Catalogue no: **ALIEN 15**

Katrina & The Waves

Biographical details: Based in Britain, this band comprises Alex Cooper, Vince de la Cruz, Kimberley Rew plus American vocalist Katrina Leskanich. Katrina & the Waves had already built up a solid live following in the Cambridgeshire and Norfolk areas of England before releasing their debut single *Que ti quiero* in November 1983. In March of the following year, the group's second single *Plasic man* appeared. In the summer of 1985 the band achieved their breakthrough with *Walking on sunshine*, which marched into the Top 10 in both Britain and the States. Like most of their material, this exurberant single was written by Rew, who had enjoyed cult status during the late Seventies and early Eighties as guitarist with the Soft Boys, an idiosyncratic psychedelic punk band; he had then joined the pre-Katrina incarnation of the Waves, who issued the 1982 singles *Nightmare* and *Brown eyed son*. The joyously frantic, 100 mph *Walking on sunshine* was one of the most upbeat and carefree celebrations of romance that has ever been released in the name of pop music. It managed to combine an instantly hummable melody and great lyrics with a raw rock energy. The group experienced some difficulty in finding the right follow-up. *Do you want crying* making only modest ripples on either side of the Atlantic. When they returned to Britain from a four-month tour of the States, they found that the reactivated *Que ti quiero* was making no greater impression on the charts than on its first outing. (Bob MacDonald, 21st Nov 1985).

DO YOU WANT CRYING
Tracks: / Do you want crying.
7" Single: Released Jul '85, on Capitol, by EMI Records. Deleted '88. Catalogue no: **CL 368**
12" Single: Released Jul '85, on Capitol, by EMI Records. Deleted '88. Catalogue no: **12CL 368**

IS THAT IT?
Tracks: / Is that it? / I really taught me to watusi.

KATRINA & THE WAVES - WALKING ON SUNSHINE (Released on Capitol)

7" Single: Released Apr '86, on Capitol, by EMI Records. Deleted '88. Catalogue no: **CL 398**
12" Single: Released Apr '86, on Capitol, by EMI Records. Deleted '88. Catalogue no: **12 CL 398**

LOVELY LINDSEY
Tracks: / Lovely Lindsey / Cry for me.
7" Single: Released Oct '86, on Capitol, by EMI Records. Deleted '87. Catalogue no: **CL 427**
12" Single: Released Oct '86, on Capitol, by EMI Records. Deleted '88. Catalogue no: **12 CL 427**

PLASTIC MAN
Tracks: / Plastic man / Animal farm.
7" Single: Released Mar '84, on Silvertown, by Silvertown Records. Catalogue no: **STS 7**
12" Single: Released Mar '84, on Silvertown, by Silvertown Records. Catalogue no: **STST 7**

QUE TE QUIERO
Tracks: / Que te quiero / Que te quiero (version) / Machine gunsmith.
7" Single: Released Nov '83, on Silvertown, by Silvertown Records. Catalogue no: **STS 6**
7" Single: Released Nov '85, on Capitol, by EMI Records. Deleted '88. Catalogue no: **CL 382**
12" Single: Released Nov '85, on Capitol, by EMI Records. Deleted '88. Catalogue no: **12 CL 382**
12" Single: Released Nov '83, on Silvertown, by Silvertown Records. Catalogue no: **STST 6**

ROCK 'N' ROLL GIRL
Tracks: / Rock 'n' roll girl / To have and to hold / Rock 'n' roll girl (ext.) (12" & CD single only.) / That's the way (CD single only.).
CD 5": Released Nov '89, on SBK, by EMI Records. Catalogue no: **CDSBK 3**
CD 5": Released Nov '89, on SBK, by EMI Records. Catalogue no: **203 610 2**
Cassingle: Released Nov '89, on SBK, by EMI Records. Catalogue no: **203 610 4**
Cassingle: Released Nov '89, on SBK, by EMI Records. Catalogue no: **TCSBK 3**
7" Single: Released Nov '89, on SBK, by EMI Records. Catalogue no: **203 610 7**
7" Single: Released Nov '89, on SBK, by EMI Records. Catalogue no: **SBK 3**
12" Single: Released Nov '89, on SBK, by EMI Records. Catalogue no: **12SBK 3**
12" Single: Released Nov '89, on SBK, by EMI Records. Catalogue no: **203 610 6**
Special: Released Nov '89, on SBK, by EMI Records. Catalogue no: **203 610 8**
Special: Released Nov '89, on SBK, by EMI Records. Catalogue no: **SBKS 3**

SUN STREAKED
Tracks: / Sun streaked / One woman.
7" Single: Released Jun '86, on Capitol, by EMI Records. Deleted '88. Catalogue no: **CL 407**
12" Single: Released Jun '86, on Capitol, by EMI Records. Deleted '88. Catalogue no: **12 CL 407**

THAT'S THE WAY
Tracks: / That's the way / Love calculator / That's the way (ext. mix) (12" & CD single only.) / Rene (CD single only.).
CD 5": Released Aug '89, on SBK, by EMI Records. Catalogue no: **203 442 2**
CD 5": Released Aug '89, on SBK, by EMI Records. Catalogue no: **CDSBK 2**
Cassingle: Released Aug '89, on SBK, by EMI Records. Catalogue no: **203 442 2**
Cassingle: Released Aug '89, on SBK, by EMI Records. Catalogue no: **TCSBK 2**
7" Single: Released Aug '89, on SBK, by EMI Records. Catalogue no: **SBK 2**
7" Single: Released Aug '89, on SBK, by EMI Records. Catalogue no: **203 442 7**
12" Single: Released Aug '89, on SBK, by EMI Records. Catalogue no: **12SBK 2**
12" Single: Released Aug '89, on SBK, by EMI Records. Catalogue no: **203 442 6**
Special: Released Sep '89, on SBK, by EMI Records. Catalogue no: **203 442 8**
Special: Released Sep '89, on SBK, by EMI Records. Catalogue no: **SBKS 2**

WALKING ON SUNSHINE (see panel above)
Tracks: / Walking on sunshine / Red wine & whisky / Do you want crying / Que te quiero / Sun Street / Is that it.
7" Single: Released Apr '85, on Capitol, by EMI Records. Deleted '88. Catalogue no: **CL 354**
12" Single: Released Apr '85, on Capitol, by EMI Records. Deleted '88. Catalogue no: **12CL 354**

Katz

VISIONS OF YOU
Tracks: / Visions of you / Flight 2605.
7" Single: Released Jun '86, on Carrere, Catalogue no: **CAR 387**

Katz Ipanema

SISTER RESISTOR
Tracks: / Sister resistor.
7" Single: Released May '87, on Official, by Official Records. Catalogue no: **OFFA 8**

Kawazu, Marie

MOUMOKO NO OKOTO (BLINDMAN)
Tracks: / Moumoko no okoto (blindman).
7" Single: Released '88, on N L Centre, Catalogue no: **Unknown**

Kay, Janet

Biographical details: This British reggae singer, born in London, was 21 years old when her single *Silly games* rocketed to No.2 on the UK chart in the summer of 1979. It was one of Britain's biggest ever reggae hits, and was a perfect example of the genre's tender soulful category known as lovers' rock. Kay was on vacation in the Netherlands at the time of the records success, unaware that *Silly games* was climbing the charts. During the late Seventies and early Eighties, reggae (including Kay's other records) was widely ignored by the radio establishment in Britain. *Silly games* had a quirky distinguishing feature, that of Janet's thin voice straining to reach the ultra-high notes of the song's climax. It remained her only pop crossover hit, but later records (such as the 1982 album *Capricorn woman*, produced by leady UK reggae wizard Dennis Bovell) continued to be well recieved in the specialist market. (Bob MacDonald, 21st Nov 1985).

CAN'T GIVE IT UP
Tracks: / Can't give it up / Imagine that.
12" Single: Released Feb '83, on Solid Groove, Catalogue no: **SG 024**

DREAMS OF EMOTION
Tracks: / Dreams of emotion / Dreams of emotion (version).
12" Single: Released Nov '87, on Body Music, by Nuclear Records. Catalogue no: **BZT 07**

ETERNALLY GRATEFUL
Tracks: / Eternally grateful.
12" Single: Released Aug '84, on Local, Catalogue no: **LR 8**

FIGHT LIFE
Tracks: / Fight life.
12" Single: Released May '85, on Soho (1), by Soho Records. Catalogue no: **SOHO 101**

I DO LOVE YOU
Tracks: / I do love you / Trench Town skank.
7" Single: Released Jan '80, on Liberty, by EMI Records. Deleted Jan '83. Catalogue no: **BP 336**

IMAGINE
Tracks: / Imagine.
12" Single: Released Dec '88, on Body Music, by Nuclear Records. Catalogue no: **BZT 019**

LOVIN YOU
Tracks: / Loving you.
12" Single: Released 30 May '87, on All Tone, Catalogue no: **AT 008**

NO EASY WALK TO FREEDOM
Tracks: / No easy walk to freedom.
12" Single: Released Aug '87, on Local, Catalogue no: **LR 012**
7" Single: Released Aug '87, on Local, Catalogue no: **7LR 012**

SILLY GAMES
Tracks: / Silly games / Dangerous.
7" Single: Released Jun '79, on Scope, Deleted '82. Catalogue no: **SC 2**
12" Single: Released Jul '89, on Pressure, Catalogue no: **ARKD 4**

SO AMAZING (PART 2)
Tracks: / So amazing / Amazing dub.
12" Single: Released Apr '87, on Body Music, by Nuclear Records. Catalogue no: **BZT 03**

WHAT LOVE CAN DO
Tracks: / What love can do / Love dunnit.
12" Single: Released Sep '82, on Sarge, Catalogue no: **LC 1001**

YOU BRING THE SUN OUT
Tracks: / You bring the Sun out.
12" Single: Released Jul '82, on Arista, by BMG Records (UK). Catalogue no: **ARIST 12 481**
12" Single: Released Aug '85, on Tom Tom, Catalogue no: **TT 3**
7" Single: Released '82, on Arista, by BMG Records (UK). Deleted '87. Catalogue no: **ARIST 481**
7" Single: Released Mar '82, on Megafunk, Deleted '85. Catalogue no: **MF 2**
7" Single: Released Feb '82, on Black Roots, Deleted Feb '87. Catalogue no: **RT 33**
12" Single: Released Mar '82, on Megafunk, Deleted '85. Catalogue no: **MFX 2**

Kay, Kathie

MOTHER OF MINE
Tracks: / Mother of mine / Old Scots mother mine.
7" Single: Released Jun '82, on Country House, by Scotdisc Records. Catalogue no: **BGC 305**

Kay, Lisa

HERE'S LOOKING AT YOU KID
Tracks: / Looking at you.
7" Single: Released Oct '89, on Arista, by BMG Records (UK). Catalogue no: **112 745**
12" Single: Released Oct '89, on Arista, by BMG Records (UK). Catalogue no: **612 745**

Kay, Yvonne

RISE UP FOR MY LOVE
Tracks: / Rise up for my love / Rise up for my love (version).
7" Single: Released Feb '88, on Carrere, Catalogue no: **CAR 422**
12" Single: Released Feb '88, on Carrere, Catalogue no: **CART 422**

Kaye, Danny

Biographical details: The golden era for this famous American entertainer was over by the time the British record charts were inaugurated in November 1952, so his only UK hit was *Wonderful Copenhagen*, which reached No 5 in early 1953. His best records were probably those he made with the Andrews Sisters, such as *Civilization (Bongo Bongo Bongo)*, *The Woody Woodpecker* and *Bread And Butter Woman*. (Bob MacDonald, November 1985.).

WONDERFUL COPENHAGEN
Tracks: / Wonderful Copenhagen.
7" Single: Released Feb '53, on Brunswick, by Decca Records. Deleted '56. Catalogue no: **05023**

Kaye, Kevin

I'M IN LOVE WITH YOU GIRL (HO HO)
Tracks: / I'm in love with you girl (Ho Ho).
7" Single: Released Oct '88, on Broadstar, by Broadstar Records. Catalogue no: **BR 1153**

Kaye Sisters

PAPER ROSES
Tracks: / Paper roses.
7" Single: Released Jul '60, on Philips, by Phonogram Ltd. Deleted '63. Catalogue no: **PB 1024**

SHAKE ME I RATTLE
Tracks: / Shake me I rattle / Alone.
7" Single: Released Jan '58, on Philips, by Phonogram Ltd. Deleted '61. Catalogue no: **PB 752**

Kayse

POSITIVE REACTION
Tracks: / Positive reaction.
12" Single: Released Aug '89, on Town Bound, by Town Bound Records. Catalogue no: **BVB 3T**

Kaz

MORE THAN I CAN SAY
Tracks: / More than I can say / Days follow days.
7" Single: Released Mar '84, on SMP (2), Catalogue no: **PASH 24**
12" Single: Released Mar '84, on SMP (2), Catalogue no: **PASH 24(12)**

YOU TAKE MY BREATH AWAY
Tracks: / You take my breath away / Cold eyes.
7" Single: Released Oct '83, on Passion, by Skratch Records. Catalogue no: **PASH 10**
12" Single: Released '88, on Passion, by Skratch Records. Catalogue no: **PASH 10(12)**

Kazino

AROUND MY DREAM
Tracks: / Around my dream.
7" Single: Released May '85, on Carrere, Catalogue no: **CAR 360**
12" Single: Released May '85, on Carrere, Catalogue no: **CART 360**

KBC Band

IT'S NOT YOU, IT'S NOT ME
Tracks: / It's not you, it's not me / It's not you, it's not me (instr).
7" Single: Released Jan '87, on I.R.S, Catalogue no: **IRS 4**
12" Single: on I.R.S, Catalogue no: **IRST 4**

K.C. Flight

PLANET E (SINGLE)
Tracks: / Planet E.
CD 5": Released Apr '89, on RCA, by BMG Records (UK). Catalogue no: **PD 49404**
7" Single: Released Mar '89, on RCA, by BMG Records (UK). Catalogue no: **PB 49403**
12" Single: Released Apr '89, on RCA, by BMG Records (UK). Catalogue no: **889 71RD**
12" Single: Released Mar '89, on RCA, by BMG Records (UK). Catalogue no: **PT 49404**

SUMMER MADNESS
Tracks: / Summer madness (love is in the air mix) (On 12" & CD single) / Summer madness (7" remix) (On 7" only) / Summer madness (sex for days mix) (On 7" & CD single.) / Summer madness (club mix) (On 12" & CD single).
CD 5": Released Sep '89, on RCA, by BMG Records (UK). Catalogue no: **PD 49336**
7" Single: Released Sep '89, on RCA, by BMG Records (UK). Catalogue no: **PB 49335**
12" Single: Released Sep '89, on RCA, by BMG Records (UK). Catalogue no: **PT 49336**

K.C. & The Sunshine

Biographical details: Masterminded by writers/producers Harry Wayne Casey ('KC') and Richard Finch, this American disco band featured a host of different musicians at various times, the most loyal players being guitarist Jerome Smith and drummer Robert Johnson. KC and Finch met at TK Studios in Florida, where both were junior employees. They began to write and produce tracks for various soul artists signed to TK Records, but often found that their word never got past the demo stage. One night they recorded a backing track called *Rock your baby* that turned out so good that they enlisted a singer called George McCrae to do the vocals, and released it as a single. Almost by accident, Casey and Finch started the Seventies disco boom - *Rock your baby* by George McCrae reached No.1 on both sides of the Atlantic in the summer of 1974 and sold an incredible ten million copies globally. The stunning success of *Rock your baby* prompted KC and Finch to assemble the Sunshine Band and exploit the new market which they had helped to create. Their dancing anthems *Queen of clubs* and *Sound your funky horn* both reached the British Top 20 in late '74. During 1975-77 they enjoyed massive American success, chalking up four US No.1 smashes with *Get down tonight, That's the way I like it, (Shake shake shake) Shake your booty* and *I'm your boogie man* plus a No.2 hit with *Keep it comin' love.* All the hits stuck closely to the formula established by *Get down tonight* - an infectious fusion of disco rhythms and pop vocals, described by one Rolling Stone critic as 'bubblegum funk'. It would be hard to imagine a more predictable band, but you could dance to their records, which is what mattered at the time. When John Travolta and the Bee Gees took the disco boom to even greater heights with the 1978 *Saturday night fever* phenomenon, KC & The Sunshine Band got it on the act by having their song *Boogie shoes* included on the soundtrack. Then followed a naff perios, but KC returned to the top at the beginning of 1980 with the uncharacteristic ballad *Please don't go,* which became his fifthe US No.1 single and a No.3 hit in Britain. KC failed to come up with a follow-up hit to *Please don't go;* the singer and his band were consigned to the archives by music observers. In January 1982 KC was seriously injured in a car crash near his Florida home - he was in a wheelchair for a long period, and it took him a year to be able to walk again. In August 1983 he returned from obscurity and achieved his first ever UK No.1 single with the ultra-lightweight but instantly hummable *Give it up;* in America, he released the song on his own independant Meca label and took it to No.18 in early 1984. The Sunshine Band now existed in name only, with Casey and Finch making the records almost entirely by themselves. (21st Nov 1985, Bob MacDonald).

ALL THROUGH THE NIGHT
Tracks: / All through the night / Don't say no.
7" Single: Released Oct '81, on Epic, by CBS Records. Deleted '85. Catalogue no: **EPC A 1722**

ARE YOU READY
Tracks: / Are you ready / Uptight / Thank you.
7" Single: Released Mar '84, on CBS, by CBS Records. Catalogue no: **A 4261**
12" Single: Released Mar '84, on CBS, by CBS Records. Catalogue no: **TA 4261**

BLOW YOUR WHISTLE
Tracks: / Blow your whistle.
7" Single: Released Mar '74, on Jay Boy, by President Records. Catalogue no: **BOY 80**

BOOGIE SHOES
Tracks: / Boogie shoes.
7" Single: Released May '78, on TK, Deleted '81. Catalogue no: **TKR 6025**

GET DOWN TONIGHT
Tracks: / Get down tonight.
7" Single: Released Mar '75, on Jay Boy, by President Records. Deleted '78. Catalogue no: **BOY 93**

GIVE IT UP
Tracks: / Give it up.
7" Single: Released Jul '83, on Epic, by CBS Records. Deleted '86. Catalogue no: **EPC A 3017**

GIVE IT UP (OLD GOLD)
Tracks: / Give it up / You said you'd gimme some more.
7" Single: Released Jan '88, on Old Gold, by Old Gold Records. Catalogue no: **OG 9745**

I'M SO CRAZY
Tracks: / I'm so crazy about you.
7" Single: Released Nov '75, on Jay Boy, by President Records. Deleted '78. Catalogue no: **BOY 101**

I'M YOUR BOOGIE MAN
Tracks: / I'm your boogie man.
7" Single: Released Apr '77, on TK, Deleted '80. Catalogue no: **XB 2167**

IT'S THE SAME OLD SONG
Tracks: / It's the same old song.
7" Single: Released Jul '78, on TK, Deleted '81. Catalogue no: **TKR 6037**

KEEP IT COMIN' LOVE
Tracks: / Keep it comin' love.
7" Single: Released Dec '76, on Jay Boy, by President Records. Deleted '79. Catalogue no: **BOY 112**

LET'S GO ROCK'N'ROLL
Tracks: / Let's go rock'n'roll / I've got the feeling.
7" Single: Released Feb '80, on TK, Deleted '83. Catalogue no: **TKR 7574**

PLEASE DON'T GO
Tracks: / Please don't go.
7" Single: Released Dec '79, on TK, Deleted '82. Catalogue no: **TKR 7558**

QUEEN OF CLUBS
Tracks: / Queen of clubs.
7" Single: Released Aug '74, on Jay Boy, by President Records. Catalogue no: **BOY 88**

QUEEN OF CLUBS (OLD GOLD)
Tracks: / Queen of clubs / Get down.
7" Single: Released Jul '82, on Old Gold, by Old Gold Records. Deleted Jul '88. Catalogue no: **OG 9178**

(SHAKE SHAKE SHAKE) SHAKE YOUR BOOTY
Tracks: / (Shake shake shake) your booty.
7" Single: Released Jul '76, on Jay Boy, by President Records. Deleted '79. Catalogue no: **BOY 110**

SOUND YOUR FUNKY HORN
Tracks: / Sound your funky horn.
7" Single: Released Nov '74, on Jay Boy, by President Records. Deleted '77. Catalogue no: **BOY 83**

SUNSHINE BAND, THE
Tracks: / Sunshine band, The.
7" Single: Released '88, on Vogue, by Vogue Records. Catalogue no: **VG 509182**

THAT'S THE WAY (I LIKE IT)
Tracks: / That's the way I like it.
7" Single: Released Aug '75, on Jay Boy, by President Records. Deleted '78. Catalogue no: **BOY 99**

YOU SAID YOU'D GIMME SOME MORE
Tracks: / You said you'd gimme some more / When you dance to the music.
7" Single: Released Sep '83, on Epic, by CBS Records. Deleted '86. Catalogue no: **EPCA 2760**
12" Single: Released Sep '83, on Epic, by CBS Records. Deleted '86. Catalogue no: **EPCA 132760**

K-Doe, Ernie

MOTHER IN LAW (SINGLE)
Tracks: / Mother-in-law.
7" Single: Released May '61, on London-American, Deleted '64. Catalogue no: **HLU 9330**

Kean, Sherry

I WANT YOU BACK
Tracks: / I want you back.
7" Single: Released Mar '84, on Capitol, by EMI Records. Deleted '88. Catalogue no: **CL 323**
12" Single: Released Mar '84, on Capitol, by EMI Records. Deleted '88. Catalogue no: **12 CL 323**

Keanan

WATERSPORT
Tracks: / Watersport.
12" Single: Released Sep '85, on Awesome Records, by Awesome Records. Catalogue no: **AOR 4**

Keane, Dolores

LION IN A CAGE
Tracks: / Lion in a cage.
CD 5": Released Oct '89, on Ringsend road, Catalogue no: **DKS 4C**
7" Single: Released Aug '89, on Ringsend road, Catalogue no: **DKS 4**
12" Single: Released Oct '89, on Ringsend road, Catalogue no: **DKS 4T**

SISTER AND BROTHER
Tracks: / Sister and brother.
7" Single: Released '88, on I&B, by I & B Records. Catalogue no: **DKS 1**

Keating, Johnny

Biographical details: This British orchestra leader, conductor and arranger enjoyed a hot streak on the UK charts in the early Sixties, just before the arrival of the Beatles and the Merseybeat explosion. He arranged several Top 10 hits for Eden Kane, and simultaneously achieved his own Top Tenner with the theme from *Z cars* - that TV police series was new in 1962 and stayed on the screen for well over a decade. Keating's orchestra subsequently became a permanent fixture on British broadcasting and in concert halls. (Bob MacDonald, 21st Nov 1985).

THEME FROM 'Z CARS'
Tracks: / 'Z Cars', Theme from.
7" Single: Released Mar '62, on Piccadilly, Deleted '65. Catalogue no: **7N 35032**

Keaton, David

GLORIA
Tracks: / Gloria / Space control.
7" Single: Released Nov '83, on Vogue, by Vogue Records. Catalogue no: **VOG 2**
12" Single: Released Nov '83, on Vogue, by Vogue Records. Catalogue no: **VOGL 2**

Keats

TURN YOUR HEART AROUND
Tracks: / Turn your heart around.
7" Single: Released Jul '84, on EMI, by EMI Records. Catalogue no: **EMI 5484**

Keeble, Papa

GOOD THE BAD AND THE UGLY
Tracks: / Good, the bad and the ugly, The / Stylus.
7" Single: Released Sep '82, on Carousel (1), by Carousel Records. Catalogue no: **CAR 02**

Keegan, Kevin

HEAD OVER HEELS IN LOVE
Tracks: / Head over heels in love.
7" Single: Released Jun '79, on EMI, by EMI Records. Deleted '82. Catalogue no: **EMI 2965**

Keegaroos

WORLD CUP 82
Tracks: / World Cup 82.
7" Single: Released Jun '82, on T.W., by T.W. Records. Catalogue no: **HIT 106**

Keel

BECAUSE THE NIGHT
Tracks: / Because the night.
7" Single: Released Mar '86, on Vertigo, by Phonogram Ltd. Deleted '87. Catalogue no: **KEEL 1**
12" Single: Released Mar '86, on Vertigo, by Phonogram Ltd. Deleted '87. Catalogue no: **KEELX 1**

Keel, Howard

BORN AGAIN
Tracks: / Born again / If.
7" Single: Released Apr '84, on Warwick, by Warwick Records. Catalogue no: **S 5137**

JR WHO DO YOU THINK YOU ARE
Tracks: / JR who do you think you are / I'll stay with you for a lifetime.
7" Single: Released May '86, on WEA, by WEA Records. Catalogue no: **W 8827**

Keene, Nelson

IMAGE OF A GIRL
Tracks: / Image of a girl.
7" Single: Released Aug '60, on H.M.V., by EMI Records. Deleted '63. Catalogue no: **POP 771**

Keene, Tommy

PLACES THAT ARE GONE
Tracks: / Places that are gone / Faith in love.
7" Single: Released Apr '86, on Geffen, by Geffen Records (USA). Catalogue no: **GEF 2**

Keep

NOT SO WONDERFUL
Tracks: / Not so wonderful.
7" Single: Released Sep '85, on One By One, by One By One Records. Catalogue no: **1 X 2**

Keep It Dark

DON'T SURRENDER
Tracks: / Don't surrender / Far from home / It's over (Extra track available on 12" version only.).
7" Single: Released May '86, on Charisma, by Virgin Records. Deleted May '88. Catalogue no: **CB 422**
12" Single: Released May '86, on Charisma, by Virgin Records. Deleted May '88. Catalogue no: **CB 42212**

DREAMER
Tracks: / Dreamer / Outsider, The / What do we need (Extra track on 12" version only.).
#
7" Single: Released Mar '86, on Virgin, by Virgin Records. Deleted '89. Catalogue no: **CB 421**
12" Single: Released Mar '86, on Virgin, by Virgin Records. Deleted '89. Catalogue no: **CB 42112**

Keia Weia

JUST ANOTHER GAME
Tracks: / Just another game / Just another game (version).
12" Single: Released Feb '89, on Black Market, Catalogue no: **BLMK 5**

Keine Ahnung

PLASTIK C'EST CHIC
Tracks: / Plastik c'est chic.
12" Single: Released Apr '84, on Cherry Red, by Cherry Red Records. Deleted '87. Catalogue no: **12 EWS 1**

Keita, Salif

NOUS PAS BOUGER
Tracks: / Nous pas bouger.
7" Single: Released Jul '89, on Mango, by Island Records. Catalogue no: **MNG 715**
12" Single: Released Jul '89, on Mango, by Island Records. Catalogue no: **12 MNG 715**

PRIMPIN
Tracks: / Primpin / Primpin (part 2) / Primpin (stretch mix) (Only on 12" version.).
7" Single: Released 27 Mar '89, on Mango, by Island Records. Catalogue no: **MNG 103**
12" Single: Released 27 Mar '89, on Mango, by Island Records. Catalogue no: **12 MNG 103**

WAMBA
Tracks: / Wamba / Souareba.
7" Single: Released 22 Aug '88, on Sterns, by Sterns African Records Centre. Catalogue no: **STERNS 720**
7" Single: Released '88, on 4th & Broadway, by Island Records. Catalogue no: **STERN 1**
7" Single: Released '88, on Sterns, by Sterns African Records Centre. Deleted Apr '89. Catalogue no: **IS 381**

YADA
Tracks: / Yada / primpin.
CD 5": Released May '89, on Mango, by Island Records. Catalogue no: **CIDM 712**

Keith

98.6
Tracks: / 98.6.
7" Single: Released Jan '67, on Mercury, by Phonogram Ltd. Deleted '70. Catalogue no: **MF 955**

TELL ME TO MY FACE
Tracks: / Tell me to my face.
7" Single: Released Mar '67, on Mercury, by Phonogram Ltd. Deleted '70. Catalogue no: **MF 968**

Keith, Brian

TOUCH ME (LOVE ME TONIGHT)
Tracks: / Touch me (love me tonight).
7" Single: Released Feb '89, on Citybeat, by Beggars Banquet Records. Catalogue no: **CBE 737**
12" Single: Released Feb '89, on Citybeat, by Beggars Banquet Records. Catalogue no: **CBE 1237**

Keith & Darrell

WORK THAT BODY
Tracks: / Work that body.
7" Single: Released Jan '84, on Motown, by BMG Records (UK). Catalogue no: **TMG 1332**
12" Single: Released Jan '84, on Motown, by BMG Records (UK). Catalogue no: **TMGT 1332**

Keith & Sonia

SHARING THE NIGHT
Tracks: / Sharing the night.
12" Single: Released Jul '83, on Melody, Catalogue no: **M 002**

TWO TIME LOVERS
Tracks: / Two time lovers / Sharing the night.
12" Single: Released Dec '83, on Melodie, Catalogue no: **M 004**

Keller, Jerry

Biographical details: This American singer and songwriter was born in Fort Smith, Arkansas, and entered showbusiness in the mid-Fifties. He worked as a resident vocalist with Jack Dalton's orchestra, and then became a Tulsa disc jockey, before beginning a solo singing career in New York. His acquaintance with Pat Boone led to him acquiring some good contacts in the music industry. As it turned out, Keller achieved fame with one hit and then quickly faded. The self-penned *Here comes Summer* reached No.14 in the States in the summer of 1959; it climbed all the way to No.1 in Britain, albeit not until October! *Here comes summer* was absolutely typical of its time - rooted in mid Fifties rock'n'roll but tempered by the rapidly mellowing sound of late Fifties-pop; its theme made it an archetypal teenage record, celebrating the freedom from high school that the summer months brought. The single was the prototype for Cliff Richard & the Shadows' 1963 UK No.1 hit *Summer holiday*. Jerry Keller was a One Hit Wonder as a performer, but he did manage to achieve a second hit as a writer - Andy Williams took the aptly titled *Almost there* to No.2 in the UK in 1965; the song peaked at No.67 in America. (Bob MacDonald, 21st Nov 1985).

HERE COMES SUMMER
Tracks: / Here comes summer.
7" Single: Released Aug '59, on London-American, Deleted '62. Catalogue no: **HLR 8890**

HERE COMES SUMMER (OLD GOLD)
Tracks: / Here comes summer.
7" Single: Released Jul '82, on Old Gold, by Old Gold Records. Catalogue no: **OG 9165**

Kelli

DOUBLE DEALING
Tracks: / Double dealing.
7" Single: Released Sep '84, on Le Cam, by Le Cam Records (USA). Catalogue no: **LC 003**

Kelly

NOTHING BUT PROMISES
Tracks: / Nothing but promises.
12" Single: Released Mar '88, on Bolts, by Bolts Records. Catalogue no: **BOLTS 15/12**

Kelly, Badamas

ONE MAN ISN'T ENOUGH
Tracks: / One man isn't enough.
12" Single: Released Aug '87, on Big Top, by Big Top Records. Deleted '88. Catalogue no: **MBT 03**

Kelly, Dave

CRYING IN THE RAIN
Tracks: / Crying in the rain.
7" Single: Released Sep '86, on BBC, by BBC Records & Tapes. Deleted 31 Aug '88. Catalogue no: **RESL 195**

HALCYON DAYS
Tracks: / Halcyon days.
7" Single: Released Sep '84, on Ethereal, Catalogue no: **MSETH 2**

LONESOME MAN BLUES
Tracks: / Lonesome man blues / Long hot summer.
7" Single: Released May '86, on BBC, by BBC Records & Tapes. Deleted 31 Aug '88. Catalogue no: **RESL 188**
12" Single: Released May '86, on BBC, by BBC Records & Tapes. Deleted 31 Aug '88. Catalogue no: **12RSL 188**
Cassingle: Released May '86, on BBC, by BBC Records & Tapes. Deleted Apr '89. Catalogue no: **ZRSL 188**

PUT YOUR MONEY WHERE YOUR MOUTH IS
Tracks: / Put your money where your mouth is / It feels right.
7" Single: Released Sep '81, on Cool King, Catalogue no: **CK 005**

RETURN TO SENDER
Tracks: / Return to sender.
7" Single: Released Apr '81, on Cool King, Catalogue no: **CK 002**

WHEN I'M DEAD AND GONE
Tracks: / When I'm dead and gone.
7" Single: Released Oct '82, on Cool King, Catalogue no: **CK 009**

Kelly, Des

TIM MAIRTINE JACK
Tracks: / Tim Mairtine Jack.
7" Single: Released '88, on Play (Ireland), Catalogue no: **PLAY 227**

Kelly Family

WHO'LL COME WITH ME
Tracks: / Who'll come with me / Join the parade.
7" Single: Released Feb '80, on Polydor, by Polydor Ltd. Deleted Feb '85. Catalogue no: **POSP 114**

Kelly, Frank

BARNET SONG
Tracks: / Barnet song / I'm drinking too much Scotch.
7" Single: Released May '84, on Ritz, by Ritz Records. Catalogue no: **RITZ 071**

CHRISTMAS COUNTDOWN
Tracks: / Christmas countdown / Yuletide moonshine.
7" Single: Released Nov '85, on Ritz, by Ritz Records. Catalogue no: **RITZ 062**

Kelly, Frankie

AIN'T THAT THE TRUTH
Tracks: / Ain't that the truth.
7" Single: Released Oct '85, on 10 Records, by Virgin Records. Deleted '89. Catalogue no: **TEN 87**
12" Single: Released Oct '85, on 10 Records, by Virgin Records. Deleted '89. Catalogue no: **TEN 87-12**

Kelly, Jerri

WALK ME 'CROSS THE RIVER
Tracks: / Walk me 'cross the river / All that shines is gold.
7" Single: Released Jan '82, on Carrere, Deleted Jan '85. Catalogue no: **CAR 251**

Kelly, Jim

WATERMELON
Tracks: / Watermelon.
12" Single: Released Nov '82, on Lucky, by Lucky Records. Catalogue no: **LSD 003**

Kelly, Keith

LISTEN LITTLE GIRL
Tracks: / Listen little girl.
7" Single: Released Aug '60, on Parlophone, by EMI Records. Deleted '63. Catalogue no: **R 4676**

TEASE ME
Tracks: / Tease me.
7" Single: Released May '60, on Parlophone, by EMI Records. Deleted '63. Catalogue no: **R 4640**

Kelly, Kin

AIN'T TOO PROUD TO BEG
Tracks: / Ain't too proud to beg / High dance, The.
7" Single: Released Jul '87, on Gipsy, by Gipsy Records. Catalogue no: **GIPSY 24**
12" Single: Released Jul '87, on Gipsy, by Gipsy Records. Catalogue no: **GIPSYT 24**

EVERY HEART
Tracks: / Every heart / Hopeless love.
7" Single: Released Feb '83, on Gipsy, by Gipsy Records. Catalogue no: **GIPSY 9**

IF I COULD HEAR YOUR VOICE
Tracks: / If I could hear your voice.
7" Single: Released Nov '80, on Gipsy, by Gipsy Records. Deleted '82. Catalogue no: **GIPSY 1**

JEANNIE
Tracks: / Jeannie / Anniversary girl.
7" Single: Released Mar '85, on Gipsy, by Gipsy Records. Catalogue no: **GIPSY 18**

JUST LIKE MARION
Tracks: / Just like Marion / When rock was king.
7" Single: Released Jul '81, on Gipsy, by Gipsy Records. Catalogue no: **GIPSY 2**

LONELY
Tracks: / Lonely / Flash Alice.
7" Single: Released Nov '81, on Gipsy, by Gipsy Records. Deleted Nov '84. Catalogue no: **GIPSY 4**

TO YOU
Tracks: / To You / Hopeless love.
7" Single: Released Jan '87, on Gipsy, by Gipsy Records. Catalogue no: **GIPSY 19**
12" Single: Released Jan '87, on Gipsy, by Gipsy Records. Catalogue no: **GIPSYT 19**

Kelly, Kris

EVERYBODY NEEDS SOMEBODY TO LOVE
Tracks: / Everybody needs somebody to love.
12" Single: Released 24 Jul '89, on Silver Heart, by Silver Heart Records. Catalogue no: **CUFF 1C**

PRISONER IN CELL BLOCK H (THEME FROM)
Tracks: / Prisoner cell block H (theme from).
7" Single: Released Jan '89, on Silver Heart, by Silver Heart Records. Catalogue no: **HEART 2**

Kelly, Luke

RAGLAN ROAD
Tracks: / Raglan Road / Scorn not his simplicity.
7" Single: Released '88, on I&B, by I & B Records. Catalogue no: **CHS 007**

Kelly, Mary Anne

GREETINGS 5
7" EP: Released Dec '88, on Materiali Sonori, Catalogue no: **MASO 70005**

Kelly, Ned

AUTOMOBILE
Tracks: / Automobile / Girls got feelings too.
7" Single: Released Oct '88, on Bark, by Bark Records. Catalogue no: **DRIVE 1**

SIGN LANGUAGE
Tracks: / Sign language.
7" Single: Released Jan '89, on Bark, by Bark Records. Catalogue no: **SIGN 1**

Kelly, Pat

BRIDGE OVER TROUBLED WATER
Tracks: / Bridge over troubled water / Bridge over troubled water (Instr).
12" Single: Released Jan '87, on Joe Frazer, Catalogue no: **BT 005**

CAN WE MAKE LOVE TONIGHT
Tracks: / Can we make love tonight / Can we make love tonight (version).
12" Single: Released 20 Jun '87, on Body Music, by Nuclear Records. Catalogue no: **BZT 04**

CRY FOR YOU NO MORE
Tracks: / Cry for you no more / What goes on in your mind.
7" Single: Released '89, on Blue Moon (1), by Magnum Music Group. Catalogue no: **BMS 003**
12" Single: Released '89, on Blue Moon (1), by Magnum Music Group. Catalogue no: **BMS 1003**

HEY BABY
Tracks: / Hey baby.
7" Single: Released Jun '83, on Ethnic, Catalogue no: **ETH 2231**

HOW I WISH IT WAS YOU
Tracks: / How I wish it was you / Radio version.
12" Single: Released Dec '85, on Three Kings, Catalogue no: **TK 055**

HOW LONG WILL IT TAKE (EP)
Tracks: / How long will it take.
10" single: Released Jul '82, on Pama Oldies, by Pama Records. Catalogue no: **PTP 1029**

I CAN DO BAD BY MYSELF
Tracks: / I can do bad by myself.
7" Single: Released 12 May '89, on Body Music, by Nuclear Records. Catalogue no: **BZT 024**

I'M SO PROUD
Tracks: / I'm so proud / Soulful love.
12" Single: Released 30 May '89, on Chanan-Jah, Catalogue no: **CJ 1003**

LET ME HAVE THE CHANCE
Tracks: / Let me have the chance.
7" Single: Released Nov '86, on Germaine, Catalogue no: **DGT 19**

LET'S GET MARRIED
Tracks: / Let's get married / Let's get married (version).
12" Single: Released Jul '82, on Lola, Catalogue no: **LOLA 21206**

LOVE THE WAY IT SHOULD BE
Tracks: / Love the way it should be.
12" Single: Released Nov '85, on Fashion, by Fashion Records. Catalogue no: **FAD 035**

ONE IN A MILLION GIRL
Tracks: / One in a million girl.
12" Single: Released Apr '82, on Paradise, Catalogue no: **PEIS 101**

ONE YOU LOVE, THE
Tracks: / One you love, The.
12" Single: Released Jun '84, on Jedi, Catalogue no: **JJ 176**

READY TO LOVE YOU AGAIN
Tracks: / Ready to love you again.
12" Single: Released Jul '84, on World Enterprise, Catalogue no: **WER/D 117**

ROCK ME TONIGHT
Tracks: / Rock me tonight (for old time's sake).
12" Single: Released May '75, on Paradise, Catalogue no: **PDIS 512**

ROSIE
Tracks: / Rosie / Flower dub.
12" Single: Released Dec '84, on Top Lady, Catalogue no: **TL 001**

SISTER LOVE
Tracks: / Sister love.
12" Single: Released Aug '84, on Ethnic, Catalogue no: **ETH 2252**

STILL WATER
Tracks: / Still water.
12" Single: Released Jul '83, on Ethnic, Catalogue no: **ETH 2235**

TALK ABOUT LOVE
Tracks: / Talk about love / I've been trying.
12" Single: Released Nov '83, on Skynote, Catalogue no: **SKY 001**

THERE'S A SONG
Tracks: / There's a song.
12" Single: on Attack, Deleted '88. Catalogue no: **TACK 18**

YOU DON'T CARE
Tracks: / You don't care.
12" Single: Released Dec '88, on Body Music, by Nuclear Records. Catalogue no: **BZT 021**

YOU MUST BELIEVE
Tracks: / You must believe / Believe in dub.
12" Single: Released Dec '83, on Ethnic, Catalogue no: **ETH 2241**

Kelly, Paul

DARLING IT HURTS
Tracks: / Darling it hurts / Desdemona, before too long.
7" Single: Released Sep '88, on A&M, by A&M Records. Deleted Feb '89. Catalogue no: **AM 459**
12" Single: Released Sep '88, on A&M, by A&M Records. Deleted Feb '89. Catalogue no: **AMY 459**

Kelly, Rick

CRY BABY
Tracks: / Cry baby / They never come back.
7" Single: Released 22 Aug '88, on Blue Moves, by Blue Moves Records. Catalogue no: **SBM 1**
12" Single: Released 22 Aug '88, on Blue Moves, by Blue Moves Records. Catalogue no: **TSBM 1**

Kelly, Roberta

ZODIACS
Tracks: / Zodiacs.
7" Single: Released Jan '78, on Oasis (USA), Deleted '81. Catalogue no: **OASIS 3**

Kelts & Kilts

REEL TO REEL
Tracks: / Reel to reel / Giving it all away.
7" Single: Released Dec '82, on Polydor, by Polydor Ltd. Deleted Dec '85. Catalogue no: **POSP 544**
12" Single: Released Dec '82, on Polydor, by Polydor Ltd. Deleted Dec '85. Catalogue no: **POSPX 544**

Kelz

CLASH OF THE BEATS
Tracks: / Clash of the beats.
12" Single: Released Nov '88, on Three Stripe, Catalogue no: **SAM 1113**

Kemp, Johnny

BIRTHDAY SUIT
Tracks: / Birthday suit / Birthday suit (7" remix) / Birthday suit (extended mix) / Birthday suit (club dub) / Birthday suit (percapella).
CD 5": Released 15 May '89, on CBS, by CBS Records. Deleted Oct '89. Catalogue no: **654 838 2**
7" Single: Released 15 May '89, on CBS, by CBS Records. Deleted Oct '89. Catalogue no: **654 838 0**
12" Single: Released 15 May '89, on CBS, by CBS Records. Deleted Oct '89. Catalogue no: **654 838 8**
12" Single: Released 15 May '89, on CBS, by CBS Records. Deleted Oct '89. Catalogue no: **654 838 7**

BIRTHDAY SUIT (HOUSE MIX)
Tracks: / Birthday suit (house mix) / Just got paid (album version) / Birthday suit (7" club mix).
12" Single: Released May '89, on CBS, by CBS Records. Catalogue no: **654 838 1**

DANCING WITH MYSELF
Tracks: / Dancing with myself / Dancing with myself (ext.) / Dancing with myself (alt. dub mix) (CD single only.) / Dancing with myself (alt. mix) (12" only.) / Just got paid (12" only.).
CD 5": Released Oct '88, on CBS, by CBS Records. Deleted 17 Apr '89. Catalogue no: **653020 2**
7" Single: Released Sep '88, on CBS, by CBS Records. Deleted 17 Apr '89. Catalogue no: **653020 7**
12" Single: Released Sep '88, on CBS, by CBS Records. Deleted 17 Apr '89. Catalogue no: **653020 6**
12" Single: Released Oct '88, on CBS, by CBS Records. Deleted 17 Apr '89. Catalogue no: **653020 1**

JUST GOT PAID
Tracks: / Just got paid / Just got paid (dub mix) / Just got paid (inst) / Penthouse lover (CD single only).

CD 5": Released 22 Aug '88, on CBS, by CBS Records. Deleted 17 Apr '89. Catalogue no: **651470 2**
7" Single: Released Jun '88, on CBS, by CBS Records. Deleted Jan '89. Catalogue no: **651470 7**
12" Single: Released May '88, on CBS, by CBS Records. Deleted Jan '89. Catalogue no: **651470 8**
12" Single: Released 14 Aug '88, on CBS, by CBS Records. Deleted 17 Apr '89. Catalogue no: **651470 6**
12" Single: Released May '88, on CBS, by CBS Records. Deleted Jan '89. Catalogue no: **651470 9**

Kendalls

THANK GOD FOR THE RADIO
Tracks: / Thank God for radio.
7" Single: Released Jun '85, on Gull, by Gull Records. Deleted '88. Catalogue no: **GULS 79**

YOU MAKE AN ANGEL WANT TO CHEAT
Tracks: / You make an angel want to cheat / Mandolin man.
7" Single: Released Apr '80, on Ovation, by Gull Records. Deleted '82. Catalogue no: **OV 1202**

Kendrick, Graham

LET THE FLAME BURN BRIGHTER
Tracks: / Let the flame burn brighter.
Cassingle: Released 21 Aug '89, on Power, Catalogue no: **CSP 30**
7" Single: Released 21 Aug '89, on Power, Catalogue no: **P 30**

Kendricks, Eddie

BOOGIE DOWN
Tracks: / Boogie down.
7" Single: Released Mar '74, on Tamla Motown, by Motown Records (UK). Deleted '77. Catalogue no: **TMG 888**

KEEP ON TRUCKIN'
Tracks: / Keep on truckin'.
7" Single: Released Nov '73, on Tamla Motown, by Motown Records (UK). Deleted '76. Catalogue no: **TMG 873**
7" Single: Released May '83, on Motown, by BMG Records (UK). Catalogue no: **TMG 985**

Kendricks, Ken

FEELS SO GOOD
Tracks: / Feels so good / Feels so good (instrumental).
12" Single: Released Apr '86, on Elite Records, by Elite Records. Deleted '88. Catalogue no: **DAZZ 51**

Kennaway, Jane

Biographical details: This British singer achieved a one-off UK chart entry in early 1981, reaching No.65 with her memorable pop/rock single *IOU*. She was accompanied on the track by Strange Behaviour, her male instrumental backing band. *IOU* received considerable airplay on BBC Radio One, and its chart placing was surprisingly modest. Later Kennaway records, appropriately released on the IOU label included *I'm missing you* and *Don't do it*. (Bob MacDonald, 22nd Nov 1985).

CELIA
Tracks: / Celia / Radio.
7" Single: Released Mar '81, on Deram, by London Records. Deleted Mar '84. Catalogue no: **DM 439**

DON'T DO IT
Tracks: / Don't do it.
7" Single: Released Nov '83, on I.O.U. (USA), by I.O.U Records (USA). Catalogue no: **IOU 1000**

I'M MISSING YOU
Tracks: / I'm missing you.
7" Single: Released Jun '83, on I.O.U. (USA), by I.O.U Records (USA). Catalogue no: **IOU 999**

I.O.U.
Tracks: / I.O.U. / Take me away.
7" Single: Released Jan '81, on Deram, by London Records. Deleted '84. Catalogue no: **DM 436**

Kennedy Express

IS THERE LIFE ON EARTH
Tracks: / Is there life on earth / Stop stop stop / Little Lolita.
7" EP: Released Mar '80, on Jet, by Jet Records. Deleted Mar '83. Catalogue no: **JET 171**

Kennedy, Gene

ABERDEEN
Tracks: / Aberdeen.
7" Single: Released Aug '83, on Rig, Catalogue no: **GSK 001**

Kennedy, Grace

ALL I WANT IS YOU
Tracks: / All I want is you.
7" Single: Released Jul '83, on Red Bus, by Red Bus Records. Catalogue no: **RBUS 81**

FANDANGO DANCING
Tracks: / Fandango dancing / My heart keeps breaking over you.
7" Single: Released Mar '80, on DJM, Deleted Mar '83. Catalogue no: **DJS 10932**

HOW MUCH LOVE DO YOU HAVE FOR ME TONIGHT
Tracks: / How much love do you have for me tonight / Love in the sunshine.
7" Single: Released Jan '82, on DJS, Deleted Jan '85. Catalogue no: **DJS 10984**

IF I'M WRONG ABOUT YOU
Tracks: / If I'm wrong about you / You cheat on me.
7" Single: Released Aug '80, on DJM, Deleted '83. Catalogue no: **DJS 10952**

I'M STARTING AGAIN (SINGLE)
Tracks: / I'm starting again / Love in the sunshine / You cheat on me.
7" Single: Released '82, on DJM, Catalogue no: **DJS 10963**
12" Single: Released '82, on DJM, Catalogue no: **DJR 10963**

MISSING YOU
Tracks: / Missing you / Love me to sleep.
7" Single: Released '82, on DJM, Catalogue no: **DJS 10971**

SLOWLY
Tracks: / Slowly / Love in the sunshine.
7" Single: Released Nov '80, on DJM, Deleted Nov '83. Catalogue no: **DJS 10959**

TAKE IT OR LEAVE IT
Tracks: / Take it or leave it / Take it or leave it (instrumental).
7" Single: Released Feb '87, on Nightmare, by Nightmare Records. Catalogue no: **MARES 14**
12" Single: Released Feb '87, on Nightmare, by Nightmare Records. Catalogue no: **MARE 14**

Kennedy, Jackie

UNDER MY SPELL
Tracks: / Under my spell.
12" Single: Released Aug '83, on Stripe Line, Catalogue no: **STRIPE 121**

Kennedy, Nigel

SUMMER (THE LAST MOVEMENT) From Vivaldi's four seasons
Tracks: / Summer - The last movement (Presto) / Summer - First movement (Allegro no molto) / Summer - Second movement (Adagio) / Summertime (CD single only.).
CD 5": Released Aug '89, on H.M.V., by EMI Records. Catalogue no: **203 513 2**
CD 5": Released Aug '89, on H.M.V., by EMI Records. Catalogue no: **CDSEASON 1**
7" Single: Released Aug '89, on H.M.V., by EMI Records. Catalogue no: **203 513 7**
7" Single: Released Aug '89, on H.M.V., by EMI Records. Catalogue no: **SEASON 1**

Kennedy, Wayne

SOMEDAY SOMEWAY
Tracks: / Someday, someway.
7" Single: Released Jan '84, on Lark, Deleted '87. Catalogue no: **LS 4**

Kennerley, Paul

FEELS SO RIGHT
Tracks: / Feels so right / Been your fool too long.

7" Single: Released Nov '81, on A&M, by A&M Records. Deleted Nov '84. Catalogue no: **AMS 8185**

JEALOUS LOVE
Tracks: / Jealous love / Death of me.
7" Single: Released May '81, on A&M, by A&M Records. Deleted May '84. Catalogue no: **AMS 8132**

TAKE THAT WOMAN AWAY
Tracks: / Take that woman away / How long.
7" Single: Released Jun '82, on A&M, by A&M Records. Deleted Jun '85. Catalogue no: **AMS 8221**

Kenny

BABY I LOVE YOU OK
Tracks: / Baby I love you ok.
7" Single: Released Jun '75, on RAK, by EMI Records. Deleted '78. Catalogue no: **RAK 207**

BUMP, THE
Tracks: / Bump, The.
7" Single: Released Dec '74, on RAK, by EMI Records. Deleted '77. Catalogue no: **RAK 186**

BUMP, THE (OLD GOLD)
Tracks: / Bump / Fancy pants.
7" Single: Released Apr '87, on Old Gold, by Old Gold Records. Deleted Sep '89. Catalogue no: **OG 9718**

FANCY PANTS
Tracks: / Fancy pants.
7" Single: Released Mar '75, on RAK, by EMI Records. Deleted '78. Catalogue no: **RAK 196**

JULIE ANN
Tracks: / Julie Ann.
7" Single: Released Aug '75, on RAK, by EMI Records. Deleted '78. Catalogue no: **RAK 214**

DAVE KENT - OUT OF MY MIND (Released on Rana)

Kenny, Gerard

Biographical details: This American singer and songwriter achieved success in Britain during the late Seventies and early Eighties while remaining relatively unknown at home. The record which made him semi-famous was *New York, New York*, a single released in the autumn of 1978. This irritating tribute to his favourite city - 'so good they named it twice' - did not seem to impress Big Apple citizens very much, for they soon adopted Frank Sinatra's *Theme from New York, New York* (a totally different song) as their anthem. Nor did it impress British record buyers very much, for it failed to chart for several weeks despite saturation UK airplay; when the single suddenly reached No.43 on the UK chart in December '78, it seemed suspicious and hyping was later alleged. In July 1979 Kenny did achieve a genuine No.19 placing on the British LP list with *Made it through the rain*, after recieving considerable TV exposure. The title track was probably his finest song, recounting his struggles to succeed in the music business. In 1981 it became an American Top 10 hit for Barry Manilow, although Big Barry amended the number so that it took on a less precise theme *I made it through the rain and kept my songs protected* was changed to *I made it through the rain and kept my world protected*. Kenny's biggest British single was the downbeat ballad *Fantasy*, which reached No.34 in 1980. *The other woman, the other man* scraped the chart in early 1984, by which time the artist had firmly established himself in the lucrative middle-of-the-road world of cabaret, variety, television and the like. (Bob MacDonald, 22nd Nov 1985).

FANTASY
Tracks: / Fantasy / No one knows.
7" Single: Released Jun '80, on RCA, by BMG Records (UK). Deleted '83. Catalogue no: **PB 5256**

GETTING TO KNOW EACH OTHER
Tracks: / Getting to know each other / Sucker for love.
7" Single: Released Mar '80, on RCA, by BMG Records (UK). Deleted '83. Catalogue no: **PB 5235**

I'VE GROWN ACCUSTOMED TO HER FACE
Tracks: / I've grown accustomed to her face.
7" Single: Released Jul '83, on Starblend, by Starblend Records. Catalogue no: **FANT 1**

MADE IT THROUGH THE RAIN (SINGLE)
Tracks: / Made it through the rain.
7" Single: Released Jan '85, on Impression, Catalogue no: **IMS 8**

MAGGIE
Tracks: / Maggie / Nickells and dimes.
7" Single: Released Sep '80, on RCA, by BMG Records (UK). Deleted Sep '83. Catalogue no: **RCA 3**

NEW YORK, NEW YORK
Tracks: / New York, New York.
7" Single: Released Sep '78, on RCA, by BMG Records (UK). Catalogue no: **PB 5117**

NO MAN'S LAND
Tracks: / No man's land.
7" Single: Released May '85, on WEA, by WEA Records. Deleted '88. Catalogue no: **YZ 38**

OTHER WOMAN, THE OTHER MAN
Tracks: / Other woman, the other man.
7" Single: Released Jan '84, on Impression, Catalogue no: **IMS 3**

WORLD FULL OF LAUGHTER
Tracks: / World full of laughter.
7" Single: Released Oct '84, on Impression, Catalogue no: **IMS 6**

Kenny (solo)

GIVE IT TO ME NOW
Tracks: / Give it to me now.
7" Single: Released Jun '73, on RAK, by EMI Records. Deleted '76. Catalogue no: **RAK 153**

HEART OF STONE
Tracks: / Heart of stone.
7" Single: Released Mar '73, on RAK, by EMI Records. Deleted '76. Catalogue no: **RAK 144**

Kent, Dave

OUT OF MY MIND
Tracks: /Out of my mind/I will be a stranger.
7" Single: Released '88, on Rana. Catalogue no. **RANA S001**

Kent, Klark

AWAY FROM HOME
Tracks: / Away from home / Office talk.
7" Single: Released 20 Jun '80, on A&M, by A&M Records. Deleted '83. Catalogue no: **AMS 7532**

DON'T CARE
Tracks: / Don't care / Office girls / Thrills.
7" Single: Released Aug '78, on A&M, by A&M Records. Deleted '81. Catalogue no: **AMS 7376**

Kent, Peter

IT'S A REAL GOOD FEELING
Tracks: / It's a real good feeling / Carrie.
7" Single: Released 20 Jun '80, on EMI, by EMI Records. Deleted '83. Catalogue no: **EMI 5080**

Kent, Steven

I COMMUTE
Tracks: / I commute / Slow dancing.
7" Single: Released Apr '80, on Pye, Deleted Apr '83. Catalogue no: **7P 184**

LONDON
Tracks: / London / Belle amour.
7" Single: Released Oct '80, on Mams, Deleted Oct '83. Catalogue no: **MAMS 205**

Kenton, Jackie

HEARTBREAKER
Tracks: / Heartbreaker.
12" Single: Released Mar '83, on Nature, Catalogue no: **NR 14**

Kenton, Janet

DRIFTING AWAY (See also Irie, Tippa)
Tracks: / Drifting away.
12" Single: Released Dec '87, on High Power, Catalogue no: **HPD 03**

GOLDEN TOUCH
Tracks: / Golden Touch / Lovely life.
12" Single: on High Power, Deleted Nov '86. Catalogue no: **HPD 01**

HONESTLY
Tracks: / Honestly.
12" Single: Released Aug '87, on Techniques, Catalogue no: **WRT 21**

I NEED YOUR LOVING
Tracks: / I need your lovin' / Cruisin'.
12" Single: Released Sep '88, on High Power, Catalogue no: **HPD 009**

Kenyon, Carol

DANCE WITH ME
Tracks: / Dance with me / Love shout.
7" Single: Released May '84, on A&M, by A&M Records. Deleted '88. Catalogue no: **AM 189**

GIVE ME ONE GOOD REASON
Tracks: / Give me one good reason / Give me one good reason (inst).
7" Single: Released 23 May '87, on Chrysalis, by Chrysalis Records. Catalogue no: **CHS 3131**
12" Single: Released 23 May '87, on Chrysalis, by Chrysalis Records. Catalogue no: **CHS 12 3131**

Keren & Chelle

SUGAR DADDY
Tracks: / Sugar Daddy / L'homme riche.
CD 5": Released Jun '89, on Funkin' Marvellous, by Steinar Records (UK). Catalogue no: **RTXC 1**
Cassingle: Released Oct '88, on Funkin' Marvellous, by Steinar Records (UK). Deleted Sep '89. Catalogue no: **RTXC 1**
7" Single: Released Oct '88, on Funkin' Marvellous, by Steinar Records (UK). Deleted Sep '89. Catalogue no: **RTX 1**
12" Single: Released Oct '88, on Funkin' Marvellous, by Steinar Records (UK). Deleted Sep '89. Catalogue no: **12RTX 1**

Keri

LOVE GOES ON
Tracks: / Love goes on.
7" Single: Released Apr '89, on W.M., Catalogue no: **NOB 1**
12" Single: Released Apr '89, on W.M., Catalogue no: **NOBE 1**

Kermitt

FLICK MY SWITCH
Tracks: / Flick my switch.
7" Single: Released Jul '82, on Eagle Music, by Eagle Music Records. Deleted Jul '85. Catalogue no: **BFB 019**

Kerr

BACK AT YA
Tracks: / Back at ya.
12" Single: Released Mar '84, on Greyhound, by Greyhound Records. Catalogue no: **GRPT 107**

Kerr, Bob Whoopee Band

REMEMBER REMEMBER
Tracks: / Remember remember / Pleasant.
7" Single: Released Oct '81, on Whoopee, by Whoopee Records. Catalogue no: **WP 106 S**

TAP DANCE MAN
Tracks: / Tap dance man / 5000 year old rock.
7" Single: Released May '79, on Whoopee, by Whoopee Records. Catalogue no: **WP 100**

WINCHESTER CATHEDRAL
Tracks: / Winchester Cathedral / Bob's fool house (Acid humour).
7" Single: Released Nov '88, on Frontier, by Frontier Records. Catalogue no: **FTR 2**

Kerr, John

THREE LEAF SHAMROCK (SINGLE)
Tracks: / Three leaf shamrock.
7" Single: Released '88, on Homespun (Ireland), by Outlet Records. Catalogue no: **HIS 14**

Kerr, Moira

MACIAIN OF GLENCOE (SINGLE)
Tracks: / Maclain of Glencoe.
7" Single: Released Jan '89, on BBC, by BBC Records & Tapes. Catalogue no: **RESL 231**

Kerr, Richard

FREE
Tracks: / Free / Somewhere in the night.
7" Single: Released May '82, on A&M, by A&M Records. Deleted '85. Catalogue no: **AMS 8215**

Kerri & Mick

SONS & DAUGHTERS
Tracks: / Sons and daughters.
7" Single: Released Apr '84, on A.1, by A.1 Records. Catalogue no: **A1 286**

Kerry, Pat

WON'T YOU BE THERE
Tracks: / Won't you be there / Come to the fair.
7" Single: Released Jan '81, on Keswick, by Loose Records. Catalogue no: **KES 003**

Kershaw, Martin

DANCE OF THE MAGPIES
Tracks: / Dance of the magpies.
7" Single: Released Mar '85, on Solid, by Solid Records. Catalogue no: **STOP 008**

Kershaw, Nik

Biographical details: This British singer, songwriter, guitarist and keyboardist hails from Ipswich. His first appearance on disc was a member of an obscure band called Fusion, who released an LP entitled *Till I hear from you* on the small Telephone label in 1980. The album is of historic interest because it contained an embryonic version of his song *Human racing*, which became the title track of his debut solo LP in February 1984. 1984 was the year of Kershaw's big breakthrough. The diminutive and previously unknown Nik was the only act in that calender year to achieve five UK Top 20 singles - *Wouldn't it be good, Dancing girls, I won't let the sun go down on me, Human racing* and *The riddle*. Kershaw proved himself to be a master of melodic and commercial pop songs, and was one of the year's top teen idols. He came to fame mere weeks after Howard Jones, an artist with whom Nik had much in common. Comparisons between the two men were heightened by their virtually simultaneous release of debut albums with similar titles: Jones' *Human's lib* and Kershaw's *Human racing* were both huge successes as was the latter's follow up LP *The riddle*. Superstar Elton John declared himself to be a great admirer of Kershaw, and insisted that he appeared on the bill for John's headlining charity concert at Wembley Stadium in June 1984. The following year, Nik played guitar on Elton's smash single *Nikita*, as well as consolidating his own position with the hit singles *Wide boy, Don Quixote* and *When a heart beats*. Unlike Howard Jones, however, Kershaw was slow to conquer America. In Britain, the girls screamed at both artists, apparently not caring that both guys were already happily married by the time they became famous. (Bob MacDonald, 22nd Nov 1985).

DANCING GIRLS (see panel below)
Tracks: / Dancing girls.
7" Pic: Released Apr '84, on MCA, by MCA Records. Catalogue no: **NIKP 3**
12" Single: Released '85, on MCA, by MCA Records. Catalogue no: **NIKT 3**

NIK KERSHAW - RADIO MUSICOLA (Released on MCA)

DON QUIXOTE
Tracks: / Don Quixote.
7" Pic: Released Aug '85, on MCA, by MCA Records. Deleted 1 Jul '89. Catalogue no: **NIKP 8**
7" Single: Released Aug '85, on MCA, by MCA Records. Catalogue no: **NIK 8**
12" Single: Released Aug '85, on MCA, by MCA Records. Catalogue no: **NIKT 8**

ELIZABETH'S EYES
Tracks: / Elizabeth's eyes.
CD 5": Released 24 Apr '89, on MCA, by MCA Records. Catalogue no: **DNIKT 13**
7" Single: Released 24 Apr '89, on MCA, by MCA Records. Catalogue no: **NIK 13**
12" Single: Released 24 Apr '89, on MCA, by MCA Records. Catalogue no: **NIKT 13**

HUMAN RACING (SINGLE)
Tracks: / Human racing.
7" Pic: Released Sep '84, on MCA, by MCA Records. Deleted 1 Jul '89. Catalogue no: **NIKP 5**
7" Single: Released Sep '84, on MCA, by MCA Records. Catalogue no: **NIK 5**
12" Single: Released Sep '84, on MCA, by MCA Records. Catalogue no: **NIKT 5**
12" Single: Released Sep '84, on MCA, by MCA Records. Catalogue no: **NIKX 5**
Special: Released Sep '84, on MCA, by MCA Records. Catalogue no: **NIKD 5**

I WON'T LET THE SUN GO DOWN ON ME
Tracks: / I won't let the sun go down on me / Dark glasses.
7" Single: Released Jun '84, on MCA, by MCA Records. Deleted '87. Catalogue no: **NIK 4**
7" Single: Released Sep '83, on MCA, by MCA Records. Catalogue no: **MCA 816**

NOBODY KNOWS
Tracks: / Nobody knows / One of our fruit machines is missing.
7" Single: Released Sep '86, on MCA, by MCA Records. Catalogue no: **NIK 10**
12" Single: Released Sep '86, on MCA, by MCA Records. Catalogue no: **NIKT 10**

ONE STEP AHEAD
Tracks: / One step ahead.
CD 5": Released 23 Jan '89, on MCA, by MCA Records. Catalogue no: **DNIK 12**
7" Single: Released 23 Jan '89, on MCA, by MCA Records. Deleted 1 Jul '89. Catalogue no: **NIK 12**
12" Single: Released 23 Jan '89, on MCA, by MCA Records. Catalogue no: **NIKT 12**

RADIO MUSICOLA (PICTURE DISC) (see panel above)
Tracks: / Radio musicola.
7" Pic: Released Dec '86, on MCA, by MCA Records. Deleted '89. Catalogue no: **NIKP 11**
7" Single: Released Dec '86, on MCA, by MCA Records. Deleted '89. Catalogue no: **NIK 11**

RIDDLE, THE (See panel on next page))
Tracks: / Riddle, The / Progress.
7" Pic: Released '84, on MCA, by MCA Records. Deleted '86. Catalogue no: **NIKP 6**
7" Single: Released '84, on MCA, by MCA Records. Catalogue no: **NIK 6**
12" Single: Released '84, on MCA, by MCA Records. Catalogue no: **NIKT 6**

WHEN A HEART BEATS
Tracks: / When a heart beats.
7" Single: Released Nov '85, on MCA, by MCA Records. Catalogue no: **NIK 9**
12" Single: Released Nov '85, on MCA, by MCA Records. Catalogue no: **NIKT 9**

WIDE BOY
Tracks: / Wide boy / So quiet.
Cassingle: Released Dec '84, on MCA, by MCA Records. Catalogue no: **NICC 7**
7" Single: Released Feb '85, on MCA, by MCA Records. Catalogue no: **NIK 7**
12" Single: Released Feb '85, on MCA, by MCA Records. Catalogue no: **NIKT 7**

WOULDN'T IT BE GOOD
Tracks: / Wouldn't it be good / Monkey business.
7" Single: Released Jan '84, on MCA, by MCA Records. Catalogue no: **NIK 2**
12" Single: Released Jan '84, on MCA, by MCA Records. Catalogue no: **NIKT 2**

Kes (band)

HAYLEY'S EYES
Tracks: / Hayley's eyes.
7" Single: Released Oct '85, on Plaza, by Plaza Records. Catalogue no: **7 PLAZA**

NIK KERSHAW - DANCING GIRLS (Released on MCA)

017

LIFE IN A BIG TOWN
Tracks: / Life in a big town.
7" Single: Released Oct '87, on Plaza, by Plaza Records. Catalogue no: **PLAZA 026**
12" Single: Released Oct '87, on Plaza, by Plaza Records. Catalogue no: **PLAZA 026T**

PARISIENNE LADY
Tracks: / Parisienne lady / Masquerade affair.
7" Single: Released Oct '88, on Plaza, by Plaza Records. Catalogue no: **PZA 033**
12" Single: Released Oct '88, on Plaza, by Plaza Records. Catalogue no: **PZA 033T**

SOMEWHERE IN THE NIGHT
Tracks: / Hayley's eyes / Somewhere in the night / Bird of prey.
7" Single: Released Jan '87, on Plaza, by Plaza Records. Catalogue no: **PLAZA 022**
12" Single: Released Feb '87, on Plaza, by Plaza Records. Catalogue no: **PLAZA 022T**

Kestral, Kate

S.O.S
Tracks: / S.O.S / It's so easy.
Cassingle: Released Oct '84, on Anderburr, by Anderburr Records. Catalogue no: **ACHX 1020**
7" Single: Released Oct '84, on Anderburr, by Anderburr Records. Catalogue no: **HX 1020**

Kevie Kev

ALL NIGHT LONG (WATERBED)
Tracks: / All night long (waterbed) / Sweet stuff.
12" Single: Released Dec '83, on Sugarhill (USA). Catalogue no: **SHL 131**

Kevin...

LOT TO LEARN
Tracks: / Lot to learn.
7" Single: Released Aug '83, on Posh, by Posh Records. Catalogue no: **POSH 009**

Kevin The Gerbil

SUMMER HOLIDAY
Tracks: / Summer holiday.
7" Single: Released Jul '84, on Rodent. Deleted '87. Catalogue no: **RAT 3**

Kewi University Of

BIGGLES
Tracks: / Biggles / Nurse.
7" Single: Released Jul '83, on Idiot (Germany). Catalogue no: **X 9716**

Key

SO MANY PEOPLE
Tracks: / So many people / Eagle's wings.
Note: In aid of Oxfam flood appeal.
7" Single: Released Dec '88, on Thin Edge Of The Wedge, by Thin Edge Of The Wedge Records. Catalogue no: **TEW 001**

Key Of Dreams

AFRICA
Tracks: / Africa / Syntha joy.
7" Single: Released Feb '83, on Baby, by New Rose Records. Catalogue no: **BABY 3**
12" Single: Released Feb '83, on Baby, by New Rose Records. Catalogue no: **BABY 312**

Key, Troyce

I GOTTA NEW CAR (SINGLE)
Tracks: / I gotta new car.
7" Single: Released May '81, on Pinnacle, by Pinnacle Records. Catalogue no: **PIN 505**

Keynotes

LET'S LET'S LET'S DANCE
Tracks: / Let's let's let's dance / Let's let's let's dance (version).
12" Single: Released Apr '88, on Kool Kat, by Kool Kat Records. Catalogue no: **KOOLT 16**

Keys

CAPTAIN KIRK'S DISCO TRACK
Tracks: / Captain Kirk's disco track / Star lover.
7" Single: Released Sep '81, on White Dove, by White Dove Records. Deleted '84. Catalogue no: **RAWD 820**

GREASY MONEY
Tracks: / Greasy money / Run, run run.
7" Single: Released Sep '81, on A&M, by A&M Records. Deleted '84. Catalogue no: **AMS 8159**

JUST A CAMERA
Tracks: / Just a camera / It ain't so.
7" Single: Released Aug '80, on A&M, by A&M Records. Deleted '83. Catalogue no: **AMS 7551**

ONE GOOD REASON
Tracks: / One good reason / Saturday to Sunday night.
7" Single: Released Apr '81, on A&M, by A&M Records. Deleted Apr '84. Catalogue no: **AMS 8121**

SUSPICIONS
Tracks: / Suspicions / Nothing.
7" Single: Released Jul '82, on A&M, by A&M Records. Deleted Jul '85. Catalogue no: **AMS 8236**

Keys, Amy

GOOD FOR YOU
Tracks: / Good for you (extended remix) / I know what's good for you (dub) / I know what's good for you (accapella).
12" Single: Released Aug '89, on Epic, by CBS Records. Catalogue no: **655 200 8**

I KNOW WHAT'S GOOD FOR YOU
Tracks: / I know what's good for you (remix) (On 7" only.) / Even now / I know what's good for you (extended remix) (On 12" only.) / I know what's good for you (LP version) (On 12" only.).
CD 5": Released 21 Aug '89, on Epic, by CBS Records. Catalogue no: **655200 2**
7" Single: Released 14 Aug '89, on Epic, by CBS Records. Catalogue no: **655200 7**
12" Single: Released 14 Aug '89, on Epic, by CBS Records. Catalogue no: **655200 6**

LOVER'S INTUITION (SINGLE)
Tracks: / Lover's intuition / Everytime I close my eyes / Precious.
CD 5": Released Apr '89, on Epic, by CBS Records. Deleted Oct '89. Catalogue no: **654 810 2**
7" Single: Released Apr '89, on Epic, by CBS Records. Deleted Oct '89. Catalogue no: **654 810 7**
12" Single: Released Apr '89, on Epic, by CBS Records. Deleted Oct '89. Catalogue no: **654 810 6**

Keytones

WHITE CHRISTMAS
Tracks: / White Christmas.
7" Single: Released Dec '84, on Key, by Key Records. Catalogue no: **KEY 25**

Khan, Chaka

Biographical details: This American singer was born Yvette Marie Stevens in Chicago, and was 21 years old when she came to fame as leader of Rufus in 1974. That raunchy soul band became one of the hottest R&B acts in America during the mid-Seventies. Khan's frenetic, fiery, funky vocal style and scintillating stage presence was so electric that later records were billed as *Rufus featuring Chaka Khan.* Chaka launched a subsidiary solo career in 1978 with dynamic hit single *I'm every woman,* which reached the Top 30 on both sides of the Atlantic. Her subsequent career was rather more erratic, with the singer following her musical heart rather than dictates of the market. Her projects included a guest appearance of a Ry Cooder LP, a duet with George Benson plus an involvement in Lenny White's Fifties jazz revival album *Echoes of an era.* Warner Bros. eventually grew impatient with Khan's musical meanderings and, in 1984, contrived a surefire smash for her to sing. They took an old Prince album track called *I feel for you,* and teamed Chaka's sexy singing with the harmonica of Stevie Wonder and the infectious rapping of Grandmaster Melle Mel. This red-hot combination of fashionable talent was supervised by the ever reliable production of studio veteran Arif Mardin - *I feel for you* gave both Mardin and Khan their first ever UK No.1 single, and reached No.3 in America. The album of the same name yielded further hit singles with *This is my night, Eye to eye* and the slow-burning success *Through the fire.* By this time, the singer had officially parted company with Rufus, having just released the glorious Rufus & Chaka Khan swansong *Ain't nobody.* (Bob MacDonald, 22nd Nov 1985).

BEST IN THE WEST
Tracks: / Best in the west / Be bop medley.
7" Single: Released Feb '83, on Warner Bros., by WEA Records. Catalogue no: **W 9753**
12" Single: Released Feb '83, on Warner Bros., by WEA Records. Catalogue no: **W 9753T**

CLOUDS
Tracks: / Clouds / What you did.
7" Single: Released May '80, on Warner Bros., by WEA Records. Deleted '83. Catalogue no: **K 17617**

EYE TO EYE
Tracks: / Eye to eye / La flamme.
7" Single: Released Apr '85, on Warner Bros., by WEA Records. Catalogue no: **W 9009**
12" Single: Released Apr '85, on Warner Bros., by WEA Records. Catalogue no: **W 9009T**

GOT TO BE THERE
Tracks: / Got to be there / Pass it on.
7" Single: Released Nov '82, on Warner Bros., by WEA Records. Catalogue no: **929881**

HEED THE WARNING
Tracks: / Heed the warning / Night moods.
7" Single: Released Apr '81, on Warner Bros., by WEA Records. Deleted '85. Catalogue no: **K 17793**
12" Single: Released Apr '81, on Warner Bros., by WEA Records. Deleted '85. Catalogue no: **K 17793T**

I FEEL FOR YOU (REMIX) (SINGLE)
Tracks: / I feel for you / I know you I live you.
CD 5": Released Sep '89, on Warner Bros., by WEA Records. Catalogue no: **W 2764 CD**
Cassingle: Released Sep '89, on Warner Bros., by WEA Records. Catalogue no: **W 2764 C**
7" Single: Released Sep '89, on Warner Bros., by WEA Records. Catalogue no: **W 2764**
12" Single: Released Sep '89, on Warner Bros., by WEA Records. Catalogue no: **W 2764 T**

I FEEL FOR YOU (SINGLE)
Tracks: / I feel for you / Chinatown.
7" Single: Released Oct '85, on Warner Bros., by WEA Records. Catalogue no: **W 9209**
12" Single: Released Oct '85, on Warner Bros., by WEA Records. Catalogue no: **W 9209T**

I KNOW YOU I LOVE YOU
Tracks: / I know you I love you.
12" Single: Released Nov '87, on Rock Mo (USA). Catalogue no: **RM 4003**

I'M EVERY WOMAN
Tracks: / I'm every woman.
7" Single: Released Dec '78, on Warner Bros., by WEA Records. Deleted '81. Catalogue no: **K 17269**

I'M EVERY WOMAN (RE-ISSUE)
Tracks: / I'm every woman / Baby me.
CD 5": Released Apr '89, on Warner Bros., by WEA Records. Catalogue no: **W 2963CD**
Cassingle: Released Apr '89, on Warner Bros., by WEA Records. Catalogue no: **W 2963MC**
7" Single: Released Apr '89, on Warner Bros., by WEA Records. Catalogue no: **W 2963**
12" Single: Released Apr '89, on Warner Bros., by WEA Records. Catalogue no: **W 2963T**

IT'S MY PARTY
Tracks: / It's my party / Where are you tonight.
7" Single: Released Jan '89, on Warner Bros., by WEA Records. Catalogue no: **W 7678**
12" Single: Released Jan '89, on Warner Bros., by WEA Records. Catalogue no: **W 7678 T**

KRUSH GROOVE (CAN'T STOP THE STREET)
Tracks: / Krush groove.
7" Single: Released Sep '85, on Warner Bros., by WEA Records. Catalogue no: **W 8923**
12" Single: Released Sep '85, on Warner Bros., by WEA Records. Catalogue no: **W 8923T**

LOVE OF A LIFETIME
Tracks: / Love of a lifetime / Coltrane dreams.
7" Single: Released Jun '86, on Warner Bros., by WEA Records. Deleted Jun '87. Catalogue no: **W 8671**
12" Single: Released Jun '86, on Warner Bros., by WEA Records. Deleted Jun '87. Catalogue no: **W 8671T**

THIS IS MY NIGHT
Tracks: / This is my night.
7" Single: Released Jan '85, on Warner Bros., by WEA Records. Catalogue no: **W 9097**
12" Single: Released Jan '85, on Warner Bros., by WEA Records. Catalogue no: **W 9097T**

THROUGH THE FIRE
Tracks: / Through the fire.
7" Single: Released Aug '85, on Warner Bros., by WEA Records. Catalogue no: **W 9025**
12" Single: Released Aug '85, on Warner Bros., by WEA Records. Catalogue no: **W 9025T**

WATCHING THE WORLD
Tracks: / Watching the world / I can't be loved.
7" Single: Released Nov '86, on Warner Bros., by WEA Records. Deleted Jun '87. Catalogue no: **W 8534**
12" Single: Released Nov '86, on Warner Bros., by WEA Records. Catalogue no: **W 8534 T**

Khan, Kay

YOUNG LOVE
Tracks: / Young love / Something coming down.
7" Single: Released Jul '82, on Chiswick Records. Deleted Jul '85. Catalogue no: **DICE 8**

Khar Tomb

SWAHILI LULLABY
Tracks: / Swahili lullaby.
7" Single: Released May '83, on Whaam. Catalogue no: **WHAAM 14**

Khin, Greg

FOR YOU
Tracks: / For you / Mood mood number.
7" Single: Released '77, on Beserkley, by Beserkley Records (USA). Catalogue no: **BZZ4**

Kia Zos

BE LIKE ME
Tracks: / Be like me.
12" Single: Released Dec '85, on Temple Records, by Temple Records (2). Catalogue no: **TOPY 005**

RAPE
Tracks: / Rape / Thank you.
7" Single: Released Sep '84, on All The Madmen, by All The Madmen Records. Catalogue no: **MAD 8**
12" Single: Released Oct '86, on All The Madmen, by All The Madmen Records. Catalogue no: **MADT 8**

Kiara

EVERY LITTLE TIME
Tracks: / Every little time (hip hop edit) / Every little time (version) / Every little time (NY mix) (Available on 12" and CD only) / Every little time (Detroit mix) (Available on 12" only) / This time (Available on CD only).
CD 5": Released Jun '89, on Arista, by BMG Records (UK). Catalogue no: **662292**
Cassingle: Released Jun '89, on Arista, by BMG Records (UK). Catalogue no: **410117**
7" Single: Released Jun '89, on Arista, by BMG Records (UK). Catalogue no: **112292**
12" Single: Released Jun '89, on Arista, by BMG Records (UK). Catalogue no: **612292**

THIS TIME
Tracks: / This time / Wait so long / Strawberry letter 23.
CD 5": Released Feb '89, on Arista, by BMG Records (UK). Catalogue no: **162 001**
7" Single: Released Feb '89, on Arista, by BMG Records (UK). Catalogue no: **112 001**
12" Single: Released 6 Mar '89, on Arista, by BMG Records (UK). Catalogue no: **612067**
12" Single: Released Feb '89, on Arista, by BMG Records (UK). Catalogue no: **612 001**

Kibibi

I AIN'T GOING OUT LIKE THAT
Tracks: / I ain't going out like that.
7" Single: Released Mar '89, on Republic, by Code Records. Catalogue no: **LICT 017**

Kick

I CAN'T LET GO
Tracks: / I can't let go / Armchair politican.
7" Single: Released Feb '86, on Countdown. Catalogue no: **VAIN 3**

LET'S GET BACK TOGETHER
Tracks: / Let's get back together.
7" Single: Released Nov '84, on Footwear. Catalogue no: **FWRO 1**

Kick Partners

IT'S TOO LATE
Tracks: / It's too late / Taking away.
7" Single: Released May '85, on CM. Catalogue no: **STEW 102**

JUST MY IMAGINATION
Tracks: / Just my imagination.
7" Single: Released Nov '83, on Raw. Catalogue no: **RAW 1**

Kick Reaction

YESTERDAY TODAY TOMORROW
Tracks: / Yesterday today and tomorrow / Stopping to speak / Friday away from the high street.
12" Single: Released Feb '86, on Precious Organisation, by Precious Organisation. Catalogue no: **12 JEWEL 1**

Kick The Can

HIDE (YOUR FEELINGS)
Tracks: / Hide (your feelings).

KID CREOLE - ANNIE I'M NOT YOUR DADDY (Released on ZE)

7" Single: Released Jul '88, on Oyster, by Oyster Records. Catalogue no: **OYS 1**

Kicking Back

KEEP ON TRYING
Tracks: / Keep on trying.
12" Single: Released Jun '89, on Desire, by Desire Records. Catalogue no: **SUBX 014**

Kicklighter, Richy

JUNGLE SONG
Tracks: / Jungle song / After you're gone / Now and then.
12" Single: Released May '88, on Ichiban, by Ichiban Records (UK). Catalogue no: **12PO 8**

Kicks

GET OFF THE TELEPHONE
Tracks: / Get off the telephone / Big boys don't cry.
7" Single: Released Feb '80, on Carrere, Deleted '83. Catalogue no: **CAR 138**

HOT STUFF
Tracks: / Hot stuff / Big kid.
7" Single: Released May '81, on RCA, by BMG Records (UK). Deleted May '84. Catalogue no: **RCA 84**

MAYBE JUST ONCE
Tracks: / Maybe just once / Polanski.
7" Single: Released Sep '80, on Polydor, by Polydor Ltd. Deleted Sep '83. Catalogue no: **POSP 177**

K.I.D.

DON'T STOP
Tracks: / Don't stop / Do it again.
7" Single: Released Feb '81, on Groove PR, by Beggars Banquet Records. Deleted '84. Catalogue no: **GP 104**
7" Single: Released Feb '81, on EMI, by EMI Records. Deleted '84. Catalogue no: **EMI 5143**
12" Single: Released Feb '81, on EMI, by EMI Records. Deleted '84. Catalogue no: **12EMI 5143**

I WANT A PIECE OF THE ACTION
Tracks: / I want a piece of the action / Shoop song.
12" Single: Released Jun '82, on Carrere, Deleted Jun '85. Catalogue no: **CART 238**

NUMBER ONE
Tracks: / Number one / You can't keep me waiting.
7" Single: Released Sep '81, on Record Shack, by Record Shack Records. Deleted '84. Catalogue no: **SHACK 5**

YOU DON'T LIKE MY MUSIC
Tracks: / You don't like my music.
7" Single: Released Jan '82, on Excaliber, by Red Bus Records. Deleted '88. Catalogue no: **EXC 515**

Kid Can't Dance

LOVE, PEACE AND UNDERSTANDING
Tracks: / Love, peace and understanding (Not on 12") / River, The (On all versions) / Love, peace and understanding (remix) (On CD & 12" only) / Love, peace and understanding (dub) (On 12" only) / Sugar in the backyard (On CD only).
CD 5": Released '88, on Siren, by Virgin Records. Catalogue no: **SRNCD 90**
7" Single: Released Sep '88, on Siren, by Virgin Records. Catalogue no: **SRN 90**
12" Single: Released Sep '88, on Siren, by Virgin Records. Catalogue no: **SRNT 90**

UP ON THE ROOFTOP
Tracks: / Up on the rooftop / In your eyes / Up on the rooftop (club) (12" only) / Up on the rooftop (extended) (12" only).
Note: "Kids Can't Dance are a young duo who met up in London's top night club, the Wag. Signed by Mark Dean, who discovered Wham, the first single, Up On The Rooftop, is a muscular pop-soul workout." (Siren Records, May 1988.)
7" Single: Released 31 May '88, on Siren, by Virgin Records. Catalogue no: **SRN 74**
12" Single: Released 31 May '88, on Siren, by Virgin Records. Catalogue no: **SRNT 74**

Kid Congo & Co

IN THE HEAT OF THE NIGHT
Tracks: / In the heat of the night.
12" Single: Released Jul '89, on Nightshift, by Nightshift Records. Catalogue no: **NISHI 208T**

Kid Creole

ANNIE I'M NOT YOUR DADDY (see panel above)
Tracks: / Annie I'm not your daddy / You had no intention.
7" Single: Released Oct '82, on ZE, by Island Records. Deleted Oct '85. Catalogue no: **WIP 6801**
7" Pic: Released Sep '82, on ZE, by Island Records. Deleted '84. Catalogue no: **PWIP 6801**

CAROLINE WAS A DROPOUT
Tracks: / Caroline was a dropout / You can't keep a good man down.
7" Single: Released Jan '86, on Sire (USA), Catalogue no: **W 8785**
12" Single: Released Jan '86, on Sire (USA), Catalogue no: **W 8785T**

DANCIN' AT THE BAINS DOUCHES
Tracks: / Dancin' at the Bains Douches / Midsummer madness (The refrain).
7" Single: Released Jul '87, on Sire (USA), Deleted Jul '88. Catalogue no: **W 8329**
12" Single: Released Jul '87, on Sire (USA), Deleted Jul '88. Catalogue no: **W 8329T**

DEAR ADDY (see panel on right)
Tracks: / Dear Addy / No fish today / Christmas on riverside drive / Yolanda (On 12" only).
7" Single: Released Dec '82, on ZE, by Island Records. Deleted Dec '85. Catalogue no: **WIP 6840**
12" Single: Released Dec '82, on Island, by Island Records. Deleted Dec '85. Catalogue no: **12WIP 6840**
7" Pic: Released Dec '82, on Island, by Island Records. Deleted Dec '85. Catalogue no: **PWIP 6840**

DON'T TAKE MY COCONUTS
Tracks: / Don't take my coconuts.
12" Single: Released Jul '84, on Island, by Island Records. Catalogue no: **12IS 190**
7" Single: Released Jul '84, on Island, by Island Records. Catalogue no: **IS 190**

ENDICOTT
Tracks: / Endicott.
12" Single: Released May '85, on Sire (USA), Catalogue no: **W 8959T**
7" Single: Released May '85, on Sire (USA), Catalogue no: **W 8959**

LATIN MUSIC
Tracks: / Latin music / Musica Americana / Going places.
7" Single: Released Oct '81, on Island, by Island Records. Deleted Oct '84. Catalogue no: **WIP 6719**
12" Single: Released Oct '81, on Island, by Island Records. Deleted Oct '84. Catalogue no: **12WIP 6719**

LIFEBOAT PARTY
Tracks: / Lifeboat party.
7" Single: Released Nov '83, on Island, by Island Records. Deleted Nov '86. Catalogue no: **IS 142**

MALADIE D'AMOUR
Tracks: / Maladie d'amour / He's not such a bad guy / There but for the grace of God go I.
7" Single: Released Aug '80, on Island, by Island Records. Deleted Aug '83. Catalogue no: **WIP 6619**
12" Single: Released Aug '80, on Island, by Island Records. Deleted Aug '83. Catalogue no: **12WIP 6619**

STOOL PIGEON
Tracks: / Stool pigeon.
7" Single: Released Jul '82, on ZE, by Island Records. Deleted Jul '85. Catalogue no: **WIP 6793**

THERE'S SOMETHING WRONG IN PARADISE
Tracks: / There's something wrong in paradise / Fireside story / Broadway rhythm.
7" Single: Released Sep '83, on Island, by Island Records. Deleted Sep '86. Catalogue no: **IS 130**

WONDERFUL THING
Tracks: / Wonderful thing / Table manners.
7" Single: Released May '82, on ZE, by Island Records. Deleted May '85. Catalogue no: **WIP 6756**
12" Single: Released Aug '82, on ZE, by Island Records. Catalogue no: **12WIP 6756**

Kid Flash

HOT LIKE FIRE
Tracks: / Hot like fire / Hot like fire (bonus beat) / Hot like fire (ext. version) (Available on 12" only) / Hot like fire (instrumental dub) (Available on 12" only).
7" Single: Released Mar '88, on Tabu, Deleted Aug '88. Catalogue no: **651521 7**
12" Single: Released Mar '88, on Tabu, Deleted Aug '88. Catalogue no: **651521 6**

Kid Montana

REVISITING YALTA
Tracks: / Revisiting Yalta / Revisiting Yalta.
12" Single: Released Jun '88, on Antler, by Antler Records (Belgium). Catalogue no: **ANT 029**

Kid 'N Play

2 HYPE (SINGLE)
Tracks: / 2 hype / 2 hype (version).
7" Single: Released Dec '88, on Cool Tempo, by Chrysalis Records. Catalogue no: **COOL 175**
12" Single: Released Dec '88, on Cool Tempo, by Chrysalis Records. Catalogue no: **COOLX 175**

DO THIS MY WAY
Tracks: / Do this my way / Do this my way (vocal) / Do this my way (inst.) / Do this my way (acapella).
7" Single: Released Mar '88, on Cool Tempo, by Chrysalis Records. Catalogue no: **COOL 164**
12" Single: Released Mar '88, on Cool Tempo, by Chrysalis Records. Catalogue no: **COOLX 164**

GETTIN' FUNKY
Tracks: / Gettin' funky (U.S. remix) / Gettin' funky (version).
7" Single: Released 16 Sep '88, on Cool Tempo, by Chrysalis Records. Catalogue no: **COOL 168**
12" Single: Released 16 Sep '88, on Cool Tempo, by Chrysalis Records. Catalogue no: **COOLX 168**

LAST NIGHT
Tracks: / Last night / Last night (inst).
7" Single: Released Jul '87, on Cool Tempo, by Chrysalis Records. Catalogue no: **COOL 148**
12" Single: Released Jul '87, on Cool Tempo, by Chrysalis Records. Catalogue no: **COOLX 148**

Kid Thomas

ROCKIN' THIS JOINT TONIGHT
Tracks: / Rockin' this joint tonight / Wail baby wail / Lookie there.
7" Single: Released May '84, on JSP, by JSP Records. Catalogue no: **JSP 4505**

Kidd, Eddie

DON'T LET THE DAY GET ANY LONGER
Tracks: / Don't let the day get any longer / Lover for life.
7" Single: Released Apr '88, on Warner Bros., by WEA Records. Catalogue no: **W 7910**
12" Single: Released Apr '88, on Warner Bros., by WEA Records. Catalogue no: **W 7910T**

FIRE ME UP
Tracks: / Fire me up / Rough diamonds.
7" Single: Released Jan '88, on Warner Bros., by WEA Records. Catalogue no: **W 7999**
12" Single: Released Jan '88, on Warner Bros., by WEA Records. Catalogue no: **W 7999T**

HEAVY METAL
Tracks: / Heavy metal / Rock 'n' roll me over.

KID CREOLE - DEAR ADDY (Released on Island)

KIDS FROM FAME - FRIDAY NIGHT (Released on RCA)

7" Single: Released May '81, on EMI, by EMI Records. Deleted May '84. Catalogue no: **EMI 5197**

Kidd Glove

GOOD CLEAN FUN
Tracks: / Good clean fun / Street angel.
7" Single: Released Mar '84, on Morocco (USA), by Motown Records (UK). Catalogue no: **TMG 1337**

Kidd, Jeremy

PETALS AND ASHES
Tracks: / Petals and ashes.
7" Single: Released Apr '85, on Self Drive, Catalogue no: **SCAR 015**
12" Single: Released Apr '85, on Self Drive, Catalogue no: **SCAR 015T**

Kidd, Johnny

ALWAYS AND EVER
Tracks: / Always and ever.
7" Single: Released Apr '64, on H.M.V., by EMI Records. Deleted '67. Catalogue no: **POP 1269**

HUNGRY FOR LOVE
Tracks: / Hungry for love.
7" Single: Released Nov '63, on H.M.V., by EMI Records. Deleted '66. Catalogue no: **POP 1228**

I'LL NEVER GET OVER YOU
Tracks: / I'll never get over you.
7" Single: Released Jul '63, on H.M.V., by EMI Records. Deleted '66. Catalogue no: **POP 1088**

LINDA LU
Tracks: / Linda Lu.
7" Single: Released Apr '61, on H.M.V., by EMI Records. Deleted '64. Catalogue no: **POP 853**

PLEASE DON'T TOUCH
Tracks: / Please don't touch.
7" Single: Released Jun '59, on H.M.V., by EMI Records. Deleted '62. Catalogue no: **POP 615**

RESTLESS
Tracks: / Restless.
7" Single: Released Oct '60, on H.M.V., by EMI Records. Deleted '63. Catalogue no: **POP 790**

SHAKIN' ALL OVER
Tracks: / Shakin' all over / Shot of rhythm and blues.
7" Single: Released Jun '60, on H.M.V., by EMI Records. Deleted '63. Catalogue no: **POP 753**
7" Single: Released Jun '80, on H.M.V., by EMI Records. Catalogue no: **POP 2005**

SHAKIN' ALL OVER (OLD GOLD)
Tracks: / Shakin' all over / I'll never get over you.
7" Single: Released Oct '83, on Old Gold, by Old Gold Records. Deleted Sep '89. Catalogue no: **OG 9366**

SHOT OF RHYTHM & BLUES, A
Tracks: / Shot of rhythm and blues, A.
7" Single: Released Jan '63, on H.M.V., by EMI Records. Deleted '66. Catalogue no: **POP 1088**

YOU GOT WHAT IT TAKES
Tracks: / You got what it takes.
7" Single: Released Feb '60, on H.M.V., by EMI Records. Deleted '63. Catalogue no: **POP 698**

Kiddo

GIVE IT UP
Tracks: / Give it up / Try my loving.
12" Single: Released Apr '83, on A&M, by A&M Records. Deleted '88. Catalogue no: **AMX 107**

Kidos Weise

SLOW DANCING
Tracks: / Slow dancing.
12" Single: Released Oct '89, on Progressive, Catalogue no: **PSP 008**

Kids

CHEERS TO THE TWO OF YOU
Tracks: / Cheers to the two of you / Roundabout.
7" Single: Released Jun '81, on EMI, by EMI Records. Deleted Jun '84. Catalogue no: **EMI 5202**

Kids From Fame

Biographical details: This American group of TV singers and actors comprised Debbie Allen (who played the dance instructress Lydia), Carlo Imperato (Danny), Valerie Landsburg (Doris), Carol Mayo (Coco), Lori Singer (Julie) and Gene Anthony Ray (Leroy). In 1980 British movie director Alan Parker made the acclaimed film *Fame*, which followed the lives of a group of starstruck students at a showbiz training school (based upon the Academy of the Performing Arts, New York). The flick was a success in the States but not in Britain. By contrast, when the spinoff television soap opera was launched in 1982, it was a bigger phenomenon in the UK than in the US. The BBC's shrewd decision to screen the series directly after 'Top of the pops' worked wonders for the program and its theme song *Fame* by Irene Cara rocketed to No.1 on the UK singles chart while the film soundtrack LP simultaneously held the top of the album list. Realising that the movie was making money out of the TV show (the theme tune was sung on television by Erica Gimpel, not Cara), the BBC got their act together and negotiated a licensing deal with RCA for an LP entitled *The Kids from Fame*, featuring the songs performed by members of the TV cast.
The television album was an immediate sensation, logging 12 weeks at No.1 on the UK LP chart, and sold a million copies in Britain alone. The music aimed straigh for the teenybopper and weeneybopper market, and was every bit as trite and insipid as the *Fame* series itself. The LP yielded two sugar-filled UK Top 5 singles, *Hi-fidelity* and *Starmaker*. In a less than bid to milk the *Fame* fever while it lasted, three further albums were released within 12 months. A live version of the crass *Friday night* gave the Kids a final UK hit single in the summer of '83. By this time plans were afoot in America to scrap the *Fame* series, on account of poor ratings. But in the event, more episodes were made; the temporary reprieve was granted because of its peculiar British popularity. Perhaps it was because the UK had given America the Bay City Rollers - the States felt that they had to get their own back! (Bob MacDonald, 22nd Nov 1985).

BODY LANGUAGE
Tracks: / Body language / Life is a celebration.
7" Single: Released Jun '83, on RCA, by BMG Records (UK). Catalogue no: **RCA 343**
12" Single: Released Jun '83, on RCA, by BMG Records (UK). Catalogue no: **RCAT 343**

FRIDAY NIGHT (see panel on left)
Tracks: / Friday night / Could we be magic like you.
7" Single: Released Feb '83, on RCA, by BMG Records (UK). Catalogue no: **RCA 320**

HI FIDELITY
Tracks: / Hi fidelity / I still believe in you.
7" Single: Released Jul '82, on RCA, by BMG Records (UK). Catalogue no: **RCA 254**

KIDS FROM FAME EP
Tracks: / Hi fidelity / Desdemona / Starmaker / It's gonna be a long night.
Cassingle: Released May '83, on RCA, by BMG Records (UK). Catalogue no: **RCXK 002**

MANNEQUIN (see panel below)
Tracks: / Mannequin / Come what may.
7" Single: Released Nov '82, on RCA, by BMG Records (UK). Catalogue no: **RCA 299**

SONGS (SINGLE)
Tracks: / Songs / Just like you.
7" Single: Released Aug '83, on RCA, by BMG Records (UK). Catalogue no: **RCA 353**

STARMAKER
Tracks: / Step up to the mike.
7" Single: Released Sep '82, on RCA, by BMG Records (UK). Catalogue no: **RCA 280**

STARMAKER (OLD GOLD)
Tracks: / Starmaker / Hi fidelity.
7" Single: Released Nov '86, on Old Gold, by Old Gold Records. Catalogue no: **OG 9643**

Kids International

REGGAE ROUND THE WORLD
Tracks: / Reggae round the world / If I had a hammer / Danny boy.
7" Single: Released Jan '82, on Magnet, by WEA Records. Deleted Jan '85. Catalogue no: **MAG 218**

YOU PROMISED ME
Tracks: / You promised me / Sing a song of love.
7" Single: Released Nov '81, on Magnet, by WEA Records. Deleted Nov '84. Catalogue no: **MAG 210**

Kidz NW10

LA LA LA LOGIC
Tracks: / La la la logic / Beep beep.
7" Single: Released May '82, on CBS, by CBS Records. Deleted '85. Catalogue no: **RUB 1**

Kiem

DON'T STOP
Tracks: / Don't stop / Moneyman.
7" Single: Released Jul '87, on Torso, by Torso Records. Catalogue no: **TORSO 70029**

MONEYMAN, THE
Tracks: / Moneyman, The.
12" Single: Released Dec '86, on Torso, by Torso Records. Catalogue no: **TORSO 12026**

Kihn, Greg

Biographical details: This American singer, songwriter and guitarist formed the Greg Kihn Band in the mid-Seventies releasing his first album in 1976. He hailed from Berkeley, California and was signed to the locally based Beserkley label. That company attracted a strong cult following in Britain in during the late Seventies, thanks mainly to the idiosyncratic exploits of Jonathon Richman and to the label's zany ads in the music press. Kihn sang backing vocals on Richman's 1977 classic *Roadrunner*.
Kihn was promoted by Beserkley as their second most important act, after Richman; but because of the company's New Wave image, the somewhat Old Wave music of Greg's group confused the public and the industry, and he failed to achieve commercial success for several years. The Greg Kihn Band broke through in 1981 with the American Top 20 single *The breakup song*, an engaging pop-rock tune that saw Kihn treading his usual territory halfway between commercial pop hooks and harder rock'n'roll leanings. 1983 brought him a US No.2 smash with the pulsating and infectious single *Jeopardy*, promoted by an expensive video on MTV. By this time the Band's UK cult status (which had never translated itself into genuine British record sales) had evaporated and *Jeopardy* could climb no higher than No.63. 1983 saw a continuation of Greg's penchant for silly name-related LP titles - *Kihnspiracy* followed hard on the heels of *Kihntinued, Rockihnroll* and *Next of Kihn*. (Bob MacDonald, 23rd Nov 1985).

BREAK UP SONG
Tracks: / Break up song / When the music stops.
7" Single: Released Aug '81, on Beserkley, by Beserkley Records (USA). Deleted '84. Catalogue no: **A 1507**

HAPPY MAN
Tracks: / Happy man / Trouble in paradise.
7" Single: Released Jul '83, on Beserkley, by Beserkley Records (USA). Catalogue no: **X 9735**
7" Single: Released Nov '82, on Beserkley, by Beserkley Records (USA). Deleted Nov '85. Catalogue no: **BSK A 2255**

KIDS FROM FAME - MANNEQUIN (Released on RCA)

JEOPARDY
Tracks: / Reunited.
7" Single: Released Oct '87, on Beserkley, by Beserkley Records (USA). Catalogue no: **7BZ 1203**
12" Single: Released Oct '87, on Beserkley, by Beserkley Records (USA). Catalogue no: **BZ 1203**
7" Single: Released Apr '83, on Beserkley, by Beserkley Records (USA). Deleted '86. Catalogue no: **E 9847**

Kikkit

HEARTBREAKER (I CAN'T UNDERSTAND)
Tracks: / Heartbreaker (I can't understand).
7" Single: Released Mar '89, on Republic, by Code Records. Catalogue no: **LICT 009**

LOVE FIXATION
Tracks: / Love fixation.
12" Single: Released 14 Aug '88, on Republic, by Code Records. Catalogue no: **LICT 002**

Kilgore Trout

BAD PUDDINGS
Tracks: / Bad puddings.
12" Single: Released Apr '89, on Thunderball, Catalogue no: **12TBL 3**

STICK IT IN THE BANK MAN
Tracks: / Quality control / English never listen / Bank / Right boys.
12" Single: Released Oct '86, on Hits & Corruption, Catalogue no: **HAC 002**

Kill Devil Hills

HERE WE GO AGAIN
Tracks: / Here we go again.
12" Single: Released Oct '88, on Roustabout, by Roustabout Records. Catalogue no: **RST 005T**

WHAT COMES AFTER
Tracks: / What comes after.
7" Single: Released 17 Oct '87, on Roustabout, by Roustabout Records. Catalogue no: **RST 002**
12" Single: Released 17 Oct '87, on Roustabout, by Roustabout Records. Catalogue no: **RST 002 T**

Kill Ugly Pop

CHURCH OF BLOODY DECEPTION
Tracks: / Church of bloody deception,The (EP).
7" EP: Released '85, on Fever, by Fever Records. Catalogue no: **UNKNOWN**

GATOR BREATH RIOT
Tracks: / Gator breath riot.
12" Single: Released Aug '84, on Fever, by Fever Records. Catalogue no: **FEV 3**

PURPLE HAZE
Tracks: / Purple haze.
12" Single: Released Aug '87, on Fever, by Fever Records. Catalogue no: **FEV 008**

Killerman Jarrett

WAR IN SOUTH AFRICA
Tracks: / War in South Africa / War in South Africa (Vocal dub Version).
12" Single: on Trojan, by Trojan Records. Deleted May '88. Catalogue no: **TRT 9086**

Killigrew

CHRISTMAS CALYPSO
Tracks: / Christmas calypso / Hush.
7" Single: Released Nov '82, on Mont, by Mont Music Records. Catalogue no: **MM 103**

Killing Joke

Biographical details: Fronted by a singer/keyboards player Jaz Coleman, this British rock band was formed in 1979. The rest of the original line-up featured Paul Ferguson, Geordie and Martin 'Pig Youth' Glover. Killing Joke's self-titled debut album was released in late 1980 and, by this time, the group had built up a sufficiently strong cult following to enable the LP to reach No.39 on the UK charts. In the same year, their *Psyche* single was a club hit in the States. Rooted in the punk era of the late Seventies, Killing Joke blasted their way through the early Eighties with a series of singles and albums that were predictable but highly energetic. Receiving strong support from BBC Radio One's John Peel, the band chalked up a string of seven minor hit singles in Britain - *Follow the leaders, Empire song, Birds of a feather, Let's all (go to the fire dances), Me or you, Eighties* and *A new day* all reached the UK Top 75 during 1981-84 but none cracked the Top 40. When Killing Joke finally achieved a solid Top 20 hit with 1985's *Love like blood,* Coleman told Record Mirror: 'I don't give a f*** what chart position it reaches, as long as people hear it'. (Bob MacDonald, 23rd Nov 1985).

ADORATION
Tracks: / Adorations / Exile / Ecstasy (On 12" Double Pack version only.).
7" Single: Released Aug '86, on E.G., by E.G. Records. Deleted '89. Catalogue no: **EGO 27**

ALMOST RED
Tracks: / Almost red / Nervous system / Are you recieving / Turn to red.
12" Single: Released Jan '80, on Island, by Island Records. Deleted Jan '85. Catalogue no: **12WIP 6550**

AMERICA
Tracks: / America / America (extended mix) (Cd & 12' only) / Jihad / Change (CD Only).
CD 5": Released Aug '88, on E.G., by E.G. Records. Catalogue no: **EGOCD 40**
7" Single: Released Apr '88, on E.G., by E.G. Records. Catalogue no: **EGO 40**
12" Single: Released Apr '88, on E.G., by E.G. Records. Catalogue no: **EGOX 40**

BIRDS OF A FEATHER
Tracks: / Birds of a feather.
7" Single: Released Oct '82, on E.G., by E.G. Records. Deleted '85. Catalogue no: **EGO 10**
12" Single: Released Oct '82, on E.G., by E.G. Records. Deleted '85. Catalogue no: **EGOX 10**

CHOP CHOP
Tracks: / Chop chop / Good samaritan.
7" Single: Released Jun '82, on E.G., by E.G. Records. Deleted Jun '85. Catalogue no: **EGO 7**

EIGHTIES
Tracks: / Eighties.
7" Single: Released Mar '84, on E.G., by E.G. Records. Deleted '87. Catalogue no: **EGO 16**
12" Single: Released Mar '84, on E.G., by E.G. Records. Catalogue no: **EGOX 16**

EMPIRE SONG
Tracks: / Empire song / Brilliant.
7" Single: Released Mar '82, on E.G., by E.G. Records. Deleted '85. Catalogue no: **EGO 4**

FOLLOW THE LEADERS
Tracks: / Follow the leader / Tension.
7" Single: Released May '81, on E.G., by E.G. Records. Deleted '84. Catalogue no: **EGMDS 101**
12" Single: Released May '81, on E.G., by E.G. Records. Deleted '84. Catalogue no: **EGMDX 101**

HA-KILLING JOKE LIVE
Tracks: / Pssyche / Sun goes down / Pandys are coming / Take take take / Unspeakable / Wardance.
Special: Released Nov '82, on Malicious Damage, Deleted '88. Catalogue no: **EGMDT 4**

KINGS AND QUEENS
Tracks: / Kings and queens / Madding crowd.
7" Single: Released Mar '85, on E.G., by E.G. Records. Deleted '89. Catalogue no: **EGO 21**
12" Single: Released Mar '85, on E.G., by E.G. Records. Deleted '89. Catalogue no: **EGOX 21**

(LET'S ALL GO TO THE) FIRE DANCES
Tracks: / (Let's all go to the) fire dances.
7" Single: Released Jun '83, on E.G., by E.G. Records. Deleted '86. Catalogue no: **EGO 11**

LOVE LIKE BLOOD, A
Tracks: / Love like blood.
7" Single: Released Jan '85, on E.G., by E.G. Records. Deleted '89. Catalogue no: **EGO 20**
12" Single: Released Jan '85, on E.G., by E.G. Records. Deleted '89. Catalogue no: **EGOX 20**

LOVE LIKE BLOOD (GESTALT MIX)
Tracks: / Love like blood (gestalt mix) / Blue feather.
7" Single: Released Mar '85, on E.G., by E.G. Records. Catalogue no: **EGOY 20**

ME OR YOU?
Tracks: / Me or you?.
7" Single: Released Oct '83, on E.G., by E.G. Records. Deleted '86. Catalogue no: **EGO 14**

MY LOVE OF THIS LAND
Tracks: / My love of this land (On all versions) / Darkness before dawn (On all versions) / Follow the leader (dub) (Not on 7") / Pssyche (live) (On 12" only) / Sun goes down (On 10" only).
10" single: Released Jul '88, on E.G., by E.G. Records. Catalogue no: **EGOT 43**
7" Single: Released Jul '88, on E.G., by E.G. Records. Catalogue no: **EGO 43**
12" Single: Released Jul '88, on E.G., by E.G. Records. Catalogue no: **EGOX 43**

NERVOUS SYSTEM
Tracks: / Nervous system / Turn to red.
7" Single: Released Nov '80, on Island, by Island Records. Deleted Nov '83. Catalogue no: **WIP 6550**
12" Single: Released Nov '80, on Island, by Island Records. Deleted Nov '83. Catalogue no: **12WIP 6550**

NEW DAY, A
Tracks: / New day, A.
7" Single: Released Jul '84, on E.G., by E.G. Records. Deleted '87. Catalogue no: **EGO 17**

PSYCHE
Tracks: / Psyche / War dance.
7" Single: Released Mar '80, on Malicious Damage, Deleted Mar '83. Catalogue no: **MD 540**

SANITY
Tracks: / Sanity / Goodbye to the village.
7" Single: Released Oct '86, on E.G., by E.G. Records. Deleted May '88. Catalogue no: **EGO 30**
12" Single: Released Oct '86, on E.G., by E.G. Records. Deleted May '88. Catalogue no: **EGOX 30**

Killjoys

THIS IS NOT LOVE
Tracks: / This is not love / In your light.
7" Single: Released Dec '82, on Clay, by Clay Records. Deleted '88. Catalogue no: **CLAY 18**

Kilometres

TWISTED WHEEL
Tracks: / Twisted wheel / SX 225.
7" Single: Released Mar '80, on Gem, Deleted '83. Catalogue no: **GEMS 22**

Kim, Andy

ROCK ME GENTLY
Tracks: / Rock me gently.
7" Single: Released Aug '74, on Capitol, by EMI Records. Deleted '77. Catalogue no: **CL 15787**

ROCK ME GENTLY (OLD GOLD)
Tracks: / Rock me gently / Games people play.
Note: Also contains:"Games people play" by Joe South
7" Single: Released Apr '87, on Old Gold, by Old Gold Records. Deleted Sep '89. Catalogue no: **OG 9717**

Kim, Susy

NEXT IN LINE
Tracks: / Next in line / Lost and found.
7" Single: Released May '80, on Active, by Active Records. Deleted '83. Catalogue no: **ACT 5**

Kimball, Bobby

ONE DAY AT A TIME
Tracks: / One day at a time.
CD 5": Released Aug '89, on AVM, by AVM Records. Catalogue no: **AVMCD 73**
7" Single: Released Aug '89, on AVM, by AVM Records. Catalogue no: **AVM 73**

Kimberly Rew

MY BABY DOES HER HAIRDO LONG
Tracks: / My baby does her hairdo long.
7" Single: Released Jul '81, on Armageddon, by Armageddon Records. Catalogue no: **AS 012**

STOMPING ALL OVER THE WORLD
Tracks: / Stomping all over the world.
7" Single: Released Jul '81, on Armageddon, by Armageddon Records. Catalogue no: **AS 004**

Kimera

FEMME SAUVAGE
Tracks: / Femme sauvage.
7" Single: Released Aug '87, on TLO (USA), by Airwave Records (USA). Catalogue no: **FEM 77**
12" Single: Released Aug '87, on TLO (USA), by Airwave Records (USA). Catalogue no: **FEMM 77**

LOST OPERA
Tracks: / Lost opera.
7" Single: Released Aug '84, on Red Bus, by Red Bus Records. Catalogue no: **RBUS 99**
12" Single: Released Aug '84, on Red Bus, by Red Bus Records. Catalogue no: **RBUSL 99**

LOST OPERATOR (THE)
Tracks: / Lost operator, The / Lost operator, The (dance mix).
12" Single: Released May '86, on Carrere, Catalogue no: **CART 394**

Kind

DON'T STOP
Tracks: / Don't stop / 999.
7" Single: Released '83, on Chrysalis, by Chrysalis Records. Deleted '87. Catalogue no: **CHS 2749**
12" Single: Released '83, on Chrysalis, by Chrysalis Records. Deleted '87. Catalogue no: **CHS 12 2749**

Kinder

MONKEY PUZZLE
Tracks: / Monkey puzzle / Double talk.
7" Single: Released Dec '83, on Amidisque, by Amidisque Records. Catalogue no: **CF 005**

Kindergarten

WARRIOR
Tracks: / Warrior.
7" Single: Released Sep '85, on Diamond, by Revolver Records. Catalogue no: **DIA 009**

WORLD TURNED UPSIDE DOWN
Tracks: / World turned upside down, The.
12" Single: Released Mar '86, on Diamond, by Revolver Records. Catalogue no: **DIAEL 014**

King

ALONE WITHOUT YOU
Tracks: / Alone without you.
7" Single: Released Aug '85, on CBS, by CBS Records. Deleted '88. Catalogue no: **A 6308**

LOVE AND PRIDE
Tracks: / Love and pride / Don't stop / Classic strangers.
7" Single: Released Jan '85, on CBS, by CBS Records. Catalogue no: **A 4988**

TASTE OF YOUR TEARS, THE
Tracks: / Taste of your tears.
7" Single: Released Oct '85, on CBS, by CBS Records. Deleted '88. Catalogue no: **A 6618**

TORTURE
Tracks: / Torture / Growing up with the king.
7" Single: Released Dec '85, on CBS, by CBS Records. Catalogue no: **A 6761**
12" Single: Released Dec '85, on CBS, by CBS Records. Deleted '87. Catalogue no: **TA 6761**

WON'T YOU HOLD MY HAND NOW
Tracks: / Won't you hold my hand now / Fish reprise / As for myself / Endlessly.
7" Single: Released Mar '85, on CBS, by CBS Records. Deleted '88. Catalogue no: **A 6094**

King, Andrew

JACK THE JOKER
Tracks: / Jack the joker / Jack the joker (version).
12" Single: Released Jul '89, on That, Catalogue no: **AJK 001**

King Austin

SOCA TAKING OVER
Tracks: / Soca taking over.
12" Single: Released Dec '84, on Charlie's, Catalogue no: **CRD 012**

King, B.B.

Biographical details: Riley B.King, better known to his fans as B.B.King the "Beale Street Blues Boy" was born in Itta Bena, Mississippi on September 16th 1925. In his early years he was influenced by musicians like T.Bone Walker and Elmore James, but in turn has himself influenced many guitarists. He started out working for his local radio but in 1947 made the move to a station in Memphis. In 1949 he made his first recording *Miss Martha King* and as a result of meeting Ike Turner obtained a contract with Modern Records and their RPM subsiduary. His first record on this label *Three o'clock blues* was an immediate No.1 hit in 1950. He gained fame as a versatile performer whose extensive appeal was the result of his capacity to adapt many different musical styles - jazz, rock, country and pop - to his own personal blues interpretation. He continues to attract multiform audiences to his numerous concert performances.

This American guitarist, vocalist and songwriter is often referred to as the King of Blues. He was born Riley B King in Itta Bena, Mississippi in 1925. He did not start to take the guitar seriously until he was eighteen. In the late Forties he worked as a disc jockey on a radio station WDIA in Memphis - it was here that he earned the nickname 'Blues boy', which got shortened to B.B. In terms of his subsequent dominance of and influence upon the blues scene, he certainly lived up to his nickname and surname. B.B's recording career began at the end of the Forties, and quickly blossomed withe the success of his first smash hit *Three o'clock blues,* which enjoyed an extended run at the top of the American rhythm-and-blues, chart in 1950.

A host of further successes followed, included 1953's *Woke up this morning* classic. By the end of the Fifties he had chalked up almost twenty entries on the US R&B charts, although virtually none crossed over to the white-dominated pop listings. King's influence upon the white rock market started to emerge during the Sixties, when such seminal players as Eric Clapton took note of his pioneering, potent guitar style. B.B's technique on tracks like *Every day I have the blues* and *Rock me baby* was heard and imitated by a mass of young upstarts including Jimmy Page and Larry Coryell. King virtually introduced the guitar to a whole generation of musicians and played a key role in its development in blues and rock. His vocal sound, which ranged from a rich thick tenor to an emotional falsetto, was mesmerising. His perpetual, workaholic concert schedule kept him on the road for most of each year, and his show was a must for anyone interested in professionalism, audience rapport and sheer classy coolness. Thanks largely to his influence on world conquering British rock performers, white Americans finally caught up with B.B.King in 1970, when his string laden *The thrill is gone* reached the US Top 20. Grateful for the wider audience he was now reaching, he continued to record and tour at an exacting rate throughout the Seventies and into the Eighties. His commitment to the blues was displayed by the fact that he was still going strong in 1985, the year of his 60th birthday. For all the respect which he has always commanded amongst the British music fraternity, B.B. has never reached the UK singles chart and did not penetrate the LP list until 1979, when *Take it home* crept to No.60. (Bob MacDonald, 24th Nov 1985).

AIN'T NOBODY HOME (see panel below)
Tracks: / Ain't nobody home / Lay another log on the fire.
CD 5": Released 24 Jul '89, on MCA, by MCA Records. Catalogue no: **DMCAT 1354**
7" Single: Released 24 Jul '89, on MCA, by MCA Records. Catalogue no: **MCA 1354**
12" Single: Released 24 Jul '89, on MCA, by MCA Records. Catalogue no: **MCAT 1354**

BIM BAM
Tracks: / Bim bam / Shake holler and run.
7" Single: Released May '81, on Ace, by Ace Records. Deleted Jun '88. Catalogue no: **NS 69**

IN THE MIDNIGHT HOUR
Tracks: / In the midnight hour / Heed my warning.
7" Single: Released Sep '87, on MCA, by MCA Records. Catalogue no: **MCA 1196**

LEGEND IN MY TIME
Tracks: / Legend in my time / Love me tender.
7" Single: Released Nov '82, on MCA, by MCA Records. Deleted Nov '85. Catalogue no: **MCA 772**

ONE OF THOSE NIGHTS
Tracks: / One of those nights / Since I met you baby.
7" Single: Released '82, on MCA, by MCA Records. Deleted '87. Catalogue no: **MCA 786**

STANDING ON THE EDGE OF LOVE
Tracks: / Standing on the edge of love / Don't tell me nothing / Let yourself in for it (Extra track on 12" release only).
7" Single: Released Mar '87, on MCA, by MCA Records. Catalogue no: **MCA 1124**
12" Single: Released Mar '87, on MCA, by MCA Records. Catalogue no: **MCAT 1124**

King Bees

MY MISTAKE
Tracks: / My mistake / One is not enough.
7" Single: Released Aug '80, on RSO, by Polydor Ltd. Deleted '82. Catalogue no: **RSO 62**

King, Ben E.

Biographical details: This American singer and songwriter was born Benjamin Earl Nelson in North Carolina. He had been working in a vocal group called the Crowns before becoming lead singer of the ever-changing Drifters in 1959. His time with the Drifters lasted only until late 1960, but it yielded some classic hits and established King as a great rhythm-and-blues vocalist. No sooner had King quit the group (bowing out with *I count the tears*) than he achieved his first solo smash *Spanish harlem*, which reached the US No.10 position in early 1961. Then came his classic hit *Stand by me*, which he co-wrote with Leiber & Stoller - this climbed to No.4 in the States and has subsequently been successfully revived by artists as diverse as Spyder Turner, John Lennon, Mickey Gilley and Maurice White. Subsequent American hits for Ben E King during the early Sixties included *Amor*, *Don't play that song* and *I (who have nothing)*. Many of his records of this era were superb soul statements. (Spanish harlem was later covered by the Queen of Soul herself, Aretha Franklin. After a period of relative obscurity during the late Sixties and early Seventies, King bounced back albeit briefly in 1975 with the US No.5 hit *Supernatural thing*. This attempt to jump onto the disco bandwagon worked well for the one single, but failed afterwards. In 1977 he teamed up with the Average White Band for the album *Benny and us* and toured Europe with them. In the early Eighties, he made a surprise decision to rejoin the Drifters, but this did not return his or their name to former glories. Britain never appreciated King's solo offerings as much as the Americans did. His best UK chart showings were *First taste of love* and *Stand by me*, which both peakeed at No.27 in 1961. (Bob MacDonald, 24th Nov 1985).

AMOR, AMOR
Tracks: / Amor, amor.
7" Single: Released Oct '61, on London-American, Deleted '64. Catalogue no: **HLK 9416**

DANCING IN THE NIGHT
Tracks: / Dancing in the night (version) / Dancing in the night.
7" Single: Released 13 Jun '87, on Syncopate, by EMI Records. Deleted Apr '88. Catalogue no: **SY 3**
12" Single: Released 13 Jun '87, on Syncopate, by EMI Records. Deleted Apr '88. Catalogue no: **12 SY 3**

FIRST TASTE OF LOVE
Tracks: / First taste of love.
7" Single: Released Feb '61, on London-American, Deleted '64. Catalogue no: **HLK 9258**

LOVER'S QUESTION
Tracks: / Lover's question / Stand by me (1987 version.) / Because of last night.
7" Single: Released Nov '87, on EMI-Manhattan, by EMI Records. Deleted 31 Jul '88. Catalogue no: **MT 33**
12" Single: Released Nov '87, on EMI-Manhattan, by EMI Records. Deleted 31 Jul '88. Catalogue no: **12MT 33**

SAVE THE LAST DANCE FOR ME (SINGLE)
Tracks: / Save the last dance for me.
7" Single: Released Jun '87, on EMI-Manhattan, by EMI Records. Deleted Jan '88. Catalogue no: **MT 25**
12" Single: Released Jun '87, on EMI-Manhattan, by EMI Records. Deleted Jan '88. Catalogue no: **12MT 25**

SPANISH HARLEM (OLD GOLD)
Tracks: / Spanish harlem / Stand by me.
7" Single: Released Jul '82, on Old Gold, by Old Gold Records. Catalogue no: **OG 9101**

SPANISH HARLEM (SINGLE)
Tracks: / Spanish Harlem / First taste of love.
Note: Includes a medley consisting of Stand by me and Don't play that song.t
7" Single: Released Mar '87, on Creole Classics, by Creole Records. Catalogue no: **CR 97**
7" Single: Released Apr '87, on Atlantic, by WEA Records. Deleted Jan '88. Catalogue no: **YZ 118**
12" Single: Released Mar '87, on Creole Classics, by Creole Records. Catalogue no: **CRT 97**
12" Single: Released Apr '87, on Atlantic, by WEA Records. Deleted Jan '88. Catalogue no: **YZ 118 T**

SPREAD MYSELF AROUND
Tracks: / Spread myself around.
7" Single: Released May '87, on Bold Reprieve (1), Catalogue no: **BRM 003**
12" Single: Released May '87, on Bold Reprieve (1), Catalogue no: **BRM 003T**

STAND BY ME (SINGLE)
Tracks: / Stand By Me / Yakety yak.
7" Single: Released Jun '61, on London-American, Deleted '64. Catalogue no: **HLK 9358**
7" Single: Released Jan '87, on Atlantic, by WEA Records. Catalogue no: **A 9361**
12" Single: Released Jan '87, on Atlantic, by WEA Records. Deleted Jul '88. Catalogue no: **A 9361 T**

King, Billy

I'M A ROCKER
Tracks: / I'm a rocker / Hey Joe.
7" Single: Released Oct '82, on Polydor, by Polydor Ltd. Deleted Oct '85. Catalogue no: **POSP 529**

WAKE UP LITTLE SUSIE
Tracks: / Wake up little Susie / Too late.
7" Single: Released Apr '82, on Minstral, Deleted Apr '85. Catalogue no: **MIN 222**

King Biscuits

LIFE SO SHORT
Tracks: / Life so short / Sophisticated lady ways.
7" Single: Released Oct '88, on Lonely Man, by Lonely Man Records. Catalogue no: **LONELY MAN 100**

King Blank

BLIND BOX
Tracks: / Blind box / Thought I was well / Fill me up.
12" Single: Released 23 Jul '88, on Situation 2, by Beggars Banquet Records. Catalogue no: **SIT 53T**

MOUTH OFF
Tracks: / Mouth off / Drunk on tears / Bagman (Track on 12" version only.).
7" Single: Released May '88, on Situation 2, by Beggars Banquet Records. Catalogue no: **SIT 51**
12" Single: Released May '88, on Situation 2, by Beggars Banquet Records. Catalogue no: **SIT 51T**

UPTIGHT
Tracks: / Uptight / Howl upside down / Slackjaw man (Only on 12".).
7" Single: Released Oct '88, on Situation 2, by Beggars Banquet Records. Catalogue no: **SIT 55**
12" Single: Released Oct '88, on Situation 2, by Beggars Banquet Records. Catalogue no: **SIT 55Z**

King, Bobby

CLOSE TO ME
Tracks: / Close to me.
7" Single: Released Aug '84, on Motown, by BMG Records (UK). Catalogue no: **TMG 1347**
12" Single: Released Aug '84, on Motown, by BMG Records (UK). Catalogue no: **TGMT 1347**

LOVEQUAKE
Tracks: / Lovequake / Fall in love.
7" Single: Released Mar '84, on Motown, by BMG Records (UK). Catalogue no: **TMG 1335**
12" Single: Released Mar '84, on Motown, by BMG Records (UK). Catalogue no: **TMGT 1335**

SEEING IS BELIEVING
Tracks: / Seeing is believing.
12" Single: Released Jan '89, on Zensor (Germany), Catalogue no: **CM 12**

King, Brenton

DON'T GIVE YOUR HEART AWAY
Tracks: / Don't give your heart away.
12" Single: Released May '84, on The Foundation, Catalogue no: **TF 014**

NEVER GIVE UP
Tracks: / Never give up.
12" Single: Released Apr '85, on Top Rank (2), Catalogue no: **TR 003**

King Brothers

6-5 JIVE
Tracks: / 6-5 jive.
7" Single: Released Mar '84, on Northwood, by Northwood Records. Catalogue no: **NW45 005**

76 TROMBONES
Tracks: / 76 trombones.
7" Single: Released Mar '61, on Parlophone, by EMI Records. Deleted '64. Catalogue no: **R 4737**

DOLL HOUSE
Tracks: / Doll house.
7" Single: Released Jan '61, on Parlophone, by EMI Records. Deleted '64. Catalogue no: **R 4715**

IN THE MIDDLE OF AN ISLAND
Tracks: / In the middle of an island.
7" Single: Released Aug '57, on Parlophone, by EMI Records. Deleted '60. Catalogue no: **R 4338**

IT'S PARTY TIME WITH .... (EP)
Tracks: / It's party time.
7" Single: Released Mar '85, on Northwood, by Northwood Records. Catalogue no: **NWEP 103**

MAIS OUI
Tracks: / Mais oui.
7" Single: Released Jul '60, on Parlophone, by EMI Records. Deleted '63. Catalogue no: **R 4672**

PUT A LIGHT IN THE WINDOW
Tracks: / Put a light in the window.
7" Single: Released Jan '58, on Parlophone, by EMI Records. Deleted '61. Catalogue no: **R 4389**

STANDING ON THE CORNER
Tracks: / Standing on the corner.
7" Single: Released Apr '60, on Parlophone, by EMI Records. Deleted '63. Catalogue no: **R 4639**

WAKE UP LITTLE SUSIE
Tracks: / Wake up little Susie.
7" Single: Released Dec '57, on Parlophone, by EMI Records. Deleted '60. Catalogue no: **R 4367**

WHITE SPORT COAT, A
Tracks: / White sports coat.
7" Single: Released May '57, on Parlophone, by EMI Records. Deleted '60. Catalogue no: **R 4310**

King Butcher

SPUD-U-LIKE
Tracks: / Spud-u-like.
12" Single: Released Oct '88, on Mashit, Catalogue no: **KING 001**

King, Calvin

NEVER GONNA FORGET YOU
Tracks: / Never gonna forget you / Never gonna forget you (disco remix).
12" Single: Released Aug '86, on Elegance, Catalogue no: **E 001**

THATS WHEN IT ALL STARTED
Tracks: / That's when it all started / Find your destiny.
12" Single: Released Oct '80, on Time, Catalogue no: **EBY 005**

B.B. KING - AIN'T NOBODY HOME (Released on MCA)

King, Carole

Biographical details: This American singer, songwriter and pianist was one of the most successful composers (for other artists) of the Sixties, and then proceeded to record one of the world's top selling albums of the Seventies. Her Sixties songwriting career and her Seventies singing career would each, on their own, be enough to ensure legendary status; but together they make Carole King one of the most successful figures in the history of the record industry and THE most successful woman.
She was born Carole Klein in Brooklyn, New York in 1942 and began playing the piano at the age of four. In the late Fifties, while attending Queen's College in New York, she befriended a number of people who shared her interest in music. Among them were Neil Sedaka - whose 1959 hit *Oh Carol* was a tribute to her despite the absence of an 'e' - and future husband Gerry Goffin, who became her permanent writing partner. When Goffin & King's song *Will you love me tomorrow* reached the US No.1 slot for the Shirelles in January 1961, it opened the floodgates for a sea of successful songs by the young writing team. Soon the charts on both sides of the Atlantic were awash with Goffin/King numbers. Their tally of American No.1 singles included Bobby Vee's *Take good care of my baby* (1961), Little Eva's *The locomotion* (1962) and Steve Lawrence's *Go away little girl* (1963). *I'm into something good* by Herman's Hermits gave the husband-and-wife team a British chart-topper in 1964. Other hits included the Chiffons' *One fine day*, the Cookies' *Don't say nothin' bad about my baby*, James Darren's *Her Royal Majesty*, Skeeter Davis' *I can't stay mad at you*, the Drifters *Up on the roof*, *Halfway to paradise (recorded by Tony Orlando in the US, Billy Fury in the UK) and Freddie Scott's Hey girl*. And those were just a few of them. The golden era for Goffin & King was the early Sixties, in the years immediately prior to the Beatles' invasion of America. They brilliantly captured the era's teenage obsession with boyfriends, girlfriends, infatuation, angst, etc. When the British revolution happened, the pair managed to get some of their songs into the repertoires of UK acts - the Animals, Manfred Mann, the Rockin' Berries and Dusty Springfield all enjoyed success with their material.
Gerry and Carole divorced in 1968, although some of their collaborative efforts had still not seen the light of day. King decided to launch a performing career, (She had enjoyed a one-off hit in 1962 with *It might as well rain until September*, but her other records of the period had flopped). After an inauspicious start wht some mediocre albums, she suddelnly made it big with her 1971 LP *Tapestry*. This classic album spent 15 weeks at No.1 in America and remained on the US chart right into the late Seventies; in Britain, it peaked at no.4 with 90 chart weeks. *Tapestry* chalked up a worldwide total of 15 million copies. It is often cited as the most important work of the singer-songwriter era; it yielded the US No.1 single *It's too late*, another track *You've got a friend* went to No.1 for her big mate James Taylor. *Tapestry* was a beautiful middle-of-the-road pop album, dealing with personal feelings and human emotions in a way that everyone could relate to. King continued to record regularly during the Seventies and Eighties, but could not match the artistic or commercial success of *Tapestry*. She continued to pop up on the American charts from time to time, the biggest of her later successes being 1974's *Jazzman* single, which released the US No.2 position. (Bob MacDonald, 24th Nov 1985).

CITY STREETS (SINGLE)
Tracks: / City streets / I can't stop thinking about you / Time heals all wounds (12" only.).
CD 5": Released Mar '89, on Capitol, by EMI Records. Deleted Oct '89. Catalogue no: **203 313 2**
CD 5": Released Mar '89, on Capitol, by EMI Records. Deleted Oct '89. Catalogue no: **CDCL 527**
7" Single: Released Mar '89, on Capitol, by EMI Records. Deleted Oct '89. Catalogue no: **CL 527**
7" Single: Released Mar '89, on Capitol, by EMI Records. Deleted Oct '89. Catalogue no: **203 313 7**
12" Single: Released Mar '89, on Capitol, by EMI Records. Deleted Oct '89. Catalogue no: **12CL 527**
12" Single: Released Mar '89, on Capitol, by EMI Records. Deleted Oct '89. Catalogue no: **203 313 6**

IT MIGHT AS WELL RAIN UNTIL SEPTEMBER (OLD GOLD)
Tracks: / It might as well rain until September.
7" Single: Released Oct '83, on Old Gold, by Old Gold Records. Catalogue no: **OG 9355**
7" Single: Released Sep '62, on London-American, Deleted '65. Catalogue no: **HLU 9591**
7" Single: Released Oct '83, on Old Gold, by Old Gold Records. Catalogue no: **OG 9355**
7" Single: Released Oct '72, on London-American, Deleted '75. Catalogue no: **HL 10391**

IT'S TOO LATE
Tracks: / It's too late.
7" Single: Released Aug '71, on A&M, by A&M Records. Deleted '74. Catalogue no: **AMS 849**

READ BETWEEN THE LINES
Tracks: / Read between the lines / Golden man.
7" Single: Released Apr '82, on Atlantic, by WEA Records. Deleted Apr '85. Catalogue no: **K 11725**

King Cotton

STICK IT TO THE GRIND
Tracks: / Stick it to the grind / Beyond Uranus.
12" Single: Released Aug '82, on Island, by Island Records. Deleted Aug '85. Catalogue no: **12WIP 6798**

King Creole

WASN'T THAT A PARTY
Tracks: / Wasn't that a party / Wanderer.
7" Single: Released May '81, on EMI, by EMI Records. Deleted May '86. Catalogue no: **EMI 5176**

King Crimson

Biographical details: Led by guitarist/keyboards player/mellotron player/composer Robert Fripp, this British art-rock band has undergone a never-ending series of personnel changes - indeed, no Crimson album between 1969 and 1974 featured the same line-up as its predecessor, so Fripp's tenacity was astounding. Amongst the noted musicians who have been King Crimson members at one time or another: Bill Bruford, Mel Collins, Mike Giles, Greg Lake, Ian McDonald and John Wetton plus many others. King Crimson came into being in 1969 and quickly established themselves at the forefront of the progressive rock scene with their experimental and extravagant (some said pompous and pretentious) music. Their first two albums, *In the court of Crimson King* (1969) and *In the wake of Poseidon* (1970, both cracked the British Top 5. With magical lyrics and colourful dynamics, these albums contained a wealth of musical elements including rock, classical, jazz, blues and psychedlic pop styles. They gave the listener an unpredictable voyage through a kingly kaleidoscope of moods, textures and dimensions; the group helped to pave the way for such pomp-rock bands as Emerson, Lake & Palmer and Yes.
After the first two releases, King Crimson never returned to the Top 10 of the British LP chart. The frequent line-up changes inevitably impaired the group's progress in both artistic and sales terms, despite the imagination and flair of the ever eccentric Fripp. Their output was pleasant but patchy. Robert decided to terminate the band in 1974, by which time he had already begun to get involved in a variety of outside projects. Both solo and collaborative works, usually of an avant garde and esoteric nature, occupied Fripp's time until the relaunch of King Crimson in 1981. The reformed band attained mediocre levels of success and were dismissed as passe in some quarters. They nonetheless displayed an admirable desire to avoid standing still. (Bob MacDonald, 24th Nov 1985).

HEARTBEAT
Tracks: / Heartbeat.
7" Single: Released Jun '82, on E.G., by E.G. Records. Deleted Jun '85. Catalogue no: **EGO 6**

MATTE KUDASAI
Tracks: / Matte Kudasai / Elephant talk.
7" Single: Released Dec '81, on E.G., by E.G. Records. Deleted Dec '84. Catalogue no: **EGO 2**

SLEEPLESS
Tracks: / Sleepless / Nuages.
7" Single: Released Mar '84, on E.G., by E.G. Records. Deleted '89. Catalogue no: **EGO 15**
12" Single: Released Mar '84, on E.G., by E.G. Records. Deleted '89. Catalogue no: **EGOX 15**

King, Danny

CHRISTMASTIME IS HERE
Tracks: / Christmastime is here.
7" Single: Released Dec '82, on JPD, Deleted '85. Catalogue no: **JPD 002**

King, Dave

CHRISTMAS AND YOU
Tracks: / Christmas and you.
7" Single: Released Dec '56, on Decca, by Decca Records. Deleted '59. Catalogue no: **F 10791**

MEMORIES ARE MADE OF THIS
Tracks: / Memories are made of this.
7" Single: Released Feb '56, on Decca, by Decca Records. Deleted '59. Catalogue no: **F 10684**

STORY OF MY LIFE, THE
Tracks: / Story of my life.
7" Single: Released Jan '58, on Decca, by Decca Records. Deleted '61. Catalogue no: **F 10973**

YOU CAN'T BE TRUE TO TWO
Tracks: / You can't be true to two.
7" Single: Released Apr '56, on Decca, by Decca Records. Deleted '59. Catalogue no: **F 10720**

King, Dee Dee

FUNKY MAN
Note: AKA Dee Dee Ramone!! Dee Dee goes in for a bit of serious rapping!
12" Single: Released 28 Sep '87, on Rock Hotel(USA), Catalogue no: **PAL 7159**

King, Denis Orchestra

WE'LL MEET AGAIN
Tracks: / We'll meet again.
7" Single: Released Jun '83, on Multi-Media, Catalogue no: **MMT 6**

King Diamond

NO PRESENTS FOR CHRISTMAS
Tracks: / No presents for Christmas.
7" Single: Released Jul '87, on Road Runner (1), by Road Runner Records. Catalogue no: **RR 125485**

King Dice

CHILDREN'S HOUR, THE
Tracks: / Children's hour, The.
7" Single: Released Feb '85, on King Dice, Catalogue no: **KD 0001**

King Dream Chorus

KING HOLIDAY
Tracks: / King holiday / (Martin Luther King Tribute song).
7" Single: Released Feb '86, on Club, by Phonogram Ltd. Catalogue no: **JAB 29**
12" Single: Released Feb '86, on Club, by Phonogram Ltd. Catalogue no: **JABX 29**

King, Ellie

SPECIAL OFFER
Tracks: / Special offer.
7" Single: Released Sep '82, on Solid, by Solid Records. Catalogue no: **STOP 004**
12" Single: Released Sep '82, on Solid, by Solid Records. Catalogue no: **12 STOP 004**

King Errisson

LIVING IT UP ON JUPITER (2 Parts)
Tracks: / Living it up on Jupiter.
7" Single: Released Feb '83, on Half Moon, by Rondelet Music & Records. Catalogue no: **SH 1962**

King, Evelyn

ACTION
Tracks: / Action / Let's get crazy.
12" Single: Released Jan '84, on RCA, by BMG Records (UK). Catalogue no: **RCAT 383**

BACK TO LOVE
Tracks: / Back to love / I can't stand it.
7" Single: Released Nov '82, on RCA, by BMG Records (UK). Catalogue no: **RCA 287**
12" Single: Released Nov '82, on RCA, by BMG Records (UK). Catalogue no: **RCAT 287**

FLIRT (SINGLE) (Radio mix)
Tracks: / Flirt / Flirt (flirt to flirt dub) / Flirt (body groove)* (*Extra track on 12" version.).
7" Single: Released 5 Apr '88, on EMI-Manhattan, by EMI Records. Deleted Nov '88. Catalogue no: **MT 37**
12" Single: Released 5 Apr '88, on EMI-Manhattan, by EMI Records. Deleted Nov '88. Catalogue no: **12MTX 37**
12" Single: Released 5 Apr '88, on EMI-Manhattan, by EMI Records. Deleted Nov '88. Catalogue no: **12MT 37**

GET LOOSE (SINGLE)
Tracks: / Get loose / I'm in love.
7" Single: Released Feb '83, on RCA, by BMG Records (UK). Catalogue no: **RCA 315**
12" Single: Released Feb '83, on RCA, by BMG Records (UK). Catalogue no: **RCAT 315**

GIVE IT UP
Tracks: / Give it up / Armies of the night.
7" Single: Released Apr '86, on Epic, by CBS Records. Catalogue no: **A 6671**
12" Single: Released Apr '86, on Epic, by CBS Records. Catalogue no: **TA 6671**

GIVE ME ONE REASON
Tracks: / Give me one reason.
7" Single: Released Feb '85, on RCA, by BMG Records (UK). Catalogue no: **RCA 474**
12" Single: Released Feb '85, on RCA, by BMG Records (UK). Catalogue no: **RCAT 474**

HIGH HORSE
Tracks: / High horse / Take a chance / High horse (remix) (on 12" only.) / Shame* (*extra track on 12" version only).
7" Single: Released Mar '86, on RCA, by BMG Records (UK). Catalogue no: **PB 49891**
12" Single: Released Mar '86, on RCA, by BMG Records (UK). Catalogue no: **PT 49892**

HOLD ON TO WHAT YOU'VE GOT
Tracks: / Hold on to what you've got / Hold on to what you've got (set it off dub) / Hold on to what you've got (ext. version) / Hold on to what you've got (radio mix) / Hold on to what you've got (instrumental).
Note: (P) 1988 Original sound recording made by EMI-Manhattan Records, a division of Capitol Records Inc. Executive producer Scott Folks.
7" Single: Released Jul '88, on EMI-Manhattan, by EMI Records. Deleted Jun '89. Catalogue no: **MT 49**
12" Single: Released Jul '88, on EMI-Manhattan, by EMI Records. Deleted Jun '89. Catalogue no: **12MTX 49**
12" Single: Released Jul '88, on EMI-Manhattan, by EMI Records. Deleted Jun '89. Catalogue no: **12MT 49**

I DON'T KNOW IF IT'S RIGHT
Tracks: / I don't know if it's right.
7" Single: Released Feb '79, on RCA, by BMG Records (UK). Deleted '82. Catalogue no: **PB 1386**

IF YOU WANT MY LOVIN'
Tracks: / If you want my lovin'.
7" Single: Released Sep '81, on RCA, by BMG Records (UK). Catalogue no: **RCA 131**
12" Single: Released Sep '81, on RCA, by BMG Records (UK). Catalogue no: **RCAT 131**

I'M IN LOVE (OLD GOLD)
Tracks: / I'm in love.
12" Single: Released Nov '87, on Old Gold, by Old Gold Records. Catalogue no: **OG 4035**

I'M IN LOVE (SINGLE)
Tracks: / I'm in love / Other side of love.
7" Single: Released Jun '81, on RCA, by BMG Records (UK). Catalogue no: **RCA 95**
12" Single: Released Jun '81, on RCA, by BMG Records (UK). Catalogue no: **RCAT 95**

LET'S GET FUNKY TONIGHT
Tracks: / Let's get funky tonight / Just a little bit of you.
7" Single: Released Nov '80, on RCA, by BMG Records (UK). Deleted '83. Catalogue no: **PB 2075**
12" Single: Released Nov '80, on RCA, by BMG Records (UK). Deleted '83. Catalogue no: **PC 2075**

LOVE COME DOWN
Tracks: / Love come down / Don't hide our love.
7" Single: Released Jul '82, on RCA, by BMG Records (UK). Catalogue no: **RCA 249**
12" Single: Released Jul '82, on RCA, by BMG Records (UK). Deleted May '89. Catalogue no: **RCAT 249**

LOVE COME DOWN (OLD GOLD)
Tracks: / Love come down / Shame.
7" Single: Released Apr '87, on Old Gold, by Old Gold Records. Catalogue no: **OG 9705**
12" Single: Released Sep '87, on Old Gold, by Old Gold Records. Catalogue no: **OG 4021**

SHAME (SINGLE)
Tracks: / Shame.
7" Single: Released May '78, on RCA, by BMG Records (UK). Deleted '81. Catalogue no: **PC 1122**

SPIRIT OF THE DANCER
Tracks: / Spirit of the dancer.
7" Single: Released Jan '82, on RCA, by BMG Records (UK). Catalogue no: **RCA 179**
12" Single: Released Jan '82, on RCA, by BMG Records (UK). Catalogue no: **RCAT 179**

YOUR PERSONAL TOUCH
Tracks: / Your personal touch.
7" Single: Released Oct '85, on RCA, by BMG Records (UK). Catalogue no: **PB 49915**
12" Single: Released Oct '85, on RCA, by BMG Records (UK). Catalogue no: **PT 49916**

King Everal

BEAT THAT SOUND
Tracks: / Beat that sound.
12" Single: Released Nov '88, on Waterhouse, Catalogue no: **UNKNOWN**

COWBOY STYLE
Tracks: / Cowboy style.
12" Single: Released Oct '83, on Cow Boy, Catalogue no: **COW BOY 1**

DREADLOCKS TIME (2 parts)
Tracks: / Dreadlocks time.
7" Single: Released Oct '83, on Jammy's, Catalogue no: **DSR 0699**

RUN DOWN
Tracks: / Run down.
12" Single: Released Nov '88, on Taurus, Catalogue no: **UNKNOWN**

SPECIAL
Tracks: / Special.
7" Single: Released Nov '88, on Taurus, Catalogue no: **UNKNOWN**

TONIGHT YOU'RE MINE
Tracks: / Tonight you're mine / Tonight you're mine (version).
12" Single: Released Jun '87, on Super Power, Catalogue no: **SPD 4**

WALK AND SKIP
Tracks: / Walk and skip.
12" Single: Released Sep '84, on Sun Set (reggae), Catalogue no: **UNKNOWN**

King, Everton & Tracy

HEAVEN
Tracks: / Heaven.
7" Single: Released Oct '84, on Legacy, by Legacy Records. Catalogue no: **LGY 5**

King, Fillmore

KEEP ON DANCIN'
Tracks: / Keep on dancing.
7" Single: Released Apr '84, on Pinnacle, by Pinnacle Records. Catalogue no: **PIN 103**

King George

OH LORD
Tracks: / Oh Lord / You are my lady.
12" Single: Released Jan '87, on Top Rank (2), Catalogue no: **TRD 025**

King, Geraldine

GROWING UP
Tracks: / Growing up / Grown up.
7" Single: Released Feb '80, on Liberty, by EMI Records. Deleted Feb '85. Catalogue no: **BP 339**

King Henrys consort

DANCERIE
Tracks: / Dancerie.
7" Single: Released Jul '84, on Rex (1), by Decca Records. Catalogue no: **REX 3**

THINGUMMY-JIG
Tracks: / Thingummy-jig / Jester.
7" Single: Released Jan '84, on Rex (1), by Decca Records. Catalogue no: **REX 1**
7" Single: Released Dec '84, on Eden, Catalogue no: **EDEN 2**

King, James

ANGELS KNOW, THE
Tracks: / Angels know, The.
12" Single: Released Jan '85, on Swamplands, by London Records. Catalogue no: **SWX 3**

BACK FROM THE DEAD
Tracks: / Back from the dead / My reward / As tears go by.
7" EP: Released Mar '81, on Virgin, by Virgin Records. Deleted Mar '84. Catalogue no: **VS 405**

EASY LOVE
Tracks: / Easy love / Heartbreak, sorrow and pain.
7" Single: Released Jun '87, on Expansion, Catalogue no: **EXPAND 8**

I TRIED
Tracks: / I tried.
7" Single: Released Sep '81, on Virgin, by Virgin Records. Deleted Sep '84. Catalogue no: **VS 454**

STORYTELLER (DANCE MIX)
Tracks: / Storyteller (dance mix) / Storyteller (version).
12" Single: Released Apr '88, on Expansion, Catalogue no: **EXPAND 12**

TEXAS LULLABY (5 track ep)
Tracks: / Texas lullaby / Sacred heart / Chance I can't deny / Until the dawn / Lost.
12" Single: Released Nov '83, on Thrush, by Thrush Records. Catalogue no: **THRUSH 2**

King, John

TRUE LIFE COUNTRY MUSIC
Tracks: / True life country music.
7" Single: Released Apr '83, on Mint, by Emerald Records. Deleted '88. Catalogue no: **CHEW 79**

King, Johnny

WAR MONGERS
Tracks: / War mongers.
12" Single: Released Nov '88, on Flick, Catalogue no: **FLK 120021**

King, Jonathan

Biographical details: This British singer, songwriter, producer, broadcaster, journalist, executive and entrepreneur is one of the great characters of the UK music industry; he is either loved or loathed by millions. He was born Kenneth King in London in 1944 and he enjoyed a privileged upbringing - he was educated at Charterhouse public school in Surrey and Cambridge University. It was while studying English at the latter institution that he shot to fame with his self-penned 1965 smash *Everyone's gone to the moon* - this whimsical, dreamy song reached No.4 in the UK and No.17 in the US. It was actually a nonsensical parody of the highly fashionable folk protest movement, but was taken seriously by many people. Jonathan quickly followed it with another self-penned ditty, *It's good news week* by Hedgehoppers Anonymous, who were a group of musical non-entities whom King manipulated to the K No.5 position. Despite these early successes, King delayed his full-time entry into the music business in order to complete his degree course. After graduation he spent the late Sixties working as a loudmouth TV personality and pop columnist, and also took a part-time post in the A&R department of Decca Records (with whom he was sporadically associated in later years). During the early Seventies King returned to active recording, songwriting and production, and hit his commercial peak at this time. As well as his own UK Top 30 hits - *Let it all hang out, Lazy bones, Hooked on a feeling* and *Flirt* - he acheived a variety of successful singles under silly pseudonyms. Bubblerock, the Piglets, Sakkarin, St.Cecilia, Shag and the Weathermen were all either the total or partial creation of Jonathan. In addition to these one-off British hits, he performed a more serious sevice to the music business by discovering 10 CC and signing them to his own UK Records. He was also involved in the early careers of Genesis and the Bay City Rollers, although those two groups did not achieve lasting success until after his association with them had finished.
During the mid-Seventies he chalked up further British biggies under his own name (*Una paloma blanca*), under the alias 100 Ton and a Feather (*It only takes a minute*) and as a producer (Brendon's *Gimme some*). There was a less happy news for his UK label, which never recovered from losing 10 CC to Mercury Records and eventually folded. During the late Seventies and early Eighties King resumed a regular broadcasting career. Casting his usual controversial eye on the music industry and on the world at large, he presented BBC Radio One's *Talkabout* and *A King in New York* programs, contributed to *Top of the Pops*; and in 1983 launched a highly acclaimed music/documentary program on BBC TV, *Entertainment USA*. He also presented a special annual Christmas show on Radio One. In 1985 King's opinions were as outspoken and idiosyncratic as ever. Writing a regular column in Britain's Sun newspaper, he dared to criticise 'Live Aid' and described Britain's Gallup-compiled official record charts as 'rubbish'. (Bob MacDonald, 25th Nov 1985).

EVERYONE'S GONE TO THE MOON
Tracks: / Everyone's gone to the moon / Summer's coming.
7" Single: Released Jul '65, on Decca, by Decca Records. Deleted '68. Catalogue no: **F 12187**
7" Single: Released Jul '82, on Old Gold, by Old Gold Records. Catalogue no: **OG 9104**

FLIRT
Tracks: / Flirt.
7" Single: Released Feb '72, on Decca, by Decca Records. Deleted '75. Catalogue no: **F 13276**

GIMME SOME
Tracks: / Gimme some / Crying again / Royal mix, The (on 12" version only).
7" Single: Released Sep '86, on Virgin, by Virgin Records. Deleted May '88. Catalogue no: **GIMME 1**
12" Single: Released Sep '86, on Virgin, by Virgin Records. Deleted May '88. Catalogue no: **GIMME 112**

GLORIA
Tracks: / Gloria.
7" Single: Released Nov '79, on Ariola, by BMG Records (UK). Deleted '82. Catalogue no: **ARO 198**

HOOKED ON A FEELING
Tracks: / Hooked on a feeling.
7" Single: Released Nov '71, on Decca, by Decca Records. Deleted '74. Catalogue no: **F 13241**

I'LL SLAP YOUR FACE
Tracks: / I'll slap your face / No speed limit.
7" Single: Released Jul '87, on BBC, by BBC Records & Tapes. Deleted Apr '89. Catalogue no: **RESL 218**

IT'S ILLEGAL, IT'S IMMORAL, IT'S UNHEALTHY...
Tracks: / It's illegal, it's immoral, it's unhealthy... / Sing your own morality.
7" Single: Released Jun '80, on WEA, by WEA Records. Deleted Jun '83. Catalogue no: **K 18257**

LAZY BONES
Tracks: / Lazybones.
7" Single: Released May '71, on Decca, by Decca Records. Deleted '74. Catalogue no: **F 13177**

LET IT ALL HANG OUT
Tracks: / Let it all hang out.
7" Single: Released Jan '70, on Decca, by Decca Records. Deleted '73. Catalogue no: **F 12988**

ONE FOR YOU ONE FOR ME
Tracks: / One for you one for me.
7" Single: Released Oct '78, on GTO, Deleted '81. Catalogue no: **GT 237**

SPACE ODDITY
Tracks: / Space oddity / Major Tom coming home / Slap your face.
7" Single: Released Apr '84, on Epic, by CBS Records. Catalogue no: **A 4335**
12" Single: Released Apr '84, on Epic, by CBS Records. Catalogue no: **TA 4335**

SUN HAS GOT HIS HAT ON, THE
Tracks: / Sun has got his hat on, The / Everyone's gone to the moon / Johnny Reggae / Mental diseases (On 12" only.).
7" Single: Released 24 Jul '89, on Ariola, by BMG Records (UK). Catalogue no: **112522**
12" Single: Released 24 Jul '89, on Ariola, by BMG Records (UK). Catalogue no: **612522**

UNA PALOMA BLANCA
Tracks: / Una paloma blanca.
7" Single: Released Sep '75, on UK, by UK Records. Deleted '78. Catalogue no: **UK 105**

WILD WORLD
Tracks: / Wild world.
7" Single: Released 21 Nov '87, on UK, by UK Records. Catalogue no: **UKP 001**
12" Single: Released 21 Nov '87, on UK, by UK Records. Catalogue no: **UKPT 001**

YOU'RE THE GREATEST LOVER
Tracks: / You're the greatest lover.
7" Single: Released Jun '79, on UK, by UK Records. Deleted '82. Catalogue no: **INT 586**

King Kobra

HOME STREET HOME
Tracks: / Home street home / Iron eagle (never say die).
12" Single: Released Jan '87, on FM-Revolver, by FM-Revolver Records. Catalogue no: **12 VHF 35**

IRON EAGLE
Tracks: / Iron eagle (never say die) / This raging fire.
7" Single: Released May '86, on Capitol, by EMI Records. Deleted '88. Catalogue no: **CL 397**

King Koen

KICKS ON THE RADIO
Tracks: / Kicks on the radio.
12" Single: Released '88, on Punk Etc., by Punk Etc. Records. Catalogue no: **PETC 015**

King Kong

CAKE OF SUCCESS
Tracks: / Cake of success / Predominant.
12" Single: Released Nov '86, on Now Generation, Catalogue no: **NG 013**

DIGITAL
Tracks: / Rambo / Digital.
12" Single: Released Mar '87, on Digikal, by Fashion Records. Catalogue no: **DIG 006**

DO NOT GET HIGH
Tracks: / Do not get high.
12" Single: Released Apr '87, on Ottey's Promotion, Catalogue no: **RMM 451**

GLAMOUR BOY IN MY LIFE
Tracks: / Glamour boy in my life / Come right in / Identify me.
12" Single: Released Nov '86, on Digikal, by Fashion Records. Catalogue no: **DIG 003**
12" Single: Released Sep '86, on Striker Lee, Catalogue no: **SLD 04**

LEGAL
Tracks: / Legal / Mix up.
12" Single: Released Mar '86, on Greensleeves, by Greensleeves Records. Catalogue no: **GRED 198**

MUST WORK ON SUNDAY
Tracks: / Must work on Sunday / Outta me way.
12" Single: Released Mar '86, on Striker Lee, Catalogue no: **SSLD 002**

NICENESS
Tracks: / Niceness / Name and number.
12" Single: Released Sep '86, on Sweetcorn, Catalogue no: **SC 12**

PARO THEM PARO
Tracks: / Paro them paro / Paronia.
12" Single: Released Sep '86, on Greensleeves, by Greensleeves Records. Catalogue no: **GRED 206**

RAGAMUFFIN A PASS
Tracks: / Ragamuffin a pass / Girl then a come.
12" Single: Released Mar '87, on New Generation, Catalogue no: **NG 016**

SENSIMANIA IS WALKING
Tracks: / Sensimania is walking / Digital sensimania.
12" Single: Released Dec '85, on Rem, Catalogue no: **REM 001**

TOOT TOOT TOO MUCH
Tracks: / Toot toot too much / Expectation / Profitable genocide.
12" Single: Released Sep '83, on Zara, Catalogue no: **ZMRD 005**
7" Single: Released Sep '83, on Zara, Catalogue no: **ZMR 005**

TROUBLE AGAIN (SINGLE)
Tracks: / Trouble again / Me lover.
Note: Features 10 tracks including the popular single and title track 'Trouble again'.The album is produced by King Jammy.
12" Single: Released Jun '86, on Greensleeves, by Greensleeves Records. Catalogue no: **GRED 201**

King Kurt

Biographical details: At the time of their greatest success, this British rock band consisted of Bert, Rory Lyons, Maggit, John Reddington, Smeg and Thwack. The loony King Kurt were formed at the beginning of 1983 and came to fame in the autumn of that year with their UK No.36 single *Destination Zululand*. Fronted by lead vocalist Smeg, the group caused much amusement on Top of the Pops with their nutty act; their live gigs became notorious because the audience were usually showered in flour! Produced by rock'n'roll stalwart Dave Edmunds, the band's debut album *Ooh wallah wallah* was a chaotic combination of raw rock'n'roll, post-punk pop and Adam Ant type tribal inflections. 1984 brought King Kurt two minor UK hit singles with a revamp of the *Mack the knife* classic plus *Banana banana*. But in 1985, with Bert and John having been replaced by bassist Dick Crippen and guitarist Jim Piper, the band were still looking for a major breakthrough. (Bob MacDonald, 25th Nov 1985).

AMERICA
Tracks: / America.
7" Pic: Released Nov '86, on Polydor, by Polydor Ltd. Deleted Aug '87. Catalogue no: **KURTP 1**
7" Single: Released Oct '86, on Polydor, by Polydor Ltd. Deleted Aug '87. Catalogue no: **KURT 1**
12" Single: Released Oct '86, on Polydor, by Polydor Ltd. Deleted Aug '87. Catalogue no: **KURTX 1**

BANANA BANANA
Tracks: / Banana banana.
7" Single: Released Jun '84, on Stiff, by Stiff Records. Catalogue no: **BUY 206**
12" Single: Released Jun '84, on Stiff, by Stiff Records. Catalogue no: **BUYIT 206**

BILLY
Tracks: / Billy.
7" Single: Released Jun '85, on Stiff, by Stiff Records. Catalogue no: **BUY 224**

DESTINATION ZULU LAND
Tracks: / Destination Zulu land / She's as hairy.

7" Single: Released Sep '83, on Stiff, by Stiff Records. Catalogue no: **BUY 189**
12" Single: Released Sep '83, on Stiff, by Stiff Records. Catalogue no: **SBUY 189**

LAND OF RING DANG DOO, THE
Tracks: / Horatio / Gather your limbs / Land of ring dang doo, The / Zulu beat (live) / Zulu beat (live at the Reading Sexadrome) / Horatio (live at the Reading Sexadrome) / Gather your limbs (live at the Reading Sexadrome).
Note: * = Extra track on 12" only
7" Set: Released May '87, on Polydor, by Polydor Ltd. Deleted Jan '88. Catalogue no: **KURTG 2**
7" Single: Released Apr '87, on Polydor, by Polydor Ltd. Deleted Jan '88. Catalogue no: **KURT 2**
12" Single: Released Apr '87, on Polydor, by Polydor Ltd. Deleted Jan '88. Catalogue no: **KURTX 2**

MACK THE KNIFE
Tracks: / Mack the knife / Wreck a party rock.
7" Pic: Released May '84, on Stiff, by Stiff Records. Catalogue no: **PBUY 199**
7" Single: Released Apr '84, on Stiff, by Stiff Records. Catalogue no: **BUY 199**
12" Single: Released Apr '84, on Stiff, by Stiff Records. Catalogue no: **SBUY 199**

ROAD TO RACK AND RUIN
Tracks: / Road to rack and ruin.
7" Single: Released Aug '85, on Stiff, by Stiff Records. Catalogue no: **BUY 230**
12" Single: Released Aug '85, on Stiff, by Stiff Records. Catalogue no: **BUYIT 230**

SLAMMERS
Tracks: / Slammers.
7" Single: Released Nov '85, on Stiff, by Stiff Records. Catalogue no: **BUY 235**
12" Single: Released Nov '85, on Stiff, by Stiff Records. Catalogue no: **BUYIT 235**

ZULU BEAT
Tracks: / Zulu beat / Rockin Kent / Ghost riders in the sky / Oedipus.
7" Single: Released Jan '87, on Thin Sliced, by Thin Sliced Records. Catalogue no: **TSR 2**
12" Single: Released Jan '87, on Thin Sliced, by Thin Sliced Records. Catalogue no: **TSR 2T**

King, Lisa

CAN'T HELP FALLING IN LOVE
Tracks: / Can't help falling in love / You've got magic.
7" Single: Released Oct '80, on Trident, Deleted '81. Catalogue no: **TR 002**

King, Marcel

HOLLYWOOD NIGHTS
Tracks: / Hollywood nights.
12" Single: Released Mar '85, on Debut, by Skratch Records. Catalogue no: **DEBT 121**

KEEP ON DANCING
Tracks: / Keep on dancing.
12" Single: Released Mar '84, on Factory (1), by Factory Records. Catalogue no: **FAC 92**

REACH FOR LOVE (REMIX)
Tracks: / Reach for love.
12" Single: Released Mar '84, on Factory (1), by Factory Records. Catalogue no: **FAC 92**
12" Single: Released Apr '85, on Factory (1), by Factory Records. Catalogue no: **FAC 92R**

King, Mark

I FEEL FREE
Tracks: / I feel free.
7" Single: Released Jun '84, on Polydor, by Polydor Ltd. Catalogue no: **MK 1**
12" Single: Released Jun '84, on Polydor, by Polydor Ltd. Catalogue no: **MKX 1**

King MC

WHAT HAVE YOU DONE FOR ME LATELY
Tracks: / What have you done for me lately.
7" Single: Released May '86, on Important, Catalogue no: **TAN 9**
12" Single: Released May '86, on Important, Catalogue no: **TANT 9**

King, Natasha

AM
Tracks: / AM / FM / Megamix.
7" Single: Released Feb '86, on Ecstasy, by Creole Records. Catalogue no: **XTC 2**
12" Single: Released Feb '86, on Ecstasy, by Creole Records. Catalogue no: **XTCT 2**

King Obstinate

HUNGRY
Tracks: / Hungry / Got a little something for you.
12" Single: Released Aug '86, on Hot Vinyl, Catalogue no: **HVT 26**

King of Hearts

QUEEN OF SPADES (2 parts)
Tracks: / Queen of spades.
7" Single: Released Feb '82, on Ritz, by Ritz Records. Catalogue no: **RITZ 011**

King of Luxembourg

PICTURE OF DORIAN GRAY, A
Tracks: / Picture of Dorian Gray, A / Hasta pronto / Lee Remick / Espadarte / Where are the prawns?.
12" Single: Released Mar '87, on El, by Cherry Red Records. Catalogue no: **GPO 24 T**

TRIAL OF DOCTOR FANCY
Tracks: / Trial of Doctor Fancy / Elusive pimpernel (le Chevalier de Londres).
7" Single: Released Oct '87, on El, by Cherry Red Records. Catalogue no: **GPO 32**

VALLERI
Tracks: / Valleri / Sketches of Luxemburg.
7" Single: Released Jul '86, on El, by Cherry Red Records. Catalogue no: **GPO 14**

King Of The Slums

BOMBS AWAY ON HARPURHEY
Tracks: / Bombs away on Harpurhey.
7" Single: Released Oct '88, on Play Hard, by Play Hard Records. Catalogue no: **DEC 013**

ENGLAND'S FINEST HOPES EP
12" Single: Released '88, on Play Hard, by Play Hard Records. Catalogue no: **DEC 008**

FANCIABLE HEADCASE
Tracks: / Fanciable headcase / Leery bleeder / Hard core pornography star / Bombs away on harpurhey.
12" Single: Released Mar '89, on Play Hard, by Play Hard Records. Catalogue no: **DEC 14**

VICIOUS BRITISH BOYFRIEND
Tracks: / Vicious British boyfriend.
12" Single: Released Oct '88, on Play Hard, by Play Hard Records. Catalogue no: **DEC 14**

King, P

HEY ROSALYN
Tracks: / Hey Rosalyn.
7" Single: Released Jul '83, on Red Bus, by Red Bus Records. Catalogue no: **RBUS 79**

King, Paul

FOLLOW MY HEART
Tracks: / Follow my heart.
Cassingle: Released Aug '87, on CBS, by CBS Records. Catalogue no: **PKING C2**
7" Single: Released Aug '87, on CBS, by CBS Records. Catalogue no: **PKING 2**
7" Single: Released Aug '87, on CBS, by CBS Records. Catalogue no: **PKING Q2**

FOLLOWING HEART
Tracks: / Following heart / Brutality.
7" Single: Released Jul '87, on CBS, by CBS Records. Catalogue no: **PKING 2**
12" Single: Released Jul '87, on CBS, by CBS Records. Deleted Nov '87. Catalogue no: **PKINGT 2**

I KNOW
Tracks: / I know / Some risks.
12" Single: Released Apr '87, on CBS, by CBS Records. Deleted Nov '87. Catalogue no: **PKINGQ 1**

I KNOW (REMIX)
Tracks: / I know (remix) / I know / Some risks.
12" Single: Released Apr '87, on CBS, by CBS Records. Deleted Nov '87. Catalogue no: **PKINGR 1**

King, Peter

BAD MEMORY
Tracks: / Bad memory.
12" Single: Released Mar '86, on Fashion, by Fashion Records. Catalogue no: **FAD 045**

NITE LIFE
Tracks: / Nite life.
7" Single: Released Sep '83, on 6 AM, by 6 AM Records. Deleted '87. Catalogue no: **AM 704**
12" Single: Released Sep '83, on 6 AM, by 6 AM Records. Deleted '87. Catalogue no: **AM 12 704**

SOMETHING WICKED
Tracks: / Something wicked / Young blood.
7" Single: Released May '86, on Spirit (1), by Spirit Records. Catalogue no: **FIRE 10**
12" Single: Released May '86, on Spirit (1), by Spirit Records. Catalogue no: **FIRET 10**

STEP ON THE GAS
Tracks: / Step on the gas.
12" Single: Released May '85, on Fashion, by Fashion Records. Catalogue no: **FAD 029**

King Pleasure

AIN'T NOBODY HERE BUT US CHICKENS (new jive version)
Tracks: / Ain't nobody here but us chickens (new jive) / Chicken rhythm / All night long.
7" Single: Released 16 Jun '89, on Big Bear, by Big Bear Records. Catalogue no: **BB 40**

King, R J

HOT SHOT
Tracks: / Hot shot.
7" Single: Released Aug '88, on Soul Sity, Catalogue no: **SITY 5**
12" Single: Released Aug '88, on Soul Sity, Catalogue no: **SITYT 5**

King, Ray

WOMAN THAT UNDERSTANDS, A
Tracks: / Woman that understands, A / Pharoah's kingdom.
7" Single: Released Jan '80, on Big Bear, by Big Bear Records. Deleted '88. Catalogue no: **BB 22**

King, Rob

YOU DON'T KNOW LIKE I KNOW
Tracks: / You don't know like I know / Blues on.
7" Single: Released Jul '87, on Soul City, by Soul City Records. Catalogue no: **SITY 1**
12" Single: Released Jul '87, on Soul City, by Soul City Records. Catalogue no: **SITYT 1**

King, Robert

PAPERHEART
Tracks: / Paperheart / Theme for love.
7" Single: Released Jun '82, on Pre, by Charisma Records. Deleted Jun '85. Catalogue no: **PRE 23**

King, Sasha

YOU CAN'T TURN ME AWAY
Tracks: / You can't turn me away / You can't turn me away (club mix).
12" Single: Released Aug '86, on Londisc, by Londisc Records. Catalogue no: **12 LDR 057**

King, Sid

BACK DOOR MAN
Tracks: / Back door man / I'd rather hear Willie.
7" Single: Released Sep '80, on Hot, Catalogue no: **HR 45 006**

King, Solomon

Biographical details: This American singer enjoyed two British hit singles in 1968 while remaining unknown at home. *She wears my ring* reached No.3 and *When we were young* peaked at No.21; between them, the two discs spent more than half the year on the UK Top 50. *She wears my ring* wa penned by Felice & Boudleaux Bryant, the American husband-and-wife songwriting team who had been responsible for many of the famous Everly Brothers hits. The production of King's records was by Peter Sullivan, who was enjoying massive success in the late Sixties with two similar cabaret-oriented balladeers, Englebert Humperdinck and Tom Jones. The UK based Solomon King tried to mine further chart success, but quickly reached the pits. (Bob MacDonald, 25th Nov 1985).

SHE WEARS MY RING
Tracks: / She wears my ring.
7" Single: Released Jan '68, on Columbia, by EMI Records. Deleted '71. Catalogue no: **DB 8325**

SHE WEARS MY RING (SINGLE)
Tracks: / She wears my ring / Pub with no beer, A.
7" Single: Released Jul '82, on Old Gold, by Old Gold Records. Deleted Jul '88. Catalogue no: **OG 9044**
7" Single: Released Mar '87, on Old Gold, by Old Gold Records. Deleted Sep '89. Catalogue no: **OG 9634**

WHEN WE WERE YOUNG
Tracks: / When we were young.
7" Single: Released May '68, on Columbia, by EMI Records. Deleted '71. Catalogue no: **DB 8402**

King Sounds

BLACK AND WHITE
Tracks: / Black and white / Black and white (version).
12" Single: Released Apr '86, on King & I, Catalogue no: **KSIDM 006**

BOOK OF RULES
Tracks: / Book of rules.
12" Single: Released Oct '84, on King 1, Catalogue no: **KSI 003**

BRAND NEW CHILD
Tracks: / Brand new child / Living dub.
7" Single: Released May '81, on Island, by Island Records. Deleted May '84. Catalogue no: **IPR 2047**

GAMES PEOPLE PLAY
Tracks: / Games people play / Games people play (version).
12" Single: Released 23 May '87, on Viza, Catalogue no: **KSID 009**

I DON'T WANT TO HURT YOU
Tracks: / I don't want to hurt you.
7" Single: Released Aug '86, on King & I, Deleted Nov '87. Catalogue no: **KS 007**
12" Single: Released Feb '85, on King & I, Deleted Aug '86. Catalogue no: **12 KS 007**

I SHALL SING
Tracks: / I shall sing.
12" Single: Released Sep '89, on Viza, Catalogue no: **VZD 003**

PATCHES
Tracks: / Patches / Happiness.
12" Single: Released Apr '80, on Island, by Island Records. Deleted '83. Catalogue no: **12WIP 6595**
7" Single: Released Apr '80, on Island, by Island Records. Deleted '83. Catalogue no: **WIP 6595**

REGGAE LOVER
Tracks: / Reggae lover.
12" Single: Released Jul '87, on Ziza, Catalogue no: **ZZD 001**

YOU ARE MY PILOT
Tracks: / You are my pilot.
12" Single: Released Dec '83, on King 1, Catalogue no: **FK 001**

King Sporty

DO YOU WANNA DANCE?
Tracks: / Do you wanna dance?.
7" Single: Released Sep '83, on Dancefloor, Catalogue no: **DF 7005**
12" Single: Released Sep '83, on Dancefloor, Catalogue no: **DFT 7005**

MEET ME AT THE DISCO
Tracks: / Meet me at the disco / L.o.v.e..
7" Single: Released May '83, on Dancefloor, Catalogue no: **DS 7003**

King Stitt

HERBSMAN SHUFFLE
Tracks: / Herbsman shuffle / Fine corner / Vigorton 2.
7" Single: on Trojan, by Trojan Records. Deleted May '88. Catalogue no: **TRO 9064**
12" Single: on Trojan, by Trojan Records. Deleted May '88. Catalogue no: **TRT 9064**

King Sun

ON THE CLUB TIP
Tracks: / On the club tip.
7" Single: Released Jun '89, on Profile (USA), by Profile Records (USA). Catalogue no: **PROF 254**
12" Single: Released Jun '89, on Profile (USA), by Profile Records (USA). Catalogue no: **PROFT 254**

King Sun-D Moet

HEY LOVE
Tracks: / Hey love / Hey love (radio version) / Flame / Rhythm King / Priority.
7" Single: Released Jun '87, on RCA, by BMG Records (UK). Catalogue no: **MELT 5**
12" Single: Released May '87, on RCA, by BMG Records (UK). Catalogue no: **MELT 5T**

King Sunny Ade

JA FUMNI
Tracks: / Ja fumni.
7" Single: Released Sep '82, on Island, by Island Records. Deleted Sep '85. Catalogue no: **WIP 6826**
12" Single: Released Sep '82, on Island, by Island Records. Deleted Sep '85. Catalogue no: **12WIP 6826**

King Swallow

SUBWAY JAM
Tracks: / Subway jam / 25 years of man.
12" Single: Released Jun '82, on Seara, Catalogue no: **SEA 1**

King Swamp

BLOWN AWAY
Tracks: / Blown away / Midnight for the world / Vigilante man (12" only).
12" Pic: Released 13 Mar '89, on Virgin, by Virgin Records. Catalogue no: **KSWP 212**
7" Single: Released 13 Mar '89, on Virgin, by Virgin Records. Catalogue no: **KSW 2**
12" Single: Released 13 Mar '89, on Virgin, by Virgin Records. Catalogue no: **KSW 212**

CD 3": Released 13 Mar '89, on Virgin, by Virgin Records. Catalogue no: **KSWCD 2**

IS THIS LOVE?
Tracks: / Is this love? / Glow.
CD 5": Released Jan '89, on Virgin, by Virgin Records. Catalogue no: **KSWCD 1**
7" Single: Released Nov '88, on Virgin, by Virgin Records. Catalogue no: **KSW 1**
12" Single: Released Nov '88, on Virgin, by Virgin Records. Catalogue no: **KSW 112**
12" Single: Released Nov '88, on Virgin, by Virgin Records. Catalogue no: **KSWG 112**

King Tee

COOLEST, THE
Tracks: / Coolest, The.
12" Single: Released Aug '87, on Techno-Hop (USA), Catalogue no: **THR 17**

King, Terry

STAY WITH ME FOR CHRISTMAS
Tracks: / Stay with me for Christmas.
7" Single: Released Oct '84, on Code, by Code Records. Catalogue no: **LOB 17**

TEARS ON MY PILLOW
Tracks: / Tears on my pillow / Lonely talking again, The / Lonely talking again, The (talkin' dub).
12" Single: Released 27 Feb '88, on Body Music, by Nuclear Records. Catalogue no: **BZT 12**

King, Tom

A.L.F.I.E.
Tracks: / A.L.F.I.E / One for the money.
7" Single: Released May '84, on Lamborghini, by Lamborghini Records. Catalogue no: **LMG 11**

King, Tracey

MAKE ME YOURS
Tracks: / Make me yours.
12" Single: Released Aug '88, on Music Scene, Catalogue no: **MKS 62548**

King Trigger

RIVER, THE (see panel below)
Tracks: / River / Push or slide / River (extended version) (Only on 12" version.) / Push or slide (extended version) (Only on 12" version.).
7" Set: Released '82, on Chrysalis, by Chrysalis Records. Catalogue no: **CHSP 2623**
7" Single: Released '82, on Chrysalis, by Chrysalis Records. Catalogue no: **CHS 2623**
12" Single: Released '83, on Chrysalis, by Chrysalis Records. Deleted '87. Catalogue no: **CHS 12 2623**

TEMPTATION
Tracks: / Temptation / Running away.
7" Single: Released Oct '82, on Chrysalis, by Chrysalis Records. Catalogue no: **CHS 2651**
12" Single: Released Oct '82, on Chrysalis, by Chrysalis Records. Catalogue no: **CHS 122641**

King Truman

LIKE A GUN
Tracks: / Like a gun / Like a gun (version).
12" Single: Released Feb '89, on Acid Jazz, by Acid Jazz Records. Catalogue no: **JAZID 9T**

King, Will

BACK UP AGAINST THE WALL (SINGLE)
Tracks: / Back up against the wall.
7" Single: Released Jun '85, on Total Experience, Catalogue no: **FB 49965**
12" Single: Released Jun '85, on Total Experience, Catalogue no: **FT 49966**

Kingdom Come

CROWN OF THORNS
Tracks: / Crown of thorns / Gone are the days.
7" Single: Released Feb '83, on Illegal, by Faulty Products Records. Catalogue no: **ILS 0035**

DO YOU LIKE IT
Tracks: / Do you like it.
CD 5": Released Apr '89, on Polydor, by Polydor Ltd. Catalogue no: **KCCDS 3**
12" Pic: Released Apr '89, on Polydor, by Polydor Ltd. Deleted Oct '89. Catalogue no: **KCPDX 3**
7" Single: Released Apr '89, on Polydor, by Polydor Ltd. Deleted Oct '89. Catalogue no: **KCS 3**
12" Single: Released Apr '89, on Polydor, by Polydor Ltd. Deleted Oct '89. Catalogue no: **KCCV 3**
12" Single: Released Apr '89, on Polydor, by Polydor Ltd. Deleted Oct '89. Catalogue no: **KCX 3**

GET IT ON
Tracks: / Get it on / 17 / Loving you (Track on 12" and CD single.).
CD 5": Released Mar '88, on Polydor, by Polydor Ltd. Catalogue no: **KCCD 1**
12" Pic: Released Mar '88, on Polydor, by Polydor Ltd. Catalogue no: **KCXP 1**
7" Single: Released Mar '88, on Polydor, by Polydor Ltd. Catalogue no: **KCS 1**
12" Single: Released Mar '88, on Polydor, by Polydor Ltd. Catalogue no: **KCX 1**

OVERRATED
Tracks: / Overrated.
CD 5": Released 18 Sep '89, on Polydor, by Polydor Ltd. Catalogue no: **KCCDS 4**
10" single: Released Sep '89, on Polydor, by Polydor Ltd. Catalogue no: **KCCVX 4**
7" Single: Released Sep '89, on Polydor, by Polydor Ltd. Catalogue no: **KCCV 4**
7" Single: Released 18 Sep '89, on Polydor, by Polydor Ltd. Catalogue no: **KCS 4**
12" Single: Released 18 Sep '89, on Polydor, by Polydor Ltd. Catalogue no: **KCX 4**

WHAT LOVE CAN BE
Tracks: / What love can be.
CD 5": Released Jul '88, on Polydor, by Polydor Ltd. Catalogue no: **KCCD2**
7" Single: Released Jul '88, on Polydor, by Polydor Ltd. Deleted 30 May '89. Catalogue no: **KCS 2**
7" Single: Released Jul '88, on Polydor, by Polydor Ltd. Deleted 30 May '89. Catalogue no: **KCSC 2**
12" Single: Released Jul '88, on Polydor, by Polydor Ltd. Deleted 30 May '89. Catalogue no: **KCXG2**
12" Single: Released Jul '88, on Polydor, by Polydor Ltd. Deleted 30 May '89. Catalogue no: **KCX 2**

KING TRIGGER - THE RIVER (Released on Chrysalis)

KING'S SINGERS - BLACKBIRD (Released on H.M.V.)

Kingdoms

HEARTLAND
Tracks: / Heartland / Stability.
7" Single: Released Feb '84, on Regard, Catalogue no: **RG 114**
12" Single: Released Feb '84, on Regard, Catalogue no: **RGT 114**

Kingfishers Catch Fire

BLUSHING RED
Tracks: / Blushing red / Never never.
7" Single: Released Sep '87, on Furry, by Furry Records. Catalogue no: **KCF 112**

RADIO KAMPALA
Tracks: / Radio Kampala / Battlescars.
7" Single: Released Jul '86, on Furry, by Furry Records. Catalogue no: **KCF 111**

Kings

SWITCH INTO GLIDE
Tracks: / Switch into glide / This beat goes on.
7" Single: Released Mar '81, on Elektra, by Elektra Records (UK). Deleted Mar '84. Catalogue no: **K 12508**

Kings Of Agreppo

AGREPPO
Tracks: / Agreppo.
12" Single: Released '88, on Antler, by Antler Records (Belgium). Catalogue no: **SUB 024**

Kings Of Oblivion

BIG FISH POPCORN (SINGLE)
7" Single: Released 23 May '87, on Bam Caruso, by Demon Records. Catalogue no: **OPRA 086**

WISE UP (EP)
Tracks: / Wise up.
7" EP: Released Sep '88, on T.C.E., Catalogue no: **TCE 007**
12" Single: Released Jul '88, on T.C.E., Catalogue no: **TCE 001**

Kings Of Swing

Biographical details: *Switched on swing* was the title of a 1982 single and album by this Australian ensemble, which both entered the UK charts in May of that year. The single reached No.48 and the LP climbed to No.28 - purchasers of the latter received eight swing medleys featuring no less than 94 tunes. The *Switched on swing* project was clearly inspired by the Royal Philharmonic Orchestra 1981 success with *Hooked on classics*. Medley mania was quickly dying by spring '82, so the KSO could not exploit the idea for very long. (Bob MacDonald, 25th Nov 1985).

SWITCHED ON SWING (SINGLE)
Tracks: / Switched on swing / Switched on swing (part 2).
7" Single: Released Mar '82, on Philips, by Phonogram Ltd. Catalogue no: **SWING 1**

Kings of the Orient

WHITE DOOR
Tracks: / White door.
7" Single: Released Oct '82, on Clay, by Clay Records. Deleted '88. Catalogue no: **CLAY 15**
12" Single: Released Oct '82, on Clay, by Clay Records. Deleted '88. Catalogue no: **12 CLAY 15**

Kings Of The Sun

BLACK LEATHER
Tracks: / Black leather / Bad love.
7" Single: Released 16 Sep '88, on RCA, by BMG Records (UK). Deleted May '89. Catalogue no: **PB 49535**
12" Single: Released 16 Sep '88, on RCA, by BMG Records (UK). Deleted May '89. Catalogue no: **PT 49536**

King's Singers

BLACKBIRD (see panel above)
Tracks: / Blackbird / Back in the USSR.
7" Single: Released May '88, on H.M.V., by EMI Records. Catalogue no: **KINGS 1**

HOME IS A SPECIAL KIND OF FEELING
Tracks: / Home is a special kind of feeling / He waves the spear around.
7" Single: Released Mar '84, on Masterchord, by Masterchord Records & Tapes. Deleted '86. Catalogue no: **MCS 413**

LET'S BEGIN AGAIN
Tracks: / Let's begin again.
7" Single: Released Nov '83, on Masterchord, by Masterchord Records & Tapes. Deleted '86. Catalogue no: **MCS 412**

MONEY, MONEY, MONEY
Tracks: / Money, money, money / Summer nights / It was almost like a song / Nouveau poor.
7" EP: Released Feb '80, on Columbia, by EMI Records. Deleted Feb '83. Catalogue no: **DB 9075**

SO LONG AGO
Tracks: / So long ago / No suspicion.
7" Single: Released Nov '81, on WEA, by WEA Records. Deleted Nov '84. Catalogue no: **K 18885**

Kingsmen

Biographical details: This American rock-band consisted of Gary Abbott, Lynn Easton, Don Gallucci, Mike Mitchell and Norman Sundholm. The Kingsmen were formed at high school in Portland, Oregon in 1957. Developing a bluesy rock'n'roll sound, they spent several years building a solid live reputation in the north-western states; by 1963 they had become the resident combo at the well-known Chase nightclub in Portland. At the end of 1963 the Kingsmen rocketed up the American charts with *Louie Louie* - this classic single constituted the 2 minutes 41 seconds of music that secured their status in the annals of rock history. It was a hard basic, punchy update of a 1956 song originally recorded by its writer Richard Berry. The Kingsmen's rendition epitomised the earthy, spontaneous sound of the garage rock groups, and was very adventurous for its era. It logged six weeks at No.2 on the US chart but failed to rise above its prolonged prince regent status and ascend to the ultimate chart throne. *Louie Louie* certainly sounded raw when compared to the two chart-toppers which prevented it from reaching No.1 - *Dominique* by the Singing Nun and *There I've said it again* by Bobby Vinton. In early 1964, just as *Louie Louie* was descending the American chart (and peaking at No.26 in Britain), the Kingsmen were swamped by the Beatles and the whole British Invasion. Although they had much in common musically with the UK best group revolution - *Louie Louie* was widely imitated, and was the direct inspiration for the Kinks' first smash *You really got me* - the Portland players could not really compete effectively in the new Brit-dominated climate. They peaked at No.16 in the US with *Money (that's what I want)*, a remake of a Barrett Strong oldie that was also part of the Beatles' repertoire, and reached No.4 with their 1965 biggie *The jolly green giant* before drifting into minor hit status. *Louie Louie* was revived by the British heavy metal band Motorhead in 1978 - it gave them their first taste of chart success. (Bob MacDonald, 25th Nov 1985).

LOUIE LOUIE (OLD GOLD)
Tracks: / Louie Louie / Jolly green giant.
7" Single: Released Sep '80, on Old Gold, by Old Gold Records. Catalogue no: **OG 9054**

LOUIE LOUIE (SINGLE)
Tracks: / Louie Louie.
7" Single: Released Jan '64, on Pye International. Deleted '67. Catalogue no: **7N 25231**

Kingsnakes

ROUNDTRIP TICKET (SINGLE)
Tracks: / Roundtrip ticket.
7" Single: Released Jun '85, on New Rose (1), by New Rose Records. Catalogue no: **NEW 57**

Kingston Trio

Biographical details: At the time of their greatest success, this American folk band consisted of Dave Guard, Nick Reynolds and Bob Shane.
Hailing not from Kingston but from San Francisco, the Trio was formed in 1957 by three college students all aged around 20. They shot to fame in November '58 with their US No.1 smash *Tom Dooley*. This was a skilful adaptation by Dave Guard of a traditional folk song about Tom Dula, who was hanged in 1968 for the alleged murder of his girlfriend. After the success of the *Tom Dooley* record, Dula's grave in North Carolina was restored. The single established a bridge between the earlier Weavers and the later sounds of Bob Dylan, Joan Baez, Peter, Paul & Mary, etc.
The Trio followed *Tom Dooley* with a string of further US Top 40 singles, but they reached progressively lower positions until the 1961 replacement of the disillusioned John Stewart. Then came *Where have all the flowers gone* (written by the Weavers' Pete Seeger), *Greenback dollar* (penned by Hoyt Axton) and the 1963 US Top Tenner *Reverend Mr.Black*. During the mid-Sixties the Trio gradually faded from the public eye, as the folk-rock style of acts like the Byrds came on the scene. In 1967 Stewart quit the group and went solo, enjoying quick success as a writer and eventual acceptance as a performer. Meanwhile Reynolds and Shane kept the Kingston Trio name going throughout the rest of the Sixties and Seventies, using various permutations of players. All four of the key members performed together in a reunion concert in 1981. In Britain the Kingston Trio's track record was limited to two chart singles. *Tom Dooley* reached No.5 and a 1959 single entitled *San Miguel* peaked at No.29. In both cases they entered the chart in the same week as a rival cover version by the shrewd British folk fanatic Lonnie Donegan - because of his huge popularity in the UK, Donegan climbed higher up the charts than the American renditions. (Bob MacDonald, 25th Nov 1985).

SAN MIGUEL
Tracks: / San Miguel.
7" Single: Released Dec '59, on Capitol, by EMI Records. Catalogue no: **CL 15073**

TOM DOOLEY (OLD GOLD)
Tracks: / Tom Dooley / Michael.
7" Single: Released Mar '87, on Old Gold, by Old Gold Records. Deleted Sep '89. Catalogue no: **OG 9641**

TOM DOOLEY (SINGLE)
Tracks: / Tom Dooley.
7" Single: Released Nov '58, on Capitol, by EMI Records. Deleted '61. Catalogue no: **CL 14951**

KINKS - BETTER THINGS (Released on Arista)

Kinkina

JUNGLE FEVER
Tracks: / Jungle fever / Scratch fever / Scratch fever (megamix) / Scratch fever (scratch mix) / Scratch fever (original mix).
12" Single: Released May '87, on Champion, by Champion Records. Catalogue no: **CHAMP 1235**

Kinks

Biographical details: At the time of their greatest success, this British band consisted of Mick Avory, Dave Davies, his elder brother Ray Davies and Peter Quaife. After playing in various small-time London groups, the four musicians jelled as the Kinks at the beginning of 1964. Their first single was a Beatle-esque remake of Little Richard's *Long tall Sally*. Both this and the second release flopped, but their third single zoomed to the UK No.1 spot in September 1964 - *You really got me* was a classic example of the burgeoning bluesy rock genre, and its commercial success (which occured before any member of the quartet had celebrated his 21st birthday) and was a notable breakthrough. Although heavily influenced by the Kingsmen's recent US smash *Louie Louie* (which had not been a major hit in Britain), *You really got me* proved Kinks leader Ray Davies to be a great songwriter. For the following three years, Ray wrote a string of successes for the combo. Of the first dozen UK hit singles, all but one reached the Top 10. These smashes included the aforementioned chart-topper *You really got me* in 1964, plus a 1965 No.1 (*tired of waiting for you*) and a 1966 summit snatcher (*Sunny afternoon*). 1967 did not produce a Kinks No.1, but nevertheless yielded what is generally regarded as their finest track - *Waterloo sunset*, which peaked at No.2 in the UK. Other great Kinks singles of the mid-Sixties included *All day and all of the night* (later acknowledged as the direct inspiration for the Doors' 1968 US No.1 *Hello I love you*, *Dedicated follower of fashion* and *Dead end street*. They reached No.1 on Britains seperate EP charts with *Kinksize session* (1965) and *Kwyet Kinks* (also '65, including the classic song *A well respected man*.
The first three of the Kinks' UK smash singles also reached the American Top 10. But the group's Stateside success subsided somewhat as the raunchy rhythm-and-blues gave way to Ray Davies' more subtle songs. He gained a reputation as a brilliant observer of the British way of life - to UK ears, his songwriting stature stood comparison with Lennon and McCartney; to US audiences, his typically English style was of no great interest. After an artistically brave but commercially disastrous period at the end of the Sixties, the Kinks hit the Top 10 on both sides of the Atlantic with 1970's *Lola*. During the mid-Seventies British record buyers totally lost interest in the Kinks but they began to build an increasingly large concert following in the States. The 1977 LP *Sleepwalker* reached the US Top 30, as did the 1978 single *A rock'n'roll fantasy*.
During the late Seventies and early Eighties, the classic songs of Ray Davies were introduced to a new generation on both sides of the Atlantic via successful cover versions by such modern bands as the Jam, the Pretenders and Van Halan. The Kinks finally reaped the rewards of this renewed acclaim in 1983, when *Come dancing*, a song that was as good as Ray's vintage material, gave the band their highest placed American hit since 1965 and their first major British success since 1972. (Bob MacDonald, 26th Nov 1985).

ALL DAY AND ALL OF THE NIGHT
Tracks: / All day and all of the night / I gotta move.
7" Pic: Released Jan '88, on PRT, by Castle Communications Records. Catalogue no: **PYS 4**
7" Pic: Released Jan '88, on PRT, by Castle Communications Records. Catalogue no: **PYS 4**
7" Pic: Released Oct '84, on PRT, by Castle Communications Records. Deleted '86. Catalogue no: **KSI 003**
7" Single: Released Oct '64, on Pye, Deleted '67. Catalogue no: **7N 15714**

APE MAN
Tracks: / Ape man.
7" Single: Released Dec '70, on Pye, Deleted '73. Catalogue no: **7N 45016**

AUTUMN ALMANAC
Tracks: / Autumn almanac.
7" Single: Released Oct '67, on Pye, Deleted '70. Catalogue no: **7N 17400**

BETTER THINGS (see panel above)
Tracks: / Better things / Massive reductions / Lola / David Watts.
7" Single: Released Jun '81, on Arista, by BMG Records (UK). Deleted '84. Catalogue no: **ARIST 415**

COME DANCING
Tracks: / Come dancing / Noise.
7" Single: Released Aug '83, on Arista, by BMG Records (UK). Catalogue no: **ARIST 502**
12" Single: Released Aug '83, on Arista, by BMG Records (UK). Deleted '84. Catalogue no: **ARIST 12502**

DAVID WATTS
Tracks: / David Watts / Where have all the good times gone / Altitudes / Victoria.
7" EP: Released Jul '80, on Arista, by BMG Records (UK). Deleted Jul '83. Catalogue no: **ARIST 360**

DAYS
Tracks: / Days.
7" Single: Released Jul '68, on Pye, Deleted '71. Catalogue no: **7N 17468**

DEAD END STREET
Tracks: / Dead End Street.
7" Single: Released Nov '66, on Pye, Deleted '69. Catalogue no: **7N 17222**

DEDICATED FOLLOWER OF FASHION
Tracks: / Dedicated follower of fashion / Autumn almanac.
7" Pic: Released 30 Mar '88, on PRT, by Castle Communications Records. Catalogue no: **PYS 7**
7" Single: Released May '86, on PRT, by Castle Communications Records. Catalogue no: **7P 355**

DEDICATED FOLLOWER OF FASHION (ORIGINAL)
Tracks: / Dedicated follower of fashion.
Note: Double A
7" Single: Released Mar '66, on PRT, by Castle Communications Records. Deleted '69. Catalogue no: **7N 17064**

DO IT AGAIN
Tracks: / Do it again.
7" Single: Released Apr '85, on Arista, by BMG Records (UK). Catalogue no: **ARIST 617**
12" Single: Released May '85, on Arista, by BMG Records (UK). Catalogue no: **ARIST 12617**

DON'T FORGET TO DANCE
Tracks: / Don't forget to dance.
7" Single: Released '83, on Arista, by BMG Records (UK). Deleted '86. Catalogue no: **ARIST 524**
12" Single: Released '83, on Arista, by BMG Records (UK). Deleted '86. Catalogue no: **ARIST 12524**

DOWN ALL THE DAYS
Tracks: / Down all the days / You really got me (live) / Entertainment (Available on 12" only).
CD 5": Released Sep '89, on London Records, by London Records. Catalogue no: **LONCD 239**
7" Single: Released Sep '89, on London Records, by London Records. Catalogue no: **LON 239**
12" Single: Released Sep '89, on London Records, by London Records. Catalogue no: **LONX 239**

EVERYBODY'S GONNA BE HAPPY
Tracks: / Everybody's gonna be happy.
7" Single: Released Mar '65, on Pye, Deleted '68. Catalogue no: **7N 15813**

HOW ARE YOU
Tracks: / How are you / Killing time / This is sleazy town (Extra track available on 12" only.).
7" Single: Released Dec '86, on London Records, by London Records. Deleted Sep '87. Catalogue no: **LON 119**
12" Single: Released Dec '86, on London Records, by London Records. Catalogue no: **LONX 119**

KINKS EP
Tracks: / Waterloo sunset / David Watts / Stop your sobbing / Well-respected man.
7" EP: Released 20 Jun '80, on Flashback, by Mainline Records. Deleted '83. Catalogue no: **FBEP 104**

LOLA (OLD GOLD)
Tracks: / Lola / Apeman.
7" Single: Released 27 Feb '89, on Old Gold, by Old Gold Records. Catalogue no: **OG 9579**

LOLA (SINGLE)
Tracks: / Lola / Celluloid heroes.
7" Single: Released May '81, on Arista, by BMG Records (UK). Deleted May '84. Catalogue no: **ARIST 404**
7" Single: Released Jul '70, on Pye, Deleted '73. Catalogue no: **7N 17961**

LOST AND FOUND
Tracks: / Lost and found / Killing time / Ray Davies interview (Extra track on 12" version.).
7" Single: Released Mar '87, on London Records, by London Records. Deleted Sep '87. Catalogue no: **LON 132**
12" Single: Released Mar '87, on London Records, by London Records. Deleted Sep '87. Catalogue no: **LONX 132**

PLASTIC MANA
Tracks: / Plastic man.
7" Single: Released Jul '68, on Pye, Deleted '71. Catalogue no: **7N 175723**

PREDICTABLE
Tracks: / Predictable / Back to front.
7" Pic: Released '82, on Arista, by BMG Records (UK). Deleted '87. Catalogue no: **ARIPD 467**
7" Single: Released Nov '81, on Arista, by BMG Records (UK). Deleted Nov '84. Catalogue no: **ARIST 467**

ROAD, THE (SINGLE)
Tracks: / Road, The / Art lover / Come dancing (* Track on 12" version only.) / Road, the (full version).
7" Single: Released 20 Feb '88, on London Records, by London Records. Deleted Feb '89. Catalogue no: **LON 165**
12" Single: Released 20 Feb '88, on London Records, by London Records. Deleted Feb '89. Catalogue no: **LONX 165**

SEE MY FRIEND
Tracks: / See my friends.
7" Single: Released Jul '65, on Pye, Deleted '68. Catalogue no: **7N 15919**

SET ME FREE
Tracks: / Set me free.
7" Single: Released May '65, on Pye. Deleted '68. Catalogue no: **7N 15759**

STATE OF CONFUSION (SINGLE)
Tracks: / State of confusion / Heart of gold.
7" Single: Released Mar '84, on Arista, by BMG Records (UK). Catalogue no: **ARIST 560**
12" Single: Released Mar '84, on Arista, by BMG Records (UK). Catalogue no: **ARIST 12560**

SUNNY AFTERNOON (OLD GOLD)
Tracks: / Sunny Afternoon / Tired of waiting for you / Sittin' on my sofa.
7" Single: Released Mar '86, on Old Gold, by Old Gold Records. Catalogue no: **OG 9577**

SUNNY AFTERNOON (ORIGINAL)
Tracks: / Sunny afternoon.
7" Single: Released Jun '66, on Pye. Deleted '69. Catalogue no: **7N 17125**

SUPERSONIC ROCKET SHIP
Tracks: / Supersonic rocket ship.
7" Single: Released May '72, on RCA, by BMG Records (UK). Deleted '75. Catalogue no: **RCA 2211**

TIRED OF WAITING FOR YOU
Tracks: / Tired of waiting for you.
7" Single: Released Jan '65, on Pye. Deleted '68. Catalogue no: **7N 15759**

TIRED OF WAITING FOR YOU (FLASHBACK)
Tracks: / Tired of waiting for you / Waterloo sunset.
7" Single: Released Jan '83, on Flashback, by Mainline Records. Catalogue no: **FBS 15**

VICTORIA
Tracks: / Victoria.
7" Single: Released Jan '70, on Pye. Deleted '73. Catalogue no: **7N 17865**

WATERLOO SUNSET
Tracks: / Waterloo sunset.
7" Single: Released May '67, on Pye. Deleted '70. Catalogue no: **7N 17321**
7" Single: Released Jun '80, on Flashback, by Mainline Records. Catalogue no: **FBEP 104**

WATERLOO SUNSET (OLD GOLD)
Tracks: / Waterloo sunset / Sunny afternoon / Lola.
CD 5": Released 27 Feb '89, on Old Gold, by Old Gold Records. Catalogue no: **OG 6117**
7" Single: Released Nov '81, on Old Gold, by Old Gold Records. Deleted Nov '84. Catalogue no: **OG 9140**

WONDERBOY
Tracks: / Wonder boy.
7" Single: Released Apr '68, on Pye. Deleted '71. Catalogue no: **7N 17468**

YOU REALLY GOT ME
Tracks: / You really got me / All day and all of the night.
7" Pic: Released Sep '83, on PRT, by Castle Communications Records. Catalogue no: **KPD 1**
7" Single: Released Feb '80, on RK, by RK Records. Deleted Feb '85. Catalogue no: **RK 1027**
7" Single: Released Jul '64, on Pye. Deleted '67. Catalogue no: **7N 15673**
7" Single: Released Apr '79, on Flashback, by Mainline Records. Catalogue no: **FBS 1**
7" Single: Released Sep '83, on PRT, by Castle Communications Records. Catalogue no: **KD 1**
12" Single: Released Sep '83, on PRT, by Castle Communications Records. Catalogue no: **DKL 1**

YOU REALLY GOT ME (OLD GOLD)
Tracks: / You really got me / All day and all of the night / Tired of waiting for you.
CD 5": Released Nov '88, on Old Gold, by Old Gold Records. Catalogue no: **OG 6102**
7" Single: Released Jun '84, on Old Gold, by Old Gold Records. Catalogue no: **OG 9408**

Kinky Foxx

SO DIFFERENT
Tracks: / So different.
7" Single: Released Dec '83, on Sound Of New York (USA), by Sound Of New York Records(USA). Catalogue no: **SNY 6**
12" Single: Released Dec '83, on Sound Of New York (USA), by Sound Of New York Records(USA). Catalogue no: **SNYL 6**

Kinney, Fern

Biographical details: This American singer first came to public attention in her native country at the end of the Seventies with her disco hit *Groove me*. This was a revival of a 1971 American Top Tenner by King Floyd. Kinney's rendition was big in the clubs but failed to cross over to the US pop Top 40. The singer did, however, manage a one-off pop smash in Britain. *Together we are beautiful*, a wimpish romantic ballad that had been a minor hit the previous year for Steve Allan, cruised to the UK No.1 slot for Fern in March 1980. Those who found the song slightly too sugary were irriated even more by Kinney's thin high voice. The failure of Fern's follow-ups placed her firmly in the One Hit Wonder bracket. The producers of *Together we are beautiful*, Tommy Couch & Wolf Stephenson, later took the singer to their own Malaco label; but Fern's flagging fortunes were not revived. (Bob MacDonald, 26th Nov 1985).

BEAUTIFUL LOVE SONG
Tracks: / Beautiful love song / Pipin' hot.
7" Single: Released Mar '83, on Malaco, by Malaco Records (UK). Deleted '88. Catalogue no: **MAL 005**
12" Single: Released Mar '83, on Malaco, by Malaco Records (UK). Deleted '88. Catalogue no: **MAL 12 005**

I WANT YOU BACK
Tracks: / I want you back / Groove me.
7" Single: Released Jun '80, on WEA, by WEA Records. Deleted Jun '83. Catalogue no: **K 791 36**

I'M READY FOR YOUR LOVE
Tracks: / I'm ready for your love.
12" Single: Released Dec '82, on Malaco, by Malaco Records (UK). Deleted '88. Catalogue no: **MAL 12 006**

I'VE BEEN LONELY FOR SO LONG
Tracks: / I've been lonely for so long / Love me.
7" Single: Released Feb '81, on WEA, by WEA Records. Catalogue no: **K 79203**
12" Single: Released Mar '81, on WEA, by WEA Records. Catalogue no: **K 79203 T**

SWEET LIFE
Tracks: / Sweet life / Tonight the night.
7" Single: Released Apr '80, on CBS, by CBS Records. Deleted Apr '83. Catalogue no: **CBS 8368**

TOGETHER WE ARE BEAUTIFUL
Tracks: / Together we are beautiful / Baby let me kiss you.
7" Single: Released Jan '80, on WEA, by WEA Records. Catalogue no: **K 79111**

TOGETHER WE ARE BEAUTIFUL (OLD GOLD)
Tracks: / Together we are beautiful.
7" Single: Released Mar '86, on Old Gold, by Old Gold Records. Catalogue no: **OG 9592**

Kino

ROOM IN MY HEART
Tracks: / Room in my heart / Ugh Ugh.
7" Single: Released Mar '86, on Chrysalis, by Chrysalis Records. Deleted '87. Catalogue no: **CHS 2974**
12" Single: Released Mar '86, on Chrysalis, by Chrysalis Records. Catalogue no: **CHS 12 2974**

Kinsman Dazz

KEEP ON ROCKIN'
Tracks: / Keep on rockin' / I searched around.
7" Single: Released Jan '80, on 20th Century, by 20th Century Records. Deleted Jan '85. Catalogue no: **TC 2417**
12" Single: Released Jan '80, on 20th Century, by 20th Century Records. Deleted Jan '85. Catalogue no: **TCD 2417**

Kintone

STATE OF EMERGENCY
Tracks: / State of emergency.
12" Single: Released Apr '86, on KMC, Catalogue no: **12 KMC 01**

Kio

HOT BLACK AND SWEET
Tracks: / Hot black and sweet / Honest men.
7" Single: Released Oct '81, on Record Shack, by Record Shack Records. Deleted Oct '84. Catalogue no: **SHACK 126**

Kipling, Anna

HAPPY ANNIVERSARY
Tracks: / Happy anniversary / Where do you go.
7" Single: Released Jul '87, on MBS, by MBS Records. Catalogue no: **MBS 002**

Kipner, Stephen

KNOCK DOWN THE WALLS
Tracks: / Knock down the walls / I had to find out for myself.

7" Single: Released Mar '80, on Elektra Asylum, by Elektra Records (USA). Deleted Mar '83. Catalogue no: **K 12411**

Kirby, Kathy

Biographical details: This British singer began to earn some attention in the music business when she appeared on the same bill as Cliff Richard & The Shadows on a 1960 tour. However, her UK chart success did not occur until 1963-64, when she chalked up four Top 20 singles plus a Top 20 LP in the space of twelve months. Like the Bachelors, she managed to win success despite being classed as a middle-of-the-road anachronism during this era dominated by the Beatles-led Merseybeat explosion. Kirby's first three Top 20 singles were plucked from the repertoires of the Shadows (a vocal version of *Dance on*), Doris Day (*Secret love*) and Teresa Brewer (*Let me go lover*) - all representatives of bygone eras in pop music. Her fourth hit was a previously unknown song called *You're the one*. The blonde heavily made-up Kirby entered the Eurovision Song Contest in 1965 with *I belong*. At that time, the United Kingdom was continually faring badly in the annual event. Kathy failed to break the mould, and her entry peaked at No.36 on the British singles chart (although her EP *A song for Europe* fared better). The UK's Eurovision breakthrough finally happened in 1967 with Sandie Shaw's winning *Puppet on a string*. Kirby, meanwhile faded from the public eye. (Bob MacDonald, 26th Nov 1985).

DANCE ON
Tracks: / Dance on.
7" Single: Released Jul '63, on Decca, by Decca Records. Deleted '66. Catalogue no: **F 11682**

HE
Tracks: / He / Nobody loves me like you do.
7" Single: Released Mar '81, on President, by President Records. Deleted Mar '84. Catalogue no: **PT 491**

I BELONG
Tracks: / I belong.
7" Single: Released Mar '65, on Decca, by Decca Records. Deleted '68. Catalogue no: **F 12087**

LET ME GO LOVER
Tracks: / Let me go lover.
7" Single: Released Feb '64, on Decca, by Decca Records. Deleted '67. Catalogue no: **F 11832**

SECRET LOVE (SINGLE)
Tracks: / Secret love / You have to want to.
7" Single: Released Nov '63, on Decca, by Decca Records. Deleted '67. Catalogue no: **F 11759**

YOU'RE THE ONE
Tracks: / You're the one.
7" Single: Released May '64, on Decca, by Decca Records. Deleted '67. Catalogue no: **F 11892**

Kirk, Richard H

HIPNOTIC
Tracks: / Hipnotic.
12" Single: Released Sep '86, on Rough Trade, by Rough Trade Records. Catalogue no: **RTT 199**

LEATHER HANDS
Tracks: / Leather hands.
12" Single: Released Oct '85, on Double Vision, by Double Vision Records. Catalogue no: **DVR 15**

Kirkland, Bo

YOU'RE GONNA GET NEXT TO ME
Tracks: / You're gonna get next to me.
7" Single: Released Jun '77, on EMI International, by EMI Records. Deleted '80. Catalogue no: **INT 532**

Kirkpatrick, John

JOGGING ALONG WITH ME REINDEER
Tracks: / Jogging along with me reindeer / King Neptune's lament.
7" Single: Released Nov '80, on Dingle's, by Dingle's Records. Catalogue no: **SID 226**

Kirkwood, Diana

VALENTINO
Tracks: / Valentino / You come into my life.
7" Single: Released Feb '86, on White Rock, Deleted '87. Catalogue no: **BOC 1**

Kirsh, Les

I'D BAKED YOU A CAKE
Tracks: / I'd baked you a cake.
7" Single: Released Jul '84, on Magic (1), by Submarine Records. Catalogue no: **MAGIC 8**

Kirton, Lew

DON'T WANNA WAIT
Tracks: / Don't wanna wait / Stuck in the middle (Between two).
7" Single: Released Jul '86, on MCA, by MCA Records. Catalogue no: **MCA 1071**
12" Single: Released Jul '86, on MCA, by MCA Records. Catalogue no: **MCAT 1071**

JUST CAN'T GET ENOUGH
Tracks: / Just can't get enough / Don't give up on your dream / Here's my love.
7" Single: Released Dec '83, on Epic, by CBS Records. Catalogue no: **A 4066**
12" Single: Released Dec '83, on Epic, by CBS Records. Catalogue no: **TA 4066**

Kirwin, Dominic

GREEN HILLS ARE ROLLING STILL, THE
Tracks: / Green hills are rolling still, The / Golden dreams / More than yesterday (Only on cassette single.) / Little cabin boy, The (Only on cassette single.).
Cassingle: Released May '89, on Ritz, by Ritz Records. Catalogue no: **RITZC 199**
7" Single: Released Apr '89, on Ritz, by Ritz Records. Catalogue no: **RITZ 199**

Kishman, Tony

STAYING WITH IT
Tracks: / Staying with it / Don't blame me.
7" Single: Released Aug '80, on RCA, by BMG Records (UK). Deleted '83. Catalogue no: **PB 5270**

STRANGE WAY
Tracks: / Strange way / There's no longer magic.
7" Single: Released Feb '81, on RCA, by BMG Records (UK). Deleted Feb '84. Catalogue no: **RCA 38**

Kiss

Biographical details: At the time of their Seventies heyday, this American rock band consisted of Peter Criss, Ace Frehley, Gene Simmons and Paul Stanley. Kiss were formed in New York in 1973, and their first two albums *Kiss* and *Hotter than hell* were issued in 1974. Always in their element on stage, it was the 1975 album *Alive!* that bought them to US Top 10 status. This pile driving concert recording demonstrated that there was plenty of good ear-shattering rock music under the band's striking visual image. The four-man heavy metal group epitomized the term 'over the top'. With 40-foot drum kits, devastating lighting effects, fire-spitting, fantasy film costumes and, most important of all, their famed horror comic make-up, Kiss stormed through the States in the Seventies, offending everyone from parents to rock critics to evangelists. Everyone, that is, except for their devoted army of fans who were amongst the most loyal for any major group, lapping up such anthems as *Rock and roll all nite*, *Shout it out loud* and the 1976 US Top 10 ballad *Beth*. In a novel move, all four members released simultaneous solo albums in 1978. Lead guitarist Frehley's effort was probably the best, yielding a US Top 20 remake of Hello's British hit *New York groove*. In 1979 Kiss were back in business with their million-selling single *I was made for lovin' you*. At the start of the Eighties, the previous unity began to break down and personnel changes started to occur. By the time of 1983's *Lick it up* LP, Frehley and drummer Criss had been respectively replaced by Vinnie Vincent and Eric Carr. The performers were now revealing their real faces instead of hiding under those masks. With the greasepaint toned down, what was left was what was always there under the make-up and smoke bombs - a competent, powerful hard rock band that had never totally caught on in Britain. Although *Destroyer* (1976) and *Creatures of the night* (1982) had reached the UK Top 30 albums, it was not until the mid-Eighties that they managed to build a solid touring and recording selling base in Britain. Their biggest UK single was 1983's *Lick it up*, which peaked at No.31. Much credit for the Kiss success story must go to their shrewd and highly professional manager Bill Aucoin who, in 1982, guided former British punk star Billy Idol to Stateside success. (Bob MacDonald, 26th Nov 1985).

2000 MAN (EP)
Tracks: / 2000 man / I was made for loving you / Sure know something.
7" EP: Released Feb '80, on Casablanca, by PolyGram UK Ltd. Deleted Feb '83. Catalogue no: **NB 1001**

CRAZY CRAZY NIGHTS (SINGLE)
Tracks: / Crazy crazy nights / No no no / Lick it up (Extra track available on 12" version only.) / Uh all night*.
Note: * extra tracks on 12" version.
12" Pic: Released Sep '87, on Vertigo, by Phonogram Ltd. Deleted Oct '88. Catalogue no: **KISSP 712**
7" Pic: Released Sep '87, on Vertigo, by Phonogram Ltd. Deleted Oct '88. Cata-

logue no: **KISSP 7**
7" Single: Released Sep '87, on Vertigo, by Phonogram Ltd. Deleted Oct '88. Catalogue no: **KISS 7**
12" Single: Released Sep '87, on Vertigo, by Phonogram Ltd. Deleted Oct '88. Catalogue no: **KISS 712**

CREATURES OF THE NIGHT (SINGLE)
Tracks: / Creatures of the night.
7" Single: Released Apr '83, on Casablanca, by PolyGram UK Ltd. Catalogue no: **KISS 4**
12" Single: Released Apr '83, on Casablanca, by PolyGram UK Ltd. Catalogue no: **KISS 412**

HEAVEN'S ON FIRE
Tracks: / Heaven's on fire.
7" Single: Released Sep '84, on Vertigo, by Phonogram Ltd. Catalogue no: **VER 12**
12" Single: Released Sep '84, on Vertigo, by Phonogram Ltd. Catalogue no: **VERX 12**

HIDE YOUR HEART
Tracks: / Hide your heart.
7" Single: Released Oct '89, on Vertigo, by Phonogram Ltd. Catalogue no: **VER 45**
12" Single: Released Oct '89, on Vertigo, by Phonogram Ltd. Catalogue no: **VERX 45**

I WAS MADE FOR LOVING YOU
Tracks: / I was made for lovin' you.
7" Single: Released Jun '79, on Casablanca, by PolyGram UK Ltd. Deleted '82. Catalogue no: **CAN 152**

I WAS MADE FOR LOVING YOU (IMPORT)
Tracks: / I was made for loving you / Hard times.
12" Single: Released Sep '88, on Casablanca (Germany), by PolyGram UK Ltd. Catalogue no: **6000562**

KILLER
Tracks: / Killer / Love it loud / I was made for lovin' you.
7" Single: Released Dec '82, on Casablanca, by PolyGram UK Ltd. Deleted Dec '87. Catalogue no: **KISS 312**

KISS: INTERVIEW PIC DISC COLLECTION
Tracks: / Interview collection picture disc / House arrest / Jack's back.
7" Set: Released 31 Oct '87, on Baktabak, by Baktabak Records. Catalogue no: **BAKPAK 1002**

LICK IT UP (SINGLE)
Tracks: / Lick it up.
7" Single: Released Oct '83, on Casablanca, by PolyGram UK Ltd. Deleted '86. Catalogue no: **KISS 005**

REASON TO LIVE
Tracks: / Reason to live / Thief in the night / Who wants to be lonely* / Thrills in the night / Tears are falling+ / Crazy crazy nights+.
Note: + tracks on CD single only.
CD 5": Released Nov '87, on Vertigo, by Phonogram Ltd. Deleted Oct '88. Catalogue no: **KISCD 8**
7" Pic: Released '88, on Vertigo, by Phonogram Ltd. Deleted Oct '88. Catalogue no: **KISSP8**
Cassingle: Released Dec '87, on Vertigo, by Phonogram Ltd. Deleted Feb '89. Catalogue no: **KISS MC8**
7" Single: Released Nov '87, on Vertigo, by Phonogram Ltd. Deleted Oct '88. Catalogue no: **KISS 8**
12" Single: Released Nov '87, on Vertigo, by Phonogram Ltd. Deleted Oct '88. Catalogue no: **KISS 812**

TEARS ARE FALLING
Tracks: / Tears are falling.
7" Single: Released Oct '85, on Vertigo, by Phonogram Ltd. Catalogue no: **KISS 6**
12" Single: Released Oct '85, on Vertigo, by Phonogram Ltd. Catalogue no: **KISS 612**

TURN ON THE NIGHT
Tracks: / Turn on the night / Hell or high water / King of the mountain (Only on 12") / Any way you slice it (Only on 12") / Crazy crazy nights / Reason to live.
CD 5": Released 22 Aug '88, on Vertigo, by Phonogram Ltd. Deleted Feb '89. Catalogue no: **KISCD 9**
7" Pic: Released Aug '88, on Vertigo, by Phonogram Ltd. Deleted 31 May '89. Catalogue no: **KISSP 9**
7" Single: Released 22 Aug '88, on Vertigo, by Phonogram Ltd. Deleted Feb '89. Catalogue no: **KISS 9**
12" Single: Released 22 Aug '88, on Vertigo, by Phonogram Ltd. Deleted Feb '89. Catalogue no: **KISS 912**

WHAT MAKES THE WORLD GO ROUND
Tracks: / What makes the world go round / Naked city.
7" Single: Released Sep '80, on Mercury, by Phonogram Ltd. Deleted '83. Catalogue no: **KISS 1**

WORLD WITHOUT HEROES, A
Tracks: / World without heroes, A / Mr. Blackwell.
7" Single: Released Feb '82, on Casablanca, by PolyGram UK Ltd. Deleted '85. Catalogue no: **KISS 2**

Kiss AMC

BIT OF..., A
Tracks: / Bit of..., A (Dance floor side.) / Raw side, The (Make sure side) / Bit of..., A (remix edit) (CD single only.) / Bit of..., A (double trouble remix) (Special product only.) / Bit of..., A (dubstrumental) (Special product only.) / Bit of..., A (amazonian mix) (Special product only.).
Note: Producer/Arranger: Chapter.i
12" Single: Released Aug '89, on Syncopate, by EMI Records. Catalogue no: **12SYX 29**

BIT OF U2, A
Tracks: / Bit of U2, A (Dance floor side.) / Raw side, The.
CD 5": Released Aug '89, on Syncopate, by EMI Records. Catalogue no: **203 417 2**
CD 5": Released Aug '89, on Syncopate, by EMI Records. Catalogue no: **CDSY 29**
12" Pic: Released Jul '89, on Syncopate, by EMI Records. Catalogue no: **12 SYP 29**
7" Pic: Released Jul '89, on Syncopate, by EMI Records. Catalogue no: **SYP 29**
7" Pic: Released Jul '89, on Syncopate, by EMI Records. Catalogue no: **203 417 0**
Cassingle: Released Aug '89, on Syncopate, by EMI Records. Catalogue no: **TCSY 29**
Cassingle: Released Aug '89, on Syncopate, by EMI Records. Catalogue no: **203 417 4**
7" Single: Released Aug '89, on Syncopate, by EMI Records. Catalogue no: **SY 29**
7" Single: Released Aug '89, on Syncopate, by EMI Records. Catalogue no: **203 417 7**
12" Single: Released Aug '89, on Syncopate, by EMI Records. Catalogue no: **12SY 29**
12" Single: Released Aug '89, on Syncopate, by EMI Records. Catalogue no: **203 417 6**

LET OFF
Tracks: / Let off (Composers Hinds/Leveridge.) / Kiss AMC (Composers Hinds/Leveridge.) / Let off (remix) (12" remix only.) / Kiss AMC (remix) (12" remix only.).
7" Single: Released Nov '88, on Syncopate, by EMI Records. Deleted Aug '89. Catalogue no: **SYG 22**
7" Single: Released Nov '88, on Syncopate, by EMI Records. Deleted Aug '89. Catalogue no: **SY 22**
12" Single: Released Dec '88, on Syncopate, by EMI Records. Deleted Aug '89. Catalogue no: **12SYX 22**
12" Single: Released Nov '88, on Syncopate, by EMI Records. Deleted Aug '89. Catalogue no: **12SY 22**

Kiss Kiss Bang Bang

HIGH HEELS
Tracks: / High heels / Kiss me on my ....
7" Single: Released Jun '87, on Magnet, by WEA Records. Deleted Jan '88. Catalogue no: **MAG 312**
12" Single: Released Jun '87, on Magnet, by WEA Records. Deleted Jan '88. Catalogue no: **MAGT 312**

Kiss Patrol

MIDNIGHT IN MOSCOW
Tracks: / Midnight in Moscow / Hit and run.
7" Single: Released Aug '80, on Sonet, by Sonet Records. Deleted '82. Catalogue no: **SON 2211**

Kiss That

MARCH OUT
Tracks: / March out / Simple girl.
7" Single: Released May '86, on Chrysalis, by Chrysalis Records. Deleted '87. Catalogue no: **CHS 2966**
12" Single: Released May '86, on Chrysalis, by Chrysalis Records. Deleted '87. Catalogue no: **CHS 12 2966**

Kiss The Blade

PARTY'S BEGUN
Tracks: / Party's begun.
12" Single: Released Feb '85, on Incision, Catalogue no: **CUT 1**

YOUNG SOLDIER
Tracks: / Young soldier.
12" Single: Released Dec '86, on Incision, Catalogue no: **CUT 3**

Kissed Air

KARIBA
Tracks: / Kariba / Kissed air.
7" Single: Released May '82, on Kabuki, Catalogue no: **KA 1**

KAWARAYA
Tracks: / Kawaraya.
12" Single: Released Jul '83, on Kabuki, Catalogue no: **KA9**

OUT OF THE NIGHT
Tracks: / Out of the night / Change of attention.
7" Single: Released Nov '82, on Kabuki, Catalogue no: **KA 3**

Kissing Bandits

CAVEMAN
Tracks: / Caveman.
7" Single: Released Mar '85, on Rogue, by Rogue Records. Catalogue no: **ROG 001**

SHAKE SOME ACTION
Tracks: / Shake some action / Jealousy.
7" Single: Released Mar '84, on WEA, by WEA Records. Catalogue no: **YZ 2**
12" Single: Released Mar '84, on WEA, by WEA Records. Catalogue no: **YZ 2T**

Kissing The Pink

Biographical details: This British band consists of Peter Barnett, Steve Cusack, Jon Kingsley-Hall, George Stewart, Jo Wells and Nick Whitecross. The roots of Kissing The Pink went back to late 1980 when Barnett, Hall and Stewart were studying at the Royal College of Music in Glasgow. After graduation the three musicians, who had previously worked under the name Ubu Roi, regrouped in London and began to assemble Kissing The Pink. This name was taken from a snooker term. The band's debut Magnet single *Mr Blunt* was released in May 1982 and received considerable airplay on BBC Radio One; it was produced by Colin Thurston of Duran Duran fame, who was also responsible for KTP's next couple of singles. *Watching their eyes* was followed by the highly distinctive *Last film*, which was their third single and first hit. *Last film* was a sleeper success - it was issued in January '83, entered the UK chart in March and reached its No.19 peak in May; all in all, the single logged 14 weeks on the UK Top 75. It was a left-field but a catchy track, militaristic in style, and slightly reminiscent of Peter Gabriel's *Games without frontiers*. Kissing The Pinks debut album *Naked* appeared in May '83, and contained several cinematic mini-agas of the *Last film* variety. Alas that song remained KTP's only hit. Despite their flair and imagination, which saw them treading pop and rock territory in an inspired manner, they were still looking for a follow-up hit to *Last film* in 1985. (Bob MacDonald)

CERTAIN THINGS ARE LIKELY (SINGLE)
Tracks: / Certain things are likely.
7" Single: Released Feb '87, on Magnet, by WEA Records. Deleted Jan '88. Catalogue no: **KTP 9**
12" Single: Released Feb '87, on Magnet, by WEA Records. Deleted Jan '88. Catalogue no: **12 KTP 9**

LAST FILM
Tracks: / Last film / Shine.
7" Set: Released Jan '83, on Magnet, by WEA Records. Deleted '86. Catalogue no: **KTP 36**
7" Single: Released Jan '83, on Magnet, by WEA Records. Deleted '86. Catalogue no: **KTP 3**
12" Single: Released Jan '83, on Magnet, by WEA Records. Deleted '86. Catalogue no: **12 KTP 3**

LOVE LASTS FOREVER
Tracks: / Love lasts forever / Underage.
7" Pic: Released Jun '83, on Magnet, by WEA Records. Catalogue no: **KTPP 4**
7" Single: Released Jun '83, on Magnet, by WEA Records. Catalogue no: **KTP 4**
12" Single: Released Jun '83, on Magnet, by WEA Records. Catalogue no: **12 KTP 4**

MAYBE THIS DAY
Tracks: / Maybe this day.
7" Single: Released Aug '83, on Magnet, by WEA Records. Catalogue no: **KTP 5**
12" Single: Released Aug '83, on Magnet, by WEA Records. Deleted '87. Catalogue no: **12 KTP 5**

MR. BLUNT
Tracks: / Mr. Blunt / Water in my eye.
7" Single: Released May '82, on Magnet, by WEA Records. Catalogue no: **KTP 1**
12" Single: Released May '82, on Magnet, by WEA Records. Catalogue no: **12 KTP 1**

NEVER TOO LATE TO LOVE YOU
Tracks: / Never too late to love you / Michael.
7" Single: Released Sep '86, on Magnet, by WEA Records. Catalogue no: **KTP 10**
12" Single: Released Sep '86, on Magnet, by WEA Records. Catalogue no: **12 KTP 10**

ONE STEP
Tracks: / One step / Footsteps / Rain never stops, The.
7" Single: Released Jul '87, on Magnet, by WEA Records. Deleted Jan '88. Catalogue no: **KTP 8**
12" Single: Released Jul '87, on Magnet, by WEA Records. Deleted Jan '88. Catalogue no: **12 KTP 8**

OTHER SIDE OF HEAVEN
Tracks: / Other side of heaven / Celestial.
7" Single: Released Mar '85, on Magnet, by WEA Records. Deleted Jan '88. Catalogue no: **KTP 7**
12" Single: Released Mar '85, on Magnet, by WEA Records. Deleted Jan '88. Catalogue no: **12 KTP 7**

RADIO ON
Tracks: / Radio on.
7" Single: Released Sep '84, on Magnet, by WEA Records. Catalogue no: **KTP 6**
12" Single: Released Sep '84, on Magnet, by WEA Records. Catalogue no: **12 KTP 6**

STAND UP
Tracks: / Stand up / Certain things are likely / What, I won't wait (12" only) / No one's on the same side (12" only).
CD 5": Released Jan '89, on WEA, by WEA Records. Catalogue no: **YZ 308 CD**
7" Single: Released Dec '88, on WEA, by WEA Records. Catalogue no: **YZ 308**
12" Single: Released Dec '88, on WEA, by WEA Records. Catalogue no: **YZ 308T**

WATCHING THEIR EYES
Tracks: / Watching their eyes / In awe of industry.
7" Single: Released Oct '82, on Magnet, by WEA Records. Catalogue no: **KTP 2**
12" Single: Released Oct '82, on Magnet, by WEA Records. Deleted '83. Catalogue no: **12 KTP 2**

Kissoon, Katie

I NEED A MAN IN MY LIFE
Tracks: / I need a man in my life.
7" Single: Released Jul '84, on Jive, by Zomba Records. Catalogue no: **JIVE 70**
12" Single: Released Jul '84, on Jive, by Zomba Records. Catalogue no: **JIVET 70**

PENNY LOVER
Tracks: / Penny lover.
7" Pic: Released Jan '84, on Jive, by Zomba Records. Catalogue no: **JIVEP 60**
7" Single: Released Jan '84, on Jive, by Zomba Records. Catalogue no: **JIVE 60**
12" Single: Released Jan '84, on Jive, by Zomba Records. Catalogue no: **JIVET 60**

YOU'RE THE ONE (YOU'RE MY NUMBER ONE)
Tracks: / You're the one.
7" Single: Released Jan '83, on Jive, by Zomba Records. Catalogue no: **JIVE 37**
12" Single: Released Jul '83, on Jive, by Zomba Records. Catalogue no: **JIVET 37**

Kissoon, Mac

CHIRPY CHIRPY CHEEP CHEEP
Tracks: / Chirpy chirpy cheep cheep.
7" Single: Released Jun '71, on Young Blood, by Young Blood Records. Deleted '74. Catalogue no: **YB 1026**

DON'T DO IT BABY
Tracks: / Don't do it baby.
7" Single: Released May '75, on State, by State Records. Deleted '78. Catalogue no: **STAT 4**

LAVENDER BLUE
Tracks: / Lavender blue / Black and white.
7" Single: Released Oct '82, on Crazy Vikings, by Crazy Vikings Records. Catalogue no: **CV 001**

LIKE A BUTTERFLY
Tracks: / Like a butterfly.
7" Single: Released Jul '75, on State, by State Records. Deleted '78. Catalogue no: **STAT 9**

LOVE AND UNDERSTANDING
Tracks: / Love and understanding / Baby you're the one.
7" Single: Released Nov '81, on Young Blood, by Young Blood Records. Catalogue no: **YB 0125**

SUGAR CANDY KISSES
(MAC AND KATIE KISSOON)
Tracks: / Sugar candy kisses.
7" EP: Released Oct '84, on Scoop 33, by Pickwick Records. Catalogue no: **7SR 5054**

SUGAR CANDY KISSES (SINGLE)
(MAC AND KATIE KISSOON)
Tracks: / Sugar candy kisses.
7" Single: Released Jan '75, on Polydor, by Polydor Ltd. Deleted '78. Catalogue no: **2058 531**

TWO OF US, THE (SINGLE)
Tracks: / Two of us, The.
7" Single: Released May '76, on State, by State Records. Deleted '79. Catalogue no: **STAT 21**

Kit

CHEATIN' MY HEART
Tracks: / My cheatin' heart.
12" Single: Released Jun '89, on Play Hard, by Play Hard Records. Catalogue no: **DEC 20**

MY DESIGN

Tracks: / My design.
12" Single: Released Jul '88, on Play Hard, by Play Hard Records. Catalogue no: **DEC 010**

Kitchen, Kevin

CRASH COURSE IN SURVIVAL
Tracks: / Crash course in survival / Where she's going.
7" Single: Released Jul '81, on Creole, by Creole Records. Catalogue no: **CR 11**

JUST HOW HIGH
Tracks: / Just how high / Get out of here.
7" Single: Released Feb '81, on Creole, by Creole Records. Catalogue no: **CR 1**

PUT MY ARMS AROUND YOU
Tracks: / Put your arms around me, honey.
7" Single: Released May '85, on China, by Polydor Ltd. Catalogue no: **WOK 1**

Kitchens Of

ELEPHANTINE
Tracks: / Elephantine.
7" Single: Released Sep '89, on One Little Indian, by One Little Indian Records. Catalogue no: **TP029**
12" Single: Released Sep '89, on One Little Indian, by One Little Indian Records. Catalogue no: **TP12029**

ESCAPE
Tracks: / Escape.
7" Single: Released Dec '87, on Gold Rush, Catalogue no: **GRR 3**

PRIZE
Tracks: / Prize, The.
7" Single: Released Oct '88, on One Little Indian, by One Little Indian Records. Catalogue no: **7TP 12**
12" Single: Released Oct '88, on One Little Indian, by One Little Indian Records. Catalogue no: **12TP 012**

THIRD TIME WE OPENED THE CAPSULE
Tracks: / Third time we opened the capsule / Four men.
7" Single: Released 28 Mar '89, on One Little Indian, by One Little Indian Records. Catalogue no: **7 TP 19**
12" Single: Released 28 Mar '89, on One Little Indian, by One Little Indian Records. Catalogue no: **12 TP 19**

Kitt, Eartha

Biographical details: Of American nationality but based in France, Eartha Kitt is best known in the UK for achieving one of the strangest chart feats of any singer. She is the only act to enjoy British singles chart success in the fifties and eighties but not the sixties or seventies. Kitt's first UK hit was *Under the bridges of Paris*, which reached no.7 in 1955 (while a rival recording of the song by Dean Martin got to no.6). After a record-setting gap of more than 28 years, she collected her second chart entry with *Where is my man*, which peaked at no.36 at the beginning of 1984. *Where is my man* saw the kitsch Kitt jumping on the then fashionable HI-NRG disco bandwagon, where anything was OK as long as it was danceable and contained the word 'man' in the title. The sexy cabaret persona which the singer had cultivated for many years was certainly ideally suited to the boystown idiom. In July she reached UK no.50 position with *I love men*. (Bob Macdonald 85).

I LOVE MEN (SINGLE)
Tracks: / I love men.
7" Single: Released Jul '84, on Record Shack, by Record Shack Records. Catalogue no: **SOHO 21**

THIS IS MY LIFE
Tracks: / This is my life.
7" Single: Released Mar '86, on Record Shack, by Record Shack Records. Catalogue no: **SOHO 61**
12" Single: Released Mar '86, on Record Shack, by Record Shack Records. Catalogue no: **SOHOT 61**

UNDER THE BRIDGES OF PARIS
Tracks: / Under the bridges of Paris.
7" Single: Released Apr '55, on H.M.V., by EMI Records. Deleted '58. Catalogue no: **B 10647**

WHERE IS MY MAN
Tracks: / Where is my man.
7" Single: Released Nov '83, on Record Shack, by Record Shack Records. Catalogue no: **SOHO 11**
12" Single: Released Nov '83, on Record Shack, by Record Shack Records. Catalogue no: **SOHOT 11**

Kitty

BENJI
Tracks: / Benji.
7" Single: Released Oct '82, on LOE, by LOE Records. Deleted '88. Catalogue no: **LOS 1**

Kiwi Sex

HOME FUCKING IS KILLING PROSTITUTION
Tracks: / Home fucking is killing prostitution.
12" Single: Released Apr '88, on Intercall, Catalogue no: **KIWI 001**

Kiwi & Tess

SHOW YOUR LOVE
Tracks: / Show your love / My heart is no liar.
7" Single: Released 25 Jul '88, on Epic, by CBS Records. Deleted Jan '89. Catalogue no: **651601 7**
12" Single: Released 25 Jul '88, on Epic, by CBS Records. Deleted Jan '89. Catalogue no: **651601 8**

Kix

COOL KIDS
Tracks: / Cool kids.
7" Single: Released Jun '83, on Atlantic, by WEA Records. Catalogue no: **A 9810**

FEAR OF FLYING
Tracks: / Fear of flying / Werewolf talking.
7" Single: Released Aug '8, on Creole, by Creole Records. Catalogue no: **CR 205**

Kjeldsen, Mark

ARE YOU READY
Tracks: / Are you ready / Something's happening.
7" Single: Released Jan '80, on Back Door (Holland), Catalogue no: **DOOR 2**

Klang, Hugo

WHEEL OF FATE
Tracks: / Wheel of fate.
7" Single: Released Oct '83, on Au-Go-Go (Australia), by Au-Go-Go Records (Australia). Catalogue no: **ANDA 24**

Klasicki, Vicki

WE'LL FIND OUR DAY
Tracks: / We'll find our day.
7" Single: Released Aug '83, on Simon, Catalogue no: **SMIKE 5**

Klass

ONE MORE CHANCE
Tracks: / One more chance.
7" Single: Released Apr '88, on OK, by Klub Records. Catalogue no: **OK 012**

Klassical Kr

BACK TO THE FUTURE
Tracks: / Back to the future.
7" Single: Released Sep '88, on Dancetrax, by BMG Records (UK). Deleted Aug '89. Catalogue no: **DRX 4**
12" Single: Released Sep '88, on Dancetrax, by BMG Records (UK). Deleted Aug '89. Catalogue no: **DRX 412**

Klassix

KNOCK THREE TIMES
Tracks: / Knock three times.
7" Single: Released Oct '82, on JKO, Catalogue no: **7 JKO 101**

PLEASE DON'T SMOKE
Tracks: / Please don't smoke / Leave it out.
7" Single: Released Mar '85, on JKO, Catalogue no: **7JKO 108**

WATCH THE WHITE BOY BOOGIE
Tracks: / Watch the white boy boogie.
12" Single: Released Jan '84, on JKO, Catalogue no: **12JKO 106**

Klaxon 5

HOT HOUSE
Tracks: / Hot house.
7" Single: Released Oct '84, on El, by Cherry Red Records. Catalogue no: **EL 2**
12" Single: Released Oct '84, on El, by Cherry Red Records. Catalogue no: **EL 2 T**

NEVER UNDERESTIMATE THE IGNORANCE OF THE RICH
Tracks: / Never underestimate the ignorance of the rich / Great railway journeys.
7" Single: Released Nov '86, on El, by Cherry Red Records. Catalogue no: **GPO 20**

Klaxons

Biographical details: During the Christmas period, the lower regions of the British charts are often dotted with novelty party hits by anonymous artists. One such single was *The clap clap sound* by a band of Belgian guys called the Klaxons; the track reached the UK No.45 position in the 1983 festive season. (Bob MacDonald, 27th Nov 1985).

CLAP CLAP SOUND
Tracks: / Clap clap sound.
7" Single: Released Jun '84, on PRT, by Castle Communications Records. Catalogue no: **7P 290**

KLE

WE GOT THE MUSIC
Tracks: / We got the music.
7" Single: Released May '89, on Underworld (USA), by Apexton Records (USA). Catalogue no: **AP 137**

Klearview Harmonix

LAUGHTER IN THE RAIN
Tracks: / Laughter in the rain / Laughter in the rain (version).
12" Single: Released Jun '88, on Roraima, by Ariwa Sounds. Catalogue no: **ROR 003**

Kleeer

Biographical details: The most successful line-up of this American soul band has been Isabelle Coles, Paul Crutchfield, Woody Cunningham, Terry Dolphin, Norman Durham, Yvette Flowers, Richard Lee, Melanie Moore and Eric Rohrbaugh. Kleeer released their debut album *I love to dance* in 1979. The LP yielded the funky albeit nondescript single *Keep your body working*, which reached No.51 on the UK singles chart at a time when the disco boom was at its height. 1981 saw the band reach the No.49 position with the equally dance-oriented *Get tough*. As the Eighties progressed, the New York-based group continued to serve the specialist sould market on both sides of the Atlantic without crossing over to the pop field in a major way. (Bob MacDonald, 27th Nov 1985).

CLOSE TO YOU
Tracks: / Close to you / Tonight's the night / I love to love.
7" Single: Released Apr '80, on Atlantic, by WEA Records. Deleted '83. Catalogue no: **LV 36**

DE KLEEER TING
Tracks: / De kleeer ting / Running back to you.
7" Single: Released Jun '81, on Atlantic, by WEA Records. Catalogue no: **K 11599**
12" Single: Released Jun '81, on Atlantic, by WEA Records. Catalogue no: **K 11599T**

GET TOUGH
Tracks: / Get tough / Hypnotised.
7" Single: Released Feb '81, on Atlantic, by WEA Records. Deleted '84. Catalogue no: **K 11560**
12" Single: Released Feb '81, on Atlantic, by WEA Records. Deleted '84. Catalogue no: **K 11560 T**

KEEP YOUR BODY WORKING
Tracks: / Keep your body working.
7" Single: Released Mar '79, on Atlantic, by WEA Records. Deleted '82. Catalogue no: **LV 21**

Klein

DIRTY TALK
Tracks: / Dirty talk / US european and canadian connections.
7" Single: Released Nov '82, on T.M.T., by T.M.T. Productions. Deleted '87. Catalogue no: **TMT 7002**
12" Single: Released Nov '82, on T.M.T., by T.M.T. Productions. Deleted '87. Catalogue no: **TMTT 7002**

K.L.F.

3AM ETERNAL
Tracks: / 3am eternal.
12" Single: Released Sep '89, on KLF, by KLF Communications. Catalogue no: **KLF 5T**

3AM ETERNAL (REMIX)
Tracks: / 3am eternal (remix).
12" Single: Released Oct '89, on KLF, by KLF Communications. Catalogue no: **KLF 5R**

BURN THE BEAT
Tracks: / Burn the beat.
12" Single: Released 5 Mar '88, on KLF, by KLF Communications. Catalogue no: **JAMS 26T**

E.TRANSCENTRAL
Tracks: / E.Transcentral.
12" Single: Released Jan '89, on KLF, by KLF Communications. Catalogue no: **KLF 008T**

KYLIE SAID TO JASON
Tracks: / Kylie said to Jason.
CD 5": Released Aug '89, on KLF, by KLF Communications. Catalogue no: **KLFO 10CD**
7" Single: Released Jul '89, on KLF, by KLF Communications. Catalogue no: **KLF 10**
12" Single: Released Aug '89, on KLF, by KLF Communications. Catalogue no: **KLFO 10P**
12" Single: Released Jul '89, on KLF, by KLF Communications. Catalogue no: **KLF 10 T**

KYLIE SAID TO JASON (REMIX)
Tracks: / Kylie said to Jason (remix).
12" Single: Released Oct '89, on KLF, by KLF Communications. Catalogue no: **KLF 10R**

LOVE TRANCE
Tracks: / Love trance.
12" Single: Released Nov '88, on KLF, by KLF Communications. Catalogue no: **KLF 006T**

LOVERS SIDE, THE
Tracks: / Lovers side, The.
12" Single: Released Sep '89, on KLF, by KLF Communications. Catalogue no: **KLF 008T**

NO MORE TEARS
Tracks: / No more tears.
7" Single: Released Nov '89, on KLF, by KLF Communications. Catalogue no: **KLF 11 G**
12" Single: Released Nov '89, on KLF, by KLF Communications. Catalogue no: **KLF 11 G T**

WHAT TIME IS LOVE
Tracks: / What time is love.
7" Single: Released Jun '89, on KLF, by KLF Communications. Catalogue no: **KLF 004**
12" Single: Released Jun '89, on KLF, by KLF Communications. Catalogue no: **KLF 004T**

Klinik

FEAR
Tracks: / Fear.
12" Single: Released Jun '88, on Antler, by Antler Records (Belgium). Deleted '88. Catalogue no: **ANT 058**

FEVER
Tracks: / Fever.
12" Single: Released Oct '88, on Antler, by Antler Records (Belgium). Catalogue no: **ANT 091**

PAIN AND PLEASURE
Tracks: / Pain & pleasure.
12" Single: Released Jun '88, on Antler, by Antler Records (Belgium). Catalogue no: **ANT 050**

Klique

I CAN'T SHAKE THIS FEELING
Tracks: / I can't shake this feeling / Dance like crazy / Pump your rump.
7" Single: Released Sep '82, on MCA, by MCA Records. Deleted Sep '85. Catalogue no: **MCA 789**
12" Single: Released Sep '82, on MCA, by MCA Records. Deleted Sep '85. Catalogue no: **MCAT 789**

Klo

FUN
Tracks: / Fun / Weirdo.
7" Single: Released Mar '84, on 101 International, Catalogue no: **INTER 1**

Klockwerke

KLOCKWERKE MIND
Tracks: / Klockwerke mind.
7" Single: Released Aug '84, on Trindisc, by Trindisc Records. Catalogue no: **TREL 001**

Klones

DISCO RHYTHM
Tracks: / Disco rhythm.
7" Single: Released Dec '81, on Secret, by Secret Records. Catalogue no: **SHH 122**

Klovn,Svart

KNUST KNEKT
Tracks: / Knust knekt.
7" Single: Released Sep '84, on Uniton Records, Catalogue no: **U 016**

Klugh, Earl

DANCE WITH ME
Tracks: / Dance with me / Living inside your love.
7" Single: Released Aug '81, on United Artists, by EMI Records. Deleted '84. Catalogue no: **UP 642**

TWINKLE
Tracks: / Twinkle / Broadway ramble / Dance with me (Only on 12" single.).
7" Single: Released Nov '81, on United Artists, by EMI Records. Deleted '84. Catalogue no: **UP 647**
12" Single: Released Nov '81, on United Artists, by EMI Records. Deleted '84. Catalogue no: **12 UP 647**

Klymaxx

I MISS YOU
Tracks: / I miss you / Video kid.
7" Single: Released Jan '86, on MCA, by MCA Records. Catalogue no: **MCA 1033**
12" Single: Released Jan '86, on MCA, by MCA Records. Catalogue no: **MCAT 1033**

MAN IN MY LIFE
Tracks: / Man in my life / Heartbreaker.

7" Single: Released Jan '83, on Elektra, by Elektra Records (UK). Catalogue no: **E9910**
12" Single: Released Jan '83, on Elektra, by Elektra Records (UK). Catalogue no: **E 9910 T**

MAN SIZE LOVE
Tracks: / Man size love / Man size love (Dub mix).
7" Single: Released Jan '87, on MCA, by MCA Records. Catalogue no: **MCA 1112**
12" Single: Released Jan '87, on MCA, by MCA Records. Catalogue no: **MCAT 1111**

WILD GIRLS
Tracks: / Wild girls / Let love just pass.
7" Single: Released Nov '82, on Solar (USA), by MCA Records. Catalogue no: **K 969955 7**
12" Single: Released Nov '82, on Solar (USA), by MCA Records. Catalogue no: **K 969955 T**

KMC

WHY DO PEOPLE LIE?
Tracks: / Why do people lie?.
12" Single: Released Jul '89, on Hammer, Catalogue no: **HZZT 2**

K.M.F.D.M.

DON'T BLOW YOUR TOP
Tracks: / Don't blow your top / No meat no man / Oh look / What a race / King Kong / No news / Oh look.
12" Single: Released '88, on Skysaw, by Skysaw Records. Catalogue no: **SKY 8**

DON'T BLOW YOUR TOP (SINGLE)
Tracks: / Don't blow your top.
12" Single: Released '88, on Skysaw, by Skysaw Records. Catalogue no: **SAW 8**

K.M.R.

BREAKING OUT
Tracks: / Breaking out.
7" Single: Released Oct '82, on Cricket International, by Cricket International Records. Catalogue no: **LBW 001**

Knack

Biographical details: This American band consisted of Berton Averre, Doug Fieger, Bruce Gary and Prescott Niles. Hailing from Los Angeles, the Knack stormed from out of the garage to the top of the US charts in the late summer of 1979. Their ludicrously catchy jerky teen-rock single *My sharona* was No.1 for six weeks in the States and reached No.6 in Britain. At the time of its success, America had largely ignoted the UK's punk rock explosion but was nonetheless looking for a fresh rock sound to offset the profusion of disco records that were saturating the charts. The Knack's music was actually rooted in the Sixties, heavily influenced by the Kingsmen's *Louie Louie* and the Beatles and Stones records; but to conservative American radio programmers, *My Sharona* represented the acceptable face of the New Wa e and they went for it.
For a few weeks the United States went Knack mad. *My Sharona* and their debut album *Get the Knack* were simultaneously No.1 on their respective lists, that had been written in one afternoon, and for an LP that had taken just 11 days to record and mix. The Knack were hailed as the new Beatles (guaranteed to be the kiss of death for any young group) and were praised for being perfect puveyors of power pop. But after one good follow-up single *Good girls don't* which reached the US No.11 position, the Knack quickly faded despite the production talents of veteran studio wizard Mike Chapman. BBC disc jockey Kid Jensen described lead vocalist Fieger as being more knowledgeable about the business side of the music industry than any other artist he had interviewed. Yet Doug could not translate that awareness into a sustained career for his band - their 1980 single *Baby talks dirty* peaked at No.38 on the Billboard Hot 100 and their 1981 album *Round trip* could do no better that No.97. The group broke up in 1982. The Knack's rise and fall was amongst the quickest and most sudden in pop history. (Bob MacDonald, 27th Nov 1985).

BABY TALKS DIRTY
Tracks: / Baby talks dirty / End of the game.
7" Single: Released Feb '80, on Capitol, by EMI Records. Deleted Feb '83. Catalogue no: **CL 16125**

GOOD GIRLS DON'T
Tracks: / Good girls don't.
7" Single: Released Oct '79, on Capitol, by EMI Records. Deleted '82. Catalogue no: **CL 16097**

I WANT YA
Tracks: / I want ya / Havin' a rave up.
7" Single: Released Mar '80, on Capitol, by EMI Records. Deleted '83. Catalogue no: **CL 16136**

KNACK - MY SHARONA (Released on Capitol)

MY SHARONA (see panel above)
Tracks: / My Sharona / Let me out.
7" Single: Released Jun '79, on Capitol, by EMI Records. Deleted '82. Catalogue no: **CL 16087**

PAY THE DEVIL (OOOO, BABY, OOO)
Tracks: / Pay the devil (Oooo, baby, ooo) / Lil Cal's big mistake.
7" Single: Released Nov '81, on Capitol, by EMI Records. Deleted Nov '84. Catalogue no: **CL 228**

Knarren, Pete

MIDNIGHT BLUE
Tracks: / Midnight blue / Without you.
7" Single: Released Feb '83, on EMI, by EMI Records. Catalogue no: **EMI 5370**

Knight, Frederick

I'VE BEEN LONELY SO LONG
Tracks: / I've been lonely for so long.
7" Single: Released Jun '72, on Stax, by Fantasy Inc (USA). Deleted '75. Catalogue no: **2025 098**
7" Single: Released Aug '87, on Stax, by Fantasy Inc (USA). Catalogue no: **STAX 811**

Knight, Gary

CRY WOLF
Tracks: / Cry wolf.
7" Single: Released Oct '83, on Button, by Musical Characters Records. Catalogue no: **BTN 110**

PRIVATE EYE
Tracks: / Private eye.
7" Single: Released Jun '84, on Works, by Works Records. Deleted '85. Catalogue no: **WK 10**

Knight, Gladys

BABY DON'T CHANGE YOUR MIND
Tracks: / Baby don't change your mind.
7" Single: Released May '77, on Buddah, by Buddah Records Inc.(USA). Deleted '80. Catalogue no: **BDS 458**

BEST THING THAT EVER HAPPENED TO ME
Tracks: / Best thing that ever happened to me / Midnight train to Georgia / Every beat of my heart.
7" Single: Released Jul '75, on Buddah, by Buddah Records Inc.(USA). Deleted '78. Catalogue no: **BDS 432**
7" Single: Released Jan '83, on Creole (Replay), by Creole Records. Catalogue no: **CR 213**

BOURGIE BOURGIE
Tracks: / Bourgie bourgie / Get the love.
7" Single: Released Nov '80, on CBS, by CBS Records. Deleted '83. Catalogue no: **CBS 9081**

CHRISTMAS EVERYDAY
Tracks: / Christmas everyday / Christmas everyday (inst).
7" Single: Released Nov '86, on MCA, by MCA Records. Catalogue no: **MCA 1104**
12" Single: Released Nov '86, on MCA, by MCA Records. Catalogue no: **MCAT 1112**

COLLECTION: GLADYS KNIGHT (4 LP SET)
Special: Released Sep '78, on Buddah, by Buddah Records Inc.(USA). Catalogue no: **11PP 602**

COME BACK & FINISH WHAT YOU STARTED
Tracks: / Come back & finish what you started.
7" Single: Released Jun '78, on Buddah, by Buddah Records Inc.(USA). Deleted '81. Catalogue no: **BDS 473**

GLADYS KNIGHT & THE PIPS (EP)
Tracks: / Midnight train to Georgia / Baby don't change your mind / Come back and finish what you started / Try to remember / Way we were, The.
CD 3": Released '88, on Special Edition, by Castle Communications Records. Catalogue no: **CD3-15**

HELP ME MAKE IT THROUGH THE NIGHT (SINGLE)
Tracks: / Help me make it through the night.
7" Single: Released Nov '72, on Tamla Motown, by Motown Records (UK). Deleted '75. Catalogue no: **TMG 830**

HERO
Tracks: / Hero / Seconds.
7" Single: Released Sep '83, on CBS, by CBS Records. Deleted '84. Catalogue no: **A 3763**
12" Single: Released Sep '83, on CBS, by CBS Records. Catalogue no: **TA 3763**

HOME IS WHERE THE HEART IS
Tracks: / Home is where the heart is.
7" Single: Released Sep '77, on Buddah, by Buddah Records Inc.(USA). Deleted '80. Catalogue no: **BDS 460**

I HEARD IT THROUGH THE GRAPEVINE
Tracks: / I heard it through the grapevine.
7" Single: Released Dec '67, on Tamla Motown, by Motown Records (UK). Deleted '70. Catalogue no: **TMG 629**

I WILL FIGHT
Tracks: / I will fight / Reach high.
7" Single: Released Apr '82, on CBS, by CBS Records. Deleted Apr '85. Catalogue no: **A 2075**

I WILL SURVIVE
Tracks: / I will survive / God is.
7" Single: Released Nov '81, on CBS, by CBS Records. Deleted Nov '84. Catalogue no: **CBS A 1772**

I'LL TAKE A MELODY
Tracks: / I'll take a melody / Way it was.
7" Single: Released Feb '81, on Buddah, by Buddah Records Inc.(USA). Deleted '84. Catalogue no: **BDS 483**

IT'S A BETTER THAN GOOD TIME
Tracks: / It's a better than good time.
7" Single: Released Sep '78, on Buddah, by Buddah Records Inc.(USA). Deleted '81. Catalogue no: **BDS 478**

JUST WALK IN MY SHOES
Tracks: / Just walk in my shoes.
7" Single: Released Jun '72, on Tamla Motown, by Motown Records (UK). Deleted '75. Catalogue no: **TMG 813**

LANDLORD
Tracks: / Landlord / We need a heart.
7" Single: Released May '80, on CBS, by CBS Records. Deleted May '83. Catalogue no: **CBS 8542**

LICENCE TO KILL
Tracks: / Licence to kill.
Cassingle: Released May '89, on MCA, by MCA Records. Catalogue no: **MCAC 1339**
CD 5": Released May '89, on MCA, by MCA Records. Catalogue no: **DMCA 1339**
12" Single: Released May '89, on MCA, by MCA Records. Catalogue no: **MCAT 1339**
7" Single: Released Jun '89, on MCA, by MCA Records. Catalogue no: **MCASP 1339**
7" Single: Released May '89, on MCA, by MCA Records. Catalogue no: **MCA 1339**

LOOK OF LOVE
Tracks: / Look of love, The.
7" Single: Released Mar '73, on Tamla Motown, by Motown Records (UK). Deleted '76. Catalogue no: **TMG 844**

LOVE OVERBOARD
Tracks: / Love overboard (women & children first remix).
7" Single: Released Jan '88, on MCA, by MCA Records. Deleted 1 Jul '89. Catalogue no: **MCA 1223**

LOVIN' ON NEXT TO NOTHIN'
Tracks: / Lovin' on next to nothin' / Lovin' on next to nothin' (instrumental) / Lovin' on next to nothin' (extended) / Lovin' on next to nothin' (extended instrumental) / Lovin' on next to nothin' (instrumental edition) / Lovin' on next to nothin' (dance remix) / Lovin' on next to nothin' (version) / Send it to me.
7" Single: Released Mar '88, on MCA Dance, by MCA Records. Catalogue no: **MCA 1237**
12" Single: Released Apr '88, on MCA, by MCA Records. Catalogue no: **MCAX 1237**
CD 5": Released Apr '88, on MCA, by MCA Records. Catalogue no: **DMCA 1237**
12" Single: Released Mar '88, on MCA Dance, by MCA Records. Catalogue no: **MCAT 1237**

LOVING ON BORROWED TIME
Tracks: / Loving on borrowed time / Angel of the city.
7" Single: Released Aug '86, on Epic, by CBS Records. Deleted '87. Catalogue no: **650062 7**

MAKE YOURS A HAPPY HOME
Tracks: / Make yours a happy home.
7" Single: Released Jul '76, on Buddah, by Buddah Records Inc.(USA). Deleted '79. Catalogue no: **BDS 447**

MIDNIGHT TRAIN TO GEORGIA (SINGLE)
Tracks: / Midnight train to Georgia.
7" Single: Released May '76, on Buddah, by Buddah Records Inc.(USA). Deleted '79. Catalogue no: **BDS 444**

NEITHER ONE OF US (SINGLE)
Tracks: / Neither one of us.
7" Single: Released May '73, on Tamla Motown, by Motown Records (UK). Deleted '78. Catalogue no: **TMG 855**

NOBODY BUT YOU
Tracks: / Nobody but you.
7" Single: Released Jan '77, on Buddah, by Buddah Records Inc.(USA). Deleted '80. Catalogue no: **BDS 451**

ONE & ONLY, THE (SINGLE)
Tracks: / One & only, The.
7" Single: Released May '78, on Buddah, by Buddah Records Inc.(USA). Deleted '81. Catalogue no: **BDS 470**

PART TIME LOVER
Tracks: / Part time lover.
7" Single: Released Nov '75, on Buddah, by Buddah Records Inc.(USA). Deleted '78. Catalogue no: **BDS 438**

SEND IT TO ME
Tracks: / Send it to me / Send it to me (acapella).
12" Single: Released Mar '87, on MCA, by MCA Records. Catalogue no: **MCAT 1122**
7" Single: Released Mar '87, on MCA, by MCA Records. Catalogue no: **MCA 1122**

SEND THE OVERTIME FOR ME
Tracks: / Send the overtime for me.
12" Single: Released Apr '83, on CBS, by CBS Records. Catalogue no: **TA 3314**
7" Single: Released Apr '83, on CBS, by CBS Records. Catalogue no: **A 3314**

SO SAD THE SONG
Tracks: / So sad the song.
7" Single: Released Nov '76, on Buddah, by Buddah Records Inc.(USA). Deleted '79. Catalogue no: **BDS 448**

STILL SUCH A THING

Tracks: / Still such a thing / We have hearts.
7" Single: Released Jan '81, on CBS, by CBS Records. Deleted Jan '84. Catalogue no: **CBS 9496**

TAKE ME IN YOUR ARMS AND LOVE ME
Tracks: / Take me in your arms and love me.
7" Single: Released Jun '67, on Tamla Motown, by Motown Records (UK). Deleted '70. Catalogue no: **TMG 604**

TASTE OF BITTER LOVE (SINGLE)
Tracks: / Taste of bitter love / Add it up.
7" Single: Released Aug '80, on CBS, by CBS Records. Deleted '83. Catalogue no: **CBS 8890**
12" Single: Released Aug '80, on CBS, by CBS Records. Deleted '83. Catalogue no: **CBS 13 8890**

THAT'LL MAKE YOU HAPPY
Tracks: / That'll make you happy / Love was made for two.
7" Single: Released Sep '81, on CBS, by CBS Records. Deleted '84. Catalogue no: **A 1534**

WAY WE WERE, THE
Tracks: / Way we were, The.
7" Single: Released Jul '80, on Flashback, by Mainline Records. Catalogue no: **FBEP 108**

WAY WE WERE, THE (OLD GOLD)
Tracks: / Way we were, The.
7" Single: Released Apr '83, on Old Gold, by Old Gold Records. Deleted Jul '88. Catalogue no: **OG 9290**

WAY WE WERE, THE/ TRY TO REMEMBER (MEDLEY)
Tracks: / Way we were, The/Try to remember (medley).
7" Single: Released May '75, on Buddah, by Buddah Records Inc.(USA). Deleted '78. Catalogue no: **BDS 428**

Knight, Holly

HEART DON'T FAIL ME NOW
Tracks: / Heart don't fail me now / Howlin' at the moon / Love is a battlefield (Available on CD single format only.).
CD 5": Released Jan '89, on CBS, by CBS Records. Deleted 10 Jul '89. Catalogue no: **652 849-2**
7" Single: on CBS, by CBS Records. Deleted 10 Jul '89. Catalogue no: **652 849-7**
7" Single: Released Jan '89, on CBS, by CBS Records. Catalogue no: **653 8497**
12" Single: Released 16 Jan '89, on CBS, by CBS Records. Deleted 10 Jul '89. Catalogue no: **652 849-8**
12" Single: Released Dec '88, on CBS, by CBS Records. Deleted 10 Jul '89. Catalogue no: **652 849-6**

Knight, Jean

MR BIG STUFF
Tracks: / Mr. Big Stuff / You think you're hot stuff / Carry on / Do me.
7" Single: Released Mar '82, on Stax, by Fantasy Inc (USA). Catalogue no: **STAX 1005**

MR. BIG STUFF (OLD GOLD)
Tracks: / Mr. Big Stuff / Do the funky chicken.
7" Single: Released Jan '87, on Old Gold, by Old Gold Records. Catalogue no: **OG 9534**

MR.BIG STUFF
Tracks: / Mr. Big Stuff / Why I keep living these memories.
7" Single: Released 13 Jun '87, on Stax, by Fantasy Inc (USA). Catalogue no: **STAX 804**
12" Single: Released Nov '87, on Stax, by Fantasy Inc (USA). Catalogue no: **STAT 804**

Knight, Jerry

I'M DOWN FOR THAT
Tracks: / I'm down for that / She's got to be a dancer.
12" Single: Released Feb '83, on Funk America, by A&M Records. Catalogue no: **USAF 1227**

OVERNIGHT SENSATION
Tracks: / Overnight sensation / Freak show.
7" Single: Released Apr '80, on A&M, by A&M Records. Deleted Apr '83. Catalogue no: **AMS 7521**

PERFECT FIT (SINGLE)
Tracks: / Perfect fit / Let me be the reason.
7" Single: Released Mar '81, on A&M, by A&M Records. Deleted Mar '84. Catalogue no: **AMS 8112**

Knight, Robert

EVERLASTING LOVE
Tracks: / Everlasting love.
7" Single: Released Jan '68, on Monument, Deleted '71. Catalogue no: **MON 1008**
7" Single: Released Mar '74, on Monument, Deleted '77. Catalogue no: **MNT 2106**

LOVE ON A MOUNTAIN TOP
Tracks: / Love on a mountain top.
7" Single: Released Nov '73, on Monument, Deleted '76. Catalogue no: **MNT 1875**

Knight, Terry

I (WHO HAVE NOTHING)
Tracks: / I (who have nothing).
7" Single: Released '66, on UNKNOWN, Deleted '69. Catalogue no: **Unknown**

Knoblock, Fred

KILLIN' TIME
Tracks: / Killin' time / Love is no friend to a fool.
7" Single: Released Mar '81, on Scotti Bros (USA), Deleted Mar '84. Catalogue no: **K 11646**

WHY NOT ME
Tracks: / Why not me / Can I get a wish.
7" Single: Released Sep '80, on Atlantic, by WEA Records. Deleted '83. Catalogue no: **K 11556**

Knockout

NEVER
Tracks: / Never / Perfect lover.
7" Single: Released Jun '87, on Karma, Deleted '88. Catalogue no: **ETH 1**

Knooks, George

WE'RE IN THIS LOVE TOGETHER
Tracks: / We're in this love together.
7" Single: Released Apr '82, on Island, by Island Records. Deleted Apr '85. Catalogue no: **WIP 6782**
12" Single: Released Apr '82, on Island, by Island Records. Deleted Apr '85. Catalogue no: **12WIP 6782**

Knopfler, David

HEART TO HEART
Tracks: / Heart to heart.
7" Single: Released May '85, on Making Waves, by Celtic Music. Catalogue no: **SURF 105**
12" Single: Released May '85, on Making Waves, by Celtic Music. Catalogue no: **SURF T105**

MADONNA'S DAUGHTER
Tracks: / Madonna's daughter / Hey Henry.
7" Single: Released Jun '84, on Fast Alley, Catalogue no: **FAR 701**

SHOCKWAVE
Tracks: / Shockwaves.
7" Single: Released Feb '86, on Making Waves, by Celtic Music. Catalogue no: **SURF 107**
12" Single: Released Feb '86, on Making Waves, by Celtic Music. Deleted Nov '87. Catalogue no: **SURFT 107**

SOUL KISSING
Tracks: / Soul kissing.
7" Single: Released Sep '83, on Peach River, Deleted '84. Catalogue no: **BBPR 7**
12" Single: Released Sep '83, on Peach River, Deleted '84. Catalogue no: **BBPR 712**

TO FEEL THAT WAY AGAIN
Tracks: / To feel that way again / Someone to believe in / Angie and Johnny.
Note: * Only on the 12" version.
7" Single: Released Jun '88, on Paris, Catalogue no: **DAVE 7**
12" Single: Released Jun '88, on Paris, Catalogue no: **DAVE 127**

WHEN WE KISS
Tracks: / When we kiss.
7" Single: Released Jan '87, on Greenhill, by Greenhill Records. Catalogue no: **GMI 9**
12" Single: Released Jan '87, on Greenhill, by Greenhill Records. Catalogue no: **GMIT 9**

Knopfler, Mark

Biographical details: This British guitarist, singer and producer is the leader and principal creative force of Dire Straits, one of the world's leading rock bands of the late Seventies and Eighties. No sooner had the band come to fame than Knopfler's distinctive and refreshing guitar style began to become an in-demand commodity for other stars' sessions - he got to play on albums by Bob Dylan (from whom, some critics suggested, he had taken singing lessons), Phil Lynott, Steely Dan and Van Morrison. During 1983, when Dire Straits took a break from studio recording, Knopfler scored the music for the movie *Local hero.* This acclaimed soundtrack yielded the beautiful instrumental single *Going home,* which surprisingly peaked at a lowly No.56 on the UK chart in March '83. The Shadows tried their luck with a cover version, but their single flopped altogether.. Also in 1983 Knopfler produced Dylan's *Infidels* LP. The following year, he earned some handy composing royalties for *Private dancer,* the title track (and eventually, a hit single) from Tinal Turner's multi platinum album. Mark's brother David Knopfler was an early member of Dire Straits, but quit to pursue an unsuccessful solo career. (Bob MacDonald, 27th Nov 1985).

COMFORT AND JOY
Tracks: / Comfort and joy.
7" Single: Released Jul '84, on Vertigo, by Phonogram Ltd. Catalogue no: **DSTR 712**

GOING HOME
Tracks: / Going home (theme from Local Hero) / Wild theme / Smooching (Extra track on 12" version only.).
7" Single: Released Feb '83, on Vertigo, by Phonogram Ltd. Deleted '85. Catalogue no: **DSTR 4**
7" Single: Released Sep '86, on Vertigo, by Phonogram Ltd. Deleted Mar '88. Catalogue no: **DSTR 14**
12" Single: Released Sep '86, on Vertigo, by Phonogram Ltd. Deleted Mar '88. Catalogue no: **DSTR 1412**

STORYBOOK LOVE Theme from The Princess Bride
Tracks: / Storybook love.
CD 5": Released Mar '88, on Vertigo, by Phonogram Ltd. Deleted Oct '88. Catalogue no: **VERCD 37**
7" Single: Released 7 Mar '88, on Vertigo, by Phonogram Ltd. Deleted Oct '88. Catalogue no: **VER 37**
12" Single: Released 7 Mar '88, on Vertigo, by Phonogram Ltd. Deleted Oct '88. Catalogue no: **VERX 37**

Knot, Kenny

WATCH HOW THE PEOPLE DANCING
Tracks: / Watch how the people dancing / A eeh do she.
12" Single: Released May '86, on Unity Sound, Catalogue no: **UN 018**

Knots In May

LIVING ON A GIRO
Tracks: / Living on a giro.
7" Single: Released Apr '83, on Ritz, by Ritz Records. Catalogue no: **RITZ 039**

Knotts, Kenny

STOP PLAYING AROUND
Tracks: / Stop playing around / Stop playing around (version).
12" Single: Released Sep '87, on Unity, Catalogue no: **UN 027**

Know

I LIKE GIRLS
Tracks: / I like girls / Out of reach.
7" Single: Released Jun '80, on Elektra Asylum, by Elektra Records (USA). Deleted Jun '83. Catalogue no: **K 12451**

Knowles, Karen

WHY WON'T YOU EXPLAIN
Tracks: / Why won't you explain / Rock me.
7" Single: Released May '81, on Piccadilly, Deleted May '84. Catalogue no: **PRT 7P 218**

Knox

GIGOLO AUNT
Tracks: / Gigolo aunt.
7" Single: Released Jul '81, on Armageddon, by Armageddon Records. Catalogue no: **AS 003**

SHE'S SO GOOD LOOKING
Tracks: / She's so good looking / Love is burning.
7" Single: Released Jan '81, on Gem, Deleted Jan '84. Catalogue no: **GEMS 46**

Knox, Buddy

Biographical details: Knox, Buddy This American singer, songwriter, guitarist and harmonica player was born Wayne Knox in a place called Happy in Texas. Before committing himself to a full time musical career, he studied accountancy and business administration with a view to joining an oil company. While at West Texas State University, he met two other musically inclined students, Jimmy Bowen and Don Lanier. They formed a group named The Rhythm Orchids in 1955. Eventually recruiting a fourth member, Dave Allred, they reached the US No.14 position in early 1957 with their single *I'm Stickin' With You.* Even more importantly, while *I'm Stickin' With You* was on the Top 20, Knox launched his solo career with an American No.1 smash *Party Doll.* Both his hits were written by Knox and Bowen; according to 'The Billboard Book of Number One Hits, Buddy thus became the first artist of the rock era to write his own US No.1 song. A tamer version by Steve Lawrence simulataneously climbed to No.5. Knox's own rendition was categorised into a new mini-genre dubbed 'Tex-Mex' music - this tag was derived from the neighbouring states of Texas and New Mexico. The latter contained producer Norman Petty's studios, which became the recording home of the young Buddy Holly after he had been impressed with the sound achieved on Buddy Knox's *Party Doll.*
Knox's musical roots were country and western and hillbilly but he played authentic rock'n'roll, so his music perfectly fitted the term 'rockabilly'. He had several follow-up hits to *Party Doll,* the biggest being *Hula Love* which reached the US No.9 position. But after 1958, he never returned to the American Top 40 save for a 1961 appearance with *Lovey Dovey.* As the sixties progressed, he moved into convential country music with only moderate success. He settled in Canada during the Seventies and has continued to work as a touring performer ever since.
In Britain *Party Doll* had to be content with a No.29 placing. Buddy's only other UK chart entry was *She's Gone,* which struggled to No.45 in August 1962. (Bob Macdonald 27/11/85).

PARTY DOLL (SINGLE)
Tracks: / Party doll.
7" Single: Released May '57, on Columbia, by EMI Records. Deleted '60. Catalogue no: **DB 3914**

SHE'S GONE
Tracks: / She's gone.
7" Single: Released Aug '62, on Liberty, by EMI Records. Deleted '65. Catalogue no: **LIB 55473**

Knuckles, Frankie

BABY WANTS TO RIDE
Tracks: / Baby wants to ride.
12" Single: Released Nov '87, on Trax (USA), Catalogue no: **TX 150**

TEARS
Tracks: / Tears / Tears (classic instrumental edit) / Tears (classic vocal/bonus beats) (Only on 12" version.).
7" Single: Released 30 May '89, on ffrr, by London Records. Catalogue no: **F 108**
12" Single: Released 30 May '89, on ffrr, by London Records. Catalogue no: **FX 108**

YOU CAN'T HIDE FROM YOURSELF
Tracks: / You can't hide from yourself (inst) / You can't hide from yourself (Chip E's house remix) (On PARTY Q1 only) / You can't hide from yourself (dub mix) (On PARTY Q1 only) / You can't hide from yourself / You can't hide from yourself(inst).
7" Single: Released Apr '87, on Portrait, by CBS Records. Deleted Nov '87. Catalogue no: **PARTY 1**
12" Single: Released May '87, on Portrait, by CBS Records. Deleted Nov '87. Catalogue no: **PARTY Q1**
12" Single: Released Apr '87, on Portrait, by CBS Records. Deleted Nov '87. Catalogue no: **PARTY T1**

YOUR LOVE
Tracks: / Your love.
12" Single: Released Oct '88, on Who's That Beat, by Play It Again Sam (Belgium). Catalogue no: **WHOS 005**

Koffie

AND I'M TELLING YOU I'M NOT GOING
Tracks: / And I'm telling you I'm not going.
7" Single: Released Nov '83, on Red Rooster, Catalogue no: **7 HEN 1**
12" Single: Released Nov '83, on Red Rooster, Catalogue no: **HEN 1**

Koffman, Moe

SWINGIN' SHEPHERD BLUES
Tracks: / Swingin' shepherd blues.
7" Single: Released Mar '58, on London-American, Deleted '61. Catalogue no: **HLJ 8549**

Kofi

BEING WITH YOU
Tracks: / Being with you.
12" Single: Released Jul '89, on Blue Chip, by Blue Chip Records. Catalogue no: **BLUEC 24**

BLACK PRIDE
Tracks: / Black pride.
12" Single: Released Sep '88, on Ariwa Sounds, by Ariwa Sounds. Catalogue no: **ARI 81**

COUNTDOWN
Tracks: / Countdown.
12" Single: Released Sep '84, on Electricity, by Electricity Records. Deleted '88. Catalogue no: **ELECT 3**

7" Single: Released Sep '84, on Electricity, by Electricity Records. Deleted '88. Catalogue no: **ELEC 3**

COUNTDOWN (1987 RE-RECORDING)
Tracks: / Countdown.
12" Single: Released 23 May '87, on Electricity, by Electricity Records. Deleted '88. Catalogue no: **TRICT 103**

DIDN'T I
Tracks: / Didn't I.
12" Single: Released Apr '88, on Ariwa Sounds, by Ariwa Sounds. Catalogue no: **ARI 73**

DON'T ASK MY NEIGHBOUR
Tracks: / Don't ask my neighbour.
12" Single: Released Sep '89, on Ariwa Sounds, by Ariwa Sounds. Catalogue no: **ARI 097**

LOOKING OVER LOVE
Tracks: / Looking over love.
7" Single: Released Apr '89, on Ariwa Sounds, by Ariwa Sounds. Catalogue no: **ARI 789**
12" Single: Released Apr '89, on Ariwa Sounds, by Ariwa Sounds. Catalogue no: **ARI 89**

PLACE IN THE SUN
Tracks: / Place in the sun, A.
12" Single: Released Jul '87, on Ariwa Sounds, by Ariwa Sounds. Catalogue no: **ARI 65**

Kojak & Mama Liza

SI DOWN PON IT
Tracks: / Si down pon it.
12" Single: Released Nov '86, on Music Track, Catalogue no: **GGD 126**

Koklin, Tony

CLAUDE MONET
Tracks: / Claude Monet / Lucky man.
7" Single: Released Jan '81, on Chiswick Records, Deleted Jan '84. Catalogue no: **CHIS 137**

Koko Pop

BRAND NEW BEAT
Tracks: / Brand new beat.
7" Single: Released Oct '85, on Motown, by BMG Records (UK). Catalogue no: **ZB 40401**
12" Single: Released Oct '85, on Motown, by BMG Records (UK). Deleted '87. Catalogue no: **ZT 40402**

I'M IN LOVE WITH YOU
Tracks: / I'm in love with you / On the beach.
7" Single: Released Dec '84, on Motown, by BMG Records (UK). Catalogue no: **TMG 1363**

Kokomo (UK)

LITTLE BIT FURTHER AWAY, A
Tracks: / Little bit further away.
7" Single: Released May '82, on CBS, by CBS Records. Deleted '85. Catalogue no: **A 2064**

Kokomo (USA)

ASIA MINOR
Tracks: / Asia minor.
7" Single: Released Apr '61, on London-American, Deleted '64. Catalogue no: **HLU 9305**

Kolbert, Cata

LIVE YOUR LIFE
Tracks: / Live your life.
7" Single: Released Sep '87, on Never More, Catalogue no: **NE 001**
12" Single: Released Sep '87, on Never More, Catalogue no: **NE 001T**

Kolsrud, Dag

JINGLE BELLS
Tracks: / Jingle bells / Stina.
7" Single: Released Dec '88, on A&M, by A&M Records. Catalogue no: **AM 489**
12" Single: Released Dec '88, on A&M, by A&M Records. Catalogue no: **AMY 489**

Kon Kan

I BEG YOUR PARDON
Tracks: / I beg your pardon.
CD 5": Released Apr '89, on Atlantic, by WEA Records. Catalogue no: **A 8969 CD**
7" Single: Released Feb '89, on Atlantic, by WEA Records. Catalogue no: **A 8969**
12" Single: Released Feb '89, on Atlantic, by WEA Records. Catalogue no: **A 8969 T**

Kongos, John

Biographical details: Kongos, John This South African singer, songwriter and multi-instrumentalist was born in Johannesburg but settled in the UK in 1969. He was taken under the wing of producer Gus Dudgeon and attracted growing interest when another of Dudgeon's charges, Elton John, started enjoying success in 1971.
Kongos came to fame with his two 1971 hits *He's Gonna Step On You Again* and *Tokoloshe Man* which both reached No.4 on the British singles chart. These were unusual and refreshing fusions of tribal African music and western rock sounds. Fleetwood Mac's internationally successful 1979 single *Tusk* was reminiscent of the Kongos hits.
In 1972 Kongos quickly drifted into obscurity and his sucesses were generally forgotten, even by oldies programmers on radio. (Bob Macdonald 27/11/85).

C.A.T.S. EYES
Tracks: / C.A.T.S eyes.
7" Single: Released May '85, on Sierra, by Sierra Records. Catalogue no: **FED 11**

HE'S GONNA STEP ON YOU AGAIN
Tracks: / He's gonna step on you again.
7" Single: Released May '71, on Fly, by Fly Records. Deleted '74. Catalogue no: **BUG 8**
7" Single: Released Aug '82, on Cube, Catalogue no: **BAK 10**

HE'S GONNA STEP ON YOU AGAIN (OLD GOLD)
Tracks: / He's gonna step on you again.
7" Single: Released Jul '82, on Old Gold, by Old Gold Records. Deleted Jul '88. Catalogue no: **OG 9231**

TOKOLOSHE MAN (OLD GOLD)
Tracks: / Tokoloshe man.
7" Single: Released Aug '82, on Old Gold, by Old Gold Records. Deleted Jul '88. Catalogue no: **OG 9231**

TOKOLOSHE MAN (SINGLE)
Tracks: / Tokoloshe man.
7" Single: Released May '71, on Fly, by Fly Records. Deleted '74. Catalogue no: **BUG 14**

Konk

FOKA TOKA MOKA
Tracks: / Foka toka moka.
7" Single: Released Feb '82, on Konk, Catalogue no: **KAY 001**

KONK PARTY
Tracks: / Konk party / Master cylinder is jam / Cylinder recycle / Uptown breakdown.
7" EP: Released Dec '82, on Konk, Catalogue no: **RT 110 T**

YOUR LIFE
Tracks: / Your life.
7" Single: Released Jun '84, on 4th & Broadway, by Island Records. Catalogue no: **BRW 7**
12" Single: Released Jun '84, on 4th & Broadway, by Island Records. Catalogue no: **12 BRW 7**

Kontini, Finzy

CHA CHA CHA
Tracks: / Cha cha cha / Bass and drums.
12" Single: Released Dec '85, on Carrere, Catalogue no: **CART 378**

Koo De Tah

TOO YOUNG FOR PROMISES
Tracks: / Too young for promises / Dancing.
7" Single: Released Feb '86, on Mercury, by Phonogram Ltd. Catalogue no: **MER 211**
12" Single: Released Feb '86, on Mercury, by Phonogram Ltd. Deleted '87. Catalogue no: **MERX 211**

Kooga

DON'T BREAK MY HEART
Tracks: / Don't break my heart / Lay down your love.
7" Single: Released 5 Mar '88, on Beserkley, by Beserkley Records (USA). Catalogue no: **KO 1**

Kool, Bo

MERRY CHRISTMAS, HAPPY NEW YEAR
Tracks: / Merry Christmas, Happy New Year.
12" Single: Released Jan '89, on Master Funk, Catalogue no: **MF 006**

SPACE INVADER
Tracks: / Space invader.
12" Single: Released Mar '82, on Master Funk, Catalogue no: **MS 1002**

Kool, D.L.

GET ON UP
Tracks: / Get on up / Get on up (inst.) (7" only.) / Get on up (dub) (12" only.) / Get on up (Hip hop mix) (12" only.) / Get on up (soundsystem mix) (Special only.) / Get on up (Kingdom mix) (Special only.) / Get on up (vibe mix) (Special only.).
7" Single: Released Sep '89, on SBK One, Catalogue no: **SBK 7001**
7" Single: Released Sep '89, on SBK One, Catalogue no: **203 488 7**
12" Single: Released Sep '89, on SBK One, Catalogue no: **203 488 6**
12" Single: Released Sep '89, on SBK One, Catalogue no: **12SBK 7001**
Special: Released Sep '89, on SBK One, Catalogue no: **203 592 6**
Special: Released Sep '89, on SBK One, Catalogue no: **12SBKX 7001**

Kool Moe Dee

GO SEE THE DOCTOR
Tracks: / Go see the doctor (almost clean version) / Monster crack (radio edit).
7" Single: Released Dec '86, on Jive, by Zomba Records. Deleted Jul '87. Catalogue no: **JIVE 136**
12" Single: Released Dec '86, on Jive, by Zomba Records. Catalogue no: **JIVET 136**

HOW D'YOU LIKE ME NOW
Tracks: / How d'you like me now / How d'you like me now (version).
7" Single: Released Jan '88, on Jive, by Zomba Records. Catalogue no: **JIVE 156**
12" Single: Released Jan '88, on Jive, by Zomba Records. Catalogue no: **JIVET 156**

I GO TO WORK
Tracks: / I go to work.
12" Single: Released Sep '89, on Jive, by Zomba Records. Catalogue no: **JIVET 223**

NO RESPECT
Tracks: / No respect / Let's go.
7" Single: Released 16 Sep '88, on Jive, by Zomba Records. Deleted '88. Catalogue no: **JIVE 183**
12" Single: Released 16 Sep '88, Deleted '88. Catalogue no: **JIVET 183**

THEY WANT MONEY
Tracks: / They want money.
7" Single: Released Jun '89, on Jive, by Zomba Records. Catalogue no: **JIVE 207**
12" Single: Released Jun '89, on Jive, by Zomba Records. Catalogue no: **JIVE T207**

WILD WILD WEST
Tracks: / Wild wild west.
7" Single: Released Apr '88, on Jive, by Zomba Records. Deleted '88. Catalogue no: **JIVE 167**
12" Single: Released Apr '88, on Jive, by Zomba Records. Deleted '88. Catalogue no: **JIVET 167**

Kool, Nat King

CHECKING OUT
Tracks: / Checking out.
7" Single: Released Sep '84, on Tia Wan, by Tania Music Records. Catalogue no: **TWD 1949**

Kool & The Gang

Biographical details: Kool & The Gang This American soul band consists of Robert 'Kool' Bell (bass gutiarist and leader), Ronald Bell, Clifford Adams, George Brown, Robert Mickens, Michael Ray, Charles Smith, James Taylor (lead vocalist), Dennis Thomas and Curtis Williams. Until 1981 there was a third Bell brother, Kevin Ball in the group.
Hailing from Jersey City, New Jersey, the nucleus of the band was formed in school in 1964 by a 14 year old Robert Bell. 1969 was the year in which Kool & The Gang officially came into being, embarked upon a serious career and signed a contract with the newly formed De-Lite label, with whom they have remained ever since. Their debut single, an instrumental workout simply titled *Kool & The Gang* made a promising showing on the US soul and pop charts in the autumn of '69.
During the early seventies, The Gang chalked up several further moderate hits, exploring the same streetwise funk territory occupied by Sly & The Family Stone and James Brown. 1973 brought them their first American Top 40 pop single in the shape of *Funky Stuff*, and they consolidated this success in 1974 with a pair of million-selling US Top 10 smashes, *Jungle Boogie* and *Hollywood Swinging*.
The group suffered an extended hiatus during the mid to late Seventies, and found themselves unable to compete effectively in the burgeoning disco market, save for the inclusion of their track *Open Sesame* on the globe conquering *Saturday Night Fever movie soundtrack. The turnaround for Kool & The Gang occurred in late 1979, with the release of the single and album Ladies' Night* - this was the first music to feature their smooth lead vocalist and frontman James Taylor and their new producer Eumir Deodato. The arrival of these guys tightened up the Gang's previously loose, communal sound and gave the group a fresh formula. The jazzy, funky and soulful elements of their past work was retained but channelled into a slick and commercial style that was dynamic on the dancefloor and irrestistibly hummable on the radio.
From 1979 onwards Kool & The Gang never looked back. They achieved a level of constistency that was the envy of ever other black band in the world. Their greatest disco tracks were the party favourite *Celebration* (a double million selling No.1 in the States) and the ultra infectious *Get Down On It* (No.3 in Britain). They also had a nice line in classy ballads, as exemplified by *Joanna* (which reached no.2 in US, No.4 in UK). Their British track record was particularly impressive - between 1979 and 1985 they collected 19 consecutive hit singles.
Many fans believed that 'Kool' referred to the personable lead singer, JT. But Kool is in fact Robert Bell, a more retiring character whose brilliant bass guitar lines have always been the backbone of the Gang's music. (Bob Macdonald 28/11/85).

BIG FUN
Tracks: / Big fun / Get down on it.
7" Single: Released Aug '82, on De-Lite, Deleted '85. Catalogue no: **DE 7**
12" Single: Released Aug '82, on De-Lite, Deleted '85. Catalogue no: **DEX 7**

CELEBRATION
Tracks: / Celebration / Morning star.
7" Single: Released Oct '80, on Kool Kat, by Kool Kat Records. Deleted Oct '83. Catalogue no: **KOOL 10**
7" Single: Released Oct '80, on De-Lite, Deleted '83. Catalogue no: **KOOL 10**
12" Single: Released Oct '80, on Kool Kat, by Kool Kat Records. Deleted Oct '83. Catalogue no: **KOOL 10 12**

CELEBRATION (OLD GOLD)
Tracks: / Celebration / Ladies night.
7" Single: Released Feb '88, on Old Gold, by Old Gold Records. Catalogue no: **OG 9766**

CELEBRATION (REMIX)
Tracks: / Celebration (SAW remix) (Remixed by Stock, Aitken & Waterman.) / Rags to riches / Celebration (Original version.).
CD 5": Released Dec '88, on Club, by Phonogram Ltd. Catalogue no: **JABCD 78**
7" Single: Released Dec '88, on Club, by Phonogram Ltd. Deleted 31 Jul '89. Catalogue no: **JAB 78**
12" Single: Released Dec '88, on Club, by Phonogram Ltd. Deleted 31 Jul '89. Catalogue no: **JABX 78**

CHERISH
Tracks: / Cherish / Celebration.
7" Single: Released Apr '85, on De-Lite, Deleted '86. Catalogue no: **DE 20**
12" Single: Released Apr '85, on De-Lite, Deleted '86. Catalogue no: **DEX 20**

EMERGENCY (SINGLE)
Tracks: / Emergency.
7" Single: Released Nov '85, on De-Lite, Deleted '88. Catalogue no: **DE 21**

FRESH
Tracks: / Fresh.
7" Single: Released Nov '84, on De-Lite, Deleted '87. Catalogue no: **DE 18**

GET DOWN ON IT
Tracks: / Get down on it / Summer madness.
7" Single: Released Dec '81, on De-Lite, Deleted '86. Catalogue no: **DE 5**
12" Single: Released Jan '82, on De-Lite, Deleted Jan '85. Catalogue no: **DEX 5**

HANGIN' OUT
Tracks: / Hangin' out.
7" Single: Released Jul '80, on De-Lite, Deleted '83. Catalogue no: **KOOL 9**
12" Single: Released Jul '80, on De-Lite, Deleted '83. Catalogue no: **KOOL 912**

HI DE HI, HI DE HO
Tracks: / Hi de hi, hi de ho / No show.
7" Single: Released Dec '82, on De-Lite, Deleted '85. Catalogue no: **DE 14**
12" Single: Released Dec '82, on De-Lite, Deleted '85. Catalogue no: **DEX 14**

JOANNA
Tracks: / Joanna.
7" Single: Released Feb '84, on De-Lite, Deleted '87. Catalogue no: **DE 16**

JOANNA (OLD GOLD)
Tracks: / Joanna / Cherish.
7" Single: Released Feb '88, on Old Gold, by Old Gold Records. Catalogue no: **OG 9777**

JONES VS JONES
Tracks: / Jones vs Jones / Summer madness.
7" Single: Released Feb '81, on De-Lite, Deleted '84. Catalogue no: **KOOL 11**

LADIES NIGHT (SINGLE)
Tracks: / Ladies night.
7" Single: Released Oct '79, on Mercury, by Phonogram Ltd. Deleted '82. Catalogue no: **KOOL 7**

MISLED
Tracks: / Misled / Rollin'.
7" Single: Released Feb '85, on De-Lite, Deleted '88. Catalogue no: **DER 19**

OOH LA LA LA (LET'S GO DANCING)
Tracks: / Ooh la la la (let's go dancing) / Stand up and sing.

7" Single: Released Oct '82, on De-Lite. Deleted '85. Catalogue no: **DE 9**
12" Single: Released Oct '82, on De-Lite. Deleted '85. Catalogue no: **DEX 9**

RAINDROPS
Tracks: / Raindrops / Amore amore / Raindrops (extended version) (Only on 12" and CD single.) / Raindrops (dub) (Only on 12" single.).
CD 5": Released Jul '89, on Mercury, by Phonogram Ltd. Catalogue no: **MERCD 293**
Cassingle: Released Jul '89, on Mercury, by Phonogram Ltd. Catalogue no: **MERMC 293**
7" Single: Released Jul '89, on Mercury, by Phonogram Ltd. Catalogue no: **MER 293**
12" Single: Released Jul '89, on Mercury, by Phonogram Ltd. Catalogue no: **MERX 293**

STEPPIN' OUT
Tracks: / Steppin' out.
7" Single: Released Oct '81, on De-Lite. Deleted '84. Catalogue no: **DE 4**

STONE LOVE
Tracks: / Stone love / Dance champion / Get down on it (ext mix) ** (** extra track on double pack single only) / Ladies night (remix)
(extra track on double pack single only).
7" Set: Released Mar '87, on Club, by Phonogram Ltd. Deleted Dec '87. Catalogue no: **JABXD 47**
7" Single: Released Feb '87, on Club, by Phonogram Ltd. Deleted Dec '87. Catalogue no: **JAB 47**
12" Single: Released Feb '87, on Club, by Phonogram Ltd. Deleted Dec '87. Catalogue no: **JABX 47**

STRAIGHT AHEAD
Tracks: / Straight ahead / Place for us.
7" Single: Released Dec '83, on De-Lite. Deleted '86. Catalogue no: **DE 15**

TAKE IT TO THE TOP
Tracks: / Take it to the top / Celebremos.
7" Single: Released May '81, on De-Lite. Deleted '84. Catalogue no: **DE 2**
12" Single: Released May '81, on De-Lite. Deleted '84. Catalogue no: **DEX 2**

TAKE MY HEART (YOU CAN HAVE IT IF YOU WANT IT)
Tracks: / Take my heart (you can have it if you want it) / Caribbean festival / Winter sadness.
7" Single: Released Mar '82, on De-Lite. Deleted '85. Catalogue no: **DE 6**
12" Single: Released Mar '82, on De-Lite. Deleted '85. Catalogue no: **DEX 6**

THROWDOWN MIX Hits medley
Tracks: / Get down on it / Ladies night / Fresh / Big fun / Celebration / Victory (7" version) / Bad woman.
12" Single: Released Dec '86, on Club, by Phonogram Ltd. Deleted Jul '87. Catalogue no: **JABXR 44**

TOO HOT
Tracks: / Too hot / Tonight's the night.
7" Single: Released Jan '80, on Mercury, by Phonogram Ltd. Deleted '83. Catalogue no: **KOOL 8**
12" Single: Released Jan '80, on Mercury, by Phonogram Ltd. Deleted Jan '85. Catalogue no: **KOOL 1812**

VICTORY (SINGLE)
Tracks: / Victory.
CD 5": Released Dec '86, on Club, by Phonogram Ltd. Deleted Jul '87. Catalogue no: **JABD 44**
Cassingle: Released Dec '86, on Club, by Phonogram Ltd. Deleted Jul '87. Catalogue no: **JABM 44**
7" Single: Released Dec '86, on Club, by Phonogram Ltd. Deleted Jul '87. Catalogue no: **JAB 44**
12" Single: Released Dec '86, on Club, by Phonogram Ltd. Deleted Jul '87. Catalogue no: **JABX 44**
12" Single: Released Dec '86, on Club, by Phonogram Ltd. Deleted Jul '87. Catalogue no: **JABXR 44**

WHEN YOU SAY YOU LOVE SOMEBODY FROM THE HEART
Tracks: / When you say you love somebody from the heart.
7" Single: Released Apr '84, on De-Lite. Deleted '87. Catalogue no: **DE 17**

Korberg, Tommy

ANTHEM
Tracks: / Anthem / Mountain duet.

7" Single: Released Nov '86, on RCA, by BMG Records (UK). Catalogue no: **CHESS 8**
12" Single: Released Nov '86, on RCA, by BMG Records (UK). Catalogue no: **CHESST 8**

Koreana

HAND IN HAND
Tracks: / Hand in hand / Victory / Hand in hand (instrumental) (Available on 12" only.).
7" Single: Released 15 Aug '88, on Polydor, by Polydor Ltd. Deleted 30 May '89. Catalogue no: **PO 13**
12" Single: Released 15 Aug '88, on Polygram, by PolyGram UK Ltd. Catalogue no: **PZ 13**

Korgis

Biographical details: Korgis Andy Davis and James Warren were the nucleus of this British band, whose melodic soft-centred pop sounds enjoyed brief success on the UK charts in the late Seventies and early Eighties. Their first hit was *If I Had You*, which reached No.13 in 1979 - this joined the ranks of oldies like B.Bumble & The Stingers' *Nut Rocker* and Eric Carmen's *All By Myself* in the category of pop hits with tunes borrowed from classical composers. 1980 brought the Korgis a UK No.5 hit with the Warren-penned *Everybody's Got To Learn Sometime*, a hummable and well produced ballad that won support from all age groups.
The slick shiny studio sound of the Korgis failed to compensate for their lack of further strong material and they quickly found themselves barking up the wrong tree. In late 1980, just as *Everybody's Got To Learn Sometime* was reaching an impressive No.18 position in the States, *If It's All Right With You Baby* was peaking at No.56 in Britain. From then onwards, a series of flops dogged their career on both sides of the Atlantic. (Bob Macdonald 28/11/85).

ALL THE LOVE IN THE WORLD
Tracks: / All the love in the world / Intimate.
7" Single: Released Jun '81, on Rialto (1), by Rialto Records. Catalogue no: **TREB 138**

BURNING QUESTIONS
Tracks: / Burning questions.
7" Single: Released Oct '85, on Marvellous. Catalogue no: **SON 2284**
12" Single: Released Oct '85, on Marvellous. Catalogue no: **SONL 2284**

DON'T LOOK BACK
Tracks: / Don't look back / Xenophobia.
7" Single: Released Jul '82, on London (Decca), by Decca International. Deleted Jul '85. Catalogue no: **LON 007**

DON'T SAY THAT IT'S OVER
Tracks: / Don't say that it's over / Drawn and quartered.
7" Single: Released Sep '81, on Rialto (1), by Rialto Records. Catalogue no: **TREB 142**

DUMB WAITERS (SINGLE)
Tracks: / Dumb waiters / Perfect hostess.
7" Single: Released Oct '80, on Rialto (1), by Rialto Records. Deleted Oct '83. Catalogue no: **TREB 122**

EVERYBODY'S GOTTA LEARN SOMETIME
Tracks: / Everybody's got to learn sometime / Dirty postcards.
7" Single: Released Apr '80, on Rialto (1), by Rialto Records. Catalogue no: **TREB 115**

EVERYBODY'S GOTTA LEARN SOMETIME (OLD GOLD)
Tracks: / Everybody's gotta learn sometime / If I had you.
7" Single: Released 24 Apr '89, on Old Gold, by Old Gold Records. Catalogue no: **OG 9889**

I JUST CAN'T HELP IT
Tracks: / I just can't help it / Oh Maxine.
7" Single: Released Jan '80, on Rialto (1), by Rialto Records. Catalogue no: **TREB 112**

IF I HAD YOU
Tracks: / If I had you.
7" Single: Released Jun '79, on Rialto (1), by Rialto Records. Deleted '82. Catalogue no: **TREB 103**

IF IT'S ALRIGHT WITH YOU BABY
Tracks: / If it's alright with you baby.
7" Single: Released Jul '80, on Rialto (1), by Rialto Records. Catalogue no: **TREB 118**

ROVERS RETURN
Tracks: / Rovers return / Wish you a merry Christmas.
7" Single: Released Nov '80, on Rialto (1), by Rialto Records. Catalogue no: **TREB 131**

TRUE LIFE CONFESSIONS
Tracks: / True life confessions.
7" Single: Released Jun '85, on Sonet, by Sonet Records. Catalogue no: **SON 2277**
12" Single: Released Jun '85, on Sonet, by Sonet Records. Catalogue no: **SONL 2277**

Kotch - Wonderful Tonight (Released on Mango)

YOUNG & RUSSIAN
Tracks: / Young & Russian.
7" Single: Released Oct '79, on Rialto (1), by Rialto Records. Catalogue no: **TREB 108**

Korn, Jiri

DAISY
Tracks: / Daisy.
7" Single: Released Sep '84, on Code, by Code Records. Catalogue no: **COD 005**

Korner, Alexis

BEIRUT
Tracks: / Beirut / Meanful.
7" Single: Released May '84, on Charisma, by Virgin Records. Deleted '89. Catalogue no: **CB 412**

Korova Milkbar

DO IT AGAIN
Tracks: / Do it again.
12" Single: Released May '89, on Subway, by Subway Records. Catalogue no: **SUBWAY 25T**

Kosmin, Lee

GETTING SO EXCITED
Tracks: / Getting so excited / My belief in you.
7" Single: Released Feb '81, on Parlophone, by EMI Records. Deleted Feb '84. Catalogue no: **R 6045**

I CAN'T GO ON
Tracks: / I can't go on / You gave yourself away.
7" Single: Released Jul '81, on Parlophone, by EMI Records. Deleted '84. Catalogue no: **R 6049**

WHAT'S IT TO YOU
Tracks: / What's it to you / Something for nothing.
7" Single: Released Jun '83, on WEA (International), by WEA Records. Catalogue no: **U 9894**

YOU ARE THE ONE FOR ME
Tracks: / You are the one for me / Your turn.
7" Single: Released Sep '80, on Parlophone, by EMI Records. Deleted '83. Catalogue no: **R 6040**

YOU CAN DO
Tracks: / You can do / Slow motion.
7" Single: Released Feb '80, on Parlophone, by EMI Records. Deleted '83. Catalogue no: **R 6031**

Kotch

OOH BABY BABY
Tracks: / Ooh baby baby / Smooth sailing.
7" Single: Released Jul '88, on Mango, by Island Records. Deleted Apr '89. Catalogue no: **IS 382**
12" Single: Released Jul '88, on Mango, by Island Records. Catalogue no: **12IS 382**

RUB A DUB OFFICER
Tracks: / Rub-a-dub officer.
12" Single: Released Oct '84, on Macca Music. Catalogue no: **Unknown**

TEARS
Tracks: / Tears / Two occasions / Banjo rock (Available on 12" format only.).
7" Single: Released Nov '88, on Mango, by Island Records. Deleted Apr '89. Catalogue no: **IS 403**
12" Single: Released Nov '88, on Mango, by Island Records. Catalogue no: **12IS 403**

WONDERFUL TONIGHT
Tracks: / Wonderful tonight / Heartbreak.
7" Single: Released 18 Apr '89, on Mango, by Island Records. Catalogue no: **MNG 104**
12" Single: Released 18 Apr '89, on Mango, by Island Records. Catalogue no: **12 MNG 104**

Koumba

WE A LEGGO
Tracks: / We a leggo / Billy.
7" Single: Released Nov '82, on Greensleeves, by Greensleeves Records. Deleted Nov '85. Catalogue no: **GRED 105**

Kova Rea

NUIT D'AMOUR
Tracks: / Nuit d'amour (night of love).
7" Single: Released Sep '89, on Battersea Power. Catalogue no: **NUIT 1**
12" Single: Released Sep '89, on Battersea Power. Catalogue no: **12 NUIT 1**

Kraftwerk

Biographical details: This West German electronic rock band consists of Karl Bartos, Wolfgang Flur, Ralf Hutter and Florian Schneider. Kraftwerk have been cited as a key influence of Britain's new technorock stars of the eighties.
Founded and dominated by the nucleus of Hutter and Schneider in 1970, the band began their recording career in the Dusseldorf studio of Conny Plank, an engineer and producer who shared their interest in experimental electronic music (and who himself became an influential force upon some UK bands of the eighties). Instead of using the new synthesiser technology to bolster conventional genres of music, as many pop and rock acts of the seventies did, Kraftwerk decided to create and define a whole new futuristic field of their own.
It was their fourth album, 1975's *Autobahn*, which brought Kraftwerk to international attention. Side one was a continuous 22 and a half minute version of the title track, a mesmerising sonic encapsulating of a drive down a motorway. Such an idea might have seem insufferably boring, but in fact it was a fascinating breakthrough in modern music that startled many listeners with its originality, especially when an edited version of *Autobahn* became a top 30 single in both Britain and America. The album reached no .4 on the UK charts. In common with fellow German pioneers Can, Kraftwerk built a solid cult following during the seventies but were not able to secure consistent commercial success. But suddenly, in February 1982,

1982, a hypnotic track called *The model*, which had been a big club favourite ever since its original 1978 release, reached no.1 on the British chart. This marked the first time that a German act had topped the UK listings. The successs of *The model* occurred at a time when such bands as New Order, The Human League, Gary Numan, Ultravox and OMD were enjoying major success by broadening the horizons of the field pioneered by Kraftwerk. The title of the German band's next UK hit single summed up their image: *Showroom dummies*. Their appearance was always contrived to look as robotic as possible, in keeping with their music. Publicity photos usually protrayed the four men wearing identical clothes and expressionless faces. They virtually never gave interviews, and their individual public profiles were anonymous. The *Computer world* album enjoyed a healthy run on the British LP list, and was followed in 1983 by their sports theme single *Tour de France*, which was a UK top 30 hit in both '83 and '84 (Bob Macdonald 85).

AUTOBAHN (SINGLE)
Tracks: / Autobahn.
7" Single: Released May '75, on Vertigo, by Phonogram Ltd. Deleted '78. Catalogue no: **6147 012**

COMPUTER LOVE
Tracks: / Computer love / Model, The.
7" Single: Released Jul '81, on EMI, by EMI Records. Deleted '84. Catalogue no: **EMI 5207**
7" Single: Released May '84, on EMI Golden 45's, by EMI Records. Deleted Nov '88. Catalogue no: **G45 16**
12" Single: Released Dec '81, on EMI, by EMI Records. Deleted Dec '84. Catalogue no: **12 EMI 5027**

KOMETEN MELODIE 2
Tracks: / Kometen melodie 2 / Vom Himmel Hoch.
7" Single: Released May '81, on Vertigo, by Phonogram Ltd. Deleted May '84. Catalogue no: **VER 3**

MUSIQUE NON STOP
Tracks: / Musique non stop.
7" Single: Released Oct '86, on EMI, by EMI Records. Deleted Jul '87. Catalogue no: **EMI 5588**
12" Single: Released Oct '86, on EMI, by EMI Records. Deleted Jul '87. Catalogue no: **12EMI 5588**

NEON LIGHTS
Tracks: / Neon lights.
7" Single: Released Oct '78, on Capitol, by EMI Records. Deleted '81. Catalogue no: **CL 15998**

POCKET CALCULATOR
Tracks: / Pocket calculator / Dentaku.
7" Single: Released May '81, on EMI, by EMI Records. Deleted '84. Catalogue no: **EMI 5175**

SHOWROOM DUMMIES (see panel below)
Tracks: / Showroom dummies / Numbers.
7" Single: Released Feb '82, on EMI, by EMI Records. Deleted '85. Catalogue no: **EMI 5272**
12" Single: Released Feb '82, on EMI, by EMI Records. Deleted '85. Catalogue no: **12EMI 5272**

TELEPHONE CALL, THE
Tracks: / Telephone call, The / Der telefon anruf (German version) / House phone (Available on 12" version only.).
Note: House Phone is an extra track only available on the 12" version.
7" Single: Released Feb '87, on EMI, by EMI Records. Catalogue no: **EMI 5602**
12" Single: Released Feb '87, on EMI, by EMI Records. Catalogue no: **12EMI 560 2**

TOUR DE FRANCE
Tracks: / Tour de France.
Cassingle: Released Aug '83, on EMI, by EMI Records. Deleted '88. Catalogue no: **TC EMI 5413**
7" Single: Released Aug '84, on EMI, by EMI Records. Deleted '88. Catalogue no: **EMI 5413**
12" Single: Released Aug '84, on EMI, by EMI Records. Catalogue no: **12EMI 5413**

Krakamaraka

EL VINO COLLAPSO
Tracks: / El vino collapso.
7" Single: Released Jun '83, on Magic Moon, Catalogue no: **KRAK 1**

K-Ram

MENAGE A TROIS
Tracks: / Menage a trois.
7" Single: Released Apr '84, on Chrysalis, by Chrysalis Records. Catalogue no: **CHS 2774**
12" Single: Released Apr '84, on Chrysalis, by Chrysalis Records. Catalogue no: **CHS 12 2774**

Kramer, Billy J.

Biographical details: Billy J Kramer & The Dakotas were part of the Beatles bandwagon of 1963-64. Like the fab four, they played at the Star Club in Hamburg before becoming famous, they were managed by Brian Epstein, produced by George Martin and signed to Parlophone Records. Unlike the fab four, they did not write their own material - most of it was supplied to them by their mentors Lennon & McCartney. Kramer was born William Ashton in Bootle, Liverpool. He worked as an apprentice engineer with British Rail for a while, during which time he fronted a small time Liverpool combo called The Coasters. Epstein discovered and liked the singer but was not so crazy about the rest of the group; he thus teamed the newly rechristened Billy J Kramer with a Manchester combo called the Dakotas. *Do you want to know a secret* became their first hit, reaching the UK no.2 spot in the summer of '63. Before the years, they chalked up their first no.1 with *Bad to me* plus a no.4 hit with *I'll keep you satisfied. Listen to Billy J Kramer*, reached no.11 on the UK album chart, logging 17 weeks on the top 20. The group's forth hit *Little children* was the first one that wsa not written by Lennon & McCartney, but that did not prevent it from becoming their second British no.1 single in March 1964. Like so many of their Merseybeat contemporaries, their records then crossed the Atlantic to become part of the British invasion. By early 1965, however, Billy J Kramer was fading fast. He was good looking but his singing style and stage personality were too ordinary to sustain an extended chart career. After a final UK top 20 entry with Burt Bacharach's *Trains and boats and planes*, the hits dried up altogether. The group remained intact until 1968, when Billy J. split from the Dakotas to pursue a steady career on the variety and cabaret circuit. He was still actively performing a making the occasional flop record - in the eighties. He was a runner in the 1984 London marathon, so there was still plenty of life in the old boy. (Bob Macdonald 85).

KRAFTWERK - SHOWROOM DUMMIES (Released on EMI)

BAD TO ME
Tracks: / Bad to me.
7" Single: Released Aug '63, on Parlophone, by EMI Records. Deleted '66. Catalogue no: **R 5049**

BAD TO ME (OLD GOLD)
Tracks: / Bad to me.
7" Single: Released Oct '83, on Old Gold, by Old Gold Records. Deleted Sep '89. Catalogue no: **OG 9372**

DO YOU WANT TO KNOW A SECRET
Tracks: / Do you want to know a secret.
7" Single: Released Oct '83, on Old Gold, by Old Gold Records. Deleted Sep '89. Catalogue no: **OG 9367**
7" Single: Released May '63, on Parlophone, by EMI Records. Deleted '66. Catalogue no: **R 5023**

FROM A WINDOW
Tracks: / From a window.
7" Single: Released Jul '64, on Parlophone, by EMI Records. Deleted '67. Catalogue no: **R 5156**

I'LL KEEP YOU SATISFIED
Tracks: / I'll keep you satisfied.
7" Single: Released Nov '63, on Parlophone, by EMI Records. Deleted '66. Catalogue no: **R 5073**

LITTLE CHILDREN
Tracks: / Little children.
7" Single: Released Feb '64, on Parlophone, by EMI Records. Deleted '67. Catalogue no: **R 5105**

ROCK IT
Tracks: / Rock it.
7" Single: Released Mar '82, on Runaway, Deleted '85. Catalogue no: **BJK 1**

SILVER DREAM
Tracks: / Silver dream / Lonely lady.
7" Single: Released Nov '80, on JM, by JM Records. Deleted '83. Catalogue no: **JM 1005**

TRAINS AND BOATS AND PLANES
Tracks: / Trains and boats and planes.
7" Single: Released May '65, on Parlophone, by EMI Records. Deleted '68. Catalogue no: **R 5285**

YOU CAN'T LIVE ON MEMORIES
Tracks: / You can't live on memories.
7" Single: Released Jun '83, on RAK, by EMI Records. Catalogue no: **RAK 359**

YOU'RE RIGHT I'M WRONG
Tracks: / You're right I'm wrong.
7" Single: Released Sep '82, on Runaway, Deleted '85. Catalogue no: **RUN 506**

Kramer, Michael

HOMETIME
Tracks: / Hometime / Hometime (version).
7" Single: Released Mar '89, on Paragon, Catalogue no: **PRE 11**

Kramer, Nancy & Solar

HALLELUJAH (SOLAR RIDER)
Tracks: / Hallelujah (solar rider).
7" Single: Released Jan '80, on Sonet, by Sonet Records. Deleted Jan '85. Catalogue no: **SON 2197**

Krankies

Biographical details: Krankies A young pre-teen girl, dressed as a boy and her long suffering adult male sparring partner constitutes this British vocal comedy duo. Soon after becoming known on television and in variety and seaside shows, the Krankies achieved a one-off UK chart entry with their 1981 single *Fan Dabi Dozi* which reached No.46. This was a half sung/ half spoken cash in on their catch phrase - if something was *Fan Dabi Dozi*, it was fantastic; if it was *Fan Dabi Double Dozi*, it was even more fantastic; if it was *Fan Dabi Triple Dozi* it was brilliant etc. etc. You know the rest. (Bob Macdonald 28/11/85).

FAN-DABI-DOZI (SINGLE)
Tracks: / Fan-dabi-dozi / Wee Jimmy Krankie.
7" Single: Released Feb '81, on Monarch, by Monarch Records. Deleted '84. Catalogue no: **MON 21**

HAND IN HAND AT CHRISTMAS
Tracks: / Hand in hand at Christmas / Grannie Krankie meets the men from Mars.
7" Single: Released Nov '84, on Relax, Catalogue no: **LAX 2**

JIMMY'S GANG
Tracks: / Jimmy's gang / We're going to Spain.
7" Single: Released Oct '81, on RCA, by BMG Records (UK). Deleted Oct '84. Catalogue no: **RCA 119**

WE'RE GOING TO SPAIN
Tracks: / We're going to Spain / Haggis song.
7" Single: Released Apr '82, on RCA, by BMG Records (UK). Deleted '85. Catalogue no: **RCA 217**

Kranz, George

DIN DAA DAA
Tracks: / Din daa daa / Din daa daa (dub version) / Din daa daa (original) (Track on 12" only).
7" Single: Released Jul '88, on 4th & Broadway, by Island Records. Deleted Apr '89. Catalogue no: **BRW 110**
12" Single: Released Jul '88, on 4th & Broadway, by Island Records. Catalogue no: **12 BRW 110**

Kray Cherubs

ROT IN HELL MOM
Tracks: / Rot in hell mom / Motor drag / Saucerman.
7" Single: Released 31 Jul '89, on Snakeskin, Catalogue no: **SS 002**

Kraze

LET'S PLAY HOUSE
Tracks: / Let's play house / Let's play house (version).
CD 5": Released May '89, on MCA, by MCA Records. Catalogue no: **DMCAT 1337**
7" Single: Released May '89, on MCA, by MCA Records. Catalogue no: **MCA 1337**
12" Single: Released May '89, on MCA, by MCA Records. Catalogue no: **MCAT 1337**

PARTY, THE
Tracks: / Party, The.
7" Single: Released Oct '88, on MCA, by MCA Records. Catalogue no: **MCA 1288**
12" Single: Released Oct '88, on MCA, by MCA Records. Catalogue no: **MCAT 1288**

SAY HELLO TO MY GIRL
Tracks: / Say hello to my girl / Friday night.
7" Single: Released Oct '80, on Double Dee, Deleted Oct '83. Catalogue no: **D-DEE 6**

Krazyhouse

KRAZYHOUSE
Tracks: / Krazyhouse / Krazyhouse (version).
7" Single: Released Jun '89, on Supreme, by Supreme Records. Catalogue no: **SUPE 145**
12" Single: Released Jun '89, on Supreme, by Supreme Records. Catalogue no: **SUPET 145**

Kreamcicle

NO NEWS IS NEWS
Tracks: / No news is news.
7" Single: Released Jul '86, on Bluebird (2), by BMG Records (UK). Deleted Jun '88. Catalogue no: **BR 25**
12" Single: Released Jul '86, on Bluebird (2), by BMG Records (UK). Catalogue no: **BRT 25**

Kreator

BEHIND THE MIRROR
Tracks: / Behind the mirror / Gangland.
12" Single: Released Oct '87, on Noise, by Dorane Records. Catalogue no: **KOISE 084T**

FLAG OF HATE
12" Pic: Released Oct '89, on Noise, by Dorane Records. Catalogue no: **NUKPD 084**
12" Single: Released Oct '89, on Noise, by Dorane Records. Catalogue no: **12NUK 047**

Kreem

TRIANGLE OF LOVE
Tracks: / Triangle of love / Triangle of love (vocal mix) / Uptown triangle beats.
7" Single: Released Jun '87, on Nine O Nine, by Creole Records. Catalogue no: **NINE 8**

Krew

PAPER HEROES
Tracks: / Paper heroes / It's for you.
7" Single: Released Apr '86, on WEA, by WEA Records. Catalogue no: **YZ 67**
12" Single: Released Apr '86, on WEA, by

WEA Records. Catalogue no: **YZ 67T**

Krew Kats

TRAMBONE
Tracks: / Trambone.
7" Single: Released Mar '61, on H.M.V., by EMI Records. Deleted '64. Catalogue no: **POP 840**

Krew Men

DO YOU WANNA TOUCH
Tracks: / Do you wanna touch.
7" Single: Released Oct '88, on Lost Moments, Catalogue no: **LM 045**

I'M GONNA GET IT
Tracks: / I'm gonna get it.
7" Single: Released Apr '85, on Lost Moments, Catalogue no: **LM 024**

MY GENERATION
Tracks: / My generation.
12" Single: Released May '88, on Lost Moments, Catalogue no: **LM 12 043**

RAMBLING
Tracks: / Rambling.
7" Single: Released Jun '85, on Lost Moments, Catalogue no: **LM 024**

WHAT ARE YOU TODAY?
Tracks: / What are you today.
7" Single: Released Nov '85, on Lost Moments, Catalogue no: **LM 034**
12" Single: Released Nov '85, on Lost Moments, Catalogue no: **LM 12 034**

Krisma

MANY KISSES
Tracks: / Many kisses / Rien ne vas plus.
7" Single: Released Sep '80, on Polydor, by Polydor Ltd. Deleted '83. Catalogue no: **POSP 165**

Kriss Kross

HOTEL
Tracks: / Hotel.
12" Single: Released Jan '84, on Midas, by Magnet Records. Catalogue no: **12 MID 6**

Krissi

LOVE MAKES A WOMAN
Tracks: / Love makes a woman* / Change in you, A / Love makes a woman (extended mix) (Only on 12" single.) / Love makes a woman (LP version) (Only on 12" version.) / Love makes a woman.
7" Single: Released Nov '85, on Secret Rendezvous, Catalogue no: **CA 100**
12" Single: Released Nov '85, on Secret Rendezvous, Catalogue no: **CA 001**

Kristeen

LIFE
Tracks: / Life.
12" Single: Released Sep '89, on Catt, by Catt Records. Catalogue no: **CATT 007**

Kristian, John

POPE JOHN PAUL
Tracks: / Pope John Paul / How come.
7" Single: Released Jul '81, on Recorded Delivery, Deleted Jul '84. Catalogue no: **RDR 001**

Kristina, Sonja

ST. TROPEZ
Tracks: / St. Tropez / Mr. Skin.
7" Single: Released May '80, on Chopper, Deleted May '80. Catalogue no: **CHOP 101**

Kristofferson, Lee

FIRE
Tracks: / Fire / Day trip to Zimbabwe.
7" Single: Released Nov '80, on Surrey Sound, Catalogue no: **HMS 2**

K-Roc

TURN IT UP
Tracks: / Turn it up.
12" Single: Released Jun '88, on Jive, by Zomba Records. Deleted '88. Catalogue no: **ZPL T2**

Krokus

Biographical details: At the time of their greatest success, this Swiss heavy metal band consisted of Mark Kohler, Steve Pace, Marc Storace, Fernando Von Arb and Chris Von Rohr. Formed in the early seventies, Krokus eventually became a credible international rock ambassador for a nation which has not been noted for it's exports to the world of pop and rock music. After many years of hard gigging, the group's debut album *Metal rendezvous* finally appeared in 1980. They built a cult following amongst headbangers throughout Europe, and by 1981 their UK following was sufficent to put the band's second LP *Hardware* in the British album chart, peaking at no.44. In the same year they scored a minor success with their *Industrial strength*" EP, the lead track of which was *Bedside radio*. Krokus *One vice at a time* album, released in 1982, reached no.28 in Britain and no.53 in America. Sticking closely to the well worn HM formula, they consolidated this success with 1983's *Headhunter*. However, their brand of Swiss rock 'n' roll fared a little more disappointingly when they issued the 1984 set *The blitz* its centrepiece single was a remake of The Sweet's *Ballroom blitz*, presumably inspired by Quiet Riot's US top 5 rendition of another glam rock classic, *Cum on feel the noize*; but the ploy failed to pay commercial dividends for Krokus. (Bob Macdonald 85).

AMERICAN WOMAN
Tracks: / American woman.
7" Single: Released '82, on Arista, by BMG Records (UK). Deleted '87. Catalogue no: **ARIST 468**

BAD BOYS RAG DOLLS
Tracks: / Bad boys rag dolls / Save me.
7" Single: Released '82, on Arista, by BMG Records (UK). Deleted '87. Catalogue no: **ARIST 451**

HEATSTROKES
Tracks: / Heatstrokes / Shy kid.
7" Single: Released Jun '80, on Ariola, by BMG Records (UK). Deleted Jun '83. Catalogue no: **ARO 233**

INDUSTRIAL STRENGTH EP
Tracks: / Bedside radio / Easy rocker / Celebration / Bye bye baby.
7" Single: Released May '81, on Ariola, by BMG Records (UK). Deleted '84. Catalogue no: **ARO 258**

ROCK CITY
Tracks: / Rock city / Mister 69 / Mad racket.
7" Single: Released Feb '81, on Ariola, by BMG Records (UK). Deleted Feb '84. Catalogue no: **ARO 254**

TOKYO NIGHT
Tracks: / Tokyo night / Bedside radio / Shy kid.
7" Single: Released Sep '80, on Ariola, by BMG Records (UK). Deleted '83. Catalogue no: **ARO 241**
12" Single: Released Sep '80, on Ariola, by BMG Records (UK). Deleted '83. Catalogue no: **AROD 241**

Kronen

KRONEN
7" EP: Released Mar '86, on Azra (USA), by Azra International (USA). Catalogue no: **A 8404**

Kronstadt Uprising

PART OF THE GAME
Tracks: / Part of the game.
7" Single: Released Jul '85, on Dog Rock, by Dog Rock Records. Catalogue no: **SD 108**

Krukutz

LOVE INSURANCE
Tracks: / Love insurance.
7" Single: Released Feb '85, on Ecstasy, by Creole Records. Catalogue no: **XTC 11**
12" Single: Released Feb '85, on Ecstasy, by Creole Records. Catalogue no: **XTCT 11**

TAKE A CHANCE TO DANCE
Tracks: / Take a chance to dance.
12" Single: Released Sep '87, on Bolts, by Bolts Records. Deleted Jun '88. Catalogue no: **BOLTS 07/12**

Kru-Pops

YUMMY YUMMY YUMMY
Tracks: / Yummy yummy yummy / Give me one more dance.
7" Single: Released Dec '82, on Electric Bubble Gum, by Electric Bubble Gum Records. Catalogue no: **EB 101**

Krush

HOUSE ARREST
Tracks: / Jack's back / House arrest.
7" Single: Released 31 Oct '87, on Phonogram, by Phonogram Ltd. Deleted Oct '88. Catalogue no: **JAB 63**
12" Single: Released 31 Oct '87, on Phonogram, by Phonogram Ltd. Deleted Oct '88. Catalogue no: **JABX 63**
12" Single: Released Oct '87, on Fon, by FON Records. Catalogue no: **KRUSH 14**

HOUSE ARREST (REMIX)
Tracks: / House arrest.
12" Single: Released Dec '87, on Club, by Phonogram Ltd. Deleted Oct '88. Catalogue no: **JABXR 63**

Krystol

PASSION FROM A WOMAN (SINGLE)
Tracks: / Passion from a woman.
7" Single: Released Aug '87, on Epic, by CBS Records. Deleted '87. Catalogue no: **A 7203**

PRECIOUS PRECIOUS
Tracks: / Precious precious / He's so jive.
7" Single: Released Nov '86, on Epic, by CBS Records. Catalogue no: **650255 7**
12" Single: Released Nov '86, on Epic, by CBS Records. Catalogue no: **650255 6**

K.S.I.

BASICALLY HE'S THE CHAMP
Tracks: / Basically he's the champ.
7" Single: Released Mar '89, on Tom Tom, Catalogue no: **TTT 03**

K.T.

KNEE DEEP IN LOVE
Tracks: / Knee deep in love / Runaround Sue / Thought of you, The (* Track on 12" version only.).
7" Single: Released May '88, on Priority, by Priority Records. Catalogue no: **SPRIT 1**
12" Single: Released May '88, on Priority, by Priority Records. Catalogue no: **12SPRIT 1**

Kudos

HOW CAN THIS BE LOVE
Tracks: / How can this be love.
7" Single: Released Oct '84, on Legacy, by Legacy Records. Catalogue no: **LGY 16**
12" Single: Released Oct '84, on Legacy, by Legacy Records. Catalogue no: **LGYT 16**

I NEED YOU
Tracks: / I need you.
7" Single: Released Oct '83, on Peninsula, by Prism Records. Catalogue no: **PEN 1**

Kudos Point

NIGHT OF THE LONG KNIVES
Tracks: / Night of the long knives / Two falling.
7" Single: Released Apr '82, on Deb, by Deb Records. Catalogue no: **DEB 103**

ZAMBIA
Tracks: / Zambia / Pictures of boys.
7" Single: Released Dec '82, on Deb, by Deb Records. Catalogue no: **DEB 106**

Kull

EYE OF DESTRUCTION
Tracks: / Eye of destruction / Operator.
7" Single: Released Mar '84, on Bomb, Catalogue no: **MAY 0037**

Kunz, Charlie

Biographical details: Of American nationality but based in Britain, this pianist began to build a reputation during his long mid-thirties residency at the Casani Club in London's Regent Street. A contemporary of singer Vera Lynn, his career blossomed during the forties. In January 1955 Kunz achieved a no.16 placing on Britain's recently inaugurated record charts with *Piano medley no.114* (Charlie was not a guy to deviate from an established formula) - this single contained a keyboard romp through some of 1954's biggest hits, namely those by Frankie Laine, Don Cornell, Doris Day, Kitty Kallen, Nat King Cole and the aforementioned Lynn. (Bob Macdonald 85).

PIANO MEDLEY NO.114
7" Single: Released Dec '54, on Decca, by Decca Records. Deleted '57. Catalogue no: **F 10419**

Kupa, Pete 'Skins'

SHTORMY WEATHER
Tracks: / Shtormy weather / All down the front of my troushers.
78 rpm: Released Jun '59, on Silberkla, by Silberkla Records. Deleted Jul '59. Catalogue no: **KUPA 1**

Kursaal Flyers

Biographical details: At the time of their one off hit, this British band consisted of Will Birch, Richie Bull, Viv Collins, Graeme Douglas and Paul Shuttleworth. Hailing from Southend, the Kursaal Flyers brand of satirical pop songs brightened up many pubs in the London area during 1974-75. They released their debut album *Chocs away* in 1975. The group flew to fame at Christmas 1976 with the UK no.14 single *Little does she know*, that told the tear jerking tale of a romance in the local launderette. It was written by Birch, Douglas and Shuttleworth, and superbly produced by the former Wombles wizard Mike Batt. *Little does she know* was an affectionate send up of the medium of the pop song but, like all the best parodies, managed to be a great pop single itself. During the early to mid seventies, mainstream British rock began to attract increwasing criticism from some quarters for being overblown, ponderous and remote. At the other end of the spectrum, there was the teenybopper syndrome with its lightwiegh pop ditties and manipulated idols. The London pub scene was viewed by many critics as a potential solution to the mid seventies malaise. But in the event, the 1976-77 punk rock explosion provided the answer. Just as the Kursaal Flyers and their ilk were being hailed as the next big thing, The Sex Pistols were hitting the charts with *Anarchy in the UK* Little does she know remained the Flyers only UK chart entry, and their final LP issued in 1977. A reunion tour was organised in 1985. (Bob Macdonald 85).

LITTLE DOES SHE KNOW
Tracks: / Little does she know.
7" Single: Released Nov '76, on CBS, by CBS Records. Deleted '79. Catalogue no: **CBS 4689**

LITTLE DOES SHE KNOW (OLD GOLD)
Tracks: / Little does she know / Have I the right.
7" Single: Released 27 Feb '89, on Old Gold, by Old Gold Records. Catalogue no: **OG 9859**

MONSTER IN LAW
Tracks: / Monster in law.
7" Single: Released Jun '85, on Waterfront, by Waterfront Music. Catalogue no: **WFS 14**

Kurtis, Gary

SHAPE I'M IN
Tracks: / Shape I'm in, The / Slow down.
7" Single: Released Jun '86, on Street Warrior, by Priority Records. Deleted Nov '87. Catalogue no: **SDW 1**

Kurts

BYE BYE BABY
Tracks: / Bye bye baby / Prussian stomp / Hey* (*Extra track on 12" version only.).
7" Single: Released 20 Feb '88, on GWR, by GWR Records. Catalogue no: **GWR 9**
12" Single: Released 20 Feb '88, on GWR, by GWR Records. Catalogue no: **GWT 9**

Kustom

LET THE GIRL DANCE
Tracks: / Let the girl dance / Arrested.
7" Single: Released Jul '82, on Red Bus, by Red Bus Records. Deleted Jul '85. Catalogue no: **RBUS 100**
7" Single: Released Jan '82, on Silhouette, Catalogue no: **KUS 100**

Kusworth, Dave

IT ONLY HAPPENS WITH HER
Tracks: / It only happens with her.
12" Single: Released Jun '88, on Kaleidoscope Sound, by Kaleidoscope Sound Records. Catalogue no: **KS 108**

Kutash, Jeff

DOWN STREET
Tracks: / Down street.
7" Single: Released Jul '83, on Magnet, by WEA Records. Catalogue no: **MAG 247**
12" Single: Released Jul '83, on Magnet, by WEA Records. Catalogue no: **12 MAG 247**

Kuti, Fela

LADY
Tracks: / Lady / Unknown soldier.
7" Single: Released Nov '83, on EMI, by EMI Records. Catalogue no: **EMI 5441**
12" Single: Released Nov '83, on EMI, by EMI Records. Catalogue no: **12 EMI 5441**

SORROW, TEARS AND BLOOD
Tracks: / Sorrow, tears and blood / Colonial mentality.
7" Single: Released May '81, on Arista, by BMG Records (UK). Deleted May '86. Catalogue no: **ARIST 408**

KV

EX-GIRLFRIEND
Tracks: / Ex-girlfriend.
12" Single: Released '88, on Citybeat, by Beggars Banquet Records. Catalogue no: **CBE 1211**

Kwick

CAN'T HELP MYSELF
Tracks: / Can't help myself
7" Single: Released Aug '80, on EMI-America, by EMI Records. Deleted '82. Catalogue no: **EA 117**
12" Single: Released Aug '80, on EMI-America, by EMI Records. Deleted '82. Catalogue no: **12EA 117**

NIGHT LIFE
Tracks: / Night life
7" Single: Released Jan '82, on EMI-America, by EMI Records. Deleted '84. Catalogue no: **EA 133**
12" Single: Released Jan '82, on EMI-America, by EMI Records. Deleted '84. Catalogue no: **12EA 133**

L

The following information was taken from the Music Master database on October 20th, 1989.

L5
I'M YOUR ASTRONAUT
Tracks: / I'm your astronaut / I was frightened / Lightning strikes.
7" Single: Released Sep '83, on Ram, by Ram Records. Catalogue no: **RAM 7002**

L. A. Danny
COUNTRY LOVING
Tracks: / Country loving.
12" Single: Released Dec '83, on The Foundation, Catalogue no: **TF 009**

L. A. Force
ACTION
Tracks: / Action.
12" Single: Released May '85, on Challenge, by Elite Records. Catalogue no: **TALL 15**

L, Gary
TIME (TO PARTY)
Tracks: / Time (to party) / Time (sensational mix).
12" Single: Released Jan '87, on Champion, by Champion Records. Deleted Aug '89. Catalogue no: **CHAMP 1228**

L. Jays
I'VE BEEN HURT
Tracks: / I've been hurt / Working for your love.
7" Single: Released Feb '82, on S & D, Catalogue no: **SD 001**

L Kage
LIKE A BUTTERFLY
Tracks: / Like a butterfly.
12" Single: Released Apr '89, on G.I., by Plastic Head Records. Catalogue no: **GI 112**

L.A.
THAT'S THE WAY
Tracks: / It's my life / That's the way.
7" Single: Released Feb '80, on Star Dust, Deleted '83. Catalogue no: **STAR 002**

La' Amour
SUNSHINE ON MY PILLOW
Tracks: / Sunshine on my pillow / Sunshine on my dub.
12" Single: Released Oct '80, on Time, Deleted Oct '83. Catalogue no: **EBY 006**

La Ban
LOVE IN SIBERIA
Tracks: / Love in Siberia / It's a fantasy.
7" Single: Released Feb '87, on Creole, by Creole Records. Catalogue no: **CR 96**
12" Single: Released Feb '87, on Creole, by Creole Records. Catalogue no: **CRT 96**

La Batterie
LET THERE BE DRUMS
Tracks: / Let there be drums / Shogun.
7" Single: Released Jan '83, on Polo, by Polo Records. Deleted '88. Catalogue no: **POLO 24**
12" Single: Released Jan '83, on Polo, by Polo Records. Deleted '88. Catalogue no: **POLO 12-24**

La Beat, Jak
IT'S SUMMERTIME
Tracks: / It's summertime (continental version) / It's summertime (British version).
7" Single: Released 18 Jul '88, on Rubber, by Mawson & Wareham Music. Catalogue no: **ADUB 20**

La Belle Epoque
BLACK IS BLACK
Tracks: / Black is black.
7" Single: Released Aug '77, on Harvest (2), by Harvest Music. Catalogue no: **HAR 5133**

La Bionda
ONE FOR YOU ONE FOR ME
Tracks: / One for you one for me.
7" Single: Released Oct '78, on Philips, by Phonogram Ltd. Deleted '81. Catalogue no: **6198 227**

La Boost
BEDASAN ON DACCA
Tracks: / Bedasan on Dacca / Rm it home.
7" Single: Released Sep '87, on Breakin', by Breakin' Records. Catalogue no: **7 BRK 1**

OUT OF TIME
Tracks: / Out of time / City on fire.
7" Single: Released Oct '88, on Breakin', by Breakin' Records. Catalogue no: **7 BRK 5**

La Boppers
BE BOP DANCING
Tracks: / Be bop dancing / Saturday.
7" Single: Released Aug '80, on Mercury, by Phonogram Ltd. Deleted '83. Catalogue no: **MER 27**
12" Single: Released Aug '80, on Mercury, by Phonogram Ltd. Deleted '83. Catalogue no: **MERX 27**

GIVE ME SOME
Tracks: / Give me some.
12" Single: Released Feb '89, on Dance Classics, Catalogue no: **LA 704**

IS THIS THE BEST
Tracks: / Is this the best / Watching life.
7" Single: Released Jun '80, on Mercury, by Phonogram Ltd. Deleted Jun '83. Catalogue no: **MER 12**
12" Single: Released Jun '80, on Mercury, by Phonogram Ltd. Deleted Jun '83. Catalogue no: **MERX 12**

LA LA MEANS I LOVE YOU
Tracks: / La la means I love you / Is this the best / Be bop dancing.
7" Single: Released May '81, on Mercury, by Phonogram Ltd. Deleted May '84. Catalogue no: **MER 71**
12" Single: Released May '81, on Mercury, by Phonogram Ltd. Deleted May '84. Catalogue no: **MERX 71**

La Bouche
ROMANTIC LOVE
Tracks: / Romantic love.
7" Single: Released Mar '85, on Safari, by Safari Records. Catalogue no: **SAFE 66**

La Campagnie Creole
LA MACHINE A DANSER
Tracks: / La machine a danser.
7" Single: Released Jul '88, on Sonet, by Sonet Records. Catalogue no: **SON 5**
12" Single: Released Jul '88, on Sonet, by Sonet Records. Catalogue no: **SONL 5**

La Chandra
SHY GIRL
Tracks: / Shy girl (radio edit) / Shy girl (dub).
7" Single: Released 23 May '87, on Syncopate, by EMI Records. Deleted Oct '87. Catalogue no: **SY 2**
12" Single: Released 23 May '87, on Syncopate, by EMI Records. Deleted Apr '88. Catalogue no: **12 SY 2**

SHY GIRL (REMIX)
Tracks: / Shy girl (remix) / Shy girl (pianopella) / Shy girl (dance mix).
7" Single: Released Jun '87, on Syncopate, by EMI Records. Catalogue no: **SYX 2**

La Compagnie
MY NUMBER ONE
Tracks: / My number one.
7" Single: Released Jun '88, on Firm (1), Catalogue no: **FK 088**

La Di Da..
LA DI DA SAMPLER
Tracks: / Suzanne: *Various artists* / Something you'll never: *Various artists* / Sea, The: *Various artists* / Say what you feel: *Various artists.*
7" Single: Released Jul '89, on LA-DI-DA, Catalogue no: **LA DI DA 004**

L.A. Dream Team
NURSERY RHYMES
Tracks: / Nursery rhymes.
7" Single: Released Sep '86, on MCA, by MCA Records. Catalogue no: **MCA 1074**
12" Single: Released Sep '86, on MCA, by MCA Records. Catalogue no: **MCAT 1074**

La Fleur
BOOGIE NIGHTS
Tracks: / Boogie nights.
7" Single: Released Jul '83, on Proto, by Proto Records. Catalogue no: **ENA 111**
12" Single: Released Jul '83, on Proto, by Proto Records. Catalogue no: **ENAT 111**

La La
WE'LL KEEP ON STRIVING
Tracks: / We'll keep striving / So in love / Love is on the money.
7" Single: Released Oct '87, on Arista, by BMG Records (UK). Deleted May '89. Catalogue no: **RIS 40**
12" Single: Released Oct '87, on Arista, by BMG Records (UK). Deleted May '89. Catalogue no: **RIST 40**

L.A. Mix
CHECK THIS OUT
Tracks: / Check this out / Check this out (sweaty Cuban mix).
Note: Towards the end of 1987, the debut single by L.A. Mix 'Don't Stop (Jammin')' topped the U.K. dance charts and made a healthy dent on the singles chart at the same time. The man behind 'Don't Stop (Jammin')', was in fact Les Adams who is one of the top DJ remixers in the country. For the past few months Les has been busy working on a follow-up single in his Worceter Park studio. The result 'Check This Out' is released on A&M's Breakout label on 9th May. Preview copies have already been circulated to the nation's clubs where the response has been as strong as ever. When making 'Don't Stop (Jammin')', Les was influenced by the Philly sound of the 70's but on 'Check This Out', he simply wanted to make the strongest dance record possible - still using samples but also adding a touch of humour. Adams explains 'There are so many records around now featuring samples and I really wanted to make something that stood apart from the rest. All the samples have been used in such a way that they make sense - each section of the record having a theme with each sample referring to the previous one'. (A & M Records, May 88).
7" Single: Released May '88, on Breakout, by A&M Records. Deleted Feb '89. Catalogue no: **USA 629**
12" Single: Released May '88, on Breakout, by A&M Records. Deleted Feb '89. Catalogue no: **USAT 629**

DON'T STOP (JAMMIN') L.A. MIX
Tracks: / Don't stop (Jammin') L.A. Mix / Don't stop (Philly jazz).
7" Single: Released Sep '87, on Breakout, by A&M Records. Catalogue no: **USA 615**

GET LOOSE
Tracks: / Get loose / Get loose (atmospheric sax dub).
12" Single: Released Jun '89, on A&M, by A&M Records. Catalogue no: **USAF 659**
12" Single: Released Jun '89, on A&M, by A&M Records. Catalogue no: **USAT 659**
7" Single: Released Jun '89, on A&M, by A&M Records. Catalogue no: **USA 659**
CD 5": Released Jun '89, on A&M, by A&M Records. Catalogue no: **USACD 659**

LOVE TOGETHER
Tracks: / Love together / Love together (American lovers edit).
12" Single: Released Aug '89, on A&M, by A&M Records. Catalogue no: **USAT 662**
12" Single: Released Sep '89, on A&M, by A&M Records. Catalogue no: **USAF 662**
CD 5": Released Aug '89, on A&M, by A&M Records. Catalogue no: **USACD 662**
7" Single: Released Aug '89, on A&M, by A&M Records. Catalogue no: **USA 662**

La Muerte
PEEP SHOW
Tracks: / Peep show.
12" Single: Released Mar '86, on Soundworks, Catalogue no: **SW 12010**

SCORPIO RISING
Tracks: / Scorpio rising.
12" Single: Released Jun '88, on Sex Wax, Catalogue no: **SW 12118**

La Rock, Scott
MEMORY OF A MAN & HIS MUSIC
Tracks: / Memory of a man & his music.
7" Single: Released '88, on B.Boy Records, by Westside Records. Catalogue no: **BBOY 2**

La Rose, Judy
LITTLE BIT OF LOVE
Tracks: / Little bit of love, A / Little bit of love, A (dub mix).
7" Single: Released Nov '86, on Champion, by Champion Records. Catalogue no: **CHAMP 19**
12" Single: Released Nov '86, on Champion, by Champion Records. Catalogue no: **CHAMP 1219**

VOODOO LOVE
Tracks: / Voodoo love.
7" Single: Released Nov '87, on Champion, by Champion Records. Deleted Jul '89. Catalogue no: **CHAMP 52**
12" Single: Released Oct '87, on Champion, by Champion Records. Deleted Aug '89. Catalogue no: **CHAMP 1252**

La Rue, Danny
ON MOTHER KELLY'S DOORSTEP
Tracks: / On mother Kelly's doorstep.
7" Single: Released Dec '68, on Page One, by Page One Records. Deleted Dec '71. Catalogue no: **POF 108**

L.A Splash
I DON'T LIKE
Tracks: / I don't like.
7" Single: Released Aug '87, on RCA, by BMG Records (UK). Catalogue no: **PB 41489**
12" Single: Released Aug '87, on RCA, by BMG Records (UK). Catalogue no: **PT 41490**

Labelle, Patti
IF YOU ASKED ME TO
Tracks: / If you asked me to.
CD 5": Released Jul '89, on MCA, by MCA Records. Catalogue no: **DMCA 1357**
7" Single: Released Jul '89, on MCA, by MCA Records. Catalogue no: **MCA 1357**
12" Single: Released Jul '89, on MCA, by MCA Records. Catalogue no: **MCAT 1357**

IF YOU ONLY KNEW
Tracks: / If you only knew / I'll never give up.
7" Single: Released Mar '84, on Philadelphia Int., by EMI Records. Catalogue no: **A 4288**
12" Single: Released Mar '84, on Philadelphia Int., by EMI Records. Catalogue no: **TA 4288**

KISS AWAY THE PAIN
Tracks: / Kiss away the pain / Kiss away the pain (inst).
7" Single: Released Mar '87, on MCA, by MCA Records. Catalogue no: **MCA 1120**
12" Single: Released Mar '87, on MCA, by MCA Records. Catalogue no: **MCAT 1120**

LADY MARMALADE (VOULEZ VOUS COUCHER AVEC MOI...)
Tracks: / Lady Marmalade.
7" Single: Released Mar '75, on Epic, by CBS Records. Deleted Mar '78. Catalogue no: **EPC 2852**

OH PEOPLE
Tracks: / Oh people / Love attack.
7" Single: Released Jul '86, on MCA, by MCA Records. Catalogue no: **MCA 1075**
12" Single: Released Jul '86, on MCA, by MCA Records. Catalogue no: **MCAT 1075**

OH PEOPLE (THE JIM MIX)
Tracks: / Oh people (the jim mix) / Love attack instrumental.
12" Single: Released Aug '86, on MCA, by MCA Records. Catalogue no: **MCAX 1075**

ON MY OWN
Tracks: / On my own / Stir it up.
7" Single: Released Apr '86, on MCA, by MCA Records. Deleted 1 Jul '89. Catalogue no: **MCA 1045**
12" Single: Released Apr '86, on MCA, by MCA Records. Catalogue no: **MCAT 1045**

POURIN' WHISKEY BLUES
Tracks: / Pourin' whiskey blues.
7" Single: Released May '85, on SPI Milan (France), Catalogue no: **S 259**

SOMETHING SPECIAL
Tracks: / Something special / Something special (accapella version).
12" Single: Released Nov '86, on MCA, by MCA Records. Catalogue no: **MCAT 1098**
7" Single: Released Nov '86, on MCA, by MCA Records. Catalogue no: **MCA 1098**

Labes, Jef

TELESTAR
Tracks: / Telestar.
7" Single: Released Jul '83, on KA, Catalogue no: **KA 19**

Labi & Jackie

ONE WORLD SONG
Tracks: / One world song / We got love.
7" Single: Released Jan '80, on EMI, by EMI Records. Deleted Jan '85. Catalogue no: **EMI 5023**

Laboum, Zsa Zsa

SOMETHING SCARY
Tracks: / Something scary.
12" Single: Released '89, on Kaos, Catalogue no: **KAOS 012**

TU VEUX OU TU VEUX PAS
Tracks: / Tu veux ou tu veux pas.
12" Single: Released '89, on Kaos, Catalogue no: **KAOS 019**
12" Single: Released May '89, on Complete Kaos, Catalogue no: **CK 3002**

Lace

MY LOVE IS DEEP
Tracks: / My love is deep (edit) (On 7" only) / My love is deep (instrumental) (On 7" only) / My love is deep (job jam) (On 12" only) / My love is deep (album groove) (On 12" only) / My love is deep (D.J. "T" mix o dub) (On 12" only).
7" Single: Released Nov '87, on Wing (USA), by PolyGram Rec.Inc.(USA). Catalogue no: **WING 1**
12" Single: Released Nov '87, on Wing (USA), by PolyGram Rec.Inc.(USA). Catalogue no: **WINGX 1**

Lacey, Martyn

CRUISING IN THE PARK
Tracks: / Cruising in the park (rap mix) / Cruising in the park (HiNRG mix).
7" Single: Released Oct '87, on Passion, by Skratch Records. Catalogue no: **PASH 80**
12" Single: Released Oct '87, on Passion, by Skratch Records. Catalogue no: **PASH 80(12)**

Lack Of Knowledge

SENTINEL
Tracks: / Sentinel.
12" Single: Released Jul '85, on Chainsaw, Deleted '88. Catalogue no: **TEXT 7**

LaCreme, Cathy

I MARRIED A CULT FIGURE FROM SALFORD
Tracks: / I married a cult figure from Salford / Tea machine dub.
7" Single: Released Oct '80, on Ovation, by Gull Records. Deleted Oct '83. Catalogue no: **OVS 1212**
7" Single: Released '80, on Rock Steady, by Rock Steady Records. Catalogue no: **MICK 009**

Ladders

GOTTA SEE JANE
Tracks: / Gotta see Jane.
7" Single: Released Jun '83, on Statik, Catalogue no: **TAK 2**
12" Single: Released Jun '83, on Statik, Catalogue no: **TAK 2-12**

Ladies Choice

FUNKY SENSATION
Tracks: / Funky sensation.
7" Single: Released Jan '86, on Sure Delight, by Sure Delight Records. Deleted Jan '89. Catalogue no: **SD 01**
12" Single: Released Jan '86, on LGR, Catalogue no: **LGR 010**

Ladly, Martha

FINLANDIA
Tracks: / Finlandia / Tasmania.
7" Single: Released Jun '81, on Dindisc, by Virgin Records. Deleted Jun '84. Catalogue no: **DIN 32**

Lads

HERE WE GO (football anthem)
Tracks: / Here we go.
7" Single: Released May '84, on FA, Deleted '85. Catalogue no: **FA 1**

Lady And The Tramp

LADY AND THE TRAMP
7" EP: Released Dec '82, on Disneyland-Vista(USA), by Disneyland-Vista Records (USA). Catalogue no: **D 307**
Special: Released Jan '85, on Whinfrey Strachan, Deleted '86. Catalogue no: **UNKNOWN**

LADY AND THE TRAMP (12")
Special: Released Dec '82, on Disneyland-Vista(USA), by Disneyland-Vista Records (USA). Catalogue no: **D 3103**

Lady Anne

INFORMER
Tracks: / Informer, The.
12" Single: Released Mar '83, on Joe Gibbs, Catalogue no: **JGM 8174**

LADY ANNE YOU'RE SWEET
Tracks: / Lady Anne you're sweet / Ball a roll.
12" Single: Released Oct '82, on Greensleeves, by Greensleeves Records. Catalogue no: **GRED 101**

MESSAGE TO EVERY HUSBAND
Tracks: / Message to every husband / Drive a taxi.
12" Single: Released Feb '84, on Mobiliser, by Jetstar Records. Catalogue no: **MM 76**

Lady B

ATTRACTIVE YOUNG MAN WANTED
Tracks: / Attractive young man wanted.
7" Single: Released Sep '83, on RCA, by BMG Records (UK). Catalogue no: **RCA 355**
12" Single: Released Sep '83, on RCA, by BMG Records (UK). Catalogue no: **RCAT 355**

Lady English

GUYS YOU CAN'T DO
Tracks: / Guys you can't do.
12" Single: Released Oct '89, on Two Friends, Catalogue no: **SIR 015**

Lady G

EVERY MAN A GET TIGHT
Tracks: / Every man a get tight.
12" Single: Released Oct '89, on Greensleeves, by Greensleeves Records. Catalogue no: **GRED 254**

NO BAD MIND
Tracks: / No bad mind.
12" Single: Released Oct '88, on Black Scorpio, Catalogue no: **VPRD 344**

Lady Love

IT'S THE SAME OLD STORY
Tracks: / It's the same old story / La la song.
7" Single: Released Nov '80, on Energy (UK), by Energy Records. Deleted Nov '83. Catalogue no: **NRG 002**

Lady Mackerel

YOU SHAPE A BADDA ME
Tracks: / You shape a badda me.
7" Single: Released Nov '88, on Taurus, Catalogue no: **UNKNOWN**

Lady Vee

GET IN DE ARMY
Tracks: / Get in de army.
12" Single: Released '85, on UNKNOWN, Deleted Jun '89. Catalogue no: **12 SKT R1**

UPTOWN
Tracks: / Uptown.
7" Single: Released Sep '87, on Uptown Records, by Uptown Records. Catalogue no: **7UTR 3**

Ladysmith Black

HELLO MY BABY
Tracks: / Hello my baby / King of Kings / Unomathemba (on 12" only) / At Golgotha.
7" Single: Released Apr '87, on Warner Bros., by WEA Records. Deleted Jan '88. Catalogue no: **W 8356**
12" Single: Released Apr '87, on Warner Bros., by WEA Records. Deleted Jan '88. Catalogue no: **W 8356T**

RAIN RAIN BEAUTIFUL RAIN
Tracks: / Rain rain beautiful rain / Black Mambazo / Ungakhowlwa rain / Wayibambezeka (12" only).
7" Single: Released Dec '88, on Warner Bros., by WEA Records. Catalogue no: **W 7630**
12" Single: Released Dec '88, on Warner Bros., by WEA Records. Catalogue no: **W 7630T**

THAT'S WHY I CHOOSE YOU
Tracks: / That's why I choose you / Pauline.
7" Single: Released Mar '87, on Serengeti, by Serengeti Records. Catalogue no: **SERS 1**

Lafayette, General

ANGEL IN BLUE
Tracks: / Angel in blue / Angel in blue (instrumental).
7" Single: Released 20 Feb '88, on Plaza, by Plaza Records. Catalogue no: **PZA 031**
12" Single: Released 20 Feb '88, on Plaza, by Plaza Records. Catalogue no: **PZA 031T**

ANGELITOS
Tracks: / Angelitos.
7" Single: Released Oct '87, on Plaza, by Plaza Records. Catalogue no: **PLAZA 027**
12" Single: Released Oct '87, on Plaza, by Plaza Records. Catalogue no: **PLAZA 027T**

CARNEVAL DO BRAZIL
Tracks: / Carneval do Brazil / Carneval do Brazil (inst).
7" Single: Released Sep '88, on Plaza, by Plaza Records. Catalogue no: **PLAZA 039**
12" Single: Released Sep '88, on Plaza, by Plaza Records. Catalogue no: **PLAZA 039T**

FOR THE GIRL WHO COULD'T FIND LOVE
Tracks: / For the girl who couldn't find love / For the girl who couldn't find love (solo mix).
7" Single: Released May '87, on Plaza, by Plaza Records. Catalogue no: **PLAZA 012**

LOVE IS A RHAPSODY (SINGLE)
Tracks: / Love is a rhapsody / Love is a rhapsody (version).
7" Single: Released 14 May '88, on Plaza, by Plaza Records. Catalogue no: **PZA 035**
12" Single: Released 14 May '88, on Plaza, by Plaza Records. Catalogue no: **PZA 035T**

REGGAE THE LONELY TRUMPET
Tracks: / Reggae the lonely trumpet.
7" Single: Released Nov '82, on Plaza, by Plaza Records. Catalogue no: **PLAZA 003**
12" Single: Released Nov '82, on Plaza, by Plaza Records. Catalogue no: **PLAZA 3-12**

SONG FOR RAY
Tracks: / Song for Ray / Song for Ray (instrumental).
7" Single: Released Oct '88, on Plaza, by Plaza Records. Catalogue no: **PZA 040**
12" Single: Released Oct '88, on Plaza, by Plaza Records. Catalogue no: **12PZA 040**

Lahiri, Bappi

ALI BABA
Tracks: / Ali Baba.
7" Single: Released Aug '89, on Hi-Hat, by BMG Records (UK). Catalogue no: **HY 007**
12" Single: Released Aug '89, on Hi-Hat, by BMG Records (UK). Catalogue no: **HYT 007**

HABIBI
Tracks: / Habibi.
Cassingle: Released Jul '88, on Hi-Hat, by BMG Records (UK). Catalogue no: **HYMC 3**
7" Single: Released Jul '88, on Hi-Hat, by BMG Records (UK). Catalogue no: **HY 3**
12" Single: Released '89, on Licensed, Catalogue no: **LD 8820**
12" Single: Released Oct '88, on Hi-Hat, by BMG Records (UK). Catalogue no: **HYT 3R**
12" Single: Released Sep '88, on Hi-Hat, by BMG Records (UK). Catalogue no: **HYT 3**

Lahost

BIG SLEEP, THE
Tracks: / Big sleep.
7" Single: Released Oct '85, on Orbitone, by Orbitone Records. Catalogue no: **ORB 010**
7" Single: Released Nov '85, on Quiet, by Quiet Records. Catalogue no: **QU 001**

Laibach

ACROSS THE UNIVERSE
Tracks: / Across the universe.
CD 5": Released Dec '88, on Mute, by Mute Records. Catalogue no: **CDMUTE 91**
7" Single: Released Dec '88, on Mute, by Mute Records. Catalogue no: **MUTE 91**
12" Single: Released Dec '88, on Mute, by Mute Records. Catalogue no: **12 MUTE 91**

BOJI
Tracks: / Boji / Sila / Brat mo.
12" Single: Released Mar '84, on Laylah, by Laylah Records. Catalogue no: **LAY 002**

DIE LIEBE
Tracks: / Die liebe.
12" Single: Released Nov '85, on Cherry Red, by Cherry Red Records. Catalogue no: **12 CHERRY 91**

DIE LIEBE/DECREE
Tracks: / Die liebe / Grosste kraft / Decree / Panorama.
CD 5": Released Jul '89, on Cherry Red, by Cherry Red Records. Catalogue no: **CDCHERRY 91**

GEBURT EINER NATION
Tracks: / Geburt einer nation / Leben heist leben.
12" Single: Released Mar '87, on Mute, by Mute Records. Catalogue no: **12 MUTE 60**

LIFE IS LIFE
Tracks: / Life is life / Germania / Leben heist leben.
7" Single: Released Jul '87, on Mute, by Mute Records. Catalogue no: **MUTE 62**
12" Single: Released Jul '87, on Mute, by Mute Records. Catalogue no: **12 MUTE 62**

PANARAMA
Tracks: / Panarama.
12" Single: Released May '84, on East-West Trading Company, by Cherry Red Records. Catalogue no: **12EWS 3**

SYMPATHY FOR THE DEVIL
Tracks: / Sympathy for the devil.
CD 5": Released Oct '88, on Mute, by Mute Records. Catalogue no: **MUTE 80 CD**
7" Single: Released Oct '88, on Mute, by Mute Records. Catalogue no: **MUTE 80**
12" Single: Released Sep '88, on Mute, by Mute Records. Catalogue no: **MUTE 80T**

Laid Back

IT'S A SHAME
Tracks: / It's a shame.
7" Single: Released Aug '87, on WEA (International), by WEA Records. Deleted Jan '88. Catalogue no: **U 8356**
12" Single: Released Aug '87, on WEA (International), by WEA Records. Deleted Jan '88. Catalogue no: **U 8356 T**

SUNSHINE REGGAE
Tracks: / Sunshine reggae / So wie so.
7" Single: Released Nov '83, on Creole, by Creole Records. Catalogue no: **CR 60**
12" Single: Released Nov '83, on Creole, by Creole Records. Catalogue no: **CR 1260**

WHITE HORSE
Tracks: / White horse.
7" Single: Released Feb '84, on Creole, by Creole Records. Catalogue no: **CR 63**
12" Single: Released Feb '84, on Creole, by Creole Records. Catalogue no: **CRT 63**

WHITE HORSE '89
Tracks: / White horse '89 / White horse '89 (version).
CD 5": Released Aug '89, on Warner Bros., by WEA Records. Catalogue no: **W 2836CD**
7" Single: Released Aug '89, on Warner Bros., by WEA Records. Catalogue no: **W 2836**
12" Single: Released Aug '89, on Warner Bros., by WEA Records. Catalogue no: **W 2836T**

Laine, Cleo

Biographical details: Laine, Cleo This British singer has been a part of the UK music business for three decades. Using jazz as her base, she has also recorded and sung in various classical and middle of the road styles. Laine's crystal clear voice has assured her of a steady and lucrative carer from the fifties through to the eighties. She has often recorded and performed with her husband, the saxophonist/clarinettist/orchestra leader John Dankworthj. Laine has pentrated the UK pop singles chart on only two occasions. *Let's Slip Away* peaked at No.42 in December 1960. *You'll Answer To Me*, a cover version of Patti Page's minor US hit, was a much bigger success for the British vocalist, reaching the UK No.5 position in 1961. On the British LP chart, Cleo's success was delayed until 1978, when the *Best of Friends* album, a collaboration with classical guitarist John Williams, reached No.18 and logged 22 listed weeks. Flutist James Galway was her partner on the 1980 LP. *Sometimes When We Touch*, which climed to No.15 and spent 14 weeks on the chart. As a solo artist Laine reached No.68 in December 1978 with an album simply entitled *Cleo*. (Bob Macdonald 30/11/85).

HOW, WHERE, WHEN
Tracks: / How, where, when / Drifting, dreaming.
7" Single: Released Apr '80, on RCA, by BMG Records (UK). Deleted Apr '83. Catalogue no: **RB 5246**

LET'S SLIP AWAY
Tracks: / Let's slip away.
7" Single: Released Dec '60, on Fontana, by Phonogram Ltd. Deleted Dec '63. Catalogue no: **H 269**

ONE MORE DAY (SINGLE)
Tracks: / One more day / Over the moon.
7" Single: Released Apr '81, on Sepia,

Deleted '85. Catalogue no: **RSS 102**

YOU'LL ANSWER TO ME
Tracks: / You'll answer to me.
7" Single: Released Sep '61, on Fontana, by Phonogram Ltd. Deleted Sep '63. Catalogue no: **H 326**

YOU'VE GOT TO DO WHAT YOU'VE GOT TO DO
Tracks: / You've got to do what you've got to do / Our relationship.
7" Single: Released Oct '80, on Sepia, Deleted Oct '83. Catalogue no: **RSS 101**

Laine, Denny

HOMETOWN GIRL (SINGLE)
Tracks: / Home town girl / Stay away.
7" Single: Released May '86, on President, by President Records. Catalogue no: **PT 544**

JAPANESE TEARS
Tracks: / Japanese tears.
7" Single: Released Aug '82, on Scratch, by Scratch Records. Catalogue no: **HS 401**

LAND OF PEACE
Tracks: / Land of peace / If I tried.
7" Single: Released Nov '86, on President, by President Records. Catalogue no: **PT 555**

SAY YOU DON'T MIND
Tracks: / Say you don't mind.
7" Single: Released Aug '82, on Scratch, by Scratch Records. Catalogue no: **HS 408**

WHO MOVED THE WORLD
Tracks: / Who moved the world.
7" Single: Released Nov '81, on Rock City, Catalogue no: **RC 7001**

WINGS ON MY FEET (SINGLE)
Tracks: / It's never too late / Wings on my feet.
7" Single: Released Sep '87, on President, by President Records. Catalogue no: **PT 565**

Laine, Frankie

ANSWER ME
Tracks: / Answer me / Jezebel.
7" Single: Released Oct '53, on Philips, by Phonogram Ltd. Deleted Oct '56. Catalogue no: **PB 196**
7" Single: Released Apr '82, on Bulldog Records, by President Records. Catalogue no: **BD 24**

BLOWING WILD
Tracks: / Blowing wild.
7" Single: Released Jan '54, on Philips, by Phonogram Ltd. Deleted Jan '57. Catalogue no: **PB 207**

COOL WATER
Tracks: / Cool water.
7" Single: Released Jun '55, on Philips, by Phonogram Ltd. Deleted Jun '58. Catalogue no: **PB 465**

GIRL IN THE WOOD
Tracks: / Girl in the wood.
7" Single: Released Mar '53, on Columbia, by EMI Records. Deleted Mar '56. Catalogue no: **DB 2907**

GOOD EVENING FRIENDS
Tracks: / Good evening friends / Up above my head.
7" Single: Released Oct '57, on Philips, by Phonogram Ltd. Deleted Oct '60. Catalogue no: **PB 708**

GRANADA
Tracks: / Granada.
7" Single: Released Mar '54, on Philips, by Phonogram Ltd. Deleted Mar '57. Catalogue no: **PB 242**

GUNSLINGER
Tracks: / Gunslinger.
7" Single: Released May '61, on Philips, by Phonogram Ltd. Deleted May '64. Catalogue no: **PB 1135**

HAWKEYE
Tracks: / Hawkeye.
7" Single: Released Nov '55, on Philips, by Phonogram Ltd. Deleted Nov '58. Catalogue no: **PB 519**

HELL HATH NO FURY
Tracks: / Hell hath no fury.
7" Single: Released May '56, on Philips, by Phonogram Ltd. Deleted May '59. Catalogue no: **PB 585**

HEY JOE
Tracks: / Hey Joe.
7" Single: Released Oct '53, on Philips, by Phonogram Ltd. Deleted Oct '56. Catalogue no: **PB 172**

HIGH MOON
Tracks: / High Moon.
7" Single: Released Jul '82, on Old Gold, by Old Gold Records. Catalogue no: **OG 9082**
7" Single: Released Apr '82, on CBS, by CBS Records. Catalogue no: **CBS 1156**

HIGH NOON
Tracks: / High noon.
7" Single: Released Nov '52, on Columbia, by EMI Records. Deleted Nov '55. Catalogue no: **DB 3113**

HIGH NOON (OLD GOLD)
Tracks: / High noon / Cool water.
7" Single: Released Nov '80, on Old Gold, by Old Gold Records. Deleted '83. Catalogue no: **OG 9082**

HUMMINGBIRD
Tracks: / Hummingbird.
7" Single: Released Nov '55, on Philips, by Phonogram Ltd. Deleted Nov '58. Catalogue no: **PB 498**

I BELIEVE
Tracks: / I believe.
7" Single: Released Apr '53, on Philips, by Phonogram Ltd. Deleted Apr '56. Catalogue no: **PB 117**

IN THE BEGINNING
Tracks: / In the beginning.
7" Single: Released Mar '55, on Philips, by Phonogram Ltd. Deleted Mar '58. Catalogue no: **PB 404**

KID'S LAST FIGHT, THE
Tracks: / Kid's last fight, The.
7" Single: Released Apr '54, on Philips, by Phonogram Ltd. Deleted Apr '57. Catalogue no: **PB 258**

LOVE IS A GOLDEN RING
Tracks: / Love is a golden ring.
7" Single: Released Apr '57, on Philips, by Phonogram Ltd. Deleted Apr '60. Catalogue no: **PB 676**

MOONLIGHT GAMBLER
Tracks: / Moonlight gambler.
7" Single: Released Mar '57, on Philips, by Phonogram Ltd. Deleted Mar '60. Catalogue no: **PB 638**

MY FRIEND
Tracks: / My friend.
7" Single: Released Jul '54, on Philips, by Phonogram Ltd. Deleted Jul '57. Catalogue no: **PB 316**

RAIN, RAIN, RAIN
Tracks: / Rain, rain, rain.
7" Single: Released Oct '54, on Philips, by Phonogram Ltd. Deleted Oct '57. Catalogue no: **PB 311**

RAWHIDE (OLD GOLD)
Tracks: / Rawhide.
7" Single: Released Jan '87, on Old Gold, by Old Gold Records. Catalogue no: **OG 9665**

RAWHIDE (SINGLE)
Tracks: / Rawhide.
7" Single: Released Nov '59, on Philips, by Phonogram Ltd. Deleted Nov '62. Catalogue no: **PB 965**

SIXTEEN TONS
Tracks: / Sixteen tons.
7" Single: Released Jan '56, on Philips, by Phonogram Ltd. Deleted Jan '59. Catalogue no: **PB 539**

STRANGE LADY IN TOWN
Tracks: / Strange lady in town.
7" Single: Released Jul '55, on Philips, by Phonogram Ltd. Deleted Jul '58. Catalogue no: **PB 478**

TELL ME A STORY
Tracks: / Tell me a story.
7" Single: Released May '53, on Philips, by Phonogram Ltd. Deleted May '56. Catalogue no: **PB 126**

THERE MUST BE A REASON
Tracks: / There must be a reason.
7" Single: Released Oct '54, on Philips, by Phonogram Ltd. Deleted Oct '57. Catalogue no: **PB 306**

WHERE THE WIND BLOWS
Tracks: / Where the wind blows.
7" Single: Released Sep '53, on Philips, by Phonogram Ltd. Deleted Sep '56. Catalogue no: **PB 167**

WOMAN IN LOVE, A
Tracks: / Woman in love.
7" Single: Released Sep '56, on Philips, by Phonogram Ltd. Deleted Sep '59. Catalogue no: **PB 617**

WOMAN IN LOVE (OLD GOLD)
Tracks: / Woman in love / Jezebel.
7" Single: Released Jul '82, on Old Gold, by Old Gold Records. Catalogue no: **OG 9079**

Laine, Jo Jo

DANCIN' MAN
Tracks: / Dancin' man / Hulk.
7" Single: Released Mar '80, on Hammer, Deleted '83. Catalogue no: **HS 305**

WHEN THE BOY'S HAPPY
Tracks: / When the boy's happy / Runaway.
7" Single: Released Aug '80, on Mercury, by Phonogram Ltd. Deleted '83. Catalogue no: **MER 30**

Laine, John

SET ME FREE
Tracks: / Set me free / Future song.
7" Single: Released Jan '86, on Radioman, by Radioman Records. Catalogue no: **RMAN 1**

TEMPTATION
Tracks: / Temptation.
7" Single: Released May '84, on Hollywood, by Hollywood Records. Catalogue no: **HWD 010**
12" Single: Released May '84, on Hollywood, by Hollywood Records. Catalogue no: **HWD 010T**

Laing, Phil

DAY AFTER DAY
Tracks: / Day after day / Don't say it's over.
7" Single: Released Jun '86, on Mix Factory, by Mix Factory Records. Deleted '88. Catalogue no: **MX 3**

Laing, Shona

BUNDLE OF NERVES
Tracks: / Bundle of nerves / I ching.
7" Single: Released Aug '81, on EMI, by EMI Records. Deleted Aug '84. Catalogue no: **EMI 5223**

DON'T TELL ME
Tracks: / Don't tell me / Across the Irish sea.
7" Single: Released Apr '80, on EMI, by EMI Records. Deleted Apr '83. Catalogue no: **EMI 5053**

GLAD I'M NOT A KENNEDY
Tracks: / Not a Kennedy / Resurrection.
7" Single: Released Jul '87, on Virgin, by Virgin Records. Deleted May '88. Catalogue no: **VS 959**
12" Single: Released Jul '87, on Virgin, by Virgin Records. Deleted May '88. Catalogue no: **VS 959-12**

OVERBOARD
Tracks: / Overboard / Timmy's goin' down.
7" Single: Released Jan '81, on EMI, by EMI Records. Deleted Jan '84. Catalogue no: **EMI 5136**

WHISTLING WALTZES
Tracks: / Whistling waltzes / No fixed abode.
7" Single: Released Oct '80, on EMI, by EMI Records. Deleted Oct '83. Catalogue no: **EMI 5111**

Laird, Christopher

DOGTANIAN
Tracks: / Three muskhounds, The.
Cassingle: Released Apr '85, on BBC, by BBC Records & Tapes. Deleted Apr '89. Catalogue no: **ZRESL 165**
7" Single: Released Apr '85, on BBC, by BBC Records & Tapes. Deleted 31 Aug '88. Catalogue no: **RESL 165**

Lake Eerie

SEX 4 DAZE

DAVE LALOR - DARLING (Released on SRS)

Tracks: / Sex 4 daze / Sex 4 daze (version).
7" Single: Released Apr '89, on Champion, by Champion Records. Catalogue no: **CHAMP 98**
12" Single: Released Apr '89, on Champion, by Champion Records. Catalogue no: **CHAMP 1298**

Lake, Greg

Biographical details: Lake, Greg This British guitarist, bassist, vocalist, songwriter and producer was a founder member of King Crimson in 1969. He took that group's pomp-rock sound with him when he became one third of Emerson Lake & Palmer in 1970. ELP took an extended break from recording and touring between 1974 and 1977, during which Lake scored a solo smash single in Britain with *I Believe In Father Christmas*. Released in 1975, it reached the UK No.2 position during that year's Yuletide; and it resurfaced in the lower reaches of the charts at a couple of later Christmases. Lushly arranged and heavily orchestrated, *I Believe In Father Christmas* was a continuation of ELP's grandiose style but was diected towards a different audience: instead of appealing to the trio's 'serious' progressive rock constituency, *Christmas* reached a broad pop audience, particularly children. Whereas ELP virtually never released singles, preferring to concentrate on albums, here was Lake with a suprise No.2 hit. *I Believe In Father Christmas* became on of Britain's all time classic Christmas standards and was regularly heard on the airways during each festive season. It tended to overshadow Lake's other solo offerings, which included the poorly received *Greg Lake* LP (1981, his first ever solo album) and *Manoeuvres* (1983). With ELP having quietly split up at the end of 1978, Lake rejoined his old colleague Carl Palmer in the supergroup Asia in 1983 while John Wetton (who returned in '85) took a lengthy break from the band.)Bob Macdonald 30/11/85).

I BELIEVE IN FATHER CHRISTMAS
Tracks: / I believe in Father Christmas / Humbug.
7" Single: Released Nov '82, on Manticore, Deleted Jul '88. Catalogue no: **K 13511**

IT HURTS
Tracks: / It hurts / Retribution drive.
7" Single: Released Feb '82, on Chrysalis, by Chrysalis Records. Deleted '85. Catalogue no: **CHS 2567**

LOVE YOU TOO MUCH
Tracks: / Love you too much / Someone.
7" Single: Released Oct '81, on Chrysalis, by Chrysalis Records. Deleted Oct. '84. Catalogue no: **CHS 2553**

Lake, Steve

IN EVERY LIFE
Tracks: / In every life.
7" EP: Released May '85, on Not So Brave, Catalogue no: **NSB 008**

RUNNING AWAY

Tracks: / Running away.
12" Single: Released 24 Apr '87, on Play It Again Sam(Belgium), by Play It Again Sam (Belgium). Catalogue no: **BIAS 050**

WELCOME TO MONKEY HOUSE
Tracks: / Welcome to monkey house.
12" Single: Released Mar '84, on Not So Brave, Catalogue no: **NSB 005**

Laker Girls

LET US FLY
Tracks: / Let us fly / Skytrain, Theme from.
7" Single: Released Mar '82, on Red Bus, by Red Bus Records. Deleted '85. Catalogue no: **RBUS 66**

Lakeside

FANTASTIC JOURNEY
Tracks: / Fantastic journey / I can't get you out of my head.
7" Single: Released Feb '81, on Solar (USA), by MCA Records. Deleted Feb '84. Catalogue no: **SO 15**
12" Single: Released Feb '81, on Solar (USA), by MCA Records. Deleted Feb '84. Catalogue no: **SOT 15**

FROM 9 UNTIL ...
Tracks: / From 9 until ... / All in my mind.
7" Single: Released Apr '80, on Solar Records, Deleted '83. Catalogue no: **SO 6**
12" Single: Released Apr '80, on Solar Records, Deleted '83. Catalogue no: **SO12-6**

OUTRAGEOUS
Tracks: / Outrageous.
7" Single: Released Apr '85, on MCA, by MCA Records. Catalogue no: **MCA 952**
12" Single: Released Apr '85, on MCA, by MCA Records. Catalogue no: **MCAT 952**

RAID
Tracks: / Raid.
7" Single: Released Mar '83, on Elektra, by Elektra Records (UK). Catalogue no: **E 9836**
12" Single: Released Mar '83, on Elektra, by Elektra Records (UK). Catalogue no: **E 9836T**

Lala

LOVE ME JUST A LITTLE
Tracks: / Love me just a little / Love me just a little (inst).
7" Single: Released Jul '87, on Arista, by BMG Records (UK). Catalogue no: **RIS 23**
12" Single: Released Jul '87, on Arista, by BMG Records (UK). Catalogue no: **RIST 23**

Lalor, Dave

DARLING (see panel o previous page)
Tracks: / Darlin' / Take me back (Take me home).
7" Single: Released Jun '87, on S.R.S., by S.R.S. Records. Catalogue no: **S 127**

Lama

LOVE ON THE ROCKS
Tracks: / Love on the rocks.
7" Single: Released Mar '84, on Carrere, Catalogue no: **CAR 309**
12" Single: Released Mar '84, on Carrere, Catalogue no: **CART 309**

Lamara

STAR OF THE SHOW
Tracks: / Star of the show / Tanesia.
12" Single: Released Dec '85, on Exclusive Productions, by Exclusive Productions. Deleted Jun '89. Catalogue no: **EPRT 2681**

Lamarr, Chris

YOUNG AND FREE
Tracks: / Young and free / 1985.
7" Single: Released Jan '83, on Crash, by Satril Records. Deleted '85. Catalogue no: **CRA 505**

Lamarr, Louise

STEVIE'S O.K
Tracks: / Stevie's OK / Waiting and hunting game.
7" Single: Released Jan '83, on Juice, by Juice Records. Deleted '88. Catalogue no: **JU 101**

Lamarr, Pepi

MAGIC
Tracks: / Magic / I got me.
7" Single: Released Jul '82, on A&M, by A&M Records. Deleted Jul '85. Catalogue no: **AMS 8232**

Lamb, Annabel

Biographical details: Lamb, Annabel This British singer, songwriter and arranger had been toying with a showbusiness career for some time, before Jermaine Jackson's 1980 hit *Let's Get Serious* finally convinced her to take the plunge. She evantually signed with A&M Records and released her debut album *Once Bitten* in February 1983. In the summer of that year she issued a pop cover version of The Doors' doomy classic *Riders On The Storm* - this single caused a storm of its own in the UK music industry, because it was launched by A&M with an accompanying video as a 'free gift', a ploy which many observers interpreted as an attempt to manipulate the record into the charts.
Riders On The Storm, did in the event, achieve a genuine No.27 placing on the UK singles chart in the early autumn. Such an apparently leightweight treatment of an established rock standard was either brave or foolhardy, depending on personal taste. Either way, it appeared to be a one off success for Lamb. Further hit singles were not forthcoming and her 1984 LP *The Flame* experienced the same reception as the first set - good press reviews but very limited commercial success. Her highly individual style, which combined elements of jazz, rock and technopop, won over the journalists but the not the record-buying public. (Bob Macdonald 2/12/85).

CHASE ACROSS THE WORLD
Tracks: / Chase across the world / Inferno / Mixing (On 12" only).
7" Single: Released Oct '87, on RCA, by BMG Records (UK). Deleted May '89. Catalogue no: **PB 41595**
12" Single: Released Oct '87, on RCA, by BMG Records (UK). Deleted May '89. Catalogue no: **PT 41596**

HEARTLAND
Tracks: / Heartland.
7" Single: Released Apr '83, on A&M, by A&M Records. Deleted '88. Catalogue no: **AM 109**
12" Single: Released Apr '83, on A&M, by A&M Records. Deleted '88. Catalogue no: **AMX 109**

ONCE BITTEN
Tracks: / Once bitten / Take me in your arms.
7" Single: Released Feb '83, on A&M, by A&M Records. Deleted '88. Catalogue no: **AMS 8310**

RIDERS ON THE STORM
Tracks: / Riders on the storm.
7" Single: Released Aug '83, on A&M, by A&M Records. Deleted Aug '86. Catalogue no: **AM 131**

Lamb, Annabelle

DAMON AND DEBBIE His song
Tracks: / Damon and Debbie (his song) / Damon and Debbie (her song).
7" Single: Released Nov '87, on Ariola, by BMG Records (UK). Deleted May '89. Catalogue no: **109 612**

Lamb, Rose

SHOPPING AROUND
Tracks: / Shopping around.
7" Single: Released Sep '81, on V-Tone, Catalogue no: **VTONE 002**

Lambert, Alistair

SCOTLAND
Tracks: / Angry as a young man / Scotland.
7" Single: Released Jun '89, on Celtic, Catalogue no: **CMT 051**

Lambrettas

Biographical details: Lambrettas This British band consisted of Jez Bird, Mark Ellis, Doug Sanders and Paul Wincer.
Together with Secret Affair, The Merton Parkas and The Chords, the Lambrettas were part of the UK's Mod Revival of 1979-80. This mini boom coincided with the 2 Tone ska scene, which was led by such acts as The Specials, Madness, The Beat and The Selecter. The two phenomena were partly linked, since both drew their inspiration from the early to mid Sixties. But because the Mod scene was essentially a revival, it was bound to be short lived.
The Lambrettas' first hit *Poison Ivy* was their biggest - this catchy remake of the Leiber & Stoller penned standard managed to reach the UK No.7 position in the spring of 1980, eight places higher than The Coasters' original version of 1959. The Lambrettas followed *Poison Ivy* with the No.12 hit *D-a-a-ance* and the No.49 entry *Another Day (another Girl)*. Their debut album *Beat Boys In The Jet Age* reached No.28 on the British LP list.
The rest of the Eighties proved to be good times for their producer Peter Collins, but not for The Lambrettas themselves. By the time they issued their 1981 album *Ambience*, the Mod Revival was a dead duck and the band quickly folded. (Bob Macdonald 2/12/85).

ANOTHER DAY (ANOTHER GIRL)
Tracks: / Another day (another girl).
7" Single: Released Aug '80, on Rocket, by Rocket Records. Deleted Aug '83. Catalogue no: **XPRESS 36**

ANYTHING YOU WANT
Tracks: / Anything you want / Ambience.
7" Single: Released Apr '81, on Rocket, by Rocket Records. Deleted '85. Catalogue no: **XPRES 52**

D-A-A-ANCE
Tracks: / D-a-a-nce / Can't you feel the beat.
7" Single: Released May '80, on Rocket, by Rocket Records. Deleted May '83. Catalogue no: **XPRESS 33**

DECENT TOWN
Tracks: / Decent town / Da a a ance / Total strangers (Only on 12" single.) / Young girls (Only on 12" single.).
7" Single: Released Aug '82, on Rocket, by Rocket Records. Deleted '84. Catalogue no: **XPRES 62**
12" Single: Released Aug '82, on Rocket, by Rocket Records. Deleted '84. Catalogue no: **XPRES 6212**

GOOD TIMES
Tracks: / Good times / Lamba samba.
7" Single: Released Mar '81, on Rocket, by Rocket Records. Deleted Mar '84. Catalogue no: **XPRES 48**

POISON IVY
Tracks: / Poison Ivy / Run around.
7" Single: Released Mar '80, on Rocket, by Rocket Records. Deleted Mar '83. Catalogue no: **XPRESS 25**

SOMEBODY TO LOVE
Tracks: / Somebody to love / Nobody's watching me.
7" Single: Released Feb '82, on Rocket, by Rocket Records. Deleted Feb '87. Catalogue no: **XPRES 74**

Lamella

WASTING YOUR TIME
Tracks: / Wasting your time.
7" Single: Released Apr '81, on Direct Records, Catalogue no: **DOB 1**

LaMotta, Stephanie

I'M HERE AT LAST (so forget the past)
Tracks: / I'm here at last.
7" Single: Released Jun '82, on Zilch, by Zilch Records. Catalogue no: **ZILCH 20**

Lamour, Gina

CONTINENTAL, THE
Tracks: / Continental, The.
12" Single: Released Aug '83, on Glamour, by Glamour Records. Catalogue no: **GLAMT 2**

I WANT TO BE ALONE
Tracks: / I want to be alone.
7" Single: Released Nov '83, on Glamour, by Glamour Records. Catalogue no: **GLAM 3**

I'M GONNA MAKE YOU WANT ME
Tracks: / I'm gonna make you want me.
7" Single: Released Aug '85, on Calibre, Deleted '86. Catalogue no: **CAB 200**
12" Single: Released Aug '85, on Calibre, Deleted '86. Catalogue no: **CABL 200**

MOVE OVER DARLING
Tracks: / Move over darling / Mad about the boy.
7" Single: Released Jul '83, on Glamour, by Glamour Records. Catalogue no: **GLAM 1**
7" Single: Released Dec '83, on Glamour, by Glamour Records. Catalogue no: **GLAM 4**
12" Single: Released Aug '83, on Glamour, by Glamour Records. Catalogue no: **GLAM 2**

YI YI YI YI I LIKE YOU VERY MUCH
Tracks: / Yi yi yi yi I like you very much.
7" Single: Released Jun '84, on Calibre, Deleted '86. Catalogue no: **CAB 125**
12" Single: Released Jun '84, on Calibre, Deleted '86. Catalogue no: **CABL 125**

L'Amour, Rudi

CALL ME On your lonely nights
Tracks: / Call me / Lonely nights.
7" Single: Released Jul '87, on Button, by Musical Characters Records. Catalogue no: **BTN 124**

Lamsie

ROSE
Tracks: / Rose.
12" Single: Released Apr '85, on White label (2), Catalogue no: **Unknown**

Lana As Covergirl

STAY WITH ME
Tracks: / Stay with me / I'm a winner.
7" Single: Released Sep '86, on Space Station, by Space Station Records. Catalogue no: **APOLLO 3**
12" Single: Released Sep '86, on Space Station, by Space Station Records. Catalogue no: **APOLLOT 3**

Lancastrians

WE'LL SING IN THE SUNSHINE
Tracks: / We'll sing in the sunshine.
7" Single: Released Dec '64, on Pye, Deleted Dec '67. Catalogue no: **7N 15732**

Lance, Major

UM UM UM UM UM UM
Tracks: / Um, um, um, um, um, um.
7" Single: Released Feb '64, on Columbia, by EMI Records. Deleted Feb '67. Catalogue no: **DB 7205**

Land Of Distraction

DISTRACTION
Tracks: / Distraction.
7" Single: Released 20 Jun '87, on Strike Back, by Strike Back Records. Catalogue no: **SBR 9**
12" Single: Released 20 Jun '87, on Strike Back, by Strike Back Records. Catalogue no: **SBR 9T**

Landes, Dee

MY LOVER BOY
Tracks: / My lover boy.
12" Single: Released Sep '85, on Londisc, by Londisc Records. Catalogue no: **LDR 050**

Landlord

I LIKE IT
Tracks: / I like it.
7" Single: Released Sep '89, on Big Shot, Catalogue no: **VS 137**

Landlord Featuring D

12" Single: Released Sep '89, on Big Shot, Catalogue no: **VS 137**

Landsborough, Charlie

I WILL LOVE YOU ALL MY LIFE
Tracks: / I will love you all my life / Listen Louise.
7" Single: Released Feb '83, on Pastafont, by Pastafont Music. Catalogue no: **PF 3008**

THANK YOU LORD
Tracks: / Thank you lord / Down to earth.
7" Single: Released Nov '82, on Pastafont, by Pastafont Music. Catalogue no: **PF 3007**

Landscape

Biographical details: Landscape This British band consisted of Richard James Burgess, Chris Heaton, Andy 'Capt. Whorlix' Pask, Peter Thomas and John Walters.
Landscape issued their eponymous debut album in 1979. They came to fame in the spring of 1981 with their UK No.5 single *Einstein a go-go*, which was a prominent part of the briefly fasionable 'futurist' movement. It helped to pave the way for a host of British technopop acts over the ensuing couple of years. Landscape's second LP *From The Tearooms of Mars...to The hellholes of Uranus* reached No.16 and logged 12 weeks on the UK album chart during 1981. But somehow the band could not capitalise on their reputation - apart from a UK No.40 placing with the follow up single to *Einstein A Go-Go*, a horro movie saga entitled *Norman Bates*, the group quickly faded into obscurity.
The band's 1982 LP *Manhatten Boogie Woogie* was a flop. An attempt to relaunch the group under the billing Landscape III with the 1983 single *So Good So Pure So Kind* was also unsuccessful. By this time, however, key member Richard James Burgess was already carving a very successful career as a producer - Spandau Ballet gave Burgess his first hir productions in 1981-2 and he also produced part of Adam Ant's 1983 album *Strip*. In 1985 he reached new heights of success with the group King. As if to prove that his production talents were not confined to trendy, clothes conscious British pop idols, Burgess broadened his profile considerably in late '85 with Colonel Abrams, a US soul artist who scored a massive dance pop hit with *Trapped*. (Bob Macdonald 2/12/85).

EASTERN GIRLS
Tracks: / Eastern girls / Back on your heads.
7" Single: Released May '82, on RCA, by BMG Records (UK). Deleted '85. Catalogue no: **RCA 219**
12" Single: Released May '82, on RCA, by BMG Records (UK). Deleted '85. Catalogue no: **RCAT 219**

EINSTEIN A GO GO
Tracks: / Einstein a go go / New religion.
7" Single: Released Feb '81, on RCA, by BMG Records (UK). Deleted Feb '84. Catalogue no: **RCA 22**
12" Single: Released Feb '81, on RCA, by

LANSCAPE - NORMAN BATES (Released on RCA)

BMG Records (UK). Deleted Feb '84. Catalogue no: **RCAT 22**
12" Single: Released Jul '89, on Old Gold, by Old Gold Records. Catalogue no: **OG 4113**

EINSTEIN A GO GO (OLD GOLD)
Tracks: / Einstein a go go / Norman Bates.
12" Single: Released 28 Mar '89, on Old Gold, by Old Gold Records. Catalogue no: **OG 4113**

EUROPEAN MAN
Tracks: / European man / Mechanical bride.
7" Single: Released Mar '80, on RCA, by BMG Records (UK). Deleted Mar '83. Catalogue no: **EDM 1**

ITS NOT MY NAME
Tracks: / It's not my name / Mistaken identity.
7" Single: Released Feb '82, on RCA, by BMG Records (UK). Deleted '85. Catalogue no: **RCAT 186**
7" Single: Released Feb '82, on RCA, by BMG Records (UK). Deleted '85. Catalogue no: **RCA 186**

NORMAN BATES (see pael above)
Tracks: / Norman Bates / From the tea rooms of mars..To the hell holes.
7" Single: Released May '81, on RCA, by BMG Records (UK). Deleted May '84. Catalogue no: **RCA 60**
12" Single: Released May '81, on RCA, by BMG Records (UK). Deleted May '84. Catalogue no: **RCAT 60**

Landscape III

SO GOOD, SO PURE, SO KIND
Tracks: / So good, so pure, so kind / Fabulous Neutrinos.
7" Single: Released Feb '83, on RCA, by BMG Records (UK). Catalogue no: **RCA 311**
12" Single: Released Feb '83, on RCA, by BMG Records (UK). Catalogue no: **RCAT 311**

YOU KNOW HOW TO HURT ME
Tracks: / You know how to hurt me.
7" Single: Released Apr '83, on RCA, by BMG Records (UK). Catalogue no: **RCA 333**
12" Single: Released Apr '83, on RCA, by BMG Records (UK). Catalogue no: **RCAT 333**

Lane, Anita

DIRTY THINGS EP
Tracks: / I'm a believer / If I should die / Lost in music / Sugar in a hurricane.
12" Single: Released May '88, on Mute, by Mute Records. Catalogue no: **12MUTE 65**

DOES IT LOOK LIKE I'VE BEEN CRYING
Tracks: / Does it look like I've been crying.
12" Single: Released Oct '87, on Mute, by Mute Records. Catalogue no: **12MUTE 65**

Lane, Arnold

BOOK OF SAND
Tracks: / Book of sand / No collar.
7" Single: Released '82, on New Dance, Catalogue no: **ND 003**

NO COLLAR
Tracks: / No collar / Book of sand.
7" Single: Released Feb '82, on New Dance. Deleted Feb '87. Catalogue no: **ND 003**

Lane, Christy

SLIPPIN' UP, SLIPPIN' AROUND
Tracks: / Slippin' up, slippin' around / He's back in town.
7" Single: Released Feb '80, on Liberty, by EMI Records. Deleted Feb '83. Catalogue no: **UP 611**

Lane, Patricia

I DREAMED A DREAM
Tracks: / I dreamed a dream / I know.
7" Single: Released Apr '86, on Carrere, Catalogue no: **CAR 389**
12" Single: Released Apr '86, on Carrere, Catalogue no: **CART 389**

Lane, Rita

PARTY'S LIVE, THE
Tracks: / Party's live, The.
12" Single: Released Oct '87, on Diamond(USA), Catalogue no: **DI 107**

Lane, Robin

DON'T CRY
Tracks: / Don't cry / Waitin' in line.
7" Single: Released May '80, on Warner Bros., by WEA Records. Deleted May '83. Catalogue no: **K 17613**

Lane, Ronnie

HOW COME (see panel on right)
Tracks: / How come / Tell everyone / Done this one before.
7" EP: Released Jan '74, on G & M, by G&M Tapes & Records. Deleted Jan '77. Catalogue no: **GMS 011**

ONE STEP TWO STEP
Tracks: / One step two step / Lad's got money.
7" Single: Released Jan '80, on Gem, Deleted Jan '83. Catalogue no: **GEMS 19**

POACHER, THE
Tracks: / Poacher, The.
7" Single: Released Jun '74, on G & M, by G&M Tapes & Records. Deleted Jun '77. Catalogue no: **GMS 024**

Lang, Don

CLOUDBURST
Tracks: / Cloudburst.
7" Single: Released Nov '55, on H.M.V., by EMI Records. Deleted Nov '58. Catalogue no: **POP 115**

SCHOOL DAY
Tracks: / School day.
7" Single: Released Jul '57, on H.M.V., by EMI Records. Deleted Jul '60. Catalogue no: **POP 350**

SINK THE BISMARCK
Tracks: / Sink the Bismarck.
7" Single: Released Mar '60, on H.M.V., by EMI Records. Deleted Mar '63. Catalogue no: **POP 714**

WITCH DOCTOR
Tracks: / Witch doctor.
7" Single: Released May '58, on H.M.V., by EMI Records. Deleted May '61. Catalogue no: **POP 488**

Lang, Gabby

1,2,3 O'CLOCK
Tracks: / 1,2,3 o'clock / Waiting.
7" Single: Released Feb '84, on Excaliber, by Red Bus Records. Deleted '88. Catalogue no: **EXC 537**
12" Single: Released Feb '84, on Excaliber, by Red Bus Records. Deleted '88. Catalogue no: **EXCL 537**

SHAME
Tracks: / Shame / Am I right.
12" Single: Released May '88, on Rise, Catalogue no: **RISET 4**

Lang, K.D.

OUR DAY WILL COME
Tracks: / Our day will come / Three cigarettes in an ashtray / Johnny get angry (Available on 12" only).
7" Single: Released Nov '88, on Warner Bros., by WEA Records. Catalogue no: **W 7697**
12" Single: Released Nov '88, on Warner Bros., by WEA Records. Catalogue no: **W 7697T**

SUGAR MOON
Tracks: / Sugar moon / Honky tonk medley (On 12" only) / I'm down to my last cigarette (On 12" only).
7" Single: Released Jun '88, on Warner Bros., by WEA Records. Catalogue no: **W 7841**
12" Single: Released Jun '88, on Warner Bros., by WEA Records. Catalogue no: **W 7841T**

Lang, Thomas

BOYS PREFER TO BE ALONE
Tracks: / Boys prefer / Cry baby (On 12" version.) / Fingers and thumbs (On 12" version only.).
7" Single: Released Oct '87, on CBS, by CBS Records. Catalogue no: **VOW 3**
12" Single: Released Oct '87, on CBS, by CBS Records. Catalogue no: **VOW T3**

HAPPY MAN, THE
Tracks: / Happy man / Envy / Injury / Logic / Sympathy / Sleep with me / Skin / Sons of / Bulgaria / Spirit.
CD 5": Released Jan '88, on Epic, by CBS Records. Deleted Jan '89. Catalogue no: **CD VOW 4**
10" single: Released Feb '88, on Epic, by CBS Records. Catalogue no: **VOW Q4**
7" Single: Released Jan '88, on Epic, by CBS Records. Deleted Aug '88. Catalogue no: **VOW 4**
12" Single: Released Jan '88, on Epic, by CBS Records. Deleted Jun '88. Catalogue no: **VOW QT4**
12" Single: Released Jan '88, on Epic, by CBS Records. Deleted Aug '88. Catalogue no: **VOW T4**

ME & MRS JONES
Tracks: / Shoelaces / Me & mrs jones.
CD 5": Released Jul '87, on Epic, by CBS Records. Catalogue no: **VOWCD 2**
7" Single: Released Jul '87, on Epic, by CBS Records. Catalogue no: **VOW 2**
12" Single: Released Jul '87, on Epic, by CBS Records. Catalogue no: **VOWT 2**

Lange, Stevie

DON'T WANT TO CRY NO MORE
Tracks: / Don't want to cry no more.
7" Single: Released Aug '83, on Jive, by Zomba Records. Catalogue no: **JIVE 23**

REMEMBER MY NAME
Tracks: / Remember my name / I don't want to know.
7" Single: Released Nov '81, on RCA, by BMG Records (UK). Catalogue no: **RCA 152**

Langer, Clive

EVEN THOUGH
Tracks: / Even though.
7" Single: Released Jun '87, on Creation, by Creation Records. Catalogue no: **CRE 042**

IT'S ALL OVER NOW
Tracks: / It's all over now / Lovely evening.
7" Single: Released 20 Jun '80, on F-Beat, by F-Beat Records. Deleted '83. Catalogue no: **XX 4**

SPLASH (SINGLE)
Tracks: / Splash / Hullo.
7" Single: Released Apr '80, on F-Beat, by F-Beat Records. Deleted '83. Catalogue no: **XX 2**

Langford, Bonnie

JUST ONE KISS
Tracks: / Just one kiss.
7" Single: Released Nov '84, on Tembo, by Tembo Records. Catalogue no: **TML 103**

Langley, Gerry

CHASING MY YOUTH AGAIN
Tracks: / Chasing my mouth again / I'm a different man.
7" Single: Released Oct '82, on Monarch, by Monarch Records. Catalogue no: **MON 034**

CROSSROADS OF MY LIFE
Tracks: / Crossroads of my life / Making it with you.
7" Single: Released Feb '80, on Monarch, by Monarch Records. Deleted Feb '83. Catalogue no: **MON 08**

Langleys

I'LL NEVER LET YOU DOWN AGAIN
Tracks: / I'll never let you down again.
7" Single: Released Aug '85, on Triangle, by Triangle Records. Catalogue no: **TRG 1**

Langton, Diane

I CAN TALK TO YOU
Tracks: / I can talk to you / If I'm wrong about you.
7" Single: Released Jul '82, on EMI, by EMI Records. Deleted '85. Catalogue no: **EMI 5321**

RONNIE LANE - HOW COME (Released on G & M)

Langton, Lloyd Group

DREAMS THAT FADE AWAY
Tracks: / Dreams that fade away / It's on me.
7" Single: Released Jul '84, on Albion, by Albion Records. Catalogue no: **12HUW 1**

WIND OF CHANGE
Tracks: / Wind of change.
7" Single: Released Jul '83, on Flicknife, by Flicknife Records. Catalogue no: **FLS 021**

Language

WE'RE CELEBRATING
Tracks: / We're celebrating.
7" Single: Released Mar '83, on Stiff, by Stiff Records. Catalogue no: **BUY 175**
12" Single: Released Mar '83, on Stiff, by Stiff Records. Catalogue no: **BUYIT 175**

Language From Memory

FORTUNE
Tracks: / Fortune / Coat.
7" Single: Released Jan '82, on Towerbell, Deleted '85. Catalogue no: **TOW 15**

Lanier & Co.

I DON'T KNOW
Tracks: / I don't know (extended version) / Dancing in the night (remix) / I don't know / Afraid of losing you.
7" Single: Released Oct '87, on Syncopate, by EMI Records. Deleted Apr '88. Catalogue no: **SY 7**
12" Single: Released Oct '87, on Syncopate, by EMI Records. Deleted Nov '88. Catalogue no: **12SY 7**

I DON'T KNOW WHAT TO DO ABOUT YOU
Tracks: / I don't know what to do about you.
12" Single: Released Mar '87, on Threeway, Catalogue no: **WAY 102T**

Lanza, Mario

Biographical details: This American singer and actor was born Alfredo Arnold Cocozza in Philadelphia; he took his stage name from his mother's maiden name Maria Lanza. His father was an admirer of the great classical tenor Enrico Caruso, and his collection of Caruso records convinced the youngster to train as a singer. In his early twenties, he was fortunate enough to recieve tuition from two of Caruso's former teachers. After a couple of years in the US Air Force, Lanza began his full time professional career in 1946, at the age 25. Lanza made his first film appearance in the 1949 movie *That midnight kiss* and achieved his first smash hit single with 1950's *Be my love* from the film "Toast of New Orleans". During the fifties he established himself as one of the world's greatest tenors, and even invoked comparison's with the man whom he portrayed in the title role of the film "The great Caruso"; the latter died in 1921, the same year that Lanza was born. Later Lanza movies included "Because you're mine", "Serenade", "Seven hills of Rome" and "For the first time". The title song from "Because you're mine" was listed on Britian's first ever record chart, published by New Musical Express on 14 November 1952; it proceeded to spend 24 weeks on that list, reaching a peak position of no.3. The singer never entered the UK top 10 again, although he did chalk up several smaller entries on the singles chart during the mid fifties. On the British LP list *The great Caruso* provided him with two top 10 successes in the late fifties and early sixties, one of which was a joint package with *The student Prince*. Lanza met an untimely death in Rome in October 1959 at the age of 38. Many posthumous LP sales were achieved. As late as 1981 the TV advertised collection *The legend of Mario Lanza* reached the top 30 of Britain's album chart. (Bob Macdonald 85).

BECAUSE YOU'RE MINE
Tracks: / Because you're mine.
7" Single: Released Nov '52, on H.M.V., by EMI Records. Deleted Nov '55. Catalogue no: **DA 2017**

DRINKING SONG
Tracks: / Drinking song.
7" Single: Released Feb '55, on H.M.V., by EMI Records. Deleted Feb '58. Catalogue no: **DA 2065**

I'LL WALK WITH GOD (SINGLE)
Tracks: / I'll walk with God.
7" Single: Released Feb '55, on H.M.V., by EMI Records. Deleted Feb '58. Catalogue no: **DA 2062**

SERENADE
Tracks: / Serenade.
7" Single: Released Sep '56, on H.M.V., by EMI Records. Deleted Sep '59. Catalogue no: **DA 2085**

Lapotaire, Jane

I'LL PUT YOU TOGETHER AGAIN
Tracks: / I'll put you together again / All rocked out.
7" Single: Released Nov '83, on DJM, Catalogue no: **DJS 8**

Lara, Derek

COME ON OVER
Tracks: / Come on over.
12" Single: Released Jan '82, on Plantation, Catalogue no: **PL 003**

HELLO STRANGER
Tracks: / Hello stranger.
7" Single: Released Nov '82, on Pama, by Pama Records. Catalogue no: **PMD 3224**

Lara, Jennifer

BE YOUR LADY
Tracks: / Be your lady / My man.
12" Single: Released Nov '86, on Uptempo, Catalogue no: **TEMP 010**

I NEVER FALL IN LOVE AGAIN
Tracks: / I never fall in love again.
12" Single: Released Aug '88, on C & E, Catalogue no: **CED 102**

I'LL GIVE YOU LOVE
Tracks: / I'll give you love.
12" Single: Released Apr '88, on Mr Moodies, Catalogue no: **RG 005**

ISLANDS IN THE STREAM
Tracks: / Islands in the stream.
12" Single: Released Jan '84, on Londisc, by Londisc Records. Catalogue no: **LD 012**

ROOTS DAUGHTER
Tracks: / Roots daughter.
12" Single: Released Sep '84, on Londisc, by Londisc Records. Catalogue no: **LDR 034**

Lard

POWER OF LARD, THE
Tracks: / Power of lard, The / Hell fudge.
CD 5": Released 9 Jan '89, on Alternative Tentacles, by Alternative Tentacles Records. Catalogue no: **VIRUS 72CD**
Cassingle: Released 9 Jan '89, on Alternative Tentacles, by Alternative Tentacles Records. Catalogue no: **VIRUS 72C**
12" Single: Released 9 Jan '89, on Alternative Tentacles, by Alternative Tentacles Records. Catalogue no: **VIRUS 72T**

Largo, Hugo

TURTLE SONG
Tracks: / Turtle song.
12" Single: Released 30 Jan '89, on Land, Catalogue no: **LANDS 501**

Lariat, Lash

DOLE QUEUE BLUES
Tracks: / Dole queue blues.
7" Single: Released Nov '85, on Big Beat, by Ace Records. Deleted '88. Catalogue no: **NS 108**
12" Single: Released Nov '85, on Big Beat, by Ace Records. Deleted '88. Catalogue no: **NST 108**

Larkins, Percy

MUSIC OF PASSION (SINGLE)
Tracks: / Music of passion.
7" Single: Released Jun '85, on Move, Catalogue no: **MVS 1**

Larks

ALL OR NOTHING GIRL
Tracks: / All or nothing girl / Whatever you say / Parents:teachers (Extra track on 12".).
7" Single: Released Oct '86, on Exaltation, by Exaltation Records. Catalogue no: **LARX 2**

BILLY GRAHAM
Tracks: / Billy Graham / Maggie, Maggie, Maggie / Phantom of the bingo hall ('Phantom of the bingo hall' is an extra track on 12" only.) / Larking with the larks (extra track on 12".).
7" Single: Released Apr '86, on R4, Catalogue no: **FOR 5**
12" Single: Released Apr '86, on R4, Catalogue no: **12 FOR 5**

PAIN IN THE NECK
Tracks: / Pain in the neck / Clean boy.
7" Single: Released Feb '87, on Exaltation, by Exaltation Records. Catalogue no: **LARX 3**
12" Single: Released Feb '87, on Exaltation, by Exaltation Records. Catalogue no: **12LARX 3**

David Lasley - Where Does That Boy Hang Out (EMI-America)

LaRosa, Julius

TORERO
Tracks: / Torero.
7" Single: Released Jul '58, on RCA, by BMG Records (UK). Deleted Jul '61. Catalogue no: **RCA 1063**

Larou, Lash

DON'T DRIVE DRUNK
Tracks: / Don't drive drunk.
12" Single: Released Nov '85, on John Dread Production, Catalogue no: **JDP 003**

Larry & Alvin

THROW ME
Tracks: / Throw me / New clothes.
12" Single: Released Sep '84, on Greensleeves, by Greensleeves Records. Catalogue no: **GRED 146**

Larry & The Actors

CRASHING THE GATE
Tracks: / Crashing the gate.
12" Single: Released Apr '89, on Plastic Head, by Plastic Head Records. Catalogue no: **PLASS 010**

THINK I'M CRAZY
Tracks: / Think I'm crazy.
12" Single: Released Mar '89, on Plastic Head, by Plastic Head Records. Catalogue no: **PLASS 010**

Larson, Kim

ROCK'N'ROLL CITY
Tracks: / Rock'n'roll city / Time bomb.
7" Single: Released Apr '82, on CBS, by CBS Records. Deleted Apr '85. Catalogue no: **A 2232**

Larson, Nicolette

BACK IN MY ARMS
Tracks: / Back in my arms / Trouble.
7" Single: Released Jan '80, on Warner Bros., by WEA Records. Deleted Jan '85. Catalogue no: **K 17550**

FOOL ME AGAIN
Tracks: / Fool me again / Arthur's theme.
7" Single: Released Mar '82, on Warner Bros., by WEA Records. Catalogue no: **K 17892**

RADIOLAND (SINGLE)
Tracks: / Radioland / How can we go on.
7" Single: Released Feb '81, on Warner Bros., by WEA Records. Deleted Feb '84. Catalogue no: **K 17752**

YOU CAN'T SAY YOU DON'T LOVE ME ANYMORE
Tracks: / You can't say you don't love me anymore.
7" Single: Released Apr '85, on MCA, by MCA Records. Catalogue no: **MCA 956**

La's

THERE SHE GOES
Tracks: / There she goes.
7" Single: Released Nov '88, on Go Discs, by Chrysalis Records. Catalogue no: **GOLAS 2**
12" Single: Released Nov '88, on Go Discs, by Chrysalis Records. Catalogue no: **GOLAS 212**

WAY OUT
Tracks: / Way out.
7" Single: Released Oct '87, on Go Discs, by Chrysalis Records. Catalogue no: **GOLAS 1**
12" Single: Released Oct '87, on Go Discs, by Chrysalis Records. Catalogue no: **GOLAS 112**

Lasalle, Denise

COME TO BED
Tracks: / Come to bed.
7" Single: Released May '83, on Malaco, by Malaco Records (UK). Deleted '88. Catalogue no: **MAL 009**
12" Single: Released May '83, on Malaco, by Malaco Records (UK). Deleted '88. Catalogue no: **MAL 12 009**

LET THE FOUR WINDS BLOW
Tracks: / Let the four winds blow.
7" Single: Released Feb '86, on Malaco, by Malaco Records (UK). Deleted '88. Catalogue no: **MAL 030**
12" Single: Released Feb '86, on Malaco, by Malaco Records (UK). Deleted '88. Catalogue no: **MAL 12 030**

MY TOOT TOOT (SINGLE)
Tracks: / My toot toot / Give me yo most strongest whiskey.
7" Single: Released Jun '85, on Epic, by CBS Records. Deleted Jun '88. Catalogue no: **A 6334**

RIGHT PLACE, RIGHT TIME (SINGLE)
Tracks: / Right place, right time / Come to bed / Let's starighten it out.
7" Single: Released Jun '84, on Malaco, by Malaco Records (UK). Deleted '88. Catalogue no: **MAL 022**
12" Single: Released Jun '84, on Malaco, by Malaco Records (UK). Deleted '88. Catalogue no: **MAL 12 012**

Lasley, David

TREAT WILLIE GOOD
Tracks: / Treat Willie good / There's gotta be somebody.

7" Single: Released Jul '82, on EMI-America, by EMI Records. Deleted Jul '85. Catalogue no: **EA 139**

WHERE DOES THAT BOY HANG OUT?
Tracks: / Where does the boy hang out / Next time.
7" Single: Released Aug '84, on EMI-America, by EMI Records. Catalogue no: **EA 179**
12" Single: Released '86, on EMI-America, by EMI Records. Deleted '87. Catalogue no: **12EA 179**

Last Chant

RUN OF THE DOVE
Tracks: / Run of the dove.
7" Single: Released Oct '81, on Chicken Jazz, Catalogue no: **JAZZ 4**

Last Few Days

KICKS
Tracks: / Kicks.
7" Single: Released Oct '88, on Product Inc., Catalogue no: **PROD 21**
12" Single: Released Oct '88, on Product Inc., Catalogue no: **PROD 21T**

LOVELY LITTLE ANGEL
Tracks: / Lovely little angel.
7" Single: Released 20 Feb '88, on Product Inc., Catalogue no: **PROD 21**
12" Single: Released Jan '88, on Product Inc., Catalogue no: **12PROD 21**

TOO MUCH IS NOT ENOUGH
Tracks: / Too much is not enough / Solemn warnings / If the bombs are not to burst.
12" Single: Released Mar '86, on Touch, by Touch Records. Catalogue no: **T9 45**

Last Flight

DANCE TO THE MUSIC
Tracks: / Dance to the music / I'm ready.
7" Single: Released Mar '81, on Heavy Metal, by FM-Revolver Records. Deleted Mar '84. Catalogue no: **HEAVY 5**

Last Gang

SPIRIT OF YOUTH
Tracks: / Spirit of youth.
7" Single: on Graduate, by Graduate Records. Deleted Jan '87. Catalogue no: **GRAD 3**

TIGER FACED LIAR
Tracks: / Tiger faced liar / Trouble with you.
7" Single: Released 27 Feb '88, on Innuendo, Catalogue no: **OOH-ER 69**

Last, James

Biographical details: This West German bandleader, conductor, arranger and producer is one of the most extraordinary phenomena of the recording industry; indeed he is virtually a recording industry all by himself. According to 'The Guinness Book Of British Hit Albums', Last chalked up no less than 43 chart LPs between 1967 and 1981; in the whole history of the UK album charts, only Elvis Presley and Frank Sinatra could boast higher totals. The bandleader's entire output has been released almost exclusively on Polydor.
Last's success has been based upon appealing to the lowest common denominator. His albums have consisted of endless medleys of non stop cover versions of familiar material, blended together into a bland whole to make all the songs sound the same. Numerous genres, from pop to classical to folk to Christmas music to reggae, have endured the Last party fodder treatment. His aforementioned 43 UK entries penetrated the Top 10: they were *This Is James Last* (No.6, 1967), *The Ten Years Non-Stop Jubilee Album* (No.5 1975), *Make The Party Last* (no.3, 1975) and *Last The Whole Night Long* (No.2 1979). The only slight aberration in Last's career was his 1980 single *The Seduction (Love Theme From 'American Gigolo')*. - this beautiful movie tune was his only hit single, reaching No.48 in Britain and No.28 in America. It was undoubtedly the best record he has ever made. (Bob Macdonald 3/12/85).

BISCAYA (SINGLE)
Tracks: / Biscaya / Lost summer.
7" Single: Released Nov '81, on Polydor, by Polydor Ltd. Deleted '84. Catalogue no: **POSP 378**

BLUEBIRD
Tracks: / Bluebird / Empty glasses.
7" Single: Released Nov '82, on Polydor, by Polydor Ltd. Deleted Nov '85. Catalogue no: **POSP 531**

FANTASY
Tracks: / Fantasy / Glow.
7" Single: Released Aug '80, on Polydor, by Polydor Ltd. Deleted '83. Catalogue no: **POSP 150**

LISTEN TO YOUR HEART
Tracks: / Listen to your heart / Champagne & caviar.
7" Single: Released Jan '87, on Polydor, by Polydor Ltd. Deleted Mar '88. Catalogue no: **POSP 846**

LONELY BULL, THE
Tracks: / Lonely bull, The / Mornings at seven.
7" Single: Released Apr '87, on Polydor, by Polydor Ltd. Deleted Jan '88. Catalogue no: **POSP 860**

MORNINGS AT SEVEN
Tracks: / Mornings at seven / Summer.
7" Single: Released Mar '80, on Polydor, by Polydor Ltd. Deleted '83. Catalogue no: **POSP 45**

SEDUCTION (SINGLE)
Tracks: / Seduction / Night drive.
7" Single: Released Apr '80, on Polydor, by Polydor Ltd. Deleted Apr '83. Catalogue no: **PD 2071**

SEDUCTION, THE
Tracks: / Seduction, The.
7" Single: Released May '80, on Polydor, by Polydor Ltd. Deleted May '83. Catalogue no: **PD 2071**

Last Party

DIE SPYRING
Tracks: / Die spyring.
12" Single: Released Nov '88, on Idol, Catalogue no: **ID 12006**

MR. HURST
Tracks: / Mr. Hurst.
7" Single: Released Feb '87, on Harvey, Catalogue no: **PR 002**

Last Rites

FASCISM MEANS WAR
Tracks: / Fascism means war.
7" Single: Released Mar '84, on Essential, Catalogue no: **ESS 04**

WE DON'T CARE
Tracks: / We don't care.
7" Single: Released Jun '83, on Flicknife, by Flicknife Records. Catalogue no: **FLS 219**

Last Touch

CLOWN TIME
Tracks: / Clown time / Social whirl.
7" Single: Released May '81, on Zilch, by Zilch Records. Deleted May '84. Catalogue no: **ZILCH 4**

Last Words

ANIMAL WORLD
Tracks: / Animal world.
7" Single: Released Aug '79, on Rough Trade, by Rough Trade Records. Catalogue no: **RT 022**

TODAYS KIDS
Tracks: / Todays kids / Something's wrong.
7" Single: Released Jan '80, on Remand, Deleted '81. Catalogue no: **REMAND 2**

TOP SECRET
Tracks: / Top secret.
7" Single: Released Jul '81, on Armageddon, by Armageddon Records. Catalogue no: **AS 002**

Laswell, Bill

WORK SONG
Tracks: / Work song.
12" Single: Released Aug '84, on Rough Trade, by Rough Trade Records. Catalogue no: **MEGA 128332**

Laszlo, Ken

TONIGHT
Tracks: / Tonight (Italian mix) / Tonight (Instr) / Hey hey guy (remix) / Tonight.
12" Single: Released Jan '87, on Greyhound, by Greyhound Records. Catalogue no: **GRY 007**

Latchkey Children

LATCHKEY CHILDREN
Tracks: / Latchkey Children / On the move.
7" Single: Released 20 Jun '80, on Virgin, by Virgin Records. Deleted '83. Catalogue no: **VS 357**

Late Show

BRISTOL STOMP
Tracks: / Bristol show.
7" Single: Released Mar '79, on Decca, by Decca Records. Deleted Mar '82. Catalogue no: **F 13822**

Latest

STARTING OVER
Tracks: / Starting over.
12" Single: Released Aug '84, on Souled Out, Catalogue no: **SOULED 1T**

Latifah

WRATH OF MY MADNESS
Tracks: / Wrath of my madness.
7" Single: Released 2 May '89, on Gee Street, by Gee Street Records. Catalogue no: **UNKNOWN**
12" Single: Released 2 May '89, on Gee Street, by Gee Street Records. Catalogue no: **UNKNOWN**

Latin Electrica

LATIN ELECTRICA
Tracks: / Latin electrica.
7" Single: Released Jun '84, on Nouveau Music, Catalogue no: **NMS 7**
12" Single: Released Jun '84, on Nouveau Music, Catalogue no: **12NMS 7**

Latin Quarter

AMERICAN FOR BEGINNERS
Tracks: / American for beginners / Sadanista.
7" Single: Released Aug '86, on Rockin' Horse, by BMG Records (UK). Catalogue no: **RH 110**
12" Single: Released Aug '86, on Rockin' Horse, by BMG Records (UK). Catalogue no: **RHT 110**

I TOGETHER
Tracks: / I together / See him / Thin white duke (extra track on 12").
7" Single: Released Jun '87, on Rockin' Horse, by BMG Records (UK). Catalogue no: **RH 114**
12" Single: Released Jun '87, on Rockin' Horse, by BMG Records (UK). Catalogue no: **RHT 114**

NEW MILLIONAIRES, THE
Tracks: / New millionaires.
7" Single: Released Jun '85, on Rockin' Horse, by BMG Records (UK). Catalogue no: **RH 104**
12" Single: Released Jun '85, on Rockin' Horse, by BMG Records (UK). Catalogue no: **RHT 104**

NO ROPE AS LONG AS TIME
Tracks: / No rope as long as time.
7" Single: Released Oct '85, on Rockin' Horse, by BMG Records (UK). Catalogue no: **RH 105**
12" Single: Released Oct '85, on Rockin' Horse, by BMG Records (UK). Catalogue no: **RHT 105**

NOMZAMO (ONE PEOPLE ONE CAUSE)
Tracks: / Nomzamo (one people one cause).
CD 5": Released Jun '89, on Rockin' Horse, by BMG Records (UK). Deleted Jul '89. Catalogue no: **RHCD 113**

RADIO AFRICA
Tracks: / Radio Africa / Voices inside / Toulouse (Extra track on 12".).
7" Single: Released Mar '85, on Rockin' Horse, by BMG Records (UK). Catalogue no: **RH 102**
7" Single: Released Oct '84, on Ignition, Catalogue no: **PUMA 8481**
12" Single: Released Mar '85, on Rockin' Horse, by BMG Records (UK). Catalogue no: **RHT 102**

SWIMMING AGAINST THE STREAM (SINGLE)
Tracks: / Swimming against the stream / Colour scheme, The / Ed Murrow (Only on 12" single.).
CD 5": Released 30 May '89, on RCA, by BMG Records (UK). Catalogue no: **PD 42664**
7" Single: Released 30 May '89, on RCA, by BMG Records (UK). Catalogue no: **PB 42663**
12" Single: Released 30 May '89, on RCA, by BMG Records (UK). Catalogue no: **PT 42664**

TOULOUSE
Tracks: / Toulouse.
7" Single: Released Jan '85, on Rockin' Horse, by BMG Records (UK). Catalogue no: **RH 101**
12" Single: Released Jan '85, on Rockin' Horse, by BMG Records (UK). Catalogue no: **RHT 101**

Latino, Gino

NO SORRY
Tracks: / No sorry.
CD 5": Released Sep '89, on RCA, by BMG Records (UK). Catalogue no: **PD 43042**
7" Single: Released Sep '89, on RCA, by BMG Records (UK). Catalogue no: **PB 43041**
12" Single: Released Sep '89, on RCA, by BMG Records (UK). Catalogue no: **PT 43042**

Latouche, Panchita

I'M MISSING YOU
Tracks: / I'm missing you / Cocksman for the dance.
7" Single: Released Nov '80, on Greensleeves, by Greensleeves Records. Deleted Nov '83. Catalogue no: **NICE 113**

SPEND SOME TIME WITH ME
Tracks: / Spend some time with me.
7" Single: Released May '82, on Paradise, Catalogue no: **PDIS 103**

Latter, Gene

ROCK BABY ROCK
Tracks: / Rock baby rock / Sweet sugar.
7" Single: Released Jul '82, on Magnet, by WEA Records. Catalogue no: **MAG 230**

Lattisaw, Stacy

Biographical details: Lattisaw, Stacy This American sisnger was born in Washington DC in November 1966.
Under the guidance of drummer/singer/songwriter/producer Narade Michael Walden, she shot to fame as a 13 year old prodigy in 1980 with her big American disco hit *Jump To The Beat*, this proceeded to become a major pop hit in Britain, reaching No.3 on the UK national chart.
Lattisaw failed to score any further significant success in the UK, but chalked up US Top 30 hits with the convincing ballad *Let Me Be Your Angel* (1980) and *Love On a Two Way Street* (1981). Thankfully, the singer's age was not overplayed in her music or marketing and her style showed considerable maturity. However, she was unable to consolidate upon her early success, and Walden could not steer her later releases to anything above mediocre sales levels.
In 1984 Lattisaw teamed with singer Johnny Gill for an album entitled *Perfect Combination* - this optimistic title was not borne out by its chart progress. But Stacy was still barely 18 years old and had plenty more years in which to return to and improve upon former glories.
(Bob Macdonald 3/12/85).

ATTACK OF THE NAME GAME
Tracks: / Attack of the name game / I could love you so divine.
7" Single: Released Nov '82, on Cotillion (Import), by WEA Records. Catalogue no: **799968 7**

BABY I LOVE YOU
Tracks: / Baby I love you / With you.
7" Single: Released Oct '81, on Atlantic, by WEA Records. Catalogue no: **K 11680**

CALL ME
Tracks: / Call me (instrumental) / Call me (extended) (12" only.) / Call me (*Track on 12" only.).
7" Single: Released Oct '88, on Motown, by BMG Records (UK). Catalogue no: **ZB 42263**
12" Single: Released Oct '88, on Motown, by BMG Records (UK). Catalogue no: **ZT 42264**

DYNAMITE
Tracks: / Dynamite / Dreaming.
7" Single: Released Aug '80, on Atlantic, by WEA Records. Deleted Aug '83. Catalogue no: **K 11554**

JUMP INTO MY LIFE
Tracks: / Jump into my life / Long shot.
7" Single: Released Jan '87, on Motown, by BMG Records (UK). Catalogue no: **ZB 41109**
12" Single: Released Jan '87, on Motown, by BMG Records (UK). Catalogue no: **ZT 41110**

JUMP TO THE BEAT
Tracks: / Jump to the beat.
7" Single: Released Jun '80, on Atlantic, by WEA Records. Deleted '84. Catalogue no: **K 11496**
12" Single: Released Jun '80, on Atlantic, by WEA Records. Catalogue no: **K 11496 T**

LOVE ON A TWO WAY STREET
Tracks: / Love on a two way street / Young girl.
7" Single: Released Jul '81, on Atlantic, by WEA Records. Catalogue no: **K 11672**

MILLION DOLLAR BASE
Tracks: / Million dollar base / Ways of love, The / Hey there lonely boy.
7" Single: Released Jan '84, on Cotillion (Import), by WEA Records. Catalogue no: **B 9819**
12" Single: Released Jan '84, on Cotillion (Import), by WEA Records. Catalogue no: **B 9819T**

NAIL IT TO THE WALL
Tracks: / Nail it to the wall / Nail it to the wall (instrumental).

7" Single: Released Sep '86, on Motown, by BMG Records (UK). Catalogue no: **ZB 40885**

SNEAKIN' OUT
Tracks: / Jump to the beat / Sneakin' out / Guys like you.
7" Single: Released Sep '82, on Cotillion (Import), by WEA Records. Catalogue no: **K 11770**
12" Single: Released Sep '82, on Cotillion (Import), by WEA Records. Catalogue no: **K 11770T**

WHAT YOU NEED (IMPORT)
Tracks: / What you need.
12" Single: Released Sep '89, on Motown (USA), by Motown Records (USA). Catalogue no: **MOT 4653**

Laugh

PAUL MCCARTNEY
Tracks: / Paul McCartney.
7" Single: Released Aug '87, on Remorse, Catalogue no: **LOSS 5**

SENSATION NO.1 (SINGLE)
Tracks: / Sensation No.1.
7" Single: Released Nov '88, on Sub Aqua, Catalogue no: **AQUA 3**
12" Single: Released Nov '88, on Sub Aqua, Catalogue no: **AQUA 312**

TAKE YOUR TIME YEAH
Tracks: / Take your time yeah.
12" Single: Released Nov '86, on Remorse, Catalogue no: **LOST 3**

TIME TO LOSE IT
Tracks: / Time to lose it.
7" Single: Released Apr '88, on Remorse, Catalogue no: **LOSS 7**
12" Single: Released Apr '88, on Remorse, Catalogue no: **LOST 7**

Laughing Apples

PARTICIPATE
Tracks: / Participate.
7" Single: Released Oct '82, on Autonomy, Catalogue no: **AUT 002**

PRECIOUS FEELING
Tracks: / Precious feeling.
7" Single: Released Mar '82, on Essential, Catalogue no: **ESS 001**

Laughing Clowns

ETERNALLY YOURS
Tracks: / Eternally yours.
7" Single: Released Mar '85, on Hot, Catalogue no: **HOT 001**
12" Single: Released Mar '85, on Hot, Catalogue no: **HOT 12001**

EVERYTHING THAT FLIES
Tracks: / Everything that flies.
12" Single: Released May '83, on Red Flame (1), by Red Flame Records. Catalogue no: **RF 1223**

LAUGHING CLOWNS
Tracks: / Laughing clowns.
12" Single: Released Aug '82, on M. Link, Catalogue no: **ING 001**

MAD FLIES MAD FLIES
Tracks: / Mad flies mad flies.
7" Single: Released Aug '82, on P.Melon, Deleted '83. Catalogue no: **PM 020**

Laughing House

DEMOCRACY
Tracks: / Democracy.
7" EP: Released Apr '87, on Sonar, by Sonar Records. Catalogue no: **SNR 3**

Laughter In The Garden

CLUTCH TIGHT
Tracks: / Clutch tight / Thgit hctulc.
7" Single: Released Dec '83, on Crash, by Satril Records. Deleted '85. Catalogue no: **CRA 601**

CORRIDOR OF STATUES
Tracks: / Corridor of statues.
12" Single: Released Aug '82, on Teatime, Deleted '86. Catalogue no: **T 999**

Lauper, Cyndi

ALL THROUGH THE NIGHT
Tracks: / All through the night.
12" Single: Released Nov '84, on Portrait, by CBS Records. Catalogue no: **TA 4849**

CHANGE OF HEART
Tracks: / Change of heart / What a thrill / Heartbeat (Available on 12" only.).
7" Single: Released Jun '84, on WEA, by WEA Records. Catalogue no: **YZ 7**
7" Single: Released Nov '86, on Portrait, by CBS Records. Catalogue no: **CYNDI 1**
12" Single: Released Jun '84, on WEA, by WEA Records. Catalogue no: **YZ 7T**

GIRLS JUST WANNA HAVE FUN (IMPORT)
Tracks: / Girls just want to have fun / Time after time.
CD 3": Released Aug '88, on Epic (USA), by CBS Records (USA). Catalogue no: **34K 05480**

GIRLS JUST WANT TO HAVE FUN
Tracks: / Girls just want to have fun.
7" Single: Released Jan '84, on Portrait, by CBS Records. Deleted '86. Catalogue no: **A 3943**
12" Single: Released Jan '84, on Portrait, by CBS Records. Catalogue no: **A 3943**

HOLE IN MY HEART
Tracks: / Hole in my heart / Boy blue.
CD 5": Released 23 Jul '88, on Epic, by CBS Records. Catalogue no: **CYN C3**
7" Single: Released 23 Jul '88, on Epic, by CBS Records. Catalogue no: **CYN 3**
12" Single: Released 23 Jul '88, on Epic, by CBS Records. Catalogue no: **CYN T3**

I DROVE ALL NIGHT
Tracks: / I drove all night / What's going on (club version) / Maybe he'll know / Time after time.
CD 5": Released 8 May '89, on Epic, by CBS Records. Catalogue no: **CYNCD 4**
CD 5": Released Apr '89, on Epic, by CBS Records. Catalogue no: **CYNC 4**
7" Pic: Released 15 May '89, on Epic, by CBS Records. Deleted Oct '89. Catalogue no: **CYN P4**
Cassingle: Released 12 Jun '89, on Epic, by CBS Records. Catalogue no: **CYN M4**
7" Single: Released Apr '89, on Epic, by CBS Records. Catalogue no: **CYN 4**
12" Single: Released Apr '89, on Epic, by CBS Records. Deleted Oct '89. Catalogue no: **CYNQT 4**
12" Single: Released Apr '89, on Epic, by CBS Records. Deleted Oct '89. Catalogue no: **CYNT 4**

MONEY CHANGES EVERYTHING
Tracks: / Money changes everything / He's so unusual / Yeah yeah / Girls just want to have fun.
7" Single: Released Feb '85, on Portrait, by CBS Records. Catalogue no: **A 6009**
12" Single: Released Feb '85, on Portrait, by CBS Records. Catalogue no: **TA 6009**

MY FIRST NIGHT WITHOUT YOU
Tracks: / My first night without you / Unabbreviated love / True colors (Only on 12" and CD single.) / Iko iko (Only on CD picture disc single.) / When you were mine (Only on CD picture disc single.) / All through the night (Only on CD single 655091 2).
CD 5": Released 14 Aug '89, on Epic, by CBS Records. Catalogue no: **655091 2**
CD 5": Released Jul '89, on Epic, by CBS Records. Catalogue no: **CYNC 5**
CD 5": Released Jul '89, on Epic, by CBS Records. Catalogue no: **CDCYN 5**
Cassingle: Released Jul '89, on Epic, by CBS Records. Catalogue no: **CYNM 5**
7" Single: Released Jul '89, on Epic, by CBS Records. Catalogue no: **CYNP 5**
7" Single: Released Jul '89, on Epic, by CBS Records. Catalogue no: **CYN 5**
12" Single: Released Jul '89, on Epic, by CBS Records. Catalogue no: **CYNT 5**

SHE BOP
Tracks: / She bop / Witness.
7" Pic: Released Aug '84, on Portrait, by CBS Records. Catalogue no: **WA 4620**
7" Single: Released Aug '84, on Portrait, by CBS Records. Deleted '87. Catalogue no: **A 4620**
12" Single: Released Aug '84, on Portrait, by CBS Records. Catalogue no: **TA 4620**

TIME AFTER TIME
Tracks: / Time after time / I'll kiss you / Girls just want to have fun (On 12" only) / Fun with V.Knutzn (On 12" only).
7" Pic: Released Mar '84, on Portrait, by CBS Records. Catalogue no: **WA 4290**
7" Single: Released Mar '84, on Portrait, by CBS Records. Deleted '87. Catalogue no: **A 4290**
12" Single: Released Mar '84, on Portrait, by CBS Records. Deleted '85. Catalogue no: **TA 4290**

WHAT'S GOING ON
Tracks: / What's going on.
7" Pic: Released Mar '87, on Portrait, by CBS Records. Deleted Nov '87. Catalogue no: **CYNP1**
7" Single: Released Feb '87, on Portrait, by CBS Records. Deleted Aug '87. Catalogue no: **CYN 1**
12" Single: Released Mar '87, on Portrait, by CBS Records. Deleted Aug '87. Catalogue no: **CYN T1**

Laurel And Hardy

Biographical details: Laurel & Hardy (UK Reggae Rappers) Certainly not related to the legendary Hollywood duo, but often just as funny this South London reggae duo first began to attract attention with their 1982 single *You're Nicked.* This took a tongue in cheek view of the strained relations between London's black youth and the Metropolitan Police, an idea that was more successfully developed by Smiley Culture's 1985 hit *Police Officer.* The pair achieved a one off Uk chart entry in April 1983, reaching No.65 on the singles chart with *Clunk Clink.*
Despite the promise of these early singles, Laurel & Hardy's subsequent toasting efforts like *Lots of Loving* and *She's Gone* and *Dangerous Shoes,* failed to sustain the initial interest. (Bob Macdonald 3/12/85).

CLUNK CLICK
Tracks: / Clunk click / You're nicked.
7" Single: Released Mar '83, on CBS, by CBS Records. Catalogue no: **A 3213**
12" Single: Released Mar '83, on CBS, by CBS Records. Catalogue no: **A 13 3213**

DANGEROUS SHOES
Tracks: / Dangerous shoes / Write me a song.
7" Single: Released Nov '83, on Upright, by Upright Records. Catalogue no: **UP 7**
12" Single: Released Nov '83, on Upright, by Upright Records. Catalogue no: **UPT 7**

LOTS OF LOVING AND SHE'S GONE
Tracks: / Lots of loving and she's gone.
7" Single: Released May '83, on CBS, by CBS Records. Catalogue no: **A 3410**
12" Single: Released May '83, on CBS, by CBS Records. Catalogue no: **TA 3410**

YOU'RE NICKED
Tracks: / You're nicked / Tell her I'm sorry.
10" single: Released Oct '82, on Top Notch, by Fashion Records. Catalogue no: **TOP 004**

Laurel & Hardy

Biographical details: Laurel & Hardy (US Comedians) Stan Laurel did not actually take up residence in the US until he was 22 years old. He was born in Ulverston in north-west England in 1890, his real name being Arthur Stanley Jefferson. He made his professional debut in Glasgow in 1906 and spent the next six years learning his trade in a variety of ways, including a spell as understudy to the then unknown Charlie Chaplin. After settling in the States in 1912 he spent a decade in vaudeville before chaning studios in Hollywood where nearly all the classic Laurel & Hardy movies were made. He died in February 1965 at the age of 74.
Oliver Hardy was born in Harlem, Georgia in 1892; his real christian name was Norvell, but the name Oliver was later added in memory of his deceased father. He got his start in showbusiness at the age of eight, touring with a troupe of entertainers. Hardy opened his own cinema in Georgia in 1910 and ran it for three years. He then spent five years working as an actor for Lubin Motion Pictures. Ollie then moved to California and spent the early Twenties supporting several prominent comedians including Buster Keaton. Like Laurel, he started work with Hal Roach in 1926. Hardy died of a stroke in August 1957 at the age of 65.
Laurel & Hardy's golden age of comedy was 1927-38. Ranging from 20 minute shorts to full length features, their most famous Hal Roach movies included 'A Perfect Day', 'Another Fine Mess', 'Below Zero', 'The Music Box', 'Their First Mistake', 'Thicker Than Water' and 'Way Out West'. The latter film, which was released in 1937, featured Stan's ridiculous rendition of *The Trail of the Lonesome Pine* which became a posthumous UK No.2 single in December 1975. In that same month *The Golden Age of Hollywood Comedy* reached No.55 on the British album chart - this was a sampler of some of the duo's funniest film excerpts, although much of the humour was impaired without the benefit of their visual antics. (Bob Macdonald 3/12/85).

SHINE ON HARVEST MOON
Tracks: / Shine on harvest moon / World is waiting for the sunrise, The (With James Finlayson) / Cuckoo song, The.
7" Single: Released Nov '86, on Columbia, by EMI Records. Deleted Oct '87. Catalogue no: **DB 9145**

TRAIL OF THE LONESOME PINE
Tracks: / Trail of the lonesome pine.
7" Single: Released Oct '75, on United Artists, by EMI Records. Catalogue no: **UP 36026**
7" Pic: Released Sep '89, on Another Fine Mess, Catalogue no: **MESS 001P**
7" Single: Released Sep '89, on Another Fine Mess, Catalogue no: **MESS 001**

Laurels

PUSH AND SHOVE
Tracks: / Push and shove / Closer.
7" Single: Released Feb '89, on No, Catalogue no: **NOS 42**

ZOOM
Tracks: / Zoom.
12" Single: Released Sep '84, on Happy, by Happy Records. Catalogue no: **LAF 1T**

Laurence, Paul

Biographical details: Although a new name to many, Paul Laurence has been responsible for creating a distinctive and very influential sound over the past couple of years in his work with Kashif, Melba Moore and Evelyn King. He composed and produced *Rock me tonight* for Freddie Jackson, named by Billboard magazine as the no.1 on the black music charts, the longest run of a single by a new artist since 1977. A debut single by Paul Laurence entitled *She's not a sleaze* was released late last year and performed well on the dance charts. Paul Laurence doesn't restrict the subject matter of his songs to the well-trodden romantic realm's of today's typical soul music but tackles issues like drug abuse *Strung out* prejudice on *Racism* and even offers a rather humerous approach to morality on *She's not a sleaze.* However, with his baptist church choir background he can deliver a scorching ballad with the best of them when he chooses, *You hooked me* being a fine example. *Haven't you heard* is produced by Paul Laurence..

SHE'S NOT A SLEAZE
Tracks: / She's not a sleaze.
7" Single: Released Sep '85, on Capitol, by EMI Records. Deleted '87. Catalogue no: **CL 378**
12" Single: Released Sep '85, on Capitol, by EMI Records. Deleted '88. Catalogue no: **12CL 378**

STRUNG OUT
Tracks: / Strung out / I'm sensitive.
7" Single: Released Feb '86, on Capitol, by EMI Records. Deleted '88. Catalogue no: **CL 393**
12" Single: Released Feb '86, on Capitol, by EMI Records. Deleted '88. Catalogue no: **12CL 393**

Laurence, Sherise

L'AMOUR DE MA VIE
Tracks: / L'amour de ma vie.
7" Single: Released Apr '86, on Arista, by BMG Records (UK). Catalogue no: **ARIST 108175**

Laurens, Rose

AFRICA
Tracks: / Africa / Broken heart.
7" Single: Released Oct '83, on WEA, by WEA Records. Catalogue no: **X 9876**

AMERICAN LOVE
Tracks: / American love.
7" Single: Released '88, on Passion, by Skratch Records. Catalogue no: **PASH 64**

AMERICAN LOVE (PASSION REMIX)
Tracks: / American love (passion remix).
12" Single: Released 21 Nov '87, on Passion, by Skratch Records. Catalogue no: **PASH 64(12)**

Laurie & Sighs

ONLY THE LONELY
Tracks: / Only the lonely / Sympathy.
7" Single: Released Jun '80, on Atlantic, by WEA Records. Deleted Jun '83. Catalogue no: **K 11484**

Laverne & Shirlie

PIG IN A SUIT
Tracks: / Pig in a suit / Rich rewards / How to smile / Thai holiday.
7" EP: Released Mar '88, on Hitback, by Hitback Records. Catalogue no: **HITBACK 1**

Laverock, Dave

JUST FOR YOU
Tracks: / Just for you / Broken wings.
7" Single: Released Jun '80, on Laser, Deleted Jun '83. Catalogue no: **LAS 29**

Lavette, Betty

EASIER TO SAY
Tracks: / Easier to say.
7" Single: Released Jul '80, on Charly, by Charly Records. Deleted '87. Catalogue no: **CTD 107**

I CAN'T STOP
Tracks: / I can't stop / Either way we lose.
7" Single: Released Jul '82, on Motown, by BMG Records (UK). Catalogue no: **TMG 1265**

YOU SEEN ONE YOU SEEN 'EM ALL
Tracks: / You seen one you seen 'em all.
7" Single: Released Mar '82, on Motown, by BMG Records (UK). Catalogue no: **TMG 1257**

Lavias

DO YOU WANNA DANCE
Tracks: / Do you wanna dance (pt.1) / Do you wanna dance (pt.2).
7" Single: Released Jul '83, on Golden Py-

ramid, by Golden Pyramid Recordsy (USA). Catalogue no: **GP 1208**

Lavin, Christine

ANOTHER WOMAN'S MAN
Tracks: / Another woman's man.
12" Single: Released Aug '88, on Philo (USA), by Rounder Records (USA). Catalogue no: **PH 002 EP**

Lavin, Les

LOVE'S AT THE BOTTOM
Tracks: / Love's at the bottom / Just like a fool.
7" Single: Released Feb '80, on Cobra. Deleted '83. Catalogue no: **COB 7**
7" Single: Released Feb '80, on EMI, by EMI Records. Deleted Feb '83. Catalogue no: **EMI 5039**

Law Lords

LIVINGSTONE RAP
Tracks: / Livingstone rap.
12" Single: Released Jun '84, on Cherry Red, by Cherry Red Records. Deleted '87. Catalogue no: **12 CHERRY 80**

Lawal, Dee

DEE DON'T PLAY, THE
Tracks: / Dee don't play, The.
12" Single: Released Oct '89, on Play Hard, by Play Hard Records. Catalogue no: **DEC 26**

Lawal, Gasper

KITA-KATA
Tracks: / Kita-kata / Oro- moro.
7" Single: Released Nov '82, on Rough Trade, by Rough Trade Records. Deleted Nov '85. Catalogue no: **RT 123**
12" Single: Released Dec '81, on C.A.P., by C.A.P. Records. Catalogue no: **CAP 1**

KOKOROKO
Tracks: / Kokoroko.
12" Single: Released Sep '86, on Hot Cat, Catalogue no: **HOTCAT 2T**

Lawnmower

THIN MAN
Tracks: / Thin man / Could have.
7" Single: Released Oct '87, on Fat Wallet, by Fat Wallet Records. Catalogue no: **FAT-CAT 2**

Lawrence, Beverly

I WILL SURVIVE
Tracks: / I will survive.
12" Single: Released 30 May '89, on Eclipse, Catalogue no: **HCF 102012**

Lawrence, Dave

ONE MORE TEAR
Tracks: / One more tear / Cleveland dealer.
7" Single: Released Jan '83, on Admiral, by Admiral Records. Catalogue no: **ADML 002**

Lawrence, Kenneth

MONEY GOT TO PAY
Tracks: / Money got to pay.
12" Single: Released Jun '83, on Firm (1), Catalogue no: **FT 002**

Lawrence, Lee

CRYING IN THE CHAPEL
Tracks: / Crying in the chapel.
7" Single: Released Nov '53, on Decca, by Decca Records. Deleted Nov '59. Catalogue no: **F 10177**

SUDDENLY THERE'S A VALLEY
Tracks: / Suddenly there's a valley.
7" Single: Released Dec '55, on Columbia, by EMI Records. Deleted Dec '58. Catalogue no: **DB 3681**

Lawrence, Stephanie

AM I ASKING TOO MUCH
Tracks: / Am I asking too much.
7" Single: Released Sep '85, on Sierra, by Sierra Records. Deleted Jun '87. Catalogue no: **FED 18**

Lawrence, Steve

Biographical details: This American singer, whose real surname is Leibowitz, was born in New York's Brooklyn district. His father was a cantor in a local synagogue and the youngster began singing there at the age of eight. His interest in music blossomed throughout his teens, though he gave up vocals for a while to concentrate on the piano. In 1952, while still in his late teens, he won first prize in one of the renowned Arthur Godfrey's talent-spotting shows; this resulted in a week of solid radio exposure and, eventually, a recording contract. Lawrencve's first single,*Poinciana*, was a reasonable success and in July 1953 he signed a contract to become a regular performer on a local New York TV show hosted by Steve Allen. The programme went from strength to strength, evolving into the nationally screened Tonight show. He stayed with Allen for several seasons during the mid-50's and married another of the programme's regular singers, Eydie Gorme. The couple hosted their own summer television series in 1958. During the late 50's and early 60's Lawrence and Gorme enjoyed US chart success as separate solo acts. Both adhered to the middle-of-the-road music they had grown up with and made few concessions to the rock 'n' roll era. Steve's biggest were *Party Doll*(a tamed rendition of Buddy Knox's rock 'n' roll No 1), Pretty Blue Eyes, Footsteps (which reached No 4 in Britain in 1960 and was his only solo UK biggie),*Portrait Of My Love*and Goffin & King's*Go Away, Little Girl*(a US No 1 smash in January '63). Under the Steve & Eydie billing, the couple achieved a UK Top Three smash in late '63 with another Goffin/King number,*I Want To Stay Here*. In 1964, with the Beatles revolution gathering momentum on both sides of the Atlantic, the pair were torpedoed out of the charts with their rapidly dating sound. But their cabaret style kept them in lucrative work on the concert and nightclub circuits and they regularly appeared on American TV. (Bob MacDonald, December 1985.).

FOOSTEPS
Tracks: / Footsteps.
7" Single: Released Apr '60, on H.M.V., by EMI Records. Deleted Apr '63. Catalogue no: **POP 726**

GIRLS GIRLS GIRLS
Tracks: / Girls, girls, girls.
7" Single: Released Aug '60, on London-American, Deleted Aug '63. Catalogue no: **HLT 9166**

Lawrence, Zack

ROCK REVOLUTION
Tracks: / Rock revolution / Interceptor boogie.
7" Single: Released 28 Jul '89, on Breakin', by Breakin' Records. Catalogue no: **7 BRK 8**

Lawrie, Edwina

BYE BYE LOVE
Tracks: / Bye bye love.
7" Single: Released Feb '83, on Springsong, Deleted '86. Catalogue no: **DAF 3**

DARK GLASSES
Tracks: / Dark glasses.
12" Single: Released Aug '84, on Panther, by MCA Records. Catalogue no: **PANT 6**
7" Single: Released Aug '84, on Panther, by MCA Records. Catalogue no: **PAN 6**

Laws, Debra

ON MY OWN
Tracks: / On my own / Long as we're together.
12" Single: Released May '81, on Elektra, by Elektra Records (UK). Deleted May '84. Catalogue no: **K 12529 T**

Laws, Eloise

LOVE FACTORY
Tracks: / Love factory.
7" Single: Released Jul '80, on Inferno (1), by Inferno Records. Catalogue no: **HEAT 15**
7" Single: Released Aug '83, on Inferno (1), by Inferno Records. Catalogue no: **HEAT 15**

Laws, Herbert

REDS (THEME FROM)
Tracks: / Reds (theme from) / Reds (theme from) (part 2).
7" Single: Released Mar '82, on CBS, by CBS Records. Deleted '85. Catalogue no; **A 2052**

Laws, Ronnie

Biographical details: Laws, Ronnie This American saxophonist, flautist, singer, songwriter and producer was briefly a member of Earth Wind & Fire during the early Seventies, and used that band's jazz influences when launching his solo career in 1975. Ronnie iss the younger brother of two other noted musicians, Hubert Laws and Eloise Laws. His first LP 1975's *Pressure Sensitive*, became the biggest selling debut album in the history of Blue Note Records; it was a smash on the Billboard jazz charts and reached No.73 on the US pop list. This, and Laws' other early albums were produced by Wayne Hendeson of Crusaders fame.
Laws never quite lived up to the success of *Pressure Sensitive*. He began producing himself in 1980, continuing to release polished and well crafted jazz funk records which achieved respectable US chart positions. He finally made his chart debut in Britain with October 1981's *Solid Ground* LP - this was listed on the UK Top 100 Albums chart for one week, at No.100! (Bob Macdonald 4/12/85).

ALWAYS THERE
Tracks: / Always there / Love is here / Goodtime ride.
12" Single: Released Mar '80, on Liberty (USA), by EMI Records. Deleted Mar '83. Catalogue no: **UP 36497**

EVERY GENERATION (SINGLE)
Tracks: / Every generation / O.T.B.A. law.
7" Single: Released May '80, on Liberty, by EMI Records. Deleted May '85. Catalogue no: **UP 626**
12" Single: Released May '80, on Liberty, by EMI Records. Deleted May '85. Catalogue no: **12UP 626**

STAY AWAKE
Tracks: / Stay awake / Heavy on easy.
12" Single: Released Sep '81, on United Artists, by EMI Records. Deleted '84. Catalogue no: **12UP 644**

THERE'S A WAY
Tracks: / There's a way / Your stuff / Always there.
7" Single: Released Jan '82, on United Artists, by EMI Records. Deleted Jan '85. Catalogue no: **UP 648**
12" Single: Released Jan '82, on United Artists, by EMI Records. Deleted Jan '85. Catalogue no: **12 UP 648**

YOUNG CHILD
Tracks: / Young child / Tomorrow.
7" Single: Released Feb '80, on Liberty, by EMI Records. Deleted Feb '85. Catalogue no: **UP 619**
12" Single: Released Feb '80, on Liberty, by EMI Records. Deleted Feb '85. Catalogue no: **12UP 619**

Lawson, Brenda

SWEET LOVE
Tracks: / Sweet love / Guts.
7" Single: Released Dec '82, on Rough Cutt, Catalogue no: **RCD 001**

Lawson, Dennis

ULTRA FANTASTICO
Tracks: / Ultra fantastico.
7" Single: Released Apr '84, on EMI, by EMI Records. Catalogue no: **EMI 5466**

Lawson, Tom

I'LL TAKE YOU HOME AGAIN KATHLEEN
Tracks: / I'll take you home again Kathleen.
7" Single: Released Aug '83, on Klub, by Klub Records. Catalogue no: **KLUB 40**

Lax

ALL MY LOVE (SINGLE)
Tracks: / All my love / Thanks but no thanks.
7" Single: Released Jan '81, on Epic, by CBS Records. Deleted Jan '84. Catalogue no: **EPC 9457**

POSSESSED
Tracks: / Possessed / Fight back.
7" Single: Released May '81, on Epic, by CBS Records. Deleted May '84. Catalogue no: **EPC A 1103**
12" Single: Released May '81, on Epic, by CBS Records. Deleted May '84. Catalogue no: **EPC 13 1103**

Lay Zee Muthas

CUT AND RUN
Tracks: / Cut and run.
12" Single: Released Apr '89, on Acid Jazz, by Acid Jazz Records. Catalogue no: **JAZID 011T**

Layne, Cynthia

STEALING LOVE
Tracks: / Stealing love.
12" Single: Released Mar '84, on Trindisc, by Trindisc Records. Catalogue no: **TRIN 009**

Laynie

DANCING IN THE SHADOWS
Tracks: / Dancing in the shadows / Dancing in the shadows (version).
7" Single: Released Dec '88, on Opium, by Opium Records. Catalogue no: **OPIN 26**
12" Single: Released Dec '88, on Opium, by Opium Records. Catalogue no: **OPINT 26**

LOVE BITES
Tracks: / Love bites / Love bites (instrumental).
7" Single: Released Jun '88, on Opium, by Opium Records. Catalogue no: **OPIN 25**
12" Single: Released Jun '88, on Opium, by Opium Records. Catalogue no: **OPINT 25**

Lazenby, Keith

KISS THE NIGHT GOODBYE
Tracks: / Kiss the night goodbye / Hearts.
7" Single: Released Aug '83, on AKA, Catalogue no: **AKA 105**

Lazlo & The Leopards

I CAN BE YOUR FRIEND
Tracks: / I can be your friend / 3 hours later.
7" Single: Released Jun '84, on Red Bus, by Red Bus Records. Catalogue no: **RBUS 91**

Lazlo, Viktor

BREATHLESS
Tracks: / Breathless / Don't say no.
7" Single: Released Aug '87, on Polydor, by Polydor Ltd. Catalogue no: **POSP 900**
12" Single: Released Aug '87, on Polydor, by Polydor Ltd. Catalogue no: **POSPX 833**

Lazy & Lisa

BAD YOUNG SISTERS
Tracks: / Bad young sisters.
12" Single: Released Jul '88, on Ahead Of Our Time, by Ahead of Our Time. Catalogue no: **CCUT 3**

Lazy Racer

JUMPING THE GUN
Tracks: / Jumping the gun / Beautiful loser.
7" Single: Released May '80, on A&M, by A&M Records. Deleted '83. Catalogue no: **AMS 7524**

L.B.W.

SOUL LIMBO
Tracks: / Soul limbo / What's your name.
12" Single: Released Jul '89, on Mango, by Island Records. Catalogue no: **12 MNG 717**
7" Single: Released Jul '89, on Mango, by Island Records. Catalogue no: **MNG 717**

LD Jam

RUDE BOYS GETTING FUNKY
Tracks: / Rude boys getting funky.
12" Single: Released Jul '89, on 1st Bass, Catalogue no: **RUFF 3**

Le Change

BACK SEAT
Tracks: / Back seat / Can't stop progress.
7" Single: Released Jun '82, on Carrere, Deleted Jun '85. Catalogue no: **CAR 244**

Le Griffe

FAST BIKES
Tracks: / Fast bikes / Where are you now / Actor, The.
7" Single: Released Jan '83, on Bullet, by Bullet Records. Deleted '88. Catalogue no: **BOL 1**
12" Single: Released Jan '83, on Bullet, by Bullet Records. Deleted '88. Catalogue no: **BOLT 1**

YOU'RE KILLING ME
Tracks: / You're killing me.
12" Single: Released Nov '83, on Bullet, by Bullet Records. Deleted '88. Catalogue no: **BOLT 7**
7" Single: Released Nov '83, on Bullet, by Bullet Records. Deleted '88. Catalogue no: **BOL 7**

Le Jete

LA CAGE AUX FOLLES
Tracks: / La cage aux folles.
7" Single: Released Dec '83, on Dance, Catalogue no: **7 SKIP 1**

Le Lu Lu

AFRICA
Tracks: / Africa / Fragile thing / Blip verts (Extra track on 12" version only.).
12" Single: Released Oct '86, on Possum, Catalogue no: **POST 1**
7" Single: Released Oct '86, on Possum, Catalogue no: **POS 1**

Le Mat

THOUGHTS OF THE FOOL
Tracks: / Thoughts of the fool / Ev'ry dream.
7" Single: Released Oct '82, on Whaam, Catalogue no: **WHAAM 08**

Le One

INCOMMUNIQUE
Tracks: / Incommunique.
12" Single: Released Nov '83, on Ricochet, Catalogue no: **RICT 1**
7" Single: Released Nov '83, on Ricochet, Catalogue no: **RIC 1**

Le Page

YOU CAN DO THE DANCIN'
Tracks: / You can do the dancin'.
7" Single: Released Oct '88, on Prism, by Prism Records. Catalogue no: **PS 2022**

Le Rock

LE ROCK

Tracks: / Le rock / Another bottle of wine.
7" Single: Released May '83, on OGP, Catalogue no: **OGP 001**

Lea, Jimmy

CITIZEN KANE
Tracks: / Citizen Kane.
7" Single: Released Nov '85, on Trojan, by Trojan Records. Deleted May '88. Catalogue no: **KANE 1**

Lea, Sandra

WHISPERING NIGHTS
Tracks: / Whispering nights / Empty town.
7" Single: Released Apr '81, on Rondercrest, by Rondercrest Records. Catalogue no: **ROND 6**

Leace

JILL THE GROOVE
Tracks: / Jill the groove.
12" Single: Released Aug '87, on Nine O Nine, by Creole Records. Catalogue no: **NINE 14**

League of Gentlemen

DISLOCATION
Tracks: / Dislocation / 1984.
7" Single: Released Mar '81, on Polydor, by Polydor Ltd. Deleted Mar '84. Catalogue no: **EGEDS 2**

HEPTAPARAPARSHINOKH
Tracks: / Heptaparaparshinokh / Marriagemuzic.
7" Single: Released Dec '80, on Polydor, by Polydor Ltd. Deleted Dec '85. Catalogue no: **EGEDS1**

Leahy, Geoff

1984
Tracks: / 1984 / Play it agian Sam.
7" Single: Released Mar '84, on K.Mosaic, Catalogue no: **MOSY 001**

Leandros, Vicky

Biographical details: Leandros, Vicky This Greek singer had not been regarded as an ambassador for her country in the same way as Nana Mouskouri or Demis Roussos have, mainly because she was raised in West Germany and won the Eurovision Song Contest for Luxembourg!
She was born in 1950 and cut her first record at the age of 15. By the time of her first Eurovision final in 1967 she was able to speak seven languages. Leaddros came fourth for Luxembourg that year and her recording of *Love Is Blue* was no great success - it was left to the French Orchestra of Paul Mauriat to make the tune an international smash.
After making a reasonable name for herself in various markets, particualarly Japan, Vicky was victorious in the 1972 Eurovision event with the dramatic *Apres Toi*. Europe; the English version was called *Come What May* and reached the UK No.2 spot. As with *Love Is Blue*, Leandros released her rendition in several different languages to suit different markets.
Like many Eurovision winners, the singer was unable to sustain her success. She carved out an adequate cabaret career, but never returned to the dizzy sales heights of *Apres Toi*. Her British follow ups included *The Love In Your Eyes* and *When Bouzoukis Played*, but neither climbed higher than No.40. However, Vicky certainly survived longer than Anne Marie David, the girl who gave Luxembourg a second consecutive Eurovision triumph in 1973 - David plunged into instant obscurity. (Bob Macdonald 4/12/85).

COME WHAT MAY
Tracks: / Come what may.
7" Single: Released Apr '72, on Philips, by Phonogram Ltd. Deleted Apr '75. Catalogue no: **6000 049**

LOVE IN YOUR EYES, THE
Tracks: / Love in your eyes.
7" Single: Released Dec '72, on Philips, by Phonogram Ltd. Deleted Dec '75. Catalogue no: **6000 081**

LOVE IS ALIVE (SINGLE)
Tracks: / Love is alive / Too many women.
7" Single: Released Apr '82, on Philips, by Phonogram Ltd. Deleted Apr '85. Catalogue no: **6005 166**

WHEN BOUZOUKIS PLAYED
Tracks: / When Bouzoukis played.
7" Single: Released Jul '73, on Philips, by Phonogram Ltd. Deleted Jul '76. Catalogue no: **6000 111**

Leanne

FANTASY
Tracks: / Fantasy / Fantasy (dub).
7" Single: Released Nov '82, on Statik, Catalogue no: **STAT 25**

LEATHERWOLF - HIDEAWAY (Released on Island)

Lear, Amanda

TIME'S UP/APHRODISIAC
Tracks: / Times up / Aphrodisiac.
12" Single: Released Apr '87, on Carrere, Catalogue no: **CART 409**

Learn Fi Dress

CUTTY BANKS
Tracks: / Cutty Banks.
12" Single: Released Mar '89, on Blue Mountain, Catalogue no: **BMD 053**

Learning Process

WHO KILLED CAROL
Tracks: / Who killed Carol.
12" Single: Released Jul '89, on Bucket, by Bucket Records. Catalogue no: **LEARN 001**

Leather Nun

506
Tracks: / 506.
12" Single: Released Jul '85, on Wire, by Wire Records. Catalogue no: **WRMS 005**

COOL SHOES
Tracks: / Cool shoes / I wish / Special agent (Only on 12" single.).
7" Single: Released Aug '87, on Wire, by Wire Records. Catalogue no: **WRS 016**
12" Single: Released Aug '87, on Wire, by Wire Records. Catalogue no: **WRMS 016**

DEMOLITION LOVE
Tracks: / Demolition love.
12" Single: Released Oct '88, on Wire, by Wire Records. Catalogue no: **WRM 021**

GIMME GIMME GIMME
Tracks: / Gimme gimme gimme / Lollipop / Gimme gimme gimme (chopper mix) (Extra track on 12" only.).
7" Single: Released May '86, on Wire, by Wire Records. Catalogue no: **WRS 009**
12" Single: Released May '86, on Wire, by Wire Records. Catalogue no: **WRMS 009**
12" Single: Released Oct '86, on Wire, by Wire Records. Catalogue no: **WRXS 009**

I CAN SMELL YOUR THOUGHTS
Tracks: / I can smell your thoughts (remix) / Falling apart / 506 (revisited).
7" Single: Released 23 May '87, on Wire, by Wire Records. Catalogue no: **WRMS 014**

LOST AND FOUND
Tracks: / Lost and found / Dance, dance, dance / Ride like a Cheyenne.
7" Single: Released Oct '87, on Wire, by Wire Records. Catalogue no: **WRS 020**
12" Single: Released Oct '87, on Wire, by Wire Records. Catalogue no: **WRMS 020**

NIGHT TRACKS EP
Tracks: / Night tracks.
12" Single: Released Oct '88, on Night Tracks, by Pinnacle Records. Catalogue no: **SFNT 014**

ON THE ROAD
Tracks: / On the road / Desolation avenue / Son of a good family (extra track on 12" version only).
7" Single: Released Feb '86, on Wire, by Wire Records. Catalogue no: **WRS 007**
12" Single: Released Feb '86, on Wire, by Wire Records. Catalogue no: **WRMS 007**

PINK HOUSE
Tracks: / Pink house / Speed of life / Lucky strike.
7" Single: Released Nov '86, on Wire, by Wire Records. Catalogue no: **WRMS 001**
12" Single: Released Nov '86, on Wire, by Wire Records. Catalogue no: **WRS 001**

PRIME MOVER
Tracks: / Prime mover / F.F.A.
7" Single: Released Jan '84, on Subterranean, Catalogue no: **SUB 40**
12" Single: Released Aug '86, on Wire, by Wire Records. Catalogue no: **WRMS 009**

SLOW DEATH
Tracks: / Slow death.
7" Single: Released May '84, on Criminal Damage, Catalogue no: **CRI 12113**

Leatherwolf

HIDEAWAY (see panel above)
Tracks: / Hide away / Too much / Rule the night (12" only).
CD 5": Released 17 Apr '89, on Island, by Island Records. Catalogue no: **CID 416**
12" Single: Released 7 Mar '89, on Island, by Island Records. Catalogue no: **12IS 416**
Special: Released Jun '89, on Island, by Island Records. Catalogue no: **ISS 416**
7" Single: Released 7 Mar '89, on Island, by Island Records. Catalogue no: **IS 416**
7" Single: Released May '89, on Island, by Island Records. Catalogue no: **ISP 416**

Leatherwood, Stu

SO TELL ME WHO'S CRAZY
Tracks: / So tell me who's crazy.
7" Single: Released Jun '85, on Tellybell, Catalogue no: **TVP 2**

Leblanc, Lenny

SOMEBODY SEND MY BABY HOME
Tracks: / Somebody send my baby home.
7" Single: Released May '81, on Capitol, by EMI Records. Deleted May '84. Catalogue no: **CL 16196**

Lecturer

BUCKLE UP
Tracks: / Buckle up.
12" Single: Released Oct '88, on Jammy's, Catalogue no: **VPRD 336**

D.J. FIND ME
Tracks: / D.J. find me.
12" Single: Released Nov '88, on Jammy's, Catalogue no: **VPRD 358**
12" Single: Released Nov '88, on Super Power, Catalogue no: **SPD 35**

IF A DJ WANT TEST
Tracks: / If a DJ want test.
12" Single: Released Dec '88, on Super Power, Catalogue no: **SPD 39**

Ledernacken

AMOK
Tracks: / Amok.
12" Single: Released Aug '87, on Strike Back, by Strike Back Records. Catalogue no: **SBR 2T**

BOOGALOO & OTHER NATTY DANCERS (SINGLE)
Tracks: / Boogaloo & other natty dancers.
12" Single: Released Mar '87, on Strike Back, by Strike Back Records. Catalogue no: **SBR 12T**

DRUMS OF MATUMBA
Tracks: / Drums of Matumba.
7" Single: Released Jun '85, on Strike Back, by Strike Back Records. Catalogue no: **SBR 7**

ICH WILL DICH ESSEN
Tracks: / Ich will dich Essen.
12" Single: Released Sep '84, on Strike Back, by Strike Back Records. Catalogue no: **SBR 4T**
7" Single: Released Sep '84, on Strike Back, by Strike Back Records. Catalogue no: **SBR 4**

I'M A DOG
Tracks: / I'm a dog.
12" Single: Released Aug '86, on Hit The Deck, Deleted '88. Catalogue no: **UNKNOWN**

LET YOURSELF GO
Tracks: / Let yourself go.
12" Single: Released May '88, on Strike Back, by Strike Back Records. Catalogue no: **SBR 16T**

MOCK & GULLEY
Tracks: / Mock & gulley / Amock / Rhythmus / Rausch.
12" Single: Released Feb '84, on Empire Records, Catalogue no: **FBR 2T**

SHIMMY & SHAKE
Tracks: / Shimmy shake / Money / Real treat.
12" Single: Released Jan '86, on Strike Back, by Strike Back Records. Catalogue no: **SBR 8T**

WHEELIN' & DEALIN'
Tracks: / Wheelin' & dealin'.
12" Single: Released Mar '89, on Deutschland Strikeback, Catalogue no: **SBR 26 T**
CD 5": Released Mar '89, on Deutschland Strikeback, Catalogue no: **SBR 26 CD**

Ledin, Tomas

NEVER AGAIN
Tracks: / Never again / Just for the fun.
7" Single: Released Oct '82, on Epic, by CBS Records. Catalogue no: **EPC A 2824**

NOT BAD AT ALL
Tracks: / Not bad at all / You've got to be kidding.
7" Single: Released Jan '80, on Epic, by CBS Records. Deleted Jan '85. Catalogue no: **EPC 8079**

RIGHT NOW
Tracks: / Right now / It's sure worth giving a try.
7" Single: Released Apr '80, on Epic, by CBS Records. Deleted Apr '83. Catalogue no: **EPC 8522**

WHAT ARE YOU DOING TONIGHT
Tracks: / What are you doing tonight / Living with the bomb.
12" Single: Released Jul '83, on Epic, by CBS Records. Catalogue no: **TA 3540**

Lee, Adrian

BLONDES AREN'T FAIR
Tracks: / Blondes aren't fair / Rich boy.
7" Single: Released Jun '82, on DJM, Deleted Jun '85. Catalogue no: **DJS 10987**

NEON, NEON
Tracks: / Neon, neon / Bodybuilding.
7" Single: Released Jan '81, on DJM, Deleted Jan '84. Catalogue no: **DJS 10962**

Lee, Albert

HUNT THEM
Tracks: / Hunt them / Have you heard the news.
7" Single: Released Feb '81, on A&M, by A&M Records. Deleted '84. Catalogue no: **AMS 8108**

RADIO GIRLS
Tracks: / Radio girls / Your boys.
7" Single: Released Jun '82, on Polydor, by Polydor Ltd. Deleted Jun '85. Catalogue no: **POSP 434**

Lee, Alvin

I DON'T WANNA STOP
Tracks: / I don't wanna stop / Heartache.
7" Single: Released Aug '81, on Avatar, by Avatar Record Corporation. Catalogue no: **AAA 106**

NUTBUSH CITY LIMITS
Tracks: / Nutbush City Limits.
7" Single: Released Mar '82, on Avatar, by Avatar Record Corporation. Catalogue no: **AAA 122**

ROCK'N'ROLL GUITAR PICKER

Tracks: / Rock 'n' roll guitar picker.
7" Single: Released Dec '81, on Avatar, by Avatar Record Corporation. Catalogue no: **AAA 117**

TAKE THE MONEY
Tracks: / Take the money / No more lonely nights.
7" Single: Released Aug '81, on Avatar, by Avatar Record Corporation. Catalogue no: **AAA 109**

Lee, Benny

WHISPERING GRASS (OLD GOLD) (See under Carless, Dorothy)
Tracks: / Whispering grass.
7" Single: Released Oct '83, on Old Gold, by Old Gold Records. Deleted Jun '89. Catalogue no: **OG 9383**

Lee, Brenda

Biographical details: Lee, Brenda This American singer was born Brenda Mae Tarpley in Atlanta, Georgia in December 1944. She was a real child prodigy, starting to sing almost before she could speak. Brenda was just six years old when she won a local talent contest. By the age of eight, she had become a regular performer on Atlanta radio and television programmes. By the time Brenda made her first record in Nashville in July 1956, she had appeared on many of America's leading network TV shows, including those hosted by Perry Como, Steve Allen and Ed Sullivan.
Lee's early records were not successful, but a 1959 season in Paris sparked off much interest in showbusiness circles and comparisons with Judy Garland were invoked. The disc that made her a major star was *Sweet Nothin's* a rock'n'roll belter that cruised to No.4 on both sides of the Atlantic in early 1960. It was followed by the ballad *I'm Sorry* which reached No.1 in America and No.12 in Britain. These two hits clearly demonstrated that a versatile and exciting young performer had been discovered. By the time she celebrated her 16th birthday, *Little Miss Dynamite*, as she was dubbed, had chalked up her second US No.1 smash with *I Want To Be Wanted*.
Between 1960 and 1964 Brenda achieved a formidable string of Top 20 singles in both the US and UK. In terms of energy and verve, she was like a junior Connie Francis; but whereas Francis tended to veer close to middle of the road material, Lee was nearer to country and rock'n'roll.
After the pop hits dried up in the mid-sixties, Lee returned to her country and western roots. She has remained active in that market ever since, scoring the occasional big hit on the American country charts and continuing to tour. She appeared at the 1985 Country Music Festival in Wembley, London. (Bob Macdonald 4/12/85).

ALL ALONE AM I (SINGLE)
Tracks: / All alone am I.
7" Single: Released Jan '63, on Brunswick, by Decca Records. Deleted Jan '66. Catalogue no: **05882**

AS USUAL
Tracks: / As usual.
7" Single: Released '80, on MCA, by MCA Records. Catalogue no: **LR 3228**
7" Single: Released Jan '64, on Brunswick, by Decca Records. Deleted Jan '67. Catalogue no: **05899**

BREAK IT TO ME GENTLY
Tracks: / Break it to me gently.
7" Single: Released Feb '62, on Brunswick, by Decca Records. Deleted Feb '65. Catalogue no: **05864**

CHRISTMAS WILL BE JUST ANOTHER LONELY DAY
Tracks: / Christmas will be just another lonely day.
7" Single: Released Dec '64, on Brunswick, by Decca Records. Deleted Dec '67. Catalogue no: **05921**

DUM DUM
Tracks: / Dum dum.
7" Single: Released Jul '61, on Brunswick, by Decca Records. Deleted Jul '63. Catalogue no: **05854**

EMOTIONS
Tracks: / Emotions.
7" Single: Released Apr '61, on Brunswick, by Decca Records. Deleted Apr '64. Catalogue no: **05847**

FOOL NUMBER ONE
Tracks: / Fool number one.
7" Single: Released Nov '61, on Brunswick, by Decca Records. Deleted Nov '64. Catalogue no: **05860**

HERE COMES THAT FEELING (SINGLE)
Tracks: / Here comes that feeling.
7" Single: Released Jun '62, on Brunswick, by Decca Records. Deleted Jun '65. Catalogue no: **05871**

I WANT TO BE WANTED
Tracks: / I want to be wanted.
7" Single: Released Oct '60, on Brunswick, by Decca Records. Deleted Oct '63. Catalogue no: **05839**

I WONDER
Tracks: / I wonder.
7" Single: Released Jul '63, on Brunswick, by Decca Records. Deleted Jul '66. Catalogue no: **05891**

I'M SORRY
Tracks: / I'm sorry.
7" Single: Released Jun '60, on Brunswick, by Decca Records. Deleted Jun '63. Catalogue no: **05833**

I'M SORRY (OLD GOLD)
Tracks: / Im sorry.
7" Single: Released Jul '82, on Old Gold, by Old Gold Records. Catalogue no: **OG 9163**

IS IT TRUE
Tracks: / Is it true.
7" Single: Released Sep '64, on Brunswick, by Decca Records. Deleted Sep '67. Catalogue no: **05915**

IT STARTED ALL OVER AGAIN
Tracks: / It started all over again.
7" Single: Released Sep '62, on Brunswick, by Decca Records. Deleted Sep '65. Catalogue no: **05876**

LET'S JUMP THE BROOMSTICK
Tracks: / Let's jump the broomstick.
7" Single: Released Jan '61, on Brunswick, by Decca Records. Deleted Apr '61. Catalogue no: **05823**

LOSING YOU
Tracks: / Losing you.
7" Single: Released Mar '63, on Brunswick, by Decca Records. Deleted Mar '66. Catalogue no: **05886**

ROCKIN' AROUND THE CHRISTMAS TREE
Tracks: / Rockin' around the Christmas tree / Bill Bailey.
7" Single: Released Nov '80, on MCA, by MCA Records. Deleted '83. Catalogue no: **MCA 556**
7" Single: Released Nov '62, on Brunswick, by Decca Records. Deleted Nov '65. Catalogue no: **05880**

SPEAK TO ME PRETTY
Tracks: / Speak to me pretty.
7" Single: Released Apr '62, on Brunswick, by Decca Records. Deleted Apr '65. Catalogue no: **05867**

SWEET IMPOSSIBLE YOU
Tracks: / Sweet impossible you.
7" Single: Released Oct '63, on Brunswick, by Decca Records. Deleted Oct '66. Catalogue no: **05896**

SWEET NOTHIN'S
Tracks: / Sweet nothin's.
7" Single: Released Mar '60, on Brunswick, by Decca Records. Deleted Mar '63. Catalogue no: **05819**

SWEET NOTHIN'S (OLD GOLD)
Tracks: / Sweet nothin's.
7" Single: Released Jul '82, on Old Gold, by Old Gold Records. Catalogue no: **OG 9162**

THANKS A LOT
Tracks: / Thanks a lot.
7" Single: Released Feb '65, on Brunswick, by Decca Records. Deleted Feb '68. Catalogue no: **05927**

THINK
Tracks: / Think.
7" Single: Released Apr '64, on Brunswick, by Decca Records. Deleted Apr '67. Catalogue no: **05903**

TOO MANY RIVERS
Tracks: / Too many rivers.
7" Single: Released Jul '65, on Brunswick, by Decca Records. Deleted Jul '68. Catalogue no: **05936**

Lee, Bruce

DIBI DIBI GIRL
Tracks: / Dibi dibi girl.
7" Single: Released Jun '88, on Yammie Music, Catalogue no: **YM 011**

Lee, Byron

FEELING IT-SOFT MAN
Tracks: / Feeling it, soft man.
12" Single: Released Jun '84, on Dynamic, Catalogue no: **DYN 1216**

HOT HOT HOT
Tracks: / Hot hot hot / Rasta chick / Six million dollar man.
12" Single: Released Aug '84, on Dynamic, Catalogue no: **DYN 1213**

SOCA GIRL (SINGLE)
12" Single: Released Jan '86, on Dynamic, Catalogue no: **D 191**

SWEET SOCA JAM
Tracks: / Sweet soca jam.
12" Single: Released Oct '88, on Dynamic, Catalogue no: **DY 203**

TINY WINEY
Tracks: / Tiny winey.
12" Single: Released Jan '85, on Dynamic, Catalogue no: **DYN 1217**
7" Single: Released Jan '85, on Dynamic, Catalogue no: **DYN 17**

Lee, Chris

THOUGHTS
Tracks: / Thoughts / Play hard.
7" Single: Released Oct '88, on Kunzel, by Gemini Enterprises. Catalogue no: **KUN 1**

Lee, Christy

BEST OF THE WOMAN IN ME
Tracks: / Best of the woman in me / T.C.L.B..
7" Single: Released Mar '80, on President, by President Records. Deleted Mar '83. Catalogue no: **PT 478**

Lee, Curtis

Biographical details: Lee, Curtis This American singer and songwriter was born in Yuma, Arizona and came to brief fame in 1961 as one of many young would be teen idols whose appeal was based as much on looks as on vocal talent. His two best known singles were *Pretty Little Angel Eyes* (No.7 in US, No.47 in UK - featuring vocal back up from bassman Arthur Crier and the Halos) and the less successful *Under The Moon of ove.* Both were good time uptempo pop records.
Unfortunately for Lee's immortality prospects, he is remembered by historians because of the other people who were associated with his hits, rather than on his own account: both tracks were early production successess for the legendary Phil Spector; and both became UK smashes in the late Seventies for th rock'n'roll revival group Showaddywaddy, *Under The Moon o Love* going all the way to No.1. (Bob Macdonald 4/12/85).

PRETTY LITTLE ANGEL EYES (SINGLE)
Tracks: / Pretty little angel eyes.
7" Single: Released Aug '61, on London-American, Deleted Aug '64. Catalogue no: **HLX 9397**

UNDER THE MOON OF LOVE
Tracks: / Under the moon of love / Pretty little angel eyes.
7" Single: Released Aug '84, on Revival, Catalogue no: **CR 219**
7" Single: Released Jun '81, on Revival, Catalogue no: **REV 6005**

Lee, Darrell

SEXY
Tracks: / Sexy (dance mix) / Sexy (radio edit & bonus mix).
12" Single: Released 18 May '89, on GEMC, Catalogue no: **12 PO 19**

Lee, Dee C

COME HELL OR WATERS HIGH
Tracks: / Come hell or waters high / I don't miss.
7" Single: Released Feb '86, on CBS, by CBS Records. Catalogue no: **A 6869**
12" Single: Released Feb '86, on CBS, by CBS Records. Catalogue no: **TA 6869**

HEY WHAT'D YA SAY
Tracks: / Hey what'd ya say / Selina wow wow.
7" Single: Released Jul '86, on CBS, by CBS Records. Catalogue no: **A 7294**
12" Single: Released Jul '86, on CBS, by CBS Records. Catalogue no: **TA 7294**

HOLD ON
Tracks: / Hold on / Welcome.
7" Single: Released May '86, on CBS, by CBS Records. Deleted '86. Catalogue no: **A 7179**
12" Single: Released May '86, on CBS, by CBS Records. Deleted '86. Catalogue no: **TA 7179**

SEE THE DAY
Tracks: / See the day.
7" Single: Released Nov '85, on CBS, by CBS Records. Deleted Nov '88. Catalogue no: **A 6570**

SELINA WOW WOW
Tracks: / Selina wow wow / Hey what do you say.
7" Single: Released Feb '84, on CBS, by CBS Records. Catalogue no: **A 4192**
12" Single: Released Feb '84, on CBS, by CBS Records. Catalogue no: **TA 4192**

YIPPEE-YI-YAY
Tracks: / Yippee-I-ay / Space and time.
12" Single: Released May '84, on CBS, by CBS Records. Catalogue no: **TA 4377**
7" Single: Released May '84, on CBS, by CBS Records. Catalogue no: **A 4377**

Lee, Des Band

DANCE DANCE DANCE
Tracks: / Dance, dance, dance.
7" Single: Released Oct '81, on Mint, by Emerald Records. Deleted '88. Catalogue no: **CHEW 54**

Lee, Dicky

I SAW LINDA YESTERDAY
Tracks: / I saw Linda yesterday / For quite a while.
7" Single: Released Jan '87, on Pinner, Catalogue no: **PRM 903**

Lee, Frankie

IT AIN'T HIM BABE
Tracks: / It ain't him babe / Birmingham.
7" Single: Released Sep '81, on Blue Velvet, Deleted '84. Catalogue no: **ZIM 100**

Lee, General

WHITE ON WHITE
Tracks: / White on white / Twenty flight rock.
7" Single: Released Jun '81, on Revolver, by FM-Revolver Records. Deleted Jun '84. Catalogue no: **REV 6**

Lee, George

SEA SHELLS
Tracks: / Sea shells.
12" Single: Released Sep '84, on Ebusia, Catalogue no: **EB 001**

Lee, Greg

GOT U ON MY MIND
Tracks: / Got u on my mind.
7" Single: Released Apr '89, on Big Shot, Catalogue no: **BR 130035**

Lee, Hubert

DON'T HIDE YOUR LOVE
Tracks: / Don't hide your love.
12" Single: Released Feb '89, on Claypot, Catalogue no: **PHD 0041**

Lee, Jack

HANGING ON THE TELEPHONE
Tracks: / Hanging on the telephone.
7" Single: Released Sep '82, on Disclexia, Catalogue no: **DXL 002**

Lee, Jacky

Biographical details: Lee, Jacky. This British female singer enjoyed two isolated UK hit singles in 1968 and 1971, both of them themes to children's TV series. The evocative *White Horses* reached No.10 and *Rupert* (singing the praises of the cartoon bear character) climbed to No.14. The latter logged an impressive total of 17 weeks on the UK top 50. On the former single the artist was billed as Jacky.
She is not to be confused with an American male vocalist called Jackie Lee, who achieved a US Top 20 hit in 1966 with *The Duck* he was better known as Earl, 50% of the Bob & Earl duo. (Bob Macdonald 4/12/85).

RUPERT
Tracks: / Rupert / Going to the circus.
7" Single: Released Dec '85, on PRT, by Castle Communications Records. Catalogue no: **7P 337**
7" Single: Released Jan '71, on Pye, Deleted Jan '74. Catalogue no: **7N 45003**

Lee, Johnny

DALLAS (MAIN THEME)
Tracks: / Dallas (Dallas dreams), Theme from / Dallas (Dallas dreams), Theme from / Loneliness in Lucy's eyes (the life Sue Ellen is living).
7" Single: Released Jan '86, on Warner Bros., by WEA Records. Catalogue no: **W 8817**

LOOKING FOR LOVE
Tracks: / Looking for love / Lyin' eyes.
7" Single: Released Aug '80, on Asylum, by WEA Records. Deleted '83. Catalogue no: **K 79153**

Lee, Katrina

BORN TOO LATE
Tracks: / Born too late / Fell into love.
7" Single: Released Jul '86, on Epic, by CBS Records. Catalogue no: **A 7300**
12" Single: Released Jul '86, on Epic, by CBS Records. Catalogue no: **TA 7300**

Lee, Laura

RIP OFF (SINGLE)
Tracks: / Rip off.
7" Single: Released Jun '84, on HDH (Holland/Dozier/Holland), by Demon Records. Catalogue no: **HDH 453**

Lee, Leapy

Biographical details: Lee, Leapy This British singer and actor was born Lee Gra-

ham in Eastbourne, Sussex in 1942. He got involved in amateur dramatics at school and, after leaving school at the age of 15, quickly developed a promising acting career at the London Palladium, The Prince's Theatre and on the television programme 'State Your Case'.
However, his showbusiness life did not quite blossom in the intended manner. Leapy Lee's only subsequent significant contribution to the entertainment world was his 1968 single *Little Arrows* - this highly commercial pop offering reached No.2 in Britain and loggd 21 weeks on the Uk charts; it peaked at No.16 in the States. *Little Arrows* was the first big break for the successful songwriting team of Albert Hammond & Mike Hazelwood; it was produced by Gordon Mills, who was more famous for managing Tom Jones and Engelbert Humperdinck.
Leapy Lee achieved one smaller UK hit - *Good Morning* which reached No.29 in early 1970 - before fading into obscurity. (Bob Macdonald 4/12/85).

GOOD MORNING
Tracks: / Good morning.
7" Single: Released Dec '69, on MCA, by MCA Records. Deleted Dec '72. Catalogue no: **MK 5021**

LITTLE ARROWS
Tracks: / Little arrows.
7" Single: Released Aug '68, on MCA, by MCA Records. Deleted Aug '71. Catalogue no: **MU 1028**

LITTLE ARROWS (OLD GOLD)
Tracks: / Little arrows.
7" Single: Released Jul '82, on Old Gold, by Old Gold Records. Deleted Nov '88. Catalogue no: **OG 9169**

Lee, Linford

MOTHER NATURE PLANNED IT SO
Tracks: / Mother nature planned it.
12" Single: Released Jun '82, on Regal, Catalogue no: **RD 011**

Lee, Maggie

RUNAROUND
Tracks: / Runaround.
7" Single: Released Jun '84, on CBS, by CBS Records. Catalogue no: **A 4343**

Lee, Miriam

MEN IN MY LIFE, THE
Tracks: / Men in my life.
12" Single: Released Sep '85, on Passion, by Skratch Records. Catalogue no: **PASH 48(12)**
7" Single: Released Sep '85, on Passion, by Skratch Records. Catalogue no: **PASH 48**

Lee, Peggy

Biographical details: Lee, Peggy This American singer, songwriter and film star was born Norma Egstrom in Jamestown, North Dakota. She began her professional career in 1938 at the age of 18, working in a Hollywood nightclub and singing with a big band. Her first big break occurred in 1941, when she joined Benny Goodman as a resident vocalist. After two years with the famous bandleader who was known as the King of Swing, she took temporary retirement from showbusiness in 1943 before commencing her own recording career.
Lee's first smash hit was *Manana*, which she co-wrote with guitarist/arranger/conductor Dave Barbour; this was one of America's biggest sellers of 1948. During the late Forties and early Fifties,when popular middle of the road singers were in their element, Lee established herself as a major star. She made her movie debut in 1951's 'Mr Music' with Bing Crosby and followed it with further hit discs like *Lover* and *This Is a Very Special Day*. After turning in an acclaimed performance in the film 'Pete Kelly's Blues' (1955), also helped to score the 1956 movie 'The Lady and the Tramp'. Peggy's rendition of the theme from the show *Mr Wonderful* (also '56) reached No.14 on the US charts and might have gone higher were it not for two other competing versions, which also made the Top 20; in Britain where she had no such competition, Lee climbed to No.5 with the song in 1957. Successfully holding her own in the face of the rock'n'roll phenomenon, she reached the Top 10 on both sides of the Atlantic with her inventive 1958 single *Fever*. In 1960 the singer enjoyed a big UK hit album with *Latin a la Lee*.
Lee faded from the record charts during the Sixties, save for a US No.11 hit with 1969's engaging and memorable *Is That All There Is*. She remained an active live performer, however, throughout the Seventies and into the Eighties. (Bob Macdonald 5/12/85).

FEVER
Tracks: / Fever.
7" Single: Released Feb '85, on EMI Golden 45's, by EMI Records. Catalogue no: **G 4538**
7" Single: Released Apr '83, on EMI (France), by EMI Records. Catalogue no: **2C 008 83378**
7" Single: Released Jul '84, on EMI (Holland), by EMI Records. Catalogue no: **1A 006 81169**

FEVER (2)
Tracks: / Fever.
7" Single: Released Aug '58, on Capitol, by EMI Records. Deleted Aug '61. Catalogue no: **CL 14902**

I DON'T WANT TO PLAY IN YOUR YARD
Tracks: / I don't want to play in your yard / Black coffee.
7" Single: Released Jun '82, on MCA, by MCA Records. Deleted Jun '85. Catalogue no: **MCA 782**

IS THAT ALL THERE IS?
Tracks: / Is that all there is?.
7" Single: Released Jul '84, on Capitol (Holland), by EMI Records. Catalogue no: **1A 006 80182**

MR. WONDERFUL
Tracks: / Mr. Wonderful.
7" Single: Released May '57, on Brunswick, by Decca Records. Deleted May '60. Catalogue no: **05671**

TILL THERE WAS YOU
Tracks: / Till there was you.
7" Single: Released Mar '61, on Capitol, by EMI Records. Deleted Mar '64. Catalogue no: **CL 15184**

Lee, Robert

LOVE ME STYLEE
Tracks: / Love me stylee.
12" Single: Released Jul '88, on Live & Love, Catalogue no: **LLD 84**

MIDNIGHT HOUR
Tracks: / Midnight hour.
12" Single: Released Jun '89, on Unity, Catalogue no: **FEA 016**

Lee Roth, David

JUST LIKE PARADISE
Tracks: / Just like paradise / Bottom line, The.
12" Single: Released Feb '88, on Warner Bros., by WEA Records. Catalogue no: **W 8119T**
7" Single: Released Feb '88, on Warner Bros., by WEA Records. Catalogue no: **W 8119**

Lee, Rude

TRUE PRINCESS
Tracks: / True princess.
12" Single: Released Nov '88, on Nubian, Catalogue no: **NRT 07**

Lee, Shako

CALL ME ANGEL
Tracks: / Call me angel.
12" Single: Released Jun '88, on Fashion, by Fashion Records. Catalogue no: **FAD 059**

Lee, Tippa

DIBI DIBI SOUND
Tracks: / Dibi dibi sound / Dibi dibi dub.
Note: Produced in Kingston Jamaica by Barry Clarke. Arranged by Carl Ayton & Gibby Morrison.
12" Single: Released May '88, on CSA, by CSA Records. Catalogue no: **12CSA 515**

Lee, Toney

Biographical details: Lee, Toney This American singer achieved a one off UK chart entry in early 1983, reaching No.64 with his dancefloor single *Reach Out*. *Love So Deep* failed to repeat the success and Lee remained relatively unknown on both sides of the Atlantic. (Bob Macdonald 5/12/85).

LOVE SO DEEP
Tracks: / Love so deep.
7" Single: Released Aug '83, on Design Communications, Catalogue no: **DEST 2**

REACH OUT
Tracks: / Reach out.

7" Single: Released Jan '83, on T.M.T., by T.M.T. Productions. Deleted '87. Catalogue no: **TMT 2**
12" Single: Released Jan '83, on T.M.T., by T.M.T. Productions. Deleted '87. Catalogue no: **TMTT 2**

Leeds United FC

LEEDS UNITED
Tracks: / Leeds United.
7" Single: Released Apr '72, on Chapter One, Deleted Apr '75. Catalogue no: **SCH 168**

Leek, Andde

DANCING QUEEN
Tracks: / Dancing queen / Woolfson Hall / Soul darling.
12" Single: Released May '84, on Fascination, Catalogue no: **FASX 602**
7" Single: Released May '84, on Fascination, Catalogue no: **FAS 602**

SOUL DANCING
Tracks: / Soul dancing.
12" Single: Released Oct '83, on Fascination, Catalogue no: **FASX 601**
7" Single: Released Oct '83, on Fascination, Catalogue no: **FAS 601**

Leek, Andy

HOLDIN' ON TO YOU
Tracks: / Holdin' on to you / Sailor song.
7" Single: Released Feb '89, on WEA, by WEA Records. Catalogue no: **A 8997**
12" Single: Released Feb '89, on WEA, by WEA Records. Catalogue no: **A 8997T**
CD 5": Released Feb '89, on WEA, by WEA Records. Catalogue no: **A 899CD**

PLEASE, PLEASE
Tracks: / Please please / Entangled hearts.
12" Single: Released Aug '88, on Atlantic, by WEA Records. Catalogue no: **A 9054 T**
7" Single: Released 30 Aug '88, on Atlantic, by WEA Records. Catalogue no: **A 9054**

Leer, Thomas

Biographical details: Thomas Leer grew up in Port Glasgow and started singing in local groups when he was 14 and somehow managed to dip into almost every conceivable style. In the mid-seventies he broke away from this dizzying circle of bands to become the wandering minstrel. When punk burst out he came down to London, forming a band called Pressure. After that he started to plan his first single. *Private plane* was eventually released on his own Oblique label, a name now resurrected for his Arista releases. Through his use of DIY technology, drum machines and synths etc. there are those that would conveniently push him into the electronic file, but this has never met with his approval. Lyrically there's a fascination with the unaccountable power of big business and syndicated crime. His first single for Arista *International* was significantly also the name of the B-side on his debut release back in 1978. (Arista).

4 MOVEMENTS (EP)
Tracks: / 4 movements.
12" Single: Released Jul '81, on Cherry Red, by Cherry Red Records. Catalogue no: **12 CHERRY 28**

ALL ABOUT YOU
Tracks: / All about you / Saving Grace.
7" Single: Released Nov '82, on Cherry Red, by Cherry Red Records. Deleted '87. Catalogue no: **CHERRY 52**
12" Single: Released Nov '82, on Cherry Red, by Cherry Red Records. Catalogue no: **12 CHERRY 52**

HEARTBEAT
Tracks: / Heartbeat / Control yourself.
12" Single: Released Mar '85, on Oblique, Catalogue no: **LEER 222**
7" Single: Released Feb '85, on Arista, by BMG Records (UK). Catalogue no: **LEER 2**
12" Single: Released Feb '85, on Arista, by BMG Records (UK). Catalogue no: **LEER 122**

INTERNATIONAL
Tracks: / International / Easy way.
7" Single: Released Jul '84, on Oblique, Catalogue no: **LEER 1**
7" Pic: Released Jul '84, on Oblique, Catalogue no: **LERPD 121**
12" Single: Released Jul '84, on Oblique, Catalogue no: **LEER 121**

NO.1
Tracks: / No.1.
12" Single: Released May '85, on Arista, by BMG Records (UK). Catalogue no: **LEER 3T**
7" Single: Released May '85, on Arista, by BMG Records (UK). Catalogue no: **LEER 3**

Lees, Ian 'Sludge'

CAN YOU DO THE BOOGIE
Tracks: / Can you do the boogie / New hand jive.
7" Single: Released Jan '83, on Swoop, Catalogue no: **RTL 005**

VIVA ENGLAND
Tracks: / Viva England.
7" Single: Released Mar '82, on Lismor, by Lismor Records. Deleted '88. Catalogue no: **LISP 2007**

Lees, Peter

DULCIMER
Tracks: / Dulcimer.
7" EP: Released Jan '81, on Goat Bag, by Goat Bag Records. Catalogue no: **GB 002**

Leesha Paradise

STAND BY ME
Tracks: / Stand by me.
7" Single: Released Sep '82, on President, by President Records. Catalogue no: **PT 507**

Leeson & Vale

LIKE A GOOD GIRL SHOULD
Tracks: / Like a good girl should / Mankiller.
7" Single: Released Sep '80, on RCA, by BMG Records (UK). Deleted Sep '83. Catalogue no: **PB 5275**

Lefevre, Raymond

SOUL COAXING
Tracks: / Soul coaxing.
7" Single: Released May '68, on Major Minor, Deleted May '71. Catalogue no: **MM 559**

Left Banke

AND ONE DAY
Tracks: / And one day.
7" Single: Released Jun '88, on Bam Caruso, by Demon Records. Catalogue no: **NRIC 041**

WALK AWAY RENEE (SINGLE)
Tracks: / Walk away Renee.
12" Single: Released Jun '88, on Bam Caruso, by Demon Records. Catalogue no: **PABL 036**
7" Single: Released Feb '84, on Bam Caruso, by Demon Records. Catalogue no: **NRIC 022**
7" Single: Released 8 Nov '88, on Bam Caruso, by Demon Records. Catalogue no: **OPRA 023**

Left Hand Side

JIMMY JIMMY JIMMY
Tracks: / Jimmy Jimmy Jimmy / Hustler.
7" Single: Released Aug '84, on Raffia, Deleted '87. Catalogue no: **BREAK 147**

Leftovers

KAISER BILLS' BATMAN
Tracks: / Kaiser Bill's batman.
7" Single: Released Nov '80, on Plaza Plastic Co, Deleted '83. Catalogue no: **ZAP 2**

Lefturno

OUT OF SIGHT
Tracks: / Out of sight.
7" Single: Released Mar '84, on MCA, by MCA Records. Catalogue no: **MCA 874**
12" Single: Released Mar '84, on MCA, by MCA Records. Catalogue no: **MCAT 874**

Legacy

DON'T WASTE THE NIGHT
Tracks: / Don't waste the night.
12" Single: Released Jun '85, on Epic, by CBS Records. Catalogue no: **TA 6407**
7" Single: Released Jun '85, on Epic, by CBS Records. Catalogue no: **A 6407**

GUILTY
Tracks: / Guilty / Guilty (inst).
7" Single: Released Mar '87, on EMI, by EMI Records. Deleted Jul '87. Catalogue no: **EMI 5586**
12" Single: Released Mar '87, on EMI, by EMI Records. Deleted Jul '87. Catalogue no: **12EMI 5586**

Legacy Of Lies

SACRIFICE THE QUEEN
Tracks: / Sacrifice the Queen / It's not really a revolution.
Note: Free 7" & poster.
12" Single: Released Nov '86, on Quiet, by Quiet Records. Catalogue no: **QST 017**

YOU & WHOSE ARMY?
Tracks: / You and whose army?.
12" Single: Released Jun '86, on Quiet, by Quiet Records. Catalogue no: **QST 013**

Legandary Hearts

IN A WORLD LIKE THIS
Tracks: / In a world like this.
12" Single: Released Apr '88, on Surfin Pict, Catalogue no: **SP 003 - 12**

Legato

BUTTERCUP
Tracks: / Buttercup.
12" Single: Released Jun '85, on Adelphi (1), Catalogue no: **ADET 002**

FOOL FOR YOUR LOVE
Tracks: / Fool for your love / I care.
12" Single: Released Apr '82, on Ital, by Ital Records. Catalogue no: **ITE 0011**

HELLO LOVE
Tracks: / Hello love.
12" Single: Released Dec '82, on Sanity,

Catalogue no: **STY 004**

IT'S A SHAME
Tracks: / It's a shame.
7" Single: Released Jun '83, on Sanity, Catalogue no: **STYS 005**
12" Single: Released Jun '83, on Sanity, Catalogue no: **STY 005**

LATELY
Tracks: / Lately.
12" Single: Released Mar '82, on Santic, Catalogue no: **SAN 0021**

Legator

HUMAN BEINGS
Tracks: / Human beings / Human beings (long version).
7" Single: Released Sep '82, on Focus, Deleted '85. Catalogue no: **FOS 4**
7" Single: Released May '82, on V-Tone, Deleted '85. Catalogue no: **VTONE 007**

Legear

CRASHIN' DOWN
Tracks: / Crashin' down / Hold me tonight.
12" Single: Released Mar '85, on Proto, by Proto Records. Catalogue no: **ENAT 124**
7" Single: Released Mar '85, on Proto, by Proto Records. Catalogue no: **ENA 124**

ONE BAD APPLE
Tracks: / One bad apple / Freeze.
7" Single: Released Jul '88, on Saturday, by Nightmare Records. Catalogue no: **7SDY 4**
12" Single: Released Jul '88, on Saturday, by Nightmare Records. Catalogue no: **SDY 4**

Legend

73 IN 83
Tracks: / 73 in 83.
7" Single: Released '88, on Creation, by Creation Records. Deleted Jul '88. Catalogue no: **CRE 001**

BALLAD, THE
Tracks: / Ballad, The.
7" Single: Released Jun '87, on Constrictor, by Constrictor Records (Germany). Catalogue no: **COLL 004**

DEATH IN THE NURSERY
Tracks: / Death in the nursey.
7" Single: Released Sep '82, on Workshop, Catalogue no: **WR 3477**

DESTROYS THE BLUES
Tracks: / Destroys the blue.
7" Single: Released Oct '84, on Creation, by Creation Records. Deleted Jul '88. Catalogue no: **CRE 010**

EVERYTHING'S COMING UP ROSES
Tracks: / Everything's coming up roses.
12" Single: Released Jul '86, on Vinyl Drip, by Vinyl Drip Records. Catalogue no: **DRIP 5**

SOME OF US STILL BURN
Tracks: / Some of us still burn.
12" Single: Released Sep '85, on Vinyl Drip, by Vinyl Drip Records. Catalogue no: **DRIP 1**

STEP ASIDE
Tracks: / Step aside.
12" Single: Released 22 Aug '88, on Constrictor, by Constrictor Records (Germany). Catalogue no: **CON 00033**

Legend, Johnny

SOUTH'S GONNA RISE AGAIN
Tracks: / South's gonna rise again, The.
7" Single: Released Apr '81, on Rondelet Music, by Rondelet Music & Records. Catalogue no: **ROUND 1002**

Legendary Dolphins

COME TOMORROW
Tracks: / Come tomorrow.
7" Single: Released '88, on Beam, by Beam Records. Catalogue no: **LD 003**

Legendary Golden

CREEPING POISON
Tracks: / Creeping poison.
7" Single: Released Apr '85, on Exile, Catalogue no: **EX 7001**

GONE FOR GOOD
Tracks: / Gone for good.
7" Single: Released Sep '85, on Exile, Catalogue no: **EX 7003**

TROUBLE BOUND EP
Tracks: / Trouble bound EP.
10" single: Released May '86, on Exile, Catalogue no: **EX 10EP 01**

Legendary Lonnie

CONSTIPATION SHAKE
Tracks: / Constipation shake / Devils guitar.
7" Single: Released Jun '81, on Nervous, by Nervous Records. Catalogue no: **NER 002**

ELEPHANT DANCE
Tracks: / Elephant dance.
7" Single: Released May '85, on Rebound, Catalogue no: **BOUNCE 5**

Legendary Pink Dots

BLACK LIST
Tracks: / Black list.
CD 5": Released Jul '89, on Play It Again Sam(Belgium), by Play It Again Sam (Belgium). Catalogue no: **BIAS 109 CD**
12" Single: Released Oct '88, on Play It Again Sam(Belgium), by Play It Again Sam (Belgium). Catalogue no: **BIAS 109**

CURIOUS GUY
Tracks: / Curious guy.
12" Single: Released Aug '86, on Play It Again Sam(Belgium), by Play It Again Sam (Belgium). Catalogue no: **BIAS 30**

PREMUNITION
Tracks: / Premunition.
7" Single: Released '88, on N L Centre, Catalogue no: **Unknown**

UNDER GLASS
Tracks: / Under glass.
12" Single: Released Oct '87, on Play It Again Sam(Belgium), by Play It Again Sam (Belgium). Catalogue no: **BIAS 074**

Legger, Nikki

MIND OVER MATTER
Tracks: / Mind over matter / We could be happy.
7" Single: Released May '86, on RCA, by BMG Records (UK). Catalogue no: **PB 40653**
12" Single: Released May '86, on RCA, by BMG Records (UK). Catalogue no: **PT 40654**

Legion Of Dynamic...

REPEL REBEL
Tracks: / Rebel rebel.
7" Single: Released Oct '88, on AVM, by AVM Records. Catalogue no: **KAK 7/11**
12" Single: Released Jan '89, on AVM, by AVM Records. Catalogue no: **KAK 12/11**

Legion Of Parasites

UNDESIRABLE GUESTS
Tracks: / Undesirable guests.
12" Single: Released May '88, on Fight Back, Catalogue no: **FIGHT 2**

Legs Akimbo

GREASY JOE'S CAFE
Tracks: / Greasy Joe's cafe.
7" Single: Released Apr '80, on Vindaloo, by Vindaloo Records. Catalogue no: **GH 1**

Legs Diamond

TURN TO STONE
Tracks: / Turn to stone / Twisted love / Right between the eyes.
12" Single: Released Jun '86, on Music For Nations, by Music For Nations Records. Catalogue no: **12 KUT 121**

Leigh, Richard

RIGHT FROM THE START
Tracks: / Right from the start / Let's do it right.
7" Single: Released Jan '81, on United Artists, by EMI Records. Deleted Jan '84. Catalogue no: **UP 638**

Leisure Process

ANXIETY
Tracks: / Anxiety / Company, The.
12" Single: Released May '83, on Epic, by CBS Records. Catalogue no: **TA 3405**
7" Single: Released May '83, on Epic, by CBS Records. Catalogue no: **A 3405**

CASHFLOW
Tracks: / Cashflow / Emigre, The.
12" Single: Released Feb '83, on Epic, by CBS Records. Catalogue no: **EPC A 13 3131**
7" Single: Released Feb '83, on Epic, by CBS Records. Catalogue no: **EPC A 3131**

WAY YOU'LL NEVER BE
Tracks: / Way you'll never be / Rachel dreams / Love cascade (on 12" only).
12" Single: Released Jun '82, on Epic, by CBS Records. Deleted Jun '85. Catalogue no: **EPCA 132478**
7" Single: Released Jun '82, on Epic, by CBS Records. Deleted Jun '85. Catalogue no: **EPCA 2478**

Leitmotiv

BIG MONEY
Tracks: / Big money.
12" Single: Released Sep '86, on Ediesta, Deleted '88. Catalogue no: **CALC 2**

SAY REMAIN
Tracks: / Say remain.
7" Single: Released Oct '85, on Cryptic, by Cryptic Records. Catalogue no: **SPYRO 98**
12" Single: Released Oct '85, on Cryptic, by Cryptic Records. Catalogue no: **RULER 98**

SILENT RUN
Tracks: / Silent run / Living in a tin.
7" Single: Released Nov '83, on Pax, by Pax Records. Catalogue no: **PAX 17**

TO THE SUFFERING
Tracks: / To the suffering.
7" Single: Released Feb '85, on Reconciliation, Catalogue no: **RECONCILE 2**

Lekakis, Paul

BOOM BOOM (LET'S GO BACK TO MY ROOM)
Tracks: / Boom boom / Boom boom (inst).
12" Single: Released May '87, on Champion, by Champion Records. Catalogue no: **CHAMP 1243**
7" Single: Released May '87, on Champion, by Champion Records. Catalogue no: **CHAMP 43**

Lelo

ALL I WANT
Tracks: / All I want / Mad Jack.
7" Single: Released Nov '80, on Club, by Phonogram Ltd. Deleted Nov '83. Catalogue no: **ABC 2**

IN CHINA
Tracks: / In China / Love in my car.
7" Single: Released Feb '81, on M.A.M, by M.A.M. Records. Deleted Feb '84. Catalogue no: **MAMS 208**

NO SAVING GRACE
Tracks: / No saving grace / I'm the suicide.
7" Single: Released May '81, on A&M, by A&M Records. Deleted May '84. Catalogue no: **MAMS 210**

TANGIERS
Tracks: / Tangiers / Bongo drum on VHF.
7" Single: Released Feb '82, on M.A.M, by M.A.M. Records. Deleted Feb '87. Catalogue no: **MAMS 213**

Lema, Ray

KAMULANG
Tracks: / Kamulang / System rules.
7" Single: Released 17 Apr '89, on Mango, by Island Records. Catalogue no: **MNG 101**
12" Single: Released 17 Apr '89, on Mango, by Island Records. Catalogue no: **12MNG 101**

Lemaire, Jo

FOLLOW ME IN THE AIR
Tracks: / Follow me in the air / Tintorella Di Lung.
7" Single: Released May '80, on Rocket, by Rocket Records. Deleted May '83. Catalogue no: **XPRES 30**

Lemarr Tony

1,2,3
Tracks: / 1-2-3 / Let's dance.
7" Single: Released Nov '82, on President, by President Records. Catalogue no: **PT 512**

COME BACK AGAIN
Tracks: / Come back again / Hit man run man.
7" Single: Released Nov '81, on President, by President Records. Catalogue no: **PT 499**

SEA CRUISE
Tracks: / Sea cruise / I wanna thank you.
7" Single: Released May '82, on President, by President Records. Catalogue no: **PT 503**

Lemon Heart

SHAKE YOURSELF
Tracks: / Shake yourself / Honey from the spoon / Fine love.
12" Single: Released May '87, on Epic, by CBS Records. Deleted Nov '87. Catalogue no: **LEMON T1**
7" Single: Released May '87, on Epic, by CBS Records. Deleted Nov '87. Catalogue no: **LEMON 1**

Lemon Kittens

CAKE BEAST
Tracks: / Cake beast.
12" Single: Released May '82, on United Dairies, Catalogue no: **UD 007**

SPOON FED AND WRITHING (EP)
Tracks: / Spoon fed and writhing.
7" Single: Released Oct '79, on Step Forward, by Faulty Products Records. Catalogue no: **SF 10**

Lemon Pipers

Biographical details: Lemon Pipers This American group consisted of Bill Albaugh, Bill Bartlett, Ivan Browne, Reg Nave and Steve Walmsley.
The Lemon Pipers were about to be dropped as no-hopers by the Buddah label, before they were rescued by the 1968 American No.1 smash *Green Tambourine*. This bubblegum ditty which was provided for them by songwriters Paul Leka and Shelley Pinz, was more overtly commercial than the psychedelia-oriented group might have wished; but beggars could not be choosers an they needed a hit. In the event *Green Tambourine* was the first chart topper for the company by names such as the Ohio Express and the 1910 Fruitgum Co. *Green Tambourine* reached No.7 in Britain. The blatantly trashy follow ups like *Rice Is Nice* and *Jelly Jungle (of orange marmalade)*, failed to pentrate the Top 40 on either side of the Atlantic. The Pipers tried to give a fillip to their flagging fortunes by producing a more serious album under their own supervision, but this was a disaster and they evantually split. (Bob Macdonald 5/12/85).

GREEN TAMBOURINE
Tracks: / Green tambourine.
7" Single: Released Feb '68, on Pye International, Deleted Feb '71. Catalogue no: **7N 25444**

GREEN TAMBOURINE (EP)
Tracks: / Green tambourine / Blueberry blue / Rice is nice / Jerry jingle.
7" Single: Released Jul '80, on Flashback, by Mainline Records. Catalogue no: **FBEP 102**

GREEN TAMBOURINE (OLD GOLD)
Tracks: / Green tambourine.
7" Single: Released Jul '84, on Old Gold, by Old Gold Records. Deleted Jul '88. Catalogue no: **OG 9415**

RICE IS NICE
Tracks: / Rice is nice.
7" Single: Released May '68, on Pye International, Deleted May '71. Catalogue no: **7N 25454**

Lemonheads

LUKA
Tracks: / Luka.
7" Single: Released Apr '89, on Taang, Catalogue no: **TAANG 031**

Lemons

MY FAVOURITE BAND
Tracks: / My favourite band.
7" Single: Released Aug '81, on Race, Deleted '83. Catalogue no: **RB 004**

Lemos, Paul

MUSIC FOR STOLEN ICON
Tracks: / Music for stolen icon.
12" Single: Released 10 Jan '87, on Sub Rosa, by Sub Rosa Records. Catalogue no: **SUB 12003-6**

Lemuria

THUNDER IN YOUR LOVE
Tracks: / Thunder in your love.
12" Single: Released Nov '84, on Street Level, by Creole Records. Catalogue no: **CRT 70**

Lena

CONNECTION
Tracks: / Connection / Connection (instrumental mix).
12" Single: Released Mar '86, on Teldec (Germany), by ASV (Academy Sound & Vision). Catalogue no: **6 20527**

Lendor, Kim

JUST WHEN I NEED YOU MOST
Tracks: / Just when I needed you most / Miss you (tough baby).
7" Single: Released 13 Jun '87, on Crystal, by President Records. Catalogue no: **7 CTL 060**
12" Single: Released 13 Jun '87, on Crystal, by President Records. Catalogue no: **12CTL 060**

Lennon, John

Biographical details: Lennon, John This British singer, songwriter, guitarist and pianist was born in Liverpool in October 1940. During the mid Fifties, right at the start of the rock'n'roll revolution, Lennon founded a group called The Quarrymen (named after the school in which they were formed); by the late Fifties, he had brought in friendsd Paul McCartney and George Harrison - it was the start of the most remarkable musical story of the 20th century. During the historic years from 1962 until 1970 Lennon was always the most controversial member of the Beatles. He was the first to break female fans' hearts by marrying; he supplemented his music with books that were dismissed as rubbish in many quarters, but which aroused huge interest; he frequently made caustic comments in public, the most famous being his misisnterpreted remark about the Beatles being bigger than Christ; and he stunned

observers by divorcing his first wife Cynthia and marrying the avant-garde Japanese artist Yoko Ono. It was Lennon's intense personal and musical relationship with Yoko that was one of the major causes of the Fab Four's break-up in the spring of 1970.
Lennon's non Beatle recording career actually began in 1968. By the end of the following year, John & Yoko had released three weird experimental albums, plus the equally adventurous but far more commercial single *Give Peace A Chance* which was recorded in a Montreal hotel bedroom with a huge cast of musical and non-musical friends who were dubbed the Plastic Ono Band. This name was used on several later Lennon records, although no such group ever really existed.
While the couple's extraordinary exploits kept their names constantly in the headlines - they later described themselves as the 'court jesters of the peace movement' - John's post Beatle musical career began in earnest with the December 1970 release of the LP *John Lennon and the Plastic Ono Band*. His next album *Imagine* reached No.1 on both sides of the Atlantic in autumn '71, the title track becoming his best known solo song. His subsequent work was somewhat more erratic in both artistic and commercial terms, although a gem was never very far away. His interest in political, sociological and humanitarian issues was fundamental to his Seventies music.
After a period of hiatus, during which he fought (and eventually won) a battle with US immigration authorities and underwent a period of separation from Yoko, John's solo career reached a new peak in the States with the No.1 success of the 1974 single *Whatever Gets You Thru The Night* and th album *Walls and Bridges*. The husband and wife were reconciled and decided to retire from the music business and escape from the public eye.
After giving birth to a son, Sean, in October 1975, John and Yoko spent five years in domestic bliss, with Ono administering their business affairs and Lennon working as a househusband. In late 1980, just after he turned 40, the couple made a comeback with the joint LP *Double Fantasy*.
In December 1980 John Lennon suffered one of the most unjust and horrible deaths imaginable - he was shot dead in cold blood outside his home, in front of his wife. The tragdy occured at a time when John and Yoko were supremely happy with their lives and their new music. (Bob Macdonald 5/12/85).

BORROWED TIME
Tracks: / Borrowed time / Your hands.
7" Single: Released Mar '84, on Polydor, by Polydor Ltd. Catalogue no: **POSP 701**
12" Single: Released Mar '84, on Polydor, by Polydor Ltd. Catalogue no: **POSPX 701**

COLD TURKEY
Tracks: / Cold turkey.
7" Single: Released Nov '69, on Apple, by Apple Records. Deleted Nov '72. Catalogue no: **APPLES 1001**

GIVE PEACE A CHANCE
Tracks: / Give peace a chance / Cold turkey.
7" Single: Released Jul '69, on Apple, by Apple Records. Deleted Jul '72. Catalogue no: **APPLE 13**
7" Single: Released Mar '84, on EMI Golden 45's, by EMI Records. Catalogue no: **G45 2**

HAPPY XMAS (WAR IS OVER)
Tracks: / Happy Xmas (war is over) / Listen the snow is falling.
7" Single: Released Nov '81, on Apple, by Apple Records. Catalogue no: **R 5970**

I'M STEPPIN OUT
Tracks: / I'm stepping out.
12" Single: Released Jul '84, on Polydor, by Polydor Ltd. Catalogue no: **POSPX 702**
7" Single: Released Jul '84, on Polydor, by Polydor Ltd. Catalogue no: **POSP 702**

IMAGINE (SINGLE)
Tracks: / Imagine / Working class hero.
7" Single: Released Oct '75, on Apple, by Apple Records. Deleted '88. Catalogue no: **R 6009**

IMAGINE (SINGLE (2))
Tracks: / Imagine / Jealous guy / Happy Xmas (war is over) / Give peace a chance.
12" Pic: Released Dec '88, on Parlophone, by EMI Records. Deleted Aug '89. Catalogue no: **12RP 6199**
7" Pic: Released Dec '88, on Parlophone, by EMI Records. Deleted Aug '89. Catalogue no: **RP 6199**
CD 5": Released Nov '88, on Parlophone, by EMI Records. Catalogue no: **CDR 6199**
12" Single: Released Nov '88, on Parlophone, by EMI Records. Deleted Aug '89. Catalogue no: **12R 6199**
7" Single: Released Nov '88, on Parlophone, by EMI Records. Deleted Aug '89. Catalogue no: **R 6199**

INSTANT KARMA
Tracks: / Instant karma.
7" Single: Released Apr '83, on EMI (France), by EMI Records. Catalogue no: **2C 008 91149**
7" Single: Released Feb '70, on Apple, by Apple Records. Deleted Feb '73. Catalogue no: **APPLES 1003**

JEALOUS GUY
Tracks: / Jealous guy.
7" Single: Released Nov '85, on Parlophone, by EMI Records. Deleted Jul '87. Catalogue no: **R 6117**
12" Single: Released Nov '85, on Parlophone, by EMI Records. Deleted Jul '87. Catalogue no: **12R 6117**

JUST LIKE STARTING OVER
Tracks: / Just like starting over / Kiss kiss kiss.
7" Single: Released Nov '80, on Geffen, by Geffen Records (USA). Deleted Nov '83. Catalogue no: **K 79186**

LOVE
Tracks: / Love / Give me some truth.
7" Single: Released Nov '82, on Parlophone, by EMI Records. Catalogue no: **R 6059**

MIND GAMES(SINGLE)
Tracks: / Mind games / Meat city.
7" Single: Released Jan '73, on Parlophone, by EMI Records. Catalogue no: **R 5994**

NO.9 DREAM
Tracks: / No.9 dream / What you got.
7" Single: Released Jan '75, on Apple, by Apple Records. Catalogue no: **R 6003**

NOBODY TOLD ME
Tracks: / Nobody told me / O sanity.
7" Single: Released Jan '84, on Polydor, by Polydor Ltd. Catalogue no: **POSP 700**

POWER TO THE PEOPLE
Tracks: / Power to the people / Open your box.
7" Single: Released Mar '71, on Parlophone, by EMI Records. Catalogue no: **R 5892**

STAND BY ME
Tracks: / Stand by me / Move over Ms.L.
7" Single: Released Apr '81, on Apple, by Apple Records. Catalogue no: **R 6005**

WATCHING THE WHEELS
Tracks: / Watching the wheels / I'm your angel.
7" Single: Released Apr '81, on Geffen, by Geffen Records (USA). Catalogue no: **K 79207**

WHATEVER GETS YOU THROUGH THE NIGHT
Tracks: / Whatever gets you through the night.
7" Single: Released Jan '74, on Parlophone, by EMI Records. Catalogue no: **R 5998**

WOMAN
Tracks: / Woman / Beautiful boy.
Cassingle: Released Jan '81, on Geffen, by Geffen Records (USA). Deleted Jan '84. Catalogue no: **MK 79195**
7" Single: Released Jan '81, on Geffen, by Geffen Records (USA). Deleted Jul '88. Catalogue no: **K 79195**

Lennon, Julian

Biographical details: John Charles Julian Lennon was born at Sefton General Hospital, Liverpool on April 8th 1963. For both of his parents, John & Cynthia, these were heady days indeed: only three weeks before Julian's birth, John and his group the Beatles had hit the number one position in the best-selling chart with their second single *Please please me*. Three days after Julian's birth, their third single *From me to you* was released and the astonishing trail of record breaking events that was to catapult John Lennon and the Beatles into a meteoric rise to international fame had begun. For Julian, infant years and childhood meant homes in transit as John and Cynthia coped with the hurly burly and astonishing speed of Beatlemania. Since Liverpool could not contain the Beatles, Julian moved, with his parents to London when he was a year old, first to a flat in West Kensington and then, as the gathering fans made life difficult for a mother and child to climb the stairs in peace, the Lennons moved to Weybridge, Surrey. These were trying times for Julian's mother. Julian was only five years old when John and Cynthia divorced in Nov 1968. The next spring, John married Yoko Ono and Julian was back living in Cheshire with his mother. His school was Kingsmead, Hoylake. It was at Hoylake that Julian forged a crucial friendship. Another pupil, Justin Clayton, shared Julian's enthusiasm for old rock'n'roll songs like *Roll over Beethoven*. Julian was keen enough to enrol for guitar tuition at school, and it wasn't long before he and Justin were forming a schoolboy group. Julian and Justin played their first date at a school entertainment evening, and the ball was rolling. Neither of them knew, at that early age, that seven years later they would be launched into a professional career. Julian went onto Ruthlin School, and therefore was unable to continue making music during schooldays, but the friendship did carry on. By the time he was 17, he and Justin Clayton had jammed around with other musicians. The news that shook the world on Dec 8th 1980 - that John Lennon had been murdered outside his New York home - struck a deep and bitter blow inside 17 year-old Julian. Within two days, he was on a plane to New York, where he spent several weeks with Yoko and Sean. After several months of mourning, Julian, living in a London flat, hit the 'young socialiste scene' - visiting London clubs, being exploited and exposed and generally living it up. It was not the happiest period for him, but his backlash behaviour was perhaps the natural reaction to a teenager whose life would from now on, forever be under the spotlight as the poor little rich boy, son of a murdered legend. Not surprisingly Julian sought refuge in music. Contrary to any belief that he was propped up by money from any sources at all, there followed many hard-up months in flats in Notting Hill, where Julian gradually gathered around him a commune of musicians and their instruments. During much of 1981 and 1982, Julian veered towards the piano, but was not completely happy about the synthesiser bands dominating the trendy rock scene. For some eighteen months, he contemplated the route his music should take, as well as the flack he could expect if he launched himself into music as a career. There was not alternative though. The call of music was in his blood - plus another factor that became increasingly strong. He saw his future role, as a songwriter and singer, as an essential family continuation of what his father did. But while he readily admits a love for so much of his father's work, and his unique voice and the influence it has on him, Julian strives for individuality. Last year Julian's manager, Dean Gordon, sent a tape of Julian's songs to Charisma's Chief Executive, Tony Stratton Smith. Stratton Smith was so impressed by the quality of Julian's writing and his strong performance that a recording and publishing contract was promptly signed. The nurturing of Julian's debut album - called *Valotte* as a mark of attachment and memory of the unique retreat that inspired the music - went into a crucial final stage. A hit single followed called *Too late for goodbyes*. (Charisma Records).

BECAUSE
Tracks: / Because.
7" Single: Released Nov '85, on EMI, by EMI Records. Catalogue no: **EMI 5538**

MIDNIGHT SMOKE
Tracks: / Midnight smoke (7" only) / Vanishing, The (7" only) / Midnight smoke (full version) (12" only) / Vanishing, The (12" only).
7" Single: on Virgin, by Virgin Records. Catalogue no: **VAD 1**
12" Single: on Virgin, by Virgin Records. Catalogue no: **VAD 112**

NOW YOU'RE IN HEAVEN
Tracks: / Now you're in heaven / Second time, The.
7" Single: Released 20 Feb '89, on Virgin, by Virgin Records. Catalogue no: **VS 1154**
12" Single: Released 20 Feb '89, on Virgin, by Virgin Records. Catalogue no: **VST 1154**
CD 3": Released Mar '89, on Virgin, by Virgin Records. Catalogue no: **VSCD 1154**

SAY YOU ARE WRONG
Tracks: / Say you are wrong.
7" Single: Released Feb '85, on Charisma, by Virgin Records. Deleted May '88. Catalogue no: **JL 3**
12" Single: Released Feb '85, on Charisma, by Virgin Records. Deleted May '88. Catalogue no: **JL 312**

STICK AROUND
Tracks: / Stick around / Always think twice.
7" Single: Released Mar '86, on Charisma, by Virgin Records. Deleted May '88. Catalogue no: **CB 420**
12" Single: Released Mar '86, on Charisma, by Virgin Records. Deleted May '88. Catalogue no: **CB 42012**

THIS IS MY DAY
Tracks: / This is my day / Everyday.
7" Single: Released May '86, on Charisma, by Virgin Records. Deleted May '88. Catalogue no: **CB 423**

TIME WILL TEACH US ALL
Tracks: / Time will teach us all / Time will teach us all (instrumental).
12" Single: Released Jul '86, on EMI, by EMI Records. Catalogue no: **12EMI 5556**
7" Single: Released Jul '86, on EMI, by EMI Records. Catalogue no: **EMI 5556**

TOO LATE FOR GOODBYES
Tracks: / Too late for goodbyes.
7" Single: Released Sep '84, on Charisma, by Virgin Records. Deleted May '88. Catalogue no: **JL 1**
12" Single: Released Sep '84, on Charisma, by Virgin Records. Catalogue no: **JL 1 12**

VALOTTE (see panel below)
Tracks: / Valotte / Let me be.
7" Single: Released Dec '84, on Charisma, by Virgin Records. Deleted May '88. Catalogue no: **JL 2**
7" Pic: Released Dec '84, on Charisma, by Virgin Records. Catalogue no: **J LS 2**
12" Single: Released Dec '84, on Charisma, by Virgin Records. Deleted May '88. Catalogue no: **JL 212**

YOU'RE THE ONE
Tracks: / You're the one / Sunday morning / Stand by me.
12" Single: Released 26 Jun '89, on Virgin, by Virgin Records. Catalogue no: **VST 1182**

JULIAN LENNON - VALOTTE (Released on Charisma)

7" Single: Released 26 Jun '89, on Virgin, by Virgin Records. Catalogue no: **VS 1182**
CD 3": Released 26 Jun '89, on Virgin, by Virgin Records. Catalogue no: **VSCD 1182**

Lennon, Kipp

SUSPENSION
Tracks: / Suspension / Something kinda funky.
7" Single: Released Mar '81, on MCA, by MCA Records. Deleted Mar '84. Catalogue no: **MCA 684**

Lennox, Annie

PUT A LITTLE LOVE IN YOUR HEART
Tracks: / Put a little love in your heart / Great big piece of love, A.
Note: This Jackie de Shannon/Randy Myers/Jimmy Holiday composition was produced by Dave Stewart and features on the forthcoming soundtrack to the new Bill Murray fim 'Scrooged' which includes tracks by Natalie Cole and Miles Davies.
7" Single: Released Oct '88, on A&M, by A&M Records. Catalogue no: **AM 484**
12" Single: Released Oct '88, on A&M, by A&M Records. Catalogue no: **AMY 484**

Lenroy, Derek

DEEP MEDITATION
Tracks: / Deep meditation / Meditation dub.
12" Single: Released Nov '82, on Body Music, by Nuclear Records. Catalogue no: **BMDIS 3**

I'LL NEVER LOVE AGAIN
Tracks: / I'll never love again / Love has gone away.
12" Single: Released Mar '85, on Raiders, Catalogue no: **LGR 007**

Leo, Phillip

FOOD OF LOVE
Tracks: / Food of love.
12" Single: Released Aug '88, on Fine Style, by Fashion Records. Catalogue no: **FS 019**

I WANNA BE LOVED BY YOU
Tracks: / I wanna be loved by you.
12" Single: Released Feb '89, on Fashion, by Fashion Records. Catalogue no: **FS 021**

WHY DO FOOLS
Tracks: / Why do fools (remix).
12" Single: Released Jun '89, on White Label (1), Catalogue no: **X 1**

WHY DO FOOLS FALL IN LOVE
Tracks: / Why do fools fall in love.
7" Single: Released Apr '89, on Fashion, by Fashion Records. Catalogue no: **FAD 065**

WHY DO FOOLS (REMIX)
Tracks: / Why do fools (remix).
12" Single: Released Jul '89, on White Label (1), Catalogue no: **X 1**

Leoi

YOU MEAN EVERYTHING TO ME
Tracks: / You mean everything to me.
7" Single: Released Oct '85, on BPOF, by BPOP Records. Deleted '86. Catalogue no: **BPOP 3**
12" Single: Released Oct '85, on BPOP, by BPOP Records. Deleted '86. Catalogue no: **12 BPOP 3**

Leon

JEALOUS HEART (SINGLE)
Tracks: / Jealous heart / Amazing grace.
7" Single: Released Apr '83, on Homespun (Ireland), by Outlet Records. Catalogue no: **HS 066**
7" Single: Released Feb '83, on Homespun (Ireland), by Outlet Records. Catalogue no: **HS 058**

WORLD NEEDS A MELODY, THE
Tracks: / World needs a melody, The / Love is a word.
7" Single: Released Oct '80, on Homespun (USA), Deleted Oct '83. Catalogue no: **HS 036**

YOU MADE MY LIFE COMPLETE
Tracks: / You made my life complete / Nobody's darling but mine.
7" Single: Released May '80, on Homespun (Ireland), by Outlet Records. Catalogue no: **HS 033**

Leon, Trisha

MY BOY LOLLIPOP
Tracks: / My boy lollipop.
7" Single: Released Aug '87, on Master Funk, Catalogue no: **MG 001**

Leonard, Deke

BIG HUNK OF LOVE
Tracks: / Big hunk of love / Marlene.
7" Single: Released May '81, on Liberty, by EMI Records. Deleted May '84. Catalogue no: **BP 400**

Leonore

FIRST TO BE A WOMAN
Tracks: / First to be a woman / Put a rainbow in your heart.
7" Single: Released Feb '80, on Polydor, by Polydor Ltd. Deleted Feb '85. Catalogue no: **POSP 116**

Leo's Sunshipp

GIVE ME THE SUNSHINE
Tracks: / Give me the sunshine / I'm back for more.
7" Single: Released Oct '80, on Grape-Vine, by Grapevine Records. Deleted Oct '83. Catalogue no: **REDC 3**
7" Single: Released Aug '86, on Expansion, Catalogue no: **EXPAND 3**

Leotis

ON A MISSION
Tracks: / On a mission / On a mission (7" remix) / On a mission (12" remix) / On a mission (A Cappella).
12" Single: Released 30 May '89, on Mercury, by Phonogram Ltd. Deleted Oct '89. Catalogue no: **MERX 289**
CD 5": Released 30 May '89, on Mercury, by Phonogram Ltd. Catalogue no: **MERCD 289**
7" Single: Released 30 May '89, on Mercury, by Phonogram Ltd. Deleted Oct '89. Catalogue no: **MER 289**

Lepke, Louis

ARGENTINA SURRENDER
Tracks: / Argentina surrender / GB destroyer.
12" Single: Released Jul '82, on Exclusive, Catalogue no: **EXC 601129**

BACK OFF
Tracks: / Back off / Can't stop the rastaman.
12" Single: Released Jan '83, on Music Works, Catalogue no: **MWRT 1298**

Leray, Ken

I WOULD DO IT ALL AGAIN
Tracks: / I would do it all again / Together we are beautiful.
7" Single: Released Mar '80, on Piccadilly, Deleted '83. Catalogue no: **7P 168**

Leroi Brothers

AIN'T I'M A DOG
Tracks: / Ain't I'm a dog / Chicken and honey.
7" Single: Released May '84, on Demon, by Demon Records. Catalogue no: **D 1027**

Leroy, Derek

LOVE HAS GONE AWAY
Tracks: / Love has gone away.
12" Single: Released Sep '84, on Raiders, Catalogue no: **LGR 005**

Lerwick Brass Band

UP-HELLY-AA (EP)
Tracks: / Up-helly-aa.
7" Single: Released Feb '82, on Galley, Deleted '84. Catalogue no: **ZET 1**

Les Afferux

HELL IS PAVED WITH GOOD INTENTIONS
Tracks: / Hell is paved with good intentions.
7" Single: Released Oct '85, on Mamba, Catalogue no: **MSA 1**

Les Enfants Terribles

LES ENFANTS TERRIBLES
Tracks: / Les enfants terribles.
7" Single: Released Sep '89, on Midnight, Catalogue no: **DING 051**
12" Single: Released Sep '89, on Midnight, Catalogue no: **DONG 051**

PATHS OF GLORY
Tracks: / Paths of glory.
12" Single: Released Apr '89, on Midnight Music, by Midnight Music Records. Catalogue no: **UNKNOWN**
7" Single: Released Apr '89, on Midnight Music, by Midnight Music Records. Catalogue no: **UNKNOWN**

Les Negresses Vertes

VOILA L'ETE
Tracks: / Viola l'ete / Zobi la mouche.
7" Single: Released Aug '89, on Rhythm King, by Mute Records. Catalogue no: **UNKNOWN**
12" Single: Released Aug '89, on Rhythm King, by Mute Records. Catalogue no: **UNKNOWN**

ZOBI LA MOUCHE
Tracks: / Zobi la mouche.
CD 5": Released Jul '89, on Rhythm King, by Mute Records. Catalogue no: **LEFT 033CD**
7" Single: Released Mar '89, on Rhythm King, by Mute Records. Catalogue no: **LEFT 033**
12" Single: Released Mar '89, on Rhythm King, by Mute Records. Catalogue no: **LEFT 033T**

Les Thugs

ELECTRIC TROUBLE
Tracks: / Electric trouble.
12" Single: Released 31 Oct '87, on Vinyl Solution, by Vinyl Solution Records. Catalogue no: **SOL 5**

RADICAL HYSTERY
7" Single: Released Mar '86, on Closer (France), Catalogue no: **CLO 761**

Les Zazous

ANOTHER TOWN
Tracks: / Another town / Against the tide / Today.
7" Single: Released Mar '87, on Spell, Catalogue no: **L 23**

Lesear, Anne

TAKE HIM BACK (TAXI)
Tracks: / Take him back (Taxi).
7" Single: Released May '84, on Allegience, Catalogue no: **ALES 4**

Leslie, Kim

LOOK UP AT THE SKY
Tracks: / Look up at the sky / Best interest at heart.
7" Single: Released Aug '80, on Piccadilly, Deleted '82. Catalogue no: **7P 197**

Lesson & Vale

UNDER MY SKIN
Tracks: / Under my skin / Rock & roll driver.
7" Single: Released Feb '81, on RCA, by BMG Records (UK). Deleted '84. Catalogue no: **RCA 37**

Lester, Ketty

Biographical details: Lester, Ketty This American singer was born in Hope, Arkansas; her initial career choice was nursing but she gave this up before completing her training in order to concentrate on music. Her big break occured when she became a resident singer with the orchestra of jazz star Cab Calloway. She later established a reputation as a nightclub performer.
In 1962 Lester came to fame with her one off smash *Love Letters* which reached No.5 in America and No.4 in Britain. Dating originally from a 1945 film of the same name, *Love Letters* beautifully displayed Ketty's soft sensuous smooth voice. Complete with a superb piano arrangement, Lester's *Love Letters* was one of the most understated yet distinctive ballad hits of the early Sixties, appealing to jazz, pop and soul fans. The song as a hit for Elvis Presley in 1966. Lester failed to achieve any further Top 40 hits on either side of the Atlantic, despite some worthy follow ups. A duet album with soulsinger Betty Everett did not revive her fortunes. (Bob Macdonald 6/12/85).

BUT NOT FOR ME
Tracks: / But not for me.
7" Single: Released Jul '62, on London-American, Deleted Jul '65. Catalogue no: **HLN 9574**

LOVE LETTERS
Tracks: / Love letters.
7" Single: Released Apr '62, on London-American, Deleted Apr '65. Catalogue no: **HLN 9527**

LOVE LETTERS (OLD GOLD)
Tracks: / Love letters.
7" Single: Released Jul '82, on Old Gold, by Old Gold Records. Catalogue no: **OG 9012**

Lester Square

PLUG, THE
Tracks: / Plug, The.
7" Single: Released Jul '84, on Thin Sliced, by Thin Sliced Records. Catalogue no: **TSR 4**
12" Single: Released Jul '84, on Thin Sliced, by Thin Sliced Records. Catalogue no: **TSR 4 T**

Let Them Eat Cake

I GET STATIC
Tracks: / I get static / Do the obvious.
12" Single: Released Aug '84, on PRT, by Castle Communications Records. Catalogue no: **SLICE 121**
7" Single: Released Aug '84, on PRT, by Castle Communications Records. Catalogue no: **SLICE 1**

Lethal Poor

TRANCE FLOOR
Tracks: / Trance floor.
12" Single: Released Sep '85, on Lethal Productions, Catalogue no: **POOR 1**

Let's Active

IN LITTLE WAYS
Tracks: / In little ways / Two you's.
12" Single: Released Jun '86, on I.R.S, Catalogue no: **IRMT 116**
7" Single: Released Jun '86, on I.R.S, Catalogue no: **IRM 116**

Let's Get Dressed

LOVE ANOTHER WAY
Tracks: / Love another way.
7" Single: Released Mar '84, on Fast, by Fast Forward Records. Catalogue no: **LGD 003**

Lets Wreck Mother

CUTS
Tracks: / Cuts.
12" Single: Released Jun '85, on Flicknife, by Flicknife Records. Catalogue no: **FLEP 105**

Lettermen

WAY YOU LOOK TONIGHT, THE
Tracks: / Way you look tonight.
7" Single: Released Nov '61, on Capitol, by EMI Records. Deleted Nov '64. Catalogue no: **CL 15222**

Letters

NOBODY LOVES ME
Tracks: / Nobody loves me / Don't want you back.
7" Single: Released '81, on Heartbeat, by Mainline Records. Catalogue no: **PULSE 9**

Levay, Rik

MISS YOU
Tracks: / Miss you / Your love you give.
12" Single: Released Aug '83, on Loose End, by MCA Records. Catalogue no: **LET 108**
7" Single: Released Aug '83, on Loose End, by MCA Records. Catalogue no: **LE108**

Level 42

Biographical details: Level 42 This British band consists of Boon Gould, Phil Gould, Mark King and Mike Lindup. Keyboards/synthesiser player Wally Badarou is an additional part-time member, and co-writes and co-produces with them.
Hailing from the Isle of Wight, Level 42 progressed from holiday camp musicians to becoming one of the UK's top funk outfits of the Eighties. They first emerged in the lower regions of the British charts in late 1980 and were part of a club-based boom that was dubbed 'Britfunk'. Soul and disco music had always been dominated by the United States, but now Level 42 and other acts like The Real Thing, Heatwave, Hi-Tension, Linx, Shakatak and The Olympic Runners were showing that the UK could become a potent force in the genre.
During 1980-83 Level 42 chalked up an acclaimed string of eight British chart singles, which all reached the Top 75 but not the Top 20.
These included such gems as *Love Games, Weave Your Spell* and *The Chinese Way*; their early albums were strong sellers and showcased the group's slickness and virtuosity. In order to ascend to the high echelons of the Uk charts, which had always just eluded them, they went to Los Angeles to record their 1983 LP *Standing In The Light* under the production aegis of Earth Wind & Fire members Larry Dunn and Verdine White; this album yielded their first UK Top 10 single *The Sun oes Down (Living It Up)*.
The group's success continued apace in '84 with the *Hot Water* single and the *True Colours* LP and 1985 proved to be Level 42's hottest year yet.
The catchy single *Something About You*, which saw them moving ever closer to mainstream pop music, reached the UK No.6 position to become their biggest single; the *World Machine* album, itself a Top 10 seller, spawned a second hit 45 in the shape of *Leaving Me Now*. The band's amiable lead singer and frontman Mark King, a veritable blond bombshell, combined an engaging media personality with musical brilliance - he was widely hailed as Britain's best bass guitarist, meriting comparison with such American bass bosses as Stanley Clarke and Robert 'Kool' Bell. (Bob Macdonald 6/12/85).

ARE YOU HEARING (WHAT I HEAR)
Tracks: / Are you hearing (what I hear) / Return of the handsome rugged man.

12" Single: Released May '82, on Polydor, by Polydor Ltd. Deleted May '85. Catalogue no: **POSPX 396**
7" Single: Released May '82, on Polydor, by Polydor Ltd. Deleted May '85. Catalogue no: **POSP 396**

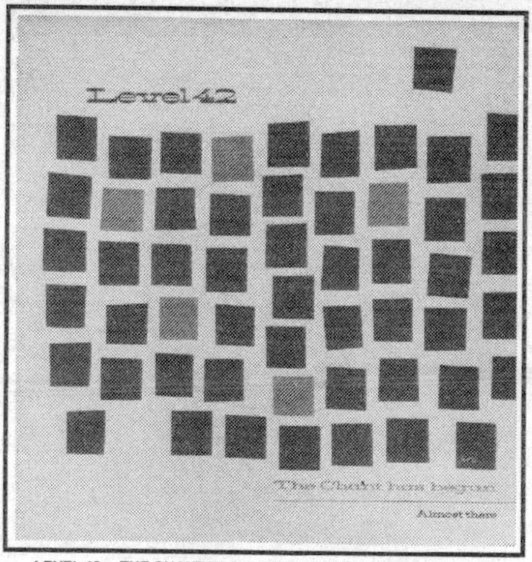

LEVEL 42 - THE CHANT HAS JUST BEGUN (Released on Polydor)

CHANT HAS JUST BEGUN, THE (see panel above)
Tracks: / Chant has just begun, The.
7" Single: Released Nov '84, on Polydor, by Polydor Ltd. Deleted Nov '87. Catalogue no: **POSP 710**

CHILDREN SAY
Tracks: / Children say (remix) / Starchild (remix) / Children say (ext. remix) (Only on cassette single.) / Something about you (Shep Pettibone remix) (Only on cassette single.) / Something about you (Only on CD single (platinum edition megamix)) / Lessons in love (Only on CD single (platinum edition megamix)) / World machine (Only on CD single (platinum edition megamix)) / Running in the family (Only on CD single (platinum edition megamix)).
CD 5": Released Dec '87, on Polydor, by Polydor Ltd. Deleted 30 Jun '89. Catalogue no: **POCD 911**
Cassingle: Released Dec '87, on Polydor, by Polydor Ltd. Deleted 30 Jun '89. Catalogue no: **POSPC 911**

CHILDREN SAY (SINGLE)
Tracks: / Children say.
7" Pic: Released Dec '87, on Polydor, by Polydor Ltd. Deleted 30 May '89. Catalogue no: **POSPP 911**
7" Single: Released 30 Nov '87, on Polydor, by Polydor Ltd. Deleted 30 May '89. Catalogue no: **POSP 911**
12" Single: Released 30 Nov '87, on Polydor, by Polydor Ltd. Deleted 30 May '89. Catalogue no: **POSPX 911**

CHINESE WAY, THE
Tracks: / Chinese way, The / 88.
7" Single: Released Jan '83, on Polydor, by Polydor Ltd. Deleted Jan '86. Catalogue no: **POSP 538**

FLYING ON THE WINGS OF LOVE
Tracks: / Flying on the wings of love / Wings of love.
7" Single: Released Nov '80, on Polydor, by Polydor Ltd. Deleted Nov '83. Catalogue no: **POSP 200**
12" Single: Released Nov '80, on Polydor, by Polydor Ltd. Deleted Nov '83. Catalogue no: **POSPX 200**

HEAVEN IN MY HANDS
Tracks: / Heaven in my hands / Heaven in my hands (extended remix) (Only on CD single & 12".) / Gresham blues / Heaven in my hands (7" mix) (Only on CD single & 12".).
7" Single: Released 22 Aug '88, on Polydor, by Polydor Ltd. Deleted 30 May '89. Catalogue no: **PO 14**
12" Single: Released 22 Aug '88, on Polydor, by Polydor Ltd. Deleted 31 May '89. Catalogue no: **PZ 14**
CD 5": Released Sep '88, on Polydor, by Polydor Ltd. Catalogue no: **PZCD 14**
12" Single: Released Aug '88, on Polydor, by Polydor Ltd. Deleted 31 May '89. Catalogue no: **PZX 14**

IT'S OVER
Tracks: / It's over / Physical presence.
Cassingle: Released Sep '87, on Polydor, by Polydor Ltd. Deleted 30 May '89. Catalogue no: **POSPC 900**
7" Single: Released Aug '87, on Polydor, by Polydor Ltd. Deleted 30 May '89. Catalogue no: **POSP 900**
12" Single: Released Aug '87, on Polydor, by Polydor Ltd. Catalogue no: **POSPX 900**

LEAVING ME NOW
Tracks: / Leaving me now.
10" single: Released Nov '85, on Polydor, by Polydor Ltd. Deleted '86. Catalogue no: **POSPT 776**
7" Single: Released Nov '85, on Polydor, by Polydor Ltd. Deleted '86. Catalogue no: **POSP 776**
12" Single: Released Nov '85, on Polydor, by Polydor Ltd. Catalogue no: **POSX 776**

LESSONS IN LOVE
Tracks: / Hot water (live) / World machine (Extra track on 12" version only) / Lessons in love.
CD 5": Released Aug '88, on Polydor (Japan), by Polydor Ltd. Catalogue no: **P10 P30 005**
7" Single: Released Apr '86, on Polydor, by Polydor Ltd. Catalogue no: **POSP 790**
12" Single: Released Apr '86, on Polydor, by Polydor Ltd. Catalogue no: **POSPX 790**

LESSONS IN LOVE (IMPORT)
Tracks: / Lessons in love / Lessons in love (remix) / Lessons in love (ext. mix) / Lessons in love (dub mix) / Running in the family.
Cassingle: Released Sep '88, on Polydor (Canada), by Polydor Ltd. Catalogue no: **LEV ELC 4**

LOVE GAMES
Tracks: / Love games.
12" Single: Released Mar '81, on Polydor, by Polydor Ltd. Deleted Mar '84. Catalogue no: **POSPX 234**
7" Single: Released Apr '81, on Polydor, by Polydor Ltd. Deleted Apr '84. Catalogue no: **POSP 234**

LOVE MEETING LOVE
Tracks: / Love meeting love / Love meeting love (part 2).
12" Single: Released Aug '80, on Polydor, by Polydor Ltd. Deleted '83. Catalogue no: **POSPX 170**
7" Single: Released Aug '80, on Polydor, by Polydor Ltd. Deleted '83. Catalogue no: **POSP 170**

MICRO KIDS
Tracks: / Micro kids.
7" Single: Released Oct '83, on Polydor, by Polydor Ltd. Deleted Oct '86. Catalogue no: **POSP 643**

OUT OF SIGHT, OUT OF MIND
Tracks: / Out of sight, out of mind.
7" Single: Released Apr '83, on Polydor, by Polydor Ltd. Deleted Apr '86. Catalogue no: **POSP 570**

PHYSICAL PRESENCE EP - FOLLOW ME
Tracks: / Physical prescence / Follow me.
7" Single: Released Jun '85, on Polydor, by Polydor Ltd. Catalogue no: **POSP 746**
12" Single: Released Jun '85, on Polydor, by Polydor Ltd. Catalogue no: **POSPX 746**

RUNNING IN THE FAMILY (SINGLE)
Tracks: / Running in the family / Dream crazy.
12" Single: Released Jan '87, on Polydor, by Polydor Ltd. Deleted 31 May '89. Catalogue no: **POSPX 842**
7" Single: Released Jan '87, on Polydor, by Polydor Ltd. Catalogue no: **POSP 842**

SOMETHING ABOUT YOU
Tracks: / Something about you.
7" Single: Released Sep '85, on Polydor, by Polydor Ltd. Deleted '86. Catalogue no: **POSP 759**
12" Single: Released Sep '85, on Polydor, by Polydor Ltd. Catalogue no: **POSPX 759**

SOMETHING ABOUT YOU (IMPORT)
Tracks: / Something about you (sisa mix).
Note: Very hard to find 'Sisa mix'.
12" Single: Released Oct '88, on Mercury (Germany), Catalogue no: **883 3621**

STARCHILD
Tracks: / Starchild / Foundation & empire.
7" Single: Released Nov '81, on Polydor, by Polydor Ltd. Deleted Nov '84. Catalogue no: **POSP 343**

SUN GOES DOWN (LIVING IT UP), THE
Tracks: / Sun goes down (living it up), The.
7" Single: Released Jul '83, on Polydor, by Polydor Ltd. Deleted Jul '86. Catalogue no: **POSP 622**

TAKE A LOOK
Tracks: / Take a look (remix) / Man / Take a look (extended mix) (Only on 12" version and CD single.).
12" Single: Released Oct '88, on Polydor, by Polydor Ltd. Deleted 31 May '89. Catalogue no: **PZ 24**
7" Single: Released Oct '88, on Polydor, by Polydor Ltd. Deleted 30 May '89. Catalogue no: **PO 24**
CD 5": Released Oct '88, on Polydor, by Polydor Ltd. Catalogue no: **PZCD 24**
7" Single: Released '88, on Polydor, by Polydor Ltd. Deleted 30 May '89. Catalogue no: **POG 24**
12" Single: Released Oct '88, on Polydor, by Polydor Ltd. Deleted 30 May '89. Catalogue no: **PZY 14**

TAKE CARE OF YOURSELF
Tracks: / Take care of yourself / Silence / Man.
CD 5": Released Oct '89, on Polydor, by Polydor Ltd. Catalogue no: **PZCD 58**
7" Single: Released Oct '89, on Polydor, by Polydor Ltd. Catalogue no: **PO 58**
12" Single: Released Oct '89, on Polydor, by Polydor Ltd. Catalogue no: **PZ 58**
Cassingle: Released Oct '89, on Polydor, by Polydor Ltd. Catalogue no: **POCS 58**

TO BE WITH YOU AGAIN
Tracks: / To be with you again / Micro kid (live) / Lessons in love (Shep Pettibone remix) (Only on 12".).
12" Single: Released Apr '87, on Polydor, by Polydor Ltd. Deleted 31 May '89. Catalogue no: **POSPX 855**
7" Pic: Released Apr '87, on Polydor, by Polydor Ltd. Deleted Aug '87. Catalogue no: **POSPP 855**
7" Single: Released Apr '87, on Polydor, by Polydor Ltd. Catalogue no: **POSP 855**

TRACIE
Tracks: / Tracie (extended mix) (Only on 12" & CD single)) / Three words / Tracie (U.S. remix) (Only on 12"(PZX 34).).
Note: (A new mix of one of the most popular tracks from the album "Staring at the Sun")S
7" Single: Released 9 Jan '89, on Polydor, by Polydor Ltd. Deleted Oct '89. Catalogue no: **POG 34**
CD 5": Released 16 Jan '89, on Polydor, by Polydor Ltd. Catalogue no: **PZCD 34**
7" Single: Released 9 Jan '89, on Polydor, by Polydor Ltd. Deleted 30 Jun '89. Catalogue no: **PO 34**
12" Single: Released Jan '89, on Polydor, by Polydor Ltd. Deleted 30 Jun '89. Catalogue no: **PZ 34**
12" Single: Released 23 Jan '89, on Polydor, by Polydor Ltd. Catalogue no: **PZX 34**

TURN IT ON
Tracks: / Turn it on.
7" Single: Released Aug '81, on Polydor, by Polydor Ltd. Deleted Aug '84. Catalogue no: **POSP 286**

WEAVE YOUR SPELL
Tracks: / Weave your spell.
7" Single: Released Oct '82, on Polydor, by Polydor Ltd. Deleted Oct '85. Catalogue no: **POSP 500**
12" Single: Released Oct '82, on Polydor, by Polydor Ltd. Deleted Oct '85. Catalogue no: **POSPX 500**

WORLD MACHINE (SINGLE)
Tracks: / World machine (remix) / World machine (dub).
12" Single: Released Jul '88, on Polydor (USA), by PolyGram Rec.Inc.(USA). Catalogue no: **8854711**

Level One

(KEEP THE) CROWD IN PEACE
Tracks: / Keep the crowd in peace.
12" Single: Released Nov '88, on UNKNOWN, Catalogue no: **SF 828**

Levellers

CARRY ME
Tracks: / Carry me / What's in the way / Last days of winter, The / England my home.
12" Single: Released May '89, on Hag, by Primitive Records. Catalogue no: **HAG 005**

OUTSIDE INSIDE
Tracks: / Outside inside.
12" Single: Released Sep '89, on Hag, by Primitive Records. Catalogue no: **HAG 006**

Levert

CASANOVA
Tracks: / Casanova.
12" Single: Released Aug '87, on Atlantic, by WEA Records. Catalogue no: **A 9217 T**
7" Single: Released Aug '87, on Atlantic, by WEA Records. Deleted Jul '88. Catalogue no: **A 9217**

POP POP POP GOES MY MIND
Tracks: / Pop pop pop goes my mind / Looking for love.
7" Single: Released Oct '87, on Atlantic, by WEA Records. Catalogue no: **A 9389**
12" Single: Released Oct '87, on Atlantic, by WEA Records. Deleted Jul '88. Catalogue no: **A 9389 T**

Levett, Dave

AFRAID OF DEEP WATER
Tracks: / Afraid of deep water.
7" Single: Released Dec '88, on Cottage Industry, Catalogue no: **CIR 4**

Levi, Barrington

SHE'S MINE
Tracks: / She's mine / She's mine (version).
12" Single: Released 27 Feb '88, on Time, Catalogue no: **12 ATR 022**

Levi, Ijahman

CLOSER TO YOU
Tracks: / Closer to you / Crazes in strange places.
12" Single: Released Jul '82, on Jahmania, Catalogue no: **JM 1**

LEND A HAND
Tracks: / Lend a hand / Closer to you.
7" Single: Released Jun '82, on Tree Roots, Catalogue no: **7 JMI 266**
12" Single: Released Jun '82, on Tree Roots, Catalogue no: **12 JMI 266**

LILLY OF MY VALLEY
Tracks: / Lilly of my valley.
12" Single: Released Jun '85, on Jahmani, Catalogue no: **JMI 501**

MADGIE
Tracks: / Madgie.
12" Single: Released 12 May '89, on Jahmani, Catalogue no: **JMID 110**

MARCUS HERO
Tracks: / Marcus Hero.
12" Single: Released Aug '87, on Tree Roots, Catalogue no: **JMI 607**

MELLOW MUSIC
Tracks: / Mellow music.
12" Single: Released May '84, on Jah Man, Catalogue no: **JMI 403**

Levi, Michael

LABAMBA
Tracks: / Labamba.
12" Single: Released Oct '89, on Power, Catalogue no: **PW 89004**

Levi, Papa

BIG 'N' BROAD
Tracks: / Big'n'broad.
7" Single: Released Oct '84, on Island, by Island Records. Catalogue no: **IS 208**
12" Single: Released Oct '84, on Island, by Island Records. Catalogue no: **12IS 208**

BONNIE AND CLYDE
Tracks: / Bonnie and Clyde.
7" Single: Released Jun '84, on Island, by Island Records. Catalogue no: **IS 176**
12" Single: Released Jun '84, on Island, by Island Records. Deleted Jul '87. Catalogue no: **12IS 176**

TROUBLE IN AFRICA
Tracks: / Trouble in Africa.
12" Single: Released Nov '85, on Mango, by Island Records. Catalogue no: **12IS 235**

Levi, Philip

MI GOD, MI KING
Tracks: / Mi god, mi king / Inna me yard.
12" Single: Released Jan '84, on Level

Vibes, by Level Vibes Records. Catalogue no: **LV 002**

Levi, Sammy

FIVE POUND OF DUBS
Tracks: / Five pound of dubs.
12" Single: Released 30 May '89, on Eclipse, Catalogue no: **HCF 102112**

HEARTBREAKER
Tracks: / Heartbreaker.
12" Single: Released Oct '88, on Eclipse, Catalogue no: **HCF 101412**

HURTING ON THE INSIDE
Tracks: / Hurting on the inside.
12" Single: Released Sep '89, on Passion, by Skratch Records. Catalogue no: **PE 3**

IT A GO DONE
Tracks: / It a go done / My love.
12" Single: Released Mar '84, on Greensleeves, by Greensleeves Records. Catalogue no: **GRED 142**

IT'S A SHAME
Tracks: / It's a shame.
7" Single: Released Jun '88, on Witty, Catalogue no: **MMD 127**

KISS & SAY GOODBYE
Tracks: / Kiss and say goodbye.
12" Single: Released Jan '89, on Eclipse, Catalogue no: **HCF 101 512**

THREE RING CIRCUS
Tracks: / Three ring circus.
12" Single: Released Oct '88, on Carron, Catalogue no: **DT 012**

TROUBLE AGAIN
Tracks: / Trouble again / Float on.
12" Single: Released 27 Feb '88, on Eclipse, Catalogue no: **HCF 1009 12**

Levi, Tatti

FESTIVAL
Tracks: / Festival / Possee are you ready.
12" Single: Released 21 Nov '87, on Blakemix, Catalogue no: **BLKM 004**

Leviathan

SANDY JEAN
Special: Released Dec '86, on Azra (USA), by Azra International (USA). Catalogue no: **A 15**

Levine, Hank

IMAGE
Tracks: / Image.
7" Single: Released Dec '61, on H.M.V., by EMI Records. Deleted Dec '64. Catalogue no: **POP 947**

Levine, Steve

BELIEVIN' IT ALL
Tracks: / Believin' it all.
7" Single: Released Mar '84, on Chrysalis, by Chrysalis Records. Catalogue no: **CHS 2775**
12" Single: Released Mar '84, on Chrysalis, by Chrysalis Records. Catalogue no: **CHS 122775**

Levy, Barrington

Biographical details: Levy, Barrington This British reggae singer released his debut album *Englishman* in 1979, and has been recording on a regular basis ever since. Like many artists of his genre, his releases have appeared at a fast and furious rate on a variety of labels. In November 1984 he issued a duet LP with another cult reggae performer *Barrington Levy meets Frankie Paul*, in addition to this joint effort, the two singers seemed to be engaged in a battle to see which of them could cram the most record releases into a single year!
In early 1985 Levy made his debut appearance on the UK pop singles chart with the memorable song *Here I Come*. Unluckily it peaked at No.41, the most tantalising and frustrating position on the British charts. Had *Here I Come* cracked the Top 40 it would have received valuable exposure on Top of The Pops and BBC Radio One. But to the exasperation of many reggae lovers, who consistently complained that their music was given unsufficient airtime by the mass media, Barrington remained on the brink of a big breakthrough. (Bob Macdonald 6/12/85).

A YA WE DEH
Tracks: / A ya we deh.
12" Single: on Burning Sounds, by Burning Sounds Records. Deleted May '88. Catalogue no: **BVD 003**

BIG BOUT YA
Tracks: / Big bout ya.
12" Single: Released Sep '84, on Corner Store, Catalogue no: **UNKNOWN**

CRUCIFIXION
Tracks: / Crucifixion / Eventide / Fire a disaster.
7" Single: Released Nov '80, on Greensleeves, by Greensleeves Records. Deleted Nov '83. Catalogue no: **GRED 40**

DO IT
Tracks: / Do it.
7" Single: Released May '89, on Power House, Catalogue no: **UNKNOWN**

ENGLISHMAN
Tracks: / Englishman / Daughter them ire.
7" Single: Released Feb '80, on Greensleeves, by Greensleeves Records. Deleted Feb '85. Catalogue no: **GRED 28**

GET UP STAND UP
Tracks: / Get up stand up / Do the dance.
12" Single: Released Dec '85, on MGR, Catalogue no: **MGR 4**

HERE I COME (SINGLE)
Tracks: / Here I come.
12" Single: Released Dec '84, on Time One, Catalogue no: **LONX 62**
7" Single: Released Dec '84, on Time One, Catalogue no: **LON 62**

JAH BLACK
Tracks: / Jah black / Leave natty business.
12" Single: Released Mar '84, on Black Roots, Catalogue no: **BR 181262**

JUGGLING SOLDIER
Tracks: / Juggling soldier.
12" Single: Released May '86, on Live & Learn (USA), by Live & Learn Records (USA). Catalogue no: **LLD 104**

LIVING DANGEROUSLY
Tracks: / Living dangerously.
7" Single: Released Oct '88, on Time, Catalogue no: **7 TR 026**
12" Single: Released Oct '88, on Time, Catalogue no: **TR 026**

MINI BUS (ON THE TELEPHONE)
Tracks: / Mini bus (on the telephone) / Red eye.
12" Single: Released Mar '84, on Kingdom, by Kingdom Records. Deleted '86. Catalogue no: **KV 8028 12**
7" Single: Released Mar '85, on Kingdom, by Kingdom Records. Deleted '87. Catalogue no: **KV 8028**

MOMMY KISSING SANTA CLAUS
Tracks: / Mommy kissing Santa Claus / Flash your dread.
7" Single: Released Dec '85, on Thunderbolt, by Magnum Music Group. Deleted '89. Catalogue no: **DSR 6752**
12" Single: Released Dec '88, on Thunderbolt, by Thunderbolt Records. Deleted '89. Catalogue no: **DSR 6753**

MONEY MOVES
Tracks: / Money moves / Give me your love.
12" Single: Released May '85, on London Records, by London Records. Catalogue no: **LONX 67**
7" Single: Released May '85, on London Records, by London Records. Catalogue no: **LON 67**

MURDERER
Tracks: / Murderer / Tell them a ready.
12" Single: Released Mar '85, on Jah Life, Catalogue no: **JL 008**

ONE FOOT JO-JO
Tracks: / One foot Jo-Jo.
12" Single: Released Aug '84, on Jah Life, Catalogue no: **JL 005**

OPEN BOOK (SINGLE)
Tracks: / Open book.
12" Single: Released Dec '82, on Oak Sound, Catalogue no: **OSD 008**

PLEASE JAH JAH
Tracks: / Please jah jah.
12" Single: Released Mar '84, on Volcano, Catalogue no: **VPRD 169**

PRISON OVAL ROCK (SINGLE) Master mix
Tracks: / Prison oval rock.
12" Single: Released Jan '84, on Greensleeves, by Greensleeves Records. Catalogue no: **GRED 136**

REAL THING, THE
Tracks: / Real thing, The.
7" Single: Released Aug '85, on Time, Catalogue no: **7 TR 012**
12" Single: Released Aug '85, on Time, Catalogue no: **TR 012**

RUN AWAY
Tracks: / Run away.
12" Single: Released 21 Nov '87, on Time, Catalogue no: **12 TR 021**

SHAOLIN TEMPLE
Tracks: / Shaolin temple.
12" Single: on His Majesty, Deleted May '88. Catalogue no: **HMD 004**

STEP UP IN LIFE
12" Single: Released 5 Jun '89, on Time One, Catalogue no: **TOR 29**

STRUGGLER
Tracks: / Struggler / Moonlight lover.
12" Single: Released Dec '86, on Time, Catalogue no: **TR 020**
7" Single: Released Mar '87, on Time One, Catalogue no: **7 TR 020**

TOMORROW IS ANOTHER DAY
Tracks: / Tomorrow is another day / Delaware.
12" Single: Released Feb '82, on Greensleeves, by Greensleeves Records. Catalogue no: **GRED 80**

UNDER ME FANCY
Tracks: / Under me fancy / Fancy dub.
12" Single: Released Aug '84, on Time, Catalogue no: **TR 005**

WARM & SUNNY DAY
Tracks: / Warm and sunny day.
12" Single: Released Apr '80, on Cha-Cha, by Cha-Cha Records. Catalogue no: **CHAD 22**

Levy, Frankie

STEADY ROCK
Tracks: / Steady rock / Bloodline connection.
12" Single: Released Dec '85, on Firm (1), Catalogue no: **FR 777**

Levy, M

MRS JONES
Tracks: / Mrs. Jones.
12" Single: Released Aug '88, on Hawkeye, by Hawkeye Records. Catalogue no: **HD 90**

Levy, Marcy

CLOSE TO HER
Tracks: / Close to her / Waiting for you.
7" Single: Released Sep '82, on Epic, by CBS Records. Deleted '85. Catalogue no: **EPCA 2076**

HELP ME
Tracks: / Help me.
7" Single: Released Nov '80, on RSO, by Polydor Ltd. Deleted Nov '83. Catalogue no: **RSO 65**

Levy, Michael

EARLY MORNING LOVER
Tracks: / Early morning lover.
12" Single: Released Jul '88, on Exodus, Catalogue no: **EX 02**

Levy, Raymond

KARMA CHAMELEON
Tracks: / Karma chameleon.
12" Single: Released May '84, on BB, Catalogue no: **BBD 155**

Levy, Trevor

THEM A WOLF
Tracks: / Them a wolf.
12" Single: Released Dec '87, on Taurus, Catalogue no: **TRS 005**

Lewie, Jona

Biographical details: Lewie, Jona This British singer, songwriter, keyboardist and multi-instrumentalist, whose real name is John Lewis, has had a lengthy and varied career which has contained three hits plus much obscurity. His musical story goes back to the late Sixties when, while studing sociology he performed some gigs with future Hawkwind guitarist/vocalist Dave Brock. He then worked as a session musician, played piano in various London clubs and worked in the studio with the US blues veteran Arthur 'Big Boy' Crudup. He then became a member of the pub rock band Brett Marvin & The Thunderbolts, who won a tour support with Eric Clapton.
Lewis' first taste of chart success occurred in the summer of 1972, when Brett Marvin & The Thunderbolts changed their name to the quaintly ridiculous Terry Dactyl & The Dinosaurs and achieved a UK No.2 smash with *Seaside Shuffle* - the disc label gave sole composing credit to Lewis, although this ultra commercial single borrowed heavily from Mungo Jerry's 1970 No.1 *In The Summertime*. After the break up of the Dinosaurs/Thunderbolts, our hero spent the mid seventies playing in various small time London bands, while keeping the wolf from the door by pursuing a number of short lived occupations.
In late 1977 he adapted his name to Jona Lewis and signed with the much talked about Stiff Records, whose policy was to take on idiosyncratic an left field acts that had been ignored by the conservative major companies. The eccentric, likeable and every grinning Lewie fitted this description; the following year, he was among the acts on one of the semi-legendary Stiff multi artist package tours.
In 1980 Jona gave Stiff two sizeable UK hits. *You'll Always Find Me In The Kitchen At Parties* reached No.16 and his acclaimed anti-war Christmas song *Stop The Cavalary* logged five weeks at No.3. These witty singles seemed to point the way towards a fruitful Eighties career for the artist, but in fact his subsequent releases lived up to the name of his record label and flopped completely, although the catchy 1981 single *Louise* did well in certain countries. The erratic career of John Lewis/Jona Lewie appeared to be over though no pundit precluded the possibility of a comeback. (Bob Macdonald 6/12/85).

BIG SHOT-MOMENTARILY
Tracks: / Big shot momentarily.
7" Single: Released Jul '80, on Stiff, by Stiff Records. Catalogue no: **BUY 85**

GOD BLESS WHO EVER MADE YOU
Tracks: / God bless who ever made you.
7" Single: Released Nov '79, on Stiff, by Stiff Records. Catalogue no: **BUY 61**

I THINK I'LL GET MY HAIR CUT
Tracks: / I think I'll get my hair cut / What have I done.
7" Single: Released Jan '82, on Stiff, by Stiff Records. Catalogue no: **BUY 139**

LOUISE WE GET IT RIGHT
Tracks: / Louise, we get it right
7" Single: Released May '81, on Stiff, by Stiff Records. Catalogue no: **BUY 110**
12" Single: Released May '81, on Stiff, by Stiff Records. Deleted May '86. Catalogue no: **SBUY 110**

LOVE DETONATOR(see panel above

JONA LEWIE - LOVE DETONATOR (Released on Stiff)

Jona Lewie - You'll Always Find Me in the Kitchen at Parties (Stiff)

Tracks: / Love detonator / Baby, she's on the street, The.
7" Single: Released '83, on Stiff, by Stiff Records. Catalogue no: **BUY 170**

LOVE DONATOR
Tracks: / Love donator / Baby she's on the up.
12" Single: Released May '83, on Stiff, by Stiff Records. Catalogue no: **SBUY 170**
7" Single: Released May '83, on Stiff, by Stiff Records. Catalogue no: **BUY 170**

RE-ARRANGING THE DECK-CHAIRS..
Tracks: / Rearranging the deckchairs on the Titanic / I'll be home.
7" Single: Released Nov '81, on Stiff, by Stiff Records. Catalogue no: **BUY 131**

SHAGGY RAGGY
Tracks: / Shaggy raggy / Shaggy raggied.
7" Single: Released Jul '81, on Stiff, by Stiff Records. Catalogue no: **BUY 122**

STOP THE CAVALRY
Tracks: / Stop the cavalry / Laughing tonight.
7" Single: Released Nov '80, on Stiff, by Stiff Records. Catalogue no: **BUY 104**

YOU'LL ALWAYS FIND ME IN THE KITCHEN AT PARTIES (see panel above)
Tracks: / You'll always find me in the kitchen at parties / Bureaucrats.
7" Single: Released Feb '80, on Stiff, by Stiff Records. Catalogue no: **BUY 73**

Lewin, Christine

BEST IN ME, THE
Tracks: / Best in me, The.
12" Single: Released Dec '88, on Kufe, Catalogue no: **EB 011**

IN THE MOOD
Tracks: / In the mood / In the mood (instrumental dub).
7" Single: Released Jan '87, on Hot Vinyl, Catalogue no: **HVT 34**

IT'S A SECRET
Tracks: / It's a secret.
12" Single: Released Dec '84, on Kufe, Catalogue no: **EB 004**

JUICY FRUIT
Tracks: / Juicy fruit.
12" Single: Released Jan '84, on Kufe, Catalogue no: **EB 002**
7" Single: Released Jan '84, on Kufe, Catalogue no: **7EB 002**

LIFE
Tracks: / Life.
12" Single: Released Sep '87, on Kuse, Catalogue no: **EB 009**

SHOW ME (WHAT LOVE CAN DO)
Tracks: / Show me (what love can do).
12" Single: Released Nov '85, on Omega, Catalogue no: **OMS 1**

Huey Lewis and the News - If This is it (Released on Chrysalis)

Lewington, Brian

WALK ON THE OUTSIDE
Tracks: / Walk on the outside.
12" Single: Released 24 Jul '89, on Silver Heart, by Silver Heart Records. Catalogue no: **CUFF 1D**

Lewis

IF THE LOVE FITS
Tracks: / If the love fits / Can't wait another minute.
12" Single: Released Apr '86, on Riva, by Riva Records. Catalogue no: **RIVAT 45**
7" Single: Released Apr '86, on Riva, by Riva Records. Catalogue no: **RIVA 45**

Lewis, Carlton

SWEET SOUL ROCKING
Tracks: / Sweet soul rocking / Golden wonder.
12" Single: Released Mar '82, on Top Notch, by Fashion Records. Catalogue no: **TOP 2**

Lewis, Cheri

I JUST DON'T KNOW WHAT TO DO WITH MYSELF
Tracks: / I just don't know what to do with myself / Somebody help me.
12" Single: Released Feb '83, on Creole, by Creole Records. Catalogue no: **CR 1245**
7" Single: Released Feb '83, on Creole, by Creole Records. Catalogue no: **CR 45**

Lewis, C.S

YOU BELONG TO ME
Tracks: / You belong to me.
12" Single: Released Aug '88, on Sound City, by Sound City Records. Catalogue no: **SOC 1**

Lewis, Dale

JUST ANOTHER LOVE
Tracks: / Just another love / Love drive.
12" Single: Released Sep '88, on London Ocean & Coastal, by London Ocean & Coastal. Catalogue no: **LOC 1201**

Lewis, Dee

BEST OF MY LOVE, THE
Tracks: / This love.
Note: A cover of the classic hit "Best of My Love" which reached number 4 in the chart in 1977 and stayed there for 9 weeks. Remixed by the brilliant Phil harding of PWL.
12" Single: Released 30 May '88, on Phonogram, by Phonogram Ltd. Deleted 31 May '89. Catalogue no: **DEE 312**
7" Single: Released 30 May '88, on Phonogram, by Phonogram Ltd. Deleted Feb '89. Catalogue no: **DEE 3**
CD 5": Released 30 May '88, on Phonogram, by Phonogram Ltd. Deleted Feb '89. Catalogue no: **DEECD 3**

DON'T MAKE ME WAIT
Tracks: / Don't make me wait / This love.
7" Single: Released Jan '88, on Mercury, by Phonogram Ltd. Deleted Oct '88. Catalogue no: **DEE 2**
12" Single: Released Jan '88, on Mercury, by Phonogram Ltd. Deleted Oct '88. Catalogue no: **DEE 212**

STUCK ON LOVE
Tracks: / Stuck on love.
7" Single: Released Aug '87, on Mercury, by Phonogram Ltd. Deleted Oct '88. Catalogue no: **DEE 4**
12" Single: Released Aug '87, on Mercury, by Phonogram Ltd. Deleted Oct '88. Catalogue no: **DEE 412**

Lewis, Earl

CLOSE TO YOU (CAN'T GET)
Tracks: / Close to you.
12" Single: Released '88, on Debut, by Skratch Records. Catalogue no: **DEBTX 3039**

Lewis, Erica

YOU DON'T KNOW
Tracks: / You don't know.
7" Single: Released May '89, on Kenyon Force, Catalogue no: **UNKNOWN**

Lewis, Gary

MY HEARTS SYMPHONY
Tracks: / My hearts symphony.
7" Single: Released Feb '75, on United Artists, by EMI Records. Deleted Feb '78. Catalogue no: **UP 35780**

Lewis & Gilbert

ENDS WITH THE SEA
Tracks: / Ends with the sea.
7" Single: Released Aug '81, on 4AD, by 4AD Records. Catalogue no: **AD 106**

Lewis, Huey

BAD IS BAD
Tracks: / Bad is bad / Giving it all up for love / Doin' it all for my baby / Back in time.
12" Single: Released 17 Oct '87, on Chrysalis, by Chrysalis Records. Catalogue no: **HUEX 9**
12" Single: Released Oct '87, on Chrysalis, by Chrysalis Records. Catalogue no: **HUEYX 9**
7" Single: Released Oct '87, on Chrysalis, by Chrysalis Records. Catalogue no: **HUEY 9**

DO YOU BELIEVE IN LOVE
Tracks: / Do you believe in love / Is it me.
7" Single: Released '82, on Chrysalis, by Chrysalis Records. Deleted '87. Catalogue no: **CHS 2589**

DOIN' IT ALL FOR MY BABY
Tracks: / Doin' it all for my baby / Jacob's ladder / I know what I like.
12" Single: Released Jul '87, on Chrysalis, by Chrysalis Records. Catalogue no: **HUEYX 8**
7" Single: Released Jul '87, on Chrysalis, by Chrysalis Records. Catalogue no: **HUEY 8**

HEART AND SOUL
Tracks: / Heart and soul / You crack me up.
7" Single: Released Nov '85, on Chrysalis, by Chrysalis Records. Catalogue no: **HUEY 2**
7" Single: Released '83, on Chrysalis, by Chrysalis Records. Catalogue no: **CHS 2748**
12" Single: Released Nov '85, on Chrysalis, by Chrysalis Records. Catalogue no: **HUEYX 2**

HEART OF ROCK'N'ROLL
Tracks: / Heart of rock 'n' roll / Hope you love me like you say you do / Tatoo (Track on 12" version only) / Bad is bad (Track on 12" version only).
7" Single: Released Apr '86, on Chrysalis, by Chrysalis Records. Catalogue no: **HUEY 4**
12" Single: Released Apr '86, on Chrysalis, by Chrysalis Records. Catalogue no: **HUEYX 4**

HIP TO BE SQUARE
Tracks: / Hip to be square / Stuck with you / Back in time / Some of my lies are true.
7" Single: Released Nov '86, on Chrysalis, by Chrysalis Records. Catalogue no: **HUEY 6**
12" Single: Released Nov '86, on Chrysalis, by Chrysalis Records. Catalogue no: **HUEYX 6**

I WANT A NEW DRUG (CALLED LOVE)
Tracks: / I want a new drug (called love) / Finally found a home.
7" Single: Released Mar '84, on Chrysalis, by Chrysalis Records. Catalogue no: **CHS 2766**
12" Single: Released Mar '84, on Chrysalis, by Chrysalis Records. Catalogue no: **CHS 2766**

IF THIS IS IT (see panel below)
Tracks: / If this is it / Change of heart.
12" Single: Released Sep '84, on Chrysalis, by Chrysalis Records. Catalogue no: **CHS 122803**
7" Single: Released Sep '84, on Chrysalis, by Chrysalis Records. Catalogue no: **CHS 2803**

IF THIS IS IT (7" EP)
Tracks: / If this is it / Change of heart / Walkin' on a thin line (live) / Workin' for a living (live).
7" EP: Released '84, on Chrysalis, by Chrysalis Records. Catalogue no: **CHSP 2803**

PERFECT WORLD
Tracks: / Perfect world / Slammin' / Workin' for a living (live) (Only on 12" picture bag single.).
12" Single: Released Jul '88, on Chrysalis, by Chrysalis Records. Catalogue no: **HUEYYX 10**
CD 5": Released Jul '88, on Chrysalis, by Chrysalis Records. Catalogue no: **CDHUEY 10**
7" Single: Released Jul '88, on Chrysalis, by Chrysalis Records. Catalogue no: **HUEY 10**

POWER OF LOVE
Tracks: / Power of love, The / Do you believe in love.
7" Single: Released Aug '85, on Chrysalis, by Chrysalis Records. Catalogue no: **HUEY 1**
12" Single: Released Aug '85, on Chrysalis, by Chrysalis Records. Catalogue no: **HUEYX 1**

SIMPLE AS THAT
Tracks: / Simple as that / Walking on a thin line / Do you believe in love* / Bad is bad* / Workin' for a livin'.
12" Single: Released Mar '87, on Chrysalis, by Chrysalis Records. Catalogue no: **HUEYX 7**
CD 5": Released Mar '87, on Chrysalis, by Chrysalis Records. Catalogue no: **CDE 2**
7" Single: Released Mar '87, on Chrysalis,

by Chrysalis Records. Catalogue no: **HUEY 7**

SMALL WORLD (SINGLE)
Tracks: / Small world.
7" Single: Released Sep '88, on Chrysalis, by Chrysalis Records. Catalogue no: **HUEY 11**

STUCK WITH YOU
Tracks: / Don't ever tell me that you love me / Heart of rock 'n' roll (Extra track on 12" version only) / Trouble in paradise (Extra track on 12" version only).
12" Single: Released Aug '86, on Chrysalis, by Chrysalis Records. Catalogue no: **HUEYX 5**
7" Single: Released Aug '86, on Chrysalis, by Chrysalis Records. Catalogue no: **HUEY 5**

(TATTOO) GIVING IT ALL UP FOR LOVE
Tracks: / (Tattoo) Giving it all up for love / Do you believe in love / Some of my lies are true.
7" Single: Released '82, on Chrysalis, by Chrysalis Records. Deleted '87. Catalogue no: **CHS 2620**

WALKING WITH THE KID
Tracks: / Walking with the kid / Bad is bad / Back in time / I wanna new drug (CD single only).
CD 5": Released Feb '89, on Chrysalis, by Chrysalis Records. Catalogue no: **HUEYCD 13**
12" Single: Released Feb '89, on Chrysalis, by Chrysalis Records. Catalogue no: **HUEYX 13**
7" Single: Released Feb '89, on Chrysalis, by Chrysalis Records. Catalogue no: **HUEY 13**

WORLD TO ME
Tracks: / World to me / It's all right (live) / Naturally (12" only).
CD 5": Released Dec '88, on Chrysalis, by Chrysalis Records. Catalogue no: **HUEYCD 12**
12" Single: Released Dec '88, on Chrysalis, by Chrysalis Records. Catalogue no: **HUEYX 12**
7" Single: Released Dec '88, on Chrysalis, by Chrysalis Records. Catalogue no: **HUEY 12**

Lewis, Jerry

ROCK A BYE YOUR BABY (WITH A DIXIE MELODY)
Tracks: / Rockabye your baby with a Dixie melody.
7" Single: Released '57, on Brunswick, by Decca Records. Deleted '60. Catalogue no: **05636**

Lewis, Jerry Lee

Biographical details: Lewis, Jerry Lee This American singer and pianist was one of the greatest of the original Fifties rock'n'rollers. He was born in Ferriday, Louisiana in 1935 and began his career in the mid Fifties; in 1956 he joined Sam Phillips' seminal Memphis based label, Sun Records, where the similarly youthful Elvis Presley had recently launched his recording career.
Lewis' first single *Crazy Arms* was issued in that same year. It flopped but the singing pianist soon gained valuable experience by touring and recording with Carl Perkins, Johnny Cash and other lesser stars. Piano was a rock'n'roll instrument in those days - guitars were not totally dominant and Jerry Lee decided that it could be used not just as a musical medium but as a dynamic stage prop. He began to develop a wild live act in which he would leap from his seated position on the piano stool, kick the chair away and play his keyboards standing up; his playing postures became more and more ludicrous and outrageous. His act was later borrowed and developed by Elton John.
The four crucial singles of Lewis' career were released in a 12 month period from mid 1957 to mid 1958. These were the four hits that made him famous in the first place and then secured his legendary status for all time. *Whole Lotta Shakin' Goin' On* (No.3 in US, No.8 in UK) and *High School Confidential* (No.21 in US, No.12 in UK) overflowed with energy and raw riotous rebellion. Both voice and piano were employed in an exuberantly intense and overtly sexual manner. Though his music was rooted in country and western, a genre to which he would later return, Jerry Lee was the ultimate rock'n'roll performer to many people.
After this brief but golden period, Lewis' musical career was overshadowed by the uncertainties of his personal life; this state of affairs has continued ever since. In the summer of '58 he attracted a wave of adverse publicity because th press disapproved of the fact that his third wife was in fact his thirteen year old cousin. Occasional musical highlights, such as his 1961 UK Top 10 version of Ray Charles *What'd I Say*, were accompanied by frequent stories of his heavy drinking, verbal abuse towards fellow musicians, and family tragedies. He attracted a reputation as one of the most unpleasant and obnoxious characters in the entertainment business; but he had much to contend with - his elder brother had been killed by a drunken driver at an early age and Jerry Lee lost two sons in accidents.
Against this unhappy backdrop, Lewis returned to his country roots during the late Sixties and early Seventies and became a major force on the US country charts. Singles like *What's Made Milwaukee Famous (has made a loser of me)*, *There Must Be More To Love Than This*, *She Even Woke Me Up To Say Goodbye* and a remake of the Big Bopper's *Chantilly Lace* were perfect vehicles for his increasisngly emotional and reflective voice. Lewis continued recording and performing throughout th Seventies and into the Eighties but his personal life did not become any happier. He teetered on the brink of death in 1981 on account of a drink related stomach illness. In 1985 two further bouts of ill health sent the 50 year old star back into hospital. (Bob Macdonald 6/12/85).

6 TRACK HITS
Tracks: / Great balls of fire / Breathless / Whole lotta shakin' goin' on / High school confidential / Good golly Miss Molly / What'd I say.
7" EP: Released Sep '83, on Scoop 33, by Pickwick Records. Catalogue no: **7SR 5014**

BABY BABY BYE BYE
Tracks: / Baby baby bye bye.
7" Single: Released Jun '60, on London-American, Deleted Jun '63. Catalogue no: **HLS 9131**

BENNIE B.
Tracks: / Bennie B. / Baby baby bye / Down the line / I'm feeling sorry.
7" EP: Released Feb '80, on Bulldog (USA), by Bulldog Records (USA). Deleted Feb '83. Catalogue no: **BDE 17**

BREATHLESS
Tracks: / Breathless / High school confidential.
12" Single: Released Nov '83, on Charly, by Charly Records. Catalogue no: **CYZ 110**

BREATHLESS (2)
Tracks: / Breathless.
7" Single: Released Apr '58, on London-American, Deleted Apr '61. Catalogue no: **HLS 8592**

CHANTILLY LACE
Tracks: / Chantilly lace.
7" Single: Released May '72, on Mercury, by Phonogram Ltd. Deleted May '75. Catalogue no: **6052 141**
7" Single: Released Jan '80, on Sun, by Charly Records. Catalogue no: **LR 0483**

EVERYDAY I HAVE TO CRY SOME
Tracks: / Everyday i have to cry some / Who will the next fool be.
7" Single: Released Jan '80, on Elektra, by Elektra Records (UK). Deleted Jan '85. Catalogue no: **K 12399**

GOOD GOLLY MISS MOLLY (SINGLE)
Tracks: / Good golly Miss Molly.
7" Single: Released Feb '58, on London-American, Deleted Feb '61. Catalogue no: **HLU 8560**
7" Single: Released Mar '63, on London-American, Deleted Mar '66. Catalogue no: **HLS 9688**

GREAT BALLS OF FIRE
Tracks: / Great balls of fire / Breathless.
7" Single: Released 25 Sep '89, on Polydor, by Polydor Ltd. Catalogue no: **PO 57**
12" Single: Released 25 Sep '89, on Polydor, by Polydor Ltd. Catalogue no: **PZ 57**

GREAT BALLS OF FIRE (CD SINGLE)
Tracks: / Great balls of fire / High school confidential / Breathless / Whole lotta shakin' goin' on.
CD 5": Released Feb '89, on Charly, by Charly Records. Catalogue no: **CDS 2**

GREAT BALLS OF FIRE (OLD GOLD)
Tracks: / Great balls of fire / Whole lotta shakin' goin' on / What'd I say ('What'd I say' extra track on 12" only.).
7" Single: Released Jul '82, on Old Gold, by Old Gold Records. Catalogue no: **OG 9110**
12" Single: Released 27 Feb '89, on Old Gold, by Old Gold Records. Catalogue no: **OG 6115**

GREAT BALLS OF FIRE (SINGLE)
Tracks: / Great balls of fire.
7" Single: Released Dec '57, on London-American, Deleted Dec '60. Catalogue no: **HLS 8529**

HIGH SCHOOL CONFIDENTIAL
Tracks: / High school confidential.
7" Single: Released Jan '80, on Sun, by Charly Records. Catalogue no: **LR 1803**
7" Single: Released Jan '59, on London-American, Deleted Jan '62. Catalogue no: **HLS 8780**

LIL' BIT OF GOLD: JERRY LEE LEWIS
Tracks: / Whole lotta shakin' goin' on / High school confidential / End of the road / What'd I say.
CD 5": Released May '88, on Rhino, by Creole Records. Catalogue no: **R 373012**

LOVIN' UP A STORM
Tracks: / Lovin' up a storm.
7" Single: Released May '59, on London-American, Deleted May '62. Catalogue no: **HLS 8840**

MY FINGERS DO THE TALKING FOREVER
Tracks: / My fingers do the talking forever / Forever forgiving.
7" Single: Released Feb '83, on MCA, by MCA Records. Catalogue no: **MCA 808**

ROCKING JERRY LEE
Tracks: / Rocking Jerry Lee / Goodtime Charlie's got the blues.
7" Single: Released Mar '80, on Elektra, by Elektra Records (UK). Deleted '83. Catalogue no: **K 12432**

SWEET LITTLE SIXTEEN
Tracks: / Sweet little sixteen.
7" Single: Released Sep '62, on London-American, Deleted Sep '65. Catalogue no: **HLS 9584**

WHOLE LOTTA SHAKIN' GOIN' ON (SINGLE)
Tracks: / Whole lotta shakin' goin' on.
7" Single: Released Jan '80, on Sun, by Charly Records. Catalogue no: **LR 8293**
7" Single: Released Sep '57, on London-American, Deleted Sep '60. Catalogue no: **HLS 8457**

Lewis, Lena

MISSUS LA GROOVE
Tracks: / Missus la groove.
7" Single: Released Jul '85, on Carrere, Catalogue no: **CAR 367**
12" Single: Released Jul '85, on Carrere, Catalogue no: **CART 367**

Lewis, Lew

1.30, 2.30, 3.35
Tracks: / 1.30, 2.30, 3.35 / Mood I'm in.
7" Single: Released Apr '80, on Stiff, by Stiff Records. Deleted Apr '83. Catalogue no: **BUY 68**

SHAME SHAME SHAME
Tracks: / Shame shame shame.
7" Single: Released Aug '87, on Epic, by CBS Records. Catalogue no: **LOG Q2**
12" Single: Released Aug '87, on Waterfront, by Waterfront Music. Catalogue no: **WFT 35**

Lewis, Linda

Biographical details: Lewis, Linda This British singer and songwriter established herself as a leading session vocalist during the early Seventies - working with such artists as David Bowie, Al Kooper and Cat Stevens - before making it big with her self-penned 1973 single *Rock A Doodle Doo*. This was a track on her third album *Fathoms Deep*. *Rock A Doodle Doo* was a catchy lightweight soul/pop single, reaching No.15 and logging 11 weeks on the UK Top 50.
Throughout the Seventies Lewis' career was a somewhat erratic affair. She chalked up three further UK chart entries at odd intervals, between which she performed further session work. Her biggest hit was a revamped oldie, *It's In His Kiss*, which achieved a British No.6 placing in 1975, the same position that *Baby I'm Yours* took Linda to No.33 in '76. After suffering a period of acute depression in the late Seventies, she was restored to health and reached No.40 with her 1979 treatment of a song from Evita, *I'd Be Suprisingly Good For You*. She sang sessions for Steve Harley & Cockney Rebel, Rick Wakeman and Rod Stewart. All in all, this background work was her real forte; her high-pitched squealing, little girl voice sounded insubstantial when exposed as a solo vehicle.
Lewis' 1983 album *A Tear and a Smile* was her first for several years; her middle of the road blend of soul influenced pop failed to win any new converts and the LP flopped. (Bob Macdonald 7/12/85).

BABY I'M YOURS
Tracks: / Baby I'm yours.
7" Single: Released Apr '76, on Arista, by BMG Records (UK). Deleted Apr '79. Catalogue no: **ARISTA 43**

CLASS STYLE
Tracks: / Class style / You turn my bitter into sweet.
7" Single: Released May '84, on Electricity, by Electricity Records. Deleted '88. Catalogue no: **TRIC 5**
12" Single: Released May '84, on Electricity, by Electricity Records. Deleted '88. Catalogue no: **TRICT 5**
12" Single: Released May '84, on Electricity, by Electricity Records. Deleted '88. Catalogue no: **RTRIC 5**
7" Pic: Released May '84, on Electricity, by Electricity Records. Deleted '88. Catalogue no: **PTRIC 5**

CLOSE THE DOOR TAKE YOUR HEART
Tracks: / Close the door take your heart.
7" Single: Released Apr '85, on Epic, by CBS Records. Catalogue no: **A 3337**

I'D BE SURPRISINGLY GOOD FOR YOU
Tracks: / I'd be surprisingly good for you.
7" Single: Released Jun '79, on Ariola, by BMG Records (UK). Deleted Jun '82. Catalogue no: **ARO 166**

IT'S IN HIS KISS
Tracks: / It's in his kiss.
7" Single: Released Jul '75, on Arista, by BMG Records (UK). Deleted Jul '78. Catalogue no: **ARISTA 17**

IT'S IN HIS KISS (OLD GOLD)
Tracks: / It's in his kiss / Remember the days of the old schoolyard.
7" Single: Released Jan '89, on Old Gold, by Old Gold Records. Catalogue no: **OG 9852**

ROCK A DOODLE DOO
Tracks: / Rock a doodle doo.
7" Single: Released Jun '75, on Raft, Deleted Jun '78. Catalogue no: **RA 18502**

SLEEPING LIKE A BABY
Tracks: / Sleeping like a baby / Rolling for a while.
7" Single: Released Feb '80, on Ariola, by BMG Records (UK). Deleted Feb '82. Catalogue no: **ARO 207**

THAT'S LOVE
Tracks: / That's love / My aphrodisiac is you.
7" Single: Released Jun '80, on Ariola, by BMG Records (UK). Deleted Jun '83. Catalogue no: **ARO 231**

WHY CAN'T I BE THE OTHER WOMAN?
Tracks: / Why can't I be the other woman ? / Come on back.
7" Single: Released Oct '82, on Kaleidoscope Sound, by Kaleidoscope Sound Records. Deleted Oct '85. Catalogue no: **KRL A2860**

Lewis, Lindell

EASY RIDER
Tracks: / Easy rider.
12" Single: Released Mar '84, on Sea View, Catalogue no: **SV 4**

Lewis, Marcus

CLUB, THE
Tracks: / Club, The / I can tell you / Club (vocal mix) (Only on 12" version.) / Club, The (dub mix) (Only on 12" version.).
7" Single: Released Mar '89, on Epic, by CBS Records. Deleted Oct '89. Catalogue no: **654661 7**
CD 5": Released Apr '89, on Epic, by CBS Records. Deleted Oct '89. Catalogue no: **654661 2**
12" Single: Released Mar '89, on Epic, by CBS Records. Deleted Oct '89. Catalogue no: **654661 8**

Lewis, Norma

I'M GONNA TELL HIM TONIGHT
Tracks: / I'm gonna tell him tonight / I'm gonna tell him tonight.
12" Single: Released Nov '87, on Key, by Key Records. Deleted '87. Catalogue no: **12 KE 1**
7" Single: Released Nov '87, on Key, by Key Records. Deleted '87. Catalogue no: **7 KE 1**

I'M INTO YOUR LOVE
Tracks: / I'm into your love.
7" Single: Released May '82, on RCA, by BMG Records (UK). Deleted '85. Catalogue no: **KR 8**
12" Single: Released May '82, on RCA, by BMG Records (UK). Deleted '85. Catalogue no: **KRT 8**

THIS FEELINGS KILLING ME
Tracks: / This feelings killing me / Girl's the fool.
12" Single: Released Jan '82, on Jive, by Zomba Records. Deleted Jan '85. Catalogue no: **JIVET 11**
12" Single: Released Dec '81, on Chal-

lenge, by Elite Records. Deleted Dec '84. Catalogue no: **LOVER 1**
7" Single: Released Jan '82, on Jive, by Zomba Records. Deleted Jan '85. Catalogue no: **JIVE 11**

Lewis, Ramsey

Biographical details: Lewis Ramsey, This American pianist was born in Chicago in 1935 and began studying the keyboards at the age of six. After an impressive childhood and adolescence, during which his prodigious talent won his scholarships and plaudits galore, he formed the Ramsey Lewis Trio in 1956. Working as a piano/bass/drums unit, the threesome spent a decade building their reputation in the field of jazz. Work included numerous gigs in nightclubs, sessions in the studio for other jazz artists, plus their own albums, the first of which was released in 1959.
The slow but steady rise of the Ramsey Lewis Trio reached its climax in 1965, when they cruised to fame on the US national pop chart with an atmospheric cover version of *The In Crowd*. This catchy song had already been a US No.13 hit for vocalist Dobie Gray earlier in the same year, but the undeterred Lewis released his bluesy jazzy instrumental rendition and watched it shoot to No.5. Realising he was onto a good thing, he recorded a version of the McCoys' current No.1 smash *Hang On Sloopy* and got to No.11. 1966 brought him a US No.29 hit with the Beatles' *A Hard Day's Night*, plus a No.19 success with *Wade In The Water*. The latter was a Lewis arrangement of an ancient slaves' song; it gave the pianist a rare and belated British hit in 1972, peaking at No.31.
Concentrating on albums rather than singles during the late Sixties and Seventies, Lewis continued to enjoy considerable commercial success by revamping well known and not so familiar material with his punchy piano panache. He retained a distinctive blend of jazz, blues, pop and sould influences in his work and never succumbed to the conveyor belt blandness of such remake merchants as James Last. Some of Ramsey's Seventies albums were produced by members and associates of Earth Wind & Fire. He was still going strong in the Eighties. (Bob Macdonald 7/12/85).

UP WHERE WE BELONG
Tracks: / Up where we belong / Chance encounter.
7" Single: Released Dec '82, on CBS, by CBS Records. Deleted Dec '87. Catalogue no: **A 2946**

WADE IN THE WATER
Tracks: / Wade in the water.
7" Single: Released Apr '72, on Chess, by Vogue Records. Deleted Apr '75. Catalogue no: **6145 004**
12" Single: Released Jun '81, on Chess, by Vogue Records. Deleted Jun '84. Catalogue no: **CHESL 101**
7" Single: Released Jun '81, on Chess, by Vogue Records. Deleted Jun '84. Catalogue no: **CHES 101**

WADE IN THE WATER (OLD GOLD)
Tracks: / Wade in the water / In crowd, The.
7" Single: Released Jan '89, on Old Gold, by Old Gold Records. Catalogue no: **OG 9848**

Lewis, Shirley

HEARTBREAKER
Tracks: / Heartbreaker / Waiting for the dawn.
7" Single: Released Aug '89, on Breakout, by A&M Records. Catalogue no: **USA 661**
12" Single: Released Aug '89, on Breakout, by A&M Records. Catalogue no: **USAT 661**

REALISTIC
Tracks: / Realistic / Realistic (R&B version).
7" Single: Released 10 Jul '89, on A&M, by A&M Records. Catalogue no: **USA 660**
12" Single: Released 10 Jul '89, on A&M, by A&M Records. Catalogue no: **USAT 660**
CD 5": Released 10 Jul '89, on A&M, by A&M Records. Catalogue no: **USACD 660**

ROMANTIC
Tracks: / Romantic (Some like it hot mix) / Romantic (romancing the street mix).
Note: In a singing career that's spanned some fifteen years, Shirley (sister of Linda and Dee) has sung with numerous major artists, including Spandau Ballet, Wham!, Pet Shop Boys and Elton John. This wealth of experience is very much in evidence on her debut breakout release. Written by Jolley/Harris/Jolley, the song is infectious Brit-funk at its best. (A&M Records, June 88)
12" Single: Released Jun '88, on Breakout, by A&M Records. Deleted Feb '89. Catalogue no: **USAT 635**
7" Single: Released Jun '88, on Breakout, by A&M Records. Deleted Feb '89. Catalogue no: **USA 635**

ROMANTIC (HOT AND BOTHERED MIX)
Tracks: / Romantic (hot and bothered mix).
7" Single: Released Jun '88, on Breakout, by A&M Records. Catalogue no: **USAF 635**

Lewis Sisters

MELTING POINT
Tracks: / Melting point / Devil made me do it, The.
12" Single: Released Oct '86, on Riva, by Riva Records. Catalogue no: **RIVAT 47**
7" Single: Released Oct '86, on Riva, by Riva Records. Catalogue no: **RIVA 47**

SO GOOD SO RIGHT
Tracks: / So good so right / Dangerous.
7" Single: Released Jan '87, on Riva, by Riva Records. Catalogue no: **RIVA 48**
12" Single: Released Feb '87, on Riva, by Riva Records. Catalogue no: **RIVAT 48**

Lewis, Webster

GIMME SOME EMOTION
Tracks: / Gimme some emotion / I want to blow my horn.
7" Single: Released Apr '80, on Epic, by CBS Records. Deleted Apr '83. Catalogue no: **EPC 8510**

Ley, Eggy

EGGY LEY'S HOTSHOTS E.C.4
12" Single: Released Aug '89, on Viaphon, Catalogue no: **V 0508**

Leyton Buzzards

Biographical details: Leyton Buzzards Hailing from east London rather than the town of Leighton Buzzard, this all male British rock band was formed in the late Seventies. Their influences were the then prevalent punk scene and the pub rock sounds of bands like Doctor Feelgood. The Leyton Buzzards attracted some favourable attention with their 1978 single *19 and Mad*, released on the fashionable independent label, Small Wonder Records. At the same time, the group won national exposure by winning the Band of Hope and Glory Contest - this was a talent competition to discover new groups, organised by BBC Radio One and the Sun newspaper.
As is often the case, an artificial stimulus like a talent contest proved to be no guarantee of a successful career. After one superb satirical single *Saturday Night Beneath The Plastic Palm Trees* which reached the UK No.53 position in March 1979, the band sunk into immediate obscurity. Abridging their name to the Buzzards in late 1979 failed to improve their status and commodities like hope and glory were in conspicuously short supply.
The Buzzards evolved into Modern Romance in 1980. Hope and glory were just around the corner after all. (Bob Macdonald 7/12/85).

SATURDAY NIGHT (BENEATH THE PLASTIC PALM TREES)
Tracks: / Saturday night (beneath the plastic palm trees).
7" Single: Released Mar '79, on Chrysalis, by Chrysalis Records. Deleted Mar '82. Catalogue no: **CHS 2288**

Leyton, Johnny

CUPBOARD LOVE
Tracks: / Cupboard love.
7" Single: Released Feb '63, on H.M.V., by EMI Records. Deleted Feb '66. Catalogue no: **POP 1122**

DOWN THE RIVER NILE
Tracks: / Down the River Nile.
7" Single: Released Aug '62, on H.M.V., by EMI Records. Deleted Aug '65. Catalogue no: **POP 1054**

I'LL CUT YOUR TAIL OFF
Tracks: / I'll cut your tail off.
7" Single: Released Jul '63, on H.M.V., by EMI Records. Deleted Jul '66. Catalogue no: **POP 1175**

JOHNNY REMEMBER ME
Tracks: / Johnny remember me.
7" Single: Released Aug '61, on Top Rank (1), Deleted Aug '64. Catalogue no: **JAR 577**

JOHNNY REMEMBER ME (OLD GOLD)
Tracks: / Johnny remember me / Wild wind / Son this is she.
CD 5": Released 27 Feb '89, on Old Gold, by Old Gold Records. Catalogue no: **OG 6116**

LONE RIDER
Tracks: / Lone rider.
7" Single: Released Mar '62, on H.M.V., by EMI Records. Deleted Feb '65. Catalogue no: **POP 992**

LONELY CITY
Tracks: / Lonely city.
7" Single: Released May '62, on H.M.V., by EMI Records. Deleted May '65. Catalogue no: **POP 1014**

MAKE LOVE TO ME
Tracks: / Make love to me.
7" Single: Released Feb '64, on H.M.V., by EMI Records. Deleted Feb '67. Catalogue no: **POP 1264**

SON THIS IS SHE
Tracks: / Son this is she.
7" Single: Released Dec '61, on H.M.V., by EMI Records. Deleted Dec '64. Catalogue no: **POP 956**

WILD WIND
Tracks: / Wild wind.
7" Single: Released Oct '61, on Top Rank (1), Deleted Oct '64. Catalogue no: **JAR 585**

LF Bass

PLAY HER WAY
Tracks: / Play her way.
12" Single: Released Nov '88, on BPM, Catalogue no: **BP 12003**

LFPD

INDEPENDENT
Tracks: / Independent.
12" Single: on Island, by Island Records. Deleted Jun '88. Catalogue no: **12IS 354**Liaison

PLAY IT WITH PASSION
Tracks: / Play it with passion / Caught in a landslide.
7" Single: Released Nov '82, on Catweazle, by Catweazle Records. Deleted Nov '85. Catalogue no: **CR 001**

Liasons Dangereuses

LOS NINOS DEL PARQUE (SINGLE)
Tracks: / Los ninos del parque / Mystere dans la Brouillard.
7" Single: Released Jul '82, on Mute, by Mute Records. Deleted Jul '85. Catalogue no: **MUTE 023**
7" Single: Released Oct '88, on Road Runner (1), by Road Runner Records. Catalogue no: **RR 125537**

Liaz

HOUSE SENSATION
Tracks: / House sensation (radio mix) / House sensation (Kevin 'Master Reese' Saunderson mix) (Edited on 7" version) / House sensation (the next phase mix) (12" only) / House sensation (magic Juan's mix) (TENR 246 only).
12" Single: Released Feb '89, on 10 Records, by Virgin Records. Catalogue no: **TENR 246**
7" Single: Released 14 Nov '88, on 10 Records, by Virgin Records. Catalogue no: **TEN 246**
12" Single: Released 14 Nov '88, on 10 Records, by Virgin Records. Catalogue no: **TENX 246**

MISSION IMPOSSIBLE
Tracks: / Mission Impossible / Mission Impossible (house mix) / Mission Impossible (secret agent mix).
12" Single: Released May '87, on Kool Kat, by Kool Kat Records. Catalogue no: **KOOLT 4**

MISSION IMPOSSIBLE (THE IMPOSSIBLE 7" MIX)
Tracks: / Mission impossible (The impossible 7" mix) / Mission impossible (radio edit).
7" Single: Released 13 Jun '87, on Kool Kat, by Kool Kat Records. Catalogue no: **KOOL 4**
12" Single: Released 13 Jun '87, on Kool Kat, by Kool Kat Records. Catalogue no: **KOOLTR 4**

Liberace

Biographical details: Liberace This American pianist, whose full name is Wladzui Valentino Liberace, has been listed in the 'Guinness Book of Records' for many years as the world's highest paid live performer. He was born in West Allis, Wisconsin. Encouraged by his musical father, he took up the piano at the age of four. Shortly after the Second World War, he became internationally famous and has remained one of the best known institutions in showbusiness ever since. Renowed for his flamboyance and ultra nice personality as much for his crisp, expressive piano virtuosity. Liberace probably spends as much money on clothes in one month as most people spend on houses in their entire lifetime. With his glittering costumes, perfect hair, plastic looking face and dazzling set of teeth, he represents the ultimate image of the archetypal sugary superstar. Liberace is, according to some (usually cynical) observers, the living embodiment of the American Dream. Much of the credit for his showbiz survival should probably go to his management, which has remained stable for almost the whole of his forty year career.
Despite his stature as a live artist, Liberace's disc success has never been spectacular. He has never reached the British album chart and his only two forays into the UK singles list were *Unchained Melody* (No.20 in June 1955) and *I Don't Care* (No.28 in October 1956). Nevertheless, subsequent big sellers of the middle of the road keyboard records - such as France's Richard Clayderman and West Germany's Klaus Wunderlich - have much to thank Liberace for. (Bob Macdonald 7/12/85).

I DON'T CARE
Tracks: / I don't care.
7" Single: Released Oct '56, on Columbia, by EMI Records. Deleted Oct '59. Catalogue no: **DB 3834**

I'LL BE SEEING YOU
Tracks: / I'll be seeing you / I'll be seeing you.
7" Single: Released Mar '87, on MCA, by MCA Records. Catalogue no: **MCA 1138**

UNCHAINED MELODY
Tracks: / Unchained melody.
7" Single: Released Jun '55, on Philips, by Phonogram Ltd. Deleted Jun '58. Catalogue no: **PB 430**

Libertines

SMITH IS LIAR
Tracks: / Smith is a liah.
12" Single: Released Oct '89, on loose fish, Catalogue no: **PIKE 001**

Liberty

OUR VOICE IS TOMORROW'S HOPE
Tracks: / Our voice is tomorrow's hope.
7" Single: Released Feb '86, on Mortarhate, by Mortarhate Records. Catalogue no: **MORT 19**

Libra Libra

I AM MUSIC
Tracks: / I am music.
12" Single: Released Sep '87, on Chicago Connection(USA), Catalogue no: **CC 8703**

I LIKE IT
Tracks: / I like it / I like it (dub mix).
12" Single: Released Jan '87, on Champion, by Champion Records. Deleted Aug '89. Catalogue no: **CHAMP 1226**
7" Single: Released Jan '87, on Champion, by Champion Records. Catalogue no: **CHAMP 26**

Lick The Tins

BELLE OF BELFAST CITY
Tracks: / Belle of belfast city / Calliope house.
7" Single: Released Aug '86, on Sedition, by Sedition Records. Catalogue no: **EDIT 3312**
12" Single: Released Aug '86, on Sedition, by Sedition Records. Catalogue no: **EDITL 3312**

CAN'T HELP FALLING IN LOVE
Tracks: / Can't help falling in love / Bad dreams.
12" Single: Released Feb '87, on Sedition, by Sedition Records. Catalogue no: **EDITL 3308**
7" Single: Released Feb '87, on Sedition, by Sedition Records. Catalogue no: **EDIT 3308**

IN THE MIDDLE OF THE NIGHT
Tracks: / In the middle of the night / Looks like you / Road to California (Extra track on 12" version.).
12" Single: Released Mar '87, on Sedition, by Sedition Records. Catalogue no: **EDITL 3323**
7" Single: Released Mar '87, on Sedition, by Sedition Records. Catalogue no: **EDIT 3323**

Licks

1970'S
Tracks: / 1970's.
7" Single: Released Nov '79, on Stortbeat, by Stortbeat Records. Catalogue no: **BEAT 8**

Lie Lie, Bunny

I MISS YOU
Tracks: / I miss you.
12" Single: Released Oct '84, on Sweetcorn, Catalogue no: **SCR 001**

LOVE ME GIRL
Tracks: / Love me girl.
12" Single: Released May '85, on Time, Catalogue no: **TR 001**

MRS BROWN
Tracks: / Mrs. Brown / My sound.

12" Single: Released Jun '86, on Sweetcorn, Catalogue no: **SC 10**

Liege Lord

WARRIOR'S FAREWELL
Special: Released Jun '87, on Iron Works (USA), by Azra International (USA). Catalogue no: **IW 1013**

Lies All Lies

STILL NIGHT AIR
Tracks: / Still night air / Armchair holiday.
7" Single: Released May '86, on Face, by Face Records & Music. Catalogue no: **LAL 17**

WONDERLAND
Tracks: / Wonderland / Poorman's knight in shining armour, A.
7" Single: Released Feb '89, on Face, by Face Records & Music. Catalogue no: **LAL 27**

Lies Damned Lies

LOVE AMONG THE RUINS
Tracks: / Love among the ruins.
7" Single: Released Sep '89, on Siren, by Virgin Records. Catalogue no: **SRN 119**
12" Single: Released Sep '89, on Siren, by Virgin Records. Catalogue no: **SRNT 119**
CD 5": Released Oct '89, on Siren, by Virgin Records. Catalogue no: **SRNCD 119**

Lieutenant Pigeon

Biographical details: Lieutenant Pigeon This British group consisted of Nigel Fletcher, Mrs Fletcher, Steve Johnson and Robert Woodward.
Having evolved from an unsuccessful combo called Stavely Makepeace, Lieutenant Pigeon shot from total obscurity to No.1 on the British chart in the autumn of 1972. Had it not been for the fact that the Royal Scots Dragoon Guards topped the charts earlier that year with *Amazing Grace*, Pigeon's *Mouldy Old Dough* would probably have been classed as the most unlikely smash of the Seventies. A pub piano pounded out an ultra-catchy, nostalgic melody, while a gruff voice occasionally interrupted to growl the worlds 'Mouldy Old Dough' (derived from the Thirties band phrase 'vo-de-o-do). The sight of a woman in her fifties playing a jolly jangly joanna while a loony stood next to her grinning and groaning the three ridiculous words, was one of the most unexpected spectacles ever witnessed on BBC TV's 'Top of the Pops'. Mrs Fletcher (Nigel's mum) looked like she had just stepped out of your local village hall.
Mouldy Old Dough was composed by Nigel in conjunction with Robert Woodward. The pair dreamed up a fast tempo follow up called *Desperate Dan* which reached the UK No.17 position in early 1973. But the gimmick could not be milked any further and the group faded into obscurity after a spell of lucrative live work. (Bob Macdonald 7/12/85).

DESPERATE DAN
Tracks: / Desperate Dan.
7" Single: Released Dec '72, on Decca, by Decca Records. Deleted Dec '75. Catalogue no: **F 13365**

MOULDY OLD DOUGH
Tracks: / Mouldy old dough / Villain.
7" Single: Released Mar '82, on Decca, by Decca Records. Deleted '88. Catalogue no: **F 13278**
7" Single: Released Apr '82, on Old Gold, by Old Gold Records. Deleted Jun '89. Catalogue no: **OG 9261**

Lieutenant Stitchie

GIRLS NOWADAYS
Tracks: / Girls nowadays / Dream lover.
12" Single: Released 27 Feb '88, on June Star, Catalogue no: **DSI 002**

TICKLE ME FANCY
Tracks: / Tickle me fancy / Missing you.
12" Single: Released 27 Feb '88, on June Star, Catalogue no: **DSI 003**

Life

ALL PLAYED OUT
Tracks: / All played out / All played out (Dub Instrumental) / Bonus beat (Extra track on 12" version only.).
7" Single: Released Mar '86, on Lovebeat Int., Catalogue no: **LOV 4**
12" Single: Released Mar '86, on Lovebeat Int., Catalogue no: **LOVT 4**

FEEL SO GOOD
Tracks: / Feel so good.
12" Single: Released Oct '89, on Prophet, Catalogue no: **12PHET 1**

OPTIMISM
Tracks: / Optimism.
7" Single: Released Jul '85, on Factory (1), by Factory Records. Catalogue no: **FAC 122**

TELL ME
Tracks: / Tell me.
7" Single: Released Jul '84, on Factory (1), by Factory Records. Catalogue no: **FAC 106**

TOO LATE
Tracks: / Too late / Castles.
7" Single: Released Aug '80, on Media, Catalogue no: **SCREEN 2**

WELL PLEASED & SATISFIED
Tracks: / Well pleased & satisfied.
12" Single: Released Aug '82, on Exclusive, Catalogue no: **EXC 611128**

Life Ahead Corporation

RICH MEN'S BURDEN
Tracks: / Rich men's burden.
12" Single: Released Apr '85, on Truth (2), Catalogue no: **TRUET 002**

Life Force

INVITATION
Tracks: / Invitation.
7" Single: Released Aug '84, on Polo, by Polo Records. Deleted '88. Catalogue no: **POLO 34**
12" Single: Released Aug '84, on Polo, by Polo Records. Deleted '88. Catalogue no: **POLO 12-34**

MAN IN A MILLION
Tracks: / Man in a million.
7" Single: Released Jun '85, on Polo, by Polo Records. Deleted '88. Catalogue no: **POLO 38**
12" Single: Released Jun '85, on Polo, by Polo Records. Deleted '88. Catalogue no: **POLO 12-38**

REACH FOR THE STARS
Tracks: / Reach for the stars.
12" Single: Released Jan '85, on Polo, by Polo Records. Deleted '88. Catalogue no: **POLO 12-37**
7" Single: Released Jan '85, on Polo, by Polo Records. Deleted '88. Catalogue no: **POLO 37**

WHAT A WAY TO GO
Tracks: / What a way to go.
12" Single: Released May '84, on Polo, by Polo Records. Deleted '88. Catalogue no: **POLO 12-33**
7" Single: Released May '84, on Polo, by Polo Records. Deleted '88. Catalogue no: **POLO 33**

Life Studies

HOMEWARD
Tracks: / Homeward.
7" Single: Released Aug '83, on Occasion, Catalogue no: **OCC 001**

Lifesighs

GET SERIOUS
Tracks: / Get serious.
7" Single: Released Oct '85, on Pressure, Catalogue no: **HAVE 1**
12" Single: Released Oct '85, on Pressure, Catalogue no: **12HAVE 1**

Lift

DON'T YOU TREAT ME LIKE A LOVER
Tracks: / Don't you treat me like a lover / Don't you treat me like a lover (extended) / Ain't it strange (rub-a-dub mix) / Love game (theme from) (On 12" single.).
12" Single: Released Nov '87, on Magnet, by WEA Records. Deleted Jan '88. Catalogue no: **MAGT 313**
7" Single: Released Nov '87, on Magnet, by WEA Records. Deleted Jan '88. Catalogue no: **MAG 313**

UNITED STATES
Tracks: / United States / L.I.F.T..
12" Single: Released Jun '87, on Magnet, by WEA Records. Deleted Jan '88. Catalogue no: **MAGT 295**
7" Single: Released Jun '87, on Magnet, by WEA Records. Deleted Jan '88. Catalogue no: **MAG 295**

Lift Up

DIAMONDS NEVER MADE A LADY
Tracks: / Diamonds never made a lady (extended mix) / Diamonds never made a lady (Inst).
12" Single: Released Jan '87, on Greyhound, by Greyhound Records. Catalogue no: **GRY 005**

Ligament Blub Brothers

BIG SHOE BOY
Tracks: / Big boy shoe.
7" Single: Released Aug '86, on Scrundle-patch, Catalogue no: **BLUB 01**

Liggett, Otis

EVERY BREATH YOU TAKE
Tracks: / Every breath you take.
12" Single: Released Oct '83, on Warehouse, by Warehouse Records. Catalogue no: **WARET 2**
7" Single: Released Oct '83, on Warehouse, by Warehouse Records. Catalogue no: **WARE 2**

Liggins, Len

HEADFUL OF ANTS, A
Note: 4-track 12" E.P.
12" Single: Released Jan '88, on AAZ, by AAZ Records. Catalogue no: **AAZ 8**

REMEDY FOR BAD NERVES, A
Tracks: / Remedy for bad nerves, A.
7" EP: Released Sep '85, on AAZ, by AAZ Records. Catalogue no: **AAZ 4**

Light

CONTRASTING STRANGERS
Tracks: / Contrasting strangers / Monument / Thinking of you (Extra track on 12" version only.).
7" Single: Released Feb '86, on Inevitable, by Inevitable Records. Catalogue no: **ZB 40149**
7" Single: Released Jun '85, on Inevitable, by Inevitable Records. Catalogue no: **ZB 70149**
12" Single: Released Jun '85, on Inevitable, by Inevitable Records. Catalogue no: **ZT 70150**
12" Single: Released Feb '86, on Inevitable, by Inevitable Records. Catalogue no: **ZT 401 50**

PRIDE IS WINNING
Tracks: / Pride of winning / Ten million years.
12" Single: Released Jun '86, on Inevitable, by Inevitable Records. Catalogue no: **ZT 407 50**
7" Single: Released Jun '86, on Inevitable, by Inevitable Records. Catalogue no: **ZB 407 49**

TURN OUT THE LIGHT
Tracks: / Turn out the light.
7" Single: Released Jan '80, on Shock Rock (Ireland), by Outlet Records. Catalogue no: **SRS 501**

Light A Big Fire

CHARLENE
Tracks: / Charlene / Hunger / Shape I'm in, The.
12" Single: Released Aug '86, on Siren, by Virgin Records. Deleted May '88. Catalogue no: **SIREN 25-12**
7" Single: Released Aug '86, on Siren, by Virgin Records. Deleted May '88. Catalogue no: **SIREN 25**

I SEE PEOPLE
Tracks: / I see people / Jonny on all fours / Mr. Twilight (live).
7" Single: Released Mar '87, on Siren, by Virgin Records. Deleted May '88. Catalogue no: **SRN 45**
12" Single: Released Mar '87, on Siren, by Virgin Records. Deleted May '88. Catalogue no: **SRN 45-12**

MR TWILIGHT
Tracks: / Mr. Twilight / Lovers.
7" Single: Released Nov '86, on Siren, by Virgin Records. Deleted May '88. Catalogue no: **SIREN 28**
12" Single: Released Nov '86, on Siren, by Virgin Records. Deleted May '88. Catalogue no: **SIREN 28-12**

Light Of The World

Biographical details: Light of The World Percussionist/vocalist Ganiyu 'Gee' Bello was the leader of this successful London based disco/soul/jazz band whose line up was a flexible and ever changing phenomenon. An assemblage of 22 musicians and vocalists contributed to the group's 1980 album *Round Trip*. Light of The World's importance lay in the fact that they were at the forefront of the Britfunk boom. Soul, disco and jazz funk music had always been dominated by the United States but, during the late Seventies and early Eighties, Light of The World and other acts like The Real Thing, Heatwave, Level 42, Heatwave, Hi-Tension, Linx, Shakatak and The onlympic Runners showed that the UK could become a potent force in the genre.
Light of The World first appeared on the British charts in the spring of 1979 with their single *Swingin'*, which reached No.45 and won them a *Top Of The Pops* appearance. A whole series of minor hits occured during 1979-81, the most successful of which the breezy ballad *I'm So Happy* (No.35). *Round Trip* reached No.73 on Britain's LP list. LOTW's success was based in the clubs, and radio play was erratic.
In early 1981, in the midst of their chart success, various members of Light of The World broke away to form two seperate spinoff bands, Beggar & Co. and Incognito. A hard core of the three members masterminded LOTW's 1982 album *Check Us Out*, but it did not achieve the unexpected commercial acceptance and the band folded. After keeping a low profile for a while, Gee Bello re-emerged in 1985 with another loose assemblage of flexible friends called The Team, who scored a big success in the discos with *Wicki Wacky House Party*. (Bob Macdonald 8/12/85).

BOYS IN BLUE
Tracks: / Boys in blue / This is this.
12" Single: Released Feb '80, on Ensign, by Ensign Records. Deleted Feb '83. Catalogue no: **ENY 36-12**
7" Single: Released Feb '80, on Ensign, by Ensign Records. Deleted Feb '83. Catalogue no: **ENY 36**

CHECK US OUT (SINGLE)
Tracks: / Check us out / I can't stop.
7" Single: Released May '82, on EMI, by EMI Records. Deleted '85. Catalogue no: **EMI 5294**
12" Single: Released May '82, on EMI, by EMI Records. Deleted '85. Catalogue no: **12 EMI 5294**

FAMOUS FACES
Tracks: / Famous faces / Get on board.
7" Single: Released Sep '82, on EMI, by EMI Records. Catalogue no: **EMI 5324**
12" Single: Released Aug '82, on EMI, by EMI Records. Catalogue no: **12 EMI 5324**

I SHOT THE SHERIFF
Tracks: / I shot the sheriff / New soft song.
7" Single: Released Jan '81, on Ensign, by Ensign Records. Deleted Jan '84. Catalogue no: **ENY 46**
12" Single: Released Nov '80, on Ensign, by Ensign Records. Deleted '83. Catalogue no: **ENY 4612**

JEALOUS LOVER
Tracks: / Jealous lover.
12" Single: Released Jul '83, on EMI, by EMI Records. Catalogue no: **12 EMI 5403**
7" Single: Released Jul '83, on EMI, by EMI Records. Catalogue no: **EMI 5403**

LONDON TOWN
Tracks: / London town / Pete's crusade.
7" Single: Released Oct '80, on Ensign, by Ensign Records. Deleted Oct '83. Catalogue no: **ENY 43**

LONDON TOWN '85
Tracks: / London Town '85.
7" Single: Released Jun '85, on Ensign, by Ensign Records. Deleted '86. Catalogue no: **ENY 518**
12" Single: Released Jun '85, on Ensign, by Ensign Records. Deleted '87. Catalogue no: **12ENY 518**

LONDON TOWN (OLD GOLD)
Tracks: / London town / Time.
12" Single: Released 30 Jan '89, on Old Gold, by Old Gold Records. Catalogue no: **OG 4095**

MIDNIGHT GROOVIN'
Tracks: / Midnight groovin'.
7" Single: Released Jul '79, on Ensign, by Ensign Records. Deleted Jul '82. Catalogue no: **ENY 29**

RIDE THE LOVE TRAIN
Tracks: / Ride the love train / Get on board.
12" Single: Released Nov '81, on EMI, by EMI Records. Deleted Nov '83. Catalogue no: **12EMI 5242**
7" Single: Released Nov '81, on EMI, by EMI Records. Deleted Nov '83. Catalogue no: **EMI 5242**

SWINGIN'
Tracks: / Swingin'.
7" Single: Released Apr '79, on Ensign, by Ensign Records. Deleted Apr '82. Catalogue no: **ENY 22**

TIME
Tracks: / Time / I'm so happy.
12" Single: Released Mar '81, on Mercury, by Phonogram Ltd. Deleted Mar '84. Catalogue no: **MERX 64**
7" Single: Released Mar '81, on Mercury, by Phonogram Ltd. Deleted Mar '84. Catalogue no: **MER 64**

Light & Shade

L'AMOUR
Tracks: / L'amour.
7" Single: Released Mar '85, on Light & Shade, Catalogue no: **LS 22**

Lightfoot, Gordon

BABY STEP BACK
Tracks: / Baby step back / Thank you for the promises.
7" Single: Released May '82, on Warner Bros., by WEA Records. Deleted May '85. Catalogue no: **K 17945**

DAYLIGHT KATY
Tracks: / Daylight Katy.
7" Single: Released Aug '78, on Warner Bros., by WEA Records. Deleted Aug '81. Catalogue no: **K 17214**

DREAM STREET ROSE (SINGLE)

Tracks: / Dream Street rose / Make way for the lady.
7" Single: Released 20 Jun '80, on Warner Bros., by WEA Records. Deleted '83. Catalogue no: **K 17637**

IF YOU COULD READ MY MIND (OLD GOLD)
Tracks: / If you could read my mind.
7" Single: Released Apr '86, on Old Gold, by Old Gold Records. Catalogue no: **OG 9572**

IF YOU COULD READ MY MIND (SINGLE)
Tracks: / If you could read my mind.
7" Single: Released '80, on Reprise, by WEA Records. Catalogue no: **LR 1178**
7" Single: Released Jun '71, on Reprise, by WEA Records. Deleted Jun '74. Catalogue no: **RS 20974**

SUNDOWN (SINGLE)
Tracks: / Sundown.
7" Single: Released Aug '74, on Sundown, by Magnum Music Group. Deleted Aug '77. Catalogue no: **K 14327**

WRECK OF THE EDMUND FITZGERALD, THE
Tracks: / Wreck of the Edmund Fitzgerald, The.
7" Single: Released Jan '77, on Reprise, by WEA Records. Deleted Jan '80. Catalogue no: **K 14451**

Lightfoot, Terry

KING KONG
Tracks: / King kong.
7" Single: Released Nov '61, on Columbia, by EMI Records. Deleted Nov '64. Catalogue no: **SCD 2165**

LONESOME
Tracks: / Lonesome / Bloodshot eyes.
7" Single: Released Jan '87, on PRT, by Castle Communications Records. Catalogue no: **PRT 7P 370**

TAVERN IN THE TOWN
Tracks: / Tavern in the town.
7" Single: Released May '62, on Columbia, by EMI Records. Deleted Jun '65. Catalogue no: **DB 4822**

TRUE LOVE
Tracks: / True love.
7" Single: Released Aug '61, on Columbia, by EMI Records. Deleted Aug '64. Catalogue no: **DB 4696**

Lightnin' Rod

DORIELLA DU FONTANE
Tracks: / Doriella du fontane.
12" Single: Released Jun '84, on Celp, Catalogue no: **CART 332**

Lightning Raiders

CITIZENS
Tracks: / Citizens / Criminal world.
7" Single: Released Sep '81, on Revenge (2), by Island Records. Deleted '84. Catalogue no: **REVS 101**

PSYCHEDELIC MUSIC
Tracks: / Psychedelic music / Views.
7" Single: Released Apr '80, on Arista, by BMG Records (UK). Deleted Apr '83. Catalogue no: **ARIST 341**

Lightning Seeds

JOY
Tracks: / Joy.
CD 5": Released Nov '89, on Ghetto, by CBS Records. Catalogue no: **GTG 6 CD**
12" Single: Released Oct '89, on Ghetto, by CBS Records. Catalogue no: **BIG 7T**
7" Single: Released Oct '89, on Ghetto, by CBS Records. Catalogue no: **BIG 7**

PURE
Tracks: / Pure.
12" Single: Released 5 Jun '89, on Ghetto (2), Catalogue no: **GTG 004 T**
7" Single: Released 5 Jun '89, on Ghetto (2), Catalogue no: **GTG 004**
CD 5": Released 5 Jun '89, on Ghetto (2), Catalogue no: **GTG 004 CD**

UPSIDE DOWN
Tracks: / Upside down.
CD 5": Released 9 Oct '89, on Ghetto, by CBS Records. Catalogue no: **GTG 7CD**
12" Single: Released 9 Oct '89, on Ghetto, by CBS Records. Catalogue no: **GTG 7T**
7" Single: Released 9 Oct '89, on Ghetto, by CBS Records. Catalogue no: **GTG 7**

Likie D

LET ME LOVE YOU NOW
Tracks: / Let me love you now.
12" Single: Released May '88, on Pioneer Muzik, Catalogue no: **PM 006**

L'il Louis

FREQUENCY
Tracks: / Frequency.
12" Single: Released Oct '87, on Media Mania (USA), Catalogue no: **DM 008**

Lilac Time

AMERICAN EYES
Tracks: / American eyes / World in her arms / Crossing the line (Only on 12" and CD single.) / Shepherd's plaid (Only on CD single.).
Note: 1988 saw the release of the Lilac Time's eponymous debut album. It was intelligent, charming, uncluttered, acoustic pop, perfectly showcasing Stephen Duffy's songwriting talents. The album and subsequent singles received almost unprecidented critical acclaim in both the music and quality press alike. By large however, it remained an undiscovered jewel. This single offers all the wry wit and intelligent dream of the debut album, but this time offers a greater depth, sophistication and variety both in terms of production and songwriting. (Phonogram, July 1989)
CD 5": Released Jul '89, on Phonogram, by Phonogram Ltd. Catalogue no: **LILCD 5**
7" Single: Released Jul '89, on Phonogram, by Phonogram Ltd. Catalogue no: **LILAC 5**
Cassingle: Released Jul '89, on Phonogram, by Phonogram Ltd. Catalogue no: **LILMC 5**
12" Single: Released Jul '89, on Phonogram, by Phonogram Ltd. Catalogue no: **LILAC 512**

BLACK VELVET
Tracks: / Black velvet / Black dawn / Tiger tea (12" only) / Street (CD only).
7" Single: Released Nov '88, on Fontana, by Phonogram Ltd. Deleted 31 May '89. Catalogue no: **LILAC 4**
7" Single: Released Nov '88, on Fontana, by Phonogram Ltd. Deleted 31 May '89. Catalogue no: **LILXM 4**
CD 5": Released Nov '88, on Fontana, by Phonogram Ltd. Catalogue no: **LILCD 4**
12" Single: Released Nov '88, on Fontana, by Phonogram Ltd. Deleted 31 May '89. Catalogue no: **LILAC 412**

DAYS OF THE WEEK, THE
Tracks: / Days of the week, The / Queen of heartless, The.
7" Single: Released Sep '89, on Fontana, by Phonogram Ltd. Catalogue no: **LILAC 6**
12" Single: Released Sep '89, on Fontana, by Phonogram Ltd. Catalogue no: **LILAC 612**
CD 5": Released Sep '89, on Fontana, by Phonogram Ltd. Catalogue no: **LILCD 6**

RETURN TO YESTERDAY
Tracks: / Return to yesterday / Trumpets from Montparnasse.
Note: The 12" and CD single feature two extra tracks.
7" Single: Released 4 Jul '88, on Phonogram, by Phonogram Ltd. Deleted Feb '89. Catalogue no: **LILAC 2**
7" Single: Released Feb '88, on Swordfish, by Swordfish Records. Catalogue no: **LILAC 1**
12" Single: Released Feb '88, on Swordfish, by Swordfish Records. Catalogue no: **12LILAC 1**
CD 5": Released 4 Jul '88, on Phonogram, by Phonogram Ltd. Deleted Feb '89. Catalogue no: **LILCD 2**
12" Single: Released 4 Jul '88, on Phonogram, by Phonogram Ltd. Deleted Feb '89. Catalogue no: **LILAC 212**

YOU'VE GOT TO LOVE
Tracks: / You've got to love / Railway bazaar / Trumpets from Montparnasse (Only on 12".).
12" Single: Released Oct '88, on Fontana, by Phonogram Ltd. Deleted Feb '89. Catalogue no: **LILAC 312**
7" Single: Released Oct '88, on Fontana, by Phonogram Ltd. Deleted Feb '89. Catalogue no: **LILAC 3**
CD 5": Released Oct '88, on Fontana, by Phonogram Ltd. Deleted Feb '89. Catalogue no: **LILCD 3**

Lilac Trumpets

SOMEONE ELSES WORLD
Tracks: / Someone else's world.
12" Single: Released 1 Oct '86, on Pink Pop, Catalogue no: **POP 001**

Liliput

DIE MATROSEN
Tracks: / Die matrosen.
7" Single: Released Jul '80, on Rough Trade, by Rough Trade Records. Catalogue no: **RT 047**

EISGERWIND
Tracks: / Eisgerwind / When the cat's away.
7" Single: Released Feb '81, on Rough Trade, by Rough Trade Records. Catalogue no: **RT 062**

YOU DID IT
Tracks: / You did it.
7" Single: Released Jul '83, on Rough Trade, by Rough Trade Records. Catalogue no: **RTD 01**

Lillo

YOU'RE A GOOD GIRL
Tracks: / You're a good girl.
12" Single: Released Aug '83, on Capitol, by EMI Records. Deleted '88. Catalogue no: **12 CL 303**
7" Single: Released Aug '83, on Capitol, by EMI Records. Deleted Jan '88. Catalogue no: **CL 303**

Limahl

Biographical details: This British singer and songwriter's real name is Chris Hamill; his stage monicker is an anagram of his surname. He had tried his hand at acting and pantomine, before shooting to fame in early 1983 as vocalist and frontman with Kajagoogoo. Having answered a classified ad, he had been the last to join the teeny-bop band; he soon became the first to leave, because his four colleagues resented the fact that he was snatching all the limelight. The acrimonous rift took place in the summer of '83, a mere six months after they had first come to fame.
Limahl launched his solo career in the autumn of that year with the self penned single *Only for love*. Not dissimilar to the group's lightweight, danceable pop style, *Only for love* reached No.16 on the UK chart. After almost a year away from the spotlight, a period interrupted only by the disappointing minor hit *Too much trouble*, the singer bounced back in late 1984 with *Never ending story*, his biggest success since Kajagoogoo's opening No.1 smash *Too shy*. The ultra-catchy *Never ending story* was written and produced by the famous workaholic Italian-born pop/disco maestro Giorgio Moroder; the vocals were actually a duet with an uncredited singer named Beth Anderson. The single became a big worldwide hit, culminating in a US Top 20 placing; it UK peak position was No.4. But the fact that Limahl required so much assistance on the record cast doubt on his ability to carve a viable long-term solo career. Apart from the continuing international success of *Story* 1985 proved to be a blank year for him. (Bob MacDonald, 12th Dec 1985).

INSIDE TO OUTSIDE
Tracks: / Inside to outside / Shock.
7" Single: Released Sep '86, on EMI, by EMI Records. Catalogue no: **EMI 5570**
12" Single: Released Sep '86, on EMI, by EMI Records. Deleted Jul '87. Catalogue no: **12 EMI 5570**

LOVE IN YOUR EYES
Tracks: / Love in your eyes / Love will tear the soul.
7" Pic: Released Apr '86, on EMI, by EMI Records. Catalogue no: **EMIP 5558**
12" Single: Released Apr '86, on EMI, by EMI Records. Catalogue no: **12 EMI 5558**
7" Single: Released Apr '86, on EMI, by EMI Records. Catalogue no: **EMI 5558**

NEVER ENDING STORY
Tracks: / Never ending story.
7" Single: Released Oct '84, on EMI, by EMI Records. Catalogue no: **LML 3**
12" Single: Released Oct '84, on EMI, by EMI Records. Deleted '87. Catalogue no: **12LML 3**

ONLY FOR LOVE
Tracks: / Only for love / O.T.T..
7" Pic: Released Oct '83, on EMI, by EMI Records. Catalogue no: **LMLP 1**
7" Single: Released Oct '83, on EMI, by EMI Records. Deleted '86. Catalogue no: **LML 1**
12" Single: Released Oct '83, on EMI, by EMI Records. Deleted '86. Catalogue no: **12LML1**

TOO MUCH TROUBLE
Tracks: / Too much trouble / You've been gone a little while.
7" Pic: Released May '84, on EMI, by EMI Records. Catalogue no: **12LMLP 2**
7" Single: Released May '84, on EMI, by EMI Records. Deleted '86. Catalogue no: **LML 2**
12" Single: Released May '84, on EMI, by EMI Records. Deleted '86. Catalogue no: **12LML 2**

Limbo

MAN UNITED
Tracks: / Man United.
7" Single: Released Feb '85, on Weasel, by Weasel Records. Catalogue no: **WR 4009**

Lime

UNEXPECTED LOVERS
Tracks: / Do your time on the planet / Profile of love / Are you being untrue tonight / Alive and well / Say you love me / My lovely angel / Unexpected lovers / I'm falling in love.
7" Single: Released Jul '85, on Boiling Point, by Polydor Ltd. Catalogue no: **POSP 755**
12" Single: Released Jul '85, on Boiling Point, by Polydor Ltd. Deleted '86. Catalogue no: **POSPX 755**

YOUR LOVE
Tracks: / Your love / Agent 406.
12" Single: Released Feb '82, on Carrere, Deleted Feb '87. Catalogue no: **CART 227**
7" Single: Released Feb '82, on Carrere, Deleted Feb '87. Catalogue no: **CAR 227**

YOUR LOVE (SINGLE)
Tracks: / Your love / Agent 406.
12" Single: Released Nov '81, on Excaliber, by Red Bus Records. Deleted Nov '84. Catalogue no: **EXCL 514**
7" Single: Released Nov '81, on Excaliber, by Red Bus Records. Deleted Nov '84. Catalogue no: **EXC 514**

Lime Spiders

WIERDO LIBIDO
Tracks: / Wierdo libido / My flash on you.
12" Single: Released Apr '87, on Zinger, Catalogue no: **ZINGIT 1**

Limelight

ASHES TO ASHES
Tracks: / Ashes to ashes / Knife in your back.
7" Single: Released Oct '82, on Future Earth, by Future Earth Records. Deleted '87. Catalogue no: **FER 010**

METAL MAN
Tracks: / Metal man / Hold me.
7" Single: Released 20 Jun '80, on Future Rights, Deleted '83. Catalogue no: **SER 006**

Limelight Orchestra

COLD WARRIOR
Tracks: / Cold warrior.
7" Single: Released Aug '84, on BBC, by BBC Records & Tapes. Deleted '87. Catalogue no: **RESL 149**

SKORPION, THE
Tracks: / Skorpion, The.
7" Single: Released Jan '83, on BBC, by BBC Records & Tapes. Deleted '87. Catalogue no: **RESL 126**

Limit

SAY YEAH!
Tracks: / Say yeah.
7" Single: Released Dec '84, on Portrait, by CBS Records. Catalogue no: **A 4808**
12" Single: Released Dec '84, on Portrait, by CBS Records. Catalogue no: **TA 4808**

SHE'S SO DIVINE
Tracks: / She's so divine.
12" Single: Released Feb '85, on Ariola, by BMG Records (UK). Catalogue no: **AROD 285**
7" Single: Released Feb '85, on Ariola, by BMG Records (UK). Catalogue no: **ARO 285**

SHOCK WAVES
Tracks: / Shockwaves / OK go.
7" Single: Released Jul '81, on Survival (1), by Survival Records. Catalogue no: **SUR 002**

TAKE IT
Tracks: / Take it.
7" Single: Released Nov '81, on Survival (1), by Survival Records. Catalogue no: **SUR 004**

Limmie & Family

DREAMBOAT
Tracks: / Dreamboat.
7" Single: Released Apr '74, on Avco-Embassy, Deleted Apr '77. Catalogue no: **6105 025**

WALKIN' MIRACLE, A
Tracks: / Walkin' miracle, A.
7" Single: Released Jan '85, on Portrait, by CBS Records. Deleted Jan '88. Catalogue no: **A 4808**

YOU CAN DO MAGIC
Tracks: / You can do magic / Walkin' miracle.
7" Single: Released Jul '73, on Avco-Embassy, Deleted Jul '76. Catalogue no: **6105 019**
7" Single: Released Oct '80, on Phonogram, by Phonogram Ltd. Deleted Oct '83. Catalogue no: **CUT 110**

YOU CAN DO MAGIC (OLD GOLD)
Tracks: / You can do magic.
7" Single: Released Jan '85, on Old Gold, by Old Gold Records. Catalogue no: **OG 9477**

Lincoln, Prince

REVOLUTIONARY MAN
Tracks: / Revolutionary man.
7" Single: Released Aug '84, on Target, by

Target Records. Catalogue no: **TAR 006**

Lincoln, Teddy

I COULD HAVE LOVED YOU
Tracks: / I could have loved you.
12" Single: Released Mar '82, on Regal, Catalogue no: **RD 002**

PLAY WITH FIRE
Tracks: / Play with fire.
12" Single: Released Feb '82, on Selena, Catalogue no: **SD 010**

SEVENTEEN
Tracks: / Seventeen.
12" Single: Released Jul '82, on Regal, Catalogue no: **RD 017**

SLAVE
Tracks: / Slave.
12" Single: Released Sep '85, on Jah Life, Catalogue no: **JL 012**

Lind, Bob

Biographical details: This American singer and songwriter was born in Baltimore, and cruised to fame in early 1966 with his reflective self-penned single *Elusive butterfly*. With its flowing poetic imagery and beautiful melody, this was one of the gentler examples of the Dylan-led folk-rock phenomenon. *Elusive butterfly* reached No.5 in the States; it was covered for the British market by the middle-of-the-road Irish vocalist Val Doonican, but the song was so strong that both versions reached the UK No.5 position! Despite being hailed as an important new artist, appealing to the folk fans and to the dawning psychedelic scene, Lind's career quickly collapsed. The follow-up single *Remember the rain* was only a minor hit on both sides of the Atlantic, and subsequent singles and albums were just too poetic and esoteric for their own good. Further hits proved to be as elusive as that butterfly. (Bob MacDonald, 12th Oct 1985).

ELUSIVE BUTTERFLY
Tracks: / Elusive butterfly.
7" Single: Released Mar '66, on Fontana, by Phonogram Ltd. Deleted Mar '99. Catalogue no: **TF 670**
7" Single: Released '80, on USA, by Charly Records. Catalogue no: **LR 3235**

REMEMBER THE RAIN
Tracks: / Remember the rain.
7" Single: Released May '66, on Fontana, by Phonogram Ltd. Deleted May '69. Catalogue no: **TF 702**

Linda C

ALL I WANT IS YOU
Tracks: / All I want is you / Don't be afraid of the dark.
7" Single: Released Oct '80, on Crash, by Satril Records. Deleted '83. Catalogue no: **POW 3**

Linda & Raymondo

RIGHT TIME RIGHT PLACE
Tracks: / Right time, right place.
12" Single: Released Nov '85, on Time, Catalogue no: **TR 026**

Linda & The Funky Boys

SOLD MY SOUL FOR ROCK 'N' ROLL
Tracks: / Sold my soul for rock 'n' roll.
7" Single: Released Jun '76, on Spark, by Spark Records. Deleted Jun '79. Catalogue no: **SRL 1139**

Linda & the Prophets

WORK
Tracks: / Work.
12" Single: Released Apr '85, on Survival (1), by Survival Records. Catalogue no: **HUM 1**

Linden C

AVENGE
Tracks: / Avenge.
7" Single: Released '89, on Living Beat, by Living Beat Records. Catalogue no: **SMASH 2**

Linden, David

EVERYBODY LOVES JOEY
Tracks: / Everybody loves Joey / Keeping it to myself.
7" Single: Released Aug '80, on Stormbringer, Deleted '83. Catalogue no: **ST 001**

Lindenberg, Udo

BERLIN
Tracks: / Berlin / Street sense / They're coming.
12" Single: Released Jun '81, on Island, by Island Records. Deleted Jun '84. Catalogue no: **12 WIP 6703**

GERMANS
Tracks: / Germans / Shadow of your smile.
7" Single: Released Apr '85, on Rockin' Horse, by BMG Records (UK). Catalogue no: **RH 103**

Lindh, Bjorn J:Son

FROM HERE TO ETERNITY
Tracks: / From here to eternity.
7" Single: Released May '83, on Sonet, by Sonet Records. Catalogue no: **SON 2254**

Lindisfarne

Biographical details: The most successful and durable line-up of this British folk-rock band has been Simon Cowe, Rod Clements, Alan Hull, Ray Jackson and Ray Laidlaw. The group took their name from an island linked by a causeway to the north-east coast England, although the group themselves hailed from the nearby city of Newcastle-upon-Tyne. Lindisfarne, the band came into being in 1967. Between then and 1971 they built up a strong live following via two of the most fashionable and important outlets of the era, colleges and festivals. This endless gigging increased the group's reputaion from local Newcastle support to a national cult following. After a well-reviewed but non-charting debut album, 1970's *Nicely out of tune*, the group sprang to stardom in 1972 with their second set *Fog on the Tyne*. This LP logged four weeks at No.1 on the UK chart and remained on the list for most of the year. It yielded the UK No.5 single *Meet me on the corner*, and the first LP became a belated biggie, logging 30 chart weeks and spawning the No.3 single *Lady Eleanor*. In much the same way as artists like Don McLean and James Taylor did in America, Lindisfarne helped to put folk firmly back on the map in the early Seventies; but the sheer Englishness of the band's music prevented them from conquering the US, despite working with noted American producer Bob Johnston.
Lindisfarne suffered an unexpectedly early rupture in 1973, because of the somewhat anticlimatic and disappointing nature of their third album *Dingly dell*. Having enjoyed a period of huge but short lived British success, Lindisfarne was reduced to Hull and Jackson while the other three musicians formed the almost but not quite successful Jack the Lad. Alan and Ray recruited a new line-up but Lindisfarne's next two albums failed to penetrate the UK Top 50. The two men's solo effort also failed to make the necessary impact, and Jackson later successfully sued EMI Records for failing to give his career the necessary attention. Having folded completed in 1975, the five members of the classic Lindisfarne line-up revived their flagging fortunes in 1978 by reforming the band. They achieved a UK Top 10 single in that year with the hackneyed but pleasing *Run for home*, and made a respectable showing with the *Back and fourth* album, the title of which referred to the fact that it was the fourth LP issued by the original membership. After making this impressive comeback, their chart success quickly diminished; but this time they decided to stick together. They remained in existence through the early and mid-Eighties, retaining a strong live following in the north of England. (Bob MacDonald, 12th Dec 1985).

ALL FALL DOWN
Tracks: / All fall down.
7" Single: Released Sep '72, on Charisma, by Virgin Records. Deleted Sep '75. Catalogue no: **CB 191**

CLEAR WHITE SPIRIT
Tracks: / Clear white spirit / Traveller, The.
7" Single: on Charisma, by Virgin Records. Catalogue no: **CB 409**

DO WHAT I WANT
Tracks: / Do what I want / Same way down.
7" Single: Released Jan '83, on LMP, Catalogue no: **FOG 2**

I MUST STOP GOING TO PARTIES
Tracks: / I must stop going to parties / See how they run.
7" Single: Released Nov '81, on Hangover, Catalogue no: **HANG 9**

I REMEMBER THE NIGHT
7" Single: Released Jun '85, on LMP, Catalogue no: **FOG 3**

JUKE BOX GYPSY
Tracks: / Jukebox gypsy.
7" Single: Released Oct '78, on Mercury, by Phonogram Ltd. Deleted Oct '81. Catalogue no: **6007 187**

LADY ELEANOR 88
Tracks: / Lady Eleanor 88 / Meet me on the corner / Lost in space (Only on 12" & CD) / Reason to be (On CD only).
Note: A completely re-recorded version of the classic seventies song by those legendary Geordies, Lindisfarne. The B-side is the original 1971 version, and the 12" contains an unreleased track.
12" Single: Released Nov '88, on Virgin, by Virgin Records. Catalogue no: **LADY 112**
CD 3": Released '88, on Virgin, by Virgin Records. Catalogue no: **LADYD 1**
7" Single: Released Nov '88, on Virgin, by Virgin Records. Catalogue no: **LADY 1**

LADY ELEANOR (SINGLE)
Tracks: / Lady Eleanor.
7" Single: Released May '72, on Charisma, by Virgin Records. Deleted May '75. Catalogue no: **CB 153**

LOVE ON THE RUN
Tracks: / Love on the run / One hundred miles to Liverpool.
7" Single: Released Feb '87, on LMP, Deleted Nov '87. Catalogue no: **LIND 2**

MEET ME ON THE CORNER
Tracks: / Meet me on the corner.
7" Single: Released Feb '72, on Charisma, by Virgin Records. Deleted Feb '75. Catalogue no: **CB 173**

MEET ME ON THE CORNER (OLD GOLD)
Tracks: / Meet me on the corner.
7" Single: Released Jul '82, on Old Gold, by Old Gold Records. Catalogue no: **OG 9005**

NIGHTS
Tracks: / Nights.
7" Single: Released Sep '82, on LMP, Catalogue no: **FOG 1**

PEEL SESSIONS:LINDISFARNE
Tracks: / Poor old Ireland / Mandolin / Lady Eleanor / Road to kingdom come.
CD 5": Released Oct '88, on Strange Fruit, by Strange Fruit Records. Catalogue no: **SFPSCD 059**
12" Single: Released Oct '88, on Strange Fruit, by Strange Fruit Records. Catalogue no: **SFPS 059**

RUN FOR HOME (see panel below)
Tracks: / Run for home / Stick together.
7" Single: Released Jun '78, on Mercury, by Phonogram Ltd. Deleted Jun '81. Catalogue no: **6007 177**

SHINE ON
Tracks: / Shine on.
7" Single: Released Sep '86, on Priority, by Priority Records. Deleted Nov '87. Catalogue no: **LIND 1**

Lindley, David

MERCURY BLUES
Tracks: / Mercury blues.
7" Single: Released Nov '81, on Elektra, by Elektra Records (UK). Deleted Nov '84. Catalogue no: **K 12573**

Lindo, Devon

SHOWER ME WITH YOUR LOVE
Tracks: / Shower me with your love.
12" Single: Released Sep '89, on Living Room, Catalogue no: **LM 031**

Lindo, Hopeton

GANG WAR
Tracks: / Gang war.
12" Single: Released Feb '89, on Digital B., Catalogue no: **VPRD 408**

SIDEWALK TRAVELLER
Tracks: / Sidewalk traveller / Bellevue patient.
12" Single: Released Dec '82, on Music Works, Catalogue no: **MWRT 52354**

Lindo, Neville

LION SLEEPS TONIGHT, THE
Tracks: / Lion sleeps tonight, The.
12" Single: Released Feb '89, on Top Rank (1), Catalogue no: **VPTRR 098**

RUB A DUB COMMANDER
Tracks: / Rub-a-dub commander / I can't believe it.
12" Single: Released Dec '84, on Negus Roots, Catalogue no: **NERT 022**

YOU'RE MY DOCTOR GIRL
Tracks: / You're my doctor girl.
12" Single: Released Jul '85, on Negus Roots, Catalogue no: **NERT 027**

Lindon, Claudius

ARMS RACE
Tracks: / Arms race / Chun-pon-nanie.
12" Single: Released Apr '84, on Sanity, Catalogue no: **STY 12011**

Lindsay, Balford

JUST BECAUSE I LOVE YOU
Tracks: / Just because I love you.
12" Single: Released Apr '85, on Londisc, by Londisc Records. Catalogue no: **LDR 043**

Lindsay, Julian

NETWORK 7 Theme from the TV series
Tracks: / Network 7 / Straight in straight out / 808 (Extra track on 12").
7" Single: Released Jul '87, on Sierra, by Sierra Records. Catalogue no: **FED 36**
12" Single: Released Jul '87, on Sierra, by Sierra Records. Catalogue no: **FED 36T**

Lindsay-Thomas, David

YOU OUGHTA BE IN PICTURES
Tracks: / You oughta be in pictures.
7" Single: Released May '83, on Modern, Catalogue no: **MOD 001**

Lindsey, Jimmy

IT'S HARD FOR A DREAD
Tracks: / It's hard for a dread / I will love you.
7" Single: Released Nov '80, on Gem, Deleted Nov '83. Catalogue no: **GEMS 41**
12" Single: Released Nov '80, on Gem, Deleted Nov '83. Catalogue no: **GEMS 12 41**

TURN OUT THE LIGHTS
Tracks: / Turn out the lights.
12" Single: Released Mar '82, on Music Hive, Catalogue no: **NHD 461**

Lindsey, Judy

FUJIYAMA MAMA
Tracks: / Fujiyama mama.
7" Single: Released Jul '83, on Seville, by President Records. Catalogue no: **SEV**

LINDISFARNE - RUN FOR HOME (Released on Mercury)

Lindsey, Steve

SHE'S LOCKED UP MY LIFE IN HER SUITCASE
Tracks: / She's locked up my life in her suitcase / Kick it out.
7" Single: Released May '82, on Rialto (1), by Rialto Records. Catalogue no: **RIA 8**

Lindt, Virna

ATTENTION STOCKHOLM
Tracks: / Attention Stockholm.
7" Single: Released Jan '85, on Compact Organisation, Deleted '86. Catalogue no: **ACT 1**

I EXPERIENCED LOVE
Tracks: / I experienced love.
7" Single: Released Sep '84, on Compact Organisation, Deleted '85. Catalogue no: **ACT 12**
12" Single: Released Sep '84, on Compact Organisation, Deleted '85. Catalogue no: **ACTX 12**

INTELLIGENCE
Tracks: / Intelligence / Letter to Sergei / Pillow talk (on 12" only).
7" Single: Released Jun '83, on Compact Organisation, Deleted '85. Catalogue no: **ACT 8**
12" Single: Released Jun '83, on Compact Organisation, Deleted '85. Catalogue no: **ACT 8X**

SHIVER (SINGLE)
Tracks: / Shiver.
7" Single: Released Jan '85, on Compact Organisation, Deleted '86. Catalogue no: **ACT 7**

WHISTLEWIND
Tracks: / Whistlewind.
7" Single: Released Apr '86, on Compact, Catalogue no: **ACTX 19**

YOUNG & HIP
Tracks: / Young & hip.
7" Single: Released Oct '81, on Compact Organisation, Deleted '83. Catalogue no: **ACT 3**

Line Line

VISION
Tracks: / Vision.
7" Single: Released Jun '84, on New Dance, Catalogue no: **ND 012**

Line Up Oona

CASSEROLE
Tracks: / Casserole.
12" Single: Released May '89, on Madagascar, Catalogue no: **MAD 002**
12" Single: Released Jul '89, on K K, by Play It Again Sam (Belgium). Catalogue no: **KK 013**

Liner

Biographical details: Fronted by Tom Farmer and Eddie Galga, who had enjoyed a UK Top 5 single in 1972 with *Standing in the road* as members of Blackfoot Sue, this British band enjoyed a brace of minor hits in 1979. *Keep reaching out for love* reached the UK No.49 position and was followed by a No.44 single *You and me.* Both were supervised by veteran American based producer Arif Mardin. The group's debut album, simply entitled *Liner,* featured a crack team of session guests. However, despite all these advantages, the LP flopped and Liner folded soon afterwards. (Bob MacDonald, 12th Dec 1985).

KEEP REACHING OUT FOR LOVE
Tracks: / Keep reaching out for love.
7" Single: Released Mar '79, on Atlantic, by WEA Records. Deleted Mar '82. Catalogue no: **K 11235**

YOU AND ME
Tracks: / You and me.
7" Single: Released May '79, on Atlantic, by WEA Records. Deleted May '82. Catalogue no: **K 11285**

Lines

HOUSE OF CRACKS
Tracks: / House of cracks.
7" Single: Released Mar '82, on R.E.D., Catalogue no: **RS 011**
12" Single: Released Mar '82, on R.E.D., Catalogue no: **RS 12011**

ON THE AIR
Tracks: / On the air.
7" Single: Released May '80, on R.E.D., Catalogue no: **RS 001**

TRANSIT
Tracks: / Transit / Transit (part 2).
7" Single: Released Aug '81, on R.E.D., Catalogue no: **RS 010**

Lingo, Laurie

CONVOY G.B.
Tracks: / Convoy G.B..
7" Single: Released Apr '76, on State, by State Records. Deleted Apr '79. Catalogue no: **STAT 23**

Linkmen

EVERY INCH A KING
Tracks: / Every inch a king.
7" Single: Released Jan '85, on Kitchenware, by Kitchenware Records. Catalogue no: **SK 17**
12" Single: Released Jun '84, on Kitchenware, by Kitchenware Records. Catalogue no: **SKX 17**

ILL WIND
Tracks: / Ill wind.
12" Single: Released Oct '85, on Spice, Catalogue no: **HERB 1**

Lino

I BELIEVE HER
Tracks: / I believe her / When Harry gets home.
7" Single: Released Aug '80, on RAK, by EMI Records. Deleted '83. Catalogue no: **RAK 319**

WAKE UP LONDON
Tracks: / Wake up London / Cruelty.
7" Single: Released Aug '81, on Pok-A-Dot, Deleted '87. Catalogue no: **POK A DOT 0102**

Linton, Slim

GOING OUT OF MY MIND
Tracks: / Goin' out of my mind / Test transmission.
12" Single: Released Feb '86, on Airwave, by Airwave Records (USA). Catalogue no: **ARW 001**

TO BE TRUE
Tracks: / To be true / Electro magnet.
12" Single: Released Aug '86, on Ariwa Sounds, by Ariwa Sounds. Catalogue no: **ARI 53**

Linx

Biographical details: Singer/percussionist David Grant and bassist Sketch (real name Peter Martin) hailed from East London, and formed the duo Linx in 1980. Prior to meeting on another, each had held a job that was connected with music - David had worked for Island records and Sketch had been a shop assistant in a West End hi-fi store. They financed their first single *You're lying* themselves, and then took the master tape to all the record companies that they could think of. None were interested, and so the two guys pressed 1000 copies and quickly sold them all via London's specialist soul market. Chrysalis then signed them up and *You're lying* reached No.15 on the UK national chart in late 1980. With the help of various back-up musicians, including producer/keyboardist Bob Carter and drummer Andy Duncan, Linx proceeded to become one of Britain's hottest black acts. Soul and disco music has traditionally been dominated by the United States; but during the late Seventies and early Eighties, bans such as the Real Thing, Heatwave, Hi Tension, Level 42, Shakatak and the Olympic Runners proved that the UK could become a potent force in the genre. Linx were part of this Britfunk boom. Although their follow-up to the catcht *You're lying,* a song called *Rise and shine,* was not a hit, they quickly compensated for this by scoring a double UK Top 10 triumph with their single and LP *Intuition.* By the end of 1981 they had placed the singles *Throw away the key* and *So this is romance* on the British charts. All were craftily concocted combinations of infectious dance rhythms and melodic pop hooks. However, just as they seemed to have everything going for them, the duo split up in 1982. Sketch - who once told a reporter that 'My real name is Preliminary Drawing but most people find that a bit of a mouthful' - faded into surprisingly rapid obscurity, but Grant embarked upon a successful solo career. The personable lad underwent a big change of image - his spectacles were exchanged for contact lenses and his jacket, white shirt and tie were traded in for fashionable sports gear and sweat bands. He also learnt to bodypop and, most importantly, teamed up with talented producer Steve Levine. After a series of solo hits, David found further success by duetting with Birmingham soul singer Jaki Graham. (Bob MacDonald, 12th Dec 1985).

CAN'T HELP MYSELF
Tracks: / Can't help myself / I'm not joking.
7" Single: Released Nov '81, on Chrysalis, by Chrysalis Records. Deleted Nov '84. Catalogue no: **CHS 2565**
12" Single: Released Nov '81, on Chrysalis, by Chrysalis Records. Deleted Nov '84. Catalogue no: **CHS 12 2565**

INTUITION (SINGLE)
Tracks: / Intuition / Together we can shine.

LINX - SO THIS IS ROMANCE (Released on Chrysalis)

7" Single: Released Mar '81, on Chrysalis, by Chrysalis Records. Deleted '86. Catalogue no: **CHS 2500**
12" Single: Released Mar '81, on Chrysalis, by Chrysalis Records. Deleted '86. Catalogue no: **CHS 12 2500**

PLAYTHING
Tracks: / Plaything / I won't play the game (remix) / Plaything (extended version) (Only on 12" version.).
12" Single: Released '82, on Chrysalis, by Chrysalis Records. Deleted '87. Catalogue no: **CHS 12 2621**
7" Single: Released Jul '82, on Chrysalis, by Chrysalis Records. Deleted '87. Catalogue no: **CHS 2621**

RISE AND SHINE
Tracks: / Rise and shine / I won't forget (instrumental).
7" Single: Released Dec '80, on Chrysalis, by Chrysalis Records. Deleted Dec '85. Catalogue no: **CHS 2480**
12" Single: Released '82, on Chrysalis, by Chrysalis Records. Deleted '87. Catalogue no: **CHS 12 2480**

SO THIS IS ROMANCE (see panel above)
Tracks: / So this is romance / So this is romance (Rio mix).
7" Single: Released '82, on Chrysalis, by Chrysalis Records. Deleted '87. Catalogue no: **CHS 2546**
12" Single: Released '82, on Chrysalis, by Chrysalis Records. Deleted '87. Catalogue no: **CHS 12 2546**

THROW AWAY THE KEY
Tracks: / Throw away the key / Ice is melting, The / Together we can shine (version) (Only on 12" version.).
12" Single: Released '82, on Chrysalis, by Chrysalis Records. Deleted '87. Catalogue no: **CHS 12 2519**
7" Single: Released '82, on Chrysalis, by Chrysalis Records. Deleted '87. Catalogue no: **CHS 2519**

YOU'RE LYING
Tracks: / You're lying / You're lying (instrumental).
12" Single: Released Sep '80, on Chrysalis, by Chrysalis Records. Deleted '85. Catalogue no: **CHS 12 2461**
7" Single: Released Sep '80, on Chrysalis, by Chrysalis Records. Deleted '85. Catalogue no: **CHS 2461**

YOU'RE LYING (OLD GOLD)
Tracks: / You're lying / Throw away the key / Intuition / So this is romance.
7" Single: Released Feb '87, on Old Gold, by Old Gold Records. Catalogue no: **OG 9694**
12" Single: Released Jan '87, on Old Gold, by Old Gold Records. Catalogue no: **OG 4018**

Lion Youth

ALECIA
Tracks: / Alecia / Chant in a dance.
7" Single: Released Nov '81, on Virgo, Catalogue no: **UG 108**

DECELIA
Tracks: / Decelia / Chant in a dance.
12" Single: Released Jun '82, on Freedom Sounds, Catalogue no: **VG 108**

LET ME ROCK YOU
Tracks: / Let me rock you / Cool but deadly rock.
12" Single: Released Nov '83, on Sunsplash, by Sunsplash Records. Deleted '87. Catalogue no: **SNS 004**

LITTLE WOMAN
Tracks: / Little woman.
12" Single: Released Mar '83, on Virgo, Catalogue no: **VG 011**

RAT A CUT BOTTLE
Tracks: / Rat a cut bottle.
12" Single: Released Sep '81, on Freedom Sounds, Deleted '89. Catalogue no: **VS 104**

Lionheart

DIE FOR LOVE
Tracks: / Die for love / Dangerous games.
7" Single: Released Jan '85, on Epic, by CBS Records. Catalogue no: **A 5001**

Lions

MARGARET THATCHER
Tracks: / Margaret Thatcher / Living the good life.
Note: Soho - 01-734 3465
7" Single: Released 30 May '87, on Soho (1), by Soho Records. Deleted Nov '87. Catalogue no: **SORE 102**
12" Single: Released 30 May '87, on Soho (1), by Soho Records. Deleted 1 Nov '87. Catalogue no: **SORE 12 102**

Lip Machine

ASTRONUT
Tracks: / Astronut.
12" Single: Released Apr '89, on DDT, by D.D.T.Records. Catalogue no: **DISP 2**

OUR WORLD
Tracks: / Our world / Lip machine.
12" Single: Released 30 May '87, on DDT, by D.D.T.Records. Catalogue no: **DISP 3**

ROCKET LOVE AND ASTRONAUT
Tracks: / Rocket love and astronaut.
12" Single: Released Feb '86, on Disposable Dance, by Fast Forward Records. Catalogue no: **DISP 2**

Lip Service

RUBY (DON'T TAKE YOUR LOVE TO TOWN)
Tracks: / Ruby (Don't take your love to town) / Jimmy Brown.
7" Single: Released Nov '80, on Zonophone, by EMI Records. Deleted '83. Catalogue no: **Z 13**

Lipps Inc.

FUNKY TOWN (OLD GOLD)
Tracks: / Funky town / Never knew love like this before.
7" Single: Released Jan '85, on Old Gold, by Old Gold Records. Catalogue no: **OG 9489**

FUNKYTOWN
Tracks: / Funky town / All night dancing.

7" Single: Released May '80, on Casablanca, by PolyGram UK Ltd. Deleted May '83. Catalogue no: **CAN 194**
12" Single: Released May '80, on Casablanca, by PolyGram UK Ltd. Deleted May '83. Catalogue no: **CANL 194**

HOW LONG
Tracks: / How long / There they are.
7" Single: Released Oct '80, on Casablanca, by PolyGram UK Ltd. Deleted Oct '83. Catalogue no: **CAN 212**

Lips

LIES
Tracks: / Lies / Silly boy.
7" Single: Released Jan '80, on Pye. Deleted Jan '83. Catalogue no: **7P 155**

Lipton, Celia

YOU'VE GOT YOUR OWN LIFE TO LIVE
Tracks: / You've got your own life to live / I've got your number.
7" Single: Released Feb '87, on Premier, by Premier Records. Catalogue no: **CELIA 1**

Liquid Gold

Biographical details: This British pop band consisted of Ellie Hope, Ray Knott, Franco Moruzzi, Wally Rothe and Syd Twynham. For a brief period during the late Seventies and early Eighties, Liquid Gold captured the candyfloss, teenybop end of the disco market. Teir first hit *Anyway you do it* reached No.41 on the UK chart at the end of 1978; the following year, its B side, *My baby's baby*, became a club hit in the States. In 1980 Liquid Gold struck solid gold with their British Top 10 smashes, *Dance yourself dizzy* (No.2) and *Substitute* (No.8). These two insipid ditties were of such a lightweight nature that they made Boney M look like intellectual giants; lead singer Ellie Hope sounded and looked like a cross between Tina Charles and a female Frankenstein. In 1981 Liquid Gold pitched their talents where they really belonged - the Eurovision Song Contest. They failed to get through to the finals, but came second in the British heats. It was a graphic illustraion of the low standard of the whole event that the group's *Don't panic*, which was bad even by their standards, came within a hair's breadth of representing the United Kingdom. *Don't panic* was rightly beaten by the only UK contender of any real quality, Bucks Fizz's *Making your mind up*; but to their credit, Liquid Gold boldly went were few established acts had gone before - by 1981 Eurovision had become the domain of unknown artists, while the big names shield away. Liquid Gold's final UK chart entry was *Where did we go wrong*, which crawled to No.56 in 1982. Its title proved prophetic, for their subsequent releases failed altogether. (Bob MacDonald, 13th Dec 1985).

ANYWAY YOU DO IT
Tracks: / Anyway you do it.
7" Single: Released Dec '78, on Creole, by Creole Records. Deleted Dec '81. Catalogue no: **CR 159**

DANCE YOURSELF DIZZY
Tracks: / Dance yourself dizzy.
12" Single: Released Feb '80, on Polo, by Polo Records. Deleted '88. Catalogue no: **POLO 12-1**
7" Single: Released Feb '80, on Polo, by Polo Records. Deleted '88. Catalogue no: **POLO 1**

DON'T PANIC
Tracks: / Don't panic.
7" Single: Released Mar '81, on Polo, by Polo Records. Deleted '88. Catalogue no: **POLO 8**
12" Single: Released Mar '81, on Polo, by Polo Records. Deleted '88. Catalogue no: **POLO 12-8**

MR.GROOVY (IT FEELS SO NICE)
Tracks: / Mr. Groovy (it feels so nice) / C'mon & dance.
7" Single: Released May '79, on Creole, by Creole Records. Catalogue no: **CR 170**

MY BABY'S BABY
Tracks: / My baby's baby.
7" Single: Released Jan '82, on Polo, by Polo Records. Deleted '88. Catalogue no: **POLO 17**
12" Single: Released Jan '82, on Polo, by Polo Records. Deleted '88. Catalogue no: **POLO 12-17**

NIGHT THE WINE & THE ROSES,THE
Tracks: / Night the wine & the roses, The.
12" Single: Released Oct '80, on Polo, by Polo Records. Deleted '88. Catalogue no: **POLO 12-6**
7" Single: Released Oct '80, on Polo, by Polo Records. Deleted '88. Catalogue no: **POLO 6**

ONE OF US FELL IN LOVE
Tracks: / One of us fell in love.
7" Single: Released Oct '81, on Polo, by Polo Records. Deleted '88. Catalogue no: **POLO 15**
12" Single: Released Oct '81, on Polo, by Polo Records. Deleted '88. Catalogue no: **POLO 12-15**

SUBSTITUTE
Tracks: / Substitute / Substitute (part 2).
7" Single: Released May '80, on Polo, by Polo Records. Deleted '88. Catalogue no: **POLO 4**
12" Single: Released May '80, on Polo, by Polo Records. Deleted '88. Catalogue no: **POLO 12-4**

SUCCESSIVE REFLEXES
7" EP: Released Feb '82, on 99. Catalogue no: **9909 EP**

TURN THE TABLES
Tracks: / Turn the tables.
7" Single: Released Sep '84, on Ecstasy, by Creole Records. Catalogue no: **XTC 9**
12" Single: Released Sep '84, on Ecstasy, by Creole Records. Catalogue no: **XTCT 9**

WHERE DID WE GO WRONG
Tracks: / Where did we go wrong / Ripping up the letter.
7" Pic: Released Jul '82, on Polo, by Polo Records. Deleted '88. Catalogue no: **POLO 23P**
7" Single: Released Jul '82, on Polo, by Polo Records. Deleted '88. Catalogue no: **POLO 23**
12" Single: Released Jul '82, on Polo, by Polo Records. Deleted '88. Catalogue no: **POLO 12-23**

Lisa

DOIN' IT
Tracks: / Doin' it (ext) / Doin' it (inst).
12" Single: Released Aug '87, on Passion, by Skratch Records. Catalogue no: **PASH 76(12)**

ROCKET TO YOUR HEART remix
Tracks: / Rocket to your heart.
12" Single: Released Apr '84, on Carrere America (USA), by PolyGram Rec.Inc.(USA). Catalogue no: **CART 328**

Lisa And The Love

MIDNIGHT LIGHTNING
Tracks: / Midnight lightning.
12" Single: Released 13 Feb '89, on Interstellar Bro. Catalogue no: **IB 002 T**

Lisa Lisa

GIT IT TOGETHER
Tracks: / Git it together (7" edit) (Only on 7" and CD single.) / Git it (beats injection mix) (Only on 7" single.) / Git it together (12" version) (Only on 12" and CD single.) / Together ruh (F.F. on the dance floor mix) (Only on 12" single.) / Just (together-pella mix) (Only on 12" single.) / I wonder if I take you home (12" version) (Only on CD single.).
CD 5": Released Jul '89, on CBS, by CBS Records. Catalogue no: **6550602**
7" Single: Released Jul '89, on CBS, by CBS Records. Catalogue no: **6550607**
12" Single: Released Jul '89, on CBS, by CBS Records. Catalogue no: **6550608**

Lisa Lisa/Cult Jam

CAN YOU FEEL THE BEAT H
Tracks: / Can you feel the beat.
7" Single: Released Oct '85, on CBS, by CBS Records. Deleted '86. Catalogue no: **A 6635**
12" Single: Released Oct '85, on CBS, by CBS Records. Deleted '86. Catalogue no: **TA 6635**

HEAD TO TOE
Tracks: / Head to toe / Head to toe (version).
12" Single: Released 20 Jun '87, on CBS, by CBS Records. Deleted Nov '87. Catalogue no: **650520 6**

I WONDER IF I TAKE YOU HOME
Tracks: / I wonder if I take you home.
7" Single: Released Aug '85, on CBS, by CBS Records. Deleted '86. Catalogue no: **A 6057**
Special: Released Aug '85, on CBS, by CBS Records. Deleted '86. Catalogue no: **QTA 6057**
12" Single: Released Aug '85, on CBS, by CBS Records. Deleted '86. Catalogue no: **TX 6057**

LITTLE JACKIE WANTS TO BE A STAR
Tracks: / Little Jackie wants to be a star / I wonder if I take you home (7" version) / Head to toe (LP version).
7" Single: Released 24 Apr '89, on CBS, by CBS Records. Catalogue no: **654781 7**
CD 5": Released 8 May '89, on CBS, by CBS Records. Catalogue no: **654781 2**
12" Single: Released 24 May '89, on CBS, by CBS Records. Catalogue no: **654781 8**

LOST IN EMOTION
Tracks: / Lost in emotion / Motion is lost.
12" Single: Released Sep '87, on CBS, by CBS Records. Catalogue no: **651 036 8**
7" Single: Released Sep '87, on CBS, by CBS Records. Catalogue no: **651 036 7**

Lise By Night

PHONE TO PHONE
Tracks: / Phone to phone.
7" Single: Released Aug '85, on EMI-Manhattan, by EMI Records. Catalogue no: **MT 4**

Lise, Inger

EVERYTHING THAT'S PART OF YOU
Tracks: / Everything that's part of you / Crazy love.
7" Single: Released Oct '80, on Satril, by Satril Records. Deleted Oct '83. Catalogue no: **HH 151**

Listen

WHATEVER
Tracks: / Whatever / Animal earth.
7" Single: Released Apr '85, on Listening Trees. Catalogue no: **LIST 1**

Lister, Grahame

FISH'N'CHIPS IN SPAIN
Tracks: / Fish'n'chips in Spain.
7" Single: Released Jul '88, on Bark, by Bark Records. Catalogue no: **SPAIN 1**

Lister,Johnny

OH MEIN PAPA
Tracks: / Oh mein papa / Falkland sound.
7" Single: Released Nov '82, on Monarch, by Monarch Records. Catalogue no: **MON 036**

REGINA CAMPAGNOLA
Tracks: / Regina campagnola.
7" Single: Released Aug '84, on Masterchord, by Masterchord Records & Tapes. Deleted '86. Catalogue no: **MCS 414**

Lite Band

EVERYBODY NEEDS SOMEBODY
Tracks: / Everybody needs somebody / Heavy heavy.
7" Single: Released Jul '87, on Creole, by Creole Records. Catalogue no: **CR 105**
12" Single: Released Jul '87, on Creole, by Creole Records. Catalogue no: **CRT 105**

Lites, Shirley

HEAT YOU UP MELT YOU DOWN
Tracks: / Heat you up melt you down.
7" Single: Released '83, on Arista, by BMG Records (UK). Deleted '86. Catalogue no: **WEND 121**

Little Acorns

HOW LUCKY YOU ARE
Tracks: / How lucky you are / Mugger, The.
7" Single: Released Jul '83, on Last Straw. Catalogue no: **SRR 021**

Little Angels

BAD OR JUST NO GOOD
Tracks: / Bad or just no good / Better than the rest / Burning me / Reach for me.
12" Single: Released 23 May '87, on L.A.Song Management, by Red Rhino Records. Catalogue no: **LAN 001**

BIG BAD EP
Tracks: / She's a little angel / Don't waste my time / Better than the rest / Sex in cars.
CD 5": Released 20 Feb '89, on Polydor, by Polydor Ltd. Catalogue no: **LTLCD 2**
7" Single: Released 20 Feb '89, on Polydor, by Polydor Ltd. Catalogue no: **LTL 2**
12" Single: Released 20 Feb '89, on Polydor, by Polydor Ltd. Catalogue no: **LTLEP 2**

BURNING ME
Tracks: / Burning me.
12" Single: Released 1 Jul '87, on Little Angels. Catalogue no: **LAN 001**

DO YOU WANNA RIOT
Tracks: / Do you wanna riot / Move in slow / Some kind of alien (Available on 12" format only).
12" Single: Released Sep '89, on Polydor, by Polydor Ltd. Catalogue no: **LTLX 3**
CD 5": Released Sep '89, on Polydor, by Polydor Ltd. Catalogue no: **LTLCD 3**
10" single: Released Sep '89, on Polydor, by Polydor Ltd. Catalogue no: **LTLXV 3**
7" Single: Released Sep '89, on Polydor, by Polydor Ltd. Catalogue no: **LTL 3**

NINETY IN THE SHADE
Tracks: / Ninety in the shade / England rocks / Big, bad world (Only on 12").
12" Single: Released 16 Sep '88, on Polydor, by Polydor Ltd. Deleted 30 Jun '89. Catalogue no: **LTLG 1**
12" Single: Released 16 Sep '88, on Polydor, by Polydor Ltd. Deleted 30 Jun '89. Catalogue no: **LTLX 1**
12" Pic: Released Oct '88, on Polydor, by Polydor Ltd. Deleted 30 Jun '89. Catalogue no: **LTLXP 1**
7" Single: Released 16 Sep '88, on Polydor, by Polydor Ltd. Deleted 30 Jun '89. Catalogue no: **LTL 1**

Little Anthony

BETTER USE YOUR HEAD
Tracks: / Better use your head.
7" Single: Released Jul '76, on United Artists, by EMI Records. Deleted Jul '79. Catalogue no: **UP 36118**

Little Benny

BUGGIN' OUT
Tracks: / Buggin' out / Buggin' out (inst) / Who comes to boogie.
7" Single: Released Aug '87, on Bluebird (2), by BMG Records (UK). Catalogue no: **BR 37**
12" Single: Released Aug '87, on Bluebird (2), by BMG Records (UK). Catalogue no: **BRT 37**

WHO COMES TO BOOGIE
Tracks: / Who comes to boogie.
12" Single: Released Jan '85, on Bluebird (2), by BMG Records (UK). Catalogue no: **BRT 13**
7" Single: Released Jan '85, on Bluebird (2), by BMG Records (UK). Catalogue no: **BR 13**

Little Big Band

WOODLAND ROCK
Tracks: / Woodland rock.
CD 5": Released Jun '89, on Factory (1), by Factory Records. Catalogue no: **FACD 207**

Little Bird

ZOLA
Tracks: / Zola.
7" Single: Released Jun '84, on Magnus Music. Catalogue no: **MGB 1**

Little Bo Bitch

I WANNA BE USED FOR LOVE
Tracks: / I wanna be used for love / My mistake.
7" Single: Released Jan '80, on Hurricane (2). Deleted Jan '85. Catalogue no: **FIRE 11**

TAKE IT EASY
Tracks: / Take it easy / Lorraine, Lorraine.
7" Single: Released Jan '80, on Cobra. Deleted Jan '83. Catalogue no: **COB 4**

Little Brother

NO RELATION
Tracks: / No relation.
7" Single: Released Apr '86, on Rouska, by Rouska Records. Catalogue no: **COME 4**

Little Clarke

MEMORIES
Tracks: / Memories.
12" Single: Released Jul '88, on Hit Room. Catalogue no: **HRS 002**

Little Clarkie

BUBBLE 'N' ROCK
Tracks: / Bubble 'n' rock.
12" Single: Released Aug '87, on Y & D. Catalogue no: **YDDO 107**

CAN'T COME A DANCE AND STAND UP
Tracks: / Can't come a dance and stand up.
7" Single: Released Apr '89, on Y & D. Catalogue no: **YDD 0134**

LIVE STOCK PARTY
Tracks: / Live stock party / Bounty hunter.
12" Single: Released Sep '86, on Jah Tubbys. Catalogue no: **JT 020**

MINI VAN DRIVER
Tracks: / Mini van driver.
12" Single: Released Apr '88, on Y & D. Catalogue no: **YDDO 122**

NEATLY
Tracks: / Neatly.
12" Single: Released Sep '89, on Y & D. Catalogue no: **YDD 0140**

SELECT HIM GOOD
Tracks: / Select him good / Bless the selector / Select the rhythm.
12" Single: Released Jan '86, on Jah Tubbys. Catalogue no. **JT 015**

Little Darlings

HE'S MY DAD
Tracks: / He's my dad / Spend a little time.
7" Single: Released Oct '82, on EMI, by EMI Records. Catalogue no: **EMI 5340**

Little, De Etta

YOU TAKE MY HEART AWAY
Tracks: / You take my heart away.
7" Single: Released Aug '77, on United Artists, by EMI Records. Deleted Aug '80. Catalogue no: **UP 36257**

Little Egypt

I DO VOODOO
Tracks: / I do voodoo / Do it right.
7" Single: Released Jul '82, on Arrival, by Blaylock Management Ltd.. Deleted '86. Catalogue no: **PIK 8**

Little Eva

Biographical details: This American singer was born Eva Narcissus Boyd in North Carolina in 1945. She had just turned 17 years old when she shot to No.1 in America and No.2 in Britain in 1962 with *The locomotion*. Penned by the hottest songwriters of the day, the husband/wife team of Gerry Goffin & Carole King, it was a party dance classic to rival Chubby Checker's *The twist*. Little Eva's leap to fame was a genuine overnight success - mere weeks before it topped the charts, she had been working as Goffin & King's babysitter; popular legend had it that the Goffins had heard her singing to herself as she walked around the house and had rushed her to a recording studio at the earliest opportunity, although King later stated they were already aware of Eva's vocal abilities before she started working for them. Little Eva dreamed up a dance routine to go with the record, and the locomotion became a short-lived but enjoyable international craze. Like most novelty hits, it was hard to follow up, but Eva managed to sustain her chart career for just over a year. *Keep your hands off my baby* reached No.12 in the US and No.30 in the UK. Then came *Let's turkey trot*, which did not have the same impact on the dance-floor as *The locomotion* but nonetheless climbed to No.20 in America and No.13 in Britain. In late 1963 she reached the US Top 40 and the UK Top 10 with a revamp of the Bing Crosby standard *Swinging on a star*, on which she dueted with male singer Big Dee Irwin. In 1964 the Beatles' invasion of America killed off Little Eva's career - her style, and that of many of her contempories suddenly became dated.
The locomotion enjoyed a revival on both sides of the Atlantic in the early Seventies. In Britain the original version re-entered the charts in 1972 and climbed to No.11. In the States the song became a No.1 smash in 1974 for the hard rock band Grand Funk, who were the last group anyone would have expected to hear performing it. (Bob MacDonald, 13th Dec 1985).

KEEP YOUR HANDS OFF MY BABY
Tracks: / Keep your hands off my baby.
7" Single: Released Jan '63, on London-American, Deleted Jan '66. Catalogue no: **HLU 9633**

LET'S TURKEY TROT
Tracks: / Let's turkey trot.
7" Single: Released Mar '63, on London-American, Deleted Mar '66. Catalogue no: **HLU 9687**

LOCOMOTION (OLD GOLD)
Tracks: / Locomotion, The / Keep your hands off my baby.
7" Single: Released Jun '88, on Old Gold, by Old Gold Records. Catalogue no: **OG 9328**

LOCO-MOTION, THE
Tracks: / Loco-motion, The / Let's turkey trot / He is the boy / Keep your hands off my baby (Extra track available on 12" version only).
7" Single: Released '88, on London Records, by London Records. Deleted May '89. Catalogue no: **H 9581**
7" Single: Released Mar '80, on London Records, by London Records. Deleted '84. Catalogue no: **HL 9581**
7" Single: Released Sep '86, on London Records, by London Records. Deleted Feb '89. Catalogue no: **LOCO 1**
12" Single: Released Sep '86, on London Records, by London Records. Deleted Feb '89. Catalogue no: **LOCOX 1**

Little Feat

Biographical details: This American rock band consisted of the following line-up at the time of the group's greatest success: Paul Barrere, Sam Clayton, Lowell George, Kenny Gradney, Richard Hayward and Bill Payne. Little Feat came into being in 1969 at the instigation of singer/songwriter/guitarist/producer Lowell George. The band enjoyed many years of critical acclaim but never quite translated their cult status into major commercial success. They possessed an eclectic rock style, which incorporated country, jazz and soul influences. Their eponymous debut album was issued in December 1970. Two further LP's, *Sailin' shoes* and *Dixie chicken*, were released before the combo temporarily broke up in October 1973. Disappointed at the band's total lack of chart recognition on both sides of the Atlantic, despite the reviewers' many plaudits, members embarked upon various artists projects. The talented George was in perennial demand as a session guitarist. The same six members decided to reform the band in May '74 and soon received their first taste of US chart success with the album *Feats don't fail me now*. A 1975 UK visit, as part of a Warner Bros. showcase, bolstered and enhanced their growing British cult following. That year's LP, *The last record album* reached N0.36 on both sides of the Atlantic.
During the mid-Seventies, George's role in Little Feat began to diminish - this situation was hastened by a bout of hepatitis, which prevented him from making a major contribution to 1977's *Time loves a hero* LP (the group's only UK Top 10 album). When he recovered, he was more interested in making his own solo album than in the group's work. Little Feat finally broke up in Aril 1979, the same month that the solo disc was released. Lowell assembled a nine-piece band and went on tour; but his itinerary was brought to an abrupt and tragic end in June 1979, when the 37 year-old Lowell George died of a drug-induced heart attack in Arlington, Virginia. With much unreleased Little Feat material still in the can, two albums were subseqently issued: *Down on the farm* came out in late '79 and the double LP *Hoy hoy* was released in 1981. The latter contained a worthy rendition of *Two trains*, which had also appeared on George's solo set. Plans for a reunion of the surviving Little Feat members were mooted but dropped. (Bob MacDonald, 13th Dec 1985).

DIXIE CHICKEN (SINGLE)
Tracks: / Dixie chicken.
7" Single: Released Mar '75, on Warner Bros., by WEA Records. Catalogue no: **K 16524**

Little Foxes

CROSSED LINE
Tracks: / Crossed line.
7" Single: Released Feb '83, on C&D, Catalogue no: **CD 2**

GOLDEN BODIES
Tracks: / Golden bodies.
7" Single: Released Jul '83, on C&D, Catalogue no: **CD 4**

Little Ginny

CHASING THE WIND
Tracks: / Chasing the wind.
7" Single: Released Jul '82, on Pastafont, by Pastafont Music. Catalogue no: **PF 3004**

MY DIXIE DARLING
Tracks: / My Dixie darling / Whisky get me gone.
7" Single: Released Nov '81, on Pastafont, by Pastafont Music. Deleted Nov '84. Catalogue no: **PF 3002**

SEA OF HEARTBREAK
7" Single: Released Mar '84, on Pastafont, by Pastafont Music. Catalogue no: **PF 3009**

Little Heroes

ONE PERFECT DAY
Tracks: / One perfect day.
7" Single: Released Jun '83, on EMI, by EMI Records. Catalogue no: **MI 5389**

YOUNG HEARTS
Tracks: / Young hearts / Saturday afternoon inside.
7" Single: Released Jan '83, on EMI, by EMI Records. Catalogue no: **EMI 5364**

Little John

BADDEST DANCE SINGER
Tracks: / Baddest dance singer.
12" Single: Released Nov '88, on Taurus, Catalogue no: **UNKNOWN**

BE MY LOVER
Tracks: / Be my lover.
7" Single: Released 12 May '89, on Black Scorpio, Catalogue no: **BS 020**

BETTER YU GWAN
Tracks: / Better yu gwan.
12" Single: Released Sep '84, on Power House, Catalogue no: **Unknown**

BRANDY
Tracks: / Brandy.
12" Single: Released Oct '82, on Music Lovers, Catalogue no: **ML 004**

BUBBLING STYLE
Tracks: / Bubbling style / Skin ase peel.
12" Single: Released Feb '85, on Black Roots, Catalogue no: **LM 241284**

BUSHMASTER CONNECTION
Tracks: / Bushmaster connection / Little girl.
12" Single: Released May '82, on Greensleeves, by Greensleeves Records. Catalogue no: **GRED 86**

CLARKE'S BOOTY (SINGLE)
Tracks: / Clarke's booty / Have to girlie girlie.
12" Single: Released Feb '86, on Unity, Catalogue no: **UN 021**

DASH RHYTHM DOWN
Tracks: / Dash rhythm down / Dash rhythm down (version).
12" Single: Released 17 Oct '87, on Legal Lights, by Legal Light Records. Catalogue no: **LLD 15**

DO MAMA
Tracks: / Do mama.
12" Single: Released Jun '85, on Hawkeye, by Hawkeye Records. Catalogue no: **HD 61**

DON'T WAIT TO BE LONELY
Tracks: / Don't wait to be lonely.
7" Single: Released Jul '84, on Jamaica Sound, Catalogue no: **SMJ 001**

FADE AWAY
Tracks: / Fade away.
12" Single: Released Nov '88, on BP International, Catalogue no: **BPKT 2**

FORM A LINE
Tracks: / Form a line / Rub and go down.
12" Single: Released Mar '84, on Greensleeves, by Greensleeves Records. Catalogue no: **GRED 139**

I DON'T WANT TO CRY OVER YOU
Tracks: / I don't want to cry over you.
12" Single: Released Nov '83, on Jah Bible, Catalogue no: **DM 008**

I HAVE WORK TO DO
Tracks: / I have work to do.
12" Single: Released Jul '83, on Gamble, Catalogue no: **GAD 02**

I WANT YOU
Tracks: / I want you.
12" Single: Released 30 May '88, on Black Scorpio, Catalogue no: **CDBA 15**

JANET SINCLAIR
Tracks: / Janet Sinclair.
12" Single: Released Aug '82, on Greensleeves, by Greensleeves Records. Catalogue no: **GRED 92**

JOKER LOVER
Tracks: / Joker lover / Scandel.
12" Single: Released Oct '82, on Greensleeves, by Greensleeves Records. Catalogue no: **GRED 102**

JOYCE GONE
Tracks: / Joyce gone / We still survive.
12" Single: Released Nov '83, on Jah Guidance, Catalogue no: **VPRD 142**

MIX UP
Tracks: / Mix up.
12" Single: Released Dec '83, on Music Parade, Catalogue no: **MP 001**

MY WOMAN IS CRYING
Tracks: / My woman is crying / Somebody lover.
12" Single: Released Mar '84, on Bebo's Music, Catalogue no: **BB 079**
12" Single: Released Oct '83, on Midnight Rock, Catalogue no: **MRO 18**

NOW MI COME
Tracks: / Now mi come.
12" Single: Released Aug '87, on Ranking Joe Universal, Catalogue no: **RJ 020**

POLICE PEGGY
Tracks: / Police Peggy.
12" Single: Released Mar '85, on Greensleeves, by Greensleeves Records. Catalogue no: **GRED 174**

RAM DANCE MASTER
Tracks: / Ram dance master / Ram dance master (version).
12" Single: Released Mar '88, on Legal Lights, by Legal Light Records. Catalogue no: **LLQ 28**

SCHOOL GIRL
Tracks: / School girl.
12" Single: Released Jun '85, on Top Rank (2), Catalogue no: **TR 007**

SLICE OF THE CAKE
Tracks: / Slice of the cake.
12" Single: Released May '85, on Rockers Forever, Catalogue no: **Unknown**

SPECIAL PRAYER
Tracks: / Special prayer.
12" Single: Released Aug '88, on Original Sounds, Catalogue no: **OS 019**

STYLE
Tracks: / Style.
12" Single: Released Nov '83, on Music Hawk, Catalogue no: **MHD 10**

TEAR DOWN THE DANCE HELL
Tracks: / Tear down the dance hell.
12" Single: Released Jan '85, on M&M, by M&M Music Company. Catalogue no: **MM 003**

TO ALL THE POSSE
Tracks: / To all the posse.
12" Single: Released Mar '84, on Volcano, Catalogue no: **VPRD 183**

WALK AWAY
Tracks: / Walk away.
12" Single: Released Aug '84, on Music Hawk, Catalogue no: **MH 15**

YES MAMA
Tracks: / Yes mama.
12" Single: Released Feb '87, on Live & Love, Catalogue no: **LLDIS 0030**

Little Kirk

MAN IN THE MIRROR
Tracks: / Man in the mirror.
7" Single: Released Oct '88, on June Star, Catalogue no: **DIS 005**

WEED THEM OUT
Tracks: / Weed them out / Weed them out (version).
12" Single: Released 17 Oct '87, on Ruddy Music, Catalogue no: **RM 015**

Little Kurk

FRIEND THEM MATE
Tracks: / Friend them mate / Don't touch the crack.
12" Single: Released Jan '87, on Jammy's, Catalogue no: **JAM 006**

Little & Large

AROUND THE OLD CAMPFIRE
Tracks: / Around the old campfire / I'm in love with Angela Rippon.
7" Single: Released Mar '81, on EMI, by EMI Records. Deleted Mar '84. Catalogue no: **EMI 5155**

ROCK STEADY
Tracks: / Rock steady / Song for the world.
7" Single: Released Apr '81, on Polydor, by Polydor Ltd. Deleted '85. Catalogue no: **2058 189**

TELEPHONE MAN
Tracks: / Telephone man.
7" Single: Released Nov '77, on Nevis, Catalogue no: **NEVS 103**

Little Lenny

GUN IN A BAGGY
Tracks: / Gun in a baggy.
12" Single: Released 24 Jul '89, on Shocking Vibes, Catalogue no: **SV 02**

NO BOTHER TROUBLE ME
Tracks: / No bother trouble me.
7" Single: Released Mar '89, on Penthouse, by Penthouse Records. Catalogue no: **PH 002**

Little Mac

IN THE MIDNIGHT HOUR
Tracks: / In the midnight hour / You can't love me in the midnight hour.
7" Single: Released Mar '80, on Atlantic, by WEA Records. Deleted '83. Catalogue no: **K 11448**

Little Nell

BEAUTY QUEEN
Tracks: / Beauty queen / Slow version.
7" Single: Released May '80, on Charisma, by Virgin Records. Deleted May '83. Catalogue no: **PRE 004**

Little Red Schoolhouse

FOUR ICED PUNS EP
7" Single: Released Jun '87, on Tim, by Tim Records. Catalogue no: **MOT 9**
12" Single: Released Jun '87, on Tim, by Tim Records. Catalogue no: **12 MOT 9**

NEARLY TRUE
Tracks: / Nearly true.
12" Single: Released '87, on Tim, by Tim Records. Catalogue no: **MOT 12009**

Little Richard

Biographical details: This American singer, pianist and songwriter was amongst the greatest of the original Fifties rock'n'rollers. He was born Richard Penniman in Macon, Georgia and was brough up as a Seventh Day Adventist; his first vocal experience was gained by singing in church choirs. After building a reputation via medicine shows and local clubs, he made his recording debut in 1951. For four years he made a series of blues and boogie discs, many of which were good although none were successful. The turning point in his career came in 1955, the year when Bill Haley, Elvis Presley and Chuck Berry were laying the groundwork for the rock'n'roll revolution. Little Richard was signed to Speciality Records in that year, and was

teamed up with the company's A&R chief and producer Robert 'Bumps' Blackwell. By the end of '55 Little Richard had hopped aboard the burgeoning rock'n'roll scene with his seminal single *Tutti frutti*. Containing his instantly recognisable, nonsensically rebellious line 'A wop-bop-a-loo-bop, a-lop-bam-boom', this single provided undisputable evidence that a vital new star had arrived. *Tutti Frutti* reached the US No.17 position in early 1956. The raucous and riotous nature of this frantic black screamer was made all the more conspicuous and exciting when compared with a sage, 'nice' cover version by white singer Pat Boone, rock's king of conservatism. Boone also recorded a toothless rendition of Richard's next hit *Long tall Sally*, and both versions reached the American Top 10. Little Richard's disc also became a British No.3 smash.
A series of UK and US hits followed during the mid to late Fifties, none deviating from his trademark style but almost all worth listening to and freaking out to. He wailed and hollered as if his life depended on it, and only Jerry Lee Lewis could rival his persecution of a poor defenceless piano. *Rip it up*, *Jenny Jenny* and Good golly Miss Molly all soured into the US Top 20. In Britain he reached Top 20 status with *She's got it*, *The girl can't help it*, *Lucille*, *Jenny Jenny*, *Good golly Miss Molly*, *Baby face* (a remake of a 1926 standard, giving Richard his biggest UK hit by reaching No.2) and *By the light of the silvery moon*. Unlike most of his best contempories, however, he never achieved a No.1 single on either side of the Atlantic
Little Richard made his movie debut in the 1956 film *Don't knock the rock*, in which he definitley stole the limelight. He quickly followed this success with appearances in *The girl can't help it* and Alan Freed's *Mr rock'n'roll*. Just as he was at the peak of his career, the wild performer decided to forsake rock'n'roll in 1958 to study to become a preacher. This astounding decision - rock'n'roll and the Christian church were hardly natural bedfellows in the late Fifties - resulted in him recording some gospel material in the early Sixties. By 1964, however, the lure of the pop world had proved irresistible. Having toured Britain with the Beatles, he notched up a UK Top 20 single in that year with *Bama lama bama loo*. The comeback was short lived, and he spent the rest of the Sixties and Seventies earning a living from his past reputation, although some of his concerts and recordings did attract good reviews. By the end of the Seventies he had returned to preaching the gospel; to this end, he became a regular on American TV chat shows. In 1985, shortly after making a much publicised visit to Britain, he was injured in a road accident. (Bob MacDonald, 13th Dec 1985).

BABY FACE
Tracks: / Baby face.
7" Single: Released Jan '59, on London-American, Deleted Jan '62. Catalogue no: **HLU 8770**

BAMA LAMA BAMA LOO
Tracks: / Bama lama bama loo.
7" Single: Released Jun '64, on London Records, by London Records. Deleted Jun '67. Catalogue no: **HL 9896**

BY THE LIGHT OF THE SILVERY MOON
Tracks: / By the light of the silvery moon.
7" Single: Released Apr '89, on London-American, Deleted Apr '62. Catalogue no: **HLU 8831**
7" Single: Released '80, on Speciality (USA), by Speciality Records (USA). Catalogue no: **LR 0214**

GIRL CAN'T HELP IT, THE
Tracks: / Girl can't help it, The / She's got it.
7" Single: Released Mar '57, on London-American, Deleted Mar '60. Catalogue no: **HLO 8382**
7" Single: Released Dec '80, on Speciality (USA), by Speciality Records (USA). Deleted Dec '85. Catalogue no: **SON 5018**

GOOD GOLLY MISS MOLLY
Tracks: / Good golly Miss Molly / Girl can't help it / Baby face.
7" Single: Released Mar '82, on Juke Box (Re-issue), Catalogue no: **JB 013**
7" Single: Released Aug '82, on Blast From The Past, by Creole Records. Catalogue no: **CR 191**

GOOD GOLLY MISS MOLLY (2)
Tracks: / Good golly Miss Molly / Rip it up.
7" Single: Released Jul '77, on Creole, by Creole Records. Deleted Jul '80. Catalogue no: **CR 140**

GOOD GOLLY MISS MOLLY (OLD GOLD)
Tracks: / Good golly Miss Molly.
7" Single: Released Jan '85, on Old Gold, by Old Gold Records. Catalogue no: **OG 9492**

GREAT GOSH A'MIGHTY
Tracks: / Great gosh a'mighty / Ride, The / Down and out in Beverly Hills (Extra track available on 12" version only).
7" Single: Released May '86, on MCA, by MCA Records. Catalogue no: **MCA 1049**
12" Single: Released May '86, on MCA, by MCA Records. Catalogue no: **MCAT 1049**

HAPPY ENDINGS
Tracks: / Happy endings / California girls.
12" Pic: Released Nov '87, on Atco, by Atlantic Recording Corp.(USA). Deleted Jul '88. Catalogue no: **B 9392 TP**
7" Single: Released 21 Nov '87, on Atco, by Atlantic Recording Corp.(USA). Deleted Jul '88. Catalogue no: **B 9392**

HE GOT WHAT HE WANTED
Tracks: / He got what he wanted.
7" Single: Released Oct '62, on Mercury (EMI), Deleted Oct '65. Catalogue no: **AMT 1189**

I'M QUITTING SHOW BUSINESS
Tracks: / I've just come from the mountain / Search me lord / Coming home / I'm quitting show business.
7" EP: Released Jun '87, on Magnum Force, by Magnum Music Group. Catalogue no: **MFEP 012**

JENNY JENNY
Tracks: / Jenny Jenny.
7" Single: Released Sep '57, on London-American, Deleted Sep '60. Catalogue no: **HLO 8470**

KANSAS CITY
Tracks: / Kansas city.
7" Single: Released Jun '59, on London-American, Deleted Jun '62. Catalogue no: **HLU 8868**

KEEP A KNOCKIN'
Tracks: / Keep a knockin'.
7" Single: Released Nov '57, on London-American, Deleted Nov '60. Catalogue no: **HLO 8509**

LIL' BIT OF GOLD: LITTLE RICHARD
Tracks: / Tutti frutti / Good golly Miss Molly / Slippin' and slidin' / Girl can't help it, The.
CD 5": Released May '88, on Rhino, by Creole Records. Catalogue no: **R 373014**

LONG TALL SALLY
Tracks: / Whole lotta shakin' goin' on / Rip it up / Baby face / Send me some lovin' / Girl can't help it ,The / Lucille / Jenny Jenny / Good golly Miss Molly / Tutti frutti / Long tall Sally / Keep a knockin' / Money honey / Hound dog / Slippin' and slidin' / Lawdy Miss Clawdy / True fine mama / She's got it.
Note: All tracks licensed from Coombe Music International Ltd. (C) 1986. Matrix number: 5 013428 111505
7" Set: Released Jul '77, on Speciality (USA), by Speciality Records (USA). Catalogue no: **SONE 1**

LONG TALL SALLY (SINGLE)
Tracks: / Long tall Sally.
7" Single: Released Feb '57, on London-American, Deleted Feb '60. Catalogue no: **HLO 8366**

LUCILLE (SINGLE)
Tracks: / Lucille.
7" Single: Released Jan '85, on Old Gold, by Old Gold Records. Catalogue no: **OG 9494**
7" Single: Released Jun '57, on London-American, Deleted Jun '60. Catalogue no: **HLO 8446**
7" Single: Released '80, on Speciality (USA), by Speciality Records (USA). Catalogue no: **LR 0781**

OOH MY SOUL (SINGLE)
Tracks: / Ooh my soul.
7" Single: Released Jul '58, on London-American, Deleted Jul '61. Catalogue no: **HLO 8647**

OPERATOR
Tracks: / Operator / Big House Reunion.
12" Single: Released Oct '86, on WEA, by WEA Records. Deleted Jun '87. Catalogue no: **YZ 89T**
7" Single: Released Oct '86, on WEA, by WEA Records. Deleted Jun '87. Catalogue no: **YZ 89**

RIP IT UP (SINGLE)
Tracks: / Rip it up / Keep on knocking.
7" Single: Released Dec '56, on London-American, Deleted Dec '59. Catalogue no: **HLO 8336**
7" Single: Released Mar '82, on Juke Box (Re-issue), Catalogue no: **JB 014**

SHE'S GOT IT
Tracks: / She's got it.
7" Single: Released Mar '57, on London-American, Deleted Mar '60. Catalogue no: **HLO 8382**

SOMEBODY'S COMING
Tracks: / One ray of sunshine.
7" Single: Released Jan '87, on WEA, by WEA Records. Deleted Sep '87. Catalogue no: **YZ 98**

TUTTI FRUTTI (OLD GOLD)
Tracks: / Tutti frutti.
7" Single: Released Jan '85, on Old Gold, by Old Gold Records. Catalogue no: **OG 9493**

TUTTI FRUTTI (SINGLE)
Tracks: / Tutti frutti.
7" Single: Released Feb '57, on London-American, Deleted Feb '60. Catalogue no: **HLO 8366**

Little River Band

IT'S NOT A WONDER
Tracks: / It's not a wonder / Reminiscing.
7" Single: Released May '80, on Capitol, by EMI Records. Deleted May '85. Catalogue no: **CL 16141**

NIGHT OWLS
Tracks: / Night owls / Suicide Boulevard.
7" Single: Released Oct '81, on Capitol, by EMI Records. Deleted Oct '84. Catalogue no: **CL 221**

OTHER GUY
Tracks: / Other guy, The / No more tears.
7" Single: Released Jan '83, on Capitol, by EMI Records. Deleted '88. Catalogue no: **CL 279**

REMINISCING
Tracks: / Reminiscing / It's a long way there.
7" Single: Released Apr '80, on Capitol, by EMI Records. Deleted '83. Catalogue no: **CL 16138**

YOU'RE DRIVING ME OUT OF MY MIND
Tracks: / You're driving me out of my mind.
7" Single: Released May '83, on Capitol, by EMI Records. Deleted '88. Catalogue no: **CL 291**

Little Roosters

I NEED A WITNESS
Tracks: / I need a witness / Age of reason.
7" Single: Released Oct '80, on AMI, by AMI Records. Deleted Oct '83. Catalogue no: **AIS 107**

SHE-CAT SISTER FLOOZIE
Tracks: / She-cat sister floozie / Roostering with intent.
7" Single: Released Jan '80, on Velvet, Deleted Jan '85. Catalogue no: **FP 152**

THAT'S HOW STRONG MY LOVE IS
Tracks: / That's how strong my love is / Suspicious.
7" Single: Released Apr '80, on AMI, by AMI Records. Deleted '83. Catalogue no: **AIS 101**

Little Roy

NATTY YARD
Tracks: / Natty yard.
12" Single: Released Feb '82, on Love Linch, Catalogue no: **LL 024**

WITHOUT MY LOVE
Tracks: / Without my love.
12" Single: Released Aug '81, on Copasetic, by Copasetic Records. Catalogue no: **COPDIS 004**

Little, Sharon

DON'T MASH UP CREATION
Tracks: / Don't mash creation.
12" Single: Released Jun '82, on One Love (USA), by Groove Time Records (USA). Catalogue no: **92567**

Little Steven

Biographical details:
Guitarist, singer, bandleader and songwriter "Miami" Steve Van Zandt was born in Boston in 1951. He gigged in bar bands in New Jersey, including Steel Mill, where he met Bruce Springsteen. He joined the Ashbury Jukes on their formation in 1975 and later that year joined Springsteen's E Street Band but stayed close to the highly-rated outfit that became Southside Johnny & The Ashbury Jukes. He was the bedrock of Springsteen's band but remained in the Boss's shadow and when the E Streets were on hold while Springsteen made *Nebraska* he adopted the name Little Steven & The Disciples of Soul for a 12-piece band which played a one-off gig at London's Marquee to critical acclaim. Like most of the best rock in the 70's and 80's his following has been a loyal cult rather than a big commercial success. He also produced LPs for Gary "US" Bonds. Leaving Springsteen in '84 he called himself Sugar Miami Steve on a Southside Johnny album, wrote songs for Jukes and Bonds and organised the *Sun City* album/concert anti-apartheid project with Springsteen, Bob Dylan, Arthur Baker, Gil Scott Heron and Stevie Wonder. He guested on some Springsteen tour dates in '85 and co-produced *Lone Justice* in '86. (Donald Clarke, January 1988.).

BITTER FRUIT
Tracks: / Bitter fruit (No Pasaran mix) / Vote! / Bitter fruit (Cana no mas dub) (Only on 12" and CD single.) / Bitter fruit / Vote!.
7" Single: Released Mar '87, on EMI-Manhattan, by EMI Records. Deleted Apr '88. Catalogue no: **MT 21**
12" Single: Released Mar '87, on EMI-Manhattan, by EMI Records. Deleted Apr '88. Catalogue no: **12 MT 21**

BITTER FRUIT (PLATANO QUEMADO MIX)
Tracks: / Bitter fruit (Platano Quemado mix) / Vote! (part3) / Vote! (world war 3).
CD 5": Released 23 May '87, on EMI-Manhattan, by EMI Records. Catalogue no: **CDMT 21 (E)**
12" Single: Released 23 May '87, on EMI-Manhattan, by EMI Records. Catalogue no: **12 MTX 21**

FOREVER
Tracks: / Forever / Men without women.
7" Single: Released Nov '82, on EMI-America, by EMI Records. Catalogue no: **EA 148**

LYIN' IN A BED OF FIRE
Tracks: / Lyin' in a bed of fire.
7" Single: Released Apr '83, on EMI-America, by EMI Records. Catalogue no: **EA 155**

NO MORE PARTIES
Tracks: / No more parties / Fruta Amarga / No more parties (party remix) (Only on 12".) / No more parties (dub) (Only on 12".) / Fruta Amarga (Spanish) (Only on 12".).
Cassingle: Released Sep '87, on EMI-Manhattan, by EMI Records. Catalogue no: **TC MT 29**
12" Single: Released Sep '87, on EMI-Manhattan, by EMI Records. Deleted Apr '88. Catalogue no: **12 MT 29**
7" Single: Released Sep '87, on EMI-Manhattan, by EMI Records. Deleted Apr '88. Catalogue no: **MT 29**

OUT OF THE DARKNESS
Tracks: / Out of the darkness / Fear.
7" Single: Released Jan '86, on EMI-America, by EMI Records. Catalogue no: **EA 174**

REVOLUTION (SINGLE)
Tracks: / Revolution.
7" Single: Released Apr '89, on RCA, by BMG Records (UK). Catalogue no: **PB 49443**
CD 5": Released Apr '89, on RCA, by BMG Records (UK). Catalogue no: **PD 49444**
12" Single: Released Apr '89, on RCA, by BMG Records (UK). Catalogue no: **PT 49414**

SOLIDARITY
Tracks: / Solidarity.
7" Single: Released Aug '83, on EMI-America, by EMI Records. Catalogue no: **EA 161**
12" Single: Released Aug '83, on EMI-America, by EMI Records. Catalogue no: **12 EA 161**

TRAIL OF BROKEN TREATIES
Tracks: / Trail of broken treaties / Native American.
7" Single: Released Nov '87, on EMI-Manhattan, by EMI Records. Deleted 31 Jul '88. Catalogue no: **MT 28**
12" Single: Released Nov '87, on EMI-Manhattan, by EMI Records. Deleted 31 Jul '88. Catalogue no: **12MT 28**

Little T

CAN YOU FEEL THE HEAT
Tracks: / Can you feel the heat / Can you feel the heat (version).
12" Single: Released Feb '89, on Midtown, Catalogue no: **MIDT 001**

Little Tom

IT'S NOT UNUSUAL
Tracks: / It's not unusual.
7" Single: Released Oct '82, on Charisma, by Virgin Records. Deleted Oct '85. Catalogue no: **CB 403**

Little Tony

TOO GOOD
Tracks: / Too good.
7" Single: Released Jan '60, on Decca, by Decca Records. Deleted Jan '63. Catalogue no: **F 11190**

Little Twitch

FREAK
Tracks: / Freak.
12" Single: Released Dec '88, on Redman International, Catalogue no: **RED 27**

GLAD SEH ME COME
Tracks: / Glad seh me come.
12" Single: Released 30 May '89, on Steely & Cleevie, Catalogue no: **VPRD 439**

TAN GOOD
Tracks: / Tan good.
7" Single: Released Apr '89, on Blue Trac, by Blue Trac Records. Catalogue no: **BTRD 036**

WEAVE ON HAIR
Tracks: / Weave on hair.
12" Single: Released Jul '88, on Vibes, by Vibes Records. Catalogue no: **VIBES 029**

Littman, Julian

YOUNG EXPLORERS
Tracks: / Young explorers / Have you got soul.
7" Single: Released Apr '81, on Harbour, by Harbour Records. Deleted '85. Catalogue no: **HRB 10**

Live...

LIVE-IN WORLD (SINGLE) (anti-heroin project)
7" Single: Released Oct '86, on EMI, by EMI Records. Catalogue no: **AHP 1**
12" Single: Released Oct '86, on EMI, by EMI Records. Catalogue no: **12 AHP 1**

Live Cinema

POP DENSITY
Tracks: / Pop density / Pop density (version).
7" Single: Released Nov '87, on High Cue, Catalogue no: **CUE 1**
12" Single: Released Nov '87, on High Cue, Catalogue no: **12CUE 1**

Live & Love

BAD CHAKA
Tracks: / Bad Chaka.
7" Single: Released Dec '88, on TSOJ, Catalogue no: **LLD 99**

Live Report

WHY DO I ALWAYS GET IT WRONG
Tracks: / Why do I always get it wrong / Take a chance on me.

7" Single: Released Apr '89, on Brouhaha, by Brouhaha Records. Catalogue no: **CUE 7**
CD 5": Released Apr '89, on Brouhaha, by Brouhaha Records. Catalogue no: **CDCUE 7**
12" Single: Released Apr '89, on Brouhaha, by Brouhaha Records. Catalogue no: **12CUE 7**

Live Skull

PUSHERMAN EP
7" Single: Released Feb '87, on Homestead, Catalogue no: **HMS 080**

Live Wire

DON'T LOOK NOW
Tracks: / Don't look now / Power.
7" Single: Released Mar '81, on A&M, by A&M Records. Deleted Mar '84. Catalogue no: **AMS 8114**

IT'S FOR YOU
Tracks: / It's for you.

12" Single: Released Oct '86, on BMW, by BMW Records. Catalogue no: **DIAL T 999**
7" Single: Released Oct '86, on BMW, by BMW Records. Catalogue no: **DIAL 999**

NO FRIGHT (SINGLE)
Tracks: / No fright / Break of day.
7" Single: Released Oct '80, on A&M, by A&M Records. Deleted Oct '83. Catalogue no: **AMS 7573**

SLEEP
Tracks: / Sleep / Breaking down my door.
7" Single: Released May '81, on A&M, by A&M Records. Deleted May '84. Catalogue no: **AMS 8139**

Live Wya

CATCH THE BEAT
Tracks: / Catch the beat.
12" Single: Released Jan '88, on Ariwa Sounds, by Ariwa Sounds. Catalogue no: **ARI 70**

Liverpool Express

Biographical details:
This British band consisted of Derek Cashin, Tony Coates, Roger Craig and Billy Kinsley Having achieved legendary status during the Sixties as the city which produced the Beatles and a host of other top acts, Liverpool's importance diminished during the Seventies. It was not until the beginning of the Eighties, with bands like Echo & The Bunnymen and the Teardrop Explodes, that the city re-established itself as a vital source of new rock talent.
When the Liverpool Express broke onto the UK charts in June 1976, at exactly the same time as fellow citizens Our Kid and the Real Thing, many observers proclaimed a new Liverpool explosion - but the disparate nature of these acts demonstrated that the so-called boom was just a figment of the record industry's imagination, and the fact that they all hailed from Liverpool was merely a coincidence.
The Liverpool Express's UK chart success began in June '76 and ended in June '77. During this time they chalked up four hit singles, all written by Craig and Kinsley. The summery ballad *You are my love* reached No.11; *Hold tight* peaked at No.46; their bombastic attempt at an epic, *Every man must have a dream* climbed to No.17; and *Dreamin'* stopped at No.40.
Their music was in a pleasant but ultimately inconsequential vein; they provided a sort of bridge between the Bay City Rollers and 10 CC.
(Bob MacDonald, 14th Dec 1985).

DREAMIN'
Tracks: / Dreamin'.
7" Single: Released Jun '77, on Warner Bros., by WEA Records. Deleted Jun '70. Catalogue no: **K 16933**

EVERY MAN MUST HAVE A DREAM
Tracks: / Every man must have a dream.
7" Single: Released Dec '76, on Warner Bros., by WEA Records. Deleted Dec '79. Catalogue no: **K 16854**

HOLD TIGHT
Tracks: / Hold tight.
7" Single: Released Oct '76, on Warner Bros., by WEA Records. Deleted Oct '79. Catalogue no: **K 16799**

IF YOU'RE OUT THERE
Tracks: / If you're out there / You are my love.
7" Single: Released May '85, on Direct (1), Catalogue no: **IF 1**

SO WHAT
Tracks: / So what / Roll over.
7" Single: Released Nov '83, on Priority, by Priority Records. Deleted Nov '87. Catalogue no: **P4**

YOU ARE MY LOVE
Tracks: / You are my love.
7" Single: Released Jun '76, on Warner Bros., by WEA Records. Deleted Jun '79. Catalogue no: **K 16743**

Liverpool Football Club

Biographical details:
Having achieved legendary status during the Sixties as the city which produced the Beatles and a host of other leading pop groups, Liverpool's musical importance diminished for a while during the Seventies.
The city's temporary rock decline coincided with the ascent of Liverpool FC, so the place remained firmly on the international entertainment map.
The soccer squad reached FA Club Final status in 1971 (against Arsenal) and again in 1974 (versus Newcastle). They were League Cup finalists in 1978 (in a showdown with the also red-hot Nottingham Forest), in 1981 (with West Ham United) and in 1982 (against Tottnham Hotspur).
Liverpool went through to the European Cup Final in three consecutive years, playing against Bruges in 1976 and 1978 and Borussia MGB in 1977. After Nottingham Forest had pulled off the Euro-double in '79 and '80, Liverpool returned in 1981 to play Spain's Real Madrid.
In 1985 Liverpool's potential triumph in European Cup Final at the Heisel Stadium in Brussels turned to disaster before the match had even begun. Football violence, which has been plaguing the UK game on a gradually increasing basis during the preceding 15 years, was exported to Brussels that night on a horrendous scale with the loss of 38 lives.
Restrictions on the overseas fixtures of English clubs were quickly imposed. It was particularly sad that Liverpool should be the team to suffer this catastrophic culmination of a long-running problem, because the club's track record over the past two decades had been excellent.
The fact that a trouble-free club should suddenly experience crowd problems, led some observers to allege that much soccer hooliganism was caused by political agitators rather than gangs of 'fans'.
During the late Seventies and early Eighties, Liverpool Football Team twice penetrated the UK singles charts.
In common with many other English squads, they realised that the acoustics of the shower-room singing sessions would transfer well to a recording studio and thus provide a handy jingoistic advertisement for the team. Liverpool's *We can do it* EP reached No.15 in 1977 - it was produced by Wayne Bickerton & Tony Waddington, the pair who had originally written the title song as a 1975 hit for the Rubettes. In 1983 the squad reached No.54 with their double A sided single *Liverpool/Anthem*.
(Bob MacDonald, 14th Dec 1985).

ANFIELD RAP
Tracks: / Anfield rap (red machine dub) (On all versions) / Anfield rap (red machine in full effect)(full time mix) (12" only).

12" Single: Released May '88, on Virgin, by Virgin Records. Catalogue no: **LFC 1-12**
7" Single: Released May '88, on Virgin, by Virgin Records. Catalogue no: **LFC 1**
7" Pic: Released '88, on Virgin, by Virgin Records. Catalogue no: **LFCY 1**

LIVERPOOL(ANTHEM)
Tracks: / Liverpool (anthem) / Paisley crazy.
7" Single: Released Mar '84, on Mean, by Mean Records. Catalogue no: **MEAN 102**

SITTING ON TOP OF THE WORLD
Tracks: / Sitting on top of the world / Running like the wind.

7" Single: Released Apr '86, on Columbia, by EMI Records. Deleted Jul '87. Catalogue no: **DB 9116**

WE CAN DO IT
Tracks: / We can do it.
7" Single: Released May '77, on State, by State Records. Deleted May '80. Catalogue no: **STAT 50**

Liverpool Philharmonic

GOD BLESS THE PRINCE OF WALES
Tracks: / God bless the Prince of Wales / Wedding march.
7" Single: Released Jul '81, on Chandos, by Chandos Records. Catalogue no: **SBRD 101**

Living Colour

CULT OF PERSONALITY
Tracks: / Cult of personality / Open letter to a landlord / Middle man(live) (12" & CD single only.) / Should I stay or should I go / What's your favourite colour.

CD 5": Released Sep '88, on Epic, by CBS Records. Deleted Jan '89. Catalogue no: **CDLCL 3**
7" Single: Released Oct '88, on Epic, by CBS Records. Deleted Jan '89. Catalogue no: **LCL B3**
12" Single: Released 24 Apr '89, on Epic, by CBS Records. Deleted Oct '89. Catalogue no: **LCL T5**
CD 5": Released 8 May '89, on Epic, by CBS Records. Deleted Oct '89. Catalogue no: **CDLCL 5**
Special: Released May '89, on Epic, by CBS Records. Deleted Oct '89. Catalogue no: **LCL P5**
7" Single: Released 24 Apr '89, on Epic, by CBS Records. Deleted Oct '89. Catalogue no: **LCL 5**
7" Single: Released Sep '88, on Epic, by CBS Records. Deleted Jan '89. Catalogue no: **LCL 3**
12" Single: Released Sep '88, on Epic, by CBS Records. Deleted Jan '89. Catalogue no: **LCL T3**

GLAMOUR BOYS
Tracks: / Glamour boys / Which way to America / Middleman (Only on 12" version.) / Rap track (conversation with Living Colour).
7" Single: Released Jul '88, on Epic, by CBS Records. Deleted Jan '89. Catalogue no: **LCL 2**
12" Single: Released Jul '88, on Epic, by CBS Records. Deleted Jan '89. Catalogue no: **LCL T2**
7" Single: Released 25 Jul '88, on Epic, by CBS Records. Deleted Jan '89. Catalogue no: **LCL G2**
CD 5": Released 18 Jul '88, on Epic, by CBS Records. Deleted Jan '89. Catalogue no: **CPLCL 2**
7" Pic: Released Jul '88, on Epic, by CBS Records. Deleted Jan '89. Catalogue no: **CTLCL 2**

GLAMOUR BOYS (2)
Tracks: / Glamour boys / Cult of personality.
CD 5": Released Sep '89, on Epic, by CBS Records. Catalogue no: **CD LCL 6**
12" Single: Released Sep '89, on Epic, by CBS Records. Catalogue no: **LCL T6**
12" Single: Released Sep '89, on Epic, by CBS Records. Catalogue no: **LCL G6**
7" Single: Released Sep '89, on Epic, by CBS Records. Catalogue no: **LCL 6**

MIDDLE MAN
Tracks: / Middle man / Desperate people / Funny vibe (Track available on 12" only.).
7" Single: Released May '88, on Epic, by CBS Records. Deleted Jan '89. Catalogue no: **LCL 1**
7" Pic: Released 13 Jun '88, on Epic, by CBS Records. Deleted Jan '89. Catalogue no: **LCL P1**
12" Single: Released May '88, on Epic, by CBS Records. Deleted Jan '89. Catalogue no: **LCL T1**
CD 5": Released 6 Jun '88, on Epic, by CBS Records. Deleted Jan '89. Catalogue no: **CPLCL 1**

OPEN LETTER (TO A LANDLORD)
Tracks: / Open letter (to a landlord) / Cult of personality (live) / Talkin' 'bout a revolution (live) (Only on 12" version.).

CD 5": Released 27 Feb '89, on Epic, by CBS Records. Catalogue no: **CDLCL 4**
7" Single: Released 27 Feb '89, on Epic, by CBS Records. Deleted 10 Jul '89. Catalogue no: **LCL 4**
12" Single: Released 27 Feb '89, on Epic, by CBS Records. Deleted 10 Jul '89. Catalogue no: **LCLT 4**
7" Single: Released Mar '89, on Epic, by CBS Records. Deleted Oct '89. Catalogue no: **LCLQ 4**

Living Daylight

COLLEEN
Tracks: / Colleen.
12" Single: Released Oct '85, on Roadrunner (Germany), Catalogue no: **RR 125486**

Living Daylights

HEART OF GOLD
Tracks: / Heart of gold.
12" Single: Released Jun '84, on In Phaze, by In Phaze Records. Catalogue no: **HAZ 5**
7" Single: Released Jun '84, on In Phaze, by In Phaze Records. Catalogue no: **7HAZ 5**

Living In A Box

BLOW THE HOUSE DOWN
Tracks: / Blow the house down / Dance the mayonnaise.
12" Single: Released Jan '89, on Chrysalis, by Chrysalis Records. Catalogue no: **LIBX 5**
7" Single: Released Feb '89, on Chrysalis, by Chrysalis Records. Catalogue no: **LIBB 5**
7" Single: Released Jan '89, on Chrysalis, by Chrysalis Records. Catalogue no: **LIB 5**
CD 5": Released Jan '89, on Chrysalis, by Chrysalis Records. Catalogue no: **LIBCD 5**

GATE CRASHING (SINGLE)
Tracks: / Gate crashing.

CD 5": Released Apr '89, on Chrysalis, by Chrysalis Records. Catalogue no: **LIBCD 6**
7" Single: Released Apr '89, on Chrysalis, by Chrysalis Records. Catalogue no: **LIV 6**
7" Single: Released Apr '89, on Chrysalis, by Chrysalis Records. Catalogue no: **LIB 6**
12" Single: Released Apr '89, on Chrysalis, by Chrysalis Records. Catalogue no: **LIBX 6**
12" Single: Released Apr '89, on Chrysalis, by Chrysalis Records. Catalogue no: **LIVX 6**

LIVING IN A BOX (SINGLE)
Tracks: / Living in a box / Living in a box (penthouse mix) / Super Heroes (Extra track on CD only).
12" Single: Released Mar '87, on Chrysalis, by Chrysalis Records. Catalogue no: **LIBX 1**
7" Single: Released Mar '87, on Chrysalis, by Chrysalis Records. Catalogue no: **LIB 1**
CD 5": Released Mar '87, on Chrysalis, by Chrysalis Records. Catalogue no: **CDE 4**

LOVE IS THE ART
Tracks: / Love is the art / Love is the art (inst.) / Love is the art (love) (Track available on 12" single only.) / Love is the art (art) (Track available on 12" single only.).
7" Single: Released Jan '88, on Chrysalis, by Chrysalis Records. Catalogue no: **LIB 4**
12" Single: Released Jan '88, on Chrysalis, by Chrysalis Records. Catalogue no: **LIBX 4**

ROOM IN YOUR HEART
Tracks: / Room in your heart.

CD 5": Released Sep '89, on Chrysalis, by Chrysalis Records. Catalogue no: **LIBCD 7**
7" Single: Released Sep '89, on Chrysalis, by Chrysalis Records. Catalogue no: **LIB 7**
12" Single: Released Sep '89, on Chrysalis, by Chrysalis Records. Catalogue no: **LIBX 7**

SCALES OF JUSTICE
Tracks: / Scales of justice / Ecstasy.
Cassingle: Released 30 May '87, on Chrysalis, by Chrysalis Records. Catalogue no: **2 LIB 2**
7" Single: Released 30 May '87, on Chrysalis, by Chrysalis Records. Catalogue no: **LIB2**
12" Single: Released 30 May '87, on Chrysalis, by Chrysalis Records. Catalogue no: **LIBX 2**

SO THE STORY GOES
Tracks: / So the story goes / Liam McCoy, The.
7" Single: Released Sep '87, on Chrysalis, by Chrysalis Records. Catalogue no: **LIB 3**
12" Single: Released Sep '87, on Chrysalis, by Chrysalis Records. Catalogue no: **LIBX 3**

Living In Texas

AND DAVID CRIED
7" Single: Released Aug '83, on Rhythmic, by Rhythmic Records. Catalogue no:

RMNS 2

GLAD BAD MAD AND SAD
12" Single: Released Sep '85, on Chainsaw, Deleted '88. Catalogue no: **TEXT 9**

GOD BLESS AMERICA
Tracks: / God bless America.
12" Single: Released Aug '84, on Chainsaw, Deleted '88. Catalogue no: **TEXT 2**

KINGDOM
Tracks: / Kingdom.
12" Single: Released Feb '84, on Chainsaw, Deleted '88. Catalogue no: **TEXT 1**
7" Single: Released Feb '84, on Chainsaw, Deleted '88. Catalogue no: **TEX 1**

MY END OF HEAVEN
Tracks: / My end of heaven.
12" Single: Released Oct '83, on Rebirth, Catalogue no: **RB 1219**

Living Legends

POPE IS A DOPE, THE
Tracks: / Pope is a dope, The.
7" Single: Released May '82, on Upright, by Upright Records. Catalogue no: **UP YOURS 2**

Living Proof

WHERE DID I GO WRONG
Tracks: / Where did I go wrong.
12" Single: Released Sep '89, on GEMC, Catalogue no: **12 PO 29**

YOU'RE THE APPLE OF MY EYE
Tracks: / You're the apple of my eye (radio edit) / You're the apple of my eye (full length).
12" Single: Released 18 May '89, on GEMC, Catalogue no: **12 PO 18**

Living Sound

SPIDERMAN
Tracks: / Spiderman / Iceman and Firestar.
7" Single: Released Nov '87, on Dulcima, by Living Productions. Catalogue no: **DLCS 102**

Livingston, Carlton

AIN'T GONNA FIGHT
Tracks: / Ain't gonna fight / Lately I found out.
12" Single: Released Feb '83, on J.B., Catalogue no: **JED 004**

ARMAGIDEON TIME
Tracks: / Armagideon time.
7" Single: Released Aug '82, on Dynamite, Catalogue no: **DYN 002**

CHALICE IN HAND
Tracks: / Chalice in hand.
7" Single: Released Jun '82, on Power House, Catalogue no: **PHO 5**

HUNDREDWEIGHT OF COLLIE WEED
Tracks: / Hundredweight of collie weed / Soundman crash.
12" Single: Released Mar '84, on Greensleeves, by Greensleeves Records. Catalogue no: **GRED 141**

MARIE
Tracks: / Marie.
7" Single: Released Feb '82, on Power House, Catalogue no: **PH 21**

MR MUSIC MAN
Tracks: / Mr. Music Man.
12" Single: Released Jul '84, on Greensleeves, by Greensleeves Records. Catalogue no: **GRED 149**

SETTLE CROWD OF PEOPLE
Tracks: / Settle crowd of people.
12" Single: Released Nov '84, on Technics, Catalogue no: **Unknown**

WHEN I'M HOT
Tracks: / When I'm hot.
12" Single: Released Sep '84, on What's Up Doc, Catalogue no: **Unknown**

YES I FEEL
Tracks: / Yes I feel.
12" Single: Released Sep '84, on Rosie Uprising, Catalogue no: **Unknown**

YOUR LOVING
Tracks: / Your loving.
12" Single: Released Jun '84, on Time, Catalogue no: **TR 003**

Livingstone, Carly

CHILDREN OF THE MOUNTAIN
Tracks: / Children of the mountain.
12" Single: Released Sep '84, on GG'S, Catalogue no: **GG 124**

Livingstone, Dandy

Biographical details: This Jamaican singer moved to Britain in the early Sixties. Just as the blue beat/ska scene was getting underway in his home country. He kept in touch with his roots by forming the ska duo Sugar'n'Dandy, who built up a cult following via regular gigs at the Flamingo club in Soho, London. As ska evolved into 'rock steady', he became a solo performer, and continued in this capacity when rock steadybecame reggae in the late Sixties. In late 1972 Livingstone became one of the many reggae artists of the era to enjoy crossover success on the British pop chart. The infectious *Suzanne beware of the devil* reached No.14. It was followed in early '73 by the double A sided hit *Big city/Think about that,* which peaked at No.26. Subsequent singles failed to make the grade, although he continued recording, and producing for other artists, right through into the Eighties. (Bob MacDonald, 15th Dec 1985).

A.M. LOVER
Tracks: / A.M. lover / A.M. lover(version).
7" Single: Released Oct '82, on Mint Music, Catalogue no: **RTD 101**

BIG CITY
Tracks: / Big city / Think about that.
7" Single: Released Jan '73, on Horse, by Trojan Records. Deleted '76. Catalogue no: **HOSS 25**

INSTANT MUSIC
Tracks: / Instant music / Living in sus.
7" Single: Released Mar '80, on EMI, by EMI Records. Deleted '83. Catalogue no: **RIC 109**
12" Single: Released Mar '80, on EMI, by EMI Records. Deleted '83. Catalogue no: **12 RIC 109**

SOMETIMES WHEN WE TOUCH
Tracks: / Sometimes when we touch / Tuff tuff.
12" Single: Released May '82, on Cartridge, Catalogue no: **CRD 12**

SUZANNE BEWARE OF THE DEVIL
Tracks: / Suzanne beware of the devil / Right on brother.
7" Single: Released Sep '72, on Horse, by Trojan Records. Deleted '75. Catalogue no: **HOSS 16**
7" Single: Released Apr '83, on Old Gold, by Old Gold Records. Catalogue no: **OG 9269**

Lixx Array

LIXX ARRAY
7" EP: Released Aug '87, on Azra (USA), by Azra International (USA). Catalogue no: **A 4086**

Lizzard

JUMP AND SPREAD OUT
Tracks: / Jump and spread out.
7" Single: Released Jul '88, on Flourgon, Catalogue no: **LLD 89**

Lizzy Borden

ME AGAINST THE WORLD
Tracks: / Me against the world.
7" Single: Released Oct '87, on Roadrunner (Germany), Catalogue no: **RR 5472**

Lizzy Lee Anne

WHISPERING ON THE PHONE
Tracks: / Whispering on the phone / If i had the world.
7" Single: Released Mar '84, on Kick, Catalogue no: **KIC 03**

LKT Band

BABY BE TRUE
Tracks: / Baby be true / My mistake.
12" Single: Released Oct '85, on Clouds, Catalogue no: **CLSD 004**

LL Cool J

GO CUT CREATOR GO
Tracks: / Bristol Hotel, The* (Available on 12" and 7" remix.) / I need love+ / Go cut creator go / Kandy.
7" Single: Released Nov '87, on Def Jam, Deleted Jun '88. Catalogue no: **LLCJ Q1**
12" Single: Released Nov '87, on Def Jam, Catalogue no: **LLCD T1**
7" Single: Released Nov '87, on Def Jam, Deleted Jun '88. Catalogue no: **LLCJ 1**
7" Single: Released Dec '87, on Def Jam, Deleted Jun '88. Catalogue no: **LLCJ P1**
7" Single: Released Nov '87, on Def Jam, Catalogue no: **LLCD 1**

GOIN' BACK TO CALIFORNIA
Tracks: / Going back to Cali / Jack the ripper / I can't live without my radio.
10" single: Released Feb '88, on Def Jam, Catalogue no: **LLCJ Q2**
7" Single: Released Feb '88, on Def Jam, Deleted Aug '88. Catalogue no: **LLCJ T2**
12" Single: Released Feb '88, on Def Jam, Deleted Jun '88. Catalogue no: **LLCJ T1**

I CAN'T LIVE WITHOUT MY RADIO (JAN 86)
Tracks: / I can't live without my radio / I can't give you no more.
7" Single: Released Jan '86, on Def Jam, Catalogue no: **A 6684**
12" Single: Released Jan '86, on Def Jam, Catalogue no: **TA 6684**

L.L. COOL J - I'M THAT TYPE OF GUY (Released on Def Jam)

I CAN'T LIVE WITHOUT MY RADIO (SEPT 86)
Tracks: / I can't live without my radio / Rock bells / You'll rock (Extra track on 12" version only.) / El Shabazz (Extra track on 12" version only).
12" Single: Released Sep '86, on Def Jam, Deleted Aug '87. Catalogue no: **650113 6**
7" Single: Released Sep '86, on Def Jam, Catalogue no: **650113 7**

I NEED LOVE
Tracks: / I need love.
7" Single: Released Aug '87, on Def Jam, Catalogue no: **651101 6**
12" Single: Released Aug '87, on Def Jam, Catalogue no: **651101 7**

I'M BAD
Tracks: / I'm bad / Get down / Dangerous (On 12" only) / Rock the bells* (*On 650 856 8) / I can't live without my radio* (*On 650 856 8 only).
7" Single: Released May '87, on Def Jam, Deleted Nov '87. Catalogue no: **650856 7**
7" Pic: Released Jun '87, on Def Jam, Deleted Nov '87. Catalogue no: **650856 8**
12" Single: Released May '87, on Def Jam, Deleted Nov '87. Catalogue no: **650856 6**

I'M THAT TYPE OF GUY (see panel above)
Tracks: / I'm that type of guy / It gets no rougher / Rock the bells.
Cassingle: Released 19 Jun '89, on Def Jam, Catalogue no: **LLCJ M3**
7" Single: Released May '89, on Def Jam, Catalogue no: **LLCJ 3**
CD 5": Released May '89, on Def Jam, Catalogue no: **CD LLCJ 3**
12" Single: Released 19 Jun '89, on Def Jam, Catalogue no: **LLCJ E3**
7" Single: Released 12 Jun '89, on Def Jam, Catalogue no: **LLCJ B3**
12" Single: Released May '89, on Def Jam, Catalogue no: **LLCJ T3**

ONE SHOT AT LOVE
Tracks: / One shot at love (edit) / Clap your hands (edit) / It gets no rougher / Clap you hands (LP version).
CD 5": Released 18 Sep '89, on Def Jam, Catalogue no: **CD LLCJ 4**
7" Single: Released 18 Sep '89, on Def Jam, Catalogue no: **LLCJ 4**
12" Single: Released 18 Sep '89, on Def Jam, Catalogue no: **LLCJ T4**

RADIO
Tracks: / I cant live without my Radio. / You cant dance. / Dear Yvette / I can give you more / Dangerous / Rock the Bells / I need a beat / You'll rock. / I want you..
Cassingle: Released Feb '86, on Def Jam, Catalogue no: **40 26745**

ROCK THE BELLS
Tracks: / Rock the Bells / El Shabazz.
7" Single: Released Mar '86, on Def Jam, Catalogue no: **A 7003**
12" Single: Released Mar '86, on Def Jam, Catalogue no: **TA 7003**

Lloyd, Allen

I KEEP LOOKING AT YOU
Tracks: / I keep looking at you.
12" Single: Released Mar '84, on Epic, by CBS Records. Catalogue no: **TA 4299**
7" Single: Released Mar '84, on Epic, by CBS Records. Catalogue no: **A 4299**

Lloyd, Andy

LIVING IN AMERICA
Tracks: / Living in america / Letters to eva.
7" Single: Released Feb '80, on Ariola, by BMG Records (UK). Deleted Feb '85. Catalogue no: **AHA 552**

Lloyd, Carol

COME SEE ABOUT ME
Tracks: / Come see about me / I just want to love you.
7" Single: Released Oct '82, on Philly World (USA), by Philly World (USA). Catalogue no: **PWS 104**
12" Single: Released Oct '82, on Philly World (USA), by Philly World (USA). Catalogue no: **PWSL 104**

Lloyd & Charmain

REMEMBER THAT SUNDAY
Tracks: / Remember that Sunday.
7" Single: Released Aug '81, on Dancebeat, Catalogue no: **DBD 1309**

Lloyd Collection

MAGGIE'S FARM
Tracks: / Maggie's Farm.
7" Single: Released Apr '86, on Mayday, Deleted '87. Catalogue no: **MAY 1**

Lloyd & Devon

BUM BALL
Tracks: / Bum ball.
12" Single: Released Sep '84, on Rosie Uprising, Catalogue no: **Unknown**

Lloyd, Floyd

SWEET LADY
Tracks: / Sweet lady / Check out your mind.
12" Single: Released Mar '82, on Echo, by Echo Records. Catalogue no: **12 ECHO 005**
7" Single: Released Mar '82, on Echo, by Echo Records. Catalogue no: **ECHO 005**

Lloyd, Geoff

AFTER LOVE
Tracks: / After love / When we meet.
7" Single: Released Feb '82, on Nectar, by Nectar Music. Catalogue no: **NRS 1**

Lloyd, Ian

DO YOU WANNA TOUCH ME
Tracks: / Do you wanna touch me / Third wave civilisation.
7" Single: Released Jan '81, on Scotti Bros (USA), Deleted Jan '84. Catalogue no: **K 11638**

LOVE STEALER
Tracks: / Love stealer / She broke your heart.
7" Single: Released Feb '80, on Scotti Bros (Germany), Deleted Feb '85. Catalogue no: **K 11410**

Lloyd, Jeremy

TEDDY BEAR
Tracks: / Teddy bear / Kenny the koala bear / My best friend / Dilys the dachshund.
7" Single: Released Jul '81, on Polydor, by Polydor Ltd. Deleted '85. Catalogue no: **POSP 252**

Lloyd, Robert

NOTHING MATTERS
Tracks: / Nothing matters.
12" Single: Released Oct '88, on In Tape, by In Tape Records. Catalogue no: **ITTI 059**
7" Single: Released Oct '88, on In Tape, by In Tape Records. Catalogue no: **IT 059**

SOMETHING NICE
Tracks: / Something nice.
12" Single: Released Jul '88, on In Tape, by In Tape Records. Catalogue no: **ITTI 056**
7" Single: Released Jul '88, on In Tape, by In Tape Records. Catalogue no: **IT 056**

Lloyd Webber, Andrew

Biographical details: This British composer and producer, born in London, recieved classical training at school and music college, and also grew up with stron interests in pop music and the theatre. He met lyricist Tim Rice in 1965 and, two years later, the young songwriting duo were asked by a London school to come up with a musical piece on any theme that would be suitable for inclusion in an end-of-term concert. They eventually dreamed up a 20-minute, embronic version of what proved to be their first hit musical, *Joseph and his amazing technicolour dreamcoat*. This 20th century treatment of a Biblical story was so imaginative, entertaining and musically exciting that it won them the financial backing to conceive an even more ambitious project with an equally eye-catching title, *Jesus Christ Superstar*.
This second production began life as one single *Superstar*, sung by Murray Head, released in Britain in late 1969. It failed to make the charts and, initially, met with similar apathy in the States. However, the full length *Jesus Christ Superstar* was premiered in America before Britain. The spectacular show opened in New York in October 1971, and in London in August '72. Despite a mixed reception from reviewers and a controversioal reaction in some religious quarters, it was a colossal success. Focusing on the final week of Christ's life, *Jesus Christ Superstar* eventually recieved the critical and religious acclaim that the public had afforded it from the outset. The show became an international phenomenon, enjoying particular success in the writers' native Britain, where it brushed aside all previous London box-office records; it was still running at London's Palace Theatre when the Seventies became the Eighties. Rice & Lloyd Webber were hailed as the saviours of British musical theatre, rescuing the genre from the terminal threat posed by cinema and television. Like *Jesus Christ Superstar*, the long-awaited follow-up project *Evita* was issued on an LP long before the opening of the theatrical production. This was strange but ultimately ingenious idea - if the public did not like what they heard on the album, Rice & Lloyd Webber could cut their losses and quietly abandon the show before embarking upon the vast overheads involved in staging it; if the record was well recieved, the resulting publicity (combined with audiences' familiarity with the songs) would create added interest in the show's premiere. The latter was certainly true with *Evita*, the songwriting duo's musical biography of Argentine history's most controversial figure, Eva Peron. The production opened in London in June 1978, some 16 months after its standout song *Don't cry for me Argentina* had become a British No.1 single. *Evita* was another extraordinary international success. Although Lloyd Webba attracted a degree of criticism for re-cycling and over-milking his best melodies - David Essex's UK Top 3 single *Oh what a circus* featured virtually the same tune as *Don't cry for me Argentina* - his status as one of Britain's greatest post-war composers could not be questioned. Lloyd Webber's next big project was his first without Rice. The pair amicably parted due to differing interests - the lyricist wanted to devote more time to pop music and the record industry, while the composer was formulating even more ambitious theatrical plans. Before embarking on *Cats*, however, Lloyd Webber found time to mastermind two other projects: *Variations*, which featured the cello work of brother Julian, became a UK No.2 LP in 1978; and he reached the runner-up position again in 1980 with *Tell me on a Sunday*, an LP/TV project in which he collaborated with lyricist Don Black and a previously unknown singer, Marti Webb. *Cats* was premiered in 1981. In traditional Webber style, it created spectacular box-office sales in both London and New York. There was little that could be described as traditional in the show itself, however: this song and dance extravaganza was inspired by the feline poems of T.S.Eliot, and boasted some wonderfully original costumes, effects, dance routines and theatrical logistics. Elaine Page belting out the big ballad *Melody* in the costume and character of a cat, might have sounded like ludicrous idea; but it worked splendidly, and gave her a UK Top 10 single as well as inspiring a host of cover versions by such big names as Barbra Streisand and Barry Manilow.
Webber's next lyrical companion was the prolific television satirist, Richard Stilgoe. Their *Starlight express* production fared respectably well, though it came nowhere near to matching the composer's usual success standards. Its awkward attempts to yield pop hit singles failed. Ironically, Webber's 1985 *Requiem* project (a Mass composed in tribute to his recently deceased father yielded an unlikely and unexpected smash single - *Pie Jesu*, sung by his wife Sarah Brightman with choirboy Paul Miles-Kingston, sped to No.3 on the UK singles chart. By this time, Webber, whose financial status had earned him the nickname 'Andrew Lloyds Band', was the proud owner of the Palace Theatre, which had for so long been the London home of *Jesus Christ Superstar*. (Bob MacDonald, 6th May 1985).

MEMORY
Tracks: / Memory / Lost variation.
7" Single: Released Apr '81, on MCA, by MCA Records. Deleted '85. Catalogue no: **MCA 698**

Lloyd Webber, Julian

RITUAL FIRE DANCE
Tracks: / Ritual fire dance / Arioso.
7" Single: Released Jan '82, on RCA Red Seal, by BMG Records (UK). Catalogue no: **RB 5445**

SWAN
Tracks: / Swan / Apres un reve.
7" Single: Released Feb '81, on Polydor, by Polydor Ltd. Deleted Feb '84. Catalogue no: **POSP 199**

Llwybr Llaethog

DULL DI DRAIS
7" EP: Released Feb '87, on Anhrefn, Catalogue no: **ANHREFN 009**

L.N.R.

WORK IT TO THE BONE
Tracks: / Work it to the bone.
7" Single: Released 22 May '89, on Kool Kat, by Kool Kat Records. Catalogue no: **KOOL 501**
12" Single: Released May '89, on Kool Kat, by Kool Kat Records. Catalogue no: **KOOL R501**
CD 5": Released 5 Jun '89, on Kool Kat, by Kool Kat Records. Catalogue no: **KOOL 501 CD**
12" Single: Released 15 May '89, on Kool Kat, by Kool Kat Records. Catalogue no: **KOOL T501**

Loaded Fourty Fours

THUNDERBIRDS ARE GO/T.V. CHILD
Tracks: / Thunderbird / T.V. child.
7" Single: Released Oct '81, on XS, Deleted '83. Catalogue no: **TL 441**

Loafers

LIVING IN A SUITCASE
Tracks: / Living in a suitcase / Postman Pat / Z cars.
12" Single: Released Feb '89, on Sticcato, Catalogue no: **12RUDE 1**

UNDERTAKER, THE
Tracks: / Undertaker, The.
12" Single: Released Jun '89, on Staccato, Catalogue no: **12 RUDE 3**

Lobban,Sandra

MAKE YOU MY MAN/MAKE DUB
Tracks: / Make you my man / Make you my man (dub).
7" Single: Released Sep '82, on Music Gallery, Catalogue no: **MG 001**

TIME IS FOR LOVE
Tracks: / Time is for love / Time is for love (version).
12" Single: Released Dec '82, on Music Gallery, Catalogue no: **MG 002**

Lobo (Holland)

Biographical details: This Dutch singer achieved a one-off UK chart entry in the summer of 1981, reaching No.8 with his medley single *The Caribbean disco show*. This was one of a host of medleys that flooded the charts at the time; the fad had been started several months earlier by Lobo's fellow countryman, Jasp Eggermont of Starsound fame. Starsound did disco mantages of the Beatles and Abba, Startraz made a Bee Gees medley, the Royal Philharmonic Orchestra scored with a classical collection, and Lobo entered the fray with a segue of Caribean calypso favourites. Using the obligatory computerised drumbeat and handclaps, he cruised through the catalogue of singalong standards like *Banana boat song* and *Angelina*. With expert timing, the record attained its UK No.8 peak position in August Bank Holiday week, thus coinciding neatly with London's Notting Hill Carnival. Lobo's attempt to be the ew Harry Belafonte worked well for that one single, but placed him in obscurity thereafter. (Bob MacDonald, 15th Dec 1985).

CARIBBEAN DISCO SHOW (SINGLE)
Tracks: / Caribbean disco show / Caribbean magic.
7" Single: Released Jul '81, on Polydor, by Polydor Ltd. Deleted '84. Catalogue no: **POSP 302**

Lobo (US)

Biographical details: This American singer, songwriter and guitarist was born Kent LaVoie in Tallahassee, Florida. He took up the guitar while at high school, and began performing on a regular basis while working his way through Florida colleges. Initially working in barrooms and nightclubs, he played with a variety of small-time groups; he eventually found himself playing in a folk trio alongside two other future stars, Jim Croce and Gram Parsons. In the late Sixties LaVoie met successful record producer Phil Gernhard, with whom he formed a long-lasting studio relationship. After perfecting his songwriting technique, the artist began a sole recording career under the name Lobo. Meaning 'wolf' in Spanish, this was chosen in order to signify his termperament as a lone wolf - even after becoming famous, he rarely undertook tours and tended to shy away from the publicity and trappings of stardom. The song that brought him fame was 1971's *Me and you and a dog named Boo*, a folk-influenced summery pop single that reached No.5 in the States and No.4 in Britain. This was a strong melodic song, although its tile temporarily placed Lobo at the children's end of the singer songwriter market.
In late 1972, eighteen months after *Me and you and a dog named Boo*, Lobo achieved a million selling US No.2 smash with his slick midtempo ballad *I'd love you to want me*. Surprisingly, this single did not reach Top 5 status in Britain until 1974, by which time he had chalked up further American Top 40 successes with *Don't expect me to be your friend, It sure took a long long time, How can I tell her* and *Standing at the end of the line*. His smooth folk-pop style invoked comparisons with Bread. He turned to a country flavour, however, when he and Gerhard produced hits for his mate Jim Stafford, notably the 1974 million seller *Spiders and snakes*. From 1976 onwards Lobo was in obscurity, as far as the record charts were concerned, but he made a steady living as a composer of jingles and commercials for radio and television. He made a brief return to chartdom in 1979 with his No.23 single *Where were you when I was falling in love*. (Bob MacDonald, 15th Dec 1985).

HOLDIN' ON FOR DEAR LOVE
Tracks: / Holdin' on for dear love / Gus the dancin' dog.
7" Single: Released Feb '80, on MCA, by MCA Records. Deleted '83. Catalogue no: **MCA 567**

I DON'T WANT TO WANT YOU
Tracks: / I don't want to want you / Come looking for me.
7" Single: Released Jan '84, on Young Blood, by Young Blood Records. Catalogue no: **LOBO 1**

I'D LOVE YOU TO WANT ME
Tracks: / I'd love you to want me.
7" Single: Released '75, on USA, by Charly Records. Catalogue no: **LR 0290**
7" Single: Released Jun '74, on UK, by UK Records. Deleted '77. Catalogue no: **UK 68**

ME AND YOU AND A DOG NAMED BOO
Tracks: / Me and you and a dog named boo.
7" Single: Released Jun '71, on Philips, by Phonogram Ltd. Deleted '74. Catalogue no: **6073 801**

ME & YOU & A DOG NAMED BOO (OLD GOLD)
Tracks: / Me & you & a dog named Boo.
7" Single: Released Sep '85, on Old Gold, by Old Gold Records. Catalogue no: **OG 9522**

WITH A LOVE LIKE OURS
Tracks: / With a love like ours / I can't believe you anymore.
7" Single: Released Nov '80, on Elektra, by Elektra Records (UK). Deleted '83. Catalogue no: **K 12484**

Local Boy Makes Good

HOROSCOPE
Tracks: / Horoscope / Hypnotic rhythm.
7" Single: Released Jan '82, on Arrival, by Blaylock Management Ltd.. Deleted '86. Catalogue no: **PIK 1**

Local Hero

DAYDREAM BELIEVER
Tracks: / Daydream believer / Why don't you / Daydream believer (extended mix) (Track on 12" only) / Daydream believer (dance mix) (Track on 12" only).
7" Single: Released Jul '88, on Ariola, by BMG Records (UK). Deleted Aug '89. Catalogue no: **111 652**
12" Single: Released Jul '88, on Ariola, by BMG Records (UK). Catalogue no: **611 652**

SON OF MY FATHER
Tracks: / Son of my father.
12" Single: Released Sep '89, on Union, Catalogue no: **12 UNION 2**
7" Single: Released Sep '89, on Union, Catalogue no: **UNION 2**

WITH A WOMAN LIKE YOU
Tracks: / With a woman like you / With a woman like you (instrumental) / With a woman like you (ext) / I would love you (12" only).
Note: Local Hero comprise of Derek Yeaman and Gorden Campbell, former members of the Scottish teenybop band, The Upstarts.
7" Single: Released 6 Feb '89, on Ariola, by BMG Records (UK). Catalogue no: **112 063**
12" Single: Released 6 Feb '89, on Ariola, by BMG Records (UK). Catalogue no: **612 063**

Locke,Joy

NEVER GIVE YOUR HEART AWAY
Tracks: / Never give your heart away.
12" Single: Released Sep '82, on Cha-Cha, by Cha-Cha Records. Catalogue no: **CHAD 38**

Locklin, Hank

Biographical details: Born Lawrence Hankins Locklin in Florida in 1918, this singer, guitarist and songwriter inherited a love of music from his parents. By the time he reached his teens he was playing and singing at school parties and local contests. Although he toured regularly from the age of 20 he didn't begin his recording career until the 50's. His 1953 single, *Let Me Be The One*, was a promising success on 4-Star Records but two years later he made a wise move by signing to RCA Victor and teaming up with the company's seminal Nashville producer/executive/guitarist Chet Atkins. Locklin proceeded to carve out a long career in country-and-western music, highlighted by two notable crossover successes: *Please Help Me, I'm Falling* reached No 8 in the States and No 9 in Britain in 1960 and his own song, *Send Me The Pillow You Dream On* was a big country hit for himself and a US Top Forty pop success for Johnny Tillotson (1962) and Dean Martin (1965). In Britain Locklin achieved a No 18 hit at the end of '62 with *We're Gonna Go Fishin'* and a No 28 in the summer of '66 with *I Feel A Cry Coming On*. (Bob MacDonald, December 1985.).

I FEEL A CRY COMING ON
Tracks: / I feel a cry coming on.
7" Single: Released May '66, on RCA, by BMG Records (UK). Deleted '69. Catalogue no: **RCA 1510**

PLEASE HELP ME I'M FALLING (OLD GOLD)
Tracks: / Pease help me from falling / Sea of heartbreak.
7" Single: Released Oct '86, on Old Gold, by Old Gold Records. Catalogue no: **OG 9621**

PLEASE HELP ME I'M FALLING (SINGLE)
Tracks: / Please help me, I'm falling.
7" Single: Released Aug '60, on RCA, by BMG Records (UK). Deleted '63. Catalogue no: **RCA 1188**

WE'RE GONNA GO FISHIN'
Tracks: / We're gonna go fishing / Please help me, I'm falling.
7" Single: Released Oct '81, on RCA, by BMG Records (UK). Catalogue no: **GOLD 537**
7" Single: Released Nov '62, on RCA, by BMG Records (UK). Deleted '65. Cata-

logue no: **RCA 1305**

Locks, Fred

FERTILE GROUND
Tracks: / Fertile ground / Fertile sound.
12" Single: Released Jul '86, on Rising Sun (1), Catalogue no: **RS 001**

GIVE JAH YOUR HEART & SOUL
Tracks: / Give Jah your heart & soul.
12" Single: Released Oct '84, on Blacker Dread, Catalogue no: **Unknown**

REDEMPTION
Tracks: / Redemption.
12" Single: Released Oct '85, on Omega, Deleted Jun '89. Catalogue no: **OMS 3**

Locksmith

UNLOCK THE FUNK
Tracks: / Unlock the funk.
Note: See under G.Q.
7" Single: Released Aug '80, on Arista, by BMG Records (UK). Deleted '83. Catalogue no: **ARIST 364**

Lockwood, Neil

TELL TALE HEART
Tracks: / Tell tale heart.
7" Single: Released Mar '83, on Red Bus, by Red Bus Records. Catalogue no: **RBUS 76**
12" Single: Released Mar '83, on Red Bus, by Red Bus Records. Catalogue no: **RBUSL 76**

Loco Lotus

DETROIT
Tracks: / Detroit.
12" Single: Released Dec '84, on Loco, by Loco Records. Catalogue no: **LL 2460 687 1**

Locomotive

RUDI'S IN LOVE
Tracks: / Rudi's in love / Never set me free.
7" Single: Released Feb '80, on EMI, by EMI Records. Deleted '83. Catalogue no: **EMI 5033**
7" Single: Released Oct '68, on Parlophone, by EMI Records. Deleted '71. Catalogue no: **R 5718**Locomotive Latenight

OUT OF RANGE
Tracks: / Out of range.
12" Single: Released '88, on KDY, by KDY Records. Catalogue no: **KDY 022T**

Lodge, Ian

BABY JUMP TO IT
Tracks: / Baby jump to it / One way out (remix).
7" Single: Released Aug '87, on ABR, by ABR Productions. Catalogue no: **ABR 004**

SHE'S MAKING MOVIES
Tracks: / She's making movies / There is only one way out / There's only one way out.
7" Single: Released Jan '86, on ABR, by ABR Productions. Catalogue no: **ABR 003**

STAY
Tracks: / Stay.
7" Single: Released Jun '85, on ABR, by ABR Productions. Catalogue no: **ABR 002**

WALKIN' TO THE BEAT
Tracks: / Walkin' to the beat / Have you ever been in love / Sheer decay (Available on 12" only).
7" Single: Released Apr '84, on President, by President Records. Catalogue no: **PT 523**
12" Single: Released Apr '84, on President, by President Records. Catalogue no: **PT 12 523**

Lodge, J.C.

GOT TO MAKE IT UP
Tracks: / Got to make it up.
12" Single: Released Jan '84, on Londisc, by Londisc Records. Catalogue no: **LD 005**

LOVE ME BABY
(J.C. LODGE & TIGER)
Tracks: / Love me baby / Love me baby (version).
12" Single: Released Aug '89, on Greensleeves, by Greensleeves Records. Catalogue no: **GRED 253**

SINCE YOU CAME INTO MY LIFE
Tracks: / Since you came into my life.
12" Single: Released Aug '88, on Greensleeves, by Greensleeves Records. Catalogue no: **GRED 227**

SOMEONE LOVES YOU HONEY
Tracks: / Someone loves you honey / Stay in tonight.
12" Single: Released Nov '86, on Greensleeves, by Greensleeves Records. Catalogue no: **GRED 205**
12" Single: on Joe Gibbs, Catalogue no: **JGM 8116**
7" Single: Released Sep '86, on Greensleeves, by Greensleeves Records. Catalogue no: **GRE 205**
12" Single: Released '87, on Greensleeves, by Greensleeves Records. Deleted Jun '89. Catalogue no: **JG 6053**

TELEPHONE LOVE
Tracks: / Telephone love.
12" Single: Released Jun '88, on Greensleeves, by Greensleeves Records. Catalogue no: **GRED 222**

TOGETHER WE WILL STAY
Tracks: / Together we will stay / Together we will stay (version).
12" Single: Released May '87, on Greensleeves, by Greensleeves Records. Catalogue no: **GRED 212**

Lodge, John

Biographical details: This British bass guitarist, cellist and singer was a founder member of the Moody Blues in 1964, but was with them for only a few weeks - he decided not to join a professional band until he had completed his City and Guild exams. It was thus left to temporary bassist Clint Warwick to perform on the Moodies' 1965 No.1 smash *Go now* and several smaller hits, before Lodge rejoined the group on a full time basis in 1966. Like most of his Moody colleagues, he hailed from Birmingham. The Moody Blues were in abeyance during the mid-Seventies, and Lodge and group leader Justin Hayward thus decided to release an LP as a duo - *Blue jays* (1975) was very much in the Moodies vein and offered a few surprises. But it was what their public wanted, and reached No.4 with 18 weeks on the UK charts. Towards the end of '75, the pair scored a British Top 10 single with the atmospheric *Blue guitar*. In common with Hayward, Lodge released his debut solo album in early 1977. *Natural Avenue* peaked at a disappointing No.38 on the UK LP list; it was merely a weak versionof the Moody Blues' style of swirling, orchestral, whimsical pomp-rock. Realising that their whole was greater than the sum of their parts, the Blues reformed in 1978, and have continued into the mid-Eighties. (Bob MacDonald, 16th Dec 1985).

STREET CAFE
Tracks: / Street cafe / Threw it all away.
7" Single: Released Oct '80, on Decca, by Decca Records. Deleted '88. Catalogue no: **F 13896**

Lodge, June

GIVE MY HUSBAND A MESSAGE
Tracks: / Give my husband a message / Selfish lover.
12" Single: Released Dec '85, on Hawkeye, by Hawkeye Records. Catalogue no: **HD 69**

OPERATOR
Tracks: / Operator.
12" Single: Released Oct '88, on Greensleeves, by Greensleeves Records. Catalogue no: **GRED 229**

SOMEONE LOVES YOU HONEY
12" Single: Released '82, on Arista, by BMG Records (UK). Deleted '87. Catalogue no: **ARIST 12477**
7" Single: Released '82, on Arista, by BMG Records (UK). Deleted '87. Catalogue no: **ARIST 477**
12" Single: Released Feb '82, on Echo, by Echo Records. Catalogue no: **ECHO 007**

STAY IN TONIGHT
Tracks: / Stay in tonight.
7" Single: Released Feb '82, on Joe Gibbs, Catalogue no: **JGM 01**

Loeb, Caroline

C'EST LA QUATE
Tracks: / C'est la quate / And so what / Paresseuse dub (Extra track on 12" only) / C'est la quate(Dean Anderson US dance remix)* (*=Extra track on 12" only).
7" Single: Released 23 May '87, on Barclay, by Decca Records. Catalogue no: **BA 3**
12" Single: Released 23 May '87, on Barclay, by Decca Records. Catalogue no: **BAX 3**

Loewenthal, Sandy

SO SAD
Tracks: / So sad.
7" Single: Released Jun '82, on Rocket, by Rocket Records. Deleted Jun '85. Catalogue no: **XPRES 80**

Lofgren, Nils

Biographical details: This American guitarist, singer, songwriter and keyboardist was born in Chicago and first attracted attention in the early Seventies as a 19 year old guitar prodigy. During this time, he played on Neil Young's highly successful 1970 LP *After the goldrush*, performed on the moderately successful eponymous debut album by Young's protege group Crazy Horse, and formed his own unsuccessful band Grin. After four albums, Lofgren gave up Grin and briefly rejoined Young with whom Nils' singing (fairly high-pitched but not as delicate as Neil's) and stylish guitar technique blended well. Lofgren's first solo LP was issued in 1975; this self0titled set attracted good reviews and a cult following. He consolidated his position with 1976's *Cry tough* LP, which reached No.32 on the US chart and shot into the British Top 10. Despite this promising acceptance, which made it seem as if there was no stopping Lofgren, his subsequent solo career achieved only moderate commercial success. His well-crafted pop-rock style was not quite strong enough to compete with the wave of bands like Boston (whom he supported on their 1976 tour), Foreigner and Kansas, who swept the American charts in the late Seventies. In Britain his music was deemed irrelevant in the era of punk. Nonetheless, songs like *I came to dance* and *Shine silently* (heavily influenced by the Beatles' *Let it be*) became popular at his concert dates. Nils continued working during the early Eighties, and rejoined Young yet again for a brief period. His career received new impetus in 1984, when he replaced Steve Van Zandt in Bruce Springsteen's E Street Band just after the release of the blockbusting *Born in the USA* album. With Springsteen reaching new heights of worldwide superstardom on account of *Born in the USA*, Nils committed himself to the Boss on a permanent basis. Amazingly, Lofgren stil found time to continue his solo recording and performing career. However, it seemed that he was destined never to become a major solo star - in 1985, while attracting acclaim for his guitar work with Springsteen, he released the seemingly ultra-commercial single *Secrets in the street* but this was only a minor hit. (Bob MacDonald, 16th Dec 1985).

ANYTIME AT ALL
Tracks: / Anytime at all / New holes in old shoes.
7" Single: Released Mar '86, on Towerbell, Catalogue no: **TOW 86**

DELIVERY NIGHT
Tracks: / Delivery night / Keith don't go.
7" Single: Released Nov '85, on Towerbell, Catalogue no: **TOW 76**
12" Single: Released Dec '85, on Towerbell, Catalogue no: **TOWT 7**

FLIP YA FLIP
Tracks: / Flip ya flip.
12" Single: Released Aug '85, on Towerbell, Catalogue no: **TOWTX 73**
7" Single: Released Jul '85, on Towerbell, Catalogue no: **TOW 73**
12" Single: Released Aug '85, on Towerbell, Catalogue no: **TOWT 73**

I GO TO PIECES
Tracks: / I go to pieces / Ancient history.
7" Single: Released Nov '81, on MCA, by MCA Records. Deleted Nov '84. Catalogue no: **MCA 757**

NIGHT FADES AWAY (SINGLE)
Tracks: / Night fades away / Anytime at all.
12" Single: Released Oct '81, on MCA, by MCA Records. Deleted Oct '84. Catalogue no: **MCAT 749**
7" Single: Released Oct '81, on MCA, by MCA Records. Deleted Oct '84. Catalogue no: **MCA 749**

SECRETS IN THE STREET
Tracks: / Secrets in the street / From the heart.
12" Single: Released May '85, on Towerbell, Catalogue no: **TOWT 68**
7" Set: Released May '85, on Towerbell, Catalogue no: **TOWG 68**
12" Single: Released Jun '85, on Towerbell, Catalogue no: **TOWRT 68**
7" Single: Released Jan '86, on Towerbell, Catalogue no: **TOW 68**

SHINE SILENTLY
Tracks: / Shine silently / Keith don't go.
7" Single: Released Apr '82, on A&M, by A&M Records. Deleted Apr '85. Catalogue no: **AMS 8211**

Loft

UP THE HILL & DOWN THE SLOPE
Tracks: / Up the hill & down the slope.
7" Single: Released Aug '85, on Creation, by Creation Records. Catalogue no: **CRE 015**
12" Single: Releasec '85, on Creation, by Creation Records. Catalogue no: **CRE 015T**

WHY DOES THE RAIN FALL?
Tracks: / Why does the rain fall?.
7" Single: Released Sep '84, on Creation, by Creation Records. Deleted Jul '88. Catalogue no: **CRE 009**

Log 10

STEP IN THE DARK
Tracks: / Step in the dark.
7" Single: Released Jun '83, on Sonic, Catalogue no: **SR 77**

YOU'RE NOT THERE
Tracks: / You're not there.
7" Single: Released May '84, on Sonic, Catalogue no: **SR 78**

Logan

STAB IN THE BACK
Tracks: / Stab in back.
12" Single: Released Mar '86, on UNKNOWN, Catalogue no: **12LOG 1**
7" Single: Released Mar '86, on UNKNOWN, Deleted Nov '87. Catalogue no: **LOG 1**

Logan, David

IT ONLY HAPPENS IN THE MOVIES
Tracks: / It only happens in the movies / Sunshine in your smile.
7" Single: Released Jan '80, on MCA, by MCA Records. Deleted Jan '85. Catalogue no: **MCA 555**

Logan, Johnny

ALL I EVER WANTED
Tracks: / All I ever wanted (Only on 7" and CD single.) / Me and my jealous heart / All I ever wanted (extended version) (Only on 12" and CD single.) / Hungry is the heart (Only on 12" and CD single.).
CD 5": Released Aug '89, on Epic, by CBS Records. Catalogue no: **654 977 2**
12" Single: Released Aug '89, on Epic, by CBS Records. Catalogue no: **654 977 8**
7" Single: Released Aug '89, on Epic, by CBS Records. Catalogue no: **654 977 7**

BECOMING ELECTRIC
Tracks: / Becoming electric / Emotional blackmail.
7" Single: Released Oct '82, on Epic, by CBS Records. Deleted Oct '85. Catalogue no: **EPC A2844**

GIVE A LITTLE MORE LOVE
Tracks: / Give a little more love / Sweet lady.
7" Single: Released Oct '80, on Epic, by CBS Records. Deleted Oct '83. Catalogue no: **EPC 9043**

HOLD ME NOW (SINGLE)
Tracks: / Hold me now.
7" Single: Released May '87, on Epic, by CBS Records. Deleted Nov '87. Catalogue no: **LOG 1**

I'M NOT IN LOVE
Tracks: / I'm not in love / Such a lady.
12" Single: Released Jul '87, on Epic, by CBS Records. Catalogue no: **LOG T2**
7" Single: Released Jul '87, on Epic, by CBS Records. Catalogue no: **LOG 2**

IN LONDON
Tracks: / In London / Sad little woman.
7" Single: Released Jun '80, on Pye, Deleted Jun '83. Catalogue no: **7P 189**

LIVING FOR LOVING
Tracks: / Living for loving.
7" Single: Released Jun '80, on Piccadilly, Deleted Jun '83. Catalogue no: **7P 186**
7" Single: Released Jul '88, on Plaza, by Plaza Records. Catalogue no: **PLA 036**

ORIENTAL EYES
Tracks: / Oriental eyes / Flames.
7" Single: Released Jul '82, on Epic, by CBS Records. Deleted Jul '85. Catalogue no: **EPC A 2553**

SAVE ME
Tracks: / Save me / Love is a small town.
7" Single: Released Aug '80, on Epic, by CBS Records. Deleted '83. Catalogue no: **EPC 8770**

WHAT'S ANOTHER YEAR
Tracks: / What's another year / Hold me now.
7" Single: Released May '80, on Epic, by CBS Records. Deleted '83. Catalogue no: **EPC 8572**
7" Single: Released 27 Feb '89, on Old Gold, by Old Gold Records. Catalogue no: **OG 9861**

Logan, Skipper

IN MY MIND
Tracks: / In my mind.
7" Single: Released Oct '88, on Dan Jam, Catalogue no: **DJ 002**

Logan, Willie

SOMETHING SPECIAL
Tracks: / Something special.
7" Single: Released '87, on Arrival, by Blaylock Management Limited Catalogue no:

PIK 18

Loggerheads

FOUR WAYS TO COOK A GOOSE
Tracks: / Four ways to cook a goose.
12" Single: Released 23 May '87, on Antenna, Catalogue no: **BUG 002T**

Loggins, Kenny

Biographical details: This American singer, guitarist and songwriter was born in Everett, Washington. He was struggling to establish a reputation in the music business, when Columbia Records signed him in September 1971. To record his debut album, he was teamed with producer Jim Messins, a former member of Buffalo Springfield and Poco. The partnership jelled so well that the pair formed a permanent due, billed simply as Loggins & Messina, and became a regular recording and touring act; both members performed guitar, and vocals and contributed to the writing, with Messina also carrying out his production role. Loggins and Messina were typical West Coast soft rockers - slick, melodic, easy on the ear, but with just enough bite to be placed in the rock category. Their peak year was 1973, when they chalked up three US Top 20 singles - *Your mama don't dance* (a million selling No.4 hit), *Thinking of you* and *My music*. After a steady string of strong-selling albums, the pair parted in '76. Loggins launched his solo career with the 1977 album *Celebrate me home*. The following year, he achieved his first big post-Messina single with the American Top 5 hit *Whenever I call you 'friend'*, on which he was given the vocal back-up from Stevie Nicks of Fleetwood Mac. This was the first of several one-off collaborations which have dotted his career. In 1979 he teamed with Doobie Brothers leader Michael McDonald to write the group's US No.1 single *What a fool believes*; McDonald returned the favour by supplying harmonies for Loggins' 1980 US No.11 single *This is it*. In 1982 Kenny joined forces with Steve Ferry, lead singer of Journey, for the American No.17 success *Don't fight it*. Loggins has profited considerably from the movie world. 1980 brought him a US Top Tenner with the catchy *I'm alright*, the theme from *Caddyshack*. In 1983 he jumped briefly on the *ET* bandwagon with his hit single *Welcome to Heartlight*. Hit title theme for the 1984 box-office biggie *Footloose*, which he co-wrote with Dean Pitchford gave him his biggest ever hit - the single logged three weeks at No.1 in America and gave him his first British chart entry, reaching the UK No.6 position. Some observers have described Loggins' post-1977 biography s a series of pleasant one-offs rather than a real career, citing his flitting from friend to friend and from one film theme to another. But he has managed to chalk up an impressive tally of American hits with his pop-filled approximation of rock. (Bob MacDonald, 16th Dec 1985).

DANGER ZONE
Tracks: / Danger zone / I'm gonna do it right.
7" Single: Released Sep '86, on CBS, by CBS Records. Catalogue no: **A 7188**

FOOTLOOSE
Tracks: / Footloose / Swear your love.
7" Single: Released Apr '84, on CBS, by CBS Records. Deleted '87. Catalogue no: **A 4101**

FOREVER
Tracks: / Forever.
7" Single: Released Jun '85, on CBS, by CBS Records. Catalogue no: **A 6369**

I'M FREE (HEAVEN HELPS THE MAN)
Tracks: / I'm free (heaven helps the man).
12" Single: Released Jun '84, on CBS, by CBS Records. Catalogue no: **TA 4495**
7" Single: Released Jun '84, on CBS, by CBS Records. Catalogue no: **A 4495**

I'M GONNA DO IT RIGHT
Tracks: / I'm gonna do it right / Danger zone / Footloose / I'm free (heaven helps the man).
12" Single: Released Sep '86, on CBS, by CBS Records. Catalogue no: **TA 7188**

I'M GONNA MISS YOU
Tracks: / I'm gonna miss you / Isabella's eyes / I'm gonna miss you (full length version) (Only on 12" version & CD single.) / This is it (Only on 12" version & CD single.) / Love will follow (Only on 12" version & CD single.).
7" Single: Released Nov '88, on CBS, by CBS Records. Deleted 17 Apr '89. Catalogue no: **653147 7**
CD 5": Released Nov '88, on CBS, by CBS Records. Deleted 17 Apr '89. Catalogue no: **653147 3**
12" Single: Released Nov '88, on CBS, by CBS Records. Deleted 17 Apr '89. Catalogue no: **653147 6**

MEET ME HALF WAY
Tracks: / Meet me half way.
7" Single: Released 30 May '87, on CBS, by CBS Records. Deleted Nov '87. Catalogue no: **650432 7**

THIS IS IT
Tracks: / This is it / Will it last.
7" Single: Released Feb '80, on CBS, by CBS Records. Deleted Feb '85. Catalogue no: **CBS 7897**

WELCOME TO HEARTLIGHT
Tracks: / Welcome to heartlight / More we try.
7" Single: Released Jan '83, on CBS, by CBS Records. Catalogue no: **A 3056**

Logic, Laura

WONDERFUL OFFER
Tracks: / Wonderful offer / Stereo.
7" Single: Released Oct '81, on Rough Trade, by Rough Trade Records. Catalogue no: **RT 087**

Logic System

BE YOURSELF
Tracks: / Be yourself.
12" Single: Released Mar '82, on EMI, by EMI Records. Catalogue no: **12 EMI 5279**
7" Pic: Released Mar '82, on EMI, by EMI Records. Catalogue no: **EMIP 5279**
7" Single: Released Mar '82, on EMI, by EMI Records. Catalogue no: **EMI 5279**

Logue, Christopher

RED BIRD EP
12" Single: Released May '84, on Evergreen, by Evergreen Records (USA). Catalogue no: **EV 1**

Loi

KEEP IT COMING
Tracks: / Keep it coming / Forever coming.
12" Single: Released Sep '84, on Diamond C, Catalogue no: **DCD 005**

ONE DRAW
Tracks: / One draw.
12" Single: Released Mar '82, on Echo, by Echo Records. Catalogue no: **12 ECHO 012**

Lok

FUNHOUSE
Tracks: / Funhouse.
7" Single: Released May '81, on Fetish, Catalogue no: **FET 001**

Lola

WAX THE VAN
Tracks: / Wax the van / Wax the van (dub).
12" Single: on Syncopate, by EMI Records. Deleted Jun '89. Catalogue no: **12SYMIX 1**
12" Single: Released Mar '87, on Syncopate, by EMI Records. Deleted Oct '87. Catalogue no: **12SY 1**
7" Single: Released Mar '87, on Syncopate, by EMI Records. Deleted Oct '87. Catalogue no: **SY 1**

Lolita Pop

BANG YOUR HEAD
Tracks: / Bang your head / Bang your head (ext. version) (Extra track on 12".) / Rain keeps pouring / Birds of ice (Extra track on 12".).
12" Single: Released Mar '88, on Virgin, by Virgin Records. Deleted '89. Catalogue no: **VST 1048**
7" Single: Released Mar '88, on Virgin, by Virgin Records. Catalogue no: **VS 1048**

Lolitas

LA FILLE QUI SE PROMENE SUR LES RAILS
Tracks: / La fille qui se promene sur les rails / La chat noir.
7" Single: Released Feb '89, on New Rose (1), by New Rose Records. Catalogue no: **NEW 122**

Lollar, Bobby

BAD BAD BOY
Tracks: / Bad bad boy.
7" Single: Released Oct '83, on Benton, Deleted '88. Catalogue no: **B-101**

London Beat

Biographical details: London Beat are a four piece - three quarters of them are quite possibly the best male voices in the UK. Comprised of Trinidad born Jimmy Chambers who's been singing forever, George Chandler from Atlanta and a big dance name in the Seventies & Jimmy Helms from Florida. Between them, these men have sung on more great records than can possibly be remembered and until recently were providing the backing vocals and appropriate dance steps - for Paul Young. They met up with the enigmatic Willy M. who is London born and bred and has spent most of his time working in The Far East, Australasia and the USA..

9 AM (THE COMFORT ZONE)
Tracks: / 9 a.m. (the comfort zone) / Talent on the make / There's an acid house going on (Track on 12" only & cassette single.) / Falling in love again (Track on CD single only.) / Up all night (Track on CD single only.) / 9 a.m. (the comfort zone) (version) (Only on cassette single.).
12" Single: Released 7 Nov '88, on Anxious, by Anxious Records. Deleted Aug '89. Catalogue no: **ANXT 008**
Cassingle: Released Dec '88, on Anxious, by Anxious Records. Catalogue no: **ANX 008 V**
7" Single: Released 7 Nov '88, on Anxious, by Anxious Records. Deleted Aug '89. Catalogue no: **ANX 008**
CD 5": Released 7 Nov '88, on Anxious, by Anxious Records. Catalogue no: **ANX 088 CD**

FAILING IN LOVE AGAIN
Tracks: / Failing in love again / Failing in love again (album version) / Jerk / Over the speed limit (Available on 12"single and CD only.).
CD 5": Released 30 Jan '89, on Anxious, by Anxious Records. Catalogue no: **ANX 007 CD**
7" Single: Released 30 Jan '89, on Anxious, by Anxious Records. Deleted Aug '89. Catalogue no: **ANX 007**
12" Single: Released 30 Jan '89, on Anxious, by Anxious Records. Deleted Aug '89. Catalogue no: **ANXT 007**

ONE BLINK
Tracks: / One blink / Beat patrol / Killer drop (Only on 12".) / 9 a.m. (the comfort zone) (Only on CD single.) / Failing in love (Only on CD single.).
CD 5": Released 22 May '89, on RCA, by BMG Records (UK). Catalogue no: **ANXCD 011**
12" Single: Released 22 May '89, on RCA, by BMG Records (UK). Catalogue no: **ANXT 011**
7" Single: Released 22 May '89, on RCA, by BMG Records (UK). Catalogue no: **ANX 011**

THERE'S A BEAT GOING ON
Tracks: / There's a beat going on / Bribe the bride.
Note: "The first single 'There's A Beat Going On' merges great vocals with elements from practically every style they've worked in and the end result is quite unique and quite brilliant. The 12" mix by Heff Moraes is unlike anything you'll have heard before, although it does have flashes which sound familiar". (Anxious Records, June 1988).
7" Single: Released 6 Jun '88, on Anxious, by Anxious Records. Deleted May '89. Catalogue no: **ANX 004**
12" Single: Released 6 Jun '88, on Anxious, by Anxious Records. Deleted Aug '89. Catalogue no: **ANXT 004**

London, Billy

WOMAN
Tracks: / Woman / Woman (part 2).
7" Single: Released Aug '81, on RSO, by Polydor Ltd. Deleted '84. Catalogue no: **RSO 80**

London Boot Mix

LONDON BOOT MIX
Tracks: / London boot mix (27 minute megamix): *Various artists*.
12" Single: Released Feb '86, on ZYX (Germany), Catalogue no: **ZYX 5376**

London Boys

HARLEM DESIRE
Tracks: / Harlem desire / Talk talk talk.
CD 5": Released Sep '89, on WEA, by WEA Records. Catalogue no: **YZ 415 CD**
12" Single: Released Sep '89, on WEA, by WEA Records. Catalogue no: **YZ 415 T**
7" Single: Released Sep '89, on WEA, by WEA Records. Catalogue no: **YZ 415**
Cassingle: Released Sep '89, on WEA, by WEA Records. Catalogue no: **YZ 415 C**

LONDON NIGHTS
Tracks: / London nights / London days / Requiem.
7" Single: Released Jun '89, on WEA, by WEA Records. Catalogue no: **YZ 393**
CD 5": Released Jun '89, on WEA, by WEA Records. Catalogue no: **YZ 393CD**
Cassingle: Released Jun '89, on WEA, by WEA Records. Catalogue no: **YZ 393C**
12" Single: Released Jun '89, on WEA, by WEA Records. Catalogue no: **YZ 393T**

REQUIEM
Tracks: / Requiem / Midi dance, The.
7" Single: Released Dec '88, on WEA, by WEA Records. Catalogue no: **YZ 345**
CD 5": Released Mar '89, on WEA, by WEA Records. Catalogue no: **YZ 345 CD**
12" Single: Released Mar '89, on WEA, by WEA Records. Catalogue no: **YZ 345 TX**
12" Single: Released Dec '88, on WEA, by WEA Records. Catalogue no: **YZ 345 T**

London Chamber Orch.

PIZZICATO
Tracks: / Pizzicato / Frolicsome finale.
7" Single: Released 30 Aug '88, on Virgin, by Virgin Records. Catalogue no: **VS 1129**

London Community

CONVERSION
Tracks: / Conversion / May day song for North Oxford.
7" Single: Released Dec '87, on RAK, by EMI Records. Catalogue no: **RAK 502**

London Cowboys

DANCE CRAZY (AND BLEED ME)
Tracks: / Dance crazy (and bleed me).
12" Single: Released 1 Nov '86, on Radioactive, Catalogue no: **HORN 002**

STREET FULL OF SOUL
Tracks: / Street full of soul.
7" Single: Released Apr '83, on Flicknife, by Flicknife Records. Catalogue no: **FLS 217**

London Film Orchestra

ANNA OF THE FIVE TOWNS
Tracks: / Anna of the five towns.
7" Single: Released Jan '85, on Sierra, by Sierra Records. Catalogue no: **FED 8**

London, Frank Kwame

JACK THE LAD (VOCAL MIX)
Tracks: / Jack the lad (vocal mix) / Jack the lad (badger mix) / Jack the lad (dub mix).
12" Single: Released Jul '87, on Nine O Nine, by Creole Records. Catalogue no: **NINE 12**

London, Jimmy

I'M YOUR PUPPET
Tracks: / I'm your puppet.
12" Single: Released Jul '89, on White, Catalogue no: **LCD 1**
12" Single: Released Jan '84, on Dancebeat, Catalogue no: **DBD 1319**

LET'S KEEP IT THAT WAY
Tracks: / Let's keep it that way.
12" Single: Released Jun '84, on GG'S, Catalogue no: **GG 121**

London, Julie

Biographical details: This American singer and actress released approximately twenty albums between the mid-Fifties and the mid-Sixties, although she is remembered by pop fans solely for her one-off hit single *Cry me a river*. This deep, bluesy ballad was perfect material for London's husky voice; the single reached No.9 in America in 1955, and crept to No.22 in Britain in 1957 after being featured in the acclaimed rock'n'roll movie *The girl can't help it". The song was revived in 1983 by British singer Mari Wilson, who peaked at No.27 on the UK chart; the 1970 rendition by another UK vocalist, Joe Cocker, which reached No.11 in America, was never a hit in Britain. London is remembered by American TV audiences as Dixie McCall in Emergency.* She also appeared on the Steve Allen and Perry Como shows and in several films. (Bob MacDonald, 16th Dec 1985).

CRY ME A RIVER
Tracks: / Cry me a river.
7" Pic: Released Feb '83, on Edsel, by Demon Records. Catalogue no: **PE 5004**
7" Single: Released Apr '57, on London-American, Deleted '60. Catalogue no: **HLU 8240**
7" Single: Released Apr '83, on EMI (France), by EMI Records. Catalogue no: **2C 008 83375**
7" Single: Released Feb '83, on Edsel, by Demon Records. Catalogue no: **E 5004**

London, Laurie

HE'S GOT THE WHOLE WORLD IN HIS HANDS (SINGLE)
Tracks: / He's got the whole world in his hands / Cradle rock.
7" Single: Released Jun '80, on H.M.V., by EMI Records. Deleted '83. Catalogue no: **POP 2008**
7" Single: Released Nov '57, on Parlophone, by EMI Records. Deleted '60. Catalogue no: **R 4359**

London Male Welsh

GOD BLESS THE PRINCE OF WALES
Tracks: / God bless the Prince of Wales.
7" Single: Released Aug '81, on PVK, by PVK Records. Catalogue no: **PV 113**

London Philharmonic

Biographical details: One of the national institutions of the British classical scene, the LPO chalked up three entries of the UK album chart during a flurry of activity in 1960-61. Their rendition of Ravel's *Bolero* reached No.15; they helped out on the London Philharmonic Choir's recording of Handel's *The Messiah*, which climbed to No.10; and *Victory at sea* cruised to No.12. In later years, they have occasionally tried their hand at pop repertoire, though without the success or regularity of their colleagues in the London Symphony Orchestra or the Royal Philharmonic Orchestra. *Diamond symphonies*, a roundup of Neil Diamond's hits, demonstrated that some material in the pop arena lent itself quite well to this treatment. The LPO's 1982 album *A classic case of funk* demonstrated even more amply that some material in the pop arena did not. (Bob MacDonald, 16th Dec 1985).

LOVE DUET
Tracks: / Love duet / Ambush.
Note: LSO conducted by Carl Davis. Torvill & dean's 'Fire & Ice'.
7" Single: Released Nov '86, on First Night, by First Night Records. Catalogue no: **SCORE 6**

WILLOW PATTERN DANCE
Tracks: / Willow pattern dance.
7" Single: Released Nov '84, on Chrysalis, by Chrysalis Records. Catalogue no: **CHS 2846**

London Posse

LONDON POSSE
Tracks: / London Posse / My beatbox reggae style.
12" Single: Released Jul '87, on Big Life, by Big Life Records. Catalogue no: **BLR 002T**

London PX

ARNOLD LAYNE Flexi disc
Tracks: / Arnold Layne.
7" Single: Released Dec '82, on Terraplane. Deleted '83. Catalogue no: **TERRAPIN 1**

ORDERS
Tracks: / Orders / Eviction.
7" Single: Released Jul '81, on London PX, Catalogue no: **NP 1**

London Rhyme Syndicate

HARD TO THE CORE
Tracks: / Hard to the core.
7" Single: Released Jul '88, on Abstract, by Abstract Sounds. Catalogue no: **LRS 001**
12" Single: Released Jul '88, on Abstract, by Abstract Sounds. Catalogue no: **12 LRS 001**

LONDON RHYME SYNDICATE
Tracks: / London rhyme syndicate.
7" Single: Released Dec '88, on Rhyme & Reason, by Priority Records. Catalogue no: **LRS 002**
12" Single: Released Dec '88, on Rhyme & Reason, by Priority Records. Catalogue no: **12LRS 002**

London String Chorale

GALLOPING HOME
Tracks: / Galloping home / Sleepy shores.
7" Single: Released Dec '73, on Polydor, by Polydor Ltd. Deleted '76. Catalogue no: **2058 280**
7" Single: Released Jun '88, on Old Gold, by Old Gold Records. Catalogue no: **OG 9792**

London Symphony...

BAKER STREET
Tracks: / Baker Street / Bring it all home.
7" Single: Released Mar '81, on Creole, by Creole Records. Catalogue no: **CR 5**

CLASSIC ROCK CLASSICS
Tracks: / Classic rock classics.
7" Single: Released Oct '82, on Towerbell, Catalogue no: **TOW 30**
12" Single: Released Oct '82, on Towerbell, Catalogue no: **12TOW 30**

CLASSIC ROCK COUNTDOWN
Tracks: / Final countdown, The / Take my breath away / You can call me Al / Lady in red / Separate lives / We don't need another hero / It's a sin / She's not there / Don't give up / You're the voice / Abbey road medley / Golden slumbers / Carry that weight / End, The.
CD 5": Released Nov '87, on CBS, by CBS Records. Catalogue no: **MOOD CD3**
7" Single: Released Nov '87, on CBS, by CBS Records. Catalogue no: **MOOD 3**
12" Single: Released Nov '87, on CBS, by CBS Records. Catalogue no: **MOOD C3**

E.T., THEME FROM
Tracks: / E.T., Theme from / Escort theme.
7" Single: Released Nov '82, on MFP, by EMI Records. Catalogue no: **FP 907**
7" Single: Released Dec '82, on Towerbell, Catalogue no: **TOW 31**

FURTHER EXPERIMENTS WITH MICE
Tracks: / Further experiments with mice / Decline and fall of a bridge.
Note: London Symphony Orchestra, narrator John Dankworth.
7" Single: Released Jul '86, on Sepia, Catalogue no: **RSRS 1**

GLORIA
Tracks: / Gloria / She's out of my life.
7" Single: Released Nov '83, on K-Tel, by K-Tel Records. Catalogue no: **CR 005**

SWITCHED ON SULLIVAN
Tracks: / Switched on Sullivan.
7" Single: Released Oct '82, on Lancaster, by Lancaster Records. Catalogue no: **C 12**

THEME FROM SUPERMAN
Tracks: / Superman, Theme from.
7" Single: Released Jan '79, on Warner Bros., by WEA Records. Deleted '82. Catalogue no: **K 17292**

YOU CAN CALL ME AL
Tracks: / You can call me Al / We don't need another hero.
7" Single: Released Nov '87, on CBS, by CBS Records. Deleted Jun '88. Catalogue no: **C ROCK 1**

London Underground

BETWEEN THE LINES
Tracks: / Between the lines.
7" Single: Released Aug '88, on On-U-Sound, by On-U-Sound Records. Catalogue no: **S3**

STRANGE
Tracks: / Strange / Why do fat man have.
10" single: Released Apr '82, on On-U-Sound, by On-U-Sound Records. Catalogue no: **ONUDP 5**

TRAIN OF THOUGHT
Tracks: / Train of thought / All too many.
7" Single: Released Oct '81, on Situation 2, by Beggars Banquet Records. Catalogue no: **SIT 9**

WATCHING WEST INDIANS IN THE COLD
Tracks: / Watching West Indians in the cold / Strange things / Conspiracy / Why do fat men have such skinny thoughts.
10" single: Released Mar '82, on On-U-Sound, by On-U-Sound Records. Catalogue no: **DP 4**

Lone Groover

JOHNNY MAKE YOU BAD SO
Tracks: / Johnny make you bad so.
12" Single: Released Feb '82, on Greensleeves, by Greensleeves Records. Catalogue no: **GRED 85**

LONE GROOVER (4 TRACK EP)
7" EP: Released Jan '82, on Charly, by Charly Records. Deleted '88. Catalogue no: **CEP 124**

Lone Justice

I FOUND LOVE
Tracks: / I found love / If you dont like the rain / Sweet Jane (Only available in double pack version.) / Don't toss us away (Only available in double pack version.).
7" Set: Released Feb '87, on Geffen, by Geffen Records (USA). Catalogue no: **GEF 18F**
7" Single: Released Feb '87, on Geffen, by Geffen Records (USA). Deleted Jan '88. Catalogue no: **GEF 18**
12" Single: Released Feb '87, on Geffen, by Geffen Records (USA). Deleted Jan '88. Catalogue no: **GEF 18T**

SHELTER (SINGLE)
Tracks: / Shelter / Can't look back / Belfry (on 12" version only).
7" Single: Released Oct '86, on Geffen, by Geffen Records (USA). Deleted Jun '87. Catalogue no: **GEF 16**
12" Single: Released Oct '86, on Geffen, by Geffen Records (USA). Deleted Jun '87. Catalogue no: **GEF 16T**

Lone Ranger

COCONUT WOMAN
Tracks: / Coconut woman / Rub-a-dub time.
12" Single: Released Jun '83, on Clair, Catalogue no: **CLAIR 006**

FOUR SEASON LOVER
Tracks: / Four season lover.
12" Single: Released Feb '85, on Silver Bullet, Catalogue no: **SB 001**

ROSEMARIE
Tracks: / Rose Marie / You make your mistakes.
7" Single: Released Nov '81, on Black Joy, Deleted '88. Catalogue no: **BH 813**

SILENT FASHION
Tracks: / Silent fashion / Lover's rock (puddy roots).
12" Single: Released Oct '83, on Technics, Catalogue no: **WR 1927**

Lone Typhoon

RHYTHM OF THE RAIN
Tracks: / Rhythm of the rain / More congas.
7" Single: Released Dec '80, on Hammer, Deleted Dec '85. Catalogue no: **HVS 312**

Lonely Hearts

DEAR HEART
Tracks: / Dear heart / Full colour guy.
7" Single: Released Mar '82, on BBC, by BBC Records & Tapes. Deleted '85. Catalogue no: **RESL 111**

Lonesome No More

TURNED INSANE
Tracks: / Turned insane / Do you think i care.
7" Single: Released May '81, on Rage, Deleted May '86. Catalogue no: **RAGE 3**

Lonesome Tone

MUM, DAD, LOVE, HATE & ELVIS
Tracks: / Mum, dad, love, hate & Elvis / Ghost town.
7" Single: Released Oct '80, on Stiff, by Stiff Records. Catalogue no: **SSH 5**

Lonewolf

NOBODY'S MOVE
Tracks: / Nobody's move / Town to town / Leave me blind.
12" Single: Released Jan '85, on Neat, by Neat Records. Catalogue no: **NEAT 44 12**

Loney, Roy

LANA LEE
Tracks: / Lana Lee / Magdalena / Goodnight.
7" Single: Released Apr '83, on Rockhouse, by Rockhouse Records (Holland). Catalogue no: **SP 8211**

Long Honeymoon

AMAZOON
Tracks: / Amazoon / Amazoon (u rap it).
7" Single: Released Apr '83, on A&M, by A&M Records. Deleted '88. Catalogue no: **AM 106**
12" Single: Released Apr '83, on A&M, by A&M Records. Deleted '88. Catalogue no: **AMX 106**

Long Pursuit

LONG PURSUIT, THE Cleary, Jon
Note: Escaping from the fall of Singapor in 1942, a strange band of soldiers and civilians, neutrals and combatants, find themselves forced to overcome their natural prejudices and personal antipathies in the face of shared dangers and all but impossible hazards. On their journey through the Dutch East Indies, as they think, away from the war, they become, by an ironic turn of fate, more deeply involved in the war than ever. Australia, for which they are making, is threatened by an attack of which they have acquired detailed intelligence. The English officer in charge of the party sees his duty plain; the drunken American bruiser who hates officers on principle is no less certain in opposing him. From the conflicts and tensions of these and other members of the party a thrilling story aquires an added dimension of tautness and excitment.
Special: Released Mar '85, on Soundings, by Soundings Records. Catalogue no: **SOUND 17**

Long Ryders

I HAD A DREAM
Tracks: / I had a dream.
7" Single: Released Mar '85, on Zippo, by Demon Records. Catalogue no: **ZIPPO 452**

I WANT YOU BAD
Tracks: / I want you bad / Ring bells / State of my union (Extra track on 12").
7" Single: Released Jun '87, on Island, by Island Records. Deleted Apr '88. Catalogue no: **IS 330**
12" Single: Released Jun '87, on Island, by Island Records. Deleted Apr '88. Catalogue no: **12IS 330**

LOOKING FOR LEWIS & CLARKE
Tracks: / Looking for Lewis and Clarke.
10" single: Released Oct '85, on Island, by Island Records. Catalogue no: **10 IS 237**
7" Single: Released Sep '85, on Island, by Island Records. Catalogue no: **IS 237**

Long, Shorty

HERE COMES THE JUDGE
Tracks: / Here comes the judge / Function at the junction.
7" Single: Released Jul '68, on Tamla Motown, by Motown Records (UK). Deleted '71. Catalogue no: **TMG 663**
7" Single: Released Apr '88, on Motown, by BMG Records (UK). Catalogue no: **ZB 41915**

Long Tall Shorty

ON THE STREETS AGAIN
Tracks: / On the streets again.
7" Single: Released Jan '85, on Diamond, by Revolver Records. Catalogue no: **DIA 002**

WHAT'S GOING ON
Tracks: / What's going on.
7" Single: Released May '86, on Diamond, by Revolver Records. Catalogue no: **DIA 005**

WIN OR LOSE
Tracks: / Win or lose / Ain't done wrong.
7" Single: Released Nov '81, on Ramkup, Catalogue no: **CAC 007**

Long Tall Texans

GET BACK, WET BACK
Tracks: / Get back, wet back / Something's cooking.
7" Single: Released Oct '88, on Razor, by Razor Records. Catalogue no: **RZ5 112**
12" Single: Released Oct '88, on Razor, by Razor Records. Catalogue no: **RZST 112**

SAINTS & SINNERS
Tracks: / Saints and sinners.
12" Single: Released 13 Jun '87, on Razor, by Razor Records. Catalogue no: **RZST 108**

SHOULD I STAY OR SHOULD I GO
Tracks: / Should I stay or should I go.
7" Single: Released 27 Feb '88, on Razor, by Razor Records. Catalogue no: **RZS 109**

Long & The Short

CHOC ICE
Tracks: / Choc ice.
7" Single: Released Dec '64, on Decca, by Decca Records. Deleted '67. Catalogue no: **F 12043**

LETTER, THE
Tracks: / Letter, The.
7" Single: Released Sep '64, on Decca, by Decca Records. Deleted '67. Catalogue no: **F 11959**

Longfellow, Baron

AMOUR
Tracks: / Amour / Chicago's queen.
7" Single: Released Aug '81, on Polydor, by Polydor Ltd. Catalogue no: **POSP 306**

Longhorns

ALL I WANT FROM YOU
Tracks: / All I want from you.
7" Single: Released '88, on Band Wagon International, Catalogue no: **BWIR 007**

Longmire, Wilbert

BLACK IS THE COLOUR
Tracks: / Black is the colour.
12" Single: Released May '86, on Streetwave, Catalogue no: **SWAVE 8**

Longpig

WHY DO PEOPLE FIND EACH OTHER STRANGE
Tracks: / Why do people find each other strange / Darkboy / Primitive sensibility (On 12" only).
7" Single: Released Mar '84, on Anagram, by Cherry Red Records. Deleted '88. Catalogue no: **ANA 21**
12" Single: Released Mar '84, on Anagram, by Cherry Red Records. Deleted '88. Catalogue no: **12 ANA 21**

Longsy D

HIP HOP REGGAE
Tracks: / Hip hop reggae.
7" Single: Released Aug '87, on Big One Records, by Big One Records. Catalogue no: **VBIG 5**
12" Single: Released Aug '87, on Big One Records, by Big One Records. Catalogue no: **VVBIG 5**

MENTAL SKA
Tracks: / Mental ska / Return to Zorba.
12" Single: Released Aug '89, on Big One Records, by Big One Records. Catalogue no: **VVBIG 16**
7" Single: Released Aug '89, on Big One Records, by Big One Records. Catalogue no: **VBIG 16**
12" Single: Released Sep '89, on Big One Records, by Big One Records. Catalogue no: **VVBIGN 16**

THIS IS SKA Skacid mix
Tracks: / This is ska.
12" Single: Released Jan '89, on Big One Records, by Big One Records. Catalogue no: **VVBIG 13**
7" Single: Released Feb '89, on Big One

Records, by Big One Records. Catalogue no: **VBIG 13**
7" Single: Released '89, on Big One Records, by Big One Records. Catalogue no: **PRE 13**

THIS IS SKA (REMIX)
Tracks: / This is ska (remix).
12" Single: Released Mar '89, on Big One Records, by Big One Records. Catalogue no: **VVBIGN 13**

TO THE RHYTHM
Tracks: / To the rhythm.
7" Single: Released Aug '88, on Big One Records, by Big One Records. Catalogue no: **VBIG 10**
12" Single: Released Aug '88, on Big One Records, by Big One Records. Catalogue no: **VVBIG 10**

ZORBA
Tracks: / Zorba.
7" Single: Released Jul '89, on Big One Records, by Big One Records. Catalogue no: **VBIGO 16**
12" Single: Released Jul '89, on Big One Records, by Big One Records. Catalogue no: **VVBIGO 16**

Longthorne, Joe

WIND BENEATH MY WINGS
Tracks: / Wind beneath my wings.
7" Single: Released Jun '89, on Telstar, by Telstar Records (UK). Catalogue no: **STAS 2367**

Look

Biographical details: Fronted by lead singer Johnny Whetstone, the Look were a British pop band of the early Eighties who promised much but delivered little. Their quirky novelty single *I am the beat* reached No.6 on the UK chart in early 1981; it was an infectious stomping pop record, ending with a specially etched loop-groove which repeated the word 'beat' ad infinitum until you lifted the stylus off the disc. With a strong vocal performance and a distinctive organ sound, *I am the beat*was indiosyncratic and refreshing. However, the four guys failed to come up with a suitable follow-up. In the late Summer of '81, *Feeding time* crept to the UK No.50 position. This was a pale rehash of the *I am the beat* sound, and other singles flopped altogether. The British Look should not be confused with an American band of the same name, who were around at the same time. (Bob MacDonald, 16th Dec 1985).

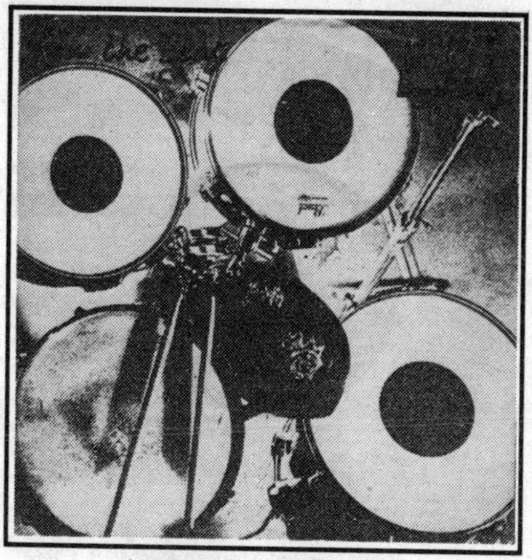

Look - I am the Beat (Released on MCA)

DRUMMING UP LOVE
Tracks: / Drumming up love.
7" Single: Released Oct '83, on Towerbell, Catalogue no: **TOW 43**

FEEDING TIME
Tracks: / Feeding time.
7" Single: Released Aug '81, on MCA, by MCA Records. Deleted '84. Catalogue no: **MCA 736**

I AM THE BEAT (see panel above)
Tracks: / I am the beat / You do these things to me.
7" Single: Released Dec '80, on MCA, by MCA Records. Deleted '83. Catalogue no: **MCA 647**

THREE STEPS AWAY
Tracks: / Three steps away / It's much too late for that.
7" Single: Released Apr '81, on MCA, by MCA Records. Deleted Apr '86. Catalogue no: **MCA 681**

TONIGHT
Tracks: / Tonight / Three steps away.
7" Single: Released Nov '81, on MCA, by MCA Records. Deleted Nov '84. Catalogue no: **MCA 756**

Look Back In Anger

CAPRICE (SINGLE)
Tracks: / Caprice / Mannequin.
7" Single: Released Aug '82, on Look Back In Anger, Catalogue no: **LBA 1**

FLOWERS
Tracks: / Flowers / Inamorta / Torment.
12" Single: Released Jan '84, on Criminal Damage, Catalogue no: **CRI 12107**

Look Before You Leap

LOOK BEFORE YOU LEAP Original cast
7" Single: Released May '84, on Royal, Catalogue no: **JBS 100**

Lookalikes

CALL ME
Tracks: / Call me / Just what you got.
7" Single: Released Sep '80, on Riva, by Riva Records. Deleted '83. Catalogue no: **RIVA 24**

CAN I TAKE YOU HOME TONIGHT?
Tracks: / Can i take you home tonight / Radio / Don't cry for me.
7" Single: Released May '80, on Riva, by Riva Records. Deleted May '85. Catalogue no: **RIVA 22**

Looking Glass

MIRROR MAN
Tracks: / Mirror man.
7" Single: Released Sep '87, on Dreamworld, by Dreamworld Records. Catalogue no: **DREAM 012**
12" Single: Released Sep '87, on Dreamworld, by Dreamworld Records. Catalogue no: **DREAM 012T**

Loop

ARC-LITE
Tracks: / Arc-lite.
12" Single: Released Nov '89, on Situation 2, by Beggars Banquet Records. Catalogue no: **SIT 64T**
CD 5": Released Nov '89, on Situation 2, by Beggars Banquet Records. Catalogue no: **SIT 64CD**
7" Single: Released Nov '89, on Situation 2, by Beggars Banquet Records. Catalogue no: **SIT 64**

BLACK SUN
Tracks: / Black swan / Black sun.
12" Single: Released Oct '88, on Chapter 22, by Chapter 22 Records. Catalogue no: **12 CHAP 32**

COLLISION
Tracks: / Collision / Crawling heart / Thief of fire / Thief.
12" Single: Released 23 Apr '88, on Chapter 22, by Chapter 22 Records. Catalogue no: **12CHAP 27**
7" Single: Released 23 Apr '88, on Chapter 22, by Chapter 22 Records. Catalogue no: **CHAP 27**

FADE OUT
Special: Released Nov '88, on Chapter 22, by Chapter 22 Records. Catalogue no: **CHAPLLP 34**

KEEP ON MOVIN'
Tracks: / Keep on movin'.
12" Single: Released Sep '87, on Rock The House, Catalogue no: **001T**

SIXTEEN DREAMS
Tracks: / Sixteen dreams.
12" Single: Released Jan '87, on Head, Catalogue no: **HEAD 5**

SPINNING PARTS
Tracks: / Spinning parts (part 1) / Spinning parts (part 2).
7" Pic: Released Jun '87, on Head, Catalogue no: **HEAD 7L**
12" Single: Released Jun '87, on Head, Catalogue no: **HEAD 7**

Looren, Jackie

LET THE BOOGIE WOOGIE ROLL
Tracks: / Let the boogie woogie roll / Love is a moment away.
7" Single: Released Mar '81, on Feelgood, by Carlin Music Corp.. Deleted Mar '84. Catalogue no: **FLG 115**

Loose Change

I WANNA HOLD ON TO YOU
Tracks: / I wanna hold on to you / Rising cost of love / Black hole (Available on 12" only.) / Big bang theory (Available on 12" only.).
7" Single: Released Mar '80, on Casablanca, by PolyGram UK Ltd. Deleted Mar '83. Catalogue no: **CAN 188**
12" Single: Released Mar '80, on Casablanca, by PolyGram UK Ltd. Deleted Mar '83. Catalogue no: **CANL 188**

Loose Ends

Biographical details: This British band consists of Jane Eugene, Macca and Steve Nichol. Hailing from Peckham in South London, Loose Ends wee at the forefront of the burgeoning UK soul scene of the mid-Eighties. The trio first began to attract attention with their 1983 single *Don't hold back your love.* To arrive at an 'authentic' funk sound, they went to America to record both of their first two albums with Philadelphia-based producer Nick Martinelli. The first, 1984's *A little spice,* yielded a trio of minor UK hit singles: *Tell me what you want* (No.74), *Emergency (dial 999)* (No 41) and *Choose me (rescue me)* (No.59). All of these would have fared even better, had they garnered national airplay instead of being confined to specialist soul programs. The second Loose Ends album, 1985's *So where are you?*, put the ever danceable group into the big league. The LP spawned two British Top 20 singles, the incredibly infectious and super-cool *Hangin' on a string* plus the inferior *Magic touch.* The former proceeded to reach No.1 on the American black music charts, the first single by a UK group to do so; it also craked the Top 50 of the US pop list, another notable coup. A messy cover version of David Bowie's *Golden years* was less successful. (Bob MacDonald, 16th Dec 1985).

CHOOSE ME (RESCUE ME)
Tracks: / Choose me (rescue me).
7" Single: Released Jul '84, on Virgin, by Virgin Records. Deleted '87. Catalogue no: **VS 697**

EMERGENCY (DIAL 999)
Tracks: / Emergency (dial 999)-extended remix / Emergency (dial 999)-dub mix.
12" Single: Released '84, on Virgin, by Virgin Records. Catalogue no: **VS 677-12**
7" Single: Released '84, on Virgin, by Virgin Records. Deleted '87. Catalogue no: **VS 677**

GOLDEN YEARS
Tracks: / Golden years.
7" Single: Released Jul '85, on Virgin, by Virgin Records. Catalogue no: **VS 795**

HANGIN' ON A STRING
Tracks: / Hangin' on a string (7" only) / Little spice, A (On all versions) / Hangin' on a string (contemplating)-extended dance mix (CD & 12" only) / Emergency (dial 999)-extended remix (CD only).
12" Single: Released '85, on Virgin, by Virgin Records. Catalogue no: **VS 748-12**
7" Single: Released '85, on Virgin, by Virgin Records. Catalogue no: **VS 748**
CD 3": Released '88, on Virgin, by Virgin Records. Catalogue no: **CDT 39**

HANGIN' ON A STRING (OLD GOLD)
Tracks: / Hangin' on a string / Emergency (dial 999).
12" Single: Released 27 Feb '89, on Old Gold, by Old Gold Records. Catalogue no: **OG 4098**

IN THE SKY
Tracks: / In the sky.
12" Single: Released May '82, on Virgin, by Virgin Records. Deleted '85. Catalogue no: **VS 497-12**
7" Single: Released May '82, on Virgin, by Virgin Records. Deleted '85. Catalogue no: **VS 497**

MAGIC TOUCH
Tracks: / Magic touch / Magic touch (instrumental).
7" Single: Released '85, on Virgin, by Virgin Records. Deleted '88. Catalogue no: **VS 761**
12" Single: Released Apr '85, on Virgin, by Virgin Records. Deleted May '88. Catalogue no: **VS 761-12**

MAGIC TOUCH (OLD GOLD)
Tracks: / Magic touch / Slow down.
CD 5": Released 28 Mar '89, on Old Gold, by Old Gold Records. Catalogue no: **OG 4108**

MASTERMIND MEGA MIX, THE
Tracks: / Mastermind mega mix, The.
12" Single: Released '89, on Virgin, by Virgin Records. Catalogue no: **VS 88413**

MR BACHELOR
Tracks: / Mr. Bachelor (NOT on 12") / Too much (NOT on CD) / Mr. Bachelor (extended remix version) (CD & 12" only) / Mr. Bachelor (dub version) (CD & 12" only) / Johnny Broadhead (part 2 remix) (CD only).
7" Single: Released 16 May '88, on Virgin, by Virgin Records. Catalogue no: **VS 1080**
CD 5": Released Aug '88, on Virgin, by Virgin Records. Catalogue no: **VSCD 1080**
12" Single: Released 16 May '88, on Virgin, by Virgin Records. Catalogue no: **VST 1080**

NIGHTS OF PLEASURE
Tracks: / Nights of pleasure (7" only) / Let's rock (7" only) / Nights of pleasure (12" full length version) (On VS 919-12 only) / Let's rock (full length version) (On 12" only) / Nights of pleasure (dub version) (On VS 919-12 only) / Nights of pleasure (12" mix by Dancing Danny Dee) (On VS 919-13 only) / Johnny Broadhead (On VS 919-13 only).
12" Single: Released '86, on Virgin, by Virgin Records. Catalogue no: **VS 919-13**
7" Single: Released Nov '86, on Virgin, by Virgin Records. Deleted May '88. Catalogue no: **VS 919**
12" Single: Released Nov '86, on Virgin, by Virgin Records. Catalogue no: **VS 919-12**

OOH, YOU MAKE ME FEEL
Tracks: / Ooh, you make me feel / Ooh, you make me feel (extended mix) (On cassette & 12" only) / Gonna make you mine (On 12" only) / Ooh, you make me feel (percussapella mix) (On cassette only) / Ooh, you make me feel (dub mix) (On cassette only).
12" Single: Released Aug '87, on Virgin, by Virgin Records. Catalogue no: **VS 991-12**
Cassingle: Released Aug '87, on Virgin, by Virgin Records. Catalogue no: **VSC 991-12**
7" Single: Released Aug '87, on Virgin, by Virgin Records. Deleted '89. Catalogue no: **VS 991**

SLOWDOWN
Tracks: / Slowdown / Slow down (instrumental) / Gonna make you mine / Slowdown (12" remix) (12" only) / Slowdown (slowjam) (12" only).
Note: *= extra tracks included in Double pack.

12" Single: Released Sep '86, on Virgin, by Virgin Records. Deleted May '88. Catalogue no: **VSD 884-12**
7" Single: Released Sep '86, on Virgin, by Virgin Records. Deleted May '88. Catalogue no: **VS 884**
12" Single: Released '86, on Virgin, by Virgin Records. Catalogue no: **VS 884-12**

STAY A LITTLE WHILE CHILD
Tracks: / Stay a little while child (7" only) / Gonna make you mine / Stay a little while child (extended version) (12" only) / Ooh, you make me feel (dub version) (12" only).
7" Single: Released May '86, on Virgin, by Virgin Records. Deleted '86. Catalogue no: **VS 819**
12" Single: Released May '86, on Virgin, by Virgin Records. Catalogue no: **VS 819-12**

TELL ME WHAT YOU WANT
Tracks: / Tell me what you want.

7" Single: Released Feb '84, on Virgin, by Virgin Records. Deleted '87. Catalogue no: **VS 658**

WATCHING YOU
Tracks: / Watching you (7" mix on all versions) / Life (7' only) / Watching you (US 12" remix) (On 12' & CD only) / Life (the complete version) (On 12" only) / Watching you (Kevin Saunderson remix) (On CD only) / Life (the complete rebirth) (On CD only).
12" Single: Released Aug '88, on Virgin, by Virgin Records. Catalogue no: **VSR 1101**
CD 5": Released '88, on Virgin, by Virgin Records. Catalogue no: **VSCD 1101**
7" Single: Released Aug '88, on Virgin, by Virgin Records. Catalogue no: **VS 1101**

WE'RE ARRIVED
Tracks: / We're arrived / In the sky.
12" Single: Released Oct '82, on Virgin, by Virgin Records. Deleted Oct '85. Catalogue no: **VS 542 12**
7" Single: Released Oct '82, on Virgin, by Virgin Records. Deleted Oct '85. Catalogue no: **VS 542**

Loose Shoes

PUT THE BLAME ON ME
Tracks: / Put the blame on me / Nobody's clown.
7" Single: Released Mar '81, on Applause, by Riva Records. Deleted Mar '84. Catalogue no: **CLAP 2**

Loose Talk

DAN DARE
Tracks: / Dan Dare / Home planet.
7" Single: Released Jul '82, on Jet, by Jet Records. Catalogue no: **JET 7025**

JUDGE DREAD
Tracks: / Judge Dread / You you you.
7" Single: Released Jan '83, on Jet, by Jet Records. Catalogue no: **JET 7033**

Looters

CROSS THE BORDER (EP)
Tracks: / Cross the border / Streets are callin', The / Rise up / Being human.
12" Single: Released Nov '86, on Alternative Tentacles, by Alternative Tentacles Records. Catalogue no: **VIRUS 54**

LOOTERS
Tracks: / Looters.
12" Single: Released Sep '86, on Alternative Tentacles, by Alternative Tentacles Records. Catalogue no: **VIRUS 54**

Lopez, Denise

SAYIN' SORRY
Tracks: / Sayin' sorry (don't make it right) / Sayin' sorry (don't make it right).
12" Single: Released Aug '88, on Breakout, by A&M Records. Catalogue no: **USAT 645**
7" Single: Released Aug '88, on Breakout, by A&M Records. Catalogue no: **USA 646**

Lopez, Trini

Biographical details:
This American singer was born in Dallas, Texas, and entered showbusiness at the age of 15 when he began performing Latin-American tunes in the local nightclubs. About five years later, having finished his studies and joined the entertainment industry on a full-time basis, he moved to Hollywood to further his career.
He spent several years building a reputation in the showbusiness mecca; in the early Sixties, while performing at P.J.'s club in Hollywood, he was offered a recording contract by Don Costs of Reprise Records. In late 1963 Lopez reached the Top 5 on both sides of the Atlantic with a cover version of the Weavers' 1958 track *If I had a hammer.* Lopez' success with this song was particularly impressive, in view of the fact that it had been an American Top Tenner for Peter, Paul and Mary merely one year before the Trini triumph. Produced and arranged by Costa, and recorded live in the enthusiastic atmosphere of P.J.'s, Lopez' distinctive treatment of *If I had a hammer* placed him in the Chicano category, a term that was used to describe artists who combined pop music with the Latin rhythms from south of the USA-Mexico border. It was Lopez' destiny to be forever associated with *If I had a hammer* for his subsequent singles were only modest hits. They included *Kansas City, Lemon tree, I'm comin' home Cindy* and Gonna get along without ya now. His albums *Trini Lopez at P.J's* (1963) and *Trini Lopez in London* (1967) were top sellers in Britain, but these seved to underline the fact that his forte was live performance rather than discs. He remained in showbusiness throughout the Sixties and Seventies, retaining a sizeable following in South America and France. In 1978 he issued the dire album *Transformed by time,* an abortive attempt to jump on the disco bandwagon.

At the end of 1981 he got into the lower regions of the British charts with the retrospective medley single *Trini tracks.* (Bob MacDonald, 18th Dec 1985).

1937 born Texan Trini Lopez is a blend od paradoxes. An Hispanic raised in Dallas, he grew up listening to R & B: yet after an uncertain start as a would-be rockabilly he finally made his mark singing commercial folk music that was driven by a bouncy Latin rhythm. There was little heavy handed social commentary in the music that Lopez interpreted. Instead, he emphasised melody and rhythm at the expense of a few potshots at the establishment. Lopez met Buddy Holly who introduced him to Norman Petty and found to Columbia in 1958. Later Lopez worked for King Records before he was heard by Frank Sinatra who signed him for a Reprise deal. Lopez landed a steady gig with his own group at PJ's Club in Hollywood, from where these recordings result. This album with the lively atmosphere spawned *If I had a hammer* which started his international chart success in 1962. The record also features five German recordings.
(Bear Family, 1988)..

GONNA GET ALONG WITHOUT YA NOW
Tracks: / Gonna get along without you now.
7" Single: Released Apr '67, on Reprise, by WEA Records. Deleted '70. Catalogue no: **R 20547**

IF I HAD A HAMMER
Tracks: / If I had a hammer / La bamba / Lemon tree (Extra track available on 12" only.) / Sunny (Extra track available on 12" only.).
7" Single: Released Apr '88, on Warner Bros., by WEA Records. Catalogue no: **W 7899**
7" Single: Released Sep '63, on Reprise, by WEA Records. Deleted '66. Catalogue no: **R 20198**
12" Single: Released Apr '88, on Warner Bros., by WEA Records. Catalogue no: **W 7899T**

IF I HAD A HAMMER (OLD GOLD)
Tracks: / If I had a hammer / La bamba.
7" Single: Released Jul '82, on Old Gold, by Old Gold Records. Catalogue no: **OG 9022**

I'M COMING HOME CINDY
Tracks: / I'm coming home Cindy.
7" Single: Released May '66, on Reprise, by WEA Records. Deleted '69. Catalogue no: **R 20455**

KANSAS CITY
Tracks: / Kansas city.
7" Single: Released Dec '63, on Reprise, by WEA Records. Deleted '66. Catalogue no: **R 20236**

TRINI TRAX
Tracks: / Trini trax / My paraguaya.
12" Single: Released Nov '81, on RCA, by BMG Records (UK). Catalogue no: **RCAT 154**
7" Single: Released Nov '81, on RCA, by BMG Records (UK). Catalogue no: **RCA 154**

L'Orange Mechanique

SYMPHONY
Tracks: / Symphony.
7" Single: Released Apr '86, on Art Pop, by Art Pop Records. Catalogue no: **POP 44**

Lorber, Jeff

FACTS OF LOVE
Tracks: / Facts of love / Sand castles / Every woman needs it.
12" Single: Released Mar '87, on Club, by Phonogram Ltd. Deleted Dec '87. Catalogue no: **JABXD 48**
7" Single: Released Mar '87, on Club, by Phonogram Ltd. Deleted Dec '87. Catalogue no: **JAB 48**
12" Single: Released Mar '87, on Club, by Phonogram Ltd. Deleted Dec '87. Catalogue no: **JABX 48**

Lorber, Jeff Fusion

FUSION JUICE (EP)
Tracks: / Fusion juice / Disco nights / Say you love me / Afterglow.
12" Single: Released Oct '80, on Arista, by BMG Records (UK). Deleted Oct '83. Catalogue no: **ARIST 12368**

MONSTER MAN
Tracks: / Monster man / magic mady.
12" Single: Released Apr '81, on Arista, by BMG Records (UK). Deleted '85. Catalogue no: **ARIST 12 410**

Lorber, Larry

SHIVERS UP MY SPINE
Tracks: / Shivers up my spine.
7" Single: Released Oct '84, on Numa, by Numa Records. Catalogue no: **NU 2**
12" Single: Released Oct '84, on Numa, by Numa Records. Catalogue no: **UM 2**

Lord, Benny

FAITHFUL TO THE FIANCE
Tracks: / Faithful to the fiance / You.
7" Single: Released Mar '80, on Magnet, by WEA Records. Deleted Mar '83. Catalogue no: **MAG 166**

Lord Cloak Inner Force

FAT WOMAN
Tracks: / Fat woman.
12" Single: Released Mar '85, on Voida, Catalogue no: **VDA 3**

Lord C.M

FLASHBACK
Tracks: / Flashback / Don't run me away.
12" Single: Released Jan '82, on RCA, by BMG Records (UK). Deleted Jan '85. Catalogue no: **RCAT 180**
7" Single: Released Jan '82, on RCA, by BMG Records (UK). Deleted Jan '85. Catalogue no: **RCA 180**

Lord Diamond

MISS LORNA
Tracks: / Miss Lorna.
7" Single: Released Sep '84, on Jama, Catalogue no: **JA 0020**
12" Single: Released Sep '84, on Jama, Catalogue no: **JAC 0020**

STOP KNOCKING ON WOOD
Tracks: / Stop knocking on wood / Party people.
12" Single: Released Aug '86, on Jazz Star, Catalogue no: **JS 003**

Lord, Jon

BACH ONTO THIS
Tracks: / Bach onto this / Going home.
7" Single: Released May '82, on Harvest (1), by EMI Records. Deleted '85. Catalogue no: **HAR 5220**

COUNTRY DIARY OF AN EDWARDIAN LADY
7" Single: Released Mar '84, on Safari, by Safari Records. Catalogue no: **SAFE 60**

Lord Laro

ROCKIN' SOCA
Tracks: / Rockin' soca.
12" Single: Released Jan '85, on Revue, by Creole Records. Catalogue no: **REV 001T**

Lord Nelson

MI LOVER
Tracks: / Mi lover / We like it.
12" Single: Released Nov '86, on Bumble Bee, Catalogue no: **BUMB 102**

Lord Of Storm

SOME PEOPLE ARE SO REAL
12" Single: Released Aug '81, on Offstreet, Catalogue no: **OSR 005**

Lord Rockingham's XI

Biographical details:
Hoots mon was one of Britain's most memorable novelty hits of the Fifties. The single reached No.1 in late 1958. It was written and produced by Scottish bandleader Harry Robinson, who had come to fame in the preceding few weeks as the resident orchestra leader on ITV's new pop show *Oh boy.* The program's creator, Jack Good, dreamed up the name Lord Rockingham's XI, and the chart-topping success of their single owed much to the weekly exposure that the ensemble were given on Good's show. *Hoots mon* was a catchy, gimmicky rock'n'roll instrumental of the kind that would be successfully performed by Johnny & The Hurricanes.

Occasionally interrupted the music, Robinson put on his thickest Scottish dialect to speak such silly lines as *Hoots mon, there's a moos loose aboot this hoos.* Like many novelty hits, it was hard to follow in February '59 he reached the UK No.16 position with another self-penned ditty *Wee Tom,* before fading into obscurity.
It is interesting to note that the band's tenor sax player was Benny Green who, in his later days as a music journalist and broadcaster, was ofter dismissive about rock'n'roll. (18th Dec 1985).

HOOTS MON
Tracks: / Hoots mon / Blue train.
7" Single: Released Oct '58, on Decca, by Decca Records. Deleted '61. Catalogue no: **F 11059**

WEE TOM
Tracks: / Wee Tom.
7" Single: Released Feb '59, on Decca, by Decca Records. Deleted '62. Catalogue no: **F 11104**

Lord Sassafrass

POCCOMANIA JUMP (SINGLE)
12" Single: Released May '85, on Horseman, Catalogue no: **UNKNOWN**

Lord Tee

NEVER ENDING LOVE
Tracks: / Never ending love.
12" Single: Released Aug '84, on Bluesville International, Catalogue no: **BI 002**

Lordan, Jerry

I'LL STAY SINGLE
Tracks: / I'll stay single.
7" Single: Released Jan '60, on Parlophone, by EMI Records. Deleted '63. Catalogue no: **R 4588**

SING LIKE AN ANGEL
Tracks: / She's like an angel.
7" Single: Released Jun '60, on Parlophone, by EMI Records. Deleted '63. Catalogue no: **R 4653**

WHO COULD BE BLUER
Tracks: / Who could be bluer.
7" Single: Released Feb '60, on Parlophone, by EMI Records. Deleted '63. Catalogue no: **R 4627**

Lords

LIKE A VIRGIN
Tracks: / Like a virgin.
12" Single: Released May '85, on Illegal, by Faulty Products Records. Catalogue no: **LORDS 12**

Lords Of Acid

I SIT IN ACID
Tracks: / I sit in acid.
12" Single: Released Dec '88, on Kaos, Catalogue no: **KAOS 008**

I SIT ON ACID
Tracks: / I sit on acid.
7" Single: Released Jul '89, on Kaos, Catalogue no: **KAOS 008-7**
CD 5": Released Jul '89, on Kaos, Catalogue no: **KAOS 008 CD**

I SIT ON ACID (REMIX)
Tracks: / I sit on acid (remix).
12" Single: Released Jul '89, on Kaos, Catalogue no: **KAOS 008R**
CD 5": Released Jul '89, on Kaos, Catalogue no: **KAOS 008RCD**

Lords Of The New

NEW CHURCH
Tracks: / New church.
7" Single: Released Apr '82, on Illegal, by Faulty Products Records. Deleted Apr '85. Catalogue no: **ILS 0028**

PSYCHO SEX
Tracks: / Psycho sex.
7" Single: Released Sep '87, on New Rose (1), by New Rose Records. Catalogue no: **BI 001**
12" Single: Released Sep '87, on New Rose (1), by New Rose Records. Catalogue no: **BI 002**

REAL BAD TIME, THE
Tracks: / Real bad time, The / Things go bump.
7" Single: Released Aug '87, on Bondage International, Catalogue no: **B1 001**

RUSSIAN ROULETTE
Tracks: / Russian roulette / Young don't cry.
7" Single: Released Nov '82, on Illegal, by Faulty Products Records. Deleted Nov '85. Catalogue no: **ILS 0033**

Lorenco Marques

WARDROBES, (THE)
Tracks: / Wardrobes, The.
7" Single: Released Sep '82, on Siren, by Virgin Records. Catalogue no: **5/82/CUS 1321**

Lori

LONELY SPY
(LORI & THE CHAMELEONS)
Tracks: / Lonely spy, The / Peru.
7" Single: Released Apr '80, on Korova, by WEA Records. Deleted '83. Catalogue no: **KOW 5**

TOUCH
Tracks: / Touch / Lonely spy / Love on the ganges (12" only).
7" Single: Released Oct '81, on Korova, by WEA Records. Deleted '85. Catalogue no: **KOW 20**
12" Single: Released Oct '81, on Korova, by WEA Records. Deleted '85. Catalogue no: **KOW 20T**
7" Single: Released Dec '79, on Sire, by Sire Records. Deleted '82. Catalogue no: **SIR 4025**

Loriana

HOLD THE DAY, HOLD THE NIGHT
Tracks: / Hold the day, hold the night / Hold the day, hold the night (inst).
7" Single: Released 23 May '87, on Explicit, by Explicit Records. Catalogue no: **XPL1**
12" Single: Released 23 May '87, on Explicit, by Explicit Records. Catalogue no:

EXP 1
12" Single: Released 23 May '87, on Explicit, by Explicit Records. Catalogue no: **XPL 1 T**

Loring, Gloria

FRIENDS & LOVERS
Tracks: / Friends and lovers / You always knew.
7" Single: Released Sep '86, on Carrere, Catalogue no: **CAR 400**
12" Single: Released Sep '86, on Carrere, Catalogue no: **CART 400**

Lorries

CRAWLING MANTRA
Tracks: / Crawling mantra / Hang man / All the same / Shout at the sky (live).
7" Single: Released Apr '87, on Red Rhino, by Red Rhino Records. Catalogue no: **RED 76**
7" Set: Released Apr '87, on Red Rhino, by Red Rhino Records. Catalogue no: **REDD 76**
12" Single: Released Apr '87, on Red Rhino, by Red Rhino Records. Catalogue no: **REDT 76**

Los Bravos

Biographical details: This Spanish pop group consisted of Manuel Fernandez, Pablo Gomez, Mike Kogel (the lead singer - he was actually German-born), Antonio Martinex and Miguel Vicens-Danus. Los Bravos came into being in 1965, having evolved from a pair of previous Spanish combos. After one of their Spanish language records caught the ear of a Decca executive in London (Ivor Raymonds), they came to Britain in Aril 1966 to record the English language song *Black is black*. This catchy number gave the group the honour of being the first Spanish combo to score a UK smash - it reached No.2 in Britain, No.4 in America and was a hit throughout Europe. The follow-up single *I don't care* peaked at No.16 on the British listings. They then drifted into obscurity, although they remained an attraction in their native country. *Black is black* was revived in 1977 by a French duo called La Belle Epoque, who gave it the disco treatment and took it to No.2 in the UK, the same position that Los Bravos had originally attained in '66. (Bob MacDonald, 18th Dec 1985).

BLACK IS BLACK
Tracks: / Black is black / I don't care.
7" Single: Released Sep '86, on Carrere, Catalogue no: **CAR 404**
7" Single: Released '66, on Decca, by Decca Records. Deleted '69. Catalogue no: **F 22419**
12" Single: Released Sep '86, on Carrere, Catalogue no: **CART 404**

BLACK IS BLACK(OLD GOLD SERIES)
Tracks: / Black is black.
7" Single: Released Nov '86, on Old Gold, by Old Gold Records. Catalogue no: **OG 9659**

I DON'T CARE
Tracks: / I don't care.
7" Single: Released Sep '66, on Decca, by Decca Records. Deleted '69. Catalogue no: **F 22484**

Los Indios Tabajaros

Biographical details: A duo comprising two Brazilian Indian Brothers stormed the charts on both sides of the Atlantic in late 1963, reaching No.6 in the US and No.5 in the UK with their acoustic guitar rendition of the 30 year-old Mexican standard *Maria Elena*. The extraordinary simplicity and tranquility of this gentle single made it one of the most surprising successes of that frenetic pop year. The brothers, Musiperi and Herundy, were born in Ceara, which lies in the north-eastern jungles of Brazil. They were sons of a Tabajaras Indian chieftain; for performing purposes, they used the names Natalicio and Antenor Lima. They had been releasing albums for the South American market since 1943. *Maria Elena* was a one off novelty hit as far as British and American pop fans were concerned, but Los Indios Tabajaras remained an active musical unit right through into the Eighties, with their distinctive guitar style. (Bob MacDonald, 18th Dec 1985).

MARIA ELENA (OLD GOLD)
Tracks: / Maria Elena / Ballad of the Green Berets.
7" Single: Released Oct '86, on Old Gold, by Old Gold Records. Catalogue no: **OG 9625**

Los Lobos

COME ON LET'S GO
Tracks: / Come on let's go.
7" Single: on London Records, by London Records. Deleted Oct '88. Catalogue no: **LASH 14**
10" single: on London Records, by London Records. Deleted Oct '88. Catalogue no: **LASHT 14**
12" Single: on London Records, by London Records. Deleted Oct '88. Catalogue no: **LASHX 14**

DONNA
Tracks: / Donna / Framed / Goodnight my love (This track is on 12" single only.).
7" Single: Released 21 Nov '87, on Slash, by London Records. Deleted Oct '88. Catalogue no: **LASH 16**
10" single: Released '88, on London Records, by London Records. Deleted Feb '89. Catalogue no: **HL 8803**
12" Single: Released 21 Nov '87, on Slash, by London Records. Deleted Oct '88. Catalogue no: **LASHX 16**

DON'T WORRY BABY
Tracks: / Don't worry baby / Will the wolf survive.
12" Single: Released Mar '85, on Slash, by London Records. Catalogue no: **LASHX 4**
7" Single: Released Mar '85, on Slash, by London Records. Catalogue no: **LASH 4**

LA BAMBA
Tracks: / La Bamba / Charlena / Rip it up* (*Extra track on 12").
12" Single: Released Jul '87, on Slash, by London Records. Deleted Oct '88. Catalogue no: **LASHX 13**
Cassingle: Released Jul '87, on Slash, by London Records. Deleted May '89. Catalogue no: **LASCS 13**
7" Single: Released Jul '87, on Slash, by London Records. Deleted Oct '88. Catalogue no: **LASH 13**

ONE TIME ONE NIGHT
Tracks: / One time one night / River of fools / Anselma / Don't worry baby.
7" Single: Released Apr '87, on Slash, by London Records. Deleted Oct '88. Catalogue no: **LASH 11**
12" Single: Released Apr '87, on Slash, by London Records. Deleted Oct '88. Catalogue no: **LASHX 11**

SET ME FREE (ROSA LEE)
Tracks: / Set me free (Rosa Lee) / Shakin' shakin' shakes / Preudeabelalama / Will the wolf survive (Only available on 12" version.).
Note: "Will the wolf survive' is an extra track only available on 12" version.
7" Single: Released Feb '87, on Slash, by London Records. Catalogue no: **LASH 10**
12" Single: Released Feb '87, on Slash, by London Records. Catalogue no: **LASHX 10**

Los Reyes

BAM BOLEO
Tracks: / Bam boleo / Corona.
7" Single: Released Jul '88, on HHO (Henry Hadaway Organisation), by Henry Hadaway Organisation. Catalogue no: **HAD 3**
12" Single: Released Jul '88, on HHO (Henry Hadaway Organisation), by Henry Hadaway Organisation. Catalogue no: **HADT 3**

Los Van Van

QUE PALO ES ESE
Tracks: / Que palo es ese / Que palo es ese (Version).
7" Single: Released Jun '89, on Mango, by Island Records. Catalogue no: **12 MNG 707**

Loss, Joe

Biographical details: This British bandleader was hailed as the most tenasious and longest-lasting person in his field when, in 1980, he celebrated his 50th year as an orchestra leader. He was never an innovative man, but his skill lay in his ability to adapt to the changing challenges of each new musical era. His band's function was to play the hits of the day for the benefit of radio listeners, record buyers and concert-goers. During the first half of the Sixties, Loss chalked up five hit singles on the UK pop charts. The classic *Wheels cha cha* reached No.21 in 1961, and logged an impressive total of 21 weeks on the Top 50. His other chart entries included *Sucu sucu*, the *Maigret* theme and *Must be Madison*. The fifth and final one was *March of the Mods*, which reached No.31 at the end of 1964 - this was the venerable bandleader's bow to one of Britain's leading youth cults of the era, although he probably had no wish to be associated with the beach hooliganism which sometimes tainted the Mods' reputation! In addition to the aforementioned singles, Loss also had two chart EP's and one chart album to his credit. (Bob MacDonald, 18th Dec 1985).

MAIGRET THEME
Tracks: / Maigret theme.
7" Single: Released Mar '62, on H.M.V., by EMI Records. Deleted '65. Catalogue no: **POP 995**

MARCH OF THE MODS
Tracks: / March of the mods.
7" Single: Released Oct '64, on H.M.V., by EMI Records. Catalogue no: **POP 1351**

MUST BE MADISON
Tracks: / Must be Madison.
7" Single: Released Nov '62, on H.M.V., by EMI Records. Deleted '65. Catalogue no: **POP 1075**

SUCU SUCU
Tracks: / Sucu sucu.
7" Single: Released Oct '61, on H.M.V., by EMI Records. Deleted '64. Catalogue no: **POP 937**

WHEELS CHA CHA
Tracks: / Wheels cha cha.
7" Single: Released May '61, on H.M.V., by EMI Records. Catalogue no: **POP 880**

Lost Boys

YOU NEVER LOVE ME
Tracks: / Feels like love / You never love me.
12" Single: Released Mar '87, on MCA, by MCA Records. Catalogue no: **MCAT 1121**
7" Single: Released Mar '87, on MCA, by MCA Records. Catalogue no: **MCA 1121**

Lost Cherries

MAN'S DUTY, A
Tracks: / Man's duty, A / Woman's place.
7" EP: Released Feb '84, on Mortarhate, by Mortarhate Records. Deleted '88. Catalogue no: **MORT 3**

NO FIGHTING NO WAR
Tracks: / No fighting no war.
7" Single: Released May '83, on Riot Clone, Catalogue no: **RCR 3**

UNWANTED CHILDREN
Tracks: / Unwanted children.
12" Single: Released Sep '85, on Mortarhate, by Mortarhate Records. Catalogue no: **MORT 12**

Lost Gringos

BARGELD
Tracks: / Bargeld / Amore.
7" Single: Released Aug '83, on Atatak, Catalogue no: **6275**

NIPPON SAMBA (EP)
12" Single: Released Aug '83, on Atatak, Catalogue no: **6260**

TROCA TROCA
12" Single: Released Jun '84, on Atatak, Catalogue no: **WR 24**

Lost In Bass

OUT ON A MISSION
Tracks: / Out on a mission.
7" Single: Released Apr '88, on Beatmaster, by Beatmaster Records. Catalogue no: **BEATM 1**
12" Single: Released Apr '88, on Beatmaster, by Beatmaster Records. Catalogue no: **BEATM 112**

Lost Jockey

PROFESSOR SLACK
Tracks: / Professor Slack.
7" Single: Released Jul '82, on Operation Twilight, Catalogue no: **OPT 011**

Lost Loved Ones

DARK THE
Tracks: / Dark, The.
7" Single: Released Sep '84, on Epic, by CBS Records. Catalogue no: **A 4718**
12" Single: Released Sep '84, on Epic, by CBS Records. Catalogue no: **TA 4718**

RAISE THE FLAG
Tracks: / Raise the flag.
12" Single: Released Feb '85, on Epic, by CBS Records. Catalogue no: **TX 5007**
7" Single: Released Feb '85, on Epic, by CBS Records. Catalogue no: **A 5007**

Lost Roberts

HELP ME
Tracks: / Help me / Shelby country.
7" Single: Released Feb '82, on Rising River, Catalogue no: **FLOOD 1**

Lost Rough Cause

VIOLENT FEW THE (EP)
7" Single: Released Sep '85, on LRC, Catalogue no: **LRC 1**

Lot 49

INNOCENT VICTIMS
Tracks: / Innocent victims.
7" Single: Released May '83, on Magic Moon, Catalogue no: **LOT 1**
12" Single: Released May '83, on Magic Moon, Catalogue no: **12 LOT 1**

Lotus Eaters

Biographical details: Peter Coyle and Jeremy Kelly were one of the numerous acts to emerge from the musically reinvigorated city of Liverpool during the early Eighties. Evolving from the Wild Swans, whose singe *A revolutionary spirit* was released on the fashionable local Zoo label in 1981, the Lotus Eaters came to fame in 1983 with their classy pop single *The first picture of you*. Released in June of that year, this was a text-book example of a summer love song. It was one of the season's biggest turntable hits, being heard incessantly on BBC Radio One; its chart progress was surprisingly slow, although it eventually edged up to the UK No.15 position. A considerable number of people named the catchy refreshing and delicate *The first picture of you* as their favourite single of '83. The Lotus Eaters failed to fulfil their early promise. Their next single *You don't need someone new* peaked at No.53 on the British listings, and their first and only album *No sense of sin* (June 1984) could only manage a No.96 placing on the LP chart. Although virtually all of their output was of high quality - good, modern pop with solid melodies and interesting lyrics - they suffered from a lack of a stable hardcore of fans, and from a slight sameness in their songs. By 1985 the charts were out of their reach and they were on the verge of splitting up. (Bob MacDonald, 18th Dec 1985).

FIRST PICTURE OF YOU, THE
Tracks: / First picture of you, The.
7" Single: Released '83, on Arista, by BMG Records (UK). Deleted '86. Catalogue no: **SYL 121**

FIRST PICTURE OF YOU, THE (OLD GOLD)
Tracks: / First picture of you, The / Hurry home.
7" Single: Released Jan '89, on Old Gold, by Old Gold Records. Catalogue no: **OG 9853**

IT HURTS
Tracks: / It hurts.
7" Single: Released Feb '85, on Sylvan, Deleted May '89. Catalogue no: **SYL 5**
12" Single: Released Feb '85, on Sylvan, Deleted May '89. Catalogue no: **SYL 125**

OUT ON YOUR OWN
Tracks: / Out on your own / Endless.
12" Single: Released Jun '84, on Sylvan, Catalogue no: **SYL 124**
7" Single: Released Jun '84, on Sylvan, Catalogue no: **SYL 4**

SET ME APART
Tracks: / Set me apart / My happy dream.
12" Single: Released Mar '84, on Sylvan, Catalogue no: **SYL 123**
7" Single: Released Mar '84, on Sylvan, Catalogue no: **SYL 3**

Lou

ROOKIES REVENGE
Tracks: / Rookies revenge / Rookies revenge (inst).
12" Single: Released Apr '88, on Supreme, by Supreme Records. Catalogue no: **SUPETX 123**
7" Single: Released Mar '88, on Supreme, by Supreme Records. Catalogue no: **SUPE 123**
12" Single: Released Mar '88, on Supreme, by Supreme Records. Catalogue no: **SUPET 123**

Lou, Bubba

LOVE YOU ALL OVER THE PLACE
Tracks: / Love you all over the place / Over you.
7" Single: Released Mar '81, on Stiff, by Stiff Records. Deleted Mar '84. Catalogue no: **BUYDJ 114**

Loudermilk, John D.

LANGUAGE OF LOVE
Tracks: / Language of love.
7" Single: Released Jan '62, on RCA, by BMG Records (UK). Deleted '65. Catalogue no: **RCA 1269**

Loudest Whisper

SPREAD YOUR WINGS
Tracks: / Spread your wings.
7" Single: Released May '86, on Ritz, by Ritz Records. Catalogue no: **RITZ 124**

Loudness

LET IT GO
Tracks: / Let it go / 1000 eyes / Ashes in the sky (Extra track on 12" version only.).
7" Single: Released Oct '86, on Atco, by Atlantic Recording Corp.(USA). Deleted Jun '87. Catalogue no: **B 9498**
12" Single: Released Oct '86, on Atco, by Atlantic Recording Corp.(USA). Deleted Jun '87. Catalogue no: **B 9498T**

ROADRACER
Tracks: / Roadracer / Shinkiro.
12" Single: Released Jun '84, on Music For Nations, by Music For Nations Records. Catalogue no: **12 KUT 110**

Loudspeaker

PSYCHOTIC MACHINE
Tracks: / Psychotic machine / Living with the dead.
12" Single: Released Aug '87, on One Little Indian, by One Little Indian Records. Catalogue no: **12TP 5**

Lougheed, Lisa

RUN WITH US
Tracks: / Run with us / Ain't no planes.
12" Single: Released Aug '88, on Ariola, by BMG Records (UK). Catalogue no: **611 713**

Louie Louie

CATHY'S CLOWN
Tracks: / Cathy's clown / Never take the blame / Cathy's clown (version) (12" only).
7" Single: Released Feb '89, on Virgin, by Virgin Records. Catalogue no: **VS 1172**
12" Single: Released Feb '89, on Virgin, by Virgin Records. Catalogue no: **VST 1172**

ONLY TIME WILL TELL
Tracks: / Only time will tell / In the packet.
12" Single: Released Aug '89, on Virgin, by Virgin Records. Catalogue no: **VST 1204**
7" Single: Released Aug '89, on Virgin, by Virgin Records. Catalogue no: **VS 1204**

Louis, Arthur

COME ON AND LOVE ME
Tracks: / Come on & love me.
7" Single: Released Aug '81, on Mainstreet, Deleted '83. Catalogue no: **MS 104**
12" Single: Released Aug '81, on Mainstreet, Deleted '83. Catalogue no: **12SP MS 104**

STILL IT FEELS GOOD
Tracks: / Still it feels good.
7" Single: Released Jul '81, on Mainstreet, Deleted '83. Catalogue no: **MS 104**

Louis, Lil

7 DAYS OF PEACE
Tracks: / 7 days of peace.
7" Single: Released Oct '88, on Dance Mania, Catalogue no: **DM 015**

FRENCH KISS (EP) The complete mix collection E.P.
Tracks: / French kiss (original mix) / French kiss (innocent until proven guilty) / French kiss (passion radio mix) / French kiss (back up your conversation mix) / French kiss (hitting virgin territory mix).
12" Single: Released Aug '89, on ffrr, by London Records. Catalogue no: **UNKNOWN**
Cassingle: Released Aug '89, on ffrr, by London Records. Catalogue no: **UNKNOWN**

FRENCH KISS (SINGLE)
Tracks: / French kiss / War games.
CD 5": Released 24 Jul '89, on ffrr, by London Records. Catalogue no: **FCD 115**
Cassingle: Released 24 Jul '89, on ffrr, by London Records. Catalogue no: **FCS 115**
12" Single: Released 24 Jul '89, on ffrr, by London Records. Catalogue no: **FX 115**

Lounge Jays

MASSAGE RAMA
Tracks: / Massage rama.
12" Single: Released Apr '89, on Mr.Modo, Catalogue no: **EMS 002T**

Loussier, Jacques

AIR ON THE G-STRING
Tracks: / Air on the G-string / Prelude no. 1.
7" Single: Released Mar '85, on Start, by Start Records Ltd.. Catalogue no: **STS 1**

KEEP LOVE ALIVE
Tracks: / Keep love alive / Whispering hope.
7" Single: Released Nov '82, on Starblend, by Starblend Records. Catalogue no: **STAR 1**

Love...

LOVE BALLADS
Special: Released Nov '84, on DM Streetsounds, Catalogue no: **ZCBAL 1**

LOVE HITS Various artists
Tracks: / Take good care of yourself: *Three Degrees* / Almost there: *Williams, Andy* / I left my heart in San Francisco: *Bennett, Tony* / How 'bout us: *Champaign* / Too much too little too late: *Williams, Deniece & Johnny Mathis* / Hurt: *Manhattans*.
7" EP: Released Mar '84, on Scoop 33, by Pickwick Records. Catalogue no: **7SR 5033**

Love Affair

Biographical details: At the time of their greatest success, this British pop group consisted of Maurice Bacon, Rex Brayley, Steve Ellis, Lynton Guest and Mick Jackson. At least, this was the official line-up; but members of the combo caused uproar across Britain in early 1968, when they admitted on Jonathan King's Saturday night TV show *Good evening* that their No.1 smash *Everlasting love* had been performed by session musicians, with the exception of the fine lead vocals of Steve Ellis. Such a practice was commonplace in the Sixties, but it was rarely admitted. In any case, the Love Affair's sound depended heavily on a big orchestra rather than upon the group's own guitar/keyboards/bass/drums line-up. The Love Affair came into being in London in late 1966, and were managed by Sid Bacon, the father of drummer Maurice. They spent the next year working on the London club circuit, including a residency at the Marquee. They then signed with CBS, and were taken under the wing of the label's top producer Mike Smith. In January '68 they shot to the UK No.1 spot with the supremely melodic *Everlasting love*, a cover version of Robert Knight's recent American hit. With predictability but shrewdness, another Knight record was chosen as the follow-up - *Rainbow Valley* reached No.5 on the British listings. The group's three final hits were all penned or co-penned by singer/songwriter Philip Goodhand-Tait, a fact which compensated for the consistent commercial failure of his own records. *A day without love* climbed to No.6 on the UK charts, *One road* peaked at No.16 and the magnificent *Bringing on back the good times* reached No.9. The fact that mattered most about Love Affair's 1968-69 hits was that they were great pop records, no matter who played on them. But as the Seventies dawned, the group's career collapsed amid a series of personnel changes and image switches. Despite an un-stable line-up, the Love Affair struggled on through the Seventies playing the cabaret and variety circuit. Upon Sid Bacon's death in 1974, his son assumed management responsibilities. A comeback attempt was launched in 1977 with the single *Private lives*; but although this was a good record, it was clearly stuck in a 1968 groove and flopped. (Bob MacDonald, 19th Dec 1985).

6 TRACK HITS
7" EP: Released Mar '84, on Scoop 33, by Pickwick Records. Catalogue no: **7SR 5037**

BRINGING ON BACK THE GOOD TIMES
Tracks: / Bringing on back the good times.
7" Single: Released Jul '69, on CBS, by CBS Records. Deleted '72. Catalogue no: **CBS 4300**

DAY WITHOUT LOVE, A
Tracks: / Day without love, A.
7" Single: Released Sep '68, on CBS, by CBS Records. Deleted '71. Catalogue no: **CBS 3674**

EVERLASTING LOVE
Tracks: / Everlasting love / Day without love, A.
7" Single: Released Jan '68, on CBS, by CBS Records. Deleted '71. Catalogue no: **CBS 3125**

EVERLASTING LOVE (OLD GOLD)
Tracks: / Everlasting love.
7" Single: Released Jul '82, on Old Gold, by Old Gold Records. Catalogue no: **OG 9194**

ONE ROAD
Tracks: / One road.
7" Single: Released Feb '69, on CBS, by CBS Records. Deleted '72. Catalogue no: **CBS 3994**

RAINBOW VALLEY
Tracks: / Rainbow valley.
7" Single: Released Jul '82, on Old Gold, by Old Gold Records. Catalogue no: **OG 9199**
7" Single: Released Apr '68, on CBS, by CBS Records. Deleted '71. Catalogue no: **CBS 3366**

WITCH QUEEN OF NEW ORLEANS
Tracks: / Witch Queen of New Orleans.
12" Single: Released Apr '87, on Hit The Deck, Deleted '88. Catalogue no: **CRUISE 1T**
7" Single: Released Jan '88, on Hit The Deck, Deleted '88. Catalogue no: **CRUISE 1**

Love, Brad

I'LL BE YOUR WARRIOR
Tracks: / I'll be your warrior / Colour me.
7" Single: Released Jan '83, on MCA, by MCA Records. Catalogue no: **MCA 807**

Love Bug

YOU CAN COUNT ON ME
Tracks: / You can count on me / You can't have it.
7" Single: Released May '86, on Roxy (1), Catalogue no: **TEASE 2**

Love Child Orchestra

WHOLE LOTTA LOVE
Tracks: / Whole lotta love / Experiment IV.
12" Single: Released May '89, on MCA, by MCA Records. Catalogue no: **HYMNT 1**
CD 5": Released May '89, on MCA, by MCA Records. Catalogue no: **DHYMN 1**
7" Single: Released May '89, on MCA, by MCA Records. Catalogue no: **HYMN 1**

Love, Darlene

CHRISTMAS (BABY PLEASE COME HOME)
Tracks: / Christmas (baby please come home) / White Christmas.
7" Single: Released Nov '82, on Spector (USA), by Spec's Music Records (USA). Catalogue no: **SPEC 1**

HE'S SURE THE MAN I LOVE
Tracks: / He's sure the man I love / Everybody needs / My heart is a clock.
7" Single: Released Jan '89, on CBS, by CBS Records. Deleted 10 Jul '89. Catalogue no: **652 935-7**
CD 5": Released Jan '89, on CBS, by CBS Records. Deleted 10 Jul '89. Catalogue no: **652 935-2**
12" Single: Released Jan '89, on CBS, by CBS Records. Deleted 10 Jul '89. Catalogue no: **652 935-6**

Love De Luxe

GOOD MUSIC
Tracks: / Good music / Keep down.
7" Single: Released Feb '81, on WEA, by WEA Records. Deleted Feb '84. Catalogue no: **K 18392**

KEEP DOWN
Tracks: / Keep down / You're a fantasy.
7" Single: Released May '80, on Atlantic, by WEA Records. Deleted May '83. Catalogue no: **K 11478**

Love Decree

SOMETHING SO REAL
Tracks: / Something so real.
12" Single: Released Sep '89, on RCA, by BMG Records (UK). Catalogue no: **612642**
CD 5": Released Sep '89, on RCA, by BMG Records (UK). Catalogue no: **662642**
7" Single: Released Sep '89, on RCA, by BMG Records (UK). Catalogue no: **112642**

Love, Geoff

LAMBETH WALK (STREET PARTY)
Tracks: / Lambeth walk.
7" Single: Released Nov '84, on Columbia, by EMI Records. Deleted '87. Catalogue no: **DB 9098**

Love, Gerald

GOING TO PARTY (HEY JULEY)
Tracks: / Going to party.
7" Single: Released May '84, on Moltwo, Catalogue no: **MOLT 1**

Love Gone Wrong

WORLD UPSIDE DOWN
Tracks: / World upside down.
7" Single: Released Nov '88, on Mighty Boy, by Mighty Boy Records. Catalogue no: **MB 20097**

Love, Joeski

PEE-WEE'S DANCE
Tracks: / Pee-Wee's dance / Pee-Wee's dance (Instrumental).
12" Single: Released '86, on Cool Tempo, by Chrysalis Records. Catalogue no: **COOLX 125**

Love Jungle

MAKE ME SPECIAL
Tracks: / Make me special.
12" Single: Released Jun '89, on Sugar Shack, by Sugar Shack Records. Catalogue no: **FOD 5**
7" Single: Released Jul '89, on Sugar Shack, by Sugar Shack Records. Catalogue no: **7 FOD 5**

Love Machine

DEPUTY OF LOVE MACHINE Featuring Rose Windross
Tracks: / Deputy of love machine, The.
12" Single: Released Jan '89, on Rap Sonic, by Rapsonic Records. Catalogue no: **YARD TR 5**

LOVE MACHINE
Tracks: / Love machine.
12" Single: Released 28 Dec '88, on Danceyard, by Danceyard Records. Catalogue no: **YARD T5**
7" Single: Released 28 Dec '88, on Danceyard, by Danceyard Records. Catalogue no: **YARD 5**
12" Single: Released Nov '88, on Pepper, by Pepper Records. Catalogue no: **PEP 2**

Love, Mary

YOU TURNED MY BITTER INTO SWEET
Tracks: / You turned my bitter into sweet / I can't get enough / This couldn't be me.
7" Single: Released Nov '82, on Kent, by Ace Records. Catalogue no: **TOWN 501**

Love, Mike

JINGLE BELL ROCK
Tracks: / Jingle bell rock / Let's party.
7" Single: Released Nov '83, on Creole, by Creole Records. Catalogue no: **CR 61**
12" Single: Released Nov '83, on Creole, by Creole Records. Catalogue no: **CR 1261**

Love & Money

CANDYBAR EXPRESS
Tracks: / Candybar express / Love and money (Dub).
7" Single: Released Apr '86, on Mercury, by Phonogram Ltd. Deleted Dec '87. Catalogue no: **MONEY1**
12" Single: Released Apr '86, on Mercury, by Phonogram Ltd. Catalogue no: **MONEY12**

DEAR JOHN
Tracks: / Dear John / Jane / Fame (Extra track on 12"version only.) / Shape of things to come.
7" Single: Released Mar '82, on Mercury, by Phonogram Ltd. Deleted '87. Catalogue no: **QUO 7**
7" Single: Released Jul '86, on Mercury, by Phonogram Ltd. Deleted '87. Catalogue no: **MER 228**
12" Single: Released Jul '86, on Mercury, by Phonogram Ltd. Deleted '87. Catalogue no: **MERX 228**

HALLELUIAH MAN
Tracks: / Hallelujah man / Love is a million miles away / She carved her name (Only on the 12" single and the CD single.) / Wanderlust 2 (Only on CD single.).
12" Single: Released Sep '88, on Mercury, by Phonogram Ltd. Deleted 31 May '89. Catalogue no: **MONEY 512**
CD 5": Released Sep '88, on Mercury, by Phonogram Ltd. Catalogue no: **MONCD 5**
7" Single: Released Sep '88, on Mercury, by Phonogram Ltd. Deleted 31 May '89. Catalogue no: **MONEY 5**

JOCELYN SQUARE
Tracks: / Jocelyn square / St. Henry / Rosemary / Candybar express / Up escalator (on MONEY 722 only) / River of people (Available on MONEY 722 only).
12" Single: Released Mar '89, on Fontana, by Phonogram Ltd. Catalogue no: **MONEY 722**
CD 5": Released 13 Mar '89, on Mercury, by Phonogram Ltd. Catalogue no: **MONEY 7 CD**
7" Single: Released 13 Mar '89, on Mercury, by Phonogram Ltd. Catalogue no: **MONEY 7**
12" Single: Released 13 Mar '89, on Mercury, by Phonogram Ltd. Catalogue no: **MONEY 712**

LOVE & MONEY
Tracks: / Love & money / Home is where the heart is.
12" Single: Released Mar '87, on Mercury, by Phonogram Ltd. Deleted Dec '87. Catalogue no: **MONEY 4-12**
7" Single: Released Mar '87, on Mercury, by Phonogram Ltd. Deleted Dec '87. Catalogue no: **MONEY 4**

RIVER OF PEOPLE
Tracks: / River of people / Desire / Candybar express (Extra track available on 12" only.).
7" Single: Released Jan '87, on Mercury, by Phonogram Ltd. Deleted Jul '87. Catalogue no: **MONEY 3**
12" Single: Released Jan '87, on Mercury, by Phonogram Ltd. Deleted Jul '87. Catalogue no: **MONEY 312**

STRANGE KIND OF LOVE (SINGLE)
Tracks: / Looking for Angeline / Scapegoat / Set the night on fire / Strange kind of love.
Special: Released Jan '89, on Phonogram, by Phonogram Ltd. Catalogue no: **MONEY 66**
CD 5": Released Jan '89, on Phonogram, by Phonogram Ltd. Catalogue no: **MONCD 6**
7" Single: Released Jan '89, on Phonogram, by Phonogram Ltd. Catalogue no: **MONEY 6**
12" Single: Released Jan '89, on Phonogram, by Phonogram Ltd. Catalogue no: **MONEY 612**

UP ESCALATOR

MONIE LOVE - I CAN DO THIS (Released on Cool Tempo)

Tracks: / Up escalator / Soon / Thistle kiss (Available on 12" format.) / History (Available on 12" format).
7" Single: Released Oct '89, on Fontana, by Phonogram Ltd. Catalogue no: **MONEY 8**
CD 5": Released Oct '89, on Fontana, by Phonogram Ltd. Catalogue no: **MONCD 8**
Cassingle: Released Oct '89, on Fontana, by Phonogram Ltd. Catalogue no: **MONMC 8**
12" Single: Released Oct '89, on Fontana, by Phonogram Ltd. Catalogue no: **MONEY 812**

Love, Monie

I CAN DO THIS (see panel above)
Tracks: / I can do this / Feels so good.
7" Single: Released Jan '89, on Cool Tempo, by Chrysalis Records. Catalogue no: **COOL 177**
12" Single: Released Feb '89, on Cool Tempo, by Chrysalis Records. Catalogue no: **COOLXR 177**
12" Single: Released Jan '89, on Cool Tempo, by Chrysalis Records. Catalogue no: **COOLX 177**

Love, Mr & Eternity

MR.LOVE
Tracks: / Mr. Love.
12" Single: Released Feb '89, on Gee Street, by Gee Street Records. Catalogue no: **GEET 13**
7" Single: Released Feb '89, on Gee Street, by Gee Street Records. Catalogue no: **GEE 13**

Love Of Life Orchestra

BEGINNING OF THE HEARTACHE
Tracks: / Beginning of the heartache / Extended niceties.
7" Single: Released Mar '81, on Beggars Banquet, by Beggars Banquet Records. Deleted Mar '84. Catalogue no: **TBET 2**

Love & Rockets

BALL OF CONFUSION
Tracks: / Ball of confusion / Inside the outside.
12" Single: Released May '85, on Beggars Banquet, by Beggars Banquet Records. Catalogue no: **BEG 132T**
7" Single: Released May '85, on Beggars Banquet, by Beggars Banquet Records. Catalogue no: **BEG 132**

IF THERE'S A HEAVEN ABOVE
Tracks: / If there's a heaven above.
12" Single: Released Aug '85, on Beggars Banquet, by Beggars Banquet Records. Catalogue no: **BEG 146T**
7" Single: Released Aug '85, on Beggars Banquet, by Beggars Banquet Records. Deleted Jan '88. Catalogue no: **BEG 146**

KUNDALINI EXPRESS
Tracks: / Kundalini Express / Lucifer Sam / Holiday on the moon.
12" Single: Released May '87, on Beggars Banquet, by Beggars Banquet Records. Catalogue no: **BEG 163T**

LAZY
Tracks: / Lazy / Dog end of a day gone by, The / Purest blue, The (12" only).
12" Single: Released 22 Aug '88, on Beggars Banquet, by Beggars Banquet Records. Catalogue no: **BEG 217T**
7" Single: Released 22 Aug '88, on Beggars Banquet, by Beggars Banquet Records. Catalogue no: **BEG 217**

LIGHT, THE
Tracks: / Light, The / Mirror people.
7" Single: Released Oct '87, on Beggars Banquet, by Beggars Banquet Records. Deleted Jun '88. Catalogue no: **BEG 186**
12" Single: Released Oct '87, on Beggars Banquet, by Beggars Banquet Records. Catalogue no: **BEG 186T**

MIRROR PEOPLE
Tracks: / Mirror people.
12" Single: Released May '88, on Beggars Banquet, by Beggars Banquet Records. Catalogue no: **BEG 213T**
7" Single: Released May '88, on Beggars Banquet, by Beggars Banquet Records. Catalogue no: **BEG 213**

MOTORCYCLE
Tracks: / Motorcycle.
12" Single: Released Dec '88, on Beggars Banquet, by Beggars Banquet Records. Catalogue no: **BEG 224T**

NO BIG DEAL
Tracks: / No big deal / No words / 1,000 watts (Available on 12" format only.).
7" Single: Released Sep '89, on Beggars Banquet, by Beggars Banquet Records. Catalogue no: **BEG 234**
12" Single: Released Sep '89, on Beggars Banquet, by Beggars Banquet Records. Catalogue no: **BEG 234T**

NO NEW TALE TO TELL
Tracks: / No new tale to tell / Earth sun moon / Seventh dream of teenage heaven (Extra track on 12" version.) / Love me (Extra track on 12" version.).
7" Single: Released Mar '88, on Beggars Banquet, by Beggars Banquet Records. Catalogue no: **BEG 209**
12" Single: Released Mar '88, on Beggars Banquet, by Beggars Banquet Records. Catalogue no: **BEG 209T**

SO ALIVE
Tracks: / So alive.
7" Single: Released Jul '89, on Beggars Banquet, by Beggars Banquet Records. Catalogue no: **BEG 229**
CD 5": Released Jul '89, on Beggars Banquet, by Beggars Banquet Records. Catalogue no: **BEG 229CD**
12" Single: Released Jul '89, on Beggars Banquet, by Beggars Banquet Records. Catalogue no: **BEG 229 T**

YIN AND YANG (THE FLOWER POT MAN)
Tracks: / Yin and Yang (The flower pot men) / Angels and Devils.
12" Single: Released Sep '86, on Beggars Banquet, by Beggars Banquet Records. Catalogue no: **BEG 166T**
7" Single: Released Sep '86, on Beggars Banquet, by Beggars Banquet Records. Deleted Jan '88. Catalogue no: **BEG 166**

Love Sculpture

Biographical details: This British rock band consisted of Dave Edmunds, Bob Jones and John Williams. Love Sculpture came into being in Cardiff in 1968, having evolved from local small-time groups. The talented instrumental trio shot to fame at the end of that year with their frantic 100mph rendition of Khachaturian's *Sabre dance*. This daring and stunning remake of a pre-pop standare reached no.5 on the charts. This was the trio's only taste of chart success - their other singles flopped,as did their interesting albums *Blues helping* (1968), and *Forms and feelings* (1969). Most of the group's work was in a boogie blues style. Love Sculpture folded after a badly organised American tour. The trio's standout musician, guitar wizard Dave Edmunds, launched a solo career in late 1970 - although his success has been spasmodic, his staying power is emphasized by the fact that his two biggest hit occurred in 1970 (his own smash *I hear you knocking*) and 1985 (as producer of Shakin' Stevens' *Merry Christmas everyone*). (Bob Macdonald, 19/12/85).

SABRE DANCE
Tracks: / Sabre dance.
7" Single: Released Nov '68, on Parlophone, by EMI Records. Deleted '71. Catalogue no: **R 5744**

SABRE DANCE (OLD GOLD SERIES)
Tracks: / Sabre dance / My white bicycle.
7" Single: Released Oct '83, on Old Gold, by Old Gold Records. Catalogue no: **OG 9386**

Love Street

GALAXY
Tracks: / Galaxy / Come on down to Love Street / Galaxy / Come on down to Love Street (Mix that mutha) (Track on 12" single only.).
Note: (P) 1988 Original sound recordings made by EMI Records Ltd.l
12" Single: Released Jul '88, on EMI, by EMI Records. Deleted Nov '88. Catalogue no: **12RX 6183**
7" Single: Released Jan '78, on MCA, by MCA Records. Deleted '81. Catalogue no: **MCA 339**
12" Single: Released Jun '88, on EMI, by EMI Records. Deleted Nov '88. Catalogue no: **12R 6183**
7" Single: Released Jun '88, on EMI, by EMI Records. Deleted Nov '88. Catalogue no: **R 6183**

Love Symphony

LET ME BE YOUR FANTASY
Tracks: / Let me be your fantasy / You're so right for me.
12" Single: Released May '81, on Excaliber, by Red Bus Records. Deleted May '84. Catalogue no: **EXCL 101**
7" Single: Released May '81, on Excaliber, by Red Bus Records. Deleted May '84. Catalogue no: **EXC 101**

Love Tractor

PARTY TRAIN
Tracks: / Party train / Got to give it up* / Rudolf Nureyev / Party train**.
Note: *Available on 12" only. **Available on 12" and also a 7" mix.
12" Single: Released Oct '87, on Big Time Records, by Big Time Records. Deleted May '89. Catalogue no: **ZT 41422**
7" Single: Released Oct '87, on Big Time Records, by Big Time Records. Deleted May '89. Catalogue no: **ZB 41421**

Love Train (group)

LIGHTEN UP
Tracks: / Lighten up / Wanting seed, The / Lighten up (extended remix) (12" only).
Note: The debut single from the 5-man combo. Lovetrain veer between eloquent rhythmic pop, which isn't afraid of melodies and persuasive, refreshingly candid tales of unrequited love. (Virgin release sheet October 88).
7" Single: Released 17 Oct '88, on Siren, by Virgin Records. Catalogue no: **SRN 96**
12" Single: Released 17 Oct '88, on Siren, by Virgin Records. Catalogue no: **SRNT 96**

RAGS TO RICHES TO RAGS
Tracks: / Rags to riches to rags / Murder on the love train express / When the breakdown comes (12" only) / Cardboard City (Only on 12" single.).
Cassingle: Released Jul '89, on Siren, by Virgin Records. Catalogue no: **SRNC 116**
CD 3": Released Jul '89, on Siren, by Virgin Records. Catalogue no: **SRNCD 116**
7" Single: Released Jul '89, on Siren, by Virgin Records. Catalogue no: **SRN 116**
12" Single: Released Jul '89, on Siren, by Virgin Records. Catalogue no: **SRNT 116**

WAY OF ALL FLESH, THE
Tracks: / Way of all flesh, The / Untitled no.1 / Jack of all hearts (Available on 12" only) / Beating like a drum (on 12" only.).
12" Single: Released 27 Mar '89, on Siren, by Virgin Records. Catalogue no: **SRNT 103**
CD 5": Released 27 Mar '89, on Siren, by Virgin Records. Catalogue no: **SRNCD 103**
7" Single: Released 27 Mar '89, on Siren, by Virgin Records. Catalogue no: **SRN 103**

Love Unlimited

Biographical details: Both Love Unlimited and the Love Unlimited Orchestra were controlled by the American musical all-rounder Barry White. While still in his late teens, he played on Bob & Earl's acclaimed 1963 single *Harlem shuffle*. He soon began to gain experience as a producer and A&R executive, and achieved a one-off British Top 20 hit in 1967 as producer and co-writer of Felice Taylor's *I feel love comin' on*. At the end of the 60's, he took three back-up singers under his wing and formed them into a female vocal trio, which he christened Love Unlimited. One member became his wife (Glodean James). White became the group's manager and mentor and spent three years grooming them for stardom. The girls broke big in 1972, hitting no.14 on both sides of the Atlantic with *Walkin' in the rain with the one I love*. This slushy single was written and produced by Barry; and it introduced the world to his lush orchestral arrangements and, via a spoken telephonic passage in the song, to his voice. *Walkin' in the rain* provided White with a launching pad on which to begin his solo career, which ran successfully throughout the 70's. Meanwhile, his success with Love Unlimited was shorter lived - although the material he provided was similar to that he recorded himself, the women's nondescript voices did not measure up to his own distinctive vocal style. After *Walkin'., the trio's only top 40 successes were I belong to you* and *It may be winter outside* (both 1975)
The Love Unlimited Orchetra was the 41-piece ensemble that White used to back his records and those of the trio. The Orchestra achieved its own smash in 74 with *Love's theme*, a beautiful single written and produced by White. This track reached no.1 in the US and no.10 in the UK; it was also the first cut on the Love Unlimited album *Under the influence of Love Unlimited*. Several of the orchestra's own LP's were released during the 70's and 80's, but like butch Barry's own discs, they quickly became stale and unnecessary. The whole Barry White package had had its roots in soul music, but veered towards and increasingly MoR style. (Bob Macdonald, 19/12/85).

HIGH STEPPIN' FELLA
Tracks: / High steppin' fella.
7" Single: Released Jan '80, on CBS, by CBS Records. Deleted Jan '83. Catalogue no: **ULG 8161**

IT MAY BE WINTER OUTSIDE
Tracks: / It may be winter outside.
7" Single: Released Jan '75, on 20th Century, by 20th Century Records. Deleted '78. Catalogue no: **BTC 2149**

LOVE'S THEME
Tracks: / Love's theme / It may be winter outside.
7" Single: Released Aug '81, on 20th Century, by 20th Century Records. Catalogue no: **GOLD 529**
7" Single: Released '74, on Pye International, Deleted '77. Catalogue no: **7N 25635**

LOVE'S THEME (OLD GOLD)
Tracks: / Love's theme / Walking in the rain with the one I love.
7" Single: Released Feb '88, on Old Gold, by Old Gold Records. Catalogue no: **OG 9769**

WALKIN' IN THE RAIN WITH THE ONE I LOVE
Tracks: / Walking in the rain with the one I love.
7" Single: Released '80, on 20th Century, by 20th Century Records. Catalogue no: **LR 1472**
7" Single: Released Jun '72, on UNI, by MCA Records. Deleted '75. Catalogue no: **UN 539**

Lovebug Starski

AMITYVILLE (THE HOUSE ON THE HILL)
Tracks: / Amityville (House on the Hill) / Amityville (Dub mix).
12" Single: Released May '86, on Def Jam, Catalogue no: **TA 7182**
7" Single: Released May '86, on Def Jam, Deleted '86. Catalogue no: **A 7182**

HOUSE ROCKER (SINGLE)
Tracks: / House rocker / House rocker (version) (On A 6952 & TA 6952 only) /

House rocker (concrete mix) (On DTA 6952 only).
12" Single: Released '86, on Epic, by CBS Records. Deleted '87. Catalogue no: **DTA 6952**
12" Single: Released '86, on Epic, by CBS Records. Deleted '87. Catalogue no: **TA 6952**
7" Single: Released '86, on Epic, by CBS Records. Deleted '87. Catalogue no: **A 6952**

SATURDAY NIGHT
Tracks: / Saturday night / Positive life.
12" Single: Released '86, on CBS, by CBS Records. Deleted '87. Catalogue no: **650112 0**
7" Single: Released '86, on CBS, by CBS Records. Deleted '87. Catalogue no: **650112 7**

Lovejoys

GIMMEEBACK
Tracks: / Gimmeeback / It ain't easy.
12" Single: Released Oct '83, on Wackies. Catalogue no: **WACKIES 707**

LET ME ROCK YOU
Tracks: / Let me rock you / Stranger.
12" Single: Released Jul '82, on Solid Groove. Catalogue no: **SG 016**

Lovelady, Bill

HOUSE OF THE RISING SUN
Tracks: / House of the rising sun / Facade.
7" Single: Released Feb '81, on Charisma, by Virgin Records. Deleted Feb '84. Catalogue no: **CB 379**

REGGAE FOR IT NOW
Tracks: / Reggae for it now.
7" Single: Released Aug '79, on Charisma, by Virgin Records. Deleted '82. Catalogue no: **CB 337**

SHE DONE ME IN
Tracks: / She done me in / Double indemnity.
7" Single: Released May '80, on Charisma, by Virgin Records. Deleted May '83. Catalogue no: **CB 361**

TOUGH GUYS DON'T DANCE
Tracks: / Tough guys don't dance / Tough guys don't dance (inst) / Why should she be different.
12" Single: Released Feb '88, on Ariola, by BMG Records (UK). Catalogue no: **609 831**
7" Single: Released Feb '88, on Ariola, by BMG Records (UK). Catalogue no: **109 831**

Loveless

KISS THAT CRAZY CORPSE
Tracks: / Kiss that crazy corpse.
7" Single: Released Aug '85, on Fragile. Deleted '88. Catalogue no: **FR 18**

Loveless, Patty

I DID
Tracks: / I did / Lonely days lonely nights.
7" Single: Released Jul '87, on MCA, by MCA Records. Catalogue no: **MCA 1158**

Lovely Eye

DON'T LOOK DOWN THE ROAD
Tracks: / Don't look down the road / Farewell.
Note: 12" includes an interview with Oracle.
7" Single: Released May '88, on Clarkesville, by Complete Music Ltd. Catalogue no: **CLARK 1**
12" Single: Released May '88, on Clarkesville, by Complete Music Ltd. Catalogue no: **12CLARK 1**

Lover Boy

BREAK IT TO ME GENTLY
Tracks: / Break it to me gently / Read my lips / Working for the weekend (Only on 12" single.).
12" Single: Released 23 Apr '88, on CBS, by CBS Records. Deleted Jan '89. Catalogue no: **651 459 8**
CD 5": Released Mar '88, on CBS, by CBS Records. Deleted Jan '89. Catalogue no: **651 459 2**
7" Single: Released Mar '88, on CBS, by CBS Records. Deleted Aug '88. Catalogue no: **651 459 7**
12" Single: Released Mar '88, on CBS, by CBS Records. Deleted Aug '88. Catalogue no: **651 459 6**

GWAN GO DANCE
Tracks: / Gwan go dance.
12" Single: Released Nov '86, on Rockas. Catalogue no: **R 005RV**

HEAVEN IN YOUR EYES
Tracks: / Heaven in your eyes / Friday night / Loving every minute of it.
Note: "= extra track on 12" version only.
7" Single: Released Jan '87, on CBS, by CBS Records. Deleted Aug '87. Catalogue no: **650144 7**

MICHAEL LOVESMITH - AIN'T NOTHIN' LIKE IT (Released on Motown)

12" Single: Released Jan '87, on CBS, by CBS Records. Deleted Aug '87. Catalogue no: **650144 6**

NOTORIOUS
Tracks: / Notorious / Wild side.
7" Single: Released Sep '87, on CBS, by CBS Records. Deleted Aug '88. Catalogue no: **651 060 7**
12" Single: Released Sep '87, on CBS, by CBS Records. Deleted Aug '88. Catalogue no: **651 060 8**
7" Pic: Released Oct '87, on CBS, by CBS Records. Deleted Aug '88. Catalogue no: **651 060 0**

THIS COULD BE THE NIGHT
Tracks: / This could be the night / It's your life.
7" Single: Released Mar '86, on CBS, by CBS Records. Catalogue no: **A 6950**

TURN ME LOOSE
Tracks: / Turn me loose / Prissy prissy.
7" Single: Released Feb '81, on CBS, by CBS Records. Deleted Feb '84. Catalogue no: **CBS 9557**
7" Single: Released Jul '81, on CBS, by CBS Records. Deleted '85. Catalogue no: **A 1371**

WORKING FOR THE WEEKEND
Tracks: / Working for the weekend / Emotional.
7" Single: Released Jan '82, on CBS, by CBS Records. Deleted Jan '85. Catalogue no: **CBS 1778**

Lover Speaks

EVERY LOVER'S SIGN
Tracks: / Every lover's sign / Every lover's sign (Dub Mix).
7" Single: Released '86, on A&M, by A&M Records. Deleted Mar '88. Catalogue no: **AM 361**
12" Single: Released '86, on A&M, by A&M Records. Deleted '88. Catalogue no: **AMY 361**

I CLOSE MY EYES AND COUNT TO TEN
Tracks: / I close my eyes and count to ten / Never forget you.
12" Single: Released Feb '87, on A&M, by A&M Records. Deleted Mar '88. Catalogue no: **AMY 378**
7" Single: Released Feb '87, on A&M, by A&M Records. Deleted Mar '88. Catalogue no: **AM 378**

NO MORE I LOVE YOUS
Tracks: / No more I love yous / Of tears / This can t go on (Extra track on 12" version only.) / Tremble dancing / I close my eyes and count to ten (Track on 12" only.).
Note: Originally released 1986.
7" Single: Released Mar '88, on A&M, by A&M Records. Deleted Feb '89. Catalogue no: **AM 438**
CD 5": Released Mar '88, on A&M, by A&M Records. Catalogue no: **CD 438**
10" single: Released Mar '88, on MCA, by MCA Records. Catalogue no: **MCAV 1236**
12" Single: Released Mar '88, on A&M, by A&M Records. Deleted Aug '88. Catalogue no: **AMY 438**

TREMBLE DANCING
Tracks: / Tremble dancing / Still faking this art of love / This could be the night / It's your life.
12" Single: Released '86, on A&M, by A&M Records. Deleted '88. Catalogue no: **AMY 347**
7" Single: Released '86, on A&M, by A&M Records. Deleted '88. Catalogue no: **AM 347**
7" Single: Released '86, on CBS, by CBS Records. Catalogue no: **A 6950**

Loverde

IKO IKO
Tracks: / Iko iko / San Francisco serenade.
7" Single: Released May '81, on EMI, by EMI Records. Deleted May '84. Catalogue no: **12 EMI 5181**

Lovesmith, Michael

AIN'T NOTHIN' LIKE IT (see panel above)
Tracks: / Ain't nothing like it / Fast girls.
7" Single: Released Sep '85, on Motown, by BMG Records (UK). Catalogue no: **ZB 40369**
12" Single: Released Sep '85, on Motown, by BMG Records (UK). Catalogue no: **ZT 40370**

BABY I WILL
Tracks: / Baby I will.
7" Single: Released Jul '83, on Motown, by BMG Records (UK). Catalogue no: **TMG 1311**
12" Single: Released Jul '83, on Motown, by BMG Records (UK). Catalogue no: **TMGT 1311**

BREAK THE ICE
Tracks: / Break the ice.
12" Single: Released Jul '85, on Motown, by BMG Records (UK). Catalogue no: **ZT 40274**
7" Single: Released Jul '85, on Motown, by BMG Records (UK). Catalogue no: **ZB 40273**

Lovett, Eddie

GYPSY GIRL
Tracks: / Gypsy girl / Heaven must be missing an angel.
12" Single: Released Dec '83, on K & K, by K & K Records. Catalogue no: **PKD 10021**

SHINING STAR
Tracks: / Shining star.
7" Single: Released Oct '81, on KR. Catalogue no: **KR 3**
12" Single: Released Oct '81, on KR. Catalogue no: **KRT 3**

Lovett, Lyle

COWBOY MAN (SINGLE)
Tracks: / Cowboy man.
7" Single: Released 21 Nov '87, on MCA, by MCA Records. Catalogue no: **MCA 1222**

SHE'S NO LADY
Tracks: / She's no lady / Pontiac / You can't resist it".
7" Single: Released May '88, on MCA, by MCA Records. Catalogue no: **MCA 1254**
12" Single: Released May '88, on MCA, by MCA Records. Catalogue no: **MCAT 1254**

STAND BY YOUR MAN
Tracks: / Stand by your man.
CD 5": Released 28 Mar '89, on MCA, by MCA Records. Catalogue no: **DMCAT 1322**
7" Single: Released 28 Mar '89, on MCA, by MCA Records. Catalogue no: **MCA 1322**

WALK THROUGH THE BOTTOMLAND
Tracks: / Walk through the bottomland (Featuring Emmylou Harris.) / Simple song / This old porch (Extra track on 12".).
12" Single: Released Feb '88, on MCA, by MCA Records. Catalogue no: **MCAT 1234**
7" Single: Released Feb '88, on MCA, by MCA Records. Catalogue no: **MCA 1234**

YOU CAN'T RESIST IT
Tracks: / You can't resist it.
7" Single: Released Jul '89, on MCA, by MCA Records. Catalogue no: **MCA 1355**
CD 5": Released Jul '89, on MCA, by MCA Records. Catalogue no: **DMCAT 1355**
7" Single: Released Jul '87, on MCA, by MCA Records. Catalogue no: **MCA 1165**

Lovette Ruff-Neck...

EMOTIONS
Tracks: / Emotions.

LENE LOVICH - LUCKY NUMBER (Released on Stiff)

12" Single: Released Oct '88, on RNB, Catalogue no: **RNB 022**

Lovich, Lene

Biographical details: This American singer, saxophonist and songwriter enjoyed a brief period of success in Britain during the late 70's and early 80's while remaining virtually unknown at home. She was born in Detroit, the daughter of a Yugoslav father and an English mother. At the age of 13 she moved to the UK with her mother but ran away from home two years later. She eventually became a pupil at London's Central school of Art where she studied sculpture; she met a fellow art school student called Les Chappell, with whom she formed a long term songwriting partnership. The pair briefly became members of a band called the Diversions, but their only LP was never released by Polydor. Lovich's big break occurred in 1978, when she joined the UK's independent Stiff label; this New Wave-orientated company's policy was to sign idiosyncratic acts who had been rejected by the conservative majors. The weird but wonderful Lovich issued her debut album *Stateless* in '78, the same year that she was the most talked about attraction on one of Stiff's legendary package tours. In a Britain that was still feeling the effects of the punk revolution, an "anything-goes" attitude was prevalent in the music press and, to a certain extent, the charts. Lene's jerky singing, quirky songwriting and theatrical appearance were sufficiently freaky to attract major interest. This reflected itself in the success of her first and biggest chart entry *Lucky number*, which sprang to no. 3 in 1979. It was followed by *Say when*, which climbed to no. 19. A series of minor hits followed but she could not sustain the interest, although her 1980 album *Flex* made a brief appearance in the UK Top 20. By this time she was married to Chappell. During the early 80's Lovich carved out a moderate acting career for herself, although she continued recording and touring. (Bob Macdonald, 19/12/85).

ANGELS
Tracks: / Angels / Fly.
12" Single: Released Jan '80, on Stiff, by Stiff Records. Deleted Jan '83. Catalogue no: **12 BUY 63**
7" Single: Released Jan '80, on Stiff, by Stiff Records. Catalogue no: **BUY 63**

BIRD SONG
Tracks: / Bird song.
7" Single: Released Sep '79, on Stiff, by Stiff Records. Catalogue no: **BUY 53**

IT'S YOU,ONLY YOU(MEIN SCHMERZ)
Tracks: / It's you,only you(mein schmerz).
7" Single: Released Oct '82, on Stiff, by Stiff Records. Catalogue no: **BUY 164**

LUCKY NUMBER
Tracks: / Lucky number / Home.
7" Single: Released Feb '79, on Stiff, by Stiff Records. Deleted '82. Catalogue no: **BUY 42**
7" Single: Released May '82, on Stiff, by Stiff Records. Catalogue no: **BUY 149**

NEW TOY
Tracks: / New toy / Cat's away.
7" Single: Released Feb '81, on Stiff, by Stiff Records. Catalogue no: **BUY 97**
12" Single: Released Feb '81, on Stiff, by Stiff Records. Catalogue no: **BUYIT 97**

SAY WHEN
Tracks: / Say when.
7" Single: Released May '79, on Stiff, by Stiff Records. Deleted '82. Catalogue no: **BUY 46**

WHAT WILL I DO WITHOUT YOU
Tracks: / What will I do without you / Joan / Monkey talk / Night / Too tender / You can't kill me.
7" Set: Released Mar '80, on Stiff, by Stiff Records. Catalogue no: **BUY 69**

Lovin' Spoonful

Biographical details: This American rock group consisted of Steve Boone, Joe Butler, John Sebastian and Zal Yanovsky. Their extraordinary name was inspired by a line in a song by bluesman Mississippi John Hurt. Formed in 1964, The Lovin' Spoonful were a refreshing combo who enjoyed brief but huge US chart success in the mid sixties by providing an imaginative alternative to the Beatles led British boom. Although the Spoonful shared the fab four's good time attitude and sense of humour, and were indeed influenced by the Beatles, their other musical components included folk rock, Beach Boys type summery sounds and thirties style jug band influence. The group's rise to fame was fairly rapid. They hit it big with their first single *Do you believe in magic?*, which reached the US no.9 position

Nick Lowe - Cruel to be Kind (Released on Radar)

in late 1965. This opened the door for a run of historic American hits, which gave the Spoonful the extraordinary achievement of hitting the US top 10 with each of their first seven singles: *Do you believe in magic* (no.9), *You didn't have to be so nice* (no.10), *Daydream* (no.2 in US and UK), *Did you ever have to make up your mind?* (no.2), *Summer in the city* (no.1 in US, no.8 in UK), *Rain on the roof* (no.10) and *Nashville cats* (no.8 in US, no.26 in UK). Lovin' Spoonful leader John Sebastion was the outfit's key songwriter; in 1967 he was commisioned the score for the first Francis Ford Coppola film *You're a big boy now* - this yielded another hit for the group in the shape of the song *Darling be home soon.* But in the same year, the combo went into sharp decline, a situation hastily accelerated by Yanovsky's San Francisco drug bust - faced with the threat of deportation, the Canadian born guitarist incriminated various other members of the city's druggy scene in order to gain his own release. The whole affair destroyed the Spoonful's image of a wholesome, good time group and caused them to be shunned by other members of the rock profession who deplored Zal's informing tactic. Some observers considered the Lovin' Spoonful to be THE group of'66, but by 1968 the hits had stopped coming and the combo collapsed. All four members drifted into obscurity. There was, however,a brief return to fame for Sebastian in 1976: ten years after his heyday, he reached no.1 in America with *Welcome back* his exuberant theme from the John Travolta TV series *Welcome back, Kotter.* (Bob Macdonald 85).

DARLING BE HOME SOON
Tracks: / Darling be home soon.
7" Single: Released Mar '67, on Kama Sutra, by Buddah Records Inc.(USA). Deleted '70. Catalogue no: **KAS 207**

DAYDREAM (OLD GOLD)
Tracks: / Daydream / Summer in the city (B side for re-issue.).
7" Single: Released Apr '83, on Old Gold, by Old Gold Records. Deleted Jul '88. Catalogue no: **OG 9291**
7" Single: Released Oct '88, on Old Gold, by Old Gold Records. Catalogue no: **OG 9799**

DAYDREAM (SINGLE)
Tracks: / Daydream.
7" Single: Released May '66, on Pye Jazz Today, Deleted '69. Catalogue no: **7N 25361**

LOVIN' SPOONFUL (EP)
Tracks: / Summer in the city / Do you believe in magic / Daydream / You didn't have to be so nice.
EP: Released 20 Jun '80, on Flashback, by Mainline Records. Deleted '83. Catalogue no: **FBEP 100**

LOVIN' SPOONFUL, THE
Tracks: / Summer in the city / Daydream / Nashville cats / Darling be home soon.
CD 3": Released '88, on Special Edition, by Castle Communications Records. Catalogue no: **CD3-11**

SUMMER IN THE CITY
Tracks: / Summer in the city.
7" Single: Released Jun '80, on Buddah, by Buddah Records Inc.(USA). Catalogue no: **FBEP 100**
7" Single: Released Jul '66, on Kama Sutra, by Buddah Records Inc.(USA). Deleted '69. Catalogue no: **KAS 200**
7" Single: Released Jul '85, on Buddah, by Buddah Records Inc.(USA). Catalogue no: **U 9023**
7" Single: Released Jul '84, on Old Gold, by Old Gold Records. Deleted Jul '88. Catalogue no: **OG 9415**
7" Single: Released Jan '83, on Flashback, by Mainline Records. Catalogue no: **FBS 22**

Lovindeer

BLUE DRAWS
Tracks: / Blue draws.
12" Single: Released Sep '84, on Sound Of Jamaica, Catalogue no: **Unknown**

COMING IN HOT
Tracks: / Coming in hot.
12" Single: Released Sep '84, on Sound Of Jamaica, Catalogue no: **Unknown**

LICKSHOT MAN
12" Single: Released Oct '84, on Sound Of Jamaica, Catalogue no: **Unknown**

MAN SHORTAGE
Tracks: / Man shortage / Bandooloo style.
7" Single: Released Oct '86, on TSOJ, Catalogue no: **TS 1**
12" Single: Released Oct '86, on TSOJ, Catalogue no: **TST 1**

WILD GILBERT
Tracks: / Wild Gilbert.
12" Single: Released May '89, on TSOJ, Catalogue no: **DSR 8776**
7" Single: Released Nov '88, on TSOJ, Catalogue no: **DSR 3776**

Low, Gary

Biographical details: This British singer achieved a one off UK chart entry in October 1983, peaking at no.52 with *I want you.* His follow up single flopped. (Bob Macdonald 86).

I WANT YOU
Tracks: / I want you.
7" Single: Released Aug '84, on Savoir Faire, Catalogue no: **FAIS 004**
12" Single: Released Aug '84, on Savoir Faire, Catalogue no: **FAIT 004**

YOU ARE A DANGER
Tracks: / You are a danger.
7" Single: Released Nov '83, on Baby, by New Rose Records. Catalogue no: **BABY 5**
12" Single: Released Nov '83, on Baby, by New Rose Records. Catalogue no: **BABY 512**

Low Noise

JUNGLELINE
Tracks: / Jungle line.
7" Single: Released Sep '81, on Happy Birthday, Catalogue no: **UR 5**

Low Over Scandinavia

SAY SOMETHING NICE
Tracks: / Say something nice / Slow boat to China.
7" Single: Released Apr '84, on Trial, by Trial Records. Catalogue no: **CASE 6**

Low Profile

CALL ME
Tracks: / Call me.
7" Single: Released Aug '83, on Buzz, Catalogue no: **BUZZ 1**
12" Single: Released Aug '83, on Buzz, Catalogue no: **BUZZT 1**

Lowe, Jim

GREEN DOOR, THE
Tracks: / Green door.
7" Single: Released Oct '56, on London-American, Deleted '59. Catalogue no: **HLD 8317**

Lowe, Nick

Biographical details: This British singer, bass guitarist, songwriter and producer has been one of the most intriguing maverick figures on the UK rock scene; his critical acclaim has outweighed his commercial success. Born in Suffolk, he had a schoolfriend called Brinsley Schwarz; after leaving school, Lowe and guitarist/vocalist Schwarz played together in an unsuccessful group named Kippington Lodge. In 1969 the band became known simply as Brinsley Schwarz, altough Lowe remained a vital part of the line up. After a disastrously overblown start, in which the band were almost hyped out of existence, Brinley Schwarz became one of the most important groups on Britain's pub rock circuit of the early to mid seventies. They did much to draw attention to this vibrant scene which spawned many noteworthy acts; but their hard work did not pay off in commercial terms and, they broke up in 1975. Many journalists still look back on Brinley Schwarz with nostalgia. Because Lowe had been at the fringes, rather than the center, of the rock establishment, he was accepted as a credible new wave artist when the punk explosion took place in 1976. That year saw the beginning of Stiff Records, the label co-founded by ex-Brinsley manager Dave Robinson - Nick's cult classic *So it goes* was the first Stiff single and cost just 45 pounds to record. In early 1977 Lowe produced the first punk album, The Damned's *Damned, damned, damned*; in the same year he was also the studio supervisor of records by Wreckless Eric and the all important new Stiff star Elvis Costello, plus Graham Parker & The Rumour and Doctor Feelgood. The red hot Nick also wrote a UK top single for his big mate, rock 'n' roll revivalist Dave Edmunds and took part in the first Stiff package tour.
Moving from Stiff to the newly formed Radar label, Lowe proceeded to produce all of Costello's output during the late seventies. At the same time Nick had a period of successas an artist in his own right. *I love the sound of breaking glass* was a UK top 10 single 1978 and, in 1979, he reached no.12 on both sides of the Atlantic with the catchy pop ditty *Cruel to be kind.* By this time, Dave Edmunds and Nick Lowe's records featured the same band of musicians, Rockpile, but legal complications forced them to release records under their individual names. When these hassles were sorted out in 1980, the group Rockpile was officially launched, but the results were, surprisingly, abortive. Now married to Carlene Carter, stepdaughter of country legend Johnny Cash, Lowe continued to make enjoyable music in the eighties but without major success.
(Bob Macdonald 86).

BORN A WOMAN (EP)
7" Single: Released May '77, on Stiff, by Stiff Records. Catalogue no: **LAST 1**

BURNING
Tracks: / Burning / Zulu kiss.
7" Single: Released Feb '82, on F-Beat, by F-Beat Records. Deleted '88. Catalogue no: **XX 20**

CRACKIN' UP
Tracks: / Crackin' up.
7" Single: Released Jun '79, on Radar, Deleted '82. Catalogue no: **ADA 34**

CRUEL TO BE KIND
Tracks: / Cruel to be kind / Endless grey ribbon.
7" Single: Released Aug '79, on Radar, Deleted '82. Catalogue no: **ADA 43**

HALF A BOY & HALF A MAN
Tracks: / Half a boy & half a man / Awesome.
12" Single: Released May '84, on F-Beat, by F-Beat Records. Deleted '88. Catalogue no: **XX 34T**
7" Single: Released May '84, on F-Beat,

by F-Beat Records. Deleted '88. Catalogue no: **XX 34**

I KNEW THE BRIDE
Tracks: / I knew the bride.
7" Single: Released Jul '85, on F-Beat, by F-Beat Records. Deleted '88. Catalogue no: **ZB 40303**
12" Single: Released Jul '85, on F-Beat, by F-Beat Records. Deleted '88. Catalogue no: **ZT 40304**

I LOVE THE SOUND OF BREAKING GLASS
Tracks: / I love the sound of breaking glass.
7" Single: Released Mar '78, on Radar, Deleted '81. Catalogue no: **ADA 1**

L.A.F.F.
Tracks: / L.A.F.F..
7" Single: Released Aug '84, on F-Beat, by F-Beat Records. Deleted '88. Catalogue no: **XX 36**
12" Single: Released Aug '84, on F-Beat, by F-Beat Records. Deleted '88. Catalogue no: **XX 36T**

MY HEART HURTS
Tracks: / My heart hurts / Pet you and hold you.
7" Single: Released Apr '82, on F-Beat, by F-Beat Records. Deleted '88. Catalogue no: **XX 23**

RAGIN EYES
Tracks: / Ragin eyes.
7" Single: Released Apr '83, on F-Beat, by F-Beat Records. Deleted '88. Catalogue no: **XX 31**
12" Single: Released Apr '83, on F-Beat, by F-Beat Records. Deleted '88. Catalogue no: **XX 31T**

SO IT GOES
Tracks: / So it goes.
7" Single: Released Sep '76, on Stiff, by Stiff Records. Deleted '80. Catalogue no: **BUY 1**

Lowe, Peter

ARABESQUE
Tracks: / Arabesque.
7" Single: Released Nov '83, on Beebee, Catalogue no: **BUZZ 2**

Lower Levels

GET IT
Tracks: / Get it / So bloody lazy.
7" Single: Released Jan '82, on Loppylugs, Deleted '87. Catalogue no: **PUSHOVER 1**

Lowery, Ian Group

NEED
Tracks: / Need / Sailor on horse / 13th floor.
7" Single: Released Jul '89, on Situation 2, by Beggars Banquet Records. Catalogue no: **SIT 059**
12" Single: Released Jul '89, on Situation 2, by Beggars Banquet Records. Catalogue no: **SIT 059T**

Lowlife

ETERNITY ROAD
Tracks: / Eternity road / Of pale yellow.
12" Single: Released Jan '88, on Nightshift, by Nightshift Records. Catalogue no: **LOLIF 005T**
7" Single: Released Jan '88, on Nightshift, by Nightshift Records. Catalogue no: **LONLIF 57**
12" Single: Released Jan '88, on Nightshift, by Nightshift Records. Catalogue no: **LOLIF 006T**

LOGIC & LUST
Tracks: / Logic & lust / Animal nightlife.
12" Single: Released Nov '82, on Clay, by Clay Records. Deleted '88. Catalogue no: **12 CLAY 19**
7" Single: Released Nov '82, on Clay, by Clay Records. Deleted '88. Catalogue no: **CLAY 19**

VAIN DELIGHTS
Tracks: / Vain delights / Hollow gut / Permanent sleep (Steel mix) / From side to side / Nightshift.
12" Single: Released Dec '86, on Lowlife, Catalogue no: **LOLIF 3T**

Lowrell

MELLOW MELLOW RIGHT ON
Tracks: / Mellow mellow right on.
7" Single: Released Nov '79, on AVI (USA), by AVI Record Production Inc.(USA). Deleted '82. Catalogue no: **AVIS 108**

LPH

ONE MORE RUB-A-DUB
Tracks: / One more rub-a-dub.
12" Single: Released Nov '84, on Guinep Roots, Catalogue no: **GPR 1001**

L.T.D.

Biographical details: At the time of their major success, this American funk band consisted of Lorenzo Carnegie, Henry Davis, Jimmie Davis John McGee, Abraham Miller, Billy Osbourne, Jeffrey Osbourne, Jake Riley, Robert Santiel and Carle Vickers. The title of the group's first album revealed that L.T.D. signified *Love, togetherness and devotion.* Though never rising to the stature of acts like Earth Wind & Fire and The Commodores, L.T.D. enjoyed a run of success on the US soul and disco during the mid seventies. Two of their singles crossed over to the pop listings - *Love ballad*, later covered even more successfully by George Benson, reached the US no.20 position in 1976; and the million selling *(Every time I turn around) Back in love again* cruised to no.4 a year later. The group's albums, *Love to the world* and *Something to love*, achieved substantial acceptance. However, their only foray in to the British charts was with *Holding on (when love is gone)*, which reached no.70 on the singles list in September 1978. L.T.D. kept functioning into the eighties, although their success faded somewhat. Shortly after they had crept into US top 40 with 1981's *Shine on*, lead singer Jeffery Osborne launched a successful solo career. (Bob Macdonald 86).

HOLDING ON (WHEN LOVE IS GONE)
Tracks: / Holding on (when love is gone).
7" Single: Released Sep '78, on A&M, by A&M Records. Deleted '81. Catalogue no: **AMS 7378**

STOP ON BY
Tracks: / Stop on by.
7" Single: Released Jul '84, on Buzz Int., Catalogue no: **VIBE 5**
12" Single: Released Jul '84, on Buzz Int., Catalogue no: **VIBE 5 T**

Lucas, Carrie

Biographical details: This American soul singer achieved moderate success on the US funk scene in the late seventies. Tracks like *I gotta keep dancin'* were competently made but not particularly distinctive. Her only UK chart entry was 1979's *Dance with you*, which peaked at no. 40. Lucas' mentor was Dick Griffey, founder of the seminal Solar label and one of the most influential figures on the American black music scene, whom she married. She has remained active in the recording studio during the eighties. (Bob Macdonald, 9/1/86).

DANCE WITH YOU
Tracks: / Dance with you.
7" Single: Released Jun '79, on Solar (USA), by MCA Records. Deleted '82. Catalogue no: **FB 1482**

IT'S NOT WHAT YOU'VE GOT
Tracks: / It's not what you've got / Keep smilin'.
12" Single: Released Oct '80, on Solar Records, Deleted Oct '83. Catalogue no: **SOT 13**
7" Single: Released Oct '80, on Solar Records, Deleted Oct '83. Catalogue no: **SO 13**

SHOW ME WHERE YOU'RE COMING FROM
Tracks: / Show me where you're coming from / Still in love.
7" Single: Released May '82, on Solar (USA), by MCA Records. Catalogue no: **K 13175**

Lucas, Cheryl

CHAMPAGNE LADY
Tracks: / Champagne lady.
7" Single: Released Aug '83, on Circle Records, by Circle Records. Catalogue no: **CIR 3**
12" Single: Released Aug '83, on Circle Records, by Circle Records. Catalogue no: **CIRT 3**

Lucas, Tammy

HEY BOY
Tracks: / Hey Boy (touch remix).
7" Single: Released Mar '89, on Republic, by Code Records. Catalogue no: **LIC 019**
12" Single: Released Mar '89, on Republic, by Code Records. Catalogue no: **LICT 019**

Lucia Joy

HEART & SOUL
Tracks: / Heart and soul.
12" Single: Released Jan '84, on ABL, by ABL Records. Catalogue no: **ABL 003**

Lucia & Project 2

LA ISLA BONITA
Tracks: / La Isla Bonita (rap version) / La Isla Bonita (version).
7" Single: Released 30 May '87, on Nine O Nine, by Creole Records. Catalogue no: **NINE 77**
12" Single: Released 30 May '87, on Nine O Nine, by Creole Records. Catalogue no: **NINE 7**

Lucienne

CARRIBBEAN
Tracks: / Carribean.
7" Single: Released Feb '80, on Pan (Switzerland), Catalogue no: **PAN 101**

Luckhurst, Reg

DOWNHEARTED
Tracks: / Downhearted.
7" Single: Released Oct '80, on Lucky, by Lucky Records. Catalogue no: **LS 12**

WAS IT RAIN
Tracks: / Was it rain.
7" Single: Released Oct '80, on Lucky, by Lucky Records. Catalogue no: **LS 17**

Lucky Saddles

BOTH HERE TODAY
Tracks: / Both here today.
7" Single: Released Aug '81, on Albion, by Albion Records. Catalogue no: **ION 1008**

Lucy Show

ELECTRIC DREAMS
Tracks: / Electric dreams / History part 1.
7" Single: Released May '84, on Piggy Bank Records, by A&M Records. Catalogue no: **BANK 999**

EMPHEMERAL
Tracks: / Emphemeral.
12" Single: Released Jul '85, on A&M, by A&M Records. Deleted '88. Catalogue no: **AMY 261**
7" Single: Released Jul '85, on A&M, by A&M Records. Deleted '88. Catalogue no: **AM 261**

LEONARDO DA VINCI
Tracks: / Leonardo da Vinci / Kill the beast.
7" Single: Released Dec '83, on Shout, by Shout Records. Catalogue no: **XS 007**

MILLION THINGS, A
Tracks: / Million things / Sojourn's end / Jam in E (Available on 12" only) / Million things.
12" Single: Released Aug '87, on Big Time Records, by Big Time Records. Catalogue no: **ZT 41398**
7" Single: Released Aug '87, on Big Time Records, by Big Time Records. Catalogue no: **ZB 41397**

NEW MESSAGE
Tracks: / New message / Sun and moon.
7" Single: Released 21 Nov '87, on Big Time Records, by Big Time Records. Catalogue no: **ZB 41603 X**
12" Single: Released 21 Nov '87, on Big Time Records, by Big Time Records. Catalogue no: **ZT 41604 X**

SEE IT GOES
Tracks: / See it goes.
12" Single: Released Sep '84, on Piggy Bank Records, by A&M Records. Catalogue no: **BANX 888**
7" Single: Released Sep '84, on Piggy Bank Records, by A&M Records. Catalogue no: **BANK 888**

UNDONE (2)
Tracks: / Undone.
7" Single: Released Oct '85, on A&M, by A&M Records. Deleted '88. Catalogue no: **AM 287**
12" Single: Released Oct '85, on A&M, by A&M Records. Deleted '88. Catalogue no: **AMY 287**

Lucy, Tom

PARIS FRANCE
Tracks: / Paris, France.
7" Single: Released Aug '82, on Bridgehouse, Deleted '88. Catalogue no: **BHS 15**

Luddites

ALTERED STATES
Tracks: / Altered states.
7" Single: Released Mar '84, on Luddites, by Red Rhino Records. Catalogue no: **EIGHT 4-001**

STRENGTH OF YOUR CRY (EP)
7" Single: Released Jul '83, on Xcentric Noise, by Xcentric Noise Records & Tapes. Catalogue no: **SECOND 1**

Ludus

DANGER CAME SMILING
Tracks: / Danger came smiling.
7" Single: Released Sep '82, on New Hormones, Catalogue no: **ORG 20**

FOUR COMPOSITIONS
Tracks: / Four compositions.
12" Single: Released Mar '80, on New Hormones, Catalogue no: **ORG 4**

MOTHERS HOUR
Tracks: / Mothers hour.
7" Single: Released Jul '81, on New Hormones, Catalogue no: **ORG 12**

MY CHERRY IS NOT SHERRY
Tracks: / My cherry is not sherry.
7" Single: Released Jul '81, on New Hormones, Catalogue no: **ORG 8**

Luft, Lorna

WHERE THE BOYS ARE
Tracks: / Where the boys are / Prove me wrong.
7" Single: Released Jun '84, on Epic, by CBS Records. Catalogue no: **A 4472**
12" Single: Released Jun '84, on Epic, by CBS Records. Catalogue no: **TA 4472**

Luin, Lars

HEAVY LOAD
Tracks: / Heavyload / How long.
12" Single: Released Jul '82, on Emporium, Catalogue no: **EMP 001**

Luke, Robin

Biographical details: This American singer, songwriter and guitarist was born in Los Angeles in 1942, and began to take a great interest in music at the age of eight. His professional career began in 1957, when he obtained work on television in Honolulu. In the autumn of '58, while still only 16, he wrote himself his first and only hit *Susie darlin*, inspired by the name of his

LUKK - ON THE ONE (Released on Important)

younger sister. This single reached no.5 in the States and no.23 in Britain. (Bob Macdonald 86).

SUSIE DARLIN' (SINGLE)
Tracks: / Susie darlin'.
7" Single: Released Oct '58, on London-American, Deleted '61. Catalogue no: **HLD 8676**

Lukk

ON THE ONE (see panel on previous page)
Tracks: / On the one / On the one (instrumental).
12" Single: Released Aug '85, on Important, Catalogue no: **TANT 6**
7" Single: Released Aug '85, on Important, Catalogue no: **TAN 6**

Lulu

Biographical details: This British singer and entertainer was born Marie McDonald McLaughlin Lawrie near Glasgow in November 1948. She began to sing almost as soon as she could speak, and grew up performing at local competitions and in local venues, and the strength of her talent was discovering by a London showbiz executive in a Glasgow nightclub in 1963. With her backing group, who became the Luvvers, Lulu released her first record *Shout* in 1964. This dynamic rendition of an old Isley Brothers single that the petite 15 year old was a vocalist of enormous power, exuberance and soulfulness. The single cruised to no.7 on the UK chart, and became a club classic - even in the eighties, it was still sufficiently popular to be classed as Britain's best selling oldie. Lulu was widely described as Scotland's answer to America's Little Miss Dynamite, Brenda Lee. 1965 brought the singer a second UK top tenner with *Leave a little love*, but her career fell into the doldrums soon afterwards. She was rescued in 1967 by two simultaneous strokes of fortune - arrival of top record producer Mickie Most, and an appearance in the Sidney Poitier movie *To Sir with love*. The title song, performed by Lulu, became a surprise smash in the States - it logged five weeks at no.1 without being a hit in Britain. Meanwhile, Most put her back on the UK hit trail with such biggies as Neil Diamond's song *The boat that I row* (1967), *Me, the peaceful heart* (1968), *I'm a tiger* (1968) and her Eurovision winning no.2 hit *Boom bang-a-bang* (1969). These singles placed her firmly in the middle of the road/light pop bracket, to the disappointment of many *Shout* fans. From the late sixties through to the eighties, Lulu remained a familiar and likeable figure in British showbusiness although her chart career dropped off. However, she showed an occasional tendency to resist the TV oriented world of sugary stardom by associating herself with trendier rock figures. Jimi Hendrix was once a guest on her regular television show; in 1970 she hit the US top 30 with *The man who sold the world*, written and produced by David Bowie. In 1981, after several years of chart absence, she reached the US top 20 and the UK top 75 with *I could never miss you (more than I do)*. Lulu was married to Maurice Gibb of The Bee Gees from 1969 till 1973. She is now married to top London hairdresser John Freida, who became her husband in 1976. (Bob Macdonald 86).

BOAT THAT I ROW
Tracks: / Boat that I row, The.
7" Single: Released Apr '67, on Columbia, by EMI Records. Deleted '70. Catalogue no: **DB 8169**

BOOM BANG-A-BANG
Tracks: / Boom bang-a-bang.
7" Single: Released Mar '69, on Columbia, by EMI Records. Deleted '72. Catalogue no: **DB 8550**

BOY
Tracks: / Boy.
7" Single: Released Jun '68, on Columbia, by EMI Records. Deleted '71. Catalogue no: **DB 8425**

HERE COMES THE NIGHT
Tracks: / Here comes the night.
7" Single: Released Nov '64, on Decca, by Decca Records. Deleted '67. Catalogue no: **F 12017**

I COULD NEVER MISS YOU (MORE THAN I DO)
Tracks: / I could never miss you (more than I do) / Dance to the feeling in your heart.
7" Single: Released Dec '81, on Alfa, Deleted '84. Catalogue no: **ALFA 1700**

I WILL DO IT FOR YOUR LOVE
Tracks: / I will do it for your love / How can I believe you.
7" Single: Released May '82, on Alfa, Deleted May '85. Catalogue no: **ALFA 2423**

IF I WERE YOU
Tracks: / If i were you / You win i lose.
7" Single: Released Feb '82, on Alfa, Deleted Feb '87. Catalogue no: **A1892**

I'M A TIGER (SINGLE)
Tracks: / I'm a tiger.
7" Single: Released Mar '69, on Columbia, by EMI Records. Deleted '72. Catalogue no: **DB 8500**

LEAVE A LITTLE LOVE
Tracks: / Leave a little love.
7" Single: Released Jun '65, on Decca, by Decca Records. Deleted '68. Catalogue no: **F 12169**

LET'S PRETEND
Tracks: / Let's pretend.
7" Single: Released Jul '67, on Columbia, by EMI Records. Deleted '70. Catalogue no: **DB 8221**

LOVE LOVES TO LOVE LOVE
Tracks: / Love loves to love love.
7" Single: Released Nov '67, on Columbia, by EMI Records. Deleted '70. Catalogue no: **DB 8295**

MAN WHO SOLD THE WORLD (OLD GOLD)
Tracks: / Man who sold the world, The / Take your mama for a ride.
7" Single: Released 24 Apr '89, on Old Gold, by Old Gold Records. Catalogue no: **OG 9887**

MAN WHO SOLD THE WORLD (SINGLE)
Tracks: / Man who sold the world, The / Watch that man.
7" Single: Released Jan '74, on Polydor, by Polydor Ltd. Deleted '77. Catalogue no: **2001 490**

ME THE PEACEFUL HEART
Tracks: / Me the peaceful heart.
7" Single: Released Feb '68, on Columbia, by EMI Records. Deleted '71. Catalogue no: **DB 8358**

MY BOY LOLLIPOP
Tracks: / My boy lollipop / It's only love.
12" Single: Released Nov '86, on Jive, by Zomba Records. Catalogue no: **LULU T 2**
7" Set: Released Nov '86, on Jive, by Zomba Records. Deleted Jul '87. Catalogue no: **LULUD 2**
7" Single: Released Nov '86, on Jive, by Zomba Records. Deleted Jul '87. Catalogue no: **LULU 2**
Special: Released Nov '86, on Jive, by Zomba Records. Deleted Jul '87. Catalogue no: **LULUX 2**

OH ME OH MY (I'M A FOOL FOR YOU BABY)
Tracks: / Oh me oh my (I'm a fool for you baby).
7" Single: Released Nov '69, on Atco, by Atlantic Recording Corp.(USA). Deleted '72. Catalogue no: **226 008**

SHOUT
7" Single: Released Jun '88, on Old Gold, by Old Gold Records. Catalogue no: **OG 9393**
7" Single: Released Mar '82, on Decca, by Decca Records. Deleted '88. Catalogue no: **F 11844**
7" Single: Released Jul '86, on Decca, by Decca Records. Deleted '88. Catalogue no: **SHOUT 1**
12" Single: Released '88, on Decca, by Decca Records. Deleted '88. Catalogue no: **LULU1**
12" Single: Released Jul '86, on Decca, by Decca Records. Deleted Feb '89. Catalogue no: **SHOUX 1**
7" Single: Released May '64, on Decca, by Decca Records. Deleted '67. Catalogue no: **F 11884**

TAKE ME TO YOUR HEART AGAIN (SINGLE)
Tracks: / Take me to your heart again / How can i love you.
7" Single: Released '82, on CBS, by CBS Records. Deleted '87. Catalogue no: **ALFA 2664**

TAKE YOUR MAMA FOR A RIDE
Tracks: / Take your mama for a ride.
7" Single: Released Apr '75, on Chelsea, Deleted '78. Catalogue no: **2005 022**

THAT'S SO
Tracks: / That's so.
7" Single: Released Mar '84, on Lifestyle, by Micrometro Ltd (Records). Catalogue no: **LIFE 9**

TO SIR WITH LOVE
Tracks: / To sir with love.
7" Single: Released '80, on United Artists, by EMI Records. Catalogue no: **LR 1766**

Lulu Boys

BOOM BOOM
Tracks: / Boom boom / Beat boy.
7" Single: Released Jun '82, on Logo, by Logo Records. Deleted Jun '85. Catalogue no: **GO 415**

Lulu Kiss Me Dead

SPEAK TO ME
Tracks: / Speak to me / Someday soon.
12" Single: Released Mar '86, on Big Fish, Deleted '88. Catalogue no: **CARP 001**

ULTIMATE SOLUTION
Tracks: / Ultimate solution / This is rock 'n' roll, this is heaven / Spade (on 12" only).
7" Single: Released May '85, on Situation 2, by Beggars Banquet Records. Catalogue no: **SIT 39**
12" Single: Released May '85, on Situation 2, by Beggars Banquet Records. Catalogue no: **SIT 39T**

Luman, Bob

Biographical details:
This American singer and guitarist was born in Nacogdoches, Texas, and became a rockabilly vocalist in the late Fifties. Despite a series of great records, all his early rock releases failed. He did, nonetheless, win an appearance in the film *Carnival Rock*. In late 1960 he suddenly became famous with *Let's think about living*, a rousing message-filled pop single which reached the top 10 on both sides of the Atlantic; it was written by Boudleaux Bryant, source of many of The Everly Brothers hits. During the rest of the sixties and seventies., Luman returned to the style that had always been at the root of his music - country and western. In view of the optimistic tone of his most famous disc, it was ironic that he should die an early death; he passed away in December 1978 at the age of 40, after a moderately successful country career. (Bob Macdonald 86).
937 Texas born Bob Luman developed early a fascination with both music and baseball. In his younger days, Luman had often listened to the *Louisiana Hayride*. His idols were Hank Williams, Webb Pierce and Johnny Horton. he desired to sound like Lefty Frizzell or Ernest Tubb. During his highschool days he formed a hillbilly band. His interests in music were radically changed from one day to the other after Bob had seen Elvis' live performances. That was the last time he tried to sound like Webb Pierce or Lefty Frizzell. He wanted to be a rock 'n' roll singer. With the Mac Curtis band he made his first demos in 1955. A couple of years later he signed a recording contract with Imperial Records. He also received an invitation to replace Johnny Cash at the *Louisiana Hayride*. He recorded the rockabilly anthems *Rd Hot* and *Red Cadillac And A Black Moustache* backed by James Burton, James Kirkland and Butch White. During this period, he also played in the movie *Varnival Rock*. Later, he was signed by Capitol, Warner Brothers, Hickory, Epic and Polydor. (Bear Family, 1988)..

GREAT SNOWMAN, THE
Tracks: / Great snowman, The.
7" Single: Released May '61, on Warner Bros., by WEA Records. Deleted '64. Catalogue no: **WB 37**

LET'S THINK ABOUT LIVING (SINGLE)
Tracks: / Let's think about living.
7" Single: Released Jun '60, on Warner Bros., by WEA Records. Deleted '63. Catalogue no: **WB 18**
7" Single: Released Apr '85, on Sundown, by Magnum Music Group. Catalogue no: **SDS 002**

STRANGER THAN FICTION
Tracks: / Stranger than fiction.
7" Single: Released Jun '80, on Rollin' Rock, Catalogue no: **45 028**

THAT'S ALRIGHT
Tracks: / That's alright.
7" Single: Released Jun '80, on Rollin' Rock, Catalogue no: **45 034**

WHY WHY BYE BYE
Tracks: / Why why bye bye.
7" Single: Released Dec '60, on Warner Bros., by WEA Records. Deleted '63. Catalogue no: **WB 28**

Lumumba

YELLOW MEALIE MEAL
Tracks: / Yellow mealie meal / Kiss kiss (sugar mama).
12" Single: Released Feb '87, on EMI, by EMI Records. Deleted Jul '87. Catalogue no: **12EMI 5600**
7" Single: Released Feb '87, on EMI, by EMI Records. Deleted Jul '87. Catalogue no: **EMI 5600**

Luna Twist

AFRICAN TIME
Tracks: / African time / So danceable.
7" Single: Released Apr '82, on Statik, Catalogue no: **STAT 14**
12" Single: Released Apr '82, on Statik, Catalogue no: **STAT 1412**

LOOK OUT
7" Single: Released Mar '83, on Statik, Catalogue no: **STAT 18**
12" Single: Released Mar '83, on Statik, Catalogue no: **STAT 1812**

Lunachicks

GET OFF THE ROAD
Tracks: / Get off the road / Sugar luv.
7" Single: Released Apr '89, on Blast First, by Blast First Records. Catalogue no: **BFFP 044**

FRINGE WITH THE FRINGE
7" Single: Released Jan '85, on Children Of The Revolution, by Revolver Records. Catalogue no: **COR 1**

WHO'S IN CONTROL
7" EP: Released Jul '82, on Ressurection, Catalogue no: **ERECT 1**

Lunatic Louise

SUMMER OF MANIACS
Tracks: / Summer of maniacs / Sing your own maniacs.
7" Single: Released 23 Jul '88, on Put It Out And Watch It Fly, Catalogue no: **LOO-1**

Lunch, Lydia

DEATH VALLEY
Tracks: / Death valley.
12" Single: Released Jan '85, on Iridescence, Catalogue no: **IRID 1-12**

STINKFIST
Tracks: / Stinkfist.
12" Single: Released 27 Feb '89, on Widowspeak, Catalogue no: **WSP 014**
CD 5": Released Jul '89, on Widowspeak, Catalogue no: **WSP 020**

Lunn, Julie

NEVER AGAIN(CARRY ON)
Tracks: / Never again(carry on) / Never again(carry on)(dub).
7" Single: Released Jun '89, on Friction, Catalogue no: **LUNN 1**

Lupone,Patti

I DREAMED A DREAM
Tracks: / I dreamed a dream / J'ai reve d'une outrevre / One more day (Extra track on 12" version only.).
12" Single: Released Dec '85, on First Night, by First Night Records. Catalogue no: **SCOREL 1**
7" Single: Released Dec '85, on First Night, by First Night Records. Catalogue no: **SCORE 1**

Lurkers

Biographical details: This British punk rock band consisted of Manic Esso, Nigel Moore, Pete Stride and Howard Wall. Hailing from Uxbridge on the outskirts of London, the Lurkers chalked up five minor UK hit singles during the latter part of the New Wave era, 1978-9. *Ain't got a clue, I don't need to tell her, Just thirteen*, the double A-sided *Out in the dark/Cyanide* and *New guitar in town* all lurked arounf the lower regions of Britain's Top 75, but the group never hit the Top 40. In similar style, the album *Fulham fallout* peaked at no. 57 in July 1978. The Lurkers enjoyed huge support from British radio's foremost champion of punk, John Peel, but could or would not break into the major league. In the early eighties, the band switched from Beggars' Banquet to Clay Records, but this did not prevent the from plunging into obscurity. (Bob Macdonald, 9/1/86).

AIN'T GOT A CLUE
Tracks: / Ain't got a clue.
7" Single: Released Jun '78, on Beggars Banquet, by Beggars Banquet Records. Deleted '81. Catalogue no: **BEG 6**

DRAG YOU OUT
Tracks: / Drag you out.
7" Pic: Released Nov '82, on Clay, by Clay Records. Catalogue no: **CLAY 17P**
7" Single: Released Nov '82, on Clay, by Clay Records. Deleted '88. Catalogue no: **CLAY 17**

FINAL VINYL
Tracks: / Final vinyl.
12" Single: Released Mar '84, on Clay, by Clay Records. Deleted '88. Catalogue no: **PLATE 7**

FRANKENSTEIN AGAIN
Tracks: / Frankenstein again / One man's meat.
7" Single: Released Feb '83, on Clay, by Clay Records. Deleted '88. Catalogue no: **CLAY 21**

I DON'T NEED TO TELL HER
Tracks: / I don't need to tell her.
7" Single: Released Aug '79, on Beggars

Banquet, by Beggars Banquet Records. Deleted Jan '88. Catalogue no: **BACK 3**
7" Single: Released Aug '78, on Beggars Banquet, by Beggars Banquet Records. Deleted '81. Catalogue no: **BEG 9**

JUST THIRTEEN
Tracks: / Just thirteen.
7" Single: Released Feb '79, on Beggars Banquet, by Beggars Banquet Records. Deleted '82. Catalogue no: **BEG 114**

LET'S DANCE NOW
Tracks: / Let's dance now / Midnight hour.
7" Single: Released May '84, on Clay, by Clay Records. Deleted '88. Catalogue no: **CLAY 32**

NEW GUITAR IN TOWN
Tracks: / New guitar in town.
7" Single: Released Nov '79, on Beggars Banquet, by Beggars Banquet Records. Deleted '82. Catalogue no: **BEG 28**

OUT IN THE DARK
Tracks: / Out in the dark / Cyanide.
7" Single: Released Jun '79, on Beggars Banquet, by Beggars Banquet Records. Deleted '82. Catalogue no: **BEG 19**

THIS DIRTY TOWN
Tracks: / This dirty town / Wolf at the door.
7" Single: Released Jun '82, on Clay, by Clay Records. Deleted '88. Catalogue no: **CLAY 12**

Lusardi, Linda

EYE CONTACT
Tracks: / Eye contact / Eye contact (club mix).
7" Single: Released Oct '86, on Polo, by Polo Records. Deleted '88. Catalogue no: **POLO 41**
12" Single: Released Oct '86, on Polo, by Polo Records. Deleted '88. Catalogue no: **POLO 12-41**

L.U.S.T.

2 HOT 2 STOP
Tracks: / 2 hot 2 stop.
12" Single: Released Mar '89, on Bass, by Champion Records. Catalogue no: **BSS 127**
7" Single: Released Mar '89, on Bass, by Champion Records. Catalogue no: **BSS 7**

Luther, Rude Boy Daddy

POP GOES THE WEASEL
Tracks: / Pop goes the weasel.
7" Single: Released Oct '89, on Blue Beat, Catalogue no: **BBSP 005**
12" Single: Released Oct '89, on Blue Beat, Catalogue no: **BBSPLS 005**

Lux, Gary

CHILDREN OF THE WORLD
Tracks: / Children of the world.
7" Single: Released May '85, on Global, by Ariola. Deleted '87. Catalogue no: **LUX 2**

WEEKEND
Tracks: / Weekend / You're all I need.
7" Single: Released Mar '85, on Global, by Ariola. Deleted '87. Catalogue no: **LUX 1**
12" Single: Released Mar '85, on Global, by Ariola. Deleted '87. Catalogue no: **12 LUX 1**

Luxuria

PUBLIC HIGHWAY
Tracks: / Public highway / Sickly thug and I / Luxuria (the wilderness mix) (on 12" only).
7" Single: Released May '88, on Beggars Banquet, by Beggars Banquet Records. Catalogue no: **BEG 211**
12" Single: Released May '88, on Beggars Banquet, by Beggars Banquet Records. Catalogue no: **BEG 211T**

REDNECK
Tracks: / Redneck.
12" Single: Released Dec '87, on Beggars Banquet, by Beggars Banquet Records. Catalogue no: **BEG 204T**
7" Single: Released Dec '87, on Beggars Banquet, by Beggars Banquet Records. Catalogue no: **BEG 204**

Luxury

BURN ME UP
Tracks: / Burn me up / Don't pretend.
7" Single: Released Jan '84, on Polydor, by Polydor Ltd. Catalogue no: **POSP 634**

LW 5

KILL OR BE KILLED
Tracks: / Kill or be killed.
12" Single: Released Oct '85, on Virgin, by Virgin Records. Deleted '89. Catalogue no: **VS 809-12**

RIPE FOR THE PICKING
Tracks: / Ripe for the picking / Last lie / Ripe for the picking (extended Hardcastle mix-April 85) (On VS 747-14 only).
7" Single: Released Jun '85, on Virgin, by Virgin Records. Deleted '86. Catalogue no: **VS 767**
12" Single: Released '85, on Virgin, by Virgin Records. Catalogue no: **VS 767-14**
12" Single: Released Jun '85, on Virgin, by Virgin Records. Deleted May '88. Catalogue no: **VS 767-12**

Lydia & Thurston

CRUMB
Tracks: / Crumb.
12" Single: Released Jul '87, on Widowspeak, Catalogue no: **WSP 13**

Lye Lye,Bunny

100% LOVING
Tracks: / 100% loving / Permanent love.
12" Single: Released Sep '86, on Rock Fort, Catalogue no: **RF 001**

Lyle, Graham

MARLEY
Tracks: / Marley / Down the subway.
7" Single: Released Jun '83, on Red Bus, by Red Bus Records. Catalogue no: **RBUS 78**

Lyles, Cynthia

CROSSOVER
Tracks: / Crossover / Crossover(Inst.).
7" Single: Released Nov '86, on GFM, Catalogue no: **GFM 107**
12" Single: Released Nov '86, on GFM, Catalogue no: **GFMT 107**

Lymon, Frankie

BABY BABY
Tracks: / Baby baby.
7" Single: Released Apr '57, on Columbia, by EMI Records. Deleted '60. Catalogue no: **DB 3878**

GOODY GOODY
Tracks: / Goody goody.
7" Single: Released Sep '57, on Columbia, by EMI Records. Deleted '60. Catalogue no: **DB 3983**

I'M NOT A JUVENILE DELINQUENT
Tracks: / I'm not a juvenile delinquent.
7" Single: Released Jan '80, on Lightning, Catalogue no: **R 0491**
7" Single: Released Mar '57, on Columbia, by EMI Records. Deleted '60. Catalogue no: **DB 3878**

WHY DO FOOLS FALL IN LOVE (2)
Tracks: / Why do fools fall in love / Goody goody / Baby baby (Not on 7".) / I want you to be my girl (CD single only.).
CD 5": Released Oct '89, on Roulette (EMI), by EMI Records. Catalogue no: **203 558 2**
7" Single: Released Oct '89, on Roulette (EMI), by EMI Records. Catalogue no: **RLTE 1**
7" Single: Released Oct '89, on Roulette (EMI), by EMI Records. Catalogue no: **203 558 7**
CD 5": Released Oct '89, on Roulette (EMI), by EMI Records. Catalogue no: **CDRLTE 1**
12" Single: Released Oct '89, on Roulette (EMI), by EMI Records. Catalogue no: **203 558 6**
12" Single: Released Oct '89, on Roulette (EMI), by EMI Records. Catalogue no: **12RLTE 1**

WHY DO FOOLS FALL IN LOVE (OLD GOLD)
Tracks: / Why do fools fall in love.
7" Single: Released Jul '84, on Old Gold, by Old Gold Records. Catalogue no: **OG 9411**

WHY DO FOOLS FALL IN LOVE (SINGLE)
Tracks: / Why do fools fall in love.
7" Single: Released Jun '56, on Columbia, by EMI Records. Deleted '59. Catalogue no: **DB 3772**
7" Single: Released Jan '80, on Lightning, Catalogue no: **LR 0491**

Lynam, Ray

BACK IN LOVE BY MONDAY (SINGLE)
Tracks: / Back in love by Monday.
7" Single: Released Jun '88, on Ritz, by Ritz Records. Catalogue no: **RITZ 189**

FIRE OF TWO OLD FLAMES
Tracks: / Fire of two old flames.
7" Single: Released '88, on Ritz, by Ritz Records. Catalogue no: **RITZ 114**

Lynch Bert & Hazel

MAMA DON'T LIKE IT/VERSION
Tracks: / Mama don't like it / Mama don't like it(version).
12" Single: Released May '82, on Sunburn, by Orbitone Records. Catalogue no: **SBD 02**

Lynch, Kenny

Biographical details: This British singer and entertainer achieved a run of mostly minor UK hit singles during the first half of the sixties. His only experience of major chart success was with two no.10 singles in 1963 *Up on the roof*, a rapid cover version of the Drifters' US biggie, and *You can never stop me loving you*. His attempts to consolidate upon these were thwarted by the onslaught of the Merseybeat boom - old fashioned solo singers like Lynch were classed as part of the previous era. After fading from the charts altogether in 1965, the singer carved out a sustained career in TV, radio, variety and cabaret shows. After doing some session vocal work for Rick Wakeman's *1984* album in 1981, Lynch made an unexpected chart comeback in 1983 with his acclaimed, self-written and self produced disco single *Half the day's gone and we haven't earned a penny*. None of Lynch's activities have made him a major star, but he has shown an impressive knack for survival and staying power; he is a mini showbusiness institution in Britain. (Bob Macdonald, 9/1/86).

BETTER DAY, A
Tracks: / Better day, A.
7" Single: Released Mar '85, on Spartan, Catalogue no: **SP 19**
12" Single: Released Mar '85, on Spartan, Catalogue no: **12SP 19**

GOTTA GET UP
Tracks: / Gotta get up / No.
7" Single: Released Mar '86, on Spartan, Catalogue no: **SP 133**
12" Single: Released Mar '86, on Spartan, Catalogue no: **12SP 133**

HALF THE DAY'S GONE AND WE HAVEN'T...(SINGLE)
Tracks: / Half the days gone & we haven't earned a penny.
12" Single: Released Aug '83, on Satril, by Satril Records. Catalogue no: **12SAT 510**
7" Single: Released Aug '83, on Satril, by Satril Records. Catalogue no: **SAT 510**

I'LL STAY BY YOU
Tracks: / I'll stay by you.
7" Single: Released Jun '65, on H.M.V., by EMI Records. Deleted '68. Catalogue no: **POP 1430**

MOUNTAIN OF LOVE
Tracks: / Mountain of love.
7" Single: Released Jun '60, on H.M.V., by EMI Records. Deleted '63. Catalogue no: **POP 751**

PUFF
Tracks: / Puff.
7" Single: Released Sep '62, on H.M.V., by EMI Records. Deleted '65. Catalogue no: **POP 1057**

STAND BY ME
Tracks: / Stand by me.
7" Single: Released Apr '64, on H.M.V., by EMI Records. Deleted '67. Catalogue no: **POP 1280**

THEY DON'T KNOW YOU
Tracks: / They don't know you / Average man.
7" Single: Released May '83, on Satril, by Satril Records. Catalogue no: **SAT 508**

UP ON THE ROOF
Tracks: / Up on the roof.
7" Single: Released Dec '62, on H.M.V., by EMI Records. Deleted '65. Catalogue no: **POP 1090**

WHAT AM I TO DO
Tracks: / What am I to do.
7" Single: Released Aug '64, on H.M.V., by EMI Records. Deleted '67. Catalogue no: **POP 1321**

Lynch, Lee

HERE I GO AGAIN
Tracks: / Here I go again / Famous Shamus.
7" Single: Released Oct '83, on Ritz, by Ritz Records. Catalogue no: **RITZ 052**

IRELAND MY ISLAND OF DREAMS
Tracks: / Ireland my island of dreams.
7" Single: Released '88, on I&B, by I & B Records. Catalogue no: **BA 005**

LOVE OF MY LIFE, THE
Tracks: / Love of my life, The.
7" Single: Released '88, on I&B, by I & B Records. Catalogue no: **BA 002**

MOLLY MAGUIRE
Tracks: / Molly Maguire.
7" Single: Released Nov '85, on Ritz, by Ritz Records. Catalogue no: **RITZ 123**

PADDY'S ON THE MOVE
Tracks: / Paddy's on the move / Darling thank you.
7" Single: Released '88, on I&B, by I & B Records. Catalogue no: **BA 003**

Lynes, Kevin

HEART ON FIRE
Tracks: / Heart on fire / Better in love.
7" Single: Released Feb '81, on RCA, by BMG Records (UK). Deleted '84. Catalogue no: **RCA 39**

Lynham, Ray

FIRE OF TWO OLD FLAMES THE
Tracks: / Fire of two old flames, The.
7" Single: Released Sep '85, on Ritz, by Ritz Records. Catalogue no: **RITZ 115**

MONA LISA LOST HER SMILE
Tracks: / Mona Lisa lost her smile / Winter time.
7" Single: Released Aug '86, on Ritz, by Ritz Records. Catalogue no: **RITZ 093**

SHE SANG THE MELODY
Tracks: / She sang the melody / Hold on.
7" Single: Released May '85, on Ritz, by Ritz Records. Catalogue no: **RITZ 099**

TO BE LOVERS
Tracks: / To be lovers / Winter time.
7" Single: Released Mar '86, on Ritz, by Ritz Records. Catalogue no: **RITZ 145**

WHAT A LIE
Tracks: / What a lie / I don't want to see another town.
7" Single: Released Apr '82, on Ritz, by Ritz Records. Catalogue no: **RITZ 013**

Lynn, Alice

YOU KEEP ME HANGIN ON
12" Single: Released Sep '82, on Pavilion, by Pavilion Records. Deleted '83. Catalogue no: **RSR 01**

Lynn, Andrea

FEEL YOUR LOVE
Tracks: / Feel your love.
12" Single: Released Aug '83, on Sanity, Catalogue no: **STY 007**

Lynn, Barbara

YOU MAKE ME SO HOT
Tracks: / You make me so hot / Sugar coated love.
12" Single: Released 23 Jul '88, on Ichiban, by Ichiban Records (UK). Catalogue no: **ICHT 704**

YOU'LL LOSE A GOOD THING
Tracks: / You'll lose a good thing.
7" Single: Released May '82, on Oval, by Oval Records. Catalogue no: **OVAL 1006**

Lynn, Cheryl

Biographical details: American soul singer Lynn was discovered on television via the much-talked-about Gong Show. This led to her receiving a million-selling disco and soul smash with the 1979 single *Got to be real*. It was such a meaty, funky, catchy record that she seemed assured of an illustrious career during the 80's. But in the event her subsequent success was fairly modest. Her two highlights were *If this world were mine*, a 1982 duet with singer-producer Luther Vandross, and the 1984 single *Encore*, which provided Lynn with her only taste of UK chart success, reaching No 68 in September of that year. (Bob MacDonald, January 1986.).

AT LAST YOU'RE MINE
Tracks: / At last you're mine.
7" Single: Released Apr '85, on Epic, by CBS Records. Catalogue no: **A 6132**

ENCORE
Tracks: / Encore.
7" Single: Released Sep '84, on Streetwave, Deleted '87. Catalogue no: **KHAN 23**

FEEL IT
Tracks: / Feel it / Chances.
7" Single: Released Feb '80, on CBS, by CBS Records. Deleted '83. Catalogue no: **CBS 8242**

FIDELITY
Tracks: / Fidelity.
7" Single: Released Jul '85, on CBS, by CBS Records. Catalogue no: **A 6373**
12" Single: Released Jul '85, on CBS, by CBS Records. Catalogue no: **TX 6373**

IF THIS WORLD WAS MINE
Tracks: / If this world was mine / I just want to be your fantasy.
7" Single: Released Jan '83, on CBS, by CBS Records. Catalogue no: **A 2952**

SHAKE IT UP TONIGHT
Tracks: / Shake it up tonight / Baby.
7" Single: Released Aug '81, on CBS, by CBS Records. Deleted '84. Catalogue no: **A 1436**
12" Single: Released Aug '81, on CBS, by CBS Records. Deleted '84. Catalogue no: **A13 1436**

Lynn, Loretta

YOU'RE LOOKING AT COUNTRY
Tracks: / You're looking at country / Coal miner's daughter.

7" Single: Released Mar '81, on MCA, by MCA Records. Deleted Mar '84. Catalogue no: **MCA 691**

Lynn, Patti

JOHNNY ANGEL
Tracks: / Johnny angel.
7" Single: Released May '62, on Fontana, by Phonogram Ltd. Deleted '65. Catalogue no: **H 391**

Lynn, Tammi

I'M GONNA RUN AWAY FROM YOU
Tracks: / I'm gonna run away from you.
7" Single: Released May '75, on Contempo. Deleted '78. Catalogue no: **CS 9026**
7" Single: Released May '71, on Mojo. Deleted '74. Catalogue no: **2092 001**

Lynn, Vera

Biographical details: This British singer was born Vera Welsh in East Ham, London in 1919. She began singing at the age of seven, joining a children's troupe at eleven, and went professional in her mid teens. She worked briefly with bandleader Joe Loss, and then experienced a valuable 18 month stint with pianist Charlie Kunz at London's Casani Club in Regent Street. In 1941 Lynn launched a solo career with the radio series *Sincerely yours*. It was at this point that Vera Lynn's star really began to shine. *Sincerely yours* became enormously popular with servicemen around the world. It's role as a morale - booster during the black days of world war II was so effective that she was dubbed "the forces sweetheart". During the remaining war years, she devoted much of her time to touring abroad singing for the troops. By the end of the second world war, she was one of Europe's most famous stars and also popular amongst American soldiers. Her psychological contribution to Britain's war effort, via her propagation of such songs as *White cliffs of Dover* and *We'll meet again*, had assured the singer of a legendary niche in British showbusiness. In 1946, the year after the end of the war, Vera Lynn took a break from the entertainment world. She returned to the spotlight in 1951 and, the following year, achieved a major success with her single *Auf wiederseh'n sweetheart*. This song reached no.1 in America in July '52, a rare event for a UK artist in pre-Beatles days. When the first British record chart was represented on the list with three different discs: *Forget me not*, *Auf wiedersehn* and *Homing waltz*. In 1954 she topped the UK chart with *My son my son*. Vera Lynn's final appearance on the British singles list was *Travellin' home*, which peaked at no.20 in 1957. She continued to be a show business legend, however, and remained in the public eye in the UK throughout the sixties and seventies and into the eighties. She remained especially popular, of course, with the war veterans. She was awarded the OBE in 1969, and became Dame Vera Lynn in 1975. (Bob Macdonald 86).

AUF WIEDERSEHEN
Tracks: / Auf wiedersehen.
7" Single: Released Nov '52, on Decca, by Decca Records. Deleted '55. Catalogue no: **F 9927**

COLOUR OF MY LIFE
Tracks: / Colour of my life / Daybreak.
7" Single: Released May '81, on PRT, by Castle Communications Records. Deleted May '84. Catalogue no: **PRT 7P 217**

FAITHFUL HUSSAR, THE
Tracks: / Faithful hussar, The.
7" Single: Released Mar '57, on Decca, by Decca Records. Deleted '60. Catalogue no: **F 10846**

FORGET ME NOT
Tracks: / Forget me not.
7" Single: Released Nov '52, on Decca, by Decca Records. Deleted '55. Catalogue no: **F 9985**

HOMING WALTZ
Tracks: / Homing waltz.
7" Single: Released Nov '52, on Decca, by Decca Records. Deleted '55. Catalogue no: **F 9959**

HOUSE WITH LOVE IN IT, A
Tracks: / House with love in it, A.
7" Single: Released Oct '56, on Decca, by Decca Records. Deleted '59. Catalogue no: **F 10799**

I LOVE THIS LAND
Tracks: / I love this land / Victory theme.
7" Single: Released Jun '82, on State, by State Records. Catalogue no: **STAT 112**

MY SON MY SON
Tracks: / My son my son.
7" Single: Released Oct '54, on Decca, by Decca Records. Deleted '57. Catalogue no: **F 10372**

TRAVELLIN' HOME
Tracks: / Travellin' home.
7" Single: Released Jun '57, on Decca, by Decca Records. Deleted '60. Catalogue no: **F 10903**

WHITE CLIFFS OF DOVER
Tracks: / White cliffs of Dover, The / Nightingale sang in Berkeley Square.
7" Single: Released May '84, on EMI, by EMI Records. Catalogue no: **EMI 5476**

WHO ARE WE
Tracks: / Who are we.
7" Single: Released Jun '56, on Decca, by Decca Records. Deleted '59. Catalogue no: **F 10715**

WINDSOR WALTZ
Tracks: / Windsor waltz.
7" Single: Released Jun '53, on Decca, by Decca Records. Deleted '56. Catalogue no: **F 10092**

Lynott, Phil

Biographical details: This Irish singer, bass guitarist and songwriter was the dominant leader of rock band Thin Lizzy from 1970 until 1983. Throughout the group's 13 year existence, he held Thin Lizzy together despite a series of personnel changes and career ups and downs. He was born in Dublin into a mainly white, Catholic community, and had the social disadvantages if being both a half caste and an illegitmate child. From the mid seventies onwards, Lynott, became a virtual institution on the British music scene. His distinctive face, voice and personality were always around. Facially resembling Jimi Hendrix, he enjoyed playing the macho rock star; he was energetic and likeable, and lived in the fast lane. While Lizzy were still in existence, Lynott launched a subsidiary solo career. His first LP, 1980's *Solo in Soho* was a strong album that tended to emphasise a softer, more romantic side of Phil than was heard on the 100mph Lizzy output. It peaked at a somewhat disappointing no.28 position on the UK charts and yielded two modest top 40 singles, *Dear Miss Lonely Hearts*, and the tasteful Elvis Presley tribute *King's call*. 1982's *The Philip Lynott album* flopped, as did its excellent but underrated single *Old town*. Somewhat more successful was the catchy *Yellow pearl*, written in collaboration with Midge Ure - this single reached the UK top 14 position in early 1982, and was known to millions of TV viewers as the theme to *Top of the pops*. After the demise of Thin Lizzy, Lynott began to assemble a new band Grand Slam. Speculation that he might be a spent force in music was neatly answered in the summer of 1985, when he achieved the biggest UK hit single of his career - the frenetic *Out in the fields*, a duet with erstwhile Lizzy guitarist Gary Moore, reached no.5 and thus became the biggest hard rock hit by any act for four years. At the same time, he was part of The Crowd's chart topping all star charity single *You'll never walk alone*. Phil Lynott's career was brought to an abrupt and tragic end when he collapsed on Christmas Day 1985. He died in a Salisbury hospital in January 1986 at the age of 35. He was, sadly, the latest in a long line rock stars felled by drink and drug abuse; a hospital spokesman stated that the cause of death was pneumonia and heart failure. Lynott, an accomplished poet as well as an expressive singer and great musician, will be much missed. (Bob Macdonald 86).

DEAR MISS LONELY HEARTS
Tracks: / Dear Miss Lonely Hearts / Solo in Soho.
7" Single: Released Apr '80, on Vertigo, by Phonogram Ltd. Deleted '83. Catalogue no: **SOLO 1**

KING'S CALL
Tracks: / King's call / Yellow pearl / Dear miss lonely hearts (Available on 12" only.).
7" Single: Released Jan '87, on Vertigo, by Phonogram Ltd. Deleted Dec '87. Catalogue no: **LYN 1**
7" Single: Released Jun '80, on Vertigo, by Phonogram Ltd. Deleted '83. Catalogue no: **SOLO 2**
12" Single: Released Jan '87, on Vertigo, by Phonogram Ltd. Deleted Dec '87. Catalogue no: **LYN 112**

OLD TOWN
Tracks: / Old town / Beat of the drum.
7" Single: Released Sep '82, on Vertigo, by Phonogram Ltd. Deleted Sep '85. Catalogue no: **SOLO 5**

YELLOW PEARL
Tracks: / Yellow pearl / Girls.
7" Single: Released Dec '81, on Vertigo, by Phonogram Ltd. Catalogue no: **SOLO 3**
12" Single: Released Dec '81, on Vertigo, by Phonogram Ltd. Deleted '85. Catalogue no: **SOLO 312**

Lynton, Jackie

DAYDREAM
Tracks: / Daydream.
12" Single: Released Aug '85, on Rock City, Catalogue no: **RCRT 7**
7" Single: Released Aug '85, on Rock City, Catalogue no: **RCR 7**

Lynx

DON'T HIT ME WITH LOVE
Tracks: / Don't hit me with love / It's my life.
7" Single: Released '83, on Chrysalis, by Chrysalis Records. Catalogue no: **CHS 2650**
12" Single: Released '83, on Chrysalis, by Chrysalis Records. Deleted '87. Catalogue no: **CHS 12 2650**

Lynyrd Skynyrd

Biographical details: The nucleus of this American rock band was lead singer Ronnie Van Zant plus the earthshaking triple lead guitars of Gary Rossington, Allen Collins and Ed King (eventually replaced by Steve Gaines). Other important players included Billy Powell and Leon Wilkeson, plus back up singer Cassie Gaines (Steve's sister). Several other members came and went. Initially founded in school, the group's strangely spelt name was derived from their unpopular PE teacher Leonard Skinner, who had a reputation as a martinet. Lynyrd Skynyrd hailed from Jacksonville, Florida. After building southern support, they released their debut album *Pronounced Leh-nerd Skin-nerd* in 1973; it was produced by the respected Al Kooper (ex-Blood, Sweat & Tears), the man who is credited with discovering them. The LP was not a immediate success, but became a sleeper smash during 1974 thanks largely to an American tour as support act to The Who. The *Pronounced* album's closing track *Freebird* became one of the most played tracks on US rock radio during the rest of the seventies - it almost rivalled the arch classic of Led Zepplin's *Stairway to heaven*. Clocking in at 9 minutes 8 seconds, *Freebird* was a mesmerising hard rock epic; it built from a slowish ballad into 100 mph triple guitar tour de force. 1974's *Second helping* LP enjoyed quicker acceptance, thanks to the success of the US top 10 single *Sweet home Alabama*. During the mid - seventies, Lynyrd Skynyrd became one of the most popular bands of the southern boogie genre; they achieved their success by sheer grit and hard work, their incessant touring schedules amounting to some 300 gigs per year. The group's career was still in the ascendant when tragedy struck in October 1977. At the start of yet another tour, their private plane crashed in a wood near Gillsburg, Mississippi; this disaster claimed the lives of Van Zant and the Gaines members. With almost unbelievable irony, the band's just released LP was entitled *Street survivors* and its cover depicted the group being engulfed by flames. In the ensuing weeks, it became a top 5 seller in the States and yielded the top 20 single *What's your name*. The surviving musicians decided to terminate the group. Some of them joined the Rossington Collins Band who were launched in 1980 with the album *Any time any place anywhere*, but this combo was no great success. Greater recognition was granted to 38 Special, a similarly styled Southern rock act led by the late Ronnie's younger brother Donnie Van Zant. Lynyrd Skynyrd's British reputation was just starting to grow when the crash happened. The group's most successful album on the UK charts was *One more for the road*: (an acclaimed 1976 live set which reached no.17) and *Street Survivors* (no.13). On the British singles list, an EP featuring *Freebird* enjoyed three seperate flights - the most successful was in 1982 when it reached no.21 and logged 9 chart weeks. (Bob Macdonald 86).

FREEBIRD
Tracks: / Freebird / Sweet home Alabama.
12" Single: Released Jan '89, on MCA, by MCA Records. Catalogue no: **MCAT 1315**
CD 5": Released Jan '89, on MCA, by MCA Records. Catalogue no: **DMCA 1315**
12" Pic: Released Dec '83, on MCA, by MCA Records. Catalogue no: **MCATP 251**
7" Single: Released Jan '89, on MCA, by MCA Records. Catalogue no: **MCA 1315**
12" Single: Released Dec '83, on MCA, by MCA Records. Catalogue no: **MCAT 251**

FREEBIRD (OLD GOLD)
Tracks: / Freebird / Sweet home Alabama.
7" Single: Released Jul '84, on Old Gold, by Old Gold Records. Catalogue no: **OG 9421**

Lyon, Barbara

LETTER TO A SOLDIER
Tracks: / Letter to a soldier.
7" Single: Released Dec '56, on Columbia, by EMI Records. Deleted '59. Catalogue no: **DB 3685**

STOWAWAY
Tracks: / Stowaway.
7" Single: Released Jun '55, on Columbia, by EMI Records. Deleted '58. Catalogue no: **DB 3619**

Lyon, Jimmy

FIRING LINE, THE
Tracks: / Firing line / Wisdom.
12" Single: Released Dec '86, on Live, Catalogue no: **ALIVE 4**

Lyons, Gerry

I AIN'T GOT NO WORK
Tracks: / I ain't got no work.
12" Single: Released Jun '85, on D.A.D., by D.A.D. Records. Catalogue no: **DR 002**

Lypbox

MY HOUSE
Tracks: / My house / This town / Wasteland (Extra track on 12".).
7" Single: Released Apr '88, on MCA, by MCA Records. Catalogue no: **IRM 157**
12" Single: Released Apr '88, on MCA, by MCA Records. Catalogue no: **IRMT 157**

Lyres

HOW DO YOU KNOW
Tracks: / How do you know.
7" Single: Released Dec '87, on New Rose (1), by New Rose Records. Catalogue no: **NEW 97**

LYRES, THE
Tracks: / Lyres, The.
12" Single: Released Jun '88, on Fundamental, by Fundamental Music Records. Catalogue no: **PRAY 008**

SOMEONE WHO'LL TREAT YOU RIGHT
Tracks: / Someone who'll treat you right / She pays the rent / You've been wrong / I'll try anyway.
7" Single: Released Dec '85, on New Rose (1), by New Rose Records. Catalogue no: **NEW 60**

Lyric By Nine

CITY LIFE
Tracks: / City life.
7" Single: Released Aug '84, on Pregnant Turtle, Catalogue no: **PREGY 1**

Lyrical

NO RUN YUH BODY SO HOT
Tracks: / No run yuh body / Ashman / Dancehall bubbling.
12" Single: Released Sep '87, on Rockas, Catalogue no: **RR 007 RV**

Lyrics, Leslie

BLIND DATE
Tracks: / Blind date.
12" Single: Released Apr '85, on UK Bubblers, by Greensleeves Records. Deleted '88. Catalogue no: **UKMC 5**

GOT TO BE REGGAE
Tracks: / Got to be reggae / Rambo killer.
12" Single: Released Dec '83, on Ghetto Tone, Catalogue no: **GT 002**

Lytie

I WANT YOU
Tracks: / I want you.
12" Single: Released Feb '89, on GT's Records, by GT'S Records. Catalogue no: **GT 004**

Lyttelton, Humphrey

BAD PENNY BLUES (SINGLE)
Tracks: / Bad penny blues.
7" Single: Released Jul '56, on Parlophone, by EMI Records. Deleted '59. Catalogue no: **R 4184**

M

The following information was taken from the Music Master database on October 20th, 1989.

M - Moonlight and Muzak (Released on MCA)

M

KEEP IT TO YOURSELF
Tracks: / Keep it to yourself / Abracadabra.
7" Single: Released Jan '81, on MCA, by MCA Records. Deleted Jan '84. Catalogue no: **MCA 666**

MOONLIGHT AND MUZAK (See panel above)
Tracks: / Moonlight and muzak / Woman make man.
7" Single: Released Dec '79, on MCA, by MCA Records. Deleted '82. Catalogue no: **MCA 541**

OFFICIAL SECRETS (SINGLE)
Tracks: / Official secrets / Maniac.
7" Single: Released Nov '80, on MCA, by MCA Records. Deleted '83. Catalogue no: **MCA 650**

POP MUZIK (See adjacent panel)
Tracks: / Pop muzik.
7" Single: Released Apr '79, on MCA, by MCA Records. Deleted '82. Catalogue no: **MCA 413**
CD 5": Released 30 May '89, on Total, Catalogue no: **FRS CDS 1**
7" Single: Released '89, on Freestyle, Catalogue no: **FRS 1**
7" Single: Released 30 May '89, on Total, Catalogue no: **FRS 1**
12" Single: Released May '89, on Total, Deleted Aug '89. Catalogue no: **12 FRSR 1**
12" Single: Released 30 May '89, on Total, Deleted Aug '89. Catalogue no: **12 FRS 1**

THAT'S THE WAY THE MONEY GOES
Tracks: / That's the way the money goes / Satisfy your lust.
7" Single: Released Mar '80, on MCA, by MCA Records. Deleted '83. Catalogue no: **MCA 570**

M 4 Alice

SHILOH
Tracks: / Shiloh.
12" Single: Released Oct '88, on Plastic Head, by Plastic Head Records. Catalogue no: **PLASS 007**

SLEEPER, THE
Tracks: / Sleeper, The.
12" Single: Released Oct '88, on Plastic Head, by Plastic Head Records. Catalogue no: **PLAS 007**

M D Emm

FANNING THE FLAMES
Tracks: / Fanning the flames.
12" Single: Released Nov '88, on Republic, by Code Records. Catalogue no: **LICT 002R**

GET BUSY (IT'S)
Tracks: / Get busy.
12" Single: Released May '88, on Republic Records, Catalogue no: **MDM 001T**

PLAYING WITH FIRE
Tracks: / Playing with fire / Playing with fire (remix) (Only on the (LICOO 4 R) 12".).
12" Single: Released Nov '88, on Republic, by Code Records. Catalogue no: **LICT 003R**
12" Single: Released Nov '88, on Republic, by Code Records. Catalogue no: **LIC 003 R**
12" Single: Released Sep '88, on Republic, by Code Records. Catalogue no: **LIC 003**

M Lisa

(See under Lisa M for details)

M & M

BLACK STATIONS
Tracks: / Black stations.
7" Single: Released Jul '84, on RCA, by BMG Records (UK). Catalogue no: **RCA 426**
12" Single: Released Jul '84, on RCA, by BMG Records (UK). Catalogue no: **RCAT 426**

COOLING THE MEDIUM
Tracks: / Cooling the medium.
12" Single: Released Sep '84, on RCA, by BMG Records (UK). Catalogue no: **RCAT 452**

GET OFF YOUR BUTT
Tracks: / Get off your butt.
12" Single: Released May '89, on Radical, by Radical Records. Catalogue no: **RADICAL 3**

SCHOOL RAP
Tracks: / School rap / Not really a school fan.
7" Single: Released Oct '86, on Carrere, Catalogue no: **CAR 406**
12" Single: Released Oct '86, on Carrere, Catalogue no: **CART 406**

SONG IN MY HEART
Tracks: / Song in my heart / Riverine.
7" Single: Released Oct '86, on RCA, by BMG Records (UK). Catalogue no: **PB 40835**
12" Single: Released Oct '86, on RCA, by BMG Records (UK). Catalogue no: **PT 40836**

M & O Band

LET'S DO THE LATIN HUSTLE
Tracks: / Let's do the latin hustle.
7" Single: Released Feb '76, on Creole, by Creole Records. Deleted '79. Catalogue no: **CR 120**

M Over M

WALK AWAY
Tracks: / Walk away / I'm scared.
7" Single: Released Dec '88, on Strike (2), Catalogue no: **STRK 2**
12" Single: Released Dec '88, on Strike (2), Catalogue no: **12 STRK 2**

M. Walking On The

PARTY IN THE CEMETERY
Tracks: / Party in the cemetery.
12" Single: Released Feb '89, on Fuego, by Fuego Records. Catalogue no: **FUEGO 1112**

Mabuse, Sipho

BURN OUT
Tracks: / Burn out / Rise.
7" Single: Released 20 Jun '87, on Virgin, by Virgin Records. Deleted May '88. Catalogue no: **VS 981**
7" Single: Released Jul '85, on Important, Catalogue no: **TAN 2**
12" Single: Released 20 Jun '87, on Virgin, by Virgin Records. Deleted May '88. Catalogue no: **VS 981-12**
12" Single: Released Jul '85, on Important, Catalogue no: **TAN T 2**

JIVE SOWETO
Tracks: / Jive Sowetto / Break dancing.
12" Single: Released Sep '86, on Important, Catalogue no: **TANT 13**

SHIKISHA
Tracks: / Shikisha / Afrodizzia.
7" Single: Released Apr '87, on Virgin, by Virgin Records. Deleted May '88. Catalogue no: **VS 953**

Mac Band

JEALOUS
Tracks: / Jealous (remix) (Only on the 7" single.) / Jealous (7" edit) (Only on the 7" version.) / Jealous (edit) (Only on the 12" version.) / Jealous (instrumental) (Only on the 12" version.).
7" Single: Released Nov '88, on MCA, by MCA Records. Deleted 1 Jul '89. Catalogue no: **MCA 1292**
CD 5": Released Nov '88, on MCA, by MCA Records. Catalogue no: **DMCA 1292**
12" Single: Released Nov '88, on MCA, by MCA Records. Catalogue no: **MCAT 1292**

ROSES ARE RED
Tracks: / Roses are red / Roses are red (instrumental) / Roses are red (extended version) (12" version only.) / Roses are red (instrumental dub) (12" version only.).
7" Single: Released Jun '88, on MCA, by MCA Records. Catalogue no: **MCA 1264**
7" Single: Released Jun '88, on MCA, by MCA Records. Catalogue no: **MCA 23791**
12" Single: Released Jun '88, on MCA, by MCA Records. Catalogue no: **MCAT 1264**

STALEMATE
Tracks: / Stalemate / Stalemate (instrumental) / Stalemate (accapella) (12" only).
12" Single: Released 30 Aug '88, on MCA, by MCA Records. Catalogue no: **MCAT 1271**
CD 5": Released Aug '88, on MCA, by MCA Records. Catalogue no: **DMCA 1271**
7" Single: Released 30 Aug '88, on MCA, by MCA Records. Deleted 1 Jul '89. Catalogue no: **MCA 1271**

Mac, Debbie

HOT FOR YOU
Tracks: / Hot for you / Words.
7" Single: Released Jan '80, on Active, by Active Records. Deleted Jan '83. Catalogue no: **ACT 1**

Mac Mac

SO SHY
Tracks: / So shy (inst) / So shy (Available on 12" version only) / Acapella Inst. (Available on 12" version only).
7" Single: Released '86, on Creole, by Creole Records. Catalogue no: **CR 91**
12" Single: Released '86, on Creole, by Creole Records. Catalogue no: **CRT 91**

TAKE ME HOME LISA LISA
Tracks: / Take me home Lisa Lisa.
12" Single: Released Sep '85, on Creole, by Creole Records. Catalogue no: **CRT 87**

M - Pop Muzik (Released on MCA)

7" Single: Released Sep '85, on Creole, by Creole Records. Catalogue no: **CR 87**

Mac, Richie

OH SCENTED ROSE
Tracks: / Oh scented rose.
12" Single: Released Jun '84, on London Gemi, Catalogue no: **LG 006**Mac Sample

HOUSE INSPECTION
Tracks: / House inspection.
12" Single: Released Sep '88, on Subway, by Subway Records. Catalogue no: **SUB 037**

McAlister, Mike

I DON'T DIG IT
Tracks: / I don't dig it / 21.
7" Single: Released Jun '80, on Rollin' Rock, Catalogue no: **45 040**

McAllisters

TOO MUCH MONEY PROPAGANDA
Tracks: / Too much money propaganda.
12" Single: Released Nov '87, on Jolly Good, Catalogue no: **JG 001**

McAnally, Mac

MINIMUM LOVE
Tracks: / Minimum love.
7" Single: Released Apr '83, on Geffen, by Geffen Records (USA). Catalogue no: **GEF 3203**

Macao Combo

MACAO MACAO
Tracks: / Macao Macao.
7" Single: Released Jun '84, on PRT, by Castle Communications Records. Catalogue no: **7P 312**

MacArthur, Neil

SHE'S NOT THERE
Tracks: / She's not there.
7" Single: Released Feb '69, on Deram, by London Records. Deleted '72. Catalogue no: **DM 225**

Macattack

ART OF DRUMS
Tracks: / Art of drums.
12" Single: Released '86, on Baad, by Baad Records. Catalogue no: **12HIPNO 1**

McAuley Schenker Group

LOVE IS NOT A GAME
Tracks: / Love is not a game / Get out.
Note: 12EMS 40 - Limited Edition 12" - with Poster.
7" Single: Released Jan '88, on EMI, by EMI Records. Deleted 31 Jul '88. Catalogue no: **EM 40**
12" Single: Released Jan '88, on EMI, by EMI Records. Deleted 31 Jul '88. Catalogue no: **12EMS 40**
12" Single: Released Jan '88, on EMI, by EMI Records. Deleted 31 Jul '88. Catalogue no: **12EM 40**

MacBeth, David

MR BLUE
Tracks: / Mr. Blue.
7" Single: Released Oct '59, on Pye, Deleted '62. Catalogue no: **7N 15231**

McBride, Frankie

Biographical details: This Irish singer and entertainer has been an institution in the showbusiness of the Emerald Isle since the sixties. During the latter part of that decade, he chalked up a pair of UK chart entries. *Five little fingers*, a cover version of a 1964 US country and western hit written and origianally recorded by Bill Anderson, reached No. 19 and logged 15 weeks of the British top 50 in 1967; the McBride rendition was produced by Tommy Scott, who was fresh from his success with the Dubliners' *Seven drunken nights*. The *Frankie McBride* album reached No 29 on the UK Lp list in early 1968. (MacDonald, Bob, 10th January 1986).

COULD I HAVE THIS DANCE (SINGLE)
Tracks: / Could I have this dance / Gentle to your senses.
7" Single: Released Jun '82, on Mint, by Emerald Records. Deleted '88. Catalogue no: **CHEW 41**

FIVE LITTLE FINGERS (SINGLE)
7" Single: Released Jun '67, on Emerald, by Emerald Records. Catalogue no: **MD 1081**

HOW ARE THINGS IN GLOCCA MORRA
Tracks: / How are things in Glocca Morra.
7" Single: Released Jan '69, on Emerald, by Emerald Records. Deleted '88. Catalogue no: **MD 1116**

I'M BEING GOOD
Tracks: / I'm being good / Laura.
7" Single: Released Nov '81, on Mint, by Emerald Records. Deleted '88. Catalogue no: **CHEW 56**

JUST BEYOND THE MOON
Tracks: / Just beyond the moon / Let's build a love together.
7" Single: Released Feb '82, on Mint, by Emerald Records. Deleted '88. Catalogue no: **CHEW 61**

Macc Lads

EH UP!
Tracks: / Eh up!.
12" Single: Released '86, on Hetic House, Catalogue no: **HH 1ST**
7" Single: Released '86, on Hetic House, Catalogue no: **HH 1S**

JINGLE BELLS
Tracks: / Jingle bells / Barrel's round.
7" Single: Released Nov '87, on FM, by FM-Revolver Records. Catalogue no: **VHF 42**

PIE TASTER
Tracks: / Pie taster / No sheep till Buxton / Dan's underpant (live) (Extra track on 12" version.).
7" Single: Released Mar '88, on FM, by FM-Revolver Records. Catalogue no: **VHF 44**
Cassingle: Released 23 Apr '88, on FM, by FM-Revolver Records. Catalogue no: **HH 9**
12" Single: Released Mar '88, on FM, by FM-Revolver Records. Deleted Jun '89. Catalogue no: **12 VHF 144**

McCafferty, Dan

OUT OF TIME
Tracks: / Out of time.
7" Single: Released Sep '75, on Mountain, Deleted '78. Catalogue no: **TOP 1**

McCaffrey, Frank

A PLACE IN MY HEART
Tracks: / Place in my heart, A / I'd rather be sorry / Blackboard of my heart / Clock in the tower, The.
7" EP: Released Jun '88, on Ritz, by Ritz Records. Catalogue no: **RITZ 188**
Cassingle: Released Jun '88, on Ritz, by Ritz Records. Catalogue no: **RITZC 188**

CANDLELIGHT AND WINE
Tracks: / Candlelight and wine / I'll take you home again Kathleen.
7" Single: Released Jan '87, on Ritz, by Ritz Records. Catalogue no: **RITZ 167**

RING YOUR MOTHER WORE, THE
Tracks: / Ring your mother wore, The.
7" Single: Released '88, on Ritz, by Ritz Records. Catalogue no: **RITZ 141**
7" Single: Released Nov '85, on Ritz, by Ritz Records. Catalogue no: **RITZ 119**

McCaffrey, Leo

RATHLIN ISLAND (EP)
Tracks: / Rathlin Island / My Lagan.
7" Single: Released Sep '82, on Mint, by Emerald Records. Deleted '88. Catalogue no: **CHEW 2**

McCall, C.W.

CONVOY
Tracks: / Convoy / Roses for mama.
7" Single: Released Feb '76, on MGM, by Polydor Ltd. Deleted '79. Catalogue no: **2006 560**
7" Single: Released Jul '84, on Old Gold, by Old Gold Records. Deleted Jun '89. Catalogue no: **OG 9452**

McCall, Toussaint

NOTHING TAKES THE PLACE OF YOU
Tracks: / Nothing takes the place of you / Foot stompin' / Duke of Earl (Avaliable on 12" only.).

Note: From the original soundtrack of Hairspray.
12" Single: Released Oct '88, on Charly, by Charly Records. Catalogue no: **CYZ 127**
7" Single: Released Oct '88, on Charly, by Charly Records. Catalogue no: **CYZ 7127**

NOTHING TAKES THE PLACE OF YOU (SINGLE)
Tracks: / Nothing takes the place of you.
7" Single: Released Jul '80, on Charly, by Charly Records. Deleted '87. Catalogue no: **CTD 124**

McCalla, Dennis

PEACE MAKER
Tracks: / Peacemaker.
12" Single: Released Mar '84, on Raintree, Catalogue no: **RTR 018**

McCalla, Noel

BEGGIN (EP)
Tracks: / Beggin' / Ain't that peculiar.
7" Single: Released Jun '80, on Epic, by CBS Records. Catalogue no: **EPC 8731**

McCallum, David

COMMUNICATION
Tracks: / Communication.
7" Single: Released Apr '66, on Capitol, by EMI Records. Deleted '69. Catalogue no: **CL 15439**

McCalmans

Biographical details: One of the world's most travelled folk groups - from Europe to The Falklands, from Australia to America - "The Macs", typical style, were quick to support the new enterprise and give some muscle to the new label. It is hard to believe that the McCalmans folk group has been around for a little over 20 years. If you go to one of their concerts or folk club appearances you will be struck by the spontancity of their approach and the freshness of their material. Scottish traditional songs are their mainstay and nobody can match the powerful vibrancy of their harmony, but these are linked with humour and laced with brand new songs, some written by members of the group, some culled from the best modern folksong writing from throughout the world. This combination has brought them countless TV appearances and radio broadcasts, including the very successful network BBC Radio program, *McCalmans and Friends*. (Greentrax, 1988).

GOD BLESS THE BIRTHDAY BOY
Tracks: / God bless the birthday boy / Seagull cry.
7" Single: Released Dec '81, on Gundog, Deleted Dec '84. Catalogue no: **GUNS 005**

McCann, Susan

BLUE JEAN
Tracks: / Blue Jean.
7" Single: Released Apr '85, on Homespun (Ireland), by Outlet Records. Catalogue no: **HS 096**

JOHNNY LOVELY JOHNNY
Tracks: / Johnny lovely Johnny / Where the river Shannon flows.
7" Single: Released May '86, on Homespun (Ireland), by Outlet Records. Catalogue no: **HS 106**

WHEN THE SUN SAYS GOODBYE TO THE MOUNTAINS(SINGLE)
7" Single: Released Nov '85, on Homespun (Ireland), by Outlet Records. Catalogue no: **HS 103**

McCarlos, Don

SWEET AFRICA
Tracks: / Sweet Africa / Sweet roots / Boy I love, The.
12" Single: Released Jul '82, on Starlight, Catalogue no: **SLD 522**

McCarthy

A LA GUILLOTINE
Tracks: / A la guillotine.
7" Single: Released May '88, on Danceteria, Catalogue no: **TUE 871**

AT WAR EP
Tracks: / At war.
12" Single: Released May '89, on Midnight Music, by Midnight Music Records. Catalogue no: **DONG 48**
CD 5": Released May '89, on Midnight Music, by Midnight Music Records. Catalogue no: **DONG 48 CD**

FRANS HALS
Tracks: / Frans Hals.
7" Single: Released Mar '87, on Pink Label, by Pink Label Records. Catalogue no: **PINKY 17**
12" Single: Released Mar '87, on Pink Label, by Pink Label Records. Catalogue no: **PINKY 17T**

IN PURGATORY
Tracks: / In purgatory.
7" Single: Released Feb '86, on Wall Of Salmon, Catalogue no: **MAC 001**

KEEP AN OPEN MIND OR ELSE
Tracks: / Keep an open mind or else.
7" Single: Released 30 Jan '89, on Midnight, Catalogue no: **DING 045**
12" Single: Released 30 Jan '89, on Midnight, Catalogue no: **DONG 045**

RED SLEEPING BEAUTY
Tracks: / Red sleeping beauty.
7" Single: Released Oct '86, on Pink, Catalogue no: **PINKY 12**
12" Single: Released Oct '86, on Pink, Catalogue no: **PINKY 12T**

SHOULD THE BIBLE BE BANNED
Tracks: / Should the bible be banned.
12" Single: Released Apr '88, on September, Catalogue no: **SEPT 5T**

THIS NELSON ROCKERFELLER
Tracks: / This Nelson Rockerfeller.
12" Single: Released 5 Mar '88, on September Records, Catalogue no: **SEPT 4T**

McCarthy,Keith

EVERYBODY RUDE
Tracks: / Everybody rude / Rambo calypso.
12" Single: Released Aug '86, on Money Disc, Catalogue no: **MDL 003**

McCartney, Paul

Biographical details: This British singer, songwriter, bass guitarist, multi-instrumentalist and producer was born James Paul McCartney in Liverpool in 1942. In his early musical years he took lessons on the trumpet, following in father's footsteps. Soon after his 14th birthday, Paul's mother died unexpectedly; his father bought him a guitar to help the lad through his grief. It was McCartney who announced to the world the news of The Beatles' breakup in April 1970. He did this via the strange medium of a self-interview in Uk promotional copies of his debut solo LP *McCartney*. Paul was incensed by the arrival of a new Beatles manager Allen Klein, and felt increasingly alienated by John Lennon's obsession with his new wife Yoko Ono; even more importantly, the individual Beatles' musical inclinations were diverging widely. The *McCartney* album cruised to No. 2 in Britain and No.1 in America; no singles were culled from it, but the two best tracks were *Maybe I'm amazed* and *Every night*. The second Lp *Ram* was credited to Paul and Linda McCartney, despite the fact that Mrs McCartney's contributions were limited to vocal harmonies and sleeve photographs. The album was slagged off by the critics, but it went to the top chart slot on both sides of the Atlantic; its strongest track, an intriguing hotchpotch of assorted ideas entitled *Uncle Albert/Admiral Halsey* became a No. 1 single in the states but was never released in Britain. In the same year, 1971, there was a Top 5 single in both the US and UK with the catchy but lightweight *Another day*. McCartney formed the band Wings in 1971, and Linda was included in the line-up despite continued carping from journalists about her limited musical talent. After a rocky and controversial start, the group got into their stride in 1973 and became one of the world's top bands. By 1980 Wings had ceased to function for all practical purposes. Ten years after *McCartney*, Paul resumed a fully fledged solo career with the LP *McCartney II*. This album entered the UK chart at NO.1, and yielded the transatlantic smash song *Coming up*. The murder of Lennon in December 1980 convinced McCartney to give up live performing altogether. He kept a low profile for a while - in 1981 he failed to release any new material, for the first time in any calendar year since the start of the Beatles' fame. He returned in 1982 with one of his strongest albums, *Tug of war*, it was a No. 1 smash in the UK and US, as was his first single *Ebony and ivory*, a bland plea for racial harmony on which he duetted with Stevie Wonder. Over the next 18 months there were two collaborations with Michael Jackson - *The girl is mine* (No. 8 in UK, No. 2 in US) and *Say say say* (No. 2 in UK and No.1 in US). 1984 brought McCartney his first solo UK No. 1 single with *Pipes of peace D*; he thus became the only artist in British history to have reached the top as a member of a quartet, a trio, a duo and as a solo performer. Later in the year McCartney finally unveiled his autobiographical feature film *Give my regards to broad street* which after being eagerly anticipated for more than 12 months, recieved a lukewarm critical reception. The soundtrack album, mainly comprising reworkings of familiar McCartney standards, was nevertheless able to reach the UK No.1 position. One of the films few new songs *No more lonely nights* was a No. 2 single and was followed by the No.3 success of *We all stand together*, a children's novelty track lifted from the film's accompanying mini-movie *Rupert and the frog song*. The everlasting appeal of this ageless superstar was reaffirmed yet again. While it is an indisputable fact that McCartney has been the most commercially successful Beatle since 1970, the general concensus is that Lennon's body of work was considerably superior. When *Imagine* is compared with *Ebony and Ivory*, or *Happy Xmas (war is over)* with *Wonderful Christmas time*, it is not hard to see why this conclusion has been reached. Where John was often incisive and profound, Paul has often been trite and superficial. But nobody can argue about the latter's ear for an infectious pop melody and his ability to churn our hit after hit after hit. With the exception of his public defence of cannabis, his image as a happy family man has not been the stuff of hell-raising rock rebellion. But McCartney has not set out to change the world; he has merely wanted to get the globe singing along. (MacDonald, Bob, 10th January 1986).

Paul McCartney - This One (Released on Parlophone)

ANOTHER DAY
Tracks: / Another day / Oh woman oh why.
7" Single: Released Mar '71, on Parlophone, by EMI Records. Catalogue no: **R 5889**

BACK SEAT OF MY CAR
Tracks: / Back seat of my car / Heart of the country.
7" Single: Released Aug '71, on EMI, by EMI Records. Catalogue no: **R 5914**

BAND ON THE RUN (SINGLE)
Tracks: / Band on the run.
7" Single: Released Jun '74, on Parlophone, by EMI Records. Catalogue no: **R 5997**

COMING UP
Tracks: / Coming up / Lunch box odd sox.
7" Single: Released Apr '80, on Parlophone, by EMI Records. Catalogue no: **R 6035**

EBONY AND IVORY
Tracks: / Ebony and ivory / Rainclouds.
12" Single: Released Mar '82, on Parlophone, by EMI Records. Deleted '88. Catalogue no: **12R 6054**
7" Single: Released Mar '82, on Parlophone, by EMI Records. Catalogue no: **R 6054**

GIRL IS MINE, THE
Tracks: / Girl is mine, The / Can't get outta the rain.
7" Single: Released Nov '82, on Epic, by CBS Records. Catalogue no: **EPC A 2729**

HELEN WHEELS
Tracks: / Helen wheels / Country dreamer.
7" Single: Released Oct '73, on EMI, by EMI Records. Catalogue no: **R 5993**

JET
Tracks: / Jet / Let me roll it.
7" Single: Released Feb '74, on Parlophone, by EMI Records. Catalogue no: **R5996**

JUNIORS FARM
Tracks: / Juniors farm / Sally G.
7" Single: Released Nov '74, on Parlophone, by EMI Records. Catalogue no: **R 5999**

MY BRAVE FACE
Tracks: / My brave face / Flying to my home / I'm gonna be a wheel someday (Not on 7".) / Ain't that a shame (Not on 7".).
7" Single: Released May '89, on Parlophone, by EMI Records. Catalogue no: **203 358 7**
CD 5": Released May '89, on Parlophone, by EMI Records. Catalogue no: **203 358 2**
7" Single: Released May '89, on Parlophone, by EMI Records. Catalogue no: **R 6213**
12" Single: Released May '89, on Parlophone, by EMI Records. Catalogue no: **203 358 6**
Cassingle: Released May '89, on Parlophone, by EMI Records. Catalogue no: **TCR 6213**
12" Single: Released May '89, on Parlophone, by EMI Records. Catalogue no: **12R 6213**
Cassingle: Released May '89, on Parlophone, by EMI Records. Catalogue no: **203 348 4**
CD 5": Released May '89, on Parlophone, by EMI Records. Catalogue no: **CDR 6213**

MY LOVE
Tracks: / My love / Mess, The.
7" Single: Released Mar '73, on Parlophone, by EMI Records. Catalogue no: **R 5985**

NO MORE LONELY NIGHTS
Tracks: / No more lonely nights.
7" Single: Released Sep '84, on Parlophone, by EMI Records. Catalogue no: **R 6080**
12" Single: Released Sep '84, on Parlophone, by EMI Records. Catalogue no: **12R 6080**

NO MORE LONELY NIGHTS (SPECIAL DANCE MIX)
Tracks: / No more lonely nights (special dance mix).
12" Single: Released Nov '84, on Parlophone, by EMI Records. Catalogue no: **12RA 6080**

ONCE UPON A LONG AGO
Tracks: / Once upon a long ago / Back on my feet / Midnight special* / Don't get around much anymore / Lawdy Miss Clawdy+ / Kansas City**.
Note: * track on 12" only. + track on 12RX 6170 only (Special Bag). ** tracks on CD single and 12RX 6170 only.
CD 5": Released Nov '87, on Parlophone, by EMI Records. Deleted Jun '89. Catalogue no: **CDR 6170**
7" Single: Released Nov '87, on Parlophone, by EMI Records. Catalogue no: **R 6170**
12" Single: Released Nov '87, on Parlophone, by EMI Records. Catalogue no: **12RX 6170**
12" Single: Released Nov '87, on Parlophone, by EMI Records. Catalogue no: **12R 6170**

ONLY LOVE REMAINS
Tracks: / Only love remains / Tough on a tightrope.
12" Single: Released Nov '86, on Parlophone, by EMI Records. Deleted Oct '87. Catalogue no: **12R 6148**
7" Single: Released Nov '86, on Parlophone, by EMI Records. Deleted Oct '87. Catalogue no: **R 6148**

PIPES OF PEACE (SINGLE)
Tracks: / Pipes of peace / So bad.
7" Single: Released Dec '83, on Parlophone, by EMI Records. Catalogue no: **R 6064**

PRESS
Tracks: / Press / It's not true / Hanglide (Extra track on 12"version only) / Press (dub) (Extra track on 12"version only) / Press (video edit).
7" Single: Released Dec '85, on Parlophone, by EMI Records. Deleted '88. Catalogue no: **R 6133**

PRETTY LITTLE HEAD
Tracks: / Pretty little head / Angry / Write away.
Cassingle: Released Nov '86, on EMI, by EMI Records. Deleted Apr '88. Catalogue no: **TCR 6145**

SPIES LIKE US
Tracks: / Spies like us.
12" Pic: Released Dec '85, on Parlophone, by EMI Records. Catalogue no: **12RP 6118**
7" Pic: Released Dec '85, on Parlophone, by EMI Records. Deleted Oct '87. Catalogue no: **RP 6118**
12" Single: Released Nov '85, on Parlophone, by EMI Records. Deleted Oct '87. Catalogue no: **12R 6118**
7" Single: Released Nov '85, on Parlophone, by EMI Records. Deleted Oct '87. Catalogue no: **R 6118**

TAKE IT AWAY
Tracks: / Take it away / I'll give you a ring.
12" Single: Released Jun '82, on Parlophone, by EMI Records. Catalogue no: **12 6056**
7" Single: Released Jun '82, on Parlophone, by EMI Records. Catalogue no: **R 6056**
12" Single: Released May '84, on EMI (Germany), by EMI Records. Catalogue no: **1C K052Z 64850**

TEMPORARY SECRETARY
Tracks: / Temporary secretary / Secret friend.
12" Single: Released Sep '80, on Parlophone, by EMI Records. Catalogue no: **12R 6039**

Paul McCartney - We All Stand Together (Released on Parlophone)

THIS ONE (See panel opposite)
Tracks: / This one / First stone, The / I wanna cry (12" & CD single only.) / I'm in love again (12" & CD single only.) / Good sign (12RX 6223 only.).
7" Single: Released Jul '89, on Parlophone, by EMI Records. Catalogue no: **RX 6223**
CD 5": Released Jul '89, on Parlophone, by EMI Records. Catalogue no: **2203 446 2**
Cassingle: Released Jul '89, on Parlophone, by EMI Records. Catalogue no: **203 446 4**
12" Single: Released Jul '89, on Parlophone, by EMI Records. Catalogue no: **203 446 0**
CD 5": Released Jul '89, on Parlophone, by EMI Records. Catalogue no: **CDR 6223**
7" Single: Released Jul '89, on Parlophone, by EMI Records. Catalogue no: **203 446 7**
7" Single: Released Jul '89, on Parlophone, by EMI Records. Catalogue no: **R 6223**
12" Single: Released Jul '89, on Parlophone, by EMI Records. Catalogue no: **12R 6223**
Cassingle: Released Jul '89, on Parlophone, by EMI Records. Catalogue no: **TCR 6223**
12" Single: Released Jul '89, on Parlophone, by EMI Records. Catalogue no: **203 446 6**
12" Single: Released Jul '89, on Parlophone, by EMI Records. Catalogue no: **12RX 6223**

TUG OF WAR(SINGLE)
Tracks: / Tug of war / Get it.
7" Single: Released Sep '82, on Parlophone, by EMI Records. Catalogue no: **R 6057**

WATERFALLS
Tracks: / Waterfalls.
7" Single: Released Jun '80, on Parlophone, by EMI Records. Deleted '83. Catalogue no: **R 6037**

WE ALL STAND TOGETHER (See panel below)
Tracks: / We all stand together / We all stand together (humming version).
Note: From the animated featurette Rupert and the Frog Song classified as Universal (suitable for all).h
7" Pic: Released Nov '85, on Parlophone, by EMI Records. Deleted '88. Catalogue no: **RP 6086**
7" Single: Released Nov '85, on Parlophone, by EMI Records. Catalogue no: **R 6086**

WONDERFUL CHRISTMAS TIME
Tracks: / Wonderful Christmas time / Rudolph the red nosed reggae.
7" Single: Released Nov '79, on Parlophone, by EMI Records. Catalogue no: **R 6029**

McClain, Charly

WHO'S CHEATIN' WHO
Tracks: / Who's cheating who / Love scenes.
7" Single: Released Apr '81, on Epic, by CBS Records. Catalogue no: **EPC A 1087**

McClain, Janice

PASSION AND PAIN
Tracks: / Passion and pain / Passion and pain (Inst).
7" Single: on MCA, by MCA Records. Catalogue no: **MCA 1109**
12" Single: Released Mar '87, on MCA, by MCA Records. Catalogue no: **MCAT 1109**

McClain, Marlon

SHAKE IT UP
Tracks: / Shake it up / Pastel.
12" Single: Released Aug '81, on Fantasy (1), by BMG Records (UK). Catalogue no: **FTCT 198**
7" Single: Released Aug '81, on Fantasy (1), by BMG Records (UK). Catalogue no: **FTC 198**

McClaine, Carla

BRINGIN' ON BACK THE GOOD TIMES
Tracks: / Bringin' on back the good times / Merry-go-round.
7" Single: Released Sep '81, on Runaway, Deleted '85. Catalogue no: **RUN 4**

McClary, Thomas

THIN WALLS
Tracks: / Thin walls / Love will find a way.
12" Single: Released Jan '85, on Motown, by BMG Records (UK). Catalogue no: **TMGT 1366**
7" Single: Released Jan '85, on Motown, by BMG Records (UK). Catalogue no: **TMG 1366**

McClean, John

SAY YOU

Kirsty MacColl - Days (Released on Virgin)

Kirsty MacColl - There's A Guy Works Down the Chip Shop (swear's he's Elvis) (Released on Polydor)

Tracks: / Say you.
12" Single: Released Jun '88, on Ariwa Sounds, by Ariwa Sounds. Catalogue no: **ARI 76**

TRULY BOWLED OVER
Tracks: / Truly bowled over.
12" Single: Released Nov '88, on Ariwa Sounds, by Ariwa Sounds. Catalogue no: **ARI 82**
7" Single: Released Nov '88, on Ariwa Sounds, by Ariwa Sounds. Catalogue no: **ARI 82 122**

McClean, Shirley

HUSTLERS SONG
Tracks: / Hustler's song.
12" Single: Released Sep '88, on Redman International, Catalogue no: **RED 35**

LET ME GO
Tracks: / Let me go.
12" Single: Released Nov '83, on Lucky Dice, Catalogue no: **LD 001**

McClen, Dee Dee

I'M IN LOVE
Tracks: / I'm in love.
12" Single: Released Oct '82, on Regal, Catalogue no: **RD 018**

McCleod, Enos

ME & MI LOVER
Tracks: / Me & mi lover.
12" Single: Released Oct '84, on Bendown, Catalogue no: **Unknown**

McClinton, Delbert

GIVING IT UP FOR YOUR LOVE
Tracks: / Giving it up for your love / My sweet baby.
7" Single: Released Jan '81, on Capitol, by EMI Records. Deleted Jan '84. Catalogue no: **CL 16185**

SHOTGUN RIDER
Tracks: / Shotgun rider / Baby ruth.
7" Single: Released Apr '81, on Capitol, by EMI Records. Deleted '85. Catalogue no: **CL 16191**

McCloskey, Sue

I REALLY NEED YOUR LOVE
Tracks: / I really need your love / Lost inside myself.
7" Single: Released Feb '81, on Carrere, Deleted '84. Catalogue no: **CAR 174**

McCloud, Caspar

MESSIN' AROUND
Tracks: / Messin' around.
7" Single: Released '79, on Rock Steady, by Rock Steady Records. Catalogue no: **MICK 007**

McCloud, Emos

HEAD MISTRESS
Tracks: / Head mistress.

Kirsty MacColl - A New England (Released on Stiff)

7" Single: Released Oct '83, on African Unity, Catalogue no: **DSR 0442**

McCluhan, Rob

GOOD MORNING
Tracks: / Good morning / Good morning (inst).
7" Single: Released Oct '88, on F2, Catalogue no: **FTW 1**
12" Single: Released Oct '88, on F2, Catalogue no: **12 FTW 1**

McClure, Bobby

IT FEELS SO GOOD (TO BE BACK HOME)
Tracks: / It feels so good (to be back home) / You never miss your water / It feels so good (radio version).
12" Single: Released Apr '87, on Debut, by Skratch Records. Catalogue no: **DEBTX 3021**

McCluskey Brothers

AWARE OF ALL
Tracks: / Aware of all / He's on the beach / Please go to sleep.
12" Single: Released Jul '86, on Thrush, by Thrush Records. Catalogue no: **THRUSH 4**

SHE SAID TO THE DRIVER
Tracks: / She said to the driver.
12" Single: Released Jan '88, on DDT, by D.D.T.Records. Catalogue no: **DISP 15T**
7" Single: Released Apr '88, Catalogue no: **DISP 15**

MacColl, Kirsty

BERLIN
Tracks: / Berlin.
7" Single: Released Aug '83, on N.O.W., by North Of Watford Records. Catalogue no: **NOW 100**
12" Single: Released Aug '83, on N.O.W., by North Of Watford Records. Catalogue no: **NOWX 100**

DAYS (See panel above)
Tracks: / Days / Happy / Still life (12" only.).
12" Single: Released 12 Jun '89, on Virgin, by Virgin Records. Catalogue no: **KMAT 2**
CD 5": Released 12 Jun '89, on Virgin, by Virgin Records. Catalogue no: **KMADX 2**
10" single: Released Jul '89, on Virgin, by Virgin Records. Catalogue no: **KMAN 2**
7" Single: Released 12 Jun '89, on Virgin, by Virgin Records. Catalogue no: **KMA 2**
CD 3": Released Jul '89, on Virgin, by Virgin Records. Catalogue no: **KMACDX 2**

FREE WORLD
Tracks: / Free world / You just haven't earned it yet,baby / Closer to God.
7" Single: Released Feb '89, on Virgin, by Virgin Records. Catalogue no: **KMA 1**
10" single: Released Feb '89, on Virgin, by Virgin Records. Catalogue no: **KMAN 1**
12" Single: Released Feb '89, on Virgin, by Virgin Records. Catalogue no: **KMAT 1**
CD 3": Released Feb '89, on Virgin, by Virgin Records. Catalogue no: **KMACD 1**

HE'S ON THE BEACH
7" Single: Released Jun '85, on Stiff, by Stiff Records. Catalogue no: **BUY 225**
12" Single: Released Jun '85, on Stiff, by Stiff Records. Catalogue no: **BUYIT 225**

INNOCENCE
Tracks: / Innocence / Clubland.
12" Single: Released Sep '89, on Virgin, by Virgin Records. Catalogue no: **12 KMA 3**
7" Single: Released Sep '89, on Virgin, by Virgin Records. Catalogue no: **KMA 3**
CD 3": Released Sep '89, on Virgin, by Virgin Records. Catalogue no: **KMACD 3**

NEW ENGLAND, A (See panel below)
Tracks: / New England, A / Patrick.
12" Single: Released Dec '84, on Stiff, by Stiff Records. Catalogue no: **BUYIT 216**
7" Single: Released Dec '84, on Stiff, by Stiff Records. Catalogue no: **BUY 216**

SEE THAT GIRL
Tracks: / See that girl / Over you.
7" Single: Released Sep '81, on Polydor, by Polydor Ltd. Deleted Sep '84. Catalogue no: **POSP 326**

TERRY
Tracks: / Terry.
12" Single: Released Oct '83, on Stiff, by Stiff Records. Catalogue no: **SBUY 190**
7" Single: Released Oct '83, on Stiff, by Stiff Records. Catalogue no: **BUY 190**

THERE'S A GUY WORKS DOWN THE CHIPSHOP (swears he's Elvis) (See panel above)
Tracks: / There's a guy works down the chip shop (swears he's Elvis) / Hard to believe.
7" Single: Released Jun '81, on Polydor, by Polydor Ltd. Deleted '82. Catalogue no: **POSP 250**

YOU STILL BELIEVE IN ME
Tracks: / You still believe in me / Queen of the high teas.
7" Single: Released Nov '81, on Polydor, by Polydor Ltd. Deleted Nov '84. Catalogue no: **POSP 368**

McComb, Dave

I DON'T NEED YOU
Tracks: / I don't need you / Willie the torch / Liberty & a thousand faces.
12" Single: Released 27 Feb '89, on Island, by Island Records. Catalogue no: **12 IS 410**
7" Single: Released 27 Feb '89, on Island, by Island Records. Catalogue no: **IS 410**

McCoo, Marilyn

Biographical details: This American singer was a member of the highly successful US vocal quintet The Fifth Dimension, for ten years starting in 1965. she and fellow member Billy Davis Jr, to whom she was married, decided to quit the group in November '75. They issued an album of duets in 1976, the title track *I hope we get to love in time* becoming a minor US hit single. Then came *You don't have to be a star (to be in my show,* which was a sleeper smash: the song entered the US top 40 in October '76 and finally hit No.1 in

January '77; in Britain, it got to No.7 in Spring '77, although its early UK progress was at the centre of an alleged chart-rigging scandal. McCoo & Davis' follow-up to *You don't have to be a star* was called *Your love*, and it peaked at No. 15 in the US. During that summer, the couple hosted their own network TV series. Like the Fifth Dimension, the pair's style was a middle-of-the-road cabaret version of soul music - this television exposure confirmed the duo's sugary showbiz orientations, and destroyed their already slender credibility amongst pop and soul fans.
Their 1978 album *Marilyn and Billy* was a turkey, although it has historical interest because in contained the first recorded version of the Gerry Goffin/Michael Masser song *Saving all my love for you* - this composition became a transatlantic smash for Whitney Houston in 1985. Marilyn tried her hand as a solo artist, but both husband and wife faded into obscurity.
(Bob MacDonald, 11th January 1986).

YOU DON'T HAVE TO BE A STAR
Tracks: / You don't have to be a star baby.
7" Single: Released Mar '77, on ABC Records, by MCA Records. Deleted '80. Catalogue no: **ABC 4147**

McCookery,Helen Book

LEAVING YOU BABY
Tracks: / Leaving you baby.
12" Single: Released Oct '86, on Pure Trash, by Pure Trash Records. Catalogue no: **PTR 002**

McCormick, Paul

ANOTHER DAY AT HOME
Tracks: / Another day at home.
12" Single: Released Apr '89, on Pink Moon Organisation, Catalogue no: **PMT 3**

McCoy, John

OH WELL
Tracks: / Oh well / Because you lied.
7" Single: Released Nov '83, on Legacy, by Legacy Records. Catalogue no: **LGY 9**

SOUND OF THUNDER, THE
Tracks: / Sound of thunder, The.
7" Single: Released Oct '84, on Legacy, by Legacy Records. Catalogue no: **LGY 17**

McCoy, Van

Biographical details: This American keyboardist, songwriter, arranger, producer, conductor and orchestra leader was a successful behind-the-scenes figure in soul and pop music during the sixties and seventies. Born in Washington DC, he took up the piano at the age of four but temporarily neglected music during his teenage years. His first key break came in 1961, when the young McCoy became an AR executive and producer for Scepter Records during his time there, he wrote The Shirelles' US top 40 single *Stop the music*. In late 1962 he was taken under the wing of the famous songwriting/production team, Jerry Leiber and Mike Stoller. He later became a staff writer for Blackwood Music and, in 1967, formed his own publishing and production company.
By the end of the sixties, his tally of hit compositions included *Giving up* (Glady's Knight and the Pips), *When you're young and in love* (Ruby and the Romantics and the Marvelettes), *Baby I'm yours* (Barbara Lewis and Peter and Gordon) and *I get the sweetest feeling* (Jackie Wilson). McCoy started the seventies by writing and producing a US No.11 hit called *5-10-15-20 (25-30 years of love)* for the Presidents; in 1971 there was *Right on the tip of my tongue* by Brenda & The Tabulations. Always geared to the smoother, sweeter side of soul music, Van was in his element when he became the arranger for the Stylistics. In 1975 McCoy had a successful studio streak with ex-Temptations member David Ruffin. During 1976-7 Van was generally more successful in Britain than America - Melba Moore's *This is it*, Gladys Knight and the Pips' *Baby don't change your mind* and his own *The Shuffle* all reached the UK Top 10. With his career far from finished, Van McCoy died suddenly of a heart attack in July 1979 in Englewood, New Jersey at the age of 39; his early passing was a considerable shock to the Ameriacan music industry. (Bob MacDonald, 11th January 1988).

CHANGE WITH THE TIMES
Tracks: / Change with the times.
7" Single: Released Nov '75, on Avco-Embassy, Deleted '78. Catalogue no: **6105 042**

HUSTLE, THE
Tracks: / Hustle, The / Shuffle, The.
7" Single: Released May '75, on Avco-Embassy, Deleted '78. Catalogue no: **6105 037**

HUSTLE, THE (OLD GOLD)
Tracks: / Hustle, The.
7" Single: Released Jul '82, on Old Gold, by Old Gold Records. Deleted Jul '88. Catalogue no: **OG 9246**

SHUFFLE, THE
Tracks: / Shuffle, The.
7" Single: Released Apr '77, on Avco-Embassy, Deleted '80. Catalogue no: **6105 076**

SOUL CHA CHA
Tracks: / Soul cha cha.
7" Single: Released Feb '77, on Avco-Embassy, Deleted '80. Catalogue no: **6105 065**

McCoys

Biographical details: This American pop combo consisted of Randy Hobbs, Bobby Peterson, Randy Zehringer and his elder brother Rick Zehringer. The latter became better known as Rick Derringer. The name of the group was inspired by by The McCoy, a track on a Ventures album. Though not an overnight success story, the McCoys were only in thier late teens when they shot to fame with their first single *Hang on Sloopy* in 1965.
Their contempories, The Strangeloves, introduced them to Bert Berns (aka Russell), who was a successful songwriter and owner of Bang Records. Berns had co-written the song *My girl Sloopy*, which had been a US No 26 hit for the Vibrations in early 1964 - he still had faith in the song, believing that it could be an even bigger success. He gave it to the McCoys under it's new title *Hang on Sloopy* and it went to No 1 in America in October '65. The record was a No. 5 hit in the UK. Sounding rather like a cross between the Beatles and The Four Seasons, and thereby capitalising upon two of the most popular styles of the era, *Hang on Sloopy* was one of the catchiest hits of '65. It was followed by *Fever* which reached No 7 in the US and No.44 in the UK.
Several more McCoys singles reached the US Hot 100, but most were only minor hits. The group had drifted into obscurity by 1969, the year that they took up residence as the house-band in a New York club. Its manager Steve Paul was able to revamp the band and team them with the up-and-coming blues-rock guitarist Johnny Winter. This combination worked well for both parties. During the early seventies, Winter's recording and concert career reached great heights; for the former *Hang on Sloopy* teenagers, the blusy material was in total contrast to the pop fodder which had made them famous.
However Johnny could not handle the superstar role that was thrust upon him; as his career went into decline, Rick Derringer (the Mccoys' former lead singer and lead guitarist) moved to the band of Johnny's younger brother, the Edgar Winter Group. Rick continued to play aporadically with both Winters until 1976. Derringer also launched a solo career, his first album being 1973's *All American boy*. Several more Lp's appeared during the rest of the seventies, but they did not achieve major success.
Nevertheless, Derringer was a uch respected figure within the music industry, both as a great guitarist and a talented producer. He kept a low profile in the eighties, but enjoyed success in 1984 as guitar player and producer of Weird Al Yankovic's Michael Jackson parody *Eat it*..

FEVER
Tracks: / Fever.
7" Single: Released Sep '65, on Immediate, Deleted '68. Catalogue no: **IM 021**

HANG ON SLOOPY
Tracks: / Hang on sloopy.
7" Single: Released Sep '80, on USA, by Charly Records. Catalogue no: **LR 8108**
12" Single: Released Nov '88, on SFM, Catalogue no: **SEA 3**
7" Single: Released Sep '65, on Immediate, Deleted '68. Catalogue no: **IM 001**

McCracklin, Jimmy

WALK, THE
Tracks: / Walk, The / I'm to blame / He knows the rules / Everybody rock.
12" Single: Released 27 Feb '89, on Charly, by Charly Records. Catalogue no: **REDZ 100**
CD 5": Released Apr '89, on Charly, by Charly Records. Catalogue no: **CDS 13**
7" Single: Released 27 Feb '89, on Charly, by Charly Records. Catalogue no: **REDZ 7100**

McCrae, George

Biographical details: This American singer takes the historical credit for pioneering the Seventies disco boom with his monster 1974 hit *Rock your baby*, a record that was virtually made by accident. He was born in West Palm Beach, Florida. He formed a couple of groups in high school, and then spent four years in the US Navy. During the late Sixties and Seventies, he struggled on the Florida club circuit and made some unsuccessful records with his singing wife Gwen. Eventually, while his spouse kept trying, George quit music to concentrate on bringing up the family. Deciding to have one more crack, however, he stumbled upon an instrumental track of *Rock your baby* at the local studios of the small TK label. *Rock your baby* by George McCrae reached No 1 on both sides of the Atlantic in the Summer of '74 and sold an incredible ten million copies globally.
His excellent falsetto vocals and the track's infection dance groove made *Rock your baby* a straightforward but brilliant moment in Seventies music. It established TK as one of the most important companies of the era, and Richard Finch. Casey and Finch proceeded to enjoy huge success as the masterminds of the disco ensemble KC and the Sunshine Band. *Rock your baby* did much for everyone else, but not a great deal for McCrae in terms of long-lasting stardom. He had six more Top 40 entries in the UK, plus a long-running chart album, all these hits were simply Casey/Finch rehashes of the *Rock your baby* formula. His wife had a big us hit with 1975's *Rockin' chair* but both singers were in obsucurity by 1977.
John Travolta and the Bee Gees took the disco boom to even greater heights with the 1978 *Saturday night fever* phenomenon, but McCrae was unable to capitalise. Suddenly, in 1984, George returned with a changed sound and made a bid for a chart comeback; but his single *One step closer (to love)* was only a minor success. George and Gwen are now divorced.
(Bob MacDonald, 12th January 1988).

GIRLS DON'T LIE
Tracks: / Girls don't lie / I have a heart / That's love (Extra track on 12" version).
7" Single: Released 20 Feb '88, on Sierra, by Sierra Records. Catalogue no: **FED 43**
12" Single: Released 20 Feb '88, on Sierra, by Sierra Records. Catalogue no: **FED 43T**

HONEY I
Tracks: / Honey I.
7" Single: Released Jan '76, on Jay Boy, by President Records. Deleted '79. Catalogue no: **BOY 107**

I AIN'T LYIN'
Tracks: / I ain't lyin'.
7" Single: Released Oct '75, on Jay Boy, by President Records. Deleted '78. Catalogue no: **BOY 105**

I CAN'T LEAVE YOU ALONE
Tracks: / I can't leave you alone.
7" Single: Released Oct '74, on Jay Boy, by President Records. Deleted '77. Catalogue no: **BOY 90**

IT'S BEEN SO LONG
Tracks: / It's been so long.
7" Single: Released Oct '75, on Jay Boy, by President Records. Deleted '78. Catalogue no: **BOY 105**

LET'S DANCE
Tracks: / Let's Dance / Never forget your eyes.
7" Single: Released Jan '86, on President, by President Records. Catalogue no: **PT 542**
12" Single: Released Jan '86, on President, by President Records. Catalogue no: **PT 12-542**

LISTEN TO YOUR HEART
Tracks: / Listen to your heart / Now that I have you.
7" Single: Released Jun '84, on President, by President Records. Catalogue no: **PT 528**
12" Single: Released Jun '84, on President, by President Records. Catalogue no: **PT 12 528**

LOVE'S BEEN GOOD TO ME
Tracks: / Love's been good to me / Out of knowhere (into my life).
7" Single: Released Sep '86, on President, by President Records. Catalogue no: **PT 549**

ONE STEP CLOSER TO LOVE (SINGLE)
Tracks: / One step closer (to love) / If it wasn't for you.
7" Single: Released Feb '84, on President, by President Records. Catalogue no: **PT 522**
12" Single: Released Feb '84, on President, by President Records. Catalogue no: **PT 12 522**

OWN THE NIGHT
Tracks: / Own the night.
12" Single: Released Sep '84, on President, by President Records. Catalogue no: **PT 12 530**
7" Single: Released Sep '84, on President, by President Records. Catalogue no: **PT 530**

ROCK YOUR BABY (SINGLE)
Tracks: / Rock your baby / Rock your baby (part 2).
12" Single: Released Feb '87, on Portrait, by CBS Records. Deleted Aug '87. Catalogue no: **650312 6**
7" Single: Released Jun '74, on Jay Boy, by President Records. Deleted '77. Catalogue no: **BOY 85**
7" Single: Released Feb '87, on Portrait, by CBS Records. Deleted Aug '87. Catalogue no: **650312 7**

SING A HAPPY SONG
Tracks: / Sing a happy song.
7" Single: Released Mar '75, on Jay Boy, by President Records. Deleted '78. Catalogue no: **BOY 95**

YOU CAN HAVE IT ALL
Tracks: / You can have it all.
7" Single: Released Dec '74, on Jay Boy, by President Records. Deleted '77. Catalogue no: **BOY 92**

McCrae, Gwen

ALL THIS LOVE THAT I'M GIVING
Tracks: / All this love that I'm giving.
7" Single: Released Mar '88, on Rhythm King, by Mute Records. Catalogue no: **MELT 7**
12" Single: Released Mar '88, on Rhythm King, by Mute Records. Catalogue no: **MELT 7T**

DO YOU KNOW WHAT I MEAN
Tracks: / Do you know what I mean.
12" Single: Released Nov '84, on Sierra, by Sierra Records. Deleted '87. Catalogue no: **FED 3T**
7" Single: Released Nov '84, on Sierra, by Sierra Records. Deleted Jun '87. Catalogue no: **FED 3**

EIGHTIES LADY
Tracks: / Eighties lady.
7" Single: Released 23 Jul '88, on Danceyard, by Danceyard Records. Catalogue no: **YARD 1**
12" Single: Released 23 Jul '88, on Danceyard, by Danceyard Records. Catalogue no: **YARD T1**

McCrarys

LOVE ON A SUMMER NIGHT
Tracks: / Love on a summer night / Miles above.
7" Single: Released Jul '82, on Capitol, by EMI Records. Deleted '85. Catalogue no: **CL 251**
12" Single: Released Jul '82, on Capitol, by EMI Records. Deleted '85. Catalogue no: **12CL 251**
12" Single: Released Nov '87, on JVS (USA), Catalogue no: **JV 941**

McCue, Bill

WHERE WE'LL NEVER GROW OLD
Tracks: / Where we'll never grow old / Count your blessings.
7" Single: Released Nov '88, on August Records, by Scotdisc Records. Catalogue no: **GBHS 7474**

McCulloch, Alan Band

SWEET DREAMS (EP)
Tracks: / Sweet dreams.
7" Single: Released Mar '84, on Linden Sounds, Catalogue no: **LS 005**

McCulloch, Cecil

PICK 'EM UP AND SHAKE 'EM UP
Tracks: / Pick 'em up and shake 'em up.
7" Single: Released Feb '80, on Detour, by Detour Records. Deleted Dec '86. Catalogue no: **DT 4501**

McCulloch, Ian

PROUD TO FALL
Tracks: / Proud to fall / Pots of gold.
Cassingle: Released Aug '89, on WEA, by WEA Records. Catalogue no: **YZ 417C**
CD 5": Released Aug '89, on WEA, by WEA Records. Catalogue no: **YZ 417CD**
7" Single: Released Aug '89, on WEA, by WEA Records. Catalogue no: **YZ 417**
12" Single: Released Aug '89, on WEA, by WEA Records. Catalogue no: **YZ 417T**

SEPTEMBER SONG
Tracks: / September song.
7" Single: Released Nov '84, on Korova, by WEA Records. Catalogue no: **KOW 40**
12" Single: Released Nov '84, on Korova, by WEA Records. Catalogue no: **KOW 40T**

McCulloch Park

DON'T LEAVE IT ALL BEHIND
Tracks: / Don't leave it all behind / Bad dreams.
7" Single: Released Apr '81, on Scratch, by Scratch Records. Deleted '85. Catalogue no: **SCR 003**

McDaniels, Gene

TOWER OF STRENGTH
Tracks: / Tower of strength.
7" Single: Released Nov '61, on London-American, Deleted '64. Catalogue no: **HLG 9448**

McDermott, Kevin

HEALING AT THE HARBOUR
Tracks: / Healing at the harbour.
12" Single: Released Sep '89, on 4th & Broadway, by Island Records. Catalogue no: **12 IS 437**
CD 5": Released Sep '89, on 4th & Broadway, by Island Records. Catalogue no: **CID 437**
7" Single: Released Sep '89, on 4th & Broadway, by Island Records. Catalogue no: **IS 437**

WHEELS OF WONDER
Tracks: / Wheels of wonder / Independence day / Mother nature's kitchen.
12" Single: Released 13 Mar '89, on Island, by Island Records. Catalogue no: **12IS 404**
CD 5": Released 13 Mar '89, on Island, by Island Records. Catalogue no: **CID 404**
7" Single: Released 13 Mar '89, on Island, by Island Records. Catalogue no: **IS 404**

WHERE WE WERE MEANT TO BE
Tracks: / Where we were meant to be / Jenny Lynn / Wheels of wonder (live) (Available on 12" and CD only).
12" Single: Released May '89, on Island, by Island Records. Catalogue no: **12 IS 423**
CD 5": Released May '89, on Island, by Island Records. Catalogue no: **CID 423**
7" Single: Released May '89, on Island, by Island Records. Catalogue no: **IS 423**

McDevitt, Chas

Biographical details: This British guitarist and singer symbolised the class of '57. The American rock 'n' roll explosion had just taken Britain by storm but, apart from the brief rock sounds of Tommy Steele and Tony Crombie, the UK had no real rock 'n' roll stars of it's own until the arrival of Cliff Richard in late 1958. The void was filled by the Lonnie Donegan - led boom in skiffle, an intriguing genre that stemmed from the first UK trad-jazz scene of the early Fifties. Skiffle was, by its very nature, amateurish - all that was needed was a rudimentary guitar, a washboard and a tea chest, plus a basic knowledge of folk and jazz music. Apart from the legions of amateur enthusiasts up and down Britain, there were only four successful professional skiffle acts: Donegan, Johnny Duncan, the Vipers and the Chas McDevitt Skiffle Group. The latter had just one significant hit - *Freight train*, an adaptation of an American folk standard, reached No.5 and logged 18 weeks on the British chart. The follow-up *Greenback dollar* peaked at No.28 in June of that year Nancy Whiskey quit in September. *Freight train* managed to reach No.40 in the States, an impressive showing for a UK act in those days. McDevitt opened a Freight train coffee bar in London, and installed a jukebox which contained a selection of obscure rock and rhythm and blues discs. The future Shadows star Hank Marvin often visited the bar, and was said to have been inspired by the records he heard. (Bob MacDonald, 12th January 1986).

FREIGHT TRAIN (OLD GOLD)
Tracks: / Freight train / Greenback dollar.
7" Single: Released Jul '82, on Old Gold, by Old Gold Records. Catalogue no: **OG 9052**

FREIGHT TRAIN
Tracks: / Freight train
7" Single: Released Apr '57, on Oriole, Deleted '60. Catalogue no: **CB 1352**

GREEN BACK DOLLAR
Tracks: / Greenback dollar.
7" Single: Released Jun '57, on Oriole, Deleted '60. Catalogue no: **CB 1371**

MacDonald, Aimii

AIN'T NOBODY GONNA TOUCH MY BODY
Tracks: / Ain't nobody gonna touch my body.
7" Single: Released Feb '81, on Spinach, by Spinach Records. Deleted '86. Catalogue no: **SPIN 007**

McDonald, Alastair

COLOMBE SHALOM
Tracks: / Colombe-shalom / White wings.
7" Single: Released Oct '83, on Corban, by Corban Records. Deleted '88. Catalogue no: **CBN 002**

WE'VE BEEN INVITED
Tracks: / We've been invited / Bruce's address.
7" Single: Released Apr '82, on McCoochley Street, Catalogue no: **MS 9**

KEVIN MCDERMOTT - WHERE WE WERE MEANT TO BE (Released on Island)

McDonald, Carl

STAR
Tracks: / Star / Skank it rub a dub style.
12" Single: Released Apr '82, on Makdon, Catalogue no: **MKD 1102**

McDonald, Country Joe

Biographical details: For biographical information see COUNTRY JOE AND THE FISH..

BLOOD ON THE ICE
Tracks: / Blood on the ice.
7" Single: Released Sep '83, on Animus, by Southern Studios Ltd.. Catalogue no: **TOUCH 1**

McDonald, Flak

JACK ME SOME CRACK
Tracks: / Jack me some crack.
7" Single: Released 20 Feb '88, on Soho (1), by Soho Records. Catalogue no: **SG 001**

MacDonald, Jeanette

IRENE
Tracks: / Irene.
7" Single: Released Jan '89, on Mac/Eddy, Catalogue no: **JN 109**

McDonald, Joe

ARE YOU DIRTY?
Tracks: / Are you dirty ? / Highland tinker, The.
7" Single: Released Oct '83, on Charly, by Charly Records. Deleted '88. Catalogue no: **CYZ 7 108**

McDonald, Michael

I GOTTA TRY
Tracks: / I gotta try.
7" Single: Released Jan '83, on Warner Bros., by WEA Records. Catalogue no: **W 9862**

I KEEP FORGETTING
Tracks: / I keep forgettin' / Losin' end.
12" Single: Released Jun '86, on Warner Bros., by WEA Records. Deleted Jun '87. Catalogue no: **K 17992 T**
7" Single: Released Jun '86, on Warner Bros., by WEA Records. Deleted Jun '87. Catalogue no: **K 17992**

NO LOOKING BACK (SINGLE)
Tracks: / I gotta try (12" version only.).
7" Single: Released Oct '86, on Warner Bros., by WEA Records. Deleted Jun '87. Catalogue no: **W 8960**
12" Single: Released Oct '86, on Warner Bros., by WEA Records. Deleted Jun '87. Catalogue no: **W 8960T**

OUR LOVE Theme to No Mercy
Tracks: / Our love / Don't let me down / Bad times (Extra track on 12" version).
12" Single: Released Mar '87, on Warner Bros., by WEA Records. Deleted Jan '88. Catalogue no: **W 8596T**
7" Single: Released Mar '87, on Warner Bros., by WEA Records. Deleted Jan '88. Catalogue no: **W 8596**

SWEET FREEDOM
Tracks: / Sweet freedom / Freedom lights,The.
7" Single: Released Aug '86, on MCA, by MCA Records. Catalogue no: **MCA 1073**

McDonald, Pete

LADY OF MINE
Tracks: / Lady of mine.
7" Single: Released Aug '83, on Creole, by Creole Records. Catalogue no: **CR 57**

LOVE UNDECIDED
Tracks: / Love undecided / Way back when.
7" Single: Released Mar '85, on Creole, by Creole Records. Catalogue no: **CR 78**

McDonald, Ralph

JAM ON THE GROOVE
Tracks: / Jam on the groove.
12" Single: Released Nov '87, on Coko (USA), Catalogue no: **CK 140**

YOU NEED MORE CALYPSO
Tracks: / You need more calypso / In the name of love.
12" Single: Released Mar '86, on London Records, by London Records. Catalogue no: **LONX 91**
7" Single: Released Mar '86, on London Records, by London Records. Catalogue no: **LON 91**

McDowall

REAPER
Tracks: / Reaper.
7" Single: Released Jun '88, on Rio Digital, by Rio Digital Records. Catalogue no: **7RDS 3**
12" Single: Released Jun '88, on Rio Digital, by Rio Digital Records. Catalogue no: **12RDS 3**

McDowell, Carrie

UH UH NO NO CASUAL SEX
Tracks: / Uh, uh, no, no casual sex / Uh, uh, no, no casual sex (part 2) / Uh, uh, no, no casual sex (dub) / Uh, uh, no, no casual sex (sunrise mix).
7" Single: Released Sep '87, on Motown, by BMG Records (UK). Catalogue no: **ZB 41501**
12" Single: Released Sep '87, on Motown, by BMG Records (UK). Catalogue no: **ZT 41502**

WHEN A WOMAN LOVES A MAN
Tracks: / When a woman loves a man.
7" Single: Released Jul '87, on Motown, by BMG Records (UK). Catalogue no: **ZB 41651**

McDowell, Rose

DON'T FEAR THE REAPER
Tracks: / Don't fear the reaper.
7" Single: Released Sep '88, on Rio Digital, by Rio Digital Records. Catalogue no: **RDS 3 A**

McElherron, Paddy

VILLAGE OF AVOCA
Tracks: / Village of Avoca.
7" Single: Released Dec '84, on Homespun (Ireland), by Outlet Records. Catalogue no: **HS 090**

McEntire, Reba

CATHY'S CLOWN
Tracks: / Cathy's clown.
CD 5": Released Apr '89, on MCA, by MCA Records. Catalogue no: **DMCAT 1336**
7" Single: Released Apr '89, on MCA, by MCA Records. Catalogue no: **MCA 1336**

WHAT AM I GONNA DO ABOUT YOU (SINGLE)
Tracks: / What am I gonna do about you / One promise too late.
7" Single: Released Mar '87, on MCA, by MCA Records. Catalogue no: **MCA 1136**

Maceo

CROSS THE TRACK (WE BETTER GO BACK)
Tracks: / Cross the track (we better go back ext version) / Parrty (part 1) / Soul power*.
Note: * = Extra track on 12" only
7" Single: Released Apr '87, on Urban, by Polydor Ltd. Deleted Jan '88. Catalogue no: **URB 1**
12" Single: Released Apr '87, on Urban, by Polydor Ltd. Deleted 30 Jun '89. Catalogue no: **URBX 1**

McEvoy, Johnny

STATEN ISLAND
Tracks: / Staten Island.
7" Single: Released '88, on Play (Ireland), Catalogue no: **PLAY 226**

WHEN WE DANCED TO AN OLD FASHIONED TUNE
Tracks: / When we danced to an old fashioned tune.
7" Single: Released '88, on Play (Ireland), Catalogue no: **PLAY 233**

YOU SELDOM COME TO SEE ME ANYMORE
Tracks: / You seldom come to see me anymore.
7" Single: Released '88, on Play (Ireland), Catalogue no: **PLAY 216**

McEvoy, Michael

GIVING GOOD FEELING
Tracks: / Giving good feeling / Love will come again.
12" Single: Released Feb '88, on Ize, Catalogue no: **MIC 1**
7" Single: Released Feb '88, on Ize, Catalogue no: **7MIC 1**

McFadden & Whitehead

AIN'T NO STOPPIN' US NOW
Tracks: / Ain't no stoppin' us now.
12" Single: Released Nov '87, on Philadelphia Int., by EMI Records. Catalogue no: **4 ZH 06923**
7" Single: Released May '79, on Philadelphia Int., by EMI Records. Deleted '82. Catalogue no: **PIR 7365**
7" Single: Released Jul '84, on Old Gold, by Old Gold Records. Catalogue no: **OG 9400**
7" Single: Released Sep '85, on Streetwave, Catalogue no: **SWAVE 2**
7" Single: Released May '84, on Buddah, by Buddah Records Inc.(USA). Catalogue no: **BDS 504**
7" Single: Released May '82, on Philadelphia Int., by EMI Records. Catalogue no: **CBS 8871**
12" Single: Released May '84, on Buddah, by Buddah Records Inc.(USA). Catalogue no: **BDSL 504**

AIN'T NO STOPPIN' US NOW (OLD GOLD)
Tracks: / Ain't no stoppin' us now.
12" Single: Released Jul '88, on Old Gold, by Old Gold Records. Catalogue no: **OG 4072**

I HEARD IT ALL IN A LOVE SONG (7")
Tracks: / I heard it all in a love song.
7" Single: Released Sep '80, on CBS, by CBS Records. Catalogue no: **PIR 8964**

I HEARD IT IN A LOVE SONG
Tracks: / I heard it in a love song / Always room for one more.
7" Single: Released Sep '80, on Philadelphia Int., by EMI Records. Deleted '83. Catalogue no: **PIR 8964**

McFarland, Billy

JENIFER JOHNSON
Tracks: / Jenifer Johnson / Little Rosa.
7" Single: Released Feb '81, on Homespun (Ireland), by Outlet Records. Catalogue no: **HS 041**

RATHLIN ISLAND
Tracks: / Rathlin island / Mama sang a song.
7" Single: Released Apr '82, on Homespun (Ireland), by Outlet Records. Cata-

logue no: **HS 057**

WHEN THE HARVEST MOON IS SHINING
Tracks: / When the harvest moon is rising / Beautiful dreamer.
7" Single: Released Mar '84, on Homespun (Ireland), by Outlet Records. Catalogue no: **HS 074**

MacFarland, C

MAGGIE'S LETTER
Tracks: / Maggie's letter.
12" Single: Released Nov '83, on Sapphire, Catalogue no: **SAP 006**

McFarland, Sandra

CRAZY IN LOVE
Tracks: / Crazy in love / Crazy dub.
12" Single: Released Jan '83, on Body Music, by Nuclear Records. Catalogue no: **BMDIS 6**

NEVER LOVE AGAIN
Tracks: / Never love again.
12" Single: Released Mar '82, on Paradise, Catalogue no: **PDIS 100**

CAUGHT YOU IN A LIE
Tracks: / Caught you in a lie.
12" Single: Released Nov '88, on Pioneer International, Catalogue no: **PI 12**

McFerrin, Bobby

DON'T WORRY BE HAPPY
Tracks: / Don't worry be happy (LP version) / Simple pleasures / From me to you (CD single only.) / Don't worry be happy (7" version).
CD 5": Released Sep '88, on EMI-Manhattan, by EMI Records. Deleted Jun '89. Catalogue no: **CDMT 56**
7" Single: Released Sep '88, on EMI-Manhattan, by EMI Records. Catalogue no: **MT 56**
12" Single: Released Sep '88, on EMI-Manhattan, by EMI Records. Deleted Oct '89. Catalogue no: **12MT 56**

GOOD LOVIN'
Tracks: / Good lovin' / There ya go.
CD 5": Released Jul '88, on EMI-Manhattan, by EMI Records. Deleted Jun '89. Catalogue no: **CDMT 42**
7" Single: Released Jun '88, on EMI-Manhattan, by EMI Records. Deleted Aug '89. Catalogue no: **MT 42**
12" Single: Released Jun '88, on EMI-Manhattan, by EMI Records. Deleted Aug '89. Catalogue no: **12MT 42**

THINKIN' ABOUT YOUR BODY For Debs
Tracks: / Thinkin' about your body / From me to you.
7" Single: Released Dec '86, on EMI, by EMI Records. Deleted Jul '87. Catalogue no: **BLUE 4**

THINKIN' ABOUT YOUR BODY (RE-ISSUE)
Tracks: / Thinkin' about your body / Don't worry be happy / From me to you(not 7") / Come to me (Only available on CD single.).
12" Single: Released Dec '88, on EMI-Manhattan, by EMI Records. Deleted Oct '89. Catalogue no: **12BLUE 6**
CD 5": Released Dec '88, on EMI-Manhattan, by EMI Records. Catalogue no: **CDBLUE 6**
7" Single: Released Dec '88, on EMI-Manhattan, by EMI Records. Catalogue no: **BLUE 6**

McGann Brothers

Biographical details: Consists of Joe (guitar), Paul (guitar and piano), Mark (guitar, piano, drums and harmonica) and Stephen McGann. Their Dad played in Irish Dance bands and their mother sang with dance bands, both semi-pro. Besides playing football together, the four boys became part of an international choir and sang at international festivals in Germany, Belgium and France, but the boys got into too many fights and wound up returning to football. Collective interest in performing arts led all the brothers (at seperate times) tinto the Everyman Youth Theatre in Liverpool. All eventually took up careers in Drama and Music but did not work together professionally until they were spotted by the director of *Yakety Yak*. The boys have a tendency to burst into song wherever there is alcohol and were doing just this at a party when Bob Walker marched over to them. They signed to Chrysalis and are now taking time out of blossoming solo careers in order to have much more fun working together. (Joe McGann, Feb '84).

SHAME ABOUT THE BOY
Tracks: / Shame about the boy / Red light.
7" Single: Released Sep '83, on Chrysalis, by Chrysalis Records. Catalogue no: **CHS 2735**

McGarrigle, Kate & Anna

Biographical details: Emerging from Canada during the mid-Seventies, the McGarrigle sisters attracted major critical acclaim but limited commercial success. They grew up in the French part of Quebec, and have regularly sung in both French and English. After making headway as songwriters, catching the ears of Linda Ronstadt and Maria Muldaur, duo's eponymous debut album was released in 1975. Featuring the assistance of some noted American West Coast sessioneers, the LP was an eclectic blend of folk, cajun and pop styles. Folk remained the bedrock of their music, however. Both sisters performed singing and songwriting roles, and both played keyboards and banjo. Kate also played guitar. The McGarrigles achieved their only UK chart entry in February 1977, when their second album *Dancer with bruised knees* peaked at No.35. Folk is not an easy genre for record companies to market in the modern pop era, so Kate & Anna have remained a cult act during the late Seventies and Eighties. Their records have been engaging and inspired, although their live conserts have not always been well reviewed. The duo's *Love over and over*, the title track from their 1982 album, was their nearest shot at a commercial pop single; but in the event, it flopped. (Bob MacDonald 12.1.86).

LOVE OVER AND OVER (SINGLE)
Tracks: / Love over and over / I cried for us.
7" Single: Released May '82, on Polydor, by Polydor Ltd. Deleted May '87. Catalogue no: **POSP 447**

McGear, Mike

Biographical details: This British singer, songwriter and comedian was an apprentice hairdresser before his part-time group, The Scaffold, turned professional in 1964. This vocal trio consisted of himself plus fellow Liverpudlians John Gorman and Roger McGough. They built up a strong cult following at colleges and arts festivals (including Edinburgh) with their zany brand of comedy. Gradually incorporating musical comedy items into their act, they chalked up several UK pop hits in the late Sixties. The first of these, *Thank U very much* (No.4 in 1967), was written by the trio's best singer Mike Gear. It was at that time that he revealed that his true name was Mike McCartney, and that he was none other than Paul McCartney's younger brother - he had changed his name in order to prove that he could make it on his own, without being accused of trading on his brother's success. In 1973 the Scaffold teamed up with some friends for larger ensemble known as Grimms. The following year, however, they hit the UK Top 10 in their usual format with the Paul McCartney-produced *Liverpool Lou*. In October 1974 McGear acheived the only UK chart entry of generally unsuccessful solo recording career - *Leave it*, once again produced by Paul, reached No.36. (Bob MacDonald 12.1.86).

ALL THE WHALES IN THE OCEAN
Tracks: / All the whales in the ocean / I juz want what you got - money.
7" Single: Released May '80, on Carrere, Catalogue no: **CAR 144**

LEAVE IT
Tracks: / Leave it.
7" Single: Released Oct '74, on Warner Bros., by WEA Records. Deleted '77. Catalogue no: **K 16446**

NO LAR DI DAR(IS LADY DI)
Tracks: / No lar di dar (is Lady Di) / God bless the gracious queen.
7" Single: Released Jul '81, on Conn, Catalogue no: **CONN 29781**

McGee, Francine

DELIRIUM
Tracks: / Delirium.
12" Single: Released Nov '83, on Bluebird (2), by BMG Records (UK). Catalogue no: **BRT 5**

McGee, Jay W

WHEN WE PARTY (UPTOWN DOWNTOWN)
Tracks: / When we party (uptown downtown).
7" Single: Released Sep '82, on Ensign, by Ensign Records. Deleted '83. Catalogue no: **ENY 231**
12" Single: Released Sep '82, on Ensign, by Ensign Records. Deleted '84. Catalogue no: **ENYT 231**

McGhee, J.

ONE DRAW
Tracks: / One draw.
12" Single: Released Mar '82, on Echo, by Echo Records. Catalogue no: **ECHO 001**

McGhee, Wes

I'LL BE THINKING OF YOU
Tracks: / I'll be thinking of you.
7" Single: Released '88, on TRP, Catalogue no: **TRPS 861**

IT'S NO USE BEIN' A FAST DRAW
Tracks: / It's no use bein' a fast draw.
7" Single: Released Aug '81, on Country Roads Records, Deleted '87. Catalogue no: **CRE 006**

WHISKY IS MY DRIVER
Tracks: / Whisky is my driver.
7" Single: Released Feb '82, on Terrapin Records, Deleted '83. Catalogue no: **TRP 8171S**

McGovern, Maureen

Biographical details: This American singer was born in Youngstown, Ohio, and came to fame in 1973 with *The morning after*, the theme from the big movie *The Poseidon adventure*. She had been working in Youngstown as a doctor's secretary and part-time folk singer during the early Seventies; out of the blue, she got the opportunity to record *The morning after* purely on the strength of a demo-tape that she sent to the boss of the record division of 20th Century. McGovern's single was a sleeper smash. After making no impression on the charts at all, it became a US No.1 hit upon winning the Oscar for Best Film Song of the Year. Maureen soon repeated the feat by singing *We may never love like this again* - this won the Academy Award as the theme to another disaster movie, *The towering inferno*. In 1976 McGovern achieved her only UK chart entry. *The continental* reached No.16 on the British singles list as part of a Forties-style revival that was happening in the UK at the time. Her only subsequent American Top 40 hit was 1979's *Different worlds*; this climbed to No.18, and was the theme from the TV series Angie. (Bob MacDonald 12.1.86).

CONTINENTAL, THE
Tracks: / Continental, The.
7" Single: Released Jun '76, on 20th Century, by 20th Century Records. Deleted '79. Catalogue no: **BTC 2222**

McGrae, Gwen

DOIN' IT
Tracks: / Doin' it / Hey world.
7" Single: Released Feb '83, on Atlantic, by WEA Records. Catalogue no: **A 9901**
12" Single: Released Feb '83, on Atlantic, by WEA Records. Catalogue no: **A 9901 T**

KEEP THE FIRE BURNING
Tracks: / Keep the fire burning / Funky....
7" Single: Released Nov '82, on Atlantic, by WEA Records. Deleted Nov '85. Catalogue no: **K 789951-7**
7" Single: Released Oct '82, on Atlantic, by WEA Records. Catalogue no: **FLAM 1**
12" Single: Released Oct '82, on Atlantic, by WEA Records. Catalogue no: **FLAM 1 T**

McGregor, Freddie

ACROSS THE BORDER (SINGLE)
Tracks: / Across the border.
12" Single: Released Sep '84, on Big Ship, Catalogue no: **Unknown**

AND SO I WILL WAIT FOR YOU
Tracks: / And so I will wait for you / Lost till you find love / And so I will wait for you (version) / Everytime you smile (On CD single only.).
7" Single: Released Nov '88, on Polydor, by Polydor Ltd. Deleted 30 May '89. Catalogue no: **PO 20**
CD 5": Released Nov '88, on Polydor, by Polydor Ltd. Catalogue no: **PZCD 20**
12" Single: Released Nov '88, on Polydor, by Polydor Ltd. Deleted 31 May '89. Catalogue no: **PZ 20**

BIG SHIP
Tracks: / Big ship / Come and take it.
12" Single: Released Jun '82, on Greensleeves, by Greensleeves Records. Catalogue no: **GRED 90**
12" Single: Released Sep '82, on Intense, by Intense Records. Catalogue no: **INT 001**

CAN'T GET YOU OUT OF MY MIND
Tracks: / Can't get you out of my mind.
7" Single: Released Nov '86, on RAS (Real Authentic Sound), by Greensleeves Records. Catalogue no: **RAS 7101**
12" Single: Released Nov '86, on RAS (Real Authentic Sound), by Greensleeves Records. Catalogue no: **RAST 7101**

COME TO ME
Tracks: / Come to me / Come to me (ext. mix) / Sorrows of my shoulder.
CD 5": Released Feb '88, on Polydor, by Polydor Ltd. Catalogue no: **POCD 905**
7" Single: Released Feb '88, on Polydor, by Polydor Ltd. Catalogue no: **POSP 905**
12" Single: Released Feb '88, on Polydor, by Polydor Ltd. Catalogue no: **POSPX 905**

GUANTANAMERA
Tracks: / Guantanamera.
12" Single: Released Sep '89, on Polydor, by Polydor Ltd. Catalogue no: **PZ 53**
7" Single: Released Sep '89, on Polydor, by Polydor Ltd. Catalogue no: **PO 53**
12" Single: Released May '84, on Tads, Catalogue no: **TRD 098**

GUANTANAMERA (RE-ISSUE)
Tracks: / Guantanamera.
12" Single: Released Aug '89, on Polydor, by Polydor Ltd. Catalogue no: **PZ 53**
7" Single: Released Aug '89, on Polydor, by Polydor Ltd. Catalogue no: **PO 53**

I JUST DON'T WANT TO BE LONELY
Tracks: / I just don't want to be lonely / I just don't want to be lonely (version).
7" Single: Released 20 Jun '87, on Germaine, Catalogue no: **DG 24**
12" Single: Released Jun '87, on Germaine, Catalogue no: **DGT 24**

LOVE BALLAD
Tracks: / Love ballad / There's no me without you.
12" Single: Released Feb '82, on Fight, Catalogue no: **FTDD 4403**
12" Single: Released Mar '82, on Exclusive, Catalogue no: **EXC 60**
7" Single: Released Feb '82, on Fight, Catalogue no: **FTD 4403**

MASHING UP HER BRAIN
Tracks: / Mashing up her brain.
10" single: Released Jul '83, on J & J, Catalogue no: **JJ 124**

MISERABLE WOMAN
Tracks: / Miserable woman / Miserable woman (Version).
12" Single: Released Aug '86, on Greensleeves, by Greensleeves Records. Catalogue no: **GRED 203**

NAME AND NUMBER
Tracks: / Name and number / Name and number (version).
12" Single: Released 23 May '87, on Tads, Catalogue no: **TRD 26187**

NEVER GET AWAY
Tracks: / Never get away.
12" Single: Released Jul '82, on Spiderman, Catalogue no: **SMD 1001**

NOT AS HAPPY
Tracks: / Not as happy / Not as happy (Solo Freddie McGregor version).
12" Single: Released Aug '88, on Greensleeves, by Greensleeves Records. Catalogue no: **GRED 226**

PRETTY WOMAN
Tracks: / Pretty woman.
12" Single: Released Apr '83, on Hawkeye, by Hawkeye Records. Catalogue no: **INT 7**

PROPHECY
Tracks: / Prophecy.
12" Single: Released Oct '89, on White Label (1), Catalogue no: **SCT 4**

PUSH COMES TO SHOVE
Tracks: / Push comes to shove / Glad you're here with me.
12" Single: Released May '86, on RAS (Real Authentic Sound), by Greensleeves Records. Catalogue no: **RAST 7016**

ROMAN SOLDIER
Tracks: / Roman soldier.
10" single: Released Oct '83, on Hitbound, Catalogue no: **JJ 127**

ROOTS MAN SKANKING
Tracks: / Roots man skanking.
12" Single: Released Feb '82, on Greensleeves, by Greensleeves Records. Catalogue no: **GRED 84**

SPECIAL LOVER
Tracks: / Special lover.
12" Single: Released Dec '82, on Music Works, Catalogue no: **MWRT 1293**

THAT GIRL (GROOVY SITUATION)
Tracks: / That girl (groovy situation) / Wando.
12" Single: Released Sep '87, on Polydor, by Polydor Ltd. Catalogue no: **POSPX 884**
7" Single: Released Sep '87, on Polydor, by Polydor Ltd. Catalogue no: **POSP 884**

TOO LONG WILL BE TOO LATE
Tracks: / Too long will be too late.
12" Single: Released Dec '83, on Tads, Catalogue no: **TRD 11183**

WINE OF VIOLENCE
Tracks: / Wine of violence / Once a man.
12" Single: Released Jan '87, on Yashemabata, Catalogue no: **YM 01**

MacGregor, Mary

Biographical details: This American singer was a part-time, unknown vocalist

Machine - Move It (Released on In Crowd)

during the mid-Seventies, her only regular studio work being commercials and jingles. Suddenly, in early 1977, MacGregor shot from obscurity to the top of the US charts with the middle-of-the-road ballad *Torn between two lovers*. The somewhat dated musical style of the single was counterbalanced by its contemporary sociological theme. The song was co-written and co-produced by Peter Yarrow of Peter, Paul & Mary fame. After reaching No.1 in the States, *Torn between two lovers* climbed to No.4 in Britain. The LP of the same name reached No.17 in the US and No.59 in the UK. No more British success was forthcoming; in the US, MacGregor had several more Hot 100 singles but only *Good friend* (No.39 in 1979, from the film Meatballs) managed to enter the Top 40. In The Billboard book of number one hits, she told writer Fred Bronson that she always hated *Torn between two lovers* - in the event, its success caused the break-up of her marriage. She became torn, not between two lovers, but between the opposing forces of her husband and her suddenly accelerated singing career. As it turned out, both were relinquished. By the Eighties, she was rearing horses and writing the occasional song on a California ranch. (Bob MacDonald 13.1.86).

GOOD FRIEND
Tracks: / Good friend / Rudy and tripper.
7" Single: Released Feb '80, on RSO, by Polydor Ltd. Deleted '83. Catalogue no: **RSO 4**

TORN BETWEEN TWO LOVERS
Tracks: / Torn between two lovers.
7" Single: Released Jul '84, on Old Gold, by Old Gold Records. Catalogue no: **OG 9455**
7" Single: Released Feb '77, on Ariola, by BMG Records (UK). Deleted '80. Catalogue no: **AA 111**
7" Single: Released Sep '82, on Ariola, by BMG Records (UK). Catalogue no: **ARO 268**

McGriff, Jimmy

ALL ABOUT MY GIRL
Tracks: / All about my girl.
7" Single: Released Apr '83, on EMI, by EMI Records. Catalogue no: **2C 008 83376**

McGuigan, Barry

SOMEBODY TO CALL MY GIRL
Tracks: / Somebody to call my girl / Somebody to call my girl (wimp mix).
7" Single: Released 17 Oct '87, on Yellow Brick Road, by Yellow Brick Road Records. Catalogue no: **YRB 4**

McGuigan, Pat

DANNY BOY
Tracks: / Danny boy.
7" Single: Released Jul '85, on Ritz, by Ritz Records. Catalogue no: **RITZ 108**

McGuiness, Joan

MOTHER TERESA'S PRAYER
Tracks: / Mother teresa's prayer / Give us the peace / Prayer before birth / Remember me.
7" Single: Released Jan '80, on Charisma, by Virgin Records. Deleted Jan '85. Catalogue no: **CB 350**

McGuinness Flint

MALT AND BARLEY BLUES
Tracks: / Malt and barley blues.
7" Single: Released May '71, on Capitol, by EMI Records. Deleted '74. Catalogue no: **CL 15682**

WHEN I'M DEAD AND GONE
Tracks: / When I'm dead and gone.
7" Single: Released Jul '84, on EMI Golden 45's, by EMI Records. Deleted 31 Jul '88. Catalogue no: **G45 29**
7" Single: Released Nov '70, on Capitol, by EMI Records. Deleted '73. Catalogue no: **CL 15662**

McGuinness, Lyle Band

ELISE
Tracks: / Elise.
7" Single: Released May '83, on Cool King, Catalogue no: **CK 011**

McGuinness,

HEARTBEAT
Tracks: / Heartbeat / Street level.
7" Single: Released Feb '80, on RCA, by BMG Records (UK). Deleted '83. Catalogue no: **PB 5224**

McGuire, Barry

Biographical details: This American singer, guitarist and songwriter was born in Oklahoma City and did not turn professional until his mid-twenties. His debut professional appearance was at a Beverly Hills club in 1961. From 1962-64 he was a member of The New Christy Minstrels, a popular group of folk bards; their biggest US hit *Green green* was co-written by McGuire, who also penned The Kingston Trio's 1963 success *Greenback dollar*. In 1965, now a solo artist, he shot to brief superstardom with one of the classic hits of the folk protest era, *Eve of destruction*. Composed by Steve Barri & P.F.Sloan, who were staff writers at Dunhill Records, the Dylan-inspired *Eve of destruction* was a catch-all diatribe against war, repression, racism and everything else that it was fashionable to protest against in 1965. McGuire's gruff voice added to the song's impact, although the version that was released was originally intended as a rough copy - the demo was leaked to local radio and proved so instantly popular that he never got around to recording the 'proper' studio version! Despite, or probably because of, the wave of controversy that *Eve of destruction* created amongst the conservative elements of society, it reached No.1 in American and No.3 in Britain. McGuire was a One Hit Wonder, although he tried his luck with several albums during the Sixties. He was immortalised in the lyrics of The mamas & Papas' 1967 hit *Creeque Alley* - this autobiographical single told the story of the group whom McGuire had discover. He became a born-again Christian in the early Seventies, and proceeded to record a series of musically mediocre gospel albums. (Bob MacDonald 13.1.86).

EVE OF DESTRUCTION (OLD GOLD)
Tracks: / Eve of destruction / Born to be wild / Woodstock.
CD 5": Released 3 May '89, on Old Gold, by Old Gold Records. Catalogue no: **OG 6141**
7" Single: Released May '89, on Old Gold, by Old Gold Records. Catalogue no: **OG 9173**

EVE OF DESTRUCTION (SINGLE)
Tracks: / Eve of destruction.
7" Single: Released Sep '65, on RCA, by BMG Records (UK). Deleted '68. Catalogue no: **RCA 1469**

McGuire, Mo

TIME AND TIME AGAIN
Tracks: / Time and time again.
7" Single: Released Oct '85, on Derelict, Catalogue no: **DRL 2**

McGuire Sisters

Biographical details: This American family vocal group consisted of Christine, Dorothy and Phyllis McGuire. The Ohio-raised Sisters sang in local church choirs in their teens, and later became regulars on local radio. In the years immediately following World War II, they gained valuable touring experience by performing at army camps and veterans' homes. After making a great impression with leading US media talent-spotter Arthur Godfrey, the girls were all in their mid-twenties when they began their run of American hits in 1954 with *Goodnight sweetheart, goodnight*. Becoming the Fifties eqivalent of those Forties favourites, The Andrews Sisters, the McGuires chalked up a lucrative string of Top 40 entries. Their peak year was 1955, when they achieved a massive US chart-topper with *Sincerly*, a watered down rendition of The Moonglows' rhythm'n'blues ballad hit. In an era when black acts were rarely heard on white-dominated pop radio, artists like the McGuire Sisters made alot of money by opportunistically releasing sweetened cover versions of black R&B records for the pop market. Other '55 hits for the Sisters included *It may sound silly*, *Something's gotta give* (from the movie Daddy Long Legs) and *He*. In 1956 they scored with the *Picnic* film theme. In 1958 they reached the US No.1 slot with *Sugartime*. 1959 brought them another Top 20 entry with *May you always* but, as if knowing that their chart days were numbered, the trio achieved their final US Top 40 entry in 1961 with the nostalgically titled *Just for old time's sake*. In Britain, the McGuire Sisters made a respectable but not spectacular impression. Of their five UK Top 30 singles, the two biggest discs both peaked at No.14: *Sincerely*(1955) and *Sugartime*(1958). (Bob MacDonald 13.1.86).

DELILAH JONES
Tracks: / Delilah Jones.
7" Single: Released Jun '56, on Vogue Coral, by Vogue Coral records. Deleted '59. Catalogue no: **Q 72161**

MAY YOU ALWAYS
Tracks: / May you always.
7" Single: Released Jul '84, on Old Gold, by Old Gold Records. Catalogue no: **OG 9418**
7" Single: Released May '59, on Coral, by MCA Records. Deleted '62. Catalogue no: **Q 72356**

NO MORE
Tracks: / No more.
7" Single: Released Apr '55, on Vogue Coral, by Vogue Coral records. Deleted '58. Catalogue no: **Q 72050**

SUGARTIME
Tracks: / Sugartime.
7" Single: Released Feb '58, on Coral, by MCA Records. Deleted '61. Catalogue no: **Q 72305**

McGurk, Colly

COLLY MCGURK
Tracks: / You're special to me / I'd rather be the one you slip around with / I would easily / Signed sealed & delivered.
7" EP: Released Mar '80, on Homespun (Ireland), by Outlet Records. Deleted '83. Catalogue no: **HS 032**

Mach 1

RIGHT STUFF, THE
Tracks: / Right stuff, The.
12" Single: Released Jul '89, on Ghetto, by CBS Records. Catalogue no: **GTGT 005**
7" Single: Released Jul '89, on Ghetto, by CBS Records. Catalogue no: **STUFF 001**

WHAT IS IT?
Tracks: / What is it?.
12" Single: Released Aug '89, on Ghetto, by CBS Records. Catalogue no: **GTST 5**

McHardy, Forbes

BANNER, THE
Tracks: / Banner, The / Love is pleasing.
7" Single: Released Nov '88, on Igus, by Klub Records. Catalogue no: **KLUB 57**

Machiavel

FLY
Tracks: / Fly / Champagne in Amsterdam.
7" Single: Released Jan '81, on EMI, by EMI Records. Deleted Jan '84. Catalogue no: **EMI 5131**

Machin, David

ICH LIEBE DICHT
Tracks: / Ich liebe dicht.
7" Single: Released Jul '81, on PVK, by PVK Records. Catalogue no: **PV 109**

SHOOT SHOOT JOHNNY
Tracks: / Shoot shoot Johnny.
7" Single: Released May '82, on PVK, by PVK Records. Catalogue no: **HIT 4**

Machinations

PRESSURE SWAY
Tracks: / Pressure sway.
12" Single: Released Jan '84, on A&M, by A&M Records. Deleted '88. Catalogue no: **AMX 169**

Machine

MOVE IT (See panel opposite)
Tracks: / Move it / Man in the moon, The.
7" Single: Released Sep '87, on In Crowd, by In Crowd Records. Catalogue no: **MWVS 008**

Machine Boys

SEX MACHINE (HOUSE)
Tracks: / Sex machine (house).
12" Single: Released Mar '88, on Nine O Nine, by Creole Records. Catalogue no: **NINE 16**

Machine Club

CREEPSHOW
Tracks: / Creepshow / Base with a beat.
7" Single: Released Aug '88, on Sonet, by Sonet Records. Catalogue no: **SON 3**

Macho Gang

NAUGHTY BOY
Tracks: / Naughty boy / Naughty boy (house) / Naughty boy (long mix) / Naughty boy (house mix).
7" Single: Released 21 Mar '88, on Nine O Nine, by Creole Records. Catalogue no: **NINE 717**
12" Single: Released 21 Mar '88, on Nine O Nine, by Creole Records. Catalogue no: **NINE 17**

Macho Man

MACHO MAN
Tracks: / Macho man.
7" Single: Released Aug '83, on Monarch, by Monarch Records. Catalogue no: **MON 047**

McHugh, Maureen

JUBILEE PAEGEANT FAIR(EP)
Tracks: / Jubilee paegeant fair / Dear lover / Jubilee year / Down at the fair.
7" Single: Released '81, on Keswick, by Loose Records. Catalogue no: **KES 004**

McIdol, Richie

SKYE BOAT SONG
Tracks: / Skye boat song.
7" Single: Released Nov '84, on Dork, by Dork Records. Catalogue no: **UR RICH 6**

McInnes Alyson

JUMP SHOUT BOOGIE
Tracks: / Jump shout boogie / Spiderwoman.
7" Single: Released Oct '81, on Happy Face, by Standard Sound Productions. Catalogue no: **MM 132**

Macintosh, C.J.

TABLES ARE TURNING, THE
Tracks: / Tables are turning, The.
12" Single: Released Aug '87, on Music Of Life, by Music Of Life Records. Catalogue no: **NOTE 4**

McIsaac, Billy

LOVE ME LIKE YOU DID BEFORE
Tracks: / Love me like you did before.
7" Single: Released Jun '85, on Sedition, by Sedition Records. Catalogue no: **EDIT 3302**
12" Single: Released Jun '85, on Sedition, by Sedition Records. Catalogue no: **EDITL 3302**

Mac,Joy

INSEPARABLE
Tracks: / Inseparable.

7" Single: Released '86, on Sierra, by Sierra Records. Catalogue no: **JOY 1**
12" Single: Released '86, on Sierra, by Sierra Records. Catalogue no: **JOY 1T 12**

MacJunior, Peter

WATER MARGIN, THE
Tracks: / Water margin, The.
7" Single: Released Oct '77, on BBC, by BBC Records & Tapes. Deleted '80. Catalogue no: **RESL 50**

Mack

I WANT YOU
Tracks: / I want you.
12" Single: Released Jul '89, on Supreme, by Supreme Records. Catalogue no: **SUPET 147**

Mack, Bunny

LET ME LOVE YOU
Tracks: / Let me love you / Love you forever.
12" Single: Released Apr '80, on Afrodisc, by RCA Records. Deleted '82. Catalogue no: **MACK 12 1**
7" Single: Released Apr '80, on Afrodisc, by RCA Records. Deleted '82. Catalogue no: **MACK 1**

LOVE SWEET LOVE
Tracks: / Love sweet love / Discolypso.
7" Single: Released Jan '81, on Rokel, Deleted Jan '84. Catalogue no: **MACK 2**

SUPAFRICO
Tracks: / Supafrico.
12" Single: Released Oct '81, on RCA, by BMG Records (UK). Deleted Oct '84. Catalogue no: **RCAT 142**

Mack, Lonnie

Biographical details: This American guitarist and singer was born Lonnie McIntosh in Harrisburg, Indiana, and possessed his first guitar at the age of four. He grew up playing country music with his sisters and brother. By the time he was twelve, he was playing local gigs. In 1955, the first year of rock 'n' roll, the 14 year-old Lonnie formed his own band. After several years of hard work, the guitarist technique and style gave him a smash single. Lonnie Mack's 1963 rendition of *Memphis* was the best instrumental version of Chuck Berry song; it reached No.5 on the US chart in the summer of that year, while it's legendary composer was languishing in jail. Mack followed *Memphis* with another instrumental single *Wham!*, which peaked at about the same time as George Michael and Andrew Ridgeley were being born. Mack never returned to the American Top 40, although he remained a respected figure in the music business for many years. During the late Sixties, he augmented his trademark guitar crispness by developing a gutsy vocal syle which combined the passion of gospel with the earthliness of blues. He became one of the most soulful and distinctive white singers around, thanks to such tracks as *Where ther's a will there's a way* and *Why*, but major fame did not come his way. He did not particulary want stardom and, during the Seventies and Eighties, his religious convictions convinced him to record only sporadically. When he released a rare new Lp in 1985, the album contained some unfortunate sexist lyrics. *Memphis* was not a hit in Britain for Mack until April 1979, when it reached No.47 in a double A sided re-issue with Chris Montez' *Let's dance*. In 1963 UK buyers had preferred to purchase the Chuck Berry original (in it's full title Memphis Tennessee) plus a cover version by the unrelated Dave Berry. (Bob MacDonald, 15th Jan 1986).

MEMPHIS
Tracks: / Memphis.
7" Single: Released Apr '79, on Lightning, Deleted '82. Catalogue no: **LIG 9011**

MEMPHIS (OLD GOLD)
Tracks: / Memphis.
7" Single: Released Jul '82, on Old Gold, by Old Gold Records. Deleted Feb '89. Catalogue no: **OG 9011**

Mack, Richie

IF I FELL
Tracks: / If I fell.
12" Single: Released Apr '83, on Solid Groove, Catalogue no: **SG 025**

Mack & The Boys

HEAVEN
Tracks: / Heaven.
7" Single: Released Oct '88, on Crammed Discs, by Crammed Discs. Catalogue no: **CRAM 16457**

Macka-B

BIBLE READER
Tracks: / Bible reader.
12" Single: Released Jun '85, on Fashion, by Fashion Records. Catalogue no: **FAD 032**

DON'T JUDGE ME
Tracks: / Don't judge me / You are the ladies.
12" Single: Released Nov '86, on Ariwa Sounds, by Ariwa Sounds. Catalogue no: **ARI 57**

WETLOOK CRAZY
Tracks: / Wet look crazy / Down inna de jungle.
12" Single: Released Jun '86, on Ariwa Sounds, by Ariwa Sounds. Catalogue no: **ARI 51**

McKane, Lorraine

LET THE NIGHT TAKE THE BLAME
Tracks: / Let the night take the blame.
7" Single: Released Jan '85, on Carrere, Catalogue no: **CAR 353**
12" Single: Released Jan '85, on Carrere, Catalogue no: **CART 353**

Mackay, Duncan

SIRIUS 3 MARK 2
Tracks: / Sirius 3 mark 2 / In the pink.
7" Single: Released May '81, on Edge, Deleted May '86. Catalogue no: **EDGE 14**

VISA (SINGLE)
Tracks: / Visa / Gin.
7" Single: Released Oct '80, on Edge, Deleted Oct '83. Catalogue no: **EDGE 5**

McKay, Freddie

CARDS ON THE TABLE
Tracks: / Cards on the table / Card tricks.
12" Single: Released Feb '84, on Castaff, Catalogue no: **CF 001**

DRUNKEN SAILOR
Tracks: / Drunken sailor / She was my lady.
12" Single: Released May '84, on Sky Juice, Catalogue no: **SJ 007**

IN TIMES OF TROUBLE
Tracks: / In times of trouble.
12" Single: Released Apr '82, on Live & Love, Catalogue no: **LLDIS 204**

MY LOVE FOR YOU
Tracks: / My love for you.
12" Single: Released Sep '84, on Thunderbar, Catalogue no: **UNKNOWN**

SING LITTLE BIRD
Tracks: / Sing little bird / Can't get no love tonight.
12" Single: Released Feb '80, on Greensleeves, by Greensleeves Records. Deleted Feb '85. Catalogue no: **NICE 106**

Mackay, Ramsay

SILENT WATER
Tracks: / Silent water / Saint Judas.
7" Single: Released Apr '80, on Magnet, by WEA Records. Deleted '82. Catalogue no: **MAG 167**

McKellar, Kenneth

Biographical details: This British singer and arranger has been an institution on the Scottish music scene since the Fifties. In 1960, the year that the UK's trade press began publishing separate EP charts, McKellar chalked up four hits on that list with *Kenneth McKellar Sings Handel*, *Handels's Arias*, *Kenneth McKellar No. 2* and *Road to the Isles*. In 1966 the singer suffered a major embarrassment when he entered that much maligned event, The Eurovision Song Contest. The BBC, who were responsible for organising the British heats to select the United Kingdom entry, had been concerned about the fact that Britain had never won the Contest despite the nation's huge international standing in the world of Sixties pop music. In an attempt to rectify this, the Beeb decided to drop the old procedure whereby regional juries voted for the UK entry from a roster of ten different songs by ten different artists (an idea that was revived a decade later). Under the new system, TV viewers selected their favourite song by postal ballot from a choice of six numbers performed by the same vocalist. This system was pioneered in 1966, the BBC choosing Kenneth McKellar as the singer to perform the six songs. The ultra-embarrassing result was that McKellar's duly selected Eurovision entry *A Man Without Love*, achieved a lower placing in the contest than any previous United Kingdom song! It also peaked at a dismal No.30 on the British charts. The BBC's red faces were finally saved in 1967, when they hired the far more contemporary Sandie Shaw to sing the six songs and won the Contest outright. McKellar was hardly a swinging pop star and, for the rest of his career returned to performing mainly Scottish and classical tunes. It was noticeable that, when Decca comiled two *World of Kenneth McKellar* collections in 1969 and 1970, *A Man Without Love* was omitted from both of them. (Bob MacDonald, 13th Jan 1986).

MAN WITHOUT LOVE, A
Tracks: / Man without love, A.
7" Single: Released Mar '66, on Decca, by Decca Records. Deleted '69. Catalogue no: **F 12341**

Macken, Steve

TWIST AND SHAKE AND JIVE AND ROCK AND ROLL
Tracks: / Twist and shake and jive and rock and roll.
12" Single: Released 24 Jul '89, on Silver Heart, by Silver Heart Records. Catalogue no: **CUFF 1E**

Mackenzie, Billy

IT'S OVER
Tracks: / It's over.
7" Single: Released May '82, on Virgin, by Virgin Records. Deleted May '85. Catalogue no: **VS 498**

McKenzie, Bob

TAKE OFF
Tracks: / Take off / Elron McKenzie.
7" Single: Released Apr '82, on Mercury, by Phonogram Ltd. Catalogue no: **HOSER 1**

McKenzie,Candi

HONESTY
Tracks: / Honesty.
7" Single: Released Jun '89, on Cool Tempo, by Chrysalis Records. Catalogue no: **COOL 186**
12" Single: Released Jun '89, on Cool Tempo, by Chrysalis Records. Catalogue no: **COOLX 186**

WANNA BE GOOD TONIGHT
Tracks: / Wanna be good tonight / Wanna be good tonight (version).
12" Single: Released Feb '89, on Cool Tempo, by Chrysalis Records. Catalogue no: **COOLX 181**
7" Single: Released Feb '89, on Cool Tempo, by Chrysalis Records. Catalogue no: **COOL 181**

McKenzie, Candy

IT MUST BE LOVE
Tracks: / It must be love.
7" Single: Released Jun '85, on Elite Records, by Elite Records. Deleted '87. Catalogue no: **DAZZ 407**
12" Single: Released Jun '85, on Elite Records, by Elite Records. Deleted '87. Catalogue no: **DAZZ 4012**

REMIND ME
Tracks: / Remind me / Different style.
12" Single: Released Oct '83, on Intense, by Intense Records. Catalogue no: **INT 010**
7" Single: Released Oct '83, on Intense, by Intense Records. Catalogue no: **INTS 010**

TURN ME UP
Tracks: / Turn me up / Last dance.
12" Single: Released Apr '86, on WEA, by WEA Records. Catalogue no: **YZ 64T**
7" Single: Released Apr '86, on WEA, by WEA Records. Catalogue no: **YZ 64**

McKenzie, Duncan

ALL OF YOU OUT THERE
Tracks: / All of you out there / Making love.
7" Single: Released Jul '83, on Outlook, Deleted '87. Catalogue no: **OUT 003**

Mackenzie, Gisele

SEVEN LONELY DAYS
Tracks: / Seven lonely days.
7" Single: Released Jul '53, on Capitol, by EMI Records. Deleted '56. Catalogue no: **CL 13920**

McKenzie, Joan

PLEASE MR. PLEASE
Tracks: / Please Mr., please.
12" Single: Released May '89, on Lemon & Lime, Catalogue no: **LLR 004**

McKenzie, Ricardo

CAN'T GET ENOUGH LOVE
Tracks: / Can't get enough love.
12" Single: Released Oct '89, on High Power, Catalogue no: **HPD 017**

McKenzie, Scott

Biographical details: This American singer's name is synonymous with the 1967 *Summer Of Love*, for his only major hit was the classic flower-power anthem *San Francisco (Be Sure To Wear Some Flowers In Your Hair)*. Born in Virginia, McKenzie's first taste of a musical career was as a member of The Journeymen, an early Sixties folk group that included singer/songwriter John Phillips and was based in New York. Phillips moved to California in the mid Sixties to found and lead the highly successful Mama & Papas quartet. In early 1967, the now famous Phillips persuaded the unsuccessful McKenzie to follow his relocation to the West Coast. Having already composed one Californian classic, the Mama's & Papas' *California Dreamin'*, John Phillips proceeded to write another. *San Francisco*, sung by Scott with a sense of naive wonderment, drew international attention to a city that was rapidly becoming the centre of Western pop culture. The single reached No.4 on the US chart, then logged four weeks at No.1 in Britain during August 1967; it also topped charts around Europe. Bland and trite in retrospect, *San Francisco* was filled with the same idealism and optimism that fuelled the whole hippie culture. The song had a great melody and a sympathetic arrangement; although dismissed by many critics as an artificial record, it probably attracted more followers to the San Francisco scene than Big Brother & The Holding Company, The Grateful Dead and The Jefferson Airplane put together. McKenzie claimed to be totally committed to the flower power philosophy so it came as no surprise that he sank into oblivion afer the Summer Of Love was over. His follow up single *Like an old time movie* peaked at No.24 in the US and No.50 in the UK, and subsequent efforts flopped. After a mediocre country-rock Lp in 1970 entitled *Stained Glass Morning*, he stopped making records altogether. (Bob MacDonald, 13th Jan 1986).

LIKE AN OLD TIME MOVIE
Tracks: / Like an old time.
7" Single: Released Nov '67, on CBS, by CBS Records. Deleted '70. Catalogue no: **CBS 3009**

SAN FRANCISCO
Tracks: / San Francisco.
7" Single: Released Apr '83, on Old Gold, by Old Gold Records. Catalogue no: **OG 9305**
7" Single: Released Jul '67, on CBS, by CBS Records. Deleted '70. Catalogue no: **CBS 2816**
7" Single: Released Apr '82, on CBS, by CBS Records. Catalogue no: **CBS 5964**

SECRET HOME
Tracks: / Secret home / Open secret.
7" Single: Released Mar '84, on Soul Stop, by Dawn Promotions. Catalogue no: **SS 3007**

McKenzies

MEALY MOUTH
Tracks: / Mealy mouth.
12" Single: Released Feb '87, on Ron Johnson, by Ron Johnson Records. Catalogue no: **ZRON 15**

MEALY MOUTH REMIX 88
Tracks: / Mealy mouth remix 88.
12" Single: Released 20 Feb '88, on Ron Johnson, by Ron Johnson Records. Catalogue no: **ZRON 18**

NEW BREED
Tracks: / New breed.
7" Single: Released Mar '86, on Ron Johnson, by Ron Johnson Records. Catalogue no: **ZRON 8**

McKenzies, Ranson

KEEP ON WORKING
Tracks: / Keep on working / Orange grooves.
12" Single: Released May '82, on Smokey, Catalogue no: **SMJD 005**

McKenzies Sings

ICE CREAM FACTORY
Tracks: / Ice cream factory / Excursions.
7" Single: Released Oct '82, on WEA, by WEA Records. Catalogue no: **MAK 1**
12" Single: Released Oct '82, on WEA, by WEA Records. Catalogue no: **MAK 1 T**

McKenzie,Tony

LOLITA
Tracks: / Lolita / This is the night of the party.
7" Single: Released Jan '86, on Portrait, by CBS Records. Catalogue no: **A 6857**
12" Single: Released Jan '86, on Portrait, by CBS Records. Catalogue no: **TA 6857**

Mackie, Sammy

I'M YER MAN pop
Tracks: / I'm yer man / Billy's boys.
7" Single: Released Apr '82, on Mint, by Emerald Records. Deleted '85. Catalogue no: **CHEW 63**

MALCOLM MCLAREN - BUFFALO GALS (Released on Charisma)

MALCOLM MCLAREN - MADAME BUTTERFLY (Released on Charisma)

Mackintosh, Ken

CREEP, THE
Tracks: / Creep, The.
7" Single: Released Jan '54, on H.M.V., by EMI Records. Deleted '57. Catalogue no: **BD 1295**

NO HIDING PLACE
Tracks: / No hiding place.
7" Single: Released Mar '60, on H.M.V., by EMI Records. Deleted '63. Catalogue no: **POP 713**

RAUNCHY
Tracks: / Raunchy.
7" Single: Released Feb '58, on H.M.V., by EMI Records. Deleted '61. Catalogue no: **POP 426**

Mack, Jimmy & The Tropics

CHRISTMAS MEMORIES
Tracks: / Christmas memories / Christmas memories (Inst.).
12" Single: Released '86, on Suntan, Catalogue no: **ST 002**

LATE IN THE EVENING
Tracks: / Late in the evening / Late in the evening (dub).
12" Single: Released '86, on Suntan, Catalogue no: **ST 001**

McKone, Vivienne

NOBODY'S FOOL
Tracks: / Nobody's fool / On the outside.
7" Single: Released Feb '83, on Cambra, by Cambra Records. Deleted '88. Catalogue no: **CMB 05**

ONE IN A MILLION
Tracks: / One in a million / Nobody's fool.
7" Single: Released Apr '83, on Cambra, by Cambra Records. Deleted '88. Catalogue no: **CMB 06**

McKown, Gene

ROCKABILLY RHYTHM
Tracks: / Rockabilly rhythm.
7" Single: Released Jun '80, on Rollin' Rock, Catalogue no: **45 041**

McLagan, Ian

LA-DI-LA
Tracks: / La-di-la / Hold on.
7" Single: Released Jan '80, on Mercury, by Phonogram Ltd. Deleted Jan '83. Catalogue no: **MER 1**

McLain, Tommy

Biographical details: McLain was part of the esoteric music scene centred round the swamplands of southern Louisiana, known as swamp pop or Cajun. Because this vibrant genre evolved in virtual isolation in one particular region, it has never become part of the pop mainstream except for the occasional crossover hit. One such hit was *Sweet Dreams*, McLain's Cajun cover version of the well-known Don Gibson song. The McLain single reached No 15 on the US national chart in the summer of 1966 and peaked at No 49 in the UK. This one-off pop success for McLain was produced by Floyd Soileau, the swamps' leading record executive. (Bob MacDonald, January 1986.).

BEFORE I GROW TOO OLD
Tracks: / Before I grow too old / Sweet dreams.
7" Single: Released May '82, on Oval, by Oval Records. Catalogue no: **OVAL 1004**

SWEET DREAMS
Tracks: / Sweet dreams / Think it over.
7" Single: Released Aug '76, on Oval, by Oval Records. Catalogue no: **OVAL 1012**
7" Single: Released Sep '66, on London-American, Deleted '69. Catalogue no: **HL 10065**

McLaren, Malcolm

Biographical details: This British manager, manipulator, entrepreneur and vocalist was one of the most important and intriguing figures on the UK rock scene during the second half o f the Seventies and the early Eighties. He was brought up by his aternal grandmother in middle- class part of London; after leaving school, he took a job as a trainee wine-taster but then spent eight years as a student at various art colleges. In the early Seventies, he opened a clothing store in the King's Road, London, which was initially known as Let It Rock, but eventually was called Sex in reflection of its growing decadence. A brief spell as manager of the pioneering and outragious New York Dolls (who broke up in 1975) inspired him to found and manage The Sex Pistols and thus begin the whole punk revolution of the mid-Seventies.

After assembling three of the four necessary members, McLaren completed the Pistols line-up by recruiting John Lyndon (whom he rechristened Johnny Rotten) who was a down-and-out often seen loitering around the Sex store. By late 1976 Malcolm's manipulation of the Sex Pistols had made the group not only a vital new force in British rock, but a source of scandal and outrage in the national media. before beginning their association with Virgin Records in 1977, the band had been hastily dropped by both EMI and A&M with the result that the Pistols and McLaren retained huge advances with barely one record released. The story was later told in the movie *The Great Rock'n'Roll Swindle*.
After the Sex Pistols had turned the UK music business on its head and set the whole New Wave phenomenon in motion, the group ended in utter chaos. McLaren proceeded to play an early role in the career of another Sex boutique customer, Adam Ant. Adam moved on to superstardom in the early Eighties, but not with his original Ants line-up - at Malcolm's suggestion, the original Ants parted company with Adam and joined forces with Annabella Lwin to form Bow Wow Wow. McLaren discovered Lwin, a 14 year old Burmese born girl, working in a London launderette. Though not as important as the Pistols, Bow Wow Wow caused almost as much controversy; their first single, for instance, was *C30, C60, C90, go*, a ditty co-written and produced by manager McLaren which proudly advocated the illegal practice of home taping, to the chagrin of the record industry.
In late 1982, just as Bow Wow Wow were severing their relationship with the irrespressible entrepreneur, he became an artist in his own right and issued his first solo single *Buffalo Gals*. Showing himself to be ahead of the trends once again, this became the first scratching record to reach the UK top 10. Scratching was a major new idea on the urban New York dance scene, and Malcolm plagiarised this and many other styles from around the globe on his cosmopolitan debut Lp *Duck Rock*. Fuelled by the exuberant Top 3 single *Double Dutch*, this Trevor Horn produced album was a major success on the British chart. It was a unique hotchpotch of other cultures, many of the ideas 'borrowed from Third World countries.
n 1984 McLaren attempted to make opera the Next Big Thing in pop music, with his UK No.13 single Madam Butterfly; this was a modern adaptation of the Puccini opera of the same name, or at least a passage from it. However, the disappointing sales of his *Fans* Lp made it clear that on this occasion, his ideas would not be followed by the rest of the music business. (Bob MacDonald, 14th Jan 1986).

BUFFALO GALS (see panel top left)
Tracks: / Buffalo gals.
12" Single: Released Nov '82, on Charisma, by Virgin Records. Deleted May '88. Catalogue no: **MALC 112**
7" Single: Released Nov '82, on Charisma, by Virgin Records. Deleted May '88. Catalogue no: **MALC 1**

CARMEN
Tracks: / Carmen / Death of a butterfly.
7" Single: Released Dec '84, on Charisma, by Virgin Records. Deleted May '88. Catalogue no: **MALC 6**
12" Single: Released Dec '84, on Charisma, by Virgin Records. Deleted May '88. Catalogue no: **MALC 612**

DOUBLE DUTCH (see panel opposite)
Tracks: / Double dutch / She's looking like a hero.
7" Single: Released Jul '83, on Charisma, by Virgin Records. Deleted May '88. Catalogue no: **MALC 3**
12" Single: Released Jul '83, on Charisma, by Virgin Records. Deleted May '88. Catalogue no: **MALC 312**

DOUBLE DUTCH (OLD GOLD)
Tracks: / Double dutch / Buffalo gals.
12" Single: Released Mar '89, on Old Gold, by Old Gold Records. Catalogue no: **OG 4111**
7" Single: Released Nov '88, on Old Gold, by Old Gold Records. Catalogue no: **OG**

MALCOLM MCLAREN - DOUBLE DUTCH (Released on Charisma)

9831

DUCK FOR THE OYSTER
Tracks: / Duck for the oyster / Legba.
12" Single: Released Sep '83, on Charisma, by Virgin Records. Deleted May '88. Catalogue no: **MALC 412**
7" Single: Released Sep '83, on Charisma, by Virgin Records. Deleted '89. Catalogue no: **MALC 4**

DUCK ROCK CHEER
Tracks: / Duck rock cheer / Boys chorus.
12" Single: Released Jan '86, on Charisma, by Virgin Records. Deleted May '88. Catalogue no: **MALC 712**
7" Single: Released Jan '86, on Charisma, by Virgin Records. Deleted May '88. Catalogue no: **MALC 7**

MADAME BUTTERFLY (See panel on previous page)
Tracks: / Madame Butterfly / First couple out (extended mix).
Special: Released Sep '84, on Charisma, by Virgin Records. Deleted '88. Catalogue no: **MALCS 5**
Cassingle: Released Sep '84, on Charisma, by Virgin Records. Deleted '88. Catalogue no: **TMALC 512**
12" Single: Released Sep '84, on Charisma, by Virgin Records. Catalogue no: **MALC 512**
7" Single: Released Sep '84, on Charisma, by Virgin Records. Deleted '88. Catalogue no: **MALC 5**
CD 3": Released Sep '84, on Charisma, by Virgin Records. Deleted '88. Catalogue no: **CDT 30**

SOMETHING'S JUMPING IN YOUR SHIRT
Tracks: / Something's jumping in your shirt / All night long / Something's jumping in your shirt (walk the body mix) (Only on 12" single.).
12" Single: Released Jul '89, on Epic, by CBS Records. Catalogue no: **WALTZT 3**
CD 5": Released Jul '89, on Epic, by CBS Records. Catalogue no: **WALTZC 3**
Cassingle: Released Jul '89, on Epic, by CBS Records. Catalogue no: **WALTZM 3**
12" Single: Released 14 Aug '89, on Epic, by CBS Records. Catalogue no: **WALTZ E3**
7" Single: Released Jul '89, on Epic, by CBS Records. Catalogue no: **WALTZ 3**

SOWETO (See panel above)
Tracks: / Soweto / Zulu's on a time bomb.
7" Single: Released Feb '83, on Charisma, by Virgin Records. Deleted May '88. Catalogue no: **MALC 2**
12" Single: Released Feb '83, on Charisma, by Virgin Records. Deleted May '88. Catalogue no: **MALC 212**

WALTZ DARLING
Tracks: / Waltz darling / All night long / Deep in vogue.
12" Single: Released 5 Jun '89, on Epic, by CBS Records. Deleted Oct '89. Catalogue no: **WALTZP 2**
7" Single: Released 15 May '89, on Epic, by CBS Records. Deleted Oct '89. Catalogue no: **WALTZ 2**
12" Single: Released 15 May '89, on Epic, by CBS Records. Catalogue no: **WALTZ T2**
12" Single: Released Jun '89, on Epic, by CBS Records. Deleted Oct '89. Catalogue no: **WALTZ Q2**
12" Single: Released Apr '89, on Epic, by CBS Records. Catalogue no: **WALTZ T1**
7" Single: Released Apr '89, on Epic, by CBS Records. Catalogue no: **WALTZ 1**
7" Single: Released 15 May '89, on Epic, by CBS Records. Deleted Oct '89. Catalogue no: **WALTZ G2**
CD 5": Released 15 May '89, on Epic, by CBS Records. Deleted Oct '89. Catalogue no: **WALTZ C2**
CD 5": Released Apr '89, on Epic, by CBS Records. Deleted Oct '89. Catalogue no: **WALTZ C1**
Cassingle: Released 15 May '89, on Epic, by CBS Records. Deleted Oct '89. Catalogue no: **WALTZ M2**
Cassingle: Released 15 May '89, on Epic, by CBS Records. Deleted Oct '89. Catalogue no: **WALTZ S2**

McLean, Don

Biographical details: This American singer, songwriter and guitarist has experienced a strangely erratic commercial career but has made several classic record along the way. He was born in New Rochesse, New York, and developed an early interest in listening to music, especially as asthma restricted his involvement in sport and other physical activities. A lover of folk music, he began his career as a folk singer in 1963 at the age of 18. After several years of hard gigging, he had built up a sufficiently strong following by the end of the Sixties to be asked by famous Pete Seeger to accompany him on a prestigious boat-tour to save the Hudson River in New York State. McLean's first album *Tapestry* was finally issued in 1970 after being rejected by a multitude of record companies. When Don McLean suddenly jumped to superstardom in early 1972, he could hardly have done so in a more dramatic fashion. He shot to No.1 in America and No.2 in Britain with *American Pie*, hailed by press and public alike as one of the most extraordinary epic tracks in pop music to date. At 8 minutes 27 seconds, it was much too long for a single but was far too brilliant to be edited; so the song appeared in a Part One/Part Two format. Although it contained many idiosyncrasies that were difficult to interpret, *American Pie* was basically a journey through rock history - its oft-repeated phrase 'the day the music died' referred to the crushing of rock 'n roll's dreams in the Fifties (the death of his idol Buddy Holly in February 1959), and secondly to the evaporation of rock's peace-love-protest ideals of the Sixties to make way for the materialistic Seventies. Its catchy chorus and bright feel belied its single *Vincent*, a tribute to painter Vincent Van Gogh - No.12 in US, No.1 in UK, was on the charts for most of the year on both sides of the Atlantic.
After *American Pie*, rock critics and consumers expected huge things from McLean, and were disappointed when he moved in a decidely folk/MOR direction thereafter. They had missed the whole point of the song, which was to say 'bye bye' to rock music - its chequered history offered no hope, and the singer wanted no part in its future. So it should have come as no surprise when his song *And I Love You So* became a 1973 hit for Perry Como, or when Don drifted off the charts altogether in the mid-seventies to concentrate on a show-bizzy concert career. When he returned to No.1 status in Britain in 1980 (and No.5 in America in 1981) with *Crying*, it was with a two-year old recording of a 19 year old Roy Orbison hit. McLean's voice was still very much intact, but his writing was not. A little while later, he achieved a moderate hit with the moving *Castles In The Air* - this was a re-recording of the opening track on his very first Lp. (Bob MacDonald 14th Jan 1986).

Malcolm McLaaren - Soweto (Released on Charisma)

AMERICAN PIE (SINGLE)
Tracks: / American pie.
7" Single: Released Apr '83, on EMI, by EMI Records. Catalogue no: **2C 008 82636**

AMERICAN PIE (SINGLE 2)
Tracks: / American pie (part 1) / American pie (part 2).
7" Single: Released Jan '72, on United Artists, by EMI Records. Deleted '75. Catalogue no: **UP 35325**
7" Single: Released Aug '80, on United Artists, by EMI Records. Catalogue no: **UP 628**

CALIFORNIA GOLD
Tracks: / California gold / Be my wife.
7" Single: Released Aug '80, on Piccadilly, Deleted '83. Catalogue no: **7P 195**

Don McLean - Castles in the Air (Released on EMI)

CASTLES IN THE AIR (See panel below)
Tracks: / Castles in the air / Crazy Eyes.
7" Single: Released Apr '82, on EMI, by EMI Records. Deleted '85. Catalogue no: **EMI 5258**

CRYING
Tracks: / Crying / Genesis.
7" Single: Released Apr '80, on EMI, by EMI Records. Deleted Oct '87. Catalogue no: **EMI 5051**

NO ROOM AT THE INN
Tracks: / No room at the inn / Home sweet loving.
7" Single: Released Nov '80, on Precision (1), Deleted Nov '83. Catalogue no: **7P 207**

VERY THOUGHT OF YOU
Tracks: / Very thought of you, The / Left for dead.
7" Single: Released Nov '82, on EMI, by EMI Records. Catalogue no: **EMI 5356**

VINCENT
Tracks: / Vincent.
7" Single: Released May '72, on United Artists, by EMI Records. Deleted '75. Catalogue no: **UP 35359**
7" Single: Released '80, on USA, by Charly Records. Catalogue no: **LR 8207**

McLean, Don (comedy)

BILLY'S BIG BASS DRUM
Tracks: / Billy's big bass drum / Al Capone.
7" Single: Released Apr '80, on Piccadilly, Deleted '83. Catalogue no: **7P 171**

MacLean, Dougie

ON A WING AND A PRAYER
Tracks: / On a wing and a prayer.
12" Single: Released Nov '86, on Ugly Man, by Ugly Man Records. Catalogue no: **UGLY 1**

McLean, Jackie

Biographical details: This American alto saxophonist and composer has been a jazz artist since the early Fifties, although his performing activities have been spasmodic.
He was given early encouragement by a famous fellow alto saxman, the legendary Charlie Parker. Born in 1932, McLean made his first records under his own name in the mid-Fifties, his first great composition being *Little Melonae*. McLean was steadily building his reputation when drug difficulties began to affect him.
During the Sixties his live work gradually diminished until, by the end of that decade, he hade ceased performing live altogether; he was barred from many New York clubs even after the problem eased. Nonetheless, he compensated for this in no uncertain terms - his 1962-67 period on the famed Blue Note label yielded what many critics consider to be his greatest disc output.
The album *Let Freedom Ring* was particularly noteworthy.
The Seventies saw him return to occasional performing. He continued beheld in high esteem in jazz circles, although he never quite entered the very top league. Late in his career, McLean achieved his only entry into the UK pop charts - *Dr Jackyll and Mr Funk*, a single featuring the assistance of a vocal back-up group, reached No.53. This was a surprising nod to the then fashionable disco scene (July 1979); by this time McLean was devoting much of his time to teaching activities and to the study and furtherance of Afro-American cultural ties.
(Bob MacDonald, 14th January 1986).

DOCTOR JACKYLL AND MISTER FUNK
Tracks: / Doctor Jackyll and Mister Funk.
7" Single: Released Jul '79, on RCA, by BMG Records (UK). Deleted '82. Catalogue no: **PB 1575**

MacLean & MacLean

DOLLI PARTEN'S TITS
Tracks: / Dolli Parten's tits.
7" Single: Released May '81, on Safari, by Safari Records. Catalogue no: **PUP 1**

McLean, Mikey

STOP DO DAT
Tracks: / Stop do dat.
12" Single: Released Feb '89, on Saxon Studio, Catalogue no: **SHF 007**

McLean, Nana

LET YOUR LOVE SHINE ON ME
Tracks: / Let your love shine on me.
12" Single: Released Sep '89, on Penthouse, by Penthouse Records. Catalogue no: **PH 023**

Mclean, Phil

SMALL SAD SAM
Tracks: / Small sad Sam.
7" Single: Released Jan '62, on Top Rank (1), Deleted '65. Catalogue no: **JAR 597**

McLean, Shirley

SUMMER HOLIDAY
Tracks: / Summer holiday / Summer holiday (inst) / Summer holiday (dub).
12" Single: Released Sep '88, on World Enterprise, Catalogue no: **WDS 01**

McLean, Tulsa

ROCK ON ELVIS
Tracks: / Rock on Elvis.
7" Single: Released Aug '81, on RCA, by BMG Records (UK). Deleted Aug '84. Catalogue no: **RCA 123**

McLean,John

COME INTO THE GARDEN
Tracks: / Come into the garden, Maud.
12" Single: Released Aug '85, on Black Starliner, Catalogue no: **BS 001**

IF I GIVE MY HEART TO YOU
Tracks: / If I give my heart to you.
12" Single: Released Jul '87, on Ariwa Sounds, by Ariwa Sounds. Catalogue no: **ARI 66**
7" Single: Released Jan '88, on Ariwa Sounds, by Ariwa Sounds. Catalogue no: **ARI 766**

OPEN MY HEART
Tracks: / Open my heart.
7" Single: Released Oct '84, on Roots Radical, by Roots Radical Records. Catalogue no: **RR 7003**
12" Single: Released Oct '84, on Roots Radical, by Roots Radical Records. Catalogue no: **RR 12003**

STARLINE
Tracks: / Starline / Dance with me / Rock to...
12" Single: Released Jul '82, on Music Lovers, Catalogue no: **ML 003**

McLean,Norman

FLOWER OF SCOTLAND & THE BONNIE DAYS OF SUMMER
Tracks: / Flower of Scotland.
7" Single: Released '81, on Lismor, by Lismor Records. Deleted '88. Catalogue no: **LISP 2002**

McLean,Ranchi

CINDERELLA
Tracks: / Cinderella / Walkin' on.
7" Single: Released Aug '83, on Dart, by President Records. Catalogue no: **DART 1**

McLelland,Sandy

NO TURNING BACK
Tracks: / No turning back / Tried to warn you.
7" Single: Released Jan '82, on Action, Catalogue no: **BACK 1**

STAY CLEAN TONIGHT
Tracks: / Stay clean tonight / Movie clean.
7" Single: Released Feb '81, on Action, Catalogue no: **A 1000**

TWO TIRED LOVERS
Tracks: / Two tired lovers / Day you left.
7" Single: Released Jul '82, on Action, Catalogue no: **A 4000**

MacLeod, John

STEEL AWAY
Tracks: / Steel away / Slow waltz - ballad of Glencoe / Wee ladies.
7" Single: Released Oct '89, on Scotdisc, by Scotdisc Records. Catalogue no: **ITV 7S 504**

MacLure, Pinkie

BITE THE HAND THAT FEEDS YOU
Tracks: / Bite the hand that feeds you.
12" Single: Released Jun '85, on Ink, by Red Flame Records. Catalogue no: **INK 1210**

WALLS OF PELVIS
Tracks: / Walls of pelvis.
12" Single: Released Jul '89, on Ink, by Red Flame Records. Catalogue no: **INK 1241**

MacManas Gang

TOWN CALLED BIG NOTHING, A
Tracks: / Town called big nothing, A / Return to big nothing.
12" Single: Released May '87, on Demon, by Demon Records. Catalogue no: **D 1052 T**
7" Single: Released May '87, on Demon, by Demon Records. Catalogue no: **D 1052**

McMann, Gerard

CRY LITTLE SISTER
Tracks: / Cry little sister / I still believe.
7" Single: Released Jan '88, on Atlantic, by WEA Records. Catalogue no: **A 9130**

McMaster, Andy

ANOTHER POLITICIAN
Tracks: / Another politician / Normal street.
Note: Pic bag
12" Single: Released 30 May '87, on GFM, Catalogue no: **GFMT 111**
7" Single: Released 30 May '87, on GFM, Catalogue no: **GFM 111**

NO JOY
Tracks: / No joy / Normal Street.
7" Single: Released 30 May '87, on GFM, Catalogue no: **GFM 111**

MacNab, Jim

CRYSTAL CHANDELIERS (SINGLE)
Tracks: / Crystal chandeliers.
7" Single: Released Apr '79, on Klub, by Klub Records. Catalogue no: **KLUB 09**

MacNab, J.J.

DO YOU RIGHT TONIGHT
Tracks: / Do you right tonight.
7" Single: Released Oct '80, on Country House, by Scotdisc Records. Deleted Jul '88. Catalogue no: **BGC 268**

McNabb, Christine

YOU TOOK YOUR LOVE AWAY
Tracks: / You took your love away.
12" Single: Released Aug '84, on Rad's, Catalogue no: **RS 101**

McNairn, John

YESTERDAY IS OVER
Tracks: / Yesterday is over.
7" Single: Released Aug '85, on Individual, by Individual Records. Catalogue no: **AIRS 102**

MacNeal, Maggie

AMSTERDAM
Tracks: / Amsterdam / Take it easy.
7" Single: Released Apr '80, on Warner Bros., by WEA Records. Deleted Apr '83. Catalogue no: **K 18214**

NIGHT TIME
Tracks: / Night time / Take it easy.
7" Single: Released Jan '80, on WEA, by WEA Records. Deleted Jan '83. Catalogue no: **K 17465**

McNeal, Rita

FLYING ON YOUR OWN
Tracks: / Flying on your own / She's called Nova Scotia.
7" Single: Released 20 Jun '87, on 10 Records, by Virgin Records. Deleted May '88. Catalogue no: **TEN 177**

McNeil, Les

IF ONLY
Tracks: / If only / You can make it possible.
12" Single: Released May '89, on Music Scene, Catalogue no: **MKS 62547**
12" Single: Released Sep '83, on Ambac, Catalogue no: **AMB 313**

LOVE MECHANIC
Tracks: / Love mechanic.
12" Single: Released Feb '82, on Solid Groove, Catalogue no: **SG 006 12**

McNeir, Ronnie

FOLLOW YOUR HEART
Tracks: / Follow your heart / Everybody's in a hurry / Love's under suspect.
7" Single: Released Nov '86, on Expansion, Catalogue no: **EXPAND 6**

I'M SO IN LOVE WITH YOU BABY
Tracks: / I'm so in love with you / Serve it up.
12" Single: Released 31 Oct '87, on Expansion, Catalogue no: **EXPAND 11**

McNichol, Kristy

FIRST LOVE
Tracks: / First love / Sister's song.
7" Single: Released Jan '83, on Polydor, by Polydor Ltd. Catalogue no: **POSP 548**

McNiel, Les

AGAIN
Tracks: / Again.
12" Single: Released Jul '82, on Ambassador, Catalogue no: **AMB 7879**

GODDESS OF LOVE
Tracks: / Goddess of love / McNiel dubonic rock.
12" Single: Released Mar '84, on Soul Patrol, Catalogue no: **SP 3120**

McPhatter, Clyde

TREASURE OF LOVE
Tracks: / Treasure of love.
7" Single: Released Aug '56, on London-American, Deleted '59. Catalogue no: **HLE 8293**

McPherson, Chris

BRAND NEW SONG
Tracks: / Brand new song / We can fly away.
7" Single: Released Oct '80, on Creole, by Creole Records. Deleted Oct '83. Catalogue no: **CR 207**

McRae, Gwen

FUNKY SENSATION
Tracks: / Funky sensation / Funky sensation (off Broadway mix).
12" Single: Released Sep '87, on Rhythm King, by Mute Records. Catalogue no: **LEFT 15T**
7" Single: Released Sep '87, on Rhythm King, by Mute Records. Catalogue no: **LEFT 15**

McShaw, Pinky

IT'S COMING SOON
Tracks: / It's coming soon / New York to Moscow.
7" Single: Released Dec '84, on Trance, Deleted '86. Catalogue no: **TRN 2001**
12" Single: Released Dec '84, on Trance, Deleted '86. Catalogue no: **TRN 2001 12**

McTell, Ralph

Biographical details: This British singer, songwriter and guitarist was born in Farnborough, Kent, and had been working in clubs for ten years before shooting to fame with his 1975 smash *Streets Of London.* He started out playing blues and ragtime music, then became a permanent folk singer. McTell's debut album *Eight Frames A Second* was released in 1968. The second Lp, 1969's *Spiral Staircase*, contained the first recorded version of the aforementioned *Streets.* During the early Seventies, the new fashionableness of solo-singer-songwriters enhanced McTell's reputation and he began to expand his folk-club base into a broader pop audience. He established himself as an excellent songwriter, building a repertoire that combined with incisive sociological comment. Despite the overall quality of his whole catalogue, the moving *Streets of London* became such a cult favourite that McTell, in a rare bow to commercial dictates, re-recorded the song with a MOR choral/string backing. The result was a UK No.2 single in early '75, plus a Top 20 entry with the *Streets* album. Within weeks of this sudden stardom, Ralph reacted by announcing that he was retreating to the United States to escape from it. By the end of the year, he was back in London.
McTell subsequently succeeded in steering a satisfactory course through the music business. He managed to play his music and live in London, which he loved, but avoid playing the pop star role which he hated. With his concert tours and occasional TV appearances, he earned a comfortable living but made sure that his success did not exceed a certain level. During the Eighties, he seemed to compromise his folk roots in favour of a more bland, easy-listening style; singles like *England* (1982) and *Winner's song* (1984) came dangerously close to the charts, but McTell had not changed his attitude to fame. In a slight career aberration, he wrote and recorded an album of children's songs, which he performed on the Granada Television program *Alphabet Zoo.* The most accomplished Lp of his career was probably 1976's *Right Side Up.* (Bob MacDonald, 14 Jan 1986).

DREAMS OF YOU
Tracks: / Dreams of you.
7" Single: Released Dec '75, on Warner Bros., by WEA Records. Deleted '78. Catalogue no: **K 16648**

ENGLAND
Tracks: / England / Grey sea strand.
7" Single: Released Jun '82, on EMI, by EMI Records. Catalogue no: **EMI 5315**

I FALL TO PIECES
Tracks: / I fall to pieces / I'm not a rock.
7" Single: Released Nov '82, on Mays, by Mays Records. Catalogue no: **ING 2**

KENNY THE KANGAROO
Tracks: / Kenny the kangaroo.
7" Single: Released May '83, on Mays, by Mays Records. Catalogue no: **ING 4**

KENNY THE KANGAROO (EP)
Tracks: / Kenny the kangaroo / Holly the hedgehog / Carmilla the camel / Nellie the newt.
7" EP: Released Dec '82, on Maze, Deleted Dec '85. Catalogue no: **NG 3**

STRANGER TO THE SEASON
Tracks: / Stranger to the season.
7" Single: Released Oct '83, on Mays, by Mays Records. Catalogue no: **ING 7**

STREETS OF LONDON
Tracks: / Streets of London.
7" Single: Released Dec '74, on Warner Bros., by WEA Records. Deleted '77. Catalogue no: **K 14380**

STREETS OF LONDON (7")
Tracks: / Streets of London.
7" Single: Released Jul '81, on Reprise (USA), Catalogue no: **K 14380**

WIND IN THE WILLOWS
Tracks: / Wind in the willows / Open road.
7" Single: Released May '84, on Red Bus, by Red Bus Records. Catalogue no: **RBUS 94**

WINNERS SONG
Tracks: / Winners song.
7" Single: Released Nov '84, on Mays, by Mays Records. Catalogue no: **ING 1**

McTells

JESSE MAN RAE
Tracks: / Jesse Man Rae.
7" Single: Released Aug '87, on Frank, Catalogue no: **TRUFFAUT 303**

WIND UP
Tracks: / Wind up.
7" Single: Released Apr '89, on Bi-Joopiter, Catalogue no: **BIJ OOP 019**

McVay

BOYS GO DANCING
Tracks: / Boys go dancing.
7" Single: Released Jul '84, on RAK, by EMI Records. Catalogue no: **RAK 375**
12" Single: Released Jul '84, on RAK, by EMI Records. Deleted '86. Catalogue no: **12RAK 375**

McVey, Morgan

LOOKING GOOD DIVING
Tracks: / Look good diving.
7" Single: Released Jan '87, on CBS, by CBS Records. Deleted Aug '87. Catalogue no: **MORG 1**
12" Single: Released Jan '87, on CBS, by CBS Records. Deleted Aug '87. Catalogue no: **MORGT 1**

McVie, Christine

GOT A HOLD ON ME
Tracks: / Got a hold on me.
12" Single: Released Feb '84, on Warner Bros., by WEA Records. Catalogue no: **W 9372 PT**
7" Single: Released Feb '84, on Warner Bros., by WEA Records. Catalogue no: **W 9372**

LOVE WILL SHOW US HOW
Tracks: / Love will show us how / Challenge.
7" Single: Released Apr '84, on Warner Bros., by WEA Records. Catalogue no: **W 9313**

McWilliams, David

Biographical details: This British singer, guitarist and songwriter was one of the nearly-men of the music business, tipped for big things but never quite making it. The track that drew most attention was *Days of Pearly Spencer*, but this did not become a hit single despite several reissues. McWilliams' only success on the UK charts was with three albums in the late Sixties: *David McWilliams Sings* reached No.38, *David McWilliams Vol 2* climbed to No.23 and *David McWilliams Vol 3* peaked at No.39. His more imaginatively titled but unsuccessful Seventies sets included *Lord Offaly, Beggar And The Priest,* and *Living Just A State Of Mind.* (Bob MacDonald, 14th Jan 1986).

DAYS OF PEARLY SPENCER
Tracks: / Days of Pearly Spencer.
7" Single: Released Apr '83, on EMI (France), by EMI Records. Catalogue no: **2C 008 05945**

McWilliams, Randy

DUMB ONE
Tracks: / Dumb one / Plastic man.
7" Single: Released Mar '84, on Switch, Catalogue no: **SW 7**

M.A.D.

SUN FEAST
Tracks: / Sun feast.
12" Single: Released Sep '84, on Criminal Damage, Catalogue no: **CRI 12121**

Mad About Sunday

DRUNK
Tracks: / Drunk.
7" Single: Released May '83, on Backs, by Backs Recording Co.. Catalogue no: **NCH 006**

Mad House

6
Tracks: / 6 / 6#24.
7" Single: Released Jun '87, on Paisley Park (USA), by WEA Records. Deleted Jul

'88. Catalogue no: **W 8485**
12" Single: Released Jun '87, on Paisley Park (USA), by WEA Records. Deleted Jul '88. Catalogue no: **W 8485T**

MAD HOUSE
Tracks: / Mad House.
12" Single: Released Jun '85, on Homestead, Catalogue no: **FOYO 12**

Mad Jocks...

GLORIA
Tracks: / Gloria.
7" Single: Released Apr '83, on DPR, Catalogue no: **DPPS 1**

JOCK MIX 1
Tracks: / House nation / Girls can jack too / Auld lang syne.
12" Single: Released '88, on Debut, by Skratch Records. Catalogue no: **DEBTX 3037**
7" Single: Released Nov '87, on Debut, by Skratch Records. Catalogue no: **DEBT 3037**

JUST LIKE KENNY (w. Kenny Dalglish)
Tracks: / Just like Kenny / Dalgleish, we're right behind you.
7" Single: Released Mar '84, on Zuma, Catalogue no: **ZOOM 2**
12" Single: Released Mar '84, on Zuma, Catalogue no: **ZOOMT 2**

Mad Lads

YOU BLEW IT
Tracks: / You blew it.
12" Single: Released Sep '85, on Champion, by Champion Records. Catalogue no: **CHAMP 123**
7" Single: Released Sep '85, on Champion, by Champion Records. Deleted Jul '89. Catalogue no: **CHAMP 3**

Mad Max

HEARTS ON FIRE
Tracks: / Hearts on fire.
7" Single: Released 21 Nov '87, on Road Runner (1), by Road Runner Records. Catalogue no: **RR 5475**

Mad Mission

ENERGY
Tracks: / Energy.
12" Single: Released May '89, on Greedy Beat, Catalogue no: **12GREED 9**

Mad Reign

SALUTE THE NEW FLAG
Tracks: / Salute the new flag.
7" EP: Released Feb '87, on Iron Works (USA), by Azra International (USA). Catalogue no: **IW 1010**

Madam X

HIGH IN HIGH SCHOOL
Tracks: / High in high school / Metal in my viens.
7" Single: Released Feb '85, on Jet, by Jet Records. Catalogue no: **JET 7044**
Special: Released Feb '85, on Jet, by Jet Records. Catalogue no: **JETP 7044**

JUST THAT TYPE OF GIRL
Tracks: / Just that type of girl / Flirt.
7" Single: Released Nov '87, on Atlantic, by WEA Records. Deleted Jul '88. Catalogue no: **A 9216**
12" Single: Released Nov '87, on Atlantic, by WEA Records. Catalogue no: **A 9216 T**

MADAM X (SINGLE)
Tracks: / Madam X.
12" Single: Released Jan '88, on Atlantic, by WEA Records. Catalogue no: **K 7817741 4**
7" Single: Released Jan '88, on Atlantic, by WEA Records. Catalogue no: **K 7817741**

Madden, Amy

MINOR DISTURBANCES EP
7" Single: Released Sep '89, on One Big

MADNESS - THE RETURN OF THE LOS PALMAS 7 (Released on Stiff)

Guitar, by One Big Guitar Records. Catalogue no: **OEG 008**
12" Single: Released Sep '89, on One Big Guitar, by One Big Guitar Records. Catalogue no: **OEG 008 T**

Madder, Gaynor Rose

ARE YOU IN PAIN
Tracks: / Are you in pain.
7" Single: Released Apr '87, on Ugly Man, by Ugly Man Records. Catalogue no: **UGLY 4**
12" Single: Released Apr '87, on Ugly Man, by Ugly Man Records. Catalogue no: **UGLY 4T**

TIES
Tracks: / Ties / Bigger than a dream.
7" Single: Released Oct '88, on Destiny Angel, Catalogue no: **GYPSY 3**

Maddison, Derek

I'LL GO WHERE YOUR MUSIC TAKES ME
Tracks: / I'll go where your music takes me.
7" Single: Released Oct '80, on Fellside, by Fellside Records. Catalogue no: **C 2018**

Maddo, Osibert

KING OF THE RING
Tracks: / King of the ring.
12" Single: Released Nov '83, on Sunsplash, by Sunsplash Records. Deleted '87. Catalogue no: **SNS 003**

Made in England

PROSPECTS
Tracks: / Stay sharp / Prospects.
Note: Featuring Ray Dorset
7" Single: Released Feb '86, on Red Bus, by Red Bus Records. Catalogue no: **RBUS 2208**

STAY SHARP
Tracks: / Stay sharp.
7" Single: Released Aug '85, on Red Bus, by Red Bus Records. Catalogue no: **RBUS 2203**
12" Single: Released Aug '85, on Red Bus, by Red Bus Records. Catalogue no: **RBUSL 2203**

Madigan, Gerry

TAKE ME BACK TO TULSA
Tracks: / Take me back to Tulsa.
7" Single: Released Sep '84, on Homespun (Ireland), by Outlet Records. Catalogue no: **HS 086**

M.A.D.M.

TO THE ACID HOUSE (WHISTLE LAMPIN)
Tracks: /To the acid house(whistle lampin).
12" Single: Released Dec '88, on Blue Chip, by Blue Chip Records. Catalogue no: **BLUECHIP 11 T**

Madness

Biographical details: The classic line-up of this British pop band was Mike Barson, Mark Bedford, Chris Foreman, Graham 'Suggs' McPherson, Carl 'Chas' Smash, Lee Thompson and Dan 'Woody' Woodgate. Crucial founder member Mike Barson quit in January 1984, but the other six guys continued withour finding a replacement. The group took their name from a 1963 track by their Jamaican idol 'Prince Buster', the pioneering purveyor of 'blue beat' and 'ska' which later gave birth to reggae. His sixties music was the key influence upon the combo's early output; their first hit *The Prince* was a tribute to him, and their second hit *One step beyond* was written and originally recorded by him. The forerunner of the London-based Madness was a band called the 'The Invaders' formed in late 1976. That group struggled to build a reputation via small-time gigs until mid-1979, when they evolved into Madness; the name change was necessitated by the existence of another small-time band called the Invaders. Madness joined 2 Tone Records, a new label founded by 'The Specials', a Coventry based band with similar musical ideas. The first Madness disc *The Prince* reached No.16 on the UK singles chart and helped to contribute to the 2 Tone label's extraordinary 100% success rate in 1979. By the time *One Step Beyond* came out, the group had switched from 2 Tone to an equally important and equally idiosyncratic label, Stiff.
From this point onwards, the Madness story can only be described as a phenomenon. From 1979-1985 the band chalked up 21 consecutive British hit singles, 15 of which reached the Top 10. They never experienced a UK flop, or even a minor hit, for the combo's least successful single peaked at No.21. The most successful was 1982's *House Of Fun*, which reached the very top of the British chart. Their many near-misses in the No.1 stakes included *Wings Of Dove* (No.2 in 1983), *My girl* and *Baggy trousers* (both No.3 in 1980), *Embarrasement* (No.4 in 1980), *Grey day* (No.4 in 1981), *It must be love* and *Driving in my car* (both No.4 in 1982). The success of 'The Nutty Boys', as they were known, inspired Stiff to launch their first ever television advertising campaign for 1982's *Complete Madness*, with the result that Madness found themselves atop the British singles and albums charts simultaneously with *House of fun* and *Complete Madness*. The group's first three ordinary studio albums had logged a total of 150 chart weeks between them. Madness were Britains most consistent pop group of the early Eighties, releasing an endless stream of mainly self-written ditties which were instantly hummable and always recognisable as Madness, yet always slightly different. The nutty boys' genius was to combine consistently interesting sociological lyrics with irresistably catchy melodies. Their zany antics belied their often incisive songwriting. Madness were among the first great video artists, backing each single with a crazy clip (No.7 in 1983).
By 1985 Madness had quit the Stiff label and founded their own Zarjazz Records. (Bob MacDonald, 15th Jan 1986).

BAGGY TROUSERS
Tracks: / Baggy trousers / Business.
7" Single: Released Sep '80, on Stiff, by Stiff Records. Catalogue no: **BUY 84**

BAGGY TROUSERS (OLD GOLD)
Tracks: / Baggy trousers / Embarrassment.
7" Single: Released Nov '88, on Old Gold, by Old Gold Records. Catalogue no: **OG 9821**

CARDIAC ARREST
Tracks: / Cardiac arrest / In the city.
7" Single: Released Feb '82, on Stiff, by Stiff Records. Catalogue no: **BUY 140**

DRIVING IN MY CAR
Tracks: / Driving in my car / Animal farm (tomorrow's dream warp mix).
7" Single: Released Jun '82, on Stiff, by Stiff Records. Deleted '85. Catalogue no: **BUY 153**
7" Pic: Released Jun '82, on Stiff, by Stiff Records. Deleted '85. Catalogue no: **PBUY 153**
7" Single: Released '85, on Virgin, by Virgin Records. Catalogue no: **VS 785**
12" Single: Released Jun '82, on Stiff, by Stiff Records. Deleted '85. Catalogue no: **SBUY 153**

EMBARRASSMENT
Tracks: / Embarrassment / Crying shame.
7" Single: Released Nov '80, on Stiff, by Stiff Records. Catalogue no: **BUY 102**

GREY DAY
Tracks: / Grey day / Memories.
Cassingle: Released Apr '81, on Stiff, by Stiff Records. Deleted '85. Catalogue no: **ZBUY 112**
7" Single: Released Apr '81, on Stiff, by Stiff Records. Deleted '85. Catalogue no: **BUY 112**

HOUSE OF FUN
Tracks: / House of fun / Don't look back.
7" Single: Released May '82, on Stiff, by Stiff Records. Deleted '85. Catalogue no: **BUY 146**
7" Pic: Released May '82, on Stiff, by Stiff Records. Deleted '85. Catalogue no: **PBUY 146**
7" Single: Released '85, on Virgin, by Virgin Records. Catalogue no: **VS 784**

IT MUST BE LOVE
Tracks: / It must be love / Shadow on the house.
7" Single: Released Nov '81, on Stiff, by Stiff Records. Catalogue no: **BUY 134**

IT MUST BE LOVE (OLD GOLD)
Tracks: / It must be love / My girl.
7" Single: Released Nov '88, on Old Gold, by Old Gold Records. Catalogue no: **OG 9826**

IT MUST BE LOVE (RE-RELEASE)
Tracks: / It must be love / Return of Los Palmas 7.
7" Single: Released May '89, on Virgin, by Virgin Records. Catalogue no: **VS 1197**

MICHAEL CAINE
Tracks: / Michael Caine / If you think there's something.
12" Single: Released Jan '84, on Stiff, by Stiff Records. Deleted '85. Catalogue no: **BUYIT 196**
7" Single: Released '85, on Virgin, by Virgin Records. Catalogue no: **VS 790**
7" Single: Released Jan '84, on Stiff, by Stiff Records. Deleted '85. Catalogue no: **BUY 196**

MY GIRL
Tracks: / My girl / Stepping into line.
12" Single: Released Jan '80, on Stiff, by Stiff Records. Deleted '85. Catalogue no: **BUYIT 62**
7" Single: Released '85, on Virgin, by Virgin Records. Catalogue no: **VS 781**
7" Single: Released Jan '80, on Stiff, by Stiff Records. Deleted '85. Catalogue no: **BUY 62**

NIGHT BOAT TO CAIRO
Tracks: / Night boat to Cairo / Deceives the eye / Young and the old, The / Don't quote me on that.
7" Single: Released '85, on Virgin, by Virgin Records. Catalogue no: **VS 782**

ONE BETTER DAY
Tracks: / One better day / Guns.
7" Pic: Released Jun '84, on Stiff, by Stiff Records. Deleted '85. Catalogue no: **PBUY 201**
7" Single: Released Jun '84, on Stiff, by Stiff Records. Deleted '87. Catalogue no: **BUY 201**
7" Single: Released '85, on Virgin, by Virgin Records. Catalogue no: **VS 791**

ONE STEP BEYOND (see panel below)
Tracks: / One step beyond / Mistakes.
7" Single: Released Oct '79, on Stiff, by Stiff Records. Catalogue no: **BUY 56**

OUR HOUSE
Tracks: / Our house / Walking with Mr.Wheeze.
7" Pic: Released Oct '82, on Stiff, by Stiff Records. Deleted '85. Catalogue no: **PBUY 163**
12" Single: Released Nov '82, on Stiff, by Stiff Records. Deleted '85. Catalogue no: **BUYIT 163**
7" Single: Released '85, on Virgin, by Virgin Records. Catalogue no: **VS 786**
7" Single: Released Oct '82, on Stiff, by Stiff Records. Deleted '85. Catalogue no: **BUY 163**

PEEL SESSIONS:MADNESS 27.8.79
12" Single: Released Oct '86, on Strange Fruit, by Strange Fruit Records. Catalogue no: **SFPS 007**
CD 5": Released Jul '88, on Strange Fruit, by Strange Fruit Records. Catalogue no: **SFPSCD 007**
Cassingle: Released 13 Jun '87, on Strange Fruit, by Strange Fruit Records. Catalogue no: **SFPSC 007**

PRINCE, THE
Tracks: / Prince, The / Madness.
7" Single: Released Sep '79, on Two-Tone, by Chrysalis Records. Deleted '84. Catalogue no: **CHS TT 3**

PRINCE, THE (OLD GOLD)
Tracks: / Madness / Prince, The.
7" Single: Released Feb '87, on Old Gold, by Old Gold Records. Catalogue no: **OG 9685**

MADNESS - ONE STEP BEYOND (Released on Stiff)

RETURN OF THE LOS PALMAS 7(see panel on previous page)
Tracks: / Return of the Los Palmas 7 / That's the way to do it.
12" Single: Released Jan '81, on Stiff, by Stiff Records. Catalogue no: **BUYIT 108**
7" Single: Released Jan '81, on Stiff, by Stiff Records. Catalogue no: **BUY 108**

SHUT UP
Tracks: / Shut up / Town with no name.
7" Single: Released Sep '81, on Stiff, by Stiff Records. Catalogue no: **BUY 126**

SUN AND THE RAIN, THE
Tracks: / Sun and the rain, The / Fireball XL5.
7" Single: Released '85, on Virgin, by Virgin Records. Catalogue no: **VS 789**
12" Single: Released Oct '83, on Stiff, by Stiff Records. Deleted '85. Catalogue no: **BUYIT 192**
7" Single: Released Oct '83, on Stiff, by Stiff Records. Deleted '85. Catalogue no: **BUY 192**
7" Pic: Released Oct '83, on Stiff, by Stiff Records. Deleted '85. Catalogue no: **PBUY 192**

SWEETEST GIRL
Tracks: / Sweetest girl, The (7" only) / Jennie (a portrait of) / Sweetest girl (dub mix) (12" only) / Sweetest girl (extended mix) (12" only).
7" Single: Released Jan '86, on Zarjazz, by Zarjazz Records. Catalogue no: **JAZZ 8**
12" Single: Released Jan '86, on Zarjazz, by Zarjazz Records. Catalogue no: **JAZZ 8-12**

TOMORROW'S (JUST ANOTHER DAY)
Tracks: / Tomorrow's (just another day) / Madness.
7" Single: Released '85, on Virgin, by Virgin Records. Catalogue no: **VS 787**
12" Single: Released Feb '83, on Stiff, by Stiff Records. Deleted '85. Catalogue no: **BUYIT 169**
7" Single: Released Feb '83, on Stiff, by Stiff Records. Deleted '85. Catalogue no: **BUY 169**
7" Pic: Released Feb '83, on Stiff, by Stiff Records. Deleted '85. Catalogue no: **PBUY 169**

UNCLE SAM
Tracks: / Uncle Sam / Please don't go.
12" Single: Released Oct '85, on Zarjazz, by Zarjazz Records. Deleted '89. Catalogue no: **JAZZ 7-12**
7" Single: Released Oct '85, on Zarjazz, by Zarjazz Records. Catalogue no: **JAZZ 7**

VICTORIA GARDENS
Tracks: / Victoria Gardens.
7" Single: Released Apr '84, on Stiff, by Stiff Records. Catalogue no: **BUY 201**

(WAITING FOR) THE GHOST TRAIN
Tracks: / (Waiting for) the ghost train / Maybe in another life / Seven year scratch (12" only).
7" Single: Released Oct '86, on Zarjazz, by Zarjazz Records. Catalogue no: **JAZZ 9**
12" Single: Released Oct '86, on Zarjazz, by Zarjazz Records. Catalogue no: **JAZZ 9-12**

WINGS OF A DOVE
Tracks: / Wings of a dove / Behind the 8 ball.
7" Single: Released Aug '83, on Stiff, by Stiff Records. Catalogue no: **BUY 181**
12" Single: Released Aug '83, on Stiff, by Stiff Records. Catalogue no: **BUYIT 181**
7" Pic: Released Aug '83, on Stiff, by Stiff Records. Catalogue no: **PBUY 181**

WORK,REST AND PLAY MADNESS
Tracks: / Night boat to Cairo / Don't quote me on that.
7" Single: Released Mar '80, on Stiff, by Stiff Records. Catalogue no: **BUY 71**

YESTERDAY'S MEN
Tracks: / Yesterday's men (7" only) / All I knew / Yesterday's men (12" version) / Yesterday's men (demo version) (12" only).
12" Single: Released Aug '85, on Zarjazz, by Zarjazz Records. Catalogue no: **JAZZ 5-12**
7" Single: Released Aug '85, on Zarjazz, by Zarjazz Records. Catalogue no: **JAZZ 5**

Madness, The

I PRONOUNCE YOU
Tracks: / I pronounce you / Patience / 4BF (CD & 12" only) / 11th hour (CD & 12" only).
CD 5": Released Aug '88, on Virgin, by Virgin Records. Catalogue no: **VSCD 1054**
12" Single: Released 7 Mar '88, on Virgin, by Virgin Records. Catalogue no: **VST 1054**
7" Single: Released 7 Mar '88, on Virgin, by Virgin Records. Catalogue no: **VS 1054**

WHAT'S THAT?
Tracks: / What's that / Be good boy (NOT on VSJ 1078) / Flashings (On VSJ & VST 1078 only).
7" Single: Released 16 May '88, on Virgin, by Virgin Records. Catalogue no: **VS 1078**
7" Pic: Released 16 May '88, on Virgin, by Virgin Records. Catalogue no: **VSJ 1078**
12" Single: Released 16 May '88, on Virgin, by Virgin Records. Catalogue no: **VST 1078**

Madoc, Ruth

FOLLOWING A STAR
Tracks: / Following a star.
7" Single: Released Dec '86, on Wattsco, Catalogue no: **WATTS C 5**

Madonna

Biographical details: This American singer, songwriter and actress was born Madonna Ciccone in Detroit, her Christian name being inherited from her mother. The girl eventually moved to New York City and, after working for a time in a doughnut shop, obtained a dance scholarship. Deciding that she would be more successful as a singer rather than a dancer, she moved to Paris to gain vocal experience. Back in the USA, her first single *Everybody* was released in late 1982 and she began to build a following in New York clubs. *Everybody* was written by the artist herself and produced by New York disc jockey Mark Kamins. Conveniently she proceeded to falll in love with the city's leading DJ and club remixer, the ultra trendy John 'Jellybean' Benitez, who produced the highly catchy track *Holiday*.
In the Autumn of '83, Madonna enjoyed her first real taste of success when a coupling of *Holiday* and the self-penned *Lucky Star* reached No.1 on the American dance charts. These tracks were a white approximation of black funk music, combining great pop hooks with an infectious disco groove. She was to continue along this route, with great success. In early 1984 *Holiday* became a Top 20 pop hit on both sides of the Atlantic, and was followed by *Borderline* (No.10 in US) and *Lucky star* (No 4 in US, No.14 in UK). All of these appeared on her first LP *Madonna* which enjoyed a prolonged sales life.
Although initially competing with the likes of Cyndi Lauper and Shannon in the race for the top new, sexually provocative female dance-pop singer, Madonna brushed all opposition with the November 1984 release of her second album *Like a virgin*. Produced by Nile Rodgers, who had just enjoyed a red-hot stread through his studio work with David Bowie and Duran Duran, the *Like a virgin* Lp cruised to the top of the US charts as did the single of the same name. That an artist called Madonna No.1 could be No.1 at Christmas with a song entitled *Like a virgin*, was ironic in view of the fact that Ms Ciccone's image and attitude were anything but reverent. The single held on to the US No.1 slot throughout January 1985, clocking up six weeks at the summit in total; it peaked at No.3 in Britain. 1985 could only be described as the year of Madonna. She became indisputably the world's hottest female performer. *Like a virgin* remained on the Lp charts in the US and UK for the entire year. *Material girl* (an apt title if ever there was one) became a US No.2 single, and was followed by the American No.1 smash *Crazy for you* (from the film soundtrack *Vision Quest*). In Britain, the 26 year old vocalist chalked up eight Top 5 singles in 1985, more than any other act has achieved in any calendar year in UK chart history. This sleazy singer's success soured to its peak on 17 August, when *Into the groove* and the reactivated *Holiday* gave her the honour of being the first American act and the first female act to hold the top two spots on the British singles chart in the same week. (Bob MacDonald, 16th Jan 1986).

ANGEL
Tracks: / Angel / Burning up / Angel (extended dance mix) (Only on 12" single.).
7" Pic: Released '87, on Sire, by Sire Records. Deleted Jun '87. Catalogue no: **W 8881 P**
12" Single: Released Sep '87, on Sire, by Sire Records. Catalogue no: **920386 0**
7" Single: Released Oct '85, on Sire, by Sire Records. Catalogue no: **W 8881**
12" Single: Released Oct '85, on Sire, by Sire Records. Deleted Jan '88. Catalogue no: **W 8881 T**

BORDERLINE
Tracks: / Borderline / Physical attraction / Borderline (dub) (Available on 12" Disc only).
12" Single: Released Jun '84, on Sire (USA), Catalogue no: **W 9260T**
7" Single: Released Jun '84, on Sire (USA), Deleted Jan '88. Catalogue no: **W 9260**
12" Pic: Released '85, on Sire (USA), Deleted Jun '87. Catalogue no: **W 9260P**

MADONNA - EXPRESS YOURSELF (Released on Sire)

BORDERLINE (U.S. REMIX)
Tracks: / Borderline (dub remix) / Physical attraction.
12" Single: Released Sep '87, on Sire, by Sire Records. Catalogue no: **920218 0**

CAUSING A COMMOTION
Tracks: / Causing a commotion / Jimmy Jimmy / Causing a commotion (silver screen mix) (Only on 12" single.) / Causing a commotion (movie house mix) (Only on 12" single.).
Note: (Cat.no.-207624) 4-track cass. single, which includes a dub mix of the title track not available in the U.K.. 12" X 3" long box packaging.
12" Single: Released Sep '87, on Warner Bros., by WEA Records. Catalogue no: **W 8224T**
12" Pic: Released Sep '87, on Warner Bros., by WEA Records. Deleted Jul '88. Catalogue no: **W 8224TP**
Cassingle: Released Nov '87, on Sire (USA), Catalogue no: **207624**
Cassingle: Released Sep '87, on Warner Bros., by WEA Records. Deleted Jul '88. Catalogue no: **W 8224C**
7" Single: Released Sep '87, on Warner Bros., by WEA Records. Catalogue no: **W 8224**

CHERISH
Tracks: / Cherish / Supernatural.
7" Single: Released Aug '89, on Sire, by Sire Records. Catalogue no: **W 2883**
Cassingle: Released Aug '89, on Sire, by Sire Records. Catalogue no: **W 2883MC**
CD 5": Released Aug '89, on Sire, by Sire Records. Catalogue no: **W 2883CD**
12" Single: Released Aug '89, on Sire, by Sire Records. Catalogue no: **W 2883T**

CRAZY FOR YOU
Tracks: / Crazy for you / I'll fall in love again.
12" Single: Released Jun '85, on Geffen, by Geffen Records (USA). Deleted '85. Catalogue no: **WA 6323P**
7" Single: Released Nov '87, on Geffen (USA), by Geffen Records (USA). Catalogue no: **GGEF 0540**
7" Single: Released Jun '85, on Geffen, by Geffen Records (USA). Catalogue no: **A 6323**

DRESS YOU UP
Tracks: / Dress you up
12" Single: Released Nov '85, on Sire, by Sire Records. Catalogue no: **W 8848 T**
12" Single: Released Jul '88, on Sire (Japan), by Sire Records. Catalogue no: **P 5202**
7" Single: Released Nov '85, on Sire, by Sire Records. Deleted Jan '88. Catalogue no: **W 8848**
Special: Released Nov '85, on Sire, by Sire Records. Catalogue no: **W 8848 P**

DRESS YOU UP (IMPORT)
Tracks: / Dress you up.
12" Single: Released Oct '88, on Sire (USA), Catalogue no: **020369**

EVERYBODY
Tracks: / Everybody / Everybody (dub version).
12" Single: Released Dec '82, on Warner Bros., by WEA Records. Catalogue no: **W 9899 T**
7" Single: Released Dec '82, on Warner Bros., by WEA Records. Catalogue no: **W 9899**

EXPRESS YOURSELF (see panel above)
Tracks: / Express yourself / Look of love, The (album version).
7" Single: Released Jun '89, on Sire, by Sire Records. Catalogue no: **W 2948 W**
CD 5": Released May '89, on Sire, by Sire Records. Catalogue no: **W 2948 CD**
Cassingle: Released May '89, on Sire, by Sire Records. Catalogue no: **W 2948 C**
12" Pic: Released May '89, on Sire, by Sire Records. Deleted '89. Catalogue no: **W 2948 TP**
7" Single: Released Jul '89, on Sire, by Sire Records. Catalogue no: **W 2948X**
12" Single: Released May '89, on Sire, by Sire Records. Catalogue no: **W 2948 T**
7" Single: Released May '89, on Sire, by Sire Records. Catalogue no: **W 2948**
7" Single: Released Jun '89, on Sire, by Sire Records. Catalogue no: **W 2948 X**

GAMBLER
Tracks: / Gambler, The / Gambler, The (instrumental).
7" Single: Released Oct '85, on Geffen, by Geffen Records (USA). Deleted '88. Catalogue no: **A 6585**
7" Single: Released Oct '85, on Geffen, by Geffen Records (USA). Deleted '88. Catalogue no: **QA 6585**
12" Single: Released Oct '85, on Geffen, by Geffen Records (USA). Deleted '88. Catalogue no: **TA 6585**

HOLIDAY
Tracks: / Holiday / Lucky star / Holiday (full length version) (Only on 12" single.).
12" Single: Released Sep '87, on Sire, by Sire Records. Catalogue no: **920176 0**
7" Single: Released Jan '84, on Sire, by Sire Records. Deleted '87. Catalogue no: **W 9405**
12" Pic: Released Jul '85, on Sire, by Sire Records. Deleted '85. Catalogue no: **W 9405 T**
12" Single: Released Nov '83, on Sire, by Sire Records. Deleted '86. Catalogue no: **W 9405 T**

NTO THE GROOVE
Tracks: / Shoo-bee-doo / Into the groove / Everybody (Only on 12" single.).
7" Single: Released Jul '85, on Warner Bros., by WEA Records. Catalogue no: **W 8934**
12" Single: Released Sep '87, on Sire, by Sire Records. Catalogue no: **920352 0**
7" Pic: Released Jul '85, on Sire, by Sire Records. Deleted '85. Catalogue no: **W 8934P**
12" Single: Released Jul '85, on Warner Bros., by WEA Records. Deleted Jan '88. Catalogue no: **W 8934 T**
Special: Released Jul '85, on Warner Bros., by WEA Records. Catalogue no: **W 9405 T**

LA ISLA BONITA
Tracks: / La Isla Bonita (remix) / La Isla Bonita (instrumental).

12" Single: Released Mar '87, on Sire (USA), Catalogue no: **W 8378T**
12" Pic: Released Mar '87, on Sire, by Sire Records. Deleted '87. Catalogue no: **W 8378TP**
7" Single: Released Mar '87, on Sire (USA), Catalogue no: **W 8378**

LIKE A PRAYER (SINGLE)
Tracks: / Like a prayer / Act of contrition.
7" Single: Released Mar '89, on Sire, by Sire Records. Catalogue no: **W 7539**
12" Pic: Released Mar '89, on Sire, by Sire Records. Deleted '89. Catalogue no: **W 7539 TP**
Cassingle: Released Mar '89, on Sire, by Sire Records. Catalogue no: **W 7539 C**
CD 5": Released Mar '89, on Sire, by Sire Records. Catalogue no: **W 7539 CD**
12" Single: Released Mar '89, on Sire, by Sire Records. Catalogue no: **W 7539 T**

LIKE A VIRGIN (SINGLE)
Tracks: / Like a virgin / Stay.
7" Single: Released Sep '84, on Sire (USA), Catalogue no: **W 9210**
12" Single: Released Sep '84, on Sire (USA), Deleted Jan '88. Catalogue no: **W 9210 T**
12" Single: Released Sep '84, on Sire (USA), Catalogue no: **920239 0**

LIVE TO TELL
Tracks: / Live to tell / Live to tell (inst) / Live to tell (Edit).
12" Pic: Released '86, on Warner Bros., by WEA Records. Deleted Jun '87. Catalogue no: **W 8717 TP**
7" Single: Released '86, on Warner Bros., by WEA Records. Catalogue no: **W 8717**
12" Single: Released '86, on Warner Bros., by WEA Records. Catalogue no: **W 8717 T**
12" Single: Released Jul '88, on Sire (USA), Catalogue no: **920461 0**

LOOK OF LOVE
Tracks: / Look of love, The / I know it / Love don't live here anymore.
12" Single: Released Nov '87, on Sire (USA), Catalogue no: **W 8115T**
7" Single: Released Nov '87, on Sire (USA), Catalogue no: **W 8115**
12" Single: Released Nov '87, on Sire (USA), Catalogue no: **W 8115TP**

LUCKY STAR
Tracks: / I know it / Lucky star / Lucky star (full length version).
12" Single: Released Sep '87, on Sire, by Sire Records. Catalogue no: **920149 0**
7" Single: Released Mar '84, on Sire (USA), Catalogue no: **W 9522**
12" Single: Released Mar '84, on Sire (USA), Deleted Jan '88. Catalogue no: **W 9522T**

MADONNA: INTERVIEW PICTURE DISC (COLLECTION)
Note: 4 x 7" picture discs in wallet.
7" Set: Released 11 Dec '88, on Baktabak, by Baktabak Records. Catalogue no: **BAK-PAK 1012**

MATERIAL GIRL
Tracks: / Pretender / Material girl / Material girl (Jellybean dance remix) (Only on 12" single.).
12" Single: Released Sep '87, on Sire, by Sire Records. Catalogue no: **920304 0**
7" Single: Released Feb '85, on Warner Bros., by WEA Records. Catalogue no: **W 9083**
12" Single: Released Feb '85, on Warner Bros., by WEA Records. Deleted Jan '88. Catalogue no: **W 9083 T**

NEW YORK 1982
Tracks: / New York 1982.
12" Pic: Released '88, on Repertoire (Germany), Catalogue no: **RR 5001 P**
CD 3": Released '88, on Repertoire (Germany), Catalogue no: **RR 6001 CS**
12" Single: Released '88, on Repertoire (Germany), Catalogue no: **RR 1002 M**

ON THE STREET
Tracks: / On the street.
12" Single: Released May '89, on Receiver, by Trojan Records. Catalogue no: **REPLAY 3008**

OPEN YOUR HEART
Tracks: / Open your heart / Lucky star / Open your heart (dub mix) (12" only.).
7" Single: Released Nov '86, on Sire (USA), Deleted Jan '88. Catalogue no: **W 8480**
12" Single: Released Nov '86, on Sire (USA), Catalogue no: **W 8480T**
12" Pic: Released Nov '86, on Sire, by Sire Records. Deleted '87. Catalogue no: **W 8480 TP**

PAPA DON'T PREACH
Tracks: / Papa don't preach / Ain't no big deal / Papa don't preach (extended version) (Only on 12" single.).
7" Single: Released '86, on Sire (USA), Catalogue no: **W 8636**
12" Pic: Released '86, on Sire, by Sire Records. Deleted '86. Catalogue no: **W 8636 TP**
12" Single: Released '86, on Sire (USA), Catalogue no: **W 8636T**

TRUE BLUE
Tracks: / True Blue / Holiday.
12" Single: Released Sep '86, on Sire (USA), Catalogue no: **W 8550 T**
12" Pic: Released Sep '86, on Sire, by Sire Records. Deleted '86. Catalogue no: **W 8550 TP**
Cassingle: Released Jul '86, on Sire (USA), Catalogue no: **WX 54 C**
7" Single: Released Sep '86, on Sire (USA), Catalogue no: **W 8550**

WHO'S THAT GIRL
Tracks: / Who's that girl / White heat.
Note: (Cat.no. 206924) Extended version of 'Who's that girl' and also 'White Heat'. Long box pack.
7" Single: Released Jul '87, on Sire (USA), Catalogue no: **W 8341**
12" Pic: Released Jul '87, on Sire, by Sire Records. Deleted '87. Catalogue no: **W 8341TP**
Cassingle: Released Nov '87, on Sire (USA), Catalogue no: **206924**
12" Single: Released Jul '87, on Sire (USA), Deleted Jul '88. Catalogue no: **W 8341T**

WILD DANCING
12" Single: Released Feb '87, on Receiver, by Trojan Records. Catalogue no: **REPLAY 3006**

Madoo

SAD MUSIC
Tracks: / Sad music.
7" Single: Released Oct '88, on Redman International, Catalogue no: **RED 37**

Madoo Ranking

WRAP UP
Tracks: / Wrap up.
12" Single: Released Nov '88, on Hurricane (2), Catalogue no: **MC 001**

Madoo, U.U.

MIX UP
Tracks: / Mix up.
12" Single: Released 5 Jun '89, on Stereo One, Catalogue no: **SOT 1**

Madskwad

BELT HAS GOT TO STAY
Tracks: / Belt has got to stay / We are the tartan army.
7" Single: Released May '82, on Pulsar, by Lismor Records. Catalogue no: **PUS 105**

Maegan

DOCTOR'S ORDERS
Tracks: / Doctor's orders / Don't sing.
7" Single: Released May '84, on Savoir Faire, Catalogue no: **FAIS 007**
12" Single: Released May '84, on Savoir Faire, Catalogue no: **FAIT 007**

Maelov,Eddie

ANOTHER TEARDROP
Tracks: / Another teardrop / At the cabaret / Times are hard (Track available on 12" only.).
7" Single: Released Nov '81, on Human (2), Catalogue no: **HUM 13**
12" Single: Released Nov '81, on Human (2), Catalogue no: **HUM 1312**

LINES
Tracks: / Lines / Last bouquet.
7" Single: Released Jul '81, on Human (1), by Accolade Music. Deleted Jul '84. Catalogue no: **HUN 912**
12" Single: Released Jul '81, on Human (2), Catalogue no: **HUM 9**
12" Single: Released Jul '81, on Human (2), Catalogue no: **MAN 3**

Mae,Thelma

WONDERMAN LOVER
Tracks: / Wonderman lover.
7" Single: Released Sep '81, on Solid Groove, Catalogue no: **SG 001**

Mafia, Leroy

LIFE IS JUST A DREAM
Tracks: / Life is just a dream / Anywhere you go.
12" Single: Released Apr '86, on Vena, Catalogue no: **VEN 006**

THERE SHE GOES AGAIN
Tracks: / There she goes again.
12" Single: Released Sep '89, on Mafia/Fluxy, Catalogue no: **M&F 010**

Magacity Four

DISTANT RELATIVES
Tracks: / Distant relatives.
7" Single: Released Dec '88, on Decoy, Catalogue no: **DYS 1**

Magazine

Biographical details: The most successful line-up of this British rock band was Barry Adamson, Dave Formula, Martin Jackson, John Mcgeoch and vocalist/founder Howard Devoto. As frontman with the Buzzcocks, Devoto had been one of the pioneers of the UK's punk rock revolution in 1976. Despite that group's increasing reputation, Devoto took the bold step of leaving the band shortly after the January 1977 release of their seminal EP *Spiral scratch*. Magazine came into being in mid-1977. Early in the following year, the new band issued one of the most critically acclaimed debut singles in the history of British rock - *Shot by both sides* was ecstatically received by the UK music press, was heavily aired by radio's leading champion of the New Wave John Peel, and was described by Rolling Stone magazine as the best rock'n' roll record of 1978, punk or otherwise. For all this, it peaked at a disappointing No.41 on the UK singles chart; for the rest of their career, Magazine's critical acceptance would continue to heavily outweigh their record sales. (Bob MacDonald, 16th Jan 1986).

ABOUT THE WEATHER
Tracks: / About the weather / In the dark.
7" Single: Released May '81, on Virgin, by Virgin Records. Deleted May '86. Catalogue no: **VS 412**

SHOT BY BOTH SIDES
Tracks: / Shot by both sides / My mind ain't so open.
7" Single: Released '77, on Virgin, by Virgin Records. Catalogue no: **VS 200**

SONG FROM UNDER THE FLOORBOARDS
Tracks: / Song from under the floorboards / Twenty years ago.
7" Single: Released Feb '80, on Virgin, by Virgin Records. Deleted '83. Catalogue no: **VS 321**

SWEETHEART CONTRACT
Tracks: / Sweetheart contract.
7" Single: Released Jul '80, on Virgin, by Virgin Records. Deleted '83. Catalogue no: **VS 368**

THANK YOU FALETTINME BE MICE ELF AGAIN
Tracks: / Thank you falettinme be mice elf again / Book.
7" Single: Released Apr '80, on Virgin, by Virgin Records. Deleted '83. Catalogue no: **VS 328**

UPSIDE DOWN
Tracks: / Upside down / Light pours out of me.
7" Single: Released May '80, on Virgin, by Virgin Records. Deleted '83. Catalogue no: **VS 334**

Magazine 60

DON QUICHOTTE
Tracks: / Don Quichotte.
7" Single: Released Jul '86, on RCA, by BMG Records (UK). Catalogue no: **PB 40771**
12" Single: Released Jul '86, on RCA, by BMG Records (UK). Catalogue no: **PT 40772**

Maggotron

WELCOME TO THE PLANET OF BASS
Tracks: / Welcome to the Planet of Bass.
12" Single: Released Nov '87, on Jamarc (USA), Catalogue no: **JMC 7729**

Maggotty, Michael

LAST DECEMBER
Tracks: / Last December / Hello Sharon.
12" Single: Released Oct '88, on Nubian, Catalogue no: **NRT 06**

Magic

CHAMPION
Tracks: / Champion.
7" Single: Released May '89, on Jammy's, Catalogue no: **UNKNOWN**

Magic Bastards

STRANGE COMMENT
Tracks: / Strange comment.
7" Single: Released '88, on Crook, Catalogue no: **BAST 001**

STRANGE GLORY
Tracks: / Strange glory
Note: Cassette single contains five tracks.
Cassingle: Released Nov '87, on Crook Cassettes, by Crook Cassettes. Catalogue no: **MAG 1**
7" Single: Released Nov '87, on Crook Cassettes, by Crook Cassettes. Catalogue no: **BAST 1**

Magic Box

I HEARD IT THROUGH THE GRAPEVINE
Tracks: / I heard it through the grapevine.
12" Single: Released Feb '85, on Kameleon, by Kameleon Records. Catalogue no: **NEON 101T**

Magic Lady

BETCHA CAN'T LOSE (WITH MY LOVE)
Tracks: / Betcha can't lose.
7" Single: Released May '88, on Motown, by BMG Records (UK). Catalogue no: **ZB 42003**
12" Single: Released May '88, on Motown, by BMG Records (UK). Catalogue no: **ZT 42004**

SEXY BODY
Tracks: / Sexy body / Get off.
7" Single: Released Aug '82, on A&M, by A&M Records. Deleted Aug '85. Catalogue no: **USAF 1222**

Magic Lanterns

EXCUSE ME BABY
Tracks: / Excuse me baby.
7" Single: Released Jul '66, on CBS, by CBS Records. Deleted '69. Catalogue no: **202094**

Magic Magic Co

TABLE TOP TAP
Tracks: / Table top tap / Kibo sassa.
7" Single: Released Feb '84, on It's Magic, Catalogue no: **MAGIC 10**

Magic Moments At Twilight

SAMPLER SINGLE: STATE OF THE ART/MMATT THEME
Tracks: / Sampler single: State of the art/Mmatt theme / Tarts.
Cassingle: Released Aug '89, on Magic Moments At Twilight Time, by Magic Moments At Twilight Time. Catalogue no: **C 4004**

WHYDOESEVERYBODYDOAXMASSINGLE?
Tracks: / WhydoeseverybodydoaXmassingle / Xmas with Jody / R.E.M..
Cassingle: Released Aug '89, on Magic Moments At Twilight Time, by Magic Moments At Twilight Time. Catalogue no: **C 4016**

Magic Pan Flutes

MAGIC OF THE PAN FLUTE
Note: Double album and cassette.
Cassingle: Released Jul '86, on Avon, by Avon Records. Catalogue no: **ADK 526**

Magical Michael

MILLIONAIRE
Tracks: / Millionaire / My friend and I.
7" Single: Released Aug '80, on Atomic, Catalogue no: **MAGIC 1**

Magician

HOUSE OF THE PURPLE MIST (1&2)
Tracks: / House of the purple mist.
7" Single: Released Aug '79, on Hobo, Catalogue no: **HOS 008**

Magna Carta

Biographical details: At the time of their only UK chart entry, this British band consisted of Tony Carr, Spike Heatley, Davey Johnstone, Barry Morgan, Chris Simpson, Glen Stuart and Lyell Tranter. The group's line-up was an ever-changing phenomenon, and guitarist/vocalist Simpson was the only constant factor. Magna Carta were one of the nearly groups of the Seventies, always tipped for success but never quite cracking it. Their eponymous debut album was issued in 1969. The follow-up, 1970's Seasons, became the only chart success of the group's carreer - it peaked at No.55 on the British LP list. This album was also notable for the presence of Rick Wakeman on keyboards, then a session musician. Songs from Wasties Orchard, produced by Gus Dudgeon of Elton John fame, was released in 1971; but, like subsequent Magna Carta albums, it reached a cult audience but no more. In that same year, guitarist Davey Johnstone became a member of Elton's backing band. Magna Carta's brand of folk and folk-rock continued to heard on albums throughout the Seventies. (Bob MacDonald, 16th Jan 1986).

HIGHWAY TO SPAIN
Tracks: / Highway to Spain.
7" Single: Released Aug '81, on Recorded Delivery, Catalogue no: **RDR 003**
7" Single: Released Oct '80, on Precision (1), Deleted Oct '83. Catalogue no: **PAR 110**

LOVE IS FOREVER
Tracks: / Love is forever.
7" Single: Released Apr '84, on Mays, by

Mays Records. Catalogue no: **ING 10**

TIGER'S EYES
Tracks: / Tiger's eyes / Long distance.
7" Single: Released 16 Sep '88, on Tempo, by Warwick Records. Catalogue no: **TML 135**

Magness, Ron

MIRACLES
Tracks: / Miracles / Emotion.
7" Single: Released Jan '83, on Towerbell, Catalogue no: **TOW 33**

STAND BY ME
Tracks: / Stand by me.
7" Single: Released Sep '82, on Towerbell, Catalogue no: **TOW 27**

Magnificent Lkage

PASSION
Tracks: / Passion / King of love song, A / One day the butterfly.
12" Single: Released Jul '89, on G.I., by Plastic Head Records. Catalogue no: **GI 12002**

Magnolia Siege

ALL WASHED UP
Tracks: / All washed up / Some kind of freak / Curtis goes to Spain.
12" Single: Released Feb '88, on Primitive, by Primitive Records. Catalogue no: **PRIME 015**

Magnum

ALL OF MY LIFE
Tracks: / All of my life / Great adventure / Invasion / Kingdom of madness.
7" Set: Released Mar '80, on Jet, by Jet Records. Deleted Mar '83. Catalogue no: **JET 175**

BACK TO EARTH
Tracks: / Back to earth.
7" Single: Released Sep '82, on Jet, by Jet Records. Catalogue no: **JET 7027**

CHANGES
Tracks: / Changes / Everybody needs.
7" Single: Released Jun '80, on Jet, by Jet Records. Deleted Jun '83. Catalogue no: **JET 188**

DAY'S OF NO TRUST
Tracks: / Day's of no trust / Day's of no trust (ext.version) (Extra track on 12" and CD.) / Maybe tonight / Spirit, The (live) (Extra track on 12".) / Two hearts (live) / How far Jerusalem (live) (Track on CD only.).
CD 5": Released Mar '88, on Polydor, by Polydor Ltd. Catalogue no: **POCD 910**
7" Single: Released Mar '88, on Polydor, by Polydor Ltd. Catalogue no: **POSP 910**
12" Single: Released Mar '88, on Polydor, by Polydor Ltd. Catalogue no: **POSPX 910**

IT MUST HAVE BEEN LOVE
Tracks: / It must have been love / Crying time / Lonely nights (live) / Just like an arrow (live) / Lights burned out (live).
12" Single: Released 20 Jun '88, on Polydor, by Polydor Ltd. Catalogue no: **POSPX 930**
7" Single: Released 20 Jun '88, on Polydor, by Polydor Ltd. Catalogue no: **POSP 930**
7" Single: Released 20 Jun '88, on Polydor, by Polydor Ltd. Catalogue no: **POSPG 930**
CD 5": Released 20 Jun '88, on Polydor, by Polydor Ltd. Catalogue no: **POCD 930**
12" Single: Released 20 Jun '88, on Polydor, by Polydor Ltd. Catalogue no: **POSXB 930**

JUST LIKE AN ARROW
Tracks: / Just like an arrow / Two hearts.
7" Single: Released Mar '85, on FM, by FM-Revolver Records. Catalogue no: **VHF 4**
12" Single: Released Mar '85, on FM, by FM-Revolver Records. Catalogue no: **12VHF 4**

LIGHTS BURNED OUT
Tracks: / Lights burned out, The.
7" Single: Released Feb '82, on Jet, by Jet Records. Catalogue no: **JET 7020**

LONELY NIGHT
Tracks: / Lonely nights.
7" Single: Released Jul '86, on Polydor, by Polydor Ltd. Deleted '89. Catalogue no: **POSP 798**

MAGNUM
Tracks: / Lights burned out, The / If I could live forever / Sacred hour.
CD 3": Released '88, on Special Edition, by Castle Communications Records. Catalogue no: **CD3-7**

MAGNUM EP
Tracks: / Invasion / Kingdom of madness / All of my life / Great adventure.
7" Single: Released Mar '80, on Jet, by Jet Records. Deleted '83. Catalogue no: **JET 175**

MIDNIGHT
Tracks: / Midnight / Back street kid.
12" Single: Released Oct '86, on Polydor, by Polydor Ltd. Deleted Aug '87. Catalogue no: **POSPX 833**
7" Single: Released Oct '86, on Polydor, by Polydor Ltd. Deleted Aug '87. Catalogue no: **POSP 833**

OH LONELY NIGHT
Tracks: / Oh lonely night / Le morts dansants (live) / Hold back your love (live).
12" Single: on Polydor, by Polydor Ltd. Deleted Mar '87. Catalogue no: **POSPX 798**
7" Single: Released Jun '86, on Polydor, by Polydor Ltd. Deleted Mar '87. Catalogue no: **POSP 798**
7" Single: on Polydor, by Polydor Ltd. Deleted Mar '87. Catalogue no: **POSPG 798**

ON A STORYTELLER'S NIGHT
Tracks: / On a storyteller's night.
7" Single: Released Jun '85, on FM, by FM-Revolver Records. Catalogue no: **VHF 10**
12" Single: Released Jun '85, on FM, by FM-Revolver Records. Catalogue no: **12 VHF 10**
7" Pic: Released May '85, on FM, by FM-Revolver Records. Catalogue no: **WKFM PD 34**

START TALKING LOVE
Tracks: / Start talking love / C'est la vie / Start talking love (ext. remix)* / Back to earth (live) / On a storytellers night (live) (on 12" and CD single only.) / Sacred hour (live) (CD single only.).
7" Single: Released Apr '88, on Polydor, by Polydor Ltd. Deleted 30 May '89. Catalogue no: **POSP 920**
12" Single: Released Apr '88, on Polydor, by Polydor Ltd. Catalogue no: **POSPX 920**
7" Single: Released Apr '88, on Polydor, by Polydor Ltd. Catalogue no: **POSPG 920**
12" Single: Released Apr '88, on Polydor, by Polydor Ltd. Catalogue no: **POSXR 920**
CD 5": Released Apr '88, on Polydor, by Polydor Ltd. Catalogue no: **POCD 920**

WHEN THE WORLD COMES DOWN
Tracks: / Vigilante / When the world comes down.
12" Single: Released Feb '87, on Polydor, by Polydor Ltd. Deleted Jan '88. Catalogue no: **POSPX 850**
7" Single: Released Feb '87, on Polydor, by Polydor Ltd. Deleted Jan '88. Catalogue no: **POSP 850**

WINGS OF HEAVEN
Tracks: / C'est la vie (On ltd edition picture disc only.).
12" Pic: Released 5 Dec '88, on Polydor, by Polydor Ltd. Catalogue no: **POLDP 5221**

Magnus, Nick

SUN ARISE
Tracks: / Sun arise.
7" Single: Released Jun '84, on Polydor, by Polydor Ltd. Catalogue no: **POSP 687**

Magoogan, Wesley

THIS GUY'S IN LOVE WITH YOU
Tracks: / This guy's in love with you / Moonshine.
12" Single: Released Nov '80, on United Artists, by EMI Records. Deleted Nov '83. Catalogue no: **12STP 5**
7" Single: Released Nov '80, on United Artists, by EMI Records. Deleted Nov '83. Catalogue no: **STP 5**

Mags & The Suspects

ERECTION
Tracks: / Erection / Thousands dead.
12" Single: Released Mar '82, on London Records, by London Records. Deleted '85. Catalogue no: **BOLX 1**
7" Single: Released Mar '82, on London Records, by London Records. Deleted '85. Catalogue no: **BOL 1**

Maguire Gang

GIMME GOOD TIMES
Tracks: / Gimme good times.
7" Single: Released Jan '85, on Real Feel, Catalogue no: **RF 001**

Mah, Marchella

I'M YOURS MAYBE (see under Marchella Mah)
Tracks: / I'm yours maybe.
7" Single: Released Oct '86, on Pink Fly, Catalogue no: **MM 001**

MAKE HAY WHILE THE SUN SHINES
Tracks: / Make hay while the sun shines / Give it up.
7" Single: Released Jun '87, on Pink Fly, Catalogue no: **PINK 99**

SHAO LIN
Tracks: / Shoa lin / Come in.
7" Single: Released Jan '82, on Rebecca, by Rebecca Records. Catalogue no: **BEC S 78**

Mahana

CRYSTAL CHANDELIERS
Tracks: / Crystal chandeliers.
7" Single: Released Nov '82, on Dawn (USA), by Biograph Records (USA). Catalogue no: **WR 4005**

Maher, Gina

BRIGHT SIDE UP
Tracks: / Bright side up.
7" Single: Released Jul '85, on Young Blood, by Young Blood Records. Catalogue no: **YB 0092**

Mahogany

RIDE ON THE RHYTHM
Tracks: / Ride on the rhythm.
7" Single: Released Jan '83, on Arista, by BMG Records (UK). Catalogue no: **ARIST 517**
12" Single: Released Jan '83, on Arista, by BMG Records (UK). Catalogue no: **ARIST 12 517**

Mahoney, Johnny

BABYLON
Tracks: / Babylon.
12" Single: Released Jan '82, on TCD Music, Catalogue no: **TCDD 016**

Mahoney, Tony

ALERT
Tracks: / Alert.
12" Single: Released Jul '89, on Mission, Catalogue no: **MIS 01**

ALL NIGHT
Tracks: / All night.
12" Single: Released Dec '81, on TCD Music, Catalogue no: **TCDD 014**

Mai Tai

AM I LOSING YOU FOREVER
Tracks: / Am I losing you forever.
12" Single: Released Oct '85, on Virgin, by Virgin Records. Deleted '86. Catalogue no: **VS 822-12**
7" Single: Released Oct '85, on Virgin, by Virgin Records. Deleted '86. Catalogue no: **VS 822**

BET THAT'S WHAT YOU SAY
Tracks: / Bet that's what you say
12" Single: Released Aug '87, on Injection Disco Dance, Catalogue no: **DJIT 1**
7" Single: Released Aug '87, on Injection Disco Dance, Catalogue no: **DJI 1**

BODY AND SOUL
Tracks: / Body and soul / What goes on / Body and soul (extended remix) (12" only).
7" Single: Released Jul '85, on Virgin, by Virgin Records. Deleted May '88. Catalogue no: **VS 801**
12" Single: Released Jul '85, on Virgin, by Virgin Records. Catalogue no: **VS 801-12**

FEMALE INTUITION
Tracks: / Female intuition / female intuition (inst).
7" Single: Released Feb '86, on Virgin, by Virgin Records. Deleted '86. Catalogue no: **VS 844**
12" Single: Released Feb '86, on Virgin, by Virgin Records. Deleted '86. Catalogue no: **VS 844-12**

HISTORY (CD SINGLE)
Tracks: / History (special dance mix) / Female intuition (compressed dance mix) / Rules of love, The (groove side) / Am I losing you forever(smooth side edit).
CD 3": Released '88, on Virgin, by Virgin Records. Catalogue no: **CDT 38**

HISTORY (OLD GOLD)
Tracks: / History / Body and soul.
12" Single: Released 27 Feb '89, on Old Gold, by Old Gold Records. Catalogue no: **OG 4104**

HISTORY (SINGLE)
Tracks: / History (7" only) / History (special dance mix) (12" only) / History (club version) (12" only) / History (instrumental version) (12" only).
7" Single: Released May '85, on Virgin, by Virgin Records. Deleted May '88. Catalogue no: **VS 773**
12" Single: Released May '85, on Virgin, by Virgin Records. Catalogue no: **VS 773-12**

WHAT GOES ON
Tracks: / What goes on.
12" Single: Released Sep '84, on Electricity, by Electricity Records. Deleted '88. Catalogue no: **TRICT 11**
7" Single: Released Sep '84, on Electricity, by Electricity Records. Deleted '88. Catalogue no: **TRIC 11**

Main Event

GONNA DO MY BEST
Tracks: / Gonna do my best / Whom ya mother takes ya home.
7" Single: Released Apr '80, on Carrere, Deleted '82. Catalogue no: **CAR 146**

Main Ingredient

DO ME RIGHT
Tracks: / Do me right / Do me right (Inst).
12" Single: Released Jun '86, on Cool Tempo, by Chrysalis Records. Catalogue no: **COOLX 126**
7" Single: Released Jun '86, on Cool Tempo, by Chrysalis Records. Catalogue no: **COOL 126**

HAPPINESS IS JUST AROUND THE BEND (OLD GOLD)
Tracks: /Happiness is just around the bend
12" Single: Released 24 Apr '89, on Old Gold, by Old Gold Records. Catalogue no: **OG 4513**

JUST DON'T WANT TO BE LONELY (OLD GOLD)
Tracks: / Just don't want to be lonely.
7" Single: Released Jan '89, on Old Gold, by Old Gold Records. Catalogue no: **OG 9851**

JUST DON'T WANT TO BE LONELY
Tracks: / Just don't want to be lonely.
7" Single: Released Jun '74, on RCA, by

MAISONETTES - HEARTACHE AVENUE (Released on Ready Steady Go)

BMG Records (UK). Deleted '77. Catalogue no: **APBO 0205**

Main T. Posse

FICKLE PUBLIC SPEAKING
Tracks: / Fickle public speaking.
7" Single: Released May '83, on Respond (2), by A&M Records. Catalogue no: **KOB 703**
12" Single: Released May '83, on Respond (2), by A&M Records. Catalogue no: **KOBX 703**

Maineeaxe

GAME, THE
Tracks: / Game, The.
7" Single: Released Oct '84, on Powerstation, by Powerstation Records. Catalogue no: **OHM 8**

GIMME YOUR LOVE
Tracks: / Gimme your love.
12" Single: Released Jan '85, on Powerstation, by Powerstation Records. Catalogue no: **OHM 10T**

GONNA MAKE YOU ROCK
Tracks: / Gonna make you rock / Snatch.
7" Single: Released Jun '84, on Powerstation, by Powerstation Records. Catalogue no: **OHM 6**

Mainframe

5 MINUTES ON
Tracks: / 5 minutes on / Eric's revenge.
12" Single: Released Jan '86, on Polydor, by Polydor Ltd. Catalogue no: **MAINF1**
7" Single: Released Jan '86, on Polydor, by Polydor Ltd. Catalogue no: **MAINA 1**

RADIO
Tracks: / Radio.
7" Single: Released Apr '83, on MC2, Catalogue no: **MC 004**

Mainline

ONE AND ONLY Jackson medley
Tracks: / One and only.
12" Single: Released Jun '84, on Malaco, by Malaco Records (UK). Deleted '88. Catalogue no: **MAL 12 025**

Maisonettes

Biographical details: This Midlands-based male/female vocal group reached No 7 in early 1983 with a Motown pastiche, Heartache Avenue. They quickly nosedived into obscurity as their follow-up attempts, in a similar style, were simply not as good. (Bob MacDonald, January 1986.).

HEARTACHE AVENUE **(see panel on previous page)**
Tracks: / Heartache Avenue
CD 3": Released Feb '89, on Ready Steady Go, by Graduate Records. Catalogue no: **CDRSG 3000**
7" Single: Released Oct '82, on Ready Steady Go, by Graduate Records. Deleted Jan '87. Catalogue no: **RSG 1**
12" Single: Released Jan '83, on Ready Steady Go, by Graduate Records. Deleted Jan '87. Catalogue no: **RSGT 1**
12" Single: Released May '88, on Graduate, by Graduate Records. Catalogue no: **12 GRAD 18**

SAY IT AGAIN
Tracks: / Say it again.
7" Single: Released Aug '83, on Ready Steady Go, by Graduate Records. Deleted Jan '87. Catalogue no: **RSG 4**
12" Single: Released Aug '83, on Ready Steady Go, by Graduate Records. Deleted Jan '87. Catalogue no: **RSGT 4**

WHERE I STAND
Tracks: / Where I stand.
7" Single: Released Mar '83, on Ready Steady Go, by Graduate Records. Deleted Jan '87. Catalogue no: **RSG 2**

Majella

ON THE INSIDE
Tracks: / On the inside / Amazing grace.
7" Single: Released Nov '88, on Igus, by Klub Records. Catalogue no: **KLUB 55**

SPINNING WHEEL
7" Single: Released Oct '82, on Klub, by Klub Records. Catalogue no: **KLUB 35**

Majesterians

IF I DIDN'T WANT YOUR LOVING
Tracks: / If I didn't want your loving.
12" Single: on Trojan, by Trojan Records. Deleted May '88. Catalogue no: **TRT 9071**

Majestics

I LOVE HER SO MUCH (IT HURTS)
Tracks: / I love her so much (it hurts).
7" Single: Released May '85, on Soul Supply, by Soul Supply Records. Catalogue no: **7SS 106**

Majesty

GIRL
Tracks: / Girl / After you.
7" Single: Released '86, on Individual, by Individual Records. Catalogue no: **AIRS 106**

NOTHING LASTS FOREVER
Tracks: / Nothing lasts forever.
7" Single: Released Jun '86, on Blue Bird (1), by Blue Sun Records (USA). Deleted Jun '88. Catalogue no: **7 BILLY 2**
12" Single: Released Jun '86, on Blue Bird (1), by Blue Sun Records (USA). Deleted Jun '88. Catalogue no: **12 BILLY 2**

WISH YOU WERE HERE
Tracks: / Wish you were here / Among the heroes.
7" Single: Released Sep '86, on Individual, by Individual Records. Catalogue no: **AIRS 105**

Major Accident

FIGHT TO WIN
Tracks: / Fight to win.
7" Single: Released Apr '83, on Flicknife, by Flicknife Records. Catalogue no: **FLS 216**

LEADERS OF TOMORROW
Tracks: / Leaders of tomorrow.
7" Single: Released Jul '83, on Flicknife, by Flicknife Records. Catalogue no: **LS 023**

MR NOBODY
Tracks: / Mr. Nobody / That's you.
7" Single: Released Jan '83, on Step Forward, by Faulty Products Records. Catalogue no: **SF 23**

RESPECTABLE
Tracks: / Respectable / Man on the wall.
7" Single: Released Apr '84, on Flicknife, by Flicknife Records. Catalogue no: **FLS 026**

Major, Dee

FIGHT TO SURVIVE
Tracks: / Fight to survive.
12" Single: Released Apr '88, on Cat, by Cat Records. Catalogue no: **CAT 002**

HOT STUFF
Tracks: / Hot stuff / Jailbreak / Socca cheata.
12" Single: Released May '89, on Catt, by Catt Records. Catalogue no: **CATT 005**

RAT RACE
Tracks: / Rat race / Human race.
12" Single: Released Dec '88, on Catt, by Catt Records. Catalogue no: **CATT 004**

Major, Gregg

YARDIE
Tracks: / Yardie / Yardie (version).
12" Single: Released Aug '88, on PLJ Records, Catalogue no: **PLJ 001**

Major Hardy

KANSAS CITY
Tracks: / Kansas City.
7" Single: Released Jun '88, on Bedrock, by Bedrock Records. Catalogue no: **BED 002**

Major Mackerel

DONKEY MEAT
Tracks: / Donkey meat.
12" Single: Released Feb '89, on Steely & Cleevie, Catalogue no: **VPRD 414**

SORRY FE BOTHA
Tracks: / Sorry fe botha.
7" Single: Released May '89, on Jammy's, Catalogue no: **UNKNOWN**
7" Single: Released 8 May '89, on Live & Love, Catalogue no: **LLD 122**

Major Major Major

PARTY UP
Tracks: / Party up / Fancy you wanting me.
12" Single: Released May '87, on A-Side, Catalogue no: **SONL 2322**
7" Single: Released May '87, on A-Side, Catalogue no: **SON 2322**

Major Problem

ACID QUEEN
Tracks: / Acid queen.
12" Single: Released Sep '88, on Antler, by Antler Records (Belgium). Catalogue no: **KAOS 003**
CD 5": Released Sep '88, on Antler, by Antler Records (Belgium). Catalogue no: **KAOS 003CD**

Majority By Four

CAROLINE
Tracks: / Caroline.
7" Single: Released Feb '80, on Waiting-In-Vain, by December Songs Records. Catalogue no: **WIV 50**

Majors, Lee

UNKNOWN STUNTMAN
Tracks: / Unknown stuntman / Lust in a lady's eyes.
7" Single: Released Feb '83, on Scotti Bros (USA), Catalogue no: **SCT A 3117**

Makadopolous

NEVER ON SUNDAY
Tracks: / Never on Sunday.
7" Single: Released Oct '60, on Palette, Deleted '63. Catalogue no: **PG 9005**

Makaton Chat

FEDERAL STATE CHANCE
Tracks: / Federal state chance / It's his life story / Communicate.
12" Single: Released Feb '83, on Statik, Catalogue no: **TRANS 202**

Makepeace, Stavely

SONGS OF YESTERDAY
Tracks: / Songs of yesterday / Storm.
7" Single: Released Apr '80, on Hammer, Deleted Apr '83. Catalogue no: **HS 304**

Makin' Time

FEELS LIKE IT'S LOVE
Tracks: / Feels like it's love.
7" Single: Released Oct '85, on Countdown, Catalogue no: **VAIN 2**
12" Single: Released Oct '85, on Countdown, Catalogue no: **12VAIN 2**

HERE IS MY NUMBER
Tracks: / Here is my number.
12" Single: Released Jun '85, on Countdown, Catalogue no: **VAIN 112**
7" Single: Released Jun '85, on Countdown, Catalogue no: **VAIN 1**

PUMP IT UP
Tracks: / Pump it up / Once again / Walk a thin line / Eating up the gold.
7" Single: Released Apr '86, on Stiff, by Stiff Records. Catalogue no: **VAIN 5**
12" Single: Released Apr '86, on Stiff, by Stiff Records. Catalogue no: **12 VAIN 5**

Malaria

MY NEW DOG
Tracks: / My new dog.
12" Single: Released Sep '82, on Les Disques Du Crepuscule(Belgium), by Les Disques Du Crepuscule(Belgium). Catalogue no: **TWI 003**

NEW YORK PASSAGE
Tracks: / New York passage.
12" Single: Released Nov '82, on Jungle, by Jungle Records. Catalogue no: **JUNG 3**

WHITE WATER WHITE SEA
Tracks: / White water white sea.
12" Single: Released Apr '82, on Les Disques Du Crepuscule(Belgium), by Les Disques Du Crepuscule(Belgium). Catalogue no: **TWI 067**

Malcolm, Carl

FATTIE BUM BUM
Tracks: / Fattie bum bum.
7" Single: Released Sep '75, on UK, by UK Records. Deleted '78. Catalogue no: **UK 108**

Malcolm, Carlos & Afro

BONANZA SKA
Tracks: / Bonanza ska.
7" Single: Released Apr '80, on Island, by Island Records. Deleted Apr '83. Catalogue no: **WIP 6563**

Malcolm, Dennis

SO MANY WAYS
Tracks: / So many ways.
12" Single: Released Jun '88, on Charm, by Charm Records. Catalogue no: **CRT 19**
7" Single: Released Jul '88, on Charm, by Charm Records. Catalogue no: **CR19**

Malcolm's Interview

FINER POINTS OF FEELING
Tracks: / Finer points of feeling / Blow the man down.
7" Single: Released Oct '87, on Special Delivery, by Topic Records. Deleted '89. Catalogue no: **SPEC 45002**

YOU DON'T LISTEN
Tracks: / You don't listen.
12" Single: Released Jun '85, on E.G., by E.G. Records. Catalogue no: **EGG 1**

Malia, Dominic

SWEETIE
Tracks: / Sweetie / Love's brown across the shore.
7" Single: Released Jul '87, on Mooncrest, by Trojan Records. Deleted May '88. Catalogue no: **MOON 1007**

Malibu

GIRLS CHAMP
Tracks: / Girls champ / Body come down.
12" Single: Released Sep '86, on VIP (2), Catalogue no: **VIPV 004**

GOLDEN RULE
Tracks: / Golden rule / One dance story.
12" Single: Released Aug '86, on Supreme, by Supreme Records. Catalogue no: **SUP 001**

KEEP WALKING
Tracks: / Keep walking.
12" Single: Released Jun '85, on RCA, by BMG Records (UK). Catalogue no: **PT 40220**
7" Single: Released Jun '85, on RCA, by BMG Records (UK). Catalogue no: **PB 40219**

Malla, Boogsie

TALK ABOUT MY BABY
Tracks: / Talk about my baby.
12" Single: Released Sep '85, on Original Sounds, Catalogue no: **OS 002**

Mallan, Peter

BONNIE MARY OF ARGYLE
Tracks: / Bonnie Mary of Argyle.
7" Single: Released Jul '81, on Klub, by Klub Records. Catalogue no: **KLUB 30**

FISHIN' SONG, THE
Tracks: / Fishing song, The.
7" Single: Released Aug '79, on Klub, by Klub Records. Catalogue no: **KLUB 19**

Mallett

C.C. RIDER
Tracks: / C.C. rider.
7" Single: Released '80, on Rox, by Rox Records. Catalogue no: **ROX 10**

Mallinder, Stephen

TEMPERATURE DROP
Tracks: / Temperature drop / Cool down.
12" Single: Released Nov '81, on Fetish, Catalogue no: **FE 12**

Malloy, Wullie

CELTIC CENTENARY EP
12" Single: Released '88, on Wullie Malloy, Catalogue no: **WULLIE 001**

OVER AND OVER
Tracks: / Over and over.
7" Single: Released '88, on Wullie Malloy, Catalogue no: **WEEWULL 001**

Malmsteen, Yngwie J.

HEAVEN TONIGHT
Tracks: / Heaven tonight / Riot in the dungeons / Rising force / Trilogy suite, Opus 5.
CD 5": Released 21 Nov '88, on Polydor, by Polydor Ltd. Catalogue no: **YJMCD 1**
12" Pic: Released 21 Nov '88, on Polydor, by Polydor Ltd. Deleted 30 May '89. Catalogue no: **YJMXP 1**
7" Single: Released 21 Nov '88, on Polydor, by Polydor Ltd. Deleted 30 May '89. Catalogue no: **YJM 1**
7" Single: Released Nov '88, on Polydor, by Polydor Ltd. Deleted 30 May '89. Catalogue no: **YJMG 1**
12" Single: Released 21 Nov '88, on Polydor, by Polydor Ltd. Deleted 30 May '89. Catalogue no: **YJMX 1**

Maloko

IN THE MIDNIGHT HOUR
Tracks: / In the midnight hour / Yawomi / In the midnight hour (version) (Only on the 12".).
7" Single: Released May '89, on London Records, by London Records. Catalogue no: **LON 229**
12" Single: Released May '89, on London Records, by London Records. Catalogue no: **LONX 229**

Malone, Bugsy & The Radix

CALL ME BABY
Tracks: / Call me baby / Call me baby (Version).
7" Single: Released Aug '86, on Taurus, Catalogue no: **TRS 003**

Malone, Debbie

RESCUE ME
Tracks: / Rescue me.
7" Single: Released Aug '89, on Krunch, Catalogue no: **KR 001**

Maloney, Bunny

BABY I'VE BEEN MISSING YOU
Tracks: / Baby I've been missing you / Easy loving.
12" Single: Released Sep '87, on Londisc, by Londisc Records. Catalogue no: **12 LDR 060**

Malvo, Anthony

CAN'T CONTROL THE FEELING
Tracks: / Can't control the feeling.
12" Single: Released May '89, on Unity, Catalogue no: **FEA 015**

COME BACK TO ME
Tracks: / Come back to me.
12" Single: Released Jul '89, on Techniques, Catalogue no: **WRT 47**

TAKE YOU TO THE DANCE
Tracks: / Take you to the dance.
12" Single: Released Sep '89, on Sound City, by Sound City Records. Catalogue no: **SCT 3**

12" Single: Released 30 May '89, on Steely & Cleevie, Catalogue no: **VPRD 452**

Mama Cass

DREAM A LITTLE DREAM OF ME
Tracks: / Dream a little dream of me.
7" Single: Released Aug '68, on RCA, by BMG Records (UK). Deleted Aug '71. Catalogue no: **RCA 1726**

IT'S GETTING BETTER
Tracks: / It's getting better / Dream a little dream of me.
7" Single: Released Aug '69, on Stateside, by EMI Records. Deleted Aug '72. Catalogue no: **SS 8021**

IT'S GETTING BETTER (OLD GOLD)
Tracks: / It's getting better / Dream a little dream of me.
CD 5": Released May '89, on Old Gold, by Old Gold Records. Catalogue no: **OG 6145**
7" Single: Released Jun '88, on Old Gold, by Old Gold Records. Catalogue no: **OG 9796**

Mama's Boys

BELFAST CITY BLUES
Tracks: / Belfast city blues / Reach for the top.
7" Single: Released Apr '82, on Scoff, Catalogue no: **DT 015**

HARD 'N' LOUD
Tracks: / Hard 'n' loud.
12" Single: Released Nov '85, on Jive, by Zomba Records. Catalogue no: **JIVET 110**

HIGHER GROUND
Tracks: / Higher ground.
7" Single: Released Jul '87, on Jive, by Zomba Records. Deleted '88. Catalogue no: **MBOY 1**
12" Single: Released Jul '87, on Jive, by Zomba Records. Deleted '88. Catalogue no: **MBOY T1**

IN THE HEAT OF THE NIGHT
Tracks: / In the heat of the night.
7" Single: Released Oct '82, on Albion, by Albion Records. Catalogue no: **ION 1038**

MAMA WE'RE ALL CRAZY NOW
Tracks: / Mama we're all crazy now.
12" Single: Released Aug '84, on Jive, by Zomba Records. Catalogue no: **G 71**

MIDNIGHT PROMISES
Tracks: / Midnight promises.
7" Single: Released Jan '84, on Spartan, Catalogue no: **SP 11**
12" Single: Released Jan '84, on Spartan, Catalogue no: **12SP 11**

NEEDLE IN THE GROOVE
Tracks: / Needle in the groove / Hard headed ways.
7" Pic: Released Jun '85, on Jive, by Zomba Records. Catalogue no: **JIVEP 96**
7" Single: Released Jan '83, on Albion, by Albion Records. Catalogue no: **ION 1041**
12" Single: Released Jan '83, on Albion, by Albion Records. Catalogue no: **12ION 1041**

WAITING FOR A MIRACLE
Tracks: / Waiting for a miracle / Lightning strikes.
7" Single: Released Sep '87, on Jive, by Zomba Records. Deleted '88. Catalogue no: **JIVE 152**
12" Single: Released Sep '87, on Jive, by Zomba Records. Catalogue no: **JIVET 152**

Mamas & Papas

Biographical details: The Mamas of this American vocal group were Cass Elliot (born Ellen Naomi Cohen) and Michelle Phillips (nee Gilliam); the Papas were Denny Doherty and John Phillips (Michelle's husband). The name of the quartet was chosen after John and Denny began calling Cass and Michelle 'Mamas' as a joke. Founded and led by their main songwriter John Phillips, who had previously been a member of an early Sixties folk group called The Journeymen, the Mama's & Papas were formed in California in 1965. They were discovered by Barry McGuire, the singer who was then enjoyin huge success with *Eve of destruction*, and he introduced them to his record company boss Lou Adler. After getting them to perform backing vocals on a McGuire LP, Adler became their producer and launched them as a recording group in their own right. The Mamas & Papas' first single established them immediately as a major pop force. *California dreamin'* reached No.4 on the US chart in early 1966 and became the best known anthem of the new flower-power generation, until being displaced in the summer of '67 by another Phillips-penned song, Scott McKenzie's *San Francisco (be sure to wear some flowers in your hair)*. The Mamas and Papas enjoyed a run of hits during 1966-67, and their brief but glorious heyday epitomised the era for many people. Combining the folk-rock of the Byrds with the infectious pop of the Beach Boys, the quartet performed memorable songs in a distinctive and 'clean' end of the hippie phenomenon. The group's hits included *Monday Monday* (No.1 in US, No.3 in UK), *I saw her again* (No.5 in US, No.11 in UK), *Words of love* (No.5. in US, No.47 in UK), *Dedicated to the one I love* (a remake of the Shirelles' 1961 hit, No.2 on both sides of the Atlantic) and the group's autobiographical *Creeque Alley* (No.5 in US, No.9 in UK). John Phillips played an important role in organising 1967's legendary Monterey Pop Festival.(Bob MacDonald, 17th Jan 1986).

CALIFORNIA DREAMIN'
Tracks: / California dreamin' / Monday monday.
7" Single: Released Apr '66, on RCA, by BMG Records (UK). Deleted '69. Catalogue no: **RCA 1503**

CALIFORNIA DREAMIN'(OLD GOLD)
Tracks: / California dreamin' / Monday Monday / Dedicated to the one I love.
CD 5": Released 30 May '89, on Old Gold, by Old Gold Records. Catalogue no: **OG 6142**
7" Single: Released Jul '82, on Old Gold, by Old Gold Records. Catalogue no: **OG 9176**

CREEQUE ALLEY
Tracks: / Creeque alley.
7" Single: Released Jul '67, on RCA, by BMG Records (UK). Deleted '70. Catalogue no: **RCA 1613**

DEDICATED TO THE ONE I LOVE
Tracks: / Dedicated to the one I love.
7" Single: Released Apr '67, on RCA, by BMG Records (UK). Deleted '70. Catalogue no: **RCA 1576**

DEDICATED TO THE ONE I LOVE (OLD GOLD)
Tracks: / Dedicated to the one I love.
7" Single: Released Jul '82, on Old Gold, by Old Gold Records. Catalogue no: **OG 9175**

I SAW HER AGAIN
Tracks: / I saw her again.
7" Single: Released Jul '66, on RCA, by BMG Records (UK). Deleted '69. Catalogue no: **RCA 1533**

MAMA'S & THE PAPAS EP
Tracks: / Monday Monday / Dalifornia dreaming / I saw her again / Creeque Alley.
7" EP: Released Jun '80, on MCA, by MCA Records. Deleted '83. Catalogue no: **MCA 601**

MONDAY MONDAY
Tracks: / Monday monday.
7" Single: Released May '66, on RCA, by BMG Records (UK). Deleted '69. Catalogue no: **RCA 1516**

WORDS OF LOVE
Tracks: / Words of love.
7" Single: Released Feb '67, on RCA, by BMG Records (UK). Deleted '70. Catalogue no: **RCA 1564**

Mamelodi

JABULANI SATURDAY NIGHT
Tracks: / Jabulani saturday night.
7" Single: Released Sep '83, on Magnet, by WEA Records. Catalogue no: **MAG 249**

Mammath

ROCK ME
Tracks: / Rock me / Rough 'n' ready.
7" Single: Released Dec '84, on Neat, by Neat Records. Catalogue no: **NEAT 42**

Mammoth

ALL THE DAYS
Tracks: / All the days.
7" Single: Released Jan '88, on Jive, by Zomba Records. Catalogue no: **MOTH 2**
12" Single: Released Jan '88, on Jive, by Zomba Records. Catalogue no: **MOTH T2**

CAN'T TAKE THE HURT
Tracks: / Can't take the hurt / None but the brave / Political animal.
7" Single: Released Feb '89, on Jive, by Zomba Records. Catalogue no: **MOTH 3**
12" Single: Released Feb '89, on Jive, by Zomba Records. Catalogue no: **MOTH T13**
CD 5": Released Jun '89, on Jive, by Zomba Records. Catalogue no: **MOTHCD 3**

FATMAN
Tracks: / Fat man / Political animal.
7" Single: Released Jul '87, on Jive, by Zomba Records. Catalogue no: **MOTH 1**
12" Single: Released Jul '87, on Jive, by Zomba Records. Catalogue no: **MOTH T1**

Man

Biographical details: An ever-changing line-up hampered the progress of this Welsh rock band, whose most important and longest-serving members were Micky Jones (guitar and vocals), Terry Williams (drums) and guitar wizard/vocalist Deke Leonard (real Christian name Roger). Evolving from an unsuccessful Merthyr Tydfil group called the Bystanders, Man came into being in 1968. Heavily influenced by the psychedelic San Francisco scene, they built up a cult following in Britain and West Germany. Albums, beginning with 1969's *Revelation*, appeared on a regular basis. During the early and mid-Seventies, Man were hotly tipped for the big league but never quite made it. Forever on the brink of stardom, their first UK chart album was *Back into the future* (No.23 in 1973); they subsequently charted with *Rhinos, winos and lunatics* (No.24 in 1974), *Maximum darkness* (No.25 in 1975) and *Welsh connection* (No.40 in 1976). Man folded in 1977, Williams enjoying success with Dave Edmunds and Nick Lowe in Rockpile. Man reformed in 1983, with the underrated Deke Leonard at the helm; this event was marked by a new live album, recorded at London's legendary Marquee venue. (Bob MacDonald, 17th Jan 1986).

ALL IN THE GAME
Tracks: / All in the game / All in the game (instrumental).
12" Single: Released Jan '84, on King Buck, Catalogue no: **KB 002**
7" Single: Released Mar '86, on RCA, by BMG Records (UK). Catalogue no: **PB 40691**

Man 2 Man

I NEED A MAN
Tracks: / I need a man / Energy is Eurobeat / Male stripper (remix) (Extra track in 12").
7" Single: Released 20 Jun '87, on Bolts, by Bolts Records. Catalogue no: **BOLTS 5**
12" Single: Released 20 Jun '87, on Bolts, by Bolts Records. Catalogue no: **BOLTS 05/7**
12" Single: Released Aug '87, on Bolts, by Bolts Records. Catalogue no: **BOLTS 12RR**

WHO KNOWS WHAT EVIL
Tracks: / Who knows what evil / Man 2 Man(instrumental).
12" Single: Released Nov '86, on Nightmare, by Nightmare Records. Catalogue no: **MARE 3**
7" Single: Released Nov '86, on Nightmare, by Nightmare Records. Catalogue no: **MARES 3**

WHO KNOWS WHAT EVIL (FRIGHTMARE MIX)
Tracks: / Who knows what evil.
12" Single: Released Feb '87, on Nightmare, by Nightmare Records. Catalogue no: **MAREX 3**

Man Called Adam

A.P.B
Tracks: / A.P.B. / A.P.B. (version).
12" Single: Released Oct '88, on Acid Jazz, by Acid Jazz Rec. Catalogue no: **JAZID 4T**

EARTHLY POWERS
12" Single: Released Jun '89, on Acid Jazz, by Acid Jazz Rec Catalogue no: **JAZID 015T**

Man Friday

PICKING UP SOUND 2 Parts
Tracks: / Picking up sound (part 1) / Picking up sound (part 2).
12" Single: Released Oct '83, on Malaco, by Malaco Records (UK). Deleted '88. Catalogue no: **MAL 12 011**

Man From Delmonte

DEBORAH ANN TURNER
Tracks: / Deborah Ann Turner.
12" Single: Released Jul '89, on Bop, Catalogue no: **UNKNOWN**

DRIVE DRIVE DRIVE
Tracks: / Drive drive drive.
7" Single: Released 1 Apr '87, on Ugly Man, by Ugly Man Records. Catalogue no: **UGLY 003**

MONDAY MORNING AFTER
Tracks: / Monday morning after.
12" Single: Released Jan '89, on Bop, Catalogue no: **BIP 502**

MY LOVE IS LIKE A GIFT YOU CAN'T RETURN
Tracks: / My love is like a gift you can't return.
12" Single: Released 24 Jul '89, on Bop, Catalogue no: **BIP 701**
Cassingle: Released Oct '89, on Bop, Catalogue no: **BIP 701C**

WATER IN MY EYES
Tracks: / Bred by you / Water in my eyes.
12" Single: Released Aug '87, on Ugly Man, by Ugly Man Records. Catalogue no: **UGLY 5T**
7" Single: Released Aug '87, on Ugly Man, by Ugly Man Records. Catalogue no: **UGLY 5**

WILL NOBODY SAVE LOUISE
Tracks: / Will nobody save Louise / Good things in life / Like a millionaire (Avaliable on 12" format only.).
7" Single: Released Mar '88, on Ugly Man, by Ugly Man Records. Catalogue no: **UGLY 7**
12" Single: Released Mar '88, on Ugly Man, by Ugly Man Records. Catalogue no: **UGLY 7T**

Man Jumping

AEROTROPICS
Tracks: / Aerotropics.
12" Single: Released Apr '85, on Cocteau, by Cocteau Records. Catalogue no: **COQT 16**

Man Machine

MAN MACHINE
Tracks: / Man machine.
12" Single: Released Jun '89, on Rhythm King, by Mute Records. Catalogue no: **MAN 001T**
7" Single: Released Jun '89, on Rhythm King, by Mute Records. Catalogue no: **MAN 001**

Man & Me

GOOD COMPANION
Tracks: / Good companion / You're my....
7" Single: Released Jan '82, on Solid Gold (1), by Creole Records. Deleted '86. Catalogue no: **SGR 115**

Man Parrish

Biographical details: This American mixer, disc jockey and producer came to mini-fame in 1983 as part of the hip hop and scratching styles that swept discos in America. His fashionable and streetwise music yielded the dynamic single Hip Hop Be Bop (Don't Stop), which became a dancefloor cult favourite and, in Britain, crossed over to No 41 on the pop chart. (Bob MacDonald, 1986.).

BOOGIE DOWN
Tracks: / Boogie down.
7" Single: Released Mar '85, on Polydor, by Polydor Ltd. Catalogue no: **POSP 731**
12" Single: Released Mar '85, on Polydor, by Polydor Ltd.. Catalogue no: **POSPX 731**

BROWN SUGAR
Tracks: / Brown sugar.
12" Single: Released Jan '88, on Bolts, by Bolts Records. Catalogue no: **BOLTS 08/12**

HIP HOP BE BOP
Tracks: / Hip hop be bop.
12" Single: Released Mar '83, on Polydor, by Polydor Ltd. Deleted '86. Catalogue no: **POSPX 575**
7" Single: Released Mar '85, on Polydor, by Polydor Ltd. Catalogue no: **POSP 575**

MALE STRIPPER
Tracks: / Male stripper.
7" Single: Released Jan '87, on Bolts, by Bolts Records. Catalogue no: **BOLTS 4 R**
12" Single: Released Jan '87, on Bolts, by Bolts Records. Catalogue no: **BOLTS 4 P**

Man upstairs

CONSUMER SONG
Tracks: / Consumer song.
7" Single: Released May '86, on Sideline, Catalogue no: **SIDE 2**

SAD IN MY HEART
Tracks: / Sad in my heart.
7" Single: Released Aug '85, on Sideline, Catalogue no: **SIDE 1**

Man With No Nuts

I RODE ACROSS THE DESERT ON A MAN WITH NO NUTS
Tracks: / I rode across the desert on a man with no nuts.
12" Single: Released Jun '88, on Massive Member, Catalogue no: **MM 001T**

Man With The...

HOOKED ON TIJUANA
Tracks: / Hooked on Tijuana.
7" Single: Released Oct '83, on Jive, by Zomba Records. Catalogue no: **LIFE 4**
12" Single: Released Oct '83, on Jive, by Zomba Records. Catalogue no: **LIFET 4**

Managers

SHAKE IT UP SHAKE IT UP
Tracks: / Shake it up shake it up.
12" Single: Released Jul '82, on Sire (USA), Catalogue no: **SIR 4056T**
7" Single: Released Jul '82, on Sire (USA), Catalogue no: **SIR 4056**

Manana

AMOR
Tracks: / Amor / Disco samba.
7" Single: Released Feb '81, on EMI, by EMI Records. Deleted Feb '84. Catalogue no: **EMI 5132**

VIDA MIA
Tracks: / Vida mia.
12" Single: Released Jan '82, on EMI, by

EMI Records. Deleted Jan '85. Catalogue no: **12 EMI 5259**
7" Single: Released Jan '82, on EMI, by EMI Records. Deleted Jan '85. Catalogue no: **EMI 5259**

Manapsara

QUEER (SINGLE)
Tracks: / Queer.
12" Single: Released '89, on Sub Rosa, by Sub Rosa Records. Catalogue no: **SUB 12006-23**

ROUTINE
Tracks: / Routine.
12" Single: Released May '89, on Sub Rosa, by Sub Rosa Records. Catalogue no: **SUB 12006 23**

Mancha, Steve

HOPELESSLY
Tracks: / Hopelessly / Hopelessly (version).
12" Single: Released 14 May '88, on Nightmare, by Nightmare Records. Catalogue no: **MARES 50**
7" Single: Released 14 May '88, on Nightmare, by Nightmare Records. Catalogue no: **MARE 50**

IT'S ALL OVER THE GRAPEVINE
Tracks: / It's all over the grapevine / It's all over the grapevine (instrumental).
7" Single: Released Aug '86, on Columbia, by EMI Records. Catalogue no: **DB 9138**
12" Single: Released Aug '86, on Columbia, by EMI Records. Catalogue no: **12DB 9138**

STANDING IN LINE
Tracks: / Standing in line / Standing in line (instrumental).
7" Single: Released Mar '87, on Nightmare, by Nightmare Records. Catalogue no: **MARES 13**
12" Single: Released Mar '87, on Nightmare, by Nightmare Records. Catalogue no: **MARE 13**

Manchanile, Amanda

LOVE AUTOMATION
Tracks: / Love automation.
12" Single: Released Jun '87, on Unit Dance, by Priority Records. Catalogue no: **12 TRA 109**

Manchester boys choir

LITTLE DRUMMER BOY
Tracks: / Little drummer boy.
7" Single: Released Nov '85, on Spirit (1), by Spirit Records. Catalogue no: **FIRE 11**

Manchester, Melissa

FIRE IN THE MORNING
Tracks: / Fire in the morning / Lights of dawn.
7" Single: Released May '80, on Arista, by BMG Records (UK). Deleted May '83. Catalogue no: **ARIST 348**

IF THIS IS LOVE
Tracks: / If this is love / Talk.
7" Single: Released Oct '80, on Arista, by BMG Records (UK). Deleted Oct '83. Catalogue no: **ARIST 375**

MUSIC OF GOODBYE, THE
Tracks: / Music of goodbye (love theme out of Africa), The / Main title / I had a farm in Africa / Have you got a story for me (Track on 12" version only).
12" Single: Released Mar '86, on MCA, by MCA Records. Catalogue no: **MCAT 1038**
7" Single: Released Mar '86, on MCA, by MCA Records. Catalogue no: **MCA 1038**

NICE GIRLS
Tracks: / Nice girls / Hey Ricky.
7" Single: Released Jan '83, on Arista, by BMG Records (UK). Catalogue no: **ARIST 511**

YOU SHOULD HEAR HOW SHE TALKS ABOUT YOU
Tracks: / You should hear how she talks about you / Race to the end.
7" Single: Released Sep '82, on Arista, by BMG Records (UK). Catalogue no: **ARIST 454**

Manchester United

Biographical details: After the England World Cup Squad reached No.1 on the British chart with their 1970 single *Back home*, jingoistic singalong singles by football teams became a regular, albeit musically insignificant, feature of the UK record listings. Clubs up and down the nation transferred their dubious vocal talents from the shower-room to the local recording studio whenever they reached FA Cup Final status or won the League. In 1985 Manchester United achieved the honour of becoming the first team to chalk up a third UK chart single - no real surprise, in view of thier probable status as THE most famous club in the post-war history of British soccer. The club's debut chart appearance, imaginatively entitled *Manchester United*, reached No.50 in May 1976; this single marked their first Cup Final appearance of the Seventies, in which they played Southampton. Their second hit occurred in 1983, the year they met Brighton & Hove Albion - *Glory glory Man Utd* climbed to No.13. The club's third and highest placing was achieved two years later, when *We all follow Man Utd* cruised to No.10, four places higher that an equally predictable choral ditty from their Cup Final opponents at Everton. It was interesting to note that the Everton disc was produced by Tony Hiller, the man who had performed the same duty on Man Utd's 1976 offering - was this guy a traitor or what? (Bob MacDonald, 17th Jan 1986).

GLORY GLORY MAN UNITED
Tracks: / Glory glory Man United.
7" Pic: Released May '83, on EMI, by EMI Records. Catalogue no: **EMIP 5390**
7" Single: Released May '83, on EMI, by EMI Records. Catalogue no: **EMI 5390**

MANCHESTER UNITED
Tracks: / Manchester United.
7" Single: Released May '76, on Decca, by Decca Records. Deleted '79. Catalogue no: **F 13633**

WE ALL FOLLOW MAN UNITED
Tracks: / We all follow Man United.
7" Pic: Released May '85, on Columbia, by EMI Records. Catalogue no: **DBP 9107**

Mancini, Henry

Biographical details: This American composer, arranger and conductor was born in Cleveland, Ohio in 1924, and was brought up in Pennsylvania. He took up the flute at the age of eight, the piano at thirteen, and began to arrange music at fifteen. He attended New York's famed Juilliard School, although his musical studies were interrupted by three years of military service in the Second World War. After a spell in the post-war, posthumous Glenn Miller Band, Mancini became an in-house composer for Universal Pictures in California in 1952. During his six years with the company, he scored approximately 150 movies.
Then came the move which made Mancini really famous. In 1958 he was engaged as the man to write, arrange and conduct the score for the NBC-TV series 'Peter Gunn'. Unlike cinema, the newer medium of television had not at that time adopted the habit of preparing original music for programs - producers simply used canned music, usually imported from Europe. All that changed with Mancini's jazz score for 'Peter Gunn'. Television themes, incidental music and soundtracks became a marketable commodity in their own right, thus serving as an excellent advertisement for the associated programs as well as being a boon for record companies. The soundtrack album until overtaken in 1986 by Miami Vice. In the very first year of the Grammy Awards, the American record industry's answer to the Oscars, the *Gunn* disc earned Mancini the prizes for Best Album and Best Arrangement. The theme became a hit single for both Ray Anthony and twangy guitarist Duanne Eddy.
Returning to films, Mancini achieved another major winner in 1961 with his score for *Breakfast at Tiffany's*. As well as being a US No.1 album, this soundtrack spawned his best known composition *Moon river*. This classic ballad, which featured lyrics by the legendary Johnny Mercer, was a Us No.11 single for both Mancini and Jerry Butler; in Britain it was a No.1 smash for Danny Williams. The composer's next big success was the 1962 film *Days of wine and roses*. In 1964 he triumphed with his insidiously *Pink Panther* theme. During the Fifties, Sixties and Seventies, Mancini clearly established himself as America's premier film composer. His tally of 20 Grammy Awards is the second highest total in the entire music business; and he has won more Oscars than any other composer or artist in the popular and middle-of-the-road fields. (Strangely, his only US No.1 single, 1969's *Love theme from Romeo and Juliet*, was lifted from a score that he did not write.) On the British charts, Mancini only ever achieved on hit LP despite the familiarity of UK audiences with his music: a *40 greatest* collection reached No.26 in October 1976. His orchestra and chorus biggest UK hit single was *How soon?*, which climbed to No.10 in 1964. In 1984, mere weeks before his 60th birthday, he reached the UK No.23 position with the main theme from the Richard Chamberlain TV serial *The Thorn Birds*. (Bob MacDonald, 17th Jan 1986).

BOLERO
Tracks: / Bolero / It's easy to say.
7" Single: Released Mar '84, on WEA, by WEA Records. Catalogue no: **K 17552**

CADE'S COUNTY THEME
Tracks: / Cade's County theme.
7" Single: Released Mar '72, on RCA, by BMG Records (UK). Deleted '75. Catalogue no: **RCA 2182**

HOW SOON
Tracks: / How soon.
7" Single: Released Sep '64, on RCA, by BMG Records (UK). Deleted '67. Catalogue no: **RCA 1414**

MOON RIVER

MANFRED MANN - DON'T KILL IT CAROL (Released on Bronze)

Tracks: / Moon river.
7" Single: Released Dec '61, on RCA, by BMG Records (UK). Deleted '64. Catalogue no: **RCA 1256**

PINK PANTHER THEME
Tracks: / Pink panther (theme from).
7" Single: Released '75, on USA, by Charly Records. Catalogue no: **LR 1208**

THORN BIRDS
Tracks: / Thorn birds / Thorn Birds - love theme (Double A-side).
7" Single: Released Aug '86, on WEA, by WEA Records. Deleted Jun '87. Catalogue no: **YZ 83**
7" Single: Released Feb '84, on Warner Bros., by WEA Records. Deleted '87. Catalogue no: **9677**

Mancrab

FISH FOR LIFE (from Karate Kid II)
Tracks: / Fish for life / Fish for life (instrumental).
12" Single: Released Aug '86, on 10 Records, by Virgin Records. Deleted May '88. Catalogue no: **TENT 140**
7" Single: Released Aug '86, on 10 Records, by Virgin Records. Deleted May '88. Catalogue no: **TEN 140**

Mandell, Robert

LORD IS MY SHEPHERD
Tracks: / Lord's my shepherd, The.
7" Single: Released Jan '83, on Pressit, Catalogue no: **LC 774**

Mandrake Paddle

STRANGE WALKING MAN
Tracks: / Strange walking man.
7" Single: Released Jun '85, on Bam Caruso, by Demon Records. Catalogue no: **PABL 033**
7" EP: Released Jun '88, on Bam Caruso, by Demon Records. Catalogue no: **NRIC 033**

Mandrell, Barbara

DARLIN'
Tracks: / Darlin' / Tears.
7" Single: Released Apr '80, on MCA, by MCA Records. Deleted '83. Catalogue no: **MCA 584**

IF LOVING YOU IS WRONG
Tracks: / If loving you is wrong / Sleeping single in a double bed.
7" Single: Released Oct '81, on MCA, by MCA Records. Deleted Oct '84. Catalogue no: **MCA 753**

OPERATOR LONG DISTANCE PLEASE
Tracks: / Operator long distance please / You're not supposed to be here.
7" Single: Released Jul '82, on MCA, by MCA Records. Deleted Jul '85. Catalogue no: **MCA 784**

Mandy

BOYS AND GIRLS
Tracks: / Boys and girls.
12" Single: Released Jun '88, on PWL, by PWL Records. Catalogue no: **PWLT 11**

GREATEST LOVE AFFAIR, THE
Tracks: / Greatest love affair.
7" Single: Released '88, on Debut, by Skratch Records. Catalogue no: **DEBT 3019**

Maneaters

NINE TO FIVE
Tracks: / Nine to five / Jerusalem.
7" Single: Released '82, on Polydor, by Polydor Ltd. Deleted '87. Catalogue no: **EGO 8**

Man-Eseke

CREEM TUBE
Tracks: / Creem tube.
12" Single: Released Sep '88, on Beat Box, by Beat Box Records. Catalogue no: **BBOXT 3**

Manfred Mann

Biographical details: The enigmatic keyboards player Manfred Mann lent his name to one of Britain's leading pop groups of the Sixties, and progressed to Manfred Mann's Earth Band, a noted rock act of the Seventies. Because he was not the lead singer, and because he was never particularly at ease in the public eye, Mann's role in both groups was that of backbone rather than frontman. He was born in Johannesburg, South Africa, but quit the country as soon as he was old enough to make his own way in the world. After studying in Vienna and New York, he moved to the UK in 1961. The following year, he formed a combo called the Mann Hugg Blues Brothers with drummer Mike Hugg; they were soon joined by vocalist Paul Jones (born Paul Pond) and, with the addition of two other guys, became simply Manfred Mann in 1963. After a couple of flops, the group surged to success in early '64 with their self-penned *5-4-3-2-1*, once it had been adopted as the theme to the key British pop TV show of the era *Ready, steady go*. The exuberent single reached No.5 on the UK chart, and was the first in a stream of 13 British Top 10 singles which kept the group's name constantly on the charts until 1969. Their hits included three UK No.1 singles: *Do wah diddy diddy* (1964), one of several singles that started life as relatively obscure American songs; *Pretty flamingo* (1966); and *Mighty Quinn* (1968), one of several Manfred Mann hits from the pen of Mann's favourite songwriter Bob Dylan. The group's first two albums sold very well, and included remakes of several rhythm-and-blues standards. *Do wah diddy diddy* reached No.1 in the Us as part of the British Invasion, although their subsequent American success was very erratic.
The group were so consistently popular and upbeat in Britain that they were even able to weather the 1966 departure of the good-looking and talented Paul Jones, who was replaced by Mike D'Abo. At the end of the Sixties, however, the combo decided that they were tired of being a singles-oriented pop group, and split up. Manfred and Huggs stayed together for a couple more years, flirting with jazz in the band Manfred Mann Chapter II and then Manfred formed the Earth Band in 1971. The latter group were never a consistent chart force, but chalked up three isolated UK Top 10 singles: *Joybringer* (1973), which borrowed a melody from Holst's *Planets*; *Blinded by the light* (1976), originally recorded by Bruce Springsteen who, like Dylan became a regular

source of Mann material; and *Davy's on the road again* (1978). *Blinded* eventually topped the American chart in 1977, thus becoming the only Springsteen song ever to reach the US No.1 slot. The Earth Band kept going through the early and mid-Eighties but, despite continued quality, were relatively unsuccessful. During his long career Manfred has always been adept at picking the right musicians, as shown by the number of now famous names that played with him at one time or another. These include Tom McGuiness, Jack Bruce, Klaus Voorman and Chris Thompson. (Bob MacDonald, 19th Jan 1986).

5 4 3 2 1
Tracks: / 5 4 3 2 1 .
7" Single: Released Mar '84, on EMI Golden 45's, by EMI Records. Deleted Oct '89. Catalogue no: **G45 15**
7" Single: Released Jan '64, on H.M.V., by EMI Records. Deleted '67. Catalogue no: **POP 1252**

BLINDED BY THE LIGHT
Tracks: / Blinded by the light.
7" Single: Released Aug '76, on Bronze, by Bronze Records. Deleted '79. Catalogue no: **BRO 29**
7" Single: Released '80, on Bronze, by Bronze Records. Catalogue no: **LR 2584**

COME TOMORROW
Tracks: / Come tomorrow.
7" Single: Released Jan '65, on H.M.V., by EMI Records. Deleted '68. Catalogue no: **POP 1381**

DAVY'S ON THE ROAD AGAIN
Tracks: / Davy's on the road again / Mighty Quinn / Don't kill it Carol.
7" Single: Released Feb '84, on Bronze, by Bronze Records. Catalogue no: **BRO 177**
12" Single: Released Feb '84, on Bronze, by Bronze Records. Catalogue no: **BROX 177**
7" Single: Released May '78, on Bronze, by Bronze Records. Deleted '81. Catalogue no: **BRO 52**

DEMOLITION MAN
Tracks: / Demolition man / It's still the same.
7" Single: Released Jan '83, on Bronze, by Bronze Records. Catalogue no: **BRO 161**

DO ANYTHING YOU WANNA DO
Tracks: / Do anything you wanna do / Crossfire.
7" Single: Released Mar '86, on 10 Records, by Virgin Records. Deleted '86. Catalogue no: **TEN 115**
12" Single: Released Mar '86, on 10 Records, by Virgin Records. Deleted '86. Catalogue no: **TEN 115-12**

DO WAH DIDDY DIDDY
Tracks: / Do wah diddy diddy
7" Single: Released Jul '64, on H.M.V., by EMI Records. Deleted '67. Catalogue no: **POP 1320**
7" Single: Released Oct '82, on EMI-Past Masters Series, by EMI Records. Deleted '83. Catalogue no: **PMS 1003**

DO WAH DIDDY DIDDY (OLD GOLD)
Tracks: / Do wah diddy diddy./ If you gotta go, go now.
7" Single: Released Jun '88, on Old Gold, by Old Gold Records. Deleted Sep '89. Catalogue no: **OG 9369**

DON'T KILL IT CAROL
Tracks: / Don't kill it Carol / Blinded by the light.
7" Single: Released Jul '79, on Bronze, by Bronze Records. Deleted '82. Catalogue no: **BRO 77**

EYES OF NOSTRADAMUS
Tracks: / Eyes of Nostradamus / Holidays end / Man in jam (Only on 12" single.).
12" Single: Released Mar '82, on Bronze, by Bronze Records. Deleted '85. Catalogue no: **BROX 141**
7" Single: Released Mar '82, on Bronze, by Bronze Records. Deleted '85. Catalogue no: **BRO 141**

FOR YOU
Tracks: / For you / Fool and I.
7" Single: Released Jan '81, on Bronze, by Bronze Records. Deleted Jan '85. Catalogue no: **BRO 113**

FOX ON THE RUN
Tracks: / Fox on the run.
7" Single: Released Dec '68, on Fontana, by Phonogram Ltd. Deleted '71. Catalogue no: **TF 985**

GERONIMO'S CADILLAC
Tracks: / Geronimo's cadillac / Two friends (from Mars & Saturn).
7" Single: Released Oct '87, on 10 Records, by Virgin Records. Deleted May '88. Catalogue no: **TEN 196**

GOING UNDERGROUND
Tracks: / Going underground / I shall be rescued.
12" Single: Released May '86, on 10 Records, by Virgin Records. Deleted May '88. Catalogue no: **TENT 121**
7" Single: Released May '86, on 10 Records, by Virgin Records. Deleted '89. Catalogue no: **TEN 121**

HA HA SAID THE CLOWN
Tracks: / Ha ha said the clown.
7" Single: Released Mar '67, on Fontana, by Phonogram Ltd. Deleted '70. Catalogue no: **TF 812**

HUBBLE BUBBLE TOIL AND TROUBLE
Tracks: / Hubble bubble toil and trouble.
7" Single: Released Apr '64, on H.M.V., by EMI Records. Deleted '67. Catalogue no: **POP 1282**

I (WHO HAVE NOTHING)
Tracks: / I (who have nothing) / Man in jam.
7" Single: Released Nov '81, on Bronze, by Bronze Records. Deleted Nov '84. Catalogue no: **BRO 137**

IF YOU GOTTA GO GO NOW
Tracks: / If you gotta go go now.
7" Single: Released Sep '65, on H.M.V., by EMI Records. Deleted '68. Catalogue no: **POP 1466**

JOYBRINGER
Tracks: / Joybringer.
7" Single: Released Sep '73, on Vertigo, by Phonogram Ltd. Deleted '77. Catalogue no: **6059 083**

JUST LIKE A WOMAN
Tracks: / Just like a woman.
7" Single: Released Aug '66, on Fontana, by Phonogram Ltd. Deleted '69. Catalogue no: **TF 730**

MIGHTY QUINN
Tracks: / Mighty Quinn.
7" Single: Released Jan '68, on Fontana, by Phonogram Ltd. Deleted '71. Catalogue no: **TF 897**

MIGHTY QUINN (OLD GOLD)
Tracks: / Mighty quinn.
7" Single: Released Jul '82, on Old Gold, by Old Gold Records. Catalogue no: **OG 9252**

MY NAME IS JACK
Tracks: / My name is Jack.
7" Single: Released Jun '68, on Fontana, by Phonogram Ltd. Deleted '71. Catalogue no: **TF 943**

OH NO NOT MY BABY
Tracks: / Oh no not my baby.
7" Single: Released Apr '65, on H.M.V., by EMI Records. Deleted '68. Catalogue no: **POP 1413**

PRETTY FLAMINGO (OLD GOLD)
Tracks: / Pretty flamingo.
7" Single: Released May '84, on Old Gold, by Old Gold Records. Catalogue no: **OG 4515**
7" Single: Released Apr '87, on Old Gold, by Old Gold Records. Catalogue no: **OG 9697**
7" Single: Released Oct '83, on Old Gold, by Old Gold Records. Deleted Jul '88. Catalogue no: **OG 9376**

PRETTY FLAMINGO (SINGLE)
Tracks: / Pretty flamingo / Come tomorrow.
7" Single: Released Apr '66, on H.M.V., by EMI Records. Deleted '69. Catalogue no: **POP 1523**
7" Single: Released '80, on Lightning. Catalogue no: **LR 1384**

RAGAMUFFIN MAN
Tracks: / Ragamuffin man.
7" Single: Released Apr '69, on Fontana, by Phonogram Ltd. Deleted '72. Catalogue no: **TF 1013**

REDEMPTION SONG
Tracks: / Redemption song / Wardream.
7" Single: Released Jul '82, on Bronze, by Bronze Records. Deleted Jul '85. Catalogue no: **BRO 150**

RUNNER, THE
Tracks: / Runner, The / No transkei.
7" Single: Released Mar '84, on Bronze, by Bronze Records. Deleted Mar '87. Catalogue no: **BRO 180**
12" Single: Released Mar '84, on Bronze, by Bronze Records. Deleted Mar '87. Catalogue no: **BROX 180**

SEMI-DETACHED SUBURBAN MR.JAMES
Tracks: / Semi-detached suburban Mr. James.
7" Single: Released Oct '66, on Fontana, by Phonogram Ltd. Deleted '69. Catalogue no: **TF 757**

SHA LA LA
Tracks: / Sha-la-la.
7" Single: Released Oct '64, on H.M.V., by EMI Records. Deleted '67. Catalogue no: **POP 1346**

SWEET PEA
Tracks: / Sweet pea.
7" Single: Released May '67, on Fontana, by Phonogram Ltd. Deleted '70. Catalogue no: **TF 828**

TRIBAL STATISTICS
Tracks: / Tribal statistics / Where do they send them.
7" Single: Released Nov '82, on Bronze, by Bronze Records. Deleted Nov '85. Catalogue no: **BRO 157**

YOU ANGEL YOU
Tracks: / You angel you.
7" Single: Released Mar '79, on Bronze, by Bronze Records. Deleted '82. Catalogue no: **BRO 68**

YOU GAVE ME SOMEBODY TO LOVE
Tracks: / You gave me somebody to love.
7" Single: Released Jul '66, on H.M.V., by EMI Records. Deleted '69. Catalogue no: **POP 1541**

Manfredo Fest

JUNGLE KITTEN
Tracks: / Jungle kitten.
7" Single: Released May '83, on Blue Bird (1), by Blue Sun Records (USA). Catalogue no: **BRT 1**

Mangaroo, Danny

BETTER THAN YARD
Tracks: / Better than yard.
12" Single: Released Feb '89, on Park Heights. Catalogue no: **PHD 0063**

WHEN THINGS GO WRONG
Tracks: / When things go wrong / Corner rock.
12" Single: Released Mar '84, on Joe Gibbs. Catalogue no: **JGM 8182**

Mangione, Chuck

FUN AND GAMES
Tracks: / Fun and games / Give it all you've got / Feels so good.
7" Single: Released May '80, on A&M, by A&M Records. Deleted '83. Catalogue no: **AMSP 7522**

GIVE IT ALL YOU'VE GOT
Tracks: / Give it all you've got / B'bye.
7" Single: Released Feb '80, on A&M, by A&M Records. Deleted '83. Catalogue no: **AMS 7508**

Manhattan Transfer

Biographical details: At the time of their greatest success this American vocal group consisted of Tim Hauser, Laurel Masse, Alan Paul and Janis Siegel. Formed in 1969, Manhattan Transfer have always been led by Hauser. Indeed, he was the only original member to stay the course after the dismal failure of the group's first album, 1971's *Jukin*. A re-shaped, re-styled Manhattan Transfer built up a cult following in New York, first in gay bars and then in more general nightclubs. When an LP called simply *Manhattan Transfer* was issued in 1975 most people were were under the impression that this second album was their first. It reached No 33 on the US chart and yielded a pair of successful singles: *Operator* reached No 22 in America and *Tuxedo Junction* climbed to No 24 in Britain as part of a Glenn Miller revival in the UK at the time. Man Tran's stock-in-trade was revivalism and chic nostalgia and it was the 40's that came most often under their microscope. With sleek professionalism the two-man/two-woman line-up developed a smooth vocal harmony sound and refined their stage act. But their commercial career was distinctly erratic. They were too middle-of-the-road to be a pop group yet too purist to be a cabaret act. Their enormous versatility was accompanied by a passion for accurate reproduction of a style or genre rather than Las Vegas-type mushiness. The quartet's chart career consisted of a series of pleasant one-offs. Manhattan Transfer's biggest British single, 1977's *Chanson D'Amour*, was a revamp of a '58 number; the remake reached the UK No 1 slot but failed to chart at all in America. Conversely, their biggest US success, *Boy From New York City*, reached No 7 in '81 but flopped in Britain where it had been recently rehashed by Darts (Bob MacDonald, 1986.

MANHATTEN TRANSFER - BIRDLAND (Released on Atlantic)

BIRDLAND
Tracks: / Birdland / Wacky dust.
7" Single: Released '79, on Atlantic, by WEA Records. Catalogue no: **K 11387**

BOY FROM NEW YORK CITY
Tracks: / Boy from New York City / World of confrontation.
7" Single: Released Apr '81, on WEA, by WEA Records. Catalogue no: **K 11585**

CHANSON D'AMOUR
Tracks: / Chanson d'amour.
7" Single: Released Feb '87, on Atlantic, by WEA Records. Deleted '80. Catalogue no: **K 10886**

CHANSON D'AMOUR (OLD GOLD)
Tracks: / Chanson d'amour.
7" Single: Released Sep '85, on Old Gold, by Old Gold Records. Catalogue no: **OG 9547**

DON'T LET GO
Tracks: / Don't let go.
7" Single: Released May '77, on Atlantic, by WEA Records. Deleted '80. Catalogue no: **K 10930**

INDEPENDENCE
Tracks: / Independence
12" Single: Released Oct '83, on Atlantic, by WEA Records. Catalogue no: **A 9766 T**
7" Single: Released Oct '83, on Atlantic, by WEA Records. Catalogue no: **A 9766**

NIGHTINGALE SANG IN BERKELEY SQUARE, A
Tracks: / Nightingale sang in Berkeley Square, A / On the boulevard.
7" Single: Released Dec '81, on Atlantic, by WEA Records. Catalogue no: **K 11685**

NOTHING YOU CAN DO ABOUT IT
Tracks: / Nothing you can do about it
7" Single: Released Sep '80, on Atlantic, by WEA Records. Deleted '83. Catalogue no: **K 11606**

ON A LITTLE STREET IN SINGAPORE
Tracks: / On a little street in Singapore.

MANIC MC ' S - MENTAL (Released on RCA)

7" Single: Released May '78, on Atlantic, by WEA Records. Deleted '81. Catalogue no: **K 11136**

SOUL FOOD TO GO
Tracks: / Soul food to go / Hear the voices.
7" Single: Released Jan '88, on Atlantic, by WEA Records. Catalogue no: **A 9156**
12" Single: Released Jan '88, on Atlantic, by WEA Records. Catalogue no: **A 9156 T**

SPICE OF LIFE
Tracks: / Spice of life.
12" Single: Released Jan '84, on Atlantic, by WEA Records. Catalogue no: **A 9728 T**
7" Single: Released Jan '84, on Atlantic, by WEA Records. Catalogue no: **A 9728**

TUXEDO JUNCTION
Tracks: / Tuxedo Junction.
7" Single: Released Feb '76, on Atlantic, by WEA Records. Deleted '79. Catalogue no: **K 10670**

TWILIGHT ZONE - TWILIGHT TONE
Tracks: / Twilight zone - twilight tone / Body & soul.
7" Single: Released May '80, on Atlantic, by WEA Records. Deleted '83. Catalogue no: **K 11476**

WALK IN LOVE
Tracks: / Walk in love.
7" Single: Released Feb '78, on Atlantic, by WEA Records. Deleted '81. Catalogue no: **K 11075**

WANTED DEAD OR ALIVE
Tracks: / Wanted dead or alive / Smile again.
7" Single: Released Jul '81, on Atlantic, by WEA Records. Deleted '84. Catalogue no: **K 11668**

WHERE DID OUR LOVE GO
Tracks: / Where did our love go / Je voulais te dire (que je t'attends).
7" Single: Released Sep '78, on Atlantic, by WEA Records. Deleted '81. Catalogue no: **K 11182**

WHO WHAT WHEN WHERE WHY
Tracks: / Who, what, when, where and why.
7" Single: Released Dec '78, on Atlantic, by WEA Records. Deleted '81. Catalogue no: **K 11233**

Manhattans

Biographical details: At the time of their greatest success, this American soul vocal group consisted of Gerald Alston, Edward 'Sonny' Bivins, Kenny Kelly, Winfred 'Blue' Lovett and Richard Taylor. The act's name was inspired by a cocktail, not by the place. The Manhattans were formed in Jersey City in 1962, and gained their first break at a 1964 talent contest at Harlem's legendary Apollo Theatre. The following year, they achieved their first minor US pop hit with *I wanna be your (everything)*. For the next ten years, the group made regular appearances on the American soul charts but could not crack the Top 40 pop list. Heavily influenced by the doo-wop singing groups of the Fifties, their repertoire included smoochy soul slowies and uptempo dancefloor records. Ballads were always their real forte, and they managed to keep performing these with considerable conviction over many years. The group's lead singer George Smith met a tragically early end in 1970, when he died of meningitis; he was replaced by Alston.
The Manhattans slowly worked their way towards a pop smash. After reaching No.43 on the US Hot 100 with *There's no me without you*(1973), and after *Don't take your love* climbed to No.37 in 1975, the group surged to the US No.1 spot in July 1976 with the Lovett-penned *Kiss and say goodbye*. Combining the butch spoken growls of Barry White with the sweet singing of the Stylistics, the Manhattans' *Kiss and say goodbye* was a perfect example of smooth Seventies soul. In Britain, where the group were previously unknown, both *Kiss and say goodbye* and the similar sounding *Hurt* reached No.4 and spent 11 weeks on the chart. The former sold two million copies in the States alone. From 1977 onwards, the Manhattans continued in their time-honoured fashion, but only returned to the American Top 40 on one occasion - the million selling *Shining star* climbed to No.5 in 1980. In 1983 they caused a minor ripple on the UK chart with *Crazy*. Two years later they found themselves on the US black charts once again with a remake of Sam Cooke's *You send me* - thus, a veteran soul group paid homage to what many historians cite as the very first soul record. (Bob MacDonald, 18th Jan 1986).

6 TRACK HITS
Tracks: / Kiss and say goodbye / There's no me without you / Don't take your love / Wonderful world of love / We never danced to a love song / La la la wish upon a star.
7" EP: Released Sep '83, on Scoop 33, by Pickwick Records. Catalogue no: **7SR 5027**

CRAZY
Tracks: / Crazy / Love is gonna find you / Kiss and say goodbye / Shining star.
7" Single: Released Aug '83, on CBS, by CBS Records. Deleted '86. Catalogue no: **A 3578**

CRAZY (OLD GOLD)
Tracks: / Crazy / You send me.
12" Single: Released 21 Nov '87, on Old Gold, by Old Gold Records. Catalogue no: **OG 4029**

HURT
Tracks: / Hurt.
7" Single: Released Oct '76, on CBS, by CBS Records. Deleted '79. Catalogue no: **CBS 4562**

IT'S YOU
Tracks: / It's you.
7" Single: Released Apr '77, on CBS, by CBS Records. Deleted '80. Catalogue no: **CBS 5093**

KISS AND SAY GOODBYE
Tracks: / Kiss and say goodbye.
7" Single: Released Jun '76, on CBS, by CBS Records. Deleted '79. Catalogue no: **CBS 4317**

KISS AND SAY GOODBYE (OLD GOLD)
Tracks: / Kiss and say goodbye.
7" Single: Released Apr '83, on Old Gold, by Old Gold Records. Catalogue no: **OG 9303**

SHINING STAR
Tracks: / Shining star.
7" Single: Released Jul '80, on CBS, by CBS Records. Deleted '83. Catalogue no: **CBS 8624**

Maniac

KILLING FOR PLEASURE
Tracks: / Killing for pleasure.
7" Single: Released 1 Apr '87, on Rent A Racket, Deleted '88. Catalogue no: **RKT 001**

Maniacs

SALUTE THE SURVIVORS
Tracks: / Salute the survivors.
7" Single: Released May '88, on Pogar, Catalogue no: **POGAR 6**

SATURDAY NIGHT
Tracks: / Saturday night.
12" Single: Released Jun '84, on 25 West (USA), by 25 West Records (USA). Catalogue no: **25 WEST 1010**

Manic MC'S

MENTAL (see panel on left)
Tracks: / Mental / Mental (version).
CD 5": Released 31 Jul '89, on RCA, by BMG Records (UK). Catalogue no: **PD 43038**
7" Single: Released 31 Jul '89, on RCA, by BMG Records (UK). Catalogue no: **PB 43037**
12" Single: Released 31 Jul '89, on RCA, by BMG Records (UK). Catalogue no: **PT 43038**

Manicured Noise

FAITH
Tracks: / Faith / Freetime.
7" Single: Released Aug '80, on Charisma, by Virgin Records. Deleted '83. Catalogue no: **PRE 006**

METRONOME
Tracks: / Metronome / Moscow.
7" Single: Released Feb '80, on Charisma, by Virgin Records. Deleted Feb '85. Catalogue no: **PRE 003**

Manilow, Barry

Biographical details: This American singer, pianist, songwriter and producer was born in Brooklyn, New York, and studied music at the New York College of Music and the Juilliard Academy. His main interests were in jazz and show music, and he was never particulary keen on the rock'n'roll explosion that affected other youngsters' lives. During the late Sixties, he worked as an arranger for Ed Sullivan's television specials and other shows, and also created commercials and jingles for TV and radio. In the early Seventies, he toured with the up-and coming sleazy singer Bette Midler as her musical director and pianist; he also arranged and co-produced her first two albums, cleaning up her act a bit. Manilow's own debut LP was released in 1973; it was not a success, although the song *Could it be magic* resurfaced after he had achieved and was also covered by Donna Summer. The number that brought Manilow to stardom was *Mandy*, which not only his first hit but also his first No.1. The song had originally been recorded as *Brandy* by it's co-writer Scott English, who had taken it into the British Top 20 in 1971. *Mandy* which topped the American chart in January '75 and became a UK No.11 hit in the Spring, established Barry as a major new middle-of-the-road crooner in the Bing Crosby/Frank Sinatra/Engelbert Humperdinck tradition.
During the mid-Seventies, Barry Manilow was America's hottest MoR star, adored by hordes of housewives and mocked by rock critics. Although he composed some of his own material, most of his big singles were carefully picked from other sources. Working with his co-producer Ron Dante, he dressed them up in epic orchestral arrangements and big production. Although his voice was criticised for lacking soulfulness, he projected it so dramaaically that the sheer power of his records could not be ignored. His biggest US singles included *I write the songs* (actually written by Bruce Johnston of the Beach Boys - No.1 for Manilow in 1976), *Looks like we made it* (No.1 in 1977) and *Can't smile without you* (No.3 in 1978). He also chalked up a string of huge-selling albums, including the US no.1 *Live* LP (July '77). Despite the early success of *Mandy*, Manilow's UK career did not really get going until the beginning of the Eighties, several years after he had peaked in his homeland. Thanks largely to the success of the shrewdly timed, TV advertised *Manilow magic* compilation, which logged 151 weeks on the UK album chart, he wooed legions of British women into buying such albums as *Barry*, *If I should love again* and the 1982 No.1. LP *Barry live in Britain*. His particular success with live albums was a reflection of the singer's extraordinary rapport with a concert audience. During the mid-Eighties, Manilow's star faded considerably on both sides of the Atlantic. This decline was partly hastened by his bizarre decision to abandon his big ballad forte (and Ron Dante) in favour of uptempo revivals of rock'n'roll hits. Who wanted to hear Manilow singing Shakin' Stevens' *Oh Julie*? Nonetheless, he has become such a showbusiness institution that his live shows will ensure that he never starves. (Bob MacDonald, 19th Jan 1986).

2AM PARADISE CAFE (SINGLE)
Tracks: / 2 a.m. paradise cafe.
7" Single: Released Aug '84, on Arista, by BMG Records (UK). Catalogue no: **ARIST 576**

BERMUDA TRIANGLE
Tracks: / Bermuda triangle.
7" Single: Released '82, on Arista, by BMG Records (UK). Deleted '87. Catalogue no: **ARIST 406**

BERMUDA TRIANGLE (OLD GOLD)
Tracks: / Bermuda triangle / Lonely together.
7" Single: Released Nov '86, on Old Gold, by Old Gold Records. Catalogue no: **OG 9652**

CAN'T SMILE WITHOUT YOU
Tracks: / Can't smile without you.
7" Single: Released May '78, on Arista, by BMG Records (UK). Deleted '81. Catalogue no: **ARISTA 176**

COULD IT BE MAGIC
Tracks: / Could it be magic.
7" Single: Released '82, on Arista, by BMG Records (UK). Deleted '87. Catalogue no: **ARIST 229**

EVEN NOW (SINGLE)
Tracks: / Even now.
7" Single: Released '82, on Arista, by BMG Records (UK). Deleted '87. Catalogue no: **ARIST 220**

HE DOESN'T CARE
Tracks: / He doesn't care (but I do) / It's all behind us now / I'm your man (Track on 12" version only.).
7" Single: Released Mar '86, on RCA, by BMG Records (UK). Catalogue no: **UPB 49877**
12" Single: Released Mar '86, on RCA, by BMG Records (UK). Catalogue no: **PT 49878**

I CAN'T SMILE WITHOUT YOU
Tracks: / I can't smile without you.
7" Single: Released '82, on Arista, by BMG Records (UK). Deleted '87. Catalogue no: **ARIST 176**

I MADE IT THROUGH THE RAIN
Tracks: / I made it through the rain / Only in Chicago.
7" Single: Released Feb '81, on Arista, by BMG Records (UK). Deleted '84. Catalogue no: **ARIST 384**

I WANNA DO IT WITH YOU (SINGLE)
Tracks: / I wanna do it with you / Heaven.
7" Single: Released Oct '82, on Arista, by BMG Records (UK). Deleted '85. Catalogue no: **ARIST 495**

IF I SHOULD LOVE AGAIN (SINGLE)
Tracks: / If I should love again / Let's take all night.
7" Single: Released '82, on Arista, by BMG Records (UK). Deleted '87. Catalogue no: **ARIST 453**

I'M GONNA SIT RIGHT DOWN AND WRITE MYSELF A LETTER
Tracks: / I'm gonna sit right down and write myself a letter / Heart of steel.
7" Single: Released Dec '82, on Arista, by BMG Records (UK). Deleted '85. Catalogue no: **ARIST 503**

I'M YOUR MAN
Tracks: / I'm your man / He doesn't love you but I do.
12" Single: Released May '86, on RCA, by BMG Records (UK). Catalogue no: **PT 49858**
7" Single: Released May '86, on RCA, by BMG Records (UK). Catalogue no: **PB 49857**

IN SEARCH OF LOVE
Tracks: / In search of love.
12" Single: Released Nov '85, on RCA, by BMG Records (UK). Catalogue no: **PT 49920**
7" Single: Released Nov '85, on RCA, by BMG Records (UK). Catalogue no: **PB 49919**

IT'S A MIRACLE
Tracks: / It's a miracle
7" Single: Released Apr '80, on Arista, by BMG Records (UK). Deleted Apr '83. Catalogue no: **ARIST 337**

LET'S HANG ON
Tracks: / Let's hang on / No other love.

7" Single: Released Sep '81, on Arista, by BMG Records (UK). Deleted '86. Catalogue no: **ARIST 429**

LONELY TOGETHER
Tracks: / Lonely together.
7" Single: Released '82, on Arista, by BMG Records (UK). Deleted '87. Catalogue no: **ARIST 373**

LOOKS LIKE WE MADE IT
Tracks: / Looks like we made it.
7" Single: Released '82, on Arista, by BMG Records (UK). Deleted '87. Catalogue no: **ARIST 120**

MAMBO
Tracks: / Mambo / Mambo (special latin remix).
12" Single: Released Apr '88, on Arista, by BMG Records (UK). Catalogue no: **609781**
7" Single: Released Apr '88, on Arista, by BMG Records (UK). Catalogue no: **109781**

MANDY (OLD GOLD)
Tracks: / Mandy.
7" Single: Released Nov '86, on Old Gold, by Old Gold Records. Catalogue no: **OG 9650**

MANDY (SINGLE)
Tracks: / Mandy.
CD 5": Released Jun '89, on Arista, by BMG Records (UK). Catalogue no: **162051**
7" Single: Released Feb '75, on Arista, by BMG Records (UK). Deleted '80. Catalogue no: **ARIST 1**

OLD SONGS, THE
Tracks: / Old songs, The / Just another New Year's Eve.
7" Single: Released '82, on Arista, by BMG Records (UK). Deleted '87. Catalogue no: **ARIST 443**

ONE THAT GOT AWAY, THE
Tracks: / One that got away, The.
12" Single: Released Sep '89, on Arista, by BMG Records (UK). Catalogue no: **112 653**
CD 5": Released Sep '89, on Arista, by BMG Records (UK). Catalogue no: **662 652**
Cassingle: Released Sep '89, on Arista, by BMG Records (UK). Catalogue no: **410 652**
7" Single: Released Sep '89, on Arista, by BMG Records (UK). Catalogue no: **112 652**

PLEASE DON'T BE SCARED
Tracks: / Please don't be scared / Little travelling music please, A / Dirt cheap.
7" Single: Released Mar '89, on Arista, by BMG Records (UK). Catalogue no: **112 186**
Cassingle: Released Apr '89, on Arista, by BMG Records (UK). Catalogue no: **409 913**
7" Single: Released Mar '89, on Arista, by BMG Records (UK). Catalogue no: **112 245**
12" Single: Released Mar '89, on Arista, by BMG Records (UK). Catalogue no: **612 246**
CD 5": Released Mar '89, on Arista, by BMG Records (UK). Catalogue no: **662 186**
12" Single: Released Mar '89, on Arista, by BMG Records (UK). Catalogue no: **612 186**

READ 'EM AND WEEP
Tracks: / Read 'em and weep / One voice.
12" Single: Released '83, on Arista, by BMG Records (UK). Deleted '86. Catalogue no: **ARIST 12551**
7" Single: Released '83, on Arista, by BMG Records (UK). Deleted '86. Catalogue no: **ARIST 551**

SOME KIND OF FRIEND
Tracks: / Some kind of friend / Oh Julie.
7" Single: Released '83, on Arista, by BMG Records (UK). Deleted '86. Catalogue no: **ARIST 516**

SOMEWHERE IN THE NIGHT
Tracks: / Somewhere in the night / Copacabana.
7" Single: Released '82, on Arista, by BMG Records (UK). Deleted '87. Catalogue no: **ARIST 196**

STAY
Tracks: / Stay / Nickles and dimes.
7" Single: Released Apr '82, on Arista, by BMG Records (UK). Deleted '85. Catalogue no: **ARIST 464**

SWING STREET EP
Tracks: / Swing street / Brooklyn blues / Sweet heaven / Who needs to dream.
7" EP: Released Nov '88, on Arista, by BMG Records (UK). Catalogue no: **111 938**
CD 5": Released Dec '88, on Arista, by BMG Records (UK). Catalogue no: **661938**

SWING STREET (SINGLE)
Tracks: / Swing street / Brooklyn blues / Sweet heaven.
10" single: Released Dec '88, on Arista, by BMG Records (UK). Catalogue no: **209 526**

YOU'RE LOOKIN' HOT TONIGHT (Live from Blenheim Palace)
Tracks: / You're looking hot tonight.
7" Single: Released Sep '83, on Arista, by BMG Records (UK). Catalogue no: **ARILE 542**
12" Single: Released '83, on Arista, by BMG Records (UK). Deleted '86. Catalogue no: **ARIST 12542**

Manish Boys

I PITY THE FOOL (EP)
Tracks: / I pity the fool.
Note: A welcome opportunity to obtain four tracks originally recorded by David Bowie in 1965. 'I pity the fool' and 'Take my tip' was Bowie's second single, credited to The Manish Boys. 'You've got a habit of leaving' and 'Baby loves that way' was the follow up, credited to Davy Jones. Both singles were released on the Parlophone label and are now extremely rare. (PS)
10" single: Released Nov '82, on Charly, by Charly Records. Deleted '88. Catalogue no: **CYM 1**

MANISH BOYS/DAVY JONES & THE LOWER THIRD
Tracks: / I pity the fool / Take my tip / You've got a habit of leaving / Baby loves that way.
Note: In the beginning there was the Manish Boys and Davy Jones, today we know him better as David Bowie - rock superstar. Though the four recordings were all recorded the same year 1965, their breadth encompasses a movement within the development of British Rock that typified the period. All four tracks were produced by ace producer Shel Talmy. The original 10" sleeve note by Dave Brown remains, which tells the story of these tracks.
12" Single: Released Jun '85, on See For Miles, by See For Miles Records. Catalogue no: **SEA 1**

Manitaza

GIMME WHAT I WANT
Tracks: / Gimme what I want.
7" Single: Released Feb '82, on Axe, Catalogue no: **AX 001**
12" Single: Released Feb '82, on Axe, Catalogue no: **AX 001 12**

Manix, Helena

HOLD TIGHT
Tracks: / Hold tight.
12" Single: Released Sep '89, on Freshbeat, by Jetstar Records. Catalogue no: **FBT 8**

Mankind

Biographical details: *Dr Who*, a single loosely based on the familiar theme tune to the top BBC-TV adventure series of the same name, was a one-off UK chart entry for this British band at the end of 1978. It peaked at No.25. The guys in the group could not find a hit follow-up to this instrumental, disco-flavoured single. It appeared that *Dr Who* was not a giant leap for Mankind, but merely a small step. (Bob MacDonald, 19th Jan 1986).

CHAIN REACTION
Tracks: / Chain reaction.
7" Single: Released Mar '79, on Firebird, by Pinnacle Records. Catalogue no: **PIN 13**

DARK STAR ANGEL
Tracks: / Dark star angel / U.F.O..
12" Single: Released Oct '80, on Ovation, by Gull Records. Deleted Oct '83. Catalogue no: **OVD 12 1216**
7" Single: Released Oct '80, on Ovation, by Gull Records. Deleted Oct '83. Catalogue no: **OVS 1216**

DOCTOR WHO
Tracks: / Doctor Who.
7" Single: Released Jan '84, on Motor, Catalogue no: **MTR 001**
7" Single: Released Nov '78, on Pinnacle, by Pinnacle Records. Deleted '81. Catalogue no: **PIN 71**
12" Single: Released Jan '84, on Motor, Catalogue no: **MTR 001T**

Mankind, Sidney

TRUTH, THE
Tracks: / Truth, The.
12" Single: Released Sep '82, on Musical Ambassador, Catalogue no: **MAPD 001**

Manklan

BOYS OF THE TERRITORY
Tracks: / Boys of the territory.
12" Single: Released Jul '85, on Wire, by Wire Records. Catalogue no: **WRMS 002**

WANTING AND WAITING VIRGINIA
Tracks: / Wanting and waiting Virginia / Man of fear.
12" Single: Released Oct '87, on Wire, by Wire Records. Catalogue no: **WRMS 018**
7" Single: Released Oct '87, on Wire, by Wire Records. Catalogue no: **WRS 018**

Manley, Cynthia

BACK IN MY ARMS AGAIN
Tracks: / Back in my arms again / That's what I want.
7" Single: Released Mar '83, on Atlantic, by WEA Records. Catalogue no: **A 9920**

Mann C.C.

HAVEN'T GOT THE TIME
Tracks: / Haven't got the time.
7" Single: Released Feb '80, on Movement 24, Deleted '82. Catalogue no: **ORR 1**

Mann, Clarence

I'LL BE AROUND
Tracks: / I'll be around.
7" Single: Released Nov '86, on Expansion, Catalogue no: **EXPAND 5**

Mann, Doug

STORY OF GREYFRIERS BOBBY, THE
Tracks: / Story of Greyfriars bobby, The.
7" Single: Released '78, on Rel, by REL Records. Catalogue no: **RES 005**

Mann, Herbie

BEND DOWN LOW
Tracks: / Bend down low / Cecilia.
7" Single: Released Aug '81, on Atlantic, by WEA Records. Deleted Aug '84. Catalogue no: **K 11677**

Mann, Johnny Singers

UP, UP AND AWAY
Tracks: / Up, up and away.
7" Single: Released Jul '67, on Liberty, by EMI Records. Deleted '70. Catalogue no: **LIB 55972**

Mann, Roberto

WITCHFINDER GENERAL
Tracks: / Witchfinder general / Both sides now.
7" Single: Released Jun '82, on Decca, by Decca Records. Deleted Jun '84. Catalogue no: **F 132904**

Mannheim Steamroller

CHRISTMAS (SINGLE)
Tracks: / Christmas.
7" Single: Released Dec '88, on Platinum Music, by Prism Leisure. Catalogue no: **AGS 1**

Manowar

ALL MEN PLAY ON 10
Tracks: / All men play on 10.
12" Single: Released Aug '84, on 10 Records, by Virgin Records. Deleted May '88. Catalogue no: **TEN 30-12**

BLOW YOUR SPEAKERS
Tracks: / Blow your speakers / Violence and bloodshed.
7" Single: Released 23 May '87, on Atlantic, by WEA Records. Deleted Jul '88. Catalogue no: **B 9463**
12" Single: Released 23 May '87, on Atlantic, by WEA Records. Deleted Jan '88. Catalogue no: **B 9463 T**

DEFENDER
Tracks: / Defender.
12" Single: Released Oct '83, on Music For Nations, by Music For Nations Records. Catalogue no: **12 KUT 102**

Mansell Chorale

SONGS OF FREEDOM
Tracks: / Songs of freedom / Enemy at the door.
7" Single: Released Feb '80, on Cube, Deleted Feb '83. Catalogue no: **BUG 88**

Manteau

PROMISES
Tracks: / Promises.
7" Single: Released Oct '84, on Riva, by Riva Records. Catalogue no: **RIVA 43**

Manton, Bob

NO TREES IN BRIXTON
Tracks: / No trees in Brixton / Brixton walkabout.
7" Single: Released Jun '81, on Mainstream, Catalogue no: **MS 101**

Mantovani

AROUND THE WORLD
Tracks: / Around the world.
7" Single: Released May '57, on Decca, by Decca Records. Deleted '60. Catalogue no: **F 10888**

LONELY BALLERINA
Tracks: / Lonely ballerina.
7" Single: Released Feb '55, on Decca, by Decca Records. Deleted '58. Catalogue no: **F 10395**

MOULIN ROUGE
Tracks: / Moulin Rouge.
7" Single: Released May '53, on Decca, by Decca Records. Deleted '56. Catalogue no: **F 10094**

SWEDISH RHAPSODY
Tracks: / Swedish rhapsody.
7" Single: Released Oct '53, on Decca, by Decca Records. Deleted '56. Catalogue no: **F 10168**

WHITE CHRISTMAS
Tracks: / White christmas.
7" Single: Released Dec '52, on Decca, by Decca Records. Deleted '55. Catalogue no: **F 10017**

Mantronix

BASSLINE
Tracks: / Bassline (7" only) / Ladies (revived) / Ladies (instrumental) (12" only) / Get stupid ('fresh' part 1) (12" only) / Bassline (stretched) (12" only).
7" Single: Released May '86, on 10 Records, by Virgin Records. Deleted '89. Catalogue no: **TEN 118**
12" Single: Released May '86, on 10 Records, by Virgin Records. Catalogue no: **TENT 118**

LADIES
Tracks: / Ladies / Ladies (instrumental) / Ladies (full length) (12" only).
7" Single: Released Feb '86, on 10 Records, by Virgin Records. Catalogue no: **TEN 116**
12" Single: Released Feb '86, on 10 Records, by Virgin Records. Catalogue no: **TEN 116-12**

SCREAM (PRIMAL SCREAM)
Tracks: / Scream (primal scream) (On all versions) / Scream (primal scream dub) (On 12" only) / Mantronix to the groove (On cassette only) / Who is it? (On cassette only) / Scream (Jack 'n' Chill mix) (On TENR 169 only).
Cassingle: Released '87, on 10 Records, by Virgin Records. Catalogue no: **TENC 169**
7" Single: Released 13 Jun '87, on 10 Records, by Virgin Records. Deleted May '88. Catalogue no: **TEN 169**
12" Single: Released '87, on 10 Records, by Virgin Records. Catalogue no: **TENR 169**
12" Single: Released 13 Jun '87, on 10 Records, by Virgin Records. Catalogue no: **TENT 169**

SIMPLE SIMON
Tracks: / Simple Simon (you gotta regard) / Simple Simon (you dubba regard) / Simple Simon (you gotta rock hard) (On 12" only) / Simple symphony (dub gotta rock hard) (On 12" only).
7" Single: Released Feb '88, on 10 Records, by Virgin Records. Catalogue no: **TEN 217**
12" Single: Released '88, on 10 Records, by Virgin Records. Catalogue no: **TENX 217**
12" Single: Released Feb '88, on 10 Records, by Virgin Records. Deleted '89. Catalogue no: **TENT 217**

SING A SONG
Tracks: / Sing a song (break it down) / Sing a song (break it down) (dub).
7" Single: Released Jan '88, on 10 Records, by Virgin Records. Catalogue no: **TEN 206**

WHO IS IT?
Tracks: / Who is it ? (dance mix) (On TENT & TENX 137 only) / Who is it? (dub version) (NOT on TENR 137) / Ladies (revived) (On TENX 137 only) / Bassline (stretched) (On TENX 137) / Who is it? (NOT on TENX & TENR 137) / Ladies (On 7" only) / Bassline (On 7" only) / Who is it? (freestyle club mix) (On TENR 137 only) / Who is it? (radio edit) (On TENR 137 only) / Who is it? (bonus beats) (On TENR 137 only).
7" Set: on 10 Records, by Virgin Records. Catalogue no: **TEND 137**
7" Single: Released Jan '87, on 10 Records, by Virgin Records. Deleted May '88. Catalogue no: **TEN 137**
12" Single: on 10 Records, by Virgin Records. Catalogue no: **TENT 137**
12" Single: Released Feb '87, on 10 Records, by Virgin Records. Catalogue no: **TENR 137**
Special: Released Jan '87, on 10 Records, by Virgin Records. Catalogue no: **TENX 137**

Manuel

Biographical details: Manuel & his Music of the Mountains is the alter ego of Geoff Love & His Orchestra. Under both guises, Love and his ensembles have been an institution on the British music scene from the late Fifties right through till the records and in concert. Through the years, a host of genres have been given the Manuel treatment, although he tends to favour the middle-ground method of doing orchestral renditions of popular MOR hits. On the British chart, Manuel & his Music of the Mountains reached No.22 with *Theme from Honeymoon* in 1959. In the following year, they were one of many orchestras to hit the chart with *Never on Sunday*. Their rendition of *Somewhere my love* made a brief appearance in '66. But their biggest single by far was the Manuel treatment of *Rodrigo's guitar concerto de aranjuez (theme from 2nd movement)*, which cruised to No.3 in 1976;

it was almost a No.1 hit, for a computer error by the chart compilers temporarily placed the single at the top, but this was corrected three hours later - thus, the Manuel disc has the distinction of being the shortest-lived No.1 of all time! On the UK Lp listings, *Music of the mountains* reached No.17 in 1960. *This is Manuel* peaked at No.18 in 1971. *Carnival* climbed to No.3 in 1976 at the same time as the smash single. (Bob MacDonald, 20th Jan 1986).

MATADOR
Tracks: / Matador.
7" Single: Released Jun '82, on Multi-Media. Catalogue no: **MMT 8**

NEVER ON SUNDAY
Tracks: / Never on Sunday.
7" Single: Released Oct '60, on Columbia, by EMI Records. Deleted '63. Catalogue no: **DB 4515**

RODRIGO'S GUITAR CONCERTO DE ARANJUEZ
Tracks: / Rodrigo's guitar concerto de Aranjuez.
7" Single: Released Jan '76, on EMI, by EMI Records. Deleted '79. Catalogue no: **EMI 2383**

SOMEWHERE MY LOVE
Tracks: / Somewhere my love.
7" Single: Released Oct '66, on Columbia, by EMI Records. Deleted '69. Catalogue no: **DB 7969**

THEME FROM HONEYMOON
Tracks: / Honeymoon, Theme from.
7" Single: Released Aug '59, on Columbia, by EMI Records. Deleted '62. Catalogue no: **DB 4323**

Manufacture

ARMED FORCES
Tracks: / Armed forces.
12" Single: Released '88, on Nettwerk, by Nettwerk Records. Catalogue no: **NT 12 3017**

AS THE END DRAWS NEAR
Tracks: / As the end draws near.
12" Single: Released '89, on Nettwerk, by Nettwerk Records. Catalogue no: **NET 009**

Manyika, Zeke

BIBLE BELT
Tracks: / Bible belt / None so blind / Huya ne kuno.
7" Single: Released Nov '88, on Parlophone, by EMI Records. Catalogue no: **R 6187**
12" Single: Released Dec '88, on Parlophone, by EMI Records. Catalogue no: **12RX 6187**
12" Single: Released Nov '88, on Parlophone, by EMI Records. Catalogue no: **12R 6187**
12" Single: Released Nov '88, on Parlophone, by EMI Records. Catalogue no: **12RG 6187**

COLD LIGHT OF DAY
Tracks: / Cold light of day.
7" Single: Released Jun '85, on Polydor, by Polydor Ltd. Catalogue no: **ZM 3**
12" Single: Released Jun '85, on Polydor, by Polydor Ltd. Catalogue no: **ZMX 3**

HEAVEN HELP US TRY
Tracks: / Heaven help us try.
7" Single: Released Jun '84, on Polydor, by Polydor Ltd. Catalogue no: **ZM 1**
12" Single: Released Jun '84, on Polydor, by Polydor Ltd. Catalogue no: **ZMX 1**

LOVE YOU FEEL
Tracks: / Love you feel (7" only.) / Was it worth it (Not on 12".) / Love you feel (a kinda 12" feeling) (Not on 7".) / Love you feel (Deep house feeling) (Not on 7".).
CD 5": Released Nov '89, on Parlophone, by EMI Records. Catalogue no: **CDR 6232**
12" Single: Released Nov '89, on Parlophone, by EMI Records. Catalogue no: **12R 6232**
7" Single: Released Nov '89, on Parlophone, by EMI Records. Catalogue no: **203 564 7**
7" Single: Released Nov '89, on Parlophone, by EMI Records. Catalogue no: **R 6232**
12" Single: Released Nov '89, on Parlophone, by EMI Records. Catalogue no: **203 564 6**
CD 5": Released Nov '89, on Parlophone, by EMI Records. Catalogue no: **203 564 2**

R.F.T.(RUNAWAY FREEDOM TRAIN)
Tracks: / R.F.T.(Runaway freedom train) / Mozambique (Manyika) / Bible belt (12" remix).
Cassingle: Released Jun '89, on Parlophone, by EMI Records. Catalogue no: **TCR 6206**
CD 5": Released Jun '89, on Parlophone, by EMI Records. Catalogue no: **CDR 6206**
Cassingle: Released Jun '89, on Parlophone, by EMI Records. Catalogue no: **203 390 4**
12" Single: Released Jun '89, on Parlophone, by EMI Records. Catalogue no: **203 390 6**
7" Single: Released Jun '89, on Parlophone, by EMI Records. Catalogue no: **203 390 7**
7" Single: Released Jun '89, on Parlophone, by EMI Records. Catalogue no: **R 6206**
CD 5": Released Jun '89, on Parlophone, by EMI Records. Catalogue no: **203 390 2**
12" Single: Released Jun '89, on Parlophone, by EMI Records. Catalogue no: **12R 6206**

Manzarek, Ray

WHEEL OF FORTUNE
Tracks: / Wheel of fortune.
7" Single: Released Jan '84, on A&M, by A&M Records. Deleted '88. Catalogue no: **AM 173**

Mapangala, Samba

MALAKO
Tracks: / Malako.
12" Single: Released Aug '84, on Earthworks, by Earthworks Records. Deleted '88. Catalogue no: **ERT 1006**

Mapfumo, Thomas

ALL MY LIFE
Tracks: / All my life / Hupenyu wangu.
12" Single: Released Apr '86, on Rough Trade, by Rough Trade Records. Catalogue no: **RTT 190**

Mar Keys

LAST NIGHT
Tracks: / Last night.
12" Single: Released Apr '80, on Atlantic, by WEA Records. Catalogue no: **ATM 1**

Mar, Marla

HERE WE GO
Tracks: / Here we go.
7" Single: Released Mar '88, on Champion, by Champion Records. Deleted Aug '89. Catalogue no: **CHAMP 65**
12" Single: Released Mar '88, on Champion, by Champion Records. Deleted Aug '89. Catalogue no: **CHAMP 1265**

Marabar Caves

SALLY'S PLACE CREW
Tracks: / Sally's place crew.
7" Single: Released Feb '85, on Tiki. Catalogue no: **MBAR 1**

Marauders

THAT'S WHAT I WANT
Tracks: / That's what I want.
7" Single: Released Aug '63, on Decca, by Decca Records. Deleted '66. Catalogue no: **F 11695**

Marble Staircase

STILL DREAMING
Tracks: / Still dreaming / Dark ages.
7" Single: Released Sep '83, on Whaam. Catalogue no: **WHAAM 11**

Marbles

Biographical details: Proteges of The Bee Gees, this British male vocal duo achieved two UK hit singles in 1968-69. *Only one woman* reached No.5, and the follow-up *The walls fell down* peaked at No.28. Both were written and produced by the three Gibb brothers, who gave the Marbles the same histrionic treatment that they were giving their own records at that time. The only thing that distinguished a Marbles singles from a Bee Gees disc was the powerful voice of Graham Bonnet, who sounded as if he would be more at home with rock material than with these pop ballads. After the demise of the Marbles in 1970, Bonnet launched a solo career with moderate European and Australian success. Graham, who is in fact a cousin of the Gibbs, had to wait until 1981 for solo British success. By that time, he had enjoyed a brief but highly successful spell as lead vocalist with Rainbow, thus fulfilling the rock potential of his voice. (Bob MacDonald, 20th Jan 1986).

ONLY ONE WOMAN
Tracks: / Only one woman.
7" Single: Released Sep '68, on Polydor, by Polydor Ltd. Deleted '71. Catalogue no: **56.272**

ONLY ONE WOMAN (OLD GOLD)
Tracks: / Only one woman.
7" Single: Released Jul '82, on Old Gold, by Old Gold Records. Catalogue no: **OG 9153**

WALLS FELL DOWN, THE
Tracks: / Walls fell down, The.
7" Single: Released Mar '69, on Polydor, by Polydor Ltd. Deleted '72. Catalogue no: **56.310**

Marc & The Crucials

CHEEK TO CHEEK
Tracks: / Cheek to cheek / Supersonic.
7" Single: Released Dec '83, on Astra, by Astra Records. Catalogue no: **ESM 1106**

Marc & The Mambas

Biographical details: Marc & The Mambas was a flexible band fronted by Leeds-raised singer-songwriter Marc Almond, both immediately before and towards the end of his 1979-84 period with the highly-successful Soft Cell. The first Mambas incarnation was, of course, in total obscurity -- it was not until the Soft Cell duo had become famous that interest was focused on Almond's other project. The group's album, Untitled, reached No 42 in the UK chart in late 1982 and was followed in '83 by the LP *Torment And Toreros*. They peaked at No 49 on the British listings with a single, *Black Heart*, in the summer of that year. Almond was certainly prolific: the first album contained one-and-a-half LP's-worth of material and the second was a fully-fledged double. However, the presence of musicians like pianist Ann Hogan and Matt Johnson (the man who is also knows as The The) failed to compensate for the synthesised sounds of David Ball, the absent Soft Cell partner who normally made Almond's histrionic, groaning vocals palatable. Marc & The Mambas' records were diverse and distinctive exercises in pop expansion but were far too disorganised to emulate Soft Cell's success. After the Mambas' termination in 1984 Almond pursued a moderately-successful solo career and scored a huge 1985 hit in duet with Bronski Beat on the remake of the Donner Summer number *I Feel Love*. (Bob MacDonald, January 1986.).

BLACK HEART
Tracks: / Black heart.
7" Single: Released Jun '83, on Some Bizzare, by Some Bizzare Records. Deleted '86. Catalogue no: **BZS 19**

Marcel

I'VE BEEN A BAD BOY
Tracks: / I've been a bad boy.
7" Single: Released Oct '82, on Red Bus, by Red Bus Records. Catalogue no: **RBUS 74**

Marcels

Biographical details: At the time of their tranatlantic No.1 smash, this American vocal group consisted of Gene Bricker, Cornelius Harp, Fred Johnson, Dick Knauss and Ronald Mundy. The group named themseves after a popular wavy hairstyle, although the style did not become their visual trademark. In 1961 the Marcels, all in their late teens and early twenties, shot from nowhere to stardom and then back to nowhere again. They actually hailed from Pittsburgh, Philadelphia, and jumped to the top of the charts on both sides of the Atlantic with *Blue moon*. This was one of the most extraordinary and unexpected cover versions of all time. The song was written in 1934 by the legendary Rodgers & Hart team, and was their only major hit not penned specifically for a stage or screen musical. Originally a slow ballad, *Blue Moon* was successfully recorded by Billy Eckstine (1948), Mel Torme (1949) and Elvis Presley *1956) before the Marcels got their zany hands on it. Changing the song out of all recognition, the group recorded it in an uptempo, gimmicky style that owed much to the black rhythm-and-blues groups of the Fifties. Typically for the genre, they made maximum use of the bass vocalist; if Johnny Cymbal's 1963 hit Mr Bass man* was sending anyone up it was the Marcels. *Blue moon* was a thoroughly enjoyable record, but hits with a novelty flavour are always hard to follow. They hit the US Top 10 with another old chestnut, *Heartaches*, in late '61; but, this time, two members had already been replaced. The British follo-up to *Blue moon* was a revamp of the Gershwin standard *Summertime*, but this peaked at No.46. While *Blue moon* remained a much-played pop classic, the Marcels themselves disappeared into the night. (Bob MacDonald, 20th Jan 1986).

BLUE MOON (OLD GOLD)
Tracks: / Blue moon.
7" Single: Released Jul '82, on Old Gold, by Old Gold Records. Catalogue no: **OG 9136**

BLUE MOON (SINGLE)
Tracks: / Blue moon.
7" Single: Released Apr '61, on Pye International. Deleted '64. Catalogue no: **7N 25073**

SUMMERTIME
Tracks: / Summertime.
7" Single: Released Jun '61, on Pye International. Deleted '64. Catalogue no: **7N 25083**

March, Little Peggy

HELLO HEARTACHE GOODBYE LOVE
Tracks: / Hello heartache goodbye love.
7" Single: Released Sep '63, on RCA, by BMG Records (UK). Deleted '66. Catalogue no: **RCA 1362**

March, Peggy

WHERE DID OUR LOVE GO
Tracks: / Where did our love go / Who needs you.
12" Single: Released Oct '86, on RCA, by BMG Records (UK). Catalogue no: **PT 40806**
7" Single: Released Aug '86, on RCA, by BMG Records (UK). Catalogue no: **PB 40805**

March Violets

CROW BABY
Tracks: / Crow baby.
7" Single: Released May '83, on Rebirth. Catalogue no: **RD 18**
12" Single: Released Mar '85, on Rebirth. Catalogue no: **RB 1812**

DEEP
Tracks: / Deep.
7" Single: Released Apr '85, on Rebirth. Catalogue no: **VRB 26**
12" Single: Released Apr '85, on Rebirth. Catalogue no: **VRB 2612**

GROOVING IN THE GREEN
Tracks: / Grooving in the green.
7" Single: Released Nov '82, on Merciful Release, by Merciful Release. Catalogue no: **MR 17**

MARCH VIOLETS (EP)
Tracks: / March violets.
7" Single: Released Aug '82, on Merciful Release, by Merciful Release. Catalogue no: **MR 13**

SNAKEDANCE
Tracks: / Snakedance.
7" Single: Released Jan '84, on Rebirth. Catalogue no: **RB 21**
12" Single: Released 13 Jun '85, on Rebirth. Deleted '87. Catalogue no: **VRB 2112**
12" Single: Released Jan '84, on Rebirth. Catalogue no: **RB 2112**

TURN TO THE SKY
Tracks: / Turn to the sky / Never look / Deep. Note: 'Deep' available on 12" version only.
7" Single: Released Sep '86, on Rebirth. Deleted Sep '87. Catalogue no: **VRB 27**
12" Single: Released Feb '86, on Rebirth. Catalogue no: **VRBX 27**

WALK IN THE SUN
Tracks: / Walk in the sun.
12" Single: Released Jun '84, on Rebirth. Catalogue no: **VRB 2412**
7" Single: Released Jun '84, on Rebirth. Catalogue no: **RB 24**

WALK INTO THE SUN
Tracks: / Walk into the sun.
7" Single: Released 13 Jun '85, on Rebirth. Deleted '87. Catalogue no: **VRB 024**

Marchand, Donny

LADIES OF THE NIGHT
Tracks: / Ladies of the night.
7" Single: Released Feb '89, on College. Catalogue no: **COLS 5939**

Marching Girls

TRUE LOVE
Tracks: / True love.
7" Single: Released Jul '81, on Pop Aural. Catalogue no: **POP 11**

Marcus, P.J.

FOR YOUR SWEET INFORMATION
Tracks: / For your sweet information / For your sweet information (Inst.).
12" Single: Released Mar '86, on ZYX (Germany). Catalogue no: **ZYX 5383**

Mardells

ONE OF A MILLION
Tracks: / One of a million.
7" Single: Released May '82, on Escape, by Escape Records. Catalogue no: **ESC 104**

Marden Hill

CURTAIN
Tracks: / Curtain / Let's make Shane & Mackenzie.
7" Single: Released Nov '86, on El, by Cherry Red Records. Catalogue no: **GPO 18**

Mardi Gras

TOO BUSY THINKING 'BOUT MY BABY
Tracks: / Too busy thinking 'bout my baby.
7" Single: Released Aug '72, on Bell. Deleted '75. Catalogue no: **BELL 1226**

Mardis, Bobby

KEEP ON
Tracks: / Keep on / Keep on (Inst.).
12" Single: Released Feb '86, on Bluebird (2), by BMG Records (UK). Deleted '86. Catalogue no: **BRT 20**

Mardonnes, Benny

INTO THE NIGHT
Tracks: / Into the night / She's so French.
7" Single: Released Jul '81, on Polydor, by Polydor Ltd. Deleted '85. Catalogue no: **POSP 303**
7" Single: Released Sep '80, on Polydor, by Polydor Ltd. Deleted '83. Catalogue no: **2095237**

Maresca, Ernie

SHOUT (KNOCK YOURSELF OUT) (SINGLE)
7" Single: Released Feb '81, on Seville, by President Records. Catalogue no: **SEV 1019**

Margo

BOYS FROM COUNTY MAYO
Tracks: / Boys from County Mayo.
7" Single: Released '88, on Homespun (Ireland), by Outlet Records. Catalogue no: **HIS 1**

COALMINERS DAUGHTER
Tracks: / Coalminers daughter / Mass rock in the glen.
7" Single: Released Apr '81, on Homespun (Ireland), by Outlet Records. Catalogue no: **HS 045**

GOLDEN JUBILEE
Tracks: / Golden jubilee.
7" Single: Released '88, on Homespun (Ireland), by Outlet Records. Catalogue no: **HIS 2**

IF WE ONLY HAD OLD IRELAND OVER HERE
Tracks: / If we only had old Ireland over here.
7" Single: Released '88, on Homespun (Ireland), by Outlet Records. Catalogue no: **HIS 15**

NEW TOMORROW, A
Tracks: / New tomorrow, A / All I have for you mum.
7" Single: Released 24 Jul '89, on I&B, by I & B Records. Catalogue no: **IRS 010**

Marias, A.C.

JUST TALK
Tracks: / Just talk / Just talk (Inst.).
12" Single: Released Aug '86, on Mute, by Mute Records. Catalogue no: **12MUTE 50**

TIME WAS
Tracks: / Time was / Something.
7" Single: Released Jan '88, on Mute, by Mute Records. Catalogue no: **MUTE 70**
12" Single: Released Jan '88, on Mute, by Mute Records. Catalogue no: **12 MUTE 70**

Marie

YOU THROW MY LOVE
Tracks: / You throw my love.
12" Single: Released Jan '82, on TCD Music. Catalogue no: **TCDD 018**

Marie &...

SALTY HOUND
Tracks: / Salty hound.
12" Single: Released Nov '86, on Ediesta. Catalogue no: **CALC 11**

Marie, Karena

RUNAWAY
Tracks: / Runaway.
7" Single: Released Apr '82, on Cask. Catalogue no: **CASK 1**

Marie, Kelly

BORN TO BE ALIVE
Tracks: / Born to be alive / Are you ready for love / Born to be alive.
7" Single: Released '88, on Passion, by Skratch Records. Catalogue no: **PASH 52**
7" Single: Released '88, on Passion, by Skratch Records. Catalogue no: **PASH 50**

BREAKOUT
Tracks: / Breakout.
12" Single: Released Jul '84, on Calibre Plus, Deleted '86. Catalogue no: **PLUSL 14**
7" Single: Released Jul '84, on Calibre Plus, Deleted '86. Catalogue no: **PLUS 14**

DON'T LET THE FLAME DIE OUT
Tracks: / Don't let the flame die out.
12" Single: Released Jun '85, on Passion, by Skratch Records. Catalogue no: **PASH 45(12)**
7" Single: Released Jun '85, on Passion, by Skratch Records. Catalogue no: **PASH 45**

DON'T TAKE YOUR LOVE TO HOLLYWOOD
Tracks: / Don't take your love to Hollywood.
7" Single: Released Oct '82, on Calibre Plus, Deleted '84. Catalogue no: **PLUS 12**
12" Single: Released Oct '82, on Calibre Plus, Deleted '84. Catalogue no: **PLUSL 12**

FEELS LIKE I'M IN LOVE (OLD GOLD)
Tracks: / Feel like I'm in love / Hot love.
7" Single: Released Mar '86, on Old Gold, by Old Gold Records. Catalogue no: **OG 9578**

FEELS LIKE I'M IN LOVE (SINGLE)
Tracks: / Feels like I'm in love / Shattered glass.
7" Single: Released May '80, on Calibre, Deleted '83. Catalogue no: **PLUS 1**
7" Single: Released Sep '86, on PRT, by Castle Communications Records. Catalogue no: **7P 365**
12" Single: Released Sep '86, on PRT, by Castle Communications Records. Catalogue no: **12P 365**
12" Single: Released May '80, on Calibre, Deleted '83. Catalogue no: **PLUSL 1**

HALF WAY TO PARADISE
Tracks: / Halfway to paradise.
7" Single: Released Oct '87, on Passion, by Skratch Records. Catalogue no: **PASH 77**
12" Single: Released Aug '87, on Passion, by Skratch Records. Catalogue no: **PASH 77(12)**

HANDS UP
Tracks: / Hands up / Hands up (Inst.).
12" Single: Released Jun '86, on Passion, by Skratch Records. Catalogue no: **PASH 56(12)**
7" Single: Released Jun '88, on Passion, by Skratch Records. Catalogue no: **PASH 56**

HOT LOVE
Tracks: / Hot love.
7" Single: Released Feb '81, on Calibre, Deleted '84. Catalogue no: **PLUS 5**

I NEED YOUR LOVE
Tracks: / I need your love / Somebody.
7" Single: Released Jan '82, on Calibre Plus, Deleted '84. Catalogue no: **PLUS 9**
12" Single: Released Jan '82, on Calibre Plus, Deleted '84. Catalogue no: **PLUSL 9**

I'M ON FIRE
Tracks: / I'm on fire.
12" Single: Released Oct '84, on Calibre Plus, Deleted '86. Catalogue no: **PLUSL 15**
7" Single: Released Oct '84, on Calibre Plus, Deleted '86. Catalogue no: **PLUS 15**

LOVE TRIAL
Tracks: / Love trial / Head for the stars.
12" Single: Released May '81, on Calibre, Deleted '84. Catalogue no: **PLUSL 7**
7" Single: Released May '81, on Calibre, Deleted '84. Catalogue no: **PLUS 7**

LOVE'S GOT A HOLD ON YOU
Tracks: / Love's got a hold on you / Heartbeat.
7" Single: Released Jul '82, on Calibre Plus, Deleted '84. Catalogue no: **PLUS 11**
12" Single: Released Jul '82, on Calibre Plus, Deleted '84. Catalogue no: **PLUSL 11**

LOVING JUST FOR FUN
Tracks: / Loving just for fun.
7" Single: Released Oct '80, on Calibre, Deleted '83. Catalogue no: **PLUS 4**

SILENT TREATMENT
Tracks: / Silent treatment.
7" Single: Released Sep '83, on Calibre Plus, Deleted '85. Catalogue no: **PLUS 13**
12" Single: Released Sep '83, on Calibre Plus, Deleted '85. Catalogue no: **PLUSL 13**

Marie, Sharon

TRICKS AND LIES
Tracks: / Tricks and lies.
12" Single: Released Jun '89, on Fine Style, by Fashion Records. Catalogue no: **FS 023**

Marie, Teena

Biographical details: This American singer, songwriter, arranger and producer has been one of the few white artists successfully operating in the US soul field. She hails from California and her real name is Mary Brocker. She was discovered in the late seventies by Mowtown chief Berry Cordy and her early career was nurtured by another of the companies rising stars Rick James. Rick and Teena duetted on the 1979 single *I'm a sucker for your love* which reached number 34 on the British Chart. It was not long before Teena Marie was writing and producing her own hits just like Rick. Both artists followed a modern danceable slinky soul path, giving their records a hard edged funk sound and, from time to time, a rock influence. Marie broke through briefly in Britain with her surprise smash *Behind the groove* which reached number 6 on the U.K. singles chart at the same time when 'groove' was the hip word in discos. The follow up *I need your loving* peaked at number 28 in late 1980 and proceeded to reach number 37 on the American pop chart. 1981's chunky *Square biz* was a moderate success for her. Apart from the uptempo material, her ability to deliver a deep and intense ballad was exemplified by *Fire and desire* a duet with James on his successful 1981 LP *Street songs*. Finding her career at an impasse, Teena switched from Motown to Epic Records for the 1983 album *Robbery*. Her next Lp, 1985's *Starchild*, was the one which yielded her first big American pop smash - *Lovergirl* climbed to No.4 on the Billboard chart but flopped in Britain. The album also contained the ballad *Dear Mr Gaye*, a stunningly soulful tribute of which the late Marvin would have been proud. Teena Marie's career has been erratic in terms of success, but not in terms of quality. (Bob MacDonald, 21st Jan 1986).

BEHIND THE GROOVE
Tracks: / Behind the groove / You're all the boogie.
12" Single: Released Apr '85, on Motown, by BMG Records (UK). Catalogue no: **TMGT 1385**
7" Single: Released Apr '85, on Motown, by BMG Records (UK). Catalogue no: **TMG 1385**
12" Single: Released Oct '81, on Motown, by BMG Records (UK). Catalogue no: **TMGT 1185**
7" Single: Released Oct '81, on Motown, by BMG Records (UK). Catalogue no: **TMG 1185**

CAN IT BE LOVE
Tracks: / Can it be love / Too many colours.
7" Single: Released Oct '81, on Motown, by BMG Records (UK). Catalogue no: **TMG 1178**

I NEED YOUR LOVIN'
Tracks: / I need your lovin'.
12" Single: Released Oct '81, on Motown, by BMG Records (UK). Catalogue no: **TMGT 1203**
7" Single: Released Oct '81, on Motown, by BMG Records (UK). Catalogue no: **TMG 1203**

I'M A SUCKER FOR YOUR LOVE
Tracks: / I'm a sucker for your love.
7" Single: Released Oct '81, on Motown, by BMG Records (UK). Catalogue no: **TMG 1146**
12" Single: Released Oct '81, on Motown, by BMG Records (UK). Catalogue no: **TMGT 1146**

IT MUST BE MAGIC (SINGLE)
Tracks: / It must be magic / Yes indeed.
7" Single: Released Nov '81, on Motown, by BMG Records (UK). Catalogue no: **TMG 1246**
12" Single: Released Nov '81, on Motown, by BMG Records (UK). Catalogue no: **TMGT 1246**

LIPS TO FIND YOU
Tracks: / Lips to find you.
7" Single: Released Jun '86, on Epic, by CBS Records. Deleted '86. Catalogue no: **A 7270**
12" Single: Released Jun '86, on Epic, by CBS Records. Deleted '86. Catalogue no: **TA 7270**

LONELY DESIRE
Tracks: / Lonely desire.
7" Single: Released Oct '81, on Motown, by BMG Records (UK). Catalogue no: **TMG 1196**

LOVE ME DOWN EASY
Tracks: / Love me down easy / Love me down easy (instrumental).
7" Single: Released Oct '86, on Epic, by CBS Records. Catalogue no: **650126 7**
12" Single: Released Oct '86, on Epic, by CBS Records. Catalogue no: **650126 6**

LOVERGIRL
Tracks: / Lovergirl.
7" Single: Released Mar '85, on Epic, by CBS Records. Catalogue no: **A 4965**

OOO LA LA LA
Tracks: / Ooo la la la / Sing one to your love / Ooo la la la (ext. mix) / Ooo la la la (slightly shorter version).
12" Single: Released Mar '88, on Epic, by CBS Records. Catalogue no: **651423 8**
7" Single: Released Mar '88, on Epic, by CBS Records. Catalogue no: **651423 0**
12" Single: Released Feb '88, on Epic, by CBS Records. Catalogue no: **651423 6**
7" Single: Released Feb '88, on Epic, by CBS Records. Catalogue no: **651423 7**

PORTUGUESE LOVE
Tracks: / Portuguese love / Ballad of cradle Rob and me.
12" Single: Released Jan '82, on Motown, by BMG Records (UK). Catalogue no: **TMGT 1251**
7" Single: Released Jan '82, on Motown, by BMG Records (UK). Catalogue no: **TMG 1251**

SQUARE BIZ
Tracks: / Square biz / Opus III (Does anybody care).
12" Single: Released Oct '81, on Motown, by BMG Records (UK). Catalogue no: **TMGT 1236**
7" Single: Released Oct '81, on Motown, by BMG Records (UK). Catalogue no: **TMG 1236**

Marietta

DO YOU WANNA DANCE
Tracks: / Do you wanna dance / Only in your eyes i see.
7" Single: Released '82, on Polydor, by Polydor Ltd. Deleted '87. Catalogue no: **POSP 483**

YOU'RE ONLY LONELY
Tracks: / You're only lonely / Making up my mind.
7" Single: Released Jan '82, on Polydor, by Polydor Ltd. Deleted '85. Catalogue no: **POSP 305**

Marillion

Biographical details: This British rock band originally consisted of lead singer Fish - (Derek Dick) plus Mark Kelly, Ian Mosley, Steve Rothery and Pete Trewavas, although Fish has since left the group, replaced by Steve Hogarth. The group came into being in 1979 as Silmarillion, inspired by J.R.R. Tolkien's posthumously published book. Emerging from Aylesbury, Buckinghamshire (except Fish, who hailed from Dalkeith in the *Heart of Lothian* in Scotland), Marillion built up a strong cult following in the early eighties through heavy gigging. After a small success with the single *Market square heroes*, they were rewarded in 1983 with two UK top 40 singles plus a successful album, *Script for a jester's tear*. With public acceptance gradually getting greater, the group consolidated their position in 1984 with the *Fugazi* LP plus the live album *Real to reel*. In 1985 they moved into the top league of British rock acts - *Misplacedchildhood* entered the UK album chart at No.1, and the band enjoyed their first two top 10 singles with *Kayleigh* (No.2) and *Lavender* (No.5). The group became a major international concert attraction, although their penetration of the US market was limited. Of all the new UK acts to break through in the eighties, Marillion were amongst the most critically derided. The music press constantly described the group as an anachronism, claiming that their pomp-rock sound was directly derived from the early seventies incarnation of Genesis, but lacked the charismatic theatrics of Peter Gabriel. Marillion's success was certainly a surprise in an era when synthesised techno-pop and danceability were the order of the day. The critics thought that their type of music had died with the 1976 advent of punk, but the public knew otherwise. (Bob Macdonald 21st Jan 1986).

ASSASSING
Tracks: / Assassing / Cinderella search.
12" Pic: Released May '84, on EMI, by EMI Records. Deleted '88. Catalogue no: **12 MARILP 2**
7" Single: Released Apr '84, on EMI, by EMI Records. Deleted '88. Catalogue no: **MARIL 2**
12" Single: Released Apr '84, on EMI, by EMI Records. Catalogue no: **12 MARIL 2**

ASSASSING (IMPORT)
Tracks: / Assassing (7" mix) / Assassing (full length) / Cinderella search.
12" Single: Released Oct '88, on EMI (Germany), by EMI Records. Catalogue no: **0622 001586**

FREAKS 'LIVE'
Tracks: / Freaks (live) / Kayleigh (live) / Childhood's end? (live) (CD single & 12" only.) / White feather (CD single & 12" only.).
7" Single: Released Nov '88, on EMI, by EMI Records. Deleted Aug '89. Catalogue no: **MARIL 9**
CD 5": Released Nov '88, on EMI, by EMI Records. Deleted Jun '89. Catalogue no: **CDMARIL 9**
12" Single: Released Nov '88, on EMI, by EMI Records. Deleted Aug '89. Catalogue no: **12MARIL 9**
7" Pic: Released Nov '88, on EMI, by EMI Records. Deleted Aug '89. Catalogue no: **MARILP 9**

GARDEN PARTY
Tracks: / Garden party.
12" Single: Released Jun '83, on EMI, by EMI Records. Catalogue no: **12 EMI 5393**
7" Single: Released Jun '83, on EMI, by EMI Records. Catalogue no: **EMI 5393**
7" Pic: Released Jun '83, on EMI, by EMI Records. Deleted '88. Catalogue no: **EMIP 5393**

HE KNOWS YOU KNOW
Tracks: / He knows you know / Charting the single.
12" Single: Released Jan '83, on EMI, by EMI Records. Catalogue no: **12 EMI 5362**
7" Single: Released Jan '83, on EMI, by EMI Records. Deleted '88. Catalogue no: **EMI 5362**

HEART OF LOTHIAN
Tracks: / Heart of Lothian / Chelsea Monday / Live at utrecht / Heart of Lothian (ext).
12" Pic: Released Nov '85, on EMI, by EMI Records. Catalogue no: **12 MARILP 5**
7" Single: Released Nov '85, on EMI, by EMI Records. Catalogue no: **MARIL 5**
12" Single: Released Nov '85, on EMI, by EMI Records. Catalogue no: **12 MARIL 5**

HOOKS IN YOU
Tracks: / Hooks in you / After me / Hooks in you (meaty mix) (12" & CD single only.).
12" Single: Released Aug '89, on EMI, by EMI Records. Catalogue no: **203 495 6**
CD 5": Released Aug '89, on EMI, by EMI Records. Catalogue no: **203 495 2**
Cassingle: Released Aug '89, on EMI, by EMI Records. Catalogue no: **203 495 4**
CD 5": Released Aug '89, on EMI, by EMI Records. Catalogue no: **CDMARIL 10**
7" Single: Released Aug '89, on EMI, by EMI Records. Catalogue no: **MARIL 10**
7" Single: Released Aug '89, on EMI, by EMI Records. Catalogue no: **203 495 7**
12" Single: Released Aug '89, on EMI, by EMI Records. Catalogue no: **12MARILP 10**
12" Single: Released Aug '89, on EMI, by EMI Records. Catalogue no: **12MARIL 10**

Cassingle: Released Aug '89, on EMI, by EMI Records. Catalogue no: **TCMARIL 10**

INCOMMUNICADO
Tracks: / Incommunicado / Going under / Sugar mice.
12" Single: Released May '87, on EMI, by EMI Records. Deleted Apr '88. Catalogue no: **12 MARIL 6**
7" EP: Released May '87, on EMI, by EMI Records. Deleted Nov '88. Catalogue no: **MARIL 6**

KAYLEIGH
Tracks: / Kayleigh.
12" Pic: Released Jun '85, on EMI, by EMI Records. Deleted '88. Catalogue no: **12 MARILP 3**
7" Pic: Released May '85, on EMI, by EMI Records. Deleted '88. Catalogue no: **MARILP 3**
7" Single: Released May '85, on EMI, by EMI Records. Catalogue no: **MARIL 3**
12" Single: Released May '85, on EMI, by EMI Records. Catalogue no: **12 MARIL 3**

LAVENDER BLUE
Tracks: / Lavender blue.
7" Single: Released Aug '85, on EMI, by EMI Records. Catalogue no: **MARIL 4**
12" Single: Released Aug '85, on EMI, by EMI Records. Catalogue no: **12 MARIL 4**

MARKET SQUARE HEROES
Tracks: / Market square heroes.
7" Single: Released Oct '82, on EMI, by EMI Records. Deleted Oct '87. Catalogue no: **EMI 5351**
12" Single: Released Oct '82, on EMI, by EMI Records. Catalogue no: **12 EMI 5351**

PUNCH AND JUDY
Tracks: / Punch and Judy.
12" Single: Released Jan '84, on EMI, by EMI Records. Catalogue no: **12 MARIL 1**
7" Single: Released Jan '84, on EMI, by EMI Records. Catalogue no: **MARIL 1**
12" Pic: Released Jan '84, on EMI, by EMI Records. Deleted '88. Catalogue no: **12 MARILP 1**

SUGAR MICE
Tracks: / Sugar mice / Tux on.
7" Pic: Released Jul '87, on EMI, by EMI Records. Deleted Apr '88. Catalogue no: **MARILP 7**
12" Pic: Released Jul '87, on EMI, by EMI Records. Deleted Apr '88. Catalogue no: **12 MARILP 7**
CD 5": Released Jul '87, on EMI, by EMI Records. Deleted Jan '88. Catalogue no: **CD MARIL 7**
7" Single: Released Jul '87, on EMI, by EMI Records. Catalogue no: **MARIL 7**
12" Single: Released Jul '87, on EMI, by EMI Records. Deleted Nov '88. Catalogue no: **12 MARIL 7**

UNINVITED GUEST
Tracks: / Uninvited guest / End of the day / Uninvited guest (12" version) (12" & CD single only.).
CD 5": Released Nov '89, on EMI, by EMI Records. Catalogue no: **203 582 2**
CD 5": Released Nov '89, on EMI, by EMI Records. Catalogue no: **CDMARIL 11**
Cassingle: Released Nov '89, on EMI, by EMI Records. Catalogue no: **203 582 4**
Cassingle: Released Nov '89, on EMI, by EMI Records. Catalogue no: **TCMARIL 11**
7" Single: Released Nov '89, on EMI, by EMI Records. Catalogue no: **203 582 7**
7" Single: Released Nov '89, on EMI, by EMI Records. Catalogue no: **MARIL 11**
12" Single: Released Nov '89, on EMI, by EMI Records. Catalogue no: **12MARIL 11**
12" Single: Released Nov '89, on EMI, by EMI Records. Catalogue no: **203 582 6**

WARM WET CIRCLES
Tracks: / Incommunicado (Live at Loreley.) / White Russian (Recorded live at Loreley.) / Warm wet circles.
CD 5": Released Nov '87, on EMI, by EMI Records. Deleted 31 Jul '88. Catalogue no: **CDMARIL 8**
7" Single: Released Oct '87, on EMI, by EMI Records. Deleted Nov '88. Catalogue no: **MARIL 8**
12" Single: Released Oct '87, on EMI, by EMI Records. Catalogue no: **12 MARIL 8**
12" Single: Released Nov '87, on EMI, by EMI Records. Deleted Apr '88. Catalogue no: **12 MARILP 8**

Marilyn

Biographical details: British singer Marilyn hit the news in late 1983 as a protege of the then red-hot Boy George. Marilyn was, like his mentor, a proponent of transvestism and his smash single, *Calling Your Name*, sounded just like a Culture Club record. The song reach No 4 on the UK chart. Marilyn received massive media coverage for a while, but his subsequent singles did not live up to sales expectations: the gospel-flavoured *Cry And Be Free* peaked at No 31 and the aptly-titled *You Don't Love Me* got to No 40. By late 1984 his star had faded. (Bob MacDonald, January 1986.).

BABY U LEFT ME
Tracks: / Baby U left me.
7" Single: Released Apr '85, on Mercury, by Phonogram Ltd. Deleted '88. Catalogue no: **MAZ 4**

CALLING YOUR NAME
Tracks: / Calling your name.
7" Single: Released Nov '83, on Mercury, by Phonogram Ltd. Deleted May '86. Catalogue no: **MAZ 1**

CRY AND BE FREE
Tracks: / Cry and be free.
7" Single: Released Feb '84, on Mercury, by Phonogram Ltd. Catalogue no: **MAZ 2**
12" Single: Released Feb '84, on Mercury, by Phonogram Ltd. Catalogue no: **MAZ 212**

YOU DON'T LOVE ME
Tracks: / You don't love me / Raining again.
12" Single: Released Apr '84, on Love-Mercury, Catalogue no: **MAZ 3 12**
7" Single: Released Apr '84, on Love-Mercury, Catalogue no: **MAZ 3**

Marine

SAME BEAT
Tracks: / Same beat.
7" Single: Released May '82, on Les Disques Du Crepuscule(Belgium), by Les Disques Du Crepuscule(Belgium). Catalogue no: **7TWI 069**

Marine Girls

DON'T COME BACK
Tracks: / Don't come back / You must be mad.
7" Single: Released Jan '83, on Cherry Red, by Cherry Red Records. Catalogue no: **CHERRY 54**

ON MY MIND
Tracks: / On my mind / Lure of the rockpools.
7" Single: Released Jan '82, on In Phaze, by In Phaze Records. Catalogue no: **COD 2**
7" Single: Released May '82, on Cherry Red, by Cherry Red Records. Deleted '87. Catalogue no: **CHERRY 40**

Mariner

TELECOMMUNICATION
Tracks: / Telecommunication / I'm coming home.
7" Single: Released Jun '82, on Tube, Catalogue no: **TUBE 2**

Marines

SAY GOODBYE
Tracks: / Say goodbye / If you're looking for love / Say goodbye (extended version) (Only on 12" and CD single.).
CD 5": Released Aug '89, on CBS, by CBS Records. Catalogue no: **WETIT C1**
7" Single: Released Aug '89, on CBS, by CBS Records. Catalogue no: **WETIT 1**
7" Pic: Released Aug '89, on CBS, by CBS Records. Catalogue no: **WETIT P1**
12" Pic: Released Aug '89, on CBS, by CBS Records. Catalogue no: **WETIT Q1**
12" Single: Released Aug '89, on CBS, by CBS Records. Catalogue no: **WETIT T1**

Marini, Marino

CIAO CIAO BAMBINA
Tracks: / Ciao ciao bambina.
7" Single: Released Apr '59, on Durium, Deleted '62. Catalogue no: **DC 16636**

VOLARE
Tracks: / Volare / Come'prima.
7" Single: Released Oct '58, on Durium, Deleted '61. Catalogue no: **DC 16632**

VOLARE (OLD GOLD)
Tracks: / Volare.
7" Single: Released Apr '86, on Old Gold, by Old Gold Records. Catalogue no: **OG 9596**

Marino, Frank

YOU GOT LIVIN'
Tracks: / You got livin' / World anthem.
7" Single: Released Jun '80, on CBS, by CBS Records. Deleted '83. Catalogue no: **CBS 8637**

Marionette

ON A NIGHT LIKE THIS
12" Single: Released Jun '85, on FM, by FM-Revolver Records. Catalogue no: **12 VHF 12**

Marion's flight

MARION'S FLIGHT
Tracks: / Marion's flight: *Various artists.*
7" EP: Released Jan '82, on Epigram, by Epigram Records. Catalogue no: **EP 1002**

Mark E

LET'S GET MARRIED
Tracks: / Let's get married.
12" Single: Released Apr '82, on UNKNOWN, Catalogue no: **DOL 001**

MARKS BROTHERS - JOE JOE'S BAR (Released on Carrere)

Mark, James & Julie

GOLDEN DUETS
Tracks: / Golden duets.
7" Single: Released Nov '81, on Rational, Catalogue no: **RATE 5**

Mark & Silly Buggers

OH DEAR I HAVE NO (SCRUPLES)
Tracks: / Oh dear I have no (scruples).
12" Single: Released Apr '82, on Zambi, Catalogue no: **BAZ 3T**

Markay, Barbara

IT'S ALL RIGHT
Tracks: / It's all right (censored version) / It's all right.
7" Single: Released Jun '80, on Fat Chance, by Fat Chance Records. Deleted '83. Catalogue no: **FC 1**

Markee

GOOD SENSIMANIA
Tracks: / Good sensimania.
12" Single: Released Jul '83, on Horsemouth, Catalogue no: **HM 002**

Markee, Dave

LET IT STAY
Tracks: / Choose life / Choose life (version) / Let it stay.
Note: Other side is by Mark Tedder.
7" Single: Released Apr '88, on Priority, by Priority Records. Deleted Sep '89. Catalogue no: **P 21**

Markham, Pigmeat

HERE COMES THE JUDGE
Tracks: / Here comes the judge.
7" Single: Released Jul '68, on Chess, by Vogue Records. Deleted '71. Catalogue no: **CRS 8077**

Markie, Biz

BIZ IS GOIN' OFF
Tracks: / Biz is goin' off / Do do, The.
7" Single: Released Mar '88, on Cold Chillin', by Cold Chillin' Records. Catalogue no: **W 7930**
12" Single: Released Mar '88, on Cold Chillin', by Cold Chillin' Records. Catalogue no: **W 7930T**

VAPOURS
Tracks: / Vapours / Do do, The
12" Single: Released Jun '88, on Cold Chillin', by Cold Chillin' Records. Catalogue no: **W 7890T**
7" Single: Released Jun '88, on Cold Chillin', by Cold Chillin' Records. Catalogue no: **W 7890**

Markopoulos, Yannis

Biographical details: This greek orchestra leader, conductor and composer enjoyed brief success in Britain during 1977-78 with his theme for the BBC-TV drama serial *Who pays the ferryman?*. The single became one of the few major hits for the BBC's subsidiary record label, reaching No.11; (Bob MacDonald, 21st Jan 1986).

WHO PAYS THE FERRYMAN (OLD GOLD)
Tracks: / Who pays the ferryman.
7" Single: Released Jan '85, on Old Gold, by Old Gold Records. Catalogue no: **OG 9413**

WHO PAYS THE FERRYMAN (SINGLE)
Tracks: / Who pays the ferryman.
7" Single: Released Dec '77, on BBC, by BBC Records & Tapes. Deleted '80. Catalogue no: **RESL 51**

Marks Brothers

JOE JOE'S BAR (see panel above)
Tracks: / Joe Joe's bar / Ronnie 'B' good.
7" Single: Released Jan '86, on Carrere, Catalogue no: **CAR 381**

Marks, Guy

LOVING YOU HAS MADE ME BANANAS
Tracks: / Loving you has made me bananas.
7" Single: Released May '78, on ABC Records, by MCA Records. Deleted '81. Catalogue no: **ABC 4211**

Marks, Louisa

6 SIX STREET
Tracks: / 6 six street.
7" Single: Released May '79, on Robot, Catalogue no: **RRS 2**
12" Single: Released May '79, on Robot, Catalogue no: **12 RRS 2**

ALL MY LOVING
Tracks: / All my loving / Lonely.
7" Single: Released Feb '81, on Voyage International, by Code Records. Catalogue no: **VOY 0016**
12" Single: Released Sep '84, on Code, by Code Records. Catalogue no: **12LOB 014**
12" Single: Released Feb '81, on Voyage International, by Code Records. Catalogue no: **12VOY 0016**

CAUGHT YOU IN A LIE
Tracks: / Caught you in a lie / Tribute to Muhammed Ali.
12" Single: Released Mar '84, on Code, by Code Records. Catalogue no: **12COD 009**
7" Single: Released Mar '84, on Code, by Code Records. Catalogue no: **COD 009**
7" Single: Released Feb '82, on Voyage International, by Code Records. Catalogue no: **VOY 0012**

HELLO THERE
Tracks: / Hello there / Hello dub.
12" Single: Released Jun '84, on Oak Sound, Catalogue no: **OSD 14**

KEEP AWAY GIRLS
Tracks: / Keep away girls / Keep away girls (version).
12" Single: Released Jul '88, on Moodies, Catalogue no: **CR 41**

MUM AND DAD
Tracks: / Mum and dad.
7" Single: Released Feb '82, on Bushay, Catalogue no: **BFM 150**

SIXTH STREET
Tracks: / Sixth street / Sixth street (Inst.).
12" Single: Released Sep '86, on Bushay, Catalogue no: **BFM 107**

BOB MARLEY AND THE WAILERS - REDEMPTION SONG (Released on Island)

Markus, Ben

SEE ME CRY
Tracks: / See me cry / Promise to show.
7" Single: Released '87, on Ooze, Catalogue no: **OZ 3**

WHITE ROOM
7" Single: Released Aug '89, on Citation, Catalogue no: **CIT 101**

Marl, Marley

HE CUTS SO FRESH
Tracks: / He cuts so fresh / Bass game.
7" Single: Released 23 May '87, on MCA, by MCA Records. Catalogue no: **MCA 1135**
12" Single: Released 23 May '87, on MCA, by MCA Records. Catalogue no: **MCAT 1135**

Marley, Bob

Biographical details: This Jamaican singer, songwriter, guitarist and percussionist was the most important and famous reggae artist ever, and the best known Jamaican citizen of all time. He was born Robert Nesta Marley in St Anne's, Jamaica in 1945, the son of a British serviceman and a local woman. His father left the scene before he was born. Marley released his first single *Judge not* in 1961 at the age of 16, at a studio in his country's capital Kingston. Over the next twelve years, he experienced many ups and downs in his struggle to establish himself as a musical force. He had several major hits in his native land, notable *Simmerdown* and *Bend down low*, and a few flops. He made many friends including Peter Tosh and Bunny Wailer (the two key early members of Marley's band, The Wailers) and such pop-reggae stars as Jimmy Cliff, Desmond Dekker and Johnny Nash; but he was often ripped off by the vagaries of the Jamaican music industry. He experienced every stage of his nation's musical evolution through blue beat, ska, rock steady and ultimately reggae. He, like many of his fellow countrymen, became a devout follower of the Rastafarian religion. By 1973 he was a leading star in the Caribbean, and was including many religious themes in his music, and was becoming quite a political force; although the great love songs were always there, too.
The most vital step in Marley's career, and an important landmark in the course of reggae music as a whole, occurred in 1973. Johnny Nash had just had a Top 20 hit in both the US and UK with Bob's song *Stir it up*, and it seemed as if Marley was ready for success in the western world, Bob Marly & The Wailers signed with Island Records, the label owned by Jamaican-born entrepreneur Chris Blackwell. Starting with the albums *Catch a fire* and *Burnin'* (both 1973), he gave this Third World band the conventional western promotional and marketing treatment. Blackwell worked hard to make Marley a favourite among critics and rock musicians, a strategy which paid off handsomely when *I shot the sheriff* (a track from *Burnin*) became a US No.1 and a UK Top 10 single in 1974 for Eric Clapton. Bob Marley & The Wailers' cult status turned into UK chart success in 1975, when *No woman no cry* reached No.22 on the singles list and *Natty dread* and *Live at the Lyceum* entered the Lp chart. Recorded at the Lyceum in London, *No woman no cry* was the most exciting live single since Little Stevie Wonder's 1963 offering *Fingertips*. The electric atmosphere at those brilliant Lyceum shows have made them legendary events in modern musical history.
Between 1976 and 1980 the band consolidated their international status by chalking up a string of hit singles and albums, many of the tracks becoming classics. One of the albums even managed to hit the Top 10 in America, a nation normally impervious to reggae artists. With great skill, Bob Marley became an international superstar without compromising his music, religion or ideals. Surviving an assassination attempt in December 1976, he later organised a symbolic handshake between Jamaica's Prime Minister and Opposition Leader in front of 20,000 concert attendees in Kingston. Marley was awarded the Third World Peace Medal at the UN. In 1980 he was invited to perform at Zimbabwe's independence celebrations by incoming Prime Minister Robert Mugabe; this event inspired Stevie Wonder to pay truibute to Marley on his smash single *Master blaster jammin')*.
When Bob Marley met a tragically early death from cancer in May 1981 at the age of 36, he was given an official Jamaican funeral attended by the Prime Minister and Leader of the Opposition. Three years later, Island's *Legend* compilation Lp logged twelve weeks at No.1 on the British charts.(Bob MacDonald, Jan 1986).

BUFFALO SOLDIER
Tracks: / Buffalo soldier.
12" Single: Released Apr '83, on Island, by Island Records. Catalogue no: **12IS 108**
7" Single: Released Apr '83, on Island, by Island Records. Deleted Dec '88. Catalogue no: **IS 108**

CLASSIC TRACKS
CD 5": Released Nov '88, on Classic Tracks, Catalogue no: **CDEP 3 C**

COULD YOU BE LOVED
Tracks: / Could you be loved / One drop / Ride Natty ride.
12" Single: Released Nov '84, on Island, by Island Records. Deleted '87. Catalogue no: **12IS 210**
7" Single: Released Jun '80, on Island, by Island Records. Deleted '83. Catalogue no: **WIP 6610**
7" Pic: Released Nov '84, on Island, by Island Records. Deleted '87. Catalogue no: **ISP 210**
7" Single: Released Nov '84, on Island, by Island Records. Deleted '87. Catalogue no: **IS 210**

EXODUS (SINGLE)
Tracks: / Exodus.
7" Single: Released Jun '77, on Island, by Island Records. Deleted '80. Catalogue no: **WIP 6390**

IS THIS LOVE
Tracks: / Is this love.
7" Single: Released Feb '78, on Island, by Island Records. Deleted '81. Catalogue no: **WIP 6420**

JAMMING
Tracks: / Jamming / Punky reggae party.
7" Single: Released Dec '77, on Island, by Island Records. Deleted '80. Catalogue no: **WIP 6410**
12" Single: Released '88, on Island, by Island Records. Deleted Dec '88. Catalogue no: **12 WIP 6410**

NATURAL MYSTIC
Tracks: / Natural / Natural mystic (version).
12" Single: Released Jan '86, on Daddy Kool, by Daddy Kool Records. Deleted Jun '89. Catalogue no: **DK 12-102**

NO WOMAN NO CRY
Tracks: / No woman no cry / Kinky reggae.
12" Single: Released Jun '81, on Island, by Island Records. Catalogue no: **12WIP 6244**
7" Single: Released Sep '75, on Island, by Island Records. Deleted '78. Catalogue no: **WIP 6244**

ONE LOVE (SINGLE)
Tracks: / One love / So much trouble (in the world).
12" Single: Released Apr '84, on Island, by Island Records. Catalogue no: **12IS 169**
12" Pic: Released Apr '84, on Island, by Island Records. Catalogue no: **12ISP 169**
7" Single: Released Apr '84, on Island, by Island Records. Deleted '87. Catalogue no: **IS 169**

RAINBOW COUNTRY
Tracks: / Rainbow country.
12" Single: Released Aug '85, on Daddy Kool, by Daddy Kool Records. Deleted Jun '89. Catalogue no: **DK 12-101**

REDEMPTION SONG
Tracks: / Redemption song / Redemption song (pt 2).
7" Single: Released Oct '80, on Island, by Island Records. Deleted Oct '83. Catalogue no: **WIP 6653**

SATISFY MY SOUL
Tracks: / Satisfy my soul.
7" Single: Released Jun '78, on Island, by Island Records. Deleted '81. Catalogue no: **WIP 6440**

SO MUCH TROUBLE IN THE WORLD
Tracks: / So much trouble in the world.
7" Single: Released Oct '79, on Island, by Island Records. Deleted '82. Catalogue no: **WIP 6510**

SOUL SHAKEDOWN PARTY
Tracks: / Soul shakedown party.
12" Single: Released Oct '83, on Trojan, by Trojan Records. Deleted May '88. Catalogue no: **TROT 9074**
7" Single: Released Oct '83, on Trojan, by Trojan Records. Deleted May '88. Catalogue no: **TRO 9074**

THANK YOU LORD
Tracks: / Thank you lord / Wisdom.
7" Single: Released Jun '81, on Trojan, by Trojan Records. Deleted May '88. Catalogue no: **TRO 9065**

THREE LITTLE BIRDS
Tracks: / Three little birds .
12" Single: Released Jun '85, on Island, by Island Records. Catalogue no: **12IS 236**
7" Single: Released Jun '85, on Island, by Island Records. Catalogue no: **IS 236**
7" Single: Released Sep '80, on Island, by Island Records. Deleted '83. Catalogue no: **WIP 6641**

WAITING IN VAIN (see panel below)
Tracks: / Waiting in vain.
7" Single: Released Sep '77, on Island, by Island Records. Deleted '80. Catalogue no: **WIP 6402**
7" Single: Released Jun '84, on Island, by Island Records. Deleted '87. Catalogue no: **IS 180**

ZIMBABWE
Tracks: / Zimbabwe / Survival / Africa unite (Only on 12" single.) / Wake up and live (Only on 12" single.).
12" Single: Released Mar '80, on Island, by Island Records. Deleted '83. Catalogue no: **12WIP 6597**
7" Single: Released Mar '80, on Island, by Island Records. Deleted '83. Catalogue no: **WIP 6597**

Marley, Rita

GOOD GIRLS CULTURE
Tracks: / Good girls culture.
7" Single: Released Mar '85, on Island, by Island Records. Catalogue no: **IS 224**
12" Single: Released Mar '85, on Island, by Island Records. Catalogue no: **12IS 224**

MUSIC FOR THE WORLD
Tracks: / Music for the world.
12" Single: Released Aug '83, on Shanachie, by Shanachie Records (USA). Catalogue no: **SHAN 5007**

ONE DRAW
Tracks: / One draw.
12" Single: Released Nov '82, on Island, by Island Records. Catalogue no: **12WIP 6841**
7" Single: Released Nov '82, on Island, by Island Records. Catalogue no: **WIP 6841**

SO MUCH THINGS TO SAY
Tracks: / So much things to say / So much things to say (version).
12" Single: Released Jul '87, on White Label (1), Catalogue no: **RMT 1**

Marley, Ziggy

LEE AND MOLLY
Tracks: / Lee and Molly (single version) (On all versions) / Dreams of home (On all versions) / Lee and Molly (live version) (On CD & 12" only)
CD 5": Released '88, on Virgin, by Virgin Records. Catalogue no: **VSCD 1148**
7" Single: Released Nov '88, on Virgin, by Virgin Records. Catalogue no: **VS 1148**
12" Single: Released Nov '88, on Virgin, by Virgin Records. Catalogue no: **VST 1148**

LOOK WHO'S DANCING
Tracks: / Look who's dancing / Pains of life / Soul II soul (12" only)
CD 5": Released Aug '89, on Virgin (USA), by Virgin Records. Catalogue no: **VUSC 5**
7" Single: Released Sep '89, on Virgin (USA), by Virgin Records. Catalogue no: **VUSP 5**
7" Single: Released Aug '89, on Virgin

BOB MARLEY AND THE WAILERS - WAITING IN VAIN (Released on Island)

(USA), by Virgin Records. Catalogue no: **VUS 5**
12" Single: Released Aug '89, on Virgin (USA), by Virgin Records. Catalogue no: **VUSX 5**
12" Single: Released Aug '89, on Virgin (USA), by Virgin Records. Catalogue no: **VUST 5**

TOMORROW PEOPLE
Tracks: / Tomorrow people (dub this) (NOT on 7") / Tomorrow people (dub a pella) (NOT on 7") / We a guh some weh (On all versions) / Tomorrow people (reggae this remix) (NOT on 7") / Tomorrow people (7" only).
CD 5": Released Aug '88, on Virgin, by Virgin Records. Catalogue no: **VSCD 1049**
12" Pic: Released '88, on Virgin, by Virgin Records. Catalogue no: **VSTY 1049**
7" Single: Released May '88, on Virgin, by Virgin Records. Catalogue no: **VS 1049**
12" Single: Released May '88, on Virgin, by Virgin Records. Catalogue no: **VST 1049**

TUMBLIN' DOWN
Tracks: / Tumblin' down (edit) (On all versions) / Have you ever been to hell (On all versions) / Tumblin' down (extended) (On 12" only) / Tumblin' down (LP version) (On CD only) / Tomorrow people (live) (CD only).
12" Single: Released Aug '88, on Virgin, by Virgin Records. Catalogue no: **VST 1098**
7" Single: Released 22 Aug '88, on Virgin, by Virgin Records. Catalogue no: **VS 1098**
7" Single: Released Aug '88, on Virgin, by Virgin Records. Catalogue no: **VSG 1098**
CD 5": Released '88, on Virgin, by Virgin Records. Catalogue no: **VSCD 1098**

Marlow, John

SISTER SOUL
Tracks: / Sister soul / Turn the lights out.
7" Single: Released Dec '81, on Situation 2, by Beggars Banquet Records. Catalogue no: **SIT 12**

Marlow, Nicholas

CITY LIFE
Tracks: / City life.
7" Single: Released Apr '82, on Avatar, by Avatar Record Corporation. Catalogue no: **AAA 124**
12" Single: Released Apr '82, on Avatar, by Avatar Record Corporation. Catalogue no: **AAA 124 T**

Marlow, Robert

CALLING ALL DESTROYERS
Tracks: / Calling all destroyers / In retrospect.
7" Single: Released May '85, on Reset, Catalogue no: **7REST 6**

CLAUDETTE
Tracks: / Claudette.
7" Single: Released Jul '84, on Reset, Catalogue no: **7REST 4**
12" Single: Released Jul '84, on Reset, Catalogue no: **12REST 4**

FACE OF DORIAN GRAY
Tracks: / Face of Dorian Gray.
7" Single: Released Jul '83, on Reset, Catalogue no: **7 REST 1**
12" Single: Released Jul '83, on Reset, Catalogue no: **12 REST 1**

I JUST WANNA DANCE
Tracks: / I just wanna dance / No heart.
7" Single: Released Oct '83, on Reset, Catalogue no: **7 REST 3**
12" Single: Released Oct '83, on Reset, Catalogue no: **12 REST 3**

Marmalade

Biographical details: At the time of their greatest success, this British pop combo consisted of Junior Campbell, Par Fairley, Dean Ford, Graham Knight and Alan Whitehead. The group originally came into being in Glasgow in 1963 under the name Dean Ford & the Gaylords. They became big in Scotland during the mid-Sixties, and released several worthy but unsuccessful singles. Their failure to become a national UK chart force led to a change in 1967 - the group evolved into the Marmalade. They dropped their previous soul-styled, Motown influenced sound in favour of an out-and-out pop approach. They were rewarded in mid-1968 with their first chart entry - *Lovin' things* reached No.6 on the British singles list.
The Marmalade's next single was a slight disappointment but, in January 1969, they reached the UK No.1 slot with *Ob-la-di ob-la-da*. Mere days after this ultra-catchy, reggae-influenced song had first appeared on the Beatles *White album*, the Marmalade had rushed into the studio to record a cover version because it was such an obvious hit. They followed it with several more Top Tenners, including a pair of singles that both reached No.3 in 1970: *Reflections of my life* (also a Top 10 hit in America) and *Rainbow*. Both of those were co-written by guitarist/keyboardist Junior Campbell, whose departure in search of solo fame occurred soon afterwards. His replacement Hughie Nicholson was the sole author of their two final UK Top 10 singles, *Cousin Norman* (1971) and *Radancer* (1972), but then he also quit. His decison effectively killed the band's chart success, a situation accelerated by a News Of The World scandal story about the group's alleged sexual adventures during tours. This left their 'pleasant pop' image in tatters. With ever changing personel, the Marmalade remained in existence throughout the Seventies and into the Eighties, playing clubs and small halls. (Bob MacDonald, 22nd Jan 1986).

6 TRACK HITS
Tracks: / Ob la di ob la da / I shall be released / Summer in the city / Loving things / Wait for me / Baby make it soon.
7" EP: Released Aug '84, on Scoop 33, by Pickwick Records. Catalogue no: **7SR 5045**

BABY MAKE IT SOON
Tracks: / Baby make it soon.
7" Single: Released Jun '69, on CBS, by CBS Records. Deleted '72. Catalogue no: **CBS 4287**

BACK ON THE ROAD (SINGLE)
Tracks: / Back on the road.
7" Single: Released Nov '71, on Decca, by Decca Records. Deleted '74. Catalogue no: **F 13251**

COUSIN NORMAN
Tracks: / Cousin Norman.
7" Single: Released Sep '71, on Decca, by Decca Records. Deleted '74. Catalogue no: **F 13214**

FALLING APART AT THE SEAMS
Tracks: / Falling apart at the seams.
7" Single: Released Feb '76, on Target, by Target Records. Deleted '79. Catalogue no: **TGT 105**

GOLDEN SHREDS
Tracks: / Golden shreds.
7" Single: Released Nov '85, on Sounds Right, Catalogue no: **MSSR 4**
12" Single: Released Nov '85, on Sounds Right, Catalogue no: **MSSRT 4**

HEARTBREAKER
Tracks: / Heartbreaker.
7" Single: Released Jun '84, on Just, Catalogue no: **JUST 1**

LOVIN' THINGS
Tracks: / Lovin' things.
7" Single: Released May '68, on CBS, by CBS Records. Deleted '71. Catalogue no: **CBS 3412**

MY LITTLE ONE
Tracks: / My little one.
7" Single: Released Mar '71, on Decca, by Decca Records. Deleted '74. Catalogue no: **F 13135**

OB LA DI OB LA DA (SINGLE)
Tracks: / Ob la di ob la da.
7" Single: Released Dec '68, on CBS, by CBS Records. Deleted '71. Catalogue no: **CBS 3892**
7" Single: Released Jul '82, on Old Gold, by Old Gold Records. Deleted Jul '88. Catalogue no: **OG 9195**

RADANCER
Tracks: / Radancer.
7" Single: Released Apr '72, on Decca, by Decca Records. Deleted '75. Catalogue no: **F 13297**

RAINBOW
Tracks: / Rainbow.
7" Single: Released Jul '70, on Decca, by Decca Records. Deleted '73. Catalogue no: **F 13035**

REFLECTIONS OF MY LIFE
Tracks: / Reflections of my life.
7" Single: Released Dec '69, on Decca, by Decca Records. Deleted '72. Catalogue no: **F 12982**
7" Single: Released Oct '80, on Decca, by Decca Records. Deleted '88. Catalogue no: **F 13898**

REFLECTIONS OF MY LIFE (OLD GOLD)
Tracks: / Reflections of my life.
7" Single: Released Oct '83, on Old Gold, by Old Gold Records. Catalogue no: **OG 9334**

WAIT FOR ME MARIANNE
Tracks: / Wait for me Marianne.
7" Single: Released Oct '68, on CBS, by CBS Records. Deleted '71. Catalogue no: **CBS 3708**

Maroon Dogs

DARK NIGHTS FALLING
Tracks: / Dark nights falling / Play the game.
7" Single: Released Aug '84, on Dux, Catalogue no: **DUX 001**

Maroon Town

POUND & THE DOLLAR, THE
Tracks: / Pound & the dollar, The.
12" Single: Released Mar '89, on Staccato, Catalogue no: **12 RUDE 2**

Marquis De Sade

CRYSTAL GRIEFF
Tracks: / Crystal grieff.
7" Single: Released Jun '82, on Out Of Town, Catalogue no: **HOOT 8**

Marra, Michael

LIKE A FRENCH MAN
Tracks: / Like a french man / There's no such thing.
7" Single: Released Aug '81, on Polydor, by Polydor Ltd. Deleted '84. Catalogue no: **POSP 301**

MIDAS TOUCH (SINGLE)
Tracks: / Midas touch / Sleepwalking.
7" Single: Released Jan '80, on Polydor, by Polydor Ltd. Deleted Jan '83. Catalogue no: **2095195**

Marrett, Bunny

TIMES ARE GETTING HARDER
Tracks: / Times are getting harder.
12" Single: Released Aug '80, on ShocWave, Catalogue no: **SRP 0004**

Marriage Of Convenience

MY YOUNG DREAMS
Tracks: / My young dreams.
7" Single: Released Oct '85, on Stranglers Information Service, Catalogue no: **SIS 002**

Marrio, Steve

UM UM SONG, THE
Tracks: / Um um song, The.
7" Single: Released Jul '89, on Trax, by Filmtrax Records. Catalogue no: **7TX 8**

Marriott, Steve

WAT'CHA GONNA DO ABOUT IT
Tracks: / Wat'cha gonna do about it.
7" Single: Released Jan '85, on Aura Records, by Aura Records. Catalogue no: **AUS 145**

M/A/R/R/S

PUMP UP THE VOLUME
Tracks: / Pump up the volume / Anitina (first time I see she dance).
Note: BAD 707R - 12" remix.
12" Single: Released Sep '87, on 4AD, by 4AD Records. Deleted Jul '88. Catalogue no: **BAD 707**
CD 5": Released Oct '87, on 4AD, by 4AD Records. Deleted Jul '88. Catalogue no: **BAD 707 CD**
7" Single: Released Sep '87, on 4AD, by 4AD Records. Deleted Jul '88. Catalogue no: **AD 707**
12" Single: Released Sep '87, on 4AD, by 4AD Records. Deleted Jul '88. Catalogue no: **BAD 707R**

PUMP UP THE VOLUME (U.S. REMIX)
Tracks: / Pump up the volume.
12" Single: Released Nov '87, on 4th & Broadway (USA), by Island Records (USA). Catalogue no: **BWAY 452**

Mars

IN THE HEAT OF THE NIGHT
Tracks: / In the heat of the night.
7" Single: Released Sep '85, on Silicon, by Silicon Records. Catalogue no: **SIL 1**

METALDROME
Tracks: / Metaldrome.
7" EP: Released Sep '87, on Azra (USA), by Azra International (USA). Catalogue no: **A 31**

Mars, Johnny

BORN UNDER A BAD SIGN
Tracks: / Born under a bad sign.
7" Single: Released Jul '84, on Lamborghini, by Lamborghini Records. Catalogue no: **LSU 2**
7" Single: Released Oct '81, on Ace, by Ace Records. Deleted Jun '88. Catalogue no: **NS 73**
12" Single: Released Jul '84, on Lamborghini, by Lamborghini Records. Catalogue no: **12LSU 2**

HOT LIPS BOOGIE
Tracks: / Hot lips boogie.
7" Single: on Sundance, by Sundance Records. Catalogue no: **SUND 004**

Mars, Jonathan

DON'T PRETEND
Tracks: / Don't pretend / Searching.
7" Single: Released Sep '80, on Atlantic, by WEA Records. Deleted '83. Catalogue no: **K 11557**

Marsden, Bernie

Biographical details: This British rock guitarist and singer achieved a one-off UK chart entry in 1981, reaching No.71 with his solo album *Look at me now*. He has however, been better known as guitarist with several bands, notable Whitesnake. In chronological order, Marsden's most important exploits included membership of an early incarnation of UFO (1972-73), playing in Cozy Powell's hitmaking band (1974), membership of Babe Ruth 91975-76), backing the Deep Purple spinoff band Paice, Ashton & Lord (1976-77) and membership of ex-Purple vocalist David Coverdale's highly successful Whitesnake (1978-81). (Bob MacDonald, 22nd Jan 1986).

SAD CLOWN
Tracks: / Sad clown / You and me.
7" Single: Released May '81, on Parlophone, by EMI Records. Deleted May '84. Catalogue no: **R 6047**

Marsden, Gerry

FERRY CROSS THE MERSEY
Tracks: / Ferry cross the Mersey.
7" Single: Released Apr '89, on PWL, by PWL Records. Catalogue no: **PWL 41**

Marsden, Lynne

COCKTAILS FOR TWO
Tracks: / Cocktails for two.
7" Single: Released May '85, on Derelict, Catalogue no: **DR 1**

Marseille

KITES
Tracks: / Kites / Some like it hot.
7" Single: Released Feb '80, on Mountain, Deleted Feb '85. Catalogue no: **TOP 51**

WALKING ON A HIGHWIRE
Tracks: / Walking on a highwire.
7" Single: Released Sep '84, on Ultranoise, by Albion Records. Catalogue no: **WALK 1**

Mars-Fenwick Band

ASH AIN'T NOTHING BUT TRASH
Tracks: / Ash ain't nothing but trash / Smoking out the Barons.
7" Single: Released Jun '86, on President, by President Records. Catalogue no: **PT 548**
12" Single: Released Jun '86, on President, by President Records. Catalogue no: **PT 12-548**

FIRE IN THE CITY (SINGLE)
Tracks: / Fire in the city.
7" Single: Released Feb '87, on President, by President Records. Catalogue no: **PT 556**

Marsh, Carl

EVERY BONE IN MY BODY
Tracks: / Every bone in my body.
CD 5": Released Jun '89, on Polydor, by Polydor Ltd. Catalogue no: **CAMCD 1**
7" Single: Released Jun '89, on Polydor, by Polydor Ltd. Catalogue no: **CAM 1**
12" Single: Released Jun '89, on Polydor, by Polydor Ltd. Catalogue no: **CAMX 1**

HERE COMES THE CRUSH
Tracks: / Here comes the crush
CD 5": Released Apr '89, on Polydor, by Polydor Ltd. Catalogue no: **CRUCD 1**
7" Single: Released Apr '89, on Polydor, by Polydor Ltd. Catalogue no: **CRUSH 1**
12" Single: Released Apr '89, on Polydor, by Polydor Ltd. Catalogue no: **CRUSX 1**

Marsh, Peter

DON'T BE FOOLISH
Tracks: / Don't be foolish / Doesn't matter.
7" Single: Released Jun '80, on Polydor, by Polydor Ltd. Deleted '83. Catalogue no: **2059251**

YOU SAY YOU WANNA LOVE ME
Tracks: / You say you wanna love me
7" Single: Released Mar '81, on Polydor, by Polydor Ltd. Deleted Mar '84. Catalogue no: **POSP 210**

Marsh, Stevie

ONLY BOY IN THE WORLD, THE
Tracks: / Only boy in the world, The.
7" Single: Released Dec '59, on Decca, by Decca Records. Deleted '62. Catalogue no: **F 11181**

Marshall, Al

BE MY GUEST
Tracks: / Be my guest / First time.
7" Single: Released Jun '83, on Tent, by BMG Records (UK). Catalogue no: **TENT 3**
7" Single: Released Mar '82, on Pavilion (USA), by CBS Records. Catalogue no: **PAV 402**

DANCE WITH ME
Tracks: / Dance with me.
7" Single: Released Jun '82, on Pavilion (USA), by CBS Records. Catalogue no: **PAV 403**
12" Single: Released Jun '82, on Pavilion (USA), by CBS Records. Catalogue no: **PAVT 403**

I'M GONNA MAKE THIS A NIGHT THAT YOU....
Tracks: / I'm gonna make this a night that

KEITH MARSHALL - SINCE I LOST MY BABY (Released on Arrival)

you... / I like the way you dance with me.
7" Single: Released Jan '83, on Tent, by BMG Records (UK). Catalogue no: **TENT 1**
12" Single: Released Jan '83, on Tent, by BMG Records (UK). Cat no: **TENTT 1**

Marshall Doktors

WORRYING KIND, THE
Tracks: / Worrying kind, The.
7" Single: Released Nov '80, on Rewind, Catalogue no: **REWIND 6**

Marshall Hain

Biographical details: Keyboardist/songwriter Julian Marshall and vocalist Kit Hain were a British pop duo who sprang from obscurity to stardom in the summer of 1978 with their straightforward and insidiously catchy single *Dancing in the city*. This reached No.3 in the UK, and was included on their promising debut album *Free ride*. The follow-up single *Coming home* was arguably one of the best records of the year - Kit used her beautiful voice to enchanting effect on this accomplished ballad. Unfortunatly, it peaked at No.39 and nothing more was heard from Marshall Hain. Kit Hain disappeared from sight altogether, but Julian Marshall found another female singer named Deborah Berg and re-emerged in 1982 under the billing Eye to eye. This duo achieved a US Top 40 single with *Nice girls*, but then faded away after a couple of albums. OVer the years, Julian's inability to find long-term success has been something of a mystery. His output has been a strong pop-orientated vein, and he has used such talented producers as Chris Neil (for Marshall Hain) and Gary Katz of Steely Dan fame (for Eye to Eye). (Bob MacDonald, 22nd Jan 1986).

COMING HOME
Tracks: / Coming home.
7" Single: Released Oct '78, on Harvest (1), by EMI Records. Deleted '81. Catalogue no: **HAR 5168**

DANCING IN THE CITY
Tracks: / Dancing in the city
12" Single: Released Aug '87, on Columbia, by EMI Records. Catalogue no: **12CD 9159**
7" Single: Released Jun '78, on Harvest (1), by EMI Records. Deleted '81. Catalogue no: **HAR 5157**
7" Single: Released Aug '87, on Columbia, by EMI Records. Catalogue no: **CD 9159**

Marshall, John

BALL OF CONFUSION
Tracks: / Ball of confusion / Down to Earth.
12" Single: Released Apr '89, on WEA, by WEA Records. Catalogue no: **WZ 389T**
CD 5": Released Apr '89, on WEA, by WEA Records. Catalogue no: **WZ 389CD**
7" Single: Released Apr '89, on WEA, by WEA Records. Catalogue no: **WZ 389**

BREAKING DOWN THE WALLS (also under Charm School)
Tracks: / Breaking down the walls / Don't want to know.
7" Single: Released Jan '88, on WEA, by WEA Records. Catalogue no: **YZ 160**
12" Single: Released Jan '88, on WEA, by WEA Records. Catalogue no: **YZ 160 T**

ONE BY ONE
Tracks: / One by one / Corridor.
7" Single: Released Feb '89, on WEA, by WEA Records. Catalogue no: **YZ 306**
12" Single: Released Feb '89, on WEA, by WEA Records. Catalogue no: **YZ 306 T**

Marshall, Joy

MORE I SEE YOU, THE
Tracks: / More I see you, The.
7" Single: Released Jun '66, on Decca, by Decca Records. Deleted '69. Catalogue no: **F 12422**

Marshall, Junior

MASSIVE MAN SKANK
Tracks: / Massive man skank.
12" Single: Released Oct '82, on Roots Rockers, Catalogue no: **RR 001**

Marshall, Keith

Biographical details: This British singer first enjoyed success during 1974-75 as a member of a UK teeny-rock band called Hello, who attempted to be a harder sounding version of the Bay City Rollers. Hello scored two Top 10 singles in Britain - *Tell him* was a revival of the 1963's chestnut, which went higher up the UK chart than either of the original hit renditions by the Exciters or Billie Davis; and *New York groove* 'borrowed' a riff from a recent hit by Hamilton Bohannon, *Disco stomp*. Both of the Hello hits were produced by Gary Glitter's songwriting partner and producer Mike Leander. *New York groove* was taken into the US Top 20 in 1979 by Kiss guitarist Ace Frehley. By 1976 Hello had waved goodbye to the charts. Marshall persued a solo career in the Eighties, which yielded just one chart success. *Only crying* reached No.12 on the UK singles list in the Spring of 1981. This breezy, laid-back pop single won considerable acclaim, but Keith could not hit upon the right follow-up. (22nd Jan 1986).

BITTEREST TASTE
Tracks: / Bitterest taste / She's in love.
7" Single: Released Apr '84, on Arrival, by Blaylock Management Ltd.. Deleted '86. Catalogue no: **PIK 14**

DEAN
Tracks: / Dean / Best of me.
7" Single: Released Jul '81, on Arrival, by Blaylock Management Ltd.. Deleted '86. Catalogue no: **PIK 6**

LIGHT YEARS
Tracks: / Light years / There goes my heart.
7" Single: Released May '82, on Arrival, by Blaylock Management Ltd.. Deleted '86. Catalogue no: **PIK 7**

ONLY CRYING
Tracks: / Only crying.
7" Single: Released Mar '81, on Arrival, by Blaylock Management Ltd.. Deleted '86. Catalogue no: **PIK 2**

SILVER AND DIAMONDS
Tracks: / Silver and diamonds.
7" Single: Released Jun '81, on Arrival, by Blaylock Management Ltd.. Deleted '86. Catalogue no: **PIK 4**

SINCE I LOST MY BABY (see panel on left)
Tracks: / Since I lost my baby / Fool's gold.
7" Single: Released Apr '83, on Arrival, by Blaylock Management Ltd.. Deleted '86. Catalogue no: **PIK 10**

Marshall Larry

HAPPINESS
Tracks: / Happiness / Happiest version.
12" Single: Released May '84, on Iyah Bingi, by Iyah Bingi Records. Catalogue no: **ND 002**

Marshall, Louisa

STOP
Tracks: / Stop.
7" Single: Released Feb '85, on Bo-Peep, Catalogue no: **BOP 100**

Marshall, Meri D

MY OBSESSION
Tracks: / My obsession.
7" Single: Released Jun '85, on WEA (International), by WEA Records. Catalogue no: **X 9074**
12" Single: Released Jun '85, on WEA (International), by WEA Records. Catalogue no: **X 9074T**

Marshall, Steve

FEEL NO WAY
Tracks: / Feel no way.
7" Single: Released 15 Aug '86, on State Of Emergency, Catalogue no: **SOE 001**

Marshall Stretch

CUT THE MUSIC
Tracks: / Cut the music.
7" Single: Released Nov '88, on Shed, by Shed Records. Catalogue no: **SHED 1**

Marshall, Tom

FILM STAR
Tracks: / Film star / Rock 'n' roll is dead.
7" Single: Released '87, on B & C, by Trojan Records. Deleted May '88. Catalogue no: **BCS 23**

Marshall, Wayne

GIVE ME THE FIX
Tracks: / Give me the fix / Mike in the hand.
12" Single: Released Dec '85, on Jah Tubbys, Catalogue no: **JT 013**

I LOVE
Tracks: / I love / Fear of Jah Jah.
7" Single: Released Oct '86, on Greensleeves, by Greensleeves Records. Catalogue no: **QP1**

PON A LEVEL
Tracks: / Pon a level / Dance baby dance / Pon a level (version).
12" Single: Released Jul '87, on Quadro Pack, Catalogue no: **QP 2**

WILD GILBERT
Tracks: / Wild Gilbert.
7" Single: Released Oct '88, on John Dread Production, Catalogue no: **DPD 12**

Marshmellow Overcoat

WHAT'S GOING ON
Tracks: / What's going on / Traffic hug / Hell.
12" Single: Released Mar '85, on Skysaw, by Skysaw Records. Catalogue no: **SKY 1**

Marte, M. C.

BEYOND CONTROL
Tracks: / Beyond control / Female force.
12" Single: Released Sep '89, on G.T.I. Records, by G.T.I. Music. Catalogue no: **GTI 006 T**

Martell Brothers

LET ME TAKE YOU IN MY ARMS AGAIN
Tracks: / Let me take you in my arms again / Let me take you in my arms again (remix).
12" Single: Released 17 Oct '87, on Mai, Deleted '88. Catalogue no: **12 MAR 1**
7" Single: Released 17 Oct '87, on Mai, Deleted '88. Catalogue no: **7 MAR 1**

Martell, Lena

Biographical details: This British singer is a stalwart of the middle-of-the-road market. Though not as talented or famous as a Shirley Bassey or a Petula Clark, her tasteful interpretations of MOR and pop hits have earned her a good living on cabaret and television, and have given her success from time to time on the UK album chart during the Seventies and Eighties. She has performed all over the world. Suddenly, in the autumn of 1979, Martell achieved the unexpected bonus of a smash single. *One day at a time*, a Kris Kristofferson number, logged three weeks at No.1 in Britain. This was a typical example of the gospel material that has always been a strong ingredient of her repertoire. The singles chart is not normally the preserve of easy listening artists, but Lena's success with *One day at a time* spurred her Lp sales considerably. (Bob MacDonald, 22nd Jan 1986).

6 TRACK HITS
Tracks: / One day at a time / Beautiful noise / Bridge over troubled water / I believe / If we only have love / Let me try again.
7" EP: Released Sep '83, on Scoop 33, by Pickwick Records. Catalogue no: **7SR 5010**
Cassingle: Released Sep '83, on Scoop 33, by Pickwick Records. Catalogue no: **7SC 5010**

DON'T CRY FOR ME ARGENTINA
Tracks: / Don't cry for me argentina / Don't remember your name.
7" Single: Released Jan '80, on Pye, Deleted Jan '85. Catalogue no: **7P157**

ONE DAY AT A TIME
Tracks: / One day at a time.
7" Single: Released Oct '79, on PRT, by Castle Communications Records. Catalogue no: **7N 46021**

ONE DAY AT A TIME (OLD GOLD)
Tracks: / One day at a time.
7" Single: Released Apr '83, on Old Gold, by Old Gold Records. Catalogue no: **OG 9295**

PRAY WITH ME
Tracks: / Pray with me / When you were sweet sixteen.
7" Single: Released Nov '81, on UNKNOWN, Deleted Nov '84. Catalogue no: **7P 225**

WHY ME LORD
Tracks: / Why me Lord / Melancholy Sunday.
7" Single: Released Nov '80, on Pye, Deleted Nov '83. Catalogue no: **7P 209**

YOU'RE MY HERO Wind beneath my wings, The
Tracks: / You're my hero (wind beneath my wings).
7" Single: Released Nov '84, on Country House, by Scotdisc Records. Catalogue no: **BGC 7S 379**

Martha & The Muffins

Biographical details: At the time of their greatest success, this Canadian band consisted of lead vocalist/keyboards player Martha Johnson plus Carl Finkle, Mark Gane, Tim Gane, Andy Haas and Martha Ladly. Like most Canadian acts, Martha & the Muffins did not find too many openings in their native country's somewhat uninspiring rock scene. They came to Britain to make it and found that in 1980, the UK climate was receptive towards their brand of slightly irreverant, avant-garde pop-rock. Their extremely catchy single *Echo Beach* became a Top 10 hit. It's parent album *Metro music* reached No.34. But despite continued press interest, no further chart entries were forthcoming. Guitarist Mark Gane, the writer of *Echo Beach*, could not come up with any more classics. With a changing line-up, the group faded into obscurity during the course of their next three albums. Then in 1984, Martha & the Muffins re-emerged under the new, abbreviated billing M+M. Their Gane/Johnson-penned single *Black stations/white stations* became a major club hit in the States, and reached No.46 on the UK pop chart. This song was an inspired protest against the American radio system, which places different genres of music into different 'formats' so that, for example, a country music station plays non-stop country 24 hours a day. Under this system, it is possible for a black soul record to sell a million in 'black' shops while only scraping the pop chart. It came as little surprise that the M+M was only a dance hit in the US, and that it was widely ignored by radio stations there. Once again the band failed to consolidate, and faded from view. They even found that their M+M monicker was poached by a pair of US dance remixers, whose surnames happened to begin with that letter. (Bob MacDonald, 22st Jan 1986).

DANSEPARC Everyday it's tomorrow
Tracks: / Danseparc.
12" Single: Released May '83, on RCA, by BMG Records (UK). Catalogue no: **RCAT 331**
7" Single: Released May '83, on RCA, by BMG Records (UK). Catalogue no: **RCA 331**

ECHO BEACH
Tracks: / Echo beach / Teddy the dink.
7" Single: Released Mar '80, on Dindisc, by Virgin Records. Deleted '83. Catalogue no: **DIN 9**

ECHO BEACH (OLD GOLD)
Tracks: / Echo beach / Women around the world at work.
7" Single: Released Nov '88, on Old Gold, by Old Gold Records. Catalogue no: **OG 9824**

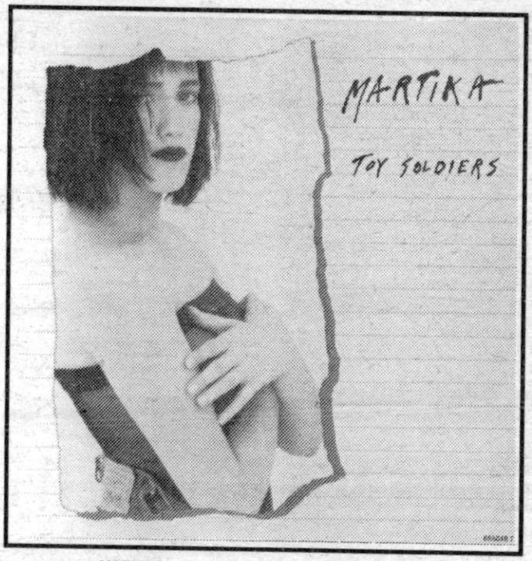

MARTIKA - TOY SOLDIERS (Released on CBS)

SAIGON
Tracks: / Saigon / Copacabana.
7" Single: Released May '80, on Dindisc, by Virgin Records. Deleted May '83. Catalogue no: **DIN 17**

Martian Dance

SITUATION
Tracks: / Situation / Boys in black.
7" Single: Released Apr '81, on EMI, by EMI Records. Deleted Apr '84. Catalogue no: **EMI 5163**

Martian School Girls

MOTION
Tracks: / Motion / La la song.
7" Single: Released Jun '81, on Albion, by Albion Records. Catalogue no: **ION 1015**

Martika

I FEEL THE EARTH MOVE
Tracks: / I feel the earth move / Alibis.
CD 5": Released Sep '89, on CBS, by CBS Records. Catalogue no: **655 294 2**
Cassingle: Released Sep '89, on CBS, by CBS Records. Catalogue no: **655 294 4**
12" Pic: Released Sep '89, on CBS, by CBS Records. Catalogue no: **655 294 8**
7" Pic: Released Sep '89, on CBS, by CBS Records. Catalogue no: **655 294 0**
7" Single: Released Sep '89, on CBS, by CBS Records. Catalogue no: **655 294 7**
12" Single: Released Sep '89, on CBS, by CBS Records. Catalogue no: **655 294 6**

MORE THAN YOU KNOW
Tracks: / More than you know / Alibis / More than you know (house mix pts. 1 & 2) (Only on 12" and CD single.).
Note: Remixed by Jellybean.
CD 5": Released 20 Mar '89, on CBS, by CBS Records. Catalogue no: **654520 2**
12" Single: Released 20 Mar '89, on CBS, by CBS Records. Catalogue no: **654520 8**
7" Single: Released 20 Mar '89, on CBS, by CBS Records. Catalogue no: **654520 7**
12" Single: Released Apr '89, on CBS, by CBS Records. Catalogue no: **TIKA 12**
12" Single: Released Nov '88, on Columbia, by EMI Records. Catalogue no: **4408 135**
12" Single: Released Apr '89, on CBS, by CBS Records. Catalogue no: **654520 1**

TOY SOLDIERS (See panel above)
Tracks: / Toy soldiers / Exchange of hearts / It's not what you're doing.
CD 5": Released Jul '89, on CBS, by CBS Records. Catalogue no: **655 049 2**
7" Single: Released Jul '89, on CBS, by CBS Records. Catalogue no: **655 049 7**
Cassingle: Released Jul '89, on CBS, by CBS Records. Catalogue no: **655 049 4**
7" Single: Released Jul '89, on CBS, by CBS Records. Catalogue no: **655 049 0**
12" Single: Released Jul '89, on CBS, by CBS Records. Catalogue no: **655 049 8**
12" Single: Released Jul '89, on CBS, by CBS Records. Catalogue no: **655 049 1**

Martin, Ansell

I'LL BE IN THE JUNGLE
Tracks: / I'll be in the jungle.
7" Single: on EMI, by EMI Records. Catalogue no: **EMI 5402**

Martin, Dadi

BODY POPPIN
Tracks: / Body poppin'.
7" Single: Released Jun '84, on VP, Catalogue no: **VPS 1002**
12" Single: Released Jun '84, on VP, Catalogue no: **VPT 1002**

Martin, Dean

Biographical details: This American singer, comedian and actor was born Dino Crocetti in Steubenville, Ohio in 1917. He held a wide array of occupations - boxer, steel worker, coal miner, gas station attendant, card dealer, drugstore clerk and mill hand - before he finally entered showbusiness professionally at the age of 27. After successfully singing in Cleveland and New York, he achieved a turning point in his career in 1946 by teaming up with the little known comedian Jerry Lewis. For the next ten years they were one of the hottest comedy-double acts in America. In additon to their stage, radio and television success, they made 16 movies together; the first was *My friend Irma* in 1949. During the late Forties and early Fifties, Martin enjoyed a successful subsidiary solo career as a singer - *I'll always love you, If, You belong to me, Kiss, That's amore, Sway* and *How so you speak to an angel* were amongst his hits. Martin and Lewis parted company in 1956, the same year that Dean had his biggest ever hit single with *Memories are made of this*. Perfect for his relaxed middle-of-the-road style, this record logged five weeks at No.1 in the US and four weeks on top in the UK. He had several more hits in the late Fifties, notable *Return to me* (No.4 in US, No.2 in UK) and *Volare* (No.12 in US and No.2 in UK). Meanwhile, he embarked on a solo film career, with big success in straight as well as comedy roles.
After six years off the charts, Martin scored a US No.1 and a UK No.11 hit with *Everybody loves somebody* in 1964. The success of this jovial ditty led to Dean getting his own weekly TV series in America, which lasted for nine series until 1974. The hit records dried up in the late Sixties, although his final British chart single was one of his biggest - *Gentle on my mind* reached the UK No.2 position in 1969. Dean Martin's notoriety as an excessive drinker has made him something of a joke figure in many quarters; but his long, very varied and highly successful career in showbusiness should not be obscured. (Bob MacDonald, 22nd Jan 1988).

DON'T GIVE UP ON ME
Tracks: / Don't give up on me / Drinking.
7" Single: Released Jul '83, on Warner Bros., by WEA Records. Catalogue no: **W 9757**

DOOR IS STILL OPEN TO MY HEART, THE
Tracks: / Door is still open, The.
7" Single: Released Nov '64, on Reprise, by WEA Records. Deleted '67. Catalogue no: **R 20307**

EVERYBODY LOVES SOMEBODY
Tracks: / Everybody loves somebody.
CD 5": Released Sep '87, on Compact Collection, Catalogue no: **76024**
7" Single: Released '80, on Reprise (USA), Catalogue no: **LR 0237**
7" Single: Released Aug '64, on Reprise, by WEA Records. Deleted '67. Catalogue no: **R 20281**

GENTLE ON MY MIND (SINGLE)
Tracks: / Gentle on my mind.
7" Single: Released Feb '69, on Reprise, by WEA Records. Deleted '72. Catalogue no: **RS 23343**

HOW DO YOU SPEAK TO AN ANGEL
Tracks: / How do you speak to an angel.
7" Single: Released Oct '54, on Capitol, by EMI Records. Deleted '57. Catalogue no: **CL 14150**

INNAMORATA
Tracks: / Innamorata.
7" Single: Released Apr '56, on Capitol, by EMI Records. Deleted '59. Catalogue no: **CL 14507**

KISS
Tracks: / Kiss.
7" Single: Released Sep '53, on Capitol, by EMI Records. Deleted '56. Catalogue no: **CL 13893**

LET ME GO LOVER
Tracks: / Let me go lover.
7" Single: Released Feb '55, on Capitol, by EMI Records. Deleted '58. Catalogue no: **CL 14226**

MAMBO ITALIANO
Tracks: / Mambo Italiano.
7" Single: Released Feb '55, on Capitol, by EMI Records. Deleted '58. Catalogue no: **CL 14227**

MAN WHO PLAYS THE MANDALINO, THE
Tracks: / Man who plays the mandalino, The.
7" Single: Released Mar '57, on Capitol, by EMI Records. Deleted '60. Catalogue no: **CL 14690**

MEMORIES ARE MADE OF THIS (ORIGINAL)
Tracks: / Memories are made of this.
7" Single: Released Feb '56, on Capitol, by EMI Records. Deleted '59. Catalogue no: **CL 14523**

MEMORIES ARE MADE OF THIS (SINGLE)
Tracks: / Memories are made of this / Return to me.
7" Single: Released Apr '87, on Old Gold, by Old Gold Records. Deleted Sep '89. Catalogue no: **OG 9715**

NAUGHTY LADY OF SHADY LANE
Tracks: / Naughty lady of shady lane.
7" Single: Released Jan '55, on Capitol, by EMI Records. Deleted '58. Catalogue no: **CL 14226**

RETURN TO ME
Tracks: / Return to me.
7" Single: Released Jun '58, on Capitol, by EMI Records. Deleted '61. Catalogue no: **CL 14844**

RIO BRAVO
Tracks: / Rio Bravo.
7" Single: Released Apr '83, on EMI (France), by EMI Records. Catalogue no: **2C 008 81168**

SWAY
Tracks: / Sway.
7" Single: Released Oct '54, on Capitol, by EMI Records. Deleted '57. Catalogue no: **CL 14138**

THAT'S AMORE
Tracks: / That's amore (Other side is It must be him - Vikki Carr.) / It must be him.
7" Single: Released May '88, on Capitol, by EMI Records. Deleted Nov '88. Catalogue no: **CL 492**

THAT'S AMORE (SINGLE)
Tracks: / That's amore.
7" Single: Released Jan '54, on Capitol, by EMI Records. Deleted '57. Catalogue no: **CL 14008**

UNDER THE BRIDGES OF PARIS
Tracks: / Under the bridges of Paris.
7" Single: Released Apr '55, on Capitol, by EMI Records. Deleted '58. Catalogue no: **CL 14255**

VOLARE
Tracks: / Volare.
7" Single: Released Aug '58, on Capitol, by EMI Records. Deleted '61. Catalogue no: **CL 14910**

YOUNG AND FOOLISH
Tracks: / Young and foolish.
7" Single: Released Mar '56, on Capitol, by EMI Records. Deleted '59. Catalogue no: **CL 14519**

Martin, Eric

INFORMATION
Tracks: / Information / I can't stop the fire.
7" Single: Released Feb '86, on Food For Thought, by Music For Nations Records. Catalogue no: **KUT 119**

Martin, Gary

COMPUTER
Tracks: / Computer / I'll give you all you ask.
7" Single: Released Mar '81, on Sonet, by Sonet Records. Deleted Mar '84. Catalogue no: **SON 2218**

Martin, Horace

AFRICA IS CALLING
Tracks: / Africa is calling / Saturday night jamboree.
12" Single: Released Apr '82, on African Youth Music, Catalogue no: **AY 001**

SUZIE
Tracks: / Suzie / Give me the vibes.
12" Single: Released Jan '87, on Music Track, Catalogue no: **D 003**

TALKIN BOUT BOOPS
Tracks: / Talkin bout Boops / Man fi you.
12" Single: Released May '86, on Reggae City, Catalogue no: **RCD 002**

TYPE OF LOVING
Tracks: / No wanga gut / Neighbourhood living / Type of loving / Mi lover.
12" Single: Released Jul '87, on Island, by Island Records. Deleted Apr '88. Catalogue no: **12IS 333**

V MAN
Tracks: / V man.
12" Single: Released Nov '85, on High Power, Catalogue no: **HPD 007**

ZUGGY ZUGGY
Tracks: / Zuggy zuggy / Sweet something.
12" Single: Released Jul '83, on Negus Roots, Catalogue no: **NERT 017**

Martin, Howard

I WILL SURVIVE
Tracks: / I will survive.
12" Single: Released 22 Apr '86, on Leeds Independent (LIL), by Revolver Records. Catalogue no: **LIL 12004**

Martin, Janis

MY BOY ELVIS
Tracks: / My boy Elvis / Cracker Jack / Love me love / Good love.
7" EP: Released Jul '80, on RCA, by BMG Records (UK). Deleted Jul '83. Catalogue no: **PE 9494**

Martin, Juan

Biographical details: This Spanish classical guitar virtuoso steadily built-up a reputation during the late Seventies and early Eighties as a player in the same class as the likes of John Williams. In early 1984 Martin reached No.10 on the UK singles chart with his *Love theme from the Thorn Birds*, thanks to the exposure that the music received on the then much talked about Richard Chamberlain TV drama serial. Martin appeared on Top of the Pops, and climbed thirteen places higher than Henry Mancini's main theme from the same series. The success of the single spurred Martin's Lp sales considerably. (Bob MacDonald, 23rd Jan 1986).

DAVID'S SONG
Tracks: / David's song.
7" Single: Released Nov '83, on WEA, by WEA Records. Catalogue no: **X 9602**

DESIRE CAUGHT BY THE TAIL
Tracks: / Desire caught by the tail / Afficionado.
7" Single: Released Nov '82, on Polydor, by Polydor Ltd. Deleted Nov '85. Catalogue no: **POSP 349**

FLIGHT TO PARADISE
Tracks: / Flight to paradise / Desired.
7" Single: Released Jan '85, on WEA, by WEA Records. Catalogue no: **YZ 19**

HARLEQUIN
Tracks: / Harlequin / Three musicians.
7" Single: Released Jan '82, on Polydor, by Polydor Ltd. Deleted Jan '85. Catalogue no: **POSP 403**

ROMEO & JULIET LOVE THEME
Tracks: / Romeo and Juliet / Desired.
7" Single: Released Apr '84, on WEA, by WEA Records. Catalogue no: **YZ 4**

THORN BIRDS - LOVE THEME
Tracks: / Thorn Birds - love theme / Last farewell.
7" Single: Released Jan '84, on WEA, by WEA Records. Deleted '87. Catalogue no: **X 9518**

Martin, Ken

ALL THE WAY
Tracks: / All the way.
12" Single: Released 31 Jul '89, on Briggie C, Catalogue no: **BC 009**

Martin, Kenny

NEVER KNOW WHAT YOU GOT
Tracks: / Never know what you got.
12" Single: Released 20 Mar '89, on Body Music, by Nuclear Records. Catalogue no: **BZT 018**

Martin, Linda

IMPOSSIBLE TO DO
Tracks: / Impossible to do / Impossible to do (trumpet solo version).
7" Single: Released Jan '89, on Plaza, by Plaza Records. Catalogue no: **PZA 041**
12" Single: Released Jan '89, on Plaza, by Plaza Records. Catalogue no: **PZA 041T**

LIFFEY TINKER
Tracks: / Liffey tinker.
7" Single: Released Jul '87, on Plaza, by Plaza Records. Catalogue no: **PZA 030**

Martin, Marilyn

NIGHT MOVES
Tracks: / Night moves / Wildest dreams.
12" Single: Released May '86, on Atlantic, by WEA Records. Catalogue no: **A 9465 T**
7" Single: Released May '86, on Atlantic, by WEA Records. Catalogue no: **A 9465**

POSSESSIVE LOVE
Tracks: / Possessive love / Homeless.
7" Single: Released Mar '88, on Atlantic, by WEA Records. Catalogue no: **A 9128**
12" Single: Released Mar '88, on Atlantic, by WEA Records. Catalogue no: **A 9128 T**

Martin & Martin

JUST ANOTHER LITTLE GIRL
Tracks: / Just another little girl / Dancin' on your own.
7" Single: Released Apr '84, on Hippodrome, by Hippodrome Records. Catalogue no: **HIPPO 5**

Martin, Mary

FALLING FOR YOU
Tracks: / Falling for you / Falling for you (inst).
7" Single: Released Jul '87, on In Touch, by In Touch Records. Catalogue no: **SEVEN 002**
12" Single: Released Jul '87, on In Touch, by In Touch Records. Catalogue no: **TWELVE 002**

WRITING'S ON THE WALL, THE
Tracks: / Writing on the wall / Part 1 (inst), part 2 (wall mix).
12" Single: Released Nov '86, on Londisc, by Londisc Records. Catalogue no: **12 LDR 058**
7" Single: Released Nov '86, on Londisc, by Londisc Records. Catalogue no: **LDR 058**

Martin, Moon

I'VE GOT A REASON
Tracks: / I've got a reason / Feeling's right.
7" Single: Released Apr '80, on Capitol, by EMI Records. Deleted '83. Catalogue no: **CL 16135**

NO CHANCE
Tracks: / No chance / Gun shy.
7" Single: Released Jan '80, on Capitol, by EMI Records. Deleted Jan '85. Catalogue no: **CL 16116**

SIGNAL FOR HELP
Tracks: / Signal for help / Rollin' in my Rolls.
7" Single: Released Oct '80, on Capitol, by EMI Records. Deleted Oct '83. Catalogue no: **CL 16170**

Martin, Patrick D.

COMPUTER DATIN'
Tracks: / Computer datin'.
7" Single: Released Oct '80, on Illegal, by Faulty Products Records. Catalogue no: **ILS 0023**

LUCY 'LECTRIC
Tracks: / Lucy 'Lectric / I like 'lectric motors / Mutant.
7" Single: Released Apr '80, on Deram, by London Records. Deleted '83. Catalogue no: **DMR 433**

Martin, Ray

BLUE TANGO
Tracks: / Blue tango.
7" Single: Released Nov '52, on Columbia, by EMI Records. Deleted '55. Catalogue no: **DB 3051**

CAROUSEL WALTZ
Tracks: / Carousel waltz.
7" Single: Released Jun '56, on Columbia, by EMI Records. Deleted '59. Catalogue no: **DB 3771**

SWEDISH RHAPSODY
Tracks: / Swedish rhapsody.
7" Single: Released Dec '53, on Columbia, by EMI Records. Deleted '56. Catalogue no: **DB 3346**

Martin, Remy

I WANT YOU
Tracks: / I want you.
12" Single: Released May '82, on Cartridge, Catalogue no: **CRD 14**

Martin, Ricky

HOLD ME TIGHT
Tracks: / Hold me tight.
7" Single: Released Apr '83, on Everest(Premier), by Everest Records. Catalogue no: **EVB 1003**

Martin, Shane

I NEED YOU
Tracks: / I need you.
Note: Composed by Jimmy Webb (McArthur Park, Witchita Lineman etc), Shane Martin's only UK single was issued on CBS in 1967 but met with no success. The disc was picked up on by the UK Northern Soul scene, and now commands a sixty-pound price tag, therefore making this reissue a very useful item. (PS)
7" Single: Released Mar '83, on Neil Rushton, Catalogue no: **510384**

Martin, Steve

DENTIST
Tracks: / Dentist.
7" Single: Released Jan '84, on Geffen, by Geffen Records (USA). Deleted Jan '88. Catalogue no: **GEF 20**

KING TUT
Tracks: / King Tut / Sally Goodin / Hoedown at Alice's.
7" Single: Released Apr '80, on Warner Bros., by WEA Records. Deleted '83. Catalogue no: **K 17216**

Martin, Teddy

KEEP LOVE NEW
Tracks: / Keep love new.
12" Single: Released Jun '89, on White Label (1), Catalogue no: **LS 013**

Martin & The Martians

MARTIANS (PART 1)
Tracks: / Martians (part 1) / Martians (part 2).
7" Single: Released Aug '80, on Risky Disc, Deleted '83. Catalogue no: **DISC 1**

Martin, Tony

BARRIERS
Tracks: / Barriers.
7" Single: Released Mar '84, on Barrier, Deleted '87. Catalogue no: **BS 101**

STRANGER IN PARADISE
Tracks: / Stranger in paradise.
7" Single: Released Apr '55, on H.M.V., by EMI Records. Deleted '58. Catalogue no: **B 10849**

WALK HAND IN HAND
Tracks: / Walk hand in hand.
7" Single: Released Jul '56, on H.M.V., by EMI Records. Deleted '59. Catalogue no: **POP 222**

Martin, Vicki

NOT GONNA DO IT
Tracks: / Not gonna do it.
7" Single: Released Mar '89, on MCA, by MCA Records. Deleted 1 Jul '89. Catalogue no: **MCA 1320**
12" Single: Released Mar '89, on MCA, by MCA Records. Catalogue no: **MCAT 1320**
CD 5": Released Apr '89, on MCA, by MCA Records. Catalogue no: **MCAX 1320**

Martin, Vince

CINDY OH CINDY
Tracks: / Cindy Oh Cindy.
7" Single: Released Dec '56, on London-American, Deleted '59. Catalogue no: **HLN 8340**

Martindale, Wink

Biographical details: This American broadcaster, whose real Christian name is Winston, began his career in Jackson, Tennessee at the age of 17. During his late teens and early twenties, he worked as a disc jockey in Memphis while simultaneously studying for a degree in speech and drama. His deep, resonant voice made him a nuatural for radio, and he eventually moved on to television. He had his own TV show *Teenage dance party* and became a game show host. His radio narration of The Elvis Presley Story series was heard around the world. To the record industry, Wink Martindale will always be known as the man who popularised the relegious recital *Deck of cards*. This spoken monologue had originally been a US country-and-western hit for its writer T.Texas Tyler in 1948. Martindale's 1959 rendition reached No.7 on the American pop chart. It told the story of a platoon of soldiers who were on a visit to church - during the worship, one serviceman brought out a pack of playing cards instead of a prayer book. When called by his superiors to explain himself, he described in detail the Christian significance of each card. The narration on the disc was accompanied by a maudlin stuing backing. While the sincerity of the writer and narrator of *Deck of cards* was not in doubt, many people described the project as sickly and sugary. For American chart-watchers, *Deck of cards* was simply a novelty hit that came and went. But British record buyers couldn't get enough of it. After origianally peaking at No.18 on the UK chart in 1959, the Martindale single re-appeared in 1960. In 1963, in total contrast to the then prevalent Beatles explosion, the single climbed to a new UK peak of No.5. Ten years later, it reached the UK No.22 position after being re-issued to compete with a new hit version by Britain's Max Bygraves. All in all, Wink Martindale's single logged 41 weeks on the British charts. (Bob MacDonald, 23rd Jan 1986).

DECK OF CARDS
Tracks: / Deck of cards / Wand'rin' star.
7" Single: Released Oct '73, on Dot (USA), by MCA Records (USA). Deleted '76. Catalogue no: **DOT 109**
7" Single: Released Dec '59, on London-American, Deleted '62. Catalogue no: **HLD 8962**
7" Single: Released Jul '82, on Old Gold, by Old Gold Records. Catalogue no: **OG 9170**

Martine

POLTERGEIST
Tracks: / Poltergeist / Imagine.
7" Single: Released Dec '83, on Ram, by Ram Records. Catalogue no: **RAM 7006**

Martinez, Nigel

BEHIND MY BACK
Tracks: / Behind my back / Doin' it.
12" Single: Released Feb '83, on Pinnacle, by Pinnacle Records. Catalogue no: **12 PIN 502**

Martinin G Special

LEAVE ME
Tracks: / Leave me.
12" Single: Released Oct '89, on UNKNOWN, Catalogue no: **BLKM 006**

Martinique

NO REGRETS
Tracks: / No regrets / Final call.
12" Single: Released Mar '85, on Young Blood, by Young Blood Records. Catalogue no: **YBT 0090**

Martino, Al

Biographical details: This American singer was born Alfred Cini in Philadelphia in 1927. He had just turned 25 years old when his single *Here in my heart* became the No.1 record on Britain's very first record sales chart, published by New Musical Express on 14 November 1952. The song stayed at the summit for nine weeks, thus making it one of the biggest UK smashes of all time as well as the first. Al was a bricklayer in his father's construction business before turning his part time singing job into a fully professional activity. A first generation Italian-American, he was a friend and protege of the great tenor Mario Lanza. The two vocalists shared a traditional operatic approach to singing *Here in my heart*, a No.1 on both sides of the Atlantic, was Martino's first major hit. It was followed with such successes as *Take my heart, Now, Rachel, Wanted* and *The story of Tina*, before the rock'n'roll explosion torpedoed him out of the charts in the mid-Fifties. After a few years in the wilderness, Martino made a strong comeback on the American charts in 1963 with *I love you because*. This rendition of a 1949 country-and-western hit reached the US No.3 position. (British record buyers consolidated his resurgence with four years of American Top 40 hits despite the rock'n'roll onslaught. One of his hit singles, 1966's *Spanish eyes*, became a belated British No.5 smash in 1973. By the latter year, he had made a well-reviewed appearance as a night club singer in the movie *The Godfather*, *To the door of the sun* and the old Italian chestnut *Volare* gave the artist his final US Top 40 singles in 1975. (Bob MacDonald, 23rd Jan 1986).

HERE IN MY HEART
Tracks: / Here in my heart.
7" Single: Released Nov '52, on Capitol, by EMI Records. Deleted '55. Catalogue no: **CL 13779**

I LOVE YOU BECAUSE
Tracks: / I love you because.
7" Single: Released Aug '63, on Capitol, by EMI Records. Deleted '66. Catalogue no: **CL 15300**

MAN FROM LARAMIE, THE
Tracks: / Man from Laramie, The.
7" Single: Released Sep '55, on Capitol, by EMI Records. Deleted '58. Catalogue no: **CL 14347**

NOW
Tracks: / Now.
7" Single: Released Jan '53, on Capitol, by EMI Records. Deleted '56. Catalogue no: **CL 13835**

RACHEL
Tracks: / Rachel.
7" Single: Released Jul '53, on Capitol, by EMI Records. Deleted '56. Catalogue no: **CL 13879**

SPANISH EYES (SINGLE)
Tracks: / Spanish eyes.
7" Single: Released Jul '84, on EMI (Holland), by EMI Records. Catalogue no: **1A 006 85133**
7" Single: Released Jan '66, on Capitol, by EMI Records. Deleted Oct '89. Catalogue no: **CL 15430**

STORY OF TINA, THE
Tracks: / Story of Tina.
7" Single: Released Oct '54, on Capitol, by EMI Records. Deleted '57. Catalogue no: **CL 14163**

SUMMERTIME
Tracks: / Summertime.
7" Single: Released Mar '60, on Top Rank (1), Deleted '63. Catalogue no: **JAR 312**

TAKE MY HEART
Tracks: / Take my heart.
7" Single: Released Nov '52, on Capitol, by EMI Records. Deleted '55. Catalogue no: **CL 13769**

Martino, Ramon

NO PROBLEM
Tracks: / No problem / Memories of Andalcia.
7" Single: Released Apr '82, on Fringe, Catalogue no: **FRI 001**

Marton, Sandy

CAMEL BY CAMEL
Tracks: / Camel by camel.
7" Single: Released Sep '85, on Carrere, Catalogue no: **CAR 370**

PEOPLE FROM IBIZA
Tracks: / People from Ibiza.
7" Single: Released Oct '84, on Carrere, Catalogue no: **CAR 347**
12" Single: Released Oct '84, on Carrere, Catalogue no: **CART 347**

Martyn, John

Biographical details: This British guitarist, singer and songwriter has been a critics' favourite since the late Sixties, but he has never translated his cult status into major commercial success. The Glasgow-born Martyn began his career on the London folk club circuit, and released his first album *London conversation* in 1968. Lp releases have appeared on a regular basis ever since. Two of these, *Stormbringer* and *The road to ruin* (both 1970), were collaborations with his wife Beverley. Gradually incorporating jazz, rock and blues influences into his music, the eclectic and intriguing Martyn really got into his artistic stride during the mid-Seventies. In February 1978 he finally achieved his first chart success with the excellent *One world* album, albeit No.54. Further forays into the British album chart included *Grace and danger* (a stark account of the breakdown of his marriage to Beverley - No.54 in 1980), the Phil Collins produced *Glorious fool* (No.25 in 1981) and *Well kept secret* (No.20 in 1982).
Island Records' initial refusal to release *Grace and danger* (it was delayed for a year, apparently because of its gloomy subject matter) caused Martyn to quit the company after a long-standing association. But he was unhappy at WEA and returned to the Island fold for the 1984 Lp *Sapphire*. Apart from a dire version of *Over the rainbow*, inexpicably issued as a single, this album showed that the artist still had some mileage in him yet. However, his excellent guitar playing and slurred, low-key vocals remained a minority taste. (Bob MacDonald 23rd Jan 1986).

ANGELINE
Tracks: / Angeline.
Note: Includes an extra track on CD single.
7" Single: Released Feb '86, on Island, by Island Records. Deleted Jul '87. Catalogue no: **IS 265**
12" Single: Released Feb '86, on Island, by Island Records. Deleted '87. Catalogue no: **12IS 265**
CD 5": Released Feb '86, on Island, by Island Records. Catalogue no: **CID 265**

GUN MONEY
Tracks: / Gun money / Hiss on the tape.
7" Single: Released Nov '82, on WEA, by WEA Records. Catalogue no: **2599877**

HISS ON THE TAPE
Tracks: / Hiss on the tape / Livin' alone.
7" Single: Released Oct '82, on WEA, by WEA Records. Catalogue no: **K 79336**

JOHNNY TOO BAD
Tracks: / Johnny too bad / Big muff.
12" Single: Released Mar '81, on Island, by Island Records. Deleted Mar '84. Catalogue no: **IPR 2046**

LONELY LOVE
Tracks: / Lonely lover / Sweet little Mystery / Fisherman's friend (12" single only.).
12" Single: Released Mar '86, on Island, by Island Records. Deleted '87. Catalogue no: **12IS 272**
7" Single: Released Mar '86, on Island, by Island Records. Deleted Jul '87. Catalogue no: **IS 272**

OVER THE RAINBOW
Tracks: / Over the rainbow.
7" Single: Released Oct '84, on Island, by

Island Records. Catalogue no: **IKS 209**

PLEASE FALL IN LOVE WITH ME
Tracks: / Please fall in love with me.
7" Single: Released Aug '81, on WEA, by WEA Records. Catalogue no: **K 79243**

SWEET LITTLE MYSTERY
Tracks: / Sweet little mystery / Johnny too bad.
7" Single: Released Jun '81, on Island, by Island Records. Deleted Jun '84. Catalogue no: **WIP 6718**

Marvelettes

Biographical details: At the time of their greatest success, this American vocal group consisted of Katherine Anderson, Juanita Cowart, Gladys Horton, Georgeanna Tillman and Wanda Young. The Marvelettes will always be remembered as the act which gave the Tamla Motown organisation its first US No.1 hit - *Please Mr Postman* in December 1961. Although the group did not become as successful or famous as Diana Ross & The Supremes or Martha Reeves & The Vandellas, they were just as good. Lead singer Gladys Horton was never given lead billing on any of the Marvelletes' discs, but her slightly gutsy and bluesy voice made her just as memorable as her better known Motown colleages. Horton formed the Marvelettes at Inkster High School in Detroit. Like so many future Tamla stars, the girls had been born in the right city at the right time. After performing well in a school talent contest, they won an audition with Motown which led to the release of the group's first single *Please Mr Postman* (featuring the up-and-coming Marvin Gaye on drums). The song was covered by the Beatles and, in 1975, became a US No.1 smash all over again for the Carpenters.
During the rest of the Sixties, the Marvelettes' contributions to the classic era of the Motown sound included *Playboy, Beechwood 4-5789, Don't mess with Bill, The hunter gets captured by the game* and *My baby must be a magician.* All of these reached the American Top.20; several were written and produced by the great Smokey Robinson. Surprisingly, the group managed only one British Top.20 single, and a cover version of a non-Motown song at that: *When you're young and in love,* written by Van McCoy and originally recorded by Ruby & The Romantics in 1964, reached No.13 in the UK in 1967. Seventeen years later, the song became a bigger British hit for the Flying Pickets. The Marvelettes' success tailed off at the end of the Sixties, by which time the group had shrunk to a quartet and then to a trio. They disbanded soon afterwards. Georgeanna Tillman died in January 1980 after a lengthy illness, at the age of 35. Attempts have been made during the Eighties to reunite the surviving members, but nothing significant has come of the idea (Bob MacDonald, 23rd Jan 1986).

TOO MANY FISH IN THE SEA
Tracks: / Too many fish in the sea / Please Mr. Postman.
7" Single: Released Apr '88, on Motown, by BMG Records (UK). Catalogue no: **ZB 41917**

WHEN YOU'RE YOUNG AND IN LOVE
Tracks: / When you're young and in love.
7" Single: Released Jun '67, on Tamla Motown, by Motown Records (UK). Deleted '70. Catalogue no: **TMG 609**
7" Single: Released Oct '81, on Tamla Motown, by Motown Records (UK). Catalogue no: **TMG 939**

Marvels

HE NEVER FAIL I YET
Tracks: / He never fail I yet / I'll follow you.
12" Single: Released Dec '82, on Pama, by Pama Records. Catalogue no: **PMD 3325**

HEAVEN MUST HAVE SENT YOU
Tracks: / Anymore / Heaven must have sent you.
10" single: Released Oct '82, on Pama, by Pama Records. Catalogue no: **PMD 3222**

NEVER LET YOUR LOVE SLIP AWAY
Tracks: / Never let your love slip away / Never let your love slip away (dub).
12" Single: Released May '86, on Toptenner, Catalogue no: **CH 503**

STAY
Tracks: / Stay / Stay (dub).
12" Single: Released May '86, on Toptenner, Catalogue no: **CH 504**

YOU MAKE ME HAPPY
Tracks: / You make me happy / I'm a hurtin' inside.
7" Single: Released Oct '80, on Liberty, by EMI Records. Deleted Oct '83. Catalogue no: **BP 373**
12" Single: Released Oct '80, on Liberty, by EMI Records. Deleted Oct '83. Catalogue no: **12BP 373**

Marvin

MARVIN
Tracks: / Marvin / Metal man.
7" Single: Released May '81, on Polydor, by Polydor Ltd. Deleted '84. Catalogue no: **POSP 261**

Marvin, Hank

Biographical details: This British guitarist, songwriter and occasional vocalist was born Brian Marvin in Newcastle in 1941. His nickname Hank was acquired at school, where a gang of four friends were all called Brian and thus needed to be distinguished. In late 1958 he took the move which changed his life - Hank and his Newcastle mate Bruce Welch, who had been living in London for about six months, became members of Cliff Richard's backing band. Cliff was just enjoying his first hit with *Move it.* From 1959 till the advent of the Beatles in 1963, Cliff Richard was Britain's top singer and his Shadows were Britain's top group. The familiar glasses and guitar of Hank Marvin became a permanent institution in the UK music industry. Marvin inspired legions of young Britons to take up the guitar, some of whom became rock stars of the Sixties and Seventies.
The permanent relationship between Cliff and the Shadows finished in 1968, although they continued to work together on an occasional basis. Hank released a self-titled solo album in 1969, which reached No.14 on the British chart. At the same time, he and Cliff scored two British Top 30 singles as a duo: *Throw down a line* and *Joy of living.* During the early Seventies Hank, Bruce and fellow guitarist/vocalist John Farrar issued a couple of albums as a trio under the billing Marvin, Welch & Farrar, but these records were commercial disappointments. So was an Lp by the duo Marvin & Farrar. Marvin's second solo album *The Hank Marvin guitar syndicate* was issued in 1977. This did not aim at the charts, but was a scholarly attempt to set up a 'guitar orchestra', featuring ten guest guitarists jamming along with Hank. His third solo set, 1982's *Words and music,* was an Lp of vocal pop ditties with a Sixties flavour - this peaked at No.66 on the UK album chart. During the Eighties, the Shadows have continued to record sporadically. (Bob MacDonald 23rd Jan 1986).

DON'T TALK
Tracks: / Don't talk / Lifeline.
7" Single: Released Mar '82, on Polydor, by Polydor Ltd. Deleted '85. Catalogue no: **POSP 420**

HAWK AND THE DOVE
Tracks: / Hawk and the dove, The / Janine.
7" Single: Released Apr '83, on Polydor, by Polydor Ltd. Catalogue no: **POSP 581**

INVISIBLE MAN
Tracks: / Invisible man, The.
7" Single: Released Jun '83, on Polydor, by Polydor Ltd. Deleted '86. Catalogue no: **POSP 618**

TROUBLE WITH ME IS YOU
Tracks: / Trouble with me is you / Captain....
7" Single: Released Feb '83, on Polydor, by Polydor Ltd. Catalogue no: **POSP 479**

Marvin, Lee

Biographical details: This American actor was born in New York in 1924 and made his Broadway debut in Billy Budd. By the time he acieved his surprise one-off hit single in 1970, he had appeared in numerous movies including Gun fury, Bad day at Black Rock, Not as a stranger and Pete Kelly's blues. The song that gave Marvin his unexpected smash was *Wand'rin star,* a tune from the 1969 movie version of the 1951 stage musical Paint your wagon by Alan Jay Lerner & Frederick Loewe. It logged three weeks at No.1 in Britain and was an international hit (though not in America), despite the fact that Lee Marvin could not sing a note. But the makers of the film, in which he starred, insisted that the song should be sung by him rather than overdubbed by a 'ghost' voice. His husky, gravelly tones seemed to suit the melancholy restlessness of the song, and the gamble paid off. The record was greeted with derision in many quarters, but no-one could argue with success. (Bob MacDonald, 24th Jan 1986).

WAND'RIN STAR
Tracks: / Wand'rin' star / I talk to the trees.
7" Single: Released Feb '70, on Paramount, Deleted '73. Catalogue no: **PARA 3004**
7" Single: Released Jul '80, on MCA, by MCA Records. Catalogue no: **MCA 703**

Marx Brothers

EVERYONE SAYS I LOVE YOU
Tracks: / Everyone says I love you.
7" Single: Released Dec '81, on MCA, by MCA Records. Deleted Dec '84. Catalogue no: **MCA 758**

Marx, Richard

ANGELIA
Tracks: / Angelia (Not on 12".) / Right here waiting (edit) / Angelia (LP version) (12" only.) / Don't mean nothing (live) (CD single only.).

MARY JANE GIRLS - ALL NIGHT LONG (Released on Motown)

12" Single: Released Oct '89, on EMI-Manhattan, by EMI Records. Catalogue no: **12MT 74**
CD 5": Released Oct '89, on EMI-Manhattan, by EMI Records. Catalogue no: **203 560 2**
CD 5": Released Oct '89, on EMI-Manhattan, by EMI Records. Catalogue no: **CDMT 74**
7" Single: Released Oct '89, on EMI-Manhattan, by EMI Records. Catalogue no: **MT 74**
7" Single: Released Oct '89, on EMI-Manhattan, by EMI Records. Catalogue no: **203 560 7**
12" Single: Released Oct '89, on EMI-Manhattan, by EMI Records. Catalogue no: **203 560 8**
12" Single: Released Oct '89, on EMI-Manhattan, by EMI Records. Catalogue no: **12MTG 74**
12" Single: Released Oct '89, on EMI-Manhattan, by EMI Records. Catalogue no: **203 560 6**
Cassingle: Released Oct '89, on EMI-Manhattan, by EMI Records. Catalogue no: **203 560 4**
Cassingle: Released Oct '89, on EMI-Manhattan, by EMI Records. Catalogue no: **TCMT 74**

DON'T MEAN NOTHING
Tracks: / Don't mean nothing / Flame of love / Should've known better (Only on CD single.) / Endless summer nights (edited version) (Only on CD single.).
12" Single: Released Jul '87, on EMI-Manhattan, by EMI Records. Deleted Nov '88. Catalogue no: **12 MT 26**
CD 5": Released Jun '88, on EMI-Manhattan, by EMI Records. Deleted Jun '89. Catalogue no: **CDMT 26**
7" Single: Released Jul '87, on EMI-Manhattan, by EMI Records. Deleted Nov '88. Catalogue no: **MT 26**
12" Single: Released Jun '88, on EMI-Manhattan, by EMI Records. Deleted Nov '88. Catalogue no: **12 MTP 26**

ENDLESS SUMMER NIGHTS
Tracks: / Endless summer nights / Should've known better (Only on 12" single.) / Have mercy / Rhythm of life.
Note: *Track on 12" version only.
CD 5": Released May '88, on EMI-Manhattan, by EMI Records. Deleted Aug '89. Catalogue no: **CDMT 39**
7" Pic: Released May '88, on EMI-Manhattan, by EMI Records. Deleted Jun '89. Catalogue no: **MTP 39**
7" Single: Released Apr '88, on EMI-Manhattan, by EMI Records. Deleted Jun '89. Catalogue no: **MT 39**
12" Single: Released Jun '88, on EMI-Manhattan, by EMI Records. Deleted Jun '89. Catalogue no: **12MT 39**
12" Single: Released May '88, on EMI-Manhattan, by EMI Records. Deleted Jun '89. Catalogue no: **12MTX 39**

HOLD ON TO THE NIGHTS
Tracks: / Hold on to the nights / Lonely heart / Hold on to the nights (live edition) (on 12" only).
7" Single: Released Aug '88, on EMI-Manhattan, by EMI Records. Deleted Jun '89. Catalogue no: **MT 53**
12" Single: Released Aug '88, on EMI-Manhattan, by EMI Records. Deleted Jun '89. Catalogue no: **12MT 53**

RIGHT HERE WAITING
Tracks: / Right here waiting (edit) (7" & cassingle only.) / Hold on to the nights (live) / That was Lulu (live) (Not on 7" & cassingle.) / Right here waiting (Not on 7" & cassingle.) / Wild life (CD single only.).
CD 5": Released Aug '89, on EMI-Manhattan, by EMI Records. Catalogue no: **203 500 2**
Cassingle: Released Aug '89, on EMI-Manhattan, by EMI Records. Catalogue no: **203 500 4**
Cassingle: Released Aug '89, on EMI-Manhattan, by EMI Records. Catalogue no: **TCMT 72**
7" Single: Released Aug '89, on EMI-Manhattan, by EMI Records. Catalogue no: **203 500 7**
12" Single: Released Aug '89, on EMI-Manhattan, by EMI Records. Catalogue no: **203 500 6**
CD 5": Released Aug '89, on EMI-Manhattan, by EMI Records. Catalogue no: **CDMT 72**
12" Single: Released Aug '89, on EMI-Manhattan, by EMI Records. Catalogue no: **12MT 72**
12" Single: Released Aug '89, on EMI-Manhattan, by EMI Records. Catalogue no: **203 500 8**
12" Single: Released Aug '89, on EMI-Manhattan, by EMI Records. Catalogue no: **12MTG 72**
7" Single: Released Aug '89, on EMI-Manhattan, by EMI Records. Catalogue no: **MT 72**

SATISFIED
Tracks: / Satisfied (LP version) (7" only.) / Should've known better (live) / Satisfied (ext rock mix) (12" only.) / Satisfied (single version).
7" Single: Released Apr '89, on EMI-Manhattan, by EMI Records. Catalogue no: **MT 64**
CD 5": Released Apr '89, on EMI-Manhattan, by EMI Records. Catalogue no: **CDMT 64**
7" Single: Released May '89, on EMI-Manhattan, by EMI Records. Catalogue no: **MTP 64**
12" Single: Released Apr '89, on EMI-Manhattan, by EMI Records. Catalogue no: **12MT 64**

SHOULD'VE KNOWN BETTER
Tracks: / Should've known better / Rhythm of life / Should've known better (ext. radio mix) (extra track on 12" and CD Single.) / Have mercy (live version) (extra track on CD Single.).
CD 5": Released Feb '88, on EMI-Manhattan, by EMI Records. Deleted Aug '89. Catalogue no: **CDMT 32**
12" Single: Released Nov '87, on EMI-Manhattan, by EMI Records. Deleted Nov '88. Catalogue no: **12MTS 32**
12" Single: Released Nov '87, on EMI-Manhattan, by EMI Records. Deleted Nov '88. Catalogue no: **12MT 32**
7" Single: Released Nov '87, on EMI-Manhattan, by EMI Records. Deleted Nov '88. Catalogue no: **MT 32**

Mary Jane Girls

Biographical details: Candi, Cheri, Jojo and Maxi, an American vocal group, are proteges of funk star Rick James. He writes, arranges and produces their material; and their streetwise, sexually risque approach is very much in keeping with James' own image. After serving as his backing vocalists, the Mary Jane Girls' self-titled debut album was released in 1983. It was a success on the US black charts and yielded the single *All night long*, which preceded the similarly named hit from fellow Motown artist Lionel Richie by some three months. In Britain *All night long* conveniently coincided with a heatwave, and its steamy, erotic invitation to 'meet me on the roof tonight' was perfect for the scorching summer nights; it thus became a UK Top 20 hit, something never achieved by Rick James' own records. Two other tracks from the Lp, *Candy man* and *Boys* were minor hits in Britain. The second Mary Jane Girls album provided both them and James with their first ever US Top 10 single - the pulsating *In my house* reached No.7 in early 1985. The Lp also contained the excellent ballad *Shadow lover*. (Bob MacDonald, 24th Jan 1986).

ALL NIGHT LONG **(See panel previous page)**
Tracks: / All night long / Musical love.
7" Single: Released Jun '83, on Motown, by BMG Records (UK). Catalogue no: **TMG 1309**
12" Single: Released Jun '83, on Motown, by BMG Records (UK). Catalogue no: **TMGT 1309**

BOYS
Tracks: / Boys / You are my heaven / All night long (on 12" only) / Candy man (on 12" only).
7" Single: Released Sep '83, on Motown, by BMG Records (UK). Deleted '85. Catalogue no: **TMG 1315**
12" Single: Released Sep '83, on Motown, by BMG Records (UK). Deleted '85. Catalogue no: **TMGT 1315**

CANDY MAN
Tracks: / Candy man.
7" Single: Released Apr '83, on Motown, by BMG Records (UK). Deleted '85. Catalogue no: **TMG 1301**
12" Single: Released Apr '83, on Motown, by BMG Records (UK). Deleted '85. Catalogue no: **TMGT 1301**

IN MY HOUSE
Tracks: / In my house.
7" Single: Released Feb '85, on Motown, by BMG Records (UK). Catalogue no: **TMG 1377**
12" Single: Released Feb '85, on Motown, by BMG Records (UK). Deleted '87. Catalogue no: **TMGT 1377**

WALK LIKE A MAN
Tracks: / Walk Like a Man / All night Long.
7" Single: Released Jul '86, on Gordy (USA), by Motown Records (UK). Deleted '87. Catalogue no: **ZB 40795**
12" Single: Released Jul '86, on Gordy (USA), by Motown Records (UK). Deleted '87. Catalogue no: **ZT 40796**

WILD AND CRAZY LOVE
Tracks: / Wild and crazy love.
7" Single: Released Aug '85, on Motown, by BMG Records (UK). Catalogue no: **ZB 40271**
12" Single: Released Aug '85, on Motown, by BMG Records (UK). Catalogue no: **ZT 40271**

Mary My Hope

IT'S ABOUT TIME
Tracks: / It's about time.
12" Single: Released Apr '83, on Silvertone, Catalogue no: **ORET 3**
7" Single: Released Apr '83, on Silvertone, Catalogue no: **ORE 3**

Mary-Lou

HERE COMES THE NIGHT
Tracks: / Here comes the night.
7" Single: Released Dec '84, on Modern, Catalogue no: **MOD 005**

LIPSTICK ON YOUR COLLAR
Tracks: / Lipstick on your collar / Fever.
7" Single: Released Jul '82, on Mint, by Emerald Records. Deleted '88. Catalogue no: **CHEW 68**

WHERE THE BOYS ARE
Tracks: / Where the boys are / Let's dance.
7" Single: Released Nov '82, on Mint, by Emerald Records. Deleted '88. Catalogue no: **CHEW 73**

Mas, Carolyne

Biographical details: This American rock singer and guitarist was born into a musical family in New York; her father played guitar and her mother was a pianist. Carolyne had mastered both instruments by her early teens. She took lessons for opera singing, but rock was really her scene; so after spells in the opera and folk worlds, she formed her own rock band in the mid-Seventies. Carlyne Mas' self-titled debut Lp was released in 1979 to a flurry of good reviews. She was hotly tipped for stardom, but it was not to be. Another female opera trainee turned rock vocalist, Pat Benatar, arrived on the scene at exactly the same time. Both artists possessed great voices, but Benatar had access to better songs and had greater charisma. Mas' second and third albums, *Hold on* (1980) and *Modern dreams*(1981 - titled *Mas hysteria* in Britain), were commercial disappointments. Her only UK chart entry was *Quote goodbye quote*, a single that peaked at No.71 in February 1980. (Bob MacDonald, 24th Jan 1986).

QUOTE GOODBYE QUOTE **(See panel below right)**
Tracks: / Quote goodbye quote / Never two without three.
7" Single: Released Feb '80, on Mercury, by Phonogram Ltd. Deleted '83. Catalogue no: **6167 873**

Mas, Jeanne

INTO THE NIGHT
Tracks: / Into the night.
7" Single: Released Aug '84, on EMI, by EMI Records. Catalogue no: **EMI 5486**

Masai

BOOGY MAN
Tracks: / Boogy man / Lets go crazy / So mad so crazy.
12" Single: Released Nov '86, on Antler, by Antler Records (Belgium). Catalogue no: **ANT 041**

STRANGER TO MYSELF
Tracks: / Stranger to myself / Lightning.
7" Single: Released Oct '82, on Turbo, Catalogue no: **TURB 001**

TONIGHT
Tracks: / Tonight.
7" Single: on Antler, by Antler Records (Belgium). Deleted '88. Catalogue no: **ANT 059**

YOU'RE THE ONE
Tracks: / You're the one.
7" Single: Released Jun '88, on Antler, by Antler Records (Belgium). Catalogue no: **ANT 045**

Masaki

DA-BA-DA
Tracks: / Da ba da.
7" Single: Released Mar '86, on LOE, by LOE Records. Deleted '88. Catalogue no: **ROSH 50**
12" Single: Released Mar '86, on LOE, by LOE Records. Deleted '88. Catalogue no: **ROSHX 50**

Mascara

BAJA
Tracks: / Baja.
12" Single: Released Oct '84, on Personal, by Personal Records. Catalogue no: **12 PER 110**

Masco

AFRICAN LOVE
Tracks: / African Love / Party jam.
7" Single: Released Sep '86, on City 1, Catalogue no: **MASC 01**
12" Single: Released Sep '86, on City 1, Catalogue no: **12 MASC 01**

DANCING PARTY
Tracks: / Dancing party / Dancing party (dub mix).
7" Single: Released Dec '87, on City 1, Catalogue no: **MASC 03**
12" Single: Released Dec '87, on City 1, Catalogue no: **12 MASC 03**

PARTY JAM
Tracks: / Party jam / Party jam (instrumental).
12" Single: Released Dec '86, on Citybeat, by Beggars Banquet Records. Catalogue no: **12 MASCO 2**

Masekela, Hugh

AFRICAN BREEZE
Tracks: / African breeze.
7" Single: Released Oct '85, on Jive, by Zomba Records. Deleted Jul '87. Catalogue no: **JIVE 100**
12" Single: Released Oct '85, on Jive, by Zomba Records. Deleted Jul '87. Catalogue no: **JIVET 100**

BRING HIM BACK HOME
Tracks: / Serengeti / Bring him back home.
7" Single: Released Feb '87, on Atlantic, by WEA Records. Deleted Jan '88. Catalogue no: **U 8466**
12" Single: Released Feb '87, on Atlantic, by WEA Records. Deleted Jan '88. Catalogue no: **U 8466 T**

DON'T GO LOSE IT BABY
Tracks: / Don't go lose it baby / African breeze# (# Track on 1988 release only, not on 1984 release.).
7" Single: Released May '84, on Jive, by Zomba Records. Catalogue no: **JIVE 64**

JEFF MASON - STRANGEWAYS (Released on Bitten by Sharks)

7" Single: Released May '88, on Jive, by Zomba Records. Deleted '88. Catalogue no: **JIVE 173**
12" Single: Released May '88, on Jive, by Zomba Records. Deleted '88. Catalogue no: **JIVET 173**
12" Single: Released May '84, on Jive, by Zomba Records. Catalogue no: **JIVET 64**

KE BALE
Tracks: / Ke bale / Bird on the wing.
7" Single: Released 13 Jun '87, on Warner Bros., by WEA Records. Catalogue no: **W 8311**
12" Single: Released 13 Jun '87, on Warner Bros., by WEA Records. Catalogue no: **W 8311T**

LADY
Tracks: / Lady.
7" Single: Released Apr '85, on Jive Africa, by Zomba Records. Catalogue no: **JIVE 94**
12" Single: Released Apr '85, on Jive Africa, by Zomba Records. Catalogue no: **JIVET 94**

PULA EA NA (IT'S RAINING)
Tracks: / Pula ea na (it's raining).
12" Single: Released Nov '84, on Jive Africa, by Zomba Records. Catalogue no: **JIVET 81**
7" Single: Released Nov '84, on Jive Africa, by Zomba Records. Catalogue no: **JIVE 81**

WIMOWEH (THE LION NEVER SLEEPS)
Tracks: / Wimoweh.
7" Single: Released Sep '84, on Jive Africa, by Zomba Records. Catalogue no: **JIVE 76**
12" Single: Released Sep '84, on Jive Africa, by Zomba Records. Catalogue no: **JIVET 76**

M.A.S.H.

Biographical details: One of the oldest quirks in the history of the UK charts was the 1980 No.1 success of *Theme from M*A*S*H (Suicide is painless)*. This was a ten year old single by an anonymous band which never actually existed - the record company billed the group as the Mash for lack of any other name. The single had been used as the theme for the 1970 20th Century Fox movie 'M*A*S*H' (Mobile army surgical hospital) starring Donald Sutherland. Though the spinoff TV series was an enormous success on both sides of the Atlantic during the Seventies and early Eighties, few people would have predicted that this single would suddenly shoot to the top of the British charts. Its success was caused by its repeated plays by BBC Radio One disc jockey Noel Edmonds, who gave it heavy exposure on his peak-time Sunday morning show. Just a few months earlier, the gimmick-loving Edmonds had been responsible for the surprise success of actor Keith Michell's *Captain Beaky*. The appeal of *Theme from M*A*S*H* was its light, folky-pop feel and its beautiful melody. Its lyrics were written by Mike Altman, the son of the movie's director Robert Altman,

CAROLYNE MAS - QUOTE GOODBYE QUOTE (Released on Mercury)

and must rank among the worst words ever commited to vinyl. Lines like 'Suicide is Painless, it brings on many cvhanges' are hardly the stuff of which epocj - making philosophy is created (Bob MacDonald, Jan 1986).

M.A.S.H. (SUICIDE IS PAINLESS) (OLD GOLD)
Tracks: / M.A.S.H., Theme / MASH march.
7" Single: Released Jan '88, on Old Gold, by Old Gold Records. Catalogue no: **OG 9759**

M.A.S.H. (SUICIDE IS PAINLESS)
Tracks: / Theme from M.A.S.H. / M.A.S.H. march.
7" Single: Released May '80, on CBS, by CBS Records. Deleted May '83. Catalogue no: **CBS 8356**

Maslon, Jimmie

TURN ME ALL AROUND
Tracks: / Turn me all around.
7" Single: Released Apr '81, on Rondelet Music, by Rondelet Music & Records. Catalogue no: **ROUND 1004**

Mason

DOUBLE-X-POSURE
Tracks: / Double-x-posure / Pour it on.
7" Single: Released Apr '87, on Elektra (USA), by Elektra Records (USA). Deleted Jan '88. Catalogue no: **EKR 56**
12" Single: Released Apr '87, on Elektra (USA), by Elektra Records (USA). Deleted Jul '88. Catalogue no: **EKR 56 T**

Mason, Barbara

Biographical details: This American soul singer and songwriter, born in Philadelphia, was barely 18 when she shot to fame in 1965 with her self-penned smoocher *Yes I'm Ready*: it reached No.5 on the US pop chart and was followed by the No.27 success of *Sad Sad Girl*. During the next few years Mason achieved strong entries on the American soul charts from time to time, though these did not become major pop hits. Tracks like *I Need Love* and *Oh How It Hurts* showed her to be a sensitive vocalist and her songs were couched in lush productions which were rich without being syrupy. She returned to the US pop Top Forty with 1973's *Give Me Your Love* and 1975's *From His Woman To You*, an answer to the Shirley Brown hit *Woman To Woman*. *Yes I'm Ready* was revived with huge success by the one-off male-female duet of KC & Teri DeSario. This million-selling cover version reached No 2 in the States, three places higher than Mason's original. She finally received an overdue glimmer of UK recognition in 1984, when *Another Man* reached No.45 on the singles chart. This somewhat controversial record bemoaned the fact that "Another man is loving mine" - it seemed that Ms Mason was discovering that she didn't know her fessa quite as well as she thought. (Bob MacDonald, January 1986.)

ANOTHER MAN
Tracks: / Another man.
7" Single: Released Jan '84, on Streetwave, Deleted '87. Catalogue no: **KHAN 3**

I'LL NEVER LOVE THE SAME WAY TWICE
Tracks: / On and off / Playing with my feelings / I'll never love the same way twice.
7" Single: Released Aug '87, on Bluebird (2), by BMG Records (UK). Catalogue no: **BR 41**
12" Single: Released Aug '87, on Bluebird (2), by BMG Records (UK). Catalogue no: **BRT 41**

ON AND OFF
Tracks: / On and off / Yes I'm ready.
7" Single: Released Mar '81, on W.M.O.T.(USA), by Virgin Records. Deleted Mar '84. Catalogue no: **WMT 103**
12" Single: Released Mar '81, on W.M.O.T.(USA), by Virgin Records. Deleted Mar '84. Catalogue no: **WMTL 103**

Mason, Barry

BERTIE THE BUS
Tracks: / Bertie the bus / Bertie to the rescue.
7" Single: Released May '83, on Mandal, Catalogue no: **BB 001**

Mason, Glen

GLENDORA
Tracks: / Glendora.
7" Single: Released Sep '56, on Parlophone, by EMI Records. Deleted '59. Catalogue no: **R 4203**

GREEN DOOR
Tracks: / Green door.
7" Single: Released Nov '56, on Parlophone, by EMI Records. Deleted '59. Catalogue no: **R 4244**

Mason, Harvey

HOW DOES IT FEEL
Tracks: / How does it feel / On and on / Till you take my love.
12" Single: Released May '81, on Arista, by BMG Records (UK). Deleted May '86. Catalogue no: **ARIST 12399**

Mason, Jeff

STRANGEWAYS
Tracks: / Strangeways / Made in Heaven.
7" Single: Released Jan '87, on Bitten By Sharks, by Bitten By Sharks Records. Catalogue no: **BBS 1**

Mason, Mary

ANGEL OF THE MORNING - ANY WAY THAT YOU WANT ME
Tracks: / Angel of the morning - any way that you want.
7" Single: Released Oct '77, on Epic, by CBS Records. Deleted '80. Catalogue no: **EPC 5552**

Mason, Sylvia

WE'VE GOTTA DANCE
Tracks: / We've gotta dance / Hello superduper star.
7" Single: Released Sep '80, on Carrere, Deleted '83. Catalogue no: **CAR 158**

(YOU'RE LIKE A) SILENT MOVIE
Tracks: / (You're like a) silent movie / Closer to heaven.
7" Single: Released Feb '80, on Carrere, Deleted Feb '85. Catalogue no: **CAR 135**

Masque

TWISTED TALES
Tracks: / Twisted tales / Confined insanity / Back with a vengeance / No light to die by.
7" Single: Released Feb '89, on RKT, Catalogue no: **CMO 121**

Masquerade

DON'T BACK BACK
Tracks: / Don't back back.
12" Single: Released Sep '84, on Pirate, Catalogue no: **PRAT 003**

EVERYBODY SAY
Tracks: / Everybody say / Everybody say (Version).
12" Single: Released Jan '87, on Streetwave, Catalogue no: **UKHAN 3**

ONE NATION
Tracks: / One nation (Note) / One nation (Inst).
12" Single: Released Dec '85, on Streetwave, Catalogue no: **MKHAX 59**
Cassingle: Released Dec '85, on Streetwave, Catalogue no: **ZCMK 59**
7" Single: Released Dec '85, on Streetwave, Deleted '88. Catalogue no: **KHAN 59**

ONE NATION (ORIGINAL STREET MIX)
Tracks: / One Nation (Original street Mix) / Set it off (original full version).
Note: Featuring dina carrol.
12" Single: Released Jan '86, on Streetwave, Catalogue no: **MKHAT 59**

(SOLUTION TO) THE PROBLEM
Tracks: / (Solution to) the problem.
7" Single: Released May '86, on Streetwave, Catalogue no: **KHAN 67**

Masqueraders

HOW
Tracks: / How.
7" Single: Released Apr '80, on Grapevine (Northern Soul), by BMG Records (UK). Catalogue no: **GRP 138**

Mass

YOU AND I
Tracks: / You and I / Cabbage.
7" Single: Released Jan '81, on 4AD, by 4AD Records. Deleted Jan '84. Catalogue no: **AD 14**

Mass Appeal

STARS ON 39-45
Tracks: / Stars on 39-45 / Tartan fling.
7" Single: Released Nov '81, on Red Bus, by Red Bus Records. Deleted Nov '84. Catalogue no: **RBUS 62**

Mass Extension

HAPPY FEE
Tracks: / Happy fee.
7" Single: Released Mar '85, on 4th & Broadway, by Island Records. Catalogue no: **GOGO 2**
12" Single: Released Mar '85, on 4th & Broadway, by Island Records. Catalogue no: **12 GOGO 2**

Mass Production

Biographical details: *Welcome To Our World (Of Merry Music)* said Mass Production in 1977. This single reached No 68 on the US pop chart and No.44 in Britain. Subsequent singles and LPs by this all-male American funk and disco band were churned out relentlessly during the late 70's and early 80's, with no great success. Only *Shante*, No.59 on the UK singles chart in 1980, went beyond a small, specialist audience. The music was so dull it seemed mass produced; but there weren't too many takers. (Bob MacDonald, January 1986.).

DIAMOND CHIP
Tracks: / Diamond chip / Bopp.
7" Single: Released Jun '81, on Cotillion, by WEA Records. Catalogue no: **K 11598**
12" Single: Released Jun '81, on Cotillion, by WEA Records. Catalogue no: **K 11598T**

SHANTE
Tracks: / Shante / You love.
7" Single: Released May '80, on Cotillion, by WEA Records. Deleted '83. Catalogue no: **K 11475**

SHE'S GOT TO HAVE IT
Tracks: / She's got to have it / We bite.
12" Single: Released May '87, on Nine O Nine, by Creole Records. Catalogue no: **NINE 6**
Cassingle: Released Mar '87, on Antilles/New Directions, by Island Records. Deleted Jun '88. Catalogue no: **ANC 8713**

WELCOME TO OUR WORLD (OF MERRY MUSIC)
Tracks: / Welcome to our world.
7" Single: Released Mar '77, on Cotillion, by WEA Records. Deleted '80. Catalogue no: **K 10898**

Mass Reaction

CAN YOU FEEL THE BEAT
Tracks: / Can you feel the beat
12" Single: Released Apr '89, on Immaculate, by Immaculate Records. Catalogue no: **12IMMAC D1**

Massara

MARGARITA
Tracks: / Margarita.
7" Single: Released Nov '80, on Champagne Records, Deleted '83. Catalogue no: **FIZZ 102**
12" Single: Released Nov '80, on Champagne Records, Deleted '83. Catalogue no: **FIZY 1002**

Massiel

LA LA LA
Tracks: / La la la.
7" Single: Released Apr '68, on Philips, by Phonogram Ltd. Deleted '71. Catalogue no: **BF 1667**

Massive Attack

ANY LOVE
Tracks: / Any love.
12" Single: Released Jul '88, on Warner Bros., by WEA Records. Catalogue no: **MASS 001**

Massive Bounds

ROUGH AND MASSIVE
Tracks: / Rough and massive / Free South Africa.
12" Single: Released Sep '89, on Republic, by Code Records. Catalogue no: **LICT 027**

Massive Dread

NICE THEM UP
Tracks: / Nice them up.
12" Single: Released Sep '81, on Upfront, by Serious Records. Catalogue no: **UPF 02**

Massive Horns

COOL & DEADLY
Tracks: / Cool & deadly.
12" Single: Released Jan '84, on Fashion, by Fashion Records. Catalogue no: **FAD 019**

Massive Sounds

I WANT YOU
Tracks: / I want you.
12" Single: Released Apr '89, on Champion, by Champion Records. Catalogue no: **CHAMP 1299**
7" Single: Released Apr '89, on Champion, by Champion Records. Catalogue no: **CHAMP 99**

Master C & J

IN THE CITY
Tracks: / In the city.
12" Single: Released Nov '87, on State Street (USA), Catalogue no: **SSR 1005**

Master Funk Band

MY BOY LOLLIPOP
Tracks: / My boy lollipop.
12" Single: Released Dec '81, on Master, Catalogue no: **MF 001**

Master Genius

LET'S DANCE
Tracks: / Let's dance.
12" Single: Released May '84, on Carrere, Catalogue no: **CART 322**

Master Jam

DANCIN' ALL NIGHT
Tracks: / Dancin' all night.
12" Single: Released Jan '83, on Proto, by Proto Records. Catalogue no: **ENAT 102**

FREAK WITH YOU (2 Parts)
Tracks: / Freak with you.
12" Single: Released May '83, on Proto, by Proto Records. Catalogue no: **ENAT108**

Master Singers

HIGHWAY CODE
Tracks: / Highway code.
7" Single: Released Apr '66, on Parlophone, by EMI Records. Deleted '69. Catalogue no: **R 5428**

WEATHER FORECAST
Tracks: / Weather forecast.
7" Single: Released Nov '66, on Parlophone, by EMI Records. Deleted '69. Catalogue no: **R 5523**

Master Twins & Blond

SQUANDER
Tracks: / Squander / Lost dreams.
12" Single: Released 17 Oct '87, on Wire, by Wire Records. Catalogue no: **12 WRS 019**
7" Single: Released 17 Oct '87, on Wire, by Wire Records. Catalogue no: **WRS 019**

Masterdon Committee

FUNK BOX PARTY
Tracks: / Funk box party.
12" Single: Released Nov '87, on Deejay (USA), Catalogue no: **BLUE 002**
7" Single: Released '88, on Champion, by Champion Records. Catalogue no: **CHAMP 33**
12" Single: Released '88, on Champion, by Champion Records. Catalogue no: **CHAMP 1233**

Mastermind

UNCLE SAM WANTS YOU
Tracks: / Uncle Sam wants you
7" Single: Released Sep '82, on Half Moon, by Rondelet Music & Records. Catalogue no: **ROUND 2004**
12" Single: Released Sep '82, on Half Moon, by Rondelet Music & Records. Catalogue no: **12 ROUND 2004**

Masterpiece

I CAN'T WAIT
Tracks: / I can't wait.
7" Single: Released Jun '87, on Serious, by Serious Records. Catalogue no: **7OUS 4**
12" Single: Released Jun '87, on Serious, by Serious Records. Catalogue no: **OUS 4**

Masterplan

STOMP
Tracks: / Stomp.
12" Single: Released Dec '88, on Crush, Catalogue no: **ONE 6601**
7" Single: Released Dec '88, on Crush, Catalogue no: **ONE 6101**

Masters, Chad

JUST A LITTLE OFF BEAT RHYTHM
Tracks: / Just a little off beat rhythm
7" Single: Released Jun '88, on Hedonic Recordings, by Hedonic Recordings. Catalogue no: **HEDON 1**

LOVE FOR EACH MOMENT
Tracks: / Love for each moment / Love hits overrider.
7" Single: Released Dec '88, on Hedonic Recordings, by Hedonic Recordings. Catalogue no: **HEDON 2**

Masters, Gerald

POOR LITTLE RICH BOY
Tracks: / Poor little rich boy / Rock and roll.
7" Single: Released Feb '80, on Pye, Deleted '83. Catalogue no: **7P 166**

Masters Of Ceremony

SEXY
Tracks: / Sexy.
7" Single: Released Mar '87, on London Records, by London Records. Deleted Sep '87. Catalogue no: **LON 129**
12" Single: Released Mar '87, on London Records, by London Records. Catalogue no: **LONX 129**

Masters Of Reality

LADY SONG, THE
Tracks: / Lady song, The / Blue garden, The.
CD 5": Released Sep '89, on Def American (USA), Catalogue no: **DEFAC 1**

Masters Of The

HE MAN
Tracks: / He man.
7" Single: Released Nov '85, on Telebell, Catalogue no: **TVP 5**

Masters, Sammy

ROCKIN' RED WING (SINGLE)
Tracks: / Rockin' red wing.
7" Single: Released Jun '82, on Revival, Catalogue no: **REV 6015**
7" Single: Released Jun '60, on Warner Bros., by WEA Records. Deleted '63. Catalogue no: **WB 10**

Mastership

ALIVE IN BRITAIN
Tracks: / Alive in Britain.
12" Single: Released Oct '84, on Londonium, Catalogue no: **DLM 1**

Masterworks

MARCH OF THE TOREADORS
Tracks: / March of the Toreadors / 1812 overture finale.
7" Single: Released Sep '80, on DJM, Deleted '83. Catalogue no: **DJS 10958**

Maston, Jimmie

HAUNT YOU BABY ROCK, THE
Tracks: / Haunt you baby rock, The.
7" Single: Released Jun '80, on Rollin' Rock, Catalogue no: **45 013**

Mata

ON YOUR BIKES
Tracks: / On your bikes.
7" Single: Released Jul '83, on Savoir Faire, Catalogue no: **FAIS 002**

Matadaruka

ODE TO JOHNNY DRUGHEAD
Tracks: / Ode to Johnny Drughead / Junk food.
12" Single: Released Nov '83, on Alligator Records, Catalogue no: **AL 501**

Matadi, Matik

MANY TIMES
Tracks: / Many times.
12" Single: Released Oct '88, on Rhythmattic, Catalogue no: **RYPPRO 2**

Matadi, Ronny

AUTOMATIC MAGIC
Tracks: / Automatic magic / Morning song.
12" Single: Released Feb '83, on Congo Matadi, Catalogue no: **TAD 1001**

Matania, Tina

LOVE ME JUST A LITTLE MORE
Tracks: / Love me just a little more.
7" Single: Released Apr '84, on WSME, Catalogue no: **WSMF 1**

Matata

MBONGO
Tracks: / Mbongo / Ulimwengu / Mbongo (maxi mix) (Only on 12" single.) / Ulimwengu (maxi mix) (Only on 12" single.).
Note: Produced by Rainer Preuss & Klaus Schmid for Violette Sound Productions, Munich. Published by Edward Kassner Music Co. Ltd. Both tracks written by P. Oluma.
7" Single: Released Jul '89, on President, by President Records. Catalogue no: **PT 579**
12" Single: Released Jul '89, on President, by President Records. Catalogue no: **PT 12 579**

Mataya

MUSIC MUSIC MUSIC
Tracks: / Music music music / Music in space.
12" Single: Released Nov '82, on Instant (1), by Instant Records. Catalogue no: **INST 112**
7" Single: Released Nov '82, on Instant (1), by Instant Records. Catalogue no: **INST 1**

Match

BOOGIE MAN
Tracks: / Boogie man.
7" Single: Released Jun '79, on Flamingo, by Airwave Records (USA). Deleted '82. Catalogue no: **FM 2**

BOOM BOOM BORIS
Tracks: / Boom boom Boris.
7" Single: Released Jul '85, on Red Bus, by Red Bus Records. Catalogue no: **RBUS 2204**

Matchbox

Biographical details: Just like another rock'n'roll revivalist, Shakin' Stevens, this British band had to toil away in clubs and halls throughout the Seventies before breaking into the UK national charts at the beginning of the Eighties. Matchbox first charted in November 1979, beating Shaky by a few months; but they were not able to sustain their fame for as long as his. Strictly speaking, Matchbox played rockabilly (the hillbilly rock that emerged from the Southern United States in the Fifties) rather than pure rock'n'roll. This fact was announced by the band's first hit single *Rockabilly rebel*, which reached the UK No.18 position; it was written by lead guitarist Steve Bloomfield. It was followed by *Buzz buzz a diddle it* (no.22) and *Midnite dynamos* (No.14). The group then achieved their only British Top Tenner with *When you ask about love*, a slick revival of a small Crickets hit (post Buddy Holly - No.27 in 1960). At Christmkas 1980 the band scored a No.15 placing with a tasteful revamp of the Judy Garland evergreen *Over the rainbow*; the guy made this into a medley with *You belong to me*. Just as Matchbox seemed to be riding high, their success declined during 1981. As they watched Shaky and the Stray Cats shoot up the charts, their own singles failed to penetrate th UK Top 40. These disappointments included another Crickets cover, *Love's made a fool of you*. Matchbox's final UK chart entry, the self-penned *One more Saturday night*, peaked at No.63 in 1982. Subsequent releases failed to strike a light. (Bob MacDonald, 24th Jan 1986).

ANGELS ON SUNDAY
Tracks: / Angels on Sunday / City women.
7" Single: Released Sep '81, on Magnet, by WEA Records. Deleted '84. Catalogue no: **MAG 196**

BABES IN THE WOOD
Tracks: / Babes in the wood / Tokyo Joe.
7" Single: Released Apr '81, on Magnet, by WEA Records. Deleted '84. Catalogue no: **MAG 193**

BUZZ BUZZ A DIDDLE IT
Tracks: / Buzz buzz a diddle it / Everybody needs a little love.
7" Single: Released Jan '80, on Magnet, by WEA Records. Deleted '83. Catalogue no: **MAG 157**

I WANT OUT
Tracks: / I want out / Heaven can wait.
7" Single: Released Jan '83, on Magnet, by WEA Records. Catalogue no: **MAG 238**

LOVE'S MADE A FOOL OF YOU
Tracks: / Love's made a fool of you / Springheel Jack.
7" Single: Released Aug '81, on Magnet, by WEA Records. Deleted '84. Catalogue no: **MAG 194**

MIDNITE DYNAMOS (SINGLE)
Tracks: / Midnite dynamos / Love is going out of fashion.
7" Single: Released May '80, on Magnet, by WEA Records. Deleted '83. Catalogue no: **MAG 169**

ONE MORE SATURDAY NIGHT
Tracks: / One more saturday night / Rollin' on.
7" Single: Released May '82, on Magnet, by WEA Records. Deleted '85. Catalogue no: **MAG 223**

OVER THE RAINBOW
Tracks: / Over the rainbow / You belong to me.
7" Single: Released Nov '80, on Magnet, by WEA Records. Deleted '83. Catalogue no: **MAG 192**

PLEASE DON'T TOUCH
Tracks: / Please don't touch / All the boys love my baby.
7" Single: Released Apr '81, on Charly, by Charly Records. Deleted '85. Catalogue no: **CYS 1074**

RIDING THE NIGHT
Tracks: / Riding the night / Mad, bad and dangerous.
7" Single: Released Jan '82, on Magnet, by WEA Records. Deleted Jan '85. Catalogue no: **MAG 231**

ROCKABILLY REBEL
Tracks: / Rockabilly rebel.
7" Single: Released Nov '79, on Magnet, by WEA Records. Deleted '82. Catalogue no: **MAG 155**

WHEN YOU ASK ABOUT LOVE
Tracks: / When you ask about love / You've made a fool of me.
7" Single: Released Sep '80, on Magnet, by WEA Records. Deleted Sep '83. Catalogue no: **MAG 191**

Matchroom Mob

SNOOKER LOOPY
Tracks: / Snooker loopy / Wallop (snookered).
12" Single: Released Apr '86, on Rockney, Catalogue no: **POT 147**
7" Single: Released Apr '86, on Rockney, Catalogue no: **POT 1**

Material

BUSTIN' OUT
Tracks: / Bustin' out / Over and over.
7" Single: Released Jun '81, on Island, by Island Records. Deleted Jun '84. Catalogue no: **WIP 6713**
12" Single: Released Jun '81, on Island, by Island Records. Deleted Jun '84. Catalogue no: **12WIP 6713**

CIGURI
Tracks: / Ciguri.
7" Single: Released Mar '82, on Reds, Catalogue no: **RS 011**
12" Single: Released Mar '82, on Reds, Catalogue no: **RS 12 011**

TEMPORY MUSIC TWO
Tracks: / Tempory music two.
12" Single: Released Aug '81, on Fresh, by Jetstar Records. Catalogue no: **RS 12008**

Mathews, Ian

DA DO RON RON
Tracks: / Da do ron ron / Shake it / Gimme an inch girl.
7" Single: Released Mar '80, on Rockburgh, Deleted '83. Catalogue no: **ROCS 221**

Mathieu, Mireille

LA DERNIERE VALSE
Tracks: / La derniere valse.
7" Single: Released Dec '67, on Columbia, by EMI Records. Deleted '70. Catalogue no: **DB 8323**

Mathis, Cathy

LATE NIGHT HOUR
Tracks: / Late night hour / Late night hour (inst).
12" Single: Released 30 May '87, on Tabu, Deleted Nov '87. Catalogue no: **650806 6**
7" Single: Released 30 May '87, on Tabu, Deleted Nov '87. Catalogue no: **650806 7**

Mathis, Johnny

Biographical details: This American singer has been a stalwart middle-of-the-road entertainer from the Fifties right through to the Eighties. Influenced by such stars as Frank Sinatra, Tony Bennett and Nat 'King' Cole, he has occasionally made minor concessions to the contemporary pop market while skilfully avoiding any major deviation from his easy-listening base. He has rarely been out of the public eye since his initial breakthrough. For many years, he held the all-time records for both the longest-running single and longest-running album on the American charts.
Born in San Francisco, Mathis was given vocal lessons by his father, a former vaudeville artist. Setting a local high-jump record at San Francisco State College, Johnny possessed the potential for an athletic career but decided upon music. In 1956 the 21 year-old singer released his first album. He initially moved in a jazz direction, but quickly switched to popular ballads at the instigation of Columbia Records' A&R wizard Mitch Miller. Defying the prevalent rock'n'roll trend of the day, *Wonderful! wonderful!* reached No.14 on the US singles charts in 1957; it remained on the Billboard listings for 39 weeks, a precedent that remained unbeaten until 1978. Also in '57, *Chances are* became a US chart-topper for Mathis.
By 1958 the singer had already enjoyed so much success that the album *Johnny's greatest hits* was issued. It logged a staggering 490 weeks on the American Lp chart, a feat that remained unequalled until 1983. Meanwhile, the US Top 40 singles kept coming until 1963, after which the Beatles and their ilk took over the singles charts. Mathis' biggest British hits of the late Fifties and early Sixties were *A certain smile* (No.4 in 1958), *Someone* (No.6 in 1959) and *My love for you* (No.9 in 1960).
Mathis made a return to the British Top 10 in 1975 with a cover version of the Stylistics' sweet soul standard *I'm stone in love with you*; this was produced and co-written the 1972 original. 18 1/2 years after he had first penetated the UK charts, Mathis achieved his first No.1 single at Christmas 1976 with the moving *When a child is born*. In 1977 and 1980 he topped the British album listings with *The Johnny Mathis collection* and *Tears and laughter* respectively. 1978 saw Mathis reach the US No.1 position with *Too much too little too late*, a duet with soul star Deniece Williams. This was the first time Johnny had ever released a duet. Its success prompted him to make records with the likes of Glady's Knight, Dionne Warwick and Natalie Cole, although none reaped the same rewards as *Too much too little too late*. In 1983, after a quarter of a century of being adored by legions of female fans, Mathis suddenly admitted that he was gay. The voice remained the same, but an important aspect of his image and charisma had been destroyed. (Bob MacDonald, 24th Jan 1986).

BEST OF EVERYTHING
Tracks: / Best of everything.
7" Single: Released Nov '59, on Fontana, by Phonogram Ltd. Deleted '62. Catalogue no: **H 218**

CERTAIN SMILE, A
Tracks: / Certain smile, A.
7" Single: Released Sep '58, on Fontana, by Phonogram Ltd. Deleted '61. Catalogue no: **H 142**

DAYDREAMIN'
Tracks: / Daydreamin' (remix) / Simple / Gone gone gone (on 7" only.) / When a child is born (Only on 7" EP.) / When a child is born (featuring Gladys Knight. Only on 7" EP.).
7" Single: Released Apr '89, on CBS, by CBS Records. Deleted Oct '89. Catalogue no: **654 7737**
7" EP: Released Dec '88, on CBS, by CBS Records. Deleted Mar '89. Catalogue no: **653 191 0**
CD 5": Released Apr '89, on CBS, by CBS Records. Deleted Oct '89. Catalogue no: **654 7732**
CD 5": Released 28 Nov '88, on CBS, by CBS Records. Deleted Mar '89. Catalogue no: **653191 2**
12" Single: Released Apr '89, on CBS, by CBS Records. Deleted Oct '89. Catalogue no: **654 7736**
7" Single: Released 21 Nov '88, on CBS, by CBS Records. Deleted Mar '89. Catalogue no: **653191 7**
7" Single: Released Apr '89, on CBS, by CBS Records. Deleted Oct '89. Catalogue no: **654 7730**
12" Single: Released 21 Nov '88, on CBS, by CBS Records. Deleted Mar '89. Catalogue no: **653191 6**

GONE GONE GONE
Tracks: / Gone gone gone.
7" Single: Released Aug '79, on CBS, by CBS Records. Deleted '82. Catalogue no: **CBS 7730**

I'LL DO IT ALL FOR YOU
Tracks: / I'll do it all for you / Lights of Rio.
7" Single: Released 20 Jun '80, on CBS, by CBS Records. Deleted '83. Catalogue no: **CBS 8696**

I'M STONE IN LOVE WITH YOU (SINGLE)
Tracks: / I'm stone in love with you / Certain smile (Available on cassingle only.) / Misty (Available on cassingle only.) / Twelth of never (Available on cassingle only.).
7" Single: Released Jan '75, on CBS, by CBS Records. Deleted '78. Catalogue no: **CBS 2653**
7" Single: Released May '82, on CBS, by CBS Records. Catalogue no: **CBS 8868**

IT MIGHT AS WELL BE SPRING
Tracks: / It might as well be spring / When a child is born.
7" Single: Released Oct '86, on CBS, by CBS Records. Catalogue no: **650196 7**

LOVE WON'T LET ME WAIT
Tracks: / Love won't let me wait / Leave me to your love.
7" Single: Released Mar '84, on CBS, by CBS Records. Catalogue no: **A 4284**

MIDNIGHT BLUE
Tracks: / Midnight blue / Just the way you are.
7" Single: Released Feb '80, on CBS, by CBS Records. Deleted '83. Catalogue no: **CBS 8253**

MISTY (SINGLE)
Tracks: / Misty.
7" Single: Released Jan '60, on Fontana, by Phonogram Ltd. Deleted '63. Catalogue no: **H 219**

MY LOVE FOR YOU
Tracks: / My love for you.
7" Single: Released Oct '60, on Fontana, by Phonogram Ltd. Deleted '63. Catalogue no: **H 267**

ONE LOVE
Tracks: / One love.
7" Single: Released May '83, on CBS, by CBS Records. Catalogue no: **A 3423**

SIMPLE
Tracks: / Simple (Note) / We were never really out of love / Lead me to your love / Gone gone gone.
7" Single: Released May '86, on CBS, by CBS Records. Deleted '86. Catalogue no: **A 7195**
12" Single: Released May '86, on CBS, by CBS Records. Deleted '86. Catalogue no: **TA 7195**
7" Single: Released Aug '84, on CBS, by CBS Records. Catalogue no: **A 4529**

SO DEEP IN LOVE
Tracks: / So deep in love / I'm glad it's you.
7" Single: Released Jul '83, on CBS, by CBS Records. Catalogue no: **A 3628**

SOMEONE
Tracks: / Someone.
7" Single: Released Aug '59, on Fontana, by Phonogram Ltd. Deleted '62. Catalogue no: **H 199**

STARBRIGHT
Tracks: / Starbright.
7" Single: Released Jul '60, on Fontana, by Phonogram Ltd. Deleted '63. Catalogue no: **H 254**

TEACHER TEACHER
Tracks: / Teacher teacher.
7" Single: Released May '58, on Fontana, by Phonogram Ltd. Deleted '61. Catalogue

no: **H 130**

TWELFTH OF NEVER (OLD GOLD)
Tracks: / Twelfth of never / Wonderful, wonderful.
7" Single: Released 27 Feb '89, on Old Gold, by Old Gold Records. Catalogue no: **OG 9857**

WHAT WILL MY MARY SAY
Tracks: / What will my Mary say.
7" Single: Released Apr '63, on CBS, by CBS Records. Deleted '66. Catalogue no: **AAG 127**

WHEN A CHILD IS BORN
Tracks: / When a child is born / Lord's Prayer, The.
7" Single: Released Dec '81, on CBS, by CBS Records. Deleted '84. Catalogue no: **CBS S 1758**

WHEN A CHILD IS BORN (OLD GOLD)
Tracks: / When a child is born / I'm stone in love with you.
7" Single: Released 24 Apr '89, on Old Gold, by Old Gold Records. Catalogue no: **OG 9874**

WHEN A CHILD IS BORN (SINGLE)
Tracks: / When a child is born.
7" Single: Released Nov '76, on CBS, by CBS Records. Deleted '79. Catalogue no: **CBS 4599**

WINTER WONDERLAND
Tracks: / Winter wonderland.
7" Single: Released Dec '58, on Fontana, by Phonogram Ltd. Deleted '61. Catalogue no: **H 165**

YOU ARE BEAUTIFUL
Tracks: / You are beautiful.
7" Single: Released Mar '60, on Fontana, by Phonogram Ltd. Deleted '63. Catalogue no: **H 234**

YOU SAVED MY LIFE
Tracks: / You saved my life / Love.
7" Single: Released Jan '80, on CBS, by CBS Records. Deleted Jan '83. Catalogue no: **CBS 8151**
7" Single: Released Sep '81, on CBS, by CBS Records. Deleted '84. Catalogue no: **A 1602**

YOU'RE ALL I NEED TO GET BY
Tracks: / You're all I need to get by.
7" Single: Released Jul '78, on CBS, by CBS Records. Deleted '81. Catalogue no: **CBS 6483**

Mathis, Kathy

GOT TO GIVE IT UP
Tracks: / Got to give it up.
12" Single: Released Nov '88, on Tabu, Catalogue no: **4 Z 9 08159**

LATE NIGHT HOUR
Tracks: / Late night hour.
7" Single: Released May '87, on Tabu, Deleted Nov '87. Catalogue no: **650806 7**

Matic 16

GET MYSELF TOGETHER
Tracks: / Get myself together.
12" Single: Released Jan '83, on LC Outernational, Catalogue no: **LC 004 12**
7" Single: Released Jan '83, on LC Outernational, Catalogue no: **LC 004**

NO MONEY TODAY
Tracks: / No money today.
12" Single: Released Oct '82, on Regent, Deleted '87. Catalogue no: **RGTDS 1001**

SAY YOU WANT ME
Tracks: / Say you want me.
12" Single: Released Jul '83, on Conqueror, Catalogue no: **CLN 1**

Matinee Idols

WHO'LL BE THE NEXT IN LINE?
Tracks: / Who'll be next in line.
7" Single: Released Nov '83, on President, by President Records. Catalogue no: **PT 520**

Matsubara, Masaki

DA-BA-DA
Tracks: / Da ba da.
7" Single: Released Jul '86, on LOE, by LOE Records. Deleted '88. Catalogue no: **ROSH 50**
12" Single: Released Jul '86, on LOE, by LOE Records. Deleted '88. Catalogue no: **ROSHX 50**

Matt Bianco

CAN'T STAND IT ANYMORE
Tracks: / Can't stand it anymore / Can't stand it anymore (inst.).
12" Single: Released Feb '86, on WEA, by WEA Records. Catalogue no: **YZ 62T**
7" Single: Released Feb '86, on WEA, by WEA Records. Catalogue no: **YZ 62**

DANCING IN THE STREET
Tracks: / Dancing in the street / Dancing in the street (inst) / Just can't stand it (live) (On 12" version only.).
7" Single: Released May '86, on WEA, by WEA Records. Deleted Jun '87. Catalogue no: **YZ 72**
12" Single: Released May '86, on WEA, by WEA Records. Deleted Jun '87. Catalogue no: **YZ 72T**

DON'T BLAME IT ON THE GIRL
Tracks: / Don't blame it on the girl / Latin house.
CD 5": Released May '88, on WEA, by WEA Records. Catalogue no: **YZ 188CD**
7" Single: Released May '88, on WEA, by WEA Records. Catalogue no: **YZ 188**
12" Single: Released May '88, on WEA, by WEA Records. Catalogue no: **YZ 188T**

GET OUT OF YOUR LAZY BED
Tracks: / Get out of your lazy bed.
7" Single: Released Feb '84, on WEA, by WEA Records. Deleted '87. Catalogue no: **BIANCO 1**

GOOD TIMES
Tracks: / Good times / Tumbao.
CD 5": Released Aug '88, on WEA, by WEA Records. Catalogue no: **YZ 302 CD**
7" Single: Released Jul '88, on WEA, by WEA Records. Catalogue no: **YZ 302**
12" Single: Released Jul '88, on WEA, by WEA Records. Catalogue no: **YZ 302 T**

HALF A MINUTE
Tracks: / Half a minute.
12" Single: Released Oct '84, on WEA, by WEA Records. Deleted Jun '87. Catalogue no: **YZ 26T**
7" Single: Released Oct '84, on WEA, by WEA Records. Catalogue no: **YZ 26**

I JUST CAN'T STAND IT
Tracks: / I just can't stand it.
7" Single: Released Mar '86, on WEA, by WEA Records. Deleted '89. Catalogue no: **YZ 62**

MORE THAN I CAN BEAR
Tracks: / More than I can bear.
12" Single: Released Feb '85, on WEA, by WEA Records. Deleted Jun '87. Catalogue no: **YZ 34T**
7" Single: Released Feb '85, on WEA, by WEA Records. Catalogue no: **YZ 34**

NERVOUS
Tracks: / Nervous / Wap bam boogie.
7" Single: Released Nov '88, on WEA, by WEA Records. Catalogue no: **YZ 328**
CD 5": Released Jan '89, on WEA, by WEA Records. Catalogue no: **YZ 328CD**
12" Single: Released Nov '88, on WEA, by WEA Records. Catalogue no: **YZ 328T**

SAY IT'S NOT TOO LATE
Tracks: / Say it's not too late.
CD 5": Released May '89, on WEA, by WEA Records. Catalogue no: **YZ 388CD**
7" Single: Released Apr '89, on WEA, by WEA Records. Catalogue no: **YZ 388**
Cassingle: Released May '89, on WEA, by WEA Records. Catalogue no: **YZ 388 C**
12" Single: Released May '89, on WEA, by WEA Records. Catalogue no: **YZ 388T**

SNEAKING OUT THE BACKDOOR
Tracks: / Sneaking out the backdoor / Matt's mood.
7" Single: Released Apr '84, on WEA, by WEA Records. Deleted '87. Catalogue no: **YZ 3**
7" Pic: Released May '84, on WEA, by WEA Records. Catalogue no: **YZ 3P**

WAP BAM BOOGIE
Tracks: / Wap bam boogie.
7" Single: Released Jul '88, on WEA, by WEA Records. Catalogue no: **YZ 188R**

YEAH YEAH
Tracks: / Yeah yeah.
7" Single: Released Sep '85, on WEA, by WEA Records. Catalogue no: **YZ 46**
12" Single: Released Sep '85, on WEA, by WEA Records. Deleted Jan '88. Catalogue no: **YZ 46T**

Mattea, Kathy

18 WHEELS & A DOZEN ROSES
Tracks: / 18 wheels and a dozen roses / Goin' gone.
Note: The current American No. 1 Country single taken from her new album "UNTASTED HONEY".
7" Single: Released 6 Jun '88, on Mercury, by Phonogram Ltd. Deleted Oct '88. Catalogue no: **MER 268**

GOIN' GONE
Tracks: / Goin' gone / Every love.
7" Single: Released Mar '88, on Mercury, by Phonogram Ltd. Deleted Oct '88. Catalogue no: **MER 260**

Matthews, Al

FOOL
Tracks: / Fool.
7" Single: Released Aug '75, on CBS, by CBS Records. Deleted '78. Catalogue no: **CBS 3429**

Matthews, Ian

CRYING IN THE NIGHT
Tracks: / Crying in the night / Live.
7" Single: Released Feb '80, on Rockburgh, Deleted Feb '83. Catalogue no: **ROCS 218**

Matthews Southern

Biographical details: At the time of their No.1 smash, this British band consisted of singer/songwriter/guitarist Ian Matthews plus Carl Barnwell, Ray Duffy, Mark Griffiths, Gordon Huntley and Andy Leigh. In 1967 Ian Matthews was a founder member of the highly influential folk group Fairport Convention. He quit in 1969 over musical differences. *Matthews' Southern Comfort* began life as the title of his first solo album, issued in January 1970. Partly written and produced by pop avengalis Ken Howard & Alan Blaikley, the Lp received sufficient critical acclaim to warrant the formation of a band bearing its title. The prolific group released two more albums before the end of 1970, *Second spring* and *Later that same year.* Working in a soft, country-rock vein, these established MSC as the UK's first West Coast type band. To crown 1970, Matthews' Southern Comfort achieved a sudden UK No.1 single in the autumn of that year with *Woodstock*, a cover version of Joni Mitchell's tribute to the legendary 1969 rock festival. The single reached No.23 in America, where Crosby, Stills, Nash & Young had already scored a hit with their hard rock rendition of the same song. In the event, MSC were a short-lived wonder. The restless Matthews broke away from the band at the end of 1970 to pursue a solo career. Barnwell led the remainder of the group, simply known as Southern Comfort, through three unsuccessful albums; the combo died a natural death in late 1972. Apart from a brief 1972 period with an unsuccessful band called Plainsong, Matthews' solo career lasted throughout the Seventies and into the Eighties. With his soft and pleasant tenor voice, he became better known for his interpretations of other people's songs than for his own compositions. Generally recording in a folk-rock manner, he was a underrated cult figure whose only taste of solo commercial success was an American Top 20 single in 1979 with *Shake it.* His limited success was probably due to his tempermental personality, which resulted in frequent changes of record company, management and backing musicians. (Bob MacDonald, 25th Jan 1986).

WOODSTOCK (OLD GOLD)
Tracks: / Woodstock / Joy to the world.
7" Single: Released Jun '88, on Old Gold, by Old Gold Records. Catalogue no: **OG 9795**

WOODSTOCK (SINGLE)
Tracks: / Woodstock.
7" Single: Released Sep '70, on MCA, by MCA Records. Deleted '73. Catalogue no: **UNS 526**
CD 5": Released Aug '89, on MCA, by MCA Records. Catalogue no: **2574542**
7" Single: Released Aug '89, on MCA, by MCA Records. Catalogue no: **2574567**
12" Single: Released Aug '89, on MCA, by MCA Records. Catalogue no: **2574540**

Mattis, Errol

ALL TIME LOVER
Tracks: / All time lover.
12" Single: Released Sep '88, on Grooveatron, Catalogue no: **GAT 05**

Matty, Marie

DREAMING
Tracks: / Dreaming / Dreaming (inst).
12" Single: Released Feb '86, on Londisc, by Londisc Records. Catalogue no: **12 LDR 053**

Matumbi

Biographical details: At the time of their sole UK pop chart entry, this British reggae band consisted of Eaton Blake, Dennis Bovell, Lloyd Donaldson, Bevin Fagan, Webster Johnson, Euton Jones and Glaister Venn. Formed in the Battersea district of London in 1971, Matumbi were at the forefront of the cult scene which imported the indigenous music of Jamaica into the inner cities of Britain. The group helped to pioneer the mellow mix of soul and reggae that eventually became known as lovers' rock. They gradually built up their following during the Seventies. As often with acts of their genre, the band's music appeared at various times on several different labels; they wet up their own Matumbi label in the late Seventies, which led to legal disputes with the famous Trojan reggae company, with whom they had previously been associated. 1979 brought the act their only taste of national chart success, when the single *Point of view* reached the UK No.35 position. Meanwhile the group's lead guitarist and vocalist Dennis Bovell (also known as Bluebeard) began to make a name for itself as one of Britain's top reggae producers. In addition to musical artists, he also nurtured the career of reggae poet Linton Kwesi Johnson. Bovell occasionally ventured into the field of rock, working in the studio with acts like The Pop Group, The Slits, The Thompson Twins and Orange Juice. Matumbi continued into the Eighties, although the distraction of Bovell's outside activities meant that the band's importance diminished somewhat. (Bob MacDonald, 25th Jan 1986).

ALIVE AND KICKING
Tracks: / Alive and kicking.
7" Single: Released Jan '84, on MR, Catalogue no: **MR 001**
12" Single: Released Jan '84, on MR, Catalogue no: **MR 12006**

IN DAYLIGHT
Tracks: / In daylight.
7" Single: Released Jul '82, on Solid Groove, Catalogue no: **SGS 013**
12" Single: Released Jul '82, on Solid Groove, Catalogue no: **SG 013**

MAN IN ME, THE
Tracks: / Man in me, The.
12" Single: on Trojan, by Trojan Records. Deleted May '88. Catalogue no: **TRT 9061**
7" Single: on Trojan, by Trojan Records. Deleted May '88. Catalogue no: **TRO 9061**

NOTHING AT ALL
Tracks: / Nothing at all / Breakdown.
7" Single: Released Oct '80, on EMI, by EMI Records. Deleted Oct '83. Catalogue no: **EMI 5116**
12" Single: Released Oct '80, on EMI, by EMI Records. Deleted Oct '83. Catalogue no: **12EMI 5116**

POINT OF VIEW
Tracks: / Point of view.
7" Single: Released Sep '79, on Matumbi Music, Deleted '82. Catalogue no: **RIC 101**

Mau Maus

FACTS OF WAR
Tracks: / Facts of war.
7" EP: Released Jun '83, on Paragon, Catalogue no: **PAX 12**

NO CONCERN
Tracks: / No concern / Clampdown / Why do.
7" Single: Released Nov '82, on Pax, by Pax Records. Catalogue no: **PAX 8**

NOWHERE TO RUN EP
Tracks: / Nowhere to run.
12" Single: Released 13 Jun '85, on Rebellion, Catalogue no: **REB 12002**

SCARRED FOR LIFE
Tracks: / Scarred for life.
12" Single: Released Jun '85, on Rebellion, Catalogue no: **REBEL 1202**

SOCIETY'S REJECTS
Tracks: / Society's rejects.
7" Single: Released Aug '82, on Pax, by Pax Records. Catalogue no: **PAX 6**

TEAR DOWN THE WALLS
Tracks: / Tear down the walls.
7" Single: Released 13 Jun '85, on Rebellion, Catalogue no: **REBEL 701**

Maughan, Susan

Biographical details: This British singer enjoyed a one-off smash single in the UK in late 1962, a hit that epitomised the uninpiring state of the country's pop establishment at that time. Maughan was launched as the next Helen Shapiro, the fifteen year old schoolgirl-turned-star who had been riding high on the British charts during the preceding 18 months. Susan stormed to No.3 in the UK with *Bobby's girl*, a quick fire cover version of a current American No.3 hit by Marcie Blane. *Bobby's girl* was a good, fun, catchy pop record; but the trouble was that both the song and singer were totally lacking in originality or imagination. It was highly signigicant that the Maughan disc entered the chart on the same week as *Love me do*, the first hit by a group called the Beatles. Their rapid impact could be witnessed by looking at the chart peaks of Susan's 1963 hits: *Hand a handkerchief to Helen* (a somewhat unwise dig at the declining fortunes of a certain other female vocalist) reached No.41 and *She's new to you* got to No.45. (Bob MacDonald, 25th Jan 1986).

BOBBY'S GIRL
Tracks: / Bobby's girl.
7" Single: Released Oct '80, on Phonogram, by Phonogram Ltd. Deleted Oct '83. Catalogue no: **CUT 102**
7" Single: Released Oct '62, on Philips, by Phonogram Ltd. Deleted '65. Catalogue no: **326544 BF**

BOBBY'S GIRL (OLD GOLD)
Tracks: / Bobby's girl.
7" Single: Released Jul '82, on Old Gold, by Old Gold Records. Deleted '87. Catalogue no: **OG 9247**

HAND A HANKERCHIEF TO HELEN
Tracks: / Hand a hankerchief to Helen.
7" Single: Released Feb '63, on Philips, by Phonogram Ltd. Deleted '66. Catalogue no: **326562 BF**

SHE'S NEW TO YOU
Tracks: / She's new to you.

7" Single: Released May '63, on Philips, by Phonogram Ltd. Deleted '66. Catalogue no: **326586 BF**

Maureen

DON'T FIGHT THE MUSIC
Tracks: / Don't fight the music.
7" Single: Released Jun '89, on Danceyard, by Danceyard Records. Catalogue no: **YARD 7**
12" Single: Released Jun '89, on Danceyard, by Danceyard Records. Catalogue no: **YARDT 7**

LOVE IS ALL
Tracks: / Love is all.
7" Single: Released Apr '80, on Klub, by Klub Records. Catalogue no: **KLUB 24**
7" Single: Released Apr '80, on Klub, by Klub Records. Deleted '83. Catalogue no: **KLUB 24**

Mauriat, Paul

Biographical details: This French orchestra leader, conductor and arranger was born in 1925 and started studying music at the age of four. The family moved from Marselle to Paris when he was ten, where Paul studied at the famed Conservatoire. He formed his first orchestra at 17, and spent several years taking it around the concert halls and cabaret venues of France and continental Europe. During the Fifties and Sixties, he became one of his country's top conductor-arrangers, thanks to his work with such singers as Charles Aznavour and to his series of albums containing orchestrated cover versions of pop hits. Maurist co-composed a pop hit in 1962, when Petula Clark achieved a European million-seller with *Chariot.* The following year the song became a US No.1 single for Little Peggy March under the title *I will follow him.*
In 1968 Paul Maurist enjoyed an international smash hit in his own right with *Love is blue*, a song that had originally been sung to no great avail by Vidky Leandros as the Luxembourg entry in the 1967 Eurovision Song Contest. Paul saw the potential of the tune, and took his instumental version to No.1 in America for five weeks and No.12 in Britain. In addition, his *Blooming hits* Lp was a big seller in the States. Despite all this success, however, Mauriat subsequently concentated on the European market once more. Like James Last in Germany, he knew he was onto a good thing with his endless albums of middle-of-the-road cover versions. (Bob MacDonald, 25th Jan 1986).

LOVE IS BLUE (SINGLE)
Tracks: / Love is blue.
7" Single: Released Feb '68, on Philips, by Phonogram Ltd. Deleted '71. Catalogue no: **BF 1637**

Maurice

THIS IS ACID (A NEW DANCE CRAZE)
Tracks: / This is acid / This is acid (version).
12" Single: Released Dec '88, on A&M, by A&M Records. Catalogue no: **USAT 650**
7" Single: Released Dec '88, on A&M, by A&M Records. Catalogue no: **USA 650**

Maurison, Oliver

IS LOVE
Tracks: / Is love / Chance on romance.
7" Single: Released Jan '80, on Authentic Records, by MHB Records. Catalogue no: **MHB 01**
12" Single: Released Jan '80, on Authentic Records, by MHB Records. Catalogue no: **MHB 1201**

Mave & Dave

DO YOU REALLY WANT MY LOVE
Tracks: / Do you really want my love / You are delicious.
7" Single: Released Nov '80, on Red Stripe, Catalogue no: **SON 2215**

Mawasi

BRIDGES
Tracks: / Bridges.
12" Single: Released Apr '85, on Londisc, by Londisc Records. Catalogue no: **LDR 040**

Max

LITTLE GHOST
Tracks: / Little ghost.
7" Single: Released Aug '87, on Chrysalis, by Chrysalis Records. Catalogue no: **CHS 3154**

Max Berlin's

ELLE ET MOI
Tracks: / Elle et moi.
7" Single: Released 1 Jun '87, on Prestige, Catalogue no: **USA 50**
12" Single: Released 1 Jun '87, on Prestige, Catalogue no: **USA 1050**

Max, Billy

TWO HUNDRED PER CENT DEVOTION
Tracks: / Two hundred per cent devotion / Sunshine.
7" Single: Released Apr '80, on AMI, by AMI Records. Deleted Apr '83. Catalogue no: **AIS 102**

Max Q

WAY OF THE WORLD
Tracks: / Way of the world / Zero 2-0 / Ghost of the year.
12" Single: Released Sep '89, on Mercury, by Phonogram Ltd. Catalogue no: **MXQ 112**
CD 5": Released Sep '89, on Mercury, by Phonogram Ltd. Catalogue no: **MXQCD 1**
Cassingle: Released Sep '89, on Mercury, by Phonogram Ltd. Catalogue no: **MXQMC 1**
7" Single: Released Sep '89, on Mercury, by Phonogram Ltd. Catalogue no: **MXQ 1**

Maxeen

IS IT MEANT TO BE THIS WAY
Tracks: / Is it meant to be this way.
12" Single: Released Jan '89, on Body Rock, Catalogue no: **12BR 2**
12" Single: Released Nov '88, on Blue Bird (1), by Blue Sun Records (USA). Catalogue no: **BRT 002**

LAST TIME
Tracks: / Last time / Last time (version).
12" Single: Released Sep '89, on Total, Catalogue no: **12SOUL 12**

Maximum Joy

DO IT TODAY
Tracks: / Do it today / Touchdown.
7" Single: Released Aug '82, on Fontana, by Phonogram Ltd. Catalogue no: **CLUB 1**

IN THE AIR
Tracks: / In the air / Simmer til done.
12" Single: Released Jul '82, on Y, Catalogue no: **12Y 26**
7" Single: Released Jul '82, on Y, Catalogue no: **Y 26**

STRETCH
Tracks: / Stretch / Silent street.
12" Single: Released Oct '81, on Y, Catalogue no: **Y 11T**
7" Single: Released Oct '81, on Y, Catalogue no: **Y 11**

WHITE AND GREEN PLACE
Tracks: / White and green place / Building bridges.
7" Single: Released Feb '82, on Y, Catalogue no: **Y 15**
12" Single: Released Feb '82, on Y, Catalogue no: **12Y 15**

WHY CAN'T WE LIVE TOGETHER
Tracks: / Why can't we live together.
7" Single: Released Apr '83, on Garage (2), by Garage Records. Catalogue no: **GAR 1**

Maximum Penetration

MAXIMUM PENETRATION
Tracks: / Maximum penetration.
7" Single: Released Jan '80, on Sidewalk, by Sidewalk Records. Deleted Jan '83. Catalogue no: **SID 115**
12" Single: Released Jan '80, on Sidewalk, by Sidewalk Records. Deleted Jan '83. Catalogue no: **12SID 115**

Maximus Three

MAXIMUS PARTY
Tracks: / Maximus party.
12" Single: Released Feb '83, on Eclipse, Catalogue no: **SG 022**

Maxine

1984
Tracks: / 1984 / In love.
7" Single: Released Jan '84, on Chrysalis, by Chrysalis Records. Catalogue no: **CHS 1984**
12" Single: Released Jan '84, on Chrysalis, by Chrysalis Records. Catalogue no: **CHS 12 1984**

TO KNOW YOU IS TO LOVE YOU
Tracks: / To know you is to love you.
7" Single: Released Oct '82, on Olympic (1), by Olympic Records. Catalogue no: **SEB 1**

Maxine, Brian

HIGHWAY FEVER
Tracks: / Highway fever.
7" Single: Released Jul '81, on Subway, by Subway Records. Catalogue no: **TUBE 001**

Maxx

COCAINE
Tracks: / Cocaine.
7" Single: Released Aug '89, on BCM Records, Catalogue no: **BCM 009**
CD 5": Released Aug '89, on BCM Records, Catalogue no: **BCM 009CD**
12" Single: Released Aug '89, on BCM Records, Catalogue no: **BCM 009X**

May, Billy

Biographical details: May, Billy This American orchestra leader, conductor and arranger was an important behind-the-scenes figure in the Los Angeles music scene during the Forties and Fifties. His imaginative arrangements graced the records of many artists on Capitol, the label for which he worked. His association with Frank Sinatra was particularly notable, as were his liaisons with Peggy Lee and Nat 'King' Cole. In 1956 May scored a one-off UK chart entry with the main title theme from *The Man With The Golden Arm.* This single reached no. 9 which compensated for the fact that in America he was beaten by a host of rival versions of the movie tune. Bob McDonald, June 1985.

MAIN TITLE THEME FROM MAN WITH THE GOLDEN ARM
Tracks: / Man with the golden arm, Theme from.
7" Single: Released Apr '56, on Capitol, by EMI Records. Deleted '59. Catalogue no: **CL 14551**

May, Brian

Biographical details: May, Brian The revered Queen guitarist, famed for his long-serving self-made 'May Axe' instrument, recorded the album *Star Fleet Project* in 1983 during a break in group activities. But it was not a solo record - he enlisted the aid of several friends in the music business including guitarist Eddie Van Halen and REO Speedwagon's drummer Alan Gratzer. *Star Fleet Project* was a mini-LP containing three tracks and 30 minutes of music. The length and loose structure of these bluesy rock cuts led to cries of self-indulgence from rock critics. It was not intended as an overtly commercial venture, so it was no surprise that the mini-album was merely a modest success. Credited to Brian May and Friends, the LP yielded the minor hit single *Star Fleet*, which reached No. 65 on the UK chart in November '83; this was an edited version of the title track. Bob McDonald, 25 January 1986.

STAR FLEET (SINGLE)
Tracks: / Star fleet.
7" Single: Released Nov '83, on EMI, by EMI Records. Deleted '86. Catalogue no: **EMI 5436**

May Day

NUDE PHOTO '88
Tracks: / Nude photo '88 / Nude photo '88 (version).
12" Single: Released Mar '88, on Kool Kat, by Kool Kat Records. Catalogue no: **KOOLT 14**

SAVE THE CHILDREN
Tracks: / Save the children.
7" Single: Released Oct '85, on Ritz, by Ritz Records. Catalogue no: **RITZ 127**

May, Mary

ANYONE WHO HAD A HEART
Tracks: / Anyone who had a heart.
7" Single: Released Feb '64, on Fontana, by Phonogram Ltd. Deleted '67. Catalogue no: **TF 440**

May, Simon

EASTENDERS
Tracks: / Eastenders.
7" Single: Released Feb '85, on BBC, by BBC Records & Tapes. Deleted '87. Catalogue no: **RESL 160**

GLORY BE (Eastenders' hymn)
Tracks: / Glory be.
7" Single: Released Nov '88, on Polydor, by Polydor Ltd. Deleted 30 May '89. Catalogue no: **RUR 2**

HOLIDAY SUITE, THE
Tracks: / Holiday suite / Holiday tracks / Holiday club (Extra track on 12" version only).
7" Single: Released Mar '86, on BBC, by BBC Records & Tapes. Deleted 31 Aug '88. Catalogue no: **RESL 181**
12" Single: Released Mar '86, on BBC, by BBC Records & Tapes. Deleted 31 Aug '88. Catalogue no: **12RSL 181**

HOWARDS WAY
Tracks: / Howards way.
7" Single: Released Oct '85, on BBC, by BBC Records & Tapes. Deleted '88. Catalogue no: **RESL 174**

OLYMPIC THEME, THE
Tracks: / Olympic theme, The (ITV).
7" Single: Released 16 Sep '88, on Polydor, by Polydor Ltd. Catalogue no: **RUR 1**
12" Single: Released 16 Sep '88, on Polydor, by Polydor Ltd. Catalogue no: **RURX 1**

SUMMER OF MY LIFE
Tracks: / Summer of my life.
7" Single: Released Oct '76, on Pye, Deleted '79. Catalogue no: **7N 45627**

WE'LL GATHER LILACS - ALL MY LOVING
Tracks: / We'll gather lilacs - all my loving.
7" Single: Released May '77, on Pye, Deleted '80. Catalogue no: **7N 45688**

Mayall, John

Biographical details: Mayall, John This British vocalist, guitarist, keyboards player, harmonica player and composer was one of the three vital catalysts of the UK's blues boom of the Sixties. The others were Graham Bond and Alexis Korner - between them, these three men fathered and nurtured a movement which produced many of Britain's leading rock and pop stars.

Born in 1933, Mayall learned piano and guitar during his teens. He grew up in Manchester. He did not become a full time professional until 1963, the year he reached the age of 30. Prior to that, he had a variety of occupations including two years' national service in the army, four years at Manchester's Regional College of Art and a job in the art studio of an advertising agency. Finally, Korner persuaded him that he could transform his passion for music into a full-time career provided he moved to London. This he did, and thus began an extraordinary saga.

From 1963 until 1970 John was the boss of John Mayall's Bluesbreakers, one of the most influential forces in the British music scene of the era. According to Pete Frame's invaluable book "Rock Family Trees", there were no less than fifteen different lineups of this band. Amongst the future stars who passed through the Bluesbreakers were John McVie (Fleetwood Mac), Hughie Flint (McGuinness Flint), Jack Bruce (Cream), Peter Green and Mick Fleetwood (both Fleetwood Mac), Aynsley Dunbar (various bands), Andy Fraser, (Free) and Mick Taylor (The Rolling Stones). But the most important of all was guitar wizard Eric Clapton, the ex-Yardbird whose performances in the Bluesbreakers led some fans to instigate a graffiti campaign proclaiming 'Clapton Is God'. Clapton's stint with the band gave Mayall his first hit album in 1966 - it was a truly remarkable achievement for a blues LP to reach the Top 10. This success paved the way for Clapton's future illustrious career.

John Mayall's Bluesbreakers enjoyed further UK Top 10 albums with *A Hard Road* and *Crusade* (both 1967), *Bare Wires* (1968) and *Empty Rooms* (1970). Because his singles were not hits, and because he made no concessions to the pop market, Mayall remained a cult figure rather than a pop star; but the music scene of the era might have looked very different without him.

He moved from London to California in 1970. The Bluesbreakers ceased to exist but, true to form, Mayall assembled a new American band with a host of never-ending personnel changes. He continued releasing albums through the Seventies, but his influence and success had waned.

Perhaps the two finest tracks of his career were *Hideaway* and *Steppin' Out* from the Eric Clapton period. Another great moment was *Stormy Monday*, which can be found on the *Looking Back* compilation. Bob McDonald, 25 January 1986.

JOHN LEE BOOGIE
Tracks: / John Lee boogie / Why worry / Mama talk to your daughter.
7" Single: Released Jun '81, on DJM, Catalogue no: **DJS 10960**
7" Single: Released '82, on DJM, Catalogue no: **DJS 10969**

Mayana

SHAKIN' ALL OVER
Tracks: / Shakin' all over / Skips a beat.
12" Single: Released Oct '83, on UNKNOWN, Catalogue no: **12 GRAFT 3**
7" Single: Released Oct '83, on UNKNOWN, Catalogue no: **GRAFT 3**

SKIPS A BEAT
Tracks: / Skips a beat / No love on the run.
7" Single: Released Jul '83, on UNKNOWN, Catalogue no: **GRAFT 2**
12" Single: Released Jul '83, on UNKNOWN, Catalogue no: **12 GRAFT 2**

Maybe Baby

HIT THE FLOOR
Tracks: / Hit the floor / Dreaming.
12" Single: Released 23 Apr '88, on Free Booze, by Magnum Music Group. Catalogue no: **PINT 1519X**
7" Single: Released Mar '88, on Free Booze, by Magnum Music Group. Catalogue no: **PINT 1519**

Mayday

DAY AFTER DAY
Tracks: / Day after day.
7" Single: Released May '80, on Reddingtons, Deleted '82. Catalogue no: **DAN 2**

Mayer, Laurie

DUST IN THE WIND
Tracks: / Dust in the wind / Bright blue Nile.
Note: Double 'A' side
7" Single: Released 30 May '87, on Y 11, by Y 11 Records. Catalogue no: **T11T 003**
12" Single: Released Jun '87, on Y 11, by Y 11 Records. Catalogue no: **Y11T 003**

Mayfair

SUMMERTIME CITY
Tracks: / Summertime city / American girls.

7" Single: Released Jul '84, on Mayfair, Catalogue no: **FAIR 1**

Mayfair Charm School

MONTAGUE TERRACE (IN BLUE)
Tracks: / Montague Terrace (in blue) / Little black dress.
7" Single: Released Nov '96, on El, by Cherry Red Records. Catalogue no: **GPO 19**

Mayfield, Curtis

Biographical details: Mayfield, Curtis This American soul singer, songwriter and producer was born in Chicago, and was only 15 years old when he formed a vocal group called The Impressions with 18-year-old singer Jerry Butler in 1958. The group quickly achieved a No. 11 hit on the US pop charts with the beautiful R&B ballad *For Your Precious Love*. Because the record was credited to Jerry Butler and the Impressions, Butler suddenly found himself with a high public profile while Mayfield was still a relatively unknown name. In the event, Jerry decided to launch a solo career while Curtis became the undisputed leader of the Impressions - both acts gave the soul world some of the greatest music of the Sixties.

Mayfield quit the Impressions in 1970 and launched a successful solo career; he also had the endless satisfaction of seeing other artists continually achievinf hits with his songs. In 1971 he registered his first solo US Top 40 single with *(Don't Worry) If There's A Hell Below, We're All Gonna Go*; the same year brought him some long overdue British recognition, when the classic *Move On Up* reached the UK No. 12 position.

In 1972 Mayfield was commissioned to score the music for 'Superfly', a movie inspired by the recent success of *Shaft* for which fellow black singer-composer Isaac Hayes had provided the soundtrack. The results for Mayfield were lucrative - his *Superfly* LP was a huge seller and spawned two US million selling singles, *Freddie's Dead* and the title track. During the mid-seventies, his own chart career faded and he concentrated on providing hits for other artists. *On And On* became a US Top 5 single for Gladys Knight and the Pips in 1974, and *Let's Do It Again* was an American No. 1 smash for the Staple Singers in 1975. In the following year Aretha Franklin reached the top of the US soul chart with *Something He Can Feel*. All of these were taken from Mayfield movie scores, which were often better than the films they accompanied. The Staples single was released on Curtom records, a label owned by Curtis which eventually folded.

Curtis Mayfield faded during the late Seventies. He tried to make a personal chart comeback with his singles *No Goodbyes* and *This Year*, but these failed to set the world alight. His decline was accelerated by the fact that, on both sides of the Atlantic, the word 'soul' was temproarily replaced by the term 'disco', a term with which Curtis had little affinity. But for what he had already achieved, Mayfield was assured of a place in musical history. Both during and after the Impressions, he had written a huge catalogue of songs that were moving and tasteful, whether he was dealing with love, religion or social issues. Bob McDonald, 25 January 1986.

BABY IT'S YOU
Tracks: / Baby it's you / Breakin' in the streets.
7" Single: Released Nov '86, on 98-6, Catalogue no: **CURT 1**
12" Single: Released Nov '86, on 98-6, Catalogue no: **CURT 1T**

IMO GIT U SUCKA
Tracks: / Imo git u sucker / He's a fly guy.
CD 5": Released May '89, on Curtom, Catalogue no: **CDCUR 102**
7" Single: Released May '89, on Curtom, Catalogue no: **7CUR 102**
12" Single: Released May '89, on Curtom, Catalogue no: **12CUR 102**

IT'S ALRIGHT
Tracks: / It's alright / Superfly.
7" Single: Released Oct '80, on Polydor, by Polydor Ltd. Catalogue no: **RSO 68**

MOVE ON UP
Tracks: / Move on up / Little child runnin' wild.
7" Single: Released Jan '83, on Flashback, by Mainline Records. Catalogue no: **FBS 23**
7" Single: Released Jul '71, on Buddah, by Buddah Records Inc.(USA). Deleted '74. Catalogue no: **2011 080**
7" Single: Released Jun '88, on Ichiban, by Ichiban Records (UK). Catalogue no: **7CUR 101**
12" Single: Released Jun '88, on Ichiban, by Ichiban Records (UK). Catalogue no: **12CUR 101**

NO GOODBYES
Tracks: / No goodbyes.
7" Single: Released Dec '78, on Atlantic, by WEA Records. Deleted '81. Catalogue no: **LV 1**

Mayhem

BLOOD RUSH
Tracks: / Blood rush / Addictive risk.
7" Single: Released Mar '85, on Vigilante, Catalogue no: **VIG 1**
12" Single: Released Mar '85, on Vigilante, Catalogue no: **VIG 1T**

GENTLE MURDER
Tracks: / Gentle murder.
7" Single: Released Aug '82, on Riot City, by Riot City Records. Catalogue no: **RIOT 13**
7" Single: Released Nov '83, on Riot City, by Riot City Records. Catalogue no: **RIOT 24**

Mayor, Ronnie

CAN'T WAIT 'TIL SUMMER COMES
Tracks: / Can't wait 'til summer comes.
7" Single: Released Aug '81, on Do-It, by Do-It Records. Catalogue no: **DUN15**

Maytals

54-46 WAS MY NUMBER
Tracks: / 54-46 was my number / Train to Skaville.
12" Single: Released Apr '84, on Trojan, by Trojan Records. Deleted May '88. Catalogue no: **TROT 9076**
7" Single: Released Apr '84, on Trojan, by Trojan Records. Deleted May '88. Catalogue no: **TRO 9076**

MONKEY MAN
Tracks: / Monkey man.
7" Single: Released Apr '70, on Trojan, by Trojan Records. Deleted '73. Catalogue no: **TR 7711**

Maytone, Vernon

MR POSTMAN
Tracks: / Mr. Postman.
12" Single: Released Sep '84, on Music Radics, Catalogue no: **Unknown**

Maywood

MOTHER HOW ARE YOU TODAY?
Tracks: / Mother how are you today / Let me know.
7" Single: Released Jun '80, on Logo, by Logo Records. Catalogue no: **GO 382**

Maze

Biographical details: Led by singer/songwriter/arranger/producer/manager Frankie Beverly (who takes a 'featuring' credit on most of the records), this American soul band have been together since the early Seventies. Success began to shine on the group during 1977-78, when they achieved entries on the US soul charts with such singles as *While I'm alone, Working together* and *Lady of magic*. Incorporating jazz influences into their music as well as straighahead funk, Maze were well able to keep pace with the always progressing needs of the black audiences. Maze made their first UK appearances in 1982, and became as big a sensation with soul fans in Britain as they were with aficionados on the other side of the Atlantic. The track *Joy and pain* became an infectious, communal anthem. By 1985 the attitudes of British music fans towards Maze fell into two distinct camps - those people who thought they were the greatest thing on Earth, and those who had never heard of them. This odd status was confirmed by the mammoth queues that gathered when tickets went on sale for their London shows - at this point eventually got one in the summer of '85 with the mediocre *Too many games*, it was the classic B side *Twilight* which garnered all the attention in discos. The mesmerising *Twilight* became the most played club record of the year, but it was widely ignored by radio.
Meanwhile, a similar story was going on in the States. The single *Back in stride* was a smash on the US black chart but barely dented the Hot 100 pop list. Beverly stated in a Billboard interview that he was in the business of playing soul music, and was not convinced that crossover to the pop charts was necessary. It would appear that he was right - 1985's *Can't stop the love* Lp was still a gold album in America. (Bob MacDonald, 26th Jan 1986).

BACK IN STRIDE
Tracks: / Back in stride.
7" Single: Released Feb '85, on Capitol, by EMI Records. Deleted '86. Catalogue no: **CL 353**
12" Single: Released Feb '85, on Capitol, by EMI Records. Catalogue no: **12CL 353**

BEFORE I LET GO
Tracks: / Before I let go / Golden time of day.
12" Single: Released Apr '82, on Capitol, by EMI Records. Deleted '85. Catalogue no: **12CL 244**
7" Single: Released Apr '82, on Capitol, by EMI Records. Deleted '85. Catalogue no: **CL 244**

CAN'T GET OVER YOU
Tracks: / Can't get over you / Africa.
12" Single: Released Aug '89, on Warner Bros., by WEA Records. Catalogue no: **W 2895 T**
7" Single: Released Aug '89, on Warner Bros., by WEA Records. Catalogue no: **W 2895**
CD 5": Released Aug '89, on Warner Bros., by WEA Records. Catalogue no: **W 2895 CD**

I WANNA BE WITH YOU
Tracks: / I wanna be with you / I wanna be with you (instrumental).
12" Single: Released Aug '86, on Capitol, by EMI Records. Deleted '88. Catalogue no: **12 CL 421**
7" Single: Released Aug '86, on Capitol, by EMI Records. Deleted '88. Catalogue no: **CL 421**

JOY & PAIN (SINGLE)
Tracks: / Joy & pain.
12" Single: Released Mar '82, on Capitol, by EMI Records. Catalogue no: **12CL 211**

JOY & PAIN (SINGLE) (2)
Tracks: / Joy and pain / Twilight (12" only.) / We are one.
CD 5": Released Jun '89, on Capitol, by EMI Records. Deleted Oct '89. Catalogue no: **203 369 2**
CD 5": Released Jun '89, on Capitol, by EMI Records. Deleted Oct '89. Catalogue no: **CDCL 531**
7" Single: Released May '89, on Capitol, by EMI Records. Catalogue no: **CL 531**
12" Single: Released May '89, on Capitol, by EMI Records. Catalogue no: **12CL 531**

LOVE IS THE KEY
Tracks: / Love is the key.
12" Single: Released Apr '83, on Capitol, by EMI Records. Deleted '88. Catalogue no: **12CL 290**
7" Single: Released Apr '83, on Capitol, by EMI Records. Deleted '88. Catalogue no: **CL 290**

TOO MANY GAMES
Tracks: / Too many games.
7" Single: Released Jul '85, on Capitol, by EMI Records. Deleted '88. Catalogue no: **CL 363**
12" Single: Released Jul '85, on Capitol, by EMI Records. Catalogue no: **12CLX 363**
12" Single: Released Jul '85, on Capitol, by EMI Records. Catalogue no: **12CL 363**

WE ARE ONE (SINGLE)
Tracks: / We are one / Right on time.
7" Single: Released Jun '83, on Capitol, by EMI Records. Deleted '88. Catalogue no: **CL 295**
12" Single: Released Jun '83, on Capitol, by EMI Records. Deleted '88. Catalogue no: **12 CL 295**

Mazelle, Kym

GOT TO GET YOU BACK
Tracks: / Got to get you back (radio mix) (Not on 12".) / Got to get you back (groovy piano mix) (CD single & 12 SY only.) / Got to get you back (amazella mix) (CD single & 12 SY only.) / Got to get you back (groovy instrumental mix) (7" & 12" only.) / Got to get you back (gettin' back mix) (12SYX only.) / Got to get you back (Saturday night special) (12SYX only.) / Got to get you back (club dub) (12SYX only.).
12" Single: Released Mar '89, on Syncopate, by EMI Records. Catalogue no: **12SY 25**
CD 5": Released Mar '89, on Syncopate, by EMI Records. Catalogue no: **CDSY 25**
7" Single: Released Mar '89, on Syncopate, by EMI Records. Catalogue no: **SY 25**
12" Single: Released Mar '89, on Syncopate, by EMI Records. Catalogue no: **12SYX 25**

I'M A LOVER
Tracks: / I'm a lover.
7" Single: Released Nov '88, on Republic, by Code Records. Catalogue no: **LIC 013**
7" Single: Released Nov '88, on Republic, by Code Records. Catalogue no: **LIC 013R**
12" Single: Released Nov '88, on Republic, by Code Records. Catalogue no: **LICT 013**

LOVE STRAIN
Tracks: / Love strain (radio version) (Not on 12".) / Love strain (sax strain) / Love strain (dub strain) (12" only.) / Love strain (Slam City club version) (CD single & 12" remix only.) / Love strain (Frankie foncett remix) (12" remix only.) / Love strain (deep dub) (12" remix only.).
12" Single: Released Sep '89, on Syncopate, by EMI Records. Catalogue no: **12SY 30**
CD 5": Released Sep '89, on Syncopate, by EMI Records. Catalogue no: **CDSY 30**
CD 5": Released Sep '89, on Syncopate, by EMI Records. Catalogue no: **203 534 2**
Cassingle: Released Sep '89, on Syncopate, by EMI Records. Catalogue no: **TCSY 30**
Cassingle: Released Sep '89, on Syncopate, by EMI Records. Catalogue no: **203 534 4**
7" Single: Released Sep '89, on Syncopate, by EMI Records. Catalogue no: **203 534 0**
7" Single: Released Sep '89, on Syncopate, by EMI Records. Catalogue no: **SY 30**
7" Single: Released Sep '89, on Syncopate, by EMI Records. Catalogue no: **SYP 30**
7" Single: Released Sep '89, on Syncopate, by EMI Records. Catalogue no: **203 534 7**
12" Single: Released Oct '89, on Syncopate, by EMI Records. Catalogue no: **12SYX 30**
12" Single: Released Oct '89, on Syncopate, by EMI Records. Catalogue no: **203 552 6**
12" Single: Released Sep '89, on Syncopate, by EMI Records. Catalogue no: **203 534 6**

USELESS (I DON'T NEED YOU NOW)
Tracks: / Useless - I don't need you now (radio mix) (7" & CD single only.) / Useless - I don't need you now (California mix) (7" only.) / Useless - I don't need you now (12" mix) (12" & CD single only.) / Useless - I don't need you now (deep house) (12" only.) / Useless - I don't need you now (ad lib dub) (12" only.) / Useless - I don't need you now (long club version) (12 special only.) / Useless - I don't need you now (after hours club) (12" special and CD single only.) / Useless - I don't need you now (dub mix) (12" special only.).
Note: Arranged, produced and mixed by Marshall Jefferson.
12" Single: Released Oct '88, on Syncopate, by EMI Records. Deleted Oct '89. Catalogue no: **12SYX 18**
CD 5": Released Oct '88, on Syncopate, by EMI Records. Deleted Oct '89. Catalogue no: **QDSY 18**
7" Single: Released Oct '88, on Syncopate, by EMI Records. Deleted Aug '89. Catalogue no: **SY 18**
12" Single: Released Oct '88, on Syncopate, by EMI Records. Deleted Oct '89. Catalogue no: **12SY 18**

MBS

OUT OF THE BLUE
Tracks: / Out of the blue / In the morning.
12" Single: Released Aug '83, on Star Track, Catalogue no: **ST 006**

M.C. Bam Bam

WIND ME UP
Tracks: / Wind me up.
7" Single: Released Oct '88, on Pow Wow (USA), Catalogue no: **PW 436**

M.C. Brooklyn

STYLE AND FASHION
Tracks: / Style and fashion / Poverty sucks.
12" Single: Released Nov '88, on Wax 'N' Butt, by Ghetto Music. Catalogue no: **POVT 1**

MC Buzz B

HOW SLEEP THE BRAVE
Tracks: / How sleep the brave / How sleep the brave (remix) (Available on 12" only).
12" Single: Released Mar '89, on Play Hard, by Play Hard Records. Catalogue no: **DEC 15**

HOW SLEEP THE BRAVE (FUTURE MIX)
Tracks: / How sleep the brave (future mix).
12" Single: Released Jul '89, on Play Hard, by Play Hard Records. Catalogue no: **DEC 16**

SLAP HEAD
Tracks: / Slap head.
12" Single: Released 14 May '88, on Play Hard, by Play Hard Records. Catalogue no: **DEC 009**

MC Choice

LET'S MAKE SOME NOISE
Tracks: / Let's make some noise.
12" Single: Released Feb '89, on Gee Street, by Gee Street Records. Catalogue no: **GEET 11**

MC Goldtop

JOURNEY INTO RAP
Tracks: / Journey into rap.
12" Single: Released Oct '88, on Gee Street, by Gee Street Records. Catalogue no: **GEE 12006**

MC & His Great...

KEEP YOUR SHOES ON
Tracks: / Keep your shoes on.
7" Single: Released May '82, on EMI, by EMI Records. Deleted '52. Catalogue no: **12 EMI 5302**
7" Single: Released May '82, on EMI, by EMI Records. Deleted '52. Catalogue no: **EMI 5302**

M.C. Mello

COMING CORRECT
Tracks: / Coming correct.

12" Single: Released 16 Jan '89, on Republic, by Code Records. Catalogue no: **LICT 007**
7" Single: Released 16 Jan '89, on Republic, by Code Records. Catalogue no: **LIC 007**

M.C. Miker "G"

CELEBRATION RAP
Tracks: / Celebration rap / Play it loud.
7" Single: Released Nov '86, on Debut, by Skratch Records. Catalogue no: **DEBT 3014**
12" Single: Released Nov '86, on Debut, by Skratch Records. Catalogue no: **DEBTX 3014**

DON'T LET THE MUSIC STOP
Tracks: / Don't let the music stop / Don't let the music stop (inst).
7" Single: Released Jul '87, on Nine O Nine, by Creole Records. Catalogue no: **NINE 79**
12" Single: Released Jul '87, on Nine O Nine, by Creole Records. Catalogue no: **NINE 9**

HOLIDAY RAP
Tracks: / Holiday rap / Holiday rap acappella / Whimsical touch / Holiday hip hop (instrumental)
12" Single: Released '88, on Debut, by Skratch Records. Catalogue no. **DEBTX 3008**

M.C. Shy D.

I'VE GOTTA BE TOUGH
Tracks: / I've gotta be tough / We don't play.
12" Single: Released Feb '87, on Champion, by Champion Records. Deleted Aug '89. Catalogue no: **CHAMP 1234**
7" Single: Released '88, on Champion, by Champion Records. Catalogue no: **CHAMP 34**

M.C. Smart

CHARGIN' WARRIOR
Tracks: / Chargin' warrior / Chargin' dub / Bonus beats.
12" Single: Released Feb '88, on Mango, by Island Records. Deleted Jun '88. Catalogue no: **12IS 355**

MCD

I AM THE LAW
Tracks: / I am the law.
Cassingle: Released Apr '88, on Bop, Catalogue no: **BIP 204**

MCIB & The Beatcreator

THUNDERBIRDS (EP)
Tracks: / Thunderbird.
12" Single: Released Apr '88, on DTI, Catalogue no: **MAC 1**

MC'S Logic

GET INVOLVED
Tracks: / Get involved.
12" Single: Released Aug '89, on Submission, by Submission Records. Catalogue no: **SUBX 013**

MCX

BUGGIN' OUT THE HOUSE
Tracks: / Buggin' out the house.
12" Single: Released Jul '88, on Beserkley, by Beserkley Records (USA). Catalogue no: **DIMC 1**
7" Single: Released Jul '88, on Beserkley, by Beserkley Records (USA). Catalogue no: **DIMCX 1**

MDC

CHICKEN SQUAWK
Tracks: / Chicken squawk.
7" Single: on R Radical, by R. Radical Records. Catalogue no: **MDC 3**

MULTI DEATH CORPORATION (EP)
Tracks: / Multideath corporation.
7" Single: Released Jan '84, on Crass, by Crass Records. Catalogue no: **CRASS 121984/5**

M.D.M.A.

EVIDENCE
Tracks: / Evidence.
12" Single: Released May '89, on Ecstatic Product, Catalogue no: **ECS 12001**
12" Single: Released 16 Sep '88, on Ediesta, Catalogue no: **CALC 054**

EYES WIDE OPEN
Tracks: / Eyes wide open.
12" Single: Released 20 Feb '88, on Ediesta, Catalogue no: **CALC 038**

GOD'S QUAD
Tracks: / God's Quad.
12" Single: Released May '87, on Ediesta, Catalogue no: **CALC 024**

GREEN RIVER WAVES
Tracks: / Green river waves.
CD 5": Released '89, on Ecstatic Product, Catalogue no: **ECSCDS 002**
12" Single: Released '89, on Ecstatic Product, Catalogue no: **ECS 12002**

M.Doc

HIS PERCUSSION
Tracks: / His percussion.
7" Single: Released Apr '88, on Jack Trax, Catalogue no: **7 JTX 13**

TIME TO GO (GOTTA GO GO HOUSE)
Tracks: / Time to go (gotta go go house).
7" Single: Released Oct '88, on DJ World Records (USA), Catalogue no: **DJW 104**

Me and You

WHO TOLD YOU SO
Tracks: / Who told you so.
12" Single: Released Jul '82, on THT, Catalogue no: **THT 001**

YOU NEVER KNOW WHAT YOU'VE GOT
Tracks: / You never know what you've got.
7" Single: Released Jul '79, on Laser, Deleted '82. Catalogue no: **LAS 8**

Me & Dean Martin

SURFING DAYS
Tracks: / Surfing days / Sweet starts and bitter ends.
7" Single: Released Feb '89, on No, Catalogue no: **NOS 44**

Me & Mex & Them

LOVE IS SAFE
Tracks: / Love is safe.
12" Single: Released Nov '88, on Warrior, by Warrior Records. Catalogue no: **STOMP 2**
7" Single: Released Nov '88, on Warrior, by Warrior Records. Catalogue no: **7 STOMP 2**

Me & You

Biographical details: The infectious You'll Never Know What You've Got gave this reggae duo a one-off UK chart entry in the summer of 1979. The melodic single reached No 31.

WE DO IT
Tracks: / We do it.
12" Single: Released May '89, on THT, Catalogue no: **THTD 005**

Meadow Mist

CHRISTMAS ISN'T CHRISTMAS
Tracks: / Christmas isn't Christmas / Love your neighbour.
7" Single: Released Nov '82, on Lorraine's, Catalogue no: **LRN 001**

LOVE YOUR NEIGHBOUR
Tracks: / Love your neighbour.
7" Single: Released Nov '83, on Lorraine's, Catalogue no: **LRN 001**

Mean St. Dealers

JAPANESE MOTABIKES
Tracks: / Japanese motabikes / Tight skirts.
7" Single: Released Jan '80, on Graduate, by Graduate Records. Deleted Jan '85. Catalogue no: **GRAD 5**

Meanies

NO SLEEP TILL BEDTIME (EP)
Tracks: / No sleep till bedtime.
7" Single: Released Sep '87, on Grinning Whale, Catalogue no: **GWR 001**

Meat Beat Manifesto

GOD O.D.
Tracks: / God O.D..
CD 5": Released Oct '88, on Crammed Discs, by Crammed Discs. Catalogue no: **SOX 039 CD**
12" Single: Released Oct '88, on Sweatbox, by Sweatbox Records. Catalogue no: **SOX 039**

I GOT THE FEAR
Tracks: / I got the fear.
12" Single: Released Feb '88, on Sweatbox, by Sweatbox Records. Catalogue no: **SOX 23R**

STRAP DOWN
Tracks: / Strap down.
12" Single: Released Jun '88, on Sweatbox, by Sweatbox Records. Catalogue no: **SOX 32**
7" Single: Released Jun '88, on Sweatbox, by Sweatbox Records. Catalogue no: **OX 32**

STRAP DOWN (REMIX)
Tracks: / Strap down (remix).
12" Single: Released 20 Jun '88, on Sweatbox, by Sweatbox Records. Catalogue no: **SOX 32R**
CD 5": Released 20 Jun '88, on Sweatbox, by Sweatbox Records. Catalogue no: **SOX 32 CD**
7" Single: Released 20 Jun '88, on Sweatbox, by Sweatbox Records. Catalogue no: **OX 32R**

SUCK HARD (SINGLE)
Tracks: / Suck hard.
12" Single: Released Jul '87, on Sweatbox, by Sweatbox Records. Catalogue no: **SOX 23**

Meat Loaf

Biographical details: This American singer and actor was born Marvin Lee Aday in Dallas; but the colossal 300-pound star is aptly known to everyone in the music business as Meat Loaf. His debut album, 1970's *Stoney and Meat Loaf*, fared so poorly that most people are under the impression that *Bat out of hell* (released October 1977 in US, January 1978 in UK) was his first Lp. During the intervening seven years, the man-mountain spent much of his time acting. He had a part in the cult-movie *The Rocky horror picture show* (1975) and became part of the touring National Lampoon show. Another Lampooner was playwright/songwriter/keyboardist/arranger Jim Steinman, whom Aday had met at an audition for one of Steinman's plays. Together with backing vocalist Ellen Foley (also a Lampooner) and noted producer Todd Rundgren, singer Meat Loaf and creator Steinman recorded the epic Lp *Bat out of hell*.
Bat out of hell was one of the most extraordinarily exciting albums in rock-history. Accurately described by Steinman as 'Wagnerian rock opera', it took the pomp-rock excesses of the early Seventies and injected them with the energy and enthusiasm of the late Seventies' New Wave. Each of the Lp's seven tracks was an apocalyptic gem, the album building into an epic adventure through the realms of Gothic fantasy. On both sides of the Atlantic, the album was a sleeper smash; its success grew and grew, gradually becoming a far bigger sales commodity than any of the singles lifted from it. By the end of 1978 it was clear that *Bat out of hell* was an all-time classic. In September '78, the 8 minute epic *Paradise by the dashboard light* became the longest ever 7-inch single to hit the US top 40. In Britain the album became a virtual industry by itself. It was listed on the UK album chart for every week of the every year from 1979 until 1984 inclusive; it stood only second to the *Sound of music* soundrack in terms of all-time chart longevity.
The success of *Bat out of hell* led to strong long-term careers for both Meat Loaf and Steinman, but not without a few hiccups inbetween. Meat Loaf - whose voice sounded equally convincing on a hushed ballad or a blistering all-out assault - toured constantly on the back of *Bat out of hell* until his voice was in ruins. He had to undergo prolonged therapy to restore it. Steinman grew so impatient that he placed the songs intended for the follow-up to *Bat* onto a solo album, *Bad for good*. When Meat Loaf's next Lp *Dead ringer* finally appeared in September 1981, it entered the UK album chart at No.1 but was a turkey in the States. The Lp spawned the singer's first UK Top 10 single *Dead ringer for love*, on which he shared lead vocals with the famous Cher.
From then onwards, Meat Loaf was always much bigger in Britain than at home. He split from Steinman and drew his subsequent material from a variety of sources. While not returning to the epic themes or dizzy commercial heights of *Bat out of hell* (which kept selling in Britain long after it had died in the States), Meat Loaf kept making powerful rock records. *Midnight at the lost and found* (1983) and *Bad attitude* (1984) were big UK sellers. He showed a remarkable capacity for soldiering on despite setbacks.(Bob MacDonald, 27th Jan 1986).

BAT OUT OF HELL (OLD GOLD)
Tracks: / Bat out of hell.
7" Single: Released Jan '88, on Old Gold, by Old Gold Records. Catalogue no: **OG 9751**

BAT OUT OF HELL (SINGLE)
Tracks: / Bat out of hell (part 1) / Bat out of hell (part 2).
7" Single: Released Feb '79, on Epic, by CBS Records. Deleted '82. Catalogue no: **EPC 7018**
12" Single: Released Oct '87, on Arista, by BMG Records (UK). Deleted May '89. Catalogue no: **RIST 41**
7" Single: Released Oct '87, on Arista, by BMG Records (UK). Catalogue no: **RIS 41**

BLIND BEFORE I STOP (SINGLE)
Tracks: / Blind before I stop.
7" Single: Released Feb '87, on Arista, by BMG Records (UK). Catalogue no: **RIS 3**
12" Single: Released Feb '87, on Arista, by BMG Records (UK). Catalogue no: **RIST 3R**
12" Single: Released Feb '87, on Arista, by BMG Records (UK). Catalogue no: **RIST 3**

DEAD RINGER FOR LOVE
Tracks: / Dead ringer for love / More than you deserve.
7" Single: Released Nov '81, on Epic, by CBS Records. Deleted '84. Catalogue no: **EPCA 1697**

GETTING AWAY WITH MURDER
Tracks: / Getting away with murder / Scot free (remix) (On 10" only) / Rock 'n' roll hero.
10" single: Released Nov '86, on Arista, by BMG Records (UK). Catalogue no: **ARIST 10683**
7" Pic: Released Nov '86, on Arista, by BMG Records (UK). Catalogue no: **ARIST 683P**
12" Single: Released Nov '86, on Arista, by BMG Records (UK). Catalogue no: **ARIST 12683**
7" Single: Released Nov '86, on Arista, by BMG Records (UK). Catalogue no: **ARIST 683**

GREATEST ORIGINAL HITS (4 Track EP)
7" Single: Released Mar '83, on Epic, by CBS Records. Catalogue no: **EPC A 2621**

IF YOU REALLY WANT TO
Tracks: / If you really want to.
7" Pic: Released Apr '83, on Epic, by CBS Records. Catalogue no: **WA 3357**
7" Single: Released Apr '83, on Epic, by CBS Records. Catalogue no: **A 3357**
12" Single: Released Apr '83, on Epic, by CBS Records. Catalogue no: **TA 3357**

I'M GONNA LOVE HER FOR BOTH OF US
Tracks: / I'm gonna love her for both of us.
7" Single: Released Sep '81, on Epic, by CBS Records. Deleted '84. Catalogue no: **EPCA 1580**

MIDNIGHT AT THE LOST AND FOUND (SINGLE)
Tracks: / Midnight at the lost and found.
7" Single: Released Sep '83, on Epic, by CBS Records. Deleted '86. Catalogue no: **A 3748**

MODERN GIRL
Tracks: / Modern girl.
7" Single: Released Oct '84, on Arista, by BMG Records (UK). Deleted '87. Catalogue no: **ARIST 585**

NOWHERE FAST
Tracks: / Nowhere fast / Clap your hands.
7" Pic: Released Dec '84, on Arista, by BMG Records (UK). Catalogue no: **ARISD 600**
7" Single: Released Dec '84, on Arista, by BMG Records (UK). Catalogue no: **ARISG 600**
7" Single: Released Dec '84, on Arista, by BMG Records (UK). Catalogue no: **ARIST 600**

PIECE OF THE ACTION
Tracks: / Piece of the action / Sailor to a siren / Bad attitude.
7" Pic: Released Mar '85, on Arista, by BMG Records (UK). Catalogue no: **ARISD 603**
7" Single: Released Mar '85, on Arista, by BMG Records (UK). Catalogue no: **ARIST 603**
12" Single: Released Mar '85, on Arista, by BMG Records (UK). Catalogue no: **ARIST 12603**

RAZORS EDGE
Tracks: / Razors edge.
7" Pic: Released Jun '83, on Epic, by CBS Records. Catalogue no: **WA 3511**
7" Single: Released Jun '83, on Epic, by CBS Records. Catalogue no: **A 3511**
7" Single: Released Jan '84, on Cleveland, Catalogue no: **A 4080**
12" Single: Released Jun '83, on Epic, by CBS Records. Catalogue no: **TA 3511**
12" Single: Released Jan '84, on Cleveland, Catalogue no: **TA 4080**

READ 'EM AND WEEP
Tracks: / Read 'em and weep / Everything is permanent.
7" Single: Released Mar '82, on Epic, by CBS Records. Deleted '85. Catalogue no: **EPCA 2012**

ROCK'N'ROLL MERCENARIES
Tracks: / Rock 'n' roll mercenaries / Revolutions per minute.
12" Pic: Released Sep '86, on Arista, by BMG Records (UK). Catalogue no: **ARIST 666 XP**
12" Pic: Released Aug '86, on Arista, by BMG Records (UK). Catalogue no: **ARIST 12666 P**
7" Pic: Released Sep '86, on Arista, by BMG Records (UK). Catalogue no: **ARIST 666 P**
7" Single: Released Aug '86, on Arista, by BMG Records (UK). Catalogue no: **ARIST 666**
12" Single: Released Aug '86, on Arista, by BMG Records (UK). Catalogue no: **ARIST 12666**

SPECIAL GIRL
Tracks: / Special girl.
CD 5": Released May '87, on Arista, by BMG Records (UK). Catalogue no: **RISCD 14**

TWO OUT OF THREE AIN'T BAD
Tracks: / Two out of three ain't bad / Paradise by the dashboard light.
7" Single: Released Aug '78, on Epic, by CBS Records. Deleted '81. Catalogue no: **EPC 6281**
CD 3": Released Aug '88, on Epic (USA), by CBS Records (USA). Catalogue no: **34K 02371**

WHAT YOU SEE IS WHAT YOU GET
Tracks: / What you see is what you get.

7" Single: Released Oct '81, on Prodigal, Catalogue no: **PROD 10**

YOU TOOK THE WORDS RIGHT OUT OF ... (OLD GOLD)
Tracks: / You took the words right out of my mouth.
7" Single: Released 27 Feb '89, on Old Gold, by Old Gold Records. Catalogue no: **OG 9865**
7" Single: Released May '78, on Epic, by CBS Records. Deleted '81. Catalogue no: **EPC 5980**

Meat Mouth

MEAT MOUTH IS MURDER
Tracks: / Meat mouth is murder.
12" Single: Released Aug '87, on Ron Johnson, by Ron Johnson Records. Catalogue no: **ZRON 30**
12" Single: Released Sep '87, on Factory (1), by Factory Records. Catalogue no: **FAC 196**

Meat Puppets

I CAN'T BE COUNTED ON
Tracks: / I can't be counted on / Paradise.
12" Single: Released 17 Oct '87, on SST (USA), by SST Records (USA). Catalogue no: **PSST 150**

IN A CAR
Tracks: / In a car.
CD 5": Released Nov '88, on SST (USA), by SST Records (USA). Catalogue no: **SSTCD 044**
7" Single: Released Jul '89, on SST (USA), by SST Records (USA). Catalogue no: **SST 044**

Meat Whiplash

DON'T SLIP UP
Tracks: / Don't slip up.
7" Single: Released Sep '85, on Creation, by Creation Records. Deleted Jul '88. Catalogue no: **CRE 020**

Mecano

UNIVITED GUEST
Tracks: / Univited guest / London.
7" Single: Released Aug '83, on CBS, by CBS Records. Catalogue no: **A 3140**

Mecca Normal

OH YES YOU CAN
Tracks: / Oh yes you can.
7" Single: Released '88, on K Records, by K Records. Catalogue no: **L 28200**

Mechanical Man

PRESSURE SITUATION
Tracks: / Pressure situation / Don't I know / One way street (Extra track on 12" version only.).
7" Single: Released Jan '86, on Arista, by BMG Records (UK). Catalogue no: **MAN 1**
12" Single: Released Jan '86, on Arista, by BMG Records (UK). Catalogue no: **MAN 121**

Mechanics

I DON'T WANNA SEE YOUR PICTURE
Tracks: / I don't wanna see your picture / Cool johnny.
7" Single: Released May '80, on Riviera (1), Deleted May '85. Catalogue no: **RR 1**

LOVE AND UNDERSTANDING
Tracks: / Love and understanding / Geraldine.
7" Single: Released Dec '81, on Bronze, by Bronze Records. Deleted Dec '84. Catalogue no: **BRO 136**

POWER OF LOVE
Tracks: / Power of love / Motorbike song.
7" Single: Released Jul '81, on Bronze, by Bronze Records. Deleted Jul '84. Catalogue no: **BRO 123**

Meco

Biographical details: This American producer, arranger, orchestra leader, trombonist and keyboardist was born in Johnsonburg, Pennsylvania in 1939. His full name is Meco Monardo. He assembled his own band while in high school, and gained a scholarship to the Eastman School of Music in Rochester, New York in 1957. He had a spell as an army cadet, then embarked on a full-time musical career in New York City. He joined bandleader Kai Winding, and spent the late Sixties and early Seventies arranging commercials and working as a session musician. His big breakthrough occurred in late 1974, when he and two colleagues established a new hitmaking formula.
The New York engineering/production team of Tony Bongiovi, Meco Monardo and Tom Moulton conceived and produced the Lp *Never can say goodbye* by Gloria Gaynor, a previously little known singer. The whole of Side One of this Lp became staple fodder for dancefloors, and was of great historic importance. The three numbers on this side - *Honey bee, Never can say goodbye* and *Reach out I'll be there* - were segued together to form one continuous dance marathon; contary to Gloria's singing, the production was manufactured and mechanical. Thus, this crew pioneered the use of extended dance mixes. The subsequent explosion in disco music owed them a lot. Gaynor's revival of *Never can say goodbye* reached No.9 on the US pop chart, and climbed No.2 in the UK. The follow up, *Reach out I'll be there*, got to No.14 in Britain. At the same time, Meco co-produced Carol Douglas' *Doctor's orders*, a US No.11 hit. Meco's career as an artist in his own right began in 1977, when he became an early fan of the legendary Star Wars movie. He loved John Williams' score, but figured that he could produce a more commercial version of the main title theme. Thus, while the London Sympony Orchestra were reaching No.10 on the US singles chart with the original rendition, Meco's discofied version rocketed to No.1. In Britain he managed to reach No.7, even in advance of the film's UK release. Meco's treatment was clever insofar as he used gimmicks, effects and snatches of tunes from the rest of the movie, as well as the theme. He subsequently worked this formula to death during the late Seventies and early Eighties - all the later John Williams themes like *Close encounters* and *ET* were given the disco treatment on Meco's singles and albums. Meco sometimes reached the US Top 40 with these, but none were as successful at *Star wars* because the original tunes were not as good and neither were Monardo's revamps. (Bob MacDonald, 27th Jan 1986).

POP GOES TO THE MOVIES
Tracks: / Pop goes to the movies.
7" Single: Released '82, on Arista, by BMG Records (UK). Deleted '87. Catalogue no: **ARIST 460**

RAIDERS MARCH
Tracks: / Raiders march / Cairo nights (Bolero de Cairo).
7" Single: Released Aug '81, on CBS, by CBS Records. Deleted '84. Catalogue no: **A 1502**

STAR WARS THEME
Tracks: / Star wars.
7" Single: Released Oct '77, on RCA, by BMG Records (UK). Deleted '80. Catalogue no: **XB 1028**

Medeiros, Glenn

LONG AND LASTING LOVE (ONCE IN A LIFETIME)
Tracks: / Long and lasting love, A / You're my woman, you're my lady / Pieces of my dream (12" only) / Nothing's gonna change my love for you (Only available on the CD single.).
CD 5": Released Aug '88, on London Records, by London Records. Catalogue no: **LONCD 202**
7" Pic: Released Aug '88, on London Records, by London Records. Deleted May '89. Catalogue no: **LONPD 202**
7" Single: Released Aug '88, on London Records, by London Records. Deleted May '89. Catalogue no: **LONP 202**
7" Single: Released 22 Aug '88, on London Records, by London Records. Deleted May '89. Catalogue no: **LON 202**
12" Single: Released Aug '88, on London Records, by London Records. Catalogue no: **LONXR 202**
12" Single: Released 22 Aug '88, on London Records, by London Records. Deleted May '89. Catalogue no: **LONX 202**

LOVE ALWAYS FINDS A REASON
Tracks: / Love always finds a reason / Love always finds a reason (version) / Long and lasting love, A (12" only).
12" Single: Released Dec '88, on London Records, by London Records. Deleted May '89. Catalogue no: **LONX 213**
CD 5": Released Nov '88, on London Records, by London Records. Catalogue no: **LONCD 213**
7" Single: Released Dec '88, on London Records, by London Records. Deleted May '89. Catalogue no: **LON 213**

NOTHING'S GONNA CHANGE MY LOVE FOR YOU
Tracks: / Nothing's gonna change my love for you / You left the loneliest heart / Nothing's gonna change my love for you (ext. version)* (Track on 12" version only.) / Nothing's gonna change my love for you (instrumental)* (Track on 12" version only.).
12" Single: Released Jul '87, on Mercury, by Phonogram Ltd. Catalogue no: **MERX 250**
7" Single: Released Jul '87, on Mercury, by Phonogram Ltd. Catalogue no: **MER 250**
12" Single: Released Jun '88, on London Records, by London Records. Deleted May '89. Catalogue no: **LONX 184**
7" Single: Released Jun '88, on London Records, by London Records. Deleted May '89. Catalogue no: **LON 184**

Media

SOUTH COAST CITY ROCKERS
Tracks: / South coast City rockers.
7" Single: Released Feb '80, on Brain Booster, Catalogue no: **BB 004**

T.V. KIDS
Tracks: / T.V. kids.
7" Single: Released Feb '80, on Brain Booster, Catalogue no: **TAOO 1**

Medicine Bow

SINCE YOU'VE BEEN GONE
Tracks: / Since you've been gone.
7" Single: Released Apr '89, on Bark, by Bark Records. Catalogue no: **SINCE 1**

Medicine Factory

SPIRIT TIMEBOMB EP
Tracks: / Breathe / Thinner / Everyman.
12" Single: Released 24 Jul '89, on House Of Dolls, Catalogue no: **HOD 008**

SYMPATHY FOR THE DEVIL
Tracks: / Sympathy for the devil / Sympathy for the devil (version) / Friction.
12" Single: Released Nov '88, on House Of Dolls, Catalogue no: **HODFW 005**

Medicine Head

Biographical details: John Fiddler and Peter Hope-Evans were the nucleus of this British band. They started as a duo on the UK underground scene in the late Sixties and early Seventies. Their debut album *New bottles, old medicine* was released on John Peel's Dandelion label in 1970, and produced by the famous talent-spotting DJ himself. The following year, they chalked up their first hit single - *(And the) pictures in the sky*, produced by ex-Yardbird Keith Relf, reached the UK No.22 position.
Switching to Polydor Records, Medicine Head enjoyed two major hits with a pair of Fidler-penned 1973 songs: *One and one is one* reached the UK No.3 position and *Rising sun* climbed to No.11. Flushed with the success of these nifty pop-rock offerings, guitarist/vocalist Fiddler and harmonica player Hop-Evans sugmented their line-up and became a six-member group. However, the expanded Medicine Head achieved just one British chart single. *Slip and slide* (No.22 in 1974), before drifting into obscurity. Like another, similar act of the era, Hudson-Ford, they were unable to hold onto a sufficiently strong following, hence their lack of acceptance in the Lp market. Medicine Head reverted to a duo in 1976, and then split. Fiddler formed an unsuccessful combo called the British Lions with some ex-members of Mott The Hoople, while Hope-Evans worked as a session harmonica player. (Bob MacDonald, 27th Jan 1986).

(AND THE) PICTURES IN THE SKY
Tracks: / (And the) pictures in the sky.
7" Single: Released Jun '71, on Dandelion, Deleted '74. Catalogue no: **DAN 7003**

ONE AND ONE IS ONE
Tracks: / One and one is one / Rising sun.
7" Single: Released May '73, on Polydor, by Polydor Ltd. Deleted '76. Catalogue no: **2001 432**

ONE AND ONE IS ONE (OLD GOLD)
Tracks: / One and one is one.
7" Single: Released Oct '88, on Old Gold, by Old Gold Records. Catalogue no: **OG 9809**

RISING SUN
Tracks: / Rising sun.
7" Single: Released Aug '73, on Polydor, by Polydor Ltd. Deleted '76. Catalogue no: **2058 389**

SLIP AND SLIDE
Tracks: / Slip and slide.
7" Single: Released Feb '74, on Polydor, by Polydor Ltd. Deleted '77. Catalogue no: **2058 436**

Meditations

CARPENTER REBUILD
Tracks: / Carpenter rebuild.
12" Single: Released Mar '82, on Jackal, Catalogue no: **JAD 1**

EASE UP FATTIE
Tracks: / Ease up fattie / Shadow man.
12" Single: Released Jul '83, on Greensleeves, by Greensleeves Records. Catalogue no: **GRED 117**

NO MORE FRIEND (SINGLE)
Tracks: / No more friend / Walla walla.
12" Single: Released Jan '83, on Greensleeves, by Greensleeves Records. Catalogue no: **GRED 113**

SIT DOWN AND REASON
Tracks: / Sit down and reason / Jam it tonight.
12" Single: Released Nov '83, on Jah Guidance, Catalogue no: **VPRD 141**

STRANGER IN LOVE
Tracks: / Stranger in love / Unity.
7" Single: Released Oct '81, on Kingdom, by Kingdom Records. Deleted '85. Catalogue no: **KV 8020**
12" Single: Released Oct '81, on Kingdom, by Kingdom Records. Deleted '82. Catalogue no: **KV 8020 12**

Medium Medium

HUNGRY SO ANGRY
Tracks: / Hungry so angry / Nadsat dream.
7" Single: Released Feb '81, on Cherry Red, by Cherry Red Records. Deleted '87. Catalogue no: **CHERRY 18**

THEM OR ME
Tracks: / Them or me.
7" Single: Released Jan '80, on APT, Catalogue no: **SAP 01**

Medium Wave Band

MY LUCK CHANGED
Tracks: / My luck changed / We've both made mistakes.
7" Single: Released Dec '88, on Astra, by Astra Records. Catalogue no: **ARC 101**

Medley, Bill

HE AIN'T HEAVY HE'S MY BROTHER
Tracks: / He ain't heavy he's my brother / Bridge, The / It's our destiny (Available on 12").
Note: * Extra track on 12 inch
CD 5": on Polydor, by Polydor Ltd. Catalogue no: **PZCD 10**
7" Single: Released 15 Aug '88, on Polydor, by Polydor Ltd. Catalogue no: **PO 10**
12" Single: Released 15 Aug '88, on Polydor, by Polydor Ltd. Catalogue no: **PZ 10**

I'M GONNA BE STRONG
Tracks: / I'm gonna be strong / Brown eyed woman / I just want to make love to you.
CD 5": Released 21 Nov '88, on Motown, by BMG Records (UK). Catalogue no: **ZD 49508**
7" Single: Released Nov '88, on RCA, by BMG Records (UK). Catalogue no: **ZB 49507**
12" Single: Released Nov '88, on RCA, by BMG Records (UK). Catalogue no: **ZT 49508**

I'VE HAD THE TIME OF MY LIFE
Tracks: / I've had the time of my life / Love is strange.
7" Single: Released Oct '87, on RCA, by BMG Records (UK). Catalogue no: **PB 49625**

Medley, Michael

REPLAY
Tracks: / Replay / Replay (bonus beats).
7" Single: Released Aug '89, on Radical, by Radical Records. Catalogue no: **RADICAL 6-7**
12" Single: Released Aug '89, on Radical, by Radical Records. Catalogue no: **RADICAL 6-12**

Medwin, Michael

SIGNATURE TUNE OF THE ARMY GAME
Tracks: / Army Game, signature tune.
7" Single: Released May '58, on H.M.V., by EMI Records. Deleted '61. Catalogue no: **POP 490**

Meechelle La Chaux

LOVE ME ALL OVER
Tracks: / Love me all over.
12" Single: Released Mar '87, on Preset, by Preset Records. Catalogue no: **12 DETAIL 3**

Meehan, Tony

SONG OF MEXICO
Tracks: / Song of Mexico.
7" Single: Released Jan '64, on Decca, by Decca Records. Deleted '67. Catalogue no: **F 11801**

Meeks, Carl

HEARD ABOUT MY LOVE
Tracks: / Heard about my love.
12" Single: Released 20 Mar '89, on Greensleeves, by Greensleeves Records. Catalogue no: **GRED 237**

TILL DAYLIGHT
Tracks: / Till daylight.
12" Single: Released Jan '89, on Redman International, Catalogue no: **VPRED 119**

WE RUN THINGS
Tracks: / We run things.
12" Single: Released Sep '88, on Redman International, Catalogue no: **RED 19**

WEH DEM FAH
Tracks: / Weh dem fah / Weh dem fah (version).
12" Single: Released 27 Feb '88, on Redman International, Catalogue no: **RED 2**

Meeson, Ian

WHO WANTS TO LIVE FOREVER?
Tracks: / Who wants to live forever ? / Who wants to live forever ? (instrumental).
7" Single: Released Aug '89, on EMI, by EMI Records. Catalogue no: **ODO 112**
12" Single: Released Aug '89, on EMI, by EMI Records. Catalogue no: **12ODO 112**

M.E.F.F.

NEVER STOP

Tracks: / Never stop.
12" Single: Released Sep '84, on Respond (2), by A&M Records. Catalogue no: **KOBX 711**

Mega City Four

LESS THAN SENSELESS
Tracks: / Less than senseless.
7" Single: Released Mar '89, on Southern, by Southern Record Dist.. Catalogue no: **DYS 2**

MILES APART
Tracks: / Miles apart / Running in darkness.
7" Single: Released Jun '88, on Primitive, by Primitive Records. Deleted '88. Catalogue no: **MC 4**
7" Single: Released Mar '88, on Primitive, by Primitive Records. Catalogue no: **PRIME 009**

Megadeth

ANARCHY IN THE UK
Tracks: / Anarchy in the UK / Liar / 502 (Only on 12" single.).
7" Pic: Released Feb '88, on Capitol, by EMI Records. Deleted Nov '88. Catalogue no: **CLP 480**
7" Single: Released Feb '88, on Capitol, by EMI Records. Deleted Jun '89. Catalogue no: **CL 480**
12" Single: Released Jun '89, on Capitol, by EMI Records. Catalogue no: **TCDETH 2**
12" Single: Released Feb '88, on Capitol, by EMI Records. Deleted Nov '88. Catalogue no: **12CL 480**
12" Single: Released Jun '89, on Capitol, by EMI Records. Catalogue no: **202 495 4**

MARY JANE
Tracks: / Mary Jane / Hook in mouth / My last words (On 12" version only.).
7" Pic: Released May '88, on Capitol, by EMI Records. Deleted Nov '88. Catalogue no: **CLP 489**
7" Single: Released Feb '88, on Capitol, by EMI Records. Deleted Jun '89. Catalogue no: **CL 489**
12" Single: Released Jun '89, on Capitol, by EMI Records. Catalogue no: **202 609 4**
12" Single: Released May '88, on Capitol, by EMI Records. Deleted Aug '89. Catalogue no: **12CL 489**
12" Single: Released Jun '89, on Capitol, by EMI Records. Catalogue no: **TCDETH 3**

WAKE UP DEAD
Tracks: / Wake up dead / Black Friday / Devils Island.
7" Pic: Released Dec '87, on EMI, by EMI Records. Deleted Apr '88. Catalogue no: **CLP 476**
7" Single: Released 7 Dec '87, on Capitol, by EMI Records. Deleted Nov '88. Catalogue no: **CL 476**
12" Single: Released Jun '89, on Capitol, by EMI Records. Catalogue no: **TCDETH 1**
12" Single: Released 7 Dec '87, on Capitol, by EMI Records. Deleted Nov '88. Catalogue no: **12 CL 476**
12" Single: Released Jun '89, on Capitol, by EMI Records. Catalogue no: **202 281 4**

Megadong, Rastas

SWING LOW
Tracks: / Swing low / What will I do when the poll tax comes in.
12" Single: Released '71, on Well Hung, Catalogue no: **WELLHUNG 1**

Megamixes

MEGAMIXES
12" Single: Released 1 Feb '88, on Total Beat Factor, Catalogue no: **TBF ONE**

Megatone

ALUMINIUM LADY
Tracks: / Aluminium lady / Die hard.
7" Single: Released Jul '81, on Hot Metal, Deleted '85. Catalogue no: **HMM 69**

Mehead

ELMER'S END
Tracks: / Elmer's end / Mummy song / Oldest man in the world / Brain collages.
12" Single: Released 21 Nov '87, on Makerite, Catalogue no: **MAKE ONE**

Meisner, Randy

GOTTA GET AWAY
Tracks: / Gotta get away / I need you bad.
7" Single: Released Dec '80, on Epic, by CBS Records. Deleted Dec '85. Catalogue no: **EPC 9354**

HEARTS ON FIRE
Tracks: / Hearts on fire / Anyway bye bye.
7" Single: Released Mar '81, on Epic, by CBS Records. Deleted Mar '84. Catalogue no: **EPC 9476**

NEVER BEEN IN LOVE
Tracks: / Never been in love / Nothing is said.

7" Single: Released Oct '82, on Epic, by CBS Records. Deleted Oct '85. Catalogue no: **EPCA A2707**

Mekons

BEATEN AND BROKEN
Tracks: / Beaten and broken / Chop that child in half / Hey Susan / Deep end.
12" Single: Released Feb '86, on Sin, by Sin Records. Catalogue no: **SIN 002**

CRIME AND PUNISHMENT
Tracks: / Crime and punishment.
12" Single: Released Jan '86, on Sin, by Sin Records. Catalogue no: **SIN 002R**

DREAM AND LIE
CD 5": Released Aug '89, on Blast First, by Blast First Records. Catalogue no: **BFFP 053CD**
10" single: Released Aug '89, on Blast First, by Blast First Records. Catalogue no: **BFFP 053**

GHOSTS OF AMERICAN ASTRONAUTS
Tracks: / Ghosts of American astronauts.
7" Single: Released Apr '88, on Cooking Vinyl, by Cooking Vinyl Records. Catalogue no: **SIN 009**
12" Single: Released Apr '88, on Cooking Vinyl, by Cooking Vinyl Records. Catalogue no: **SIN 009T**

GREETINGS EIGHT
Tracks: / Greetings eight.
12" Single: Released Nov '88, on Materiali Sonori, Catalogue no: **MASO 70008**

HELLO CRUEL WORLD
Tracks: / Hello cruel world.
7" Single: Released Jun '86, on Sin, by Sin Records. Catalogue no: **SIN 004**

HOLE IN THE GROUND
Tracks: / Hold in the ground / Sin city / Prince of darkness.
12" Single: Released Oct '87, on Cooking Vinyl, by Cooking Vinyl Records. Catalogue no: **SIN 007T**

NEVER BEEN IN A RIOT
Tracks: / Never been in a riot.
7" Single: Released Sep '79, on Fast, by Fast Forward Records. Catalogue no: **FAST 1**

SLIGHTLY SOUTH OF THE BORDER
Tracks: / Sightly south of the border.
10" single: Released Sep '86, on Sin, by Sin Records. Catalogue no: **SIN 005**

SNOW
Tracks: / Snow.
7" Single: Released 26 Jun '85, on Red Rhino, by Red Rhino Records. Deleted '88. Catalogue no: **RED 007**

SPORTING LIFE
Tracks: / Sporting life.
7" Single: Released Nov '82, on CNT, Catalogue no: **CNT 008**

TEETH
Tracks: / Teeth / Guardian / Kill / Stay cool.
7" Single: Released Apr '80, on Virgin, by Virgin Records. Deleted '83. Catalogue no: **VS 101**

WHERE WERE YOU
Tracks: / Where were you.
7" Single: Released Sep '79, on Fast, by Fast Forward Records. Catalogue no: **FAST 7**

Mel & Kim

F.L.M. (SINGLE)
Tracks: / F.L.M. / F.L.M. (remix).
7" Single: Released Jun '87, on Supreme, by Supreme Records. Catalogue no: **SUPE 113**
12" Single: Released Jun '87, on Supreme, by Supreme Records. Catalogue no: **SUPET 113**

I'M THE ONE WHO REALLY LOVES YOU
Tracks: / I'm the one who really loves you.
7" Single: Released Sep '87, on Supreme, by Supreme Records. Catalogue no: **SUPE 117**
12" Single: Released Sep '87, on Supreme, by Supreme Records. Catalogue no: **SUPET 117**

RESPECTABLE
Tracks: / Respectable (The tabloid mix) / Respectable (The 7"mix) / Respectable (Extra beats version).
7" Single: Released Feb '87, on Supreme, by Supreme Records. Catalogue no: **SUPE 111**
12" Single: Released Mar '87, on Supreme, by Supreme Records. Catalogue no: **SUPETP 111**
12" Single: Released Feb '87, on Supreme, by Supreme Records. Catalogue no: **SUPET 111**
12" Single: Released Mar '87, on Supreme, by Supreme Records. Catalogue no: **SUPETX 111**

SHOWING OUT
Tracks: / Showing out / System (House version) / Showing out (Mortgage Mix).
7" Single: Released Sep '86, on Supreme, by Supreme Records. Catalogue no: **SUPE 107**

JOHN MELLENCAMP - POP SINGER (Released on Mercury)

12" Single: Released Sep '86, on Supreme, by Supreme Records. Catalogue no: **SUPETX 107**
12" Single: Released Oct '86, on Supreme, by Supreme Records. Catalogue no: **SUPETP 107**
12" Single: Released Sep '86, on Supreme, by Supreme Records. Catalogue no: **SUPET 107**

THAT'S THE WAY IT IS
Tracks: / That's the way it is / I'm the one who really loves you / You changed my life.
12" Pic: Released Mar '88, on Supreme, by Supreme Records. Catalogue no: **SUPETP 117**
7" Single: Released 5 Mar '88, on Supreme, by Supreme Records. Catalogue no: **SUPE 117**
12" Single: Released Mar '88, on Supreme, by Supreme Records. Catalogue no: **SUPETZ 117**
12" Single: Released Mar '88, on Supreme, by Supreme Records. Catalogue no: **SUPETX 117**
12" Single: Released 5 Mar '88, on Supreme, by Supreme Records. Catalogue no: **SUPET 117**

Mel & Tim

BACKFIELD IN MOTION (OLD GOLD)
Tracks: / Back field in motion / I feel love comin' on.
Note: Mel and Tim is correct.
7" Single: Released Jun '88, on Old Gold, by Old Gold Records. Catalogue no: **OG 9784**

STARTING ALL OVER AGAIN
Tracks: / Starting all over again / It hurts to want it so bad.
7" Single: Released Sep '87, on Stax, by Fantasy Inc (USA). Catalogue no: **STAX 816**
7" Single: Released Mar '82, on Stax, by Fantasy Inc (USA). Catalogue no: **STAX 1006**

Melachrino Orchestra

AUTUMN CONCERTO
Tracks: / Autumn concerto.
7" Single: Released Oct '56, on H.M.V., by EMI Records. Deleted '59. Catalogue no: **B 10958**

Melanie

Biographical details: This American singer, songwriter and guitarist was born Melanie Safka in New York City of Ukrainian-Italian parentage. During her rebellious teenage years she gained valuable experience performing in Greenwich Village coffee shops and New Jersey clubs. She also studied to be an actress. Legend has it that, while seeking an audition for a small part in a play, she stumbled into the wrong office and met recording executive Neil Bogart and budding record producer Peter Schekeryk. The relationship between Melanie and Peter blossomed in both professional and personal terms - he becam her long-term producer and her long-term husband.
Melanie's first two albums, *Born to be* and *Affectionately Melanie*, were released in 1969. Her career really took off when she performed at that year's legendary Woodstock Festival, where her folk influenced songs of peace, love and the simple life fitted perfectly. Although the 22 year old's air of innocence and bewilderment sometimes bordered on childlike naivete, her reputation was enhanced by her distinctive jazzy voice (sometimes compared with the French chanteuse style of Edith Piaf) and her delectable looks. With her long-flowing locks and acoustic guitar, Melanie was the epitome of the flower child.
One particular incident at Woodstock, when the vast crowd lit candles as a gesture of defiance against the pouring rain and the approach of darkness inspired Melanie's first US Top 40 single. *Lay down (candles in the rain)*, on which she was backed by the gospel strains of The Edwin Hawkins Singers, reached the US No.6 position in 1970; that year's *Candles in the rain* album became a smash in Britain, logging 27 weeks on the Lp chart and peaking at No.5. The singer enjoyed several more big-selling albums during the early Seventies. Unfortunately, her only other major hit single was *Brand new key*, which was America's Christmas No.1 of 1971 and reached No.4 in the UK in early 1972. Although the lyrics of this novelty song were open to a sexual interpretation, the record really emphasised the schoolgirl side of Melanie's image. The song was given an unlikely new adaption in 1976, when the Wurzels reached No.1 in Britain with *Combine harvester*. (Melanie herself had another single that was big in Britain but not the States - a remake of the Rolling Stones' *Ruby Tuesday*.)
Being very much a product of her era, Melanie slipped into obscurity in the mid-Seventies. She quit performing for a while to concentrate on raising a family. She has made several subsequent comeback attempts,showing a more mature incarnation of her folk-pop sound; but of these, only 1983's acclaimed single *Every breath of the way* (No.70 in UK) recieved any glimmer of public recognition. (Bob MacDonald, 28th Jan 1986).

BRAND NEW KEY
Tracks: / Brand new key / Ruby Tuesday.
7" Single: Released Jan '83, on Flashback, by Mainline Records. Catalogue no: **FBS 26**
7" Single: Released Jan '72, on Buddah, by Buddah Records Inc.(USA). Deleted '75. Catalogue no: **2011 105**

DIDN'T YOU EVER LOVE SOMEBODY
Tracks: / Didn't you ever love somebody.
7" Single: Released Nov '83, on Neighborhood (USA), by CBS Records (USA). Catalogue no: **NB 2**

EVERY BREATH OF THE WAY
Tracks: / Every breath of the way.
7" Single: Released Sep '83, on Neighborhood (USA), by CBS Records (USA). Catalogue no: **NB 1**
12" Single: Released Sep '83, on Neighborhood (USA), by CBS Records (USA). Catalogue no: **NBT 1**
7" Pic: Released Sep '83, on Neighborhood (USA), by CBS Records (USA). Catalogue no: **NBP 1**

RUBY TUESDAY
Tracks: / Ruby Tuesday.
CD 5": Released Mar '89, on Silvertone, Catalogue no: **CDYUM 117**
7" Single: Released Sep '70, on Buddah, by

Buddah Records Inc.(USA). Deleted '73. Catalogue no: **2011 038**
12" Single: Released Mar '89, on Silvertone, Catalogue no: **12 YUM 117**
7" Single: Released Mar '89, on Silvertone, Catalogue no: **YUM 117**

WHAT HAVE THEY DONE TO MY SONG MA
Tracks: / What have they done to my song Ma.
7" Single: Released Jan '71, on Buddah, by Buddah Records Inc.(USA). Deleted '74. Catalogue no: **2011 038**

WILL YOU LOVE ME TOMORROW
Tracks: / Will you love me tomorrow.
7" Single: Released Feb '74, on Neighborhood (USA), by CBS Records (USA). Deleted '77. Catalogue no: **NBH 9**

Melissa

GET YOUR LOVE RIGHT
Tracks: / Get your love right / Don't give up on love.
7" Single: Released May '82, on Index, Catalogue no: **IND 5**

TEDDY BEAR
Tracks: / Teddy bear.
7" Single: Released Oct '82, on Identity, by Identity Records. Catalogue no: **ID 002**

Mellaa & Co

BE FREE
Tracks: / Be free.
12" Single: Released Nov '87, on Dancefloor (USA), Catalogue no: **DF 1209**

Melle Mel

MESSAGE 2 (SURVIVAL)
Tracks: / Message 2 (survival) / Message 2 (survival) (instrumental).
Note: Writers: S.Robinson/M.Glover/J.Robinson, Jr. Sugarhill Music Publ. Ltd. Produced by Sylvia Inc.
12" Single: Released '82, on Sugarhill (USA), Deleted '86. Catalogue no: **SHL 119**
7" Single: Released '82, on Sugarhill (USA), Deleted '86. Catalogue no: **SH 119**

Mellencamp, John

AUTHORITY SONG
Tracks: / Authority song / Hurts so good / Thundering hearts (on 12" only).
7" Single: Released Feb '84, on Riva, by Riva Records. Catalogue no: **JCM 2**

CHECK IT OUT
Tracks: / Check it out / Check it out (live) (track on CD single.) / We are the people / Shama lama ding dong (Track on 12") / Pretty ballerina (track on 12" version.) / Pink houses (acoustic version).
CD 5": Released Feb '88, on Mercury, by Phonogram Ltd. Deleted Oct '88. Catalogue no: **JCMCD 10**
7" Single: Released Feb '88, on Mercury, by Phonogram Ltd. Deleted Oct '88. Catalogue no: **JCM 10**
12" Single: Released Feb '88, on Mercury, by Phonogram Ltd. Deleted Oct '88. Catalogue no: **JCMX 10**

CHERRY BOMB
Tracks: / Cherry bomb.
CD 5": Released Nov '87, on Phonogram, by Phonogram Ltd. Deleted Oct '88. Catalogue no: **JCMCD 9**
7" Single: Released Nov '87, on Mercury, by Phonogram Ltd. Deleted Oct '88. Catalogue no: **JCM 9**
12" Single: Released Nov '87, on Mercury, by Phonogram Ltd. Deleted Oct '88. Catalogue no: **JCMX 9**

CRUMBLIN' DOWN
Tracks: / Crumblin' down / Golden gates.
7" Single: Released Nov '83, on Riva, by Riva Records. Catalogue no: **JCM 1**
12" Single: Released Nov '83, on Riva, by Riva Records. Catalogue no: **JCM 112**

HAND TO HOLD ON TO
Tracks: / Hand to hold on to / Hurts so good.
12" Single: Released Jan '83, on Riva, by Riva Records. Catalogue no: **RIVA 38 T**
7" Single: Released Jan '83, on Riva, by Riva Records. Catalogue no: **RIVA 38**

HURT SO GOOD
Tracks: / Hurt so good / Close enough.
7" Single: Released May '82, on Riva, by Riva Records. Catalogue no: **RIVA 36**

JACK AND DIANE
Tracks: / Jack and Diane / Danger list / Need a lover.
7" Single: Released Sep '82, on Riva, by Riva Records. Catalogue no: **RIVA 37**
12" Single: Released Sep '82, on Riva, by Riva Records. Catalogue no: **RIVA 37T**

LONELY OL' NIGHT
Tracks: / Lonely ol' night.
7" Single: Released Oct '85, on Riva, by Riva Records. Catalogue no: **JCM 4**
12" Single: Released Oct '85, on Riva, by Riva Records. Catalogue no: **JCMX 4**

PAPER IN FIRE
Tracks: / Paper in fire / Never too old.
12" Single: Released Sep '87, on Mercury, by Phonogram Ltd. Deleted Oct '88. Catalogue no: **JCMX 8**
7" Single: Released Sep '87, on Mercury, by Phonogram Ltd. Deleted Oct '88. Catalogue no: **JCM 8**

PINK HOUSES
Tracks: / Pink houses / Warmer place to sleep.
7" Single: Released Jun '84, on Riva, by Riva Records. Catalogue no: **JCM 3**

POP SINGER (See panel previous page)
Tracks: / Pop singer / JM's question / Like a rolling stone (live) / Check it out (live).
7" Single: Released 30 May '89, on Mercury, by Phonogram Ltd. Deleted Oct '89. Catalogue no: **JCM 12**
12" Single: Released 30 May '89, on Mercury, by Phonogram Ltd. Deleted Oct '89. Catalogue no: **JCM 1212**
CD 5": Released 30 May '89, on Mercury, by Phonogram Ltd. Catalogue no: **JCMCD 12**

ROCK IN THE USA
Tracks: / Rock in the USA / Under the boardwalk.
12" Single: Released Apr '86, on Riva, by Riva Records. Catalogue no: **JCMX 6**
7" Single: Released Apr '86, on Riva, by Riva Records. Catalogue no: **JCM 6**

ROOTY TOOT TOOT
Tracks: / Rooty toot toot / Check it out (live) / Pretty ballerina (On 12" only).
12" Single: Released Jul '88, on Mercury, by Phonogram Ltd. Deleted Feb '89. Catalogue no: **JCMX 11**
7" Single: Released Jul '88, on Mercury, by Phonogram Ltd. Deleted Feb '89. Catalogue no: **JCM 11**
CD 5": Released Jul '88, on Mercury, by Phonogram Ltd. Deleted Feb '89. Catalogue no: **JCMCD 11**

SMALL TOWN
Tracks: / Small town.
7" Set: Released Jan '86, on Riva, by Riva Records. Deleted Dec '87. Catalogue no: **JCMDP 5**
7" Single: Released Jan '86, on Riva, by Riva Records. Catalogue no: **JCM 5**
7" Set: Released Jan '86, on Riva, by Riva Records. Catalogue no: **JCMXD 5**
12" Single: Released Jan '86, on Riva, by Riva Records. Catalogue no: **JCMX 5**

Mello Colly Man

DON'T SAY GOODBYE
Tracks: / Don't say goodbye.
7" Single: Released Mar '89, on Tom Tom, Catalogue no: **TTT 04**

Mellow, Locksley

COME AND DINE WITH ME
Tracks: / Come and dine with me.
12" Single: Released Apr '82, on Scarlet, Catalogue no: **L 109**

ICE WATER
Tracks: / Ice water.
12" Single: Released Jun '82, on Scarlet, Catalogue no: **L 1010**

Mellow 'N' Roots

BRING BACK MY LOVE
Tracks: / Bring back my love / Well capable.
12" Single: Released Dec '84, on K & K, by K & K Records. Catalogue no: **KK 62**

Mellow Rose

LET ME BE THE ONE
Tracks: / Let me be the one.
12" Single: Released Nov '80, on Nice, Deleted '82. Catalogue no: **NICE 111**

Melly, George

HOMETOWN (SINGLE)
Tracks: / Hometown.
7" Single: Released Nov '86, on PRT, by Castle Communications Records. Catalogue no: **7P 368**

MASCULINE WOMEN FEMININE MEN
Tracks: / Masculine women feminine men.
7" Single: Released Oct '84, on PRT, by Castle Communications Records. Catalogue no: **7P 318**

Melodians

Biographical details: The main reason why this Jamaican reggae band are known amongst European pop fans is that theirs was the best known version of *Rivers of Babylon* prior to the taditional song becoming a monster hit for Boney M in 1978. The Melodians' rendition of this religious, melodic and catchy song was a huge hit in Jamaica in 1970; it was produced by one of the Island's top behind-the-scenes men of the era, Leslie Kong who was also responsible for Desmond Dekker's **The Israelites**. The wonderful state-of-the-art reggae sounds of the Melodians only enjoyed one small taste of British chart success: *Sweet sensation* a single issued in the UK on the reggae-orientated Trojan label reached No. 41 in January 1970. Being a traditional spiritual song, the Melodians did not of course make any money out of the later renditions of *Rivers of Babylon* by Don McLean (an adaptation appeared appeared on his 1971 LP *American Pie*) or Boney M . But their version is fondly remembered by all reggae enthusiasts. (Bob Macdonald 28.1.86).

SWEET SENSATION (SINGLE)
Tracks: / Sweet sensation.
7" Single: Released Jan '70, on Trojan, by Trojan Records. Deleted '73. Catalogue no: **TR 695**

Melody

PEOPLE LIKE YOU
Tracks: / People like you.
Note: Theme from the BBC TV program 'People'
7" Single: Released Jul '88, on BBC, by BBC Records & Tapes. Catalogue no: **RESL 225**

Melody, Bobby

DREWS LAND ROCK
Tracks: / Drews land rock.
10" single: Released Jul '82, on Pama, by Pama Records. Catalogue no: **PMD 3217**

GOT TO BE SERTN
Tracks: / Got to be sertn.
12" Single: Released Nov '82, on Music Works, Catalogue no: **MW 012**

KEEP ON TRYING
Tracks: / Keep on trying.
12" Single: Released Mar '82, on Negus Roots, Catalogue no: **NERT 012**

KISSING AND LOVING
Tracks: / Kissing and loving / Party tonight.
12" Single: on Negus Roots, Catalogue no: **NERT 025**

ROCKERS TILL THE MORNING
Tracks: / Rockers 'till the morning.
12" Single: Released Oct '84, on Nura, Catalogue no: **Unknown**

TRUE TRUE LOVING
Tracks: / True true loving.
12" Single: Released Apr '81, on Negus Roots, Catalogue no: **NERT 102**

Melody, Courtney

1, 2, 3 ROCK
Tracks: / 1,2,3 rock.
12" Single: Released Jun '89, on Living Room, Catalogue no: **OH 14**

BAD BOY
Tracks: / Bad boy / Bad boy (version).
12" Single: Released Nov '87, on Techniques, Catalogue no: **WR 22**

BILLY BOY
Tracks: / Billy boy.
12" Single: Released Sep '89, on Mixing Lab, Catalogue no: **MXL 26**

CALL ME
Tracks: / Call me.
12" Single: Released Jun '88, on Charm, by Charm Records. Catalogue no: **CRT 16**

FALLING IN LOVE
Tracks: / Falling in love.
12" Single: Released Oct '88, on Sir George, Catalogue no: **SG 051T**

FEEL THE PRESSURE
Tracks: / Feel the pressure.
12" Single: Released Feb '89, on Jammy's, Catalogue no: **VPRD 400**

GIRL YOU TURN ME ON
Tracks: / Girl you turn me on.
12" Single: Released Apr '88, on Pioneer International, Catalogue no: **PM 002**

I REMEMBER
Tracks: / I remember.
12" Single: Released Mar '89, on Pickout, Catalogue no: **PICK 04**

LIVE MY LIFE ALONE
Tracks: / Live my life alone.
12" Single: Released Nov '88, on Digital B., Catalogue no: **VPRD 365**

MY LADY
Tracks: / My lady.
12" Single: Released Sep '88, on Redman International, Catalogue no: **RED 36**

STRAIGHT FROM MY HEART
Tracks: / Straight from my heart.
12" Single: Released Jul '88, on Buzz Rock, Catalogue no: **BR 1654**

TELL THEM
Tracks: / Tell them.
7" Single: Released Nov '88, on Taurus, Catalogue no: **UNKNOWN**

THEM SOFT
Tracks: / Them soft.
12" Single: Released Sep '88, on Black Scorpio, Catalogue no: **VPRD 345**

Melody, Delroy

LIVE AND DIRECT
Tracks: / Live and direct.
12" Single: Released Sep '84, on Sun Set (reggae), Catalogue no: **Unknown**

MY LOVER
Tracks: / My lover.
12" Single: Released Sep '83, on Sun Set (reggae), Catalogue no: **Unknown**

POSSEE ARE YOU READY ?
Tracks: / Possee are you ready.
12" Single: Released May '85, on Rhino, by Creole Records. Catalogue no: **RNO 2**

SCHOOL GIRL
Tracks: / School girl.
12" Single: Released May '85, on Rhino, by Creole Records. Catalogue no: **RNO 1**

Melody Four

LITTLE PICTURES
Tracks: / Little pictures.
7" Single: Released Apr '87, on Essex, by Essex Records. Catalogue no: **OH 15**

Melody, Lilly

JUMB
Tracks: / Jumb / Good good lover.
12" Single: Released Jun '86, on Firehouse, Catalogue no: **FH 009**

OLDER THAN ME
Tracks: / Older than me / Pressure me.
12" Single: Released May '86, on Firehouse, Catalogue no: **FH 006**

Melody Makers

CHILDREN PLAYING IN THE STREETS
Tracks: / Children playing in the streets / Dubbing in the streets.
7" Single: Released Dec '80, on Korova, by WEA Records. Deleted Dec '85. Catalogue no: **KOW 12**

MET HER ON A RAINY DAY
Tracks: / Met her on a rainy day / Can't be what you want to be.
7" Single: Released Apr '84, on EMI-America, by EMI Records. Catalogue no: **EA 171**

ROCK IT, BABY
Tracks: / Rock it baby.
7" Single: Released Sep '84, on EMI-America, by EMI Records. Catalogue no: **EA 180**

Melody, Mikey

GILBERT
Tracks: / Gilbert.
12" Single: Released Oct '88, on Dennis Star, Catalogue no: **DSI 008**

JUMBOS WE JUMBO
Tracks: / Jumbos we Jumbo / Ungrateful girl.
12" Single: Released Aug '86, on Taurus, Catalogue no: **TRS 004**

MARANDA MY GIRL
Tracks: / Maranda my girl.
7" Single: Released Jun '88, on Dennis Star, Catalogue no: **DSI 01**

UNDER ME FAT THING BOOGSIE
Tracks: / Under me fat thing boogsie / Reggae music.
12" Single: Released May '85, on Jah Life, Catalogue no: **JL 010**

Melon

FUNKASIA
Tracks: / Only tonight / Funkasia.
12" Single: Released Feb '87, on Epic, by CBS Records. Deleted Aug '87. Catalogue no: **MELON T1**

GATE OF JAPANESIA
Tracks: / Gate of Japanesia.
7" Single: Released Mar '87, on Epic, by CBS Records. Catalogue no: **MELON 2**
12" Single: Released Mar '87, on Epic, by CBS Records. Catalogue no: **MELON T2**

HARDCORE HAWAIIAN
Tracks: / Hardcore Hawaiian / Hawaiian break / Only tonight.
12" Single: Released Jul '87, on Epic, by CBS Records. Catalogue no: **MELON Q3**

SERIOUS JAPAN
Tracks: / Serious Japan.
12" Single: Released Aug '85, on 10 Records, by Virgin Records. Deleted '86. Catalogue no: **TEN 60-12**
7" Single: Released Aug '85, on 10 Records, by Virgin Records. Deleted May '86. Catalogue no: **TEN 60**

Melting Bear

IT MAKES NO DIFFERENCE
Tracks: / It makes no difference.
12" Single: Released Aug '85, on Beggars Banquet, by Beggars Banquet Records. Deleted Jan '88. Catalogue no: **BEG 144T**
7" Single: Released Aug '85, on Beggars Banquet, by Beggars Banquet Records. Deleted Jan '88. Catalogue no: **BEG 144**

Melton, Barry

Biographical details: For Biographical information see COUNTRY JOE AND THE FISH..

ROBBERY
Tracks: / Robbery.

7" Single: Released Jan '82, on Rag Baby, Catalogue no: **BRAG 104**

Melvin, Harold

Biographical details: Despite his perennial star billing in the American soul vocal group Harold Melvin & The Blue Notes, Melvin himself has never been the lead singer. On most of their classic hits, that role was taken by Teddy Pendergrass (real forename - Theodore). But since the group's inception in Philadelphia in 1956, he has been the only constant factor in an otherwise changing line-up. Starting out as a street-corner doo-wop group, they sampled their first tastes of modest success with the singles *If you love me* (1956) and *My hero* (1960). During the Sixties, the group adopted a slicker style and worked on the white-dominated cabaret and supper club circuits, while releasing sporadic singles.
The move took the tenacious Melvin and his cohorts from relative obscurity to stardom was their 1972 decision to sign with Philadelphia International Records. As well as the obvious attraction of this label being based in Melvin's home town, the company was just beginning to establish a 'Philly' soul sound. With the help of Harold Melvin & The Blue Notes plus other acts like Archie Bell & The Drells, the O'Jays and MFSB, the Philly hit machine became to black music in the Seventies what Tamla Motown had been in the Sixties. During 1972-77 the Blue Notes chalked up a run a great soul and disco hits, ranging from punchy uptempo numbers like *The love I lost* and *Satisfaction guaranteed* to intense ballads such as *I miss you* to the social consciousness of *Wake up everybody*. Their biggest American hit was the heartrendingly sad *If you don't know me by now* (No.3 in 1972); their most successful UK single was *Don't leave me this way* (No.5 in 1977, a US No.1 for Thelma Houston). The key elements of these records were the rich, deeply soulful vocals of Pendergrass, and the writing/production talents of Philly father figures Kenny Gamble & Leon Huff (who were responsible for the vast majority of the Blue Notes' hits during this period).
Friction set in towards the end of this time, particulary between Melvin and Pendergrass; the latter thought he deserved the star billing. Pendergrass embarked upon a successful solo career in 1977, staying with the Philly camp, while Melvin took the Bue Notes to ABC Records with new lead voclaist David Ebo. The musical and commercial results were little short of disastrous, and they were left stranded without a recording contract in the early Eighties. But Melvin displayed his usual grit and, after keeping busy via live concerts, returned the group to moderate success in 1984 with the singles *Don't give me up* and *Today's your lucky day*. (Bob MacDonald, 28th Jan 1986).

6 TRACK HITS

Tracks: / Love I lost, The / Wake up everybody / If you don't know me by now / Don't leave me this way / Satisfaction guaranteed / I miss you.
7" EP: Released Sep '83, on Scoop 33, by Pickwick Records. Catalogue no: **7SR 5028**

DON'T GIVE ME UP

Tracks: / Don't give me up.
12" Single: Released Apr '84, on London Records, by London Records. Catalogue no: **LONX 47**
7" Single: Released Apr '84, on London Records, by London Records. Catalogue no: **LON 47**

DON'T LEAVE ME THIS WAY

Tracks: / Don't leave me this way.
7" Single: Released Jan '77, on Philadelphia Int., by EMI Records. Deleted '80. Catalogue no: **PIR 4909**
7" Single: Released May '79, on Philadelphia Int., by EMI Records. Catalogue no: **PIR 8867**

DON'T LEAVE ME THIS WAY (OLD GOLD)

Tracks: / Don't leave me this way / If you don't know me by now.
7" Single: Released Apr '83, on Old Gold, by Old Gold Records. Catalogue no: **OG 9306**

GET OUT (AND LET ME CRY)

Tracks: / Get out.
7" Single: Released Nov '83, on Inferno (1), by Inferno Records. Catalogue no: **674327**
7" Single: Released May '75, on Route, Deleted '78. Catalogue no: **ROUTE 06**

I SHOULD BE YOUR LOVER

Tracks: / I should be your lover / Prayin'.
7" Single: Released May '80, on Source, Deleted '83. Catalogue no: **SRC 104**
12" Single: Released May '80, on Source, Deleted '83. Catalogue no: **12SRC 104**

IF YOU DON'T KNOW ME BY NOW

Tracks: / If you don't know me by now.
7" Single: Released Jan '73, on CBS, by CBS Records. Deleted '76. Catalogue no: **CBS 8496**

LOVE I LOST, THE

Tracks: / Love I lost, The / Love I lost (part 2), The.
7" Single: Released Jan '74, on Philadelphia Int., by EMI Records. Deleted '77. Catalogue no: **PIR 1879**

PRAYIN'

Tracks: / Prayin' (1986 remix) / Prayin' (instrumental) / Gospel (acappela mix) (Extra track on 12" version only.) / Your love is taking me on a journey.
12" Single: Released May '86, on Source, Catalogue no: **12 SOURCE 2**
7" Single: Released May '86, on Source, Catalogue no: **SOURCE 2**
7" Single: Released Jan '80, on Source, Deleted Jan '85. Catalogue no: **SRC 102**
12" Single: Released Jan '80, on Source, Deleted Jan '85. Catalogue no: **12 SRC 102**

REACHING FOR THE WORLD

Tracks: / Reaching for the world.
7" Single: Released Apr '77, on ABC Records, by MCA Records. Deleted '80. Catalogue no: **ABC 4161**

SATISFACTION GUARANTEED (OR TAKE YOUR LOVE BACK)

Tracks: / Satisfaction guaranteed.
7" Single: Released Apr '74, on Philadelphia Int., by EMI Records. Deleted '77. Catalogue no: **PIR 2187**

TODAY'S YOUR LUCKY DAY

Tracks: / Today's your lucky day.
7" Single: Released Aug '84, on Philly World (USA), by Philly World (USA). Deleted '87. Catalogue no: **LON 52**

WAKE UP EVERYBODY

Tracks: / Wake up everybody.
7" Single: Released Feb '76, on Philadelphia Int., by EMI Records. Deleted '79. Catalogue no: **PIR 3866**

Members

Biographical details: At the time of their greatest success, this British rock band consisted of Nigel Bennett, Jean-Marie Carroll, Adrian Lillywhite, Chris Payne and Nicky Tesco. Formed by lead vocalist Tesco in 1977 in the Surrey town of Camberley, the Members were part of the UK's burgeoning punk rock scene. True to the spirit of the movement, their music was loud and brash with uncompromising lyrics; but, in common with the Clash, they also incorporated a reggae feel in some of their songs. This dual approach was demonstrated by their only two UK hit singles: *The sound of the suburbs* (No.12 in 1979) was a classic headbanging punk anthem, and *Offshore banking business* (No.31 in 1979) was a subtle, well-crafted attempt at white man's reggae. Their debut album *At the Chelsea nightclub* reached the UK No.45 position in 1979. Everything seemed to be looking up for the Members in '79, but their success immediately vanished. By 1980 punk had lost it's freshness, and the punters who wanted reggae with their rock were buying from the new new 2 Tone bands (such as the Specials and the Selector) rather than the Members. After disappearing altogether, the Members reemerged in 1982 with the unsuccessful but worthy album *Uprhythm, downbeat* (later retitled *Going West*). Tesco quit in 1963, effectively ending the band. It was somewhat surprising that the Members never achieved greater success than they did, especially in view of their use of such talented producers as Steve Lillywhit, Rupert Hine and Martin Rushent. (Bob MacDonald, 28th Jan 1986).

GOING WEST

Tracks: / Going west.
12" Single: Released Aug '83, on Albion, by Albion Records. Catalogue no: **12ION 153**
7" Single: Released Aug '83, on Albion, by Albion Records. Catalogue no: **ION 153**

MEMBERS EP

Tracks: / Flying again / Disco oui oui / Love in a life / Rat up a drainpipe.
7" Single: Released May '80, on Virgin, by Virgin Records. Deleted '83. Catalogue no: **VS 352**

OFFSHORE BANKING BUSINESS (See panel above right)

Tracks: / Offshore banking business / Solitary confinement.
7" Single: Released Apr '79, on Virgin, by Virgin Records. Deleted '82. Catalogue no: **V 248**

RADIO

Tracks: / Radio / Can't stand up.
7" Single: Released May '82, on Island, by Island Records. Deleted '85. Catalogue no: **WIP 6773**

ROMANCE

Tracks: / Romance / Ballad of John and Martin.
7" Single: Released Apr '80, on Virgin, by Virgin Records. Deleted '83. Catalogue no: **VS 2333**

SOUND OF THE SUBURBS

Tracks: / Sound of the suburbs, The.
7" Single: Released Feb '79, on Virgin, by

MEMBERS - OFFSHORE BANKING BUSINESS (Released on Virgin)

Virgin Records. Deleted '82. Catalogue no: **VS 242**

WORKING GIRL

Tracks: / Working girl.
7" Single: Released May '81, on Albion, by Albion Records. Catalogue no: **ION 1012**
7" Single: Released Jul '83, on Albion, by Albion Records. Catalogue no: **ION 1050**
12" Single: Released Jul '83, on Albion, by Albion Records. Catalogue no: **12ION 1050**
12" Single: Released May '81, on Albion, by Albion Records. Catalogue no: **12ION 1012**

Members Of The House

SHARE THIS HOUSE

Tracks: / Share this house (radio edit mix) (7" only) / Share this house (radio version) / Share this house (house mix) (12" only) / Share this house (accapella) (12" only) / Share this house (bonus beats) (12" only).
Note: "The first single to be culled from the forthcoming double album Techno: The Dance Sound of Detroit." (Virgin Records, June 1988).
7" Single: Released Jun '88, on 10 Records, by Virgin Records. Catalogue no: **TEN 233**
12" Single: Released Jun '88, on 10 Records, by Virgin Records. Catalogue no: **TENX 233**

Members' Radio

IF YOU CAN'T STAND UP

Tracks: / If you can't stand up / Radio.
12" Single: Released Apr '82, on Island, by Island Records. Deleted Apr '85. Catalogue no: **12WIP 6773**

Membranes

DEATH IN TRAD ROCK

Tracks: / Death in trad rock.
12" Single: Released Dec '84, on Criminal Damage, Catalogue no: **CRI 12125**

EUROPIG V. AUTOFLESH

Tracks: / Europig v. Autoflesh.
12" Single: Released Jul '89, on Vinyl Drip, by Vinyl Drip Records. Catalogue no: **SUK 8**

EVERYTHING'S BRILLIANT

Tracks: / Everything's brilliant.
7" Single: Released Mar '86, on In Tape, by In Tape Records. Catalogue no: **IT 029**
12" Single: Released Mar '86, on In Tape, by In Tape Records. Catalogue no: **ITT 029**

KENNEDY '63

Tracks: / Kennedy '63 / Spike Milligan's tape recorder.
7" Single: Released Mar '87, on Constrictor, by Constrictor Records (Germany). Catalogue no: **COLL 002**

MUSCLES

Tracks: / Muscles / All roads lead to Norway / Entertaining friends.
7" Single: Released Jan '82, on Vinyl Drip, by Vinyl Drip Records. Deleted Jan '85. Catalogue no: **VD 007**
7" Single: Released May '82, on Rondelet Music, by Rondelet Music & Records. Catalogue no: **ROUND 19**
12" Single: Released May '82, on Rondelet Music, by Rondelet Music & Records. Catalogue no: **12 ROUND 19**

PINSTRIPE HYPE

Tracks: / Pinstripe hype.
7" Single: Released Nov '82, on Rondelet Music, by Rondelet Music & Records. Catalogue no: **ROUND 28**

SPIKE MILLIGAN'S TAPE RECORDER

Tracks: / Spike Milligan's tape recorder.
7" Single: Released Jun '84, on Criminal Damage, Catalogue no: **CRI 115**
12" Single: Released Sep '86, on Constrictor, by Constrictor Records (Germany). Catalogue no: **CON 9**

Memphis (Group)

YOU SUPPLY THE ROSES

Tracks: / You supply the roses / Apres ski / I supply the wine ((12" only)).
12" Single: Released Jan '85, on Swamplands, by London Records. Catalogue no: **SWX 4**
7" Single: Released Jan '85, on Swamplands, by London Records. Deleted '86. Catalogue no: **SWP 4**

Memphis Tenorc's

BIG AS MEMPHIS

Tracks: / Big as Memphis / Rock 'n' roll hall of fame.
7" Single: Released Aug '80, on Hot Rock, by Hot Rock Records. Catalogue no: **HR45 005**

Men 2nd

INTERCORPSE

Tracks: / Intercorpse.
12" Single: Released Sep '86, on Anything But, Catalogue no: **ABR 013**

Men At Play

DOCTOR JAM (IN THE SLAM)

7" Single: Released Sep '83, on Design Communications, Catalogue no: **DES 1**
12" Single: Released Sep '83, on Design Communications, Catalogue no: **DEST 1**

Men At Work

Biographical details: At the time of their greatest success, this Australian band consisted of Greg Ham, Colin Hay, John Rees, Jerry Speiser and Ron Strykert. Various members of the group began to get to know each other at Melbourne University in the mid-Seventies, but 1979 was the year that Men At Work officially came into being. After being turned down by virtually every record company in existence, the band were eventually signed up by CBS thanks to the persistence of one individual employee of the company, Peter Karpin. He teamed the band with an American producer called Peter MClan. The results were incredible. Men at Work's first Lp *Business as usual* was released in 1982. It reached No.1 in their native Australia, as did the first two singles lifted from the album, *Who can it be now* and *Down under*. Men at Work were duly proclaimed the top new band in Australia. More remarkably, the three aforementioned records then proceeded to reach No.1 in America, with a little help from the new US 24-hour rock video channel MTV. *Business as usual* ascended to the top of the American Lp chart on 13 November 1982 and stayed there for 15 weeks - this made it the most successful debut album in Billboard chart history, smashing the previous record set by the Monkees. *Who can it be now?* was only a minor hit in Britain, but *Down under* and *Business as usual* reached the UK No.1

MEN AT WORK - DOWN UNDER (Released on Epic)

position in early 1983. Indeed at one point, *Down under* and *Business as usual* were simultaneously at the summit of both the singles and albums charts in both Britain and America - this extraordinary quadruple grand slam is normally reserved for long-established superstars such as Barbara Streisand (1980), Michael Jackson, (1983) and Phil Collins (1985), and even then it is rare enough.
Although Men At Work were often knocked for sounding too much like the Police, the truth was that their success lay in the sheer freshness and quality of their music. It was, simply, catchy melodic pop-rock with a hint of New Wave. Most of their material was written by lead vocalist/guitarist Colin Hay. Deliberately making international capital out of their nationality, *Down under* was virtually a new Australian national anthem; but because it was one of the most exuberant and infectious pop singles of all time, its theme became universal. Men At Work seemed to be spearheading a new boom in Aussie bands, but in the event this explosion did not live up to its promise. As for the Men themselves, their task of following up *Business as usual* proved predictably impossible. Although the *Cargo* album and its three international hit singles were respectable successes, they were clearly not quite as good as what had come before. Men at Work dispppeared from the scene in 1984. When a depleted line-up returned in 1985, with the Lp *Two hearts*, the results were a calamity. This third album was merely a pale imitation of its predecessors, and it was a dismal commercial failure. (Bob MacDonald, 28th Jan 1986).

BE GOOD JOHNNY
Tracks: / Be good Johnny / Who can it be now.
7" Single: Released Feb '84, on Epic, by CBS Records. Catalogue no: **A 4119**
12" Single: Released Feb '84, on Epic, by CBS Records. Catalogue no: **TA 4119**
7" Set: Released Feb '84, on Epic, by CBS Records. Catalogue no: **DA 4119**

DOCTOR HECKYLL AND MR. JIVE
Tracks: / Doctor Heckyll and Mr. Jive.
7" Single: Released Sep '83, on Epic, by CBS Records. Deleted '86. Catalogue no: **EPC A 3668**

DOWN UNDER (See panel above)
Tracks: / Down under / Crazy.
7" Single: Released Feb '79, on Epic, by CBS Records. Deleted '82. Catalogue no: **EPC A 2392**

IT'S A MISTAKE
Tracks: / It's a mistake.
7" Pic: Released Jun '83, on Epic, by CBS Records. Catalogue no: **WA 3475**
12" Single: Released Jun '83, on Epic, by CBS Records. Catalogue no: **TA 3475**
7" Single: Released Jun '83, on Epic, by CBS Records. Catalogue no: **A 3475**

MARIA
Tracks: / Maria.
7" Single: Released Aug '85, on Epic, by CBS Records. Catalogue no: **A 6464**
12" Single: Released Aug '85, on Epic, by CBS Records. Catalogue no: **TX 6464**

OVERKILL
Tracks: / Overkill.
7" Single: Released Apr '83, on Epic, by CBS Records. Catalogue no: **EPC A 3220**

WHO CAN IT BE NOW
Tracks: / Who can it be now / Anyone for tennis.
7" Single: Released Oct '82, on Epic, by CBS Records. Deleted '85. Catalogue no: **EPC A 2392**

Men From The Mountains

TREMBLING
Tracks: / Tremblin'.
12" Single: Released Sep '85, on 1 In 12, by Backs Recording Co.. Catalogue no: **1IN 12 120**

Men In Progress

BUSTRIP, THE
Tracks: / Bustrip, The.
12" Single: Released May '89, on Who's That Beat, by Play It Again Sam (Belgium). Catalogue no: **WHOS 16**

Men Men

NATIVES DANCE
Tracks: / Natives dance.
7" Single: Released Jun '84, on Gnu, Catalogue no: **GNU 1**

Men Of Courage

COLD WINTER
Tracks: / Cold winter.
7" Single: Released 22 Aug '88, on Far Out Recording Company, by Far Out Recording Company. Catalogue no: **FAROUT 003**

LOST SOUL
Tracks: / Lost souls.
7" Single: Released '88, on Far Out Recording Company, by Far Out Recording Company. Catalogue no: **FAROUT 002**

Men Of Harlech

CHARLIE'S GETTING MARRIED AT LAST
Tracks: / Charlie's getting married at last / Tribute.
7" Single: Released May '81, on Epic, by CBS Records. Deleted May '84. Catalogue no: **A 1274**

Men They Couldn't Hang

COLOURS, THE (REMIX)
Tracks: / Colours, The / Rory's grave / Big iron (On 12" and CD only) / Colours, The (full remix) (On CD only).
7" Single: Released 14 Mar '88, on Magnet, by WEA Records. Deleted Jun '88. Catalogue no: **SELL 6**
12" Single: Released 14 Mar '88, on Magnet, by WEA Records. Deleted Jun '88. Catalogue no: **SELLT 6**
CD 5": Released 14 Mar '88, on Magnet, by WEA Records. Catalogue no: **CDSELL 6**

CREST, THE
Tracks: / Crest, The / Time at the bar / Goodbye t'Jane / Iron masters (On CD single only).
7" Single: Released May '88, on WEA, by WEA Records. Catalogue no: **YZ 193**
12" Single: Released May '88, on WEA, by WEA Records. Catalogue no: **YZ 193T**
CD 5": Released Jun '88, on WEA, by WEA Records. Catalogue no: **YZ 193 CD**

EVENING SHOW EP: MEN THEY COULDN'T HANG
Tracks: / Going back to Coventry / Ghosts of cable street, The / Dancing on the pier / Tiny tin soldiers.
12" Single: Released Jul '88, on Strange Fruit, by Strange Fruit Records. Catalogue no: **SFNT 012**

GHOSTS OF CABLE STREET
Tracks: / Dream machine / Liverpool lullaby (On 12" only).
Cassingle: Released Apr '87, on MCA, by MCA Records. Catalogue no: **SELLC 3**
7" Single: Released Feb '87, on MCA, by MCA Records. Catalogue no: **SELL 3**
12" Single: Released Apr '87, on MCA, by MCA Records. Catalogue no: **SELLT 3**

GOLD RUSH
Tracks: / Gold rush / Ghost of cable street, The / Walkin' talkin' (Extra track on 12" version only.).
12" Single: Released Jun '86, on MCA, by MCA Records. Catalogue no: **SELLT 1**
7" Single: Released Jun '86, on MCA, by MCA Records. Catalogue no: **SELL 1**

GREEN BACK DOLLAR
Tracks: / Greenback dollar.
7" Single: Released Nov '85, on Demon, by Demon Records. Catalogue no: **D 1040**
12" Single: Released Nov '85, on Demon, by Demon Records. Catalogue no: **D 1040 T**

GREEN FIELDS OF FRANCE
Tracks: / Green fields of France.
7" Single: Released Oct '84, on Imp, by Demon Records. Catalogue no: **IMP 003**
12" Single: Released Oct '84, on Imp, by Demon Records. Catalogue no: **IMP 003T**

IRON MASTERS
Tracks: / Iron masters.
12" Single: Released Jun '85, on Imp, by Demon Records. Catalogue no: **IMP 005T**
7" Single: Released Jun '85, on Imp, by Demon Records. Catalogue no: **IMP 005**

ISLAND IN THE RAIN
Tracks: / Island in the rain / Country song / Silver dagger / Restless highway.
7" Pic: Released Oct '87, on Magnet, by WEA Records. Deleted Jun '88. Catalogue no: **SELLP 5**
12" Single: Released Oct '87, on Magnet, by WEA Records. Deleted Jun '88. Catalogue no: **SELLT 5**
7" Single: Released Oct '87, on Magnet, by WEA Records. Deleted Jun '88. Catalogue no: **SELL 5**

PLACE IN THE SUN, A
Tracks: / Place in the sun, A / Rosettes.
CD 5": Released May '89, on Silvertone, Catalogue no: **ORECD 7**
12" Single: Released May '89, on Silvertone, Catalogue no: **ORET 7**
7" Single: Released May '89, on Silvertone, Catalogue no: **ORE 7**

RAIN, STEAM & SPEED
Tracks: / Rain, steam & speed.
12" Single: Released Feb '89, on Silvertone, Catalogue no: **ORET 4**
7" Single: Released Feb '89, on Silvertone, Catalogue no: **ORE 4**
CD 5": Released Feb '89, on Silvertone, Catalogue no: **ORECD 4**

SHIRT OF BLUE
Tracks: / Shirt of blue / Johnny come home / Night to remember / Whisky with me giro (Extra track on 12" version only.) / Scarlet ribbons (Extra track on 12" version only.).
7" Single: Released Oct '86, on MCA, by MCA Records. Catalogue no: **SELL 2**
12" Single: Released Oct '86, on MCA, by MCA Records. Catalogue no: **SELLT 2**

Men Without Hats

Biographical details: Hailing from Canada, this intriguingly named Montreal band were around at the same time as Australia's Men At Work (although an amalgam of the two names - Men Without Work - might have been more appropriate to the international economic climate of the era). Men Without Hats came to fame with their quirky oddball pop-rock single *The safety dance*, supported by a memorable promo video. This single first saw the light of day at the beginning of 1983, but was a sleeper smash. It eventually reached No.3 in America and No.6 in Britain in the autumn of that year. The electo pop sound of Men Without Hats was furthered explored on the albums *Rhythm of youth* and *Folk of the Eighties*. But the *Safety dance* was essentially a one off novelty hit, and the trio's other releases failed to arouse interest. (Bob MacDonald, 28th Jan 1986).

ANTARCTICA
Tracks: / Antarctica.
7" Single: Released Mar '82, on Statik, Catalogue no: **STAT 13**

I'VE GOT THE MESSAGE
Tracks: / I've got the message / Out of space / Freeway.
7" Single: Released Dec '83, on Statik, Catalogue no: **TAK 14**
12" Single: Released Dec '83, on Statik, Catalogue no: **TAK 1412**

LIVING IN CHINA
Tracks: / Living in China.
12" Single: Released Jan '84, on Statik, Catalogue no: **TAK 3-12**
7" Single: Released Jan '84, on Statik, Catalogue no: **TAK 3**

POP GOES THE WORLD
Tracks: / Pop goes the world / End of the world.
CD 5": on Mercury, by Phonogram Ltd. Deleted Oct '88. Catalogue no: **MERCD 257**
12" Single: Released Nov '87, on Mercury, by Phonogram Ltd. Deleted Oct '88. Catalogue no: **MERX 257**
7" Single: Released Nov '87, on Mercury, by Phonogram Ltd. Deleted Oct '88. Catalogue no: **MER 257**

SAFETY DANCE
Tracks: / Safety dance / I got the message.
7" Single: Released Mar '83, on Statik, Catalogue no: **TAK 1**
12" Single: Released Mar '83, on Statik, Catalogue no: **TAK 112**

WHERE DO THE BOYS GO?
Tracks: / Where do the boys go.
7" Single: Released Jun '84, on Statik, Catalogue no: **TAK 15**
12" Single: Released Jun '84, on Statik, Catalogue no: **TAK 15/12**

Mena, Billy

SHUT UP YER GOB
Tracks: / Shut up yer gob / Football frolics.
7" Single: Released Apr '81, on Mint, by Emerald Records. Deleted '88. Catalogue no: **CHEW 49**

Menace

YOUNG ONES, THE
Tracks: / Young ones, The.
7" Single: Released Apr '81, on Fresh, by Jetstar Records. Catalogue no: **FRESH 14**

Menage

MEMORY
Tracks: / Memory.
12" Single: Released Jul '83, on Carrere America (USA), by PolyGram Rec.Inc.(USA). Catalogue no: **CART 283**

Mendes, Sergio

Biographical details: This American pianist, conductor, arranger, bandleader and producer was signed up by A&M Records in 1966 together with his band Brasil '66. These Latin stylists were designed to complement but not compete with Herb Alpert & The Tijuana Brass in the easy listening stakes. Alpert, the co-owner of A&M became Mendes' producer in the early days. Mendas & Brasil '66 enjoyed a US No.4 smash in 1968 with their single *The look of love*, from the movie 'Casino Royale'. They followed this with two more American Top 20 singles during 1968: these were cover versions of the Beatles' *The fool on the hill* and Simon and Garfunkel's *Scarborough fair*.
Having built up a sturdy reputation in the music business, Mendes never starved after this. But he did not return to the US Top 40 until 1983, when the middle-of-the-road ballad *Never gonna let you* (featuring vocals by Joe Bixxulo and Leza Miller) reached No.4; it thus tied the 1968 peak of his previous shot, *The look of love.. This single provided Mendes (who no longer used the name Brasil '66 for his group) whith his only UK chart entry - it peaked at No.45. In 1984 he reached the US No.29 position with Alibis.* Ostensibly operating in the realms of Latin pop, jazz and rythm-and-blues, Mendes' music has really been too conservative and middle-of-the-road to be of interest to fans of those genres. (Bob MacDonald, 28th Jan 1986).

MAS QUE NADA
Tracks: / Mas qeu nada.
12" Single: Released Aug '89, on Breakout, by A&M Records. Catalogue no: **USAT 672**
7" Single: Released Aug '89, on Breakout, by A&M Records. Catalogue no: **USA 672**

MY SUMMER LOVE
Tracks: / My summer love / Life in the movies.
7" Single: Released Aug '82, on A&M, by A&M Records. Deleted Aug '85. Catalogue no: **AMS 8249**

NEVER GONNA LET YOU GO
Tracks: / Never gonna let you go.
7" Single: Released Jul '83, on A&M, by A&M Records. Deleted '86. Catalogue no: **AM 118**

NON STOP
Tracks: / Non stop / Flower of Bahia / Never gonna let you go (Extra track on 12" version only.).
7" Single: Released Aug '86, on A&M, by A&M Records. Deleted '87. Catalogue no: **AM 341**
12" Single: Released Aug '86, on A&M, by A&M Records. Deleted '87. Catalogue no: **AMY 341**

Mendez Prey

ON TO THE BORDERLINE
Tracks: / On to the borderline / Runnin' for you.
7" Single: Released Jan '83, on MP, Catalogue no: **AM 076**

WONDERLAND
Tracks: / Wonderland / Can you believe it.
7" Single: Released Feb '86, on Wag, Catalogue no: **WAG 2**
12" Single: Released Feb '86, on Wag, Catalogue no: **12 WAG 2**

Mengalomania

FIVE FINGER SHUFFLE
Tracks: / Five finger shuffle / Panic station.
12" Single: Released Nov '81, on Magnet, by WEA Records. Catalogue no: **12 MAG 209**
7" Single: Released Nov '81, on Magnet, by WEA Records. Catalogue no: **MAG 209**

Meno, Roger

I FIND THE WAY
Tracks: / I find the way / Do you really go.
12" Single: Released Dec '85, on ZYX (Germany), Catalogue no: **ZYX 5352**

Mental As Anything

EGYPT
Tracks: / Egypt / Pork is not a gift.
7" Single: Released May '80, on Virgin, by Virgin Records. Deleted May '83. Catalogue no: **VS 348**

HE'S JUST NO GOOD FOR YOU
Tracks: / He's just no good for you / Ruby baby.
Note: ANY Q4 - Special: Dye-cut Picture Bag.
Special: Released Jan '88, on Epic, by CBS Records. Deleted Aug '88. Catalogue no: **ANY Q4**
7" Single: Released Dec '87, on Epic, by CBS Records. Deleted Jun '88. Catalogue no: **ANY 4**
7" Pic: Released Jan '88, on Epic, by CBS Records. Deleted Aug '88. Catalogue no: **ANY P4**
12" Single: Released Dec '87, on Epic, by CBS Records. Deleted Jun '88. Catalogue no: **ANY T4**

IF YOU LEAVE CAN I COME TOO?
Tracks: / If you leave can I come too / Let's cook.
7" Single: Released Nov '82, on CBS, by CBS Records. Deleted Nov '85. Catalogue no: **CBS 8265**

IF YOU LEAVE ME CAN I COME TOO (SINGLE)
Tracks: / If you leave me can I come too / I'm glad.
12" Single: Released Jun '88, on Epic, by CBS Records. Deleted Jan '89. Catalogue no: **ANYT 5**
7" Single: Released Jun '88, on Epic, by CBS Records. Deleted Jan '89. Catalogue no: **ANY 5**

LET'S GO TO PARADISE
Tracks: / Let's go to paradise / My hands are tied.
7" Single: Released Jul '87, on Epic, by CBS Records. Catalogue no: **ANY P3**
12" Single: Released 13 Jun '87, on Epic, by CBS Records. Deleted Nov '87. Catalogue no: **ANY T3**
7" Single: Released Jun '87, on Epic, by CBS Records. Deleted Nov '87. Catalogue no: **ANY 3**

LIVE IT UP
Tracks: / Live it up / Good Friday.
7" Single: Released Mar '86, on Epic, by CBS Records. Deleted '86. Catalogue no: **A 6797**
7" Pic: Released Mar '86, on Epic, by CBS Records. Deleted '86. Catalogue no: **WA 6797**
12" Single: Released Mar '86, on Epic, by CBS Records. Deleted '87. Catalogue no: **TX 6797**
12" Single: Released Jan '87, on Epic, by CBS Records. Deleted Aug '87. Catalogue no: **ANUT 1**
7" Single: Released Jan '87, on Epic, by CBS Records. Deleted Aug '87. Catalogue no: **ANY 1**

NIPS ARE GETTING BIGGER
Tracks: / Nips are getting bigger / Instrumental as anything.
7" Single: Released Feb '80, on Virgin, by Virgin Records. Deleted '83. Catalogue no: **VS 309**

ROCK'N'ROLL MUSIC
Tracks: / Rock'n'roll music.
12" Single: Released Oct '89, on Epic, by CBS Records. Catalogue no: **ANY T6**
7" Pic: Released Oct '89, on Epic, by CBS Records. Catalogue no: **ANY Q6**
CD 5": Released Oct '89, on Epic, by CBS Records. Catalogue no: **CDANY 6**
7" Single: Released Oct '89, on Epic, by CBS Records. Catalogue no: **ANY 6**

YOU'RE SO STRONG
Tracks: / You're so strong / Bus ride / Live it up / Good Friday / Take stars to your place.
7" Single: Released May '86, on Epic, by CBS Records. Deleted '86. Catalogue no: **A 7138**
12" Single: Released May '86, on Epic, by CBS Records. Deleted '86. Catalogue no: **TA 7138**
7" Single: Released May '87, on Epic, by CBS Records. Deleted Nov '87. Catalogue no: **ANY D2**

Mental, Ella

LIGHT UP MY LIFE
Tracks: / Light up my life / Song for Jenny.
7" Single: Released Aug '89, on Warner Bros., by WEA Records. Catalogue no: **W 2839**

Menticide

BATHROOM IDEAS EXHIBITION EP
Tracks: / Bathroom ideas exhibition EP.
7" Single: Released Mar '86, on Pink Flag, by Pink Flag Records. Catalogue no: **MENT 001**

Menudo

IF YOU'RE NOT HERE(BY MY SIDE)
Tracks: / If you're no here (by my side).
7" Single: Released Oct '84, on RCA, by BMG Records (UK). Catalogue no: **RCA 462**

Merc & Monk

BABY FACE
Tracks: / Baby face.
7" Single: Released May '85, on EMI-Manhattan, by EMI Records. Catalogue no: **MT 3**
12" Single: Released May '85, on EMI-Manhattan, by EMI Records. Catalogue no: **12 MT 3**

Mercenary Skank

NO MORE DANCING (EP)
Tracks: / No more dancing.
7" Single: Released Oct '84, on Criminal Damage, Catalogue no: **CRI 12122**

WORKERS GIANTS
Tracks: / Workers giants.
12" Single: Released Sep '85, on Before The Storm, Catalogue no: **STORM 1**

Merchant

ROCK IT
Tracks: / Rock it / Pan in danger.
12" Single: Released Jul '86, on Hot Vinyl, Deleted Mar '87. Catalogue no: **POSPX 764**
7" Single: Released Jul '86, on Hot Vinyl, Deleted Mar '87. Catalogue no: **POSP 764**

Merchant Sugar

GONE SHE GONE
Tracks: / Gone she gone.
12" Single: Released Jul '89, on White, Catalogue no: **KUFF 1**

TEARS OF A CLOWN
Tracks: / Tears of a clown / Raggamuffin.
12" Single: Released Jul '86, on UK Bubblers, by Greensleeves Records. Deleted '88. Catalogue no: **UKMC 15**

Mercurian

SHOT DOWN IN FLAMES
Tracks: / Shot down in flames.
7" Single: Released Jan '82, on Arcadia, Catalogue no: **ARA2**

Mercury

TOO HOT
Tracks: / Too hot.
7" Single: Released Feb '85, on La Fell, Catalogue no: **FEL 2**
12" Single: Released Feb '85, on La Fell, Catalogue no: **FEL 2 T**

Mercury, Eric

GIMME A CALL SOMETIME
Tracks: / Gimme me a call sometime / Include me out.
7" Single: Released Oct '81, on Capitol, by EMI Records. Deleted Oct '84. Catalogue no: **CL 216**

Mercury, Freddie

BARCELONA
Tracks: / Barcelona / Exercises in free love / Barcelona (extended version).
12" Single: Released Oct '87, on Polydor, by Polydor Ltd. Catalogue no: **POSPX 887**
12" Pic: Released Oct '87, on Polydor, by Polydor Ltd. Deleted 30 May '89. Catalogue no: **POSPP 887**
Cassingle: Released Oct '87, on Polydor, by Polydor Ltd. Deleted 30 May '89. Catalogue no: **POSPC 887**
7" Single: Released Oct '87, on Polydor, by Polydor Ltd. Catalogue no: **POSP 887**

GOLDEN BOY, THE
Tracks: / Golden boy, The / Fallen priest, The / Golden boy, The (instrumental).
CD 5": Released Oct '88, on Polydor, by Polydor Ltd. Catalogue no: **PZCD 23**
12" Single: Released Oct '88, on Polydor, by Polydor Ltd. Deleted 31 May '89. Catalogue no: **PZ 23**
7" Single: Released Oct '88, on Polydor, by Polydor Ltd. Deleted 30 May '89. Catalogue no: **PO 23**

GREAT PRETENDER
Tracks: / Great pretender, The / Exercises in free love.
7" Single: Released Feb '87, on Parlophone, by EMI Records. Deleted Jul '87. Catalogue no: **RP 6151**
7" Single: Released Feb '87, on Parlophone, by EMI Records. Deleted Apr '88. Catalogue no: **R 6151**
7" Single: Released Feb '87, on Parlophone, by EMI Records. Deleted Apr '88. Catalogue no: **12R 6151**

HOW CAN I GO ON
Tracks: / How can I go on / Overture piccante / Guide me home* (*Extra track on 12" & CD singles).
Note: (New single from "Barcelona" album)h
12" Single: Released 23 Jan '89, on Polydor, by Polydor Ltd. Deleted 30 Jun '89. Catalogue no: **PZ 29**
7" Single: Released 23 Jan '89, on Polydor, by Polydor Ltd. Deleted 30 Jun '89. Catalogue no: **PO 29**
7" Pic: Released 30 Jan '89, on Polydor, by Polydor Ltd. Deleted 30 Jun '89. Catalogue no: **POP 29**
CD 5": Released 23 Jan '89, on Polydor, by Polydor Ltd. Catalogue no: **PZCD 29**

I WAS BORN TO LOVE YOU
Tracks: / I was born to love you.
7" Single: Released Apr '85, on CBS, by CBS Records. Deleted '88. Catalogue no: **A 6019**

LIVING ON MY OWN
Tracks: / Living on my own.
7" Single: Released Sep '85, on CBS, by CBS Records. Deleted '88. Catalogue no: **A 6555**

LOVE KILLS
Tracks: / Love kills / Rotwang's party.
7" Single: Released Sep '84, on CBS, by CBS Records. Deleted '87. Catalogue no: **A 4735**

MADE IN HEAVEN
Tracks: / Made in heaven.
7" Single: Released Jul '85, on CBS, by CBS Records. Deleted '88. Catalogue no: **A 6413**

TIME
Tracks: / Time.
7" Single: Released May '86, on EMI, by EMI Records. Deleted '89. Catalogue no: **EMI 5559**

Mercy Mercy

IT MUST BE HEAVEN
Tracks: / It must be heaven.
7" Single: Released Oct '84, on Ensign, by Ensign Records. Deleted '86. Catalogue no: **ENY 515**
12" Single: Released Oct '84, on Ensign, by Ensign Records. Deleted '85. Catalogue no: **12ENY 515**

WHAT ARE WE GONNA DO ABOUT IT (See panel above)
Tracks: / What are we gonna do about it / What are we gonna do about it (dub/mix).
7" Single: Released Aug '85, on Ensign, by Ensign Records. Deleted '86. Catalogue no: **ENY 522**
12" Single: Released Aug '85, on Ensign, by Ensign Records. Deleted '87. Catalogue no: **12ENY 522**

MERCY MERCY - WHAT ARE WE GONNA DO ABOUT IT? (Released on Ensign)

Mercyful Fate

BLACK FUNERAL
Tracks: / Black funeral / Black masses.
12" Single: Released Nov '83, on Music For Nations, by Music For Nations Records. Catalogue no: **12 KUT 106**

Merican, Mikey

CONTROL THE DANCE HALL
Tracks: / Control the dance hall.
12" Single: Released Feb '87, on Unity, Catalogue no: **UN 011**

Merlin

BORN FREE
Tracks: / Born free.
12" Single: Released Sep '88, on Rhythm King, by Mute Records. Catalogue no: **LEFT 022 T**
7" Single: Released Oct '88, on Rhythm King, by Mute Records. Catalogue no: **LEFT 022**

DROP THE WEAPON EP
Tracks: / Drop the weapon.
7" Single: Released Sep '89, on Rhythm King, by Mute Records. Catalogue no: **LEFT 32**

WEEKEND GIRL
Tracks: / Weekend girl / Drop the weapon / Drop the pressure / Bust da move.
7" Single: Released Jun '89, on Rhythm King, by Mute Records. Catalogue no: **LEFT 032**
12" Single: Released Jun '89, on Rhythm King, by Mute Records. Catalogue no: **LEFT 032T**
Cassingle: Released Oct '89, on Rhythm King, by Mute Records. Catalogue no: **LEFT 032C**

WIZARD MIX
Tracks: / Wizard mix.
CD 5": Released 23 Jan '89, on Rhythm King, by Mute Records. Catalogue no: **LEFTCD 22**
12" Single: Released Dec '88, on Rhythm King, by Mute Records. Catalogue no: **LEFT 022TR**

Merran

OH CHIMERA
Tracks: / Oh chimera.
7" Single: Released Aug '85, on Siren, by Virgin Records. Deleted '89. Catalogue no: **SIREN 5**
12" Single: Released Aug '85, on Siren, by Virgin Records. Deleted May '88. Catalogue no: **SIREN 5-12**

SEE YOU LATER
Tracks: / See you later / Out of my hands.
7" Single: Released '85, on Siren, by Virgin Records. Catalogue no: **SIREN 10**

Merrell, Ray

BIG JOHN WAYNE
Tracks: / Big John Wayne / Movin' on down.
7" Single: Released Apr '81, on President, by President Records. Catalogue no: **PT 493**

BINGO COWBOYS

MERRAN - SEE YOU LATER (Released on Siren)

Tracks: / Bingo cowboys / Seeds.
7" Single: Released Sep '82, on President, by President Records. Catalogue no: **PT 508**

I WILL LOVE YOU
Tracks: / I will love you / Little white lies.
7" Single: Released Dec '83, on Satril, by Satril Records. Catalogue no: **RM 005**

Merrick & Tibbs

CALL OF THE WILD
Tracks: / Tiger tiger.
7" Single: Released Feb '83, on CBS, by CBS Records. Catalogue no: **MAT 1**
12" Single: Released Feb '83, on CBS, by CBS Records. Catalogue no: **MAT 131**

Merrick, Tony

LADY JANE
Tracks: / Lady Jane.
7" Single: Released Jun '66, on Columbia, by EMI Records. Deleted '69. Catalogue no: **DB 7913**

Mersaide

NON STOP DANCING
Tracks: / Non stop dancing.
7" Single: Released Sep '87, on Legal Lights, by Legal Light Records. Catalogue no: **LLD 26**

Merseybeats

Biographical details: At the time of their greatest success, this British pop combo consisted of John Banks, Tony Crane, Johnny Gustafson and Aaron Williams. Hailing from Liverpool, they were named after the Beatles-led boom in best groups, and were a much acclaimed part of that boom. They apparently obtained permission from the Merseybeat newspaper before choosing that name. Initially known as the Mavericks (1960) and then the Pacifics, they became the Merseybeats in 1962. They built up a reputation at the Cavern and this spread to Merseyside as a whole. Their first single *It's love that really counts* reached No.24 on the British chart in late 1963. The Merseybeats enjoyed their peak year in 1964, with four hit singles, two hit Ep's and one hit album. The biggest single was *I think of you*, which reached the UK No.5 position..
For all the praise that they received, The Merseybeats were somewhat underrated by the public. Their chart success fizzled out during 1965-66, as did many of the Mersey boom combos who were not able to achieve wider international success. After the termination of the group in February 1966, Crane and Billy Kinsley (an earlier Merseybeat member who had quit and rejoined the group) abandoned their instruments and became a vocal duo known as the Merseys. In the summer of '66, they enjoyed one UK No.4 hit with *Sorrow* (originally recorded by the McCoys in 1965, immortalised by David Bowie in 1973). Despite having no further chart success after *Sorrow*, the duo stayed together for several years and made a steady living via cabaret. (Bob MacDonald, 28th Jan 1986).

DON'T TURN AROUND
Tracks: / Don't turn around.
7" Single: Released Apr '64, on Fontana, by Phonogram Ltd. Deleted '67. Catalogue no: **TF 459**

I LOVE YOU, YES I DO
Tracks: / I love you, yes I do.
7" Single: Released Oct '65, on Fontana, by Phonogram Ltd. Deleted '68. Catalogue no: **TF 607**

I STAND ACCUSED
Tracks: / I stand accused.
7" Single: Released Jan '66, on Fontana, by Phonogram Ltd. Deleted '69. Catalogue no: **TF 645**

I THINK OF YOU
Tracks: / I think of you.
7" Single: Released Jan '64, on Old Gold, by Old Gold Records. Deleted '67. Catalogue no: **TF 431**

I THINK OF YOU (OLD GOLD)
Tracks: / I think of you.
7" Single: Released Jul '82, on Old Gold, by Old Gold Records. Catalogue no: **OG 9251**

IT'S LOVE THAT REALLY COUNTS
Tracks: / It's love that really counts.
7" Single: Released Sep '63, on Fontana, by Phonogram Ltd. Deleted '66. Catalogue no: **TF 412**

LAST NIGHT
Tracks: / Last night.
7" Single: Released Nov '64, on Fontana, by Phonogram Ltd. Deleted '67. Catalogue no: **TF 504**

THIS IS MERSEYBEAT (MEDLEY)
Tracks: / This is merseybeat.
7" Single: Released Oct '81, on Tudor, Catalogue no: **CR 23**
12" Single: Released Oct '81, on Tudor, Catalogue no: **CR 12 23**

WISHIN' AND HOPIN'
Tracks: / Wishin' and hopin'.
7" Single: Released Jul '64, on Fontana, by Phonogram Ltd. Deleted '67. Catalogue no: **TF 482**

Merseys

SORROW
Tracks: / Sorrow.
7" Single: Released Jun '88, on Fontana, by Phonogram Ltd. Catalogue no: **TF 694**

SORROW (OLD GOLD)
Tracks: / Sorrow / You've got to hide your love away.
7" Single: Released Jun '88, on Old Gold, by Old Gold Records. Catalogue no: **OG 9787**

Mertens, Wim

EDUCES ME (SINGLE)
Tracks: / Educes me.
7" Single: Released 13 Jun '87, on Factory (1), by Factory Records. Catalogue no: **FAC 190**

HIROSE
Tracks: / Hirose / Noli me tangere.
7" Single: Released Dec '86, on Les Disques Du Crepuscule(Belgium), by Les Disques Du Crepuscule(Belgium). Catalogue no: **7TWI 593**

Merton Parkas

Biographical details: One of a considerable number of bands to appear and disappear during Britain's short-lived Mod revival of 1979/80, the Merton Parkas -- Neil Hurrell, Simon Smith, Danny Talbot and Mick Talbot -- had just one chart hit when the single, *You Need Wheels*, peaked at No.40 in the summer of '79. Coincidentally, keyboards player Mick Talbot was also a member of the Chords, another Mod revival band who reached No 40 with their biggest single, Maybe Tomorrow. The Merton Parkas faded into history but Talbot's career reached a new level in '83: having previously played keyboards on some Jam sessions he teamed with Paul Weller on that group's disbandment and the new duo, Style Council, quickly began a string of Top Twenty hits. (Bob MacDonald, January 1986.).

FLAT 19
Tracks: / Flat 19 / Band of gold.
7" Single: Released Nov '83, on Well Suspect, by Well Suspect Records. Catalogue no: **BLAM 002**

PUT ME IN THE PICTURE
Tracks: / Put me in the picture / In the midnight hour.
7" Single: Released Jul '80, on Beggars Banquet, by Beggars Banquet Records. Deleted Jul '83. Catalogue no: **BEG 43**

YOU NEED WHEELS
Tracks: / You need wheels.
7" Single: Released Apr '66, on Beggars Banquet, by Beggars Banquet Records. Deleted '69. Catalogue no: **BEG 22**

YOU NEED WHEELS (5 TRACK EP)
Tracks: / You need wheels.
12" Single: Released Apr '83, on Beggars Banquet, by Beggars Banquet Records. Deleted Jan '88. Catalogue no: **BEG 93E**

Mervyn, Junior

APARTHEID (SINGLE)
Tracks: / Apartheid.
12" Single: Released May '86, on Greensleeves, by Greensleeves Records. Catalogue no: **GRED 199**

Mesh

MEET EVERY SITUATION HEAD ON
Tracks: / Meet every situation head on.
7" Single: Released 8 Nov '88, on Castalia, Catalogue no: **STAB 1**
12" Single: Released '88, on Castalia, Catalogue no: **TAB 1**

Mesple Mady

CANTILENA ARIA (CANTILENA)
Tracks: / Cantilena aria (cantilena).
7" Single: Released Jun '85, on EMI, by EMI Records. Catalogue no: **EMI 5522**

Message People

AFRICAN PEOPLE (SINGLE)
Tracks: / African people.
12" Single: Released Mar '87, on Music For Nations, by Music For Nations Records. Catalogue no: **12 KUT 112GV**

Messenger, Ian

LIVING IN THE NIGHT
Tracks: / Living in the night / Love active.
7" Single: Released Dec '85, on Warner Bros., by WEA Records. Catalogue no: **W 8900**

Messenger Service

GET STREETWISE
Tracks: / Get streetwise.
12" Single: on Silver Screen, by Creole Records. Catalogue no: **MIXT 3**

Messengers

GREAT INSTITUTIONS
Tracks: / Great institutions.
7" Single: Released Jun '84, on Music Fest, by Chrysalis Records. Catalogue no: **MUST 1**
12" Single: Released Jun '84, on Music Fest, by Chrysalis Records. Deleted '85. Catalogue no: **MUSTX 1**

I TURN IN (TO YOU)
Tracks: / I turn in (to you) / Semi-professionals, The (Theme No.1).
12" Single: Released '83, on Chrysalis, by Chrysalis Records. Deleted '87. Catalogue no: **CHS 2663**
7" Single: Released '83, on Chrysalis, by Chrysalis Records. Catalogue no: **CHS 2663**

Messiah Force

SEQUEL, THE
Tracks: / Sequel, The.
7" Single: Released Oct '88, on Bold Reprive (2), by Bold Reprive Records. Catalogue no: **7BRM 021**
12" Single: Released Oct '88, on Bold Reprive (2), by Bold Reprive Records. Catalogue no: **BRMT 021**

Messina, Jim

DO YOU WANNA DANCE (OLD GOLD)
Tracks: / Do you wanna dance / Love will follow.
12" Single: Released Sep '88, on Old Gold, by Old Gold Records. Catalogue no: **OG 4501**

Metal Boys

SWEET MARILYN
Tracks: / Sweet Marilyn / Fugue for a darkening.
7" Single: Released Jun '79, on Rough Trade, by Rough Trade Records. Catalogue no: **RT 016**

Metal Doughnut Band

LAURA NORDER
Tracks: / Laura Norder.
12" Single: Released Apr '85, on Vuggum, Catalogue no: **BAAD 1**

Metal Mickey

DO THE FUNKY ROBOT
Tracks: / Do the funky robot.
7" Single: Released Oct '82, on Mickey-pops, Catalogue no: **METMIK 3**

I WANT TO HOLD YOUR HAND
Tracks: / I want to hold your hand.
7" Single: Released Mar '83, on Hollywood, by Hollywood Records. Catalogue no: **HWD 008**

METAL MICKEY MAGIC
Tracks: / Metal Mickey magic.
7" Single: Released Oct '82, on Mickey-pops, Catalogue no: **METMIK 1**

METAL MICKEY THEME
Tracks: / Metal Mickey theme / Fruit bat rap.
7" Single: Released Jan '83, on Hollywood, by Hollywood Records. Catalogue no: **HWD 004**

PARIS MAQUIS
Tracks: / Paris maquis / Cle de contact.
7" Single: Released Jan '79, on Rough Trade, by Rough Trade Records. Catalogue no: **RTG 001**

SILLYCON CHIPP
Tracks: / Sillycon chip.
7" Single: Released Oct '82, on Mickey-pops, Catalogue no: **METMIK 2**

Metalgon

METALGON
Special: Released Jun '87, on Azra (USA), by Azra International (USA). Catalogue no: **A 30**

Metallica

CREEPING DEATH
Tracks: / Creeping death / Am I evil / Blitzkrieg.
7" Single: Released Mar '86, on Music For Nations, by Music For Nations Records. Catalogue no: **TKUT 112**
12" Single: Released Nov '84, on Music For Nations, by Music For Nations Records. Catalogue no: **12 KUT 112**
12" Pic: Released Nov '84, on Music For Nations, by Music For Nations Records. Catalogue no: **P12KUT 112**

HARVESTER OF SORROW
Tracks: / Harvester of sorrow / Breadfan / Prince, The.
12" Single: Released 15 Aug '88, on Vertigo, by Phonogram Ltd. Deleted Feb '89. Catalogue no: **METAL 212**
CD 5": Released 15 Aug '88, on Vertigo, by Phonogram Ltd. Deleted Feb '89. Catalogue no: **METCD 2**

JUMP IN THE FIRE
Tracks: / Jump in the fire.
7" Pic: Released Mar '86, on Music For Nations, by Music For Nations Records. Catalogue no: **KUT 105P**
12" Single: Released Jan '84, on Music For Nations, by Music For Nations Records. Catalogue no: **12 KUT 105**
Cassingle: Released Apr '87, on Music For Nations, by Music For Nations Records. Catalogue no: **T 12 KUT 105**

METALLICA: INTERVIEW PICTURE DISC (COLLECTION)
Note: 4 x 7" picture discs in wallet.
7" Set: Released 11 Dec '88, on Baktabak, by Baktabak Records. Catalogue no: **BAKPAK 1015**

ONE
Tracks: / One / Seek & destroy (live) (Not available on 12" and CD single) / For whom the bell tolls (On 12" and CD 5" only) / Welcome home (sanitarium) (On 12" and CD 5" only).
10" single: Released Apr '89, on Vertigo, by Phonogram Ltd. Deleted 31 Jul '89. Catalogue no: **METPD 5**
7" Single: Released Apr '89, on Vertigo, by

Phonogram Ltd. Deleted 31 Jul '89. Catalogue no: **METAL 5**
CD 5": Released Apr '89, on Vertigo, by Phonogram Ltd. Deleted Oct '89. Catalogue no: **METCD 5**
12" Single: Released Apr '89, on Vertigo, by Phonogram Ltd. Deleted 31 Jul '89. Catalogue no: **METAL 512**
12" Single: Released Apr '89, on Vertigo, by Phonogram Ltd. Deleted 31 Jul '89. Catalogue no: **METG 512**

WHIPLASH
Tracks: / Whiplash.
7" EP: Released Aug '87, on Megaforce (USA), Catalogue no: **MRS04**
7" EP: Released Aug '87, on Megaforce (USA), Deleted Oct '87. Catalogue no: **MRS04P**

Meteors

Biographical details: A sort of British answer to American cult band the Cramps, the Meteors built up an underground following in the 80's by playing "psychobilly" music. This is a strange, idiosyncratic brand of rockabilly revivalism, incorporating comic-book and horror-film themes. They were also sometimes described as "punkabilly", as they were influenced by the raucously energetic, undisciplined attitudes of the punk rock scene in which they had grown up. The Meteors first, minor, taste of UK chart success came in 1983, when an unlikely version of John Leyton's *Johnny Remember Me* reached No 66. (Bob MacDonald, January 1986.).

BAD MOON RISING
Tracks: / Bad moon rising.
7" Single: Released Sep '85, on Mad Pig, Catalogue no: **PORK 3**

DON'T TOUCH THE BANG BANG FRUIT (SINGLE)
Tracks: / Dateless nites / Corpse grinder (On 12" single only.) / Don't touch the bang bang fruit.
7" Single: Released Oct '87, on Anagram, by Cherry Red Records. Catalogue no: **ANA 39**
12" Single: Released Oct '87, on Anagram, by Cherry Red Records. Catalogue no: **12 ANA 39**

FIRE FIRE
Tracks: / Fire fire.
12" Single: Released Apr '85, on Mad Pig, Catalogue no: **PORK 2T**
7" Single: Released Apr '85, on Mad Pig, Catalogue no: **PORK 2**

GO BUDDY GO
Tracks: / Go buddy go / Wildkat ways / You crack me up.
7" Single: Released Jun '87, on Anagram, by Cherry Red Records. Catalogue no: **ANA 35**
12" Single: Released Jun '87, on Anagram, by Cherry Red Records. Catalogue no: **12 ANA 35**

I'M JUST A DOG
Tracks: / I'm just a dog.
7" Single: Released Oct '84, on Mad Pig, Catalogue no: **PORK 1**
12" Single: Released Oct '84, on Mad Pig, Catalogue no: **PORK 1T**

JOHNNY REMEMBER ME
Tracks: / Johnny remember me / Wreckin'.
7" Single: Released Jan '83, on I.D., by I.D. Records. Catalogue no: **EYE 1**

MUTANT ROCK
Tracks: / Mutant rock / Hills have eyes, The.
7" Single: Released Aug '82, on WXYZ, Catalogue no: **ABCD 5**
12" Single: Released Feb '89, on I.D., by I.D. Records. Catalogue no: **EYE 010T**

RADIOACTIVE KID
Tracks: / Radioactive kid / Graveyard stomp.
7" Single: Released May '81, on Chiswick Records, Deleted May '84. Catalogue no: **CHIS 147**
7" Single: Released Nov '81, on Chiswick Records, Catalogue no: **NS 74**

RAWHIDE
Tracks: / Rawhide / Surfin' on the planet Zorch / Little Red Riding Hood (Only available on 12" format.).
12" Single: Released Oct '88, on Anagram, by Cherry Red Records. Catalogue no: **12 ANA 43**
7" Single: Released 3 Oct '88, on Anagram, by Cherry Red Records. Catalogue no: **ANA 43**

SOMEBODY PUT SOMETHING IN MY DRINK
Tracks: / Somebody put something in my drink.
12" Single: Released 20 Feb '88, on Anagram, by Cherry Red Records. Catalogue no: **12 ANA 41**

SURF CITY
Tracks: / Surf city.
12" Single: Released Aug '86, on Anagram, by Cherry Red Records. Catalogue no: **12 ANA 31**
7" Single: Released Aug '86, on Anagram, by Cherry Red Records. Catalogue no: **ANA 31**

VOODOO RHYTHM
Tracks: / Voodoo rhythm.
7" Single: Released Jul '81, on Chiswick Records, Catalogue no: **MAD 1**

VOODOO RHYTHM (EP)
Tracks: / Voodoo rhythm / Maniac rockers from hell / My daddy is a vampire / You can't keep a good man down.
7" EP: Released Mar '81, on Ace, by Ace Records. Deleted Mar '84. Catalogue no: **SW 65**

WRECKIN' CREW (SINGLE)
Tracks: / Wrecking crew / Johnny remember me / I dont worry about it / Wild thing.
Note: All tracks Licensed from Head Music Pub. Ltd.
7" Single: Released Sep '86, on I.D., by I.D. Records. Catalogue no: **EYET 10**
12" Single: Released Aug '86, on Archive 4, by Castle Communications Records. Catalogue no: **TOF 106**

Meters

LOOK KA PY PY
Tracks: / Look ka py py / Tippi toes.
7" Single: Released Jul '80, on Charly, by Charly Records. Deleted '87. Catalogue no: **CTD 113**

Metheny, Pat

ARE YOU GOING WITH ME
Tracks: / Are you going with me / Au lait.
7" Single: Released Jun '82, on ECM, Catalogue no: **ECM 7 29999**

Method

CHANCES
Tracks: / Chances / Little lasers.
7" Single: Released Jan '81, on Red Lightnin', by Red Lightning Records. Deleted Jan '84. Catalogue no: **MET 2**

PINK PANTHER THEME
Tracks: / Pink panther (theme from) / Taking liberties.
7" Single: Released Aug '80, on Red Lightnin', by Red Lightning Records. Catalogue no: **MET 1**

Method Actors

COMMOTION
Tracks: / Commotion / Bleeding.
12" Single: Released Nov '82, on Armageddon, by Armageddon Records. Catalogue no: **P 2004**

RANG-A-TANG
Tracks: / Rang-a-tang.
7" Single: Released Jul '86, on Press, by Compendium Int.Records. Catalogue no: **P 1004**

ROUND WORLD
Tracks: / Round world / E.Y.E.
7" Single: Released Oct '81, on Armageddon, by Armageddon Records. Catalogue no: **AS 011**

THIS IS IT
Tracks: / This is it.
7" Single: Released Jul '81, on Armageddon, by Armageddon Records. Catalogue no: **AS 006**

Metro

AMERICA IN MY HEAD
Tracks: / America in my head / Alone.
7" Single: Released Jul '81, on Polydor, by Polydor Ltd. Deleted '85. Catalogue no: **POSP 280**

GEMINI
Tracks: / Gemini / Face.
7" Single: Released Apr '80, on EMI, by EMI Records. Deleted '83. Catalogue no: **EMI 5057**

Metro, Anthony

WATERPUMPEE NEW STYLE
Tracks: / Waterpumpee new style.
12" Single: Released Oct '84, on Stylaman, Catalogue no: **SM 1**

Metro Glider

DO IT RIGHT
Tracks: / Do it right / Consequences.
7" Single: Released Nov '80, on Racket (Germany), Deleted Nov '83. Catalogue no: **RKT 1**

Metro, Peter

ACCIDENT
Tracks: / Accident.
7" Single: Released Mar '89, on Penthouse, by Penthouse Records. Catalogue no: **PH 007**

BOSANOVA
Tracks: / Bosanova.
7" Single: Released Oct '83, on Dynamite, Catalogue no: **DSR 0324**

CALYPSO CALYPSO
Tracks: / Calypso calypso / Seven heroes.
12" Single: Released Dec '83, on Greensleeves, by Greensleeves Records. Catalogue no: **GRED 135**

DEBI DEBI GIRL
Tracks: / Debi Debi girl.
12" Single: Released May '88, on Taurus, Catalogue no: **TRS 007**

DON, THE
Tracks: / Don, The.
12" Single: Released Apr '85, on Striker Lee, Catalogue no: **BL 19**

DON'T RUN HIM DOWN
Tracks: / Don't run him down / Don't touch the crack.
12" Single: Released Feb '87, on Revolutionary Sounds, Catalogue no: **RS 001**

FRONTLINE GET RAID
Tracks: / Frontline get raid.
12" Single: Released Apr '85, on Striker Lee, Catalogue no: **BL 20**

IN THE ARMY
Tracks: / In the army.
10" single: Released Sep '82, on Dynamite, Catalogue no: **DYN 003**

LIFE MUD UP
Tracks: / Life mud up.
12" Single: Released Mar '89, on Penthouse, by Penthouse Records. Catalogue no: **PH 001**

NU SELL YUSELF
Tracks: / Nu sell yuself / Nu sell yuself (version).
12" Single: Released Jul '87, on Greensleeves, by Greensleeves Records. Catalogue no: **GRED 214**

SHOULDER MOVE
Tracks: / Shoulder move.
12" Single: Released Mar '84, on Marlon Ranks, Catalogue no: **MR 001**

TOGETHER
Tracks: / Together.
12" Single: Released Aug '87, on People Unite, by People Unite Records. Catalogue no: **12 PU 008**

WARN THEM TEACH THEM
Tracks: / Warn them teach them.
12" Single: Released Sep '82, on Greensleeves, by Greensleeves Records. Catalogue no: **GRED 97**

YES DADDY
Tracks: / Yes daddy.
12" Single: Released May '87, on Power House, Catalogue no: **DSR 8372**

Metro Trinity

DIE YOUNG
Tracks: / Die young.
12" Single: Released Jul '87, on Cafeteria, by Cafeteria Records. Catalogue no: **CTA 0001**

Metrophase

IN BLACK
Tracks: / In black.
7" Single: Released Apr '81, on Fresh, by Jetstar Records. Catalogue no: **FRESH 6**

Metropolis

DUBLIN (Theme from liberty)
Tracks: / Dublin (Double A).
7" Single: Released Dec '85, on Havoc House, by Havoc House Records. Catalogue no: **SHH 01**

Metros

LOVE ME TOMORROW
Tracks: / Love me tomorrow.
7" Single: Released Aug '81, on Montivideo, Catalogue no: **M 1**

Mex

HAPPY LIFE
Tracks: / Happy life / Veins.
7" Single: Released Dec '84, on Lost Moments, Catalogue no: **LM 005**

Mexicano

DALLAS
Tracks: / Dallas / Night life groove.
12" Single: Released Jul '80, on Mercury, by Phonogram Ltd. Deleted Jul '83. Catalogue no: **MERX 29**
7" Single: Released Jul '80, on Mercury, by Phonogram Ltd. Deleted Jul '83. Catalogue no: **MER 29**

ISRAELITES COME DANCE SOME MORE
Tracks: / Israelites come dance some more / Every step I made.
7" Single: Released Feb '80, on Ice, by Ice Records. Deleted '83. Catalogue no: **GUY 35**

MOVE UP STARSKY (SINGLE)
Tracks: / Move up Starsky.
7" Single: Released Aug '83, on Creole, by Creole Records. Catalogue no: **CR 58**
12" Single: Released Aug '83, on Creole, by Creole Records. Catalogue no: **CR 12 58**

TRIAL BY TELEVISION
Tracks: / Trial by television.
7" Single: Released Sep '80, on Stiff, by Stiff Records. Catalogue no: **BUY 93**
12" Single: Released Sep '80, on Stiff, by Stiff Records. Catalogue no: **BUYIT 93**

Meyer, Anita

WHY TELL ME WHY
Tracks: / Why tell me why / Places where we used to be.
7" Single: Released Nov '81, on Epic, by CBS Records. Deleted Nov '84. Catalogue no: **EPC A 1774**

Meyers, Augie

I'M NOT SOMEONE YOU WANT
Tracks: / I'm not someone you want / Money.
7" Single: Released Apr '84, on Sonet, by Sonet Records. Catalogue no: **SON 2264**

JUST YOU AND ME
Tracks: / Just you and me / Sitting up all night.
7" Single: Released May '82, on Sonet, by Sonet Records. Catalogue no: **SON 2242**

YOU'RE ON MY MIND
Tracks: / You're on my mind / Peace of mind.
7" Single: Released Apr '86, on Sonet, by Sonet Records. Catalogue no: **SON 2301**

Meyers, Steve

LOVE'S GONNA LAST (SINGLE)
Tracks: / Love's gonna last / Back alley shuffle.
7" Single: Released Apr '86, on Pressure, Catalogue no: **HAVE 6**
12" Single: Released Apr '86, on Pressure, Catalogue no: **12 HAVE 6**

Mezzoforte

Biographical details: At the time of their greatest success, this Icelandic instrumental jazz-funk band consisted of Johann Asmundsson, Gunnlauger Briem, Eythor Gunnarsson, Fridrik Karlsson and Dristinn Svavarsson. In 1983 Mezzoforte achieved the notable feat of becoming the first act from their country to hit the British charts. The band had already existed for six years up to that point, having first been formed in 1977 in an Icelandic school. The single that took them to No.17 on the UK chart was *Garden party*, one of the most exuberant and catchy instrumental hits of the decade. *Garden party* was taken into the US Hot 100 by no less a jazzman than Herb Alpert, but unfortunately his rendition was soporific in comparison to the bright uptempo original version. It was reported that Alpert learnt *Garden party* off a British import 12-inch single, which he played at the standard US speed of 33 rpm (whereas UK 12-inch singles should be played at 45 rpm). He apparently based his version on the accidentally slowed down Mezzoforte sound, believing this to be correct.
Mezzoforte did not really sustain their UK breakthrough, although they became popular in Japan. The only subsequent British hit single for the band, who compose their own material, was *Rockall* - this pulsating track spent just one week on the UK Top 75 at No.75! But never fear - *Rockall* was adopted as the theme music for top-rated chart countdown programs on TROS Radio in Holland and BBC Radio One. After the success of *Garden party*, Mezzoforte moved from Iceland to live in Essex, England. (Bob MacDonald, 28th Jan 1986).

CRYING IN THE DARK
Tracks: / Crying in the dark.
7" Single: Released Jul '82, on Suspect, Catalogue no: **SUS 4**

GARDEN PARTY
Tracks: / Garden party / Early autumn.
7" Single: Released Jul '85, on Steinar, by Steinar Records (UK). Catalogue no: **STE 780**
12" Single: Released Jul '85, on Steinar, by Steinar Records (UK). Catalogue no: **STE 1280**

MIDNIGHT SUN
Tracks: / Midnight sun.
12" Single: Released Jan '84, on Steinar, by Steinar Records (UK). Catalogue no: **STE 1215**
7" Single: Released Jan '84, on Steinar, by Steinar Records (UK). Catalogue no: **STE 715**

NO LIMIT (SINGLE)
Tracks: / No limit / EG blues.
7" Single: Released Mar '87, on Funkin' Marvellous, by Steinar Records (UK). Deleted Nov '87. Catalogue no: **MEZZ 02**
12" Single: Released Mar '87, on Funkin' Marvellous, by Steinar Records (UK). Deleted Nov '87. Catalogue no: **12MEZZ 02**

NOTHING LASTS FOREVER
Tracks: / Nothing lasts forever / Joy ride.
CD 5": Released Nov '86, on Mezzoforte, Catalogue no: **CD MEZZ 01**
7" Single: Released Nov '86, on Mezzoforte, Catalogue no: **MEZZ 01**
12" Single: Released Nov '86, on Mezzoforte, Catalogue no: **12 MEZZ 01**

ROCKALL
Tracks: / Rockall.
7" Single: Released May '83, on Steinar, by Steinar Records (UK). Catalogue no: **STE 710**
12" Single: Released May '83, on Steinar, by Steinar Records (UK). Catalogue no: **STE 1210**
7" Pic: Released May '83, on Steinar, by Steinar Records (UK). Catalogue no: **STE 710P**

SHOOTING STAR
Tracks: / Shooting star / Dreamland.
12" Single: Released Jun '82, on Steinar, by Steinar Records (UK). Catalogue no: **STE 1202**
7" Single: Released Jun '82, on Steinar, by Steinar Records (UK). Catalogue no: **STE 02**

SPRING FEVER
Tracks: / Spring fever / Summer dream.
7" Single: Released Apr '84, on Steinar, by Steinar Records (UK). Catalogue no: **STE 720**
12" Single: Released Apr '84, on Steinar, by Steinar Records (UK). Catalogue no: **STE 1220**

TAKING OFF
Tracks: / Taking off / Take off.
12" Single: Released Mar '85, on Steinar, by Steinar Records (UK). Catalogue no: **STE 1260**
7" Single: Released Mar '85, on Steinar, by Steinar Records (UK). Catalogue no: **STE 760**
7" Single: Released Oct '84, on Steinar, by Steinar Records (UK). Catalogue no: **STE 750**
12" Single: Released Oct '84, on Steinar, by Steinar Records (UK). Catalogue no: **STE 1250**

THIS IS THE NIGHT
Tracks: / This is the night.
7" Single: Released Sep '85, on Steinar, by Steinar Records (UK). Catalogue no: **STE 790**
12" Single: Released Sep '85, on Steinar, by Steinar Records (UK). Catalogue no: **STE 1290**

MFSB

Biographical details: MFSB (Mothers, Fathers, Sisters, Brothers) were a racially intergrated band of studio musicians who provided musical backing on almost all the Philadelphia International hits of the Seventies. Philly, as the label became known, was founded in 1971 by the writing/production team of Kenny Gamble and Leon Huff. During the following few years, the 'Philly' sound took over from Tamla Motown as the most prominent force in black music. Like Motown in the Sixties, Philly's artists were predominantly vocalists. Thus, a regular in-house band of session musicians (varying from 28 to 40 in number) was the most economic way of organising the backing music on the records. In 1973 MFSB released an album in their own right, featuring not just soul music but also jazz and easy listening styles. In the following year, the massed studio ensemble scored a US No.1 smash with the single *TSOP (The sound of Philadelphia), after the track had been used as the theme for the 'Soul train' television show. This vibrant and infectious single also served as the theme for the Philly label itself. The record was mainly instrumental, except for some vocals at the end by the Three Degrees whose career was given a considerable boost by the success of TSOP.* The single reached No.22 in the UK.
MFSB issued a series of moderately successful albums during the rest of the Seventies, containing mostly disco-funk. They chalked up chart singles in Britain with *Sexy* (No.37 in 1975) and *Mysteries of the world* (No.41 in 1981). (Bob MacDonald, 28th Jan 1986).

MYSTERIES OF THE WORLD (SINGLE)
Tracks: / Mysteries of the world
12" Single: Released Jan '81, on Philadelphia Int., by EMI Records. Deleted '84. Catalogue no: **13-9501**
7" Single: Released Jan '81, on Philadelphia Int., by EMI Records. Deleted '84. Catalogue no: **PIR 9501**

SEXY
Tracks: / Sexy.
7" Single: Released Jul '75, on Philadelphia Int., by EMI Records. Deleted '78. Catalogue no: **PIR 3381**

SOUND OF PHILADELPHIA
Tracks: / Sound of Philadelphia
Note: Originally recorded in the 1970's.
12" Single: Released Oct '87, on Philadelphia Int., by EMI Records. Catalogue no: **4ZHA 06924**

T.S.O.P.
Tracks: / T.S.O.P..
7" Single: Released Apr '74, on Philadelphia Int., by EMI Records. Deleted '77. Catalogue no: **PIR 2289**
7" Single: Released '80, on Philadelphia Int., by EMI Records. Catalogue no: **LR 0564**

T.S.O.P. (OLD GOLD)
Tracks: / T.S.O.P. / Live is the message.
7" Single: Released 24 Apr '9, on Old Gold, by Old Gold Records. Catalogue no: **OG 9869**

MG

CAN'T GET ENOUGH (OF THAT FUNKY STUFF)
Tracks: / Can't get enough (of that funky stuff).
7" Single: Released Dec '87, on Rhythm Attack (Germany), Catalogue no: **RTM 1**
12" Single: Released Dec '87, on Rhythm Attack (Germany), Catalogue no: **RTMS 1**

Miami

YOU ARE TEMPTATION
Tracks: / You are temptation / You are temptation (instrumental).
7" Single: Released Feb '86, on Grana, Catalogue no: **GRANA 001**
12" Single: Released Feb '86, on Grana, Catalogue no: **GRANAT 001**

Miami Sound Machine

BAD BOY
Tracks: / Bad boys / Monies.
12" Single: Released Mar '86, on Epic, by CBS Records. Deleted '87. Catalogue no: **TA 6537**
7" Single: Released Mar '86, on Epic, by CBS Records. Deleted '87. Catalogue no: **A 6537**

DOCTOR BEAT
Tracks: / Doctor Beat.
7" Single: Released Aug '84, on Epic, by CBS Records. Deleted '87. Catalogue no: **A 4614**
12" Single: Released Aug '88, on Old Gold, by Old Gold Records. Catalogue no: **OG 4078**

FALLING IN LOVE
Tracks: / Falling in love / Surrender paradise / Falling in love (remix) / Paradise.
7" Single: Released Jul '86, on Epic, by CBS Records. Deleted '87. Catalogue no: **A 6956**
7" Single: Released Nov '86, on Epic, by CBS Records. Catalogue no: **650251 7**
12" Single: Released Jul '86, on Epic, by CBS Records. Deleted '86. Catalogue no: **TA 6956**
12" Single: Released Aug '86, on Epic, by CBS Records. Deleted '87. Catalogue no: **QTA 6956**

Miamis

VAMOS A LA PLAYA
Tracks: / Vamos a la playa.
7" Single: Released Sep '83, on Carrere America (USA), by PolyGram Rec.Inc.(USA). Catalogue no: **CAR 290**
12" Single: Released Sep '83, on Carrere America (USA), by PolyGram Rec.Inc.(USA). Catalogue no: **CART 290**

Miaow

BELLE VUE
Tracks: / Belle vue.
7" Single: Released Mar '86, on Venus, Catalogue no: **VENUS 1**
12" Single: Released Mar '86, on Venus, Catalogue no: **VENUS 1T**

BREAK THE CODE
Tracks: / Break the code / Stolen ears.
7" Single: Released 31 Oct '87, on Factory (1), by Factory Records. Catalogue no: **FAC 189**

WHEN IT ALL COMES DOWN
Tracks: / When it all comes down.
7" Single: Released Feb '87, on Factory (1), by Factory Records. Catalogue no: **FAC 179 (7)**
12" Single: Released Feb '87, on Factory (1), by Factory Records. Catalogue no: **FAC 179**

Michael

MICHAEL (I'M MICHAEL)
Tracks: / Michael (I'm Michael).
7" Single: Released Sep '84, on Disques Du Grand Michel, by December Songs Records. Catalogue no: **MLGS 001X**

SECESSION
Tracks: / Secession / All the animals come out at night / Helter skelter.
7" Single: Released Jun '86, on Siren, by Virgin Records. Deleted '89. Catalogue no: **SIREN 23**
12" Single: Released Jun '86, on Siren, by Virgin Records. Deleted '89. Catalogue no: **SIREN 23-12**

Michael, Dene

HOLY CITY
Tracks: / Holy City, The.
7" Single: Released Dec '83, on Posh, by Posh Records. Catalogue no: **POSH 011**

Michael, George

CARELESS WHISPER
Tracks: / Careless Whisper.
7" Single: Released Aug '84, on Epic, by CBS Records. Deleted '87. Catalogue no: **A 4603**
7" Pic: Released Aug '84, on Epic, by CBS Records. Catalogue no: **WA 4603**
12" Single: Released May '8, on Columbia (USA), by CBS Records (USA). Catalogue no: **4405170**
12" Single: Released Aug '84, on Epic, by CBS Records. Catalogue no: **QTA 4603**

DIFFERENT CORNER, A
Tracks: / Different corner, A / Different corner, A (instrumental).
7" Single: Released Mar '86, on Epic, by CBS Records. Catalogue no: **A 7033**
12" Single: Released Mar '86, on Epic, by CBS Records. Catalogue no: **TA 7033**

FAITH (SINGLE)
Tracks: / Faith / Faith (instrumental) / Hard day / Hand to mouth.Hard day (Shep pettibone remix) (Extra tracks available on 12" and CD single only.) / Last request (I want your sex, part 3) (on 12" and CD single only.)
12" Pic: Released Jul '87, on Epic, by CBS Records. Deleted Aug '88. Catalogue no: **EMU P3**
Cassingle: Released Oct '87, on Epic, by CBS Records. Catalogue no: **EMU C3**
7" Single: Released Oct '87, on Epic, by CBS Records. Deleted Aug '88. Catalogue no: **EMU 3**
12" Single: Released Oct '87, on Epic, by CBS Records. Deleted Aug '88. Catalogue no: **EMU T3**

FATHER FIGURE
Tracks: / Father figure / Love's in need of love today / Father figure (instrumental).
CD 3": Released Sep '88, on Epic/Sony (Japan), by CBS Records. Catalogue no: **108P 3008**
CD 5": Released Dec '87, on Epic, by CBS Records. Deleted Jan '89. Catalogue no: **CD EMU 4**
12" Single: Released Dec '87, on Epic, by CBS Records. Deleted Aug '88. Catalogue no: **EMUT 4 R**
7" Pic: Released Jan '88, on Epic, by CBS Records. Deleted Jun '88. Catalogue no: **EMU P4**
7" Single: Released Dec '87, on Epic, by CBS Records. Deleted Aug '88. Catalogue no: **EMU 4 R**
7" Single: Released Dec '87, on Epic, by CBS Records. Deleted Aug '88. Catalogue no: **EMU 4**
12" Single: Released Dec '87, on Epic, by CBS Records. Deleted Aug '88. Catalogue no: **EMU T4**

I WANT YOUR SEX
Tracks: / I want your sex / I want your sex (inst).
7" Single: Released 30 May '87, on Epic, by CBS Records. Deleted Nov '87. Catalogue no: **LUST 1**
12" Single: Released 30 May '87, on Epic, by CBS Records. Catalogue no: **QT1**
12" Single: Released 30 May '87, on Epic, by CBS Records. Deleted Nov '87. Catalogue no: **LUST T1**

I WANT YOUR SEX (MONOGAMY MIX)
Tracks: / Rhythm 1 - Lust / Rhythm 2 - Brass in love / Rhythm 3 - A last request.
CD 5": Released 20 Jun '87, on Epic, by CBS Records. Deleted Nov '87. Catalogue no: **CDLUST 1**
Cassingle: Released 27 Jun '87, on Epic, by CBS Records. Deleted Nov '87. Catalogue no: **LUST C1**
7" Pic: Released 20 Jun '87, on Epic, by CBS Records. Deleted Nov '87. Catalogue no: **LUST P1**

KISSING A FOOL
Tracks: / Kissing a fool / Kissing a fool (instrumental) / Last request
CD 5": Released 21 Nov '88, on Epic, by CBS Records. Deleted 17 Apr '89. Catalogue no: **CD EMU 7**
12" Single: Released 21 Nov '88, on Epic, by CBS Records. Deleted 17 Apr '89. Catalogue no: **EMU T7**
7" Single: Released 21 Nov '88, on Epic, by CBS Records. Deleted 17 Apr '89. Catalogue no: **EMU 7**

MONKEY
Tracks: / Monkey / Monkey (extended version) (On 12" & CD versions only.) / Monkey (a'capella) / Monkey (extra beats) (On 12" & CD versions only.) / Monkey (7-inch edit) (On CD only.).
CD 5": Released Jun '88, on Epic, by CBS Records. Deleted Jan '89. Catalogue no: **CDEMU 6**
12" Single: Released Jun '88, on Epic, by CBS Records. Deleted Jan '89. Catalogue no: **EMUT 6**
7" Single: Released 18 Jul '88, on Epic, by CBS Records. Deleted Jan '89. Catalogue no: **EMU G6**
7" Single: Released Jun '88, on Epic, by CBS Records. Deleted Jan '89. Catalogue no: **EMU 6**

ONE MORE TRY
Tracks: / One more try / Look at your hands.
12" Single: Released Apr '88, on Epic, by CBS Records. Deleted Jan '89. Catalogue no: **EMUT 5**
7" Single: Released Apr '88, on Epic, by CBS Records. Deleted Jan '89. Catalogue no: **EMU 5**
CD 5": Released Apr '88, on Epic, by CBS Records. Deleted Jan '89. Catalogue no: **CPEMU 5**
CD 5": Released Apr '88, on Epic, by CBS Records. Deleted Jan '89. Catalogue no: **651532 2**
7" Single: Released Apr '88, on Epic, by CBS Records. Deleted Jan '89. Catalogue no: **EMU B5**

Michael, Gordon

THINKING ABOUT MY GIRL
Tracks: / Thinking about my girl.
12" Single: Released Aug '87, on Fine Style, by Fashion Records. Catalogue no: **FS 013**

Michaela

H.A.P.P.Y. RADIO
Tracks: / Happy radio / Time flies / Happy radio (extended version) (Only on 12" single.).
12" Single: Released Aug '89, on London Records, by London Records. Catalogue no: **HHPX 1**
7" Single: Released Aug '89, on London Records, by London Records. Catalogue no: **HHP 1**

Michaels, Billy

SHAKE IT AND DANCE
Tracks: / Shake it and dance / US male.
7" Single: Released Mar '81, on Warner Bros., by WEA Records. Deleted Mar '84. Catalogue no: **K 17763**

Michell, Keith

CAPTAIN BEAKY (SINGLE)
Tracks: / Captain Beaky / Wilfred the weasel / Blanche.
7" Single: Released Jan '80, on Polydor, by Polydor Ltd. Deleted '83. Catalogue no: **POSP 106**

I'LL GIVE YOU THE EARTH
Tracks: / I'll give you the earth.
7" Single: Released Mar '71, on Spark, by Spark Records. Deleted '74. Catalogue no: **SRL 1046**

TRIAL OF HISSING SID
Tracks: / Trial of Hissing Sid / Looking for Hissing Sid.
7" Single: Released Mar '80, on Polydor, by Polydor Ltd. Deleted '83. Catalogue no: **HISS 1**

Michelle And Renato

MR. MAYBE
Tracks: / Mr. Maybe.
7" Single: Released Feb '87, on President, by President Records. Catalogue no: **PT 554**

Michelle, Karen

WHEN WILL I
Tracks: / When will I / Hey.
7" Single: Released Apr '88, on Debut, by Skratch Records. Catalogue no: **DEBT 3046**
12" Single: Released '88, on Debut, by Skratch Records. Catalogue no: **DEBTX 3046**

Michelle & WW 4

LEAVE IT ALL BEHIND
Tracks: / Leave it all behind.
7" Single: Released Jul '89, on Big Life, by Big Life Records. Catalogue no: **BLR 011**
12" Single: Released Jul '89, on Big Life, by Big Life Records. Catalogue no: **BLR 011 T**
CD 5": Released Jul '89, on Big Life, by Big Life Records. Catalogue no: **BLR 011 CD**

Michigan & Smiley

DISEASES
Tracks: / Diseases / Dance hall style.
12" Single: Released Feb '82, on Greensleeves, by Greensleeves Records. Catalogue no: **GRED 72**

ONE LOVE JAM DOWN
Tracks: / One love jam down / Dub down.
7" Single: Released Jul '80, on Island, by Island Records. Deleted Jul '83. Catalogue no: **WIP 6636**

REGGAE SKA
Tracks: / Reggae ska.

BETTE MIDLER - WIND BENEATH MY WINGS (Released on Atlantic)

12" Single: Released Jun '84, on RAS (Real Authentic Sound), by Greensleeves Records. Catalogue no: **RAS 7005**

SUGAR DADDY (SINGLE)
Tracks: / Sugar daddy / What a life.
12" Single: Released Mar '84, on RAS (Real Authentic Sound), by Greensleeves Records. Catalogue no: **RAS 7033**

Mick & Pat

LET'S ALL CHANT
Tracks: / Let's all chant.
7" Single: Released Apr '88, on PWL, by PWL Records. Catalogue no: **PWL 10**
12" Single: Released Apr '88, on PWL, by PWL Records. Catalogue no: **PWLT 10**

Mickey Rourke's Fridge

MICKEY ROURKE'S FRIDGE PRESENTS
7" Single: Released Jul '89, Catalogue no: **MRF 2**

Microbe

GROOVY BABY
Tracks: / Groovy baby / Your turn.
7" Single: Released May '69, on CBS, by CBS Records. Deleted '72. Catalogue no: **CBS 4158**

Microbes

COMPUTER
Tracks: / Computer / Ministry of space.
7" Single: Released Jun '80, on DJM, Deleted '83. Catalogue no: **DJS 10944**

Microdisney

BIRTHDAY GIRL
Tracks: / Birthday girl.
12" Single: Released Sep '85, on Rough Trade, by Rough Trade Records. Catalogue no: **RTT 185**
7" Single: Released Sep '85, on Rough Trade, by Rough Trade Records. Catalogue no: **RT 185**

GALE FORCE WIND
Tracks: / Gale force wind (On all versions) / I can't say no (Betty Lou version) (On all versions) / No, I can't say (thank you for speaking to me Mustapha) (CD & 12' only) / Can't I say no (Hackney aid) (12" only) / Town to town (CD only) / Irish national anthem, The (Cassette only) / Say "No I can't" (Cassette only).
Cassingle: Released '88, on Virgin, by Virgin Records. Catalogue no: **VSTC 1044**
7" Single: Released Feb '88, on Virgin, by Virgin Records. Catalogue no: **VS 1044**
CD 5": Released Aug '88, on Virgin, by Virgin Records. Catalogue no: **VSCD 1044**
12" Single: Released Feb '88, on Virgin, by Virgin Records. Catalogue no: **VST 1044**

HELLO RASCALS
Tracks: / Hello rascals.
7" Single: Released Sep '82, on Kabuki, Catalogue no: **KAMD 2**

MICRODISNEY IN THE WORLD
Tracks: / Microdisney in the world.
12" Single: Released Mar '85, on Rough Trade, by Rough Trade Records. Catalogue no: **RTT 175**

PINK SKINNED MAN
Tracks: / Pink skinned man.
7" Single: Released May '83, on Kabuki, Catalogue no: **KAMD 4**

SINGER'S HAMPSTEAD HOME
Tracks: / Singer's Hampstead home / She only gave in to her anger / Brother Olaf (12" only).
7" Single: Released Oct '87, on Virgin, by Virgin Records. Deleted May '88. Catalogue no: **VS 1014**
12" Single: Released Oct '87, on Virgin, by Virgin Records. Catalogue no: **VST 1014**

TOWN TO TOWN
Tracks: / Town to town / Little town of Ireland / Genius ((Extra track on 12" version only)) / Bullwhip Road ((Extra track on 12" version only)).
12" Single: Released Jan '87, on Virgin, by Virgin Records. Catalogue no: **VS 927-12**
7" Single: Released Jan '87, on Virgin, by Virgin Records. Deleted May '88. Catalogue no: **VSD 927**

Microdot

YOU'RE MY EXTACY
Tracks: / You're my extacy / You're my extasy (version).
12" Single: Released Jan '89, on Microdot, Catalogue no: **MIC 1**

Microphone Prince

ROCK HOUSE
Tracks: / Rock house.
12" Single: Released Jan '88, on Magnetic Dance, by Magnet Records. Deleted Jun '88. Catalogue no: **MAGDT 11**
7" Single: Released Jan '88, on Magnetic Dance, by Magnet Records. Deleted Jun '88. Catalogue no: **MAGD 11**

WHO'S THE CAPTAIN
Tracks: / Who's the captain.
7" Single: Released Apr '87, on Music Of Life, by Music Of Life Records. Catalogue no: **7 NOTE 2**
12" Single: Released Apr '87, on Music Of Life, by Music Of Life Records. Catalogue no: **NOTE 2**

Midas

CAN'T STOP LOVING YOU
Tracks: / Can't stop loving you / Power in the sky.
7" Single: Released Feb '83, on Small Run, Catalogue no: **SRR 0008**

DON'T WANNA DANCE
Tracks: / Don't wanna dance / Living independent.
7" Single: Released Jun '81, on Rialto (1), by Rialto Records. Deleted Jun '84. Catalogue no: **TREB 137**

Midas Touch

TOO MUCH LOVE TO SOON
Tracks: / Too much love too soon / Gotta get back to you.
7" Single: Released May '81, on Champagne (DJM), Deleted May '86. Catalogue no: **FUNK 3**

Middle Of The Road

CHIRPY CHIRPY CHEEP CHEEP
Tracks: / Chirpy chirpy cheep cheep / Soley soley.
7" Single: Released May '82, on RCA, by BMG Records (UK). Deleted May '89. Catalogue no: **GOLD 543**
7" Single: Released Jun '71, on RCA, by BMG Records (UK). Deleted '74. Catalogue no: **RCA 2047**

CHIRPY CHIRPY CHEEP CHEEP (OLD GOLD)
Tracks: / Chirpy chirpy cheep cheep / Tweedle dee tweedle dum.
7" Single: Released Nov '86, on Old Gold, by Old Gold Records. Catalogue no: **OG 9632**

PARTY TIME MEDLEY
Tracks: / Party time medley / Postcard.
7" Single: Released Jan '82, on Pulsar, by Lismor Records. Catalogue no: **PUS 103**

SACRAMENTO
Tracks: / Sacramento.
7" Single: Released Apr '72, on RCA, by BMG Records (UK). Deleted '75. Catalogue no: **RCA 2184**

SAMSON AND DELILAH
Tracks: / Samson and Delilah.
7" Single: Released Jul '72, on RCA, by BMG Records (UK). Deleted '75. Catalogue no: **RCA 2237**

SOLEY SOLEY
Tracks: / Soley soley.
7" Single: Released Dec '71, on RCA, by BMG Records (UK). Deleted '74. Catalogue no: **RCA 2151**

STEAL A PIECE OF MY HEART
Tracks: / Steal a piece of my heart / Lonely.
7" Single: Released Oct '80, on OK, by Klub Records. Catalogue no: **OK 002**

TWEEDLE DEE TWEEDLE DUM
Tracks: / Tweedle Dee, Tweedle Dum.
7" Single: Released Sep '71, on RCA, by BMG Records (UK). Deleted '74. Catalogue no: **RCA 2110**

Midland Phil

BRASS PINAFORE
Tracks: / Brass Pinafore / March of the Austrian navy.
7" Single: Released Mar '81, on Transatlantic, by Transatlantic Records. Deleted Mar '84. Catalogue no: **BIG 569**

Midler, Bette

BIG NOISE FROM WINNETKA
Tracks: / Big noise from Winnetka / Rain.
7" Single: Released Jan '81, on Stiff, by Stiff Records. Deleted Jan '84. Catalogue no: **K 11412**

FIRE DOWN BELOW
Tracks: / Fire down below / You can't get what you want.
7" Single: Released May '81, on Atlantic, by WEA Records. Deleted May '84. Catalogue no: **K 11592**

ROSE, THE (SINGLE)
Tracks: / Rose, The / Stay with me.
7" Single: Released Apr '80, on Atlantic, by WEA Records. Deleted Apr '83. Catalogue no: **K 11459**

UNDER THE BOARDWALK
Tracks: / Under the boardwalk / Otto Titsling.
7" Single: Released Sep '89, on Atlantic, by WEA Records. Catalogue no: **A 8976**
12" Single: Released Sep '89, on Atlantic, by WEA Records. Catalogue no: **A 8976T**
CD 5": Released Sep '89, on Atlantic, by WEA Records. Catalogue no: **A 8976CD**

WHEN A MAN LOVES A WOMAN
Tracks: / When a man loves a woman / Have me with a feeling.
7" Single: Released Jan '80, on Atlantic, by WEA Records. Deleted Jan '83. Catalogue no: **K 11433**

WIND BENEATH MY WINGS (See panel above left)
Tracks: / Wind beneath my wings / On industry / I think it's going to rain today.
12" Single: Released Jun '89, on Atlantic, by WEA Records. Catalogue no: **A 8972T**
7" Single: Released Jun '89, on Atlantic, by WEA Records. Catalogue no: **A 8972**

YOU'RE MY FAVOURITE WASTE OF TIME
Tracks: / You're my favourite waste of time / My eye on you.
7" Single: Released Jan '84, on Atlantic, by WEA Records. Catalogue no: **A 9761**

Midnight

EASY PROMISE TO BREAK
Tracks: / Easy promise to break / Easy promise to break (instrumental).
12" Single: Released Feb '86, on Polo, by Polo Records. Deleted '88. Catalogue no: **POLO 12-40**
7" Single: Released Feb '86, on Polo, by Polo Records. Deleted '88. Catalogue no: **POLO 40**

KING OF THE MOUNTAIN
Tracks: / King of the mountain / Too high.
7" Single: Released Jul '87, on Epic, by CBS Records. Catalogue no: **GADS G2**
12" Single: Released Jun '87, on Epic, by CBS Records. Deleted Nov '87. Catalogue no: **GADS T2**
7" Single: Released Jun '87, on Epic, by CBS Records. Deleted Nov '87. Catalogue no: **GADS 2**

RUN WITH YOU
Tracks: / Everything.
7" Single: Released Feb '87, on Epic, by CBS Records. Deleted Aug '87. Catalogue no: **GADS 1**
12" Single: Released Feb '87, on Epic, by CBS Records. Deleted Aug '87. Catalogue no: **GADS T1**

Midnight blue

ENJOY WITH ME
Tracks: / Enjoy with me.
7" Single: Released Jul '83, on New York Connexion, Catalogue no: **NYC 100**
12" Single: Released Jul '83, on New York Connexion, Catalogue no: **NYCX 100**

Midnight Choir

HALLELUJAH
Tracks: / Hallelujah.
7" EP: Released Sep '85, on Native (1), by Native Records. Catalogue no: **NTV 1**

KISS
Tracks: / Kiss.
12" Single: Released Nov '83, on Golden Dawn, Catalogue no: **GD 1201**
7" Single: Released Nov '83, on Golden Dawn, Catalogue no: **GD 701**

Midnight Cowboy

Biographical details: Midnight Cowboy Eleven years after the film was made, John Barry's original theme from the movie 'Midnight Cowboy' became a UK chart single, reaching No. 47 in November 1980. This sudden success was caused by repeated plays by BBC Radio One disc jockey Noel Edmonds, who suddenly decided to give the beautiful theme heavy exposure on his peak-time Sunday morning show. Bob MacDonald, 28 January 1986..

MIDNIGHT COWBOY (SINGLE)
Tracks: / Midnight cowboy.
7" Single: Released Nov '80, on United Artists, by EMI Records. Deleted '83. Catalogue no: **UP 634**

Midnight Flyer

ROUGH TRADE
Tracks: / Rough trade.
7" Single: Released Apr '81, on Swansong, Deleted Apr '85. Catalogue no: **SSK 19423**

WAITING FOR YOU
Tracks: / Waiting for you / Rock'n'roll party.
7" Single: Released Nov '82, on Swansong, Deleted Nov '85. Catalogue no: **SSK 19426**

Midnight Oil

BEDS ARE BURNING
Tracks: / Beds are burning / Gun barrel highway / Hercules (Track on 12" and CD only.) / Power and the passion.
12" Single: Released 13 Mar '89, on CBS, by CBS Records. Deleted Oct '89. Catalogue no: **OILT 3**
12" Single: Released Feb '88, on CBS, by CBS Records. Deleted Aug '88. Catalogue no: **OILT 1**
CD 5": Released 13 Mar '89, on CBS, by CBS Records. Deleted Oct '89. Catalogue no: **CDOIL 3**
CD 5": Released Mar '88, on CBS, by CBS Records. Deleted Jan '89. Catalogue no: **CDOIL 1**
7" Single: Released 13 Mar '89, on CBS, by CBS Records. Deleted Oct '89. Catalogue no: **OIL 3**
7" Single: Released Feb '88, on CBS, by CBS Records. Deleted Aug '88. Catalogue no: **OIL 1**
Special: Released Mar '88, on CBS, by CBS Records. Deleted Jan '89. Catalogue no: **OILQ 1**
Special: Released 13 Mar '89, on CBS, by CBS Records. Deleted Oct '89. Catalogue no: **OILQ 3**

BEST OF BOTH WORLDS
Tracks: / Best of both worlds.
7" Single: Released Jul '85, on CBS, by CBS Records. Catalogue no: **A 6383**
12" Single: Released Jul '85, on CBS, by CBS Records. Catalogue no: **TX 6383**

DEAD HEART, THE
Tracks: / Dead heart, The / Kosciusko / Whoah / Dead heart, The (extended version) / Beds are burning (tamarama mix) / Progress (on 12" and CD 5" only.) / Blossom & blood (on EP only.) / Pictures (on EP only.).
Note: 12" single is a picture bag edition.
CD 5": Released Jun '89, on CBS, by CBS Records. Catalogue no: **CD OIL 4**
7" EP: Released Jun '89, on CBS, by CBS Records. Catalogue no: **OIL EP 4**
12" Single: Released Jun '89, on CBS, by CBS Records. Catalogue no: **OIL T4**
12" Single: Released Jun '88, on CBS, by CBS Records. Deleted Jan '89. Catalogue no: **OILQT 2**
CD 5": Released 13 Jun '88, on CBS, by CBS Records. Deleted Jan '89. Catalogue

no: **CD OIL 2**
Cassingle: Released Jul '89, on CBS, by CBS Records. Catalogue no: **OILC4**
7" Single: Released Jun '89, on CBS, by CBS Records. Catalogue no: **OIL 4**
7" Single: Released 13 Jun '88, on CBS, by CBS Records. Deleted Jan '89. Catalogue no: **OIL 2**
12" Single: Released 13 Jun '88, on CBS, by CBS Records. Deleted Jan '89. Catalogue no: **OIL T2**

US FORCES
Tracks: / U.S. forces.
7" Single: Released May '83, on CBS, by CBS Records. Catalogue no: **A 3343**
12" Single: Released May '83, on CBS, by CBS Records. Catalogue no: **TA 3343**

WHEN THE GENERALS TALK
Tracks: / When the generals talk.
7" Single: Released Sep '85, on CBS, by CBS Records. Catalogue no: **A 6583**

Midnight Star

CURIOUS
Tracks: / Curious / Body snatchers.
7" Single: Released Mar '85, on MCA, by MCA Records. Catalogue no: **MCA 961**
12" Single: Released Mar '85, on MCA, by MCA Records. Catalogue no: **MCAT 961**

ENGINE NO.9
Tracks: / Engine no.9 / (US mix).
7" Single: Released Jan '87, on MCA, by MCA Records. Catalogue no: **MCA 1117**
12" Single: Released Jan '87, on MCA, by MCA Records. Catalogue no: **MCAT 1117**

ENGINE NO.9 (EXTENDED VERSION)
Tracks: / Les Adams (mega mix) / Engine no.9 (extended version).
12" Single: Released Feb '87, on MCA, by MCA Records. Catalogue no: **MCAX 1117**

FEELS SO GOOD
Tracks: / Feels so good / Slow jam.
7" Single: Released Mar '84, on Elektra, by Elektra Records (UK). Catalogue no: **E 9775**

HEADLINES (SINGLE)
Tracks: / Headlines.
7" Single: Released Jul '86, on MCA, by MCA Records. Catalogue no: **MCA 1065**
12" Single: Released Jul '86, on MCA, by MCA Records. Catalogue no: **MCAX 1065**

MAKE IT LAST
Tracks: / Make it last / Follow the path.
12" Single: Released Mar '80, on Solar Records, Deleted '83. Catalogue no: **SO 12-5**

MIDAS TOUCH
Tracks: / Midas touch (extended remix) / Midas touch (acappella).
7" Single: Released Sep '86, on MCA, by MCA Records. Catalogue no: **MCA 1096**
12" Single: Released Sep '86, on MCA, by MCA Records. Catalogue no: **MCAT 1096**

MIDAS TOUCH (OLD GOLD)
Tracks: / Midas touch / Operator.
12" Single: Released 30 May '89, on Old Gold, by Old Gold Records. Catalogue no: **OG 4114**

OPERATOR
Tracks: / Operator.
7" Single: Released Feb '85, on Solar Records, Deleted '88. Catalogue no: **MCA 942**

WET MY WHISTLE
Tracks: / Wet my whistle / Curious / Freak-a-zoid / Headlines (extra extra mix).
12" Single: Released Apr '87, on MCA, by MCA Records. Catalogue no: **MCAT 1127**
7" Single: Released Apr '87, on MCA, by MCA Records. Catalogue no: **MCA 1127**

Midnight Sunrise

IN AT THE DEEP END
Tracks: / In at the deep end (instrumental).
12" Single: Released Feb '87, on Nightmare, by Nightmare Records. Catalogue no: **MARE 11**
7" Single: Released Feb '87, on Nightmare, by Nightmare Records. Catalogue no: **MARES 11**

ON THE HOUSE
Tracks: / On the house / On the house (remix).
7" Single: Released Sep '86, on Crossover, Catalogue no: **7CROSS 1**
12" Single: Released Sep '86, on Crossover, Catalogue no: **CROSS 1**

ON THE HOUSE REMIX
Tracks: / On the house remix.
12" Single: Released Oct '86, on Crossover, Catalogue no: **CROSSX1**

Midnite

LOVE COMES LOVE GROWS
Tracks: / Love comes love grows / I'm doin' alright.
7" Single: Released Mar '80, on Gem, Deleted Mar '83. Catalogue no: **GEMS 24**

NEVER GONNA STOP
Tracks: / Never gonna stop.
12" Single: Released Jun '83, on Tivoli, by Tivoli Records. Catalogue no: **TIV 2**
7" Single: Released Jun '83, on Tivoli, by Tivoli Records. Catalogue no: **TIVT 2**

PARADISE DRIVE
Tracks: / Paradise drive / Don't come easy.
12" Single: Released Feb '83, on Tivoli, by Tivoli Records. Catalogue no: **TIVT 1**
7" Single: Released Feb '83, on Tivoli, by Tivoli Records. Catalogue no: **TIV 1**

Midnite Follies

KICKING THE GONG AROUND
Tracks: / Kicking the gong around / Snake hips.
7" Single: Released Mar '81, on ASV (Academy Sound & Vision), by Academy Sound & Vision Records. Deleted Mar '84. Catalogue no: **ASV 102**

Midway

SET IT OUT
Tracks: / Set it out.
12" Single: Released Nov '84, on Personal, by Personal Records. Catalogue no: **12 PER 108**
7" Single: Released Nov '84, on Personal, by Personal Records. Catalogue no: **PERS 108**

Mighty Avengers

SO MUCH IN LOVE
Tracks: / So much in love.
7" Single: Released Nov '64, on Decca, by Decca Records. Deleted '67. Catalogue no: **F 11962**

Mighty Ballistics...

GHOST TRAIN
Tracks: / Ghost train / Spring hill Jack / Back gold.
12" Single: Released May '86, on Criminal Damage, Catalogue no: **CRI 1235**

MATCHLESS TRIPLE A
Tracks: / Matchless triple, A (3 track).
12" Single: Released Jun '86, on Criminal Damage, Catalogue no: **CRI 12135**

Mighty Caesars

BABY WHAT'S WRONG
Tracks: / Baby what's wrong / 10 bears of the Commanchees.
7" Single: Released Feb '86, on Empire Records, Catalogue no: **LWC 604Q**

LITTLE BY LITTLE
Tracks: / Little by little / Swag, The / I want what you got / Cyclonic.
7" Single: Released Feb '86, on Media Burn, by Media Burn Records. Catalogue no: **MB 5**

Mighty Clouds Of Dust

CHAMPION THE WONDER HORSE
Tracks: / Champion the wonder horse.
12" Single: Released Sep '89, on Rogue, by Rogue Records. Catalogue no: **12FMS 108**

MR. CUSTER
Tracks: / Mr. Custer / Flowers on the wall.
7" Single: Released Jan '84, on Dead On Productions, Catalogue no: **DOR 001**

Mighty Diamonds

BAD BOY
Tracks: / Bad boy.
7" Single: Released Nov '83, on Mobiliser, by Jetstar Records. Catalogue no: **MM 73**

BROTHER MAN
Tracks: / Brother man.
12" Single: Released Oct '83, on Reggae, Catalogue no: **REG 22 1923**

DANGER IN YOUR EYES
Tracks: / Danger in your eyes.
12" Single: Released Oct '88, on EAD, Catalogue no: **BG 004**

DAY IN DAY OUT
Tracks: / Day in, day out.
12" Single: Released Sep '85, on Blue Trac, by Blue Trac Records. Catalogue no: **BTR 011**

GATES OF ZION
Tracks: / Gates of Zion / Zion in dub.
12" Single: Released Nov '80, on Greensleeves, by Greensleeves Records. Catalogue no: **GRED 45**

HEY GIRL
Tracks: / Hey girl / Fade away root man.
12" Single: Released Dec '83, on Jama, Catalogue no: **JADC 0014**

I AM NOT TO BE BLAMED
Tracks: / I am not to be blamed / I wanna love you.
12" Single: Released Dec '86, on Rockers Plantation, Catalogue no: **PL 20**

IF YOU LOOKING FOR TROUBLE (SINGLE)
Tracks: / If you looking for trouble / Love, love come get me tonight.
12" Single: Released Jul '86, on Live & Learn (USA), by Live & Learn Records (USA). Catalogue no: **LLD 101**

I'M REALLY PICKNEY
Tracks: / I'm really pickney.
12" Single: Released Dec '82, on Music Works, Catalogue no: **MWRT 52353**

JUST CAN'T FIGURE IT OUT
Tracks: / Just can't figure it out.
12" Single: on Trojan, by Trojan Records. Catalogue no: **CSY 2**
7" Single: on Trojan, by Trojan Records. Deleted May '88. Catalogue no: **7 CSY 2**

JUVENILE CHILD
Tracks: / Juvenile child / Same knife, The.
12" Single: Released Dec '85, on Revolutionary Germain, Catalogue no: **RGD 500**

KEPT OUT
Tracks: / Kept out.
12" Single: Released Jun '86, on Germaine, Catalogue no: **DGT 16**

LAST DANCE
Tracks: / Last dance / Lucky.
12" Single: Released Nov '82, on KR, Catalogue no: **KRT 16**
12" Single: Released Sep '82, on J.G., by JG Recordings. Catalogue no: **JBD 040**
7" Single: Released Dec '82, on KR, Deleted Dec '87. Catalogue no: **KR 16**

LET THE DOLLAR CIRCULATE
Tracks: / Let the dollar circulate.
12" Single: Released May '82, on Thunderbolt, by Magnum Music Group. Deleted '89. Catalogue no: **TBD 03**

MARY MACK
Tracks: / Mary Mack.
12" Single: Released Jun '84, on Kingdom, by Kingdom Records. Deleted '86. Catalogue no: **KV 8030 12**

MORGAN THE PIRATE
Tracks: / Morgan the pirate / Blackbeard.
12" Single: Released Dec '82, on Mobiliser, by Jetstar Records. Catalogue no: **MM 66**

NEVER SAY GOODBYE
Tracks: / Never say goodbye.
12" Single: Released Oct '84, on Bad Gong, Catalogue no: **UNKNOWN**

PASTAKOUCHIE
Tracks: / Pastakouchie / Party time.
7" Single: Released Jan '82, on Jetstar, by Jetstar Records. Catalogue no: **RT 100**

PRETTY WOMAN
Tracks: / Pretty woman.
12" Single: Released Mar '82, on Reggae, Catalogue no: **REG 04**

SET ME FREE
Tracks: / Set me free.
12" Single: Released Aug '85, on SMJ, Catalogue no: **SMJ 003**

WE'VE ONLY JUST BEGUN
Tracks: / We've only just begun.
12" Single: Released 27 Feb '88, on Germaine, Catalogue no: **DGT 29**

WHA DO YUH SO
Tracks: / Wha do yuh so / Wha do yuh so (alternative version).
12" Single: Released Jul '86, on SRI, Catalogue no: **SRIM 001**

WHO'S SORRY NOW
Tracks: / Who's sorry now.
12" Single: Released Jul '83, on Mobiliser, by Jetstar Records. Catalogue no: **MM 69**

Mighty Faith

LITTLE GIRL
Tracks: / Little girl.
12" Single: Released Sep '84, on Fulani, Catalogue no: **FW 15A**

Mighty Force

THRASHING A DEAD HOUSE
Tracks: / Thrashing a dead house.
12" Single: Released Nov '88, on Vinyl Drip, by Vinyl Drip Records. Catalogue no: **SUK 3**

Mighty Gabby

JACK
Tracks: / Jack.
7" Single: Released Jul '83, on Ice, by Ice Records. Catalogue no: **ICE 59**
12" Single: Released Jul '83, on Ice, by Ice Records. Catalogue no: **ICET 59**
12" Single: Released Sep '82, on Seara, Catalogue no: **SEA 5**

Mighty General

MY COMMANDED WIFE
Tracks: / My commanded wife / Are you gonna run.
12" Single: Released Aug '86, on Ragin' Lion Music, Catalogue no: **RL 006**

PROUD OF ME COUNTRY
Tracks: / Proud of me country.
12" Single: Released Aug '87, on Digikal, by Fashion Records. Catalogue no: **DIG 007**

Mighty Grynner

STINGIN' BEES
Tracks: / Stingin' bees / Mr. T.
12" Single: Released May '85, on Ensign, by Ensign Records. Deleted '86. Catalogue no: **12ENY 516**
7" Single: Released May '85, on Ensign, by Ensign Records. Deleted '86. Catalogue no: **ENY 516**

Mighty Jungle Beasts

TRUMPETING OF MIGHTY JUNGLE BEASTS
Tracks: / Trumpeting of Mighty Jungle Beasts.
12" Single: Released 29 Sep '86, on Good Bloke, Deleted '88. Catalogue no: **JP 501**

Mighty Lemon Drops

FALL DOWN (LIKE THE RAIN)
Tracks: / Fall down (like the rain) / Paint it black / Laughter* (*Track on cassingle only) / Happy head (Track on cassingle only) / Hollow inside* (*Track on cassingle only).
12" Single: Released 23 Apr '88, on Blue Guitar, by Blue Guitar Records. Catalogue no: **AZURX 9**
7" Single: Released 23 Apr '88, on Blue Guitar, by Blue Guitar Records. Catalogue no: **AZUR 9**
CD 5": Released 23 Apr '88, on Blue Guitar, by Blue Guitar Records. Catalogue no: **AZURCD 9**
Cassingle: Released 23 Apr '88, on Blue Guitar, by Blue Guitar Records. Catalogue no: **ZAZURX 9**

INSIDE OUT
Tracks: / Inside out / Head on the block (Available on 12" only) / Shine.
7" Single: Released Jan '88, on Blue Guitar, by Blue Guitar Records. Catalogue no: **AZUR 6**
12" Single: Released Jan '88, on Blue Guitar, by Blue Guitar Records. Catalogue no: **AZURX 6**

INTO THE HEART OF LOVE
Tracks: / Into the heart of love / Rumble train.
7" Single: Released Aug '89, on Blue Guitar, by Blue Guitar Records. Catalogue no: **AZUR 12**
12" Single: Released Aug '89, on Blue Guitar, by Blue Guitar Records. Catalogue no: **AZURX 12**
CD 5": Released Aug '89, on Blue Guitar, by Blue Guitar Records. Catalogue no: **AZURCD 12**
Cassingle: Released Sep '89, on Blue Guitar, by Blue Guitar Records. Catalogue no: **AZURMC 12**
7" Single: Released Sep '89, on Blue Guitar, by Blue Guitar Records. Catalogue no: **AZURB 12**

LIKE AN ANGEL
Tracks: / Like an angel.
12" Single: Released Dec '85, on Dreamworld, by Dreamworld Records. Catalogue no: **DREAM 005**

MY BIGGEST THRILL
Tracks: / My biggest thrill / Open mind.
7" Single: Released '86, on Blue Guitar, by Blue Guitar Records. Catalogue no: **AZUR 3**
12" Single: Released '86, on Blue Guitar, by Blue Guitar Records. Catalogue no: **AZURX 3**

NIGHT TRACKS EP
Tracks: / Night tracks.
12" Single: Released Jul '87, on Night Tracks, by Pinnacle Records. Catalogue no: **SFNT 004**

OTHER SIDE OF YOU, THE
Tracks: / Other side of you, The / Uptight / Pass you by (Extra track on 12" version only).
7" Single: Released Aug '86, on Blue Guitar, by Blue Guitar Records. Catalogue no: **AZUR 1**
12" Single: Released Aug '86, on Blue Guitar, by Blue Guitar Records. Catalogue no: **AZURX 1**

Mighty Maytones

I DON'T KNOW WHY
Tracks: / I don't know why / Mr. Gate Man.
12" Single: Released Oct '83, on GG'S, Catalogue no: **GG 119**

Mighty Micro

REPLACED BY A MICRO CHIP
Tracks: / Replaced by a micro chip.
7" Single: Released Jan '80, on WEA, by WEA Records. Deleted Jan '85. Catalogue no: **K18134**

Mighty Mighty

BORN IN A MAISONETTE
Tracks: / Born in a maisonette.
12" Single: Released Jan '88, on Chapter 22, by Chapter 22 Records. Catalogue no: **12CHAP 21**
7" Single: Released Jan '88, on Chapter 22, by Chapter 22 Records. Catalogue no: **CHAP 21**

BUILT LIKE A CAR
Tracks: / Built like a car / I don't need you anymore / Twilight (On 12" only) / Love so strong (On 12" only).
7" Single: Released 23 May '87, on Chapter 22, by Chapter 22 Records. Catalogue no: **CHAP 12**

12" Single: Released 23 May '87, on Chapter 22, by Chapter 22 Records. Catalogue no: **12 CHAP 12**

EVERYBODY KNOW THE MONKEY
Tracks: / Everybody knows the monkey / You're on my mind.
7" Single: Released Apr '86, on Girlie, Catalogue no: **GAY 1**

IS THERE ANYONE OUT THERE
Tracks: / Is there anyone out there.
7" Single: Released Aug '86, on Girlie, Catalogue no: **XGAY2**

ONE WAY
Tracks: / One way.
12" Single: Released Oct '87, on Chapter 22, by Chapter 22 Records. Catalogue no: **12CHAP 19**
7" Single: Released Oct '87, on Chapter 22, by Chapter 22 Records. Catalogue no: **CHAP 19**

THROWAWAY
Tracks: / Throwaway / Ceiling to the floor / Ghost of love (track on 12" version only).
7" Single: Released Dec '86, on Chapter 22, by Chapter 22 Records. Catalogue no: **CHAP 10**
12" Single: Released Dec '86, on Chapter 22, by Chapter 22 Records. Catalogue no: **12 CHAP 10**

Mighty Rudo

SKANK AT THE PARTY
Tracks: / Skank at the party.
12" Single: Released Nov '83, on Greensleeves, by Greensleeves Records. Catalogue no: **GRED 132**
7" Single: Released Oct '83, on Jammy's, Catalogue no: **DSR 0349**

SUNSHINE
Tracks: / Sunshine.
12" Single: Released Nov '83, on Chartbound, Catalogue no: **COO 1**

WATERHOUSE
Tracks: / Waterhouse.
12" Single: Released Dec '83, on CF, Catalogue no: **CFD 007**

Mighty Seven

PUSH THE BUTTON TO THE BEAT
Tracks: / Push the button to the beat / Call me.
7" Single: Released Nov '84, on EMI, by EMI Records. Deleted Oct '87. Catalogue no: **PUSH 1**
12" Single: Released Nov '84, on EMI, by EMI Records. Deleted Oct '87. Catalogue no: **12PUSH 1**

Mighty Shamrocks

CONDOR WOMAN
Tracks: / Condor woman / Stand up in public.
7" Single: Released Sep '81, on Independent, by Independent Records. Catalogue no: **WR 1**

Mighty Swallow

DON'T STOP THE PARTY
Tracks: / Don't stop the party.
12" Single: Released Dec '84, on White label (2), Catalogue no: **Unknown**

SOCA UP THE PARTY
Tracks: / Soca up the party.
12" Single: Released Mar '83, on Sunburn, by Orbitone Records. Catalogue no: **SBD 28**

Mighty Wah

COME BACK
Tracks: / Come back.
12" Single: Released Jun '84, on Beggars Banquet, by Beggars Banquet Records. Catalogue no: **BEG 111T**
7" Single: Released Jun '84, on Beggars Banquet, by Beggars Banquet Records. Catalogue no: **BEG 111**

PEEL SESSIONS:MIGHTY WAH
Tracks: / Basement blues; the story of the blues / Better scream / Weekends / Yuh learn.
12" Single: Released Sep '87, on Strange Fruit, by Strange Fruit Records. Catalogue no: **SFPS 035**

WEEKENDS
Tracks: / Weekends / Shambeko / Body and soul (on 12" only) / Something wrong with Eddie (on 12" only).
12" Single: Released Sep '84, on Beggars Banquet, by Beggars Banquet Records. Deleted Jan '88. Catalogue no: **BEG 117T**
7" Single: Released Sep '84, on Beggars Banquet, by Beggars Banquet Records. Deleted Jan '88. Catalogue no: **BEG 117**

Migil 5

MOCKIN' BIRD HILL
Tracks: / Mockin' bird hill.
7" Single: Released Mar '64, on Pye, Deleted '67. Catalogue no: **7N 15597**

NEAR YOU
Tracks: / Near you.
7" Single: Released Jun '64, on Pye, Deleted '67. Catalogue no: **7N 15645**

Mijn-alarm

MIJN-ALARM (BENIFIT)
Tracks: / Mijn-alarm (benifit).
7" Single: Released Jun '88, on Antler, by Antler Records (Belgium). Catalogue no: **ANT 044**

Mikado

ROMANCE
Tracks: / Romance / Ce garcon la.
7" Single: Released Feb '83, on Operation Twilight, Catalogue no: **OPT 016**

Mike Morton Orchestra

WINDS OF WAR
Tracks: / Winds of war.
7" Single: Released Nov '83, on M&H, Catalogue no: **M&H 1002**

Mike T

DO IT ANY WAY YOU WANNA
Tracks: / Do it anyway you wanna.
7" Single: Released Sep '81, on Blue Inc, Catalogue no: **INC 13**
12" Single: Released Sep '81, on Blue Inc, Catalogue no: **INCD 13**

Mike & The Mechanics

ALL I NEED IS A MIRACLE
Tracks: / All I need is a miracle / You are the one / Call to arms, The (on 12" version only).
12" Single: Released Apr '86, on WEA, by WEA Records. Deleted Jun '87. Catalogue no: **U 8765T**
7" Single: Released Apr '86, on WEA, by WEA Records. Deleted Jun '87. Catalogue no: **U 8765**

LIVING YEARS, THE (SINGLE)
Tracks: / Living years, The / Too many friends.
12" Single: Released Jan '89, on Atlantic, by WEA Records. Catalogue no: **U 7717 T**
7" Single: Released Jan '89, on Atlantic, by WEA Records. Catalogue no: **U 7717**

NOBODY KNOWS
Tracks: / Nobody knows.
7" Single: Released Apr '89, on WEA, by WEA Records. Catalogue no: **U 7602**
12" Single: Released Apr '89, on WEA, by WEA Records. Catalogue no: **U 7602T**
CD 5": Released Apr '89, on WEA, by WEA Records. Catalogue no: **U 7602CD**

NOBODY'S PERFECT
Tracks: / Nobody's perfect / Nobody knows / All I need is a miracle (Available on 12" only.).
12" Single: Released Oct '88, on WEA (International), by WEA Records. Catalogue no: **U 7789 T**
CD 3": Released Oct '88, on WEA, by WEA Records. Catalogue no: **U 7789 CD**
7" Single: Released Oct '88, on WEA (International), by WEA Records. Catalogue no: **U 7789**

SILENT RUNNING (ON DANGEROUS GROUND) (SINGLE)
Tracks: / Silent running (on dangerous ground) / I get the feeling / Too far gone (only on 12").
12" Single: Released Oct '85, on WEA, by WEA Records. Deleted Jun '87. Catalogue no: **U 8908T**
7" Single: Released Oct '85, on WEA, by WEA Records. Deleted Jun '87. Catalogue no: **U 8908**

Mike-D And The LA

I GET ROUGH
Tracks: / I get rough.
12" Single: Released Nov '87, on Public (USA), Catalogue no: **PAO 12**

Mikey, D

MY TELEPHONE
Tracks: / My telephone / Bust a rhyme mike (vocal).
7" Single: Released Apr '87, on 10 Records, by Virgin Records. Deleted May '88. Catalogue no: **TEN 172**
12" Single: Released Apr '87, on 10 Records, by Virgin Records. Deleted May '88. Catalogue no: **TENT 172**

Miki & Griff

Biographical details: *Hold Back Tomorrow* (No 26 in 1959), *Rockin' Alone* (No 44 in '60), *Little Bitty Tear* (No 16 in '62) and *I Wanna Stay Here* (No 23 in '63) gave UK hit singles to this British male/female pair. The last two titles were, respectively, bigger hits for Burl Ives and Steve Lawrence & Eydie Gorme. Miki & Griff also had a big-selling EP in 1960. The duo subsequently pursued a concert and cabaret career, playing middle-of-the-road and country music. (Bob MacDonald, January 1986.).

HOLD BACK TOMORROW
Tracks: / Hold back tomorrow.
7" Single: Released Oct '59, on Pye, Deleted '62. Catalogue no: **7N 15213**

I WANNA STAY HERE
Tracks: / I wanna stay here.
7" Single: Released Aug '63, on Pye, Deleted '66. Catalogue no: **7N 15555**

LITTLE BITTY TEAR
Tracks: / Little bitty tear, A.
7" Single: Released Feb '62, on Pye, Deleted '65. Catalogue no: **7N 15412**

ROCKIN' ALONE
Tracks: / Rockin' alone.
7" Single: Released Oct '60, on Pye, Deleted '63. Catalogue no: **7N 15296**

Miko & The Vat Men

OH JOE!
Tracks: / Oh Joe! / Don't kiss me again.
7" Single: Released Apr '80, on CBS, by CBS Records. Deleted Apr '83. Catalogue no: **CBS 8369**

Mile End

UNCLE BILLY SE2
Tracks: / Uncle Billy SE2 / I don't wanna miss your Christmas.
7" Single: Released Dec '85, on Toffee, Catalogue no: **TOF 001**

Mile High Club

WALKING BACKWARDS
Tracks: / Walking backwards.
12" Single: Released Nov '84, on Aalto, by Aalto Records. Catalogue no: **AAL 003**

Miles, Carol

FASHION JUNKY
Tracks: / Fashion junky (radio mix) / Fashion junky (club mix) / Fashion junky (jazz mix) / Fashion junky (dance 'crazy' mix).
12" Single: Released Oct '87, on FM Dance, by FM-Revolver Records. Catalogue no: **12 VHF 41**

Miles, John

Biographical details: Miles, John. This British singer, songwriter, guitarist, keyboardist and multi-instrumentalist hailed from Jarrow in north-east England, and was one of the most hotly-tipped artists of the mid-Seventies. His *Rebel* LP, produced by the noted Alan Parsons, was hailed as one of the best debut albums of the era. It reached No. 9 on the British LP chart, and contained two hit singles: *High Fly* (No. 17) and *Music* (No. 3). The epic *Music*, which was released just after Queen's *Bohemian Rhapsody* had made the six minute single a fashionable commodity, was one of the most ambitious singles of 1976. Its brief lyrics explained in direct terms Miles' love for music; the remainder of the track consisted of lengthy instrumental segments that sounded as though they were intended for a rock opera or a dramatic movie soundtrack.

For a short period Miles seemed to be Britain's brightest new hope; but things did not turn out that way. He experienced two problems. Firstly, he peaked too early and could not live up to the success of *Music*. Secondly, the punk rock explosion in late 1976 effectively categorised him as a member of the overblown Old Wave, despite the fact that he had not been around for very long.

There was one more major success for Miles - the frenetic rock-disco single *Slow Down* reached the UK Top 10 in 1977 and became his only Top 40 single in America (where it was also very big in the clubs). After that, he faded from prominence. He continued releasing albums on a fairly regular basis during the late Seventies and Eighties, and remained an active concert artist. Bob MacDonald, 28 January 1986..

HIGH FLY
Tracks: / High fly.
7" Single: Released Oct '75, on Decca, by Decca Records. Deleted '78. Catalogue no: **F 13595**

I NEED YOUR LOVE
Tracks: / I need your love / Watching over me / Run (Track on 12" version only).
7" Single: Released Jun '86, on Valentino, Catalogue no: **B 9528**
12" Single: Released Jun '86, on Valentino, Catalogue no: **B 9528 T**

MUSIC (OLD GOLD)
Tracks: / Music / Slow down.
7" Single: Released Jun '88, on Old Gold, by Old Gold Records. Catalogue no: **OG 9339**

MUSIC (SINGLE)
Tracks: / Music.
7" Single: Released Mar '76, on Decca, by Decca Records. Deleted '79. Catalogue no: **F 13627**
12" Single: Released Sep '82, on Decca, by Decca Records. Deleted '88. Catalogue no: **MILE X1**
7" Single: Released Sep '82, on Decca, by Decca Records. Deleted '88. Catalogue no: **MILE 1**

REMEMBER YESTERDAY
Tracks: / Remember yesterday.
7" Single: Released Oct '76, on Decca, by Decca Records. Deleted '79. Catalogue no: **F 13667**

RIGHT TO SING
Tracks: / Right to sing.
7" Pic: Released Apr '83, on EMI, by EMI Records. Catalogue no: **EMIP 5386**
7" Single: Released Apr '83, on EMI, by EMI Records. Catalogue no: **EMI 5386**

SLOW DOWN
Tracks: / Slow down.
7" Single: Released Jun '77, on Decca, by Decca Records. Deleted '80. Catalogue no: **F 13709**

SONG FOR YOU
Tracks: / Song for you, A.
7" Single: Released Jul '83, on EMI, by EMI Records. Catalogue no: **EMI 5411**

Militant Dee

MEN OF TODAY
Tracks: / Men of today / Technology.
12" Single: Released May '86, on Ragin' Lion Music, Catalogue no: **RL 005**

Militent Red

AND THEN A VOICE
Tracks: / And then a voice.
7" Single: Released Feb '82, on Vital, Deleted '83. Catalogue no: **VTL 1203**

Milk & Honey

ELECTRIC MONEY
Tracks: / Electric money / Black and white.
7" Single: Released Nov '80, on Bellaphon, Deleted Nov '83. Catalogue no: **BPS 010**

HALLELUJAH
Tracks: / Hallelujah.
7" Single: Released Apr '79, on Polydor, by Polydor Ltd. Deleted '82. Catalogue no: **2001 870**

Milk Monitors

DANCE WITH ME
Tracks: / Dance with me / When all else fails / Drag you down / Don't lean on me.
12" Single: Released Apr '88, on Vinyl Solution, by Vinyl Solution Records. Catalogue no: **VS 9**

Milkshakes

AMBASSADORS OF LOVE
Tracks: / Ambassadors of love.
7" Single: Released Dec '84, on Big Beat, by Ace Records. Deleted '88. Catalogue no: **SW 105**

BRAND NEW CADILLAC
Tracks: / Brand new cadillac.
7" Single: Released Mar '83, on Big Beat, by Ace Records. Deleted '88. Catalogue no: **NS 94**

LET ME LOVE YOU
Tracks: / let me love you.
7" Single: Released Aug '86, on Empire Records, Catalogue no: **SYF 895**

PLEASE DON'T TELL MY BABY
Tracks: / Please don't tell my baby.
7" Single: Released May '82, on Bilk-O Records, Catalogue no: **BILK O**

SOLDIER OF LOVE
Tracks: / Soldier of love.
7" Single: Released Mar '83, on Upright, by Upright Records. Catalogue no: **UP 6**

Milla, Yolanda

WHEN THE PIECES FALL
Tracks: / When the pieces fall / When the pieces fall (version).
12" Single: Released Mar '89, on Champion, by Champion Records. Catalogue no: **CHAMP 1296**
7" Single: Released Mar '89, on Champion, by Champion Records. Catalogue no: **CHAMP 96**

Millar, Sam

HOW DID YOU KNOW
Tracks: / How did you know / Tropical girl.
7" Single: Released Sep '86, on Yellow Brick Road, by Yellow Brick Road Records. Catalogue no: **YBR 1**

Miller, Cat

READY OR NOT
Tracks: / Ready or not.
12" Single: Released Sep '84, on Creole, by Creole Records. Catalogue no: **CRT 67**
7" Single: Released Sep '84, on Creole, by Creole Records. Catalogue no: **CR 67**
12" Single: Released Mar '85, on Street Level, by Creole Records. Catalogue no: **CRT 87**

Miller, Count Prince

COME TO ME SOFTLY
Tracks: / Come to me softly / It ain't no big thing.
12" Single: Released Dec '86, on Hot Vinyl, Catalogue no: **HVT 31**

MULE TRAIN
Tracks: / Mule train.
12" Single: Released Nov '87, on Mango, by Island Records. Catalogue no: **12IS 346**
7" Single: Released Nov '87, on Mango, by Island Records. Deleted Jun '88. Catalogue no: **IS 346**

Miller, David

SWING AND DINE (DANCE ALL THE TIME)
Tracks: / Swing and dine (dance all the time) / Slipping away.
12" Single: Released Feb '83, on LGR, Catalogue no: **LGR 001**

Miller Family

THIS THING COULD GROW
Tracks: / This thing could grow / This thing could grow (inst).
7" Single: Released 30 May '87, on Carrere, Catalogue no: **CAR 414**
12" Single: Released 30 May '87, on Carrere, Catalogue no: **CART 414**

Miller, Frankie

Biographical details: Miller, Frankie. This British singer, guitarist and songwriter was born in Glasgow and was playing gigs by the time he was 14. After brief periods in a variety of small-time bands, he moved to London in 1971; once there, he became a member of the short-lived Jude, a group formed by ex-Procol Harum guitarist Robin Trower. That project did not work out, so Miller embarked upon a solo recording career.

Miller's first album *Once In A Blue Moon* was released in 1973. His backing band on the LP was Brinsley Schwarz, one of the most important groups on Britain's pub rock circuit of the early Seventies. From then onwards, Frankie used different musicians and a different producer on virtually every LP. Throughout the Seventies and early Eighties, he strove to find the right sound; but he never achieved lasting commercial success, and seemed to be stuck in the nearly-man category. Nonetheless, his material was covered by several 'name' artists. Miller's own best asset was his bluesy voice, which was influenced by such gutsy singers as Otis Redding, Joe Cocker, Wilson Pickett and Bob Seger.

Frankie's 1977 album *Full House* (which was also the name of his backing band for a time) yielded his first UK chart single - the earthy, acclaimed, R&B orientated *Be Good To Yourself* reached No. 27 and won him a "Top of the Pops" appearance. In late 1978 he suddenly moved in an out-and-out pop direction with the singalong single *Darlin'.* This gave him a one-off UK Top Tenner, but the similar-sounding follow-up *When I'm Away From You* peaked at No. 42. Miller's career as a pop star was over almost before it had begun.

Always at his musical best when performing in a bluesy rock vein, Miller's career has been erratic, with much chopping and changing. But there have been some good tracks along the way. When not occupied with music, he had pursued a subsidiary career as an actor. Bob MacDonald, 29 January 1986..

BE GOOD TO YOURSELF
Tracks: / Be good to yourself.
7" Single: Released Jun '77, on Chrysalis, by Chrysalis Records. Deleted '80. Catalogue no: **CHS 2147**

DARLIN'
Tracks: / Darlin' / Drunken nights in the city.
7" Single: Released Nov '81, on Chrysalis, by Chrysalis Records. Catalogue no: **CHS 2255**

DARLIN' (OLD GOLD)
Tracks: / Darlin' / Be good to yourself.
7" Single: Released Feb '87, on Old Gold, by Old Gold Records. Catalogue no: **OG 9688**

I'D LIE TO YOU FOR YOUR LOVE
Tracks: / I'd lie to you for your love / Dancing in the rain / Do it till we drop.
12" Single: Released Mar '86, on Vertigo, by Phonogram Ltd. Catalogue no: **VERX 25**
7" Single: Released Mar '86, on Vertigo, by Phonogram Ltd. Catalogue no: **VER 25**

SO YOUNG, SO YOUNG
Tracks: / So young, so young / Tears.
7" Single: Released May '80, on Chrysalis, by Chrysalis Records. Deleted May '83. Catalogue no: **CHS 2436**

STANDING IN THE OTHER SIDE
Tracks: / Standing in the other side / Fire in the furnace.
7" Single: Released Jul '81, on Good Foot, by Good Foot Records (USA). Catalogue no: **GFR 003**

TO DREAM THE DREAM
Tracks: / To dream the dream / Don't stop.
7" Single: Released Jun '82, on Capitol, by EMI Records. Deleted Jun '85. Catalogue no: **CL 253**

WHEN I'M AWAY FROM YOU
Tracks: / When I'm away from you.
7" Single: Released Jan '79, on Chrysalis, by Chrysalis Records. Deleted '82. Catalogue no: **CHS 2276**

Miller, Gary

GARDEN OF EDEN
Tracks: / Garden of Eden.
7" Single: Released Jan '57, on Pye Nixa, Deleted '60. Catalogue no: **N 15070**

ROBIN HOOD
Tracks: / Robin Hood.
7" Single: Released Jan '56, on Nixa, by Pye Records. Deleted '59. Catalogue no: **N 15020**

STORY OF MY LIFE
Tracks: / Story of my life.
7" Single: Released Jan '58, on Pye Nixa, Deleted '61. Catalogue no: **N 15120**

THERE GOES THAT SONG AGAIN
Tracks: / There goes that song again / Night is young, The.
7" Single: Released Dec '61, on Pye, Deleted '64. Catalogue no: **7N 15404**

WONDERFUL WONDERFUL
Tracks: / Wonderful wonderful.
7" Single: Released Jul '57, on Pye Nixa, Deleted '60. Catalogue no: **N 15094**

Miller, Glenn

Biographical details: Born in Clarinda, Iowa, USA on Ist March 1904, Glenn Alton Miller first learned to play cornet and mandolin, only graduating to trombone so that he could play in the town band in Grant City, Missouri, to where the family had moved. His interest in arranging evolved in the early 1920's and he worked for Max Fischer and Ben Pollack before arranging freelance for Broadway shows. He joined the Dorsey Brothers Orchestra in 1934, leaving them after one year to work with, first, Ray Noble and then with Glen Gray and the Casa Loma Band. He formed his own band in 1937, cut some sides for Decca and began playing the ballrooms although not with much success. The band only really gained popularity in the latter half of 1938. On August 1st 1939 the band recorded it's biggest hit "In The Mood". Miller made two films - "Sun Valley Serenade" and "Orchestra Wives". In 1942 he volunteered for the army, becoming Captain Glenn Miller and formed an all-star band, touring first the USA and then England in 1944. The plane carrying him to a concert in France was lost over the English Channel on December 15th 1944. No trace of the wreckage was ever found and Glenn Miller was declared missing, presumed dead, by the United States government.
This American orchestra leader, conductor, arranger and trombonist was one of the most famous and successful musical figures of the 20th century. He was born in Clarinda, Iowa in 1904, and grew up in Platts, Nebraska. He acquired his first trombone at the age of 13. Miller attended the University of Colorado from 1924 until 1926. The following nine years were spent working for various bandleaders of the era, such as Ben Pollack, Paul Ash, Red Nichols and Victor Young; he travelled across America during this period, working on both the West and West Coasts. In 1935 he teamed up with British bandleader Ray Noble, helping to organise Noble's new band when the latter arrived in America. This experience proved valuable when Miller began to set up his own ensemble in 1937.
After a few hiccups, Glenn Miller's orchestra got into gear in mid-1938. Success was not long in coming. After a series of one-nighters in the New York area, the ensemble gained some plum residencies. By 1941 Miller was the top bandleader in the world. Adhering to a 'popular' danceband format rather than the authentic jazz stance of such contemporaries as Duke Ellington, the Miller magic popularised a host of tunes - *Little Brown Jug, In The Mood, Tuxedo Junction* and *Moonlight Serenade* (which he composed himself, and used as his theme tune) became synonymous with his name. When Billboard magazine published the world's first ever record chart in July 1940, Miller had three tunes in the Top 10: *Imagination* (No. 3), *Fools Rush In* (No. 5) and *Pennsylvania 6-5000* (No. 7).
In 1942, while Glenn was at the peak of his career, the Second World War beckoned. During his time in the US Forces, first as Captain and later as a Major, he continued to be one of the most popular musical figures in the world; his role as a morale-booster enhanced his already high reputation. He was stationed in Britain in 1944. In December of that year, while his plane was en route from France to the UK amid thick fog, Major Miller perished as his craft disappeared over the English Channel; he was aged 40.
Ten years after his passing, a biographical movie entitled 'The Glenn Miller Story' was released by Universal Pictures, with James Stewart in the title role. Miller's music lived on, not only in this film but throughout ensuing decades. During the Sixties and Seventies, seven separate Glenn Miller albums registered on the British LP chart. In 1976, more than thirty years after his death, he became an unlikely recipient of a Top 20 placing on the UK singles chart when a brief but enjoyable Glenn Miller revival took place in British discos, thus introducing his music to a new generation. Bob MacDonald, 29 January 1986..

IN THE MOOD (OLD GOLD)
Tracks: / In the mood / String of pearls.
7" Single: Released Jun '88, on Old Gold, by Old Gold Records. Catalogue no: **OG 9602**

IN THE MOOD (SINGLE)
Tracks: / In the mood.
7" Single: Released Jan '76, on RCA, by BMG Records (UK). Catalogue no: **RCA 2644**

MOONLIGHT SERENADE (OLD GOLD)
Tracks: / Moonlight serenade / Tuxedo Junction.
7" Single: Released Nov '86, on Old Gold, by Old Gold Records. Catalogue no: **OG 9651**

MOONLIGHT SERENADE (SINGLE)
Tracks: / Moonlight serenade / Sunrise serenade.
7" Single: Released Jul '85, on MCA, by MCA Records. Catalogue no: **MCA 985**
7" Single: Released Jan '76, on RCA, by BMG Records (UK). Deleted '79. Catalogue no: **RCA 2644**
7" Single: Released Mar '54, on H.M.V., by EMI Records. Deleted '57. Catalogue no: **BD 5942**
7" Single: Released '80, on Lightning, Catalogue no: **LR 1158**
12" Single: Released Jul '85, on MCA, by MCA Records. Catalogue no: **MCAV 985**

Miller, Grant

COLDER THAN ICE
Tracks: / Colder than ice / Red for love.
12" Single: Released Dec '85, on ZYX (Germany), Catalogue no: **ZYX 5341**

Miller, Herb

TUXEDO JUNCTION
Tracks: / Tuxedo Junction / Anchors aweigh / American patrol.
7" Single: Released Nov '81, on Miller, Catalogue no: **MEP 001**

Miller, Jacob

SILVERBELLS
Tracks: / Silver bells.
12" Single: Released Dec '88, on Echo, by Echo Records. Catalogue no: **TRID 001**

Miller, Jimmy

SIZZLIN' HOT
Tracks: / Sizzlin' hot.
7" Single: Released Mar '84, on Northwood, by Northwood Records. Catalogue no: **NW 45 001**

Miller, Jody

HOME OF THE BRAVE
Tracks: / Home of the brave.
7" Single: Released Oct '65, on Capitol, by EMI Records. Deleted '68. Catalogue no: **CL 15415**

Miller, Mitch

Biographical details: Miller, Mitch. This American producer, arranger, conductor, oboist and executive was one of the key figures in the Amercian music industry of the Fifties. He was born in Rochester, New York on Independence Day 1911. He started to play piano at the age of six and took up his main instrument, the oboe, at eleven. During his eens he studied at the Eastman School of Music and, after graduation, joined the Rochester Philharmonic Orchestra as an oboist. After spending many years progressing through various orchestras, he joined Mercury Records in 1947 as head of popular music. In this capacity he was associated with the careers of stars like Frankie Laine and Patti Page.
In 1950, Miller took the move which made him a real big gun. He became head of Artists and Repertoire for Columbia Records. He quickly boosted the company's lacklustre fortunes. overseeing and developing the careers of many of the top popular singers of the early Fifties. He was conspicuously adept at both guiding established stars and spotting new talent. In addition to Laine (who moved with him), Miller's roster of artists included Tony Bennett, Rosemary Clooney, Doris Day, The Four Lads, Johnny Mathis, Guy Mitchell and Johnny Ray. Mitch's productions were never far from the top of the American charts. After the British listings were inaugurated in November 1952, Miller chalked up a staggering total of 17 No. 1 production credits on the UK singles chart between 1953 and 1958; even after more than 30 years of British chart history, his tally of 17 has only been bettered by two other producers.
Miller was known in the business as a strong critic of rock 'n' roll, the music that revolutionised the record industry (and therefore undermined his domination of it) in the mid-Fifties. But though he ignored it and then fought against it, he watched helplessly as his middle-of-the-road crooners were gradually nudged out of the charts by an array of young rock 'n' roll upstats.
However, Miller's position and standing in the music business was not diminished - he continued to shine brightly, but from another angle. He became a performing act in his own right. Mitch Miller's Orchestra and Chorus logged six weeks at No. 1 in America, and reached No. 2 in Britain, with an adaptation of a song originally dated from 1853, *The Yellow Rose Of Texas.* Its success was not lost on Mitch - in 1958 he began releasing an endless series of *Sing Along With Mitch* albums, containing masses of familiar songs performed by *iller's chorus. The idea proved so successful that NBC television gave him his own networked singalong series, which ran from 1960 till 1966. Lyrics were flashed on the screen, to encourage viewers to join in the spirit of the show. Bob MacDonald, 29 January 1986..*

YELLOW ROSE OF TEXAS
Tracks: / Yellow rose of Texas.
7" Single: Released Oct '55, on Nixa, by Pye Records. Deleted '58. Catalogue no: **N 15004**
7" Single: Released Oct '55, on Philips, by Phonogram Ltd. Deleted '58. Catalogue no: **PB 505**
7" Single: Released '80, on Impact, by Ace Records. Catalogue no: **LR 1775**

Miller, Ned

Biographical details: Miller, Ned. This American singer, songwriter and guitarist was born in Raines, Utah in 1925. After periods as a US marine and as a pipefitter, he enjoyed success in 1957 as writer of *Dark Moon.* This song was simultaneously in the American Top 10 for both Bonnie Guitar and Gale Storm; in Britain, it was successfully covered by Tony Brent.
In that same year Miller decided to record his own version of another of his songs, *From A Jack To A King.* This single was initially a flop, but it suddenly became a big hit when re-issued in 1963: it reached No. 6 in the States and zoomed to No. 2 in Britain.

Working in a country bop vein, Miller chalked up success as a singer and more often as a songwriter on the US C&W charts during the late Fifties and the Sixties. Amongst his better known compositions were *Invisible Tears, Southbound* and *Do What You Do Do Well,* the latter gave him a UK No. 48 hit in 1965. Bob MacDonald, 29 January 1988..

DO WHAT YOU DO DO WELL
Tracks: / Do what you do do well.
7" Single: Released Feb '65, on London-American, Deleted '68. Catalogue no: **HL 9937**

FROM A JACK TO A KING
Tracks: / From a jack to a king / Parade of broken hearts.
7" Single: Released Feb '63, on London-American, Deleted '66. Catalogue no: **HL 9648**
7" Single: Released Mar '82, on Decca, by Decca Records. Deleted '88. Catalogue no: **F 13910**

FROM A JACK TO A KING (OLD GOLD)
Tracks: / From a jack to a king / Do what you do do well.
7" Single: Released Oct '83, on Old Gold, by Old Gold Records. Deleted Sep '89. Catalogue no: **OG 9340**

STEVE MILLER BAND - ABRACADABRA (Released on Mercury)

Miller O.C

HOW CAN I LOVE AGAIN
Tracks: / How can I love again / Oh what a feeling.
12" Single: Released Feb '84, on Orbitone, by Orbitone Records. Deleted Feb '87. Catalogue no: **DORB 7**

Miller, Roger

Biographical details: Miller, Roger. This American singer, songwriter and guitarist was born in Fort Worth, Texas, and was brought up in Erick, Oklahoma. He worked for several years in Nashville, striving to gain recognition, before coming to fame in 1964 with his first hit *Dang Me*. Prior to this breakthrough, he had achieved a UK No. 2 smash in 1962 with *Swiss Maid* - this was written by Miller and performed by Del Shannon.

Dang Me was the first of a series of American hit singles for Miller, a run which lasted until 1968. His records were a blend of country, folk and pop styles. Initially, the accent was on humour and wit, as with *Dang Me* and *Chug-A-Lug*. His biggest success, 1965's *King Of The Road* (No. 4 in US, a No. 1 smash in UK), was also a good comedy record. But as time progressed, they became less and less amusing, and more and more schmaltzy. *England Swings*, a yukky 1965 tribute to the then world centre of fashion and youth culture, was a bigger hit in America than in the subject country. By the time *Little Green Apples* came along in 1968, many people were staring into their sick bowls and praying that this would be Miller's final Top 40 hit on both sides of the Atlantic. In the event, it was. He gradually faded from prominence, and devoted much of his energy to proprietorship of the King Of The Road Inn, the largest hotel in Nashville. Bob MacDonald, 29 January 1986..

ENGINE ENGINE NO.9
Tracks: / Engine no.9.
7" Single: Released Jun '65, on Philips, by Phonogram Ltd. Deleted '68. Catalogue no: **BF 1416**

ENGLAND SWINGS
Tracks: / England swings.
7" Single: Released Dec '65, on Philips, by Phonogram Ltd. Deleted '68. Catalogue no: **BF 1456**

KANSAS CITY STAR
Tracks: / Kansas City star.
7" Single: Released Oct '65, on Philips, by Phonogram Ltd. Deleted '68. Catalogue no: **BF 1437**

KING OF THE ROAD
Tracks: / King of the road / England swings / Little green apples.
7" Single: Released Mar '65, on Philips, by Phonogram Ltd. Deleted '68. Catalogue no: **BF 1397**

KING OF THE ROAD (OLD GOLD)
Tracks: / King of the road.
7" Single: Released Jan '85, on Old Gold, by Old Gold Records. Catalogue no: **OG 9480**

LITTLE GREEN APPLES (SINGLE)
Tracks: / Little green apples.
7" Single: Released Mar '68, on Mercury, by Phonogram Ltd. Deleted '71. Catalogue no: **MF 1021**

Miller, Steve

Biographical details: The Steve Miller Band has survived every musical trend since its formation in the late Sixties, when Miller's childhood friend Boz Scaggs featured on the first album, *I*Children Of The Future'*D*. However, he soon left in pursuit of a solo career. Despite many such line-up changes (and despite Miller's frequent bouts of illness) the band has been enourmously successful in the U.S.A. (number one with *I*The joker'*D*), and moderately popular in Britain, where the biggest hit came after a long break in the late Seventies; *I*Abracadabra'*D* reached number Two in the Summer of 1982. (Robert Cohen, 1/5/87)..

ABRACADABRA (SINGLE) (See panel above)
Tracks: / Abracadabra / Never say no.
7" Single: Released Jun '82, on Mercury, by Phonogram Ltd. Deleted '85. Catalogue no: **STEVE 3**

GIVE IT UP
Tracks: / Give it up / Rock 'n' me.
7" Single: Released Oct '82, on Mercury, by Phonogram Ltd. Deleted Oct '85. Catalogue no: **STEVE 5**

HEART LIKE A WHEEL
Tracks: / Heart like a wheel / Threshold / Jet airliner.
7" Single: Released Nov '81, on Mercury, by Phonogram Ltd. Deleted '84. Catalogue no: **STEVE 1**

I WANT TO MAKE THE WORLD TURN AROUND
Tracks: / I want to make the world turn around / Slinky.
12" Single: Released Mar '87, on Capitol, by EMI Records. Deleted Apr '88. Catalogue no: **12CL 444**
7" Single: Released Mar '87, on Capitol, by EMI Records. Deleted '88. Catalogue no: **CL 444**

JOKER, THE (SINGLE)
Tracks: / Joker / Living in the USA / My dark hour.
7" Single: Released Jan '83, on Capitol, by EMI Records. Deleted '88. Catalogue no: **CL 258**

KEEPS ME WONDERING WHY
Tracks: / Keeps me wondering why.
7" Single: Released Sep '82, on Mercury, by Phonogram Ltd. Deleted '85. Catalogue no: **STEVE 4**

MACHO CITY
Tracks: / Macho city.
7" Single: Released Feb '82, on Mercury, by Phonogram Ltd. Catalogue no: **STEVE 2**

ROCK'N ME
Tracks: / Rock'n me.
7" Single: Released Oct '76, on Mercury, by Phonogram Ltd. Deleted '79. Catalogue no: **6078 804**

TAKE THE MONEY AND RUN
Tracks: / Take the money and run / Joker (live).
7" Single: Released Apr '83, on Mercury, by Phonogram Ltd. Catalogue no: **STEVE 6**
12" Single: Released Apr '83, on Mercury, by Phonogram Ltd. Catalogue no: **STEVE 612**

YA YA
Tracks: / Ya ya / Filthy McNasty.
Note: Remixed by Steve Weiss.
7" Single: Released Sep '88, on Capitol, by EMI Records. Deleted Jun '89. Catalogue no: **CL 506**
12" Single: Released Sep '88, on Capitol, by EMI Records. Deleted Jun '89. Catalogue no: **12CL 506**

Miller, Suzi

HAPPY DAYS AND LONELY NIGHTS
Tracks: / Happy days and lonely nights.
7" Single: Released Jan '55, on Decca, by Decca Records. Deleted '58. Catalogue no: **F 10389**

Miller, Tracy

BABY IT TAKES TWO
Tracks: / Baby it takes two / Yours confidentially.
7" Single: Released May '82, on Peachtown, by Peachtown Records. Catalogue no: **PT 101**

Miller, Vallin

HIT BACK
Tracks: / Hit back.
12" Single: Released Nov '86, on Governor, Catalogue no: **GVR 007**

Milli Vanilli

ALL OR NOTHING (SINGLE)
Tracks: / All or nothing.
12" Single: Released May '89, on Cool Tempo, by Chrysalis Records. Catalogue no: **COOLX 180**
7" Single: Released May '89, on Cool Tempo, by Chrysalis Records. Catalogue no: **COOL 180**

BABY, DON'T FORGET MY NUMBER
Tracks: / Too much monkey business / Baby don't forget my number (radio mix) (Only available on 12" version.).
Special: Released Jan '89, on Cool Tempo, by Chrysalis Records. Catalogue no: **COOLXR 178**
12" Single: Released Dec '88, on Cool Tempo, by Chrysalis Records. Catalogue no: **COOLX 178**
CD 5": Released Jan '89, on Cool Tempo, by Chrysalis Records. Catalogue no: **COOLCD 178**
7" Single: Released Dec '88, on Cool Tempo, by Chrysalis Records. Catalogue no: **COOL 178**

BLAME IT ON THE RAIN
Tracks: / Blame it on the rain / Money.
Cassingle: Released Jul '89, on Cool Tempo, by Chrysalis Records. Catalogue no: **COOLMC 180**
7" Single: Released Jun '89, on Cool Tempo, by Chrysalis Records. Catalogue no: **COOL 180**
CD 5": Released Jun '89, on Cool Tempo, by Chrysalis Records. Catalogue no: **COOLCD 180**
12" Single: Released Jun '89, on Cool Tempo, by Chrysalis Records. Catalogue no: **COOLX 180**

GIRL I'M GONNA MISS YOU
Tracks: / Girl I'm gonna miss you / Can't you feel my love.
CD 5": Released Sep '89, on Cool Tempo, by Chrysalis Records. Catalogue no: **COOLCD 191**
Cassingle: Released Sep '89, on Cool Tempo, by Chrysalis Records. Catalogue no: **COOLMC 191**
12" Single: Released Sep '89, on Cool Tempo, by Chrysalis Records. Catalogue no: **COOLX 191**
7" Single: Released Sep '89, on Cool Tempo, by Chrysalis Records. Catalogue no: **COOL 191**

GIRL YOU KNOW IT'S TRUE
Tracks: / Girl you know it's true (DJ edit) / Magic touch.
7" Single: Released Jun '88, on Cool Tempo, by Chrysalis Records. Catalogue no: **COOL 170**
12" Single: Released Jun '88, on Cool Tempo, by Chrysalis Records. Catalogue no: **COOLX 170**

Millican & Nesbitt

Biographical details: Millican and Nesbitt. An eponymously titles LP gave this British comedy duo a Top 3 smash on the UK album chart in 1974. They followed this in 1975 with the slightly less successful album *Everybody Knows Millican And Nesbitt*. On the singles chart, the vocal pair reached No. 20 at the end of 1973 with a remake of the 20 year-old Les Paul and Mary Ford hit *Vaya Con Dios*; in 1974 they peaked at No. 38 with *For Old Time's Sake*. The guys did not penetrate the charts again. Bob MacDonald, 29 January 1986..

FOR OLD TIMES SAKE
Tracks: / For old times sake.
7" Single: Released May '74, on Pye, Deleted '77. Catalogue no: **7N 45357**

VAYA CON DIOS
Tracks: / Vaya con dios.
7" Single: Released Dec '73, on Pye, Deleted '76. Catalogue no: **7N 45310**

Millie

Biographical details: Millie. This Jamaican singer was born Millicent Small in the island's parish of Clarendon in 1948. After winning a Kingston talent contest at the age of 12, Millie became a juvenile star in her home country via such singles as *We'll Meet*. Millie was barely 16 years old when she came to fame in Britain and America with *My Boy Lollipop* in 1964, an update of a 1956 song.

On the face of it *My Boy Lollipop*, which reached No. 2 in both the UK and US, was simply an enjoyable, catchy novelty pop hit. But in fact, its significance was greater than that. It gave pop listerners on both sides of the Atlantic their first insight into 'blue beat' or 'ska', the Jamaican music that was later to evolve into reggae. It was an early talent-spotting success for Chris Blackwell, the entrepreneur whose Island label became the most important international outlet for Jamaican sounds. It was also the first taste of chart success for Rod Stewart, and up-and-coming 19 year old who played the harmonica on *My Boy Lollipop*.

There were great times ahead for reggae, Blackwell and Stewart, but not for Millie Small. After a moderately successful follow-up hit, *Sweet William* (No. 30 in UK, No. 40 in US), she vanishes from the public eye. *My Boy Lollipop*, now a party classic, resurfaced in 1982 as *My Girl Lollipop* in a new British Top 10 version by Bad Manners. Bob MacDonald, 29 January 1986..

BLOODSHOT EYES
Tracks: / Bloodshot eyes.
7" Single: Released Nov '65, on Fontana, by Phonogram Ltd. Deleted '68. Catalogue no: **TF 617**

MY BOY LOLLIPOP
Tracks: / My boy lollipop / Oh Henry.
12" Single: Released Jul '87, on Island, by Island Records. Deleted Apr '88. Catalogue no: **12WIP 6574**
7" Single: Released Mar '64, on Fontana, by Phonogram Ltd. Deleted '67. Catalogue no: **TF 449**
Cassingle: Released Jul '87, on Island, by Island Records. Deleted Apr '89. Catalogue no: **CWIP 6574**
7" Single: Released Jul '87, on Island, by Island Records. Catalogue no: **WIP 6574**

SWEET WILLIAM
Tracks: / Sweet William / Wings of a dove.
7" Single: Released Jun '64, on Fontana, by Phonogram Ltd. Deleted '67. Catalogue no: **TF 479**
7" Single: Released Aug '82, on Island, by Island Records. Catalogue no: **WIP 6811**

Milligan, Spike

Biographical details: Milligan, Spike. This British comedian, whose real first name is Terence, came to fame as a member of 'The Goon Show' team; this was the most acclaimed BBC radio comedy show of the Fifties. After the Fifties heyday of 'The Goons', all three members enjoyed solo success. Milligan, their main scriptwriter, assailed the nation with such multi-media projects as 'Adolf Hitler - My Part In His Downfall'. Though he did not enjoy the same record success as his former colleagues, Harry Secombe and Peter Sellers, he chalked up two entries on the UK album chart: *Milligan Preserved* reached No. 11 in 1961, and *The Snow Goose* (on which he was backed by the London Symphony Orchestra) peaked at No. 49 in December 1976. He has remained a national institution in British showbusiness, and is perhaps best described as a professional eccentric. The best insights into the ultra-weird Spike can be found in his semi-autobiographical books about his wartime experiences, 'Adolf Hitler - My Part In His Downfall' (Spike played his own father in the movie version) and 'Monty - His Part In My Victory'. Bob MacDonald, 30 January 1986..

HIMAZAS
Tracks: / Himazas / There ain't no morning.
7" Single: Released Nov '83, on Paramount, Catalogue no: **PARA 101**

STICKY
Tracks: / Sticky / None today thank you.
7" Single: Released Oct '82, on Spike, Catalogue no: **STICKY 1**

Million, Jeb

SECOND TIME AROUND
Tracks: / Second time around / Welcome to love.
12" Single: Released Aug '86, on WEA, by WEA Records. Catalogue no: **YZ 77T**
7" Single: Released Aug '86, on WEA, by WEA Records. Deleted Jun '87. Catalogue no: **YZ 77**

SPEED UP MY HEARTBEAT
Tracks: / Speed up my heartbeat / Who send you.
7" Single: Released Oct '86, on WEA, by WEA Records. Deleted Jun '87. Catalogue no: **YZ 82**
12" Single: Released Oct '86, on WEA, by WEA Records. Deleted Jun '87. Catalogue no: **YZ 82T**

Million, Max

TOO SKINNY
Tracks: / Too skinny.
7" Single: Released Oct '85, on Anubis, Catalogue no: **ANU 002**

WALK MY WAY
Tracks: / Walk my way.
7" Single: Released Jul '84, on Button, by Musical Characters Records. Catalogue no: **BTN 119**

Million Miles

HEART, THE
Tracks: / Heart, The.
7" Single: Released 5 Mar '88, on Exile, Catalogue no: **EX 7009**

Millionaires

DON'T MESS WITH MY LOVE
Tracks: / Don't mess with my love / This is love.
7" Single: Released Aug '89, on Ardent, by Ardent Records. Catalogue no: **ADS 9003**

Millions Like Us

GUARANTEED FOR LIFE
Tracks: / Guaranteed for life (Not on 12") / Heaven help the child (On all versions) / Guaranteed for life (limited warranty mix) (Not on 7").
12" Single: Released Sep '87, on Circa, by Virgin Records. Catalogue no: **YRT 7**
7" Single: Released Sep '87, on Circa, by Virgin Records. Catalogue no: **YR 7**
Cassingle: Released '87, on Circa, by Virgin Records. Catalogue no: **YRC 7**

IN LOVE WITH YOURSELF
Tracks: / In love with yourself (NOT on 12") / Heartbroken man (On all versions) / In love with yourself (vanity version) (CD & 12" only) / In love with yourself (distortion dub) (12" only) / Guaranteed for life (CD only).
7" Single: Released Feb '88, on Circa, by Virgin Records. Catalogue no: **YR 9**
12" Single: Released Feb '88, on Circa, by Virgin Records. Catalogue no: **YRT 9**
CD 5": Released Aug '88, on Virgin, by Virgin Records. Catalogue no: **YRCD 9**

ONE WORLD (IDEAL WORLD)
Tracks: / One world (ideal world) / What you want is what you get / One world (ideal world) (ideal home version) (12" only).
Note: "Millions like us release the killer cut from their forthcoming album, Millions Like Us (CIRCA 1), and it's a catchy mid-tempo R & B number guaranteed to garner the airplay they so richly deserve." (Virgin Records, May 1985.)
12" Single: Released 31 May '88, on Circa, by Virgin Records. Catalogue no: **YRT 14**
7" Single: Released 31 May '88, on Circa, by Virgin Records. Catalogue no: **YR 14**

Millions Of Dead

CHICKEN SQWAWK
7" Single: Released Dec '84, on Radical, by Radical Records. Deleted '86. Catalogue no: **MOC 3**

Mills, Barbara

QUEEN OF FOOLS
Tracks: / Queen of fools / Make it last.
7" Single: on Soul Supply, by Soul Supply Records. Catalogue no: **7SS 103**
7" Single: Released Aug '82, on Inferno (1), by Inferno Records. Catalogue no: **HEAT 9**

Mills Brothers

Biographical details: Mills Brothers. The Mills Brothers were one of the leading close harmony vocal groups of the Thirties and Forties. John, Herbert, Harry and Donald were born in Piqua, Ohio, and started their career singing on a Cincinatti radio station. That was in 1930; over the following few years, the group became steady record sellers and made several film appearances. In 1934 their version of *Tiger Rag*, a 1917 Dixieland tune, made them internationally famous.

John died in 1935, and his place was taken by the group's father John Mills Sr. The group achieved their biggest success in 1942 with *Paper Doll*, a mammouth US No. 1; this was a surprise remake of a 1915 song. 1944 brought the Mills Brothers another American chart-topper with *You Always Hurt The One You Love*, a song successfully revived in the pop era by Connie Francis and Clarence 'Frogman' Henry. In 1948 the group scored a smash with their rendition of Hoagy Carmichael's *Lazy River*. Soon after the November 1952 inception of the British record charts, the Brothers reached the UK No. 10 position in January 1953 with their revival of the classic chestnut *Glow Worm*. Despite the onset of the rock 'n' roll era, they managed to hit the US Top 40 in 1957 with *Queen Of The Senior Prom* and in 1958 with *Get A Job*. They then disappeared from the charts, but made a surprise comeback in 1968 with their US No. 23 single *Cab Driver*.

Although their heyday was over by the time the rock era began in the mid-Fifties, the Mills Brothers' harmony singing had a considerable influence on the early development of pop and rock music, particularly the black rhythm and blues groups of the Fifties. The same could be said of the Brothers' contemporaroes, The Ink Spots. Henry Milles died in June 1982 at the age of 68. His father, John Sr., passed away in December 1967 at the age of 85. Bob MacDonald, 30 January 1986..

GLOW WORM
Tracks: / Glow worm.
7" Single: Released Jan '53, on Brunswick, by Decca Records. Deleted '56. Catalogue no: **05007**

Mills, Eleonore

MR. RIGHT
Tracks: / Mr. Right / Mr. Right (Right mix).
Note: Pic bag
12" Single: Released Apr '87, on Debut, by Skratch Records. Catalogue no: **DEBTX 3020**
7" Single: Released Apr '87, on Debut, by Skratch Records. Catalogue no: **DEBT 3020**

YOU CAN'T HAVE MY DREAMS
Tracks: / You can't have my dreams / You can't have my dreams (dub) / You can't have my dreams (club mix) (Featured on 12" version only.) / You can't have my dreams (radio mix) (Featured on 12" version only.) / You can't have my dreams (sax dub) (Featured on 12" version only.) / You can't have my dreams (bonus beats) (Featured on 12" version only.).
7" Single: Released 14 Mar '88, on Debut, by Skratch Records. Catalogue no: **DEBT 3043**
12" Single: Released 14 Mar '88, on Debut, by Skratch Records. Catalogue no: **DEBTX 3043**

Mills, Eric

GO YOUR WAY
Tracks: / Go your way.
12" Single: Released Jun '86, on Amanda, Catalogue no: **AMD 004**

Mills, Erica

I'D RATHER GO BLIND
Tracks: / I'd rather go blind.
7" Single: Released Oct '84, on Code, by Code Records. Catalogue no: **LOB 019**
12" Single: Released Oct '84, on Code, by Code Records. Catalogue no: **12LOB 019**

Mills, Garry

I'LL STEP DOWN
Tracks: / I'll step down.
7" Single: Released Jun '61, on Decca, by Decca Records. Deleted '64. Catalogue no: **F 11358**

LOOK FOR A STAR
Tracks: / Look for a star.
7" Single: Released Mar '87, on Old Gold, by Old Gold Records. Catalogue no: **OG 9648**

TOP TEEN BABY
Tracks: / Top teen baby.
7" Single: Released Oct '60, on Top Rank (1), Deleted '63. Catalogue no: **JAR 500**

Mills, Hayley

LET'S GET TOGETHER
Tracks: / Let's get together.
7" Single: Released Oct '61, on Decca, by Decca Records. Deleted '64. Catalogue no: **F 11396**

Mills, John

YOUNG AT HEART
Tracks: / Young at heart.
7" Single: Released May '80, on Chips, Deleted '83. Catalogue no: **CHI 103**

Mills & Mckenna

STRIKE IT RICH
Tracks: / Strike it rich / Millionaire mix.
7" Single: Released Jan '86, on BBC, by BBC Records & Tapes. Deleted Apr '89. Catalogue no: **RESL 177**

Mills, Mrs.

Biographical details: The ultra-jolly piano style of Mrs Mills, containing endless medleys of familiar age-old standards, sold particularly well in the 60's: *Come To My Party*, *Mrs Mills' Party Pieces* and *Let's Have Another Party* all registered on the British album chart. At Christmas 1961 she had a one-off UK Top Twenty single with Mrs Mills' Medley. (Bob MacDonald, January 1986.).

MRS.MILLS' MEDLEY
Tracks: / Mrs. Mills medley.
7" Single: Released Dec '61, on Parlophone, by EMI Records. Deleted '64. Catalogue no: **R 4856**

Mills, Stephanie

Biographical details: This American singer and actress first came to fame as a teenager in 1975, via her starring role in the successful Broadway show 'The Wiz'. This was an acclaimed revival of 'The Wizard Of Oz' (although it should be emphasised that Mills was not involved in the 1978 flop film of 'The Wiz'). Stephanie's debut album *For The First Time* was issued on Motown and was written and arranged by Bacharach and David, but was not a success.

Mills' recording career did not really get into gear until 1979, by which time she was with the 20th Century label. *What'cha Gonna Do With My Lovin'* reached No. 22 on the US Hot 100 singles chart in that year. She peaked in 1980 with exuberant pop-soul single *Never Knew Love Like This Before*, a Top 10 smash in both the US and UK. The following year, she achieved a moderate success in both countries with *Two Hearts*, a duet with soul veteran Teddy Pendergrass.

Subsequently Mills has drifted along in the second division, struggling to retrieve the reputation she won with *Never Knew Love Like This Before*. She did well in 1984 with the catchy single *The Medecine Song*, a club winner that returned her to the UK Top 30. But 1985's *Bit By Bit* was a bit of a disappointment. Bob MacDonald, 30 January 1986..

D-A-N-C-I-N-G
Tracks: / D-A-N-C-I-N-G / Better than ever.
12" Single: Released Aug '80, on 20th Century, by 20th Century Records. Deleted '83. Catalogue no: **TCD 2464**

I FEEL GOOD ALL OVER
Tracks: / I feel good all over / Secret lady.
12" Single: Released 21 Nov '87, on MCA, by MCA Records. Catalogue no: **MCAT 1213**
7" Single: Released Oct '87, on MCA, by MCA Records. Catalogue no: **MCA 1213**

MEDICINE SONG
Tracks: / Medicine song.
12" Single: Released Aug '84, on Club, by Phonogram Ltd. Catalogue no: **JABX 8**

NEVER KNEW LOVE LIKE THIS BEFORE (OLD GOLD)
Tracks: / Never knew love like this before.
7" Single: Released Jan '85, on Old Gold, by Old Gold Records. Catalogue no: **OG 9489**
12" Single: Released Oct '80, on 20th Century, by 20th Century Records. Deleted Oct '83. Catalogue no: **TCD 2460**
7" Single: Released Oct '80, on 20th Century, by 20th Century Records. Deleted Oct '83. Catalogue no: **TC 2460**

SOMETHING IN THE WAY (IMPORT)
Tracks: / Something in the way.
12" Single: Released May '89, on MCA, by MCA Records. Catalogue no: **MCA 23941**

SWEET SENSATION
Tracks: / Sweet sensation / Wish that you were mine.
7" Single: Released May '80, on 20th Century, by 20th Century Records. Deleted May '85. Catalogue no: **TCD 2449**

TWO HEARTS
Tracks: / Two hearts / Just wanna say.
7" Single: Released May '81, on 20th Century, by 20th Century Records. Deleted '84. Catalogue no: **TC 2492**
12" Single: Released May '81, on 20th Century, by 20th Century Records. Deleted '84. Catalogue no: **TCD 2492**

YOU CAN'T RUN FROM MY LOVE
Tracks: / You can't run from my love.
7" Single: Released Jul '82, on Phonogram, by Phonogram Ltd. Catalogue no: **CAN 1011**
12" Single: Released Jul '82, on Phonogram, by Phonogram Ltd. Catalogue no: **CANX 1011**

YOU'RE PUTTIN' A RUSH ON ME
Tracks: / Rush on me, A (You're puttin') / Rush on me, A (You're puttin') (Inst).
12" Single: Released Aug '87, on MCA, by MCA Records. Catalogue no: **MCAT 1187**
12" Single: Released Aug '87, on MCA (USA), by MCA Records (USA). Deleted Oct '87. Catalogue no: **MCA 23774**
7" Single: Released Aug '87, on MCA, by MCA Records. Catalogue no: **MCA 1187**

Mills, Warren

FLAME IN THE FIRE
Tracks: / Flame in the fire.
12" Single: Released Aug '86, on Jive, by Zomba Records. Deleted '87. Catalogue no: **JIVET 127**
7" Single: Released Aug '86, on Jive, by Zomba Records. Deleted '87. Catalogue no: **JIVE 127**

MICKIES MONKEY
Tracks: / Mickies monkey.
7" Pic: Released Jan '84, on Jive, by Zomba Records. Catalogue no: **JIVES 57**
12" Single: Released Jan '84, on Jive, by Zomba Records. Catalogue no: **JIVET 57**
7" Single: Released Jan '84, on Jive, by Zomba Records. Catalogue no: **JIVE 57**

SUNSHINE
Tracks: / Sunshine.
7" Single: Released Aug '85, on Jive, by Zomba Records. Catalogue no: **JIVE 99**
12" Single: Released Jan '85, on Jive, by Zomba Records. Catalogue no: **JIVET 99**

TELL ME WHAT YOU WANT
Tracks: / Tell me what you want / Angel eyes / Sunshine (remix) (Extra track on 12" version only).
12" Single: Released Feb '86, on Jive, by Zomba Records. Catalogue no: **JIVET 112**
7" Single: Released Feb '86, on Jive, by Zomba Records. Catalogue no: **JIVE 112**

Milltown Brothers

COMING FROM THE MILL 1989
Tracks: / Coming from the mill 1989.
CD 5": Released Feb '89, on Big Round, Catalogue no: **BIGR 101CD**
12" Single: Released Feb '89, on Big Round, Catalogue no: **BIG R101T**
7" Single: Released Feb '89, on Big Round, Catalogue no: **BIG R101**

Milner, John

I FEEL FREE
Tracks: / I feel free.
7" Single: Released Jul '83, on Purple Plum, Catalogue no: **PUR 101**

Milnes, Sherrill

LARGO AL FACTOTUS
Tracks: / Largo al factotum.
7" Single: Released Jun '79, on Decca, by Decca Records. Deleted '88. Catalogue no: **F 13849**

Milsap, Ronnie

Biographical details: Born in Robinsville, North Carolina, and raised by his grandparents until he was five, Ronnie Milsap began taking chances early. He was kicked out of music class at the Governor Morehead School for the Blind in Raleigh for playing rock'n'roll instead of classical music. After attending Young-Harris Junior College near Atlanta, Georgia for two years, he turned down a scholarship to Emory University School of Law in favor of playing music for a living. For awhile, that chance didn't look as if it was going to pan out. For the next few years, success seemed always to be just around the corner. In 1965, Ronnie was living in Atlanta, working as a sideman and playing sessions when two significant events occurred: he married Joyce, and he signed to New York based Scepter Records as an R&B artist. His first Scepter single *Never had it so good* was a top five R&B hit. Nonetheless, although Ronnie continued to record for Scepter throughout the '60's, he never had another big record, and by the end of the decade, he had formed his own band and moved to Memphis, where his was the house band at T.J.'s club. The most notable thing that happened to Milsap in Memphis was that he caught the attention of Elvis Presley, who asked Ronnie to play at his private New Year's Eve party and to do some session work for him - the most famous of the Milsap/Presley sessions was for Elvis's *Kentucky rain*. Still Ronnie didn't feel that he could ensure a secure future for his family - for by then he and Joyce had a son, Todd - by continuing his career in Memphis. Bedeviled by management problems and without a record label, the Milsap family moved to Nashville, Tennessee in 1972. Ronnie Milsap's first Nashville job was playing four shows a night at the rooftop club of Roger Miller's King of the Road Hotel, and those shows became legendary in Nashville. There were lines at the elevators every night, and everybody who was anybody in Nashville flocked to see the blind guy at the King of the Road. By the year's end, however, 'that blind guy' had a recording contract with RCA and everybody knew his name. Ronnie Milsap's first RCA single *Altogether now (let's fall apart)* sold a hundred thousand copies. From there on, there was no looking back; it became a rare occurrence for a Ronnie Milsap single or album not to be a hit, beginning with his first number one single *Pure love*. First, Ronnie established himself solidly in the country music field, and rapidly acquired a loyal legion of fans with hits like *Daydreams about night things* and *(I'm a) stand by my woman man*. He won his first CMA award for Best Male Vocalist only a year after signing with RCA. The hits and the awards kept coming, the Milsap style kept developing and in 1977, he had his first big crossover pop hit with the Archie Jordan composition *It was almost like a song*. After that it became almost routine for a Milsap hit to find itself on pop adult contemporary and country radio. In 1980, there was *Smokey mountain rain* and in 1981, it was *There's no gettin' over me*. In 1982, there were *Any day now* (Billboard Adult Contemporary Song Of The Year), *He got you* and *Inside*. Of course the biggest challenge Ronnie Milsap has faced in his life is his blindness, a handicap with which he was born. Put in the larger context of his career, however, Ronnie's blindness seems like one challenge too many, rather than the central dilemma of his existence. (May 1983).

I WOULDN'T HAVE MISSED IT FOR THE WORLD
Tracks: / I wouldn't have missed it for the world / It happens every time.
7" Single: Released Nov '81, on RCA, by BMG Records (UK). Deleted Nov '84. Catalogue no: **RCA 168**

MY HEART
Tracks: / My heart / Silent night.
7" Single: Released 20 Jun '80, on RCA, by BMG Records (UK). Deleted '83. Catalogue no: **PB 1952**

SMOKY MOUNTAIN RAIN
Tracks: / Smoky mountain rain / Crystal fallin' rain.
7" Single: Released Mar '81, on RCA, by BMG Records (UK). Deleted Mar '84. Catalogue no: **RCA 41**

STRANGER IN MY HOUSE
Tracks: / Stranger in my house.
7" Single: Released May '83, on RCA, by BMG Records (UK). Catalogue no: **RCA 338**

Milton

LOVE IS LIKE A VIOLENCE
Tracks: / Love is like a violence.
12" Single: Released Jan '85, on Embryo, by Embryo Records. Catalogue no: **CELE 2T**

Milton, Ted

ODE: OH TO BE SEEN THROUGH YOUR EYES
Tracks: / Ode: oh to be seen through your eyes.
12" Single: Released Nov '85, on Toeblock, Catalogue no: **TBL 001**

Mimi

GET READY
Tracks: / Get ready.
12" Single: Released '88, on Passion, by Skratch Records. Catalogue no: **PASH 69(12)**

MAN'S SO REAL
Tracks: / Man's so real.
12" Single: Released Mar '84, on Challenge, by Elite Records. Catalogue no: **TAL 8**

NO MORE
Tracks: / No more / No more (inst).
12" Single: Released Jun '87, on Big Top, by Big Top Records. Deleted '88. Catalogue no: **MBT 01**

TOUCH SENSITIVE
Tracks: / Touch sensitive.
12" Single: Released Jun '85, on Challenge, by Elite Records. Catalogue no: **TALL 16**

Mimms, Garnet

WHAT IT IS
Tracks: / What it is / What it is (instrumental).
7" Single: Released Jun '77, on Arista, by BMG Records (UK). Deleted '80. Catalogue no: **109**

Mind Over Muesli

JUST WALK AWAY
Tracks: / Just walk away / Just walk away (inst).
12" Single: Released 20 Jun '87, on GFM, Catalogue no: **GFMT 114**
7" Single: Released 20 Jun '87, on GFM, Catalogue no: **GFM 114**

Mindbenders

Biographical details: Wayne Fontana and The Mindbenders (comprising vocalist Wayne Fontana plus backing musicians Bob Land, Ric Rothwell and Eric Stewart) enjoyed major success during 1964-65 as part of the Manchester wing of the Merseybeat explosion. However, having reached No. 2 in Britain and No. 1 in America in early 1965 with *Game Of Love*, their next two singles were markedly less successful. With Fontana and the Mindbenders blaming each other, the vocalist and the group parted company at the end of the year.

While their ex-leader gained two UK Top 20 hits with *Come On Home* and *Pamela Pamela*, the Mindbenders fared better by reaching No. 2 on both sides of the Atlantic with *A Groovy Kind Of Love*. Confusingly, the combo recorded for the Fontana label.

A Groovy Kind Of Love was a pleasant beat ballad written by the US team Toni Wine and Carole Bayer (later known as Carole Bayer Sager). The group used the same source for *Ashes To Ashes*, which reached the UK No. 14 position in late 1966. However, the group's subsequent releases failed to sustain their success and the Mindbenders broke up in 1968.

Rothwell quit the music business to open an antique shop, and Land subsequently moved into the hi-fi business. Guitarist Eric Stewart, who had taken over from Wayne on vocals, embarked upon an illustrious career with Hotlegs and then 10CC. Bob MacDonald, 30 January 1986..

ASHES TO ASHES
Tracks: / Ashes to ashes.
7" Single: Released Jun '66, on Fontana, by Phonogram Ltd. Deleted '69. Catalogue no: **TF 731**

CAN'T LIVE WITH YOU (CAN'T LIVE WITHOUT YOU)
Tracks: / Can't live with you (can't live without you).
7" Single: Released May '66, on Fontana, by Phonogram Ltd. Catalogue no: **TF 697**

GROOVY KIND OF LOVE, A
Tracks: / Groovy kind of love.
7" Single: Released Jan '66, on Fontana, by Phonogram Ltd. Catalogue no: **TF 644**
7" Single: Released Jul '82, on Old Gold, by Old Gold Records. Catalogue no: **OG 9266**

LETTER, THE
Tracks: / Letter, The.
7" Single: Released Sep '67, on Fontana, by Phonogram Ltd. Deleted '70. Catalogue no: **TF 869**

Mindel, David

DISTRICT NURSE
Tracks: / District nurse.
7" Single: Released Mar '84, on Savoir Faire, Catalogue no: **FAIS 006**

Mineo, Sal

START MOVIN'
Tracks: / Start movin'.
7" Single: Released Jul '57, on Philips, by Phonogram Ltd. Deleted '60. Catalogue no: **PB 707**

Minerbi, Marcello

Biographical details: This Italian orchestra leader achieved a one-off UK chart entry in 1965, reaching No. 6 with his single *Zorba's Dance*. This was taken from 'Zorba The Greek', a movie released in the same year. The film theme became a US No. 11 hit for Herb Alpert ad the Tijuana Brass. Bob MacDonald, 30 January 1986..

ZORBA'S DANCE
Tracks: / Zorba's dance.
7" Single: Released Jul '82, on Old Gold, by Old Gold Records. Catalogue no: **OG 9055**
7" Single: Released Jul '65, on Durium, Deleted '68. Catalogue no: **DRS 54001**

Ming, Maurice

BUBBLING
Tracks: / Bubbling.
12" Single: Released Oct '84, on Tracey, Catalogue no: **TR 001**

Ming, Sexton

MAN WHO CREATED HIMSELF, THE
Special: Released Jun '88, on Hangman, by Hangman Records. Catalogue no: **WORDUP 002**

Minimal Compact

IMMIGRANTS SONGS
Tracks: / Immigrants songs.
Note: E.P.
12" Single: Released Feb '87, on Crammed Discs, by Crammed Discs. Catalogue no: **CRAM 050**

IT TAKES A LIFETIME
Tracks: / It takes a lifetime / Intrespection.
7" Single: Released May '83, on Crammed Discs, by Crammed Discs. Deleted '88. Catalogue no: **CRAM 7457**

MY WILL
Tracks: / My will.
7" Single: Released '88, on Crammed Discs, by Crammed Discs. Catalogue no: **CRAM 11457**

NEXT ONE IS REAL, THE (SINGLE)
Tracks: / Next one is real, The.
12" Single: Released Oct '84, on Crammed Discs, by Crammed Discs. Catalogue no: **CRAM 032**
7" Single: Released '88, on Crammed Discs, by Crammed Discs. Catalogue no: **CRAM 8457**

NIL NIL
Tracks: / Nil nil / Inner station / Traitor.
12" Single: Released Dec '87, on Materiali Sonori, Catalogue no: **MASO 20031**

SCENT OF LOVE
Tracks: / Scent of love.
7" Single: Released Sep '87, on Crammed Discs, by Crammed Discs. Catalogue no: **CRAM 14457**

LIZA MINNELLI - LOSING MY MIND (Released on Epic)

Minimal Man

MOCK HONEYMOON
Tracks: / Mock honeymoon.
12" Single: Released 3 Jun '87, on Play It Again Sam(Belgium), by Play It Again Sam (Belgium). Catalogue no: **BIAS 059**

SEX TEACHER
Tracks: / Sex teacher.
12" Single: Released Jan '86, on Play It Again Sam(Belgium), by Play It Again Sam (Belgium). Catalogue no: **BIAS 022**

Mini-Mode

MAKING DEALS
Tracks: / Making deals.
12" Single: Released May '89, on Escalator, Catalogue no: **ESCA 4501**

Miniplot

MINIPLOT
Tracks: / Miniplot: *Various artists*.
Note: Best of 'Miniplot' LP with Sonic Yoof, Das Damen and two others.
CD 5": Released Jul '89, on SST (USA), by SST Records (USA). Catalogue no: **SSTCD 234**

Minipops

ADVENTURES OF SANTA CLAUS
Tracks: / Adventures of Santa Claus / Christmas Scenes / Ring a bell for Christmas / Rock baby Jesus.
7" Single: Released Dec '86, on Creole, by Creole Records. Catalogue no: **CR 95**

SONGS FOR CHRISTMAS '88
Tracks: / Songs for Christmas 88.
7" Single: Released Dec '88, on Bright, by Bright Records. Catalogue no: **BUB 12**

SONGS FOR XMAS 88
12" Single: Released Dec '88, on Bright, by Bright Records. Catalogue no: **BULB 12**

THANKS FOR GIVING US CHRISTMAS
Tracks: / Thanks for giving us Christmas / Man in red, The / Christmas time around the world / Shine on bright.
7" Single: Released Dec '87, on Bulb, Catalogue no: **BULB 9**

VIDEO KILLED THE RADIO STAR
Tracks: / Video killed the radio star / Stupid ....
7" Single: Released Nov '81, on RCA, by BMG Records (UK). Catalogue no: **RCA 167**

WHEN YOU WISH UPON A STAR
Tracks: / When you wish upon a star / Why can't we love each other.
7" Single: Released Jan '84, on Bright, by Bright Records. Catalogue no: **BULB 5**

Minister Of Noise

ONE TRACK SYSTEM
Tracks: / One track system / Rock real show.
12" Single: Released Jul '89, on Sinister Groove, Catalogue no: **TAO 002**

Ministry

Biographical details: Al Jourgensen and Ministry first hit the map in 1982 with a song called *Cold life*, released on the independent Chicago label, Wax Trax and in Britain by Beggar's Banquet off-shoot, Situation 2. Almost against Jourgensen's will, he found he had a hit on his hands. Though still in his early twenties, Al had already become disillusioned with the music bis after time he spent playing in a Chicago-based group called Special Effect. Special Effect were courted by several large American record companies, but Jourgensen had had enough - he retired to a life of deejaying and managing a record store. And of course banging out to the odd song, but Wax Trax supremo Jim Nash, heard a tape of *Cold Life* and insisted turning it into a hit single. Following the success of *Cold life* on the American Rockpool chart, Arista moved in for the kill and signed them up. They have also released singles *Work for love* and *I wanted to tell her*. (Arista, Feb '84).

COLD LIFE
Tracks: / Cold life.
12" Single: Released Mar '82, on Situation 2, by Beggars Banquet Records. Catalogue no: **SIT 17T**

I WANTED TO TELL HER
Tracks: / I wanted to tell her.
7" Single: Released '83, on Arista, by BMG Records (UK). Deleted '86. Catalogue no: **ARIST 533**

NATURE OF LOVE
Tracks: / Nature of love.
12" Single: Released Oct '85, on Wax Trax, by Wax Trax Records. Catalogue no: **WAXUK 009**

REVENGE
Tracks: / Revenge.
7" Single: Released '83, on Arista, by BMG Records (UK). Deleted '86. Catalogue no: **ARIST 549**
12" Single: Released '83, on Arista, by BMG Records (UK). Deleted '86. Catalogue no: **ARIST 12549**

Ministry of Love

BURNIN' AND LOOTIN
Tracks: / Brothers & sisters / John y na blame rasta / Burnin' and lootin'.
12" Single: Released Jun '86, on Midnight Music, by Midnight Music Records. Catalogue no: **DONG 22**

Mink

YOU WERE THE ONE TOO LATE
Tracks: / You were the one too late.
12" Single: Released Jul '85, on Streetwave, Catalogue no: **MKHAN 49**

Mink Deville

EACH WORDS A BEAT OF MY HEART
Tracks: / Each words a beat of my heart / River of tears / Harlem nocturne / Maybe tomorrow.
12" Single: Released Apr '84, on Atlantic, by WEA Records. Catalogue no: **A 9750 T**
7" Single: Released Apr '84, on Atlantic, by WEA Records. Catalogue no: **A 9750**

HEART OF THE CITY
Tracks: / Heart of the city.
7" Single: Released Jun '85, on Polydor, by Polydor Ltd. Catalogue no: **POSP 745**
12" Single: Released Jun '85, on Polydor, by Polydor Ltd. Catalogue no: **POSPX 745**

I MUST BE DREAMING
Tracks: / I must be dreaming.

KYLIE MINOGUE & JASON DONOVAN - ESPECIALLY FOR YOU (Released on PWL)

12" Single: Released Oct '85, on Polydor, by Polydor Ltd. Catalogue no: **POSPX 773**
7" Single: Released Oct '85, on Polydor, by Polydor Ltd. Catalogue no: **POSP 773**

SPANISH STROLL
Tracks: / Spanish stroll.
7" Single: Released Aug '77, on Capitol, by EMI Records. Deleted '80. Catalogue no: **CLX 103**
7" Single: Released Jul '84, on EMI Golden 45's, by EMI Records. Catalogue no: **G 4527**

THIS MUST BE THE NIGHT
Tracks: / This must be the night / Mixed up, shook up girl / Lipstick traces.
7" Single: Released Apr '80, on Capitol, by EMI Records. Deleted '83. Catalogue no: **CL 16134**

Minnelli, Liza

Biographical details: This American actress and singer followed in the career footsteps of her legendary mother, the late Judy Garland. The triumph of Minelli's career was the 1972 movie musical 'Cabaret', whose soundtrack LP reached No. 13 on the UK chart in 1973. Also in the same year, her album *Liza With a Z* was a Top 10 item; this was a TV soundtrack. In the following year, Liza performed some vocals on Alice Cooper's *Muscle Of Love* LP. Bob MacDonald, 30 January 1986..

DON'T DROP BOMBS
Tracks: / Don't drop bombs / Don't drop bombs (instrumental).
CD 5": Released Sep '89, on Epic, by CBS Records. Catalogue no: **ZEE C2**
12" Single: Released Sep '89, on Epic, by CBS Records. Catalogue no: **ZEE T2**
7" Single: Released Sep '89, on Epic, by CBS Records. Catalogue no: **ZEE 2**
7" Pic: Released Sep '89, on Epic, by CBS Records. Catalogue no: **ZEE QT2**
Cassingle: Released Sep '89, on Epic, by CBS Records. Catalogue no: **ZEE M2**
7" Single: Released Sep '89, on Epic, by CBS Records. Catalogue no: **ZEE P2**

LOSING MY MIND (See panel on previous page)
Tracks: / Losing my mind / Tonight is for ever / Losing my mind (extended remix) (Only on 12" and CD single.).
CD 5": Released Jul '89, on Epic, by CBS Records. Catalogue no: **ZEEC 1**
7" Single: Released Jul '89, on Epic, by CBS Records. Catalogue no: **ZEE 1**
12" Single: Released Jul '89, on Epic, by CBS Records. Catalogue no: **ZEET 1**
Cassingle: Released Jul '89, on Epic, by CBS Records. Catalogue no: **655144**

Minnie & The Metros

CHARLIE'S ANGELS
Tracks: / Charlie's angels / Don't say you love me.
7" Single: Released May '81, on EMI, by EMI Records. Deleted May '84. Catalogue no: **EMI 5191**

Minnypops

DOLPHIN SPURT
Tracks: / Dolphin spurt.
7" Single: Released Mar '81, on Factory (1), by Factory Records. Catalogue no: **FAC 31**

EIN KUS
Tracks: / Ein kus.
7" Single: Released Jun '84, on Les Temps Modernes, Catalogue no: **CSBT 4/5**

FOOTSTEPS
Tracks: / Footsteps.
7" Single: Released Jun '79, on Pleurex, Deleted '84. Catalogue no: **AO 5**

Mino

KAMA SUTRA
Tracks: / Kama sutra / All because of reggae.
7" Single: Released Feb '81, on Edge, Deleted Feb '84. Catalogue no: **EDGE 9**
12" Single: Released Feb '81, on Edge, Deleted Feb '84. Catalogue no: **EDGE 9T**

Minogue, Kylie

ESPECIALLY FOR YOU (See panel above)
Tracks: / Especially for you.
7" Single: Released Dec '88, on PWL, by PWL Records. Catalogue no: **PWL 24**
12" Single: Released Dec '88, on PWL, by PWL Records. Catalogue no: **PWLT 24**

GOT TO BE CERTAIN
Tracks: / Got to be certain.
12" Single: Released May '88, on PWL, by PWL Records. Catalogue no: **PWLT 12**
CD 5": Released May '88, on PWL, by PWL Records. Catalogue no: **PWCD 12**
7" Single: Released May '88, on PWL, by PWL Records. Catalogue no: **PWL 12**

HAND ON YOUR HEART
Tracks: / Hand on your heart.
Cassingle: Released Apr '89, on PWL, by PWL Records. Catalogue no: **PWMC 35**
7" Single: Released Apr '89, on PWL, by PWL Records. Catalogue no: **PWL 35**
12" Single: Released Apr '89, on PWL, by PWL Records. Catalogue no: **PWLT 35**

I SHOULD BE SO LUCKY (See panel opposite)
Tracks: / I should be so lucky / I should be so lucky (inst).
7" Single: Released Jan '88, on PWL, by PWL Records. Catalogue no: **PWL 8**

JE NE SAIS PAS POURQUOI
Tracks: / Je ne sais pas pourquoi / Made in heaven.
7" Single: Released Oct '88, on PWL, by PWL Records. Catalogue no: **PWL 21**
12" Single: Released Oct '88, on PWL, by PWL Records. Catalogue no: **PWLT 21**

LOCOMOTION, THE
Tracks: / Locomotion, The.
7" Single: Released Jul '88, on PWL, by PWL Records. Catalogue no: **PWL 14**
12" Single: Released Jul '88, on PWL, by PWL Records. Catalogue no: **PWLT 14**

WOULDN'T CHANGE A THING
Tracks: / Wouldn't change a thing.

CD 5": Released 24 Jul '89, on PWL, by PWL Records. Catalogue no: **PWLCD 42**
Cassingle: Released 24 Jul '89, on PWL, by PWL Records. Catalogue no: **PWLMC 42**
7" Single: Released 24 Jul '89, on PWL, by PWL Records. Catalogue no: **PWL 42**
12" Single: Released 24 Jul '89, on PWL, by PWL Records. Catalogue no: **PWLT 42**

Minor Classics

SIGN LANGUAGE
Tracks: / Sign language / This side of paradise.
7" Single: Released Mar '82, on Chiswick Records, Catalogue no: **DICE 4**

Minor Detail

TAKE IT AGAIN
Tracks: / Take it again / 20th century.
7" Single: Released Mar '84, on Polydor, by Polydor Ltd. Catalogue no: **POSP 679**

Minor Threat

SALAD DAYS
Tracks: / Salad days.
7" Single: on Dischord, by Dischord Records. Catalogue no: **DISCHORD 15**

Minott, Echo

BUBBLIN' SHE WANT
Tracks: / Bubblin' she want.
12" Single: Released Oct '84, on Black Joy, Catalogue no: **DH 834**

HOLD ME BABY
Tracks: / Hold me baby.
12" Single: Released Dec '87, on Taurus, Catalogue no: **TRS 006**

I AM BACK
Tracks: / I am back.
7" Single: Released Jan '89, on Jammy's, Catalogue no: **Unknown**

MY FAT MILLIE
Tracks: / My fat Millie.
12" Single: Released Jul '84, on Fu-Manchu, Catalogue no: **TC 8684**

ONE MAN ONE
Tracks: / One man one.
12" Single: Released Mar '86, on Twin Explosion, Catalogue no: **TE 101**

SWEET DREAMS
Tracks: / Sweet dreams / Bam bam.
12" Single: Released Dec '84, on Greensleeves, by Greensleeves Records. Catalogue no: **GRED 165**

WHAT THE HELL
Tracks: / Don't touch boops / One scotch / What the hell.
12" Single: Released Jul '86, on Unity, Catalogue no: **UN 020**

WHEN MY LITTLE GIRL IS SMILING
Tracks: / When my little girl is smiling.
7" Single: Released Apr '89, on Blue Trac, by Blue Trac Records. Catalogue no: **BTRD 037**

Minott, Robert

ALL I HAVE IS LOVE
Tracks: / All I have is love.
7" Single: Released Oct '88, on Wackies, Catalogue no: **JACK 140**

I NEED YOUR LOVE
Tracks: / I need your love.
7" Single: Released 22 May '89, on Fameous, Catalogue no: **UNKNOWN**

Minott, Sugar

Biographical details: This Jamaican reggae singer and songwriter was born in Lincoln Minott in Kingston. He bagan his career in a group called the African Brothers in the mid-Seventies, who enjoyed two JA hit singles with *Party Night* and *Youth Of Today*. After the band split in 1977, Sugar sang and played sessions for other reggae artists and also embarked on a solo career. In 1978 Minott founded his own Black Roots label, to further his own career and that of other up and coming talent.

Despite the existance of his label, Sugar's records have appeared in Britain on a wide variety of labels; and like most Jamaican reggae artists, his release schedule is frantically prolific. Thus, a Sugar Minott collector has the twin trouble of keeping up with a mass of product coming at him from all directions. Minott's first British single *Hard Time Pressure* reached the top of the UK regae chart in 1979. The biggest success of Sugar's career occurred in 1981, when his revival of an old Jackson Five track called *Good Thing Going* enjoyed an extended run at the top of the reggae listings and became a UK No. 4 pop smash. This was a classic example of lovers' rock, the mellow reggae sub-genre at which Sugar excelled. He has also recorded many political tracks. He remains one of reggae's most repected vocalists. Bob MacDonald, 30 January 1986..

AFTER THE STORM
Tracks: / After the storm.
12" Single: Released Nov '88, on Taurus, Catalogue no: **UNKNOWN**

ALL DAY & NIGHT
Tracks: / All day & night.
12" Single: Released Aug '85, on Burning Sounds, by Burning Sounds Records. Catalogue no: **BSD 063**

ANOTHER MAN'S GIRL
Tracks: / Another man's girl.
12" Single: Released Aug '88, on Skengdon, Catalogue no: **SKD 082**

BOSS BOSS
Tracks: / Boss boss.
12" Single: Released May '85, on Kings & Lions, Catalogue no: **KLSM 004**

BUY OFF THE BAR
Tracks: / Buy off the bar.
12" Single: Released '89, on Power House, Catalogue no: **PHT 25**

BUY OUT THE BEAR
Tracks: / Buy out the bear.
12" Single: Released Oct '83, on Black Roots, Catalogue no: **LML 13358**

CAN YOU REMEMBER
Tracks: / Can you remember.
12" Single: Released May '83, on BFM, Catalogue no: **BFM 50**

CAN'T STOP LOVE IT
Tracks: / Can't stop love it.
12" Single: Released Jan '89, on Exterminator, Catalogue no: **VPRD 392**

CHRISTMAS HOLIDAY
Tracks: / Christmas holiday.
12" Single: Released Dec '84, on Tom Tom, Catalogue no: **Unknown**

CHRISTMAS TIME
Tracks: / Christmas time.
7" Single: Released Nov '82, on Black Roots, Catalogue no: **BR 7001**

COME AGAIN

KYLIE MINOGUE - WOULD'NT CHANGE A THING (Released on PWL)

Tracks: / Dubbing a storm / Come again.
12" Single: Released Jun '86, on SMP (2), Catalogue no: **SMP 003**

DANCE HALL WE DEH
Tracks: / Dancehall we deh.
12" Single: Released Jun '84, on Tads, Catalogue no: **TRD 51684**

DEVIL'S PICKNEY
Tracks: / Devil's pickney.
12" Single: Released Dec '83, on Taxi (1), Catalogue no: **IPR 2068**

DOING THE DUB
Tracks: / Doing the dub.
12" Single: Released Jun '88, on Wackies, Catalogue no: **NJ 22**

DON'T CRY
Tracks: / Don't cry.
12" Single: Released Jan '85, on W.O.W., Catalogue no: **WOW 101**

DON'T DISTRESS
Tracks: / Don't distress / Heard about my love.
7" Single: Released Apr '89, on Greensleeves, by Greensleeves Records. Catalogue no: **GRED 237**

EASY SQUEEZE
Tracks: / Easy squeeze.
12" Single: Released Jun '82, on Black Roots, Catalogue no: **BRST 10 12**
7" Single: Released Jun '82, on Black Roots, Catalogue no: **BRST 10**

FALSE RUMOUR
Tracks: / False rumour / Struggle.
12" Single: Released Oct '82, on Exile, Catalogue no: **EX 009**

FUNKING SONG
Tracks: / Funking song.
12" Single: Released Nov '88, on Greensleeves, by Greensleeves Records. Catalogue no: **GRED 231**

GHETTO-OLOGY
Tracks: / Ghetto-ology.
12" Single: on Trojan, by Trojan Records. Deleted May '88. Catalogue no: **TRT 9069**

GIMME THE TU SHUNG PENG
Tracks: / Gimme the tu shung peng.
12" Single: Released Jun '85, on SMJ, Catalogue no: **SMJ 001**

GOOD THING GOING
Tracks: / Good thing going.
7" Single: Released Mar '81, on RCA, by BMG Records (UK). Catalogue no: **RCA 58**
12" Single: Released Mar '81, on RCA, by BMG Records (UK). Catalogue no: **RCAT 58**

HARBOUR SHARK
Tracks: / Harbour shark.
12" Single: Released Apr '83, on Guidance, Catalogue no: **VPRD 119**

HEARTBREAKER
Tracks: / Heartbreaker / Up to date.
12" Single: Released Feb '83, on Black Roots, Catalogue no: **BRT 1003**

HERBMAN HUSTLING (12")
Tracks: / Herbman hustling.
12" Single: Released Dec '84, on Black Roots, Catalogue no: **LML 201 284**

HI, HELLO
Tracks: / Hi, hello / Sax man special.
12" Single: Released May '85, on Wackies, Catalogue no: **WACKIES 965**
12" Single: Released May '85, on Kings & Lions, Catalogue no: **KLSM 005**

HIGH UP ABOVE
Tracks: / High up above.
12" Single: Released Jul '83, on S & G (2), Catalogue no: **SG 29**

HOW COULD I LET YOU GET AWAY
Tracks: / How could I let you get away / Runaway version.
12" Single: Released Mar '83, on Thompson Sound, Catalogue no: **TS 2**

I KNOW THEM LOVE IT
Tracks: / I know them love it.
12" Single: Released Jul '85, on Striker Lee, Catalogue no: **BL 25**

I MAN HAVE NO LUCK IN GAMBLING
Tracks: / I man have no luck in gambling.
12" Single: Released Aug '84, on Music Rock, Catalogue no: **ROCK 001**

I REMEMBER MAMA
Tracks: / Sound design / I remember mama.
7" Single: Released Mar '85, on Sound Design Studio, Catalogue no: **SDS 001**
12" Single: Released Nov '85, on Sound Design Studio, Catalogue no: **SDS 121**

I WANNA GIVE MY LOVE
Tracks: / I wanna give my love.
12" Single: Released May '84, on M&M, by M&M Music Company. Catalogue no: **MM 002**

IN A DIS YAH TIME
Tracks: / In a dis yah time.
12" Single: Released Mar '82, on Live & Love, Catalogue no: **LLV 201**

INDECA
Tracks: / Indeca.
12" Single: Released Sep '87, on Youth Promotion, Catalogue no: **YP 001**

IT WAS GOOD IT WAS BAD
Tracks: / It was good it was bad.
12" Single: Released Feb '85, on Hitbound, Catalogue no: **JJ 222**

IT'S ALL IN THE GAME
Tracks: / It's all in the game.
12" Single: Released Oct '86, on Revue, by Creole Records. Catalogue no: **REV 036T**
7" Single: Released Oct '86, on Revue, by Creole Records. Catalogue no: **REV 736**

JAH LOVE IS PEOPLE
Tracks: / Jah love is people.
12" Single: Released Dec '82, on Music Works, Catalogue no: **MWRT 1294**

JAMMING IN THE STREET (SINGLE)
Tracks: / Jamming in the street.
12" Single: Released Jun '85, on Black Roots, Catalogue no: **Unknown**
12" Single: Released May '84, on Wackies, Catalogue no: **WACKIES 717**

JUST DON'T WANNA BE LONELY
Tracks: / Just don't want to be lonely / Sing a happy song.
12" Single: Released Mar '84, on Black Roots, Catalogue no: **BR 181 261**

LEVEL VIBES
Tracks: / Level vibes.
12" Single: Released Sep '83, on Tads, Catalogue no: **TRD 8754**

LICK SHOT
Tracks: / Lick shot.
12" Single: Released Oct '84, on Brand X, Catalogue no: **BPRD 200**

LIKE A CHILD
Tracks: / Like a child.
12" Single: Released Jan '88, on Josiah, Catalogue no: **KJ 002**

LOOKING FOR A HOME (EP)
Tracks: / Looking for a home.
7" Single: Released Aug '82, on Future Times, Catalogue no: **FT 001**

LOVE MACHINE
Tracks: / Love machine.
12" Single: Released Mar '89, on Bun Gem, Catalogue no: **BG 0037**

LOVE ME WITH FEELING
Tracks: / Love me with feeling.
12" Single: Released Nov '88, on Phaze 1, Catalogue no: **PRF 4**

LOVERS RACE
Tracks: / Lover's race / Mix-up.
10" single: Released Dec '82, on Black Roots, Catalogue no: **BRT 02**

LOVING YOU
Tracks: / Loving you / Tip of my tongue.
12" Single: Released May '85, on EAD, Catalogue no: **GEM 0023**

MEMORIES (MEDLEY)
Tracks: / Memories (medley).
12" Single: Released Nov '85, on Striker Lee, Catalogue no: **SLD 02**

MIND BLOWING DECISIONS
Tracks: / Mind blowing decisions / Brother man.
12" Single: Released Jun '85, on W.O.W., Catalogue no: **WOW 102**
7" Single: Released Jun '85, on W.O.W., Catalogue no: **WOW 7102**

MORE WE ARE TOGETHER
Tracks: / More we are together.
12" Single: Released Jul '82, on Black Roots, Catalogue no: **BRD 02**

MR. DC
Tracks: / Mr. DC.
12" Single: Released May '82, on KG, Catalogue no: **KG 003**

NEVER CAN SAY GOODBYE
Tracks: / Never can say goodbye / Singer style.
12" Single: Released Feb '83, on Carousel (1), by Carousel Records. Catalogue no: **CAR 5**

NEVER MY LOVE
Tracks: / Never my love.
7" Single: Released Oct '81, on RCA, by BMG Records (UK). Deleted '84. Catalogue no: **RCA 138**

NEW GIRLS
Tracks: / New girls.
12" Single: Released Nov '82, on Black Roots, Catalogue no: **BR 008**

NO WICKED
Tracks: / No wicked.
7" Single: Released Jul '87, on Charm, by Charm Records. Catalogue no: **CRT 11**

NOW THAT I'VE FOUND YOU
Tracks: / Now that I've found you.
12" Single: Released Dec '84, on Scom, Catalogue no: **BD 004**

NOW WE KNOW
Tracks: / Now we know.
12" Single: Released Jun '84, on Black Roots, Catalogue no: **BR 181 264**

RUN COME
Tracks: / Run come.
12" Single: Released Sep '85, on Hawkeye, by Hawkeye Records. Catalogue no: **HD 64**

SANDY
Tracks: / Sandy.
12" Single: Released 30 May '89, on Rub A Dub, Catalogue no: **KR 001**

SAVE YOUR LOVING FOR ME
Tracks: / Ain't nobody moves me.
12" Single: Released Mar '86, on Island, by Island Records. Deleted Jul '87. Catalogue no: **12IS 275**

SEE ME YAH
Tracks: / See me yah.
12" Single: Released Nov '85, on Omega, Deleted Jun '89. Catalogue no: **OMS 201**

SHE JUST A BUBBLE
Tracks: / She just a bubble / Bubble up dubba - S M band.
7" Single: Released Jan '88, on Rockers Plantation, Catalogue no: **PL 23**

SHERIFF JOHN BROWN
Tracks: / Sheriff John Brown.
12" Single: Released Dec '87, on Black Victory, Catalogue no: **ADM 095**

SMILE
Tracks: / Smile.
12" Single: Released Feb '89, on Steely & Cleevie, Catalogue no: **VPRD 412**

SO MUCH TROUBLE
Tracks: / So much trouble.
12" Single: Released Dec '84, on Vena, Catalogue no: **VEN 701**

SOMETHING WRONG
12" Single: Released '87, on Uptempo, Deleted Jun '89. Catalogue no: **TEMP 003**

STICK & STONE
Tracks: / Stick & stone.
12" Single: Released Sep '85, on Crystal, by President Records. Catalogue no: **BM 006**

STILL IN LOVE WITH ME
Tracks: / Still in love with me.
12" Single: Released Feb '89, on Techniques, Catalogue no: **WRT 901**

TAKE A SET
Tracks: / Take a set / No way.
12" Single: Released Sep '83, on Wackies, Catalogue no: **WACKIES 712**

THAT WAY YOU MAKE ME FEEL
Tracks: / That way you make me feel.
7" Single: Released Jun '88, on L & M, Catalogue no: **LM 0002**

THEY HAVE TO COME WE
Tracks: / They have to come we.
12" Single: Released Jun '85, on Striker Lee, Catalogue no: **BL 22**

TOO MUCH BACKBITING
Tracks: / Too much backbiting.
12" Single: Released Sep '82, on J & J, Catalogue no: **JJ 046**

UPON THE LEVEL
Tracks: / Upon the level.
12" Single: Released Oct '84, on African Museum, Catalogue no: **BTR 007**

WE HAVE FI LIVE
Tracks: / We have fi live.
12" Single: Released Dec '83, on Live & Learn (USA), by Live & Learn Records (USA). Catalogue no: **LL 106**

WHAT A FEELING
Tracks: / Riot inna Brixton / Candy man / What a feeling.
12" Single: Released Feb '86, on CSA, by CSA Records. Deleted '88. Catalogue no: **12CSA 509**

WHO CORK THE DANCE
Tracks: / Who cork the dance.
12" Single: Released May '85, on Kings & Lions, Catalogue no: **KLSM 002**

WHOLE HEAP A MAN
Tracks: / Whole heap a man.
12" Single: Released Feb '89, on Steely & Cleevie, Catalogue no: **VPRD 413**

WICKED A GO FEEL IT (SINGLE)
12" Single: Released Nov '83, on Wackies, Catalogue no: **DISCO 589**

YOU LICK ME FIRST
Tracks: / Insert kitchen / You lick me first.
7" Single: Released Jul '86, on Live & Learn (USA), by Live & Learn Records (USA). Catalogue no: **LLDIS 0013**

YOUR LOVE
Tracks: / Your love.
12" Single: Released Nov '86, on Germaine, Catalogue no: **DGT 18**

Mint Addicts

CHICKEN CHASING
Tracks: / Chicken chasing.
7" Single: Released Oct '87, on Constrictor, by Constrictor Records (Germany). Catalogue no: **CON 00025**

Mint Juleps

DOCKLANDS
Tracks: / Docklands / Under pressure.
12" Single: Released May '88, on Stiff, by Stiff Records. Catalogue no: **BUYIT 264**
7" Single: Released May '88, on Stiff, by Stiff Records. Catalogue no: **BUY 264**

EVERY KINDA PEOPLE
Tracks: / Every kinda people / Best of both worlds / Ain't seen nothing yet (*Exrta track on 12").
Note: *Ain't seen nothing yet* on 12" only.
12" Single: Released May '87, on Stiff, by Stiff Records. Catalogue no: **BUYIT 257**
7" Single: Released May '87, on Stiff, by Stiff Records. Catalogue no: **BUY 257**

GIRL TO THE POWER OF SIX, THE
Tracks: / Girl to the power of 6, The / Set me free.
7" Single: Released Aug '87, on Stiff, by Stiff Records. Catalogue no: **BUY 263**
12" Single: Released Aug '87, on Stiff, by Stiff Records. Catalogue no: **BUYIT 263**

ONLY LOVE CAN BREAK YOUR HEART
Tracks: / Moving closer / Shout (Extra track on 12" version only).
7" Single: Released Feb '86, on Stiff, by Stiff Records. Catalogue no: **BUY 241**
12" Single: Released Feb '86, on Stiff, by Stiff Records. Catalogue no: **BUYIT 241**

Minus One

WHY
Tracks: / Why.
12" Single: Released Jun '89, on Premiere UK, Catalogue no: **ERET 505**
7" Single: Released Jun '89, on Premiere UK, Catalogue no: **ERE 505**

Minutemen

OK ALRIGHT
Tracks: / OK alright.
12" Single: Released Sep '89, on Music Man, Catalogue no: **MMPT 12007**
7" Single: Released Sep '89, on Music Man, Catalogue no: **MMPS 7007**

PARANOID TIME (EP)
Tracks: / Paranoid time.
CD 5": Released Dec '88, on SST (USA), by SST Records (USA). Catalogue no: **SSTCD 002**
12" Single: Released Mar '83, on SST (USA), by SST Records (USA). Catalogue no: **SST 2**

TOUR SPIEL (LIVE EP)
7" Single: Released Apr '85, on Homestead, Catalogue no: **REFLEX L**

Miracle

AFRICA
Tracks: / Africa / Eritrea.
7" Single: Released Mar '88, on Round, Catalogue no: **TRR 786**
12" Single: Released Mar '88, on Round, Catalogue no: **12TRR 786**

Miracle Legion

BACKYARD
Tracks: / Until she talks.
7" Single: Released Feb '86, Catalogue no: **SURF 112**

YOU'RE THE ONE
Tracks: / You're the one.
7" Single: Released Feb '89, on Rough Trade, by Rough Trade Records. Catalogue no: **RT 226**
12" Single: Released Feb '89, on Rough Trade, by Rough Trade Records. Catalogue no: **RTT 226**

YOU'RE THE ONE LEE
Tracks: / You're the one Lee.
7" Single: Released Apr '89, on Rough Trade, by Rough Trade Records. Catalogue no: **RTT 226**

Miracles

Biographical details: After a decade of stardom as Smokey Robinson and the Miracles, this American soul vocal group began life afresh in 1972 when Billy Griffin replaced the departing Smokey as leader. .
Griffin was an excellent singer, but the group were lost without Smokey Robinson The Miracles' career was generally disappointing in musical and commercial terms, except for two flashes of light. The firstwas *Do It Baby,* which reached No. 13 on the US

singles chart in 1974. The second was *Love Machine*, a pulsating funk throbber that was perfect for the dance floors. This single was an American No. 1 smash in 1976, and reached No. 3 in Britain; few listeners or dancers were aware that it was part of a concept album called *City Of Angels* examining the Hollywood star system, for which the group members themselves wrote all the songs.

After *Love Machine* the Miracles vanishes into surprisingly rapid obscurity, a situation accelerated by their disasterous decision to leave Motown in favour of Columbia Records.

With the group defunct, Griffin launched a fairly successful solo career in early 1983. Bob MacDonald, 30 January 1986..

LOVE MACHINE
Tracks: / 25 miles / Love machine.
7" Single: Released Oct '81, on Motown, by BMG Records (UK). Catalogue no: **TMG 1015**

LOVE MACHINE (PART 1)
Tracks: / Love machine (part 1).
7" Single: Released Apr '88, on Motown, by BMG Records (UK). Catalogue no: **ZB 41919**

Mirage

Biographical details: This American group of one-hit wonders (to date) were led by Roy Gayle, and made the U.K. singles charts in January 1984 with *I Give Me The Night'D.* (Robert Cohen, 1/5/87).

Mirage are a band of studio session vocalists and musicians under the supervision of keyboards/synthesiser player and producer Nigel Wright (of Shakatak fame). During the Eighties Mirage have been doing on singles what Music For Pleasure and other budget-price LP companies gave been doing for many years on albums - imitating contemporary chart artists. The first of these 'substitute' singles to reach the UK chart was *Give Me The Night*, a George Benson soundalike medley featuring the voice of Roy Gayle; this peaked at No. 49 in 1984. Mirage then tried an Earth, Wind and Fire medley but this did not reach the chart, possibly because EWF had not achieved any success in the preceding year. In 1985 the studio team had better luck with a Madonna montage, featuring the hits of the hottest star of the day. Bob MacDonald, 30 January 1986..

AS FROM NOW
Tracks: / As from now / Luckiest people.
12" Single: Released Jun '82, on Copasetic, by Copasetic Records. Catalogue no: **COP DIS 6**
12" Single: Released Dec '81, on Solid Gold (1), by Creole Records. Deleted '86. Catalogue no: **COPD 156**
7" Single: Released Jun '82, on Copasetic, by Copasetic Records. Catalogue no: **COP 005**

DRUGBUSTIN' MUSIC-POP MUSIC
Tracks: / Drugbustin' - music pop music.
12" Single: Released Nov '85, on Debut, by Skratch Records. Catalogue no: **DEBT 10(12)**

GET DOWN ON IT
Tracks: / Get down on it / Our song.
12" Single: Released Mar '85, on Debut, by Skratch Records. Catalogue no: **DEBT 01(12)**

GIVE ME THE NIGHT (George Benson Medley)
Tracks: / Give me the night.
7" Single: Released '88, on Passion, by Skratch Records. Catalogue no: **PASH 15**
12" Single: Released Dec '83, on Passion, by Skratch Records. Catalogue no: **PASH 15(12)**

HOUSE ATTACK
Tracks: / House attack.
CD 5": Released Feb '89, on Debut, by Skratch Records. Catalogue no: **DEBTX 3062**
12" Single: Released Feb '89, on Debut, by Skratch Records. Catalogue no: **DEBT 3062**

INTO THE GROOVE MEDLEY (Madonna medley)
Tracks: / Into the groove medley.
12" Single: Released Oct '85, on Debut, by Skratch Records. Catalogue no: **DEBTX 09(12)X**
7" Single: Released Oct '85, on Debut, by Skratch Records. Catalogue no: **DEBT 09X**

JACK MIX Featuring Jack your body
Tracks: / Jack mix (featuring jack your body) / Showing out / Move on out.
12" Single: Released Feb '87, on Debut, by Skratch Records. Catalogue no: **DEBTX 3015**

JACK MIX 7
Tracks: / Jack mix 7.
12" Single: Released 5 Mar '88, on Debut, by Skratch Records. Catalogue no: **DEBTX 3042**

JACK MIX II
Tracks: / Jack mix II / Move on out.
12" Single: Released Apr '87, on Debut, by Skratch Records. Catalogue no: **DEBTX 3022**

JACK MIX III
Note: Feat. Living in a box/Respectable/Male stripper/Can U dance/Jack your body/Showing out/Axel F/Jackin'/Do it properly/House Nation/Under water/Let yourself go/Move on out. Yes! All your favourites transformed into one interminable jack mix!
12" Single: Released Jun '87, on Debut, by Skratch Records. Catalogue no: **DEBTR 3022**

JACK MIX IV
Tracks: / Jack mix IV / Here it is get into it.
7" Single: Released Oct '87, on Debut, by Skratch Records. Catalogue no: **DEBT 3035**
12" Single: Released Oct '87, on Debut, by Skratch Records. Catalogue no: **DEBTX 3035**

JACK MIX V
Tracks: / Jack mix V / Jack mix.
12" Single: Released '88, on Debut, by Skratch Records. Catalogue no: **DEBTR 3035**

LET'S GROOVE (Earth Wind & Fire medley)
Tracks: / Let's groove.
7" Single: Released Mar '84, on Passion, by Skratch Records. Catalogue no: **PASH 20**
12" Single: Released Mar '84, on Passion, by Skratch Records. Catalogue no: **PASH 20(12)**

NO MORE NO WAR
Tracks: / No more no war.
7" Single: Released Jul '85, on Proto, by Proto Records. Catalogue no: **ENA 128**
12" Single: Released Jul '85, on Proto, by Proto Records. Catalogue no: **ENAT 128**

PUSH THE BEAT
Tracks: / Push the beat / Big heat.
Note: "A side comprises of a medley of 14 songs on 7" - 21 on 12". These include, Beat Dis, Push Beat, Just a Mirage, Let's all chant, I want you back, Set it off, Theme from S-Express, Bust this house down, Doctorin' the house, Rok da house, Tired of getting pushed around, Bass (How low can you go), Got to be certain, That's the way it is." (Music Week, June 1988)
12" Single: Released Jun '88, on Debut, by Skratch Records. Catalogue no: **DEBTX 3050**
7" Single: Released Jun '88, on Debut, by Skratch Records. Catalogue no: **DEBT 3050**

SERIOUS MIX
Note: Inc:Serious/Keep your eye on me/What have you done for me lately/Diamons/Looking for a new love/Chicago/Chicago song/Down in one
12" Single: Released Jul '87, on Debut, by Skratch Records. Catalogue no: **DEBTX 3028**
7" Single: Released Jul '87, on Debut, by Skratch Records. Catalogue no: **DEBT 3028**
12" Single: Released Aug '87, on Debut, by Skratch Records. Catalogue no: **DEBTR 3028**

Mirah

MYSTERY MAN
Tracks: / Mystery man.
7" Single: Released Nov '83, on Baskerville, Catalogue no: **BAS 3**

Miranda

JUMP TO THE BEAT
Tracks: / Jump to the beat.
12" Single: Released Oct '88, on Blue Chip, by Blue Chip Records. Catalogue no: **BLUE-CHIP 5 T**

Mirandi, Mike

HOLIDAY
Tracks: / Holiday.
7" Single: Released Aug '84, on Lady London, by Lady London Records. Catalogue no: **LLP 004**

Miri

TRAKBAK
Tracks: / Trakbak / Trakbak (Instrumental).
7" Single: Released Aug '86, on Mcasso, Deleted '87. Catalogue no: **MCASSO 1**

Miro Miroe

ISLAND
Tracks: / Island / Frolix 8.
12" Single: Released Oct '82, on CBS, by CBS Records. Deleted Oct '85. Catalogue no: **A 132797**
7" Single: Released Oct '82, on CBS, by CBS Records. Deleted Oct '85. Catalogue no: **A 2797**

NIGHTS OF ARABIA
Tracks: / Nights of Arabia / Do androids dream.
7" Single: Released Aug '82, on CBS, by CBS Records. Deleted Aug '85. Catalogue no: **A 2429**
12" Single: Released Aug '82, on CBS, by CBS Records. Deleted Aug '85. Catalogue no: **A 132429**

READY STEADY
Tracks: / Ready steady.
12" Single: Released Mar '83, on CBS, by CBS Records. Catalogue no: **A 13 3144**
7" Single: Released Mar '83, on CBS, by CBS Records. Catalogue no: **A 3144**

Mirror

REFLECTED GLORY
Tracks: / Reflected glory.
12" Single: Released Mar '86, on Bam Caruso, by Demon Records. Catalogue no: **PABL 042**

WE'VE GOT ALL THE TIME IN THE WORLD
Tracks: / We've got all the time in the world.
7" Single: Released May '83, on Magnet, by WEA Records. Catalogue no: **MAG 242**

Mirror Crack'd

DANDY WALLFLOWER
Tracks: / Dandy wallflower / Comfort of strangers.
7" Single: Released Mar '84, on Carrere, Catalogue no: **CAR 307**
12" Single: Released Mar '84, on Carrere, Catalogue no: **CART 307**

Mirror, Danny

I REMEMBER ELVIS PRESLEY King is dead, The
Tracks: / I remember Elvis Presley.
7" Single: Released Sep '77, on Sonet, by Sonet Records. Deleted '80. Catalogue no: **SON 2121**

SUSPICION (Elvis Medley)
Tracks: / Suspicion.
7" Single: Released Nov '81, on Albion, by Albion Records. Catalogue no: **MIR 123**

Mirror Image

JACK IT UP
Tracks: / Jack it up.
12" Single: Released Mar '88, on Bolts, by Bolts Records. Catalogue no: **BOLTS 14/12**

Mirror Mile

RHYMING MAN
Tracks: / Rhyming man / Last night.
7" Single: Released Jan '82, on Lunar 2, Deleted Jan '85. Catalogue no: **MOON 2**

Mirrors Over Kiev

DIFFERENT GIRL
Tracks: / Different girl / Love's colder days / Not the last time (Avaliable on 12" format only.) / In this mess (Avaliable on 12" format only.).
7" Single: Released Apr '88, on Playtime, by Playtime Records. Catalogue no: **AMUSE 1**
12" Single: Released Apr '88, on Playtime, by Playtime Records. Catalogue no: **AMUSE 1T**

HOLE IN THE MIDDLE
Tracks: / Hole in the middle.
12" Single: Released Sep '88, on Playtime, by Playtime Records. Catalogue no: **AMUSE 4T**

TAKE ME DOWN
Tracks: / Take me down / Don't leave me.
7" Single: Released 31 Oct '87, on Imaginary, by Imaginary Records. Catalogue no: **MIRAGE 004**

Misacres

SO FINALLY SWEET
Tracks: / So finally sweet.
7" Single: Released Sep '86, on Cherry Red, by Cherry Red Records. Catalogue no: **CHERRY 95**

Mischievous Deeds

ON YOUR BIKE ARGENTINA
Tracks: / On your bike Argentina.
7" Single: Released May '82, on Firestar, Catalogue no: **FIRE 1**

WISHING YOU WELL
Tracks: / Wishing you well / You've got it wrong.
7" Single: Released Jul '82, on Safari, by Safari Records. Catalogue no: **SAFE 44**

Mi-Sex

BLUE DAY
Tracks: / Blue day / Don't look back in anger.
7" Single: Released Jun '84, on CBS, by CBS Records. Catalogue no: **A 4302**

COMPUTER GAMES
Tracks: / Computer games / Wot do you want.
7" Single: Released May '83, on CBS, by CBS Records. Catalogue no: **A 3437**
12" Single: Released May '83, on CBS, by CBS Records. Catalogue no: **TA 3437**
7" Single: Released Feb '80, on CBS, by CBS Records. Deleted '83. Catalogue no: **CBS 7985**

Misfits

BEWARE
Tracks: / Beware.
7" Single: Released Jul '81, on Plan 9, by Armageddon Records. Catalogue no: **PLP 9**

DIE DIE MY DARLING
Tracks: / Die die my darling.
12" Single: Released Nov '87, on Plan 9, by Armageddon Records. Catalogue no: **PL 903**

RAIN VOICES
Tracks: / Rain voices.
7" Single: Released Dec '86, on Misfit, Catalogue no: **MISFIT 1**
12" Single: Released Dec '86, on Misfit, Catalogue no: **MISFIT T 1**

Misha

IMAGINATION, (USE YOUR)
Tracks: / Imagination, (Use your) / Radio heartbreak.
7" Single: Released Mar '85, on Nu-Disk, by Pan Polychord Records. Catalogue no: **MISHA 1**

Miss P

DON'T RUSH ME
Tracks: / Don't rush me / Impatient.
12" Single: Released Mar '83, on Plantation, Catalogue no: **PL 012**

Miss X

CHRISTINE
Tracks: / Christine.
7" Single: Released Aug '63, on ember, Deleted '66. Catalogue no: **S 175**

Missing Link

TOO YOUNG TO ROCK N ROLL
Tracks: / Too yolung to rock n roll / Why me ?.
7" Single: Released Jul '81, on RCA, by BMG Records (UK). Deleted '85. Catalogue no: **RCA 96**

Missing Persons

DESTINATION UNKNOWN
Tracks: / Destination unknown / Hello, I love you.
7" Single: Released Oct '82, on Capitol, by EMI Records. Deleted Oct '85. Catalogue no: **CL 269**

I CAN'T THINK ABOUT DANCING WITHOUT YOU
Tracks: / I can't think about dancing without you / Face to face.
12" Single: Released Aug '86, on Capitol, by EMI Records. Deleted Apr '88. Catalogue no: **12CL 417**
7" Single: Released Aug '86, on Capitol, by EMI Records. Deleted Apr '88. Catalogue no: **CL 417**

I LIKE BOYS
Tracks: / I like boys / Words.
7" Single: Released May '82, on Capitol, by EMI Records. Deleted May '85. Catalogue no: **CL 247**

WORDS
Tracks: / Words / I like boys.
12" Single: Released Feb '83, on Capitol, by EMI Records. Deleted '88. Catalogue no: **12 CL 283**
7" Single: Released Feb '83, on Capitol, by EMI Records. Deleted '88. Catalogue no: **CL 283**

Mission

BEYOND THE PALE
Tracks: / Beyond the pale / Tadeusz (1912-1988) / Love me to death (Extra track on 12".) / For ever more (Extra track on 12".).
7" Single: Released Mar '88, on Mercury, by Phonogram Ltd. Deleted Oct '88. Catalogue no: **MYTH 6**
12" Single: Released Mar '88, on Mercury, by Phonogram Ltd. Deleted Oct '88. Catalogue no: **MYTHX 6**
CD 5": Released Mar '88, on Mercury, by Phonogram Ltd. Deleted Oct '88. Catalogue no: **MTHCD 6**

BEYOND THE PALE (ARMAGEDDON MIX)
Tracks: / Beyond the pale (Armageddon mix) / Forever more / Tadeusz (1912-1988).
12" Single: Released Apr '88, on Mercury, by Phonogram Ltd. Catalogue no: **MYTHX 622**

LIKE A HURRICANE
Tracks: / Like a Hurricane / Garden of delight / Over the hills and far away (Extra tracks on 12"version only) / Crystal ocean, The (Extra tracks on 12" version only.).
7" Single: Released Jul '86, on Chapter 22, by Chapter 22 Records. Catalogue no: **CHAP 7**
Special: Released Jul '86, on Chapter 22, by Chapter 22 Records. Catalogue no: **L12 CHAP 7**
12" Single: Released Jul '86, on Chapter 22, by Chapter 22 Records. Catalogue no: **12 CHAP 7**

MISSION: INTERVIEW PICTURE

DISC
12" Single: Released '87, on Talkies, Catalogue no: **MISSION 1**

SERPENTS KISS
Tracks: / Serpents kiss / Naked and savage / Wake (rsv).
12" Single: Released May '86, on Chapter 22, by Chapter 22 Records. Catalogue no: **CHAP 6**
7" Single: Released May '86, on Chapter 22, by Chapter 22 Records. Catalogue no: **CHAP 67**

SEVERINA
Tracks: / Severina / Tomorrow never knows / Wishing well (Extra track "Wishing Well" only on 12" version).
7" Single: Released Feb '87, on Mercury, by Phonogram Ltd. Deleted Dec '87. Catalogue no: **MYTH 3**
12" Single: Released Feb '87, on Mercury, by Phonogram Ltd. Deleted Dec '87. Catalogue no: **MYTHX 3**

STAY WITH ME
Tracks: / Stay with me / Blood brothers / Island in a stream (Extra track on 12" version only).
7" Single: Released Oct '86, on Mercury, by Phonogram Ltd. Deleted Dec '87. Catalogue no: **MYTH 1**
12" Single: Released Oct '86, on Mercury, by Phonogram Ltd. Deleted Dec '87. Catalogue no: **MYTHX 1**

TOWER OF STRENGTH
Tracks: / Tower of strength / Tower of strength (ext. version) / Fabienne / Dream on (track on 12" only.) / Breath / Breath (version) (Instrumental on 12" & CD only).
7" Single: Released Feb '88, on Mercury, by Phonogram Ltd. Deleted Oct '88. Catalogue no: **MYTH 4**
12" Single: Released Feb '88, on Mercury, by Phonogram Ltd. Deleted Oct '88. Catalogue no: **MYTHX 4**
CD 5": Released Feb '88, on Mercury, by Phonogram Ltd. Deleted Oct '88. Catalogue no: **MTHCD 4**

WASTELAND
Tracks: / Wasteland / Shelter from the storm / Dancing barefoot (Extra track on 12" version only).
7" Single: Released Jan '87, on Mercury, by Phonogram Ltd. Catalogue no: **MYTH 2**

Mission Impossible

COLLECTING THE MONEY
Tracks: / Collecting the money.
12" Single: Released '88, on Subway, by Subway Records. Catalogue no: **SUB 012**

Mission USA

SHOW A LITTLE LOVE
Tracks: / Show a little love / Sensuous mood / Show a little love (instrumental) (On 12" version only.).
7" Single: Released Oct '87, on CBS, by CBS Records. Deleted Jun '88. Catalogue no: **651 222 7**
12" Single: Released Oct '87, on CBS, by CBS Records. Deleted Jun '88. Catalogue no: **651 222 6**

Mista E

DON'T BELIEVE THE HYPE
Tracks: / Don't believe the hype.
7" Single: Released Dec '88, on Urban, by Polydor Ltd. Deleted 30 May '89. Catalogue no: **URB 28**
12" Single: Released Dec '88, on Urban, by Polydor Ltd. Deleted 30 May '89. Catalogue no: **URBX 28**
12" Single: Released Dec '88, on Urban, by Polydor Ltd. Deleted 30 Jun '89. Catalogue no: **URBA 28**

Mistaken Identity

ANSWER
Tracks: / Answer.
12" Single: Released Apr '85, on Ram, by Ram Records. Catalogue no: **12CHP 7010**

Mister Murray

DOWN CAME THE RAIN
Tracks: / Down came the rain / Whatever happened to music.
7" Single: Released Nov '81, on WHB, Deleted '83. Catalogue no: **WHB 001**

Mister Spaulding

SKANK IN THE DARK
Tracks: / Skank in the dark.
12" Single: Released Sep '85, on Roots Rockers, Catalogue no: **RRD 001**

Mister Steve

CHRISTMAS SONG, THE
Tracks: / Christmas song, The.
7" Single: Released Nov '83, on Town & Country, Deleted '84. Catalogue no: **T & C 1**

ONE ROAD
Tracks: / One road.

7" Single: Released Jul '84, on Albion, by Albion Records. Catalogue no: **ION 1066**

Mistrals Daughter

MISTRALS DAUGHTER
Tracks: / Teddy's theme / Mistral's theme.
7" Single: Released Feb '86, on Carrere, Catalogue no: **CAR 382**

Mistura

FLASHER, THE
Tracks: / Flasher, The.
7" Single: Released May '76, on Route, Deleted '79. Catalogue no: **RT 30**

Misty D

OUT ON A LIMB
Tracks: / Out on a limb / Out on a limb (instrumental) (On 7" only) / U better think (On 12" only).
7" Single: Released Aug '89, on Mango Street, by Island Records. Catalogue no: **IS 425**
12" Single: Released Aug '89, on Mango Street, by Island Records. Catalogue no: **12 IS 425**

Misty In Roots

ATOMIC ENERGY
Tracks: / Atomic energy / Set me free.
7" Single: Released Dec '81, on People Unite, by People Unite Records. Catalogue no: **PU NAT 001**

JAH JAH BLESS AFRICA
Tracks: / Jah Jah bless Africa.
7" Single: Released Feb '82, on People Unite, by People Unite Records. Catalogue no: **PUAS 01**

OWN THEM CONTROL THEM
Tracks: / Own them control them.
7" Single: Released Nov '86, on People Unite, by People Unite Records. Catalogue no: **PU 007 S**
12" Single: Released Nov '86, on People Unite, by People Unite Records. Catalogue no: **PU 007 T**

PEACE AND LOVE
Tracks: / Peace and love / Ball out.
7" Single: Released Jul '81, on People, Catalogue no: **PU 005 S**
12" Single: Released Jul '81, on People, Catalogue no: **PU 005**

POOR AND NEEDY
Tracks: / Poor and needy / Follow fashion.
12" Single: Released Jun '83, on People Unite, by People Unite Records. Catalogue no: **PU 103 T**
7" Single: Released Jun '83, on People Unite, by People Unite Records. Catalogue no: **PU 103 S**

RICH MAN
Tracks: / Rich man / Salvation.
12" Single: Released Feb '80, on People, Catalogue no: **PU 002**

TOGETHER
Tracks: / Together / Together (dub).
7" Single: Released Jan '88, on Misty In Roots, Catalogue no: **PUM 3**

UPTOWN DOWNTOWN
Tracks: / Uptown downtown / No need to....
7" Single: Released Dec '81, on People Unite, by People Unite Records. Catalogue no: **PU JEN 001**

VIVA ZAPATTA
Tracks: / Viva zapatta.
7" Single: Released Jan '81, on People Unite, by People Unite Records. Catalogue no: **PU/S 004**

WANDERING WANDERER
Tracks: / Wandering wanderer / Wandering wanderer.
7" Single: Released Feb '85, on People Unite, by People Unite Records. Deleted '88. Catalogue no: **PU 006 S**
12" Single: Released Sep '88, on People Unite, by People Unite Records. Catalogue no: **PU 006 T**

Misunderstood

CHILDREN OF THE SUN (EP)
Tracks: / Children of the sun / Who do you love / I can take you to the sun.
7" Single: Released Jan '81, on Cherry Red, by Cherry Red Records. Deleted '87. Catalogue no: **CHERRY 22**

GOLDEN GLASS (SINGLE)
Tracks: / Golden glass.
12" Single: Released Jun '84, on Cherry Red, by Cherry Red Records. Deleted '87. Catalogue no: **12 THYME 1**

SHAKE YOUR MONEY MAKER
Tracks: / Shake your moneymaker.
12" Single: Released Jul '84, on Cherry Red, by Cherry Red Records. Catalogue no: **THYME 1 12**

Mitchell, Brenda

SIZZLIN
Tracks: / Sizzlin'.
12" Single: Released Jul '85, on Ecstasy, by Creole Records. Catalogue no: **XTCT 17**
7" Single: Released Jul '85, on Ecstasy, by Creole Records. Catalogue no: **XTC 17**

Mitchell/ Coe

SOMETHING INSIDE US IS DYING
Tracks: / Something inside us is dying.
7" Single: Released Sep '80, on RCA, by BMG Records (UK). Deleted Sep '83. Catalogue no: **PB 5284**

Mitchell, George

LONDON'S EAST END
Tracks: / London's east end / Lovely hot pies / Snuggle up / Girls are lovely.
7" Single: Released May '80, on Pye, Deleted '83. Catalogue no: **7P 177**

Mitchell, Guy

Biographical details: This American singer and actor was born Al Cernick in Detroit of Yugoslavian parents. The family moved to Los Angeles when he was 11. He was given a contract with Warner Bros and, with child stardom in mind, received all round singing, acting and dancing training. However, when his parents moved away from LA again, his stardom had to be delayed until adulthood. In 1946 the 19 year old lad joined the US Navy for 16 months. He then had a spell as avocalists with Carmen Cavallaro's orchestra, before winning one of Arthur odfrey's TV talent shows in 1949.

The big break in Mitchell's career occurred in 1950, when he signed with Columbia Records. The company's A&R department had just been taken over by producer/arranger/conductor Mitch Miller, who dreamed up the singer's stage name. Miller became the dominant behind the scenes figure in the American record industry during the first half of the Fifties, and was the undisputed king of the middle of the road ballad market which rock 'n' roll eventually rebelled against. Guy Mitchell was one of the key stars of the Mitch Miller empire.

Mitchell's first smash *My Heart Cries For You* reached the US No. 2 position in 1950, and was recorded by Guy at the last minute when Frank Sinatra turned it down. 1951 brought Guy further US Top 5 biggies with *The Roving Kind* and *My Truly, Truly Fair.* The latter was penned by songwriter Bob Merrill, who provided Mitchell with many of his hits including two 1953 UK No. 1 smashes, *She Wears Red Feathers* and *Look At That Girl.* Concurrent with his chart success, Mitchell made many forays into acting. Two of his 1954 Top Tenners, *Chicka Boom* and *A Dime And A Dollar,* came from the films 'Those Redheads From Seattle' and 'Red Garters' respectively.

The hits had kept on coming until this point, but in 1956 Mitchell's career was in need of a boost. Mitch Miller thus gave a reluctant nod to the new rock 'n' roll music by adding a rock beat to his charge's next single, *Singing The Blues.* This ultra catchy single became the most sensational success of Guy's career, logging a staggering 10 weeks at No. 1 in America and three weeks at the summit in Britain. Its UK success inspired a jaunty cover version by Britain's Tommy Steele, which also climbed to No. 1 in the UK.

After *Singing The Blues,* the American singer achieved one more chart topper on each side of the Atlantic. In Britain he attempted to be trendy with *Rock-A-Billy* in 1957 (which reached No. 10 in the US); in America, he snatched the summit with *Heartaches By The Number* in 1959 (which climbed to No. 5 in the UK). As the Sixties dawned, Mitchell faded into obscurity. He was dropped by Columbia in 1962, and thereafter pursued a career in cabaret. Bob Macdonald, 30 January 1986..

ALWAYS ON MY MIND
Tracks: / Always on my mind / Wind beneath my wings.
7" Single: Released Aug '87, on Top Hat, Catalogue no: **TPH 2**

CALL ROSIE ON THE PHONE
Tracks: / Call Rosie on the phone.
7" Single: Released Oct '57, on Philips, by Phonogram Ltd. Deleted '60. Catalogue no: **PB 743**

CHIKA BOOM
Tracks: / Chika boom.
7" Single: Released Nov '53, on Philips, by Phonogram Ltd. Deleted '56. Catalogue no: **PB 178**

CLOUD LUCKY SEVEN
Tracks: / Cloud lucky seven.
7" Single: Released Dec '53, on Philips, by Phonogram Ltd. Deleted '56. Catalogue no: **PB 210**

CUFF OF MY SHIRT
Tracks: / Cuff of my shirt.
7" Single: Released Feb '54, on Philips, by Phonogram Ltd. Deleted '57. Catalogue no: **PB 225**

DIME AND A DOLLAR
Tracks: / Dime and a dollar.
7" Single: Released May '54, on Philips, by Phonogram Ltd. Deleted '57. Catalogue no: **PB 248**

FEET UP
Tracks: / Feet up.
7" Single: Released Nov '52, on Columbia, by EMI Records. Deleted '55. Catalogue no: **DB 3151**

HEARTACHES BY THE NUMBER
Tracks: / Heartaches by the number.
7" Single: Released Nov '59, on Philips, by Phonogram Ltd. Deleted '62. Catalogue no: **PB 964**

IN THE MIDDLE OF A DARK DARK NIGHT
Tracks: / In the middle of a dark dark night / Sweet stuff.
7" Single: Released Jul '57, on Philips, by Phonogram Ltd. Deleted '60. Catalogue no: **PB 712**

KNEE DEEP IN THE BLUES
Tracks: / Knee deep in the blues.
7" Single: Released Feb '57, on Philips, by Phonogram Ltd. Deleted '60. Catalogue no: **PB 669**

LOOK AT THAT GIRL
Tracks: / Look at that girl.
7" Single: Released Aug '53, on Philips, by Phonogram Ltd. Deleted '56. Catalogue no: **PB 162**

PRETTY LITTLE BLACK EYED SUSIE
Tracks: / Pretty little black-eyed Susie.
7" Single: Released Apr '53, on Columbia, by EMI Records. Deleted '56. Catalogue no: **DB 3255**

ROCKABILLY
Tracks: / Rockabilly / Knee deep in the blues.
7" Single: Released Apr '57, on Philips, by Phonogram Ltd. Deleted '60. Catalogue no: **PB 685**
7" Single: Released Jul '82, on Old Gold, by Old Gold Records. Deleted Jul '88. Catalogue no: **OG 9092**

SHE WEARS RED FEATHERS
Tracks: / She wears red feathers.
7" Single: Released Feb '53, on Columbia, by EMI Records. Deleted '56. Catalogue no: **DB 3238**

SINGING THE BLUES
Tracks: / Singing the blues / Heartaches by the number.
7" Single: Released Dec '56, on Philips, by Phonogram Ltd. Deleted '59. Catalogue no: **PB 650**
7" Single: Released Jul '82, on Old Gold, by Old Gold Records. Catalogue no: **OG 9073**

SIPPIN' SODA
Tracks: / Sippin' soda.
7" Single: Released Feb '54, on Philips, by Phonogram Ltd. Deleted '58. Catalogue no: **PB 210**

Mitchell, Joni

Biographical details: This Canadian singer, songwriter, guitarist, pianist and painter was born Roberta Joan Anderson in Alberta. While studying at the Alberta College of Art in the early Sixties, Joni became deeply interested in folk music. The folk boom was happening all over North America at that time, and she was inspired to take up performing. Her dirst taste of success occurred in 1966, when the critically acclaimed folk artist Tom Rush achieved a local hit in New England with Joni's song *Urge For Going.* He then used her moving number *The Circle Game* as the title track for his highly successful 1967 LP. This acceptance happened to Joni when she was married to a guy called Chuck Mitchell; thus Mitchell became established as her surname within the music business, and it was retained throughout her career even though she soon separated from Chuck.

In 1968 Judy Collins, anoher folkie with a lovely voice, championed Joni's cause by reaching the American Top 10 with *Both Sides Now* (also known as *Clouds*). Arguably Mitchell's best ever song, *Both Sides Now* became a belated British Top 20 hit for Collins in 1970.

Mitchell's own eponymous debut LP, produced by ex-Byrd David Crosby, was released in 1968. From that moment onwards, she was one of the most critically respected artists in the world. Throughout the late Sixties and early Seventies, her albums were compulsive listening. With disarming frankness, she bared her soul and told the world about her rpivate life and her personal philosophies. In songs like *I Had A King, Marriage Too Soon* and *Willy,* Mitchell brought a new meaning to the phrase "kiss and tell" - the ups and downs of every love affair were recounted in great detail. But in doing this, Mitchell employed touching sincerity rather than opportunistic sensationalism. *Songs To Ageing Children Come* was a devastating statement about the condition of her generation. *Free Man In Paris* talked about getting away from the pressures of her fame and success. *Joni Mitchell, Clouds, Ladies Of The Canyon, Blue, For The Roses* and *Court And Spark* were excellent, and in many cases commercially successful, albums.

Cover versions of Mitchell material abounded. *Woodstock*, Joni's tribute to the legendary 1969 rock festival, was given sharply contrasting readings by Crosby, Stills, Nash and Young (Top 20 in US) and Matthews' Southern Comfort (No. 1 in Britain). *This Flight Tonight* became a UK Top 20 hit for rock band Nazareth in 1973. And *Both Sides Now* was recorded by virtually avery MOR singer in the business. Being an album orientated artist, Mitchell herself had just one Top 20 single in the US and UK: the American hit was *Help Me* in 1974, and the British one was *Big Yellow Taxi* in 1970.

From 1965 onwards, Mitchell moved away from her folk and rock roots abd moved in a jazz direction. This meant a decline in her commercial fortunes; but the jazzy feel made interesting listening, particularly on *Hejira* (1976) and the tribute album *Mingus* (1979, dedicated to jazz legend Charles Mingus). In the Eighties she devoted more time to her passionate hobby, painting (she has always been her own sleeve artist). But she resurfaced occasionally on disc, returning to her old style for the albums *Wild Things Run Fast* (1982) and *Dog Eat Dog* (1985). Bob MacDonald, 30 January 1986..

BIG YELLOW TAXI
Tracks: / Big yellow taxi.
7" Single: Released Jun '70, on Reprise, by WEA Records. Deleted '73. Catalogue no: **RS 20906**

CHINESE CAFE
Tracks: / Chinese cafe / Ladies man.
7" Single: Released Feb '83, on Geffen, by Geffen Records (USA). Catalogue no: **GEF A 3122**

I DON'T CARE
Tracks: / I don't care / Love.
7" Single: Released Nov '82, on Geffen, by Geffen Records (USA). Deleted Nov '85. Catalogue no: **GEFA 2950**

MY SECRET PLACE
Tracks: / My secret place / Number one / Chinese cafe* / Good friends*.
Note: From the album Chalk Mark In The Rain. Chorus features Peter Gabriel. *Extra tracks on 12in only.
7" Single: Released May '88, on Geffen, by Geffen Records (USA). Catalogue no: **GEF 37**
12" Single: Released May '88, on Geffen, by Geffen Records (USA). Catalogue no: **GEF 37T**

SHINING TOYS
Tracks: / Shining toys / Three great stimulants.
7" Single: Released Apr '86, on Geffen, by Geffen Records (USA). Deleted '86. Catalogue no: **A 7124**
12" Single: Released Apr '86, on Geffen, by Geffen Records (USA). Deleted '86. Catalogue no: **TA 7124**

WHY DO FOOLS FALL IN LOVE
Tracks: / Why do fools fall in love / Black crow.
7" Single: Released Oct '80, on Elektra, by Elektra Records (UK). Deleted Oct '83. Catalogue no: **K 12478**

Mitchell, Kim

GO FOR SODA
Tracks: / Go for soda.
7" Single: Released May '85, on Bronze, by Bronze Records. Catalogue no: **BRO 192**
12" Single: Released May '85, on Bronze, by Bronze Records. Catalogue no: **BROX 192**

Mitchell, Lauren

ALL THAT I CAN BE
Tracks: / All that I can be / S.C.R.A.T.C.H..
12" Single: Released May '89, on Trax, by Filmtrax Records. Catalogue no: **12TX 6**
7" Single: Released May '89, on Trax, by Filmtrax Records. Catalogue no: **7TX 6**

Mitchell, Neville

PREACHING LOVE
Tracks: / Preaching love.
12" Single: Released Dec '83, on King Jam, Catalogue no: **KJ 079**

Mitchell, Phillip

HURT SO GOOD
Tracks: / Hurt so good / Loving is good.
7" Single: Released Sep '81, on Magnet, by WEA Records. Deleted '84. Catalogue no: **MAG 23**

Mitchell, Sharon

HANDSOME STRANGER
Tracks: / Handsome stranger.
12" Single: Released Jun '84, on Malaco, by Malaco Records (UK). Deleted '88. Catalogue no: **MAL 12 023**

Mitchell, Willie

Biographical details: This American producer, arranger, conductor, composer and trumpeter was a seminal cornerstone on the Memphis rhythm and blues and soul scene during the Sixties and Seventies. Born in Ashland, Mississippi in 1928, he was raised in Memphis and learned trumpet at high school there. He spent his late teens and early twenties playing professionally with local dance bands, and formed his own R&B group in 1954. His combo's pulsating, danceable sound backed several R&B stars on disc.

Mitchell joined the Memphis-based Hi label in the early Sixties, and became a regular fixture on the US soul charts with his driving instrumentals. When Bill Black, leader of the hitmaking Hi band Bill Black's Combo, died in 1965, Mitchell assumed responsibility for the combo and added them to his own existing pool of musicians. Altough Hi records lived in the shadow of their local rivals at Stax/Volt during the Sixties, Mitchell borrowed a few tricks of the trade from Stax's Booker T & The MGs and carved out his own niche in black music. Two of his instrumental singles crossed over to the American pop Top 40: *20-75* reached No. 31 in 1964 abd *Soul Serenade* climbed to No. 23 in 1968. The latter also reached No. 43 in Britain.

Hi Records and Willie Mitchell enjoyed their greatest period of success from 1969 until the mid-Seventies, thanks to Willie's production of two new soul singers, Al Green and Ann Peebles. Green, in particular, was a huge success. Between 1971 and 1974, Al chalked up eight million-selling smash singles in the States. With Mitchell remaining at the production desk, most of these hits were written by Green in conjunction with Mitchell and Al Jackson (of Booker T & The MGs fame). By 1975 Mitchell's distinctive 'Memphis Sound' was wearing thin. He became a less important figure at this stage, although he had the unexpected bonus in December 1976 of a British chart entry with his instrumental single *The Champion*.

Becoming President of Hi Records, Mitchell's creative career tailed off during the late Seventies, after more than twenty years of great soul music. Bob MacDonald, 30 January 1986..

CHAMPION, THE
Tracks: / Champion, The.
7" Single: Released Jan '76, on London-American, Catalogue no: **HLU 10545**

EVERYTHING IS GONNA BE ALRIGHT
Tracks: / Everything is gonna be alright.
7" Single: Released '65, on London-American, Catalogue no: **HLU 10004**

SOUL SERENADE
Tracks: / Soul serenade.
7" Single: Released Apr '68, on London Records, by London Records. Deleted '71. Catalogue no: **HLU 10186**

THAT DRIVING BEAT (SINGLE)
Tracks: / That driving beat. .
7" Single: Released Jun '80, on Hi-Cream, by Demon Records. Catalogue no: **HCS 104**
7" Single: Released Mar '85, on Spindrift, by Celtic Music. Catalogue no: **SBG 44**

Mitchell,Eddie

HOLD ME
Tracks: / Hold me.
7" Single: Released Nov '86, on Mooncrest, by Trojan Records. Deleted May '88. Catalogue no: **MOON 1004**

Mitchigan

RAPTURE OF LOVE
Tracks: / Rapture of love.
12" Single: Released 24 Jul '89, on Live & Love, Catalogue no: **LLD 125**

Mitchum, Arthur

ARRIBA TACO GRANDE
Tracks: / Arriba taco grande / Strange goodbye.
7" Single: Released Jul '82, on Pastafont, by Pastafont Music. Catalogue no: **PF 3006**

Mite, Colonel

THIS SIDE UP
Tracks: / This side up.
12" Single: Released Jun '88, on Y & D, Catalogue no: **YDDO 118**

Mitsouko, Rita

C'EST COMME CA
Tracks: / C'est comme ca / Andy / C'est comme ca (extended version) (12" only) / Andy (extended instrumental version) (12" only).
12" Single: Released Mar '87, on Virgin, by Virgin Records. Catalogue no: **VS 946-12**
7" Single: Released Mar '87, on Virgin, by Virgin Records. Deleted May '88. Catalogue no: **VS 946**

MARCIA BAILA
Tracks: / Marcia Baila / Marcia Baila (French version) / Marcia Baila (extended version) (12" only) / Marcia Baila (extended French version) (12" only).
7" Single: Released Jul '86, on Virgin, by Virgin Records. Catalogue no: **VS 889**
12" Single: Released Jul '86, on Virgin, by Virgin Records. Catalogue no: **VS 889-12**

SINGING IN THE SHOWER
Tracks: / Singing in the shower / Smog / Hip kit.
12" Single: Released Dec '88, on Virgin, by Virgin Records. Catalogue no: **VST 1163**
CD 3": Released Feb '89, on Virgin, by Virgin Records. Catalogue no: **VSCD 1163**
7" Single: Released Dec '88, on Virgin, by Virgin Records. Catalogue no: **VS 1163**

TONGUE DANCE
Tracks: / Tongue dance / Perfect eyes.
12" Single: Released Aug '89, on Virgin, by Virgin Records. Catalogue no: **VST 1212**
7" Single: Released Aug '89, on Virgin, by Virgin Records. Catalogue no: **VS 1212**

Mittoo, Jackie

NEVER CAN SAY GOODBYE
Tracks: / Never can say goodbye / Finger style.
12" Single: Released May '83, on Carousel (1), by Carousel Records. Catalogue no: **12 CAR 5**

REGGAE MAGIC
Tracks: / Reggae magic.
7" Single: Released May '89, on Studio One, Catalogue no: **UNKNOWN**

THESE EYES
Tracks: / These eyes / Wall Street.
12" Single: Released Aug '81, on Rough Trade, by Rough Trade Records. Catalogue no: **RTT 082**
7" Single: Released Aug '81, on Rough Trade, by Rough Trade Records. Catalogue no: **RT 082**

Mitty, Walter

BRAVE NEW ENGLAND
Tracks: / Brave new England / Good boys from the south.
7" Single: Released Jul '82, on RCA, by BMG Records (UK). Catalogue no: **RCA 161**

Mix blood

TOOT LAST TRAIN TO SKAVILLE
Tracks: / Toot last train to Skaville / Move & move.
7" Single: Released Apr '80, on Creole, by Creole Records. Deleted Apr '83. Catalogue no: **CR 201**

Mix it up

MICKY REFORM
Tracks: / Close silence / 4 U my love / Cloud 9 / Micky reform.
12" Single: Released Feb '87, on Antworm, Catalogue no: **ANTWORM 001**

Mix Masters

HIT ME, HIT ME
Tracks: / Hit me, hit me / Hit me, hit me (version).
7" Single: Released Jun '88, on Town Bound, by Town Bound Records. Catalogue no: **BVB 1T**

Mixmaster

GRAND PIANO
Tracks: / Grand piano.
7" Single: Released Oct '89, on BCM Records, Catalogue no: **BCM 344**
12" Single: Released Oct '89, on BCM Records, Catalogue no: **BCMX 344**
CD 5": Released Oct '89, on BCM Records, Catalogue no: **BCM 344CD**

Mixtures

Biographical details: Scooters, motorbikes and cars have had their fair share of pop songs written about them over the years. And Burt Bacharach and Hal David immortalised three forms of transport in one fell swoop when they composed their hit *Trains And Boats And Planes*. But riders of the musically neglected pedal cycle, who improve their own health and create no pollution for others, have been the subject of just one pop smash. The ultra-catchy *Pushbike Song* by an Australian band called Te Mixtures reached No. 2 on the UK chart in 1971, logging 21 weeks on the Top 50. It was in the runner-up spot for four consecutive weeks in February of that year. The single that was No. 1 for all of that time was *My Sweet Lord* by George Harrison, who later became greatly interested in that most dangerous manifestation of man's obsession with wheels, Grand Prix motor racing.

The Pushbike Song peaked at No. 44 in the States. It was the group's only chart success on either side of the Atlantic, and the Mixture immediately plunged back into onscurity from whence they had come. But in watching other pop stars enjoying he sustained recording careers that they themselves were denied, the guys could at least take comfort from the fact that they were physically fit. The greatest exercise that many pop stars ever get is the walk from the hotel lift to the waiting limousine. Bob MacDonald, 31 January 1986..

PUSHBIKE SONG
Tracks: / Pushbike song.
7" Single: Released Jul '82, on Old Gold, by Old Gold Records. Catalogue no: **OG 9153**
7" Single: Released Jan '71, on Polydor, by Polydor Ltd. Deleted '74. Catalogue no: **2058 083**

Mizarolli,John

GRANNY DID IT
Tracks: / Granny did it / Make up and live.
7" Single: Released Apr '83, on Carrere, Catalogue no: **CAR 262**

Mizell, Hank

Biographical details: This American singer and guitarist's story was one of the oddest in rock history. When the rock 'n' roll explosion happened in the mid-Fifties, he was, like numerous other youngsters of the era, inspired to have a go at playing the music himself. He formed a local band and became a proficient amateur. He and his mates concocted some songs, one of which was called *Jungle Rock*. They recorded this number in a garage, which was the standard alternative for those rockers who could not afford to book a studio. The record was made and forgotten, Hank Mizell did not become a star, and he continued living an ordinary life.

Suddenly in 1976, *Jungle Rock* was unearthed by Charly Records, a UK label with an enthusiastic penchant for re-discovering and re-issuing old rock 'n' roll material. For some inexplicable reason, this particular single zoomed onto the British chart and climbed to No. 3. No-one had ever heard of Hank Mizell, and the sound quality was pretty primitive - but the strength of the song and the untainted enthusiasm of the performance won through. Its success neatly coincided with an organised march on the BBC by rock 'n' roll fanatics, who cited the national UK acceptance of the Mizell single as evidence that a specialist programme was required; their demonstration proved successful.

Mizell knew nothing about the success of *Jungle Rock* until it was high on the chart. It took several weeks to track down this most obscure of hit performers; but when he was finally located in the United States, he came over to Britain for a publicity visit, and also recorded an album. Bob MacDonald, 31 January 1988..

I'M READY
Tracks: / I'm ready.
7" Single: Released Jul '85, on Juke Box (Re-issue), Catalogue no: **JB 501**

JUNGLE ROCK/BURNING EYES
Tracks: / Jungle rock / Burning eyes.
7" Single: Released Jul '82, on Old Gold, by Old Gold Records. Catalogue no: **OG 9115**
7" Single: Released Mar '76, on Charly, by Charly Records. Deleted '79. Catalogue no: **CS 1005**

Mizelle,Cyndi

THIS COULD BE THE NIGHT
Tracks: / This could be the night.
7" Single: Released Mar '85, on Atlantic, by WEA Records. Deleted '86. Catalogue no: **A 9635**

MLK Project

I HAVE A DREAM
Tracks: / I have a dream.
7" Single: on 4th & Broadway, by Island Records. Deleted Jun '88. Catalogue no: **BRW 93**
12" Single: on 4th & Broadway, by Island Records. Deleted Apr '89. Catalogue no: **12 BRW 93**

MMC

IT'S OUR THING(LET'S GET IT)
Tracks: / It's our thing(let's get it).
7" Single: Released Oct '87, on After Sunset, by After Sunset Music Promotions. Catalogue no: **ASMP 001**

Mo

FRED ASTAIRE
Tracks: / Fred Astaire / Band with bassoon.
7" Single: Released May '81, on Carrere, Deleted May '84. Catalogue no: **CAR 190**

Mob

CRYING AGAIN
Tracks: / Crying again / Youth / No doves / Gates of hell / What's going on.
12" Single: Released Oct '86, on All The Madmen, by All The Madmen Records. Catalogue no: **MAD 13**

NO DOVES FLY HERE

MOBILES - AMOUR AMOUR (Released on Rialto)

Tracks: / No doves fly here / I hear you laughing.
7" Single: Released Apr '82, on Crass, by Crass Records. Catalogue no: **321984/7**

Mobiles

Biographical details: When the idiosyncratic and worthy single *Drowing In Berlin* shot the previously unknown British band called the Mobiles into the national Top 10 in early 1982, the members of the group were sacked from their day-jobs for taking time off to appear on Top Of The Pops. At first, it seemed as though the band had made the right choice - the success of *Drowning In Berlin*, a slice of modern pop with a female lead vocal that was rather similar to Toyah, seemed to suggest that the guys and gals in the Mobiles would not need the security of a "proper job". But the quirky follow-up *Amour Amour* peaked at No. 45 on the UK singles chart, and subsequent releases flopped altogether.
In late 1984, having switched from Rialto to MCA Records, the Brighton-based band had another crack with *Lost Without Your Love*; but it seemed that the group were no longer upwardly mobile. Bob MacDonald, 31 January 1988..

AMOUR AMOUR (See panel above)
Tracks: / Amour amour / Skeleton dance.
7" Single: Released Mar '82, on Rialto (1), by Rialto Records. Catalogue no: **RIA 5**

BUILD ME UP BUTTERCUP
Tracks: / Build me up buttercup / Don't pay the axeman.
7" Single: Released Mar '83, on Rialto (1), by Rialto Records. Catalogue no: **RIA 15**

DROWNING IN BERLIN
Tracks: / Drowning in Berlin / 7 Teen.
7" Single: Released 24 Apr '89, on Old Gold, by Old Gold Records. Catalogue no: **OG 9890**
7" Single: Released Nov '81, on Rialto (1), by Rialto Records. Catalogue no: **RIA 3**

LOST WITHOUT YOUR LOVE
Tracks: / Lost without your love.
7" Single: Released Oct '84, on Panther, by MCA Records. Catalogue no: **PAN 10**
12" Single: Released Oct '84, on Panther, by MCA Records. Catalogue no: **PANT 10**

PARTNERS IN CRIME
Tracks: / Partners in crime / Snow man.
7" Single: Released Sep '82, on Rialto (1), by Rialto Records. Catalogue no: **RIA 10**

YOU'RE NOT ALONE
Tracks: / You're not alone / Struth.
7" Single: Released Oct '82, on Rialto (1), by Rialto Records. Catalogue no: **MOB 3**

Mobster

PERFECT MAN
Tracks: / Perfect man / Trinidad.
7" Single: Released May '81, on RCA, by BMG Records (UK). Deleted May '84. Catalogue no: **ENY 209**
12" Single: Released May '81, on RCA, by BMG Records (UK). Deleted May '84. Catalogue no: **ENYT 209**

Moby Dick

WHEN THE TIME COMES (See panel opposite)
Tracks: / When the time comes / All enough now.
7" Single: Released Oct '86, on Red House, by Sonet Records. Catalogue no: **SON 2310**

SONG FROM THE RADIO
Tracks: / Song from the radio / Reunion.
7" Single: Released Aug '88, on Red House, by Sonet Records. Catalogue no: **RH 7**

Mock Turtles

POMONA
Tracks: / Pomona.
12" Single: Released Jun '87, on Imaginary, by Imaginary Records. Catalogue no: **MIRAGE 003**

WICKER MAN
Tracks: / Wicker man.
12" Single: Released May '89, on Imaginary, by Imaginary Records. Catalogue no: **MIRAGE 009**

Mockers

YOU'RE A MOCKER
Tracks: / You're a mocker.
7" Single: Released Feb '84, on Dead Dog, by Dead Dog Records. Deleted '86. Catalogue no: **DOG 1**

M.O.D.

SURFIN' M.O.D.
Tracks: / Surfin' U.S.A. / Surf's up / Sgt. Drexall / Mr. Oofus.
7" EP: Released Dec '88, on Road Runner (1), by Road Runner Records. Catalogue no: **RR 2452 1**
CD 5": Released Dec '88, on Road Runner (1), by Road Runner Records. Catalogue no: **RR 2452 2**

Model 500

CHASE, THE
Tracks: / Chase, The.
12" Single: Released Oct '89, on Kool Kat, by Kool Kat Records. Catalogue no: **KOOLT 507**
7" Single: Released Oct '89, on Kool Kat, by Kool Kat Records. Catalogue no: **KOOL 507**

SOUND OF STEREO
Tracks: / Sound of stereo.
12" Single: Released Nov '87, on Metroplex (USA), Catalogue no: **MO 11**

Models

LOCAL AND/OR GENERAL
Tracks: / Local and/or general / Bantam had.
7" Single: Released Feb '82, on A&M, by A&M Records. Deleted Feb '87. Catalogue no: **AMS 8204**

OUT OF MIND OUT OF SIGHT (SINGLE)
Tracks: / Out of mind out of sight.
7" Single: Released Mar '86, on Geffen, by Geffen Records (USA). Catalogue no: **GEF 1**
12" Single: Released Mar '86, on Geffen, by Geffen Records (USA). Catalogue no: **GEF 1 T**

UNHAPPY
Tracks: / Unhappy / Rate of change.
7" Single: Released Apr '82, on A&M, by A&M Records. Deleted Jan '85. Catalogue no: **AMS 8212**

Moderates

EMILE
Tracks: / Emile / For what it's worth.
7" Single: Released Feb '82, on Hyped, Catalogue no: **BMRB 53**

YES TO THE NEUTRON BOMB
Tracks: / Yes to the neutron bomb / Bus girl.
7" Single: Released Apr '81, on Hyped, Catalogue no: **BMRB 51**

Modern Art

DREAMS TO LIVE
Tracks: / Dreams to live.
7" Single: Released Feb '85, on Color Disc, by Color Disc & Tapes. Catalogue no: **COLORS 1**

Modern English

BREAKING AWAY
Tracks: / Breaking away.
7" Single: Released Apr '84, on 4AD, by 4AD Records. Catalogue no: **AD 406**
12" Single: Released Apr '84, on 4AD, by 4AD Records. Catalogue no: **BAD 406**

CHAPTER 12
Tracks: / Chapter 12.
7" Single: Released Jan '84, on 4AD, by 4AD Records. Catalogue no: **AD 401**
12" Single: Released Jan '84, on 4AD, by 4AD Records. Catalogue no: **BAD 401**

GATHERING DUST
Tracks: / Gathering dust / Tranquility of a summer moment.
7" Single: Released Dec '80, on 4AD, by 4AD Records. Catalogue no: **AD 15**

I MELT WITH YOU
Tracks: / I melt with you.
7" Single: Released Aug '82, on 4AD, by 4AD Records. Catalogue no: **AD 212**

LIFE IN THE GLADHOUSE
Tracks: / Life in the gladhouse / Choicest veiw.
7" Single: Released May '82, on 4AD, by 4AD Records. Catalogue no: **BAD 208**

MODERN ENGLISH
Tracks: / Modern English.
12" Single: Released Jun '83, on 4AD, by 4AD Records. Catalogue no: **BAD 306**

SMILES AND LAUGHTER
Tracks: / Smiles and laughter / Mesh and lace.
7" Single: Released Aug '81, on 4AD, by 4AD Records. Catalogue no: **AD 110**

SOMEONE'S CALLING
Tracks: / Someone's calling / Life in the gladhouse.
7" Single: Released Sep '83, on 4AD, by 4AD Records. Catalogue no: **AD 309**
12" Single: Released Sep '83, on 4AD, by 4AD Records. Catalogue no: **BAD 309**

Modern Eon

Biographical details: This British band consisted of Alix (known solely by his first name), Danny Hampshire, Cliff Hewitt, Tim Lever and Bob Wakelin. The *Fiction Tales* album provided Modern Eon with their sole week of UK chart glory, reaching No 65 in the middle of June 1981. It had been preceded by a 1980 single called Euthenics. (Bob MacDonald, January 1986.).

EUTHENICS
Tracks: / Euthenics / Cardinal sides.
7" Single: Released Mar '81, on Dindisc, by Virgin Records. Deleted Mar '84. Catalogue no: **DIN 30**
7" Single: Released Nov '80, on Inevitable, by Inevitable Records. Catalogue no: **INEV 003**

MECHANIC
Tracks: / Mechanic / Splash.
7" Single: Released Sep '81, on Dindisc, by Virgin Records. Deleted Sep '84. Catalogue no: **DIN 35**

Modern Jazz

IN MY SLEEP
Tracks: / In my sleep / Sheep B side.
7" Single: Released Feb '81, on Magnet, by WEA Records. Deleted '84. Catalogue no: **MAG 185**

IVORY TOWERS
Tracks: / Ivory towers / I'm in reverse.
7" Single: Released May '81, on Magnet, by WEA Records. Deleted May '84. Catalogue no: **MAG 201**

Modern Lovers

MORNING OF OUR LIVES, THE
Tracks: / Morning of our lives, The.
7" Single: Released Jan '78, on Beserkley, by Beserkley Records (USA). Deleted '81. Catalogue no: **BZZ 7**

Modern Man

ALL THE LITTLE IDIOTS
Tracks: / All the little idiots / Advance.
7" Single: Released Aug '80, on M.A.M, by M.A.M. Records. Deleted '83. Catalogue no: **MAMS 204**

BODY MUSIC
Tracks: / Body music / I couldn't stop.
7" Single: Released Oct '80, on M.A.M, by M.A.M. Records. Deleted Oct '83. Catalogue no: **MAMS 206**

THINGS COULD BE BETTER
Tracks: / Things could be better / Wasteland.
7" Single: Released Feb '81, on Mams, Deleted Feb '84. Catalogue no: **MAM 207**

Modern Rocketry

CUBA LIBRE
Tracks: / Cuba libre / Homosexuality.
12" Single: Released Jan '87, on Greyhound, by Greyhound Records. Catalogue no: **GRY 003**

HOMOSEXUALITY (REMIX)
Tracks: / Homosexuality.
12" Single: Released Nov '85, on ZYX (Germany), Catalogue no: **ZYX 5311**

Modern Romance

Biographical details: At the time of their greatest success, this British pop band consisted if Paul Gendler, Robbie James, David Jaymes, Andy Kyriacou, Michael J Mullins and John du Prez.

The Leyton Buzzards, a London rock band of the late Seventies, evolved into Modern Romance in 1980. They soon built up a strong following, and spearheaded a mini-boom in salsa music with their first hit -

MOBY DICK - WHEN THE TIME COMES (Released on Red House)

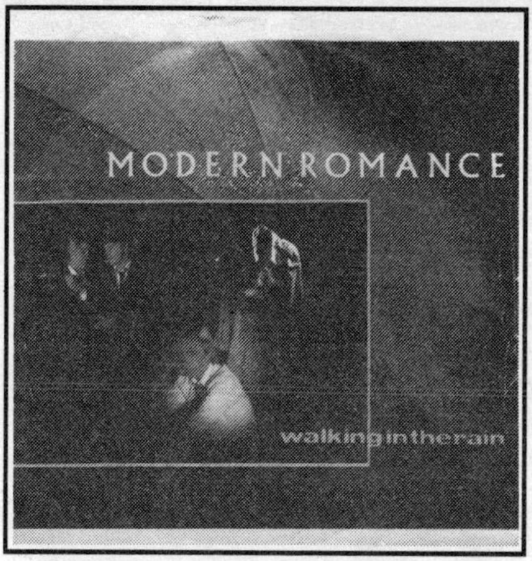

MODERN ROMANCE - WALKING IN THE RAIN (Released on WEA)

Everybody Salsa reached No. 12 on the UK singles chart in 1981. They followed it with the almost identical *Ay Ay Ay Ay Moosey*, which amazingly outflanked its predecessor by climbing to No. 10. At this point they were chic and trendy albeit calculating; they espoused a smart collar and tie image. Modern Romance's salsa songs were even accepted in South America, from whence came their inspiration.

The group's career slumped in early 1982, but they rectified this in the autumn of that year by going for a more overtly pop approach. They did a vocal version of *Cherry Pink And Apple Blosom White*, which had been a monster instrumental hit in 1955. The Modern Romance rendition reached No. 15 on the UK chart. The band's trumpeter, John du Prez, claimed that he used the very same instrument played by Eddie Calvert on his 1955 record.

In early 1983 the band enjoyed their biggest UK single, climbing to No. 4 with their exuberant party celebration *Best Years Of Our Lives*. As with *Everybody Salsa*, they followed it with a clone - but *High Life* nonetheless reached No. 8. These hits came from the Tony Visconti produced album *Trick Of The Light*, which also yielded further biggies with *Don't Stop That Crazy Rhythm* and *Walking In The Rain*.

Modern Romance played unashamedly good-time, ightweight pop. But the party was over by the end of 1983, and they moved into the world of making commercials. They tried to return to the British charts in the summer of 1985 with *Tarzan Boy*, but the original version by Baltimora got there first. Bob MacDonald, 31 January 1986..

AY AY AY AY MOOSEY
Tracks: / Ay ay ay ay moosey.
12" Single: Released Nov '81, on WEA, by WEA Records. Deleted '84. Catalogue no: **K 18883T**
7" Single: Released Nov '81, on WEA, by WEA Records. Deleted '84. Catalogue no: **K 18883**

BEST YEARS OF OUR LIVES (See panel bottom right)
Tracks: / Best years of our lives / We've got them running (the counting song).
7" Single: Released Nov '82, on WEA, by WEA Records. Deleted '85. Catalogue no: **ROM 1**
12" Single: Released Nov '82, on WEA, by WEA Records. Deleted '85. Catalogue no: **ROM 1T**

BURN IT
Tracks: / Burn it.
12" Single: Released Jan '85, on RCA, by BMG Records (UK). Catalogue no: **RCAT 473**
7" Single: Released Jan '85, on RCA, by BMG Records (UK). Catalogue no: **RCA 473**

BY THE WAY
Tracks: / By the way.
12" Single: Released Jun '82, on WEA, by WEA Records. Catalogue no: **K 19185T**
7" Single: Released Jun '82, on WEA, by WEA Records. Catalogue no: **K 19185**

CHERRY PINK AND APPLE BLOSSOM WHITE
Tracks: / Cherry pink and apple blossom white / Who is John Du Prez?.
12" Single: Released Aug '82, on WEA, by WEA Records. Catalogue no: **K19245T**
7" Single: Released Aug '82, on WEA, by WEA Records. Catalogue no: **K19245**

DON'T STOP THAT CRAZY RHYTHM
Tracks: / Don't stop that crazy rhythm.
7" Single: Released Apr '83, on WEA, by WEA Records. Catalogue no: **ROM 3**
12" Single: Released Apr '83, on WEA, by WEA Records. Catalogue no: **ROM 3T**
7" Pic: Released Apr '83, on WEA, by WEA Records. Catalogue no: **ROM 3P**

EVERYBODY SALSA
Tracks: / Everybody salsa / Salsa rhapsody.
7" Single: Released Jul '81, on WEA, by WEA Records. Catalogue no: **K 18815**

HIGHLIFE
Tracks: / High life / Just can't kill the beat.
12" Single: Released Feb '83, on WEA, by WEA Records. Catalogue no: **ROM 2T**
7" Single: Released Feb '83, on WEA, by WEA Records. Catalogue no: **ROM 2**

MODERN ROMANCE
Tracks: / Modern romance / I believe in me.
7" Single: Released Sep '80, on WEA, by WEA Records. Catalogue no: **K 18329**

QUEEN OF THE RAPPING SCENE
Tracks: / Queen of the rapping scene / Can you move.
7" Single: Released Jan '82, on WEA, by WEA Records. Deleted '85. Catalogue no: **K 18929**

TARZAN BOY
Tracks: / Tarzan boy.
12" Single: Released Jul '85, on Carrere, Catalogue no: **CART 368**
7" Single: Released Jul '85, on Carrere, Catalogue no: **CAR 368**

TONIGHT
Tracks: / Tonight / Fever.
7" Single: Released Mar '81, on WEA, by WEA Records. Catalogue no: **K 18467**
12" Single: Released Mar '81, on WEA, by WEA Records. Catalogue no: **K 18467T**

WALKING IN THE RAIN (See panel above)
Tracks: / Walking in the rain / Walking in the rain (blues).
7" Single: Released Jul '83, on WEA, by WEA Records. Catalogue no: **X 9733**
12" Single: Released Jul '83, on WEA, by WEA Records. Deleted '84. Catalogue no: **X 9733T**

Modern Sound

SAFARI
Tracks: / Safari / Safari (part 2).
7" Single: Released Feb '80, on Epic, by CBS Records. Deleted '83. Catalogue no: **EPC 8209**
12" Single: Released Feb '80, on Epic, by CBS Records. Deleted '83. Catalogue no: **13-8209**

Modern Talking

ATLANTIS IS CALLING SOS for love
Tracks: / Atlantis is calling / You're my heart, you're my soul.
7" Pic: Released Sep '86, on RCA, by BMG Records (UK). Catalogue no: **PB 40969P**
7" Single: Released Sep '86, on RCA, by BMG Records (UK). Catalogue no: **PB 40969**
12" Single: Released Sep '86, on RCA, by BMG Records (UK). Deleted May '89. Catalogue no: **PT 40970**

BROTHER LOUIE
Tracks: / Brother Louie / Brother Louie (instrumental).
CD 5": Released Jun '89, on RCA, by BMG Records (UK). Catalogue no: **162054**
7" Single: Released Sep '86, on RCA, by BMG Records (UK). Deleted May '89. Catalogue no: **PB 40875**
12" Single: Released Sep '86, on RCA, by BMG Records (UK). Catalogue no: **PT 40876**

GIVE ME PEACE ON EARTH
Tracks: / Give me peace on Earth / Cheri cheri lady / Just we too! (Extra track on 12" version only.).
7" Single: Released Nov '86, on RCA, by BMG Records (UK). Catalogue no: **PB 41071**
12" Single: Released Nov '86, on RCA, by BMG Records (UK). Catalogue no: **PT 41072**

YOU CAN WIN IF YOU WANT
Tracks: / You can win if you want.
7" Single: Released Sep '85, on Magnet, by WEA Records. Deleted '87. Catalogue no: **MAG 282**
12" Single: Released Sep '85, on Magnet, by WEA Records. Deleted '87. Catalogue no: **MAGT 282**

YOU'RE MY HEART, YOU'RE MY SOUL
Tracks: / You're my heart, you're my soul.
7" Single: Released Mar '85, on Magnet, by WEA Records. Catalogue no: **MAG 277**
12" Single: Released Mar '85, on Magnet, by WEA Records. Deleted '87. Catalogue no: **MAGT 277**

Modern Trouble

SAVE OUR SEOUL
Tracks: / Save our Seoul / S.O.S..
12" Single: Released Sep '88, on MIL, by MIL Records. Catalogue no: **121003**

Modernaires

BEND
Tracks: / Bend.
12" Single: Released Mar '82, on Illuminated, Deleted '85. Catalogue no: **ILL 812**

BEND (EP)
Tracks: / Bend.
7" Single: Released Feb '82, on Illuminated, Catalogue no: **ILL 8**
12" Single: Released Feb '82, on Illuminated, Catalogue no: **ILL 812**

LIFE IN OUR TIMES
Tracks: / Life in our times.
7" Single: Released Nov '80, on Illuminated, Catalogue no: **ILL 2**

WE DID IT AGAIN
Tracks: / We did it again / And again.
7" Single: Released Apr '81, on Illuminated, Catalogue no: **ILL 4**

Modernique

LOVE'S GONNA GET YOU
Tracks: / Love's gonna get you / Love's gonna get you (instrumental).
7" Single: Released Sep '86, on 10 Records, by Virgin Records. Deleted May '88. Catalogue no: **TEN 123**
12" Single: Released Sep '86, on 10 Records, by Virgin Records. Deleted '89. Catalogue no: **TENT 123**

Modesty

NOEL
Tracks: / Noel.
7" Single: Released Dec '81, on FX, Catalogue no: **FX 7**

Mo-Dettes

Biographical details: At the time of their success, this British band consisted of Ramona Carlier, Kate Coris. Jane Crockford and June Miles.

The Mo-Dettes grew from the London punk scene of the late Seventies; two of the four girls had been pals of various members of the Sex Pistols. The group's first single *White Mice* was issued in 1979 to good press reviews. Two of their later singles reached the UK chart: *Paint It Black*, a punky revamp of the Rolling Stones' 1966 chart-topper, climbed to No. 42 in 1980; and *Tonight* peaked at No. 68 in 1981. Their only album *The Story So Far* was released in November 1980, but was not a success.

The Mo-Dettes were falling apart by the end of 1981. They might hace been bigger if they had come along a couple of years earlier. Drummer/vocalist June Miels, who became known as Junes Miles-Kingston, was part of the Fun Boy Three's backing band on their seminal 1983 album *Waiting*. She then attempted a solo career. Bob MacDonald, 31 January 1986..

DARK PARK CREEPING
Tracks: / Dark park creeping / Two can play / White mice.
7" Single: Released Oct '80, on Deram, by London Records. Catalogue no: **DET 2**

PAINT IT BLACK
Tracks: / Paint it black.
7" Single: Released Jun '80, on Deram, by London Records. Catalogue no: **DET/R 1**

TONIGHT
Tracks: / Tonight / Waltz in blue minor.
7" Single: Released Jun '81, on Deram, by London Records. Catalogue no: **DET 3**

WHITE MICE
Tracks: / White mice.
7" Single: Released Jul '81, on Human (2), Catalogue no: **HUM 10**

Modugno, Domenico

CIAO CIAO BAMBINA
Tracks: / Ciao ciao bambina.
7" Single: Released Mar '59, on Oriole, Deleted '62. Catalogue no: **CB 1489**

VOLARE
Tracks: / Volare.
7" Single: Released Sep '58, on Oriole, Deleted '61. Catalogue no: **CB 5000**

MODERN ROMANCE - BEST YEARS OF OUR LIFES (Released on WEA)

Moe Dee, Kool

HOW YA LIKE ME NOW (SINGLE)
Tracks: / How ya like me now.
7" Single: Released Oct '87, on Jive, by Zomba Records. Deleted '88. Catalogue no: **JIVE 156**
12" Single: Released Nov '87, on Jive (USA), by Zomba Records. Catalogue no: **10731 JD**
12" Single: Released Jul '87, on Jive, by Zomba Records. Deleted '88. Catalogue no: **JIVET 156**

Moev

ALIBIS
Tracks: / Alibis.
12" Single: Released 17 Jul '87, on Nettwerk, by Nettwerk Records. Catalogue no: **11 NTWK 012**
12" Single: Released Sep '85, on Ink, by Red Flame Records. Catalogue no: **INK 1212**

CAPITAL HEAVEN
Tracks: / Capital heaven.
12" Single: Released Feb '88, on Nettwerk, by Nettwerk Records. Catalogue no: **NTL 12-3012**

TOOK OUT THE LACE
Tracks: / Took out the lace.
12" Single: Released 17 Jul '87, on Nettwerk, by Nettwerk Records. Catalogue no: **NT12-3001**

WANTING
Tracks: / Wanting.
12" Single: Released 17 Jul '87, on Network, by CBS Records. Catalogue no: **NT12-3006**

YEAH, WHATEVER (REMIX)
Tracks: / Yeah, whatever (remix).
12" Single: Released Aug '88, on Nettwerk, by Nettwerk Records. Catalogue no: **NT 12 3020**

Moffitt, Matt

MISS THIS TONIGHT
Tracks: / Miss this tonight / Save your worry.
7" Single: Released Jun '86, on CBS, by CBS Records. Deleted May '87. Catalogue no: **A 6685**
12" Single: Released Sep '86, on CBS, by CBS Records. Deleted May '87. Catalogue no: **TA 6685**

Moffs

TRAVELLER, THE
Tracks: / Traveller, The.
7" Single: Released Jan '88, on Citadel (UK), by Citadel Records. Catalogue no: **CIT 033**

Mogodons

ZUVENBIE
Tracks: / Zuvenbie.
7" Single: Released Jul '82, on TD (USA), Catalogue no: **MOG 1**

Mohamed

HAM SAFAR
Tracks: / Ham safar.
CD 5": Released 24 Jul '89, on Fun Factory, Catalogue no: **FUNFACMCD 1912**
12" Single: Released 24 Jul '89, on Fun Factory, Catalogue no: **FUNFACM 1912**

Mohawks

CHAMP, THE
Tracks: / Champ, The.
12" Single: Released Jan '87, on Pama, by Pama Records. Catalogue no: **PMT 1**
7" Single: Released Jan '87, on Pama, by Pama Records. Catalogue no: **PM 1**

Moho Pack

LET US TOUCH
Tracks: / Neve stellung fun / Warpath / Let us touch.
Note: *=Extra track on 12" only
7" Single: Released Feb '87, on Fun After All, by Music For Nations Records. Catalogue no: **FAA 107**

Moja

MEK-WE-ROCK (2 parts)
Tracks: / Mek we rock (part 1) / Mek we rock (part 2).
7" Single: Released Jun '83, on Ethnic, Catalogue no: **ETH 2233**

Moja Nya

UP RISE
Tracks: / Up rise.
12" Single: Released Jun '84, on Streetwise, Catalogue no: **STRW 22229**

Mojo

DANCE ON
Tracks: / Dance on / It's a game.
7" Single: Released Aug '81, on Creole, by Creole Records. Deleted '84. Catalogue no: **CR 17**

Mojos

Biographical details: At the time of their greatest success, this British pop combo consisted of Nicky Crouch, Stu James, Keith Karlson, John Konrad and Terry O'Toole.

Formed in 1962 as the Nomads, they became the Mojos the following year. Hailing from Liverpool, the group were typical of the Merseybeat genre - their repertoire on stage was harder and more R&B orientated than the pop material which was heard on their hit singles. Their first single *Forever* was released in October 1963. It was not a hit, so they trekked to where many of their Mersey peers had gone before - the Star Club, Hamburg. While in Germany they recorded their second single, and what a goodie it was.

Everything's Alright reached No. 9 on the British chart in the Spring of 1964, and was one of the best loved singles of the beat boom. However, after a couple more UK Top 30 singles in 1964 (*Why Not Tonight* and *Seven Daffodils*), the Mojos disintegrated. James and Crouch spent the following two years touring the UK with a new lineup. Using his real name Stuart Slater, James moved into the business side of the music businessm including a lengthy period of service with Chrysalis. Bob MacDonald, 31 January 1986..

EVERYTHING'S ALLRIGHT
Tracks: / Everything's alright / Give your lovin' to me.
7" Single: Released Apr '82, on Decca, by Decca Records. Deleted '88. Catalogue no: **F 11853**

SEVEN DAFFODILS
Tracks: / Seven daffodils.
7" Single: Released Sep '64, on Decca, by Decca Records. Deleted '67. Catalogue no: **F 11959**

WHY NOT TONIGHT
Tracks: / Why not tonight.
7" Single: Released Jun '64, on Decca, by Decca Records. Deleted '67. Catalogue no: **F 11918**

Molly Hatchet

SATISFIED MAN
Tracks: / Satisfied man.
12" Single: Released Jan '85, on Epic, by CBS Records. Catalogue no: **TA 4848**
7" Single: Released Jan '85, on Epic, by CBS Records. Catalogue no: **A 4848**

Moloney, Chris

GALTEE SONG
Tracks: / Galtee song.
7" Single: Released Aug '82, on Disc International, by Disc International Records. Catalogue no: **INT 2**

Molzen, Gerty

WALK ON THE WILD SIDE
Tracks: / Walk on the wild side.
7" Single: Released Apr '85, on 10 Records, by Virgin Records. Deleted '89. Catalogue no: **TEN 47**

Moment

1,2 THEY FLY
Tracks: / 1,2 they fly.
7" Single: Released Sep '85, on Diamond, by Revolver Records. Catalogue no: **KIA 006**

IN THIS TOWN
Tracks: / In this town / Just once.
7" Single: Released Apr '85, on Diamond, by Revolver Records. Catalogue no: **DIA 004**

ONE TWO THEY FLY
Tracks: / One two, they fly.
7" Single: Released Feb '89, on Diamond, by Revolver Records. Catalogue no: **DIA 006**

READY TO FALL
Tracks: / Ready to fall / Carpenter of life / Who the hell / Poor Mr. Diamond.
12" Single: Released Mar '89, on Big Stuff, Catalogue no: **STUFF 1**

Moment Of Ecstacy

WANNA GET OUT
Tracks: / Wanna get out.
CD 5": Released Jul '89, on Kaos, Catalogue no: **KAOS 15CD**
12" Single: Released Apr '89, on Kaos, Catalogue no: **KAOS 15**

YOU AND ME
Tracks: / You and me.
12" Single: Released Nov '88, on Kaos, Catalogue no: **KAOS 005**

Moments

Biographical details: The Moments were a sweet soul vocal trio who first began to attract attention in the late Sixties with such singles as *Sunday*. 1970 brought them a US million seller with *Love On A Two Way Street*, which reached NO. 3. Signed to Sylvia Robinson's All Platinum organisation (the forerunner of Sugarhill Records), the Moments were regular visitors to the American soul charts during the first half of the Seventies, operating in the same soul ballad territory as acts like the Delfonics and the Stylistics.

In 1974 the Moments returned to the Top 20 of the US pop charts with *Sexy Mama*. The following year, with he All Platinum label gaining momentum in Britain, the trio zoomed to the UK No. 3 position with the breezy mid-tempo offering *Girls*. The lyrics of that song would undoubtedly be classed as sexist in the Eighties. In the summer of 1975, a second consecutive British Top Tenner was achieved with the exuberant *Dolly My Love*. A slightly dated sound called *Jack In The Box* reached No. 7 in Britain in 1977. Shortly afterwards, the three performers who comprised the group at that time - Harry Ray, Al Goodman and Billy Brown - decided to abandon the Moments billing and record as Ray, Goodman and Brown.

During the Eighties RG&B continued as before, with their beautiful vocal harmonisation as good as ever. 1980 brought them their biggest American single for ten years - this beautiful million seller scored a US No. 5 placing, and was called *Special Lady*. Strangely, none of the threesome's major successes were big hits on both sides of the Atlantic; it was always either the US or the UK. *Special Lady* continued this trend.

Ahowing that they could still cut it when they wanted to, Ray, Goodman and Brown released an exquisite soul smoocher, *Who's Gonna Make The First Move*, but this was unfortunately underrated in 1985. Bob MacDonald, 31 January 1986..

DOLLY MY LOVE
Tracks: / Dolly my love.
7" Single: Released Jul '75, on All Platinum, Deleted '78. Catalogue no: **6146 306**

GIRLS
Tracks: / Girls / Dolly my love.
7" Single: Released Mar '75, on All Platinum, Deleted '78. Catalogue no: **6146 302**
7" Single: Released Jan '83, on Flashback, by Mainline Records. Catalogue no: **FBS 16**

JACK IN THE BOX
Tracks: / Jack in the box.
7" Single: Released Jan '77, on All Platinum, Deleted '80. Catalogue no: **6146 318**

LOOK AT ME (I'M IN LOVE)
Tracks: / Look at me (I'm in love).
7" Single: Released Oct '75, on All Platinum, Deleted '78. Catalogue no: **6146 309**

Momus

HAIRSTYLE OF THE DEVIL
Tracks: / Hairstyle of the devil.
12" Single: Released 16 Jan '89, on Creation, by Creation Records. Catalogue no: **CRE 063LT**
7" Single: Released 16 Jan '89, on Creation, by Creation Records. Catalogue no: **CRE 063L**

LIFESTYLES OF THE RICH & FAMOUS
Tracks: / Lifestyles of the rich & famous.
12" Single: Released Oct '89, on Creation, by Creation Records. Catalogue no: **UNKNOWN**
CD 3": Released Oct '89, on Creation, by Creation Records. Catalogue no: **UNKNOWN**
7" Single: Released Oct '89, on Creation, by Creation Records. Catalogue no: **UNKNOWN**

MURDERERS THE HOPE OF WOMEN
Tracks: / Murderers,the hope of women.
12" Single: Released Mar '87, on Creation, by Creation Records. Catalogue no: **CRE 037 T**
7" Single: Released Mar '87, on Creation, by Creation Records. Catalogue no: **CRE 037**

NICKY
Tracks: / Nicky / Don't leave / See a friend in tears.
12" Single: Released Jul '86, on El, by Cherry Red Records. Catalogue no: **GPO 9T**

Monae, Tia

DON'T KEEP ME WAITING (DUB MIX)
Tracks: / Don't keep me waiting.
7" Single: on Carrere, Catalogue no: **CAR 320**
12" Single: on Carrere, Catalogue no: **CART 320**

Monchhichi

MONCHHICHI'S SONG
Tracks: / Monchhichi's song / Monchhichi in space.
7" Single: Released Jun '82, on WEA, by WEA Records. Deleted Jun '85. Catalogue no: **K 18445**

Mondays

FORTUNE & GLORY (SINGLE)
Tracks: / Fortune and glory.
7" Single: Released Feb '88, on Unicorn Records, by Unicorn Records. Catalogue no: **PHZ 14**

Mondo Cane

EVERLASTING LOVE
Tracks: / Everlasting love / Everlasting love (instrumental).
12" Single: Released Nov '86, on Lisson, by PWL Records. Catalogue no: **DOLEQ 6**
7" Single: Released Nov '86, on Lisson, by PWL Records. Catalogue no: **DOLE 6**

NEW YORK AFTERNOON
Tracks: / New York afternoon / Manhattan morning.
7" Single: Released Aug '86, on Lisson, by PWL Records. Catalogue no: **DOLE 2**
12" Single: Released Aug '86, on Lisson, by PWL Records. Catalogue no: **DOLEQ 2**

Mondo Rock

COOL WORLD
Tracks: / Cool world / Step up step out.
7" Single: Released May '82, on Atlantic, by WEA Records. Deleted May '85. Catalogue no: **K 11732**

MODERN BOP, THE (New York remix)
Tracks: / Modern bop, The.
7" Single: Released Jul '85, on Polydor, by Polydor Ltd. Catalogue no: **POSP 748**
12" Single: Released Jul '85, on Polydor, by Polydor Ltd. Catalogue no: **POSPX 748**

PRIMITIVE LOVE RITES
Tracks: / Primitive love rites / Under lights.
7" Single: Released Jul '87, on Polydor, by Polydor Ltd. Deleted Mar '88. Catalogue no: **POSP 874**
12" Single: Released Jul '87, on Polydor, by Polydor Ltd. Deleted Mar '88. Catalogue no: **POSPX 874**

SEARCHING FOR MY BABY
Tracks: / Searching for my baby / Send me someone.
7" Single: Released Jan '80, on EMI, by EMI Records. Deleted Jan '83. Catalogue no: **EMI 5024**

STATE OF THE HEART
Tracks: / State of the heart / Mona Lisa.
7" Single: Released Jan '82, on Atlantic, by WEA Records. Deleted Jan '85. Catalogue no: **K 11579**

Money, Eddie

I WANNA GO BACK
Tracks: / I wanna go back / Broken down Chevy.
7" Single: Released Mar '87, on CBS, by CBS Records. Catalogue no: **650321 7**
12" Single: Released Mar '87, on CBS, by CBS Records. Catalogue no: **650321 6**

RUNNING BACK
Tracks: / Running back / Satin angel.
7" Single: Released Sep '80, on CBS, by CBS Records. Deleted '83. Catalogue no: **CBS 8924**

TAKE ME HOME TONIGHT
Tracks: / Take me home tonight / Be my baby / Take me home tonight (version) / Calm before the storm / Baby hold on.
7" Single: Released Nov '86, on CBS, by CBS Records. Catalogue no: **650042 7**
12" Single: Released Nov '86, on CBS, by CBS Records. Catalogue no: **650042 6**

WALK ON WATER
Tracks: / Walk on water / Take me home tonight / Dancing with Mr. Jitters.
7" Single: Released 16 Jan '89, on CBS, by CBS Records. Deleted 10 Jul '89. Catalogue no: **653 033-7**
12" Single: Released 16 Jan '89, on CBS, by CBS Records. Deleted 10 Jul '89. Catalogue no: **653 033-8**
CD 5": Released 16 Jan '89, on CBS, by CBS Records. Deleted 10 Jul '89. Catalogue no: **653 033-2**

Money, Zoot

Biographical details: Backed by his Big Roll Band, this quality named artist was a major attraction on Britain's soul and R&B circuit of the Sixties. Zoot Money (real name George Bruno) was never really able to translate his big live following into record chart success. His only two UK chart entries (both 1966) were *Big Time Operator* (No. 25 single) and *Zoot* (No. 23 album). Several important musicians passed through the ranks of the Big Roll Band, most noteably Andy Somers; with the spelling of his surname changed to Summers, this guitarist re-emerged in the late Seventies as a member of the Police. Bob MacDonald, 31 January 1986..

BIG TIME OPERATOR
Tracks: / Big time operator.
7" Single: Released Aug '66, on Columbia, by EMI Records. Deleted '69. Catalogue no: **DB 7975**

TWO OF US
Tracks: / Two of us, The / Ain't nothing shaking.
7" Single: Released Jun '82, on Magic

Moon, Catalogue no: **MACH 6**

YOUR FEET'S TOO BIG
Tracks: / Your feet's too big.
7" Single: Released Sep '80, on Magic Moon, Catalogue no: **MACH 3**

Moneymakers

BIG HIT
Tracks: / Big hit.
12" Single: Released Aug '89, on Subway, by Subway Records. Catalogue no: **SUB 067**

Monfungo

EL SALVADOR PLUS 2 (EP)
Tracks: / El Salvador plus 2.
7" Single: Released Aug '82, on Rough Trade, by Rough Trade Records. Catalogue no: **RT 103**

Monica

HE'S THE ONE
Tracks: / He's the one.
12" Single: Released May '82, on Rosie, by Rosie Records. Catalogue no: **RR 004**

Monique

I CHOOSE YOU
Tracks: / I choose you.
12" Single: Released Jun '89, on Blaka Mix International, Catalogue no: **BLKM 005**

VALERIE
Tracks: / Valerie / Pump up the Valerie.
7" Single: Released Oct '88, on Hard, by Hard Records. Catalogue no: **BRAT 1**

Monk, T.S.

Biographical details: The son of the legendary jazz pianis and composer Thelonious Monk, this American artist emerged as a funk performer during the early Eighties. The highly danceable singe *Bon Bon Vie* was a minor hit on both sides of the Atlantic in 1981. In the same year, he chalked up a second minor UK chart entry with *Candidate For Love*. Both tracks appeared on his sophisticated funk album *House Of Music*. However, his next album *More Of The Good Life* was a stiff, and Monk quickly disappeared from view. Bob MacDonald, 2 February 1986..

BON BON VIE
Tracks: / Bon bon vie / Stay free of his love.
7" Single: Released Mar '81, on Mirage (USA), Deleted '84. Catalogue no: **K 11653**

CANDIDATE FOR LOVE
Tracks: / Candidate for love / Last of the wicked romances.
7" Single: Released Apr '81, on Mirage (USA), Deleted '84. Catalogue no: **K 11648**

TOO MUCH TOO SOON
Tracks: / Too much too soon / First lady of love.
7" Single: Released Jan '82, on Mirage (USA), Deleted Jan '85. Catalogue no: **K 11693**

Monkees

Biographical details: This contrived pop group consisted of Mickey Dolenz, Mike Nesmith Peter Tork (born Peter Thorkelson) and the only non-American, Manchester born Davy Jones.
One of the most shrewdly conceived and brilliantly executed marketing exercises in pop history, the Monkees were launched onto an unsuspecting public in 1966. The idea was the brainchild of two American producers Bob Rafelson and Bert Schneider, who wanted to create a television sitcom series that would capitalise on the phenomenal Beatles-led boom in pop groups. Out of 437 applicants who answered the producers' ad in the showbusiness press, two former child actors and two former folk singers were chosen. All four were in their late teens or early twenties. When NBC TV in America showed the first episodes in September 1966, 'The Monkees' became an immediate sensation. With the help of top music publisher Don Kirshner, whose roster of talent included many of America's leading pop songwriters, the Monkees concept became a huge cross-marketing success: the television programme was a sensation, and vast quantities of records were sold.
The Monkees unashamedly imitated the Beatles, from the name onwards. The zany image and clowning around that characterised the TV programmes were directly inspired by the films 'A Hard Day's Night' and 'Help!'. The music was closely modelled on the Liverpool heroes' 1962-66 period. Some journalists extended the links with the Fab Four still further by dubbing the Monkees 'the Fabricated Four'. As the Monkees' hits exploded onto the charts in America in late 1966, and the rest of the world in early 1967, it became a source of public indignation that the four lads merely sang on their records - the instruments that they appeared to play on screen were in fact played on disc by some of the West Coast's top session musicians. The outcry that greeted this disclosure overlooked the fact that the Monkees' members were hired primarily to be actors.
The Monkees' discs were great pop records, regardless of who played the backing tracks. The single that launched them in the States was *Last Train To Clarksville*, which reached No. 1 in late 1966. Then came their biggest smash, written by up and coming singer/songwriter Neil Diamond: *I'm A Believer* logged seven weeks at the top in America and four weeks in Britain. Diamond was also the source of the follow up hit *A Little Bit Me, A Little Bit You*, which got to No. 2 in the US and No. 3 In the UK. The joyous *Daydream Believer* appeared at the end of 1967, clocking up four weeks at No. 1 in America and reaching No. 5 in Britain. Their other biggest hits included *Pleasant Valley Sunday* and *Valleri*. On the album front, *The Monkees* and *More Of The Monkees* were No. 1 on both sides of the Atlantic; their third and fourth sets, *Headquarters* and *Pisces, Aquarius, Capricorn & Jones Ltd*, reached No. 1 in America and the Top 5 in Britain.
In both television and chart terms, the Monkees phenomenon was over by 1969. It was inevitable that such an exercise could not be popular for very long; and the group, particularly Nesmith, had grown increasingly frustrated at their lack of control over the project. After the group's demise, Nesmith became a moderately successful country-rock artist, and later turned into a video director. Dolenz eventually moved to Britain to become a successful TV and stage producer. Jones and Tork faded into obscurity.
'The Monkees' is still repeated regularly on television in America, the United Kingdom and Japan. Bob MacDonald, 1 February 1986..

6 TRACK HITS: MONKEES
Tracks: / I'm a believer / Alternate title / Somebody man / Little bit me, a little bit you / Valleri / Pleasant valley Sunday.
7" EP: Released Mar '84, on Scoop 33, by Pickwick Records. Catalogue no: **7SR 5035**

ALTERNATE TITLE
Tracks: / Alternate title.
7" Single: Released Jun '67, on RCA, by BMG Records (UK). Deleted '70. Catalogue no: **RCA 1604**

DAYDREAM BELIEVER (OLD GOLD)
Tracks: / Daydream believer / Last train to Clarksville.
7" Single: Released Jun '88, on Old Gold, by Old Gold Records. Catalogue no: **OG 9117**

DAYDREAM BELIEVER
Tracks: / Daydream believer / Monkees, theme from / Little bit me, a little bit you.
7" Single: Released Nov '67, on RCA, by BMG Records (UK). Deleted '70. Catalogue no: **RCA 1645**
CD 5": Released Mar '89, on Arista, by BMG Records (UK). Catalogue no: **662 157**
10" single: Released Mar '89, on Arista, by BMG Records (UK). Catalogue no: **112 157**

D.W. WASHBURN
Tracks: / D.W. Washburn.
7" Single: Released Jun '68, on RCA, by BMG Records (UK). Deleted '71. Catalogue no: **RCA 1706**

I'M A BELIEVER
Tracks: / I'm a believer.
7" Single: Released Jan '67, on RCA, by BMG Records (UK). Deleted '70. Catalogue no: **RCA 1560**
7" Single: Released Jul '82, on Old Gold, by Old Gold Records. Catalogue no: **OG 9123**
7" Single: Released Aug '82, on Arista, by BMG Records (UK). Catalogue no: **ARIST 487**

LAST TRAIN TO CLARKSVILLE
Tracks: / Last train to Clarksville / I'm a believer / Pleasant valley sunday.
7" EP: Released Apr '89, on Arista, by BMG Records (UK). Catalogue no: **112 158**
CD 5": Released Jun '89, on Arista, by BMG Records (UK). Catalogue no: **162053**
7" Single: Released Jan '67, on RCA, by BMG Records (UK). Deleted '70. Catalogue no: **RCA 1547**
12" Single: Released Apr '89, on Arista, by BMG Records (UK). Catalogue no: **662 158**

LITTLE BIT ME A LITTLE BIT YOU, A
Tracks: / Little bit me, a little bit you.
7" Single: Released Apr '67, on RCA, by BMG Records (UK). Deleted '70. Catalogue no: **RCA 1580**

MONKEES EP, THE
7" Single: Released Feb '80, on Arista, by BMG Records (UK). Catalogue no: **ARIST 326**

MONKEES EP, VOL 2, THE
Tracks: / I'm not your stepping stone / Pleasant Valley Sunday / Alternate title
7" Single: Released Jun '81, on Arista, by BMG Records (UK). Catalogue no: **ARIST 402**

MONKEES THEME (EP)
Tracks: / Monkees theme.
7" EP: Released '82, on Arista, by BMG Records (UK). Deleted '87. Catalogue no: **ARIST 487**

PLEASANT VALLEY SUNDAY
Tracks: / Pleasant valley Sunday.
7" Single: Released Aug '67, on RCA, by BMG Records (UK). Deleted '70. Catalogue no: **RCA 1620**

SOME DAY MAN
Tracks: / Some day man.
7" Single: Released Jun '69, on RCA, by BMG Records (UK). Deleted '72. Catalogue no: **RCA 1824**

TEARDROP CITY
Tracks: / Teardrop city.
7" Single: Released Mar '69, on RCA, by BMG Records (UK). Deleted '72. Catalogue no: **RCA 1802**

THAT WAS THEN, THIS IS NOW
Tracks: / That was then, this is now / Monkees (theme from) / Pleasant valley sunday / Last train to Clarksville.
7" Single: Released Sep '86, on Arista, by BMG Records (UK). Catalogue no: **ARIST 673**
12" Single: Released Sep '86, on Arista, by BMG Records (UK). Catalogue no: **ARIST 12 673**

VALLERI
Tracks: / Valleri.
7" Single: Released Mar '68, on RCA, by BMG Records (UK). Deleted '71. Catalogue no: **RCA 1679**

Monkey Run

BLOOD OF A CIVIL SERVANT
Tracks: / Blood of a civil servant.
7" Single: Released 29 Jul '86, on Intense, by Intense Records. Catalogue no: **INT 001**

FALLING UPSTAIRS
Tracks: / Falling upstairs.
7" Single: Released 6 Apr '87, on Intense, by Intense Records. Catalogue no: **INT 003**

WAITING FOR A 409
Tracks: / Waiting for a 409 / Waiting for a 409 (version).
12" Single: Released Oct '87, on Intense, by Intense Records. Deleted '88. Catalogue no: **INT 004**

Monkman, Francis

DWELLER ON THE THRESHOLD
Tracks: / Dweller on the threshold / Margarita.
7" Single: Released Oct '81, on Maya, Deleted '85. Catalogue no: **MAY 001**

PULU PSHU
Tracks: / Pulu pshu.
7" Single: Released Feb '82, on Maya, Deleted '85. Catalogue no: **MAY 002**

Monks

I CAN DO ANYTHING YOU LIKE
Tracks: / I can do anything you like.
7" Single: Released Nov '81, on Eagle (London), by Eagle (London) Records. Deleted '88. Catalogue no: **ERS 012**

NICE LEGS, SHAME ABOUT HER FACE
Tracks: / Nice legs, shame about her face.
7" Single: Released Apr '79, on Carrere, Deleted '82. Catalogue no: **CAR 104**

Monks, Jah

CHEAP WOK
Tracks: / Cheap wok.
7" Single: Released '88, on Kickers Prod., Catalogue no: **K 181955**

Mono, Niki

DAUDA & THE CROW
Tracks: / Dauda & the crow / I am a feeling / Wild pleasures / Clouds in cages.
12" Single: Released Jan '89, on Antler, by Antler Records (Belgium). Catalogue no: **ANT 095**

Monochrome

TEMPTATION
Tracks: / Temptation / Fire in the sun.
7" Single: Released Jan '82, on Stiletto, by Fast Forward Distribution. Deleted Jan '85. Catalogue no: **STC 3**

Monochrome Set

Biographical details: At the time of their only UK chart entry, this British rock band consisted of Bid (known solely by that name), J D Haney, Lester Square and Andy Warren. A non-musical fifth member was film maker and projectionist Tony Potts, who supplied visual material at the group's gigs.
The Monochrome Set were formed in 1978 and became a typically eccentric, unpredictable and flippant art-school rock group. Their first single *He's Frank* was released in January 1979. The band's diverse debut album *Strange Boutique* reached No. 62 on the British LP chart in 1980, but this remained their sole chart appearance.
The minority appeal of the Monochrome Set has meant that they have moved from one record label to another, but they have retained a modest cult following into the mid-Eighties. Bob MacDonald, Feb 1986..

405 LINES
Tracks: / 405 lines / Goodbye Joe.
7" Single: Released Jul '80, on Dindisc, by Virgin Records. Deleted Jul '83. Catalogue no: **DIN 23**

APOCALYPSE
Tracks: / Apocalypse / Fiasco bongo.
7" Single: Released Oct '80, on Dindisc, by Virgin Records. Deleted Oct '83. Catalogue no: **DIN 26**

CAST A LONG SHADOW
Tracks: / Cast a long shadow / Bridge.
7" Single: Released Oct '82, on Cherry Red, by Cherry Red Records. Deleted '87. Catalogue no: **CHERRY 51**

EINE SYMPHONIE DES GRAUENS
Tracks: / Eine symphonie des grauens.
7" Single: Released Jun '79, on Rough Trade, by Rough Trade Records. Catalogue no: **RT 019**

HE'S FRANK
Tracks: / He's Frank.
7" Single: Released Jan '80, on Rough Trade, by Rough Trade Records. Catalogue no: **BL 1**
7" Single: Released Jan '79, on Rough Trade, by Rough Trade Records. Catalogue no: **RT 005**

JET SET JUNTA
Tracks: / Jet set junta.
7" Single: Released May '83, on Cherry Red, by Cherry Red Records. Catalogue no: **CHERRY 60**

MATING GAME
Tracks: / Mating game / J.D.H.A.N.E.Y..
7" Single: Released Jul '82, on Cherry Red, by Cherry Red Records. Catalogue no: **CHERRY 42**

MONOCHROME SET, THE
Tracks: / Monochrome set, The.
7" Single: Released Sep '79, on Rough Trade, by Rough Trade Records. Catalogue no: **RTO 28**

STRANGE BOUTIQUE (SINGLE)
Tracks: / Strange boutique / Surfing SW12.
7" Single: Released May '80, on Dindisc, by Virgin Records. Deleted May '83. Catalogue no: **DIN 18**

WALLFLOWER
Tracks: / Wallflower / Big Ben bongo.
7" Single: Released May '85, on Blanco Y Negro, by Blanco Y Negro Records. Deleted '86. Catalogue no: **NEG 12**

Monopoly, Tony

Biographical details: This Australian middle of the road singer became a reasonable successful figure in British showbiz during the Seventies and Eighties. His run of the mill appearances on television and in concert caused a one-off UK chart entry in 1976 - a self titled LP reached No. 25. Bob MacDonald, 1 February 1986..

GOLDEN HAIRED BOY FROM THE VALLEY
Tracks: / Golden haired boy from the valley
12" Single: Released Jul '83, on President, by President Records. Catalogue no: **PTE 3**

Monos

SOUND OF YOUR RADIO
Tracks: / Sound of your radio
7" Single: Released May '80, on RCA, by BMG Records (UK). Deleted May '83. Catalogue no: **PB 5254**

UH-OH-UH-OH
Tracks: / Uh-oh-uh-oh / Mad lover.
7" Single: Released Feb '80, on RCA, by BMG Records (UK). Deleted Feb '85. Catalogue no: **PB 5232**

Monro

SOME GIRLS
7" Single: Released Mar '87, on Spellbound, by Spellbound Records. Catalogue no: **SPELL 11**
12" Single: Released Mar '87, on Spellbound, by Spellbound Records. Catalogue no: **SPELT 11**

Monro, Matt

Biographical details: The former London bus driver who died of cancer in 1985 was often talked of as 'England's answer to Frank Sinatra'. Shooting to fame with *I Portrait Of*

My Love'D in 1960, he was rarely out of the charts during the first half of that decade; contracted to Parlophone, home of the Beatles, he had one of his greatest triumphs with a version of /Yesterday'D and was immortalised on celluloid by the theme song of /From Russia With love'D. (Robert Cohen, 1/5/87).

This British singer enjoyed a run of hit singles in the UK from 1960 until 1965, not by adhering to the trends of the day but by singing in the age-old midle of the road tradition and simply doing it well. His first and biggest hit was *Portrait Of My Love*, which reached No. 3. His second was *My Kind Of Girl* (No. 5 in 1961), which also managed to penetrate the American Top 20 - a rare feat for any British vocalist in pre-Beatles days. His subsequent UK Top Tenners included *Softly As I Leave You* (1962) and *Walk Away* (1964).

In late 1965 Monro achieved a feat that, with the benefit of hindsight, can be reviewed as historic. When it became clear that Parlophone were not going to issue the Beatles' *Yesterday* as a single in Britain (in keeping with a common UK policy of the era that singles should not be lifted off previously released albums), Monro recorded his own version. It reached the UK No. 8 position. His was the first cover version of a song which subsequently attracted over 2500 remakes, making it the most recorded song in history.

Yesterday was Matt's final British chart single, apart from a one-off return in December 1973 with the No. 28 hit *And You Smiled.* However, his fine voice ensured that he remained a showbusiness institution. Living in London, he continued to be a performer of international repute. In 1980 a TV-advertised compilation album called *Heartbreakers* climbed to No. 5 on the British LP chart. Matt Monro died of cancer in early 1985. Bob MacDonald, 1 February 1986.

Matt Monro, UK vocalist, died in February 1985 aged 54. He made a successful career as a romantic ballad singer both in Britain and America in an age dominated by raucous pop singers.

His rise to fame against the Elvis Presley tide was a singular achievement for a small man with no stage background. One under his real name of Terry Parsons he was a London bus driver. He worked the No.27 route from Highgate to Teddington via Kentish Town. In recent years he worked chiefly in America, dividing his life between homes in Florida and West London. Earlier, he had represented Britain in the European Song Contest coming second in Copenhagen in 1964 with *I Love The Little Things*. He made numerous discs with 15 hits in the UK though he never topped the charts. His songs included *Portrait of My Love, Born Free, From Russia With Love.* His career was as romantic as his songs. He was born in Shoreditch, London and brought up in a council flat. His father died with he was three and his mother, left with four sons and a daughter became a Mrs Mopp to keep the family together. For a while Matt, the youngest son, was in an orphanage and began work in a tobacco factory later working as a plaster's labourer and a plumber's mate before bus driving. On leaving the Army he found the competition of show businesss tough but he gained his first break in 1956 when he became the resident singer with the BBC Show Band. The pianist, Winifred Attwell, had helped him make a record. (Daily Telegraph February 8th 1985).

AND YOU SMILED
Tracks: / And you smiled.
7" Single: Released Nov '73, on EMI, by EMI Records. Deleted '76. Catalogue no: **EMI 2091**

BORN FREE
Tracks: / Born free / We're gonna change the world.
7" Single: Released Mar '80, on Capitol, by EMI Records. Deleted '83. Catalogue no: **CL 16126**

DIANA
Tracks: / Diana / Beyond the hill.
7" Single: Released May '81, on EMI, by EMI Records. Deleted May '84. Catalogue no: **EMI 5194**

FOR MAMA
Tracks: / For mama.
7" Single: Released Dec '64, on Parlophone, by EMI Records. Deleted '67. Catalogue no: **R 5215**

FROM RUSSIA WITH LOVE
Tracks: / From Russia with love.
7" Single: Released Nov '63, on Parlophone, by EMI Records. Deleted '66. Catalogue no: **R 5068**

GONNA BUILD A MOUNTAIN
Tracks: / Gonna build a mountain.
7" Single: Released Sep '61, on Parlophone, by EMI Records. Deleted '64. Catalogue no: **R 4819**

MY KIND OF GIRL
Tracks: / MY kind of girl.
7" Single: Released Mar '61, on Parlophone, by EMI Records. Deleted '64. Catalogue no: **R 4755**

MY LOVE AND DEVOTION
Tracks: / My love and devotion.
7" Single: Released Nov '62, on Parlophone, by EMI Records. Deleted '65. Catalogue no: **R 4954**

PORTRAIT OF MY LOVE
Tracks: / Portrait of my love.
7" Single: Released Dec '60, on Parlophone, by EMI Records. Deleted '63. Catalogue no: **R 4714**

SOFTLY AS I LEAVE YOU (SINGLE)
Tracks: / Softly as I leave you.
7" Single: Released Feb '62, on Parlophone, by EMI Records. Deleted '65. Catalogue no: **R 4868**

WALK AWAY
Tracks: / Walk away.
7" Single: Released Sep '64, on Parlophone, by EMI Records. Deleted '67. Catalogue no: **R 5171**

WHEN LOVE COMES ALONG
Tracks: / When love comes along.
7" Single: Released Jun '62, on Parlophone, by EMI Records. Deleted '65. Catalogue no: **R 4911**

WHY NOT NOW
Tracks: / Why not now / Can this be love.
7" Single: Released May '61, on Parlophone, by EMI Records. Deleted '64. Catalogue no: **R 4775**

WITHOUT YOU
Tracks: / Without you.
7" Single: Released Mar '65, on Parlophone, by EMI Records. Deleted '68. Catalogue no: **R 5251**

YESTERDAY
Tracks: / Yesterday.
7" Single: Released Oct '65, on Parlophone, by EMI Records. Deleted '68. Catalogue no: **R 5348**

Monroe

YOU CAN'T TRUST A WOMAN
Tracks: / You can't trust a woman / Who needs you.
7" Single: Released Nov '80, on Polydor, by Polydor Ltd. Deleted '83. Catalogue no: **POSP 189**

Monroe, Gerry

CRY
Tracks: / Cry.
7" Single: Released Sep '70, on Chapter One, Deleted '73. Catalogue no: **CH 128**

GIRL OF MY DREAM
Tracks: / Girl of my dreams.
7" Single: Released Feb '72, on Chapter One, Deleted '75. Catalogue no: **CH 159**

IT'S A SIN TO TELL A LIE
Tracks: / It's a sin to tell a lie.
7" Single: Released Apr '71, on Chapter One, Deleted '74. Catalogue no: **CH 144**

LITTLE DROPS OF SILVER
Tracks: / Little drops of silver.
7" Single: Released Aug '71, on Chapter One, Deleted '74. Catalogue no: **CH 152**

MY PRAYER
Tracks: / My prayer.
7" Single: Released Nov '70, on Chapter One, Deleted '73. Catalogue no: **CH 132**

SALLY
Tracks: / Sally.
7" Single: Released May '70, on Chapter One, Deleted '73. Catalogue no: **CH 122**

Monroe, Jesus

LOVE AMERICAN STYLE
Tracks: / Love American style.
12" Single: Released Oct '88, on Ediesta, Catalogue no: **CALC 070T**

Monroe, Marilyn

I WANNA BE LOVED BY YOU
Tracks: / I wanna be loved by you.
7" Single: Released Apr '83, on EMI (France), by EMI Records. Catalogue no: **2C 008 83377**
7" Single: Released Feb '79, on United Artists, by EMI Records. Catalogue no: **UP 36484**

WHEN I FALL IN LOVE
Tracks: / Heatwave / Diamonds are a girl's best friend* / When I fall in love.
Note: *=Extra track on 12" only
7" Pic: Released Feb '87, on Zuma, Catalogue no: **ZOOMP 6**
7" Single: Released Feb '87, on Zuma, Catalogue no: **ZOOM 6**
12" Single: Released Feb '87, on Zuma, Catalogue no: **ZOOMT 6**

MONROES - SUNDAY PEOPLE (Released on EMI)

Monroes

CHEERIO
7" Single: Released Nov '86, on EMI, by EMI Records. Catalogue no: **EMI 5590**

JEANETTE Stay with me -
Tracks: / Jeanette / Jeanette (Stay with me) - / How strong is your love?.
7" Single: Released Mar '86, on Parlophone, by EMI Records. Catalogue no: **R 6122**
12" Single: Released Mar '86, on Parlophone, by EMI Records. Catalogue no: **12R 6122**

LET'S GO
Tracks: / Let's go.
7" Single: Released Aug '85, on Parlophone, by EMI Records. Catalogue no: **R 6105**
12" Single: Released Aug '85, on Parlophone, by EMI Records. Catalogue no: **12R 6105**

SUNDAY PEOPLE(see panel above)
Tracks: / Sunday people / Move in closer.
7" Single: on EMI, by EMI Records. Catalogue no: **EMI 5450**

WHAT DO ALL THE PEOPLE KNOW
Tracks: / What do all the people know / Yamarock.
7" Single: Released '82, on CBS, by CBS Records. Deleted '87. Catalogue no: **ALFA2468**

WISH YOU WERE HERE
Tracks: / Wish you were here / Lady on 5th avenue.
7" Single: Released Jun '86, on EMI, by EMI Records. Catalogue no: **EMI 5576**
12" Single: Released Jun '86, on EMI, by EMI Records. Catalogue no: **12EMI 5576**

Monsoon

Biographical details: This British band consisted of Sheila Chandra, Steve Coe, Dari Mankoo and Martin Smith.

With much originality and imagination, Monsoon married the traditional Eastern sounds of the Indian sub-continent with Western pop. Formed in early 1981, the group was led by lovely teenage singer Sheila Chandra, who was of Indian origin and had had a part in the BBC TV school soap opera Grange Hill. Also of Eastern blood was Dari Mankoo, who played sitar and tabla. Smith played convential rock guitar and Coe was responsible for keyboards, co-production and writing the material as well as forming the band in the first place. Monsoon's first single *Ever So Lonely* was a flop at first, but eventually reached the UK No. 12 position in the Spring of 1982. The follow-up *Shakti (The Meaning Of Within* peaked at No. 41. The band faded surprisingly quickly, perhaps because the idea was not so new after all - the third single was a remake of the Beatles' 1966 track *Tomorrow Never Knows*, conceived when the Fab Four were in the midst of their Eastern phase. The only Monsoon album *Third Eye*, issued in August 1983, was not a commercial success, and the band was defunct by the end of the year.

In 1984 Sheila Chandra released her first solo LP *Out On My Own*, one of the most acclaimed indie albums of the year; its cult acceptance did not spread to the national charts but, with the singer still only 20 years old, it suggested that her promising and individual talent had much more to offer in laer years. Bob MacDonald, 1 February 1986..

EVER SO LONELY
Tracks: / Ever so lonely / Sunset over the Ganges.
7" EP: Released Jun '81, on Indipop, by Indipop Records. Catalogue no: **IND 1**
7" Single: Released Apr '82, on Phonogram, by Phonogram Ltd. Deleted '85. Catalogue no: **CORP 2**

SHATKI (THE MEANING OF WITHIN)
Tracks: / Shatki (the meaning of within).
7" Single: Released May '82, on Mobile Suit Corporation, Catalogue no: **CORP 4**
12" Single: Released May '82, on Mobile Suit Corporation, Catalogue no: **CORP 4 12**

TOMORROW NEVER KNOWS
Tracks: / Tomorrow never knows.
7" Single: Released Oct '82, on Mobile Suit Corporation, Catalogue no: **CORP 6**
12" Single: Released Oct '82, on Mobile Suit Corporation, Catalogue no: **CORP 612**

WINGS OF THE DAWN
Tracks: / Wings of the dawn.
7" Single: Released May '83, on Mobile Suit Corporation, Catalogue no: **CORP 7**
12" Single: Released May '83, on Mobile Suit Corporation, Catalogue no: **CORP 7 12**

Montage

WHEN I CLOSE MY EYES
Tracks: / When I close my eyes / Where are you now?.
7" Single: Released Aug '86, on Reekus, by Reekus Records. Catalogue no: **RKS 018**

Montana, June

I NEED YOUR LOVE
Tracks: / I need your love / I need your love (te queiro) / I need your love (extended) (Only on 12".) / I need your love (full length club remix) (Only on CD single.).
CD 5": Released Jul '89, on ffrr, by London Records. Catalogue no: **FFRCD 28**
7" Single: Released Jun '89, on ffrr, by London Records. Catalogue no: **FFR 28**
12" Single: Released Jun '89, on ffrr, by London Records. Catalogue no: **FFRX 28**

Montana, Kid

SPOOKY
Tracks: / Spooky.
7" Single: Released Dec '86, on Les Disques Du Crepuscule(Belgium), by Les Disques Du Crepuscule(Belgium). Catalogue no: **7TWI 805**

STILL COLOUR WAITING
Tracks: / Still colour waiting / Spooky.
7" Single: Released May '87, on Les Disques Du Crepuscule(Belgium), by Les Disques Du Crepuscule(Belgium). Catalogue no: **7TWI 812**
12" Single: Released Apr '87, on Les Dis-

ques Du Crepuscule(Belgium), by Les Disques Du Crepuscule(Belgium). Catalogue no: **TWI 812**

Montana Sextet

Biographical details: The club favourite *Heavy Vibes* provided this American band with a one-off UK chart entry in January 1983 - it reached No. 59 on the singles chart. Bob MacDonald, 1 February 1986..

HEAVY VIBES
Tracks: / Heavy vibes (On all versions) / Heavy heavy vibes (On TENR 204) / Heavy vibes (club mix) (On 12" only) / Heavy vibes (radio edit) (On TENT 204) / It keeps me coming back / I wanna know.
7" Single: Released Jan '83, on Virgin, by Virgin Records. Deleted '86. Catalogue no: **VS 560**
7" Single: on 10 Records, by Virgin Records. Catalogue no: **TEN 204**
12" Single: on 10 Records, by Virgin Records. Catalogue no: **TENR 204**
12" Single: Released Sep '87, on Unidisc (Canada). Catalogue no: **SPEC 1248**
12" Single: on 10 Records, by Virgin Records. Catalogue no: **TENT 204**

WHO NEEDS ENEMIES (WITH A FRIEND LIKE...)
Tracks: / Who needs enemies (with a friend like...).
7" Single: Released Jun '83, on Virgin, by Virgin Records. Deleted '89. Catalogue no: **VS 600**
12" Single: Released Jun '83, on Virgin, by Virgin Records. Deleted '89. Catalogue no: **VS 600-12**

Montellas

PROTECTION
Tracks: / Protection / Rut, The.
Note: *Extra track on 12" version only.
CD 5": Released 23 Jul '88, on Arista, by BMG Records (UK). Catalogue no: **661 585**
7" Single: Released Jul '88, on Arista, by BMG Records (UK). Catalogue no: **111585**
7" Single: Released Jun '88, on Arista, by BMG Records (UK). Catalogue no: **ARISTA 109491**
12" Single: Released Jul '88, on Arista, by BMG Records (UK). Catalogue no: **611585**
12" Single: Released Jun '88, on Arista, by BMG Records (UK). Catalogue no: **ARISTA 609491**

STOP TALKING
Tracks: / Stop talking / Gone searching / Better the devil.
CD 5": Released Mar '88, on Arista, by BMG Records (UK). Catalogue no: **659 755**
7" Single: Released 20 Feb '88, on Arista, by BMG Records (UK). Catalogue no: **109755**
12" Single: Released 20 Feb '88, on Arista, by BMG Records (UK). Catalogue no: **609755**

Montenegro, Hugo

Biographical details: This American orchestra leader, conductor, arranger and composer was born in New York in 1925. He spent two years in the US Navy, during which he helped to arrange music for service bands. He moved to California and spent thirteen years (1955-1968) scoring films, releasing unsuccessful orchestral albums, and acting as arranger-conductor for the highly successful Harry Belafonte.
At the age of 43 Montenegro achieved fame in his own right with the title theme from the Clint Eastwood spaghetti western 'The Good, the Bad and the Ugly'. Composed by Ennio Morricone, Montenegro's arrangement of this tune was highly original. He employed an array of unusual instruments, including electric violin, piccolo trumpet and ocarina; a whistler and some grunting vocals were also used. *The Good, The Bad And The Ugly* by Hugo Montenegro and his Orchestra and Chorus reached No. 2 in the States in the Spring of 1968, and logged four weeks at No. 1 in Britain towards the end of that year.

Montenegro also recorded the theme for the next Eastwood flick 'Hang 'em High'; this single peaked at a more modest No. 50 in the UK in January 1969. The success of *The Good, The Bad And The Ugly* did of course mean that Hugo was in great demand for future film soundtracks.

Hugo Montenegro died in February 1981 at the age of 55. Bob MacDonald, 1 February 1986..

GOOD, THE BAD AND THE UGLY, (THE)
Tracks: / Good, the bad and the ugly, The / Fistful of dollars.
7" Single: Released Sep '68, on RCA, by BMG Records (UK). Deleted '71. Catalogue no: **RCA 1727**
7" Single: Released Jul '81, on RCA, by BMG Records (UK). Deleted May '89. Catalogue no: **GOLD 518**
7" Single: Released Oct '86, on Old Gold, by Old Gold Records. Catalogue no: **OG 9604**

HANG 'EM HIGH
Tracks: / Hang 'em high.
7" Single: Released Jan '69, on RCA, by BMG Records (UK). Deleted '72. Catalogue no: **RCA 1771**

Montez, Chris

Biographical details: This American singer and guitarist was born in Los Angeles in 1943, and was a protege of srock 'n' roll star Ritchie Valens. Both artists espoused the 'Chicano' style, a term that was used to describe artists who combined pop music with the Latin rhythms from south of the USA-Mexico border. In 1960, a year after the young Valens was killed in the Buddy Holly plane crash, Montez cut his first record *She's My Rocking Baby*. After graduating from high school in 1961, Montez (real name Montanez) met writer/producer Jim Lee.
Lee was responsible for the single that made Montez famous. *Let's Dance*, with its wild and crazy keyboard part and its celebratory approach cruised to No. 4 in the US in the autumn of 1962. It fared even better in Britain, surging to No. 2 and logging 18 weeks on the chart. *Let's Dance* became a party classic.

Montez' follow-up *Some Kinda Fun*, was also bigger in the UK - it reached No. 10 in Britain but failed to crack the American Top 40. While *Some Kinda Fun* was riding high in the UK, Montez toured Britain in a bill that also included Tommy Roe and the up and coming Beatles. This gave Chris a foretaste of what was to come, for the Beatles-led British conquest of the international pop scene torpedoed Montez out of the charts on both sides of the Atlantic until 1966.

Montez finally bounced back in 1966 with *Call Me* (No. 22 in US) and *The More I See You* (No. 6 in US, a No. 3 smash in Britain). The latter was an intensely jolly revamp of a 1945 number, and it demonstrated that Montez was now firmly a middle of the road performer.

Montez then faded from the charts once more, but remained an active live artist into the Seventies. Meanwhile, *Let's Dance* continued to light up dancefloors, particularly in Britain. The single was introduced to a new generation when it hit the UK Top 10 on re-issue in 1972. It made another brief appearance in April 1979, when the re-issued disc peaked at No. 47 in the UK. Bob MacDonald, 1 February 1986..

LET'S DANCE (OLD GOLD)
Tracks: / Let's dance / You're the one / Some kinda fun.
CD 5": Released 27 Feb '89, on Old Gold, by Old Gold Records. Catalogue no: **OG 6120**
7" Single: Released Nov '86, on Old Gold, by Old Gold Records. Deleted Jun '88. Catalogue no: **OG 9660**

LET'S DANCE
7" Single: Released Oct '62, on London Records, by London Records. Deleted '65. Catalogue no: **HLU 9596**

MORE I SEE YOU, THE
Tracks: / More I see you, The.
7" Single: Released Jun '66, on Pye International, Deleted '69. Catalogue no: **7N 25369**
7" Single: Released Jul '82, on Old Gold, by Old Gold Records. Catalogue no: **OG 9146**

SOME KINDA FUN
Tracks: / Some kinda fun.
7" Single: Released Jan '63, on London Records, by London Records. Deleted '66. Catalogue no: **HLU 9650**

THERE WILL NEVER BE ANOTHER YOU
Tracks: / There will never be another you.
7" Single: Released Sep '66, on Pye International, Deleted '69. Catalogue no: **7N 25381**

Montgomery, Jack

DEARLY BELOVED
Tracks: / Dearly beloved / That's no way to treat a girl.
7" Single: Released Apr '85, on Kent, by Ace Records. Catalogue no: **TOWN 102**

Montgomery, Mandy

IN MY FANTASY
Tracks: / In my fantasy / Sail away.
7" Single: Released Feb '82, on Rocket, by Rocket Records. Deleted Feb '87. Catalogue no: **XPRES 72**

Montgomery, Monty

BAD REPUTATION
Tracks: / Bad reputation / Irie.
12" Single: Released Mar '87, on Mango, by Island Records. Deleted Apr '88. Catalogue no: **12IS 321**

Montrose

Biographical details: The first and most successful line-up of this American rock band consisted of guitarist Ronnie Montrose plus Denny Carmassi, Bill Church and Sammy Hagar. Formed in 1973 by one of the West Coast's top session guitar players, the group were moderately successful exponents of heavy metal. Their eponymous debut album was released in '73 to be followed next year by *Paper Money*. Singer Hagar quit in '75 for a solo career: he struggled for a few years but his luck changed in '79 and, in 1985, he became lead vocalist with Van Halen.
Meanwhile Hagar's replacement in Montrose was Bob James and the band continued to play run-of-the-mill boogie rock throughout the 70's. Their final album, 1978's *Open Fire* was produced by Edgar Winter, in whose group Ronnie Montrose had once played. In '79 Montrose evolved into Gamma, another hard rock band who failed to rise above the crowd.
Montrose's only chart album in Britain was the self-titled *Montrose*, which reached No 43 in June '74. Two tracks from this set, *Space Station* No 5 and *Good Rockin' Tonight*, became a belated double-A-sided hit single in 1980 as part of a Warners Brothers heavy metal reissue campaign: the pairing reached the UK No 71 position. (Bob MacDonald, February 1986.).

SPACE STATION NO. 5
Tracks: / Space station no. 5 / Good rockin' tonight.
7" Single: Released Jun '80, on Warner Bros., by WEA Records. Deleted '83. Catalogue no: **HM 9**

Monty

T-T-T-TOTTENHAM
Tracks: / T-T-T-Tottenham.
Note: Royalties to be divided between the Jarrett/Groce & Blacklock families.
7" Single: Released Mar '86, on Forest, Catalogue no: **MOT 01**

Monty M.C's

HOLIDAY RAP WITH A CAPITAL C
Tracks: / Holiday rap with a capital C / Monty says don't scratch the B side.
7" Single: Released Oct '86, on Debut, by Skratch Records. Catalogue no: **DEBT 3011**
12" Single: Released Oct '86, on Debut, by Skratch Records. Catalogue no: **DEBTX 3011**

Monty Python

Biographical details: This British comedy group consisted of Graham Chapman, John Cleese, Terry Gilliam, Eric Idle, Michael Palin and Terry Williams. In their early days, the group and the television programme were known by the fuller name of Monty Python's Flying Circus. According to the sleeve notes on one of the early albums, the name was inspired by the fact that was no such person as Monty Python, it had nothing to do with flying, and it was not a circus.

Following in a long tradition of surreal and satirical British humour, the Monty Python team was formed in 1969 and emerged as the most impotant UK comedy act of the Seventies. Highly innovative and original in content and presentation, the team's BBC TV shows somehow managed to become mass entertainment without ever losing a 'cult following' status. Accompanying albums were regularly released, and seven of these registered on the British LP chart between 1971 and 1980; *Live At Drury Lane* (1974) and *Contractual Obligation Album* (1980) were the biggest, reaching Nos. 19 and 13 respectively. Sketches like *The Spam Song*, *Pet Shop* (that's the one about the dead parrot) and *Election Special* became classics.
Despite the Englishness of their material and style, Monty Python attracted a considerable following in the States. A bunch of English university graduates dealing in puns, double talk, weird animation, lumberjacks, transvestism and occasional obscenity garnered a surprisingly international audience.
In the mid-Seventies, the members of the team branched out into a variety of individual projects. The most notable was John Cleese's Fawlty Towers, a classic BBC TV situation comedy which ran spasmodically from 1975 through into the early Eighties. The Monty Python team remained intact on a part-time basis, moving from television to films. These cinematic exploits included 'Monty Python and the Holy Grail (1975), the controversial quasi-religious parody 'Life of Brian' (1979) and the generally disappointing 'Meaning Of Life' (1983). 'Life Of Brian' was financed by ex-Beatle George Harrison, after EMI withdrew its support. Harrison's film production company was also responsible for Terry Gilliam's 'Time Bandits' (1981) and Michael Palin's 'The Missionary' (1982). Bob MacDonald, 1 February 1986..

ALWAYS LOOK ON THE BRIGHT SIDE OF LIFE
Tracks: / Always look on the bright side of things / Brian.
7" Single: Released Dec '88, on Warner Bros., by WEA Records. Catalogue no: **W 7653**

GALAXY SONG
Tracks: / Galaxy song / Every sperm is sacred.
7" Single: Released Jun '83, on CBS, by CBS Records. Catalogue no: **A 3495**
7" Single: Released Jun '83, on CBS, by CBS Records. Catalogue no: **WA 3495**

I LIKE CHINESE
Tracks: / I like chinese / I bet they won't play this song on the radio.
7" Single: Released Oct '80, on Charisma, by Virgin Records. Deleted Oct '83. Catalogue no: **CB 374**

Monyaka

Biographical details: The catchy *Go Deh Yaka*-- Swahili for "Go to the top" -- gave this New York-based band a one-off UK chart entry in the autumn of 1983. It reached No 14 on the singles chart and appealed to fans of both funk and reggae. The band, who spoke fluent Swahili, seemed fresh and interesting, but the follow-up single, Reggae-matic-funk, sounded over-similar to its predecessor and the group faded into obscurity. (Bob MacDonald, February 1986.).

GO DE YAKA (GO TO THE TOP)
Tracks: / Go Deh Yaka (Go to the top)(1986 style) / Go Deh Yaka (Go to the top)(1986 style)(Instrumental).
7" Single: Released Sep '83, on Polydor, by Polydor Ltd. Deleted '86. Catalogue no: **POSP 641**
12" Single: Released Aug '83, on Polydor, by Polydor Ltd. Catalogue no: **POSPX 641**
7" Single: Released Sep '86, on Boiling Point, by Polydor Ltd. Deleted Mar '87. Catalogue no: **POSP 820**
12" Single: Released Sep '86, on Boiling Point, by Polydor Ltd. Deleted Mar '87. Catalogue no: **POSPX 820**

REGGAE-MATIC-FUNK
Tracks: / Reggae-matic-funk.
7" Single: Released Nov '83, on Polydor, by Polydor Ltd. Catalogue no: **POSP 658**
12" Single: Released Nov '83, on Polydor, by Polydor Ltd. Catalogue no: **POSPX 658**

ROUND THE CORNER
Tracks: / Round the corner.
12" Single: Released Mar '85, on Kaya, Catalogue no: **KA 005**

Mood

Biographical details: Operating in a pop-rock style, British group Mood -- Eric James, Mark James and John Moore -- had three minor hit singles in 1982. The first, *Don't Stop*, went to No 59 on the British chart. *Paris Is One Day Away* reached No 42 and *Passion In Dark Rooms* peaked at No 74. All three were well-crafted offerings that were very much in tune with the times and Mood had a fashionably dapper image: their failure to break through in a major way was something of a mystery.

They tried again in 1984 with *I Don't Need Your Love Now*, but this single missed the chart altogether. (Bob MacDonald, February 1986.).

DON'T STOP
Tracks: / Don't stop / Watching time.
7" Single: Released Jan '82, on RCA, by BMG Records (UK). Deleted '84. Catalogue no: **RCA 171**
12" Single: Released Jan '82, on RCA, by BMG Records (UK). Catalogue no: **RCAT 171**

IS THERE A REASON?
Tracks: / Is there a reason / Waves in motion.
7" Single: Released Sep '81, on RCA, by BMG Records (UK). Deleted Sep '84. Catalogue no: **RCA 129**
12" Single: Released Sep '81, on RCA, by BMG Records (UK). Deleted Sep '84. Catalogue no: **RCAT 129**

PARIS IS ONE DAY AWAY
Tracks: / Paris is one day away / No one left to blame.
7" Single: Released Apr '82, on RCA, by BMG Records (UK). Catalogue no: **RCA 211**
12" Single: Released Apr '82, on RCA, by BMG Records (UK). Catalogue no: **RCAT 211**

PASSION IN DARK ROOMS
Tracks: / Passion in dark rooms.
7" Single: Released Oct '82, on RCA, by BMG Records (UK). Catalogue no: **RCA 276**

12" Single: Released Oct '82, on RCA, by BMG Records (UK). Catalogue no: **RCAT 276**

Mood Elevators

ANNAPURNA
Tracks: / Annapurna / Driving by night.
7" Single: Released Apr '81, on Go Feet, Deleted '85. Catalogue no: **FEET 7**

GEORGIE GIRL
Tracks: / Georgie girl.
7" Single: Released '82, on R.E.D., Catalogue no: **RS 013**

Mood Mosaic

TOUCH OF VELVET-A STING OF BRASS
Tracks: / Touch of velvet - a sting of brass / Bond Street.
7" Single: Released Nov '83, on Soul Supply, by Soul Supply Records. Catalogue no: **7SS 102**

Mood Six

I SAW THE LIGHT
Tracks: / I saw the light / Flowers and boxes / Light music (Extra track on 12" version only.) / Chase, The, Theme from (Extra track on 12" version only.).
7" Single: Released May '87, on Cherry Red, by Cherry Red Records. Catalogue no: **CHERRY 97**
12" Single: Released May '87, on Cherry Red, by Cherry Red Records. Catalogue no: **12 CHERRY 97**

PLASTIC FLOWERS
Tracks: / Plastic flowers.
7" Single: Released May '85, on Psycho, Deleted '88. Catalogue no: **PSYCHO 2001**

PLASTIC FLOWERS (EP) 5-track EP
12" Single: Released May '85, on Psycho, Deleted '88. Catalogue no: **PSYCHO 4001**

WHAT HAVE YOU DONE
Tracks: / What have you done.
12" Single: Released Aug '86, on Cherry Red, by Cherry Red Records. Catalogue no: **12 CHERRY 94**

Moodie

DO THE JAM
Tracks: / Do the jam.
7" Single: Released '89, on Seven Seals, Catalogue no: **UNKNOWN**
12" Single: Released '89, on Seven Seals, Catalogue no: **LRM 132**

GIVE ME LOVE
Tracks: / Give me love.
12" Single: Released Sep '86, on Port, Catalogue no: **PORT 002**

HOLD ME TIGHT
Tracks: / Hold me tight.
12" Single: Released Mar '82, on LRM, Catalogue no: **LRM 001**

I LOVE YOU
12" Single: Released '89, on Seven Seals, Catalogue no: **TCD 019**

JANIE GOES TO PARIS
Tracks: / Janie goes to Paris.
12" Single: Released '89, on Seven Seals, Catalogue no: **LRM 132**

LOVE IS A WONDERFUL THING
12" Single: Released Sep '85, on Port, Catalogue no: **PORT 003**

STICKSMAN
12" Single: Released Sep '85, on Port, Catalogue no: **PORT 004**

Moodists

DISCIPLES KNOW
Tracks: / Disciples know.
7" Single: Released Mar '83, on Red Flame (1), by Red Flame Records. Catalogue no: **RF 721**

ENOUGH LEGS TO LIVE ON
Tracks: / Enough legs to live on.
7" Single: Released Oct '84, on Red Flame 10, by Virgin Records. Catalogue no: **RFB 41**

GONE DEAD
Tracks: / Gone dead.
7" Single: Released Oct '83, on Au-Go-Go (Australia), by Au-Go-Go Records (Australia). Catalogue no: **ANDA 18**

HEY LITTLE GARY
Tracks: / Hey little Gary / Someone's got to give / Somebody to love (On 12" only) / It takes a thief (On 12" only).
7" Single: Released May '87, on Tim, by Tim Records. Catalogue no: **MOT 5**
12" Single: Released May '87, on Tim, by Tim Records. Catalogue no: **12 MOT 5**

JUSTICE & MONEY TOO
Tracks: / Justice & money too.
7" Single: Released Nov '85, on Creation, by Creation Records. Deleted Jul '88. Catalogue no: **CRE 023**

12" Single: Released Nov '85, on Creation, by Creation Records. Deleted Jul '88. Catalogue no: **CRE 023T**

RUNAWAY
Tracks: / Runaway / Chevrolet rise.
7" Single: Released May '84, on Red Flame 10, by Virgin Records. Catalogue no: **RFB 39**
12" Single: Released May '84, on Red Flame 10, by Virgin Records. Catalogue no: **RFB 3912**

TAKE THE RED CARPET OUT OF TOWN
Tracks: / Take the red carpet out of town / Jack o' diamonds / Everybody don't tell her.
12" Single: Released Sep '86, on Tim, by Tim Records. Catalogue no: **12 MOT 1**

Moody Blues

Biographical details: The classic line-up of this British rock band was Graeme Edge, Justin Hayward, John Lodge, Mike Pinder and Ray Thomas. Formed as a rhythm-and-blues combo in Birmingham in 1964, they shot to No 1 on the UK chart with their second single, *Go Now*, in January '65. This magnificent record, a cover version of a 1963 song recorded by Bessie Banks, reached No 10 in the States. At that time the line-up comprised Edge, Pinder and Thomas plus Denny Laine and Clint Warwick. Their next three singles all reached the British Top Fifty but failed to crack the Top Twenty. The rapid decline accelerated during 1966, causing Laine and Warwick to quit: Warwick faded into oblivion while Laine became Paul McCartney's most important cohort in Wings during the 70's. The departing pair's replacements were Justin Hayward and John Lodge; the latter had been an original member for a few weeks in '64 but had delayed joining on a full-time basis in order to complete his City and Guild exams. The revamped group did not immediately turn round their fortune and the next four singles flopped. The revival began at the end of '77 when Decca's Deram label decided they liked the new complex, classically-influenced direction the Moodies were hinting at. To promote a new stereo recording system they had developed the company hired the group to record their own version of Dvorak's New World Symphony with the London Festival Orchestra. Showing admirable cheek and nerve, the group persuaded arranger-producer Peter Knight to let them record their own concept album instead. An initially disgruntled Deram released this classical-rock fusion LP, *Days Of Future Passed*, in November '67. Early in the following year the epic single *Nights In White Satin* sneaked to No 19 on the UK chart and its parent album reached 27. A single from the album, Tuesday Afternoon, reached the American Top Thirty. Realising they had stumbled on a promising formular, the Moody Blues developed their symphonic pop sound even further and became the first kings of pomp-rock. During the late 60's and early 70's they were one of the world's most successful bands. In Britain they chalked up six Top Five entries during this period, including three No 1 sets, *On The Threshold Of A Dream* ('69), *A Question Of Balance* ('70) and *Every Good Boy Deserves Favour* ('71). The masterly single, *Question*, reached the UK No 2 position in 1970. *Nights In White Satin* surged belatedly to No 2 in the States in '72, causing it to rebound to Britain and reach the UK Top Ten for the first time. The Moodies paved the way for Yes, Rick Wakeman, Genesis, ELO and all the other progressive pomp-rock bands of the early 70's. The Moody Blues were in abeyance from 1973 until 1978 to make way for individual projects. They successfully returned in '78 with the *Octave* album and enjoyed one of their biggest-ever American successes with the chart-topping 1981 album *Long Distance Voyager*. The Present, in '83, was a musical and commercial disappointment but the group kept going. In late '84 they embarked on a national UK benefit tour in aid of children's charities and at the same time a compilation album, *Voices In The Sky*, was released. Who would have thought, 20 years earlier, that they would be transformed from a beat combo to classic rock stalwarts? (Bob MacDonald, February 1986.).

BLUE WORLD
Tracks: / Blue world.
7" Single: Released Aug '83, on Threshold (1), by Threshold Records. Catalogue no: **TH 30**
12" Single: Released Aug '83, on Threshold (1), by Threshold Records. Catalogue no: **THX 30**

BOULEVARD DE LA MADELAINE
Tracks: / Boulevard de la Madelaine.
7" Single: Released '66, on Decca, by Decca Records. Deleted '88. Catalogue no: **F 12598**

EVERYDAY
Tracks: / Everyday.
7" Single: Released Nov '65, on Decca, by Decca Records. Deleted '68. Catalogue no: **F 12266**

FLY ME HIGH
Tracks: / Fly me high.
7" Single: Released May '67, on Decca, by Decca Records. Deleted '88. Catalogue no: **F 12607**

FROM THE BOTTOM OF MY HEART
Tracks: / From the bottom of my heart.
7" Single: Released Nov '65, on Decca, by Decca Records. Deleted '68. Catalogue no: **F 12166**

GEMINI DREAM
Tracks: / Gemini dream / Painted smile.
7" Single: Released Jun '81, on Threshold (1), by Threshold Records. Deleted Jun '84. Catalogue no: **TH 27**

GO NOW
Tracks: / Go now.
7" Single: Released Dec '64, on Decca, by Decca Records. Deleted '67. Catalogue no: **F 12022**
7" Single: Released Sep '85, on Old Gold, by Old Gold Records. Catalogue no: **OG 9509**

I DON'T WANT TO GO ON WITHOUT YOU
Tracks: / I don't want to go on without you.
7" Single: Released Mar '65, on Decca, by Decca Records. Deleted '68. Catalogue no: **F 12095**

I KNOW YOU'RE OUT THERE SOMEWHERE
Tracks: / I know you're out there somewhere / Miracle / I know you're out there somewhere (Ext. Remix) (12" & CD only) / Rock 'n' roll over you (live) (12" & CD only).
CD 5": Released May '88, on Polydor, by Polydor Ltd. Catalogue no: **POCD 921**
7" Single: Released May '88, on Polydor, by Polydor Ltd. Catalogue no: **POSP 921**
12" Single: Released May '88, on Polydor, by Polydor Ltd. Catalogue no: **POSPX 921**

I'M JUST A SINGER (IN A ROCK'N'ROLL BAND)
Tracks: / I'm just a singer (in a rock and roll band).
7" Single: Released Feb '73, on Threshold (1), by Threshold Records. Deleted '76. Catalogue no: **TH 13**

ISN'T LIFE STRANGE
Tracks: / Isn't life strange.
7" Single: Released May '72, on Threshold (1), by Threshold Records. Deleted '75. Catalogue no: **TH 9**

MEANWHILE
Tracks: / Meanwhile / Twenty two thousand days.
7" Single: Released May '81, on Threshold (USA), by London Records. Deleted May '84. Catalogue no: **TH 26**

NIGHTS IN WHITE SATIN
Tracks: / Nights in white satin.
7" Single: Released '67, on Deram, by London Records. Catalogue no: **DM 161**

NIGHTS IN WHITE SATIN (OLG GOLD)
Tracks: / Nights in white satin / Cities.
7" Single: Released Jun '88, on Old Gold, by Old Gold Records. Catalogue no: **OG 9349**

NO MORE LIES
Tracks: / No more lies / Rivers of endless love / Other side of life, The (live) (Track available on 12" single only.).
7" Single: Released 14 Nov '88, on Polydor, by Polydor Ltd. Deleted 30 May '89. Catalogue no: **PO 27**
12" Single: Released 14 Nov '88, on Polydor, by Polydor Ltd. Deleted 30 May '89. Catalogue no: **PZ 27**

OTHER SIDE OF LIFE (SINGLE)
Tracks: / Other side of life, The
7" Single: Released Oct '86, on Polydor, by Polydor Ltd. Deleted Aug '87. Catalogue no: **POSP 830**
12" Single: Released Oct '86, on Polydor, by Polydor Ltd. Deleted Aug '87. Catalogue no: **POSPX 830**

QUESTION
Tracks: / Question.
7" Single: Released May '70, on Threshold (1), by Threshold Records. Deleted '73. Catalogue no: **TH 4**
7" Single: Released Oct '83, on Old Gold, by Old Gold Records. Deleted Jul '88. Catalogue no: **OG 9348**

RIDE MY SEE-SAW
Tracks: / Ride my see-saw.
7" Single: Released Dec '68, on Deram, by London Records. Deleted '71. Catalogue no: **DM 213**

SITTING AT THE WHEEL
Tracks: / Sitting at the wheel.
7" Single: Released Oct '83, on Threshold (1), by Threshold Records. Catalogue no: **TH 31**
12" Single: Released Oct '83, on Threshold (1), by Threshold Records. Catalogue no: **THX 31**

TALKING OUT OF TURN
Tracks: / Talking out of turn / Veteran cosmic rocker.
7" Pic: Released Oct '81, on Threshold (1), by Threshold Records. Deleted '85. Catalogue no: **THPD 29**
7" Single: Released Oct '81, on Threshold (1), by Threshold Records. Deleted '85. Catalogue no: **TH 29**

VOICE, THE
7" Single: Released Nov '84, on Threshold (1), by Threshold Records. Catalogue no: **TH 33**

VOICES IN THE SKY (SINGLE)
Tracks: / Voices in the sky.
7" Single: Released Aug '68, on Deram, by London Records. Deleted '71. Catalogue no: **DM 196**

YOUR WILDEST DREAM
Tracks: / Your wildest dream / Talkin' talkin'.
7" Single: Released Mar '86, on Polydor, by Polydor Ltd. Catalogue no: **POSP 787**
12" Single: Released Mar '86, on Polydor, by Polydor Ltd. Deleted Aug '87. Catalogue no: **POSPX 787**

Moody Boys

ACID RAPPIN'
Tracks: / Acid rappin' / Acid rappin' (version).
7" Single: Released Oct '88, on Citybeat, by Beggars Banquet Records. Catalogue no: **CBE 730**
12" Single: Released Oct '88, on Citybeat, by Beggars Banquet Records. Catalogue no: **CBE 1230**

FIRST NATIONAL RAPPA, THE
Tracks: / First national rappa, The / First national rappa, The (version) / Funk Zulu you're so fresh.
12" Single: Released Jul '89, on Citybeat, by Beggars Banquet Records. Catalogue no: **CBE 1239**

Moody, George

I'M IN LOVE WITH A MEMORY
Tracks: / I'm in love with a memory / Michelle.
7" Single: Released Dec '82, on Marina, Catalogue no: **DBWS 022**

Moon, Johnny

FORWARD LOVE
Tracks: / Forward love / Something inside of me.
7" Single: Released '86, on Swoop, Catalogue no: **RTLS 015**

OH CAROL
Tracks: / Oh Carol / Why can't you stay.
7" Single: Released '67, on Swoop, Catalogue no: **RTLS 010**

Moondogs

IMPOSTER
Tracks: / Imposter / Baby snatcher.
7" Single: Released Apr '81, on Real, by WEA Records. Deleted '85. Catalogue no: **ARE 16**

TALKING IN THE CANTINE
Tracks: / Talking in the cantine / Make her love me.
7" Single: Released Feb '81, on Real, by WEA Records. Deleted '84. Catalogue no: **ARE 14**

WHO'S GONNA TELL MARY ?
Tracks: / Who's gonna tell Mary ? / Overcaring parents.
7" Single: Released Oct '80, on Real, by WEA Records. Deleted Oct '83. Catalogue no: **ARE 13**

Moone, Maggie

HAPPY EVERYTHING
Tracks: / Happy everything
7" Single: Released May '80, on GTO, Deleted May '83. Catalogue no: **GT 270**

Mooney, Eddie

I BOUGHT 3 EGGS
Tracks: / I bought 3 eggs.
7" Single: Released Nov '79, on TJM, Deleted '82. Catalogue no: **TJM 16**

Moonflowers

WE DIG YOUR EARTH
Tracks: / We dig your earth.
7" Single: Released May '89, on Electric Stars, Catalogue no: **ESTT 001**
12" Single: Released May '89, on Electric Stars, Catalogue no: **ESTT 1**

Moonliters

OH WHAT A NIGHT
Tracks: / Oh what a night / Miss you

/ Lonely boy (Available on CD single only.).
CD 5": Released Nov '88, on WEA, by WEA Records. Catalogue no: **YZ 327CD**
7" Single: Released Nov '88, on WEA, by WEA Records. Catalogue no: **YZ 327**
12" Single: Released Nov '88, on WEA, by WEA Records. Catalogue no: **YZ 327T**

Moontrekkers

NIGHT OF THE VAMPIRE
Tracks: / Night of the vampire.
7" Single: Released Nov '61, on Parlophone, by EMI Records. Deleted '64. Catalogue no: **R 4814**

Moontwist

SIGHT & SOUND
Tracks: / Sight and sound.
7" Single: Released Oct '85, on Certain, by Certain Records. Catalogue no: **ACERT 4**
12" Single: Released Oct '85, on Certain, by Certain Records. Catalogue no: **12 ACERT 4**

TALKING ABOUT THE WEATHER
Tracks: / Talking about the weather / Love in a war zone / Venus on the wing (Extra track on 12" version only).
7" Single: Released Mar '87, on London Records, by London Records. Deleted Sep '87. Catalogue no: **LON 124**
12" Single: Released Mar '87, on London Records, by London Records. Catalogue no: **LONX 124**

Moore, Christy

BACK HOME IN DERRY (SINGLE)
Tracks: / Back home in Derry.
7" Single: Released '88, on WEA (Ireland), by WEA Records. Catalogue no: **IR 9241**

BIKO DRUM
Tracks: / Biko drum / Derby day.
7" Single: Released Jul '87, on WEA, by WEA Records. Catalogue no: **YZ 135**

DELERIUM TREMENS (SINGLE)
Tracks: / Delerium tremens.
7" Single: Released '88, on WEA (Ireland), by WEA Records. Catalogue no: **IR 8831**

DELIRIUM TREMENS
Tracks: / Delirium tremens.
7" Single: Released Aug '85, on WEA (Ireland), by WEA Records. Catalogue no: **IR 8993**

DON'T FORGET YOUR SHOVEL (SINGLE)
Tracks: / Don't forget your shovel.
7" Single: Released '88, on WEA (Ireland), by WEA Records. Catalogue no: **IR 9718**

DYING SOLDIER, THE (SINGLE)
Tracks: / Dying soldier, The.
7" Single: Released '88, on WEA (Ireland), by WEA Records. Catalogue no: **IR 8176**

KNOCK SONG, THE (SINGLE)
Tracks: / Knock song, The.
7" Single: Released '88, on WEA (Ireland), by WEA Records. Catalogue no: **IR 9591**

LISDOONVARNA (SINGLE)
Tracks: / Lisdoonvarna.
7" Single: Released '88, on WEA (Ireland), by WEA Records. Catalogue no: **IR 9353**

MESSENGER BOY (SINGLE)
Tracks: / Messenger boy.
7" Single: Released '88, on WEA (Ireland), by WEA Records. Catalogue no: **IR 8167**

ORDINARY MAN (SINGLE)
Tracks: / Ordinary man.
7" Single: Released '88, on WEA (Ireland), by WEA Records. Catalogue no: **IR 8923**
7" Single: Released Sep '86, on Demon, by Demon Records. Catalogue no: **D 1045**

RIDE ON (7")
Tracks: / Ride on / Lakes of Pontchartrain.
7" Single: Released Aug '84, on WEA, by WEA Records. Catalogue no: **X 9374**

RIDE ON (SINGLE)
Tracks: / Ride on.
7" Single: Released '88, on WEA (Ireland), by WEA Records. Catalogue no: **IR 9374**

VOYAGE, THE
Tracks: / Voyage, The.
7" Single: Released Sep '89, on WEA, by WEA Records. Catalogue no: **YZ 416**
12" Single: Released Sep '89, on WEA, by WEA Records. Catalogue no: **YZ 416T**

Moore, Dorothy

Biographical details: Based at Malaco Records in Jackson, Mississippi, this American soul singer shot to fame in 1976 with the straightforward, sensual ballad *Misty Blue*. It reached No 3 in America and No 5 in Britain and the album of the same name was a US top seller, yielding a further UK Top Forty single: Willie Nelson's *Funny How Time Slips Away* provided an interesting link between a country song and a soul singer. In 1977 Moore climbed to No 27 in the States and No 20 in Britain with a cut of the Addrisi Brothers' *I Believe You*. She subsequently faded from prominence due to lacklustre material: she couldn't find further ballads to live up to the standard of her hits. (Bob MacDonald, February 1986.).

FUNNY HOW TIME SLIPS AWAY
Tracks: / Funny how time slips away.
7" Single: Released Oct '76, on Contempo, Deleted '79. Catalogue no: **CS 2092**

I BELIEVE YOU
Tracks: / I believe you.
7" Single: Released Oct '77, on Epic, by CBS Records. Deleted '80. Catalogue no: **EPC 5573**

LAUGH IT OFF
Tracks: / Laugh it off / 1,2,3, you and me.
7" Single: Released Feb '83, on Malaco, by Malaco Records (UK). Deleted '88. Catalogue no: **MAL 003**

MISTY BLUE
Tracks: / Misty blue.
7" Single: Released Nov '61, on Contempo, Deleted '64. Catalogue no: **CS 2087**
7" Single: Released Oct '83, on Old Gold, by Old Gold Records. Catalogue no: **OG 9362**
7" Single: Released Jul '82, on Malaco, by Malaco Records (UK). Catalogue no: **MAL 1029**

TALK TO ME
Tracks: / Talk to me / Every beat of my heart / Lonely.
7" Single: Released Mar '80, on Epic, by CBS Records. Deleted Mar '83. Catalogue no: **EPC 8343**

THERE'LL NEVER BE ANOTHER NIGHT LIKE THIS
Tracks: / There'll never be another night like this / Crazy in love.
7" Single: Released Aug '80, on Epic, by CBS Records. Deleted '83. Catalogue no: **EPC 8836**

Moore, Dudley

Biographical details: British actor, comedian and pianist Moore first became famous via his long-lasting association with Peter Cook, though he had earlier been known as a fine jazz pianist and -- with Jonathan Miller, Alan Bennett and Cook -- as one of the four-strong cast of the seminal review Beyond The Fringe. It was with Cook that he first hit the British charts, peaking at No 18 in summer '65 with *Goodbye-ee*. Neither hit the singles chart again but Moore's skills as a serious pianist resurfaced on his two 1966 UK Top Twenty albums: *The Other Side of Dudley Moore* reached No 11 and *Genuine Dud* (credited to the Dudley Moore Trio) peaked at No 13. Pete 'n' Dud enjoyed a British LP chart entry together in May '66. The double act established themselves as one of Britain's most successful comedy teams, notably with their TV series 'Not Only But Also'. Later came their notorious Derek and Clive period: *Derek And Clive Live* reached No 12 and logged 25 weeks on the British LP chart in 1976 and the follow-up album, *Derek And Clive Come Again*, got to No 18. The diminutive Moore's burning desire for Hollywood stardom led to the duo splitting up. And he got what he wanted, becoming a major international star and a Hollywood sex symbol! His most notable triumph was the 1981 film 'Arthur', in which he starred with Liza Minelli and John Gielgud. Moore's skill on piano has led to collaborations with such musical heavyweights as John Williams (1973) and Cleo Laine (1982). (Bob MacDonald, February 1986.).

STRICTLY FOR THE BIRDS
Tracks: / Strictly for the birds / Smiling through.
7" Single: Released Nov '82, on CBS, by CBS Records. Catalogue no: **A 2947**

Moore, Gary

Biographical details: Irish rock guitarist and singer Gary Moore began his career in the late 60's, playing in a Dublin band, Skid Row. The line-up included, at one time, future Thin Lizzy leader Phil Lynott, though he did not play the two unsuccessful Skid Rown albums released in 1970 and 1971. Moore's debut solo album, *Grinding Stone*, was issued in 1973. It was no great success and in January '74 he began the first of three separate periods of membership of Thin Lizzy. At that time Lizzy were in the doldrums after failing to consolidate the success of their first hit, *Whiskey In The Jar*. Moore quit the band in April of that year because of musical difficulties. A year later he joined drummer Jon Hiseman and others in Colosseum II, a mid-70's outfit that failed to win the acclaim of Hiseman's original blues/jazz/rock fusion band Colosseum. During a break in the activities of Colosseum II, Moore spent the first five months of 1977 in his old role of temporary guitarist with Thin Lizzy: Lynott's band were now enjoying consistent success and much of this period was spent on an American tour as support act to Queen. Moore switched from Colosseum II to Thin Lizzy on a permanent basis in August '78. This time he hung around long enough to play on a successful Lizzy album, *Black Rose (A Rock Legend)*, for which he wrote a lot of material and which climbed to No 2 on the British album chart in 1979. At the same time Moore enjoyed his own UK Top Ten single with *Parisienne Walkways*, on which Lynott contributed bass guitar and guest vocals. This track, taken from his second solo album, *Back On The Streets*, was a great vehicle for Moore's guitar prowess. Just as everything seemed to be running smoothly Moore was sacked from Thin Lizzy halfway through a 1979 American tour for missing a couple of concerts. He formed his own band G Force, who released one eponymous album in 1980. Then, in '82, Moore reached No 30 on the UK charts with his third solo album, *Corridors Of Power*, a set featuring guest assistance from such familiar hard-rock players as Jack Bruce, Neil Murray and Ian Paice. A Top Twenty placing was garnered by his '84 album, *Victims Of The Future*, which yielded the minor hit singles *Hold On To Your Love* and *Empty Rooms*. The bitter friction between Lynott and Moore, which had lasted for several years, was finally knocked on the head in 1985. After patching up their differences the pair released the frenetic duet single *Out In The Fields*, which stormed to the UK No 5 position, the biggest hard-rock hit for four years. This led to a remodelled rendition of *Empty Rooms* becoming a Top Thirty hit for Moore, the latest stage in a worthy but erratic rock career. In January 1986 his old friend and sparring partner Phil Lynott died. (Bob MacDonald, February 1986.).

AFTER THE WAR (SINGLE)
Tracks: / After the war / This thing called love / Over the hills and far away (live) (on 12" only) / Emerald (on CD only) / Thunder rising (live) (on CD only).
7" Single: Released Jan '89, on Virgin, by Virgin Records. Catalogue no: **GMS 1**
7" Single: Released Dec '88, on Virgin, by Virgin Records. Catalogue no: **GMSG 1**
7" Single: Released '88, on Virgin, by Virgin Records. Catalogue no: **VS 1153**
12" Single: Released Jan '89, on Virgin, by Virgin Records. Catalogue no: **GMST 1**
12" Single: Released Dec '88, on Virgin, by Virgin Records. Catalogue no: **VST 1153**
CD 3": Released '88, on Virgin, by Virgin Records. Catalogue no: **VSCD 1153**
CD 3": Released 30 Jan '89, on Virgin, by Virgin Records. Catalogue no: **GMSCD 1**

ALWAYS GONNA LOVE YOU
Tracks: / Always gonna love you / Cold hearted.
7" Single: Released Sep '82, on Virgin, by Virgin Records. Deleted Sep '85. Catalogue no: **VS 528**

DON'T LET ME BE MISUNDERSTOOD
Tracks: / Don't let me be misunderstood.
7" Single: Released Jun '84, on Jet, by Jet Records. Catalogue no: **JET 7043**

EMPTY ROOMS
Tracks: / Empty rooms (summer 1985 version) (On all versions) / Out of my system (NOT on CD) / Murder in the skies (live) (On double 7" set only) / Parisienne walkways (live) (On CD & double 7" set only) / Empty rooms (long version) (On CD only).
7" Set: on 10 Records, by Virgin Records. Catalogue no: **TEND 58**
7" Single: Released Jul '85, on 10 Records, by Virgin Records. Catalogue no: **TEN 58**
CD 3": Released '88, on Virgin, by Virgin Records. Catalogue no: **CDT 35**

FALLING IN LOVE WITH YOU
Tracks: / Falling in love with you.
7" Single: Released Feb '83, on Virgin, by Virgin Records. Deleted '89. Catalogue no: **VS 564**
12" Single: Released Feb '83, on Virgin, by Virgin Records. Deleted '89. Catalogue no: **VS 564-12**

FRIDAY ON MY MIND
Tracks: / Friday on my mind (On 7" only) / Reach for the sky (live version) (On all versions) / Friday on my mind (12" version) (On CD & 12" only) / Friday on my mind (kool rap version) (On CD & 12" only) / Parisienne walkways (live) (On CD only).
CD 5": Released 23 May '87, on 10 Records, by Virgin Records. Catalogue no: **KERRY 164**
7" Pic: Released '87, on 10 Records, by Virgin Records. Catalogue no: **TENP 164**
7" Single: Released Apr '87, on 10 Records, by Virgin Records. Catalogue no: **TEN 164**
12" Single: Released Apr '87, on 10 Records, by Virgin Records. Catalogue no: **TENT 164**

GARY MOORE
Tracks: / Don't let me be misunderstood / Parisienne / White knuckles.
CD 3": Released '88, on Special Edition, by Castle Communications Records. Catalogue no: **CD3-4**

HOLD ON TO LOVE
Tracks: / Hold on to love.
7" Single: Released Jan '84, on 10 Records, by Virgin Records. Deleted '87. Catalogue no: **TEN 13**

LED CLONES
Tracks: / Led clones.
7" Single: Released Jun '89, on Virgin (USA), by Virgin Records. Catalogue no: **UNKNOWN**

LONER, THE
Tracks: / Loner, The (On all versions) / Johnny Boy (On all versions) / Loner, The (extended version) (Cassette only) / Loner, The (live at Hammersmith Odeon) (12" only).
Cassingle: Released '87, on 10 Records, by Virgin Records. Catalogue no: **TENC 178**
7" Single: Released '87, on 10 Records, by Virgin Records. Catalogue no: **TEN 178**
12" Single: Released '87, on 10 Records, by Virgin Records. Catalogue no: **TENT 178**

NUCLEAR ATTACK
Tracks: / Nuclear attack.
12" Single: Released Oct '81, on Jet, by Jet Records. Catalogue no: **JET 127 016**

OUT IN THE FIELDS
Tracks: / Out in the fields / Military man / Still in love with you (12" only).
7" Single: Released May '85, on 10 Records, by Virgin Records. Catalogue no: **TEN 49**
12" Single: Released May '85, on 10 Records, by Virgin Records. Catalogue no: **TEN 49-12**

OVER THE HILLS AND FAR AWAY
Tracks: / Over the hills and far away (NOT on CDT 16) / Crying in the shadows (On all versions) / Over the hills and far away (extended) (On CD's & 12" only) / Out in the fields (live) (On TENCD & TEND 134 only) / All messed up (live at Milton Keynes) (On TEND, TENT & CDT 16 only).
7" Pic: Released '88, on 10 Records, by Virgin Records. Catalogue no: **TENP 134**
7" Single: Released '88, on 10 Records, by Virgin Records. Catalogue no: **TENDJ 134**
7" Single: Released Dec '86, on 10 Records, by Virgin Records. Catalogue no: **TEN 134**
12" Single: Released Dec '86, on 10 Records, by Virgin Records. Catalogue no: **TENT 134**
CD 5": Released '88, on 10 Records, by Virgin Records. Catalogue no: **TENCD 134**
7" Set: Released '88, on 10 Records, by Virgin Records. Catalogue no: **TEND 134**
CD 3": Released '88, on 10 Records, by Virgin Records. Catalogue no: **CDT 16**
Special: Released '88, on 10 Records, by Virgin Records. Catalogue no: **TENG 134**

PARISIENNE WALKWAYS (SINGLE)
Tracks: / Parisienne walkways.
7" Single: Released Apr '79, on MCA, by MCA Records. Deleted '82. Catalogue no: **MCA 419**

READY FOR LOVE
Tracks: / Ready for love / Wild frontier / Loner, The (on 12" only).
CD 5": Released Apr '89, on Virgin, by Virgin Records. Catalogue no: **GMSDX 2**
12" Single: Released 6 Mar '89, on Virgin, by Virgin Records. Catalogue no: **GMST 2**
CD 5": Released Apr '89, on Virgin, by Virgin Records. Catalogue no: **GMSCD 2**
7" Single: Released 6 Mar '89, on Virgin, by Virgin Records. Catalogue no: **GMS 2**
12" Single: Released 6 Mar '89, on Virgin, by Virgin Records. Catalogue no: **GMSTG 2**

TAKE A LITTLE TIME
Tracks: / Take a little time / Out in the fields / All messed up (live) / Thunder rising (live).
7" Set: Released 21 Nov '87, on 10 Records, by Virgin Records. Catalogue no: **TEND 190**

WILD FRONTIER (SINGLE)
Tracks: / Wild frontier (On all versions) / Run for cover (live version) (On all versions) / Wild version (extended version) (On 12" only) / Wild frontier (live) (On TEND & TENT 159 only) / Murder in the skies (live) (On TEND 159 only) / Over the hills and far away (On CD only) / Empty rooms (On CD only) / Out in the fields (On CD only) / Shapes of things (On CD only).
CD 5": on 10 Records, by Virgin Records. Catalogue no: **KERRY 159**
12" Single: on 10 Records, by Virgin Records. Catalogue no: **TENT 159**
7" Set: on 10 Records, by Virgin Records. Catalogue no: **TEND 159**
7" Single: on 10 Records, by Virgin Records. Catalogue no: **TEN 159**

Moore, Geoffrey

SLEEP WITH ME (TONIGHT)
Tracks: / Sleep with me (tonight) / Place in your heart, A.
7" Single: Released 20 Jun '87, on Hit Or Miss, Deleted Oct '87. Catalogue no: **HOM 2**
12" Single: Released 20 Jun '87, on Hit Or Miss, Deleted Oct '87. Catalogue no: **12 HOM 2**

Moore, Grace

WAY OF LIFE
Tracks: / Way of life.

12" Single: Released Jun '86, on Stallion, Catalogue no: **SM 001**

Moore, Jackie

HOLDING BACK
Tracks: / Holding back.
7" Single: Released Apr '83, on Satril, by Satril Records. Catalogue no: **SAT 506**
12" Single: Released Apr '83, on Satril, by Satril Records. Catalogue no: **12SAT 506**

THIS TIME BABY
Tracks: / This time baby.
7" Single: Released Sep '79, on CBS, by CBS Records. Deleted '82. Catalogue no: **CBS 7722**
7" Single: Released Aug '84, on CBS, by CBS Records. Catalogue no: **A 4694**

Moore, Jackson

ONE LOOK
Tracks: / One look.
12" Single: Released Apr '88, on Mega (Supermusic), by Pinnacle Records. Catalogue no: **ELET 2**

Moore, John

FRIENDS
Tracks: / Friends.
12" Single: Released 31 Jul '89, on Polydor, by Polydor Ltd. Catalogue no: **JMEX 2**
7" Single: Released 31 Jul '89, on Polydor, by Polydor Ltd. Catalogue no: **JMEP 2**
7" Single: Released 31 Jul '89, on Polydor, by Polydor Ltd. Catalogue no: **JMEG 2**
CD 5": Released 31 Jul '89, on Polydor, by Polydor Ltd. Catalogue no: **JMECD 2**
7" Single: Released 31 Jul '89, on Polydor, by Polydor Ltd. Catalogue no: **JME 2**

OUT OF MY MIND
Tracks: / Out of my mind.
12" Single: Released 20 Feb '89, on Polydor, by Polydor Ltd. Deleted Aug '89. Catalogue no: **XWYZ 1**
7" Single: Released 20 Feb '89, on Polydor, by Polydor Ltd. Deleted Aug '89. Catalogue no: **XWY 1**

SOMETHING ABOUT YOU GIRL
Tracks: / Something about you girl.
12" Single: Released '89, on Polydor, by Polydor Ltd. Catalogue no: **JEMP 1**
7" Single: Released 2 May '89, on Polydor, by Polydor Ltd. Deleted Oct '89. Catalogue no: **JME 1**
CD 5": Released 2 May '89, on Polydor, by Polydor Ltd. Catalogue no: **JMECD 1**
12" Single: Released 2 May '89, on Polydor, by Polydor Ltd. Deleted Oct '89. Catalogue no: **JMEX 1**
12" Single: Released 2 May '89, on Polydor, by Polydor Ltd. Catalogue no: **JMEP 1**
7" Single: Released Apr '89, on Polydor, by Polydor Ltd. Catalogue no: **JMEG 1**

WAIT A MINUTE
Tracks: / Wait a minute.
12" Single: Released May '89, on Living Room, Catalogue no: **LM 022**

Moore, Johnny Darrow

STILL CAN'T SHAKE YOUR LOVE
Tracks: / Still can't shake your love / Lady loves to dance.
7" Single: Released Feb '80, on Magnet, by WEA Records. Deleted Feb '83. Catalogue no: **MAG 162**

YOUR BROKEN HEART
Tracks: / Your broken heart / Soul of love.
12" Single: Released Oct '82, on Towerbell, Catalogue no: **12TOW 28**
Special: Released Oct '82, on Towerbell, Catalogue no: **TOW 28**

Moore, Kim

YOU'RE A FOOL
Tracks: / You're a fool / 100 times a hour.
7" Single: Released Nov '80, on DB, by DB Records. Catalogue no: **DBS 4**

Moore, Larry

MEANT TO BE
Tracks: / Meant to be / Promises.
7" Single: Released 20 Jun '80, on Piccadilly, Deleted '83. Catalogue no: **7P 188**

Moore, Melba

Biographical details: This American singer and actress was a member of the original Broadway cast of the legendary musical 'Hair' in 1968, and was one of the featured vocalists on the songs *Ain't got no, Air, White boys* and *Good morning starshine.* She did not capitalise on the stunning success of the 'Hair' soundtrack LP quite as quickly as fellow cast member Ronnie Dyson, and had to wait until 1976 for her real breakthrough as a solo recording artist. When it occurred, it was courtesy of the famous disco writer/producer Van McCoy - he masterminded her exuberant single *This is it* which reached No.9 on the UK pop chart. Melba Moore has never reached the American pop Top 40 but sufaced on the British chart at three-yearly intervals, working each time with noted disco maestros. In 1979 she teamed up with McFadden & Whitehead who wrote and produced her single *Pick me up, I'll dance* (in similar style to the duo's own *Ain't no stoppin' us now*), which peaked at No.48 in Britain. In 1982 she cruised to the UK No.15 position with the punchy *Love's comin' at ya*, masterminded by Paul Lawrence Jones III who was enjoying simultaneous success with Evelyn King's *Love come down.* In early 1983 Melba's album *The other side of the rainbow* yielded two smaller UK hits, *Mind up tonight* and *Underlove.* In the States, Moore often penetrated the soul and dance charts but, in common with many other black artists, found it difficult to cross over to white-dominated pop radio. With her shrill, screechy voice growing more mature as the years went by. (Bob MacDonald, 4th February 1986).

I CAN'T BELIEVE IT (IT'S OVER)
Tracks: / I can't believe it (it's over).
7" Single: Released Oct '85, on Capitol, by EMI Records. Deleted '88. Catalogue no: **CL 381**
12" Single: Released Oct '85, on Capitol, by EMI Records. Deleted '88. Catalogue no: **12CL 381**

LET'S STAND TOGETHER
Tracks: / Let's stand together / Each second.
7" Single: Released Mar '82, on EMI-America, by EMI Records. Deleted '85. Catalogue no: **EA 137**
12" Single: Released Mar '82, on EMI-America, by EMI Records. Deleted '85. Catalogue no: **12EA 137**

LOVE'S COMIN' AT YA
Tracks: / Love's comin' at ya / Let's go back to lovin'.
7" Single: Released Oct '82, on EMI-America, by EMI Records. Deleted '85. Catalogue no: **EA 146**
12" Single: Released Oct '82, on EMI-America, by EMI Records. Deleted '85. Catalogue no: **12EA 146**

MAGIC TOUCH, THE
Tracks: / Magic touch / Pretty part of you, The.
7" Single: Released Jun '88, on Horaces, Catalogue no: **HORACE 1**

MIND UP TONIGHT
Tracks: / Mind up tonight / Other side of the rainbow.
7" Single: Released Jan '83, on Capitol, by EMI Records. Deleted '88. Catalogue no: **CL 272**
12" Single: Released Oct '82, on Capitol, by EMI Records. Deleted '88. Catalogue no: **12CL 272**

PICK ME UP, I'LL DANCE
Tracks: / Pick me up.
7" Single: Released May '79, on Epic, by CBS Records. Deleted '82. Catalogue no: **EPC 7234**

THIS IS IT
Tracks: / This is it.
7" Single: Released May '76, on Buddah, by Buddah Records Inc.(USA). Deleted '79. Catalogue no: **BDS 443**
7" Single: Released Jan '83, on Flashback, by Mainline Records. Catalogue no: **FBS 23**

UNDERLOVE
Tracks: / Underlove / Don't go away.
7" Single: Released Feb '83, on Capitol, by EMI Records. Deleted '88. Catalogue no: **CL 281**
12" Single: Released Feb '83, on Capitol, by EMI Records. Deleted '88. Catalogue no: **12CL 281**

YOU STEPPED INTO MY LIFE
Tracks: / You stepped into my life / Hard not to like you.
12" Single: Released Sep '88, on Old Gold, by Old Gold Records. Catalogue no: **OG 4504**

Moore, Nicky

OTHER SIDE
Tracks: / Other side, The / Long time.
7" Single: Released May '82, on Street Tunes, by Street Tunes Records. Catalogue no: **STS 008**

Moore, Sam

SOUL MAN
Tracks: / Soul man / Sweet Sarah.
7" Single: Released Jan '87, on A&M, by A&M Records. Deleted Mar '88. Catalogue no: **AM 364**

Moore, Seamus

JCB SONG
Tracks: / JCB song / Paidins party / 6ft 7in woman (Only on cassette.) / Town of Ballybay, The (Only on cassette.).
Cassingle: Released Jan '88, on I&B, by I & B Records. Catalogue no: **IRMC 005**
7" Single: Released Jan '88, on I&B, by I & B Records. Catalogue no: **IRS 005**

Moore, Ray

BOG EYED JOG
Tracks: / Bog eyed jog.
7" Single: Released Oct '87, on Play, by Play Records. Catalogue no: **PLAY 224**

OH MY FATHER HAD A RABBIT
Tracks: / Oh my father had a rabbit / Oh my father had a rabbit (inst).
7" Single: Released Oct '86, on Play, by Play Records. Catalogue no: **PLAY 213**

Moose, Ade & Walker

LOUNGE AROUND
Tracks: / Lounge around.
7" Single: Released Oct '84, on Lost Moments, Catalogue no: **LOM 008**

Morales, Michael

WHO DO YOU GIVE YOUR LOVE TO
Tracks: / Who do you give your love to / Won't you come home.
7" Single: Released Jul '89, on Wing (USA), by PolyGram Rec.Inc.(USA). Catalogue no: **WING 6**
12" Single: Released Jul '89, on Wing (USA), by PolyGram Rec.Inc.(USA). Catalogue no: **887 743 1**

Moran, Shaun

MOTORBIKIN
Tracks: / Motorbikin'.
7" Single: Released Dec '84, on Wat, Deleted '86. Catalogue no: **MB 41**

Mordred

EVERYDAY'S A HOLIDAY
7" Single: Released Jun '89, on Noise, by Dorane Records. Catalogue no: **7 MORD 5**

More

Biographical details: Bashing out heavy metal at a 100 mph tempo, and making it loud and hard, British all-male rock group More reached the UK No 59 position in March 1981 with their flag-waving single *We Are The Band*, from their debut album, *Warhead.* Next year they released another album, *Blood And Thunder*, before fading from the scene. (Bob MacDonald, February 1986.).

WE ARE THE BAND
Tracks: / We are the band / Atomic rock.
7" Single: Released Mar '81, on Atlantic, by WEA Records. Deleted '84. Catalogue no: **K 11561**

More, Anthony

INDUSTRIAL DRUMS
Tracks: / Industrial drums / Conference.
7" Single: Released Jun '84, on Parlophone, by EMI Records. Catalogue no: **R 6072**

WORLD SERVICE (SINGLE)
Tracks: / World service / Run right back.
7" Single: Released May '82, on Do-It, by Do-It Records. Catalogue no: **DUN 22**
12" Single: Released May '82, on Do-It, by Do-It Records. Catalogue no: **DUN IT 22**

More, Junior

COMING UP LOVE
Tracks: / Coming up love.
12" Single: Released May '89, on Steppa, Catalogue no: **STEPPA 1201**

More, Kenny

LOVE IS THE KEY
Tracks: / Love is the key.
CD 5": Released Apr '89, on Anxious, by Anxious Records. Catalogue no: **CDNERV 3**
7" Single: Released Apr '89, on Anxious, by Anxious Records. Catalogue no: **NERV 3**
12" Single: Released Feb '89, on Anxious, by Anxious Records. Catalogue no: **NERVT 3**

More, Nicky

YEAR OF THE LIE
Tracks: / Year of the lie / Smokin' / Walks like a lady.
7" EP: Released May '81, on Street Tunes, by Street Tunes Records. Deleted May '84. Catalogue no: **STS 006**

Moreno, Azucar

BREATHLESS(AUNQUE ME FALTE EL AIRE)
Tracks: / Breathless(Aunque me falte el aire).
7" Single: Released Aug '88, on Epic, by CBS Records. Catalogue no: **652885 7**
12" Single: Released Aug '88, on Epic, by CBS Records. Deleted Jan '89. Catalogue no: **652885 6**

Morgan

ONE MORE DAY
Tracks: / One more day / Princeton.
7" Single: Released Mar '80, on Evolution, by Evolution Records. Deleted '83. Catalogue no: **EV 3**

Morgan, Barry

BOOF
Tracks: / Boof.
12" Single: Released Jun '88, on JC Records, Catalogue no: **EJC 1001**

Morgan, Bob

MARGUERITE
Tracks: / Marguerite / Stepping out.
7" Single: Released Jan '80, on Gem, Deleted Jan '85. Catalogue no: **GEMS 17**

Morgan, Denroy

HAPPY FEELING
Tracks: / Happy feeling / Instrumental version.
7" Single: Released Nov '82, on Beckett, Deleted '84. Catalogue no: **BKS 6**
12" Single: Released Nov '82, on Beckett, Deleted '84. Catalogue no: **BKSL 6**

Morgan, Dermot

MR. EASTWOOD
Tracks: / Mr. Eastwood.
7" Single: Released '88, on I&B, by I & B Records. Catalogue no: **DOS 187**

THANK YOU MR. EASTWOOD
Tracks: / Thank you Mr. Eastwood.
7" Single: Released '88, on Ritz, by Ritz Records. Catalogue no: **RITZ 131**

THANK YOU VERY MUCH MR EASTWOOD
Tracks: / Thank you very much Mr. Eastwood.
7" Single: Released Mar '86, on Stiff, by Stiff Records. Catalogue no: **BUY 246**

Morgan, Derrick

Biographical details: This Jamaican singer and songwriter was a prism mover on his country's music scene throughout the Sixties, being part of the evolution from blue beat to ska to rock steady to reggae. He first came to fame with *Fat man,* a single recorded while he was still a teenager. Subsequent successes included *Look before you leap,* the suggestive *Kill me dead, Tougher than tough, Court dismiss, Do the beng beng* and *Woman a grumble.* In duet with his sister Patsy, he enjoyed success with *Housewives choice* and *Troubles.* At one point, Derrick found himself engaged in an extraordinary vinyl feud with his Jamaican contemporary and fellow legend Prince Buster; the latter attacked Morgan with singles like *Black head chinaman,* while Derrick retorted with *Blazing fire* and *Let them talk.* At the end of the Sixties, reggae became popular with British skinheads, just had ska had been with the UK Mod movement. In recognition of this, some Jamaican artists began making records specially for the skinheads. Morgan's *Moon hop* was one such example, and it provided him with a one-off UK chart entry - the single reached No.49 in January 1970. During the Seventies Morgan's importance diminished, although singles such as *Rasta don't fear* kept him on the Jamaican charts from time to time.. (B. M., Feb 1986)

MOON HOP
Tracks: / Moon hop.
7" Single: Released Jan '70, on Crab, Deleted '73. Catalogue no: **CRAB 32**

SEVEN LETTERS/FIRST TASTE OF LOVE
10" single: Released Oct '82, on Pama, by Pama Records. Catalogue no: **PMD 3220**

Morgan, Jane

DAY THE RAINS CAME, THE
Tracks: / Day the rains came, The.
7" Single: Released Dec '58, on London-American, Deleted '61. Catalogue no: **HLR 8751**
7" Single: Released Jul '82, on Old Gold, by Old Gold Records. Catalogue no: **OG 9206**

IF ONLY I COULD LIVE MY LIFE AGAIN
Tracks: / If only I could live my life again.
7" Single: Released May '59, on London-American, Deleted '62. Catalogue no: **HLR 8810**

ROMANTICA
Tracks: / Romantica.
7" Single: Released Jul '60, on London-American, Deleted '63. Catalogue no: **HLR 9120**

Morgan, Maria

BEST PART OF BREAKING UP
Tracks: / Best part of breaking up.
7" Single: Released Aug '85, on President, by President Records. Catalogue no: **PT 533**

FULL CIRCLE
Tracks: / Full circle / You got my number.
7" Single: Released May '80, on President, by President Records. Catalogue no: **PT 485**

RUPERT THE BEAR
Tracks: / Rupert the bear.
7" Single: Released Sep '79, on President, by President Records. Catalogue no: **PT 480**

Morgan, Meli'sa

DO ME BABY (SINGLE)
Tracks: / Do me baby.
7" Single: Released Nov '85, on Capitol, by EMI Records. Deleted '88. Catalogue no: **CL 385**
12" Single: Released Nov '85, on Capitol, by EMI Records. Deleted '88. Catalogue no: **12CL 385**

FOOLS' PARADISE
Tracks: / Fools' paradise
7" Single: Released Jul '86, on Capitol, by EMI Records. Deleted Oct '87. Catalogue no: **CL 415**
12" Single: Released Jul '86, on Capitol, by EMI Records. Deleted Oct '87. Catalogue no: **12 CL 415**

GOOD LOVE (SINGLE)
Tracks: / Good love / Here comes the night / Good love (album version) (on 12" only.) / Good love (extended version) (on CD single only.) / Fool's paradise.
CD 5": Released Jun '88, on Capitol, by EMI Records. Deleted Jun '89. Catalogue no: **CDCL 483**
7" Single: Released Jun '88, on Capitol, by EMI Records. Deleted Jun '89. Catalogue no: **CL 483**
12" Single: Released Jun '88, on Capitol, by EMI Records. Deleted Jun '89. Catalogue no: **12CL 483**

IF YOU CAN DO IT I CAN TOO
Tracks: / If you can do it I can to / If you can do it I can too / Fools paradise / Feeling lucky lately (This track is available on 12" single only.).
7" Single: Released 21 Nov '87, on Capitol, by EMI Records. Deleted Apr '88. Catalogue no: **CL 475**
12" Single: Released 21 Nov '87, on Capitol, by EMI Records. Deleted Jun '89. Catalogue no: **12CL 475**

WANTING YOU
Tracks: / Wanting you / Wanting you (radio version) / Wanting you (dub version).
12" Single: Released 20 Jun '87, on Master Mix. Catalogue no: **12 CHE 8413**

Morgan, Portia

INFATUATION
Tracks: / Infatuation.
12" Single: Released May '82, on Afrik. Catalogue no: **AK 137**

Morgan, Ray

LONG AND WINDING ROAD, THE
Tracks: / Long and winding road, The.
7" Single: Released Jul '70, on B & C, by Trojan Records. Deleted '73. Catalogue no: **CB 128**

Morgan, Tony

GET IT RIGHT
Tracks: / Get it right.
7" Single: Released Sep '84, on Cougar (USA), by Cougar Records (USA). Catalogue no: **BC 50002**

Morgan, Vicki

ALWAYS ON MY MIND
Tracks: / Always on my mind (Not on 12".) / Always on my mind (remix) / Always on my mind (12" remix).
CD 5": Released Sep '89, on Parlophone, by EMI Records. Catalogue no: **CDR 6231**
CD 5": Released Sep '89, on Parlophone, by EMI Records. Catalogue no: **203 546 2**
7" Single: Released Sep '89, on Parlophone, by EMI Records. Catalogue no: **R 6231**
7" Single: Released Sep '89, on Parlophone, by EMI Records. Catalogue no: **RP 6231**
7" Single: Released Sep '89, on Parlophone, by EMI Records. Catalogue no: **203 546 8**
7" Single: Released Sep '89, on Parlophone, by EMI Records. Catalogue no: **203 546 7**
12" Single: Released Sep '89, on Parlophone, by EMI Records. Catalogue no: **12R 6231**
12" Single: Released Sep '89, on Parlophone, by EMI Records. Catalogue no: **203 546 6**

Morgana

PANTHER
Tracks: / Panther / Panther (version).
7" Single: Released May '89, on Plaza, by Plaza Records. Catalogue no: **PZA 45**
12" Single: Released May '89, on Plaza, by Plaza Records. Catalogue no: **PZA 45T**

Morgan,Alan

TAKE THEM TO SCHOOL
Tracks: / Take them to school / Take them to school (instumental).
7" Single: Released Feb '87, on Total Eclipse, by Total Eclipse Records. Catalogue no: **TECLR 3**

Morgan,Brett

EVERYTHING IT TAKES
Tracks: / Everything it takes / If you want it you've got it.
7" Single: Released Jan '86, on Lady. Catalogue no: **LADY 1**

Morgan,Carlton B

SUPERNORMAL THING, THE
Tracks: / Supernormal thing, The.
12" Single: Released Oct '86, on Tim, by Tim Records. Catalogue no: **12 MOT 3**

Morgan,Tandy band

ACTION
Tracks: / Action.
7" Single: Released Feb '86, on FM, by FM-Revolver Records. Catalogue no: **VHF 26**
12" Single: Released Feb '86, on FM, by FM-Revolver Records. Catalogue no: **12 VHF 26**

Morley Morgan

FOREVER AND EVER (THE LORD'S PRAYER)
Tracks: / Forever and ever / Forever for you.
7" Single: Released Dec '88, on Spartan. Catalogue no: **DSP 1**

Morley Tom

WHO BROKE THAT LOVE
Tracks: / Who broke that love.
7" Single: Released Sep '85, on Zarjazz, by Zarjazz Records. Deleted May '88. Catalogue no: **JAZZ 6**
12" Single: Released Sep '85, on Zarjazz, by Zarjazz Records. Deleted May '88. Catalogue no: **JAZZ 6-12**

Morningstar,Jackie

ALABAMA ROCKABILITY
Tracks: / Alabama rockability.
7" EP: Released May '83, on Spade, by Rollercoaster Records. Deleted Dec '88. Catalogue no: **SPADE EP 102**

Moroder, Giorgio

CALL ME
Tracks: / Call me.
7" Single: Released Apr '80, on Chrysalis, by Chrysalis Records. Catalogue no: **CHS 2414**

CHASE
Tracks: / Chase.
7" Single: Released Mar '79, on Casablanca, by PolyGram UK Ltd. Deleted '82. Catalogue no: **CAN 144**

FROM HERE TO ETERNITY
Tracks: / From here to eternity.
7" Single: Released Sep '77, on Oasis. Deleted '80. Catalogue no: **OASIS 1**

NIGHT DRIVE
Tracks: / Night drive / Apartment.
7" Single: Released 20 Jun '80, on Polydor, by Polydor Ltd. Deleted '83. Catalogue no: **POSP 134**

NOW YOU'RE MINE
Tracks: / Now you're mine.
7" Single: Released Nov '84, on Virgin, by Virgin Records. Deleted '89. Catalogue no: **VS 710**
12" Single: Released Nov '84, on Virgin, by Virgin Records. Deleted '89. Catalogue no: **VS 710-12**

PAUL'S THEME
Tracks: / Paul's theme / Cat people.
7" Single: Released Jul '82, on MCA, by MCA Records. Catalogue no: **MCA 770**
12" Single: Released Jul '82, on MCA, by MCA Records. Catalogue no: **MCAT 770**

REACH OUT
Tracks: / Reach out.
7" Single: Released Aug '84, on CBS, by CBS Records. Catalogue no: **A 4570**

TOGETHER IN ELECTRIC DREAMS (OLD GOLD)
Tracks: / Together in electric dreams / Goodbye bad times.
7" Single: Released Nov '88, on Old Gold, by Old Gold Records. Catalogue no: **OG 9825**

TOGETHER IN ELECTRIC DREAMS (see panel above)
Tracks: / Together in electric dreams /
7" Single: Released Sep '84, on Virgin, by Virgin Records. Catalogue no **VS 713**

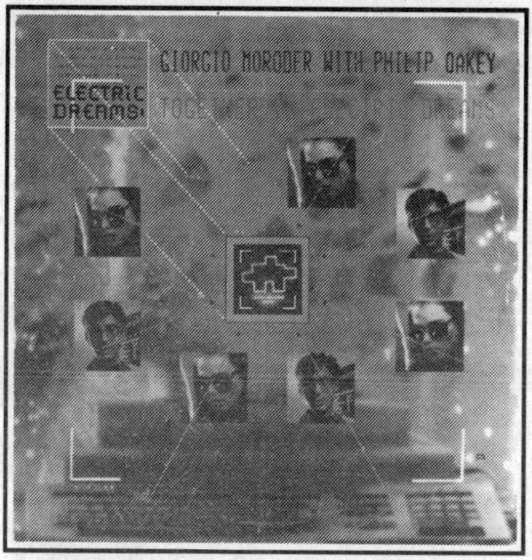

GEORGIO MORODER - TOGETHER IN ELECTRIC DREAMS (Released on Virgin)

Moronic Surveyor

I SPY(FOR THE DTI)
Tracks: / I spy (for the DTI).
7" Single: Released Oct '85, on Farse. Catalogue no: **DTI 7**
12" Single: Released Oct '85, on Farse. Catalogue no: **DTIT 7**

Morons

MORONS FROM OUTER SPACE
Tracks: / Morons from outer space.
7" Single: Released Mar '85, on EMI, by EMI Records. Deleted '86. Catalogue no: **MORON 1**
12" Single: Released Mar '85, on EMI, by EMI Records. Deleted '86. Catalogue no: **12 MORON 1**

Moross, Reg

LITTLE ONE
Tracks: / Little one / All the time & everywhere.
7" Single: Released Mar '80, on WEA, by WEA Records. Deleted '83. Catalogue no: **K 18155**

Morricone, Ennio

Biographical details: This Italian orchestra leader, conductor and composer was responsible for numerous film themes during the Sixties and Seventies. His most successful movie composition was hit title tune for the Clint Eastwood spaghetti western *The good, the bad and the ugly* in 1968. However, this number was taken into the charts not by his orchestra but by Hugo Montenegro & his Orchestra & Chorus: it reached No.2 in the States and No.1 in Britain. Earlier in the decade, Morricone backed Paul Anka on his on his 1964 smash *Ogni volta*, which became only the second single to sell a million copies in Italy alone.
In 1981 Morricone enjoyed an unexpected bonus, when BBC television dug up an old track of his called *Chi mai* and used it as the theme for their historical drama 'The life and times of David Lloyd George'. It was such a beautifully composed and arranged melody that orders for the track flooded in immediately. *Chi mai* leapt into the UK singles chart at No.19 and sped to its No.2 peak a couple of weeks later. (Bob MacDonald, January 1986).

CHI MAI (SINGLE)
Tracks: / Chi mai / Come maddalena.
7" Single: Released Apr '81, on BBC, by BBC Records & Tapes. Deleted '84. Catalogue no: **RESL 92**
7" Single: Released Jan '85, on Old Gold, by Old Gold Records. Catalogue no: **OG 9413**

ON EARTH AS IT IS IN HEAVEN
Tracks: / On earth as it is in heaven / Gabriel's oboe.
Note: 'Gabriel's Obe' is an extra track on 12" version only.
7" Single: Released Oct '86, on Virgin, by Virgin Records. Deleted May '88. Catalogue no: **VS 909**
12" Single: Released Oct '86, on Virgin, by Virgin Records. Deleted May '88. Catalogue no: **VS 909-12**

ONCE UPON A TIME IN THE WEST
Tracks: / Once upon a time in the West / Secret.
7" Single: Released Jun '81, on BBC, by BBC Records & Tapes. Deleted Jun '84. Catalogue no: **RESL 93**

SAHARA
Tracks: / Sahara.
7" Single: Released Mar '84, on Red Bus, by Red Bus Records. Catalogue no: **RBUS 88**

Morris, Ainsley

MY TERMS ONLY
Tracks: / My terms only / Continuation.
7" Single: Released Mar '84, on CBM. Catalogue no: **CBM 001**

Morris And The Minors

STATE THE OBVIOUS EP
Tracks: / State the obvious.
7" Single: Released Feb '80, on Round. Catalogue no: **MOR 1**

Morris, Byron

KITTY BEY
Tracks: / Kitty Bey / Brother Davies Miles / Bottom end, The.
12" Single: Released 22 Aug '88, on Acid Jazz, by Acid Jazz Records. Catalogue no: **JAZID 2T**

Morris, Chris

CROSS MY PALM
Tracks: / Cross my palm / Something so right.
7" Single: Released Nov '83, on Tivoli, by Tivoli Records. Catalogue no: **TIV 4**

Morris, David

SATURDAY NIGHT
Tracks: / Saturday night.
7" Single: Released Aug '82, on Beckett. Deleted '84. Catalogue no: **BKS 4**
12" Single: Released Aug '82, on Beckett. Deleted '84. Catalogue no: **BKSL 4**

Morris, Gary

SECOND HAND HEART (SINGLE)
Tracks: / Second hand heart.
7" Single: Released Feb '86, on Warner Bros., by WEA Records. Catalogue no: **W 8781**

TRY GETTING OVER YOU
Tracks: / Try getting over you / Back in her arms again.
7" Single: Released Mar '86, on Warner Bros., by WEA Records. Deleted Jun '87. Catalogue no: **W 8720**

Morris, Gee

NATURAL THING
Tracks: / Natural thing.
7" Single: Released Sep '89, on Collision. Catalogue no: **CIR 7003**
12" Single: Released Sep '89, on Collision. Catalogue no: **CIR 12003**

TOUCH A HAND MAKE A FRIEND
Tracks: / Touch a hand make a friend / Gee's groove.
CD 5": Released Dec '88, on Indi-go, by Indi-go Records. Catalogue no: **INDCD 2**
7" Single: Released Dec '88, on Indi-go, by Indi-go Records. Catalogue no: **INDS 2**
12" Single: Released Dec '88, on Indi-go, by Indi-go Records. Catalogue no: **INDX 2**

Morris, Jenny

YOU I KNOW
Tracks: / You I know / Tested sentences / Broke the leather (Only on 12" version.).
7" Single: Released May '88, on WEA, by WEA Records. Catalogue no: **YZ 187**
12" Single: Released May '88, on WEA, by WEA Records. Catalogue no: **YZ 187T**

Morris, Johnny

MORE IT SNOWS
Tracks: / More it snows / King's breakfast, The.
7" Single: Released Dec '81, on M&W, by Mawson & Wareham Music. Deleted '83. Catalogue no: **ADUB 17**

Morris, Kenny

MAIN MORT, (LA)
Tracks: / La main mort.
12" Single: Released Mar '87, on Temple Records, by Temple Records (2). Catalogue no: **TOPY 011**

Morris Minor

STUTTER RAP
Tracks: / Stutter rap (no sleep til bedtime) / Another boring 'B' side / Stutter rap (no sleep til bedtime) (12" only).
7" Single: Released Jul '87, on 10 Records, by Virgin Records. Catalogue no: **TEN 203**
12" Single: Released Jul '87, on 10 Records, by Virgin Records. Catalogue no: **TENT 203**

THIS IS THE CHORUS
Tracks: / This is the chorus / This is the chorus (On all versions) / This is the chorus (30cm mix) (On CD & 12" only) / Stutter rap (no sleep til bedtime) (On CD only).
CD 5": Released '88, on 10 Records, by Virgin Records. Catalogue no: **TENCD 229**
7" Single: Released Jul '88, on 10 Records, by Virgin Records. Catalogue no: **TEN 229**
12" Single: Released Jul '88, on 10 Records, by Virgin Records. Catalogue no: **TENX 229**

Morris, Naggo

FALSE RASTA
Tracks: / False rasta / Two time girl.
12" Single: Released Jan '83, on S & G (2), Catalogue no: **SG 23**

Morris, Sarah Jane

CAN'T GET TO SLEEP WITHOUT YOU
Tracks: / Can't get to sleep without you.
7" Single: Released Aug '88, on Jive, by Zomba Records. Catalogue no: **SJM 1**
12" Single: Released Aug '88, on Jive, by Zomba Records. Catalogue no: **SJMT 1**

ME & MRS JONES
Tracks: / Me & Mrs Jones.
CD 5": Released Feb '89, on Jive, by Zomba Records. Catalogue no: **SJMCD 3**
7" Single: Released Feb '89, on Jive, by Zomba Records. Catalogue no: **SJM 3**
12" Single: Released Feb '89, on Jive, by Zomba Records. Catalogue no: **SJMT 3**

RAINS HAVE FAILED AGAIN, THE
Tracks: / Rains have failed again, The.
CD 5": Released Jun '89, on Jive, by Zomba Records. Catalogue no: **SJMCD 2**
7" Single: Released Nov '88, on Jive, by Zomba Records. Catalogue no: **SJM 2**
12" Single: Released Nov '88, on Jive, by Zomba Records. Catalogue no: **SJMX 2**

Morris & The Minors

MORRIS MINOR
Tracks: / Morris Minor / So near yet so far.
7" Single: Released Apr '89, on Pacific, by Pacific Records. Catalogue no: **MINOR 1**

Morrison, Bruce

EYES OF SUSPICION
Tracks: / Eyes of suspicion / Count the tears.
7" Single: Released Aug '83, on Compact Organisation, Deleted '85. Catalogue no: **ACT 9**

Morrison, Julie

LOVE'S MY FAVOURITE LESSON
Tracks: / Body language / Love's my favorite lesson (extended version) (On 12" version only.).
7" Single: Released Oct '87, on Hit Or Miss, Deleted Apr '88. Catalogue no: **HOM 4**
12" Single: Released Oct '87, on Hit Or Miss, Deleted Apr '88. Catalogue no: **12 HOM 4**

Morrison, Junie

Biographical details: See Clinton, George for biographical details..

TECHNO-FREQS
Tracks: / Techno-freqs / T-fregan.
7" Single: Released May '84, on ZE, by Island Records. Catalogue no: **IS 171**
12" Single: Released May '84, on ZE, by Island Records. Catalogue no: **12IS 171**

Morrison, Tommy

HOW COME THE WEAK MAN LOOKS SO STRONG
Tracks: / How come the weak man looks so strong / Just lately.
7" Single: Released Nov '83, on His Cadillac, by His Cadillac Records. Catalogue no: **HIC 001**

WHEN THIS PUB CLOSES
Tracks: / When this pub closes.
7" Single: Released '78, on Real, by WEA Records. Catalogue no: **ARE 8**

Morrison, Van

Biographical details: This British singer, songwriter, pianist, guitarist and saxophonist was born George Ivan in Belfast, Northern Ireland. He came to fame as leader of the group Them, a combo which lasted from 1963 till 1966 and which hit it's commercial peak in 1965. Morrison's solo career began in 1967, and continued throughout the Seventies and into the Eighties. He is a classic example of an artist whose critical acclaim has heavily outweighted his commercial success; he has always resided in credibility corner'. He launched his solo journey in fine form with the classic single *Brown eyed girl.,which reached No.10 in America but flopped in the UK. It was produced by American whizz-kid Bert Berns (aka Russell), a leading songwriter and owner of Bang Records; he had been one of the guiding forces in Them's career. When Berns died of a heart attack in December 1967, Morrison moved to Warner Bros and came up with the classic album Astral weeks.* When DJ and pop journalist Paul Gambaccini polled an international panel of rock critics in 1977, Morrison's *Astral weeks* was voted 4th best LP of all time. This album emphasised all of the artists best points, particulary his tender but urgent songwriting and his soulful, blues-inflected singing. This LP marked the most extreme example of the aforementioned discrepency between reviewers and record buyers' opinions - *Astral weeks* was Morrison's most acclaimed album of all and yet sold very modestly, failing to enter the UK LP chart in any position. During the early Seventies Morrison managed to chalk up his four final US Top 40 singles: *Come running* (No.39 from the album *Moondance, Domino* and *Blue money* (Nos.9 and 23 repectively) from his *Band and street choir.* and *Wild night* (No.28, from *Tupelo honey*). Operating in an eclectic manner his music has embraced blue-eyed soul, rock, blues, jazz and folk - he retained a sizeable concert following throughout the Seventies, particulary in the States. There was a three-year hiatus in his recording career in the mid-Seventies: after the idiosynercratic *Veedon fleece* album (1974), no new material appeared until the release of the LP *A period of transition* (1977). He then continued in good form with *Wavelength* (1978), which contained the exquisite but unsuccessful single *Natalia.* In late 1979 Morrison achieved his ludiocrously overdue debut solo entry on the British singles chart - but even then, the uplifting *Bright side of the road* peaked at No.63. This single came from the *Into the music* album which reached the UK No.21 position, his highest placing to that date. In 1982 Dexy's Midnight Runners scored a UK No.5 single with his tribute to the great soul artist Jackie Wilson - 'Jackie Wilson said (I'm in heaven when you smile)' first appeared on Morrison's 1972 album *St Dominic's preview.*(Bob MacDonald, 5th February 1986).

ALAN WATTS BLUES
Tracks: / Did ye get healed / Alan Watts blues.
7" Single: Released Aug '87, on Mercury, by Phonogram Ltd. Catalogue no: **MER 254**

BRIGHT SIDE OF THE ROAD
Tracks: / Bright side of the road.
7" Single: Released Oct '79, on Mercury, by Phonogram Ltd. Deleted '82. Catalogue no: **6001 121**

CELTIC SWING
Tracks: / Celtic swing / Mr. Thomas.
7" Single: Released May '83, on Mercury, by Phonogram Ltd. Catalogue no: **MER 141**
12" Single: Released May '83, on Mercury, by Phonogram Ltd. Catalogue no: **MERX 141**

CRY FOR HOME
Tracks: / Cry for home / Summertime in England.
7" Single: Released Feb '83, on Mercury, by Phonogram Ltd. Catalogue no: **MER 132**
12" Single: Released Feb '83, on Mercury, by Phonogram Ltd. Catalogue no: **MERX 132**

DWELLER ON THE THRESHOLD
Tracks: / Dweller on the threshold / Scandinavia.
7" Single: Released Apr '84, on Mercury, by Phonogram Ltd. Catalogue no: **MER 159**

HAVE I TOLD YOU LATELY
Tracks: / Have I told you lately that I love you / Contacting my angel / Listen to the lion / Irish heartbeat.
CD 5": Released 5 Jun '89, on Polydor, by Polydor Ltd. Catalogue no: **VANCD 1**
7" Single: Released 5 Jun '89, on Polydor, by Polydor Ltd. Catalogue no: **VANS 1**
12" Single: Released 5 Jun '89, on Polydor, by Polydor Ltd. Catalogue no: **VANX 1**

I'LL TELL ME MA
Tracks: / Ta mo chleamhnas deanta / I'll tell me ma / Carrickfergus (on 12" and CD only.).
Note: "The first single from a major new project consisting the extraordinary talents of Van Morrison and Irelands foremost traditional ensemble, the Chieftans." (Phonogram Records, May 1988).
7" Single: Released 6 Jun '88, on Mercury, by Phonogram Ltd. Deleted Feb '89. Catalogue no: **MER 262**
12" Single: Released Jun '88, on Mercury, by Phonogram Ltd. Deleted Feb '89. Catalogue no: **MERX262**
CD 5": Released Jun '88, on Mercury, by Phonogram Ltd. Deleted Feb '89. Catalogue no: **MERCD 262**

ORANGEFIELD
Tracks: / Orangefield / These are the days / And the healing has begun (On CD only.).
CD 5": Released Sep '89, on Polydor, by Polydor Ltd. Catalogue no: **VANCD 3**
7" Single: Released Sep '89, on Polydor, by Polydor Ltd. Catalogue no: **VANS 3**
12" Single: Released Sep '89, on Polydor, by Polydor Ltd. Catalogue no: **VANX 3**

QUEEN OF THE SLIP STREAM
Tracks: / Queen of the slipstream / Spanish steps.
7" Single: Released Apr '88, on Mercury, by Phonogram Ltd. Deleted Oct '88. Catalogue no: **MER 261**

SOMEONE LIKE YOU
Tracks: / Someone like you / Celtic excavation.
7" Single: Released Nov '87, on Mercury, by Phonogram Ltd. Deleted Oct '88. Catalogue no: **MER 258**

Morrisons

MORRISONS EP, THE
12" Single: Released Oct '87, on Play Room Discs, by Play Room Discs. Catalogue no: **PLAYD 002-12**

Morrissey

EVERY DAY IS LIKE SUNDAY
Tracks: / Everyday is like Sunday / Disappointed / Sister I'm a poet (Only on 12", cassette and CD single.) / Will never marry (Only on 12", cassette and CD single.).
CD 5": Released Jun '88, on Parlophone, by EMI Records. Catalogue no: **CDPOP 1619**
Cassingle: Released Jun '88, on Parlophone, by EMI Records. Catalogue no: **TCPOP 1619**
7" Single: Released 31 May '88, on Parlophone, by EMI Records. Deleted Oct '89. Catalogue no: **POP 1619**
12" Single: Released 31 May '88, on Parlophone, by EMI Records. Catalogue no: **12POP 1619**

INTERESTING DRUG
Tracks: / Interesting drug / Such a little thing makes such a big difference (Morrissey/Street.) / Sweet and tender hooligan (Recorded live at the Wolverhampton Civic, December 1988.).
CD 5": Released Apr '89, on EMI, by EMI Records. Catalogue no: **CDPOP 1621**
CD 5": Released Apr '89, on EMI, by EMI Records. Catalogue no: **203 301 2**
Cassingle: Released Apr '89, on EMI, by EMI Records. Catalogue no: **TCPOP 1621**
Cassingle: Released Apr '89, on EMI, by EMI Records. Catalogue no: **203 301 4**
7" Single: Released Apr '89, on EMI, by EMI Records. Catalogue no: **203 301 7**
7" Single: Released Apr '89, on EMI, by EMI Records. Catalogue no: **POP 1621**
12" Single: Released Apr '89, on EMI, by EMI Records. Catalogue no: **203 301 6**
12" Single: Released Apr '89, on EMI, by EMI Records. Catalogue no: **12POP 1621**
Special: Released Apr '89, on EMI, by EMI Records. Catalogue no: **203 301 8**
Special: Released Apr '89, on EMI, by EMI Records. Catalogue no: **12POPS 1621**

LAST OF THE FAMOUS INTERNATIONAL PLAYBOYS, THE
Tracks: / Last of the famous international playboys / Lucky lisp / Michael's bones (Not on 7".).
CD 5": Released Jan '89, on Parlophone, by EMI Records. Deleted Aug '89. Catalogue no: **CDPOP 1620**
Cassingle: Released Jan '89, on Parlophone, by EMI Records. Catalogue no: **TCPOP 1620**
7" Single: Released Jan '89, on Parlophone, by EMI Records. Catalogue no: **POP 1620**
12" Single: Released Jan '89, on Parlophone, by EMI Records. Catalogue no: **12POP 1620**

OUIJA BOARD, OUIJA BOARD
Tracks: / Ouija board, ouija board / Yes I am blind / East West (12" & CD single only.).
CD 5": Released Nov '89, on H.M.V., by EMI Records. Catalogue no: **203 615 2**
CD 5": Released Nov '89, on H.M.V., by EMI Records. Catalogue no: **CDPOP 1622**
Cassingle: Released Nov '89, on H.M.V., by EMI Records. Catalogue no: **TCPOP 1622**
Cassingle: Released Nov '89, on H.M.V., by EMI Records. Catalogue no: **203 615 4**
7" Single: Released Nov '89, on H.M.V., by EMI Records. Catalogue no: **203 615 7**
7" Single: Released Nov '89, on H.M.V., by EMI Records. Catalogue no: **POP 1622**
12" Single: Released Nov '89, on H.M.V., by EMI Records. Catalogue no: **12POP 1622**
12" Single: Released Nov '89, on H.M.V., by EMI Records. Catalogue no: **203 615 6**

SUEDEHEAD
Tracks: / Suedehead / I know very well how I got my name / Hairdresser on fire / Oh well, I'll never learn.
CD 5": Released Feb '88, on EMI, by EMI Records. Deleted Aug '89. Catalogue no: **CDPOP 1618**
Cassingle: Released Feb '88, on EMI, by EMI Records. Deleted 31 Jul '88. Catalogue no: **TCPOP 1618**
7" Single: Released Feb '88, on EMI, by EMI Records. Deleted Oct '89. Catalogue no: **POP 1618**
12" Single: Released Feb '88, on EMI, by EMI Records. Catalogue no: **12POP 1618**

Morrissey, Louise

HILLS OF KILLENAULE, THE
Tracks: / Hills of Killenaule, The.
7" Single: Released '88, on I&B, by I & B Records. Catalogue no: **CMR 84**

Morrissey Mullen

Biographical details: Saxophonist Dick Morrissey and guitarist Jim Mullen are a jazz-funk duo who released their first album *Up* in 1977. Prior to this, both men had been gaining experience in various guises for a decade. Morrissey started out on the London jazz club circuit, principally the famous Ronnie Scott's Club. He played with many visiting jazz stars, toured with Cannonball Adderley, and became a session recording musician for such names as John Dankworth and Georgie Fame. He formed his own band If, who made a string of albums during the early Seventies. Mullen was based in Glasgow in the late Sixties, and moved his musical activities to London in the early Seventies. He played with Brian Auger, Vinegar Joe and Kokomo. It was while Dick was in New York with If and Jim was there working with the Average White Band and Herbie Mann, that the two guys met. Members of AWB guested on *Up.* The duo's second album *Cape wrath* was issued in 1979. As the Eighties dawned, Morrissey Mullen found themselves part of the UK's burgeoning jazz-funk scene. Attracting interest from disco audiences, they reached No.43 on the British LP chart with *Badness* (1981) and No.47 with *Life on the wire* (1982)...(Bob MacDonald, 5th Feb 1986).

BLADE RUNNER
Tracks: / Bladerunner / I pull the strings.
7" Single: Released Nov '82, on Beggars Banquet, by Beggars Banquet Records. Deleted Jan '88. Catalogue no: **BEG 87**
12" Single: Released Nov '82, on Beggars Banquet, by Beggars Banquet Records. Deleted Jan '88. Catalogue no: **BEG 87T**

COME AND GET ME
Tracks: / Come and get me.
7" Single: Released Feb '82, on Beggars Banquet, by Beggars Banquet Records. Deleted Jan '88. Catalogue no: **BEG 73**
12" Single: Released Feb '82, on Beggars Banquet, by Beggars Banquet Records. Deleted Jan '88. Catalogue no: **BEG 73T**

LIFE ON THE WIRE (SINGLE)
Tracks: / Life on the wire / Brazil nut.
7" Single: Released Apr '82, on Beggars Banquet, by Beggars Banquet Records. Deleted Jan '88. Catalogue no: **BEG 75**

OLD SAX AND CAPTAIN AXE
Tracks: / Ol' sax and Captain Axe.
7" Single: Released Jul '83, on Beggars Banquet, by Beggars Banquet Records. Deleted Jan '88. Catalogue no: **BEG 97**
12" Single: Released Jul '83, on Beggars Banquet, by Beggars Banquet Records. Deleted Jan '88. Catalogue no: **BEG 97T**

SO SO FINE
Tracks: / So so fine.
7" Single: Released Apr '83, on Beggars Banquet, by Beggars Banquet Records. Deleted '88. Catalogue no: **EG 94**

STAY AWHILE
Tracks: / Stay awhile.
7" Single: Released Sep '81, on Beggars Banquet, by Beggars Banquet Records. Deleted Jan '88. Catalogue no: **BEG 63**
12" Single: Released Sep '81, on Beggars Banquet, by Beggars Banquet Records. Deleted Jan '88. Catalogue no: **BEG 63T**

Morrisseys

HOME TO AHERLOW
Tracks: / Home to Aherlow.
7" Single: Released '88, on I&B, by I & B Records. Catalogue no: **CMR 73**

Morrow, Buddy

NIGHT TRAIN
Tracks: / Night train.
7" Single: Released Mar '53, on H.M.V., by EMI Records. Deleted '56. Catalogue no: **B 10347**

Mortis

IS NOTHING SACRED
7" EP: Released May '88, on Masque, by Azra International (USA). Catalogue no: **MSQ 8702**

Morton, Ivan

YOU BETTER COME HOME
Tracks: / You better come home / Sellafield rap.
7" Single: Released Jun '86, on Mint, by Emerald Records. Deleted '88. Catalogue no: **CHEW 106**

Morton, Mike

CHRISTMAS CRACKERS
Tracks: / Christmas crackers / Santa's wein er diner.
7" Single: Released Dec '83, on M&H, Catalogue no: **MH 1004**

FIDDLER ON THE GROOVE
Tracks: / Fiddler on the groove / Eine kleine.
12" Single: Released Nov '83, on M&H, Catalogue no: **12MH 1003**
7" Single: Released Nov '83, on M&H, Catalogue no: **MH 1003**

UNFORGETTABLE CHRISTMAS (SINGLE)
Tracks: / Unforgettable Christmas.
12" Single: Released Dec '83, on M&H, Catalogue no: **ZCMH 203**

WINDS OF WAR LOVE THEME
Tracks: / Winds of war (Love theme.) / Berlin beat.
7" Single: Released Oct '83, on M&H, Catalogue no: **MH 1002**

WINDS OF WAR (THEME)
Tracks: / Winds of war.
7" Single: Released Jul '85, on Sounds Right, Catalogue no: **MSBW 2**

Morton, Milt

SPIRIT OF THE THING
Tracks: / Spirit of the thing.
7" Single: Released Oct '83, on Maze, Catalogue no: **ING 7**

Morton Music Machine

CRAZY MUSIC
Tracks: / Crazy music / Reel to reel.
7" Single: Released Nov '82, on EMI, by EMI Records. Deleted Nov '85. Catalogue no: **EMI 5353**
12" Single: Released Nov '82, on EMI, by EMI Records. Deleted Nov '85. Catalogue no: **12EMI 5353**

Morty

HONEYMOON IN BABYLON
Tracks: / Honeymoon in Babylon / Little Miss World.
7" Single: Released Nov '80, on Bellaphon, Deleted Nov '83. Catalogue no: **BPS 008**

Morwells

KINGSTON TWELVE TUFFIE
Tracks: / Kingston twelve tuffie.
12" Single: on Attack, Deleted '88. Catalogue no: **TACK 5**

Moscow

GABRIEL
Tracks: / Gabriel.
7" Single: Released Jul '83, on Amazing (USA), by Amazing Records (USA). Catalogue no: **MOS 0003**

Moscow, Harry

STEP ON
Tracks: / Step on / Sexy dancer.
7" Single: Released Feb '81, on Soulville, by Soulville Records. Catalogue no: **SA 003**

Moses, Joshua

DOMINICA INDEPENDENCE FEVER
Tracks: / Dominica independence fever.
7" Single: Released Aug '80, on Shoc-Wave, Catalogue no: **SRP 0001**

JOE LE TAXI
Tracks: / Joe le taxi.
12" Single: Released 5 Mar '88, on Shoc-Wave, Catalogue no: **SRP 12X**

PRETTY GIRL
Tracks: / Pretty girl.
12" Single: Released Aug '80, on Shoc-Wave, Catalogue no: **SRP 0002**

Moses, P

TWIGHLIGHT ZONE
Tracks: / Twilight zone / Twilight zone (AA mix) / Twighlight zone (A mix) (Only on 12" version.) / Twighlight zone (radio version) (Only on 12" version.).
CD 5": Released Feb '89, on Arista, by BMG Records (UK). Catalogue no: **161 943**
7" Single: Released Feb '89, on Arista, by BMG Records (UK). Catalogue no: **111 943**
12" Single: Released Feb '89, on Arista, by BMG Records (UK). Catalogue no: **611 943**

Moses, Pablo

DUBBING IS A MUST
Tracks: / Dubbing is a must / Revolutionary step.
12" Single: Released Mar '80, on Island, by Island Records. Deleted '83. Catalogue no: **12WIP 6570**

Moses, Rick

IF I COULD JUST FALL IN LOVE
Tracks: / If I could just fall in love.
12" Single: Released Mar '86, on Teldec (1), by ASV (Academy Sound & Vision). Catalogue no: **620516**

Mosiah

RUMOURS OF WAR
Tracks: / Rumours of war.
7" Single: Released Aug '79, on Big Records, Catalogue no: **SOLD 6**

Mosquitos

HOW COULD THEY KNOW
Tracks: / How could they know.
7" Single: Released May '83, on Discovery (1), by Oryx Records. Catalogue no: **DIK 003**

Moss Poles

10,000 MILES
Tracks: / 10,000 miles.
7" Single: Released Nov '88, on Ediesta, Catalogue no: **CALC 064**
12" Single: Released Nov '88, on Ediesta, Catalogue no: **CALC 064T**

ONE SUMMER
Tracks: / One summer / Go down / Blissful.
7" Single: Released Jul '87, on Idea, by Idea Records. Catalogue no: **IDEA 006**
12" Single: Released Jul '87, on Idea, by Idea Records. Catalogue no: **IDEAT 006**

UNDERGROUND
Tracks: / Underground.
7" Single: Released 20 Feb '88, on Idea, by Idea Records. Catalogue no: **IDEA 012**
12" Single: Released 20 Feb '88, on Idea, by Idea Records. Catalogue no: **IDEAT 012**

Most, Mickie

MISTER PORTER
Tracks: / Mister Porter.
7" Single: Released Jul '63, on Decca, by Decca Records. Deleted '66. Catalogue no: **F 11664**

Motello, Elton

20TH CENTURY FOX
Tracks: / 20th century fox / Falling like a domino.
7" Single: Released Oct '80, on Edge, Deleted Oct '83. Catalogue no: **EDGE 4**

Motels

Biographical details: At the time of their major American success, this US rock band consisted of Martha Davies, Brian Glascock, Michael Goodroe, Marty Jourard and Guy Perry. Although placed in the New Wave bracket by both music press and the group's marketing team, lead singer and main songwriter Martha Davis formed the first incarnations of the Motels in the early Seventies. Moving from Berkeley to Los Angeles, the California girl spent the middle of the decade experimenting with different styles and various personnel. The line-up stabilised at last (with four of the above five members) in 1978, whereupon the Motels began to build a name for themselves on the LA club scene. They were one of a handful of bands who offered an antidote to the traditional soft-rock slickness associated with that West Coast city. The Motel's self-titled debut album was released in 1979 to good reviews. It was followed in 1980 by the *Careful* LP, which spawned two minor British hit singles with *Whose problem?* and *Day's are OK*; these peaked at Nos 42 and 41 respectively, an unlucky sequence of events in view of the fact that the UK mass media's chart coverage focuses on the Top 40! The Motels failed to consolidate this toehold, and Britain lost interest in the group. After faring quite well in Australia, the band found their major audience in their native country. The spring of 1982 was just the right tie for the Motels to break through in America. Joan Jett and the Blackhearts were No.1 on the singles chart while the Go-go's headed the album list. After years of conversatism US radio was suddenly receptive to 'new music' bands, particularly those with female leaders. Accordingly, Martha's Motels cruised to No.9 on the Billboard Hot 100 with *Only the lonely* (not the Roy Orbison hit) and reached No.16 with their third album *All four one*. In 1983 they reached No.9 again with *Suddenly last summer*from the LP *Little robbers*. The focal point of the band's sound was the deep, dour voice of Davis set against a lean and unimposing backing. However, the Motels' fifth album fared disappointingly in 1985. It seemed that their detached coolness required some new ingredients to restore interest. (Bob MacDonald, 5th Feb 1986).

DANGER
Tracks: / Danger / Envy / Total control.
7" Single: Released Feb '81, on Capitol, by EMI Records. Deleted Feb '84. Catalogue no: **CL 16185**
12" Single: Released Feb '81, on Capitol, by EMI Records. Deleted Feb '84. Catalogue no: **12 CL 16185**

DAYS ARE O.K.
Tracks: / Days are o.k. / Slow town.
7" Single: Released Jan '81, on Capitol, by EMI Records. Deleted '84. Catalogue no: **CL 16149**

ONLY THE LONELY
Tracks: / Only the lonely / Mission of mercy.
7" Single: Released Jan '82, on Capitol, by EMI Records. Deleted Jan '85. Catalogue no: **CL 263**

SHAME
Tracks: / Shame.
7" Single: Released Sep '85, on Capitol, by EMI Records. Deleted '88. Catalogue no: **CL 373**
12" Single: Released Sep '85, on Capitol, by EMI Records. Deleted '88. Catalogue no: **12CL 373**

SUDDENLY LAST SUMMER
Tracks: / Suddenly last summer / Some-things never change.
7" Single: Released Oct '83, on Capitol, by EMI Records. Deleted Jan '88. Catalogue no: **CL 308**

TAKE THE L OUT OF LOVER
Tracks: / Take the L out of lover / Change my mind.
7" Single: Released May '82, on Capitol, by EMI Records. Deleted '85. Catalogue no: **CL 245**

TOTAL CONTROL
Tracks: / Total control / Love don't help.
7" Single: Released Jan '80, on Capitol, by EMI Records. Deleted Jan '83. Catalogue no: **CL 16113**

WHOSE PROBLEM?
Tracks: / Whose problem / Cry baby.
7" Single: Released Oct '80, on Capitol, by EMI Records. Deleted '83. Catalogue no: **CL 16162**

Mother Cube

DO THE KAMA SUTRA
Tracks: / Do the kama sutra.
7" Single: Released Oct '85, on Strange, by Strange Records. Catalogue no: **WIERD 5**
12" Single: Released Oct '85, on Strange, by Strange Records. Catalogue no: **WIERD 5T**

YOU MAKE MY HEART GO
Tracks: / You make my heart go.
7" Single: Released Oct '85, on Strange, by Strange Records. Catalogue no: **WIERD 2**
12" Single: Released Oct '85, on Strange, by Strange Records. Catalogue no: **WIERD 2T**

Mothers Ruin

SAY IT'S NOT TRUE
Tracks: / Say it's not true / It's illogical.
7" Single: Released May '82, on Spectra, by Spectra Records. Deleted '87. Catalogue no: **SPC 7**

STREETFIGHTERS
Tracks: / Streetfighters / Leaving you.
7" Single: Released Sep '81, on Spectra, by Spectra Records. Deleted '87. Catalogue no: **SPC 1**

STREETLIGHTS
Tracks: / Streetlights / Turn a corner.
7" Single: Released Jan '82, on Spectra, by Spectra Records. Deleted '87. Catalogue no: **SPC 6**

Mothmen

DOES IT MATTER IRENE
Tracks: / Does it matter Irene / Please let it go.
7" Single: Released Sep '82, on Absurd, by Absurd Records. Catalogue no: **ABS 6**

TEMPTATION
Tracks: / Temptation / People people.
7" Single: Released Oct '81, on Do-It, by Do-It Records. Deleted Oct '84. Catalogue no: **DUN 14**

Moti Special

COLD DAYS HOT NIGHTS
Tracks: / Cold days hot nights.
7" Single: Released Jun '85, on Carrere, Catalogue no: **CAR 364**
12" Single: Released Jun '85, on Carrere, Catalogue no: **CART 364**

Motion

WALK ON BY
Tracks: / Crazy deep / Walk on by.
12" Single: Released Feb '87, on Bluebird (2), by BMG Records (UK). Catalogue no: **BRT 30**

Motion Pictures

JON
Tracks: / Jon / Audio scan.
7" Single: Released Jul '81, on State, by State Records. Deleted '84. Catalogue no: **STAT 104**

TWISTED AVENUES
Tracks: / Twisted avenues.
7" Single: Released Nov '80, on State, by State Records. Deleted '83. Catalogue no: **STAT 100**

Motivation

DON'T PLAY THAT SONG
Tracks: / Don't play that song.
7" Single: Released Oct '84, on Rock City, Catalogue no: **RCR 3**
12" Single: Released Oct '84, on Rock City, Catalogue no: **RCRT 3**

GIVE THE GIFT OF MUSIC
Tracks: / Give the gift of music / Color blind.
7" Single: Released Sep '83, on De-Lite, Catalogue no: **DE 12**
12" Single: Released Sep '83, on De-Lite, Catalogue no: **DEX 12**

SO LONELY
Tracks: / So lonely.
7" Single: Released Jul '84, on Rock City, Catalogue no: **RCR 1**

Motivators

I WISH IT WOULD RAIN
Tracks: / I wish it would rain.
7" Single: Released Jan '85, on Contraband, by Contraband Records. Catalogue no: **GEO 41**

Motley Crue

GIRLS, GIRLS, GIRLS (SINGLE)
Tracks: / Girls, girls, girls / Sumthin' for nuthin' / Smokin' in the boys room (live)* (Extra track on 12").
7" Single: Released Jul '87, on Elektra (USA), by Elektra Records (USA). Deleted Jul '88. Catalogue no: **EKR 59**
12" Single: Released Jul '87, on Elektra (USA), by Elektra Records (USA). Catalogue no: **EKR 59 T**

LOOKS THAT KILL
Tracks: / Looks that kill.
12" Single: Released Jul '84, on Elektra, by Elektra Records (UK). Deleted '87. Catalogue no: **E 9756**

MOTLEY CRUE: INTERVIEW PICTURE DISC
12" Single: Released '87, on Talkies, Catalogue no: **MOTLEY 1**

SMOKIN' IN THE BOYS ROOM
Tracks: / Smokin' in the boys room / Home sweet home / Shout at the devil (* Extra track available on 12" version only.).
7" Single: Released Sep '84, on Elektra (USA), by Elektra Records (USA). Deleted Sep '87. Catalogue no: **EKR 16**
7" Single: Released Aug '85, on Elektra, by Elektra Records (UK). Catalogue no: **E 9625**
7" Single: Released Jan '86, on Elektra (USA), by Elektra Records (USA). Deleted Jun '87. Catalogue no: **EKR 33**
12" Single: Released Aug '85, on Elektra, by Elektra Records (UK). Catalogue no: **E 9625T**
12" Single: Released Jan '86, on Elektra (USA), by Elektra Records (USA). Deleted Jun '87. Catalogue no: **EKR 33 T**

TOO YOUNG TO FALL IN LOVE (REMIX)
Tracks: / Too young to fall in love.
7" Single: Released Oct '84, on Elektra, by Elektra Records (UK). Catalogue no: **E 9732**
12" Single: Released Oct '84, on Elektra, by Elektra Records (UK). Catalogue no: **E 9732T**

WILD SIDE
Tracks: / Wild side / Five years dead.
Note: In full colour picture sleeve. B-side is 'Five Years Dead'.
7" Single: Released Nov '87, on Elektra (USA), by Elektra Records (USA). Catalogue no: **769449**

YOU'RE ALL I NEED
Tracks: / You're all I need / Wild side / Home sweet home (On 12" only) / Looks that kill (On 12" only).
7" Single: Released Feb '88, on Elektra, by

Elektra Records (UK). Catalogue no: **EKR 65**
12" Single: Released Feb '88, on Elektra, by Elektra Records (UK). Deleted Jul '88. Catalogue no: **EKR 65T**

Motor Boys Motor

DRIVE FRIENDLY
Tracks: / Drive friendly / Fasr'n bulbows / Brow fins.
7" Single: Released Oct '80, on Silent (1), by Silent Records. Deleted Oct '83. Catalogue no: **SSH 4**

Motor City Crew

SCRATCH BREAK (GLOVE STYLE)
Tracks: / Scratch break (glove style) / Let's break.
12" Single: Released Nov '83, on Motown, by BMG Records (UK). Catalogue no: **TMGT 1325**

Motor City Raiders

1-2-3-
Tracks: / 1-2-3.
7" Single: Released Nov '84, on Magnet, by WEA Records. Deleted '87. Catalogue no: **MAG 264**

AIN'T THAT PECULIAR
Tracks: / Ain't that peculiar.
7" Single: Released Aug '87, on Magnet, by WEA Records. Catalogue no: **MAG 261**
12" Single: Released Aug '87, on Magnet, by WEA Records. Catalogue no: **MAGT 261**

Motor Cycle Boy

BIG ROCK CANDY MOUNTAIN
Tracks: / Big rock candy mountain.
7" Single: Released Sep '87, on Rough Trade, by Rough Trade Records. Catalogue no: **RT 210**
12" Single: Released Sep '87, on Rough Trade, by Rough Trade Records. Catalogue no: **RTT 210**

TRYING TO BE KIND
Tracks: / Trying to be kind / World falls into place / Trying to be kind(version) / Will you love me tomorrow (12" only).
7" Single: Released Jun '89, on Chrysalis, by Chrysalis Records. Catalogue no: **CHS 3310**
12" Single: Released Jun '89, on Chrysalis, by Chrysalis Records. Catalogue no: **CHS 123310**

YOU AND ME AGAINST THE WORLD
Tracks: / You and me against the world / Under the bridge / Some girls (Available on 12" only).
7" Single: Released Sep '89, on Chrysalis, by Chrysalis Records. Catalogue no: **CHS 3398**
12" Single: Released Sep '89, on Chrysalis, by Chrysalis Records. Catalogue no: **CHS 123398**

Motorhead

Biographical details: Although Lemmy Kilminster formed Motorhead in 1975, several years of label-changing ensued before they became the most successful Heavy Metal band in Britain. Considerable chart achievement (notably *Ace of Spades*) has been coupled with a formidable on-stage reputation which resulted in the live L.P., *No Sleep Till Hammersmith'*. In addition to conventional successes, projects with female collaborators have obtained mixed results; despite the *St. Valentine's Day Massacre* E.P. with Girlschool, hitting the Top Five, the combined power of Motorhead and The Nolans (A.K.A. *The Young and Moody Band*) only succeeded in dragging *Don't Do That* to Number 63. (Robert Cohen, 1/5/87).
At the time of their greatest success, this British heavy metal band consisted of 'Fast' Eddie Clarke, Lemmy (real name Ian Kilminster) and Phil Taylor. The group were founded by Lemmy, who named them after *Motorhead*, the title of the final song he wrote for his previous group Hawkwind; it was also an American slang term for a speed freak. Motorhead came into being in 1975, with the classic Lemmy/Phil/Eddie line-up stabilising the following year. Showing extraordinary tenacity and faith in themselves, the band slogged away with their music despite the fact that their early days coincided with the dawn of the punk explosion, a phenomenon which made heavy metal distinctly unfashionable. 1976-78 were full of hiccups, hassles and headaches; but they did manage to get some tracks released, and a glimmer of hope was provided by the brief appearance of their eponymous debut album in the UK Top 50 in September 1977. Gradually building up a loyal army of fans, the band wone their first BBC TV 'Top of the pops' appearance in September '78 with *Louie Louie*, a revival of the 1963 Kingsmen hit which took Motorhead to No.68 on the British singles chart. The aptly titled *Overkill* single and album gave Motorhead their first taste of UK Top 40 success in 1979. Helping to pave the way for a major HM resurgence on the British charts, the band became one of the most uncompromisingly heavy acts in the history of rock. While avoiding the demonic references that were often associated with the genre, they were in a class of their own as far as fast, heavy, riff-laden, earshattering music was concerned. They possessed a lively sense of humour, and their sound was more strongly influenced by Fifties rock'n'roll that that of some of their HM peers. 1980-81 were the group's peak years. They chalked up UK Top 10 singles with *The golden years* EP and *Motorhead (Live)* and Top 10 albums with *Ace of spades* and *No sleep till Hammersmith* (a frenetic live LP that entered the British chart at N0.1 in June 1981). In the same year, they enjoyed a Top 5 single in duet with all-girl metal group Girlschool. Somewhat less expected was the trio's one-off collaboration with another female act, the middle-of-the-road Nolans!
After the *Iron fist* album, which reached the UK Top 10 in spring '82, Clarke quit Motorhead in the middle of an American tour; he took exception to the group's strange collaborations, especially Lemmy's cover version of *Stand by your man* in duet with singer Wendy O'Williams. Clarke proceeded to form Fastway, and was replaced with Brian Robertson (former guitarist with Thin Lizzy and Wild Horses). The new line-up continued bashing away, but lost some of their commercial edge. In 1984 a double compilation album was issued; released under the title *No remorse*, it came with the optional bonus of a deluxe leather sleeve. (Bob MacDonald, 5th Feb 1986).

ACE OF SPADES (SINGLE)
Tracks: / Ace of spades.
7" Single: Released Nov '80, on Bronze, by Bronze Records. Deleted '83. Catalogue no: **BRO 106**

BEER DRINKERS AND HELL RAISERS
Tracks: / Beer drinkers and hell raisers / On patrol / I'm your witchdoctor.
7" Single: Released Oct '80, on Big Beat, by Ace Records. Deleted '88. Catalogue no: **SWT 61**

BOMBER
Tracks: / Bomber / Over the top.
7" Single: Released Dec '82, on Bronze, by Bronze Records. Catalogue no: **BRO 85**

DEAF FOREVER
Tracks: / Deaf forever / On the road.
7" Single: Released Jul '86, on GWR, by GWR Records. Catalogue no: **GWR 2**
12" Single: Released Jul '86, on GWR, by GWR Records. Catalogue no: **GWT 2**

EAT THE RICH
Tracks: / Eat the rich / Cradle to the grave.
12" Single: Released 31 Oct '87, on GWR, by GWR Records. Catalogue no: **GWR 6**

GOLDEN YEARS EP
Tracks: / Dead men tell no tales / Too late too long / Leaving here / Stone dead forever.
7" EP: Released May '80, on Bronze, by Bronze Records. Deleted '83. Catalogue no: **BRO 92**

I GOT MINE
Tracks: / I got mine.
7" Single: Released May '83, on Bronze, by Bronze Records. Deleted '86. Catalogue no: **BRO 165**

IRON FIST (SINGLE)
Tracks: / Iron fist / Remember me, I'm gone.
7" Single: Released Apr '82, on Bronze, by Bronze Records. Deleted '85. Catalogue no: **BRO 146**

KILLED BY DEATH
Tracks: / Killed by death.
7" Single: Released Sep '84, on Bronze, by Bronze Records. Deleted '87. Catalogue no: **BRO 185**

LEAVING HERE
Tracks: / Leaving here / Stone dead forever / Dead men tell no tales / Too late, too late.
7" Single: Released Apr '80, on Bronze, by Bronze Records. Deleted Apr '83. Catalogue no: **BRO 92**
12" Single: Released Apr '80, on Bronze, by Bronze Records. Deleted Apr '83. Catalogue no: **12BRO 92**

LOUIE LOUIE
Tracks: / Louie louie / Tear ya down.
7" Single: Released Sep '78, on Bronze, by Bronze Records. Deleted '81. Catalogue no: **BRO 60**

MOTORHEAD (EP)
Tracks: / Ace of spades / Bomber / Motorhead / Overkill.
CD 3": Released '88, on Special Edition, by Castle Communications Records. Catalogue no: **CD3-10**

MOTORHEAD (LIVE)
Tracks: / Motorhead (live) / Over the top.
7" Single: Released Jul '81, on Bronze, by Bronze Records. Deleted '84. Catalogue no: **BRO 124**
12" Single: Released Jul '81, on Bronze, by Bronze Records. Deleted Jul '84. Catalogue no: **BROP 124**

MOTORHEAD (SINGLE)
Tracks: / Motorhead / City kids.
7" Single: Released Feb '82, on Chiswick Records. Catalogue no: **NSP 13**

NO CLASS
Tracks: / No class / Like a nightmare.
7" Single: Released Jun '79, on Bronze, by Bronze Records. Deleted '82. Catalogue no: **BRO 78**

OVERKILL (SINGLE)
Tracks: / Overkill / Too late, too late.
7" Single: Released Mar '79, on Bronze, by Bronze Records. Deleted '82. Catalogue no: **BRO 67**

SHINE
Tracks: / Shine / I'm your hoochie coochie man / (Don't need) religion.
7" Single: Released Jul '83, on Bronze, by Bronze Records. Deleted '86. Catalogue no: **BRO 167**

Motorhead Girlschool

Biographical details: In early 1981 one of Britain's hottest heavy metal bands, Motorhead, teamed up with their up-and-coming Bronze labelmates Girlschool to recor the *St Valentine's Day massacre* EP. The combination of the all-male HM group and the equally hard-rocking all-female combo was predictably frentic. Hilled as Headgirl for short, the explosive alliance rocketed to the UK No.5 position. The lead track was *Please don't touch*, originally a hit for Johnny Kidd. The Motorhead/Girschool duet version complemented the original superbly, and reaffirmed the fact that Motorhead were more strongly influenced by Fifties rock'n'roll than many of their HM peers. In October of the same year, 1981, Motorhead picked a rather less obvious all-girl group to record with. But weird though it may sound, they teamed up with that easy listening family group, the Nolans (Bob MacDonald, 5th Feb 1986).

ST. VALENTINES DAY MASSACRE (see panel below)
Tracks: / Please don't touch / Emergency / Bomber.
7" EP: Released '81, on Bronze, by Bronze Records. Catalogue no: **BRO 116**

Motorpool

SOLDIER BOY
Tracks: / Soldier boy / 6 K skip.
7" Single: Released Dec '88, on Strike (2), Catalogue no: **STRK 5**
12" Single: Released Dec '88, on Strike (2), Catalogue no: **12 STRK 5**

Motors

Biographical details: At the time of their greatest success, this British rock band consisted of Nick Garvey, Andy McMaster, Ricky Slaughter-Wernham and Bram Tchaikovsky (real name Peter Bramall). Emerging from the ashes of former pub-rock bands Ducks Deluxe and the Snakes, the Motors came into being in January 1977. The punk explosion was just taking place, and the Morots came into being in January 1977. The punk explosion was just taking place, and the Motors combined the enthusiasm and energy of the New Wave with a more traditional rock'n'roll approach. They came to public attention in late '77 with their powerhouse single *Dancing the night away*, which reached the UK No.42 position and became a hot critics favourite. BBC Radio One's influential DJ John Peel named *Dancing the night away* as his favourite 45 of the year. The band's eponymous debut album peaked at No.46.
With Garvey and McMaster at the songwriting helm, the Motors went in an out-and-out pop direction in 1978. This approach yielded the smash hit *Airport* which climbed to No.4 on the UK chart in the summer of that year. The follow-up single *Forget about you* was strongly reminiscent of White Plains' 1970 hit *My baby loves lovin'* but nonetheless reached No.13. Just as everything seemed to be going great for the Motors, Slaughter and Tchaikovsky quit. While the former drifted into oblivion, the latter guy launched his own career. This yielded just one success - Bram Tchaikovsky's criminally underated pop single *Girl of my dreams* crept into the US Top 40 in the summer of '79, but flopped in Britain. (Bob MacDonald 5th Feb 1986).

AIRPORT
Tracks: / Airport / Forget about you.
7" Single: Released Jun '78, on Virgin, by Virgin Records. Deleted '81. Catalogue no: **VS 219**
7" Single: Released Nov '88, on Old Gold, by Old Gold Records. Catalogue no: **OG 9830**

DANCING THE NIGHT AWAY
Tracks: / Dancing the night away.
7" Single: Released Sep '77, on Virgin, by Virgin Records. Deleted '80. Catalogue no: **VS 186**

FORGET ABOUT YOU
Tracks: / Forget about you.
7" Single: Released Aug '78, on Virgin, by Virgin Records. Deleted '81. Catalogue no: **VS 222**

LOVE AND LONELINESS
Tracks: / Love and loneliness / Time for make up.
7" Single: Released Apr '80, on Virgin, by Virgin Records. Deleted '83. Catalogue no: **VS 263**

METROPOLIS
Tracks: / Metropolis / Love round the corner.
7" Single: Released Oct '80, on Virgin, by Virgin Records. Deleted Oct '83. Catalogue no: **VS 363**

THAT'S WHAT JOHN SAID
Tracks: / That's what John said
7" Single: Released May '80, on Virgin, by Virgin Records. Deleted '83. Catalogue no: **VS 349**

Mott The Hoople

Biographical details: At the time of their

MOTORHEAD GIRLSCHOOL - ST . VALENTINES DAY MASSACRE (Released on Bronze)

greatest success, this British band consisted of Dale Griffin, Ian Hunter, Mick Ralphs and Peter 'Overend' Watts. The group's name was chosen by Guy Stevens, the A&R executive who discovered them; it was taken from a novel by Willard Manus. Formed in Herefordshire in 1969, Mott the Hoople built up a cult following with their powerful concerts. Working in a bluesy rock vein, the early Mott music was heavily influenced by Bob Dylan's 1966-style output; this was particularly true of lead singer/guitarist/pianist Ian Hunter, whose intense and grating vocals gave the group and ear-catching focal point. Their first three albums - *Mott the Hoople, Mad shadows* and *Wild life* - all reached the lower regions of the British chart, but their sales performance fell far short of the ecstatic reviews that were being heaped upon the band's records and concerts by rock journalists. Mott the Hoople's fourth album *Brain capers* failed to enter the charts at all, and the group dicided to jack the whole thing in in March 1972. However, the rising superstar David Bowie declared himself to be a big fan of the band, achieved the success they deserved, he offered them one of his best new songs. They accepted, and Bowie proceeded to produce the band's recording of that song - *All the young dudes* was indeed a surefire smash, cruising to No.3 in Britain in autumn '72 and going to No.37 in the States. David's gererous gesture achieved its purpose - Mott the Hoople stayed together to enjoy a string of successful singles and albums over the ensuing couple of years. The biggest and best LP was *Mott*, a UK Top 10 seller in 1973. Ian Hunter penned their two 1973 Top 10 singles, *All the way from Memphis* and *Roll away the stone*. Mott the Hoople's albums and concerts fared well in America as well as in Britain. In an era when there was a considerable divide between singles-oriented 'commercial' pop and album-orientated 'progressive' rock, Hunter's boys appealed to both camps. Their brash, rough-st-the-edges approach caused Karen Carpenter to describe them as one of the most amateurish acts in the business! The Mott the Hoople party did not last all that long. Following Hunter's hospitalisation through exhaustion, thus causing a European tour to be cancelled, the band folded in December 1974. Hunter launched a moderately successful solo career (with a little help from famous guitarist Mick Ronson), while several other members tried unsuccessfully to continue as Mott. Dale Griffin (also known as Buffin) later joined BBC Radio One, engineering many sessions for the John Peel show. Meanwhile, Mott The Hoople received much posthumous praise from the New Wave of British punk musicians, who cited the band as a major influence. (Bob MacDonald, 5th Feb 1986).

ALL THE WAY FROM MEMPHIS (SINGLE)
Tracks: / All the way from Memphis.
7" Single: Released Sep '73, on CBS, by CBS Records. Deleted '76. Catalogue no: **CBS 1764**

ALL THE YOUNG DUDES
Tracks: / All the young dudes / One of the boys.
7" Single: Released Aug '72, on CBS, by CBS Records. Deleted '75. Catalogue no: **CBS 8271**
7" Single: Released Jul '84, on CBS, by CBS Records. Catalogue no: **A 4581**

ALL THE YOUNG DUDES (2)
Tracks: / All the young dudes / Roll away the....
7" Single: Released Apr '83, on Old Gold, by Old Gold Records. Catalogue no: **OG 9312**

FOXY FOXY
Tracks: / Foxy foxy.
7" Single: Released Jun '74, on CBS, by CBS Records. Deleted '77. Catalogue no: **CBS 2439**

GOLDEN AGE OF ROCK AND ROLL
Tracks: / Golden age of rock and roll.
7" Single: Released Mar '74, on CBS, by CBS Records. Deleted '77. Catalogue no: **CBS 2177**

HONALOOCHIE BOOGIE
Tracks: / Honaloochie boogie.
7" Single: Released Jun '73, on CBS, by CBS Records. Deleted '76. Catalogue no: **CBS 1530**

ROLL AWAY THE STONE
Tracks: / Roll away the stone.
7" Single: Released Nov '73, on CBS, by CBS Records. Deleted '76. Catalogue no: **CBS 1895**

SATURDAY GIG
Tracks: / Golden age of rock and roll.
7" Single: Released Nov '74, on CBS, by CBS Records. Deleted '77. Catalogue no: **CBS 2754**

Motto, Denise

DOING IT PROPERLY IS XTC
Tracks: / Doing it properly is XTC / Imnxtc (2 mixes).
Note: Full artist title: Denise Motto, Scobby Swift, 2 Brummies, a Cockney and a Mancunian. Can this record be for real!
12" Single: Released Jul '87, on Kool Kat, by Kool Kat Records. Catalogue no: **KOOLTR 2**

IMNXTC (JACK YOUR BODY TO THE BEAT)
Tracks: / Imnxtc (jack your body to the beat) / Imnxtc (extended vocal version) / Imnxtc (instrumental version) / Imnxtc (dub mix) / Imnxtc (scratch mix (radio edit)).
12" Single: Released Mar '87, on Kool Kat, by Kool Kat Records. Catalogue no: **DOOLT 1**

Mould, Bob

SEE A LITTLE LIGHT
Tracks: / See a little light.
CD 5": Released Sep '89, on Virgin (USA), by Virgin Records. Catalogue no: **VUSCD 2**
7" Single: Released Sep '89, on Virgin (USA), by Virgin Records. Catalogue no: **VUS 2**
12" Single: Released Sep '89, on Virgin (USA), by Virgin Records. Catalogue no: **VUST 2**

Moulin Rouge

MY BABY HOLDS THE KEY
Tracks: / My baby holds the key / Bluer than blue.
7" Single: Released Sep '83, on Polo, by Polo Records. Deleted '88. Catalogue no: **POLO 27**
12" Single: Released Sep '83, on Polo, by Polo Records. Deleted '88. Catalogue no: **POLO 12-27**

Mountaineers

MAGIC BOOTS
Tracks: / Magic boots / Foreign tongue.
7" Single: Released Jun '82, on Swift, by 77 Records. Catalogue no: **BIRD 1**
12" Single: Released Jun '82, on Swift, by 77 Records. Catalogue no: **BIRD 12-1**

Mounten,Liberty

I'M JUST A CHILD AGAIN
Tracks: / I'm just a child again.
7" Single: Released Nov '85, on Climber, by Climber Records. Deleted '86. Catalogue no: **CLIS 5**

Mournblade

EIN HELDENTRAUM a heros dream
Tracks: / Ein heldentraum.
12" Single: Released Dec '85, on Vanishing Tower, by Vanishing Tower Records. Catalogue no: **TVC 03**

Mouse, John

TRICKSTER
Tracks: / Trickster / Lyrical brain.
12" Single: Released Sep '86, on Magnificent Master Blaster, Catalogue no: **12 MMB 2**

WE RAGGAMUFFIN
Tracks: / We raggamuffin.
7" Single: Released May '89, on Digital B., Catalogue no: **UNKNOWN**

Mouskouri, Nana

Biographical details: This Greek singer was born in Athens in 1936, and made her first record in 1959. She became a star in Greece in the early Sixties, and has been one of the top showbusiness ambassadors for her country ever since. The record that really broke her was her 1961 recording of of *Weisse rosen aus Athen* (The white rose of Athens), a German language adaptation from an old Greek song. Mouskouri's somewhat plaintive voice made her one of Europe's leading middle-of-the-road singers, a status she has maintained ever since. Her long-term viability has not been in any way affected by her rather severe appearance; her ever-present thick-rimmed spectacles and long, straight, dark hair have always made Mouskouri look more like a school matron than a showbiz personality. Mouskouri first reached the British album chart in 1969, when the *Over and over* LP peaked at No.10. Amazingly, it logged 105 weeks on the survey. During the early Seventies, the singer achieved a run of entries on the UK album chart including *The exquisite Nana Mouskouri, Recital '70, Turn on the sun, British concert, Songs from her TV series* and *Spotlight on Nana Mouskouri*. In August 1976 she cruised to the UK No.3 position with the *Passport* album. Surprisingly, Nan did not register her first appearance on the British singles chart until 1986 , (Bob MacDonald, 6th Feb 1986).

COME WITH ME (SINGLE)
Tracks: / Come with me / Lullaby of love.
7" Single: Released Mar '81, on RCA, by BMG Records (UK). Deleted Mar '84. Catalogue no: **RCA 45**

FORGIVE AND FORGET
Tracks: / Forgive and forget / To me.
7" Single: Released Feb '88, on Philips, by Phonogram Ltd. Deleted Feb '89. Catalogue no: **870 120-7**

I HAVE A DREAM
Tracks: / I have a dream / Recuerdos / White rose of Athens, The / White rose of Athens, The (Extra track on 12" version only.) / Bridge over troubled water (Extra track on 12" version only.).
7" Single: Released Feb '86, on Philips, by Phonogram Ltd. Catalogue no: **PH 39**
12" Single: Released Feb '86, on Philips, by Phonogram Ltd. Catalogue no: **PH 3912**

MOONDANCE
Tracks: / Moondance / Missing.
Note: Produced by Tony Visconti
7" Single: Released Oct '87, on Phonogram, by Phonogram Ltd. Catalogue no: **PH 42**

ONLY LOVE
Tracks: / Only love / White rose of Athens, The (12" version only.) / Bridge over troubled water (12" version only.).
7" Single: Released Oct '85, on Carrere, Catalogue no: **CAR 376**
7" Single: Released Feb '86, on Philips, by Phonogram Ltd. Catalogue no: **PH 38**
12" Single: Released Oct '85, on Carrere, Catalogue no: **CART 376**
12" Single: Released Feb '86, on Philips, by Phonogram Ltd. Catalogue no: **PH 3812**

ONLY TIME WILL TELL
Tracks: / Only time will tell / White rose of Athens, The.
7" Single: Released Sep '88, on Philips, by Phonogram Ltd. Deleted 31 May '89. Catalogue no: **PH 44**

WHY WORRY? (SINGLE)
Tracks: / Why worry.
7" Single: Released Oct '86, on Philips, by Phonogram Ltd. Deleted '87. Catalogue no: **PH 41**

Mouth

OOH AH YEAH OOH
Tracks: / Ooh ah yeah ooh / Ooh?.
7" Single: Released Jan '82, on Recreational, by Revolver Records. Catalogue no: **SPORT 3**

TO WHOM IT MAY CONCERN
Tracks: / To whom it may concern / Bull face.
7" Single: Released Jun '82, on Sheet, Catalogue no: **BULL 4**

WHO'S HOT
Tracks: / Who's hot / Catch a cab.
10" single: Released May '82, on Y, Catalogue no: **10Y20**
7" Single: Released May '82, on Y, Catalogue no: **Y 20**

Mouth In Motion

FIGHT TIME
Tracks: / Fight time / Fight time (alternative mix).
12" Single: Released Nov '88, on G.T.I. Records, by G.T.I. Music. Catalogue no: **GT 1002T**

Mouth & MacNeal

I SEE A STAR
Tracks: / I see a star.
7" Single: Released May '74, on Decca, by Decca Records. Deleted '77. Catalogue no: **F 13504**

Mouzon, Alphonse

DON'T WANT TO LOSE THIS FEELING
Tracks: / Don't want to lose this feeling / Don't want to lose this feeling (part 2).
7" Single: Released Mar '82, on London Records, by London Records. Deleted '86. Catalogue no: **LON 003**
12" Single: Released Mar '82, on London Records, by London Records. Deleted '85. Catalogue no: **LONX 003**

I'M GLAD THAT YOU'RE HERE
Tracks: / I'm glad that you're here.
7" Single: Released Nov '81, on London (Decca), by Decca International. Deleted Nov '84. Catalogue no: **HL 10581**
12" Single: Released Nov '81, on London (Decca), by Decca International. Deleted Nov '84. Catalogue no: **HLX 10581**

Move

Biographical details: At the time of their greatest success, this British pop combo consisted of Roy Wood, Bev Bevan, Trevor Burton and Carl Wayne. Formed in Birmingham in 1965, they started out as a kind of "supergroup" of the city's best young pop musicians. The following year they secured a residency at London's hallowed Marquee Club. In the first week of 1967 they entered the UK singles chart for the first time and they remained a regular force on the list for the next five years. An out-and-out pop singles group with just the right amount of psychedelia, the Move's success was built on the superb songwriting skills of Roy Wood. After their first hit, *Night Of Fear* (No 2), Wood's pastiche on Tchaikovsky's 1812 Overture, he was careful to include botanical references in his lyrics in order to appease flower power devotees: *Can Hear The Grass Grow, Flowers In The Rain and Blachberry Way* were all part of this policy. *Flowers*, which reached No 2 in autumn '67 was the first record played by BBC Radio One when the national pop station began broadcasting on 30 September '67, and has since assumed classic status. At the time it was more notorious for its publicity material, which depicted Prime Minister Harold Wilson naked in the bath; the PM was not amused and successfully sued the group for libel with the result that all the single's royalties went to charity. The early Move hits featured the lead voice of Carl Wayne, but from *Fire Brigade* (No 3 in '68) onwards, the increasingly dominant Wood took over. A long line of personnel upheavels began to plague the band, but Wood kept coming up with the hits, *Blackberry Way* becoming the combo's only UK No 1 single in February '69. During the early 70's, with psychedelia forgotten, Wood found a new bandwagon to jump on -- *Brontosaurus, Tonight* and *California Man* were all pop approximations to heavy metal. By this time Wood and newcomer Jeff Lynne, who were acting as the group's producers, felt increasingly frustrated by the Move's "niche" on the British singles chart. Unable to make sufficient inroads into the album listings or the American charts, they and Bev Bevan launched the Electric Light Orchestra in 1972.(Bob MacDonald, February 1986.).

BLACKBERRY WAY (OLD GOLD)
Tracks: / Blackberry way / Brontosaurus.
7" Single: Released Jul '82, on Old Gold, by Old Gold Records. Catalogue no: **OG 9227**

BLACKBERRY WAY
Tracks: / Blackberry way / I can hear the grass grow.
7" Single: Released Dec '68, on Regal Zonophone, by EMI Records. Deleted '71. Catalogue no: **RZ 3015**
7" Single: Released Sep '82, on Dakota, Catalogue no: **BAK 6**

BRONTOSAURUS
Tracks: / Brontosaurus.
7" Single: Released Apr '70, on Regal Zonophone, by EMI Records. Deleted '73. Catalogue no: **RZ 3026**

CALIFORNIA MAN
Tracks: / California man.
7" Single: Released May '72, on Harvest (1), by EMI Records. Deleted '75. Catalogue no: **HAR 5050**

CHINATOWN
Tracks: / Chinatown.
7" Single: Released Oct '71, on Harvest (1), by EMI Records. Deleted '74. Catalogue no: **HAR 5043**

CURLY
Tracks: / Curly.
7" Single: Released Jul '69, on Regal Zonophone, by EMI Records. Deleted '72. Catalogue no: **RZ 3021**

FIRE BRIGADE
Tracks: / Fire brigade.
7" Single: Released Feb '68, on Regal Zonophone, by EMI Records. Deleted '71. Catalogue no: **RZ 3005**

FLOWERS IN THE RAIN
Tracks: / Flowers in the rain / Brontosaurus.
7" Single: Released Sep '67, on Regal Zonophone, by EMI Records. Deleted '70. Catalogue no: **RZ 3001**
7" Single: Released Aug '82, on Cube, Catalogue no: **BAK 8**

FLOWERS IN THE RAIN (OLD GOLD)
Tracks: / Flowers in the rain / Fire brigade.
7" Single: Released Jul '82, on Old Gold, by Old Gold Records. Catalogue no: **OG 9226**

I CAN HEAR THE GRASS GROW
Tracks: / I can hear the grass grow
7" Single: Released Apr '67, on Deram, by London Records. Deleted '70. Catalogue no: **DM 117**
12" Single: Released Sep '86, on Archive 4, by Castle Communications Records. Catalogue no: **TOF 111**

NIGHT OF FEAR
Tracks: / Night of fear.
7" Single: Released Jan '67, on Deram, by London Records. Deleted '70. Catalogue no: **DM 109**
7" Single: Released Aug '82, on Dakota, Catalogue no: **BAK 7**

NIGHT OF FEAR (2)

MOVING FEELINGS - SUBWAY AND THE STAIRS (Released on Sonet)

Tracks: / Night of fear
7" Single: Released Jul '82, on Dakota, Catalogue no: **OG 9228**

TONIGHT
Tracks: / Tonight.
7" Single: Released Jul '71, on Harvest (1), by EMI Records. Deleted '74. Catalogue no: **HAR 5038**

Move Into Soul

MOVE INTO SOUL EP
12" Single: Released Sep '85, on Move, Catalogue no: **MVLP 4**

Movement

MAGIC
Tracks: / Magic / Magic (7" version)
7" Single: Released May '87, on Debut, by Skratch Records. Catalogue no: **DEBTX 3023**

Movie Land

POSTCARD OF NEW YORK
Tracks: / Postcard of New York / Dreamtime.
7" Single: Released Jun '86, on RCA, by BMG Records (UK). Catalogue no: **PB 49853**
12" Single: Released Jun '86, on RCA, by BMG Records (UK). Catalogue no: **PT 49854**

Movie Stars

NO TIME TO KILL
Tracks: / No time to kill.
7" Single: Released Oct '82, on Lancaster, by Lancaster Records. Catalogue no: **LG 10**

Movies

CLOCKWISE INTO THE SUN
Tracks: / Clockwise into the sun / Slavery time.
7" Single: Released Sep '81, on RCA, by BMG Records (UK). Deleted '84. Catalogue no: **RCA 111**

HAVE ANOTHER BODY
Tracks: / Have another body / Bardot.
7" Single: Released May '80, on Gem, Deleted May '83. Catalogue no: **GEMS 29**

LOVE IS A SACRIFICE
Tracks: / Love is a sacrifice / Fat girl.
7" Single: Released Feb '80, on Gem, Deleted Feb '83. Catalogue no: **GEMS 20**

Moving Fingers

DOUBLE VISION
Tracks: / Double vision / Single vision.
7" Single: Released Mar '82, on French, Catalogue no: **TFL 001**

EVERYTHING CHANGES
Tracks: / Everything changes.
7" Single: Released Jul '87, on Sonet, by Sonet Records. Catalogue no: **SON 2292**

FINAL WORD OF HISTORY
Tracks: / Final word of history / Love is.
7" Single: Released Sep '86, on Sonet, by Sonet Records. Catalogue no: **SON 2308**

KAREN
Tracks: / Karen / Chlorophyll (in my eyes).
7" Single: Released Mar '86, on Sonet, by Sonet Records. Catalogue no: **SON 2298**

LOCKED ONTO LOVE
Tracks: / Locked onto love / Eye contact / Shot first.
12" Single: Released Feb '85, on KSV, by Kingsley Sound & Vision Records. Catalogue no: **MF 001**

ROME LIES BURNING
Tracks: / Rome lies burning / Heartland.
7" Single: Released May '87, on Sonet, by Sonet Records. Catalogue no: **SON 2321**

SINK LIKE A STONE
Tracks: / Sink like a stone.
7" Single: Released May '85, on Sonet, by Sonet Records. Catalogue no: **SON 2282**

SUBWAY AND THE STARS (see panel above)
Tracks: / Subway and the stars / Lock up your heart.
7" Single: Released Nov '86, on Sonet, by Sonet Records. Catalogue no: **SON 2314**

Moving Hearts

2-1 FREDDIE
Tracks: / 2-1 Freddie.
7" Single: Released May '83, on 51%, Catalogue no: **MH 010**

LET SOMEBODY KNOW
Tracks: / Let somebody know.
7" Single: Released Sep '82, on WEA, by WEA Records. Catalogue no: **K 19273**

Moving Pictures

PARTY NIGHT
Tracks: / Party night.
7" Single: Released Jul '82, on Runaway, Deleted '85. Catalogue no: **RUN 1**

WHAT ABOUT ME
Tracks: / What about me / Joni and the Romeo.
7" Single: Released Dec '82, on Epic, by CBS Records. Catalogue no: **EPC A 3004**

Mowatt, Judy

MY MY PEOPLE
Tracks: / My my people / Black woman.
7" Single: Released Jan '81, on Island, by Island Records. Deleted Jan '84. Catalogue no: **WIP 6670**

Mowrey,Irvin

QUEEN OF MAYBE
Tracks: / Queen of maybe / Fat city.
7" Single: Released '80, on Initial, Catalogue no: **IRS 001**

Moxham,Steve

LOVE AT FIRST SIGHT
Tracks: / Love at first sight / Light aircraft.
7" Single: Released Aug '82, on Rough Trade, by Rough Trade Records. Catalogue no: **RT 085**

Moyet, Alison

ALL CRIED OUT
Tracks: / All cried out.
7" Single: Released Sep '84, on CBS, by CBS Records. Deleted '86. Catalogue no: **A 4757**
12" Single: Released Sep '84, on CBS, by CBS Records. Deleted '85. Catalogue no: **TA 4757**

INVISIBLE
Tracks: / Invisible / Hitch hiker / Love resurrection / Baby I do.
7" Set: Released Dec '84, on CBS, by CBS Records. Catalogue no: **A 4930**

IS THIS LOVE
Tracks: / Is this love / Blow wind blow.
7" Single: Released Nov '86, on CBS, by CBS Records. Catalogue no: **MOYET 1**

LOVE LETTERS
Tracks: / Love letters / This house / Love letters (ext. version) / Ne me quitte pas (live) (on CD single only.).
CD 5": Released Nov '87, on CBS, by CBS Records. Deleted Jan '89. Catalogue no: **MOYET C5**
7" Single: Released Nov '87, on CBS, by CBS Records. Deleted Jun '88. Catalogue no: **MOYET 5**
12" Single: Released Nov '87, on CBS, by CBS Records. Deleted Jun '88. Catalogue no: **MOYET T5**

LOVE RESURRECTION
Tracks: / Love resurrection.
7" Single: Released Jun '84, on CBS, by CBS Records. Catalogue no: **A 4497**
12" Single: Released Jun '84, on CBS, by CBS Records. Deleted '85. Catalogue no: **TA 4497**

ORDINARY GIRL
Tracks: / Ordinary girl / Palm of your hand.
7" Single: Released 23 May '87, on CBS, by CBS Records. Deleted Nov '87. Catalogue no: **MOYET 3**
12" Single: Released 23 May '87, on CBS, by CBS Records. Deleted Nov '87. Catalogue no: **MOYET T3**

SLEEP LIKE BREATHING
Tracks: / Sleep like breathing / Love resurrection (live) / Ne me quitte pas (live) (on 12" only.).
7" Single: Released Sep '87, on CBS, by CBS Records. Catalogue no: **MOYET 4**
12" Single: Released Sep '87, on CBS, by CBS Records. Catalogue no: **MOYET T4**

THAT OLD DEVIL CALLED LOVE
Tracks: / That ole devil called love
7" Single: Released Mar '85, on CBS, by CBS Records. Deleted '86. Catalogue no: **A 6044**
12" Single: Released Mar '85, on CBS, by CBS Records. Deleted '86. Catalogue no: **TA 6044**

WEAK IN THE PRESENCE OF BEAUTY
Tracks: / To work on you / Take my imagination to bed (12" only).
7" Single: Released Feb '87, on CBS, by CBS Records. Deleted Aug '87. Catalogue no: **MOYET 2**
12" Single: Released Feb '87, on CBS, by CBS Records. Deleted Aug '87. Catalogue no: **MOYET T2**

Mr Abie

NOTHING LEFT TO SAY BUT GOODBYE
Tracks: / Nothing left to say but goodbye
7" Single: Released Dec '82, on Igus, by Klub Records. Catalogue no: **KLUB 37**

Mr. Barleywine

OPEN DOOR
Tracks: / Open door.
7" Single: Released Jan '85, on Top Dog, Deleted '86. Catalogue no: **TDR 0001**

Mr Big

FEEL LIKE CALLING HOME
Tracks: / Feel like calling home.
7" Single: Released May '77, on EMI, by EMI Records. Deleted '80. Catalogue no: **EMI 2610**

ROMEO
Tracks: / Romeo.
7" Single: Released Feb '77, on EMI, by EMI Records. Deleted '80. Catalogue no: **EMI 2567**

Mr. Big Noise

DROP THAT GHETTO BLASTER
Tracks: / Drop that ghetto blaster.
CD 5": Released Oct '88, on Sampler Et Sans Reproches, Catalogue no: **SSR 90CD**
7" Single: Released Nov '88, on Sampler Et Sans Reproches, Catalogue no: **SSR 90**
12" Single: Released Oct '88, on Sampler Et Sans Reproches, Catalogue no: **12 SSR 90**

Mr. Bloe

GROOVIN' WITH MR. BLOE
Tracks: / Groovin' with Mr. Bloe.
7" Single: Released May '70, on DJM, Deleted '73. Catalogue no: **DJS 216**

GROOVIN' WITH MR. BLOE (OLD GOLD)
Tracks: / Groovin' with Mr. Bloe / Sinful.
7" Single: Released Jul '82, on Old Gold, by Old Gold Records. Deleted Jul '88. Catalogue no: **OG 9002**

Mr. Burns

WHEN I'M ASLEEP
Tracks: / When I'm asleep / Third degree burns.
7" Single: Released Aug '80, on Korova, by WEA Records. Catalogue no: **KOW 9**

Mr. Easy

MARY MARY (IMPORT)
Tracks: / Mary Mary.
12" Single: Released Oct '89, on Two Friends, Catalogue no: **SIR 017**

RHINESTONE COWBOY
Tracks: / Rhinestone cowboy.
12" Single: Released May '89, on Living Room, Catalogue no: **LM 0025**

Mr. Fingers

SLAM DANCE (EP)
Tracks: / Slam dance / Acid attacks / Stars / Waterfalls / I'm strong / For so long.
12" Single: Released Jan '88, on Jack Trax, Catalogue no: **12TRAX 10**

Mr. Horse

CRISIS SITUATION
Tracks: / Crisis situation.
12" Single: Released Nov '88, on Subway, by Subway Records. Catalogue no: **SUB 041**

Mr Lee

COME TO HOUSE
Tracks: / Come to house.
12" Single: Released Oct '87, on Trax (USA), Catalogue no: **TX 140**

I CAN'T FORGET
Tracks: / I can't forget / I can't forget (dub).
7" Single: Released Aug '87, on Breakout, by A&M Records. Deleted Mar '88. Catalogue no: **USA 607**
12" Single: Released Aug '87, on Breakout, by A&M Records. Deleted Mar '88. Catalogue no: **USAT 607**

PUMP UP LONDON
Tracks: / Pump up London / Pump up Chicago.
7" Single: Released Aug '88, on Breakout, by A&M Records. Catalogue no: **USA 639**
12" Single: Released Aug '88, on Breakout, by A&M Records. Catalogue no: **USAT 639**

ROCK THIS PLACE
Tracks: / Rock this place.
12" Single: Released Dec '88, on Kool Kat, by Kool Kat Records. Catalogue no: **KOOLT 23**

THIS GIRL IS MY LOVER
Tracks: / This girl is my lover / Miss Mavis.
12" Single: Released Feb '86, on Unity Sound, Catalogue no: **UN 013**

Mr Love Mr Love

MR LOVE MR LOVE
Tracks: / Mr. Love Mr. Love.
CD 5": Released 16 Jan '89, on Gee Street, by Gee Street Records. Catalogue no: **GEECD 13**
7" Single: Released 16 Jan '89, on Gee Street, by Gee Street Records. Catalogue no: **GEE 13**
12" Single: Released 16 Jan '89, on Gee Street, by Gee Street Records. Catalogue no: **GEET 13 R**
12" Single: Released 16 Jan '89, on Gee Street, by Gee Street Records. Catalogue no: **GEET 13**

Mr Mertha

WONDER
Tracks: / Wonder.
12" Single: Released Sep '86, on Fundamental, by Fundamental Music Records. Catalogue no: **PRAY 4**

Mr. Mister

BROKEN WINGS
Tracks: / Broken wings.
CD 5": Released Jun '89, on RCA, by BMG Records (UK). Catalogue no: **PD 49449**
7" Single: Released Jul '85, on RCA, by BMG Records (UK). Catalogue no: **PB 49945**
12" Single: Released Jul '85, on RCA, by BMG Records (UK). Deleted May '89. Catalogue no: **PT 49946**

HEALING WATERS
Tracks: / Healing waters / Control
7" Single: Released Nov '87, on RCA, by BMG Records (UK). Catalogue no: **PB 49606**
12" Single: Released Nov '87, on RCA, by BMG Records (UK). Catalogue no: **PT**

49607

HUNTERS OF THE NIGHT
Tracks: / Hunters of the night / I get lost sometimes.
7" Single: Released Apr '84, on RCA, by BMG Records (UK). Catalogue no: **RCA 402**
12" Single: Released Apr '84, on RCA, by BMG Records (UK). Catalogue no: **RCAT 402**

IS IT LOVE?
Tracks: / Is it love? / Thirty two / Is it love (dance mix) (Extra track available on 12" version only.) / Is it love (dub mix) (Extra track available on 12" version only.).
7" Single: Released Apr '86, on RCA, by BMG Records (UK). Catalogue no: **PB 49861**
12" Single: Released Apr '86, on RCA, by BMG Records (UK). Catalogue no: **PT 49862**

KYRIE
Tracks: / Kyrie (edited version) / Kyrie (full version) / Hunters of the night (Available on 12" version only.).
7" Single: Released Feb '86, on RCA, by BMG Records (UK). Catalogue no: **PB 49927**
12" Single: Released Feb '86, on RCA, by BMG Records (UK). Catalogue no: **PT 49928**

SOMETHING REAL
Tracks: / Something real / Bare my soul / Something real (rock dance mix) (on 12" only) / Something real (instrumental) (on 12" only).
7" Single: Released Sep '87, on RCA, by BMG Records (UK). Catalogue no: **PB 49629**
12" Single: Released Sep '87, on RCA, by BMG Records (UK). Catalogue no: **PT 49630**

Mr. Monday

KEEP ON
Tracks: / Keep on / Don't stop.
12" Single: Released May '89, on Greedy Beat, Catalogue no: **12GREED 7**

Mr & Mrs Dale

IT'S YOU
Tracks: / It's you.
7" Single: Released Sep '89, on Big Shot, Catalogue no: **VS 134**

Mr & Mrs Yellowman

WHERE IS SANTA CLAUS
Tracks: / Where is Santa Claus.
12" Single: Released Nov '85, on Greensleeves, by Greensleeves Records. Catalogue no: **GRED 192**

Mr. Palmer

MIXED ME PROPERLY
Tracks: / Mixed me properly / Under me ganja.
12" Single: Released Apr '85, on Sweetcorn, Catalogue no: **SW 005**

RIBIBONSCAN
Tracks: / Ribibonscan.
12" Single: Released Sep '84, on Melody, Catalogue no: **M 005**

Mr. Rhymes

STOP BREAKIN'
Tracks: / Stop breakin'.
7" Single: Deleted Aug '87. Catalogue no: **POSP 832**
12" Single: Deleted Aug '87. Catalogue no: **POSPX 832**

Mr Snowman

MR SNOWMAN
Tracks: / Mr. Snowman / Christmas is coming.
7" Single: Released Dec '83, on Solid, by Solid Records. Catalogue no: **STOP 005**

Mr Spalding

ROCKY ROAD
Tracks: / Rocky road / Rocky dub.
12" Single: Released Jun '86, on Rocky Road, Catalogue no: **RR 001**

Mr. X & Mr. Z

MR. X AND MR. Z
Tracks: / Mr. X and Mr. Z.
7" Single: Released '87, on Citybeat, by Beggars Banquet Records. Deleted Jul '88. Catalogue no: **CBE 717**

Mra Sleeping Figures

HANDFUL OF HEART
Tracks: / Handful of heart.
7" Single: Released Mar '83, on Kapac, Catalogue no: **LYNX 2**

Mr.Amir

REASONS TO LIVE
Tracks: / Reasons to live / Oh no oppressor.
7" Single: Released Nov '83, on Probe Plus, by Probe Plus Records. Catalogue no: **PP 6**

Ms Melodie

WAKE UP
Tracks: / Wake up.
12" Single: Released Sep '89, on Jive, by Zomba Records. Catalogue no: **JIVET 224**

M.S.G.

GIMME YOUR LOVE
Tracks: / Gimme your love / Rock 'till you're crazy.
12" Pic: Released Oct '87, on EMI, by EMI Records. Deleted Nov '88. Catalogue no: **12EMP 30**
7" Single: Released Oct '87, on EMI, by EMI Records. Deleted 31 Jul '88. Catalogue no: **EM 30**
12" Single: Released Oct '87, on EMI, by EMI Records. Deleted 31 Jul '88. Catalogue no: **12EM 30**

MSO

MUSIC MAN
Tracks: / Music man.
7" Single: Released Aug '81, on Mainstreet, Catalogue no: **MS 103**
12" Single: Released Aug '81, on Mainstreet, Deleted '83. Catalogue no: **12SP MS 103**

M.T Quarter

CRUCIAL LOVER
Tracks: / Crucial lover.
12" Single: Released Apr '85, on Illuminated, Catalogue no: **ILL 5912**

Mtoto, Mungu

GHETTO CHILDREN
Tracks: / Ghetto children.
12" Single: Released Dec '84, on Ghetto Tears, Catalogue no: **GT 001**

Mtume

Biographical details: Dominated by keyboardist/percussionist/songwriter/producer James Mtume (pronounced Em-too-may), this flexible American soul band surged to fame in 1983 with the intoxicating ballad *Juicy fruit*. This single peaked at No.34 in the UK and failed to even crack the Top 40 of the US pop chart, but was a monster hit on the American black charts. *Juicy fruit* was No.1 on that list for two months, selling a million copies in the process - the fact that such a sale was possible without the single becoming a pop smash, was an indictment of white-dominated pop radio in the States and of the American formats/crossover system which dictates the charts there. *Juicy fruit* was one of the sexiest and most beautiful soul singles of the Eighties; it sounded rather like a more genuinely erotic version of Jane Birkin & Serge Gainsbourg's *Je t'aime*, which of course added to its problems on the UK pop radio. In 1984 Mtume chalked up further hits on the US soul chart with *You, me and him* and *Prime time*; the latter reached No.57 on the UK pop chart. Prior to *Juicy fruit*, James Mtume was a well-established musician, producer and songwriter. He cut his teeth playing with jazz masters like Miles Davis and Larry Coryell and, as jazz developed a closer relationship with funk, progressed to such acts as the Players Association and the O'Jays. In 1980 he saw two of his soul compositions become Top 5 pop hits in Britain: *Back together again* by Roberta Flack & Donny Hathaway and *Never knew love like this before* by Stephanie Mills. He co-wrote those two successes with is long-time musical partner Reggie Lucas, who beame well-known in his own right for producing Madonna's first LP. The first Mtume album, 1980's *In search of the rainbow seekers*, provided valuable experience for such up-and-coming soul talents as Hubert Eaves (later of D Train fame), Gwen Guthrie and Luther Vandross. In 1985 James Mtume undertook an interesting but underrated collaboration with a UK rock band, the Comsat Angels, on the single *I'm falling*. (Bob MacDonald, 6th Feb 1986).

BREATHLESS
Tracks: / Breathless / Theatre of the mind, Theme from.
7" Single: Released May '86, on Epic, by CBS Records. Deleted '86. Catalogue no: **A 7159**
12" Single: Released May '86, on Epic, by CBS Records. Deleted '86. Catalogue no: **TA 7159**

JUICY FRUIT
Tracks: / Juicy fruit / Prime time / Just be good to me / Weekend girl.
12" Single: Released Jan '89, on Old Gold, by Old Gold Records. Catalogue no: **OG 4002**

JUICY FRUIT (PART 1)
Tracks: / Juicy fruit (part 1).
7" Single: Released May '83, on Epic, by CBS Records. Catalogue no: **A 3424**
12" Single: Released May '83, on Epic, by CBS Records. Catalogue no: **TA 3424**

PRIME TIME
Tracks: / Prime time / Juicy fruit / You, me and he (on 12" only).
7" Single: Released Sep '84, on Epic, by CBS Records. Deleted '87. Catalogue no: **A 4720**

SO YOU WANT TO BE A STAR
Tracks: / So you want to be a star / Mrs sippi.
7" Single: Released Dec '80, on Epic, by CBS Records. Deleted Dec '85. Catalogue no: **EPC 9337**
12" Single: Released Dec '80, on Epic, by CBS Records. Deleted Dec '85. Catalogue no: **EPC 12 9337**

YOU CAN'T WAIT FOR LOVE
Tracks: / You can't wait for love / Everything good to me.
7" Single: Released Jun '81, on Epic, by CBS Records. Deleted Jun '84. Catalogue no: **EPCA 1025**

Mud

Biographical details: This British pop band consisted of Rob Davies, Les Gray, Dave Mount and Ray Stiles. Hailing from Carshalton, Surrey, the four members of Mud were all about 20 years old when they came together in 1966. They turned professional two years later. They spent the late Sixties and early Seventies on the club circuit, and released a few flop records along the way. They had become a very entertaining and polished outfit by the time they were spotted by Mickie Most in late 1972. Most, one of Britain's best known commercial pop svengalis and owner of the RAK label, brought the songwriting team Nicky Chinn & Mike Chapman up to the Social Club in Nottingham to see the group. Because the band were not interested in writing their own material at that time, they were happy to be signed up. The results were hugely successful. with the Chinnichap team producing as well as writing, Mud became one of the UK's most successful acts of the mid-Seventies. The Mud/Chinnichap/RAK alliance chalked up eleven British chart singles during 1973-75. These included three No.1 smashes, each of which displayed different aspects of the Mud/Chinnichap team's talents: *Tiger feet*, the UK's best-selling single of 1974, was an all-out good-time stomper that becamed one of the all-time greatest dance-floor fillers; *Lonely this Christmas* was one of several Mud hits that made clever use of lead vocalist Gray's Elvis Presley impersonations;l and *Oh boy* was an imaginative remake of the 1958 Crickets standard, which featured strong vocal harmonies from Mud. Mud were the crowning gory of Chinnichap's phenomenally successful roster of acts. Another of their groups, the Sweet, quit the stable in early 1975. Mud followed suit later in the year, because they wanted to exercise greater control over their output and reap a greater financial return. This policy was successful for a while, yielding four UK Top 20 singles on the Private Stock label with the same variety of stompers, ballads and imaginative cover versions. But the hits stopped coming in early 1977, although Gray proceeded to achieve one modest solo success. the closely knit quartet stayed together during the late Seventies and Eighties, enthusiastically gigging all over the place and releasing the occasional flop record. The wheel had turned.full circle. (Bob MacDonald, 6th Feb 1986).

CAT CREPT IN, THE
Tracks: / Cat crept in, The.
7" Single: Released Apr '74, on RAK, by EMI Records. Deleted '77. Catalogue no: **RAK 170**

CRAZY
Tracks: / Crazy.
7" Single: Released Mar '73, on RAK, by EMI Records. Deleted '76. Catalogue no: **RAK 146**

DYNA-MITE
Tracks: / Dyna-mite.
7" Single: Released Oct '73, on RAK, by EMI Records. Deleted '76. Catalogue no: **RAK 159**

HYPNOSIS
Tracks: / Hypnosis.
7" Single: Released Jun '73, on RAK, by EMI Records. Deleted '76. Catalogue no: **RAK 152**

LEAN ON ME
Tracks: / Lean on me.
7" Single: Released Nov '76, on Private Stock, Deleted '79. Catalogue no: **PVT 85**

L-L-LUCY
Tracks: / L-L-Lucy.
7" Single: Released Oct '75, on Private Stock, Deleted '78. Catalogue no: **PVT 41**

LONELY THIS CHRISTMAS
Tracks: / Lonely this Christmas.
7" Single: Released Nov '85, on RAK, by EMI Records. Deleted Oct '87. Catalogue no: **RAK 187**
12" Single: Released Nov '85, on RAK, by EMI Records. Catalogue no: **12 RAK 187**

MOONSHINE SALLY
Tracks: / Moonshine Sally.
7" Single: Released Jun '75, on RAK, by EMI Records. Deleted '78. Catalogue no: **RAK 208**

OH BOY
Tracks: / Oh boy.
7" Single: Released Apr '75, on RAK, by EMI Records. Deleted '78. Catalogue no: **RAK 201**

ONE NIGHT
Tracks: / One night.
7" Single: Released Apr '75, on RAK, by EMI Records. Deleted '78. Catalogue no: **RAK 201**

ROCKET
Tracks: / Rocket.
7" Single: Released Jul '74, on RAK, by EMI Records. Deleted '77. Catalogue no: **RAK 178**

SECRETS THAT YOU KEEP, THE
Tracks: / Secrets that you keep, The.
7" Single: Released Feb '75, on RAK, by EMI Records. Deleted '78. Catalogue no: **RAK 194**

SHAKE IT DOWN
Tracks: / Shake it down.
7" Single: Released May '76, on Private Stock, Deleted '79. Catalogue no: **PVT 65**

SHOW ME YOU'RE A WOMAN
Tracks: / Show me you're a woman.
7" Single: Released Nov '75, on Private Stock, Deleted '78. Catalogue no: **PVT 45**

TIGER FEET
Tracks: / Tiger feet.
7" Single: Released Jan '74, on RAK, by EMI Records. Deleted '77. Catalogue no: **RAK 166**
7" Single: Released Jan '77, on RAK Replay, by EMI Records. Catalogue no: **RR 6**

Mudhoney

BURN IT CLEAN
Tracks: / Burn it clean.
7" Single: Released Aug '89, on Glitterhouse, Catalogue no: **GR 0060**

Mudlarks

BOOK OF LOVE
Tracks: / Book of love.
7" Single: Released Jun '58, on Columbia, by EMI Records. Deleted '61. Catalogue no: **DB 4133**

LOLLIPOP
Tracks: / Lollipop.
7" Single: Released May '58, on Columbia, by EMI Records. Deleted '61. Catalogue no: **DB 4099**

LOVE GAME, THE
Tracks: / Love game, The.
7" Single: Released Feb '59, on Columbia, by EMI Records. Deleted '62. Catalogue no: **DB 4250**

Muerte, La

SERIALIST MYSTERY
Tracks: / Serialist mystery.
12" Single: Released Oct '84, on Red Rhino, by Red Rhino Records. Catalogue no: **RED 51**

SURREALIST MYSTERY
Tracks: / Surrealist mystery.
12" Single: Released 27 Jun '85, on Red Rhino, by Red Rhino Records. Catalogue no: **REDT 051**

Mugshots

SHY
Tracks: / Shy / Don't understand.
7" Single: Released Sep '80, on Liberty, by EMI Records. Deleted Sep '83. Catalogue no: **BP 368**

TOO OLD FOR FAIRY TALES
Tracks: / Too old for fairy tales.
7" Single: Released Oct '82, on Lancaster, by Lancaster Records. Catalogue no: **LG 11**

Muhammad, Idris

Biographical details: American drummer, percussionist and occasional singer, Idris Muhammad released a series of soul albums between 1972 and 1980, starting with Black Rhythm Revolution. *Power Of Soul* (1974) was, perhaps, the best of them. *Turn This Mutha Out* ('77) yielded a one-off UK chart entry with the single *Could Heaven Ever Be Like This?* -- the song reached No 42 after picking up strong play in the clubs; it peaked at No 76 in the States. On the whole, Muhammad's talents have been put to better use as a sidesman that as a performer in his own right. Among artists he worked with during the 70's were Merry Clayton, Hank Crawford, Roberta Flack, Bob James and Grover Washington Jr. Like fellow percussionist Ralph McDonald he varied his schedule by working with both jazz and soul performers. (Bob MacDonald, February 1986.).

COULD HEAVEN EVER BE LIKE THIS

MUNGO JERRY - BABY JUMP (Released on Dawn)

Tracks: / Could heaven ever be like this / Turn this mutha out.
7" Single: Released Sep '77, on Kudu. Deleted '80. Catalogue no: **935**

FOR YOUR LOVE
Tracks: / Fot your love / New Orleans.
7" Single: Released Nov '80, on Fantasy (1), by BMG Records (UK). Deleted Nov '83. Catalogue no: **FTC 191**
12" Single: Released Oct '80, on Fantasy (1), by BMG Records (UK). Deleted Oct '83. Catalogue no: **FTCT 191**

Muldaur, Maria
Biographical details: This American singer, violinist and percussionist was born Maria Grazia Rosa Domenica d'Amato in New York City in 1943, and started her career in jug bands. This good-time, somewhat amateurish genre provided a training ground for many folk-influenced artists. Maria spent the mid-Sixties as a member of Jim Kweskin's Jug Band, where she met fellow singer Geoff Muldaur. Maria married Geoff (who was also a solo artist in his own right). The couple recorded a pair of duet albums, *Pottery pie* and *Sweet potatoes*, in the early Seventies. The marriage ended in 1973, whereupon Geoff resumed his undistinguished solo career. Maria's solo journy was launched with an eponymous debut LP in 1974. This contained her hit single *Midnight at the oasis*, which reached No.6 in the States and No.21 in Britain. This record typified the hybrid jazz/folk/pop style which characterised Muldeur's whole career. The most important ingredient was her subtle, sensual, serene singing. She achieved another US Top 20 pop hit in 1975 with *I'm a woman*. Selecting her material from diverse sources, Muldaur continued issuing albums through the rest of the Seventies and during the Eighties, but did not achieve any further major chart success. She never escaped the tag of being 'the woman who did *Midnight at the oasis*.' Always careful to maintain the integrity of her craft regardless of commercial dictates, Maria ran the gamut of styles from blues to MoR on her later releases. (Bob MacDonald, 6th Feb 1986).

MIDNIGHT AT THE OASIS
Tracks: / Midnight at the oasis.
7" Single: Released Jun '74, on Reprise, by WEA Records. Deleted '77. Catalogue no: **K 14331**

TENDERNESS
Tracks: / Tenderness / Noche de amour.
7" Single: Released May '81, on Polydor, by Polydor Ltd. Deleted May '84. Catalogue no: **POSP 259**

Mullane, Mick
COMPLETELY
Tracks: / Completely / Completely (version).
7" Single: Released Apr '88, on Legal Lights, by Legal Light Records. Catalogue no: **7LLQ 25**
12" Single: Released Apr '88, on Legal Lights, by Legal Light Records. Catalogue no: **LLQ 25**

Mullen, Morrissey
DO LIKE YOU
Tracks: / Do like you / Badness.
7" Single: Released Jul '81, on Beggars Banquet, by Beggars Banquet Records. Deleted '84. Catalogue no: **BEG 60**

Muller,Egon
GO GO GO MAN GO/LET'S DANCE THE ROCK 'N' ROLL
7" Single: Released Nov '83, on President, by President Records. Catalogue no: **PT 521**

Muller-Steger, Gila
LOVERS, THE
Tracks: / Lovers, The / Together.
7" Single: Released Jun '87, on First Time, by First Time Records. Catalogue no: **FTR 5452**

Multicoloured Shades
2000 LIGHT YEARS FROM HOME
Tracks: / 2000 light years from home.
12" Single: Released Aug '87, on ABC (indie). Catalogue no: **ABCS 014T**

TEEN SEX TRANSFUSION
Tracks: / Teen sex transfusion / Roses / Miss Terry shade (Extra track available on 12" version only.).
7" Single: Released Nov '86, on Situation 2, by Beggars Banquet Records. Catalogue no: **SIT 43**
12" Single: Released Nov '86, on Situation 2, by Beggars Banquet Records. Catalogue no: **SIT 43T**

Multicoloured World
BOLERO FOR PEACE
Tracks: / Bolero for peace.

7" Single: Released Jun '82, on Oblivion. Catalogue no: **PAPA 1**

Multi-Story
BREAKING NEW GROUND
Tracks: / Breaking new ground.
7" Single: Released Sep '85, on FM, by FM-Revolver Records. Catalogue no: **VHF 18**

CARRIE
Tracks: / Carrie.
7" Single: Released Apr '85, on FM, by FM-Revolver Records. Catalogue no: **VHF 9**

Multivizion
WORK TO LIVE DON'T LIVE TO WORK
Tracks: / Work to live don't live to work.
7" Single: Released Jul '81, on Situation 2, by Beggars Banquet Records. Catalogue no: **SIT 8**
12" Single: Released Jul '81, on Situation 2, by Beggars Banquet Records. Catalogue no: **SIT 8T**

Mummy Calls
BEAUTY HAS HER WAY
Tracks: / Beauty has her way / Messages on your door.
7" Single: Released Feb '86, on Geffen, by Geffen Records (USA). Catalogue no: **A 6884**
12" Single: Released Feb '86, on Geffen, by Geffen Records (USA). Catalogue no: **TX 6884**

LET'S GO
Tracks: / Let's go / Jane I'll kiss you in the desert.
7" Single: Released Apr '86, on Geffen, by Geffen Records (USA). Catalogue no: **A 7088**
12" Single: Released Apr '86, on Geffen, by Geffen Records (USA). Catalogue no: **TA 7088**

MARY I SWEAR
Tracks: / Mary I swear.
7" Single: Released Nov '83, on Mummy Calls, by Backs Recording Co.. Catalogue no: **MC 12**

Munch, D.J.
PARTY ROCK
Tracks: / Party rock.
12" Single: Released Jul '87, on FM Dance, by FM-Revolver Records. Catalogue no: **12 VHF 39**

Munch, Frankie
DON'T LET MY FUNK DIE
Tracks: / Don't let my funk die.
12" Single: Released Nov '88, on Flim Flam, Catalogue no: **LURV 001 T**

Mundy, Reg
BE MY SQUEEZE
Tracks: / Be my squeeze.
7" Single: Released Jun '81, on EMI, by EMI Records. Deleted Jun '84. Catalogue no: **EMI 5179**
12" Single: Released May '81, on EMI, by EMI Records. Deleted May '84. Catalogue no: **12 EMI 5179**

Mungo Jerry
Biographical details: At the time of their greatest success, this British band consisted of Mike Cole, Ray Dorset, Colin Earl and Paul King. The group's name was taken from one of the cats in T.S.Eliot's famous feline verses. Dominated by lead singer/songwriter/multi-instrumentalist Ray Dorset, Mungo Jerry came into being in the late Sixties. Playing a good-time combination of jug band and skiffly styles, quite out of keeping with the times, the group suddenly surged from obscurity to showstopping status when they became the hit of the Hollywood Festival in Newcastle, England in the early summer of 1970. Within a few weeks, the band stormed to the top of the UK chart with *In the summertime* and stayed at No.1 for seven weeks, the longest run at the summit by any single during the first half of the Seventies.
The success of *In the summertime* was quite phenomenal, especially coming from an act who had been unknown mere weeks earlier. It went to No.1 in more than twenty countries. In France it was one of the fastest selling records of all time. In America the single reached No.3 and sold a million copies in the US alone. It was the best summer anthem since the heyday of the Beach Boys, and its universal appeal can simply be attributed to the fact that it was an infectiously catchy folk-pop ditty, brilliant in its sheer straightforwardness. The song's bright, optimistic flavour was a welcome ingredient in a pop world where, in 1970 the Beatles and several other big acts were splitting, and no-one knew what the Seventies had in store.
Mungo Jerry never, of course, enjoyed another hit on the scale of *In the summertime*, but for several years, the group chalked up a string of hit singles in Britain and Continental Europe. These included the wild workout *Baby jump* (a second UK No.1) and the Marc Bolan-style song *Lady Rose*. Most of the Mungo hits were penned by Dorset, the exception being *Alright alright alright* (No 3 in the UK in 1973), a translation of a 1966 French song. After 1974's *Long legged woman dressed in black*, Mungo Jerry's fresh and quirky pop approach finally faded from the British charts. They devoted much of their subsequent time to live work on the Continent before folding in the late Seventies. The Dorset story did not end there, however. In 1980 Kelly Marie reached the British No.1 slot with his song *Feels like I'm in love*. In 1983 he tried in vain to resurrect Mungo Jerry with the single *There goes my heart again*. (Bob MacDonald, 6th Feb 1988).

ALRIGHT ALRIGHT ALRIGHT
Tracks: / Alright alright alright.
7" Single: Released Jul '73, on Dawn, by Pye Records. Deleted '76. Catalogue no: **DNS 1037**

BABY JUMP (See panel above left)
Tracks: / Baby jump / Man behind the piano, The / Live from Hollywood.
7" Single: Released Feb '71, on Dawn, by Pye Records. Deleted '74. Catalogue no: **DNX 2505**
7" Single: Released Jul '82, on Old Gold, by Old Gold Records. Deleted Jul '88. Catalogue no: **OG 9139**

IN THE SUMMERTIME (See panel below)
Tracks: / In the summertime / Long legged woman dressed in black.
CD 5": Released 24 Apr '89, on Old Gold, by Old Gold Records. Catalogue no: **OG 6139**

IN THE SUMMERTIME (7" EP)
Tracks: / In the summertime / Mighty man / Dust pneumonia blues.
7" EP: Released '70, on Dawn, by Pye Records. Catalogue no: **DNX 2502**

IN THE SUMMERTIME (SINGLE)
Tracks: / In the summertime / Mighty man.
7" Single: Released Aug '87, on Illegal, by Faulty Products Records. Catalogue no: **MUNG 1**
7" Single: Released Apr '79, on Flashback, by Mainline Records. Catalogue no: **FBS 7**
7" Single: Released Apr '83, on Old Gold, by Old Gold Records. Catalogue no: **OG 9292**
12" Single: Released Jul '87, on Illegal, by Faulty Products Records. Catalogue no: **MUNGT 1**

LADY ROSE
Tracks: / Lady Rose.
7" Single: Released May '71, on Dawn, by Pye Records. Deleted '74. Catalogue no: **DNX 2510**

LONG LEGGED WOMAN DRESSED IN BLACK
Tracks: / Long legged woman dressed in black.
7" Single: Released Apr '74, on Dawn, by Pye Records. Deleted '77. Catalogue no: **DNS 1061**

MUNGO'S SUMMER FUN PACKAGE

MUNGO JERRY - IN THE SUMMER TIME (Released on Old Gold)

(EP)
7" Single: Released Aug '82, on Scratch, by Scratch Records. Catalogue no: **HS 406**

OPEN UP
Tracks: / Open up.
7" Single: Released Apr '72, on Dawn, by Pye Records. Deleted '75. Catalogue no: **DNX 2514**

SUNSHINE REGGAE
Tracks: / Sunshine reggae.
7" Single: Released Jun '85, on Orbit, by Orbit Records. Catalogue no: **TRIP 4**

THERE GOES MY HEART AGAIN
Tracks: / There goes my heart again.
7" Single: Released Jun '83, on Mach 1, by Mach 1 Records. Catalogue no: **MAGIC 8**

WILD LOVE
Tracks: / Wild love.
7" Single: Released Nov '73, on Dawn, by Pye Records. Deleted '76. Catalogue no: **DNS 1051**

YOU DON'T HAVE TO BE IN THE ARMY
Tracks: / You don't have to be in the army to fight in the war.
7" Single: Released Sep '71, on Dawn, by Pye Records. Deleted '74. Catalogue no: **DNX 2513**

Munich Machine

GET ON THE FUNK TRAIN
Tracks: / Get on the funk train.
7" Single: Released Dec '77, on Oasis, Deleted '80. Catalogue no: **OASIS 2**

Munro, Lee

STEREO HEADPHONES (I'VE GOT)
Tracks: / Stereo headphones (I've got) / Give me your love.

7" Single: Released Jan '87, on Numa, by Numa Records. Catalogue no: **NU 20**

Munroe, Caroline

PUMP ME UP
Tracks: / Pump me up.
7" Single: Released Apr '85, on Numa, by Numa Records. Catalogue no: **NU 5**
12" Single: Released Apr '85, on Numa, by Numa Records. Catalogue no: **NUM 5**

Munsey, Adrian

MAIN THEME
Tracks: / Main theme.
7" Single: Released May '81, on Armageddon, by Armageddon Records. Catalogue no: **AS 015**

Muppets

Biographical details: The launch of Jim Henson's *The Muppet Show* on American television in the mid-Seventies was a major movement in the history of children's entertainment. Kermit the Frog, Miss Piggy, Robin, Animal, Fozzie Bear, Rolf and all their fellow puppets gave new impetus to kids' shows, injecting a zany wit that also appealed to adults without compromising the main purpose of keeping the youngsters entertained. A whole cult following developed for *The Muppet Show*, and stars like Diana Ross and John Denver willingly subjected themselves to the tender mercies of the unpredictable television animals. When the Muppets became hugely popular on ITV in Britain in 1977, the effects of their appeal were felt on the record charts. *The Muppet Show* reached No.1 on the UK album chart in June of that year, dethroning a Beatles live album in the process! It contained the Top 10 single *Halfway down the stairs*, a rendition of the A.A.Milne standard performed by Kermit the Frog's nephew Robin (actually sung by Jerry Nelson). After logging 35 weeks on the British album chart, *The Muppet Show* was replaced on the list by the logically titled LP *The Muppet Show vol 2*. This album reached No.16 and logged 10 weeks on the survey. *The Muppet Show music hall* EP reached No.19 on the UK singles chart - one of the four standards featured on this disc was *Waiting at the church* which continued the perennial sparring between the amorous but ugly Miss Piggy and the programe's M.C. Kermit, who repeatedly rejected her advances. An unexpected beneficiary of Muppet Mania was the Italian orchestra/chorus leader and composer Piero Umiliani, whose dotty ditty *Mah na mah na* became a UK Tp 10 single after a cover version was adopted as the Muppets' theme. (Bob MacDonald, 7th Feb 1986).

HALFWAY DOWN THE STAIRS
Tracks: / Halfway down the stairs.
7" Single: Released May '77, on PRT, by Castle Communications Records. Catalogue no: **7N 45698**

MUPPET SHOW MUSIC HALL
Tracks: / Don't dilly dally on the way / Waiting at the church / Boy in the gallery / Wotcher (knocked 'em in the Old Kent Road).
7" EP: Released Dec '77, on Pye, Deleted '80. Catalogue no: **7NX 8004**
7" Single: Released Sep '80, on IMS, by Polydor Ltd. Catalogue no: **LR 4375**

Mur, Mona

JESZCHE POLSKE
Tracks: / Jeszche polske.
12" Single: Released Sep '81, on Supermax (Germany), Catalogue no: **MAX 02**

Murder Murder Suicide

CHRISTIANS
12" Single: Released Oct '87, on Major (Australia), Catalogue no: **MRLP 008**

Murdock, Lydia

Biographical details: This American singer was totally unknown before she hit the US black and dance charts and the UK pop chart with her autumn 1983 single *Superstar*. Though not mentioned by name on the record the *Superstar* in question ('you know just who you are') was clearly Michael Jackson. Murdock believed that Michael's recent worldwide smash *Billie Jean* was a sexist song, so she recorded this answer disc on which she declared 'I'm Billie Jean and I'm mad as hell'. The single reached No.14 on the UK chart; and in one particular week, it was placed side by side on the Top 20 with a Michael Jackson single. The success of *Superstar* briefly revived the answer disc phenomenon, a chart genre that was more common in the Fifties and early Sixties than in the Eighties. Cleverly, the melody and feel of Lydia's single were very similar to *Billie Jean* without being a direct copy. Despite the fact that he was given label credit as a cowriter of *Superstar*, there were rumours flying around at the time that Jackson was threatening to sue. These proved unfounded, which was just as well because Michael might have found himself on shaky ground - in the summer of '83, and Italian act called Clubhouse had reached the UK No.11 position by pointing out the similarity between *Billie Jean* and Steely Dan's *Do it again*! Murdock herself quickly faded into oblivion after her enjoyable hit; her 1984 single *Love on the line* flopped. (Bob MacDonald, 7th Feb 1986).

SUPERSTAR
Tracks: / Superstar.
7" Single: Released Sep '83, on Korova, by WEA Records. Deleted '86. Catalogue no: **KOW 30**

Murdock, Shirley

AS WE LAY
Tracks: / As we lay (remix) (Side A) / Danger zone (Side B).
7" Single: Released Mar '87, on Elektra (USA), by Elektra Records (USA). Deleted Jan '88. Catalogue no: **EKR 53**
12" Single: Released Mar '87, on Elektra (USA), by Elektra Records (USA). Deleted Jan '88. Catalogue no: **EKR 53 T**

NO MORE
Tracks: / No more / One I need, The / Truth or dare (Extra track on 12" version only.).
7" Single: Released Aug '86, on Elektra (USA), by Elektra Records (USA). Deleted Jun '87. Catalogue no: **EKR 43**
12" Single: Released Aug '86, on Elektra (USA), by Elektra Records (USA). Deleted Jun '87. Catalogue no: **EKR 43 T**

TRUTH OR DARE
Tracks: / Truth or dare / Go on without you.
7" Single: Released Feb '86, on Elektra (USA), by Elektra Records (USA). Deleted Jun '87. Catalogue no: **EKR 36**
12" Single: Released Feb '86, on Elektra (USA), by Elektra Records (USA). Deleted Jun '87. Catalogue no: **EKR 36 T**

Murphey, Elliott

EYES OF THE CHILDREN OF MARIA
Tracks: / Eyes of the children of Maria.
7" Single: Released Jul '88, on New Rose (1), by New Rose Records. Catalogue no: **NEW 113**

Murphy, Eddie

BOOGIE IN YOUR BUTT
Tracks: / Boogie in your butt / Party all the time.
12" Single: Released Sep '88, on Old Gold, by Old Gold Records. Catalogue no: **OG 4505**

HOW COULD IT BE (SINGLE)
Tracks: / How could it be.
7" Single: Released Apr '86, on CBS, by CBS Records. Deleted '86. Catalogue no: **A 6890**

PARTY ALL THE TIME
Tracks: / Party all the time.
7" Single: Released Dec '85, on CBS, by CBS Records. Deleted '87. Catalogue no: **A 4457**
12" Single: Released Dec '85, on CBS, by CBS Records. Deleted '87. Catalogue no: **TX 4457**

PUT YOUR MOUTH ON ME
Tracks: / Put your mouth on me / Party all the time.
7" Pic: Released Sep '89, on CBS, by CBS Records. Catalogue no: **655266 7**
7" Single: Released Sep '89, on CBS, by CBS Records. Catalogue no: **655266 0**
7" Single: Released Sep '89, on CBS, by CBS Records. Catalogue no: **655266 6**
12" Single: Released Sep '89, on CBS, by CBS Records. Catalogue no: **655266 2**

Murphy, James

PLACE IN YOUR HEART, A
Tracks: / Place in your heart, A.
7" Single: Released Jul '88, on Illegal, by Faulty Products Records. Catalogue no: **ILS 1001**

Murphy, Michael Martin

WHAT'S FOREVER FOR?
Tracks: / What's forever for? / Crystal.
7" Single: Released Sep '82, on Liberty, by EMI Records. Deleted '85. Catalogue no: **UP 656**

Murphy, Noel

MURPHY AND THE BRICKS
Tracks: / Murphy and the bricks / From Clare to here.
7" Single: Released Mar '87, on Murphy's, Catalogue no: **STACK 1**

Murphy, Peter

ALL NIGHT LONG
Tracks: / All night long / Funtime (Extra track on 12").
7" Single: Released Feb '88, on Beggars Banquet, by Beggars Banquet Records. Catalogue no: **BEG 207**
12" Single: Released Feb '88, on Beggars Banquet, by Beggars Banquet Records. Catalogue no: **BEG 207 T**

BLUE HEART
Tracks: / Blue heart / Canvas beauty.
7" Single: Released Jun '86, on Beggars Banquet, by Beggars Banquet Records. Catalogue no: **BEG 162 T**
7" Single: Released Jun '86, on Beggars Banquet, by Beggars Banquet Records. Deleted Jan '88. Catalogue no: **BEG 162**

FINAL SOLUTION, THE
Tracks: / Final solution, The.
12" Pic: Released Nov '85, on Beggars Banquet, by Beggars Banquet Records. Catalogue no: **BEG 143TP**
7" Single: Released Nov '85, on Beggars Banquet, by Beggars Banquet Records. Deleted Jan '88. Catalogue no: **BEG 143**
12" Single: Released Nov '85, on Beggars Banquet, by Beggars Banquet Records. Catalogue no: **BEG 143T**

INDIGO EYES
Tracks: / Indigo eyes / God sends (live) / Confessions (live).
Note: * extra track on 12" only
7" Single: Released May '88, on Beggars Banquet, by Beggars Banquet Records. Catalogue no: **BEG 210B**
7" Single: Released Apr '88, on Beggars Banquet, by Beggars Banquet Records. Catalogue no: **BEG 210**
12" Single: Released Apr '88, on Beggars Banquet, by Beggars Banquet Records. Catalogue no: **BEG 210T**

SHOULD THE WORLD FAIL TO FALL APART
Tracks: / Should the world fail to fall apart.
12" Single: Released Jan '87, on Beggars Banquet, by Beggars Banquet Records. Deleted Jun '88. Catalogue no: **BEG 179 T**

TALE OF THE TONGUE
Tracks: / Tale of the tongue / Should the world fail to fall apart.
7" Single: Released Oct '86, on Beggars Banquet, by Beggars Banquet Records. Deleted Jan '88. Catalogue no: **BEG 174**
12" Single: Released Oct '86, on Beggars Banquet, by Beggars Banquet Records. Catalogue no: **BEG 174 T**

Murphy, Walter

Biographical details: This American keyboardist, multi-instrumentalist, composer and arranger was raised on classical music while growing up in the Manhattan area. During the early Seventies, he earned a steady living as a TV arranger and as a writer of jingles and commercials. Intrigued by the way in which pop records occasionally borrowed their tunes from the classical sphere (e.g. the Toys' *A lover's concerto* and Deodato's revamp of *Also sprach Zarathustra*), he came up with the idea of presenting familiar classic themes in a way that would appeal to the burgeoning disco market. Despite a series of refusals by record companies, Murphy's idea worked as a treat for a short while. His single *A fifth of Beethoven*, based on Beethoven's Fifth Symphony, glided gracefully up the American chart in 1976. When it reached No.1 in October, it was part of a string of five consecutive disco charttoppers that also included such dancefloor favourites as the Bee Gees and KC & The Sunshine Band. The single reached No.28 in Britain. It was initially credited to Walter Murphy & The Big Apple Band, depite the fact that Murphy himself played most of the instruments; this billing was eventually dropped when it was discovered that another band's name was being duplicated. The fact that Walter Murphy had been accepted into the disco marketplace was not lost on the compilers of the Bee Gees-dominated *Saturday night fever* soundtrack. *A fifth of Beethoven* was included on that double album, which dominated world markets in 1978 and sold 25 million copies. Attempts by Murphy to repeat the appeal of *A fifth Beethoven* were only marginally successful, although he scored a US Top 50 hit in 1982 with a medley of themes from John Williams *ET* music. Walter's style had a strong influence on Britains's Royal Philharmonic Orchestra who achieved an international Top 10 hit in 1981 with their discofied medley *Hooked on classics*. (Bob MacDonald, 7th Feb 1986).

DANCE TO THEMES FROM E.T.
Tracks: / Dance to themes from E.T. / Your planet or mine.
7" Single: Released Nov '82, on MCA, by MCA Records. Catalogue no: **MCA 791**
12" Single: Released Nov '82, on MCA, by MCA Records. Deleted Nov '85. Catalogue no: **MCAT 791**

FIFTH OF BEETHOVEN, A
Tracks: / Fifth of Beethoven, A.
7" Single: Released Jul '76, on Private Stock, Deleted '79. Catalogue no: **PVT 59**

MOSTLY MOZART
Tracks: / Mostly Mozart / Classical dancin'.
7" Single: Released Feb '80, on New York, Catalogue no: **FB 1773**

Murrain,Marie

HOW CAN LOVE BE SO CRUEL
Tracks: / How can love be so cruel / Cruel version.
12" Single: Released Mar '86, on Body Music, by Nuclear Records. Catalogue no: **BMD 155**

Murray, Anne

Biographical details: This Canadian singer was born in Springhill, Nova Scotia, and worked as a qualified physical education teacher for a year before entering the music business professionally in the mid-Sixties. She started out as a regular Canadian TV show *Sngslong jubilee*. Its musical director Brian Ahern persuaded her to try her hand at recording. He became her studio producer, and her first album *This was my way* was released on the small Arc label. She then went to Toronto to sign with Capitol Records, with whom she has remained ever since.
Murray's first album for Capital spawned *Snowbird*, the single that made her famous in 1970. *Snowbird* reached No.8 on the American pop chart, and was also a sizeable country hit; it was the first ever record by a Canadian female artist to sell a million copies in the US. Ever since then, she has continued to work in a pleasant middle-of-the-road vein, incorporating tinges of country and folk into her style. Her American Top 20 singles included Kenny Loggins' *Danny's song* (No.7 in 1973), *Love song* (No.12 in 1974) and a cover version of a the Beatles *You won't see me* (No.8 in 1974). After a break in the middle of the Seventies to start a family, she returned in 1978 with her biggest hit, the slow building US No.1 ballad *You needed me*. During 1979-80 the singer chalked up three US Top 20 hits which all peaked at No.12: *I just fall in love again*, *Broken hearted me* and a revival of the Monkee's *Daydream believer*. During the early Eighties, she scaled down her concentration on ballads in favour of a more uptempo approach; her chart success, in terms of both singles and albums, suffered markedly as a result. Throughout her career, Murray has often been criticised for submerging her deep, potentially intense voice in a lukewarm sea of middle-of-the-road blendness. She has chosen her material from a wide variety of sources, including many remakes of Beatles oldies and other standards. Never in the top league of easy listening perfomers, she has nonetheless been highly successful. In Britain, only *Snowbird* and *You needed me* reached the Top 40. She finally achieved UK Top 20 status in 1981 with a TV advertised *Very best of* album. (Bob MacDonald, 7th Feb 1986).

COULD I HAVE THIS DANCE
Tracks: / Could I have this dance.
7" Single: Released Nov '80, on Capitol, by EMI Records. Deleted '83. Catalogue no: **CL 16175**

DAYDREAM BELIEVER
Tracks: / Daydream believer / Do you think of me?.
7" Single: Released Apr '80, on Capitol, by EMI Records. Deleted '83. Catalogue no: **CL**

6123

DESTINY
Tracks: / Destiny.
7" Single: Released Oct '72, on Capitol, by EMI Records. Deleted '75. Catalogue no: **CL 15734**

I JUST FALL IN LOVE AGAIN
Tracks: / I just fall in love again.
7" Single: Released Apr '80, on Capitol, by EMI Records. Deleted '83. Catalogue no: **CL 16069**

LITTLE GOOD NEWS
Tracks: / Little good news, A.
7" Single: Released Oct '83, on Capitol, by EMI Records. Deleted Jan '88. Catalogue no: **CL 309**

LUCKY ME
Tracks: / Lucky me / You set my dreams to music.
7" Single: Released May '80, on Capitol, by EMI Records. Deleted '83. Catalogue no: **CL 16144**

NOBODY LOVES ME LIKE YOU DO
Tracks: / Nobody loves me like you do.
7" Single: Released Oct '84, on Capitol, by EMI Records. Deleted '88. Catalogue no: **CL 340**

NOW AND FOREVER
Tracks: / Now and forever (you and me) / I don't wanna spend another night without you.
7" Single: Released Mar '86, on Capitol, by EMI Records. Deleted '88. Catalogue no: **CL 391**

SNOWBIRD (SINGLE)
Tracks: / Snowbird.
7" Single: Released Oct '70, on Capitol, by EMI Records. Deleted '73. Catalogue no: **CL 15654**
7" Single: Released '80, on Capitol, by EMI Records. Catalogue no: **LR 1245**

WHERE DO YOU GO WHEN YOU DREAM (SINGLE)
Tracks: / Where do you go when you dream / Only dream.
7" Single: Released Mar '81, on Capitol, by EMI Records. Deleted Mar '84. Catalogue no: **CL 16192**

YOU NEEDED ME
Tracks: / You needed me.
7" Single: Released Sep '78, on Capitol, by EMI Records. Catalogue no: **CL 16011**

Murray, David

Biographical details: One of the best-selling artists on Black Saint, David Murray, born in Berkeley, California, in 1955, is a talented musician and composer, playing tenor and soprano sax and flute. His style favours Albert Ayler and he has played with Cecil Taylor, Don Cherry and Anthony Braxton. He names his major influences as Charlie Parker, Sonny Rollins, Albert Ayler, Ben Webster and Coleman Hawkins. (IMS, September 1985.).

LET THE GREAT BIG WORLD KEEP TURNING
Tracks: / Let the great big world keep turning / Let the great big world keep turning (Instrumental) (Double 'A' side.).
7" Single: Released Nov '85, on Pectcode, Deleted '86. Catalogue no: **PECM 3**

Murray, Pauline

Biographical details: Born in Durham, singer-songwriter Murray achieved huge press acclaim and moderate commercial success during 1977-79 as leader of punk rock band Penetration. She embarked on a solo career in 1980 and, although her backing musicians were men, released records under the billing Pauline Murray & The Invisible Girls. The first, the promising *Dream Sequence (One)*, peaked at No 67 on the British singles chart in August 1980 and an LP, Pauline Murray & The Invisible Girls, reached No 25. To support the album the band toured Britain with punk poet John Cooper Clarke. She then drifted into obscurity, returning in '84 with a single, *Holocaust*, under the billing Pauline Murray & Storm. (Bob MacDonald, February 1986.).

DREAM SEQUENCES
Tracks: / Dream sequence (1) / Dream sequence (2).
7" Single: Released Aug '80, on Illusive, Deleted '83. Catalogue no: **IVE 1**

HOLOCAUST
Tracks: / Holocaust.
7" Single: Released Oct '84, on Polestar, Catalogue no: **PSTR 001**
12" Single: Released Oct '84, on Polestar, Catalogue no: **PSTR 12001**

HONG KONG
Tracks: / Hong Kong (A side).
12" Single: Released Feb '87, on Polestar, Catalogue no: **PSTR 12002**

NEW AGE
Tracks: / New age / Body music.
12" Single: Released Oct '86, on Polestar, Catalogue no: **PSTR 12003**
7" Single: Released Oct '86, on Polestar, Catalogue no: **PSTR 003**

SEARCHING FOR HEAVEN
Tracks: / Searching for heaven / Animal crazy / Vistor (12" only).
7" Single: Released Apr '81, on Illusive, Deleted '85. Catalogue no: **IVE 3**
12" Single: Released Apr '81, on Illusive, Deleted '85. Catalogue no: **IVEX 3**

THIS THING CALLED LOVE
Tracks: / This thing called love.
12" Single: Released May '89, on Cat & Mouse, by Cat & Mouse Records. Catalogue no: **ABBO 9T**

Murray, Ruby

Biographical details: This British singer, though of no great importance in the overall development of music, holds a special place in the hearts of pop historians for the way in which she dominated the British charts in one particular year, 1955. When American star Madonna had a similarly tight grip on the UK listings 30 years later chartologists often stated that she was the first female singer to achieve such a feat since Ruby Murray. But the comparison with Madonna ends there. Murray was a reserved young woman whose music and personality neatly conformed with the conventional standards of middle-of-the-road balladeers of the day. She was described, somewhat patronisingly with hindsight, as "the shy little songstress from Belfast". She was still in her late teens when her gentle, melodic voice first penetrated the charts in December 1954. That first hit, *Heartbeat*, reached No.3 in early '55. Consolidation of her breakthrough was swift and her roll call of British hit singles in '55 continued with *Softly Softly* (No.1), *Happy Days And Lonely Nights* (No.6), *Let Me Go, Lover* (No.5), *If Anyone Finds This, I Love You* (No.4), *Evermore* (No.3) and *I'll Come When You Call* (No.6). At one point, in the week of 18 March, Murray placed five of these hits in the Top Twenty simultaneously. With her songs mainly supplied by Tin Pan Alley, Murray epitomised the conservative state of Britain's popular music taste in 1955. As the rock 'n' roll explosion swept across the Atlantic over the following couple of years she felt the effects along with many of her peers. Having achieved seven Top Tenners in one calendar year, she failed to crack the Top Ten once during 1956-58. Her fortunes were briefly revived in '59 when *Goodbye, Jimmy, Goodbye*, a cover version of Kathy Linden's American hit, reached the No.10 position. But in the event the "goodbye" theme was appropriate: as the 50's ended Ruby Murray faded from the public eye. (Bob MacDonald, February 1986.).

EVERMORE
Tracks: / Evermore.
7" Single: Released Jul '55, on Columbia, by EMI Records. Deleted '58. Catalogue no: **DB 3617**

GOODBYE JIMMY GOODBYE
Tracks: / Goodbye Jimmy goodbye.
7" Single: Released Jun '59, on Columbia, by EMI Records. Deleted '62. Catalogue no: **DB 4305**

HAPPY DAYS AND LONELY NIGHTS
Tracks: / Happy days and lonely nights.
7" Single: Released Feb '55, on Columbia, by EMI Records. Deleted '58. Catalogue no: **DB 3577**

HEARTBEAT
Tracks: / Heartbeat.
7" Single: Released Dec '54, on Columbia, by EMI Records. Deleted '57. Catalogue no: **DB 3542**

IF ANYONE FINDS THIS I LOVE YOU
Tracks: / If anyone finds this I love you.
7" Single: Released Mar '55, on Columbia, by EMI Records. Deleted '58. Catalogue no: **DB 3580**

I'LL COME WHEN YOU CALL
Tracks: / I'll come when you call.
7" Single: Released Aug '56, on Columbia, by EMI Records. Deleted '59. Catalogue no: **DB 3643**

LET ME GO LOVER
Tracks: / Let me go lover.
7" Single: Released Mar '55, on Columbia, by EMI Records. Deleted '58. Catalogue no: **DB 3577**

REAL LOVE
Tracks: / Real love.
7" Single: Released Dec '58, on Columbia, by EMI Records. Deleted '61. Catalogue no: **DB 4192**

SOFTLY SOFTLY
Tracks: / Softly softly.
7" Single: Released Jan '55, on Columbia, by EMI Records. Deleted '58. Catalogue no: **DB 3558**

MUSICAL YOUTH - SIXTEEN (Released on MCA)

YOU ARE MY FIRST LOVE
Tracks: / You are my first love.
7" Single: Released Aug '56, on Columbia, by EMI Records. Deleted '59. Catalogue no: **DB 3770**

Murrell, Kris

CHERRY PIE
Tracks: / Cherry pie / I shall be free.
7" Single: Released Mar '85, on Birdland, by Birdland Records. Catalogue no: **1 NEST**

RAWHIDE
Tracks: / Rawhide / Rawhide (version).
7" Single: Released Jul '88, on Legacy, by Legacy Records. Catalogue no: **LGY 64**
12" Single: Released Jul '88, on Legacy, by Legacy Records. Catalogue no: **LGYT 64**

WHO'S WITH YOU
Tracks: / Who's with you.
7" Single: Released Sep '85, on Survival (1), by Survival Records. Catalogue no: **EST 2**

Murrin,Jelly Belly

BACK FROM L.A.
Tracks: / Back from L.A. (Swed Mix) / Murrin rap (Jacko Mix).
7" Single: Released Apr '86, on Greyhound, by Greyhound Records. Catalogue no: **GUT 1**

Murrumbridgee Whalers

GIVING WAY TO TRAINS
Tracks: / Giving way to trains / In a garden.
7" Single: Released Aug '89, on Island, by Island Records. Catalogue no: **MOBY 1**

Murvin,Junior

Biographical details: This Jamaican reggae singer has made many average records over the years, but is really known for his one classic *Police and thieves*. First released in 1976, this political reggae song attracted a cult following in both Jamaica and Britain. In 1977 it was covered by the Clash on their seminal debut album, thus establishing an important link between reggae and the UK's burgeoning punk scene. The connection was confirmed at the end of the year when Bob Marley & The Wailers released the song *Punk reggae party*. For several years Murvin's track was a classic 'one that got away', but Junior's *Police and thieves* finally entered the UK singles chart in 1980, reaching No.23. (Bob MacDonald, 7th Feb 1986).

BAD MAN POSSE (SINGLE)
Tracks: / Bad man posse.
12" Single: Released Jul '82, on Dread At The Controls, Catalogue no: **DATC 009**

POLICE AND THIEVES
Tracks: / Police and thieves / Soldier and police dub.
7" Single: Released May '80, on Island, by Island Records. Deleted '83. Catalogue no: **WIP 6539**
12" Single: Released May '80, on Island, by Island Records. Deleted '83. Catalogue no: **12WIP 6539**

POLICE & THIEVES (SINGLE)
Tracks: / Police and thieves.
7" Single: Released Jul '81, on Island, by Island Records. Catalogue no: **WIP 6539**
12" Single: Released Apr '80, on Island, by Island Records. Catalogue no: **12WIP 6539**

Muscle Shoal

IF THE WEATHER GETS ME DOWN
Tracks: / If the weather gets me down.
12" Single: Released Jul '88, on Roustabout, by Roustabout Records. Catalogue no: **RST 003T**

SUMMER'S HERE
Tracks: / Summer's here.
7" Single: Released Aug '88, on Treasure Island Discs, by Treasure Island Discs. Catalogue no: **TID 001**
12" Single: Released Aug '88, on Treasure Island Discs, by Treasure Island Discs. Catalogue no: **12 TID 001**

Music Academy

RINGING THE BELL
Tracks: / Ringing the bell.
7" Single: Released Mar '85, on Record Shack, by Record Shack Records. Catalogue no: **SOHO 36**
12" Single: Released Mar '85, on Record Shack, by Record Shack Records. Catalogue no: **SOHOT 36**

Music For...

MUSIC FOR THE SEASONS Various orchestras
Special: Released Apr '82, on Ronco, Catalogue no: **4C RTL 2075A/D**
Special: Released Apr '82, on Ronco, Catalogue no: **RTL 2075A/D**

Music for Aborigines

SITTING ON A BISCUIT TIN
Tracks: / Sitting on a biscuit tin / Faith / Ragbone man.
12" Single: Released 30 May '87, on Spartan, Catalogue no: **12SP 148**

Music For Boys

MUSIC FOR BOYS
Tracks: / Music for boys / Samba some day.
7" Single: Released Jan '82, on Logo, by Logo Records. Deleted '85. Catalogue no: **GO 407**

Music For Pleasure

CHROME HIT CORROSION
Tracks: / Chrome hit corrosion.
12" Single: Released May '84, on Whirlpool, Catalogue no: **WH 4**

DARK CRASH
Tracks: / Dark crash / Urban poison / Black.
7" Single: Released Jun '83, on Polydor, by Polydor Ltd. Catalogue no: **POSP 594**
12" Single: Released Jun '83, on Polydor, by Polydor Ltd. Catalogue no: **POSPX 594**

DISCONNECTION
Tracks: / Disconnection / Whiplash caress.
7" Single: Released Jan '84, on Whirlpool, Catalogue no: **WH 1**

FUEL TO THE FIRE
Tracks: / Fuel to the fire / Debris.
7" Single: Released Feb '81, on DJM, Deleted '84. Catalogue no: **RAGE 2**

LIGHT
Tracks: / Light / Malefice.
7" Single: Released Oct '82, on Polydor, by Polydor Ltd. Catalogue no: **POSP 533**
12" Single: Released Oct '82, on Polydor, by Polydor Ltd. Deleted Nov '85. Catalogue no: **POSPX 533**

LIGHT (2)
Tracks: / Light / Nostalgia.
12" Single: Released Oct '82, on Polydor, by Polydor Ltd. Catalogue no: **POSPX 533**

TIME
Tracks: / Time.
7" Single: Released Jan '83, on Polydor, by Polydor Ltd. Catalogue no: **POSP 553**
12" Single: Released Jan '83, on Polydor, by Polydor Ltd. Catalogue no: **POSPX 553**

Music from a Small

LOVE SACRIFICE
Tracks: / Love sacrifice.
12" Single: Released Jul '84, on Safari, by Safari Records. Catalogue no: **MP 121**

Music Machine

WHITER SHADE OF PALE, A
Tracks: / Whiter shade of pale, A.
7" Single: Released Nov '78, on Oasis, Deleted '81. Catalogue no: **OASIS 5**

Musical Youth

Biographical details: Ranging in age from 11 to 15, British reggae band Musical Youth were brothers Kelvin and Michael Grant, brothers Junior and Patrick Waite and a friend, Dennis Seaton. Five black lads of West Indian extraction, they came together as a group in their native Birmingham in 1980, at the instigation of the Grants' father, who had been a singer in Jamaica. They spent a couple of years gigging in the youth clubs of Birmingham and made some demos which attracted the attention of pioneering DJ John Peel. In August 1982 they played a gig at London's annual celebratory ethnic melting pot, the Notting Hill Carnival. They were snapped up by MCA Records and paired with the highly successful pop producer Peter Collins. Within a month Musical Youth entered the UK singles chart with the bubbly *Pass The Dutchie*, an adaption of the reggae standards *Pass The Kutchie* (slang for "pass the joint") which the band changed to the more universally acceptable *Pass The Dutchie* ("pass the cooking pot" in Jamaican patois). The single's success was phenominally quick for a new band -- it zoomed onto the UK list at the end of September and rocketed to No.1 a week later. The combination of an exuberantly catchy sound and the novelty element of the band's 11 - 15 age range, proved irresistible to the British public. And they remained "credible" with the music press, avoiding the sugary sweetness that has sometimes afflicted kiddie groups. *Pass The Dutchie* reached No.10 in the States in early '83, exposing reggae to a nation often impervious to the genre. The group consolidated British success with a hit album, *Youth Of Today*, which contained a further Top Ten single in *Never Gonna Give You Up*. Then followed a series of smaller hits which lasted until early '84, plus a collaboration with Donna Summer on the UK No 14 single *Unconditional Love*. Late that year they worked under the production of famous pop-reggae artist Eddie Grant, but this association proved fruitless and the band were already in obscurity. But they had lasted much longer than many would have predicted after the novelty success of *Pass The Dutchie* and they still had long and potentially productive lives ahead of them. (Bob MacDonald, February 1986.).

007
Tracks: / 007.
7" Single: Released Oct '83, on MCA, by MCA Records. Deleted '86. Catalogue no: **YOU 6**

HEARTBREAKER
Tracks: / Heartbreaker.
7" Single: Released Apr '83, on MCA, by MCA Records. Deleted '86. Catalogue no: **YOU 4**

NEVER GONNA GIVE YOU UP
Tracks: / Never gonna give you up / Rub'n'dub / Jim'll fix it.
7" Single: Released Feb '83, on MCA, by MCA Records. Deleted '86. Catalogue no: **YOU 3**

PASS THE DUTCHIE
Tracks: / Pass the dutchie / Give love a chance.
7" Single: Released Sep '82, on MCA, by MCA Records. Deleted '85. Catalogue no: **YOU 1**
12" Single: Released Sep '82, on MCA, by MCA Records. Deleted '85. Catalogue no: **YOUT 1**

PASS THE DUTCHIE (OLD GOLD)
Tracks: / Pass the Dutchie / Never gonna give you up.
7" Single: Released Apr '86, on Old Gold, by Old Gold Records. Deleted Jul '88. Catalogue no: **OG 9597**

POLITICAL
Tracks: / Political / General.
7" Single: Released Oct '82, on 021 Records, by Avatar Record Corporation. Deleted '84. Catalogue no: **OTO 6**

SHE'S TROUBLE
Tracks: / She's trouble / Tell Jack.
7" Single: Released Apr '84, on MCA, by MCA Records. Catalogue no: **YOU 8**
12" Single: Released Apr '84, on MCA, by MCA Records. Catalogue no: **YOUT 8**

SIXTEEN (See panel on previous page)
Tracks: / Sixteen / Strictly vibes.
7" Pic: Released Jan '84, on MCA, by MCA Records. Catalogue no: **YOUP 7**
7" Single: Released Jan '84, on MCA, by MCA Records. Catalogue no: **YOU 7**
12" Single: Released Jan '84, on MCA, by MCA Records. Catalogue no: **YOUT 7**

TELL ME WHY
Tracks: / Tell me why.
7" Single: Released Jul '83, on MCA, by MCA Records. Deleted '86. Catalogue no: **YOU 5**

YOUTH OF TODAY (SINGLE)
Tracks: / Youth of today / Gone straight.
7" Single: Released Nov '82, on MCA, by MCA Records. Deleted '85. Catalogue no: **YOU 2**

Musique

IN THE BUSH
Tracks: / In the bush.
7" Single: Released Nov '78, on CBS, by CBS Records. Deleted '81. Catalogue no: **CBS 6791**

Mustard, Doc

NUCLEAR BOOGIE
Tracks: / Nuclear boogie / Don't give up.
7" Single: Released May '84, on Joy, by President Records. Catalogue no: **KIC 04**

Muta Baruka

HARD TIME LOVE
Tracks: / Hard time love / Nah I give up.
12" Single: Released Jun '82, on Hightide, Catalogue no: **HT 02**

Mutant Rockers

CLASSICAL SCRATCH
Tracks: / Classical scratch.
7" Single: Released Jan '85, on Beggars Banquet, by Beggars Banquet Records. Deleted '86. Catalogue no: **BEG 127**
12" Single: Released Jan '85, on Beggars Banquet, by Beggars Banquet Records. Deleted Jun '87. Catalogue no: **BEG 127T**

Mutants

BOSS MAN
Tracks: / Boss man.
7" Single: Released '78, on Rox, by Rox Records. Catalogue no: **ROX 2**

HARD TIMES
Tracks: / Hard times.
7" Single: Released '79, on Rox, by Rox Records. Catalogue no: **ROX 5**

Mute Drivers

BOOMTOWN
Tracks: / Boomtown.
12" Single: Released Dec '88, on Irradiated, Catalogue no: **RAD 12001**

IMPOSSIBILITIES
Tracks: / Impossibilities.
12" Single: Released Jul '89, on Irradiated, Catalogue no: **RAD 12002**

Mutha Hood

TEAR THE ROOF OFF
Tracks: / Tear the roof off / Love or money?.
7" Single: Released Oct '88, on Dancetrax, by BMG Records (UK). Deleted Aug '89. Catalogue no: **DRX 5**
12" Single: Released Oct '88, on Dancetrax, by BMG Records (UK). Catalogue no: **DRXT 512**
12" Single: Released Oct '88, on Dancetrax, by BMG Records (UK). Catalogue no: **DRX 512**

Mwab

IS MICHAEL BUM AN APPLE
Tracks: / Is Michael Bum an apple / Angus Yung.
7" Single: Released Jan '84, on MWAB, by Red Rhino Records. Catalogue no: **MWAB 001**

Mwamba, Murial

NO ARMS
Tracks: / No arms / Tomorrow is too late.
7" Single: Released Jun '88, on Bold Reprieve (1), Catalogue no: **BRM 012**

MWRT Sound

BAD BEHAVIOUR
Tracks: / Bad behaviour / Unruly pickney.
12" Single: Released Dec '82, on MWRT, Catalogue no: **MWRT 52353**

My Baby's Arm

HUNG IN THE PLAYGROUND
Tracks: / Primitive kind / Hung in the playground.
7" Single: Released Feb '87, on Kasper, Catalogue no: **KAT 2**

My Bloody Valentine

FEED ME WITH YOUR KISS
Tracks: / Feed me with your kiss.
12" Single: Released Nov '88, on Creation, by Creation Records. Catalogue no: **CRE 061 T**
7" Single: Released Nov '88, on Creation, by Creation Records. Catalogue no: **CRE 061**

NEW RECORD BY, A
Tracks: / New record by, A.
12" Single: Released Sep '86, on Kaleidoscope Sound, by Kaleidoscope Sound Records. Catalogue no: **KS 101**

NO PLACE TO GO
Tracks: / No place to go.
12" Single: Released Mar '86, on Fever, by Fever Records. Catalogue no: **FEV 5**

STRAWBERRY WINE
Tracks: / Strawberry wine.
12" Single: Released Jul '87, on Lazy, Catalogue no: **LAZY 07T**

SUNNY SUNDAE SMILE
Tracks: / Sunny sundae smile (A-side).
12" Single: Released Mar '87, on Lazy, Catalogue no: **LAZY 04T**

YOU MADE ME REALISE
Tracks: / You made me realise.
12" Single: Released Aug '88, on Creation, by Creation Records. Catalogue no: **CRE 055 T**
12" Single: Released Nov '88, on Creation, by Creation Records. Catalogue no: **CRE 061T**
7" Single: Released Nov '88, on Creation, by Creation Records. Catalogue no: **CRE 061**
7" Single: Released Aug '88, on Creation, by Creation Records. Catalogue no: **CRE 055**

My Brilliant Career

MESSAGE OF LOVE
Tracks: / Message of love.
12" Single: Released Oct '84, on Dingbat, Deleted '87. Catalogue no: **DBT 1**

My Captains

FALL
Tracks: / Fall / Converse / History / Nothing.
7" Single: Released Aug '81, on 4AD, by 4AD Records. Catalogue no: **AD 103**

My Life ...

SOME HAVE TO DANCE, SOME HAVE TO KILL
Tracks: / Some have to dance, some have to kill.
12" Single: Released May '89, on Wax Trax, by Wax Trax Records. Catalogue no: **WAXUK 055**

My Mine

HYPNOTIC TANGO
Tracks: / Hypnotic tango.
7" Single: Released Jun '84, on Sonet, by Sonet Records. Catalogue no: **SON 2267**

Myami, George

WE'RE HAVIN' A PARTY
Tracks: / We're having a party / First time.
7" Single: Released Feb '84, on Passion, by Skratch Records. Catalogue no: **PASH 18**
12" Single: Released Feb '84, on Passion, by Skratch Records. Catalogue no: **PASH 18(12)**

Mycron

MARCH OF THE SPACE INVADERS
Tracks: / March of the space invaders / Flight of the space invaders.
7" Single: Released Dec '82, on Multi-Media, Catalogue no: **MMT 2**

Myers, Alicia

APPRECIATION
Tracks: / Appreciation / Say that.
12" Single: Released Mar '85, on MCA, by MCA Records. Catalogue no: **MCAT 933**
7" Single: Released Mar '85, on MCA, by MCA Records. Catalogue no: **MCA 933**

I WANT TO THANK YOU
Tracks: / I want to thank you.
12" Single: Released Nov '87, on M & A (USA), Catalogue no: **MA 1101**

YOU GET THE BEST FROM ME
Tracks: / You get the best from me.
12" Single: Released Aug '84, on MCA, by MCA Records. Catalogue no: **MCAT 914**

Myers, Stanley

DIANA
Tracks: / Diana / Huntress, The.
7" Single: Released Jan '84, on BBC, by BBC Records & Tapes. Deleted '87. Catalogue no: **RESL 141**

NANCY ASTOR THEME
Tracks: / Nancy Astor theme / Virginia.
7" Single: Released Jan '82, on BBC, by BBC Records & Tapes. Deleted Jan '85. Catalogue no: **RESL 110**

Myhill, Richard

IT TAKES TWO TO TANGO
Tracks: / It takes two to tango.
7" Single: Released Apr '78, on Mercury, by Phonogram Ltd. Deleted '81. Catalogue no: **TANGO 1**

LULLABY LOVE
Tracks: / Lullaby love / Those beautiful girls.
7" Single: Released Dec '80, on Bronze, by Bronze Records. Deleted Dec '85. Catalogue no: **BRO 111**

Mynk

GET UP AND DANCE (DANCE WITH ME)
Tracks: / Get up and dance.
12" Single: Released May '82, on Cricket International, by Cricket International Records. Catalogue no: **HOWZAT 101**

Myofist

HOT SPIKES (SINGLE)
Tracks: / Hot spikes / It's a sin.
7" Single: Released Oct '80, on A&M, by A&M Records. Deleted Oct '83. Catalogue no: **AMS 7565**

Myriam, Marie

L'OISEAU ET L'ENFANT
Tracks: / L'ouiseau et l'enfant.
7" Single: Released May '77, on Polydor, by Polydor Ltd. Deleted '80. Catalogue no: **2056 634**

Myrick, Gary

SHE TALKS IN STEREO
Tracks: / She talks in stereo / Model.
7" Single: Released Sep '80, on Epic, by CBS Records. Deleted '83. Catalogue no: **EPC 8972**

Mystere Five

SHAKE SOME ACTION
Tracks: / Shake some action / No message.
7" Single: Released Apr '80, on Flicknife, by Flicknife Records. Catalogue no: **FL 1**

Mysteriods

SANTA CLAUS IS COMING TO TOWN
Tracks: / Santa Claus is coming to town.
7" Single: Released Nov '81, on Superville, Catalogue no: **SV 3001**

Mysterious Art

OMEN PART 1, THE
Tracks: / Omen part 1, The (7" remix) (On 7" only) / Omen part 1, The (instrumental 7" remix) (On 7" only) / Omen part 1, The (extended remix) (On 12" only.) / Das omen (German 12" mix) (On 12" only.) / Omen part 1, The (extended instrumental remix) (On 12" only.) / Das Omen 1 (On CD single only.) / Das Omen 1 (instrumental) (On CD single only.) / Das Omen 1 (radio version) (On CD single only.).
12" Single: Released 14 Aug '89, on CBS, by CBS Records. Catalogue no: **654966 6**
CD 5": Released 21 Aug '89, on CBS, by CBS Records. Catalogue no: **654966 3**
7" Single: Released 14 Aug '89, on CBS, by CBS Records. Catalogue no: **654966 7**

Mysterious, William

SECURITY OF NOISE
Tracks: / Security of noise / Alright.
7" Single: Released Apr '82, on Mezzanine, Catalogue no: **MEZ 1**

Mystery

MYSTERY GIRL
Tracks: / Mystery girl.
12" Single: Released Nov '87, on Trax (USA), Catalogue no: **TX 138**

Mystery Boys

LOUIE LOUIE
Tracks: / Louie Louie / Sixty minutes.
7" Single: Released Nov '82, on President, by President Records. Catalogue no: **NRG 10**

Mystery Girls

ASH IN DRAG

Tracks: / Ash in drag / Ash in drag (Version) / Fire in monsters.
12" Single: Released Jan '84, on A&M, by A&M Records. Deleted '88. Catalogue no: **AMX 175**
7" Single: Released Jan '84, on A&M, by A&M Records. Deleted '88. Catalogue no: **AM 175**

I PROMISE TO ROCK YOU FOREVER
Tracks: / I promise to rock you forever / Nuthin' to do / Swing and slide (extended mix) / Call of the wild.
12" Single: Released Apr '88, on Mystery Girls. Catalogue no: **MGSTP 2**

SWING AND SLIDE
Tracks: / Swing and slide.
7" Single: Released 5 Mar '88, on Mystery Girls. Catalogue no: **MGS 1**

Mystery Guests

SPARROW THAT ATE NEW YORK
Tracks: / Sparrow that ate New York.
7" Single: Released Jul '81, on Boys Own. Catalogue no: **BO 3**

Mystery Slang

I'M MAD AT YOU
Tracks: / I'm mad at you.
12" Single: Released Sep '89, on Foundation. Catalogue no: **TFL 003T**

Mystic Angels

CHEATING IN THE NEXT ROOM
Tracks: / Cheating in the next room / It's all in the game.
7" Single: Released Nov '82, on S & D. Deleted Nov '85. Catalogue no: **SD 004**
12" Single: Released Nov '82, on S & D. Catalogue no: **SDL 004**

Mystic Feat

SPECIAL LOVING
Tracks: / Special loving / Dub.
12" Single: Released Aug '82, on Ariwa Sounds, by Ariwa Sounds. Catalogue no: **ARI 006**

Mystic Harmony

LIVING IN THE COUNTRY
Tracks: / Living in the country / Independent lady.
12" Single: Released Aug '84, on Clouds. Catalogue no: **CLSD 008**

NIGHT OVER EGYPT
Tracks: / Night over Egypt / Out in London.
7" Single: Released May '83, on Clouds. Catalogue no: **CLSD 001**

PHONE LINE
Tracks: / Phone line / Line.
12" Single: Released Sep '81, on SS, by SS Records. Catalogue no: **SSMD 004 12**

STAY WITH ME
Tracks: / Stay with me.
12" Single: Released Mar '82, on SS, by SS Records. Catalogue no: **SSMD 005**

SWEET FEELINGS
Tracks: / Sweet feelings.
12" Single: Released May '82, on SS, by SS Records. Catalogue no: **LLSD 015**

Mystic Man

STAND BY ME
Tracks: / Stand by me.
12" Single: Released May '89, on Living Room. Catalogue no: **LM 0021**

SWEET TENDER LOVE
Tracks: / Sweet tender love.
12" Single: Released May '89, on Living Room. Catalogue no: **LM 0016**

Mystic Merlin

Biographical details: *Just Can't Give You Up* provided a one-off UK chart entry for this American funk band -- it reached No.20 on the singles list in 1980. The slick, breezy single was catchy and danceable and its sound had an influence on Imagination, the British group soon to enjoy a run of disco smashes. But Mystic Merlin, who combined a magical act with their musical wares, were unable to conjure up any further hits and the guys vanished into thin air. (Bob MacDonald, February 1986.).

60 THRILLS A MINUTE
Tracks: / 60 thrills a minute / Got to make it better.
12" Single: Released Mar '81, on Capitol, by EMI Records. Deleted Mar '84. Catalogue no: **12 CL 16190**
7" Single: Released Mar '81, on Capitol, by EMI Records. Deleted Mar '84. Catalogue no: **CL 16190**

JUST CAN'T GIVE YOU UP
Tracks: / Just can't give you up / Burned to learn / Got to make the best of a love situation.
7" Single: Released Apr '80, on Capitol, by EMI Records. Deleted '83. Catalogue no: **CL 16133**
12" Single: Released Mar '80, on Capitol, by EMI Records. Deleted '83. Catalogue no: **12CL 16133**

Mystic Radics

NATIONWIDE
Tracks: / Nationwide.
12" Single: Released Sep '84, on Water Mount. Catalogue no: **WMT 1**

Mystic Revelations...

DRUMMER BOY
Tracks: / Drummer boy / Drummer boy (Version).
12" Single: Released Dec '86, on Star Apple. Catalogue no: **STRAP 120010**

Mystic Touch

GET YOURSELF TOGETHER
Tracks: / Get yourself together / Party people.
12" Single: Released Feb '81, on Champagne (USA), by Goldbond Recording (USA). Deleted Feb '84. Catalogue no: **FIZY 505**
7" Single: Released Feb '81, on Champagne (USA), by Goldbond Recording (USA). Deleted Feb '84. Catalogue no: **FIZZ 505**

Mystical Maniacs

SIDA
Tracks: / Sida.
12" Single: Released May '89, on Rodger. Catalogue no: **RODGER 8**

Mystique

HEARTBREAKER
Tracks: / Heartbreaker.
7" Single: Released 5 Jun '89, on Republic, by Code Records. Catalogue no: **LIC 009**
12" Single: Released 5 Jun '89, on Republic, by Code Records. Catalogue no: **LICT 009**

Mystral

PUSHING BACK THE HANDS OF TIME
Tracks: / Pushing back the hands of time / Twilight / Pushing back the hands of time (Radio mix).
7" Single: Released Mar '86, on Citybeat, by Beggars Banquet Records. Deleted Jun '87. Catalogue no: **CBE 702**
12" Single: Released Jan '86, on T-Mac, by T-Mac Records. Deleted '88. Catalogue no: **UEZT 2**
12" Single: Released Mar '86, on Citybeat, by Beggars Banquet Records. Catalogue no: **CBE 1202**

Mythra

DEATH AND DESTINY
Tracks: / Death and destiny.
7" Single: Released Oct '82, on Guardian. Catalogue no: **GRM 16**

Myton, Cedric

CAN'T TAKE IT AWAY
Tracks: / Can't take it away / When he leads.
7" Single: Released Sep '81, on Go Feet. Deleted '84. Catalogue no: **FEET 1210**

N

The following information was raken from the Music Master database on October 20th, 1989

N 93

BUS STOP
Tracks: / Bus stop / Bus stop (version).
7" Single: Released Dec '88, on Rhyme & Reason, by Priority Records. Deleted Aug '89. Catalogue no: **RNR 1**
12" Single: Released Dec '88, on Rhyme & Reason, by Priority Records. Deleted Aug '89. Catalogue no: **12 RNR 1**

Naafi Sandwich

D'Y HEAR ME
Tracks: / D'y hear me / Freddies fever.
7" Single: Released Oct '81, on Naffi Productions, Deleted '83. Catalogue no: **RUN 5**

Nab, Christine

FOR YOUR EYES ONLY
Tracks: / For your eyes only.
12" Single: Released Aug '88, on Class One, Catalogue no: **CO 002**

Nabay

BELIEVE IT OR NOT
Tracks: / Believe it or not / Believe it or not (part 2).
7" Single: Released Jun '80, on Grapevine (Northern Soul), by BMG Records (UK). Deleted '83. Catalogue no: **GRP 143**

Nacht Und Nebel

TABLE FOR TWO
Tracks: / Table for two.
7" Single: Released Jun '88, on Antler, by Antler Records (Belgium). Catalogue no: **ANT 032**

ZAFARI
Tracks: / Zafari.
7" Single: Released Jun '88, on Antler, by Antler Records (Belgium). Catalogue no: **ANT 017**

Nadine

JAGGED EDGE OF A BROKEN HEART
Tracks: / Jagged edge of a broken heart.
12" Single: Released 24 Jul '89, on Silver Heart, by Silver Heart Records. Catalogue no: **CUFF 1F**

Naffis

SLICE TWO
Tracks: / Slice two / Slice one.
7" Single: Released Oct '82, on Relentless, Catalogue no: **RS 200**

Nagamatzu

SPACE SHUTTLE SHUFFLE
Tracks: / Space shuttle shuffle / Space shuttle shuffle (version).
12" Single: Released May '88, on Motorcade, Catalogue no: **CADE 1T**

Nail, Jimmy

LOVE DON'T LIVE HERE ANYMORE
Tracks: / Love don't live here anymore / Night for day / Love don't live here anymore (extended version) (12" only).
7" Single: Released Mar '85, on Virgin, by Virgin Records. Deleted May '88. Catalogue no: **VS 764**
12" Single: Released Mar '85, on Virgin, by Virgin Records. Catalogue no: **VS 764-12**

THAT'S THE WAY LOVE IS
Tracks: / That's the way love is / Way out west, The.

7" Single: Released Oct '86, on Virgin, by Virgin Records. Deleted May '88. Catalogue no: **VS 915**
12" Single: Released Oct '86, on Virgin, by Virgin Records. Deleted May '88. Catalogue no: **VS 915-12**

Naima

YOU NEVER HAD A LOVE LIKE MINE
Tracks: / You never had a love like mine.
7" Single: Released Mar '85, on 10 Records, by Virgin Records. Deleted '86. Catalogue no: **TEN 42**

12" Single: Released Mar '85, on 10 Records, by Virgin Records. Deleted '89. Catalogue no: **TEN 42-12**

Nairobi

SOUL MAKOSSA (2 PARTS)
Tracks: / Soul makossa.
7" Single: Released Nov '82, on London Records, by London Records. Catalogue no: **LON 17**
12" Single: Released Nov '82, on London Records, by London Records. Catalogue no: **LONX 17**

Naisha

ONE STEP AT A TIME
Tracks: / One step at a time.
7" Single: Released May '89, on PWL, by PWL Records. Catalogue no: **PWL 40**
12" Single: Released May '89, on PWL, by PWL Records. Catalogue no: **PWLT 40**

Najee

PERSONALITY
Tracks: / Personality / Sweet love.
7" Single: Released Aug '88, on EMI-Manhattan, by EMI Records. Deleted Nov '88. Catalogue no: **MT 47**
12" Single: Released Aug '88, on EMI-Manhattan, by EMI Records. Deleted Nov '88. Catalogue no: **12MT 47**

Naked Eyes

Biographical details: Pete Byrne and Rob Fisher were a British twosome who came to brief fame in America in 1983, while they remained in relative obscurity in their native country. They were very much a product of their era, for technopop duos had been springing up like mushrooms in Britain during the early Eighties. In particular, Soft Cell had popularised the vocalist/synthesiser player line-up - Naked Eyes followed suit. And Tears for Fears had made it fashionable to come from the city of Bath - Naked Eyes followed suit. The duo had actually been together since 1979; the two guys had attempted to recruit other musicians and develop into a larger ensemble, but had reverted to a duo in late 1981. They were signed to EMI in May 1982 and teamed with producer Tony Mansfield, noted for his work with New Musik and Captain Sensible. The first product of their labours was an extraordinarily catchy reworking of the Burt Bacharach/Hal David standard *Always something there to remind me*, which had been a UK No.1 for Sandie Shaw in 1964 but was never a major hit for anybody in the States. Perhaps for this reason, the Naked Eyes rendition flopped in Britain when first released in September 1982 (later climbing to a modest No.60) but cruised to No.8 in America in the summer of '83. The duo followed this success with three further US Top 40 singles, all of them original songs: *Promises promises*, *When the lights go out* and *(What) in the name of love*. The British charts continued to be a blind spot for Naked Eyes and they soon lost sight of their American success too. (Bob MacDonald, 8th Feb 1986).

ALWAYS SOMETHING THERE TO REMIND ME
Tracks: / Always something there to remind me.

7" Single: Released Jul '83, on RCA, by BMG Records (UK). Deleted '86. Catalogue no: **RCA 348**

IN THE NAME OF LOVE
Tracks: / In the name of love.
7" Single: Released Aug '84, on Parlophone, by EMI Records. Catalogue no: **R 6078**

THERE'S ALWAYS SOMETHING THERE TO REMIND ME
Tracks: / There's always somethig there to remind me / Pitstop.

7" Single: Released Sep '82, on EMI, by EMI Records. Deleted '85. Catalogue no: **EMI 5334**
12" Single: Released Sep '82, on EMI, by EMI Records. Deleted '85. Catalogue no: **12EMI 5334**

VOICES IN MY HEAD
Tracks: / Voices in my head / Sweet poison.
7" Single: Released Jan '83, on EMI, by EMI Records. Catalogue no: **EMI 5363**

Naked In Paris

CAZA
Tracks: / Caza / No no hey hey.
7" Single: Released Jul '83, on VM, by VM Records. Catalogue no: **VMS 001**

Naked Lunch

MAKE BELIEVE
Tracks: / Make believe / Breathe.
7" Single: Released Mar '85, on Plezure, by Plezure Records. Catalogue no: **PLZS 843**

RABIES
Tracks: / Rabies / Slipping again.
7" Single: Released May '81, on Ramkup, Catalogue no: **PAP 003**

YOU TIE ME DOWN
Tracks: / You tie me down / Laugh your mind away.
7" Single: Released Apr '84, on Plezure, by Plezure Records. Catalogue no: **PLZS 841**

Naked Voice

DREAM HOUSE
Tracks: / Dream house.
7" Single: Released Sep '85, on Lambs To The Slaughter, by Prism Records. Catalogue no: **LTS 10**

Name

DANGEROUS TIMES (SINGLE)
Tracks: / Dangerous times (LP version) (Track on 12" only) / Driving rain.
7" Single: Released 5 Apr '88, on China, by Polydor Ltd. Catalogue no: **CHINA 3**
12" Single: Released 5 Apr '88, on China, by Polydor Ltd. Catalogue no: **CHINAX 3**

JESUS AND THE DEVIL
Tracks: / Great depression / Great depression.
7" Single: Released Sep '87, on Chrysalis, by Chrysalis Records. Catalogue no: **WOK 15**
12" Single: Released Sep '87, on Chrysalis, by Chrysalis Records. Catalogue no: **WOKX 15**

LAST WAR SONG
Tracks: / Last war song / Jesus and the devil (live) / Calm before the storm (live) / Dangerous times (live).
CD 5": Released Mar '89, on China, by Polydor Ltd. Catalogue no: **CHICD 15**
7" Single: Released Mar '89, on China, by Polydor Ltd. Deleted Oct '89. Catalogue no: **CHINA 15**
12" Single: Released Mar '89, on China, by Polydor Ltd. Deleted Oct '89. Catalogue no: **CHINX 15**

MAYBE SOMEDAY
Tracks: / Maybe someday (U.S.Remix) / Calm before the storm / Dangerous times (U.S.Remix) (Track on 12" only).
7" Single: Released 22 Aug '88, on China, by Polydor Ltd. Deleted 30 May '89. Catalogue no: **CHINA 8**
12" Single: Released 22 Aug '88, on China, by Polydor Ltd. Deleted 30 Jun '89. Catalogue no: **CHINX 8**

Name Escapes Me, The

HEARTBEAT
Tracks: / Heartbeat.
7" Single: Released Oct '87, on Piranha, Catalogue no: **NEM 1**

Names

NIGHTSHIFT
Tracks: / Nightshift / I wish I could speak your language.
7" Single: Released Jan '81, on Factory (1), by Factory Records. Catalogue no: **FAC 29**

POSTCARDS
Tracks: / Postcard / Calcutta.
7" Single: Released Feb '82, on Factory (1), by Factory Records. Catalogue no: **FAC 9**

Nan Tuck Five

NAN TUCK'S AXE
Tracks: / Nan Tuck's axe.

7" EP: Released Sep '83, on Brickyard, by Brickyard Records. Deleted Oct '85. Catalogue no: **NT 5**

Nancy Boys

I LIKE I LIKE I LIKE
Tracks: / I like I like I like / Do you wanna touch.
7" Single: Released Apr '83, on Red Sky, by Red Sky Records. Catalogue no: **RO 12**

Nancy & Lee

DID YOU EVER
Tracks: / Did you ever.
7" Single: Released Aug '71, on Reprise (USA), Deleted Aug '74. Catalogue no: **K 14093**

Naomi

HEATWAVE
Tracks: / Heatwave.
12" Single: Released May '82, on Rosie, by Rosie Records. Catalogue no: **RR 002**

Napalm Death

MENTALLY MURDERED
Tracks: / Mentally murdered.
CD 5": Released 29 Aug '89, on Earache, by Earache Records. Catalogue no: **MOSH 14 CD**
7" Single: Released 29 Aug '89, on Earache, by Earache Records. Catalogue no: **MOSH 14**
12" Single: Released 29 Aug '89, on Earache, by Earache Records. Catalogue no: **MOSH 14 T**

PEEL SESSIONS:NAPALM DEATH
Note: Session material from John Peel's programme on BBC Radio 1.
CD 5": Released Apr '89, on Strange Fruit, by Strange Fruit Records. Catalogue no: **SFPDSCD 049**
Cassingle: Released Apr '89, on Strange Fruit, by Strange Fruit Records. Catalogue no: **SFPDSMC 049**
12" Single: Released May '88, on Strange Fruit, by Strange Fruit Records. Catalogue no: **SFPS 049**

PROMO SINGLE
7" Single: Released Feb '89, on Earache, by Earache Records. Catalogue no: **7MOSH 008**

Napalm Stars

FICTION
Tracks: / Fiction.
7" Single: Released Jun '85, on Stranded, by Stranded Records. Catalogue no: **XLNT 2**

WORK HARD
Tracks: / Work hard.
7" Single: Released Jul '85, on Stranded, by Stranded Records. Catalogue no: **XLNT 3**

Napoleon XIV

Biographical details: The one-off novelty hit has always been a feature of pop music - while most acts who reach the chart strive to create a long term career in the hallowed bestseller listings, there are always gimmicks, fads and oddities which give brief prominence to more unlikely hitmakers. One of the weirdest examples of all time was *They're coming to take me away ha-haaa* by Napoleon XIV, which was a Top 5 hit on both sides of the Atlantic in August 1966. Despite the fact that the composer of the single was billed on the label as N. Bonaparte, the disc had nothing to do with France and everything to do with a New York engineer called Jerry Samuaels. Jerry, a previously unknown studio worker, was responsible for writing, recording and producing this idiosyncratic offering. Set against an insistent military beat *They're coming to take me away ha-haaa* was a spoken recital by a man supposedly going insane and waiting for the men in the white coats to arrive. As Napolion sank deeper and deeper into the abyss of madness, his voice grew higher and higher by means of tape tricks - eventually his sounded like the Chipmunks. Although *They're coming to take me away ha-haaa* reached No.3 on the American charts, it only remained on Billboard's Top 40 for five weeks - the single was deemed to be in bad taste by many US radio stations who consequently banned it, and in any case such an out-and-out comedy record was bound to

NASH THE SLASH - 19th NERVOUS UPRISING (Released on Dindisc)

tire the public quickly. Britain however, found it somewhat durable: it logged ten weeks on the UK Top 50, including three weeks in its No.4 peak position. Using a mask and a backing band, Samuels took Napoleon XIV on the road; but he and his band were soon forgotton. (Bob MacDonald, 8th Feb 1986).

THEY'RE COMING TO TAKE ME AWAY (OLD GOLD)
Tracks: / They're coming to take me away.
7" Single: Released '85, on Old Gold, by Old Gold Records. Catalogue no: **OG 9551**

THEY'RE COMING TO TAKE ME AWAY (SINGLE)
Tracks: / They're coming to take me away.
7" Single: Released Aug '66, on Warner Bros., by WEA Records. Deleted '69. Catalogue no: **WB 5831**

Napoli, Francesco

BALLA BALLA
Tracks: / Balla balla / Stay the night.
7" Single: Released Nov '87, on Carrere, Catalogue no: **CAR 418**
12" Single: Released Sep '87, on Carrere, Catalogue no: **CART 418**

Naptali, Raymond

ANY RIDDIM
Tracks: / Any riddim.
12" Single: Released Aug '85, on Patmans Studio, Catalogue no: **SD 001**

DIRTY RAT
Tracks: / Dirty rat / ABC.
12" Single: Released Oct '82, on Solid Gold (1), by Creole Records. Catalogue no: **SG 003**

Napti, Karin

BAD BAD BOY
Tracks: / Bad bad boy.
12" Single: Released Jun '85, on RCR, Catalogue no: **RCR 0521**

Narada

CAN'T GET YOU OUTTA MY HEAD
Tracks: / Can't get you outta my head / We still have a dream.
7" Single: Released Sep '88, on Reprise/Slash (USA), by WEA Records. Catalogue no: **W 7767**
12" Single: Released Sep '88, on Reprise/Slash (USA), by WEA Records. Catalogue no: **W 7767T**

Nardini, Norman

BURNIN' UP
Tracks: / Burnin' up / Stay away from him / Ready Freddy.
7" Single: Released May '80, on Tiger, by Legend Music Group. Deleted May '83. Catalogue no: **TIG 001**

Nardini, Peter

THINK YOU'RE GREAT
Tracks: / Think you're great.
7" Single: Released Dec '81, on Kettle, Catalogue no: **KS 701**

WE JUST MIGHT WIN
Tracks: / We just might win / Stop it I like it.
7" Single: Released May '82, on Kettle, Catalogue no: **KS 702**

Nasa

SEROPHIA
Tracks: / Serophia / Wild ways / Burning gold / Bad tan.
7" Single: Released Dec '87, on Fun After All, by Music For Nations Records. Catalogue no: **FAA 109**
12" Single: Released Dec '87, on Fun After All, by Music For Nations Records. Catalogue no: **12 FAA 109**

SHAH SHAH
Tracks: / Shah shah / Power to love / Cruisin' Persion (Only on 12" version.).
7" Single: Released Sep '88, on Fun After All, by Music For Nations Records. Catalogue no: **FAA 111**
12" Single: Released Oct '88, on Fun After All, by Music For Nations Records. Catalogue no: **12 TAA 111**

Nash, Billy

COME ON
Tracks: / Come on / Mikey's Rap.
7" Single: Released Jul '86, on Laurel, by Laurel Records. Catalogue no: **BSN 101**

JUST WANNA BE LOVED
Tracks: / Just wanna be loved.
Note: 5 track EP.
7" EP: Released Feb '87, on Laurel, by Laurel Records. Catalogue no: **EPC 102**

Nash, Johnny

6 TRACK HITS: JOHNNY NASH
Tracks: / There are more questions than answers / Tears on my pillow / You got soul / Stir it up / Hold me tight / Cupid.
7" EP: Released Sep '83, on Scoop 33, by Pickwick Records. Catalogue no: **7SR 5020**

CUPID
Tracks: / Cupid.
7" Single: Released Apr '69, on Major Minor, Deleted '72. Catalogue no: **MM 603**

HOLD ME TIGHT
Tracks: / Hold me tight.
7" Single: Released Aug '68, on Regal Zonophone, by EMI Records. Deleted '71. Catalogue no: **RZ 3010**

HOLD ME TIGHT (OLD GOLD)
Tracks: / Hold me tight.
7" Single: Released Jul '84, on Old Gold, by Old Gold Records. Deleted Jul '88. Catalogue no: **OG 9396**

I CAN SEE CLEARLY NOW (SINGLE)
Tracks: / I can see clearly now.
CD 5": Released Apr '89, on Epic, by CBS Records. Deleted Oct '89. Catalogue no: **CDJN 1**
7" Single: Released May '82, on CBS, by CBS Records. Catalogue no: **CBS 3964**
7" Single: Released Jun '72, on CBS, by CBS Records. Deleted '75. Catalogue no: **CBS 8113**
7" Single: Released Apr '89, on Epic, by CBS Records. Deleted Oct '89. Catalogue no: **JN 1**
12" Single: Released Apr '89, on Epic, by CBS Records. Deleted Oct '89. Catalogue no: **JNT 1**

LET'S BE FRIENDS
Tracks: / Let's be friends.
7" Single: Released Oct '75, on CBS, by CBS Records. Deleted '78. Catalogue no: **CBS 3597**

ROCK ME BABY
Tracks: / Rock me baby.
7" Single: Released Oct '85, on Sierra, by Sierra Records. Catalogue no: **FED 19**
12" Single: Released Oct '85, on Sierra, by Sierra Records. Catalogue no: **FED 19T**

STIR IT UP (SINGLE)
Tracks: / Stir it up.
7" Single: Released Apr '72, on CBS, by CBS Records. Deleted '75. Catalogue no: **CBS 7800**

TEARS ON MY PILLOW (OLD GOLD)
Tracks: / Tears on my pillow.
7" Single: Released Jul '82, on Old Gold, by Old Gold Records. Catalogue no: **OG 9196**

TEARS ON MY PILLOW (SINGLE)
Tracks: / Tears on my pillow.
7" Single: Released May '82, on CBS, by CBS Records. Catalogue no: **CBS 5956**
7" Single: Released Jun '75, on CBS, by CBS Records. Deleted '78. Catalogue no: **CBS 3220**

THERE ARE MORE QUESTIONS THAN ANSWERS
Tracks: / There are more questions than answers.
7" Single: Released Oct '72, on CBS, by CBS Records. Deleted '75. Catalogue no: **CBS 8351**

WHAT A WONDERFUL WORLD
Tracks: / What a wonderful world.
7" Single: Released Jun '76, on Epic, by CBS Records. Deleted '79. Catalogue no: **EPC 4294**

YOU GOT SOUL
Tracks: / You got soul.
7" Single: Released Jan '69, on Major Minor, Deleted '72. Catalogue no: **MM 586**

Nash, Neville

WIND ME UP
Tracks: / Wind me up / King hearted.
7" Single: Released Sep '82, on Kaleidoscope Sound, by Kaleidoscope Sound Records. Deleted Sep '94. Catalogue no: **KRLA 2612**

Nash The Slash

Biographical details: This Canadian violinist, multi instrumentalist and vocalist is a professional eccentric, who wraps himself in all manner of weird masks and bandages and produces music of a highly experimental nature. He picked up a brief cult following in Britain during the early Eighties when, after being discovered by Gary Numan, he was signed up by Dindisc/Virgin Records. His debut LP *Children of the night* made a one-off appearance on the UK charts, reaching No.61 in February 1981. This contained his own compositions plus his freaky interpretations of classics like Jan & Deans *Dead man's curve* and the Rolling Stones *19th nervous breakdown*. In the same year he guested on Numans *Dance* album. Leaving Dindisc and returning to Canada, Nash the Slash's subsequent albums only reached a small audience but were an interesting and esoteric contribution to the world of techno-rock. (Bob MacDonald, 8th Feb 1986).

19TH NERVOUS BREAKDOWN (See panel above left)
Tracks: / 19th Nervous breakdown / Danger zone.
7" Single: Released Mar '81, on Dindisc, by Virgin Records. Deleted '89. Catalogue no: **DIN 29**

DEAD MAN'S CURVE
Tracks: / Dead man's curve / Reactor no.2.
7" Single: Released Jan '81, on Dindisc, by Virgin Records. Deleted '89. Catalogue no: **DIN 28**

NOVEL ROMANCE
Tracks: / Novel romance / In a glass eye.
7" Single: Released Jul '81, on Dindisc, by Virgin Records. Catalogue no: **DIN 33**

Nashville Teens

FIND MY WAY BACK HOME
Tracks: / Find my way back home.
7" Single: Released Mar '65, on Decca, by Decca Records. Deleted '68. Catalogue no: **F 12089**

GOOGLE EYE
Tracks: / Google eye.
7" Single: Released Oct '64, on Decca, by Decca Records. Deleted '67. Catalogue no: **F 12000**

HARD WAY, THE
Tracks: / Hard way, The.
7" Single: Released Feb '66, on Decca, by Decca Records. Deleted '69. Catalogue no: **F 12316**

MIDNIGHT
Tracks: / Midnight.
7" Single: Released Mar '82, on Butt, by Butt Records. Deleted '86. Catalogue no: **GO 2**

THIS LITTLE BIRD
Tracks: / This little bird.
7" Single: Released May '65, on Decca, by Decca Records. Deleted '68. Catalogue no: **F 12143**

TOBACCO ROAD
Tracks: / Tobacco road.
7" Single: Released Jul '64, on Decca, by Decca Records. Deleted '67. Catalogue no: **F 11930**
7" Single: Released '80, on IMS, by Polydor Ltd. Catalogue no: **LR 0620**
7" Single: Released Feb '85, on EMI Golden 45's, by EMI Records. Catalogue no: **G 4543**
7" Single: Released Feb '84, on Butt, by Butt Records. Catalogue no: **MGLS 1**

Nasmak

PLASTER
Tracks: / Plaster / Me rex.
7" Single: Released Jun '83, on Aura Records, by Aura Records. Deleted '88. Catalogue no: **AUS 138**

Nasty Facts

DRIVE MY CAR
Tracks: / Drive my car / Gotta get to you / Crazy 'bout you.
7" Single: Released Dec '82, on 5th Column, by Graduate Records. Deleted Jan '87. Catalogue no: **FC 2**

Nasty Rox Inc.

ESCAPE FROM NEW YORK
Tracks: / Escape from New York / Escape from New York (version).
7" Single: Released Apr '88, on Stiff, by Stiff Records. Catalogue no: **NRO 1**
12" Single: Released Apr '88, on Stiff, by Stiff Records. Catalogue no: **NROX 1**

Nasty Savage

NO MORE (REMIX BY FROGGY)
Tracks: / No more / Heartbreak.
7" Single: Released Jul '87, on Columbia, by EMI Records. Catalogue no: **DB 9149**
12" Single: Released Jul '87, on Columbia, by EMI Records. Deleted Oct '87. Catalogue no: **DBX 9149**

Nasty Thoughts

ROCK THE HOUSE
Tracks: / Rock the house.
12" Single: Released Aug '89, on Kaos, Catalogue no: **KAOS 018**
12" Single: Released May '89, on Complete Kaos, Catalogue no: **CK 3001**

SEX
Tracks: / Sex.
12" Single: Released Nov '88, on Kaos, Catalogue no: **KAOS 006**

Natalie, Ann

DOCTOR GAMES
Tracks: / Doctor Games.
7" Single: Released Sep '84, on Spellbound, by Spellbound Records. Catalogue no: **SPELL 9**

Natasha

Biographical details: This British singer embarked on a solo career in 1980 after a spell in a girl group called the Flirts. After releasing the flop single *Strangest feeling* she zoomed to success in the summer of 1982 with *Iko iko* which reached the UK No.10 position. This singalong chant was made famous by the Dixie Cups in 1965. Another all-girl group called the Belle Stars had the same idea at the same time as Natasha. Although the Stars' version was undoubtedly superior, Natasha's rendition was more danceable and therefore won the race. Natasha's follow-up single *The boom boom room* peaked at No.44 on the British charts, and her debut LP *Captured* reached No.53. This contained a blend of oldies and original compositions, but Natasha England's talent was too lightweight and unoriginal to sustain a career. It was left to Tracey Ullman in 1983 to be derivative in a much more imaginative way. But because she was the wife of Bob England, the owner of her record label Towerbell, Natasha was able to continue releasing records at liberty, (Bob MacDonald, 8th Feb 1986).

BOOM BOOM ROOM
Tracks: / Boom boom room / I casually.
7" Pic: Released Aug '82, on Towerbell, Catalogue no: **TOWX 25**
7" Single: Released Aug '82, on Towerbell, Catalogue no: **TOW 25**

DON'T WALK AWAY
:

HOME LANDS
Tracks: / Homeland / Living my dream.

7" Single: Released Mar '84, on Towerbell, Catalogue no: **TOW 50**
12" Single: Released Mar '84, on Towerbell, Catalogue no: **12 TOW50**

I CAN'T HOLD ON
Tracks: / I can't hold on / Tonight.
7" Single: Released Jan '83, on Towerbell, Catalogue no: **TOW 34**
12" Single: Released Mar '84, on Towerbell, Catalogue no: **12 TOW 34**

I WANT YOU TO BE MY BABY
Tracks: / I want you to be my baby.
7" Single: Released Oct '83, on Towerbell, Catalogue no: **TOW 41**
12" Single: Released Oct '83, on Towerbell, Catalogue no: **12 TOW 41**

IKO IKO
Tracks: / Iko Iko / I should have known / I still love you.
12" Pic: Released May '82, on Towerbell, Catalogue no: **TOWX 122**
7" Single: Released May '82, on Towerbell, Catalogue no: **TOW 22**
12" Single: Released May '82, on Towerbell, Catalogue no: **TOWX 22**

PATA PATA
Tracks: / Pata pata / Tease.
7" Single: Released Oct '82, on Towerbell, Catalogue no: **TOW 29**

STAY WITH ME
Tracks: / Stay with me.
7" Single: Released Jun '84, on Towerbell, Catalogue no: **TOW 56**
12" Single: Released Jun '84, on Towerbell, Catalogue no: **TOW 56**

STRANGEST FEELING
Tracks: / Strangest feeling / Maybe.
7" Single: Released Oct '81, on Towerbell, Catalogue no: **TOW 12**

Natashe

BABY LOVE
Tracks: / Baby love.
7" Single: Released Feb '82, on Mass Media, Catalogue no: **MMM 7 1001**

Nation

WONDATIME
Tracks: / Wondatime.
12" Single: Released Nov '85, on Sweet Release, Catalogue no: **SR 01**

National Euphoria

DANCABILITY
Tracks: / Dancability.
7" Single: Released Dec '83, on Amidisque, by Amidisque Records. Catalogue no: **CF 003**

National Pastime

IT'S ALL A GAME
Tracks: / It's all a game / It's all a game (extended mix) (Only on 12" version.) / Idle threats / Idle threats (extended version) (Only on 12" version.).
7" Single: Released Feb '85, on Spellbound, by Spellbound Records. Catalogue no: **SPELL 10**
12" Single: Released Feb '85, on Spellbound, by Spellbound Records. Catalogue no: **SPELT 10**

LUNACY
Tracks: / Lunacy / It's all a game / Built to break (on 12" only).
7" Single: Released May '84, on Spellbound, by Spellbound Records. Catalogue no: **SPELL 4**
12" Single: Released May '84, on Spellbound, by Spellbound Records. Catalogue no: **SPELT 4**

National Shinguard

I'M FOREVER BLOWING BUBBLES
Tracks: / I'm forever blowing bubbles / Here comes the fleet.
7" Single: Released May '80, on Philips, by Phonogram Ltd. Deleted May '83. Catalogue no: **WEST 1**

National Youth Jazz...

LONDON
Tracks: / London.
7" Single: Released Jul '85, on N.Y.J.O., by National Youth Jazz Orchestra. Catalogue no: **2NYJ**

WHY DON'T THEY WRITE SONGS LIKE THIS ANYMORE
Tracks: / Why don't they write songs like this anymore.
7" Single: Released Aug '83, on SRT, by SRT Records. Catalogue no: **NYJO SRTS 1**

Native

BLACK TRACKS
Tracks: / Black tracks / When the master is dead.
7" Single: Released Apr '81, on GTO, Deleted '85. Catalogue no: **GT 288**

Native Hipsters

LARRY'S COMING BACK
Tracks: / Larry's coming back.
7" Single: Released Jul '83, on Plattekop, by Volume Records. Catalogue no: **KOP 1**

TENDERLY HURT ME
Tracks: / Tenderly hurt me / Stuck.
7" Single: Released Feb '82, on Illuminated Glass, Catalogue no: **HIP 1**

THERE GOES CONCORDE AGAIN
Tracks: / There goes concorde again.
7" Single: Released Oct '80, on Heater, Catalogue no: **HVR 003**

Native Tongue

HISTORY
Tracks: / History.
7" Single: Released Jul '84, on Squanderlust, Catalogue no: **LUST 3**

Natives

HERE IS THE NEWS
Tracks: / Here is the news.
7" Single: Released Jul '84, on Fearless, Deleted '87. Catalogue no: **FEAR 2**

Natty Papa

DON'T KNOW WHY I LOVE YOU
Tracks: / Don't know why I love you / Dance hall rock.
12" Single: Released Mar '85, on Natural Sounds, Catalogue no: **NS 001**

Natural Beauty

YOU WANNA BE LOVED
Tracks: / You want to be loved / Toshoong-peng.
12" Single: Released Dec '83, on Must Dance, Catalogue no: **MD 005**

Natural, Clive

JUICY WATER MELON
Tracks: / Juicy water melon / Juicy water melon (Version).
12" Single: Released Sep '86, on W.I.R.L., Catalogue no: **WIRL 002**

Natural Ites

BLACK ROSES
Tracks: / Black roses.
12" Single: Released Jul '84, on Realistic, Catalogue no: **RR 03**

HAPPEN ALL OVER AGAIN
Tracks: / Happen all over again.
12" Single: Released May '89, on Realistic, Catalogue no: **RRO 15**

JUST THE TWO OF US
Tracks: / Just the two of us.
12" Single: Released Oct '88, on Realistic, Catalogue no: **RR 11**

LATELY
Tracks: / Lately.
12" Single: Released Nov '86, on Realistic, Catalogue no: **RR 04**

LION INNA JUNGLE
Tracks: / Lion inna jungle.
7" Single: Released Apr '85, on CSA, by CSA Records. Catalogue no: **CSA 504**
12" Single: Released Apr '85, on CSA, by CSA Records. Deleted '88. Catalogue no: **12CSA 504**

PICTURE ON THE WALL
12" Single: Released Apr '83, on Realistic, Catalogue no: **RR 02**

PICTURE ON THE WALL (SINGLE)
Tracks: / Picture on the wall / Jah works mamma.
7" Single: Released Jun '86, on CSA, by CSA Records. Catalogue no: **CSA 501**
12" Single: Released Jun '86, on CSA, by CSA Records. Catalogue no: **12CSA 501**

Natural Mystic

GROOVE ROCKING
12" Single: Released Jun '84, on Starlight, Catalogue no: **SLD 533**

JUST A LITTLE LOVIN'
Tracks: / Just a little lovin'.
7" Single: Released Nov '87, on Mixdown, Catalogue no: **MIXD 002**

LITTLE BIT MAYBE, A
Tracks: / Little bit maybe, A / Little bit maybe, A (dub version).
12" Single: Released Jan '86, on Starlight, Catalogue no: **SLD 536**

Natural Mystique

GENERALS
Tracks: / Generals / In this time.
7" Single: Released May '82, on Dune, Catalogue no: **DUNE 2**

Natural, Neil

ON A STRING
Tracks: / On a string.
12" Single: Released Jul '89, on Street Vibes, Catalogue no: **SV 010**

Natural Roots

KNOW YOURSELF
Tracks: / Know yourself / Ain't got no money.
12" Single: Released Aug '82, on Fasim, Catalogue no: **FF 103**

Natural Scientists

SEE THROUGH YOU
Tracks: / See through you / Liar.
7" Single: Released Apr '85, on Dental, by Dental Records. Catalogue no: **MOLAR 2**

Natural Sound

LET ME BE YOUR LOVER
Tracks: / Let me be your lover / Night long.
7" Single: Released Feb '81, on Volume (1), by Volume Records. Deleted Feb '84. Catalogue no: **CR 2**

Natural Touch

GIMME GOOD LOVING
Tracks: / Gimme good loving / Gimme good loving (instrumental).
12" Single: Released Dec '83, on Neville King, by Neville King Records. Catalogue no: **NKRD 0016**

HOLD ME TIGHT
Tracks: / Hold me tight.
12" Single: Released May '85, on NK Music, Catalogue no: **NKRD 027**

LET'S GET IT ON
Tracks: / Let's get it on / Get it off.
12" Single: Released Nov '83, on NK Music, Catalogue no: **NKRD 017**

LIVIN IT UP
Tracks: / Living it up.
12" Single: Released Dec '84, on Neville King, by Neville King Records. Catalogue no: **NKRD 0026**

THAT FUNNY FEELING
Tracks: / That funny feeling.
12" Single: Released Mar '84, on NK Music, Catalogue no: **NKRD 018**

YOU MAKE ME FEEL SO RIGHT
Tracks: / You make me feel so right / I don't want to be alone tonight.
12" Single: Released Aug '84, on MK, Catalogue no: **MKRD 0019**

Naturally

SUNNY GETS BLUE
Tracks: / Sunny gets blue.
12" Single: Released Jul '89, on Ottey's Promotion, Catalogue no: **OTD 001**

Naturals

FUNKY RASTA (YA EDIT)
Tracks: / Funky rasta (ya edit) / Organ jam.
7" Single: Released Jan '87, on Cool Tempo, by Chrysalis Records. Catalogue no: **COOL 140**
12" Single: Released Jan '87, on Cool Tempo, by Chrysalis Records. Catalogue no: **COOLX 140**

I SHOULD HAVE KNOWN BETTER
Tracks: / I should have known better.
7" Single: Released Aug '64, on Parlophone, by EMI Records. Deleted '67. Catalogue no: **R 5165**

SIX GIRLS AND ALICE
Tracks: / Six girls and Alice / Your bravery.
7" Single: Released Nov '82, on Logo, by Logo Records. Deleted Nov '85. Catalogue no: **GO 414**

Nature's Creation

FREAK UNIQUE
Tracks: / Freak unique.
12" Single: Released Mar '86, on Capitol City, Catalogue no: **CCR 123**

LET'S FIRE IT UP
Tracks: / Let's fire it up (instrumental).
12" Single: Released Mar '86, on Sound Makers, Catalogue no: **SM 3008**

Naughtiest Girl...

ALL THE NAKED HEROES
Tracks: / All the naked heroes.
7" Single: Released Nov '80, on Aardvark, by Aardvark Records. Catalogue no: **STEAL 4**

FRONT
Tracks: / Front / No sensation.
7" Single: Released Sep '81, on Illumination, Catalogue no: **NGWAM 1**

IS ALL I NEED
Tracks: / Is all I need.
7" Single: Released Feb '82, on Dining Out, by Dining Out Records. Catalogue no: **TUX 22**

Naughton, David

MAKIN' IT
Tracks: / Makin' it.
7" Single: Released Aug '74, on RSO, by Polydor Ltd. Deleted '82. Catalogue no: **RSO 32**

Naughty Culture

ONCE UPON A TIME
Tracks: / Once upon a time / Doing O.K..
7" Single: Released Jan '81, on Charisma, by Virgin Records. Deleted Jan '84. Catalogue no: **CB 378**

SOMEDAY SUNDAY
Tracks: / Someday Sunday.
7" Single: Released May '81, on Charisma, by Virgin Records. Deleted May '84. Catalogue no: **CB 381**

Naughty Thoughts

WEEKDAYS
Tracks: / All or nothing / Weekdays.
7" Single: Released Jun '82, on Maestro (1), by Maestro Records. Catalogue no: **MR 004**

Navah

SEVEN WAYS TO HEAVEN
Tracks: / Seven ways to heaven / Seven ways to heaven (version).
7" Single: Released Sep '89, on CNB, Catalogue no: **P 26**
12" Single: Released Sep '89, on CNB, Catalogue no: **PX 26**

WELCOME TO THE NIGHT

JERRY NAYLOR - FOR OLD TIMES SAKE (Released on West Records)

Tracks: / Welcome to the night / Only time.
7" Single: Released May '83, on RCA, by BMG Records (UK). Catalogue no: **RC 110**

Naylor, Jerry

FOR OLD TIME SAKE (See panel on previous page)
Tracks: / For old time sake.
7" Single: Released '86, on West Records, Catalogue no: **W 723**

Nazareth

BAD BAD BOY
Tracks: / Bad bad boy.
7" Single: Released Jul '73, on Mooncrest, by Trojan Records. Deleted '76. Catalogue no: **MOON 9**

BROKEN DOWN ANGEL
Tracks: / Broken down angel / Hair of the dog.
7" Single: Released May '73, on Mooncrest, by Trojan Records. Deleted '76. Catalogue no: **MOON 1**
7" Single: Released Jan '80, on IMS, by Polydor Ltd. Catalogue no: **LR 8197**

DREAM ON
Tracks: / Dream on / Juicy Lucy.
7" Single: Released Jun '83, on Nems, by Castle Communications Records. Catalogue no: **NIS 103**

DRESSED TO KILL
Tracks: / Dressed to kill.
7" Single: Released Mar '81, on Nems, by Castle Communications Records. Catalogue no: **NES 301**

GAMES
Tracks: / Games / You love another.
7" Single: Released Jan '83, on Nems, by Castle Communications Records. Catalogue no: **NIS 102**

GONE DEAD TRAIN
Tracks: / Gone dead train.
7" Single: Released Feb '78, on Mountain, Deleted '81. Catalogue no: **NAZ 002**

HEARTS GROWN COLD (2 DISC SET)
Tracks: / Hearts grown cold / Razamanaz / Hair of the dog / Talkin' to one of the boys.
7" Set: Released Jan '81, on Nems, by Castle Communications Records. Deleted Jan '84. Catalogue no: **BSD 1**

HOLIDAY
Tracks: / Holiday / Talkin' 'bout love.
7" Single: Released Feb '80, on Mountain, Deleted '83. Catalogue no: **TOP 50**

HOLY ROLLER
Tracks: / Holy roller.
7" Single: Released Nov '75, on Mountain, Deleted '78. Catalogue no: **TOP 3**

HOT TRACKS EP
Tracks: / Love hurts / This flight tonight / Broken down angel / Hair of the dog.
7" Single: Released Sep '77, on Mountain, Deleted '80. Catalogue no: **NAZ 1**

LOVE HURTS
Tracks: / Love hurts / Bad bad boy.
7" Single: Released Oct '88, on Old Gold, by Old Gold Records. Catalogue no: **OG 9803**

LOVE HURTS (EP)
Tracks: / Love hurts / This flight tonight / Broken down angel / Hair of the dog.
7" EP: Released Jul '80, on Mountain, Deleted Jul '83. Catalogue no: **HOT 1**
7" Pic: Released Jan '83, on Nems, by Castle Communications Records. Catalogue no: **NEP 2**

LOVE LEADS TO MADNESS
Tracks: / Love leads to madness.
7" Single: Released Jul '82, on Nems, by Castle Communications Records. Catalogue no: **NS 101**

MAY THE SUNSHINE
Tracks: / May the sunshine.
7" Single: Released Jan '79, on Mountain, Deleted '82. Catalogue no: **NAZ 003**

MORNING DEW
Tracks: / Morning dew / Juicy Lucy.
7" Single: Released Aug '81, on Nems, by Castle Communications Records. Catalogue no: **NES 302**

MY WHITE BICYCLE
Tracks: / My white bicycle.
7" Single: Released Jun '75, on Mooncrest, by Trojan Records. Deleted '78. Catalogue no: **MOON 47**

NAZARETH (EP)
Tracks: / This flight tonight / Broken down angel / Bad bad boy / Love hurts.
CD 3": Released '88, on Special Edition, by Castle Communications Records. Catalogue no: **CD3-17**

PLACE IN YOUR HEART
Tracks: / Place in your heart, A.
7" Single: Released May '78, on Mountain, Deleted '81. Catalogue no: **TOP 37**

RUBY TUESDAY
Tracks: / Ruby Tuesday.
7" Single: Released Sep '84, on Vertigo, by Phonogram Ltd. Catalogue no: **VER 13**
12" Single: Released Sep '84, on Vertigo, by Phonogram Ltd. Catalogue no: **VERX 13**

SHANGHAI'D IN SHANGHAI
Tracks: / Shanghai'd in Shanghai.
7" Single: Released Mar '74, on Mooncrest, by Trojan Records. Deleted '77. Catalogue no: **MOON 22**

STAR
Tracks: / Star.
7" Single: Released Jul '79, on Mountain, Deleted '82. Catalogue no: **TOP 45**

THIS FLIGHT TONIGHT
Tracks: / This flight tonight.
7" Single: Released Oct '73, on Mooncrest, by Trojan Records. Deleted '76. Catalogue no: **MOON 14**

THIS FLIGHT TONIGHT (OLD GOLD)
Tracks: / This flight tonight / Broken down angel.
7" Single: Released Oct '88, on Old Gold, by Old Gold Records. Catalogue no: **OG 9801**

Nazz Nasko

NO MORE
Tracks: / No more / Heartbreak.
7" Single: Released Feb '87, on Columbia, by EMI Records. Deleted Oct '87. Catalogue no: **DB 9149**
12" Single: Released Feb '87, on Columbia, by EMI Records. Deleted Oct '87. Catalogue no: **12DB 9149**

N'dour, Youssou

RUBBER BAND MAN
Tracks: / Rubber band man, The / Nelson Mandela.
12" Single: Released Mar '86, on Rough Trade, by Rough Trade Records. Catalogue no: **ET 004**

Ndugu

SHADOW DANCING
Tracks: / Shadow dancing / Love anew.
7" Single: Released May '80, on Epic, by CBS Records. Deleted May '85. Catalogue no: **EPC 8371**
12" Single: Released May '80, on Epic, by CBS Records. Deleted May '85. Catalogue no: **13-8371**

Nearly Normal

BEDTIME
Tracks: / Bedtime / Die baby die.
7" Single: Released May '82, on Insurrection, Catalogue no: **IN 1**

Nebula One

NEBULA 1
Tracks: / Nebula 1.
7" Single: Released Nov '88, on Gee Street, by Gee Street Records. Catalogue no: **GEE 12002**

Negative Trend

WE DON'T PLAY WE RIOT
Tracks: / We don't play we riot.
7" Single: Released Dec '84, on Subterranean, Catalogue no: **SUB 32**

Negatives

ELECTRIC WALTZ
Tracks: / Electric waltz / Money talk.
7" Single: Released Nov '80, on Aardvark, by Aardvark Records. Catalogue no: **STEAL 1**

Negro, J Walter

COST OF LIVING (2 PARTS)
Tracks: / Cost of living.
12" Single: Released May '83, on Albion, by Albion Records. Catalogue no: **12ION 1044**

SHOOT THE PUMP
Tracks: / Shoot the pump.
7" Single: Released Dec '81, on Island, by Island Records. Catalogue no: **WIP 6765**
12" Single: Released Dec '81, on Island, by Island Records. Catalogue no: **12WIP 6765**

Negus, Peter

I WON'T BE AROUND
Tracks: / I won't be around / I won't be around (dub version).
10" single: Released Jul '82, on Progressive, Catalogue no: **PROG 03**

PLACE IN THE SUN
Tracks: / Place in the sun, A / Dusty road.
12" Single: Released Aug '82, on Progressive, Catalogue no: **PROG 04**

Neighbour Hoods

PURE & EASY
Tracks: / Pure and easy.
7" Single: Released Oct '87, on Roadrunner (Germany), Catalogue no: **EM 5505**

NEIL - HOLE IN MY SHOE (Released on WEA)

Neighbourhood

A - THE TIME (B - THE INCLINATION)
Tracks: / A - the time (B - the inclination) / Certain attitude, A (instrumental) / I must have faith (10", Cass. single, CD single only.) / That way (10", Cass. single, CD single only.) / A - the time (B - the inclination) (12" remix).
CD 5": Released Sep '88, on Parlophone, by EMI Records. Deleted Aug '89. Catalogue no: **CDR 6188**
10" single: Released Sep '88, on Parlophone, by EMI Records. Deleted Aug '89. Catalogue no: **10R 6188**
Cassingle: Released Sep '88, on Parlophone, by EMI Records. Deleted Jan '89. Catalogue no: **TCAB 1**
7" Single: Released Sep '88, on Parlophone, by EMI Records. Deleted Aug '89. Catalogue no: **R 6188**
12" Single: Released Sep '88, on Parlophone, by EMI Records. Deleted Aug '89. Catalogue no: **12RX 6188**
12" Single: Released Sep '88, on Parlophone, by EMI Records. Deleted Aug '89. Catalogue no: **12R 6188**

MISSING OUT
Tracks: / Missing out / That way (CD single only.) / That way (instrumental) (7" & 12" only.) / Certain attitude, A (CD single only.) / Tell me (CD single only.).
Note: Producer/Arranger:- Mario Tavares.
CD 5": Released Mar '89, on Parlophone, by EMI Records. Deleted Aug '89. Catalogue no: **CDR 6208**
7" Single: Released Mar '89, on Parlophone, by EMI Records. Deleted Aug '89. Catalogue no: **R 6208**
12" Single: Released Mar '89, on Parlophone, by EMI Records. Deleted Aug '89. Catalogue no: **12R 6208**

Neighbourhood Watch

DEATH AT THE HANDS OF TIME
Tracks: / Death at the hands of time.
7" Single: Released 20 Feb '88, on Real World, Catalogue no: **RWR 002**

Neighbours

WHOLE IN YOUR LIFE
Tracks: / Whole in your life.
7" Single: Released Mar '86, on Closer (France), Catalogue no: **CLO 752**

Neil

HOLE IN MY SHOE (See panel above)
Tracks: / Hole in my shoe / Hurdy gurdy mushroom man.
Note: I'd just like to say thanks a lot to Alan MacGowan, doing this record was one of the worst things thats ever happened to me. It started out like it was going to be a really mellow experience until this Dave Stuart guy started to bring the whole thing down and like using tape recorders and computers and got in this heavy technology freak Ted Hayton and Barbara Breadhead Gaskin to do backing vocals and ruined what could have been a totally accoustic experience, not to mention the capitalist media gonzos who got into all the packaging and design and marketing, Kate Hepburn, Fiona Doulton and photos Nobby Clarke. Anyway you're all going to hate it anyway because it's me singing and I wrote all the lyrics except somebody said thy're exactly the same as the lyrics of a song which has got exactly the same tune and also happens to be called 'Hole in my shoe' by Dave Mason. (Neil 1987)
7" Pic: Released Jun '84, on WEA, by WEA Records. Catalogue no: **YZ 10P**
7" Single: Released Jul '84, on WEA, by WEA Records. Deleted '87. Catalogue no: **YZ 10**

Neill, Kevin

THIRD MAN THEME
Tracks: / Third man theme / Black eyes.
7" Single: Released May '81, on EMI, by EMI Records. Deleted May '84. Catalogue no: **EMI 5196**

Nelson, Big Pete

DO IT!
Tracks: / As time goes by / Do it.
7" Single: Released Jun '86, on Debut, by Skratch Records. Catalogue no: **DEBTX 3006**

Nelson, Bill

ACCELERATION
Tracks: / Acceleration / Hard facts from the fiction factory.
7" Pic: Released Jun '85, on Cocteau, by Cocteau Records. Catalogue no: **COQT 15**
7" Single: Released Aug '84, on Cocteau, by Cocteau Records. Catalogue no: **CCQ 15**

BANAL
Tracks: / Banal / Mr. Magnetism himself.
7" Single: Released Mar '81, on Mercury, by Phonogram Ltd. Deleted Mar '84. Catalogue no: **WILL 1**
12" Single: Released Mar '81, on Mercury, by Phonogram Ltd. Deleted Mar '84. Catalogue no: **WILL 1 12**

BE BOP DELUXE
Tracks: / Be bop deluxe.
12" Single: Released Jul '85, on Cocteau, by Cocteau Records. Catalogue no: **COQT 7**

BROND (THEME FROM)
Tracks: / Brond.
12" Single: Released May '87, on Cocteau, by Cocteau Records. Catalogue no: **COQT 21**

DO YOU DREAM IN COLOUR
Tracks: / Do you dream in colour / Ideal homes / Instantly yours / Atom Man loves Radium Girl.
7" Single: Released Aug '80, on Cocteau, by Cocteau Records. Deleted '83. Catalogue no: **COQ 1**

EROS ARRIVING
Tracks: / Eros arriving / Haunting in my head.
7" Set: Released Apr '82, on Mercury, by Phonogram Ltd. Deleted '83. Catalogue no: **WILL 44**
7" Single: Released Apr '82, on Mercury, by Phonogram Ltd. Catalogue no: **WILL 4**

FLAMING DESIRE

BILL NELSON - DO YOU DREAM IN COLOUR? (Released on Cocteau Records)

Tracks: / Flaming desire / Passion, The.
12" Single: Released Jul '82, on Mercury, by Phonogram Ltd. Catalogue no: **WILL 5 12**
7" Single: Released Jul '82, on Mercury, by Phonogram Ltd. Catalogue no: **WILL 5**

FURNITURE MUSIC
Tracks: / Furniture music.
7" Single: Released Feb '79, on Harvest (1), by EMI Records. Deleted '82. Catalogue no: **HAR 5176**

LIFE IN YOUR HANDS
Tracks: / Life in your hands / Do you dream in colour / Get out of that hole (12" only) / Dream Demon (12" only).
12" Single: Released Dec '88, on Cocteau, by Cocteau Records. Catalogue no: **COQT 22**
CD 5": Released Dec '88, on Cocteau, by Cocteau Records. Catalogue no: **COQTCD 22**

LIVING IN MY LIMOUSINE
Tracks: / Living in my limousine / Birds of tin / Love in the abstract / White sound.
7" Single: Released Sep '81, on Mercury, by Phonogram Ltd. Deleted Sep '84. Catalogue no: **WILL 3**
12" Single: Released Sep '81, on Mercury, by Phonogram Ltd. Deleted Sep '84. Catalogue no: **WILL 312**

PERMANENT FLAME
Tracks: / Permanent flame.
7" Single: Released Jul '85, on Cocteau, by Cocteau Records. Catalogue no: **JEAN 1**

REVOLT INTO STYLE
Tracks: / Revolt into style / Stay young / Furniture music.
7" Single: Released Feb '83, on Cocteau, by Cocteau Records. Catalogue no: **COQT 8**
7" Single: Released May '79, on Harvest (1), by EMI Records. Deleted '82. Catalogue no: **HAR 5183**

TOUCH AND GLOW
Tracks: / Touch and glow / Dancing in the wind / Love without fear.
7" Single: Released Aug '83, on Cocteau, by Cocteau Records. Catalogue no: **COQ 10**

WILDEST DREAMS
Tracks: / Widest dreams.
7" Single: Released Mar '86, on Portrait, by CBS Records. Catalogue no: **A 6928**
12" Single: Released Mar '86, on Portrait, by CBS Records. Catalogue no: **TA 6928**

YOUTH OF NATION ON FIRE
Tracks: / Youth of nation of fire.
7" Single: Released Jun '81, on Mercury, by Phonogram Ltd. Deleted '84. Catalogue no: **BILL 2**

Nelson, Grace

CONVERSATION
Tracks: / Conversation.
12" Single: Released Jul '88, on Exodus, Catalogue no: **EX 01**

Nelson, Jackie

BOY WITH A FUTURE
Tracks: / Midnight in heaven.
7" Single: Released Oct '86, on August (USA), by Rounder Records (USA). Catalogue no: **GBH 7S 421**

DEAREST MOTHER MINE
Tracks: / Dearest mother mine.
7" Single: Released Sep '84, on Country House, by Scotdisc Records. Catalogue no: **BGC 7S 361**

FOOL SUCH AS I
Tracks: / Fool such as I, A / Legend in my time.
7" Single: Released Jun '81, on Mint, by Emerald Records. Deleted '88. Catalogue no: **CHEW 50**

LET THERE BE PEACE
Tracks: / Let there be peace / Holy City, The.
7" Single: Released 14 Aug '88, on Scotdisc, by Scotdisc Records. Catalogue no: **ITV 7S 458**

WALKING TALKING DOLLY
Tracks: / Silent night / Walking talking dolly.
7" Single: Released Nov '81, on Mint, by Emerald Records. Deleted '88. Catalogue no: **CHEW 44**

Nelson, Juliet

ME A NO BOOPSIE
Tracks: / Me a no boopsie / Me a no boopsie(version).
7" Single: Released Dec '87, on Orbitone, by Orbitone Records. Catalogue no: **OR 725**
12" Single: Released Dec '87, on Orbitone, by Orbitone Records. Catalogue no: **OR 1225**

Nelson, Larry

TOO MUCH GROUND
Tracks: / Too much ground.
7" Single: Released May '84, on Artic, Catalogue no: **SART 001**

Nelson, Nick

DON'T LOOK AT ME
Tracks: / Don't look at me / Loser, babe, is you.
7" Single: Released Jan '81, on Capitol, by EMI Records. Deleted Jan '84. Catalogue no: **CL 16177**

Nelson, Phyllis

Biographical details: This American singer and songwriter has experienced an erratic areer in soul and disco music during the Eighties. Hailing from Philadelphia, she attracted considerable attention with her 1980 single *Don't stop the train*, which became a substantial hit on the US dance chart. Her voice sounded rough on that track, but it greatly improved over the following few years as she struggled to carve a long-term career for herself. After several failures with other people's material, Nelson wrote her own soul ballad *Move closer*. Originally released in April 1984 by the London office of the French-owned Carrere label, this single became one of the great sleeper smashes of the Eighties. *Move closer* flopped at first but, by early 1985, was picking up heavy airplay on Tony Blackburn's influential specialist soul show on BBC Radio London. The persistent faith in the single by Blackburn and Carrere MD Freddy Cannon eventually paid off. After slowly working its way up the UK Top 75, *Move Closer* reached No.1 in May 1985. In so doing, it becaime the only UK chart-topping single of the year to scale the summit without the benefit of a promotional video clip. Given that Nelson was no oil painting, the No.1 status of *Move closer* was a heartening triumph for the age-old values of a good singer and a great song. It ended up as Britain's 7th best-seller of the year. Combining a beautiful melody with suggestive lyrics, *Move closer* was ultra-sexy without resorting to smut; it became a classic lights-down smoocher in discos. Incredibly, *Move closer* was not released in the singer's native America during 1985. Instead towards the end of the year, she issued an uptempo self-penned ditty entitle *I like you*. Somewhat reminiscent of Dead or Alive's *You spin me round*, this exuberant single was a phenomenon in American clubs and attracted a strong dancefloor response in all the diverse types of US discos. *I like you* reached No.1 on the Billboard club play chart, and logged a staggering eight weeks on top of the disco 12-inch singles chart. In February 1986 *I like you* gave Nelson her first entry on the US pop ratings. But Phyllis 'One nation' Nelson had not mastered the art of simultaneously pleasing both American and British audiences: *Move closer* had been a smashin the UK and nowhere else, and the US dance success of *I like you* failed to cross the Atlantic. (Bob MacDonald, 8th Feb 1986).

CHEMICAL REACTION
Tracks: / Stop don't do this to me / Chemical reaction.
7" Single: Released Oct '86, on Carrere, Catalogue no: **CAR 401**
12" Single: Released Oct '86, on Carrere, Catalogue no: **CART 401**

I LIKE YOU
Tracks: / I like you.
7" Single: Released Jul '86, on Carrere, Catalogue no: **CAR 365**
12" Single: Released Jul '86, on Carrere, Catalogue no: **CART 365**

MOVE CLOSER (SINGLE)
Tracks: / Move closer.
7" Single: Released Feb '85, on Carrere, Catalogue no: **CAR 337**
12" Single: Released Feb '85, on Carrere, Catalogue no: **CART 337**

STOP DON'T DO THIS TO ME
Tracks: / Stop don't do this to me.
12" Single: Released Jul '83, on Carrere America (USA), by PolyGram Rec.Inc.(USA). Catalogue no: **CART 286**

Nelson, Ricky

Biographical details: This American singer, guitarist, songwriter and actor was born Eric Hilliard Neson in Teaneck, New Jersey in 1940. Showbusiness was ingrained in his family - his father was a bandleader and his mother a vocalist, and the couple began their own radio series *The adventures of Ozzie and Harriet* in 1944. For the first five years of this 'ongoing autobiography', the parts of Ricky and his elder brother David were portrayed by child actors; but in 1949 the real boys joined, thus marking the beginning of a long career in showbusiness for Ricky. The series transferred from radio to ABC Television in 1952. The program continued apace through the mid-Fifties, while Ricky received his education at Hollywood High School. In the Spring of 1957, a year after Elvis Presley had exploded onto the scene, Nelson launched a recording career via the TV series. He was given an image that was defenitely rock'n'roll, but not so rebellious as to be a real danger to the establishment - his stance and style were a neat middle-ground between Presley and Pat Boone. Ricky's first single and first hit, *I'm walking*, reached No.17 on the US charts; but the flipside *A teenager's romance* soon took on a life of its own and zoomed to No.2. It was merely the opening gambit in a vast string of Top 40 singles, which kept Nelson constantly in the charts on both sides of the Atlantic until 1964. He developed a tradition of performing a song at the end of every episode of the *Oozie and Harriet* show thus guaranteeing a perennial promotional outlet for his latest releases. Ricky Nelson was one of the major pop stars of his era, but there were several reasons why he was not regarded as highly as he should have been by journalists, critics and lovers of 'authentic rock'n'roll'. He never had to struggle for his fame and fortune - stardom was handed to him on a plate. Because of his showbusiness contacts, he had access to the best songwriters and backing musicians, most notably the ace guitarist James Burton (who later joined Elvis' group). Ricky's voice was good, but not great. The relentless corn and showbizzy schmaltz of the *Ozzie and Harriet* program was always associated with Ricky in the minds of many people, even though he managed to shake this off when he entered the recording studio. For all the criticism that was levelled at him, he amply proved that he was far more than just a pretty face. No-one has 35 well crafted American Top 40 singles without major talent. Ricky's two biggest US hits were *Poor little fool* (No.1 on the first ever Billboard Hot 100 in August 1958) and *Travelin' man* (No.1 in 1961). His biggest British smashes were *It's late* (No.3 in 1959), later revived by Shakin' Stevens) and Gene Pitney's *Hello Mary Lou* (No.2 in 1961). Just after this hit, he shortened his name from 'Ricky' to 'Rick' in recognition of his 21st birthday.
Nelson faded from the charts in the mid-Sixties, but formed the Stone Canyon Band and moved into the country-rock arna with moderate success. His old fans were reluctant to allow him to change his style, as shown by his disastrous appearance at a rock'n'roll revival show at New York's Madison Square Garden. He responded to this in defiant mood on his million-selling one-off comeback smash in 1972, *Garden party*. Still working in a countrified vein, Ricky Nelson remained an active concert performer until his tragic death in a plane crash in December 1985 at the age of 45. He, and several members of the Stone Canyon Band, lost their lives in poor weather en route to a New Year's Eve gals concert. (Bob MacDonald, 9th Feb 1986).

BELIEVE WHAT YOU SAY
Tracks: / Believe what you say / Do the best you can.
7" Single: Released Mar '81, on Capitol, by EMI Records. Deleted Mar '84. Catalogue no: **CL 16188**

EVERLOVIN'
Tracks: / Everlovin'.
7" Single: Released Nov '61, on London-American, Deleted '64. Catalogue no: **HLP 9440**

FOOLS RUSH IN
Tracks: / Fools rush in.
7" Single: Released Oct '63, on Brunswick, by Decca Records. Deleted '66. Catalogue no: **05895**

FOR YOU
Tracks: / For you.
7" Single: Released Jan '64, on Brunswick, by Decca Records. Deleted '67. Catalogue no: **05900**

GARDEN PARTY (SINGLE)
Tracks: / Garden party.
7" Single: Released Oct '72, on MCA, by MCA Records. Deleted '75. Catalogue no: **MU 1165**

HELLO MARY LOU
Tracks: / Hello Mary Lou / Travellin' man.
7" Single: Released Jun '61, on London-American, Deleted '64. Catalogue no: **HLP 9347**
7" Single: Released Jul '84, on EMI Golden 45's, by EMI Records. Deleted Nov '88. Catalogue no: **G45 31**
7" Single: Released Oct '80, on United Artists, by EMI Records. Catalogue no: **UP 36522**

I WANNA BE LOVED
Tracks: / I wanna be loved.
7" Single: Released Jan '60, on London-American, Deleted '63. Catalogue no: **HLP 9021**

IT'S LATE
Tracks: / It's late.
7" Single: Released Apr '59, on London-American, Deleted '62. Catalogue no: **HLP 8817**
7" Single: Released '80, on Imperial, by K-Tel Records. Catalogue no: **LR 2018**

IT'S UP TO YOU
Tracks: / It's up to you.
7" Single: Released Jan '63, on London-American, Deleted '66. Catalogue no: **HLP 9648**

JUST A LITTLE TOO MUCH
Tracks: / Just a little too much.
7" Single: Released Sep '59, on London-American, Deleted '62. Catalogue no: **HLP 8927**

JUST A LITTLE TOO MUCH (RE-RELEASE)
Tracks: / Just a little too much / Waitin' in school.
7" Single: Released Sep '80, on United Artists, by EMI Records. Deleted '83. Catalogue no: **UP 633**

NEVER BE ANYONE ELSE BUT YOU
Tracks: / Never be anyone else but you.
7" Single: Released May '59, on London-American, Deleted '62. Catalogue no: **HLP 8817**
7" Single: Released '80, on Imperial, by K-Tel Records. Catalogue no: **LR 4142**

POOR LITTLE FOOL
Tracks: / Poor little fool.
7" Single: Released Aug '58, on London-

American, Deleted '61. Catalogue no: **HLP 8670**

SOMEDAY
Tracks: / Someday / I got a feeling.
7" Single: Released Nov '58, on London-American, Deleted '61. Catalogue no: **HLP 8732**

STOOD UP
Tracks: / Stood up.
7" Single: Released Feb '58, on London-American, Deleted '61. Catalogue no: **HLP 8542**

SWEETER THAN YOU
Tracks: / Sweeter than you.
7" Single: Released Sep '59, on London-American, Deleted '62. Catalogue no: **HLP 8927**

TEENAGE IDOL
Tracks: / Teenage idol.
7" Single: Released Aug '62, on London-American, Deleted '65. Catalogue no: **HLP 9583**

YOUNG EMOTIONS
Tracks: / Young emotions.
7" Single: Released Aug '60, on London-American, Deleted '63. Catalogue no: **HLP 9121**

YOUNG WORLD
Tracks: / Young world.
7" Single: Released Mar '62, on London-American, Deleted '65. Catalogue no: **HLP 9524**

Nelson, Sandy

DRUMMIN' UP A STORM
Tracks: / Drummin' up a storm.
7" Single: Released Jul '62, on London-American, Deleted '65. Catalogue no: **HLP 9558**

DRUMS ARE MY BEAT
Tracks: / Drums are my beat.
7" Single: Released Mar '62, on London-American, Deleted '65. Catalogue no: **HLP 9521**

LET THERE BE DRUMS
Tracks: / Let there be drums / Teen beat.
7" Single: Released Dec '61, on London-American, Deleted '64. Catalogue no: **HLP 9466**
7" Single: Released 21 Nov '87, on Old Gold, by Old Gold Records. Deleted Sep '89. Catalogue no: **OG 9732**
7" Single: Released '80, on Imperial, by K-Tel Records. Catalogue no: **LR 8208**

TEEN BEAT
Tracks: / Teen beat.
7" Single: Released Nov '59, on Top Rank (1), Deleted '62. Catalogue no: **JAR 197**

Nelson, Shara

LOVE HITS YOU
Tracks: / Love hits you / Dub hit you.
12" Single: Released Oct '82, on Disco Tex, Catalogue no: **DT 4**

Nelson, Sharon

AIMING AT YOUR HEART
Tracks: / Aiming at your heart.
12" Single: Released Dec '83, on On-U-Sound, by On-U-Sound Records. Catalogue no: **ONUMIX 2**

Nelson, Shelley

FOLLOW THE WIND
Tracks: / Follow the wind / Follow the wind (instrumental).
7" Single: Released Jan '89, on Bonnymove, by Bonnymove Records. Catalogue no: **BONS 2**

Nelson, Tyka

MARC ANTHONY'S TUNE
Tracks: / Marc Anthony's tune / Be good to me / This girl is gonna fall in love (On 12" only).
Note: Prince's sister makes a very smooth and competant debut with this lush ballad and without any help from her brother. Produced by Preston Glass. (Music Week, July 1988)
CD 5": Released Jun '88, on Cool Tempo, by Chrysalis Records. Catalogue no: **COOLCD 166**
7" Single: Released Jun '88, on Cool Tempo, by Chrysalis Records. Catalogue no: **COOL 166**
12" Single: Released Jun '88, on Cool Tempo, by Chrysalis Records. Catalogue no: **COOLX 166**

Nelson, Vicki

ONLY A FOOL
Tracks: / Only a fool.
7" Single: Released Jan '82, on Lunar (Ireland), by Lunar Records (Ireland). Catalogue no: **MOON 1**

Nelson, Willie

Biographical details: Nelson, Willie (b 30 Apr. '33, Abbott, Texas). Country singer, guitarist and songwriter who achieved superstar status in late '70s. Raised by grandparents after parents were divorced; bagan on guitar as a child and played in local honky tonk bands as a teenager, also in polka bands favoured by local Czech community.

Served in USAF in Korea, worked in Waco as a farm labourer, vacuum cleaner salesman, then as DJ on local radio station. Next he had a daytime country show in Fort Worth, played in honky tonks evenings; he'd begun writing songs and sold his early efforts *Family Bible* and *Night Life* for less than $200 (the former was a top 10 country hit by Claude Gray '60; *Night Life* reached top 30 by Ray Price '64, no. 31 by Gray '68).
He moved to Nashville '60, joined Ray Price's Cherokee Cowboys on bass, had more writing success: *Funny (How Time Slips Away)* (top 15 pop hit '64 and Joe Hinton's biggest; he died 13 Aug. '68), *Hello Walls* (no. 1 country hit '61 by Faron Young), *Crazy* (no. 2 country hit by Patsy Cline '61), more. He had recorded in Texas, mainly demos; signed with Liberty '62, made 2 LPs incl. *And Then I Wrote* '63, top 10 hit *Touch Me* same year; recorded for Monument Oct. '64 but nothing was released; joined RCA in Dec. and made some 18 albums in eight years, incl. *Country Music Concert* '66 (reissued '76 as *Willie Nelson Live*), *Texas In My Soul* '68, *Laying My Burdens Down* '70, *Yesterday's Wine* '71, *The Words Don't Fit The Picture* '73; also had minor hit singles *The Party's Over* '67, *Little Things* '68, *Bring Me Sunshine* '69. His songs tended to be more complex technically than the usual country tune; he sang in a highly personal, yet lackadaisical and almost conversational way.
He grew tired of the increasing slickness of Nashville; when his house in Ridgetop, Tenn. burned to the ground he took advantage of the opportunity to move back to Texas '71.

He organised the first 4th of July Festival '72 in Dripping Springs, near Austin; it was a financial disaster, but subsequent events were more successful until '80, when they were so successful they were too big to be what they were intended to be, and were abandoned. Meanwhile, he had changed his image: growing long hair and a beard and wearing jeans, he signed with Atlantic, made LPs *Shotgun Willie* and *Phases And Stages*, which brought recognition from the rock press (the latter LP made the pop album chart when reissued '76); he had hit country singles *Stay All Night, Bloody Mary Morning*, duet ith Tracy Nelson (no relation) *After The Fire Is Gone*, all '73-4.
When Atlantic closed their Nashville office he signed with Columbia (CBS) and concept LP *Redheaded Stranger* '75: it was the first (of 33 '75-85) to make the pop album chart; first single *Blue Eyes Cryin' In The Rain* was no. 1 country hit, also made pop top 20; his old labels began scrabbling in their vaults and he had eight singles in the country charts on three labels '76, with *If You've Got The Money, I've Got The Time* (on Columbia) hitting no. 1. He had achieved success by refusing to be limited by commercial considerations, and carried on: he made a gospel set *The Troublemaker* '76, tribute to Lefty Frizzell *To Lefty From Willie* '77,
Willie And Family Live '78 recorded in Lake Tahoe, 2-disc *One For The Road* '79 with Leon Russell. The new mood in country music was already being called the 'Outlaw' movement; RCA released *Wanted: The Outlaws* '76 with tracks by Nelson, Waylon Jennings, Tompall Glaser and Jessi Colter: it was the first country LP to sell a million copies. The same year *Good Hearted Woman*, a duet by Waylon and Willie, was No. 1 country, made the pop top 30 and was named CMA single of the year. *Stardust* '78 on CBS was his first set of standards, prod. by Booker T Jones; it stayed in the pop album chart 117 weeks, sold millions, including No. 1 country hits with Hoagy Carmichael's *Georgia On My Mind* and Irving Berlin's *Blue Skies*. The first *Waylon And Willie* album on Jennings' label RCA including No. 1 hit with Ed bruce song *Mammas Don't Let Your Boys Grow Up To Be Cowboys*, which also won a Grammy '78; they toured together and outgrossed every other country act, released further duet LPs /W-WIID '82 on RCA, /Take It To The LimitD '83 on CBS.

Nelson moved into films: 'Electric Horseman' '79 (soundtrack LP had one side by Willie, the other instrumental), 'Honeysuckle Rose' '80 (soundtrack LP no. 11, with hit single /On The Road AgainD), 'Thief' '81, 'Barbarosa' '82, 'Songwriter' '85 (with Kris Kristofferson; LP charted)
. He made duet LPs /Angel EyesD '84 with guitarist Jackie King, /San Antonio RoseD '80 with his old boss Price, /Brand On My HeartD with Hank Snow, /Old FriendsD with roger Miller, /In The Jailhouse NowD with Webb Pierce, /Funny How Time Slips AwayD with Faron Young; /Half Nelson D '85 is a selection of duets, but the most successful duet set apart from those with Jennings was /Poncho & LeftyD with Merle Haggard '83, a top 40 pop LP and CMA album of the year, the title track no. 1 country hit.

Among much Nelson material recycled by RCA was /Before His TimeD '77, remixed by Jennings; other Columbia LPs incl. /The Sound In Your MindD '76, /Somewhere Over The RainbowD '81, /Always On My MindD '82 (pop hit LP for 99 weeks reaching no. 2; title single a top 5 hit), /Tougher Than LeatherD and /Without A SongD '83. Nelson could make a songwriter a lot of money by including a song on an album; /City Of New OrleansD '84 incl. title song by Stephen Goodman, when that much-loved singer/songwriter was dying of leukaemia. /Me And PaulD '85 had title song about his drummer, Paul English; /The PromiselandD followed in '86. Among reissues and compilations on many labels are /Once More With FeelingD and /Good Hearted WomanD, both 2-disc sets on Pair '86; Columbia USA had issued a limited edition 10-disc boxed set, a tribute to an artist who not only crosses over but flattens the fence. Donald Clarke, 17 Feb 1987.

One of the all time greats of country music. Willie Nelson was born in Texas in 1933 and began his career in the 50's as a country and western DJ on a Fort Worth radio station.
He got a job as bass player in the band of top C & W artist Ray Price and his song, *Night life*, was adopted as Price's theme tune. Nelson's reputation as a songwriter grew enormously during the early '60's, when three of his songs became hits for other country artists and came to be regarded as standards. Patsy Cline recorded *Crazy*, Jimmy Elledge won success with *Funny how time slips away* and Faron Young scored with *Hello Walls*. With these successes under his belt, Nelson began releasing albums in his own right in 1962.
Throughout the rest of the '60's he pursued a successful though not particulary stunning career in Nashville. Like most of his peers he was signed to RCA, the dominant country label, and was a regular performer at the Grand Ole Opry. But with his rough edged musical style and tough image he grew increasingly frustrated with the constraints of the Nashville establishment.
As the city's studio productions became increasingly smooth, sweet and homogenised, the dissatisfied Nelson resolved to free himself from his RCA contract. In 1972 he took the revolutionary step of signing with Atlantic Records, a company totally unused to handling country arts. Now based in Texas once more, he became a leader of the so called 'Outlaws', a group of like minded performers, who established a separate country music base away from Nashville. This grouping of artists included Waylon Jennings, Tompall Glaser and Jessi Colter. Thus, just when he was turning 40, Nelson entered the best part of his career with the 1973 albums *Phases and stages* and *Shotgun Willie*. Switching to Columbia Records, Nelson began his period of greatest commercial success with the deeply thoughtful '75 album *Red headed stranger*, yielding the single *Blue eyes crying in the rain*, which crossed over to reach No. 21 on the US pop chart. These records earned Nelson a sizeable following among rock and blues fans and did much to propogate the country gospel. He has always had a penchant for duetting with other singers, his collaborations with his great friend Waylon Jennings usually being the best - they had a US Top 30 pop hit together in '76 with *Good hearted woman*. Nelson's forays into films have included a prominent appearance in *Honeysuckle rose* (1980), which yielded his big theme hit *On the road again*, and a starring role in *Barbarosa* (1983).

In 1982 his stunning version of the Elvis Presley hit *Always on my mind* provided him with his biggest ever triumph: it reached No. 5 in the States and gave him a ludicrously over-due British chart debut, albeit No. 49. His most ludicrous duet was in 1984, when he hit the Top Twenty on both sides of the Atlantic with the smiling Spaniard Julio Iglesias on *To all the girls I've loved before*. The following year he teamed with Jennings again, plus fellow country legends Johnny Cash and Kris Kristofferson for the highly successful single and album *Highway man*. With his tremulous, evocative voice and rugged appearance, Willie 'Mr Headband' Nelson has remained one of country's most distinctive and distinguished performers. His role as a bridge between country and pop was reaffirmed in 1985 when he teamed with rock star John Cougar Mellencamp to organise the huge Farm Aid benefit concert, featuring a host of top acts from both country and rock spheres. (Bob MacDonald, February 1986).

ALWAYS ON MY MIND (OLD GOLD)
Tracks: / Always on my mind / Blue eyes.
7" Single: Released Jan '88, on Old Gold, by Old Gold Records. Catalogue no: **OG 9755**

ALWAYS ON MY MIND (SINGLE)
Tracks: / Always on my mind / Autumn leaves.
7" Single: Released May '84, on CBS, by CBS Records. Catalogue no: **A 4455**
7" Single: Released Jul '82, on CBS, by CBS Records. Deleted '85. Catalogue no: **A 2511**

BLUE SKIES (SINGLE)
Tracks: / Blue skies / Funny how time slips away.
7" Single: Released May '81, on CBS, by CBS Records. Deleted May '84. Catalogue no: **CBS A 1248**

CITY OF NEW ORLEANS
Tracks: / City of New Orleans
7" Single: Released Jan '85, on CBS, by CBS Records. Catalogue no: **A 4707**

CRY
Tracks: / Cry.
7" Single: Released Oct '84, on CBS, by CBS Records. Catalogue no: **A 4830**

HONDO'S SONG
Tracks: / Hondo's song / I'd have to be crazy.
7" Single: Released Dec '81, on Young Blood, by Young Blood Records. Deleted Dec '84. Catalogue no: **YB 122**

MY HEROES HAVE ALWAYS BEEN COWBOYS
Tracks: / My heroes have always been cowboys / Rising stars.
7" Single: Released Mar '80, on CBS, by CBS Records. Deleted Mar '83. Catalogue no: **CBS 8316**

ON THE ROAD AGAIN
Tracks: / On the road again / Jumpin' cotton eyed Joe.
7" Single: Released Oct '81, on CBS, by CBS Records. Deleted Oct '84. Catalogue no: **CBSA 1632**

STARDUST (SINGLE)
Tracks: / Stardust / Funny how time slips away.
7" Single: Released Mar '81, on CBS, by CBS Records. Deleted Mar '84. Catalogue no: **A 1083**

THEY ALL WENT TO MEXICO
Tracks: / They all went to Mexico.
7" Single: Released May '83, on CBS, by CBS Records. Catalogue no: **A 3359**

TO ALL THE GIRLS I'VE LOVED BEFORE
Tracks: / To all the girls I've loved before.
7" Single: Released Mar '84, on CBS, by CBS Records. Catalogue no: **A 4252**

UNCHAINED MELODY
Tracks: / Unchained melody.
7" Single: Released May '83, on CBS, by CBS Records. Catalogue no: **A 3408**

Nena

Biographical details: When they reached the UK No. 1 position with *99 red balloons*, Nena became only the fourth act from West Germany ever to top the UK chart. Strangely the first three of three of these were crammed into one frantic period of Kraut activity in 1982 when Kraftwerk , the part-German Goombay Dance Band and the Eurovision-winning Nicole all made No. 1 within four months. Lyric listeners noted that whereas the previous German chart topper pleased for *A Little Peace* , *99 red balloons* gloomily predicted the onset of war. In its original German lingo version entitled *99 luftballons*, Nena's single was one of the biggest Eurohits of 1983 and steamed to No. 2 in the States. The band was pursuaded to translate the song into English solely for the UK market, a graphic example of stubbornness of the British when it comes to tolerating foreign languages. Despite impressions to the contrary, Nena was the name of the whole band (i.e. four guys and one girl), not just the lead vocalist - her name was Gabrielle Kerner. The follow-up single *Just a dream* was a sizeable hit in some European countries but stiffed in the UK and US. The accomplished but underrated 1985 single *It's all in the game* failed to revive the group's reputation, so their imaginative and original pop-rock offerings could not sustain Nenamania. (Bob MacDonald, 9th Feb 1986).

99 RED BALLOONS
Tracks: / 99 red balloons.
7" Single: Released Feb '84, on Epic, by CBS Records. Deleted '87. Catalogue no: **A 4074**
12" Single: Released Jan '84, on Epic, by CBS Records. Catalogue no: **TA 4074**

ICH LIEBE DICHT
Tracks: / Ich liebe dicht.
7" Single: Released Jul '84, on Epic, by CBS Records. Catalogue no: **A 4617**
12" Single: Released Jul '84, on Epic, by CBS Records. Catalogue no: **TA 4617**

JUST A DREAM
Tracks: / Just a dream / Indiana.
7" Pic: Released Apr '84, on Epic, by CBS Records. Catalogue no: **WA 3249**
7" Single: Released Apr '84, on Epic, by CBS Records. Catalogue no: **A 3249**
7" Single: Released Mar '83, on Epic, by CBS Records. Catalogue no: **EPC A 2349**
12" Single: Released Apr '84, on Epic, by CBS Records. Catalogue no: **TA 3249**

Nenad

HIS LATEST FLAME
Tracks: / His latest flame / Sanja.
7" Single: Released Jul '82, on Camab, Deleted '84. Catalogue no: **TMA 1**

Neon

COMMUNICATION WITH SOUND
Tracks: / Communication with sound / Remote control.
7" Single: Released Jul '81, on Carrere, Deleted '84. Catalogue no: **CAR 201**

Neon Barbs

BREAK YOUR CHAINS
Tracks: / Break your chains.
7" Single: Released Jul '81, on Logic Step, Catalogue no: **LSO 1**

Neon Blondes

MIRROR FREAK
Tracks: / Mirror freak.
7" Single: Released Nov '81, on 4 Series, Catalogue no: **NB 1**

Neon Judgement

AWFUL DAY
Tracks: / Awful day.
12" Single: Released 25 Sep '86, on Play It Again Sam(Belgium), by Play It Again Sam (Belgium). Catalogue no: **BIAS 038**

FACTORY WALK
Tracks: / Factory walk.
7" Single: Released Jun '88, on Antler, by Antler Records (Belgium). Deleted '88. Catalogue no: **ANT 009**

GAMES OF LOVE
Tracks: / Games of love.
7" Single: Released Sep '89, on Play It Again Sam(Belgium), by Play It Again Sam (Belgium). Catalogue no: **BIAS 133**
12" Single: Released Sep '89, on Play It Again Sam(Belgium), by Play It Again Sam (Belgium). Catalogue no: **12 BIAS 133**

MAN AIN'T NO MAN IF A MAN AIN'T GOT NO HORSE MAN, A
Tracks: / Man ain't no man if a man ain't got no horse man, A.
CD 5": Released Aug '88, on Play It Again Sam(Belgium), by Play It Again Sam (Belgium). Catalogue no: **CDBIAS 65**
12" Single: Released 3 Jun '87, on Play It Again Sam(Belgium), by Play It Again Sam (Belgium). Catalogue no: **BIAS 065**

MISS BROWN
Tracks: / Miss Brown.
7" Single: Released 31 Oct '87, on Play It Again Sam(Belgium), by Play It Again Sam (Belgium). Catalogue no: **BIAS 77**
12" Single: Released 31 Oct '87, on Play It Again Sam(Belgium), by Play It Again Sam (Belgium). Catalogue no: **BIAS 77T**

TOMORROW
Tracks: / Tomorrow.
7" Single: Released '89, on Play It Again Sam(Belgium), by Play It Again Sam (Belgium). Catalogue no: **BIAS 018**

TOMORROW IN THE PAPERS
Tracks: / Tomorrow in the papers.
CD 5": Released Aug '88, on Play It Again Sam(Belgium), by Play It Again Sam (Belgium). Catalogue no: **BIAS 14CD**
12" Single: Released Nov '85, on Play It Again Sam(Belgium), by Play It Again Sam (Belgium). Catalogue no: **BIAS 014**

TV TREATED
Tracks: / T.V. treated / Fashion party.
12" Single: Released Dec '88, on Licensed, Catalogue no: **LD 8824**

VOODOO NIPPLEFIELD
Tracks: / Voodoo nipplefield.

12" Single: Released May '86, on Play It Again Sam(Belgium), by Play It Again Sam (Belgium). Catalogue no: **BIAS 026**

Neon Leon

LAS PALMAS
Tracks: / Las Palmas / Heart of stone.
7" Single: Released Feb '83, on Tansing, Catalogue no: **TANSIN 007**

Neon Tetra

TIGHTROPE
Tracks: / Tightrope / Night boat to Amsterdam.
7" Single: Released Aug '82, on Deeda, Catalogue no: **DD 001**

Nerious, Joseph

SENSI CRISIS
Tracks: / Sensi crisis.
12" Single: Released Jun '85, on Fashion, by Fashion Records. Catalogue no: **FAD 034**

Nero & The Gladiators

ENTRY OF THE GLADIATORS
Tracks: / Entry of the gladiators.
7" Single: Released Mar '61, on Decca, by Decca Records. Deleted '64. Catalogue no: **F 11329**

IN THE HALL OF THE MOUNTAIN KING
Tracks: / In the hall of the mountain king.
7" Single: Released Sep '61, on Decca, by Decca Records. Deleted '64. Catalogue no: **F 11367**

Nerve

I'LL GIVE YOU UP
Tracks: / I'll give you up.
7" Single: Released Jul '83, on Future Earth, by Future Earth Records. Deleted '87. Catalogue no: **FER 016**

LITTLE BIT OF JAZZ, A
Tracks: / Little bit of jazz, A / It only takes a minute.
12" Single: Released May '87, on Sedition, by Sedition Records. Catalogue no: **EDITL 3325**

WELCOME TO YOUR T.V.
Tracks: / Welcome to your T.V..
12" Single: Released Apr '86, on D.M.D., Catalogue no: **DMD 001**

Nervex

REBECCA
Tracks: / Rebecca / Ha ha ha.
7" Single: Released Feb '85, on Lost Moments, Catalogue no: **LM 007**

Nervous Choir

ALSTATIONS EP
Tracks: / Alstations.
7" Single: Released Feb '89, on Cathexis, by Cathexis Records. Catalogue no: **CRN 5407**

Nervous Eaters

LORETTA
Tracks: / Loretta / Get stuffed.
7" Single: Released Oct '80, on Elektra, by Elektra Records (UK). Deleted Oct '83. Catalogue no: **K 12481**

Nervous Germans

THESE BOOTS ARE MADE FOR WALKING
Tracks: / These boots are made for walking / Watch out.
7" Single: Released May '82, on Rondelet Music, by Rondelet Music & Records. Catalogue no: **ROUND 3000**

Nervous, Joseph

MOVE ON UP
Tracks: / Move on up.
12" Single: Released Aug '87, on Fine Style, by Fashion Records. Catalogue no: **FS 012**

Nervus Rex

I THANK YOU
Tracks: / I thank you / Not easy being me.
7" Single: Released May '82, on EMI, by EMI Records. Deleted May '85. Catalogue no: **EMI 5292**

THERE SHE GOES
Tracks: / There she goes / Incredible crawling eye.
7" Single: Released Aug '80, on Dreamland, Deleted '83. Catalogue no: **DLSP 3**

Nesmith, Michael

RIO
Tracks: / Rio.
7" Single: Released Mar '77, on Island, by Island Records. Deleted '80. Catalogue no: **WIP 6373**
7" Single: Released Apr '89, on Awareness, by Awareness Records. Catalogue no: **AWP 014**

Netto, Loz

FADEAWAY
Tracks: / Fade away.
12" Single: Released Jul '83, on 21 Records, by Polydor Ltd. Catalogue no: **POSPX 526**
7" Single: Released Jul '83, on 21 Records, by Polydor Ltd. Catalogue no: **POSP 526**

WE TOUCH
Tracks: / Do what you want / We touch.
7" Single: Released Aug '86, on Atlantic, by WEA Records. Deleted Jun '87. Catalogue no: **A 9399**
12" Single: Released Aug '86, on Atlantic, by WEA Records. Deleted Jun '87. Catalogue no: **A 9399 T**

YOU ARE RHYTHM
Tracks: / You are rhythm.
7" Single: Released May '84, on 21 Records, by Polydor Ltd. Catalogue no: **POSP 682**

Netwerk

IT'S A SHAME
Tracks: / It's a shame.
7" Single: Released Aug '89, on Blue Chip, by Blue Chip Records. Catalogue no: **BLUEC 28**

Network 3

DANGEROUS GAME
Tracks: / Dangerous game / Come go with me.
7" Single: Released Jul '81, on EMI, by EMI Records. Deleted '84. Catalogue no: **EMI 5205**

LAST TRAIN HOME
Tracks: / Last train home / Lifeline.
7" Single: Released Jan '81, on EMI, by EMI Records. Deleted Jan '84. Catalogue no: **EMI 5120**

Neue Sachlichkeit

ICE
Tracks: / Ice / Ice.
7" Single: Released Jun '88, on Antler, by Antler Records (Belgium). Deleted '88. Catalogue no: **ANT 001**

Neurotics

LIVING WITH UNEMPLOYEMENT
Tracks: / Living with umemployment / Airstrip 1 / My death / Oh no / Mindless violence / Porky the poet / Peter Campbell.
7" Single: Released Jun '86, on Jungle, by Jungle Records. Catalogue no: **JUNG 29**
12" Single: Released Jun '86, on Jungle, by Jungle Records. Catalogue no: **JUNG 29T**

NEVER THOUGHT
Tracks: / Never thought / Screaming (live) / Stand by me / Mind of Valerie's / Sects / My death.
12" Single: Released Mar '88, on Jungle, by Jungle Records. Catalogue no: **JUNG 39T**

Nevada

Biographical details: A version of the Christmas standard *In the bleak midwinter* gave one solitary week of UK chart glory to this British band of mixed sexes. The single reached No.71 in January 1983, and was reactivated without success, the following year. (Bob MacDonald, 10th Feb 1986).

IN THE BLEAK MID WINTER
Tracks: / In the bleak mid winter / Pictures in the fire.
7" Single: Released Jan '83, on Polydor, by Polydor Ltd. Deleted '86. Catalogue no: **POSP 203**

YOU KNOW I LIKE IT
Tracks: / You know I like it / Once in a lifetime.
7" Single: Released Feb '81, on Polydor, by Polydor Ltd. Deleted '84. Catalogue no: **POSP 229**

Never Mind The

NEVER MIND THE JACKSONS...HERE'S THE POLLOCKS
Tracks: / Never mind the Jacksons...here's the Pollocks: *Various artists*.
12" Single: Released Mar '85, on Abstract, by Abstract Sounds. Catalogue no: **12 ABS 030**

Never Never

AMERICANA
Tracks: / Americana.
7" Single: Released Feb '87, on Round, Catalogue no: **NN 001**

Nevil, Robbie

BACK ON HOLIDAY
Tracks: / Back on holiday / Too soon / Back on holiday (Ibiza mix) (12" only.) / Back on holiday (Montego Bay mix) (12" only.).
CD 5": Released Oct '88, on EMI-Manhattan, by EMI Records. Deleted Aug '89. Catalogue no: **CDMT 58**
7" Single: Released Oct '88, on EMI-Manhattan, by EMI Records. Deleted Aug '89. Catalogue no: **MTP 58**
7" Single: Released Oct '88, on EMI-Manhattan, by EMI Records. Deleted Aug '89. Catalogue no: **MT 58**
12" Single: Released Oct '88, on EMI-Manhattan, by EMI Records. Deleted Aug '89. Catalogue no: **12MT 58**

C'EST LA VIE (EXT. REMIX)
Tracks: / C'est la vie (ext remix) / Time waits for no one.
Note: Side A extended remix by Michael Braver.
12" Single: Released Dec '86, on EMI-Manhattan, by EMI Records. Catalogue no: **12 MTX 14**

C'EST LA VIE (SINGLE)
Tracks: / C'est la vie / Time waits for no one.
7" Single: Released Nov '86, on EMI-Manhattan, by EMI Records. Deleted Oct '87. Catalogue no: **MT 14**
12" Single: Released Dec '86, on EMI-Manhattan, by EMI Records. Deleted '88. Catalogue no: **12 MT 14**

DOMINOES
Tracks: / Dom dom domino dub / C'est la vie*.
7" Single: Released Mar '87, on EMI-Manhattan, by EMI Records. Deleted Apr '88. Catalogue no: **MT 19**
12" Single: Released Mar '87, on EMI-Manhattan, by EMI Records. Catalogue no: **12 MT 19**

DOMINOES (EXT VOCAL MIX)
Tracks: / Dominoes (ext vocal mix) / C'est la vie (Steve Street mix) / Dominoes (Dom dom domino dub) / Dominoes (Dance mix).
CD 5": Released 23 May '87, on EMI-Manhattan, by EMI Records. Deleted Jul '87. Catalogue no: **CDMT 19**
7" Set: Released Apr '87, on EMI-Manhattan, by EMI Records. Catalogue no: **12 MTD 12**

WHAT'S IT TO YA
Tracks: / What's it to ya / What's it to ya (remix).
7" Single: Released 20 Jun '87, on EMI-Manhattan, by EMI Records. Deleted Apr '88. Catalogue no: **MT 24**
12" Single: Released 20 Jun '87, on EMI-Manhattan, by EMI Records. Deleted Apr '88. Catalogue no: **12 MT 24**

WOT'S IT TO YA? (EXT TO YA REMIX)
Tracks: / Wot's it to ya / C'est la vie (Steve Street mix) / Dominoes (Ext).
Cassingle: Released Jul '87, on EMI-Manhattan, by EMI Records. Catalogue no: **TC-MT 24**

WOT'S IT TO YA (RUSTY'S 12" DANCE MIX)
Tracks: / Wot's it to ya (Rusty's 12" dance mix) / Wot's it to ya (dub to ya mix) / Wot's it to ya (to ya remix).
12" Single: Released Jul '87, on EMI-Manhattan, by EMI Records. Deleted Oct '87. Catalogue no: **12 MTX 24**

Neville, Aaron

TELL IT LIKE IT IS
Tracks: / Fever / Iko Iko / Fortune teller.
7" Single: Released Jun '88, on Charly Groove, by Charly Records. Catalogue no: **CYZ 7 124**
7" Single: Released Jul '80, on Charly, by Charly Records. Deleted '87. Catalogue no: **CTD 124**
12" Single: Released Jun '88, on Charly Groove, by Charly Records. Catalogue no: **CYZ 124**

Neville Brothers

CHANGE IS GONNA COME, A
Tracks: / Change is gonna come, A / Sister Rosa.
7" Single: Released Apr '89, on A&M, by A&M Records. Catalogue no: **USAT 656**
7" Single: Released Apr '89, on A&M, by A&M Records. Catalogue no: **USA 656**

SISTER ROSA
Tracks: / Sister Rosa.
7" Single: Released May '89, on A&M, by A&M Records. Catalogue no: **USA 656**
12" Single: Released May '89, on A&M, by A&M Records. Catalogue no: **USAT 656**

YELLOW MOON (SINGLE)
Tracks: / Yellow moon / With God on our side.
CD 5": Released Oct '89, on A&M, by A&M Records. Catalogue no: **USACD 657**
7" Single: Released 5 Jun '89, on A&M, by A&M Records. Catalogue no: **USA 657**
12" Single: Released 5 Jun '89, on A&M, by A&M Records. Catalogue no: **USAT 657**

Neville, Ivan

FALLING OUT OF LOVE
Tracks: / Falling out of love.
7" Single: Released 20 Mar '89, on Polydor, by Polydor Ltd. Deleted Oct '89. Catalogue no: **PO 39**
12" Single: Released 20 Mar '89, on Polydor, by Polydor Ltd. Catalogue no: **PZ 39**

NOT JUST ANOTHER GIRL
Tracks: / Not just another girl / Up to you / Never should have told me.
7" Single: Released Jan '89, on Polydor, by

Polydor Ltd. Deleted 30 Jun '89. Catalogue no: **PO 30**
12" Single: Released Jan '89, on Polydor, by Polydor Ltd. Deleted 30 Jun '89. Catalogue no: **PZ 30**

PRIMITIVE MAN
Tracks: / Primitive man / After all this time / Not just another girl.
CD 5": Released Jul '89, on Polydor, by Polydor Ltd. Catalogue no: **PXCD 50**
7" Single: Released Jul '89, on Polydor, by Polydor Ltd. Catalogue no: **PO 50**
12" Single: Released Jul '89, on Polydor, by Polydor Ltd. Catalogue no: **PZ 50**

New Adventures

COM'ON
Tracks: / Com'on / Back to the pit.
7" Single: Released Feb '80, on WEA, by WEA Records. Deleted Feb '83. Catalogue no: **K 18151**

DRIVE ME WILD
Tracks: / Drive me wild / Late late show.
7" Single: Released Sep '80, on Polydor, by Polydor Ltd. Deleted '83. Catalogue no: **POSP 169**

New Age

JANE FONDA
Tracks: / Jane Fonda / Radio show.
7" Single: Released Sep '81, on Dining Out, by Dining Out Records. Catalogue no: **TUX 14**

LIVING FOR NOW (EP)
Tracks: / Living for now / My love.
12" Single: Released Feb '82, on Dining Out, by Dining Out Records. Catalogue no: **TUX 18**

New Age Steppers

MY LOVE
12" Single: Released Jul '81, on Statik, Catalogue no: **STAT 612**

New Apartment

CATCH 22
Tracks: / Catch 22.
7" Single: Released Jul '81, on Demon, by Demon Records. Deleted '88. Catalogue no: **D 1008**

New Band

HAPPY NEW YEAR
Tracks: / Happy new year.
7" Single: Released Feb '85, on RPM, Catalogue no: **RPM 1**

New Beat Connection

SOUND OF B., THE
Tracks: / Sound of B., The.
12" Single: Released '89, on Rodger, Catalogue no: **RODGER 002**

New Beat Sensation

ROBBIN' & STEALIN'
Tracks: / Robbin' & stealin'.
12" Single: Released '88, on Subway, by Subway Records. Catalogue no: **SUB 031**

SUCK THAT BEAT
Tracks: / Suck that beat.
12" Single: Released Oct '88, on Subway, by Subway Records. Catalogue no: **SUB 038**

New Belgian...

COLD SENSATION
Tracks: / Cold sensation.
12" Single: Released Apr '89, on Subway, by Subway Records. Catalogue no: **SUB 062**

New Christs

DETRITUS EP
Tracks: / Born out of time / No next time / Like a curse / Sun God.
12" Single: Released Feb '87, on What Goes On, by What Goes On Records. Catalogue no: **GOES ON 09T**

New Edition

Biographical details: In 1983 the 25 year old Michael Jackson was unquestinably the globe's hottest star. In that same year, writer/producer Maurice Starr launched a group of five Boston teenagers onto an unsuspecting marketplace, who were directly modelled on the early days of the Jackson Five circa 1970. Although New Edition's falsetto lead singer Ralph Tresvant lacked the precocious talent of the juvenile Michael, their smash single *Candy Girl* was so cleverly crafted that even those listeners who hated it couldn't stop singing it. *Candy Girl* was like a rerun of *I Want You Back* or *ABC*, but with 1983's arrangement and production touches. With the five young vocalists billed as New Edition, there could be absolutely no doubt about what they were supposed to be a new edition of. *Candy Girl* reached No.1 on the American black charts and climbed approximately halfway up the Hot 100 pop chart. In Britain, where no such musical formats exist for radio and chart purposes, *Candy Girl* cruised to No.1 on the national singles chart. The follow up, *Popcorn Love*, peaked at No.44 on the UK chart. Britain then forgot about New Edition for a while. Back in the States, the group decided to wrest themselves from Maurice Starr's dominance, with the result that their second album was a pot-pourri of different tracks by various producers and songwriters. Starr's ensuing legal action threatened, at one point, to rob the group of their name. But the quintet's exposure to the bitter adult world of lawsuits and courtrooms made no difference to their music, which sounded as lightweight and kidlike as ever. At the beginning of 1985 they acheived a US million seller with the No.1 black and No.4 pop hit *Cool It Now*. It was followed by the Ray Parker Jr song and production *Mr.Telephone Man*, which restored New Edition to the British Top 20 and was another No.1 Black smash in the States. The Brantley/Timas writing and producing team, who had been responsible for *Cool It Now*, came up with another Top 10 Black hit *Count Me Out* in late 1985. New Edition's approximations of soul and dance music had begun as a novelty and ended up as a long-term career. Their success paved the way for Britain's similar sounding Five Star.(N.B. New Edition are not to be confused with a UK group of the same name who were associated with the Seaside Special TV show in the 70's) (Bob Macdonald 2/86).

CANDY GIRL (SINGLE)
Tracks: / Candy girl.
7" Single: Released Apr '83, on London Records, by London Records. Catalogue no: **LON 21**
12" Single: Released Apr '83, on London Records, by London Records. Catalogue no: **LONX 21**

COOL IT NOW
Tracks: / Cool it now.
12" Single: Released Apr '85, on MCA, by MCA Records. Catalogue no: **MCAT 963**
7" Single: Released Apr '85, on MCA, by MCA Records. Catalogue no: **MCA 963**
12" Single: Released Oct '84, on MCA, by MCA Records. Catalogue no: **MCAT 922**
7" Single: Released Oct '84, on MCA, by MCA Records. Catalogue no: **MCA 922**

CRUCIAL
Tracks: / Crucial.
7" Single: Released Apr '89, on MCA, by MCA Records. Catalogue no: **MCA 1333**
12" Single: Released Apr '89, on MCA, by MCA Records. Catalogue no: **MCA 23934**
12" Single: Released Apr '89, on MCA, by MCA Records. Catalogue no: **MCAT 1333**

EARTH ANGEL (SINGLE)
Tracks: / Earth angel / With you all the way.
7" Single: Released Nov '86, on MCA, by MCA Records. Catalogue no: **MCA 1103**
12" Single: Released Nov '86, on MCA, by MCA Records. Catalogue no: **MCAT 1103**

IF IT ISN'T LOVE
Tracks: / If it isn't love / If it isn't love (instrumental) / If it isn't love (dubapella) (on 12" only).
7" Single: Released 22 Aug '88, on MCA, by MCA Records. Catalogue no: **MCA 1269**
12" Single: Released 22 Aug '88, on MCA, by MCA Records. Catalogue no: **MCAT 1269**

IS THIS THE END
Tracks: / Is this the end.
7" Single: Released Oct '83, on London Records, by London Records. Catalogue no: **LON 35**
12" Single: Released Oct '83, on London Records, by London Records. Catalogue no: **LONX 35**

LITTLE BIT OF LOVE, A (IS ALL IT TAKES)
Tracks: / Little bit of love, A / Sneakin' around / Little bit of love, A / Little bit of love, A (Inst).
7" Single: Released Feb '86, on MCA, by MCA Records. Catalogue no: **MCA 1032**
12" Single: Released Feb '86, on MCA, by MCA Records. Catalogue no: **MCAT 1032**

MR TELEPHONE MAN
Tracks: / Mr. Telephone man.
7" Single: Released Feb '85, on MCA, by MCA Records. Catalogue no: **MCA 938**
12" Single: Released Feb '85, on MCA, by MCA Records. Catalogue no: **MCAT 938**

POPCORN LOVE
Tracks: / Popcorn love.
7" Single: Released Aug '83, on London Records, by London Records. Catalogue no: **LON 31**
12" Single: Released Aug '83, on London Records, by London Records. Catalogue no: **LONX 31**

New Experience

PROVE IT TO ME
Tracks: / Prove it to me.
7" Single: Released Jul '85, on Boiling Point, by Polydor Ltd. Catalogue no: **POSP 736**
12" Single: Released Jul '85, on Boiling Point, by Polydor Ltd. Catalogue no: **POSPX 736**

New Fast Automatic ...

LIONS
Tracks: / Lions.
12" Single: Released Jul '89, on Playtime, by Playtime Records. Catalogue no: **12 AMUSE 4 T**

New Generation...

SMOKEY BLUES AWAY
Tracks: / Smokey blues away.
7" Single: Released Jun '68, on Spark, by Spark Records. Deleted '71. Catalogue no: **SRL 1007**

New Grass Revival

CAN'T STOP NOW
Tracks: / Can't stop now / Unconditional love.
7" Single: Released Jun '88, on Capitol, by EMI Records. Deleted Nov '88. Catalogue no: **CL 499**

New Guys On The Block

ON THE DANCE FLOOR
Tracks: / On the dance floor.
7" Single: Released Jun '83, on Sugarhill (USA), Catalogue no: **SH 126**
12" Single: Released Jun '83, on Sugarhill (USA), Catalogue no: **SHL 126**

New Horizon

HERE WITH YOU
Tracks: / Here with you.
12" Single: Released Sep '89, on Quartz, by Quartz Records. Catalogue no: **QMW 002**

WALK ON
Tracks: / Walk on / Landscapes.
7" Single: Released Oct '81, on Red Bus, by Red Bus Records. Catalogue no: **RBUS 61**

New Jersey Connection

LOVE DON'T COME EASY
Tracks: / Love don't come easy.
7" Single: Released Nov '82, on Nite Life, Deleted '84. Catalogue no: **LIFE 1**
12" Single: Released Nov '82, on Nite Life, Deleted '85. Catalogue no: **LIFE 112**

New Jersey Mass Choir

DONALD
Tracks: / Donald / I want to know what love is / Jesus is right on.
7" Single: Released Nov '86, on Prelude, Catalogue no: **ZB 41029**
12" Single: Released Nov '86, on Prelude, Catalogue no: **ZT 41030**

I WANT TO KNOW WHAT LOVE IS
7" Single: Released Jan '85, on Prelude, Catalogue no: **MHS 103**
12" Single: Released Jan '85, on Prelude, Catalogue no: **MHST 103**

New Kids On The Block

HANGIN' TOUGH (SINGLE)
Tracks: / Hangin' tough / Didn't I (blow your mind) / Hangin' tough (LP version) (Only on 12" single.) / Wat'cha gonna do (about it) / Hangin' tough (tougher mix) (Only on 12" and CD single.).
CD 5": Released Aug '89, on CBS, by CBS Records. Catalogue no: **BLOCK C1**
7" Pic: Released Sep '89, on CBS, by CBS Records. Catalogue no: **BLOCK P1**
12" Single: Released Aug '89, on CBS, by CBS Records. Catalogue no: **BLOCK T1**
7" Single: Released Sep '89, on CBS, by CBS Records. Catalogue no: **BLOCKS 1**
Cassingle: Released Sep '89, on CBS, by CBS Records. Catalogue no: **BLOCKM 1**
7" Single: Released Aug '89, on CBS, by CBS Records. Catalogue no: **BLOCK 1**

PLEASE DON'T GO GIRL
Tracks: / Please don't go girl / Please don't go girl (ext. version) (12" and CD only) / Watcha gonna do about it (dub mix) (12" and CD only).
7" Single: Released Aug '88, on CBS, by CBS Records. Deleted 17 Apr '89. Catalogue no: **652992 7**
CD 5": Released Aug '88, on CBS, by CBS Records. Deleted 17 Apr '89. Catalogue no: **652992 2**
12" Single: Released Aug '88, on CBS, by CBS Records. Deleted 17 Apr '89. Catalogue no: **652992 6**

YOU GOT IT (THE RIGHT STUFF)
Tracks: / You got it (the right stuff) / Whatcha gonna do about it / You got it (the right stuff) remix.
CD 5": Released 6 Feb '89, on CBS, by CBS Records. Catalogue no: **653169 2**
7" Single: Released 30 Jan '89, on CBS, by CBS Records. Catalogue no: **653169 7**
12" Single: Released 30 Jan '89, on CBS, by CBS Records. Catalogue no: **653169 8**

New London Chorale

EVERY VALLEY
Tracks: / Every valley / He was despised.
7" Single: Released Mar '80, on RCA, by BMG Records (UK). Deleted Mar '83. Catalogue no: **PB 5225**

UNTO US A CHILD IS BORN
Tracks: / Unto us a child is born / Who shall abide.
7" Single: Released Dec '82, on RCA, by BMG Records (UK). Catalogue no: **RCA 297**

New Marketts

M.A.S.H., THEME FROM
Tracks: / M.A.S.H., Theme from.
7" Single: Released Jun '80, on Satril, by Satril Records. Deleted Jun '83. Catalogue no: **HH 149**

New Model

CHILEAN WARNING
Tracks: / Chilean warning / World thru our eyes, The / Totalitarian.
7" Single: Released Sep '83, on Mr.Clean, Catalogue no: **MRC 001**

New Model Army

51ST STATE
Tracks: / 51st state / Ten commandments / Liberal education, A / No rest / No man's land.
7" Set: Released Nov '86, on EMI, by EMI Records. Catalogue no: **EMI 12NMAD 4**
7" Single: Released Oct '86, on EMI, by EMI Records. Deleted Oct '87. Catalogue no: **NMA 4**

BETTER THAN THEM
Tracks: / Better than them / No sense.
7" Set: Released Jul '85, on EMI, by EMI Records. Catalogue no: **NMAD 2**
7" Single: Released Jul '85, on EMI, by EMI Records. Catalogue no: **NMA 2**
12" Single: Released Jul '85, on EMI, by EMI Records. Catalogue no: **12NMA 2**

BITTERSWEET
Tracks: / Bittersweet / Betcha / Tension.
7" Single: Released Jan '86, on Quiet, by Quiet Records. Catalogue no: **QS 002**

BRAVE NEW WORLD
Tracks: / Brave new world.
7" Set: Released Nov '85, on EMI, by EMI Records. Catalogue no: **12NMAD 3**
7" Single: Released Nov '85, on EMI, by EMI Records. Catalogue no: **NMA 3**
12" Single: Released Nov '85, on EMI, by EMI Records. Catalogue no: **12 NMA 3**

GREAT EXPECTATIONS
Tracks: / Great expectations.
7" Single: Released Nov '83, on Abstract, by Abstract Sounds. Catalogue no: **ABS 020**

GREEN AND GREY
Tracks: / Green and grey / Charge, The (live).
CD 5": Released May '89, on EMI, by EMI Records. Catalogue no: **203 388 2**
CD 5": Released May '89, on EMI, by EMI Records. Catalogue no: **CDNMA 9**
Cassingle: Released Jun '89, on EMI, by EMI Records. Catalogue no: **TCNMA 9**
7" Single: Released May '89, on EMI, by EMI Records. Catalogue no: **203 388 7**
7" Single: Released May '89, on EMI, by EMI Records. Catalogue no: **NMA 9**
7" Pic: Released May '89, on EMI, by EMI Records. Catalogue no: **NMAPD 9**
12" Single: Released May '89, on EMI, by EMI Records. Catalogue no: **203 388 8**
12" Single: Released May '89, on EMI, by EMI Records. Catalogue no: **12NMA 9**
12" Single: Released May '89, on EMI, by EMI Records. Catalogue no: **203 388 6**
Cassingle: Released Jun '89, on EMI, by EMI Records. Catalogue no: **203 388 4**
12" Single: Released May '89, on EMI, by EMI Records. Catalogue no: **12NMAP 9**
7" Pic: Released May '89, on EMI, by EMI Records. Catalogue no: **203 338 0**

NO REST
Tracks: / No rest / Heroin.
7" Single: Released Apr '85, on EMI, by EMI Records. Catalogue no: **NMA 1**
12" Single: Released Apr '85, on EMI, by EMI Records. Catalogue no: **12NMA 1**

POISON STREET
Tracks: / Courage / All of this (Live at The Ritz, New York) (Extra track on double pack only) / My country (Live) (Live at Coventry Poly.).
7" Set: Released Feb '87, on EMI, by EMI Records. Catalogue no: **12 NMAD**
12" Single: Released Feb '87, on EMI, by EMI Records. Deleted Oct '87. Catalogue no: **12 NMA 5**
7" Single: Released Feb '87, on EMI, by EMI Records. Deleted Oct '87. Catalogue no: **NMA 5**

PRICE, THE

NEW MUSIC - SANCTURY (Released on GTO)

Abstract Sounds. Catalogue no: **ABS 028**
12" Single: Released Oct '84, on Abstract, by Abstract Sounds. Catalogue no: **12 ABS 028**

STUPID QUESTIONS
Tracks: / Stupid questions / Nothing touches / 51st state (live) (CD single only.) / Betcha (live) (CD single & 12" only.) / Stupid questions (stupid mix) (12" only.).
7" Single: Released Jan '89, on EMI, by EMI Records. Catalogue no: **NMAG 7**
12" Single: Released Jan '89, on EMI, by EMI Records. Deleted Oct '89. Catalogue no: **12NMA 7**
7" Single: Released Jan '89, on EMI, by EMI Records. Deleted Aug '89. Catalogue no: **NMA 7**
12" Single: Released Jan '89, on EMI, by EMI Records. Deleted Aug '89. Catalogue no: **12NMAP 7**
CD 5": Released Jan '89, on EMI, by EMI Records. Catalogue no: **CDNMA 7**

VAGABONDS
Tracks: / Vagabonds (edit) (7" only) / Vagabonds (Sullivan) (12" & CD single oly.) / Deadeye / White coats (12" only.) / Lights go out (ext.) (CD single only.).
CD 5": Released Feb '89, on EMI, by EMI Records. Catalogue no: **CDNMA 8**
7" Pic: Released Feb '89, on EMI, by EMI Records. Deleted Aug '89. Catalogue no: **NMAP 8**
12" Single: Released Feb '89, on EMI, by EMI Records. Deleted Aug '89. Catalogue no: **12NMAS 8**
7" Single: Released Feb '89, on EMI, by EMI Records. Catalogue no: **NMA 8**
12" Single: Released Feb '89, on EMI, by EMI Records. Catalogue no: **12NMA 8**
7" Single: Released Feb '89, on EMI, by EMI Records. Catalogue no: **NMAG 8**

WHITE COATS
Tracks: / White coats / Charge, The / Chinese whispers / My country.
7" Single: Released Sep '87, on EMI, by EMI Records. Deleted Apr '88. Catalogue no: **NMA 6**
12" Single: Released Sep '87, on EMI, by EMI Records. Deleted Nov '88. Catalogue no: **12NMAG 6**

New Musik

Biographical details: As the 70's gave way to the 80's and ushered in a new era of synthesised technopop, New Musik -- Clive Gates, Tony Hibbert, Tony Mansfield and Phil Towner -- provided an archetypal foretaste of the sound that would fill much of the British singles chart during the early 80's. Dominated by singer/guitarist/keyboards player/sythesiser player/songwriter/producer Mansfield, the British band emphasised the catchy, hummable and melodic aspects of the synth's potential. Straight Lines provided New Musik with their first taste of UK chart success, reaching No 53 on the singles list in late '79, and in 1980 Mansfield and his studio colleagues reached No 13 with the timely *Living By Numbers* and peaked at No 31 with two other singles, *This World Of Water* and *Sanctuary*. All these songs appeared on their first and best album, *From A To B*, which peaked at a surprisingly low No 35 position on the British LP chart. With their somewhat faceless image New Musik did not corner the Technopop market as successfully as the Ultravoxes or Soft Cells of this world: their second album, *Anywhere*, reached No 68 in 1981 and 1982's *Warp* flopped altogether. New Musik folded and Mansfield embarked on a successful career as a producer for other artists. He immediately struck lucky with Captain Sensible's No 1 smash *Happy Talk* (July '82) and followed it with further Captain hits plus a UK Top Tenner for Mari Wilson *Just What I Always Wanted* '82 and a US Top Tenner for Naked Eyes *Always Something There To Remind Me* '83. (Bob MacDonald, February 1986.).

ALL YOU NEED IS LOVE
Tracks: / All you need is love / Twelth house.
7" Single: Released Feb '82, on Epic, by CBS Records. Deleted Feb '87. Catalogue no: **EPC A1976**

LIVING BY NUMBERS
Tracks: / Living by numbers.
7" Single: Released Jan '80, on GTO. Deleted '83. Catalogue no: **GT 261**

LUXURY
Tracks: / Luxury / Office.
7" Single: Released Feb '81, on GTO. Deleted '84. Catalogue no: **GT 284**

PLANET DOESN'T MIND
Tracks: / Planet doesn't mind / Twenty four hours from culture.
7" Single: Released Sep '81, on GTO. Deleted Sep '84. Catalogue no: **GT 302**

SANCTUARY
Tracks: / Sanctuary / She's a magazine / Chik music / Magazine musik.
7" Single: Released Jul '80, on GTO. Deleted '83. Catalogue no: **GT 275**

STRAIGHT LINES
Tracks: / Straight lines.
7" Single: Released Oct '79, on GTO. Deleted '82. Catalogue no: **GT 255**

THIS WORLD OF WATER
Tracks: / This world of water / Missing persons / Tell me something new.
7" Single: Released Apr '80, on GTO. Deleted '83. Catalogue no: **GT 268**

WARP (SINGLE)
Tracks: / Warp / Here come the people.
7" Single: Released Jun '82, on Epic, by CBS Records. Deleted Jun '85. Catalogue no: **EPCA 2424**

WHILE YOU WAIT
Tracks: / While you wait / From the village / Guitars.
12" Single: Released Apr '81, on GTO. Deleted Apr '84. Catalogue no: **GT 291**

New Number Two

NEW NUMBER TWO
Tracks: / New number two.
12" Single: Released Aug '82, on Lightbeat. Catalogue no: **LIGHT 004**

New Order

Biographical details: This British rock band -- Bernard Dickin (aka Bernard Albrecht), Gillian Gilbert, Peter Hook and Stephen Morris -- evolved from the legendary cult band Joy Division, who received huge critical acclaim from early 1978 until the May 1980 suicide of vocalist Ian Curtis. After that tragic event the three surviving men decided to continue working, but under a name which was designed to imply a new beginning. Dickin assumed the role of vocalist and keyboards player Gillian Gilbert was recruited. They remained with the indie record company Factory Records in Manchester. While keeping Joy Division's rigid independence and detachment from the mainstream rock business, New Order went on to achieve greater commercial success. Despite their wish to continue mainly on new repertoire, the first New Order single, *Ceremony*, was actually from the Joy Division set: it reached No 34 on the UK chart in March '81 and was followed in the autumn by the double-A-sided single *Procession/Everything's Gone Green* (No 38). Their first album, *Movement*, reached No 30. All these records retained the dark, eerie and pensive style of the group's previous incarnation. A new, more optimistic and more danceable sound began to emerge in 1982 with the acclaimed single *Temptation*. This reached the UK No 29 position, in spite of the fact that the band were still ignored by the bulk of the daytime radio establishment. However, stations were finally forced to succumb to *Blue Monday*, the '83 track which initiated the group's policy of issuing singles in the 12-inch format only. *Blue Monday* was not only the perfect crystallisation of the group's new rhythmic sound but became one of the surprise monster hits of '83. It was at first a UK hit in the spring, when it peaked at No 12 and logged 17 chart weeks. It then became a club favourite in America and a pop smash in Europe during the summer. With returning British holidaymakers giving the song a new lease of life on the UK charts the seven-minute single amazingly chalked up a further 17-week run and attained a new peak of No 9. It became the biggest-selling 12-inch single to that date, though Frankie Goes To Hollywood later overtook New Order in this respect. New Order's 1983 album, *Power, Corruption and Lies*, was also a British Top Ten smash, and the single *Confusion* peaked at No 12. The last stage of the quartet's hit streak was the excellent melodic single *Thieves Like Us*, which reached the UK No 18 position in spring '84. Thereafter they found success a little harder to come by, due to the increasing predictability of their music and the economic resurgence of the major record companies at the expense of indies like Factory. The *Low Life* album, issued in '85, made the British Top Ten but their singles of this period failed to crack the Top Forty. (Bob MacDonald, February 1986.).

BEG STEAL OR BORROW
Tracks: / Beg steal or borrow.
7" Single: Released Mar '72, on Polydor, by Polydor Ltd. Deleted '75. Catalogue no: **2058 201**

BIZZARE LOVE TRIANGLE
Tracks: / Bizzare love triangle.
7" Single: Released Nov '86, on Factory (1), by Factory Records. Catalogue no: **FAC 1637**
12" Single: Released Nov '86, on Factory (1), by Factory Records. Catalogue no: **FAC 163**

BLUE MONDAY
Tracks: / Blue Monday.
7" Single: Released Mar '83, on Factory (1), by Factory Records. Deleted '86. Catalogue no: **FAC 73**

BLUE MONDAY 1988
Tracks: / Blue Monday 1988 (1988 version re-mixed by Quincy Jones.) / Beach buggy / Touched by the hand of God / Blue Monday 1988 (remix).
12" Single: Released May '88, on Qwest (USA), by Qwest Records (USA). Catalogue no: **020869**
12" Single: Released Apr '88, on Factory (1), by Factory Records. Catalogue no: **FACT 73 R**
12" Single: Released May '88, on Factory (1), by Factory Records. Catalogue no: **FAC 7312**

CEREMONY
Tracks: / Ceremony.
7" Single: Released Mar '81, on Factory (1), by Factory Records. Catalogue no: **FAC 33**

CONFUSION
Tracks: / Confusion.
7" Single: Released Jul '83, on Factory (1), by Factory Records. Catalogue no: **FAC 93**
12" Single: Released Jul '83, on Factory (1), by Factory Records. Catalogue no: **FAC 9312**

EVERYTHINGS GONE GREEN
Tracks: / Everything's gone green.
12" Single: Released 23 Jul '88, on Factory Benelux, by Rough Trade Records. Catalogue no: **FBN 008**
7" Single: Released Sep '81, on Factory (1), by Factory Records. Catalogue no: **FAC 53**

FINE TIME
Tracks: / Fine time.
12" Single: Released Dec '88, on Factory (1), by Factory Records. Catalogue no: **FACT 223**
7" Single: Released Dec '88, on Factory (1), by Factory Records. Catalogue no: **FAC 2237**

MURDER
Tracks: / Murder / Thieves like us.
12" Single: Released Jun '84, on Factory Benelux, by Rough Trade Records. Catalogue no: **FBN 22**

PEEL SESSIONS:NEW ORDER I 1.6.82
Tracks: / Turn the heater on / We all stand / Too late / 5.8.6.
CD 5": Released Aug '88, on Strange Fruit, by Strange Fruit Records. Catalogue no: **SFPSCD 001**
12" Single: Released 30 May '87, on Strange Fruit, by Strange Fruit Records. Catalogue no: **SFPS 001**

PEEL SESSIONS:NEW ORDER II
CD 5": Released Mar '88, on Strange Fruit, by Strange Fruit Records. Catalogue no: **SFPSCD 039**
12" Single: Released Jul '87, on Strange Fruit, by Strange Fruit Records. Catalogue no: **SFPS 039**

PERFECT KISS
Tracks: / Perfect kiss, The.
7" Single: Released Nov '85, on Factory (1), by Factory Records. Catalogue no: **FAC 123**
12" Single: Released Nov '85, on Factory (1), by Factory Records. Catalogue no: **FAC 1237**

PROCESSION
Tracks: / Procession / Everything's gone green.
7" Single: Released Oct '81, on Factory (1), by Factory Records. Deleted '84. Catalogue no: **FAC 53**

ROUND AND ROUND
Tracks: / Round and round / Best & Marsh.
12" Single: Released Mar '89, on Factory (1), by Factory Records. Catalogue no: **FAC 263 R**
7" Single: Released Mar '89, on Factory (1), by Factory Records. Catalogue no: **FAC 2637**
CD 3": Released Mar '89, on Factory (1), by Factory Records. Catalogue no: **FACD 263 R**
12" Single: Released Mar '89, on Factory (1), by Factory Records. Catalogue no: **FAC 263**
CD 5": Released Mar '89, on Factory (1), by Factory Records. Catalogue no: **FACD 263**
CD 3": Released Apr '89, on Factory (1), by Factory Records. Catalogue no: **FACD 163R**

RUN
Tracks: / Run.
7" Single: Released Sep '89, on Factory (1), by Factory Records. Catalogue no: **FAC 273**
12" Single: Released Sep '89, on Factory (1), by Factory Records. Catalogue no: **12 FAC 273**

SHELLSHOCK
Tracks: / Shellshock.
7" Single: Released Mar '86, on Factory (1), by Factory Records. Catalogue no: **FAC 143**
12" Single: Released Mar '86, on Factory (1), by Factory Records. Catalogue no: **FAC 14312**

STATE OF THE NATION
Tracks: / State of the Nation.
7" Single: Released Aug '86, on Factory (1), by Factory Records. Catalogue no: **FAC 153**

SUB-CULTURE
Tracks: / Sub-culture.
12" Single: Released Nov '85, on Factory (1), by Factory Records. Catalogue no: **FAC 13312**
7" Single: Released Nov '85, on Factory (1), by Factory Records. Catalogue no: **FAC 133**

TEMPTATION (SINGLE)
Tracks: / Temptation.
12" Single: Released May '82, on Factory

(1), by Factory Records. Catalogue no: **FAC 63 12**
7" Single: Released May '82, on Factory (1), by Factory Records. Catalogue no: **FAC 63**

THIEVES LIKE US
Tracks: / Thieves like us.
7" Single: Released Apr '84, on Factory (1), by Factory Records. Deleted '87. Catalogue no: **FAC 103**
12" Single: Released May '84, on Factory (1), by Factory Records. Catalogue no: **FAC 103T**

TOUCHED BY THE HAND OF GOD
Tracks: / Touched by the hand of god.
7" Single: Released Dec '87, on Factory (1), by Factory Records. Catalogue no: **FAC 1937**
12" Single: Released Dec '87, on Factory (1), by Factory Records. Catalogue no: **FAC 193**

TRUE FAITH
Tracks: / True faith / 1963 / True faith (remix) / True faith (dub) / Paradise (r.rasic remix).
12" Single: Released Jul '87, on Factory (1), by Factory Records. Catalogue no: **FAC 183**
12" Single: Released Jul '88, on Factory (Australia), Catalogue no: **FACAUS 183R**
12" Single: Released Aug '87, on Factory (1), by Factory Records. Catalogue no: **FAC 183R**
7" Single: Released Jul '87, on Factory (1), by Factory Records. Catalogue no: **FAC 1837**

TRUE FAITH (REMIX)
Tracks: / True faith (remix).
12" Single: Released Dec '88, on Qwest (USA), by Qwest Records (USA). Catalogue no: **020733**

New Philharmonic...

BODY TALK
Tracks: / Bodytalk.
7" Single: Released Jun '84, on Red Bus, by Red Bus Records. Catalogue no: **RBUS 96**
12" Single: Released Jun '84, on Red Bus, by Red Bus Records. Catalogue no: **RBUSL 96**

New Rollers

PARTY HARTY
Tracks: / Party harty / Before the edge / Electric on heels / Ninety-nine in the shade / Bye bye, baby (12" only) (* Track on 12" version only.).
7" Single: Released May '88, on Fast Edge, Catalogue no: **BAY 1**
12" Single: Released May '88, on Fast Edge, Catalogue no: **BAY 1T**

New Sacristi

DOWN BELOW
Tracks: / Down below.
12" Single: Released '88, on K K, by Play It Again Sam (Belgium). Catalogue no: **KK 005**

New Seekers

Biographical details: This British-based pop combo comprised Eve Graham, Paul Layton and Lyn Paul (allBritish), plus Marty Kristian (born in Germany, raised in Australia) and Peter Doyle (from Australia). They were formed in 1969 by Keith Potger who was anxious to fill the market gap left by the demise of the original Seekers, the 60's hit-making group of which he had been a member. He was not involved in the new outfit's hit records and his initiation work was the only physical link between the two groups. Both enjoyed similar levels of success but whereas the old Seekers blended folk and pop the new act went for an out-and-out pop approach. Surprisingly, the New Seekers' first major success was in America: they recorded Melanie's song, *Look What They've Done To My Song, Ma* and took it to the US Top Twenty in late 1970. Thereafter American acceptance was more limited and their career took off in Britain and the rest of the world. In summer '71 the New Seekers reached No 2 in Britain with *Never-Ending Song of Love*, a rapid cover version of a US hit by Delaney & Bonnie & Friends. In January '72 they logged four weeks at the top of the UK charts with the record that proved to be their biggest British and worldwide hit. *I'd Like To Teach The World To Sing* started life as a Coca-Cola ad sung by the Hillside Singers under the title *I'd Like To Buy The World A Coke*. The New Seekers' version was an international monster, winning them a huge concert and TV audience around the globe. The follow-up hit, *Beg, Steal Or Borrow* (No 2 in Britain) was the UK's unsuccessful entry in the 1972 Eurovision Song Contest. Subsequent hits in their singalong, middle-of-the-road pop fashion included Harry Chapin's *Circles*, a revival of the Fleetwoods' *Come Softly To Me*, a dire attempt at a Who-style Tommy medley, *Pinball Wizard - See Me, Feel Me, You Won't Find Another Fool Like Me* (No 1 in UK January '74) and *I Get A Little Sentimental Over You*. The group split up in May '74 to pursue solo careers, all conspicuously underwhelming in their public impact. They had been bold to end the group while on top but it did not work out. Minus Lyn Paul, they reformed in 1976 and achieved one modest hit per year until 1978. (Bob MacDonald, February 1986.).

ANTHEM (ONE DAY IN EVERY WEEK)
Tracks: / Anthem (one day in every week).
7" Single: Released Aug '78, on CBS, by CBS Records. Deleted '81. Catalogue no: **CBS 6413**

CIRCLES (SINGLE)
Tracks: / Circles.
7" Single: Released Jan '72, on Polydor, by Polydor Ltd. Deleted '75. Catalogue no: **2058 242**

COME SOFTLY TO ME
Tracks: / Come softly to me.
7" Single: Released Dec '72, on Polydor, by Polydor Ltd. Deleted '75. Catalogue no: **2058 313**

GOODBYE IS JUST ANOTHER WORD
Tracks: / Goodbye is just another word.
7" Single: Released Jun '73, on Polydor, by Polydor Ltd. Deleted '76. Catalogue no: **2058 368**

I GET A LITTLE SENTIMENTAL OVER YOU
Tracks: / I get a little sentimental over you.
7" Single: Released Mar '74, on Polydor, by Polydor Ltd. Deleted '77. Catalogue no: **2058 439**

I WANNA GO BACK
Tracks: / I wanna go back.
7" Single: Released Jan '77, on CBS, by CBS Records. Deleted '80. Catalogue no: **CBS 4786**

I'D LIKE TO TEACH THE WORLD TO SING
Tracks: / I'd like to teach the world to sing / Gentle on my mind.
7" Single: Released Jun '82, on Polydor, by Polydor Ltd. Deleted Jun '85. Catalogue no: **POSP 453**
7" Single: Released Dec '71, on Polydor, by Polydor Ltd. Deleted '74. Catalogue no: **2058 184**

IT'S SO NICE (TO HAVE YOU HOME)
Tracks: / It's so nice (to have you home).
7" Single: Released Aug '76, on CBS, by CBS Records. Deleted '79. Catalogue no: **CBS 4391**

LET THE BELLS RING OUT FOREVER
7" Single: Released Nov '85, on Tom Cat, Deleted Nov '87. Catalogue no: **TNS 1**

NEVER ENDING SONG OF LOVE (SINGLE)
Tracks: / Never ending song of love.
7" Single: Released Sep '71, on Philips, by Phonogram Ltd. Deleted '74. Catalogue no: **6006 125**

NEVERTHELESS
Tracks: / Nevertheless.
7" Single: Released Apr '73, on Polydor, by Polydor Ltd. Deleted '76. Catalogue no: **2068 340**

PINBALL WIZARD - SEE ME FEEL ME
Tracks: / Pinball wizard - see me, feel me.
7" Single: Released Feb '73, on Polydor, by Polydor Ltd. Deleted '76. Catalogue no: **2058 338**

TELL ME
Tracks: / Tell me / What've you got to lose.
7" Single: Released Mar '80, on EMI, by EMI Records. Deleted Mar '83. Catalogue no: **EMI 5050**

WHAT HAVE THEY DONE TO MY SONG MA
Tracks: / What have they done to my song ma.
7" Single: Released Oct '70, on Philips, by Phonogram Ltd. Deleted '73. Catalogue no: **6006 027**

YOU WON'T FIND ANOTHER FOOL LIKE ME
Tracks: / You won't find another fool like me.
7" Single: Released Nov '73, on Polydor, by Polydor Ltd. Deleted '76. Catalogue no: **2058 421**

New Statesman

I WALK IN THE LIGHT
Tracks: / I walk in the light / Low life.
7" Single: Released Mar '82, on Underground Music, Catalogue no: **UMA 002**

New Swingle Singers

RONDO
Tracks: / Rondo / Swan.
7" Single: Released Jul '80, on Columbia, by EMI Records. Deleted Jul '83. Catalogue no: **DB 9081**

New Tactics

EASE UP
Tracks: / Ease up / Ease off.
12" Single: Released Jul '88, on Redman International, Catalogue no: **RED 4**

New Vaudeville Band

Biographical details: A deliberate and cheeky anachronism, the New Vaudeville Band revived a poular vocal and instrumental style of the Twenties and Thirties, and succesfully presented it to the totally different pop market of 1966-67. The Band's first and biggest hit *Winchester Cathedral* reached No.4 in America. *Peek a boo* and *Finchley Central* also cracked the British Top 20, but after *Green Street Green* had peaked at No.37 in August 1967, the Band's chart success finished altogether. But with the huge American success of *Winchester Cathedral* behind them, they were able to spend a year pumping out their quaint ditties of English geography at the Aladdin Hotel in Las Vegas. After returning to the UK, they moved into cabaret and adopted a more mainstream MoR approach. *Winchester Cathedral* and the other hits by the New Vaudeville Band were the brainchild of writer/producer Geoff Stephens, whose previous chart compostions included *The crying game* (Dave Berry) and *Tell me when* (The Applejacks). Using megaphones, he created the adeonoidal singing sound himself on *Winchester Cathedral* and used session musicians to record the instrumental track. When the single became a smash, a real group had to be formed for live performances. Being a behind-the-scenes man by nature, Stephens chose not to go out on the road; his place was taken by Alan Klein, who adopted the title 'Tristram, seventh Earl of Cricklewood'. But Stephens kept writing and producing the hits. The other recruited members of the New Vaudeville Band were Henry Harrison, Stan Heywood, Robert 'Pops' Kerr, Neil Korner, Hugh Watts and Mick Wilsher. Stephens continued churning out numerous pop hits for the likes of Herman's Hermits, The New Seekers and many others. (Bob MacDonald, 11th Feb 1988).

6 TRACK HITS
7" EP: Released Aug '84, on Scoop 33, by Pickwick Records. Catalogue no: **7SR 5044**

FINCHLEY CENTRAL
Tracks: / Finchley central.
7" Single: Released May '67, on Fontana, by Phonogram Ltd. Deleted '70. Catalogue no: **TF 824**

GREEN STREET GREEN
Tracks: / Green street green.
7" Single: Released Aug '67, on Fontana, by Phonogram Ltd. Deleted '70. Catalogue no: **TF 853**

PEEK A BOO
Tracks: / Peek-a-boo.
7" Single: Released Jan '67, on Fontana, by Phonogram Ltd. Deleted '70. Catalogue no: **TF 784**

WINCHESTER CATHEDRAL
Tracks: / Winchester Cathedral.
7" Single: Released Sep '66, on Fontana, by Phonogram Ltd. Deleted '69. Catalogue no: **TF 741**

WINCHESTER CATHEDRAL (OLD GOLD)
Tracks: / Winchester Cathedral / I was Kaiser Bill's Batman.
7" Single: Released Oct '88, on Old Gold, by Old Gold Records. Catalogue no: **OG 9805**

New Walk

PRESSURE POINT
Tracks: / Pressure point.
7" Single: Released Nov '83, on Web, by Web Records. Catalogue no: **WEB 22**

New World

I TALK TO MY CAR
Tracks: / I talk to my car.
7" Single: Released Oct '83, on Slipped Discs, by Slipped Discs Records. Catalogue no: **HD 106**

KARA KARA
Tracks: / Kara Kara.
7" Single: Released Dec '71, on RAK, by EMI Records. Deleted '74. Catalogue no: **RAK 123**

ROOF TOP SINGING
Tracks: / Roof top singing.
7" Single: Released May '73, on RAK, by EMI Records. Deleted '76. Catalogue no: **RAK 148**

SISTER JANE
Tracks: / Sister Jane.
7" Single: Released May '72, on RAK, by EMI Records. Deleted '75. Catalogue no: **RAK 130**

TOM TOM TURNAROUND
Tracks: / Tom Tom turnaround.
7" Single: Released Jul '71, on RAK, by EMI Records. Deleted '74. Catalogue no: **RAK 117**

New World Philharmonic

DYNASTY, THEME FROM
Tracks: / Dynasty (theme from).
7" Single: Released Sep '84, on Red Bus, by Red Bus Records. Catalogue no: **RBUS 100**

New York City

I'M DOIN' FINE NOW
Tracks: / I'm doin' fine now.
7" Single: Released Jul '73, on RCA, by BMG Records (UK). Deleted '76. Catalogue no: **RCA 2351**

New York Dolls

LOOKING FOR A KISS
Tracks: / Looking for a kiss.
12" Single: Released '87, on Dolls, Catalogue no: **DOLLS 12002CV**

NEW YORK DOLLS
CD 5": Released Nov '88, on Counterpoint, Catalogue no: **CDEP 14 C**

PERSONALITY CRISIS
Tracks: / Personality crisis.
12" Single: Released '87, on Dolls, Catalogue no: **DOLLS 12001CV**

PERSONALITY CRISIS EP
Tracks: / Personality crisis / Subway train / Bad girl / Looking for a kiss.
12" Single: Released Feb '86, on Kamera, Catalogue no: **ERA 013/12**

PILLS
Tracks: / Pills.
7" Single: Released Oct '84, on Fan Club, by New Rose Records. Catalogue no: **NYD 1**

RED PATENT LEATHER (SINGLE)
Tracks: / Red patent leather.
7" Single: Released Sep '84, on Fan Club, by New Rose Records. Catalogue no: **CF 007**

New York New York

NEW YORK NEW YORK EXPERIENCE
Tracks: / New York experience.
12" Single: Released Sep '85, on Beat Culture, Catalogue no: **BC 002**

ROGER WILSON SAID
Tracks: / Roger Wilson said.
7" Single: Released Nov '83, on Urchin, Catalogue no: **NY 2001**

New York Pig Funkers

HOTHOUSE ORGAN
Tracks: / Hothouse organ / Tomato grosso.
12" Single: Released Jan '87, on Pasta Spectacular, Catalogue no: **PASTA 001 T**

New York Sensation

HOOKED ON YOU
Tracks: / Hooked on you / Hooked on you (dub).
7" Single: Released Aug '86, on 10 Records, by Virgin Records. Deleted May '88. Catalogue no: **TEN 152**
12" Single: Released Aug '86, on 10 Records, by Virgin Records. Deleted May '88. Catalogue no: **TENT 152**

New York Skyy

Biographical details: American male/female group Skyy were known as New York Skyy in Britain to avoid confusion with the British classical-rock fusion band Sky. NYS's sole UK chart entry was *Let's Celebrate*, reaching No 67 on the singles chart in January 1982. This "bass bin trembler", popular in the clubs, was not sufficiently melodic or catchy to cross over to the wider pop market. A few weeks later, however, they managed to climb to No 26 on the US pop chart with *Call Me*. A series of albums kept the dancefloors happy in the early 80's, with Skyyline the most successful . Randy Muller (of Brass Construction) and Solomon Roberts Jr masterminded the eight-piece band. (Bob MacDonald, February 1986.).

CALL ME
Tracks: / Call me / Jam the box.
7" Single: Released Mar '82, on Epic, by CBS Records. Deleted '85. Catalogue no: **EPCA 2151**
12" Single: Released Mar '82, on Epic, by CBS Records. Deleted '85. Catalogue no: **EPCA 132151**

GIVIN' IT (TO YOU)
Tracks: / Givin' it (to you) / Givin' it (to you) (Dub remix).

7" Single: Released Jun '86, on Capitol, by EMI Records. Deleted '88. Catalogue no: **CL 401**
12" Single: Released May '86, on Capitol, by EMI Records. Deleted '88. Catalogue no: **12CL 401**

HERE'S TO YOU
Tracks: / Here's to you / No music.
7" Single: Released Feb '81, on Excaliber, by Red Bus Records. Deleted '84. Catalogue no: **EXCL 504**

HIGH
Tracks: / High / First time around.
7" Single: Released May '80, on Salsoul, Deleted May '85. Catalogue no: **SAL 12-1**

LET LOVE SHINE
Tracks: / Let love shine / Won't you be mine.
7" Single: Released Nov '82, on Epic, by CBS Records. Deleted Nov '85. Catalogue no: **EPCA 2975**
12" Single: Released Nov '82, on Epic, by CBS Records. Deleted Nov '85. Catalogue no: **EPCA 13 2975**

LET'S CELEBRATE
Tracks: / Let's celebrate / Call me.
7" Single: Released Jan '82, on Epic, by CBS Records. Deleted '85. Catalogue no: **EPC A 1898**

NON-STOP
Tracks: / Non-stop / Tell her you care.
7" Single: Released Sep '86, on Capitol, by EMI Records. Deleted '88. Catalogue no: **CL 434**
12" Single: Released Sep '86, on Capitol, by EMI Records. Deleted '88. Catalogue no: **12CL 434**

SUPER LOVE
Tracks: / Super love / I can't get enough / Take it easy (on 12" only).
7" Single: Released Mar '81, on Excaliber, by Red Bus Records. Deleted Mar '84. Catalogue no: **EXC 507**
12" Single: Released Mar '81, on Excaliber, by Red Bus Records. Deleted Mar '84. Catalogue no: **EXCL 507**

New York Spice

SET IT OFF
Tracks: / Set it off / Set it off.
7" Single: Released '86, on Champion, by Champion Records. Catalogue no: **CHAMP 4**
12" Single: Released Oct '85, on Champion, by Champion Records. Catalogue no: **CHAMP 124**

New York Sweet...

SINCERELY YOURS
7" Single: Released Jun '89, on Atlantic, by WEA Records. Catalogue no: **AN 246**
12" Single: Released Jun '89, on Atlantic, by WEA Records. Catalogue no: **AN 246T**

New You

NEVER MEET AGAIN
Tracks: / Never meet again / London.
7" Single: Released Nov '88, on NY, Catalogue no: **NY 002**

TO HAVE AND HAVE NOT
Tracks: / To have and have not / Walking on air.
Cassingle: Released Nov '88, on NY, Catalogue no: **NYC 01**

Newbeats

Biographical details: Nashville is usually associated with country music but in 1964 the city produced this pop trio -- Larry Henley and Dean and Mark Mathis -- with a punchy rock edge. With their falsetto vocals and upbeat style, they were influenced by Jimmy Jones, Lou Christie and the Four Seasons. The record that brought them fame was *Bread And Butter*, which cruised to No 2 on the US chart in late 1964 and reached No 15 in the UK. By the end of '65 they had chalked up further American Top Forty hits with *Everything's Alright* (No 16), *Break Away (From That Boy)* (No 40) and *Run Baby Run (Back Into My Arms)* (No 12). The Newbeats then faded into obscurity and Henley eventually went solo. Neither he, nor Dean and Mark, who stayed together, had any success. A strange footnote to the Newbeats' career was the sudden British acceptance of *Run Baby Run* in 1971: the single had made no impression in the UK on its first '65 outing, but climbed to No 10 in late '71 as part of a spate of reactivated oldies that went charging up the British charts. (Bob MacDonald, February 1986.).

BREAD AND BUTTER
Tracks: / Bread and butter / Everything's alright.
7" Single: Released Jun '87, on WEA, by WEA Records. Deleted Jul '88. Catalogue no: **YZ 140**
12" Single: Released Jun '87, on WEA, by WEA Records. Catalogue no: **YZ 140T**

BREAD AND BUTTER (ORIGINAL)
Tracks: / Bread and butter.
7" Single: Released Sep '64, on Hickory, by Bear Family Records (Germany). Deleted '67. Catalogue no: **HICKORY 1269**

RUN BABY RUN
Tracks: / Run baby run.
7" Single: Released Oct '71, on London-American, Deleted '74. Catalogue no: **HL 10341**
7" Single: Released Aug '82, on Inferno (1), by Inferno Records. Catalogue no: **HEAT 9**

Newberry, Booker III

Biographical details: American singer Newberry jumped from obscurity to brief stardom in summer 1983 when British soul club disc jockeys began playing import copies of his dance single *Love Town*. As soon as it received a UK release *Love Town* jumped straight into the Top Twenty and peaked at No 6. It was an excellent, punchy record which combined a disco backing track with great vocals from the colossal Newberry. The follow-up single, *Teddy Bear*, was aptly titled in view of thee singer's build but sounded too similar to *Love Town* to make the same impact: it peaked at No 44 on the British chart. Nobody knows what happened to Booker Newberry Nos 1 and 2, and Booker III soon faded from memory. (Bob MacDonald, February 1986.).

LOVE TOWN (OLD GOLD)
Tracks: / Love town / Murphy's law.
12" Single: Released Feb '88, on Old Gold, by Old Gold Records. Catalogue no: **OG 4047**

LOVE TOWN (SINGLE)
Tracks: / Love town.
7" Single: Released May '83, on Polydor, by Polydor Ltd. Deleted '86. Catalogue no: **POSP 613**

SHADOWS
Tracks: / Shadows.
7" Single: Released Oct '84, on Malaco, by Malaco Records (UK). Deleted '88. Catalogue no: **MAL 028**
12" Single: Released Oct '84, on Malaco, by Malaco Records (UK). Deleted '88. Catalogue no: **MAL 12 028**

TAKE A PIECE OF ME
Tracks: / Take a piece of me.
12" Single: Released Apr '86, on Omni (USA), by First String Records (USA). Catalogue no: **12 OMN 1**
7" Single: Released Apr '86, on Omni (USA), by First String Records (USA). Catalogue no: **OMN 1**

TEDDYBEAR
Tracks: / Teddybear.
7" Single: Released Oct '83, on Polydor, by Polydor Ltd. Deleted '86. Catalogue no: **POSP 637**

Newbury, Mickey

Biographical details: Newbury, Mickey (b Milton S. Newbury Jr, 19 May '40, Houston, Texas). Singer/songwriter who wrote many hits for others. Began writing songs in high school, also singing tenor in a harmony quartet; joined USAF '58 and was stationed in England; returned to Galveston '63 and worked on shrimp boats. Moved to Nashville '65 as he took his writing seriously; got a contract with Acuff-Rose (Wesly Rose was listed in his ASCAP biography as chief collaborator). He slept in the back of his car for a few months; eventually had songs recorded by Eddy Arnold *Here Comes The Rain Baby*), Don Gibson (*Funny, Familiar, Forgotten Feelings*, later a pop hit by Tom Jones), Carl Smith (*How I Do Love Them Old Songs*). Signed to RCA for two LPs '67-8: *Harlequin Melodies* and *Sings His Own* incl. songs that defy categorisation but often ended up in the pop charts (e.g. *Just Dropped In* by Kenny Rogers and the First Edition). He went to Mercury, made highly praised *Looks Like Rain* '69, incl. classics ,*She Even Woke Me Up To Say Goodbye*, *San Francisco Mabel Joy* and *I Don't Think Much About Her No More*. Moved to Elektra for series of albums that again generated large praise, small sales, incl. *Frisco Mabel Joy* '71, *I Came To Hear The Music* '72, *Heaven Help The Child* '73, *Live At Montezume/Looks Like Rain* '74. He had a top 30 pop hit with his *An American Trilogy* '71, based on three Civil War songs, also recorded by Elvis Presley live in Las Vegas '72; his *Sunshine* made the Hot 100 '73. He provided hits for Johnny Rodriguez Tompall and the Glaser Brothers, Roger Miller, Waylon Jennings, Marie Osmond and many others, but big stardom eluded him. Further LPs incl. *Rusty Tracks, Eye On The Sparrow* and *The Sailor* '77-9 on ABC-Hickory (now MCA), *After All These Years* '81 on Mercury. Donald Clarke, 17 Feb '87..

AMERICAN TRILOGY
Tracks: / American trilogy.
7" Single: Released Jul '72, on Elektra, by Elektra Records (UK). Deleted '75. Catalogue no: **K 12047**

Newcleus

Biographical details: *Jam On Revenge (The Wikki Wikki Song)* provided this American funk band with a one-off British chart entry in 1983. This engaging, novelty-flavoured single reached No 44 in the UK and enjoyed a cult following in discos on both sides of the Atlantic. It was one of the best examples of the streetwise electro sound to emerge from New York's Bronx district. Newcleus' subsequent singles, *Jam On It* and *Computer Age*, were well received in the clubs but did not enjoy any crossover success. The group's debut album, *Jam On Revenge*, issued in 1984, was full of futuristic and robotic themes. (Bob MacDonald, February 1986.).

COMPUTER AGE
Tracks: / Computer age.
7" Single: Released Sep '84, on Sunny View (USA), by Sunnyview Records (USA). Catalogue no: **SUNY 107**
12" Single: Released Sep '84, on Sunny View (USA), by Sunnyview Records (USA). Catalogue no: **SUNYL 107**

JAM ON IT
Tracks: / Jam on it.
12" Single: Released Apr '84, on Sunny View (USA), by Sunnyview Records (USA). Catalogue no: **SUNYL 103**
7" Single: Released Apr '84, on Sunny View (USA), by Sunnyview Records (USA). Catalogue no: **SUNY 103**

JAM ON REVENGE (THE WIKKI WIKKI SONG)
Tracks: / Jam on revenge (the wikki wikki song).
7" Single: Released Aug '83, on Beckett, Deleted '84. Catalogue no: **BKS 8**
12" Single: Released Aug '83, on Beckett, Deleted '84. Catalogue no: **BKSL 8**

Newell Martin

WHEN THE FIRE BURNS DREAMS
Tracks: / When the fire burns dreams / Amateur paranoic.
Cassingle: Released Jan '84, on Matol, Catalogue no: **MATOL 000**

YOUNG JOBLESS
Tracks: / Young jobless / Sylvie in town.
7" Single: Released Mar '81, on Liberty, by EMI Records. Deleted Mar '84. Catalogue no: **BP 392**
7" Single: Released May '83, on Offstreet, Catalogue no: **OSR 001**

Newley, Anthony

Biographical details: Actor, singer and playwright Newley was born in Hackney, London, and became a successful child actor. Among his best-known early films were Peter Ustinov's Vice Versa, in which he performed alongside child star Petula Clark, and 1948's Oliver Twist, in which the 17-year-old Newley played the Artful Dodger. He then established himself as an adult actor. Newley's career as a pop singer began as an offshoot of the 1959 movie Idle On Parade. The film told the story of a rock 'n' roll singer conscripted into the army: ostensibly the principal character was fictitious but it was clearly inspired by the recent abortive army career of here-today-gone-tomorrow rock 'n' roller Terry Dene and was also topical because of Elvis Presley's military service. It gave Newley a spin-off smash single with the catchy rock parody *I've Waited So Long*, written by Jerry Jordan, which reached the UK No 3 position in mid-'59 and also appeared on the *Idle On Parade* EP which climbed to No 13. During the next two years Newley chalked up a further six British Top Ten singles, including two No 1 smashes in 1960: a cover version of Frankie Avalon's US chart-topper *Why?* and Lionel Bart's *Do You Mind?* Most of his hits were ballads rather than rock. Newley's chart career was already over by the time the Beatles era began, but he had other fish to fry. After playing the title role in the TV series The World Of Gurney Slade he co-wrote and starred in the 1961 musical *Stop The World, I Want To Get Off.* The London cast of this smash stage musical reached No 8 on the British album chart. In 1963 he enjoyed another Top Ten seller with the cast album of *Fool Britannia*, in which he starred alongside Peter Sellers and Joan Collins, to whom he was then married. Newley subsequently enjoyed further theatrical success plus stints as a Las Vegas all-round nightclub entertainer. His Cockney vocal manner exerted a considerable influence on David Bowie. An example of this can be heard on the 1967 single *The Laughing Gnome*, which was a flop for Bowie at the time of release but resurfaced successfully in 1973, to Bowie's embarrassment. (Bob MacDonald, February 1986.).

AND THE HEAVENS CRIED
Tracks: / And the heavens cried.
7" Single: Released Mar '61, on Decca, by Decca Records. Deleted '64. Catalogue no: **F 11331**

D DARLING
Tracks: / D darling.
7" Single: Released Jan '62, on Decca, by Decca Records. Deleted '65. Catalogue no: **F 11419**

DO YOU MIND
Tracks: / Do you mind.
7" Single: Released Mar '60, on Decca, by Decca Records. Deleted '63. Catalogue no: **F 112220**

IDLE ON PARADE
Tracks: / I've waited so long / Idle rock a boogie / Idle on parade / Saturday night rock a boogie.
7" EP: Released May '59, on Decca, by Decca Records. Deleted '62. Catalogue no: **DFE 6566**

I'VE WAITED SO LONG
Tracks: / I've waited so long.
7" Single: Released May '59, on Decca, by Decca Records. Deleted '62. Catalogue no: **F 11127**

PERSONALITY
Tracks: / Personality.
7" Single: Released Jun '59, on Decca, by Decca Records. Deleted '62. Catalogue no: **F 11142**

POP GOES THE WEASEL
Tracks: / Pop goes the weasel / Bee bom.
7" Single: Released Jun '61, on Decca, by Decca Records. Deleted '64. Catalogue no: **F 11362**

STRAWBERRY FAIR
Tracks: / Strawberry fair.
7" Single: Released Nov '60, on Decca, by Decca Records. Deleted '63. Catalogue no: **F 11295**

THAT NOISE
Tracks: / That noise.
7" Single: Released Jul '62, on Decca, by Decca Records. Deleted '65. Catalogue no: **F 11486**

WHAT KIND OF FOOL AM I
Tracks: / What kind of fool am I.
7" Single: Released Aug '61, on Decca, by Decca Records. Deleted '64. Catalogue no: **F 11376**

WHY
Tracks: / Why / Anything you wanna do.
7" Single: Released Jan '60, on Decca, by Decca Records. Deleted '63. Catalogue no: **F 11194**

Newman, Brad

SOMEBODY TO LOVE
Tracks: / Somebody to love.
7" Single: Released Feb '62, on Fontana, by Phonogram Ltd. Deleted '65. Catalogue no: **H 357**

Newman, Carlton

MY GIRL
Tracks: / My girl.
12" Single: Released Mar '89, on Tuff Link, Catalogue no: **99 KOSB**

Newman, Colin

BETTER LATER THAN NEVER
Tracks: / Better later than never.
12" Single: Released May '88, on Crammed Discs, by Crammed Discs. Catalogue no: **CRAM 17457**

FEIGNED HEARING
Tracks: / Feigned hearing.
7" Single: Released Oct '86, on Crammed Discs, by Crammed Discs. Catalogue no: **CRAM 13457**

INVENTORY
Tracks: / Inventory / This picture.
7" Single: Released Mar '81, on Beggars Banquet, by Beggars Banquet Records. Deleted Mar '84. Catalogue no: **BEG 52**

WE MEAN WE STARTS
Tracks: / We mean we starts / Not too (remix).
7" Single: Released May '82, on 4AD, by 4AD Records. Catalogue no: **AD 209**

Newman, Dave

LION SLEEPS TONIGHT, THE
Tracks: / Lion sleeps tonight, The.
7" Single: Released Apr '72, on Pye, Deleted '75. Catalogue no: **7 N 45134**

Newman, Randy

BLUES, THE
Tracks: / Blues, The / Same girl / Simon Smith.
7" Single: Released Jan '83, on Warner Bros., by WEA Records. Catalogue no: **W 9803**
12" Single: Released Jan '83, on Warner Bros., by WEA Records. Catalogue no: **W 9803T**

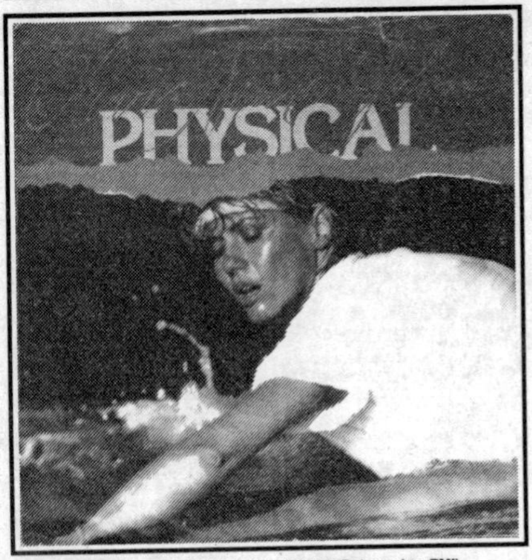

OLIVIE NEWTON-JOHN - PHYSICAL (Released on EMI)

FALLING IN LOVE
Tracks: / Falling in love / Bad news from home.
12" Single: Released Jan '89, on Warner Bros., by WEA Records. Catalogue no: **W 7578 T**
CD 5": Released Jan '89, on Warner Bros., by WEA Records. Catalogue no: **W 7578 CD**
7" Single: Released Jan '89, on Warner Bros., by WEA Records. Catalogue no: **W 7578**

I LOVE L.A.
Tracks: / I love L.A. / Song for the dead.
7" Single: Released 23 May '87, on Warner Bros., by WEA Records. Deleted 1 Jan '88. Catalogue no: **W 9687**

IT'S MONEY THAT MATTERS
Tracks: / It's money that matters.
12" Single: Released Oct '88, on Warner Bros., by WEA Records. Catalogue no: **W 7709 T**
7" Single: Released Oct '88, on Warner Bros., by WEA Records. Catalogue no: **W 7709**

Newman, Richard

JUVENILE CITY
Tracks: / Juvenile city / So lovely.
7" Single: Released Apr '80, on PVK, by PVK Records. Deleted Apr '83. Catalogue no: **PV 38**

Newmantics

TEARS OF CLOWN
Tracks: / Tears of a clown.
7" Single: Released Aug '82, on Music International, by Music International Records. Catalogue no: **M 10015**
12" Single: Released Aug '82, on Music International, by Music International Records. Catalogue no: **12 M 10015**

Newport,Kim

I NEED A LOVER
Tracks: / I need a lover.
7" Single: Released Feb '82, on Sun Set (reggae), Catalogue no: **SUN 007**

News

Biographical details: No relation to Huey Lewis & The News -- who became famous shortly after this group's only hit -- the News reached No 52 on the UK singles chart in 1981 with *Audio Video*. Subsequent singles by this all-male American band fell on deaf ears. (Bob MacDonald, February 1986.).

50% REDUCTION
Tracks: / 50% reduction / High society.
7" Single: Released Apr '80, on Polydor, by Polydor Ltd. Deleted '83. Catalogue no: **POSP 129**

AUDIO VIDEO
Tracks: / Audio video.
7" Single: Released Sep '81, on KA, Catalogue no: **GEORGE 1**

HOLE IN MY SHOE
Tracks: / Hole in my shoe.
7" Single: Released Nov '82, on KA, Catalogue no: **KA 9**

MODERN TOYS
Tracks: / Modern toys / Feed the meter.
7" Single: Released Aug '80, on Polydor, by Polydor Ltd. Deleted '83. Catalogue no: **POSP 152**

WORLD WITHOUT LOVE
Tracks: / World without love.
7" Single: Released Oct '81, on KA, Catalogue no: **NEWS 1**

Newsboys

BRING ME THE NEWS BOY
Tracks: / Bring me the news boy / Alternative.
7" Single: Released Sep '80, on Epic, by CBS Records. Deleted '83. Catalogue no: **EPC 8793**

Newton Family

DON QUIXOTE
Tracks: / Don Quixote / Te quiero.
7" Single: Released Nov '81, on White Dove, by White Dove Records. Catalogue no: **RAS 821**

Newton, Juice

Biographical details: Born in Virginia, singer and guitarist Newton began releasing albums in 1975 under the billing Juice Newton & The Silver Spur. By the end of the 70's the outfit had issued five albums containing a blend of country, rock and pop, but Newton lacked the quality and gusto of an artist like Emmylou Harris. Newton dropped the group billing and her career turned around in 1981 with the rlease of the LP *Juice*. She now went for an overtly commercial country-pop approach which fitted in perfectly with the country genre's move away from its roots and into the mainstream, a phenomenon which was taking place in the wake of the movie Urban Cowboy. The *Juice* album yielded two million-selling US Top Five singles, both remakes: *Angel Of The Morning* had been recorded in 1968 by Merrilee Rush & The Turnabouts and P.P. Arnold, and *Queen Of Hearts* had been a British hit for Dave Edmunds. *Juice* reached No 20 on the Billboard album chart as did Newton's '82 set *Quiet Lies*, which spawned the US No 7 single, the ultra-catchy *Love's Been A Little Hard On Me*. All in all she enjoyed seven American Top Forty singles from 1981-83. Country music was elbowed out of the pop charts during the mid-80's but the singer was well able to compete on the specialist country listings and hit No 1 on the Billboard country singles chart in February '86 with *Hurt*. One of the flaws of Newton's style was that her voice, while pleasant, lacked conviction: she often sounded more like a session singer with a job to do than a creative artist seeking to make her personal mark. Her only UK chart entry was *Angel Of The Morning*, which peaked at No 43 in 1981. (Bob MacDonald, February 1986.).

ANGEL OF THE MORNING
Tracks: / Angel of the morning / Headin' for a heartache.
7" Single: Released May '81, on Capitol, by EMI Records. Deleted '84. Catalogue no: **CL 16189**

CAN'T WAIT ALL NIGHT
Tracks: / Little love, A / One that gets you / Can't wait all night / Restless heart / Easy way out / Let's dance / He's gone / You don't know me / Eye of the hurricane / Waiting for the sun.
7" Single: Released Sep '84, on RCA, by BMG Records (UK). Catalogue no: **RCA 441**

DIRTY LOOKS
Tracks: / Dirty looks / Twenty years ago.
7" Single: Released Nov '83, on Capitol, by EMI Records. Deleted Jan '88. Catalogue no: **CL 311**

HEART OF THE NIGHT
Tracks: / Heart of the night / Love sail away.
7" Single: Released Feb '83, on Capitol, by EMI Records. Deleted '88. Catalogue no: **CL 278**

LOVE'S BEEN A LITTLE BIT HARD ON ME
Tracks: / Love's been a bit hard on me / Ever true.
7" Single: Released May '82, on Capitol, by EMI Records. Deleted '88. Catalogue no: **CL 248**

QUEEN OF HEARTS
Tracks: / Queen of hearts / River of love.
7" Single: Released Jun '81, on Capitol, by EMI Records. Deleted Jun '84. Catalogue no: **CL 204**

SWEETEST THING
Tracks: / Sweetest thing / Shot full of love.
7" Single: Released Feb '82, on Capitol, by EMI Records. Deleted Feb '87. Catalogue no: **CL 217**

Newton-John, Olivia

Biographical details: This British singer and actress was born in Cambridge, raised in Melbourne, Australia, achieved fame in Britain and went on to become a huge star in America. Olivia "Neutron Bomb", as she is sometimes affectionately called, has been aided throughout her career by her stunning good looks. The blonde bombshell is one of the biggest female heart-throbs in showbusiness history, though she has usually emphasised a demure girl-next-door approach rather than a sexy image. Newton-ohn came from an academic family background. Her grandfather was a Nobel Prize-winning physicist, her father a potential opera singer who opted instead for a scholarly life. When Olivia was born he was teaching at the famed King's College, Cambridge; when she was five he landed a job as the dean of Ormond College in Melbourne. Olivia grew up with an interest in music, although she received no formal training. On leaving school she won a talent contest held by Australian TV singer Johnny O'Keefe. The prize was a trip to London, which she took up, and the late 60's were spent working round the pubs and clubs of Britain with singer Pat Carroll (who married Olivia's producer, John Farrar). Newton-John came to fame in 1971, thanks to two UK Top Ten singles -- *If Not For You* and *Banks Of The Ohio* -- and to her regular appearances on Cliff Richard's television show. A couple of further Top Twenty hits consolidated her position as a pleasant pop/ middle-of-the-road singer and a reasonably though not spectacularly successful star. In early '74 two simultaneous events symbolised the turning point of her career. She represented the UK in the Eurovision Song Contest with the dated *Long Live Love* and came a disappointing fourth: as the event was held in Brighton she was seen to have humiliated the host nation and was promptly forgotten by British record buyers. At the same time -- and much more importantly -- she achieved her first American Top Ten hit with *Let Me Be There*, a single which emphasised the country element in her style. This breakthrough paved the way for huge US stardom, where she successfully bridged the country, pop and middle-of-the-road spheres. Newton-John's run of US million-sellers during 1974-75 -- which included the No 1 hits *I Honestly Love You* and *Have You Never Been Mellow?* -- later led to success on an even greater scale. She starred with John Travolta in the 1978 film *Grease*, which proved to be one of the biggest box-office sensations of all time, yielding *You're The One That I Want* (No 1 in US and UK) and *Summer Nights* (No 5 in US, No 1 in UK). Between them these two duets logged 16 weeks at No 1 in Britain, putting her firmly back on top in her native country where she was awarded the OBE soon afterwards. In 1980 the cinematic disaster of the film *Xanadu* was compensated for by the success of its music, which provided Newton-John with a British No 1 single (the title track, in collaboration with ELO) and an American chart-topper (Magic, written and produced by her consistently shrewd mentor, John Farrar). She finally shook off her sweet image in late '81, achieving the biggest triumph of her career with *Physical*. The punchy single, which fitted in perfectly with the new aerobics craze, was banned on some US radio stations for its highly suggestive lyrics. *Physical* was No 1 in America for 10 consecutive weeks , making it one of the four biggest US hits in the rock era. *Make A Move On Me* , *Heart Attack* and *Twist Of Fate* -- a big hit from the flop film *Two Of A Kind* -- continued Newton-John's endless American success into the mid-80's. Then she married actor-dancer Matt Lattanzi and millions of male hearts were crushed. (Bob MacDonald, February 1986.)
Born 26 September 1948, Cambridge, England. MOR singer. Grandfather was Nobel prize winning scientist; grew up in Australia, formed school girl vocal quartet; solo, she won talent contest sponsored by Johnny O Keefe (the Australian Elvis) with return to the UK as prize. Worked there with Australian Pat O Carroll (who later married Olivia's producer, John Farrar) as Pat and Olivia before Carroll's work permit ran out. Then joined Tomorrow, Monkee creator Don Kirshner's manufactured two boy/two girl vocal group, went solo when planned TV series fell through. Sugary version of Bob Dylan's *If not for you* reached No. 7 UK and No. 25 USA; country flavoured pop hits in UK helped by connection with producer/fiance Shadows guitarist Bruce Welsh, which led to showcase on Cliff Richard TV spots: *Banks of Ohio*, George Harrison's *What is life*, John Denver's *Take me home country roads* all hits 71-73. Surprise breakthrough in the USA with *Let me be there* '73, MCA LP of same title (which included six tracks from two year old LP on Universal), coming after Eurovision flop with strident *Long live love*, led to swift relocation westward; when the hit won a grammy for 'Best Country Vocalist' success seemed assured (though '76 MCA award for Best Female Vocalist led to resignations). Split with Welsh personally/professionally led to his former associate (in Marvin Welsh and Farrar) taking over as producer. Of four Top 5 hits in USA '74-75 including two at No. 1 only one charted in UK; big hit USA albums included *If you love me, Let me know, Have you ever been mellow, Clearly love, Come on over, Don't stop believin', Making a good thing better, Greatest hits* set all 75-77 on MCA. She raunched up her image playing leather clad role in *Grease* '78 and scored big hits both solo and with John Travolta, singles plus the soundtrack LP *Totally hot* '78 was another hit album; soundtrack *Xanadu* '80 with then fashionable Electric Light Orchestra was a hit album with three hit singles (including duet *Suddenly* with Richard), although the film flopped; then she slid further into raunch, pushing aerobic sex in *Physical* '81 No. 1 title single ; No. 5 with *Make a move on me*. *Heart attack* was a No. 3 single '82, included in *Greatest hits vol II*; soundtrack *Two of a kind* included four tracks by her (*Twist of fate* a Top 5 hit). By '85 she had posed half topless with riding crop in Helmut Newton photo for sleeve of *Soul kiss*: title track reached Top 20 LP chart placing in USA since '77: time for another change of image for the charismatic warbler with the unremarkable voice. (Donald Clarke 1987)l.

BANKS OF THE OHIO
Tracks: / Banks of the Ohio.
7" Single: Released Oct '71, on Pye International, Deleted '74. Catalogue no: **7N 25568**

DEEPER THAN THE NIGHT
Tracks: / Deeper than the night.
7" Single: Released Jun '79, on EMI, by EMI Records. Deleted '82. Catalogue no: **EMI 2954**

HEART ATTACK
Tracks: / Heart attack.
7" Single: Released Oct '82, on EMI, by EMI Records. Deleted '85. Catalogue no: **EMI 5347**

HOPELESSY DEVOTED TO YOU
Tracks: / Hopelessly devoted to you.
7" Single: Released Nov '78, on RSO, by Polydor Ltd. Deleted '81. Catalogue no: **RSO 17**

I HONESTLY LOVE YOU
Tracks: / I honestly love you / Physical.
7" Single: Released Oct '74, on EMI, by EMI Records. Deleted '77. Catalogue no: **EMI 2216**
7" Single: Released Jan '83, on EMI, by EMI Records. Catalogue no: **EMI 5360**
12" Single: Released Jan '83, on EMI, by EMI Records. Catalogue no: **12 EMI 5360**

IF NOT FOR YOU
Tracks: / If not for you.
7" Single: Released Mar '71, on Pye International, Deleted '75. Catalogue no: **7N 25543**

LANDSCAPE
Tracks: / Landscape.
7" Single: Released Jan '82, on EMI, by EMI Records. Deleted '85. Catalogue no: **EMI 5257**

LANDSLIDE
Tracks: / Landslide / Falling.
7" Single: Released Jan '82, on EMI, by EMI Records. Deleted '85. Catalogue no: **EMI 5257**

LITTLE MORE LOVE, A
Tracks: / Little more love, A / Borrowed time.
7" Single: Released Dec '78, on EMI, by EMI Records. Deleted '81. Catalogue no: **EMI 2879**

LONG LIVE LOVE (SINGLE)
Tracks: / Long live love.
7" Single: Released Mar '74, on Pye International, Deleted '77. Catalogue no: **7N 25638**

MAGIC
Tracks: / Magic / Whenever you're away from me.
7" Single: Released Aug '80, on Jet, by Jet Records. Deleted '83. Catalogue no: **JET 196**

MAKE A MOVE ON ME
Tracks: / Make a move on me / Strangers touch.
7" Single: Released Apr '82, on EMI, by EMI Records. Deleted '85. Catalogue no: **EMI 5291**

PHYSICAL (SINGLE)
Tracks: / Promise, The (dolphin song) / Physical.
7" Single: Released '81, on EMI, by EMI Records. Catalogue no: **EMI 5234**

RUMOUR, THE (SINGLE)
Tracks: / Rumour, The / Winter angel.
12" Single: Released Sep '88, on Mercury, by Phonogram Ltd. Deleted 31 Jul '89. Catalogue no: **MERX 272**
CD 5": Released Sep '88, on Mercury, by Phonogram Ltd. Catalogue no: **MERCD 272**
7" Single: Released Sep '88, on Mercury, by Phonogram Ltd. Deleted 31 May '89. Catalogue no: **MER 272**

SAM
Tracks: / Sam.
7" Single: Released Jun '77, on EMI, by EMI Records. Deleted '80. Catalogue no: **EMI 2616**

SOUL KISS (SINGLE)
Tracks: / Soul kiss / Electric.
7" Single: Released Feb '86, on Mercury, by Phonogram Ltd. Catalogue no: **MER 210**
12" Single: Released Feb '86, on Mercury, by Phonogram Ltd. Catalogue no: **MERX 210**

SUDDENLY
Tracks: / Suddenly / You made me love you.
7" Single: Released Oct '80, on Jet, by Jet Records. Deleted '83. Catalogue no: **JET 7002**

TAKE ME HOME COUNTRY ROADS
Tracks: / Take me home country roads.
7" Single: Released Jan '73, on Pye International, Deleted '76. Catalogue no: **7N 25599**

TIED UP
Tracks: / Tied up / Silvery rain.
7" Single: Released Mar '83, on EMI, by EMI Records. Catalogue no: **EMI 5375**

TWIST OF FATE
Tracks: / Twist of fate.
7" Single: Released Oct '83, on EMI, by EMI Records. Catalogue no: **EMI 5438**

WHAT IS LIFE
Tracks: / What is life.
7" Single: Released Mar '72, on Pye International, Deleted '75. Catalogue no: **7N 25575**

XANADU
Tracks: / Xanadu / Fool country.
7" Single: Released Jun '80, on Jet, by Jet Records. Deleted '83. Catalogue no: **JET 185**

Newtown Neurotics

BLITZKRIEG BOP
7" Single: Released Aug '83, on Razor, by Razor Records. Catalogue no: **RZS 107**

KICK OUT THE TORIES
Tracks: / Kick out the tories.
7" Single: Released May '82, on CNT, Catalogue no: **CNT 005**

LICENCING HOURS
Tracks: / Licencing hours / No sanctury.
7" Single: Released Dec '82, on CNT, Catalogue no: **CNT 010**

SUZI
Tracks: / Suzi.
7" Single: Released Nov '84, on No Wonder, Catalogue no: **NOW 6**
12" Single: Released Nov '84, on No Wonder, Catalogue no: **NOW 6T**

WHEN THE OIL RUNS OUT
Tracks: / When the oil runs out.
7" Single: Released Oct '84, on No Wonder, Catalogue no: **NOW 4**

Newtrament

LONDON BRIDGE IS FALLING DOWN
Tracks: / London bridge is falling down.
7" Single: Released Jul '83, on Jive, by Zomba Records. Catalogue no: **JIVE 43**
12" Single: Released Jul '83, on Jive, by Zomba Records. Catalogue no: **JIVET 43**

Next Generation

IN MY BABY'S ARMS (IMPORT)
Tracks: / In my baby's arms.
12" Single: Released Sep '89, on Mass Media, Catalogue no: **MAR 1032**

Next Step

CRUSHED BY THE CRISIS
7" Single: Released Oct '84, on Trial, by Trial Records. Catalogue no: **CASE 8**

Nexus 21

STILL LIFE KEEPS MOVING
Tracks: / Still life keeps moving.
12" Single: Released Sep '89, on Blue Chip, by Blue Chip Records. Catalogue no: **BLUEC 41**

Niah,George

SWEETA JAMAICA
Tracks: / Sweeta Jamaica.
12" Single: Released Nov '81, on Freedom Sounds, Catalogue no: **VG 107**

WALKING IN THE RAIN
Tracks: / Walking in the rain.
12" Single: Released Jul '82, on Future Times, Catalogue no: **FT 002**

Nicci

CAN'T GET CLOSE TO YOU
Tracks: / Can't get close to you / Close to who?.
7" Single: Released Feb '86, on Debut, by Skratch Records. Catalogue no: **DEBT 3002**

RESPECT
Tracks: / Respect.
7" Single: Released May '87, on Sedition, by Sedition Records. Catalogue no: **EDIT 3321**
12" Single: Released May '87, on Sedition, by Sedition Records. Catalogue no: **EDITL 3321**

SO IN LOVE
Tracks: / So in love.
12" Single: Released Oct '85, on Boiling Point, by Polydor Ltd. Catalogue no: **POSPX 774**
7" Single: Released Aug '85, on Debut, by Skratch Records. Catalogue no: **DEBT 07**
12" Single: Released Aug '85, on Debut, by Skratch Records. Catalogue no: **DEBT 07(12)**
7" Single: Released Oct '85, on Boiling Point, by Polydor Ltd. Catalogue no: **POSP 774**

Nice

AMERICA
Tracks: / America / Diamond hard apples of the moon.
7" Single: Released Dec '82, on Immediate, Catalogue no: **IMS 068**

Nice And Wild

DIAMOND GIRL
Tracks: / EMU 2 / Diamond girl.
12" Single: Released May '87, on Atlantic, by WEA Records. Deleted Jan '88. Catalogue no: **A 9362 T**
7" Single: Released May '87, on Atlantic, by WEA Records. Deleted Jan '88. Catalogue no: **A 9362**

Nice, Chippy

TOO USE TO ME
Tracks: / Too use to me.
7" Single: Released May '89, on Rockers Master International, Catalogue no: **UNKNOWN**

Nice Men

SENILE YOUTH
Tracks: / Senile youth.
7" Single: Released Apr '82, on Demon, by Demon Records. Deleted '88. Catalogue no: **D 1007**

Nice Music

TALKING PICTURES (EP)
Tracks: / Talking pictures.
12" Single: Released Apr '88, on Saturn, Catalogue no: **BTE 1T2**

Nicely, Nick

D.C.T. DREAMS
Tracks: / D.C.T. dreams / Tree line.
7" Single: Released Jan '81, on Hansa, by Hansa Records. Deleted Jan '84. Catalogue no: **AHA 569**

Nicholas, Neil

DEEP INSIDE
Tracks: / Deep inside / Dance the waltz of men.
12" Single: Released Feb '88, on Elecstar, by Elecstar Records. Deleted Nov '88. Catalogue no: **VCLT 020**
7" Single: Released Feb '88, on Elecstar, by Elecstar Records. Deleted Nov '88. Catalogue no: **VCL 020**

TO BUSY EARNING A LIVING (TO EARN ANY MONEY)
Tracks: / To busy earning a living (to earn any money) / Fly away.
7" Single: Released May '89, on Pyramid, by Pyramid Records. Catalogue no: **PYR 11**
12" Single: Released May '89, on Pyramid, by Pyramid Records. Catalogue no: **12PYR 11**

Nicholas, Paul

Biographical details: This British actor and singer began his career in 1964 when, at the tender age of 16, he became a member of the Savages, the group employed by the tender mercies of cult hero Screaming Lord Sutch. Nicholas' theatrical career began in earnest in 1968 when he joined the first London cast of the legendary musical *Hair*. He was in the role of Claude for a couple of years, then later moved on to *Jesus Christ Superstar* and the pre-film stage version of *Grease*. Moving into cinema, he was involved in three 1975 projects: *Stardust* with David Essex, *Tommy* with the Who and *Lisztomania* with Rick Wakeman. With these acting and musical successes behind him, Nicholas decided to take a leaf out of Essex's book and bid for a subsidiary career as a pop singer. Accordingly, he teamed up with songwriters Dominic Bugatti & Frank Musker and producer Christopher Neil to create four excruciatingly winsome hit singles. *Reggae like it used to be*, *Dancing with the captain* and *Grandma's party* all became British Top 20 hits in 1976. Although the fourth one, *Heaven on the 7th floor* was a relative failure in Britain, its disappointing UK performance was compensated by its unexpected Top 10 success in the States in late '77. Having got these ultra-lightweight ditties out of his system, and having grinned away to his heart's content on 'Top of the Pops', Nicholas concentrated his energies on acting once more as his later records flopped. Starting with *Two up two down* (1978), he included a substantial amount of television work in his schedule. In the early Eighties his theatrical work included Andrew Lloyd Webber's *Cat's* and Tim Rice's *Blondel*. (Bob MacDonald, 12th Feb 1986).

DANCING WITH THE CAPTAIN
Tracks: / Dancing with the captain.
7" Single: Released Oct '76, on RSO, by Polydor Ltd. Deleted '79. Catalogue no: **2090 206**

GRANDMA'S PARTY
Tracks: / Grandma's party.
7" Single: Released Dec '76, on RSO, by Polydor Ltd. Deleted '79. Catalogue no: **2090 216**

HEAVEN ON THE 7TH FLOOR
Tracks: / Heaven on the 7th floor.
7" Single: Released Jul '77, on RSO, by Polydor Ltd. Deleted '80. Catalogue no: **2090 249**

HOUSE OF ROCK
Tracks: / House of rock.
7" Single: Released Oct '83, on Flying, by Flying Records. Catalogue no: **FLY 108**
12" Single: Released Oct '83, on Flying, by Flying Records. Catalogue no: **FLYT 108**

JUST GOOD FRIENDS
Tracks: / Just good friends
7" Single: Released Dec '84, on Flying, by Flying Records. Catalogue no: **FLY 109**

LEAST OF MY TROUBLES
Tracks: / Least of my troubles, The / Running back for more.
7" Single: Released Jan '84, on MCA, by MCA Records. Catalogue no: **MCA 851**

MAGICAL MR. MISTOFFELEES
Tracks: / Magical Mr. Mistoffelees / Old Deuteronomy.
7" Single: Released Jan '81, on Polydor, by Polydor Ltd. Deleted Jan '84. Catalogue no: **POSP 204**

NO NEWS
Tracks: / No news / American woman.
7" Single: Released Jun '81, on RSO, by Polydor Ltd. Deleted Jun '84. Catalogue no: **RSO 76**

REGGAE LIKE IT USED TO BE
Tracks: / Reggae like it used to be.
7" Single: Released Apr '76, on RSO, by Polydor Ltd. Deleted '79. Catalogue no: **2090 185**

Nicholl, Derek

PATRON
Tracks: / Patron.
7" Single: Released Oct '82, on Clubland, Catalogue no: **SJP 830**

Nicholl, Phil

ONE WAY
Tracks: / One way / Newsprint.
7" Single: Released Dec '82, on Mont, by Mont Music Records. Catalogue no: **MM 102**

Nicholls, Sue

WHERE WILL YOU BE
Tracks: / Where will you be.
7" Single: Released Jul '68, on Pye, Deleted '71. Catalogue no: **7 N 17565**

Nicholson, Hugh

LOVE, YOU MADE A FOOL OF ME
Tracks: / Love you made a fool of me / I wonder if I'm making it.
7" Single: Released Jan '85, on Zuma, Catalogue no: **ZOOM 4**

Nick & Nock

HELPERS OF SANTA CLAUS
Tracks: / Helpers of Santa Claus.
7" Single: Released Nov '86, on Custard Pie, Catalogue no: **CUS 501**

Nick O Teen

SMOKE THAT CIGARETTE
Tracks: / Smoke that cigarette.
7" Single: Released '79, on White Rose, by White Rose Records. Deleted '80. Catalogue no: **WRO 3**

Nicks, Stevie

Biographical details: This American singer and songwriter recorded a 1973 album with boyfriend Linsey Buckingham under the billing *Buckingham Nicks* before they both joined Fleetwood Mac in 1975. The input of these two Americans into a fading British rock group, transformed Mac into world superstars and produced one of the world's top-selling albums of all-time, *Rumours*. Nicks wrote that LP's biggest single, *Dreams*. Nicks became Fleetwood Mac's most prominent vocalist, being the only member who did not play any instrument. Partly because of this high profile, and partly because of the strength of her songwriting, she became the most successful individual member when the group took time off for solo projects in the early Eighties. Her first album *Bella donna* was a long-running No.3 LP in the States during late 1981, becoming one of the year's biggest sellers; coincidentally, its first single *Stop draggin' my heart around* (a duet with Tom Petty & The Heartbreakers) also had a lengthy stint at No.3. The second single *Leather and lace* (No.6 in US in early 1982) was a collaboration with ex-Eagle Don Henley. In Britain *Bella donna* reached No.11 and logged 15 weeks on the album chart. Becoming the most prolific individual Fleetwood Mac person as well as the most successful, Stevie's subsequent albums *The wild heart* (1983) and *Rock a little* (1985) achieved their expected platinum status in America. The former yielded the Top 5 single *Stand back*, and the latter spawned the similarly successful *Talk to me*. Nicks' records were tailor-made for American radio - crisply produced melodic fare with a sufficiently raunchy feel to be described as rock, but falling far shor of heavy metal. Stevie's slightly nasal voice became a distinctive commodity; it sounded delicate yet daring. Before *Bella donna* saw the light of day, it graced a pair of big American hits in a guest capacity. .(Bob MacDonald, 12th Feb 1986).

EDGE OF 17
Tracks: / Edge of 17 / Outside the rain.
7" Single: Released Apr '82, on WEA, by WEA Records. Deleted Apr '85. Catalogue no: **K 79264**

HAS ANYONE EVER WRITTEN ANYTHING FOR YOU
Tracks: / Has anyone ever written anything for you / I can't wait / No spoken word.
12" Single: Released Aug '86, on EMI, by EMI Records. Deleted Jul '87. Catalogue no: **12EMI 5574**
7" Single: Released Aug '86, on EMI, by EMI Records. Deleted Jul '87. Catalogue no: **EMI 5574**

I CAN'T WAIT
Tracks: / I can't wait / Rock a little.
12" Single: Released Jan '86, on Parlophone, by EMI Recs. Catalogue no: **12 R**

NICKY & THE DOTS - NEVER BEEN SO STUCK (Released on Small Wonders)

6110
7" Single: Released Jan '86, on Parlophone, by EMI Records. Catalogue no: **R 6110**

LEATHER AND LACE
Tracks: / Leather and lace / Outside the rain.
7" Single: Released Oct '81, on WEA, by WEA Records. Deleted Oct '84. Catalogue no: **K 79265**

LONG WAY TO GO
Tracks: / Long way to go / Real tears / Long way to go (remix) (Not on 7" or cassingle.) / No spoken word (CD single only.).
Note: Produced by Rupert Hine.
Cassingle: Released Jul '89, on EMI, by EMI Records. Catalogue no: **203 431 4**
7" Single: Released Jul '89, on EMI, by EMI Records. Catalogue no: **203 431 7**
7" Single: Released Jul '89, on EMI, by EMI Records. Catalogue no: **EM 97**
Cassingle: Released Jul '89, on EMI, by EMI Records. Catalogue no: **TCEM 97**
CD 5": Released Jul '89, on EMI, by EMI Records. Catalogue no: **203 431 2**
12" Single: Released Jul '89, on EMI, by EMI Records. Catalogue no: **12EM 97**
12" Single: Released Jul '89, on EMI, by EMI Records. Catalogue no: **12EMG 97**
12" Single: Released Jul '89, on EMI, by EMI Records. Catalogue no: **203 431 6**
CD 5": Released Jul '89, on EMI, by EMI Records. Catalogue no: **CDEM 97**
12" Single: Released Jul '89, on EMI, by EMI Records. Catalogue no: **203 431 8**

NIGHT BIRD
Tracks: / Night bird.
7" Single: Released Jan '84, on WEA (International), by WEA Records. Catalogue no: **U 9690**

ROOMS ON FIRE
Tracks: / Rooms on fire / Alice / Has anyone ever written anything for you (Nicks/Olsen) (12" & CD single only.).
Cassingle: Released Apr '89, on EMI, by EMI Records. Catalogue no: **TCEM 90**
12" Single: Released Apr '89, on EMI, by EMI Records. Catalogue no: **12EMP 90**
7" Single: Released Apr '89, on EMI, by EMI Records. Catalogue no: **EM 90**
12" Single: Released Apr '89, on EMI, by EMI Records. Catalogue no: **12EM 90**
CD 5": Released Apr '89, on EMI, by EMI Records. Catalogue no: **CDEM 90**

STOP DRAGGIN' MY HEART AROUND
Tracks: / Stop draggin' my heart around.
7" Single: Released Aug '81, on WEA, by WEA Records. Deleted '84. Catalogue no: **K 79231**

TALK TO ME
Tracks: / Talk to me / One more big time rock 'n' roll star / Imperial hotel (Extra track available on 12" version only.).
12" Single: Released Mar '86, on Parlophone, by EMI Records. Catalogue no: **12 R 6124**
7" Single: Released Mar '86, on Parlophone, by EMI Records. Catalogue no: **R 6124**

WHOLE LOTTA TROUBLE
Tracks: / Whole lotta trouble / Edge of seventeen (Not on CD) / Beauty and the beast (live) (Not on 7" or cassingle.) / Rooms on fire (CD single only.).
Cassingle: Released Oct '89, on EMI, by EMI Records. Catalogue no: **203 583 4**
7" Single: Released Oct '89, on EMI, by EMI Records. Catalogue no: **EM 114**
CD 5": Released Oct '89, on EMI, by EMI Records. Catalogue no: **2203 583 2**
12" Single: Released Oct '89, on EMI, by EMI Records. Catalogue no: **12EMP 114**
12" Single: Released Oct '89, on EMI, by EMI Records. Catalogue no: **12EM 114**
12" Single: Released Oct '89, on EMI, by EMI Records. Catalogue no: **203 583 6**
7" Single: Released Oct '89, on EMI, by EMI Records. Catalogue no: **203 583 7**
CD 5": Released Oct '89, on EMI, by EMI Records. Catalogue no: **CDEM 114**
Cassingle: Released Oct '89, on EMI, by EMI Records. Catalogue no: **TCEM 114**
12" Single: Released Oct '89, on EMI, by EMI Records. Catalogue no: **203 583 0**

Nicky & The Dots

NEVER BEEN SO STUCK (see panel above)
Tracks: / Never been so stuck / Linoleum walk.
7" Single: Released '79, on Small Wonder, by Small Wonder Records. Catalogue no: **SMALL 12**

Nico

HEROES
Tracks: / Heroes / One more chance.
7" Single: Released Jun '83, on Aura Records, by Aura Records. Deleted '88. Catalogue no: **AUS 137**

I'M NOT SAYING
Tracks: / I'm not saying / Last mile.
7" Single: Released May '82, on Immediate, Catalogue no: **IMS 003**

LIVE: NICO
Tracks: / Live:Nico.
12" Single: Released Feb '87, on Archive 4, by Castle Communications Records. Catalogue no: **TOF 110**

MY FUNNY VALENTINE
Tracks: / My funny valentine.
7" Single: Released Jun '85, on Beggars Banquet, by Beggars Banquet Records. Deleted '86. Catalogue no: **BEG 139**
12" Single: Released Jun '85, on Beggars Banquet, by Beggars Banquet Records. Deleted Jun '88. Catalogue no: **BEG 139T**

PEEL SESSIONS:NICO
CD 5": Released Nov '88, on Strange Fruit, by Strange Fruit Records. Catalogue no: **SFPSCD 064**
12" Single: Released Nov '88, on Strange Fruit, by Strange Fruit Records. Catalogue no: **SFPS 064**

PROCESSION
Tracks: / Procession / All tomorrows parties.
7" Single: Released '82, on Pinnacle, by Pinnacle Records. Deleted '87. Catalogue no: **REC 1**

SAETA
Tracks: / Saeta.
7" Single: Released Sep '81, on Flicknife, by Flicknife Records. Catalogue no: **FLS 206**

WAITING FOR THE MAN
Tracks: / Waiting for the man.
7" Single: Released Oct '85, on Aura Records, by Aura Records. Catalogue no: **AUS 147**

Nicodemus

BONE CONNECTION
Tracks: / Bone connection / All of my love.
12" Single: Released Feb '82, on Greensleeves, by Greensleeves Records. Catalogue no: **GRED 75**

GUN MAN CONNECTION
Tracks: / Gun man connection.
12" Single: Released Dec '81, on Cha-Cha, by Cha-Cha Records. Catalogue no: **CHAD 44**

Nicole

Biographical details: West German singer and guitarist Nicole was just 17 when she gave her country its first-ever Eurovision Song Contest winner: the year was 1982, the song *A Little Peace* and the venue Harrogate, Yorkshire, England. Nicole had first hit the German charts with *Flieg Nicht So Hoch Mein Freund ("Don't fly so high my friend")*, which led to her Eurovision chance with *A Little Peace*, her second single. She was born Nicole Hohloch in Saarbrucken, where she was still living when fame struck, and she was back there for the start of the new term within days of winning the contest, determined to finish her exam course in preference to consolidating her musical career. With her flowing golden hair and charming, innocent face, Nicole looked as though she had stepped out of a children's fairytale, but if the Saarbrucken schoolgirl epitomised the middle-of-the-road blandness of Eurovision for many people, she also exuded a natural intelligence. When she performed the encore of the winning song at the end of the contest she did so in four European languages in quick succession. The multi-lingual call for "a little peace" was a sensible use of the Continent-wide TV link-up and provided one of the few moving moments in the generally insipid history of the contest. In Britain, where the lyrics were particularly pertinent to a nation locked in the Falklands War, she logged up the 500th No 1 single since the inception of the charts. Predictably, the record was No 1 all over Europe and equally predictably -- and in the best Eurovision tradition -- the singer faded into obscurity soon afterwards. Nicole's British follow-up, *Give Me More Time*, did not live up to its title and peaked at No 75 and her album, *A Little Peace*, stopped at No 85. There was even less luck for Ralph Siegel, co-writer of *A Little Peace*, who was later sued for plagiarism. It should be noted that the West German Nicole is not to be confused with the American soul singer of the same name, who reached No 41 in Britain in early 1966 with New York Eyes. (Bob MacDonald, February 1986.).

BUTTERFLY
Tracks: / Butterfly / Where have all my heroes gone.
7" Single: Released Oct '82, on CBS, by CBS Records. Deleted Oct '85. Catalogue no: **A 2873**

CANTO
Tracks: / Canto / Esoterix.
12" Single: Released Jan '88, on Priority, by Priority Records. Deleted Mar '88. Catalogue no: **PX 18**
7" Single: Released Jan '88, on Priority, by Priority Records. Catalogue no: **P 18**

DON'T YOU WANT MY LOVE
Tracks: / Don't you want my love / Shy boy.
7" Single: Released Feb '86, on Portrait, by CBS Records. Deleted '86. Catalogue no: **A 6933**
12" Single: Released Feb '86, on Portrait, by CBS Records. Catalogue no: **TA 6933**

GIVE ME MORE TIME
Tracks: / Give me more time / Take away the heartaches.
7" Single: Released Aug '82, on CBS, by CBS Records. Deleted '85. Catalogue no: **A 2467**

HAPPINESS
Tracks: / Happiness.
7" Single: Released Sep '89, on Sleeping Bag, by Sleeping Bag Records. Catalogue no: **SBUK12**
12" Single: Released Sep '89, on Sleeping Bag, by Sleeping Bag Records. Catalogue no: **SBUK12T**

HORSE CALLS
Tracks: / Horse calls / It happens every night.
7" Single: Released Oct '86, on Portrait, by CBS Records. Deleted '87. Catalogue no: **650129 7**

JAM PACKED (AT THE WALL)
Tracks: / Jam packed (at the wall) / Don't you want my love / Jam packed (at the wall) (club mix) (Available on 12" only) / Jam packed (at the wall) (house mix)(12" only) (Available on 12" only).
7" Single: Released Jun '88, on Portrait, by CBS Records. Deleted Jan '89. Catalogue no: **652822 7**
12" Single: Released Jun '88, on Portrait, by CBS Records. Deleted Jan '89. Catalogue no: **652822 6**

LITTLE PEACE, A
Tracks: / Little peace, A / Thank you mercy.
7" Single: Released May '82, on CBS, by CBS Records. Deleted '85. Catalogue no: **A 2365**

NEW YORK EYES
Tracks: / New York eyes / New York eyes (remix)(12" only).
12" Single: Released Dec '85, on Portrait, by CBS Records. Catalogue no: **QTA 6805**
7" Single: Released Dec '85, on Portrait, by CBS Records. Deleted '87. Catalogue no: **A 6805**

WHAT ABOUT ME
Tracks: / Don't you want my love
12" Single: Released Jun '86, on Portrait, by CBS Records. Catalogue no: **TA 7266**
7" Single: Released Jun '86, on Portrait, by CBS Records. Deleted '86. Catalogue no: **A 7266**

Nielsen & Pearson

IF YOU SHOULD SAIL
Tracks: / If you should sail / Don't forget.
7" Single: Released Oct '80, on Capitol, by EMI Records. Deleted Oct '83. Catalogue no: **CL 16172**

SUN AIN'T GONNA SHINE ANYMORE
Tracks: / Sun ain't gonna shine anymore, The / Don't let me go.
7" Single: Released Oct '81, on Capitol, by EMI Records. Deleted Oct '84. Catalogue no: **CL 224**

Nielsson, Carol

ELEVEN O'CLOCK IN MY LIFE
7" Single: Released Jul '84, on Safari, by Safari Records. Catalogue no: **SAFE 63**

Nigger Mikey

DEPEND PON MAN
Tracks: / Depend pon man.
12" Single: Released 31 Jul '89, on Shocking Vibes, Catalogue no: **SV 03**

TING DEH
Tracks: / Ting deh.
7" Single: Released Mar '89, on Penthouse, by Penthouse Records. Catalogue no: **PH 008**

Night

COLD WIND ACROSS MY HEART
Tracks: / Cold wind across my heart / You ain't pretty enough.
7" Single: Released Feb '80, on Elektra Asylum, by Elektra Records (USA). Deleted Feb '83. Catalogue no: **K 12420**

IT'S GOOD TO BE BACK IN YOUR ARMS
Tracks: / It's good to be back in your arms / Look at you.
7" Single: Released Feb '81, on Planet, Deleted Feb '84. Catalogue no: **K 12507**

LOVE ON THE AIRWAVES
Tracks: / Love on the airwaves / Day after day.
7" Single: Released Jan '81, on Planet, Deleted Jan '84. Catalogue no: **K 12492**

Night & Day

NIGHT AND DAY (SINGLE)
Tracks: / Night and day: *Various artists.*
12" Single: Released Oct '89, on Two Friends, Catalogue no: **SIR 023**

Night Flight

GROWING UP
Tracks: / Growing up.
7" Single: Released Aug '84, on Iguana (1), by Iguana Records. Catalogue no: **HRSL 003**

Night Force

HOLD THE NIGHT
Tracks: / Hold the night.
12" Single: Released Jul '83, on Carrere America (USA), by PolyGram Rec.Inc.(USA). Catalogue no: **CART 278**
7" Single: Released Jul '83, on Carrere America (USA), by PolyGram Rec.Inc.(USA). Catalogue no: **CAR 278**

Night in Cologne

JUST A WHISPER (IN THE AIR)
Tracks: / Just a whisper (in the night).

7" Single: Released Jan '85, on LD, by LD Records. Catalogue no: **LD 5005**

Night Moves

TRANSDANCE
Tracks: / Transdance / You can take my love.
12" Single: Released Dec '84, on GC, Catalogue no: **GCT 1001**
12" Single: Released May '83, on GC, Catalogue no: **GCT 2**
7" Single: Released May '83, on GC, Catalogue no: **GC 2**

Night People

WE LOVE BULLDOG BOBBY
Tracks: / We love bulldog Bobby / Disco party.
7" Single: Released Mar '82, on PRT, by Castle Communications Records. Catalogue no: **7 235**

Night Ranger

COLOUR OF YOUR SMILE
Tracks: / Colour of your smile / Girls will like it / When you close your eyes (live) / Don't tell me you love me (live).
7" Single: Released Apr '87, on MCA, by MCA Records. Catalogue no: **MCA 1125**
12" Single: Released Apr '87, on MCA, by MCA Records. Catalogue no: **MCAT 1125**

DON'T TELL ME YOU LOVE ME
Tracks: / Don't tell me you love me.
7" Single: Released Mar '83, on Epic, by CBS Records. Catalogue no: **EPC A 3210**

SECRET OF MY SUCCESS, THE
Tracks: / Secret of my success, The / Carry on / Sister Christian (live) (Extra track on 12").
7" Single: Released 20 Jun '87, on MCA, by MCA Records. Catalogue no: **MCA 1163**
12" Single: Released 20 Jun '87, on MCA, by MCA Records. Catalogue no: **MCAT 1163**

SENTIMENTAL STREET
Tracks: / Sentimental Street / Night machine.
12" Single: Released May '85, on MCA, by MCA Records. Catalogue no: **MCAT 973**
7" Single: Released May '85, on MCA, by MCA Records. Catalogue no: **MCA 973**

SISTER CHRISTIAN (SINGLE)
Tracks: / Sister Christian / Chippin' away.
7" Single: Released Jun '84, on MCA, by MCA Records. Catalogue no: **MCA 881**

Night Shift

DANCE IN THE MOONLIGHT
Tracks: / Dance in the moonlight / Don't rush the good things.
7" Single: Released Jan '81, on Harvest (1), by EMI Records. Deleted Jan '84. Catalogue no: **HAR 5214**

DON'T RUSH THE GOOD THINGS
Tracks: / Don't rush the good things / Change in the weather.
7" Single: Released Feb '80, on Harvest (2), by Harvest Music. Deleted Feb '83. Catalogue no: **HAR 5197**

SENDING ME
Tracks: / Sending me / Silly boy.
7" Single: Released Aug '80, on Harvest (1), by EMI Records. Deleted '83. Catalogue no: **HAR 5211**

Night Swimmers

SHE STARTS LAUGHING
Tracks: / She starts laughing.
7" Single: Released '88, on Witness Records, Catalogue no: **WIT 001**

Night Time Flyer

OUT WITH A VENGEANCE
Tracks: / Out with a vengeance.
7" Single: Released Sep '80, on Red Eye, by Red Eye Records. Catalogue no: **EYE 2**

Nightblooms

GO ELIZA
Tracks: / Go Eliza.
7" Single: Released '88, on Dingo Records, Catalogue no: **DING D001**

Nightcatchers

I CAN'T BELIEVE
Tracks: / I can't believe.
12" Single: Released Jun '85, on RCA, by BMG Records (UK). Catalogue no: **PT 40126**
7" Single: Released Jun '85, on RCA, by BMG Records (UK). Catalogue no: **PB 40125**

Nightdoctor

JUST ENOUGH
Tracks: / Just enough / Hit and miss affair.
7" Single: Released Feb '82, on Race, Deleted '83. Catalogue no: **RB 001**

MUSIC LIKE DIRT
Tracks: / Music like dirt / Dirty dub.
7" Single: Released Oct '80, on Young Blood, by Young Blood Records. Deleted Oct '83. Catalogue no: **YB 105**

Nightfall

SALSA NIGHTS
Tracks: / Salsa nights / Tightrope.
7" Single: Released Feb '80, on EMI, by EMI Records. Deleted '83. Catalogue no: **EMI 5036**

Nightingale, Maxine

LEAD ME ON
Tracks: / Lead me on / Love me like you meant it.
7" Single: Released Feb '80, on Liberty, by EMI Records. Deleted Feb '80. Catalogue no: **BP 337**

LOVE HIT ME (SINGLE)
Tracks: / Love hit me.
7" Single: Released Mar '77, on United Artists, by EMI Records. Deleted '80. Catalogue no: **UP 36215**

RIGHT BACK WHERE WE STARTED FROM (OLD GOLD)
Tracks: / Right back where we started from.
7" Single: Released Mar '87, on Old Gold, by Old Gold Records. Deleted Sep '89. Catalogue no: **OG 9656**
7" Single: Released Nov '75, on United Artists, by EMI Records. Deleted '78. Catalogue no: **UP 36015**

TAKE YOUR HEART
Tracks: / Take your heart / I'm givin' it all to you.
7" Single: Released Jan '81, on Liberty, by EMI Records. Deleted Jan '84. Catalogue no: **BP 384**

WORK ON IT
Tracks: / Work on it / All night with me.
7" Single: Released Oct '80, on Liberty, by EMI Records. Deleted Oct '83. Catalogue no: **BP 375**

Nightingale, Pamela

I'LL NEVER FALL IN LOVE AGAIN
Tracks: / I'll never fall in love again.
7" Single: Released Mar '85, on Carrere, Catalogue no: **CAR 361**
12" Single: Released Mar '85, on Carrere, Catalogue no: **CART 361**

Nightingales

CAKEHOLE
Tracks: / Urban ospreys / Cakehole.
7" Single: Released Feb '83, on Cherry Red, by Cherry Red Records. Deleted '87. Catalogue no: **CHERRY 56**

CRAFTY FAG
Tracks: / Crafty fag / How to age.
7" Single: Released Nov '83, on Ink, by Red Flame Records. Catalogue no: **INK 71**

CRUNCH, THE
Tracks: / Crunch, The.
7" EP: Released May '84, on Vindaloo, by Vindaloo Records. Catalogue no: **YUS 1**

IDIOT STRENGTH
Tracks: / Idiot strength / Seconds.
7" Single: Released Apr '81, on Rough Trade, by Rough Trade Records. Catalogue no: **RT 075**

IT'S A CRACKER
Tracks: / It's a cracker.
7" Single: Released Jan '85, on Vindaloo, by Vindaloo Records. Catalogue no: **GH 9**

PARAFFIN BRAIN
Tracks: / Paraffin brain.
7" Single: Released Apr '82, on Cherry Red, by Cherry Red Records. Deleted '87. Catalogue no: **CHERRY 38**

START FROM SCRATCH
Tracks: / Start from scratch / Butter bricks / Torn / 12 years.
12" Single: Released Jul '88, on Strange Fruit, by Strange Fruit Records. Catalogue no: **SFPS 052**

USE YOUR LOAF (EP)
Tracks: / Use your loaf.
7" Single: Released Feb '82, on Cherry Red, by Cherry Red Records. Deleted '87. Catalogue no: **CHERRY 34**

WHAT A CARRY ON
Tracks: / What a carry on.
12" Single: Released Sep '85, on Vindaloo, by Vindaloo Records. Catalogue no: **YUS 4**

WHICH HI-FI?
Tracks: / Which hi-fi / My brilliant career / Son of God's mate / Give 'em time.
12" Single: Released Jul '82, on Cherry Red, by Cherry Red Records. Deleted '87. Catalogue no: **12 CHERRY 44**

Nightmare

EVOLUTION
Tracks: / Evolution / Ruth Ellis.
7" Single: Released Apr '80, on PVK, by PVK Records. Deleted Apr '83. Catalogue no: **PV 37**

NINE BELOW ZERO - AIN'T COMIN' BACK (Released on A&M)

I WANNA BE A MONSTER IN A MOVIE
Tracks: / I wanna be a monster in a movie / Boogi bogi man.
7" Single: Released '86, on Swoop, Catalogue no: **RTLS 011**

I WANNA BE SHOT
Tracks: / I wanna be shot / Ruth Ellis.
7" Single: Released '87, on PVK, by PVK Records. Catalogue no: **PV 119**

NEW ORLEANS
Tracks: / New Orleans / Drac's back.
7" Single: Released '85, on Swoop, Catalogue no: **RTL 001**
7" Single: Released Jan '83, on Swoop, Catalogue no: **RTL 001**

Nightwing

BARREL OF PAIN
Tracks: / Barrel of pain.
7" Single: Released Jul '80, on Ovation, by Gull Records. Deleted '88. Catalogue no: **OVS 1209**

NIGHT OF MYSTERY
Tracks: / Night of mystery / Dressed to kill.
7" Single: Released Feb '84, on Gull, by Gull Records. Deleted '88. Catalogue no: **GULS 77**

STRANGERS ARE WELCOME
7" Set: Released Jun '85, on Gull, by Gull Records. Deleted '88. Catalogue no: **GULS 80**

TREADING WATER
Tracks: / Treading water.
7" Single: Released Jun '85, on Gull, by Gull Records. Deleted '88. Catalogue no: **GULS 75**

Nightwriters

OVER YOU
Tracks: / Over you.
12" Single: Released Apr '89, on Jack Trax, Catalogue no: **JTX 24**

Nikki

UH UH NO WAY (MUCHO MACHO)
Tracks: / Uh uh no way (mucho macho).
7" Single: Released Aug '89, on Total/Swanyard, Catalogue no: **SYR 5**
12" Single: Released Aug '89, on Total/Swanyard, Catalogue no: **SYRT 5**

Nikola & Eugene

LONGEST REVOLUTION
Tracks: / Longest revolution / Work these fields.
7" Single: Released Nov '88, on America First, Catalogue no: **BISON 001**

Nile, Willie

VAGABOND MOON
Tracks: / Vagabond moon / Old men sleeping in the Bowery.

7" Single: Released Jun '80, on Arista, by BMG Records (UK). Deleted Jun '83. Catalogue no: **ARIST 352**

Niles,Tessa

PRESIDENT'S GIRL, THE
Tracks: / President's girl, The.
7" Single: Released Nov '85, on Rainbow, by Rainbow Records. Catalogue no: **RBR 3**

TOUGH GIRLS
Tracks: / Tough girls (part 2) / Directable JJT / Bowling funth mix, The / Play by Harold Punter, A (12" only).
7" Single: Released May '86, on Rainbow, by Rainbow Records. Catalogue no: **RBR 6**
12" Single: Released May '86, on Rainbow, by Rainbow Records. Catalogue no: **RBRT 6**

Nilsson, Harry

ALL I THINK ABOUT IS YOU
Tracks: / All I think about is you.
7" Single: Released Aug '77, on RCA, by BMG Records (UK). Deleted '80. Catalogue no: **PB 9104**

COCONUT
7" Single: Released Jun '72, on RCA, by BMG Records (UK). Deleted '75. Catalogue no: **RCA 2214**

EVERYBODY'S TALKIN'
Tracks: / Everybody's talkin'.
7" Single: Released Sep '69, on RCA, by BMG Records (UK). Deleted '72. Catalogue no: **RCA 1876**

RAIN
Tracks: / Rain / Bright side of life.
7" Single: Released Oct '80, on Mercury, by Phonogram Ltd. Deleted Oct '83. Catalogue no: **MER 44**

WITHOUT YOU
Tracks: / Without you / Everybody's talking.
7" Single: Released Feb '72, on RCA, by BMG Records (UK). Deleted '75. Catalogue no: **RCA 2165**
7" Single: Released Oct '76, on RCA, by BMG Records (UK). Deleted '79. Catalogue no: **RCA 2733**
7" Single: Released Jul '81, on RCA Golden Grooves, by BMG Records (UK). Catalogue no: **GOLD 503**
CD 5": Released Jun '89, on RCA, by BMG Records (UK). Catalogue no: **PD 49461**

WITHOUT YOU (OLD GOLD)
Tracks: / Without you.
7" Single: Released Jul '88, on Old Gold, by Old Gold Records. Catalogue no: **OG 9630**

Nina & Frederick

LISTEN TO THE OCEAN
Tracks: / Listen to the ocean.
7" Single: Released Mar '60, on Columbia, by EMI Records. Deleted '63. Catalogue no: **DB 4332**

LITTLE DONKEY
Tracks: / Little donkey.
7" Single: Released Nov '60, on Columbia, by EMI Records. Deleted '63. Catalogue no: **DB 4536**

LONGTIME BOY
Tracks: / Longtime boy.
7" Single: Released Sep '61, on Columbia, by EMI Records. Deleted '64. Catalogue no: **DB 4703**

NINE BELOW ZERO - WIPE AWAY YOUR KISS (Released on A&M)

MARY'S BOY CHILD
Tracks: / Mary's boy child.
7" Single: Released Dec '59, on Columbia, by EMI Records. Deleted '62. Catalogue no: **DB 4375**

SUCU SUCU
Tracks: / Sucu sucu.
7" Single: Released Oct '61, on Columbia, by EMI Records. Deleted '64. Catalogue no: **DB 4632**

Nine Below Zero

Biographical details: This British band consisted of Stix Burkey, Peter Clark, Mark Feltham and Dennis Greaves. Drummer Burkey replaced Kenny Bradley in 1980. Nine Below Zero began to attrcat attention in 1979, thanks to an independently issued EP entitled *Packed Fair & Square.* After the signing with A&M Records, they made their LP debut in 1980 with *Live At The Marquee.* Both the EP and LP contained a collection of remakes of old rhythm and blues songs. The band were r&b lovers, and simply played their favourite music, regardless of the fact that it was unfashionable. The challenge of making the first studio album was met in early 1981, by which time Dennis Greaves, the groups guitarist and frontman, had written some original material. *Don't Point Your Finger* was produced by the famous veteran Glyn Johns, and reached No.56 on the UK album chart. The follow-up album, 1982's *Third Degree*, showed a definate move away from r&b and into the rock mainstream; but nevertheless, it did not climb higher than No.38 on Britain's national listings. None of their singles charted and, by the end of 82, the group was defunct. Nine Below Zero were enthusiastic, energetic and sharp, and received some very favourable reviews - but r&b has never been a major commercial proposition on the British charts and, at a time when synthesisers and technopop were becoming the primary force, the public were not particularly interested in traditional guitar/bass/drums line up.(Bob Macdonald 7/4/88).

AIN'T COMIN' BACK (See panel on previous page)
Tracks: / Ain't comin' back / Liquor Lover.
7" Single: Released Apr '81, on A&M, by A&M Records. Deleted '88. Catalogue no: **AMS 8127**

HELEN
Tracks: / Helen / You can't please all the people all the time.
7" Single: Released Jun '81, on A&M, by A&M Records. Deleted '88. Catalogue no: **AMS 8136**

HOMEWORK
Tracks: / Homework / Is that you.
7" Single: Released Jun '80, on A&M, by A&M Records. Deleted Jun '83. Catalogue no: **AMS 7531**

SUGARBEAT
Tracks: / Sugarbeat / East Street, SE 17.
7" Single: Released May '82, on A&M, by A&M Records. Deleted May '85. Catalogue no: **AMS 8224**

THREE TIMES CAUGHT
Tracks: / Three times caught / Doghouse.
7" Single: Released Mar '81, on A&M, by A&M Records. Deleted '88. Catalogue no: **AMS 8110**

WHY DON'T YOU TRY ME TONIGHT?
Tracks: / Why don't you try me tonight?.
7" Single: Released Oct '81, on A&M, by A&M Records. Deleted '88. Catalogue no: **AMS 8171**

WIPE AWAY YOUR KISS (See panel above)
Tracks: / Wipe away your kiss / True love is a crime.
7" Single: Released '82, on A&M, by A&M Records. Catalogue no: **AMS 8210**

Nine Nine

ALL OF ME FOR ALL OF YOU
Tracks: / All of me for all of you.
12" Single: Released Jun '85, on RCA, by BMG Records (UK). Catalogue no: **PT 49951**
7" Single: Released Jun '85, on RCA, by BMG Records (UK). Catalogue no: **PB 49951**

Nine Nine Nine

Biographical details: This British rock band consists of Nick Cash, Guy Days, Pablo Labritain and John Watson. 999 came to public attention during the UK's New Wave/Punk explosion of the late Seventies. The group's debut eponymous album was released in March 1978. It reached No.53 on the British chart, and proved to be the only chart LP that the band would have. They chalked up four minor hit singles however, begun with the biggest in late '78: *Homicide* reached No.40 and was the opening track on their second album, *Separates.* 999's third LP *The Biggest Prize In Sport* came out in 1980, and was followed by 1981's *Concrete.* Also in '81, the combo acheived those three other entries on the UK singles chart - Obsessed and an irreverent interpretation of the Lil Red Riding Hood story were followed by a no-holds-barred rendition of *Indian Reservation*, the John D.Loudermilk song first made famous by Don Fardon. The groups 1983 albu, 13th Floor Madness followed the prevailing musical wind towards dance orientation, but made very little impact. Perhaps the band's best offering was *Emergency*, a 1978 single that earned the group a cult following but failed to gain commercial success. 999 have never been able truly to build upon that following. (Bob Macdonald 4/85).

13TH FLOOR MADNESS
Tracks: / 13th floor madness.
7" Single: Released Oct '83, on Albion, by Albion Records. Catalogue no: **ION 155**
12" Single: Released Oct '83, on Albion, by Albion Records. Catalogue no: **12ION 155**

FOUND OUT TOO LATE
Tracks: / Found out too late.
7" Single: Released Sep '79, on Radar, Catalogue no: **ADA 46**

HOMICIDE
Tracks: / Homicide.
7" Single: Released '78, on United Artists, by EMI Records. Catalogue no: **UP 36467**

INDIAN RESERVATION
Tracks: / Indian reservation.
7" Single: Released Nov '81, on Albion, by Albion Records. Catalogue no: **ION 1023**

LIL RED RIDING HOOD
Tracks: / Lil' red riding hood / Wait for your numbers to be called.
7" Single: Released Aug '81, on Albion, by Albion Records. Deleted '84. Catalogue no: **ION 1017**

OBSESSED
Tracks: / Obsessed / Change / Lie lie lie.
7" Single: Released Apr '78, on Albion, by Albion Records. Catalogue no: **ION 1011**

TROUBLE
Tracks: / Trouble / Made a fool of you.
7" Single: Released Feb '80, on Polydor, by Polydor Ltd. Deleted '83. Catalogue no: **POSP 99**

WILD SUN
Tracks: / Wild sun / Scandal in the city / Bongos on the Nile / Don't you know I need you.
12" Single: Released Jun '82, on Albion, by Albion Records. Catalogue no: **12ION 1033**
Cassingle: Released Jun '82, on Albion, by Albion Records. Catalogue no: **CION 1033**
7" Single: Released Jun '82, on Albion, by Albion Records. Catalogue no: **ION 1033**

Nine O Nine Section

CLASSICAL JACK
Tracks: / Classical Jack.
12" Single: Released Aug '87, on Nine O Nine, by Creole Records. Catalogue no: **NINE 13**

Nine Out Of Ten Cats

SOUND OF MUSIC
12" Single: Released Nov '84, on Slaughter, Catalogue no: **ROAST 4T**

Nine, Sadie

LET'S WORK IT OUT
Tracks: / Let's work it out.
12" Single: Released Feb '87, on Record Shack, by Record Shack Records. Catalogue no: **SOHOT 74**
7" Single: Released Feb '87, on Record Shack, by Record Shack Records. Catalogue no: **SOHO 74**

Nineteen Nineteen

CAGED
Tracks: / Caged / After the fall.
7" Single: Released Jun '82, on Red Rhino, by Red Rhino Records. Deleted '88. Catalogue no: **RED 14**

CRY WOLF
Tracks: / Cry wolf / Storm / Dream / Repulsion / Tear down these walls.
7" Single: Released Sep '83, on Abstract, by Abstract Sounds. Catalogue no: **ABS 016**
12" Single: Released Sep '83, on Abstract, by Abstract Sounds. Catalogue no: **12 ABS 016**

EARTHSONG EP, THE
Tracks: / Earthsong.
12" Single: Released Jul '84, on Abstract, by Abstract Sounds. Catalogue no: **12 ABS 026**

REPULSION
Tracks: / Repulsion / Tear down these walls.
7" Single: Released Oct '82, on Red Rhino, by Red Rhino Records. Catalogue no: **RED 22**

Nineteen Sixty-Nine

APOLLO 11
Tracks: / Apollo 11.
12" Single: Released Aug '89, on Big One Records, by Big One Records. Catalogue no: **VVBIG 15**

Nineteen Ten Fruitgum

SIMON SAYS
Tracks: / Simon says.
7" Single: Released Mar '68, on Pye International, Deleted '71. Catalogue no: **7N 25447**

SIMON SAYS (OLD GOLD)
Tracks: / Simon says / Yummy yummy yummy (B side on re-issue.).
7" Single: Released Oct '88, on Old Gold, by Old Gold Records. Catalogue no: **OG 9798**
7" Single: Released Apr '83, on Old Gold, by Old Gold Records. Deleted Jul '88. Catalogue no: **OG 9293**

Nineteen Twenty Seven

IF I COULD
Tracks: / If i could / Not talking / All the people (Only on CD and 12") / Willing and able (Only on CD and 12") / If I could (version).
7" Single: Released Jun '89, on WEA, by WEA Records. Catalogue no: **YZ 402**
CD 5": Released Jun '89, on WEA, by WEA Records. Catalogue no: **YZ 402CD**
12" Single: Released Jun '89, on WEA, by WEA Records. Catalogue no: **YZ 402T**

THAT'S WHAT I THINK OF YOU
Tracks: / That's what I think of you.
12" Single: Released Jan '89, on WEA, by WEA Records. Catalogue no: **YZ 351 T**
7" Single: Released Jan '89, on WEA, by WEA Records. Catalogue no: **YZ 351**

Nineteen Twenty-Seven

YOU'LL NEVER KNOW
Tracks: / You'll never know / Willing and able / Give the kid a break (On 12" and CD single only.) / Mess, The (On 12" and CD single only.).
7" Single: Released Aug '89, on WEA, by WEA Records. Catalogue no: **YZ 412**
12" Single: Released Aug '89, on WEA, by WEA Records. Catalogue no: **YZ 412T**
Cassingle: Released Aug '89, on WEA, by WEA Records. Catalogue no: **YZ 412C**
CD 5": Released Aug '89, on WEA, by WEA Records. Catalogue no: **YZ 412CD**

Ninety Nine Point Nine

DO IT AGAIN (PART 1)
Tracks: / Do it again (part 1) / I still don't believe it.
Note: A side contains a medley of 9 songs. Produced by Nigel Wright.
12" Single: Released '88, on Debut, by Skratch Records. Catalogue no: **DEBTX 3048**
7" Single: Released Jun '88, on Debut, by Skratch Records. Catalogue no: **DEBT 3048**

Nini

INSTANT ATTITUDE
Tracks: / Instant attitude / Instant attitude (version).
7" Single: Released Apr '88, on Groove & Move, by Groove & Move Records. Catalogue no: **GMT 5**
12" Single: Released Apr '88, on Groove & Move, by Groove & Move Records. Catalogue no: **GMT 125**

Ninja

EYE ON YOU
Special: Released Apr '87, on Iron Works (USA), by Azra International (USA). Catalogue no: **IW 1015**

Ninja Man

HONG KONG FLU
Tracks: / Hong Kong flu.
12" Single: Released Feb '89, on Redman International, Catalogue no: **VPRED 123**

LAUGH AND GRIN
Tracks: / Laugh and grin.
12" Single: Released Nov '88, on Jammy's, Catalogue no: **VPRD 359**

SEND THREAT TO ME
Tracks: / Send threat to me.
7" Single: Released Jan '89, on Exterminator, Catalogue no: **Unknown**

STUMBLING BLOCK
Tracks: / Stumbling block.
12" Single: Released Dec '88, on Blue Mountain, Catalogue no: **BMD 040**

TELL ME
Tracks: / Tell me.
7" Single: Released Jan '89, on Pickout, Catalogue no: **Unknown**

Ninty Nine Point

CHECK OUT THE GROOVE
Tracks: / Check out the groove: Strut you funky stuff / Get boogie / Turn the music up / Love ranger.
12" Single: Released Sep '88, on Debut, by Skratch Records. Catalogue no: **DEBTX 3054**

Nips

ALL THE TIME IN THE WORLD
Tracks: / All the time in the world.
7" Single: Released '79, on Soho (1), by Soho Records. Deleted '82. Catalogue no: **SH 4**

GABRIELLE
Tracks: / Gabrielle.
7" Single: Released Nov '79, on Soho (1), by Soho Records. Deleted '82. Catalogue no: **SH 9**

HAPPY SONG
Tracks: / Happy song.
7" Single: Released Oct '81, on Burning Rome, Catalogue no: **TP 5**

Nirvana

BLACK AND WHITE OR COLOUR
Tracks: / Black and white or colour / Tall trees and mansions.
7" Single: Released Feb '82, on Zilch, by Zilch Records. Catalogue no: **ZILCH15**

BLACK FLOWER
Tracks: / Black flower / Save my soul.

7" Single: Released Apr '87, on Bam Caruso, by Demon Records. Catalogue no: **OPRA 078**

LOVE BUZZ
Tracks: / Nirvana.
7" Single: Released '88, on Sub Pop, Catalogue no: **SP 023**

PICTURE OF DORIAN GRAY
Tracks: / Picture of Dorian Gray / No it isn't.
7" Single: Released Sep '81, on Zilch, by Zilch Records. Deleted Sep '84. Catalogue no: **ZILCH 8**

RAINBOW CHASER
Tracks: / Rainbow chaser.
7" Single: Released May '68, on Island, by Island Records. Deleted '71. Catalogue no: **WIP 6029**

Nirvana Devils

SECRET AGENT GIRL
Tracks: / Secret agent girl.
7" Single: Released Sep '85, on Exile, Catalogue no: **EX 7004**

SOME FOREIGN SHORE
Tracks: / Some foreign shore.
7" Single: Released Apr '85, on Exile, Catalogue no: **EX 7002**

TWISTED TALES EP
Tracks: / Twisted tales EP.
10" single: Released May '86, on Exile, Catalogue no: **EX 10EP 02**

Niteflyte

IF YOU WANT IT
Tracks: / If you want it / I wonder if I'm falling in love.
7" Single: Released Feb '80, on Ariola, by BMG Records (UK). Deleted '83. Catalogue no: **ARO 220**

Nitro Deluxe

THIS BRUTAL HOUSE
Tracks: / This brutal house / This brutal house (dub) / This brutal house (mega mix) / (original US mix).
7" Single: Released Jan '88, on Cool Tempo, by Chrysalis Records. Catalogue no: **COOL 142**
12" Single: Released Jan '88, on Cool Tempo, by Chrysalis Records. Catalogue no: **COOLX 142**

Nitros

RUNNING OUT OF TIME (EP)
Tracks: / Running out of time.
7" Single: Released Sep '89, on Raucous, Catalogue no: **RAUC 009**

Nits

IN THE DUTCH MOUNTAINS
Tracks: / In the Dutch mountains / Strangers of the night / Moon and stars (12" only) / Magic of Lassie II (12" only).
7" Single: Released Jan '88, on Epic, by CBS Records. Deleted Aug '88. Catalogue no: **NITS 1**
12" Single: Released Jan '88, on Epic, by CBS Records. Deleted Aug '88. Catalogue no: **NITS T1**

NESCIO
Tracks: / Nescio.
7" Single: Released May '83, on Epic, by CBS Records. Catalogue no: **A 3201**

Nitty Gritty

BORDERLINE
Tracks: / Borderline / In Africa / 007.
12" Single: Released Jul '86, on Uptempo, Catalogue no: **TEMP 006**

CREATOR
Tracks: / Creator / Love fever.
12" Single: Released Jul '86, on SMJ, Catalogue no: **SMJ 004**

GIMME SOME OF YOU SOMETHING
Tracks: / Gimme some of you something.
12" Single: Released Nov '85, on Greensleeves, by Greensleeves Records. Catalogue no: **GRED 193**

HOG IN A MINTY
Tracks: / Hog in a minty.
12" Single: Released Aug '85, on Greensleeves, by Greensleeves Records. Catalogue no: **GRED 187**

LETTING OF STEAM
12" Single: Released Mar '89, on Live & Love, Catalogue no: **LLD 113**

LICK HIM,KILL HIM
Tracks: / Lick him, kill him.
12" Single: Released Nov '86, on Bowl, Catalogue no: **BL 001**

LOVING FEELING
Tracks: / Loving feeling.
12" Single: Released Mar '86, on Twin Explosion, Catalogue no: **TE 102**

MAN IN A HOUSE
Tracks: / Man in a house / False Alarm.

12" Single: Released Apr '86, on Greensleeves, by Greensleeves Records. Catalogue no: **GRED 195**

ORIGINAL BANGA RANG
Tracks: / Original banga rang / Original banga rang (Version).
12" Single: Released Jul '86, on Jammy's, Catalogue no: **PIADIS 001**

SO THEM COME SO THEY GO
Tracks: / So them come so they go.
12" Single: Released Feb '87, on Live & Love, Catalogue no: **LLDIS 0025**

SWEET REGGAE MUSIC
Tracks: / Sweet reggae music / Politician.
12" Single: Released Dec '85, on Unity Sound, Catalogue no: **UN 009**

USED TO BE MY LOVER
Tracks: / Used to be my lover / Used to be my dubber.
12" Single: Released Mar '86, on Uptempo, Deleted Jun '89. Catalogue no: **TEMP 001**

WE RUN THINGS
Tracks: / We run things.
12" Single: Released Sep '88, on Blue Trac, by Blue Trac Records. Catalogue no: **BTRD 025**

Niven

YESTERDAY
Tracks: / Yesterday / I hope you'll always be my friend.
7" Single: Released Jan '89, on Woosh, by Woosh Records. Catalogue no: **WOOSH 5**

Niven, Kristina

MAMMY BLUE
Tracks: / Mammy blue / Wait until tomorrow.
7" Single: Released Aug '86, on Amidisque, by Amidisque Records. Catalogue no: **NIVEN 1**

Nkomo, Pablo

WICKED MURDERER
Tracks: / Wicked murderer.
12" Single: Released Sep '84, on Sun Set (reggae), Catalogue no: **Unknown**

No Choice

SADIST DREAM
Tracks: / Sadist dream.
7" EP: Released Feb '83, on Riot City, by Riot City Records. Catalogue no: **RIOT 20**

No Comment

IN MY MIND
Tracks: / In my mind.
7" Single: Released Mar '82, on Spectrum (1), Deleted '86. Catalogue no: **KRO 003**

No Corridor

SOFT TARGET
Tracks: / Soft target / Last time, The.
7" Single: Released May '86, on UNKNOWN, Catalogue no: **A 1001**

No Cover

TWO HUNDRED VOICES
Tracks: / Two hundred voices.
7" Single: Released Jul '83, on Northeast Music, by Northeast Music Records. Catalogue no: **GRC 136**

No Dakota

OUTOFTHISWORLD
Tracks: / Out of this world.
7" Single: Released Aug '89, on NOH, Catalogue no: **NOH 1**

No Deposit

MOUNTAIN LAKE
Tracks: / Mountain lake / Jazz radio.
7" Single: Released Jul '80, on Shoc-Wave, Catalogue no: **SRP 0006**

No Dice

COME DANCING
Tracks: / Come dancing.
7" Single: Released May '79, on EMI, by EMI Records. Deleted '82. Catalogue no: **EMI 2927**

ONE MORE NIGHT
Tracks: / One more night.
7" Single: Released Sep '82, on Seara, Catalogue no: **SEA 005**

No Exit

CASABLANCAN NIGHT
Tracks: / Casablancan night.
7" Single: Released Oct '83, on Slug, Catalogue no: **CUS 1786**

No Fears 55

CREATURES OF THE NIGHT
Tracks: / Creatures of the night.

12" Single: Released '87, on Sampler Et Sans Reproches, Catalogue no: **12SSR 8080**

NOEL - SILENT MORNING (Released on 4th and Broadway)

No Hat Moon

I LOVE TODAY
Tracks: / I love today / It's only the rain.
7" Single: Released Apr '86, on Towerbell, Catalogue no: **TOW 85**

WON'T YOU DANCE WITH ME
Tracks: / Won't you dance with me.
7" Single: Released Nov '85, on Towerbell, Catalogue no: **TOW 78**

No Idea

RUSSIAN ROULETTE
Tracks: / Russian roulette.
7" Single: Released Mar '83, on Paro, by Paro Records. Catalogue no: **PARO 55**

No Jaz

SIX FLIGHTS OF STAIRS
Tracks: / Six flights of stairs.
7" Single: Released Aug '84, on Fleeced, Catalogue no: **FLC 1**

No Man Is An Island

GIRL FROM MISSOURI EP, THE
Tracks: / Girl from Missouri.
12" Single: Released Jun '89, on Plastic Head, by Plastic Head Records. Catalogue no: **PLASS 012**

No Man's Band

HEY JOE
Tracks: / Hey Joe.
7" Single: Released Jul '82, on Energy (USA), by Bulldog Records (USA). Catalogue no: **NRG 006**

No Man's Land

SPLASH
Tracks: / Splash / Building a road.
7" Single: Released Oct '86, on Future Earth, by Future Earth Records. Deleted '87. Catalogue no: **FER 024**

No Means No

DAY EVERYTHING BECAME NOTHING, THE
Tracks: / Day everything became nothing, The.
12" Single: Released Apr '88, on Alternative Tentacles, by Alternative Tentacles Records. Catalogue no: **VIRUS 062**

No More Ecstacy

GOD IS DEAD
Tracks: / God is dead.

12" Single: Released Apr '89, on Rodger, Catalogue no: **RODGER 7**

No Quarter

SURVIVORS
Tracks: / Survivors.
12" Single: Released Nov '83, on Reel, Catalogue no: **REEL 1**

No Smoke

KORRO KORRO
12" Single: Released Aug '89, on Warriors Dance, by Warriors Dance Records. Catalogue no: **WAFT 11**

No Sovereign

SHOWDOWN
Tracks: / Showdown / Know love so well.
7" Single: Released Apr '87, on Geffen, by Geffen Records (USA). Deleted Jan '88. Catalogue no: **GEF 21**
12" Single: Released Apr '87, on Geffen, by Geffen Records (USA). Deleted Jan '88. Catalogue no: **GEF 21T**

No Trend

HEART OF DARKNESS
Tracks: / Heart of darkness.
12" Single: Released Oct '85, on Widowspeak, Catalogue no: **WSP 3**

No Way Jose

TEQUILA
Tracks: / Tequila.
12" Single: Released Aug '85, on 4th & Broadway, by Island Records. Catalogue no: **12 BRWX 28**
12" Single: Released Aug '85, on 4th & Broadway, by Island Records. Deleted Jul '87. Catalogue no: **12 BRW 28**
7" Single: Released Aug '85, on 4th & Broadway, by Island Records. Catalogue no: **BRW 28**
7" Pic: Released Aug '85, on 4th & Broadway, by Island Records. Catalogue no: **PBRW 28**

Noah House Of Dread

MURDER
Tracks: / Murder.
12" Single: Released Jun '82, on On-U-Sound, by On-U-Sound Records. Catalogue no: **DP 6**

Noah Noah

UTOPIA
Tracks: / Utopia.
7" Single: Released Jul '85, on Exclusive, Catalogue no: **EXC 1402**
12" Single: Released Jul '85, on Exclusive, Catalogue no: **EXCL 1402**

Noble, Kara

ALL I WANT (IS TO SEE YOU SMILE)
Tracks: / All I want (is to see you smile).
7" Single: Released Oct '82, on Towerbell, Catalogue no: **TOW 20**

MUMMY
Tracks: / Mummy / It's over.
7" Single: Released May '82, on Towerbell, Catalogue no: **TOW 20**

Nobody's Fool

ROCK ON RADIO
Tracks: / Rock on radio / I'm in the mood.
7" Single: Released Mar '88, on Bad, by Bad Records. Catalogue no: **BAD 3**

Nocera

LET'S GO
Tracks: / Let's go.
12" Single: Released Oct '87, on Sleeping Bag, by Sleeping Bag Records. Catalogue no: **SLX 29**

SUMMERTIME SUMMERTIME
Tracks: / Summertime summertime / Sum-

mertime summertime (hard summer dub).
7" Single: Released Oct '86, on 4th & Broadway, by Island Records. Catalogue no: **BRW 54**
12" Single: Released Oct '86, on 4th & Broadway, by Island Records. Deleted Apr '88. Catalogue no: **12 BRW 54**
12" Single: Released 11 Sep '89, on Sleeping Bag, by Sleeping Bag Records. Catalogue no: **SBUK 12T**

Nocturnal Emissions

NO SACRIFICE
Tracks: / No sacrifice.
12" Single: Released Sep '84, on Sterile, Catalogue no: **SR 6**

Nod & Friends

DAD
Tracks: / Dad.
7" Single: Released Oct '82, on Red Rhino, by Red Rhino Records. Deleted '88. Catalogue no: **RED 16**

Noel (Group)

SILENT MORNING (See panel on previous page)
Tracks: / Silent morning (12" club mix) / Silent morning (1018 dub mix) / Silent morning (hearthrob mix) / Silent morning / Silent morning (percapella).
7" Single: Released Sep '87, on 4th & Broadway, by Island Records. Deleted Jun '88. Catalogue no: **BRW 76**
12" Single: Released Sep '87, on 4th & Broadway, by Island Records. Deleted Jun '88. Catalogue no: **12 BRW 76**

Noh Rodeo

SUBTERRANEAN, THE
Tracks: / Subterranean, The.
7" Single: Released Jun '88, on Antler, by Antler Records (Belgium). Catalogue no: **ANT 051**

Nohumaneye

WET YOUR LIPS
Tracks: / Wet your lips / Owners lose a package.
7" Single: Released Oct '82, on Rhodium, by Rhodium Records. Catalogue no: **TT 826**

Noise Boyz

BOYZ-GO SCRATCH
Tracks: / Boyz-go scratch / Lean Street.
12" Single: Released Sep '86, on Citybeat, by Beggars Banquet Records. Catalogue no: **CBE 1207**

NO WAY BACK
Tracks: / No way back / No way back (alt. dance mix).
12" Single: Released 20 Jun '87, on City-beat, by Beggars Banquet Records. Catalogue no: **CBE 1212**

Noiseworks

NO LIES
Tracks: / No lies / Learning to swim / No lies (ext) (track on 12").
7" Single: Released May '88, on Epic, by CBS Records. Deleted Jan '89. Catalogue no: **650369 7**
7" Single: Released May '87, on Epic, by CBS Records. Catalogue no: **TENSE C2**
12" Single: Released May '88, on Epic, by CBS Records. Deleted Jan '89. Catalogue no: **650369 6**

SIMPLE MAN
Tracks: / Simple man / Letter / Love somebody (Only on 12" and CD single.) / No lies (Only on 12" and CD single.).
CD 5": Released Jul '89, on Epic, by CBS Records. Catalogue no: **6548452**
7" Single: Released Jul '89, on Epic, by CBS Records. Catalogue no: **6548457**
12" Single: Released Jul '89, on Epic, by CBS Records. Catalogue no: **6548458**

TAKE ME BACK
Tracks: / Take me back / Don't wait.
7" Single: Released Feb '88, on Epic, by CBS Records. Deleted Aug '88. Catalogue no: **650775 7**
12" Single: Released Feb '88, on Epic, by CBS Records. Deleted Aug '88. Catalogue no: **650775 6**

TOUCH (SINGLE)
Tracks: / Touch / 5 more days / Welcome to the world / River of tears.
12" Pic: Released Jun '89, on Epic, by CBS Records. Deleted Oct '89. Catalogue no: **653010 9**
7" Single: Released 8 May '89, on Epic, by CBS Records. Deleted Oct '89. Catalogue no: **653010 0**
12" Single: Released 24 Apr '89, on Epic, by CBS Records. Deleted Oct '89. Catalogue no: **653010 8**
7" Single: Released Apr '89, on Epic, by CBS Records. Deleted Oct '89. Catalogue no: **653010 7**
CD 5": Released Apr '89, on Epic, by CBS Records. Deleted Oct '89. Catalogue no: **653010 2**

Nola

LOVE STRIKER
Tracks: / Love striker.
7" Single: Released Dec '83, on Chantel, by Chantel Records. Catalogue no: **CHA 1**

Nolan, Denise

DON'T YA SAY IT
Tracks: / Don't ya say it / Aching heart.
7" Single: Released Jun '81, on Mercury, by Phonogram Ltd. Deleted Jun '84. Catalogue no: **MER 74**

GIRLS DO IT, BOYS DO IT
Tracks: / Girls do it, boys do it / Just can't stop the feeling.
7" Single: Released May '82, on Mercury, by Phonogram Ltd. Deleted '85. Catalogue no: **MER 103**

IN LOVE WITH LOVE
Tracks: / In love with love / My mind is made up on you.
7" Single: Released Nov '82, on Mercury, by Phonogram Ltd. Deleted Nov '85. Catalogue no: **MER 125**

Nolan, Dennis

PILLOW TALK
Tracks: / Pillow talk / Killer thriller.
7" Single: Released Jul '87, on Blakemix, Catalogue no: **BLKM 003**

Nolan, Jerry

TAKE A CHANCE WITH ME
Tracks: / Take a chance with me / Pretty baby.
7" Single: Released Feb '83, on Tansing, Catalogue no: **TANSIN 006**

Nolan, Kenny

US AND LOVE
Tracks: / Us and love / You're so beautiful tonight.
7" Single: Released Mar '80, on Casablanca, by PolyGram UK Ltd. Deleted '86. Catalogue no: **CAN 186**

Nolans

Biographical details: Originally known as the Nolan Sisters, this Anglo-Irish family vocal group first came to fame in Britain in the mid-Seventies via the television shows of Cliff Richard and Mike Yarwood. The quintet's sweet, inoffensive middle-of-the-road style was ideal for the Saturday night TV audience. Although a career in cabaret seemed an obvious route for the girls to take, it was decided that they should first establish themselves on the record charts. Accordingly, an album entitled *20 giant hits* was ensembled and given a TV advertising campaign; containing the Sisters' bland renditions of familiar pop standards, the LP reached No.3 on the UK charts. One girl was lead singer, while four harmonised. This success paved the way for a breakthrough in the singles market, to fill the gap left by fading chart careers of the Brotherhood Of Man and the Dooleys. After a modest Top.40 entry with *Spirit, body and soul*, the girls shortened their billing to the Nolans and chalked up seven UK Top 20 singles during 1980-82. The first and biggest was *I'm in the mood for dancing* (No.3), heavily influenced by Tina Charles' *I love to love (but my baby loves to dance)*. Subsequent singles included *Don't make waves, Gotta pull myself together, Who's gonna rock you* (co-written by Billy Ocean), *Attention to me, Chemistry* and *Don't love me too hard*. All of these peaked on the UK charts somewhere between No.9 and No.15; the group's singles usually took a long time climbing Top 75, but they reached the higher echelons in the end. The Nolans' gently danceable MoR/pop sound also sold many albums during this period - four releases clocked up 61 LP chart weeks between them. Things started to decline in mid-1982 when the aptly titled single *Crashing down* flopped and the group's membership fluctuated between four and five as Anne and then Denise came and went confusing regularity. Their 1983 single *Dressed to kill* was excluded from the UK singles chart by Gallup, to the girls' embarrassment, because of suspicious marketing methods by the record company. With their succession of hits now over, the Nolans concentrated on the cabaret circuit with great success. They enjoyed particular popularity in Japan. In 1985 the Nolans played a prominent part in the Crowd's UK chart-topping charity single *You'll never walk alone*. (Bob MacDonald, 13th Feb 1986)r.

6 TRACK HITS
Tracks: / Bright eyes / Lead me on / Thankyou for the music / Chemistry / Don't make waves / Miss you nights.
7" EP: Released Mar '84, on Scoop 33, by Pickwick Records. Catalogue no: **7SR 5032**

ATTENTION TO ME
Tracks: / Attention to me / Old feelings again.
7" Single: Released Mar '81, on Epic, by CBS Records. Deleted '84. Catalogue no: **EPC 9571**

CHEMISTRY
Tracks: / Chemistry / Are you still thinking of me.
7" Single: Released Aug '81, on Epic, by CBS Records. Deleted '84. Catalogue no: **EPC A 1485**

CRASHING DOWN
Tracks: / Crashing down / If it takes me all night.
7" Single: Released May '82, on Epic, by CBS Records. Deleted May '85. Catalogue no: **EPCA 2387**

DON'T LOVE ME TOO HARD
Tracks: / Don't love me too hard / Simple case of loving you.
7" Single: Released Feb '82, on Epic, by CBS Records. Deleted '85. Catalogue no: **EPC A 1927**

DON'T MAKE WAVES
Tracks: / Don't make waves / Don't let me be the last to know.
7" Single: Released Apr '80, on Epic, by CBS Records. Deleted '83. Catalogue no: **EPC 8349**

DRAGONFLY
Tracks: / Dragonfly / Every little thing.
7" Single: Released Oct '82, on Epic, by CBS Records. Deleted '85. Catalogue no: **EPCA 2864**

GOODBYE NOTHING TO SAY
Tracks: / Goodbye nothing to say.
7" Single: Released Jun '85, on Towerbell, Catalogue no: **TOW 70**
12" Single: Released Jun '85, on Towerbell, Catalogue no: **TOWT 70**

GOTTA PULL MYSELF TOGETHER
Tracks: / Gotta pull myself together / Directions of love.
7" Single: Released Sep '80, on Epic, by CBS Records. Deleted '83. Catalogue no: **EPC 8878**

GREATEST ORIGINAL HITS 4 Track EP
Tracks: / I'm in the mood for dancing / Who's gonna rock you / Don't love me too hard / Gotta pull myself together.
7" Single: Released Mar '83, on Epic, by CBS Records. Catalogue no: **EPC A 2625**

I'M IN THE MOOD FOR DANCING (CASS)
Tracks: / I'm in the mood for dancing / Who's gonna rock you now / Gotta pull myself together / Don't love me too hard.
Cassingle: Released Sep '82, on Epic, by CBS Records. Deleted Sep '85. Catalogue no: **EPCA40 2625**

I'M IN THE MOOD FOR DANCING (SINGLE)
Tracks: / I'm in the mood for dancing / No question.
12" Single: Released Jul '89, on A.1, by A.1 Records. Catalogue no: **12A1 312**
7" Single: Released Jul '89, on A.1, by A.1 Records. Catalogue no: **A1 312**
7" Single: Released Dec '79, on Epic, by CBS Records. Deleted '82. Catalogue no: **EPC 8068**

LET'S SPEND THE NIGHT TOGETHER
Tracks: / Let's spend the night together / When I fall in love.
7" Single: Released Mar '86, on Spartan, Catalogue no: **SP 130**

SPIRIT BODY AND SOUL
Tracks: / Spirit body and soul.
7" Single: Released Oct '79, on Epic, by CBS Records. Deleted '82. Catalogue no: **EPC 7796**

WHO'S GONNA ROCK YOU
Tracks: / Who's gonna rock you / Better late than never.
7" Single: Released Dec '80, on Epic, by CBS Records. Deleted '83. Catalogue no: **EPC 9325**

Nolen & Crossley

READY OR NOT
Tracks: / Ready or not / Place in my heart.
12" Single: Released Apr '82, on Motown, by BMG Records (UK). Catalogue no: **TMGT 1261**
7" Single: Released Apr '82, on Motown, by BMG Records (UK). Catalogue no: **TMG 1261**

Nomad

RAGAMUFFIN NUMBER, THE
Tracks: / Ragamuffin number, The / It really doesn't matter (bonus beats).
12" Single: Released Apr '89, on Rumour, Catalogue no: **RUMAT 2**
7" Single: Released Apr '89, on Rumour, Catalogue no: **RUMA 2**

Nomad, Naz

I HAD TOO MUCH TO DREAM (LAST NIGHT)
Tracks: / I had too much to dream (last night) / Cold turkey.
7" Single: Released Mar '84, on Ace, by Ace Records. Catalogue no: **NS 93**

Nomad Pop!

DIGNITY
Tracks: / Dignity / Best man.
7" Single: Released May '86, on Redhouse, by Redhouse Records. Catalogue no: **RHR 1**

Nomads

16 FOREVER
Tracks: / 16 forever / Come on / You're gonna miss me.
12" Single: Released 1 Aug '89, on Play It Again Sam(Belgium), by Play It Again Sam (Belgium). Catalogue no: **LD 876**
12" Single: Released 23 May '87, on Wire, by Wire Records. Catalogue no: **WIMS 001**

SHE PAYS THE RENT
Tracks: / She pays the rent.
7" Single: Released Nov '85, on Wire, by Wire Records. Catalogue no: **TNMS 66**

SOMETHING BAD
Tracks: / Something bad.
7" Single: Released May '85, on Soul Supply, by Soul Supply Records. Catalogue no: **7SS 105**

Nomi, Klaus

DING DONG THE WITCH IS DEAD
Tracks: / Ding dong the witch is dead.
7" Single: Released Oct '82, on RCA, by BMG Records (UK). Catalogue no: **RCA 289**

LIGHTNING STRIKES
Tracks: / Lightning strikes / Falling in love again.
7" Single: Released Jan '82, on RCA, by BMG Records (UK). Catalogue no: **RCA 175**

Non

OUT OUT OUT
Tracks: / Out out out.
7" Single: Released Jan '82, on Mute, by Mute Records. Catalogue no: **MUTE 15**

Nooks, George

BE YOUR LOVER
Tracks: / Be your lover.
12" Single: Released Dec '85, on Moa Anbessa, Catalogue no: **MA 009**

FREEDOM BLUES
Tracks: / Freedom blues / Call it off.
12" Single: Released Sep '83, on Oak Sound, Catalogue no: **OSD 012**

FRET NOT YOURSELF
Tracks: / Fret not yourself.
12" Single: Released Jan '84, on CF, Catalogue no: **CF 008**

ROCKING TIMES
Tracks: / Rocking times.
12" Single: Released Oct '83, on Hitbound, Catalogue no: **BG 005**

TIME FOR LOVE
Tracks: / Time for love, A.
7" Single: Released Oct '82, on J.B., Deleted '84. Catalogue no: **JBD 042**

Noone, Peter

I'M INTO SOMETHING GOOD
Tracks: / I'm into something good / God knows.
7" Single: Released Feb '89, on Cypress, by Sonet Records. Catalogue no: **YY 5004**

OH YOU PRETTY THING
Tracks: / Oh you pretty things.
7" Single: Released May '71; on RAK, by EMI Records. Deleted '74. Catalogue no: **RAK 114**

Nordland

JUST KEEP IT AWAY
Tracks: / Just keep it away.
7" Single: Released May '88, on Nord, Catalogue no: **NORD 002**

Norfolk & Good

KRISTMAS KRACKER
Tracks: / Kristmas kracker.
7" Single: Released Dec '81, on Gipsy, by Gipsy Records. Catalogue no: **GIPSY 5**

Norma

LIFE IS THE REASON
Tracks: / Life is the reason / We're gonna make it together.
12" Single: Released Nov '83, on ERC, Catalogue no: **ERCL 108**
7" Single: Released Nov '83, on ERC, Catalogue no: **ERC 108**

Norma Jean

HIGH SOCIETY

Tracks: / High society / Hold me lonely boy.
7" Single: Released Mar '80, on Island, by Island Records. Deleted Mar '83. Catalogue no: **WIP 6559**
12" Single: Released Mar '80, on Island, by Island Records. Deleted Mar '83. Catalogue no: **12 WIP 6559**

HOW DEEP
Tracks: / How deep / How deep (inst.).
7" Single: Released Jan '88, on Uptown Records, by Uptown Records. Catalogue no: **7 UTR 6**
12" Single: Released Jan '88, on Uptown Records, by Uptown Records. Catalogue no: **12 UTR 6**

MEGA STAR HIT ONE
Tracks: / Mega star hit one.
12" Single: Released Aug '87, on Uptown Records, by Uptown Records. Catalogue no: **12 UTR 4**
7" Single: Released Aug '87, on Uptown Records, by Uptown Records. Catalogue no: **7 UTR 4**

Normal

TVOD
Tracks: / T.V.O.D..
7" Single: Released Nov '79, on Mute, by Mute Records. Catalogue no: **MUTE 1**

Norman, Chris

LOVE IS A BATTLEFIELD
Tracks: / Love is a battlefield.
7" Single: Released Jan '84, on RCA, by BMG Records (UK). Catalogue no: **RCA 386**

MIDNIGHT LADY
Tracks: / Midnight lady / Woman.
7" Single: Released Aug '86, on Arista, by BMG Records (UK). Catalogue no: **ARIST 670**
12" Single: Released Aug '86, on Arista, by BMG Records (UK). Catalogue no: **ARIST 12670**

MY GIRL AND ME
Tracks: / My girl and me.
7" Single: Released Aug '84, on RCA, by BMG Records (UK). Catalogue no: **RCA 427**

Norman, Jessye

AMAZING GRACE
Tracks: / Amazing grace / He's got the whole world in his hands.
CD 5": Released Jun '88, on Philips, by Phonogram Ltd. Catalogue no: **422 227-2**
7" Single: Released Jun '88, on Philips, by Phonogram Ltd. Catalogue no: **JESS 1**

Norman, Neil

INDIANA JONES AND THE TEMPLE OF DOOM
Tracks: / Indiana Jones and the Temple of Doom.
7" Single: Released Aug '84, on PRT, by Castle Communications Records. Catalogue no: **7P 315**

Normil Hawaiians

BEAT GOES ON
Tracks: / Beat goes on.
7" Single: Released Jun '81, on Dining Out, by Dining Out Records. Catalogue no: **TUX 13**

GALA FAILED
Tracks: / Gala failed.
12" Single: Released 27 Jun '85, on Red Rhino, by Red Rhino Records. Catalogue no: **REDT 008**

STILL OBEDIENT
Tracks: / Still obedient / Should you forget.
7" Single: Released Dec '81, on KSV, by Kingsley Sound & Vision Records. Deleted Dec '84. Catalogue no: **ILL 7**

Nort

COOL ON THE LOOP
Tracks: / Cool on the loop.
7" Single: Released '88, on Ediesta, Catalogue no: **CALC 045**
12" Single: Released Feb '88, on Ediesta, Catalogue no: **CALC 045T**

North, Christopher

STRAY
Tracks: / Stray.
7" Single: Released Nov '86, on North Corporation, Catalogue no: **CNC 001**

North, Ian

HOLLYWOOD BABYLON
Tracks: / Hollywood Babylon / No sound from 25.
7" Single: Released Feb '80, on Aura Records, by Aura Records. Deleted Feb '83. Catalogue no: **AUS 115**

NO SOUND FROM 25
Tracks: / No sound from 25 / Hollywood Babylon.
7" Single: Released May '80, on Aura Records, by Aura Records. Deleted '83. Catalogue no: **AUS 115**

North West Ten

YOU'VE GOT ALL NIGHT
Tracks: / You've got all night.
12" Single: Released Jun '85, on Ensign, by Ensign Records. Deleted '86. Catalogue no: **12ENY 519**
7" Single: Released Jun '85, on Ensign, by Ensign Records. Deleted '86. Catalogue no: **ENY 519**

Northern Sky

I WANNA BE WITH YOU
Tracks: / I wanna be with you / Thursday girl.
7" Single: Released Jul '88, on Square One, Catalogue no: **SQR 2**
12" Single: Released Jul '88, on Square One, Catalogue no: **12SQR 2**

TAKE IT ON TRUST
Tracks: / Take it on trust.
7" Single: Released Oct '85, on Rebound, Catalogue no: **BOUNCE 7**

Norum, John

LOVE IS MEANT
Tracks: / Love is meant / In chase of the wind / Don't believe a word / Love is meant (extended mix).
7" Single: Released Mar '88, on Epic, by CBS Records. Deleted Aug '88. Catalogue no: **651493 7**
12" Single: Released Mar '88, on Epic, by CBS Records. Deleted Aug '88. Catalogue no: **651493 6**

Norwood

I CAN'T LET YOU GO
Tracks: / I can't let you go / Don't let love / Should have been us together / Lady in love / I can't live without you / Give it up / Feels so good / Glad I found you / Come back my lover.
7" Single: Released Apr '87, on MCA, by MCA Records. Catalogue no: **MCA 1115**
12" Single: Released Apr '87, on MCA, by MCA Records. Catalogue no: **MCAT 1115**

SHOULD HAVE BEEN US TOGETHER
Tracks: / Should have been us together / Come back my lover.
7" Single: Released Aug '87, on MCA, by MCA Records. Catalogue no: **MCA 1180**

Norwood B

YOUR ON THE ONE (YOU ON THE MONEY)
Tracks: / Your on the one (you on the money) / Your on the one (you on the money) (part 2).
7" Single: Released Jul '82, on Philly World (USA), by Philly World (USA). Catalogue no: **PWS 102**
12" Single: Released Jul '82, on Philly World (USA), by Philly World (USA). Catalogue no: **PWSL 102**

Nose Flutes

LEARNING TO SPRAY WITH CATARRH
Tracks: / Learning to spray with catarrah.
12" Single: Released Nov '85, on Reflex, by Reflex Records. Catalogue no: **12 RE 11**

LEG FULL OF ALCOHOL
Tracks: / Leg full of alcohol.
12" Single: Released Feb '87, on Ron Johnson, by Ron Johnson Records. Catalogue no: **ZRON 19**

RAVERS, THE
Tracks: / Ravers, The.
12" Single: Released Mar '87, on Ron Johnson, by Ron Johnson Records. Catalogue no: **ZRON 19**

Nostromo

BLACK HOLE Theme from Jabbar
Tracks: / Black hole.
7" Single: Released Jan '80, on Bronze, by Bronze Records. Deleted Jan '85. Catalogue no: **BRO 86**
12" Single: Released Jan '80, on Bronze, by Bronze Records. Deleted Jan '85. Catalogue no: **12 BRO 86**

Not The Nine O'Clock

Biographical details: The team of this British satirial television program consisted of Rowan Atkinson, Griff Rhys Jones, Mel Smith and Pamela Stephenson. On Monday nights during the early Eighties, the BBC 1 channel's traditional 'Nine o'clock news' slot was rivalled on BBC 2 by the acclaimed topical comedy show *Not the nine o'clock news*. On the air for approximately a dozen weeks in each year, each 30-minute programme cast an irreverent eye over the preceding seven days' events; final inserts and edits often took place as late as 8.30 on Monday evening. Its success led to a series of spinoff albums on the BBC label, the first two of which both reached No.5 and logged over 20 weeks on the UK chart: *Not the nine o'clock news* was released in late *980, and *Hedgehog sandwich* appeared on record shop shelves in late 1981. Pop music was always anintegral part of the show, be it political comedy set to music (e.g. *The Ayatollah song*) or parodies of musical stars (e.g. the Barry Manilow send-up *Because I'm wet and lonely. Not the nine o'clock news* made stars of all four of the principal participants. The memorable face and hands of Atkinson enjoyed an idiosyncratic career as a one-man stand-up comic, and also starred in his own eccentric comedy drama serial on TV called *The black adder*. The outrageous Stephenson carved a television series *Alas Smith and Jones* whose title parodied the old American western series *Alias Smith and Jones*. (Bob MacDonald, 13th Feb 1986).

AYATOLLAH SONG
Tracks: / Ayatollah song / Gob on you.
7" Single: Released Dec '80, on BBC, by BBC Records & Tapes. Deleted '87. Catalogue no: **RESL 88**

Not The US...

NOT THE US PRESIDENTIAL PRESS....
Tracks: / Not the US presidential press: *Various artists*.
7" Single: Released Oct '84, on BBC, by BBC Records & Tapes. Deleted '87. Catalogue no: **RESL 150**

Notch, Kenny

RING UP MY NUMBER
Tracks: / Ring up my number / Ring up my number (Version).
12" Single: Released Dec '86, on Unity Sound, Catalogue no: **UN 022**

Notch, Trevor

BIP BIP BIP BIP BOP BOP BOP
Tracks: / Bip bip bip bip bop bop bop / Just cool.
7" Single: Released Feb '86, on Island, by Island Records. Deleted '87. Catalogue no: **12IS 264**

FAMILY COURT
Tracks: / Family court.
12" Single: Released Feb '87, on Sound Disc, Catalogue no: **SDR 001**

Notes, Freddie

MONTEGO BAY
Tracks: / Montego Bay.
7" Single: Released Mar '78, on Trojan, by Trojan Records. Deleted '81. Catalogue no: **TR 7791**

Nothing But Happiness

COULDN'T MAKE YOU MINE
Tracks: / Couldn't make you mine / Narcotics day.
12" Single: Released Jun '86, on Remorse, Catalogue no: **LOST 1**

NARCOTICS DAY
Tracks: / Narcotics day.
7" Single: Released Feb '89, on Justine, Catalogue no: **JUS 002**

Notorious Garter Kids

LEAVE ME ALONE
Tracks: / Leave me alone.
12" Single: Released Nov '87, on Fourth Floor (USA), Catalogue no: **FF 687**

Notsensibles

I AM THE BISHOP
Tracks: / I am the bishop.
7" Single: Released May '81, on Snotty Snail, Deleted '83. Catalogue no: **NEL COL 6**

I THOUGHT YOU WERE DEAD
Tracks: / I thought you were dead.
7" Single: Released Aug '80, on Snotty Snail, Deleted '82. Catalogue no: **NEL COL 3**

MARGARET THATCHER
Tracks: / Margaret Thatcher.
7" Single: Released May '80, on Snotty Snail, Deleted '81. Catalogue no: **NEL COL 1**

Nottingham Forest FC

WE'VE GOT THE WHOLE WORLD IN OUR HANDS
Tracks: / We've got the whole world in our hands.
7" Single: Released Mar '78, on Warner Bros., by WEA Records. Deleted '81. Catalogue no: **K 17710**

Nova

BLACK HOLE Theme from Over The Moon
Tracks: / Black hole.
7" Single: Released Jan '80, on Epic, by CBS Records. Deleted Jan '85. Catalogue no: **EPC 8145**

IT'S ONLY YOU
Tracks: / It's only you / Cry myself.
7" Single: Released Nov '87, on Caprice Records, by BMG Records (UK). Catalogue no: **CAPR 11303**

Nova, Aldo

HOLD BACK THE NIGHT
Tracks: / Hold back the night.
7" Single: Released Jan '84, on Portrait, by CBS Records. Catalogue no: **A 4189**
12" Single: Released Jan '84, on Portrait, by CBS Records. Catalogue no: **DA 4189**
12" Single: Released Jan '84, on Portrait, by CBS Records. Catalogue no: **TA 4189**

Nova Casper

TURNED ON TO YOU
Tracks: / Turned on to you / Turned on to you (inst.).
7" Single: Released Jul '86, on Bluebird (2), by BMG Records (UK). Catalogue no: **BR 24**
12" Single: Released Jul '86, on Bluebird (2), by BMG Records (UK). Catalogue no: **BR 24T**

Nova, Nancy

Biographical details: This British singer achieved a one-off UK chart entry in September 1982, when her single *No, no, no) reached No.63. After that, the record-buying public said non no no to Nova. (Bob MacDonald, 13th Feb 1986).*

LIFELINE
Tracks: / Lifeline.
7" Single: Released Aug '83, on EMI, by EMI Records. Catalogue no: **EMI 5404**

MADE IN JAPAN
Tracks: / Made in Japan / Jealousy.
7" Single: Released May '82, on EMI, by EMI Records. Deleted '85. Catalogue no: **EMI 5290**

NO NO NO
Tracks: / No no no.
7" Single: Released Sep '82, on EMI, by EMI Records. Deleted '85. Catalogue no: **EMI 5328**

Nova, Paul

FAMOUS BOYS
Tracks: / Famous boys.
7" Single: Released Jul '83, on Exhibit One, Catalogue no: **EX 002**

Novak, Sean

THIS IS YOUR CAPTAIN
Tracks: / This is your captain.
7" Single: Released Sep '84, on Priority, by Priority Records. Catalogue no: **P9**
12" Single: Released Sep '84, on Priority, by Priority Records. Deleted Nov '87. Catalogue no: **PX 9**

Novelle, Jay

IF THIS AIN'T LOVE
Tracks: / If this ain't love.
7" Single: Released Aug '84, on Club, by Phonogram Ltd. Catalogue no: **JAB 6**
12" Single: Released Aug '84, on Club, by Phonogram Ltd. Catalogue no: **JABX 6**

November One

BIG BOY LITTLE BOY
Tracks: / Big boy little boy / Running for your love / Big boy little boy (ext. mix) (on 12" version only) / Running for your love (long version) (on 12" version only).
Note: * extra trfack on 12" version.
7" Single: Released Apr '88, on Epic, by CBS Records. Deleted Jan '89. Catalogue no: **NOV 1**
12" Single: Released Apr '88, on Epic, by CBS Records. Deleted Jan '89. Catalogue no: **NOV T1**

GET CLOSER
Tracks: / Get closer / Never give up.
CD 5": Released Aug '88, on Epic, by CBS Records. Deleted 17 Apr '89. Catalogue no: **CDNOV 2**
7" Single: Released 18 Jul '88, on Epic, by CBS Records. Deleted Jan '89. Catalogue no: **NOV 2**
12" Single: Released 23 Jul '88, on Epic, by CBS Records. Deleted Jan '89. Catalogue no: **NOVT 2**
12" Single: Released Aug '88, on Epic, by CBS Records. Deleted 17 Apr '89. Catalogue no: **NOVQT 2**

SOMEONE SPECIAL
Tracks: / Someone special / Running for your love / Someone special (special 12" mix) (12" & CD single only.) / Running for your love (long version) (12" & CD single only.).
CD 5": Released Oct '88, on Epic, by CBS Records. Deleted 17 Apr '89. Catalogue no: **CD NOV 3**
7" Single: Released Nov '88, on Epic, by CBS Records. Deleted 17 Apr '89. Catalogue no: **NOVB 3**
7" Single: Released Oct '88, on Epic, by CBS Records. Deleted 17 Apr '89. Catalogue no: **NOV 3**

12" Single: Released Oct '88, on Epic, by CBS Records. Deleted 17 Apr '89. Catalogue no: **NOV T3**

Novik,Bridget

DANUBE
Tracks: / Danube / Neutron.
12" Single: Released Jun '82, on Stiff, by Stiff Records. Catalogue no: **SBUY 151**
7" Single: Released Jun '82, on Stiff, by Stiff Records. Catalogue no: **BUY 151**

WEDDING DANCE
Tracks: / Wedding dance / Abracadabra.
12" Single: Released Oct '82, on Stiff, by Stiff Records. Catalogue no: **BUYIT 166**
7" Single: Released Oct '82, on Stiff, by Stiff Records. Catalogue no: **BUY 166**

Novo

EXTREMIX (INSTRUMENTAL)
Tracks: / Extremix.
7" Single: Released Apr '84, on Carrere, Catalogue no: **CAR 315**
12" Single: Released Apr '84, on Carrere, Catalogue no: **CART 315**

Novo Combo

TATTOO
Tracks: / Tattoo / Light of the world.
7" Single: Released Feb '82, on Polydor, by Polydor Ltd. Deleted Feb '87. Catalogue no: **POSP 404**

UP PERISCOPE
Tracks: / Up periscope / Do you wanna shake.
7" Single: Released Sep '81, on Polydor, by Polydor Ltd. Deleted '84. Catalogue no: **POSP 329**

Novocento

MOVIN' ON
Tracks: / Movin' on.
7" Single: Released Jan '85, on WEA, by WEA Records. Catalogue no: **X 9427**

Now (group)

DEVELOPMENT CORPORATIONS
Tracks: / Development corporations.
7" Single: Released Jun '81, on Ultimate, by Ultimate Records. Catalogue no: **ULT 401**

Nowomowa

NOWOMOWA
Tracks: / Nowomowa / 801, Urbania St / Museum of memories.
12" Single: Released Dec '88, on Coda, by Coda Records. Catalogue no: **CODS 25T**

NRBQ

Biographical details: NRBQ. Eclectic American band playing nearly everything, formed '67 in Miami, Fla. as New Rhythm and Blues Quintet: without a single hit, still have a loyal cult following 20 years later. Original lineup: Terry Adams on keyboards and harmonica, guitarist Steve Ferguson, both from Louisville, Ky.; Joey Stampinato on bass and vocalist Frank Gadler, both from nyc; Tom Staly on drums, from Ft. Lauderdale, Fla. They all sang except Staley. Encouraged by Slim Harpo, they played a club in NYC and were signed to Colombia (CBS/USA) who mismanaged their potential: albums *NRBQ* '69 and *Boppin The Blues* '70 with Carl Perkins didn't do much at the time. Guitarist Al Anderson (led Connecticut country-rock band Wildweeds) joined '71; *Scraps* '72 and *Workshop* '74 came out on Kama Sutra; Ferguson and Gadler left, Tom Ardolino joined on drums and the Whole Wheat Horns became a more or less permanent fixture (saxes Gary Windo and Keith Spring, Adam's brother Donn on trombone); they formed their own Red Rooster label and released *All Hopped Up* '77 followed by *At Yankee Stadium* '78 on Mercury *Kick Me Hard* '79 on Red Rooster (distributed by Rounder), *Tiddleywinks* '80 on Rounder, *Grooves In Orbit* '83 on Bearsville; *Tapdancin' Bats* c.'84, *She Sings They Play* '86 with Skeeter Davis and EP *Christmas Wish* '86 on Rounder.
The Kama Sutra LPs have been reissued on an obscure label, *Scraps* on Rounder, and the first Columbia album and the Mercury are still in print: their incessant touring, insouciant stage presence keeps the fans loyal. They perform covers, originals, sometimes anything the audience asks for; Adams has written songs covered by Dave Edmunds, Bonnie Raitt; Windo and Adams toured with Carla Bley '77, played on her Watt LPs *European Tour 1977* and *Musique Mechanique* '78, Windo playing bass clarinet on the latter as well as tenor sax. Donald Clarke, 17 Feb. 1987..

CHRISTMAS WISH
Tracks: / Christmas wish.
CD 5": Released '88, on Rounder (USA), by Rounder Records (USA). Catalogue no: **ROUNDER 2501C**
12" Single: Released '88, on Rounder (USA), by Rounder Records (USA). Catalogue no: **ROUNDER 2501**

N.T.Gang

NO WAM BAM
Tracks: / No wam bam / We're gonna rock you.
7" Single: Released Mar '88, on Cool Tempo, by Chrysalis Records. Catalogue no: **COOL 163**
12" Single: Released Mar '88, on Cool Tempo, by Chrysalis Records. Catalogue no: **COOLX 163**

THERE'S A NOISE GOING ON
Tracks: / There's a noise going on / Lonely.
7" Single: Released Feb '89, on Cool Tempo, by Chrysalis Records. Catalogue no: **COOL 174**
12" Single: Released Feb '89, on Cool Tempo, by Chrysalis Records. Catalogue no: **COOLX 174**

Nu Romance Crew

TONIGHT
Tracks: / Tonight / Tonight (sax version).
7" Single: Released May '87, on EMI, by EMI Records. Deleted Oct '87. Catalogue no: **EA 233**
12" Single: Released May '87, on EMI, by EMI Records. Catalogue no: **12 A 233**

Nu Shooz

I CAN'T WAIT
Tracks: / I can't wait / Make your mind up.
7" Single: Released May '86, on Atlantic, by WEA Records. Deleted Jan '88. Catalogue no: **A 9446**
12" Single: Released May '86, on Atlantic, by WEA Records. Deleted Jan '88. Catalogue no: **A 9446 T**

POINT OF NO RETURN, THE
Tracks: / Point of no return / Going through the motions.
7" Single: Released Jul '86, on Atlantic, by WEA Records. Deleted Jun '87. Catalogue no: **A 9392**
12" Single: Released Jul '86, on Atlantic, by WEA Records. Deleted Jun '87. Catalogue no: **A 9392 T**

SHOULD I SAY YES?
Tracks: / Should I say yes? / Monte Carlo nite.
7" Single: Released May '88, on Atlantic, by WEA Records. Catalogue no: **A 9108**
12" Single: Released May '88, on Atlantic, by WEA Records. Catalogue no: **A 9108 T**

Nuance

LOVERIDE
Tracks: / Loveride.
7" Single: Released Jan '85, on 4th & Broadway, by Island Records. Deleted '88. Catalogue no: **BRW 20**

TAKE A CHANCE
Tracks: / Take a chance.
12" Single: Released Apr '84, on 4th & Broadway, by Island Records. Catalogue no: **12 BRW 4**

Nuclear Assault

BRAIN DEATH
Tracks: / Brain death / Final flight / Demolition.
12" Single: Released Jan '87, on Under One Flag, by Music For Nations Records. Catalogue no: **12 FLAG 102**

FIGHT TO BE FREE
Tracks: / Fight to be free / Equal rights / Stand up.
Cassingle: Released Aug '88, on Under One Flag, by Music For Nations Records. Catalogue no: **T 12 FLAG 105**
12" Single: Released Aug '88, on Under One Flag, by Music For Nations Records. Catalogue no: **12 FLAG 105**
12" Single: Released Aug '88, on Under One Flag, by Music For Nations Records. Catalogue no: **PB 12 FLAG 105**

GOOD TIMES BAD TIMES
Tracks: / Good times bad times / Hang the Pope (Live) / Lesbians / My America / Happy days.
12" Single: Released 24 Jul '89, on Under One Flag, by Music For Nations Records. Catalogue no: **12 FLAG 107**

Nuclear Socketts

PLAY LOUD
Tracks: / Play loud.
7" Single: Released Jul '81, on Subversive, Catalogue no: **Unknown**

Nude, Miss

TASTE MY ACID FRUIT
Tracks: / Taste my acid fruit.
12" Single: Released Dec '88, on Kaos, Catalogue no: **KAOS 011**

Nugent, Ted

Biographical details: This American guitarist, songwriter and vocalist has been bashing away in the field of hard and heavy rock since the late 60's. It has often been reported that he wears ear plugs in concert while submitting his loyal legion of fans to unrelenting heavy metal. He once said his motto was "If it's too loud you're too old". Born in Detroit, Nugent obtained his first guitar at the age of eight. In 1965, when 16, he became a member of a band called the Amboy Dukes. They spent the rest of the 60's playing a combination of psychedelic pop and rock 'n' roll, releasing their debut album in 1968. In the same year they enjoyed a one-off US Top Twenty single with *Journey To The Center Of The Mind.* The band were without a recording contract for a couple of years in the early 70's but eventually re-emerged under the billing Ted Nugent & The Amboy Dukes. As Nugent, the self-styled extrovert, assumed an increasingly dominant role (a trend which began as early as the mid-60's) the group billing was finally dropped altogether in '75 -- to mark this his LP of that year was simply called *Ted Nugent.* It was at this point that Nugent began to enjoy the steady commercial success that had previously eluded him. Each of his next three albums reached a higher position on the American chart than its predecessor. Ted Nugent peaked at No 28, *Free For All* got to No 24 in 1976 and *Cat Scratch Fever* climbed to No 17 in '77. This last album represented his peak: the title track became his only US Top Thirty single and the LP gave him his only Top Thirty success in Britain. *Double Live Gonzo!*, a two-disc concert album released in '78, provided an excellent sampler for headbangers who had only recently discovered Nugent. He continued with his usual formula during the late 70's and early 80's, though his success gradually declined. (Bob MacDonald, February 1986.).

FLESH AND BLOOD
Tracks: / Flesh and blood / Motor city madness.
7" Single: Released Jun '80, on Epic, by CBS Records. Deleted '83. Catalogue no: **EPC 8640**
12" Single: Released Jun '80, on Epic, by CBS Records. Deleted '83. Catalogue no: **12 8640**

TIED UP IN LOVE
Tracks: / Tied up in love / Lean mean r'n'r machine.
7" Single: Released Feb '84, on Atlantic, by WEA Records. Catalogue no: **A 9705**

Null & Void

STILL
Tracks: / Still.
7" Single: Released 14 Jun '85, on Not So Brave, Catalogue no: **NSB 003**

Numan, Gary

Biographical details: This British singer, synthesiser player, songwriter, producer and guitarist was the first superstar of the new synthesised electropop phenomenon which took off at the end of the 70's. London-born Numan, whose real surname is Webb, was 18 when the punk explosion happened in 1976 : it was the liberating effect of this New Wave movement on the music business that made his later exploits possible. His first band, a punk outfit called the Lasers, was formed in '76 and evolved into Tubeway Army by the end of the following year. After building a cult following, first on the London live circuit and then via a few records, Tubeway Army entered the UK national charts in May '79 with the single *Are Friends Electric?* Written and produced by Numan, this mesmerising record was No 1 by the end of the following month. It was soon joined at the top by the No 1 album, *Replicas*, an extraordinary double coup for a previously unknown act. Tubeway Army were, in fact, defunct by the time these successes took place. The charismatic Numan now totally dominated proceedings and subsequent records were released under his name. He quickly consolidated his newfound fame with a second consecutive UK No 1 single, *Cars*, and a chart-topping LP, *The Pleasure Principle*: once again, the two No 1 placings were achieved simultaneously. By chalking up two No 1 singles and two No 1 albums in just three months, Gary Numan became Britain's fastest-rising star since the Beatles. But for all his rapid and incredible impact, his detractors claimed he was totally derivative: there is no doubt that his image owed a considerable debt to David Bowie and Numan himself freely admitted that his main musical influence was John Foxx of Ultravox. Numan may not have been the originator of his bleak, robotic, futuristic style, but he certainly popularised it in a skilful and imaginative way. In the autumn of '79 he decided to embark on a British tour. He formed a backing band called Dramatis and the itinerary was eventually extended to include, Europe, Japan, Australasia and America. The backing musicians simply did their job and nothing more -- the spectacular visual appeal of the shows came from the elaborate, extravagent neon stage sets and from Numan's enigmatic charisma. However, he could not maintgain the momentum of his 1979 breakthrough much beyond mid-'80. He had a US Top Ten hit with *Cars*, but this proved to be a one-off. The 1980 *Telekon* album was briefly No 1 in the UK. From 1980 onwards Numan simply repeated himself over and over again, with each single virtually indistinguishable from its predecessor. These endless offerings appealed to his army of fans but did not make much impact with anyone else, least of all journalists. For example his '82 single, *We Take Mystery*, entered the British Top Seventy-Five at No 9, dropped to No 11 the next week and only managed a total of four weeks on the chart. His peak positions gradually became lower and he was missing the Top Forty by 1985. Having "retired" from live performances in 1981, in order to devote more time to studio and video work and to develop his much-publicised interest in flying, Numan decided to resume live work in late '83. At about the same time he started up his own Numan label which he ran in conjunction with his ever-reliable father (his manager) and mother (his press officer). (Bob MacDonald, February 1986.)
Born Gary Webb, 8th March in 1958 in London. UK singer, synthesiser player. Joined the Lasers at 16, changed name to Tubeway Army in 1977: lineup Numan, vocals and guitar; Paul Gardiner, bass; Numan's uncle Jess Lidyard, drums; made two singles *That's not it* and *Bombers*, recruited second guitar Sean Burke, replaced Lidyard with Barry Benn, disbanded mid '78. Reformed Army to cut demos (issued as *Tubeway Army* '79 on Beggars Banquet). He'd doubled on keyboards before, but interest in synth was timely (inspired by Euro-rock groups Can, Kraftwerk): stream of keyboard bands followed him into the charts as punk faded. LP *Replicas* '79 developed ideas further, though singing was suitable punk monotone. Single *Are friends electric* with insidious synth hook over relentless rhythm was surprise No.1, abetted by picture disc format; album followed suit; *Cars* also No. 1 and with album *The pleasure principle* credited to Numan solely, now backed by Gardiner, Ced Sharpley (ex Druid) on drums, Chris Payne on keyboards and viola. *Cars* also made top 10 USA. He added guitarist Russell Bell, keyboardist Billie Curry (the latter from Ultravox, another influence); '79 stage shows included robots, florescent tubes and other novelties, but sound was somewhat two-dimensional. Collaborated with Robert Palmer on his *Clues* '79, writing *I dream of wires.* His own *Telekon* '80 was No. 1 LP, single *I die, you die* No. 6, but signs that interest was flagging and music press critism led to retirement from live performance: *Living ornaments 1979-80* made No. 2 in the album chart by being available for one month, then deleted. The new decade was littered with synth bands; backing group now called Dramatis, with Dennis Hines replacing Currie, failed to carve own niche despite Numan fronting them for Top 40 single *Love needs no disguise*; he summed up his career on *Newman Numan*, came back with albums *Dance* '81, *I assasin* '82, *Warriors* '83; number of guests on these LPs included guitarist Bill Nelson , drummer Roger Taylor from Queen, Jim Morrisey on sax, Pino Palladino on bass, etc. suggests that he was held in esteem by fellow musicians. Hard core fans remained to give him Top 20 hits with *We take mystery to bed* (Top 10), *Music for chameleons* and *White boys and heroes* '82, *Warriors* and *Sister surprise* '83; Top 40 *Berserker* '84 was the first release on his own Numa label, also impressive, place as synth pioneer assured; if it seems he has wrung maximum mileage from his ideas, refreshing duet *Change your mind* '85 with Shakatak keyboardist Bill Sharpe showed possible willingness to adapt. He is also well known for interest in flying and owns several vintage planes. (Donald Clarke, February 1987)1.

1978/79 VOL.2
12" Single: Released Mar '85, on Beggars Banquet, by Beggars Banquet Records. Catalogue no: **BEG 123E**

1978/79 VOL.3 6-track EP
12" Single: Released Feb '85, on Beggars Banquet, by Beggars Banquet Records. Catalogue no: **BEG 124E**

AMERICA
Tracks: / America / Respect / New anger (Available on 12" format only.).
CD 5": Released Nov '88, on Illegal, by Faulty Products Records. Catalogue no: **ILSCD 1004**
7" Pic: Released Nov '88, on Illegal, by Faulty Products Records. Catalogue no: **ILSPD 1004**
7" Single: Released Nov '88, on Illegal, by Faulty Products Records. Catalogue no: **ILS**

1004
12" Single: Released Nov '88, on Illegal, by Faulty Products Records. Catalogue no: **ILST 1004**

ARE FRIENDS ELECTRIC
Tracks: / Are friends electric / Berserker / Cars / We are glass.
7" EP: Released Apr '85, on Numa, by Numa Records. Catalogue no: **NUM 7**
7" Single: Released Apr '85, on Numa, by Numa Records. Catalogue no: **NU 7**

BERSERKER
7" Single: Released Oct '84, on Numa, by Numa Records. Catalogue no: **NU 4**
12" Single: Released Oct '84, on Numa, by Numa Records. Catalogue no: **NUM 4**

CALL OUT THE DOGS
Tracks: / Call out the dogs.
7" Single: Released Sep '85, on Numa, by Numa Records. Catalogue no: **NU 11**
12" Single: Released Sep '85, on Numa, by Numa Records. Catalogue no: **NUM 11**

CARS
Tracks: / Cars / Are friends electric / We are glass (On 12" version only.) / I die you die (On 12" version only.).
7" Pic: Released Sep '87, on Beggars Banquet, by Beggars Banquet Records. Catalogue no: **BEG 199 P**
Cassingle: Released Apr '81, on WEA, by WEA Records. Deleted Apr '86. Catalogue no: **SPC 7**
7" Single: Released Aug '79, on Beggars Banquet, by Beggars Banquet Records. Catalogue no: **BEG 23**

CARS (E REG MODEL)
Tracks: / Are "friends" electric? / I die, you die / We are glass / Cars (E reg model) (Ext.) (Available on 12" only.) / Motorway mix.
7" Single: Released Aug '87, on Beggars Banquet, by Beggars Banquet Records. Catalogue no: **BEG 199**
12" Single: Released Aug '87, on Beggars Banquet, by Beggars Banquet Records. Catalogue no: **BEG 199 T**

COMPLEX
Tracks: / Complex.
7" Single: Released Nov '79, on Beggars Banquet, by Beggars Banquet Records. Deleted '82. Catalogue no: **BEG 29**

I CAN'T STOP
Tracks: / I can't stop / Faces.
10" single: Released Jun '86, on Numa, by Numa Records. Catalogue no: **NUDJ 17**
12" Pic: Released Jun '86, on Numa, by Numa Records. Catalogue no: **NUMP 17**
7" Pic: Released Jun '86, on Numa, by Numa Records. Catalogue no: **NUP 17**
7" Single: Released Jun '86, on Numa, by Numa Records. Catalogue no: **NU 17**
12" Single: Released Jun '86, on Numa, by Numa Records. Catalogue no: **NUM 17**

I DIE - YOU DIE
Tracks: / I die - you die / Down in the park (piano version).
7" Single: Released Aug '80, on Beggars Banquet, by Beggars Banquet Records. Deleted Jan '88. Catalogue no: **BEG 46**

I STILL REMEMBER
Tracks: / I still remember / Puppets.

Note: All royalties to RSPCA.
12" Pic: Released Dec '86, on Numa, by Numa Records. Catalogue no: **NUMP 21**
7" Single: Released Nov '86, on Numa, by Numa Records. Catalogue no: **NU 21**
7" Single: Released Dec '86, on Numa, by Numa Records. Catalogue no: **NUP 21**

LOVE NEEDS NO DISGUISE
Tracks: / Love needs no disguise / Take me home.
7" Single: Released Nov '81, on Beggars Banquet, by Beggars Banquet Records. Deleted Jan '88. Catalogue no: **BEG 68**
12" Single: Released Nov '81, on Beggars Banquet, by Beggars Banquet Records. Deleted Jan '88. Catalogue no: **BEG 68 T**

MIRACLES
Tracks: / Miracles.
7" Single: Released Nov '85, on Numa, by Numa Records. Catalogue no: **NU 13**
12" Single: Released Nov '85, on Numa, by Numa Records. Catalogue no: **NUM 13**

MUSIC FOR CHAMELEONS
Tracks: / Music for chameleons / Noise noise.
7" Single: Released Mar '82, on Beggars Banquet, by Beggars Banquet Records. Deleted Jan '88. Catalogue no: **BEG 70**
12" Single: Released Mar '82, on Beggars Banquet, by Beggars Banquet Records. Deleted Jan '88. Catalogue no: **BEG 70 T**

MY DYING MACHINE
Tracks: / My dying machine / Here I am / She cries (on 12" only).

7" Single: Released Dec '84, on Numa, by Numa Records. Catalogue no: **NU 6**
12" Single: Released Dec '84, on Numa, by Numa Records. Catalogue no: **NUM 6**

NEW ANGER
Tracks: / New anger / I don't believe / Children (Only on 12").
CD 5": Released Sep '88, on Illegal, by Faulty Products Records. Catalogue no: **ILSCD 1003**
7" Single: Released Sep '88, on Illegal, by Faulty Products Records. Catalogue no: **ILS 1003**
7" Single: Released Sep '88, on Illegal, by Faulty Products Records. Catalogue no: **ILSP 1003**
12" Single: Released Sep '88, on Illegal, by Faulty Products Records. Catalogue no: **ILST 1003**
12" Single: Released Sep '88, on Illegal, by Faulty Products Records. Catalogue no: **ILSG 1003**

RADIO HEART
Tracks: / Radio heart / Radio heart (Instrumental).
7" Pic: Released Mar '87, on GFM, Catalogue no: **GFMP 109**
7" Single: Released Apr '87, on GFM, Catalogue no: **GFM 109**
12" Pic: Released Mar '87, on GFM, Catalogue no: **GFMX 109**
12" Single: Released Apr '87, on GFM, Catalogue no: **GFMR 109**

SHE'S GOT CLAWS
Tracks: / She's got claws.
7" Single: Released Aug '81, on Beggars Banquet, by Beggars Banquet Records. Deleted '84. Catalogue no: **BEG 62**

SISTER SURPRISE
Tracks: / Sister surprise / Poetry and power / Love letters (12" only).
7" Single: Released Oct '83, on Beggars Banquet, by Beggars Banquet Records. Deleted Jan '88. Catalogue no: **BEG 101**
12" Single: Released Oct '83, on Beggars Banquet, by Beggars Banquet Records. Deleted Jan '88. Catalogue no: **BEG 101T**

THAT'S TOO BAD
Tracks: / That's too bad.
12" Single: Released Apr '83, on Beggars Banquet, by Beggars Banquet Records. Catalogue no: **BEG 92 E**

THIS IS LOVE
Tracks: / This is love / Survival.
7" Pic: Released Apr '86, on Numa, by Numa Records. Catalogue no: **NUP 16**
12" Pic: Released Apr '86, on Numa, by Numa Records. Catalogue no: **NUMP 16**
7" Single: Released Apr '86, on Numa, by Numa Records. Catalogue no: **NU 16**
12" Single: Released Apr '86, on Numa, by Numa Records. Catalogue no: **NUM 16**

THIS WRECKAGE
Tracks: / This wreckage / Photograph.
7" Single: Released Nov '80, on Beggars Banquet, by Beggars Banquet Records. Deleted Jan '88. Catalogue no: **BEG 50**

TUBEWAY ARMY/DANCE
Note: 2 CD Pack.
Special: Released Dec '87, on Beggars Banquet, by Beggars Banquet Records. Catalogue no: **BEGA 4CD**

WARRIORS (SINGLE)
Tracks: / Warriors.

7" Pic: Released Sep '83, on Beggars Banquet, by Beggars Banquet Records. Deleted Jan '88. Catalogue no: **BEG 95P**
7" Single: Released Aug '83, on Beggars Banquet, by Beggars Banquet Records. Deleted Jan '88. Catalogue no: **BEG 95**
12" Single: Released Aug '83, on Beggars Banquet, by Beggars Banquet Records. Deleted Jan '88. Catalogue no: **BEG 95T**

WE ARE GLASS
Tracks: / We are glass / Trois gymnopedies.
7" Single: Released May '80, on Beggars Banquet, by Beggars Banquet Records. Deleted Jan '88. Catalogue no: **BEG 35**

WE TAKE MYSTERY
Tracks: / We take mystery to bed / Image is.
12" Single: Released May '82, on Beggars Banquet, by Beggars Banquet Records. Deleted Jan '88. Catalogue no: **BEG 77T**
7" Single: Released May '82, on Beggars Banquet, by Beggars Banquet Records. Deleted Jan '88. Catalogue no: **BEG 77**

WHITE BOYS AND HEROES
Tracks: / White boys and heroes.
7" Single: Released Aug '82, on Beggars Banquet, by Beggars Banquet Records. Deleted Jan '88. Catalogue no: **BEG 81**
12" Single: Released Aug '82, on Beggars Banquet, by Beggars Banquet Records. Deleted Jan '88. Catalogue no: **BEG 81T**

YOUR FASCINATION
Tracks: / Your fascination.

12" Single: Released Aug '85, on Numa, by Numa Records. Catalogue no: **NUM 9**
12" Pic: Released Aug '85, on Numa, by Numa Records. Catalogue no: **NUMP 9**
7" Pic: Released Aug '85, on Numa, by Numa Records. Catalogue no: **NUP 9**
7" Single: Released Aug '85, on Numa, by Numa Records. Catalogue no: **NU 9**

Numarx

RHYMES SO DEF
Tracks: / Rhymes so def / Rhymes so def (ext mix).

12" Single: Released Apr '87, on Bluebird (2), by BMG Records (UK). Catalogue no: **BRT 39**

YOU KNOW IT'S TRUE
Tracks: / You know it's true / Rhymes so def.
7" Single: Released Jun '88, on Bluebird (2), by BMG Records (UK). Catalogue no: **BR 50**
12" Single: Released Jun '88, on Bluebird (2), by BMG Records (UK). Catalogue no: **BRT 50**

Number Four Joy Street

STEPHANIE
Tracks: / Stephanie.

7" Single: Released Sep '87, on Golden Pathway, Catalogue no: **GPV 010**

WATCH THE WORLD
Tracks: / Watch the world.
7" Single: Released Aug '86, on Golden Pathway, Catalogue no: **GPV 004**

Numbers

FIVE LETTER WORD
Tracks: / Five letter word / Alone.

7" Single: Released Sep '81, on RCA, by BMG Records (UK). Deleted '84. Catalogue no: **RCA 74**

I DON'T KNOW
Tracks: / I don't know / Mr. President.
7" Single: Released Jan '82, on RCA, by BMG Records (UK). Catalogue no: **RCA 169**

Numero Uno

TORA TORA TORA
Tracks: / Tora tora tora / Tiger.
7" Single: Released Mar '85, on Starblend, by Starblend Records. Catalogue no: **STAR 5**

Nunn, Bobby

DON'T KNOCK IT
Tracks: / Don't knock it.
7" Single: Released Jan '84, on Motown, by BMG Records (UK). Catalogue no: **TMG 1323**
12" Single: Released Jan '84, on Motown, by BMG Records (UK). Catalogue no: **TMGT 1323**

Nuns

SINGLE WILD
7" Single: Released Feb '82, on Butt, by Butt Records. Deleted '84. Catalogue no: **FUN 2**

SUN IS GOING TO GET TO ME, THE
Tracks: / Sun is going to get to me, The.

12" Single: Released May '87, on Hive, Catalogue no: **HIVE 8**

Nuptown Corporation

DISCO CHRISTMAS
Tracks: / Disco Christmas.
7" Single: Released Dec '82, on Springsong, Deleted '86. Catalogue no: **DAF 1**

Nuptown Keys

BEST OF CHRISTMAS
Tracks: / Best of Christmas / Superstar

7" Single: Released Nov '81, on EMI, by EMI Records. Deleted Nov '84. Catalogue no: **EMI 5248**

Nurse With Wound

BRAINED BY FALLING MASONRY
Tracks: / Brained by falling masonry / Short dip in the glory hole.
12" Single: Released Dec '84, on Laylah, by Laylah Records. Catalogue no: **LAY 007**

CUT GLASS POISON
Tracks: / Cut glass poison.
12" Single: Released Jun '88, on United Dairies, Catalogue no: **UD 027**

FAITH'S FAVOURITES
Tracks: / Faith's favourites.
12" Single: Released Jul '88, on Yankhi, Catalogue no: **YANKHI 02**

TERMITE QUEEN,THE
Tracks: / Termite queen, The.
7" Single: Released Mar '87, on Crystal, by President Records. Catalogue no: **WW 001**

Nutmeg

AND IN ENGLAND THEY'RE GOING MENTAL
Tracks: / And in England they're going mental / You're the only one / Walking in the rain.
12" Single: Released May '87, on Molesworth, by New Leaf Records. Catalogue no: **HUNTS 3**

WHY YOU LIE
Tracks: / Why you lie / I'm in the mood.
7" Single: Released Mar '88, on Fenrock, Catalogue no: **FEN 001**

Nuts, Professor

WOMAN DEH YA
Tracks: / Woman deh ya.
12" Single: Released 31 Oct '87, on Fashion, by Fashion Records. Catalogue no: **FAD 049**

Nutwood Pals

RUPERT
Tracks: / Rupert.
7" Single: Released Oct '83, on Rose, by Rose Records. Deleted '87. Catalogue no: **RRS 1**

Nux Nemo

HIROSHIMA
Tracks: / Hiroshima.
12" Single: Released Jul '87, on Clip, Deleted '88. Catalogue no: **DS 5462**

NV

IT'S ALRIGHT
Tracks: / It's alright.
12" Single: Released Jan '84, on Sire (USA), Catalogue no: **SIR 4060T**

N.W.A

EXPRESS YOURSELF
Tracks: / Express yourself / Straight outta Compton / Express yourself (bonus beats) (On 12" only) / Bitch is a bitch (On 12" only).

Cassingle: Released Aug '89, on 4th & Broadway, by Island Records. Catalogue no: **BRCA 144**
7" Single: Released Aug '89, on 4th & Broadway, by Island Records. Catalogue no: **BRW 144**
12" Single: Released Aug '89, on 4th & Broadway, by Island Records. Catalogue no: **12 BRW 144**

N.W.Ten

COOL COOL LOVING
Tracks: / Cool cool loving.
12" Single: Released Dec '81, on P.R.O., Catalogue no: **PRO D 003**

Nya, Sis

FEEL IT
Tracks: / Feel it / Five star version.
12" Single: Released May '86, on Fivestar, Catalogue no: **FS 003**

Nyah Fearties

GOOD, BAD AND ALKIES
Tracks: / Good, bad and alkies.
12" Single: Released Jan '88, on DDT, by D.D.T.Records. Catalogue no: **DISP 14T**

Nyam Nyam

ARCHITECT
Tracks: / Architect.
12" Single: Released Mar '85, on Situation 2, by Beggars Banquet Records. Catalogue no: **SIT 37T**

Nylon, Judy

CARLOTTA
Tracks: / Carlotta.
7" Single: Released Feb '82, on Demon, by Demon Records. Deleted '88. Catalogue no: **D 1011**

Nylons

KISS HIM GOODBYE
Tracks: / Kiss him goodbye / It's what they call magic

7" Single: Released Jul '87, on A&M, by A&M Records. Deleted Mar '88. Catalogue no: **AM 404**
12" Single: Released Jul '87, on A&M, by A&M Records. Deleted Mar '88. Catalogue no: **AMY 404**

MILLION WAYS
Tracks: / Million ways.
7" Single: Released Sep '82, on Noir, by Noir Records. Catalogue no: **NYLON 1**

PRINCE OF DARKNESS
Tracks: / Prince of darkness.
7" Single: Released Mar '83, on Noir, by Noir Records. Catalogue no: **NYLON 2**

Nyman, Michael

IN RE DON GIOVANNI
Tracks: / In re don giovanni.
7" Single: Released Feb '82, on Piano, Deleted '83. Catalogue no: **BULL 3**

O

The following information was taken from the Music Masters database on October 20th, 1989

O, Alexander

WILL IT ALWAYS BE LIKE THIS
Tracks: / Will it always be like this.

7" Single: Released 8 Apr '88, on Intown, by Intown Records. Catalogue no: **7 INTX 1**
12" Single: Released 8 Apr '88, on Intown, by Intown Records. Catalogue no: **12 INTX 1**

O, Bobby

GIVING IT UP
Tracks: / Giving it up.
7" Single: Released Dec '83, on Design Communications, Catalogue no: **DES 6**

O Dev

100 TIMES A WHORE
Tracks: / 100 times a whore.
7" Single: Released Oct '87, on Constrictor, by Constrictor Records (Germany). Catalogue no: **COLL 006**

O Veux

LA LA BOLIVIA
Tracks: / La la Bolivia.
12" Single: Released 15 Sep '86, on Stoker, Catalogue no: **TORPO 005**

Oak Ridge Boys

BOBBIE SUE (SINGLE)
Tracks: / Bobbie sue / I wish you were here.
7" Single: Released May '82, on MCA, by MCA Records. Deleted '85. Catalogue no: **MCA 773**

ELVIRA
Tracks: / Elvira / Woman like you.
7" Single: Released Jun '81, on MCA, by MCA Records. Deleted Jun '84. Catalogue no: **MCA 727**

FANCY FREE (SINGLE)
Tracks: / Fancy free / How long has it been.
7" Single: Released Oct '81, on MCA, by MCA Records. Deleted Oct '84. Catalogue no: **MCA 747**

I GUESS IT NEVER HURTS SOMETIMES
Tracks: / I guess it never hurts sometimes / Through my eyes.
7" Single: Released Mar '84, on MCA, by MCA Records. Catalogue no: **MCA 879**

THANK GOD FOR KIDS
Tracks: / Thank God for kids.
7" Single: Released Nov '84, on MCA, by MCA Records. Catalogue no: **MCA 929**

XMAS IS PAINTING THE TOWN
Tracks: / Xmas is painting the town / Thank God for kids.
7" Single: Released Nov '82, on MCA, by MCA Records. Deleted Nov '85. Catalogue no: **MCA 796**

Oakey, Philip

GOODBYE BAD TIMES
Tracks: / Goodbye bad times.
7" Single: Released Jun '85, on Virgin, by Virgin Records. Deleted '88. Catalogue no: **VS 772**

TOGETHER IN ELECTRIC DREAMS
Tracks: / Together in electric dreams (7" only) / Together in electric dreams (instumental) / Together in electric dreams (extended) (12" only).
7" Single: Released Sep '84, on Virgin, by Virgin Records. Catalogue no: **VS 713**
12" Single: Released Sep '84, on Virgin, by Virgin Records. Catalogue no: **VS 713-12**

Oakley, Glenroy

IF IT AIN'T ONE THING IT'S ANOTHER
Tracks: / If it ain't one thing it's another.
12" Single: Released Nov '82, on Exclusive, Catalogue no: **EXC 60 11**

Oakville Tune

HEADIN' HOME
Tracks: / Headin' home.

7" Single: Released Aug '87, on Shark, by Shark Records. Deleted '88. Catalogue no: **SH 1002**

Oasis

CHRISTMAS REGGAE TIME
Tracks: / Christmas reggae time.
7" Single: Released Dec '85, on Oasis, Catalogue no: **ZEL SPS 436**

Ob Jay Da

ALWAYS FOREVER
Tracks: / Always forever.
7" Single: Released Feb '89, on Burning Ice, by Burning Ice Records. Catalogue no: **OJD 74**

ICE/SECRETS
Tracks: / Ice / Secrets.
7" Single: Released Aug '89, on Burning Ice, by Burning Ice Records. Catalogue no: **OJD 75**

Obeah

ZOOM ZOOM
Tracks: / Zoom zoom.
12" Single: Released Jul '89, on Blue Mountain, Catalogue no: **BMD 056**

Obernkirchen

HAPPY WANDERER
Tracks: / Happy wanderer, The.
7" Single: Released Jan '54, on Parlophone, by EMI Records. Deleted '57. Catalogue no: **R 3799**

O'Brien, Dermot

Biographical details: This Irish singer and accordian player is one of the veterans of the Eire music scene. Because much of his material has been available in Britain either at budget price or via mail order, he has never shown up on the UK album chart. He achieved a one-off British chart single in October 1966, reaching No.46 with *The merry ploughboy*. (Bob MacDonald, 14th Feb 1986).

MERRY PLOUGHBOY, THE (SINGLE)
Tracks: / Merry ploughboy, The.
7" Single: Released Oct '66, on Envoy, Deleted '69. Catalogue no: **ENV 016**

WHAT'S GOING TO HAPPEN TO US
Tracks: / What's going to happen to us / Bunch of thyme.
7" Single: Released Aug '82, on Ritz, by Ritz Records. Catalogue no: **RITZ 021**

O'Brien, Michael

ACTION MAN
Tracks: / Action man / Seven quid a week.
7" Single: Released Apr '82, on Zilch, by Zilch Records. Catalogue no: **ZILCH 17**

VEIL OF WHITE LACE
Tracks: / Veil of white lace.
7" Single: Released '88, on I&B, by I & B Records. Catalogue no: **FACS 1001**

ZYLOPHONE JET
Tracks: / Zylophone jet.
7" Single: Released Nov '81, on Zilch, by Zilch Records. Catalogue no: **ZILCH 14**

O'Brien, Paddy

I'M ALWAYS TRUE TO THE ONE I LOVE
Tracks: / I'm always true to the one I love.
7" Single: Released '88, on I&B, by I & B Records. Catalogue no: **CMR 71**

O'Brien, Richard

SHOCK TREATMENT
Tracks: / Shock treatment.
7" Single: Released Jan '82, on Warner Bros., by WEA Records. Deleted Jan '85. Catalogue no: **K 17882**

O'Brien, Stuart

LIVE TO BE OLD
Tracks: / Live to be old / Live to be old (Instrumental).
7" Single: Released Feb '86, on AGR, Deleted '87. Catalogue no: **AGR 4**

O'Bryan

I'M FREAKY
Tracks: / I'm freaky.
7" Single: Released Apr '83, on Capitol, by EMI Records. Deleted '88. Catalogue no: **12 CL 286**
7" Single: Released Apr '83, on Capitol, by EMI Records. Deleted '88. Catalogue no: **CL 286**

STILL WATER
Tracks: / Still water / Can't live without your love.
7" Single: Released Apr '82, on Capitol, by EMI Records. Deleted Apr '85. Catalogue no: **CL 240**
12" Single: Released Apr '82, on Capitol, by EMI Records. Deleted Apr '85. Catalogue no: **12CL 240**

Obscur, Clair

SMURF IN THE GULAG
Tracks: / Smurf in the gulag / La ballade de genes heureux.
12" Single: Released Oct '86, on Cathexis, by Cathexis Records. Catalogue no: **CRC 069**

Obscured By Degrees

I'M DYING
Tracks: / I'm dying / Woman like you.
7" Single: Released Mar '82, on KA, Catalogue no: **KA 10**

Ocasek, Ric

EMOTION IN MOTION
Tracks: / Emotion in motion / P.F.J. / Step by step (Extra track on 12' version only.).
7" Single: Released Oct '86, on Geffen, by Geffen Records (USA). Deleted Jan '88. Catalogue no: **GEF 9**
12" Single: Released Oct '86, on Geffen, by Geffen Records (USA). Deleted Jan '88. Catalogue no: **GEF 9 T**

Occult Chemistry

OCCULT CHEMISTRY
Tracks: / Occult chemistry.
7" Single: Released Jun '81, on Dining Out, by Dining Out Records. Catalogue no: **TUX 4**

Ocean

LIFE IS GOOD
Tracks: / Life is good.
7" Single: Released Dec '84, on New Stars, by New Stars Records. Catalogue no: **BRIGHT 1**

YOU ARE
Tracks: / You are.
12" Single: Released 8 Aug '88, on Ocean (1), by Ocean Records. Catalogue no: **001088**

YOU ARE TO BE MINE
Tracks: / You are to be mine.
12" Single: Released Jul '88, on Ocean (1), by Ocean Records. Catalogue no: **GPS 001**

Ocean, Billy

Biographical details: This British singer, songwriter, producer and multi-instrumentalist was born Leslie Charles in Trinidad but moved with his family to the East End of London when he was seven. One of six children, he grew up with a love of calypso, soul and pop music and while building his early career by singing in club groups he worked by day as a Savile Row tailor. His success began in early 1976 after he teamed up with record producer Ben Findon. Choosing the name Billy Ocean simply because he thought it easily memorable for the public, he chalked up four UK Top Twenty singles during 1976-77, all written by him and Findon and produced by Findon. The first and fourth hits -- *Love Really Hurts Without You* and *Red Light Spells Danger* -- both reached No 2 and the former was also an American Top Thirty hit. Ocean's singles of this period were highly catchy slices of pop-soul which relived the Motown sound of the 60's while meeting contemporary disco demands. Ocean did not achieve another major success until 1984 and at one time he considered quitting the music business. But his morale and reputation were sustained by a batch of assorted mini-triumphs. His singles *American Hearts* and *Are You Ready?* were minor UK hits in '79 and '80 respectively and in early '81 the Nolans cruised to No 12 on the British listings with a cover version of his *Who's Gonna Rock You?* Late in '81 Ocean achieved a substantial success on the American soul chart and a modest showing on the Hot Hundred pop list with *Nights (Feel Like Getting Down)*. When he released *European Queen (No More Love On The Run)* in Britain in May '84 the underwhelming response suggested that this single was going the same way as his other recent releases. But on changing its title to *Caribbean Queen*, this excellent record became a monster in the States. In addition to hitting No 1 on the soul and dance charts it knocked Stevie Wonder off the top of the Billboard Hot Hundred in November of that year. The success rebounded to Britain, where it reached No 6. Working with producer/co-writer Keith Diamond (also born in Trinidad), Ocean quickly consolidated his renaissance: the *Suddenly* album was a big seller on both sides of the Atlantic and yielded the 1985 single smashes *Loverboy* and the title track, *Suddenly*. In early '86 Ocean produced a UK Top Thirty hit for Ruby Turner & Jonathan Butler with a remake of the Staple Singers' hit *If You're Ready (Come Go With Me)*. Now bigger than ever, Ocean simultaneously achieved his first-ever British No 1, and another US monster, with a song which perhaps summed up his own career -- *When The Going Gets Tough, The Tough Get Going*. (Bob MacDonald, February 1986.).

6 TRACK HITS
Tracks: / Love really hurts without you / Who's gonna rock you / Are you ready / American hearts / Stop me / Red light spells danger.
7" EP: Released Sep '83, on Scoop 33, by Pickwick Records. Catalogue no: **7SR 5024**

AMERICAN HEARTS
Tracks: / American hearts.
7" Single: Released Jan '79, on GTO, Deleted '82. Catalogue no: **GT 244**

ARE YOU READY
Tracks: / Are you ready.
7" Single: Released Jan '80, on GTO, Deleted '83. Catalogue no: **GT 259**

BITTERSWEET
Tracks: / Bitter sweet / Bittersweet (inst.).
7" Single: Released Oct '86, on Jive, by Zomba Records. Catalogue no: **JIVE 133**
12" Single: Released Oct '86, on Jive, by Zomba Records. Catalogue no: **JIVET 133**

CALYPSO CRAZY
Tracks: / Calypso crazy / Let's get back together.
CD 5": Released May '88, on Jive, by Zomba Records. Deleted '88. Catalogue no: **BOSSCD 2**
7" Single: Released 23 Apr '88, on Jive, by Zomba Records. Deleted '88. Catalogue no: **BOS 2**
12" Single: Released 23 Apr '88, on Jive, by Zomba Records. Deleted '88. Catalogue no: **BOST 2**

CARIBBEAN QUEEN
Tracks: / Caribbean queen.
Cassingle: Released Sep '84, on Jive, by Zomba Records. Catalogue no: **JIVEK 77**
7" Single: Released Sep '84, on Jive, by Zomba Records. Deleted '88. Catalogue no: **JIVE 77**
12" Single: Released Sep '84, on Jive, by Zomba Records. Deleted '87. Catalogue no: **JIVET 77**

COLOUR OF LOVE
Tracks: / Colour of love.
CD 5": Released 23 Jul '88, on Jive, by Zomba Records. Deleted '88. Catalogue no: **BOSCD 3**
7" Single: Released 23 Jul '88, on Jive, by Zomba Records. Deleted '88. Catalogue no: **BOS 3**
12" Single: Released 23 Jul '88, on Jive, by Zomba Records. Deleted '88. Catalogue no: **BOST 3**

EUROPEAN QUEEN (NO MORE LOVE ON THE RUN)
Tracks: / European queen (no more love on the run).
7" Single: Released May '84, on Jive, by Zomba Records. Catalogue no: **JIVE 55**
12" Single: Released Jun '84, on Jive, by Zomba Records. Catalogue no: **JIVEC 55**
12" Single: Released May '84, on Jive, by

Zomba Records. Catalogue no: **JIVET 55**

GET OUT OF MY DREAMS, GET INTO MY CAR
Tracks: / Get out of my dreams, get into my car / Showdown.
7" Single: Released Jan '88, on Jive, by Zomba Records. Deleted '88. Catalogue no: **BOS 1**
12" Single: Released Jan '88, on Jive, by Zomba Records. Deleted '88. Catalogue no: **BOST 1**
Special: Released Jan '88, on Jive, by Zomba Records. Deleted '88. Catalogue no: **BOSR 1**

I CAN'T STOP
Tracks: / I can't stop / Inner feelings.
7" Single: Released Jun '82, on Epic, by CBS Records. Deleted Jun '85. Catalogue no: **EPCA 2453**

LICENCE TO CHILL
Tracks: / Licence to chill.
CD 5": Released Sep '89, on Jive, by Zomba Records. Catalogue no: **BOSCD 5**
7" Single: Released Sep '89, on Jive, by Zomba Records. Catalogue no: **BOS 5**
12" Single: Released Sep '89, on Jive, by Zomba Records. Catalogue no: **BOST 5**

L.O.D. (LOVE ON DELIVERY)
Tracks: / L.O.D. (love on delivery).
7" Single: Released Jul '76, on GTO. Deleted '79. Catalogue no: **GT 62**

LOVE IS FOREVER
Tracks: / Love is forever / Suddenly / Loverboy (Extra track on 12" version only.).
7" Single: Released Dec '86, on Jive, by Zomba Records. Deleted Jul '87. Catalogue no: **JIVE 134**
12" Single: Released Dec '86, on Jive, by Zomba Records. Catalogue no: **JIVET 134**

LOVE REALLY HURTS WITHOUT YOU (OLD GOLD)
Tracks: / Love really hurts without you.
7" Single: Released Jul '82, on Old Gold, by Old Gold Records. Catalogue no: **OG 9197**

LOVE REALLY HURTS WITHOUT YOU (SINGLE)
Tracks: / Love really hurts without you (cupid mix) / Love really hurts without you (dub mix) / Love really hurts without you (1986 7" mix) / Love really hurts without you (instrumental) / Red light spells danger / Love really hurts without you.
7" Single: Released Nov '86, on Supreme, by Supreme Records. Catalogue no: **SUPE 110**
7" Single: Released Feb '76, on GTO. Deleted '79. Catalogue no: **GT 52**
12" Single: Released Nov '86, on Supreme, by Supreme Records. Catalogue no: **SUPET 110**
12" Single: Released Nov '86, on Supreme, by Supreme Records. Catalogue no: **SUPETX 010**

LOVE ZONE (SINGLE)
Tracks: / Love zone.
7" Single: Released Jul '86, on Jive, by Zomba Records. Catalogue no: **JIVE 124**
12" Single: Released Jul '86, on Jive, by Zomba Records. Deleted '87. Catalogue no: **JIVET 124**

LOVER BOY
Tracks: / Loverboy.
7" Pic: Released Jan '85, on Jive, by Zomba Records. Catalogue no: **JIVES 80**
7" Single: Released Jan '85, on Jive, by Zomba Records. Deleted Jul '87. Catalogue no: **JIVE 80**

MYSTERY LADY
Tracks: / Mystery lady.
Cassingle: Released Aug '85, on Jive, by Zomba Records. Catalogue no: **JIVEK 98**
7" Single: Released Jan '85, on Jive, by Zomba Records. Catalogue no: **JIVE 98**
12" Single: Released Aug '85, on Jive, by Zomba Records. Catalogue no: **JIVET 98**

NIGHTS
Tracks: / Nights / Everlasting love.
7" Single: Released Oct '80, on GTO. Deleted Oct '83. Catalogue no: **GT 286**
7" Single: Released Feb '81, on GTO. Deleted '84. Catalogue no: **GT13 286**

NIGHTS (FEEL LIKE GETTING DOWN) (SINGLE)
Tracks: / Nights (feel like getting down) / Nights (feel like getting down) (pt 2).
7" Single: Released Sep '81, on GTO. Deleted Sep '84. Catalogue no: **GT 13 303**

RED LIGHT SPELLS DANGER
Tracks: / Red light spells danger.
7" Single: Released Mar '77, on GTO. Deleted '80. Catalogue no: **GT 85**

STAND AND DELIVER
Tracks: / Stand and deliver / Pleasure.
CD 5": Released Oct '88, on Jive, by Zomba Records. Deleted '88. Catalogue no: **BOSCD 4**
7" Single: Released Oct '88, on Jive, by Zomba Records. Deleted '88. Catalogue no: **BOS 4**
12" Single: Released Oct '88, on Jive, by Zomba Records. Deleted '88. Catalogue no: **BOST 4**

STAY THE NIGHT
Tracks: / Stay the night / What you doing to me.
7" Single: Released Apr '80, on GTO. Deleted '83. Catalogue no: **GT 271**

STOP ME (IF YOU'VE HEARD IT ALL BEFORE)
Tracks: / Stop me (if you've heard it all before).
7" Single: Released Nov '76, on GTO. Deleted '79. Catalogue no: **GT 72**

SUDDENLY (SINGLE)
Tracks: / Suddenly / Lover boy / Caribbean queen / Stay the night / Are you ready / Lucky man.
7" Single: Released Mar '85, on Jive, by Zomba Records. Deleted '88. Catalogue no: **JIVE 90**
12" Single: Released May '85, on Jive, by Zomba Records. Deleted '87. Catalogue no: **JIVET 90**

THERE'LL BE SAD SONGS (TO MAKE YOU CRY)
Tracks: / There'll be sad songs (to make you cry) / If I should lose you.
7" Single: Released Apr '86, on Jive, by Zomba Records. Deleted Jul '87. Catalogue no: **JIVE 117**
12" Single: Released Apr '86, on Jive, by Zomba Records. Deleted Jul '87. Catalogue no: **JIVET 117**

WHEN THE GOING GETS TOUGH (THE TOUGH GET GOING)
Tracks: / When the going gets tough (the tough get going).
7" Set: Released Jun '86, on Jive, by Zomba Records. Deleted '88. Catalogue no: **JIVED 114**
7" Pic: Released Jan '86, on Jive, by Zomba Records. Deleted '87. Catalogue no: **JIVES 114**
7" Single: Released Jan '86, on Jive, by Zomba Records. Deleted '88. Catalogue no: **JIVE 114**
12" Single: Released Jan '86, on Jive, by Zomba Records. Deleted '87. Catalogue no: **JIVET 114**
12" Single: Released Jan '86, on Jive, by Zomba Records. Catalogue no: **JIVER 114**

Oceans

PACIFIC DREAMING
Tracks: / Pacific dreaming / Good guy bad guy.
7" Single: Released Mar '82, on Record Shack, by Record Shack Records. Catalogue no: **SHACK 129**

Oceans Eleven

THIS SPORTING LIFE
Tracks: / This sporting life.
12" Single: Released Jun '85, on Compact Organisation. Deleted '86. Catalogue no: **ACTX 16**

O'Connor, Des

Biographical details: This British singer and comedian is to the vocal chords what Bert Weedon is to the guitar -- the butt of everyone's jokes and a veteran institution of UK show business. Both are successful and likeable, and have taken the ridicule in the right spirit. Born in 1932, O'Connor turned his 60's career as a TV entertainer into a subsidiary pop singer career in late '67. *Careless Hands*, originally an American hit for Sammy Kaye in 1949, reached the UK No 6 spot for Des. In '68 he logged 36 weeks on the British Top Fifty with his No 1 smash *I Pretend*, written for him by ace middle-of-the-road composers Les Reed and Barry Mason. O'Connor's hits were as bland and corny as his television jokes, but they lasted until 1970 and included such titles as *One, Two, Three O'Leary* and *Dick-A-Dum-Dum*. From 1971 onwards there were no further hit singles, but O'Connor popped up in the Top Thirty of the album chart from time to time. *Sing A Favourite Song* reached the list in '72, *Just For You* made its mark in '80 and Des O'Connor Now charted in '84. The latter was typical of his recorded output: remakes of mainly recent middle-of-the-road and pop hits. Throughout his career he has chosen not to commit comic material to vinyl -- although, listening to the above albums, there are those who might disagree. (Bob MacDonald, February 1986.).

1 2 3 O LEARY
Tracks: / 1 2 3 O Leary.
7" Single: Released Nov '68, on Columbia, by EMI Records. Deleted '71. Catalogue no: **DB 8492**

CARELESS HANDS (RE-RELEASE)
Tracks: / Careless hands / I pretend.
7" Single: Released Jun '80, on H.M.V., by EMI Records. Deleted '83. Catalogue no: **POP 2006**

HAZEL O'CONNOR - D-DAYS (Released on Albion)

CARELESS HANDS (SINGLE)
Tracks: / Careless hands.
7" Single: Released Nov '67, on Columbia, by EMI Records. Deleted '70. Catalogue no: **DB 8275**

DICK A DUM DUM (KING'S ROAD)
Tracks: / Dick a dum dum.
7" Single: Released May '69, on Columbia, by EMI Records. Deleted '72. Catalogue no: **DB 8566**

I PRETEND (SINGLE)
Tracks: / I pretend.
7" Single: Released May '68, on Columbia, by EMI Records. Deleted '71. Catalogue no: **DB 8397**

I'LL GO ON HOPING
Tracks: / I'll go on hoping.
7" Single: Released Mar '70, on Columbia, by EMI Records. Deleted '73. Catalogue no: **DB 8661**

LONELINESS
Tracks: / Loneliness.
7" Single: Released Nov '69, on Columbia, by EMI Records. Deleted '72. Catalogue no: **DB 8632**

NEIGHBOURS
Tracks: / Neighbours / Stay in love.
7" Single: Released 7 Mar '88, on Columbia, by EMI Records. Deleted Nov '88. Catalogue no: **DB 9166**

TIPS OF MY FINGERS, THE
Tracks: / Tips of my fingers, The.
7" Single: Released Sep '70, on Columbia, by EMI Records. Deleted '73. Catalogue no: **DB 8713**

TRUE LOVE WAYS (SINGLE)
Tracks: / True love ways.
7" Single: Released Oct '87, on Ariola, by BMG Records (UK). Deleted May '89. Catalogue no: **109 513**

O'Connor, Hazel

Biographical details: British singer, songwriter and actress Hazel O'Connor shot to fame in 1980 via the punk rock feature film *Breaking Glass*, an account of the trials, traumas and rip-offs associated with trying to make it in the music business. The movie was highly praised and the soundtrack album, composed entirely by O'Connor, enjoyed a 37-week run on the British LP chart. It yielded two UK Top Ten singles, *Eighth Day*, a dramatic rock number, and *Will You?*, a slow and powerful love song featuring a moving sax solo by Wesley Magoogan. Born in Coventry, O'Connor left school at 16 in 1971 and dropped out of art college the following year. Dancing and English teaching occupied her for the next three years, during which she travelled round Europe, North Africa, Tokyo and Beirut. She took up singing in the mid-70's, in Germany and France and then London, signing with Albion Records in 1978 (although the *Breaking Glass* work appeared on A & M). After coming to fame with the film O'Connor only achieved one other major hit: *D-Days* reached the UK No 10 position in 1981. The *Cover Plus* album, which peaked at No 32, yielded the underrated singles (*Cover Plus*) *We're All Grown Up* and *Hanging Around*. The disappointment surrounding her career was heightened during 1982-83 when she failed to release any new records. She was locked in a bitter dispute with Albion Records, was in the process of changing her management and felt unhappy with the pressures of stardom and the resulting intrusions on her privacy. She occupied some time with theatrical work and the television series *Jangles*. With a new RCA contract she returned to recording, without success, in 1984. (Bob MacDonald, February 1986.).

AND I DREAM
Tracks: / And I dream / Wake me oh wake me.
7" Single: Released Oct '87, on First Night, by First Night Records. Catalogue no: **SCORE 13**

CALLS THE TUNE
Tracks: / Calls the tune / Eighth day / Give me an inch.
7" Single: Released Jan '82, on A&M, by A&M Records. Deleted '85. Catalogue no: **AMS 8203**

COMPACT HITS: HAZEL O'CONNOR
Tracks: / Eighth day / Calls the tune / Give me an inch / Will you?.
CD 5": Released Apr '88, on A&M, by A&M Records. Deleted Feb '89. Catalogue no: **AMCD 902**

COVER PLUS (SINGLE)
Tracks: / Cover plus - we're all grown up.
7" Single: Released Jul '81, on Albion, by Albion Records. Catalogue no: **ION 1018**
12" Single: Released Jul '81, on Albion, by Albion Records. Catalogue no: **12ION 1018**

D-DAYS (See panel above)
Tracks: / D-days / Time is free.
7" Single: Released Mar '81, on Albion, by Albion Records. Catalogue no: **ION 1009**
12" Single: Released Mar '81, on Albion, by Albion Records. Catalogue no: **12ION 1009**
Cassingle: Released Mar '81, on Albion, by Albion Records. Catalogue no: **CION 1009**

DON'T TOUCH ME
Tracks: / Don't touch me.
7" Single: Released Jan '84, on RCA, by BMG Records (UK). Catalogue no: **RCA 387**
12" Single: Released Jan '84, on RCA, by BMG Records (UK). Catalogue no: **RCAT 387**
7" Pic: Released Jan '84, on RCA, by BMG Records (UK). Catalogue no: **ACAP 387**

EIGHTH DAY
Tracks: / Eighth day / Monster in disguise.
7" Single: Released Aug '80, on A&M, by A&M Records. Deleted '83. Catalogue no: **AMS 7553**

FIGHTING BACK
Tracks: / Fighting back / Reach.
12" Single: Released Jul '86, on BBC, by BBC Records & Tapes. Deleted 31 Aug '88. Catalogue no: **12 RSL 182**
7" Single: Released Jul '86, on BBC, by BBC Records & Tapes. Deleted 31 Aug '88. Catalogue no: **RESL 182**

GIVE ME AN INCH
Tracks: / Give me an inch.
7" Single: Released Oct '80, on A&M, by A&M Records. Deleted '83. Catalogue no: **AMS 7569**

HANGING AROUND
Tracks: / Hanging around.
7" Single: Released Sep '81, on Albion, by Albion Records. Catalogue no: **ION 1022**

JUST GOOD FRIENDS
Tracks: / Just good friends.
12" Single: Released Jun '84, on RCA, by BMG Records (UK). Catalogue no: **RCAT 422**
7" Single: Released Jun '84, on RCA, by BMG Records (UK). Catalogue no: **RCA 422**

PUSH AND SHOVE
Tracks: / Push and shove.
7" Single: Released Jun '85, on Greenpeace, Catalogue no: **FND 1**
12" Single: Released Jun '85, on Greenpeace, Catalogue no: **FND 12**

THAT'S LIFE
Tracks: / That's life.
7" Single: Released Apr '82, on Albion, by Albion Records. Catalogue no: **ION 1032**

TIME
Tracks: / Time.
7" Single: Released Nov '80, on Albion, by Albion Records. Catalogue no: **ION 1006**
12" Single: Released Dec '80, on Albion, by Albion Records. Catalogue no: **12ION 1006**

TODAY COULD BE SO GOOD
Tracks: / Today could be so good / We tried.
7" Single: Released Mar '86, on Red Bus, by Red Bus Records. Catalogue no: **RBUS 2209**

WILL YOU?
Tracks: / Will you? / Sons and lovers.
7" Single: Released May '81, on A&M, by A&M Records. Deleted May '84. Catalogue no: **AMS 8131**

WILL YOU? (OLD GOLD)
Tracks: / Will you? / Eighth day.
7" Single: Released Jun '88, on Old Gold, by Old Gold Records. Catalogue no: **OG 9544**

WRITING ON THE WALL
Tracks: / Writing on the wall / Big brother.
7" Single: Released 20 Jun '80, on A&M, by A&M Records. Deleted '83. Catalogue no: **AMS J7530**

O'Connor, Karen

GIRL IN THE UNIFORM
Tracks: / Girl in the uniform.
7" Single: Released May '83, on Legacy, by Legacy Records. Catalogue no: **LGY 2**

O'Connor, Sinead

I WANT YOUR (HANDS ON ME)
Tracks: / I want your (hands on me) / I want your (hands on me) (Knee trembler mix)* / I want your (hands on me) (Hickey on me neck mix)* / Just call me Joe.
Note: * extra track on 12" version.
CD 5": Released Apr '88, on Ensign, by Ensign Records. Catalogue no: **ENY CD 613**
7" Single: Released Apr '88, on Ensign, by Ensign Records. Catalogue no: **ENY 613**
12" Single: Released Apr '88, on Ensign, by Ensign Records. Catalogue no: **ENYX 613**

JUMP IN THE RIVER
Tracks: / Jump in the river / Never get old.
7" Single: Released Oct '88, on Ensign, by Ensign Records. Catalogue no: **ENY 618**
12" Single: Released Oct '88, on Ensign, by Ensign Records. Catalogue no: **ENYX 618**

MANDINKA
Tracks: / Mandinka / Drink before the war / Mandinka (extended) / Mandinka (dub mix/drink before the war).
CD 5": Released Dec '87, on Ensign, by Ensign Records. Catalogue no: **ENY CD 611**
7" Single: Released Dec '87, on Ensign, by Ensign Records. Catalogue no: **ENY 611**
12" Single: Released Dec '87, on Chrysalis, by Chrysalis Records. Catalogue no: **ENYX 611**

TROY
Tracks: / Troy / Still listening.
7" Single: Released Oct '87, on Ensign, by Ensign Records. Catalogue no: **ENY 610**
12" Single: Released Oct '87, on Ensign, by Ensign Records. Catalogue no: **ENYX 610**

O'Connor, Tom

FESTIVAL SONG
Tracks: / Festival song.
7" Single: Released Apr '84, on Mayfield, Catalogue no: **MA 104**

Octavia

2 THE LIMIT
Tracks: / 2 the limit.
7" Single: Released Sep '86, on Cool Tempo, by Chrysalis Records. Deleted '87. Catalogue no: **COOL 131**
12" Single: Released Sep '87, on Pow Wow (USA), Catalogue no: **PW 415**
12" Single: Released Sep '86, on Cool Tempo, by Chrysalis Records. Catalogue no: **COOLX 131**

October 9

SIREN, THE
Tracks: / Siren, The / Is this the end.
7" Single: Released Feb '86, on Gold Direction, Catalogue no: **FADB 1**

October, Gene

DON'T QUIT
Tracks: / Don't quit.
7" Single: Released Jan '84, on Slipped Discs, by Slipped Discs Records. Catalogue no: **SPLAT 001**

SUFFERING IN THE LAND
Tracks: / Sufferin' in the land.
7" Single: Released Jan '83, on Illegal, by Faulty Products Records. Catalogue no: **ILS 0034**

O'Cuthbert, Martin

BUG-EYED MONSTERS
Tracks: / Bug eyed monsters.
7" Single: Released Jul '78, on Esoteric, by Esoteric Records. Catalogue no: **EEE 1**

CELEBRATE OR DEGENERATE
Tracks: / Celebrate or degenerate.
7" EP: Released Jun '83, on Esoteric, by Esoteric Records. Catalogue no: **EEE 6**

NAVIGATOR THROUGH NOWHERE
Tracks: / Navigator through nowhere.
7" Single: Released Nov '79, on Esoteric, by Esoteric Records. Catalogue no: **EEE 3**

OH GOD
Tracks: / Oh God.
7" Single: Released Apr '85, on Esoteric, by Esoteric Records. Catalogue no: **EEE 7**

SERENE MACHINES
Tracks: / Serene machines.
7" Single: Released Dec '78, on Esoteric, by Esoteric Records. Catalogue no: **EEE 2**

SONGS FOR SQUARE PEGS
Tracks: / Songs for square pegs.
7" EP: Released May '81, on Esoteric, by Esoteric Records. Catalogue no: **EEE 5**

VOCAL VIGILANTE
Tracks: / Vocal vigilante.
7" Single: Released Apr '80, on Esoteric, by Esoteric Records. Catalogue no: **EEE 4**

O'Day, Alan

Biographical details: This American songwriter, singer and pianist was born an only child in Hollywood in 1940, and grew up suffering from bronchial pneumonia. O'Day spent the Sixties working in small-time groups, working for recording studios and scoring music for B movies. The latter gave him the experience he needed to branch out into the world of songwriting. Alan's first taste of substantial songwriting success occurred in 1971, when Bobby Sherman took *The drum* to No.29 on the US charts. O'Day suddenly hit a hot streak in mid-1974, when Cher climbed to No.27 with *Train of thought* and the Righteous Brothers surged to No.3 with *Rock'n'roll heaven*. O'Day's rise was capped by the No.1 success of *Angie baby*, which Helen Reddy took to the top of the American chart in the final week of 1974; the single became a British No.5 hit in early 1975. The song told the harrowing tale of a mixed up girl besotted by her radio, who is eventually transfized by the mirage of a guy (perhaps a disc jockey) who appears from nowhere and then disappears back into the radio. Having written a No.1 song for somebody else, O'Day did the same favour for himself in 1977. *Undercover angel*, another mixture of fantasy and real life, took him to the top slot on the Billboard Hot 100 in July of that year. The song's apparent sexual references caused it to be banned by some radio stations. Musically it was a pleasant pop ditty that made much use of studio echo. As a performer, it was O'Day's only significant hit; the song peaked at No.43 in Britain. Alan did not come up with any further hit songs of the stature of *Rock'n'roll heaven*, *Angie baby* or *Undercover angel*. But he remained in the music business and, in 1985, began composing the music for Jim Henson's latest Muppets project. (Bob MacDonald, 18th Feb 1986).

SKINNY GIRLS
Tracks: / Skinny girls / Love at first sight.
7" Single: Released Apr '80, on Pacific, by Pacific Records. Deleted '83. Catalogue no: **K 11457**

UNDERCOVER ANGEL
Tracks: / Undercover angel.
7" Single: Released Jul '77, on Atlantic, by WEA Records. Deleted '80. Catalogue no: **K 10926**

Odd

LAST TIME I SAW YOU
Tracks: / Last time I saw you / Look into my eyes.
7" Single: Released Apr '84, on OK, by Klub Records. Catalogue no: **OK 007**

Odds

DREAD IN MY BED
Tracks: / Dread in my bed.
7" Single: Released Jul '81, on JSO, Deleted '87. Catalogue no: **EAT 7**

SATURDAY NIGHT
Tracks: / Saturday night.
7" Single: Released 26 Jun '85, on Red Rhino, by Red Rhino Records. Deleted '88. Catalogue no: **RED 001**

Oderant, Roland D

MIDNIGHT EXPRESS
Tracks: / Midnight express / Karl the washerwoman.
Note: This zany group release their debut single, which promises to be a real smash. This talented all male combo, which already boasts a small cult following are currently working on an album.
7" Single: Released Oct '88, on Rana, Catalogue no: **MUM 40**

O'Donnell, Daniel

DON'T FORGET TO REMEMBER (SINGLE)
Tracks: / Don't forget to remember.
7" Single: Released Oct '87, on Ritz, by Ritz Records. Catalogue no: **RITZ 180**

FAR FAR FROM HOME
Tracks: / Far far from home.
Cassingle: Released '88, on Ritz, by Ritz Records. Catalogue no: **RITZC 197**

I NEED YOU (SINGLE)
Tracks: / I need you / Your friendly irish way.
7" Single: Released Jan '87, on Ritz, by Ritz Records. Catalogue no: **RITZ 169**

MY SHOES KEEP WALKING BACK TO YOU
Tracks: / My shoes keep walking back to you.
7" Single: Released Apr '89, on Ritz, by Ritz Records. Catalogue no: **RITZ 197**

TAKE GOOD CARE OF HER
Tracks: / Take good care of her / I wonder where you are tonight / Summertime in Ireland / My side of the road.
Cassingle: Released Jul '87, on Ritz, by Ritz Records. Catalogue no: **RITZC 150**
7" Single: Released Jul '87, on Ritz, by Ritz Records. Catalogue no: **RITZ 150**

TWO'S COMPANY
Tracks: / Two's company / Home sweet / Violet and the rose, The / Streets of Baltimore.
7" Single: Released Apr '88, on Ritz, by Ritz Records. Catalogue no: **RITZ 185**
Cassingle: Released Apr '88, on Ritz, by Ritz Records. Catalogue no: **RITZC 185**

VEIL OF WHITE LACE, A
Tracks: / Veil of white lace / Your friendly Irish way.
7" Single: Released Oct '86, on Ritz, by Ritz Records. Catalogue no: **RITZ 155**

YOUR OLD LOVE LETTERS
Tracks: / Your old love letters.
7" Single: Released '88, on Ritz, by Ritz Records. Catalogue no: **RITZ 132**

Ods Band

RED ARROWS THEME - FLY
Tracks: / Red Arrows theme - fly / Hypercharge.
7" Single: Released Aug '81, on BBC, by BBC Records & Tapes. Deleted '87. Catalogue no: **RESL 95**

Odyssey

Biographical details: Dominated by singing sisters Lillian and Louise Lopez, this black American soul vocal group was initially a quintet but later settled into a two-woman/one-man trio format. They came to fame in early 1978 with *Native New Yorker*, an evocative and well-crafted single which appealed to both dancefloor and radio audiences. Written by Sandy Linzer and Denny Randell, it reached No 21 in the States and cruised to No 5 in Britain. Linzer and Randell had been responsible for several of the Four Seasons' hits of the 60's. Britain's Daily Mail described Odyssey as "the sound and group of 1978" but in fact they had to wait until 1980 for their next success, *Use It Up And Wear It Out*, a straightforward disco ditty with a slight calypso feel, which zoomed to No 1 in the UK. It was, once again, co-written by Linzer, who also produced it. During the early 80's Odyssey became far better known in Britain than in America. Although their early records regularly reached the US disco and soul charts they did not cross over to white-dominated pop radio and thus failed to crack the US Top Forty. In Britain, where no such formats and "crossover" systems operated, Odyssey achieved several memorable pop smashes, including the strong, long-running ballad *If You're Lookin' For A Way out* (No 6 in '80), *Lamont Dozier's Going Back To My Roots* (No 4 in '81) and *Inside Out* (No 3 in '82). After three years out of the limelight, Odyssey returned in 1985 with *Joy (I Know It)*. This single, the group's first release since 1982, was mediocre in both musical and sales terms. (Bob MacDonald, February 1986)..

DON'T TELL ME TELL HER
Tracks: / Don't tell me tell her / Use it up wear it out.
12" Single: Released Jun '80, on RCA, by BMG Records (UK). Deleted '83. Catalogue no: **PB 1962**

EASY COME EASY GO
Tracks: / Easy come easy go.
7" Single: Released Oct '82, on RCA, by BMG Records (UK). Catalogue no: **RCA 295**
12" Single: Released Oct '82, on RCA, by BMG Records (UK). Catalogue no: **RCAT 295**

GOING BACK TO MY ROOTS
Tracks: / Going back to my roots / Bawa awa / Roots suite (on 12" only).
7" Single: Released May '81, on RCA, by BMG Records (UK). Deleted '84. Catalogue no: **RCA 85**
12" Single: Released May '81, on RCA, by BMG Records (UK). Deleted '84. Catalogue no: **RCAT 85**

HANG TOGETHER (SINGLE)
Tracks: / Hang together / Down boy.
7" Single: Released Jan '81, on RCA, by BMG Records (UK). Deleted '84. Catalogue no: **RCA 23**

I KNOW IT
Tracks: / I know it.
7" Single: Released Jul '85, on Mirror (USA), by Mirror Records Inc.(USA). Catalogue no: **BUTCH 1**
12" Single: Released Jul '85, on Mirror (USA), by Mirror Records Inc.(USA). Catalogue no: **BUTCH 12**

IF YOU'RE LOOKIN' FOR A WAY OUT
Tracks: / If you're looking for a way out / Never had it all.
7" Single: Released Sep '80, on RCA, by BMG Records (UK). Deleted '83. Catalogue no: **RCA 5**
12" Single: Released Sep '80, on RCA, by BMG Records (UK). Deleted '83. Catalogue no: **RCA 12-5**

INSIDE OUT
Tracks: / Native New Yorker (Manhattan flute mix) / Inside out (inside club mix) / Inside out (straight remix) / Inside out / Inside out (edited remix).
7" Single: Released Sep '87, on RCA, by BMG Records (UK). Catalogue no: **PB 49623**
7" Single: Released Jun '82, on RCA, by BMG Records (UK). Deleted '85. Catalogue no: **RCA 226**
12" Single: Released Sep '87, on RCA, by BMG Records (UK). Catalogue no: **PT 49624**
12" Single: Released May '82, on RCA, by BMG Records (UK). Deleted '85. Catalogue no: **RCAT 226**

IT WILL BE ALRIGHT
Tracks: / It will be alright / Oh no not my baby.
7" Single: Released Sep '81, on RCA, by BMG Records (UK). Deleted '84. Catalogue no: **RCA 128**
12" Single: Released Sep '81, on RCA, by BMG Records (UK). Deleted '84. Catalogue no: **RCAT 128**

JOY I KNOW IT
Tracks: / Joy I know it.
7" Single: Released Aug '85, on Mirror (1), by Priority Records. Deleted '88. Catalogue no: **BUTCH 12**

MAGIC TOUCH (REMIX)
Tracks: / Magic touch / Happy people.
7" Single: Released Aug '82, on RCA, by BMG Records (UK). Catalogue no: **RCA 275**
12" Single: Released Aug '82, on RCA, by BMG Records (UK). Catalogue no: **RCAT 275**

NATIVE NEW YORKER
Tracks: / Native New Yorker.
7" Single: Released Dec '77, on RCA, by BMG Records (UK). Deleted '80. Catalogue no: **PC 1129**
7" Single: Released Jul '81, on RCA, by BMG Records (UK). Catalogue no: **GOLD 517**

USE IT UP WEAR IT OUT
Tracks: / Use it up wear it out.
CD 5": Released Jun '89, on RCA, by BMG Records (UK). Catalogue no: **PD 49457**
7" Single: Released Jun '80, on RCA, by

BMG Records (UK). Deleted '83. Catalogue no: **PB 1962**

USE IT UP WEAR IT OUT (OLD GOLD)
Tracks: / Use it up wear it out / Inside out.
7" Single: Released Nov '88, on Old Gold, by Old Gold Records. Catalogue no: **OG 9835**

Ofanchi

LET'S MAKE LOVE
Tracks: / Let's make love / Yesterday's affair.
7" Single: Released Jul '80, on RCA, by BMG Records (UK). Deleted Jul '83. Catalogue no: **PB 5263**

Ofarim, Esther & Abi

CINDERELLA ROCKEFELLER
Tracks: / Cinderella rockefeller.
7" Single: Released Oct '80, on Phonogram, by Phonogram Ltd. Deleted Oct '83. Catalogue no: **CUT 107**
7" Single: Released Feb '68, on Philips, by Phonogram Ltd. Deleted '71. Catalogue no: **BF 1640**

CINDERELLA ROCKEFELLER (OLD GOLD)
Tracks: / Cinderella rockefeller.
7" Single: Released Jan '85, on Old Gold, by Old Gold Records. Catalogue no: **OG 9481**

ONE MORE DANCE
Tracks: / One more dance.
7" Single: Released Jun '68, on Philips, by Phonogram Ltd. Deleted '71. Catalogue no: **BF 1678**

O'Farrell, Frank

I USED TO ROCK YOU
Tracks: / I used to rock you.
7" Single: Released May '80, on Ark, by Ark Records (UK). Deleted May '83. Catalogue no: **AR 1001**

O.F.B.

SATURDAY NIGHTS AND SUNDAY MORNINGS
Tracks: / Saturday nights and Sunday mornings.
7" Single: Released Sep '78, on DJM, Catalogue no: **DJS 10910**

Off

ELECTRICA SALSA
Tracks: / Electrica salsa / Electrica salsa (inst).
7" Single: Released Apr '88, on Sonet, by Sonet Records. Catalogue no: **SON 1**
7" Single: Released May '87, on Sonet, by Sonet Records. Catalogue no: **SON 2323**
12" Single: Released Apr '88, on Sonet, by Sonet Records. Catalogue no: **SONL 1**
12" Single: Released May '87, on Sonet, by Sonet Records. Catalogue no: **SONL 2323**

Off Broadway Cast

STAY IN TIME
Tracks: / Stay in time / Full moon turn my head around.
7" Single: Released Feb '80, on Atlantic, by WEA Records. Deleted '83. Catalogue no: **K 11446**

Offenders

WAIT FOR ME
Tracks: / Wait for me / Trevor's trousers (slop out mix).
7" Single: Released Sep '89, on Release, Catalogue no: **P 25**
12" Single: Released Sep '89, on Release, Catalogue no: **PX 25**

Office Boy

GIMME A BREAK
Tracks: / Gimme a break.
7" Single: Released Jul '81, on Rel, by REL Records. Catalogue no: **RES 008**

HOW CAN I
Tracks: / How can I / I get excited.

7" Single: Released Nov '82, on Holyrood, by REL Records. Deleted '87. Catalogue no: **HOLLY 002**

Officers & Gentlemen

THAT'S LIFE AND LOVE
Tracks: / That's life and love / Noise.
7" Single: Released Jun '85, on G.A.P., Catalogue no: **GAP 001**

Offshore

ALL WORK AND NO PLAY
Tracks: / All work and no play / All work and no play (version).
12" Single: Released Dec '88, on Reflections, by Decca Records. Catalogue no: **FLE 5**

Offspring

NOT A SAD SONG
Tracks: / Not a sad song.
7" Single: Released Sep '84, on Offspring Promotions, by Offspring Promotions. Catalogue no: **OP 001**

O'Flaherty, Tyrone

PARTY TING
Tracks: / Party ting.
12" Single: Released Jul '83, on Sunburn, by Orbitone Records. Catalogue no: **SBD 36**

Ogdens

IT'S A BEAUTIFUL DAY
Tracks: / It's a beautiful day / Shades of green.
7" Single: Released 23 Jul '88, on Casca, Catalogue no: **CASC 701**

RACHEL PUT YOUR ARMS AROUND ME
Tracks: / Rachel put your arms around me.
7" Single: Released Jun '89, on Casca, Catalogue no: **CASC 1202**

Oggy

CLOG DANCE
Tracks: / Clog dance.
7" Single: Released Oct '82, on Taurus, Catalogue no: **OG 100**

Oh Romeo

ONCE IS NOT ENOUGH
Tracks: / Once is not enough.
12" Single: Released Oct '84, on Personal, by Personal Records. Catalogue no: **12PER 109**

SAVING MYSELF (FOR THE ONE I LOVE)
Tracks: / Saving myself (for the one I love).
12" Single: Released Nov '85, on ZYX (Germany), Catalogue no: **ZYX 5328**

Oh Well

OH WELL
Tracks: / Oh well / Rio De janeiro / Oh well - remix (12" only.).
7" Single: Released Sep '89, on Parlophone, by EMI Records. Catalogue no: **202 992 7**
7" Single: Released Sep '89, on Parlophone, by EMI Records. Catalogue no: **R 6236**
12" Single: Released Sep '89, on Parlophone, by EMI Records. Catalogue no: **12R 6236**
12" Single: Released Sep '89, on Parlophone, by EMI Records. Catalogue no: **203 323 6**

OH WELL (REMIX)
Tracks: / Oh well (12" ext. mix) / Oh well ('89 dance floor mix) (Not on 12RXS 6236.) / Oh well (U.K. mix) (12RXS 6236 only.) / Rio de Janeiro.
CD 5": Released Oct '89, on Parlophone, by EMI Records. Catalogue no: **CDR 6236**
CD 5": Released Oct '89, on Parlophone, by EMI Records. Catalogue no: **203 589 2**
12" Single: Released Oct '89, on Parlophone, by EMI Records. Catalogue no: **12RX 6236**
12" Single: Released Oct '89, on Parlophone, by EMI Records. Catalogue no: **203 589 8**
12" Single: Released Oct '89, on Parlophone, by EMI Records. Catalogue no: **203 589 6**
12" Single: Released Oct '89, on Parlophone, by EMI Records. Catalogue no: **12RXS 6236**

O'Hara, Mary

Biographical details: Singer and harpist Mary O'Hara established herself as a successful television and concert artist during the second half of the 70's with her classically-influenced middle-of-the-road style. She penetrated the UK album chart in '78, reaching No 37 with *Mary O'Hara At The Royal Festival Hall*, which ranged from interpretations of pop standards like *Bridge Over Troubled Water* and *When I Need You* to Christian offerings such as *Morning Has Broken* and *Lord Of The Dance*. Her 1979 album, *Tranquillity: 20 Songs Of Life*, glided to No 12. (Bob MacDonald, February 1986.).

MESSENGER
Tracks: / Messanger.
7" Single: Released Apr '85, on Valentine, by Valentine Records. Catalogue no: **VALS 124**

ROSE
Tracks: / Rose / Colours of my life.
7" Single: Released Nov '81, on Images, by Images Records. Catalogue no: **IMGS 0001**

YOU ARE THE NEW DAY
Tracks: / You are the new day / Scent of the roses.

7" Single: Released Dec '80, on Chrysalis, by Chrysalis Records. Deleted Dec '85. Catalogue no: **CHS 2475**

O'Hara, Mary Margaret

BODY'S IN TROUBLE
Tracks: / Body's in trouble / Year in song, The.
7" Single: Released Feb '89, on Virgin, by Virgin Records. Catalogue no: **MMOS 1**

O'Hare, Pat

TRAVELLING MAN
Tracks: / Travelling man.
7" Single: Released May '82, on Pax, by Pax Records. Catalogue no: **VAT 1**

Ohi Ho Bang Bang

THREE, THE
Tracks: / Three, The.
12" Single: Released Oct '89, on Mute, by Mute Records. Catalogue no: **MUTE 72**

Ohio Express

Biographical details: The official line-up of this American pop group was Tim Corwin, Douglas Grassel, Dean Kastran, Jim Player and Dale Powers. Those were the people who promoted the records on television and in concert halls, but the discs were in fact created in the studio by vocalist Joey Levine, songwriters Levine and Artie Resnick plus a team of session musicians, all under the supervision of producers Jerry Kasenetz and Jeff Katz. Ohio Express were one of the first successful acts in the bubblegum genre. This form of pop was created by Kasenetz and Katz and yielded a string of hits in the late 60's. The main business brain behind bubblegum was Neil Bogart, founder of Buddah Records, and the style's trademarks were a pounding, simple, dance beat, a repetitive singalong chorus, nasal vocals and semi-moronic lyrics. It was designed to appeal to children and the words were written accordingly -- cartoons, games, comics, sweets and bubblegum itself were standard subjects. Super K, the production company of Kasenetz and Katz, were also responsible for successful offerings by the 1910 Fruitgum Co, the Music Explosion and several lesser names. At a time when hippies and "progressive" rockers were taking music more seriously bubblegum represented the opposite end of the spectrum. The first Ohio Express success was *Beg, Borrow And Steal*, which reached No 29 on the US chart in late 1967, but they are best remembered for *Yummy Yummy Yummy*, perhaps the most irritating record of 1968, a million-selling No 4 hit in the States and No 5 in Britain. There were no further UK hits for Ohio Express but subsequent US Top Forty singles included *Down At Lulu's*, the million-selling *Chewy Chewy and Mercy*. When Bubblegum died in 1970 the artificially-created Ohio Express died with it. (Bob MacDonald, February 1986.).

YUMMY YUMMY YUMMY
Tracks: / Yummy yummy yummy.
7" Single: Released Jun '68, on Pye International, Deleted '71. Catalogue no: **7N 25459**
7" Single: Released Feb '75, on Buddah, by Buddah Records Inc.(USA). Catalogue no: **BDS 416**

YUMMY YUMMY YUMMY (OLD GOLD)
Tracks: / Yummy yummy yummy.
7" Single: Released Apr '83, on Old Gold, by Old Gold Records. Deleted Jul '88. Catalogue no: **OG 9293**

Ohio Players

Biographical details: At the time of their greatest success this American funk band consisted of William Beck, Leroy Bonner, Marshall Jones, Ralph Middlebrooks, Marvin Pierce, Clarence Satchell and James Williams. The roots of the Ohio Players go back to 1959, when Jones and Satchell were members of a Dayton, Ohio, combo called the Ohio Untouchables. That group backed the Falcons on their 1962 single, *I Found A Love*, which was a success on the American R & B chart. Marshall and Clarence later formed the Ohio Players, who recorded several unsuccessful singles in the late 60's. After working hard at their raunchy soul sound during the early 70's, they came to fame in 1973 with the novelty US Top Twenty single *Funky Worm*. It was the first of a series of American million-sellers for the Ohio Players during the mid-70's, all in the freaky funk-rock mould developed by James Brown and Sly & The Family Stone. *Skin Tight* ('74) was followed by a pair of US No 1 smashes: *Fire* scorched up the charts in early '75 and *Love Rollercoaster* rolled to the top in early '76. The band's hits were composed collectively in the studio, with all seven members contributing to spontaneous studio jam sessions and production work. In addition to their highly danceable music the group became notorious for their less-than-subtle LP covers which depicted scantily-dressed models in a variety of sexy poses. Having been in at the start of the disco boom, the Ohio Players did not capitalise on its later development. Their last great moment was *Who'd She Coo?*, which reached No 18 on the US singles chart in 1976 -- it was also their only UK chart entry, reaching No 43 in July of that year. Afterwards their sound became increasingly repetitive and predictable, though they continued recording into the early 80's. (Bob MacDonald, February 1986.).

FIRE (SINGLE)
Tracks: / Fire.
7" Single: Released '80, on Mercury (USA), by PolyGram Rec.Inc.(USA). Catalogue no: **LR 0870**

FOLLOW ME
Tracks: / Follow me.
7" Single: Released Mar '85, on Air, by Chrysalis Records. Catalogue no: **AIR 3700 7**
12" Single: Released Mar '85, on Air, by Chrysalis Records. Catalogue no: **AIR 3700 12**

WHO'D SHE COO
Tracks: / Who'd she coo.
7" Single: Released Jul '76, on Mercury, by Phonogram Ltd. Deleted '79. Catalogue no: **PLAY 001**

Oi Polloi

RESIST THE ATOMIC MENACE
Tracks: / Resist the atomic manace.
7" Single: Released May '86, on Endangered Musik, Catalogue no: **EDR 5**

Oingo Boingo

ONLY A LAD (SINGLE)
Tracks: / Only a lad / Ain't this the life.
7" Single: Released May '81, on A&M, by A&M Records. Deleted May '84. Catalogue no: **PFP 1002**

PRIVATE LIFE
Tracks: / Private life / Wild sex.
7" Single: Released Aug '82, on A&M, by A&M Records. Deleted Aug '85. Catalogue no: **AMS 8244**

O'Jays

Biographical details: At the time of their greatest success this soul vocal group consisted of Eddie Levert, William Powell and Walter Williams. They were named after disc jockey Eddie O'Jay, who became their manager. Levert, Powell and Williams formed the group -- initially named the Triumphs, then the Mascots -- in Canton, Ohio, in 1958 with two other singers, Bill Isles and Bobby Massey. They became the O'Jays in the early 60's. Working with producer H.B. Barnum they achieved their first US Hot Hundred entry with 1963's *Lonely Drifter*, followed by several other modestly successful entries on the pop and R & B charts. But the group were down on their luck by 1968, causing Isles to quit. The following six years were much the same as the previous six: a batch of moderate chart ripples, raised hopes and disappointments. Massey resigned in '72, leaving the O'Jays as a trio. Their career experienced a dramatic turnaround in that year, when they signed with Philadelphia International Records. Teaming with that label's key writing/production team Kenny Gamble and Leon Huff, the group became one of the most consistent exponents of the Philly soul sound of the 70's. Together with such acts as Harold Melvin & The Blue Notes, the Three Degrees and MFSB, the O'Jays helped Philly to become to the 70's what Motown was to the 60's. Between '72 and '78 the O'Jays' US million-selling singles included *Backstabbers* (No 9 in '74), *I Love Music* (No 5 in '76) and *Used To Be My Girl* (No 4 in '78). Four of their records also reached the British Top Twenty, the biggest being *Love Train*, No 9 in '73. Powell was stricken with cancer in 1976 and died in May of the following year at the age of 35; he was replaced by Sammy Strain. From 1979 onwards the O'Jays drifted into the minor league as Philadelphia International lost its grip of the market. *Sing A Happy Song* (No 39 in the UK in '83), *Forever Mine* (No 26 in America in '80) and the classy *Put Our Heads Together* (No 45 in Britain, '83) showed that they could still make good records from time to time, but they were no longer the force they had once been. (Bob MacDonald, February 1986.).

BACK STABBERS
Tracks: / Back stabbers.
7" Single: Released Sep '72, on CBS, by CBS Records. Deleted '75. Catalogue no: **CBS 8270**

BRANDY
Tracks: / Brandy.
7" Single: Released Sep '78, on Philadelphia Int., by EMI Records. Deleted '81. Catalogue no: **PIR 6658**

DARLIN' DARLIN' BABY (SWEET TENDER LOVE)

Tracks: / Darlin' darlin' baby (sweet tender love).
7" Single: Released Feb '77, on Philadelphia Int., by EMI Records. Deleted '80. Catalogue no: **PIR 4834**

DON'T TAKE YOUR LOVE AWAY
Tracks: / Don't take your love away / I just want somebody to love me.
7" Single: Released Sep '87, on Philadelphia Int., by EMI Records. Deleted Jan '88. Catalogue no: **PIR 5**
12" Single: Released Sep '87, on Philadelphia Int., by EMI Records. Deleted Jan '88. Catalogue no: **12PIR 5**

EXTRAORDINARY GIRL (SINGLE)
Tracks: / Extraordinary girl / I really need you now.
7" Single: Released Apr '84, on Philadelphia Int., by EMI Records. Catalogue no: **A 4387**
12" Single: Released Apr '84, on Philadelphia Int., by EMI Records. Catalogue no: **TA 4387**

I JUST WANT TO SATISFY
Tracks: / I just want to satisfy / Don't walk away mad.
7" Single: Released May '82, on Philadelphia Int., by EMI Records. Deleted May '85. Catalogue no: **PIRA 2247**

I LOVE MUSIC
Tracks: / I love music / Used to be my girl.
7" Single: Released Apr '78, on Philadelphia Int., by EMI Records. Deleted '82. Catalogue no: **PIR 6093**
7" Single: Released Apr '82, on Philadelphia Int., by EMI Records. Catalogue no: **CBS 8869**
7" Single: Released Jan '76, on Philadelphia Int., by EMI Records. Deleted '79. Catalogue no: **PIR 3879**

I LOVE MUSIC (OLD GOLD)
Tracks: / I love music.
7" Single: Released Nov '87, on Old Gold, by Old Gold Records. Catalogue no: **OG 9728**

JUST ANOTHER LONELY NIGHT
Tracks: / Just another lonely night.
7" Single: Released Sep '85, on Philadelphia Int., by EMI Records. Catalogue no: **PIR 1**
12" Single: Released Sep '85, on Philadelphia Int., by EMI Records. Catalogue no: **12 PIR**

LOVE TRAIN
Tracks: / Love train / I love music.
7" EP: Released Oct '84, on Scoop 33, by Pickwick Records. Catalogue no: **7SR 5053**
Cassingle: Released Oct '84, on Scoop 33, by Pickwick Records. Catalogue no: **7SC 5053**
7" Single: Released Mar '73, on CBS, by CBS Records. Deleted '76. Catalogue no: **CBS 1181**
7" Single: Released May '86, on Portrait, by CBS Records. Deleted '86. Catalogue no: **A 7235**

LOVE TRAIN (OLD GOLD)
Tracks: / Love train.
7" Single: Released Apr '83, on Old Gold, by Old Gold Records. Catalogue no: **OG 9310**

LOVIN' YOU
Tracks: / Loving you / Don't take your love away (ext. remix) / Don't let the dream get away.
7" Single: Released Feb '88, on Philadelphia Int., by EMI Records. Deleted 31 Jul '88. Catalogue no: **PIR 6**
12" Single: Released Feb '88, on Philadelphia Int., by EMI Records. Deleted Nov '88. Catalogue no: **12PIR 6**

MY FAVOURITE PERSON
Tracks: / Summer fling / My favourite person.
7" Single: Released Sep '87, on Epic, by CBS Records. Catalogue no: **OJAY 1**
12" Single: Released Aug '87, on Epic, by CBS Records. Catalogue no: **OJAY T 1**

PUT OUR HEADS TOGETHER
Tracks: / Put our heads together / Letter to my friend.
7" Single: Released Jul '83, on Philadelphia Int., by EMI Records. Deleted '86. Catalogue no: **A 3642**

PUT YOUR HANDS TOGETHER (OLD GOLD)
Tracks: / Put your hands together / I love music.
12" Single: Released Sep '87, on Old Gold, by Old Gold Records. Catalogue no: **OG 4023**

SING A HAPPY SONG
Tracks: / Sing a happy song.
7" Single: Released Sep '79, on Philadelphia Int., by EMI Records. Deleted '82. Catalogue no: **PIR 7825**

SUMMER FLING
Tracks: / Summer fling / Extraordinary girl.
7" Single: Released Jul '84, on Philadelphia Int., by EMI Records. Catalogue no: **A 4613**

SUMMER FLING (OLD GOLD)
Tracks: / Summer fling.
12" Single: Released Jul '88, on Old Gold, by Old Gold Records. Catalogue no: **OG 4073**

USED TA BE MY GIRL
Tracks: / Used ta be my girl.
7" Single: Released Jun '78, on Philadelphia Int., by EMI Records. Deleted '81. Catalogue no: **PIR 6332**

O.K.?

O.K.?
Tracks: / OK?: *Various artists.*
7" Single: Released May '77, on Polydor, by Polydor Ltd. Deleted May '80. Catalogue no: **2001 714**

OK Jive

ON ROUTE
Tracks: / On route / Congo Kwela.
7" Single: Released Jan '82, on Epic, by CBS Records. Deleted Jan '85. Catalogue no: **EPC A 1934**

TAKE IT EASY
Tracks: / Take it easy / Why won't you dance with me.
7" Single: Released Oct '82, on Epic, by CBS Records. Deleted Oct '85. Catalogue no: **A 2873**

TO YOU
Tracks: / To you / I watch the clock.
7" Single: Released Aug '81, on Epic, by CBS Records. Deleted '84. Catalogue no: **EPCA 1472**

O'Kanes

OH DARLING
Tracks: / Oh darling / When I found you.
7" Single: Released Apr '87, on CBS, by CBS Records. Catalogue no: **650777 7**

Okossun, Sonny

MOTHER AND CHILD
Tracks: / Mother and child.
12" Single: Released Nov '82, on OTI, Catalogue no: **OTID 030**

Oku, Onuara

WI A COME
Tracks: / Wi a come.
12" Single: Released Jul '85, on Heartbeat, by Mainline Records. Catalogue no: **HB 12002**

Old Gold Decades

OLD GOLD DECADES (11)
Tracks: / All I have to do is dream: *Everly Brothers* / To know him is to love him: *Teddy Bears* / Donna: *Valens, Ritchie* / Born too late: *Poni-Tails* / Tammy: *Reynolds, Debbie.*
7" EP: Released May '86, on Old Gold, by Old Gold Records. Deleted Feb '89. Catalogue no: **OG 5011**

OLD GOLD DECADES (12)
Tracks: / Girl can't help it, The: *Little Richard* / Great balls of fire: *Lewis, Jerry Lee* / Ain't that a shame: *Domino, Fats* / Be bop a lula: *Vincent, Gene* / Rave on: *Holly, Buddy.*
7" EP: Released May '86, on Old Gold, by Old Gold Records. Deleted Jun '89. Catalogue no: **OG 5012**

OLD GOLD DECADES (13)
Tracks: / Tom Dooley: *Kingston Trio* / Sixteen tons: *Ford, Tennessee Ernie* / Love letters in the sand: *Boone, Pat* / When: *Kalin Twins* / Whole lotta woman: *Rainwater, Marvin.*
7" EP: Released May '86, on Old Gold, by Old Gold Records. Deleted Jun '89. Catalogue no: **OG 5013**

OLD GOLD DECADES (14)
Tracks: / Sailor: *Clark, Petula* / Sealed with a kiss: *Hyland, Brian* / Run to him: *Vee, Bobby* / Rhythm of the rain: *Cascades* / Soldier boy: *Shirelles.*
7" EP: Released May '86, on Old Gold, by Old Gold Records. Deleted Jun '89. Catalogue no: **OG 5014**

OLD GOLD DECADES (15)
Tracks: / Poetry in motion: *Tillotson, Johnny* / Locomotion, The: *Little Eva* / Let's dance: *Montez, Chris* / He's so fine: *Chiffons.*
7" EP: Released May '86, on Old Gold, by Old Gold Records. Deleted Nov '88. Catalogue no: **OG 5015**

OLD GOLD DECADES (17)
Tracks: / How do you do it: *Gerry & The Pacemakers* / Do you want to know a secret: *Kramer, Billy J. & The Dakotas* / I'm into something good: *Herman's Hermits* / Hippy hippy shake: *Swinging Blue Jeans* / I'm alive: *Hollies.*
7" EP: Released May '86, on Old Gold, by Old Gold Records. Deleted Nov '88. Catalogue no: **OG 5017**

OLD GOLD DECADES (18)
Tracks: / She's not there: *Zombies* / For your love: *Yardbirds* / All or nothing: *Small Faces* / Out of time: *Farlowe, Chris* / Go now: *Moody Blues.*
7" EP: Released May '86, on Old Gold, by Old Gold Records. Deleted Jun '89. Catalogue no: **OG 5018**

OLD GOLD DECADES (19)
7" EP: Released May '86, on Old Gold, by Old Gold Records. Deleted Nov '88. Catalogue no: **OG 5019**

OLD GOLD DECADES (20)
Tracks: / From a jack to a king: *Miller, Ned* / Green green grass of home: *Jones, Tom* / Release me: *Humperdinck, Engelbert* / She wears my ring: *King, Solomon* / Honey: *Goldsboro, Bobby.*
7" EP: Released May '86, on Old Gold, by Old Gold Records. Deleted Dec '88. Catalogue no: **OG 5020**

Old Men

SACK
Tracks: / Sack.
7" Single: Released Jun '86, on Black Lagoon, by Black Lagoon Records. Deleted '88. Catalogue no: **INC 006**

Old Pals Act

TWO UP FOR TROUBLE With Peter Blake
Tracks: / Two up for trouble / Fathers and sons.
7" Single: Released May '80, on EMI, by EMI Records. Deleted May '85. Catalogue no: **EMI 5073**

Old People Are Mad

TRUST
Tracks: / Trust.
7" Single: Released Feb '85, on Wrinkley, by Revolver Records. Catalogue no: **WRINK 888**

Oldfield, Mike

Biographical details: Multi-instrumentalist, composer and producer Oldfield was born in Reading, Berkshire, in 1953 and was only 20 when he came to fame with his prodigious 1973 masterwork *Tubular Bells*. He had begun his career at 14 with his elder sister, Sally, as a folk duo: they released an acoustic album, *Sallyangie*, in 1968. The next few years of his life were spent working as a stand-in musician in the orchestra for the Hair musical and as guitarist/bassist with Kevin Ayres & The Whole World. In 1971 he concocted a 50-minute demo tape which was rejected by all the major record companies -- it formed the basis of *Tubular Bells*, which was chosen by up-and-coming entepreneur Richard Branson as the disc to launch his new label, Virgin Records. *Tubular Bells* was the result of almost a year's work by Oldfield at the Manor studios in Oxfordshire, where he recorded this symphonic LP by playing 21 instruments himself and repeatedly dubbing one layer of sound onto another. The only other people involved were a chorus of singers, a flautist, a string bassist, a drummer, two co-producers and an MC. It was a triumphant fusion of rock and classical music and was hailed as one of the greatest albums of the decade. Its association with the film *The Exorcist* yielded a spin-off Top Ten single in America and assured the album's US success. The album fared even better in Oldfield's native Britain, where it logged 247 weeks on the album chart. There was a memorable four-week period in autumn '74 when the follow-up LP, *Hergest Ridge*, was No 1 in the UK for three weeks and was then dethroned by *Tubular Bells*. Hergest Ridge and the third album, *Ommadawn*, continued to develop the classical-rock symphony idea and each was successful without achieving the mega-sales of the first epic. Oldfield, a previously album-orientated artist, then proceeded to enjoy a couple of surprise hit singles: his exuberant rendition of the Christmas carol *In Dulci Jubilo* (coupled with On Horseback) reached the UK No 4 in 1975 and the traditional *Portsmouth* climbed to No 3 the following Christmas. After two years out of the limelight Oldfield returned in late '78 with the *Incantations* album, yielding the hit single *Guilty* which was Oldfield's attempt at a disco record. During the early 80's he moved closer to the pop mainstream while still retaining a hint of his old esoteric self. *Five Miles Out* ('82), *Crises* ('83) and *Discovery* ('84) were all big-selling albums and he also enjoyed a run of hit singles featuring the golden voice of Maggie Reilly, whose crystal clear singing was perfectly suited to his multi-textured instrumental sound. One of these was *Family Man*, which became a Top Twenty hit on both sides of the Atlantic for Daryl Hall & John Oates in 1983. In that same year Oldfield achieved Europe's best-selling single of '83 with *Moonlight Shadow*, which caused him to break his pledge never to appear on television's Top Of The Pops! In 1984 he and Reilly scored another big Eurohit with *To France*. Oldfield unintentially contributed to one of 1985's biggest hits, when a melody from *Tubular Bells* was "borrowed" for Paul Hardcastle's *Nineteen*: Oldfield claimed, and eventually received, inclusion in the writing credits and a portion of the royalties. (Bob MacDonald, February 1986.).

ARRIVAL
Tracks: / Arrival / Polka.
7" Single: Released Sep '80, on Virgin, by Virgin Records. Deleted Sep '83. Catalogue no: **VS 374**

BLUE PETER
Tracks: / Blue Peter.
7" Single: Released Dec '79, on Virgin, by Virgin Records. Deleted '82. Catalogue no: **VS 317**

BOXED Tubular bells/Hergest ridge/Ommadawn/Collaborations
Tracks: / Tubular bells (part 1) / Tubular bells (part 2) / Hergest ridge (part 1) / Ommadawn (part 1) / Ommadawn (part 2) / Phaeacian games, The / Star's end (extract) / Rio Grande / First excursion / Algiers / Portsmouth / In dulci jubilo / Speak (tho you only say farewell) / Hergest ridge (part 2).
Note: Tubular Bells & Hergest Ridge are remixes
Special: Released '85, on Virgin, by Virgin Records. Catalogue no: **VBOX 1**

CRIME OF PASSION
Tracks: / Crime of passion.
7" Single: Released Jan '84, on Virgin, by Virgin Records. Deleted '87. Catalogue no: **VS 648**

EARTH MOVING (SINGLE)
Tracks: / Earth moving / Bridge to paradise.
7" Single: Released Jul '89, on Virgin, by Virgin Records. Catalogue no: **VS 1189**
12" Single: Released Jul '89, on Virgin, by Virgin Records. Catalogue no: **VST 1189**

FAMILY MAN
Tracks: / Family man.
7" Single: Released Jun '82, on Virgin, by Virgin Records. Deleted '85. Catalogue no: **VS 489**

FIVE MILES OUT (SINGLE)
Tracks: / Five miles out.
7" Single: Released Mar '82, on Virgin, by Virgin Records. Deleted '85. Catalogue no: **VS 464**

FLYING START
Tracks: / Flying start (Vocals - Kevin Ayers) / Wind chimes, The (part 2-edit) / Flying start (12" version) (Vocals - Kevin Ayers).
7" Single: Released Feb '88, on Virgin, by Virgin Records. Catalogue no: **VS 1047**
12" Single: Released Feb '88, on Virgin, by Virgin Records. Catalogue no: **VST 1047**

GUILTY
Tracks: / Guilty.
7" Single: Released Apr '79, on Virgin, by Virgin Records. Deleted '82. Catalogue no: **VS 245**

IN DULCE JUBILO
Tracks: / In dulci jubilo / On horseback.
7" Single: Released Dec '75, on Virgin, by Virgin Records. Deleted '78. Catalogue no: **VS 131**

IN HIGH PLACES
Tracks: / In high places / Poison arrows.
7" Single: Released May '87, on Virgin, by Virgin Records. Deleted May '88. Catalogue no: **VS 955**
12" Single: Released May '87, on Virgin, by Virgin Records. Deleted May '88. Catalogue no: **VS 955-12**

INNOCENT
Tracks: / Innocent.
CD 5": Released Oct '89, on Virgin, by Virgin Records. Catalogue no: **VSCD 1214**
7" Single: Released '89, on Virgin, by Virgin Records. Catalogue no: **VS 1214**
12" Single: Released '89, on Virgin, by Virgin Records. Catalogue no: **VST 1214**

ISLANDS (SINGLE)
Tracks: / Islands / When the wind chimes / When the night's on fire.
CD 5": Released Aug '88, on Virgin, by Virgin Records. Deleted '88. Catalogue no: **CDEP 6**
Cassingle: Released Sep '87, on Virgin, by Virgin Records. Deleted May '88. Catalogue no: **VSC 990-12**
7" Single: Released Sep '87, on Virgin, by Virgin Records. Deleted May '88. Catalogue no: **VS 990**
12" Single: Released Sep '87, on Virgin, by Virgin Records. Deleted May '88. Catalogue no: **VS 990-12**

KILLING FIELDS, THE (SINGLE) Original
Tracks: / Killing fields, The / Etude / Evacuation.
7" Single: Released Nov '84, on Virgin, by

Virgin Records. Deleted '85. Catalogue no: **VS 731**
12" Single: Released Nov '84, on Virgin, by Virgin Records. Deleted May '88. Catalogue no: **VS 731-12**

MIKE OLDFIELD'S SINGLE Theme from Tubular Bells
Tracks: / Mike Oldfield's single.
7" Single: Released Jul '74, on Virgin, by Virgin Records. Deleted '77. Catalogue no: **VS 101**

MOONLIGHT SHADOW
Tracks: / Moonlight shadow / Rite of man (On all versions) / Moonlight shadow (extended version) (CD & 12" only) / To France (CD only) / Jungle gardenia (CD only).
7" Pic: Released Jun '83, on Virgin, by Virgin Records. Deleted '84. Catalogue no: **VSP 586**
7" Single: Released Jun '83, on Virgin, by Virgin Records. Catalogue no: **VS 586**
12" Single: Released Jun '83, on Virgin, by Virgin Records. Deleted '89. Catalogue no: **VS 586-12**
CD 3": Released Jun '88, on Virgin, by Virgin Records. Catalogue no: **CDT 7**

PICTURES IN THE DARK
Tracks: / Pictures in the dark.
7" Single: Released Nov '85, on Virgin, by Virgin Records. Deleted '86. Catalogue no: **VS 836**
12" Single: Released Nov '85, on Virgin, by Virgin Records. Deleted '86. Catalogue no: **VS 836-12**

PORTSMOUTH
Tracks: / Portsmouth.
7" Single: Released Nov '76, on Virgin, by Virgin Records. Deleted '79. Catalogue no: **VS 163**

SHEBA
Tracks: / Sheba / Wonderful land.
7" Single: Released Dec '80, on Virgin, by Virgin Records. Deleted Dec '85. Catalogue no: **VS 387**

SHINE
Tracks: / Shine / Past, The / Shine (extended version) (12" only).
7" Single: Released Apr '86, on Virgin, by Virgin Records. Deleted '86. Catalogue no: **VS 863**
12" Single: Released Apr '86, on Virgin, by Virgin Records. Catalogue no: **VS 863-12**

TAKE 4
Tracks: / Portsmouth / In dulci jubilo / Wrekorder wrondo / Sailors hornpipe.
7" EP: Released Dec '78, on Virgin, by Virgin Records. Deleted '81. Catalogue no: **VS 163**

TIME HAS COME, THE
Tracks: / Time has come, The / Final extract from the Wind Chimes.
7" Single: Released Nov '87, on Virgin, by Virgin Records. Deleted May '88. Catalogue no: **VS 1013**
12" Single: Released Nov '87, on Virgin, by Virgin Records. Deleted '89. Catalogue no: **VST 1013**

TO FRANCE
Tracks: / To France (extended version) (Vocals:Maggie Reilly) / In the pool (instrumental) / Bones (instrumental).
7" Single: Released Jun '84, on Virgin, by Virgin Records. Deleted '87. Catalogue no: **VS 686**
: by Virgin Records.

Oldfield, Sally

Biographical details: British singer, songwriter and multi-instrumentalist Sally is the elder sister of world-famous Mike Oldfield. They began their careers together as a folk duo, Sallyangie, who released one album in 1968. When Mike released the legendary *Tubular Bells* LP in '73 she was listed on the cover as part of the "girlie chorus"; she also guested on several of his subsequent albums. Sally's other vocal sessions included an appearance on Steve Hackett's successful '75 album *Voyage Of The Acolyte*. At the end of 1978 Sally achieved a one-off UK chart entry in her own right. The uplifting *Mirrors* single, a Christmas offering which displayed a slight Kate Bush influence, reached No 19 and logged 13 weeks on the British chart. During the late 70's and early 80's Sally issued a series of solo albums with little success. Many of these saw her caught in a 60's folk/hippie timewarp, although 1983's *Strange Day In Berlin* (produced by Hans Zimmer) represented an entry into the Kraftwerk-type Germanic electropop stakes. (Bob MacDonald, February 1986.).

MANDALA
Tracks: / Mandala / Woman of the night.
7" Single: Released Sep '80, on Bronze, by Bronze Records. Deleted '83. Catalogue no: **BRO 104**

MIRRORS
Tracks: / Mirrors.
7" Single: Released Dec '78, on Bronze, by Bronze Records. Deleted '81. Catalogue no: **BRO 66**

MORNING OF MY LIFE
Tracks: / Morning of my life / Blue water.
7" Single: Released Jan '81, on Bronze, by Bronze Records. Deleted Jan '84. Catalogue no: **BRO 114**

SILVER DAGGER
Tracks: / Silver dagger / Sometimes I'm a woman.
7" Single: Released May '88, on CBS, by CBS Records. Deleted Jan '89. Catalogue no: **650814 7**
12" Single: Released May '88, on CBS, by CBS Records. Deleted Jan '89. Catalogue no: **650814 8**

SONG OF THE LAMP
Tracks: / Song of the lamp / Rare lightning.
7" Single: Released Nov '81, on Bronze, by Bronze Records. Deleted Nov '84. Catalogue no: **BRO 138**

Oldfield, Terry

MAIN THEME FROM JOHN SILVER'S TREASURE ISLAND
Tracks: / John Silver's return to Treasure Island (main theme) / Isabella / Island of dreams.
7" Single: Released Jul '86, on Towerbell, Catalogue no: **TVP 8**

Oldland Montano

JUST A GAME
Tracks: / Just a game (On all versions) / Old man (On all versions) / Just a game (extended version) (CD & 12" only) / Whatever happened to (me & you boy)? (CD only).
CD 5": Released Jul '88, on Siren, by Virgin Records. Catalogue no: **SRNCD 79**
7" Single: Released Jul '88, on Siren, by Virgin Records. Catalogue no: **SRN 79**
12" Single: Released Jul '88, on Siren, by Virgin Records. Catalogue no: **SRNT 79**

LOVE DIMENSION
Tracks: / Love dimension / Secrets.
7" Single: Released Nov '87, on Siren, by Virgin Records. Deleted May '88. Catalogue no: **SRN 67**
12" Single: Released Nov '87, on Siren, by Virgin Records. Deleted '89. Catalogue no: **SRNT 67**

SOMETIMES BLACK, SOMETIMES WHITE
Tracks: / Sometimes black, sometimes white (7" & CD only) / You're losing me (7" & CD only) / Dance in the dark (12" & CD only) / I've got to use my imagination (CD only) / Sometimes black, sometimes white (extended) (12" only) / You're losing me (extended) (12" only).
Note: Oldland Montano are fronted by Michael Oldland & Kay Montano whose debut album "The Time Has Come" has been well received. This track is a different version than that found on the album.
CD 5": Released 17 Oct '88, on Siren, by Virgin Records. Catalogue no: **SRNCD 94**
7" Single: Released 17 Oct '88, on Siren, by Virgin Records. Catalogue no: **SRN 94**
12" Single: Released 17 Oct '88, on Siren, by Virgin Records. Catalogue no: **SRNT 94**

SUGAR MONEY
Tracks: / Sugar money / Whatever happened to (me & you boy)? / Imagination (12" only).
7" Single: Released Sep '87, on Siren, by Virgin Records. Deleted '89. Catalogue no: **SRN 63**
12" Single: Released Sep '87, on Siren, by Virgin Records. Catalogue no: **SRN 63-12**

Ole Ole

CONSPIRACY
Tracks: / Conspiracy.
7" Single: Released Aug '84, on CBS, by CBS Records. Catalogue no: **A 4628**
12" Single: Released Aug '84, on CBS, by CBS Records. Catalogue no: **TA4628**

O'Leary, Kim

PUT THE PIECES BACK
Tracks: / Put the pieces back / Kids downtown, The.
7" Single: Released Jun '87, on Motown, by BMG Records (UK). Catalogue no: **ZB 41411**
12" Single: Released Jun '87, on Motown, by BMG Records (UK). Catalogue no: **ZT 41412**

O'Leary, Tony

ROAD TO HELL
Tracks: / Road to hell.
7" Single: Released Jun '84, on Blue Stack, Catalogue no: **BSR 001**

Olho Seco

OLHO SECO EP
Tracks: / Olho seco.
7" EP: Released May '88, on Pogar, Catalogue no: **POGAR 7**

O'List, David

FALLOUT LOVE
Tracks: / Fallout love / Talking pictures.
7" Single: Released Jul '82, on Underground Music, Deleted Jul '85. Catalogue no: **UMA 004**

Oliver

GOOD MORNING STARSHINE
Tracks: / Good morning starshine.
7" Single: Released Aug '69, on CBS, by CBS Records. Deleted '72. Catalogue no: **CBS 4435**

Oliver, Hayley

SAINT OF THE ORPHANS
Tracks: / Saint of the orphans.
7" Single: Released Jul '87, on Record Shack, by Record Shack Records. Catalogue no: **HALEY 1**

Oliver, James

WHAT WE SAY WITH OUR EYES
Tracks: / What we say with our eyes / I'm not in love with you.
7" Single: Released Apr '85, on Ritz, by Ritz Records. Catalogue no: **RITZ 100**

Oliver, Laurence

TIME, THEME FROM
Tracks: / Time, Theme from.
10" single: Released Nov '85, on EMI, by EMI Records. Deleted Oct '87. Catalogue no: **10 EMI 5539**
7" Single: Released Nov '85, on EMI, by EMI Records. Catalogue no: **EMI 5539**

Oliver, Valerie

GET THE MONEY
Tracks: / Get the money.
12" Single: Released Oct '83, on I.R.S, Catalogue no: **PFSX 1028**

Ollie & Jerry

BREAKIN' ... THERE'S NO STOPPIN' US (OLD GOLD)
Tracks: / Breakin' ... there's no stoppin' us / You can dance if you want to.
12" Single: Released 28 Aug '89, on Old Gold, by Old Gold Records. Catalogue no: **OG 4131**

BREAKIN' THERE'S NO STOPPING US
Tracks: / Breakin' there's no stopping us / Breakin' there's no stopping us (instr.).
7" Single: Released Jun '84, on Polydor, by Polydor Ltd. Deleted '87. Catalogue no: **POSP 690**

ELECTRIC BOOGALOO
Tracks: / Electric boogaloo / Physical clash.
7" Single: Released Mar '85, on Polydor, by Polydor Ltd. Deleted '88. Catalogue no: **POSP 730**

Olton, Mike

FAVOURITE FLAVOURS
Tracks: / Favourite flavours / Love's a gamble.
7" Single: Released Nov '86, on UK Sunshine Records, by UK Sunshine Records. Catalogue no: **7 UKS 1**
12" Single: Released Nov '86, on UK Sunshine Records, by UK Sunshine Records. Catalogue no: **UKS 1**

Olympic Orchestra

Biographical details: The television theme *Reilly, Ace Of Spies* provided Britain's Olympic Orchestra with a one-off UK chart entry in late 1983. The single reached No 26: this was its peak position during an erratic 15-week residency on the Top Seventy-Five, in which it kept going up and down in yo-yo fashion. (Bob MacDonald, February 1986.).

REILLY - ACE OF SPIES
Tracks: / Reilly, ace of spies - theme / Canon in D.
7" Single: Released Sep '83, on Red Bus, by Red Bus Records. Catalogue no: **RBUS 82**

Olympic Runners

Biographical details: With a nucleus comprising keyboards player/vocalist Pete Wingfield, guitarist Joe Jammer and percussionist/producer Mike Vernon, this flexible funk outfit released a series of disco albums between 1974 and 1979. The first few of these, such as *Put The Music Where Your Mouth Is* and *Don't Let Up*, were well received in the clubs but were not great commercial successes and Wingfield found greater acceptance with his international solo hit *Eighteen With A Bullet*. The Runners got into their commercial stride during 1978-79 when *Get It While You Can, Sir Dancealot* and *The Bitch* all sneaked into the Top Forty of the British singles chart. But by the end of '79, with the disco era starting to fade, the Olympic Runners reached the end of their tracks. Most of the members were music business veterans with other projects. Wingfield's next activity was, coincidentally, with another group of (unrelated) Runners: he was the producer of the very successful 1980 output by Dexy's Midnight Runners. The Olympic Runners were particularly notable because they were one of the first British acts to jump on the American-driven disco bandwagon. (Bob MacDonald, February 1986.).

BITCH, THE
Tracks: / Bitch, The.
7" Single: Released Jul '79, on Polydor, by Polydor Ltd. Deleted '82. Catalogue no: **POSP 63**

GET IT WHILE YOU CAN
Tracks: / Get it while you can.
7" Single: Released Oct '78, on Polydor, by Polydor Ltd. Deleted '81. Catalogue no: **RUN 7**

SIR DANCEALOT
Tracks: / Sir Dancealot.
7" Single: Released Jan '79, on Polydor, by Polydor Ltd. Deleted '82. Catalogue no: **POSP 17**

WHATEVER IT TAKES
Tracks: / Whatever it takes.
7" Single: Released May '78, on RCA, by BMG Records (UK). Deleted '81. Catalogue no: **PC 5078**

Olympic Sideburns

OLYMPIC SIDEBURNS (SINGLE)
Tracks: / Olympic sideburns.
12" Single: Released Aug '85, on New Rose (1), by New Rose Records. Catalogue no: **NEW 54**

Olympic Smiles

SOMETHING'S PUSHING ME
Tracks: / Something's pushing me.
7" Single: Released Aug '84, on Slipped Discs, by Slipped Discs Records. Catalogue no: **SPLAT 002**

Olympics

Biographical details: This American R & B vocal group consisted of Charles Fizer, Melvin King, Eddie Lewis and Walter Ward. Founded and led by Ward, the Los Angeles quartet were imitators of the comedy R & B style of the Coasters, one of the hottest acts in the business in 1958, the year the Olympics reached No 8 in the States and No 12 in the UK with their novelty single *Western Movies*. Though they were a good group the Olympics' tales of teenage American life could not really compete with those of the Coasters, who had the talented writing/production team of Jerry Leiber and Mike Stoller behind them. After *Western Movies* the only significant successes for the Olympics were *I Wish I Could Shimmy Like My Sister Kate* (No 45 in Britain in January '61) and *The Bounce* (No 40 in US in June '83). (Bob MacDonald, February 1986.).

I WISH I COULD SHIMMY LIKE MY SISTER KATE
Tracks: / I wish I could shimmy like my sister Kate.
7" Single: Released Jan '61, on Vogue, by Vogue Records. Deleted '64. Catalogue no: **V 9174**

WESTERN MOVIES
Tracks: / Western movies.
7" Single: Released Oct '58, on H.M.V., by EMI Records. Deleted '61. Catalogue no: **POP 528**

Omar & The Howlers

GET IT OUT OF YOUR SYSTEM
Tracks: / Get it out of your system / Get it out of your system (instrumental).
12" Single: Released Aug '86, on Kongo, by Kongo Records. Catalogue no: **DPST 3**

HARD TIMES IN THE LAND OF PLENTY (SINGLE)
Tracks: / Don't rock me the wrong way / Hard times in the land of plenty.
7" Single: Released Dec '87, on CBS, by CBS Records. Catalogue no: **651 138 7**
12" Single: Released Dec '87, on CBS, by CBS Records. Deleted Jun '88. Catalogue no: **651 138 6**

I DON'T MIND THE WAITING
Tracks: / I don't mind the waiting.
7" Single: Released 21 Apr '89, on Kongo, by Kongo Records. Catalogue no: **DPS 5**
12" Single: Released 31 Jul '89, on Kongo, by Kongo Records. Catalogue no: **DPSTR 5**
12" Single: Released 21 Apr '89, on Kongo, by Kongo Records. Catalogue no: **DPST 5**

MR POSTMAN
Tracks: / Mr. Postman / Rap hash.
12" Single: Released May '85, on Kongo, by Kongo Records. Catalogue no: **DPS 002**

YOU AND ME
Tracks: / You and me.
12" Single: Released Feb '89, on Kongo, by

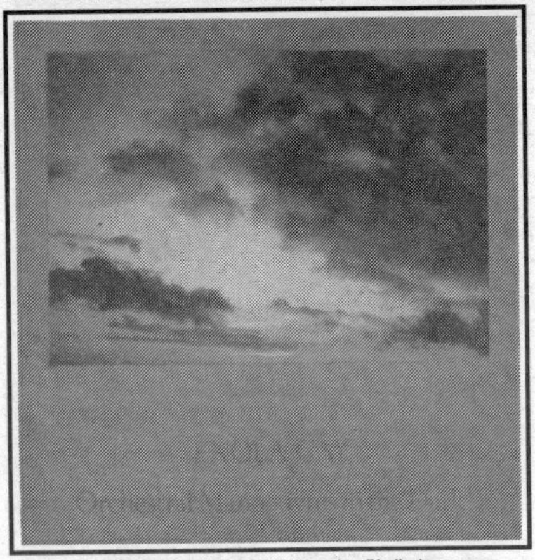

O.M.D. - ENOLA GAY (Released on Dindisc)

Kongo Records. Catalogue no: **DPST 4**

Omari

AFTER LOVING YOU
Tracks: / After loving you.
7" Single: Released Nov '88, on Silhouette, Catalogue no: **SILH 001**
12" Single: Released Nov '88, on Silhouette, Catalogue no: **SILHT 001**
12" Single: Released Nov '85, on Recent Future, Catalogue no: **12 RFR 001**
12" Single: Released Feb '84, on Beau-Jolly, Deleted '86. Catalogue no: **12 BJ 1001**

O.M.D.

Biographical details: Known as OMD for short, Paul Humphreys and Andy McCluskey have always been the nucleus of this British electropop band. In their early days the line-up comprised And and Paul plus a tape recorder known as Winston which was given its own spotlight on stage! The duo later grew into a quartet. Emerging from a short-lived band called the Id, OMD came into being in 1978 and went on to become one of the most successful acts to emerge from the second Liverpool invasion and one of the most successful of the many synthesiser duos to srrive on the British charts during the early 80's. Like many of their Merseyside peers they made their first appearances at Eric's Club in Matthew Street, Liverpool, the late 70's equivalant of the Cavern in the early 60's. They managed to impress the independently-minded entepreneur Tony Wilson, who offered them a one-off single release on his seminal new Factory label. That single was the joyously catchy technopop anthem *Electricity*, which was re-issued in late '79 when the duo signed with Dindisc Records, a subsidiary of Virgin. *Electricity*, which sounded like Johnny & The Hurricanes let loose in Kraftwerk's studios, became a cult favourite and one of the first classics of the new synthesiser pop boom. But, unlike all the subsequent OMD singles, it did not reach the British charts. The rise of OMD was steady and sustained. They logged their first chart single with *Red Flame, White Light*, followed by their first Top Twenty hit *Messages* and their first Top Ten song *Enola Gay*, named after the plane which dropped the atom bomb on Hiroshima. OMD's crowning glory was a run of three consecutive UK Top Fivers, *Souvenir, Joan Of Arc* and *Maid Of Orleans*, all lifted from their third successful LP, *Architecture And Morality*, released in late '81. However, 1983's experimental Dazzle Ships set saw a faltering in their chart fortunes, with the New Order-ish Genetic Engineering only just scraping the Top Twenty and the Telegraph single sinking to minor hit status. This aberration was rectified in 1984 by the highly successful *Junk Culture* album, which yielded four chart singles. *So In Love and Secret* were the hit singles from 1985's *Crush* album. Their somewhat lukewarm reception in Britain was compensated by the fact that they gave OMD their first significant taste of American success. (Bob MacDonald, February 1986.).

BRIDES OF FRANKENSTEIN
Tracks: / Brides of Frankenstein.
12" Single: Released Nov '88, on A&M, by A&M Records. Catalogue no: **SP 12285**

DIN 6
Tracks: / Red frame/White light / I betray my friends.
7" Single: Released '80, on Dindisc, by Virgin Records. Catalogue no: **DIN 6**

DREAMING
Tracks: / Dreaming (Not on 10" & 12") / Satellite (Not on 10") / Gravity never failed (Not on 10" & 12") / Dreaming (extended mix) (Not on 7' & 12') / Dreaming (The William Orbit remix) (On 10" only).
CD 5": Released Apr '88, on Virgin, by Virgin Records. Catalogue no: **VSCD 987**
12" Pic: Released '88, on Virgin, by Virgin Records. Catalogue no: **VSY 987-12**
CD 5": Released '88, on Virgin, by Virgin Records. Catalogue no: **VSCDX 987**
10" single: Released '88, on Virgin, by Virgin Records. Catalogue no: **VS 987-10**
12" Single: Released May '88, on Virgin, by Virgin Records. Catalogue no: **VS 987-12**
7" Single: Released '88, on Virgin, by Virgin Records. Catalogue no: **VS 987**
7" Single: Released May '88, on Virgin, by Virgin Records. Deleted '89. Catalogue no: **VSG 987**

ELECTRICITY
Tracks: / Electricity / Almost.
7" Single: Released Apr '80, on Dindisc, by Virgin Records. Catalogue no: **DIN 2**

ENOLA GAY (See panel above)
Tracks: / Enola Gay / Annexe.
7" Single: Released '80, on Dindisc, by Virgin Records. Catalogue no: **DIN 22**

ENOLA GAY (OLD GOLD)
Tracks: / Enola gay / Electricity.
12" Single: Released 27 Feb '89, on Old Gold, by Old Gold Records. Catalogue no: **OG 4099**

EXTENDED SOUVENIR
Tracks: / Extended souvenir / Motion & heart amazon version / Sacred heart.
10" single: Released '89, on Dindisc, by Virgin Records. Catalogue no: **DIN 2410**

(FOREVER) LIVE AND DIE
Tracks: / (Forever) live and die / This town / (Forever) live and die (extended mix) (On 12" only).
7" Single: Released Aug '86, on Virgin, by Virgin Records. Catalogue no: **VS 888**
12" Single: Released '86, on Virgin, by Virgin Records. Catalogue no: **VS 888-13**
12" Single: Released Aug '86, on Virgin, by Virgin Records. Deleted '89. Catalogue no: **VS 888-12**

GENETIC ENGINEERING
Tracks: / Genetic engineering / 4 neu.
7" Single: Released Feb '83, on Virgin, by Virgin Records. Deleted '86. Catalogue no: **VS 527**

IF YOU LEAVE
Tracks: / If you leave (7" only) / 88 seconds in Greensboro' / If you leave (extended version) (12" only) / Locomotion (live) (12" only).
7" Single: Released Apr '86, on Virgin, by Virgin Records. Catalogue no: **VS 843**
12" Single: Released Apr '86, on Virgin, by Virgin Records. Catalogue no: **VS 843-12**

JOAN OF ARC
Tracks: / Joan of Arc / Romance of the telescope, The.
7" Single: Released '81, on Dindisc, by Virgin Records. Catalogue no: **DIN 36**

LA FEMME ACCIDENT
Tracks: / La femme accident (7" version) / Firegun / La femme accident (12" version).
7" Single: Released Oct '85, on Virgin, by Virgin Records. Deleted '86. Catalogue no: **VS 811**
12" Single: Released Oct '85, on Virgin, by Virgin Records. Catalogue no: **VS 811-12**

LOCOMOTION
Tracks: / Locomotion, The / Her body in my soul / Avenue, The (On 12" & CD only).
7" Single: Released '84, on Virgin, by Virgin Records. Catalogue no: **VS 660**
12" Single: Released '84, on Virgin, by Virgin Records. Catalogue no: **VS 660-12**
CD 3": Released Jun '88, on Virgin, by Virgin Records. Catalogue no: **CDT 12**

MAID OF ORLEANS The waltz Joan of Arc
Tracks: / Maid of Orleans(The waltz Joan of Arc) / Navigation / Joan of Arc (CD only) / Of all the things we've made (CD only).
7" Single: Released '82, on Dindisc, by Virgin Records. Catalogue no: **DIN 40**
CD 3": Released '88, on Virgin, by Virgin Records. Catalogue no: **CDT 27**

MESSAGES
Tracks: / Messages / Taking sides again.
7" Single: Released '80, on Dindisc, by Virgin Records. Catalogue no: **DIN 15**

NEVER TURN AWAY
Tracks: / Never turn away.
7" Single: Released Oct '84, on Virgin, by Virgin Records. Deleted '89. Catalogue no: **VS 727**
12" Single: Released Oct '84, on Virgin, by Virgin Records. Deleted '89. Catalogue no: **VS 727-12**

RED FRAME WHITE LIGHT
Tracks: / Red frame/White light / I betray my friends.
7" Single: Released Feb '80, on Dindisc, by Virgin Records. Deleted '83. Catalogue no: **DIN 6**

SECRET
Tracks: / Secret (7" only) / Drift / Secret (extended mix) (12" only).
7" Single: Released Jul '85, on Virgin, by Virgin Records. Deleted '89. Catalogue no: **VS 796**
12" Single: Released Jul '85, on Virgin, by Virgin Records. Catalogue no: **VS 796-12**

SHAME
Tracks: / Shame (re-recorded version) (Not on CD) / Goddess of love (On all versions) / Shame (extended re-recorded version) (CD & 12' only) / (Forever) live and die (12" mix) (CD only) / Messages (10" mix) (CD only).
CD 5": Released May '87, on Virgin, by Virgin Records. Catalogue no: **MIKE 93812**
7" Single: Released Apr '87, on Virgin, by Virgin Records. Catalogue no: **VS 938**
12" Single: Released Apr '87, on Virgin, by Virgin Records. Catalogue no: **VS 938-12**

SO IN LOVE WITH YOU
Tracks: / So in love with you.
7" Single: Released May '85, on Virgin, by Virgin Records. Deleted '86. Catalogue no: **VS 766**
12" Single: Released May '85, on Virgin, by Virgin Records. Deleted '89. Catalogue no: **VS 766-12**

SOUVENIR
Tracks: / Souvenir / Motion & heart (Amazon version).
7" Single: Released '81, on Dindisc, by Virgin Records. Catalogue no: **DIN 24**

SOUVENIR (OLD GOLD)
Tracks: / Souvenir / Talking loud and clear.
12" Single: Released 28 Mar '89, on Old Gold, by Old Gold Records. Catalogue no: **OG 4109**

TALKING LOUD AND CLEAR
Tracks: / Talking loud and clear (7" only) / Julia's song (7" only) / Talking loud and clear (extended version) (12" only) / Julia's song (extended version) (12" only).
7" Single: Released Jun '84, on Virgin, by Virgin Records. Catalogue no: **VS 685**
12" Single: Released Jun '84, on Virgin, by Virgin Records. Catalogue no: **VS 685-12**

TELEGRAPH
Tracks: / Telegraph.
7" Single: Released Apr '83, on Virgin, by Virgin Records. Deleted '86. Catalogue no: **VS 580**

TESLA GIRLS (See panel below)
Tracks: / Tesla girls / Garden city / Telegraph (live).
7" Single: Released Aug '84, on Virgin, by Virgin Records. Deleted '86. Catalogue no: **VS 705**
12" Single: Released Aug '84, on Virgin, by Virgin Records. Catalogue no: **VS 705-12**

WE LOVE YOU
Tracks: / We love you / We love you (dub) / We love you (extended) (On 12" only) / If you leave (On 7" set only) / 88 seconds in Greensboro' (On 7" set only).
7" Set: Released Nov '86, on Virgin, by Virgin Records. Catalogue no: **VSD 911**
7" Single: Released Nov '86, on Virgin, by Virgin Records. Deleted '89. Catalogue no: **VS 911**
12" Single: Released Nov '86, on Virgin, by Virgin Records. Catalogue no: **VS 911-12**

Omega Theatre

ROBOTS MACHINES AND SILICON DREAMS
Tracks: / Robots machines and silicon dreams / Power of advertising.
7" Single: Released Nov '82, on Sunny, by Sunny Records. Catalogue no: **EON 100**

Omega Tribe

ANGRY SONGS
Tracks: / Angry songs.
7" Single: Released Jun '83, on Crass, by Crass Records. Catalogue no: **CRASS 221984/10**

IT'S A HARD LIFE
Tracks: / It's a hard life.
7" Single: Released Sep '84, on Corpus

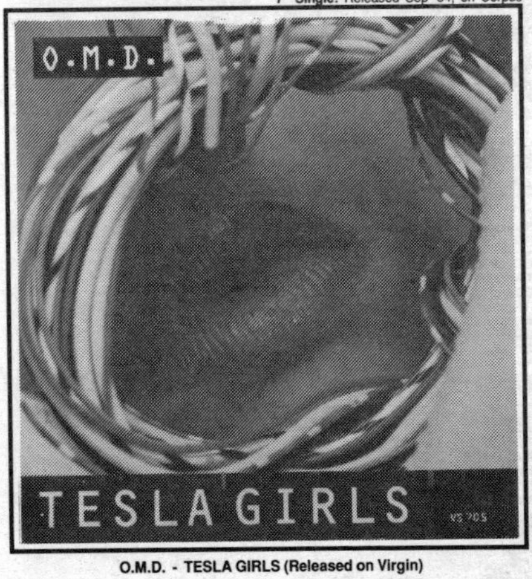

O.M.D. - TESLA GIRLS (Released on Virgin)

Christi, by Corpus Christi Records. Catalogue no: **CHRIST 12**
12" Single: Released Sep '84, on Corpus Christi, by Corpus Christi Records. Catalogue no: **CHRIST 12T**

Omen

SATISFACTION
Tracks: / Satisfaction.
7" Single: Released Mar '89, on Debut, by Skratch Records. Catalogue no: **DEBT 3065**
12" Single: Released Mar '89, on Debut, by Skratch Records. Catalogue no: **DEBTX 3065**

On The Air

ANOTHER PLANET
Tracks: / Another planet / Typically.
7" Single: Released Dec '80, on WEA, by WEA Records. Deleted Dec '85. Catalogue no: **K 18376**

READY FOR ACTION
Tracks: / Ready for action / Crazy and youth.
7" Single: Released Jun '80, on WEA, by WEA Records. Deleted Jun '83. Catalogue no: **K 18242**

On The Case

SHIKISHA Featuring Cousin Rachel
Tracks: / Shikisha / Shikisha (version).
7" Single: Released Oct '88, on Supreme, by Supreme Records. Catalogue no: **SUPE 135**
12" Single: Released Oct '88, on Supreme, by Supreme Records. Catalogue no: **SUPET 135**

On The House

GIVE ME BACK THE LOVE
Tracks: / Give me back the love.
7" Single: Released Jun '87, on Serious, by Serious Records. Catalogue no: **7OUS 5**
12" Single: Released Jun '87, on Serious, by Serious Records. Catalogue no: **12OUS 5**

On The One

WHO'S REALLY BAD
Tracks: / Who's really bad.
12" Single: Released Oct '87, on Bassment (USA). Catalogue no: **BM 0061**

On The Waterfront

KIDS ARE ALRIGHT, THE
Tracks: / Kids are alright, The / Never surrender / Far from the madding crowd / Mrs. Harrington.
7" Single: on Sierra, by Sierra Records. Catalogue no: **WIZZ 1**

One

I'LL WAIT
Tracks: / I'll wait.
7" Single: Released Jun '89, on Chrysalis, by Chrysalis Records. Catalogue no: **CHS 3375**
12" Single: Released Jun '89, on Chrysalis, by Chrysalis Records. Catalogue no: **CHS 123375**

SON OF THE SUN
Tracks: / Son of the sun / Somebody.
7" Single: Released Sep '89, on Chrysalis, by Chrysalis Records. Catalogue no: **CHS 3426**
12" Single: Released Sep '89, on Chrysalis, by Chrysalis Records. Catalogue no: **CHS 123426**

One 2 Many

ANOTHER MAN
Tracks: / Another man / You're the reason.
CD 5": Released Feb '89, on A&M, by A&M Records. Catalogue no: **CDEE 490**
7" Single: Released Jan '89, on A&M, by A&M Records. Catalogue no: **AM 490**
12" Single: Released Jan '89, on A&M, by A&M Records. Catalogue no: **AMY 490**
Special: Released Jan '89, on A&M, by A&M Records. Catalogue no: **ANX 490**

DOWNTOWN
Tracks: / Downtown.
CD 5": Released May '89, on A&M, by A&M Records. Catalogue no: **CDEE 476**
7" Single: Released Oct '88, on A&M, by A&M Records. Catalogue no: **AM 476**
12" Single: Released Oct '88, on A&M, by A&M Records. Catalogue no: **AMY 476**

WRITING ON THE WALL
Tracks: / Writing on the wall / Writing on the wall (instrumental).
CD 5": Released Jul '89, on A&M, by A&M Records. Catalogue no: **CDEE 518**
7" Single: Released Jul '89, on A&M, by A&M Records. Catalogue no: **AM 518**
12" Single: Released Jul '89, on A&M, by A&M Records. Catalogue no: **AMY 518**

One Beat

DREAMING (OF YOU)
Tracks: / Dreaming (of you).
12" Single: Released Feb '88, on Submission, by Submission Records. Catalogue no: **SUBX 03**

One Blood

BE THANKFUL
Tracks: / Be thankful.
12" Single: Released Aug '84, on Sound City, by Sound City Records. Catalogue no: **KNO 001**
12" Single: Released Feb '82, on Sound City, by Sound City Records. Catalogue no: **KCD 001**

CHRISTMAS PRESENT, THE
Tracks: / Christmas present, The / Don't have to fight.
12" Single: Released Dec '86, on Level Vibes, by Level Vibes Records. Catalogue no: **LV 12**

DON'T STOP LOVIN'
Tracks: / Don't stop loving me / When I'm with you.
12" Single: Released Jun '86, on Level Vibes, by Level Vibes Records. Catalogue no: **LV 11**

GET IN TOUCH
Tracks: / Get in touch / No tears woman.
7" Single: Released Feb '84, on Sound City, by Sound City Records. Catalogue no: **SC 011**
12" Single: Released Feb '84, on Sound City, by Sound City Records. Catalogue no: **SCD 011**

I CAN MAKE YOU HAPPY
Tracks: / I can make you happy / Girl I adore.
12" Single: Released Jan '83, on Neville King, by Neville King Records. Catalogue no: **NKRD 0012**

I WILL NEVER FALL IN LOVE AGAIN
Tracks: / I will never fall in love again.
12" Single: Released Dec '88, on Neville King, by Neville King Records. Catalogue no: **NKR 004**

I'M A CHANGED MAN
Tracks: / I'm a changed man / It's a romance.
12" Single: Released Feb '86, on Level Vibes, by Level Vibes Records. Catalogue no: **LV 10**

I'M YOUR FOOL
Tracks: / I'm your fool.
12" Single: Released Apr '82, on Neville King, by Neville King Records. Catalogue no: **NKRD 005**

MY LOVE DON'T COME EASY
Tracks: / At the dance / My love don't come easy.
12" Single: Released Dec '86, on King's Records. Catalogue no: **KRD 002**

RUNNING AROUND
Tracks: / Running around / Cool down woman.
7" Single: Released Mar '85, on Sound City, by Sound City Records. Catalogue no: **SS 013**
12" Single: Released Mar '85, on Sound City, by Sound City Records. Catalogue no: **SCD 013**

SHOW SOME LOVE
Tracks: / Show some love.
12" Single: Released Oct '81, on NK Music. Catalogue no: **NKRD 003**

YOU'RE WORTH IT
Tracks: / You're worth it.
12" Single: Released Sep '82, on Neville King, by Neville King Records. Catalogue no: **NKRD 008**

One By One

I KEPT MY PROMISE
Tracks: / I kept my promise.
7" Single: Released Mar '85, on Discovery (1), by Oryx Records. Catalogue no: **DIS 001**

One Child

ALWAYS
Tracks: / Always / Rebel eyes.
7" Single: Released '88, on Savage, by Savage Records. Catalogue no: **7VAG 901**

One Destiny

NO REGRETS
Tracks: / We've found love / No regrets.
Note: Featuring Dennis Gregory.
12" Single: Released Dec '86, on UK Bubblers, by Greensleeves Records. Deleted '88. Catalogue no: **UKMC 19**

TREASURE
Tracks: / Treasure.
12" Single: Released 31 Oct '87, on Sound City, by Sound City Records. Catalogue no: **SCD 019**

One Force

CRUISIN'
Tracks: / Cruisin'.
12" Single: Released May '82, on After Lord. Catalogue no: **AL 001**

One Gang Logic

ALIENATE
Tracks: / Alienate.
7" Single: Released Oct '79, on Stark. Deleted '80. Catalogue no: **STARK 1**

One Hand One Heart

MIRACLE HEART
Tracks: / Miracle heart / Too close for comfort.
CD 5": Released Aug '88, on Epic, by CBS Records. Deleted 17 Apr '89. Catalogue no: **CDWUN 1**
7" Single: Released 22 Aug '88, on Epic, by CBS Records. Deleted 17 Apr '89. Catalogue no: **WUN Q1**
7" Single: Released Aug '88, on Epic, by CBS Records. Deleted 17 Apr '89. Catalogue no: **WUN 1**
12" Single: Released Aug '88, on Epic, by CBS Records. Deleted 17 Apr '89. Catalogue no: **WUNT 1**

ONE STEP CLOSER
Tracks: / One step closer.
CD 5": Released Dec '88, on Epic, by CBS Records. Deleted 10 Jul '89. Catalogue no: **CDWUN 2**
7" Single: on Epic, by CBS Records. Deleted 10 Jul '89. Catalogue no: **WUN G2**
7" Single: Released Dec '88, on Epic, by CBS Records. Deleted 10 Jul '89. Catalogue no: **WUN 2**
12" Single: Released Dec '88, on Epic, by CBS Records. Deleted 10 Jul '89. Catalogue no: **WUN T2**

ONE STEP CLOSER (BOXED SINGLES SET)
7" Set: Released Jan '89, on Epic, by CBS Records. Catalogue no: **WUN B2**

One Hundred Percent

GREEN FOR GO
Tracks: / Green for go.
7" Single: Released Apr '82, on Backstop. Deleted '88. Catalogue no: **SHOP 1**

One Hundred Proof

SOMEBODYS BEEN SLEEPING IN MY BED
Tracks: / Somebody's been sleeping in my bed.
7" Single: Released May '84, on HDH (Holland/Dozier/Holland), by Demon Records. Catalogue no: **HDH 455**

One Hundred Ton & A

IT ONLY TAKES A MINUTE
Tracks: / It only takes a minute.
7" Single: Released Jun '76, on UK, by UK Records. Deleted '79. Catalogue no: **UK 135**

One Hundred & Twenty

ALLO
Tracks: / Allo.
7" Single: Released Jul '81, on JSO. Deleted '87. Catalogue no: **EAT 8**

One Hundredth...

BOUNCY BOUNCY
Tracks: / Bouncy bouncy.
7" Single: Released Sep '85, on Wooltown. Deleted '86. Catalogue no: **Unknown**

One Last Fight

MENAGE A TROIS
Tracks: / Menage a trois.
12" Single: Released Jun '86, on Skysaw, by Skysaw Records. Catalogue no: **SKY 4**

One Million Fuzz

MENS HEARTS
Tracks: / Mens hearts.
7" Single: Released May '83, on Monsters In Orbit. Deleted '84. Catalogue no: **TV EYE 008**

ONE MILLION FUZZ GUITARS
Tracks: / One million fuzz guitars.
7" Single: Released Jan '82, on Monsters In Orbit. Deleted '83. Catalogue no: **TV EYE 003**

One Nation

LOVE IS JUST AN EMOTION
Tracks: / Love is just an emotion / Truth runs deeper, The / For better or worse (12" only).
7" Single: Released 31 Jul '89, on I.R.S. Catalogue no: **EIRS 120**
12" Single: Released 31 Jul '89, on I.R.S. Catalogue no: **EIRST 120**

MY COMMITMENT
Tracks: / My commitment / For better or worse / My commitment (demo) (Not on 7".).
CD 5": Released Mar '89, on I.R.S. Catalogue no: **EIRSCD 103**
7" Single: Released Mar '89, on I.R.S. Catalogue no: **EIRS 103**
12" Single: Released Mar '89, on I.R.S. Catalogue no: **EIRST 103**

WHAT YOU SEE IS WHAT YOU'VE GOT
Tracks: / What you see is what you've got / Wot you see blues.
CD 5": Released May '89, on I.R.S. Catalogue no: **EIRSCD 112**
7" Single: Released May '89, on I.R.S. Catalogue no: **EIRS 112**
12" Single: Released May '89, on I.R.S. Catalogue no: **EIRST 112**

One O'clock Gang

CLOSE YOUR EYES (AND THINK OF ENGLAND)
Tracks: / Close your eyes (and think of England).
7" Single: Released Mar '85, on Arista, by BMG Records (UK). Catalogue no: **JOIN 2**
12" Single: Released Mar '85, on Arista, by BMG Records (UK). Catalogue no: **JOIN 122**

TRIGGER HAPPY
Tracks: / Trigger happy / Testify.
7" Single: Released May '85, on Arista, by BMG Records (UK). Catalogue no: **JOIN 3**
12" Single: Released May '85, on Arista, by BMG Records (UK). Catalogue no: **JOIN 123**

One Of You

DON'T BE DESPERATE
Tracks: / Don't be desperate.
7" Single: Released Oct '82, on Scarab. Catalogue no: **SCARAB 2**

One On One

BODY MUSIC
Tracks: / Body music.
7" Single: Released Mar '81, on RCA, by BMG Records (UK). Deleted Mar '84. Catalogue no: **RCA 46**
12" Single: Released Mar '81, on RCA, by BMG Records (UK). Deleted Mar '84. Catalogue no: **RCAT 46**

YOU'RE MY TYPE (MAKE YOUR BODY MOVE)
Tracks: / You're my type (make you body move).
7" Single: Released '89, on 10 Records, by Virgin Records. Catalogue no: **TEN 281**
12" Single: Released '89, on 10 Records, by Virgin Records. Catalogue no: **TENR 281**
12" Single: Released '89, on 10 Records, by Virgin Records. Catalogue no: **TENX 281**
CD 3": Released '89, on 10 Records, by Virgin Records. Catalogue no: **TENCD 281**

One Plus One

AUTUMN LEAVES
Tracks: / Autumn leaves.
7" Single: Released Nov '82, on RCA, by BMG Records (UK). Catalogue no: **RBS 212**

One Shots

GOODBYE CAROLINE
Tracks: / Goodbye Caroline: *Various artists.*
7" Single: Released Aug '80, on East Anglian Productions, by East Anglian Productions. Catalogue no: **JR 6**
Cassingle: Released Aug '80, on East Anglian Productions, by East Anglian Productions. Catalogue no: **C 6**

One Syntax One

FEEL NO TOUCH
Tracks: / Feel no touch.
7" Single: Released Mar '84, on Proteus. Catalogue no: **PRT 101**

One Take..

ONE TAKE NO DUBS
Tracks: / One take no dubs: *Various artists.*
Note: Featuring Hellenbach/Avenger/Black Rose/Alien.
12" Single: Released '88, on Neat, by Neat Records. Catalogue no: **NEAT 25 12**

One The Juggler

ARE YOU THE ONE
Tracks: / Are you the one.
7" Single: Released Jan '84, on Regard. Catalogue no: **RG 113**
12" Single: Released Jan '84, on Regard. Catalogue no: **RGT 113**

DAMAGE IS DONE
Tracks: / Damage is done.
7" Single: Released Jul '83, on Regard. Catalogue no: **RG 109**
12" Single: Released Jul '83, on Regard. Catalogue no: **RGT 109**

DJANGO'S COMING
Tracks: / Django's coming / Rip the cat / Nearly a sin (on 12" only) / Far away (from London) (on 12" only).
7" Single: Released Sep '83, on Regard. Catalogue no: **RG 111**
12" Single: Released Sep '83, on Regard. Catalogue no: **RGT 111**

HOURS AND HOURS
Tracks: / Hours and hours.
7" Single: Released Apr '85, on RCA, by BMG Records (UK). Catalogue no: **RCA 482**
12" Single: Released Apr '85, on RCA, by

BMG Records (UK). Catalogue no: **RCAT 482**

IT HURT'S
Tracks: / It hurt's.
7" Single: Released Aug '84, on Regard. Catalogue no: **RG 115**
12" Single: Released Aug '84, on Regard. Catalogue no: **RGT 115**

PASSION KILLER
Tracks: / Passion killer / Dangerous daze.
7" Single: Released Jan '83, on Regard. Catalogue no: **RG 107**
12" Single: Released Jan '83, on Regard. Catalogue no: **RGT 107**

One Thousand Mexicans

ART OF LOVE
Tracks: / Art of love.
7" Single: Released Sep '83, on Whaam. Catalogue no: **WHAAM 12**

CRIMINAL
Tracks: / Criminal / Running down.
7" Single: Released May '85, on Play It Again Sam(Belgium), by Play It Again Sam (Belgium). Catalogue no: **BIAS 009**

DIVING FOR PEARLS
Tracks: / Diving for pearls.
12" Single: Released Nov '84, on Fire, by Fire Records. Catalogue no: **FIRE 1**

LAST POP SONG
Tracks: / Last pop song / Chinese whispers.
7" Single: Released Jan '84, on Abstract, by Abstract Sounds. Catalogue no: **ABS 021**
12" Single: Released Jan '84, on Abstract, by Abstract Sounds. Catalogue no: **12 ABS 021**

UNDER CONSTRUCTIONS
Tracks: / Under construction.
12" Single: Released Jul '84, on Abstract, by Abstract Sounds. Catalogue no: **12 ABS 024**

One Thousand OHM

YOU LOOSE
Tracks: / You lose.
7" Single: Released Jun '88, on Antler, by Antler Records (Belgium). Deleted '88. Catalogue no: **ANT 014**

One Thousand Violins

ALL ABOARD THE LOVE-MOBILE
Tracks: / All aboard the love mobile / Place to surf, A / Only time I got to rock was in my..., The.
7" Single: Released Oct '88, on Immaculate, by Immaculate Records. Deleted '89. Catalogue no: **IMMAC 7**
12" Single: Released Oct '88, on Immaculate, by Immaculate Records. Catalogue no: **12IMMAC 7**

HALYCON DAYS
Tracks: / Halycon days.
12" Single: Released Jul '85, on Dreamworld, by Dreamworld Records. Catalogue no: **DREAM 2**

IF I WERE A BULLET (THEN FOR SURE...)
Tracks: / If I were a bullet (then for sure...) / Almost dead & nigh on forty years to go / Poet, The.
Note: Full title: If I were a bullet (then for sure I'd find a way to your heart).
7" Single: Released Nov '87, on Report, by Report Records. Deleted '89. Catalogue no: **REPX 1**
12" Single: Released Nov '87, on Report, by Report Records. Catalogue no: **REPX 1T**

IF ONLY WORDS (COULD LET ME CONQUER YOU)
Tracks: / If only words (could let me conquer you) / Orange sunshine ride / I left my mind in San Fransisco.
7" Single: Released Apr '89, on Immaculate, by Immaculate Records. Catalogue no: **IMMAC 9**
12" Single: Released Apr '89, on Immaculate, by Immaculate Records. Catalogue no: **12IMMAC 9**

LOCKED-OUT OF THE LOVE-IN
Tracks: / Locked out of the love in.
7" Single: Released Sep '87, on Dreamworld, by Dreamworld Records. Catalogue no: **DREAM 014**
12" Single: Released Sep '87, on Dreamworld, by Dreamworld Records. Catalogue no: **DREAM 014T**

PLEASE DON'T SAND BLAST MY HOUSE
Tracks: / Please don't sand blast my house / Time I broke down / Though it poured the next day I never noticed (*=Extra track on 12" only) / You ungrateful bastard (Extra track on 12" only).
7" Single: Released Oct '86, on Dreamworld, by Dreamworld Records. Catalogue no: **DREAM 008**
12" Single: Released Oct '86, on Dreamworld, by Dreamworld Records. Catalogue no: **DREAM 008 T**

UNGRATEFUL BASTARD
Tracks: / I remember when everyone used to ride bikes / Ungrateful bastard.
7" Single: Released Feb '87, on Constrictor, by Constrictor Records (Germany). Deleted '88. Catalogue no: **COLL 001**

One To One

ANGEL IN MY POCKETS
Tracks: / Angel in my pockets / Where's the answer.
7" Single: Released Jun '86, on Bonaire, by Bonaire Records. Deleted '88. Catalogue no: **BON 3**
12" Single: Released Jun '86, on Bonaire, by Bonaire Records. Deleted '88. Catalogue no: **BON 123**

THERE WAS A TIME
Tracks: / There was a time.
7" Single: Released Oct '85, on Bonaire, by Bonaire Records. Deleted '88. Catalogue no: **BON 1**
12" Single: Released Oct '85, on Bonaire, by Bonaire Records. Deleted '88. Catalogue no: **BON 121**

One Touch

DON'T THROW AWAY YOUR LOVE
Tracks: / Don't throw your love away.
7" Single: Released Feb '86, on Sierra, by Sierra Records. Deleted Jun '87. Catalogue no: **FED 21**
12" Single: Released Feb '86, on Sierra, by Sierra Records. Deleted Jun '87. Catalogue no: **FED 21T**

One Two Three

LOVE REIGN
Tracks: / Love reign / Love reign (version).
7" Single: Released Aug '89, on Total. Catalogue no: **STRAD 2**
12" Single: Released Aug '89, on Total. Catalogue no: **12STRAD 2**

One Way

Biographical details: This American vocal and instrumental group, with male and female members, is fronted by lead singer Al Hudson. They first attracted public attention in the mid-70's under the name Al Hudson & The Soul Partners and chalked up a handful of entries on the US soul and disco charts with their brand of soulful dance music, winning particular acclaim with their 1977 album*Cherish*. Although they failed to cross over to the American pop market they managed top score a trio of entries on Britain's national Top Seventy-Five singles chart during 1979-79. The first was a double-A-sided single,*Dance.Get Down/How Do You Do?*, which reached No 57. In recognition of the fact that they were now, in keeping with the times, more of a disco act than soul, the group were simply known as Al Hudson & The Partners during this period. It was under this billing that they scored a UK Top Twenty hit in autumn '79: *You Can Do It*, an infectious and sleek single, took them to No 15. Having established their name on the UK pop charts and the US soul listings with the Partners billing they then took the strange decision to change their name again. Music reached No 56 on the British chart at the end of '79 and was credited to One Way, featuring Al Hudson. They stuck to this name -- or simply One Way -- during the 80's and continued to achieve sporadic successes on the American black listings, all featuring Hudon's smooth, understated vocals. Hudson's group have always made competent and professional music but, with the exception of *You Can Do It*, have never released anything of particularly outstanding quality. (Bob MacDonald, April 1985.).

MUSIC
Tracks: / Music.
7" Single: Released Dec '79, on MCA, by MCA Records. Deleted '82. Catalogue no: **MCA 542**

WHO'S FOOLING WHO
Tracks: / Who's fooling who / Sweet lady.
7" Single: Released May '82, on MCA, by MCA Records. Deleted '85. Catalogue no: **MCA 768**
12" Single: Released May '82, on MCA, by MCA Records. Deleted '85. Catalogue no: **MCAT 768**One Way System

CUM ON FEEL THE NOIZE
Tracks: / Cum on feel the noize.
7" Single: Released Jul '83, on Anagram, by Cherry Red Records. Deleted '88. Catalogue no: **ANA 9**

JERUSALEM
Tracks: / Jerusalem / Jackie was a junkie.
7" Single: Released Dec '82, on Anagram, by Cherry Red Records. Deleted '88. Catalogue no: **ANA 5**

JUST ANOTHER HERO
Tracks: / Just another hero / Give us a future.
7" Single: Released Aug '82, on Anagram, by Cherry Red Records. Deleted '88. Catalogue no: **ANA 1**

STAB THE JUDGE
Tracks: / Stab the judge.
7" Single: Released Jun '82, on Lightbeat. Catalogue no: **WAY 1**

THIS IS THE AGE
Tracks: / This is the age.
7" Single: Released Sep '83, on Anagram, by Cherry Red Records. Deleted '88. Catalogue no: **ANA 14**

VISIONS OF ANGELS
Tracks: / Visions of angels.
7" Single: Released Mar '84, on Anagram, by Cherry Red Records. Deleted '88. Catalogue no: **ANA 19**
12" Single: Released Mar '84, on Anagram, by Cherry Red Records. Deleted '88. Catalogue no: **12 ANA 19**

O'Neal, Alexander

BROKEN HEART CAN'T MEND
Tracks: / Broken heart can mend, A / If you were here tonight.
7" Single: Released Mar '86, on Tabu. Catalogue no: **QA 6244**
7" Single: Released Apr '86, on Tabu. Deleted '89. Catalogue no: **A 6244**
12" Single: Released Mar '86, on Tabu. Catalogue no: **QTA 6244**

CHRISTMAS SONG, THE
Tracks: / Christmas song, The / Thank you for a good year / Sleigh ride (*Not on 7" version.).
12" Single: Released 28 Nov '88, on Tabu. Catalogue no: **653182 6**
CD 5": Released 28 Nov '88, on Tabu. Catalogue no: **653182 2**
7" Single: Released 28 Nov '88, on Tabu. Catalogue no: **653182 7**
7" Single: Released Dec '88, on Tabu. Catalogue no: **653182 0**

CRITICIZE
Tracks: / Criticize / Criticize (critical edit) / Criticize (nag mix) / Criticize (remix) (On 12" version only.) / Criticize (critical mix) (On 12" version only.) / Criticize (critical dub) (On 12" version only.) / Criticize (acapella).
7" Single: Released Oct '87, on Epic, by CBS Records. Deleted Aug '88. Catalogue no: **651211 7**
10" single: Released Nov '87, on Epic, by CBS Records. Catalogue no: **651211 8**
12" Single: Released Nov '87, on Tabu. Deleted Aug '88. Catalogue no: **651211 9**
12" Single: Released Oct '87, on CBS, by CBS Records. Deleted Aug '88. Catalogue no: **651211 6**

FAKE
Tracks: / Fake / Look at us now / Fake (extended version).
Cassingle: Released 23 May '87, on Tabu. Catalogue no: **650891 8**
7" Single: Released 23 May '87, on Tabu. Deleted Nov '87. Catalogue no: **650891 7**
12" Single: Released 23 May '87, on Tabu. Catalogue no: **650891 6**

FAKE '88
Tracks: / Fake '88 / Innocent / Fake '88 (short house mix) (652949 0 only.).
7" Single: Released Sep '88, on Tabu. Deleted 17 Apr '89. Catalogue no: **652949 7**
CD 5": Released Sep '88, on Tabu. Deleted 17 Apr '89. Catalogue no: **652949 2**
7" Single: Released Sep '88, on Tabu. Deleted 17 Apr '89. Catalogue no: **652949 0**
12" Single: Released Sep '88, on Tabu. Deleted 17 Apr '89. Catalogue no: **652949 6**

FAKE (ORIGINAL EXTENDED VERSION)
Tracks: / Fake (original extended version) / Fake 88 (hop mix) / Fake 88 (acapella) / Innocent.
12" Single: Released 19 Sep '88, on Tabu. Deleted 18 Apr '89. Catalogue no: **652949 8**

HEARSAY 89 (SINGLE)
Tracks: / Hearsay / You were meant to be my lady / Hearsay 89 (Extended remix) / Hearsay 89 (Club instrumental).
12" Single: Released Feb '89, on Tabu. Deleted 10 Jul '89. Catalogue no: **654 667-6**
7" Single: Released Feb '89, on Tabu. Deleted 10 Jul '89. Catalogue no: **654 667-7**
CD 5": Released Feb '89, on Tabu. Deleted 10 Jul '89. Catalogue no: **654 667-2**
12" Single: Released 20 Feb '89, on Tabu. Deleted 10 Jul '89. Catalogue no: **654 667-8**

IF YOU WERE HERE TONIGHT
Tracks: / If you were here tonight / If you were here tonight (remix) / Soft version.
12" Single: Released Feb '86, on Tabu. Catalogue no: **QTA 6391**
7" Single: Released Feb '86, on Tabu. Deleted '87. Catalogue no: **A 6391**

LOVERS, THE
Tracks: / Lovers, The / Lovers, The (inst.) / Lovers, The (extended version) (track on 12".) / Lovers, The (acapella) (track on 12".) / Lovers, The (bonus beats).
7" Single: Released May '88, on Tabu. Deleted Jan '89. Catalogue no: **651595 7**
CD 5": Released May '88, on Tabu. Deleted Jan '89. Catalogue no: **651595 2**
7" EP: Released 6 Jun '88, on Tabu. Deleted Jan '89. Catalogue no: **651595 9**
12" Single: Released May '88, on Tabu. Deleted Jan '89. Catalogue no: **651595 6**

NEVER KNEW LOVE LIKE THIS
Tracks: / Never knew love like this (ext. version) / Never knew love like this (inst.) / Never knew love like this (reprise).
12" Single: Released Jan '88, on Tabu. Deleted Aug '88. Catalogue no: **651382 6**
7" Single: Released Jan '88, on Tabu. Deleted Aug '88. Catalogue no: **651382 7**
CD 5": Released Feb '88, on Tabu. Deleted Jan '89. Catalogue no: **651382 2**
7" Single: Released Jan '88, on Tabu. Deleted Aug '88. Catalogue no: **651382 9**
10" single: Released Jan '88, on Tabu. Catalogue no: **651382 0**

SUNSHINE
Tracks: / Sunshine (edit) / Do you wanna like I do / Crying overtime (On 12" & CD single.) / Broken heart can mend, A (On 12" & CD single.).
CD 5": Released 21 Aug '89, on Tabu. Catalogue no: **655191 2**
7" Single: Released 21 Aug '89, on Tabu. Catalogue no: **655191 7**
12" Single: Released Aug '89, on Tabu. Catalogue no: **655191 6**

THANK YOU FOR A GOOD YEAR
Tracks: / Thank you for a good year / Sleigh ride / Christmas song, The.
12" Single: Released Jan '89, on Tabu. Deleted 10 Jul '89. Catalogue no: **653 182-8**
7" Single: Released Jan '89, on Tabu. Deleted 10 Jul '89. Catalogue no: **653 182-9**
CD 5": Released Jan '89, on Tabu. Deleted 10 Jul '89. Catalogue no: **654 533-2**

(WHAT CAN I SAY) TO MAKE YOU LOVE ME
Tracks: / (What can I say) to make you love me / Broken heart can mend, A / You were mean't to be my lady (not my girl)*
Note: * Only available on the CD single and the 12 inch version.
CD 5": Released Jul '88, on Tabu. Deleted Jan '89. Catalogue no: **652852 2**
12" Single: Released Aug '88, on Tabu. Catalogue no: **652652 8**
7" Single: Released Jul '88, on Tabu. Deleted Jan '89. Catalogue no: **652852 7**
12" Single: Released Jul '88, on Tabu. Deleted Jan '89. Catalogue no: **652852 6**

WHAT'S MISSING
Tracks: / What's missing / Do you wanna.
7" Single: Released May '86, on Tabu. Deleted '86. Catalogue no: **A 7191**
12" Single: Released May '86, on Tabu. Deleted '86. Catalogue no: **TA 7191**

YOU WERE MEANT TO BE MY LADY
Tracks: / You were meant to be my lady.
12" Single: Released Aug '86, on Tabu. Catalogue no: **650048 6**
7" Single: Released Aug '86, on Tabu. Deleted '87. Catalogue no: **650048 7**

One-A-Way

SUFFERER
Tracks: / Sufferer.
12" Single: Released Oct '84, on Route. Catalogue no: **Unknown**

O'Neil, Dyer

ROBBERY
Tracks: / Robbery.
12" Single: Released Dec '82, on Cha-Cha, by Cha-Cha Records. Catalogue no: **CHAD 50**

O'Neil, John

ELIZABETH
Tracks: / Elizabeth.
7" Single: Released May '85, on August (USA), by Rounder Records (USA). Catalogue no: **GBH 7S 387**

TAKE GOOD CARE OF HER
Tracks: / Take good care of her / Ring your mother wore, The.
7" Single: Released Oct '89, on Scotdisc, by Scotdisc Records. Catalogue no: **ITV 7S 503**

O'Neill, Aura

WITCHERY WOODS
Tracks: / Witchery woods.
7" Single: Released Jul '84, on Uncanny, by Uncanny Records. Catalogue no: **UN 1**

O'Neill, Jonjo

I STILL LOVE HER
Tracks: / I still love her / Horse.
7" Single: Released Mar '81, on OBM, by RK Records. Deleted '83. Catalogue no: **OBM 1007**

O'Neill, Sean

CITY BY THE LAGAN SIDE

Tracks: / City by the Lagan side / Rose of Mooncoin.
7" Single: Released Mar '84, on Homespun (Ireland), by Outlet Records. Catalogue no: **HS 077**

Oneness

EVERYBODY LOVES A BEAUTIFUL WOMAN
Tracks: / Everybody loves a beautiful woman.
12" Single: Released Oct '85, on Fantasy (1), by BMG Records (UK). Catalogue no: **F 0001**

Oneness Of Juju

EVERYWAY BUT LOOSE
Tracks: / Every way but loose / Higher / Always have to say goodbye / Make a change / Run away bay / Love's wonderland.
7" Single: Released Apr '82, on Buddah, by Buddah Records Inc.(USA). Catalogue no: **BDS 497**
12" Single: Released Apr '82, on Buddah, by Buddah Records Inc.(USA). Catalogue no: **BDSL 497**

One-O-One'ers

KEY'S TO YOUR HEART
Tracks: / Keys to your heart.
7" Single: Released Aug '83, on Big Beat, by Ace Records. Deleted '88. Catalogue no: **NS 3**

SWEET REVENGE
Tracks: / Sweet revenge / Rabies from the dogs of love.
7" Single: Released Jan '81, on Big Beat, by Ace Records. Deleted '88. Catalogue no: **NS 63**

Onidis, Nicky

BABY I LOVE YOU
Tracks: / Baby I love you / I will give you my heart.
7" Single: Released Jan '83, on Carrere, Catalogue no: **CAR 259**

Onike

BUSH WOMAN
Tracks: / Bush woman.
12" Single: on Earthworks, by Earthworks Records. Deleted '88. Catalogue no: **12003**

Onlookers

YOU AND I
Tracks: / You and I.
7" Single: Released Mar '82, on Demon, by Demon Records. Deleted '88. Catalogue no: **D 1012**

Only After Dark

GHOSTS OF ROMANCE
Tracks: / Ghosts of romance / Lover of outrage.
7" Single: Released Apr '82, on Disclexia, Catalogue no: **DXL 001**

Only Child

SAVE A PLACE IN MY HEART
Tracks: / Save a place in my heart / Shot heard around the world.
7" Single: Released Oct '88, on Savage, by Savage Records. Catalogue no: **7VAG 002**

Only Connect

KHAN
Tracks: / Khan / Bop / Catharsis.
12" Single: Released Mar '86, on Only Connect, Catalogue no: **KB 1**

Only Lonely

TEENAGE LOVE
Tracks: / Teenage love / Rainbow.
12" Single: Released Aug '86, on Sierra, by Sierra Records. Catalogue no: **FED 25 T**
7" Single: Released Aug '86, on Sierra, by Sierra Records. Catalogue no: **FED 25**

Only Ones

Biographical details: This British rock band consisted of Mike Kellie, Alan Mair, Peter Perrett and John Perry. Their front man, vocalist/guitarist/songwriter Peter-Perrett had been trying to get a viable band off the ground for several years before this group stabilised in 1977. The Only Ones' arrival coincided with the punk explosion and Perrett's band became one of the most critically-acclaimed constituents of the New Wave scene. Their debut single was an independently-released 12-inch offering called *Lovers Of Today*, whose 500 copies were rapidly sold. They then signed with CBS. But they never achieved the major success they deserved. None of their singles charted and their three albums received modest runs on the British LP listings: *The Only Ones* ('78) reached No 56, *Even Serpents Shine* ('79) peaked at No 42 and *Baby's Got A Gun* ('80) climbed to No 37. The group broke up in early 1981. Their first album contained the single *Another Girl, Another Planet*, one of the best records produced by the New Wave era. With a vocal style influenced by Marc Bolan and Lou Reed, Perrett recorded this song superbly. It was included on the soundtrack of the 1979 punk nostalgia film *That Summer!* and was one of the most memorable non-hit singles of the late 70's. (Bob MacDonald, February 1986.).

FOOLS
Tracks: / Fools / Castle built on sand.
7" Single: Released May '80, on CBS, by CBS Records. Deleted May '85. Catalogue no: **CBS 8535**

TROUBLE IN THE WORLD
Tracks: / Trouble in the world / Your chosen life.
7" Single: Released Jan '80, on CBS, by CBS Records. Deleted Jan '85. Catalogue no: **CBS 7963**

Ono, Yoko

Biographical details: Japanese singer, songwriter and producer Ono was married to John Lennon from March 1969 until his murder in December 1980. Born in Tokyo in 1933, she moved to New York with her affluent parents at the age of 14. During the early 60's she became a substantial figure on the city's avant-garde art scene as a film maker, poet and conceptual artist. John Lennon first met Ono at her art exhibition in a London gallery in November '66. Their relationship blossomed in '68, the year they released their first album together, *Two Virgins*: the title was not, of course, materially accurate, as both were already married with a child apiece by the time they first met. Having divorced their partners, the couple married in Gibraltar in March 1969. Thirteen months later Paul McCartney announced the break-up of the Beatles. John and Yoko's obsession, in both musical and personal terms, was widely blamed for the event although there were several other contributory factors. During the late 60's and early 70's Lennon and Ono indulged in a series of weird headline-grabbing stunts in the name of peace and love -- they later described themselves as "court jesters of the peace movement". One of their bizarre activities was the formation of the Plastic Ono Band, a non-existent "group" whose members comprised John, Yoko and whoever else was around at the time of recording or performing. The Plastic Ono Band was launched in the summer of '69 with *Give Peace A Chance*, a smash single recorded in a Montreal hotel room during one of the couple's famous "bed-ins". While Lennon introduced Ono to the world of rock music, she led him to the worlds of electronic experimentation and improvised jazz. When the pair worked together on albums, as on 1972's *Sometime In New York City*, the musical results were extraordinary and often unsatisfactory. Many Lennon fans preferred it when she let her husband proceed with his music in an unimpeded fashion, as on *Instant Karma* ('70) when she simply sat knitting on BBC TV's Top Of The Pops while John sat at the piano. But even on some of Lennon's best songs her influence could be clearly heard -- many of the lines in *Imagine*, for example, were inspired by Ono's 1970 book of poems, Grapefruit. Yoko's contributions to Plastic Ono Band performances often consisted of little more than grunting and screeching from the inside of a bag into which she would climb before going on stage. She released several solo albums during the early 70's, all of which were far too deliberately esoteric to attain commercial success. Some of her music was interesting feminist and/or sociological rock, but much was quite unlistenable. After the couple's 1973-74 separation it was Yoko who persuaded John that he should quit the music business for the sake of his happiness. The pair were reconciled, had a son named Sean in 1975 and spent the following five years in domestic bliss. When they returned to the spotlight in 1980 with the *Double Fantasy* album Ono contributed seven of the 14 songs and gave the world some of her most accessible music to date. After the brutal killing of Lennon, Yoko Ono bore her bereavement with enormous courage and dignity. One of her first actions was to complete *Walking On Ice*, the song they had been working on in the days immediately before John's death. This excellent track gave Yoko her first solo UK chart entry in early 1981, albeit a surprisingly low No 35; it failed to reach the American Top Forty, suffering as usual from the Oko stamp of weirdness. Her 1981 album, *Season Of Glass*, peaked at No 47 on the UK charts. Further idiosyncratic albums followed during the 80's. In early '84 the *Milk And Honey* LP was issued. Masterminded by Ono, this was a substandard re-run of the *Double Fantasy* formula using some of Lennon's previously unreleased songs. Maenwhile Yoko Ono has continued to perform her traditional role of managing and administering the highly complicated Lennon finances. (Bob MacDonald, February 1986.).

OPERATING THEATRE - QUEEN OF NO HEART (Released on Mother)

MY MAN
Tracks: / My man / Let the tears dry.
7" Single: Released Dec '82, on Polydor, by Polydor Ltd. Catalogue no: **POSP 541**

WALKING ON THIN ICE
Tracks: / Walking on thin ice / It happened.
7" Single: Released Feb '81, on Geffen, by Geffen Records (USA). Deleted '84. Catalogue no: **K 79202**

Onslaught

LET THERE BE ROCK
Tracks: / Let there be rock / Shellshock / Metal forces (on 12" only.).
7" Single: Released Apr '89, on London Records, by London Records. Catalogue no: **LON 224**
12" Single: Released Apr '89, on London Records, by London Records. Catalogue no: **LONX 224**
12" Single: Released 31 Oct '87, on Under One Flag, by Music For Nations Records. Catalogue no: **12 FLAG 103**
12" Single: Released Apr '89, on London Records, by London Records. Catalogue no: **LONXP 224**
Special: Released Apr '89, on London Records, by London Records. Catalogue no: **LONB 224**
CD 5": Released Apr '89, on London Records, by London Records. Catalogue no: **LONCD 224**

SHELL SHOCK
Tracks: / Shellshock / Confused / H-eyes.
12" Single: Released Dec '88, on London Records, by London Records. Deleted 26 Jun '89. Catalogue no: **LONX 215**

WELCOME TO DYING
Tracks: / Welcome to dying / Nice 'n' sleazy / Atomic punk (Only on 12" single.).
12" Single: Released Jul '89, on London Records, by London Records. Catalogue no: **LONX 198**

7" Single: Released Jul '89, on London Records, by London Records. Catalogue no: **LON 198**

Onuora, Oku

I A TELL
Tracks: / I a tell.
12" Single: Released Apr '82, on Kuya, Catalogue no: **SK 002**

Ony

GIVE IT TO THEM
Tracks: / Give it to them.
7" Single: Released Sep '84, on HR, Catalogue no: **BM 003**

Onyeka

TRINA FOUR (HIGHLAND TOWN)
Tracks: / Trina four (Highland Town) / Ekive.
12" Single: Released Feb '85, on Mother Africa, Deleted '86. Catalogue no: **MAS 1201**

7" Single: Released Feb '85, on Mother Africa, Deleted '87. Catalogue no: **MAS 01**

Opal

NORTHERN LINE
Tracks: / Northern line / Empty bottles / Soul giver.
12" Single: Released Jan '86, on One Big Guitar, by One Big Guitar Records. Catalogue no: **OBG 002 T**

Operating Theatre

QUEEN OF NO HEART (See panel above)
Tracks: / Queen of no hearts / Spring is coming with a strawberry in the mouth / Part of my make-up (Track on 12" version only) / Atlanteon (Track on 12" version only) / Satonosa (Track on 12" version only).
7" Single: Released Apr '86, on Mother, by Mother Records. Catalogue no: **MUM 4**
12" Single: Released Apr '86, on Mother, by Mother Records. Catalogue no: **12 MUM 4**

Ophiuchus

SERPENT & THE BEARDED KING
Tracks: / Serpent & the bearded king.
7" Single: Released Jul '88, on Ophiuchus, Catalogue no: **OPH 001**

Opium Monks

SECRETS OF AFRIKA
Tracks: / Secrets of Afrika.
12" Single: Released 23 Apr '88, on Subway, by Subway Records. Catalogue no: **SUB 020**

O.P.M.

MOVE THAT BODY
Tracks: / Move that body.

7" Single: Released Jun '83, on Ram, by Ram Records. Catalogue no: **RAM 7001**
12" Single: Released Jun '83, on Ram, by Ram Records. Catalogue no: **RAM 001-12**

Oppenheimer, Andie

NEW MEXICO
Tracks: / New Mexico.
Cassingle: Released Sep '83, on JTN, Catalogue no: **JTN 1**

Opposition

Biographical details: Consisting of Mark Long (guiarist & singer), Marcus Bell (bass guitar) and Ralph Hall (drums). They were born in a Bermondsey basement, inexperienced lured the group into a premature deal with Ariola and the clutches of the marketing men. Their 1980 single *This year* was a hit in France. They left Ariola and formed their own *Double Vision* label, releasing an album in France called *Breaking the silence* and the follow-up *Intimacy*. They signed to Charisma and released the EP *My room is white* and the overdue British release of *Intimacy* was shortly followed. Guarded press acclaim in the U.K. was accompanied by guarded sales, as the album got lost in distribution problem and Mark's health. They gigged a lot and also released *Promises* another LP from Charisma. (Charisma, March '84).

5 MINUTES
Tracks: / 5 minutes.
7" Single: Released Jun '85, on Charisma,

by Virgin Records. Deleted May '88. Catalogue no: **OPPS 3**

INNOCENT
Tracks: / Innocent.
7" Single: Released Jul '84, on Charisma, by Virgin Records. Deleted May '88. Catalogue no: **OPPS 2**
12" Single: Released Jul '84, on Charisma, by Virgin Records. Catalogue no: **OPPS 212**

MY ROOM IS WHITE 4 track EP
Tracks: / My room is white.
12" Single: Released Apr '83, on Charisma, by Virgin Records. Deleted '89. Catalogue no: **CB 41012**

SOMEONE TO TALK TO
Tracks: / Someone to talk to.
7" Single: Released Sep '85, on Virgin, by Virgin Records. Deleted May '88. Catalogue no: **OPPS 4**
12" Single: Released Sep '85, on Virgin, by Virgin Records. Deleted May '88. Catalogue no: **OPPS 4-12**

STRANDED
Tracks: / Stranded.
7" Single: Released Mar '84, on Virgin, by Virgin Records. Deleted May '88. Catalogue no: **OPPS 1**
12" Single: Released Mar '84, on Virgin, by Virgin Records. Catalogue no: **OPPS 1-12**

THIS YEAR
Tracks: / This year / Punishment of luxury.
7" Single: Released Feb '80, on Ariola, by BMG Records (UK). Deleted Feb '83. Catalogue no: **AHA 558**

Oppressed

NEVER SAY DIE
Tracks: / Never say die.
7" Single: Released Aug '83, on Firm (2), Catalogue no: **NICK 001**

WORK TOGETHER
Tracks: / Work together.
7" Single: Released Dec '83, on UNKNOWN, Catalogue no: **OPPO 1**

Optimists

MULL OF KINTYRE
Tracks: / Mull of Kintyre.
7" Single: Released Jul '81, on Armageddon, by Armageddon Records. Catalogue no: **AS 018**

Opus

FLYIN' HIGH
Tracks: / Flyin' high.
7" Single: Released Aug '85, on Polydor, by Polydor Ltd. Catalogue no: **POSP 757**
12" Single: Released Aug '85, on Polydor, by Polydor Ltd. Catalogue no: **POSPX 757**

LIVE IS LIFE (SINGLE)
Tracks: / Live is life.
7" Single: Released Jun '85, on Polydor, by Polydor Ltd. Deleted '88. Catalogue no: **POSP 743**

WHITELAND
Tracks: / Walking along with you / Whiteland / Whiteland (extended version) / Walking along with you (7" version) / Shut up already. Note: *Available on 12" only.
7" Single: Released Nov '87, on Polydor, by Polydor Ltd. Catalogue no: **POSP 895**
12" Single: Released Nov '87, on Polydor, by Polydor Ltd. Catalogue no: **POSPX 895**

Orange Juice

Biographical details: Orange Juice -- the name was chosen because their music was supposed to sound fresh -- were Edwin Collins, David McClymont, Zeke Manyika and Malcolm Ross. Originally formed in Glasgow in late 1977 they came to the attention of the British music press during 1980-81 as part of a wave of Scottish bands signed to Alan Horne's Postcard label. Although other impressive acts like Aztek Camera and Josef K were also part of this mini-boom, Orange Juice garnered the most praise thanks to such singles as *Falling And Laughing* and *Poor Old Soul*. They built upon this by supporting the Undertones on tour. In a bid to make the jump from cult status to national chart success, Orange Juice switched from the independent Postcard label to one of the major companies, Polydor. The band's time with Polydor proved a period of frustrated anticipation when they always seemed to be on the brink of major success. Between 1981 and 1984 they reached the UK Top Seventy-Five with nine different singles but only one, 1983's *Rip It Up*, cracked the Top Forty. The No 8 position of *Rip It Up* (not the Little Richard/Bill Haley hit) was the lone beacon that towered above the 41-75 placings of the other singles. The problem was that while their music contained charm and perkiness on first hearing it was really a lightweight rehash of mid-60's pop influences. Their singles chart performance was compensated in part by the Top Forty placings of their albums, *You Can't Hide Your Love Forever* and *Rip It Up*. Orange Juice folded in 1985, by which time leader Edwin Collins had reaffirmed his credibility by duetting with Paul Quinn on the acclaimed single *Pale Blue Eyes*. (Bob MacDonald, February 1986.).

BRIDGE
Tracks: / Bridge.
12" Single: Released Jan '84, on Polydor, by Polydor Ltd. Catalogue no: **OJX 5**
7" Single: Released Jan '84, on Polydor, by Polydor Ltd. Catalogue no: **OJ 5**

FELICITY
Tracks: / Felicity / In a nut shell / You old eccentric (Only on 12" single.).
7" Single: Released Jan '82, on Polydor, by Polydor Ltd. Deleted '85. Catalogue no: **POSP 386**
12" Single: Released Jan '82, on Polydor, by Polydor Ltd. Deleted '85. Catalogue no: **POSPX 386**

FLESH OF MY FLESH
Tracks: / Flesh of my flesh.
12" Single: Released May '83, on Polydor, by Polydor Ltd. Catalogue no: **OJX 4**
7" Single: Released May '83, on Polydor, by Polydor Ltd. Catalogue no: **OJ 4**

I CAN'T HELP MYSELF
Tracks: / I can't help myself / Tongues begin to wag / Barbeque (Available on 12" only).
12" Single: Released Oct '82, on Polydor, by Polydor Ltd. Deleted '85. Catalogue no: **POSPX 522**
7" Single: Released Oct '82, on Polydor, by Polydor Ltd. Deleted '85. Catalogue no: **POSP 522**

LEAN PERIOD
Tracks: / Lean period.
7" Single: Released Oct '84, on Polydor, by Polydor Ltd. Deleted '87. Catalogue no: **OJ 7**

L.O.V.E. LOVE
Tracks: / L.O.V.E. love / Intuition told me.
12" Single: Released Oct '81, on Polydor, by Polydor Ltd. Deleted '84. Catalogue no: **POSPX 357**
7" Single: Released Nov '81, on Polydor, by Polydor Ltd. Deleted '84. Catalogue no: **POSP 357**

RIP IT UP (SINGLE)
Tracks: / Rip it up.
7" Single: Released Feb '83, on Polydor, by Polydor Ltd. Deleted '86. Catalogue no: **POSP 547**
7" Set: Released Feb '83, on Polydor, by Polydor Ltd. Catalogue no: **POSPD 547**

WHAT PRESENCE
Tracks: / What presence.
7" Single: Released Jun '84, on Polydor, by Polydor Ltd. Catalogue no: **OJC 6**
12" Single: Released Apr '84, on Polydor, by Polydor Ltd. Catalogue no: **OJX 6**
7" Single: Released Apr '84, on Polydor, by Polydor Ltd. Catalogue no: **OJ 6**

Orange Lemon

DREAMS OF SANTA ANNA, THE
Tracks: / Dreams of Santa Anna, The / Texican, The.
12" Single: Released May '88, on Champion, by Champion Records. Deleted Aug '89. Catalogue no: **CHAMP 1278**
7" Single: Released May '88, on Champion, by Champion Records. Catalogue no: **CHAMP 78**

Orange, Richard

ONE WRONG MOVE
Tracks: / One wrong move / So full of tears.
7" Single: Released 24 Jul '89, on Supertrack, Catalogue no: **YAP 1**

Orbidoig

NOCTURNAL OPERATION
Tracks: / Nocturnal operation / Down periscope.
7" Single: Released Dec '81, on Situation 2, by Beggars Banquet Records. Catalogue no: **SIT 15**

Orbison, Roy

Biographical details: Born and raised in Texas, singer/guitarist/songwriter Orbison was interested in music from early childhood and formed his first group, the Wink Westerners, at the age of 13. His first recording session took place at Norman Petty's studio in Clovis, New Mexico, in 1955, and the following year he became part of Sam Phillips' Sun Records, the legendary Memphis label that launched the careers of Elvis Presley, Johnny Cash, Jerry Lee Lewis and Carl Perkins. The Sun period gave him his first US Hot Hundred entry with Ooby Dooby. Phillips pushed Orbison in a rock 'n' roll direction but because his voice was not suited to this his later Sun singles were unsuccessful: he preferred to record in a ballad style. Orbison's first taste of major success came in 1958 when the Everly Brothers recorded his song *Claudette* (dedicated to his wife) and placed it on the flipside of their classic *All I Have To Do Is Dream*. Orbison then signed with Monument Records and after a couple of hiccups began a string of hit records in 1980. The first was the classic *Only The Lonely* which reached No 2 in the States and No 1 in Britain. During the first five years of the 60's the Big O -- as he became known -- was rarely off the charts on both sides of the Atlantic. Writing either alone or with a co-writer (Joe Melson or Bill Dees), his biggest successes included *Blue Angel, Crying, In Dreams, Falling and Blue Bayou*. Combining the emotional openness of country music with the infectious melodies of the best pop songs, Orbison managed to convey tear-jerking, lovelost numbers without resort to cloying sentimentality. He was virtually motionless on stage but his expressive voice always carried the day. Even the brighter, uptempo songs were infused with emotion. During his career Orbison enjoyed two American No 1 singles, *Running Scared* (1961) and *Oh Pretty Woman* (1964, another song inspired by *Claudette*). And he was even more popular in Britain, where he won high praise from and toured with the Beatles. Between August '63 and November '64 his *It's Over* and *Oh Pretty Woman* were the only American records to reach No 1 on the British charts. The sheer strength of his talent withstood the UK explosion in an impressive fashion while the careers of many of his US peers were blown sky high. Orbison's singing and songwriting styles clearly reflected the influence of country pop star Don Gibson and in recognition of this he issued in 1966 Gibson's *Too Soon To Know*, which reached No 3 in Britain, plus a Gibson-penned LP. But that year was marred by the death in a motorcycle accident of his wife, *Claudette*: two years later his personal tragedy was compounded by the death of two of his sons in a house fire. He remarried in 1969. Having first entered the British singles charts in 1960, Orbison neatly ended his UK singles chart career by falling of the final listing of 1969. This "tidiness" was maintained when he attempted a UK come-back in 1985 -- *Wild Hearts*, a single released on Trevor Horn's fashionable ZTT label, missed the UK Top Seventy-Five singles chart by peaking at No 76... In the meantime he had reached No 1 on the British album chart in January '76 with the TV-advertised compilation *The Best Of Roy Orbison*. During the late 70's and early 80's he embarked on a fresh career on the US country scene, enjoying a substantial duet success with Emmylou Harris on 1980's *That Loving You Feeling*. And his oldies lived on: *Blue Bayou* was a US No 3 for Linda Ronstadt in '77; *Crying* was given a stunning new treatment by Don McLean, who took it to No 1 in Britain in 1980 and No 5 in the States in '81; and Van Halen reached No 12 in America the following year with a rock remake of *Oh Pretty Woman*. Roy Orbison died from a heart attack in December 1988. (Bob MacDonald June 1986) .

ALMOST EIGHTEEN
Tracks: / Almost eighteen / Jolie / Sweet and innocent / Bug, The (with the bug) ((Previously unissued)) / Paper boy ((Previously unissued)) / Seems to me.
7" EP: Released Sep '82, on Bear Family, by Bear Family Records (Germany). Catalogue no: **BFE 15019**

BLUE ANGEL
Tracks: / Blue angel.
7" Single: Released Oct '60, on London-American, Deleted '63. Catalogue no: **HLU 9207**

BLUE BAYOU
Tracks: / Blue bayou / Mean woman blues.
7" Single: Released Sep '63, on London-American, Deleted '66. Catalogue no: **HLU 9777**

BORNE ON THE WIND
Tracks: / Borne on the wind.
7" Single: Released Feb '64, on London-American, Deleted '67. Catalogue no: **HLU 9845**

BREAKIN' UP IS BREAKIN' MY HEART
Tracks: / Breakin' up is breakin' my heart.
7" Single: Released Jan '66, on London-American, Deleted '69. Catalogue no: **HL 10015**

CALIFORNIA BLUE
Tracks: / California blue / Blue bayou (live) / Leah (live) (Only on 12" and CD single.) / In dreams (live) (Only on CD single.).
12" Single: Released Jul '89, on Virgin, by Virgin Records. Catalogue no: **VST 1193**
7" Single: Released Jul '89, on Virgin, by Virgin Records. Catalogue no: **VS 1193**
CD 3": Released Jul '89, on Virgin, by Virgin Records. Catalogue no: **VSCD 1193**

CRAWLIN' BACK
Tracks: / Crawling back.
7" Single: Released Nov '65, on London-American, Deleted '68. Catalogue no: **HLU 10000**

CROWD, THE
Tracks: / Crowd, The.
7" Single: Released Jun '62, on London-American, Deleted '65. Catalogue no: **HLU 9561**

CROWD, THE (OLD GOLD)
Tracks: / Crowd, The / Lana.
7" Single: Released 27 Feb '89, on Old Gold, by Old Gold Records. Catalogue no: **OG 9888**

CRYING (SINGLE)
Tracks: / Crying.
7" Single: Released '80, on Monument, Catalogue no: **LR 0675**
7" Single: Released Sep '61, on London-American, Deleted '64. Catalogue no: **HLU 9405**

DREAM BABY
Tracks: / Dream baby.
7" Single: Released Mar '62, on London-American, Deleted '65. Catalogue no: **HLU 9511**

DREAM BABY (OLD GOLD)
Tracks: / Dream baby / Pretty paper.
7" Single: Released 27 Feb '89, on Old Gold, by Old Gold Records. Catalogue no: **OG 9885**

FALLING
Tracks: / Falling.
7" Single: Released May '63, on London-American, Deleted '66. Catalogue no: **HLU 9727**

GOODNIGHT
Tracks: / Goodnight.
7" Single: Released Feb '65, on London-American, Deleted '68. Catalogue no: **HLU 9951**

HEARTACHE
Tracks: / Heartache.
7" Single: Released Sep '68, on London-American, Deleted '71. Catalogue no: **HLU 10222**

IN DEUTSCHLAND
Tracks: / San Fernando / Mama.
12" Single: Released 6 Apr '89, on Bear Family, by Bear Family Records (Germany). Catalogue no: **BFM 15352**

IN DREAMS (OLD GOLD)
Tracks: / In dreams / Falling.
7" Single: Released 27 Feb '89, on Old Gold, by Old Gold Records. Catalogue no: **OG 9883**

IN DREAMS (SINGLE)
Tracks: / In dreams.
7" Single: Released May '87, on Virgin, by Virgin Records. Deleted May '88. Catalogue no: **ROY 1**
7" Single: Released Feb '63, on London-American, Deleted '66. Catalogue no: **HLU 9676**
7" Single: Released May '82, on Monument, Catalogue no: **CBS 076**

IT'S OVER
Tracks: / It's over.
7" Single: Released Apr '64, on London-American, Deleted '67. Catalogue no: **HLU 9882**

IT'S OVER (OLD GOLD)
Tracks: / It's over / Blue bayou.
7" Single: Released 27 Feb '89, on Old Gold, by Old Gold Records. Catalogue no: **OG 9879**

LANA
Tracks: / Lana.
7" Single: Released Jun '66, on London-American, Deleted '69. Catalogue no: **HL 10051**

MY FRIEND
Tracks: / My friend.
7" Single: Released Apr '69, on London-American, Deleted '72. Catalogue no: **HL 10261**

OH PRETTY WOMAN (OLD GOLD)
Tracks: / Oh pretty woman / Mean woman blues.
7" Single: Released 27 Feb '89, on Old Gold, by Old Gold Records. Catalogue no: **OG 9881**

OH PRETTY WOMAN (SINGLE)
Tracks: / Oh pretty woman.
7" Single: Released '80, on Monument, Catalogue no: **F 8110**
7" Single: Released Sep '64, on London-American, Deleted '67. Catalogue no: **HLU 9919**

ONLY THE LONELY (OLD GOLD)
Tracks: / Only the lonely / Blue angel.
7" Single: Released 27 Feb '89, on Old Gold, by Old Gold Records. Catalogue no: **OG 9870**

ONLY THE LONELY (SINGLE)
Tracks: / Only the lonely.

7" **Single:** Released Jan '80, on Monument, Catalogue no: **LR 8210**
7" **Single:** Released Jul '60, on London-American, Deleted '63. Catalogue no: **HLU 9149**

PENNY ARCADE
Tracks: / Penny arcade.
7" **Single:** Released Sep '69, on London-American, Deleted '72. Catalogue no: **HL 10285**

PRETTY PAPER
Tracks: / Pretty paper.
7" **Single:** Released Nov '64, on London-American, Deleted '67. Catalogue no: **HLU 9930**

RIDE AWAY
Tracks: / Ride away.
7" **Single:** Released Sep '65, on London-American, Deleted '68. Catalogue no: **HLU 9986**

ROY ORBISON: VINTAGE INTERVIEW PIC DISC
7" **Single:** Released Jun '89, on Baktabak, by Baktabak Records. Catalogue no: **VBAK 3002**

RUNNING SCARED
Tracks: / Running scared.
7" **Single:** Released Jan '80, on Monument, Catalogue no: **LR 1760**
7" **Single:** Released May '61, on London-American, Deleted '64. Catalogue no: **HLU 9342**

RUNNING SCARED (OLD GOLD)
Tracks: / Running scared / Crying.
7" **Single:** Released 27 Feb '89, on Old Gold, by Old Gold Records. Catalogue no: **OG 9872**

(SAY) YOU'RE MY GIRL
Tracks: / (Say) you're my girl.
7" **Single:** Released Jul '65, on London-American, Deleted '68. Catalogue no: **HLU 9978**

SHE'S A MYSTERY TO ME
Tracks: / She's a mystery to me / Crying / Dream baby (12" only).
7" **Single:** Released 6 Mar '89, on Virgin, by Virgin Records. Catalogue no: **VS 1173**
12" **Single:** Released 6 Mar '89, on Virgin, by Virgin Records. Catalogue no: **VST 1173**
CD 3": Released Feb '89, on Virgin, by Virgin Records. Catalogue no: **VSCD 1173**

SO GOOD
Tracks: / So good.
7" **Single:** Released Feb '67, on London-American, Deleted '70. Catalogue no: **HL 10113**

THERE WON'T BE MANY COMING HOME
Tracks: / There won't be many coming home.
7" **Single:** Released Dec '66, on London-American, Deleted '69. Catalogue no: **HL 10096**

TOO SOON TO KNOW
Tracks: / Too soon to know.
7" **Single:** Released Sep '66, on London-American, Deleted '69. Catalogue no: **HLU 10067**

TWINKLE TOES
Tracks: / Twinkle toes.
7" **Single:** Released Apr '66, on London-American, Deleted '69. Catalogue no: **HLU 10034**

WALK ON
Tracks: / London records.
7" **Single:** Released Jul '68, on London-American, Deleted '71. Catalogue no: **HLU 10206**

WILD HEARTS
Tracks: / Wild hearts / Time.

7" **Set:** Released Jun '85, on ZTT, by ZTT Records. Catalogue no: **DZTAS 9**
12" **Single:** Released Jun '85, on ZTT, by ZTT Records. Deleted '87. Catalogue no: **12 ZTAS 9**
7" **Single:** Released Jun '85, on ZTT, by ZTT Records. Catalogue no: **ZTAS 9**
12" **Single:** Released '87, on ZTT, by ZTT Records. Deleted Jun '88. Catalogue no: **12 ZTS 9**

WORKIN' FOR THE MAN
Tracks: / Working for the man.
7" **Single:** Released Nov '62, on London-American, Deleted '65. Catalogue no: **HLU 9607**

YOU GOT IT
Tracks: / You got it / Only one, The / Crying out (Available on 12" format only.).

7" **Single:** Released Dec '88, on Virgin, by Virgin Records. Catalogue no: **VS 1166**
12" **Single:** Released Dec '88, on Virgin, by Virgin Records. Catalogue no: **VST 1166**
CD 3": Released 30 Jan '89, on Virgin, by Virgin Records. Catalogue no: **VSCD 1166**

Orbit

BEAT GOES ON
Tracks: / Beat goes on.
12" **Single:** Released Jan '83, on Arista, by BMG Records (UK). Catalogue no: **ARIST 12514**
7" **Single:** Released Jan '83, on Arista, by BMG Records (UK). Catalogue no: **ARIST 514**

FEEL LIKE JUMPIN'
Tracks: / Feel like jumpin' / Blue Street.
12" **Single:** Released 23 May '87, on MCA, by MCA Records. Catalogue no: **WORBT 2**
7" **Single:** Released 23 May '87, on MCA, by MCA Records. Catalogue no: **WORB 2**

Orbit, William

LOVE MY WAY
Tracks: / Love my way.
12" **Single:** Released Aug '87, on MCA, by MCA Records. Catalogue no: **WORBT 1**
7" **Single:** Released Aug '87, on MCA, by MCA Records. Catalogue no: **WORB 1**

Orbitone

POLLUTION
Tracks: / Pollution.
12" **Single:** Released Sep '89, on Orbitone, by Orbitone Records. Catalogue no: **OR 1240**

Orbitone Allstars

THIS LOVE OF MINE (PART 2)
Tracks: / This love of mine.
12" **Single:** Released Jan '85, on Orbitone, by Orbitone Records. Catalogue no: **DORB 9**

Orchard

SECRET, A
Tracks: / Secret, A / Birds of passage.
7" **Single:** Released Apr '85, on Swan, by Rollercoaster Records. Catalogue no: **CYGNET 001**

Orchards

UNDERNEATH THE WINDOW, UNDERNEATH THE SINK
Tracks: / Underneath the window, underneath the sink.
7" **Single:** Released Nov '88, on Sarah, Catalogue no: **SARAH 11**

Orchestere De Chambre

VIETNAM, THEME FROM
Tracks: / Vietnam, Theme from.
7" **Single:** Released Aug '88, on Debut, by Skratch Records. Catalogue no: **DEBT 3053**

Orchestra Arcana

SEX PSYCHE
Tracks: / Sex psyche.
12" **Single:** Released May '85, on Cocteau, by Cocteau Records. Catalogue no: **COQT 19**

Orchestra J.B.

ON A LOVE GROOVE
Tracks: / On a love groove / There's a riot goin' on.
12" **Single:** Released Apr '88, on Metro Music International, Catalogue no: **12MMI 1**
CD 5": Released Jun '88, on Metro Music International, Catalogue no: **CDMMI 1**
7" **Single:** Released Apr '88, on Metro Music International, Catalogue no: **MM 1**

Orchestra Makassy

MAMBO BADO
Tracks: / Mambo bado.
7" **Single:** Released Sep '82, on Virgin, by Virgin Records. Deleted '89. Catalogue no: **VS 526**
12" **Single:** Released Sep '82, on Virgin, by Virgin Records. Deleted '89. Catalogue no: **VS 526-12**

Orchestra Suisse

INTERMEZZO
Tracks: / Intermezzo / El gato montes.
7" **Single:** Released Mar '84, on Polydor, by Polydor Ltd. Catalogue no: **POSP 675**

Orchestral Fever

CHRISTMAS STARS AND MORE
Tracks: / Christmas stars and more.
7" **Single:** Released Nov '81, on State, by State Records. Deleted Nov '84. Catalogue no: **STAT 109**

Orchestre Jazira

HAPPY DAY (CELEBRATION)
Tracks: / Happy day (celebration).
7" **Single:** Released Jul '84, on Beggars Banquet, by Beggars Banquet Records. Deleted '87. Catalogue no: **BEG 114**
12" **Single:** Released Jul '84, on Beggars Banquet, by Beggars Banquet Records. Deleted '87. Catalogue no: **BEG 114T**

LOVE
Tracks: / Love.
7" **Single:** Released Sep '82, on Earthworks, by Earthworks Records. Deleted '88. Catalogue no: **DIG 1**

SAKABO
Tracks: / Sakabo.
7" **Single:** Released Jan '84, on Beggars Banquet, by Beggars Banquet Records. Deleted '87. Catalogue no: **BEG 104**
12" **Single:** Released Jan '84, on Beggars Banquet, by Beggars Banquet Records. Deleted '87. Catalogue no: **BEG 104T**

Orchestre Super Moth

SALT OF THE EARTH (Song of praise)
Tracks: / Salt of the earth / Simbomba / Slow Benga.
12" **Single:** Released Sep '88, on Rogue, by Rogue Records. Catalogue no: **12FMS 106**

WORLD AT SIXES AND SEVENS, THE
Tracks: / World at sixes and sevens, The.
12" **Single:** Released Jul '89, on Rogue, by Rogue Records. Catalogue no: **12FMS 67**

Orchids

BOY CAN'T DANCE, THE
Tracks: / Boy can't dance, The / Daughters of Babylon.
7" **Single:** Released Jun '80, on MCA, by MCA Records. Deleted '83. Catalogue no: **MCA 586**

I'VE GOT A HABIT
Tracks: / I've got a habit.
7" **Single:** Released Jan '88, on Sarah, Catalogue no: **SARAH 002**

LYCEUM
10" **single:** Released Aug '89, on Sarah, Catalogue no: **SARAH 401**

WHAT WILL WE DO NEXT
Tracks: / What will we do next.
7" **Single:** Released Oct '89, on Sarah, Catalogue no: **SARAH 23**

Ordinary Man

I CAN'T BELIEVE IT'S COME TO THIS
Tracks: / I can't believe it's come to this / Goodbye America.
7" **Single:** Released Jul '87, on EMI, by EMI Records. Deleted Oct '87. Catalogue no: **EM 12**
12" **Single:** Released Jul '87, on EMI, by EMI Records. Deleted Oct '87. Catalogue no: **12 EM 12**

Ore

YOUR TIME WILL COME
Tracks: / Your time will come.
7" **Single:** Released Sep '82, on Bandit, by Bandit Records. Catalogue no: **BR 003**

Organiser

BANDIT
Tracks: / Bandit.
7" **Single:** Released Apr '89, on Soca, Catalogue no: **SOT 004**

Organum

TOWER OF SILENCE
Tracks: / Tower of silence.
12" **Single:** Released Oct '88, on Laylah, by Laylah Records. Catalogue no: **LAY 012**

Original...

ORIGINAL MIXED UP KID
Tracks: / Original mixed up kid: *Various artists*.
7" **Single:** Released Jul '81, on Fried Egg, by Fried Egg Records. Deleted '87. Catalogue no: **EGG 9**

Original Concept

CHARLIE SEZ
Tracks: / Charlie sez / Runnin yo' mouth / Gottanotha funky break 4 U hit it! (12" only.).
12" **Single:** Released Oct '88, on Def Jam, Deleted 17 Apr '89. Catalogue no: **653032 6**
7" **Single:** Released Oct '88, on Def Jam, Deleted 17 Apr '89. Catalogue no: **653032 7**

Original Mirrors

BOYS CRY
Tracks: / Boys cry / Chains of love.
7" **Single:** Released Feb '80, on Mercury, by Phonogram Ltd. Deleted Feb '83. Catalogue no: **MER 5**

DANCING WITH THE REBELS
Tracks: / Dancing with the rebels / Sure yeah / On Broadway.
7" **Single:** Released Mar '81, on Mercury, by Phonogram Ltd. Deleted Mar '84. Catalogue no: **MER 65**
12" **Single:** Released Mar '81, on Mercury, by Phonogram Ltd. Deleted Mar '84. Catalogue no: **MERX 65**

Original Oldies

ORIGINAL OLDIES (1) 6 track EP
Tracks: / Personality: *Price, Lloyd* / In the still of the night: *Five Satins* / At my front door: *Eldorados* / One summer night: *Danleers* / Keep a knockin': *Little Richard* / Sunday kind of love: *Harptones*.
7" **EP:** Released Nov '84, on Original Oldies, Catalogue no: **MD 501**

ORIGINAL OLDIES (2) 6 track EP
Tracks: / Hush-a-bye: *Mystics* / Earth angel: *Penguins* / Angels listened, The: *Crest* / Donna: *Valens, Ritchie* / Churchbells may ring, The: *Willows* / Just a dream: *Clanton, Jimmy*.
7" **EP:** Released Nov '84, on Original Oldies, Catalogue no: **MD 502**

ORIGINAL OLDIES (3) 6 track EP
Tracks: / Blue Monday: *Domino, Fats* / Little darlin': *Diamonds* / To the aisle: *Five Satins* / Teenager in love: *Dion & The Belmonts* / Everybody loves to cha cha: *Cooke, Sam* / Good golly Miss Molly: *Little Richard*.
7" **EP:** Released Nov '84, on Original Oldies, Catalogue no: **MD 503**

ORIGINAL OLDIES (4) 6 track EP
Tracks: / Kansas City: *Harrison, Wilbert* / Desiree: *Charts* / La bamba: *Valens, Ritchie* / Cherry pie: *Marlin & Johnny* / Stagger lee: *Price, Lloyd* / Twilight time: *Platters*.
7" **EP:** Released Nov '84, on Original Oldies, Catalogue no: **MD 504**

ORIGINAL OLDIES (5) 6 track EP
Tracks: / Tutti frutti: *Little Richard* / Eddie my love: *Teen Queens* / Great pretender, The: *Platters* / Blanche: *Three Friends* / Tiger: *Fabian* / Oh what a night: *Dells*.
7" **EP:** Released Nov '84, on Original Oldies, Catalogue no: **MD 505**

ORIGINAL OLDIES (6) 6 track EP
Tracks: / Sweet little sixteen: *Berry, Chuck* / Most of all: *Moonglows* / There goes my baby: *Drifters* / Bobby sox to stockings: *Avalon, Frankie* / Sea cruise: *Falcons* / You're so fine: *Falcons* / It was I: *Skip and Flip*.
7" **EP:** Released Nov '84, on Original Oldies, Catalogue no: **MD 506**

ORIGINAL OLDIES (7) 6 track EP
Tracks: / Sea Cruise: *Ford, Frankie* / You send me: *Cooke, Sam* / Hey little girl: *Clark, Dee* / Why don't you write: *Jacks* / Rockin' robin: *Day, Bobby* / Happy happy birthday baby: *Tune Weavers*.
7" **EP:** Released Nov '84, on Original Oldies, Catalogue no: **MD 507**

ORIGINAL OLDIES (8) 6 track EP
Tracks: / I'm gonna get married: *Price, Lloyd* / Only you: *Platters* / Stormy weather: *Spaniels* / Six nights a week: *Crests* / Let the good times roll: *Shirley & Lee* / Dedicated to the one I love: *Various artists*.
7" **EP:** Released Nov '84, on Original Oldies, Catalogue no: **MD 508**

ORIGINAL OLDIES (9) 6 track EP
Tracks: / Sincerely: *Moonglows* / Book of love: *Monotones* / My true love: *Scott, Jack* / Alone: *Shepherd Sisters* / Tragedy: *Wayne, Thomas* / Blueberry Hill: *Domino, Fats*.
7" **EP:** Released Nov '84, on Original Oldies, Catalogue no: **MD 509**

ORIGINAL OLDIES (10) 6 track EP
Tracks: / Maybellene: *Berry, Chuck* / Western movies: *Olympics* / It's just a matter of time: *Benton, Brook* / Seven little girls sitting in the back seat: *Evans, Paul* / You were mine: *Fireflies* / For your precious love: *Butler, Jerry & The Impressions*.
7" **EP:** Released Nov '84, on Original Oldies, Catalogue no: **MD 510**

ORIGINAL OLDIES (11) 6 track EP
Tracks: / Yakety yak: *Coasters* / Smoke gets in your eyes: *Platters* / Only sixteen: *Cooke, Sam* / Come go with me: *Del-Vikings* / Lavender blue: *Turner, Sammy*.
7" **EP:** Released Nov '84, on Original Oldies, Catalogue no: **MD 511**

ORIGINAL OLDIES (12) 6 track EP
Tracks: / Rip it up: *Little Richard* / My prayer: *Platters* / Primrose Lane: *Wallace, Jerry* / Sea of love: *Phillips, Phil* / Rockin' pneumonia and the boogie woogie flu: *Smith, Huey "Piano"* / Turn me loose: *Fabian*.
7" **EP:** Released Nov '84, on Original Oldies, Catalogue no: **MD 512**

ORIGINAL OLDIES (13) 6 track EP
Tracks: / I met him on a Sunday: *Various artists* / Year ago tonight, A: *Crests* / Goodnight my love: *Belvin, Jesse* / Dance with me Henry: *James, Etta* / Love is strange: *Mickey & Sylvia* / Stranded in the jungle: *Cadets*.
7" **EP**· Released Nov '84, on Original Oldies, Catalogue no: **MD 513**

ORIGINAL OLDIES (14) 6 track EP
Tracks: / Love potion No.9: *Clovers* / You've got the magic touch: *Platters* / Where were you on our wedding day: *Price, Lloyd* / I'll be home: *Flamingos* / Up on the mountain: *Magnificents* / My girl Josephine: *Domino, Fats*.
7" **EP:** Released Nov '84, on Original Oldies, Catalogue no: **MD 514**

ORIGINAL OLDIES (15) 6 track EP
Tracks: / My true story: *Jive Five* / Lonely

teenager: *Dion* / Those oldies but goodies: *Little Caesar & The Romans* / Will you love me tomorrow: *Shirelles* / Rhythm of the rain: *Cascades* / Duke of Earl: *Clanton, Jimmy*.
7" EP: Released Nov '84, on Original Oldies, Catalogue no: **MD 601**

ORIGINAL OLDIES (16) 6 track EP
Tracks: / Angel baby: *Rosie & The Originals* / Runaway: *Shannon, Del* / Venus in blue jeans: *Clanton, Jimmy* / Once in a while: *Chimes* / Raindrops: *Clark, Dee* / Soldier boy: *Shirelles*.
7" EP: Released Nov '84, on Original Oldies, Catalogue no: **MD 602**

ORIGINAL OLDIES (17) 6 track EP
Tracks: / Louie Louie: *Kingsmen* / Till: *Angels* / Baby it's you: *Various artists* / Where or when: *Dion & The Belmonts* / Ya ya: *Dorsey, Lee* / Love you so: *Holden, Ron*.
7" EP: Released Nov '84, on Original Oldies, Catalogue no: **MD 603**

ORIGINAL OLDIES (18) 6 track EP
Tracks: / He's so fine: *Chiffons* / Wonderful world: *Cooke, Sam* / You can't sit down: *Dovells* / He will break your heart: *Butler, Jerry* / All in my mind: *Brown, Maxine* / Any day now: *Jackson, Chuck*.
7" EP: Released Nov '84, on Original Oldies, Catalogue no: **MD 604**

ORIGINAL OLDIES (19) 6 track EP
Tracks: / Watermelon: *Santamaria* / Every beat of my heart: *Knight, Gladys & The Pips* / Tossin' and turnin': *Lewis, Bobby* / Denise: *Randy & The Rainbows* / Million to one, A: *Charles, Jimmy* / I know: *George, Barbara*.
7" EP: Released Nov '84, on Original Oldies, Catalogue no: **MD 605**

ORIGINAL OLDIES (20) 6 track EP
Tracks: / What's your name: *Don & Juan* / Runaround Sue: *Dion* / Tonight's the night: *Various artists* / Mockingbird: *Foxx, Nez* / Barefootin': *Parker, Robert* / Till then: *Classics*.
7" EP: Released Nov '84, on Original Oldies, Catalogue no: **MD 606**

ORIGINAL OLDIES (21) 6 track EP
Tracks: / Chapel of love: *Dixie Cups* / Funny: *Brown, Maxine* / I like it like that: *Kenner, Chris* / Please love me forever: *Cathy, Jean & Room mates* / Shoop shoop song: *Everett, Betty* / Yesterday's gone: *Chad & Jeremy*.
7" EP: Released Nov '84, on Original Oldies, Catalogue no: **MD 607**

ORIGINAL OLDIES (22) 6 track EP
Tracks: / Remember (walking in the sand): *Various artists* / Don't let the sun catch you crying: *Gerry & The Pacemakers* / I'm so lonesome I could cry: *Thomas, B.J.* / It ain't me babe: *Turtles* / Foolish little girl: *Various artists* / Surfer girl: *Beach Boys*.
7" EP: Released Nov '84, on Original Oldies, Catalogue no: **MD 608**

ORIGINAL OLDIES (23) 6 track EP
Tracks: / Hats off to Larry: *Shannon, Del* / Mama said: *Various artists* / Let it be me: *Butler, Jerry & Betty Everett* / Every breath I take: *Pitney, Gene* / Surfin' safari: *Beach Boys*.
7" EP: Released Nov '84, on Original Oldies, Catalogue no: **MD 609**

ORIGINAL OLDIES (24) 6 track EP
Tracks: / Oh no not my baby: *Brown, Maxine* / I saw her standing there: *Beatles* / Expressway to your heart: *Soul Survivors* / Summer song: *Chad & Jeremy* / Leader of the pack: *Shangri-Las* / What in the world's come over you: *Scott, Jack*.
7" EP: Released Nov '84, on Original Oldies, Catalogue no: **MD 610**

ORIGINAL OLDIES (25) 6 track EP
Tracks: / She'd rather be with me: *Turtles* / Duck, The: *Lee, Jacky* / Ferry cross the Mersey: *Gerry & The Pacemakers* / Tell it like it is: *Neville, Aaron* / Hooked on a feeling: *Thomas, B.J.* / Boy from New York City: *Ad Libs*.
7" EP: Released Nov '84, on Original Oldies, Catalogue no: **MD 611**

ORIGINAL OLDIES (26) 6 track EP
Tracks: / Raindrops keep falling on my head: *Thomas, B.J.* / Sweet talking guy: *Chiffons* / Get on up: *Esquires* / Iko iko: *Dixie Cups* / My own true love: *Durprees* / Love makes the world go round: *Jackson, Deon*.
7" EP: Released Nov '84, on Original Oldies, Catalogue no: **MD 612**

ORIGINAL OLDIES (27) 6 track EP
Tracks: / Surfin': *Beach Boys* / Have you heard: *Durples* / Judy in disguise: *Fred, John & The Playboys* / Take me for a little while: *Sands, Evie* / I'm in the mood for love: *Chimes* / Foot stompin': *Flares*.
7" EP: Released Nov '84, on Original Oldies, Catalogue no: **MD 613**

ORIGINAL OLDIES (28) 6 track EP
7" EP: Released Nov '84, on Original Oldies, Catalogue no: **MD 614**

ORIGINAL OLDIES (29) 6 track EP
Tracks: / I'm gonna be strong: *Various artists* / Five o'clock world: *Various artists* / I fought the law: *Various artists* / California sun: *Various artists* / Harbour lights: *Various artists*.
7" EP: Released Nov '84, on Original Oldies, Catalogue no: **MD 615**

ORIGINAL OLDIES (30) 6 track EP
Tracks: / Town without pity: *Various artists* / You belong to me: *Various artists* / Sunny: *Various artists* / Traces: *Various artists* / Backfield in motion: *Various artists* / Moon river: *Various artists*.
7" EP: Released Nov '84, on Original Oldies, Catalogue no: **MD 616**

ORIGINAL OLDIES (31) 6 track EP
Tracks: / Kind of a drag: *Buckinghams* / Till there was you: *Beatles* / Tighten up: *Bell, Archie & The Drells* / Misty: *Price, Lloyd* / Make it easy on yourself: *Butler, Jerry* / Twist and shout: *Isley Brothers*.
7" EP: Released Nov '84, on Original Oldies, Catalogue no: **MD 617**

ORIGINAL OLDIES (32) 6 track EP
Tracks: / Knock on wood: *Various artists* / Up on the roof: *Various artists* / Man who shot Liberty Valance: *Various artists* / One track mind: *Various artists* / Mother-in-law: *Various artists*.
7" EP: Released Nov '84, on Original Oldies, Catalogue no: **MD 618**

Original Party Mix

ORIGINAL PARTY MIX
Tracks: / Original party mix: *Various artists*.
12" Single: Released Nov '87, on Awesome (USA), Catalogue no: **AW 200**

Original Red Box

NEVER TRUST YOUR SOUL
Tracks: / Never trust your soul.
12" Single: Released Jul '84, on Polo, by Polo Records. Deleted '88. Catalogue no: **POLO 12-30**
7" Single: Released Jul '84, on Polo, by Polo Records. Deleted '88. Catalogue no: **POLO 30**

Original Sin

SHADOW, THE
Tracks: / Shadow, The.
12" Single: Released May '84, on Original Sin, Catalogue no: **SIN 1**

Original Wailers

MUSIC LESSON
Tracks: / Music lesson / Nice time.
12" Single: Released Mar '86, on Tuff Gong, Catalogue no: **TG 12001**
7" Single: Released Mar '86, on Tuff Gong, Catalogue no: **TG 7001**

Orioles

WHAT ARE YOU DOING NEW YEAR'S EVE
Tracks: / What are you doing New Year's Eve / Lonely Christmas.
7" Single: Released Jan '81, on President, by President Records. Deleted Jan '84. Catalogue no: **PT 488**

Orion

INSANE IN ANOTHER WORLD
Tracks: / Insane in another world.
7" Single: Released Jul '84, on Lost Moments, Catalogue no: **LM 002**

MEN FROM WHITEHALL, THE
Tracks: / Men from Whitehall, The.
7" Single: Released Jan '85, on County Cat, Catalogue no: **CAT 1**

Orion the Hunter

SO YOU RAN
Tracks: / So you ran.
7" Single: Released Jul '84, on Portrait, by CBS Records. Catalogue no: **A 4530**
12" Single: Released Jul '84, on Portrait, by CBS Records. Catalogue no: **TA 4530**

Or-Kestral-Line

CRAZY ROMANCE
Tracks: / Crazy romance.
7" Single: Released Jan '85, on Riviere, Catalogue no: **RIVI 01**

Orlando, Johnny

IT BURNS INSIDE
Tracks: / It burns inside.
12" Single: Released Aug '88, on Orbitone, by Orbitone Records. Catalogue no: **R 1232**

LET'S GIVE LOVE A TRY
Tracks: / Let's give love a try / Let's give love a try (Inst).
12" Single: Released Nov '86, on Orbitone, by Orbitone Records. Catalogue no: **OR 1218**

LOOKING BACK ON MY LIFE
Tracks: / Looking back on my life.
12" Single: Released Nov '85, on Orbitone, by Orbitone Records. Catalogue no: **DORB 12**

TELL ME WHEN
Tracks: / Tell me when / In and out (instrumental).
12" Single: Released May '86, on Orbitone, by Orbitone Records. Catalogue no: **DORB 15**

Orlando, Tony

Biographical details: Michael Anthony Orlando Cassivitis was born in New York City in 1944. He became interested in singing during childhood and, at 13, was hired by music publisher Don Kirshner to record demo tapes. Later he was launched as a singer in his own right and at 17 he had a pair of US Top Forty singles. The first was *Halfway To Paradise*, penned by the young husband-wife songwriting team Gerry Goffin and Carole King: Orlando took it to No 39 but it was a much bigger British hit for Billy Fury. The second, *Bless You* -- which Orlando took to No 15 in the States and No 5 in the UK -- was the first successful collaboration between Barry Mann and Cynthia Weil, who became another of Kirshner's hottest songwriting partnerships. Orlando's next single, *Happy Days Are Here To Stay*, was only a minor hit. His first period of pop stardom was over by his 18th birthday and for the rest of the 60's he worked for various music publishers. He staged a bried return to the US Top Forty in 1969 as leader of a faceless studio group called Wind, whose *Make Believe* reached No 28. By 1970 he had risen to a management position in Columbia Records' publishing division, April Blackwood. In that same year Orlando began his real return to the chart scene by becoming lead singer with Dawn. With worldwide smashes like *Knock Three Times* and *Tie A Yellow Ribbon Round The Old Oak Tree*, Orlando and the two Dawn girls became one of the top middle-of-the-road acts of the early 70's. This phase of his career was more lucrative but less interesting than his *Bless You* days. (Bob MacDonald, February 1986.).

BLESS YOU (OLD GOLD)
Tracks: / Bless you / Halfway to paradise.
7" Single: Released Jul '82, on Old Gold, by Old Gold Records. Deleted Jul '88. Catalogue no: **OG 9190**

BLESS YOU (SINGLE)
Tracks: / Bless you.
7" Single: Released Oct '61, on Fontana, by Phonogram Ltd. Deleted '64. Catalogue no: **H 330**

THEY'RT PLAYING OUR SONG
Tracks: / They're playing our song / Moonlight.
7" Single: Released Oct '80, on Casablanca, by PolyGram UK Ltd. Deleted Oct '83. Catalogue no: **CAN 207**

Orlons

DON'T HANG UP
Tracks: / Don't hang up.
7" Single: Released Dec '62, on Cameo Parkway, by Pye Records. Deleted '65. Catalogue no: **C 231**

Orme, Joey

GOOD OL BIRD
Tracks: / Good ol bird / Come on and love me.
7" Single: Released Jul '87, on ORM, Catalogue no: **ORM 10**

Ornamental

CRYSTAL NIGHTS
Tracks: / Crystal nights.
7" Single: Released Dec '88, on One Little Indian, by One Little Indian Records. Catalogue no: **7TP 18**
12" Single: Released Dec '88, on One Little Indian, by One Little Indian Records. Catalogue no: **12TP 18**

NO PAIN
Tracks: / No pain.
12" Single: Released Apr '88, on Gramm, Catalogue no: **GRAMM 28**

Orphan

JULIE ISN'T JULIE IN THE BATH
Tracks: / Julie isn't Julie in the bath / Time bomb.
Note: Originally released Apr '84.
7" Single: Released Jul '87, on Brilliant, by Brilliant Records. Catalogue no: **HIT 6**

LOVE ON THE LICHFIELD LINE
Tracks: / Love on the Lichfield line / Ambition.
7" Single: Released '85, on Swoop, Catalogue no: **RTL 004**

NERVOUS
Tracks: / Nervous / Little England.
Note: Le Matt Music 0789 750474/0494 36301
7" Single: Released Sep '86, on Swoop, Catalogue no: **RTLS 013**

R.S.V.P.U.
Tracks: / R.S.V.P.U. / Mouth to mouth.
7" Single: Released Oct '82, on Swoop, Catalogue no: **RTLS 008**

Orr, Benjamin

STAY THE NIGHT
Tracks: / Stay the night / That's the way.
12" Single: Released Jan '87, on Elektra (USA), by Elektra Records (USA). Deleted Jan '88. Catalogue no: **EKR 48 T**
7" Single: Released Jan '87, on Elektra (USA), by Elektra Records (USA). Deleted Jan '88. Catalogue no: **EKR 48**

Orrall, Robert Ellis

ACTUALLY
Tracks: / Actually / Let's eat / What she's doin' to me.
7" Single: Released May '81, on RCA, by BMG Records (UK). Deleted May '84. Catalogue no: **WHY 2**

I COULDN'T SAY NO
Tracks: / I couldn't say no / Next time.
7" Single: Released Feb '83, on Why-Fi, by Why-Fi Records. Catalogue no: **WHY 10**

TELL ME IF IT HURTS
Tracks: / Tell me if it hurts / I'm a bargain you're no steal.
7" Single: Released Sep '82, on RCA, by BMG Records (UK). Deleted Sep '85. Catalogue no: **WHY 9**

Orson Family

BALL AND CHAIN
Tracks: / Ball and chain / You shake my soul.
7" Single: Released Jul '83, on Orson, Catalogue no: **OE 1**

HEARTBEAT
Tracks: / Heartbeat / You shake my soul.
7" Single: Released Jun '83, on Orson, Catalogue no: **OE 1**

SWEETEST EMBRACE
Tracks: / Sweetest embrace.
7" Single: Released Oct '84, on Orson, Catalogue no: **OE 2**

Osborne, Jeffrey

Biographical details: This American singer, drummer and songwriter first came to fame in the mid-70's as leader of soul/disco band LTD, enjoying sizeable US pop hits with *Love Ballad* and *Back In Love Again*. He launched his solo career in 1982, enjoying a major black hit and moderate American pop hit with *I Really Don't Need No Light*. From late '82 until early '84 Osborne's strong soul voice graced three varied US Top Thirty singles: the soaring ballad *On The Wings Of Love*, the dancefloor shuffler *Don't You Get So Mad* and the quirky dance boppper *Stay With Me Tonight*. In Britain the steady increase of soul exposure on the airwaves bore fruit for Osborne in 1984. *Stay With Me Tonight* reached No 18 on the UK pop chart and *On The Wings Of Love* climbed belatedly to No 11. After a series of worthy records he slipped back somewhat with the disappointing material on his *Don't Stop* album, issued in late '84. His output was produced by the noted George Duke. (Bob MacDonald, February 1986.).

BORDERLINE
Tracks: / Borderline.
12" Single: Released Jan '85, on A&M, by A&M Records. Deleted '88. Catalogue no: **AMY 230**
7" Single: Released Jan '85, on A&M, by A&M Records. Deleted '88. Catalogue no: **AM 230**

DON'T STOP (SINGLE)
Tracks: / Don't stop.
12" Single: Released Oct '84, on A&M, by A&M Records. Deleted '88. Catalogue no: **AMX 222**
7" Single: Released Oct '84, on A&M, by A&M Records. Deleted '88. Catalogue no: **AM 222**

DON'T YOU GET SO MAD
Tracks: / Don't you get so mad.
7" Single: Released Sep '83, on A&M, by A&M Records. Deleted '86. Catalogue no: **AM 140**

EENIE MEENIE
Tracks: / Eenie meenie / You were made to love.
7" Single: Released Aug '82, on A&M, by A&M Records. Deleted Aug '85. Catalogue no: **USAF 1223**

I REALLY DON'T NEED NO LIGHT
Tracks: / I really don't need no light / One million kisses.
7" Single: Released Jul '82, on A&M, by A&M Records. Deleted Jul '85. Catalogue no: **AMS 8234**
12" Single: Released Jul '82, on A&M, by A&M Records. Deleted Jul '85. Catalogue no: **AMS 128234**

ON THE WINGS OF LOVE

Tracks: / On the wings of love / I'm begging.
12" Single: Released Jun '84, on A&M, by A&M Records. Deleted '85. Catalogue no: **AMX 198**
7" Single: Released Jun '84, on A&M, by A&M Records. Deleted '88. Catalogue no: **AM 198**
12" Single: Released Jan '83, on Funk America, by A&M Records. Catalogue no: **USAF 1225**
7" Single: Released Jan '83, on Funk America, by A&M Records. Catalogue no: **USA 1225**

ON THE WINGS OF LOVE (OLD GOLD)
Tracks: / On the wings of love / Stay with me tonight.
12" Single: Released Nov '88, on Old Gold, by Old Gold Records. Catalogue no: **OG 4088**

ROOM WITH A VIEW
Tracks: / Room with a view / Power.
7" Single: Released Sep '86, on A&M, by A&M Records. Deleted '87. Catalogue no: **AM 352**
12" Single: Released Sep '86, on A&M, by A&M Records. Deleted '87. Catalogue no: **AMY 352**

SHE'S ON THE LEFT
Tracks: / She's on the left / Plane love.
12" Single: Released Oct '88, on Breakout, by A&M Records. Catalogue no: **USAT 643**
7" Single: Released Oct '88, on Breakout, by A&M Records. Catalogue no: **USA 643**

SOWETO
Tracks: / Soweto / Plain love.
7" Single: Released Jul '86, on A&M, by A&M Records. Deleted '88. Catalogue no: **AM 334**
12" Single: Released Jul '86, on A&M, by A&M Records. Deleted '87. Catalogue no: **AMY 334**

STAY WITH ME TONIGHT (SINGLE)
Tracks: / Stay with me tonight / Baby.
7" Single: Released Oct '83, on A&M, by A&M Records. Deleted '88. Catalogue no: **AM 157**
12" Single: Released Oct '83, on A&M, by A&M Records. Deleted '88. Catalogue no: **AMX 157**
7" Single: Released Apr '84, on A&M, by A&M Records. Deleted '87. Catalogue no: **AM 188**

YOU SHOULD BE MINE
Tracks: / You should be mine / Eenie / Stay with me tonight (* Extra tack on 12" version only).
7" Single: Released May '86, on A&M, by A&M Records. Deleted '88. Catalogue no: **AM 311**
12" Single: Released May '86, on A&M, by A&M Records. Deleted '88. Catalogue no: **AMY 311**

Osborne, Leroy

AIN'T NOTHING STRONGER THAN LOVE
Tracks: / Ain't nothing stronger than love.
7" Single: Released Jun '84, on Excaliber, by Red Bus Records. Deleted '88. Catalogue no: **EXC 538**
12" Single: Released Jun '84, on Excaliber, by Red Bus Records. Deleted '88. Catalogue no: **EXCL 538**

Osbourne, Johnny

BABY I LOVE YOU
Tracks: / Baby I love you / Gwan black hot summer.
12" Single: Released Nov '86, on Vibes & Vibes, Catalogue no: **VAV 11**

BABY LOVE
Tracks: / Baby love.
12" Single: Released May '84, on Tads, Catalogue no: **TRD 099**

BACK OFF
Tracks: / Back off.
12" Single: Released May '81, on Greensleeves, by Greensleeves Records. Catalogue no: **GRED 50**

BEDTIME STORY
Tracks: / Bedtime story.
12" Single: Released Jul '83, on D-Music, Catalogue no: **D Music**

BRING YOUR DAUGHTER
Tracks: / Bring your daughter.
12" Single: Released Dec '84, on Tads, Catalogue no: **TRB 31384**

CAN'T LEAVE JAH
Tracks: / Can't leave Jah.
12" Single: Released Aug '82, on Black Joy, Catalogue no: **DH 823**

COME IN A DANCE
Tracks: / Come in a dance.
12" Single: Released Mar '85, on Music Tab, Catalogue no: **Unknown**

CROSS BREED
Tracks: / Cross breed.
12" Single: Released Jun '84, on D-Music, Catalogue no: **HR 3**

DO IT AGAIN
Tracks: / Do it again / More cut.
7" Single: Released Jun '82, on Plantation, Deleted Jun '85. Catalogue no: **PL 06**
12" Single: Released May '82, on Plantation, Catalogue no: **PL 006**

DON'T BITE THE HAND
Tracks: / Don't bite the hand.
10" single: Released Feb '83, on Simba, Catalogue no: **SIM 002**

DON'T YOU KNOW THAT I LOVE YOU?
Tracks: / Don't you know I love you / Dub wise.
12" Single: Released May '84, on D-Music, Catalogue no: **MR 4**

DUB PLATE PLAYING
Tracks: / Dub plate playing.
12" Single: Released Nov '86, on Greensleeves, by Greensleeves Records. Catalogue no: **GRED 208**

FOR THE LONGEST TIME
Tracks: / For the longest time.
12" Single: Released Jul '84, on Tads, Catalogue no: **TRD 18684**

GET CRACKING
Tracks: / Get cracking / Soul and inspiration.
12" Single: Released Mar '84, on Londisc, by Londisc Records. Catalogue no: **LD 016**

GOOD QUALITY
Tracks: / Good quality.
12" Single: Released May '89, on Black Scorpio, Catalogue no: **BS 021**

GOOD TIME ROCK
Tracks: / Good time rock.
12" Single: Released Feb '89, on Digital B., Catalogue no: **VPRD 410**

GROOVING
Tracks: / Groovin'.
12" Single: Released Jul '84, on Dancefloor, Catalogue no: **DFT 7008**

GUNSHOT
Tracks: / Gunshot.
12" Single: Released Sep '89, on Digital B., Catalogue no: **VPRD 477**

HERE I COME AGAIN
Tracks: / Here I come again.
12" Single: Released Dec '83, on Foundation, Catalogue no: **TF 12**

HILL AND GULLEY
Tracks: / Hill and gulley.
12" Single: Released Aug '87, on Moodies, Catalogue no: **MR 007**

I DON'T WANT TO BE LONELY
Tracks: / I don't want to be lonely.
12" Single: Released Sep '85, on Hawkeye, by Hawkeye Records. Catalogue no: **HD 63**

I SHALL NOT BE REMOVED
Tracks: / I shall not be removed.
12" Single: Released Sep '89, on Exodus, Catalogue no: **EX 013**

IF JAH DIDN'T LOVE YOU
Tracks: / If Jah didn't love you / Who fa fay a the best.
12" Single: Released May '85, on Rockers Forever, Catalogue no: **HR 006**

IF YOU LOVE DE RUB-A-DUB SAY FORWARD
Tracks: / If you love de rub-a-dub say forward / Chanting til morning.
12" Single: Released Dec '83, on Selection, Catalogue no: **SEL 311183**

I'M MOVING UP
Tracks: / I'm moving up.
12" Single: Released Jun '89, on Living Room, Catalogue no: **OH 17**

IN THE AREA (SINGLE)
Tracks: / In the area / Saying goodbye.
12" Single: Released Dec '84, on Greensleeves, by Greensleeves Records. Catalogue no: **GRED 168**

JOY
Tracks: / Joy.
7" Single: Released Apr '89, on Rock Star (2), Catalogue no: **RSD 003**

JUGGLING STEEP
Tracks: / Juggling steep.
12" Single: Released Jul '89, on Live & Love, Catalogue no: **LLD 123**

LEND ME A CHOPPER
Tracks: / Lend me a chopper.
12" Single: Released Feb '83, on Starlight, Catalogue no: **SLD 526**

MY SOUND
Tracks: / My sound.
12" Single: Released Nov '88, on Steely & Cleevie, Catalogue no: **VPRD 355**

NO SOUND LIKE WE
Tracks: / No sound like we.
12" Single: Released Nov '85, on Greensleeves, by Greensleeves Records. Catalogue no: **GRED 190**

ONE MORE RUB-A-DUB
Tracks: / One more rub-a-dub.
12" Single: Released Jun '83, on Tads, Catalogue no: **TRD 1583**

ONE RUB-A-DUB FOR THE ROAD
Tracks: / One rub-a-dub for the road.
12" Single: Released Mar '85, on Top Rank (2), Catalogue no: **TR 001**
12" Single: Released 30 May '89, on Black Scorpio, Catalogue no: **CDBS 13**

ORIGINAL REWIND, THE
Tracks: / Original rewind , The.
12" Single: Released Apr '85, on Unity Sound, Catalogue no: **UN 003**

PUT IT BY NUMBER 1
Tracks: / Put it by number 1.
12" Single: Released Jul '85, on Unity, Catalogue no: **UN 006**

QUASAI
Tracks: / Quasai / I've lost that love.
12" Single: Released Dec '83, on Cha-Cha, by Cha-Cha Records. Catalogue no: **CHAD 58**

REGGAE ON BROADWAY (SINGLE)
Tracks: / Reggae on Broadway.
12" Single: Released Nov '82, on Black Music, Catalogue no: **BM 707**

REWIND
Tracks: / Rewind.
12" Single: Released Sep '84, on Jammy's, Catalogue no: **Unknown**

ROCK AND COME ON YA
Tracks: / Rock and come on ya.
12" Single: Released Jul '82, on Black Joy, Catalogue no: **DH 818**

ROCK-A-DUB
Tracks: / Rock a dub.
12" Single: Released Oct '85, on Germaine, Catalogue no: **Unknown**

SHOW ME YOUR SIGN
Tracks: / Show me your sign / Six for a nine.
12" Single: Released Aug '86, on Unity Sound, Catalogue no: **UN 021**

SWEET MOUTH
Tracks: / Sweet mouth.
7" Single: Released 12 May '89, on Greensleeves, by Greensleeves Records. Catalogue no: **GRED 244**

T.K.O.
Tracks: / T.K.O..
12" Single: Released May '83, on Roots Radical, by Roots Radical Records. Catalogue no: **RR 12055**

TRICKSTER
Tracks: / Trickster.
12" Single: Released Nov '88, on Greensleeves, by Greensleeves Records. Catalogue no: **GRED 232**

TROUBLEMAKER
Tracks: / Trouble maker / Angel in my arms.
12" Single: Released Nov '83, on Greensleeves, by Greensleeves Records. Catalogue no: **GRED 130**

UPFRONT LOVER
Tracks: / Upfront lover.
7" Single: Released Oct '83, on Top Rank (2), Catalogue no: **DSR 0488**

WATER PUMPING (SINGLE)
Tracks: / Water pumping.
12" Single: Released Aug '83, on CF, Catalogue no: **CF 003**

WHAT ABOUT ME
Tracks: / What about me.
12" Single: Released Mar '89, on Charm, by Charm Records. Catalogue no: **CRT 28**
12" Single: Released Feb '89, on Top Rank (1), Catalogue no: **VPTRR 099**

WIPE OUT APARTHEID
Tracks: / Wipe out apartheid / Wipe out apartheid (version).
12" Single: Released Feb '86, on Top Rank (2), Catalogue no: **TRD 018**

YO YO
Tracks: / Yo yo.
12" Single: Released Oct '82, on Oak Sound, Catalogue no: **OS 007**

YOU SEXY THING
Tracks: / You sexy thing.
12" Single: Released Dec '88, on Top Rank (2), Catalogue no: **TRD 031**
12" Single: Released Apr '89, on Top Rank (2), Catalogue no: **TRD 032**

Osbourne, Ozzy

Biographical details: This British singer and songwriter (whose real forename is John) hailed from Aston, Birmingham and was a founder member of Black Sabbath in 1969. They became one of the world's foremost heavy metal acts of the early Seventies, and Ozzy enjoyed superstar status as their truly crazy frontman. In 1978 Osbourne quit the banew band. His uncompromising musical stance continued - he played out-and-out heavy metal combining frantically powerful guitar riffs and chords with lyrics about occult, rebellion, death, destruction and the like. His first post-Sabbath album was released in 1980, the same year that BS released their first LP with new vocalist Ronnie James Dio. Thus commenced an intriguing vinyl battle in which each side tried to out-metal the other. Black Sabbath had the upper hand at first, as their *Heaven and hell* LP outflanked Ozzy Osbourne's *Blizzard of Oz* (this was initially the name of his band, though later records were simply creditied to Ozzy Osbourne). But as the Eighties progressed, Ozzy clearly emerged as the winner.
Osbourne's 1981 album *Diary of a madman* reached No.14 in Britain and No.16 in the States. 1982's *Talk of the devil* climbed to No.21 in the UK and No.14 in the US. 1983's *Bark at the moon* reached No.19 in America and yielded his first solo British Top 30 singles: *Bark at the moon* (No.21) and *So tired* (No.20). For his fifth solo offering, the lunatic rocker decided to spend much longer in the studio - he hired talented producer Ron Nevison for *The ultimate sin*, which was a Top 20 item on both sides of the Atlantic in early 1986. This latter LP spawned the catchy single *Shot in the dark*, which reached the UK No.20 position; this song was the most accessible track of Ozzy's solo career, and represented the closest he could get to the mainstream pop. Controversy was a perpetual feature of his career during the Eighties. He became notorious amongst animal lovers for his on-stage stunt of biting the head of a dead bat. Then in April 1982, he suffered the death of his talented guitarist and sidekick Randy Rhoads. The blatantly provocative nature of many of Ozzy's lyrics made him a prime target for American bodies like the Moral Majority and the Parents' Music Resource Centre - these self-appointed guardians of the nation's morals cited many heavy metal acts as evil propagators of the devil's ideology and as a corrupting influence upon young people. A new furor greeted Osbourne when the bitter parents of a deceased American lad took the vocalist to court, claiming that his track *Suicide solution* had prompted their son to take his own life (Bob MacDonald, 21st Feb 1986)o.

BARK AT THE MOON (SINGLE)
Tracks: / Bark at the moon.
7" Single: Released Nov '83, on Epic, by CBS Records. Deleted '86. Catalogue no: **A 3915**

CRAZY TRAIN
Tracks: / Crazy train.
7" Single: Released Sep '80, on Jet, by Jet Records. Deleted '83. Catalogue no: **JET 197**
7" Single: Released 20 Jun '87, on Epic, by CBS Records. Deleted Nov '87. Catalogue no: **650943 7**
12" Single: Released 20 Jun '87, on Epic, by CBS Records. Deleted Nov '87. Catalogue no: **650943 6**

FLYING HIGH AGAIN
Tracks: / Flying high again / I don't know.
7" Single: Released Oct '81, on Jet, by Jet Records. Deleted Oct '84. Catalogue no: **JET 12107**

LIVE E.P.
7" EP: Released '88, on Jet (Canada), Catalogue no: **12 EXP 37640**

MIRACLE MAN
Tracks: / Miracle man / Crazy babies / Liar, The (Only on 12" & CD single.).
7" Pic: Released Nov '88, on Epic, by CBS Records. Deleted 17 Apr '89. Catalogue no: **653063 9**
CD 5": Released Oct '88, on Epic, by CBS Records. Deleted 17 Apr '89. Catalogue no: **653063 2**
12" Single: Released Nov '88, on Epic, by CBS Records. Deleted 17 Apr '89. Catalogue no: **653063 8**
7" Single: Released Oct '88, on Epic, by CBS Records. Deleted 17 Apr '89. Catalogue no: **653063 0**
12" Single: Released Oct '88, on Epic, by CBS Records. Deleted 17 Apr '89. Catalogue no: **653063 6**

MR. CROWLEY
Tracks: / Mr. Crowley / You said it all / Suicide solution (On 12" only).
12" Single: Released Nov '80, on Jet, by Jet Records. Deleted '83. Catalogue no: **JET 12-7003**
7" Single: Released Nov '80, on Jet, by Jet Records. Deleted '83. Catalogue no: **JET 7003**

OVER THE MOUNTAIN
Tracks: / Over the mountain / I don't know.
7" Single: Released Dec '81, on Jet, by Jet Records. Deleted Dec '84. Catalogue no: **JET 7017**
12" Single: Released Dec '81, on Jet, by Jet

Records. Deleted Dec '84. Catalogue no: **JET 12017**

SHOT IN THE DARK
Tracks: / Shot in the dark / Rock 'n' roll rebel.
7" Single: Released Jan '86, on Epic, by CBS Records. Catalogue no: **A 6859**
7" Single: Released Jan '86, on Epic, by CBS Records. Catalogue no: **QA 6859**
12" Single: Released Jan '86, on Epic, by CBS Records. Catalogue no: **TA 6859**

SO TIRED
Tracks: / So tired / Forever / Waiting for darkness (On 12" only) / Paranoid (On 12" only).
7" Single: Released Jun '84, on Epic, by CBS Records. Deleted '87. Catalogue no: **A 4452**
7" Single: Released Jun '84, on Epic, by CBS Records. Catalogue no: **A 4460**
12" Single: Released Jun '84, on Epic, by CBS Records. Catalogue no: **WA 4460**
12" Single: Released Mar '84, on CBS, by CBS Records. Catalogue no: **TA 4260**
7" Set: Released Mar '84, on CBS, by CBS Records. Catalogue no: **DA 4260**

SYMPTON OF THE UNIVERSE
Tracks: / Symptom of the universe nib / Iron man / Children of the grave.
12" Pic: Released Dec '82, on Jet, by Jet Records. Deleted Dec '87. Catalogue no: **JETP 7030**
7" Single: Released Dec '82, on Jet, by Jet Records. Deleted Dec '87. Catalogue no: **JET 12030**

ULTIMATE SIN (SINGLE)
Tracks: / Ultimate sin / Bark at the moon / Mr. Crowley / Diary of a madman.
12" Single: Released 25 Jul '88, on CBS, by CBS Records. Deleted Jan '89. Catalogue no: **652 875-6**
CD 5": Released 25 Jul '88, on CBS, by CBS Records. Deleted Jan '89. Catalogue no: **652 875-2**

ULTIMATE SIN (SINGLE)
Tracks: / Ultimate sin / Lightning strikes.
7" Single: Released Jul '86, on Epic, by CBS Records. Deleted '87. Catalogue no: **A 7311**

Osbourne, Tony

MAN FROM MADRID
Tracks: / Man from Madrid.
7" Single: Released Feb '61, on H.M.V., by EMI Records. Deleted '64. Catalogue no: **POP 827**

SHEPHERD'S SONG, THE
Tracks: / Shepherd's song.
7" Single: Released Feb '73, on Philips, by Phonogram Ltd. Deleted '76. Catalogue no: **6006 266**

Oscur, Clair

BLUME
Tracks: / Blume.
7" Single: Released '88, on Visa (1), Catalogue no: **VISAUF 006**

Oshama

HIGHWAY
Tracks: / Highway.
12" Single: Released Aug '82, on Smokey, Catalogue no: **SMJD 007**

Osibisa

Biographical details: The first and most successful line-up of this multi-international band comprised saxophonist/founder/leader Teddy Osei, his brother Mac Tontoh and Sol Amargio (all from Ghana), Loughty Amao (from Nigeria), Robert Bailey (from Trinidad), Spartacus R (from Grenada) and Wendel Richardson (from Antigua). The band's music was summed up by their name, which meant 'criss-cross rhythms that explode with happiness'. Formed in London in 1970, Osei's intention with Osibisa was to promote and popularise African music on the western rock scene. They achieved this handsomely on their first two albums - *Osisbisa* and *Woyaya* (1971 and 1972 respectively) both reached No.11 on the British LP charts, and received substantial critical acclaim. In 1974 the band were responsible for the soundtrack of the movie *Superfly TNT*. Although Osibisa never quite lived up to the quality of their first two releases, they continued to tour prolifically through the mid-seventies. Their live shows were spectacular from a visual standpoint, as well as being an educational experience for music fans weaned on pop or classical. 1976 brought Osibisa a pair of UK Top 40 singles: *Sunshine day*, a singalong ditty that epitomised their optimistic stance, reached No.17 and *Dance the body music* peaked at No.31. Their music was joyous, and they chose not to export Third World. Britain and Europe largely forgot them, and it was left to others to continue the process of black music propagation in those areas. 1981 was particulary productive for Osibisa - they embarked upon large benefit tours of Kenya and Zimbabwe and enjoyed huge success with an album and tour in India. (Bob MacDonald, 21st Feb 1986).

DANCE THE BODY MUSIC
Tracks: / Dance the body music.
7" Single: Released Jun '76, on Bronze, by Bronze Records. Deleted '79. Catalogue no: **BRO 26**

OREBA Magic people
Tracks: / Oreba / Moving on.
7" Single: Released Nov '80, on Calibre, Deleted '83. Catalogue no: **CAB 106**
12" Single: Released Nov '80, on Calibre, Deleted '83. Catalogue no: **CABL 106**

PATA-PATA
Tracks: / Pata-pata / Jumbo.
12" Single: Released Jan '80, on Pye, Deleted Jan '83. Catalogue no: **12P 5013**
7" Single: Released Jan '80, on Pye, Deleted Jan '83. Catalogue no: **7P 5013**

RAGHUPATI RAGHAVA RAGARAM
Tracks: / Raghupati raghava ragaram.
7" Single: Released Mar '83, on AVM, by AVM Records. Deleted '87. Catalogue no: **AVM 1003**

SUNSHINE DAY
Tracks: / Sunshine day.
7" Single: Released Jan '76, on Bronze, by Bronze Records. Deleted '79. Catalogue no: **BRO 20**

WOOLY BULLY
Tracks: / Wooly bully.
12" Single: Released Aug '85, on Sierra, by Sierra Records. Deleted Jun '87. Catalogue no: **FED 14T**
7" Single: Released Aug '85, on Sierra, by Sierra Records. Deleted Jun '87. Catalogue no: **FED 14**

Osiris

WAR ON THE BULLSHIT (SINGLE)
Tracks: / War on the bullshit.
12" Single: Released Jun '86, on Cherry Red, by Cherry Red Records. Catalogue no: **12 ATTACK 2**

Oskar, Lee

FEELIN' HAPPY
Tracks: / Feelin' happy / More than words can say.
7" Single: Released Mar '80, on MCA, by MCA Records. Deleted Mar '83. Catalogue no: **MCA 576**

Oslin, K.T.

EIGHTIES LADIES (SINGLE)
Tracks: / Eighties ladies / Two hearts.
7" Single: Released 6 Jun '88, on RCA, by BMG Records (UK). Deleted Aug '89. Catalogue no: **PB 49545**

WALL OF TEARS
Tracks: / Wall of tears / Doctor Doctor.
7" Single: Released 23 Apr '88, on RCA, by BMG Records (UK). Deleted May '89. Catalogue no: **PB 49559**

YOUNGER MEN
Tracks: / Younger men / I'll always come back.
7" Single: Released Jul '88, on RCA, by BMG Records (UK). Deleted May '89. Catalogue no: **PB 49531**

Osman, Sophie

WITH ALL MY HEART
Tracks: / With all my heart / Heavy heart (On 7" only) / Come on (Charlie Brown) (On 12" only).
7" Single: Released May '86, on Fresh, by Jetstar Records. Catalogue no: **CN 001**
12" Single: Released Nov '86, on Fresh, by Jetstar Records. Catalogue no: **FBT 001**

Osmond Brothers

I THINK ABOUT YOUR LOVIN'
Tracks: / I think about your lovin'.
7" Single: Released Mar '85, on Range, by Range Records. Catalogue no: **RANS 74**

Osmond, Donny

DEEP PURPLE (SINGLE)
Tracks: / Deep purple.
7" Single: Released Jan '76, on MGM, by Polydor Ltd. Deleted '79. Catalogue no: **2006 561**

GROOVE
Tracks: / Groove / Only heaven knows / Groove (club mix) (CD only) / Only heaven knows (alternate mix) (CD only) / I'm in it for love (CD only (radio remix)).
7" Single: Released Oct '87, on Virgin, by Virgin Records. Deleted May '88. Catalogue no: **VS 1016**
CD 5": Released Aug '88, on Virgin, by Virgin Records. Catalogue no: **CDEP 15**
12" Single: Released Oct '87, on Virgin, by Virgin Records. Deleted May '88. Catalogue no: **VST 1016**

IF IT'S LOVE THAT YOU WANT
Tracks: / If it's love that you want / Come down / If it's love that you want (extended remix) (12" only).
Note: Taken from the forthcoming album this is the follow up to "Soldier of Love".
12" Single: Released 17 Oct '88, on Virgin, by Virgin Records. Catalogue no: **VST 1140**
7" Single: Released 17 Oct '88, on Virgin, by Virgin Records. Catalogue no: **VS 1140**

I'M IN IT FOR LOVE
Tracks: / I'm in it for love / Keep me hummin' / What am I here for.
Cassingle: Released Aug '87, on Virgin, by Virgin Records. Deleted May '88. Catalogue no: **VSC 994-12**
7" Single: Released Aug '87, on Virgin, by Virgin Records. Deleted May '88. Catalogue no: **VS 994**
12" Single: Released Aug '87, on Virgin, by Virgin Records. Deleted May '88. Catalogue no: **VS 994-12**

I'M LEAVING IT ALL UP TO YOU (SINGLE)
Tracks: / I'm leaving it all up to you.
7" Single: Released Aug '74, on MGM, by Polydor Ltd. Deleted '77. Catalogue no: **2006 446**

MAKE THE WORLD GO AWAY (SINGLE)
Tracks: / Make the world go away.
7" Single: Released Jun '75, on MGM, by Polydor Ltd. Deleted '78. Catalogue no: **2006 523**

MORNING SIDE OF THE MOUNTAIN
Tracks: / Morning side of the mountain.
7" Single: Released Dec '74, on MGM, by Polydor Ltd. Deleted '77. Catalogue no: **2006 474**

PUPPY LOVE
Tracks: / Puppy love.
7" Single: Released Jun '72, on MGM, by Polydor Ltd. Deleted '75. Catalogue no: **2006 104**

SACRED EMOTION
Tracks: / Sacred emotion.
7" Single: Released Jul '89, on Virgin, by Virgin Records. Catalogue no: **VS 1211**
12" Single: Released Sep '89, on Virgin, by Virgin Records. Catalogue no: **12 VS 1211**

SOLDIER OF LOVE
Tracks: / Soldier of love (On all versions) / Time can't erase (On all versions) / Soldier of love (dub mix) (On CD & 12" only) / Groove (On CD only).
Note: "'Soldier of Love' sees 'Donny Osmond' in rockin' good form, which shows a depth and maturity which should silence any critics. Don't be put off by the name - Donny is back - in a big way." (Virgin, July 1988)
12" Pic: Released '88, on Virgin, by Virgin Records. Catalogue no: **VSTY 1094**
7" Single: Released May '89, on Virgin, by Virgin Records. Catalogue no: **VS 1094**
CD 5": Released May '89, on Virgin, by Virgin Records. Catalogue no: **VSCD 1094**
12" Single: Released May '89, on Virgin, by Virgin Records. Catalogue no: **VST 1094**

TOO YOUNG (SINGLE)
Tracks: / Too young.
7" Single: Released Sep '72, on MGM, by Polydor Ltd. Deleted '75. Catalogue no: **2006 113**

TWELFTH OF NEVER
Tracks: / Twelfth of never.
7" Single: Released Mar '73, on MGM, by Polydor Ltd. Deleted '76. Catalogue no: **2006 199**

WHEN I FALL IN LOVE
Tracks: / When I fall in love.
7" Single: Released Nov '73, on MGM, by Polydor Ltd. Deleted '76. Catalogue no: **2006 365**

WHERE DID ALL THE GOOD TIMES GO
Tracks: / Where did all the good times go.
7" Single: Released Nov '74, on MGM, by Polydor Ltd. Deleted '77. Catalogue no: **2006 468**

WHY
Tracks: / Why.
7" Single: Released Nov '72, on MGM, by Polydor Ltd. Deleted '75. Catalogue no: **2006 119**

YOUNG LOVE
Tracks: / Young love.
7" Single: Released Aug '73, on MGM, by Polydor Ltd. Deleted '76. Catalogue no: **2006 300**

Osmond, Jimmy

I'M GONNA KNOCK ON YOUR DOOR
Tracks: / I'm gonna knock on your door.
7" Single: Released Mar '74, on MGM, by Polydor Ltd. Deleted '77. Catalogue no: **2006 389**

LONG HAIRED LOVER FROM LIVERPOOL
Tracks: / Long haired lover from Liverpool.
7" Single: Released Nov '72, on MGM, by Polydor Ltd. Deleted '75. Catalogue no: **2006 109**

TWEEDLE DEE
Tracks: / Tweedle dee.
7" Single: Released Mar '73, on MGM, by Polydor Ltd. Deleted '76. Catalogue no: **2006 175**

Osmond, Marie

GET ME TO HEAVEN
Tracks: / Get me to heaven / La song.
7" Single: Released Apr '80, on Polydor, by Polydor Ltd. Deleted Apr '83. Catalogue no: **POSP 147**

PAPER ROSES (SINGLE)
Tracks: / Paper roses.
7" Single: Released Nov '73, on MGM, by Polydor Ltd. Deleted '76. Catalogue no: **2006 315**

THERE'S NO STOPPING YOUR HEART (SINGLE)
Tracks: / There's no stopping your heart / Love will find it's way to you.
7" Single: Released Mar '86, on Capitol, by EMI Records. Deleted '88. Catalogue no: **CL 390**

Osmonds

Biographical details: One of the most successful families in the history of showbusiness, the Utah-based Osmonds enjoyed hits on both sides of the Atlantic in five different membership combinations: Donny, Marie, Donny & Marie, Little Jimmy and, simply, The Osmonds (Alan, Wayne, Merrill, Jay and Donny). The first four of these acts concentrated on cover versions of old pop standards; the latter originated much of its own material (usually provided by the Alan/Wayne/Merrill team) or else recorded new, unfamiliar songs from other sources. Parents George and Olive Osmond nurtured and encouraged the early careers of their offspring, and travelled with them on many of their tours. In order of birth, the couple's eight sons and one daughter comprised: Virl, Tom, Alan, Wayne, Merrill, Jay, Donny, Marie and Jimmy. The two eldest sons suffered from hearing defects, and thus did not become performers but helped to administer the family's business affairs.

The first Osmonds to make their mark in music were Alan, Wayne, Merrill and Jay (born between 1949 and 1955). The foursome's first professional engagement was a residency at Disneyland in Los Angeles in 1962. In December of that year, they began a 4 1/2 year run of regular appearances on Andy Williams' networked US television show; they initially sang in harmony as a barber shop quartet but, with the addition of Donny (born 1957) in December 1963, they adopted a more contemporary style. From 1967-69 they appeared regularly on Jerry Lewis' TV variety show. Despite their prodigious fame during the Sixties, the Osmonds' discs of this era failed.

The family's career in pop music began in earnest in early 1971, when the five brothers logged five weeks at No. 1 in America with *One Bad Apple*. Though this single was clearly an imitation of the red-hot Jackson Five, it ushered in a series of further US Top 20 hits over the following couple of years. Hailed by the pin-up magazines as the best looking and most interesting Osmond, Donny was launched as a solo artist in mid-1971 with the aptly titled *Sweet And Innocent*. It was followed by the Number One revival of the Steve Lawrence 1963 hit *Go Away Little Girl*. In a similar manner to the group, Donny enjoyed a run of American hits during 1971-71. He became the arch-rival of David Cassidy (from the Partridge Family) in the teenybopper stakes.

In the cases of both Cassidy and the Osmonds, the acts peaked in the States during 1971-71 and enjoyed their British zenith between late '72 and 1974. Donny was phenomenally successful in the UK, enjoying No. 1 hits with *Puppy Love* (originally a hit for Paul Anka in 1960), *The Twelfth Of Never* (Johnny Mathis in 1957, Cliff Richard in 1964 - this was Donny's first hit with a broken voice) and *Young Love* (Tab Hunter in 1957. Marie (born 1959) reached No. 2 in the UK and No. 5 in the US with *Paper Roses* (a country music standard). The excrucating Jimmy was only nine years old when he reached the UK No. 1 slot with *Long Haired Lover From Liverpool* (originally composed at the height of Beatlemania and the Merseybeat explosion). Donny & Marie's biggest duet was *I'm Leaving It Up To You* (No. 4 in US, No. 2 in UK) - this was a remake of Dale & Grace's 1963 biggie.

The family's best records were undoubtedly made by the five brothers' group. Their originals like *Crazy Horses* and *Goin' Home* were pop-rock singles of the highest order,

Let Me In was a fine self-penned ballad and *Love Me For A Reason* (No. 1 in Britain) was a strong rendition of a Johnny Bristol soul song. These records should have received a far better judgement from the critics, who were put off by the family's pure-as-gold weenybopper image. The closely knit Osmonds adhered to the Mormon faith, the strict disciplinary aspects of which were emphasised by the press at the time.

The Osmonds' bubble burst in the mid-Seventies and their public profile had witherd completely by 1978, the year that Donny got married. During the Eighties Donny and Jimmy moved into field of television and video direction with moderate success, while the elder brothers became a country band and met with lukewarm approval. Surprisingly it was Marie who emerged as the real survivor - her country music career took off in a big way with *Meet Me In Montana*, a 1985 duet with Dan Seals. That single reached No. 1 on the Billboard country chart, as did her solo 1986 offering *There's No Stopping Your Heart*. Bob MacDonald, 21 February 1986..

CRAZY HORSES (SINGLE)
Tracks: / Crazy horses.
7" Single: Released Nov '72, on MGM, by Polydor Ltd. Deleted '75. Catalogue no: **2006 142**

DOWN BY THE LAZY RIVER
Tracks: / Down by the lazy river.
7" Single: Released Mar '72, on MGM, by Polydor Ltd. Deleted '75. Catalogue no: **2006 096**

GOING HOME
Tracks: / Going home.
7" Single: Released Aug '73, on MGM, by Polydor Ltd. Deleted '76. Catalogue no: **2006 288**

HAVING A PARTY
Tracks: / Having a party.
7" Single: Released Mar '75, on MGM, by Polydor Ltd. Deleted '78. Catalogue no: **2006 492**

I CAN'T LIVE A DREAM
Tracks: / I can't live a dream.
7" Single: Released Oct '76, on Polydor, by Polydor Ltd. Deleted '79. Catalogue no: **2391 236**

I CAN'T STOP
Tracks: / I can't stop.
7" Single: Released Apr '74, on MCA, by MCA Records. Deleted '77. Catalogue no: **MCA 129**

I'M STILL GONNA NEED YOU (SINGLE)
Tracks: / I'm still gonna need you.
7" Single: Released Nov '75, on MGM, by Polydor Ltd. Deleted '78. Catalogue no: **2006 551**

LET ME IN
Tracks: / Let me in.
7" Single: Released Oct '73, on MGM, by Polydor Ltd. Deleted '76. Catalogue no: **2006 321**

LOVE ME FOR A REASON (SINGLE)
Tracks: / Love me for a reason.
7" Single: Released Aug '74, on MGM, by Polydor Ltd. Deleted '77. Catalogue no: **2006 458**

ONE BAD APPLE
Tracks: / One bad apple.
12" Single: Released Sep '88, on Polydor, by Polydor Ltd. Catalogue no: **PZ 18**
7" Single: Released Sep '88, on Polydor, by Polydor Ltd. Catalogue no: **PO 18**

PROUD ONE, THE
Tracks: / Proud one, The.
7" Single: Released May '75, on MGM, by Polydor Ltd. Deleted '78. Catalogue no: **2006 520**

Ostrogoth

FULL MOONS EYES
Tracks: / Full moons eyes.
12" Single: Released Aug '84, on Mausoleum, by Mausoleum Records. Catalogue no: **BONE 128310**

Osu

LIGHT UP MY FIRE
Tracks: / Light up my fire.
7" Single: Released Aug '84, on Shaka, Catalogue no: **XAKA 2**

O'Sullivan, Gilbert

Biographical details: This Irish singer, songwriter and pianist was born Raymond Edward O'Sullivan in waterford, Eire. He moved with his family to the English town of Swindon at the age of 13. He went to Art College with a view to pursuing a career in graphic design, but his interest in music proved irresistible. O'Sullivan entered the music business in 1965 at the age of 19. After a series of failed discs on CBS and then Major Minor, he signed with Gordon Mills' newly formed MAM company in 1970. Mills had enjoyed huge success in the Sixties as manager of Tom Jones and Engelbert Humperdinck; he rechristened his new charge Gilbert O'Sullivan, thus creating the same prestigious musical association that had worked with Humperdinck. Mills became Gilbert's producer as well as manager.

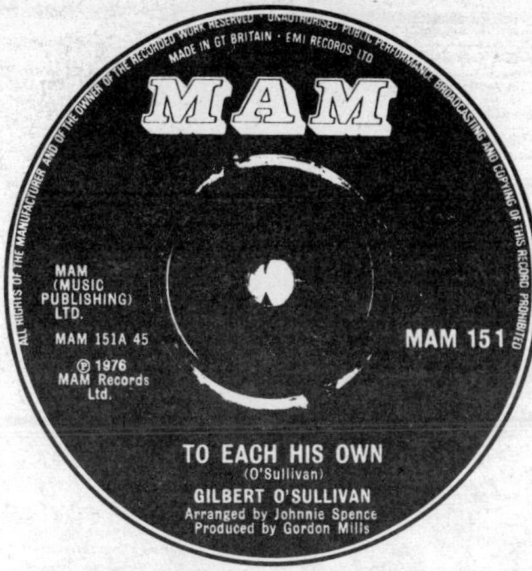

GILBERT O'SULLIVAN - TO EACH HIS OWN (Released on M.A.M)

Gilbert O'Sullivan came to fame at the end of 1970 with his first British hit *Nothing Rhymed*, a whimsical and memorable single that peaked at No. 8. It was followed into the Top 20 by two 1971 hits, *Me Will* and *No Matter How I Try*. Gilbert's image at this time was a deliberate and total anachronism - he appeared on television as the caricature of a working-class lad, with short trousers, short hair, cloth cap, grey shirt and an oil lamp perched on his piano. When he began to have success in America, this very English look was dropped in favour of a totally contemporary 1972 style - he took off his cap, grew his hair and donned fashionable jumpers with the letter 'G' prominently plastered on them. The deeply reflective ballad *Alone Again (Naturally)* was the record which made him an international superstar, logging six weeks at No. 1 in America as well as reaching No. 3 in Britain.

O'Sullivan's first UK No. 1 was *Clair* in November 1972, a song inspired by Mills' baby daughter. Gilbert's red hot streak continued with a UK No. 1 album, *Back To Front*, in January 1973, and a second British No. 1 single in April '73 with the bouncy *Get Down*. Both *Clair* and *Get Down* reached the Top 10 in Amwrica. His stateside success then tailed off, but he remained a regular visitor to the British Top 20 until 1975. With a musical style that was roughly halfway between pop and easy listening, he could write as strong a ballad as Elton John; but Gilbert lacked Elton's versatility and showmanship, and jolly ditties like *Ooh-wakka-doo-wakka-day* could match up to John's out-and-out rockers like *Saturday Night's Alright For Fighting*.

Gilbert O'Sullivan's career collapsed in 1976, as he totally lost the art of writing good songs. After several years out of the limelight, and after severing his ties with Gordon Mills, he achieved a one-off comeback hit in 1980 with the UK Top 20 single *What's In a Kiss?* on CBS. During the early Eighties, O'Sullivan and Mills were locked in an acrimonious and widely publicised court battle over royalties. The law came down in Gilbert's favour in 1982, but this did not inspire any long term return to musical form. Bob MacDonald, 21 February 1986..

ALONE AGAIN (NATURALLY)
Tracks: / Alone again (naturally).
7" Single: Released Mar '72, on M.A.M, by M.A.M. Records. Deleted '75. Catalogue no: **MAM 66**

CAN'T GET ENOUGH OF YOU
Tracks: / Can't get enough of you / Or so they say.
7" Single: Released Apr '81, on CBS, by CBS Records. Deleted Apr '86. Catalogue no: **A 1118**

CHRISTMAS SONG
Tracks: / Christmas song / Ave maria / Do you hear what i hear / Silent night.
7" Single: Released Dec '80, on Flashback, by Mainline Records. Deleted Dec '85. Catalogue no: **FBEP 110**
7" Single: Released Dec '74, on M.A.M, by M.A.M. Records. Deleted '77. Catalogue no: **MAM 124**

CLAIR
Tracks: / Clair.
7" Single: Released Oct '72, on M.A.M, by M.A.M. Records. Deleted '75. Catalogue no: **MAM 84**

CLAIR (OLD GOLD)
Tracks: / Claire / Alone again naturally.
7" Single: Released Jul '82, on Old Gold, by Old Gold Records. Catalogue no: **OG 9132**

GET DOWN
Tracks: / Get down.
7" Single: Released Mar '73, on M.A.M, by M.A.M. Records. Deleted '76. Catalogue no: **MAM 96**

GET DOWN (OLD GOLD)
Tracks: / Get down / Nothing rhymed.
7" Single: Released Jul '82, on Old Gold, by Old Gold Records. Catalogue no: **OG 9145**

HAPPINESS IS ME AND YOU
Tracks: / Happiness is me and you.
7" Single: Released Feb '74, on M.A.M, by M.A.M. Records. Deleted '77. Catalogue no: **MAM 114**

HELLO, IT'S GOODBYE
Tracks: / Hello, it's goodbye / Break it to me gently.
7" Single: Released Jan '81, on CBS, by CBS Records. Deleted Jan '84. Catalogue no: **CBS 9462**

I DON'T LOVE YOU BUT I THINK I LIKE YOU
Tracks: / I don't love you but I think I like you.
7" Single: Released Jun '75, on M.A.M, by M.A.M. Records. Deleted '78. Catalogue no: **MAM 130**

I LOVE IT BUT
Tracks: / I love it but / Help is on the way.
7" Single: Released Nov '80, on CBS, by CBS Records. Catalogue no: **CBS 9355**

MINUTE OF YOUR TIME
Tracks: / Minute of your time / In other words.
7" Single: Released Jun '82, on CBS, by CBS Records. Deleted Jun '85. Catalogue no: **CBSA 2452**

NO MATTER HOW I TRY
Tracks: / No matter how I try.
7" Single: Released Nov '71, on M.A.M, by M.A.M. Records. Deleted '74. Catalogue no: **MAM 53**

NOTHING RHYMED
Tracks: / Nothing rhymed.
7" Single: Released Nov '70, on M.A.M, by M.A.M. Records. Deleted '73. Catalogue no: **MAM 3**

OOH BABY
Tracks: / Ooh baby.
7" Single: Released Sep '73, on M.A.M, by M.A.M. Records. Deleted '76. Catalogue no: **MAM 107**

OOH WAKKA DOO WAKKA DAY
Tracks: / Ooh wakka doo wakka day.
7" Single: Released Jun '72, on M.A.M, by M.A.M. Records. Deleted '75. Catalogue no: **MAM 78**

TO EACH HIS OWN (See panel opposite)
Tracks: / To each his own / Can't get you out of my mind.
7" Single: Released '76, on M.A.M, by M.A.M. Records. Catalogue no: **MAM 151**

UNDERNEATH THE BLANKET GO
Tracks: / Underneath the blanket go.
7" Single: Released Apr '71, on M.A.M, by M.A.M. Records. Deleted '74. Catalogue no: **MAM 13**

WE WILL
Tracks: / We will.
7" Single: Released Jul '71, on M.A.M, by M.A.M. Records. Deleted '74. Catalogue no: **MAM 30**

WHAT'S IN A KISS
Tracks: / What's in a kiss / Down down down.
7" Single: Released Sep '80, on CBS, by CBS Records. Deleted '83. Catalogue no: **CBS 8929**

WHY OH WHY OH WHY
Tracks: / Why oh why.
7" Single: Released Nov '73, on M.A.M, by M.A.M. Records. Deleted '76. Catalogue no: **MAM 111**

WOMAN'S PLACE, A
Tracks: / Woman's place, A.
7" Single: Released Sep '74, on M.A.M, by M.A.M. Records. Deleted '77. Catalogue no: **MAM 122**

Other Ones

WE ARE WHAT WE ARE
Tracks: / We are what we are / Dark ages.
7" Single: Released Jan '87, on Virgin, by Virgin Records. Deleted May '88. Catalogue no: **VS 931**
12" Single: Released Jan '87, on Virgin, by Virgin Records. Deleted May '88. Catalogue no: **VS 931-12**

Other People

HAVE A NICE DAY
Tracks: / Have a nice day / Another day, another dollar.
7" Single: Released Dec '84, on Arcadia, Catalogue no: **OTHER 1**
12" Single: Released Dec '84, on Arcadia, Catalogue no: **OTHER 12**

Otis, Byron

BRING BACK MY BABY
Tracks: / Bring back my baby.
12" Single: Released Mar '82, on Ital, by Ital Records. Catalogue no: **ITD 005**

SO YOU SAY
Tracks: / So you say / So you dub.
12" Single: Released '82, on Shashanane, Catalogue no: **SHA 0010**

Otis, Johnny

Biographical details: This American band leader, drummer, pianist, vibraphonist, songwriter and singer has often been described as the Godfather of Rhythm-and-Blues. This predominantly black music was championed by the white Otis, son of Greek immigrant parents. He was born in California in 1921, his real surname being Veliotes. Initially inspired by big band jazz, he built up his instrumental skills during his teens and twenties. After forming his own 16-piece swing ensemble, Otis chalked up his first national US hit in 1946 with *Harlem Nocturne*. After touring with such names as Nat King Cole, The Ink Spots and Louis Jordan, he arrived in Los Angeles in 1948 to open the city's first club devoted entirely to R&B. While running the Barrelhouse Club, he discovered two important talents: Little Esther, the 13-year-old prodigy who was later known as Esther Phillips, and the Robins, who evolved into the Coasters. As a duo, Little Esther and Johnny Otis achieved five Top 10 singles on the American R&B charts during 1950.

Also during the early Fifties, Otis pioneered the phenomenon that really made his name. He set in motion a multi-artist touring revue that was dubbed The Johnny Otis R&B Caravan; it was later called the Johnny Otis Show. This became the top showcase for rhythm-and-blues music during the Fifties. It gave a boost to the early careers of many of the genre's top artists including Johnny Ace, Hank Ballard, Etta James, Little Willie John, Sugar Pie De Santo, Big mama Thornton and Jackie Wilson. The success of the show paved the way for many later black music package tours, especially those by Tamla

Motown.

During 1957-58 the Johnny Otis Show chalked up three substantial pop hits in its own right, two in Britain and one in America. *Ma, He's Making Eyes At Me*, a song that dated from 1921, surged to the UK No. 2 position; this featured vocals by Marie Adams and the Three Tons of Joy. Adams also sang on Otis' own song *Bye Bye Baby*, which peaked at No. 20 on the British chart. Another of Johnny's self-penned numbers, *Willie And The Hand Jive*, became a US No. 9 hit. *Willie* became Otis' best known track, and was successfully covered in Britain by Cliff Richard; the song was strongly influenced by Bo Diddley's eponymous anthem. All this pop success was a reflection of the fact that Otis had taken the new rock 'n' roll music on board.

Having made a huge contribution to R&B in the Fifties, the Sixties were a largely uninspiring period for Johnny Otis. After spending most of the decade as a backroom producer-arranger, he made an impressive comeback in 1969 with the *Cold Shot* LP. This fine album introduced the talents of his son Shuggie Otis, who carved out his own successful career as a blues guitarist. Johnny revived his revue for the Monterey Jazz Festival in 1970, featuring Esther Phillips and a host of other greats; a live album, capturing the event, was released. After several more years on the road with renewed vigour, Otis faded from view during the mid-Seventies. But the shoe came back yet again in 1982. Bob MacDonald, 23 February 1986..

BYE BYE BABY
Tracks: / Bye bye baby.
7" Single: Released Jan '58, on Capitol, by EMI Records. Deleted '61. Catalogue no: **CL 14817**

MA, HE'S MAKING EYES AT ME
Tracks: / Ma, he's making eyes at me.
7" Single: Released Nov '57, on Capitol, by EMI Records. Deleted '60. Catalogue no: **CL 14794**

MA, HE'S MAKING EYES AT ME (OLD GOLD)
Tracks: / Ma, he's making eyes at me / Fever.
7" Single: Released Apr '87, on Old Gold, by Old Gold Records. Deleted Sep '89. Catalogue no: **OG 9720**

REASON WHY
Tracks: / Reason why / Secret agent.
7" Single: Released Jun '83, on Sonet, by Sonet Records. Catalogue no: **SON 2253**

Otis, Jon

IN THE MIDDLE OF THE NIGHT
Tracks: / In the middle of the night.
12" Single: Released Jul '88, on Splash, by Splash Records. Catalogue no: **CPST**

IS THIS REALLY LOVE
Tracks: / Is this really love.
7" Single: Released Nov '88, on Libido, Catalogue no: **URGE 1**
12" Single: Released Nov '88, on Libido, Catalogue no: **URGET 1**

Otitis

FOUR O'CLOCK ROCK
Tracks: / Four o'clock rock / Thailand.
7" Single: Released Jan '83, on Sonet, by Sonet Records. Catalogue no: **SON 2250**

NEANDERTHAL MAN
Tracks: / Neanderthal man / Boy.
7" Single: Released Dec '83, on Sonet, by Sonet Records. Catalogue no: **SON 2260**

NEXT TIME
Tracks: / Next time.
7" Single: Released Nov '83, on Sonet, by Sonet Records. Catalogue no: **SON 2259**

O'Toole, Shameless

ALBERT & MARY
Tracks: / Albert & Mary / Forever.
7" Single: Released Aug '83, on Crazy Viking, by Crazy Vikings Records. Catalogue no: **CV 004**

Ottawan

Biographical details: Almost every summer, there are one or two big European hits that British holidaymakers fall in love with and, wishing to recapture the mood of their vacation, push into the UK chart in the early Autumn. 1980's example was *D.I.S.C.O.* by the French boy-girl vocal duo Ottawan. This supremely catchy pop single was perfect for parties. It reached No. 2 in the UK, logging 18 weeks on the chart and giving the French-owned Carrere label one of its biggest British successes.

Almost as infectious, and almost as successful was 1981's *Hands Up, (Give Me Your Heart)*. This reached the UK No. 3 position and chalked up 15 chart weeks. Ottawan also had a couple of minor hits, but most of their other output was pretty dire and they faded into obscurity. Bob MacDonald, 23 February 1986..

CRAZY MUSIC
Tracks: / Crazy music / Sha-la-la song.
12" Single: Released Mar '83, on Carrere, Catalogue no: **CART 268**
7" Single: Released Mar '83, on Carrere, Catalogue no: **CAR 68**

D.I.S.C.O
Tracks: / D.I.S.C.O. / Hands up.
7" Single: Released Mar '85, on Carrere, Catalogue no: **CAR 356**
12" Single: Released Mar '85, on Carrere, Catalogue no: **CART 356**

D.I.S.C.O. (2)
Tracks: / D.I.S.C.O. / You're ok.
7" Single: Released Sep '80, on Carrere, Catalogue no: **CAR 161**
12" Single: Released Sep '80, on Carrere, Catalogue no: **CAR 161T**

HANDS UP
Tracks: / Hands up.
12" Single: Released Aug '81, on Carrere, Catalogue no: **CAR 183T**
7" Single: Released Aug '81, on Carrere, Catalogue no: **CAR 183**

HELLO RIO
Tracks: / Hello Rio / Sha-la-la-song.
12" Single: Released Nov '82, on Carrere, Deleted Nov '85. Catalogue no: **CART 235**
7" Single: Released Nov '82, on Carrere, Deleted Nov '85. Catalogue no: **CAR 235**

OUR DAUGHTER'S WEDDING - LAWNCHAIRS (Released on EMI)

HELP, GET ME SOME HELP
Tracks: / Help, get me some help / Siesta for two.
7" Single: Released Dec '81, on Carrere, Deleted '84. Catalogue no: **CAR 215**

YOU'RE OK
Tracks: / You're OK / D.I.S.C.O..
7" Single: Released Dec '80, on Carrere, Deleted '83. Catalogue no: **CAR 161**

Otway & Barrett

BIRTHDAY BOY
Tracks: / Birthday boy / What a woman.
7" Single: Released Apr '80, on Polydor, by Polydor Ltd. Deleted Apr '83. Catalogue no: **POSP 143**

LAST OF THE MOHICANS, THE
Tracks: / Last of the mohicans / Fashion.
7" Single: Released 17 Oct '87, on VM, by VM Records. Catalogue no: **VM 6**

Otway, John

DK 50-80
Tracks: / DK 50-80.
7" Single: Released Jul '80, on Polydor, by Polydor Ltd. Deleted '83. Catalogue no: **2059 250**

GREEN GREEN GRASS OF HOME (See panel below opposite)
Tracks: / Green green grass of home / Wednesday club.
7" Single: Released Oct '80, on Stiff, by Stiff Records. Catalogue no: **BUY 101**

HEADBUTTS JINGLE
Tracks: / Headbutts jingle / Racing cars jingle / Best dream jingle / Auld lang sanity.
7" Single: Released Dec '81, on Buyalot, Deleted Dec '84. Catalogue no: **STIN 1**
12" Single: Released Aug '82, on Empire Records, Catalogue no: **HAM 5T**

IN DREAMS
Tracks: / In dreams / You aint seen nothing yet.
7" Single: Released Oct '82, on Empire Records, Catalogue no: **HAM 3**

MASS COMMUNICATION
Tracks: / Mass communication.
7" Single: Released May '83, on Empire Records, Catalogue no: **HAM 6**

MIDDLE OF WINTER
Tracks: / Middle of winter.
7" Single: Released Dec '84, on Strike Back, by Strike Back Records. Catalogue no: **SBR 1**

NEW JERUSALEM
Tracks: / New Jerusalem / Tyger, The.
7" Single: Released Nov '86, on WEA, by WEA Records. Deleted Jan '88. Catalogue no: **YZ 95**

REALLY FREE
Tracks: / Really free.
7" Single: Released Dec '77, on Polydor, by Polydor Ltd. Deleted '80. Catalogue no: **2058 951**

TURNING POINT
Tracks: / Turning point / Too much air, not enough oxygen.
7" Single: Released Apr '81, on Stiff, by Stiff Records. Catalogue no: **BUY 115**

WHOOPS APOCALYPSE
Tracks: / Losing / Whoops apocalypse.
7" Single: Released Mar '87, on WEA, by WEA Records. Deleted Jan '88. Catalogue no: **YZ 111**
12" Single: Released Mar '87, on WEA, by WEA Records. Catalogue no: **YZ 111 T**

O-Two-One

POP SONG
Tracks: / Pop song / Aversion.
7" Single: Released Sep '82, on UK Pop, Deleted '83. Catalogue no: **UK 0201**

Ouba

BEST IS YET TO COME
Tracks: / Best is yet to come, The / Storm before the calm.

7" Single: Released May '86, on Capitol, by EMI Records. Deleted '88. Catalogue no: **CL 4056**

Oui

IS THAT ALL THERE IS
Tracks: / Is that all there is.
7" Single: Released Sep '83, on Jet, by Jet Records. Catalogue no: **JET 7039**

Ouida & The Numbers

RUNAWAY
Tracks: / Runaway / Yeah yeah yeah.
7" Single: Released May '80, on Modern, Deleted May '83. Catalogue no: **STP 1**

Our Daughters Wedding

Biographical details: This American synthesiser band consisted of Layne Rico, Keith Silva and Scott Simon. The trio took their name from a section divider in a greetings card display stand.
Injecting a sense of quirky fun into the technopop revolution, Our Daughter's Wedding lay somewhere between Devo and Gary Numan. Ater releasing an indie single entitled *Nightlife*, they reached a wider audience with the catchy, oddball offering *Lawnchairs*. This single became a disco hit in the States and provided the threesome with a one-off UK pop chart entry - *Lawnchairs* reached No. 49 in Britain in the summer of 1981, on EMI America. That year also saw the release of the 12 inch EP *Digital Cowboy*, produced by Britain's Colin Thurston. Our Daughter's Wedding debut full-scale album *Moving Windows*, issued in late 1982, was somewhat average and the band faded from view. Bob MacDonald, 23 February 1986..

AUTO MUSIC
Tracks: / Auto music / Track me down.
12" Single: Released Aug '82, on EMI, by EMI Records. Catalogue no: **12 EA 144**
7" Single: Released Aug '82, on EMI, by EMI Records. Catalogue no: **EA 144**

LAWNCHAIRS (See panel above)
Tracks: / Lawnchairs / Airline.
7" Single: Released Aug '81, on EMI-Ameri-

JOHN OTWAY - GREEN GREEN GRASS (Released on Stiff)

OUTBAR SQUEEK - DISCO EDDIE (Released on ca, by EMI Records. Deleted '84. Catalogue no: **EA 124**

Our Heroes

NOW THE SCARS ARE HEALING
Tracks: / Now the scars are healing.
12" Single: Released Oct '84, on Icon, Catalogue no: **IC 004**

Our Jim

ME & THE WIFE & TRACY
Tracks: / Me & the wife & Tracy / Come uppance.
7" Single: Released Jul '81, on Carrere, Deleted '85. Catalogue no: **CAR 205**

Our Kid

YOU JUST MIGHT SEE ME CRY
Tracks: / You just might see me cry.
7" Single: Released May '76, on Polydor, by Polydor Ltd. Deleted '79. Catalogue no: **2058 729**

Our Man In Tokyo

SET UP
Tracks: / Set up.
7" Single: Released May '82, on Shakey Joe, Deleted '83. Catalogue no: **SJD 0001**

Out

BETTER THE DEVIL
Tracks: / Better the devil.
7" Single: Released Jul '81, on Cargo, Catalogue no: **CRS 014**

TOUGH ENOUGH
Tracks: / Tough enough.
12" Single: Released Feb '85, on Illuminated, Catalogue no: **ILL 4612**

WHO IS INNOCENT
Tracks: / Who is innocent.
7" Single: Released Sep '82, on Rabid, by Rabid Records. Catalogue no: **TOSH 113**

Out Bar Squeek

AWAY FROM THE HEART
Tracks: / Away from the heart./Gate gate.
7" Single: Released Sep '84, on EMI, by EMI Records. Catalogue no: **EMI 5492**
12" Single: Released Sep '84, on EMI, by EMI Catalogue no: **EMI 5553**

DISCO EDDIE (See panel above)
Tracks: / Disco Eddie / Where the people meet.
12" Single: Released Jun '84, on EMI, by EMI Records. Catalogue no: **12EMI 5479**
7" Single: Released Jun '84, on EMI, by EMI

WHEN THE BAD MEN COME (HAKI-BO SADO-BO)
Tracks: / When the bad men come (Haki-bo sado-bo) / When the bad men come (inst).
12" Single: Released May '86, on EMI, by EMI Records. Catalogue no: **12 EMI 5553**
7" Single: Released May '86, on EMI, by EMI Records. Catalogue no: **EMI 5553**
Records. Catalogue no: **EMI 5479**

Out Of The Blue

HOW MUCH IS THAT DOGGY IN THE WINDOW
Tracks: / How much is that doggie in the window / Chewed off stump.
7" Single: Released Nov '82, on PRT, by Castle Communications Records. Catalogue no: **7P 256**

Out Of The Ordinary

DREAM, THE (GET INTO MAGIC MIX)
Tracks: / Dream, The (Get into magic mix) / Dream, The (Get into magic mix)/(version).
7" Single: Released Aug '89, on Radical, by Radical Records. Catalogue no: **RADC 4**

Outcasts

1969
Tracks: / 1969.
7" Single: Released Jul '85, on New Rose (1), by New Rose Records. Catalogue no: **NEW 52**

ANGEL FACE
Tracks: / Angel face / Gangland warfare.
7" Single: Released Jun '82, on Outcast, Deleted '83. Catalogue no: **OO 200**

JUST ANOTHER TEENAGE REBEL
Tracks: / Just another teenage rebel.
7" Single: Released Aug '79, on Good Vibration, by Good Vibrations Records. Catalogue no: **GOT 3**

NOWHERE LEFT TO RUN
Tracks: / Nowhere left to run.
7" Single: Released Jun '83, on Abstract, by Abstract Sounds. Catalogue no: **ABS 017**
12" Single: Released Sep '83, on Anagram, by Cherry Red Records. Deleted '88. Catalogue no: **12 ANA 12**
7" Single: Released Sep '83, on Anagram, by Cherry Red Records. Deleted '88. Catalogue no: **ANA 12**
12" Single: Released Jun '83, on Abstract, by Abstract Sounds. Catalogue no: **12 ABS 017**

SELF CONCIOUS OVER YOU
Tracks: / Self concious over you.
7" Single: Released Nov '79, on Good Vibration, by Good Vibrations Records. Catalogue no: **GOT 17**

SEVEN DEADLY SINS (SINGLE)
Tracks: / Seven deadly sins / Swamp fever.
7" Single: Released Aug '84, on New Rose (1), by New Rose Records. Catalogue no: **NEW 38**

Outcasts Only

PROGRAMME LOVE
Tracks: / Programme love.
7" Single: Released Nov '81, on Outcast, Deleted '83. Catalogue no: **OO 001**

Outer Limits

CHASE, THE
Tracks: / Chase, The.
7" Single: Released Sep '84, on SD, Catalogue no: **SD 106**

CRUISIN'
Tracks: / Cruisin.
12" Single: Released Jul '85, on Sir George, Catalogue no: **SG 028T**

EDGE OF TIME
Tracks: / Edge of time.
12" Single: Released Jul '85, on Dog Rock, by Dog Rock Records. Catalogue no: **SD 107**

Outfield

ALL THE LOVE IN THE WORLD
Tracks: / All the love in the world / Taking my chances.
7" Single: Released Aug '86, on CBS, by CBS Records. Catalogue no: **A 7243**
12" Single: Released Aug '86, on CBS, by CBS Records. Catalogue no: **TA7243**

ALL THE LOVE IN THE WORLD (II)
Tracks: / All the love in the world / Mystery man.
7" Single: Released Sep '86, on CBS, by CBS Records. Deleted '87. Catalogue no: **650053 7**

SINCE YOU'VE BEEN GONE
Tracks: / Since you've been gone / Better than nothing.
7" Single: Released Jul '87, on CBS, by CBS Records. Catalogue no: **650 932 7**
12" Single: Released Jul '87, on CBS, by CBS Records. Catalogue no: **650 932 6**

VOICES OF BABYLON (SINGLE)
Tracks: / Voices of Babylon / Inside your skin / All the love in the world / Since you've been gone.
7" Single: Released Apr '89, on CBS, by CBS Records. Deleted Oct '89. Catalogue no: **654739 7**
12" Single: Released Apr '89, on CBS, by CBS Records. Deleted Oct '89. Catalogue no: **654739 6**
CD 5": Released Apr '89, on CBS, by CBS Records. Deleted Oct '89. Catalogue no: **654739 2**

YOUR LOVE
Tracks: / Your love / 61 seconds / Mystery man (Extra track on 12" only).
12" Single: Released May '86, on CBS, by CBS Records. Catalogue no: **TA 6942**
7" Single: Released Apr '86, on CBS, by CBS Records. Deleted '87. Catalogue no: **A 6942**

Outlaw Posse

ORIGINAL DOPE
Tracks: / Original dope.
12" Single: Released Sep '89, on Gee Street, by Gee Street Records. Catalogue no: **GEET 021**

PARTY
Tracks: / Party / Outlaws in effect.
12" Single: Released Sep '88, on Gee Street, by Gee Street Records. Catalogue no: **GEE 12001**

Outlaws

AMBUSH
Tracks: / Ambush.
7" Single: Released Jun '61, on H.M.V., by EMI Records. Deleted '64. Catalogue no: **POP 877**

GHOST RIDERS IN THE SKY (SINGLE)
Tracks: / Ghost riders in the sky / Devils road.
7" Single: Released Feb '81, on Arista, by BMG Records (UK). Deleted Feb '84. Catalogue no: **ARIST 396**

SWINGIN' LOW
Tracks: / Swingin' low.
7" Single: Released Apr '61, on H.M.V., by EMI Records. Deleted '64. Catalogue no: **POP 844**

Outline

I LIKE THE BLUEBEAT
Tracks: / I like the bluebeat / Hit the road Jack.
7" Single: Released Feb '80, on Ariola-Hansa, by Hansa Records. Deleted '83. Catalogue no: **AHA 560**

Out-Patients

SUBWAY ART
Tracks: / Subway art.
12" Single: Released May '88, on Unstable Pop Corp, Catalogue no: **UPC 001**

Outside Edge

HEARTBEAT AWAY
Tracks: / Heartbeat away / Out of my head / Soldier boy (Extra track on 12" version only).
12" Single: Released Mar '86, on 10 Records, by Virgin Records. Deleted '89. Catalogue no: **TEN 92-12**
7" Single: Released Mar '86, on 10 Records, by Virgin Records. Deleted '86. Catalogue no: **TEN 92**

Outsiders

HANDFULS OF NOTHING (Give me lots of money)
Tracks: / Handfuls of nothing (Give me lots of money) / Love you to death.
7" Single: Released 31 Jul '89, on Redd Armadillo, Catalogue no: **UNKNOWN**

THAT CAR
Tracks: / That car / Careless talk.
7" Single: Released Aug '82, on Impact, by Ace Records. Catalogue no: **ACT 4**

Outskirts

DOWN
Tracks: / Down.
7" EP: Released May '86, on Glass, by Glass Records. Catalogue no: **GLAEP 103**

TOO BAD
Tracks: / Too bad.
7" Single: Released Mar '86, on Glass, by Glass Records. Catalogue no: **GLASS 047**

Ovaltineys

HAPPY DAYS ARE HERE AGAIN
Tracks: / Happy days are here again.
7" Single: Released Oct '80, on CJM, by Wellard Dist.. Catalogue no: **OVA 1**

Ovation

LOVE WILL GROW AGAIN
Tracks: / Love will grow again / Can't imagine / Anytime anywhere anyhow / So long.
7" EP: Released May '83, on Small Run, Catalogue no: **SRR 0015**

Ovationz

FOREVER LOVE
Tracks: / Forever love / Girl i love.
7" Single: Released Feb '82, on Dread At The Controls, Catalogue no: **DCD 005**

SECRET ADMIRER
Tracks: / Secret admirer.
12" Single: Released Apr '82, on Live & Love, Catalogue no: **LLDIS 203**

Overdraft

SAVE YOUR LOVE
Tracks: / Save your love.
7" Single: Released Aug '85, on Pay, Deleted '86. Catalogue no: **PAY 1**
12" Single: Released Aug '85, on Pay, Deleted '86. Catalogue no: **12PAY 1**

Overkill

FUCK YOU (SINGLE)
Tracks: / Fuck you.
12" Single: Released Jul '87, on Under One Flag, by Music For Nations Records. Catalogue no: **12 FLAG 104**

Overlanders

Biographical details: At the time of their greatest success, this British combo consisted of Paul Arnold, Peter Bartholomew, Laurie Mason, David Walsh and Terry Widlake.
Initially formed as a threesome in 1963, the Overlanders were supposed to be a UK answer to the Kingston trio. But their folk incarnation was not particularly successful - their singles flopped in Britain, and their only taste of American acceptance was *Yesterday's Gone*, a No. 75 hit that was beaten to the US Top 30 by Chad & Jeremy's version. Having branched into a quintet, the Overlanders came to fame in early 1966 with a cover version of the Beatles *Michelle*. This catchy, gentle and unusual ballad, partly sung in French, first appeared on the Fab Four's Christmas '65 LP *Rubber Soul*. It was such a strong song that the Overlanders ruched their remake, produced by pop maestro Tony Hatch onto the market as quickly as possible. (The Beatkes had not thought the song suitable for their own single release.) The Overlanders logged three weeks at No. 1 in Britain, beating off a rival rendition by David & Johnathan which peaked at No. 11. In the States, however, the duo climbed to No. 18 while the group failed to crack the Hot 100.
Even with a No. 1 smash behind them, the Overlander's subsequebt singles flopped and they passed into the chart history bookes as a One Hit Wonder. Bob MacDonald, 23 February 1986.s.

MICHELLE
Tracks: / Michelle.
7" Single: Released Jan '66, on Pye, Deleted '69. Catalogue no: **7 N 17034**

MICHELLE (OLD GOLD)
Tracks: / Michelle / Where are you now.
7" Single: Released Jul '82, on Old Gold, by Old Gold Records. Deleted Jul '88. Catalogue no: **OG 9138**

Overload

WHO ARE YOU
Tracks: / Who are you / Drift away.
7" Single: Released Jan '81, on MCA, by MCA Records. Deleted Jan '84. Catalogue no: **MCA 656**

Overlord X

EARTH IS MOVING, THE
Tracks: / Earth is moving, The / Rough in Hackney.
7" Single: Released May '88, on Mango

Street, by Island Records. Deleted Apr '89. Catalogue no: **IS 372**
12" Single: Released 16 May '88, on Mango Street, by Island Records. Deleted Apr '89. Catalogue no: **12 IS 372**

FOURTEEN DAYS IN MAY
Tracks: / Fourteen days in May.
12" Single: Released Jun '88, on Hardcore, Catalogue no: **HAKX 12**
12" Single: Released Apr '88, on Hardcore, Catalogue no: **HAKT 12**

RADICAL KICKIN'
Tracks: / Radical kicking / Weapon is my lyric (remix) / Kickbag (Only on 12" version.).
7" Single: Released Apr '89, on Mango Street, by Island Records. Catalogue no: **IS 415**
12" Single: Released Apr '89, on Mango Street, by Island Records. Catalogue no: **12 IS 415**

TOO BAD
Tracks: / Too bad / Too bad (inst) / Too bad (bonus beats) (Only on 12") / Now I'm here (Only on 12").
12" Single: Released 17 Oct '88, on Mango Street, by Island Records. Deleted Apr '89. Catalogue no: **12 IS 387**
7" Single: Released 17 Oct '88, on Mango Street, by Island Records. Deleted Apr '89. Catalogue no: **IS 387**

Oville, Helena

AMOUREUX BLUER THAN BLUE
Tracks: / Amoureux bluer than blue.
12" Single: Released Oct '82, on Fid Def, Catalogue no: **FD 7822**

Owen, Bill

COMPO'S GONE AND LOST HIS WELLIES
Tracks: / Compo's gone and lost his wellies / Friends.
7" Single: Released Feb '83, on Look, by Look Records. Catalogue no: **LKSP 6681**

NORA BATTY'S STOCKINGS (see also Kathy Staff)
Tracks: / Nora Batty's stockings / Last of the summer wine.
7" Single: Released Mar '83, on AVM, by AVM Records. Deleted '87. Catalogue no: **AVM 1004**

Owen, Danny

KISS AN ANGEL GOOD MORNING
Tracks: / Kiss an angel good morning.
7" Single: Released Jun '80, on Hammer, Deleted Jun '83. Catalogue no: **HS 308**

Owen, Glyn

I WISH I COULD LOVE YOU AGAIN
Tracks: / I wish I could love you again / I wish I could love you again (version) / Theme for Jack & Vanessa (instrumental).
7" Single: Released Sep '89, on Telstar, by Telstar Records (UK). Catalogue no: **STAS 295**

Owen, Reg

MANHATTAN SPIRITUAL
Tracks: / Manhattan spiritual.
7" Single: Released Feb '59, on Pye International, Deleted '62. Catalogue no: **7N 25009**

OBSESSION
Tracks: / Obsession.
7" Single: Released Oct '60, on Palette, Deleted '63. Catalogue no: **PG 9004**

Owens, Buck

CRYING TIME
Tracks: / Crying time / I've got a tiger by the tail.
7" Single: Released '80, on Capitol (USA), by Capitol (USA) Records. Catalogue no: **LR 1859**

HOT DOG
Tracks: / Don't let her know / A-11 / Summertime blues / Memphis / Hot dog / Put a quarter in the jukebox / Under your spell again / Second fiddle / Sweethearts in heaven / Keys in the mailbox, The.
7" Pic: Released Jul '88, on P.E.P., Catalogue no: **PEP 8017**

O'Williams, Wendy

IT'S MY LIFE
Tracks: / It's my life / Priestus.
7" Single: Released May '84, on Music For Nations, by Music For Nations Records. Catalogue no: **KUT 111**
12" Single: Released May '84, on Music For Nations, by Music For Nations Records. Catalogue no: **12 KUT 111**

Owusu, Steve

NEGATIVE REALITY
Tracks: / Negative reality.
12" Single: Released Jan '85, on Trinity House, Catalogue no: **THR 10**

Oxley, Louie

GO GO GADGET
Tracks: / Go go gadget / Go go gadget (not so long version).
7" Single: Released Apr '86, on Cool Tempo, by Chrysalis Records. Catalogue no: **COOL 121**
12" Single: Released Apr '86, on Cool Tempo, by Chrysalis Records. Catalogue no: **COOLX 121**

Oxo

WHIRLY GIRLS
Tracks: / Whirly girls / In the stars.
7" Single: Released Mar '83, on Geffen, by Geffen Records (USA). Catalogue no: **GEFA 3206**

Oxy & The Morons

WORK
Tracks: / Work / Good life.
7" Single: Released Apr '82, on Music For The Deaf, Deleted '84. Catalogue no: **MFD 2**

Oyster Band

HAL-AN-TOW
Tracks: / Hal-an-tow / Ashes to ashes.
7" Single: Released Oct '86, on Cooking Vinyl, by Cooking Vinyl Records. Catalogue no: **FRY 001**

LOST AND FOUND, THE
Tracks: / Lost and found.
7" Single: Released Jan '89, on Cooking Vinyl, by Cooking Vinyl Records. Catalogue no: **FRY 006**
12" Single: Released Jan '89, on Cooking Vinyl, by Cooking Vinyl Records. Catalogue no: **FRY 006T**

LOVE VIGILANTES
Tracks: / Love vigilantes.
7" Single: Released Sep '89, on Cooking Vinyl, by Cooking Vinyl Records. Catalogue no: **FRY 012**
CD 5": Released Oct '89, on Cooking Vinyl, by Cooking Vinyl Records. Catalogue no: **FRYCD 012**
12" Single: Released Sep '89, on Cooking Vinyl, by Cooking Vinyl Records. Catalogue no: **FRYT 012**

NEW YORK GIRLS
Tracks: / New York girls.
12" Single: Released Apr '89, on Cooking Vinyl, by Cooking Vinyl Records. Catalogue no: **FRY 009T**
7" Single: Released Apr '89, on Cooking Vinyl, by Cooking Vinyl Records. Catalogue no: **FRY 009**

ROSE OF ENGLAND
Tracks: / Rose of England / Dawn run.
7" Single: Released Oct '87, on Cooking Vinyl, by Cooking Vinyl Records. Catalogue no: **CHEF 001**

Ozo

I'M GONNA MAKE YOU MINE FOREVER
Tracks: / I'm gonna make you mine forever.
12" Single: Released Aug '89, on WEA, by WEA Records. Catalogue no: **YZ 423T**
7" Single: Released Aug '89, on WEA, by WEA Records. Catalogue no: **YZ 423**

LISTEN TO THE BUDDAH (SINGLE)
Tracks: / Listen to the Buddah / Spirits of Africa.
7" Single: Released Feb '84, on Sphinx, by Sphinx Records. Catalogue no: **BBSP 01**
12" Single: Released Feb '84, on Sphinx, by Sphinx Records. Catalogue no: **BBSP 1201**

SKINTIGHT (NO ROOM TO MOVE UP)
Tracks: / Skintight (no room to move up).
12" Single: Released Aug '82, on Sphinx, by Sphinx Records. Catalogue no: **SPS 1201**
7" Single: Released Aug '82, on Sphinx, by Sphinx Records. Catalogue no: **SPS 01**

WHY WASTE (ZAINAB)
Tracks: / Why waste (zainab) / Dreaming.
12" Single: Released Feb '85, on Mother Africa, Deleted '87. Catalogue no: **MAS 1202**
7" Single: Released Feb '85, on Mother Africa, Deleted '87. Catalogue no: **MAS 02**

Ozo Theatre Company

ARMADA '88
Tracks: / Oye como va / Thurrock bridge.
12" Single: Released Aug '88, on Galaxy (1), by Galaxy Records. Catalogue no: **GALS 12003**
7" Single: Released Aug '88, on Galaxy (1), by Galaxy Records. Catalogue no: **GALS 003**

Ozone

DO WHAT'CHA WANNA DO
Tracks: / Do what'cha wanna do / Come on in.
12" Single: Released Apr '82, on Motown, by BMG Records (UK). Catalogue no: **TMGT 1259**
7" Single: Released Apr '82, on Motown, by BMG Records (UK). Catalogue no: **TMG 1259**

GIGOLETTE
Tracks: / Gigolette.
12" Single: Released Nov '81, on Motown, by BMG Records (UK). Catalogue no: **TMGT 1249**
7" Single: Released Nov '81, on Motown, by BMG Records (UK). Catalogue no: **TMG 1249**

WALK ON
Tracks: / Walk on / This is funkin insane

7" Single: Released Oct '81, on Motown, by BMG Records (UK). Catalogue no: **TMG 1192**

Ozone Farm

OZONE FARM, THE
Tracks: / Ozone Farm, The / Sail the sea.
7" Single: Released Oct '88, on 2 DN, by 2 DN Records. Catalogue no: **UNKNOWN**

P

The following information was taken from the Music Master database on October 20th, 1989.

P, Johnny

BIG CHAT
Tracks: / Big chat.
12" Single: Released Mar '89, on Blue Mountain, Catalogue no: **BMD 051**

EVERY POSSE FOLLOW ME
Tracks: / Every posse follow me.
12" Single: Released Mar '89, on Penthouse, by Penthouse Records. Catalogue no: **PH 004**

EXPENSIVE AND DEAR
Tracks: / Expensive and dear.
12" Single: Released Jun '89, on Living Room, Catalogue no: **OH 15**

GAL MAN
Tracks: / Gal man.
12" Single: Released May '89, on Blue Mountain, Catalogue no: **BMD 059**

IF YOU LOVE ME
Tracks: / If you love me.
12" Single: Released 31 Jul '89, on Live & Love, Catalogue no: **LLD 130**

JUMP AND SPREAD OUT
Tracks: / Jump and spread out.
12" Single: Released Nov '88, on Jammy's, Catalogue no: **VPRD 357**

MINE YOU GET A LICK
Tracks: / Mine you get a lick.
12" Single: Released Aug '88, on Skengdon, Catalogue no: **SKD 058**

POST THEM OUT
Tracks: / Post them out.
12" Single: Released Feb '89, on Jammy's, Catalogue no: **VPRD 394**
12" Single: Released Feb '89, on Digital B., Catalogue no: **VPRD 409**

READ AND WRITE
Tracks: / Read and write.
12" Single: Released Sep '89, on Penthouse, by Penthouse Records. Catalogue no: **PH 025**

RUDE BOY
Tracks: / Rude boy.
12" Single: Released Jan '89, on Unity, Catalogue no: **FEA 07**

STICK BY ME
Tracks: / Stick by me.
7" Single: Released May '89, on Live & Love, Catalogue no: **LLD 117**

TRUE LOVE
Tracks: / True love.
7" Single: Released 21 Apr '89, on Steely & Cleevie, Catalogue no: **VPRD 434**

WINE AND RUSHENE
Tracks: / Wine and rushene.
12" Single: Released Nov '88, on Digital B., Catalogue no: **VPRD 366**

YOUNG AND SHE GREEN
Tracks: / Young and she green.
12" Single: Released Nov '88, on Techniques, Catalogue no: **WRT 37**

P Lion

HAPPY CHILDREN
Tracks: / Happy children.
7" Single: Released Oct '84, on Carrere, Catalogue no: **CAR 346**
12" Single: Released Oct '84, on Carrere, Catalogue no: **CART 346**

Pablo

BO MBANDA
Tracks: / Bo mbanda / Ma coco. .
12" Single: Released Apr '82, on Island, by Island Records. Deleted Apr '85. Catalogue no: **12WIP 6734**
7" Single: Released Apr '82, on Island, by Island Records. Deleted Apr '85. Catalogue no: **WIP 6734**

MADELINA
Tracks: / Madelina / Bongo Mokomzie.
7" Single: Released May '82, on Island, by Island Records. Deleted '85. Catalogue no: **WIP 6772**
12" Single: Released May '82, on Island, by Island Records. Deleted '85. Catalogue no: **12 WIP 6772**

Pablo, Augustus

EASTERN PROMISE
Tracks: / Eastern promise (Dub) / Sukiyaki / Eastern promise (Version).
12" Single: Released Jan '87, on Island, by Island Records. Deleted Jul '87. Catalogue no: **12IS 308**

EL ROCKERS CHAPTERS 1-4
Tracks: / El rockers chapters 1-4.
7" Single: Released Feb '80, on Greensleeves, by Greensleeves Records. Deleted Feb '85. Catalogue no: **GRED 29**

PABLO MEETS MR. BASIE
Tracks: / Pablo meets Mr. Basie.
7" Single: Released Jan '79, on Rough Trade, by Rough Trade Records. Catalogue no: **RT 002**

SUKIYAKI
Tracks: / Sukiyaki / Easter promise / Sukiyaki (dub).
12" Single: Released Nov '86, on Mango, by Island Records. Deleted Jul '87. Catalogue no: **12IS 308**

Pace, Papa

JAMMING
Tracks: / Jamming / Modeller.
12" Single: Released Jul '83, on Fashion, by Fashion Records. Catalogue no: **TOP 006**

Pace, Thom

MAYBE
Tracks: / Maybe.
7" Single: Released May '79, on RSO, by Polydor Ltd. Deleted '82. Catalogue no: **RSO 34**

Pacific

BAWNOON HILL
Tracks: / Bawnoon Hill.
12" Single: Released Oct '88, on Creation, by Creation Records. Catalogue no: **CRE 058 T**
7" Single: Released Oct '88, on Creation, by Creation Records. Catalogue no: **CRE 058**

SEA OF SAND
Tracks: / Sea of sand.
7" Single: Released '88, on Creation, by Creation Records. Catalogue no: **CRE 058**
12" Single: Released '88, on Creation, by Creation Records. Catalogue no: **CRE 058T**

SHAFT
Tracks: / Shaft, Theme from.
7" Single: Released 6 Feb '89, on Creation, by Creation Records. Catalogue no: **CRE 064**
12" Single: Released 6 Feb '89, on Creation, by Creation Records. Catalogue no: **CRE 064 T**

SHRIFT
Tracks: / Shrift.
7" Single: Released Mar '89, on Creation, by Creation Records. Catalogue no: **CRE 064L**
12" Single: Released Mar '89, on Creation, by Creation Records. Catalogue no: **CRE 064LT**

Pacific Ethno Techno

C'MON A MY HOUSE
Tracks: / C'mon a my house.
7" Single: Released Aug '83, on Dakota, Catalogue no: **DAK 12**

Pack

LONG LIVE THE PAST
Tracks: / Long live the past.
7" Single: Released Apr '82, on Cyclops, Deleted '82. Catalogue no: **CYC 1**

MUCHAS GRACIAS
Tracks: / Muchas gracias / Limelight.
7" Single: Released Aug '81, on Escape, by Escape Records. Deleted '82. Catalogue no: **ESC 102**

NUMBER 12
Tracks: / Number 12.
7" Single: Released Nov '79, on Rough Trade, by Rough Trade Records. Deleted '82. Catalogue no: **RT 025**

Packabeats

GYPSY BEAT
Tracks: / Gypsy beat.
7" Single: Released Feb '61, on Parlophone, by EMI Records. Deleted '64. Catalogue no: **R 4729**

Packman

I'M A PACKMAN
Tracks: / I'm a packman / Play it again Sam.
12" Single: Released Nov '83, on Malaco, by Malaco Records (UK). Deleted '88. Catalogue no: **MAL 12 014**

Pad Anthony

BORN LOVER MAN
Tracks: / Born lover man.
7" Single: Released Nov '88, on Taurus, Catalogue no: **UNKNOWN**

Padden, Bernard

MASS MOVEMENT
Tracks: / Mass movement / Career advice.
7" Single: Released Nov '83, on Dancing Sideways, by Dancing Sideways Records. Catalogue no: **DS 6 XA**

Paddy

MY ROCKA ROCKA GOOCHI GOOCHI WOMAN YEH
Tracks: / My rocka rocka goochi goochi woman yeh / Blue waters.
7" Single: Released Dec '83, on Little Acorns, by Little Acorns Records. Catalogue no: **LSMC 0020**

Paddy Goes To Hollywood

GREEN GREEN GRASS OF HOME
Tracks: / Green green grass of home.
7" Single: Released 21 Nov '87, on Rage, Catalogue no: **PADDY 1**

Paddy's Dream

OLD FRIENDS
Tracks: / Galtee mountain boy / Old friends.
7" Single: Released Jul '86, on Homespun (Ireland), by Outlet Records. Catalogue no: **HS 109**

Pagan Ritual

PAGAN DANCE
Tracks: / Pagan dance.
7" Single: Released Mar '84, on Backs, by Backs Recording Co.. Catalogue no: **MANE 1002**

Page Boys

YOU'RE MY KIND OF GIRL
Tracks: / You're my kind of girl.
7" Single: Released Sep '83, on Whaam, Catalogue no: **WHAAM 10**

Page, Cleo

I LOVE TO EAT IT
Tracks: / I love to eat it.
7" Single: Released Jan '79, on JSP, by JSP Records. Catalogue no: **JSP 4502**

Page, Hal

GOING BACK TO MY HOME TOWN
Tracks: / Going back to my home town.
7" Single: Released Aug '60, on Melodisc, Deleted '63. Catalogue no: **MEL 1553**

Page, Ian

DOGS IN THE YARD
Tracks: / Dogs in the yard / Spanish waiter.
7" Single: Released Feb '81, on Mercury, by Phonogram Ltd. Deleted Feb '84. Catalogue no: **MER 50**

UNITY STREET (Page, Ian & Bop)
Tracks: / Unity street.
7" Single: Released Aug '84, on Parlophone, by EMI Records. Catalogue no: **PAGE 2**

Page, Jimmy

Biographical details: This British guitarist, songwriter and producer had already enjoyed an impressive career before founding and leading Led Zepplin in 1968. Born in Heston, West London in 1944, he was one of Britain's most important session guitarists of the mid-Sixties. Amongst the many records he played on were hits by Jet Harris & Tony Meehan, Herman's Hermits, the Who and the Kinks; he was also heard on discs by Georgie Fame, Petula Clarke, Billy Fury, Dave Berry and the Everley Brothers. Meanwhile, Page was also a member of several small-time groups including Carter-Lewis & The Southerners, Mickey Flinn and the Blue Men and Neil Christian and the Crusaders. Jimmy's first release under his own name was a 1965 single entitled *She Just Satisfies*; it was not a hit.With all his session work, versatility was name of Page's game. He had to be able to play in whatever style was required at the time. In the pop world of the Sixties it was commonplace for studio musicians to replace the official members of a group on disc, especially if a producer was working with a new combo and thought that a particular player was inexperienced or unsuitable; the practice was rarely admitted in public, but many ruthless substitutions took place in recording studios. Page was rarely credited, but often heard.In 1966 Page became a member of the Yardbirds, initially working with fellow guitarist Jeff Beck. When the group folded in 1968, circumstances left Jimmy holding the baby. He formed a quartet known as the New Yardbirds to meet contractual obligations, and they soon became Zepplin. After a decade of superstardom, the death of drummer John Bonham caused the termination of Led Zep in 1980. Since then, the Page profile has been relatively low. His records have enjoyed only minor hit status, coming nowhere near the sales levels of Zepplin or of the band's former singer Robert Plant. Page's first project was the composing and recording of the soundtrack for Michael Einner's 1982 movie 'Death Wish II' (starring Charles Bronson); this saw Jimmy making prominent use if the guitar synthesiser for the first time. 1984 saw the release of the album *No Introduction Necessary*, credited to Jimmy Page & Friends. In 1985, Page was featured on the LP *Whatever Happened to 1214 AD*, a collaboration with veteran cult figure Roy Harper; in the same year, he played at Live Aid as part of a one-off Led Zep reunion. Bob MacDonald, 23 February 1986..

1972 INTERVIEW (2)
12" Single: Released '89, on Wax, by Wax Records. Catalogue no: **RAMBLE 3P**

WASTING MY TIME
Tracks: / Wasting my time / Writes of winter.
7" Single: Released Jun '88, on Geffen, by Geffen Records (USA). Catalogue no: **GEF 41**

Page, Larry

STAY AWHILE
Tracks: / Stay awhile / Late nights.
7" Single: Released Oct '82, on Page One, by Page One Records. Catalogue no: **POR 005**

Page, Patti

Biographical details: Patti Page was born Clara Ann Fowler, in 1927 in Oklahoma; she sang with Benny Goodman combo on Chicago radio in 1947; her distinctive vocal colour and good diction made her a natural star of the era of pop singers. She had more than 70 hits 1948-62 on the Mercury label, many top tens 1950-4. She will always be associated with Pee Wee King's *Tennesse Waltz*, number one in the USA for 13 weeks in 1950. (Donald Clarke 15.5.87) .

HOW MUCH IS THAT DOGGIE IN THE WINDOW (OLD GOLD)
Tracks: / How much is that doggie in the window.
7" Single: Released Jan '85, on Old Gold, by Old Gold Records. Catalogue no: **OG 9482**
7" Single: Released Mar '53, on Oriole, Deleted '56. Catalogue no: **CB 1156**

Page, Stu

ARE YOU STILL IN LOVE WITH ME
Tracks: / Are you still in love with me / Motor radio.
7" Single: Released '88, on Barge, by Barge Records. Catalogue no: **BGE 7 1005**

PAINTED WORLD - INDEPENDENCE DAY (Released on Mother)

Page, Tommy

SHAG, THE
Tracks: / Shag / Hard to be normal.
12" Single: Released 16 Sep '88, on Warner Bros., by WEA Records. Catalogue no: **W 7739T**
7" Single: Released 16 Sep '88, on Warner Bros., by WEA Records. Catalogue no: **W 7739**

SHOULDER TO CRY ON
Tracks: / Shoulder to cry on / Hard to be normal.
12" Single: Released May '89, on Warner Bros., by WEA Records. Catalogue no: **W 2999 T**
CD 5": Released May '89, on Warner Bros., by WEA Records. Catalogue no: **W 2999 CD**
7" Single: Released May '89, on Warner Bros., by WEA Records. Catalogue no: **W 2999**

ZILLION KISSES, A
Tracks: / Zillion kisses, A / I love london.
7" Single: Released Aug '89, on Sire, by Sire Records. Catalogue no: **W 2866**
12" Single: Released Aug '89, on Sire, by Sire Records. Catalogue no: **W 2866T**
Cassingle: Released Aug '89, on Sire, by Sire Records. Catalogue no: **W 2866C**
CD 5": Released Aug '89, on Sire, by Sire Records. Catalogue no: **W 2866CD**

Pagliaro

LOVING YOU AIN'T EASY
Tracks: / Loving you ain't easy.
7" Single: Released Feb '72, on Pye, Deleted '75. Catalogue no: **7 N 45111**

Pagoda

FINDERS KEEPERS
Tracks: / Finders keepers / We're alright tonight / Go back (Only on 12" version.).
7" Single: Released Jun '83, on Chrysalis, by Chrysalis Records. Catalogue no: **CHS 2714**
12" Single: Released '83, on Chrysalis, by Chrysalis Records. Deleted '87. Catalogue no: **CHS 12 2714**

Paiao, Carlos

PLAYBACK
Tracks: / Playback.
7" Single: Released Apr '81, on EMI, by EMI Records. Deleted Apr '86. Catalogue no: **EMI 5174**

Paige, Elaine

Biographical details: This British singer and actress first achieved major fame in the late Seventies, and has subsequently become an institution on the UK's MOR scene. She made her name in 1978 in the title role of 'Evita', the incredibly successful musical by Tim Rice and Andrew Lloyd Webber; as Eva Peron she was responsible for, amongst many other things, singing the tour de force *Don't Cry For Me Argentina*, which had originally been taken to the UK No. 1 position by Julie Covington. After several months in the opening London run of 'Evita', Elaine dropped out to concentrate on launching a career as a pop singer. This was only partially successful, for the bland single *Don't Walk Away Till I Touch You* peaked at No. 46 on the British chart. Still a theatrical animal first and foremost, Paige's talents continues to be favoured by both Lloyd Webber and Rice. The famous twosome went their seperate ways after 'Evita', but both guys made good use of Elaine. Lloyd Webber's 'Cats', a highly imaginative production inspired by the feline poems of T. S. Eliot, was introduced to the public by Paige's disc rendition of the show's standout song *Memory*. This showstopping number took her to No. 6 on the UK singles chart in mid-1981. In 1985 her involvement in Rice's 'Chess' project yielded the smash hit *I Know Him So Well*, a Paide duet with fellow middle-of-the-road vocalist Barbara Dickson; this single logged four weeks at No. 1, becoming Britain's second biggest selling single of the year. During the mid-Eighties Elaine enjoyed three huge selling solo albums. *Stages* was a tasteful compilation of show songs, containing not only her best work from 'Evita' and 'Cats' but also her cover versions of standards from such productions as 'Hair and 'Annie'. *Cinema* collected together a series of film classics, and *Love Hurts* was an LP of lovey dovey numbers. These three albums confirmed Paige's prominence in the easy listening field, but marked something of a departure for producer Tony Visconti; he was a veteran of the rock and pop spheres, and was best known for his work with such names as David Bowie, Marc Bolan and the Boomtown Rats - Tony was partly responsible for Paige's longevity on the UK LP charts, making sure that her records were made in a catch-all manner that appealed to the broadest possible audience. Bob MacDonald, 23 February, 1986..

AVE MARIA
Tracks: / Ave Maria / Rocking.
7" Single: Released Dec '82, on WEA, by WEA Records. Catalogue no: **X 9939**

DON'T WALK AWAY TILL I TOUCH YOU
Tracks: / Don't walk away till I touch you.
7" Single: Released Oct '78, on EMI, by EMI Records. Deleted '81. Catalogue no: **EMI 2862**

FALLING DOWN TO EARTH
Tracks: / Falling down to earth / Up so high.
7" Single: Released Apr '81, on Arista, by BMG Records (UK). Deleted Apr '84. Catalogue no: **ARIST 405**

FATHER CHRISTMAS EYES
Tracks: / Father Christmas eyes / Winters tale, A.
7" Single: Released Nov '87, on WEA, by WEA Records. Catalogue no: **YZ 167**

FOR YOU
Tracks: / For you / Don't cry for me Argentina (Available on 12" version only.).
7" Single: Released Jan '86, on WEA, by WEA Records. Catalogue no: **YZ 52**
12" Single: Released Jan '86, on WEA, by WEA Records. Catalogue no: **YZ 52T**

HEAVEN HELP MY HEART
Tracks: / Heaven help my heart / Argument / Russian and Molokov (available on 12" version only.) / Where I want to be (available on 12" version only.).
7" Single: Released Sep '86, on RCA, by BMG Records (UK). Catalogue no: **CHESS 5**
12" Single: Released Sep '86, on RCA, by BMG Records (UK). Catalogue no: **CHESST 5**

I GET A KICK OUT OF YOU
Tracks: / I get a kick out of you.
7" Single: Released Jun '89, on First Night, by First Night Records. Catalogue no: **SCORE 18**

I KNOW HIM SO WELL
Tracks: / I know him so well.
7" Single: Released Jan '85, on RCA, by BMG Records (UK). Deleted '88. Catalogue no: **CHESS 3**

IF YOU DON'T WANT MY LOVE
Tracks: / If you don't want my love.
7" Single: Released Jan '81, on Arista, by BMG Records (UK). Deleted Jan '84. Catalogue no: **ARIST 381**

IS ANYONE THERE
Tracks: / Is anyone there / Whose baby blue are you?.
7" Single: Released Jul '81, on EMI, by EMI Records. Deleted '84. Catalogue no: **EMI 5212**

ISLAND
Tracks: / We're only flesh and blood.
7" Single: Released Jun '86, on Inspiration, Deleted '87. Catalogue no: **WHS 101**

LIKE AN IMAGE PASSING BY
Tracks: / Like an image passing by.
7" Single: Released Jan '84, on Epic, by CBS Records. Catalogue no: **A 3892**

MEMORY
Tracks: / Memory / Overtures.
7" Single: Released May '81, on Polydor, by Polydor Ltd. Deleted 30 May '89. Catalogue no: **POSP 279**

MEMORY (OLD GOLD)
Tracks: / Memory / Take that look off your face.
7" Single: Released Oct '88, on Old Gold, by Old Gold Records. Deleted Nov '88. Catalogue no: **OG 9797**

MY KNIGHTS IN BLACK LEATHER
Tracks: / My knights in black leather / Falling down to earth.
7" Single: Released Jun '82, on WEA, by WEA Records. Deleted Jun '85. Catalogue no: **K 19186**

NOBODY'S SIDE
Tracks: / Nobody's side.
12" Single: Released Oct '84, on RCA, by BMG Records (UK). Catalogue no: **CHEST 2**
12" Single: Released Apr '86, on RCA, by BMG Records (UK). Catalogue no: **CHESST 7**
7" Single: Released Apr '86, on RCA, by BMG Records (UK). Catalogue no: **CHESS 7**
7" Single: Released Oct '84, on RCA, by BMG Records (UK). Catalogue no: **CHESS 2**

RADIO GA GA
Tracks: / Radio ga ga / Love of my life.
7" Single: Released Dec '88, on Siren, by Virgin Records. Catalogue no: **SRN 110**

RUNNING BACK FOR MORE
Tracks: / Running back for more.
7" Single: Released Jan '84, on WEA, by WEA Records. Catalogue no: **X 9530**

SECOND TIME
Tracks: / Second time / If you don't want my love.
7" Single: Released Feb '82, on WEA, by WEA Records. Deleted Feb '87. Catalogue no: **K 18966**

SECOND TIME, THE
Tracks: / Second time, The / All things considered.
7" Single: Released Sep '87, on WEA, by WEA Records. Catalogue no: **YZ 163**

SOMETIMES (THEME FROM CHAMPIONS)
Tracks: / Sometimes (theme from Champions) / I'm going to live.
7" Single: Released Apr '84, on Island, by Island Records. Deleted '87. Catalogue no: **IS 174**

TAKE ME BACK Theme from 'Classmates'
Tracks: / Take me back (Theme from 'Classmates') / Everybody's singing love songs.
7" Single: Released Jul '88, on Siren, by Virgin Records. Deleted '89. Catalogue no: **SRNP 89**
7" Single: Released Jul '88, on Siren, by Virgin Records. Catalogue no: **SRN 89**

TONIGHT IS THE NIGHT
Tracks: / Tonight is the night.
7" Single: Released Mar '85, on Avatar, by Avatar Record Corporation. Catalogue no: **AVAT 12**

WALKING IN THE AIR
Tracks: / Thirty two feet and eight little tails / Walking in the air.
7" Single: Released Nov '86, on WEA, by WEA Records. Deleted Jan '88. Catalogue no: **YZ 94**

WINDMILLS OF MY MIND
Tracks: / Windmills of your mind.
7" Single: Released Jan '85, on WEA, by WEA Records. Catalogue no: **YZ 25**

Paige, Raiana

OPEN UP YOUR HEART
Tracks: / Open up your heart.
7" Single: Released 2 May '89, on Sleeping Bag, by Sleeping Bag Records. Catalogue no: **SBUK 010**
12" Single: Released 2 May '89, on Sleeping Bag, by Sleeping Bag Records. Catalogue no: **SBUK 010T**
CD 5": Released 2 May '89, on Sleeping Bag, by Sleeping Bag Records. Catalogue no: **SBUKSCD 010**

Paige, Sharon

TONIGHT'S THE NIGHT
Tracks: / Tonight's the night.
7" Single: Released Mar '80, on Source, Deleted Mar '83. Catalogue no: **SRC 103**
12" Single: Released Mar '80, on Source, Deleted Mar '83. Catalogue no: **12SRC 103**

Pailhead

I WILL REFUSE
Tracks: / I will refuse / No bunny.
12" Single: Released 21 Nov '87, on Wax Trax, by Wax Trax Records. Catalogue no: **WAXUK 031**

TRAIT (SINGLE)
Tracks: / Trait.
12" Single: Released Dec '88, on Wax Trax, by Wax Trax Records. Catalogue no: **WAXUK 047**

Pain Famine

LIQUID LIGHT
Tracks: / Liquid light.
7" Single: Released Sep '86, on AV, by Priority Records. Catalogue no: **Unknown**

STARVISION
Tracks: / Vanity fair / Starvision.
7" Single: Released Apr '86, on AV, by Priority Records. Catalogue no: **AVS 1**

STATE OF THE ART, THE
7" Single: Released Jul '88, on AV, by Priority Records. Catalogue no: **AVS 3**

Painted Word

INDEPENDENCE DAY (see panel top left)
Tracks: / Letter from Jackie / State of mind (Available on 12" version only.) / Independance day.
7" Single: Released Jun '86, on Mother, by Mother Records. Catalogue no: **MUM 5**
12" Single: Released Jun '86, on Mother, by Mother Records. Catalogue no: **12 MUM 5**

THAT'S THE REASON I'M ALIVE
Tracks: / That's the reason I'm alive / This is going to be my world / That's the reason I'm alive (extended mix) (on 12" only) / Perfect timing (on 12" and CD 5" only).
7" Single: Released Jul '89, on RCA, by BMG Records (UK). Catalogue no: **PB 42963**
7" Single: Released Jul '89, on RCA, by BMG Records (UK). Catalogue no: **PB 42917**
CD 5": Released Jul '89, on RCA, by BMG Records (UK). Catalogue no: **PD 42918**
12" Single: Released Jul '89, on RCA, by BMG Records (UK). Catalogue no: **PT 42918**

WORLDWIDE
Tracks: / Worldwide / I found love today / My darkest hour.
CD 5": Released Apr '89, on RCA, by BMG Records (UK). Catalogue no: **PD 42704**
12" Single: Released Apr '89, on RCA, by BMG Records (UK). Catalogue no: **PT 42704**
7" Single: Released Apr '89, on RCA, by BMG Records (UK). Catalogue no: **PB 42703**
12" Single: Released May '89, on RCA, by BMG Records (UK). Catalogue no: **PT 42840**
7" Single: Released Apr '89, on RCA, by BMG Records (UK). Catalogue no: **PB 42807**

Pair Of Blue Eyes

YOU USED TO GO TO MY HEAD
Tracks: / You used to go to my head / Duty free.
7" Single: Released Sep '87, on CBS, by CBS Records. Catalogue no: **PBE 1**
12" Single: Released Sep '87, on CBS, by CBS Records. Catalogue no: **PBE T1**

Paiton, Tony

FEELING IS GONE, THE
Tracks: / Feeling is gone, The / Message (in a bottle), The.
7" Single: Released 17 Oct '87, on Light & Shade, Catalogue no: **LS 2**

GOT A MESSAGE (IN A BOTTLE)
Tracks: / Got a message (in a bottle) / Got a message (in a bottle) version.
7" Single: Released Sep '88, on Ellorac, Catalogue no: **ELL 1**
12" Single: Released Sep '88, on Ellorac, Catalogue no: **ELLT 1**

TRUST ME BABY
Tracks: / Love / Trust me baby.
7" Single: Released Jul '86, on Gipsy, by Gipsy Records. Catalogue no: **GIPSY 22**

WHERE DID IT GO
Tracks: / Where did it go / Where did it go (part 2).
7" Single: Released Apr '89, on Ellorac, Catalogue no: **ELL 2**
12" Single: Released Apr '89, on Ellorac, Catalogue no: **ELL T2**

Pajah, Paulette

COZ YOU LOVE ME BABY
Tracks: / Coz you love me baby.
7" Single: Released Aug '84, on Raiders, Catalogue no: **LGR 7004**

Pal

TALK WE DON'T
Tracks: / Talk we don't (inst) / Talk we don't (club mix) (Available on 12" version only) / Talk we don't (tribal mix) (inst) (Available on 12" version only.) / Talk we don't (safari mix) (Available on 12" version only.) / Talk we don't (jungletalk mix) (Available on 12" only.).
7" Single: Released Mar '86, on Motown, by BMG Records (UK). Catalogue no: **ZB 40561**
12" Single: Released Mar '86, on Motown, by BMG Records (UK). Catalogue no: **ZT 40562**

Palace Of Light

CITY OF GOLD
Tracks: / City of gold.
12" Single: Released Mar '87, on Bam Caruso, by Demon Records. Catalogue no: **PABL 053**

SAFER
Tracks: / Safer.
7" Single: Released 8 Nov '88, on Bam Caruso, by Demon Records. Catalogue no: **OPRA 035**

Palais Schaumburg

BEAT OF TWO
Tracks: / Beat of two / Milt Raskin.
7" Single: Released Apr '84, on Mercury, by Phonogram Ltd. Catalogue no: **MER 158**

HOCKEY
Tracks: / Hockey.
7" Single: Released Aug '83, on Mercury, by Phonogram Ltd. Catalogue no: **PASCH 1**
12" Single: Released Aug '83, on Mercury, by Phonogram Ltd. Catalogue no: **PASCH 112**

WIR BAUNEN EINE NEUE STADT
Tracks: / Wir baunen eine neue stadt.
7" Single: Released Jun '82, on Kamera, Deleted '88. Catalogue no: **ERA 005**

Pale Fountains

Biographical details: The classy, Sixties-influenced pop single *Thank You* provideed this four-piece all male British band with a one-off UK chart entry in late 1982 - it reached No. 48. It was their first release on Virgin, having previously issued an indie single called *Something On my Mind*. Later output from the Pale Fountains consisted of competent MOR-tinged pop, but was not sufficiently strong to garber chart action. *Thank You* remained their best track. Bob MacDonald, 23 February 1986.u.

DON'T LET YOUR LOVE START A WAR
Tracks: / Don't let your love start a war / Love situation.
12" Single: Released Mar '84, on Virgin, by Virgin Records. Deleted '89. Catalogue no: **VS 668-12**
7" Single: Released Mar '84, on Virgin, by Virgin Records. Deleted '89. Catalogue no: **VS 668**

FROM ACROSS THE KITCHEN TABLE (SINGLE)
Tracks: / Across the kitchen table.
7" Single: Released Jun '85, on Virgin, by Virgin Records. Deleted '89. Catalogue no: **VS 750**

JEAN'S NOT HAPPENING
Tracks: / Jean's not happening / Bicycle thieves.
12" Single: Released Dec '84, on Virgin, by Virgin Records. Deleted '86. Catalogue no: **VS 735-12**

SOMETHING ON MY MIND
Tracks: / Something on my mind / Just a girl.
7" Single: Released Jul '82, on Operation Twilight, Catalogue no: **OPT 009**

THANK YOU
Tracks: / Thank you / Meadow of love.
7" Single: Released Nov '82, on Virgin, by Virgin Records. Deleted '85. Catalogue no: **VS 557**

UNLESS
Tracks: / Unless.
7" Single: Released Jan '84, on Virgin, by Virgin Records. Deleted '89. Catalogue no: **VS 614**

Pale Red Competitor

FUTURE LOST
Tracks: / Future lost.
7" Single: Released Mar '84, on UNKNOWN, Catalogue no: **PRC 001**

Pale Saints

BARGING INTO THE PRESENCE OF GOD
Tracks: / Barging into the presence.
12" Single: Released Sep '89, on 4AD, by 4AD Records. Catalogue no: **BAD 910**
CD 5": Released Sep '89, on 4AD, by 4AD Records. Catalogue no: **BAD 910CD**

Palladin, Patti

BABY IT'S YOU
Tracks: / Baby it's you.
7" Single: Released Nov '88, on Jungle, by Jungle Records. Catalogue no: **JUNG 44**
12" Single: Released Nov '88, on Jungle, by Jungle Records. Catalogue no: **JUNG 44T**

SIAMESE LOVERS
Tracks: / Siamese lovers.
12" Single: Released Feb '83, on Love Corporation, Catalogue no: **LOVE 004**

Pallas

ARRIVE ALIVE (SINGLE)
Tracks: / Arrive alive / Stranger.
7" Single: Released Jun '82, on Granite Wax, Deleted Jun '85. Catalogue no: **GWS 1**

EYES IN THE NIGHT (ARRIVE ALIVE)
Tracks: / Eyes in the night.
7" Pic: Released Feb '84, on EMI, by EMI Records. Catalogue no: **PLSP 1**

PARIS IS BURNING
Tracks: / Paris is burning.
12" Single: Released Apr '83, on Cool King, Catalogue no: **12 CK 010**
7" Single: Released Apr '83, on Cool King, Catalogue no: **CK 010**

STRANGERS
Tracks: / Strangers / Nightmare / Sanctuary.
12" Single: Released Apr '85, on Harvest (1), by EMI Records. Catalogue no: **12PLS 3**
7" Pic: Released Apr '85, on Harvest (1), by EMI Records. Catalogue no: **12PLSP 3**
7" Single: Released Apr '85, on Harvest (1), by EMI Records. Catalogue no: **PLS 3**

THROWING STONES AT THE WINDOW
Tracks: / Cut and run / Crown of thorns (available on 12" version only.) / Throwing stones at the window.
7" Single: Released Jan '86, on Harvest (1), by EMI Records. Catalogue no: **PLS 4**
12" Single: Released Jan '86, on Harvest (1), by EMI Records. Catalogue no: **12PLS 4**

WIN OR LOSE
Tracks: / Just a memory / Win or lose.
7" Single: Released Apr '86, on EMI, by EMI Records. Catalogue no: **PLS 5**
12" Single: Released Apr '86, on EMI, by EMI Records. Catalogue no: **12PLS 5**

Pallas, Laura

CRY TO THE WIND
Tracks: / Cry to the wind.
12" Single: Released Aug '86, on MDM, by MDM Communications. Deleted May '88. Catalogue no: **MDM 10-12**
7" Single: Released Aug '86, on MDM, by MDM Communications. Deleted May '88. Catalogue no: **MDM 10**

EMERGENCY
Tracks: / Emergency.
12" Single: Released Mar '84, on Record Shack, by Record Shack Records. Catalogue no: **SOHOT 16**
7" Single: Released Mar '84, on Record Shack, by Record Shack Records. Catalogue no: **SOHO 16**

HANDS OFF
Tracks: / Hands off.
12" Single: Released Oct '84, on Record Shack, by Record Shack Records. Catalogue no: **SOHOT 29**
7" Single: Released Oct '84, on Record Shack, by Record Shack Records. Catalogue no: **SOHO 29**

IN THE NIGHT
Tracks: / In the night.
12" Single: Released Nov '82, on Solo, Catalogue no: **SOL 001 12**

SKIING IN THE SNOW
Tracks: / Skiing in the snow.
7" Single: Released Nov '83, on Record Shack, by Record Shack Records. Catalogue no: **SOHO 12**
12" Single: Released Nov '83, on Record Shack, by Record Shack Records. Catalogue no: **SOHOT 12**

SWEET CONFUSION
Tracks: / Sweet confusion.
7" Single: Released Apr '86, on MDM, by MDM Communications. Deleted '86. Catalogue no: **MDM 6**

Palm, Anna

DANCE
Tracks: / Dance / Dance (instrumentals).
7" Single: Released Dec '87, on Dynamite Discs, by Dynamite Discs. Catalogue no: **DYD 2**

MASQUERADE
Tracks: / Masquerade.
12" Single: Released Oct '88, on One Little Indian, by One Little Indian Records. Catalogue no: **12TP 013**

Palma, Triston

CAN'T EXPLAIN
Tracks: / Can't explain.
12" Single: Released Aug '84, on World Enterprise, Catalogue no: **WER/D 114**

DANCE HALL FAN
Tracks: / Dance hall fan.
12" Single: Released Sep '84, on Black Solidarity, Catalogue no: **Unknown**

DOLLARS FE A PIECE
Tracks: / Dollars fe a piece.
12" Single: Released Oct '88, on Bun Gem, Catalogue no: **BG 0027**

DREAM OF ME
Tracks: / Dream of me / Let it be me.
12" Single: Released Dec '84, on Oak Sound, Catalogue no: **SD 016**

ENTERTAINMENT
Tracks: / Entertainment.
12" Single: Released Aug '81, on Greensleeves, by Greensleeves Records. Catalogue no: **GRED 66**

HEARTBREAKER
Tracks: / Heartbreaker.
12" Single: Released Oct '88, on Bun Gem, Catalogue no: **BG 0029**

HOW CAN A MAN BE HAPPY
Tracks: / How can a man be happy / Time is cold.
12" Single: Released Mar '81, on Attack, Deleted '88. Catalogue no: **TACK 25**

I'M LEAVING
Tracks: / I'm leaving.
12" Single: Released Nov '83, on Sharp Axe, Catalogue no: **SA 005**

IT'S NOT WHAT YOU SAY
Tracks: / It's not what you say.
12" Single: Released Sep '83, on Londisc, by Londisc Records. Catalogue no: **LD 002**

JOKER SMOKER (SINGLE)
Tracks: / Joker smoker / Loafter smoker.
12" Single: Released Jul '82, on Greensleeves, by Greensleeves Records. Deleted '87. Catalogue no: **GRED 93**

MR FALSE PREACHER
Tracks: / Mr. False preacher.
12" Single: Released Feb '82, on Greensleeves, by Greensleeves Records. Catalogue no: **GRED 79**

NO SHOT, NO FIRE
Tracks: / No shot, no fire / Jukes and watch.
12" Single: Released Aug '83, on Greensleeves, by Greensleeves Records. Catalogue no: **GRED 126**

RAVING
Tracks: / Raving.
12" Single: Released Feb '82, on Midnight Rock, Catalogue no: **MR 005**

ROCK WITH ME
Tracks: / Rock with me.
12" Single: Released Oct '88, on Bun Gem, Catalogue no: **BG 0028**

SETTLE DOWN
Tracks: / Settle down.
12" Single: Released Apr '83, on Trojan, by Trojan Records. Deleted May '88. Catalogue no: **TROT 9068**

THEM WOUNDED
Tracks: / Them wounded.
12" Single: Released '88, on Bun Gem, Catalogue no: **BG 0025**

TRASH AND READY
Tracks: / Trash and ready.
12" Single: Released Jan '85, on Blue Trac, by Blue Trac Records. Catalogue no: **BTR 005**

UNDER MI NOSE
Tracks: / Under mi nose.
12" Single: Released Oct '88, on Bun Gem, Catalogue no: **BG 008**

UPTOWN GIRL
Tracks: / Uptown girl.
12" Single: Released Sep '84, on High Music, Catalogue no: **Unknown**

WOMAN WOMAN
Tracks: / Woman woman.
12" Single: Released Mar '83, on Rusty International, Catalogue no: **RI 008**

Palmer, Barry

DOO WAH DIDDY
Tracks: / Do wah diddy.
7" Single: Released Aug '88, on Pyramid, by Pyramid Records. Catalogue no: **PYR 4**
12" Single: Released Aug '88, on Pyramid, by Pyramid Records. Catalogue no: **12 PYR 4**

GOD BLESS THE CHILDREN
Tracks: / God bless the children.
Note: The song that was performed at the Albert Hall in 1987 at the Miss World Final. All artist royalties will be donated to the Save The Children Fund.
7" Single: Released Mar '88, on Pyramid, by Pyramid Records. Catalogue no: **PYR 2**
12" Single: Released Mar '88, on Pyramid, by Pyramid Records. Catalogue no: **12 PYR 2**

HOUSE OF THE RISING SUN
Tracks: / House of the rising sun.
12" Single: Released Feb '87, on Starblend, by Starblend Records. Catalogue no: **12 STAR 10**
7" Single: Released '87, on Starblend, by Starblend Records. Catalogue no: **STAR 10**

SHE'S LEAVING HOME
Tracks: / She's leaving home / Unknown singer.
7" Single: Released Sep '80, on Aura Records, by Aura Records. Deleted Sep '83. Catalogue no: **AUS 119**

WHEN ONE DOOR CLOSES
Tracks: / When one door closes / Love at first sight.
7" Single: Released Mar '85, on Venom, Deleted '86. Catalogue no: **VENOM 1**
12" Single: Released Mar '85, on Venom, Deleted '86. Catalogue no: **12VENOM 1**

Palmer Dog

DON'T SMOKE THE SEED
Tracks: / Don't smoke the seed / Black rose.
12" Single: Released Oct '83, on Hitbound, Catalogue no: **JJ 141**
12" Single: Released Jun '84, on Jedi, Catalogue no: **JJ 171**

Palmer, Florrie

HI FI LOVE
Tracks: / Hi fi love / When he shines.
7" Single: Released Feb '81, on Hansa, by Hansa Records. Deleted Feb '84. Catalogue no: **HANSA 1**

Palmer, Joe

JUST ONE MORE CHANCE
Tracks: / Just one more chance / Carrickfergus.
7" Single: Released Mar '88, on Etude, by Etude Records. Catalogue no: **ET 1**

Palmer, Michael

BUS STOP
Tracks: / Bus stop.
12" Single: Released Sep '84, on Power House, Catalogue no: **Unknown**

DONE WITH IT
Tracks: / Done with it.
12" Single: Released Sep '84, on Greensleeves, by Greensleeves Records. Catalogue no: **GRED 155**

GHETTO DANCE
Tracks: / Ghetto dance.
12" Single: Released Nov '83, on Greensleeves, by Greensleeves Records. Catalogue no: **GRED 131**

GUN SHOT AUGUST
Tracks: / Gun shot August.
12" Single: Released Apr '84, on Power

ROBERT PALMER - SWEET LIES (Released on Island)

ROBERT PALMER - NOT A SECOND TIME (Released on Island)

House, Catalogue no: **Unknown**

HAPPY MERRY CHRISTMAS
Tracks: / Happy merry Christmas.
12" Single: Released Dec '83, on Greensleeves, by Greensleeves Records. Catalogue no: **GRED 134**

I'M STILL DANCING
Tracks: / I'm still dancing / No war.
12" Single: Released Mar '84, on Greensleeves, by Greensleeves Records. Catalogue no: **GRED 144**

JAIL HOUSE ROCK
Tracks: / Jailhouse rock.
12" Single: Released Apr '85, on Londisc, by Londisc Records. Catalogue no: **LDR 042**

JUBIE ROCK
Tracks: / Jubie rock / Ready, she no ready.
12" Single: Released Dec '84, on Greensleeves, by Greensleeves Records. Catalogue no: **GRED 166**

MY NIGHT
Tracks: / My night.
12" Single: Released Oct '84, on Uptempo, Catalogue no: **UT 007**

NO TIME FOR ME
Tracks: / No time for me.
12" Single: Released Jul '85, on Rockers Forever, Catalogue no: **Unknown**

ONE MORE YOUTH GET SHOT
Tracks: / One more youth get shot / Don't worry yourself.
12" Single: Released May '85, on Scom, Catalogue no: **BD 016**

PULL IT UP NOW
Tracks: / Pull it up now
12" Single: Released May '85, on Greensleeves, by Greensleeves Records. Catalogue no: **GRED 179**

SHE HAS FE GET IT
Tracks: / She has fe get it.
12" Single: Released Jan '85, on Vibes, by Vibes Records. Catalogue no: **VV 006**

SHE NO READY YET
Tracks: / She no ready yet.
12" Single: Released Oct '84, on Jammy's, Catalogue no: **Unknown**

SHOW ME YOUR COMPANY
Tracks: / Show me your company.
12" Single: Released Dec '84, on Vena, Catalogue no: **VEN 002**

Palmer, Mr.

CLICK CLICK
Tracks: / See ninja deh / Click click.
12" Single: Released Jun '86, on Sweetcorn, Catalogue no: **SC 11**

NA GO DEH SO
Tracks: / Na go deh so.
12" Single: Released Jan '88, on Sure Spin, Catalogue no: **SPN 002**

TELEVISION
Tracks: / Television / Age of the gangster.
12" Single: Released Dec '85, on Mab, Catalogue no: **MAB 006**

Palmer, Robert

Biographical details: Born in Batley, west Yorkshire,in 1949 singer, songwriter, producer and multi-instrumentalist Palmer enjoyed many years of cult acclaim before achieving substantial record and international success. His main interests have always been in soul and rock music and he has fused the two genres throughout his career. Palmer first started to attract attention as vocalist with the Alan Bown Set in 1968. In the early 70's he shared lead vocals with the up-and-coming Elkie Brooks in two bands, Dada and Vinegar Joe. All these groups attracted strong concert followings but did not sell records. Vinegar Joe folded in 1974, with both singers embarking on solo careers. Palmer eventually achieved commercial success, but not as quickly as Brooks. Beginning a long-term solo association with Chris Blackwell's Island label, Palmer released his first album, *Sneakin' Sally Through The Alley*, in 1974. This was recorded in New Orleans and New York and it was American record buyers who gave modest chart acceptance to early Palmer albums like *Pressure Drop* (1975) and *Some People Can Do What They Like* (1976). Signs of stronger success came in 1978-79, when *Double Fun* and *Secrets* yielded a pair of US Top Twenty singles, *Every Kinda People* and *Bad Case Of Loving You (Doctor, Doctor)* respectively. *The Clues* LP, of 1980, spawned Palmer's first two British Top Fifty singles, the seminal *Johnny and Mary* (regarded by many as his best-ever track) and *Looking For Clues*. In '82 he finally cracked the UK Top Twenty with *Some Guys Have All The Luck*, later an even bigger hit for Rod Stewart. The excellent title track of 1983's *Pride* album failed as a single but the album yielded a couple of minor hits with cover versions borrowed from black funk acts, *You Are In My System* (The System) and *You Can Have It (Take My Heart)* (Kool & The Gang). Most of Palmer's product during the late 70's and early 80's was self-produced. Throughout this period he lived in Nassau in the Bahamas, which caused many observers to accuse him of taking an over-casual attitude to his work and to reviewers describing him as an under-achiever. In 1985, however, he achieved his biggest international success by teaming up with teenybop superstars Andy Taylor, John Taylor (Duran Duran) and Chic drummer Tony Thompson: Palmer was vocalist with this "supergroup" which was called Power Station after the famous New York studios. Having completed the band's successful album, he chose to return to his solo recording career rather than join them on tour and he was replaced on the road by the lesser known Michael Des Barres. (Bob MacDonald, February 1986.)
He was born in 1949, in Batley, West Yorkshire. The white soul singer, songwriter, producer has achieved international success, gained slowly during some years of cult stardom. (Donald Clarke 15.5.87).

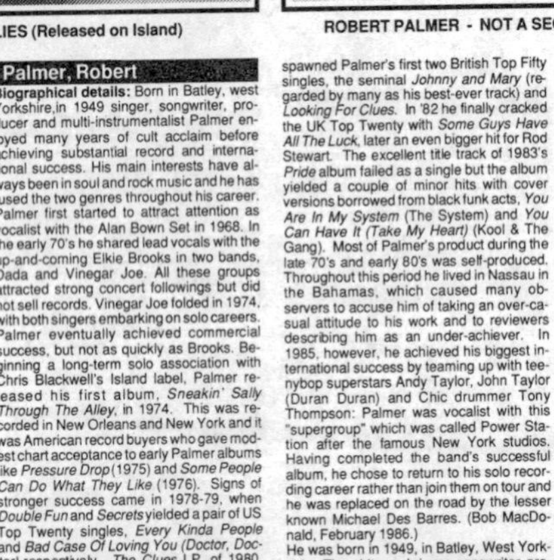

ROBERT PALMER - SHE MAKES MY DAY (Released on EMI)

ADDICTED TO LOVE
Tracks: / Remember to remember / You are in my system (Available on 12" version only.) / Addicted to love (12" mix) (Only on 12" and CD single.) / Addicted to love.
12" Single: on Island, by Island Records. Deleted Jun '88. Catalogue no: **12IS 270**
7" Single: Released Apr '86, on Island, by Island Records. Catalogue no: **IS 270**
CD 3": Released Sep '88, on Polystar (Japan), Catalogue no: **P15 D37004**

BAD CASE OF LOVIN' YOU (DOCTOR DOCTOR)
Tracks: / Bad case of lovin' you (doctor doctor).
7" Single: Released Jul '79, on Island, by Island Records. Deleted '82. Catalogue no: **WIP 6481**

BAD CASE OF LOVIN' YOU (REMIX)
Tracks: / Bad case of loving you (remix) / Sweet lies / What's it take (On 12" only).
CD 5": Released Jun '89, on Island, by Island Records. Catalogue no: **CID 438**
12" Single: Released Jun '89, on Island, by Island Records. Catalogue no: **12 IS 438**
7" Single: Released Jun '89, on Island, by Island Records. Catalogue no: **IS 438**

CHANGE HIS WAYS
Tracks: / Change his ways (Not on 12".) / Change his ways (Wed. 9PM mix) (Not on 7".) / Change his ways (Rock mix) (12" only.) / More than ever / She makes my day (CD single only.).
7" Single: Released Mar '89, on EMI, by EMI Records. Deleted Oct '89. Catalogue no: **EM 85**
12" Single: Released Mar '89, on EMI, by EMI Records. Deleted Oct '89. Catalogue no: **12EM 85**
CD 5": Released Mar '89, on EMI, by EMI Records. Catalogue no: **CDEM 85**
7" Pic: Released Mar '89, on EMI, by EMI Records. Deleted Oct '89. Catalogue no: **203 295 0**
7" Pic: Released Mar '89, on EMI, by EMI Records. Deleted Oct '89. Catalogue no: **EMPD 85**

DISCIPLINE OF LOVE
Tracks: / Dance for me / Addicted to love / Remember to remember / Wake up laughing.
12" Single: Released Oct '86, on Island, by Island Records. Deleted Jul '87. Catalogue no: **12IS 242**
7" Single: Released Oct '86, on Island, by Island Records. Deleted '89. Catalogue no: **IS 242**
12" Single: Released Oct '86, on Island, by Island Records. Catalogue no: **12ISX 242**

EVERY KINDA PEOPLE
Tracks: / Every kinda people.
7" Single: Released May '78, on Island, by Island Records. Deleted '81. Catalogue no: **WIP 6425**

I DIDN'T MEAN TO TURN YOU ON
Tracks: / Get it through your heart / Back in arms / Johnny and Mary (Doublepack.) /

Trick bag (live) (Doublepack.) / No not much (live).
7" Single: Released Jul '86, on Island, by Island Records. Deleted Apr '88. Catalogue no: **IS 283**
7" Single: Released Jan '86, on Island, by Island Records. Catalogue no: **IS 256**
7" Set: Released Jan '86, on Island, by Island Records. Deleted Jul '87. Catalogue no: **ISD 256**
12" Single: Released Jan '86, on Island, by Island Records. Catalogue no: **12IS 256**
12" Single: Released Jul '86, on Island, by Island Records. Deleted Apr '88. Catalogue no: **12IS 283**

IT COULD HAPPEN TO YOU
Tracks: / It could happen to you / Change his ways / Early in the morning (get up mix) (12" & CD single only.) / Casting a spell (CD single only.).
12" Single: Released Aug '89, on EMI, by EMI Records. Catalogue no: **203 490 6**
12" Single: Released Aug '89, on EMI, by EMI Records. Catalogue no: **12EM 99**
7" Single: Released Aug '89, on EMI, by EMI Records. Catalogue no: **EM 99**
CD 5": Released Aug '89, on EMI, by EMI Records. Catalogue no: **CDEM 99**
CD 5": Released Aug '89, on EMI, by EMI Records. Catalogue no: **203 490 2**
Cassingle: Released Aug '89, on EMI, by EMI Records. Catalogue no: **203 490 4**
Cassingle: Released Aug '89, on EMI, by EMI Records. Catalogue no: **TCEM 99**
7" Single: Released Aug '89, on EMI, by EMI Records. Catalogue no: **203 490 7**

JOHNNY & MARY
Tracks: / Johnny and Mary / What's it take.
7" Single: Released Aug '80, on Island, by Island Records. Catalogue no: **WIP 6638**

LOOKING FOR CLUES
Tracks: / Looking for clues / Good care of you / Style kills.
12" Single: Released Nov '80, on Island, by Island Records. Deleted '83. Catalogue no: **12WIP 6651**
7" Single: Released Nov '80, on Island, by Island Records. Deleted '83. Catalogue no: **WIP 6651**

NOT A SECOND TIME (See panel on previous page)
Tracks: / Not a second time / Woke up laughing.
7" Single: Released '80, on Island, by Island Records. Catalogue no: **WIP 6678**

PRIDE
Tracks: / Pride.
7" Pic: Released Dec '82, on Island, by Island Records. Deleted Dec '87. Catalogue no: **PWIP 6833**
12" Single: Released Nov '82, on Island, by Island Records. Deleted Nov '85. Catalogue no: **12WIP 6833**
7" Single: Released Nov '82, on Island, by Island Records. Deleted Nov '85. Catalogue no: **WIP 6833**

RIPTIDE
Tracks: / Riptide / Hyperactive / Addicted to love / Trick bag / Get it through your heart / I didn't mean to turn you on / Flesh wound / Discipline of love / Riptide (reprise).
7" Set: Released Nov '85, on Island, by Island Records. Catalogue no: **ISD 9801**
7" Single: Released Nov '85, on Island, by Island Records. Catalogue no: **IS 9801**
12" Single: Released Nov '85, on Island, by Island Records. Catalogue no: **12IS 9801**

SHE MAKES MY DAY (See panel on previous page)
Tracks: / She makes my day / Disturbing behaviour / Simply irresistible (ext. remix) (Only on 12").
Note: Produced by Robert Palmer for Remlap Co. Inc. Executive producer David Harper. Mixed by Eric 'E.T.' Thorngren.
12" Single: Released Oct '88, on EMI, by EMI Records. Deleted Oct '89. Catalogue no: **12EM 65**
CD 5": Released Oct '88, on EMI, by EMI Records. Catalogue no: **CDEM 65**
7" Single: Released Oct '88, on EMI, by EMI Records. Catalogue no: **EM 65**

SIMPLY IRRESISTIBLE
Tracks: / Simply irresistible / Nova / Simply irresistible (extended version) (Only on 12"'s and CD single.) / Simply irresistible (instrumental) (Only on 12"'s and CD single.).
12" Single: Released 31 May '88, on EMI, by EMI Records. Deleted Aug '89. Catalogue no: **12EM 61**
Special: Released 31 May '88, on EMI, by EMI Records. Deleted Aug '89. Catalogue no: **12EMS 61**
CD 5": Released Jun '88, on EMI, by EMI Records. Catalogue no: **CDEM 61**
7" Single: Released 31 May '88, on EMI, by EMI Records. Deleted Aug '89. Catalogue no: **EM 61**
7" Pic: Released Jun '88, on EMI, by EMI Records. Deleted Aug '89. Catalogue no: **EMP 61**

SOME GUYS HAVE ALL THE LUCK
Tracks: / Some guys have all the luck.
12" Single: Released Feb '82, on Island, by Island Records. Deleted '85. Catalogue no: **12 WIP 6754**
7" Single: Released Feb '82, on Island, by Island Records. Deleted '85. Catalogue no: **WIP 6754**

SWEET LIES (See panel on previous page)
Tracks: / Sweet lies / Sweet lies (extended remix).
12" Single: Released Mar '88, on Island, by Island Records. Deleted Jun '88. Catalogue no: **12 IS 352**
7" Single: Released Mar '88, on Island, by Island Records. Deleted Jun '88. Catalogue no: **IS 352**

YOU ARE IN MY SYSTEM
Tracks: / You are in my system.
7" Single: Released Apr '83, on Island, by Island Records. Deleted '86. Catalogue no: **IS 104**

YOU CAN HAVE IT (TAKE MY HEART)
Tracks: / You can have it (take my heart).
7" Single: Released Jun '83, on Island, by Island Records. Deleted '86. Catalogue no: **IS 121**

Palmer, Sinclair

GROWING UP TOO YOUNG
Tracks: / Growing up too young / Almost grown.
7" Single: Released Nov '83, on Carrere America (USA), by PolyGram Rec.Inc.(USA). Catalogue no: **CAR 293**
12" Single: Released Nov '83, on Carrere America (USA), by PolyGram Rec.Inc.(USA). Catalogue no: **CART 293**

Palmer, Teddy

NOBODY LOVES LIKE AN IRISHMAN
Tracks: / Nobody loves like an Irishman / First love never dies.
7" Single: Released Nov '82, on Mint, by Emerald Records. Deleted '88. Catalogue no: **CHEW 75**

Palmer, Wayne

COME SEE ME YA
Tracks: / Suzie.
12" Single: Released May '86, on Firm (1), Catalogue no: **FH 007**

Palmer,Trudi

ANYTHING CAN HAPPEN
Tracks: / Anything can happen / Fool with a bottle / Wheel of life.
7" Single: Released Apr '83, on Thunderbay, Catalogue no: **TBR 015**
Cassingle: Released Oct '82, on Thunderbay, Deleted Oct '85. Catalogue no: **TBC 001**

FOOL WITH A BOTTLE
Tracks: / Fool with a bottle.
7" Single: Released Apr '83, on Thunderbay, Catalogue no: **TBR 017**

WHEEL OF LIFE
Tracks: / Wheel of life.
7" Single: Released Apr '83, on Thunderbay, Catalogue no: **TBR 016**

Palookas

CLEAR DAY
Tracks: / Clear day, A.
12" Single: Released Jul '85, on Prophet, Catalogue no: **PROFIT 11**

HIT THE BOTTLE(SINGLE)
Tracks: / Hit the bottle.
12" Single: Released Nov '87, on Hollow Planet, Catalogue no: **HOP 001**

RUN RABBIT
Tracks: / Run rabbit run / Happy song.
12" Single: Released Jan '88, on Hollow Planet, Catalogue no: **HOP 001**
7" Single: Released Nov '87, on Hollow Planet, Catalogue no: **HOP 001 2**

Pam

TYPING POOL
Tracks: / Typing pool / Dear Katie.
7" Single: Released Apr '80, on EMI, by EMI Records. Deleted Apr '83. Catalogue no: **EMI 5015**

Pam 'n' Pat

TO BE SUPERMAN
Tracks: / To be superman / It's all music.
12" Single: Released Apr '82, on RCA, by BMG Records (UK). Deleted Apr '85. Catalogue no: **RCAT 207**
7" Single: Released Apr '82, on RCA, by BMG Records (UK). Deleted Apr '85. Catalogue no: **RCA 207**

Pan Assembly

GOODBYE MY LOVE
Tracks: / Mr. Magic / Goodbye my love.
7" Single: Released Mar '86, on Carotte, Catalogue no: **Unknown**

Panache

HEROES
Tracks: / Heroes / Lucinda.
7" Single: Released Jun '83, on Mach 1, by Mach 1 Records. Catalogue no: **MAGIC 6**
7" Single: Released May '84, on Mach 1, by Mach 1 Records. Catalogue no: **MAGIC 15**

HOW CAN I BE SURE
Tracks: / How can I be sure / Mayfair.
7" Single: Released Aug '82, on KJM, Catalogue no: **MAGIC 1**

I WANNA DANCE
Tracks: / I wanna dance / Crazy for your love.
7" Single: Released Jan '83, on Mach 1, by Mach 1 Records. Catalogue no: **MAGIC 4**

Panama

IF YOU'RE LEAVING NOW
Tracks: / If you're leaving now / All night long.
7" Single: Released Sep '82, on Jive, by Zomba Records. Catalogue no: **JIVE 21**

WILL YOU LOVE ME TOMORROW
Tracks: / Will you love me tomorrow.
7" Single: Released Mar '82, on Jive, by Zomba Records. Catalogue no: **JIVE 15**
12" Single: Released Mar '82, on Jive, by Zomba Records. Catalogue no: **JIVET 15**

Panatella, Slim

SWEET NICOTINA
Tracks: / Sweet nicotina / Lime rock.
7" Single: Released Feb '88, on Acoustics, by Acoustics Records. Catalogue no: **ACS 007**

Pancoute & Trinity

IF LOVING JAH IS WRONG
Tracks: / If loving jah is wrong.
12" Single: Released Jan '83, on September, Catalogue no: **SEP 003**

Pandora

MARIANNE
Tracks: / Marianne / Gaels' song.
7" Single: Released Aug '82, on Oscar, Catalogue no: **OSC 2**

Pandora's Box

IT'S ALL COMING BACK TO ME NOW
Tracks: / It's all coming back to me now / Pray lewd.
7" Single: Released Sep '89, on Virgin, by Virgin Records. Catalogue no: **VS 1216**
12" Single: Released Sep '89, on Virgin, by Virgin Records. Catalogue no: **VST 1216**

Pandy, Darryl

ANIMAL MAGNETISM
Tracks: / Animal magnetism (inst) / Tearing up the house (Remix) (Available on 12" version only.) / Animal magnetism.
12" Single: Released Oct '86, on Nightmare, by Nightmare Records. Catalogue no: **MARE 2**
7" Single: Released Oct '86, on Nightmare, by Nightmare Records. Catalogue no: **MARES 2**

FREE MAN
Tracks: / Free man.
12" Single: Released Oct '87, on DJ Int.(USA), Catalogue no: **DJ 955**

I PUT MY LOVE ON THE LINE
Tracks: / I put my love on the line.
7" Single: Released 23 May '87, on Nightmare, by Nightmare Records. Catalogue no: **MARES 27**

Panic

SHE'S NOT THERE
Tracks: / She's not there.
12" Single: Released Jan '83, on PRT, by Castle Communications Records. Catalogue no: **12P 259**
7" Single: Released Jan '83, on PRT, by Castle Communications Records. Catalogue no: **7P 259**

TICKET TO THE TROPICS
Tracks: / Ticket to the tropics.
12" Single: Released Jun '83, on PRT, by Castle Communications Records. Catalogue no: **12P 275**
7" Single: Released Jun '83, on PRT, by Castle Communications Records. Catalogue no: **7P 275**

Panic Stations

DEM BONES
Tracks: / Dem bones / Mine bones.
7" Single: Released May '83, on Crash, by Satril Records. Deleted '85. Catalogue no: **CRA 507**

Pankow

ART AND MADNESS
Tracks: / Art and madness.
12" Single: Released Feb '89, on Contempo, Catalogue no: **TEMPO 130**

GOD'S DENEUVE
Tracks: / God's deneuve.
12" Single: Released Nov '88, on Contempo, Catalogue no: **KGR 6**

PLAY THE HITS OF THE NINETIES
Tracks: / Play the hits of the nineties.
12" Single: Released Jan '88, on Contempo, Deleted '88. Catalogue no: **TEMPO 117**

SEX MINS
Tracks: / Sex mins.
12" Single: Released Jul '88, on Contempo, Catalogue no: **TEMPO 123**

Panorama

DREAM HOME
Tracks: / Dream home / Revisited.
7" Single: Released Jun '82, on Kamera, Deleted '88. Catalogue no: **ERA 009**

Panther Burns

BLOW YOUR TOP
Tracks: / Blow your top.
12" Single: Released Nov '82, on Rough Trade, by Rough Trade Records. Catalogue no: **RT 114T**

TRAIN KEPT A ROLLIN'
Tracks: / Train kept a rollin' / Red-headed woman.
7" Single: Released Oct '81, on Rough Trade, by Rough Trade Records. Catalogue no: **R007**

Panza Division

WE'LL ROCK THE WORLD
Tracks: / We'll rock the world / Standing on....
7" Single: Released Apr '82, on Panza Trax, by Panza Trax Records. Catalogue no: **PTO 1**

Paola

CINEMA
Tracks: / Cinema / Juke box.
7" Single: Released Apr '80, on CBS, by CBS Records. Deleted Apr '83. Catalogue no: **CBS 8504**

Paolo,Frankie

QUE PASA?MANANA!
Tracks: / Que pasa?Manana!.
12" Single: Released Jun '85, on Sonet, by Sonet Records. Catalogue no: **SONL 2283**
7" Single: Released Jun '85, on Sonet, by Sonet Records. Catalogue no: **SON 2283**

Papa Bemsie

DANCING FEVER
Tracks: / Dancing fever.
12" Single: Released May '85, on Music Rock, Catalogue no: **ROCK 003**

SETTLEMENT
Tracks: / Settlement.
12" Single: Released May '85, on Creole, by Creole Records. Catalogue no: **CRT 82**

Papa Biggie

NU GI HIM THE BODY
Tracks: / Nu gi him the body.
12" Single: Released Jun '88, on Uptempo, Catalogue no: **TEMP 026**

UNDER THE PLANE WING
Tracks: / Under the plane wing.
12" Single: Released Sep '84, on Taxi (1), Catalogue no: **UNKNOWN**

Papa Face

GIRLS
Tracks: / Girls / Dance pon de corner.
12" Single: Released Sep '82, on Fashion, by Fashion Records. Catalogue no: **TOP 003**

IN A JAMAICA STYLE
Tracks: / In a Jamaica style / Forward style.
12" Single: Released Feb '82, on Top Notch, by Fashion Records. Catalogue no: **TOP 001**

WE'RE BUBBLING HOT
Tracks: / We're bubbling hot / Pon the street.
12" Single: Released Sep '84, on Fashion, by Fashion Records. Catalogue no: **FAD 021**

Papa San

D.J. BUSINESS
Tracks: / D.J. business.
12" Single: Released Jul '88, on Fashion, by Fashion Records. Catalogue no: **FAD 058**

GIRL YOU LOVE ME
Tracks: / Girl you love me.
12" Single: Released 20 Mar '89, on Greensleeves, by Greensleeves Records. Catalogue no: **GRED 236**

NUH JOKE ME A MEK, A

Tracks: / Nuh joke me a mek, A.
12" Single: Released 20 Mar '89, on Steely & Cleevie, Catalogue no: **VPRD 440**

WHA' DEM A TRY
Tracks: / Wha' dem a try.
12" Single: Released Apr '88, on Super Power, Catalogue no: **SPD 26**

WHAT KIND A FART
Tracks: / What kind a fart.
12" Single: Released Jun '88, on Fashion, by Fashion Records. Catalogue no: **FAD 056**

Papa Winnie

ROOTSIDE AND BOOTSIE
Tracks: / Rootside and bootsie.
7" Single: Released Jul '89, on Epic, by CBS Records. Catalogue no: **6546717**
12" Single: Released Jul '89, on Epic, by CBS Records. Catalogue no: **6546711**

Papa's New Faith

SHINE
Tracks: / Shine.
12" Single: Released Jul '87, on Garage 27, Catalogue no: **GAR 001**

THROUGH THE ROOF
Tracks: / Through the roof / Mystery train medley / Every trip (demo).
12" Single: Released Apr '88, on Garage 27, Catalogue no: **GAR 002**

Paper Bags

JOSS BAY
Tracks: / Joss bay / Drat.
7" Single: Released Jan '80, on Retread, Deleted Jan '85. Catalogue no: **TREAD 1**

Paper Dolls

Biographical details: The catchy *Something Here In My Heart (Keeps A-Tellin' Me No)* provided this British female vocal trio with a one-off UK chart entry in 1968; the single, which gave full vent to the girls' somewhat whiny singing, reached No. 11. With their blond wigs, matching satin dresses and rather lightweight musical talent, the group's name was appropriate. The song was penned by the ace team of Tony Macaulay and John McLeod, who had scored back-to-back UK No. 1 singles in 1967 with the Foundations' *Baby Now That I've Found You* and Long John Baldry's *Let The Heartaches Begin*. It was produced by Macaulay, one of the leading behind-the-scenes figures in British commercial pop. Bob MacDonald, 23 February 1986..

SOMETHING HERE IN MY HEART
Tracks: / Something here in my heart.
7" Single: Released Jan '85, on Old Gold, by Old Gold Records. Catalogue no: **OG 9470**
7" Single: Released Jan '83, on Flashback, by Mainline Records. Catalogue no: **FBS 20**
7" Single: Released Mar '68, on Pye, Deleted '71. Catalogue no: **7 N 17456**

Paper Lace

Biographical details: This British pop band consisted of Cliff Fish, Chris Morris, Carlo Santanna (a guitarist who bore no relation to another guitar player with a similar name!), Michael Vaughan and Philip Wright (a drummer who also sang lead vocals, thereby beating Phil Collins to the idea!). Hailing from Nottinghm, Fish and Wright formed Paper Lace in 1969. The above lineup stabilised in early 1974, the time that they won ITV's talent contest Opportunity Knocks. Thanks to that show they were quickly signed by ace songwriters/producers Mitch Murray and Pater Callender who had recently started their own Bus Stop label. They immediately provided Paper Lace with the smash hit *Billy Don't Be A Hero* - this ear-catching story, about a fictional soldier in the American Civil War and his pleading sweetheart, logged three weeks at No. 1 on the British Chart in March 1974. An equally catchy story song, this time concerning Al Capone, reached the UK No. 3 position; it was called *The Night Chicago Died*. A third Murray/Callender hit, *The Black Eyed Boys*, took Paper Lace to No. 11 in late 1974. Shortly afterwards, the group broke away from Bus Stop in the hope of getting a big-time deal from another company. Instead paper Lace plunged into obscurity amidst a flurry of lawsuits from their former mentors; an out-of-court settlement was reached, with the group coming off worse. Continuing to work live, they made a brief return to the Top 30 in 1978 with a revival of *We've Got The Whole World In Our Hands* - this was a studio collaboration with the dubious vocal talents of their favourite football team, the red-hot Nottingham Forest. With their American subject matter (albeit somewhat trite), it was logical that *Billy Don't Be A Hero* and *The Night Chicago Died* should become US hits. But Paper Lace had to be content with a No. 96 placing for *Billy*, a rapid and opportunistic cover version was rushed onto the market by the American group Bo Donaldson and the Heywoods, who reached the US No. 1 spot in June '74. In August of that year, however, Paper Lace enjoyed their own American chart-topper with *Chicago*. Bob MacDonald, 23 February 1986.h.

BILLY, DON'T BE A HERO
Tracks: / Billy don't be a hero.
7" Single: Released Feb '74, on Bus Stop, Deleted '77. Catalogue no: **BUS 1014**

BILLY, DON'T BE A HERO (OLD GOLD)
Tracks: / Billy, don't be a hero / Night Chicago died, The.
7" Single: Released Jun '88, on Old Gold, by Old Gold Records. Catalogue no: **OG 9028**

BLACK EYED BOYS, THE
Tracks: / Black eyed boys, The.
7" Single: Released Aug '74, on Bus Stop, Deleted '77. Catalogue no: **BUS 1019**

NIGHT CHICAGO DIED, THE
Tracks: / Night Chicago died, The.
7" Single: Released May '74, on Bus Stop, Deleted '77. Catalogue no: **BUS 1016**

Paper Toys

WHEN THERE'S TWO OF YOU
Tracks: / When there's two of you / Love in me.
7" Single: Released Apr '89, on Armada, Catalogue no: **ARMA 1**

Papers

B.M.X BANDITS
Tracks: / B.M.X. bandits.
7" Single: Released Jun '84, on Creole, by Creole Records. Catalogue no: **CR 64**

REGGAE ON THE RADIO
Tracks: / Reggae on the radio.
7" Single: Released Aug '81, on Radioactive, Catalogue no: **RAD 2**

Papparazzi

DON'T STAY ALL NIGHT
Tracks: / Don't stay all night.
7" Single: Released May '84, on MCA, by MCA Records. Catalogue no: **PAPA 1**
12" Single: Released May '84, on MCA, by MCA Records. Catalogue no: **PAPAT 1**

Parachute Club

LOVE IS FIRE
Tracks: / Love is fire / Zeljo Mojo / Waves.
12" Single: Released Mar '87, on RCA, by BMG Records (UK). Catalogue no: **PT 41095**
7" Single: Released Mar '87, on RCA, by BMG Records (UK). Deleted '87. Catalogue no: **PB 41095**

RISE UP
Tracks: / Rise up / Tabago style.
7" Single: Released Jul '85, on Magnet, by WEA Records. Catalogue no: **MAG 262**
12" Single: Released Jul '85, on Magnet, by WEA Records. Catalogue no: **MAGT 262**

Parachute Men

IF I COULD WEAR YOUR JACKET
Tracks: / If I could wear your jacket.
12" Single: Released Oct '88, on Fire, by Fire Records. Catalogue no: **BLAZE 30T**
7" Single: Released Oct '88, on Fire, by Fire Records. Catalogue no: **BLAZE 30**

LEEDS STATION
Tracks: / Leeds station.
12" Single: Released May '89, on Fire, by Fire Records. Catalogue no: **BLAZE 33 T**
7" Single: Released May '89, on Fire, by Fire Records. Catalogue no: **BLAZE 33**
CD 5": Released May '89, on Fire, by Fire Records. Catalogue no: **BLAZE 33 CD**

SOMETIMES IN VAIN
Tracks: / Sometimes in vain.
12" Single: Released May '88, on Fire, by Fire Records. Catalogue no: **BLAZE 27T**

Paradaema, Paula

ONLY TIME
Tracks: / Only time / Only time (instrumental).
7" Single: Released Oct '88, on Destiny Angel, Catalogue no: **GYPSY 1**

Parade Ground

CUT UP (SINGLE)
Tracks: / Cut up.
CD 5": Released Oct '88, on Play It Again Sam(Belgium), by Play It Again Sam (Belgium). Catalogue no: **BIAS 93CD**

DUAL PERSPECTIVE
Tracks: / Dual perspective.
12" Single: Released 20 Jun '87, on Play It Again Sam(Belgium), by Play It Again Sam (Belgium). Catalogue no: **BIAS 060**

HOLLYWOOD
Tracks: / Hollywood.
12" Single: Released '88, on Play It Again Sam(Belgium), by Play It Again Sam (Belgium). Catalogue no: **BIAS 92**

Parade World

STRANGE WORLD
Tracks: / Strange world.
12" Single: Released Dec '87, on Play It Again Sam(Belgium), by Play It Again Sam (Belgium). Catalogue no: **BIAS 081**

Paradine Express

HUNGRY FOR YOUR LOVE
Tracks: / Hungry for your love.
12" Single: Released Jul '87, on Priority, by Priority Records. Deleted Jan '88. Catalogue no: **12 PARS 1**
7" Single: Released Jul '87, on Priority, by Priority Records. Catalogue no: **PARS 1**
12" Single: Released Oct '86, on Parasound, Deleted '88. Catalogue no: **PARS T 1**

Paradis, Vanessa

JOE LE TAXI
Tracks: / Joe le taxi / Varvara Pavlovna / Joe le taxi (ext. mix) (extra track on 12").
12" Single: Released Feb '88, on Polydor, by Polydor Ltd. Catalogue no: **POSPX 902**
7" Single: Released Feb '88, on Polydor, by Polydor Ltd. Catalogue no: **POSP 902**

MARILYN & JOHN (SINGLE)
Tracks: / Marilyn & John / Soldat (On 12" only).
7" Single: Released 22 Aug '88, on Polydor, by Polydor Ltd. Catalogue no: **PO 16**
12" Single: Released 22 Aug '88, on Polydor, by Polydor Ltd. Catalogue no: **PZ 16**

MAXOU
Tracks: / Maxou.
12" Single: Released 2 May '89, on Polydor, by Polydor Ltd. Catalogue no: **PZ 38**
CD 5": Released 2 May '89, on Polydor, by Polydor Ltd. Catalogue no: **871 225 2**
7" Single: Released 2 May '89, on Polydor, by Polydor Ltd. Catalogue no: **PO 38**

Paradise

Biographical details: This British soul band -- David Aiyeola, Bobby Clarke, Raymond Dennis, Carl Edwards, Junior Edwards, Philip Edwards, Paul Johnson and Doug Williams -- had a one-off UK chart entry in September 1983, reaching No 42 with the single *One Mind, Two Hearts*. This was taken from their debut album, *Love Is The Answer*. They were a classy black soul group with some gospel influence, but none of their other efforts matched *One Mind, Two Hearts*. (Bob MacDonald, February 1986.).

GUARDIAN ANGEL
Tracks: / Guardian angel.
12" Single: Released Aug '89, on Spirtual House, Catalogue no: **BBLS 003**
7" Single: Released Aug '89, on Spirtual House, Catalogue no: **BBSP 003**

HEARTSTRINGS
Tracks: / Heartstrings.
7" Single: Released Jul '85, on Priority, by Priority Records. Deleted Nov '87. Catalogue no: **P 12**
12" Single: Released Jul '85, on Priority, by Priority Records. Deleted Nov '87. Catalogue no: **PX 12**

LOVE IS THE ANSWER (SINGLE)
Tracks: / Love is the answer.
12" Single: Released Nov '83, on Priority, by Priority Records. Catalogue no: **PX 6**
7" Single: Released Nov '83, on Priority, by Priority Records. Deleted Nov '87. Catalogue no: **P 6**

ONE MIND TWO HEARTS
Tracks: / One mind two hearts.
7" Single: Released Aug '83, on Priority, by Priority Records. Deleted Nov '87. Catalogue no: **P 1**
12" Single: Released Aug '83, on Priority, by Priority Records. Catalogue no: **PX 1**

Paradise Alley

WARMIN' UP
Tracks: / Warmin' up / Can't do without.
7" Single: Released Jun '81, on Epic, by CBS Records. Deleted Jun '84. Catalogue no: **EPCA 1292**

Paradise, Leesha

WAITING
Tracks: / Waiting.
7" Single: Released Mar '83, on EMI, by EMI Records. Catalogue no: **EMI 5379**
12" Single: Released Mar '83, on EMI, by EMI Records. Catalogue no: **12 EMI 5379**

Paradise, Lisa

DO BEE DOO BE DO
Tracks: / Do bee doo be do / Do the rock.
7" Single: Released Feb '80, on Epic, by CBS Records. Deleted '83. Catalogue no: **EPC 8277**

Paradise Regained

GARAGE SOUND OF NEW YORK VOL II
Tracks: / Garage sound of New York Vol II.
12" Single: Released Jul '89, on Republic, by Code Records. Catalogue no: **LICT 020**

Paradise, Sal

Biographical details: Like his namesake in the Jack Kerouac novel, Sal Paradise spent much of his youth on the road. He travelled throughout Asia and Africa writing and living in such countries as Nepal and Morocco. He became absorbed with the alien sounds and rhythms of Arabic and Asian music, and in particular the music of Morroco; with its meandering tmpos and subtle drum sounds. Sal recorded much of this material while he travelled, with the intention of applying many of it's qualities in a fusion with Western melody and lyric. In December '81, Sal returned to Morroco, to learn from traditional musicians in the towns and villages, how to play the various drums needed to create the moods and sounds he required. Upon his return to England he combined these instruments with synthesiser and sim drums. Working with producer Simon Heyworth, Sal recorded his first single, *Living in a dreamboat* in which he played as many as twenty instruments. These include two unique Morrocan drums, the Shenai and the long and short drums and an Indian clarinet which sounds similar to bagpipes. The track also features Asian bongos, miniature steel drums and an assortment of tambourines. This sound has been described by its composer as 'original body music' that makes you want to shake instead of dance and it certainly produces that effect. Sal has also worked with other musicians, many from Asia and Africa, and has experimented with Ethiopian music using female voices to create beat and rhythm..

LIVING IN A DREAM BOAT
Tracks: / Living in a dream boat.
12" Single: Released '83, on Arista, by BMG Records (UK). Deleted '86. Catalogue no: **ARIST 12525**
7" Single: Released '83, on Arista, by BMG Records (UK). Deleted '86. Catalogue no: **ARIST 525**

SLOW PASSION
Tracks: / Slow passion.
7" Single: Released Mar '82, on Abstract, by Abstract Sounds. Catalogue no: **ABS 007**

THERE IS A UNIVERSE
Tracks: / There is a universe / Olipopo kalimar.
12" Single: Released Mar '84, on Arista, by BMG Records (UK). Catalogue no: **ARIST 12555**
7" Single: Released Mar '84, on Arista, by BMG Records (UK). Catalogue no: **ARIST 555**

Paradox

WE CAN'T LET MAGGIE GO
Tracks: / We can't let Maggie go / Cabinet shuffle.
7" Single: Released Jun '87, on Gipsy, by Gipsy Records. Catalogue no: **MAGGIE 1**

Paragon, Steve

TERRA COTTA WARRIORS
Tracks: / Terra cotta warriors / Boys know best.
7" Single: Released Apr '82, on Scratch, by Scratch Records. Catalogue no: **SCR 007**

Paragons

MODELING CROWD
Tracks: / Modeling crowd.
12" Single: Released Jul '82, on Starlight, Catalogue no: **SLD 521**

Parallel

WORKING
Tracks: / Working.
7" Single: Released Sep '84, on Swagman, Catalogue no: **CY 2**

Paramedics Squad

MOVEMENT IN TIME
Tracks: / Movement in time.
7" Single: Released Aug '82, on Gargoyle, Catalogue no: **GRGL 2**

Paramor, Norrie

Biographical details: This British producer, arranger, executive, orchestra leader and conductor was born in 1914. He left school at 15 and soon played accompaniment for Gracie Fields then with top dance bands, he was music director for the Ralph Reader Gang shows during WW11 but was perhaps best known for his association with the career of Cliff Richard, a connection which lasted from Richard's 1958 beginnings until the early 70's. But Paramor's greatest achievement of all was his chart-topping

status as a producer. According to the Guinness Book Of Five Hundred Number One Hits he chalked up 27 UK No 1 singles in an exact 15-year period from 8 January 1954 until 8 January 1969. Nobody else had ever produced so many British chart-toppers until George Martin gained his 27th No 1 credit in January 1984. All but one of Paramor's No 1 smashes were attained while he was a staff producer at EMI Records, but for many years he headed up the company's Columbia label, one of the major forces in British pop music of the 50's and 60's. Among the artists benefitting from his golden touch were Eddie Calvert, Ruby Murray, Michael Holliday, Cliff Richard, the Shadows, Ricky Valance, Helen Shapiro, Frank Ifield and the Scaffold. During the late 60's Paramor's assistant for three years was Tim Rice, the future star lyricist. Paramor's orchestra achieved a couple of minor UK hit singles in its own right: *Theme From A Summer Place* reached No 36 in 1960 and *Theme From Z Cars* got to No 33 in 1962; both were eclipsed by simultaneous versions from other ensembles. For many years Paramor oversaw the BBC's Midland Radio Orchestra. He died in 1979. (Bob MacDonald, February 1986.)
This conductor, composer, arranger and producer, was born in 1914. He left school at 15 and soon played accompaniment for Gracie Fields, then with top dance bands; he was music director for the Ralph Reader Gang shows during WWII and teamed postwar with tenor saxist Harry Gold in *Pieces of Eight*. He became best known in his A&R role at EMI Records through the 1950's to 1968. (Donald Clarke 15.5.87) .

SUMMER PLACE, A
Tracks: / Summer place, A (theme from).
7" Single: Released Mar '60, on Columbia, by EMI Records. Deleted '63. Catalogue no: **DB 4419**

Z CARS
Tracks: / Z cars.
7" Single: Released Mar '62, on Columbia, by EMI Records. Deleted '65. Catalogue no: **DB 4789**

Paramounts

POISON IVY
Tracks: / Poison ivy.
7" Single: Released Jan '64, on Parlophone, by EMI Records. Deleted '67. Catalogue no: **R 5093**

Paranoia

SHATTERED GLASS (SINGLE)
Tracks: / Shattered glass / Dead man's dreams.
7" Single: Released Jul '84, on Rot, by Rot Records. Catalogue no: **ASS 8**

Paranoics

I'VE BEEN WAITIN'
Tracks: / I've been waitin'.
7" Single: Released Apr '89, on Play It Again Sam(Belgium), by Play It Again Sam (Belgium). Catalogue no: **BIAS 128**

Paranoid Visions

AUTONOMY
Tracks: / Autonomy.
7" Single: Released Jun '88, on F.O.A.D., Catalogue no: **FOAD 5**

CITY OF SCREAMS
Tracks: / City of screams / City of screams (version).
12" Single: Released Nov '88, on F.O.A.D., Catalogue no: **FOAD 1000**

ROBOT HAS RUN AMOK
Tracks: / Robot has run amok (EP).
7" EP: Released Oct '86, on All The Madmen, by All The Madmen Records. Catalogue no: **FOAD 1**

Paranoids

LOVE JOB
Tracks: / Love job / Theme from gravity's rainbow.
7" Single: Released May '80, on Hurricane (1), Deleted May '83. Catalogue no: **FIRE 14**

Parchman

NEW GOSPEL
Tracks: / New gospel.
12" Single: Released Oct '88, on Kollective Mind, Catalogue no: **KOM 001**

Parchman, Kenny

TREAT ME RIGHT
Tracks: / Treat me right.
7" Single: Released Jan '85, on Bison Bop, by Bear Family Records (Germany). Catalogue no: **J 16**

Parchment

Biographical details: Light Up The Fire provided this British gospel band with a one-off UK chart entry in 1972: it reached No 31. (Bob MacDonald, February 1986.).

LIGHT UP THE FIRE
Tracks: / Light up the fire.
7" Single: Released Sep '72, on Pye, Deleted '75. Catalogue no: **7 N 45178**

Parchment, Mikki

WHERE DO BROKEN HEARTS GO
Tracks: / Where do broken hearts go.
12" Single: Released Nov '88, on Parish, Catalogue no: **UNKNOWN**

Paris

Biographical details: While songwriter, arranger and producer Andy Hill was masterminding the career of Bucks Fizz, with help from his wife, Nichola Martin, the couple were also themselves recording under the name Paris. Their singing efforts yielded just one modest UK chart entry: *No Getting Over You* reached No 49 on the singles chart in 1982. In view of their Bucks Fizz hits this was a rather poor track record, though one of their earlier singles, *Have You Ever Been In Love?*, was covered and taken into the UK Top Ten by Leo Sayer, also in 1982. (Bob MacDonald, February 1986.).

ANOTHER SAD AFFAIR
Tracks: / Another sad affair.
7" Single: Released Jul '83, on RCA, by BMG Records (UK). Catalogue no: **RCA 351**

CENSORED
Tracks: / Censored.
7" Single: Released Jan '83, on RCA, by BMG Records (UK). Catalogue no: **RCA 288**
12" Single: Released Jan '83, on RCA, by BMG Records (UK). Catalogue no: **RCAT 288**

HAVE YOU EVER BEEN IN LOVE
Tracks: / Have you ever been in love / One touch.
7" Single: Released Feb '82, on Hansa, by Hansa Records. Deleted '85. Catalogue no: **HANSA7**
7" Single: Released Mar '82, on RCA, by BMG Records (UK). Catalogue no: **RCA 210**

I CHOOSE YOU
Tracks: / I choose you / Punkin' funkin'.
12" Single: Released 20 Jun '87, on Bluebird (2), by BMG Records (UK). Catalogue no: **BRT 38**
7" Single: Released 20 Jun '87, on Bluebird (2), by BMG Records (UK). Catalogue no: **BR 38**
7" Single: Released Oct '84, on Bluebird (2), by BMG Records (UK). Catalogue no: **BR 9**
12" Single: Released Oct '84, on Bluebird (2), by BMG Records (UK). Catalogue no: **BRT 9**

LEARN TO LOVE
Tracks: / Learn to love.
12" Single: Released May '89, on DJ International, by Westside Records. Catalogue no: **DJINT 9**

NO GETTING OVER YOU
Tracks: / No getting over you / Fighting for the country.
7" Single: Released Apr '82, on RCA, by BMG Records (UK). Catalogue no: **RCA 222**

Paris 9

24 HOUR SURVEILLANCE
Tracks: / 24 hour surveillance / Never keep a promise.
7" Single: Released Apr '81, on RCA, by BMG Records (UK). Deleted '85. Catalogue no: **RCA 53**

BUZZ
Tracks: / Buzz / Lady.
7" Single: Released Apr '80, on RCA, by BMG Records (UK). Deleted Apr '83. Catalogue no: **PB 5247**

DON'T LET ME DIE
Tracks: / Don't let me die / I hear you're leavin' now.
7" Single: Released Oct '80, on RCA, by BMG Records (UK). Deleted Oct '83. Catalogue no: **PB 5272**

Paris France Transit

CHILD
Tracks: / Child.
12" Single: Released Mar '83, on Vogue, by Vogue Records. Catalogue no: **12VJ 103**
7" Single: Released Mar '83, on Vogue, by Vogue Records. Catalogue no: **7VJ 103**

Paris Grey

REACH FOR YOUR DREAMS
Tracks: / Reach for your dreams.
12" Single: Released Oct '87, on Future Sounds, Catalogue no: **FSR 1001**

Paris, Mica

BREATHE LIFE INTO ME
Tracks: / Breathe life into me (Radio mix Only on 12") / In the city / Breathe life into me (extended mix) (Only on 12" single.) / Breathe life into me (alt).
12" Single: Released 29 Sep '88, on 4th & Broadway, by Island Records. Catalogue no: **12 BRW 115**
7" Single: Released 29 Sep '88, on 4th & Broadway, by Island Records. Catalogue no: **BRW 115**

LIKE DREAMERS DO Featuring Courtney Pine
Tracks: / Like dreamers do / Wicked / Like dreamers do (freeway mix) (Available on 12" only).
Note: * Only available on the 12" version.
7" Single: Released Jun '88, on 4th & Broadway, by Island Records. Deleted Apr '89. Catalogue no: **BRW 108**
7" Single: Released Jun '88, on 4th & Broadway, by Island Records. Deleted Apr '89. Catalogue no: **BRWG 108**
CD 5": Released Jun '88, on 4th & Broadway, by Island Records. Catalogue no: **BRCDP 108**
12" Pic: Released Aug '88, on 4th & Broadway, by Island Records. Catalogue no: **12 BRP 108**
12" Single: Released Jun '88, on 4th & Broadway, by Island Records. Deleted Apr '89. Catalogue no: **12 BRW 108**

MY ONE TEMPTATION (REMIX)
Tracks: / My one temptation (remix).
12" Single: Released '88, on 4th & Broadway, by Island Records. Deleted Apr '89. Catalogue no: **12 BRX 85**

MY ONE TEMPTATION
Tracks: / My one temptation / Rock together.
7" EP: Released Apr '88, on 4th & Broadway, by Island Records. Deleted Apr '89. Catalogue no: **BRWEP 85**
12" Single: Released 23 Apr '88, on 4th & Broadway, by Island Records. Deleted Apr '89. Catalogue no: **12 BRW 85**
7" Single: Released 23 Apr '88, on 4th & Broadway, by Island Records. Deleted Apr '89. Catalogue no: **BRW 85**

Paris, Ryan

DOLCE VITA
Tracks: / Dolce vita.
7" Single: Released Sep '83, on Carrere America (USA), by PolyGram Rec.Inc.(USA). Catalogue no: **CAR 289**
12" Single: Released Sep '83, on Carrere America (USA), by PolyGram Rec.Inc.(USA). Catalogue no: **CART 289**

FALL IN LOVE
Tracks: / Fall in love.
7" Single: Released Jan '84, on Carrere America (USA), by PolyGram Rec.Inc.(USA). Catalogue no: **CAR 300**
12" Single: Released Jan '84, on Carrere America (USA), by PolyGram Rec.Inc.(USA). Catalogue no: **CART 300**

Paris Sisters

I LOVE HOW YOU LOVE ME
Tracks: / I love how you love me.
7" Single: Released Oct '83, on Old Gold, by Old Gold Records. Deleted Jul '88. Catalogue no: **OG 9361**

Park

KICKING STONES
Tracks: / Kicking stones.
7" Single: Released Apr '83, on C&D, Catalogue no: **CD 3**

PUTTING ON HER MAKEUP
Tracks: / Putting on her make up.
7" Single: Released Oct '83, on C&D, Catalogue no: **CD 7**

SINGER, THE
Tracks: / Singer, The.
12" Single: Released Aug '83, on C&D, Catalogue no: **CD 512**
7" Single: Released Aug '83, on C&D, Catalogue no: **CD 5**

Park, Andy

SILK STOCKINGS
Tracks: / Silk stockings.
7" Single: Released Sep '83, on Blue Hat, by Blue Hat Records. Catalogue no: **BHR 16**

Park Avenue

LOOKING FOR NUMBER ONE
Tracks: / Looking for number one / Perfumed bore.
7" Single: Released Jul '81, on Offstreet, Catalogue no: **OSR 002A**

Park, Simon

EYE LEVEL
Tracks: / Eye level.
7" Single: Released Nov '72, on Columbia, by EMI Records. Deleted '75. Catalogue no: **DB 8946**

EYE LEVEL(OLD GOLD)
7" Single: Released Apr '86, on Old Gold, by Old Gold Records. Deleted Jun '89. Catalogue no: **OG 9600**

Parker, Belinda

DON'T MAKE WAVES
Tracks: / Don't make waves.
12" Single: Released Nov '84, on B.B. Music, Catalogue no: **BBD 160**

DREAM LOVER
Tracks: / Dream lover.
12" Single: Released Mar '85, on B.B. Music, Catalogue no: **BBD 163**

GYPSY LOVE
Tracks: / Gypsy love.
12" Single: Released Mar '83, on Sunburn, by Orbitone Records. Catalogue no: **SBD 16**

HOLD TIGHT
Tracks: / Hold tight.
12" Single: Released Apr '84, on Whiplash, Deleted '86. Catalogue no: **WLD 003**

RED RED WINE
Tracks: / Red red wine.
12" Single: Released Oct '83, on Sunburn, by Orbitone Records. Catalogue no: **SBD 38**

Parker, Cecil

REALLY, REALLY LOVE YOU
Tracks: / Really, really love you.
7" Single: Released Jul '80, on EMI, by EMI Records. Deleted Jul '83. Catalogue no: **EMI 5086**

WHAT IT IS
Tracks: / What it is / You were there.
12" Single: Released Feb '81, on EMI, by EMI Records. Deleted '84. Catalogue no: **12EMI 5139**
7" Single: Released Feb '81, on EMI, by EMI Records. Deleted '84. Catalogue no: **EMI 5139**

Parker, Graham

Biographical details: British rock singer, guitarist and songwriter Parker was born in London in 1950 and started playing in groups in his early teens. In 1965, at 15, he fronted a short-lived mod group. After dropping out of music for a couple of years he experimented with acid rock and rhythm-and-blues and during the early 70's he began to be involved in the pub-rock scene then blossoming in London. After meeting entepreneur Dave Robinson, one of the prime movers on that scene, he formed Graham Parker & The Rumour in 1975. Included in the line-up was guitarist Brinsley Schwarz, one of the pioneers of the pub-rock pnenomenon. Throughout the band's career critical acclaim heavily outweighed commercial success. This was particularly true of the first two albums, *Howlin' Wind* and *Heat Treatment* (both '76), which received ecstatic reviews but barely dented the national UK chart. His music was rooted in R & B, while containing elements of rock 'n' roll and the new punk sound. Journalists cited comparisons with such illustrious names as Bob Dylan, Van Morrison and Bruce Springsteen and were particularly impressed by Parker's strong, intense vocal style. The *Pink Parker* EP (1977, featuring a remake of the Trammps' *Hold Back The Night*) and *Hey Lord, Don't Ask Me Questions* ('78) provided Graham Parker & The Rumour with a pair of UK Top Forty singles. Later albums -- *Stick To Me*, *The Parkerilla*, *Squeezing Out Sparks* and *The Up Escalator* -- were not quite as good as the first two but all four achieved brief runs in the British Top Twenty. And the band enjoyed a strong concert reputation. After disintegration of the Rumour, Parker launched a solo career in 1982. *Another Grey Area*, containing the minor hit *Temporary Beauty*, was a modest success on the British album chart. His 1983 set *The Real Macaw* was one of his best efforts but was, as often, very underrated; it contained his exuberant love song *Love Gets Better*, a flop single that saw him in his happiest-ever mood. In 1985 he launched a new band, Graham Parker & The Shot. Im America most of Parker's work has raised minor chart ripples without breaking into the big league. (Bob MacDonald, February 1986.).

HEY LORD DON'T ASK ME QUESTIONS
Tracks: / Hey Lord don't ask me questions.
7" Single: Released Apr '78, on Vertigo, by Phonogram Ltd. Deleted '81. Catalogue no: **PARK 002**

LIFE GETS BETTER
Tracks: / Life gets better.
12" Single: Released Jul '83, on RCA, by BMG Records (UK). Catalogue no: **RCAT 346**
7" Single: Released Jul '83, on RCA, by BMG Records (UK). Catalogue no: **RCA 346**

LOVE WITHOUT GREED
Tracks: / Love without greed.
7" Single: Released Jun '80, on Stiff, by Stiff Records. Catalogue no: **BUY 82**

NO MORE EXCUSES
Tracks: / No more excuses / Hit the spot / Another grey area.
7" EP: Released Jul '82, on RCA, by BMG Records (UK). Catalogue no: **RCA 243**

GRAHAM PARKER -STUPEFACTION (Released on Stiff)

PINK PARKER, THE
Tracks: / Hold back the night / (Let me get) sweet on you / White honey / Soul shoes.
7" EP: Released Mar '77, on Vertigo, by Phonogram Ltd. Deleted '80. Catalogue no: **PARK 001**

STEADY NERVES
Tracks: / Break them down / Might rivers / Lunatic fringe / Wake up (next to you) / When you do that to me / Weekend's too short / Take everything back / Black lincoln continental / Canned laughter / Everyone's hand is on the switch / Locked into grgeen.
Note: Digital stereo recording.
12" Single: Released Apr '85, on Elektra, by Elektra Records (UK). Deleted '86. Catalogue no: **EKT 4C**

STUPEFACTION (See panel above)
Tracks: / Stupefaction / Women in charge.
7" Single: Released '80, on Stiff, by Stiff Records. Catalogue no: **BUY 72**

TEMPORARY BEAUTY
Tracks: / Temporary beauty / No more excuses.
7" Single: Released Mar '82, on RCA, by BMG Records (UK). Deleted '85. Catalogue no: **PARK 100**

YOU CAN'T TAKE LOVE FOR GRANTED
Tracks: / You can't take love for granted.
7" Single: Released Oct '83, on RCA, by BMG Records (UK). Catalogue no: **RCA 361**

Parker, Greg

BLACK DOG
Tracks: / Future perfect / Black dog.
7" Single: Released Nov '86, on Mec, Catalogue no: **MEC 143**
12" Single: Released Nov '86, on Mec, Catalogue no: **MEC 12143**

Parker, Ken

BEFORE & AFTER
Tracks: / Before and after.
7" Single: Released May '89, on Studio One, Catalogue no: **UNKNOWN**

GOD BLESS OUR LOVE
Tracks: / God bless our love / Dubbers of blessing.
12" Single: Released Dec '82, on Pama, by Pama Records. Catalogue no: **PMD 3327**

JIMMY BROWN
Tracks: / Holy holy medley / Jimmy Brown.
12" Single: Released Jan '87, on Time, Catalogue no: **TR 031**

THREE BELLS
Tracks: / Three bells, The.
12" Single: Released Jan '84, on Clouds, Catalogue no: **CLSD 007**

Parker, Louis

IS THAT YOU
Tracks: / Is that you.
7" Single: Released Sep '85, on Red Bus, by Red Bus Records. Catalogue no: **RBUS 2202**

Parker, Paul

DESIRE
Tracks: / Desire.
12" Single: Released Mar '84, on Technique, Catalogue no: **TECT 101**
7" Single: Released Mar '84, on Technique, Catalogue no: **TEC 101**

Parker, Pop

JUST ASK NICK AYLING
Tracks: / Just ask Nick Ayling.
7" Single: Released Sep '86, on Golden Pathway, Catalogue no: **GPV 009**

Parker, Ray Jnr.

Biographical details: This American guitarist, multi-instrumentalist, singer, songwriter and producer has become to soul music what Eddy Grant has become to reggae - transforming the genre into such an out-and-out pop format that it is barely recognisable. Both artists create their records in their own studios, and totally dominate the proceedings; both artists have become adept at producing records whose music and lyrics are so simple that they sound like nursery rhymes.

Born in Detroit in 1954, Parker was already a proficient player of several instruments by the time he took up the guitar at the age of 12. During the early Seventies he was a musical prodigy, becoming one of America's leading session guitarists. By the time he launched his own band Raydio in 1978, he had played on discs by Freda Payne, the Honey Cone, Labelle, Gene Page, Boz Scaggs and Barry White amongst many others. He had also played guitar for Marvin Gaye and Stevie Wonder, and had enjoyed his first songwriting success via Rufus and Chaka Khan's recording of *You Got The Love* (No. 11 in US in 1974). Raydio's first hit was, quite literally, a reworking of a nursery rhyme: *Jack And Jill*, a catchy and classy single, reached No. 8 in the US and No. 11 in the UK. The group also hit the American Top Ten with *You Can't Change That* (1979) and *A Woman Needs Love* (1981). Having the billed the records as Raydio and then Ray Parker Junior & Raydio, Parker went the whole hog in 1982 and simply released the discs under his own name. The first product of this policy was *The Other Woman*, a sparse slice of rock-funk that became yet another US Top 10 smash. After several smaller American hits, Ray reached the peak of his career in 1984 with his monster hit single *Ghostbusters*. Hurriedly written and recorded in the space of 72 hours, this title theme from the Dan Ackroyd/Bill Murray movie (which became the biggest comedy film ever) was Parker's first No. 1 single in America, excluding session work. *Ghostbusters* gave him his first British hit since 1978, and enjoyed two seperate visits to the UK Top 10: it logged three weeks at No. 2 in advance of the film's release, and bounced back to No. 6 after the movie had reached British cinemas. The *Ghostbusters* single sold a staggering worldwide total of 12 million copies. The song was a great personal triumph for Parker, despite the fact that it inspired charges of plagiarism from the writers of two previous biggies: M's *Pop Muzik* and Huey Lewis & The News' *I Want A New Drug*. In late 1985 Parker came up with the moderate hit single *Girls Are More Fun*; this was a tongue-in-cheek but distinctly unfunny crusdae against homosexuality. Earlier in that year, he wrote and produced a sizeable hit for New Edition - *Mr Telephone Man*. Bob MacDonald, 24 February 1986.

GHOSTBUSTERS
Tracks: / Ghostbusters.
12" Single: Released Nov '84, on Arista, by BMG Records (UK). Catalogue no: **ARIST 12580**
7" Pic: Released Nov '84, on Arista, by BMG Records (UK). Catalogue no: **ARISD 580**
12" Pic: Released Nov '84, on Arista, by BMG Records (UK). Deleted '85. Catalogue no: **ARIPD 12580**
7" Single: Released Nov '84, on Arista, by BMG Records (UK). Catalogue no: **ARIST 580**

GHOSTBUSTERS (OLD GOLD)
Tracks: / Ghostbusters / Jack & Jill / You can't change that.
12" Single: Released Jan '88, on Old Gold, by Old Gold Records. Catalogue no: **OG 4041**

GIRLS ARE MORE FUN
Tracks: / Girls are more fun / I'm in love / Ghost busters.
12" Single: Released Dec '85, on Arista, by BMG Records (UK). Catalogue no: **ARIST 12641**
7" Single: Released Nov '85, on Arista, by BMG Records (UK). Catalogue no: **ARIST 641**

I DON'T THINK THAT MAN SHOULD SLEEP ALONE
Tracks: / I don't think that man should sleep alone / After midnite.
12" Single: Released Sep '87, on Geffen, by Geffen Records (USA). Catalogue no: **GEF 27 T**
12" Pic: Released Sep '87, on Geffen, by Geffen Records (USA). Deleted Jul '88. Catalogue no: **GEF 27 TP**
7" Single: Released Sep '87, on Geffen, by Geffen Records (USA). Deleted Jul '88. Catalogue no: **GEF 27**

OTHER WOMAN (SINGLE)
Tracks: / Other woman, The / Stay the night.
7" Single: Released '82, on Arista, by BMG Records (UK). Deleted '87. Catalogue no: **ARIST 466**
12" Single: Released '82, on Arista, by BMG Records (UK). Deleted '87. Catalogue no: **ARIST 12466**

OVER YOU
Tracks: / Over you / Loving you.
7" Single: Released Jan '88, on Geffen, by Geffen Records (USA). Catalogue no: **GEF 33**
12" Single: Released Jan '88, on Geffen, by Geffen Records (USA). Catalogue no: **GEF 33T**

WOMAN NEEDS A LOVE, A
Tracks: / Woman needs love, A / So into you / Still in the groove.
12" Single: Released Jul '81, on Arista, by BMG Records (UK). Deleted '85. Catalogue no: **ARIST 12392**

YOU CAN'T CHANGE THAT
Tracks: / You can't change that / Bad boy.
7" Single: Released Feb '83, on Arista, by BMG Records (UK). Catalogue no: **ARIST 512**
12" Single: Released Feb '83, on Arista, by BMG Records (UK). Catalogue no: **ARIST 12 512**

YOU SHOULDA KEPT A SPARE
Tracks: / You shoulda kept a spare / I love your daughter.
12" Single: Released Apr '88, on Geffen, by Geffen Records (USA). Catalogue no: **GEF 36T**
7" Single: Released Apr '88, on Geffen, by Geffen Records (USA). Catalogue no: **GEF 36**

Parker, Robert

Biographical details: Alto saxist, singer and songwriter Robert Parker was born in New Orleans in 1930 and began a career as a sax session player on the city's rhythm-and-blues scene in 1949. As one of the most reliable studio musicians, he played with numerous R & B notables over the years, being heard on discs by such as Irma Thomas, Joe Tex, Professor Longhair and Ernie K-Doe. Despite several tries Parker had just one successful record in his own right -- *Barefootin'*, a self-penned dancefloor belter, reached No 7 on the US pop charts in '66 and peaked at No 24 in the UK. (Bob MacDonald, February 1986.).

BAREFOOTIN'
Tracks: / Barefootin' / Duke of earl / Let's go baby (where the action is) / Hiccup, The (on 12" only.).
12" Single: Released Jul '87, on Charly, by Charly Records. Catalogue no: **CYZ 121**
7" Single: Released Aug '86, on Important, Catalogue no: **TAN 12**
7" Single: Released Aug '66, on Island, by Island Records. Deleted '69. Catalogue no: **WI 286**
7" Single: Released Aug '84, on Creole (Replay), by Creole Records. Catalogue no: **CR 218**
7" Single: Released Jul '87, on Charly, by Charly Records. Catalogue no: **CYZ 7121**
7" Single: Released Jul '80, on Charly, by Charly Records. Deleted '87. Catalogue no: **CTD 123**

Parker, Shan Lee

WORK IT OUT
Tracks: / Work it out.
7" Single: Released Jun '84, on VP, Catalogue no: **VPS 003**

Parker, Wesley

FUGITIVE FROM BROKEN DREAMS
Tracks: / Fugitive from broken dreams.
7" Single: Released Jan '86, on Garden Isle, by Garden Isle Records. Catalogue no: **SRT 5KS 571**

MONTANA SKIES
Tracks: / Montana skies.
7" Single: Released Jun '85, on Garden Isle, by Garden Isle Records. Catalogue no: **5KS 451**

SUSQUEHANNA RIVER VALLEY SONG
Tracks: / Susquehanna river valley song.
7" Single: Released Apr '83, on President, by President Records. Catalogue no: **PT 515**

WHITE LINES NORTH
Tracks: / White lines north.
7" Single: Released Mar '85, on Garden Isle, by Garden Isle Records. Catalogue no: **AKS 333**

Parkes, Clarence

RUN UP AND DOWN IN THE DARK
Tracks: / Run up and down in the dark.
12" Single: Released Aug '82, on Red Lightnin', by Red Lightning Records. Catalogue no: **RL 002**

TAKE A MIRACLE
Tracks: / Take a miracle / Take a miracle (version).
7" Single: Released Aug '82, on Red Lightnin', by Red Lightning Records. Catalogue no: **RR 01**

Parkings, Juliet

SAY YES
Tracks: / Say yes.
12" Single: Released Nov '88, on Charm, by Charm Records. Catalogue no: **CRT 25**

Parkinson, Jimmy

GREAT PRETENDER, THE
Tracks: / Great pretender, The.
7" Single: Released Mar '56, on Columbia, by EMI Records. Deleted '59. Catalogue no: **DB 3729**

IN THE MIDDLE OF THE HOUSE
Tracks: / In the middle of the house.
7" Single: Released Nov '56, on Columbia, by EMI Records. Deleted '59. Catalogue no: **DB 3833**

WALK HAND IN HAND
Tracks: / Walk hand in hand.
7" Single: Released Aug '56, on Columbia, by EMI Records. Deleted '59. Catalogue no: **DB 3775**

Parkinson, Michael

BEER IS BEST
Tracks: / Beer is best / Two heads are better than one.
7" Single: Released Nov '83, on Paramount, Deleted '88. Catalogue no: **PARA 102**

Parkinson, Philip

CONTROL THEM
Tracks: / Control them / Take us home.
12" Single: Released Sep '83, on Twinkle, by Twinkle Records. Catalogue no: **NG 963**

Parks, Lloyd

AIN'T TOO PROUD TO BEG
Tracks: / Ain't too proud to beg.
12" Single: Released Jul '88, on Exodus, Catalogue no: **EX 04**

GEORGIA
Tracks: / Georgia.
12" Single: Released Sep '89, on Charm, by Charm Records. Catalogue no: **CRT 36**

HELLO
Tracks: / Hello.
12" Single: Released Jul '84, on Tads, Catalogue no: **TRD 23784**

NO WAR IN THE DANCE
Tracks: / No war in the dance / Rock.
12" Single: Released Aug '82, on Plantation, Catalogue no: **PL O11**

Parks, Steve

ONE WHO REALLY LOVES YOU, THE
Tracks: / One who really loves you, The.
12" Single: Released Nov '87, on Dancefloor (USA), Catalogue no: **DF 1210**

Parliament

Biographical details: See Clinton, George for biographical details..

AGONY OF DEFEAT
Tracks: / Agony of defeat / Freeze.
12" Single: Released Apr '81, on Casablanca, by PolyGram UK Ltd. Deleted Apr '84. Catalogue no: **CANL 223**
7" Single: Released Apr '81, on Casablanca, by PolyGram UK Ltd. Deleted Apr '84. Catalogue no: **CAN 223**

I CALL MY BABY PUSSYCAT
Tracks: / I call my baby pussycat.
7" Single: Released Dec '84, on HDH (Holland/Dozier/Holland), by Demon Records. Catalogue no: **HDH 457**

PARTY PEOPLE
Tracks: / Party people / Tear the roof off the sucker / Flashlight.
12" Single: Released Jan '80, on Casablanca, by PolyGram UK Ltd. Deleted '85. Catalogue no: **NBL 2222**
7" Single: Released Jan '80, on Casablanca, by PolyGram UK Ltd. Deleted '85. Catalogue no: **NR 2222**

Parma, Edward Jnr

KING KONG IN HONG KONG
Tracks: / King Kong in Hong Kong.
7" Single: Released Sep '82, on Code, by Code Records. Catalogue no: **COD 004**

Parr, John

NAUGHTY NAUGHTY
Tracks: / Naughty naughty / Revenge / Everything they say is true (Extra track on 12" version only.).
12" Single: Released Jan '86, on London Records, by London Records. Catalogue no: **LONX 80**
7" Single: Released Jan '86, on London Records, by London Records. Catalogue no: **LON 80**

RESTLESS HEART
Tracks: / Restless heart.
CD 5": Released Jun '89, on UNKNOWN, Deleted Aug '89. Catalogue no: **CDTX 2**
12" Single: Released Sep '88, on UNKNOWN, Deleted Aug '89. Catalogue no: **12TX 2**
7" Single: Released Sep '88, on UNKNOWN, Deleted Aug '89. Catalogue no: **7TX 2**

ST. ELMO'S FIRE
Tracks: / St. Elmo's fire.
7" Single: Released Sep '85, on London Records, by London Records. Deleted '88. Catalogue no: **LON 73**

TWO HEARTS
Tracks: / Two hearts / Two hearts (version) / Somebody stole my thunder (Extra track on 12" version only.).
12" Single: Released Sep '86, on London Records, by London Records. Deleted Sep '87. Catalogue no: **LONX 100**
7" Single: Released Sep '86, on London Records, by London Records. Deleted '87. Catalogue no: **LON 100**

Parris, Jackie

THOSE GUYS
Tracks: / Those guys.
12" Single: Released Jun '88, on Starlight, Catalogue no: **SLD 546**

Parrish, Dean

Biographical details: *I'm On My Way* was a one-off UK chart entry for American singer Parrish, reaching No 38 on the singles chart in early 1975, released by Jonathan King's UK label. (Bob MacDonald, February 1986.).

I'M ON MY WAY
Tracks: / I'm on my way.
7" Single: Released Feb '78, on RK, by RK Records. Deleted '82. Catalogue no: **RK 1004**
7" Single: Released Feb '75, on UK, by UK Records. Deleted '78. Catalogue no: **USA 2**

Parrots

PHOTOGRAPHY SONG
Tracks: / Photography song / Home sweet home / Breaking up new ground / Serious thing.
12" Single: Released Aug '80, on Attrix, by Attrix Records. Catalogue no: **ARI 12**

Parry, Bernie

'A' TO 'Z' OF LONDON
Tracks: / 'A' to 'Z' of London.
7" Single: Released Oct '81, on Celtic Music, Catalogue no: **CMS 100**

Parry, Big John

MARIA
Tracks: / Maria / Romeo.
7" Single: Released Dec '83, on Lady London, by Lady London Records. Catalogue no: **ST 45 GEMA**

Parsons, Alan Project

Biographical details: Although named after producer/engineer/songwriter/keyboardist /guitarist Alan Parsons, the other half of this British studio ensemble is equally vital to its success: he is songwriter/ideas man/keyboardist/manager/occasional vocalist Eric Woolfson, who met Parsons in 1974 at London's legendary Abbey Road studios. Both men were employees of that hallowed building at the time, and they have chosen to make it their home ever since. Parsons had been an assistant engineer on several albums by the Beatles and Wings, and was nominated for a Grammy for his engineering work on Pink Floyd's 1973 mega-classic *The Dark Side Of The Moon.* He then became a record producer, enjoying back-to-back UK No. 1 singles in February 1975 with Pilot's *January* and Steve Harley and Cockney Rebel's *Make Me Smile (Come Up And See Me).* He also produced successfully for John Miles and Al Stewart. Despite the fact that their first album was released in 1976, the year of the punk explosion, the Alan Parsons Project have always operated in the musical territory that used to be termed 'progressive rock'. Wilfully disregarding the dictates of modern fashions, they are the masters of the 'concept album'. Because Britain is perpetually at the forefront of the lastest developments and fads in pop music, it is perhaps not surprising that the Alan Parsons Project have found less acceptance for their music in their native UK than in many other territories of the globe. They have been particularly big in America and West Germany. The Project's first LP *Tales Of Mystery And Imagination* was based on a series of short stories by Edgar Allan Poe; it was a Top 40 seller in the states. 1977's futuristic *I Robot* album was a US Top 10 smash. By contrast, 1978's *Pyramid* provided a histroical glance, with a nod to Isaac Asimov. *Eve* (1979) concerned relationships with, and the role of, women. 1980's *The Turn Of A Friendly Card* examined the role of fate, the role of the subconscious and the power of choice; it yielded the Project's first US Top 20 singles, with *Games People Play (lead vocal by Lenny Zakatek) and the beautiful ballad Time* (lead vocal by Woolfson). The Orwellian *Eye In The Sky* album, issued in 1982 was the Project's biggest yet. It reached No. 7 in the US and No. 28 in the UK, and the title track (lead vocal by Woolfson) became a Top 3 single in the states. It also yielded the Project's first ever UK hit single, albeit No. 74, with the reflective *Old And Wise* (lead vocal by Colin Blunstone, superb sax by Mel Collins). The Project hit a sticky patch in the mid-Eighties, experiencing reduced sales and haggles with their record company over royalties for compact discs (a piece of technology for which their music was tailor-made). Bob MacDonald, 24 February 1986..

DON'T ANSWER ME
Tracks: / Don't answer me / You don't believe / Games people play (on 12" only) / Old and wise (on 12" only).
12" Single: Released Feb '84, on Arista, by BMG Records (UK). Catalogue no: **ARIST 12553**
7" Pic: Released Feb '84, on Arista, by BMG Records (UK). Catalogue no: **ARISD 553**
7" Single: Released Feb '84, on Arista, by BMG Records (UK). Catalogue no: **ARIST 553**

EYE IN THE SKY (SINGLE)
Tracks: / Eye in the sky.
7" Single: Released '82, on Arista, by BMG Records (UK). Deleted '87. Catalogue no: **ARIST 470**

GAMES PEOPLE PLAY
Tracks: / Games people play / Ace of swords.
7" Single: Released Jan '81, on Arista, by BMG Records (UK). Deleted Jan '84. Catalogue no: **ARIST 386**

LET'S TALK ABOUT ME
Tracks: / Let's talk about me.
7" Single: Released Jan '85, on Arista, by BMG Records (UK). Catalogue no: **ARIST 588**
12" Single: Released Jan '85, on Arista, by BMG Records (UK). Catalogue no: **ARIST 12588**

OLD AND WISE
Tracks: / Old and wise / Children of the moon.
7" Single: Released Nov '82, on Arista, by BMG Records (UK). Catalogue no: **ARIST 494**

PRIME TIME
Tracks: / Prime time.
7" Single: Released Jun '84, on Arista, by BMG Records (UK). Catalogue no: **RIST 572**
12" Single: Released Jun '84, on Arista, by BMG Records (UK). Catalogue no: **ARIST 12572**

STEREOTOMY
Tracks: / Stereotomy / Urbania (instrumental) / Beaujolais / Urbania (instrumental) / Limelight / In the real world / Where's the walrus? (instrumental) / Light of the world / Chinese whispers (instrumental) / Stereotomy two.
Note: Produced by Alan Parsons.Features guest vocalists John Miles,Chris Rainbow,Gary Brooker(Procul Harum).Also features the Philharmonia Orchestra.
12" Single: Released Mar '86, on Arista, by BMG Records (UK). Catalogue no: **ARIST 12 654**
7" Single: Released Mar '86, on Arista, by BMG Records (UK). Catalogue no: **ARIST 654**

TURN OF A FRIENDLY CARD (SINGLE)
Tracks: / Turn of a friendly card / Maybe a price to pay.
7" Single: Released Oct '80, on Arista, by BMG Records (UK). Deleted Oct '83. Catalogue no: **ARIST 374**

YOU DON'T BELIEVE
Tracks: / You don't believe.
7" Single: Released '83, on Arista, by BMG Records (UK). Deleted '86. Catalogue no: **ARIST 548**

Parsons, Bill

ALL AMERICAN BOY
Tracks: / All American boy.
7" Single: Released Apr '59, on London Records, by London Records. Deleted '62. Catalogue no: **HL 8798**

Parsons, Gram

Biographical details: Gram Parsons was born Cecil Ingram Connor on 5 November 1946, in Winterhaven, Florida; he died on 19 September 1973 in a motel room near the Joshua Tree National Monument in California, one of his favourite spots. The singer, songwriter, guitarist, keyboardist and bandleader invented the genre of country rock as we know it today, bequeathing it to his friend Emmylou Harris, who took it heights of commercial and artistic success that Parsons did not have in his lifetime. His iconoclasm and alcoholism could have come from a novel by William Faulkner: his mother's family were wealthy, while his father was a guitarist/songwriter and ranch hand called Bull Dog Connor, who committed suicide when Gram was 13, his mother married a man named Parsons and died of alcoholism on the day Gram graduated from high school. He sang in a folk group with Kent Lavoie (see listing for Lobo); his first pro group was the Shilos (tracks later issued as *The Early Years* 1963-65 on Sierra); he formed the International Submarine Band in Cambridge, Massachusetts to make *Cosmic American Music*: album *Safe At Home* was produced in 1967 by Lee Hazlewood. Parsons joined the Bryds and helped them to make history as the first rock band to play the Grand Ole Opry, and with their most important album, *Sweetheart Of The Rodeo* in 1968. With ex-Byrd Chris Hillman he formed the Flying Burrito Brothers, his LPs with them their finest moments: *The Gilded Palace Of Sin* and *Burrito Deluxe* in 1969-70; their later issues *Close Up The Honky Tonks* (1974) and *Sleepless Nights* (1976) also included Parsons material. He influenced the songwriting of Mick Jagger and Keith Richards (*Dead Flowers, Wild Horses*; he sang backup on *Sweet Virginia* in 1972). Parson's own album *GP* in 1973 featured duets with Emmylou, as well as James Burton on guitar, Glen D. Hardin on piano, bassist Rik Grech. He was recording another album with Harris when he died. He had expressed a wish to be cremated and his ashes strewn at Cap Rock, the nearby natural monument; his road manager Phil Kaufman stole the body from a railway platform and carried out these wishes (they were fined $750; it wasn't against the law to steal a corpse). *The Return of the Grievous Angel* and *Gram Parsons and The Fallen Angels Live 1973* were released postumously. Tributes to Parsons inclued Harris's *Boulder To Birmingham* (on her album *Pieces Of The Sky* 1975), Bernie Leadon's *My Men* (on the Eagles album On The Border 1974), Richie Furay's *Crazy Eyes* (title track of 1973 Poco LP). Elvis Costello wrote the sleeve note for *The Best of Gram Parsons* (1982) and included Parsons songs in his *Almost Blue* album. (Donald Clarke 15.5.87).

WITH EMMYLOU HARRIS
7" Single: Released Feb '83, on Sierra (USA), by Sierra Records (USA). Catalogue no: **GP/EP 104**

Partisans

17 YEARS OF HELL (EP)
Tracks: / 17 years of hell.
7" Single: Released Jun '82, on No Future, Deleted '87. Catalogue no: **01 12**

BLIND AMBITION
Tracks: / Blind ambition / Come clean / Change.
7" Single: Released Oct '83, on Cloak & Dagger, Deleted '87. Catalogue no: **PART 1**

BOOGALOO IN YAZAZOO
Tracks: / Boogaloo in Yazazoo.
7" Single: Released Jun '88, on Antler, by Antler Records (Belgium). Catalogue no: **ANT 039**
12" Single: Released Jun '88, on Antler, by Antler Records (Belgium). Catalogue no: **ANT 038**

POLICE STORY
Tracks: / Police story.
7" Single: Released Jul '82, on No Future, Deleted '87. Catalogue no: **01 2**

Partland Brothers

SOUL CITY
Tracks: / Soul city / Outside the city.
7" Single: Released Aug '87, on Capitol, by EMI Records. Deleted Jan '88. Catalogue no: **CL 454**
12" Single: Released Aug '87, on Capitol, by EMI Records. Deleted Jan '88. Catalogue no: **12CL 454**

Partners In Crime

MIRACLES
Tracks: / Miracles.
7" Single: Released Jan '85, on Epic, by CBS Records. Catalogue no: **A 5040**

Parton, David

ISN'T SHE LOVELY
Tracks: / Isn't she lovely.
7" Single: Released Jan '77, on Pye, Deleted '80. Catalogue no: **7 N 45663**

Parton, Dolly

Biographical details: Dolly Parton is a country singer, songwriter and actress, born in 1946 in Sevier County, Tennessee, one of 12 children. She became the best known female country star of the 1970s-80s. She appeared as a child star on Cas Walker's TV show in Knoxville 1956-9, recorded for an obscure label around 1960 and headed for Nashville after graduating from high school in 1964; she wrote songs with her uncle Bill Owen including hits for Bill Phillips and Hank Williams Jr. and signed with Monument; she had minor country hits in 1967 including *Dumb Blonde*, but joined the syndicated Porter Wagoner TV show that year, replacing Norma Jean, and signed to RCA same year: she had many hits of her own and duet hits with Wagoner; her excellent songwriting began to attract attention: he produced her classic hits including the autobiographical *Coat of Many Colors, Touch Your Woman* and the international hit *Jolene* in 1972-74, but their split was eventually acrimonious because she felt he was holding her back: she left him in 1974, but he still had a contract to produce her records, including more country hits, but she wanted to reach a wider audience: her last album to reach the USA pop chart has been *Joshua* in 1971;she relocated to the West Coast and recorded *New Harvest . . . First Gathering*, her first album to crack the top 100 pop albums in the USA (in 1977); single *Light Of A Clear Morning* failed to reach country top 10 but made the pop Hot 100; *Here You Come Again* 1978 was a top 20 pop LP with title track at No. 1 country, No. 3 pop, followed by consecutive country No.1 hits *Two Doors Down, Heartbreaker, Baby I'm Burnin'* '78, all also in pop top 40. She was the Academy of Country Music's Entertainer of the Year 1977, the Country Music Association's in '78; in demand for TV shows for her personality, figure-hugging outfits, blonde wigs and delightful knack for kidding herself. She made her film debut in 9 to 5 in 1980 (title song a no. 1 USA pop hit), co-starred with Burt Reynolds in The Best Little Whorehouse in Texas in 1982 (including new version of *I Will Always Love You*), Sylvester Stallone in

Rhinestone 1984. Her hits continued and in 1984 she teamed with Kenny Rogers for tours, TV specials, hit single *Islands In The Stream* in 1984 (written and produced by the Bee Gees. A shrewd business lady, Dolly Parton (rather than somebody else) is doing well from all her many talents. In 1987 *Trio* was released, her long-awaited collaboration with Emmylou Harris and Linda Ronstadt. (Donald Clarke 15.5.87)

This American singer, songwriter, guitarist and actress became one of the greats of country music, and then moved onto all-round showbiz stardom in the pop, middles-of-the-road and movie worlds. She was born in Tennessee, the fourth of twelve children. Showing an early aptitude for music, she mae her first appearance at Nashville's Grand Ole Opry at the age of 12; at around the same time, she made her debut television appearance and cut her first record. She did not become a child star, however - after graduating from school at 18, Parton made Nashville her home and had to struggle for three years before etting her big break, despite being related to country singer Buck Owens. Dolly's country career began in earnest in 1967 when she joined the entourage of one of the genre's leading stars, Porter Wagoner. She and Wagoner recorded a series of memorable duets during the late Sixties and early Seventies, while Parton simultaneously launched a solo recording career. She regularly appeared on his TV show as Miss Dolly, thereby introducing fans to her stunning physique - her giant bosoms were accompanied by an only marginally less eye-catching cascading blonde wig. During the first few years of the Seventies, several of Parton's country hits became standards. These included *Joshua*, *Coat Of Many Colours* and *Light Of A Clear Blue Morning*. With her fine, expressive voice and her perceptive songwriting skill, Dolly became one of the best storytellers in country music; she portrayed her music with clarity and passion, without resorting to schmaltzy sentimentality. In 1976, two years after its Stateside success, the classic *Jolene* gave Parton a one-off Top 10 smash in Britain. In 1977 the good ol' Southern girl decided to aim for major pop stardom, and hired new management in Los Angeles. She recorded *Her You Come Again*, penned by ace pop songwriters Barry Mann and Cynthia Weil, and achieved a million-selling US No. 3 smash. It was followed by such lightweight ditties as *Two Doors Down* (No. 19 in 1978) and the disco offering *Baby I'm Burnin'* (No. 25 in 1979). In 1981 she moved into acting, playing the role of Doralee the molested secretary in '9 To 5'; her co-stars in the film included Jane Fibonda and Lily Tomlin. Dolly's self-penned theme song for '9 To 5' became her first US No. 1 pop hit. Her transition was now complete. She proceeded to land starring roles alongside Burt Reynolds and Sylvester Stallone. In late 1983 she teamed up with fellow country crossover star Kenny Rogers for the duet single *Islands In The Stream*, written and produced by the Bee Gees' stable. This became America's biggest selling single of the year, shifting two million copies in the States alone; it peaked at No. 7 in the UK, her biggest British success since *Jolene*.

Parton's showbiz status offended the country purists, of course, but she ensured that enough country-ish product was released to keep many of her old fans happy. In early 1986, for example, she scored a big hit on the specialist charts with *Think About Love*. The trouble with her megastardom was that her eye-catching figure became her principal asset in the public mind; she became the butt of every comedian's jokes, a fact which tended to obscure awareness of the musical talent that had made her known in the first place. She had been one of country music's best singers and songwriters, a far more noteworthy achievement than the size of her tits. Bob MacDonald, 24 February 1986..

9 TO 5
Tracks: / 9 to 5 / Sing for the common man.
7" Single: Released Feb '81, on RCA, by BMG Records (UK). Deleted '84. Catalogue no: **RCA 25**
CD 5": Released Jun '89, on RCA, by BMG Records (UK). Catalogue no: **PD 49447**

CHRISTMAS WITHOUT YOU
Tracks: / Christmas without you.
7" Single: Released Nov '84, on RCA, by BMG Records (UK). Catalogue no: **RCA 465**

EVERYTHING IS BEAUTIFUL
Tracks: / Everything is beautiful / Here comes that rainbow again.
7" Single: Released Dec '82, on Monument, Deleted Dec '85. Catalogue no: **MNT A 2983**

HERE YOU COME AGAIN
Tracks: / Here you come again / Potential new boyfriend / Love is like a butterfly.
7" Single: Released Apr '84, on RCA, by BMG Records (UK). Deleted '87. Catalogue no: **RCA 395**

I KNOW YOU BY HEART
Tracks: / I know you by heart / Could I have your autograph / Make love work.
7" Single: Released Mar '88, on CBS, by CBS Records. Deleted Aug '88. Catalogue no: **DOLLY 1**
12" Single: Released Mar '88, on CBS, by CBS Records. Deleted Aug '88. Catalogue no: **DOLLY T1**
7" Single: Released Mar '88, on CBS, by CBS Records. Deleted Aug '88. Catalogue no: **DOLLY Q1**

I WILL ALWAYS LOVE YOU
Tracks: / I will always love you / Do I ever.
7" Single: Released Nov '82, on RCA, by BMG Records (UK). Deleted May '89. Catalogue no: **RCA 270**

I WILL ALWAYS LOVE YOU (OLD GOLD)
Tracks: / I will always love you / Love is like a butterfly.
7" Single: Released Jan '87, on Old Gold, by Old Gold Records. Catalogue no: **OG 9667**

JOLENE
Tracks: / Jolene / Love is like a butterfly.
7" Single: Released Apr '76, on RCA, by BMG Records (UK). Catalogue no: **RCA 2675**

JOLENE (OLD GOLD)
Tracks: / Bargain store / Jolene.
7" Single: Released Oct '86, on Old Gold, by Old Gold Records. Catalogue no: **OG 9603**

ME AND LITTLE ANDY
Tracks: / Me and little Andy / Cowgirl and the dandy.
7" Single: Released Apr '80, on RCA, by BMG Records (UK). Deleted '83. Catalogue no: **PB 9526**

POTENTIAL NEW BOYFRIEND
Tracks: / Potential new boyfriend.
7" Single: Released May '83, on RCA, by BMG Records (UK). Catalogue no: **RCA 335**

RIVER UNBROKEN, THE
Tracks: / River unbroken, The / More than I can say.
7" Single: Released Jan '88, on CBS, by CBS Records. Deleted Jan '89. Catalogue no: **651 202 7**
12" Single: Released Jan '88, on CBS, by CBS Records. Deleted Jan '89. Catalogue no: **651 202 6**

SAVE THE LAST DANCE FOR ME (SINGLE)
Tracks: / Save the last dance for me.
7" Single: Released Jan '84, on RCA, by BMG Records (UK). Catalogue no: **RCA 391**

STARTING OVER AGAIN
Tracks: / Starting over again / Sweet agony.
7" Single: Released Jun '80, on RCA, by BMG Records (UK). Deleted Jun '83. Catalogue no: **PB 1926**

THINK ABOUT LOVE
Tracks: / Think about love / I can't be true.
7" Single: Released Apr '85, on RCA, by BMG Records (UK). Catalogue no: **PB 49995**

TO KNOW H
Tracks: / To know H.
7" Single: Deleted Jan '88. Catalogue no: **W 8492**

WHY'D YOU COME IN HERE LOOKING LIKE THAT
Tracks: / Why'd you come in here looking like that / Wait till I get you home / River unbroken, The (Available on CD only) / Make love work (on CD 5" only.).
CD 5": Released Jun '89, on CBS, by CBS Records. Catalogue no: **DOLLY C2**
7" Single: Released Jun '89, on CBS, by CBS Records. Catalogue no: **DOLLY 2**

Parton, Stella

Biographical details: One of 11 siblings of country superstar Dolly Parton, Stella was born in Sevier County, Tennessee, in 1949. She made her radio debut with Dolly in 1955, later achieving her own smaller success. She sang in local clubs in '66 before going to Nashville in '72. Her own song, Ode to Olivia, was a 1975 defence of Olivia Newton-John, who had won CMA awards amid protests that she wasn't country. She recorded for Country, Soul & Blues label, had country hits in '75-'76, switched to Elektra and hit the US Top Twenty and the British Top Forty with Danger Of A Stranger, written by Shel Silverstein. More hits followed in the late 70's and she then worked in television and theatre and recorded for the Town House label in California. (Donald Clarke, May 1987.) This American singer, the sister of superstar Dolly Parton, launched her own career in the mid-Seventies. She tried to follow Dolly's lead into the country and pop spheres but failed pretty dismally. Her albums were not significant sellers in the States; and her only taste of UK chart success was the ultra-bland 1977 single *The Danger Of A Stranger*. Written by Shel Silverstein and Even Stevens, better known for their work for Dr Hook, this singles peaked at Mo. 35 on the British listings. Stella was learly not particularly talented, and merely decided to have a stab in view of her sister's success. The two Partons, certainly came from a large family - Dolly was the fourth of twelve children. Bob MacDonald, 24 February 1986. Stella Parton was born in Sevier County, Tennessee in 1949, one of 11 siblings of country superstar Dolly Parton: she made her radio debut with Dolly in 1955, but achieved her own smaller success. Sang in local clubs '66, moved to Nashville '72, recorded her own song *Ode To Olivia* '75, in defence of Olivia Newton-John, who had won CMA awards amid protests that she wasn't country. Recorded for Country, Soul & Blues label, had country hits '75-6; switched to elektra and had a top 20 with *Danger Of A Stranger* (top 40 UK), written by Shel Silverstein, others in late 1970s. Then worked on TV, in theatres, recorded for Town House label in California. (Donald Clarke).e.

DANGER OF A STRANGER, THE
Tracks: / Danger of a stranger, The.
7" Single: Released Oct '77, on Elektra, by Elektra Records (UK). Deleted '80. Catalogue no: **K 12272**

Partridge, Don

BLUE EYES
Tracks: / Blue eyes.
7" Single: Released May '68, on Columbia, by EMI Records. Deleted '71. Catalogue no: **DB 8416**

BREAKFAST ON PLUTO
Tracks: / Breakfast on Pluto.
7" Single: Released Feb '69, on Columbia, by EMI Records. Deleted '72. Catalogue no: **DB 8538**

ROSIE
Tracks: / Rosie.
7" Single: Released Feb '68, on Columbia, by EMI Records. Deleted '71. Catalogue no: **DB 8330**

Partridge Family

BREAKING UP IS HARD TO DO
Tracks: / Breaking up is hard to do.
7" Single: Released Jul '72, on Bell, Deleted '75. Catalogue no: **MABEL 1**

I THINK I LOVE YOU
Tracks: / I think I love you.
7" Single: Released Feb '71, on Bell, Deleted '74. Catalogue no: **BELL 1130**

IT'S ONE OF THOSE NIGHTS (YES LOVE)
Tracks: / It's one of those nights (yes love).
7" Single: Released Feb '72, on Bell, Deleted '75. Catalogue no: **BELL 1203**

LOOKING THROUGH THE EYES OF LOVE
Tracks: / Looking through the eyes of love.
7" Single: Released Feb '73, on Bell, Deleted '76. Catalogue no: **BELL 1278**

WALKING IN THE RAIN
Tracks: / Walking in the rain.
7" Single: Released May '73, on Bell, Deleted '76. Catalogue no: **BELL 1293**

Party

CHRISTMAS CRACKERS
Tracks: / Christmas crackers.
7" Single: Released Dec '81, on Rox, by Rox Records. Catalogue no: **PARTY 1**

ROXY BEAT
Tracks: / Roxy beat.
12" Single: Released May '89, on Rodger, Catalogue no: **RODGER 6**

Party Boy

TWILIGHT ZONE
Tracks: / Twilight zone (UK radio edit) / Twilight zone (industrial mix) / Twilight zone (Bam bam's corrosion mix) (12" only).
7" Single: Released Nov '88, on Urban, by Polydor Ltd. Deleted 30 May '89. Catalogue no: **URB 27**
12" Single: Released Nov '88, on Urban, by Polydor Ltd. Deleted 30 May '89. Catalogue no: **URBX 27**

Party Boys

HE'S GONNA STEP ON YOU AGAIN
Tracks: / He's gonna step on you again / She's a mystery / He's gonna step on you again (stomp mix) (Only 12" single.) / She's a mystery (On 12" version.).
7" Single: Released Oct '87, on CBS, by CBS Records. Deleted Jun '88: Catalogue no: **651230 7**
12" Single: Released Oct '87, on CBS, by CBS Records. Deleted Jun '88. Catalogue no: **651230 6**
7" Pic: Released Nov '87, on Epic, by CBS Records. Catalogue no: **651230 0**

Party Day

GLASSHOUSE (EP)
Tracks: / Glasshouse.
12" Single: Released Nov '85, on Rouska, by Rouska Records. Catalogue no: **COME 1T**

ROW THE BOAT ASHORE
Tracks: / Row the boat ashore.
7" Single: Released Aug '83, on Party Day, Catalogue no: **FX 301**

SPIDER, THE
Tracks: / Spider, The.
7" Single: on Party Day, Catalogue no: **FX 302**

Party People

FUNKY WAY TO TREAT SOMEBODY
12" Single: Released May '88, on Hi-Hut, by Hi-Hut Records. Catalogue no: **HH 003**

RED WHITE & BLUE
Tracks: / Red white & blue / Red white & blue (version).
12" Single: Released 5 Mar '88, on Hi-Hut, by Hi-Hut Records. Catalogue no: **HH 2**

SUPERMAN SYMSONIC DANCE
Tracks: / Superman symsonic dance.
12" Single: Released Aug '87, on Hi-Hut, by Hi-Hut Records. Catalogue no: **HH 1**

Pasadena Roof Orchestra

WAY WE GET IT TOGETHER
Tracks: / Way we get it together.
7" Single: Released May '82, on T. E. R., by That's Entertainment Records. Catalogue no: **TER 002 EP**

Pasadenas

ENCHANTED LADY
Tracks: / Enchanted lady / New love (original version) / New love (instrumental) (Only on 12" version.) / Tribute (right on) (Only on CD single.) / Riding on a train (segue mix) (Only on CD single.).
12" Single: Released Nov '88, on CBS, by CBS Records. Deleted 17 Apr '89. Catalogue no: **PASAT 3**
7" Single: Released Nov '88, on CBS, by CBS Records. Deleted 17 Apr '89. Catalogue no: **PASA 3**
CD 5": Released Nov '88, on CBS, by CBS Records. Deleted 17 Apr '89. Catalogue no: **CDPASA 3**
7" Single: Released Nov '88, on CBS, by CBS Records. Deleted 17 Apr '89. Catalogue no: **PASA B3**
12" Single: Released 28 Nov '88, on CBS, by CBS Records. Deleted 17 Apr '89. Catalogue no: **PASA Q3**

RIDING ON A TRAIN
Tracks: / Riding on a train (7" only) / My baby don't love me no more / Riding on a train (ext. version) (12" only) / Riding on a train (Clapham Jct. demo mix) (12" and CD only) / Riding on a train (full version) / Riding on a train (dub version) / Little love, A.
CD 5": Released Aug '88, on CBS, by CBS Records. Deleted 17 Apr '89. Catalogue no: **CDPASA 2**
12" Single: Released Oct '88, on CBS, by CBS Records. Deleted 17 Apr '89. Catalogue no: **PASAT PT2**
12" Single: Released Sep '88, on CBS, by CBS Records. Deleted 17 Apr '89. Catalogue no: **PASAT 2**
7" Single: Released Aug '88, on CBS, by CBS Records. Deleted 17 Apr '89. Catalogue no: **PASA Q2**
7" Single: Released Aug '88, on CBS, by CBS Records. Deleted 17 Apr '89. Catalogue no: **PASA 2**
12" Single: Released Aug '88, on CBS, by CBS Records. Deleted 17 Apr '89. Catalogue no: **PASA QT2**

TRIBUTE
Tracks: / Tribute / I believe / Tribute (right on) (the screaming cat mix) (12" and CD5" only.) / I believe (live) (on 12" and CD5" only.) / All night long (live)(12" and CD only.) / Enchanted lady (Acappella version)(12" only.).
CD 5": Released May '88, on CBS, by CBS Records. Deleted Jan '89. Catalogue no: **PASAC 1**
12" Single: Released 14 May '88, on CBS, by CBS Records. Deleted 17 Apr '89. Catalogue no: **PASA T1**
12" Single: Released May '88, on CBS, by CBS Records. Deleted Jan '89. Catalogue no: **PASA QT1**
7" Pic: Released May '88, on CBS, by CBS Records. Deleted Jan '89. Catalogue no: **PASAP 1**
7" Single: Released May '88, on CBS, by CBS Records. Deleted Jan '89. Catalogue no: **PASAB 1**
7" Single: Released May '88, on CBS, by CBS Records. Catalogue no: **PASA S1**

PASSION PUPPETS - LIKE DUST (Released On Stiff)

7" Single: Released 14 May '88, on CBS, by CBS Records. Deleted Jan '89. Catalogue no: **PASA 1**

Pascal, Francoise

I CAN'T GET ENOUGH
Tracks: / I can't get enough / Make love to me.
7" Single: Released Feb '81, on RCA, by BMG Records (UK). Deleted Feb '84. Catalogue no: **RCA 35**

Pasha

NOW WE ARE FRIENDS
Tracks: / Now we are friends.
7" Single: Released Dec '83, on Floating World, by Floating World Records. Catalogue no: **YUN 01**

Pask, Morgan

OVERKILL (Theme from The Bill)
Tracks: / Overkill.
7" Single: Released Jan '85, on Columbia, by EMI Records. Deleted Jul '87. Catalogue no: **DB 9100**

Pasquez, Emilio

SOUNDS FROM THE PINK SANDBOX
Tracks: / Sounds from the pink sandbox / Do it again, Emilio.
12" Single: Released May '88, on WEA, by WEA Records. Catalogue no: **YZ 180T**
7" Single: Released May '88, on WEA, by WEA Records. Catalogue no: **YZ 180**

Passage

DEVILS AND ANGELS
Tracks: / Devils and angels / Watching you dance.
7" Single: Released Feb '81, on Virgin, by Virgin Records. Deleted Feb '84. Catalogue no: **AMPM 2400**

TABOOS
Tracks: / Taboos.
12" Single: Released Nov '81, on Cherry Red, by Cherry Red Records. Deleted '87. Catalogue no: **12 CHERRY 30**

WAVE
Tracks: / Wave / Angel land.
7" Single: Released Oct '82, on Cherry Red, by Cherry Red Records. Deleted '87. Catalogue no: **CHERRY 50**
12" Single: Released Oct '82, on Cherry Red, by Cherry Red Records. Deleted '87. Catalogue no: **12 CHERRY 50**

XOYO
Tracks: / Xoyo / Born every minute.
12" Single: Released Jun '82, on Cherry Red, by Cherry Red Records. Deleted '87. Catalogue no: **12 CHERRY 35**
7" Single: Released Apr '82, on Cherry Red, by Cherry Red Records. Deleted '87. Catalogue no: **CHERRY 35**

Passengers

HE SPEEDY LIKE GONZALES
Tracks: / He speedy like Gonzales / Hot leather.
7" Single: Released Feb '81, on Carrere. Deleted Feb '84. Catalogue no: **CAR 177**

HELL TO HEAVEN
Tracks: / Hell to heaven / Frances farmer's song / World outside, The.
7" Single: Released Aug '88, on True, by True Records. Catalogue no: **PASS 001**

Passion

DON'T STOP MY LOVE
Tracks: / Don't stop my love / Don't stop my love (part 2).
12" Single: Released Sep '82, on Prelude. Deleted '85. Catalogue no: **PRLA 13-27**
7" Single: Released Sep '82, on Prelude. Deleted '85. Catalogue no: **PRLA 2704**

ONCE UPON A TIME
Tracks: / Once upon a time.
12" Single: Deleted Nov '87. Catalogue no: **PX 11**

SUNSET & VINE(THE VERY FIRST TIME)
Tracks: / Sunset & vine(The very first time) / La pornographique.
7" Single: Released Feb '86, on Wag. Catalogue no: **WAG 1**
12" Single: Released Feb '86, on Wag. Catalogue no: **12 WAG 1**

Passion All Stars

PASSION MEDLEY
Tracks: / Passion medley.
12" Single: Released Feb '85, on Passion, by Skratch Records. Catalogue no: **PASH 40(12)**

Passion Day

MALE SLUTS
Tracks: / Male sluts / Weapon of work.
7" Single: Released Feb '84, on Red Energy Dynamo, by Red Energy Dynamo Records. Catalogue no: **S 201**

Passion Fodder

LUZ BLANCA
Tracks: / Luz Blanca / Tomorrow is a long time / Dirt (12" only) ("Extra track on 12") / God couldn't fight his way out of a wet brown bag (on 12" only.).
12" Single: Released Jul '87, on Beggars Banquet, by Beggars Banquet Records. Catalogue no: **BEG 191T**
7" Single: Released Jul '87, on Beggars Banquet, by Beggars Banquet Records. Catalogue no: **BEG 191**

ORWELL COOKS
Tracks: / Orwell cooks.
7" Single: Released Jun '88, on Beggars Banquet, by Beggars Banquet Records. Catalogue no: **BEG 216**
12" Single: Released Jun '88, on Beggars Banquet, by Beggars Banquet Records. Catalogue no: **BEG 216T**

SPOKANE
Tracks: / Spokane / Blood thicker than love / Heart hunters / Girl that I marry, The.
12" Single: Released Oct '88, on Beggars Banquet, by Beggars Banquet Records. Catalogue no: **BEG 222 T**
7" Single: Released Oct '88, on Beggars Banquet, by Beggars Banquet Records. Catalogue no: **BEG 222**

Passion Puppets

Biographical details: Formed by Micki Screene and Ray Burmiston who met in school. In 1977 we formed the Camden-based band The Limit. This five piece signed to Private Stock Records and released one single *Please please me/My world at night*. When the Limit bit the dust Miki and I continued to write using a four track tape machine donated by ex-Pistol Steve Jones. This resulted in the formation of their new vision, which was eventually to become the Passion Puppets. Consciously going against the abundance of synths they decided to use guitars. To further this aim, local heroes Andy P and David Rollins were drafted in. After many changes in the drum dept ex Drowning Craze drummer Simon Godfrey finalised the line up in Easter '82. Since then they have been gigging around London. (Island Records, Feb 1984).

BEYOND THE TALE
Tracks: / Beyond the pale / Like dust / Terminal culture / New way / Playground / Voices / Fear of being touched / Child / Memories / In your eyes.
12" Single: Released May '84, on Stiff, by Stiff Records. Catalogue no: **SBUY 203**
7" Single: Released May '84, on Stiff, by Stiff Records. Catalogue no: **BUY 203**

LIKE DUST (See panel opposite)
Tracks: / Like dust / House of love.
7" Single: Released Jul '83, on Stiff, by Stiff Records. Catalogue no: **BUY 178**
12" Single: Released Jul '83, on Stiff, by Stiff Records. Catalogue no: **SBUY 178**

VOICES
Tracks: / Voices / Powder monkeys / We are the dead.
12" Single: Released Sep '83, on Stiff, by Stiff Records. Catalogue no: **SBUY 188**
7" Single: Released Sep '83, on Stiff, by Stiff Records. Catalogue no: **BUY 188**

Passion Spent

SOMEONE TO TALK TO
Tracks: / Wildlife.
12" Single: Released Feb '87, on Paragon. Catalogue no: **PSS 1**

Passionate Friends

TIME BANDITS
Tracks: / Time bandits / Time and tide.
7" Single: Released Apr '83, on T.Toons. Catalogue no: **TEN 02**

Passions

Biographical details: At the time of their chart success, this British band consisted of David Agar, Barbara Gogan, Clive Timperley and Richard Williams.

The Passions were formed in 1978 from the ashes of various small-time bands. They had just experienced the punk explosion, and they combined this influence with a sparse art-rock approach. They supported the similarly styled Cure on tour, and released their debut album *Michael And Miranda* in 1980. In the following year, the Passions chalked up their only hit single - *I'm In Love With A German Film Star* reached the UK No. 25 position. This was a slightly eerie and very appealing track which made full use of Gogan's ethereal voice. It appeared on the group's only chart album *Thirty Thousand Feet Over China*, which peaked at No. 92 in October 1981.

The Passions were an interesting band with a lot of potential, which was never really fulfilled. Their 1982 album *Sanctuary* received reasonable praise from the critics, but the band then faded into obscurity. Bob MacDonald, 25 February 1986..

AFRICA MINE
Tracks: / Africa mine / I feel cheap.
7" Single: Released Jan '82, on Polydor, by Polydor Ltd. Deleted Jan '85. Catalogue no: **POSP 384**

I'M IN LOVE WITH A GERMAN FILM STAR
Tracks: / I'm in love with a German film star / Don't talk to me.
7" Single: Released Jan '81, on Polydor, by Polydor Ltd. Deleted '84. Catalogue no: **POSP 222**

JUMP FOR JOY
Tracks: / Jump for joy / Story.
7" Single: Released May '82, on Polydor, by Polydor Ltd. Deleted '85. Catalogue no: **POSP 435**

SANCTUARY (SINGLE)
Tracks: / Sanctuary / Tempting fate.
7" Single: Released Sep '82, on Polydor, by Polydor Ltd. Deleted Sep '85. Catalogue no: **POSP 487**

SKIN DEEP
Tracks: / Skin deep / I radiate / Small stones (On 12" only).
12" Single: Released Jul '81, on Polydor, by Polydor Ltd. Deleted Jul '84. Catalogue no: **POSPX 256**
7" Single: Released Jul '81, on Polydor, by Polydor Ltd. Deleted Jul '84. Catalogue no: **POSP 256**

SWIMMER
Tracks: / Swimmer / Some fun.
7" Single: Released Sep '81, on Polydor, by Polydor Ltd. Deleted '84. Catalogue no: **POSP 325**

Passmore Sisters

DANCE THE HOUSE DOWN
Tracks: / Dance the house down.
7" Single: Released Nov '85, on Sharp, by Sharp Records. Catalogue no: **CAL 3**

EVERY CHILD IN HEAVEN
Tracks: / Every child in heaven.
12" Single: Released Jun '87, on Sharp, by Sharp Records. Catalogue no: **CAL 6T**
7" Single: Released Jun '87, on Sharp, by Sharp Records. Catalogue no: **CAL 6**

SAFE PLACE TO HIDE, A
Tracks: / Safe place to hide, A.
12" Single: Released 12 Oct '87, on Sharp, by Sharp Records. Catalogue no: **CAL 007T**
7" Single: Released 12 Oct '87, on Sharp, by Sharp Records. Catalogue no: **CAL 007**

VIOLENT BLUE
Tracks: / Violent blue.
12" Single: Released Aug '86, on Sharp, by Sharp Records. Catalogue no: **CAL 4**

Passport

NEW MOON
Tracks: / New moon / Abakus.
7" Single: Released Dec '82, on WEA, by WEA Records. Catalogue no: **K11768**

Pasta Rock

MONUMENT
Tracks: / Monument / Trial.
7" Single: Released Feb '82, on Polygram, by PolyGram UK Ltd. Deleted Feb '87. Catalogue no: **PN 1**

Pastels

BABY YOU'RE JUST YOU
Tracks: / Baby you're just you.
12" Single: Released 16 Jan '89, on Chapter 22, by Chapter 22 Records. Catalogue no: **12 CHAP 37**
7" Single: Released 16 Jan '89, on Chapter 22, by Chapter 22 Records. Catalogue no: **CHAP 37**

COMING THROUGH
Tracks: / Coming through.
7" Single: Released Oct '87, on Glass, by Glass Records. Catalogue no: **GLASS 053**
12" Single: Released Oct '87, on Glass, by Glass Records. Catalogue no: **GLASS 12053**

CRAWL BABIES
Tracks: / Crawl babies.
7" Single: Released Mar '87, on Glass, by Glass Records. Catalogue no: **GLASS 050**
12" Single: Released Mar '87, on Glass, by Glass Records. Catalogue no: **GLASS 12050**

GLASS 12048 & 12050 PACKAGE
12" Single: Released Dec '87, on Glass, by Glass Records. Catalogue no: **PASTEL 001**

HEAVENS ABOVE
Tracks: / Heavens above / Teatime tales.
7" Single: Released Oct '82, on Whaam. Catalogue no: **WHAAM 05**
7" Single: Released Mar '85, on Villa. Catalogue no: **21VILLA 1**

I WONDER WHY
Tracks: / I wonder why.
7" Single: Released Oct '83, on Rough Trade, by Rough Trade Records. Catalogue no: **RT 114**

I'M ALRIGHT WITH YOU
Tracks: / I'm alright with you.
12" Single: Released Nov '85, on Creation, by Creation Records. Deleted Jul '88. Catalogue no: **CRE 022T**
7" Single: Released Nov '85, on Creation, by Creation Records. Deleted Jul '88. Catalogue no: **CRE 022**

MILLION TEARS, A
Tracks: / Million tears, A.
12" Single: Released Oct '84, on Creation, by Creation Records. Catalogue no: **CRE 011T**

SOMETHING'S GOING ON
Tracks: / Something's going on.
7" Single: Released Mar '84, on Rough Trade, by Rough Trade Records. Deleted Jul '88. Catalogue no: **CRE 005**

TRUCK TRAIN TRACTOR
Tracks: / Truck train tractor / Breaking lines / Truck train tractor (2).
7" Single: Released Jun '86, on Glass, by Glass Records. Catalogue no: **GLASS 048**

12" Single: Released Jun '86, on Glass, by Glass Records. Catalogue no: **GLASS 12048**

Pastiche

WHERE DID THAT SOUL GO
Tracks: / Where did that soul go.
12" Single: Released Nov '83, on Inferno (1), by Inferno Records. Catalogue no: **12 BURN 6**
7" Single: Released Nov '83, on Inferno (1), by Inferno Records. Catalogue no: **BURN 6**

Pat 'n' Mick

I HAVNE'T STOPPED DANCING YET
Tracks: / I haven't stopped dancing yet.
7" Single: Released Mar '89, on PWL, by PWL Records. Catalogue no: **PWL 33**
12" Single: Released Mar '89, on PWL, by PWL Records. Catalogue no: **PWLT 33**

Patea Maori Club

POI-E
Tracks: / POI-E.
7" Single: Released Feb '85, on Sonet, by Sonet Records. Catalogue no: **SON 2278**

Patience & Prudence

GONNA GET ALONG WITHOUT YOU NOW
Tracks: / Gonna get along without you now.
7" Single: Released Mar '57, on London-American, Deleted '60. Catalogue no: **HLU 8369**

TONIGHT YOU BELONG TO ME
Tracks: / Tonight you belong to me.
7" Single: Released Nov '56, on London-American, Deleted '59. Catalogue no: **HLU 8321**

Patinkin, Mandy

YOUNGER THAN SPRINGTIME
Tracks: / Younger than Springtime (From 'South Pacific'.) / I'm gonna wash that man right out-a my hair.
7" Single: Released Oct '86, on CBS, by CBS Records. Deleted '87. Catalogue no: **650124 7**

Pato

ALLO TOSH
Tracks: / Allo tosh.
12" Single: Released Feb '85, on Don Christie, Catalogue no: **DCR 1**

Pato & Roger

AGO TALK
Tracks: / Ago talk / Cool entertainer / Tappy lappy dub (Only on 12" single.).
12" Single: Released '82, on Go Feet, Deleted '87. Catalogue no: **FEET 1214**
7" Single: Released '82, on Go Feet, Deleted '87. Catalogue no: **FEET 14**

Paton, Dave

NO TIES, NO STRINGS
Tracks: / No ties, no strings / Stop and let go.
7" Single: Released May '80, on EMI, by EMI Records. Deleted May '83. Catalogue no: **EMI 5063**

Patric

MESSAGE, THE
Tracks: / Message, The.
12" Single: Released 6 Feb '89, on Orange (1), by Orange Records. Catalogue no: **JOOS 001 T**

Patrick

IMMIGRANT
Tracks: / Immigrant.
7" Single: Released Apr '85, on Patrick, Catalogue no: **Patrick 1**

Patrick, Bobby

DALLAS
Tracks: / Dallas / Waltons.
7" Single: Released Mar '80, on Monza, Catalogue no: **MONZA 004**

Patrick, Chris

STAND FOR
Tracks: / Stand for.
12" Single: Released Jul '89, on Collision, Catalogue no: **UNKNOWN**
7" Single: Released Jul '89, on Collision, Catalogue no: **UNKNOWN**

Patrick, Keith

NIGHT TO REMEMBER,A
Tracks: / Night to remember,A / Nioght to remember, A (Instrumental).
7" Single: Released Nov '86, on In Recordings, Catalogue no: **INR 2**
12" Single: Released Nov '86, on In Recordings, Catalogue no: **INRT 2**

Patrick, Rikki

CLEAR THE WAY
Tracks: / Clear the way.
12" Single: Released Jan '85, on CBS, by

BILLY PAUL - LATELY (Releaserd on Total Experiance)

CBS Records. Catalogue no: **TX5039**

I NEVER THOUGHT IT WOULD COME TO THIS
Tracks: / I never thought it would come to this.
7" Single: Released Jun '84, on CBS, by CBS Records. Catalogue no: **A 4414**

NIGHT MOVES
Tracks: / Night moves / Night moves (remix) / Break point.
12" Single: Released Mar '87, on DMC, Deleted '87. Catalogue no: **DECKS 125**
12" Single: Released Mar '84, on CBS, by CBS Records. Catalogue no: **TA 4144**
7" Single: Released Mar '84, on CBS, by CBS Records. Catalogue no: **A 4144**
7" Single: Released Mar '87, on DMC, Deleted '87. Catalogue no: **DECK 5**
12" Single: Released Mar '87, on DMC, Deleted '87. Catalogue no: **DECK 125**

Patris

LOVE OASIS
Tracks: / Love oasis.
12" Single: Released Nov '85, on MDM, by MDM Communications. Catalogue no: **DMD 2-12**

Patterns

PART 2 - THE BISHOPS'S IN THE FRIDGE
Tracks: / Bishop's in the fridge, The (part 2).
7" Single: Released Aug '80, on Heater, Catalogue no: **HVR 002**

Patterns in Peru

THIS IS THE NIGHT
Tracks: / This is the night / Playing games.
12" Single: Released Feb '86, on WEA, by WEA Records. Catalogue no: **YZ 60 T**
7" Single: Released Feb '86, on WEA, by WEA Records. Catalogue no: **YZ 60**

Patterson, Colin

CAN'T RUSH LOVE
12" Single: Released Jul '89, on White Label (1), Catalogue no: **STD 10**

Patterson, Kellee

IF IT DON'T FIT DON'T FORCE IT
Tracks: / If it don't fit don't force it.
7" Single: Released Feb '78, on EMI International, by EMI Records. Deleted '81. Catalogue no: **INT 544**

Patterson, Ottilie

CARELESS LOVE
Tracks: / Careless love / Georgia grind.
7" Single: Released Nov '82, on Fat Hen, by Fat Hen Records. Catalogue no: **FM 001**

Patterson, Rosie

LOVING YOU AIN'T EASY
Tracks: / Loving you ain't easy.
7" Single: Released Apr '89, on Frontier, by Frontier Records. Catalogue no: **FTR 4**

SHOO-RAH, SHOO-RAH!
Tracks: / Shoo-rah-shoo-rah / If you like it (don't fight it).
12" Single: Released 16 Sep '88, on Frontier, by Frontier Records. Catalogue no: **12FTR 1**
7" Single: Released 16 Sep '88, on Frontier, by Frontier Records. Catalogue no: **FTR 1**

Patterson, Sir Les

GIVE HER ONE FOR CHRISTMAS
Tracks: / Give her one for Christmas.
7" Single: Released Dec '85, on Towerbell, Catalogue no: **TOW 82**
12" Single: Released Dec '85, on Towerbell, Catalogue no: **TOWT 82**

Patterson, Sunshine

LINES See under Maelov, Eddie
Tracks: / Lines / Last bouquet.
7" Single: Released Jul '81, on Human (1), by Accolade Music. Deleted Jul '84. Catalogue no: **HUN 912**

Patti, Guesch

ETIENNE
Tracks: / Une espoir / Etienne / Etienne (English version).
7" Single: Released Feb '88, on Columbia, by EMI Records. Deleted Nov '88. Catalogue no: **DB 9165**
12" Single: Released Feb '88, on Columbia, by EMI Records. Deleted Nov '88. Catalogue no: **12DB 9165**

LET BE MUST THE QUEEN
Tracks: / Let be must the queen / Etienne / Tout seul (12" only) (Only on 12" single.).
12" Single: Released Jun '88, on Columbia, by EMI Records. Deleted Nov '88. Catalogue no: **12DB 9170**

7" Single: Released Jun '88, on Columbia, by EMI Records. Deleted Nov '88. Catalogue no: **DB 9170**

Patti & The Dep Band

BIKO
Tracks: / Biko / Try me.
7" Single: Released Aug '86, on Important, Catalogue no: **TAN 11**
12" Single: Released Aug '86, on Important, Catalogue no: **TANT 11**

Patto

BLACK AND WHITE
Tracks: / Black and white.
12" Single: Released Aug '84, on Teldec (1), by ASV (Academy Sound & Vision). Catalogue no: **PAT 1**

Patton, Robbie

DON'T GIVE IT UP
Tracks: / Don't give it up / When love dissapears.
7" Single: Released Oct '81, on United Artists, by EMI Records. Deleted '85. Catalogue no: **UP 643**

Patty

RED LIGHT
Tracks: / Red light / Red light (Instrumental).

12" Single: Released May '86, on Spartan, Catalogue no: **12SP 137**
7" Single: Released May '86, on Spartan, Catalogue no: **SP 137**

Paul, Andrew

CRAZY
Tracks: / Crazy / What the police can do.
12" Single: Released Aug '86, on Fashion, by Fashion Records. Catalogue no: **FAD 046**

HUSTLE THEM A HUSTLE
Tracks: / Hustle them a hustle / Bad boys.
12" Single: Released Nov '85, on Fashion, by Fashion Records. Catalogue no: **FAD 038**

TOO STUSH
Tracks: / Too stush / Gunshot a flow.
12" Single: Released Mar '87, on Digikal, by Fashion Records. Catalogue no: **DIG 004**

UNDER ME SENSIMA
Tracks: / Under me sensima.
12" Single: Released 8 Aug '88, on Y & D, Catalogue no: **YDDO 126**

WHAT POLICE CAN DO
Tracks: / What police can do / Crazy.
12" Single: Released Sep '86, on Digikal, by Fashion Records. Catalogue no: **DIG 001**

WHO'S GONNA MAKE THE DANCE RAM
Tracks: / Who's gonna make the dance ram.
12" Single: Released Jun '85, on Fashion, by Fashion Records. Catalogue no: **FAD 033**

Paul, Andy

BUILD ME UP BUTTERCUP
Tracks: / Build me up buttercup / I believe.
7" Single: Released 20 Jun '87, on Face, by Face Records & Music. Catalogue no: **FR 102**

HEARTBREAK SITUATION
Tracks: / Heartbreak situation.
7" Single: Released Jun '83, on Sticky, Catalogue no: **STICK 102**

NOW THAT I'VE FOUND YOU
Tracks: / Now that I've found you / Boys dont cry / Now that I've found you (re-mix).
7" Single: Released May '88, on Nine O Nine, by Creole Records. Catalogue no: **NINE 719**
12" Single: Released May '88, on Nine O Nine, by Creole Records. Catalogue no: **NINE 19**

Paul, Ashley

WHEN BOYS CRY
Tracks: / When boys cry / When boys cry (dub) / When boys cry (devastating mix).
12" Single: Released May '88, on Nine O Nine, by Creole Records. Catalogue no: **NINE 18**
7" Single: Released May '88, on Nine O Nine, by Creole Records. Catalogue no: **NINE 718**

Paul, Billy

Biographical details: This American singer has always been known as a soul artist, although his voice also contains a jazzy element. Although he began his sining career at the age of 11, he had to wait until 38 for his first hit. He was boen Paul Williams in Philadelphia in 1934, and grew up listening to his mother's collection of jazz 78s. He started performing on a local radio station at 11, and later studied music at two specialist colleges. Given early encouragement by jazz legend Charlie Parker, who told Paul to stick to his musical career for as long as it took to succeed, he formed his own trio and released his first record *Why Am I* in 1955. After being drafted into the Army, his resumed his career at the end of the Fifties. The Sixties proved to be a decade of struggles; he was briefly a member of Harold Melvin & The Blue Notes and, a few years later, formed a friendship with the songwriting/production pair Kenny Gamble and Leon Huff. After owning a couple of shortlived labels in the Sixties, Gamble and Huff struck upon lasting success with Philadelphia International company in the early Seventies. Both Billy and Harold Melvin's Blue Notes became part of that success. In December 1972, in the same week that Harold Melvin & The Blue Notes were No. 3 on the American charts with their first smash *If You Don't Know Me By Now*, Billy Paul climbed to No. 1 with his breakthrough hit *Me And Mrs Jones*. There were three important elements in the success of this single: the immaculate production of Gamble and Huff, whose 'Philly' soul sound became one of the key forces in the black music of the Seventies; the characteristically colourful and passionate vocal delivery by Billy; and the striking lyrics, which made *Me And Mrs Jones* the first pop smash to focus on an adulterous relationship. Although *Me And Mrs Jones* remained Paul's biggest hit on both sides of the Atlantic (peaking at No. 12 in Britain), his association with Philly yielded some further memorable records during the Seventies. Gamble and Huff gave him spicy lyrics once again on *Let's Make A Baby*, which reached the UK Top 30 in 1976 despite a BBC ban. Socially conscious lyrics, well suited to Billy's intense style, were heard on tracks like *Only The Strong Survive*, *Everybody's Breakin' Up* and *Bring The Family Back*. In 1977 he scored with superb soul remakes of two pop hits: Paul McCartney's *Let 'Em In* (featuring excerpts of speeches by Martin Luther King) and Elton John's *Your Song*. During the early Eighties Billy Paul took an extended break from recording to recharge his batteries; he spent part of this time taking renewed tuition in musical theory, mastering such skils as counterpointing. He made a disappointing comeback attempt in 1985 with *Sexual Therapy*, a carbon copy of Marvin Gaye's *Sexual healing*. In 1986 he played some concert dates with up-and-coming soul singer Joana Gardner. Bob MacDonald, 25 February 1986..

6 TRACK HITS
Tracks: / Me & Mrs Jones / Let's make a baby / Thanks for saving my life / Let 'em in / Don't give up on us / Brown baby.
7" EP: Released Sep '83, on Scoop 33, by Pickwick Records. Catalogue no: **7SR 5019**

BRING THE FAMILY BACK
Tracks: / Bring the family back.
7" Single: Released Jul '79, on Philadelphia Int., by EMI Records. Deleted '82. Catalogue no: **PIR 7456**
12" Single: Released Sep '85, on Streetwave, Catalogue no: **SWAVE 2**

LATELY
Tracks: / Lately.
12" Single: Released Jan '86, on RCA, by BMG Records (UK). Catalogue no: **FT 49900**
7" Single: Released Jan '86, on RCA, by BMG Records (UK). Catalogue no: **FB 49899**

LATELY (SINGLE) (See panel on previous page)
Tracks: / Lately / I search no more.
7" Single: Released Jan '86, on Total Experience, Catalogue no: **FB 49899**

LET 'EM IN
Tracks: / Let 'em in.
7" Single: Released Apr '77, on Philadelphia Int., by EMI Records. Deleted '80. Catalogue no: **PIR 5143**

LET'S MAKE A BABY
Tracks: / Let's make a baby.
7" Single: Released May '76, on Philadelphia Int., by EMI Records. Deleted '79. Catalogue no: **PIR 4144**

LET'S MAKE A BABY (OLD GOLD)
Tracks: / Let's make a baby / America / Malorie.
12" Single: Released Aug '88, on Old Gold, by Old Gold Records. Catalogue no: **OG 4074**

ME & MRS JONES
Tracks: / Me & Mrs Jones.
7" Single: Released Jan '73, on Epic, by CBS Records. Deleted '76. Catalogue no: **EPC 1055**

ME & MRS JONES (OLD GOLD)
Tracks: / Me & Mrs Jones / Let's make a baby.
7" Single: Released Apr '83, on Old Gold, by Old Gold Records. Catalogue no: **OG 9308**

ONLY THE STRONG SURVIVE (SINGLE)
Tracks: / Only the strong survive.
7" Single: Released Nov '77, on Philadelphia Int., by EMI Records. Deleted '80. Catalogue no: **PIR 5699**

SEXUAL THERAPY
Tracks: / Sexual therapy.
7" Single: Released Sep '85, on Total Experience, Catalogue no: **PB 49933**
12" Single: Released Sep '85, on Total Experience, Catalogue no: **PT 49934**

THANKS FOR SAVING MY LIFE
Tracks: / Thanks for saving my life.
7" Single: Released Jan '74, on Philadelphia Int., by EMI Records. Deleted '77. Catalogue no: **PIR 1928**

WE COULD HAVE BEEN
Tracks: / We could have been / Wide open / Dirty laundry (12" only).
12" Single: Released 1 May '89, on Ichiban, by Ichiban Records (UK). Catalogue no: **ICHT 705**
7" Single: Released 1 May '89, on Ichiban, by Ichiban Records (UK). Catalogue no: **ICHS 705**

YOUR SONG
Tracks: / Your song.
7" Single: Released Jul '77, on Philadelphia Int., by EMI Records. Deleted '80. Catalogue no: **PIR 5391**

YOU'RE MY SWEETNESS
Tracks: / You're my sweetness / Me and mrs jones.
7" Single: Released Feb '80, on Epic, by CBS Records. Deleted Feb '85. Catalogue no: **EPC 8202**

Paul, Chris

BACK IN MY ARMS
Tracks: / Back in my arms (radio edit) / City nights.
12" Single: Released Nov '87, on Syncopate, by EMI Records. Deleted Nov '88. Catalogue no: **12SYX 5**
12" Single: Released Oct '87, on Syncopate, by EMI Records. Catalogue no: **12 SY 5**
7" Single: Released Oct '87, on Syncopate, by EMI Records. Deleted Nov '88. Catalogue no: **SY 5**

EXPANSIONS '86 (EXPAND YOUR MIND)
Tracks: / Expansions '86 (expand your mind)(remix) / Expansions '86 / Broadway boulevard.
7" Single: Released May '86, on 4th & Broadway, by Island Records. Catalogue no: **BRW 48**
12" Single: Released May '86, on 4th & Broadway, by Island Records. Catalogue no: **12 BRW 48**
12" Single: Released Jul '86, on 4th & Broadway, by Island Records. Catalogue no: **12 BRWX 48**

TURN THE MUSIC UP
Tracks: / Turn the music up / House on the move / Turn the music up (acidic dub) (Available on 12" only).
Note: * Only on the 12" version.
7" Single: Released Aug '88, on Syncopate, by EMI Records. Deleted Aug '89. Catalogue no: **SY 13**
12" Single: Released Aug '88, on Syncopate, by EMI Records. Deleted Aug '89. Catalogue no: **12SY 13**
12" Single: Released Aug '88, on Syncopate, by EMI Records. Deleted Aug '89. Catalogue no: **12SYX 13**

Paul, Eugene

CHILDREN GO TO SCHOOL
Tracks: / Children go to school / Time.
7" Single: Released Mar '81, on Ensign, by Ensign Records. Deleted Mar '84. Catalogue no: **ENY 205**
12" Single: Released Mar '81, on Ensign, by Ensign Records. Deleted Mar '84. Catalogue no: **ENYT 205**

THERE'S AN ISLAND
Tracks: / There's an island / There's an island (part 2).
12" Single: Released Dec '84, on Hot Vinyl, Catalogue no: **HVD 006**

Paul, Frankie

A NO NUTTEN
Tracks: / A no nutten.
12" Single: Released Aug '88, on Fashion, by Fashion Records. Catalogue no: **FAD 060**

ACID
Tracks: / Acid.
12" Single: Released Feb '89, Catalogue no: **BD 89005**

AFRICAN PRINCESS
Tracks: / African princess.
12" Single: Released Jun '84, on Ethnic, Catalogue no: **ETH 2246**

AGONY
Tracks: / Agony.
12" Single: Released Mar '88, on Ujama, Catalogue no: **UJ 2**

ALESHA
Tracks: / Alesha.
12" Single: Released Dec '86, on Power House, Catalogue no: **PHT 13**

BAD MAN PICNEY
Tracks: / Bad man picney.
7" Single: Released Jan '88, on White Label (1), Catalogue no: **TD 0014**

BE MINE TONIGHT
Tracks: / Be mine tonight.
12" Single: Released Feb '89, on Jammy's, Catalogue no: **VPRD 411**

BEGINNING, THE
Tracks: / Beginning, The.
7" Single: Released Dec '84, on Scom, Catalogue no: **Unknown**

BROKEN HEART REFUGE
Tracks: / Broken heart refuge.
12" Single: Released Sep '85, on High Power, Catalogue no: **HPD 006**

CASANOVA (SINGLE)
Tracks: / Casanova.
12" Single: Released Feb '88, on Live & Love, Catalogue no: **LLD 64**

CLOSER I GET TO YOU
Tracks: / Closer I get to you, The.
12" Single: Released Jun '85, on Greensleeves, by Greensleeves Records. Catalogue no: **GRED 182**

COME ON GIRL
Tracks: / Come on girl.
12" Single: Released Jul '88, on Live & Love, Catalogue no: **LLD 82**

COME TO ME
Tracks: / Come to me.
12" Single: Released 5 Mar '88, on Germaine, Catalogue no: **DGT 31**

DO GOOD
Tracks: / Do good.
12" Single: Released Nov '84, on Greensleeves, by Greensleeves Records. Catalogue no: **GRED 160**

EAGLES FEATHER
Tracks: / Eagles feather.
12" Single: Released Dec '86, on SMP (2), Catalogue no: **SMP 004**

FIONA
Tracks: / Fiona.
7" Single: Released Jul '87, on Pioneer International, Catalogue no: **PI 49**

FIRE DEDE A MUS MUS TAIL
Tracks: / Fire dede a mus mus tail.
12" Single: Released Aug '84, on Blacker Dread, Catalogue no: **SCOMBD 0058**

FOOLS FIGHTING
Tracks: / Fools fighting.
12" Single: Released Sep '85, on Greensleeves, by Greensleeves Records. Catalogue no: **GRED 189**

FOREIGN MIND
Tracks: / Foreign mind.
12" Single: Released Sep '84, on Greensleeves, by Greensleeves Records. Catalogue no: **GRED 158**

GET READY
Tracks: / Get ready / Get ready (version).
12" Single: Released 17 Oct '87, on Supreme, by Supreme Records. Catalogue no: **SUPT 1**

GUN SHOT
Tracks: / Gun shot / Gun shot (version).
12" Single: Released Jun '87, on Skengdon, Catalogue no: **SKDL 018**
12" Single: Released Jun '87, on Sweatbox, by Sweatbox Records. Catalogue no: **SOX 20**

HONEY GIRL
Tracks: / Honey girl.
7" Single: Released 12 May '89, on Blue Trac, by Blue Trac Records. Catalogue no: **BTRD 038**

I AM YOUR LOVER
Tracks: / Baby come on / I am your lover.
12" Single: Released Jan '87, on Fingers, Catalogue no: **TD 007**

I KNOW THE SCORE
Tracks: / I know the score.
12" Single: Released Aug '88, on Live & Love, Catalogue no: **LLD 79**

I WANNA SAY I LOVE YOU
Tracks: / I wanna say I love you.
12" Single: Released Feb '89, on Techniques, Catalogue no: **WRT 41**

I WRITE THE SONGS
Tracks: / I write the songs.
7" Single: Released Jan '89, on Exterminator, Catalogue no: **Unknown**

INFERIORITY COMPLEX
Tracks: / Inferiority complex.
12" Single: Released Aug '85, on Blue Mountain, Catalogue no: **BM 005**

IT'S YOU I LOVE
Tracks: / It's you I love.
12" Single: Released Aug '84, on Londisc, by Londisc Records. Catalogue no: **LDR 021**

JAMAICA SOCA
Tracks: / Jamaica soca.
12" Single: Released Dec '88, on Hawkeye, by Hawkeye Records. Catalogue no: **HD 93**

JUST BE MY LADY
Tracks: / Just be my lady.
12" Single: Released Jun '84, on Real Wax, Catalogue no: **JGMD 8197**

KEEP ON DANCING
Tracks: / Keep on dancing / Dancing dub.
12" Single: Released Feb '86, on Greensleeves, by Greensleeves Records. Catalogue no: **GRED 194**

KICK UP RUMPUS
Tracks: / Kick up rumpus.
12" Single: Released May '87, on Power House, Catalogue no: **PHD 16**

LITTLE WALTER
Tracks: / Little Walter.
12" Single: Released Oct '88, on Blue Mountain, Catalogue no: **BMD 049**
12" Single: Released Oct '88, on Fashion, by Fashion Records. Catalogue no: **FAD 061**

LOVE BEEN TAKEN
Tracks: / Love been taken.
12" Single: Released Jul '88, on Youth Promotion, Catalogue no: **YP 0030**

LOVE OF MY LIFE
Tracks: / Love of my life.
12" Single: Released Sep '89, on Techniques, Catalogue no: **WRT 56**

MIDNIGHT RAVER
Tracks: / Midnight raver.
12" Single: Released Jun '85, on Hornpipe, Catalogue no: **HD 59**

MOVING UP
Tracks: / Moving up.
12" Single: Released Jun '88, on Techniques, Catalogue no: **WRT 33**

NEVER GONNA GIVE YOU UP
Tracks: / Never gonna give you up.
12" Single: Released Jul '88, on Exterminator, Catalogue no: **VPRD 313**

NO TOUCH NO STYLEE
Tracks: / No touch no stylee.
12" Single: Released Oct '85, on Black Address, Catalogue no: **SCOMBD 021**

OLD NIGGER
12" Single: Released Sep '84, on Cornerstone, Catalogue no: **Unknown**

ONE LITTLE ROMANCE
Tracks: / One little romance.
12" Single: Released Jul '89, on Reality, Catalogue no: **REAL 002**

ONLY YOU (BABY BABY)
Tracks: / Only you (baby baby).
12" Single: on Sir Coxsone, Catalogue no: **BD 88001**

PASS ME THE SCALE
Tracks: / Pass me the scale / Island rock (Top Rank Players).
12" Single: Released Jan '86, on Top Rank (2), Catalogue no: **TRD 012**
12" Single: Released Oct '84, on Top Rank (2), Catalogue no: **Unknown**

RIDE ON
Tracks: / Ride on.
12" Single: Released Mar '85, on Top Rank (2), Catalogue no: **TR 002**

RIDE THE RHYTHM
Tracks: / Ride the rhythm.
12" Single: Released Dec '84, on Time, Catalogue no: **TR 008**

ROCK YOU STEADY
Tracks: / Rock you steady.
7" Single: Released Oct '88, on Pioneer Muzik, Catalogue no: **PM 010**

SARAH
Tracks: / Sarah.
12" Single: Released Sep '87, on Live & Love, Catalogue no: **LLD 467**

SHINE ON
Tracks: / Shine on.
12" Single: Released Apr '88, on Ujama, Catalogue no: **UJ 12**

SHINING STAR
Tracks: / Shining star.
12" Single: Released Jul '85, on Tonos, Catalogue no: **TON 007**

SHUB IN
Tracks: / Shub in.
12" Single: on Trojan, by Trojan Records. Deleted May '88. Catalogue no: **PA 2**
7" Single: on Trojan, by Trojan Records. Deleted May '88. Catalogue no: **7 PA 2**

SLOW DOWN
Tracks: / Slow down.
7" Single: Released Jun '88, on Redman International, Catalogue no: **RED 13**

SOUTH AFRICA
Tracks: / South Africa.
12" Single: Released Oct '84, on Fu-Manchu, Catalogue no: **PC 004**

SOUVENIR
Tracks: / Souvenir.
12" Single: Released Jan '89, on Tonos, Catalogue no: **TAAC 8**

TELL ME YOU LOVE ME
Tracks: / Tell me you love me.
12" Single: Released 5 Mar '88, on Germaine, Catalogue no: **DGT 32**

THRILLER
Tracks: / Thriller.
12" Single: Released May '85, on Ranking Joe Universal, Catalogue no: **RT 008**

THROUGHOUT THE YEARS
Tracks: / Throughout the years.
12" Single: Released May '88, on Blue Trac, by Blue Trac Records. Catalogue no: **BRTD 016**

TIDAL WAVE (SINGLE)
Tracks: / Tidal wave.
12" Single: Released Mar '85, on Greensleeves, by Greensleeves Records. Cata-

logue no: **GRED 170**

TOUCH ME
Tracks: / Touch me.
12" Single: Released Aug '88, on Living Room, Catalogue no: **LM 007**

WE'VE ONLY JUST BEGUN
Tracks: / We've only just begun.
12" Single: Released Mar '88, on Charm, by Charm Records. Catalogue no: **CRT 12**

YOU'RE MY KIND
Tracks: / You're my kind.
12" Single: Released Feb '89, on Briggie C, Catalogue no: **BC 001T**

YOU'RE SO GOOD TO ME
Tracks: / You're so good to me / Bald head, treat your woman good.
12" Single: Released Nov '86, on Technique, Catalogue no: **WRT 010**

Paul, Les

Biographical details: Les paul was born Lester Polfus in Waukesha, Wisconsin in 1915; he has done more for the electric guitar than anyone else except Charlie Christian, with whom he was sometimes compared. He began playing on the radio in Wisconsin, then Chicago; he played country music as Hot Rod Red and Rhubarb Red; formed a jazz-oriented Les Paul Trio in 1936 and led it for nearly a decade (a few tracks now on Guitar Genius on Charly). He also recorded with Bing Crosby and the Andrews Sisters on the American Decca label; by the time he toured with Jazz At The Philharmonic in the late '40s he was building his own guitars; he took the first solid-body electric guitar to Gibson in 1946, and the Les Paul model became one of the most famous guitars in the world. *Lover/Brazil* '48 was a two-sided hit on Capitol, overdubbed until it sounded like six guitars; he broke his right elbow in a car crash and had it reset at an angle so he could still play; the instrumental hits continued through 1953, including *Nola* (a piano novelty from 1919) with Paul playing both electric and Spanish guitars. Meanwhile he met country singer Mary Ford (born Colleen Summers in 1928; they married in 1949, seperated in 1963and she died in 1977). Les Paul and Mary Ford were among the biggest hitmakers of the early '50s in the USA; 28 hits 1950-57 three at no. 2, *How High the Moon* and *Vaya Con Dios* at no.1, the latter for 11 weeks in 1953. Les Paul's Capitol recordings used technology that was ahead of its time, most recorded in his own studio using an 8-track desk of his design, both his guitar and her voice overdubbed, and they stand up very well today. He retired to his work bench except for the album in 1968, but became active again in the mid-'70s, performing and promoting his guitars for Gibson; he moved full circle back to country picking, recording with his old friend Chet Atkins, winning a Grammy for *Chester And Lester* in 1977, followed by *Guitar Monsters* '78. He was featured in a TV documentary, The Wizard of Waukesha, in 1980. (Donald Clarke 15.5.87).

HOW HIGH THE MOON
10" single: Released Feb '83, on Capitol, by EMI Records. Deleted '88. Catalogue no: **10 CL 282**
7" Single: Released Feb '83, on Capitol, by EMI Records. Deleted '88. Catalogue no: **CL 282**

VAYA CON DIOS
Tracks: / Vaya con dios.
7" Single: Released Nov '53, on Capitol, by EMI Records. Deleted '56. Catalogue no: **CL 13943**

Paul, Lyn

Biographical details: This British singer enjoyed international fame as a member of the New Seekers during the early Seventies. Born in 1949, she had previously tried her hand at being a singer, dancer and comedienne in a variety of short-lived groups. The three guy/two girl lineup of the New Seekers was formed in 1969 and lasted until May 1974, when the group split up to pursue solo careers. These individual ventures were so underwhelming in their impact on the public that Lyn Paul's No. 37 showing with 1975's *It Outghta Sell A Million* was he only UK chart entry by any solo New Seeker. Perhaps because of this distinction, Lyn was the only member who chose not to rejoin the group when they reformed in 1976. In common with the New Seekers' biggest British and worldwide hit *I'd Like To Teach The World To Sing*, *It Oughta Sell A Million* started life as a Coca-Cola jingle. It was a catchy enough song, but Paul's voice was not suffiently strong or distinctive on its own to puch the single into the higher echelons of the charts. Her other efforts flopped altogether, and she faded into obscurity. After a decade out of the limelight, Lyn Paul suddenly popped up in the summer of 1985 in an article contained in one of Britain's popular daily tabloid newspapers. In what appeared to be an attempt to regain some publicity, she namedropped several celebrities and spread some tittle-tattle about them; disc jockey Tony Blackburn, whom she described as the most boring person she had ever dated, gave a hilarious in-depth response on his Radio London show. Also in 1985, Lyn made the news as the fiancee of Mike Nolan, singer with Eighties New Seekers-type group Bucks Fizz. Bob MacDonald, 25 February 1986..

ECHOES OF LOVE
Tracks: / Echoes of love / You never told me it love hurts.
7" Single: Released Jul '83, on Crash, by Satril Records. Deleted '85. Catalogue no: **CRA 509**

T OUGHTA SELL A MILLION
Tracks: / It oughta sell a million.
7" Single: Released Jun '75, on Polydor, by Polydor Ltd. Deleted '78. Catalogue no: **2058 602**

MAKE THE NIGHT
Tracks: / Make the night / Everything that's part of you.
7" Single: Released Sep '84, on Mute, by Mute Records. Catalogue no: **CRA 607**

Paul, Owen

BRING ME BACK THAT SPARK
Tracks: / Bring me back that spark / Feeling, A / Feeling, A.
12" Single: Released Mar '87, on Epic, by CBS Records. Catalogue no: **OWEN T6**
7" Single: Released Mar '87, on Epic, by CBS Records. Catalogue no: **OWEN 6**

MAD ABOUT THE GIRL
Tracks: / Mad about the girl / Going solo.
7" Single: Released Sep '87, on NBR, Catalogue no: **OWP 1**
12" Single: Released Sep '87, on NBR, Catalogue no: **12 OWP 1**

MY FAVOURITE WASTE OF TIME
Tracks: / My favourite waste of time / Just another day.
12" Single: Released May '86, on Epic, by CBS Records. Deleted '86. Catalogue no: **TA 7125**
7" Single: Released May '86, on Epic, by CBS Records. Deleted '86. Catalogue no: **A 7125**

ONE WORLD
Tracks: / One world / Pleased to meet you.
7" Single: Released Oct '86, on Epic, by CBS Records. Deleted '87. Catalogue no: **OWEN 5**
12" Single: Released Oct '86, on Epic, by CBS Records. Deleted '87. Catalogue no: **OWENT 5**

ONLY FOR THE YOUNG
Tracks: / Only for the young / Another homeland.
7" Single: Released Jan '86, on Epic, by CBS Records. Catalogue no: **A 6847**
12" Single: Released Jan '86, on Epic, by CBS Records. Catalogue no: **TX 6847**

PLEASED TO MEET YOU
Tracks: / Pleased to meet you / Sunny.
12" Single: Released Sep '86, on Epic, by CBS Records. Deleted '87. Catalogue no: **650097 6**
7" Single: Released Sep '86, on Epic, by CBS Records. Deleted '87. Catalogue no: **650097 7**

Paul & Paula

Biographical details: Paul (whose real name was Ray Hildebrand) and Paula (Jill Jackson) were in their early twenties when they shot from nowhere to stardom in early 1963 with *Hey Paula*. This starry eyed vocal duo typified the innocence and optimistic romance of the American pop music of that era, soon to be swept aside by the Beatles and the British invasion. Paul & Paula were a couple of college students from Texas who happened to sing together one day for a cancer benefit show on local radio. The combination clicked, and Hildebrand's song *Hey Paula* became their first record. It reached No. 1 in America and No. 8 in Britain. The similar sounding follow-up *Young Lovers*, written by Ray in collaboration with Jill's mother, climbed to No. 6 in the US and No. 9 in the UK. For some of their appearances, the duo wore unisex sweaters with the letter 'P' embalzoned on them; this sparked off a craze. Subsequent singles were less and less successful, and the duo soon disappeared. They were never romantically linked in real life, and settled down with separate partners in different parts of America. Bob MacDonald, 25 February 1986..

HEY PAULA
Tracks: / Hey Paula.
7" Single: Released Feb '63, on Philips, by Phonogram Ltd. Deleted '66. Catalogue no: **304012 BF**

YOUNG LOVERS
Tracks: / Young lovers.
7" Single: Released Apr '63, on Philips, by Phonogram Ltd. Deleted '66. Catalogue no: **304016 BF**

Paul, PK

JUMPED THE GUN
Tracks: / Jump the gun / Picking up the pieces.
7" Single: Released Jul '82, on Pastafont, by Pastafont Music. Catalogue no: **PF 3005**

Paula

BEE BOP DANCING
Tracks: / Bee bop dancing.
12" Single: Released Sep '85, on Rock'n'Groove, Catalogue no: **RNG 004**

DYNAMIC
Tracks: / Dynamic.
7" Single: Released Sep '85, on Rhino, by Creole Records. Catalogue no: **RNO 4**

JAZZY
Tracks: / Jazzy / You want my man.
12" Single: Released Nov '84, on Rock'n'Groove, Catalogue no: **RNG 001**

Paulette

MY ONLY LOVE
Tracks: / My only love / My only love (version).
7" Single: Released Nov '82, on Solomonic (1), by Solomonic Records. Catalogue no: **SM 004**

Pause

IT'S JUST AMAZING
Tracks: / It's just amazing.
12" Single: Released Mar '89, on White Label (1), Catalogue no: **CLICK 1**

Pavarotti, Luciano

Biographical details: This Italian classical and operatic singer has become one of the greatest worldwide names in his profession. Together with names like Kiri Te Kanawa and Placido Domingo, he has achieved success on a scale which has brought many previously unconverted listeners to appreciation of classical music. *Pavarotti's Greatest Hits* reached No. 95 on the UK album chart in May 1982, he has been a huge success in America, where such albums as *Passions* and Verdi's *Masked Ball* have maintained his sales prowess into the mid-Eighties. Pavarotti's single releases in Britain have included *Ave Maria* and *If We Were In Love.* Bob MacDonald, 25 February 1986..

AVE MARIA
Tracks: / Ave Maria / Oh come all ye faithful.
7" Single: Released Oct '80, on Decca, by Decca Records. Deleted '88. Catalogue no: **PAVO 1**

IF I WERE IN LOVE
Tracks: / If I were in love / None shall sleep.
7" Single: Released Feb '83, on Decca, by Decca Records. Deleted '88. Catalogue no: **PAVO 2**

Pavillion, Percy

CRICKET IN THE JUNGLE, THE
Tracks: / Cricket in the jungle, The.
7" Single: Released Jul '83, on Paviloned in Splendour, Deleted '84. Catalogue no: **PIS 1**

GOWER POWER
Tracks: / Gower power.
7" Single: Released Jun '84, on Dead Good Dolly Platters, Catalogue no: **DMS 002**

Pavone, Rita

HEART
Tracks: / Heart.
7" Single: Released Dec '66, on RCA, by BMG Records (UK). Deleted '69. Catalogue no: **RCA 1553**

YOU ONLY YOU
Tracks: / You only you.
7" Single: Released Jan '67, on RCA, by BMG Records (UK). Deleted '70. Catalogue no: **RCA 1561**

Pawlak, Andy

MERMAIDS
Tracks: / Mermaids / No compromise / Squeaky clean (Only on 12") / Winter time (Only on CD single).
Note: The debut single from Tyneside's Andy Pawlack. He is a singer, songwriter in the tradition of Van Morrison, Elvis Costello and Aztec Camera and Mermaid's has a clean modern edge - which means it's an obvious contender for the charts. He has supported The Pogues, The Blow Monkeys and Wet Wet Wet. (Phonogram, Oct 1988)
12" Single: Released Oct '88, on Phonogram, by Phonogram Ltd. Deleted 31 May '89. Catalogue no: **PAWL 112**
12" Single: Released Oct '88, on Phonogram, by Phonogram Ltd. Deleted 31 May '89. Catalogue no: **PAWL 1212**
CD 5": Released Oct '88, on Phonogram, by Phonogram Ltd. Catalogue no: **PAWCD 1**
7" Single: Released Oct '88, on Phonogram, by Phonogram Ltd. Deleted 31 May '89. Catalogue no: **PAWL 1**

SECRETS
Tracks: / Secrets / Bulldogs / Lullaby / For better or worse (Available on CD single format only.).
7" Single: Released Jan '89, on Phonogram, by Phonogram Ltd. Deleted 31 Jul '89. Catalogue no: **PAWL 2**
12" Single: Released Jan '89, on Phonogram, by Phonogram Ltd. Deleted 31 Jul '89. Catalogue no: **PAWL 212**
CD 5": Released Jan '89, on Phonogram, by Phonogram Ltd. Catalogue no: **PAWCD 2**

SHE KEPT A HOLD OF LOVE Mothers day
Tracks: / She kept a hold of love (Mothers day) / Turn again / Eskimo kissing / She kept a hold of love (Acoustic version).
7" Single: Released 30 May '89, on Phonogram, by Phonogram Ltd. Deleted Oct '89. Catalogue no: **PAWL 3**
12" Single: Released 30 May '89, on Phonogram, by Phonogram Ltd. Deleted Oct '89. Catalogue no: **PAWL 312**
CD 5": Released 30 May '89, on Phonogram, by Phonogram Ltd. Catalogue no: **PAWCD 3**

Paxton, Tom

Biographical details: Paxton was born in 1937. His sense of humour and personable stage presence has kept him popular as a live attraction, and he has continued recording on his own Mountain Railroad label. (Donald Clarke 15.5.87) This American folk singer, songwriter and guitarist was born in Chicago and, after studying at the University of Oklahoma and undergoing his military service, became one of the many folkies on the Greenwich Village scene of the early Sixties. He took the same route as many of his peers - built up a cult following in the coffeehouses of that famous suburb of New York, and then signed with Elektra Records. The title track of his first album 1964's *Ramblin' Boy*, became a folk standard. Many other strong compositions followed, in a career which spawned much recordable material for other artists but little disc success for Paxton himself. Paxton became a regular commentator on political and social issues. His early protest numbers included *Daily News* and *Lyndon Johnson Told The Nation*. Later examples of the singer's running commentary on news events were *Talking Vietnam Pot Luck Blues* (1968), *The Hostage* (1973), *All Clear In Harrisburg* (1980) and *Be A Sport* (1981) amongst many others. His memorable love songs included *The Last Thing On My Mind, My Lady's A Wild Flying Dove* and *Leaving London*. His other strengths included travelling songs (e.g. *Bound For The Mountains And The Sea* and *I Can't Help But Wonder Where I'm Bound*) and children's numbers (such as *We're All Going To The Zoo* and *Katie*). Paxton's acclaimed performance at the 1971 Isle Of Wight Festival earned him a cult following in Britain. Three of his albums registered on the UK Top 50 during the early Seventies: *No. 6* (No. 23), *The Compleat Tom Paxton* (No. 18) and *Peace Will Come* (No. 47, produced by the famous Tony Visconti). These successes aside, his general lack of major chart action on both sides of the Atlantic is explained by the fact that he has remained true to his folk roots, and has resisted the temptation to seek wider fame in the pop, rock or MOR spheres. He has continued recording into the Eighties. Bob MacDonald, 25 February 1986..

BAD OLD DAY'S
Tracks: / Bad old days.
7" Single: Released Nov '85, on Cherry Lane, by Cherry Lane Productions. Deleted '86. Catalogue no: **PIP 719**

BE A SPORT AFGHANISTAN
Tracks: / Be a sport Afghanistan / Outlaw.
7" Single: Released Jun '80, on Evolution, by Evolution Records. Deleted '83. Catalogue no: **EV 8**

FEED THE CHILDREN
Tracks: / Feed the children / That's the way it seems to me.
7" Single: Released Apr '80, on Evolution, by Evolution Records. Deleted '83. Catalogue no: **EV 5**

Payback VS Atmosfear

KICKIN' IT
Tracks: / Kickin' it (alkaline mix) / Cut like a knife (radical rebel mix).
12" Single: Released Mar '88, on Jam Today, by Jam Today Records. Catalogue no: **12CHIL 6**

Payne, Devin

EXCUSE ME (SINGLE)
Tracks: / Excuse me / Confess.

7" Single: Released Mar '81, on Polydor, by Polydor Ltd. Deleted Mar '84. Catalogue no: **POSP 237**

Payne, Freda

Biographical details: A fine jazz and soul singer, Freda Payne was born in Detroit in 1945. She will always be famous for her huge 1970 hit Band Of Gold. Earlier she had sung with Quincy Jones and Duke Ellington. After her success on Holland-Dozier-Holland's Invictus label she reverted to jazz, hosted a USA TV show and remained popular in clubs. (Donald Clarke, May 1987.).

BAND OF GOLD
Tracks: / Band of gold / Easiest way to fall.
7" Single: Released Jan '81, on Champagne Records, Deleted Jan '84. Catalogue no: **VAT 301**
7" Single: Released Sep '70, on Invictus, Deleted '73. Catalogue no: **INV 502**
12" Single: Released Jan '81, on Champagne Records, Deleted Jan '84. Catalogue no: **VATS 301**
7" Single: Released Jun '89, on hgh, Catalogue no: **HGH 451**

CHERISH WHAT IS DEAR TO YOU
Tracks: / Cherish what is dear to you.
7" Single: Released Mar '71, on Invictus, Deleted '74. Catalogue no: **INV 509**

DEEPER & DEEPER
Tracks: / Deeper and deeper.
7" Single: Released Nov '70, on Invictus, Deleted '73. Catalogue no: **INV 505**

IN MOTION
Tracks: / In motion.
7" Single: Released Nov '82, on Buddah, by Buddah Records Inc.(USA). Deleted Nov '85. Catalogue no: **BDS 498**

Payne, John

FLY AWAY
Tracks: / Fly away / Coming home.
7" Single: Released Dec '83, on Arrival, by Blaylock Management Ltd.. Deleted '86. Catalogue no: **PIK 13**

GONNA GIVE HER ALL THE LOVE I'VE GOT
Tracks: / Gonna give her all the love I've got / Looking at your picture.
7" Single: Released Mar '84, on Arrival, by Blaylock Management Ltd.. Deleted '86. Catalogue no: **PIK 15**

Payne, Les

WHO WILL BE THE WINNER
Tracks: / Who will be the winner / Over to you.
7" Single: Released May '82, on Polydor, by Polydor Ltd. Deleted '85. Catalogue no: **POSP 418**

Payne, Scherrie

CHASING ME INTO SOMEONE ELSE'S ARMS
Tracks: / Chasing me into someone else's arms.
12" Single: Released Feb '87, on Nightmare Gold, Catalogue no: **NGR 8**

I'M NOT IN LOVE
Tracks: / I'm not in love / Girl you're in love.
7" Single: Released Dec '82, on Record Shack, by Record Shack Records. Catalogue no: **SOHO 1**

Payola, Lola

SCHOOL GIRL SONG
Tracks: / School girl song / I got married to a man from outer space.
7" Single: Released Aug '81, on Epic, by CBS Records. Deleted Aug '84. Catalogue no: **EPCA 1499**

Payolas

CHINA BOYS
Tracks: / China boys / Rose.
7" Single: Released May '81, on A&M, by A&M Records. Deleted May '84. Catalogue no: **PFP 1001**

JUKE BOX
Tracks: / Jukebox / T.N.T.
7" Single: Released Feb '81, on Illegal, by Faulty Products Records. Catalogue no: **ILS 0024**

Payton, Walter

WOLVERINE BLUES See also under Teddy Riley & Jim Duggan
Tracks: / Wolverine blues.
7" Single: Released Nov '87, on Nola, Catalogue no: **JB (S) 5**

Paz

ALWAYS THERE
Tracks: / Right moment, The / Big shot / Angels delight / For art / I can see you / You've got something / Be natural / Hold back / Always there.

7" Single: Released Mar '86, on Coda, by Coda Records. Catalogue no: **CODS 16**
12" Single: Released Mar '86, on Coda, by Coda Records. Catalogue no: **CODS 16 T**

Peabody, Dave

CATS WHISKERS
7" EP: Released Oct '88, on Waterfront, by Waterfront Music. Catalogue no: **WFEP 01**

Peace Band

WISHES
Tracks: / Wishes.
7" Single: Released May '84, on Southbank-GLC, Catalogue no: **GLC 1**

Peach, Dixie

GET UP AND SKANK
Tracks: / Get up and skank / Skank with me.
12" Single: Released May '87, on Y & D, Catalogue no: **YDDO 106**

LOVE BONDAGE
Tracks: / Love bondage.
12" Single: Released 20 Mar '89, on Music Scene, Catalogue no: **MKS 62580**

LOVE IS A THING
Tracks: / Love is a thing.
12" Single: Released Nov '86, on Jah Tubbys, Catalogue no: **JT 022**

PURE WORRIES
Tracks: / Pure worries.
12" Single: Released Jul '85, on Jah Tubbys, Catalogue no: **JT 011**

SLAUGHTER
Tracks: / Slaughter / Slaughter mix.
12" Single: Released Jul '86, on Jah Tubbys, Catalogue no: **JT 018**

SPIN SPIN
Tracks: / Spin spin.
12" Single: Released Dec '85, on Jah Tubbys, Catalogue no: **JT 014**

TONIGHT IS THE NIGHT
Tracks: / Tonight is the night / Tonight is the night (7"version).
12" Single: Released 17 Oct '87, on Y & D, Catalogue no: **YDDO 112**

Peaches

FOR THE LOVE OF YOU
Tracks: / For the love of you / Your love is king.
12" Single: Released Apr '85, on Peaches, Catalogue no: **PEACH IT**

SWEET TALK
Tracks: / Sweet talk.
12" Single: Released May '83, on Starlite, by Titan Int. Prod.. Catalogue no: **SLD 5027**

WHY
Tracks: / Why.
12" Single: Released Sep '83, on Peaches, Catalogue no: **PE 001**

YOUR LOVE IS KING
Tracks: / Your love is king.
12" Single: Released May '84, on Arena, Catalogue no: **AR 31**

Peaches & Herb

Biographical details: After achieving a handful of successful soul records in the late Sixties, this American vocal duo disappeared into obscurity for a decade; then Herb suddenly returned with a new Peaches at the end of the Seventies and enjoyed a pair of even bigger hits.

Discovered by the talented behind the scenes man Van McCoy, Herb Fame (real name Herbert Feemster) and Francine 'Peaches' Barker began recording together in 1966. One of their tracks *Let's Fall In Love* rose from the status of a B side to become their first hit single: it peaked at No. 21 on the US pop chart in early 1967. Then followed a No. 8 hit entitled *Close Your Eyes. For Your Love, Love Is Strange* and *Two Little Kids* kept the duo's name on the Top 40 of the American pop and soul charts during 1967-68. As their success tailed off, Herb quit the music business in 1970 and joined the Washington police force. While Barker faded from view, Herb decided to attempt a comeback. Teaming with a new female singing partner, Linda Greene (another McCoy discovery), he bounced back in 1979 with the infectious dancefloor burner *Shake Your Groove Thing*. Released at the peak of the disco boom, this single sold a million copies in the States alone and reached No. 5 on the US pop chart; in Britain, where the Sixties hits had been overlooked, *Shake Your Groove Thing* reached No. 26. It was quickly followed by the biggest Peaches and Herb hit of all, *Reunited*. This beautiful ballad was an instant classic, widely hailed as one of the greatest sweet soul records of all time. *Reunited* sold two million units in America and logged four weeks at No. 1; it reached No. 4 in the UK. The high artistic quality and fantastic commercial success of *Shake Your Groove Thing* and *Reunited* seemed to suggest a sustained renaissance for Peaches and Herb. But in fact, their subsequent singles and albums (excepting 1980's *I Pledge My Love* - No. 19 in US) returned them to obscurity. Herbert Feemster had enjoyed two separate, short-lived and worthy musical careers. Bob MacDonald, 25 February 1986..

FREEWAY
Tracks: / Freeway / Picking up the pieces.
7" Single: Released Sep '81, on Polydor, by Polydor Ltd. Deleted '84. Catalogue no: **POSP 330**

ONE CHILD OF LOVE
Tracks: / One child of love / Fun time.
7" Single: Released Nov '80, on Polydor, by Polydor Ltd. Deleted Nov '83. Catalogue no: **POSP 198**
12" Single: Released Nov '80, on Polydor, by Polydor Ltd. Deleted Nov '83. Catalogue no: **POSPX 198**

REUNITED
Tracks: / Reunited.
12" Single: Released Nov '82, on Polydor, by Polydor Ltd. Deleted Nov '85. Catalogue no: **POSPX 604**
7" Single: Released Apr '79, on Polydor, by Polydor Ltd. Deleted '82. Catalogue no: **POSP 43**

REUNITED (OLD GOLD)
Tracks: / Reunited / Shake your groovy thing.
7" Single: Released Jul '84, on Old Gold, by Old Gold Records. Catalogue no: **OG 9441**

SHAKE YOUR GROOVE THING
Tracks: / Shake your groove thing.
7" Single: Released Jan '79, on Polydor, by Polydor Ltd. Deleted '82. Catalogue no: **2066 992**

Peacock, Annette

Biographical details: Singer, composer and multi-instrumentalist Peacock moved from jazz to jazz-rock to free form, always from a position of feminist integrity. She eloped, at 19, with bassist Gary Peacock, met Paul Bley and succeeded Carla Bley as his chief composer. Bley's 1967 trio album, Ballads, used her themes entirely and helped to set the style of the new ECM label. He has recorded about 35 of her songs and they were among the first to use synthesisers in jazz-fusion, in concert with Hans Bennink and others. She also invented a way to sing through the synth. Peacock's own debut LP, Revenge, released in 1972, was made with Bley's trio. Three albums on Aura included jazz-rock jams with Bill Bruford and she sessioned on Bruford's Feels Good To Me in '78. The first LP for her own Ironic label that year was Sky-skating, live concert recordings on which she played all the instruments, acoustic, electric, synth and percussion. In 1987 she toured Europe and performed with Karlheinz Stockhausen. (Donald Clarke, May 1987.).

DON'T BE CRUEL
Tracks: / Don't be cruel.
7" Single: Released May '78, on Aura Records, by Aura Records. Deleted '88. Catalogue no: **AUS 102**

LOVE'S OUT TO LUNCH
Tracks: / Love's out to lunch / Rubber hunger.
7" Single: Released Nov '82, on Aura Records, by Aura Records. Deleted '88. Catalogue no: **AUS 113**

SKY-SKATING (SINGLE)
7" Single: Released Dec '81, on Ironic, by Ironic Records. Catalogue no: **IRONIC 1**

Pearce, Gerry

THESE THINGS
Tracks: / These things.
12" Single: Released Nov '88, on Blue Chip, by Blue Chip Records. Catalogue no: **BLUE-CHIP 8 T**

THESE THINGS (CARMINE ST. REMIX)
Tracks: / These things.
12" Single: Released '88, on Blue Chip, by Blue Chip Records. Catalogue no: **BLUE CHIP 8R**

WHY CAN'T WE BE LOVERS
Tracks: / Why can't we be lovers.
12" Single: Released Jul '88, on Blue Chip, by Blue Chip Records. Catalogue no: **BLUE-CHIP 3 T**
7" Single: Released Jul '88, on Blue Chip, by Blue Chip Records. Catalogue no: **BLUE-CHIP 3**

Pearce, Paulette

LIVE AND LEARN
Tracks: / Live and learn.
12" Single: Released Oct '84, on Small Acts, Catalogue no: **Unknown**

Pearl, Leslie

IF THE LOVE FITS WEAR IT
Tracks: / If the love fits wear it / Anything but yes is still a no.
7" Single: Released Sep '82, on RCA, by BMG Records (UK). Deleted '85. Catalogue no: **RCA 261**

Pearls

GUILTY
Tracks: / Guilty.
7" Single: Released Jun '74, on Bell, Deleted '77. Catalogue no: **BELL 1352**

THIRD FINGER LEFT HAND
Tracks: / Third finger left hand.
7" Single: Released May '72, on Bell, Deleted '75. Catalogue no: **BELL 1217**

YOU ARE EVERYTHING
Tracks: / You are everything.
7" Single: Released Mar '73, on Bell, Deleted '76. Catalogue no: **BELL 1284**

YOU CAME YOU SAW YOU CONQUERED
Tracks: / You came you saw you conquered.
7" Single: Released Sep '72, on Bell, Deleted '75. Catalogue no: **BELL 1254**

Pearson, Chris

LET ME BE YOUR SUNNY DAY
Tracks: / Let me be your sunny day / Write you a letter.
7" Single: Released 27 Feb '88, on Dingle's, by Dingle's Records. Catalogue no: **SID 240**

Pearson, Johnny

Biographical details: Thsi British pianist, composer, arranger, orchestra leader and conductor was born in Plaistow, London in 1925. He took up the piano at the age of seven, and won a scholarship to the London Academy of Music two years later. He was giving classical recitals by the time he entered his teens, but then switched to jazz. After serving in the Army, he spent six years in a successful jazz trio which played in clubs around Europe. This introduced him to the world of television, which was later to become the key element in his career. After the termination of the trio in 1954, he spent ten years working with many leading middle of the road and pop singers. In 1964 he enjoyed two British No. 1 singles as musical director for Cilla Black. In the following year, Pearson enjoyed a Top 10 single on both sides of the Atlantic as leader of Sounds Orchestral: that ensembl's *Cast Your Fate To The Wind* was one of the year's biggest instrumental hits. Pearson's long-standing association with BBC television got into full swing in the mid-Sixties. He became one of the leading composers of themes and incidental music for British TV programmes, and his orchestra was regularly heard on shows ranging from 'Top Of The Pops' to drama serials. One of his most successful and beautiful themes was *Sleepy Shores* - this was written for 'Owen MD', a twice weekly BBC1 soap opera about a doctor which was transmitted in the early evenings. Like *Caste Your Fate To The Wind*, the reflective *Sleepy Shores* was a light classical singles with broad appeal; the theme assumed a life of its own, reaching No. 8 on the UK chart in early 1972. Instead of being in the backroom, Johnny thus appeared on 'Top Of The Pops' himself!

Having written the music for a serial about a practising doctor, one of the best of Pearson's later themes was his music for veterinary surgeon series 'All Creatures Great And Small'. These adaptations of the James Herriot sagas began in January 1978 and finished their regular run in 1981. For a time, Johnny had his own 'Johnny Pearson Show' on BBC Rdio. Bob MacDonald, 26 February 1986..

SLEEPY SHORES
Tracks: / Sleepy shores.
7" Single: Released Jul '82, on Old Gold, by Old Gold Records. Deleted Jul '88. Catalogue no: **OG 9050**
7" Single: Released Dec '71, on Penny Farthing, by Penny Farthing Records. Deleted '74. Catalogue no: **PEN 778**

TRIANGLE
Tracks: / Triangle (love theme) / Triangle (introduction).
7" Single: Released Mar '81, on Rampage (USA), Deleted Mar '84. Catalogue no: **RAM 49**

Pearson, Keith

BABY YOU'VE FALLEN IN LOVE AGAIN
Tracks: / Baby you've fallen in love again.
7" Single: Released Jun '84, on Mix, by Mix Records. Catalogue no: **MREP 001**

PEECH BOYS - DON'T MAKE ME WAIT (Released on T.M.T.)

Pearson, Maureen

HANDSOME
Tracks: / Handsome.
12" Single: Released Sep '84, on Jammy's, Catalogue no: **Unknown**

RAIN OR SHINE
Tracks: / Rain or shine (Inst) / Rain or shine.
12" Single: Released Nov '86, on Virgo, Catalogue no: **VG 015**

SOULFUL LOVER BABY
Tracks: / Soulful lover baby.
7" Single: Released Mar '82, on Echo, by Echo Records. Catalogue no: **12 ECHO 002**

Peaston, David

TWO WRONGS DON'T MAKE A RIGHT
Tracks: / Two wrongs don't make a right / Thank you for the moment.
7" Single: Released Jul '89, on Geffen, by Geffen Records (USA). Catalogue no: **GEF 58**
12" Single: Released Jul '89, on Geffen, by Geffen Records (USA). Catalogue no: **GEF 58 T**

Pebbles

DO IT
Tracks: / Do it.
12" Single: Released Feb '84, on Sapphire, Catalogue no: **SAP 0011**

DO ME RIGHT
Tracks: / Do me right.
7" Single: Released Jan '89, on MCA, by MCA Records. Catalogue no: **MCA 8040**

GIRLFRIEND
Tracks: / Girlfriend / Girlfriend(Inst.) / Girlfriend(ext.) (Track on 12") / Girlfriend(ext. inst) (Track on 12") / Girlfriend(vocal edit) / Girlfriend (Dance remix) / Love / Hate (Radio edit).
12" Single: Released Mar '88, on MCA Dance, by MCA Records. Catalogue no: **MCAX 1223**
12" Single: Released Mar '88, on MCA Dance, by MCA Records. Catalogue no: **MCAT 1233**
CD 5": Released Apr '88, on MCA, by MCA Records. Catalogue no: **DMCA 1233**
7" Single: Released Mar '88, on MCA Dance, by MCA Records. Deleted 1 Jul '89. Catalogue no: **MCA 1233**

MERCEDES BOY
Tracks: / Mercedes boy / Love hate / Mercedes boy (extended version) / Love hate (extended version).
7" Single: Released May '88, on MCA, by MCA Records. Catalogue no: **MCA 1248**
12" Single: Released May '88, on MCA, by MCA Records. Catalogue no: **MCAT 1248**
CD 5": Released 14 May '88, on MCA, by MCA Records. Catalogue no: **DMCA 1248**

Peck, Gregory

MODEL AND POSE
Tracks: / Model and pose.
12" Single: Released 30 May '89, on Steely & Cleevie, Catalogue no: **VPRD 437**

OVER SIZE MAMPIE
Tracks: / Over size mampie.
12" Single: Released 24 Jul '89, on Steely & Cleevie, Catalogue no: **VPRD 438**

STUD 100
Tracks: / Stud 100.
7" Single: Released '88, on Black Solidarity, Catalogue no: **BSI 20**

WATCH YOUR FRIEND
Tracks: / Watch your friend.
12" Single: Released Aug '88, on Black Solidarity, Catalogue no: **BSI 12**

Peddie, Dennis

TRULY
Tracks: / Truly.
12" Single: Released Oct '89, on Ariwa Sounds, by Ariwa Sounds. Catalogue no: **ARI 093**

Peddle, Wendy

GONNA GET OVER YOU
Tracks: / Gonna get over you.
12" Single: Released Jul '88, on Blue Chip, by Blue Chip Records. Catalogue no: **BLUECHIP 2 T**
7" Single: Released Jul '88, on Blue Chip, by Blue Chip Records. Catalogue no: **BLUECHIP 2**

Peddlers

BIRTH
Tracks: / Birth.
7" Single: Released Aug '69, on CBS, by CBS Records. Deleted '72. Catalogue no: **CBS 4449**

GIRLIE
Tracks: / Girlie.
7" Single: Released Jan '70, on CBS, by CBS Records. Deleted '73. Catalogue no: **CBS 4720**

LET THE SUN SHINE IN
Tracks: / Let the sun shine in.
7" Single: Released Jan '65, on Philips, by Phonogram Ltd. Deleted '68. Catalogue no: **FB 1375**

Pedestrians

COMMUTER FANTASY
Tracks: / Commuter fantasy / 1984.
7" Single: Released May '81, on Metropolis (2), by Red Bus Records. Deleted May '86. Catalogue no: **MET 1**

Pedro

GOOD FOOTIN
Tracks: / Good footin'.
12" Single: Released Apr '88, on Bum, Catalogue no: **UM 001**

Pee Bee Squad

RUGGED AND MEAN BUTCH AND ONSCREEN
Tracks: / Rugged and mean, butch and on screen.
7" Single: Released Sep '85, on Project, Catalogue no: **PRO 3**
12" Single: Released Sep '85, on Project, Catalogue no: **12PRO 3**

SCARS AND STRIPES
Tracks: / Scars and stripes / D.J. talking the blues (part 2) / Main event mix.
7" Single: Released Apr '86, on Legacy, by Legacy Records. Catalogue no: **LGY 50**
12" Single: Released Apr '86, on Legacy, by Legacy Records. Catalogue no: **LGYT 50**

Peebles, Ann

Biographical details: This American soul singer was born in East St Louis and was raised on church music. She grew up singing in her father's Baptist choir, and was a big fan of gospel vocalist Mahalia Jackson. Peebles' big break occurred in 1969 when, at the age of 22, she signed with Memphis-based producer/arranger/conductor/trumpeter Willie Mitchell and his Hi label.

The Peebles/Mitchell alliance yielded a lengthy run of hits on the US soul charts during the first half of the Seventies. Together with stablemate Al Green, who was another Mitchell protege, Ann helped to shape a new Memphis soul sound for the Seventies; in many ways Hi carried on the good work that the city's Stax/Volt labels had done in the Sixties.

Peebles' bold, earthy vocal style was not as accessible to non-soul lovers as the more laid-back Green approach, so she did not enjoy his pop crossover success. Her highest pop chart showing was for *I Can't Stand The Rain*, which reached No. 38 in the US in December 1973 and No. 41 in Britain in May 1974. But her two best known tracks later became pop smashes for other artists: *I Can't Stand The Rain* became a British and American Top 20 hit for Eruption in 1978, and was included on Tina Turner's multi-platinum 1984 album *Private Dancer*, and *I'm Gonna Tear Your Playhouse Down*, which was originally recorded by Ann in 1972, became a UK and US Top 20 hit for Paul Young in 1984-85.

By 1975 Mitchell's distinctive 'Memphis Sound' was wearing thin, a fact which began to impair the careers of both Green and Peebles. Having repeated the formula too often, Peebles faded into obscurity. Bob MacDonald, 26 February 1986..

I CAN'T STAND THE RAIN (SINGLE)
Tracks: / I can't stand the rain / Love vibration, A.
7" Single: Released Mar '85, on Hi, by Demon Records. Catalogue no: **HIUK 45 7002**
12" Single: Released Mar '85, on Hi, by Demon Records. Catalogue no: **HIUK 45 7002 T**
7" Single: Released Apr '74, on London-American, Deleted '77. Catalogue no: **HL 10428**

Peech Boys

Biographical details: *Don't Make Me Wait* provided this British disco-rock band with a one-off UK chart entry in late 1982 - it reached No. 49 on the singles listings, and became a cult record in clubs on both sides of the Atlantic. Subsequent efforts, produced in New York, were not quite so successful. Bob MacDonald, 26 February 1986.
The Peech Boys are in the vanguard of New York's dance music renaisssance. The group is an offshoot of the city's most serious dance hall, The Paradise Garage. P-Boy producers Larry Levan and Michael De Benedictus to play records and synthesiser together at the Garage: Levan is the essence of the modern record mixer who understands the music so well that he ends up making his own records. Well known for his studio mixes his own records. The nucleus of the band is DeBenedictus on keyboards, Robert Kapser on guitar, Steve Brown on drums, Darryl Short on bass and R. Bernard Fowler on vocals, played together as a group for four years before connecting with Levan and The Garage. They are a multi-racial bandm with all possiblities for a colour blind music that comes from their diverse backgrounds. The appeal of the Peech Boys is black/white, gay/straight. It defies the traditional segmentation of the music industry. (Island Records, Feb 1984).

DON'T MAKE ME WAIT
Tracks: / Don't make me wait / Don't make me wait (alt. version).
12" Single: Released Oct '82, on T.M.T., by T.M.T. Productions. Deleted '87. Catalogue no: **TMTT 7001**
7" Single: Released Oct '82, on T.M.T., by T.M.T. Productions. Deleted '87. Catalogue no: **TMT 7001**

Peek, Kevin

Biographical details: This Australian guitarist, multi-instrumentalist and composer, based in the UK, was one of Britain's most respected session guitarists of the Seventies. In 1978 he became a founder member of the classical/rock fusion group Sky; the band's other guitarist was another expatriate Aussie who had settles in Britain, John williams. With their debut album released in 1979, Sky were an immediate success and continued to enjoy strong sales throughout the early Eighties. Peek arranged their smash 1980 single *Toccata*, a Bach adaptation. As a subsidiary to Sky, Peek launches a solo career with the 1980 album *Guitar Junction*. His next LP *Awakening*, reached No. 52 on the UK album chart in March 1981. His 1982 offering, *Life And Other Games*, contained a re-working of the Jimi Hendrix classic *Hey Joe*; but generally speaking, Peek's solo records contained fewer rock influences than the Sky sets, and were less successful. Bob MacDonald, 26 February 1986..

COMING ON
Tracks: / Coming on / Awakening.
7" Single: Released Jul '81, on Ariola, by BMG Records (UK). Deleted '84. Catalogue no: **ARO 265**

DRIFTING
Tracks: / Drifting / Capricorn 2.
7" Single: Released May '82, on Ariola, by BMG Records (UK). Deleted '85. Catalogue no: **ARO 279**

HEY JOE
Tracks: / Hey Joe / Hunter's theme.
7" Single: Released '82, on Ariola, by BMG Records (UK). Deleted '87. Catalogue no: **ARO 283**

SAILPLANE
Tracks: / Sailplane / Sidewinder.
7" Single: Released Feb '81, on Ariola, by BMG Records (UK). Deleted Feb '84. Catalogue no: **ARO 255**

Peek, Paul

ROCK-A-ROUND
Tracks: / Rock a round / Sweet skinny Jenny / Olds-mo-William / Gee but I miss that girl.
7" EP: Released Aug '86, on Rollercoaster, by Rollercoaster Records. Catalogue no: **RCEP 103**

Peelers

DODGER, THE
Tracks: / Dodger, The.
7" Single: Released Sep '84, on Etude, by Etude Records. Catalogue no: **DODGE 1**

JOHN O'DREAMS
Tracks: / John O'Dreams / Dicey Rielly.
7" Single: Released Jun '83, on After Hours, Deleted '88. Catalogue no: **AFT 11**

WIND IN THE WILLOWS
Tracks: / Wind in the willows / Sweet memories.
7" Single: Released Nov '82, on Masquerade, Catalogue no: **MASQ 1**

Peep Show

SETTING ME UP
Tracks: / Setting me up.
7" Single: Released Jan '85, on Boff, Catalogue no: **BOF 1**

Peers, Donald

Biographical details: This veteran British middle of the road singer reached No. 3 on the UK chart in 1969 with *Please Don't Go*, a single produced and co-written by the highly talented Les Reed who had written material for such MOR greats as Tom Jones and Engelbert Humperdinck. In 1972 Peers reached the UK No. 36 position with *Give Me One More Chance*. Bob MacDonald, 26 February 1986..

GIVE ME ONE MORE CHANCE
Tracks: / Give me one more chance.
7" Single: Released Jun '72, on Decca, by Decca Records. Deleted '75. Catalogue no: **F 13302**

PLEASE DON'T GO
Tracks: / Please don't go.
7" Single: Released Dec '68, on Columbia, by EMI Records. Deleted '71. Catalogue no: **DB 8502**

Pegg, Dave

COCKTAIL COWBOY
Tracks: / Cocktail cowboy / Swirling pit.
7" Single: Released Sep '83, on Projection, Catalogue no: **WRS 101**

Peking man

ROOM THAT ECHOES
Tracks: / Room that echoes (round and around) / Vision high.
7" Single: Released Feb '87, on Epic, by CBS Records. Deleted Aug '87. Catalogue no: **650432 7**
12" Single: Released Feb '87, on Epic, by CBS Records. Deleted Aug '87. Catalogue no: **650423 6**

Pellay, Alan

DEMONIC FORCES
Tracks: / Demonic forces / Hostage in Iran.
7" Single: Released May '81, on On-U-Sound, by On-U-Sound Records. Catalogue

no: **SOUND 2**

Pellay, Lana

PISTOL IN MY POCKET
Tracks: / Pistol in my pocket / Pistol in my pocket (Instrumental) / Dirty Harry.
7" Single: Released Feb '86, on Sublime, Catalogue no: **LIME 101**
12" Single: Released Feb '86, on Sublime, Catalogue no: **LIMET 101**

Pencils

IF YOU REALLY WANNA HURT SOMEBODY
Tracks: / If you really wanna hurt somebody.
7" Single: Released Sep '82, on Next, by Next Records. Catalogue no: **NEX 703**

PICTURES OF PARIS
Tracks: / Pictures of Paris.
7" Single: Released Apr '83, on Next, by Next Records. Catalogue no: **NEX 705**

WATCHING THE TEARS
Tracks: / Watching the tears / You say you.
7" Single: Released Jul '82, on Next, by Next Records. Catalogue no: **NEX 701**

Pender, Mike

IT'S OVER
Tracks: / It's over / Brothers & sisters.
12" Single: Released Jun '86, on Sierra, by Sierra Records. Deleted Jun '87. Catalogue no: **FED 23T**
7" Single: Released Jun '86, on Sierra, by Sierra Records. Deleted Jun '87. Catalogue no: **FED 23**

Pendergrass, Teddy

Biographical details: This American soul singer was born Theodore Pendergrass in Philadelphia, and came to fame in the early Seventies as part of the Philly soul boom created by songwriters/producers Kenny Gamble and Leon Huff and their Philadelphia International company. Between 1972 and 1977 Pendergrass made his name as lead singer with Harold melvin & The Blue Notes. The inevitable friction that resulted from the discrepancy between Melvin's star billing and Pendergrass' role as principal vocalist, caused a rupture in the group in 1977. Melvin took the Blue Notes to ABC records with new lead singer David Ebo, a move whose musical and commercial results were little short of disasterous; meanwhile Teddy embarked upon a successful solo career, staying with Philly and Gamble & Huff. Pendergrass injected the same passion and power into his solo records as he had into those of his former group. Despite the fact that they were in the dominant position of writing and producing the material, Gamble & Huff and their Philly assistants showed great musical integrity by leaving ample room for Teddy's vocal talents to shine. With his romantic style and good looks, he became one of the top sex symbols amongst balck women on both sides of the Atlantic; his management and promoters cultivated this by sometimes organising 'ladies only' concerts. Although the artist enjoyed great success on the American soul charts during the late Seventies, he did not receive the same pop crossover acceptance that he had achieved in the Blue Notes' heyday. This was because the disco boom, with its emphasis on beats per minute and its reliance on the bass and drums, was not so interested in a performer whose appeal was founded upon rich, deeply soulful singing. Thus Pendergrass' 1978 single *Close The Door* sold a million copies in the States, while only climbing to No. 25 on the American pop chart. In Britain his pop success was limited to *The Whole Town's Laughing At Me* (No. 44 in 1977) and the double A sided *Only You/Close The Door* (No. 41 in 1978). *Two Hearts*, a 1981 duet with Stephanie Mills, reached No. 49. In March 1982, Pendergrass was seriously injured in a car accident, suffering major internal and spinal wounds. With admirable courage, he fought his way back to recovery and returned to the recording scene. His strong 1984 single *Hold Me* was a duet with the up and coming Whitney Houston, thus helping to pave the way for her subsequent solo success. This track, produced and co-written by the ballad-orientated Michael Masser, belatedly entered the British pop chart in 1986. Bob MacDonald, 26 February 1986..

2 AM
Tracks: / 2 am.
7" Single: Released Nov '88, on Elektra, by Elektra Records (UK). Catalogue no: **EKR 83**
12" Single: Released Nov '88, on Elektra, by Elektra Records (UK). Catalogue no: **EKR 83T**

I JUST CALLED TO SAY
Tracks: / I just called to say / Reach out and touch.
7" Single: Released Feb '82, on Philadelphia Int., by EMI Records. Deleted Feb '87. Catalogue no: **PIRA 2047**

JOY (SINGLE)
Tracks: / Joy / Let me be closer.
7" Single: Released May '88, on Elektra, by Elektra Records (UK). Catalogue no: **EKT 75**
12" Single: Released May '88, on Elektra, by Elektra Records (UK). Catalogue no: **EKT 75T**

ONLY YOU
Tracks: / Only you / Close the door.
7" Single: Released Oct '78, on Philadelphia Int., by EMI Records. Deleted '81. Catalogue no: **SPIR 6713**

SHOUT AND SCREAM
Tracks: / Shout and scream / Close the door.
7" Single: Released Feb '80, on Philadelphia Int., by EMI Records. Deleted '83. Catalogue no: **PIR 8183**

WHOLE TOWN'S LAUGHING AT ME
Tracks: / Whole town's laughing at me, The / Love t.k.o..
7" Single: Released Apr '81, on Philadelphia Int., by EMI Records. Deleted Apr '86. Catalogue no: **PIRA 1089**
7" Single: Released May '77, on Philadelphia Int., by EMI Records. Deleted '80. Catalogue no: **PIR 5116**

Pendragon

RED SHOES
Tracks: / Searching / Contact (Extra track on 12" only.).
7" Single: Released Feb '87, on Awareness, by Awareness Records. Deleted '88. Catalogue no: **AWS 101**
12" Single: Released Feb '87, on Awareness, by Awareness Records. Deleted '88. Catalogue no: **AWSX 101**

Pendulum

JINGLES
Tracks: / Jingles.
7" Single: Released Nov '82, on Monarch, by Monarch Records. Catalogue no: **MON 038**

PUT THE CLOCK BACK
Tracks: / Put the clock back / White confetti.
7" Single: Released Oct '82, on Monarch, by Monarch Records. Deleted Oct '85. Catalogue no: **MON 035**

WHITE CONFETTI
Tracks: / White confetti.
7" Single: Released Oct '82, on Monarch, by Monarch Records. Catalogue no: **MON 035**

Penfield, Holly

ONLY HIS NAME
Tracks: / Only his name / Eyes behind your eyes.
7" Single: Released Sep '80, on Dreamland, Deleted '83. Catalogue no: **DLSP 5**

Penfold, Jim

DREAM ON
Tracks: / Dream on.
7" Single: Released Oct '85, on Water, Catalogue no: **WAT 1**

HOLE IN MY ROOM
Tracks: / Hole in my room / Velvet cushion / Hand on my heart (Available on 12" only.) / Hole in my room (Available on 12" version only.).
7" Single: Released Feb '88, on Big Time Records, by Big Time Records. Deleted May '89. Catalogue no: **ZB 41731**
12" Single: Released Feb '88, on Big Time Records, by Big Time Records. Deleted May '89. Catalogue no: **ZT 41732**

Penguin Cafe Orchestra

Biographical details: This British group were formed in the late 70's by multi-instrumentalist and composer Simon Jeffes, who was born in London in 1948. He studied music in London in the 60's and visited Japan in 1972. A friend gave him a tape of African music in '73. Along the way he arranged the strings for Sid Vicious' *My Way* and tutored Adam Ant on Burundi drumming. He says the PCO is for "people capable of enjoying Wilson Pickett, Beethoven, the Rolling Stones, choral music from West Africa, Bach, Stravinsky, Irish bagpipe music and even Abba on the odd occasion". The album Broadcasting From Home includes *Music For A Found Harmonium*, used in TV commercials for the national daily paper The Independent in 1986. The music sounds "roughly like a string quartet letting its hair down at some mysteriously-located barn dance of the future," wrote Robert Sandall in the Sunday Times. The string band of up to seven people may include Helen Liebman on cello, Gavyn Wright, Elizabeth Perry and Bob Lovejoy on violins, Steve Nye on keyboards, Neil Rennie on cuatro and ukelele, Jeffes playing everything including tapes, plus other guests on percussion etc. The gently insidious, often foot-tapping result could be called New Age music -- but it's better than that. (Donald Clarke, May 1987.).

DIRT
Tracks: / Dirt / Air a danser / Air (Extra track on 12" only).
7" Single: Released May '87, on Virgin, by Virgin Records. Deleted May '88. Catalogue no: **EDS 2**
12" Single: Released May '87, on Virgin, by Virgin Records. Catalogue no: **EDSX 2**

MUSIC FOR A FOUND HARMONIUM
Tracks: / Music for a sound harmonian / In the back of a taxi / Bean fields (Extra track on 12" version.) / Penguin cafe single (Extra track on 12" version).
12" Single: Released Mar '87, on E.G., by E.G. Records. Catalogue no: **EDSX 1**
7" Single: Released Mar '87, on E.G., by E.G. Records. Deleted May '88. Catalogue no: **EDS 1**

Penk, Steve

ITSY BITSY TEENIE WEENIE YELLOW POLKADOT BIKINI
Tracks: / Itsy bitsy teeny weeny yellow polkadot bikini / Trash can.
7" Single: Released 24 Jul '89, on Dot, Catalogue no: **DOT 1**

Pennies From Heaven

LOVE IS GOOD FOR ANYTHING
Tracks: / Love is good for anything that ails you / Life is just a bowl of cherries.
7" Single: Released Jun '82, on Warner Bros., by WEA Records. Catalogue no: **K 17963**

Penning, Les

SHOULD HAVE BEEN FOREVER
Tracks: / Should have been forever / Merlin's welcome home.
7" Single: Released Dec '83, on Plant Life, by Plant Life Records. Catalogue no: **PLRS 004**

WILLOW FAIR
Tracks: / Willow fair.
7" Single: Released Jun '83, on Plant Life, by Plant Life Records. Catalogue no: **PLRS 003**

Pennington, Barbara

Biographical details: American soul singer Barbara Pennington had been active in the music business for a decade before achieving a modest British hit with the bright, catchy 1985 single *On A Crowded Street*. This was a club favourite and it received much airplay on London's soul radio. (Bob MacDonald, February 1986.) Originally brought to the UK by Northern Soul DJ and producer Ian Levine in 1975 as part of the same package that launched Evelyn Thomas and LJ Johnson, she had a minor hit on Island with I Can't Escape The Thoughts Of You, followed by Running In Another Direction in 76. A change of labels to UA later in the year produced the superb 24 Hours A Day single, a huge Northern Soul favourite. Returned to the scene in the mid-80's with a string of hi-energy tracks, produced again by Ian Levine. (P.Smith).

ALL AMERICAN BOY
Tracks: / All American boy / Sorry, wrong number / Skiing in the snow.
12" Single: Released Feb '88, on Record Shack, by Record Shack Records. Catalogue no: **SOHOB 6**
12" Single: Released Sep '84, on Record Shack, by Record Shack Records. Catalogue no: **SOHOT 28**
7" Single: Released Sep '84, on Record Shack, by Record Shack Records. Catalogue no: **SOHO 28**

DON'T STOP THE WORLD
Tracks: / Don't stop the world.
12" Single: on Nightmare, by Nightmare Records. Catalogue no: **MARE 8**
7" Single: Released Feb '87, on Nightmare, by Nightmare Records. Catalogue no: **MARES 8**

FAN THE FLAME
Tracks: / Fan the flame.
7" Single: Released Mar '85, on Record Shack, by Record Shack Records. Catalogue no: **SOHO 37**
12" Single: Released Mar '85, on Record Shack, by Record Shack Records. Catalogue no: **SOHOT 37**

ON A CROWDED STREET
Tracks: / On a crowded street.
7" Single: Released Aug '85, on Record Shack, by Record Shack Records. Catalogue no: **SOHO 49**
12" Single: Released Aug '85, on Record Shack, by Record Shack Records. Catalogue no: **SOHOT 49**
12" Single: Released Aug '85, on Record Shack, by Record Shack Records. Catalogue no: **SOHORT 49**

THERE ARE BRIGHTER DAYS
Tracks: / There are brighter days / There are brighter days (version).
7" Single: Released Apr '88, on Nightmare, by Nightmare Records. Catalogue no: **MARES 49**
12" Single: Released Apr '88, on Nightmare, by Nightmare Records. Catalogue no: **MARE 49**

WAYDOWN DEEP IN MY SOUL
Tracks: / Waydown deep in my soul.
7" Single: Released Jan '85, on Record Shack, by Record Shack Records. Catalogue no: **SOHO 33**
12" Single: Released Jan '85, on Record Shack, by Record Shack Records. Catalogue no: **SOHOT 33**

Penny Arcade

CALLIN' YOU
Tracks: / Callin' you / Midnight train.
7" Single: Released May '82, on Brilliant, by Brilliant Records. Catalogue no: **HIT 3**

CALLING YOU
Tracks: / Calling you / Midnight train.
7" Single: Released May '82, on Brilliant, by Brilliant Records. Deleted '85. Catalogue no: **HIT 3**

I DO LOVE YOU
Tracks: / I do love you / London lights.
7" Single: Released '86, on PVK, by PVK Records. Catalogue no: **PV 115**

RADIO STATION
Tracks: / Radio station / Alright on the night.
7" Single: Released '86, on PVK, by PVK Records. Catalogue no: **PV 118**

Penny & The Rims

JUMP AND JERK
Tracks: / Jump and jerk.
7" Single: Released Jan '81, on Electro, Catalogue no: **GRC 61**

Penrose, Charles

LAUGHING POLICEMAN
Tracks: / Laughing policeman, The / Window cleaner / Lion and Albert, The.
7" Single: Released Dec '72, on Columbia, by EMI Records. Catalogue no: **DB 8959**

Pentangle

Biographical details: This British folk band consisted of Terry Cox, Bert Jansch, Jacqui McShee, John Renbourn and Danny Thompson.

Pentangle (sometimes called the Pentangle) were formed in 1967 by guitarists Jansch and Renbourn, who had already established themselves as virtuosos and who had released a duet album the previous year. Both men continued to issue solo albums throughout Pentangl's lifespan. Cox (drums) and Thompson (bass) had been busy session musicians in blues and jazz music, and had played together in Alexis Korner's Blues Incorporated. Lead singer McShee had emerged from the folk club circuit. Starting out at the same time as Fairport Convention, Pentangle interpreted folk music in a very different manner to their contemporaries. Pentagle's key word was fusion: they aimed to bring blues, jazz and gospel influences under the general banner of folk. The band's eponymous debut album was released in 1968 and reached No. 21 on the British chart. It was quickly followed by the ambitious double LP set *Sweet Child*. The group hit their commercial peak in 1969 with the album *Basket Of Light*; this reached No. 5 and logged 28 weeks on the UK LP listings, fuelled by the chart singles *Once I Had A Sweetheart* and *Light Flight* (the theme from the important BBC TV series 'Take Three Girls'). For a while the name Pentangle was on everyone's lips and the band looked set for superstardom. But their next albu, *Cruel Sister*, issued in late 1970, peaked at No. 51 and the group never saw chart action again. In artistic and commercial terms, they had peaked early; their Seventies output could only repeat what had gone before. Pentangle folded in 1973, and the members resumed the same activities that they had been engaged in previously. The same five musicians reformed for the 1982 Cambridge Folk Festival, but the reunion was short-lived. Bob MacDonald, 26 February 1986..

LIGHT FLIGHT
Tracks: / Light flight.
7" Single: Released Feb '70, on Big T, Deleted '73. Catalogue no: **BIG 128**

ONCE I HAD A SWEETHEART
Tracks: / Once I had a sweetheart.
7" Single: Released May '69, on Big T, Deleted '72. Catalogue no: **BIG 124**

Penthouse 4

BUST THIS HOUSE DOWN
Tracks: / Bust this house down (John Shaft's radio mix) / Easy B side / Bust this house

down (John Shaft's mix) (Track on 12" single only.) / Bust this house down (John Shaft's dub mix) (Track on 12" single and 12" remix.).
12" Single: Released 5 Apr '88, on Syncopate, by EMI Records. Deleted Nov '88. Catalogue no: **12SY 10**
12" Single: Released 11 Apr '88, on Syncopate, by EMI Records. Deleted Nov '88. Catalogue no: **12 SYX 10**
7" Single: Released 5 Apr '88, on Syncopate, by EMI Records. Deleted Nov '88. Catalogue no: **SY 10**

SLAVE (TO THE HOUSE OF LOVE)
Tracks: / Slave (house of love) / I'd rather b / Slave (to the house of love).
7" Single: Released Sep '88, on Dynatrack, Catalogue no: **DYNA 102**
12" Single: Released Sep '88, on Dynatrack, Catalogue no: **DYNAT 102**

Penumbrah

HOW GOOD IT IS
Tracks: / How good it is / I love you so.
12" Single: Released Dec '83, on Jah Observers, Catalogue no: **JAH 003**

People

MUSICAL MAN
Tracks: / Musical man / Songs and daughters.
7" Single: Released May '81, on Race, Deleted '83. Catalogue no: **RB 003**

People In Control

WHEN IT'S WAR
Tracks: / When it's war.
7" Single: Released Apr '83, on Crammed Discs, by Crammed Discs. Catalogue no: **CRAM 1457**

People In Progress

THIS IS MY SONG
Tracks: / This is my song (part 1) / This is my song (part 2).
7" Single: Released Nov '86, on Polydor, by Polydor Ltd. Catalogue no: **POSP 829**
12" Single: Released Nov '86, on Polydor, by Polydor Ltd. Deleted Aug '87. Catalogue no: **POSPX 829**

People Like Us

DELIVERANCE
Tracks: / Deliverance / Midnight lover.
12" Single: Released '88, on Passion, by Skratch Records. Catalogue no: **PASH 68(12)**
12" Single: Released Nov '86, on Passion, by Skratch Records. Catalogue no: **PASH 63(12)**

FIGHTING FOR OUR LIVES
Tracks: / Fighting for our lives.
12" Single: Released '88, on Passion, by Skratch Records. Catalogue no: **PASH 78(12)**

MIDNIGHT LOVER
Tracks: / Midnight lovers / Midnight lovers (Instrumental).
12" Single: Released Feb '86, on Passion, by Skratch Records. Catalogue no: **PASH 51(12)**

REINCARNATION (COMING BACK FOR LOVE)
Tracks: / Reincarnation.
7" Single: Released Aug '85, on Passion, by Skratch Records. Catalogue no: **PASH 46**
12" Single: Released Aug '85, on Passion, by Skratch Records. Catalogue no: **PASH 46(12)**

RESTLESS HEARTS
Tracks: / Restless hearts.
12" Single: Released '88, on Passion, by Skratch Records. Catalogue no: **PASH 55(12)**
7" Single: Released '88, on Passion, by Skratch Records. Catalogue no: **PASH 55**

People Of The World

PEOPLE OF THE WORLD
Tracks: / People of the world.
12" Single: Released Feb '83, on Carousel (1), by Carousel Records. Catalogue no: **CAR 6**

Peoples Choice

DO IT (ANYWAY YOU WANNA)
Tracks: / Do it anyway you wanna.
7" Single: Released Sep '75, on Philadelphia Int., by EMI Records. Deleted '78. Catalogue no: **PIR 3500**
7" Single: Released Sep '85, on Old Gold, by Old Gold Records. Deleted Jul '88. Catalogue no: **OG 9564**

JAM JAM JAM
Tracks: / Jam jam jam.
7" Single: Released Jan '78, on Philadelphia Int., by EMI Records. Deleted '81. Catalogue no: **PIR 5891**

Pepper

ICKIE FASHION
Tracks: / Ickie fashion.
12" Single: Released 31 Jul '89, on Clarkey & Blakey, Catalogue no: **CB 002**

Pepper and Maureen

WINDSONG
Tracks: / Windsong.
12" Single: Released Dec '82, on Holly Cone, by Ariwa Sounds. Catalogue no: **HC 101**

Pepper, Jim

WITCHITIATO
Tracks: / Witchitiato / Ya na ho / Custer gets it (Extra track on 12").
12" Single: Released Feb '88, on Antilles/New Directions, by Island Records. Deleted Jun '88. Catalogue no: **12 ANN 1**
7" Single: Released Feb '88, on Antilles/New Directions, by Island Records. Deleted Jun '88. Catalogue no: **ANN 1**

Peppermint, Danny

PEPPERMINT TWIST
Tracks: / Peppermint twist.
7" Single: Released Jan '62, on London-American, Deleted '65. Catalogue no: **HLL 9478**

Peppers

Biographical details: *Pepper box* gave this anonymous French all-male instrumental band a one-off UK chart entry in late 1974 - the infectious single climbed to No.6 after becoming a club hit and after being heavily featured by BBC Radio disc jockey Johnnie Walker.(Bob MacDonald 5.3.86).

PEPPER BOX
Tracks: / Pepper box.
7" Single: Released '80, on IMS, by Polydor Ltd. Catalogue no: **LR 0183**
7" Single: Released Oct '74, on Spark, by Spark Records. Deleted '77. Catalogue no: **SRL 1100**

Peppers, Nancy

FIRST NIGHT
Tracks: / First night.
7" Single: Released Nov '85, on Sounds Right, Catalogue no: **MSSR 2**

I BELIEVE
Tracks: / I believe / Where did we go wrong.
7" Single: Released Jan '82, on Fresh, by Jetstar Records. Deleted '85. Catalogue no: **NBP 1**

JESUS WILL OUTSHINE THEM ALL
Tracks: / Jesus will outshine them all / I never go around mirrors.
7" Single: Released Apr '80, on Liberty, by EMI Records. Deleted '82. Catalogue no: **BP 353**

Peppertree, Ricky

BABY IT'S NICE TO SEE YOU
Tracks: / Baby it's nice to see you.
7" Single: Released Feb '82, on Mekaliteit, by Mekaliteit Music. Catalogue no: **MTM 1001**

Pepsi & Shirlie

ALL RIGHT NOW (SINGLE)
Tracks: / All right now / Feels like the first time / All right now (ext. remix) (Extra track available on cassette and CD only.).
7" Pic: Released Dec '87, on Polydor, by Polydor Ltd. Catalogue no: **POSPP 896**
Cassingle: Released Dec '87, on Polydor, by Polydor Ltd. Catalogue no: **POSPC 896**
CD 5": Released Dec '87, on Polydor, by Polydor Ltd. Catalogue no: **POCD 896**
12" Single: Released Dec '87, on Polydor, by Polydor Ltd. Catalogue no: **POSPX 896**

CAN'T GIVE ME LOVE
Tracks: / Can't give me love / It's a shame.
7" Single: Released Aug '87, on Polydor, by Polydor Ltd. Catalogue no: **POSP 885**
12" Single: Released Aug '87, on Polydor, by Polydor Ltd. Catalogue no: **POSPX 885**
Cassingle: Released Sep '87, on Polydor, by Polydor Ltd. Catalogue no: **POSPC 885**

GOODBYE STRANGER
Tracks: / Goodbye stranger.
12" Single: Released May '87, on Polydor, by Polydor Ltd. Catalogue no: **POSPX 856**
7" Single: Released May '87, on Polydor, by Polydor Ltd. Catalogue no: **POSP 865**

HEARTACHE
Tracks: / Heartache.
7" Single: Released Jan '87, on Polydor, by Polydor Ltd. Deleted Mar '88. Catalogue no: **POSP 837**
12" Single: Released Jan '87, on Polydor, by Polydor Ltd. Deleted Mar '88. Catalogue no: **POSPX 837**

HIGHTIME
Tracks: / Hightime (Jellybean remix) (Available on 12" only.) / Lover's revolution / Hightime (Jellybean 12" remix) (on 12" only.) / Hightime (7" mix) (on 12" only.).
Note: Many people's favourite track from the "All Right Now" album, specially remixed by the hottest club name- "Jellybean" Benitez. Supported by extensive club promotion and ads in Smash Hits, Just 17 and No.1. As featured on the 1988 Montreux rock festival, where Pepsi & Shirlie were the stars of the show. (Polydor records, June 88)
7" Single: Released Jun '88, on Polydor, by Polydor Ltd. Catalogue no: **PO 1**
12" Single: Released Jun '88, on Polydor, by Polydor Ltd. Catalogue no: **PZ 1**

Percival, Lance

SHAME AND SCANDAL IN THE FAMILY
Tracks: / Shame and scandal in the family.
7" Single: Released Oct '65, on Parlophone, by EMI Records. Deleted '68. Catalogue no: **R 5335**

Percival, Norman

FIGHTER PILOT
Tracks: / Fighter pilot / Valley Welsh.
7" Single: Released Jan '83, on Splash, by Splash Records. Catalogue no: **SP 26**

Pere Ubu

BREATH
Tracks: / Breath / Bang the drum / Over my head (live) (Available on 12" only) / Universal vibration (live) (Available on 12" only) / Humour me (live) (Available on CD single only.).
7" Single: Released Aug '89, on Fontana, by Phonogram Ltd. Catalogue no: **UBU 4**
12" Single: Released Aug '89, on Fontana, by Phonogram Ltd. Catalogue no: **UBU 412**
CD 5": Released Aug '89, on Fontana, by Phonogram Ltd. Catalogue no: **UBUCD 4**

WAITING FOR MARY (what are we doing here)
Tracks: / Waiting for Mary (what are we doing here) / Wine dark sparks.
7" Single: Released 20 Mar '89, on Phonogram, by Phonogram Ltd. Deleted 31 Jul '89. Catalogue no: **UBU 2**
12" Single: Released 20 Mar '89, on Phonogram, by Phonogram Ltd. Deleted 31 Jul '89. Catalogue no: **UBU 212**
CD 5": Released 20 Mar '89, on Phonogram, by Phonogram Ltd. Catalogue no: **UBUCD 2**

WE HAVE THE TECHNOLOGY
Tracks: / We have the technology.
7" Single: Released 28 Jul '88, on Phonogram, by Phonogram Ltd. Deleted Feb '89. Catalogue no: **UBU 1**
12" Single: Released 28 Jul '88, on Phonogram, by Phonogram Ltd. Deleted Feb '89. Catalogue no: **UBU 112**
CD 5": Released 28 Jul '88, on Phonogram, by Phonogram Ltd. Deleted Feb '89. Catalogue no: **UBUCD 1**

Perennial Divide

BEE HEAD
Tracks: / Bee head.
12" Single: Released Mar '88, on Sweatbox, by Sweatbox Records. Catalogue no: **SOX 020**

BURN DOWN
Tracks: / Burn down.
12" Single: Released Oct '86, on Sweatbox, by Sweatbox Records. Catalogue no: **SOX 018**

LEATHER NECKS
Tracks: / Leather necks.
12" Single: Released Oct '88, on Sweatbox, by Sweatbox Records. Catalogue no: **SOX 036**
CD 5": Released Oct '88, on Sweatbox, by Sweatbox Records. Catalogue no: **SOX 036 CD**

Perfect Alibi

NOT AT HOME TO HEARTACHE
Tracks: / Not at home to heartache / Pretty boy blue / Not at home to heartache (majestic mix) (Only on 12" version.).
7" Single: Released Oct '87, on RCA, by BMG Records (UK). Deleted May '89. Catalogue no: **PB 41517**
12" Single: Released Oct '87, on RCA, by BMG Records (UK). Deleted May '89. Catalogue no: **PT 41518**

Perfect Crime

I FEEL LIKE AN ESKIMO
Tracks: / I feel like an Eskimo / No drums.
7" Single: Released Jan '84, on MCA, by MCA Records. Catalogue no: **MCA 854**
12" Single: Released Jan '84, on MCA, by MCA Records. Catalogue no: **MCAT 854**

Perfect Day

JANE
Tracks: / Jane.
7" Single: Released Mar '89, on London Records, by London Records. Deleted Jul '89. Catalogue no: **LON 188**
12" Single: Released Mar '89, on London Records, by London Records. Deleted Jul '89. Catalogue no: **LONX 188**
CD 5": Released Mar '89, on London Records, by London Records. Catalogue no: **LONCD 188**

LIBERTY TOWN
Tracks: / Liberty town / On the right side / Liberty town (the good,the bad + the extended) (Extra track on CD single only) / Liberty town (*Extra track on 12" single only).
7" Single: Released Jan '89, on London Records, by London Records. Deleted 26 Jun '89. Catalogue no: **LON 214**
12" Single: Released '89, on London Records, by London Records. Deleted 26 Jun '89. Catalogue no: **LONXP 214**
12" Single: Released Jan '89, on London Records, by London Records. Deleted 26 Jun '89. Catalogue no: **LONX 214**
CD 5": Released Jan '89, on London Records, by London Records. Catalogue no: **LONCD 214**

THIS IS AMERICA
Tracks: / This is America / Stateside / This is America (full version) (Only on 12" and CD single.).
CD 5": Released Oct '88, on London Records, by London Records. Catalogue no: **LONCD 207**
7" Single: Released Oct '88, on London Records, by London Records. Deleted May '89. Catalogue no: **LONB 207**
12" Single: Released Oct '88, on London Records, by London Records. Deleted May '89. Catalogue no: **LONX 207**
7" Single: Released Oct '88, on London Records, by London Records. Deleted May '89. Catalogue no: **LON 207**

Perfect Daze

BUBBLEGUM
Tracks: / Bubblegum / Picture of you / She revs me up / Blue horizon / Love you kill the bomb drops.
Special: Released Mar '87, on Vinyl Solution, by Vinyl Solution Records. Catalogue no: **SOL 1**

REGULAR JAILBREAK EP
Tracks: / Regular jailbreak.
12" Single: Released May '88, on Vinyl Solution, by Vinyl Solution Records. Catalogue no: **VS 11**

Perfect Disaster

BLUE BELL
Tracks: / Blue bell.
12" Single: Released Nov '87, on Glass, by Glass Records. Catalogue no: **GLAEP 109**

TIME TO KILL
Tracks: / Time to kill.
7" Single: Released Nov '88, on Fire, by Fire Records. Catalogue no: **BLAZE 31**
12" Single: Released Nov '88, on Fire, by Fire Records. Catalogue no: **BLAZE 31T**

TV (GIRLS ON FIRE)
12" Single: Released May '88, on Fire, by Fire Records. Catalogue no: **BLAZE 28T**

Perfect End

SWEET DREAM
Tracks: / Sweet dream / Natural causes.
7" Single: Released Apr '82, on Hellfire Disc, Catalogue no: **HELL 1**

Perfect Fit

IF YOU ONLY KNEW
Tracks: / If you only knew / Heartbreaking.
12" Single: Released Sep '86, on Move, Catalogue no: **MS 16**

Perfect Strangers

I DON'T WANNA FIGHT
Tracks: / I don't wanna fight / It's all over your face (it's all over).
7" Single: Released Feb '88, on RAK, by EMI Records. Catalogue no: **RAK 504**
12" Single: Released Feb '88, on RAK, by EMI Records. Catalogue no: **12RAK 504**

LOVE THAT TURNED AWAY
Tracks: / Love that turned away / 15 minutes.
7" Single: Released Jun '83, on Best, Catalogue no: **BEST 1**

WITHOUT YOU
Tracks: / Without you / My kind of love / Without you (extended version) (Only on 12" version.).
7" Single: Released '83, on Chrysalis, by Chrysalis Records. Deleted '87. Catalogue no: **CHS 2702**
12" Single: Released '83, on Chrysalis, by Chrysalis Records. Deleted '87. Catalogue no: **CHS 12 2702**

Perfect Vision

OUR BROKEN CROWN (EP)
Tracks: / Our broken crown.
7" Single: Released Sep '84, on Leave It

Art, Catalogue no: **LIAR 002**

THIS HOOK
Tracks: / This hook.
12" Single: Released Jul '84, on Perfect Vision, Catalogue no: **LIAR 2**

Perfect Zebras

ANOTHER LOVE STORY
Tracks: / Another love story.
7" Single: Released Oct '82, on Focus, Catalogue no: **FOS 3**

RUNNING WITH ZEBRAS
Tracks: / Running with zebras / Man or machine.
12" Single: Released May '82, on Focus, Catalogue no: **FOS 112**
7" Single: Released May '82, on Focus, Catalogue no: **FOS 1**

TOUCHING MY HEART AGAIN
Tracks: / Touching my heart again.
7" Single: Released Jul '82, on Focus, Catalogue no: **FOS 2**
12" Single: Released Jul '82, on Focus, Catalogue no: **FOS 2 12**

Perfectly Ordinary

PERFECTLY ORDINARY PEOPLE, THEME FROM
Tracks: / Perfectly ordinary people, Theme from (radio edition) (On single only.) / Perfectly ordinary people, Theme from (acid edit) (On single only.) / Perfectly ordinary people, Theme from (club remix) (Only on 12" single.) / Perfectly ordinary people, Theme from (12" acid rundown mix) (Only on 12" single.).
7" Single: Released Sep '88, on Urban, by Polydor Ltd. Deleted 30 May '89. Catalogue no: **URB 25**
12" Single: Released Sep '88, on Urban, by Polydor Ltd. Deleted 30 Jun '89. Catalogue no: **URBX 25**

Performance

WISH I WAS FREE AGAIN
Tracks: / Wish I was free again / Free again.
7" Single: Released Mar '86, on Clay, by Clay Records. Deleted '88. Catalogue no: **CLAY 47**

Performing Ferrets

PERFORMING FERRETS(EP)
Tracks: / Performing ferrets.
7" Single: Released Nov '82, on Dead Happy, by Dead Happy Records. Catalogue no: **DHR 3**

Pericoli, Emilio

AL DI LA
Tracks: / Al di la.
7" Single: Released Jun '62, on Warner Bros., by WEA Records. Deleted '65. Catalogue no: **WB 69**

Perils of Plastic

LOVE I LOVE, THE
Tracks: / Love I love, The / What love can do for you.
7" Single: Released Sep '87, on WEA, by WEA Records. Deleted Jul '88. Catalogue no: **YZ 153**
12" Single: Released Sep '87, on WEA, by WEA Records. Deleted Jul '88. Catalogue no: **YZ 153 T**

RING A DING RING
Tracks: / Ring a Ding Ring (7" and 12" A side) / Debile Matin.
7" Single: Released May '86, on WEA, by WEA Records. Deleted Jun '87. Catalogue no: **YZ 61**
12" Single: Released May '86, on WEA, by WEA Records. Deleted Jun '87. Catalogue no: **YZ 61T**

WOMANHOOD
Tracks: / Womanhood / Moth Music.
12" Single: Released Sep '86, on WEA, by WEA Records. Deleted Jun '87. Catalogue no: **YZ 80T**
7" Single: Released Sep '86, on WEA, by WEA Records. Deleted Jun '87. Catalogue no: **YZ 80**

Perkins, Carl

Biographical details: Carl Perkins, the jazz pianist, was born in 1928 in Indianapolis, Indiana; his life was shortened by narcotics addiction and he died in 1958. He was a very fine and influential post-bop West Coast musician. His left hand was slightly handicapped by polio; his compensating for this may partly account for his heavier blues feeling than that of most other modern jazz pianists. He played with an early edition of the famous Max Roach-Clifford Brown quintet, was a key member of Curtis Counce quintet; played and recorded with Harold Land (his tune *Grooveyard* on a 1958 Land LP became a modern jazz standard); he only made three or four albums as a leader, which are now highly prized. (Donald Clarke 25.5.87)

The name of this American singer, songwriter and guitarist is indelibly associated in everybody's minds with *Blue suede shoes*. Perkins wrote and recorded the original version of this rock'n'roll classic in 1956, soon after joining Sam Phillips' Sun label in Memphis. It logged four weeks at No.2 on the American charts and reached No.10 in Britain. However, the song was quickly covered by Elvis Presley who made the song his own thus tended to overshadow Perkins. A series of peronal problems prevented Perkins from building on the sucess of *Blue Suede Shoes*, and it remained his only pop hit. He subsequently went back to his country roots, and spent much of his time touring with Johnny Cash. During the late Seventies and early Eighties, Carl was a regular live performer in his own right.(Bob MacDonald 5.3.86).

BLUE SUEDE SHOES
Tracks: / Blue suede shoes / Raunchy.
7" Single: Released '80, on USA, by Charly Records. Catalogue no: **LR 0693**

BLUE SUEDE SHOES (CD SINGLE)
Tracks: / Blue suede shoes / Boppin' the blues / Honey don't / Everybody's trying to be my baby.
CD 5": Released Feb '89, on Charly, by Charly Records. Catalogue no: **CDS 9**

BLUE SUEDE SHOES (OLD GOLD)
Tracks: / Blue suede shoes.
7" Single: Released Nov '87, on Old Gold, by Old Gold Records. Catalogue no: **OG 9737**

BLUE SUEDE SHOES (ORIGINAL)
Tracks: / Blue suede shoes.
7" Single: Released May '56, on London-American, Deleted '59. Catalogue no: **HLU 8271**

LIL' BIT OF GOLD: CARL PERKINS
Tracks: / Blue suede shoes / Honey don't / Everybody's trying to be my baby / Matchbox.
CD 5": Released May '88, on Rhino, by Creole Records. Catalogue no: **R 373015**

ROCK AND ROLL & COUNTRY SOUL
Tracks: / Didn't the 50's rock / Country soul / I don't like what I'm seeing in you.
Note: Collection of seventies material from the rock and roll legend
7" EP: on Magnum Force, by Magnum Music Group. Catalogue no: **MFEP 013**

TURNAROUND (SINGLE)
Tracks: / Turnaround / Blue suede shoes / Lovesick blues / Miss misunderstood.
7" Single: Released Nov '80, on Jet, by Jet Records. Deleted '83. Catalogue no: **JET 182**

Perkins, Jonathan

BELIEVE IN ME
Tracks: / Believe in me.
7" Single: Released Feb '85, on Checkmount, Catalogue no: **CHK 2**

I'LL LAY MY SILVER SPURS
Tracks: / I'll lay my silver spurs.
12" Single: Released Sep '83, on RCA, by BMG Records (UK). Catalogue no: **SPURT 1**
7" Single: Released Sep '83, on RCA, by BMG Records (UK). Catalogue no: **SPUR 1**

Perkins, Laura Lee

GONNA ROCK MY BABY TONIGHT
Tracks: / Gonna rock my baby tonight.
7" Single: Released Feb '81, on Detour, by Detour Records. Deleted Dec '86. Catalogue no: **DT 4502**

Perkins, Luther

TENNESSEE SATURDAY NIGHT
Tracks: / Tennessee Saturday night / Million dollar quartet.
7" Single: Released Aug '80, on Magic (1), by Submarine Records. Deleted '83. Catalogue no: **101**

Perks

REGGAE SUE
Tracks: / Reggae Sue / Keep on doing it.
7" Single: Released May '80, on Virgin, by Virgin Records. Deleted May '83. Catalogue no: **VS 335**

Perks, Katie

COLD STONE
Tracks: / Cold stone / Small.
7" Single: Released Nov '83, on Plastic Head, by Plastic Head Records. Catalogue no: **PLAS 001**

Pernell Lovers

BLACK IS THE BEST
Tracks: / Black is the best.

12" Single: Released Jun '82, on Export, Catalogue no: **EX 715**

Peron, Carlos

DIRTY SONG, A
Tracks: / Dirty song, A.
12" Single: Released Dec '88, on Play It Again Sam(Belgium), by Play It Again Sam (Belgium). Catalogue no: **BIAS 115**

HIT SONG, A
Tracks: / Hit song, A.
12" Single: Released Aug '89, on Bbat, Catalogue no: **BBAT 004T**
CD 5": Released Aug '89, on Bbat, Catalogue no: **BBAT 004CD**

TALKS TO THE NATION
Tracks: / Talks to the nation.
12" Single: Released 20 Feb '88, on Licensed, Catalogue no: **LD 8712**

Peroux

WHEELS KEEP TURNIN'
Tracks: / Wheels keep turnin'.
12" Single: Released Oct '88, on Razor, by Razor Records. Catalogue no: **PPR 1**

Perrett, Peter

BABY'S GOT A GUN
Tracks: / Baby's got a gun.
7" Single: Released Jan '83, on Vengeance, Catalogue no: **VEN 002**

Perri

FALL IN LOVE
Tracks: / Fall in love.
CD 5": Released Oct '88, on MCA, by MCA Records. Catalogue no: **DMCA 1293**
12" Single: Released Oct '88, on MCA, by MCA Records. Catalogue no: **MCA T1293**
7" Single: Released Oct '88, on MCA, by MCA Records. Deleted 1 Jul '89. Catalogue no: **MCA 1293**

FEEL SO GOOD
Tracks: / Feel so good / Feel so good (instrumental) / Feel so good (extended).
CD 5": Released Oct '89, on Motown, by BMG Records (UK). Catalogue no: **ZD 43084**
12" Single: Released Oct '89, on Motown, by BMG Records (UK). Catalogue no: **ZT 43084**
7" Single: Released Oct '89, on Motown, by BMG Records (UK). Catalogue no: **ZB 43083**

I'M THE ONE
Tracks: / I'm the one.
CD 5": Released Apr '89, on MCA, by MCA Records. Catalogue no: **DMCAT 1311**
12" Single: Released Apr '89, on MCA, by MCA Records. Catalogue no: **MCAT 1311**
7" Single: Released Apr '89, on MCA, by MCA Records. Catalogue no: **MCA 1311**

Perri, Lorna

JUST A MEMORY
Tracks: / Just a memory.
12" Single: Released May '83, on Ital, by Ital Records. Catalogue no: **ITD 0020**

Perrier, Cher

I WANNA DANCE
Tracks: / I wanna dance.
12" Single: Released Nov '86, on Musik, Catalogue no: **12 MUK 1**
7" Single: Released Nov '86, on Musik, Catalogue no: **MUK 1**
12" Single: Released Feb '87, on Musik, Catalogue no: **12 MUK 4**
7" Single: Released Feb '87, on Musik, Catalogue no: **MUK 4**

Perry, Lee 'Scratch'

ALL THINGS ARE POSSIBLE
Tracks: / All things are possible / Sexy lady.
7" Single: Released Sep '86, on Trojan, by Trojan Records. Deleted May '88. Catalogue no: **TRO 9082**

JUNGLE (RADIO PLATE)
Tracks: / Jungle (radio plate) / Jungle (radio plate) (Rhythm mix) / Music and science (12" only).
7" Single: Released Sep '87, on Syncopate, by EMI Records. Deleted Jan '88. Catalogue no: **SY 6**
12" Single: Released Sep '87, on Syncopate, by EMI Records. Deleted Jan '88. Catalogue no: **12SY 6**
10" single: Released Sep '87, on Syncopate, by EMI Records. Deleted Jan '88. Catalogue no: **10SY 6**

MASTER OF THE UNIVERSE
Tracks: / Master of the universe.
12" Single: Released May '89, on Arkwell, Catalogue no: **ARK 03**

MERRY CHRISTMAS, HAPPY NEW YEAR
Tracks: / Merry Christmas, The (dub mix) / I am a mad man / Mad men dub wise * / Merry Christmas, Happy New Year / Return of Django / All things are Possible (Only available on 12" version (Ltd Edition with photo insert)) / Happy Birthday (Only available on 12" version (Ltd Edition with photo insert)).

12" Single: Released Dec '86, on Trojan, by Trojan Records. Deleted May '88. Catalogue no: **TROT 9095**
12" Single: Released Dec '85, on Trojan, by Trojan Records. Deleted May '88. Catalogue no: **TROT 9080**
7" Single: Released Dec '85, on Trojan, by Trojan Records. Deleted May '88. Catalogue no: **TRO 9080**
7" Single: Released Dec '86, on Trojan, by Trojan Records. Deleted May '88. Catalogue no: **TRO 9095**

Perry, Steve

FOOLISH HEART
Tracks: / Foolish heart.
7" Single: Released Feb '85, on CBS, by CBS Records. Catalogue no: **A 6017**

SHE'S MINE
Tracks: / She's mine.
7" Single: Released Aug '84, on CBS, by CBS Records. Catalogue no: **A 4636**

STEP BY STEP
Tracks: / Step by step.
7" Single: Released Aug '60, on H.M.V., by EMI Records. Deleted '63. Catalogue no: **POP 745**

Perry, Tyren

DON'T RUSH IT (IMPORT)
Tracks: / Don't rush it.
12" Single: Released Jul '89, on Columbia, by EMI Records. Catalogue no: **FC 45151**

Persian Flowers

SOMEBODY ELSE'S SIN
Tracks: / Somebody else's sin.
7" Single: Released Mar '84, on 4th. Dimension, by 4th. Dimension Records. Catalogue no: **FDF 02**

Persian Gulf

TRAILER, THE
12" Single: Released Oct '86, on Tim, by Tim Records. Catalogue no: **MT 12002**

Persian Risk

RIDIN' HIGH
Tracks: / Ridin' high / Hurt you.
7" Single: Released Mar '83, on Neat, by Neat Records. Catalogue no: **NEAT 24**

Persian Rugs

BURNING PASSION PAIN
Tracks: / Burning passion pain.
7" Single: Released Mar '82, on Phoenix (1), by Phoenix Records. Catalogue no: **PSP 11**

SHE SAID
Tracks: / She said.
7" Single: Released Jan '84, on Plus One, Catalogue no: **RUG 1**
12" Single: Released Jan '84, on Plus One, Catalogue no: **RUG 1-12**

Persion Risk

TOO DIFFERENT, TWO PEOPLE
12" Single: Released Jul '84, on Zebra (1), by Zebra Records (1). Catalogue no: **12 RA 3**

Persistant Gods

ASH GARDEN (EP)
Tracks: / Ash garden.
7" Single: Released Feb '82, on Alternative, Deleted '88. Catalogue no: **ALT 0098**

COME INTO THE ASH GARDEN
Tracks: / Come into the ash garden / Fair / Genetic engineering.
7" Single: Released Apr '82, on Alternative, Deleted '88. Catalogue no: **ALT 008**

Person To Person

HIGH TIME
Tracks: / High time.
7" Single: Released May '85, on Epic, by CBS Records. Catalogue no: **A 4630**

REPUTATION
Tracks: / Reputation.
7" Single: Released Jan '85, on Epic, by CBS Records. Catalogue no: **A 6001**
12" Single: Released Jan '85, on Epic, by CBS Records. Catalogue no: **TX 6001**

Personal Column

STRICTLY CONFIDENTIAL
Tracks: / Strictly confidential / Here's looking at you.
7" Single: Released Apr '84, on Stiff, by Stiff Records. Catalogue no: **BUY 202**

Persuasion

TIME IS RIGHT, THE
Tracks: / Time is right.
12" Single: Released Apr '89, on Zoo Experience, by Zoo Experience Records. Catalogue no: **JTYG 0121**

Persuasions

I WOKE UP IN LOVE THIS MORNING

Tracks: / I woke up in love this morning.
7" Single: Released Apr '85, on Demon, by Demon Records. Catalogue no: **D 1036**

Pertwee, Jon

Biographical details: One of Britain's best known actors, Pertwee played the title role in Southern Television's Worzel Gummidge during the late Seventies and early Eighties. This adaptation of Barbara Euphan Todd's children's literary classic spawned the minor hit single *Worzel's song*, which reached the UK No.33 position in 1980. Fans of the legendary BBC TV programme Doctor Who remember Pertwee for his portrayal of the title role in that series between 1970 and 1974. Following in the footsteps of William Hartnell and Patrick Troughton, Pertwee was the third and possibly most notable Doctor. He was succeeded in 1974 by Tom Baker.(Bob MacDonald 5.3.86).

NEVER EVER TALK TO A STRANGER Worzel's warning

Tracks: / Never ever talk to a stranger / Worzel's world.
7" Single: Released Mar '87, on Splash, by Splash Records. Catalogue no: **CPS 1009**

SING THE BEATLES WHEN I'M 64

Tracks: / Sing the Beatles when I'm 64 / Yesterday.
7" Single: Released Apr '84, on Flightstream, Catalogue no: **IM 64 A**

SPOTTYMAN SONG

Tracks: / Spotty man song.
7" Single: Released Jan '84, on Rainbow, by Rainbow Records. Catalogue no: **TED 1**

WHO IS THE DOCTOR

Tracks: / Who is the doctor.
7" Single: Released Jun '85, on Safari, by Safari Records. Catalogue no: **DOCTOR 1**

WORZEL'S SONG

Tracks: / Worzel's song / Who'd be a scarecrow.
7" Single: Released Mar '80, on Decca, by Decca Records. Deleted '83. Catalogue no: **F 13885**

Peryglus, Eirin

BRONSON

Tracks: / Bronson.
7" Single: Released May '87, on Welsh Celtic & Worldwide, Catalogue no: **OFN 03**

DASYBB YN GWNEUDTERFUN

Tracks: / Dasybb yn gwneudterfun.
7" Single: Released '88, on OFN, Catalogue no: **OFN 006**

Pestalozzi Int'...

IMAGINE

Tracks: / Imagine / Give peace a chance.
7" Single: Released Dec '81, on Contact, by RK Records. Catalogue no: **CON 8**

Pet Hate

BLOWN OUT AGAIN

Tracks: / Blown out again.
12" Single: Released Mar '84, on Trapper, Catalogue no: **EARFITS 1**

GIRLS GROW UP TOO FAST

Tracks: / Girls grow up too fast.
7" Single: Released Apr '85, on Fobik, Catalogue no: **VHF 8**

ROLL AWAY THE STONE

Tracks: / Roll away the stone.
12" Single: Released Jul '84, on FM, by FM-Revolver Records. Catalogue no: **12 VHF 2**

Pet Shop Boys

ALWAYS ON MY MIND

Tracks: / Always on my mind (extended dance version) / Do I have to? / Always on my mind / Always on my mind (7" version) / Always on my mind (dub).
7" Single: Released Nov '87, on Parlophone, by EMI Records. Deleted '88. Catalogue no: **RS 6171**
12" Single: Released Dec '87, on Parlophone, by EMI Records. Deleted 31 Jul '88. Catalogue no: **12 RX 6171**
12" Single: Released Nov '87, on Parlophone, by EMI Records. Deleted '88. Catalogue no: **12RS 6171**
12" Single: Released Nov '87, on Parlophone, by EMI Records. Catalogue no: **12R 6171**
CD 3": Released Aug '88, on EMI (Japan), by EMI Records. Catalogue no: **XP 102002**
7" Single: Released Nov '87, on Parlophone, by EMI Records. Deleted Oct '89. Catalogue no: **R 6171**

DOMINO DANCING

Tracks: / Domino dancing / Don Juan / Domino dancing (disco mix) (12" & CD single only.) / Domino dancing (alternative mix) (12" & CD single only.) / Don Juan (disco mix) (12" & CD single only.) / Domino dancing (bass mix) (12RX 6190 only.).
CD 5": Released Sep '88, on Parlophone, by EMI Records. Catalogue no: **CDR 6190**

PET SHOP BOYS - IT'S ALRIGHT (Released on Parlophone)

7" Single: Released Sep '88, on Parlophone, by EMI Records. Deleted Aug '89. Catalogue no: **RS 6190**
7" Single: Released Sep '88, on Parlophone, by EMI Records. Deleted Aug '89. Catalogue no: **R 6190**
12" Single: Released Sep '88, on Parlophone, by EMI Records. Catalogue no: **12R 6180**
12" Single: Released Sep '88, on Parlophone, by EMI Records. Deleted Aug '89. Catalogue no: **12RX 6190**
12" Single: Released Sep '88, on Parlophone, by EMI Records. Deleted Aug '89. Catalogue no: **12RS 6190**
Cassingle: Released Sep '88, on Parlophone, by EMI Records. Deleted Aug '89. Catalogue no: **TCR 6190**

DOMINO DANCING (IMPORT)

Tracks: / Domino dancing.
12" Single: Released Dec '88, on EMI-Manhattan, by EMI Records. Catalogue no: **V 56116**

HEART

Tracks: / Heart* (*This version on 7" only.) / Heart (disco mix) / Heart (dance mix) / Heart (12" remix) / Heart (dub mix)* / I get excited (you get excited too)*.
CD 5": Released 21 Mar '88, on Parlophone, by EMI Records. Catalogue no: **CDR 6177**
Cassingle: Released 21 Mar '88, on Parlophone, by EMI Records. Deleted 31 Jul '88. Catalogue no: **TC R6177**
12" Single: Released 5 Apr '88, on Parlophone, by EMI Records. Deleted Aug '89. Catalogue no: **12RX 6177**
12" Single: Released 21 Mar '88, on Parlophone, by EMI Records. Catalogue no: **12R 6177**
7" Single: Released 21 Mar '88, on Parlophone, by EMI Records. Deleted Oct '89. Catalogue no: **R 6177**

INTROSPECTIVE

Tracks: / Left to my own devices / I want a dog / Domino dancing / I'm not scared / Always on mind / It's alright / In my house.
Special: Released Nov '88, on Parlophone, by EMI Records. Deleted Jan '89. Catalogue no: **PCSX 7325**

IT'S A SIN

Tracks: / It's a sin / You know where you went wrong / It's a sin (disco mix) (Extra track on CD).
CD 5": Released Jul '87, on Parlophone, by EMI Records. Catalogue no: **CDR 6158**
Cassingle: Released Jun '87, on Parlophone, by EMI Records. Deleted '88. Catalogue no: **TCR 6158**
12" Single: Released Jun '87, on Parlophone, by EMI Records. Catalogue no: **12R 6158**
7" Single: Released Jun '87, on Parlophone, by EMI Records. Deleted Oct '89. Catalogue no: **R 6158**

IT'S A SIN (REMIX)

Tracks: / It's a sin (remix) / You know where you went wrong (rough mix).

12" Single: Released Jul '87, on Parlophone, by EMI Records. Catalogue no: **12 RX 6158**

IT'S ALRIGHT (See panel above)

Tracks: / It's alright / One of the crowd / Your funny uncle / It's alright (ext. disco mix) (12" & CD single only.) / It's alright (It's acid) / It's alright (underground mix) / It's alright (tyree mix) (Special product only.) / It's alright (sterling void mix) (Special product only.).
Note: Producer/Arranger: Trevor Horn
CD 5": Released Jun '89, on Parlophone, by EMI Records. Catalogue no: **203 420 2**
10" single: Released Jul '89, on Parlophone, by EMI Records. Catalogue no: **203 420 8**
CD 5": Released Jun '89, on Parlophone, by EMI Records. Catalogue no: **CDR 6220**
Cassingle: Released Jun '89, on Parlophone, by EMI Records. Catalogue no: **203 420 4**
Cassingle: Released Jun '89, on Parlophone, by EMI Records. Catalogue no: **TCR 6220**
7" Single: Released Jun '89, on Parlophone, by EMI Records. Catalogue no: **R 6220**
7" Single: Released Jun '89, on Parlophone, by EMI Records. Catalogue no: **203 420 7**
7" Single: Released Jun '89, on Parlophone, by EMI Records. Catalogue no: **RS 6220**
7" Single: Released Jun '89, on Parlophone, by EMI Records. Catalogue no: **203 433 7**
12" Single: Released Jun '89, on Parlophone, by EMI Records. Catalogue no: **12RS 6220**
12" Single: Released Jun '89, on Parlophone, by EMI Records. Catalogue no: **203 420 6**
12" Single: Released Jun '89, on Parlophone, by EMI Records. Catalogue no: **203 433 6**
12" Single: Released Jun '89, on Parlophone, by EMI Records. Catalogue no: **12R 6220**
Special: Released Jul '89, on Parlophone, by EMI Records. Catalogue no: **12RX 6220**
10" single: Released Jul '89, on Parlophone, by EMI Records. Catalogue no: **10R 6220**

LEFT TO MY OWN DEVICES

Tracks: / Left to my own devices / Sound of the atom splitting / Left to my own devices (disco mix) (Not on 7".).
CD 5": Released Nov '88, on Parlophone, by EMI Records. Catalogue no: **CDR 6198**
7" Single: Released Nov '88, on Parlophone, by EMI Records. Deleted Aug '89. Catalogue no: **R 6198**
7" Single: Released Nov '88, on Parlophone, by EMI Records. Deleted Aug '89. Catalogue no: **RS 6198**
12" Single: Released Nov '88, on Parlophone, by EMI Records. Deleted Aug '89. Catalogue no: **12RS 6198**
12" Single: Released Nov '88, on Parlophone, by EMI Records. Catalogue no: **12R 6198**
Cassingle: Released Nov '88, on Parlophone, by EMI Records. Deleted Oct '89. Catalogue no: **TCR 6198**

LOVE COMES QUICKLY

Tracks: / Love comes quickly / That's my impression / Love comes quickly (dance mix 12" only). / That's my impression (disco mix) (on 12" only).
12" Single: Released Mar '86, on Parlophone, by EMI Records. Catalogue no: **12R 6116**
7" Single: Released Mar '86, on Parlophone, by EMI Records. Deleted Jul '87. Catalogue no: **R 6116**

MEGAMIX

Tracks: / Megamix.
CD 5": Released Dec '88, on ZYX (Germany), Catalogue no: **ZYX 85995**

MEGAMIX (EP)

Tracks: / Megamix / West End - sunglasses / One more chance / West End girls / West End girls (remix '86) / One more chance (hurricane mix).
12" Single: Released Sep '88, on ZYX (Germany), Catalogue no: **ZYX 5995**

ONE MORE CHANCE

Tracks: / One more chance / West End Girls / Alive and kicking.
12" Single: Released May '88, on RCA (USA), Catalogue no: **76441 RD**
12" Single: Released May '88, on Virgin (Germany), by Virgin Records. Catalogue no: **602 038**
12" Single: Released May '88, on Bobkat (USA), by Bobkat Records (USA). Catalogue no: **4Z905019**

ONE MORE CHANCE (REMIX)

Tracks: / One more chance (hurricane mix) / Theme for the 'Pet Shop Boys' (part 2).
Note: A brand new 1988 remix of their fine track 'One more chance'. Remixed by Tess, the 'Hurricane mix is 5 mins long.
CD 3": Released Sep '88, on ZYX (Germany), Catalogue no: **ZYX 85401**

OPPORTUNITIES

Tracks: / Opportunities (Lets make lots of money) / Was that what it was.
7" Single: Released Jun '85, on Parlophone, by EMI Records. Catalogue no: **12R 6097**
7" Single: Released Jun '85, on Parlophone, by EMI Records. Catalogue no: **R 6097**
12" Single: Released May '86, on Parlophone, by EMI Records. Catalogue no: **12R 6129**
7" Single: Released May '86, on Parlophone, by EMI Records. Deleted Oct '87. Catalogue no: **R 6129**

OPPORTUNITIES (IMPORT)

Tracks: / Opportunities.
12" Single: Released Dec '88, on EMI-America, by EMI Records. Catalogue no: **S 75146**

PANINARO

Tracks: / Paninaro.
Note: Italian-only 12" featuring two versions of 'Paninaro'. Limited edition, picture bag.
12" Single: Released Nov '87, on Parlophone (Italy), by EMI Records. Catalogue no: **2015626**

RENT

Tracks: / Rent / I want a dog.
CD 5": Released Nov '87, on Parlophone, by EMI Records. Catalogue no: **CDR 6168**
7" Single: Released Oct '87, on Parlophone, by EMI Records. Deleted Aug '89. Catalogue no: **R 6168**
12" Single: Released Oct '87, on Parlophone, by EMI Records. Catalogue no: **12R 6168**

SUBURBIA

Tracks: / Suburbia / Jack the lad / Love comes quickly / Paninaro.
7" Set: Released Sep '86, on Parlophone, by EMI Records. Deleted Oct '87. Catalogue no: **RD 6140**
7" Single: Released Sep '86, on Parlophone, by EMI Records. Deleted Oct '87. Catalogue no: **R 6140**
12" Single: Released Sep '86, on Parlophone, by EMI Records. Catalogue no: **12R 6140**

WEST END GIRLS

Tracks: / West End girls / West End dub / Man could get arrested, A.
10" single: Released Dec '85, on Parlophone, by EMI Records. Deleted '88. Catalogue no: **10R 6115**
7" Pic: Released Dec '85, on Parlophone, by EMI Records. Deleted '88. Catalogue no: **RP 6115**
12" Single: Released Oct '85, on Parlophone, by EMI Records. Catalogue no: **12R 6115**
12" Single: Released Jan '86, on Parlophone, by EMI Records. Deleted 31 Jul '88. Catalogue no: **12RA 6115**
7" Single: Released Oct '85, on Parlophone, by EMI Records. Catalogue no: **R 6115**

WEST END GIRLS (DANCE MIX)

Tracks: / West End girls (dance mix) / Man could get arrested, A / West End girls (dub).
12" Single: Released Jul '88, on EMI-Ameri-

ca, by EMI Records. Catalogue no: **VI 9206**

WEST END - SUNGLASSES
Tracks: / West End - sunglasses / One more chance (dub mix).
Note: A special mix of 'West End girls' and 'Sunglasses at night'. No UK release.
CD 3": Released Aug '88, on ZYX (Germany), Catalogue no: **ZYX 85196**

WHAT HAVE I DONE TO DESERVE THIS? (Pet shop boys and Dusty Springfield)
Tracks: / What have I done to deserve this? (Shep Pettibone mix) / What have I done to deserve this? (Extended mix) (CD only) / New life, A (CD only) / What have I done to deserve this (Disco mix) (CD only).
CD 5": Released Sep '87, on Parlophone, by EMI Records. Catalogue no: **CDR 6163**
7" Single: Released Aug '87, on Parlophone, by EMI Records. Deleted Oct '89. Catalogue no: **R 6163**
12" Single: Released Aug '87, on Parlophone, by EMI Records. Catalogue no: **12R 6163**
Cassingle: Released Aug '87, on Parlophone, by EMI Records. Deleted '88. Catalogue no: **TCR 6163**

Peter & Gordon

Biographical details: A young British duo comprising Peter Asher and Gordon Waller had a very useful connection during the early Sixties - Peter's sister Jane was dating Paul McCartney. Thus, in the Spring of 1964, the unknown Peter & Gordon jumped to No.1 in the UK with one of Lennon & McCartney's strongest songs, *A world without love*. The Beatles never recorded this song, and Asher and Waller were therefore able to take full advantage of its international potential. *A world without love* proceeded to reach No.1 in America as part of the British Invasion. Then followed a series of hits on both sides of the Atlantic, including Lennon & McCartney's *Nobody I Know* and McCartney's *Woman* plus remakes of classics by Buddy Holly and The Teddy Bears. After the duo split up in 1967, Peter became a successful manager and producer; amongst the acts who came under his wing were James Taylor, Linda Ronstadt and Joni Mitchell. Gordon made his mark as Pharoah in Tim Rice & Andrew Lloyd Webber's *Joseph and his amazing technicolour dreamcoat*, and later left the music industry.(Bob MacDonald 5.3.86).

BABY I'M YOURS
Tracks: / Baby I'm yours.
7" Single: Released Oct '65, on Columbia, by EMI Records. Deleted '68. Catalogue no: **DB 7729**

LADY GODIVA
Tracks: / Lady Godiva.
7" Single: Released Sep '66, on Columbia, by EMI Records. Deleted '69. Catalogue no: **DB 8003**

NOBODY I KNOW
Tracks: / Nobody I know.
7" Single: Released Jun '64, on Columbia, by EMI Records. Deleted '67. Catalogue no: **DB 7292**

TO KNOW YOU IS TO LOVE YOU
Tracks: / To know you is to love you.
7" Single: Released Jun '65, on Columbia, by EMI Records. Deleted '68. Catalogue no: **DB 7617**

TRUE LOVE WAYS
Tracks: / True love ways.
7" Single: Released Apr '65, on Columbia, by EMI Records. Deleted '68. Catalogue no: **DB 7524**

WOMAN
Tracks: / Woman.
7" Single: Released Feb '66, on Columbia, by EMI Records. Deleted '69. Catalogue no: **DB 7834**

WORLD WITHOUT LOVE (OLD GOLD)
Tracks: / World without love.
7" Single: Released Oct '83, on Old Gold, by Old Gold Records. Deleted Jun '89. Catalogue no: **OG 9381**

WORLD WITHOUT LOVE (SINGLE)
Tracks: / World without love.
7" Single: Released Jul '84, on See For Miles, by See For Miles Records. Catalogue no: **1A 066 07025**
7" Single: Released Mar '64, on Columbia, by EMI Records. Deleted '67. Catalogue no: **DB 7225**

Peter, Paul & Mary

Biographical details: Peter Yarrow, from New York, Paul Stookey, Baltimore, Maryland, and Mary Travers, Louisville, Kentucky -- all born 1937-38 -- formed as a folk-protest trio in New York in 1961. They were put together by Albert Grossman before he managed Bob Dylan and were immediately successful, one critic describing them as "the Kingston Trio with sex appeal". True folkies regarded their act as musically watered down but they championed Dylan's songs for a very big audience, his *Blowin' In The Wind* being one of their biggest hits at No 2 in 1963. *Puff The Magic Dragon*, also No 2 that year, is still a popular children's song, though some thought it was a drugs song at the time. Their biggest hit was a surprise: John Denver's *Leaving' On A Jet Plane* was American No 1 in late '69, British No 2 early '70. They split up in the early 70's and re-formed in '78. (Meanwhile Yarrow wrote *Torn Between Two Lovers*, a smash international hit in 1977 for Mary McGregor.) Mary Travers has never stopped protesting: she now sings songs about El Salvador but the sentiments are the same and she tours, sings and lectures for the benefit of Soviet Jews. (Donald Clarke, May 1987.)
Peter Yarrow, Paul Stookey and Mary Travers became one of the most famous acts on the American folk protest scene of the early to mid-Sixties. Formed in New York's Greenwich in 1961, the trio's biggest hits were *Puff the magic dragon* and Bob Dylan's *Blowing in the wind* - these both reached No.2 on the US charts in 1963. After their success tailed off somewhat, towards the end of the Sixties, the threesome's final single proved to be their biggest hit of all: their rendition of John Denver's *Leavin' on a jet plane* reached No.1 in America in December 1969 and climbed to No.2 in Britain in early 1970.
Some people complained that Peter, Paul & Mary's middle-of-the-road style watered down the impact of the protest movement, but they should be given credit for taking the music to a broke pop audience in advance of Dylan and many others. The trio broke up in the early Seventies, but reformed in 1978. In the meantime, Yarrow co-wrote and co-produced Mary MacGregor's 1977 smash *Torn between two lovers*, which reached No.1 in the US and No.4 in the UK. (Bob MacDonald 5.3.86).

BLOWING IN THE WIND
Tracks: / Blowing in the wind.
7" Single: Released Oct '63, on Warner Bros., by WEA Records. Deleted '66. Catalogue no: **WB 104**

LEAVING ON A JET PLANE
Tracks: / Leaving on a jet plane.
7" Single: Released Jan '70, on Warner Bros., by WEA Records. Deleted '73. Catalogue no: **WB 7340**
7" Single: Released May '80, on Warner Bros.(USA), by WEA Records. Catalogue no: **LR 1044**

PUFF THE MAGIC DRAGON
Tracks: / Puff the magic dragon.
7" Single: Released Jul '81, on Warner Bros., by WEA Records. Catalogue no: **K 17809**

TELL IT ON THE MOUNTAIN
Tracks: / Tell it on the mountain.
7" Single: Released Apr '64, on Warner Bros., by WEA Records. Deleted '66. Catalogue no: **WB 127**

TIMES THEY ARE A CHANGIN', THE
Tracks: / Times they are a-changin'.
7" Single: Released Oct '64, on Warner Bros., by WEA Records. Deleted '67. Catalogue no: **WB 142**

Peter & The Test....

BANNED FROM THE PUB
Tracks: / Banned from the pub.
7" Single: Released Jul '82, on No Future, Deleted '87. Catalogue no: **01 4**

JINX
Tracks: / Jinx.
7" Single: Released Mar '85, on Trapper, Catalogue no: **EARS 2**
12" Single: Released Mar '85, on Trapper, Catalogue no: **EARS 12002**

KEYS TO THE CITY
Tracks: / Keys to the city / Keith Moon / Work hard.
7" Single: Released Jun '86, on Hairy Pie, Catalogue no: **TTB 1**
12" Single: Released Jun '86, on Hairy Pie, Catalogue no: **TTB 121**

PRESSED FOR CASH
Tracks: / Pressed for cash / Peace and quiet.
12" Single: Released Mar '85, on Trapper, Catalogue no: **EARFIT 1**

ROTTING IN THE FART SACK
Tracks: / Rotting in the fart sack.
12" Single: Released May '85, on Metal Knob, Catalogue no: **JUNG 21T**

RUN LIKE HELL
Tracks: / Run like hell.
7" Single: Released Jul '82, on No Future, Deleted '87. Catalogue no: **01 15**

WHIMPEEZ
Tracks: / Whimpeez.
7" Single: Released Dec '85, on Trapper, Catalogue no: **EARS 3**

ZOMBIE CREEPING FLESH
Tracks: / Zombie creeping flesh.
7" Single: Released Mar '85, on Trapper, Catalogue no: **EARS 1**

Peter-Paul

COO CA CHOO
Tracks: / Coo ca choo.
7" Single: Released 21 Nov '87, on Spectec, Catalogue no: **TEC 002**

TURNING POINT
Tracks: / Turning point / Way I'm feeling.
12" Single: Released Jul '82, on Kingdom, by Kingdom Records. Deleted '85. Catalogue no: **KV 8024-12**
7" Single: Released Jun '82, on Kingdom, by Kingdom Records. Deleted Jun '85. Catalogue no: **KV 8024**

Peters, Bernadette

GEE WHIZZ
Tracks: / Gee whizz / I never thought I'd break.
7" Single: Released May '80, on MCA, by MCA Records. Deleted May '85. Catalogue no: **MCA 590**

Peters, Chris

CAUGHT IN THE ACT (SINGLE)
Tracks: / Caught in the act.
12" Single: Released Jul '85, on Ecstasy, by Creole Records. Catalogue no: **XTCT 18**
7" Single: Released Jul '85, on Ecstasy, by Creole Records. Catalogue no: **XTC 18**

LOVE INSURANCE
Tracks: / Love insurance.
7" Single: Released Jul '86, on Titania, by Creole Records. Catalogue no: **TNA 1**

LOVE TRAP
Tracks: / Love trap (megamix) / Caught in the act (remix).
12" Single: Released Jan '87, on Titania, by Creole Records. Catalogue no: **TNA 2T**

PHANTOM OF THE BASSLINE, THE
Tracks: / Phantom of the bassline, The.
12" Single: Released Aug '87, on Nine O Nine, by Creole Records. Catalogue no: **NINE 15**

Peters, Eddie

JOCK MIX 2
Tracks: / Jock mix 2.
12" Single: Released Aug '87, on Rhino, by Creole Records. Catalogue no: **RNO 9**

Peters & Lee

BY YOUR SIDE (SINGLE)
Tracks: / By your side.
7" Single: Released Nov '73, on Philips, by Phonogram Ltd. Deleted '76. Catalogue no: **6006 339**

DON'T STAY AWAY TOO LONG
Tracks: / Don't stay away too long.
7" Single: Released Apr '74, on Philips, by Phonogram Ltd. Deleted '77. Catalogue no: **6006 388**

FAMILIAR FEELINGS
Tracks: / Familiar feelings / Guess you'll never know.
7" Single: Released Oct '86, on A.1, by A.1 Records. Catalogue no: **A1 295**

HEY MR. MUSIC MAN
Tracks: / Hey Mr. Music man.
7" Single: Released Mar '76, on Philips, by Phonogram Ltd. Deleted '79. Catalogue no: **6006 502**

I UNDERSTAND
Tracks: / I understand / Tommorrow's here today.
7" Single: Released May '80, on Pye, Deleted May '83. Catalogue no: **7P 176**

ISLE OF DEBRIS
Tracks: / Isle of debris / Wings on my feet.
7" Single: Released Jun '89, on President, by President Records. Catalogue no: **PT 583**

OCEAN & BLUE SKY
Tracks: / Ocean & blue sky / What have I got, I got you babe.
7" Single: Released Nov '80, on Celebrity, Deleted '83. Catalogue no: **ACS 4**

RAINBOW (SINGLE)
Tracks: / Rainbow.
7" Single: Released Aug '74, on Philips, by Phonogram Ltd. Deleted '77. Catalogue no: **6006 406**

WELCOME HOME
Tracks: / Welcome home.
7" Single: Released May '73, on Philips, by Phonogram Ltd. Deleted '76. Catalogue no: **6006 307**

WELCOME HOME (OLD GOLD)
Tracks: / Welcome home.
7" Single: Released Jul '82, on Old Gold, by Old Gold Records. Catalogue no: **OG 9254**

Peters, Lennie

KEY LARGO
Tracks: / Key largo.
7" Single: Released Nov '85, on Relax, Catalogue no: **LAX 5**

THIS IS A RECORD MY LOVE
Tracks: / This a record of my love / I just need you.
7" Single: Released Apr '81, on EMI, by EMI Records. Deleted '85. Catalogue no: **EMI 5164**

WHY ME
Tracks: / Why me.
7" Single: Released Dec '82, on Lifestyle, by Micrometro Ltd (Records). Catalogue no: **LIFE 1**

Peterson, Ray

Biographical details: This American singer had a handful of hits in the late 50's and early 60's, including *Corrina Corrina* (No 9 in US, No 41 in UK) which was produced by the up-and-coming Phil Spector. Peterson himself never meant much in Britain, but two of his numbers became No 1 hits in the UK for other artists: the sick death disc *Tell Laura I Love Her* was recorded by Welshman Ricky Valance in 1960 and the big ballad *The Wonder Of Love was* a British chart-topper for Elvis Presley in 1970. (Bob MacDonald March 1986.).

ANSWER ME
Tracks: / Answer me.
7" Single: Released Mar '60, on RCA, by BMG Records (UK). Deleted '63. Catalogue no: **RCA 1175**

CORRINE CORRINA
Tracks: / Corina Corina.
7" Single: Released '80, on MGM, by Polydor Ltd. Catalogue no: **LR 4754**
7" Single: Released Jan '61, on London-American, Deleted '64. Catalogue no: **HLX 9246**

WONDER OF YOU, THE
Tracks: / Wonder of you, The.
7" Single: Released Sep '59, on RCA, by BMG Records (UK). Deleted '62. Catalogue no: **RCA 1131**

Pete's Dragon

PETE'S DRAGON (EP)
Tracks: / Pete's dragon: *Various artists*.
7" EP: Released Dec '82, on Disneyland, by Disneyland Records. Catalogue no: **D 369**

Petit Cheval

ONCE IN A LIFETIME
Tracks: / Once in a lifetime.
7" Single: Released Feb '86, on WEA, by WEA Records. Catalogue no: **X 8790**

Petrie, Anne

PERSONALITIES
Tracks: / Personalities / Forecast for 1982.
7" Single: Released Nov '81, on Stars, Deleted '86. Catalogue no: **STARS 1 12**

Pets Of Friction

CAREER IN THE MORNING
Tracks: / Career in the morning.
7" Single: Released Dec '82, on Turn Blue, Deleted '83. Catalogue no: **TB 1**

Petters, Steve

NOT LOVE ON THE RUN
Tracks: / Not love on the run / Change of heart.
7" Single: Released Mar '82, on RCA, by BMG Records (UK). Deleted '85. Catalogue no: **CHEAP 39**

Pettus, Giorge

MY NIGHT FOR LOVE
Tracks: / My night for love.
7" Single: Released 23 Apr '88, on MCA, by MCA Records. Catalogue no: **MCA 1251**
12" Single: Released 23 Apr '88, on MCA, by MCA Records. Catalogue no: **MCAT 1251**

Petty, Tom

Biographical details: Formed in Los Angeles in 1976, Tom Petty & The Heartbreakers were initially marketed as a New Wave punk band but soon took their rightful place in the FM rock school. Despite a British cult following they never really consolidated the early UK success they enjoyed in 1977 with the singles *Anything That's Rock 'n' Roll* and *American Girl*. Instead they became staple fodder for American rock fans and their albums and singles were regular items in the US charts during the late 70's and through the 80's. Although they have never quite been in the megastar league of Bruce Springsteen and Foreigner, their sound has successfully combined elements of both these acts. Petty & The Heartbreakers are energetic rockers in concert and make well-crafted but not over-slick records. The band's biggest American hit was 1981's *Stop Draggin' My Heart Around*, a collaboration with Stevie Nicks which logged six consecutive weeks in the US No 3 position. (Bob MacDonald 5.3.86)

Tom Petty was in Florida in 1951 and formed the Heartbreakers in 1975 with guitarist Mike Campbell, Benmont Tench on keyboards (both colleagues from Mudcrutch, a Florida band), plus Stan Lynch on drums, Ron Blair on bass; they supported Nils Lofgren on a UK tour and at first were more successful in the UK than at home, but soon hit the big time: their third LP *Damn the torpedoes* was No.2 in the USA in 1979, the next three all top ten. They backed Bob Dylan on his Australian tour in 1986; Tench backed Elvis Costello in live shows in 1987. (Donald Clarke 15.5.87).

ALL MIXED UP
Tracks: / All mixed up / Let me up (I've had enough) / Little bit o'soul*.
Note: * Extra track on 12" version only. 12" contains alternative (album) version of 'All Mixed Up'.
7" Single: Released Sep '87, on MCA, by MCA Records. Catalogue no: **MCA 1190**
12" Single: Released Sep '87, on MCA, by MCA Records. Catalogue no: **MCAT 1190**

AMERICAN GIRL
Tracks: / American girl.
7" Single: Released Aug '77, on Shelter (1), Deleted '80. Catalogue no: **WIP 6403**

ANYTHING THAT'S ROCK 'N' ROLL
Tracks: / Anything that's rock 'n' roll.
7" Single: Released Jun '77, on Shelter (1), Deleted '80. Catalogue no: **WIP 6396**

CHANGE OF HEART
Tracks: / Change of heart.
7" Single: Released Apr '83, on MCA, by MCA Records. Catalogue no: **MCA 814**

DON'T COME AROUND HERE NO MORE
Tracks: / Don't come around here no more / Trailer.
7" Single: Released Apr '85, on MCA, by MCA Records. Deleted '88. Catalogue no: **MCA 926**

DON'T DO ME LIKE THAT
Tracks: / Don't do me like that / Century city.
7" Single: Released Jun '80, on MCA, by MCA Records. Deleted '83. Catalogue no: **MCA 596**

I WON'T BACK DOWN
Tracks: / I won't back down.
CD 5": Released 24 Apr '89, on MCA, by MCA Records. Catalogue no: **DMCAX 1334**
CD 5": Released 24 Apr '89, on MCA, by MCA Records. Catalogue no: **DMCAT 1334**
7" Single: Released 24 Apr '89, on MCA, by MCA Records. Catalogue no: **MCA 1334**
12" Single: Released 24 Apr '89, on MCA, by MCA Records. Catalogue no: **MCAT 1334**

JAMMIN' ME
Tracks: / Jammin' me / Let me up (I've had enough) / Make that collection.
7" Single: Released Apr '87, on MCA, by MCA Records. Catalogue no: **MCA 1148**
12" Single: Released Apr '87, on MCA, by MCA Records. Catalogue no: **MCAT 1148**

REFUGEE
Tracks: / Refugee / Don't do me like that / Here comes the girl / Waiting, The.
12" Single: Released Apr '86, on MCA, by MCA Records. Catalogue no: **MCAT 1047**
7" Single: Released Feb '80, on MCA, by MCA Records. Deleted Feb '83. Catalogue no: **MCA 559**

RUNNIN' DOWN A DREAM
Tracks: / Runnin' down a dream.
CD 5": Released 31 Jul '89, on MCA, by MCA Records. Catalogue no: **DMCAX 1359**
CD 5": Released 31 Jul '89, on MCA, by MCA Records. Catalogue no: **DMCAT 1359**
12" Single: Released 31 Jul '89, on MCA, by MCA Records. Catalogue no: **MCAT 1359**
Cassingle: Released 31 Jul '89, on MCA, by MCA Records. Catalogue no: **MCAC 1359**
7" Single: Released 31 Jul '89, on MCA, by MCA Records. Catalogue no: **MCA 1359**

SO YOU WANT TO BE A ROCK 'N' ROLL STAR
Tracks: / American girl / Spike.
7" Single: Released Feb '86, on MCA, by MCA Records. Catalogue no: **MCA 1028**
12" Single: Released Feb '86, on MCA, by MCA Records. Catalogue no: **MCAT 1028**

STRAIGHT INTO DARKNESS
Tracks: / Straight into darkness / Wasted life.
7" Single: Released Dec '82, on MCA, by MCA Records. Deleted Dec '87. Catalogue no: **MCA 805**

WAITING
Tracks: / Waiting / Nightwatchman.
7" Single: Released Apr '81, on MCA, by MCA Records. Deleted Apr '86. Catalogue no: **MCA 669**

YOU GOT LUCKY
Tracks: / You got lucky / Between two worlds.
7" Single: Released Nov '82, on MCA, by MCA Records. Deleted Nov '85. Catalogue no: **MCA 801**

Peyr

FOURTH REICH
Tracks: / Fourth reich.
12" Single: Released Oct '82, on Shout, by Shout Records. Catalogue no: **XW 1202**

Peyton, Craig

BE THANKFUL FOR WHAT YOU GOT
Tracks: / Be thankful for what you got.
12" Single: Released Jun '83, on Elite Records, by Elite Records. Deleted '85. Catalogue no: **DAZZ 20**

Pfeifer, Diane

JUST WHEN I NEEDED A LOVE SONG
Tracks: / Just when I needed a love song / Wishful drinkin'.
7" Single: Released Oct '80, on Capitol, by EMI Records. Deleted Oct '83. Catalogue no: **CL 16169**

Pfeiffer, Michelle

COOL RIDER
Tracks: / Cool rider / Do it for our country.
7" Single: Released Jan '82, on RSO, by Polydor Ltd. Deleted Jan '85. Catalogue no: **RSO 93**

P-Funk All Stars

HYDRAULIC PUMP
Tracks: / Hydraulic pump / Hydraulic pump (part 2).
12" Single: Released Mar '82, on Virgin, by Virgin Records. Deleted '85. Catalogue no: **VS 48712**
7" Single: Released Mar '82, on Virgin, by Virgin Records. Deleted '85. Catalogue no: **VS 487**

Phantom

LAZY FASCIST
Tracks: / Lazy fascist.
7" Single: Released Jul '83, on Cool Ghoul, by Cool Ghoul Records. Catalogue no: **COOL 1**

LOVE ME
Tracks: / Love me.
7" Single: Released Mar '85, on DJ Jamboree, Catalogue no: **45 16056**

MOVE GROOVE
Tracks: / Move groove / Move groove (version).
12" Single: Released Apr '89, on Big City, by Pinnacle Records. Catalogue no: **BCITY 0121**

Phantom, Rocker &

MEN WITHOUT SHAME
Tracks: / Men without shame.
12" Single: Released Nov '85, on EMI-America, by EMI Records. Catalogue no: **12EA 209**
7" Single: Released Nov '85, on EMI-America, by EMI Records. Catalogue no: **EA 209**

MY MISTAKE
Tracks: / My mistake / Runnin' from the hounds.
7" Single: Released Mar '86, on EMI-America, by EMI Records. Catalogue no: **EA 212**

Phantom Tollbooth

VALLEY OF THE GWANGI
Tracks: / Flip your lid / Wailing ultimate, The.
7" Single: Released Dec '86, on Homestead, Catalogue no: **HMS 067**
7" Single: Released Sep '86, on Homestead, Catalogue no: **HMS 058**

Pharaohs

BROKEN HEART, CRYING EYES
Tracks: / Broken heart, crying eyes.
7" Single: Released Aug '86, on Big Beat, by Ace Records. Deleted Jun '88. Catalogue no: **SW 116**

IN THE MIDNIGHT HOUR
Tracks: / In the midnight hour / Berta.
7" Single: Released Mar '80, on Laser, Deleted '83. Catalogue no: **LAS 26**

VIGILANTE
12" Single: Released Jun '87, on Nervous, by Nervous Records. Catalogue no: **12 NEP 005**
12" Single: Released Jun '87, on Nervous, by Nervous Records. Catalogue no: **12 NEP 005**

PHD - I WON'T LET YOU DOWN (Released on WEA)

Phare, Rory

LAUGHING INSIDE
Tracks: / Laughing inside / Laughing inside (version).
7" Single: Released 27 Feb '88, on Parlophone, by EMI Records. Catalogue no: **RP 1**

Phase 2

MYSTERY
Tracks: / Mystery.
12" Single: Released Nov '87, on Quark (USA), Catalogue no: **QK 007**

REACHIN'
Tracks: / Reachin' / It's a mystery.
7" Single: Released Jan '89, on Republic, by Code Records. Catalogue no: **LIC 006**
12" Single: Released Oct '88, on Republic, by Code Records. Catalogue no: **LICT 006**
12" Single: Released 16 Jan '89, on Republic, by Code Records. Catalogue no: **LICT 006 X**

ROXY
Tracks: / Roxy.
7" Single: Released May '83, on Celluloid (USA), by Celluloid Records (USA). Catalogue no: **CYZ 102**

Phase 111 Mod Bands

PHASE 111 MOD BANDS
Tracks: / Phase 111 Mod Bands: *Various artists.*
Note: Featuring: Manual Scan, City Motors, The Pictures, XL.
7" Single: Released 23 May '87, on Unicorn-Kanchana, by Unicorn - Kanchana Records. Catalogue no: **PHZ 6**

Phase III Project

FOUR-BANK INTERNATIONAL EP
Tracks: / Naked City / Look in your eyes / Jobs for the boys / Love someone.
7" Single: Released Jan '87, on Unicorn-Kanchana, by Unicorn - Kanchana Records. Catalogue no: **PHZ 4**

PHASE III PROJECT
Tracks: / Phase III project: *Various artists.*
12" Single: Released Oct '87, on Unicorn-Kanchana, by Unicorn - Kanchana Records. Catalogue no: **PHZ 13**

PhD

Biographical details: Classically trained pianist Tony Hymas and singer Jim Diamond had both had many years of experience in the music business before formed the duo PhD in early 1981. Their first single *I won't let you down*, issued in early '82, was an internation smash. It was a highly memorable synthesised pop single, combining Hymas' keyboard expertise with Diamond's melodramatic vocals. *I won't let you down* was a big hit in many countries around the world, America being a notable exception; its UK peak position was No.3, and the pair's self-titled debut LP reached No.33.

PhD did not have anything as good as *I won't let you down* at their disposal, and faded into obscurity. Diamond re-emerged as a solo star in late 1984, reaching No.1 in Britain with *I should have known better*; he enjoyed another big hit in early 1986 with *Hi ho Silver.* (Bob MacDonald 5.3.86).

I DIDN'T KNOW
Tracks: / I didn't know / Theme for Jenny.
7" Single: Released Mar '83, on WEA (International), by WEA Records. Catalogue no: **U 9996**
12" Single: Released Apr '83, on WEA (International), by WEA Records. Catalogue no: **U 9996 T**

I WON'T LET YOU DOWN (see panel above)
Tracks: / I won't let you down / Hideaway.
7" Single: Released Feb '82, on WEA, by WEA Records. Deleted Jul '88. Catalogue no: **K 79209**

LITTLE SUZIE'S ON THE UP
Tracks: / Little Suzie's on the up / I'm gonna take you to the top.
7" Single: Released Jun '82, on WEA, by WEA Records. Deleted Jun '85. Catalogue no: **K 79233**

Phenomena

DANCE WITH THE DEVIL
Tracks: / Dance with the devil.
7" Single: Released Jun '85, on Bronze, by Bronze Records. Catalogue no: **BRO 193**
12" Single: Released Jun '85, on Bronze, by Bronze Records. Catalogue no: **BROX 193**

Phenomena II

DID IT ALL FOR LOVE
Tracks: / Did it all for love / Double 6, 55, 44....
7" Single: Released Oct '87, on Arista, by BMG Records (UK). Deleted May '89. Catalogue no: **RIS 42**
12" Single: Released Oct '87, on Arista, by BMG Records (UK). Deleted May '89. Catalogue no: **RIST 42**

Philadelphia Five

BUMP
Tracks: / Bump.
12" Single: Released 23 Apr '88, on K K, by Play It Again Sam (Belgium). Catalogue no: **KK 002**

I AM SHARED
Tracks: / I am shared.
12" Single: Released Oct '88, on K K, by Play It Again Sam (Belgium). Catalogue no: **KK 007**

WATCH OUT (REMIX & ACID RETURN)
Tracks: / Watch out.
12" Single: Released '89, on K K, by Play It Again Sam (Belgium). Catalogue no: **KK 014**

Philadelphia Int...

LET'S CLEAN UP THE GHETTO
Tracks: / Let's clean up the ghetto.
12" Single: Released Jul '85, on Streetwave, Catalogue no: **SWAVE 1**
7" Single: Released Aug '77, on Philadelphia Int., by EMI Records. Deleted '80. Catalogue no: **PIR 5451**

Philharmonic Orchestra

THUS SPAKE ZARATHUSTRA
Tracks: / Thus spake zarathustra.
7" Single: Released Jul '69, on Columbia, by EMI Records. Deleted '72. Catalogue no: **DB 607**

Philippe, Louis

ANTHONY BAY
Tracks: / Anthony Bay / What if a day.
7" Single: Released Oct '87, on El, by Cherry Red Records. Catalogue no: **GPO 31**

GUESS I'M DUMB
Tracks: / Guess I'm dumb / Smash hit wonder / Cantilena.
7" Single: Released Nov '88, on El, by Cherry Red Records. Catalogue no: **GPO 40**

LA PLUIE FAIT DES CLAQUETTES
Tracks: / La pluie fait des claquettes / Touch of evil / You're missing someone / Siren's call / Red roses and red noses.
12" Single: Released Apr '86, on El, by Cherry Red Records. Catalogue no: **GPO 6 T**

LIKE NOBODY DO
Tracks: / Like nobody do / Twangy twangy.
7" Single: Released Jul '86, on El, by Cherry Red Records. Catalogue no: **GPO 15**

YOU MARY YOU
Tracks: / You Mary you / With and without you / Little pad (Available on 12" only) / Blue roofs of Ispahan.
7" Single: Released Mar '87, on El, by Cherry Red Records. Catalogue no: **GPO 23**
12" Single: Released Mar '87, on El, by Cherry Red Records. Catalogue no: **GPO 23 T**

Philips, Anthony

ANTHEM FROM TARKA
Tracks: / Anthem from Tarka.
7" Pic: Released Nov '88, on PRT, by Castle Communications Records. Catalogue no: **PYS 18**
CD 5": Released Nov '88, on PRT, by Castle Communications Records. Catalogue no: **PYD 18**

Phill & Company

TRA LA LA
Tracks: / Tra la la / Hey how do you do.
7" Single: Released Apr '85, on Sonet, by Sonet Records. Catalogue no: **SON 2279**

Phillinganes, Greg

BEHIND THE MASK
Tracks: / Behind the mask / Only you.
12" Single: Released Mar '85, on Planet, Catalogue no: **RPST 110**
7" Single: Released Mar '85, on Planet, Deleted '87. Catalogue no: **RPS 110**

Phillip & His...

TELL ME WHAT IS THE BANE OF YOUR LIFE
Tracks: / Tell me what is the bane of your life.
7" Single: Released Jan '82, on Self Immolation, by Some Bizzare Records. Catalogue no: **OMBKX 07**

Phillips, Anthony

PRELUDE '84
Tracks: / Prelude '84 / Anthem 1984.
7" Single: Released Jul '81, on RCA, by BMG Records (UK). Deleted '85. Catalogue no: **RCA 102**

SALLY
Tracks: / Sally.
12" Single: Released Feb '84, on Street Tunes, by Street Tunes Records. Catalogue no: **STS 009**

Phillips, Dave

NEXT STOP
Tracks: / Next stop / Dancin' shoes.
7" Single: Released Mar '84, on Kix 4U (Holland), by Rockhouse Records (Holland). Catalogue no: **KIX4U 4545**

Phillips, Esther

Biographical details: This British exercise and dance teacher reached No.41 on the UK album chart in the late 1982 with *Keep in shape system* (KISS to its friends). The LP was part of the aerobics and popmobility craze that took off on both sides of the Atlantic during the early Eighties. Unlike actresses Jane Fonda and Felicity Kendall, newscaster Angela Rippon and disc-jockey Peter Powell, Phillips was a professional tutor; her album was therefore somewhat more authorative than those of the aforementioned persons. (Bob MacDonald 5.3.86)

Born Esther May Jones, this American blues, jazz and soul singer was discovered at the age of 13 by musician and entrepreneur Johnny Otis. Billed as Little Esther, she enjoyed a run of Top 10 collaborations with Otis on the US rhythm and blues charts during the following year (1950). An occasional visitor to the US pop charts, Phillips reached No. 8 in 1962 with *Release Me* (a country and western song that was later turned into an even bigger hit by Engelbert Humperdinck) and climbed to No. 20 in America and No. 6 in Britain with 1975's *What A Difference A Day Made*. She died in August 1984 at the age of 48. Bob MacDonald, 5 March 1986..

WHAT A DIFFERENCE A DAY MAKES (SINGLE)
Tracks: / What a difference a day made.
7" Single: Released Oct '75, on Kudu, Deleted '78. Catalogue no: **KUDU 925**

Phillips, Ken

ANGELINA
Tracks: / Angelina / Rambling man.
7" Single: Released Mar '84, on Dakota, Catalogue no: **DAK 17**

Phillips, Noel

YOUTHMAN
Tracks: / Youthman.
12" Single: Released Apr '82, on KG, Catalogue no: **J 7001**

Phillips, Sam

FLAME
Tracks: / Flame.
7" Single: Released Jun '89, on Virgin (USA), by Virgin Records. Catalogue no: **UNKNOWN**

Phillips, Sian

BEWITCHED
Tracks: / Bewitched / What is a man.
7" Single: Released Oct '80, on Chrysalis, by Chrysalis Records. Deleted Oct '83. Catalogue no: **CHS 2470**

Phillips, West

I'M JUST A SUCKER FOR A PRETTY FACE
Tracks: / I'm just a sucker for a pretty face.
12" Single: Released Mar '84, on Trans Q, Catalogue no: **BUBT 401**

LOOKING FOR THE SAME THING
Tracks: / Looking for the same thing / Another pretty face.
12" Single: Released 21 Nov '87, on Ichiban, by Ichiban Records (UK). Catalogue no: **12PO 5**

TELL ME
Tracks: / Tell me.
12" Single: Released Aug '87, on Kool Kat, by Kool Kat Records. Catalogue no: **KOOLT 7**

Philly Cream

COWBOYS TO GIRLS
Tracks: / Cowboys to girls / No time like now.
7" Single: Released Feb '81, on W.M.O.T.(USA), by Virgin Records. Deleted '84. Catalogue no: **WMT 101**
12" Single: Released Feb '81, on W.M.O.T.(USA), by Virgin Records. Deleted '84. Catalogue no: **WMTL 101**

NO TIME LIKE NOW (SINGLE)
Tracks: / No time like now / Who do.
12" Single: Released Jul '80, on Calibre, Deleted Jul '83. Catalogue no: **CABL 504**
7" Single: Released Jul '80, on Calibre, Deleted Jul '83. Catalogue no: **CAB 504**

Phoenix

EVERYBODY (GET LOOSE)
Tracks: / Everybody (get loose) / Everybody (get loose) acidic bam bam mix (Availble on 12" only).
Note: Features samples from Players Association, Kashif, Michael Jackson and Phyllis Hyman.e
7" Single: Released Jul '88, on Urban, by Polydor Ltd. Catalogue no: **URB 22**
12" Single: Released Jun '88, on Urban, by Polydor Ltd. Catalogue no: **URBX 22**

JULIET
Tracks: / Juliet / I'm in love.
7" Single: Released May '80, on Charisma, by Virgin Records. Deleted May '83. Catalogue no: **CB 359**

JUST ANOTHER DAY
Tracks: / Just another day / You don't fool me.
7" Single: Released Feb '80, on Charisma, by Virgin Records. Deleted '83. Catalogue no: **CB 352**

SUSPICION
Tracks: / Suspicion.
12" Single: Released Oct '87, on Fate, Catalogue no: **FATE 001**
7" Single: Released Oct '87, on Fate, Catalogue no: **FATE 700**

Phoenix, Paul

NUNC DIMITTIS
Tracks: / Nunc dimittis.
7" Single: Released Nov '79, on Different, Deleted '82. Catalogue no: **HAVE 20**

Phorphazade

AAH YOU ARE AS LIGHT AS A FEATHER
Tracks: / Aah you are as light as a feather.
12" Single: Released May '85, on Crackle & Corkette, Catalogue no: **CRACK ONE**

Photofit

ANOTHER ALIAS
Tracks: / Another alias.
7" Single: Released Nov '83, on Raffia, Deleted '85. Catalogue no: **RAF 005**

Photoglo

WE'RE MEANT TO BE LOVERS
Tracks: / We're meant to be lovers.
7" Single: Released Jun '80, on 20th Century, by 20th Century Records. Deleted Jun '83. Catalogue no: **TC 2446**

Photos

Biographical details: This British band consisted of Steve Eagles, Oily Harrison, Dave Sparrow and Wendy Wu.

Lead vocalist Wendy Wu tried to be a dark haired British answer to Debbie Harry of Blondie, who was red hot at the time of the Photo's brief success. The Photos' brand of post punk yielded one hit single and hit album on the UK charts: the single *Irene* peaked at No. 56 in the summer of 1980; and the eponymous album fared more impressively, reaching No. 4 just after the single's success. Bob MacDonald, 5 March 1986..

IRENE
Tracks: / Irene / Cridsilla.
7" Single: Released May '80, on Epic, by CBS Records. Deleted '83. Catalogue no: **EPC 8517**

LIFE IN A DAY
Tracks: / Life in a day / More than a friend.
7" Single: Released Feb '81, on Epic, by CBS Records. Deleted Feb '84. Catalogue no: **EPC A 1010**

THERE'S ALWAYS WORK
Tracks: / There's always work.
12" Single: Released Apr '83, on Rialto (1), by Rialto Records. Catalogue no: **12 RIA 16**
7" Single: Released Apr '83, on Rialto (1), by Rialto Records. Catalogue no: **RIA 16**

WE'LL WIN
Tracks: / We'll win / You won't get to me.
7" Single: Released Jul '81, on Epic, by CBS Records. Deleted '84. Catalogue no: **EPCA 1369**

Phranc

AMAZON
Tracks: / Amazon.
7" Single: Released Nov '85, on Stiff, by Stiff Records. Catalogue no: **BUY 233**
12" Single: Released Nov '85, on Stiff, by Stiff Records. Catalogue no: **BUYIT 233**

LONESOME DEATH OF HAPPIE CARROLL
Tracks: / Lonesome death of Hattie Carroll / El Salvador.
7" Single: Released Mar '86, on Stiff, by Stiff Records. Catalogue no: **BUY 247**

Phuture

ACID TRAX
Tracks: / Acid trax.
CD 5": Released '89, on Who's That Beat, by Play It Again Sam (Belgium). Catalogue no: **WHOS 006CD**
12" Single: Released Oct '88, on Who's That Beat, by Play It Again Sam (Belgium). Catalogue no: **WHOS 006**
12" Single: Released Nov '87, on Trax (USA), Catalogue no: **TX 142**

SLAM
Tracks: / Slam.
7" Single: Released Oct '88, on Low Fat Vinyl, by Low Fat Vinyl Records. Catalogue no: **LFV 1**

Physical Blue

BACK ON TOP
Tracks: / Back on the top / Day of glory.
7" Single: Released May '89, on MTG, Catalogue no: **MTG 5**

CELEBRATION
Tracks: / Celebration / One arrow.
7" Single: Released Dec '87, on MTG, Catalogue no: **MTG 3**

DAY OF GLORY
Tracks: / Day of glory / Day of glory (instrumental).
7" Single: Released Apr '86, on MTG, Catalogue no: **MTG 1**

LOVE LIES WAITING
Tracks: / Love lies waiting / One arrow.
7" Single: Released Apr '88, on MTG, Catalogue no: **MTG 4**

ONE ARROW
Tracks: / One arrow / Hot sun.
7" Single: Released Sep '87, on MTG, Catalogue no: **MTG 2**

Physicals

BE LIKE ME
Tracks: / Be like me / Pain in love.
7" Single: Released Feb '80, on Chiswick Records, Deleted '83. Catalogue no: **NS 58**

Pia

DANCE OUT OF MY HEAD
Tracks: / Dance out of my head / I really like you (not him) / Dance out of my head (the dressed-down mix) (12" & CD single only.) / Dance out of my head (dub version) (12" only.) / Dance out of my head (house groove vocal) (CD single only.) / Dance out of my head (jam & lewis remix) (Only on (6528661) 12", (9531236) 12" & CD single.) / Dance out of my head (dubacella) / Dance out of my head (Ben Liebrand remix) (Only on the 12" version (653 123 6)).
CD 5": Released Oct '88, on Epic, by CBS Records. Deleted 17 Apr '89. Catalogue no: **652866 2**
7" Single: Released 21 Nov '88, on Epic, by CBS Records. Deleted 17 Apr '89. Catalogue no: **652866 0**
7" Single: Released Oct '88, on Epic, by CBS Records. Deleted 17 Apr '89. Catalogue no: **652866 7**
12" Single: Released Oct '88, on Epic, by CBS Records. Deleted 17 Apr '89. Catalogue no: **652866 1**
12" Single: Released Oct '88, on Epic, by CBS Records. Deleted 17 Apr '89. Catalogue no: **652866 8**
12" Single: Released Nov '88, on Epic, by CBS Records. Deleted 17 Apr '89. Catalogue no: **653123 6**
CD 5": Released Nov '88, on Epic, by CBS Records. Deleted 17 Apr '89. Catalogue no: **653123 3**

Piaf, Edith

Biographical details: One of the greatest talents ever to emerge from France, this singer was born Edith Giovanna Gassion in Belleville, Paris in 1915. Her mother absconded when Edith was two months old. For much of her childhood, she was in the care of her grandmother in Bernay, Normandy; but also toured with her father, who was a circus acrobat. Edith's childhood was blemished by blindness, which lasted from the age of 3 until she was cured at 7.

Edith began her singing career in her father's circus, and headed for Paris at the age of 15 to try and make a name for herself. After performing on the streets for mere pennies, she was offered work by cabaret proprietor Louis Leplee who changed her name to Piaf (a Parisian colloquialism for 'sparrow'). She made a good impression at his distinguished establishment for six months, but the engagement ended when Leplee was brutally murdered in a robbery. After various other engagements, she began to reach a wider public at the age of 20 by becoming a successful performer at one of Paris' most important vaudeville theatres.

The husky, powerful, slightly melancholy voice of Edith Piaf was at the peak of its success from 1945 until the early Sixties. The singer's best known numbers during her heyday were *Les Trois Cloches* (translated into English as *The Three Bells*, and later made into a US No. 1 hit by the Browns) and *La Vie En Rose* (successfully covered many years later by Grace Jones). Another Piaf recording, *Milord*, reached No. 24 on the British chart at the end of 1960. logging 15 weeks on the Top 50.

Edith Piaf died in October 1963, at the age of 47, after fighting illness and struggling to maintain her career regardless for five years. Bob MacDonald, 5 March 1986..

MILORD (SINGLE)
Tracks: / Milord.
7" Single: Released May '60, on Columbia, by EMI Records. Deleted '63. Catalogue no: **DC 754**

NON JE NE REGRETTE RIEN
Tracks: / Non, je ne regrette rien / No regrets.
7" Single: Released Oct '76, on EMI, by EMI Records. Catalogue no: **EMI 2544**

Pianos

BE A FOOL FOR YOU
Tracks: / Be a fool for you / Slow dancing.
7" Single: Released Feb '81, on Plaza Plastic Co, Deleted '83. Catalogue no: **ZAP 3**

Piccadilly Dance...

SANTA CLAUS IS COMING TO TOWN

Tracks: / Santa Claus is coming to town.
7" Single: Released Dec '88, on PRT, by Castle Communications Records. Catalogue no: **DNS 1**

Pick A Number

GROOVY
Tracks: / Groovy.
12" Single: Released Jul '89, on Subway dance, Catalogue no: **SD 4003**

Pick-A-Pow

I BELIEVE IN YOU
Tracks: / I believe in you.
7" Single: Released Aug '89, on Sunjam, Catalogue no: **SR 0008**

Pickett, Bobby 'Boris'

Biographical details: One of the silliest and most successful novelty hits of all time was *Monster Mash* by Massachusetts-born Bobby "Boris" Pickett and his backing group, the Crypt-Kickers. It reached No 1 in America in October 1962 and enjoyed a second visit to the Billboard Hot Hundred in 1970. *Monster Mash* returned yet again in '73, climbing to the US No 10 position. In that same year the single became a hit in Britain for the first time -- the BBC had considered this "graveyard smash" to be too offensive for airplay in 1962, but played it heavily when it became a UK No 3. (Bob MacDonald, March 86.).

MONSTER MASH
Tracks: / Monster mash / Monster mash party.
7" Single: Released Feb '82, on Decca, by Decca Records. Deleted '88. Catalogue no: **F 13917**
7" Single: Released Sep '73, on London-American, Deleted '76. Catalogue no: **HL 10320**

Pickett, Phil

DESTINY
Tracks: / Destiny.
7" Single: Released Jul '84, on MCA, by MCA Records. Catalogue no: **MCA 901**
12" Single: Released Jul '84, on MCA, by MCA Records. Deleted '85. Catalogue no: **MCAT 901**

FAREWELL TO BERLIN
Tracks: / Farewell to Berlin.
7" Single: Released Jul '83, on BBC, by BBC Records & Tapes. Deleted '87. Catalogue no: **RESL 133**

Pickett, Wilson

Biographical details: Born in Prattville, Alabama, in 1941, soul singer and songwriter Pickett was one of the major black artists on the 60's. After a period as leader of the Detroit-based vocal group the Falcons, he launched his solo career in 1963 and soon released *If You Need Me* and *It's Too Late*, which were successful on the US rhythm-and-blues charts. But his real breakthrough came in '65 when he journeyed to Memphis and recorded the superb *In The Midnight Hour*. Written by Pickett and Stax/Volt soul man Steve Cropper, *In The Midnight Hour* crossed over from the American soul chart to the pop listings, where it reached No 21, and it was No 12 in Britain. It came to be regarded as one of the great 60's soul classics and paved the way for a run of Pickett hits which lasted until '69 (UK) and '72 (US). Though he never reached the pop Top Five in either country, Pickett's bold, gutsy, distinctive vocal style made him a regular chart name thanks to hits like *Land Of A Thousand Dances* and *Mustang Sally*. In early '69 he scored with an inspired reworking of the Beatles' recent smash *Hey Jude*.
His American hits of the early 70's included *Engine Number Nine, Don't Let The Green Grass Fool You* and *Don't Knock My Love*, then his success tailed off. Along with stars like Otis Redding and Sam & Dave, he will always be remembered as one of the best of the non-Motown soul acts of his era. (Bob MacDonald, March 1986.).

634-5789
Tracks: / 634-5789.
7" Single: Released Mar '66, on Atlantic, by WEA Records. Deleted '69. Catalogue no: **AT 4072**

DON'T FIGHT IT
Tracks: / Don't fight it.
7" Single: Released Nov '65, on Atlantic, by WEA Records. Deleted '68. Catalogue no: **AT 4052**

DON'T UNDERESTIMATE THE POWER OF LOVE
Tracks: / Don't underestimate the power of love / Ain't gonna give you no more / I want you (On 12" only).
12" Single: Released Feb '81, on EMI-America, by EMI Records. Deleted '84. Catalogue no: **12EA 120**
7" Single: Released Feb '81, on EMI-America, by EMI Records. Deleted '84. Catalogue no: **EA 120**

FUNKY BROADWAY
Tracks: / Funky broadway.
7" Single: Released Sep '67, on Atlantic, by WEA Records. Deleted '70. Catalogue no: **584 130**

HEY JUDE
Tracks: / Hey Jude.
7" Single: Released Jan '69, on Atlantic, by WEA Records. Deleted '72. Catalogue no: **584 236**

I'M A MIDNIGHT MOVER
Tracks: / I'm a midnight mover.
7" Single: Released Sep '68, on Atlantic, by WEA Records. Deleted '71. Catalogue no: **584 203**

IN THE MIDNIGHT HOUR
Tracks: / In the midnight hour / In the midnight hour (12") (on 12" only.) / In the midnight hour (dub) (on 12" only.).
7" Single: Released '87, on WEA, by WEA Records. Deleted Jul '88. Catalogue no: **YZ 169**
7" Single: Released Sep '65, on Atlantic, by WEA Records. Deleted '68. Catalogue no: **AT 4036**
7" Single: Released Nov '87, on Motown, by BMG Records (UK). Catalogue no: **ZB 41583**
12" Single: Released Nov '87, on Motown, by BMG Records (UK). Catalogue no: **ZT 41584**
7" Single: Released Sep '65, on Atlantic, by WEA Records. Deleted '68. Catalogue no: **AT 4036**

LAND OF 1000 DANCES
Tracks: / Land of 1000 dances / In the midnight hour / You don't know like I know / Soul man.
7" Single: Released Apr '80, on Atlantic, by WEA Records. Deleted Apr '83. Catalogue no: **ATM 7**
7" Single: Released Sep '66, on Atlantic, by WEA Records. Deleted '69. Catalogue no: **584 039**

MUSTANG SALLY
Tracks: / Mustang Sally.
7" Single: Released Dec '66, on Atlantic, by WEA Records. Deleted '69. Catalogue no: **584 066**

SECONDS
Tracks: / Second / Second (inst).
7" Single: Released Feb '88, on New York 42, by Satril Records. Catalogue no: **NY 101**
12" Single: Released Feb '88, on New York 42, by Satril Records. Catalogue no: **NYT 101**

SHAMELESS
Tracks: / Shameless / Superstar.
7" Single: Released Apr '80, on EMI-America, by EMI Records. Deleted Apr '83. Catalogue no: **EA 107**

Pickettywitch

Biographical details: Proteges of the pop songwriting team Tony Macauley and John McLeod -- composers of such smashes as the Foundations *Baby, Now That I've Found You* and Long John Baldry's *Let The Heartaches Begin* -- this British pop group enjoyed three UK Top Thirty singles during 1970. Their first and most catchy hit was the lightweight *That Same Old Feeling*, which reached No 5. It was followed by *(It's Like A) Sad Old Kinda Movie*, which got to No 16, and *Baby I Won't Let You Down*, which peaked at No 27. All were produced by McLeod. Lead singer of Pickettywitch was Polly Brown, who proceeded to go solo: she enjoyed a surprise American Top Twenty single in 1975 with *Up In A Puff Of Smoke* but her other records flopped. She was succeeded in the group by Sheila Rossall who, many years after the public had forgotten about them, made headlines during 1980-81 when it was reported that she was languishing in an American hospital suffering from a comprehensive allergy to 20th century life. Her rare condition caused several benefits to be organised within the music industry, including a charity single by Brown. (Bob MacDonald, March 1986.).

BABY I WON'T LET YOU DOWN
Tracks: / Baby I won't let you down.
7" Single: Released Nov '70, on Pye, Deleted '73. Catalogue no: **7 N 45002**

(IT'S LIKE A) SAD OLD KINDA MOVIE
Tracks: / (It's like a) sad old kinda movie.
7" Single: Released Jul '70, on Pye, Deleted '73. Catalogue no: **7 N 17951**

THAT SAME OLD FEELING
Tracks: / That same old feeling.
7" Single: Released Feb '70, on Pye, Deleted '73. Catalogue no: **7 N 17887**

THAT SAME OLD FEELING (OLD GOLD)
Tracks: / That same old feeling.
7" Single: Released Jan '85, on Old Gold, by Old Gold Records. Catalogue no: **OG 9470**

Pickford, Gary

WHY (THE SONG)
Tracks: / Why (the song) / Story, The.
7" Single: Released Nov '86, on Spartan, Catalogue no: **SP 143**
12" Single: Released Dec '86, on Spartan, Catalogue no: **12SP 143**

Pickles, Lion John

WHAT'S THE MATTER WITH THE WORLD
Tracks: / What's the matter with the world.
7" Single: Released Oct '83, on Future Earth, by Future Earth Records. Deleted '87. Catalogue no: **FER 017**

Picnic at The Whitehouse

EAST RIVER
Tracks: / East River / Clockwork blue.
7" Single: Released Jun '86, on Portrait, by CBS Records. Deleted '87. Catalogue no: **A 7093**
12" Single: Released Jun '86, on Portrait, by CBS Records. Catalogue no: **TA 7093**

SUCCESS
Tracks: / Success / I wanna be.
12" Single: Released Mar '87, on Portrait, by CBS Records. Deleted Aug '87. Catalogue no: **CIA T1**
7" Single: Released Mar '87, on Portrait, by CBS Records. Deleted Aug '87. Catalogue no: **CIA 1**

WE NEED PROTECTION
Tracks: / We need protection / We need protection (Inst.) / We need protection (Mother mix) / Little lady.
Note: 'We need protection' and 'Little lady' available on 12" version only.
12" Single: Released Feb '86, on Portrait, by CBS Records. Deleted '87. Catalogue no: **QTX 6783**
12" Single: Released Feb '86, on Portrait, by CBS Records. Catalogue no: **TA 6783**
7" Single: Released Feb '86, on Portrait, by CBS Records. Catalogue no: **A 6783**

Picnic Boys

WHITE HOTEL
Tracks: / White hotel / Dawn patrol.
7" Single: Released Nov '82, on Challet, Deleted '87. Catalogue no: **BEAN 001**

Picture Frame

GOOD ENOUGH (FOR ME)
Tracks: / Good enough (for me).
7" Single: Released Jun '84, on Soso, Catalogue no: **SO 033**

Pictures

WHAT DO WE WANT
Tracks: / What do we want / It's all over.
7" Single: Released Jun '81, on KRL, by Kaleidoscope Records (UK). Deleted Jun '84. Catalogue no: **A 1224**

Pictures In A Dark

ANIMALS IN MUSIC, SPIDERS IN PIANOS
Tracks: / Animals in music, spiders in pianos.
7" Single: Released '83, on Zone To Zone, by Zone To Zone Records. Catalogue no: **ZON 01**

LOVE IS FIRE
Tracks: / Love is fire.
7" Single: Released '83, on Zone To Zone, by Zone To Zone Records. Catalogue no: **ZON 07**

VOLUNTEERS
Tracks: / Volunteers / Arabia.
7" Single: Released Jun '82, on Tube, Catalogue no: **TUBE 5**

Pictures Like This

NIGHT VENDETTA
Tracks: / Night vendetta.
7" Single: Released Apr '83, on T.W., by T.W. Records. Catalogue no: **HIT 112**

Pictures of Innocence

NO ONE CRYING
Tracks: / No one crying / Love and war.
7" Single: Released Oct '84, on Little Prince, by Little Prince Records. Catalogue no: **LIP 1**

Pieces

WINNERS
Tracks: / Winners.
7" Single: Released Oct '83, on CBS, by CBS Records. Deleted '84. Catalogue no: **PC 55055**

Pieces Of A Dream

RISING TO THE TOP
Tracks: / Rising to the top / Ain't my love enough / Rising to the top (U.K. remix) (12" only.) / Rising to the top (radio version) (12" only.) / Ain't my love enough (12" version) (12" only.).
7" Single: Released Sep '88, on EMI-Manhattan, by EMI Records. Deleted Jun '89. Catalogue no: **MT 54**
12" Single: Released Sep '88, on EMI-Manhattan, by EMI Records. Deleted Jun '89. Catalogue no: **12MT 54**

SAY LA LA
Tracks: / Say la la / Outside in.
7" Single: Released Jul '86, on EMI-Manhattan, by EMI Records. Catalogue no: **MT 12**
12" Single: Released Jul '86, on EMI-Manhattan, by EMI Records. Catalogue no: **12 MT 12**

WARM WEATHER
Tracks: / Warm weather / Mount Airey groove.
7" Single: Released Sep '82, on Elektra, by Elektra Records (UK). Catalogue no: **K 13201**
12" Single: Released Sep '82, on Elektra, by Elektra Records (UK). Catalogue no: **K 13201T**
7" Single: Released Nov '81, on Elektra, by Elektra Records (UK). Deleted '84. Catalogue no: **K 12569**

Pied Piper Of Hamelin

PIED PIPER OF HAMELIN
Tracks: / Pied piper: *Various artists* / Ugly duckling, The: *Various artists*.
7" EP: Released Aug '83, on Mr.Pickwick, Deleted '85. Catalogue no: **MP 9042**

Pie'N'Ears

CUSTARD PIE SONG
Tracks: / Custard pie song / Year of the pie.
7" Single: Released Nov '81, on Towerbell, Catalogue no: **TOW 17**

Pierce, Jeffrey Lee

FLAMINGO (EP)
Tracks: / Flamingo.
7" Single: Released Nov '85, on Statik, Catalogue no: **STAB 5**

LOVE & DESPERATION
Tracks: / Love & desperation.
7" Single: Released Aug '85, on Statik, Catalogue no: **TAK 36**
12" Single: Released Aug '85, on Statik, Catalogue no: **TAK 36/12**

Pierre, Marie

CHOOSE ME
Tracks: / Choose me.
7" Single: on Trojan, by Trojan Records. Deleted May '88. Catalogue no: **TRO 9060**

NOTHING GAINED
Tracks: / Nothing gained.
12" Single: on Attack, Deleted '88. Catalogue no: **TACK 4**

WALK AWAY
Tracks: / Walk away.
12" Single: Released '86, on Trojan, by Trojan Records. Deleted Aug '89. Catalogue no: **TRT 9057**
12" Single: Released Apr '82, on Trojan, by Trojan Records. Deleted May '88. Catalogue no: **TROT 9066**
7" Single: Released Apr '82, on Trojan, by Trojan Records. Deleted May '88. Catalogue no: **TRO 9066**

Pig

NEVER FOR FUN
Tracks: / Never for fun.
12" Single: Released Jun '88, on Wax Trax, by Wax Trax Records. Catalogue no: **WAXUK 045**

SICK CITY
Tracks: / Sick city.
12" Single: Released 5 Jun '89, on Sweatbox, by Sweatbox Records. Catalogue no: **SOX 044**
CD 5": Released 5 Jun '89, on Sweatbox, by Sweatbox Records. Catalogue no: **SOX 044 CD**

Pig Bros

BABY FACE
Tracks: / Baby face.
12" Single: Released Sep '87, on Cake, by Cake Records. Catalogue no: **12 PIECES**

BLUBBERHOUSE
Tracks: / Blubberhouse.
12" Single: Released Nov '85, on Vinyl Drip, by Vinyl Drip Records. Catalogue no: **DRIP 3**

CHEAP LIFE
Tracks: / Cheap life / In doubt / Bad attitude.
12" Single: Released Sep '86, on Backs, by Backs Recording Co.. Catalogue no: **12 NCH 110**

JUST CALL ME GOD
Tracks: / Just call me God.
12" Single: Released Dec '87, on Cake, by Cake Records. Catalogue no: **12 PIECE 5**

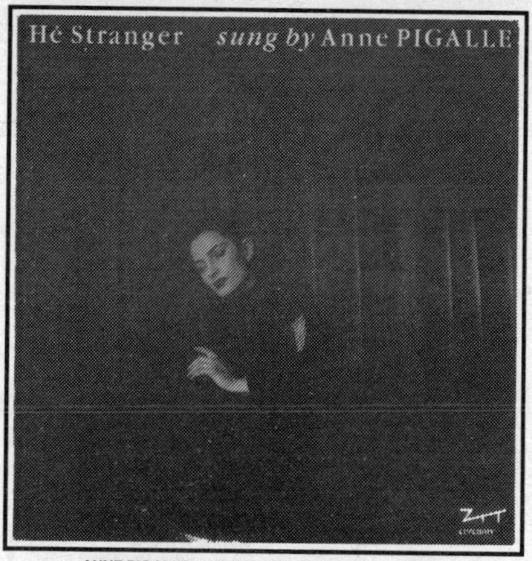

ANNE PIGALLE - HE STRANGER (Released on ZTT)

Pig, Clive

ONE NIGHT IN GREECE WITH AN AMERICAN
Tracks: / One night in Greece with an American.
12" Single: Released May '85, on Pig Enterprises, Catalogue no: **PIG 9**

WHALE ZOO, THE
Tracks: / Whale zoo, The.
7" EP: Released Jun '88, on Bam Caruso, by Demon Records. Catalogue no: **NRIC 020**

Pig, Martin

LOVELY RITA
Tracks: / Lovely Rita.
7" Single: Released Jun '83, on Rough Trade, by Rough Trade Records. Catalogue no: **RT 092**

Pigalle, Anne

HE STRANGER (see panel above)
Tracks: / He stranger.
12" Single: Released Apr '85, on ZTT, by ZTT Records. Catalogue no: **12 CERT 1**
7" Single: Released Apr '85, on ZTT, by ZTT Records. Catalogue no: **CERT 1**

WHY DOES IT HAVE TO BE THIS WAY
Tracks: / Why does it have to be this way.
7" Single: Released Nov '85, on ZTT, by ZTT Records. Catalogue no: **CERT 2**
12" Single: Released Nov '85, on ZTT, by ZTT Records. Catalogue no: **12 CERT 2**

Pigbag

Biographical details: This British band consisted of Chippie Carpenter, Roger Freeman, James Johnstone, Chris Leigh, Ollie Moore and Simon Underwood. The six young instrumentalists emerged from the Gloucestershire and Avon area of England in early 1981 and their debut single, *Papa's Got A Brand New Pigbag*, was issued in May of that year. This was a quirky, oddball cheeky and very catchy instrumental track, the title of which was oviously a reference to the famous James Brown hit Papa's *Got A Brand New Bag*. The Pigbag single became one of the most extraordinary sleeper smashes of the 80's. It bubbled under the British chart for nine months, selling in small but steady numbers week by week and by the time it finally entered the Top Seventy-Five in April 1982 two other Pigbag singles *Sunny Day and Getting Up* had been released and had become minor hits. The way in which *Papa's Got A Brand New Pigbag* finally reached the chart was a headline grabber within the industry. The band's record company, the small Y label, deleted the single for several weeks in order to allow a backlog of orders to accumulate: the steady demand showed no signs of slowing down. Y then reactivated the record and the backlog pushed the single straight to No 50 on the following week's chart. The momentum was maintained and it eventually peaked at No 3. Pigbag's first album, *Dr Heckle And Mr Jive*, climbed to No 18 and logged 14 weeks on the UK chart. Y Records' marketing tactic was extremely shrewd but did little to advance the band's long-term career. Their follow-up single, another instrumental called *The Big Bean*, peaked at No 40. They disbanded in 1983. (Bob MacDonald, March 1986.).

BIG BEAN
Tracks: / Big bean / Sounds.
7" Single: Released Jun '82, on Y, Catalogue no: **Y 24**
12" Single: Released Jun '82, on Y, Deleted Jun '85. Catalogue no: **12Y 24**

GETTING UP
Tracks: / Getting up / Giggling mud / Go cat.
12" Single: Released Feb '82, on Y, Catalogue no: **Y 1612**
7" Single: Released Jan '81, on Y, Catalogue no: **Y 16**

HIT THE 'O' DECK
Tracks: / Hit the 'o' deck / Six of one.
7" Single: Released Feb '83, on Y, Catalogue no: **Y 101**
12" Single: Released Feb '83, on Y, Catalogue no: **YT 101**

PAPA'S GOT A BRAND NEW PIG BAG
Tracks: / Papa's got a brand new pig bag
12" Single: Released Mar '82, on Y, Catalogue no: **Y 10T**
7" Single: Released Mar '82, on Y, Catalogue no: **Y 10**

SUNNY DAY
Tracks: / Sunny day.
7" Single: Released Oct '81, on Y, Catalogue no: **Y 12**

Piglets

JOHNNY REGGAE
Tracks: / Johnny reggae.
7" Single: Released Nov '71, on Bell, Deleted '74. Catalogue no: **BELL 1180**

P.I.L.(Public Image Ltd.)

WARRIOR
Tracks: / Warrior / U.S.L.S.1 / Warrior (version).
7" Single: Released Jul '89, on Virgin, by Virgin Records. Catalogue no: **VSG 1195**
12" Single: Released Jul '89, on Virgin, by Virgin Records. Catalogue no: **VSTX 1195**
12" Single: Released Jul '89, on Virgin, by Virgin Records. Catalogue no: **VST 1195**
CD 3": Released Jul '89, on Virgin, by Virgin Records. Catalogue no: **VSCD 1195**
7" Single: Released Jul '89, on Virgin, by Virgin Records. Catalogue no: **VS 1195**

Pilditch, Colin

TAKE A HAND
Tracks: / Take a hand.
7" Single: Released Jan '83, on Thunderbay, Catalogue no: **TBR 026**

Pilgrim, Billy

THEY ARE COMING TO GET US
Tracks: / They are coming to get us.
7" Single: Released '83, on Zone To Zone, by Zone To Zone Records. Catalogue no: **ZON 04**

Pilkington,Foster

IN THE TOWN OF FORGOTTEN TALENT
Tracks: / In the town of forgotten talent / Last tango.
12" Single: Released Mar '86, on Rockin' Horse, by BMG Records (UK). Catalogue no: **RHT 106**
7" Single: Released Mar '86, on Rockin' Horse, by BMG Records (UK). Catalogue no: **RH 106**

LISTENING LAND
Tracks: / Listening land / Art of being shy, The.
7" Single: Released Jul '86, on Rockin' Horse, by BMG Records (UK). Catalogue no: **RH 111**
12" Single: Released Jul '86, on Rockin' Horse, by BMG Records (UK). Catalogue no: **RHT 111**

Pilot

Biographical details: Pilot At the time of their chart success, this British pop band consisted of Ian Bairnson, Billy Lyall, David Paton and Stuart Tosh.
The classy Pilot did not last as long as everyone expected. They came to fame at the end of 1974 with the memorable *Magic*, a single that lived up to its name and reached No.11 on the UK chart; it later climbed to No.5 in America and sold a million copies in the States alone. *Magic* was followed by the more bland but even more catchy *January* - this polished single was written by Paton and produced by Alan Parsons, and zoomed to No.1 on the British charts in February 1975. Pilot looked set to become one of the major success stories of the mid Seventies, but the next single *Call Me Round* peaked at No.34 on the UK chart. This was a pale rehash of the *January* formula, but even the exuberant *Just A Smile* (a re-promotion of one of their early singles) could only reach No.31.
Pilot disintegrated. Bairnson and Paton worked as session musicians on Kate Bush's first album *The Kick Inside* and became long standing members of Parsons' highly successful studio ensemble, the Alan Parsons Project. Tosh also played with the Project for a while and joined 10cc after the departure of Godley & Creme. (Bob Macdonald 5/3/86).

CALL ME ROUND
Tracks: / Call me round.
7" Single: Released Apr '75, on EMI, by EMI Records. Deleted '78. Catalogue no: **EMI 2287**

JANUARY
Tracks: / January.
7" Single: Released Jan '75, on EMI, by EMI Records. Deleted '78. Catalogue no: **EMI 2255**

JANUARY (OLD GOLD)
Tracks: / Magic / January.
Note: Also contains:"Magic" by Pilot
7" Single: Released Apr '87, on Old Gold, by Old Gold Records. Deleted Sep '89. Catalogue no: **OG 9723**

JUST A SMILE
Tracks: / Just a smile.
7" Single: Released Sep '75, on EMI, by EMI Records. Deleted '78. Catalogue no: **EMI 2338**

MAGIC
Tracks: / Magic.
7" Single: Released Nov '74, on EMI, by EMI Records. Deleted '77. Catalogue no: **EMI 2217**

Piltdown Men

GOODNIGHT MRS FLINTSTONE
Tracks: / Goodnight Mrs. Flintstone.
7" Single: Released Mar '61, on Capitol, by EMI Records. Deleted '64. Catalogue no: **CL 15186**

MACDONALD'S CAVE
Tracks: / Macdonald's cave.
7" Single: Released Sep '60, on Capitol, by EMI Records. Deleted '63. Catalogue no: **CL 15149**

PILTDOWN RIDES AGAIN
Tracks: / Piltdown rides again.
7" Single: Released Jan '61, on Capitol, by EMI Records. Deleted '64. Catalogue no: **CL 15175**

PILTDOWN RIDES AGAIN (OLD GOLD)
Tracks: / Piltdown rides again / Macdonalds cave.
7" Single: Released Mar '87, on Old Gold, by Old Gold Records. Deleted Sep '89. Catalogue no: **OG 9646**

Pinchers

ABRACADABRA
Tracks: / Abracadabra / Trouble and problem.
12" Single: Released Jun '86, on Blue Trac, by Blue Trac Records. Catalogue no: **BTR 004**

AGONY (SINGLE)
Tracks: / Agony.
12" Single: Released Feb '87, on Live & Love, Catalogue no: **LLDIS 0029**

ARDENT FAN
Tracks: / Ardent fan.
7" Single: Released Nov '88, on Supreme, by Supreme Records. Catalogue no: **UNKNOWN**

GIRLS GIRLS
Tracks: / Girls, girls, girls.
7" Single: Released Jan '89, on Exterminator, Catalogue no: **Unknown**

KINGSTON 13
Tracks: / Kingston 13 / Kingston 13 (version).
12" Single: Released 27 Feb '88, on Love People, Catalogue no: **LPD 1006**

LADY
Tracks: / Lady.
12" Single: Released Aug '88, on Jammie, Catalogue no: **JM 001**

POSE UP
Tracks: / Pose up.
12" Single: Released Feb '89, on Supreme, by Supreme Records. Catalogue no: **VPRD 386**

ROUGH NECK
Tracks: / Rough neck / Rough neck (version).
12" Single: Released Jun '87, on Revolutionary Sounds, Catalogue no: **RS 009**

SIT DOWN PON IT
Tracks: / Sit down pon it / Sit down pon it (version).
12" Single: Released Mar '87, on Live & Love, Catalogue no: **LLDIS 0032**

Pine, Courtney

Biographical details: The various activities of Courtney Pine -- born in London in 1964 -- are the most encouraging development in British jazz in a long time. The press refers to the hype surrounding him, but the press itself is responsible: Pine is a serious man ("I'm not going to spend my life playing *Stella By Starlight* in some wine bar") with enough talent to make any hype superfluous. He formed the Brixton-based big band Jazz Warriors, featuring black British musicians of all ages, many of whom had been stuck in reggae bands but who are now playing gloriously exciting original music. Pine's first album was a strong debut, showing the influences of John Coltgrane and Wayne Shorter. Future albums will all be exciting and they will all be different. (Donald Clarke, May 1987.).

CHILDREN OF THE GHETTO
Tracks: / Children of the ghetto / E.F.P. / When, where, how and why (Available on 12" version only.) / E.S.P. / Courtney Pine talks to Robert Elms (Part 1).
Cassingle: Released Nov '86, on Island, by Island Records. Deleted Jul '87. Catalogue no: **CIS 301**
12" Single: Released Oct '86, on Island, by Island Records. Deleted Jul '87. Catalogue no: **12IS 301**
7" Single: Released Oct '86, on Island, by Island Records. Catalogue no: **IS 301**

SACRIFICE
Tracks: / Sacrifice / Mark of the time.
10" single: Released Mar '88, on Antilles/New Directions, by Island Records. Catalogue no: **10 ANN 3**

TRADITIONS BECKONING
Tracks: / Traditions beckoning.
7" Single: Released 12 Sep '88, on Antilles/New Directions, by Island Records. Deleted Apr '89. Catalogue no: **ANN 4**
10" single: Released 12 Sep '88, on Antilles/New Directions, by Island Records. Deleted Apr '89. Catalogue no: **10 ANN 4**

Pineapple Party

WALK AWAY
Tracks: / Walk away.
7" Single: Released May '85, on Anubis, Catalogue no: **ANU 001**

Ping Ping & Al

SUCU SUCU
Tracks: / Sucu sucu.
7" Single: Released Sep '61, on Oriole, Deleted '64. Catalogue no: **CB 1589**

Pink

SOUL FLIGHT (SINGLE)
Tracks: / Ramon night / Jim Taihoshizukiyo.
7" Single: Released Jan '87, on Rime, by Rime Records. Deleted '88. Catalogue no: **RIM 2**
12" Single: Released Jan '87, on Rime, by Rime Records. Deleted '88. Catalogue no: **RIME 2**

Pink And Black

SOMETIMES I WISH
Tracks: / Sometimes I wish.

12" Single: Released Feb '85, on Illuminated, Catalogue no: **ILL 4912**

Pink Flamingos

HIT THE DECK
Tracks: / Hit the deck.
12" Single: Released Jul '85, on Prophet, Catalogue no: **PROFIT 10**

Pink Floyd

Biographical details: Cult figures on the late 60's underground scene -- and later one of the most successful of all rock bands -- Pink Floyd, formed in 1966, were initially fronted by singer/songwriter/guitarist Syd Barrett, born in 1946. His whimsical lyrics and engaging melodies won substantial UK chart successes in '67. *Arnold Layne* and *See Emily Play* hit the Top 20 singles lists and their debut album, *Piper At The Gates Of Dawn*, reached No 6. Barrett's increasingly erratic behaviour, largely caused by his drug-taking habits, forced his exit in early '68 and he was replaced by Dave Gilmour (born 1945), other members of the band being Nick Mason, Roger Waters and Richard Wright (all born 1944-45). Syd pursued a moderately successful solo career and is remembered with affection by many fans who regard the early Floyd incarnation as the group's best period. Virtually ignoring the singles market, the Barrett-less Pink Floyd concentrated on albums. It was a highly successful policy, for every one of the band's LPs reached the British Top Ten, two of them -- *Atom Heart Mother* ('70) and *Wish You Were Here* ('75) -- zooming to No 1. The fact that the legendary *Dark Side Of The Moon* album only reached No 2 is scarcely relevant: it logged 294 weeks in the chart and thus became the fifth longest-running album of all time. In America *Dark Side Of The Moon* (released in spring '73) chalked up its 600th chart week in late '85. *Money* was the best-known track on *Dark Side Of The Moon*, but the whole album passed into the history books as an all-time classic and the epitome of the progressive rock era. It emphasised the extent to which the bleak songwriting of bassist Roger Waters had come to dominate the band. He successfully led Pink Floyd through a series of subsequent albums, most notably 1979's *The Wall*. This yielded a rare single, *Another Brick In The Wall*, which became Britain's Christmas No 1 of that year and logged another five weeks at the top. In the US 1980 proved an incredible year for the Floyd: *Another Brick In The Wall* was on top for four weeks and *The Wall* was No 1 album for a staggering 15 weeks. *The Wall* concept was the basis of a spectacular series of live shows and was later made into a film starring Bob Geldof which was a more moderate success. Pink Floyd albums had been appearing on a less and less frequent basis so it came as little surprise that their chart-topping 1983 set *The Final Cut* lived up to its title. Waters and Gilmour released solo albums with modest success although Gilmour became better known for other activities: his stunning guitar solos on the outros of Kate Bush's Wuthering Heights ('78), the Floyd's own *Another Brick In The Wall* ('79) and Paul McCartney's *No More Lonely Nights* ('84) reaffirmed his instrumental virtuosity, and in 1985 he co-produced Dream Academy's international smash single *Life In A Northern Town*. (Bob MacDonald, March 1986.) Gilmour, Mason, Waters and Wright all born '44-5, Barrett born '46. A USA newspaper report in 1986 said that *Dark side of the moon* was still in the album charts, had sold 19 million copies; that the CD edition is a USA best-seller, and that Gilmour, Mason and Wright were recording together as Pink Floyd, Waters trying to stop them. (Donald Clarke 21.5.88).

ANOTHER BRICK IN THE WALL
Tracks: / Another brick in the wall.
7" Single: Released Nov '79, on Harvest (1), by EMI Records. Catalogue no: **HAR 5194**

ANOTHER BRICK IN THE WALL (PART 2)
Tracks: / Another brick in the wall (part 2) / One of my turns.
CD 3": Released Aug '88, on Columbia (USA), by CBS Records (USA). Catalogue no: **38K03118**

ARNOLD LAYNE
Tracks: / Arnold Layne.
7" Single: Released Mar '67, on Columbia, by EMI Records. Deleted '70. Catalogue no: **DB 8156**

FREE FOUR
Tracks: / Free four.
7" Single: Released '80, on Lightning, Catalogue no: **LR 0703**

LEARNING TO FLY
Tracks: / Learning to fly (edited version) / One slip (Edited version) / Terminal frost (LP version) / Terminal frost (dyol version) / Learning to fly.
CD 5": Released Aug '87, on EMI, by EMI Records. Deleted Nov '88. Catalogue no: **CDEM 26**

MONEY
Tracks: / Money / Let there be more light.
7" Single: Released Apr '83, on EMI (France), by EMI Records. Catalogue no: **2 C 008 95368**
12" Single: Released Dec '81, on Harvest (1), by EMI Records. Deleted Dec '84. Catalogue no: **12 HAR 5217**

NOT NOW JOHN
Tracks: / Not now John.
12" Single: Released May '83, on Harvest (1), by EMI Records. Catalogue no: **12 HAR 5224**
7" Single: Released May '83, on Harvest (1), by EMI Records. Catalogue no: **HAR 5224**

ON THE TURNING AWAY
Tracks: / On the turning away (Live) / Run like hell (live) (Recorded live at Atlanta, November 5th, 1987) / On the turning away / On the turning away (album version).
CD 5": Released Dec '87, on EMI, by EMI Records. Deleted Aug '89. Catalogue no: **CDEM 34**
7" Single: Released 7 Dec '87, on EMI, by EMI Records. Deleted Nov '88. Catalogue no: **EM 34**
12" Single: Released Dec '87, on EMI, by EMI Records. Catalogue no: **12EMP 34**
12" Single: Released 7 Dec '87, on EMI, by EMI Records. Deleted Nov '88. Catalogue no: **12EM 34**
7" Single: Released 7 Dec '87, on EMI, by EMI Records. Deleted Apr '88. Catalogue no: **EMP 34**

ONE OF THESE DAYS
Tracks: / One of these days.
7" Single: on Lightning, Catalogue no: **LR 0702**

ONE SLIP
Tracks: / One slip / Terminal frost / Dogs of war "live", The (Extra track available on 12" only).
Note: (P) 1987 **except** 'B' (2) (P) 1988 original sound recordings made by Pink Floyd Music Ltd under exclusive licence to EMI Records Ltd.
CD 5": Released Jun '88, on EMI, by EMI Records. Catalogue no: **CDEM 52**
7" Single: Released May '88, on EMI, by EMI Records. Deleted Jan '89. Catalogue no: **EM 52**
12" Single: Released Jun '88, on EMI, by EMI Records. Deleted Aug '89. Catalogue no: **12EMP 52**
12" Single: Released May '88, on EMI, by EMI Records. Deleted Jan '89. Catalogue no: **12EM 52**
7" Single: Released Jun '88, on EMI, by EMI Records. Deleted Jun '89. Catalogue no: **EMG 52**

POINT ME AT THE SKY
Tracks: / Point me at the sky.
7" Single: Released '80, on Lightning, Catalogue no: **LR 0701**

SEE EMILY PLAY
Tracks: / See Emily play.
7" Single: Released Jun '67, on Columbia, by EMI Records. Deleted '70. Catalogue no: **DB 8214**

SHINE ON YOU CRAZY DIAMOND
Tracks: / Shine on you crazy diamond.
7" Single: Released '80, on Lightning, Catalogue no: **LR 8198**

WHEN THE TIGERS BROKE FREE
Tracks: / When the tigers broke free.
7" Single: Released Jul '82, on Harvest (1), by EMI Records. Catalogue no: **HAR 5222**

Pink Industry

DON'T LET GO
Tracks: / Don't let go.
12" Single: Released Nov '87, on Cathexis, by Cathexis Records. Catalogue no: **CRL 16**

THIS IS THE END
Tracks: / This is the end / Don't let go.
7" Single: Released Feb '82, on Zulu, by Zulu Records. Deleted Feb '87. Catalogue no: **ZULU 1**

WHAT I WOULDN'T GIVE
Tracks: / What I wouldn't give.
7" Single: Released Jun '85, on Zulu, by Zulu Records. Catalogue no: **RA 8**

Pink Military

DID YOU SEE HER
Tracks: / Did you see her / Everyday.
7" Single: Released 20 Jun '80, on Virgin, by Virgin Records. Deleted '83. Catalogue no: **ERS 005**

Pink Noise

EVERYTHING
Tracks: / Everything.
12" Single: Released Jul '88, on Reasonable, by Reasonable Records. Catalogue no: **JRR 006**

MOVE FOR YOU
Tracks: / Move for you.
12" Single: Released 12 Apr '88, on Reasonable, by Reasonable Records. Catalogue no: **JRR 006**

THIN END OF THE WEDGE
Tracks: / Thin end of the wedge, The / Face away.
7" Single: Released Jan '88, on Reasonable, by Reasonable Records. Catalogue no: **JRR 004**

Pink Peg Slax

DRIPPING My love for you
Tracks: / Dripping.
7" Single: Released Mar '84, on Black Fish, Catalogue no: **BF 101**

SELF PITYING
Tracks: / Self pitying.
7" Single: Released Jan '85, on Half Cut, Catalogue no: **HC 59**

SOUND OF THE MEANWOOD VALLEY
Tracks: / Sound of the Meanwood Valley.
12" Single: Released Jan '87, on Half Cut, Catalogue no: **HC 63**

Pink Project

DISCO PROJECT MEDLEY
Tracks: / Disco project medley / Mammagamma serious.
7" Single: Released Feb '83, on Baby, by New Rose Records. Catalogue no: **BABY 2**
12" Single: Released Feb '83, on Baby, by New Rose Records. Catalogue no: **BABY 212**

Pink Rhythm

INDIA
Tracks: / India.
7" Single: Released Sep '85, on Beggars Banquet, by Beggars Banquet Records. Deleted Jun '87. Catalogue no: **BEG 149**
12" Single: Released Sep '85, on Beggars Banquet, by Beggars Banquet Records. Deleted Jun '87. Catalogue no: **BEG 149T**

Pink Turns Blue

YOUR MASTER IS CALLING
Tracks: / Your master is calling.
12" Single: Released Jul '89, on Fun Factory, Catalogue no: **M 3915**
CD 5": Released Jul '89, on Fun Factory, Catalogue no: **CD 3915**

Pink Umbrellas

RASPBERRY RAINBOWS
Tracks: / Raspberry rainbows.
7" Single: Released Apr '83, on Ready Steady Go, by Graduate Records. Deleted Jan '87. Catalogue no: **RSG 3**

Pinkees

Biographical details: A somewhat inglorious career was experienced by this 60's-influenced pop band. The Pinkees, an all-male British combo, chalked up just one UK chart entry, which became the subject of a hype scandal. The single *Danger Games* was released in August 1982, entered the British Top Seventy-Five in September and hovered in the mid-chart region for a few weeks. Just as it seemed to be peaking at No 27 it suddenly zoomed to No 8, but in the following week it slipped back to No 12, making the sudden surge even more suspicious. It transpired that collusion had taken place between Creole Records and an employee of the UK chart compilers, the British Market Research Bureau. Police at Scotland Yard were called in to investigate, a very unusual move in a chart-rigging scandal, but the affair did not make any long-term difference to the record industry for the BMRB had already given notice that they were to lose the chart compilation contract to Gallup. *Danger Games* was a pleasant pop ditty, but No 27 was a more accurate reflection of its quality than No 8. The Pinkees' other records were not as strong and they faded into obscurity. (Bob MacDonald, March 1986.).

DANGER GAMES
Tracks: / Danger games / Keep on loving you.
7" Single: Released Aug '82, on Creole, by Creole Records. Catalogue no: **CR 39**

GONNA BE LONELY AGAIN
Tracks: / Gonna be lonely again.
7" Single: Released May '82, on Creole, by Creole Records. Catalogue no: **CR 33**

HOLDING ME TIGHT
Tracks: / Holding me tight / Girl in a million.
7" Single: Released Nov '82, on Creole, by Creole Records. Catalogue no: **CR 42**

I'LL BE THERE
Tracks: / I'll be there / Rocking with the band.
7" Single: Released Feb '83, on Creole, by Creole Records. Catalogue no: **CR 46**

OPEN COMMUNE
Tracks: / Open commune / Target searching.
7" Single: Released Nov '82, on 021 Records, by Avatar Record Corporation. Deleted Nov '85. Catalogue no: **OTO 7**

Pinkertons Assorted...

Biographical details: Full title of the group is **Pinkertons Assorted Colours**
At the time of their chart success this British pop group consisted of Barrie Bernard, Dave Holland, Samuel "Pinkerton" Kemp -- the group's singer and frontman -- Tom Long and Tony Newman. With their sickly bright pink jackets (a good case, if ever there was one, for the preservation of black-and-white television) Pinkertons Assorted Colours zoomed into the UK chart in early 1966 with the Newman-penned *Mirror Mirror*. This peaked at No 9 but proved to be the Colours' only taste of major success. *Don't Stop Loving Me, Baby* could only manage a No 50 placing and they faded away. (Bob MacDonald, March 1986.).

DON'T STOP LOVIN' ME BABY
Tracks: / Don't stop loving me.
7" Single: Released Apr '66, on Decca, by Decca Records. Deleted '69. Catalogue no: **F 12377**

MIRROR MIRROR (OLD GOLD)
Tracks: / Mirror mirror.
7" Single: Released Oct '83, on Old Gold, by Old Gold Records. Catalogue no: **OG 9357**

MIRROR MIRROR
Tracks: / Mirror mirror / Smile a little smile for me / When you walk in the room / Don't stop loving me.
7" Single: Released Jan '66, on Decca, by Decca Records. Deleted '88. Catalogue no: **F 12307**
7" EP: Released Jan '83, on Explosion, by Orbit Records. Catalogue no: **BANG 2**

Pinkie & His Band

BURN THE CITADEL DOWN
Tracks: / Burn the citadel down.
7" EP: Released Mar '85, on Fluffy, Catalogue no: **FLUFF 1**

Pinkney, St Clair

DO YOU LIKE IT (SINGLE)
Tracks: / Do you like it / As we like it / Shake you down.
12" Single: Released 31 Oct '87, on Ichiban, by Ichiban Records (UK). Catalogue no: **ICHT 701**

Pinnock, Delroy

I DON'T KNOW WHY
Tracks: / I don't know why / No dub.
7" Single: Released Nov '81, on Solid Groove, Catalogue no: **SG 7**

Pinnock, Dennis

DRIFTER
Tracks: / Drifter.
12" Single: Released Nov '88, on Uptempo, Catalogue no: **TEMP 028**

IN AND OUT OF LOVE
Tracks: / In and out of love (dub disco).
12" Single: Released Feb '87, on Disco Tex, Catalogue no: **DT 18**

WOMAN BE FAIR
Tracks: / Woman be fair.
12" Single: Released Jul '88, on Disco Tex, Catalogue no: **DT 24A**

Pinpoint

WAKING UP TO MORNING
Tracks: / Waking up to morning.
7" Single: Released Sep '80, on Albion, by Albion Records. Catalogue no: **ION 1002**

YO YO
Tracks: / Yo yo.
7" Single: Released Jan '81, on Albion, by Albion Records. Catalogue no: **ION 1007**

Pinski Zoo

SWEET AUTOMATIC
Tracks: / Sweet automatic (acid mix) / New lunacy.
7" Single: Released Jan '89, on JCR, Catalogue no: **JCR 901**

Pint, Junior

DANCE HALL YOU HAVE TO FIT
Tracks: / Dance hall you have to fit.
12" Single: Released Nov '88, on Digital English, Catalogue no: **DE 008**

Pintev, Stefan

MORNING SUN
Tracks: / Morning sun / Let there be some love.
7" Single: Released '86, on Memoir, by Memoir Records. Catalogue no: **MEM 1**

PIRANHAS - I DON'T WANT MY BODY (Released on Sire)

PARANHAS - JILLY (Released on Attrix)

Pioneer Core

PIONEER BOY
Note: 4-track EP
12" Single: Released Jan '88, on Nightshift, by Nightshift Records. Catalogue no: **NISHI 201T**

Pioneers

Biographical details: In 1969 this Jamaican vocal group reached No 21 in Britain with *Long Shot Kick De Bucket* it made a brief return to the chart in early 1980 during the Two-Tone explosion. Their recording of Jimmy Cliff's *Let Your Yeah Be Yeah* reached the UK No 5 position in summer '71. (Bob MacDonald, March 1986.).

DO IT RIGHT
Tracks: / Do it right.
7" Single: on Trojan, by Trojan Records. Catalogue no: **TRO 9084**

GIVE AND TAKE
Tracks: / Give and take.
7" Single: Released Jan '72, on Trojan, by Trojan Records. Deleted '75. Catalogue no: **TR 7846**

LET YOUR YEAH BE YEAH
Tracks: / Let your yeah be yeah.
7" Single: Released Jul '71, on Trojan, by Trojan Records. Deleted '74. Catalogue no: **TR 7825**

LONG SHOT KICK THE BUCKET
Tracks: / Long shot kick the bucket.
7" Single: Released Oct '69, on Trojan, by Trojan Records. Deleted '72. Catalogue no: **TR 672**
7" Single: Released Mar '80, on Trojan, by Trojan Records. Deleted '83. Catalogue no: **TRO 9063**

LONG SHOT KICK THE BUCKET (OLD GOLD)
Tracks: / Long shot kick the bucket.
7" Single: Released Apr '83, on Old Gold, by Old Gold Records. Deleted Jul '88. Catalogue no: **OG 9273**

REGGAE IN LONDON CITY
Tracks: / Reggae in London city / My woman.
12" Single: Released '86, on Trojan, by Trojan Records. Deleted May '88. Catalogue no: **TROT 9090**
7" Single: Released '86, on Trojan, by Trojan Records. Deleted May '88. Catalogue no: **TRO 9090**

ROCK MY SOUL
Tracks: / Rock my soul.
7" Single: Released Apr '85, on Creole, by Creole Records. Catalogue no: **CR 73**

Pipe Dreams

QUICK SILVER
Tracks: / Quick silver.
7" Single: Released Nov '83, on Design Communications, Catalogue no: **DES 6**
12" Single: Released Nov '83, on Design Communications, Catalogue no: **DEST 6**

Pipkins

Biographical details: *Gimme Dat Ding* was a one-off UK chart entry for this British vocal duo in the spring of 1970. Written by Albert Hammond and Mike Hazelwood, the novelty number reached No 6 in Britain and, more surprisingly, climbed to No 9 in America. The lead voice was Tony Burrows, Britain's hottest session singer of the time. By the time the Pipkins' single clicked he had already performed lead vocal duties on three 1970 Top Tenners: Edison Lighthouse's *Love Grows (Where My Rosemary Goes), White Plains', My Baby Loves Lovin'* and Brotherhood of Man's *United We Stand.* And the year wasn't even half over... (Bob MacDonald, March 1986.).

GIMME DAT DING
Tracks: / Gimme dat ding.
7" Single: Released '80, on Lightning, Catalogue no: **LR 8138**
7" Single: Released Mar '70, on Columbia, by EMI Records. Deleted '73. Catalogue no: **DB 8662**

Pippanannakim

CASTLES IN THE AIR
Tracks: / Castles in the air.
7" Single: Released Jun '84, on Dakota, Catalogue no: **DAK 19**

Piranhas

Biographical details: At the time of their greatest success this British pop band consisted of Boring Bob Grover, Johnny Helmer, Graham Preskett, Dick Slexia plus two gentlemen known only as Reg and Zoot. These Brighton boys zoomed onto the UK charts in the summer of 1980 with a remake of *Tom Hark*, the exuberantly catchy tune that had been a smash in 1958 for Elias & His Zig Zag Jive Flutes. The Piranhas gave it the same novelty appeal but added some lyrics instead of treating it as an instrumental. These included such profundities as *You have to laugh or else you cry* and *You have to live or else you die.* The band's self-titled LP reached the UK No 69 position. Not a group to take themselves too seriously, the Piranhas bounced back in 1982 with a second 50's remake: *Zambesi*, which again featured new words, climbed to No 17 on the British chart and featured Boring Bob Grover's attempt to be Eddie Calvert. (Bob MacDonald, March 1986.).

I DON'T WANT MY BODY (See panel top left)
Tracks: / I don't want my body / (I'm gonna get) Well away.
7" Single: Released '80, on Sire, by Sire Records. Catalogue no: **SIR 4046**

JILLY (See panel above)
Tracks: / Jilly / Coloured music.
7" Single: Released '78, on Attrix, by Attrix Records. Catalogue no: **RB 04 SUE**

KWELA (See panel below)
Tracks: / Tom Hark / Getting beaten up / Boyfriend.
7" Single: Released '80, on Sire, by Sire Records. Catalogue no: **SIR 4044**

PIRANHAS - KWELA (Released on Sire)

TOM HARK
Tracks: / Tom Hark.
7" Single: Released Aug '80, on Sire, by Sire Records. Deleted '83. Catalogue no: **SIR 4044**

VIGELEGELE
Tracks: / Vigelegele / Nobody.
7" Single: Released Dec '81, on Dakota, Deleted Dec '84. Catalogue no: **DAK 2**
12" Single: Released Dec '81, on Dakota, Deleted Dec '84. Catalogue no: **12 DAK 2**

ZAMBESI
Tracks: / Zambesi.
7" Single: Released Oct '82, on Dakota, Deleted '84. Catalogue no: **DAK 6**

Pirates

Biographical details: Frank Farley, Mick Green and Johnny Spence - former backing group of the late, great rock 'n' roller Johnny Kidd, reformed for a series of albums in the late 70's and early 80's, featuring remakes of rock standards plus a batch of new songs. Only the first LP reached the charts: *Out Of Their Skulls* peaked at No 57 in their native Britain in late 1977. (Bob MacDonald, March 1986.).

PETER GUNN EP
Tracks: / Peter Gunn / Just another party / Cap in hand / Something very strange.
7" Single: Released Aug '82, on Charly, by Charly Records. Deleted '88. Catalogue no: **CYX 204**

Pisces

UP THE MARINERS
Tracks: / Up the mariners / Mariners memories.
7" Single: Released Mar '81, on Humber, by Humber Records. Deleted Mar '84. Catalogue no: **HRSP 050**

Pitman, Donnell

CHOCOLATE LOVER
Tracks: / Chocolate lover.
12" Single: Released Oct '87, on Pana, Catalogue no: **PRI 2007**

Pitney, Gene

Biographical details: Pitney, Gene Born in Hartford, Connecticut, this American singer and songwriter was a consistent chart force on both sides of the Atlantic from 1961 until the late Sixties. His strong tenor voice was well suited to both his own material and that of other writers. He never achieved a No.1 single in America or Britain, but reached No.2 in the States with *Only Love Can Break A Heart* (1962) and No.2 in the UK with Barry Mann & Cynthia Weil's *I'm Gonna Be Strong* (1964) and Randy Newman's *Nobody Needs Your Love* (1966). By the time of the latter hit he was, like Roy Orbison, more popular in Britain than at home; this fact was reflected by his 1967 UK No.5 smash *Something's Gotten Hold Of My Heart* which was penned by the UK songwriting team Roger Cook & Roger Greenaway.
Pitney's lack of a chart topper was compensated by the fact that he wrote a No.1 smash

for somebody else. *He's A Rebel* topped the US chart for Phil Spector's puppet group the Crystals in 1962. Another Pitney composition *Hello Mary Lou* was a British No.2 smash for Ricky Nelson in 1961. (Bob Macdonald 6/3/86).

6 TRACK HITS
Tracks: / 24 hours from Tulsa / Looking through the eyes of love / Town without pity / Something's gotten hold of my heart / Just one smile / Man who shot Liberty Valance.
7" EP: Released Sep '83, on Scoop 33, by Pickwick Records. Catalogue no: **7SR 5003**

24 HOURS FROM TULSA (OLD GOLD)
Tracks: / 24 hours from from Tulsa.
7" Single: Released Nov '88, on Old Gold, by Old Gold Records. Catalogue no: **OG 6107**

24 HOURS FROM TULSA (OLD GOLD CD SINGLE)
Tracks: / 24 hours from Tulsa / Looking through the eyes of love / I'm gonna be strong.
CD 5": Released Nov '88, on Old Gold, by Old Gold Records. Catalogue no: **OG 6107**

24 HOURS FROM TULSA (SINGLE)
Tracks: / 24 hours from Tulsa.
7" Single: Released Dec '63, on United Artists, by EMI Records. Deleted '66. Catalogue no: **UP 1035**

24 SYCAMORE
Tracks: / 24 sycamore.
7" Single: Released Apr '73, on Pye International, Deleted '76. Catalogue no: **7N 25606**

BACKSTAGE
Tracks: / Backstage.
7" Single: Released Feb '66, on Stateside, by EMI Records. Deleted '69. Catalogue no: **SS 490**

BLUE ANGEL
Tracks: / Blue angel.
7" Single: Released Nov '74, on Bronze, by Bronze Records. Deleted '77. Catalogue no: **BRO 11**

I MUST BE SEEING THINGS
Tracks: / I must be seeing things.
7" Single: Released Feb '65, on Stateside, by EMI Records. Deleted '68. Catalogue no: **SS 390**

I WANNA LOVE MY LIFE AWAY
Tracks: / I wanna love my life away.
7" Single: Released Mar '61, on London Records, by London Records. Deleted '64. Catalogue no: **HL 9270**

I'M GONNA BE STRONG (SINGLE)
Tracks: / I'm gonna be strong.
7" Single: Released Nov '64, on Stateside, by EMI Records. Deleted '67. Catalogue no: **SS 358**
7" Single: Released Aug '82, on Dakota, Catalogue no: **BAK 14**

IT HURTS TO BE IN LOVE
Tracks: / It hurts to be in love.
7" Single: Released Oct '64, on United Artists, by EMI Records. Deleted '67. Catalogue no: **UP 1063**

IT'S OVER IT'S OVER
Tracks: / It's over it's over / Walkin' in the sun / Something's gotten hold of my heart (Only on 12" version.) / 24 hours from Tulsa (Only on 12" version.).
CD 5": Released Mar '89, on Epic, by CBS Records. Deleted Oct '89. Catalogue no: **654749 2**
7" Single: Released 6 Mar '89, on Epic, by CBS Records. Deleted Oct '89. Catalogue no: **654749 7**
12" Single: Released Mar '89, on Epic, by CBS Records. Deleted Oct '89. Catalogue no: **654749 6**

JUST ONE SMILE
Tracks: / Just one smile.
7" Single: Released Nov '66, on Stateside, by EMI Records. Deleted '69. Catalogue no: **SS 558**

MARIA ELENA
Tracks: / Maria Elena.
7" Single: Released Mar '69, on Stateside, by EMI Records. Deleted '71. Catalogue no: **SS 2142**

NOBODY NEEDS YOUR LOVE (SINGLE)
Tracks: / Nobody needs your love.
7" Single: Released Jun '66, on Stateside, by EMI Records. Deleted '69. Catalogue no: **SS 518**

PRINCESS IN RAGS
Tracks: / Princess in rags.
7" Single: Released Nov '65, on Stateside, by EMI Records. Deleted '68. Catalogue no: **SS 471**

SHADY LADY
Tracks: / Shady lady.
7" Single: Released Oct '70, on Stateside, by EMI Records. Deleted '73. Catalogue no: **SS 2177**

SOMETHING'S GOTTEN HOLD OF MY HEART (SINGLE)
Tracks: / Something's gotten hold of my heart.
7" Single: Released Nov '67, on Stateside, by EMI Records. Deleted '70. Catalogue no: **SS 2060**

SOMEWHERE IN THE COUNTRY
Tracks: / Somewhere in the country.
7" Single: Released Apr '68, on Stateside, by EMI Records. Deleted '71. Catalogue no: **SS 2013**

STREET CALLED HOPE
Tracks: / Street called hope, A.
7" Single: Released Mar '70, on Stateside, by EMI Records. Deleted '73. Catalogue no: **SS 2164**

THAT GIRL BELONGS TO YESTERDAY
Tracks: / That girl belongs to yesterday.
7" Single: Released Mar '64, on United Artists, by EMI Records. Deleted '67. Catalogue no: **UP 1045**

TOWN WITHOUT PITY
Tracks: / Town without pity.
7" Single: Released Mar '62, on H.M.V., by EMI Records. Deleted '65. Catalogue no: **POP 952**

YOURS UNTIL TOMORROW
Tracks: / Yours until tomorrow.
7" Single: Released Nov '68, on Stateside, by EMI Records. Deleted '71. Catalogue no: **SS 2131**

Pits

THERE'S ALWAYS SOMETHING THERE TO REMIND ME
Tracks: / There's always something there to remind me / Botswana beach dance.
7" Single: Released Jun '81, on Zilch, by Zilch Records. Deleted Jun '84. Catalogue no: **ZILCH 5**

Pitt, William

CITY LIGHTS
Tracks: / City lights.
7" Single: Released 31 Oct '87, on Sierra, by Sierra Records. Catalogue no: **FED 41**
12" Single: Released 31 Oct '87, on Sierra, by Sierra Records. Catalogue no: **FED 41 T**

Pixies

GIGANTIC
Tracks: / Gigantic / River Euphrates / Vamos / Heaven (Lady in the radiator song).
Note: 4-track EP.
CD 5": Released 30 Aug '88, on 4AD, by 4AD Records. Catalogue no: **BAD 805CD**
12" Single: Released 30 Aug '88, on 4AD, by 4AD Records. Catalogue no: **BAD 805**

HERE COMES YOUR MAN
Tracks: / Here comes my man / Into the white / Wave of mutilation / Bailey's walk.
CD 5": Released Jun '89, on 4AD, by 4AD Records. Catalogue no: **AD 909 CD**
7" Single: Released Jun '89, on 4AD, by 4AD Records. Catalogue no: **AD 909**
12" Single: Released Jun '89, on 4AD, by 4AD Records. Catalogue no: **BAD 909**

MONKEY GONE TO HEAVEN
Tracks: / Monkey gone to heaven.
CD 5": Released 27 Feb '89, on 4AD, by 4AD Records. Catalogue no: **BAD 904 CD**
7" Single: Released 27 Feb '89, on 4AD, by 4AD Records. Catalogue no: **AD 904**
12" Single: Released 27 Feb '89, on 4AD, by 4AD Records. Catalogue no: **BAD 904**

Pizarrio, Kevin

LONELINESS
Tracks: / Loneliness.
CD 5": Released Feb '89, on Champion, by Champion Records. Catalogue no: **CHAMPX 1293**
7" Single: Released Nov '88, on Champion, by Champion Records. Catalogue no: **CHAMP 93**
12" Single: Released Nov '88, on Champion, by Champion Records. Catalogue no: **CHAMP 1293**

P.J.O.

DON'T JIVE ME
Tracks: / Don't jive me / You cheat on me.
7" Single: Released '82, on DJM, Catalogue no: **DJS 10968**

Placebo

PAYING HOMAGE
Tracks: / Paying homage.
7" Single: Released Mar '82, on Aura Records, by Aura Records. Deleted '88. Catalogue no: **AUS 131**

POPPY DANCE
Tracks: / Poppy dance.
7" Single: Released Jun '82, on Aura Records, by Aura Records. Deleted '88. Catalogue no: **AUS 133**

Plague

OUT WITH ME ALL NIGHT
Tracks: / Out with me all night / Er? / I don't want to be ike Jimmy.
7" Single: Released Apr '80, on Evolution, by Evolution Records. Deleted '83. Catalogue no: **EV 4**

Plague Dogs

I DON'T FEEL NO PAIN ANYMORE
Tracks: / I don't feel no pain anymore / Rowf / Snitter run to the sea.
7" Single: Released Nov '82, on CBS, by CBS Records. Deleted Nov '85. Catalogue no: **A 2917**

Plague Of Fools

FOOLS ALL DAY
Tracks: / Fools all day.
12" Single: Released Mar '85, on Partizan Pestilenti, Catalogue no: **PART 001**

HEART OF HEARTS
Tracks: / Heart of hearts.
12" Single: Released Aug '85, on Partizan Pestilenti, Catalogue no: **PART 002**

Plain Characters

MENIAL TASKS
Tracks: / Menial tasks / Conversation piece.
7" Single: Released Nov '81, on Abstract, by Abstract Sounds. Catalogue no: **ABS 005**

Plain Clothes

AH FEELING RO ROCK
Tracks: / Ah feeling ro rock.
12" Single: Released Feb '89, on Hot Vinyl, Catalogue no: **HVT 54**

MAXI TAXI
Tracks: / Maxi taxi.
12" Single: Released Dec '84, on Charlie's, Catalogue no: **CRD 013**

Plain Jane

ONE LOOK
Tracks: / One look / Loving you.
7" Single: Released Aug '81, on Avatar, by Avatar Record Corporation. Catalogue no: **AAA 102**

TOO SERIOUS
Tracks: / Too serious / Made in Hong Kong.
7" Single: Released Jan '81, on Creole, by Creole Records. Deleted Jan '84. Catalogue no: **CR 220**

Plain Sailing

EASY
Tracks: / Easy / Northbound train.
7" Single: Released Apr '80, on Chrysalis, by Chrysalis Records. Deleted '83. Catalogue no: **CHS 2386**

SATELLITE
Tracks: / Satellite / Call your name.
7" Single: Released Jun '80, on Chrysalis, by Chrysalis Records. Deleted '83. Catalogue no: **CHS 2433**

Plan B

I DON'T KNOW
Tracks: / I don't know.
7" Single: Released Sep '84, on Racket Manufacture, Catalogue no: **RKT 1**

Planer,Nigel

ROUGH WITH THE SMOOTH
Tracks: / Rough with the smooth (Side A) / Nicholas Craig and Max (Nigel Planer,Nicholas Craig and Max(Hugh Cornwall)).
7" Single: Released '86, on Columbia, by EMI Records. Catalogue no: **DB 9140**

Planet Ha Ha

HOME
Tracks: / Home / Home (part 2).
7" Single: Released Nov '82, on EMI, by EMI Records. Deleted Nov '85. Catalogue no: **EMI 5358**

Planet P Project

WHY ME
Tracks: / Why me.
7" Single: Released May '83, on Geffen, by Geffen Records (USA). Catalogue no: **A 3204**
12" Single: Released May '83, on Geffen, by Geffen Records (USA). Catalogue no: **TA 3204**

Planet Patrol

Biographical details: Planet Patrol The club hit *Cheap Thrills* gave this American all male band a one off UK chart entry in 1983 - the single reached No.64. The record was notable for the state of the art production techniques by engineering/mixing svengali Arthur Baker, one of the key names in Eighties disco music. (Bob Macdonald 6/3/86)
In 1982, independent producer, Arthur Baker, took an 'already successful' recording act in Boston, Massachusetts, and with them developed an exciting and highly unusual entertainment concept. Planet Patrol consist of five superb singers, a futuristic sound and songs that won't let you sit down. Planet Patrol's career was beginning to take off, but it was not until later that same year, when the group released their first single on Polydor Records, that their career was launched into orbit. The hit song *Play at your own risk* skyrocketed to the top of Billboard's US R&B charts in just a few weeks, making Planet Patrol an overnight success. Success is not stranger to the five men who make up the Planet Patrol squad. Melvin Franklin, Rodney Butler, Michael Jones, Herb Jackson and Joseph Lite have all had many previous successes, both as international entertainers and as former recording artists for Atlantic Records. (Polydor Records, August 1983).

CHEAP THRILLS
Tracks: / Cheap thrills.
7" Single: Released Sep '83, on Polydor, by Polydor Ltd. Deleted '86. Catalogue no: **POSP 639**

PLAY AT YOUR OWN RISK
Tracks: / Play at your own risk / Rock at your own risk.
7" Single: Released Nov '82, on 21 Records, by Polydor Ltd. Catalogue no: **POSP 535**
12" Single: Released Nov '82, on 21 Records, by Polydor Ltd. Deleted '85. Catalogue no: **POSPX 535**

Planet Wilson

TAKEN FOR A RIDE
Tracks: / Taken for a ride.
7" Single: Released Jan '89, on Records Of Achievement, Catalogue no: **PLAN 2**
12" Single: Released Jan '89, on Records Of Achievement, Catalogue no: **12PLAN 2**

WHITE LIES
Tracks: / White lies / Vision on / Big wheel, The (12" only).
7" Single: Released 7 Mar '88, on Virgin, by Virgin Records. Catalogue no: **VS 1053**
12" Single: Released 7 Mar '88, on Virgin, by Virgin Records. Catalogue no: **VST 1053**

Planets

Biographical details: *Lines* (1979) and *Don't Look Down* (1980) provided this all male British band with a couple of modest UK hit singles. They were signed to Rialto Records, but could not quite match the success of their stablemates, the Korgis. (Bob Macdonald 6/3/86).

BREAK IT TO ME GENTLY
Tracks: / Break it to me gently / Minute ago.
7" Single: Released Jan '80, on Rialto (1), by Rialto Records. Deleted Jan '83. Catalogue no: **TREB 114**

DON'T LOOK DOWN
Tracks: / Don't look down / I wanna touch you.
7" Single: Released Oct '80, on Rialto (1), by Rialto Records. Deleted '83. Catalogue no: **TREB 116**

INTENSIVE CARE
Tracks: / Intensive care / Earth.
7" Single: Released Feb '81, on Rialto (1), by Rialto Records. Deleted Feb '84. Catalogue no: **TREB 133**

LET ME FALL
Tracks: / Let me fall / Follow the leader.
7" Single: Released Apr '81, on Rialto (1), by Rialto Records. Deleted '85. Catalogue no: **TREB 135**

LINES
Tracks: / Lines.
7" Single: Released Aug '79, on Rialto (1), by Rialto Records. Deleted '82. Catalogue no: **TREB 104**

PLANETS
Tracks: / Too late / Lines / Break it to me gently / Iron for the iron.
12" Single: Released Apr '80, on Rialto (1), by Rialto Records. Deleted Apr '83. Catalogue no: **TREB 501**

Planning By Numbers

LIVING NEON
Tracks: / Living neon / Kinetic.
7" Single: Released Dec '82, on Beggars Banquet, by Beggars Banquet Records. Deleted Jan '88. Catalogue no: **BEG 72**

Plant, Robert

Biographical details: Former Led Zeppelin vocalist Plant issued highly successful solo albums in America and in his native Britain with *Pictures At Eleven* and *The Principle Of Moments*. Principle, released in 1983, contained the hit single *Big Log*, a pensive track which was acclaimed, though questions were asked as to why it was called *Big Log* when the words appeared nowhere in the lyrics. Plant took an unexpected musical

PLASMATICS - MONKEY SUIT (Released on Stiff)

direction in late '84, when he became the front-man of a part-time band called the Honeydrippers. The all-star line-up featured the talents of former Led Zep colleague Jimmy Page plus Jeff Beck and famed US producer Nile Rodgers. Their remake of Phil Phillips & The Twilights' 1959 hit *Sea Of Love* reached No 3 on the US chart, just one place lower than the original; it also reached No 1 on the Billboard adult contemporary (MoR) listing, an unprecedented feat for Page and Plant, the pioneers of heavy metal. This achievement may have cost Plant the support of some of his rock fans, for his 1985 solo album did not fare as well as its predecessors. The surviving members of Led Zeppelin reformed for Live Aid in July 1985. (Bob MacDonald, March 1986.).

BIG LOG
Tracks: / Big log.
7" Single: Released Jul '83, on WEA, by WEA Records. Catalogue no: **B 9848**
12" Single: Released Jul '83, on WEA, by WEA Records. Catalogue no: **B 9848 T**

BURNING DOWN ONE SIDE
Tracks: / Burning down one side / Moonlight.
7" Single: Released Sep '82, on Swansong, Catalogue no: **SSK 19429**
12" Single: Released Sep '82, on Swansong, Catalogue no: **SSK 19249 T**

HEAVEN KNOWS
Tracks: / Heaven knows / Walking toward paradise.
7" Single: Released Jan '88, on Es Paranza (USA), Catalogue no: **A 9373**
12" Single: Released Jan '88, on Es Paranza (USA), Catalogue no: **A 9373 T**

IN THE MOOD
Tracks: / In the mood / Pledge pin.
7" Single: Released Nov '83, on Es Paranza (USA), Catalogue no: **PLANT 2**
12" Single: Released Jan '84, on Es Paranza (USA), Catalogue no: **B 6970 T**

LITTLE BY LITTLE
Tracks: / Little by little.
7" Single: Released Aug '85, on Es Paranza (USA), Catalogue no: **B 9621**
12" Single: Released Aug '85, on Es Paranza (USA), Catalogue no: **B 9621 T**

PINK AND BLACK
Tracks: / Pink and black / Trouble your money.
7" Single: Released May '85, on Es Paranza (USA), Catalogue no: **B 9640**
12" Single: Released May '85, on Es Paranza (USA), Catalogue no: **B 9640 T**

SHIP OF FOOLS
Tracks: / Ship of fools / Helen of Troy / Heaven knows (live) (Only on 12") / Dimples (live) (Only on CD single).
CD 5": Released Sep '88, on Atlantic, by WEA Records. Catalogue no: **A 9281 CD**
7" Single: Released Sep '88, on Atlantic, by WEA Records. Catalogue no: **A 9281**
12" Single: Released Sep '88, on Atlantic, by WEA Records. Catalogue no: **A 9281 T**

TALL COOL ONE
Tracks: / Tall cool one / White, clean and neat.
7" Single: Released May '88, on Atlantic, by WEA Records. Catalogue no: **A 9348**
12" Single: Released May '88, on Atlantic, by WEA Records. Catalogue no: **A 9348 T**

Plasmatics

Biographical details: At the time of their UK chart success, this American rock band consisted of Wes Beach, Jean Beauvoir, Stu Deutsch, Richard Stotts and Wendy O. Williams. Fronted by the outrageous and controversial Williams, the Plasmatics took the most brash elements of punk and heavy metal and wielded them into a startling, blatantly sexual stage spectacle. They were conceived in New York in 1979 and attracted a cult following in Britain in 1980 which resulted in the single *Butcher Baby* and the album *New Hope For The Wretched* reaching No 55 on their respective UK charts. Thereafter they attracted controversy on both sides of the Atlantic, though never becoming a major chart force. One of Williams' many crazy antics was a duet with Lemmy, of Motorhead: the pair recorded a cover version of Tammy Wynette's *Stand By Your Man...* (Bob MacDonald, March 1986.).

BUTCHER BABY
Tracks: / Butcher baby.
7" Single: Released Jun '80, on Stiff, by Stiff Records. Catalogue no: **BUY 76**
12" Single: Released Jun '80, on Stiff, by Stiff Records. Catalogue no: **BUYIT 76**

MONKEY SUIT (See panel above)
Tracks: / Monkey suit / Squirm.
7" Single: Released Sep '80, on Stiff, by Stiff Records. Catalogue no: **BUY 91**

Plastic Bertrand

CA PLANE POUR MOI
Tracks: / Ca plane pour moi.
7" Single: Released May '78, on Sire, by Sire Records. Deleted '81. Catalogue no: **6078 616**

SHA LA LA LA LEE
Tracks: / Sha-la-la-la-lee.
7" Single: Released Aug '78, on Vertigo, by Phonogram Ltd. Deleted '81. Catalogue no: **6059 209**

Plastic Flies

SENSE OF TIME
Tracks: / Sense of time / Millions just like you.
7" Single: Released Oct '82, on Y Finto, Catalogue no: **SHARP 1**

Plastic Ono Band

Biographical details: Though credited on many John Lennon records, the Plastic Ono Band was a figment of the weird imaginations of John and Yoko. The band never existed as a conventional working line-up but was merely an umbrella title for whichever musicians and friends happened to be playing on the records. The name was launched on the classic 1969 single *Give Peace A Chance*, which was recorded in a Montreal hotel bedroom by Lennon and Ono plus an army of musical and non-musical friends and acquaintances. The catch-all nature of the Plastic Ono Band was emphasised at the project's press launch -- journalists who arrived expecting the unveiling of an exciting new rock band merely saw themselves on a large film screen. (Bob MacDonald, March 1986.).

POWER TO THE PEOPLE
Tracks: / Power to the people.
7" Single: Released '80, on Apple, by Apple Records. Catalogue no: **LR 1861**

Plastic Penny

EVERYTHING I AM
Tracks: / Everything I am.
7" Single: Released Jan '68, on Page One, by Page One Records. Deleted '71. Catalogue no: **POF 051**

Plastic Surgery

TORMENT
Tracks: / Surgery looks nice (at a price).
7" Single: Released Jan '87, on Watch Out!, by Watch Out Records. Catalogue no: **PSG 1**

Plasticland

EUPHORIC TRAPDOOR BLUES
Tracks: / Euphoric trapdoor blues.
7" Single: Released Mar '84, on Scadillac (USA), Catalogue no: **SC 05**

Plastics

DIAMOND HEAD
Tracks: / Diamond head / Peace.
7" Single: Released Apr '81, on Island, by Island Records. Deleted '85. Catalogue no: **NIP 1**

Platinum Blonde

DOESN'T REALLY MATTER
Tracks: / Doesn't really matter / All fall down.
7" Single: Released Jul '84, on Epic, by CBS Records. Catalogue no: **A 4454**

Platinum Hook

STANDING ON THE VERGE OF GETTING IT ON
Tracks: / Standing on the verge of getting it on.
7" Single: Released Sep '78, on Motown, by BMG Records (UK). Deleted '81. Catalogue no: **TMG 1115**

Platters

Biographical details: At the time of their greatest success, this American vocal group comprised Tony Williams, David Lynch, Herbert Reed, Paul Robi and Zola Taylor, a line-up that stabilised in 1954, a year after the group's formation. They were managed by Buck Ram, a domineering individual who also served as the group's producer. Under his supervision the Platters became one of the first black acts to break out of the rhythm-and-blues ghetto in which US radio and charts kept black music during the 50's -- and they were the first black group to reach No 1 on the American pop charts. Regarded as a vital part of the rock 'n' roll era -- though their forte was the big ballad -- they enjoyed a long stretch of American hits during the last five years of the 60's, including four No 1 smashes, *The Great Pretender* and *My Prayer* (both '56), *Twilight Time* ('58) and *Smoke Gets In Your Eyes* ('59). The latter, a revival of the 1933 Jerome Kern-Otto Harbach standard, was also a chart-topper in Britain. Another Platters smash on both sides of the Atlantic was *Only You*, successfully revived in the mid-70's by Ringo Starr. Shortly after their classic rendition of *Smoke Gets In Your Eyes* the Platters' career was impaired by a sex-and-drugs scandal. The four male members were accused -- and later acquitted -- of soliciting prostitutes and taking drugs, charges which tarnished their image. A bigger blow, however, was the 1960 exit of the strong lead singer, Tony Williams. After a couple of other personnel changes, the Platters chalked up two comeback hits in the American Top Forty in 1966 and 1967. (Bob MacDonald, March 1986.) USA vocal group of the 1950's created by vocal coach Buck Ram, who was born in Chicago in 1907. He was a successful songwriter and arranger during the Swing Era, formed a talent agency in Los Angeles in 1954; his group the Penguins were the first black vocal group of the era to reach the pop top 10 with *Earth Angel* in 1955, but the Platters were far more successful. Ram took them from Ralph Bass's Federal label, where they had recorded Ram's song *Only you*; by the time they had recorded for Mercury (in a deal that included the Penguins, who never had another hit) the lineup included lead singer Tony Williams (born in 1928 in Elizabeth, New Jersey), David Lynch (1929-81), Hebert Reed, Paul Robi and Zola Taylor, whom Ram had added from another of his acts (called Shirley Gunther and the Queens), making an unusual lineup then of four guys and a girl. They re-recorded *Only you*, this time reaching the No.1 R&B slot and No.5 in the pop chart (despite a white cover by the Hilltoppers), their next, *The great pretender*, was No.1 in both charts, still in 1955: it is an immortal hit or the era, further immortalised in being satirised by Stan Freberg for its slow 'kling-kling-kling' piano, and more recently by a fine, impressionist rendering as the title track of an album by trumpeter Lester Bowie. Their records were the best smooch records of the decade for slow dancing at parties; they were the first black act of the era to reach No.1 in the pop chart and helped smash the industry's white monopoly through covers. 35 Hot 100 hits on Mercury through '62 incl. *(You've got) The magic touch*, old standards *My Prayer*, *Twilight time* (with words by Ram), *Smoke gets in your eyes* (by Jerome Kern and Otto Harbach), *Harbor Lights*, *I'll never smile again*, *To each his own*, *If I didn't care*, etc. Four of these were also Top 10 in the UK. The group retained a cleancut image even though members were arraigned on vice charges in 1959 (aquitted). Williams left in 1961, but they came back for a few more hits on Musicor '66-7 with Sonny Turner singing lead. Subsequently there were many editions of the group; Ram had tried to prevent the Ink Spots syndrome by setting up The Five Platters Inc. in 1956, with members of the group owning shares but not allowed to use the name when they left, but it didn't work: lawsuits and injunctions were flying in the 1980's. The original recordings sold 50,000,000 records, are now the property of Polydor (Mercury, Phillips, etc)..

6 TRACK HITS
Tracks: / Great pretender, The / Only you / Smoke gets in your eyes / I'm sorry / Twilight time / My prayer.
7" EP: Released Sep '83, on Scoop 33, by Pickwick Records. Catalogue no: **7SR 5006**

GREAT PRETENDER
Tracks: / Great pretender, The / Only you.
78 rpm: Released '56, on Mercury (Pye), Deleted '58. Catalogue no: **MT 117**

HARBOUR LIGHTS
Tracks: / Harbour lights.
7" Single: Released Jan '60, on Mercury (EMI), Deleted '63. Catalogue no: **AMT 1081**

I'M SORRY
Tracks: / I'm sorry.
78 rpm: Released '57, on Mercury (Pye), Deleted '58. Catalogue no: **MT 145**

MY PRAYER
Tracks: / My prayer.
78 rpm: Released '56, on Mercury (Pye), Deleted '58. Catalogue no: **MT 120**

ONLY YOU (OLD GOLD)
Tracks: / Only you / Great pretender, The.
7" Single: Released Jun '88, on Old Gold, by Old Gold Records. Catalogue no: **OG 9485**

ONLY YOU (SINGLE)
Tracks: / Only you.
7" Single: Released '80, on Mercury, by Phonogram Ltd. Catalogue no: **LR 8234**

REMEMBER WHEN (SINGLE)
Tracks: / Remember when.
7" Single: Released Aug '59, on Mercury (EMI), Deleted '62. Catalogue no: **AMT 1053**

SMOKE GETS IN YOUR EYES
Tracks: / Smoke gets in your eyes.
7" Single: Released '80, on Mercury, by Phonogram Ltd. Catalogue no: **LR 8142**
7" Single: Released Jan '59, on Mercury (EMI), Deleted '62. Catalogue no: **AMT 1016**

SMOKE GETS IN YOUR EYES (OLD GOLD)
Tracks: / Smoke gets in your eyes.
7" Single: Released Jan '85, on Old Gold, by Old Gold Records. Catalogue no: **OG 9486**

TWILIGHT TIME
Tracks: / Twilight time.
78 rpm: Released '58, on Mercury (Pye), Deleted '58. Catalogue no: **MT 214**

YOU'LL NEVER NEVER KNOW
Tracks: / You'll never never know / It isn't right.
78 rpm: Released '57, on Mercury (Pye), Deleted '58. Catalogue no: **MT 130**

Play

CHASING THE SUN
Tracks: / Chasing the sun / This little girl / Deeper than blue.
12" Single: Released Oct '82, on Survival (1), by Survival Records. Catalogue no: **SUR 12 008**

IN MY MIND
Tracks: / In my mind.
7" Single: Released Jun '84, on Survival (1), by Survival Records. Catalogue no: **SUR 022**
12" Single: Released Jun '84, on Survival (1), by Survival Records. Catalogue no: **SUR 12 022**

YOU DON'T LOOK THE SAME

Tracks: / You don't look the same.
7" Single: Released Aug '83, on Survival (1), by Survival Records. Catalogue no: **SUR 015**
12" Single: Released Aug '83, on Survival (1), by Survival Records. Catalogue no: **SUR 12 015**

Play Dead

BREAK
Tracks: / Break / Bloodstains.
7" Single: Released Apr '84, on Clay, by Clay Records. Deleted '88. Catalogue no: **CLAY 31**
12" Single: Released Apr '84, on Clay, by Clay Records. Deleted '88. Catalogue no: **12 CLAY 31**

BURNING DOWN
Tracks: / Burning down.
12" Single: Released Apr '86, on Tanz, Catalogue no: **TANZ 2**

CONSPIRACY
Tracks: / Conspiracy.
7" Single: Released Oct '84, on Clay, by Clay Records. Deleted '88. Catalogue no: **CLAY 40**
12" Single: Released Oct '84, on Clay, by Clay Records. Catalogue no: **12 CLAY 40**

IN THE BEGINNING
Tracks: / In the beginning / 1981 singles, The / Poison takes a hold / Introduction / T.V. eye / Final epitaph.
12" Single: Released Feb '86, on Jungle, by Jungle Records. Catalogue no: **JUNG 26T**

ISABEL
Tracks: / Isabel / Solace.
7" Single: Released May '84, on Clay, by Clay Records. Deleted '88. Catalogue no: **CLAY 35**
12" Single: Released May '84, on Clay, by Clay Records. Deleted '88. Catalogue no: **12 CLAY 35**

POISON TAKES A HOLD
Tracks: / Poison takes a hold.
7" Single: Released Jan '84, on Fresh, by Jetstar Records. Catalogue no: **FRESH 29**

PROPAGANDA
Tracks: / Propaganda.
7" Single: Released Nov '82, on Jungle, by Jungle Records. Catalogue no: **JUNG 2**
12" Single: Released Sep '84, on Jungle, by Jungle Records. Catalogue no: **JUNG 17**

SACROSANCT
Tracks: / Sacrosanct.
7" Single: Released Feb '85, on Clay, by Clay Records. Catalogue no: **CLAY 42**
12" Single: Released Feb '85, on Clay, by Clay Records. Catalogue no: **12 CLAY 42**

SHINE
Tracks: / Shine / Promise / Gaze.
7" Single: Released Sep '83, on Situation 2, by Beggars Banquet Records. Catalogue no: **SIT 28**
12" Single: Released Sep '83, on Situation 2, by Beggars Banquet Records. Catalogue no: **SIT 28T**

THIS SIDE OF HEAVEN
Tracks: / This side of heaven.
12" Single: Released Sep '85, on Tanz, Catalogue no: **TANZ 1**

T.V. EYE
Tracks: / T.V. eye / Final epitath.
7" Single: Released Jan '84, on Fresh, by Jetstar Records. Catalogue no: **FRESH 38**

Playback

SPACE INVADERS
Tracks: / Space invaders / Menacing glow in the sky.
7" Single: Released Dec '80, on WEA, by WEA Records. Deleted Dec '85. Catalogue no: **K70002**

Player

AM I A DREAMER
Tracks: / Am I a dreamer / I'll never forget you / I'll cry for you tonight (Extra track on 12" version only).
7" Single: Released Apr '86, on Rainbow, by Rainbow Records. Catalogue no: **RBR 5**
12" Single: Released Apr '86, on Rainbow, by Rainbow Records. Catalogue no: **RBR 512**

BABY COME BACK
Tracks: / Baby come back.
7" Single: Released Feb '78, on RSO, by Polydor Ltd. Deleted '81. Catalogue no: **RSO 2090 254**

IT'S FOR YOU
Tracks: / It's for you / Tip of the iceberg.
7" Single: Released Aug '80, on Casablanca, by PolyGram UK Ltd. Deleted '83. Catalogue no: **CAN 202**

Player, M.C.

RHYMING RAMPAGE
Tracks: / Rhyming rampage.
12" Single: Released Sep '87, on 4 Sight (USA), Catalogue no: **FS 68719**

Player One

SPACE INVADERS
Tracks: / Space invaders / Menacing glow in the sky.
7" Single: Released Mar '80, on WEA, by WEA Records. Deleted '83. Catalogue no: **K 70002**

Players Association

Biographical details: The pedestrian but infectious single *Turn The Music Up* gave this American disco group a British smash in 1979. It reached the UK No 8 position and was followed by the minor hits *Ride The Groove* and *We Got The Groove. Turn The Music Up* clicked at the height of the disco boom, when the beats per minute were far more important than the melody of the song or the faces of the band. (Bob MacDonald, March 1986.).

GET DOWN MELLOW MELLOW SOUND
Tracks: / Get down mellow mellow sound / More than a little bit.
7" Single: Released Mar '80, on Vanguard, by Start Records Ltd.. Deleted Mar '83. Catalogue no: **VS 5017**
12" Single: Released Mar '80, on Vanguard, by Start Records Ltd.. Deleted Mar '83. Catalogue no: **VSL 5017**

GET ON UP NOW
Tracks: / Get on up now / Let your body go.
7" Single: Released May '81, on Vanguard, by Start Records Ltd.. Deleted May '84. Catalogue no: **VSL 5020**

RIDE THE GROOVE
Tracks: / Ride the groove.
7" Single: Released May '79, on Vanguard, by Start Records Ltd.. Deleted '82. Catalogue no: **VS 5012**

TURN THE MUSIC UP (OLD GOLD)
Tracks: / Turn the music up / Ride the groove / Get down mellow sound, The.
12" Single: Released 28 Aug '89, on Old Gold, by Old Gold Records. Catalogue no: **OG 4130**

TURN THE MUSIC UP (SINGLE)
Tracks: / Turn the music up.
7" Single: Released Mar '79, on Vanguard, by Start Records Ltd.. Deleted '82. Catalogue no: **VS 5011**

WE GOT THE GROOVE
Tracks: / We got the groove / I like it.
7" Single: Released Feb '80, on Vanguard, by Start Records Ltd.. Deleted '83. Catalogue no: **VS 5016**

Playground

SEEKING THE TRUTH
Tracks: / Seeking the truth / Violence for violence sake / Final.
7" Single: Released Aug '88, on 4th. Dimension, by 4th. Dimension Records. Catalogue no: **FDS 18**

Playing At Trains

WALK ON WATER
Tracks: / Walk on water.
7" Single: Released May '89, on Octopus, Catalogue no: **OCT 5**

WORLD WITHOUT LOVE, A
Tracks: / World without love.
7" Single: Released '80, on IMS, by Polydor Ltd. Catalogue no: **LR 1860**
7" Single: Released May '87, on Idea, by Idea Records. Catalogue no: **IDT 001**

Playmates

WASTED YEARS
Tracks: / Wasted years.
7" Single: Released Jun '86, on What Goes On, by What Goes On Records. Catalogue no: **GOES ON 07**

Playn Jayn

I LOVE YOU LIKE I LOVE MYSELF
Tracks: / I love you like I love myself.
7" Single: Released Aug '85, on ABC (indie), Catalogue no: **ABCS 007**
12" Single: Released Aug '85, on ABC (indie), Catalogue no: **ABCS 007T**

JULIETTE
Tracks: / Juliette / Something died / Strange.
7" Single: Released Mar '85, on A&M, by A&M Records. Deleted '88. Catalogue no: **AM 241**
12" Single: Released Mar '85, on A&M, by A&M Records. Deleted '88. Catalogue no: **AMY 241**

Plaza

DON'T LOOK BACK
Tracks: / Don't look back.
7" Single: Released Nov '85, on Record Shack, by Record Shack Records. Catalogue no: **SOHO 54**
7" Single: Released Jul '86, on Record Shack, by Record Shack Records. Catalogue no: **SOHO 70**
12" Single: Released Nov '85, on Record Shack, by Record Shack Records. Catalogue no: **SOHOT 54**
12" Single: Released Jul '86, on Record Shack, by Record Shack Records. Catalogue no: **SOHOT 70**

MOVING ON
Tracks: / Moving on.
7" Single: Released Jul '85, on Record Shack, by Record Shack Records. Catalogue no: **SOHO 50**
12" Single: Released Jul '85, on Record Shack, by Record Shack Records. Catalogue no: **SOHOT 50**

Plaza, Martin

CONCRETE AND CLAY
Tracks: / Concrete and clay / New shoes / I could be so good (Extra track on 12" version only) / Concrete and clay / New suit.
7" Single: Released Jul '86, on Epic, by CBS Records. Deleted Aug '87. Catalogue no: **A 7274**
12" Single: Released Jul '86, on Epic, by CBS Records. Deleted Aug '87. Catalogue no: **TA 7274**

Please Y'self

DON'T GIMME NON O' THAT COYOTE
Tracks: / Don't gimme non o' that coyote.
7" Single: Released Feb '85, on Green Fringe, by Green Fringe Records. Catalogue no: **SKIFF 85**

POISON SONG, THE
Tracks: / Poison song, The.
7" Single: Released Feb '87, on Green Fringe, by Green Fringe Records. Catalogue no: **SKIFF 871**

SKIFFLE PARTY
Tracks: / Skiffle party.
7" Single: Released Feb '84, on Green Fringe, by Green Fringe Records. Catalogue no: **S83 CUS 2029**

SURFIN' UK
Tracks: / Surfin' UK.
7" Single: Released Aug '84, on Green Fringe, by Green Fringe Records. Catalogue no: **SKIFF 841**

Pleasurama

COME DANCE WITH ME
Tracks: / Come dance with me / Modern times.
7" Single: Released May '85, on Sedition, by Sedition Records. Catalogue no: **EDIT 3301**
12" Single: Released May '85, on Sedition, by Sedition Records. Catalogue no: **EDITL 3301**

MAGGIE
Tracks: / Maggie / Forever amber.
7" Single: Released May '87, on D & M, Catalogue no: **DMR 001**

TEMPTATION
Tracks: / Temptation / Stop the world / Modern times (Extra track on 12" version only).
7" Single: Released Oct '86, on Sedition, by Sedition Records. Catalogue no: **EDIT 3318**
12" Single: Released Oct '86, on Sedition, by Sedition Records. Catalogue no: **EDITL 3318**

Pleasure

PAIN
Tracks: / Pain / Basic black / Yield not to temptation / Remember you're.
CD 5": Released Jun '89, on Anxious, by Anxious Records. Catalogue no: **CSNERV 7**
7" Single: Released Jun '89, on Anxious, by Anxious Records. Catalogue no: **NERV 7**
12" Single: Released Jun '89, on Anxious, by Anxious Records. Catalogue no: **NERVT 7**

YELLOWFIELD
Tracks: / Yellowfield / Don't stop to think about it.
CD 5": Released Sep '89, on Anxious, by Anxious Records. Catalogue no: **CDNERV 9**
7" Single: Released Sep '89, on Anxious, by Anxious Records. Catalogue no: **NERV 9**
12" Single: Released Sep '89, on Anxious, by Anxious Records. Catalogue no: **NERVT 9**

Pleasure Crew

I COULD BE SO GOOD FOR YOU
Tracks: / I could be so goos for you.
12" Single: Released Jun '87, on Factory (1), by Factory Records. Catalogue no: **FAC 169**

Pleasure Garden

ON A MIDNIGHT PICNIC
Tracks: / On a midnight picnic.
7" Single: Released 27 Jun '86, on Don't Knock Your Granny While...., by Don't Knock Your Granny While..... Deleted '88. Catalogue no: **4TH SHAVE**

Pleasure Pump

FANTASISE ME
Tracks: / Pleasure pump.
7" Single: Released Jun '87, on Serious, by Serious Records. Catalogue no: **7OUS 6**
12" Single: Released Jun '87, on Serious, by Serious Records. Catalogue no: **OUS 6**

Pleasure & The Beast

DOCTOR SEX
Tracks: / Doctor Sex.
7" Single: Released May '83, on Carrere America (USA), by PolyGram Rec.Inc.(USA). Catalogue no: **CAR 276**
12" Single: Released May '83, on Carrere America (USA), by PolyGram Rec.Inc.(USA). Catalogue no: **CART 276**

GOD'S EMPTY CHAIR
Tracks: / God's empty chair / Sometimes.
12" Single: Released Jun '84, on Carrere, Catalogue no: **CART 326**

Pleasure Thieves

CHASING THE RUNAWAY
Tracks: / Chasing the runaway.
7" Single: Released Apr '89, on Minta, by Minta Records. Catalogue no: **MINTA 1**

Pleasure Zone

ALL THE KINGS HORSES
Tracks: / All the king's horses / My baby talks to me.
7" Single: Released Mar '84, on Carrere, Catalogue no: **CAR 305**
12" Single: Released Mar '84, on Carrere, Catalogue no: **CART 305**

Pleasureheads

DON'T FAKE IT
Tracks: / Don't fake it.
7" Single: Released Jul '86, on Molesworth, by New Leaf Records. Catalogue no: **HUNTS 2**

HOLDING ON EP, THE
Tracks: / Holding on EP, The.
12" Single: Released Nov '86, on Ediesta, Catalogue no: **CALC 10**

TREASURE
Tracks: / Treasure.
12" Single: Released Aug '87, on Ediesta, Catalogue no: **CALC 025**

Pliers

HER LOVE IS BURNING
Tracks: / Her love is burning.
12" Single: Released Sep '88, on Pickout, Catalogue no: **PICK 10**

HOLIDAYS
Tracks: / Holidays.
7" Single: Released May '89, on Rockers Master International, Catalogue no: **UNKNOWN**

IN YOUR EYES
Tracks: / In your eyes.
12" Single: Released Apr '89, on Legal Lights, by Legal Light Records. Catalogue no: **LLQ 31**
12" Single: Released Feb '89, on Pickout, Catalogue no: **VPRD 377**

MURDER SHE WROTE
Tracks: / Murder she wrote.
7" Single: Released Oct '88, on Pioneer Muzik, Catalogue no: **PM 011**

SESSION LOVER
Tracks: / Session lover.
7" Single: Released 21 Apr '89, on Music Scene, Catalogue no: **TK 0094**

Plimsouls

MILLION MILES AWAY
Tracks: / Million miles away / I'll get lucky.
7" Single: Released May '82, on Bomp International, Catalogue no: **BOMP 2**

NOW
Tracks: / Now / When you find it.
7" Single: Released Apr '81, on Planet, Deleted Apr '86. Catalogue no: **K 12519**

Plod

LAUGHING POLICEMAN
Tracks: / Laughing policeman, The.
7" Single: Released Oct '83, on MFP, by EMI Records. Catalogue no: **FP 999**

Plop Plops

U THANT
Tracks: / U Thant.
7" Single: Released Sep '87, on Anhrefn, Catalogue no: **THANT 001**

Plum

TOO MUCH AIN'T ENOUGH (FAT IS BACK)
Tracks: / Too much ain't enough (fat is back).
7" Single: Released Mar '83, on Stiff, by Stiff

Records. Catalogue no: **FAT 1**
12" Single: Released Mar '83, on Stiff, by Stiff Records. Catalogue no: **FAT 112**

Plum And Youth

I GOT YOU BABE
Tracks: / I got you babe.
7" Single: Released Oct '84, on Checkmount, Catalogue no: **CHK 001**

Plummer, Paul

LOVE REVOLUTION
Tracks: / Love revolution / Love revolution (instrumental).
12" Single: Released Apr '86, on New Jerusalem, Catalogue no: **Unknown**

Plus One

IT'S HAPPENIN'
Tracks: / It's happenin'.
12" Single: Released Oct '89, on White Label (1), Catalogue no: **DJV 001**

Plush

FREE AND EASY
Tracks: / Free and easy.
12" Single: Released Feb '89, on UNKNOWN, Catalogue no: **PL 703**

Pluto

Biographical details: Pluto Jamaican singer Pluto Shervington took his gentle and infectious brand of comedy reggae into the British singles chart on three occasions. *Dat* climbed to No.6 in early 1976 and *Ram Goat Liver* peaked at No.43 in the same year. *Your Honour* was recorded at the same time as the other two hits, but had to wait until 1982 before reaching the UK Top 20. (Bob Macdonald 8/3/86).

I MAN BITTER
Tracks: / I man bitter / Bitterness.
7" Single: Released May '82, on KR, Catalogue no: **KR 7**
12" Single: Released May '82, on KR, Catalogue no: **KRT 7**

YOUR HONOUR
Tracks: / Your honour / No honour among tiefs.
7" Single: Released Jan '82, on KR, Catalogue no: **KR 4**
12" Single: Released Jan '82, on KR, Catalogue no: **KRT 4**

Plyers

BIAS THEM BIAS
Tracks: / Bias them bias.
12" Single: Released Jul '88, on Black Scorpio, Catalogue no: **VPRD 296**

SWEET SHERENE (SINGLE)
Tracks: / Sweet Sherene.
12" Single: Released Nov '88, on Dennis Star, Catalogue no: **DS 009**

Plytas, Nick

HOT SEGAS (EP)
Tracks: / Hot segas.
10" single: Released Oct '82, on Illuminated, Catalogue no: **ILL 1210**

PM

YOU GOT ME ROCKIN'
Tracks: / You got me rockin' / Go for it.
7" Single: Released Apr '80, on Ariola, by BMG Records (UK). Deleted Apr '83. Catalogue no: **ARO 217**

Poacher

ENGLAND FOREVER
Tracks: / England forever / Buttermarket.
7" Single: Released Mar '80, on RK, by RK Records. Deleted Mar '83. Catalogue no: **RK 1029**

SUZY LOVES YOU NO MORE
Tracks: / Suzy loves you no more.
7" Single: Released Nov '83, on Ritz, by Ritz Records. Catalogue no: **RITZ 054**

YOU ARE NO ANGEL
Tracks: / You are no angel / Look up to me.
7" Single: Released Nov '82, on Ritz, by Ritz Records. Catalogue no: **RITZ 030**
7" Single: Released Mar '86, on Ritz, by Ritz Records. Catalogue no: **RITZ 139**

Pocket Rockets

VIDEO KID KO
Tracks: / Video kid KO / Rock socket.
7" Single: Released May '87, on MCA, by MCA Records. Catalogue no: **MCA 1140**
12" Single: Released May '87, on MCA, by MCA Records. Catalogue no: **MCAT 1140**

Poco

Biographical details: Poco was a country rock band formed in 1968 by Buffalo Springfield alumni Richie Furay and Jim Messina. They recruited steel guitarist Rusty Young, who played on the last Springfield LP, and he recommended drummer George Grantham and bass player Randy Meisner, from

THE POGUES - MISTY MORNING, ALBERT BRIDGE (Released on WEA)

Colorado groups. The band was first called Pogo, after a comic strip, but its creator sued. They auditioned for Apple, then Epic. After their first album *Pickin' Up The Pieces* in '69, Meisner quit to join Rick Nelson and was replaced by Tim Schmit. Messina left after *Poco* and the live album *Deliverin' The Goods* ('70-'71), to be replaced by ex-Illinois Speed Press singer-guitarist Paul Cotton. This was the most creative line-up, with both Cotton and Furay being prolific songwriters. But Furay left after *From The Inside* ('71) and *A Good Feelin' To Know* and *Crazy Eyes* ('71-'73) to join ill-fated supergroup Souther Hillman Furay. Young's steel guitar helped replace Furay's voice in the vocal blend and with more changes they kept selling in the new, lucrative West Coast rock market. *Legend* in '78, was their top seller in America but earlier albums stayed the course as they descended into Eagles-style FM radio music. They broke up in 1982. Furay rejoined for a reunion album in 1984 on Atlantic, but it didn't sell. (Donald Clarke, May 1987.).

ROSE OF CIMARRON (SINGLE)
Tracks: / Rose of Cimarron / Legend.
7" Single: Released May '80, on MCA, by MCA Records. Deleted '83. Catalogue no: **MCA 589**

UNDER THE GUN
Tracks: / Under the gun / Reputation.
7" Single: Released Aug '80, on MCA, by MCA Records. Deleted '83. Catalogue no: **MCA 635**

Poeme Electronique

ECHOES FADE
Tracks: / Echoes fade / V.o.i.c.e..
7" Single: Released Mar '82, on Carrere America (USA), by PolyGram Rec.Inc.(USA). Catalogue no: **CAR 228**

Poesie Noire

RADIO ACTIVE FLOOD, THE
Tracks: / Radio active flood, The.
12" Single: Released Jun '88, on Antler, by Antler Records (Belgium). Catalogue no: **ANT 052**

TIMBER
Tracks: / Timber.
12" Single: Released Jun '88, on Antler, by Antler Records (Belgium). Catalogue no: **ANT 062**

TRAGEDY
Tracks: / Tragedy.
7" Single: Released '88, on Antler, by Antler Records (Belgium). Catalogue no: **ANT 074-7**

Poet, Peter

MY WAY
Tracks: / My way.
7" Single: Released Apr '89, on House, Catalogue no: **HWHT 1**

SONG FOR THE ANIMALS, A
7" Single: Released Sep '89, on Hits With Heart, Catalogue no: **UNKNOWN**

Poets

I LOVE HER STILL
Tracks: / I love her still.
7" Single: Released 8 Nov '88, on Bam Caruso, by Demon Records. Catalogue no: **OPRA 088**

NOW WE'RE THRU
Tracks: / Now we're thru.
7" Single: Released Oct '64, on Decca, by Decca Records. Deleted '67. Catalogue no: **F 11995**

Pogues

BOYS FROM THE COUNTRY HELL
Tracks: / Boys from the country hell / Repeal of the licensing laws.
7" Single: Released Oct '84, on Stiff, by Stiff Records. Catalogue no: **BUY 212**

DARK STREETS OF LONDON
Tracks: / Dark streets of London / Band played waltzing Matilda, The.
7" Single: Released Jun '84, on Stiff, by Stiff Records. Catalogue no: **BUY 207**

DIRTY OLD TOWN
Tracks: / Dirty old town / Pistol for Paddy Garcia, A / Parting glass, The.
7" Single: Released Aug '85, on Stiff, by Stiff Records. Catalogue no: **BUY 229**
12" Single: Released Aug '85, on Stiff, by Stiff Records. Catalogue no: **BUYIT 229**

FAIRYTALE OF NEW YORK
Tracks: / Fairytale of New York / Battle march / Shanne Bradley.
7" Single: Released 21 Nov '87, on Pogue Mahone, by Rough Trade Records. Catalogue no: **NY 7**
12" Single: Released 21 Nov '87, on Pogue Mahone, by Rough Trade Records. Catalogue no: **NY 12**
CD 5": Released 21 Nov '87, on Pogue Mahone, by Rough Trade Records. Catalogue no: **CDNY 1**

FIESTA
Tracks: / Fiesta / Sketches of Spain.
7" Single: Released Jul '88, on Pogue Mahone, by Rough Trade Records. Catalogue no: **FG 2**
12" Single: Released Jul '88, on Pogue Mahone, by Rough Trade Records. Catalogue no: **FG 212**

GOOD, THE BAD AND THE UGLY, THE
Tracks: / Good, the bad and the ugly, The / Rak at the gates of hell.
12" Single: Released Jun '87, on Hell, Catalogue no: **BLOODY 1**
7" Single: Released Jun '87, on Hell, Catalogue no: **BLOOD 1**

HAUNTED
Tracks: / Haunted / Junk theme / Hot dogs with everything (Extra track on 12" version only).
7" Single: Released Aug '86, on MCA, by MCA Records. Catalogue no: **MCA 1084**
12" Single: Released Aug '86, on MCA, by MCA Records. Catalogue no: **MCAT 1084**

IF I SHOULD FALL FROM GRACE WITH GOD(REMIX)
Tracks: / If I should fall from grace with God(Remix) / If I should fall from grace with God(7"Remix) / Sally Maclannan / Pair of brown eyes, A / Dirty old town (12" limited edition special bag only).
Special: Released 8 Mar '88, on Pogue Mahone, by Rough Trade Records. Catalogue no: **FGG 112**
7" Single: Released Feb '88, on Stiff, by Stiff Records. Catalogue no: **FG 1**
12" Single: Released Feb '88, on Stiff, by Stiff Records. Catalogue no: **FG 112**
CD 5": Released 7 Mar '88, on Stiff, by Stiff Records. Catalogue no: **CDFG 1**

IRISH ROVER, THE
Tracks: / Irish rover, The / Rare ould mountain dew, The / Dubliners fancy, The (Extra track on 12" version only.).
7" Single: Released Mar '87, on Stiff, by Stiff Records. Catalogue no: **BUY 258**
12" Single: Released Mar '87, on Stiff, by Stiff Records. Catalogue no: **BUYIT 258**

MISTY MORNING ALBERT BRIDGE (See panel opposite)
Tracks: / Cotton fields / Train of love (12" only) / Young ned of the hill (12" only) / Misty morning Albert bridge.
12" Single: Released Jun '89, on WEA, by WEA Records. Catalogue no: **YZ 407 TW**
Cassingle: Released Jun '89, on WEA, by WEA Records. Catalogue no: **YZ 407C**
7" Single: Released Jun '89, on WEA, by WEA Records. Catalogue no: **YZ 407X**
7" Single: Released Jun '89, on WEA, by WEA Records. Catalogue no: **YZ 407**
12" Single: Released Jun '89, on WEA, by WEA Records. Catalogue no: **YZ 407T**

PAIR OF BROWN EYES
Tracks: / Pair of brown eyes, A / Whiskey of a devil / Muirshin durkin.
7" Single: Released Mar '85, on Stiff, by Stiff Records. Catalogue no: **BUY 220**
12" Single: Released Mar '85, on Stiff, by Stiff Records. Catalogue no: **BUYIT 220**

POGUETRY IN MOTION EP; LONDON GIRL
Tracks: / Poguetry in motion / Body of an American, The / Rainy night, A / Planxy / Noel / Hill.
12" Single: Released Feb '86, on Stiff, by Stiff Records. Catalogue no: **BUYIT 243**
7" Single: Released Feb '86, on Stiff, by Stiff Records. Catalogue no: **BUY 243**

SALLY MACLANNAN
Tracks: / Sally Maclannan / Wild rover / Leaving of Liverpool (Exta track available on 12" version only.).
12" Single: Released Jun '85, on Stiff, by Stiff Records. Catalogue no: **BUYIT 223**
7" Single: Released Jun '85, on Stiff, by Stiff Records. Catalogue no: **BUY 223**

WHITE CITY
Tracks: / White city / Every man is a king.
7" Single: Released Aug '89, on WEA, by WEA Records. Catalogue no: **YZ 409**
CD 5": Released Aug '89, on WEA, by WEA Records. Catalogue no: **YZ 409CD**
Cassingle: Released Aug '89, on WEA, by WEA Records. Catalogue no: **YZ 409C**
12" Single: Released Aug '89, on WEA, by WEA Records. Catalogue no: **YZ 409T**

YEAH YEAH YEAH YEAH YEAH
Tracks: / Yeah yeah yeah / Limeriks rake / Honky tonk women (Only on 12" and CD single.).
12" Single: Released Dec '88, on Pogue Mahone, by Rough Trade Records. Catalogue no: **YZ 355 T**
7" Single: Released Dec '88, on Pogue Mahone, by Rough Trade Records. Catalogue no: **YZ 355**

Poiema

MARY'S SONG
Tracks: / Mary's song / You make me see.
7" Single: Released Aug '84, on World, by World Records. Catalogue no: **WR TWO**

Poindexter, Buster

HOT HOT HOT
Tracks: / Hot hot hot / Cannibal.
7" Single: Released Jun '88, on RCA, by BMG Records (UK). Deleted May '89. Catalogue no: **PB 49581**
12" Single: Released Jun '88, on RCA, by BMG Records (UK). Deleted May '89. Catalogue no: **PT 49582**

Point

METROPOLIS
Tracks: / Metropolis.
7" Single: Released May '82, on Pendulum, Deleted '83. Catalogue no: **PT 002**

RIGHT TO THE POINT
Tracks: / Right to the point / Starlight.
7" Single: Released Dec '81, on Sonet, by Sonet Records. Deleted Dec '84. Catalogue no: **SONEL 2235**

Point 3 FM

PICKS ME UP (YOUR LOVE)
Tracks: / Picks me up (your love) / Picks me up (your love)(remix).
12" Single: Released 30 May '87, on Hard-

core, Catalogue no: **HAKT 1**

Pointer, Anita

OVERNIGHT SUCCESS
Tracks: / Overnight success / Love me like you do / Overnight success (dance) (Track on 12" single only) / Overnight success (ii) (Track available on 12" single only.).
Note: Tracks on 12" version only.
7" Single: Released Nov '87, on RCA, by BMG Records (UK). Deleted May '89. Catalogue no: **PB 49615**
12" Single: Released Nov '87, on RCA, by BMG Records (UK). Deleted May '89. Catalogue no: **PT 49616**

Pointer, Bonnie

DEEP INSIDE MY SOUL
Tracks: / Deep inside my soul / I love to sing to you.
7" Single: Released Apr '80, on Motown, by BMG Records (UK). Deleted Apr '83. Catalogue no: **TMG 184**

HEAVEN MUST HAVE
Tracks: / Heaven must have / Deep inside my soul.
7" Single: Released Apr '85, on Motown, by BMG Records (UK). Catalogue no: **TMG 1363**
12" Single: Released Apr '85, on Motown, by BMG Records (UK). Catalogue no: **TMGT 1383**

I CAN'T HELP MYSELF
Tracks: / I can't help myself / When I'm gone.
7" Single: Released Oct '81, on Motown, by BMG Records (UK). Catalogue no: **TMG 1171**

Pointer, June

DON'T MESS WITH BILL (I WILL UNDERSTAND)
Tracks: / Don't mess with Bill.
7" Single: Released Jun '83, on Planet, Catalogue no: **RPS 103**
12" Single: Released Jun '83, on Planet, Catalogue no: **RPST 103**

Pointer, Noel

CLASSY LADY
Tracks: / Classy lady / There's a feeling.
7" Single: Released Oct '81, on United Artists, by EMI Records. Deleted Oct '84. Catalogue no: **UP 645**

Pointer Sisters

Biographical details: This black Californian family vocal group -- Ruth, Anita, Bonnie and June, all born in Oakland between 1946 and 1954 -- came to fame via three US Top Twenty singles during 1973-75. *Yes We Can Can* , *Fairytale* and *How Long?* demonstrated their versatility and proved they were capable of recording jazz, soul, country and cabaret styles. There then followed an extended hiatus, during which Bonnie split to pursue a solo career. As a trio the Pointer Sisters got into their real commercial stride in 1979, when they began a long liaison with producer Richard Perry and his Planet label. Moving in a streetwise rock-pop-dance direction they scored US million-sellers with Bruce Springsteen's *Fire*('79) and the Doobie-ish *He's So Shy* ('80). The following year's smooth and sensual *Slow Hand* logged three consecutive weeks at No 2 in the States and gave the group their first British Top Ten hit; it came from the hit album *Black And White* , whose title reflcted the Pointers' blend of soul and rock. In 1984 the trio enjoyed a run of hit singles from the long-running *Breakout* LP, including *Automatic ,Jump (For My Love), Neutron Dance (used in the smash movie Beverly Hills Cop) and I'm So Excited* (which was grafted onto Breakout after first appearing on the less-successful '82 album *So Excited.* In 1985 the Contact album yielded the transAtlantic Top Twenty hit *Dare Me* but its other singles were less satisfactory. (Bob MacDonald, March 1986.).

AMERICAN MUSIC
Tracks: / American music / I want to do it with you.
7" Single: Released Sep '82, on Planet, Deleted '85. Catalogue no: **RPS 101**

AUTOMATIC (See panel above)
Tracks: / Automatic.
CD 5": Released Jun '89, on RCA, by BMG Records (UK). Catalogue no: **PD 49469**
7" Single: Released '84, on Planet, Catalogue no: **RSP 105**

AUTOMATIC (OLD GOLD)
Tracks: / Automatic / Jump.
7" Single: Released Jun '88, on Old Gold, by Old Gold Records. Catalogue no: **OG 4028**
12" Single: Released 21 Nov '87, on Old Gold, by Old Gold Records. Catalogue no: **OG 4028T**

AUTOMATIC (SINGLE)
Tracks: / Automatic / Nightline.

POINTER SISTERS - AUTOMATIC (Released on RCA)

7" Single: Released Apr '84, on Planet, Deleted '87. Catalogue no: **RPS 105**

AUTOMATIC-THE RITCHIE
Tracks: / Automatic-The Ritchie.
CD 5": Released Aug '89, on RCA, by BMG Records (UK). Catalogue no: **PD 43036**
7" Single: Released Aug '89, on RCA, by BMG Records (UK). Catalogue no: **PB 43035**
12" Single: Released Aug '89, on RCA, by BMG Records (UK). Catalogue no: **PT 43036**

BACK IN MY ARMS AGAIN
Tracks: / Back in my arms again / Dance electric / Dare me (remix) (Track on 12" version only).
7" Single: Released May '86, on RCA, by BMG Records (UK). Catalogue no: **PB 49865**
12" Single: Released May '86, on RCA, by BMG Records (UK). Catalogue no: **PT 49866**

BE THERE From Beverly Hills cop II
Tracks: / Be there / Be there (Acappella) / Be there (Ext. Version).
7" Single: Released Jun '87, on MCA, by MCA Records. Catalogue no: **MCA 1181**
12" Single: Released Jun '87, on MCA, by MCA Records. Catalogue no: **MCAT 1181**

COULD I BE DREAMIN'
Tracks: / Could I be dreamin' / Evie.
7" Single: Released Feb '81, on Planet, Deleted Feb '84. Catalogue no: **K 12505**

DARE ME
Tracks: / Dare me.
7" Single: Released Jul '85, on RCA, by BMG Records (UK). Deleted '88. Catalogue no: **PB 49957**

EVERYBODY IS A STAR
Tracks: / Everybody is a star.
7" Single: Released Feb '79, on Planet, Deleted '82. Catalogue no: **K 12324**

FIRE
Tracks: / Fire / Should I do it.
7" Single: Released Mar '79, on Planet, Deleted '82. Catalogue no: **K 12339**

FREEDOM
Tracks: / Freedom.
7" Single: Released Nov '85, on RCA, by BMG Records (UK). Catalogue no: **PB 49913**
12" Single: Released Nov '85, on RCA, by BMG Records (UK). Catalogue no: **PT 49914**

GOLDMINE (SINGLE)
Tracks: / Sexual power / Goldmine.
7" Single: Released Nov '86, on Planet, Catalogue no: **PB 40987**
12" Single: Released Nov '86, on Planet, Catalogue no: **PB 40988**

HEART TO HEART
Tracks: / Heart to heart.
7" Single: Released Sep '82, on Planet, Catalogue no: **RPS 102**
12" Single: Released Sep '82, on Planet, Catalogue no: **RPST 102**

HE'S SO SHY
Tracks: / He's so shy / Happiness.
7" Single: Released Nov '82, on Planet, Catalogue no: **E 9924**

I NEED YOU
Tracks: / I need you / So excited / Slow hand.
7" Single: Released Aug '84, on Planet, Deleted '87. Catalogue no: **RPS 107**
7" Single: Released Nov '83, on Planet, Catalogue no: **RST 104**
12" Single: Released Aug '84, on Planet, Catalogue no: **RPST 107**

I'M SO EXCITED (SINGLE)
Tracks: / I'm so excited.
7" Single: Released Oct '84, on Planet, Deleted Aug '89. Catalogue no: **RPS 108**
12" Single: Released Oct '84, on Planet, Deleted Aug '89. Catalogue no: **RPST 108**

JUMP (for my love)
Tracks: / Jump / Heartbeat.
7" Single: Released Jun '84, on Planet, Deleted Aug '89. Catalogue no: **RPS 106**
12" Single: Released Jun '84, on Planet, Deleted May '89. Catalogue no: **RPST 106**

NEUTRON DANCE
Tracks: / Neutron dance / Telegraph for your love / I feel for you.
7" Single: Released Dec '84, on Planet, Catalogue no: **RPS 109**
12" Single: Released Dec '84, on Planet, Catalogue no: **RPST109**

SAVE THIS NIGHT FOR LOVE
Tracks: / Save this night for love / Special things.
7" Single: Released Nov '80, on Planet, Catalogue no: **K 12484**

SHOULD I DO IT
Tracks: / Should I do it / Sweet lover man.
7" Single: Released Dec '81, on Reprise, by WEA Records. Deleted '84. Catalogue no: **K 12578**

SLOW HAND (See panel below)
Tracks: / Slow hand / Holdin' out for love.
7" Single: Released '81, on Planet, Catalogue no: **K 12530**

SLOW HAND (OLD GOLD)
Tracks: / Slow hand / Fire / Everybody is a star / I'm in love.
12" Single: Released Nov '87, on Old Gold, by Old Gold Records. Catalogue no: **OG 4034**

SOMEDAY WE WILL BE TOGETHER
Tracks: / Someday we will be together / Special things.
7" Single: Released Feb '82, on WEA, by WEA Records. Deleted '85. Catalogue no: **K12591**

WHO DO YOU LOVE
Tracks: / Who do you love / We turned up.
7" Single: Released Jan '80, on Planet, Catalogue no: **K 12406**

Poison

CRY TOUGH
Tracks: / Cry tough.
7" Single: Released Aug '87, on Music For Nations, by Music For Nations Records. Catalogue no: **KUT 127**
12" Single: Released Aug '87, on Music For Nations, by Music For Nations Records. Catalogue no: **12 KUT 127**

EVERY ROSE HAS ITS THORN
CD 5": Released Feb '89, on Capitol, by EMI Records. Deleted Aug '89. Catalogue no: **CDCL 520**
7" Pic: Released Jan '89, on Capitol, by EMI Records. Deleted Aug '89. Catalogue no: **CLS 520**
7" Pic: Released Jan '89, on Capitol, by EMI Records. Deleted Aug '89. Catalogue no: **CLP 520**
12" Single: Released Jan '89, on Capitol, by EMI Records. Deleted Aug '89. Catalogue no: **12CLG 520**

FALLEN ANGEL
Tracks: / Fallen angel / Bad to be good / Open up and say ..... interview (12" only.).
Note: Producer Tom Werman. Engineered by Duane Baron.
12" Pic: Released Oct '88, on Capitol, by EMI Records. Catalogue no: **12CLP 500**
7" Single: Released Oct '88, on Capitol, by EMI Records. Deleted Oct '89. Catalogue no: **CLS 500**
7" Single: Released Oct '88, on Capitol, by EMI Records. Deleted Aug '89. Catalogue no: **CL 500**
12" Single: Released Oct '88, on Capitol, by EMI Records. Deleted Oct '89. Catalogue no: **12CL 500**

NOTHIN' BUT A GOOD TIME
Tracks: / Nothin' but a good time / Look but

POINTER SISTERS - SLOW HAND (Released on Planet)

you can't touch / Livin' for the minute.
Note: "Track on 12" version only.
7" Single: Released Apr '88, on Capitol, by EMI Records. Deleted Jun '89. Catalogue no: **CLP 486**
7" Single: Released May '88, on Capitol, by EMI Records. Deleted Oct '89. Catalogue no: **CLZ 486**
7" Single: Released Apr '88, on Capitol, by EMI Records. Deleted Jun '89. Catalogue no: **CL 486**
12" Single: Released Apr '88, on Capitol, by EMI Records. Deleted Jun '89. Catalogue no: **12CL 486**
12" Single: Released May '88, on Capitol, by EMI Records. Deleted Aug '89. Catalogue no: **12CLG 486**

NOTHIN' BUT A GOOD TIME (RE-ISSUE)
Tracks: / Nothin' but a good time / Livin' for the minute / Look what the cat dragged in (12" & CD single only.).
CD 5": Released Jul '89, on Capitol, by EMI Records. Catalogue no: **CDCL 539**
CD 5": Released Jul '89, on Capitol, by EMI Records. Catalogue no: **203 432 2**
Cassingle: Released Jul '89, on Capitol, by EMI Records. Catalogue no: **203 432 4**
Cassingle: Released Jul '89, on Capitol, by EMI Records. Catalogue no: **TCCL 539**
7" Single: Released Jul '89, on Capitol, by EMI Records. Catalogue no: **CL 539**
7" Single: Released Jul '89, on Capitol, by EMI Records. Catalogue no: **203 432 7**
12" Single: Released Aug '89, on Capitol, by EMI Records. Catalogue no: **12CLG 539**
12" Single: Released Jul '89, on Capitol, by EMI Records. Catalogue no: **12CLPD 539**
12" Single: Released Aug '89, on Capitol, by EMI Records. Catalogue no: **203 499 8**
12" Single: Released Jul '89, on Capitol, by EMI Records. Catalogue no: **203 432 6**
12" Single: Released Jul '89, on Capitol, by EMI Records. Catalogue no: **12CL 539**
12" Single: Released Jul '89, on Capitol, by EMI Records. Catalogue no: **203 432 0**
Special: Released Jul '89, on Capitol, by EMI Records. Catalogue no: **203 432 8**
Special: Released Jul '89, on Capitol, by EMI Records. Catalogue no: **CLX 539**

POISON INTERVIEW 86
10" single: Released Jul '89, on Wax, by Wax Records. Catalogue no: **POISON 10**
7" Pic: Released Jul '89, on Wax, by Wax Records. Catalogue no: **POISON 7P**

TALK DIRTY TO ME
Tracks: / Talk dirty to me / Want some, need some / Poison interview.
7" Pic: Released May '87, on Music For Nations, by Music For Nations Records. Catalogue no: **P12KUT 125**
7" Single: Released May '87, on Music For Nations, by Music For Nations Records. Catalogue no: **KUT 125**
12" Single: Released May '87, on Music For Nations, by Music For Nations Records. Catalogue no: **12 KUT 125**

YOUR MAMA DON'T DANCE
Tracks: / Your mama don't dance / Tearin' down the walls / Love on the rocks.
CD 5": Released Apr '89, on Capitol, by EMI Records. Catalogue no: **CDCL 523**
CD 5": Released Apr '89, on Capitol, by EMI Records. Catalogue no: **203 264 2**
7" Single: Released Apr '89, on Capitol, by EMI Records. Deleted Oct '89. Catalogue no: **CLS 523**
7" Single: Released Apr '89, on Capitol, by EMI Records. Catalogue no: **CL 523**
7" Single: Released Apr '89, on Capitol, by EMI Records. Catalogue no: **203 264 7**
7" Single: Released Apr '89, on Capitol, by EMI Records. Deleted Oct '89. Catalogue no: **203 264 0**
12" Single: Released Apr '89, on Capitol, by EMI Records. Deleted Oct '89. Catalogue no: **203 264 8**
12" Single: Released Apr '89, on Capitol, by EMI Records. Deleted Oct '89. Catalogue no: **12CLB 523**
12" Single: Released Apr '89, on Capitol, by EMI Records. Catalogue no: **12CL 523**
12" Single: Released Apr '89, on Capitol, by EMI Records. Catalogue no: **203 264 6**

POLECATS - JOHN I'M ONLY DANCING (Released on Mercury)

Poison Girls

ALL SYSTEMS GO
Tracks: / All systems go.
7" Single: Released Oct '81, on Crass, by Crass Records. Catalogue no: **421984/8**

ARE YOU HAPPY NOW (REMIX)
Tracks: / Are you happy now.
12" Single: on Illuminated, Catalogue no: **ILL 312**

ARE YOU HAPPY NOW (SINGLE)
Tracks: / Are you happy now / Cream dream.
7" Single: Released Mar '85, on Illuminated, Catalogue no: **ILL 25**
12" Single: Released Mar '85, on Illuminated, Catalogue no: **ILL 3312**

(I'M NOT A) REAL WOMAN
Tracks: / I'm not a real woman.
7" Single: Released Nov '84, on X Centrix, Catalogue no: **XN 2009**
12" Single: Released Nov '84, on X Centrix, Catalogue no: **12XN 2009**

ONE GOOD REASON
Tracks: / One good reason / Cinnamon gardens.
7" Single: Released Mar '85, on Illuminated, Catalogue no: **ILL 23**

PERSONS UNKNOWN
Tracks: / Persons unknown.
7" Single: Released Oct '81, on Crass, by Crass Records. Catalogue no: **421984/1**

PRICE OF GRAIN, THE
Tracks: / Price of grain, The.
12" Single: Released Nov '85, on Upright, by Upright Records. Catalogue no: **UPT 12**

Poison Ivy

SECRETS
Tracks: / Secrets / Other side of you, The / Satisfy / Grounded.
7" Single: Released Feb '89, on Far Out Recording Company, by Far Out Recording Company. Catalogue no: **SRT 8KS**

Poison No.9

LAY ALL YOUR LOVE ON ME
Tracks: / Lay all your love on me.
7" Single: Released Mar '87, on Boy, Catalogue no: **BOY 001**
12" Single: Released Jan '87, on Boy, Catalogue no: **LEYBOY 001**

Polecats

ALL NIGHT LONG
Tracks: / All night long / Big green car / John I'm only dancing.
7" Single: Released Apr '81, on Mercury, by Phonogram Ltd. Deleted '85. Catalogue no: **POLE 10**

JEEPSTER
Tracks: / Jeepster.
7" Single: Released Aug '81, on Mercury, by Phonogram Ltd. Deleted '84. Catalogue no: **POLE 3**

JOHN I'M ONLY DANCING (See panel above)
Tracks: / John, I'm only dancing / Big green car.
7" Single: Released Mar '81, on Mercury, by Phonogram Ltd. Deleted '84. Catalogue no: **POLE 1**

MAKE A CIRCUIT WITH ME
Tracks: / Make a circuit with me / Juvenile delinquents / Red ready amber (Only on 12" single.).
7" Single: Released Jan '83, on Mercury, by Phonogram Ltd. Catalogue no: **POLE 4**
12" Single: Released Jan '83, on Mercury, by Phonogram Ltd. Catalogue no: **POLE 412**

ROCKABILLY GUY
Tracks: / Rockabilly guy / Don't cry baby.

7" Single: Released May '81, on Mercury, by Phonogram Ltd. Deleted '84. Catalogue no: **POLE 2**

Poles

GROW OLD WITH ME
Tracks: / Grow old with me.
7" Single: Released Jul '88, on Warm, by Warm Records. Catalogue no: **WARM 1A**

Police

Biographical details: Police were the most successful pop band of the early 80's. Drummer-songwriter Stewart Copeland was born in 1952 in Alexandria, Virginia. His father, who worked for the CIA, sent him to school in England. He played in the art-rock band Curved Air then recruited singer-bassist Sting -- real name Gordon Sumner, born in Northumberland, 1951 -- who had played in the Newcastle jazz-rock outfit Last Exit, and guitarist Henry Padovani. Their first single was released on brother Miles Copeland's label, Illegal. Guitarist Andy Summers was added to make a quartet. Born in Blackpool in 1942, he had played with Eric Burden, Zoot Money and Kevin Ayers. Padovani soon left, leaving the trio to storm the world's pop charts with their "white reggae" sound. *Ghost In The Machine* is probably

POLICE - WRAPPED AROUND YOUR FINGER (Released on A&M)

POLICE - EVERY BREATH YOU TAKE (Released on A&M)

the best of their five albums, three of which entered the British charts at No 1 and were also in the American Top Five. Thanks to Miles Copeland's stewardship they became very wealthy. Sting has gone solo as an actor, songwriter and bandleader. An abortive reunion of the trio resulted in only one remake of an old hit, included in the compilation *Every Breath You Take*. Summers has collaborated with Robert Fripp and Copeland has recorded solo and worked on the soundtrack of the film Rumblefish. (Donald Clarke, May 1987.).

CAN'T STAND LOSING YOU
Tracks: / Can't stand losing you / Dead end job.
7" Single: Released Jan '84, on A&M, by A&M Records. Catalogue no: **AMS 7381**

COMPACT HITS: POLICE
Tracks: / Roxanne / Canary in a coalmine / Bed's too big without you, The / Can't stand losing you.
CD 5": Released Apr '88, on A&M, by A&M Records. Deleted Feb '89. Catalogue no: **AMCD 905**

DE DO DO DO DE DA DA DA
Tracks: / De do do do De da da da / Sermon.
7" Single: Released Nov '80, on A&M, by A&M Records. Catalogue no: **AMS 7578**

DON'T STAND SO CLOSE TO ME
Tracks: / Don't stand so close to me (live) / Don't stand so close to me / Friends.
7" Single: Released Sep '80, on A&M, by A&M Records. Catalogue no: **AMS 7564**
7" Single: Released Oct '86, on A&M, by A&M Records. Deleted '88. Catalogue no: **AM 354**
12" Single: Released Oct '86, on A&M, by A&M Records. Deleted '88. Catalogue no: **AMY 354**

EVERY BREATH YOU TAKE (See panel on previous page)
Tracks: / Every breath you take / Murder by numbers.
7" Pic: Released Jun '83, on A&M, by A&M Records. Deleted '88. Catalogue no: **AMSP 117**
7" Single: Released Jun '83, on A&M, by A&M Records. Deleted '88. Catalogue no: **AM 117**

EVERY LITTLE THING SHE DOES IS MAGIC
Tracks: / Every little thing she does is magic / Flexible strategies.
7" Single: Released Oct '81, on A&M, by A&M Records. Deleted Mar '88. Catalogue no: **AMS 8174**

FALL OUT
Tracks: / Fall out.
7" Single: Released Oct '77, on Illegal, by Faulty Products Records. Catalogue no: **IL 001**

INVISIBLE SUN
Tracks: / Invisible sun / Shambelle.
7" Single: Released Sep '81, on A&M, by A&M Records. Deleted '84. Catalogue no: **AMS 8164**

KING OF PAIN
Tracks: / King of pain.
7" Single: Released Jan '84, on A&M, by A&M Records. Deleted '88. Catalogue no: **AM 176**
12" Single: Released Jan '84, on A&M, by A&M Records. Deleted '85. Catalogue no: **AMX 176**

MESSAGE IN A BOTTLE
Tracks: / Message in a bottle / Landlord.
7" Single: Released Sep '79, on A&M, by A&M Records. Catalogue no: **AMS 7474**

ROXANNE
Tracks: / Synchronicity II.
7" Single: Released Mar '79, on A&M, by A&M Records. Catalogue no: **AMS 7348**
7" Single: Released Nov '86, on A&M, by A&M Records. Deleted Mar '88. Catalogue no: **AM 363**

SIX PACK
Tracks: / Bed's too big without you, The / Roxanne / Message in a bottle / Walking on the moon / So lonely / Can't stand losing you.
7" Set: Released Jun '80, on A&M, by A&M Records. Deleted '83. Catalogue no: **AMPP 6001**

SO LONELY
Tracks: / No time this time / So lonely.
7" Single: Released '78, on A&M, by A&M Records. Catalogue no: **AMS 7402**

SPIRITS IN THE MATERIAL WORLD
Tracks: / Spirits in the material world / Low life.
7" Single: Released Dec '81, on A&M, by A&M Records. Deleted Mar '88. Catalogue no: **AMS 8194**

SYNCHRONICITY II
Tracks: / Synchronicity II.
7" Single: Released Nov '83, on A&M, by A&M Records. Deleted '86. Catalogue no: **AM 153**

WALKING ON THE MOON
Tracks: / Walking on the Moon.
7" Single: Released Dec '79, on A&M, by A&M Records. Deleted '82. Catalogue no: **AMS 7494**

WRAPPED AROUND YOUR FINGER (See panel on previous page)
Tracks: / Wrapped around your finger / Someone to talk to.
7" Single: Released Aug '83, on A&M, by A&M Records. Deleted '86. Catalogue no: **AM 127**

Politburo

EUPHORIA
Tracks: / Euphoria.
12" Single: Released Jun '86, on Skysaw, by Skysaw Records. Catalogue no: **SKY 3**

RADIO
Tracks: / Radio / Money.
7" Single: Released Aug '81, on Avatar, by Avatar Record Corporation. Catalogue no: **AAA 101**

Political Asylum

WINTER
Tracks: / Winter.
7" Single: Released Apr '85, on Children Of The Revolution, by Revolver Records. Catalogue no: **COR 5**

Polka Dots

OH ROSEMARY
Tracks: / Oh Rosemary / Don't love me at all.
7" Single: Released Apr '82, on RCA, by BMG Records (UK). Catalogue no: **RCA 227**

Pollard, Su

COME TO ME (I am woman)
Tracks: / You don't really want me / Come to me.
7" Single: Released Oct '85, on Rainbow, by Rainbow Records. Deleted '88. Catalogue no: **RBR 1**
7" Single: Released Feb '87, on Rainbow, by Rainbow Records. Catalogue no: **RBR 11**

STARTING TOGETHER
Tracks: / Starting together / Good news.
7" Single: Released Jan '86, on Rainbow, by Rainbow Records. Catalogue no: **RBR 4**

WIVES WILL ALWAYS BE THE LAST TO KNOW
Tracks: / Wives will always be the last to know / Too late.
7" Single: Released Oct '86, on Rainbow, by Rainbow Records. Catalogue no: **RBR 9**

YOU'VE LOST THAT LOVING FEELING
Tracks: / You've lost that lovin' feeling / Too late rainbow.
7" Single: Released Jul '86, on Rainbow, by Rainbow Records. Catalogue no: **RBR 7**
12" Single: Released Jul '86, on Rainbow, by Rainbow Records. Catalogue no: **RBRT 7**

Pollen

NURTURING DESIRE
Tracks: / Nurturing desire.
7" Single: Released May '89, on Danceteria, Catalogue no: **7 DAN 012**
12" Single: Released May '89, on Danceteria, Catalogue no: **12 DAN 012**

Polo, Jimi

FREE YOURSELF
Tracks: / Free yourself / Better days.
7" Single: Released Apr '89, on Urban, by Polydor Ltd. Catalogue no: **URB 36**
12" Single: Released Apr '89, on Urban, by Polydor Ltd. Deleted Oct '89. Catalogue no: **URBX 36**

Polyrock

ROMANTIC ME
Tracks: / Romantic me / You dragging feet.
7" Single: Released Feb '81, on RCA, by BMG Records (UK). Deleted '84. Catalogue no: **RCA 31**

Polystyrene

TALK IN TOYTOWN
Tracks: / Talk in toytown / Sub-tropical.
7" Single: Released Sep '80, on Liberty (USA), by EMI Records. Deleted '83. Catalogue no: **BP 370**

Ponce, Daniel

NO COMPRENDO
Tracks: / No comprendo.
12" Single: Released 20 Feb '88, on Antilles/New Directions, by Island Records. Deleted Jun '88. Catalogue no: **12 ANN 2**

Poni-Tails

BORN TOO LATE
Tracks: / Born too late.
7" Single: Released Sep '58, on H.M.V., by EMI Records. Deleted '61. Catalogue no: **POP 516**

POOKAH MAKES THREE - TAKE IT BACK (Released on 10 records)

BORN TOO LATE (OLD GOLD)
Tracks: / Born to late.
7" Single: Released Jul '82, on Old Gold, by Old Gold Records. Catalogue no: **OG 9164**

EARLY TO BED
Tracks: / Early to bed.
7" Single: Released Apr '59, on H.M.V., by EMI Records. Deleted '62. Catalogue no: **POP 596**

Ponsar, Serge

I WANT MONEY
Tracks: / I want money.
7" Single: Released Nov '83, on WEA (International), by WEA Records. Catalogue no: **U 9756**
12" Single: Released Nov '83, on WEA (International), by WEA Records. Catalogue no: **U 9756 T**

OUT IN THE NIGHT
Tracks: / Out in the night / Gotta get outside.
7" Single: Released Jul '83, on WEA (International), by WEA Records. Catalogue no: **U 9852**
12" Single: Released Jul '83, on WEA (International), by WEA Records. Catalogue no: **U 9852 T**

Ponty, Jean Luc

Biographical details: Jean-Luc Ponty was born in 1942 in Normandy, France. He took time off from school to practice several hours a day on the violin, played as a teenager in the Lamoureaux Symphony Orchestra, turned to jazz, then jazz-rock. He used an amplifier from the beggining and soon explored the electronic possibilities of the sound. He played in the Mahavishnu Orchestra with John McLaughlin, also with Frank Zappa and George Duke, as well as making his own albums. (Donald Clarke 15.5.87)..

BEACH GIRL
Tracks: / Beach girl / Somerset Drive.
7" Single: Released Jan '80, on Atlantic, by WEA Records. Deleted Jan '83. Catalogue no: **K 11430**

DEMAGOMANIA
Tracks: / Demagomania / Happy robots.
7" Single: Released Jan '81, on Atlantic, by WEA Records. Deleted Jan '84. Catalogue no: **K 11643**

Poody

THIS PARTY CYAR DONE
Tracks: / This party cyar done.
12" Single: Released Sep '89, on Sica, Catalogue no: **SOT 007**

Pookah Makes Three

LUCKY LUCKY LUCKY
Tracks: / Lucky lucky lucky / Fanfare for a cowboy.
7" Single: Released Feb '84, on 10 Records, by Virgin Records. Deleted '86. Catalogue no: **TEN 15**
12" Single: Released Feb '84, on 10 Records, by Virgin Records. Deleted '86. Catalogue no: **TEN 15-12**

TAKE IT BACK (See panel above)
Tracks: / Take it back / I can do anything.
7" Single: Released Sep '84, on 10 Records, by Virgin Records. Deleted '89. Catalogue no: **TEN 31**
12" Single: Released Sep '84, on 10 Records, by Virgin Records. Deleted '86. Catalogue no: **TEN 31-12**

WAVING A FLAME
Tracks: / Waving a flame / This.
7" Single: Released Mar '85, on 10 Records, by Virgin Records. Deleted '86. Catalogue no: **TEN 40**

Pookiesnackenburger

JUST ONE CORNETTO
Tracks: / Just one cornetto / Turkist bath.
7" Single: Released Jan '82, on Stiff, by Stiff Records. Catalogue no: **BUY 138**

Pool Sharks

DESTINATION UNKNOWN
Tracks: / Destination unknown / Sunshine / Mercyless.
7" Single: Released Apr '88, on Strike (1), by Strike Records. Catalogue no: **KIK 011**

SUNSHINE
Tracks: / Sunshine / Destination unknown.
7" Single: Released Dec '87, on Strike (1), by Strike Records. Catalogue no: **KIK 010**

Poole, Brian

CANDY MAN
Tracks: / Candy man.
7" Single: Released Jan '64, on Decca, by Decca Records. Deleted '67. Catalogue no: **F 11823**

DO YOU LOVE ME?
Tracks: / Do you love me?.
7" Single: Released Sep '63, on Decca, by Decca Records. Deleted '66. Catalogue no: **F 11739**
7" Single: Released Apr '83, on Outlook, Catalogue no: **OUT 100K**

DO YOU LOVE ME? (OLD GOLD)
Tracks: / Do you love me?.
7" Single: Released Oct '83, on Old Gold, by Old Gold Records. Catalogue no: **OG 9331**

I CAN DANCE
Tracks: / I can dance.
7" Single: Released Nov '63, on Decca, by Decca Records. Deleted '66. Catalogue no: **F 11771**

I WANT CANDY
Tracks: / I want candy.
7" Single: Released Jun '65, on Decca, by Decca Records. Deleted '68. Catalogue no: **F 12197**

SOMEONE SOMEONE
Tracks: / Someone, someone.
7" Single: Released May '64, on Decca, by Decca Records. Deleted '67. Catalogue no: **F 11893**
7" Single: Released Nov '83, on Sumatra, by Sumatra Records. Catalogue no: **SUM 4**

THREE BELLS
Tracks: / Three bells, The.

7" Single: Released Jan '65, on Decca, by Decca Records. Deleted '68. Catalogue no: **F 12037**

TWELVE STEPS TO LOVE
Tracks: / Twelve steps to love.
7" Single: Released Aug '64, on Decca, by Decca Records. Deleted '67. Catalogue no: **F 11951**

TWIST & SHOUT (SINGLE)
Tracks: / Twist and shout.
7" Single: Released Oct '80, on Decca, by Decca Records. Deleted '88. Catalogue no: **F 13893**

Poole, Glyn

MILLY MOLLY MANDY
Tracks: / Milly Molly Mandy.
7" Single: Released Oct '73, on York. Deleted '76. Catalogue no: **SYK 565**

Poor Howard

MAYBE TOMORROW
Tracks: / Maybe tomorrow.
7" Single: Released Apr '84, on Self Drive. Catalogue no: **SCAR 012**

Poorboys

MOVE BABY MOVE
Tracks: / Move baby move / Wild girl / My baby don't agree / Dancin' with the rebels.
7" Single: Released Nov '82, on Ace, by Ace Records. Deleted Jun '88. Catalogue no: **SW 81**

POORBOY SHUFFLE
Tracks: / Poorboy shuffle / Waterfront girls / Wolfman moan.
7" Single: Released Jan '86, on El Panzon. Catalogue no: **ELP 001**

Poors Of Reign

CHERISH
Tracks: / Cherish.
7" Single: Released Aug '86, on Low Type. Catalogue no: **LYT 001**

PLENTY
Tracks: / Plenty / Finchley bitch / Yellow flame / Going home / Last American socialist / Wilderness.
12" Single: Released 20 Feb '88, on Probe Plus, by Probe Plus Records. Catalogue no: **LT 005**

Poorsah

GO RIGHT UP IN DEY
Tracks: / Go right up in dey / Up in dey jam.
7" Single: Released Mar '84, on Trindisc, by Trindisc Records. Catalogue no: **TRIN 008**

Poovey, Groovey Joe

LIFE'S AMBITION
Tracks: / Life's ambition.
7" Single: Released Jun '80, on Rollin' Rock. Catalogue no: **45 030**

YOU ARE MY SUNSHINE
Tracks: / You are my sunshine / Lightning 'cross the sky.
7" Single: Released Nov '81, on President, by President Records. Deleted Nov '84. Catalogue no: **PT 497**

Pop Art

NEVER NO
Tracks: / Never no.
7" Single: Released Mar '89, on Blue Moves, by Blue Moves Records. Catalogue no: **SBM 2**
12" Single: Released Mar '89, on Blue Moves, by Blue Moves Records. Catalogue no: **TSBM 2**

Pop Black

BLACK AND WHITE RAG
Tracks: / Black and white rag.
7" Single: Released May '80, on Weasel, by Weasel Records. Catalogue no: **WR 4002**

Pop Guns

LANDSLIDE
Tracks: / Landslide.
12" Single: Released '89, on Medium Cool, by Medium Cool Records. Catalogue no: **MC 019T**

Pop Icons

BOY LEAVES CITY
Tracks: / Boy leaves city (double mix) / Boy leaves city nothing.
7" Single: Released 17 Oct '87, on Huge Big. Catalogue no: **ICON 1**

SAME OLD STORY
Tracks: / Same old story / Devil and the deep blue sea / Same old situation.
7" Single: Released Jan '86, on Vital Spark. Catalogue no: **VSC 101**

Pop, Iggy

Biographical details: Pop Iggy. This American singer and songwriter was born James Jewel Osterberg in Michigan. He changed his stage name to Iggy (the 'Pop' came later) and performed with a Detriot band named the Prime Movers. Iggy came to notoriety in the late Sixties when he became leaders of The Stooges, an outrageously incompetent rock group who were later cited as the prototype punk band. Iggy & The Stooges were no commercial success, but their ludicrously over the top stage performance won them a cult following. Iggy would whack his face with the microphone, and draw blood from his own chest. His blend of masochism, madness, showmanship and anarchy made Johnny Rotten's later exploits seem tame by comparison.
The Stooges fell into obscurity during the mid-Seventies, but Iggy was suddenly rediscovered in 1977, thanks to the twin tributes of David Bowie and the new British punk bands. Because it was now 'hip' to like Iggy Pop in Britain, three albums hurtled into the UK Top 50 during 1977 - *Raw Power* was a reactivated Stooges LP but *The Idiot* and *Lust For Life* were brand new sets produced by Mr Bowie. He toured with Bowie during this period and enjoyed great critical acclaim. At the end of the Seventies, Iggy's status declined again; but his 1982 album *Zombie Birdhouse*, produced by Blondie's Chris Stein, showed that Pop could still make a good chaotic rock record when he wanted to. Bob Macdonald 4.11.85.

BANG BANG
Tracks: / Bang bang / Sea of love.
7" Single: Released May '81, on Arista, by BMG Records (UK). Deleted May '84. Catalogue no: **ARIST 407**

COLD METAL
Tracks: / Cold metal / Instinct / Tough baby (On 12" only).
12" Pic: Released Aug '88, on A&M, by A&M Records. Catalogue no: **AMP 452**
7" Single: Released 22 Aug '88, on A&M, by A&M Records. Catalogue no: **AM 452**
12" Single: Released 22 Aug '88, on A&M, by A&M Records. Catalogue no: **AMY 452**

COMPACT HITS: IGGY POP
Tracks: / Real wild child / Isolation / Cry for love / Shades.
CD 5": Released Apr '88, on A&M, by A&M Records. Deleted Feb '89. Catalogue no: **AMCD 909**

CRY FOR LOVE
Tracks: / Cry for love / Winners and losers.
7" Single: Released Oct '86, on A&M, by A&M Records. Deleted '87. Catalogue no: **AM 358**
12" Single: Released Oct '86, on A&M, by A&M Records. Deleted '87. Catalogue no: **AMY 358**

FIRE GIRL
Tracks: / Fire girl / Blah-blah-blah (live).
7" Single: Released Apr '87, on A&M, by A&M Records. Deleted Mar '88. Catalogue no: **AM 392**
12" Single: Released Apr '87, on A&M, by A&M Records. Deleted Mar '88. Catalogue no: **AMY 392**

HIGH ON YOU
Tracks: / High on you / Squarehead.
7" Single: Released Dec '88, on A&M, by A&M Records. Catalogue no: **AM 475**
12" Single: Released Dec '88, on A&M, by A&M Records. Catalogue no: **AMY 475**

ISOLATION
Tracks: / Isolation / Shades (live) / Fire girl (remix) (on 12" only.).
7" Single: Released Jun '87, on A&M, by A&M Records. Deleted Mar '88. Catalogue no: **AM 397**
12" Single: Released Jun '87, on A&M, by A&M Records. Deleted Mar '88. Catalogue no: **AMY 397**

PASSENGER, THE
Tracks: / Passenger, The / Nightclubbing.
7" Single: Released May '82, on RCA, by BMG Records (UK). Catalogue no: **GOLD 549**

REAL WILD CHILD
Tracks: / Little Miss Emperor / Real wild child.
7" Single: Released Nov '86, on A&M, by A&M Records. Deleted Mar '88. Catalogue no: **AM 368**
12" Single: Released Nov '86, on A&M, by A&M Records. Deleted Mar '88. Catalogue no: **AMY 368**

RUN LIKE A VILLAIN
Tracks: / Run like a villain / Platonic.
7" Single: Released '82, on Chrysalis, by Chrysalis Records. Deleted '87. Catalogue no: **CHFLY 2634**

SHADES
Tracks: / Baby it can't fall / Cry for love (12" only).
Note: One of Iggy's greatest ever songs and easily the most underrated single of 1987.
7" Single: Released Feb '87, on A&M, by A&M Records. Deleted Mar '88. Catalogue no: **AM 374**
12" Single: Released Feb '87, on A&M, by A&M Records. Deleted Mar '88. Catalogue no: **AMY 374**

TAKE CARE OF ME
Tracks: / Take care of me / Locomosquito.
7" Single: Released Feb '80, on Arista, by BMG Records (UK). Deleted Feb '85. Catalogue no: **ARIST327**

Pop Man..

PIRATE
Tracks: / Pirate.
12" Single: Released Jul '89, on DTI. Catalogue no: **DT 12**

Pop Man & The Raging

FIELDS IN MOTION
Tracks: / Fields in motion / Hustlin' man.
7" Single: Released Aug '87, on MCA, by MCA Records. Catalogue no: **MCA 1185**
12" Single: Released Aug '87, on MCA, by MCA Records. Catalogue no: **MCAT 1185**

NEW FEELINGS
Tracks: / New feelings / Friends & lovers.
7" Single: Released Aug '88, on Greensleeves, by Greensleeves Records. Catalogue no: **GRE 223**
12" Single: Released Aug '88, on Greensleeves, by Greensleeves Records. Catalogue no: **GRED 223**

Pop Tarts

POP TARTS '88
Tracks: / Pop tarts '88.
12" Single: Released Aug '88, on World, by World Records. Catalogue no: **WOW 188**

Pop & The Beagle

NAME THAT TUNE
Tracks: / Name that tune.
7" Single: Released Mar '80, on Venture (1). Catalogue no: **EAR 726**

Pop Tops

MAMY BLUE
Tracks: / Mamy blue.
7" Single: Released Oct '71, on A&M, by A&M Records. Deleted '74. Catalogue no: **AMS 859**

Pop Wallpaper

OVER YOUR SHOULDER
Tracks: / Over your shoulder.
12" Single: Released Aug '84, on Spark, by Spark Records. Catalogue no: **SPARK 001**

STRAWBERRY LETTER 23
Tracks: / Strawberry letter 23 / Nothing can call me back.
12" Single: Released Apr '86, on Rosebud. Catalogue no: **SPARK 2**

Pop Will Eat Itself

BEAVER PATROL
Tracks: / Beaver patrol / Bubbles.
7" Single: Released Sep '87, on Chapter 22, by Chapter 22 Records. Catalogue no: **LCHAP 16**
7" Single: Released Sep '87, on Chapter 22, by Chapter 22 Records. Catalogue no: **CHAP 16**
12" Single: Released Sep '87, on Chapter 22, by Chapter 22 Records. Catalogue no: **12 CHAP 16**

CAN U DIG IT
Tracks: / Can U dig it / Poison to the mind / Radio PWEI (12" only.) / Fuses have been lit, The (on 12" only).
CD 5": Released Jan '89, on RCA, by BMG Records (UK). Deleted Jul '89. Catalogue no: **PD 42620**
7" Single: Released Feb '89, on RCA, by BMG Records (UK). Catalogue no: **PB 42619**
7" Single: Released Jan '89, on RCA, by BMG Records (UK). Catalogue no: **PB 42621**
12" Single: Released Jan '89, on RCA, by BMG Records (UK). Catalogue no: **PT 42620**

DEF CON ONE Very metal noise pollution (EP)
Tracks: / Def con one / Preaching to the converted.
CD 5": Released Sep '89, on RCA, by BMG Records (UK). Catalogue no: **PD 42884**
CD 5": Released Jul '88, on Chapter 22, by Chapter 22 Records. Catalogue no: **PWEICD 001**
Cassingle: Released Sep '89, on RCA, by BMG Records (UK). Catalogue no: **PK 43023**
Cassingle: Released Sep '89, on RCA, by BMG Records (UK). Catalogue no: **PK 43024**
7" Single: Released Sep '89, on RCA, by BMG Records (UK). Deleted Sep '89. Catalogue no: **PB 43021**
7" Single: Released Sep '89, on RCA, by BMG Records (UK). Catalogue no: **PB 42883**
7" Single: Released Jul '88, on Chapter 22, by Chapter 22 Records. Catalogue no: **PWEI 001**
12" Single: Released Sep '89, on RCA, by BMG Records (UK). Catalogue no: **PT 43022**
12" Single: Released Sep '89, on RCA, by BMG Records (UK). Catalogue no: **PT 42884**
12" Single: Released Jul '88, on Chapter 22, by Chapter 22 Records. Catalogue no: **PWEIL 12001**
Special: Released Jul '88, on Chapter 22, by Chapter 22 Records. Catalogue no: **LPWEI 001**

LOVE MISSILE F1-11
Tracks: / Love missile F1-11 / Orgone accumulator / Everything that rises* (Available on 12" only) / Like an angel (Available on 12" only).
7" Single: Released 23 May '87, on Chapter 22, by Chapter 22 Records. Catalogue no: **CHAP 13**
12" Single: Released 23 May '87, on Chapter 22, by Chapter 22 Records. Catalogue no: **12 CHAP 13**

LOVE MISSILE F1-11 (REMIX)
Tracks: / Love missile F1-11 (remix) / Everything that rises (remix) / Orgone accumulator / Like an angel.
12" Single: Released Jun '87, on Chapter 22, by Chapter 22 Records. Catalogue no: **L 12CHAP 13**

POPPIECOCK
Note: 5 track EP
7" Single: Released Nov '86, on Chapter 22, by Chapter 22 Records. Catalogue no: **CHAP 9**
12" Single: Released Nov '86, on Chapter 22, by Chapter 22 Records. Catalogue no: **12CHAP 9**

SWEET SWEET PIE
Tracks: / Devil Inside / Runaround.
7" Single: Released Jan '87, on Chapter 22, by Chapter 22 Records. Catalogue no: **CHAP 11**
12" Single: Released Jan '87, on Chapter 22, by Chapter 22 Records. Catalogue no: **12 CHAP 11**

THERE IS NO LOVE BETWEEN US ANYMORE
Tracks: / There is no love between us anymore / Picnic in the sky / On the razor edge (12" only.) / Kiss that girl (Only on 12" single.).
7" Pic: Released Jan '88, on Chapter 22, by Chapter 22 Records. Catalogue no: **LCHAP 20**
7" Single: Released Jan '88, on Chapter 22, by Chapter 22 Records. Catalogue no: **CHAP 20**
12" Single: Released Jan '88, on Chapter 22, by Chapter 22 Records. Catalogue no: **12CHAP 20**
Special: Released Jan '88, on Chapter 22, by Chapter 22 Records. Catalogue no: **L12 CHAP 20**

WISE UP SUCKER
Tracks: / Wise up sucker / Orgyone stimulator / Wise up sucker (12" mix) (Only on 10" and 12" single.) / Can U dig it? (Riffs mix) (12" version only.) / Wise up sucker (7" mix) (Only on 10" and 12" single.).
12" Single: Released Apr '89, on RCA, by BMG Records (UK). Catalogue no: **PT 42762**
CD 5": Released Apr '89, on RCA, by BMG Records (UK). Catalogue no: **PD 42762**
10" single: Released Apr '89, on RCA, by BMG Records (UK). Catalogue no: **PJ 42762**
7" Pic: Released Apr '89, on RCA, by BMG Records (UK). Catalogue no: **PB 42793**
7" Single: Released Apr '89, on RCA, by BMG Records (UK). Catalogue no: **PB 42761**

Pope, Jana

I'M LOSING YOU (REMIX)
Tracks: / You won't believe it.
7" Single: Released Feb '87, on Polydor, by Polydor Ltd. Deleted Jan '88. Catalogue no: **POSP 852**
12" Single: Released Feb '87, on Polydor, by Polydor Ltd. Deleted Aug '87. Catalogue no: **POSPX 852**

Pope, Maldwyn

FIREMAN SAM
Tracks: / Fireman Sam / Sam Tan.
7" Single: Released May '88, on BBC, by BBC Records & Tapes. Catalogue no: **RESL 224**

Pope, Tim

I WANT TO BE A TREE
Tracks: / I want to be a tree.
7" Single: Released Jun '84, on Fiction, by Fiction Records. Catalogue no: **FICS 21**
12" Single: Released Jun '84, on Fiction, by Fiction Records. Catalogue no: **FICSX 21**

Popinjays

DON'T GO BACK

Tracks: / Don't go back / So close / Move to perish.
12" Single: Released Aug '88, on Big Cat, by Big Cat Records. Catalogue no: **BBAO 2**

Popman & The Raging

JUST LIKE A WOMAN
Tracks: / Just like a woman / Casual aquaintance.
12" Single: Released Aug '86, on MCA, by MCA Records. Catalogue no: **REGYT 1**

Poppies

THERE'S A PAIN IN MY HEART
Tracks: / There's a pain in my heart.
7" Single: Released '79, on Inferno (1), by Inferno Records. Catalogue no: **NR 2**

Poppin, Keith

ENVIOUS
Tracks: / Envious.
12" Single: Released Jun '86, on UNKNOWN, Catalogue no: **unknown**

Poppy, Andrew

32 FRAMES FOR ORCHESTRA
Tracks: / 32 frames for orchestra / Impossible.
12" Single: Released Sep '86, on ZTT, by ZTT Records. Catalogue no: **12 ZTIS 200**

AMUSEMENT, THE
Tracks: / Amusement, The / Listening in / Kink konk presto (Only on 12" single.) / East fragment / Kink konk adagio (*Extra tracks on 12" only.).
7" Single: Released Feb '87, on ZTT, by ZTT Records. Deleted Apr '88. Catalogue no: **ZTPS 3**
12" Single: Released Feb '87, on ZTT, by ZTT Records. Catalogue no: **12 ZTPS 3**

Poppy Family

WHICH WAY YOU GOIN' BILLY
Tracks: / Which way are you going.
7" Single: Released Aug '70, on Decca, by Decca Records. Deleted '73. Catalogue no: **F 22976**
7" Single: Released '69, on Decca, by Decca Records. Deleted '88. Catalogue no: **F 22976**

Poppy Fields

ALIEN
Tracks: / Alien.
12" Single: Released Feb '85, on Illuminated, Catalogue no: **ILL 2912**

Poppy Heads

CREMATION TOWN
Tracks: / Cremation town.
7" Single: Released Apr '88, on Sarah, Catalogue no: **SARAH 006**

Pops, Charlie

DON'T TEASE THE ANIMALS
Tracks: / Don't tease the animals / Don't just stand there babe / Oh what a gas.
7" EP: Released May '82, on JSO, Deleted '87. Catalogue no: **EAT 13**

Popticians

MOBILE HOME
Tracks: / Mobile home / Spare pear.
7" Single: Released Jun '84, on Off The Kerb, Catalogue no: **DAD 1**

Poptones

WOODEN HEART
Tracks: / Wooden heart / Appliances.
7" Single: Released Nov '80, on Square, Catalogue no: **SQS 4**

Popular Front

FALLING OUT
Tracks: / Falling out.
7" Single: Released 23 May '87, on Midnight Music, by Midnight Music Records. Catalogue no: **DONG 32**

LIBERTE+EGALITE+DANSABILITE
Tracks: / Liberte + egalite + dansabilite (EP) / Did the earth move? / Listening / Buffet of forbidden fruit, A / La position soixante-huit.
7" Single: Released Jun '86, on Midnight Music, by Midnight Music Records. Catalogue no: **DONG 26**

Popular History Of Signs

BODY AND SOUL
7" Single: Released Oct '84, on Jungle, by Jungle Records. Deleted '88. Catalogue no: **JUNG 19**
12" Single: Released Oct '84, on Jungle, by Jungle Records. Deleted '88. Catalogue no: **JUNG 19T**

HOUSE
Tracks: / House / Ladderjack.
12" Single: Released Mar '84, on Jungle, by Jungle Records. Catalogue no: **JUNG 10**

IF SHE WAS A CAR
12" Single: Released Sep '83, on Jungle, by Jungle Records. Catalogue no: **JUNG 6**

Pork Dukes

FILTHY AND THE NASTY, THE
Tracks: / Filthy and the nasty, The.
7" Single: Released Oct '89, on Damaged Goods, Catalogue no: **FNARR 8**

Porridge People

EXTENSION 38 (EP)
7" Single: Released May '83, on Oat, Catalogue no: **OAT 1**

Porter, Hugh

LITTLE LOVE, A
Tracks: / Little love, A / Black man.
12" Single: Released May '85, on Reggae, Catalogue no: **REGGAE 001**

WOMAN (FEELING THE FEELING)
Tracks: / Woman (feeling the feeling).
12" Single: Released Dec '83, on Intense, by Intense Records. Catalogue no: **INT 011**

Portion Control

GO TALK
Tracks: / Go talk / Upside down.
12" Single: Released Mar '85, on Illuminated, Catalogue no: **ILL 4312**

GREAT DIVIDE, THE
Tracks: / Great divide, The.
7" Single: Released Jul '85, on Rhythmic, by Rhythmic Records. Catalogue no: **7 RMIC 007**
12" Single: Released Jul '85, on Rhythmic, by Rhythmic Records. Catalogue no: **12 RMIC 007**

LIVE IN EUROPE
Tracks: / Live In Europe.
10" single: Released Sep '87, on Big Noise In Archgate, by Big Noise In Archgate Records. Catalogue no: **BNIA ONE**

PURGE
Tracks: / Purge.
12" Single: Released Aug '86, on Deadman's Curve, by Deadman's Curve Records. Catalogue no: **DMC 001**

RAISE THE PULSE
Tracks: / Raise the pulse / Collapse / Bite my head.
12" Single: Released Mar '85, on Illuminated, Catalogue no: **ILL 2612**

ROUGH JUSTICE
Tracks: / Rough justice.
12" Single: Released Mar '84, on Illuminated, Catalogue no: **ILL 3212**

SURFACE TO BE SEEN (EP)
Tracks: / Surface to be seen.
12" Single: Released Mar '82, on In Phaze, by In Phaze Records. Catalogue no: **IP 006**

Portnoy, Gary

CHEERS THEME
Tracks: / Cheers theme / Jenny.
7" Single: Released Jan '84, on Starblend, by Starblend Records. Catalogue no: **CHEER 1**

Port-O-Spain

PHYSICAL CONTACT
Tracks: / Physical contact.
7" Single: Released Jul '83, on Vista Sounds, by Vista Sounds Records. Catalogue no: **JC 7002**

Portraits

HAZARDS IN THE HOME
Tracks: / Hazards in the home / Never let go.
7" Single: Released Mar '80, on Ariola, by BMG Records (UK). Deleted '83. Catalogue no: **ARO 206**

Portsmouth Sinfonia

CLASSICAL MUDDLEY
Tracks: / Classical muddley.
7" Single: Released Sep '81, on Springtime, by Springtime Records. Deleted '84. Catalogue no: **WIP 6736**

Posey, Sandy

BORN A WOMAN (SINGLE)
Tracks: / Born a woman.
7" Single: Released Sep '66, on MGM, by Polydor Ltd. Deleted '69. Catalogue no: **MGM 1321**

SINGLE GIRL
Tracks: / Single girl / Born a woman.
7" Single: Released Mar '86, on Old Gold, by Old Gold Records. Catalogue no: **OG 9584**

SINGLE GIRL (ORIGINAL)
Tracks: / Single girl.
7" Single: Released Sep '75, on MGM, by Polydor Ltd. Deleted '78. Catalogue no: **2006 533**
7" Single: Released Jan '67, on MGM, by Polydor Ltd. Deleted '70. Catalogue no: **MGM 1330**

WHAT A WOMAN IN LOVE WON'T DO
Tracks: / What a woman in love won't do.
7" Single: Released Apr '67, on MGM, by Polydor Ltd. Deleted '70. Catalogue no: **MGM 1335**

Posh

LETTER TO LINDA
Tracks: / Letter to Linda.
7" Single: Released Aug '81, on Marathon, by Marathon Records. Deleted '83. Catalogue no: **RUN 1**

SAND IN MY FACE
Tracks: / Sand in my face.
7" Single: Released Aug '83, on Marathon, by Marathon Records. Deleted '83. Catalogue no: **JOG 1**

Posie Noire

STARVATION OF A MIND
Tracks: / Starvation of a mind.
7" Single: Released Jun '88, on Antler, by Antler Records (Belgium). Deleted '88. Catalogue no: **ANT 043**

Posit, Jean Pierre

SANTA MONICA
Tracks: / Santa Monica / You.
7" Single: Released Mar '84, on Ferroway, Catalogue no: **1 JPP 1**
12" Single: Released Mar '84, on Ferroway, Catalogue no: **12 JPP 1**

Positive

CHANGE THIS CIRCUS
Tracks: / Change this circus.
12" Single: Released 13 Feb '89, on SSR, Catalogue no: **12 SSR 92**

Positive Action

BREAD NOT BOMBS
Tracks: / Bread not bombs.
7" Single: Released 24 Jun '86, on Positive Action, Catalogue no: **BNB 001**

Positive Force

WE GOT THE FUNK
Tracks: / We got the funk / Rappers delight.
7" Single: Released Sep '75, on Sugarhill (USA), Deleted '78. Catalogue no: **SHL 102**
12" Single: Released Dec '85, on Streetwave, Catalogue no: **SWAVE 6**

Positive Noise

DISTANT FIRES
Tracks: / Distant fires.
7" Single: Released Jun '85, on Statik, Catalogue no: **TAK 32**
12" Single: Released Jun '85, on Statik, Catalogue no: **TAK 3212**

GET UP AND GO
Tracks: / Get up and go.
7" Single: Released Sep '82, on Statik, Catalogue no: **STAT 23**
12" Single: Released Sep '82, on Statik, Catalogue no: **STAT 2312**

MILLION MILES AWAY
Tracks: / Million miles away.
7" Single: Released Aug '84, on Statik, Catalogue no: **TAK 22**
12" Single: Released Aug '84, on Statik, Catalogue no: **TAK 22-12**

WHEN THE LIGHTNING STRIKES
Tracks: / When the lightning strikes.
7" Single: Released Sep '83, on Statik, Catalogue no: **TAK 8**
12" Single: Released Sep '83, on Statik, Catalogue no: **TAK 8-12**

Positive Two

DIAMONDS AND GOLD
Tracks: / Diamonds and gold / Diamonds and gold (instrumental).
12" Single: Released Sep '89, on Gold Key, Catalogue no: **12 PO 24**

Posse, George

TOUCH A FOUR LEAF CLOVER
Tracks: / Touch a four leaf clover / Every nigger.
12" Single: Released Sep '84, on Sir George, Catalogue no: **SG 015T**

Post, Mike

AFTERNOON OF THE RHINO
Tracks: / Afternoon of the rhino.
7" Single: Released Aug '75, on Warner Bros., by WEA Records. Deleted '78. Catalogue no: **K 16588**

A-TEAM, THEME FROM
Tracks: / A Team, Theme from / 6 slash 24.
7" Single: Released Sep '84, on RCA, by BMG Records (UK). Deleted '87. Catalogue no: **RCA 443**

HILL STREET BLUES
Tracks: / Hill Street blues / Aarons theme.
7" Pic: Released Nov '85, on Elektra, by Elektra Records (UK). Catalogue no: **K 12576T**
7" Single: Released Nov '85, on Elektra, by Elektra Records (UK). Deleted Sep '87. Catalogue no: **K 12576**
7" Single: Released Sep '85, on Old Gold, by Old Gold Records. Catalogue no: **OG 9515**

MAGNUM P.I.
Tracks: / Magnum P.I / Rockford files.
7" Single: Released Apr '82, on Elektra, by Elektra Records (UK). Catalogue no: **K 13167**

ROCKFORD FILES
Tracks: / Rockford files / Gumbus bus.
7" Single: Released Mar '82, on Elektra, by Elektra Records (UK). Deleted '85. Catalogue no: **K 12606**

Post Mortem

AGAINST ALL ODDS (EP)
Tracks: / Against all odds.
7" Single: Released Aug '84, on Flowmotion, Catalogue no: **FM 006**

POST MORTEM (EP)
Tracks: / Post mortem.
7" Single: Released May '83, on Lightbeat, Catalogue no: **POST 1**

Post War Nudes

SO NOW
Tracks: / So now.
7" Single: Released Jan '83, on Virgin, by Virgin Records. Deleted '89. Catalogue no: **VS 550**

Postethwaite, David

RULY TRULY FALSE
Tracks: / Ruly truly false.
7" Single: Released Jul '89, on Sol, Catalogue no: **SOL 802**

Postman Pat

POSTMAN PAT
7" Single: Released '82, on Post Music, Catalogue no: **PP 001**

Potato Five

DO THE JERK
Tracks: / Do the jerk / Reburial.
7" Single: Released Jul '89, on Rhyme & Reason, by Priority Records. Catalogue no: **RNR 5**
12" Single: Released Jul '89, on Rhyme & Reason, by Priority Records. Catalogue no: **12 RNR 5**

GOTTO GO
Tracks: / Gotto go / Burning fire.
12" Single: Released 17 Oct '87, on Rackit, Catalogue no: **SPUD 001**

SKA DANGER
Tracks: / Dead boring (DUB).
Note: Self-20 Porchester Terrace,W.2., phone:01-723-5435
7" Single: Released Jan '87, on Drolltone, Catalogue no: **TPF 001**

SPIN YOUR HEAD
Tracks: / Spin your head.
12" Single: Released Nov '85, on Gaz's, Catalogue no: **12GAZ 001**

WESTERN SPECIAL
Tracks: / Western special / Big city.
7" Single: Released Mar '86, on Gaz's Rockin' Records, by Stiff Records. Catalogue no: **GAZ 001**

Potential Threat

BRAINWASHED
Tracks: / Brainwashed.
7" Single: Released Apr '85, on Children Of The Revolution, by Revolver Records. Catalogue no: **COR 6**

WHAT'S SO GREAT ABOUT BRITAIN (EP)
7" Single: Released Jun '82, on Out Of Town, Catalogue no: **HOOT 7**

Potion

CATCH THE FEELING
Tracks: / Catch the feelin' / Showstopper.
7" Single: Released Jun '81, on Champagne (USA), by Goldbond Recording (USA). Deleted Jun '84. Catalogue no: **FUNK 5**
12" Single: Released Jun '81, on Champagne (USA), by Goldbond Recording (USA). Deleted Jun '84. Catalogue no: **FUNKY 5**

LIFE
Tracks: / Life / City.
7" Single: Released Sep '81, on Champagne (DJM), Deleted '84. Catalogue no: **FUNK 6**
12" Single: Released Sep '81, on Champagne (DJM), Deleted '84. Catalogue no: **FUNKY 6**

Potter, Nic

DOLPHINS
Tracks: / Dolphins.
7" Single: Released '82, on Butt, by Butt

Records. Catalogue no: **FUN 1**

Potters

WE'LL BE WITH YOU
Tracks: / We'll be with you.
7" Single: Released Apr '72, on Pye. Deleted '75. Catalogue no: **JT 100**

Powder Blues

BOPPIN' WITH THE BLUES
Tracks: / Boppin' with the blues / Hear that guitar ring.
7" Single: Released Sep '80, on RCA, by BMG Records (UK). Deleted Sep '83. Catalogue no: **PB 9597**

Powell, Andrew

LUCIFER (AND MAMA GAMMA)
Tracks: / Lucifer (and mama gamma).
7" Single: Released Jul '83, on EMI, by EMI Records. Catalogue no: **EMI 5399**

Powell, Cozy

DANCE WITH THE DEVIL
Tracks: / Dance with the devil.
7" Single: Released Dec '73, on RAK, by EMI Records. Deleted '76. Catalogue no: **RAK 165**
7" Single: Released Jul '84, on EMI Golden 45's, by EMI Records. Catalogue no: **G45 30**

LONER
Tracks: / Loner / El Sid.
7" Single: Released Feb '80, on Ariola, by BMG Records (UK). Deleted '83. Catalogue no: **ARO 205**

MAN IN BLACK, THE
Tracks: / Man in black, The.
7" Single: Released May '74, on RAK, by EMI Records. Deleted '77. Catalogue no: **RAK 173**

NA NA NA
Tracks: / Na na na.
7" Single: Released Aug '74, on RAK, by EMI Records. Deleted '77. Catalogue no: **RAK 180**

SOONER OR LATER
Tracks: / Sooner or later / Blister.
7" Single: Released Sep '81, on Polydor, by Polydor Ltd. Deleted Sep '84. Catalogue no: **POSP 328**

THEME ONE
Tracks: / Theme one.
7" Single: Released Nov '79, on Ariola, by BMG Records (UK). Deleted '82. Catalogue no: **ARO 189**

Powell, Doc

GIVE IT UP
Tracks: / Give it up / What I like.
7" Single: Released Nov '87, on Club, by Phonogram Ltd. Catalogue no: **JAB 61**
12" Single: Released Nov '87, on Club, by Phonogram Ltd. Catalogue no: **JABX 61**

Powell, Picker

DANCING FEELING
Tracks: / Dancing feeling / Dancing feeling (version).
12" Single: Released Jul '86, on Sunjam, Catalogue no: **SR 001**

Powell, Shezwae

ACT OF WAR
Tracks: / Act of war.
7" Single: Released Feb '87, on Nightmare, by Nightmare Records. Catalogue no: **MARES 10**
12" Single: Released Feb '87, on Nightmare, by Nightmare Records. Catalogue no: **MARE 10**

BACK TRACK
Tracks: / Back track / Back track (inst).
7" Single: Released 13 Jun '87, on Nightmare, by Nightmare Records. Catalogue no: **MARES 34**
12" Single: Released 13 Jun '87, on Nightmare, by Nightmare Records. Catalogue no: **MARE 34**

Powell, Verna Lee

LET'S SIT DOWN AND TALK ABOUT IT
Tracks: / Let's sit down and talk about it / Let's sit down and talk about it(instrumental).
7" Single: Released Feb '81, on B & C, by Trojan Records. Deleted '84. Catalogue no: **BCS 22**

Power

GROOVIN'
Tracks: / Groovin' / Hot.
7" Single: Released Jun '82, on Malaco, by Malaco Records (UK). Deleted '88. Catalogue no: **MAL 001**

PLAY IT AGAIN SAM
Tracks: / Play it again Sam / Play it again Sam (inst.).
7" Single: Released Oct '81, on Malaco, by Malaco Records (UK). Deleted '88. Catalogue no: **MAL 1204**
7" Single: Released Oct '81, on Malaco, by Malaco Records (UK). Deleted '88. Catalogue no: **MAL 012**
12" Single: Released Oct '81, on Malaco, by Malaco Records (UK). Deleted '88. Catalogue no: **12MAL 1204**
12" Single: Released Oct '81, on Malaco, by Malaco Records (UK). Deleted '88. Catalogue no: **MAL 12 012**

SEVENTEEN
Tracks: / Seventeen / In a world / US remix (Extra track on 12" version only) / Acapella mix (Extra track on 12" version only).
7" Single: Released Aug '86, on Arista, by BMG Records (UK). Catalogue no: **ARIST 668**
12" Single: Released Aug '86, on Arista, by BMG Records (UK). Catalogue no: **ARIST 12668**

SOUL IN MY SHOES
Tracks: / Soul in my shoes / Sad boy / Soul in my shoes (dance mix) (Track on 12" version only).
7" Single: Released Jan '86, on Arista, by BMG Records (UK). Catalogue no: **ARIST 649**
12" Single: Released Jan '86, on Arista, by BMG Records (UK). Catalogue no: **ARIST 12649**

TRY A LITTLE TENDERNESS
Tracks: / Try a little tenderness / In a world.
7" Single: Released Oct '86, on Arista, by BMG Records (UK). Catalogue no: **ARIST 680**
12" Single: Released Oct '86, on Arista, by BMG Records (UK). Catalogue no: **ARIST 12680**

WORK HARD
Tracks: / Work hard / Work hard (soul party mix) / Callous love.
7" Single: Released Aug '85, on Arista, by BMG Records (UK). Catalogue no: **ARIST 630**
7" Single: Released Mar '86, on Arista, by BMG Records (UK). Catalogue no: **ARIST 661**
12" Single: Released Aug '85, on Arista, by BMG Records (UK). Catalogue no: **ARIST 12630**
12" Single: Released Mar '86, on Arista, by BMG Records (UK). Catalogue no: **ARIST 12661**
12" Single: Released May '86, on Arista, by BMG Records (UK). Catalogue no: **ARIST 22661**

Power Cut Crew

POWER CUTS
Tracks: / Power cuts.
7" Single: Released Jul '88, on Vinyl Lab, Catalogue no: **VL 0003**

Power Farm

WHICH WAY USA
Tracks: / Which way USA / Glass.
7" Single: Released Nov '83, on Boob, Deleted '85. Catalogue no: **MM 2**

Power Heddy

I DON'T BELIEVE IT
Tracks: / I don't believe it.
7" Single: Released May '85, on Sandos Music, Deleted '86. Catalogue no: **DACC 1**

Power Station

Biographical details: Power Station is a marriage of four major talents with impeccable track records: the distinctive vocal style of Robert Palmer coupled with Duran Duran's bassist John Taylor and lead guitarist Andy Taylor plus "Serious moonlight tour" drummer Tony Thompson. John Taylor met Robert Palmer in Birmingham following Duran Duran's 1984 US tour and after meeting with producer Bernard Edwards the project was confirmed. The power station album was recorded at the studio of the same name in New York in 1985.

COMMUNICATION
Tracks: / Communication / Murderess.
7" Single: Released Oct '85, on Parlophone, by EMI Records. Catalogue no: **R 6114**
12" Single: Released Oct '85, on Parlophone, by EMI Records. Catalogue no: **12R6114**

GET IT ON
Tracks: / Get it on.
7" Single: Released Apr '85, on Parlophone, by EMI Records. Catalogue no: **R 6096**
12" Single: Released Apr '85, on Parlophone, by EMI Records. Catalogue no: **12R 6096**

SOME LIKE IT HOT
Tracks: / Some like it hot / Heat is on.
7" Pic: Released Mar '85, on Parlophone, by EMI Records. Catalogue no: **RP 6091**
7" Pic: Released Apr '85, on Parlophone, by EMI Records. Catalogue no: **12RP 6091**

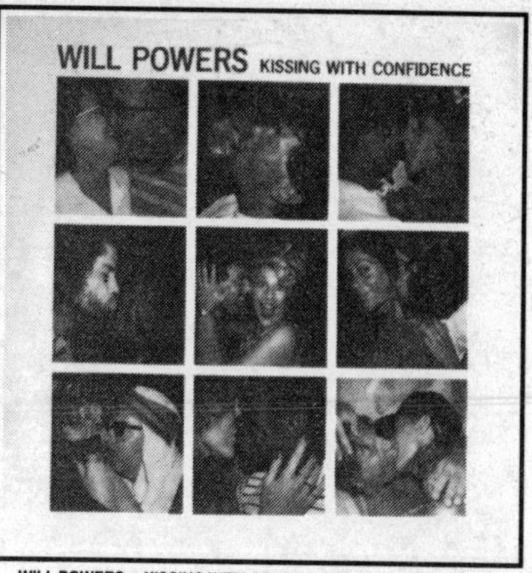

WILL POWERS - KISSING WITH CONFIDENCE (Released on Island)

7" Single: Released Feb '85, on Parlophone, by EMI Records. Catalogue no: **R 6091**
12" Single: Released Feb '85, on Parlophone, by EMI Records. Catalogue no: **12R 6091**

Power Supply

LATIN COOKING
Tracks: / Latin cooking / All right by me.
Cassingle: Released Feb '83, on Rapture, Deleted '85. Catalogue no: **RAPS 1**

Power To Dream

BODIES GONE
Tracks: / Bodies gone.
12" Single: Released Feb '85, on Illuminated, Catalogue no: **ILL 3512**

FAITH HEALER
Tracks: / Faith healer.
12" Single: Released Mar '85, on Illuminated, Catalogue no: **ILL 5112**

FRANTIC
Tracks: / Frantic.
7" Single: Released Oct '86, on Illuminated, Catalogue no: **LEV 73**
12" Single: Released Oct '86, on Illuminated, Catalogue no: **12 LEV 73**

Power, Wonder & Love

AFRO ACID
Tracks: / Afro acid / Entertainment for everyone.
12" Single: Released May '88, on Hardcore, Catalogue no: **HAKT 14**

Powerhouse

ON THE FLOOR
Tracks: / On the floor / Lost in space / Cut it up parts 1-5 (Avaliable on 12" format only.).
7" Single: Released Apr '88, on Champion, by Champion Records. Catalogue no: **CHAMP 69**
12" Single: Released Apr '88, on Champion, by Champion Records. Catalogue no: **CHAMP 1269**

Powerline

WATCHING YOU
Tracks: / Watching you / Watching you (inst.).
7" Single: Released Jul '82, on PLR, Deleted '83. Catalogue no: **PLR 1**
12" Single: Released Jul '82, on PLR, Deleted '83. Catalogue no: **12PLR 1**

YOU'RE THE GIRL (2 parts)
Tracks: / You're the girl.
7" Single: Released Apr '83, on Plant Life, by Plant Life Records. Catalogue no: **PLRS 212**

Powers, Johnny

LONG BLOND HAIR
Tracks: / Long blond hair / Mama rock / Rock rock / Waiting for you.
7" EP: Released Aug '89, on Rollercoaster, by Rollercoaster Records. Catalogue no: **RCEP 107**

Powers, Will

Biographical details: Lynn Goldsmith is best known as one of America's finest photographers. For the past two years however she has been plotting the rise of Will Powers. Will is solely her creation, a direct outgrowth of Lynn's own career, personality and experiences. Will Powers is the mild-mannered king of self-help dance/rock: *Dancing for mental health* is his first album. Lynn, born in Detroit, is a graduate of the University of Michigan where she studied television and film production. After college there was a short stint teaching English at Miami Beach High School before moving to New York City, where Lynn landed a job as National Publicity Director for Elektra Records. From Elektra, Lynn joined up with producer Josua White to form Joshus Television; together they developed a video-magnification system first used at Madison Square Garden and the Hollywood Bowl for rock concerts. This led to a job at America's ABC TV, directing the first late-night rock show In Concert. Lynn at the age of 24, was the youngest member of the Director's guild. It was during this period, the mid-Seventies, that Lynn developed her interest in photography. She placed her first nationally published rock photo - a performance shot of James Brown in Zaire - for Newsweek magazine. Diversity remained a key element in Lynn's career. In 1974, for instance she helped revive the prospects of a band that had gone defunct - Grand Funk Railroad. She brought in Todd Rundgren as producer, giving the band a new credibility. In 1977 Lynn Goldsmith had honed her various interests into a primary direction, a burgeoning career as a photographer. In the years since she has done album covers for such artists as Carly Simon and Frank Zappa, building a reputation as one of America's most in demand photographers. Throughout this odyssey however, Lynn has kept an abiding interest in the music itself, writing songs and even singing backups on friends albums. The Will Powers album includes contributions from artists Steve Winwood, Carly Simon, David Sanborn, Tom Bailey, Todd Rundgren and Nile Rodgers, though Will is very much the mainman. (Island Records, February 1984.).

ADVENTURES IN SUCCESS
Tracks: / Adventures in success / Adventures in success (dub).
7" Single: Released Jan '84, on Island, by Island Records. Catalogue no: **IS 156**

KISSING WITH CONFIDENCE (See panel above)
Tracks: / Kissing with confidence / All thru history.
7" Single: Released Oct '83, on Island, by Island Records. Deleted '86. Catalogue no: **IS 134**

Pozitiv Noize

I FEEL FINE
Tracks: / I feel fine.

7" Single: Released 20 Feb '89, on Polydor, by Polydor Ltd. Deleted Aug '89. Catalogue no: **URB 30**
12" Single: Released 20 Feb '89, on Polydor, by Polydor Ltd. Deleted Aug '89. Catalogue no: **URBX 30**

PRATT & MCLEAN - HAPPY DAYS (Released on Reprise)

P.P.G.

JACK THE BEAT
Tracks: / Jack the beat / Jack the beat (version).
7" Single: Released May '88, on Quazar, Catalogue no: **QUA 7**
12" Single: Released Apr '88, on Quazar, Catalogue no: **QUAT 7**

Prado, Perez

Biographical details: Perez Prado (1918-83) was born in Cuba and led one of the most popular mambo bands. His best-known mambos were numbered: *Mambo No.5*, *Mambo No.8*; his big international hits were *Cherry Pink And Apple Blossom White* and *Patricia* in 1955-58. (Donald Clarke 15.5.87)..

CHERRY PINK AND APPLE BLOSSOM WHITE
Tracks: / Cherry pink and apple blossom white.
7" Single: Released Mar '55, on H.M.V., by EMI Records. Deleted '58. Catalogue no: **B 10833**
7" Single: Released Oct '86, on Old Gold, by Old Gold Records. Catalogue no: **OG 9610**

PATRICIA
Tracks: / Patricia.
7" Single: Released Jul '58, on RCA, by BMG Records (UK). Deleted '61. Catalogue no: **RCA 1067**

Prams

BLACK SHEEP
Tracks: / Black sheep / Classic quotes.
7" Single: Released Mar '86, on Classic Quotes, Deleted '88. Catalogue no: **CLASS 1**

DON'T DROP ANY BOMBS ON ME
Tracks: / Don't drop any bombs on me.
7" Single: Released Aug '81, on Wabbit, Catalogue no: **WWS 1025**

Prats

GENERAL DAVIS
Tracks: / General Davis / Alliance.
7" Single: Released Nov '81, on Rough Trade, by Rough Trade Records. Catalogue no: **RT 080**

Pratt, Andy

CARRY YOU
Tracks: / Carry you / Modern police.
7" Single: Released Aug '83, on Lamborghini, by Lamborghini Records. Catalogue no: **LMG 2**

Pratt & McClain

HAPPY DAYS (See panel above)
Tracks: / Happy days / Cruisin' with the Fonz.
7" Single: Released Oct '77, on Reprise (USA), Catalogue no: **K 14435**

Prayers

SISTER, GOODBYE
Tracks: / Sister, goodbye.
7" Single: Released Nov '88, on Egg, Catalogue no: **EGG 001**

Praying Mantis

ALL DAY AND ALL OF THE NIGHT
Tracks: / All day and all of the night / Beads of ebony.
7" Single: Released Mar '81, on Arista, by BMG Records (UK). Deleted Mar '84. Catalogue no: **ARIST 397**

CAPTURED CITY
Tracks: / Captured city / Johnny cool / Ripper (On 12" only).
7" Single: Released Feb '80, on Harvest (1), by EMI Records. Deleted Feb '83. Catalogue no: **12HAR 5201**
7" Single: Released Feb '80, on Harvest (1), by EMI Records. Deleted Feb '83. Catalogue no: **HAR 5201**

CHEATED
Tracks: / Cheated / 30 pieces of silver / Free live single / Flirting with suicide / Panic in the streets.
7" EP: Released '82, on Arista, by BMG Records (UK). Deleted '87. Catalogue no: **ARIST 378**

PRAYING MANTIS (SINGLE)
Tracks: / Praying Mantis / High roller.
7" Single: Released Jul '80, on Gem, Deleted Jul '83. Catalogue no: **GEMS 36**

TELL ME THE NIGHTMARE'S WRONG
Tracks: / Tell me the nightmare's wrong / Turn the tables / Question of time.
7" Single: Released Sep '82, on Jet, by Jet Records. Deleted '85. Catalogue no: **JET 7026**

Preacher Harry

DEVIL IN THE PRIEST HALL
Tracks: / Devil in the priest hall.
7" Single: Released Jul '87, on Golden Pathway, Catalogue no: **POS 001**

Preachers Of Twilight

ON THE RAZOR EDGE
Tracks: / On the razor edge.
12" Single: Released Dec '88, on Receiver, by Trojan Records. Catalogue no: **12EDIT 2**

Precinct

DON'T GO
Tracks: / Don't go.
7" Single: Released Jun '85, on Calibre, Catalogue no: **CAB 204**
12" Single: Released Jun '85, on Calibre, Deleted '86. Catalogue no: **CABL 204**

SHINING STAIR
Tracks: / Shining stair.
7" Single: Released Aug '84, on Passion, by Skratch Records. Catalogue no: **PASH 32**
12" Single: Released '88, on Passion, by Skratch Records. Catalogue no: **PASH 32(12)**
12" Single: Released Aug '84, on Passion, by Skratch Records. Catalogue no: **PASH 32(12)**

Precious

DEFINITION OF A TRACK
Tracks: / Definition of a track.
12" Single: Released Jun '89, on Big Beat, by Ace Records. Catalogue no: **BB 0007**

IN MOTION
Tracks: / In motion.
CD 5": Released Jul '89, on MCA, by MCA Records. Catalogue no: **DMCA 1349**
7" Single: Released Jul '89, on MCA, by MCA Records. Catalogue no: **MCA 1349**
12" Single: Released Jul '89, on MCA, by MCA Records. Catalogue no: **MCAT 1349**

TABOO
Tracks: / Taboo.
12" Single: Released May '84, on Passion, by Skratch Records. Catalogue no: **PASH 28(12)**

Precious Little

GIVE IT TO ME NOW
Tracks: / Give it to me now / Clean living.
7" Single: Released Feb '81, on Rock On, Deleted Feb '84. Catalogue no: **ROR 2**

LET'S TOUCH DANCE
Tracks: / Let's touch dance.
7" Single: Released Sep '83, on Speed, Catalogue no: **SPEED 18**

ON AND ON SONG
Tracks: / On and on song / On and on and on.
7" Single: Released Sep '82, on Precious Organisation, by Precious Organisation. Catalogue no: **AVE 4**
7" Single: Released Nov '82, on KA, Catalogue no: **KA 14**

Precious Metal

MOVIN' MOUNTAINS
Tracks: / Movin' mountains.
7" Single: Released Sep '88, on Savage, by Savage Records. Catalogue no: **7VAG 001**

STAND UP AND SHOUT
Tracks: / Stand up and shout / Sweet sweet.
7" Single: Released Jan '89, on Savage, by Savage Records. Catalogue no: **7VAG 902**

Prediction

AFTER THIS DANCE IS THROUGH
Tracks: / After this dance is through.
12" Single: Released Feb '85, on Adelphi (1), Catalogue no: **ADET 001**

PRETTY LADY
Tracks: / Pretty lady / Dub that lady.
12" Single: Released Mar '83, on Prediction, Catalogue no: **PTN 001**

THROUGH IT ALL
Tracks: / Through it all.
12" Single: Released Oct '84, on Sanity, Catalogue no: **ES 001**

WAY WE WERE
Tracks: / Way we were, The / Way we were (dub version).
7" Single: Released Mar '82, on Student, Catalogue no: **STUDENT 008**

WONDERLAND
Tracks: / Wonderland.
7" Single: Released Oct '85, on Adelphi (1), Catalogue no: **ADET 003**

Prefab Sprout

Biographical details: Prefab Sprout. This new wave pop group was formed in Newcastle in 1978 by singer/songwriter/guitarist Paddy (Patrick) McAloon (born 1957), with brother Martin on drums (born 1962) and second vocalist Wendy Smith. The name came from the phrase 'pepper sprout' in Nancy Sinatra's *Jackson*, misheard by McAloon. The initials of first self-financed single *Lions In My Garden (Exit Someone)* spelled Limges, where his girlfriend had gone to study, pointing out a tendancy to wordplay. They signed to the local Kitchenware label; their second LP *Steve McQueen* had to be retitled *Two Wheels Good* in the USA when the late film-star's widow complained; it was produced by Thomas Dolby, who also played keyboards, and led to critical as well as popular success with their first hit single *When Love Breaks Down*. (Donald Clarke 15.5.87).

APPETITE (See panel below)
Tracks: / Appetite / Heaven can wait.
7" Single: Released '85, on CBS, by CBS Records. Catalogue no: **SK 23**

CARS AND GIRLS
Tracks: / Cars and girls / Faron Young (truckin' mix) / Real life (just around the corner) / Vendetta.
CD 5": Released Sep '88, on CBS, by CBS Records. Deleted 17 Apr '89. Catalogue no: **CDD SK 35**
CD 5": Released Feb '88, on Kitchenware, by Kitchenware Records. Deleted 17 Apr '89. Catalogue no: **CD SK35**
7" Single: Released Feb '88, on Kitchenware, by Kitchenware Records. Deleted 17 Apr '89. Catalogue no: **SK 35**
12" Single: Released Feb '88, on Kitchenware, by Kitchenware Records. Deleted 17 Apr '89. Catalogue no: **SKX 35**

COULDN'T BEAR TO BE SPECIAL
Tracks: / Couldn't bear to be special / Spinning Belinda.
7" Single: Released Mar '84, on Kitchenware, by Kitchenware Records. Catalogue no: **SK 10**
12" Single: Released Mar '84, on Kitchenware, by Kitchenware Records. Catalogue no: **SK 1012**

DEVIL HAS ALL THE BEST TUNES, THE
Tracks: / Devil has all the best tunes, The.
7" Single: Released Oct '83, on Kitchenware, by Kitchenware Records. Catalogue no: **SK 7**
7" Single: Released Jun '86, on Kitchenware, by Kitchenware Records. Catalogue no: **SK 8**

DON'T SING
Tracks: / Don't sing / Green Isaac II.
7" Single: Released Jan '84, on Kitchenware, by Kitchenware Records. Catalogue no: **SK 9**
12" Single: Released Jan '84, on Kitchenware, by Kitchenware Records. Catalogue no: **SK 912**

FARON YOUNG (See panel on next page)
Tracks: / Faron Young / Silhouettes.
7" Single: Released Jul '85, on Kitchenware, by Kitchenware Records. Deleted '88. Catalogue no: **SK 22**

PREFAB SPROUT - APPETITE (Released on CBS)

PREFAB SPROUT - FARON YOUNG (Released on Kitchenware)

PREFAB SPROUT - JOHNNY JOHNNY (Released on Kitchenware)

GOLDEN CALF, THE (EDIT)
Tracks: / Golden calf (edit) / Venus of the soup kitchen, The / Bonny (Only on 12" version and CD single.) / Golden calf (long version) (Only on 12" version and CD single.).
CD 5": Released 27 Feb '89, on Kitchenware, by Kitchenware Records. Deleted 10 Jul '89. Catalogue no: **CDSK 41**
7" Pic: Released Apr '89, on Kitchenware, by Kitchenware Records. Deleted Oct '89. Catalogue no: **SKP 41**
7" Single: Released 27 Feb '89, on Kitchenware, by Kitchenware Records. Deleted 10 Jul '89. Catalogue no: **SK 41**
12" Single: Released Apr '89, on Kitchenware, by Kitchenware Records. Deleted Oct '89. Catalogue no: **SKEP 41**
12" Single: Released 27 Feb '89, on Kitchenware, by Kitchenware Records. Deleted 10 Jul '89. Catalogue no: **SKX 41**

HEY MANHATTAN
Tracks: / Hey Manhattan / Tornado / Hey Manhattan (JFK version) (Only available on 12" and CD single.) / Donna Summer (Only available on 12" and CD single.).
CD 5": Released Jul '88, on Kitchenware, by Kitchenware Records. Deleted Jan '89. Catalogue no: **CDSK 38**
7" Single: Released 18 Jul '88, on Kitchenware, by Kitchenware Records. Deleted Jan '89. Catalogue no: **SKB 38**
7" Single: Released Jul '88, on Kitchenware, by Kitchenware Records. Deleted Jan '89. Catalogue no: **SK 38**
12" Single: Released Jul '88, on Kitchenware, by Kitchenware Records. Deleted Jan '89. Catalogue no: **SKGT 38**
12" Single: Released Jul '88, on Kitchenware, by Kitchenware Records. Deleted Jan '89. Catalogue no: **SKX 38**

JOHNNY JOHNNY (See panel top right)
Tracks: / Johnny Johnny / Wigs.
7" Single: Released Jan '86, on Kitchenware, by Kitchenware Records. Catalogue no: **SK 24**
12" Single: Released Jan '86, on Kitchenware, by Kitchenware Records. Catalogue no: **SKX 24**

KING OF ROCK AND ROLL
Tracks: / King of rock and roll / Moving river / Dandy of the Danube (Included on 12" single) / Tin can pot (Included on 12" single) / He'll have to go (Included on CD single).
CD 5": Released 23 Apr '88, on Kitchenware, by Kitchenware Records. Deleted Jan '89. Catalogue no: **CDSK 37**
7" Single: Released 23 Apr '88, on Kitchenware, by Kitchenware Records. Deleted Jan '89. Catalogue no: **SKB 37**
7" Single: Released 23 Apr '88, on Kitchenware, by Kitchenware Records. Deleted Jan '89. Catalogue no: **SKQ 37**
7" Single: Released 23 Apr '88, on Kitchenware, by Kitchenware Records. Deleted Jan '89. Catalogue no: **SK 37**
12" Single: Released 23 Apr '88, on Kitchenware, by Kitchenware Records. Deleted Jan '89. Catalogue no: **SKX 37**

LIONS IN MY OWN GARDEN
Tracks: / Lions in my own garden / Radio love / Devil has all the best tunes / Walk on.
7" Single: Released Aug '82, on Candle. Deleted '83. Catalogue no: **CANDLE 001**
12" Single: Released Dec '83, on Kitchenware, by Kitchenware Records. Deleted '85. Catalogue no: **SK8**

NIGHTINGALES
Tracks: / Nightingales / Nightingales (full version) (Only on 7" single and CD single.) / Life of surprises (Only on 12" single and CD single.) / King of rock and roll (Only on 12" version.) / Bearpark (Only on 12" version and CD single.).
CD 5": Released Nov '88, on CBS, by CBS Records. Deleted 17 Apr '89. Catalogue no: **CDSK 39**
7" Single: Released Nov '88, on CBS, by CBS Records. Deleted 17 Apr '89. Catalogue no: **SK 39**
12" Single: Released Nov '88, on CBS, by CBS Records. Deleted 17 Apr '89. Catalogue no: **SKX 39**

NIGHTINGALES (EDIT)
Tracks: / Nightingales (edit) / Lions in my own garden / Devil has all the best tunes.
7" Single: Released 21 Nov '88, on Kitchenware, by Kitchenware Records. Deleted 17 Apr '89. Catalogue no: **SK EP 39**

WHEN LOVE BREAKS DOWN
Tracks: / When love breaks down / Yearning loins.
7" Single: Released Nov '85, on Kitchenware, by Kitchenware Records. Deleted '88. Catalogue no: **SK 21**

Preface

AMERICAN YOUTH
Tracks: / American youth.
7" Single: Released Sep '82, on Bumtickler. Catalogue no: **BUM 1**

NOTHING SURPRISES ME ANYMORE
Tracks: / Nothing surprises me anymore.
7" Single: Released Mar '83, on Bumtickler. Catalogue no: **BMTK 2**

Prefects

GOING THROUGH THE MOTIONS
Tracks: / Going through the motions.
7" Single: Released Jul '80, on Rough Trade, by Rough Trade Records. Catalogue no: **RTO 40**

LOVE IS ALL AROUND
Tracks: / Love is all around / I saw the night.
7" Single: Released Dec '82, on Variety. Deleted '83. Catalogue no: **BBVY 402**

PEEL SESSIONS:PREFECTS 8.1.79
12" Single: Released Apr '87, on Strange Fruit, by Strange Fruit Records. Catalogue no: **SFPS 025**

YOUNG WORLD
Tracks: / Young world / I saw the night.
7" Single: Released Oct '81, on Rag Baby. Catalogue no: **PRIVY 504**

Prelude

AFTER THE GOLDRUSH (OLD GOLD)
Tracks: / After the goldrush.
7" Single: Released Jan '89, on Old Gold, by Old Gold Records. Catalogue no: **OG 9839**

AFTER THE GOLDRUSH (RE-RECORDING)
Tracks: / After the goldrush / I have no answers.
7" Single: Released Apr '82, on After Hours. Deleted '88. Catalogue no: **AFT 02**

AFTER THE GOLDRUSH (SINGLE)
Tracks: / After the goldrush.
7" Single: Released Jan '74, on Dawn (USA), by Biograph Records (USA). Deleted '77. Catalogue no: **DNS 1052**

CITY TONIGHT
Tracks: / City tonight / Freedom.
7" Single: Released Oct '82, on After Hours. Deleted '88. Catalogue no: **AFT 07**

FREEDOM
Tracks: / Freedom.
7" Single: Released Aug '83, on Black Crow, by Mawson & Wareham Music. Catalogue no: **CROS 1**

ONLY THE LONELY
Tracks: / Only the lonely (know the way I feel) / One broken heart for sale.
7" Single: Released Jul '82, on After Hours. Deleted '88. Catalogue no: **AFT 06**

PLATINUM BLONDE
Tracks: / Platinum blonde / Wonderful life.
7" Single: Released Apr '80, on EMI, by EMI Records. Deleted '83. Catalogue no: **EMI 5046**

SILENT NIGHT
Tracks: / Silent night.
7" Single: Released Nov '82, on After Hours. Deleted '88. Catalogue no: **AFT 08**

TRICK OF THE LIGHT
Tracks: / Trick of the light / Man in the moon.
7" Single: Released Jul '80, on EMI, by EMI Records. Deleted Jul '83. Catalogue no: **EMI 5090**

WHEN TWO WORLDS COLLIDE
Tracks: / When two worlds collide / America.
7" Single: Released Mar '81, on MCA, by MCA Records. Deleted Mar '84. Catalogue no: **MCA 2001**

Premiere Classe

POUPEE FLASH
Tracks: / Poupee flash.
7" Single: Released Feb '83, on Carrere America (USA), by PolyGram Rec.Inc.(USA). Catalogue no: **CAR 252**
12" Single: Released Feb '83, on Carrere America (USA), by PolyGram Rec.Inc.(USA). Catalogue no: **CART 252**

Pren, Ceffyl

COLLASANT EU GWAED
Tracks: / Collasant eu gwaed.
7" Single: Released May '84, on Anthem. Catalogue no: **ANTHEM 1**

Prentiss, Lee

SWEETHEARTS
Tracks: / Sweethearts / U + me (Einstein song) / Love this way (Extra track on cassette only).
Cassingle: Released May '87, on Funkin' Marvellous, by Steinar Records (UK). Deleted Jul '87. Catalogue no: **MARVC 7**
7" Single: Released May '87, on Funkin' Marvellous, by Steinar Records (UK). Deleted Jul '87. Catalogue no: **MARV 7**
12" Single: Released May '87, on Funkin' Marvellous, by Steinar Records (UK). Deleted Nov '87. Catalogue no: **12MARV 7**

U + ME (The Einstein song)
Tracks: / U + me (special New York dance mix) / U + me (extended club version) / U + me (Einstein dub mix).
12" Single: Released Mar '87, on Funkin' Marvellous, by Steinar Records (UK). Deleted May '87. Catalogue no: **12MARVX 6**

WINDOW SHOPPING
Tracks: / Window shopping / Sweetheart.
Cassingle: Released Aug '87, on Funkin' Marvellous, by Steinar Records (UK). Deleted Jan '88. Catalogue no: **MARVC 8**
7" Single: Released Aug '87, on Funkin' Marvellous, by Steinar Records (UK). Deleted Jan '88. Catalogue no: **MARV 8**
12" Single: Released Aug '87, on Funkin' Marvellous, by Steinar Records (UK). Deleted Jan '88. Catalogue no: **12MARV 8**

YOU PLUS ME
Tracks: / You plus me.
7" Single: Released Mar '87, on Funkin' Marvellous, by Steinar Records (UK). Deleted Nov '87. Catalogue no: **MARV 6**
12" Single: Released Mar '87, on Funkin' Marvellous, by Steinar Records (UK). Deleted May '87. Catalogue no: **12 MARV 6**

Presage

PRODUCT 1: LOCOMOTION
Tracks: / S.O.S..
7" Single: Released Dec '86, on Presage. Deleted '87. Catalogue no: **PRES 1**
12" Single: Released Dec '86, on Presage. Deleted '87. Catalogue no: **PREST 1**

Prescott, Brenda

I WANT TO BE WITH YOU
Tracks: / I want to be with you / Orient Express.
7" Single: Released Jan '80, on Active, by Active Records. Deleted '83. Catalogue no: **ACT 8**

Present

DANCE AWAY
Tracks: / Dance away.
7" Single: Released Dec '84, on Plezure, by Plezure Records. Catalogue no: **PLZS 844**

Preset

MONKEY SHOP
Tracks: / Monkey shop / I want to taste your love.
12" Single: Released Sep '87, on Carrere. Catalogue no: **CART 419**

President

EUROPEAN SUMMER
Tracks: / European summer pt.1 / European

summer pt.2.
7" Single: Released Jul '87, on Rekords UK. Catalogue no: **RUK 1**

President President

ALL GOOD MEN
Tracks: / All good men / Skin of the salamander.
7" Single: Released Feb '82, on Magnet, by WEA Records. Deleted Feb '87. Catalogue no: **MAG 219**
12" Single: Released Feb '82, on Magnet, by WEA Records. Deleted Feb '87. Catalogue no: **12MAG 219**

President Reagan...

FROM THIS TO THAT
Tracks: / From this to that.
12" Single: Released Jun '86, on Hyena. Catalogue no: **HAHA 001**

Presidents Men

OUT IN THE OPEN
Tracks: / Out in the open.
7" Single: Released Jul '81, on Oily, by Oily Records. Catalogue no: **SLICK 4**

REASONS FOR LEAVING
Tracks: / Reasons for leaving.
7" Single: Released Mar '81, on Oily, by Oily Records. Catalogue no: **SLICK 5**

Presley, Elvis

50TH ANNIVERSARY
12" Single: Released Jan '85, on RCA International, by BMG Records (UK). Catalogue no: **RCAT 459**

AIN'T THAT LOVING YOU BABY
Tracks: / Ain't that loving you baby.
7" Single: Released Oct '64, on RCA, by BMG Records (UK). Deleted '67. Catalogue no: **RCA 1422**

AIN'T THAT LOVING YOU BABY (RE-ISSUE)
Tracks: / Ain't that loving you baby / Bossa nova baby / Rock a hula (Extra track on 12" version).
7" Single: Released Mar '87, on RCA, by BMG Records (UK). Catalogue no: **PB 49745**
12" Single: Released Mar '87, on RCA, by BMG Records (UK). Catalogue no: **PT 49746**

ALL SHOOK UP original release
Tracks: / All shook up / That's when your heartaches begin.
7" Single: Released '57, on H.M.V., by EMI Records. Deleted '57. Catalogue no: **POP 359**

ALL SHOOK UP (RE-ISSUE)
Tracks: / All shook up / Heartbreak hotel.
7" Single: Released '77, on RCA, by BMG Records (UK). Catalogue no: **RCA 2694**

ALL THAT I AM
Tracks: / All that I am.
7" Single: Released Oct '66, on RCA, by BMG Records (UK). Deleted '69. Catalogue no: **RCA 1545**

ALWAYS ON MY MIND (OLD GOLD)
Tracks: / Always on my mind / Burning love.
7" Single: Released Jan '88, on Old Gold, by Old Gold Records. Catalogue no: **OG 9744**

ALWAYS ON MY MIND (SINGLE)
Tracks: / Always on my mind.
7" Single: Released '85, on RCA, by BMG Records (UK). Deleted '87. Catalogue no: **PB 49943**
7" Single: Released '72, on RCA, by BMG Records (UK). Deleted '75. Catalogue no: **RCA 2304**

AMERICAN TRILOGY
Tracks: / American trilogy.
7" Single: Released Jun '72, on RCA, by BMG Records (UK). Deleted '75. Catalogue no: **RCA 2229**

AMERICAN TRILOGY (OLD GOLD)
Tracks: / American trilogy / Until it's time for you to go.
7" Single: Released Jun '88, on Old Gold, by Old Gold Records. Catalogue no: **OG 9624**

AMERICAN TRILOGY (RE-ISSUE)
Tracks: / American trilogy / Suspicious minds.
7" Single: Released '81, on RCA Golden Grooves, by BMG Records (UK). Deleted May '89. Catalogue no: **GOLD 506**

ANYTHING THAT'S PART OF YOU
Tracks: / Anything that's part of you.
7" Single: Released May '77, on RCA, by BMG Records (UK). Catalogue no: **RCA 2704**

ARE YOU LONESOME TONIGHT (OLD GOLD)
Tracks: / Are you lonesome tonight / Wooden heart.
7" Single: Released Apr '87, on Old Gold, by Old Gold Records. Catalogue no: **OG 9702**

ARE YOU LONESOME TONIGHT (ORIGINAL ISSUE)
Tracks: / Aré you lonesome tonight / I gotta know.
7" Single: Released Jan '61, on RCA, by BMG Records (UK). Deleted '64. Catalogue no: **RCA 1216**

ARE YOU LONESOME TONIGHT (RE-ISSUE)
Tracks: / Are you lonesome tonight / From a jack to a king.
7" Single: Released '82, on RCA, by BMG Records (UK). Deleted '85. Catalogue no: **RCA 196**

ARE YOU SINCERE
Tracks: / Are you sincere.
7" Single: Released '80, on RCA, by BMG Records (UK). Catalogue no: **LR 4996**

BABY I DON'T CARE
Tracks: / Baby I don't care.
7" Single: Released Apr '83, on RCA, by BMG Records (UK). Catalogue no: **RCA 332**
12" Single: Released Apr '83, on RCA, by BMG Records (UK). Catalogue no: **RCAT 332**

BIG HUNK O LOVE, A
Tracks: / Big hunk o love, A.
7" Single: Released Jul '59, on RCA, by BMG Records (UK). Deleted '62. Catalogue no: **RCA 1136**

BLUE CHRISTMAS
Tracks: / Blue Christmas.
7" Single: Released Dec '64, on RCA, by BMG Records (UK). Deleted '67. Catalogue no: **RCA 1430**

BLUE HAWAII (SINGLE) Film soundtrack
7" Single: Released '80, on RCA, by BMG Records (UK). Catalogue no: **LR 5194**

BLUE MOON original release
Tracks: / Blue moon / I don't care if the sun don't shine.
7" Single: Released '56, on H.M.V., by EMI Records. Deleted '57. Catalogue no: **POP 272**
7" Single: Released '80, on RCA, by BMG Records (UK). Catalogue no: **LR 1281**

BLUE MOON (OLD GOLD)
Tracks: / Blue moon / I don't care if the sun don't shine.
7" Single: Released Oct '86, on Old Gold, by Old Gold Records. Catalogue no: **OG 9620**

BLUE RIVER
Tracks: / Blue river.
7" Single: Released Dec '66, on RCA, by BMG Records (UK). Deleted '69. Catalogue no: **RCA 1504**
7" Single: Released '75, on RCA, by BMG Records (UK). Catalogue no: **LR 0709**

BLUE SUEDE SHOES
Tracks: / Blue suede shoes.
7" Single: Released '75, on RCA, by BMG Records (UK). Catalogue no: **LR 8132**

BLUE SUEDE SHOES (SINGLE) original release
Tracks: / Blue suede shoes / Tutti frutti.
7" Single: Released '56, on H.M.V., by EMI Records. Deleted '57. Catalogue no: **7M 405**
78 rpm: Released '56, on H.M.V., by EMI Records. Deleted '57. Catalogue no: **POP 213**

BOSSA NOVA BABY
Tracks: / Bossa nova baby.
7" Single: Released '80, on RCA, by BMG Records (UK). Catalogue no: **LR 1198**
7" Single: Released Oct '63, on RCA, by BMG Records (UK). Deleted '66. Catalogue no: **RCA 1374**

BURNING LOVE
Tracks: / Burning love.
7" Single: Released Sep '72, on RCA, by BMG Records (UK). Deleted '75. Catalogue no: **RCA 2267**
7" Single: Released '80, on RCA, by BMG Records (UK). Catalogue no: **LR 1898**

CAN'T HELP FALLING IN LOVE (OLD GOLD)
Tracks: / Can't help falling in love / Rock a hula baby.
Note: Full title: "Can't help falling in love"
7" Single: Released Jan '88, on Old Gold, by Old Gold Records. Catalogue no: **OG 9754**

CLEAN UP YOUR OWN BACK YARD
Tracks: / Clean up your own backyard.
7" Single: Released Sep '69, on RCA, by BMG Records (UK). Deleted '72. Catalogue no: **RCA 1869**

COLLECTOR'S GOLD
7" Single: Released Oct '82, on RCA, by BMG Records (UK). Catalogue no: **RCX 3**

CRYING IN THE CHAPEL
Tracks: / Crying in the chapel.
7" Single: Released May '77, on RCA, by BMG Records (UK). Deleted May '89. Catalogue no: **RCA 2708**
7" Single: Released May '65, on RCA, by BMG Records (UK). Deleted '68. Catalogue no: **RCA 1455**

DANNY BOY
Tracks: / Danny boy.
7" Single: Released '80, on RCA, by BMG Records (UK). Catalogue no: **LR 5195**

DEVIL IN DISGUISE
Tracks: / Devil in disguise.
7" Single: Released Jul '63, on RCA, by BMG Records (UK). Deleted '66. Catalogue no: **RCA 1355**
7" Single: Released May '77, on RCA, by BMG Records (UK). Catalogue no: **RCA 2707**

DO THE CLAM
Tracks: / Do the clam.
7" Single: Released Mar '65, on RCA, by BMG Records (UK). Deleted '68. Catalogue no: **RCA 1443**

DON'T
Tracks: / Don't.
7" Single: Released Feb '58, on RCA, by BMG Records (UK). Deleted '61. Catalogue no: **RCA 1043**
7" Single: Released '80, on RCA, by BMG Records (UK). Catalogue no: **LR 0711**

DON'T BE CRUEL (RE-ISSUE)
Tracks: / Don't be cruel / Hound dog.
7" Single: Released Jun '78, on RCA, by BMG Records (UK). Catalogue no: **PB 9265**

DON'T CRY DADDY
Tracks: / Don't cry daddy.
7" Single: Released Feb '70, on RCA, by BMG Records (UK). Deleted '73. Catalogue no: **RCA 1916**
7" Single: Released '80, on RCA, by BMG Records (UK). Catalogue no: **LR 1896**

DON'T (OLD GOLD)
Tracks: / Don't / Wear my ring around your neck.
7" Single: Released Jan '88, on Old Gold, by Old Gold Records. Catalogue no: **OG 9752**

ELVIS EP COLLECTION NO.2
7" EP: Released Oct '82, on RCA, by BMG Records (UK). Catalogue no: **EP 2**

ELVIS (MEDLEY)
Tracks: / Elvis (medley).
7" Single: Released Jan '85, on RCA, by BMG Records (UK). Deleted '87. Catalogue no: **RCA 476**

ELVIS PRESLEY: INTERVIEW PICTURE DISC COLLECTION
7" Set: Released Apr '88, on Baktabak, by Baktabak Records. Catalogue no: **BAKPAK 1008**
7" Single: on Talkies, Catalogue no: **ELVIS 1**

ELVIS SAILS
Note: Various press interviews prior to sailing to Germany in 1958 for U.S. army service
7" EP: Released '58, on RCA, by BMG Records (UK). Catalogue no: **RCX 131**

FLAMING STAR (EP)
Tracks: / Flaming star.
7" EP: Released Oct '82, on RCA, by BMG Records (UK). Catalogue no: **RCX 7205**

FOLLOW THAT DREAM (EP)
Tracks: / Follow that dream / Angel / What a wonderful life / I'm not the marrying kind.
7" EP: Released Jun '62, on RCA, by BMG Records (UK). Deleted '65. Catalogue no: **RCX 211**
7" EP: Released Feb '82, on RCA, by BMG Records (UK). Catalogue no: **RCX 7196**

FOOL
Tracks: / Fool.
7" Single: Released Aug '73, on RCA, by BMG Records (UK). Deleted '76. Catalogue no: **RCA 2393**

FOOL SUCH AS I, A
Tracks: / Fool such as I, A / Need your love tonight.
7" Single: Released Apr '59, on RCA, by BMG Records (UK). Deleted '62. Catalogue no: **RCA 1113**
7" Single: Released May '77, on RCA, by BMG Records (UK). Catalogue no: **RCA 2697**

FRANKIE AND JOHNNY (SINGLE)
Tracks: / Frankie and Johnny.
7" Single: Released Apr '66, on RCA, by BMG Records (UK). Deleted '69. Catalogue no: **RCA 1509**
7" Single: Released Jan '80, on RCA, by BMG Records (UK). Catalogue no: **LR 1282**

G.I. BLUES (EP) The alternate takes
Tracks: / Shoppin' around / Big boots / Tonight's all right for love / Frankfurt special.
7" EP: Released '82, on RCA, by BMG Records (UK). Deleted May '89. Catalogue no: **RCX 1**

GIRL OF MY BEST FRIEND
Tracks: / Girl of my best friend.
7" Single: Released Sep '76, on RCA, by BMG Records (UK). Deleted '79. Catalogue no: **RCA 2729**
7" Single: Released Jul '81, on RCA Golden Grooves, by BMG Records (UK). Catalogue no: **GOLD 500**

GOOD LUCK CHARM
Tracks: / Good luck charm.
7" Single: Released May '62, on RCA, by BMG Records (UK). Deleted '65. Catalogue no: **RCA 1280**
7" Single: Released May '77, on RCA, by BMG Records (UK). Catalogue no: **RCA 2704**

GOOD ROCKIN' TONIGHT
Tracks: / Good rockin' tonight.
7" Single: Released Oct '81, on RCA Golden Grooves, by BMG Records (UK). Catalogue no: **GOLD 534**

GOOD ROCKIN' TONIGHT (EP)
Tracks: / Good rockin' tonight / Blue moon of Kentucky / Milkcow blues boogie / Just because.
7" EP: Released '57, on H.M.V., by EMI Records. Deleted '57. Catalogue no: **7EG 8256**

GREEN GREEN GRASS OF HOME
Tracks: / Green green grass of home / Release me / Solitaire.
7" Single: Released Nov '75, on RCA, by BMG Records (UK). Deleted '78. Catalogue no: **RCA 2674**
7" Single: Released May '84, on RCA, by BMG Records (UK). Catalogue no: **RCA 405**

GUITAR MAN (SINGLE)
Tracks: / Guitar man / Faded love.
7" Single: Released Feb '81, on RCA, by BMG Records (UK). Catalogue no: **RCA 43**
7" Single: Released Feb '68, on RCA, by BMG Records (UK). Deleted '71. Catalogue no: **RCA 1663**

HARD HEADED WOMAN
Tracks: / Hard headed woman.
7" Single: Released Jul '58, on RCA, by BMG Records (UK). Deleted '61. Catalogue no: **RCA 1070**
7" Single: Released Jan '80, on RCA, by BMG Records (UK). Catalogue no: **LR 0715**

HEARTBREAK HOTEL (CD SINGLE)
Tracks: / Heartbreak Hotel.
CD 5": Released Jun '89, on RCA, by BMG Records (UK). Catalogue no: **PD 49467**

HEARTBREAK HOTEL (EP)
Tracks: / Heartbreak hotel / Money honey / I was the one / I forgot to remember to forget.
7" EP: Released '82, on RCA, by BMG Records (UK). Catalogue no: **RCX 7189**

HEARTBREAK HOTEL (OLD GOLD)
Tracks: / Heartbreak hotel / All shook up.
7" Single: Released '87, on Old Gold, by Old Gold Records. Catalogue no: **OG 9704**

HEARTBREAK HOTEL (RE-ISSUE)
Tracks: / Heartbreak Hotel / Hound dog.
7" Single: Released Jul '71, on RCA, by BMG Records (UK). Deleted '74. Catalogue no: **RCA 2104**

HEARTBREAK HOTEL (SINGLE) original release
Tracks: / Heartbreak hotel / I was the one.
7" Single: Released '56, on H.M.V., by EMI Records. Deleted '57. Catalogue no: **7M 385**
78 rpm: Released '56, on H.M.V., by EMI Records. Deleted '57. Catalogue no: **POP 182**

HIS LATEST FLAME
Tracks: / His latest flame / Little sister.
7" Single: Released '77, on RCA, by BMG Records (UK). Catalogue no: **RCA 2702**
7" Single: Released Oct '86, on Old Gold, by Old Gold Records. Catalogue no: **OG 9622**
7" Single: Released '61, on RCA, by BMG Records (UK). Deleted '64. Catalogue no: **RCA 1258**

HOUND DOG (OLD GOLD)
Tracks: / Hound dog / Don't be cruel.
7" Single: Released Apr '87, on Old Gold, by Old Gold Records. Catalogue no: **OG 9700**

HOUND DOG (SINGLE) original release
Tracks: / Hound dog / Don't be cruel.
7" Single: Released '56, on H.M.V., by EMI Records. Deleted '57. Catalogue no: **POP 249**

HURT
Tracks: / Hurt.
7" Single: Released May '76, on RCA, by BMG Records (UK). Deleted '79. Catalogue no: **RCA 2674**

I CAN HELP (SINGLE)
Tracks: / I can help.
7" Single: Released '83, on RCA, by BMG

ELVIS PRESLEY - IT'S ONLY LOVE (Released on RCA)

Records (UK). Catalogue no: **RCA 369**

I DON'T CARE IF THE SUN DON'T SHINE
Tracks: / I don't care if the sun don't shine.
7" Single: Released Jan '80, on RCA, by BMG Records (UK). Catalogue no: **LR 1216**

I GOT A THING ABOUT YOU BABY
Tracks: / I got a thing about you baby.
7" Single: Released Jul '74, on RCA, by BMG Records (UK). Deleted '77. Catalogue no: **APBO 0196**

I GOT STUNG
Tracks: / I got stung.
7" Single: Released May '77, on RCA, by BMG Records (UK). Catalogue no: **RCA 2696**

I JUST CAN'T HELP BELIEVIN'
Tracks: / I just can't help believing.
7" Single: Released Dec '61, on RCA, by BMG Records (UK). Deleted '64. Catalogue no: **RCA 21578**
7" Single: Released Jul '81, on RCA Golden Grooves, by BMG Records (UK). Deleted May '89. Catalogue no: **GOLD 510**

I NEED YOU SO
Tracks: / I need you so.
7" Single: Released Oct '82, on RCA, by BMG Records (UK). Catalogue no: **RCX 7200**

I NEED YOUR LOVE TONIGHT
Tracks: / I need your love tonight.
7" Single: Released May '77, on RCA, by BMG Records (UK). Catalogue no: **RCA 2697**

I WANT YOU, I NEED YOU, I LOVE YOU original release
Tracks: / I want you, I need you, I love you / My baby left me.
7" Single: Released '56, on H.M.V., by EMI Records. Deleted '57. Catalogue no: **7M 424**
7" Single: Released Jan '80, on RCA, by BMG Records (UK). Catalogue no: **LR 0710**
78 rpm: Released '56, on H.M.V., by EMI Records. Deleted '57. Catalogue no: **POP 235**

IF EVERY DAY WAS LIKE CHRISTMAS
Tracks: / If every day was like Christmas / Blue Christmas.
7" Single: Released Dec '66, on RCA, by BMG Records (UK). Deleted '69. Catalogue no: **RCA 1557**
7" Single: Released Nov '81, on RCA Golden Grooves, by BMG Records (UK). Catalogue no: **GOLD 541**

IF I CAN DREAM
Tracks: / If I can dream.
7" Single: Released Feb '69, on RCA, by BMG Records (UK). Deleted '72. Catalogue no: **RCA 1795**
7" Single: Released Jan '80, on RCA, by BMG Records (UK). Catalogue no: **LR 2707**

IF YOU TALK IN YOUR SLEEP
Tracks: / If you talk in your sleep.
7" Single: Released Jul '74, on RCA, by BMG Records (UK). Deleted '77. Catalogue no: **APBO 0280**

I'M LEAVIN'
Tracks: / I'm leaving.
7" Single: Released Oct '71, on RCA, by BMG Records (UK). Deleted '74. Catalogue no: **RCA 2125**
7" Single: Released Jan '80, on RCA, by BMG Records (UK). Catalogue no: **LR 0732**

I'M LEFT YOU'RE RIGHT SHE'S GONE
Tracks: / I'm left you're right she's gone.
7" Single: Released Jan '58, on H.M.V., by EMI Records. Deleted '61. Catalogue no: **POP 428**

IN THE GHETTO
Tracks: / In the ghetto.
7" Single: Released '75, on RCA, by BMG Records (UK). Catalogue no: **LR 8111**
7" Single: Released Jun '69, on RCA, by BMG Records (UK). Deleted '72. Catalogue no: **RCA 1831**

IN THE GHETTO (OLD GOLD)
Tracks: / In the ghetto / Suspicious minds.
7" Single: Released Oct '86, on Old Gold, by Old Gold Records. Catalogue no: **OG 9616**

INDESCRIBABLY BLUE
Tracks: / Indescribably blue.
7" Single: Released Feb '67, on RCA, by BMG Records (UK). Deleted '70. Catalogue no: **RCA 1565**

IT WON'T SEEM LIKE CHRISTMAS WITHOUT YOU(SINGLE)
Tracks: / It won't seem like christmas without you.
7" Single: Released Nov '79, on RCA, by BMG Records (UK). Catalogue no: **PB 9464**

IT'S NOW OR NEVER (OLD GOLD)
Tracks: / It's now or never / Surrender.
7" Single: Released '88, on Old Gold, by Old Gold Records. Catalogue no: **OG 9742**

IT'S NOW OR NEVER (SINGLE)
Tracks: / It's now or never / Make me know it.
7" Single: Released '60, Deleted '63. Catalogue no: **RCA 1207**
7" Single: Released '83, on RCA, by BMG Records (UK). Catalogue no: **PC 60033**
7" Single: Released '77, on RCA, by BMG Records (UK). Catalogue no: **RCA 2698**

IT'S ONLY LOVE (See panel above)
Tracks: / It's only love / Beyond the reef.
7" Single: Released Aug '80, on RCA, by BMG Records (UK). Deleted '83. Catalogue no: **RCA 4**
12" Single: Released Oct '80, on RCA, by BMG Records (UK). Deleted Oct '83. Catalogue no: **RCAT 4**

I'VE LOST YOU
Tracks: / I've lost you.
7" Single: Released Nov '70, on RCA, by BMG Records (UK). Deleted '73. Catalogue no: **RCA 1999**
7" Single: Released Jan '80, on RCA, by BMG Records (UK). Catalogue no: **LR 0727**

JAILHOUSE ROCK (EP)
Tracks: / Jailhouse rock / Young and beautiful / I want to be free / Don't leave me now / Baby I don't care.
7" EP: Released '82, on RCA, by BMG Records (UK). Catalogue no: **RCX 7193**
7" EP: Released '58, on RCA, by BMG Records (UK). Deleted '61. Catalogue no: **RCX 106**

JAILHOUSE ROCK (OLD GOLD)
Tracks: / Jailhouse rock / Treat me nice.
7" Single: Released Jan '88, on Old Gold, by Old Gold Records. Catalogue no: **OG 9740**

JAILHOUSE ROCK (SINGLE)
Tracks: / Jailhouse rock.
Note: Various re-issues
7" Pic: Released '83, on RCA, by BMG Records (UK). Catalogue no: **RCAP 1028**
7" Single: Released '83, on RCA, by BMG Records (UK). Catalogue no: **RCA 1028**
7" Single: Released Dec '71, on RCA, by BMG Records (UK). Deleted '74. Catalogue no: **RCA 2153**
7" Single: Released Sep '77, on RCA, by BMG Records (UK). Deleted '80. Catalogue no: **PB 2695**
7" Single: Released '58, on RCA, by BMG Records (UK). Deleted '61. Catalogue no: **RCA 1028**

KENTUCKY RAIN
Tracks: / Kentucky rain.
7" Single: Released May '70, on RCA, by BMG Records (UK). Deleted '73. Catalogue no: **RCA 1949**
7" Single: Released Jan '80, on RCA, by BMG Records (UK). Catalogue no: **LR 4058**

KID GALAHAD (EP)
Tracks: / King of the whole wide world / This is living / Riding the rainbow / Home is where the heart is / I got lucky / Whistling tune.
7" EP: Released '82, on RCA, by BMG Records (UK). Catalogue no: **RCX 7197**

KING CREOLE (OLD GOLD)
Tracks: / King Creole / Hard headed woman.
7" Single: Released Jan '88, on Old Gold, by Old Gold Records. Catalogue no: **OG 9750**

KING CREOLE (SINGLE) original release
Tracks: / King Creole / Dixieland rock.
7" Single: Released '58, on RCA, by BMG Records (UK). Deleted '61. Catalogue no: **RCA 1081**

KING CREOLE VOL.1 (EP)
Tracks: / King Creole / New Orleans / As long as I have you / Lover doll.
7" EP: Released '82, on RCA, by BMG Records (UK). Catalogue no: **RCX 7194**

KING CREOLE VOL.2 (EP)
7" EP: Released '82, on RCA, by BMG Records (UK). Catalogue no: **RCX 7201**

KISS ME QUICK
Tracks: / Kiss me quick.
7" Single: Released Dec '63, on RCA, by BMG Records (UK). Deleted '66. Catalogue no: **RCA 1375**

KISSIN' COUSINS (SINGLE)
Tracks: / Kissin' cousins.
7" Single: Released Jun '64, on RCA, by BMG Records (UK). Deleted '67. Catalogue no: **RCA 1404**
7" Single: Released Jan '80, on RCA, by BMG Records (UK). Catalogue no: **LR 1262**

LAST FAREWELL, THE
Tracks: / Last farewell, The.
7" Single: Released Oct '84, on RCA, by BMG Records (UK). Deleted '87. Catalogue no: **RCA 459**

LAWDY MISS CLAWDY (SINGLE)
Tracks: / Lawdy Miss Clawdy / Tryin' to get to you.
7" Single: Released '57, on H.M.V., by EMI Records. Deleted '57. Catalogue no: **POP 408**

LONG LEGGED GIRL
Tracks: / Long legged girl with the short dress on.
7" Single: Released Sep '67, on RCA Victor, by BMG Records (UK). Deleted '70. Catalogue no: **RCA 1616**

LOVE IN LAS VEGAS
Tracks: / Love in Las Vegas.
7" Single: Released Oct '82, on RCA, by BMG Records (UK). Catalogue no: **RCX 7206**

LOVE LETTERS
Tracks: / Love letters.
7" Single: Released Jul '66, on RCA, by BMG Records (UK). Deleted '69. Catalogue no: **RCA 1526**
7" Single: Released Jan '80, on RCA, by BMG Records (UK). Catalogue no: **LR 1156**

LOVE ME TENDER (EP)
Tracks: / Love me tender / We're gonna move / Let me / Poor boy.
7" EP: Released '82, on RCA, by BMG Records (UK). Catalogue no: **RCX 7191**
7" EP: Released '56, on H.M.V., by EMI Records. Deleted '57. Catalogue no: **7EG 8199**

LOVE ME TENDER (OLD GOLD)
Tracks: / Love me tender / Teddy bear.
7" Single: Released '86, on Old Gold, by Old Gold Records. Catalogue no: **OG 9626**

LOVE ME TENDER (SINGLE) original release
Tracks: / Love me tender / Anyway you want me.
7" Single: Released '56, on H.M.V., by EMI Records. Deleted '57. Catalogue no: **POP 253**
7" Single: Released Aug '87, on RCA, by BMG Records (UK). Deleted May '89. Catalogue no: **ARON 2**
12" Single: Released Aug '87, on RCA, by BMG Records (UK). Deleted May '89. Catalogue no: **ARON T2**

LOVIN' ARMS
Tracks: / Lovin' arms / You asked me to.
7" Single: Released '81, on RCA, by BMG Records (UK). Catalogue no: **RCA 48**

LOVING YOU (OLD GOLD)
Tracks: / Loving you / Paralysed.
7" Single: Released Jan '88, on Old Gold, by Old Gold Records. Catalogue no: **OG 9746**

LOVING YOU (SINGLE) Re-issue
Tracks: / Loving you.
7" Single: Released Jan '80, on RCA, by BMG Records (UK). Catalogue no: **LR 0714**
7" Single: Released Feb '82, on RCA, by BMG Records (UK). Catalogue no: **RCX 7192**

MEAN WOMAN BLUES
Tracks: / Mean woman blues / I beg of you / Mean woman blues (dub) (On 12" and CD single only.) / Party (On 12" and CD single only.).
CD 5": Released Jan '89, on RCA, by BMG Records (UK). Deleted Jul '89. Catalogue no: **PD 49474**
7" Single: Released Jan '89, on RCA, by BMG Records (UK). Catalogue no: **PB 49473**
12" Single: Released Jan '89, on RCA, by BMG Records (UK). Catalogue no: **PT 49474**

MEMORIES
Tracks: / Memories.
7" Single: Released Jan '80, on RCA, by BMG Records (UK). Catalogue no: **LR 4059**

MESS OF BLUES, A
Tracks: / Mess of blues, A.
7" Single: Released Jul '60, on RCA, by BMG Records (UK). Deleted '63. Catalogue no: **RCA 1194**

MOODY BLUE (SINGLE)
Tracks: / Moody blue / Way down.
7" Single: Released Mar '77, on RCA, by BMG Records (UK). Deleted '80. Catalogue no: **PB 0857**
7" Single: Released May '82, on RCA Golden Grooves, by BMG Records (UK). Deleted May '89. Catalogue no: **GOLD 544**

MY BABY LEFT ME
Tracks: / My baby left me.
7" Single: Released Jan '80, on RCA, by BMG Records (UK). Catalogue no: **LR 0710**

MY BOY
Tracks: / My boy.
7" Single: Released Nov '74, on RCA, by BMG Records (UK). Deleted '77. Catalogue no: **RCA 2458**

MY BOY (OLD GOLD)
Tracks: / My boy / My way.
7" Single: Released Jan '88, on Old Gold, by Old Gold Records. Catalogue no: **OG 9756**

MY WAY
Tracks: / My way.
7" Single: Released Jun '78, on RCA, by BMG Records (UK). Deleted '81. Catalogue no: **PB 1165**

MYSTERY TRAIN original issue
Tracks: / Mystery train / Love me.
7" Single: Released '57, on H.M.V., by EMI Records. Deleted '57. Catalogue no: **POP 295**
7" Single: Released Jan '80, on RCA, by BMG Records (UK). Catalogue no: **LR 1289**

OLD SHEP
Tracks: / Old Shep.
7" Single: Released Jan '79, on RCA, by BMG Records (UK). Catalogue no: **PB 9334**

ONE BROKEN HEART FOR SALE
Tracks: / One broken heart for sale.
7" Single: Released Feb '63, on RCA, by BMG Records (UK). Deleted '66. Catalogue no: **RCA 1337**

ONE NIGHT original issue
Tracks: / One night / I got stung.
7" Single: Released Jan '59, on RCA, by BMG Records (UK). Deleted '62. Catalogue no: **RCA 1100**
7" Single: Released Jan '80, on RCA, by BMG Records (UK). Catalogue no: **LR 8280**

PARALYSED
Tracks: / Paralysed / When my blue moon turns to gold again.
7" Single: Released '57, on H.M.V., by EMI Records. Deleted '57. Catalogue no: **POP 378**

PARTY original issue
Tracks: / Party / Got a lot of livin' to do.
7" Single: Released Oct '57, on RCA, by BMG Records (UK). Deleted '60. Catalogue no: **RCA 1020**

PARTY (OLD GOLD)
Tracks: / Party / Got a lot of livin' to do.
7" Single: Released Oct '86, on Old Gold, by Old Gold Records. Catalogue no: **OG 9618**

PEACE IN THE VALLEY
Tracks: / Peace in the valley / It is no secret / Take my hand precious Lord / I believe.
7" EP: Released '57, on RCA, by BMG Records (UK). Deleted '62. Catalogue no: **RCX 101**
7" EP: Released '82, on RCA, by BMG Records (UK). Catalogue no: **RCX 7199**

PORK SALAD ANNIE
Tracks: / Pork salad Annie.
7" Single: Released May '73, on RCA, by BMG Records (UK). Deleted '76. Catalogue no: **RCA 2359**

PROMISED LAND (SINGLE)
Tracks: / Promised land.
7" Single: Released Jan '75, on RCA, by BMG Records (UK). Deleted '78. Catalogue no: **PB 10074**
7" Single: Released Jan '80, on RCA, by BMG Records (UK). Catalogue no: **LR 0730**

RAGS TO RICHES
Tracks: / Rags to riches.
7" Single: Released May '71, on RCA, by BMG Records (UK). Deleted '74. Catalogue no: **RCA 2084**
7" Single: Released Jan '80, on RCA, by BMG Records (UK). Catalogue no: **LR 4138**

RAISED ON ROCK
Tracks: / Raised on rock.
7" Single: Released Nov '73, on RCA, by BMG Records (UK). Deleted '76. Catalogue no: **RCA 2435**

REAL ELVIS
Tracks: / Real Elvis.
7" Single: Released Feb '82, on RCA, by BMG Records (UK). Catalogue no: **RCX 7190**

RETURN TO SENDER (SINGLE)
Tracks: / Return to sender.
7" Single: Released '77, on RCA, by BMG Records (UK). Catalogue no: **RCA 2706**
7" Single: Released '62, on RCA, by BMG Records (UK). Deleted '65. Catalogue no: **RCA 1320**

RIP IT UP
Tracks: / Rip it up.
7" Single: Released Mar '57, on H.M.V., by EMI Records. Deleted '60. Catalogue no: **POP 305**

ROCK A-HULA BABY
Tracks: / Rock a hula baby / Can't help falling in love.
7" Single: Released '77, on RCA, by BMG Records (UK). Catalogue no: **RCA 2703**
7" Single: Released '62, on RCA, by BMG Records (UK). Deleted '65. Catalogue no: **RCA 1270**

SANTA BRING MY BABY BACK (TO ME)
Tracks: / Santa bring my baby back to me.
7" Single: Released Nov '57, on RCA, by BMG Records (UK). Deleted '60. Catalogue no: **RCA 1025**

SANTA CLAUS IS BACK IN TOWN
Tracks: / Santa Claus is back in town / I believe.
7" Single: Released Nov '80, on RCA, by BMG Records (UK). Catalogue no: **RCA 16**

SHAKE RATTLE AND ROLL
Tracks: / Shake, rattle and roll.
7" Single: Released Oct '82, on RCA, by BMG Records (UK). Catalogue no: **RCX 7198**

SHE'S NOT YOU
Tracks: / She's not you.
7" Single: Released Aug '62, on RCA, by BMG Records (UK). Deleted '65. Catalogue no: **RCA 1303**
7" Single: Released May '77, on RCA, by BMG Records (UK). Catalogue no: **RCA 2705**

SOUND OF YOUR CRY (SINGLE)
Tracks: / Sound of your cry / I'll never know.
7" Single: Released '82, on RCA, by BMG Records (UK). Catalogue no: **RCA 232**

STRICTLY ELVIS (EP)
Tracks: / Old Shep / Anyplace is paradise / Paralysed / Is it so strange.
7" Single: Released Feb '60, on RCA, by BMG Records (UK). Deleted '63. Catalogue no: **RCX 175**

STUCK ON YOU
Tracks: / Stuck on you / Anyway you want me.
CD 5": Released Jun '89, on RCA, by BMG Records (UK). Deleted Aug '89. Catalogue no: **PD 49596**
7" Single: Released '60, on RCA, by BMG Records (UK). Deleted '63. Catalogue no: **RCA 1187**
7" Single: Released Jan '88, on RCA, by BMG Records (UK). Deleted Aug '89. Catalogue no: **PB 49595**

SUCH A NIGHT
Tracks: / Such a night.
7" Single: Released Aug '64, on RCA, by BMG Records (UK). Deleted '67. Catalogue no: **RCA 1411**
7" Single: Released Feb '82, on RCA, by BMG Records (UK). Catalogue no: **RCX 7195**

SURRENDER
Tracks: / Surrender.
7" Single: Released Mar '61, on RCA, by BMG Records (UK). Deleted '64. Catalogue no: **RCA 1227**
7" Single: Released May '77, on RCA, by BMG Records (UK). Catalogue no: **RCA 2701**

SUSPICION
Tracks: / Suspicion.
7" Single: Released Nov '76, on RCA, by BMG Records (UK). Catalogue no: **RCA 2768**

SUSPICIOUS MINDS (SINGLE)
Tracks: / Suspicious minds.
7" Single: Released '80, on RCA, by BMG Records (UK). Catalogue no: **LR 1152**
7" Single: Released '69, on RCA, by BMG Records (UK). Deleted '72. Catalogue no: **RCA 1900**

TEDDY BEAR
Tracks: / Teddy bear / Loving you.
7" Single: Released Jul '57, on RCA, by BMG Records (UK). Deleted '60. Catalogue no: **RCA 1013**

TELL ME WHY
Tracks: / Tell me why.
7" Single: Released Nov '65, on RCA, by BMG Records (UK). Deleted '68. Catalogue no: **RCA 1489**
7" Single: Released Jan '80, on RCA, by BMG Records (UK). Catalogue no: **LR 4065**

THAT'S ALL RIGHT MAMA
Tracks: / That's alright mama / Harbour lights.
7" Single: Released Aug '81, on RCA Golden Grooves, by BMG Records (UK). Deleted May '89. Catalogue no: **GOLD 520**

THERE GOES MY EVERYTHING
Tracks: / There goes my everything.
7" Single: Released Mar '71, on RCA, by BMG Records (UK). Deleted '74. Catalogue no: **RCA 2060**

TOO MUCH
Tracks: / Too much / Playing for keeps.
7" Single: Released '57, on H.M.V., by EMI Records. Deleted '57. Catalogue no: **POP 330**

TOUCH OF GOLD - VOL.1 (EP)
7" EP: Released '82, on RCA, by BMG Records (UK). Catalogue no: **RCX 7202**

TOUCH OF GOLD - VOL.2 (EP)
7" EP: Released '82, on RCA, by BMG Records (UK). Catalogue no: **RCX 7203**

TOUCH OF GOLD - VOL.3 (EP)
7" EP: Released '82, on RCA, by BMG Records (UK). Catalogue no: **RCX 7204**

T.R.O.U.B.L.E.
Tracks: / T.R.O.U.B.L.E..
7" Single: Released May '75, on RCA, by BMG Records (UK). Deleted '78. Catalogue no: **RCA 2562**

UNCHAINED MELODY
Tracks: / Unchained melody.
7" Single: Released '80, on RCA (USA), Catalogue no: **LR 4590**

UNTIL IT'S TIME FOR YOU TO GO
Tracks: / Until it's time for you to go.
7" Single: Released Apr '72, on RCA, by BMG Records (UK). Deleted '75. Catalogue no: **RCA 2188**
7" Single: Released '80, on RCA (USA), Catalogue no: **LR 1897**

U.S. MALE (SINGLE)
Tracks: / U.S. male.
7" Single: Released '80, on RCA, by BMG Records (UK). Catalogue no: **LR 1133**
7" Single: Released '68, on RCA, by BMG Records (UK). Deleted '71. Catalogue no: **RCA 1688**

VIVA LAS VEGAS
Tracks: / Viva Las Vegas.
7" Single: Released Mar '64, on RCA, by BMG Records (UK). Deleted '67. Catalogue no: **RCA 1390**
7" Single: Released '80, on RCA (USA), Catalogue no: **LR 1266**

WAY DOWN
Tracks: / Way down.
7" Single: Released Aug '77, on RCA, by BMG Records (UK). Deleted '80. Catalogue no: **PB 0998**

WAY DOWN (OLD GOLD)
Tracks: / Way down / Moody blue.
7" Single: Released Jan '88, on Old Gold, by Old Gold Records. Catalogue no: **OG 9758**

WEAR MY RING AROUND YOUR NECK
Tracks: / Wear my ring around your neck.
7" Single: Released May '58, on RCA, by BMG Records (UK). Deleted '61. Catalogue no: **RCA 1058**
7" Single: Released '80, on RCA (USA), Catalogue no: **LR 0712**

WILD IN THE COUNTRY (OLD GOLD)
Tracks: / Wild in the country / I feel so bad.
7" Single: Released Apr '87, on Old Gold, by Old Gold Records. Catalogue no: **OG 9706**

WILD IN THE COUNTRY (SINGLE) original issue
Tracks: / Wild in the country / I feel so bad.
7" Single: Released '61, on RCA, by BMG Records (UK). Deleted '64. Catalogue no: **RCA 1244**

WONDER OF YOU, THE
Tracks: / Wonder of you, The.
7" Single: Released Sep '77, on RCA, by BMG Records (UK). Deleted '80. Catalogue no: **PB 2709**
7" Single: Released Jul '70, on RCA, by BMG Records (UK). Deleted '73. Catalogue no: **RCA 1974**

WONDER OF YOU, THE (OLD GOLD)
Tracks: / Wonder of you, The / If I can dream.
7" Single: Released Jan '88, on Old Gold, by Old Gold Records. Catalogue no: **OG 9761**

WOODEN HEART
Tracks: / Wooden heart.
7" Single: Released Mar '61, on RCA, by BMG Records (UK). Deleted '64. Catalogue no: **RCA 1226**
7" Single: Released May '77, on RCA, by BMG Records (UK). Deleted May '89. Catalogue no: **RCA 2700**

YOU DON'T HAVE TO SAY YOU LOVE ME
Tracks: / You don't have to say you love me.
7" Single: Released Jan '71, on RCA, by BMG Records (UK). Deleted '74. Catalogue no: **RCA 2046**
7" Single: Released '80, on RCA (USA), Catalogue no: **LR 0728**

YOU GOTTA STOP
Tracks: / You gotta stop / Love machine.
7" Single: Released May '67, on RCA, by BMG Records (UK). Deleted '70. Catalogue no: **RCA 1593**

YOU'LL NEVER WALK ALONE (SINGLE)
Tracks: / You'll never walk alone.
7" Single: Released Oct '68, on RCA, by BMG Records (UK). Deleted '71. Catalogue no: **RCA 1747**

YOU'RE A HEARTBREAKER
Tracks: / You're a heartbreaker.
7" Single: Released '80, on RCA (USA), Catalogue no: **LR 1279**

YOU'RE TIME HASN'T COME YET BABY
Tracks: / You're time hasn't come yet baby.
7" Single: Released Jul '68, on RCA, by BMG Records (UK). Deleted '71. Catalogue no: **RCA 1714**

Presley, Sid

COLD TURKEY
Tracks: / Cold turkey.
7" Single: Released Dec '84, on S.P.E., Catalogue no: **SPE 41**

HUP TWO THREE FOUR
Tracks: / Hup two three four / Public enemy no. 1.
7" Single: Released May '84, on I.D., by I.D. Records. Catalogue no: **EYE 4**
12" Single: Released May '84, on I.D., by I.D. Records. Catalogue no: **EYET 4**

Press Gang

51ST STATE
Tracks: / 51st state / You know full well / Who are you trying to kid.
12" Single: Released Mar '85, on Admiralty, Catalogue no: **GANG 00112**

JAMES WHERE ARE YOU NOW?
Tracks: / James where are you now?.
12" Single: Released Nov '85, on Admiralty, Catalogue no: **ABM 212**

MONEY
Tracks: / Money / Money (version).
7" Single: Released Apr '89, on T.M.T., by T.M.T. Productions. Deleted Sep '89. Catalogue no: **TTT 1003**
12" Single: Released Apr '89, on T.M.T., by T.M.T. Productions. Deleted Sep '89. Catalogue no: **12TTT 1003**

Press Men

READ ALL ABOUT IT
Tracks: / Read all about it.
7" Single: Released Dec '88, on UNKNOWN, Catalogue no: **FM 001**

Press The Flesh

IN THE HEAT OF THE NIGHT
Tracks: / In the heat of the night / Invisible (remix).
7" Single: Released Jul '87, on Offshore, by Offshore Records. Catalogue no: **PED 002**
12" Single: Released Jul '87, on Offshore, by Offshore Records. Catalogue no: **12PED 002**

INVISIBLE
Tracks: / Invisible / Streetwise girl.
7" Single: Released Aug '86, on Offshore, by Offshore Records. Catalogue no: **PED 001**
12" Single: Released Aug '86, on Offshore, by Offshore Records. Catalogue no: **PEDT 001**

Presser, Gabor

BALLETTA, LA
Tracks: / Balletta, La.
7" Single: Released Mar '83, on EMI, by EMI Records. Catalogue no: **EMI 5376**

Pressure

CAN YOU FEEL IT
Tracks: / Can you feel it / That's the thing to do.
7" Single: Released Apr '80, on MCA, by MCA Records. Deleted Apr '83. Catalogue no: **MCA 574**

PRESSURE
Tracks: / Pressure.
12" Single: Released May '83, on Anagram, by Cherry Red Records. Deleted '88. Catalogue no: **12 ANA 06**

SLIDE
Tracks: / Slide / Real thing.
7" Single: Released Jul '81, on Fantasy (1), by BMG Records (UK). Deleted '85. Catalogue no: **FTCT 196**

YOU TALK WE TALK
Tracks: / You talk we talk.
12" Single: Released Nov '82, on Anagram, by Cherry Red Records. Deleted '88. Catalogue no: **12 ANA 02**

Pressure Drop

007 (SHANTY TOWN)
Tracks: / 007 (shanty town) / Samfi man / Rivers of Babylon / Monkey man.
7" Single: Released Jun '89, on Mango, by Island Records. Catalogue no: **MNG 711**
CD 5": Released Jun '89, on Mango, by Island Records. Catalogue no: **CIDM 711**
12" Single: Released Jun '89, on Mango, by Island Records. Catalogue no: **12 MNG 711**

FROM HERE TO ETERNITY
Tracks: / From here to eternity.
7" Single: Released Jun '83, on Noose, Catalogue no: **END 001**

PRESSURE DROP EP
Tracks: / Pressure drop: *Toots & The Maytals* / Guns of Navarone: *Skatalites* / Long shot kick de bucket: *Pioneers* / Hard road to travel: *Cliff, Jimmy*.
CD 5": Released 27 Feb '89, on Mango, by Island Records. Catalogue no: **MBCD 25**
7" Single: Released 27 Feb '89, on Mango, by Island Records. Catalogue no: **MNG 25**
7" EP: Released 27 Feb '89, on Mango, by Island Records. Catalogue no: **MBDJ 25**
12" Single: Released 27 Feb '89, on Mango, by Island Records. Catalogue no: **12 MNG 25**

PRESSURE DROP (SINGLE)
Tracks: / Shanty town: *Various artists* / Samfi man: *Various artists* / Rivers of Babylon: *Various artists* / Monkey man: *Various artists*.
7" Single: Released Jul '89, on Mango, by Island Records. Catalogue no: **MNG 711**
12" Single: Released Jul '89, on Mango, by Island Records. Catalogue no: **12MNG 711**
CD 5": Released Jul '89, on Mango, by Island Records. Catalogue no: **CIDM 711**

Pressure Point

DREAMING (SINGLE)
Tracks: / Dreaming.
7" Single: Released May '89, on Viceroy, by Viceroy Records. Deleted Sep '89. Catalogue no: **VICE 2**
12" Single: Released May '89, on Viceroy,

PRETENDERS - BRASS IN POCKET (Released on WEA)

by Viceroy Records. Catalogue no: **12VICE 2**

MELLOW MOODS
Tracks: / Mellow moods / I need your love.
7" Single: Released Aug '85, on Viceroy, by Viceroy Records. Catalogue no: **7VICE 001**
12" Single: Released Nov '86, on Hardback, by Hardback Records. Catalogue no: **BOSS 1**
7" Single: Released Nov '86, on Hardback, by Hardback Records. Catalogue no: **7 BOSS 1**
12" Single: Released Aug '85, on Viceroy, by Viceroy Records. Catalogue no: **12VICE 001**

Pressure Zone

BACKSTABBERS
Tracks: / Backstabbers.
12" Single: Released Mar '89, on Tam Tam, Catalogue no: **TTT 05**

Prestigee

SAY YOU KNOW
Tracks: / Say you know.
7" Single: Released Jan '84, on Rebound, Catalogue no: **BOUNCE 3**

Preston, Billy

Biographical details: Born in Houston, Texas, in 1946, singer and keyboards man Billy Preston toured Europe with Little Richard, Sam Cooke and Ray Charles and sessioned with the Beatles, the Rollings Stones and many others. His solo career began on Apple, sponsored by George Harrison, and he played on the Concert For Bangla Desh concert/album, organised by Harrison, in 1972. He also had hits with A & M before turning to Motown. (Donald Clarke, May 1987.).

AND DANCE
Tracks: / And dance / Kick in.
12" Single: Released Jun '84, on ERC, Catalogue no: **ERCL 116**

BILLY'S BAG (OLD GOLD)
Tracks: / Billy's bag.
7" Single: Released Jul '82, on Old Gold, by Old Gold Records. Catalogue no: **OG 9030**

CHANGE IS GONNA COME, A
Tracks: / Change is gonna come, A / You.
7" Single: Released Oct '81, on Motown, by BMG Records (UK). Deleted '83. Catalogue no: **TMG 1231**

GO FOR IT
Tracks: / Go for it.
7" Single: Released Oct '81, on Motown, by BMG Records (UK). Deleted '83. Catalogue no: **TMG 1139**

HOPE
Tracks: / Hope / Give it up, hot.
7" Single: Released Oct '81, on Motown, by BMG Records (UK). Deleted '83. Catalogue no: **TMG 1224**
12" Single: Released Oct '81, on Motown, by BMG Records (UK). Deleted '83. Catalogue no: **TMGT 1224**

I'M NEVER GONNA SAY GOODBYE
Tracks: / I'm never gonna say goodbye.
7" Single: Released Oct '82, on Motown, by BMG Records (UK). Deleted '84. Catalogue no: **TMG 1283**

IT WILL COME IN TIME
Tracks: / It will come in time / All i wanted was you.
7" Single: Released Oct '81, on Motown, by BMG Records (UK). Deleted '83. Catalogue no: **TMG 1175**

NEW WAY TO SAY I LOVE YOU
Tracks: / New way to say I love you / Hey you.
7" Single: Released Feb '83, on Motown, by BMG Records (UK). Deleted '85. Catalogue no: **TMG 1291**
12" Single: Released Feb '83, on Motown, by BMG Records (UK). Deleted '85. Catalogue no: **TMGT 1291**

ONE MORE TIME FOR LOVE
Tracks: / One more time for love / Dance for me children.
7" Single: Released Oct '81, on Motown, by BMG Records (UK). Deleted '83. Catalogue no: **TMG 1138**

OUTA SPACE
Tracks: / Outa space.
7" Single: Released Sep '72, on A&M, by A&M Records. Deleted '75. Catalogue no: **AMS 7007**

PLEASE STAY
Tracks: / Please stay / Signed, sealed and delivered, I'm yours.
7" Single: Released Oct '81, on Motown, by BMG Records (UK). Deleted '83. Catalogue no: **TMG 1211**

THAT'S THE WAY GOD PLANNED IT
Tracks: / That's the way God planned it.
7" Single: Released Jul '69, on Apple, by Apple Records. Deleted '72. Catalogue no: **APPLE 12**

WITH YOU I'M BORN AGAIN
Tracks: / With you I'm born again.
7" Single: Released Mar '83, on Motown, by BMG Records (UK). Catalogue no: **TMG 1159**

Preston, Ellis

WARM WEATHER
Tracks: / Warm weather.
7" Single: Released 17 Jul '89, on MCA, by MCA Records. Catalogue no: **MCA 1356**

Preston, Helen

DALEY
Tracks: / Daley / Something you're not saying.
7" Single: Released Aug '84, on Dux, Catalogue no: **DUX 002**

Preston, Jimmy

ROCK THE JOINT (EP)
Tracks: / Rock the joint / Do the bump / Hucklebuck Daddy / Let's hang on tonight.
Note: This EP has a picture bag with a previously unissued photograph of Bill Haley, with a personal note on it from Haley to two of the men working at GOTHAM. The EP commemorates the fact that Jimmy Preston first cut 'Rock the Joint' (before Haley covered it)...and recorded probably the first rock'n'roll disc..in 1949...almost two years Brenston's ROCKET 88.
7" EP: Released Jul '88, on Krazy Kat, by Interstate Music. Catalogue no: **KKEP 01**

Preston, Johnny

CHARMING BILLY
Tracks: / Charming Billy.
7" Single: Released Dec '60, on Mercury (EMI), Deleted '63. Catalogue no: **AMT 1114**

CRADLE OF LOVE
Tracks: / Cradle of love.
7" Single: Released Apr '60, on Mercury (EMI), Deleted '63. Catalogue no: **AMT 1092**

FEEL SO FINE
Tracks: / Feel so fine.
7" Single: Released Aug '60, on Mercury (EMI), Deleted '63. Catalogue no: **AMT 1104**

I'M STARTING TO GO STEADY
Tracks: / I'm starting to go steady.
7" Single: Released Jul '60, on Mercury (EMI), Deleted '63. Catalogue no: **AMT 1104**

RUNNING BEAR (OLD GOLD)
Tracks: / Running bear.
7" Single: Released Jan '85, on Old Gold, by Old Gold Records. Catalogue no: **OG 9461**

RUNNING BEAR
Tracks: / Running bear.
7" Single: Released Feb '60, on Mercury (EMI), Deleted '63. Catalogue no: **AMT 1079**
7" Single: Released '80, on Mercury, by Phonogram Ltd. Catalogue no: **LR 8077**

Preston, Mike

I'D DO ANYTHING
Tracks: / I'd do anything.
7" Single: Released Aug '60, on Decca, by Decca Records. Deleted '63. Catalogue no: **F 11255**

MARRY ME
Tracks: / Marry me.
7" Single: Released Mar '61, on Decca, by Decca Records. Deleted '64. Catalogue no: **F 11335**

MR BLUE
Tracks: / Mr. Blue.
7" Single: Released Oct '59, on Decca, by Decca Records. Deleted '62. Catalogue no: **F 11167**

TOGETHERNESS
Tracks: / Togetherness.
7" Single: Released Dec '60, on Decca, by Decca Records. Deleted '63. Catalogue no: **F 11287**

Preston, Robert

I WON'T SEND ROSES
Tracks: / I won't send roses.
7" Single: Released Nov '82, on ABC Records, by MCA Records. Catalogue no: **MCA 795**

Pretenders

Biographical details: British rock group the Pretenders were formed in 1978 by singer, songwriter and guitarist Chrissie Hynde, born in Ohio in '51. Hynde came to London, wrote for New Musical Express, worked in the USA and France with various groups, returned to London and took part in projects with Mick Jones, who later co-formed Clash, Malcolm McClaren's Masters of the Backside -- later to become the Damned -- and with Steve Strange in the shortlived Moors Murderers, who made just one single. She formed the Pretenders with bassist Pete Farndon (born '53 in Hereford, died '83 of drugs) and guitarist James Honeyman-Scott (born '57, Hereford, died '82, drugs). With drummer Gerry Mackleduff they issued their first Top Forty hit, a cover of Ray Davies' *Stop Your Sobbin'* in early 1979. Martin Chambers was the drummer on their first album *Pretenders* No 1 in '80, which showed Hynde to be a very good rhythm guitarist with a great variety of pace, from full-tilt rock 'n ' roll to ballads. The Pretenders have been highly regarded -- by both critics and public -- ever since. (Donald Clarke, May 1987.).

2000 MILES
Tracks: / 2000 miles.
7" Single: Released Nov '83, on Real, by WEA Records. Deleted '86. Catalogue no: **ARE 20**

BACK ON THE CHAIN GANG
Tracks: / Back on the chain gang / My city was gone.
7" Single: Released Oct '82, on Real, by WEA Records. Deleted '85. Catalogue no: **ARE 19**
12" Single: Released Oct '82, on Real, by WEA Records. Deleted '85. Catalogue no: **ARE 19T**

BRASS IN POCKET (see panel oppoisite)
Tracks: / Brass in pocket / Swinging London / Nervous but shy / Talk of the town.
Cassingle: Released Apr '81, on WEA, by WEA Records. Deleted Apr '86. Catalogue no: **SPC 5**
7" Single: Released Nov '79, on Real, by WEA Records. Deleted Jan '88. Catalogue no: **ARE 11**

DAY AFTER DAY
Tracks: / Day after day / In the sticks.
7" Single: Released Sep '81, on Real, by WEA Records. Deleted '84. Catalogue no: **ARE 17**

DON'T GET ME WRONG
Tracks: / Don't get me wrong / Dance.
7" Single: Released Sep '86, on WEA, by WEA Records. Deleted Jan '88. Catalogue no: **YZ 85**
12" Single: Released Sep '86, on WEA, by WEA Records. Deleted Jan '88. Catalogue no: **YZ 85T**

HYMN TO HER
Tracks: / Room Full of Mirrors.
7" Single: Released Nov '86, on Real, by WEA Records. Deleted Jan '88. Catalogue no: **YZ 93**
12" Single: Released Nov '86, on Real, by WEA Records. Deleted Jan '88. Catalogue no: **YZ 93T**

I GO TO SLEEP
Tracks: / I go to sleep / English roses.
7" Single: Released Nov '81, on Real, by WEA Records. Deleted '84. Catalogue no:

PRETENDERS - TALK OF THE TOWN (Released on Real)

ARE 18

IF THERE WAS A MAN
Tracks: / If there was a man.
7" Single: Released Aug '87, on WEA, by WEA Records. Deleted Jul '88. Catalogue no: **YZ 149**
12" Single: Released Aug '87, on WEA, by WEA Records. Deleted Jul '88. Catalogue no: **YZ 149T**

KID
Tracks: / Kid (remix) / Stop your sobbing (Original Demo version.) / What you gonna do about it (Included in Picture bag.).
7" Single: Released Jul '79, on Real, by WEA Records. Deleted '82. Catalogue no: **ARE 9**
12" Single: Released 17 Oct '87, on WEA, by WEA Records. Deleted Jul '88. Catalogue no: **WZ 156 T**
7" Single: Released 17 Oct '87, on WEA, by WEA Records. Deleted Jul '88. Catalogue no: **WZ 156**

MESSAGE OF LOVE
Tracks: / Message of love / Porcelain.
7" Single: Released Feb '81, on Real, by WEA Records. Deleted '84. Catalogue no: **ARE 15**

MIDDLE OF THE ROAD
Tracks: / Middle of the road.
7" Single: Released Feb '84, on Real, by WEA Records. Catalogue no: **ARE 21**
12" Single: Released Feb '84, on Real, by WEA Records. Catalogue no: **ARE 12T**

MY BABY
Tracks: / My baby / Tradition of love (remix).
12" Single: Released Mar '87, on Real, by WEA Records. Deleted Jan '88. Catalogue no: **YZ 110T**
7" Single: Released Mar '87, on Real, by WEA Records. Deleted Jan '88. Catalogue no: **YZ 110**

STOP YOUR SOBBING
Tracks: / Stop your sobbing / Kid.
Cassingle: Released Apr '81, on WEA, by WEA Records. Deleted Apr '86. Catalogue no: **SPC 1**
7" Single: Released Feb '79, on Real, by WEA Records. Deleted '82. Catalogue no: **ARE 6**

TALK OF THE TOWN
Tracks: / Talk of the town / Cuban slide.
7" Single: Released Apr '80, on Real, by WEA Records. Deleted '83. Catalogue no: **ARE 12**

THIN LINE BETWEEN LOVE AND HATE
Tracks: / Thin line between love and hate / Time the avenger.
7" Single: Released Jun '84, on Real, by WEA Records. Deleted '87. Catalogue no: **ARE 22**

WINDOWS OF THE WORLD
Tracks: / Windows of the world / 1969.
CD 3": Released Apr '89, on Polydor, by Polydor Ltd. Catalogue no: **PRECD 69**
7" Single: Released Apr '89, on Polydor, by Polydor Ltd. Deleted Oct '89. Catalogue no: **PRE 69**

Pretty Boy

JUNCTION DISASTER
Tracks: / Junction disaster.
12" Single: Released Aug '89, on Pantomime, Catalogue no: **PR 247**

Pretty Maids

LOVE GAMES
Tracks: / Love games / Needles in the dark / Yellow rain (Extra track on 12" only).
7" Single: Released May '87, on Epic, by CBS Records. Deleted Nov '87. Catalogue no: **650437 7**
12" Single: Released May '87, on Epic, by CBS Records. Deleted Nov '87. Catalogue no: **650437 8**

Pretty Poison

CATCH ME (I'M FALLING) (SINGLE)
Tracks: / Catch me (I'm falling) (radio mix) (7" only) / Catch me (I'm falling) (arsenic mix) (12" only) / Catch me (I'm falling) (dub version) (12" only) / Catch me (I'm falling) (Spanish mix) (7" only) / Catch me (I'm falling) (Belladonna mix) (12" only).
7" Single: Released Jun '88, on Virgin, by Virgin Records. Catalogue no: **VS 1099**
7" Single: Released Oct '87, on 10 Records, by Virgin Records. Deleted '89. Catalogue no: **TEN 187**
12" Single: Released Jun '88, on Virgin, by Virgin Records. Catalogue no: **VST 1099**
12" Single: Released Sep '87, on 10 Records, by Virgin Records. Deleted '89. Catalogue no: **TENT 187**

NIGHTIME
Tracks: / Nightime (7" only) / Nightime (Spanish mix) (7" only) / Nightime (Shep Pettibone remix) (12" only) / Nightime (dub) (12" only) / Nightime (cold house mix) (12" only).
7" Single: Released May '88, on Virgin, by Virgin Records. Catalogue no: **VS 1068**
12" Single: Released May '88, on Virgin, by Virgin Records. Catalogue no: **VST 1068**

Pretty Ricky Boo-ski

IT'S MINE
Tracks: / It's mine.
12" Single: Released Apr '86, on Cherry Red, by Cherry Red Records. Deleted '87. Catalogue no: **12 DANCE 1**

Pretty Things

Biographical details: This British rhythm-and-blues band was formed at Sidcup Art School in Kent in 1963 by bassist Dick Taylor -- an original member of the Rolling Stones -- and singer Phil May. Taylor soon switched to lead guitar and the group, modelled very much on the Stones, had many changes of personnel and styles over the years, from blues through psychedelic and progressive rock. The orthodox critical theory is that they were several bands, with May as the only constant factor. Their first two albums were *The Pretty Things* (an album of R & B covers which reached No 6 in the UK) and *Get The Picture*. Few of their LPs charted but the spate of 80's reissues testifies to the high regard in which they are still held in the history of rock. Their concept album *SF Sorrow* in 1968, written by May and Taylor, is held to be the first rock opera and the inspiration for the Who's more successful *Tommy*; *Parachute*, in '69, was highly praised but flopped commercially, and polished AOR albums *Silk Torpedo* and *Savage Eye* ('74 and '75) were the only ones to chart in the US but are the least interesting in retrospect. *Let Me Hear The Choir Sing* anthologises their early singles; *Closed Restaurant Blues* portrays them emerging from their blues period. In 1985 May was playing in pubs with young musicians as the Pretty Things while Taylor played with former Leeds punks the Mekons. (Donald Clarke, May 1987.).

COME SEE ME
Tracks: / Come see me.
7" Single: Released May '66, on Fontana, by Phonogram Ltd. Deleted '69. Catalogue no: **TF 688**

CRY TO ME
Tracks: / Cry to me.
7" Single: Released Jul '65, on Fontana, by Phonogram Ltd. Deleted '68. Catalogue no: **TF 585**

DON'T BRING ME DOWN
Tracks: / Don't bring me down.
7" Single: Released Oct '64, on Fontana, by Phonogram Ltd. Deleted '67. Catalogue no: **TF 503**

DON'T BRING ME DOWN (OLD GOLD)
Tracks: / Don't bring me down.
7" Single: Released Jul '82, on Old Gold, by Old Gold Records. Catalogue no: **OG 9237**

EVE OF DESTRUCTION
Tracks: / Eve of destruction.
7" Single: Released Sep '89, on Trax, by Filmtrax Records. Catalogue no: **7TX 12**
12" Single: Released Sep '89, on Trax, by Filmtrax Records. Catalogue no: **12TX 12**

FALLING AGAIN
Tracks: / Falling again / She don't.
7" Single: Released Oct '80, on Warner Bros., by WEA Records. Deleted Oct '83. Catalogue no: **K 17702**

HONEY I NEED
Tracks: / Honey I need.
7" Single: Released Feb '65, on Fontana, by Phonogram Ltd. Deleted '68. Catalogue no: **TF 537**

HOUSE IN THE COUNTRY
Tracks: / House in the country.
7" Single: Released Jul '66, on Fontana, by Phonogram Ltd. Deleted '69. Catalogue no: **TF 722**

MIDNIGHT TO SIX MAN
Tracks: / Midnight to six man.
7" Single: Released Jan '66, on Fontana, by Phonogram Ltd. Deleted '69. Catalogue no: **TF 647**

ROSALYN
Tracks: / Rosalyn.
7" Single: Released Jun '64, on Fontana, by Phonogram Ltd. Deleted '67. Catalogue no: **TF 469**

Previn, Lovely

FROM A TO B
Tracks: / From A to B.
7" Single: Released Jun '81, on Secret, by Secret Records. Catalogue no: **SHH 114**

I'LL NEVER GET OVER YOU
Tracks: / I'll never get over you.
7" Single: Released Jul '82, on Secret, by Secret Records. Catalogue no: **SHH 124**

WASTED LOVE
Tracks: / Wasted love.
7" Single: Released Jul '82, on Secret, by Secret Records. Catalogue no: **SHH 135**
12" Single: Released Aug '82, on Secret, by Secret Records. Catalogue no: **SHH 135 12**

Prewitt, James

YOU'RE INSATIABLE
Tracks: / You're insatiable.
12" Single: Released Jul '86, on Move, Catalogue no: **MS 14**

Price, Alan

BABY OF MINE
Tracks: / Baby of mine / Just for you.
7" Single: Released Feb '79, on Jet, by Jet Records. Deleted '82. Catalogue no: **JET 135**

BEAT OUT DAT RHYTHM ON A DRUM
Tracks: / Beat out dat rhythm on a drum / Geordie melody.
7" Single: Released Dec '80, on Key, by Key Records. Deleted '87. Catalogue no: **KEY 2000**

CHANGES
Tracks: / Changes / Vegetable (come and get it) / Jarrow song (Only on CD single.).
CD 5": Released 30 May '89, on RCA, by BMG Records (UK). Catalogue no: **6 59911**
7" Single: Released 15 May '89, on RCA, by BMG Records (UK). Catalogue no: **1 09911**
12" Single: Released 15 May '89, on RCA, by BMG Records (UK). Deleted Aug '89. Catalogue no: **6 09911**

CLAIR DE LUNE
Tracks: / Clair de lune.
7" Single: Released Jun '84, on Safari, by Safari Records. Catalogue no: **ALAN 1**

DON'T STOP THE CARNIVAL
Tracks: / Don't stop the carnival.
7" Single: Released Jan '68, on Decca, by Decca Records. Deleted '71. Catalogue no: **F 12731**

FOOL'S IN LOVE
Tracks: / Fools in love.
7" Single: Released Aug '89, on Ariola, by BMG Records (UK). Catalogue no: **112 491**
12" Single: Released Aug '89, on Ariola, by BMG Records (UK). Catalogue no: **612 491**

HI LILO HI LO
Tracks: / Hi lili hi lo.
7" Single: Released Jul '66, on Decca, by Decca Records. Deleted '69. Catalogue no: **F 12442**

HOUSE OF THE RISING SUN
Tracks: / House of the rising sun / Wake up.
7" Single: Released Apr '80, on Jet, by Jet Records. Deleted Apr '83. Catalogue no: **JET 177**

HOUSE THAT JACK BUILT, THE
Tracks: / House that Jack built, The.
7" Single: Released Aug '67, on Decca, by Decca Records. Deleted '70. Catalogue no: **F 12641**

I PUT A SPELL ON YOU
Tracks: / I put a spell on you.
7" Single: Released Mar '66, on Decca, by Decca Records. Deleted '69. Catalogue no: **F 12367**

JARROW SONG
Tracks: / Jarrow song.
7" Single: Released May '74, on Warner Bros., by WEA Records. Deleted May '77. Catalogue no: **K 16372**

JARROW SONG (OLD GOLD)
Tracks: / Jarrow song.
7" Single: Released Jul '82, on Old Gold, by Old Gold Records. Deleted Jul '88. Catalogue no: **OG 9114**

JARROW SONG (RE-ISSUE)
Tracks: / Between today & yesterday / Jarrow song.
7" Single: Released Nov '86, on Mooncrest, by Trojan Records. Deleted May '88. Catalogue no: **MOON 1005**
12" Single: Released Nov '86, on Mooncrest, by Trojan Records. Deleted May '88. Catalogue no: **T MOON 1005**

JUST FOR YOU
Tracks: / Just for you.
7" Single: Released Apr '78, on Jet, by Jet Records. Deleted '81. Catalogue no: **UP 36358**
7" Single: Released May '78, on Jet, by Jet Records. Catalogue no: **JET 108**

LOVE IS A MIRACLE
Tracks: / Love is a miracle.
7" Single: Released Aug '81, on Key, by Key Records. Deleted '87. Catalogue no: **KEY 2001**

LOVE YOU TRUE
Tracks: / Love you true / Mr sunbeam.
7" Single: Released Feb '80, on Jet, by Jet Records. Deleted Feb '85. Catalogue no: **JET 170**

PAPERS
Tracks: / Papers / Frozen moments.
7" Single: Released Mar '86, on Trojan, by Trojan Records. Deleted May '88. Catalogue no: **TRO 9083**

SHAME
Tracks: / Shame.
7" Single: Released Nov '67, on Decca, by Decca Records. Deleted '70. Catalogue no: **F 12691**

SIMON SMITH & HIS AMAZING DANCING BEAR(OLD GOLD)
Tracks: / Simon Smith and the amazing dancing bear / I put a spell on you / Jarrow song.
CD 5": Released 28 Mar '89, on Old Gold, by Old Gold Records. Catalogue no: **OG 6127**
7" Single: Released May '86, on Old Gold, by Old Gold Records. Catalogue no: **OG 9594**
7" Single: Released Mar '67, on Decca, by Decca Records. Deleted '70. Catalogue no: **F 12570**

Price, Lloyd

Biographical details: A major voice in early rock 'n' roll, via New Orleans rhythm-and-blues, singer- songwriter Price was born in New Orleans in 1934. He wrote *Lawdy Miss Clawdy* in 1952 for an advertisement and it was a No 1 R & B hit with a New Orleans studio sound by Dave Bartholomew and a pianist who may have been Fats Domino; the song was covered by Elvis Presley and others. He had more R & B hits on Specialty. After military service he started his own record company and came back with big hits in the late 50's. He recorded *Just Because* and leased it to ABC for a No 4 R & B and Top Twenty pop hit. Signed directly to ABC, he had a No 1 smash on both R & B and pop -- also Top Ten in the UK -- with *Stagger Lee*, a reworking of the traditional *Stagolee*. Price then turned towards a bigger studio pop sound with *Personality* (also UK Top Ten), and *I'm Gonna Get Married* (both No 1 R & B, Top Three pop in USA), and there were several more hits through to '60. During the 60's he operated a club and his own record labels and had a few minor hits. (Donald Clarke, May 1987.).

I'M GONNA GET MARRIED
Tracks: / I'm gonna get married.
7" Single: Released Sep '59, on H.M.V., by EMI Records. Deleted '62. Catalogue no: **POP 650**

LADY LUCK
Tracks: / Lady luck.
7" Single: Released Apr '60, on H.M.V., by EMI Records. Deleted '63. Catalogue no: **POP 712**

PERSONALITY
Tracks: / Personality.
7" Single: Released Jun '59, on H.M.V., by EMI Records. Deleted '62. Catalogue no: **POP 626**

STAGGERLEE
Tracks: / Staggerlee / Personality / Where were you.
7" Single: Released Nov '80, on Creole (Replay), by Creole Records. Catalogue no: **CR 211**
7" Single: Released Feb '59, on H.M.V., by EMI Records. Deleted '62. Catalogue no: **POP 580**
7" Single: Released Aug '82, on Dakota, Catalogue no: **BAK 11**

WHERE WERE YOU
Tracks: / Where were you.
7" Single: Released May '59, on H.M.V., by EMI Records. Deleted '62. Catalogue no: **POP 598**

Price, Ray

DIAMONDS IN THE STARS (SINGLE)
Tracks: / Diamonds in the stars / Let it rain, let her cry.
7" Single: Released Nov '81, on Young Blood, by Young Blood Records. Deleted Nov '84. Catalogue no: **YB 121**

Price, Wilson

FORWARD & TYAKE
Tracks: / Forward & tyake.
12" Single: Released Feb '82, on Castro Brown, Catalogue no: **CB 011**

Price & Wright

COME ON DOWN
Tracks: / Come on down.
7" Single: Released Jul '85, on Young Blood, by Young Blood Records. Catalogue no: **YB 0091**

Pride

WHAT'S LOVE
Tracks: / What's love.
7" Single: Released Mar '85, on Pride Productions, Catalogue no: **PRD 0001**

Pride, Charley

Biographical details: Charley was one of 11 children born to the family of Sledge, Mississippi - a small town 60 miles south of Memphis. He earned his living picking cotton (for $3-00 per 100 pounds) alongside his brothers and sisters until he was 17 years old. At the time Charley made a bid for what, as a child, had been his first love - baseball. He played in the Negro American League with Detroit and Memphis Red Sox until entering the military during the late '50's. Returning to baseball, he made it to the Major league for a brief period in 1961, playing outfield and pitching for the Los Angeles Angels. Although the career in baseball never fully materialised, his dreams of playing have never died. Charley goes to spring training with the Texas Rangers every year. Attracted to music (along with baseball), at an early age, Charley learned the songs he heard on his family's radio, which was usually tuned to WSM Radio in Nashville. His attraction to country music grew stronger with age, and he eventually purchased a Sears' Silvertone guitar and started singing along. Charley likes to downplay his importance in the music world, but his low key, straight forward style speaks for itself. He had not only established himself as an industry leader, but has been instrumental in the careers of country artists Dave & Sugar, Ronnie Milsap, Gary Stewart, Johnny Duncan and Johnny Russell. (RCA, Feb 1984).

CRYSTAL CHANDELIERS
Tracks: / Crystal chandeliers / Honky tonk blues.
7" Single: Released Apr '80, on RCA, by BMG Records (UK). Deleted '83. Catalogue no: **PB 9528**

CRYSTAL CHANDELIERS (OLD GOLD)
Tracks: / Crystal chandeliers / Does my ring hurt your finger.
7" Single: Released 27 Feb '89, on Old Gold, by Old Gold Records. Catalogue no: **OG 9608**

DO WHAT YOU DO, DO WELL
Tracks: / Do what you do do well / If we're just killing time (Let's love it to death).
7" Single: Released Oct '88, on Ritz, by Ritz Records. Catalogue no: **RITZ 196**

DO WHAT YOU DO WELL
Tracks: / Do what you do well.
7" Single: Released '88, on Ritz, by Ritz Records. Catalogue no: **RITZ 192**

EVERY HEART SHOULD HAVE ONE
Tracks: / Every heart should have one / Lovin' it up.
7" Single: Released Mar '84, on RCA, by BMG Records (UK). Catalogue no: **RCA 393**

HAVE I GOT SOME BLUES FOR YOU
Tracks: / Have I got some blues for you / Even knowin'.
7" Single: Released 30 May '87, on Ritz, by Ritz Records. Catalogue no: **RITZ 175**

ROLL ON MISSISSIPPI (SINGLE)
Tracks: / Roll on Mississippi / Fall back on me.
7" Single: Released Mar '81, on RCA, by BMG Records (UK). Deleted Mar '84. Catalogue no: **RCA 49**

YOU TOOK ME THERE
Tracks: / You took me there / One of these days.
7" Single: Released Jan '88, on Ritz, by Ritz Records. Catalogue no: **RITZ 183**

Pride, Dickie

PRIMROSE LANE
Tracks: / Primrose lane.
7" Single: Released Oct '59, on Columbia, by EMI Records. Deleted '62. Catalogue no: **DB 4340**

Pride Of Nashville

COUNTRY SYMPHONY
Tracks: / Country symphony.
7" Single: Released Jan '81, on Thumbs Up, Catalogue no: **TU 102**

Pride Of The Cross

TOMMY'S BLUE VALENTINE
Tracks: / Tommy's blue valentine.
7" Single: Released Apr '85, on Big Beat, by Ace Records. Deleted '88. Catalogue no: **NS 106**
12" Single: Released Apr '85, on Big Beat, by Ace Records. Deleted '88. Catalogue no: **NST 106**

Pridesmen

GENE STUART
Tracks: / Gene Stuart / Shores of Lough Neagh.
7" Single: Released Feb '80, on Foyle Folk, by Outlet Records. Deleted '83. Catalogue no: **FR 1981**

Priest, Maxi

CRAZY LOVE
Tracks: / Crazy love / Pretty little girl.
7" Single: Released Oct '86, on 10 Records, by Virgin Records. Catalogue no: **TEN 135**
12" Single: Released Oct '86, on 10 Records, by Virgin Records. Deleted '89. Catalogue no: **TENT 135**

CRAZY LOVE (WITH FLUTES)
Tracks: / Crazy love (with flutes)(extended version) / Pretty little girl (longer version) / Strollin on (part 1 of the maxi medley) / Pretty little girl (part 2 of the maxi medley) / Should I (part 3 of the maxi medley) / In the springtime (part 4 of the maxi medley) / Bubble (we ah go bubble)(part 5 of the maxi me / You're safe (part 6 of the maxi medley) / Bubble (we ah go bubble)(in a different stylee).
Special: on 10 Records, by Virgin Records. Catalogue no: **TENX 135**

DANCIN' MOOD
Tracks: / Dancin' mood.
7" Single: Released Jul '85, on 10 Records, by Virgin Records. Deleted May '88. Catalogue no: **MAXS 2**
12" Single: Released Jul '85, on 10 Records, by Virgin Records. Deleted May '88. Catalogue no: **MAXT 2**

GOODBYE TO LOVE AGAIN
Tracks: / Goodbye to love again (7"version not on TENXY 238) / Angel (On all versions) / Wild world (On TENB 238 only) / Wild world (re-edit) (On CD only) / Goodbye to love (long version) (On CD & 12" only).
Note: 7" version of *Goodbye to love again* not on 12" picture single. *Wild world* on 7" single only. *Wild world (re-edit)* on CD only and *Goodbye to love (long version)* on CD and 12" only.
CD 5": Released Aug '88, on 10 Records, by Virgin Records. Catalogue no: **TENCD 238**
12" Pic: Released '88, on 10 Records, by Virgin Records. Catalogue no: **TENXY 238**
7" Single: Released '88, on 10 Records, by Virgin Records. Catalogue no: **TENB 238**
7" Single: Released Aug '88, on 10 Records, by Virgin Records. Catalogue no: **TENP 238**
7" Single: Released Aug '88, on 10 Records, by Virgin Records. Catalogue no: **TEN 238**
12" Single: Released Aug '88, on 10 Records, by Virgin Records. Catalogue no: **TENX 238**

HOW CAN WE EASE THE PAIN
Tracks: / How can we ease the pain / Love don't come easy / Ready posse sings revival selection, The (CD & 12" only) / How can we ease the pain (instrumental) (CD only).
Note: *Ready posse sings revival selection, The* on CD & 12" only and *How can we ease the pain (in an instrumental style)* on CD only.
CD 5": Released Aug '88, on 10 Records, by Virgin Records. Catalogue no: **TENCD 207**
7" Single: Released Feb '88, on 10 Records, by Virgin Records. Catalogue no: **TEN 207**
12" Single: Released Feb '88, on 10 Records, by Virgin Records. Deleted '89. Catalogue no: **TENT 207**

IN THE SPRINGTIME
Tracks: / In the springtime (summertime remix) / Bubble (we ah go bubble) / Should I (roots mix) (12" only).
Note: *Should I (roots mix)* on 12" only.n
7" Single: Released Jun '86, on 10 Records, by Virgin Records. Catalogue no: **TEN 127**
12" Single: Released Jun '86, on 10 Records, by Virgin Records. Deleted May '88. Catalogue no: **TENT 127**

LET ME KNOW
Tracks: / Let me know / I dream / Let me know (extended version) (On 12" only) / I dream (sax version) (On 12" only) / Cry me a river (remix) (On 12" only).
Note: *Let me know (extended version), I dream (sax version)* and *Cry me a river (remix)* on 12" only.c
7" Single: Released Mar '87, on 10 Records, by Virgin Records. Deleted May '88. Catalogue no: **TEN 156**
12" Single: Released Mar '87, on 10 Records, by Virgin Records. Deleted May '88. Catalogue no: **TENT 156**
Special: Released '87, on 10 Records, by Virgin Records. Catalogue no: **TENX 156**

SOME GUYS HAVE ALL THE LUCK
Tracks: / Some guys have all the luck (On 7" only) / Festival time (On all versions) / Some guys have all the luck (extended version) (NOT on 7") / Let me know (NOT on 7") / Some guys have all the luck (radio edit) (Not on TEN & TENR 198).
CD 5": Released Aug '88, on Virgin, by Virgin Records. Catalogue no: **GUYSCD 198**
Cassingle: Released '87, on 10 Records, by Virgin Records. Catalogue no: **TENC 198**
7" Single: Released Oct '87, on 10 Records, by Virgin Records. Catalogue no: **TEN 198**
12" Single: Released '87, on 10 Records, by Virgin Records. Catalogue no: **TENR 198**
12" Single: Released Oct '87, on 10 Records, by Virgin Records. Catalogue no: **TENT 198**

STROLLIN' ON
Tracks: / Strollin' on (re-mix) / Dancing mood / Strollin' on (extended re-mix) (12" only) / Strollin' on (roots version) (12" only).
Note: *Strollin' on (extended re-mix)* and *Strollin' on (roots version)* on 12" only.
7" Single: Released Mar '86, on 10 Records, by Virgin Records. Deleted May '88. Catalogue no: **TEN 84**
12" Single: Released Mar '86, on 10 Records, by Virgin Records. Catalogue no: **TEN 84-12**

THROW MY CORN
Tracks: / Throw me corn / Strolling on.
12" Single: Released May '84, on Level Vibes, by Level Vibes Records. Catalogue no: **LV 003**

WILD WORLD
Tracks: / Wild world (NOT on TENX 221) / On and on / Wild world (instrumentally saxed) (NOT on 7") / Some guys have the luck (On CD only) / How can we ease the pain (Only on TENC 221) / Wild world (long & saxy) (Only on TENX 221).
Note: "Yes, it is the Cat Stevens song, and it is a fabulous cover version by one of South Londons finest - Maxi Priest. 'Wild World' is sure to bring Maxi more chart success, and if there's any justice in this world, should take him all the way to number 1". (Virgin Records May 88)
CD 5": Released '88, on 10 Records, by Virgin Records. Catalogue no: **TENCD 221**
7" Single: Released May '88, on 10 Records, by Virgin Records. Catalogue no: **TEN 221**
12" Single: Released Jul '88, on 10 Records, by Virgin Records. Deleted '89. Catalogue no: **TENTP 221**
12" Single: Released May '88, on 10 Records, by Virgin Records. Catalogue no: **TENX 221**
Cassingle: Released '88, on 10 Records, by Virgin Records. Catalogue no: **TENC 221**

WOMAN IN YOU
Tracks: / Woman in you / Problems / Must be a way (recorded in concert) (12" only) / I dream (live) (12" only).
Note: *Must be a way (recorded in concert)* and *I dream (recorded in concert)* on 12" only.
7" Single: Released Jun '87, on 10 Records, by Virgin Records. Deleted May '88. Catalogue no: **TEN 175**
12" Single: Released Jun '87, on 10 Records, by Virgin Records. Catalogue no: **TENT 175**

Prima, Louis

Biographical details: Trumpeter, novelty vocalist and bandleader Prima was born in New Orleans in 1910 and died there in 1978. He wrote *Sing, Sing, Sing*, interpolated by Benny Goodman in 1937 with *Christopher Columbus* for one of the biggest hits of the era. Other well-known compositions included *It's The Rhythm In Me* and *Sunday Kind Of Love*. His own hits were an entertaining, almost nonsensical mixture of jivespeak and Neapolitan slang with solid trumpet playing, including *Robin Hood, Bellbottom Trousers, Civilization* and *Oh Babe* (1944-50). He married his fourth wife, Keely Smith, in 1952, signed to Capitol with a combo featuring Sam Butera on tenor sax and soon became a hot attraction in Las Vegas. Smith sang in a straight jazz style, poker-faced with a Tonto haircut, while Prima perpetrated his familiar ebullient nonsense. Their interpolation of *I Ain't Got Nobody/Just A Gigolo* was a hit on EP (copied by David Lee Roth for a single hit in '85) and *That Old Black Magic* and *I've Got You Under My Skin* also charted. They made films in 1959, switched to the Dot label and had more hits, including Prima's version of *Wonderful By Night*. The marriage failed. Smith had a successful vocal career while Prima worked in Vegas and provided the voice for the cartoon orangutan in the '69 Disney film The Jungle Book. He fell into a coma in 1975 and lingered for three years in a nursing home before his death. (Donald Clarke, May 1987.).

BUONA SERA
Tracks: / Buona sera.
7" Single: Released Jul '84, on EMI (Holland), by EMI Records. Catalogue no: **1A 006 80935**

BUONA SERA (SINGLE)
Tracks: / Buona Sera.
7" Single: Released Feb '58, on Capitol, by EMI Records. Deleted '61. Catalogue no: **CL 14841**

JUST A GIGOLO
Tracks: / Just a gigolo.
7" Single: Released Apr '83, on EMI (France), by EMI Records. Catalogue no: **2C 008 81166**

Prima Tanz Musik

PRIMA TANZ MUSIK
Special: Released Jun '82, on Polydor, by Polydor Ltd. Catalogue no: **1040 232**

Primadonna

FLASHING ON THE FLOOR
Tracks: / Flashing on the floor.
12" Single: Released Dec '85, on ZYX (Germany), Catalogue no: **ZYX 5197**

GOT TO BE YOU
Tracks: / Got to be you / Let's take our chances.
7" Single: Released Oct '80, on Ariola, by BMG Records (UK). Deleted Oct '83. Catalogue no: **ARO 244**

LOVE ENOUGH FOR TWO
Tracks: / Love enough for two / Missing out on love.
7" Single: Released Apr '80, on Ariola, by BMG Records (UK). Deleted '83. Catalogue no: **ARO 221**

Primal Scene

LIVING HELL
Tracks: / Living hell.
7" Single: Released Mar '88, on Waterfront, by Waterfront Music. Catalogue no: **DAMP 062**

Primal Scream

ALL FALL DOWN
Tracks: / All fall down.
7" Single: Released May '85, on Creation, by Creation Records. Deleted Jul '88. Catalogue no: **CRE 017**

CRYSTAL CRESCENT
Tracks: / Crystal crescent / Velocity girl / Sirea - X (Extra track available on 12" version only.).
Note: *Sirea - X* is an extra track on 12" only.
7" Single: Released May '86, on Creation, by Creation Records. Catalogue no: **CRE 026**
12" Single: Released May '86, on Creation, by Creation Records. Catalogue no: **CRE 026 T**

GENTLE TUESDAY
Tracks: / Gentle Tuesday / Black star carnival.
7" Single: Released 13 Jun '87, on WEA, by WEA Records. Deleted Jul '88. Catalogue no: **ACID3**
12" Single: Released 13 Jun '87, on WEA, by WEA Records. Deleted Jul '88. Catalogue no: **ACID3T**

IMPERIAL
Tracks: / Imperial / Star fruit surf rider / So sad about us / There's no holding back / Lonely man.
Note: *So sad about us* on 12" only.
7" Single: Released Sep '87, on Elevation, Deleted Jul '88. Catalogue no: **ACID 5**
12" Single: Released Sep '87, on Elevation, Catalogue no: **ACID 5T**

IVY IVY IVY
Tracks: / Ivy ivy ivy.
CD 5": Released Jul '89, on Creation, by Creation Records. Catalogue no: **CRE 067 CD**
7" Single: Released Jul '89, on Creation, by Creation Records. Catalogue no: **CRE 067**
12" Single: Released Jul '89, on Creation, by Creation Records. Catalogue no: **CRE 067 T**

Primary

RADIO SILENCE
Tracks: / Radio silence.
7" Single: Released May '84, on Peeved, by Peeved Records. Catalogue no: **GOLDFISH 002**

Primary Industry

AT GUNPOINT
Tracks: / At gunpoint / Perversion.
7" Single: Released Feb '86, on Niss, Catalogue no: **CSBTVV**

CICATRICE
Tracks: / Cicatrice.
12" Single: Released Nov '85, on Sweatbox, by Sweatbox Records. Catalogue no: **SOX 007**

HEART OF GLASS
Tracks: / Heart of glass.
12" Single: Released Aug '87, on Sweatbox, by Sweatbox Records. Catalogue no: **SOX 22**

WYNDHAM LEWIS
Tracks: / Wyndham Lewis.

12" Single: Released Mar '88, on Sweatbox, by Sweatbox Records. Catalogue no: **SOX 26**

Prime Movers

DARK WESTERN NIGHT
Tracks: / Dark western night / Lost in your world / Museum (Extra track available on 12" version only.).
Note: *Museum* on 12" only.M
7" Single: Released Mar '86, on Island, by Island Records. Catalogue no: **IS 271**
12" Single: Released Mar '86, on Island, by Island Records. Catalogue no: **12IS 271**

ON THE TRAIL
Tracks: / On the trail / Strong as I am.
7" Single: Released Jan '86, on Island, by Island Records. Deleted Jul '87. Catalogue no: **IS 263**
12" Single: Released Jan '86, on Island, by Island Records. Catalogue no: **12IS 263**

Primevals

FERTILE MIND
Tracks: / Fertile mind.
7" Single: Released Apr '88, on New Rose (1), by New Rose Records. Catalogue no: **NEW 015**

HEYA
Tracks: / Heya.
7" Single: Released Jul '87, on New Rose (1), by New Rose Records. Catalogue no: **NEW 93**
12" Single: Released Jul '87, on New Rose (1), by New Rose Records. Catalogue no: **NEW 92**

PEEL SESSIONS:PRIMEVALS
12" Single: Released '87, on Strange Fruit, by Strange Fruit Records. Catalogue no: **SFPS 014**

Primitives

CRASH
Tracks: / Crash / I'll stick with you / Crash (demo) (*Extra track on 12" version only.) / Things get in the way.
Note: *Crash (demo)* on 12" only.t
7" Single: Released Feb '88, on RCA, by BMG Records (UK). Deleted Aug '89. Catalogue no: **PB 41761**
12" Single: Released Feb '88, on RCA, by BMG Records (UK). Catalogue no: **PT 41762**

OUT OF REACH
Tracks: / Out of reach / Dreamwalk baby / Really stupid (live) / Crash (live) / Crash (album version) / Out of reach (album version).
Note: *Crash (album version)* and *Out of reach (album version)* on 12" only. Limited edition free poster with 12".
CD 5": Released Apr '88, on RCA, by BMG Records (UK). Deleted Jul '89. Catalogue no: **PD 42012**
7" Single: Released Apr '88, on RCA, by BMG Records (UK). Deleted May '89. Catalogue no: **PB 42011**
7" Single: Released Apr '88, on RCA, by BMG Records (UK). Deleted May '89. Catalogue no: **PB 42011 LE**
12" Single: Released Apr '88, on RCA, by BMG Records (UK). Deleted May '89. Catalogue no: **PT 42012**

REALLY STUPID
Tracks: / Really stupid / We found a way to the sun / Where the wind blows.
7" Single: Released Oct '86, on Lazy. Catalogue no: **LAZY 02**

SECRETS
Tracks: / Secrets / I almost touched you / Secrets (Demo) / Dizzy heights.
CD 5": Released Sep '89, on RCA, by BMG Records (UK). Catalogue no: **PD 43174**
Cassingle: Released Sep '89, on RCA, by BMG Records (UK). Catalogue no: **PK 43174**
7" Single: Released 24 Sep '89, on Lazy. Catalogue no: **PB 43209**
7" Single: Released Sep '89, on RCA, by BMG Records (UK). Catalogue no: **PB 43173**
12" Single: Released 23 Sep '89, on Lazy. Catalogue no: **PT 43212**
12" Single: Released Sep '89, on RCA, by BMG Records (UK). Catalogue no: **PT 43174**

SICK OF IT (See panel above)
Tracks: / Sick of it / Noose / I'll be your mirror (on 12" and CD single only).
CD 5": Released Jul '89, on RCA, by BMG Records (UK). Catalogue no: **PD 42948**
7" Single: Released Jul '89, on RCA, by BMG Records (UK). Catalogue no: **PB 42993**
7" Single: Released Jul '89, on RCA, by BMG Records (UK). Catalogue no: **PB 42947**
12" Single: Released Jul '89, on RCA, by BMG Records (UK). Catalogue no: **PT 42948**

STOP KILLING ME

THE PRIMITIVES - SICK OF IT (Released on RCA)

Tracks: / Buzz, buzz, buzz. / Laughing up my sleeve.
Note: *Laughing up my sleeve* on 12" only.
7" Single: Released Feb '87, on Lazy. Catalogue no: **LAZY 03**
12" Single: Released Feb '87, on Lazy. Catalogue no: **LAZY 03T**

THRU THE FLOWERS
Tracks: / Thru the flowers / Everything shining bright / Across my shoulder (Extra track available on 12" picture bag only.).
Note: *Across my shoulder* on 12" only.
7" Single: Released Aug '87, on Lazy. Catalogue no: **LAZY 06**
7" Single: Released Aug '87, on Lazy. Catalogue no: **LAZY 6L**
12" Single: Released Aug '87, on Lazy. Catalogue no: **LAZY 06T**
12" Single: Released May '86, on Lazy. Catalogue no: **LAZY 01**

WAY BEHIND ME
Tracks: / Way behind me.
7" Single: Released 30 Aug '88, on RCA, by BMG Records (UK). Deleted Aug '89. Catalogue no: **PB 42209**
12" Single: Released Sep '88, on Lazy. Deleted Aug '89. Catalogue no: **PT 42210**

Primitons

DON'T GO AWAY
Tracks: / Something on my mind / Come what may.
12" Single: Released Dec '86, on What Goes On, by What Goes On Records. Catalogue no: **GOES ON 13T**

Prince

Biographical details: Son of a jazz pianist and singer, Prince was born Prince Rogers Nelson in Minneapolis, Minnesota, in 1960. As a soul singer, songwriter and bandleader he rivals Bruce Springsteen in chart and critical success in 1980's rock music. Self-taught on piano, guitar and drums, he formed a local group, Grand Central, later called Champagne, and made demos under the patronage of a local studio owner. He was signed by WEA while still in his teens and his early albums and singles were a curious mixture of religious and sexual/secular impulses, often banned from the radio. But the double album *1999* in 1982 (Top Ten in America, originally released as a single LP in Britain) included commercial soul tracks that could be played on the air: *Little Red Corvette, Delirious* and *1999*, were all big hits, the title track reaching the UK Top Twenty Five. *The Purple Rain* album and film in '84 put him into rock's first division: the LP was No 1 in the US though the film was widely panned. Critics are irritated by his behaviour. He has threatened to retire as many times as David Bowie. In 1987 he was rehearsing for a British tour and hadn't bothered to tell WEA/UK he was in the country. But his impact and influence cannot be denied. (Donald Clarke, May 1987.).

1999 (SINGLE)
Tracks: / 1999 / Uptown (Available on cassingle only.) / Controversy (Available on cassingle only.) / Dirty minds (Available on cassingle only.) / Sexuality (Available only cassingle only.).
7" Single: Released Jan '83, on Warner Bros., by WEA Records. Deleted '86. Catalogue no: **W 9896**

1999/LITTLE RED CORVETTE
Tracks: / 1999 / Little red corvette.
7" Single: Released Jan '85, on Warner Bros., by WEA Records. Deleted '88. Catalogue no: **W 1999**

ALPHABET STREET
Tracks: / Alphabet Street / Alphabet Street (version) / This is not music, this is a trip.
Note: *This is not music, this is a trip* on 12" only.
7" Single: Released 23 Apr '88, on Paisley Park (USA), by WEA Records. Catalogue no: **W 7900**
12" Single: Released 23 Apr '88, on Paisley Park (USA), by WEA Records. Catalogue no: **W 7900T**

ANOTHERLOVERHOLEINYOHEAD
Tracks: / Anotherloverholenyohead / I wanna be your lover.
Note: (Cat.no. 205160) 12" Import.
12" Single: Released Nov '87, on Warner Bros.(USA), by WEA Records. Catalogue no: **205160**
12" Single: Released Oct '86, on Paisley Park (USA), by WEA Records. Deleted Jan '88. Catalogue no: **W 8521T**
7" Single: Released Oct '86, on Paisley Park (USA), by WEA Records. Deleted Jun '87. Catalogue no: **W 8521**

BATDANCE (See panel below)
Tracks: / Batdance / 200 balloons.
7" Single: Released Jun '89, on Warner Bros., by WEA Records. Catalogue no: **W 2924**
12" Single: Released Jun '89, on Warner Bros., by WEA Records. Catalogue no: **W 2924 T**
CD 5": Released Jun '89, on Warner Bros., by WEA Records. Catalogue no: **W 2924CD**
12" Pic: Released Jul '89, on Warner Bros., by WEA Records. Catalogue no: **W 2924TP**
CD 3": Released Jul '89, on Warner Bros., by WEA Records. Catalogue no: **W 2924CDX**
Cassingle: Released Jun '89, on Warner Bros., by WEA Records. Catalogue no: **W 2924 C**

CONTROVERSY (SINGLE)
Tracks: / Controversy / When you're mine.
7" Single: Released Oct '81, on Warner Bros., by WEA Records. Deleted Oct '84. Catalogue no: **K 17866**

DO IT ALL NIGHT
Tracks: / Do it all night / Head.
7" Single: Released Mar '81, on Warner Bros., by WEA Records. Deleted Mar '84. Catalogue no: **K 17768**
12" Single: Released Mar '81, on Warner Bros., by WEA Records. Deleted Mar '84. Catalogue no: **K 17768T**

GIRLS AND BOYS
Tracks: / Girls and Boys / Under the cherry moon / She's always in my hair / 17 days / Erotic city.
7" Set: Released Aug '86, on Paisley Park (USA), by WEA Records. Deleted Jan '88. Catalogue no: **W 8586**
7" Pic: Released Aug '86, on Paisley Park (USA), by WEA Records. Deleted Jun '87. Catalogue no: **W 8586P**
12" Single: Released Aug '86, on Paisley Park (USA), by WEA Records. Catalogue no: **W 8586T**
12" Single: Released Nov '87, on Paisley Park (Germany), by WEA Records. Catalogue no: **920 532 0**

GLAM SLAM
Tracks: / Glam slam / Escape.
7" Single: Released Jul '88, on Paisley Park (USA), by WEA Records. Catalogue no: **W 7806**
CD 5": Released Jul '88, on Paisley Park (USA), by WEA Records. Catalogue no: **W 7806CD**
12" Single: Released Jul '88, on Paisley Park (USA), by WEA Records. Catalogue no: **W 7806T**

GOTTA STOP
Tracks: / Gotta stop / I wanna be your lover.
7" Single: Released Jun '81, on Warner Bros., by WEA Records. Deleted Jun '84. Catalogue no: **K 17819**

I COULD NEVER TAKE THE PLACE OF YOUR MAN
Tracks: / I could never take the place of your man / Hot thing (edit).
Note: (Cat.no. 207284) 4 track cassette single of the new Prince release. Also includes three versions of 'Hot Thing'. Long Box pack.

PRINCE - BATDANCE (Released on Warner bros.)

Cassingle: Released Jul '87, on Paisley Park (USA), by WEA Records. Deleted Jul '88. Catalogue no: **W 8288C**
7" Single: Released Jul '87, on Paisley Park (USA), by WEA Records. Catalogue no: **W 8288**
12" Single: Released Nov '87, on Paisley Park (Germany), by WEA Records. Catalogue no: **920728 0**
12" Single: Released Jul '87, on Paisley Park (USA), by WEA Records. Catalogue no: **W 8288T**
Cassingle: Released Nov '87, on Paisley Park (USA), by WEA Records. Catalogue no: **20728 4**

I WANNA BE YOUR LOVER
Tracks: / I wanna be your lover / Just as long as we're together.
7" Single: Released Jan '80, on Warner Bros., by WEA Records. Deleted '83. Catalogue no: **K 17537**

I WISH U HEAVEN
Tracks: / I wish U heaven / Scarlet pussy.
CD 5": Released Oct '88, on Paisley Park (USA), by WEA Records. Catalogue no: **W 7745CD**
12" Single: Released Oct '88, on Paisley Park (USA), by WEA Records. Catalogue no: **W 7745T**
7" Single: Released Oct '88, on Paisley Park (USA), by WEA Records. Catalogue no: **W 7745**

I WOULD DIE 4 U
Tracks: / I would die 4 U.
7" Single: Released Dec '84, on Warner Bros., by WEA Records. Deleted '87. Catalogue no: **W 9121**

IF I WAS YOUR GIRLFRIEND
Tracks: / If I was your girlfriend / Shock Adelica.
7" Single: Released Jun '87, on Paisley Park (USA), by WEA Records. Deleted Jul '88. Catalogue no: **W 8334**
Cassingle: Released Jun '87, on Paisley Park (USA), by WEA Records. Deleted Jul '88. Catalogue no: **W 8334C**
12" Single: Released Nov '87, on Paisley Park (USA), by WEA Records. Catalogue no: **20697 0**
12" Single: Released Jun '87, on Paisley Park (USA), by WEA Records. Catalogue no: **W 8334T**

KISS
Tracks: / Kiss / Love or money.
Note: (Cat. No. 9204420 - 12" Import single in picture bag.
12" Single: Released Nov '87, on Paisley Park (Germany), by WEA Records. Catalogue no: **920442 0**
7" Pic: Released Feb '86, on Paisley Park (USA), by WEA Records. Deleted Jun '87. Catalogue no: **W 8751P**
7" Single: Released Feb '86, on Paisley Park (USA), by WEA Records. Catalogue no: **W 8751**
12" Single: Released Feb '86, on Paisley Park (USA), by WEA Records. Catalogue no: **W 8751T**

LET'S GO CRAZY
Tracks: / Let's go crazy / Take me with U.
Note: In picture bag.
12" Single: Released Nov '87, on Warner Bros.(USA), by WEA Records. Catalogue no: **202460**
7" Single: Deleted Jun '87. Catalogue no: **W 2000**

LET'S WORK
Tracks: / Let's work / Ronnie talk to Russia.
7" Single: Released Apr '82, on Warner Bros., by WEA Records. Deleted Apr '85. Catalogue no: **K 17922**

LITTLE RED CORVETTE
Tracks: / Little red corvette.
7" Single: Released Nov '83, on Warner Bros., by WEA Records. Deleted '86. Catalogue no: **W 9436**
12" Single: Released May '88, on Warner Bros.(Germany), by WEA Records. Catalogue no: **920107 0**
7" Single: Released Apr '83, on Warner Bros., by WEA Records. Deleted '86. Catalogue no: **W 9688**

MOUNTAINS
Tracks: / Mountains / Alexa de Paris.
12" Single: Released May '88, on Paisley Park (USA), by WEA Records. Catalogue no: **20465 0**
7" Single: Released May '86, on Warner Bros., by WEA Records. Deleted Jun '87. Catalogue no: **W 8711**
12" Single: Released May '86, on Warner Bros., by WEA Records. Deleted Jan '88. Catalogue no: **W 8711 T**
12" Pic: Released May '86, on Warner Bros., by WEA Records. Deleted Jun '87. Catalogue no: **W 8711 TP**

PAISLEY PARK (See panel above)
Tracks: / Paisley Park / She's always in my hair.
7" Single: Released May '85, on WEA, by WEA Records. Deleted '88. Catalogue no: **W 9052**
12" Single: Released Jan '85, on Warner Bros., by WEA Records. Deleted Jan '88. Catalogue no: **W 9052 T**

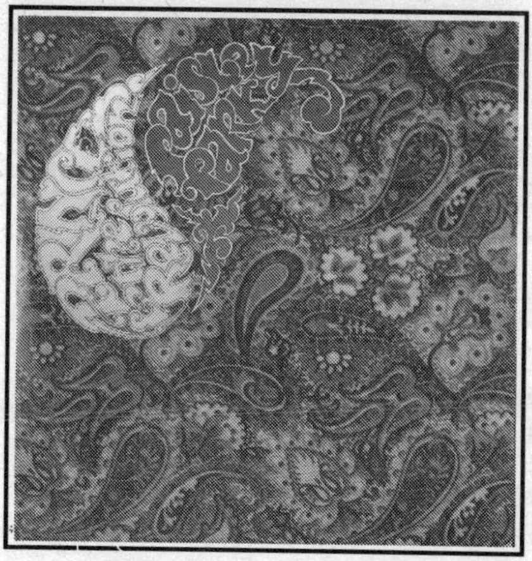

PRINCE - PAISLEY PARK (Released on WEA)

PARTY-MAN
Tracks: / Party-man / Feel U up.
Cassingle: Released Aug '89, on Warner Bros., by WEA Records. Catalogue no: **W 2814MC**
7" Single: Released Aug '89, on Warner Bros., by WEA Records. Catalogue no: **W 2814**
12" Single: Released Aug '89, on Warner Bros., by WEA Records. Catalogue no: **W 2814T**
CD 5": Released Aug '89, on Warner Bros., by WEA Records. Catalogue no: **W 2814CD**

POP LIFE
Tracks: / Pop life.
7" Single: Released Oct '85, on Paisley Park (USA), by WEA Records. Deleted '88. Catalogue no: **W 8858**
12" Single: Released Oct '85, on Paisley Park (USA), by WEA Records. Deleted Jan '88. Catalogue no: **W 8858 T**

PRINCE INTERVIEW 86
12" Single: Released '89, on Wax, by Wax Records. Catalogue no: **PRINCE 212**
7" Pic: Released '89, on Wax, by Wax Records. Catalogue no: **PRINCE 2P**
7" Single: Released '89, on Wax, by Wax Records. Catalogue no: **PRINCE 2**

PRINCE: INTERVIEW PICTURE DISC (COLLECTION)
Note: 4 x 7" picture discs in wallet.
7" Set: Released 11 Dec '88, on Baktabak, by Baktabak Records. Catalogue no: **BAKPAK 1014**

PURPLE RAIN (SINGLE)
Tracks: / Purple rain.
7" Single: Released Sep '84, on Warner Bros., by WEA Records. Deleted '87. Catalogue no: **W 9174**
12" Single: Released Nov '87, on Warner Bros., by WEA Records. Catalogue no: **920267 0**

RASPBERRY BERET
Tracks: / Raspberry beret.
7" Single: Released '87, on Paisley Park (USA), by WEA Records. Deleted Jun '87. Catalogue no: **W 8929**

SEXY DANCER
Tracks: / Sexy dancer / Bambi.
7" Single: Released Apr '80, on Warner Bros., by WEA Records. Deleted Apr '83. Catalogue no: **K 17590**

SIGN OF THE TIMES (SINGLE)
Tracks: / Sign of the times / La la la la he he he he.
Note: (Cat.no. 206480) 12" single (Import).
12" Single: Released Feb '87, on Paisley Park (USA), by WEA Records. Catalogue no: **W 8399T**
7" Single: Released Feb '87, on Paisley Park (USA), by WEA Records. Catalogue no: **W 8399**
12" Single: Released Nov '87, on Paisley Park (USA), by WEA Records. Catalogue no: **20648 0**

U GOT THE LOOK
Tracks: / U got the look.
Note: (Cat.no. 207274) 4 track cassette single, in long box pack. 2 versions of the title track, together with 2 versions of 'Housequake'. (Cat.no. 207270) 12" single Import.
7" Single: Released Aug '87, on Warner Bros., by WEA Records. Catalogue no: **W 8289**
12" Single: Released Nov '87, on Paisley Park (USA), by WEA Records. Catalogue no: **20727 0**
12" Single: Released Aug '87, on Warner Bros., by WEA Records. Catalogue no: **W 8289 T**
Cassingle: Released Nov '87, on Paisley Park (USA), by WEA Records. Catalogue no: **20727 4**

WHEN DOVES CRY
Tracks: / When doves cry / 17 days / 1999 (Cassingle only.) / DMSR (Cassingle only.).
7" Single: Released '85, on Paisley Park (USA), by WEA Records. Deleted Jan '88. Catalogue no: **W 9286**

Prince Aley

KEEP ON TRYING
Tracks: / Keep on trying.
12" Single: Released Aug '88, on Slick, by Slick Records. Catalogue no: **SLICK 02**

Prince Buster

Biographical details: Born in Kingston, Jamaica, this vocalist and songwriter (real name Buster Campbell) had boxing as his original career. It was this pugnacious aspect of his character that won him the title 'Prince'. During the early and mid-Sixties he came to prominence in his home country by being one of the foremost pioneers of a style that was initially known as 'blue beat' and then called 'ska'. This was an infectious ethnic music that relied heavily on its persistent rhythm and later gave birth to reggae.
The striking feature of his early success such as *I Feel The Spirit*, *Thirty Pieces Of Silver* and *Sammy Dead*, was the fact that they won recognition not only in Jamaica but also amongst the white Mod movement in Britain. Later in the decade, his cult status in the UK spread to the skinhead movement. By that time his music was no longer called 'ska' but was given a new name, 'rock steady'. The followers of this genre were known as 'rude boys', a Jamaican term that had now become fashionable in Britain too. In 1967 Prince Buster scored his only chart success in the latter country: *Al Capone*, an account of Jamaican gangster violence, was a steady seller, reaching No. 18 and logging 13 weeks on the UK Top 50 singles list. The content of his songs was often politically motivated and socially aware.
In the Seventies he switched from recording to producing other artists on the Jamaican scene. He also ran his own chain of record shops and made a cameo appearance in the early Seventies reggae movie *The Harder They Come*.
Though *Al Capone* remains his best known number, this solitary British chart appearance is a scant reflection of his influence on British music. His Sixties recording career was one of the major catalysts that led to the development of reggae, a form that Jamaica has always exported to the UK more successfully than to any other nation in the industrialised world.
Another more unexpected sign of his influence began in 1972, when British comedian Judge Dread scored a long-running UK chart success with his outrageous single *Big Six*. This was a continuation of Buster's Sixties track *Big Five*, which had been equally lewd. The Prince had also recorded a number called *Judge Dread*, thus inspiring both the name and the hit record of another artist. The new Judge Dread made several more sequels: *Big Seven*, *Big Eight* and *Big Ten* were all British Top 20 hits despite being banned by the BBC.
In 1979 a ska revival got underway in Britain. The first hit produced by this new movement was the Specials' *Gangsters*, a Top 10 single that was a re-working of *Al Capone*, on which group leader Jerry Dammers cheekily claimed sole composer credit. Although new lyrics were added, there is no doubt as to the source of inspiration for *Gangsters*. The Specials' 2 Tone record label also launched the careers of other ska-influenced acts, namely the Selecter, Madness, the Beat and the Bodysnatchers and managed to sustain an incredible 100% UK hit rate for a time. Allied to this resurgence was a simultaneous Mod revival; the protagonists of this movement also gave Buster recognition, as indeed they had done in their original heyday of the Sixties. In the wake of all this new acclaim, Prince Buster attempted to make a recording comeback, but with little success. This did not matter, for the influence of his previous work had already made him something of a legend. Perhaps the best tribute to him was Madness' first hit, released by 2 Tone Records in the summer of 1979, simply entitled, *The Prince*. (Bob MacDonald)..

AL CAPONE
Tracks: / One step beyond / Al capone.
12" Single: Released Feb '87, on Spartan, Catalogue no: **12SP 145**
7" Single: Released Feb '87, on Spartan, Catalogue no: **SP 145**

FINGER
Tracks: / Finger / Finger (version).
7" Single: Released Jun '81, on Arista, by BMG Records (UK). Deleted Jun '84. Catalogue no: **ARIST 411**

Prince Charles

I CAN'T STOP LOVING YOU
Tracks: / I can't stop loving you.
12" Single: Released Apr '87, on Carrere, Catalogue no: **CART 411**

WE CAN MAKE IT HAPPEN
Tracks: / We can make it happen / Chaka beat / We can make it happen (vocal mix) (Track on Picture disc only) / Radio live (Track on Picture disc only) / Saxxy licks (Track on Picture disc only).
7" Single: Released Mar '86, on PRT, by Castle Communications Records. Catalogue no: **7P 348**
7" Pic: Released Mar '86, on PRT, by Castle Communications Records. Catalogue no: **12PD 348**
12" Single: Released Mar '86, on PRT, by Castle Communications Records. Catalogue no: **12P 348**

Prince Far-I

EIGHTY THREE STRUGGLE
Tracks: / Eighty three struggle / Weeping wailing.
12" Single: Released Oct '80, on Charisma, by Virgin Records. Deleted Oct '83. Catalogue no: **PRE 11 12**

VIRGIN
Tracks: / Virgin / Danger.
7" Single: Released Apr '82, on On-U-Sound, by On-U-Sound Records. Deleted '85. Catalogue no: **DP 1**

Prince Hammer

DANCE HALL STYLE
Tracks: / Dance hall style.
12" Single: Released Jul '84, on Progressive, Catalogue no: **UNKNOWN**

Prince, Ian

AMERICAN GIRL
Tracks: / American girl / Rotation / American girl (dance mix) (12" only).
Note: Highly respected songwriter gaining rapid & widespread acclaim in the US.His songs have been performed by such people as Earth,Wind & Fire,Al Jarreau,Gladys Knight & Elisa Fiorillo,to name but a few.'American Girl'is Ian's debut single for Virgin.
7" Single: Released 21 Mar '88, on Virgin, by Virgin Records. Catalogue no: **VS 1057**
12" Single: Released 21 Mar '88, on Virgin, by Virgin Records. Catalogue no: **VST 1057**

MASTER OF THE GAME

Tracks: / Master of the game.
7" Single: Released Apr '87, on Virgin, by Virgin Records. Deleted May '88. Catalogue no: **VS 966**
12" Single: Released Apr '87, on Virgin, by Virgin Records. Deleted '89. Catalogue no: **VS 966-12**

TOO MUCH TOO SOON
Tracks: / Too much too soon / Let the music play.
7" Single: Released Aug '83, on London Records, by London Records. Catalogue no: **LON 30**
12" Single: Released Aug '83, on London Records, by London Records. Catalogue no: **LONX 30**

Prince JJ

I BELIEVE
Tracks: / I believe / Haunting memory.
7" Single: Released Nov '81, on JSO, Deleted '87. Catalogue no: **EAT 12**

Prince Junior & Mannings

FREE MANDELA!
Tracks: / Free Mandela (version).
12" Single: Released Nov '86, on Metrosound, Catalogue no: **PBL 004**

Prince Lessa Lassan

DJALENGA
Tracks: / Djalenga.
12" Single: Released Aug '83, on Swahili, by Albion Records. Catalogue no: **12 SWAH 001**

Prince Lincoln

I MAN FEEL IT
Tracks: / I man feel it.
12" Single: Released Jun '83, on MSR, Catalogue no: **MSRD A1**

ROOTS MAN BLUES
Tracks: / Root man blues / You make me feel alright.
12" Single: Released Mar '84, on Target, by Target Records. Catalogue no: **TAR 3**

Prince Lover Dalu

LET ME MAKE LOVE TO YOU
Tracks: / Let me make love to you / Let me make love to you (instrumental).
7" Single: Released Feb '89, on Breakout, by A&M Records. Catalogue no: **USA 641**
12" Single: Released Feb '89, on Breakout, by A&M Records. Catalogue no: **USAT 641**

Prince, Michael

DANCE YOUR LOVE AWAY
Tracks: / Dance your love away.
12" Single: Released Feb '86, on Bolts, by Bolts Records. Deleted Jan '87. Catalogue no: **BOLT 3**

Prince Oliver

RUNAWAY GIRL
Tracks: / Runaway girl.
12" Single: Released Mar '85, on Ariwa Sounds, by Ariwa Sounds. Catalogue no: **ARI 1036**

Prince Phalms

I LOVE YOUR STYLE
Tracks: / I love your style.
12" Single: Released Jun '85, on Tropical Sunset, Catalogue no: **CPP 002**

Prince, Steve

SHOULD HAVE BEEN YOU
Tracks: / Should have been you.
12" Single: Released Nov '83, on Pyramid, by Pyramid Records. Catalogue no: **PAD 001**

Princes Of Peace

X-RAY PROVED
Tracks: / X-ray proved.
7" Pic: Released Feb '88, on Shadowline, Catalogue no: **SR 0686**

Princess

AFTER THE LOVE HAS GONE
Tracks: / After the love has gone / After the dub has gone.
7" Set: Released Oct '85, on Supreme, by Supreme Records. Catalogue no: **SUPETD 103**
7" Single: Released Oct '85, on Supreme, by Supreme Records. Catalogue no: **SUPE 103**
7" Single: Released Jan '86, on Supreme, by Supreme Records. Catalogue no: **SUPETG 103**
12" Single: Released Oct '85, on Supreme, by Supreme Records. Catalogue no: **SUPET 103**
12" Single: Released Oct '85, on Supreme, by Supreme Records. Catalogue no: **SUPETX 103**

I CANNOT CARRY ON
Tracks: / I cannot carry on / I can't say goodbye.
7" Single: Released 31 Oct '87, on Polydor, by Polydor Ltd. Catalogue no: **POSP 893**
12" Single: Released 31 Oct '87, on Polydor, by Polydor Ltd. Catalogue no: **POSPX 893**

I'LL KEEP ON LOVING YOU
Tracks: / I'll keep on loving you / I'll keep on loving you (instrumental) / Say dub it / Keep on scratching (mix) / Chad's scratch mix.
Note: 7" shrinkwrapped together with SUPE 105 and SUPE 103. 12" gatefold sleeve.
12" Single: Released Apr '86, on Supreme, by Supreme Records. Catalogue no: **SUPETX 105**
7" Set: Released Apr '86, on Supreme, by Supreme Records. Catalogue no: **SUPED 105**
12" Single: Released Apr '86, on Supreme, by Supreme Records. Catalogue no: **SUPET 105**
12" Pic: Released May '86, on Supreme, by Supreme Records. Catalogue no: **SUPETP 105**
7" Single: Released Apr '86, on Supreme, by Supreme Records. Catalogue no: **SUPE 105**

IN THE HEAT OF A PASSIONATE MOMENT
Tracks: / In the heat of a passionate moment / I'll keep loving you (Extra track available on 12" version only.).
Note: *I'll keep loving you* on 12" only.t
7" Single: Released Sep '86, on Supreme, by Supreme Records. Catalogue no: **SUPE 108**
12" Single: Released Sep '86, on Supreme, by Supreme Records. Catalogue no: **SUPET 108**

LOVER DON'T GO
Tracks: / Lover don't go.
7" Single: Released 31 Jul '89, on Touch Tone, Catalogue no: **OUC 1**
12" Single: Released 7 Jul '89, on Touch Tone, Catalogue no: **OUCTR 1**
12" Single: Released 31 Jul '89, on Touch Tone, Catalogue no: **OUCT 1**

RED HOT
Tracks: / Red hot / Programmed to love you / Red hot (ext. mix) (Track on 12" only.) / Red hot (dub mix) (Track on 12" only.) / Red hot (inferno mix) (Track on 12" remix version only.).
Note: *Red hot (ext. mix)* and *red hot (dub mix)* on 12" only.
7" Single: Released May '87, on Polydor, by Polydor Ltd. Deleted Jan '88. Catalogue no: **POSP 868**
12" Single: Released May '87, on Polydor, by Polydor Ltd. Deleted Jan '88. Catalogue no: **POSPA 868**
12" Single: Released 30 May '87, on Polydor, by Polydor Ltd. Deleted Jan '88. Catalogue no: **POSPX 868**

SAY I'M YOUR NUMBER ONE
Tracks: / Say I'm your number one / Senza voce version / Funky sisters (Remix).
7" Single: Released Jul '85, on Supreme, by Supreme Records. Catalogue no: **SUPE 101**
12" Single: Released Jul '85, on Supreme, by Supreme Records. Catalogue no: **SUPET 101**
12" Single: Released Jul '85, on Supreme, by Supreme Records. Catalogue no: **SUPETX 101**
12" Single: Released Jul '85, on Supreme, by Supreme Records. Catalogue no: **SUPETZ 101**

TELL ME TOMORROW
Tracks: / Tell me tomorrow.
7" Single: Released Jun '86, on Supreme, by Supreme Records. Catalogue no: **SUPE 106**
12" Single: Released Jun '86, on Supreme, by Supreme Records. Catalogue no: **SUPET 106**

Princess Tinymeat

ANGELS IN PAIN
Tracks: / Angels in pain.
7" Single: Released Apr '87, on Rough Trade, by Rough Trade Records. Catalogue no: **RT 187**
12" Single: Released Apr '87, on Rough Trade, by Rough Trade Records. Catalogue no: **RTT 187**

BUN IN THE OVEN, A
Tracks: / Bun in the oven, A / Wigs on the green.
7" Single: Released Jan '86, on Rough Trade, by Rough Trade Records. Catalogue no: **RT 163**

SLOBLANDS
Tracks: / Sloblands / Fairest of them all.
12" Single: Released Mar '85, on Rough Trade, by Rough Trade Records. Catalogue no: **RTT 160**

Princess UFO

HI-FLYER
Tracks: / Hi-flyer.
7" Single: Released Jan '85, on Young Blood, by Young Blood Records. Catalogue no: **YB 0088**

LILI MARLENE
Tracks: / Lili Marlene / Mean to me / Hobellied, The / Annie doesn't live here anymore / You have my heart / Surrey with the fringe on top / Time on my hands / Taking a chance on love / Must I go / Miss Otis regrets / You have taken my soul / I couldn't sleep a wink last night.
7" Pic: Released Nov '84, on Young Blood, by Young Blood Records. Catalogue no: **YBP 0088**
7" Single: Released Nov '84, on Young Blood, by Young Blood Records. Catalogue no: **YB 0088**
12" Single: Released Nov '84, on Young Blood, by Young Blood Records. Catalogue no: **YBT 0088**

Principle

THIS IS NOT A SONG BY TALKING HEADS
Tracks: / This is not a song by Talking Heads / Nursery crime / I can tell.
12" Single: Released May '87, on Principle, by Principle Records. Catalogue no: **SRT 7KL 1074**

Principle, Jamie

BABY WANTS TO RIDE
Tracks: / Baby wants to ride / Baby wants to ride(dub).
7" Single: Released Feb '88, on ffrr, by London Records. Deleted Oct '88. Catalogue no: **FFR 1**
12" Single: Released Nov '87, on DJ Int.(USA), Catalogue no: **DJ 903**
12" Single: Released Feb '88, on ffrr, by London Records. Deleted Oct '88. Catalogue no: **FFRX 1**

I'M GONNA MAKE YOU SCREAM
Tracks: / I'm gonna make you scream.
7" Single: Released Oct '88, on DJ World Records (USA), Catalogue no: **DJW 102**

REBELS (GET RIGHTEOUS)
Tracks: / Rebels (get righteous) / Baby wants to ride / Rebels (get righteous) - (acid mix) / Rebels (get righteous) - (house of trix mix).
Note: This brand-new single from the 'Godfather of House' has been mixed by former chart-topper Steve 'Silk' Hurley and appeared in its original form on the album 'House Sound of London - IV'.
7" Single: Released Sep '88, on ffrr, by London Records. Deleted May '89. Catalogue no: **FFRXR 10**
7" Single: Released Sep '88, on ffrr, by London Records. Deleted May '89. Catalogue no: **FFR 10**
12" Single: Released Sep '88, on ffrr, by London Records. Deleted May '89. Catalogue no: **FFRX 10**

WAITING ON MY ANGEL
Tracks: / Waiting on my angel.
12" Single: Released Dec '85, on ZYX (Germany), Catalogue no: **ZYX 5303**

Prior, Maddy

Biographical details: She achieved great success with the folk-rock band, Steeleye Span, before going it alone with albums released on Plant Life, and then after a period of consolidation of her own writing, an album called *Going for glory* (Making Waves, April 1984).

DEEP IN THE DARKEST NIGHT
Tracks: / Deep in the darkest night / Western movies.
7" Single: Released Nov '83, on RCA, by BMG Records (UK). Catalogue no: **RCA 379**
7" Single: Released Jan '86, on Making Waves, by Celtic Music. Catalogue no: **SURF 109**

FACE TO FACE
Tracks: / Face to face.
7" Single: Released Oct '82, on Plant Life, by Plant Life Records. Catalogue no: **PLRS 001**

STOOKIE
Tracks: / Stookie.
7" Single: Released Sep '85, on Making Waves, by Celtic Music. Catalogue no: **SURF 108**

Prism

YOU WALKED AWAY AGAIN
Tracks: / You walked away again / N-n-n-no.
7" Single: Released Mar '80, on Capitol, by EMI Records. Deleted Mar '83. Catalogue no: **CL 16132**

Prisoners

ELECTRIC FIT
Tracks: / Electric fit.
7" Single: Released Aug '84, on Ace, by Ace Records. Deleted Jun '88. Catalogue no: **SW 98**

HURRICANE
Tracks: / Hurricane.
7" Single: Released Nov '83, on Big Beat, by Ace Records. Catalogue no: **NS 90**

WHENEVER I'M GONE
Tracks: / Whenever I'm gone / Promised land / Gravedigger (Extra track on 12" version only.).
Note: *Gravedigger* on 12" only.
7" Single: Released Mar '86, on Countdown, Catalogue no: **VAIN 4**
12" Single: Released Mar '86, on Countdown, Catalogue no: **12 VAIN 4**

Prister, Jerome

SAY YOU'LL BE
Tracks: / Say you'll be.
12" Single: Released Jan '88, on Sure Delight, by Sure Delight Records. Catalogue no: **SDT 4**
12" Single: Released 28 Sep '87, on Tuff City (USA), Catalogue no: **TUF 120008**

WHERE IS SHE NOW
Tracks: / Where is she now / Let me tell you about my girl.
12" Single: Released Feb '89, on Tuff City (USA), Catalogue no: **TUF 128035**
7" Single: Released Mar '89, on Sure Delight, by Sure Delight Records. Catalogue no: **SD 7**
12" Single: Released Mar '89, on Sure Delight, by Sure Delight Records. Catalogue no: **SDT 7**

Pritchard,Bill

INVISIBLE STATE
Tracks: / Invisible state.
7" Single: Released Aug '89, on Play It Again Sam(Belgium), by Play It Again Sam (Belgium). Catalogue no: **BIAS 132-7**

PAS DE PLAISANTERIE
Tracks: / Pas de plaisanterie / Angelique / Born blonde.
7" Single: Released 23 Apr '88, on Third Mind, by Third Mind Records. Catalogue no: **TMS 07**

TOMMY & CO
Tracks: / Tommy & co.
7" Single: Released Mar '89, on Play It Again Sam(Belgium), by Play It Again Sam (Belgium). Catalogue no: **BIAS 104-7**

Private Collection

DREAMERS
Tracks: / Dreamers.
12" Single: Released Sep '89, on Mafia/Fluxy, Catalogue no: **MF 011**

IT'S HOPELESS
Tracks: / It's hopeless.
7" Single: Released Jul '82, on Gallery, Catalogue no: **GAL 003**

Private Constable

TOWN AND COUNTRY
Tracks: / Town and country.
12" Single: Released Jul '88, on Vibes, by Vibes Records. Catalogue no: **VIBES 032**

Private Eye

I CRY FOR YOU
Tracks: / I cry for you.
7" Single: Released Oct '83, on Spider, by Spider Records. Deleted '86. Catalogue no: **SPY00/A**

Private I.D

COLD COLD SWEAT
Tracks: / Cold cold sweat.
12" Single: Released Oct '84, on W.A.R., by W.A.R. Records. Catalogue no: **12 WAR 3**
7" Single: Released Oct '84, on W.A.R., by W.A.R. Records. Catalogue no: **WAR 3**

Private Is

DO I WORRY
Tracks: / Do I worry?.
12" Single: Released Aug '81, on Dub Vendor, Deleted '88. Catalogue no: **TND 002**

Private Joy

COOLIN' OUT
Tracks: / Coolin' out / Coolin' out (inst).
12" Single: Released 20 Jun '87, on Champion, by Champion Records. Deleted Aug '89. Catalogue no: **CHAMP 1249**
7" Single: Released Jun '87, on Champion, by Champion Records. Catalogue no: **CHAMP 49**

Private Life

TIME TO RIDE
Tracks: / Time to ride.
12" Single: Released Jul '88, on Pirate, Catalogue no: **PRY 1T**

Private Line

ISN'T IT MAGIC
Tracks: / Isn't it magic / Don't hang up.
7" Single: Released Apr '80, on Red Bus, by Red Bus Records. Deleted Apr '83. Cata-

logue no: **RBUS 51**

Private Lives

BECAUSE YOU'RE YOUNG
Tracks: / Because you're young / Because you're young (part 2).
7" Single: Released Feb '82, on Chrysalis, by Chrysalis Records. Catalogue no: **CHS 2564**
12" Single: Released Feb '82, on Chrysalis, by Chrysalis Records. Catalogue no: **CHS 12 2564**

LIVING IN A WORLD (TURNED UP-SIDE DOWN)
Tracks: / Living in a world turned upside down.
7" Single: Released Feb '84, on EMI, by EMI Records. Deleted '87. Catalogue no: **PRIV 2**

MEMORY OF YOUR NAME
Tracks: / Memory of your name / Swim away / Stranger the love.
Note: *Memory of your name (dub)* on 12" only.
7" Single: Released '82, on Chrysalis, by Chrysalis Records. Deleted '87. Catalogue no: **CHS 2628**
12" Single: Released '82, on Chrysalis, by Chrysalis Records. Deleted '87. Catalogue no: **CHS 12 2628**
7" Single: Released Nov '81, on Chrysalis, by Chrysalis Records. Deleted Nov '84. Catalogue no: **CHS 2564**

Private Party

CHANGE
Tracks: / Change.
7" Single: Released Nov '83, on Button, by Musical Characters Records. Catalogue no: **BTN 112**

IT TEARS ME UP
Tracks: / It tears me up.
7" Single: Released May '85, on Shoestring (2), by Shoestring Records. Catalogue no: **LACE 004**

TENNENTS
Tracks: / Tennents.
12" Single: Released 1 Aug '87, on I.M.W., by I.M.W. Records. Catalogue no: **IMW 1201**

Private Possession

THIS TIME
Tracks: / This time / Rap, The.
Note: Featuring Hunter Hayes.
12" Single: Released Nov '86, on 4th & Broadway, by Island Records. Deleted Jul '87. Catalogue no: **12 BRW 55**

Private Sector

LIKE A TON OF BRICKS (IT'S HIT ME)
Tracks: / Like a ton of bricks (it's hit me).
12" Single: Released Jun '83, on Food For Thought, by Music For Nations Records. Catalogue no: **YUMT 103**

Private Slim

THERE I GO AGAIN
Tracks: / There I go again / I'm in full gear.
12" Single: Released Jun '89, on Rhyme & Reason, by Priority Records. Catalogue no: **12RNR 3**

Private Tabby

JAILHOUSE
Tracks: / Jailhouse / If you leave me.
Note: double A single.
12" Single: Released Sep '86, on Trojan, by Trojan Records. Deleted May '88. Catalogue no: **TROT 9087**

Private View

WALLS
Tracks: / Walls.
7" Single: Released Jun '84, on New Label, Catalogue no: **GNO 100**

Privates

ASHAMED TO BE WHITE
Tracks: / Ashamed to be white.
7" Single: Released May '82, on Dune, Catalogue no: **DUNE 1**

Prize Guys

THATS WHAT I CALL LOVIN'
Tracks: / That's what I call lovin'.
7" Single: Released Aug '81, on Castle, by Castle Communications Records. Catalogue no: **CAS 002**

Pro Arte Orchestra

BOX OF DELIGHTS
Tracks: / Box of delights / Carol symphony.
7" Single: Released Dec '84, on BBC, by BBC Records & Tapes. Deleted Apr '89. Catalogue no: **RESL 162**

Proby, P.J.

Biographical details: Born James Marcus Smith in Houston, Texas, 1938, Proby is a rock singer who had hits in the UK and made the tabloids with his trouser-splitting act. He made demos for Elvis Presley in the late 1950's, played bit parts in western films and toured under the name of Jet Powers. He was discovered by British TV producer Jack Good and impressed viewers of a '64 Beatles television special with his flamboyant image: pony tail, frilled shirt, tight trousers. His several hits up to '68 included a frantic revival of the pre-war ballad Hold Me. The variety of his material indicated a lack of direction rather than eclecticism. He challenged Tom Jones to a singing contest (it didn't happen) and played Iago in Good's Catch My Soul (a rock version of Othello) in London in '71. He re-emerged from cabaret to play Presley in Elvis On Stage in '78. He made an album, *Focus Con Proby* in 1978 with the Dutch jazz-rock band Focus and one-off singles included a cover of Joy Division's doom-laden new wave anthem *Love Will Tear Us Apart* in '85. (Donald Clarke, May 1987.).

HOLD ME
Tracks: / Hold me / Tip of my fingers.
7" Single: Released May '64, on Decca, by Decca Records. Deleted '67. Catalogue no: **F 11904**

I APOLOGISE
Tracks: / I apologise.
7" Single: Released Feb '65, on Liberty, by EMI Records. Deleted '68. Catalogue no: **LIB 10188**

I CAN'T MAKE IT ALONE
Tracks: / I can't make it alone.
7" Single: Released Oct '66, on Liberty, by EMI Records. Deleted '69. Catalogue no: **LIB 10250**

IT'S YOUR DAY TODAY
Tracks: / It's your day today.
7" Single: Released Mar '68, on Liberty, by EMI Records. Deleted '71. Catalogue no: **LBF 15046**

LET THE WATER RUN DOWN
Tracks: / Let the water run down.
7" Single: Released Aug '65, on Liberty, by EMI Records. Deleted '68. Catalogue no: **LIB 10206**

LOVE WILL TEAR US APART
Tracks: / Love will tear us apart.
7" Single: Released Nov '85, on Savoy, by Savoy Records. Catalogue no: **PJS 2**
12" Single: Released Nov '85, on Savoy, by Savoy Records. Catalogue no: **PJS 212**

MARIA
Tracks: / Maria.
7" Single: Released Nov '65, on Liberty, by EMI Records. Deleted '68. Catalogue no: **LIB 10218**

SOMEWHERE (SINGLE)
Tracks: / Somewhere / Maria.
7" Single: Released Mar '82, on Juke Box (Re-issue), Catalogue no: **JB 08**
7" Single: Released Dec '64, on Liberty, by EMI Records. Deleted '67. Catalogue no: **LIB 10182**

TAINTED LOVE
Tracks: / Tainted love.
7" Single: Released Oct '85, on Savoy, by Savoy Records. Catalogue no: **PJS 1**

THAT MEANS A LOT
Tracks: / That means a lot.
7" Single: Released Sep '65, on Liberty, by EMI Records. Deleted '68. Catalogue no: **LIB 10215**

TO MAKE A BIG MAN CRY
Tracks: / To make a big man cry.
7" Single: Released Jun '66, on Liberty, by EMI Records. Deleted '69. Catalogue no: **LIB 10236**

TOGETHER
Tracks: / Together.
7" Single: Released Sep '64, on Decca, by Decca Records. Deleted '67. Catalogue no: **F 11967**

YOU'VE COME BACK
Tracks: / You've come back.
7" Single: Released Feb '66, on Liberty, by EMI Records. Deleted '69. Catalogue no: **LIB 10223**

Process

SOMETHING INTERNATIONAL
Tracks: / Something international / Triple echo.
7" Single: Released Jul '80, on Mercury, by Phonogram Ltd. Deleted Jul '83. Catalogue no: **MER 26**

Proclaimers

I'M GONNA BE (500 MILES)
Tracks: / I'm gonna be (500 miles) / Better days / Teardrops (12" version only.).
7" Single: Released 15 Aug '88, on Chrysalis, by Chrysalis Records. Catalogue no: **CLAIM 2**
12" Single: Released 15 Aug '88, on Chrysalis, by Chrysalis Records. Catalogue no: **CLAIMX 2**

I'M ON MY WAY
Tracks: / I'm on my way / Over and done with (live).
CD 5": Released Jan '89, on Chrysalis, by Chrysalis Records. Catalogue no: **CLAMCD 4**
7" Single: Released Jan '89, on Chrysalis, by Chrysalis Records. Catalogue no: **CLAIM 4**
12" Single: Released Jan '89, on Chrysalis, by Chrysalis Records. Catalogue no: **CLAIMX 4**

LETTER FROM AMERICA
Tracks: / Letter from America (band version) / Letter from America (acoustic version) / I'm lucky / Just because / Twenty flight rock.
10" single: Released May '88, on Chrysalis (Australia), by Chrysalis Records. Catalogue no: **X 14575**
7" Single: Released Oct '87, on Chrysalis, by Chrysalis Records. Catalogue no: **CHS 3178**
12" Single: Released Oct '87, on Chrysalis, by Chrysalis Records. Catalogue no: **CHS 12 3178**

MAKE MY HEART FLY
Tracks: / Make my heart fly / Wish I could say / I'm gonna burn your playhouse down (track on 12" only.) / Throw the 'R' away (track on 12" only.).
7" Single: Released Feb '88, on Chrysalis, by Chrysalis Records. Catalogue no: **CLAIM 1**
12" Single: Released Feb '88, on Chrysalis, by Chrysalis Records. Catalogue no: **CLAIMX 1**

SUNSHINE ON LEITH (SINGLE)
Tracks: / Sunshine on Leith / Leaving home / First attack (Only on 12".) / Letter from America (live) (Only on 12".).
CD 5": Released Oct '88, on Chrysalis, by Chrysalis Records. Catalogue no: **CLAM CD 3**
7" Single: Released Oct '88, on Chrysalis, by Chrysalis Records. Catalogue no: **CLAIM 3**
12" Single: Released Oct '88, on Chrysalis, by Chrysalis Records. Catalogue no: **CLAIMX 3**

THROW THE R AWAY
Tracks: / Throw the R away / Train went past the window, A / Long gone lonesome (live) (Available on 12" only) / I can't be myself (live).
7" Single: Released 23 May '87, on Chrysalis, by Chrysalis Records. Catalogue no: **CHS 3144**
12" Single: Released 23 May '87, on Chrysalis, by Chrysalis Records. Catalogue no: **CHS 12 3144**

Procul Harum

Biographical details: This British rock band began as the Paramounts in the early 1960's, playing R & B covers in Southend. Members were Gary Brooker (piano and vocals), Robin Trower (guitar), Chris Copping (bass) -- all born in 1945 -- and Barrie (B.J.) Wilson (drums), born in 1947. Brooker's bluesy, Ray Charles-influenced voice combined with a tune by Bach and mysterious words by Keith Reid to make *A Whiter Shade Of Pale*, with Mathew Fisher (born 1946) on organ and other session players: it was No 1 in the UK, No 5 in America and will always be associated with the 1967 "Summer of Love". They had another hit with *Homburg* the same year but the scratch band fell apart and Trower and Wilson were recruited to finish the album *Procol Harum*, also in 1967. The name of the group was either Latin for "beyond these things" or the name of somebody's cat. They were typecast as one-hit wonders because of the impact of their first hit but they had many fans and were influential for their two-keyboard approach. *Shine On Brightly* and *A Salty Dog* in '68-'69 are now regarded as 60's classics. Their other big hit single was *Conquistador* in '72. Fisher went solo in 1969 and made four albums between '73 and '81. Brooker also recorded solo. (Donald Clarke, May 1987.).

CONQUISTADOR
Tracks: / Conquistador / Salty dog.
7" Single: Released Aug '72, on Chrysalis, by Chrysalis Records. Deleted '75. Catalogue no: **CHS 2003**
7" Single: Released Aug '72, on Chrysalis, by Chrysalis Records. Deleted '77. Catalogue no: **CHS 2244**

CONQUISTADOR (OLD GOLD)
Tracks: / Pandora's box.
7" Single: Released Feb '87, on Old Gold, by Old Gold Records. Catalogue no: **OG 9692**

HOMBURG
Tracks: / Homburg.
7" Single: Released Oct '67, on Regal Zonophone, by EMI Records. Deleted '70. Catalogue no: **RZ 3003**
7" Single: Released Aug '82, on Cube, Catalogue no: **BAK 2**

PANDORA'S BOX
Tracks: / Pandora's box / Pipers tune, The.
7" Single: Released Aug '75, on Chrysalis, by Chrysalis Records. Deleted '80. Catalogue no: **CHS 2073**

PROCUL HARUM (CD SINGLE)
Tracks: / Whiter shade of pale, A / Homburg / Conquistador / Salty dog.
CD 3": Released '88, on Special Edition, by Castle Communications Records. Catalogue no: **CD3-14**

QUITE RIGHTLY SO
Tracks: / Quite rightly so.
7" Single: Released Apr '68, on Regal Zonophone, by EMI Records. Deleted '71. Catalogue no: **RZ 3007**

SALTY DOG (SINGLE)
Tracks: / Salty dog.
7" Single: Released Jun '69, on Regal Zonophone, by EMI Records. Deleted '72. Catalogue no: **RZ 3019**

WHITER SHADE OF PALE, A (OLD GOLD)
Tracks: / Whiter shade of pale, A / Homburg.
7" Single: Released Jun '88, on Old Gold, by Old Gold Records. Catalogue no: **OG 9225**

WHITER SHADE OF PALE (SINGLE)
Tracks: / Whiter shade of pale, A.
7" Single: Released May '67, on Deram, by London Records. Deleted '70. Catalogue no: **DM 126**
7" Single: Released Aug '82, on Cube, Catalogue no: **BAK 1**
7" Single: Released Apr '72, on Magnifly, by Fly Records. Deleted '75. Catalogue no: **ECHO 10**
7" Single: Released Aug '82, on Cube, Catalogue no: **BUG 77**
12" Single: Released Aug '82, on Cube, Catalogue no: **GBUG**

Producers

RADIO
Tracks: / Radio.
7" Single: Released Jul '79, on Hobo, Catalogue no: **HOS 003**

WALK RIGHT BACK
Tracks: / Walk right back.
7" Single: Released Nov '80, on Magic (1), by Submarine Records. Catalogue no: **MACH 4**

Product

STYLE WARS
Tracks: / Style wars.
12" Single: Released Jul '81, on Clay, by Clay Records. Deleted '88. Catalogue no: **PLATE 1**

Product, Clive

HONEST IT'S PRODUCT
Tracks: / Drastic haircut of Mr. Doomedalright / Future of our lives, The / Honest it's product / Chair, The / Western hampster.
7" EP: Released Mar '82, on Nuclear, by Nuclear Records. Catalogue no: **CLEAR 003**

Product Of Reason

MAN OF YOUR DREAMS
Tracks: / Man of your dreams.
7" Single: Released Mar '83, on T. E. R., by That's Entertainment Records. Catalogue no: **LYNX 1**

Production House

COMING ROUND
Tracks: / Coming round.
12" Single: Released Jun '85, on Production House (1). Catalogue no: **PH 1**

Profane, Benny

DEVIL LAUGHING
Tracks: / Devil laughing.
12" Single: Released Jul '87, on Ediesta, Catalogue no: **CALC 026**

PARASITE
Tracks: / Parasite / Kamikaze drinking / Holy cow / Little god.
12" Single: Released May '88, on Ediesta, Catalogue no: **CALC 048**

ROB A BANK
Tracks: / Rob a bank.
7" Single: Released Aug '88, on Ediesta, Catalogue no: **CALC 061**
12" Single: Released Aug '88, on Ediesta, Catalogue no: **CALC 061T**

SKATEBOARD TO OBLIVION
Tracks: / Skateboard to oblivion.
12" Single: Released 30 May '89, on Play Hard, by Play Hard Records. Catalogue no: **DEC 24**

WHERE IS PIG
Tracks: / Where is pig.
12" Single: Released May '86, on Sub Pop,

Catalogue no: **PURE 1**

Professionals

1-2-3
Tracks: / 1-2-3 / White light, white heat.
7" Single: Released Oct '80, on Virgin, by Virgin Records. Deleted '83. Catalogue no: **VS 376**

JOIN THE PROFESSIONALS
Tracks: / Join the professionals.
7" Single: Released Jun '81, on Virgin, by Virgin Records. Deleted Jun '84. Catalogue no: **VS 426**

Professor Lee

FREEDOM TO BANDAGE
Tracks: / Freedom to bandage.
12" Single: Released Nov '85, on Serious, by Serious Records. Catalogue no: **SV 001**

Professor Nuts

CRISIS
Tracks: / Crisis.
12" Single: Released Oct '84, on Gorgon, Catalogue no: **UNKNOWN**

RAGAMUFFIN NATTY DREAD
Tracks: / Ragamuffin natty dread / Ragamuffin natty dread (version).
12" Single: Released Jan '88, on Fashion, by Fashion Records. Catalogue no: **FAD 051**

Profil

HEY MUSIC MAN
Tracks: / Hey music man / He, he, M'sieurs Dames.
7" Single: Released Apr '80, on CBS, by CBS Records. Deleted Apr '83. Catalogue no: **CBS 8574**

Profile

HIP HOP
Tracks: / Hip hop.
12" Single: Released May '88, on Kufe, Catalogue no: **EB 010**

Progoganda For Frankie

MEDLEY WITH RELAX
Tracks: / Medley with relax / Dee Jay.
7" Single: Released Jul '86, on Record Shack, by Record Shack Records. Catalogue no: **SOHO 71**
12" Single: Released Jul '86, on Record Shack, by Record Shack Records. Catalogue no: **SOHOT 71**

Project

LOVE RESCUE
Tracks: / Love rescue.
7" Single: Released Apr '81, on Creole, by Creole Records. Deleted '85. Catalogue no: **CR 4**
12" Single: Released Apr '81, on Creole, by Creole Records. Deleted '85. Catalogue no: **CR 124**

Project 4

LIFE AFTER LIVE
Tracks: / Life after live.
7" Single: Released Jan '82, on Never, Deleted '84. Catalogue no: **NEV 1001**

Project Club

AMNESIA
Tracks: / Dance with the devil / Amnesia.
7" Single: Released Jun '88, on Supreme, by Supreme Records. Catalogue no: **SUPE 131**
12" Single: Released Jun '88, on Supreme, by Supreme Records. Catalogue no: **SUPET 131**

HOW LOW CAN YOU GO
Tracks: / How low can you go.
12" Single: Released Apr '88, on Supreme, by Supreme Records. Catalogue no: **SUPETX 125**

Project Future

RAY-GUN-OMICS
Tracks: / Ray-gun-omics.
7" Single: Released Aug '83, on Capitol, by EMI Records. Deleted Jan '88. Catalogue no: **CL 305**
12" Single: Released Aug '83, on Capitol, by EMI Records. Deleted '88. Catalogue no: **12 CL 305**

Project One

PLAY PLAY GIRL
Tracks: / Play play girl.
12" Single: Released Aug '85, on Sea View, Catalogue no: **SVR 09**

Projection

DON'T FAKE MY LOVE
Tracks: / Don't fake my love.
7" Single: Released Sep '86, on Elite Records, by Elite Records. Deleted '88. Catalogue no: **DAZZ 55**

LOVE STRUCK
Tracks: / Lovestruck / Turn your love (right around).
12" Single: Released May '89, on Jam Today, by Jam Today Records. Catalogue no: **12CHIL 13**

LOVESTRUCK
Tracks: / Lovestruck (wireless mix) / Dumbstruck.
12" Single: Released May '89, on Jam Today, by Jam Today Records. Catalogue no: **12 CHIL 13**
12" Single: Released Dec '86, on Elite Records, by Elite Records. Deleted '88. Catalogue no: **DAZZ 63**

TURN YOUR LOVE (RIGHT AROUND)
Tracks: / Turn your love (right around) / Hardrock soul remix / Allstars (Remix).
12" Single: Released Mar '86, on Elite Records, by Elite Records. Deleted '88. Catalogue no: **DAZZ 48**

TURN YOUR LOVE (RIGHT AROUND) (RE-ISSUE)
Tracks: / Turn your love (right around).
12" Single: Released May '89, on Jam Today, by Jam Today Records. Catalogue no: **12CHIL 13**

WHAT'S YOUR PROBLEM
Tracks: / What's your problem / What's your problem (version).
7" Single: Released Oct '88, on Jam Today, by Jam Today Records. Catalogue no: **CHIL 8**
12" Single: Released Sep '88, on Jam Today, by Jam Today Records. Catalogue no: **12CHIL 8**

Projection Brothers

CRYSTAL EYES
Tracks: / Crystal eyes.
7" Single: Released Jul '83, on Flying, by Flying Records. Catalogue no: **FLY 107**

Proletariat

MARKETPLACE
Tracks: / Marketplace.
7" Single: Released Aug '86, on Homestead, Catalogue no: **HMS 037**

Promise

AWAY AWAY
Tracks: / Away away.
12" Single: Released Oct '84, on Inner Vision, Catalogue no: **IVSTR 3**

Promises

I SEE NO REASON
Tracks: / I see no reason.
12" Single: Released Apr '82, on Jama, Catalogue no: **JADC 018**

Promises,Promises

CAN YOU TAKE THE RISK
Tracks: / Can you take the risk? / Empty rooms and echos.
7" Single: Released Sep '86, on Fend For Yourself, Catalogue no: **FFY 001**

SHUT OUT THE LIGHT
Tracks: / Shut out the light / Apocalypse of fashion.
7" Single: Released Sep '86, on Fend For Yourself, Catalogue no: **FFY 002**

Propaganda

DOCTOR MABUSE
Tracks: / Doctor Mabuse.
7" Single: Released Mar '84, on ZTT, by ZTT Records. Catalogue no: **ZTAS 2**
12" Single: Released Mar '84, on Island, by Island Records. Catalogue no: **12ZTAS 2**

DUEL
Tracks: / Duel.
7" Single: Released May '85, on ZTT, by ZTT Records. Catalogue no: **DUAL 1**
7" Single: Released Apr '85, on ZTT, by ZTT Records. Catalogue no: **ZTAS 8**
12" Single: Released Apr '85, on ZTT, by ZTT Records. Catalogue no: **12 ZTAS 8**

NINE LIVES OF DR. MABUSE EP
Tracks: / Nine lives of Dr. Mabuse.
Cassingle: Released May '84, on ZTT, by ZTT Records. Catalogue no: **CTIS 101**

P MACHINERY
Tracks: / P machinery.
7" Single: Released Nov '85, on ZTT, by ZTT Records. Deleted Jun '88. Catalogue no: **ZTAS 21**
12" Single: Released Nov '85, on ZTT, by ZTT Records. Deleted Jun '88. Catalogue no: **12 ZTS 12**
12" Single: Released Nov '85, on ZTT, by ZTT Records. Catalogue no: **12 ZTAS 21**

P MACHINERY (BETA MIX)
Tracks: / P machinery.
12" Single: Released Aug '85, on ZTT, by ZTT Records. Catalogue no: **12 XZTAS 15**

Propellors

DAMBUSTERS
Tracks: / Dambusters / Pomp and circumstance.
7" Single: Released Mar '81, on Carve Up, by Red Lightning Records. Catalogue no: **CU 1**

Prophet

SOUND OF A BREAKING HEART
Tracks: / Sound of a breaking heart / Asylum / Hard lovin' man (On 12" only).
7" Single: Released May '88, on Atlantic, by WEA Records. Catalogue no: **A 9082**
12" Single: Released May '88, on Atlantic, by WEA Records. Catalogue no: **A 9082 T**

Prophet, Michael

BODY FUSION
Tracks: / Body fusion.
12" Single: Released Jul '89, on Passion, by Skratch Records. Catalogue no: **PE 2**

BOOM HIM UP NOW
Tracks: / Boom him up now / Trouble nobody.
12" Single: Released May '82, on Greensleeves, by Greensleeves Records. Catalogue no: **GRED 87**

BUBBLE DOWN BUBBLE DOWN
Tracks: / Bubble down bubble down / Touch me back.
12" Single: Released Mar '85, on Greensleeves, by Greensleeves Records. Catalogue no: **GRED 173**

CEASE FIRE (SINGLE)
Tracks: / Cease fire.
12" Single: Released Jun '85, on Live & Learn (USA), by Live & Learn Records (USA). Catalogue no: **LLD 001**

COME ON LOVE ME TONIGHT
Tracks: / Come on love me tonight.
12" Single: Released Mar '83, on Simba, Catalogue no: **SM 004**

COME ON OVER
Tracks: / Come on over.
12" Single: Released May '87, on C & E, Catalogue no: **CED 120**

CRY ME A RIVER
Tracks: / Cry me a river.
12" Single: Released Feb '89, on BP International, Catalogue no: **BP 25**

FIGHT TO THE TOP
Tracks: / Fight to the top / Love and unity / Mash down Rome.
12" Single: Released Apr '80, on Island, by Island Records. Deleted Apr '83. Catalogue no: **12 WIP 6583**

GIRLS A FI MI
Tracks: / Girls a fi mi / Girls a fi mi (Version) (Techniques Posse).
12" Single: Released Oct '86, on Techniques, Catalogue no: **WRT 10**

HELP THEM PLEASE
Tracks: / See Baba Joe / Help them please.
12" Single: Released Nov '80, on Greensleeves, by Greensleeves Records. Catalogue no: **GRED 44**

HERE COMES THE BRIDE
Tracks: / Here comes the bride.
12" Single: Released Feb '82, on Greensleeves, by Greensleeves Records. Catalogue no: **GRED 73**
7" Single: Released Mar '82, on Greensleeves, by Greensleeves Records. Catalogue no: **NIGHT 1**

IMAGINE ME
Tracks: / Imagine me.
12" Single: Released Jul '88, on World Enterprise, Catalogue no: **WED 54**

JANE
Tracks: / Jane / Banana spliff.
12" Single: Released Dec '85, on Impact, by Ace Records. Catalogue no: **IM 001**

JUST TALKING
Tracks: / Just talking / Thru me.
12" Single: Released Nov '82, on Greensleeves, by Greensleeves Records. Catalogue no: **GRED 104**

MY LOVE WILL YEARS CARRY ON
Tracks: / My love will years carry on.
12" Single: Released May '88, on Blue Trac, by Blue Trac Records. Catalogue no: **BRTD 018**

RICH AND POOR
Tracks: / Rich and poor.
12" Single: Released Oct '84, on Thunderbolt, by Magnum Music Group. Deleted '89. Catalogue no: **UNKNOWN**

RICH MAN POOR MAN
Tracks: / Rich man poor man.
12" Single: Released Apr '83, on CSA, by CSA Records. Deleted '88. Catalogue no: **SPCSA 12003**

ROCK ME BABY
Tracks: / Rock me baby / Don't throw stones.
7" Single: Released Sep '82, on WLN, Catalogue no: **WLN 03**

SETTLE YU FE SETTLE
Tracks: / Settle yu fe settle / Accept me live.
12" Single: Released May '86, on Live & Learn (USA), by Live & Learn Records (USA). Catalogue no: **LLD 009**

WEY U A DO OVER DEY
Tracks: / Wey u a do over dey.
12" Single: Released May '85, on Kings Of Jazz, Catalogue no: **KLMP 001**

YOUR HEART
Tracks: / Your heart.
12" Single: Released May '88, on Skengdon, Catalogue no: **SKD 067**

Prophets

BACK TO THE BURNER
Tracks: / Back to the burner / Back to Siberia.
7" Single: Released Oct '81, on KSV, by Kingsley Sound & Vision Records. Catalogue no: **KSV 1**

Prosser, Alan

ROYAL DAVID'S CITY
Tracks: / Royal David's City.
7" Single: Released Dec '81, on Phantom, by Mean Records. Catalogue no: **PHAN 2**

Protagonist

28 NEIN
Tracks: / 28 nein.
12" Single: Released Oct '85, on Snak, Catalogue no: **SNAK 6**

Protector

MASS FANTASY
Tracks: / Mass fantasy.
12" Single: Released Dec '84, on Charlie's, Catalogue no: **CRD 001**

Protest

VINYL OVERLOAD
7" EP: Released Nov '83, on Xcentric Noise, by Xcentric Noise Records & Tapes. Catalogue no: **FOURTH 1**

Protex

PLACE IN YOUR HEART
Tracks: / Palce in your heart / Jeepster.
7" Single: Released Apr '80, on Polydor, by Polydor Ltd. Deleted Apr '83. Catalogue no: **2059245**

Protheroe, Brian

PINBALL
Tracks: / Pinball.
7" Single: Released Sep '74, on Chrysalis, by Chrysalis Records. Deleted '77. Catalogue no: **CHS 2043**

Protocol

THERE'S NO HOLDING BACK
Tracks: / Lonely man.
7" Single: Released Aug '87, on Hit The Deck, Deleted '88. Catalogue no: **CRUISE 3**

Proton Plus

PAY UP
Tracks: / Pay up.
7" Single: Released Jun '81, on Champagne Records, Deleted Jun '84. Catalogue no: **FUNK 4**
12" Single: Released Jun '81, on Champagne Records, Deleted Jun '84. Catalogue no: **FUNKY 4**
12" Single: Released Apr '84, on Yew Wood, Catalogue no: **UWOOD 2**

Proud, Peter

ANGEL BABY
Tracks: / Angel baby / Overacting.
7" Single: Released Apr '81, on State, by State Records. Deleted Apr '86. Catalogue no: **STAT 103**

HYPNOTIST
Tracks: / Hypnotist / Crazy.
7" Single: Released Jan '81, on State, by State Records. Deleted Jan '84. Catalogue no: **STAT 102**

THAT GIRL
Tracks: / That girl / Angel baby / Crazy.
7" Single: Released Sep '81, on State, by State Records. Deleted '84. Catalogue no: **STAT 108**

Proudlove

MIDAS TOUCH
Tracks: / Midas touch.
7" Single: Released Nov '83, on KRP, Catalogue no: **KRP 101**

Provine, Dorothy

CRAZY WORDS CRAZY TUNE
Tracks: / Crazy words crazy tune.
7" Single: Released Jun '62, on Warner Bros., by WEA Records. Deleted '65. Catalogue no: **WB 70**

DON'T BRING LULU

PSEUDO ECHO - LISTENING (Released on EMI)

Tracks: / Don't bring Lulu.
7" Single: Released Dec '61, on Warner Bros., by WEA Records. Deleted '64. Catalogue no: **WB 53**

P.R.S.

54-46 (THAT'S MY NUMBER)
Tracks: / 54-46 (that's my number).
12" Single: Released Oct '89, on Hysteria, by Hysteria Records. Catalogue no: **HYSTX 100**

Prudes

LIGHTHOUSE KEEPER'S DAUGHTER, THE
Tracks: / Lighthouse keeper's daughter, The / P.S. I'm leaving you.
7" Single: Released Feb '89, on Yo Yo, by Yo Yo Records. Catalogue no: **PRU 1**

PS I'M LEAVING (SINGLE)
Tracks: / PS I'm leaving.
12" Single: Released Sep '89, on Imaginary, by Imaginary Records. Catalogue no: **MIRAGE 14**

Pryor, Renee

ON BROADWAY
Tracks: / On Broadway / You want my love.
7" Single: Released Feb '80, on Polydor, by Polydor Ltd. Deleted '83. Catalogue no: **POSP 109**

P.S. Personal

SHOOT ME DOWN
Tracks: / Shoot me down.
7" Single: Released Aug '83, on New World, by President Records. Catalogue no: **NEW 1**

Pseudo Echo

FUNKY TOWN
Tracks: / Funky town / Lies are nothing.
7" Single: Released Jul '87, on RCA, by BMG Records (UK). Deleted May '89. Catalogue no: **PB 49705**
12" Single: Released Jul '87, on RCA, by BMG Records (UK). Catalogue no: **PB 49706**

LISTENING (See panel above)
Tracks: / Listening / From the shore.
7" Single: Released '84, on EMI, by EMI Records. Deleted '88. Catalogue no: **EMI 5512**

LIVING IN A DREAM
Tracks: / Living in a dream / Don't go.
7" Single: Released Oct '87, on RCA, by BMG Records (UK). Deleted May '89. Catalogue no: **PB 49753**
12" Single: Released Oct '87, on RCA, by BMG Records (UK). Catalogue no: **PT 49754**

LOVE AND ADVENTURE (ALL TIED UP)
Tracks: / Love and adventure (all tied up).
7" Single: Released May '86, on EMI, by EMI Records. Catalogue no: **EMI 5550**

Pseudo Elektronixx

ROTE GEFAHR 5 track EP
12" Single: Released Dec '83, on Rocky Road, Catalogue no: **ROCK TREND 300**

Psyche

LIVE
Tracks: / Live.
12" Single: Released Jul '88, on New Rose (1), by New Rose Records. Catalogue no: **PSYCHE 2**

NEVER LAUGH
Tracks: / Never laugh.
7" Single: Released Jun '83, on Burning Bing, Catalogue no: **BWP 001**

PRISONER OF DESIRE
Tracks: / Prisoner of desire.
12" Single: Released Aug '87, on New Rose (1), by New Rose Records. Catalogue no: **PSYCHE 1**

UNCIVILISED
Tracks: / Uncivilised.
12" Single: Released Jan '88, on New Rose (1), by New Rose Records. Catalogue no: **NEW 99**

UNCIVILISED (REMIX)
Tracks: / Uncivilised (remix).
7" Single: Released Apr '88, on New Rose (1), by New Rose Records. Catalogue no: **NEW 109**

UNVEILING THE SECRET (SINGLE)
Tracks: / Unveiling the secret.
CD 5": Released Apr '89, on New Rose (1), by New Rose Records. Catalogue no: **NEAT 4CD**
12" Single: Released 13 Jun '87, on New Rose (1), by New Rose Records. Catalogue no: **NEW 84**

Psychedelic Furs

Biographical details: With a name inspired by Velvet Underground's Venus In Furs, this new wave band were formed in London in 1977 by Richard "Butler Rep" Butler, vocals, with brother Tim Butler, bass, Duncan Kilburn, sax, and Roger "Dog" Morris, guitar. After a session on John Peel's BBC show led to a deal with CBS they recruited ex-Photons guitarist John Ashton and drummer Vince Ely in 1979. Steve Lillywhite produced their first two Top Thirty albums, *Psychedelic Furs* and *Talk Talk Talk* in '80 and '81: the music owed much to 60's groups like the Velvets while Butler's monotone sounded like John Rotten/Lydon. Singles were not big hits. Butler streamlined the band and made *Forever Now*, produced by Todd Rundgren in America with dubbed brass and strings. *Mirror Moves* in '84, was produced by Keith Forsey with a Euro-disco influence. *Midnight To Midnight* ('86) included a remake of *Pretty In Pink*, a hit film theme. They are now just Butler/Butler/Ashton and session players, heavily stylised. (Donald Clarke, May 1987.).

ALL THAT MONEY WANTS
Tracks: / All that money wants / Birdland / No easy street (live) (Only on 12" version.) / No tears (Only on 12" and CD single.) / Heaven (live) (Available on EP only).
Note: ** CD version only. *** EP version only.
7" EP: Released Jul '88, on CBS, by CBS Records. Deleted Jan '89. Catalogue no: **FURSEP 4**
CD 5": Released Jun '88, on CBS, by CBS Records. Deleted Jan '89. Catalogue no: **CDFURS 4**
7" Single: Released Jun '88, on CBS, by CBS Records. Deleted Jan '89. Catalogue no: **FURS 4**
12" Single: Released Jun '88, on CBS, by CBS Records. Deleted Jan '89. Catalogue no: **FURST 4**

ANGELS DON'T CRY
Tracks: / No release / We love you / Pretty in pink / Love my way.
7" Set: Released Jan '87, on CBS, by CBS Records. Deleted Aug '87. Catalogue no: **FURS D 3**
7" Single: Released Jan '87, on CBS, by CBS Records. Catalogue no: **FURS 3**
7" Single: Released Jan '87, on CBS, by CBS Records. Deleted Aug '87. Catalogue no: **FURS C 3**

DANGER
Tracks: / Danger / Shadow.
7" Single: Released Oct '82, on CBS, by CBS Records. Deleted Oct '85. Catalogue no: **A 2665**

DUMB WAITERS
Tracks: / Dumb waiters.
7" Single: Released May '81, on CBS, by CBS Records. Deleted '84. Catalogue no: **CBS 1166**

GHOST IN YOU
Tracks: / Ghost in you / Calypso dub.
7" Pic: Released May '84, on CBS, by CBS Records. Catalogue no: **WA 4470**
7" Single: Released May '84, on CBS, by CBS Records. Catalogue no: **A 4470**
12" Single: Released May '84, on CBS, by CBS Records. Catalogue no: **TA 4470**

GREATEST ORIGINAL HITS
7" EP: Released Mar '83, on CBS, by CBS Records. Catalogue no: **A 2909**

HEARTBREAK BEATS
Tracks: / Heartbreak beats / New Dream.
7" Single: Released Oct '86, on CBS, by CBS Records. Deleted Aug '87. Catalogue no: **650 183 7**
12" Single: Released Oct '86, on CBS, by CBS Records. Deleted Aug '87. Catalogue no: **650 186 6**

HEAVEN
Tracks: / Heaven / Heartbeat.
7" Single: Released Mar '84, on CBS, by CBS Records. Catalogue no: **A 4300**
12" Single: Released Mar '84, on CBS, by CBS Records. Catalogue no: **TA 4300**

LOVE MY WAY
Tracks: / Love my way / Aeroplant.
7" Single: Released Jul '82, on CBS, by CBS Records. Deleted '85. Catalogue no: **A 2549**

MR. JONES
Tracks: / Mr. Jones / Susan strange.
7" Single: Released Oct '80, on CBS, by CBS Records. Deleted Oct '83. Catalogue no: **CBS 9059**

PRETTY IN PINK
Tracks: / Pretty in pink / Love my way.
7" Single: Released Jun '81, on CBS, by CBS Records. Deleted '84. Catalogue no: **A 1327**
7" Single: Released Jul '86, on CBS, by CBS Records. Deleted '87. Catalogue no: **A 7242**
12" Single: Released Jul '86, on CBS, by CBS Records. Deleted '87. Catalogue no: **TA 7242**

SISTER EUROPE
Tracks: / Sister Europe / Pretty in pink / Dumb waiters / Love my way.
Cassingle: Released Jan '80, on CBS, by CBS Records. Deleted Jan '83. Catalogue no: **A40 2909**
7" Single: Released Jan '80, on CBS, by CBS Records. Deleted Jan '83. Catalogue no: **CBS 8179**

Psychic TV

GODSTAR
Tracks: / Godstar / Godstar (B.J. mix).
7" Single: Released Mar '86, on Temple Records, by Temple Records (2). Catalogue no: **TOPY 009**
12" Single: Released Mar '86, on Temple Records, by Temple Records (2). Catalogue no: **TOPY 009T**

GOOD VIBRATIONS
Tracks: / Good vibrations / Roman P.
7" Single: Released Sep '86, on Temple Records, by Temple Records (2). Deleted '89. Catalogue no: **TOPY 23**

JUST DRIFTING
Tracks: / Just drifting / Breakthrough.
7" Single: Released Dec '82, on Some Bizzare, by Some Bizzare Records. Catalogue no: **PTV 1**
12" Single: Released Dec '82, on Some Bizzare, by Some Bizzare Records. Catalogue no: **PTV 1T**

MAGICK DEFENDS ITSELF
Tracks: / Magick defends itself.
12" Single: Released Mar '87, on Temple Records, by Temple Records (2). Catalogue no: **TOPY 022**

ROMAN P
Tracks: / Roman P / Good vibrations.
7" Single: Released Jun '84, on Sordide Sentimental (France), Catalogue no: **SS 33009**
7" Single: Released Sep '86, on Temple Records, by Temple Records (2). Catalogue no: **TOPY 23**

TUNE (IN TO THE) ACID HOUSE
Tracks: / Tune (in to the) acid house.
12" Single: Released Jul '88, on Temple Records, by Temple Records (2). Catalogue no: **TOP 037**

UNCLEAN
Tracks: / Unclean.
12" Single: Released Aug '84, on Temple Records, by Temple Records (2). Catalogue no: **TOPY 001**

Psycho Surgeons

BOOK OF JOB
Tracks: / Book of job.
7" Single: Released Mar '89, on Q.T.A., Catalogue no: **QTA 1**

GIVE A MAN A BADGE
Tracks: / Give a man a badge / Diagnosis.
7" Single: Released Oct '86, on Flexible Response, Deleted '88. Catalogue no: **FR 003**

Psyclones

PANIC IN DETROIT
Tracks: / Panic in Detroit.
7" Single: Released '88, on Gigantic, by Gigantic Records. Catalogue no: **GI 002**

Psycon

MAKE YOURSELF SCARCE
Tracks: / Make yourself scarce.
7" Single: Released Sep '84, on Interdisc, by Interdisc Records. Catalogue no: **IN 12**
12" Single: Released Sep '84, on Interdisc, by Interdisc Records. Catalogue no: **12IN 12**

Psycons

RUN TO THE STRANGER
Tracks: / Run to the stranger.
7" Single: Released Apr '86, on Crystal, by President Records. Catalogue no: **CRYSTAL 10**

Psylons

ALL THE THINGS WE NEED
Tracks: / All the things we need.
7" Single: Released Jun '87, on Iron Lung, Catalogue no: **IL 001**

MOCKERY OF DECLINE, THE
Tracks: / Mockery of decline, The / Clear sky.
7" Single: Released Aug '86, on E-Type, Catalogue no: **E-TYPE 1**

Pub Singer

I SINK THEM MY WAY
Tracks: / I sink them my way / Rock on the Rocks.
7" Single: Released Jul '86, on PRT, by Castle Communications Records. Catalogue no: **7P 363**
12" Single: Released Jul '86, on PRT, by Castle Communications Records. Catalogue no: **12P 363**

Public

SUSSEX
Tracks: / Sussex / How can I tell you.
7" Single: Released Nov '80, on MCA, by MCA Records. Deleted '83. Catalogue no: **MCA 654**

Public Bar...

CHRISTMAS CRACKERS MEDLEY
Tracks: / Christmas crackers medley.
7" Single: Released Nov '81, on Chrysalis, by Chrysalis Records. Deleted Nov '84. Catalogue no: **CHS 2566**

Public Disgrace

TOXTETH
Tracks: / Toxteth.
7" Single: Released May '82, on Probe Plus, by Probe Plus Records. Catalogue no: **PP 2**

Public Enemy

BRING THE NOISE
Tracks: / Bring the noise / Sophisticated / Bring the noise (no noise version) (Only on 12" version.) / Bring the noise (acappella) (Only on 12" version.) / Sophisticated (instrumental) (Only on 12" version.).
7" Single: Released Dec '87, on Def Jam, Deleted Jun '88. Catalogue no: **651335 7**
12" Single: Released Dec '87, on Def Jam, Deleted Aug '88. Catalogue no: **651335 6**

DON'T BELIEVE THE HYPE

Tracks: / Don't believe the hype / Prophets of rage / Rhythm, the rebel (a capella), The (12" only) / Prophets of rage (vocal) (12" only) / Prophets of rage (power version) (12" only) / Bring the noise (CD only).
CD 5": Released 27 Jun '88, on Def Jam, Deleted Jan '89. Catalogue no: **652833 2**
7" Single: Released Jun '88, on Def Jam, Deleted Jan '89. Catalogue no: **652833 7**
7" Single: Released Jun '88, on Def Jam, Deleted Jan '89. Catalogue no: **652833 0**
7" Single: Released Jun '88, on Def Jam, Catalogue no: **WS4 07934**
12" Single: Released 20 Jun '88, on Def Jam, Deleted Jan '89. Catalogue no: **652833 6**
12" Single: Released Jun '88, on Def Jam, Catalogue no: **652822 6**

FIGHT THE POWER
Tracks: / Fight the power / Fight the power (Radio edit) / Fight the power (12" version) (Only on 12" single.) / Fight the power (Slavor flav meets) (Only on 12 single (ZK 42878).).
Cassingle: Released Jul '89, on Motown, by BMG Records (UK). Catalogue no: **ZK 42878**
7" Single: Released Jun '89, on Motown, by BMG Records (UK). Catalogue no: **ZB 42877**
12" Single: Released Jun '89, on Motown, by BMG Records (UK). Catalogue no: **ZT 42878**

NIGHT OF THE LIVING BASEHEADS
Tracks: / Night of the living baseheads / Night of the living baseheads / Night of the living baseheads (instrumental) (Terminator X meets DST & Chuck Chill Out Ins.) / Terminator X to the edge of panic (No need to panic radio v) (CD single.).
CD 5": Released Oct '88, on Def Jam, Deleted 17 Apr '89. Catalogue no: **653046 2**
7" Single: Released Oct '88, on Def Jam, Deleted 17 Apr '89. Catalogue no: **653046 7**
7" Single: Released Oct '88, on Def Jam, Deleted 17 Apr '89. Catalogue no: **653046 0**
7" Single: Released Oct '88, on Def Jam, Deleted 17 Apr '89. Catalogue no: **653046 9**
12" Single: Released Oct '88, on Def Jam, Deleted 17 Apr '89. Catalogue no: **653046 8**

PUBLIC ENEMY NO.1
Tracks: / Public enemy no.1 / Time bomb / Son of public enemy.
7" Single: Released Mar '87, on Def Jam, Deleted Aug '87. Catalogue no: **650049 7**
12" Single: Released Mar '87, on Def Jam, Catalogue no: **650049 6**

REBEL WITHOUT A PAUSE
Tracks: / Rebel without a pause / Terminator X speaks with his hands (on 12" only) / Sophisticated bitch (on 12" only).
CD 5": Released Dec '87, on Def Jam, Deleted Jun '88. Catalogue no: **651245 0**
7" Single: Released Nov '87, on Def Jam, Deleted Jun '88. Catalogue no: **651245 7**
12" Single: Released Nov '87, on Def Jam, Deleted Jun '88. Catalogue no: **651245 6**

YOU'RE GONNA GET YOURS
Tracks: / You're gonna get yours / Miuzi weighs a ton.
7" Single: Released 20 Jun '87, on Def Jam, Catalogue no: **650975 7**
12" Single: Released 20 Jun '87, on Def Jam, Catalogue no: **650975 6**

Public Heirs

RUN FOXY RUN
Tracks: / Run foxy run / Stomping in the pit.
7" Single: Released 23 May '87, on Quiet, by Quiet Records. Catalogue no: **Q5 014**

WHAT'S GOING ON?
Tracks: / What's going on?.
12" Single: Released Jun '86, on Quiet, by Quiet Records. Catalogue no: **QST 012**

Public Image Ltd (PIL)

Biographical details: Public Image Ltd, aka PIL, were a new wave act but are now a concept, not a group. They were formed by John Lydon -- Johnny Rotten reverting to his real name after the demise of the Sex Pistols -- and featured the bizarre guitar of Keith Levene Jr, an original member of Clash, reggae-influenced bassist Jah Wobble (John Wordle) and Canadian ex-Furies drummer Jim Walker. The concept of the group showed how much Lydon had learned from Malcolm McLaren about merchandising pop music. Metal Box, in 1979, later reissued as a two-disc Second Edition, originally came as three 12in singles in a metal box. Flowers Of Romance ('81) was named after Pistol Sid Vicious' first group. The two-disc Live In Tokyo was a Rotten self-indulgence. He swore he'd never play again after a 1981 riot in New York when P.I.L. played behind a screen to tapes. By 1984 Levene, Wobble and drummer/co-writer Martin Atkins had gone and Lydon used pick-up musicians on tours, played the Pistols' "greatest hit", Anarchy In The UK, and lived in America, contrary to everything he didn't stand for. Album in '86 (it was also called Cassette or Compact Disc as the case may be) was produced by Bill Laswell, who called Lydon "the Ornette Coleman of new wave singers". The sleeve contained no names of personnel, the idea being to seek judgement without names. US magazine Downbeat gave it a good review, despite the "snotty, annoying, venemous sounds" from the "snarling gap" of the "quintessential Johnny One-Note", for the backing which included Ginger Baker or Tony Williams on drums, Steve Vai for guitar aficianados, L. Shankar on violin, Ryuichi Sakomoto (Yellow Magic Orchestra) on keyboards and acoustic bass by Malachai Favors on one track. The sight of Lydon miming on Top of the Pops was unforgettable, as if punk had never been. The lad who once wanted to destroy music may leave a positive mark if he does as he's told. Now a movie star -- in Harvey Keitel's Cop Killer -- he can wheel out phoney groups whenever he feels like it. (Donald Clarke, May 1987.).

BAD LIFE
Tracks: / Bad life / Question mark.
7" Single: Released May '84, on Virgin, by Virgin Records. Deleted '87. Catalogue no: **VS 675**

BODY, THE
Tracks: / Body, The / Angry / Religion.
7" Single: Released Oct '87, on Virgin, by Virgin Records. Deleted May '88. Catalogue no: **VS 1010**
12" Single: Released Oct '87, on Virgin, by Virgin Records. Catalogue no: **VST 1010**

DEATH DISCO
Tracks: / Death disco (7" only) / No birds do sing (7" only) / Death disco (1/2 mix) (12" only) / Death disco (mega mix) (12" only).
7" Single: Released '79, on Virgin, by Virgin Records. Catalogue no: **VS 274**
12" Single: Released '79, on Virgin, by Virgin Records. Catalogue no: **VS 274-12**

DISAPPOINTED
Tracks: / Disappointed / Same old story / Disappointed (version) (12" only).
CD 5": Released May '89, on Virgin, by Virgin Records. Catalogue no: **VSCD 1181**
7" Single: Released 28 Apr '89, on Virgin, by Virgin Records. Catalogue no: **VSG 1181**
7" Single: Released 28 Apr '89, on Virgin, by Virgin Records. Catalogue no: **VS 1181**
12" Single: Released 28 Apr '89, on Virgin, by Virgin Records. Catalogue no: **VST 1181**

FLOWERS OF ROMANCE (SINGLE)
Tracks: / Flowers of romance.
7" Single: Released Apr '81, on Virgin, by Virgin Records. Deleted '84. Catalogue no: **VS 397**

HOME
Tracks: / Home / Round.
7" Single: Released Apr '86, on Virgin, by Virgin Records. Deleted '86. Catalogue no: **VS 856**
12" Single: Released Apr '86, on Virgin, by Virgin Records. Deleted May '88. Catalogue no: **VS 856-12**

MEMORIES
Tracks: / Memories / Another.
7" Single: Released Oct '79, on Virgin, by Virgin Records. Deleted '82. Catalogue no: **VS 299**
12" Single: Released '79, on Virgin, by Virgin Records. Catalogue no: **VS 299-12**

PUBLIC IMAGE (SINGLE)
Tracks: / Public image / Cowboy song.
7" Single: Released Sep '78, on Virgin, by Virgin Records. Catalogue no: **VS 228**

RISE
Tracks: / Rise / Rise (instrumental).
7" Single: Released Jan '86, on Virgin, by Virgin Records. Catalogue no: **VS 841**
12" Single: Released Jan '86, on Virgin, by Virgin Records. Catalogue no: **VS 841-12**

SEATTLE
Tracks: / Seattle / Suit, The / Selfish rubbish.
Cassingle: Released Aug '87, on Virgin, by Virgin Records. Deleted May '88. Catalogue no: **VSC 988-12**
7" Single: Released Aug '87, on Virgin, by Virgin Records. Deleted May '88. Catalogue no: **VS 988**
12" Single: Released Aug '87, on Virgin, by Virgin Records. Catalogue no: **VS 988-12**

THIS IS NOT A LOVE SONG
Tracks: / This is not a love song (remixed version) (CD & 12" only) / Public image (On all versions) / This is not a love song (On all versions) / Blue water (CD & 12" only).
7" Single: Released Aug '83, on Virgin, by Virgin Records. Catalogue no: **VS 529**
12" Single: Released Aug '83, on Virgin, by Virgin Records. Catalogue no: **VS 529-12**
CD 3": Released Jun '88, on Virgin, by Virgin Records. Catalogue no: **CDT 14**

THIS IS NOT A LOVE SONG (OLD GOLD)
Tracks: / This is not a love song / Public image.
7" Single: Released Nov '88, on Old Gold, by Old Gold Records. Catalogue no: **OG 9823**

Public, Joe

WHAT I WANT
Tracks: / What I want / Why did you make me care.
7" Single: Released Dec '83, on Knocked Back, Catalogue no: **KB 123**

Puckett, Gary & Union Gap

LADY WILLPOWER
Tracks: / Lady willpower.
7" Single: Released Aug '68, on CBS, by CBS Records. Deleted '71. Catalogue no: **CBS 3551**

WOMAN WOMAN
Tracks: / Woman woman.
7" Single: Released Aug '68, on CBS, by CBS Records. Deleted '71. Catalogue no: **CBS 3100**

YOUNG GIRL
Tracks: / Young girl.
7" Single: Released Jun '74, on CBS, by CBS Records. Deleted '77. Catalogue no: **CBS 8202**
7" Single: Released Apr '68, on CBS, by CBS Records. Deleted '71. Catalogue no: **CBS 3365**

YOUNG GIRL (OLD GOLD)
Tracks: / Young girl / Lady willpower.
7" Single: Released Apr '83, on Old Gold, by Old Gold Records. Catalogue no: **OG 9304**

Puff, Tony

I'LL HAVE TO GET YOU
Tracks: / I'll have to get you.
12" Single: Released Jul '84, on GG'S, Catalogue no: **GG 080**

Pullen, Whitey

DRINKIN' WINE
Tracks: / Drinkin' wine.
7" Single: Released Jun '80, on Rollin' Rock, Catalogue no: **45 010**

LET'S ALL GO WILD
Tracks: / Let's all go wild.
7" Single: Released Jun '80, on Rollin' Rock, Catalogue no: **45 005**

Pullens, Vern

BOP CRAZY BALL
7" EP: Released May '88, on Rockstar (1), Catalogue no: **RSREP 2011**

Pullins, Leroy

I'M A NUT (SINGLE)
Tracks: / I'm a nut.
7" Single: Released May '80, on MCA (USA), by MCA Records (USA). Catalogue no: **LR 4127**

Pulp

DOGS ARE EVERYWHERE
Tracks: / Dogs are everywhere.
7" Single: Released Jun '86, on Fire, by Fire Records. Catalogue no: **BLAZE 10**

EVERYBODY'S PROBLEM
Tracks: / Everybody's problem.
7" Single: Released Sep '83, on Red Rhino, by Red Rhino Records. Catalogue no: **RED 37**

LITTLE GIRL WITH BLUE EYES
Tracks: / Little girl with blue eyes.
12" Single: Released Dec '85, on Fire, by Fire Records. Catalogue no: **FIRE 5**

MASTER OF THE UNIVERSE
Tracks: / Master of the universe.
7" Single: Released Mar '87, on Fire, by Fire Records. Catalogue no: **BLAZE 21**
12" Single: Released Mar '87, on Fire, by Fire Records. Catalogue no: **BLAZE 21T**

MY LIGHTHOUSE
Tracks: / My lighthouse / Looking for life.
7" Single: Released May '83, on Red Rhino, by Red Rhino Records. Catalogue no: **RED 32**

THEY SUFFOCATE AT NIGHT
Tracks: / Tunnel.
7" Single: Released Jan '87, on Fire, by Fire Records. Catalogue no: **BLAZE 17**
12" Single: Released Jan '87, on Fire, by Fire Records. Catalogue no: **BLAZE 17T**

Pulsallama

QUI QUI
Tracks: / Qui qui.
7" Single: Released Mar '83, on Y, Catalogue no: **Y 103**
12" Single: Released Mar '83, on Y, Catalogue no: **YT 103**

UNGAWA PART 2
Tracks: / Ungawa / Devil lives in my husband's body, The.
7" Single: Released Jul '82, on Y, Catalogue no: **Y 25**
12" Single: Released Jul '82, on Y, Catalogue no: **Y 25T**

Pulse

SHUT UP ALREADY
Tracks: / Shut up already (Fierce mix) / Shut up already (pulsating mix) / Shut up already (samplepella mix) (12" only) / Shut up already (piano dub) (12" only).
7" Single: Released Nov '87, on Urban, by Polydor Ltd. Catalogue no: **URB 12**
12" Single: Released Nov '87, on Urban, by Polydor Ltd. Catalogue no: **URBX 12**

WHOLE LOT OF LOVE
Tracks: / Whole lot of love / Ultra-V.
7" Single: Released 16 May '88, on Son, by Son Records. Deleted Apr '89. Catalogue no: **BUA 881**
12" Single: Released 16 May '88, on Son, by Son Records. Deleted Apr '89. Catalogue no: **12 BUA 881**

Pumphouse Gang

JUDY TURN OUT THE LIGHT
Tracks: / Judy turn out the light / Girl like you.
7" Single: Released Apr '80, on Splash, by Splash Records. Deleted Apr '83. Catalogue no: **SP 010**

Punching Holes

LA MER
Tracks: / La mer / Mad mother.
7" Single: Released Dec '82, on Firebird, by Pinnacle Records. Deleted Dec '85. Catalogue no: **FLAME 13**

Punilux

HOLD ME (NEVER MOULD ME)
Tracks: / Hold me (never mould me).
7" Single: Released 13 Jun '85, on Red Rhino, by Red Rhino Records. Catalogue no: **RED 033**

Punishment of luxury

LAUGHING ACADEMY
Tracks: / Laughing academy / Baby don't jump.
7" Single: Released Feb '80, on Liberty (USA), by EMI Records. Deleted Feb '83. Catalogue no: **BP 317**

Punk...

PUNK DEAD NAH MUTE
Tracks: / Punk dead nah mute: *Various artists.*
12" Single: Released '85, on Pax, by Pax Records. Catalogue no: **PAX 7**

Punters Choir

WORLD CUP SPECIAL, THE
Tracks: / World cup special, The.
7" Single: Released May '86, on Scotdisc, by Scotdisc Records. Catalogue no: **ITV 7S 415**

Pure DJ

PROMISES
Tracks: / Promises.
12" Single: Released Apr '89, on Pure, Catalogue no: **PURE T44**

Pure Energy

LOVE GAME
Tracks: / Love game / Love game (remix) / Love game (original mix).
12" Single: Released Mar '86, on ZYX (Germany), Catalogue no: **ZYX 5395**

Pure Glass

DON'T TAKE YOUR LOVE
Tracks: / Don't take your love / Portrait of years.
7" Single: Released May '85, on R4, Deleted '86. Catalogue no: **FOR 1**
12" Single: Released May '85, on R4, Deleted '86. Catalogue no: **12FOR 1**

MATTER OF TIME
Tracks: / Matter of time (Ext. Edit.) (Only on 7" single (TLM 5)) / Flip the lid / Matter of time.
7" Single: Released Jan '87, on Legend (1), by Legend Records (UK). Catalogue no: **LM 5**
7" Single: Released Jan '87, on Legend (1), by Legend Records (UK). Catalogue no: **LM 5**
7" Single: Released Feb '87, on Legend (1), by Legend Records (UK). Deleted Jun '88. Catalogue no: **TLM 5**
12" Single: Released Jan '87, on Legend (1), by Legend Records (UK). Catalogue no: **12LM 5**
12" Single: Released Jan '87, on Legend (1), by Legend Records (UK). Catalogue no: **12LM 5**

Pure Prairie League

I'M ALMOST READY
Tracks: / I'm almost ready / My true love.
7" Single: Released Oct '80, on Casablanca, by PolyGram UK Ltd. Deleted Oct '83. Catalogue no: **CAN 029**

STILL RIGHT HERE IN MY HEART
Tracks: / Still right here in my heart / Don't keep me hangin'.
7" Single: Released Jun '81, on Casablanca, by PolyGram UK Ltd. Deleted Jun '84. Catalogue no: **CAN 1003**

Pure Silk

BABY IT'S YOU AND I
Tracks: / Baby it's you and I.
12" Single: Released Jun '89, on Sir George, Catalogue no: **SG 055**

BLUES AWAY
Tracks: / Blues away / Blues away (Instrumental).
12" Single: Released Aug '86, on Raiders, Catalogue no: **LGR 011**

EVERYBODY PLAYS THE FOOL
Tracks: / Everybody plays the fool.
12" Single: Released Oct '89, on Pure Silk, Catalogue no: **SG 065**

IT AIN'T EASY
Tracks: / It ain't easy.
12" Single: Released Nov '86, on Sir George, Catalogue no: **SG 040T**

IT'S TOO LATE
Tracks: / It's too late.
7" Single: Released 12 May '89, on Sir George, Catalogue no: **SG 057**

LADY IN RED
Tracks: / Lady in red / Electronic.
7" Single: Released Aug '86, on Champion, by Champion Records. Catalogue no: **CHAMP 20**
12" Single: Released Aug '86, on Champion, by Champion Records. Catalogue no: **CHAMP 1220**

RONI
Tracks: / Roni.
12" Single: Released Oct '89, on Sir George, Catalogue no: **SG 064**

THIS LOVE AFFAIR
Tracks: / This love affair.
12" Single: Released Jul '89, on Sir George, Catalogue no: **SG 059**

Pure Vision

COSMOPOLITAN
Tracks: / Cosmopolitan.
7" Single: Released Jul '85, on LBA, Catalogue no: **LBA 108**

Purify, James

I'M YOUR PUPPET
Tracks: / I'm your puppet.
7" Single: Released Apr '76, on Mercury, by Phonogram Ltd. Deleted '79. Catalogue no: **6167 324**

MORNING GLORY
Tracks: / Morning glory.
7" Single: Released Aug '76, on Mercury, by Phonogram Ltd. Deleted '79. Catalogue no: **6167 380**

SHAKE A TAIL FEATHER
Tracks: / Shake a tail feather.
7" Single: Released Mar '83, on Neil Rushton, Catalogue no: **CC 3**

Purple Hearts

JIMMY
Tracks: / Jimmy / What am i.
7" Single: Released Mar '80, on Fiction, by Fiction Records. Deleted '83. Catalogue no: **FICS 9**

MILLIONS LIKE US
Tracks: / Millions like us.
7" Single: Released Sep '79, on Fiction, by Fiction Records. Deleted '82. Catalogue no: **FICS 003**

MY LIFE'S A JIGSAW
Tracks: / My life's a jigsaw.
7" Single: Released '81, on Safari, by Safari Records. Catalogue no: **SAFE 30**

SCHOOBY DOO
Tracks: / Schooby doo.
7" Single: Released Jul '82, on Roadrunner (Germany), Catalogue no: **RR 1**

Purple Helmets

BRAND NEW CADILLAC
Tracks: / Brand new cadillac / Under the sun / Baby (on 12" only).
7" Single: Released Sep '89, on Anagram, by Cherry Red Records. Catalogue no: **ANA 50**
12" Single: Released Sep '89, on Anagram, by Cherry Red Records. Catalogue no: **12 ANA 50**

Purple Things

DEEP IN THE MIND OF THE PURPLE THINGS
Tracks: / Deep in the mind of the purple things.
12" Single: Released Dec '85, on Media Burn, by Media Burn Records. Catalogue no: **MB 4**

KING SNAKE
Tracks: / King snake.
7" Single: Released Aug '87, on Absolutely Free, Catalogue no: **FREE 001**

OUT OF THE DEEP
Tracks: / Out of the deep.
12" Single: Released May '86, on Media Burn, by Media Burn Records. Catalogue no: **MB 7**

Purpleman

LEVEL VIBES PUMPING
Tracks: / Level vibes pumping.
7" Single: Released Oct '83, on Jammy's, Catalogue no: **DSR 0695**

Pursey, James T.

IF ONLY BEFORE
Tracks: / If only before / Reveng is not the password'.
12" Single: on An Eskimo Green Production, Catalogue no: **CODE 02**

Pursey, Jimmy

ANIMALS HAVE MORE FUN
Tracks: / Animals have more fun / Sus.
7" Single: Released Jul '81, on Epic, by CBS Records. Deleted '85. Catalogue no: **EPC A 1336**

LUCKY MAN
Tracks: / Lucky man / Black & white rock reggae.
7" Single: Released Sep '80, on Polydor, by Polydor Ltd. Deleted Sep '83. Catalogue no: **POSP 154**

NAUGHTY BOYS LIKE NAUGHTY GIRLS
Tracks: / Naughty boys like naughty girls / Who's making you happy.
7" Single: Released Dec '81, on Epic, by CBS Records. Deleted Dec '84. Catalogue no: **EPC A 1830**

ZAP POW
Tracks: / Zap pow.
7" Single: Released Sep '86, on Videocat, Catalogue no: **JIMM 1**
12" Single: Released Sep '86, on Videocat, Catalogue no: **JIMMYT 1**

Pursuit Of Happiness

SHE'S SO YOUNG
Tracks: / She's so young.
CD 5": Released Jun '89, on Chrysalis, by Chrysalis Records. Catalogue no: **POHCD 1**
7" Single: Released Jun '89, on Chrysalis, by Chrysalis Records. Catalogue no: **CHS 3370**
12" Single: Released Jun '89, on Chrysalis, by Chrysalis Records. Catalogue no: **CHS 123370**

Push

MIDNIGHT
Tracks: / Midnight.
7" Single: Released May '83, on Excaliber, by Red Bus Records. Deleted '88. Catalogue no: **EXC 532**
12" Single: Released May '83, on Excaliber, by Red Bus Records. Deleted '88. Catalogue no: **EXCL 532**

MY HEART
Tracks: / My heart.
7" Single: Released Oct '82, on Excaliber, by Red Bus Records. Deleted '88. Catalogue no: **EXC 524**
12" Single: Released Oct '82, on Excaliber, by Red Bus Records. Deleted '88. Catalogue no: **EXCL 524**

Pusmort Sampler

PUSMORT SAMPLER
7" EP: on Pusmort, by Pusmort Records. Catalogue no: **PUS 007-02**

Pussy Jews

SHE'S BOTH
Tracks: / She's both.
12" Single: Released 16 Sep '88, on Kaos, Catalogue no: **KAOS 002**

Pussycat

BLUE LIGHTS IN MY EYES
Tracks: / Blue lights in my eyes / I don't wanna rock and roll.
7" Single: Released Jul '81, on EMI, by EMI Records. Deleted '84. Catalogue no: **EMI 5208**

DOING LA BAMBA
Tracks: / Doing la bamba / On the corner of my life.
7" Single: Released Nov '80, on Logo, by Logo Records. Deleted Nov '83. Catalogue no: **GO 395**

MISSISSIPPI
Tracks: / Mississippi.
7" Single: Released '80, on EMI (Europe), by EMI Records. Catalogue no: **LR 2230**
7" Single: Released Aug '76, on Sonet, by Sonet Records. Deleted '79. Catalogue no: **SON 2077**

MISSISSIPPI (OLD GOLD)
Tracks: / Smile / Mississippi.
7" Single: Released Mar '87, on Old Gold, by Old Gold Records. Deleted Sep '89. Catalogue no: **OG 9695**

SMILE
Tracks: / Smile.
7" Single: Released Dec '76, on Sonet, by Sonet Records. Deleted '79. Catalogue no: **SON 2096**

Pussyfoot

I WANT TO BE ME
Tracks: / I want it to be me / What'll we do with the money.
7" Single: Released Mar '80, on EMI, by EMI Records. Deleted Mar '83. Catalogue no: **EMI 5045**

Putrone, Patrick

DIAMONDS ARE A BOY'S BEST FRIEND
Tracks: / Diamonds are a boy's best friend.
7" Single: Released Aug '85, on Ideal Music, by Ideal Music Records. Catalogue no: **IDEAL 1**

Putsch

SOLIDARITY
Tracks: / Solidarity / Four horsemen.
7" Single: Released Mar '82, on Pip, by Pip Records. Catalogue no: **PIP 8202**

Puzzle

I LOVE FUNKIN'
Tracks: / I love funkin'.
7" Single: Released Aug '84, on Steinar, by Steinar Records (UK). Catalogue no: **PUZZ 1**
12" Single: Released Aug '84, on Steinar, by Steinar Records (UK). Catalogue no: **PUZZ 12**

Puzzler

DREAMING
Tracks: / Dreaming.
7" Single: Released Jul '80, on Rk, by RK Records. Deleted Jul '83. Catalogue no: **RK 1030**

Pyjama Sutra

ALL HARD WORK
Tracks: / All hard work.
7" Single: Released Aug '85, on Plastic Head, by Plastic Head Records. Catalogue no: **PLASS 003**

TEN SECOND TAN
Tracks: / Ten second tan / When killed time / Song of sixpence, A.
12" Single: Released Nov '86, on Plastic Head, by Plastic Head Records. Catalogue no: **PLASS 005**

Pylon

BEEP
Tracks: / Beep.
7" Single: Released Jul '86, on DB, by DB Records. Catalogue no: **DB 62**

COOL
Tracks: / Cool.
10" single: Released Feb '81, on Armageddon, by Armageddon Records. Catalogue no: **AEP 12004**

CRAZY
Tracks: / Crazy.
7" Single: Released Jul '86, on DB, by DB Records. Catalogue no: **DB 61**

Pyramids

TRAIN TOUR TO RAINBOW CITY
Tracks: / Train tour to rainbow city.
7" Single: Released Nov '67, on President, by President Records. Deleted '70. Catalogue no: **PT 161**

Python Lee Jackson

IN A BROKEN DREAM (OLD GOLD)
Tracks: / In a broken dream.
7" Single: Released Jul '82, on Old Gold, by Old Gold Records. Catalogue no: **OG 9004**

IN A BROKEN DREAM (SINGLE)
Tracks: / In a broken dream.
7" Single: Released Jul '87, on Bold Reprieve (1), Catalogue no: **BRM 004**
12" Single: Released Jul '87, on Bold Reprieve (1), Catalogue no: **BRM 004T**
7" Single: Released Sep '72, on Young Blood, by Young Blood Records. Deleted '75. Catalogue no: **YB 1002**
7" Single: Released Jul '80, on Young Blood, by Young Blood Records. Catalogue no: **YB 0089**
12" Single: Released Jul '80, on Young Blood, by Young Blood Records. Catalogue no: **YBT 0089**

Pzazz

SKY TRAIN
Tracks: / Sky train.
7" Single: Released Jul '80, on Magenta, Catalogue no: **MAG 001**

SWITCH, THE
Tracks: / Switch, The.
7" Single: Released Nov '83, on Keytone, Catalogue no: **KY 6727**
12" Single: Released Nov '83, on Keytone, Catalogue no: **KYT 6727**

Q

The following information was taken from the Music Master database on October 20th, 1989.

Q

PLAYBACK
Tracks: / Playback / Music's gone.
7" Single: Released Oct '82, on Cocteau, by Cocteau Records. Catalogue no: **COQ 6**

VOICE OF Q
Tracks: / Voice of Q / Voice of Q(Part 2)
7" Single: Released Oct '82, on Philly World (USA), by Philly World (USA). Catalogue no: **PWS 106**
12" Single: Released Oct '82, on Philly World (USA), by Philly World (USA). Catalogue no: **PWSL 106**

Q5

STEEL THE LIGHT (SINGLE)
Tracks: / Steel the light / That's alright with you.
12" Single: Released May '85, on Music For Nations, by Music For Nations Records. Catalogue no: **12 KUT 115**

Q Feel

DANCING IN HEAVEN
Tracks: / Dancing in heaven / At the top.
7" Single: Released Apr '82, on Jive, by Zomba Records. Deleted Apr '85. Catalogue no: **JIVE 7**
12" Single: Released Apr '82, on Jive, by Zomba Records. Deleted Apr '85. Catalogue no: **JIVET 7**

DOCTOR ON THE RADIO
Tracks: / Doctor on the radio.
7" Single: Released Jul '81, on Jive, by Zomba Records. Deleted '85. Catalogue no: **JIVE 001**

Q, Pete

SHIFTING SANDS (LOVE SO HOT)
Tracks: / Shifting sands / Oh yeah.
7" Single: Released Jul '88, on Premiere, by Premiere Records. Catalogue no: **ERE 502**
12" Single: Released Jul '88, on Premiere, by Premiere Records. Catalogue no: **ERET 502**

Q, Stacey

TWO OF HEARTS
Tracks: / Two of hearts / Dancing nowhere.
7" Single: Released Aug '86, on Atlantic, by WEA Records. Deleted Sep '87. Catalogue no: **A 9381**
12" Single: Released Aug '86, on Atlantic, by WEA Records. Deleted Sep '87. Catalogue no: **A 9381 T**

WE CONNECT
Tracks: / We connect / Don't break my heart.
7" Single: Released Jun '87, on Atlantic, by WEA Records. Deleted Jul '88. Catalogue no: **A 9331**
12" Single: Released Jun '87, on Atlantic, by WEA Records. Deleted Jul '88. Catalogue no: **A 9331 T**

Q, Suzy

CAN'T LIVE WITHOUT YOUR LOVE
Tracks: / Can't live without your love / Can't live without your iove(special bell mix).
12" Single: Released 8 Aug '88, on Carrere, Catalogue no: **CART 428**

Q.A.X.

DOES ME GOOD
Tracks: / Does me good / Does me good (version).
7" Single: Released Jan '84, on Vinyl Beat, by Vinyl Beat Records. Catalogue no: **VB 001**

Q.E.D.

I CAN'T WAIT TO GET ON THE BEACH
Tracks: / I can't wait (to get on the beach) / I can't wait (to get on the beach)(Street level beach mix).
7" Single: Released Jul '86, on Climber, by Climber Records. Deleted '87. Catalogue no: **CLIS 6**

SANTA'S GOING TO MISS ME
Tracks: / Santa's going to miss me / Solace.
7" Single: Released Nov '87, on Dingle's, by Dingle's Records. Catalogue no: **SID 241**

SUNNY DAYS
Tracks: / Sunny days.
7" Single: Released Jul '89, on Dingle's, by Dingle's Records. Catalogue no: **SID 243**

YUPPIE SONG
Tracks: / Yuppie song / Wacky mix / Yuppie song (version)*.
Note: *extra track on 7/88 single
7" Single: Released 30 May '87, on Dingle's, by Dingle's Records. Catalogue no: **SID 239**

Q-Pid

MY LATIN LOVER
Tracks: / My latin lover.
7" Single: Released Oct '86, on Rhythm King, by Mute Records. Catalogue no: **LEFT 1**
12" Single: Released Oct '86, on Rhythm King, by Mute Records. Catalogue no: **LEFT 1T**

Q-Tips

LOVE HURTS
Tracks: / Love hurts / I wish it would rain.
7" Single: Released Oct '81, on Rewind, Deleted '85. Catalogue no: **REWIND 10**

MAN CAN'T LOSE
Tracks: / Man can't lose / Some kinda wonderful.
7" Single: Released Sep '80, on Chrysalis, by Chrysalis Records. Deleted Sep '83. Catalogue no: **CHS 2456**

STAY THE WAY YOU ARE
Tracks: / Stay the way you are / Sweet talk / Looking for some action.
7" Single: Released May '81, on Chrysalis, by Chrysalis Records. Deleted May '86. Catalogue no: **CHS 2518**

S.Y.S.L.J.F.M.
Tracks: / S.Y.S.L.J.F.M. / Dance.
7" Single: Released Mar '80, on Shotgun, Deleted Mar '83. Catalogue no: **SHOT 1**

TRACKS OF MY TEARS
Tracks: / Tracks of my tears / Different world.
7" Single: Released Jul '80, on Chrysalis, by Chrysalis Records. Deleted Jul '83. Catalogue no: **CHS 2420**

Quads

GOTTA GET A JOB
Tracks: / Gotta get a job / Gang of kids.
7" Single: Released Apr '81, on Big Bear, by Big Bear Records. Deleted '85. Catalogue no: **BB 32**

THERE MUST BE THOUSANDS
Tracks: / There must be thousands.
7" Single: Released Sep '79, on Big Bear, by Big Bear Records. Deleted '82. Catalogue no: **BB 23**

Quake, Glen

THEN YOU CAME
Tracks: / Then you came.
12" Single: Released Nov '82, on Third Kind, Deleted Nov '85. Catalogue no: **TKD 0002**

Quando Quango

GO EXCITING
Tracks: / Go exciting / Tingle.
12" Single: Released Dec '82, on Factory (1), by Factory Records. Deleted Dec '85. Catalogue no: **FAC 67**

Quantize

SUN AIN'T GONNA SHINE ANYMORE
Tracks: / Sun ain't gonna shine anymore, The / Sun ain't gonna shine anymore, The (inst).
12" Single: Released Jun '88, on Passion, by Skratch Records. Catalogue no: **PASH 83(12)**

Quantum Jump

LONE RANGER, THE
Tracks: / Lone ranger, The.
7" Single: Released Jun '79, on Electric, Deleted '82. Catalogue no: **WOT 33**

Quarks

MECHANICAL
Tracks: / Mechanical / Working model.
7" Single: Released Oct '81, on Magnet, by WEA Records. Deleted Oct '84. Catalogue no: **MAG 212**
12" Single: Released Oct '81, on Magnet, by WEA Records. Deleted Oct '84. Catalogue no: **12MAG 212**

Quarterflash

Biographical details:
Quarterflash, a USA AOR group formed in Portland, Oregon in 1980. Lineup: Rindy Ross, vocals and sax; Mary Ross and Jack Charles, guitars and vocals; Rick Gooch, bass; David Willis, drums. The Rosses were husband and wife; they quit teaching in 1977 and recruited ex-members of Pilot (not the UK group) to form SeafoodMMama; their new name came from an Australian colloquialism. *Harden My Heart*was first hit (number 3 USA; number 1 in Japan, Australia, Italy, France). They sounded like Fleetwood Mac. *Back Into Blue* was produced in France by Culture Club producer Steve Levine, the band slimmed down to Rosses, Gooch and willis: a sanitised sound that sparkles but lacks passion. (Donald Clarke)..

FIND ANOTHER FOOL
Tracks: / Find another fool / Cruisin' with the Duece.
7" Single: Released Nov '82, on Geffen, by Geffen Records (USA). Deleted Nov '85. Catalogue no: **GEF A 2276**

HARDEN MY HEART
Tracks: / Harden my heart / Don't be lonely.
7" Single: Released Feb '82, on Geffen, by Geffen Records (USA). Deleted '85. Catalogue no: **GEFA 1838**

RIGHT KIND OF LOVE
Tracks: / Right kind of love / You're holding me back.
7" Single: Released Aug '82, on Geffen, by Geffen Records (USA). Deleted Aug '85. Catalogue no: **GEFA 2635**

Quartermain, Andrew

RIU RIU
Tracks: / Riu Riu / Children's voices.
7" Single: Released '88, on Virgin, by Virgin Records. Catalogue no: **VS 1161**

Quartlock

NO REGRETS
Tracks: / No regrets.
7" Single: Released Mar '88, on Reflection, by Nightmare Records. Catalogue no: **7FLE 1**
12" Single: Released Mar '88, on Reflection, by Nightmare Records. Catalogue no: **FLE 1**

Quartz

MELTDOWN (CLUB MIX)
Tracks: / Meltdown (club mix) / R.U. ready (for this) (divine club mix).
12" Single: Released Sep '89, on I.T.M., Catalogue no: **ITMR 101**

SATAN'S SERENADE
Tracks: / Satan's serenade / Bloody fool.
7" Single: Released 20 Jun '80, on Logo, by Logo Records. Deleted '83. Catalogue no: **GO 387**
12" Single: Released 20 Jun '80, on Logo, by Logo Records. Deleted '83. Catalogue no: **GOT 387**

STAND UP AND FIGHT
Tracks: / Stand up and fight / Charlie Snow.
7" Single: Released Jan '81, on MCA, by MCA Records. Deleted Jan '84. Catalogue no: **MCA 661**

Quartz, Jakie

A LA VIE, A L'AMOUR
Tracks: / A la vie, a l'amour / Bye bye l'ennui.
7" Single: Released Mar '89, on PWL, by PWL Records. Catalogue no: **PWL 30**
12" Single: Released Mar '89, on PWL, by PWL Records. Catalogue no: **PWLT 30**

Quasar

LIFE IN THE DISTANCE
Tracks: / Life in the distance / You don't believe in me.
7" Single: Released May '80, on Pulsar, by Lismor Records. Deleted May '85. Catalogue no: **PIS 101**

Quasimodo

I CAN IMAGINE
Tracks: / I can imagine.
7" Single: Released May '82, on Fore, Deleted '85. Catalogue no: **FORE 1**

Quatro, Suzi

Biographical details:
Suzi Quatro is a singer and bassist born in 1950 in Detroit. She gigged with her sisters in Detroit; in 1971 Mickie Most (touring with Jeff Beck) offered her a solo deal. Her first single flopped; she toured supporting Slade; soon donned leather, screamed and hollered with a neanderthal band in support; all that was missing ws material, soon supplied by bubblegum kings Chinn & Chapman: 7 Top 40 hits incl. chart-toppers *Can The Can* and *Devil Gate Drive* in 1973-4, all nonsense lyrics delivered hysterically over relentless thumping. The rise of punk suddenly rendered her less interesting: she changed her image, appeared on USA children's TV as Leather Tuscadero, played roles in *Minder* and *Dempsey & Makepeace* on TV; her songs became more reflective: *Stumblin' In*, a singalong strummer with Smokie's Chris Norman, was her only USA hit (number 4 in 1979. She played Annie Oakley in Andrew Lloyd Webber production of *Annie Get Your Gun*. (Donald Clarke)..

48 CRASH
Tracks: / 48 crash.
7" Single: Released Jul '73, on RAK, by EMI Records. Deleted '75. Catalogue no: **RAK 158**

BABY YOU'RE A STAR
Tracks: / Baby you're a star / Baby you're a star (Version).
7" Single: Released Jun '89, on WEA, by WEA Records. Catalogue no: **YZ 406**
12" Single: Released Jun '89, on WEA, by WEA Records. Catalogue no: **YZ 406T**

CAN THE CAN
Tracks: / Can the can.
7" Single: Released May '73, on RAK, by EMI Records. Deleted '75. Catalogue no: **RAK 150**
7" Single: Released Jul '84, on EMI Golden 45's, by EMI Records. Catalogue no: **G45 35**

DAYTONA DEMON
Tracks: / Daytona demon.
7" Single: Released Oct '73, on RAK, by EMI Records. Deleted '76. Catalogue no: **RAK 161**

DEVIL GATE DRIVE
Tracks: / Devil gate drive.
7" Single: Released Feb '74, on RAK, by EMI Records. Deleted '77. Catalogue no: **RAK 167**

GLAD ALL OVER
Tracks: / Glad all over / Ego in the night.
7" Single: Released Jan '81, on Dreamland, Deleted Jan '84. Catalogue no: **DLSP 8**

HEART OF STONE
Tracks: / Heart of stone.
7" Single: Released Nov '82, on Polydor, by Polydor Ltd. Deleted '85. Catalogue no: **POSP 477**

IF YOU CAN'T GIVE ME LOVE
Tracks: / If you can't give me love.
7" Single: Released Mar '78, on RAK, by EMI Records. Deleted '81. Catalogue no: **RAK 271**

I'VE NEVER BEEN IN LOVE
Tracks: / I've never been in love / Starlight lady.
7" Single: Released Apr '80, on RAK, by EMI Records. Deleted '83. Catalogue no: **RAK 307**

LIPSTICK
Tracks: / Lipstick / Woman cry.
7" Single: Released May '81, on Polydor, by Polydor Ltd. Deleted May '84. Catalogue no: **DOSP 10**

LOST IN HIS ARMS

7" Single: Released Sep '86, on First Night, by First Night Records. Catalogue no: **SCORE 3**

MAMA'S BOY
Tracks: / Mama's boy / Mind demons.
7" Single: Released Jan '80, on RAK, by EMI Records. Deleted '83. Catalogue no: **RAK 303**

RACE IS ON, THE
Tracks: / Race is on, The.
7" Single: Released Jul '78, on RAK, by EMI Records. Deleted '81. Catalogue no: **RAK 278**

ROCK HARD
Tracks: / Rock hard / State of king.
7" Single: Released Oct '80, on Dreamland, Deleted '83. Catalogue no: **DLSP 6**

SHE'S IN LOVE WITH YOU
Tracks: / She's in love with you.
7" Single: Released Oct '79, on RAK, by EMI Records. Deleted '82. Catalogue no: **RAK 299**

STUMBLIN' IN
Tracks: / Stumblin' in.
7" Single: Released Nov '78, on RAK, by EMI Records. Deleted '81. Catalogue no: **RAK 285**

TEAR ME APART
Tracks: / Tear me apart.
7" Single: Released Mar '77, on RAK, by EMI Records. Deleted '80. Catalogue no: **RAK 248**

TOO BIG
Tracks: / Too big.
7" Single: Released Jun '74, on RAK, by EMI Records. Deleted '77. Catalogue no: **RAK 175**

WILD ONE, THE
Tracks: / Wild one.
7" Single: Released Nov '74, on RAK, by EMI Records. Deleted '77. Catalogue no: **RAK 185**

WILD THING
Tracks: / Wild thing / I don't want you.
12" Single: Released Nov '86, on PRT, by Castle Communications Records. Catalogue no: **12P 367**
7" Single: Released Nov '86, on PRT, by Castle Communications Records. Catalogue no: **7P 367**

YOUR MAMA WON'T LIKE ME
Tracks: / Your mama won't like me.
7" Single: Released Feb '75, on RAK, by EMI Records. Deleted '78. Catalogue no: **RAK 191**

Quay, Judy

GOOD AS GOLD
Tracks: / Good as gold.
Note: Official Sport Aid disc
7" Single: Released May '86, on Musik, Catalogue no: **MRGG 104**

Queen

Biographical details: Formed in 1972 from various small-time outfits, Queen's line-up -- Freddie Mercury, John Deacon, Brian May and Roger Taylor -- has remained unchanged. The four very different individuals have withstood the pressures of success admirably. Each makes a positive contribution: though Mercury and May are the main songwriters, Deacon and Taylor also provide material and with four songwriters on board the band enjoy built-in versatility and variety. As well as having a stable line-up, Queen have consistently remained with EMI throughout their career. The band's first single and album, *Keep Yourself Alive* and *Queen*, respectively, were released in 1973 to an underwhelming response. But their two '74 albums, *Queen 2* and *Sheer Heart Attack* reached the British Top Ten and spawned ther similarly successful singles, *Seven Seas Of Rye* and *Killer Queen*. The latter gave them their first Top Twenty single in the States. Queen's ascending career reached a new point in late '75 with the release of the stunning single *Bohemian Rhapsody* and the impeccable album *A Night At The Opera*, which both reached No 1 in Britain. *Bohemian Rhapsody* was the first single for 18 years to log nine weeks at the top and this six-minute, multi-faceted epic was notable for two more reasons: it was the longest track to reach No.1 since the Beatles' *Hey Jude* and it was the first instance of a promotional video helping to spark sales, a trend which was to explode in the early 80's. *Bohemian Rhapsody* was perhaps the ultimate progressive rock track, progressing from "opera" to plaintiff balladry to hard rock in the space of six minutes. Mercury (whose real surname is Bulsara) was a flamboyant and charismatic showman. Often outrageous and sometimes ridiculous, he was hailed as a hero by some and derided as a prat by others. The more introverted May was one of the best guitar virtuosos on the UK rock scene. The onslaught of the British punk revolution in 1976-77 made no dent on Queen's popularity and during the late 70's and early 80's they consolidated their position as one of the world's biggest bands. *Somebody To Love, We Are The Champions* and *Crazy Little Thing Called Love* all reached No.2 on the UK singles chart and they hit the top of the British album list with *A Day At The Races, The Game* and the phenominally successful Greatest Hits collection. *Under Pressure*, an excellent 1981 collaboration with David Bowie, topped the UK singles chart; the multi-million-selling *Another One Bites The Dust* reached No.1 on the Hot Hundred and *The Game* topped the American LP chart. In 1984 Queen achieved back-to-back UK Top Five singles for the first time with the Taylor-penned *Radio Ga-Ga* and *I Want To Break Free*, written by Deacon. With the Top Twenty success of Mercury's *It's A Hard Life* and May's *Hammer To Fall*, the same year's *The Works* became their biggest-ever album in terms of spin-off singles. The only blot on the group's perenially rosy global landscape was the declining American fortune, a source of many observers. Queen's set at Live Aid was one of the most acclaimed acts at the July 1985 mega-concert, and they commemorated the event with a single, *One Vision*. (Bob MacDonald, March 1986.)

A UK rock band, with lineup unchanged since 1971: vocalist Freddie Mercury (born Frederick Bulsara in 1946 in Zanzibar), Brian May on guitar, John Deacon on bass, Roger Taylor on drums. One of the UK's most enduring bands despite entrenched critical hostility, they plugged a gap in the pre-punk scene and reflected the music hall aspect of UK rock evident ever since the Beatles. Their first big hit was *A Night At The Opera* in 1975 said to have been the most expensive UK LP production since *Sergeant Pepper* '67; its hit *Bohemian Rhapsody* was 6-minute magnum opus with balladry, hard rock, heavy metal: something for everybody made it the longest running UK No. 1 for 20 years (and top 10 in the USA), with a video that for good or ill was probably seminal. Their soundtrack for *Flash Gordon* in 1980 the first score for a major film by a rock band; in 1981 they were criticised for appearing in South Africa's Sun City; their *Greatest Hits* album remained in UK album charts for several years. Taylor wrote the world-wide number one hit *Radio Ga-Ga*; Taylor and May have also made successful solo albums. (Donald Clarke)..

ANOTHER ONE BITES THE DUST
Tracks: / Another one bites the dust / Dragon attack / Las palabras de amor (CD single only.).
7" Single: Released Aug '80, on EMI, by EMI Records. Deleted Oct '89. Catalogue no: **EMI 5102**
CD 3": Released Nov '88, on EMI, by EMI Records. Catalogue no: **QUEENCD 8**
CD 3": Released Nov '88, on EMI, by EMI Records. Catalogue no: **QUECD 8**

BACK CHAT
Tracks: / Back chat / Staying power.
7" Single: Released Jul '82, on EMI, by EMI Records. Deleted '85. Catalogue no: **EMI 5325**
12" Single: Released Jul '82, on EMI, by EMI Records. Deleted '85. Catalogue no: **12 EMI 5325**

BICYCLE RACE
Tracks: / Bicycle race / Fat bottomed girls.
7" Single: Released Oct '78, on EMI, by EMI Records. Deleted '81. Catalogue no: **EMI 2870**

BODY LANGUAGE
Tracks: / Body language / Life is real.
7" Single: Released May '82, on EMI, by EMI Records. Deleted '85. Catalogue no: **EMI 5293**

BOHEMIAN RHAPSODY
Tracks: / Bohemian rhapsody / I'm in love with my car / You're my best friend (CD single only.).
7" Single: Released Oct '75, on EMI, by EMI Records. Catalogue no: **EMI 2375**
CD 3": Released Nov '88, on EMI, by EMI Records. Catalogue no: **QUEENCD 3**
CD 3": Released Nov '88, on EMI, by EMI Records. Catalogue no: **QUECD 3**

BREAKTHRU
Tracks: / Breakthru / Stealin' / Breakthru (12" version) (12" & CD single only.).
CD 5": Released Jun '89, on Parlophone, by EMI Records. Catalogue no: **CDQUEEN 11**
CD 5": Released Jun '89, on Parlophone, by EMI Records. Catalogue no: **203 421 2**
7" Pic: Released Jun '89, on Parlophone, by EMI Records. Catalogue no: **203 421 0**
7" Pic: Released Jun '89, on Parlophone, by EMI Records. Catalogue no: **QUEENPD 11**
Cassingle: Released Jun '89, on Parlophone, by EMI Records. Catalogue no: **203 421 4**
Cassingle: Released Jun '89, on Parlophone, by EMI Records. Catalogue no: **TCQUEEN 11**
7" Single: Released Jun '89, on Parlophone, by EMI Records. Catalogue no: **203 4221 7**
7" Single: Released Jun '89, on Parlophone, by EMI Records. Catalogue no: **QUEEN 11**
12" Single: Released Jun '89, on Parlophone, by EMI Records. Catalogue no: **12QUEEN 11**
12" Single: Released Jun '89, on Parlophone, by EMI Records. Catalogue no: **203 421 6**

CRAZY LITTLE THING CALLED LOVE
Tracks: / Crazy little thing called love / We will rock you (live).
12" Single: Released May '88, on EMI (Germany), by EMI Records. Catalogue no: **05263317**

CRAZY LITTLE THING CALLED LOVE (CD)
Tracks: / Crazy little thing called love / Spread your wings (Deacon) / Flash's theme.
CD 3": Released Nov '88, on EMI, by EMI Records. Catalogue no: **QUEENCD 7**
CD 3": Released Nov '88, on EMI, by EMI Records. Catalogue no: **QUECD 7**

CRAZY LITTLE THING CALLED LOVE (SINGLE)
Tracks: / Crazy little thing called love.
7" Single: Released Oct '79, on EMI, by EMI Records. Deleted '82. Catalogue no: **EMI 5001**

DON'T STOP ME NOW
Tracks: / Don't stop me now.
7" Single: Released Feb '79, on EMI, by EMI Records. Deleted '82. Catalogue no: **EMI 2910**

FLASH
Tracks: / Flash / Football fight.
7" Single: Released Dec '80, on EMI, by EMI Records. Deleted '83. Catalogue no: **EMI 5126**

FRIENDS WILL BE FRIENDS
Tracks: / Friends will be friends / Seven seas of Rhye.
7" Pic: Released Jun '86, on EMI, by EMI Records. Catalogue no: **QUEENP 8**
7" Single: Released Jun '86, on EMI, by EMI Records. Deleted Oct '87. Catalogue no: **QUEEN 8**
12" Single: Released Jun '86, on EMI, by EMI Records. Deleted Oct '87. Catalogue no: **12 QUEEN 8**

GOOD OLD-FASHIONED LOVER BOY
Tracks: / Good old-fashioned lover boy / Death on two legs / Tenament funster (Only on CD single.) / White Queen (as it began) (Only on CD single.).
7" Single: Released May '77, on EMI, by EMI Records. Deleted Nov '88. Catalogue no: **EMI 2623**

HAMMER TO FALL
Tracks: / Hammer to fall / Tear it up.
7" Single: Released Sep '84, on EMI, by EMI Records. Deleted Oct '89. Catalogue no: **QUEEN 4**
12" Single: Released Sep '84, on EMI, by EMI Records. Catalogue no: **12 QUEEN 4**

I WANT IT ALL (See panel above)
Tracks: / I want it all / Hang on in there / I want it all (album version) (Not on 7".).
CD 5": Released May '89, on Parlophone, by EMI Records. Catalogue no: **203 360 2**
CD 5": Released May '89, on Parlophone, by EMI Records. Catalogue no: **CDQUEEN 10**
Cassingle: Released May '89, on Parlophone, by EMI Records. Catalogue no: **TCQUEEN 10**
Cassingle: Released May '89, on Parlophone, by EMI Records. Catalogue no: **203 360 4**
7" Single: Released May '89, on Parlophone, by EMI Records. Catalogue no: **203 360 7**
7" Single: Released May '89, on Parlophone, by EMI Records. Catalogue no: **QUEEN 10**
12" Single: Released May '89, on Parlophone, by EMI Records. Catalogue no: **203 360 6**
12" Single: Released May '89, on Parlophone, by EMI Records. Catalogue no: **12QUEEN 10**

I WANT TO BREAK FREE
Tracks: / I want to break free / Machines (or back to humans) / It's a hard life (CD single only.).
7" Single: Released Apr '84, on EMI, by EMI Records. Catalogue no: **QUEEN 2**
12" Single: Released Apr '84, on EMI, by EMI Records. Deleted Oct '89. Catalogue no: **12 QUEEN 2**
CD 3": Released Nov '88, on EMI, by EMI Records. Catalogue no: **QUEENCD 11**
CD 3": Released Nov '88, on EMI, by EMI Records. Catalogue no: **QUE CD 11**

INVISIBLE MAN, THE
Tracks: / Invisible man, The / Hijack my heart / Invisible man, The (12" version) (12"s only.).
CD 5": Released Aug '89, on Parlophone, by EMI Records. Catalogue no: **203 487 2**
CD 5": Released Aug '89, on Parlophone, by EMI Records. Catalogue no: **CDQUEEN 12**
Cassingle: Released Aug '89, on Parlophone, by EMI Records. Catalogue no: **203 487 4**
Cassingle: Released Aug '89, on Parlophone, by EMI Records. Catalogue no: **TCQUEEN 12**
7" Single: Released Aug '89, on Parlophone, by EMI Records. Catalogue no: **203 487 7**
7" Single: Released Aug '89, on Parlophone, by EMI Records. Catalogue no: **QUEEN 12**
7" Single: Released Aug '89, on Parlophone, by EMI Records. Catalogue no: **QUEENX 12**
7" Single: Released Aug '89, on Parlophone, by EMI Records. Catalogue no: **203 487 8**
12" Single: Released Aug '89, on Parlophone, by EMI Records. Catalogue no: **203 487 6**
12" Single: Released Aug '89, on Parlophone, by EMI Records. Catalogue no: **203**

QUEEN - I WANT IT ALL (Released on Parlophone)

QUEEN - WE ARE THE CHAMPIONS (Released on EMI)

QUEEN IDA - CELIMENE (Released on Sonet)

487 0
12" Single: Released Aug '89, on Parlophone, by EMI Records. Catalogue no: **12QUEEN 12**
12" Single: Released Aug '89, on Parlophone, by EMI Records. Catalogue no: **12QUEENX 12**

IT'S A HARD LIFE
Tracks: / It's a hard life.
12" Pic: Released Aug '84, on EMI, by EMI Records. Deleted '88. Catalogue no: **12 QUEENP 3**
7" Single: Released Jul '84, on EMI, by EMI Records. Deleted Oct '89. Catalogue no: **QUEEN 3**
12" Single: Released Aug '84, on EMI, by EMI Records. Deleted Jun '89. Catalogue no: **12 QUEEN 3**

KILLER QUEEN (CD SINGLE)
Tracks: / Killer queen / Flick of the wrist / Brighton rock.
CD 3": Released Nov '88, on EMI, by EMI Records. Catalogue no: **QUEENCD 2**
CD 3": Released Nov '88, on EMI, by EMI Records. Catalogue no: **QUECD 2**

KILLER QUEEN (SINGLE)
Tracks: / Killer queen / You're my best friend.
7" Single: Released Oct '74, on EMI, by EMI Records. Deleted '77. Catalogue no: **EMI 2229**
7" Single: Released Mar '84, on EMI Golden 45's, by EMI Records. Catalogue no: **G45 1**

KIND OF MAGIC, A (CD)
Tracks: / Kind of magic, A / Dozen red roses for my darling, A / One vision.
CD 3": Released Nov '88, on EMI, by EMI Records. Catalogue no: **QUEENCD 12**
CD 3": Released Nov '88, on EMI, by EMI Records. Catalogue no: **QUE CD 12**

KIND OF MAGIC, A (SINGLE)
Tracks: / Kind of magic, A / Don't lose your head (inst.) / Kind of magic, A (ext.) (12" only.).
12" Pic: Released Mar '86, on EMI, by EMI Records. Deleted '88. Catalogue no: **12 QUEENT 7**
7" Single: Released Mar '86, on EMI, by EMI Records. Deleted Oct '89. Catalogue no: **QUEEN 7**
12" Single: Released Mar '86, on EMI, by EMI Records. Deleted Jun '89. Catalogue no: **12 QUEEN 7**

LAS PALABRAS DE AMOUR
Tracks: / Las palabras de amor / Cool cat.
7" Single: Released Jun '82, on EMI, by EMI Records. Catalogue no: **EMI 5316**

LOVE OF MY LIFE
Tracks: / Love of my life.
7" Single: Released Jul '79, on EMI, by EMI Records. Deleted '82. Catalogue no: **EMI 2959**

NOW I'M HERE
Tracks: / Now I'm here.
7" Single: Released Jan '75, on EMI, by EMI Records. Deleted '78. Catalogue no: **EMI 2256**

ONE VISION
Tracks: / One vision.
7" Single: Released Nov '85, on EMI, by EMI Records. Catalogue no: **EMI 5535**
7" Single: Released Nov '85, on EMI, by EMI Records. Deleted Aug '89. Catalogue no: **QUEEN 6**
12" Single: Released Nov '85, on EMI, by EMI Records. Deleted Oct '89. Catalogue no: **12 QUEEN 6**

PLAY THE GAME
Tracks: / Play the game / Human body.
7" Single: Released Jun '80, on EMI, by EMI Records. Deleted '83. Catalogue no: **EMI 5076**

QUEEN'S FIRST EP
Tracks: / Good-old fashioned lover boy / Death on two legs / Tenement funster / White Queen (as it began).
7" EP: Released Jun '77, on EMI, by EMI Records. Deleted '80. Catalogue no: **EMI 2623**
CD 3": Released Nov '88, on EMI, by EMI Records. Catalogue no: **QUEENCD 5**
CD 3": Released Nov '88, on EMI, by EMI Records. Catalogue no: **QUECD 5**

RADIO GA GA
Tracks: / Radio ga ga / I go crazy / Hammer to fall (CD single only.).
7" Single: Released Jan '84, on EMI, by EMI Records. Deleted Oct '89. Catalogue no: **QUEEN 1**
12" Single: Released Jan '84, on EMI, by EMI Records. Deleted Oct '89. Catalogue no: **12 QUEEN 1**
CD 3": Released Nov '88, on EMI, by EMI Records. Catalogue no: **QUEENCD 10**
CD 3": Released Nov '88, on EMI, by EMI Records. Catalogue no: **QUE CD 10**

SAVE ME
Tracks: / Save me / Let me entertain you.
7" Single: Released Feb '80, on EMI, by EMI Records. Deleted '83. Catalogue no: **EMI 5022**

SCANDAL
Tracks: / Scandal / My life has been saved / Scandal (12" version) (12" & CD single only.).
CD 5": Released Oct '89, on Parlophone, by EMI Records. Catalogue no: **CDQUEEN 14**
CD 5": Released Oct '89, on Parlophone, by EMI Records. Catalogue no: **203 544 2**
Cassingle: Released Oct '89, on Parlophone, by EMI Records. Catalogue no: **TCQUEEN 14**
Cassingle: Released Oct '89, on Parlophone, by EMI Records. Catalogue no: **203 544 4**
7" Single: Released Oct '89, on Parlophone, by EMI Records. Catalogue no: **203 544 7**
7" Single: Released Oct '89, on Parlophone, by EMI Records. Catalogue no: **203 544 8**
7" Single: Released Oct '89, on Parlophone, by EMI Records. Catalogue no: **QUEEN 14**
7" Single: Released Oct '89, on Parlophone, by EMI Records. Catalogue no: **QUEENP 14**
12" Single: Released Oct '89, on Parlophone, by EMI Records. Catalogue no: **203 544 6**
12" Single: Released Oct '89, on Parlophone, by EMI Records. Catalogue no: **12QUEEN 14**
Special: Released Oct '89, on Parlophone, by EMI Records. Catalogue no: **203 544 0**
Special: Released Oct '89, on Parlophone, by EMI Records. Catalogue no: **12QUEENS 14**

SEVEN SEAS OF RHYE
Tracks: / Seven seas of rhye / See what a fool I've been / Funny how love is.
CD 3": Released Nov '88, on EMI, by EMI Records. Catalogue no: **QUEENCD 1**
CD 3": Released Nov '88, on EMI, by EMI Records. Catalogue no: **QUECD 1**

SEVEN SEAS OF RHYE (SINGLE)
Tracks: / Seven seas of Rhye.
7" Single: Released Mar '74, on EMI, by EMI Records. Deleted '77. Catalogue no: **EMI 2121**

SOMEBODY TO LOVE
Tracks: / Somebody to love.
7" Single: Released Oct '76, on EMI, by EMI Records. Deleted '79. Catalogue no: **EMI 2565**
7" Single: Released '80, on EMI, by EMI Records. Catalogue no: **LR 2755**

SOMEBODY TO LOVE (CD SINGLE)
Tracks: / Somebody to love / White man / Tie your mother down.
CD 3": Released Nov '88, on EMI, by EMI Records. Catalogue no: **QUEENCD 4**
CD 3": Released Nov '88, on EMI, by EMI Records. Catalogue no: **QUECD 4**

SOUL BROTHER
Tracks: / Soul brother.
12" Single: Released Jul '84, on EMI (Germany), by EMI Records. Catalogue no: **ICK 052 64626**

SPREAD YOUR WINGS
Tracks: / Spread your wings.
7" Single: Released Feb '78, on EMI, by EMI Records. Deleted '81. Catalogue no: **EMI 2757**

THANK GOD IT'S CHRISTMAS
Tracks: / Thank God it's Christmas.
7" Single: Released Nov '84, on EMI, by EMI Records. Catalogue no: **QUEEN 5**
12" Single: Released Nov '84, on EMI, by EMI Records. Catalogue no: **12 QUEEN 5**

TIE YOUR MOTHER DOWN
Tracks: / Tie your mother down.
7" Single: Released Mar '77, on EMI, by EMI Records. Deleted '80. Catalogue no: **EMI 2593**

UNDER PRESSURE
Tracks: / Under pressure / Soul brother / Body language (CD single only.).
CD 3": Released Nov '88, on EMI, by EMI Records. Catalogue no: **QUEENCD 9**
CD 3": Released Nov '88, on EMI, by EMI Records. Catalogue no: **QUECD 9**
7" Single: Released Nov '81, on EMI, by EMI Records. Catalogue no: **EMI 5250**

WE ARE THE CHAMPIONS (See panel above left)
Tracks: / We are the champions / We will rock you.
7" Single: Released Oct '77, on EMI, by EMI Records. Catalogue no: **EMI 2708**
CD 3": Released Nov '88, on EMI, by EMI Records. Catalogue no: **QUEENCD 6**
CD 3": Released Nov '88, on EMI, by EMI Records. Catalogue no: **QUECD 6**

WHO WANTS TO LIVE FOREVER?
Tracks: / Who wants to live forever / Kind of magic, A / Killer Queen / Who wants to live forever (piano version) (Track on 12" only).
7" Single: Released Sep '86, on EMI, by EMI Records. Deleted Oct '87. Catalogue no: **QUEEN 9**
12" Single: Released Sep '86, on EMI, by EMI Records. Deleted Oct '87. Catalogue no: **12 QUEEN 9**

YOU'RE MY BEST FRIEND
Tracks: / You're my best friend.
7" Single: Released Jul '76, on EMI, by EMI Records. Deleted '79. Catalogue no: **EMI 2494**
7" Single: Released Mar '84, on EMI Golden 45's, by EMI Records. Catalogue no: **G 45 1**
7" Single: Released '80, on EMI (Europe), by EMI Records. Catalogue no: **LR 2255**

Queen Ida

Biographical details: Grammy Award winner Queen Ida is one of America's most colourful musical characters. She hails from Louisiana's bayou area and her Bon Temps Zydeco band play an exhilarating mixture of good time dance sounds, sung in a mixture of French and English. Queen Ida, who plays accordion and sings, is the only woman leading a Louisiana zydeco band, and is rapidly gaining an international following with prestigious festival appearances in the USA and Europe and a cameo appearance in the film *Rumble fish*. (Sonet).

CELIMENE (See panel above)
Tracks: / Celimene / Fais deaux deaux.
7" Single: Released '83, on Sonet, by Sonet Records. Catalogue no: **SON 2261**

Queen Latifah

DANCE FOR ME
Tracks: / Dance for me.
7" Single: Released 22 May '89, on Gee Street, by Gee Street Records. Catalogue no: **GEE 016**
7" Single: Released May '89, on Gee Street, by Gee Street Records. Catalogue no: **GEE 16**
12" Single: Released 22 May '89, on Gee Street, by Gee Street Records. Catalogue no: **GEE T016**
12" Single: Released 22 May '89, on Gee Street, by Gee Street Records. Catalogue no: **GEET 016 R**
12" Single: Released May '89, on Gee Street, by Gee Street Records. Catalogue no: **GEET 16**

LADIES FIRST
Tracks: / Ladies first.
7" Single: Released Nov '89, on Gee Street, by Gee Street Records. Catalogue no: **GEE 23**
12" Single: Released Nov '89, on Gee Street, by Gee Street Records. Catalogue no: **GEET 23**

PRINCESS OF THE POSSE
Tracks: / Princess of the posse.

12" Single: Released Jul '89, on Gee Street, by Gee Street Records. Catalogue no: **GEET 020**

Queensryche

EYES OF A STRANGER
Tracks: / Eyes of a stranger / Queen of the Reich / Walk in the shadows (12" only.) / Take hold of the flame (12" only.) / Prophecy.
CD 5": Released Apr '89, on EMI-Manhattan, by EMI Records. Catalogue no: **CDMT 65**
7" Single: Released Apr '89, on EMI-Manhattan, by EMI Records. Catalogue no: **MT 65**
12" Single: Released Apr '89, on EMI-Manhattan, by EMI Records. Catalogue no: **12MTG 65**
12" Single: Released Apr '89, on EMI-Manhattan, by EMI Records. Catalogue no: **12MT 65**

GONNA GET CLOSE TO YOU
Tracks: / Gonna get close to you / Prophecy / Queen of the Reich (On 7" set only) / Deliverance (On 7" set only).
7" Set: Released Aug '86, on EMI, by EMI Records. Catalogue no: **EAD 22**
7" Single: Released Aug '86, on EMI, by EMI Records. Catalogue no: **EA 22**

OVERSEEING THE OPERATION Excerpts from "Operation: Mindcrime"
Tracks: / I remember now / Revolution calling / Operation: Mindcrime / Breaking the silence / Eyes of a stranger / Suite Sister Mary.
10" single: Released Oct '88, on EMI-Manhattan, by EMI Records. Catalogue no: **10 QR 1**

Quest for Life

BABY DON'T STOP ME
Tracks: / Baby don't stop me / Acapella mix.
7" Single: Released Jun '86, on MDM, by MDM Communications. Deleted '89. Catalogue no: **MDM 9**
12" Single: Released Jun '86, on MDM, by MDM Communications. Deleted May '88. Catalogue no: **MDM 9-12**

Question Mark

96 TEARS
Tracks: / 96 tears.
7" Single: Released Nov '66, on Cameo Parkway, by Pye Records. Deleted '69. Catalogue no: **C 428**

Questionaires

LOOK OUT
Tracks: / That's what you're doing to me.
7" Single: Released Jan '87, on Shark, by Shark Records. Deleted '88. Catalogue no: **SH 1001**

Questions

PRICE YOU PAY
Tracks: / Price you pay, The.
7" Single: Released Apr '83, on Respond (2), by A&M Records. Deleted '86. Catalogue no: **KOB 702**

TEAR SOUP
Tracks: / Tear soup.
7" Single: Released Sep '83, on Respond (2), by A&M Records. Deleted '86. Catalogue no: **KOB 705**

TUESDAY SUNSHINE
Tracks: / Tuesday sunshine / No one / House that Jack built (on 12" only).
7" Single: Released Mar '84, on Respond (2), by A&M Records. Deleted '87. Catalogue no: **KOB 707**

WORK AND PLAY
Tracks: / Work and play.
7" Single: Released Feb '82, on Respond (1), by Respond Records. Deleted Feb '87. Catalogue no: **RESP 7**
12" Single: Released Feb '82, on Respond (1), by Respond Records. Deleted Feb '87. Catalogue no: **RESPX 7**

Queue Dance

NOT THE ONE FOR ME
Tracks: / Not the one for me.
12" Single: Released May '87, on Pylon, Catalogue no: **ALI 001**

Quick

BED OF NAILS
Tracks: / Bed of nails / Guarantee, The / Down the wire (learn to dance mix) (Track on 12" only).
7" Single: Released Mar '86, on A&M, by A&M Records. Deleted '88. Catalogue no: **AM 304**
12" Single: Released Mar '86, on A&M, by A&M Records. Deleted '88. Catalogue no: **AMY 304**

DOWN THE WIRE
Tracks: / Down the wire / Specialist, The.
7" Single: Released '88, on A&M, by A&M Records. Catalogue no: **KWIK 1**

HIP, SHAKE, JERK!
Tracks: / Hip, shake, jerk! / Expresso bongo.
7" Single: Released Oct '80, on Epic, by CBS Records. Deleted Oct '83. Catalogue no: **EPC 9032**

I NEEDED YOU
Tracks: / I needed you / You reach for me no more / Heaven & earth*.
Note: *This track on 12"version only
7" Single: Released Feb '87, on A&M, by A&M Records. Deleted '88. Catalogue no: **AM 379**
12" Single: Released Feb '87, on A&M, by A&M Records. Deleted '88. Catalogue no: **AMY 379**

RHYTHM OF THE JUNGLE
Tracks: / Rhythm of the jungle.
7" Single: Released May '82, on Epic, by CBS Records. Deleted '85. Catalogue no: **A 2013**

SHIP TO SHORE
Tracks: / Ship to shore / Eastern promise.
7" Single: Released May '80, on Epic, by CBS Records. Deleted May '85. Catalogue no: **EPC 8539**

TOUCH
Tracks: / Touch / Twisted.
7" Single: Released Aug '82, on Epic, by CBS Records. Deleted Aug '85. Catalogue no: **EPCA 2669**

WE CAN LEARN FROM THIS
Tracks: / We can learn from this / All you want is heaven / Blow the man down / My King will come (Track on 12" only).
7" Single: Released Jul '86, on A&M, by A&M Records. Deleted '88. Catalogue no: **AM 328**
12" Single: Released Jul '86, on A&M, by A&M Records. Deleted '88. Catalogue no: **AMY 328**

YOUNG MEN DRIVE FAST
Tracks: / Young men drive fast / Small blond box.
7" Single: Released Jan '81, on Epic, by CBS Records. Deleted Jan '84. Catalogue no: **EPC 9466**

ZULU
Tracks: / Zulu / Eat your words.
7" Single: Released May '81, on Epic, by CBS Records. Deleted May '84. Catalogue no: **EPC A 1119**
12" Single: Released Oct '81, on Epic, by CBS Records. Deleted '85. Catalogue no: **EPC A 13 1739**
12" Single: Released May '81, on Epic, by CBS Records. Deleted May '84. Catalogue no: **EPC A 13 1119**

Quickly, Tommy

WILD SIDE OF LIFE
Tracks: / Wild side of life.
7" Single: Released Oct '64, on Pye, Deleted '67. Catalogue no: **7 N 15708**

Quiet Boys

LET THE GOOD TIMES ROLL
Tracks: / Let the good times roll.
12" Single: Released Feb '89, on Acid Jazz, by Acid Jazz Records. Catalogue no: **JAZID 10 T**

Quiet Five

HOMEWARD BOUND
Tracks: / Homeward bound.
7" Single: Released Apr '66, on Parlophone, by EMI Records. Deleted '69. Catalogue no: **R 5421**

WHEN THE MORNING SUN DRIES THE DEW
Tracks: / When the morning sun dries the dew.
7" Single: Released May '65, on Parlophone, by EMI Records. Deleted '68. Catalogue no: **R 5273**

Quiet Riot

Biographical details: A USA heavy rock band formed in Los Angeles in 1975 by vocalist Kevin DuBrow, Randy Rhoads on guitar, Rudy Sarzo on bass; Frankie Banazi on drums. They claimed an affinity with Status Quo, whose Rick Parfitt suggested name. Made LPs *Quiet Riot* and *Quiet riot II* '77-8 for Japan-only release; they're now collectors items, though band have since disowned them. Rhoads left to join Ozzy Osbourne; Sarzo left and duo carried on as BuBrow, but changed name back to *Quiet Riot*, adding guitarist Carlos Cavazo, commenced recording *Metal Health* '83, Sarzo rejoining during sessions; *QRIII* in 1986 had new bassist Chuck Wright. (Donald Clarke)..

METAL HEALTH (SINGLE)
Tracks: / Metal health / Cum on feel the noize.
7" Single: Released Dec '83, on Epic, by CBS Records. Deleted '86. Catalogue no: **A 3968**

WILD AND THE YOUNG
Tracks: / Wild and the young / Rise or fall.
7" Single: Released Sep '86, on Epic, by CBS Records. Catalogue no: **A 7280**
12" Single: Released Sep '86, on Epic, by CBS Records. Catalogue no: **TA 7280**

Quinn, Aileen

TOMORROW
Tracks: / Tomorrow / Let's go to the movies.
7" Single: Released Jul '82, on CBS, by CBS Records. Deleted Jul '85. Catalogue no: **CBS A 2409**

Quinn, Anthony

LIFE ITSELF WILL LET YOU KNOW
Tracks: / Life itself will let you know / All my life.
7" Single: Released Nov '81, on WEA, by WEA Records. Deleted Nov '84. Catalogue no: **K 79240**

Quinn, Brendan

CAN'T HOLD BACK THE YEARS
Tracks: / Can't hold back the years.
7" Single: Released Aug '86, on Ritz, by Ritz Records. Catalogue no: **RITZ 153**

HUSTLER (SINGLE)
Tracks: / Mamma she's crazy.
7" Single: Released Jan '87, on Ritz, by Ritz Records. Catalogue no: **RITZ 168**

IRISH HEARTBEAT
Tracks: / Irish heartbeat / Right or wrong.
7" Single: Released Jan '86, on Ritz, by Ritz Records. Catalogue no: **RITZ 129**

Quinn, Paul

PALE BLUE EYES
Tracks: / Pale blue eyes.
7" Single: Released Aug '84, on Swamplands, by London Records. Deleted '87. Catalogue no: **SWP 1**

Quint

NIGHTMARE
Tracks: / Nightmare / Only time can tell.
7" Single: Released Feb '80, on RCA, by BMG Records (UK). Deleted '83. Catalogue no: **PB 5219**

Quireboys

7 O'CLOCK
Tracks: / 7 o'clock / Pretty girls / How do you feel (Not on 7".).
CD 5": Released Oct '89, on Parlophone, by EMI Records. Catalogue no: **CDR 6230**
CD 5": Released Oct '89, on Parlophone, by EMI Records. Catalogue no: **203 540 2**
7" Pic: Released Oct '89, on Parlophone, by EMI Records. Catalogue no: **RPD 6230**
7" Pic: Released Oct '89, on Parlophone, by EMI Records. Catalogue no: **2203 540 0**
Cassingle: Released Oct '89, on Parlophone, by EMI Records. Catalogue no: **203 540 4**
Cassingle: Released Oct '89, on Parlophone, by EMI Records. Catalogue no: **TCR 6230**
7" Single: Released Oct '89, on Parlophone, by EMI Records. Catalogue no: **203 540 7**
7" Single: Released Oct '89, on Parlophone, by EMI Records. Catalogue no: **RG 6230**
7" Single: Released Oct '89, on Parlophone, by EMI Records. Catalogue no: **R 6230**
7" Single: Released Oct '89, on Parlophone, by EMI Records. Catalogue no: **203 540 8**
12" Single: Released Oct '89, on Parlophone, by EMI Records. Catalogue no: **203 543 8**
12" Single: Released Oct '89, on Parlophone, by EMI Records. Catalogue no: **12R 6230**
12" Single: Released Oct '89, on Parlophone, by EMI Records. Catalogue no: **12RP 6230**

MAYFAIR
Tracks: / Mayfair / Misled / Man on the loose (12" single only.).
7" Single: Released 14 May '88, on Survival (1), by Survival Records. Catalogue no: **SUR 043**
12" Single: Released 14 May '88, on Survival (1), by Survival Records. Catalogue no: **SUR 12 043**

THERE SHE GOES AGAIN
Tracks: / There she goes again / How do ya feel / Sex party (12" only.).
7" Pic: Released Dec '88, on Survival (2), Deleted Oct '89. Catalogue no: **PDSUR 46**
7" Single: Released Oct '88, on Survival (2), Deleted Oct '89. Catalogue no: **SUR 46**
12" Single: Released Oct '88, on Survival (2), Catalogue no: **12SUR 46**
12" Single: Released Oct '88, on Survival (2), Deleted Aug '89. Catalogue no: **SURT 46**

Quiz

AND THE WORLD
Tracks: / And the world / Call on you.
7" Single: Released Jul '81, on Hit City, Deleted '85. Catalogue no: **HCR 1**

R

This information was taken from the Music Master database on October 20th, 1989

R & D

IN BERLIN
Tracks: / In Berlin.
7" Single: Released Nov '84, on Sonet, by Sonet Records. Catalogue no: **SON 2274**
12" Single: Released Nov '84, on Sonet, by Sonet Records. Catalogue no: **SONL 2274**

R & R

ACID OFF A WAY
Tracks: / Acid off a way / Funky man (you better run).
12" Single: Released Sep '88, on Three Stripe, Catalogue no: **SAM 1112**

FUNKY MAN (YOU BETTER RUN)
Tracks: / Funky man (you better run).
7" Single: Released Oct '88, on Three Stripe, Catalogue no: **SAM 112**

Ra Ra Rawhide

I START COUNTING
12" Single: Released Aug '88, on Mute, by Mute Records. Catalogue no: **MUTE 81**

Raaw

ORDINARY MAN
12" Single: Released '87, on UNKNOWN, Deleted Jun '89. Catalogue no: **TEMD 22**

Rabbitt, Eddie

Biographical details:
Eddie Rabbitt a pop/country vocalist and songwriter born in 1941 in Brooklyn. He wrote hits for others including Elvis Presley (*Kentucky Rain* in 1970), Ronnie Milsap (*Pure Love* in 1974); began having his own hits on Elektra 1974-5 including the film song *Every Which Way But Loose*, several country number ones and all pop cross-overs; he was the biggest selling country artist in the USA in 1980-2; a WB compilation in 1985 was entirely number one hits. He switched to RCA in 1985 with mor contemporary styling, slicker production. (Donald Clarke)..

DIM DIM THE LIGHTS
Tracks: / Dim dim the lights / Nobody loves me like my baby.
7" Single: Released Jan '82, on Mercury, by Phonogram Ltd. Deleted Jan '85. Catalogue no: **MER 88**

EVERY WHICH WAY BUT LOOSE
Tracks: / Every which way but loose.
7" Single: Released Jan '79, on Elektra, by Elektra Records (UK). Catalogue no: **K 12331**

I LOVE A RAINY NIGHT
Tracks: / I love a rainy night / Short road to love.
7" Single: Released Feb '81, on Elektra, by Elektra Records (UK). Deleted '84. Catalogue no: **K 12498**

STEP BY STEP (SINGLE)
Tracks: / Step by step / My only wish.
7" Single: Released Sep '81, on Mercury, by Phonogram Ltd. Deleted Sep '84. Catalogue no: **MER 81**

YOU AND I
Tracks: / You and I / All my life, all my love.
7" Single: Released Dec '82, on Mercury, by Phonogram Ltd. Deleted '85. Catalogue no: **MER 123**

Rabid

BLOODY ROAD TO GLORY
Tracks: / Bloody road to glory.
7" Single: Released May '88, on Fall Out, Catalogue no: **FALL 007**

BRING OUT YOUR DEAD
Tracks: / Bring out your dead.
12" Single: Released May '88, on Fall Out, Catalogue no: **FALL 12009**

Rabin, Trevor

TAKE ME TO A PARTY
Tracks: / Take me to a party / Looking for a lady.
7" Single: Released Mar '81, on Chrysalis, by Chrysalis Records. Deleted Mar '84. Catalogue no: **CHS 2508**

Rabitts Wedding

COMING
Tracks: / Coming.
7" Single: Released Jan '88, on Waterfront, by Waterfront Music. Catalogue no: **DAMP 58**

Race

SHOW ME THE WAY
Tracks: / Show me the way.
7" Single: Released Nov '82, on London (Decca), by Decca International. Deleted Nov '85. Catalogue no: **LON 16**
12" Single: Released Nov '82, on London (Decca), by Decca International. Deleted Nov '85. Catalogue no: **LONX 16**

Race, Steve

PIED PIPER (THE BEEJE)
Tracks: / Pied piper.
7" Single: Released Feb '63, on Parlophone, by EMI Records. Deleted '66. Catalogue no: **R 4981**

Racey

BOY OH BOY (See panel opposite)
Tracks: / Boy oh boy / Sensational buzz.
7" Single: Released Aug '79, on RAK, by EMI Records. Deleted '82. Catalogue no: **RAK 297**

LAY YOUR LOVE ON ME
Tracks: / Lay your love on me.
7" Single: Released Nov '78, on RAK, by EMI Records. Deleted '81. Catalogue no: **RAK 284**

NOT TOO YOUNG TO GET MARRIED
Tracks: / Not too young to get married / Love games.
7" Single: Released Sep '82, on RAK, by EMI Records. Deleted '85. Catalogue no: **RAK 348**

REST OF MY LIFE
Tracks: / Rest of my life / Cry baby cry.
7" Single: Released Jul '80, on RAK, by EMI Records. Deleted Jul '83. Catalogue no: **RAK 317**

RUNAROUND SUE
Tracks: / Runaround Sue / Hold me close.
7" Single: Released Dec '80, on RAK, by EMI Records. Deleted '83. Catalogue no: **RAK 325**

SHAME
Tracks: / Shame / Let me take you home tonight.
7" Single: Released Mar '81, on RAK, by EMI Records. Deleted Mar '84. Catalogue no: **RAK 329**

SOME GIRLS
Tracks: / Some girls.
7" Single: Released Mar '79, on RAK, by EMI Records. Deleted '82. Catalogue no: **RAK 291**

THERE'S A PARTY GOING
Tracks: / There's a party going / High Street sunset.
7" Single: Released Dec '81, on RAK, by EMI Records. Deleted Dec '84. Catalogue no: **RAK 338**

Rachet, Don

SWEET ROSIE
Tracks: / Sweet Rosie / Sweet Rosie (version).
12" Single: Released Jun '87, on Startime, Catalogue no: **ST 001**

Racing Cars

THEY SHOOT HORSES DON'T THEY
Tracks: / They shoot horses don't they / Four wheel drive.
7" Single: Released Feb '77, on Chrysalis, by Chrysalis Records. Deleted '82. Catalogue no: **CHS 2129**

THEY SHOOT HORSES DON'T THEY (OLD GOLD)
Tracks: / They shoot horses don't they / Gonna capture your heart.
Note: Double 'A' side
7" Single: Released Apr '87, on Old Gold, by Old Gold Records. Catalogue no: **OG 9699**

RACEY - BOY OH BOY (Released on RAK)

Radcliffe, Jimmy

LONG AFTER TONIGHT IS ALL OVER
Tracks: / Long after tonight is all over.
7" Single: Released Feb '65, on Stateside, by EMI Records. Deleted '68. Catalogue no: **SS 374**

Radford, Phil

TELL ME
Tracks: / Tell me / Smiling moon.
7" Single: Released Aug '86, on Excaliber, by Red Bus Records. Deleted '88. Catalogue no: **EXC 1404**
12" Single: Released Aug '86, on Excaliber, by Red Bus Records. Deleted '88. Catalogue no: **EXCL 1404**

Radha Krishna Temple

GOVINDA
Tracks: / Govinda.
7" Single: Released Mar '70, on Apple, by Apple Records. Deleted '73. Catalogue no: **APPLE 25**

HARE KRISHNA MANTRA
Tracks: / Hare Krishna mantra.
7" Single: Released Sep '69, on Apple, by Apple Records. Deleted '72. Catalogue no: **APPLE 15**

Radiators

ENEMIES
Tracks: / Enemies / Teenager in love / Television screen / Psychotic reaction.
7" Single: Released Feb '80, on Chiswick Records, Deleted '83. Catalogue no: **SW 57**

UNDER CLEARY'S CLOCK
Tracks: / Under Cleary's clock.
7" Single: Released Jan '89, on Chiswick-Ace, by Ace Records. Catalogue no: **NS 128**
12" Single: Released Jan '89, on Chiswick-Ace, by Ace Records. Catalogue no: **NST 128**

Radical Dance

SURVIVE THE DAY
Tracks: / Survive the day.
7" Single: Released Sep '86, on Bite Back, Catalogue no: **BB 009**

Radicals

RUMTREE
Tracks: / Rumtree / Radics in dub / Give me loving.
12" Single: Released Jun '86, on Blue Trac, by Blue Trac Records. Catalogue no: **BTR 003**

Radics, Jack

ROUGH LIFE
Tracks: / Rough life.
12" Single: Released Nov '87, on Mango, by Island Records. Deleted Apr '88. Catalogue no: **12IS 345**

Radio 5

THREE COLOURS
Tracks: / Three colours / Animal connections.
7" Single: Released May '80, on Rockburgh, Deleted May '85. Catalogue no: **ROCS 225**

Radio Earth

DISTANT LAND (BA-DO-BOMB-BOMB)
Tracks: / Distant land (ba-do-bomb-bomb) / Race.
7" Single: Released May '87, on WEA, by WEA Records. Deleted Jul '88. Catalogue no: **YZ 115**
12" Single: Released May '87, on WEA, by WEA Records. Deleted Jul '88. Catalogue no: **YZ 115T**

NEVER TO MAKE YOU CRY
Tracks: / Never to make you cry.
7" Single: Released Aug '87, on Priority, by Priority Records. Catalogue no: **P 16**
7" Single: Released Aug '87, on WEA, by WEA Records. Deleted Jul '88. Catalogue no: **YZ 146**
12" Single: Released Aug '87, on WEA, by WEA Records. Deleted Jul '88. Catalogue no: **YZ 146T**
12" Single: Released Aug '87, on Priority, by Priority Records. Catalogue no: **PZ 16**

Radio Heart

ALL ACROSS THE NATION
Tracks: / All across the nation.
CD 5": Released Nov '87, on NBR, Catalogue no: **CDNBRK 1**
7" Single: Released Oct '87, on NBR, Catalogue no: **NBR 1**
12" Single: Released Oct '87, on NBR, Catalogue no: **12 NBR 1**

LONDON TIMES
Tracks: / London Times / Rumour, The.
12" Pic: Released Jun '87, on GFM, Catalogue no: **GFMX 112**
7" Pic: Released Jun '87, on GFM, Cata-

logue no: **GFMP 112**
7" Single: Released 23 May '87, on GFM, Catalogue no: **GFM 112**
12" Single: Released 23 May '87, on GFM, Catalogue no: **GFMT 112**

Radio Stars

GOOD PERSONALITY
Tracks: / Good personality / Talkin' 'bout you.
7" Single: Released Jun '82, on Moonlight, by Lithon Recording & Music Publishing. Deleted Jun '85. Catalogue no: **MNS 001**

MY MOTHER SAID
Tracks: / My mother said / Two minutes Mr. Smith.
7" Single: Released Nov '82, on Snat, Deleted Nov '85. Catalogue no: **ECG 1**

NERVOUS WRECK
Tracks: / Nervous wreck.
7" Single: Released Feb '78, on Chiswick Records, Deleted '81. Catalogue no: **NS 23**

Radioactive

RADIOACTIVE 7" singles set
7" Set: Released Sep '86, on Fall Out, Deleted '88. Catalogue no: **FALLBOX 040**

Rae, Fonda

OVER LIKE A FAT RAT
Tracks: / Over like a fat rat.
7" Single: Released Jul '82, on Vanguard, by Start Records Ltd.. Deleted Jul '85. Catalogue no: **VS 5023**
12" Single: Released Jul '82, on Vanguard, by Start Records Ltd.. Deleted Jul '85. Catalogue no: **VSL 5023**

TUCH ME
Tracks: / Tuch me.
7" Single: Released Oct '84, on Streetwave, Deleted '87. Catalogue no: **KHAN 28**

Rae, Jamie

MYSTERY GIRL
Tracks: / Mystery girl / Mystery girl (inst).
7" Single: Released Feb '88, on Bluebird (2), by BMG Records (UK). Catalogue no: **BR 46**
12" Single: Released Feb '88, on Bluebird (2), by BMG Records (UK). Catalogue no: **BRT 46**

SHE'S THE ONE
Tracks: / She's the one / Sad song.
7" Single: Released Jun '84, on Stiff, by Stiff Records. Catalogue no: **BUY 204**

Rae, Jesse

D.E.S.I.R.E.
Tracks: / D.E.S.I.R.E. / Sky diver.
7" Single: Released Oct '81, on Radial Choice, by Virgin Records. Deleted Oct '84. Catalogue no: **TIC 7**

HOU-DI-NI
Tracks: / Hou-di-ni / Idio-syn-crazy.
7" Single: Released Apr '87, on WEA, by WEA Records. Deleted Jan '88. Catalogue no: **YZ 116**
12" Single: Released Apr '87, on WEA, by WEA Records. Deleted Jan '88. Catalogue no: **YZ 116T**

IT'S JUST THE DOG IN ME
Tracks: / It's just the dog in me / Be yourself.
12" Single: Released Dec '88, on Edition 100, Catalogue no: **EDIT 84.5**
12" Single: Released Dec '84, on Supreme Int.Editions, by Supreme Int.Records. Catalogue no: **EDITION 84-5**

OVER THE SEA
Tracks: / Over the sea / Party crackers.
7" Single: Released May '85, on Scotland The What, Deleted '88. Catalogue no: **YZ 36**

THAT KIND O'GIRL
Tracks: / That kind o' girl.
7" Single: Released Jul '87, on WEA, by WEA Records. Deleted Jul '88. Catalogue no: **YZ 138**
12" Single: Released Jul '87, on WEA, by WEA Records. Deleted Jul '88. Catalogue no: **YZ 138T**

Rae, Stacey

PRISONER CELL BLOCK-H (THEME FROM)
Tracks: / Prisoner cell block H (theme from) / Goodnews (inst).
7" Single: Released Nov '87, on Humber, by Humber Records. Catalogue no: **CELL-1**

Raemon

PRIVATE JOY
Tracks: / Private joy / Private joy (Radio mix) / Whirly gig.
12" Single: Released Oct '85, on T-Mac, by T-Mac Records. Deleted '88. Catalogue no: **UEZT 1**

RAF

CHANGE YOUR WAYS
Tracks: / Change your ways / Waiting for the weekend.
7" Single: Released Oct '80, on A&M, by A&M Records. Deleted Oct '83. Catalogue no: **AMS 7572**

GERRY RAFFERTY - NIGHT OWL (Released on United Artists)

R.A.F. (band)

CHANGE YOUR MIND
Tracks: / Change your mind / She's a criminal.
7" Single: Released Jan '85, on Carrere, Catalogue no: **CAR 355**
12" Single: Released Jan '85, on Carrere, Catalogue no: **CART 355**

EASY COME, EASY GO
Tracks: / Easy come, easy go / Heat's on.
7" Single: Released Apr '81, on A&M, by A&M Records. Deleted Apr '84. Catalogue no: **AMS 8122**

SELF CONTROL PART 1
Tracks: / Self control part 1 / Self control part 2.
7" Single: Released May '84, on Carrere, Catalogue no: **CAR 324**
12" Single: Released May '84, on Carrere, Catalogue no: **CART 324**

WOMAN LIKE YOU
Tracks: / Woman like you, A / It's only love.
7" Single: Released Nov '86, on Aura Records, by Aura Records. Catalogue no: **AUS 151**

Rafferty, Gerry

Biographical details: Gerry Rafferty was born in 1947 in Paisley, Scotland; he is a folk-rock singer/songwriter and guitarist. He worked with Billy Connolly in the Humblebums; then *Can I Have My Money Back* in 1971 (some say still his best), then formed Stealer's Wheel with folksinger Rab Noakes, who soon bowed out; the act centered around Rafferty, vocalist/keyboardist/co-writer Joe Egan; after three Stealer's LPs he went solo again with *City To City* in 1978, which critics like to pan, but the public made it a number one album in the USA, *Baker Street* a number two single (sax solo by Raphael Ravenscroft). *Night Owl* in 1979 was top 30 *Snakes And Ladders* in 1980 did less well, *Sleepwalking* in 1982 did not chart. he produced an LP for Richard and Linda Thompson in 1982 (not released), sang on one track on Mark Knopfler's *Local Hero* in 1983. (Donald Clarke)..

BAKER STREET
Tracks: / Baker Street.
7" Single: Released Feb '78, on United Artists, by EMI Records. Catalogue no: **UP 36346**
7" Single: Released Apr '83, on EMI (France), by EMI Records. Catalogue no: **2C 008 60574**

BRING IT ALL HOME
Tracks: / Bring it all home / In transit.
7" Single: Released Mar '80, on United Artists, by EMI Records. Deleted '83. Catalogue no: **BP 340**

CHANGE OF HEART
Tracks: / Change of heart / Good intentions.
7" Single: Released Nov '82, on United Artists, by EMI Records. Catalogue no: **BP 415**

GET IT RIGHT NEXT TIME
Tracks: / Get it right next time.
7" Single: Released Aug '79, on United Artists, by EMI Records. Deleted '82. Catalogue no: **BP 301**

NIGHT OWL (SINGLE) (See panel above)
Tracks: / Night owl / Why won't you talk to me.
7" Single: Released May '79, on United Artists, by EMI Records. Deleted '82. Catalogue no: **UP 36512**

ROYAL MILE
Tracks: / Royal mile / Wastin' away.
7" Single: Released Jun '80, on United Artists, by EMI Records. Deleted '83. Catalogue no: **BP 354**

SHIPYARD TOWN
Tracks: / Shipyard town / Hearts desire.
CD 5": on London Records, by London Records. Deleted Oct '88. Catalogue no: **LONCD 170**
7" Single: Released Mar '88, on London Records, by London Records. Deleted Oct '88. Catalogue no: **LON 170**
12" Single: Released Mar '88, on London Records, by London Records. Deleted Oct '88. Catalogue no: **LONX 170**

SLEEPWALKING
Tracks: / Sleepwalking / When I rest.
7" Single: Released Aug '82, on Liberty, by EMI Records. Catalogue no: **BP 413**

Rafferty, Jim

BOGEY MAN
Tracks: / Bogey man / Salt Lake city.
7" Single: Released Nov '80, on Charisma, by Virgin Records. Deleted '83. Catalogue no: **CB 377**

Rafferty, Paul

MAN BEHIND THE SCENES
Tracks: / Man behind the scenes / Start at the bottom.
7" Single: Released May '81, on EMI, by EMI Records. Deleted May '84. Catalogue no: **EMI 5169**

Raffles

TURNED INTO THE EVERLY'S
Tracks: / Turned into the Everly's / Motorbike boys.
7" Single: Released Nov '82, on Spartan, Deleted Nov '85. Catalogue no: **S 3**
7" Single: Released Oct '82, on Paro, by Paro Records. Catalogue no: **PARO 53**

Rage

INVISIBLE HORIZONS
Tracks: / Invisible horizons.
12" Single: Released Sep '89, on Noise, by Dorane Records. Catalogue no: **12RAGE 6**

LOOKING FOR YOU
Tracks: / Looking for you / Come on now / Great balls of fire (Extra track on 12" version only) / Hallelujah I love her so (Extra track on 12" version only).
7" Single: Released Aug '87, on ERC, Catalogue no: **RAGE 1**
12" Single: Released May '86, on Diamond, by Revolver Records. Catalogue no: **BIG RAGE 1**

MONEY
Tracks: / Money / Thank that woman.
7" Single: Released Sep '80, on Carrere, Deleted '83. Catalogue no: **CAR 159**

NEVER BEFORE
Tracks: / Never before / Rock fever.
7" Single: Released Oct '83, on Carrere, Catalogue no: **CAR 291**

OUT OF CONTROL (SINGLE)
Tracks: / Out of control / Double dealer.
7" Single: Released Mar '81, on Carrere, Deleted Mar '84. Catalogue no: **CAR 182**

WOMAN
Tracks: / Woman.
7" Single: Released Jul '82, on Carrere America (USA), by PolyGram Rec.Inc.(USA). Catalogue no: **CAR 240**

Ragged Reggie

FALLING DOWN THE HOLE
Tracks: / Falling down the hole / Bridgetown.
7" Single: Released Jan '83, on ESR, by ESR Records. Catalogue no: **SSR 0006**

Ragland, Lou

I TRAVEL ALONE
Tracks: / Travel alone / Didn't I tell you? / Since you said you'd be mine.
7" Single: Released Dec '83, on Inferno (1), by Inferno Records. Catalogue no: **BURN 4**

Rags

NIGHT MUSIC
Tracks: / Night music / Stones.
7" Single: Released Jan '80, on MCA, by MCA Records. Deleted Jan '83. Catalogue no: **MCA 546**

Rags & Ritches

SESSIONS
Tracks: / Sessions / Your loving.
12" Single: Released Nov '82, on Oak Sound, Catalogue no: **OSD 007**

Ragtimers

STING, THE
Tracks: / Sting, The.
7" Single: Released Mar '74, on Pye, Deleted '77. Catalogue no: **7 N 45323**

Rah Band

ACROSS THE BAY
Tracks: / Jammin' on the byte / Take some thyme.
7" Single: Released Jan '87, on RCA, by BMG Records (UK). Catalogue no: **PB 41099**
12" Single: Released Jan '87, on RCA, by BMG Records (UK). Catalogue no: **PT 41100**

ARE YOU SATISFIED (FUNKA NOVA)
Tracks: / Are you satisfied (Funka nova) / Shadow of your love.
7" Single: Released Dec '84, on RCA, by BMG Records (UK). Catalogue no: **RCA 470**
12" Single: Released Dec '84, on RCA, by BMG Records (UK). Catalogue no: **RCAT 470**

CLOUDS ACROSS THE MOON
Tracks: / Clouds across the moon.
7" Single: Released Mar '85, on RCA, by BMG Records (UK). Catalogue no: **PB 40025**
12" Single: Released Mar '85, on RCA, by BMG Records (UK). Catalogue no: **PT 40025**

CRUNCH, THE
Tracks: / Crunch, The.
7" Single: Released Jul '77, on Good Earth, Deleted '80. Catalogue no: **GD 7**
7" Single: Released Nov '85, on RCA, by BMG Records (UK). Catalogue no: **PB 40481**
12" Single: Released Nov '85, on RCA, by BMG Records (UK). Catalogue no: **PT 40482**

DOWNSIDE UP
Tracks: / Downside up / Dream on.
7" Single: Released '82, on DJM, Catalogue no: **DJS 10967**
12" Single: Released '82, on DJM, Catalogue no: **DJR 10967**

FALCON
Tracks: / Falcon / Falcon 2 / Toyko flyer.
7" Single: Released '82, on DJM, Catalogue no: **DJS 10954**
12" Single: Released Sep '80, on D.E.M., Deleted '83. Catalogue no: **DJR 18014**

MESSAGES FROM THE STARS
Tracks: / Messages from the stars.
7" Single: Released Jul '83, on T.M.T., by T.M.T. Productions. Deleted '87. Catalogue no: **TMT 5**
12" Single: Released Jul '83, on T.M.T., by T.M.T. Productions. Deleted '87. Catalogue

no: **TMTT 5**

PERFUMED GARDEN
Tracks: / Perfumed garden / Funk me down.
7" Single: Released Apr '82, on KR, Catalogue no: **KR 5**
12" Single: Released Apr '82, on KR, Catalogue no: **KRT 5**

QUESTIONS (WHAT YOU GONNA DO)
Tracks: / Questions / Falcon 2 (on 12" only).
7" Single: Released Nov '83, on S.O.U.N.D Recordings, by S.O.U.N.D. Recordings. Catalogue no: **SND 1**
12" Single: Released Nov '83, on S.O.U.N.D Recordings, by S.O.U.N.D. Recordings. Catalogue no: **SNDS 1**

RUN FOR THE SUN
Tracks: / Run for the sun / Life after love.
7" Single: Released Jul '87, on RCA, by BMG Records (UK). Catalogue no: **PB 41413**
12" Single: Released Jul '87, on RCA, by BMG Records (UK). Catalogue no: **PT 41413**

SAM THE SAMBA MAN
Tracks: / Sam the samba man.
7" Single: Released Jun '84, on S.O.U.N.D Recordings, by S.O.U.N.D. Recordings. Catalogue no: **RAHS 901**
7" Single: Released Apr '83, on T.M.T., by T.M.T. Productions. Deleted '87. Catalogue no: **TMT 3**
12" Single: Released Jun '84, on S.O.U.N.D Recordings, by S.O.U.N.D. Recordings. Catalogue no: **RAHXL 901**
12" Single: Released Apr '83, on T.M.T., by T.M.T. Productions. Deleted '87. Catalogue no: **TMTT 3**

SILVERBIRD
Tracks: / Silverbird.
7" Single: Released Aug '89, on Total/Icy, Catalogue no: **EAGLE 12**

SLIDE
Tracks: / Slide / Drat that cat.
7" Single: Released '82, on DJM, Catalogue no: **DJS 10964**
12" Single: Released '82, on DJM, Catalogue no: **DJR 10964**

SORRY DOESN'T MAKE IT ANYMORE
Tracks: / Sorry doesn't make it anymore.
7" Single: Released Jun '85, on RCA, by BMG Records (UK). Catalogue no: **PB 40191**
12" Single: Released Jun '85, on RCA, by BMG Records (UK). Catalogue no: **PT 40192**

SWEET FORBIDDEN
Tracks: / Sweet forbidden / Perfect stranger.
7" Single: Released Jun '86, on RCA, by BMG Records (UK). Catalogue no: **PB 40779**
12" Single: Released Jun '86, on RCA, by BMG Records (UK). Catalogue no: **PT 40780**

TEARS AND RAIN
Tracks: / Tears and rain / Hungry for your jungle love / Party games.
7" Single: Released Jul '82, on KR, Catalogue no: **KR 10**
12" Single: Released Jul '82, on KR, Catalogue no: **KRT 10**

TIME KEEPS TEARING US APART
Tracks: / Time keeps tearing us apart / Adventures of E-man, The / Aliens are coming (inst.mix).
7" Single: Released 17 Oct '88, on Nine O Nine, by Creole Records. Catalogue no: **NINE 721**
12" Single: Released 17 Oct '88, on Nine O Nine, by Creole Records. Catalogue no: **NINE 21**

TOKYO FLYER
Tracks: / Tokyo flyer / Tokyo flyer (instrumental).
7" Single: Released '82, on DJM, Catalogue no: **DJS 10930**

WHAT'LL BECOME OF THE CHILDREN
Tracks: / What'll become of the children.
7" Single: Released Sep '85, on RCA, by BMG Records (UK). Catalogue no: **PB 40373**
12" Single: Released Sep '85, on RCA, by BMG Records (UK). Catalogue no: **PT 40374**

Raheem

DANCEFLOOR
Tracks: / Dancefloor.
7" Single: Released 22 Aug '88, on Breakout, by A&M Records. Catalogue no: **USA 642**
12" Single: Released 22 Aug '88, on Breakout, by A&M Records. Catalogue no: **USAT 642**

Raid

CITY HEAT
Tracks: / City heat.
7" Single: Released '88, on Debut, by Skratch Records. Catalogue no: **DEBT 3036**

HIGH NOON
Tracks: / High noon.
12" Single: Released Nov '85, on Nervous, by Nervous Records. Catalogue no: **12 NEP 002**

Raiders

TWO COLD POTATOES AND A BOTTLE OF WINE
Tracks: / Two cold potatoes and a bottle of wine.
12" Single: Released May '86, on Lost Moments, Catalogue no: **LM 12 038**

Rail, D

PETROL SUNSET
Tracks: / Petrol sunset.
12" Single: Released Sep '85, on Survival (1), by Survival Records. Catalogue no: **SURT 35**

Railway Children

BRIGHTER
Tracks: / Brighter.
7" Single: Released Feb '87, on Factory (1), by Factory Records. Catalogue no: **FAC 167**
12" Single: Released Feb '87, on Factory (1), by Factory Records. Catalogue no: **FAC 167T**

GENTLE SOUND
Tracks: / Gentle sound.
7" Single: Released Sep '86, on Factory (1), by Factory Records. Catalogue no: **FAC 162**

IN THE MEANTIME
Tracks: / In the meantime / Merciless / Second nature (CD & 12" only) / Swallowed (12" only) / I caught you (CD only).
CD 5": Released Aug '88, on Virgin, by Virgin Records. Catalogue no: **VSCD 1070**
7" Single: Released Mar '88, on Virgin, by Virgin Records. Catalogue no: **VS 1070**
12" Single: Released Mar '88, on Virgin, by Virgin Records. Catalogue no: **VST 1070**

OVER AND OVER
Tracks: / Over and over (remix edit) (7" & 12" only) / Gentle sound, A (original demo) (On all versions) / Union city blue (live at the Hacienda) (On CD & 12" only) / Over and over (full remix) (On CD only) / Big hands of freedom (live at the Hacienda) (On CD only).
CD 5": Released '88, on Virgin, by Virgin Records. Catalogue no: **VSCD 1115**
7" Single: Released 15 Aug '88, on Virgin, by Virgin Records. Catalogue no: **VS 1115**
12" Single: Released 15 Aug '88, on Virgin, by Virgin Records. Catalogue no: **VST 1115**

SOMEWHERE SOUTH
Tracks: / Somewhere south / Listen on / Darkness and colour (12" only).
Note: This is the second single taken from the Railway Children's album Recurrence.t
7" Single: Released Jun '88, on Virgin, by Virgin Records. Catalogue no: **VS 1084**
12" Single: Released Jun '88, on Virgin, by Virgin Records. Catalogue no: **VST 1084**

Rain

BURT REYNOLDS
Tracks: / Burt Reynolds.
12" Single: Released May '88, on Serene, Catalogue no: **RAIN 001**

FIRST OF MAY
Tracks: / First of May.
7" Single: Released Jun '88, on Medium Cool, by Medium Cool Records. Catalogue no: **MC 012**
12" Single: Released Jun '88, on Medium Cool, by Medium Cool Records. Catalogue no: **MC 012T**

ONCE
Tracks: / Once.
7" Single: Released Jun '85, on Jive Alive, by Zomba Records. Catalogue no: **JA 002**

Rain Gods

ARMOUR
Tracks: / Armour / Raining hearts.
12" Single: Released 5 Mar '88, on RCA, by BMG Records (UK). Deleted May '89. Catalogue no: **PT 41758**
7" Single: Released 5 Mar '88, on RCA, by BMG Records (UK). Deleted May '89. Catalogue no: **PB 41757**

TEARS IN THE RAIN
Tracks: / Tears in the rain / Stars go out, The / Tidal wave (on 12" only) / In my town (on 12" only).
7" Single: Released May '88, on RCA, by BMG Records (UK). Deleted May '89. Catalogue no: **PB 42015**
12" Single: Released May '88, on RCA, by BMG Records (UK). Deleted May '89. Catalogue no: **PT 42016**

Rain Parade

YOU ARE MY FRIEND
Tracks: / You are my friend.
7" Single: Released Feb '85, on Zippo, by Demon Records. Catalogue no: **ZIPPO 451**

Rain People

LITTLE BIT OF TIME
Tracks: / Little bit of time / Hiding out / I'm changing.
CD 5": Released 15 May '89, on Epic, by CBS Records. Deleted Oct '89. Catalogue no: **654 823 2**
7" Single: Released 15 May '89, on Epic, by CBS Records. Deleted Oct '89. Catalogue no: **654 823 0**
12" Single: Released 15 May '89, on Epic, by CBS Records. Deleted Oct '89. Catalogue no: **654 823 6**

Rain & Tears

I HAD A FRIEND
Tracks: / I had a friend / Music has a way.
7" Single: Released Oct '86, on MCA, by MCA Records. Catalogue no: **KNOC 1**
12" Single: Released Oct '86, on MCA, by MCA Records. Catalogue no: **KNOCT 1**

Rainbirds

Biographical details: Over 400,000 copies of the debut Rainbirds albums have been sold in Germany - and this band are truly the European phenomenon of 1988. "Rainbirds" showcases both the crystal clear vocals of band leader Katharina Frank, as well as the simple, uncluttered, semi-acoustic sound of her band. Compared in the press to Adele Bertei, Suzanne Vega and Tracy Chapman, media interest is already building. A startling performance at this year's Montreux Pop Festival has gained great reactions. WIth live shows in the U.K. later this summer, The Rainbirds are well set to take the U.K. by storm. (Phonogram Records, July 1988)..

BLUEPRINT
Tracks: / Blueprint.
Note: Fronted by vocalist/guitarist Katharina Franck.
CD 5": Released 23 May '88, on Mercury, by Phonogram Ltd. Deleted Oct '88. Catalogue no: **MERCD 264**
7" Single: Released 23 May '88, on Mercury, by Phonogram Ltd. Deleted Oct '88. Catalogue no: **MER 264**
12" Single: Released 23 May '88, on Mercury, by Phonogram Ltd. Deleted Oct '88. Catalogue no: **MERX 264**

BOYS ON THE BEACH
Tracks: / Boys on the beach / Just a simple matter / Compartments (Only on 12").
Note: "Rainbirds are the most successful German band of 1988 and stand a greater chance of belonging to tomorrow than any previous German band. Taking a commercial sense in order of Eurythmics or Pretenders with Throwing Muses or Sugarcubes, they could soar into unanimous rhythmic acceptance. Possibly what we have here is big news. Certainly what we have is one of those voices, which cold find a national heart." (Melody Maker, June 1988).
CD 5": Released 22 Aug '88, on Mercury, by Phonogram Ltd. Catalogue no: **MERCD 274**
7" Single: Released 22 Aug '88, on Mercury, by Phonogram Ltd. Catalogue no: **MER 274**
12" Single: Released 22 Aug '88, on Mercury, by Phonogram Ltd. Catalogue no: **MERX 274**

SEA OF TIME
Tracks: / Sea of time (parts I, II & III) / Messy (12" & CD single only) / Responsible (12" & CD single only).
CD 5": Released 15 May '89, on Phonogram, by Phonogram Ltd. Deleted Oct '89. Catalogue no: **MERCD 287**
7" Single: Released 15 May '89, on Phonogram, by Phonogram Ltd. Deleted Oct '89. Catalogue no: **MER 287**
12" Single: Released 15 May '89, on Phonogram, by Phonogram Ltd. Deleted Oct '89. Catalogue no: **MERX 287**

Rainbow

ALL NIGHT LONG
Tracks: / All night long / Weiss heim.
7" Single: Released Feb '80, on Polydor, by Polydor Ltd. Deleted '83. Catalogue no: **POSP 104**

CAN'T HAPPEN HERE
Tracks: / Can't happen here / Jealous lover.
7" Single: Released Jun '81, on Polydor, by Polydor Ltd. Deleted '84. Catalogue no: **POSP 251**

CAN'T LET YOU GO
Tracks: / Can't let you go.
7" Single: Released Nov '83, on Polydor, by Polydor Ltd. Deleted '86. Catalogue no: **POSP 654**

I SURRENDER
Tracks: / I surrender / Veilleicht das nachester zeit.
7" Single: Released Jan '81, on Polydor, by Polydor Ltd. Deleted '84. Catalogue no: **POSP 221**

KILL THE KING
Tracks: / Kill the king / Man on the silver mountain / Mistreated.
7" Single: Released Jul '81, on Polydor, by Polydor Ltd. Deleted '84. Catalogue no: **POSP 274**
7" Single: Released Sep '77, on Polydor, by Polydor Ltd. Deleted '80. Catalogue no: **2066 845**

L.A. CONNECTION
Tracks: / L.A. connection / Lady of the lake.
7" Single: Released Jul '81, on Polydor, by Polydor Ltd. Deleted '85. Catalogue no: **POSP 274**
7" Single: Released Sep '78, on Polydor, by Polydor Ltd. Deleted '81. Catalogue no: **2066 968**

LONG LIVE ROCK 'N' ROLL (SINGLE)
Tracks: / Long live rock 'n' roll.
7" Single: Released Jul '81, on Polydor, by Polydor Ltd. Deleted '85. Catalogue no: **POSP 276**
7" Single: Released Apr '78, on Polydor, by Polydor Ltd. Deleted '81. Catalogue no: **2066 913**

SINCE YOU'VE BEEN GONE
Tracks: / Since you've been gone / Bad girl.
7" Single: Released Sep '79, on Polydor, by Polydor Ltd. Deleted '82. Catalogue no: **POSP 70**

SINCE YOU'VE BEEN GONE (OLD GOLD)
Tracks: / Since you've been gone / All night long.
7" Single: Released Feb '88, on Old Gold, by Old Gold Records. Catalogue no: **OG 9772**

STONE COLD
Tracks: / Stone cold / Rock fever.
7" Single: Released Apr '82, on Polydor, by Polydor Ltd. Deleted '85. Catalogue no: **POSP 421**

STREET OF DREAMS
Tracks: / Street of dreams.
7" Single: Released Aug '83, on Polydor, by Polydor Ltd. Deleted '86. Catalogue no: **POSP 631**

Rainbow, Chris

BODY MUSIC (SINGLE)
Tracks: / Body music / Girl in collision.
7" Single: Released Sep '81, on EMI, by EMI Records. Deleted '84. Catalogue no: **EMI 5215**

Rainbow Cottage

I'M ALIVE
Tracks: / I'm alive / Fantasy / Let 'em in.
7" Single: Released Aug '81, on Castle, by Castle Communications Records. Catalogue no: **CAS 011**

SEAGULL
Tracks: / Seagull.
7" Single: Released Mar '76, on Penny Farthing, by Penny Farthing Records. Deleted '79. Catalogue no: **PEN 906**

Rainbow Kids

CHILDREN POWER
Tracks: / Children power / Happy Christmas (War is over).
7" Single: Released Dec '87, on Rainbow World, Deleted Jan '88. Catalogue no: **RWR 1**

Rainbow People

LIVING IN A DREAM WORLD
Tracks: / Living in a dreamworld / Nobody knows what's going on.
Note: Coupled with 'Nobody knows what's going on in my mind but me' by Tammy St.John
7" Single: Released Nov '79, on Casino Classics, by RK Records. Catalogue no: **CC 14**

Rainbow, Tucker

JAH IS COMING
Tracks: / Jah is coming / Hard to be.
12" Single: Released Jun '86, on Melody, Catalogue no: **MEL 007**

Rainbow Valley

DO IT FOR THE CHILDREN
Tracks: / Do it for the children (Inst.) / Do it for the children.
7" Single: Released Sep '82, on Half Moon, by Rondelet Music & Records. Catalogue no: **ROUND 2005**
12" Single: Released Sep '82, on Half Moon, by Rondelet Music & Records. Catalogue no: **12 ROUND 2005**

Raincoats

ANIMAL RHAPSODY
Tracks: / Animal rhapsody / No one's little honey / Honey-mad woman.
12" Single: Released Nov '83, on Rough

Trade, by Rough Trade Records. Catalogue no: **RTT 153**

FAIRYTALE IN THE SUPERMARKET
Tracks: / Fairytale in the supermarket.
7" Single: Released Jan '79, on Rough Trade, by Rough Trade Records. Catalogue no: **RT 013**

RUNNING AWAY
Tracks: / Running away / No one's little girl.
7" Single: Released Jul '82, on Rough Trade, by Rough Trade Records. Catalogue no: **RT 093**

Rainmakers

DOWN STREAM
Tracks: / Down stream / Carpenter's son / Drinking on the job (On 12" only).
7" Single: Released May '87, on Mercury, by Phonogram Ltd. Deleted Dec '87. Catalogue no: **MER 246**
12" Single: Released May '87, on Mercury, by Phonogram Ltd. Deleted Dec '87. Catalogue no: **MERX 246**

LET MY PEOPLE GO
Tracks: / Nobody knew / Kissing time (Only on 12" single.).
12" Single: Released Jan '87, on Mercury, by Phonogram Ltd. Deleted Dec '87. Catalogue no: **MERX 238**
7" Single: Released Jan '87, on Mercury, by Phonogram Ltd. Catalogue no: **MER 238**

SMALL CIRCLES
Tracks: / Small circles / Lakeview man, The / Rockabilly standard / Small circles (acoustic version) (track on CD single.).
CD 5": Released Feb '88, on Mercury, by Phonogram Ltd. Deleted Oct '88. Catalogue no: **MERCD 259**
7" Single: Released Feb '88, on Mercury, by Phonogram Ltd. Deleted Oct '88. Catalogue no: **MER 259**
12" Single: Released Feb '88, on Mercury, by Phonogram Ltd. Deleted Oct '88. Catalogue no: **MERX 259**

SNAKEDANCE
Tracks: / Snakedance / Tornado of love / Kisses from St. Louis (not on 7" single) / Amazing grace (not on 7" single) / Let my people go go (not on 7" single).
Note: 7" EP has 4 tracks including previously unreleased "Kisses from St Louis" and the live "Let my people go-go"- only previously available on the US bootleg album.
7" EP: Released 27 Jun '88, on Mercury, by Phonogram Ltd. Deleted Feb '89. Catalogue no: **MEREP 265**
CD 5": Released 27 Jun '88, on Mercury, by Phonogram Ltd. Deleted Oct '88. Catalogue no: **MERCD 265**
12" Single: Released 27 Jun '88, on Mercury, by Phonogram Ltd. Deleted Oct '88. Catalogue no: **MERX 165**

Rainpools

NEW DAY, A
Tracks: / New day, A.
7" Single: Released Sep '87, on Rainpool, Catalogue no: **JPL 1001**

Rainwater, Marvin

Biographical details: Marvin Rainwater was born Marvin Percy in 1925 in Wichita, Kansas. the country singer/songwriter took his mother's name when he turned to music and paraded as a full blooded Cherokee in regalia. He won a talent show with own song, *Gonna Find Me A Bluebird*, subsequently a big hit in 1957. He toured the UK in 1971 for the first time in 12 years and found new fans, made a LP with London-based Country Fever (Albert Lee on guitar). (Donald Clarke)..

HENRYETTA...
Tracks: / Henryetta... / City of angels.
7" Single: Released Apr '81, on Sonet, by Sonet Records. Catalogue no: **SON 2225**

I DIG YOU BABY
Tracks: / I dig you baby / Dance me daddy.
7" Single: Released Jun '58, on MGM, by Polydor Ltd. Deleted '61. Catalogue no: **MGM 980**
7" Single: Released '80, on MGM, by Polydor Ltd. Catalogue no: **LR 4268**

WHOLE LOTTA MARVIN
Tracks: / Mr. Blues / Hot and cold / Tennesse hound dog yodel / I dig you baby.
Note: Limited quantities.
7" Single: Released Jul '88, on Southern, by Southern Record Dist.. Catalogue no: **SEP 1001**

WHOLE LOTTA WOMAN
Tracks: / Whole lotta woman.
7" Single: Released Mar '58, on MGM, by Polydor Ltd. Deleted '61. Catalogue no: **MGM 974**

WHOLE LOTTA WOMAN (OLD GOLD)
Tracks: / Whole lotta woman.
7" Single: Released Jul '84, on Old Gold, by Old Gold Records. Catalogue no: **OG 9446**

Rainy Day

PAINTING PICTURES
Tracks: / Painting pictures / Welche farbe hat de sonnenschein?.
7" Single: Released Mar '84, on EMI, by EMI Records. Catalogue no: **EMI 5472**

Raising Cain

SILENCE
Tracks: / Silence / Rawhid Mix.
12" Single: Released Aug '87, on Arcane, Catalogue no: **CANE 001T**

Raitt, Bonnie

Biographical details: Bonnie Raitt was born in 1949 in Burbank, California; she is a blues/rock singer, songwriter and guitarist with a country rock feel. (Her father John Raitt starred in the first production of Rodgers & Hammerstein's *Carousel* in 1945; also starred in *Pyjama Game* in 1954, film '57). She olayed the blues in clubs, touring in accoustic duo with Freebo on tuba/fretless bass, who later played on some of the albums; joined ex-Little Feat Paul Barrere in Bluesbusters. She went solo, shared bills with real bluespeople Sippie Wallace, Fred McDowell, Son House (all abiding influences); her mature voice belied her years and her fine guitar technique (especially on slide) also marked her out. Every one of her albums has fine things on it and they went as high as number 25 in the USA charts; but she changed lineups and producers constantly. She wrote songs herself, chose others by Allen Toussaint, James Taylor, Wallace, Isaac Hayes & David Porter, J.D. Souther, Eric Kaz etc; she helped blues friends by hiring them as support, was active in MUSE anti-nuclear campaign with Jackson Browne. After a hiatus she came back with *Nine Lives* in 1986 and had completely lost her touch: its overproduced, unswinging music and undistinguished songs were typical of pop in the 1980s and totally unlike her best work. (Donald Clarke)..

BABY MINE
Tracks: / Baby mine.
7" Single: Released Oct '88, on A&M, by A&M Records. Catalogue no: **AM 485**

ME AND THE BOYS
Tracks: / Me and the boys / Keep this heart.
7" Single: Released Apr '82, on Warner Bros., by WEA Records. Catalogue no: **K 17943**

NICK OF TIME (SINGLE)
Tracks: / Nick of time / Road's my middle name, The / I ain't gonna let you break my heart again (Lasley/Lasley) (12" only.).
CD 5": Released Apr '89, on Capitol, by EMI Records. Deleted Oct '89. Catalogue no: **CDCL 530**
7" Single: Released Apr '89, on Capitol, by EMI Records. Deleted Oct '89. Catalogue no: **CL 530**
7" Single: Released Apr '89, on Capitol, by EMI Records. Deleted Oct '89. Catalogue no: **203 345 7**
12" Single: Released Apr '89, on Capitol, by EMI Records. Deleted Oct '89. Catalogue no: **203 345 6**
12" Single: Released Apr '89, on Capitol, by EMI Records. Deleted Oct '89. Catalogue no: **12CL 530**
CD 5": Released Apr '89, on Capitol, by EMI Records. Deleted Oct '89. Catalogue no: **203 345 2**

Raj Quartet

WHOOPS, WHAT A PALAVER
Tracks: / Whoops, what a palaver.
Note: Introducing Lord Clifton.
12" Single: Released Mar '87, on El, by Cherry Red Records. Catalogue no: **GPO 26 T**

Rajan

TIME
Tracks: / Time / Time (instrumental).
12" Single: Released Jan '85, on St.James, Deleted '86. Catalogue no: **SAINT 1**

Ralls, Tony

HOLDIN' ON
Tracks: / Holdin' on / Burnin' alive.
7" Single: Released Feb '80, on Calibre, Deleted '83. Catalogue no: **CAB 150**

Ralph, Sheryl Lee

IN THE EVENING
Tracks: / In the evening / Ready or not.
7" Single: Released Jan '85, on Arista, by BMG Records (UK). Catalogue no: **ARIST 595**
12" Single: Released Jan '85, on Arista, by BMG Records (UK). Catalogue no: **ARIST 12595**

Ram Jam

BLACK BETTY
Tracks: / Black Betty.
7" Single: Released Sep '77, on Epic, by CBS Records. Deleted '80. Catalogue no: **EPC 5492**
7" Single: Released Jul '84, on CBS, by CBS Records. Catalogue no: **A 4585**

BLACK BETTY (OLD GOLD)
Tracks: / Black Betty / Keep your hands on the wheel.
7" Single: Released Jul '82, on Old Gold, by Old Gold Records. Catalogue no: **OG 9193**

FREETOWN
Tracks: / Freetown / Do what.
7" Single: Released Sep '81, on White Line, by White Line Records. Deleted '87. Catalogue no: **JAM 001**

Ram Ram Kino

TANTRIC ADVANTAGE 1.5
Tracks: / Tantric advantage 1.5.
12" Single: Released Dec '85, on Temple Records, by Temple Records (2). Catalogue no: **TOPY**

Ram & Tan

MARKET PLACE
Tracks: / Market place / Market place (Dub inst.).
12" Single: Released Aug '84, on Hyphen, Catalogue no: **HY 002**

MY NIGHTS
Tracks: / My nights.
12" Single: Released Sep '89, on Hyphen, Catalogue no: **HLP 11**

Ramblers

BECAUSE IT'S SPRING
Tracks: / Because it's spring / Mountain shall sing forever.
7" Single: Released Mar '81, on EMI, by EMI Records. Deleted Mar '84. Catalogue no: **EMI 5150**

PLAIN AND SIMPLE LIFE
Tracks: / Plain and simple life.
7" Single: Released Sep '81, on Smile, Catalogue no: **SRO 34**

SONG FOR MOTHER
Tracks: / Song for mother / Let there be peace.
7" Single: Released Oct '83, on EMI, by EMI Records. Catalogue no: **EMI 5422**

SPARROW, THE
Tracks: / Sparrow, The / Lollipops and skipping rope.
7" Single: Released Sep '79, on Decca, by Decca Records. Deleted '88. Catalogue no: **F 13860**

WRIGGLY WRIGGLY WORMS
Tracks: / Wriggly wriggly worms / Goodbye.
7" Single: Released May '80, on Decca, by Decca Records. Deleted May '83. Catalogue no: **F 13887**

Ramblin Rod

I CAN DO THE MOLLY DANCE
Tracks: / I can do the Molly dance / Beggar boys.
7" Single: Released Mar '84, on New Leaf, by New Leaf Records. Catalogue no: **SVC 2692**

Rambow, Philip

STAR(IN HER OWN RIGHT)
Tracks: / Star(in her own right) / Night out.
7" Single: Released Jun '81, on Parlophone, by EMI Records. Deleted Jun '84. Catalogue no: **R 6048**

Ramming Speed

WHEN YOU WALK IN THE ROOM
Tracks: / When you walk in the room.
12" Single: Released Apr '84, on Proto, by Proto Records. Catalogue no: **ENAT 115**

Ramones

Biographical details: The Ramones, NYC punk band formed in 1974 with Joey (Jeffry Hyman) on vocals, Johnny (John Cummings) on guitar, bassist Dee Dee (Douglas Colvin), drummer Tommy (Tom Erdelyi). Their blitzkreig brand of nonstop two-minute riffing influenced punk in the UK, especially after a headline gig at London's Roundhouse in 1976. Critics liked their cartoon vision of rock 'n' roll; Tommy quit in 1977, replaced by Marky (Mark Bell); they appeared in trashy exploitation film *Rock 'N' Roll High School* '79, ideally suiting their image. Just as their gimmick was starting to wear thin, Phil Spector produced *End Of The Century* in 1980, their best-sounding LP, with affectionate *Do You Remember Rock 'N' Roll Radio?* and cover of the Ronette' *Baby I Love You*. They retain a devoted cult following: time will tell whether they represented everything that went wrong in '70s music or were a crucial element in saving it. (Donald Clarke)..

BABY I LOVE YOU
Tracks: / Baby I love you / Don't come close.
Cassingle: Released Apr '81, on WEA, by WEA Records. Deleted Apr '86. Catalogue no: **SPC 6**
7" Single: Released Jan '80, on Sire, by Sire Records. Deleted '83. Catalogue no: **SIR 4031**

BONZO GOES TO BITBURG
Tracks: / Bonzo goes to Bitburg / Daytime dilemma / Go home Ann (on 12" only.).
7" Single: Released Jun '85, on Beggars Banquet, by Beggars Banquet Records. Deleted Jun '87. Catalogue no: **BEG 140**
12" Single: Released Jun '85, on Beggars Banquet, by Beggars Banquet Records. Catalogue no: **BEG 140T**

CHASING THE NIGHT
Tracks: / Chasing the night / Howlin' at the moon / Smash you / Street fighting.
12" Single: Released Mar '85, on Beggars Banquet, by Beggars Banquet Records. Deleted Jun '88. Catalogue no: **BEG 128TP**

CRUMMY STUFF
Tracks: / Crummy stuff / She belongs to me / I don't want to live t:'s life (Track on 12" only).
12" Single: Released Jul '86, on Beggars Banquet, by Beggars Banquet Records. Catalogue no: **BEG 167T**

DO YOU REMEMBER ROCK'N'ROLL RADIO
Tracks: / Do you remember rock 'n' roll radio? / I want you around.
7" Single: Released Apr '80, on Sire, by Sire Records. Deleted '83. Catalogue no: **SIR 4037**

DON'T COME CLOSE
Tracks: / Don't come close.
7" Single: Released Sep '78, on Sire, by Sire Records. Deleted '81. Catalogue no: **SRE 1031**

HOWLING AT THE MOON (SHA LA LA)
Tracks: / Howlin' at the moon (sha la la) / Chasing the night / Smash you / Street fighting.
7" Set: Released Mar '85, on Beggars Banquet, by Beggars Banquet Records. Deleted Jun '87. Catalogue no: **BEG 128D**
7" Single: Released Jan '85, on Beggars Banquet, by Beggars Banquet Records. Catalogue no: **BEG 128**
12" Single: Released Jan '85, on Beggars Banquet, by Beggars Banquet Records. Catalogue no: **BEG 128T**

I JUST WANT TO HAVE SOMETHING TO DO
Tracks: / I just want to have something to do / Here today gone tomorrow / I wanna be your boyfriend.
7" Single: Released Dec '80, on WEA, by WEA Records. Deleted Dec '85. Catalogue no: **SREP 1**

I WANNA BE SEDATED
Tracks: / I wanna be sedated / Return of Jackie and Judy.
7" Single: Released Jan '81, on RSO, by Polydor Ltd. Deleted Jan '84. Catalogue no: **RSO 70**

I WANNA LIVE
Tracks: / I wanna live / Merry Christmas (I don't want to fight tonight).
Note: Double A sided single
7" Single: Released Nov '87, on Beggars Banquet, by Beggars Banquet Records. Catalogue no: **BEG 201**
12" Single: Released Nov '87, on Beggars Banquet, by Beggars Banquet Records. Catalogue no: **BEG 201 T**

PET CEMETARY
Tracks: / Pet cemetary / All screwed up.
7" Single: Released Sep '89, on Chrysalis, by Chrysalis Records. Catalogue no: **CHS 3423**
12" Single: Released Sep '89, on Chrysalis, by Chrysalis Records. Catalogue no: **CHS 123423**

REAL COOL TIME
Tracks: / Real cool time / Life goes on / Indian giver.
Note: * track on 12" version only.
7" Single: Released Sep '87, on Beggars Banquet, by Beggars Banquet Records. Deleted Jun '88. Catalogue no: **BEG 198**
12" Single: Released Sep '87, on Beggars Banquet, by Beggars Banquet Records. Catalogue no: **BEG 198T**

ROCK'N'ROLL HIGH SCHOOL
Tracks: / Rock 'n' roll high school.
7" Single: Released Sep '79, on Sire, by Sire Records. Deleted '82. Catalogue no: **SIR 4021**

SHEENA IS A PUNK ROCKER
Tracks: / Sheena is a punk rocker.
7" Single: Released May '77, on Sire, by Sire Records. Deleted '80. Catalogue no: **RAM 001**

SHE'S A SENSATION
Tracks: / She's a sensation / All's quiet on the Eastern Front.
7" Single: Released Oct '81, on Sire, by Sire

RANCH - PUT YOUR LOVE IN ME (Released on Sedition)

Records. Deleted Oct '84. Catalogue no: **SIR 4052**

SOMETHING TO BELIEVE IN
Tracks: / Something to believe in / Somebody put something in my drink / Can't say anything nice.
7" Single: Released May '86, on Beggars Banquet, by Beggars Banquet Records. Deleted Jun '88. Catalogue no: **BEG 157**
12" Single: Released May '86, on Beggars Banquet, by Beggars Banquet Records. Catalogue no: **BEG 157T**

SWALLOW MY PRIDE
Tracks: / Swallow my pride.
7" Single: Released Aug '77, on Sire, by Sire Records. Deleted '80. Catalogue no: **6078 607**

TIME HAS COME TODAY
Tracks: / Time has come today / Psycho therapy / Baby I love you (on 12" only) / Don't come close (on 12" only).
7" Single: Released Jun '83, on Sire (USA), Catalogue no: **W 9606**
12" Single: Released Jun '83, on Sire (USA), Catalogue no: **W 9606T**

WE WANT THE AIRWAVES
Tracks: / We want the airwaves / You sound like your sick.
7" Single: Released Jul '81, on Sire, by Sire Records. Deleted '85. Catalogue no: **SIR 4051**

Ramrods

GHOST RIDERS IN THE SKY
Tracks: / Ghost riders in the sky.
7" Single: Released Feb '61, on London-American, Deleted '64. Catalogue no: **HLU 9282**
7" Single: Released '80, on USA, by Charly Records. Catalogue no: **LR 3363**

Ranch

PUT YOUR LOVE IN ME (see panel above)
Tracks: / Put your love in me / Specialist, The.
7" Single: Released Mar '85, on Sedition, by Sedition Records. Catalogue no: **EDIT 3300**
12" Single: Released Mar '85, on Sedition, by Sedition Records. Catalogue no: **EDITL 3300**

Ranch, Martini

HOW CAN THE LABOURING MAN FIND TIME FOR SELF-CULTURE
Tracks: / How can the labouring man find time for self-culture / Back at the ranch / Fallen, idols (Track on 12" only).
7" Single: Released Jul '86, on Warner Bros., by WEA Records. Deleted Jun '87. Catalogue no: **W 8651**
12" Single: Released Jul '86, on Warner Bros., by WEA Records. Deleted Jun '87. Catalogue no: **W 8651T**

REACH
Tracks: / Reach / Richard Cory.
7" Single: Released Jul '88, on WEA, by WEA Records. Catalogue no: **W 7985**
12" Single: Released Jul '88, on WEA, by WEA Records. Catalogue no: **W 7985T**

Rancid Hell Spawn

FESTERING PUS
Tracks: / Festering pus.
7" Single: Released Dec '88, on Wrench, Catalogue no: **STUNCH 001**

Randall, Alan

HOOKED ON FORMBY
Tracks: / Mystic vibes.
7" Single: Released Dec '86, on Superb, by Priority Records. Catalogue no: **FORMB 1**

Randell, Denny

E.T. MEDLEY THEME
Tracks: / E.T. medley theme / Over the moon.
7" Single: Released Nov '82, on Elektra, by Elektra Records (UK). Deleted Nov '85. Catalogue no: **EET 1**
12" Single: Released Nov '82, on Elektra, by Elektra Records (UK). Deleted Nov '85. Catalogue no: **EET 1T**

Randell, Helen

MANY HAPPY HANGOVERS TO YOU
Tracks: / Many happy hangovers to you / God walks these hills with me.
7" Single: Released Dec '88, on August Records, by Scotdisc Records. Catalogue no: **GBH 7S 471**

SWEETEST THING, THE
Tracks: / Sweetest thing.
7" Single: Released Oct '85, on August (USA), by Rounder Records (USA). Catalogue no: **GBH 7S 402**

Randell, Lynne

STRANGER IN MY ARMS
Tracks: / Stranger in my arms.
7" Single: Released Mar '83, on Neil Rushton, Catalogue no: **510147**

Randells

MARTIAN HOP
Tracks: / Martian hop.
7" Single: Released '80, on USA, by Charly Records. Catalogue no: **LR 0017**

Randle, Alan

EEH BAH GUM GIVE IT SOME CLOG
Tracks: / Eeh bah gum give it some clog.
12" Single: Released Jul '85, on Legacy, by Legacy Records. Catalogue no: **LGYT 27**

Randolph, Barbara

I GOT A FEELING
Tracks: / I got a feeling.
7" Single: Released Oct '81, on Motown, by BMG Records (UK). Catalogue no: **TMG 1133**

Random, Eric

DOW CHEMICAL COMPANY
Tracks: / Dow chemical company.
7" Single: Released Jul '81, on New Hormones, Catalogue no: **ORG 11**

FLOOD
Tracks: / Flood.
12" Single: Released Oct '84, on Double Vision, by Double Vision Records. Catalogue no: **DVR 7**

THAT'S WHAT I LIKE ABOUT ME
Tracks: / That's what I like about me.
12" Single: Released Jul '81, on New Hormones, Catalogue no: **ORG 6**

Random Hold

MARCH
Tracks: / March / Dance feeling.
7" Single: Released Oct '81, on RCA, by BMG Records (UK). Deleted Oct '84. Catalogue no: **RCA 132**

WALKING ON THE EDGE
Tracks: / Walking on the edge / Shining smile.
7" Single: Released Jun '81, on RCA, by BMG Records (UK). Deleted Jun '84. Catalogue no: **RCA 92**
7" Single: Released Feb '82, on RCA, by BMG Records (UK). Deleted Feb '87. Catalogue no: **RCA 176**

WHAT HAPPENED
Tracks: / What happened / Cause and effect.
7" Single: Released Feb '80, on Polydor, by Polydor Ltd. Deleted Feb '83. Catalogue no: **POSP 12**

Rank Outsiders

THAT IS THAT
Tracks: / That is that / Crazy things.
7" Single: Released Aug '81, on Good Foot, by Good Foot Records (USA). Deleted Aug '84. Catalogue no: **GFR 004**

Rankin, Amsha

GILBERT
Tracks: / Gilbert.
12" Single: Released Jul '89, on Jetstar, by Jetstar Records. Catalogue no: **ST 10013**

Rankin, Joe

DISCO SKATE (SINGLE)
Tracks: / Disco skate.
12" Single: Released Jul '81, on Copasetic, by Copasetic Records. Catalogue no: **COP DIS 5**

Rankin, Kenny

ON AND ON
Tracks: / On and on.
7" Single: Released Jun '89, on Atlantic (USA), by WEA Records. Catalogue no: **LD 735**

Rankin, Louie

PROUD A WE
Tracks: / Proud a we.
12" Single: Released Jul '88, on Carron, Catalogue no: **BW 001**

Rankine, Alan

LAST BULLET
Tracks: / Last bullet.
7" Single: Released Dec '86, on Les Disques Du Crepuscule(Belgium), by Les Disques Du Crepuscule(Belgium). Catalogue no: **7TWI 762**

SANDMAN
Tracks: / Sandman.
7" Single: Released Oct '87, on Virgin, by Virgin Records. Deleted May '88. Catalogue no: **VS 1003**
7" Single: Released Sep '86, on Himalaya, Catalogue no: **7TWI 598**
12" Single: Released Oct '87, on Virgin, by Virgin Records. Deleted May '88. Catalogue no: **VST 1003**
12" Single: Released Sep '86, on Himalaya, Catalogue no: **TWI 598**

WORLD BEGINS TO LOOK HER AGE
Tracks: / World begins to look her age.
7" Single: Released Aug '87, on Virgin, by Virgin Records. Deleted May '88. Catalogue no: **VS 971**
12" Single: Released Aug '87, on Virgin, by Virgin Records. Deleted May '88. Catalogue no: **VS 971-12**

Ranking Copper

FRIENDS
Tracks: / Friends.
12" Single: Released Jun '89, on Blue Mountain, Catalogue no: **BMD 062**

Ranking, Dicky

PARTY PEOPLE
Tracks: / Party people.
12" Single: Released May '89, on Live & Love, Catalogue no: **LLD 121**

Ranking Dread

FATTIE BOOM BOOM
Tracks: / Fattie boom boom / Dub boom.
7" Single: Released Dec '81, on Greensleeves, by Greensleeves Records. Deleted Dec '84. Catalogue no: **FATTIE 1**

IF NANNY WAS HERE
Tracks: / If nanny was here.
12" Single: Released Jul '82, on Greensleeves, by Greensleeves Records. Deleted '85. Catalogue no: **GRED 91**

MY MAMMY
Tracks: / My mammy / Mammy mammy.
12" Single: Released Oct '82, on Greensleeves, by Greensleeves Records. Deleted Oct '85. Catalogue no: **GRED 96**

Ranking, Luxley

REGGAE FEVER
Tracks: / Reggae Fever / Warm and easy.
12" Single: Released Jul '86, on King Jam, Catalogue no: **KJ 088**

Ranking, Morris

FRIENDS
Tracks: / Friends / Friends (Version).
12" Single: Released Jun '89, on Blue Mountain, Catalogue no: **BMD 062**

Ranking Peter

BEVERLEY BLACK
Tracks: / Beverley black / Walk and talk.
12" Single: Released Nov '82, on Greensleeves, by Greensleeves Records. Deleted Nov '85. Catalogue no: **GRED 98**

JAH STANDING OVER ME
Tracks: / Jah standing over me.
12" Single: Released Sep '82, on Silver Camel, Catalogue no: **SC 016**

Ranking Predigas

MURDERER
Tracks: / Murderer.
12" Single: Released Sep '83, on Tads, Catalogue no: **TRD 4983**

Ranking, Ricky

DIGITAL ROCK
Tracks: / Digital rock / Digital rock (dub version).
12" Single: Released Apr '86, on Conqueror, Catalogue no: **DOND 008**

Ranking Roger

IN LOVE WITH YOU
Tracks: / In love with you.
7" Single: Released Oct '88, on I.R.S, Catalogue no: **IRM 174**
12" Single: Released Oct '88, on I.R.S, Catalogue no: **IRMT 174**

SO EXCITED
Tracks: / So excited.
12" Single: Released Jun '88, on I.R.S, Catalogue no: **IRMT 166**
7" Single: Released Jun '88, on I.R.S, Catalogue no: **IRM 166**

Ranking, Shortie

SCHOOL GIRL
Tracks: / School girl.
7" Single: Released Sep '89, on Roots Connection, Catalogue no: **RCON 003**

Ranking Superstar

HOT ME HOT
Tracks: / Hot me hot.
12" Single: Released Mar '82, on Roots Rockers, Catalogue no: **SS 008**

Ranking Tiny

DANCE STYLE
Tracks: / Dance style.
12" Single: Released Dec '81, on TCD Music, Catalogue no: **TCDD 017**

OLD TIME RELIGION
Tracks: / Old time religion.
12" Single: Released Jan '82, on TCD Music, Catalogue no: **TCDD 015**

Ranking, Tippa

FEEL IT FOR THEM
Tracks: / Feel it for them / One time selector.
12" Single: Released Sep '86, on Virgo, Catalogue no: **VG 013**

Ranking Toyan

PANTS AND BLOUSES
Tracks: / Pants and blouses.
12" Single: Released Jul '82, on Grim Bim, Catalogue no: **GB 001**

TROD ALONG
Tracks: / Trod along.
12" Single: Released Feb '82, on Black Roots, Catalogue no: **BR 034**

Ranking Tranny

VAN MAN
Tracks: / Van man.
7" Single: Released Oct '83, on Top Rank (2), Catalogue no: **DSR 0545**

Ranking Trevor

BLOOD SHED
Tracks: / Blood shed.
12" Single: Released Oct '80, on Skengdon, Catalogue no: **SKD 090**

IRON LADY Maggie May
Tracks: / Iron lady.
12" Single: Released Jun '83, on Trojan, by Trojan Records. Deleted May '88. Catalogue no: **TROT 9072**

Ranks, Andrew

MASSIVE SKANK
Tracks: / Massive skank.
12" Single: Released Dec '83, on Wackies, Catalogue no: **LB 781**

Ranks, Goldie

KILL UP A SOUND
Tracks: / Kill up a sound / Answer me question.
12" Single: Released Nov '85, on Roots Connection, Catalogue no: **CON 002**

Ranks, Junie

CRY SEE ME BOOPS
Tracks: / Cry see me boops / Cry see me boops (Version).
12" Single: Released Aug '86, on Technique, Catalogue no: **WRT 05**

NEW GIRLS
Tracks: / New girls / Jah jah rule.
12" Single: Released Nov '82, on Technique, Deleted Nov '85. Catalogue no: **TC 002**

NO READY FI WOMAN
Tracks: / No ready fi woman.
7" Single: Released May '89, on Kool Vibes, Catalogue no: **UNKNOWN**

Ranks, Nardo

JUMP UP, JUMP UP
Tracks: / Jump up, jump up.
12" Single: Released 30 May '89, on Steely & Cleevie, Catalogue no: **VPRD 435**

Ranks, Oliver

85 SHACK
Tracks: / 85 shack.
12" Single: Released Jul '85, on High Power, Catalogue no: **HPD 004**

Ranks, S.

WHO SHE LOVES
Tracks: / Who she loves.
7" Single: Released Feb '89, on Live & Love, Catalogue no: **11D 103**

Ranks, Scringer

DUN WID KIFF
Tracks: / Dun wid kiff.
12" Single: Released Jul '88, on FM Force, Catalogue no: **FM 005**

Ranks, Shaba

ARE YOU SURE? (IMPORT)
Tracks: / Are you sure.
12" Single: Released Oct '89, on Digital B., Catalogue no: **VPRD 473**

BEST BABY FATHER
Tracks: / Best baby father.
12" Single: Released Feb '89, on Digital B., Catalogue no: **VPRD 405**

CAN'T DO THE WORK
Tracks: / Can't do the work.
12" Single: Released Nov '88, on Steely & Cleevie, Catalogue no: **VPRD 372**

GET UP STAND UP
Tracks: / Get up stand up.
12" Single: Released Nov '88, on Jammy's, Catalogue no: **VPRD 371**

MAAMA MAN
Tracks: / Maama man.
12" Single: Released Oct '88, on Jammy's, Catalogue no: **VPRD 339**

MUSIC LOVER
Tracks: / Music lover.
12" Single: Released Aug '88, on Live & Love, Catalogue no: **LLD 83**
7" Single: Released 6 Aug '88, on Live & Love, Catalogue no: **LLP 83**

NO BOGARISM
Tracks: / No bogarism.
7" Single: Released May '89, on Music Master, Catalogue no: **UNKNOWN**

NO BOTHER DIS (SOUNDBOY)
Tracks: / No bother dis (soundboy).
12" Single: Released Nov '88, on Greensleeves, by Greensleeves Records. Catalogue no: **GRED 234**

PUNANNY BAD
Tracks: / Punanny bad.
12" Single: Released 8 Aug '88, on Witty, Catalogue no: **MMD 138**

WHAT CAN YOU DO?
Tracks: / What can you do?.
12" Single: Released Sep '89, on Digital B., Catalogue no: **VPRD 469**

WICKED IN BED
Tracks: / Wicked in bed.
12" Single: Released Oct '89, on Digital B., Catalogue no: **DBT 1**

Ranks, Sluggy

TAKE THE SLUG
Tracks: / Take the slug.
12" Single: Released May '89, on Lemon & Lime, Catalogue no: **LR 001**

Raped

PRETTY PAEDOPHILES (EP)
Tracks: / Pretty paedophiles.
7" Single: Released Sep '82, on Parole, by Parole Records. Deleted '87. Catalogue no: **KNIT 1**

Rapeman

BUDD
Tracks: / Budd.
7" Single: Released Oct '88, on Blast First, by Blast First Records. Catalogue no: **BFFP 27**

Raphael, Lori

ALWAYS
Tracks: / Always.
12" Single: Released Aug '87, on Roddy's Music, Catalogue no: **RM 0010**

Rapid Dance

FRAGMENTS OF YOUTH
Tracks: / Fragments of youth.
7" Single: Released Jul '82, on Resolute, Catalogue no: **RO 1**

Rapids

RAID, THE
Tracks: / Raid, The / Silver bullet / High noon / Eighties girl.
12" Single: Released Dec '85, on Nervous, by Nervous Records. Catalogue no: **12 NEP 003**

Rapiers

CLOSING THEME, THE
Tracks: / Closing, The / Still I cry.
7" Single: Released Feb '86, on Off-Beat (1), Catalogue no: **NS 112**

Rapologists

KIDS RAP
Tracks: / Kids rap / Party rap street mix.
7" Single: Released Jun '84, on Billy Boy, by Blue Sun Records (USA). Deleted Jun '88. Catalogue no: **7WHIZ 1**
12" Single: Released Jun '84, on Billy Boy, by Blue Sun Records (USA). Deleted Jun '88. Catalogue no: **WHIZ 1**

Rappa Robert

HALF KEY DRIVE
Tracks: / Half key drive.
12" Single: Released Jul '89, on Greensleeves, by Greensleeves Records. Catalogue no: **GRED 248**

Rappin' Reverend

I AIN'T INTO THAT
Tracks: / I ain't into that / Original rap.
7" Single: Released 30 May '87, on Cool Tempo, by Chrysalis Records. Catalogue no: **COOL 145**
12" Single: Released 30 May '87, on Cool Tempo, by Chrysalis Records. Catalogue no: **COOLX 145**

Rapski

CONNECTION
Tracks: / Connection.
12" Single: Released Jul '88, on Positive Beat, by Positive Beat Records. Catalogue no: **PBEP 1**

Rare Bird

SYMPATHY (OLD GOLD)
Tracks: / Sympathy.
7" Single: Released Jul '82, on Old Gold, by Old Gold Records. Deleted Jul '88. Catalogue no: **OG 9040**

SYMPATHY (SINGLE)
Tracks: / Sympathy.
7" Single: Released Feb '70, on Charisma, by Virgin Records. Deleted '73. Catalogue no: **CB 120**

Rare Moods

DANCIN' THRO THE NIGHT
Tracks: / Dancin' thro the night / Dancin' thro the night (dub).
7" Single: Released Mar '86, on Creole, by Creole Records. Catalogue no: **CR 89**
12" Single: Released Mar '86, on Creole, by Creole Records. Catalogue no: **CRT 89**

I'VE GOT LOVE
Tracks: / I've got love.
7" Single: Released Sep '86, on AGR, Deleted '87. Catalogue no: **AGR 5**
12" Single: Released Sep '86, on AGR, Deleted '87. Catalogue no: **12 AGR 5**

Rarebell, Herman

ROCK YOUR ALL
Tracks: / Rock your all / Pancake.
7" Single: Released Jan '82, on Harvest (1), by EMI Records. Deleted Jan '85. Catalogue no: **HAR 5218**

Rasheda

PSALM 61
Tracks: / Psalm 61 / Psalm 61 (version).
12" Single: Released Jul '87, on Shaka, Catalogue no: **SHAKA 862**

Raspberries

OVERNIGHT SENSATION (SINGLE)
Tracks: / Overnight sensation.
7" Single: Released Feb '89, on Zap, by Blaylock Management Ltd.. Catalogue no: **DRB 001**

Rasps

PUT YOUR MONEY WHERE YOUR MOUTH IS
Tracks: / Put your money where your mouth is / Ice cream.
7" Single: Released Apr '80, on RCA, by BMG Records (UK). Deleted Apr '83. Catalogue no: **PB 5244**

Rasses

AIN'T NOBODY HERE BUT ME
Tracks: / Ain't nobody here but me / Kingston II.
7" Single: Released Jan '80, on Liberty (USA), by EMI Records. Deleted Jan '83. Catalogue no: **SRK 4031**

Rat Patrol

LAST OFFENSIVE
Tracks: / Last offensive.
7" Single: Released Dec '83, on Si Jenn, by Si Jenn Records. Catalogue no: **MSPI 002**

Ratchet, Dan

BIG RUMPUS
Tracks: / Big rumpus.
12" Single: Released 8 Aug '88, on Y & D, Catalogue no: **YDDO 129**

RAGAMUFFIN GIRL
Tracks: / Ragamuffin girl.
12" Single: Released Jul '89, on Fresh Blood, Catalogue no: **FB 001**

Ratcliff, John

KERRY GIRL
Tracks: / Kerry girl.
Cassingle: Released Jan '84, on OGP, Catalogue no: **OGP 062C**
7" Single: Released Jan '84, on OGP, Catalogue no: **OGP 002**
12" Single: Released Jan '84, on OGP, Catalogue no: **OGP 002T**

Ratt

ROUND AND AROUND
Tracks: / Round and around / You think you're tough / Sweet cheater.
7" Single: Released Sep '84, on Atlantic, by WEA Records. Deleted '87. Catalogue no: **A 9693**

YOU'RE IN LOVE
Tracks: / You're in love / Between the eyes.
7" Single: Released Jan '86, on Atlantic, by WEA Records. Catalogue no: **A 9502**

Rattlers

I DON'T WANT YOU
Tracks: / I don't want you.
7" Single: Released Jul '84, on Lost Moments, Catalogue no: **LOM 3**

Rattles

WITCH, THE
Tracks: / Witch, The / Geraldine.
7" Single: Released Mar '82, on Decca, by Decca Records. Deleted '88. Catalogue no: **F 23058**

WITCH, THE (OLD GOLD)
Tracks: / Witch, The.
7" Single: Released Sep '85, on Old Gold, by Old Gold Records. Catalogue no: **OG 9533**

Rattlesnake Annie

Biographical details: Rattlesnake Annie was born Annie McGowan in 1941 in Paris, Tennessee; she is a country singer and songwriter who has long been highly regarded by stars like Merle Haggard and Willie Nelson; David Allen Coe recorded her *Texas lullably*. She has released an album on Supraphon in Czechoslavakia, as well as two on ther own Rattlesnake label; the last called *Country livin*, included a duet with Nelson on Long Black Limousine; it has been picked up and issued on CBS as *Rattlesnake Annie* with some different tracks. The album and single *Callin' your bluff* reached the country charts in the USA. About half the songs on her LP's are her own; she is at last receiving long-overdue wider recognition. (Donald Clarke 21.5.88).

LONG BLACK LIMOUSINE
Tracks: / Long black limousine / Goodbye to a river.
7" Single: Released 6 Jun '88, on CBS, by CBS Records. Deleted Jan '89. Catalogue no: **651679 7**

SIXTEEN TONS
Tracks: / Sixteen tons / Somewhere south of Macon.
7" Single: Released Jan '87, on CBS, by CBS Records. Deleted Aug '88. Catalogue no: **651 350 7**

TENNESSEE WALTZ
Tracks: / Tennessee waltz.
7" Single: Released Aug '83, on Mint, by Emerald Records. Deleted '88. Catalogue no: **CHEW 82**

Raunch Hands

STOMP IT
Tracks: / Stomp it.
7" Single: Released Feb '88, on Shadowline, Catalogue no: **E 01**

Rave Two Thousand And

SEDUCE ME
Tracks: / Seduce me.
12" Single: Released 24 Jul '89, on Institute, Catalogue no: **12 INS 005**

Ravell, David

YOU GOT ME NOW
Tracks: / You got me now.
12" Single: Released Sep '89, on Soul Train, Catalogue no: **STD 17**

Raven

BORN TO BE WILD
Tracks: / Born to be wild / Inquisitor.
7" Pic: Released Aug '83, on Neat, by Neat Records. Catalogue no: **NEAT 29P**
7" Single: Released Aug '83, on Neat, by Neat Records. Catalogue no: **NEAT 29**
12" Single: Released Aug '83, on Neat, by Neat Records. Catalogue no: **NEAT 29 12**

BREAK THE CHAIN
Tracks: / Break the chain / Ballad of Marshall Stack.
7" Single: Released May '83, on Neat, by Neat Records. Catalogue no: **NEAT 28**

CRASH BANG WALLOP (EP)
Tracks: / Crash bang wallop / Firepower / Run them down / Rock hard.
12" Single: Released Oct '82, on Neat, by Neat Records. Catalogue no: **NEAT 15 12**

DON'T NEED YOUR MONEY
Tracks: / Don't need your money / Wiped out.
7" Single: Released Aug '80, on Neat, by Neat Records. Catalogue no: **NEAT 06**

GIMME SOME LOVIN'
Tracks: / Gimme some lovin' / One on.
7" Single: Released Feb '86, on Atlantic, by WEA Records. Catalogue no: **A 9453**

HARD RIDE
Tracks: / Hard ride / Crazy world.
7" Single: Released Nov '81, on Neat, by Neat Records. Catalogue no: **NEAT 11**

Raven Maize

FOR EVER TOGETHER
Tracks: / Together forever.
7" Single: Released Jul '89, on Republic, by Code Records. Catalogue no: **LIC 014**
7" Single: Released Jul '89, on Quark (USA), Catalogue no: **QU 017**
12" Single: Released Jul '89, on Republic, by Code Records. Catalogue no: **LICT 014**

Raven, Marsha

CATCH ME (I'M FALLING IN LOVE)
Tracks: / Catch me (I'm falling in love).
7" Single: Released Mar '85, on Passion, by Skratch Records. Catalogue no: **PASH 07**
12" Single: Released Mar '85, on Passion, by Skratch Records. Catalogue no: **PASH 07(12)**

DOCTOR DJ
Tracks: / Doctor DJ.
12" Single: Released Oct '84, on Record Shack, by Record Shack Records. Catalogue no: **SOHO 31**

FALSE ALARM
Tracks: / False alarm.
7" Single: Released Jun '84, on Passion, by Skratch Records. Catalogue no: **PASH 29**
12" Single: Released Jun '84, on Passion, by Skratch Records. Catalogue no: **PASH 29(12)**

I LIKE PLASTIC
Tracks: / I like plastic / Angel 43.
7" Single: Released May '82, on Red Bus, by Red Bus Records. Catalogue no: **RBUS 68**

12" Single: Released May '82, on Red Bus, by Red Bus Records. Catalogue no: **RBUSL 68**

STRANGER IN DISGUISE
Tracks: / Stranger in disguise.
7" Single: Released May '85, on Record Shack, by Record Shack Records. Catalogue no: **SOHO 43**
12" Single: Released May '85, on Record Shack, by Record Shack Records. Catalogue no: **SOHOT 43**

YOU MAKE ME FEEL LIKE LOVING YOU
Tracks: / You make me feel like loving you.
7" Single: Released May '83, on Big Boy, by Big Boy Records. Catalogue no: **BB 1**
12" Single: Released May '83, on Big Boy, by Big Boy Records. Catalogue no: **BB 112**

Ravenna & The

FEEL SO GOOD
Tracks: / Feel so good / 6918 peach.
7" Single: Released Jan '82, on Rondelet Music, by Rondelet Music & Records. Deleted '85. Catalogue no: **ROUND 1007**

MEAN MEAN MAN
Tracks: / Mean little man / Mean little mama.
7" Single: Released Apr '81, on Rondelet Music, by Rondelet Music & Records. Catalogue no: **ROUND 1001**

Ravenscroft

HOLD ON (THIS IS CLIVE'S SONG)
Tracks: / Hold on.
Note: All royalties to 'Search 88' fund.
7" Single: Released Jul '87, on Columbia, by EMI Records. Deleted Apr '88. Catalogue no: **DB 9157**
12" Single: Released Jul '87, on Columbia, by EMI Records. Deleted Apr '88. Catalogue no: **12 DB 9157**

Ravenscroft, Raf

LIFELINE
Tracks: / Lifeline.
7" Single: Released Nov '81, on Nems, by Castle Communications Records. Catalogue no: **NES 303**

MAXINE
Tracks: / Maxine / Two of us.
7" Single: Released Jul '85, on Solid, by Solid Records. Catalogue no: **STOP 007**
12" Single: Released Jul '85, on Solid, by Solid Records. Catalogue no: **STOPT 007**

Ravin

LOVE TIME LOVE
Tracks: / Love time love.
12" Single: Released Mar '89, on Living Room, Catalogue no: **LM 0012**

R.A.W.

R.A.W. GROOVE
Tracks: / R.A.W. theme.
12" Single: Released Sep '89, on Rumour, Catalogue no: **RUMAT 4**

Raw And Alive

BIRDHOUSE
Tracks: / Birdhouse.
7" Single: Released Dec '88, on Vinyl Solution, by Vinyl Solution Records. Catalogue no: **GROO 36**

Raw Deal

LONE WOLF
Tracks: / Lone wolf / Take the sky.
7" Single: Released Nov '81, on Neat, by Neat Records. Catalogue no: **NEAT 12**

Raw Herbs

DON'T BURY ME YET
Tracks: / Don't bury me yet.
7" Single: Released 17 Oct '87, on Medium Cool, by Medium Cool Records. Catalogue no: **MC 006**
12" Single: Released 17 Oct '87, on Medium Cool, by Medium Cool Records. Catalogue no: **MC 006 T**

OLD JOE
Tracks: / Old Joe.
Special: Released Nov '86, on Medium Cool, by Medium Cool Records. Catalogue no: **MC 002**

SECOND TIME, THE
Tracks: / Second time, The / He's blown in.
7" Single: Released 14 May '88, on Rooster (Indie), Catalogue no: **BOC 1**
12" Single: Released 14 May '88, on Rooster (Indie), Catalogue no: **BOC 1 T**

SHE'S A NURSE
Tracks: / She's a nurse.
7" Single: Released 6 Apr '87, on Media Burn, by Media Burn Records. Catalogue no: **MC 003**

Raw Sex Pure Energy

STOP THE WAR
Tracks: / Stop the war / Give sheep a chance.
7" Single: Released Jun '82, on Island, by Island Records. Deleted Jun '85. Catalogue no: **WIP 6797**
12" Single: Released Jun '82, on Island, by Island Records. Deleted Jun '85. Catalogue no: **12WIP 6797**

Raw Silk

DO IT TO THE MUSIC
Tracks: / Do it to the music.
7" Single: Released Sep '82, on KR, Catalogue no: **KR 14**
12" Single: Released Sep '82, on KR, Catalogue no: **KRT 14**

JUST IN TIME
Tracks: / Just in time.
7" Single: Released Sep '83, on West End, Deleted '86. Catalogue no: **WEND 2**
12" Single: Released '83, on West End, Deleted '86. Catalogue no: **WEND 122**

Rawe Deal

HEARTBEAT
Tracks: / Heartbeat.
7" Single: Released Aug '85, on Passion, by Skratch Records. Catalogue no: **PASH 47**
12" Single: Released Aug '85, on Passion, by Skratch Records. Catalogue no: **PASH 47(12)**

Rawe, Jackie

Biographical details: See under Midnight Sunrise &....

I BELIEVE IN DREAMS
Tracks: / I believe in dreams.
7" Single: Released Jul '85, on Fanfare, by Captain Billy's Music. Catalogue no: **FAN 3**
12" Single: Released Jul '85, on Fanfare, by Captain Billy's Music. Catalogue no: **12 FAN 3**

Rawes, Peter

WHY SHOULD I ASK HER TO STAY?
Tracks: / Why should I ask her to stay / Shark, Theme from / Forever.
7" Single: Released Jan '86, on Official, by Official Records. Catalogue no: **OFFA 5**

Raw-Ho

BE ME
Tracks: / Be me / Pay the mother.
7" Single: Released Jan '86, on Roarecords, by Roarecords. Catalogue no: **Z 222**

SUMMER
Tracks: / Summer.
7" Single: Released Jul '84, on Roarecords, by Roarecords. Catalogue no: **Z 1111**

Rawls, Lou

Biographical details: Rawls, Lou was born in Chicago in 1935. He is a singer and an actor with a soulful voice; initially popular in black charts, his commercial delivery soon crossed over and he has been successful in MOR music since the mid '60s. He signed with Capitol in 1962 and had two LPs in the top 10 in 1966; since then he has won two Grammies and has had a total of more than 20 chart album. (Donald Clarke 21.5.88).

ARE YOU WITH ME?
Tracks: / Are you with me / Are you with me (Instrumental).
7" Single: Released Mar '86, on Epic, by CBS Records. Catalogue no: **A 6966**
12" Single: Released Mar '86, on Epic, by CBS Records. Catalogue no: **TA 6966**

SIT DOWN AND TALK TO ME (SINGLE)
Tracks: / Sit down and talk to me / When you get home.
7" Single: Released Feb '80, on Philadelphia Disco, by Soulville Records. Deleted Feb '83. Catalogue no: **PIR 8201**

STOP ME FROM STARTING THIS FEELING
Tracks: / Stop me from starting this feeling / Love all your blues away / See you when I get there (Extra track on 12" version only.) / Natural man (Extra track on 12" version only).
7" Single: Released Jun '86, on Epic, by CBS Records. Catalogue no: **A 7263**
12" Single: Released Jun '86, on Epic, by CBS Records. Catalogue no: **TA 7263**

YOU'LL NEVER FIND ANOTHER LOVE LIKE MINE
Tracks: / You'll never find another love like mine.
7" Single: Released Jul '76, on Philadelphia Int., by EMI Records. Deleted '79. Catalogue no: **PIR 7372**

YOU'LL NEVER FIND ANOTHER LOVE LIKE MINE (OLD GOLD)
7" Single: Released Sep '85, on Old Gold, by Old Gold Records. Catalogue no: **OG 9560**

Raww

DON'T YOU TRY IT
Tracks: / Don't you try it / Don't you try it (Dub version).
12" Single: Released Oct '86, on Debut, by Skratch Records. Catalogue no: **DEBTX 3009**

Ray, Danny

HOW 'BOUT US?
Tracks: / How 'bout us? / Back in my arms.
12" Single: Released Apr '83, on Black Jack, Catalogue no: **12 BJ 016**

IF YOU WANNA BE HAPPY
Tracks: / If you wanna be happy.
7" Single: Released '85, on UNKNOWN, Deleted Jun '89. Catalogue no: **JA 1980**

JAMAICA, I HEAR YOU CALLING
Tracks: / Jamaica, I hear you calling / Gilbert blues / Jamaica I hear you calling (club mix).
12" Single: Released Nov '88, on Black Jack, Catalogue no: **BJ 022**

KINGSTON TOWN
12" Single: Released Jun '88, on Black Jack, Catalogue no: **BJ 020**

PLAYBOY
Tracks: / Playboy (*12BJ 18 also has part 2 & part 3.) / Fire redder than red (Track on BJD 4506 but not on 12BJ 18.).
12" Single: Released Jan '81, on Black Jack, Catalogue no: **BJD 4506**
12" Single: Released Mar '85, on Black Jack, Catalogue no: **12 BJ 018**

SPRING AGAIN
Tracks: / Spring again / Birdman, The (Dub).
12" Single: Released Apr '82, on Black Jack, Catalogue no: **BJ 013**

Ray, David

STRIKES
Tracks: / Strikes.
7" Single: Released Jun '80, on Rollin' Rock, Catalogue no: **45 036**

Ray, Fay

FAMILY AFFAIRS
Tracks: / Family affairs / Didn't have to say that.
7" Single: Released Jan '81, on Surrey Sound, Catalogue no: **HMS 5**

WAITING FOR THE HEATWAVE
Tracks: / Waiting for the heatwave / I wish.
7" Single: Released Apr '82, on WEA, by WEA Records. Catalogue no: **K 79290**

Ray, Goodman & Brown

SPECIAL LADY
Tracks: / Special lady / Deja vu.
7" Single: Released Mar '80, on Mercury, by Phonogram Ltd. Deleted '83. Catalogue no: **6008800**

Ray, Harry

LOVE IS A GAME
Tracks: / Love is a game / Sweet baby.
7" Single: Released Feb '83, on Sugarhill (USA), Deleted '88. Catalogue no: **SH 122**
12" Single: Released Feb '83, on Sugarhill (USA), Catalogue no: **SHL 122**

Ray, James

MEXICO SUNDOWN BLUES
Tracks: / Mexico sundown blues.
12" Single: Released Jul '86, on Merciful Release, by Merciful Release. Catalogue no: **MRAY 52**

TEXAS
Tracks: / Texas.
7" Single: Released 20 Jun '87, on Merciful Release, by Merciful Release. Catalogue no: **MRAY 38**
12" Single: Released 20 Jun '87, on Merciful Release, by Merciful Release. Catalogue no: **MRAY 38T**

Ray, Jamey

PRETTY ONE
Tracks: / Pretty one.
7" Single: Released Feb '85, on Stiff, by Stiff Records. Catalogue no: **BUY 219**
12" Single: Released Feb '85, on Stiff, by Stiff Records. Catalogue no: **BUYIT 219**

Ray, Johnnie

Biographical details: Johnnie Ray was born in Rosebud, Oregon in 1927. The pop singer was partially deaf since childhood; he became a huge star in 1951 *Cry and The little white cloud* with the Four Lads backing, produced by Mitch Miller; number one for 11 weeks, his emotional delivery becoming a staple for stand-up comics and mimics. He hit with good old songs such as *Please Mr Sun, Here I am broken-hearted and Walkin' my baby back home, Somebody stole my girl etc.* He acted in the Irving Berlin musical film *There's no business like show business* in 1954; his delivery of *Alexander's ragtime band* was the best part of long, bizarre production number based on the one song, but his acting was outclassed by the rest of the cast. He had 25 top 30 hits in the USA 1951-7 and has always been popular in the UK. (Donald Clarke 21.5.88).

AIN'T MISBEHAVIN'
Tracks: / Ain't misbehavin'.
7" Single: Released Apr '56, on Philips, by Phonogram Ltd. Deleted '59. Catalogue no: **PB 580**

BUILD YOUR LOVE
Tracks: / Build your love.
7" Single: Released Sep '57, on Philips, by Phonogram Ltd. Deleted '60. Catalogue no: **PB 721**

CRY
Tracks: / Cry / Goodnight sleepyhead.
7" Single: Released Nov '80, on Celebrity, Deleted '83. Catalogue no: **ACS 5**

FAITH CAN MOVE MOUNTAINS
Tracks: / Faith can move mountains.
7" Single: Released Dec '52, on Columbia, by EMI Records. Deleted '55. Catalogue no: **DB 3154**

HERNANDO'S HIDEAWAY
Tracks: / Hernando's hideaway.
7" Single: Released Oct '55, on Philips, by Phonogram Ltd. Deleted '58. Catalogue no: **PB 495**

HEY THERE
Tracks: / Hey there.
7" Single: Released Oct '55, on Philips, by Phonogram Ltd. Deleted '58. Catalogue no: **PB 495**

IF YOU BELIEVE
Tracks: / If you believe.
7" Single: Released Apr '55, on Philips, by Phonogram Ltd. Deleted '58. Catalogue no: **PB 379**

I'LL NEVER FALL IN LOVE AGAIN
Tracks: / I'll never fall in love again.
7" Single: Released Dec '59, on Philips, by Phonogram Ltd. Deleted '62. Catalogue no: **PB 952**

JUST WALKIN' IN THE RAIN
Tracks: / Just walking in the rain.
7" Single: Released Oct '56, on Philips, by Phonogram Ltd. Deleted '59. Catalogue no: **PB 624**

LOOK HOMEWARD ANGEL
Tracks: / Look homeward angel.
7" Single: Released Feb '57, on Philips, by Phonogram Ltd. Deleted '60. Catalogue no: **PB 655**

PATHS OF PARADISE
Tracks: / Paths of paradise.
7" Single: Released May '55, on Philips, by Phonogram Ltd. Deleted '58. Catalogue no: **PB 441**

SOMEBODY STOLE MY GAL
Tracks: / Somebody stole my gal.
7" Single: Released Apr '53, on Philips, by Phonogram Ltd. Deleted '56. Catalogue no: **PB 123**

SONG OF THE DREAMER
Tracks: / Song of the dreamer.
7" Single: Released Oct '55, on Philips, by Phonogram Ltd. Deleted '58. Catalogue no: **PB 516**

SUCH A NIGHT
Tracks: / Such a night.
7" Single: Released Apr '54, on Philips, by Phonogram Ltd. Deleted '57. Catalogue no: **PB 244**

WALKING MY BABY BACK HOME
Tracks: / Walkin' my baby back home.
7" Single: Released Nov '52, on Columbia, by EMI Records. Deleted '55. Catalogue no: **DB 3060**

WHO'S SORRY NOW
Tracks: / Who's sorry now.
7" Single: Released Feb '56, on Philips, by Phonogram Ltd. Deleted '59. Catalogue no: **PB 546**

YES TONIGHT JOSEPHINE
Tracks: / Yes tonight Josephine.
7" Single: Released May '57, on Philips, by Phonogram Ltd. Deleted '60. Catalogue no: **PB 686**

YES TONIGHT JOSEPHINE (OLD GOLD)
Tracks: / Yes tonight Josephine / Just walkin' in the rain.
7" Single: Released Jul '82, on Old Gold, by Old Gold Records. Catalogue no: **OG 9075**

YOU DON'T OWE ME A THING
Tracks: / You don't owe me a thing.
7" Single: Released Jan '57, on Philips, by Phonogram Ltd. Deleted '60. Catalogue no: **PB 655**

Ray, Mercy

SHE'LL BE HOME LATER TONIGHT
Tracks: / She'll be home later tonight / She's

happy.
7" Single: Released Oct '85, on Charisma, by Virgin Records. Deleted May '88. Catalogue no: **CB 416**
12" Single: Released Oct '85, on Charisma, by Virgin Records. Deleted May '88. Catalogue no: **CB 41612**

Ray O'Sunshine

HAPPY PARTY TIME
Tracks: / Happy party time.
7" Single: Released Nov '83, on A.1, by A.1 Records. Deleted '88. Catalogue no: **A1 281**

Ray, Reuben

BET'CHA DON'T REMEMBER
Tracks: / Bet'cha don't remember.
12" Single: Released Oct '88, on Groovea-tron, Catalogue no: **GAT 04**

Rayband

MAKES YOU WANNA DANCE
Tracks: / Makes you wanna dance / Reggae music / D-d-do-it.
7" Single: Released Jun '85, on Buffalo (UK), by M.I.S.Records. Catalogue no: **MSBUF 1**

Raybeats

GUITAR BEAT (SINGLE)
Tracks: / Guitar beat.
7" Single: Released Jun '81, on Don't Fall Off The Mountain, by Don't Fall Off The Mountain Records. Catalogue no: **Z 8**

HOLIDAY INN, SPAIN
Tracks: / Holiday Inn, Spain / Cocktails.
7" Single: Released Aug '81, on Don't Fall Off The Mountain, by Don't Fall Off The Mountain Records. Catalogue no: **Z10**

ROPING WILD BEARS
Tracks: / Roping wild bears / Searching.
12" Single: Released Jan '81, on Don't Fall Off The Mountain, by Don't Fall Off The Mountain Records. Catalogue no: **Y 4**

Raydio

IS THIS A LOVE THING
Tracks: / Is this a love thing.
7" Single: Released Jul '78, on Arista, by BMG Records (UK). Deleted '81. Catalogue no: **ARISTA 193**

JACK AND JILL
Tracks: / Jack and Jill.
Note: See under Parker, Ray Jnr.
7" Single: Released '82, on Arista, by BMG Records (UK). Deleted '87. Catalogue no: **ARIST 161**

JACK AND JILL (OLD GOLD)
Tracks: / You can't change that / Jack and Jill.
7" Single: Released Jun '88, on Old Gold, by Old Gold Records. Catalogue no: **OG 9782**

TWO PLACES AT THE SAME TIME (SINGLE)
Tracks: / Two places at the same time / For those who like to groove.
7" Single: Released Mar '80, on Arista, by BMG Records (UK). Deleted '83. Catalogue no: **ARIST 334**

WOMAN NEEDS LOVE, A
Tracks: / Woman needs love, A.
7" Single: Released '82, on Arista, by BMG Records (UK). Deleted '87. Catalogue no: **ARIST 392**

Raymond & Townsend

THAT'S RIGHT
Tracks: / That's right / I feel great.
12" Single: Released Feb '88, on Cake, by Cake Records. Catalogue no: **12 PIECE 6**

Raymonde

DESTINATION BREAKDOWN
Tracks: / Destination breakdown / Destination breakdown (version).
7" Single: Released Nov '88, on Immaculate, by Immaculate Records. Deleted '89. Catalogue no: **IMMAC 8**
12" Single: Released Nov '88, on Immaculate, by Immaculate Records. Catalogue no: **12IMMAC 8**

RAYMONDE
Tracks: / Raymonde / These boots are made for walking.
7" Single: Released Mar '86, on Desire, by Desire Records. Deleted '89. Catalogue no: **WANT 5**
12" Single: Released Mar '86, on Desire, by Desire Records. Deleted '89. Catalogue no: **WANTX 5**

SOLID STATE SOUL
Tracks: / Solid state soul / Eulogy to Harvey Milk.
7" Single: Released Sep '87, on Blue Guitar, by Blue Guitar Records. Catalogue no: **AZUR 5**
12" Single: Released Sep '87, on Blue Guitar, by Blue Guitar Records. Catalogue no: **AZURX 5**

STOP KICKIN' MY HEART AROUND
Tracks: / Stop kickin' my heart around / Fool of fortune / Sex, love, security.
7" Single: Released 21 Mar '88, on Blue Guitar, by Blue Guitar Records. Catalogue no: **AZUR 7**
12" Single: Released 21 Mar '88, on Blue Guitar, by Blue Guitar Records. Catalogue no: **AZURX 7**

Raymus

SUMMER HOLIDAY
Tracks: / Summer holiday.
12" Single: Released Aug '88, on Living Room, Catalogue no: **LM 008**

Rayvan

SWEET & PETTY
Tracks: / Sweet & petty.
12" Single: Released Aug '88, on Living Room, Catalogue no: **LM 006**

Rayvons

I'D RATHER BOP
Tracks: / I'd rather bop / Next in line.
7" Single: Released Aug '89, on Tribute, Catalogue no: **TRIB 5**
12" Single: Released Aug '89, on Tribute, Catalogue no: **12TRIB 5**

Razberry Holiday Band

HANGOVER SQUARE
Tracks: / Hangover square.
7" Single: Released May '89, on Caleche, Catalogue no: **LIS 1**

Raze

BREAK 4 LOVE
Tracks: / Break 4 love / Break 4 love (version).
CD 5": Released May '88, on Champion, by Champion Records. Catalogue no: **CHAMP CD 67**
7" Single: Released May '88, on Champion, by Champion Records. Catalogue no: **CHAMP 67**
12" Single: Released Aug '89, on Champion, by Champion Records. Catalogue no: **CHAMPX 1267**
12" Single: Released May '88, on Champion, by Champion Records. Catalogue no: **CHAMP 1267**

CAUGHT U CHEATIN'
Tracks: / Caught u cheatin' / Caught u cheatin' (version) / Jack the groove (remix) (Available on 12" only).
7" Single: Released Dec '87, on Champion, by Champion Records. Catalogue no: **CHAMP 58**
12" Single: Released Dec '87, on Champion, by Champion Records. Catalogue no: **CHAMP 1258**

JACK THE GROOVE
Tracks: / Jack the groove / Bonus beats / Oh song (On 12" only.) / Jump in your dance (Available on 12" only).
7" Single: Released Oct '86, on Champion, by Champion Records. Catalogue no: **CHAMP 23**
12" Single: Released Oct '86, on Champion, by Champion Records. Catalogue no: **CHAMP 1223**

LET IT ROLL
Tracks: / Let it roll.
12" Single: Released May '89, on Champion, by Champion Records. Catalogue no: **CHAMP 12204**
12" Single: Released Apr '89, on Grove Street, Catalogue no: **GSR 018**
7" Single: Released Jul '89, on Atlantic, by WEA Records. Catalogue no: **A 8866**
7" Single: Released May '89, on Champion, by Champion Records. Catalogue no: **CHAMP 204**
7" Single: Released Jun '89, on Atlantic, by WEA Records. Catalogue no: **086407**
12" Single: Released Jul '89, on Atlantic, by WEA Records. Catalogue no: **A 8866 T**

LET THE MUSIC MOVE U
Tracks: / Get down / Let the music move U.
7" Single: Released Feb '87, on Champion, by Champion Records. Catalogue no: **CHAMP 27**
12" Single: Released Jan '87, on Champion, by Champion Records. Catalogue no: **CHAMP 1227**

Razette

READY 4 LOVE
Tracks: / Ready 4 love / Ready 4 love (version).
7" Single: Released Jul '89, on Champion, by Champion Records. Deleted Aug '89. Catalogue no: **CHAMP 207**
12" Single: Released Jul '89, on Champion, by Champion Records. Deleted Aug '89. Catalogue no: **CHAMP 12207**

Razorcuts

BIG PINK CAKE
Tracks: / Big pink cake.
7" Single: Released Feb '89, on Subway Organisation, Catalogue no: **SUBWAY 005**

I HEARD YOU THE FIRST TIME
Tracks: / I heard you the first time.
7" Single: Released Jun '87, on Flying Nun, Catalogue no: **FNUK 9**
12" Single: Released Jul '87, on Flying Nun, Catalogue no: **FNUK 9T**

I'LL STILL BE THERE
Tracks: / I'll still be there / Big pink cake.
7" Single: Released May '86, on Subway, by Subway Records. Catalogue no: **SUBWAY 5**

SORRY TO EMBARASS YOU
Tracks: / Sorry to embarass you.
7" Single: Released Nov '86, on Subway, by Subway Records. Catalogue no: **SUBWAY 8**
12" Single: Released Nov '86, on Subway, by Subway Records. Catalogue no: **SUBWAY 8T**

Razz

ALRIGHT TONIGHT
Tracks: / Alright tonight.
7" Single: Released May '85, on Lady London, by Lady London Records. Catalogue no: **MSLLR 7**

WHEN YOU FALL IN LOVE
Tracks: / When you fall in love / Everything you do.
7" Single: Released Jan '85, on Lady London, by Lady London Records. Catalogue no: **MSLLR 6**

RB Method

QUANTUM HOP
Tracks: / Quantum hop.
12" Single: Released Apr '85, on Survival (1), by Survival Records. Catalogue no: **SUR 12 029**

RB's

EXPLAIN
Tracks: / Explain / Let me feel it.
7" Single: Released Nov '80, on Phoenix (1), by Phoenix Records. Catalogue no: **PSP 21**

URUGUAY
Tracks: / Uruguay / Time.
7" Single: Released Apr '82, on Hansa, by Hansa Records. Catalogue no: **HANSA 14**
12" Single: Released Apr '82, on Hansa, by Hansa Records. Catalogue no: **HANSA 1214**

Rea, Chris

Biographical details: Chris Rea is the English Bruce Springsteen. Content to compose his own music in his own way and in his own time, Chris Rea has seen his popularity increase in leaps and bounds without any real effort on his part. 1985 sees him with a huge international following round Europe with Top 10 chart success all over the continent. Ever increasing album sales and a top 75 hit *I can hear your heartbeat* ensure that this half Irish/half Italian gruff voiced songster will soon be back in the limelight in his home country. A spring 1985 tour with Eric Clapton to coincide with the release of a new single *Stainsby Girls* sets the scene for both a full-scale concert hall tour in May and June and another superbly crafted LP set for release late spring. Chris Rea was born and bred in the Geordie land of Middlesborough, one of eight children. He left school at 18 with little more than an affinity for Newcastle Brown Ale, and found himself grafting a living by either labouring or helping his father out in his many catering ventures. Chris was always delegated the job of bouncing the local villains. Two broken noses later he discovered the benefits of weight training. This period gave Chris the taste of real street-life, which has subsequently proved endlessly fruitful as a source of lyrical ideas for his totally down-to-earth, life orientated songwriting. Inspired by music after hearing a Joe Walsh record one Friday night, he went out and bought a slide guitar the following day. Rea's first band (initially named Magdalene, which then changed to Beautiful Losers) included the young David Coverdale (who now fronts Whitesnake) and which soon earned Melody Maker's 'Best New Comer" award for 1975. 1976 saw Chris Rea signing to Magnet Records and releasing his debut album *Whatever happened to Benny Santini*. *Fool if you think it's over* was written for his youngest sister to help her recover from a broken romance, and reached no.30 in the UK charts and no.5 in the US charts earning Chris Rea a grammy nomination for 'Most Promising New Artist'. Until the early 80's Chris found himself a well-respected cult artist. His second coming happened in 1983 when Magent released *I can hear your heartbeat* a single which not only breached the UK chart, but hit the top twenty in nearly every other European Territory. *Watersign* notched up sales of over half a million. This encouraged Chris Rea to tour Europe for the first time. His current band lineup includes Sade percussionist Martin Ditcham, ex-Jeff Beck keyboard man Max Middleton and Mel Collins on sax. (Press Office release, February 1984).

ACE OF HEARTS (SPECIAL MIX)
Tracks: / Ace of hearts (special mix).
Cassingle: Released Nov '85, on Magnet, by WEA Records. Deleted '87. Catalogue no: **ZCMAG 269**
7" Single: Released Nov '85, on Magnet, by WEA Records. Catalogue no: **MAG 269**
12" Single: Released Nov '85, on Magnet, by WEA Records. Deleted '87. Catalogue no: **MAGT 269**

BOMBOLLINI
Tracks: / Bombollini / True love.
7" Single: Released May '84, on Magnet, by WEA Records. Catalogue no: **MAG 259**
12" Single: Released May '84, on Magnet, by WEA Records. Catalogue no: **MAGT 259**

DANCING GIRLS
Tracks: / Dancing girls / Friends across the water.
7" Single: Released May '80, on Magnet, by WEA Records. Deleted '83. Catalogue no: **MAG 176**

DIAMONDS
Tracks: / Diamonds.
7" Single: Released Apr '79, on Magnet, by WEA Records. Deleted '82. Catalogue no: **MAG 144**

DRIVING HOME FOR CHRISTMAS
Tracks: / Hello friend / Driving home for Christmas.
7" Single: Released Dec '86, on Magnet, by WEA Records. Catalogue no: **298**

DRIVING HOME FOR CHRISTMAS (EP)
Tracks: / Driving home for Christmas / Footsteps in the snow / Joys of Christmas / Smile.
7" EP: Released Dec '88, on WEA, by WEA Records. Catalogue no: **YZ 325**
12" Single: Released Dec '88, on WEA, by WEA Records. Catalogue no: **YZ 325 T**
CD 3": Released Dec '88, on WEA, by WEA Records. Catalogue no: **YZ 325 CD**

EVERY BEAT OF MY HEART
Tracks: / Every beat of my heart / Don't look back.
7" Single: Released May '82, on Magnet, by WEA Records. Deleted '85. Catalogue no: **MAG 225**

FOOL IF YOU THINK IT'S OVER
Tracks: / Fool if you think it's over / Midnight love.
7" Single: Released Oct '78, on Magnet, by WEA Records. Deleted '81. Catalogue no: **MAG 111**

HELLO FRIEND
Tracks: / Hello friend / Driving home for Christmas / It's all gone (Recorded live at Montreaux - Track on 7" only) / Steel river (Track on 7" only).
7" Set: Released Nov '86, on Magnet, by WEA Records. Deleted '87. Catalogue no: **MAG 298 D**
7" Single: Released Nov '86, on Magnet, by WEA Records. Catalogue no: **MAG 298**
12" Single: Released Nov '86, on Magnet, by WEA Records. Catalogue no: **MAGT 298**

I CAN HEAR YOUR HEART BEAT
Tracks: / I can hear your heartbeat / Loving you again (live) / Divenry (Only on 12").
CD 5": Released Oct '88, on WEA, by WEA Records. Catalogue no: **YZ 320CD**
7" Single: Released Oct '83, on Magnet, by WEA Records. Deleted '86. Catalogue no: **MAG 244**
7" Single: Released Oct '88, on WEA, by WEA Records. Catalogue no: **YZ 320**
12" Single: Released Oct '88, on WEA, by WEA Records. Catalogue no: **YZ 320T**

I DON'T KNOW WHAT IT IS BUT I LOVE IT / MYSTERY MAN
Tracks: / I don't know what it is but I love it / Mystery man.
7" Single: Released Feb '84, on Magnet, by WEA Records. Catalogue no: **MAG 255**
12" Single: Released Feb '84, on Magnet, by WEA Records. Deleted '87. Catalogue no: **MAGT 255**

IT'S ALL GONE
Tracks: / It's all gone / Bless them all / Crack that mould (Extra track on 12" version only.) / Look out for me (Extra track on 12" version only.) / Let's dance (Extra track on 12" version only.).
Cassingle: Released Mar '86, on Magnet, by WEA Records. Deleted '87. Catalogue no: **ZCMAG 283**
7" Single: Released Mar '86, on Magnet, by WEA Records. Deleted '87. Catalogue no: **MAG 283**
12" Single: Released Mar '86, on Magnet,

Chris Rea - Fool if you Think it's Over (Released on Magnet)

by WEA Records. Deleted '87. Catalogue no: **MAGT 283**

JOSEPHINE
Tracks: / Josephine.
7" Single: Released Jun '85, on Magnet, by WEA Records. Catalogue no: **MAG 280**
12" Single: Released Jun '85, on Magnet, by WEA Records. Deleted '87. Catalogue no: **MAGT 280**

JOYS OF CHRISTMAS
Tracks: / Joys of Christmas / Driving home for Christmas / Hello friend (On 12" and CD only) / Yes I do (On CD only).
CD 5": Released 21 Nov '87, on Magnet, by WEA Records. Catalogue no: **CD MAG 314**
7" Single: Released Nov '87, on Magnet, by WEA Records. Deleted Jun '88. Catalogue no: **MAG 314**
12" Single: Released Nov '87, on Magnet, by WEA Records. Deleted Jun '88. Catalogue no: **MAGT 314**

LET'S DANCE
Tracks: / Let's dance / I don't care anymore / Let's dance (12" Special mix) / Josephine (extended French re-record) Extra track on Compact Disc and Cassingle.).
CD 5": Released Mar '87, on Magnet, by WEA Records. Deleted Jun '88. Catalogue no: **CD MAG 299**
Cassingle: Released Mar '87, on Magnet, by WEA Records. Deleted '87. Catalogue no: **ZCMAG 299**
7" Single: Released May '87, on Magnet, by WEA Records. Deleted Jun '88. Catalogue no: **MAG 299**
12" Single: Released May '87, on Magnet, by WEA Records. Deleted '87. Catalogue no: **MAGT 299**

LOVE'S STRANGE WAYS
Tracks: / Love's strange ways / Smile.
7" Single: Released Jul '83, on Magnet, by WEA Records. Catalogue no: **MAG 245**

LOVING YOU
Tracks: / Loving you / Let me be the one.
7" Single: Released Mar '82, on Magnet, by WEA Records. Deleted '85. Catalogue no: **MAG 215**

LOVING YOU AGAIN
Tracks: / Loving you again / Donahue's broken wheel.
7" Single: Released Aug '87, on Magnet, by WEA Records. Deleted '87. Catalogue no: **MAG 300**
12" Single: Released Aug '87, on Magnet, by WEA Records. Deleted '87. Catalogue no: **MAGT 300**

ON THE BEACH (SINGLE)
Tracks: / It's all gone (Recorded live in Montreaux) / On the beach / I'm taking the day out / One golden rule (live) (Tracks on 7" Double pack only.) / Midnight (Live) (Tracks on 7" Double pack only.).
CD 5": Released Jul '88, on WEA, by WEA Records. Catalogue no: **YZ 195CD**
7" Set: Released May '86, on Magnet, by WEA Records. Deleted Jun '88. Catalogue no: **MAG 294 D**
7" Single: Released May '86, on Magnet, by WEA Records. Deleted '89. Catalogue no: **MAG 294**
7" Single: Released Jul '88, on WEA, by WEA Records. Catalogue no: **YZ 195**
12" Single: Released Jul '88, on WEA, by WEA Records. Catalogue no: **YZ 195T**
12" Single: Released May '86, on Magnet, by WEA Records. Deleted Jun '88. Catalogue no: **MAGT 294**

QUE SERA
Tracks: / Que sera / Se sequi / Let's dance (the remix) (Available on 12" only.) / Que sera (down under mix) (Available on 12" only.) / One sweet tender touch (Track available only on CD.).
CD 5": Released Jan '88, on Magnet, by WEA Records. Catalogue no: **CD MAG 318**
7" Single: Released Jan '88, on Magnet, by WEA Records. Deleted Jun '88. Catalogue no: **MAG 318**
12" Single: Released Jan '88, on Magnet, by WEA Records. Deleted Jun '88. Catalogue no: **MAGT 318**

ROAD TO HELL
Tracks: / Road to hell / Josephine.
CD 5": Released Sep '89, on WEA, by WEA Records. Catalogue no: **YZ 431CD**
Cassingle: Released Sep '89, on WEA, by WEA Records. Catalogue no: **YZ 431C**
7" Single: Released Sep '89, on WEA, by WEA Records. Catalogue no: **YZ 431**
12" Single: Released Sep '89, on WEA, by WEA Records. Catalogue no: **YZ 431T**

STAINSBY GIRLS
Tracks: / Stainsby girls.
7" Single: Released Mar '85, on Magnet, by WEA Records. Deleted '87. Catalogue no: **MAG 276**
12" Single: Released Mar '85, on Magnet, by WEA Records. Deleted Jun '88. Catalogue no: **MAGT 276**

TENNIS (SINGLE)
Tracks: / Tennis / If you really love me.
7" Single: Released Mar '80, on Magnet, by WEA Records. Deleted '83. Catalogue no: **MAG 163**

TOUCHE D'AMOUR
Tracks: / Touche d'amour.
7" Single: Released Jul '84, on Magnet, by WEA Records. Catalogue no: **MAG 260**
12" Single: Released Jul '84, on Magnet, by WEA Records. Catalogue no: **MAGT 260**

WORKING ON IT
Tracks: / Working on it / One golden rule.

CD 5": Released Jan '89, on WEA, by WEA Records. Catalogue no: **YZ 350CD**
7" Single: Released Jan '89, on WEA, by WEA Records. Catalogue no: **YZ 350**
12" Single: Released Jan '89, on WEA, by WEA Records. Catalogue no: **YZ 350T**

React

LOVE REACTION
Tracks: / Love reaction / Invisible (dub) / Love reaction (version).
12" Single: Released Sep '87, on Citybeat, by Beggars Banquet Records. Catalogue no: **CBE 1216**

Reaction

MAKE UP YOUR MIND
Tracks: / 4 x 4.
7" Single: Released Feb '87, on Waterloo Sunset, by Waterloo Sunset Records. Catalogue no: **RUSS 015**

Reaction, Junior C

BETTER MUST COME
Tracks: / Better must come / Better must come (Dub version).
7" Single: Released Mar '86, on Cool Tempo, by Chrysalis Records. Catalogue no: **COOL 120**
12" Single: Released Mar '86, on Cool Tempo, by Chrysalis Records. Catalogue no: **COOLX 120**

IF IT DON'T FIT DON'T FORCE IT
Tracks: / If it don't fit don't force it / I am.
7" Single: Released Sep '86, on Chrysalis, by Chrysalis Records. Catalogue no: **CHS 3051**
12" Single: Released Sep '86, on Chrysalis, by Chrysalis Records. Catalogue no: **CHS 123 051**

Read, Darryl

LIVING ON BORROWED TIME
Tracks: / Living on borrowed time / West end girl.
7" Single: Released Sep '80, on Monarch, by Monarch Records. Deleted Sep '83. Catalogue no: **MON 16**

Read, John Dawson

I AM WITH YOU MARY
Tracks: / I am with you Mary.
7" Single: Released Jun '84, on Open Space, Catalogue no: **OS 91**

Read, Mike

TELL ME I'M WRONG
Tracks: / Tell me I'm wrong / Have your own way.
7" Single: Released Apr '84, on MCA, by MCA Records. Catalogue no: **MCA 884**
12" Single: Released Apr '84, on MCA, by MCA Records. Catalogue no: **MCAT 884**

Read:All:Over

HARD TO LOVE
Tracks: / Hard to love.
7" Single: Released Jun '85, on Station, Catalogue no: **TA 001**

OUTSIDE TO THE OTHER WORLD
Tracks: / Outside to the other world.
7" Single: Released '87, on Station, Catalogue no: **STA 002**

Reading, Bertice

DON'T BOTHER TO KNOCK
Tracks: / Don't bother to knock / Don't bother to knock (instrumental).
7" Single: Released Feb '89, on Rotunda, Catalogue no: **7TUN 001**
12" Single: Released Feb '89, on Rotunda, Catalogue no: **12TUN 001**

STAND BY ME
Tracks: / Stand by me / I'm a woman.
7" Single: Released Oct '80, on Chrysalis, by Chrysalis Records. Deleted Oct '83. Catalogue no: **CHS 2437**

YOU'RE GONNA SUFFER
Tracks: / You're gonna suffer / Nightmare (Dub mix).
12" Single: Released Oct '86, on Sublime, Catalogue no: **LIME T 103**

Ready For The World

LOVE YOU DOWN
Tracks: / Human toy / Love you down.
7" Single: Released Feb '87, on MCA, by MCA Records. Catalogue no: **MCA 1110**
12" Single: Released Feb '87, on MCA, by MCA Records. Catalogue no: **MCAT 1110**

MARY GOES ROUND
Tracks: / Mary goes round / It's all a game.
7" Single: Released 23 May '87, on MCA, by MCA Records. Catalogue no: **MCA 1144**

OH SHEILA
Tracks: / Oh Sheila / I'm the one who loves you (Extra track in double pack.) / Side over.
7" Single: Released Sep '85, on MCA, by MCA Records. Catalogue no: **MCA 1005**
7" Single: Released May '86, on MCA, by MCA Records. Catalogue no: **RFT WD 1**
12" Single: Released Sep '85, on MCA, by MCA Records. Catalogue no: **MCAT 1005**
12" Single: Released May '86, on MCA, by MCA Records. Catalogue no: **RFT WX 1**

Reaganstein

BLOOD NATION
Tracks: / Blood nation / Ignore it.
7" Single: Released Jun '88, on F.O.A.D., Catalogue no: **FOAD 6**

Real Life

CATCH ME I'M FALLING
Tracks: / Catch me I'm falling / Exploding bullets.

7" Single: Released Apr '84, on MCA, by MCA Records. Catalogue no: **MCA 885**
12" Single: Released Apr '84, on MCA, by MCA Records. Catalogue no: **MCAT 885**

FACE TO FACE
Tracks: / Face to face / Flame / Face to face (instrumental) (Extra track on 12" version only.).

7" Single: Released Jan '86, on MCA, by MCA Records. Catalogue no: **MCA 1011**
12" Single: Released Jan '86, on MCA, by MCA Records. Catalogue no: **MCAT 1011**

SEND ME AN ANGEL
Tracks: / Send me an angel / Like a gun.
CD 5": Released 29 Jul '89, on RCA, by BMG Records (UK). Catalogue no: **ZD 42962**
7" Single: Released 29 Jul '89, Catalogue no: **ZB 42961**
12" Single: Released 29 Jul '89, on RCA, by BMG Records (UK). Catalogue no: **ZT 42962**

Real Macarbe

ALICE IS DRESSED IN GREY
Tracks: / Alice is dressed in grey.
7" Single: Released Oct '86, on Dacarpo, Catalogue no: **AD 15C**

EMOTION
Tracks: / Emotion / Dance, The.
7" Single: Released Dec '85, on Push, Catalogue no: **PUSH 1**
12" Single: Released Dec '85, on Push, Catalogue no: **PUSH 1T**

WHITE HORSES(REMIX)
Tracks: / White horses (remix) / Call (The).
12" Single: Released Dec '85, on Push, Catalogue no: **PUSH 2T**

Real Roxanne

LET'S GO-GO (BANG ZOOM)
Tracks: / (Bang zoom) Let's go go / Howie's teed off.
12" Single: Released Jun '86, on Cool Tempo, by Chrysalis Records. Catalogue no: **COOLX 124**
7" Single: Released Jun '86, on Cool Tempo, by Chrysalis Records. Catalogue no: **COOL 124**

RESPECT
Tracks: / Respect / Her bad self.
12" Single: Released Oct '88, on Cool Tempo, by Chrysalis Records. Catalogue no: **COOLX 176**
7" Single: Released Oct '88, on Cool Tempo, by Chrysalis Records. Catalogue no: **COOL 176**

ROXANNE'S ON A ROLL
Tracks: / Roxanne's on a roll.

12" Single: Released 5 Jun '89, on Urban, by Polydor Ltd. Catalogue no: **URBX 42**
CD 5": Released 5 Jun '89, on Urban, by Polydor Ltd. Catalogue no: **URCD 42**
7" Single: Released 5 Jun '89, on Urban, by Polydor Ltd. Catalogue no: **URB 42**

Real Sounds

WALK FOR THE WORLD
Tracks: / Walk for the world / Dynamos vs Tornados (On 12" only).
Note: Guests: Desmond Dekker & The London Community Gospel Choir

7" Single: Released 23 May '87, on Cooking Vinyl, by Cooking Vinyl Records. Catalogue no: **FRY 003**
12" Single: Released 23 May '87, on Cooking Vinyl, by Cooking Vinyl Records. Catalogue no: **FRY 003T**

Real Thing

BOOGIE DOWN (GET FUNKY NOW)
Tracks: / Boogie down (get funky now).
7" Single: Released Jul '79, on Pye, Deleted '82. Catalogue no: **7 P 109**

CAN YOU FEEL THE FORCE
Tracks: / Can you feel the force(1986 Mix) / Love's such a wonderful thing / Lightning strikes (Extra track on 12" version only.).
7" Single: Released Feb '79, on Pye, Catalogue no: **7N 46147**
7" Single: Released Aug '86, on PRT, by Castle Communications Records. Catalogue no: **7P 358**
12" Single: Released May '79, on Pye, Catalogue no: **12P 105**
12" Single: Released Aug '86, on PRT, by Castle Communications Records. Catalogue no: **12P 358**

CAN YOU FEEL THE FORCE (2)
Tracks: / Can you feel the force.
7" Single: Released May '89, on PRT, by Castle Communications Records. Catalogue no: **PYS 26**
12" Single: Released May '89, on PRT, by Castle Communications Records. Catalogue no: **PYT 26**

CAN YOU FEEL THE FORCE (LP)
Tracks: / Can you feel the force.
7" Single: Released Apr '79, on Pye,

Deleted Apr '84. Catalogue no: **NSPH 18601**

CAN YOU FEEL THE FORCE (OLD GOLD)
Tracks: / Can you feel the force / You to me are everything.
12" Single: Released 30 Jan '89, on Old Gold, by Old Gold Records. Catalogue no: **OG 4090**

CAN YOU FEEL THE FORCE (OLD GOLD) (2)
Tracks: / Can you feel the force / Whenever you want my love.
7" Single: Released Jan '89, on Old Gold, by Old Gold Records. Catalogue no: **OG 9837**

CAN'T GET BY WITHOUT YOU
Tracks: / Can't get by without you.
7" Single: Released Sep '76, on Pye, Deleted '79. Catalogue no: **7 N 45618**
7" Single: Released May '86, on PRT, by Castle Communications Records. Catalogue no: **7P 352**
12" Single: Released May '86, on PRT, by Castle Communications Records. Catalogue no: **12P 352**

CRIME OF LOVE
Tracks: / Crime of love / Baby don't go.
CD 5": Released 24 Jul '89, on RCA, by BMG Records (UK). Catalogue no: **PD 42848**
7" Single: Released 24 Jul '89, on RCA, by BMG Records (UK). Catalogue no: **PB 42847**
12" Single: Released 24 Jul '89, on RCA, by BMG Records (UK). Catalogue no: **PT 42848**

FOOT TAPPIN'
Tracks: / Foot tappin'.
7" Single: Released Nov '81, on Calibre, Deleted Nov '84. Catalogue no: **CAB 110**
12" Single: Released Nov '81, on Calibre, Deleted Nov '84. Catalogue no: **CABL 110**

HARD TIMES
Tracks: / Children of the ghetto.
7" Single: Released Feb '87, on Jive, by Zomba Records. Deleted Jul '87. Catalogue no: **JIVE 137**
12" Single: Released Feb '87, on Jive, by Zomba Records. Catalogue no: **CIVET 137**

I BELIEVE IN YOU
Tracks: / I believe in you
7" Single: Released Jun '81, on Calibre, Deleted '83. Catalogue no: **CAB 109**
12" Single: Released Jun '81, on Calibre, Deleted '83. Catalogue no: **CABL 109**

I CAN'T HELP MYSELF
Tracks: / I can't help myself / Hard times.
7" Single: Released Aug '87, on Jive, by Zomba Records. Catalogue no: **JIVE 147**
12" Single: Released Aug '87, on Jive, by Zomba Records. Deleted Nov '87. Catalogue no: **JIVET 147**

LET'S GO DISCO
Tracks: / Let's go disco.
7" Single: Released Jun '78, on Pye, Deleted '81. Catalogue no: **7 N 46078**

LOVE TAKES TWO
Tracks: / Love takes tears / Going for the....
7" Single: Released Jan '82, on Calibre, Deleted '84. Catalogue no: **CAB 112**
12" Single: Released Jan '82, on Calibre, Deleted '84. Catalogue no: **CABL 112**

LOVE'S SUCH A WONDERFUL THING
Tracks: / Love's such a wonderful thing.
7" Single: Released Jul '77, on Pye, Deleted '80. Catalogue no: **7 N 45701**

RAININ' THROUGH MY SUNSHINE
Tracks: / Raining through my sunshine / Can you feel the force / You to me are everything / Can't get by without you.
7" Single: Released Aug '78, on Pye, Deleted '81. Catalogue no: **7 N 46113**
7" Single: Released May '80, on Pye, Deleted May '85. Catalogue no: **7P 178**

SAINT ON SINNER
Tracks: / Saint on sinner / We gotta take it to the second stage.
7" Single: Released Feb '80, on Pye, Deleted Feb '83. Catalogue no: **7P 161**
12" Single: Released Feb '80, on Pye, Deleted Feb '83. Catalogue no: **12P 161**

SEEN TO SMILE
Tracks: / Seen to smile / Look up to the sky.
7" Single: Released Aug '82, on EMI, by EMI Records. Deleted Aug '85. Catalogue no: **EMI 5337**
12" Single: Released Aug '82, on EMI, by EMI Records. Deleted Aug '85. Catalogue no: **12EMI 5337**

SHE'S A GROOVY FREAK
Tracks: / She's a groovy freak / It's the real thing.
7" Single: Released Nov '80, on Calibre, Deleted '82. Catalogue no: **CAB 105**
12" Single: Released Nov '80, on Calibre, Deleted '82. Catalogue no: **CABL 105**

STRAIGHT TO THE HEART
Tracks: / Straight to the heart / Mystique.
7" Single: Released Oct '86, on Jive, by Zomba Records. Catalogue no: **JIVE 129**
12" Single: Released Oct '86, on Jive, by Zomba Records. Catalogue no: **JIVET 129**

WHENEVER YOU WANT MY LOVE
Tracks: / Whenever you want my love.
7" Single: Released Mar '78, on Pye, Deleted '81. Catalogue no: **7 N 46045**

YOU TO ME ARE EVERYTHING
Tracks: / You to me are everything / You to me are everything(decade remix '76-78) / Foot tappin / Children of the Ghetto (original '78 vintage version).
7" Single: Released Jul '76, on PRT, by Castle Communications Records. Catalogue no: **7N 25709**
7" Single: Released Feb '86, on PRT, by Castle Communications Records. Catalogue no: **7P 349**
12" Single: Released Feb '86, on PRT, by Castle Communications Records. Catalogue no: **12P 349**

YOU TO ME ARE EVERYTHING (OLD GOLD)
Tracks: / You to me are everything / Can't get by without you.
7" Single: Released Jun '88, on Old Gold, by Old Gold Records. Catalogue no: **OG 9294**

YOU'LL NEVER KNOW WHAT YOU'RE MISSING
Tracks: / You'll never know what you're missing.
7" Single: Released Feb '77, on Pye, Deleted '80. Catalogue no: **7 N 45662**

Real To Reel

BLUE
Tracks: / Blue / Wind up man.
7" Single: Released Sep '80, on R.E.D., Deleted '83. Catalogue no: **REDS 006**

LOVE ME LIKE THIS (see panel on page R14)
Tracks: / Love me like this / Taking the long way home
7" Single: Released Apr '84, on Arista, by BMG Records (UK). Catalogue no: **ARIST 565**
12" Single: Released Apr '84, on Arista, by BMG Records (UK). Catalogue no: **ARIST 12565**

MR & MRS
Tracks: / Mr. & Mrs. / Not the one.
7" Single: Released Feb '81, on Red Shadow, Catalogue no: **REDS 101**

WHITE MAN REGGAE
Tracks: / White man reggae / One of these days.
7" Single: Released Mar '80, on R.E.D., Deleted '83. Catalogue no: **REDS 001**

Realistic Band

I DON'T MIND
Tracks: / I don't mind.
12" Single: Released 24 Jul '89, on Realistic, Catalogue no: **RRO 14**

Realistics

FEELIN' FINE
Tracks: / Feelin' fine.
7" Single: Released May '82, on Spinach, by Spinach Records. Deleted '86. Catalogue no: **SPIN 004**
12" Single: Released May '82, on Spinach, by Spinach Records. Deleted '86. Catalogue no: **SPIN 004 12**

JAMAICA YOU'VE LOST YOUR MAKER
Tracks: / Jamaica you've lost your maker.
7" Single: Released Aug '81, on 101, Catalogue no: **UR 1**

Reality

BLIND TO THE TRUTH (EP)
Tracks: / Blind to the truth.
7" Single: Released Dec '82, on Subversive, Catalogue no: **SUB 006**

STAND UP AND BE COUNTED
Tracks: / Stand up and be counted.
7" Single: Released Oct '81, on Romantic, Catalogue no: **MCA 750**
12" Single: Released Oct '81, on Romantic, Catalogue no: **MCAT 750**

WHAT'S GOING ON IN YOUR MIND
Tracks: / What's going on in your mind / O.K. / Stepping out (on 12" only).
7" Single: Released Mar '81, on MCA, by MCA Records. Deleted Mar '84. Catalogue no: **MCA 683**
12" Single: Released Mar '81, on MCA, by MCA Records. Deleted Mar '84. Catalogue no: **MCAT 683**

WHO KILLED THE GOLDEN GOOSE?
Tracks: / Who killed the golden goose / Lonely shadow.
7" Single: Released Jun '84, on Fight Back, Catalogue no: **FIGHT 3**

Reality Band

STEP INTO MY LIFE
Tracks: / Step into my life.
7" Single: Released Oct '80, on Record Shack, by Record Shack Records. Catalogue no: **GALD 004**

Reality Control

REPRODUCTION OF HATE
Tracks: / Reproduction of hate / Sunny outlook / Another surprise.
7" Single: Released Oct '83, on Volume (1), by Volume Records. Catalogue no: **VOL 7**

Really 4 Real

SHINE ON
Tracks: / Shine on / Cinderella.
7" Single: Released 22 Aug '88, on PRT, by Castle Communications Records. Catalogue no: **GEL 1**
12" Single: Released 22 Aug '88, on PRT, by Castle Communications Records. Catalogue no: **12GEL 1**

Really Schmaltzy

OUTTA SIGHT OUTTA MIND
Tracks: / Outta sight outta mind.
7" Single: Released May '89, on Pyramid, by Pyramid Records. Catalogue no: **PYR 10**
12" Single: Released May '89, on Pyramid, by Pyramid Records. Catalogue no: **12PYR 10**

Reasonable Strollers

TOOLS FOR AFRICA
Tracks: / Tools for Africa / Smile / No wasting.
7" Single: Released Mar '82, on Robust, Deleted '83. Catalogue no: **TRS 001**

Reasonable, Wooly

YOU'RE THE ONLY ONE
Tracks: / You're the only one / You're the only one (Instrumental).
7" Single: Released Mar '87, on Club, by Phonogram Ltd. Deleted Dec '87. Catalogue no: **JAB 45**
12" Single: Released Mar '87, on Club, by Phonogram Ltd. Deleted Dec '87. Catalogue no: **JABX 45**

Rebel

VALENTINO
Tracks: / Valentino / Lonely traveller.
7" Single: Released Sep '86, on Flying Pig, by Flying Pig Records. Deleted '87. Catalogue no: **REBS 1**

Rebel C & LA

RUGGED
Tracks: / Rugged.
7" Single: Released '88, on Champion, by Champion Records. Catalogue no: **CHAMP 72**
12" Single: Released '88, on Champion, by Champion Records. Catalogue no: **CHAMP 1272**

Rebel Christening

TRIBAL EYE
Tracks: / Tribal eye / Desire and glory
12" Single: Released Aug '85, on Clay, by Clay Records. Deleted '88. Catalogue no: **12 CLAY 44**

Rebel MC

COCKNEY RHYTHM
Tracks: / Cockney rhythm.
12" Single: Released Sep '88, on B-Ware, by B/Ware Records. Catalogue no: **UM 004**

STREET TUFF
Tracks: / Street tuff.
7" Single: Released Sep '89, on Desire, by Desire Records. Catalogue no: **WANT 18**
12" Single: Released Sep '89, on Desire, by Desire Records. Catalogue no: **WANTX 18**

Rebel, Tony

MUSIC FRATERNITY
Tracks: / Music fraternity.
12" Single: Released Oct '89, on Penthouse, by Penthouse Records. Catalogue no: **PH 016**

Rebels

YOU CAN MAKE IT
Tracks: / You can make it.
12" Single: Released Nov '84, on Carrere, Catalogue no: **CART 348**

Rebirth

GUILTY
Tracks: / Guilty / Guilty version.
12" Single: Released Oct '84, on Roots Radical, by Roots Radical Records. Catalogue no: **RR 12006**

Recipe

OUTBOARD
Tracks: / Outboard / Home's over.
12" Single: on Survival (1), by Survival Records. Catalogue no: **ERT 8R12**

Reckless

HOT 'N' READY
Tracks: / Hot 'n' ready.
7" Single: Released Aug '85, on FM, by FM-Revolver Records. Catalogue no: **VHF 16**

NITTY GRITTY
Tracks: / Nitty gritty / Deadly game.
7" Single: Released Mar '87, on Valentino, Deleted Jan '88. Catalogue no: **B 9458**

VICTIM OF TIME
Tracks: / Victim of time / All night woman.
7" Single: Released Oct '80, on EMI, by EMI Records. Deleted Oct '83. Catalogue no: **EMI 5113**

Reckless Sleepers

IF WE NEVER MEET AGAIN
Tracks: / If we never meet again.
7" Single: Released May '89, on I.R.S, Catalogue no: **EIRS 114**
12" Single: Released May '89, on I.R.S, Catalogue no: **EIRST 114**

Reco, Ezz

KING OF KINGS
Tracks: / King of kings.
7" Single: Released Mar '64, on Columbia, by EMI Records. Deleted '67. Catalogue no: **DB 7217**

Recognitions

BIM BAM BOM
Tracks: / Bim bam bom.
7" Single: Released Feb '85, on Blue Train, Catalogue no: **COACH 4**

FIRST DANCE
Tracks: / First dance.
7" Single: Released Mar '84, on Blue Train, Catalogue no: **COACH 1**

TOO MUCH FICTION
Tracks: / Too much fiction / Smokey Joes.
7" Single: Released May '81, on Ryme Time, by Lismor Records. Catalogue no: **WRS 801**

Recommended...

VARIOUS RECOMMENDED ARTISTS
7" Single: Released Jun '82, on Recommended, by Recommended Records. Catalogue no: **RRR 1982**

Record Players

MONEY WORRIES
Tracks: / Money worries
7" Single: Released May '84, on Wreckord, by Wreckord Records. Catalogue no: **WEK 3003**

Recordiau Priod

MADOG Y MORWR
Tracks: / Madog y morwr.
7" Single: Released May '84, on Recordiau Priod, by Recordiau Priod. Catalogue no: **REP 001**

Records

HEARTS IN HER EYES
Tracks: / Hearts in her eyes / So sorry.
7" Single: Released May '80, on Virgin, by Virgin Records. Deleted May '83. Catalogue no: **VS 330**

IMITATION JEWELLERY
Tracks: / Imitation jewellery.
7" Single: Released Aug '81, on Virgin, by Virgin Records. Deleted '84. Catalogue no: **VS 442**

Red

DANCING
Tracks: / Dancing.
7" Single: Released May '84, on RGM, by RGM Records. Catalogue no: **RGM 2030**

I CAN FLY
Tracks: / I can fly.
7" Single: Released Feb '87, on Lost Moments, Catalogue no: **LMR 021**
12" Single: Released Apr '85, on Lost Moments, Catalogue no: **LMR 12 021**

LET HER GO
Tracks: / Let her go.
7" Single: Released Jan '84, on RGM, by RGM Records. Catalogue no: **RGM 2010**
12" Single: Released Jan '84, on RGM, by RGM Records. Catalogue no: **RGMT 2010**

NAOMI
Tracks: / Naomi.
12" Single: Released Jan '84, on RGM, by RGM Records. Catalogue no: **RGMT 2020**

PROMISES SAIL AWAY
Tracks: / Promises sail away.
12" Single: Released Apr '86, on Lost Moments, Catalogue no: **LM 12 037**

THOSE WHO TRY
Tracks: / Those who try.
12" Single: Released Apr '87, on Lost Moments, Catalogue no: **LM 12 042**

Red Alert

BREAK THE RULES
Tracks: / Break the rules / What do you do for laughs.
7" Single: Released Sep '80, on State, by State Records. Deleted '83. Catalogue no: **STAT 101**

CITY EVASION
Tracks: / City evasion.
7" Single: Released Jan '83, on No Future, Deleted '87. Catalogue no: **01 20**

IN BRITAIN (EP)
Tracks: / In Britain.
7" Single: Released Jul '82, on No Future, Deleted '87. Catalogue no: **01 5**

TAKE NO PRISONERS
Tracks: / Take no prisoners.
7" Single: Released Jul '82, on No Future, Deleted '87. Catalogue no: **01 13**

THERE'S A GUITAR BURNING (EP) (6-track EP)
Tracks: / There's a guitar burning.
12" Single: Released Dec '83, on No Future, Catalogue no: **12 01 27**

WILD DOGS
Tracks: / Wild dogs / Back in the band / Red skies / Baby Jane.
7" Single: Released May '80, on EMI, by EMI Records. Deleted May '83. Catalogue no: **EMI 12-5074**

Red Assassin

RISE (EP)
Tracks: / Rise.
12" Single: Released Oct '84, Catalogue no: **R.A.A.1**

Red Bamboo

DANCE OF LOVE
Tracks: / Dance of love / On the line.
7" Single: Released Jul '86, on EMI, by EMI Records. Catalogue no: **EMI 5561**
12" Single: Released Jul '86, on EMI, by EMI Records. Catalogue no: **12EMI 5561**

Red Beans & Rice

THAT DRIVING BEAT
Tracks: / That driving beat / Throw it in the grass.
7" Single: Released Mar '80, on Chiswick Records, Deleted '83. Catalogue no: **CHIS 124**

Red Beards From Texas

GUDBUY T'JANE
Tracks: / Gudbuy T'Jane.
7" Single: Released Nov '86, on Receiver, by Trojan Records. Deleted May '88. Catalogue no: **RRS 1001**

I DIDN'T KNOW I LOVED YOU Till I saw you rock'n'roll
Tracks: / I didn't know I loved you till I saw you rock'n'roll / Rockin' and boppin'.
7" Single: Released Jul '87, on Receiver, by Trojan Records. Deleted May '88. Catalogue no: **RRS 1002**

I SAW HER STANDING THERE
Tracks: / I saw her standing there / Poker with the boys.
7" Single: Released May '86, on Receiver, by Trojan Records. Deleted May '88. Catalogue no: **RRS 1000**

Red Beat

DREAM
Tracks: / Dream.
12" Single: Released Feb '82, on Red Beat, Deleted '83. Catalogue no: **RB 003**

SURVIVAL
Tracks: / Survival.
7" Single: Released Jun '81, on Red Beat, Deleted '83. Catalogue no: **RB 002**

Red Box

CHENKO
Tracks: / Chenko / Valley, The.
7" Single: Released Jan '84, on Cherry Red, by Cherry Red Records. Catalogue no: **CHERRY 73**
7" Single: Released Jan '86, on WEA, by WEA Records. Deleted Jul '88. Catalogue no: **YZ 59**
12" Single: Released Jan '84, on Cherry Red, by Cherry Red Records. Catalogue no: **12 CHERRY 73**
12" Single: Released Jan '86, on WEA, by WEA Records. Deleted Jul '88. Catalogue no: **YZ 59T**

CHENKO (TENKO-LO)
Tracks: / Chenko / Speeches / Heart of the sun (slash and burn) (Available on 12" only).
7" Single: Released Jul '87, on WEA, by WEA Records. Catalogue no: **YZ 125**
12" Single: Released Jul '87, on WEA, by WEA Records. Catalogue no: **YZ 125T**

FOR AMERICA
Tracks: / For America / R'n'a / Ain't got no.
7" Single: Released Oct '86, on WEA, by WEA Records. Deleted Sep '87. Catalogue no: **YZ 84**
12" Single: Released Oct '86, on WEA, by WEA Records. Deleted Jan '88. Catalogue no: **YZ 84T**

HEART OF THE SUN
Tracks: / Enjoy (solid gold easy amex) / Lean on me*.
7" Single: Released Jan '87, on WEA, by WEA Records. Deleted Jan '88. Catalogue no: **YZ 100**
12" Single: Released Jan '87, on WEA, by WEA Records. Deleted Jan '88. Catalogue no: **YZ 100T**

LEAN ON ME
Tracks: / Lean on me.
7" Single: Released Aug '85, on Sire (USA), Catalogue no: **W 8926**
12" Single: Released Aug '85, on Sire (USA), Catalogue no: **W 8926T**

SASKATCHEWAN
Tracks: / Saskatchewan.
7" Single: Released Dec '84, on WEA, by WEA Records. Catalogue no: **W 9157**
12" Single: Released Dec '84, on WEA, by WEA Records. Catalogue no: **W 9157 T**

Red Cloud

DOUBLE TALK
Tracks: / Double talk / I want to be free.
7" Single: Released Jun '83, on Dancefloor, Catalogue no: **DF 7004**
12" Single: Released Jun '83, on Dancefloor, Catalogue no: **DFT 7004**

JOANNA
Tracks: / Joanna.
7" Single: Released Dec '88, on Safe House, Catalogue no: **SASH 006**
12" Single: Released Dec '88, on Safe House, Catalogue no: **SASH 006T**

WHEN A MAN LOVES A WOMAN
Tracks: / When a man loves a woman.
7" Single: Released Mar '82, on Echo, by Echo Records. Catalogue no: **ECHO 004**
12" Single: Released Mar '82, on Echo, by Echo Records. Catalogue no: **12 ECHO 004**

Red Dogs

RUBY RED
Tracks: / Ruby red.
12" Single: Released Aug '89, on Total/Episode, Catalogue no: **12LUS 2**

Red Dragon

BUST BLANK
Tracks: / Bust blank.
12" Single: Released 10 Jul '89, on Dragon, by Dragon Records. Catalogue no: **DRT 2**
12" Single: Released 30 May '88, on Dragon, by Dragon Records. Catalogue no: **VPRD 453**

DUCK DANCE
Tracks: / Duck dance.
12" Single: Released Aug '88, on Live & Love, Catalogue no: **LLD 78**

GAL WINER
Tracks: / Gal winer.
12" Single: Released Jan '89, on Redman International, Catalogue no: **VPRED 122**

HOL A FRESH
Tracks: / Hol a fresh.
12" Single: Released 20 Jun '87, on Technics, Catalogue no: **WRT 18**

LOOK YOUR SIZE
Tracks: / Look your size.
12" Single: Released Apr '88, on Redman International, Catalogue no: **RED 11**

LOVE OONUH
Tracks: / Love oonuh.
12" Single: Released Feb '89, on Dragon, by Dragon Records. Catalogue no: **VPRD 418**

POPULAR
Tracks: / Popular / Youths & youths.
12" Single: Released Sep '87, on Rockas, Catalogue no: **RR 008RV**

WILD RIDER
Tracks: / Wild rider.
12" Single: Released Nov '88, on Redman International, Catalogue no: **VPRED 118**

Red Fox

CRABLOUISE MAN
Tracks: / Crablouise man.
12" Single: Released Jul '88, on Eclipse, Catalogue no: **HCF 1013**

Red, Georgie

GET IN TOUCH
Tracks: / Get in touch (inst) / Night time (is the right time).
7" Single: Released Feb '87, on WEA (International), by WEA Records. Deleted Jan '88. Catalogue no: **X 8598**
12" Single: Released Feb '87, on WEA (International), by WEA Records. Deleted Jan '88. Catalogue no: **X 8598 T**

REDHEAD KINGPIN - DO THE RIGHT THING (Released on 10 Records)

Red Guitars

AMERICA AND ME
Tracks: / America and me / Marianna / America and me (12" version).
7" Single: Released May '86, on Virgin, by Virgin Records. Deleted May '88. Catalogue no: **VS 858**
12" Single: Released May '86, on Virgin, by Virgin Records. Catalogue no: **VS 858-12**

BE WITH ME
Tracks: / Be with me.
7" Single: Released Mar '85, on One Way, Catalogue no: **OW 1**
12" Single: Released Mar '85, on One Way, Catalogue no: **OW 1 T**

BLUE CARAVAN
Tracks: / Blue caravan / Suspicion & fear.
7" Single: Released Oct '86, on Virgin, by Virgin Records. Deleted May '88. Catalogue no: **VS 899**
12" Single: Released Oct '86, on Virgin, by Virgin Records. Deleted May '88. Catalogue no: **VS 899-12**

FACT
Tracks: / Fact / Live (guys).
7" Single: Released Nov '83, on Self Drive, Catalogue no: **SD 007**

GOOD TECHNOLOGY
Tracks: / Good technology / Fact (On 12" SD 008 only) / Paris France (On 12" SD 008 only).
7" Single: Released Jun '83, on Self Drive, Catalogue no: **SD 006**
7" Single: Released May '84, on Self Drive, Catalogue no: **SD 009**
12" Single: Released Jan '84, on Self Drive, Catalogue no: **SD 008**
12" Single: Released May '84, on Self Drive, Catalogue no: **SD 009T**

MARIMBA JIVE
Tracks: / Marimba jive.
7" Single: Released Sep '84, on Self Drive, Catalogue no: **SCAR 014**
12" Single: Released Sep '84, on Self Drive, Catalogue no: **SCAR 014T**

NATIONAL AVENUE
Tracks: / National Avenue (Sunday afternoon) / King and country / Things I want.
7" Single: Released Feb '86, on Virgin, by Virgin Records. Deleted '89. Catalogue no: **VS 832**
12" Single: Released Feb '86, on Virgin, by Virgin Records. Deleted '89. Catalogue no: **VS 832-12**

STEELTOWN
Tracks: / Steeltown.
7" Single: Released Jun '84, on Self Drive, Catalogue no: **SCAR 010**
12" Single: Released Jun '84, on Self Drive, Catalogue no: **SCAR 010T**

Red Gun

I WAS ONLY NINETEEN
Tracks: / I was only nineteen.
7" Single: Released Jun '85, on CBS, by CBS Records. Catalogue no: **A 6418**

Red Harvest

MURDER
Tracks: / Murder / Fifty years / Burning party.
7" Single: Released Aug '87, on Quiet, by Quiet Records. Catalogue no: **QS 019**

Redhead Kingpin

DO THE RIGHT THING (See panel above)
Tracks:/Do the right thing/Shade of red.
7" Single: Released Jul '89, on 10 Records by 10 Records. Catalogue no: **TEN 271**
12" Singles: Released Jul '89, on 10 Records, by 10 Records. Catalogue no:**TENX 271**
12" Single: Released Jul '89, on 10 Records, by 10 Records. Catalogue no: **TENR 271**
Cassingle: Released Jul '89, on 10 Records by 10 Records. Catalouge no: **TENC 271**

Red Hot Chili Peppers

ABBEY ROAD EP, THE
Tracks: / Backwoods / Catholic school girls rule (on 12" version only) / Hollywood (Africa) / True men don't kill Coyotes.
7" Single: Released 16 May '88, on EMI-Manhattan, by EMI Records. Deleted Nov '88. Catalogue no: **MT 41**
12" Single: Released 16 May '88, on EMI-Manhattan, by EMI Records. Deleted Jun '89. Catalogue no: **12MT 41**

FIGHT LIKE A BRAVE
Tracks: / Fight like a brave (mofo mix) / Fight like a brave (knucklehead mix) / Fight like a brave (LP version) / Fire.
12" Pic: Released Feb '88, on EMI-America, by EMI Records. Deleted Nov '88. Catalogue no: **12EAP 241**
7" Single: Released Jan '88, on EMI-America, by EMI Records. Deleted 31 Jul '88. Catalogue no: **EA 241**
12" Single: Released Jan '88, on EMI-America, by EMI Records. Deleted Nov '88. Catalogue no: **12EA 241**

HIGHER GROUND
Tracks: / Higher ground (CD single only.) / Politician (mini rap) (12" only.) / Higher ground (Munchkin mix) / Higher ground (dub mix) (12" only.) / Mommy where's daddy / Millionaires against hunger (Not on 12").
CD 5": Released Nov '89, on EMI-Manhattan, by EMI Records. Catalogue no: **203 572 2**
CD 5": Released Nov '89, on EMI-Manhattan, by EMI Records. Catalogue no: **CDMT 75**
7" Single: Released Nov '89, on EMI-Manhattan, by EMI Records. Catalogue no: **MT 75**
7" Single: Released Nov '89, on EMI-Manhattan, by EMI Records. Catalogue no: **203 572 7**
12" Single: Released Nov '89, on EMI-Manhattan, by EMI Records. Catalogue no: **12MT 75**
12" Single: Released Nov '89, on EMI-Manhattan, by EMI Records. Catalogue no: **203 572 6**

KNOCK ME DOWN
Tracks: / Knock me down / Punk rock classic / Pretty little ditty (7" & Picture Disc only.) / Special secret song inside (12" only.) / Magic Johnson (12" & CD single only.) / Jungle man (Avaliable on CD single only).
CD 5": Released Aug '89, on EMI-Manhattan, by EMI Records. Catalogue no: **CDMT 70**
CD 5": Released Aug '89, on EMI-Manhattan, by EMI Records. Catalogue no: **203 476 2**
7" Pic: Released Aug '89, on EMI-Manhattan, by EMI Records. Catalogue no: **203 476 8**
7" Pic: Released Aug '89, on EMI-Manhattan, by EMI Records. Catalogue no: **MTPD 70**
7" Single: Released Aug '89, on EMI-Manhattan, by EMI Records. Catalogue no: **MT 70**
7" Single: Released Aug '89, on EMI-Manhattan, by EMI Records. Catalogue no: **203 476 7**
12" Single: Released Aug '89, on EMI-Manhattan, by EMI Records. Catalogue no: **12MT 70**
12" Single: Released Aug '89, on EMI-Manhattan, by EMI Records. Catalogue no: **203 476 6**

Red Letter Day

RELEASED EMOTIONS
Tracks: / Released emotions.
12" Single: Released Aug '86, on Quiet, by Quiet Records. Catalogue no: **QST 015**

TAKE ME IN YOUR ARMS
Tracks: / Take me in your arms / Moving on.
7" Single: Released Jul '87, on Quiet, by Quiet Records. Catalogue no: **QS 018**

WHEREVER YOU MAY RUN
Tracks: / Wherever you may run / Susie's bombed out tonite.
7" Single: Released Mar '86, on Last Generation, Catalogue no: **LG 003**

Red Lipstique

DRAC'S BACK
Tracks: / Drac's back / Drac's back (part 2).
7" Single: Released Mar '82, on Magnet, by WEA Records. Catalogue no: **MAG 221**
12" Single: Released Mar '82, on Magnet, by WEA Records. Catalogue no: **12 MAG 221**

OSCAR WILDE
Tracks: / Oscar Wilde / More GDM.
7" Single: Released Feb '83, on Charly, by Charly Records. Deleted '86. Catalogue no: **7 WILDE 1**
12" Single: Released Feb '83, on Charly, by Charly Records. Deleted '86. Catalogue no: **12 WILDE 1**

SHAME SHAME SHAME
Tracks: / Shame shame shame / Shame shame shame (special NY mix).
7" Single: Released Oct '83, on Disco Int., by Charly Records. Catalogue no: **CYZ 7 109**
12" Single: Released Oct '83, on Disco Int., by Charly Records. Catalogue no: **CYZ 109**

Red London

STEN GUNS IN SUNDERLAND
Tracks: / Sten guns in Sunderland / This is England.
7" Single: Released Jul '83, on Razor, by Razor Records. Catalogue no: **RZS 105**

Red Lorry Yellow Lorry

BEATING MY HEAD
Tracks: / Beating my head.
7" Single: Released Sep '82, on Red Rhino, by Red Rhino Records. Catalogue no: **RED 20**

CHANCE
Tracks: / Chance.
7" Single: Released Mar '85, on Red Rhino, by Red Rhino Records. Catalogue no: **RED 55**
12" Single: Released Mar '85, on Red Rhino, by Red Rhino Records. Catalogue no: **REDT 55**

CUT DOWN
Tracks: / Cut down / Running fever / Pushed me.
7" Single: Released Oct '86, on Red Rhino, by Red Rhino Records. Catalogue no: **RED 73**
12" Single: Released Oct '86, on Red Rhino, by Red Rhino Records. Catalogue no: **REDT 73**

HE'S RED
Tracks: / He's red / See the fire.
7" Single: Released Oct '83, on Red Rhino, by Red Rhino Records. Catalogue no: **RED 39**

HOLLOW EYES
Tracks: / Hollow eyes.
7" Single: Released Oct '84, on Red Rhino, by Red Rhino Records. Catalogue no: **RED 052**
12" Single: Released Oct '84, on Red Rhino, by Red Rhino Records. Catalogue no: **REDT 052**

MONKEYS ON JUICE
Tracks: / Monkeys on juice.
7" Single: Released Jun '84, on Red Rhino, by Red Rhino Records. Catalogue no: **RED 49**
12" Single: Released Jun '84, on Red Rhino, by Red Rhino Records. Catalogue no: **REDT 49**

NOTHING WRONG
Tracks: / Nothing wrong / Do you understand / Calling (Extra track on 12".) / Big stick / Hands off me / She said / Sayonara / World around / Hard-away / Only dreaming / Never know / Pushing on / Time is tight.
7" Single: Released Mar '88, on Situation 2, by Beggars Banquet Records. Catalogue no: **SIT 50**
12" Single: Released Mar '88, on Situation 2, by Beggars Banquet Records. Catalogue no: **SIT 50T**

ONLY DREAMING (WIDE AWAKE)
Tracks: / Only dreaming (wide awake) / Rise, The.
7" Single: Released 16 Sep '88, on Situation 2, by Beggars Banquet Records. Catalogue no: **SIT 54**
12" Single: Released 16 Sep '88, on Situation 2, by Beggars Banquet Records. Catalogue no: **SIT 54T**

OPEN UP
Tracks: / Open up / Another side / You only get what you pay for (Available on 12" only). Note: * track on 12" version only.
7" Single: Released Oct '87, on Situation 2, by Beggars Banquet Records. Deleted Jul '88. Catalogue no: **SIT 49**
12" Single: Released Oct '87, on Situation 2, by Beggars Banquet Records. Deleted Jul '88. Catalogue no: **SIT 49T**

SPINNING ROUND
Tracks: / Spinning around.
7" Single: Released Sep '85, on Red Rhino, by Red Rhino Records. Catalogue no: **RED 60**
12" Single: Released Sep '85, on Red Rhino, by Red Rhino Records. Catalogue no: **REDT 60**

TAKE IT ALL
Tracks: / Take it all / Happy.
7" Single: Released Apr '83, on Red Rhino, by Red Rhino Records. Catalogue no: **RED 28**

TEMPTATION
Tracks: / Temptation.
7" Single: Released Aug '89, on Situation 2, by Beggars Banquet Records. Catalogue no: **SIT 060**
12" Single: Released Aug '89, on Situation 2, by Beggars Banquet Records. Catalogue no: **SIT 060T**

THIS TODAY
Tracks: / This today.
7" Single: Released Mar '84, on Red Rhino, by Red Rhino Records. Catalogue no: **RED 048**
12" Single: Released Mar '84, on Red Rhino, by Red Rhino Records. Catalogue no: **REDT 048**

WALKING ON YOUR HANDS
Tracks: / Walking on your hands.
7" Single: Released May '86, on Red Rhino, by Red Rhino Records. Catalogue no: **RED 66**
12" Single: Released May '86, on Red Rhino, by Red Rhino Records. Catalogue no: **REDT 66**

Red Rider

WHAT HAVE YOU GOT TO DO
Tracks: / What have you got to do / Laughing man.
7" Single: Released Jan '82, on Capitol, by EMI Records. Deleted Jan '85. Catalogue no: **CL 229**

WHITE HOT
Tracks: / White hot / Avenue 'A'.
7" Single: Released May '80, on Capitol, by EMI Records. Deleted May '83. Catalogue no: **CL 16139**

Red Rockers

CHINA
Tracks: / China / Voice of America.
7" Single: Released May '83, on CBS, by CBS Records. Catalogue no: **A 3245**
12" Single: Released May '83, on CBS, by CBS Records. Catalogue no: **TA 3245**

EVE OF DESTRUCTION
Tracks: / Eve of destruction / T.D.F. the truth.
7" Single: Released Jan '85, on CBS, by CBS Records. Catalogue no: **A 4816**

Red Rose

DANCE PAN FIRE
Tracks: / Dance pan fire.
7" Single: Released Apr '89, on Pickout, Catalogue no: **PICK 22**

IT'S REALLY LOVE
Tracks: / It's really love / Them a shock out.
12" Single: Released Nov '88, on Steely & Cleevie, Catalogue no: **VPRD 353**

LOVE IS SO AMAZING
Tracks: / Love is so amazing.
12" Single: Released Nov '88, on Steely & Cleevie, Catalogue no: **VPRD 352**

Red Shark

SOUR MASH
Tracks: / Sour mash.
7" Single: Released Jun '86, on Bite Back, Catalogue no: **BB 006**

Red Shoes

ALL FALL DOWN
Tracks: / All fall down.
7" Single: Released Nov '85, on Stepping Out, Catalogue no: **STEP EP1**

BY THE TIME IT GETS DARK
Tracks: / By the time it gets dark / Her song / Room with a view.
7" Single: Released May '87, on Mooncrest, by Trojan Records. Deleted May '88. Catalogue no: **MOON 1006**

Red, Snowy

I'M HURT
Tracks: / I'm hurt.
7" Single: Released Apr '82, on New Dance, Deleted Apr '85. Catalogue no: **DANCE 7002**

LONG RUN
Tracks: / Long run, The / Psychoscratch.
7" Single: Released Mar '84, on Soundworks, Catalogue no: **SW 7005**

Red Sovine

TEDDY BEAR
Tracks: / Teddy bear / Daddy.
7" Single: Released May '81, on RCA, by BMG Records (UK). Deleted May '84. Catalogue no: **RCA 80**

Red Star Belgrade

MAD DOGS AND ENGLISHMEN
Tracks: / Mad dogs and Englishmen / Barracadies.
7" Single: Released Apr '82, on Stagecoach, Catalogue no: **MAIL 36**

Red Sun

CINDERELLA ROCKAFELLA
Tracks: / Cinderella Rockafella / Superwoman.
7" Single: Released Feb '81, on Oliver D, Catalogue no: **OD 4141**

Red Turns To

DEEP SLEEP
Tracks: / Deep sleep.
12" Single: Released May '85, on Factory (1), by Factory Records. Catalogue no: **FAC 116T**

Red, White & Blues

WE'RE BRINGING THE WORLD CUP HOME
Tracks: / We're bringing the world cup home / Si si.
7" Single: Released Mar '82, on EMI, by EMI Records. Deleted '85. Catalogue no: **EMI 5282**

Redbone

WITCH QUEEN OF NEW ORLEANS
Tracks: / Witch Queen of New Orleans.
7" Single: Released Sep '71, on Epic, by CBS Records. Deleted '74. Catalogue no: **EPC 7351**
7" Single: Released Jan '80, on Lightning, Catalogue no: **LR 8272**

WITCH QUEEN OF NEW ORLEANS (OLD GOLD)
Tracks: / Witch Queen of New Orleans / Maggie.
7" Single: Released 27 Feb '89, on Old Gold, by Old Gold Records. Catalogue no: **OG 9868**

Redd Holt Unlimited

I SHOT THE SHERIFF
Tracks: / I shot the sheriff.
7" Single: Released Jul '80, on Charly, by Charly Records. Catalogue no: **CTD 123**

Redd, Sharon

CAN YOU HANDLE IT?
Tracks: / Can you handle it / Leaving you is easier said than done.
7" Single: Released Feb '81, on Epic, by CBS Records. Catalogue no: **EPC 9572**
12" Single: Released Feb '81, on Epic, by CBS Records. Catalogue no: **EPC 13-9572**
12" Single: Released Sep '87, on Prelude (Canada), Catalogue no: **SPEC 1209**

IN THE NAME OF LOVE
Tracks: / In the name of love / Send your love / Can you handle it.
7" Single: Released Jan '83, on Prelude, Deleted '86. Catalogue no: **PRLA 2905**

LOVE HOW YOU FEEL
Tracks: / Love how you feel.
7" Single: Released Oct '83, on Prelude, Deleted '86. Catalogue no: **A 3868**

LOVE IS GOING TO GET YOU
Tracks: / Love is going to get you / It's a lie.
7" Single: Released May '81, on Epic, by CBS Records. Deleted May '84. Catalogue no: **EPC A 1210**

NEVER GIVE YOU UP
Tracks: / Never give you up.
7" Single: Released Oct '82, on Prelude, Deleted '85. Catalogue no: **PRLA 2755**

TAKING A CHANCE ON LOVE
Tracks: / Taking a chance on love / You're the....
7" Single: Released Mar '83, on Prelude, Catalogue no: **PRLA 3197**
12" Single: Released Mar '83, on Prelude, Catalogue no: **PRLA 13 3197**

YOU'RE A WINNER
Tracks: / You're a winner / Activate.
7" Single: Released Jan '84, on Prelude, Catalogue no: **A 4127**
12" Single: Released Jan '84, on Prelude, Catalogue no: **TA 4127**

Redding, Otis

Biographical details: The great American soul singer and songwriter was born in 1941, one of a church minister's six children. Like many soul stars his early musical training was in the local church choir. When he began his secular vocal career at the end of the 50's his main influences were Little Richard -- who had emerged from Redding's home town of Macon, Georgia -- and Sam Cooke. After a few flops Redding had his first taste of success in the spring of 1963 with the self-penned ballad *These Arms Of Mine*, which entered both the US rhythm-and-blues and pop lists. He consolidated this chart toehold with his second single, *Pain In My Heart*. Both tracks were recorded at the seminal Stax/Volt studios in Memphis with the help of Booker T & The MGs. In the black music world of the 60's the Stax/Volt label provided the main challenge to the dominance of Tamla Motown. During 1965-67 Redding was the biggest and most important star of that stable. His forte was the soulful slowie: hits like *That's How Strong My Love Is*, *I've Been Loving You Too Long* and *Try A Little Tenderness* demonstrated his ability to discover every last drop of emotion in a song and convey it to the listener. But there were good uptempo numbers too -- he belted his way through stompers such as *I Can't Turn You Loose* and *Hard To Handle*. Tramps featured Redding in a successful collaboration with fellow soul singer Carla Thomas. In summer '67 he enjoyed two smashes in quick succession, as a writer for other artists: *Sweet Soul Music* was a US No 2 and UK Top Ten hit for his protege Arthur Conley, who composed the song with Redding, and Redding's hit *Respect* was successfully covered by Aretha Franklin, who took it to No 1 in American and the Top Ten in Britain. Sadly, Redding's only No 1 in his own right came after his death. While at the peak of his career the 26-year-old superstar was killed in a place crash in Lake Monona, Wisconsin, in December 1967. Several members of his backing group, the Bar-Kays, also lost their lives. Three days before his death he had recorded a track called *Sitting On The Dock Of The Bay.* Written and produced by famous Stax man Steve Cropper, *Dock Of The Bay* reached the top of the US chart in March '68 and climbed to No 3 in Britain, where an album of the same name was a posthumous No 1. Otis Redding's name lives on, and the best buy for any convert is the *Otis Blue* LP. Recorded in 1965 this is arguably the greatest soul album of the 60's. (Bob MacDonald, February 1986.)
Otis Redding was born in 1941 in Georgia; he was killed in a plane crash in December 1967. He was perhaps the greatest of male soul singers, the most popular black act of his time except for James Brown, and a fine songwriter as well. He first recorded at the tail end of a Stax recording session that had not gone well; he had 15 R&B hits in his lifetime, most in the top 10; many also crossed over to the pop Hot 100. He wrote and recorded *Respect* in 1965 an even bigger hit by Aretha Franklin two years later. His appearance at the Monterey Pop Festival in 1967 astonished a largely white audience and was captured on film; the festival inspired the beautiful *Sitting on the dock of the bay* (co-written with Steve Cropper), which was no one on both pop and R&B charts after he died. His plane crashed in the icy waters of one of Madison, Wisconsin's lakes,

1967 astonished a largely white audience and was captured on film; the festival inspired the beautiful *Sitting on the dock of the bay* (co-written with Steve Cropper), which was no one on both pop and R&B charts after he died. His plane crashed in the icy waters of one of Madison, Wisconsin's lakes, on the way to a gig there; four members of his backing group 'The Bar-Kays' were also killed. (Donald Clarke 21.5.88)

During the Sixties, the main rival to the Motown sound of Detroit came from Memphis' Stax/Volt labels. To of the latter's stars were Otis Redding and Carla Thomas, who were brought together in 1967 for a duet album entitled *King And Queen*. In terms of importance to and influence upon soul music, Otis truly deserved such an accolade; but in spite of her handful of memorable records, Carla certainly did not live up to the title. Nonetheless, *King And Queen* was a strong and successful soul LP which yielded a pair of Top 40 singles on both sides of the Atlantic - their rendition of Lowell Fulsom's *Tramp* reached No. 26 in the US and No. 18 in the UK, and the duo's remake of Eddie Floyd's *Knock On Wood* peaked at No. 30 in America an No. 35 in Britain.

A more accurate King/Queen alliance occured, also in 1967, when the true Queen of Soul Aretha Franklin scored a smash hit with her recording of Redding's *Respect*. Bob MacDonald, 21 February 1986..

DAY TRIPPER
Tracks: / Day tripper.
7" Single: Released Mar '67, on Stax, by Fantasy Inc (USA). Deleted '70. Catalogue no: **601 005**

DOCK OF THE BAY (SINGLE)
Tracks: / (Sittin' on) the dock of the bay.
7" Single: Released '74, on Atlantic, by WEA Records. Deleted '79. Catalogue no: **K 10126**

FA FA FA FA FA (SAD SONG)
Tracks: / Fa fa fa fa fa (sad song).
7" Single: Released Nov '66, on Atlantic, by WEA Records. Deleted '69. Catalogue no: **584 049**

HAPPY SONG
Tracks: / Happy song.
7" Single: Released May '68, on Stax, by Fantasy Inc (USA). Deleted '71. Catalogue no: **601 040**

HARD TO HANDLE
Tracks: / Hard to handle.
7" Single: Released Jul '68, on Atlantic, by WEA Records. Deleted '71. Catalogue no: **584 199**

I CAN'T TURN YOU LOOSE
Tracks: / I can't turn you loose.
7" Single: Released Aug '66, on Atlantic, by WEA Records. Deleted '69. Catalogue no: **584 030**

I CAN'T TURN YOU LOOSE (EP)
Tracks: / I can't turn you loose / Dock of the bay / Respect / Think.
7" EP: Released Apr '80, on Atlantic, by WEA Records. Deleted '83. Catalogue no: **ATM 2**

KNOCK ON WOOD
Tracks: / Knock on wood.
7" Single: Released Oct '67, on Stax, by Fantasy Inc (USA). Deleted '70. Catalogue no: **601 021**

LET ME COME ON HOME
Tracks: / Let me come on home.
7" Single: Released Mar '67, on Stax, by Fantasy Inc (USA). Deleted '70. Catalogue no: **601 007**

LOVE MAN (SINGLE)
Tracks: / Love man.
7" Single: Released Jul '69, on Atco, by Atlantic Recording Corp.(USA). Deleted '72. Catalogue no: **226 001**

MY GIRL
Tracks: / My girl.
7" Single: Released Nov '65, on Atlantic, by WEA Records. Deleted '68. Catalogue no: **AT 4050**
7" Single: Released '80, on Atlantic, by WEA Records. Catalogue no: **LR 1042**
7" Single: Released Feb '68, on Atlantic, by WEA Records. Deleted '71. Catalogue no: **584 092**
7" Single: Released Mar '84, on Atlantic, by WEA Records. Catalogue no: **K 10601**

MY LOVER'S PRAYER
Tracks: / My lover's prayer.
7" Single: Released Jul '66, on Atlantic, by WEA Records. Deleted '69. Catalogue no: **584 019**

SATISFACTION
Tracks: / Satisfaction.
7" Single: Released Apr '66, on Atlantic, by WEA Records. Deleted '69. Catalogue no: **AT 4080**

SHAKE
Tracks: / Shake.
7" Single: Released Jun '67, on Stax, by Fantasy Inc (USA). Deleted '70. Catalogue no: **601 011**

(SITTIN' ON THE) DOCK OF THE BAY
Tracks: / (Sittin' on) the dock of the bay.
7" Single: Released Oct '84, on Atlantic, by WEA Records. Deleted Jun '87. Catalogue no: **A 9607**
7" Single: Released Feb '68, on Stax, by Fantasy Inc (USA). Deleted '71. Catalogue no: **601 031**

(SITTIN' ON THE) DOCK OF THE BAY (OLD GOLD)
Tracks: / (Sittin' on) the dock of the bay / You don't miss your water.
7" Single: Released Jan '85, on Old Gold, by Old Gold Records. Catalogue no: **OG 9500**

TRY A LITTLE TENDERNESS
Tracks: / Try a little tenderness / I've been loving you too long / Hard to handle (On 12" only).
Note: Pic bag
7" Single: Released Jan '67, on Atlantic, by WEA Records. Deleted '70. Catalogue no: **584 070**
7" Single: Released May '87, on Atlantic, by WEA Records. Deleted Jan '88. Catalogue no: **YZ 117**
12" Single: Released May '87, on Atlantic, by WEA Records. Deleted Jan '88. Catalogue no: **YZ 117 T**

Redding, Otis & Carla

TRAMP
Tracks: / Tramp / Ooh Otis ooh Carla.
7" Single: Released Jul '67, on Stax, by Fantasy Inc (USA). Deleted '70. Catalogue no: **601 012**
12" Single: Released Apr '80, on Atlantic, by WEA Records. Catalogue no: **ATM 5**

Redding,George

GIVE ME YOUR BODY
Tracks: / Give me your body.
7" Single: Released Oct '85, on Solida, by Solida Leisure Records. Deleted Jun '89. Catalogue no: **SOLIDS 100**
12" Single: Released Oct '85, on Solida, by Solida Leisure Records. Deleted Jun '89. Catalogue no: **SOLIDT 100**

I WISH
Tracks: / I wish / Let's give love a try.
7" Single: Released Nov '81, on Major Record, by The Major Record Company. Catalogue no: **IHS 3711**

Reddings

PARASITE
Tracks: / Parasite / In my pants.
7" Single: Released Jul '85, on Boiling Point, by Polydor Ltd. Catalogue no: **POSP 738**
12" Single: Released Jul '85, on Boiling Point, by Polydor Ltd. Catalogue no: **POSPX 738**

REMOTE CONTROL
Tracks: / Remote control / Awakening.
7" Single: Released Jan '81, on Epic, by CBS Records. Deleted Jan '84. Catalogue no: **EPC 9360**

Reddington, Amanda

FATAL ATTRACTION
Tracks: / Fatal attraction / Fatal attraction (version).
CD 5": Released Aug '89, on RCA, by BMG Records (UK). Catalogue no: **PD 42908**
7" Single: Released Aug '89, on RCA, by BMG Records (UK). Catalogue no: **PB 42907**
12" Single: Released Aug '89, on RCA, by BMG Records (UK). Catalogue no: **PT 42908**

Redds & The Boys

MOVIN' AND GROOVIN'
Tracks: / Movin' and groovin' / Movin' and groovin' (Crackdown version).
7" Single: Released Feb '85, on Washington Go Go, Deleted '86. Catalogue no: **GOGO 1**
12" Single: Released Feb '85, on Washington Go Go, Deleted '86. Catalogue no: **12 GOGO 1**

PUT YOUR RIGHT HAND IN THE AIR
Tracks: / Put your right hand in the air put your left hand down your (...underwear.) / Rare essence / Soo-be-doo-wop.
7" Single: Released Jun '85, on London Records, by London Records. Catalogue no: **GOEP 1**

Reddy, Helen

Biographical details: Helen Reddy was born in 1942 in Melbourne, Australia; she was a favourite singer on USA FM radio while pop music went through a sedate period: she had 14 top 40 hits in the USA 1971-1977. She came from a show-biz family, made her stage debut at age 4 and won a talent contest prixe in 1966: A trip to the USA. Her 1977 album *Ear Candy* might have been named after the type of FM programming she was (perhaps unfairly) identified with. As big hits stopped she also worked as a TV actress. (Donald Clarke 21.5.88).

REDSKINS - BRING IT DOWN (Released on Decca)

ANGIE BABY
Tracks: / Angie baby.
7" Single: Released Jan '75, on Capitol, by EMI Records. Deleted '78. Catalogue no: **CL 15799**
7" Single: Released '80, on Capitol, by EMI Records. Catalogue no: **LR 0385**

I CAN'T SAY GOODBYE TO YOU
Tracks: / I can't say goodbye to you / Save me.
7" Single: Released Sep '81, on MCA, by MCA Records. Catalogue no: **MCA 744**

LOOKS LIKE LOVE
Tracks: / Looks like love / Yesterday can't....
7" Single: Released Feb '83, on MCA, by MCA Records. Catalogue no: **MCA 809**

TAKE WHAT YOU FIND
Tracks: / Take what you find / Love's not the question.
7" Single: Released May '80, on Capitol, by EMI Records. Deleted May '85. Catalogue no: **CL 16147**

TAKE WHAT YOU FIND (SINGLE)
Tracks: / Take what you find / Take what you find (pt 2).
7" Single: Released Jun '80, on Capitol, by EMI Records. Deleted Jun '83. Catalogue no: **12CL 16147**

Rednite

GUY LIKE ME
Tracks: / Crying over you.
7" Single: Released Jan '87, on Free Booze, by Magnum Music Group. Catalogue no: **PINT 2734**

Redrose, Anthony

BANG AROUND
Tracks: / Bang around / Elegant lover / Teazer.
12" Single: Released Apr '86, on Firehouse, Catalogue no: **FH 003**

CAN'T DRESS
Tracks: / Can't dress.
12" Single: Released Jul '89, on Sir Coxsone, Catalogue no: **BD 8911**

CAN'T KNOCK ME
Tracks: / Can't knock me / Gwan talk / Stay with me.
12" Single: Released Apr '86, on Firehouse, Catalogue no: **FH 001**

CANTA
Tracks: / Canta / Up lender.
12" Single: Released Apr '86, on Firehouse, Catalogue no: **FH 004**

FRAID A PRISON
Tracks: / Fraid a prison / Josephine.
12" Single: Released Jun '86, on Toughest, Catalogue no: **RRD 54**

LAUNCH AND ATTACK
Tracks: / Launch and attack / Visit, The.
12" Single: Released Oct '86, on Aces Music, Catalogue no: **ACES 004**

ME NO WANT NO BOOPS
Tracks: / Me no want no boops / No call me no boops.
12" Single: Released Jul '86, on Firehouse, Catalogue no: **FH 008**

OH CAROL
Tracks: / Oh Carol.
7" Single: Released May '89, on Power House, Catalogue no: **UNKNOWN**

SHAKA ZULU
Tracks: / Shaka Zulu.
12" Single: Released May '88, on Pioneer Muzik, Catalogue no: **PM 007**

SOUND BOY GET NERVOUS
Tracks: / Sound boy get nervous / Love me country.
12" Single: Released Jul '86, on BP International, Catalogue no: **BPNINT 001**

TEMPO
Tracks: / Tempo.
12" Single: Released Nov '85, on Firehouse, Catalogue no: **Unknown**

TENDER LOVE
Tracks: / Tender love.
12" Single: Released Feb '88, on Live & Love, Catalogue no: **LLD 62**

Reds

DANGER/DO YOU PLAY THE GAME
Tracks: / Danger / Do you play the game.
7" Single: Released Oct '81, on Kingdom, by Kingdom Records. Deleted '83. Catalogue no: **KV 8019**

Redskins

BRING IT DOWN (THIS INSANE THING) (See panel above)
Tracks: / Bring it down (this insane thing) / You want it? They've got it.
7" Single: Released Jun '85, on Decca, by Decca Records. Deleted '88. Catalogue no: **F2**
12" Single: Released Jun '85, on Decca, by Decca Records. Deleted '88. Catalogue no: **FX2**

IT CAN BE DONE
Tracks: / It can be done / Koko / Let's make it work / Plateful of hate, A.
10" single: Released May '86, on Decca, by Decca Records. Deleted '88. Catalogue no: **FXT 4**
7" Single: Released May '86, on Decca, by Decca Records. Deleted '88. Catalogue no: **F4**

KEEP ON KEEPING ON
Tracks: / Keep on keeping on.
7" Single: Released Oct '84, on Decca, by Decca Records. Deleted '88. Catalogue no: **F1**
12" Single: Released Oct '84, on Decca, by Decca Records. Deloted '88. Catalogue no: **FX1**

KICK OVER THE STATUES
Tracks: / Kick over the statues.

7" Single: Released Nov '85, on Abstract Dance, by Priority Records. Deleted Nov '87. Catalogue no: **AD 6**

LEAN ON ME
Tracks: / Lean on me / Unionize.
7" Single: Released Jul '83, on CNT, Catalogue no: **CNT 016**
12" Single: Released Jul '83, on CNT, Catalogue no: **CNTX 016**

LEV BRONSTEIN
Tracks: / Lev Bronstein / Peasant army, The.
7" Single: Released Jul '82, on CNT, Catalogue no: **CNT 007**

PEEL SESSIONS:REDSKINS 9.10.82
12" Single: Released Jun '87, on Strange Fruit, by Strange Fruit Records. Catalogue no: **SFPS 030**

POWER IS YOURS, THE
Tracks: / Power is yours, The / 99 1/2 (won't do) / Take 3 / Take your goods and buy them.
7" Set: Released Feb '86, on London Records, by London Records. Catalogue no: **FXT 3**
7" Single: Released Feb '86, on London Records, by London Records. Catalogue no: **F 3**
12" Single: Released Feb '86, on London Records, by London Records. Catalogue no: **FX 3**

Redtone, Leon

SEDUCED
Tracks: / Seduced / Te na na.
7" Single: Released Jun '81, on City, by City Records. Deleted Jun '84. Catalogue no: **K 11589**

Reducers

AIRWAYS
Tracks: / Airways / Waiting for no one.
7" Single: Released Feb '80, on EMI, by EMI Records. Deleted '83. Catalogue no: **EMI 5028**

Redundants

ON YER BIKE/MY BABY'S GONE
Tracks: / On yer bike / My baby's gone.
7" Single: Released May '82, on Leo Records, by Leo Records. Catalogue no: **LEO 1003**

Redway, Mike

COME ON HOME
Tracks: / Come on home / Georgie Sunday.
7" Single: on Aveca, Catalogue no: **AVECA 003**

DON'T PUT ME ON HOLD
Tracks: / Don't put me on hold / Good morning.
7" Single: Released Mar '88, on Redrock, by Redrock Records. Catalogue no: **RR 501**

DON'T WANNA BE FAMOUS/BLUE SUNRISE
Tracks: / Don't wanna be famous / Blue sunrise.
7" Single: Released Sep '82, on Go Ahead, by Go Ahead Records. Catalogue no: **GA 114**

IT TAKES ONLY A MOMENT
Tracks: / It takes only a moment.
7" Single: Released Feb '89, on Redrock, by Redrock Records. Catalogue no: **REDR 6**

MORRIS MINOR/HAPPY BIRTHDAY TO YOU
Tracks: / Morris minor / Happy birthday to you.
7" Single: Released Nov '81, on Button, by Musical Characters Records. Catalogue no: **BTN 101**

OUR ANNIVERSARY OF LOVE (SINGLE)
Tracks: / Our anniversary of love / Someday the loving will be.
7" Single: Released Jun '86, on Aveca, Catalogue no: **AVECA 001**

ROCK AND ROLL YOU'RE BEAUTIFUL
Tracks: / What are you like love / Rock and roll you're beautiful.
7" Single: Released Jan '82, on Go Ahead, by Go Ahead Records. Catalogue no: **GA 0112**
7" Single: Released Jan '87, on Aveca, Catalogue no: **AVECA 002**

SHOW IS OVER
Tracks: / Show is over, The.
7" Single: Released May '83, on Go Ahead, by Go Ahead Records. Catalogue no: **GA 116**

TOO MANY HEARTACHES
Tracks: / Too many heartaches / Eva's song.
7" Single: Released Oct '88, on Redrock, by Redrock Records. Catalogue no: **REDR 5**

WEDDING BELLS
Tracks: / Wedding Bells / I'm yours.
7" Single: Released Jun '81, on Crystal, by President Records. Deleted Jun '82. Catalogue no: **CR 7032**

WHAT ARE YOU LIKE LOVE/HEAVEN ONLY KNOWS
Tracks: / What are you like love / Heaven only knows.
7" Single: Released Aug '83, on Go Ahead, by Go Ahead Records. Catalogue no: **GA 117**

Reece

YOU'RE MINE
Tracks: / You're mine.
7" Single: Released Aug '89, on Kool Kat, by Kool Kat Records. Catalogue no: **KOOL 506**
12" Single: Released Aug '89, on Kool Kat, by Kool Kat Records. Catalogue no: **KOOLT 506**

Reed, Al

I AM FED UP WITH THIS MUSIC
Tracks: / I am fed up with this music.
12" Single: Released Mar '82, on Ice Cube (1), Catalogue no: **C 5926**

Reed, Curtis

EXIT 23
Tracks: / Exit 23.
7" Single: Released Oct '87, on Expansion, Catalogue no: **EXPAND 9**

Reed, Dan

GET TO YOU
Tracks: / Get to you(12" mix) (Only on 12" version & CD single.) / Forgot to make her mine / Get to you (album mix) (Only on CD single.) / Halfway round the world (LP version) (Only on the CD single.).
CD 5": Released Oct '88, on Mercury, by Phonogram Ltd. Catalogue no: **MERCD 269**
7" Single: Released Oct '88, on Mercury, by Phonogram Ltd. Deleted 31 May '89. Catalogue no: **MER 269**
12" Single: Released Oct '88, on Mercury, by Phonogram Ltd. Deleted 31 May '89. Catalogue no: **MERX 269**

TIGER IN A DRESS
Tracks: / Tiger in a dress / Affection / Seven sisters (Available on 12" only) / Get to you (Available on CD and MC single only).
CD 5": Released Sep '89, on Mercury, by Phonogram Ltd. Catalogue no: **DRNCD 1**
Cassingle: Released Sep '89, on Mercury, by Phonogram Ltd. Catalogue no: **DRNMC**
7" Single: Released Sep '89, on Mercury, by Phonogram Ltd. Catalogue no: **DRN 1**
12" Single: Released Sep '89, on Mercury, by Phonogram Ltd. Catalogue no: **DRN 112**

Reed, Herb

EVERYBODY GET TOGETHER
Tracks: / Everybody get together / Ruby let me down.
7" Single: Released Feb '80, on PVK, by PVK Records. Deleted Feb '83. Catalogue no: **PV 34**

Reed, Jimmy

Biographical details: Reed, Jimmy was born Mathis James Reed in 1925 in Mississippi; he suffered from epilepsy from the mid-'50's and died in his sleep in 1976 in California, but not before becoming a much-loved and influential blues singer and songwriter; he also played guitar and harmonica. He signed with Vee-Jay in Chicago and had 13 influential R&B hits 1956-61 (including 12 crossovers to the pop Hot 100); *Baby what you want me to do* was covered by Elvis Presley, and *Honest I do* by Aretha Franklin and the Rolling Stones. Vee-Jay went broke; Reed came back to the R&B chart in 1966 on Exodus with *Knocking at your door.* His laid-back style avoided the menace and dread of some other bluesmen, he was one of the first to use a neck mount so that he could play mouth harp and guitar at the same time. His wife Mary Lee 'Mama' Reed wrote many of his songs. (Donald Clarke 21.5.88).

SHAME SHAME SHAME
Tracks: / Shame shame shame / Big boss man.
7" Single: Released Sep '64, on Stateside, by EMI Records. Deleted '67. Catalogue no: **SS 330**
7" Single: Released Jul '80, on Charly, by Charly Records. Deleted '87. Catalogue no: **CTD 105**

Reed, Junior

RUBBA DUBBING
Tracks: / Rubba dubbing / Rubba dubbing (instrumental).
7" Single: Released Sep '84, on Black Roots, Catalogue no: **BR 330**

THANKS AND PRAISE
Tracks: / Thanks and praise / Dub praises.
12" Single: Released Jan '85, on W.O.W., Catalogue no: **WOW 103**

REAL TO REEL - LOVE ME LIKE THIS (Released on Arista)

Reed, Les

MAN OF ACTION
Tracks: / Man of action.
7" Single: Released '80, on Decca, by Decca Records. Catalogue no: **LR 4684**

Reed, Lou

Biographical details: Reed, Lou was born Louis Firbank in 1943 in New York. The influential singer, songwriter and guitarist came to fame as a founder member of the Velvet Underground 1965-70 after studying poetry and journalism at Syracuse (NY) University. His departure from the Velvets during sessions for Loaded was acrimonious; after a period of hibernation he distanced himself from the NYC scene which until then had fueled his writing muse; he went to England to make Lou Reed in 1972, perhaps too smooth to be convincing: his customary venom was lost. Transformer in 1972 saw him back in form, probably still his best album; produced by David Bowie and his guitarist Mick Ronson, both longtime fans, it had decadence written all over it: *Walk on the wild side* was a shock No.10 UK/16 USA hit, despite a line about 'giving head' that the censors missed. The concept LP *Berlin* in 1973 totally lacked his self-mocking humour and failed to sell, is now seen as lost masterpiece. Disillusioned by critical/public nonacceptance of *Berlin,* he went heavy metal for the live *Rock 'n' roll animal* (revamped versions of old hits) and the disco-fied *Sally can't dance*; after *Lou Reed Live* in 1975, he made a perverse 2-disc set of white noise *Metal machine music,* winning a release from his RCA contract after the mellower *Coney Island Baby* in 1976. His LP's for Arista lacked originality in the late '70's, except for the title track of *Street Hassle*; his second marriage in 1980 seemed to revitalise his muse and the best of his later albums was *Mistrial* in 1984, with its hit single *I Love you Suzanne.* At it's best his narrative songwriting is harrowing, and certainly unique. (Donald Clarke 21.5.88).

BLUE MASK (SINGLE)
Tracks: / Blue mask / Walk on the wild side.
12" Single: Released Dec '83, on RCA, by BMG Records (UK). Catalogue no: **PC 9352**

DIRTY BOULEVARD
Tracks: / Dirty boulevard / Last great American whale / Room, The.
7" Single: Released Feb '89, on Sire, by Sire Records. Catalogue no: **W 7547**
12" Single: Released Feb '89, on Sire, by Sire Records. Catalogue no: **W 7547T**

I LOVE YOU, SUZANNE
Tracks: / I love you, Suzanne / Vicious / Walk on the wild side.
7" Single: Released May '84, on RCA, by BMG Records (UK). Catalogue no: **RCA 417**
12" Single: Released May '84, on RCA, by BMG Records (UK). Deleted '87. Catalogue no: **RCAT 417**

NO MONEY DOWN
Tracks: / No money down / Don't hurt a woman / No money down (ext. version) / No money down (Dub version).
7" Single: Released Jun '86, on RCA, by BMG Records (UK). Deleted May '89. Catalogue no: **RCA 501**
12" Single: Released Sep '86, on RCA (Germany), Catalogue no: **PT 49844**
12" Single: Released Jun '86, on RCA, by BMG Records (UK). Catalogue no: **RCAT 501**

SEPTEMBER SONG
Tracks: / September song.
7" Single: Released Oct '85, on A&M, by A&M Records. Deleted '88. Catalogue no: **AM 283**

WALK ON THE WILD SIDE (OLD GOLD)
Tracks: / Walk on the wild side.
7" Single: Released Mar '89, on Old Gold, by Old Gold Records. Catalogue no: **OG 9635**

WALK ON THE WILD SIDE (SINGLE)
Tracks: / Walk on the wild side / Vicious.
CD 5": Released Jun '89, on RCA, by BMG Records (UK). Catalogue no: **PD 49453**
7" Single: Released Aug '81, on Golden Grooves, by BMG Records (UK). Deleted May '89. Catalogue no: **GOLD 523**
7" Single: Released May '73, on RCA, by BMG Records (UK). Deleted '76. Catalogue no: **RCA 2303**

Reed, Marc

ONE BODY
Tracks: / One body / One body (remix).
7" Single: Released May '86, on 20/20, by 20/20 Records. Catalogue no: **MR 1**
12" Single: Released May '86, on 20/20, by 20/20 Records. Catalogue no: **MRT 1**

Reed, Mike

CHARLIE NOT SO GOOD
Tracks: / Charlie not so good.
7" Single: Released Dec '86, on Red Bus, by Red Bus Records. Deleted '88. Catalogue no: **RBUS 2210**

Reedy, Winston

AMBITION
Tracks: / Ambition.
12" Single: Released Sep '85, on DEP International, by DEP International Records. Deleted '89. Catalogue no: **DEP 21-12**

BABY LOVE
Tracks: / Baby love.
12" Single: Released Oct '84, on Inner Light, Catalogue no: **DTL 104**

BEING WITH YOU
Tracks: / Being with you.
7" Single: Released Nov '81, on P.R.O., Catalogue no: **PRO 002**
12" Single: Released Nov '81, on P.R.O., Catalogue no: **PRO D 002**

DAUGHTER OF ZION
Tracks: / Daughter of Zion.
12" Single: Released Mar '82, on S & G (2), Catalogue no: **SG 17**

DIM THE LIGHT
Tracks: / Dim the light / Showers of rain.
7" Single: Released Feb '3, on Carousel (1),

by Carousel Records. Catalogue no: **7 CAR 4**

EVERY DAY I WRITE THE BOOK
Tracks: / Everyday I write the book.
7" Single: Released Aug '86, on Priority, by Priority Records. Deleted Nov '87. Catalogue no: **P 14**
12" Single: Released Aug '86, on Priority, by Priority Records. Deleted Nov '87. Catalogue no: **PX 14**

LEAVING ME
Tracks: / Leaving me.
12" Single: Released 21 Nov '87, on J.R. Production, Catalogue no: **TKJR 34**

MOI EMMA OH
Tracks: / Moi Emma oh / Lend me.
12" Single: Released Aug '83, on Inner Light, Catalogue no: **IN 001**

PARADISE IN YOUR EYES
Tracks: / Paradise in your eyes.
12" Single: Released Aug '82, on Dasala, Catalogue no: **DAS 001**

PERSONALLY SPEAKING
Tracks: / Personally speaking.
12" Single: Released May '84, on Inner Light, Catalogue no: **DLT 102**

REGGAE MAN
Tracks: / Reggae man / Everyday I write the book.
7" Single: Released Jul '87, on Priority, by Priority Records. Deleted Nov '87. Catalogue no: **P 16**
7" Single: Released Mar '87, on I.R.S, Catalogue no: **P 16**
12" Single: Released Jul '87, on Priority, by Priority Records. Deleted Nov '87. Catalogue no: **PX 16**

SUPERSTAR
Tracks: / Superstar / Baby love.
7" Single: Released Mar '85, on DEP International, by DEP International Records. Deleted '89. Catalogue no: **DEP 17**
12" Single: Released Mar '85, on DEP International, by DEP International Records. Deleted '89. Catalogue no: **DEP 17-12**

TALKING BLUES
Tracks: / Talking blues.
12" Single: Released Sep '88, on One & One, Catalogue no: **DW 001**

Reego & Yvonne

PATTERNS
Tracks: / Patterns / Rise above the cloud.
7" Single: Released Aug '82, on Medical (USA), Catalogue no: **MED 1**

Reegs

SEE MY FRIENDS
Tracks: / See my friends.
12" Single: Released Apr '89, on Imaginary, by Imaginary Records. Catalogue no: **MIRAGE 006**

Reels

PREFAB HEART
Tracks: / Prefab heart / Spot the ridge.
7" Single: Released Mar '80, on Back Door (Holland), Deleted '83. Catalogue no: **DOOR 3**

Rees, Tony

VIVA EL FULHAM
Tracks: / Viva el Fulham.
7" Single: Released May '75, on Sonet, by Sonet Records. Deleted '78. Catalogue no: **SON 2059**

Reese & Santonio

BACK TO THE BEAT (WITH THE SOUND)
Tracks: / Back to the beat / Rock to the beat (shortened beats) / Sound, The (acid remix) (Only on 12" single.).
Note: The original house sound of Detroit, recently imitated on the New York club scene, now re-recorded by techno-genius producer Kevin Saunderson.
7" Single: Released Jun '88, on Polygram, by PolyGram UK Ltd. Deleted Oct '88. Catalogue no: **FFR 7**
12" Single: Released Jun '88, on Polygram, by PolyGram UK Ltd. Deleted Oct '88. Catalogue no: **FFRX 7**

SOUND, THE
Tracks: / Sound, The / How to play our music.
12" Single: Released 27 Feb '88, on Kool Kat, by Kool Kat Records. Catalogue no: **KOOLT 15**

STRUCTURE
Tracks: / Structure / Truth of self-evidence / Grab the beat (12" only).
7" Single: Released Nov '88, on ffrr, by London Records. Deleted May '89. Catalogue no: **FFR 15**
12" Single: Released Nov '88, on ffrr, by London Records. Deleted 29 Jun '89. Catalogue no: **FFRXR 15**
12" Single: Released Nov '88, on ffrr, by London Records. Deleted 29 Jun '89. Catalogue no: **FFRX 15**

Reeves, Chris

DINING AT DZERZHINSKY'S
Tracks: / Dining at Dzerzhinsky's / Floor show at Dzerzhinsky's.
7" Single: Released Jun '82, on Y, Catalogue no: **Y 23**
12" Single: Released Jun '82, on Y, Catalogue no: **12 Y 23**

Reeves, Dianne

Biographical details: Dianne Reeves was born in 1956 in Detroit. She is a jazz singer with a lovely contalto voice and a range of 3.5 octaves. She grew up in Denver, was discovered at 17 by Clarke Terry and sang with his band; moved to Los Angeles and worked with Sergio Mendez, Harry Belafonte and others; she was a sensation at a Monterey Jazz Festival backed by Tito Puente. After two LP's on Palo Alto she made her Blue Note debut in 1987. (Donald Clarke 21.5.88).

BETTER DAYS
Tracks: / Better days (Exta track on 12" version only.) / Better days (re-mix) / That's all.
Note: * extra track on 12" version.
7" Single: Released May '88, on Blue Note, by EMI Records. Deleted Nov '88. Catalogue no: **BLUE 5**
12" Single: Released May '88, on Blue Note, by EMI Records. Deleted Nov '88. Catalogue no: **12BLUE 5**

Reeves, Jim

Biographical details: Reeves, Jim was born in Galloway, Texas in 1924; he died in a plane crash in 1964. He was the first big country crossover artist, and one of the most popular of all time he removed the the sound of steel guitar and fiddles from his sound and created a pop-country style which scored international hits. He played baseball with the st Louis cardinals, but a leg injury stopped his sports career; he became a DJ and newsreader in Texas and soon performed on the Louisiana Hayride. His first hits were on Abbott, scoring a number one country hit with *Mexican Joe*, a number two with *Bimbo*; RCA bought his contract including the Abbott masters; he scored more than 40 top ten hits in the country chart altogether, 25 hits in pop Hot 100. First RCA hit with his own song *Yonder comes a sucker* in 1955; top tens included his own *Am I losing you?* and *Four walls* in 1957 (latter written by Marvin Moore and George Campbell; his biggest pop hit at number two in both country and pop charts); *Billy Bayou, He'll have to go, I guess I'm crazy* were all number ones. After his death he had number one country hits; the hits continued through the 1970's many given new updated backing tracks. Deborah Allen duetted with a Reeves record for top 10 hit *Take me in your arms and hold me* in 1980; Owen Bradley created duets on tape by superstars Reeves and Patsy Cline, who never recorded together when they were alive including top 10 *Have you ever been lonely* in 1981. (Donald Clarke 21.5.88).

ADIOS AMIGO
Tracks: / Adios amigo / Guilty.
7" Single: Released Jun '62, on RCA (USA), Deleted '65. Catalogue no: **RCA 1293**
7" Single: Released '80, on RCA (USA), Catalogue no: **LR 1213**

ANGEL'S DON'T LIE
Tracks: / Angel's don't lie.
7" Single: Released Sep '70, on RCA, by BMG Records (UK). Deleted '73. Catalogue no: **RCA 1997**

BUT YOU LOVE ME DADDY
Tracks: / But you love me daddy.
7" Single: Released Oct '69, on RCA, by BMG Records (UK). Deleted '72. Catalogue no: **RCA 1899**

DISTANT DRUMS (OLD GOLD)
Tracks: / Distant drums.
7" Single: Released Oct '86, on Old Gold, by Old Gold Records. Catalogue no: **OG 9612**

DISTANT DRUMS (SINGLE)
Tracks: / Distant drums.
7" Single: Released Aug '66, on RCA, by BMG Records (UK). Deleted '69. Catalogue no: **RCA 1537**

FOUR WALLS
Tracks: / Four walls / Bimbo.
7" Single: Released '80, on RCA (USA), Catalogue no: **LR 1283**

GUILTY
Tracks: / Guilty.
7" Single: Released Oct '63, on RCA, by BMG Records (UK). Deleted '66. Catalogue no: **RCA 1364**

HE'LL HAVE TO GO
Tracks: / He'll have to go.
7" Single: Released Mar '60, on RCA, by BMG Records (UK). Deleted '63. Catalogue no: **RCA 1168**
7" Single: Released '80, on RCA (USA), Catalogue no: **LR 1264**

HOW LONG HAS IT BEEN
Tracks: / How long has it been.
7" Single: Released May '65, on RCA, by BMG Records (UK). Deleted '68. Catalogue no: **RCA 1445**

I HEARD A HEART BREAK LAST NIGHT
Tracks: / I heard a heart break last night.
7" Single: Released Nov '67, on RCA, by BMG Records (UK). Deleted '70. Catalogue no: **RCA 1643**

I LOVE YOU BECAUSE (OLD GOLD)
Tracks: / I love you because / He'll have to go.
7" Single: Released Oct '86, on Old Gold, by Old Gold Records. Catalogue no: **OG 9607**

I LOVE YOU BECAUSE (SINGLE)
Tracks: / I love you because / He'll have to go / Moonlight and roses.
7" Single: Released Jun '71, on RCA, by BMG Records (UK). Deleted '74. Catalogue no: **RCA 2092**
7" Single: Released Feb '64, on RCA, by BMG Records (UK). Deleted '67. Catalogue no: **RCA 1385**

I WON'T COME IN WHILE HE'S THERE
Tracks: / I won't come in while he's there.
7" Single: Released Feb '67, on RCA, by BMG Records (UK). Deleted '70. Catalogue no: **RCA 1563**

I WON'T FORGET YOU
Tracks: / I won't forget you.
7" Single: Released Jun '64, on RCA, by BMG Records (UK). Deleted '67. Catalogue no: **RCA 1400**

I'M GONNA CHANGE EVERYTHING
Tracks: / I'm gonna change everything.
7" Single: Released Nov '62, on RCA, by BMG Records (UK). Deleted '65. Catalogue no: **RCA 1317**

IS IT REALLY OVER
Tracks: / Is it really over.
7" Single: Released Nov '65, on RCA, by BMG Records (UK). Deleted '68. Catalogue no: **RCA 1488**

IT HURTS SO MUCH
Tracks: / It hurts so much to see you go.
7" Single: Released Feb '65, on RCA, by BMG Records (UK). Deleted '68. Catalogue no: **RCA 1437**

NOBODY'S FOOL
Tracks: / Nobody's fool.
7" Single: Released Mar '70, on RCA, by BMG Records (UK). Deleted '73. Catalogue no: **RCA 1915**

NOT UNTIL THE NEXT TIME
Tracks: / Not until the next time.
7" Single: Released Apr '65, on RCA, by BMG Records (UK). Deleted '68. Catalogue no: **RCA 1446**

PRETTY BROWN EYES
Tracks: / Pretty brown eyes.
7" Single: Released Mar '68, on RCA, by BMG Records (UK). Deleted '71. Catalogue no: **RCA 1672**

THERE'S A HEARTACHE FOLLOWING ME
Tracks: / There's a heartache following me.
7" Single: Released Nov '64, on RCA, by BMG Records (UK). Deleted '67. Catalogue no: **RCA 1423**

THIS WORLD IS NOT MY HOME
Tracks: / This world is not my home.
7" Single: Released Jul '65, on RCA, by BMG Records (UK). Deleted '68. Catalogue no: **RCA 1412**

TRYING TO FORGET
Tracks: / Trying to forget.
7" Single: Released Jul '67, on RCA, by BMG Records (UK). Deleted '70. Catalogue no: **RCA 1611**

WELCOME TO MY WORLD (OLD GOLD)
Tracks: / Welcome to my world.
7" Single: Released Nov '86, on Old Gold, by Old Gold Records. Catalogue no: **OG 9649**

WELCOME TO MY WORLD (SINGLE)
Tracks: / Welcome to my world.
7" Single: Released Jun '63, on RCA, by BMG Records (UK). Deleted '66. Catalogue no: **RCA 1342**
7" Single: Released Oct '81, on RCA Golden Grooves, by BMG Records (UK). Catalogue no: **GOLD 539**

WHEN TWO WORLDS COLLIDE
Tracks: / When two worlds collide.
7" Single: Released Jun '69, on RCA, by BMG Records (UK). Deleted '72. Catalogue no: **RCA 1830**

WHISPERING HOPE
Tracks: / Whispering hope.
7" Single: Released Mar '61, on RCA, by BMG Records (UK). Deleted '64. Catalogue no: **RCA 1223**

YOU'RE FREE TO GO
Tracks: / You're free to go.
7" Single: Released Feb '72, on RCA, by BMG Records (UK). Deleted '75. Catalogue no: **RCA 2174**

YOU'RE THE ONLY GOOD THING
Tracks: / You're the only good thing.
7" Single: Released Nov '61, on RCA, by BMG Records (UK). Deleted '64. Catalogue no: **RCA 1261**

Reeves, Martha & The

Biographical details: At the time of their greatest success, this American vocal group consisted of lead singer Martha Reeves plus Rosalind Ashford and Betty Kelly. In the later stages of their career, the group were credited as Martha Reeves & The Vandellas rather than just Martha & the Vandellas. They were so named because they started out as backing vocalists on Marvin Gaye's records, and were jokingly accused of stealing the limelight from him - thus vandals became Vandellas.
Martha Reeves was born in the right place at the right time. Born in Detroit in 1941, she was at just the right age when the city's Tamla Motown organisation grew into a major musical force in the early Sixties. She actually joined the company as a secretary and a demo-tape singer. She and the other girls got their chance to sing on a Gaye disc (*Stubborn kind of fellow*) when somebody else fell ill. After several more Marvin tracks, Martha & The Vandellas became a group in their own right. The trio's second single *Come and get these memories* became their first US Top 40 single in 1963. Over the next two years, they chalked US Top smashes with *Heatwave, Quicksand, Dancing in the streets* and *Nowhere to run*. Biggies like *I'm ready for love* and *Jimmy Mack* kept the hits going till the late Sixties. Although overshadowed by another Motown female vocal threesomes, Diana Ross and the Supremes, the slightly raunchier sound of Martha Reeves & The Vandellas was a vital part of the label's classic Sixties era. Martha's bluesy voice was one of the company's best assets. Their material was drawn from several sources, including Tamla's legendary Holland/Dozier/Holland team and Marvin Gaye, who co-wrote the group's biggest and most famous hit *Dancing in the street* (No.2 in US in 1964 and, belatedly, No.4 in UK in 1969). This ecstatic anthem was covered in 1985 by David Bowie and Mick Jagger, whose excellent record and video of the song was one of the most memorable contributions to Live Aid.
As the group's star faded in the States during the late Seventies, Britain was only just waking up to them. Several old hits became UK successes anew, and 1971's *Forget me not*, which had only been a minor US hit, reached No.11 in the UK. The advice of that title was not heede by the public, and the group were eventually forgotten on both sides of the Atlantic. They split in 1973. Martha pursued a solo career on various labels during the mid to late Seventies, but this was quite unsuccessful. (Bob MacDonald, 22nd Jan 1986).

BLESS YOU
Tracks: / Bless you.
7" Single: Released Jan '72, on Tamla Motown, by Motown Records (UK). Deleted '75. Catalogue no: **TMG 794**

DANCING IN THE STREET
Tracks: / Dancing in the street.
7" Single: Released Oct '64, on Stateside, by EMI Records. Deleted '67. Catalogue no: **SS 345**
7" Single: Released Jan '69, on Tamla Motown, by Motown Records (UK). Deleted '72. Catalogue no: **TMG 684**
7" Single: Released Jun '83, on Motown, by BMG Records (UK). Catalogue no: **TMG 1176**

FORGET ME NOT
Tracks: / Forget me not / I'm ready.
7" Single: Released Mar '83, on Motown, by BMG Records (UK). Catalogue no: **TMG 983**
7" Single: Released Feb '71, on Tamla Motown, by Motown Records (UK). Deleted '74. Catalogue no: **TMG 762**

HONEY CHILE
Tracks: / Honey chile.
7" Single: Released Jan '68, on Tamla Mo-

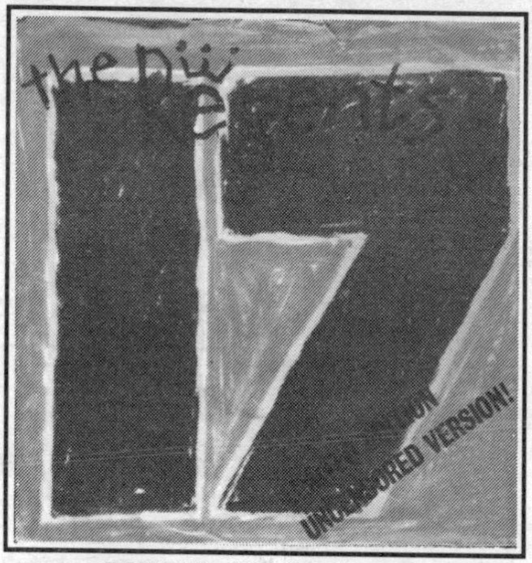

THE REGENTS - 7 TEEN (Released on Rialto)

town, by Motown Records (UK). Deleted '71. Catalogue no: **TMG 636**

I'M READY FOR LOVE
Tracks: / I'm ready for love.
7" Single: Released Dec '66, on Tamla Motown, by Motown Records (UK). Deleted '69. Catalogue no: **TMG 582**

JIMMY MACK
Tracks: / Jimmy Mack / Third finger left hand.
7" Single: Released Oct '81, on Motown, by BMG Records (UK). Catalogue no: **TMG 599**

NOWHERE TO RUN
Tracks: / Nowhere to run / Forget me not.
7" Single: Released Apr '65, on Tamla Motown, by Motown Records (UK). Deleted '68. Catalogue no: **TMG 502**
7" Single: Released Apr '69, on Tamla Motown, by Motown Records (UK). Deleted '72. Catalogue no: **TMG 694**
7" Single: Released Apr '88, on Motown, by BMG Records (UK). Catalogue no: **ZB 41921**

Reflections

FOUR COUNTRIES
Tracks: / Four countries.
7" Single: Released Dec '81, on Cherry Red, by Cherry Red Records. Deleted '87. Catalogue no: **CHERRY 33**

JUST LIKE ROMEO AND JULIET
Tracks: / Just like Romeo and Juliet.
7" Single: Released Oct '81, on Motown, by BMG Records (UK). Catalogue no: **TMG 907**

SEARCHING
Tracks: / Searching.
7" Single: Released Jan '84, on Cherry Red, by Cherry Red Records. Deleted '87. Catalogue no: **CHERRY 75**

Reflections A.O.B

ONLY IN MY DREAMS
Tracks: / Only in my dreams.
12" Single: Released Oct '86, on Keep It, Catalogue no: **KEEP ONE 12**

Re-Flex

POLITICS OF DANCING, THE
Tracks: / Politics of dancing, The.
7" Single: Released Jan '84, on EMI, by EMI Records. Deleted '87. Catalogue no: **FLEX 2**

Reform Club

BOOK OF REASONS
Tracks: / Book of reasons.
12" Single: Released Feb '89, on G.I., by Plastic Head Records. Catalogue no: **GI 12001**

Refugee

I'M NOT LIKE YOU
Tracks: / I'm not like you / When I was young.
7" Single: Released Oct '81, on New World, by President Records. Catalogue no: **NW 104**

Regal, Norace

STRUGGLE
Tracks: / Struggle.
12" Single: Released May '84, on Sirron Music, Catalogue no: **SRN 001**

Regan, Joan

HAPPY ANNIVERSARY
Tracks: / Happy anniversary.
7" Single: Released Feb '60, on Pye, Deleted '63. Catalogue no: **7 N 15238**

IF I GIVE MY HEART TO YOU
Tracks: / If I give my heart to you.
7" Single: Released Oct '54, on Decca, by Decca Records. Deleted '57. Catalogue no: **F 10373**

MAY YOU ALWAYS
Tracks: / May you always.
7" Single: Released May '59, on H.M.V., by EMI Records. Deleted '62. Catalogue no: **POP 593**

MUST BE SANTA
Tracks: / Must be Santa.
7" Single: Released Jan '61, on Pye, Deleted '64. Catalogue no: **7 N 15303**

ONE OF THE LUCKY ONES
Tracks: / One of the lucky ones.
7" Single: Released Nov '60, on Pye, Deleted '63. Catalogue no: **7 N 15310**

OPEN UP YOUR HEART
Tracks: / Open up your heart.
7" Single: Released May '55, on Decca, by Decca Records. Deleted '58. Catalogue no: **F 10474**

PAPA LOVES MAMA
Tracks: / Papa loves mama.
7" Single: Released Jul '60, on Pye, Deleted '63. Catalogue no: **7 N 15278**

PRIZE OF GOLD
Tracks: / Prize of gold.
7" Single: Released Mar '55, on Decca, by Decca Records. Deleted '58. Catalogue no: **F 10432**

RICOCHET
Tracks: / Ricochet.
7" Single: Released Dec '53, on Decca, by Decca Records. Deleted '56. Catalogue no: **F 10193**

SOMEONE ELSE'S ROSES
Tracks: / Someone else's roses.
7" Single: Released May '54, on Decca, by Decca Records. Deleted '57. Catalogue no: **F 10257**

WAIT FOR ME
Tracks: / Wait for me.
7" Single: Released Nov '54, on Decca, by Decca Records. Deleted '57. Catalogue no: **F 10362**

YOU NEEDED ME
Tracks: / You needed me / Together again.
7" Single: Released Jun '89, on Nectar, by Nectar Music. Catalogue no: **JOAN 1**

Regan, Riff

HARD HEART DON'T CRY
Tracks: / Hard heart don't cry / Miss mid West farmer's daughter.
7" Single: Released Apr '81, on Epic, by CBS Records. Deleted '85. Catalogue no: **EPC 1124**

ONLY ONE
Tracks: / Only one / Lucky dub.
7" Single: Released Apr '80, on MCA, by MCA Records. Deleted Apr '83. Catalogue no: **MCA 573**

YOU CALL ME LUCKY
Tracks: / You call me lucky / Jacoby island.
7" Single: Released Jan '80, on MCA, by MCA Records. Deleted Jan '85. Catalogue no: **MCA 548**

Regents

7 TEEN (See panel opposite)
Tracks: / 7 teen.
7" Single: Released Dec '79, on Rialto (1), by Rialto Records. Deleted '82. Catalogue no: **TREB 111**

JUST A LITTLE
Tracks: / Just a little / Dance Don.
7" Single: Released Jan '81, on Arista, by BMG Records (UK). Deleted Jan '84. Catalogue no: **ARIST 369**

RIDE COWBOY RIDE
Tracks: / Ride cowbot ride / London London.
7" Single: Released Apr '81, on MCA, by MCA Records. Deleted '85. Catalogue no: **MCA 2002**

SEE YOU LATER
Tracks: / See you later / Oh terrys.
7" Single: Released Jun '80, on Arista, by BMG Records (UK). Deleted '83. Catalogue no: **ARIST 350**

Reggae...

ALLSTAR REGGAE
Tracks: / Allstar reggae.
7" Single: Released Oct '81, on Spitfire, by Spitfire Records. Deleted '86. Catalogue no: **SFS 1001**
12" Single: Released Oct '81, on Spitfire, by Spitfire Records. Deleted '86. Catalogue no: **SFS 1001 12**

LOVE AND HATE
Tracks: / Love and hate / Without you / Love and hate (dub) / Without you (wisdom mix).
12" Single: Released 27 Feb '89, on Mango, by Island Records. Catalogue no: **12 MNG 100**
CD 5": Released 27 Feb '89, on Mango, by Island Records. Catalogue no: **MNCD 100**
7" Single: Released 27 Feb '89, on Mango, by Island Records. Catalogue no: **MNG 100**

REGGAE CHARTBUSTERS
7" EP: Released Jun '84, on Scoop 33, by Pickwick Records. Catalogue no: **7SR 5042**

Reggae George

EVERYBODY BALLING
Tracks: / Everybody balling.
12" Single: Released Jan '84, on Sky Juice, Catalogue no: **SJ 002**

THREE TIMES A LADY
Tracks: / Three times a lady.
12" Single: Released Jan '84, on Lion Kingdom, Catalogue no: **LK 005**

THREE WICKED MEN
Tracks: / Three wicked men.
12" Single: Released Sep '82, on Yvonne's, Catalogue no: **YS 011**

YOU'LL NEVER KNOW
Tracks: / You'll never know / We still survive.
12" Single: Released Jan '83, on Greensleeves, by Greensleeves Records. Catalogue no: **GRED 114**

Reggae Philharmonic

MINNIE THE MOOCHER
Tracks: / Minnie the moocher / Dangling / Minnie the moocher (version) (Only on 12").
7" Single: Released 30 Oct '88, on Mango, by Island Records. Catalogue no: **IS 378**
12" Single: Released 30 Oct '88, on Mango, by Island Records. Catalogue no: **12IS 378**

Reggae Regulars

BLACK STARLINER
Tracks: / Black starliner.
12" Single: Released Jun '78, on Greensleeves, by Greensleeves Records. Catalogue no: **GRED 2**

GHETTO ROCK (SINGLE)
Tracks: / Ghetto rock / Tribute to the D.J..
12" Single: Released Mar '84, on Greensleeves, by Greensleeves Records. Catalogue no: **GRED 138**

HOUSE PARTY
Tracks: / House party / Dub party / House bag.
12" Single: Released Feb '82, on Greensleeves, by Greensleeves Records. Catalogue no: **GRED 83**

Reggie

I DON'T PLAY THE GAME
Tracks: / I don't play the game.
12" Single: Released 19 Jan '87, on Licensed, Catalogue no: **LD 872**

Regiment

STEP OUT
Tracks: / Step out / Burning world.
7" Single: Released Nov '80, on Flamingo, by Airwave Records (USA). Deleted Nov '83. Catalogue no: **FM 9**

Regimental Band...

SILVER SERENADE
Tracks: / Silver serenade / Victory salute / Tchaike on parade.
7" Single: Released '86, on Help The Aged, Deleted '87. Catalogue no: **HA 001**

Regina

BABY LOVE
Tracks: / Baby love / Baby love (Inst).
7" Pic: Released '86, on Funkin' Marvellous, by Steinar Records (UK). Catalogue no: **PMARV 01**
7" Single: Released '86, on Funkin' Marvellous, by Steinar Records (UK). Catalogue no: **MARV 01**
12" Single: Released '86, on Funkin' Marvellous, by Steinar Records (UK). Catalogue no: **12MARV 01**
12" Single: Released '86, on Funkin' Marvellous, by Steinar Records (UK). Catalogue no: **MARVR 01**

Regist, Ronnie

TIME TO PLAY
Tracks: / Time to play.
7" Single: Released Aug '84, on Oscar, Catalogue no: **OSCAR 1**
12" Single: Released Aug '84, on Oscar, Catalogue no: **OSCAR 121**

Regular Guys

DIVINE HELP
Tracks: / Divine help.
12" Single: Released Jun '88, on Vinyl Drip, by Vinyl Drip Records. Catalogue no: **DRIP 6**

Regulars

DON'T STAY OUT LATE
Tracks: / Don't stay out late / Rude boy gone jail.
7" Single: Released Feb '80, on CBS, by CBS Records. Deleted '83. Catalogue no: **CBS 8150**

RUDE BOY GONE JAIL
Tracks: / Rude boy gone jail / Don't stay out late.
7" Single: Released Apr '80, on Epic, by CBS Records. Deleted Apr '83. Catalogue no: **EPC 8356**

Rehnbein, Herbert

BEAUTIFUL MORNING
Tracks: / Beautiful morning / Late evening.
7" Single: Released Sep '80, on Piccadilly, Deleted '83. Catalogue no: **7 P 204**

Reid

GOOD TIMES
Tracks: / Good times (Santa Monica mix) (Not on remix.) / Good times (radio version) (Not on remix.) / Good times (worlds end dub) (Not on remix.) / Good times (red shiny mix) (Remix only.) / Good times (red shiny transformer dub) (Remix only.).
CD 5": Released Apr '89, on Syncopate, by EMI Records. Catalogue no: **CDSY 27**
7" Single: Released Apr '89, on Syncopate, by EMI Records. Catalogue no: **SY 27**
12" Single: Released Apr '89, on Syncopate, by EMI Records. Catalogue no: **12SYX 27**
12" Single: Released Apr '89, on Syncopate, by EMI Records. Catalogue no: **12SY 27**

LOVIN' ON THE SIDE
Tracks: / Lovin' on the side (radio version) (Not on 12".) / Lovin' on the side (flute version) (Not on 12".) / Lovin' on the side (sky king version) (12" & CD single only.) / Lovin' on the side (12" version) (12" only.) / Lovin' on the side (Full length flute version) (12" only.).
CD 5": Released Oct '89, on Syncopate, by EMI Records. Catalogue no: **203 551 2**
CD 5": Released Oct '89, on Syncopate, by EMI Records. Catalogue no: **CDREID 1**
Cassingle: Released Oct '89, on Syncopate, by EMI Records. Catalogue no: **TCREID 1**
Cassingle: Released Oct '89, on Syncopate, by EMI Records. Catalogue no: **203 551 4**
7" Single: Released Oct '89, on Syncopate, by EMI Records. Catalogue no: **REID 1**
7" Single: Released Oct '89, on Syncopate, by EMI Records. Catalogue no: **203 551 8**
7" Single: Released Oct '89, on Syncopate, by EMI Records. Catalogue no: **REIDP 1**
7" Single: Released Oct '89, on Syncopate, by EMI Records. Catalogue no: **203 551 7**
12" Single: Released Oct '89, on Syncopate, by EMI Records. Catalogue no:

12REIDX 1
12" Single: Released Oct '89, on Syncopate, by EMI Records. Catalogue no: **12REID 1**
12" Single: Released Oct '89, on Syncopate, by EMI Records. Catalogue no: **203 581 6**
12" Single: Released Oct '89, on Syncopate, by EMI Records. Catalogue no: **203 551 6**

ONE WAY OUT
Tracks: / One way out (12" only.) / One way out (radio edit) / One way out (dub) / One way out (The U-turn mix) (12" special only.) / One way out (The U-turn dub) (12" special only.).
CD 5": Released Sep '88, on Syncopate, by EMI Records. Deleted Oct '89. Catalogue no: **CDSY 16**
Cassingle: Released Sep '88, on Syncopate, by EMI Records. Deleted Oct '89. Catalogue no: **TCSY 16**
7" Single: Released Sep '88, on Syncopate, by EMI Records. Deleted Oct '89. Catalogue no: **SYP 16**
7" Single: Released Sep '88, on Syncopate, by EMI Records. Deleted Oct '89. Catalogue no: **SY 16**
12" Single: Released Sep '88, on Syncopate, by EMI Records. Deleted Oct '89. Catalogue no: **12SY 16**
Special: Released Sep '88, on Syncopate, by EMI Records. Deleted Oct '89. Catalogue no: **12SYX 16**

REAL EMOTION
Tracks: / Real emotion (7" only.) / Real emotion (workout version) (Not on 7") / Real emotion (Flat Top House version) (Not on 7") / Real emotion (Flat Top House edit) (7" only.) / Real emotion (radio version) (CD single only.) / Real emotion (Motortown meltdown) / Real emotion (Detroit meets Bedford).
CD 5": Released Jan '89, on Syncopate, by EMI Records. Catalogue no: **CDSY 24**
7" Single: Released Jan '89, on Syncopate, by EMI Records. Deleted Oct '89. Catalogue no: **SY 24**
12" Single: Released Jan '89, on Syncopate, by EMI Records. Catalogue no: **12SYX 24**
12" Single: Released Jan '89, on Syncopate, by EMI Records. Catalogue no: **12SY 24**

Reid, Fire

CAN'T GET MI LOVE
Tracks: / Can't get mi love.
7" Single: Released May '89, on Black Gold, Catalogue no: **UNKNOWN**

Reid, Junior

BANK CLERK
Tracks: / Bank clerk / Youth man.
12" Single: Released Mar '85, on Rusty International, Catalogue no: **RI 018**

BOOM SHACK A LACK (SINGLE)
Tracks: / Boom shack a lack.
12" Single: Released Nov '84, on Greensleeves, by Greensleeves Records. Catalogue no: **GRED 163**

CHANTING
Tracks: / Chanting.
12" Single: Released Nov '85, on UNKNOWN, Catalogue no: **Unknown**

JAILHOUSE
Tracks: / Jailhouse.
12" Single: Released Apr '82, on KG, Catalogue no: **KG 008**

MOVIE STAR
Tracks: / Movie star / Let sleeping dogs lie.
12" Single: Released Mar '84, on Dove, Catalogue no: **DOVE 008**

ONE BLOOD
Tracks: / One blood.
12" Single: Released Jun '89, on White Label (1), Catalogue no: **JR 01**

ORIGINAL FOREIGN MIND, THE
Tracks: / Original foreign mind, The.
12" Single: Released Feb '85, on Black Roots, Catalogue no: **LML 211 284**

PALAVING STREET
Tracks: / Palaving street / Grey eye woman.
12" Single: Released Dec '83, on Chartbound, Catalogue no: **CB 003**

POOR MAN TRANSPORTATION
Tracks: / Poor man transportation.
12" Single: Released Mar '85, on Rockers Forever, Catalogue no: **Unknown**

RUB-A-DUBBING
Tracks: / Rub-a-dubbing.
12" Single: Released Nov '84, on Black Roots, Catalogue no: **BRUK 002**

TURN THE RADIO ON
Tracks: / Turn the radio on / Sufferation.
12" Single: Released '86, on Hard Rock, Catalogue no: **HRR 001**

WHAT YOU KNOW
Tracks: / What you know.
12" Single: Released Jan '84, on Black Roots, Catalogue no: **LML 6663**

Reid, Mike

PATIENT'S LAMENT (bed pan song)
Tracks: / Patient's lament / I've got to go.
7" Single: Released Nov '80, on Pel, Deleted '81. Catalogue no: **CAT POO 3**

UGLY DUCKLING, THE
Tracks: / Ugly duckling, The.
7" Single: Released Mar '75, on Pye, Deleted '78. Catalogue no: **7 N 45434**

Reid, Neil

MOTHER OF MINE
Tracks: / Mother of mine.
7" Single: Released Jan '72, on Decca, by Decca Records. Deleted '75. Catalogue no: **F 13264**

MOTHER OF MINE (OLD GOLD)
Tracks: / Mother of mine.
7" Single: Released Sep '85, on Old Gold, by Old Gold Records. Catalogue no: **OG 9538**

THAT'S WHAT I WANT TO BE
Tracks: / That's what I want to be.
7" Single: Released Apr '72, on Decca, by Decca Records. Deleted '75. Catalogue no: **F 13300**

Reid, Pam

MYSTERIOUS YOU
Tracks: / Mysterious you.
7" Single: Released May '89, on Studio One, Catalogue no: **UNKNOWN**

Reid, Richard

HOW DOES IT FEEL
Tracks: / How does it feel / Groove Train.
7" Single: Released Nov '81, on Solid Groove, Catalogue no: **SG 004**
12" Single: Released Nov '81, on Solid Groove, Catalogue no: **SG 004 12**

Reid, Sandra

DON'T LET IT GO
Tracks: / Don't let it go / Rave on.
12" Single: Released '86, on Sir George, Catalogue no: **SG 035T**

DON'T TELL ME TELL HER
Tracks: / Don't tell me tell her.
12" Single: Released Sep '83, on Sir George, Catalogue no: **SG 004T**

FEELS SO GOOD (SINGLE)
Tracks: / Feels so good / Don't go.
7" Single: Released Apr '84, on Sir George, Catalogue no: **SG 014**

IN A LIE
Tracks: / In a lie.
12" Single: Released Sep '85, on Sir George, Catalogue no: **SG 030T**

LOOK IN YOUR EYES
Tracks: / Look in your eyes.
12" Single: Released Nov '82, on Sir George, Catalogue no: **SG 002T**

LOVE EACH OTHER
Tracks: / Love each other.
12" Single: Released May '85, on Sir George, Catalogue no: **SG 025T**

MAKE ME LOVE THE RAIN
Tracks: / Make me love the rain.
12" Single: Released Mar '84, on Sir George, Catalogue no: **SG 005T**

OOH BOY
Tracks: / Ooh boy / Lovers rock.
7" Single: Released Jul '82, on Sir George, Catalogue no: **TRY 3**
12" Single: Released Jul '82, on Sir George, Catalogue no: **12 TRY 3**

WE BELONG TOGETHER
Tracks: / We belong together.
12" Single: Released Nov '84, on Sir George, Catalogue no: **SG 018T**

Reilly, David

LIFE ON EARTH
Tracks: / Life on Earth / Firing line.
7" Single: Released May '82, on DJM, Deleted '85. Catalogue no: **DJS 10985**

WINGS OVER AMERICA
Tracks: / Wings over america / Trick of the light.
7" Single: Released Feb '82, on DJM, Deleted '85. Catalogue no: **DJS 10982**

Reilly, Maggie

AS TEARS GO BY
Tracks: / As tears go by / Syonara.
7" Single: Released Apr '84, on Arista, by BMG Records (UK). Catalogue no: **ARIST 563**
12" Single: Released Apr '84, on Arista, by BMG Records (UK). Catalogue no: **ARIST 12563**

LIFE AFTER JOHN
Tracks: / Life after John / Meanwhile back at my heart.
7" Single: Released Dec '87, on Adventure, by Adventure Records. Deleted Aug '89. Catalogue no: **ADV 1**

MANHATTAN DANCE THEME
Tracks: / Manhatten dance theme.
12" Single: Released May '88, on Adventure, by Adventure Records. Catalogue no: **ADT 1**

Reilly, Paddy

FIELDS OF ATHENRY (single)
Tracks: / Fields of Athenry.
7" Single: Released Oct '84, on Ritz, by Ritz Records. Catalogue no: **RITZ 088**

Reilly, Vinny

TWO TRIANGLES
Tracks: / Two triangles.
12" Single: Released Jul '82, on Factory Benelux, by Rough Trade Records. Catalogue no: **FBN 10**

Rein, Paul

HOLD BACK YOUR LOVE
Tracks: / Hold back your love / Ce mej en chans.
12" Single: Released '85, on ZYX (Germany), Catalogue no: **ZYX 5339**

STOP
Tracks: / Stop.
7" Single: Released Jan '88, on Champion, by Champion Records. Deleted Aug '89. Catalogue no: **CHAMP 56**
12" Single: Released Jan '88, on Champion, by Champion Records. Catalogue no: **CHAMP 1256**

Reincarnate

TAKE IT OR LEAVE IT
Tracks: / Take it or leave it / Metal in disguise.
7" Single: Released Feb '83, on Zipp, Deleted '84. Catalogue no: **REIN 001**

Reininger, Blaine

EL PASO
Tracks: / El Paso.
7" Single: Released Oct '88, on Normal, by Jungle Records. Deleted '89. Catalogue no: **NORMAL 72**
12" Single: Released Oct '88, on Normal, by Jungle Records. Deleted '89. Catalogue no: **NORMAL 72T**
CD 3": Released Oct '88, on Normal, by Jungle Records. Deleted '89. Catalogue no: **NORMAL 72CD**

Reja Bumu

REJA BUMU
Tracks: / Reja bumu.
12" Single: Released Aug '82, on Eon, Catalogue no: **EON S1**

Rejects

BACK TO THE START
Tracks: / Back to the start / Leave it.
7" Single: Released Mar '85, on FM, by FM-Revolver Records. Catalogue no: **VHF 7**

Relations

BIG MANS SHOES
Tracks: / Big mans shoes.
7" Single: Released '86, on Hush, Catalogue no: **HCP 001**

BRAINWASHED & BLOWDRIED
Tracks: / Brainwashed & blowdried / Come home (Tell us everything).
7" Single: Released '86, on Hush, Catalogue no: **HCP 002**

Relatives

MY TIME
Tracks: / My time.
12" Single: Released May '89, on Radio City, Catalogue no: **RCR 001**

Release

IT'S NOT FAIR
Tracks: / It's not fair.
7" Single: Released Jul '84, on EMI, by EMI Records. Catalogue no: **RLSE 1**
12" Single: Released Jul '84, on EMI, by EMI Records. Deleted 31 Jul '88. Catalogue no: **12RLSE 1**

Release The Bats

UNACCEPTABLE BEHAVIOUR
Tracks: / Unacceptable behaviour.
7" Single: Released Apr '85, on Belfry, Deleted Jun '88. Catalogue no: **BELF 001**

Relf, Keith

MR ZERO
Tracks: / Mr. Zero.
7" Single: Released May '66, on Columbia, by EMI Records. Deleted '69. Catalogue no: **DB 7920**

Relford, Sammie

LOVE YOU ALL OVER
Tracks: / Lover you all over / Lover you all over (instrumental).
12" Single: Released Sep '89, on Evejim, Catalogue no: **12 PO 25**

Relief

WE ARE THE WORLD
Tracks: / We are the world.
12" Single: Released Jul '85, on Dough Boy, Catalogue no: **DBT 1**

Religious Overdose

25 MINUTES
Tracks: / 25 minutes.
7" Single: Released Sep '82, on Glass, by Glass Records. Deleted '83. Catalogue no: **GLASS 004**

GIRL WITH THE DISAPPEARING HEAD
Tracks: / Girl with the disappearing head / In this century.
12" Single: Released Jun '82, on Glass, by Glass Records. Deleted '83. Catalogue no: **GLASS 018**

I SAID GO
Tracks: / I said go / Alien to you.
7" Single: Released Sep '81, on Glass, by Glass Records. Deleted '83. Catalogue no: **GLASS 009**

Rell, M.C.

IN THE FUTURE
Tracks: / In the future / My vision.
12" Single: Released Nov '88, on Criminal (1), by Criminal Records. Catalogue no: **BUST 15**

Reluctant Stereotypes

NIGHTMARES
Tracks: / Nightmares / Factory wit.
7" Single: Released Apr '81, on WEA, by WEA Records. Deleted '85. Catalogue no: **K 18721**

PLANS FOR TODAY
Tracks: / Plans for today / Subway.
7" Single: Released Sep '80, on WEA, by WEA Records. Deleted Sep '83. Catalogue no: **K 18335**

ROUNDS, THE
Tracks: / Rounds, The.
7" Single: Released May '82, on Oval, by Oval Records. Catalogue no: **OVAL 1013**

R.E.M.

Biographical details: A rock group formed in 1980 in Athens, Georgia: vocalist Michael Stipe, Peter Buck on guitar, Michael Mills on bass, Bill Berry on drums. They became critics; favourites with a revivalist style: their early sound was reminiscent of Byrds; band acknowledged influences, enriched by stipes mysterious lyrics, Buck's eclectic guitar. *Life's rich pageant* in 1986 was a stronger, less dreamy-sounding album; *Dead letter office* collected B sides, live tracks and covers; then *Number 5. Document* in 1987 was also more outward looking. (Donald Clarke 21.5.88).

CAN'T GET THERE FROM HERE
Tracks: / Can't get there from here.
7" Single: Released Jul '85, on I.R.S, Catalogue no: **IRM 102**
12" Single: Released Jul '85, on I.R.S, Catalogue no: **IRT 102**

FALL ON ME
Tracks: / Fall on me / Rotary ten / Toys in the attic (Available on 12" version only).
7" Single: Released '86, on I.R.S, Catalogue no: **IRM 121**
12" Single: Released '86, on I.R.S, Catalogue no: **IRMT 121**

FINEST WORKSONG
Tracks: / Finest worksong (LP version) / Finest worksong (Lengthy club mix) / Time after time medley / It's the end of the world as we know it (and I feel fine).
Note: Medley: Time After Time/Red Rain/S.Central Rain. LP version on 7" and CD. Lengthy Club Mix on 12". * Track on CD only.
CD 5": Released May '88, on IRS (Holland), Catalogue no: **6513202**
CD 5": Released Apr '88, on MCA, by MCA Records. Catalogue no: **DIRM 161**
7" Single: Released Apr '88, on MCA, by MCA Records. Deleted 1 Jul '89. Catalogue no: **IRM 161**
12" Single: Released Apr '88, on MCA, by MCA Records. Catalogue no: **IRMT 161**

IT'S THE END OF THE WORLD AS WE KNOW IT (AND I FEEL FINE)
Tracks: / It's the end of the world as we know it (and I feel fine) / This one goes out (live) / Maps and legends (live)*.
Note: * track on 12" version
7" Single: Released Aug '87, on I.R.S, Catalogue no: **IRM 145**
12" Single: Released Aug '87, on I.R.S, Catalogue no: **IRMT 145**

ONE I LOVE, THE

Tracks: / One I love, The / Last date / Disturbance at the Heron House*.
Note: * extra track on 12" version only.
CD 5": Released Oct '88, on I.R.S, Catalogue no: **DIRM 173**
7" Single: Released Oct '88, on I.R.S, Catalogue no: **IRM 173**
7" Single: Released Oct '87, on MCA, by MCA Records. Deleted '88. Catalogue no: **IRM 146**
12" Single: Released Oct '88, on I.R.S, Deleted 1 Jul '89. Catalogue no: **IRMT 173**
12" Single: Released Oct '87, on MCA, by MCA Records. Deleted '88. Catalogue no: **IRMT 146**

ORANGE CRUSH
Tracks: / Orange crush / Ghost riders in the sky / Dark globe (Only on 12" and CD single.).
7" Single: Released May '89, on WEA, by WEA Records. Catalogue no: **W 2960**
12" Single: Released May '89, on WEA, by WEA Records. Catalogue no: **W 2960 T**
CD 3": Released May '89, on WEA, by WEA Records. Catalogue no: **W 2960 CD**

STAND
Tracks: / Stand / Memphis train blues / Pop song '89 (acoustic version) (On re-issue only) / Skin tight (On CD single only).
CD 5": Released 31 Jul '89, on Warner Bros., by WEA Records. Catalogue no: **W 2833CD**
CD 5": Released Jan '89, on Warner Bros., by WEA Records. Catalogue no: **W 7577CD**
7" Single: Released 31 Jul '89, on Warner Bros., by WEA Records. Catalogue no: **W 2833**
7" Single: Released Jan '89, on Warner Bros., by WEA Records. Catalogue no: **W 7577**
12" Single: Released 31 Jul '89, on Warner Bros., by WEA Records. Catalogue no: **W 2833C**
12" Single: Released Jan '89, on Warner Bros., by WEA Records. Catalogue no: **W 7577T**

SUPERMAN
Tracks: / Superman / White tornado / Femme fatale (Only available on 12" version.).
7" Single: Released Mar '87, on I.R.S, Catalogue no: **IRM 128**
12" Single: Released Mar '87, on I.R.S, Catalogue no: **IRMT 128**

TALK ABOUT THE PASSION
Tracks: / Talk about the passion.
12" Single: Released Nov '83, on I.R.S, Catalogue no: **PFSX 1026**

WENDELL GEE
Tracks: / Wendell Gee.
7" Set: Released Oct '85, on I.R.S, Catalogue no: **IRMD 105**
7" Single: Released Oct '85, on I.R.S, Catalogue no: **IRM 105**
12" Single: Released Oct '85, on I.R.S, Catalogue no: **IRT 105**

Rema

GERMAINE
Tracks: / Germaine.
7" Single: Released '86, on Gas, Catalogue no: **GAS 1011**

Rema Rema

WHEEL IN THE ROSES
Tracks: / Wheel in the roses (4 Track EP.) / Macho man.
12" Single: Released '86, on 4AD, by 4AD Records. Catalogue no: **BAD 5**

Remayns

REMAYNS EP
7" EP: Released Jun '88, on Bam Caruso, by Demon Records. Catalogue no: **NRIC 029**

Remmler, Stephan

I DON'T GO TO USA
Tracks: / I don't go to USA / Kine sterne in Athen (Janet in Sankt Katreine) / Die zeit ohne stimmer (Extra track on 12").

7" Single: Released Jul '87, on Mercury, by Phonogram Ltd. Catalogue no: **MER 249**
12" Single: Released Jul '87, on Mercury, by Phonogram Ltd. Catalogue no: **MERX 249**

Remote

FEELS SO GOOD
Tracks: / Feels so good / Feels so good (remix).
12" Single: Released Jul '87, on FM Dance, by FM-Revolver Records. Catalogue no: **12 VHF 38**

Remote Start

AUTOMATED MAN
Tracks: / Automated man / Debutante.
7" Single: Released Mar '82, on UNKNOWN, Catalogue no: **JIG 5**

Renaissance

Biographical details: A UK rock band of the 1970's. Original group formed in 1969 by Yardbirds vocalist Keith Relf (1943-76) and Jim McCarty; they recruited bassist Louis Cennamo, ex-Nashville Teens keyboardist John Hawken and relf's vocalist sister Jane to make an eponymous folky Lp for Island. The ex-Yardbirds left; by the time of *Prologue* '72 personnel was entirely new: Annie Haslam, vocals; Jon Camp, bass; John Tout, keyboards; Rob Hendry, guitar; Terry Sullivan, drums. Hendry was replaced by Mick Dunford, who rarely used the electric guitar, preferring acoustic; corresponding with one Betty Thatcher by post, he set her words for *Ashes are burning* and *Turn of the cards* in 1973-4, which charted the UK; *Scheherezade and other stories* in 1975 was a heavily orchestrated 'contempory version' of Rimsky-Korsakov's classic, a top 50 LP in the USA where they went for two years: at home they were stuck on college circuit, 2-discs *Live at Carnege Hall* in 1976 (with NY Philharmonic) emphasising difference. Their sound based on tout's keyboards, Haslams's classical rock wailing; After Novella *A song for all seasons* and *Azure d'or* '77-9, Peter Gosling bucking fashion with *Camera camera* and *Time line* in the '80's. Haslam made solo *Annie in wonderland* '78; Relf Cennamo and Hawken from first band formed Illusion (two Lps '77-78) but Relf was electrocuted. Like fellow pomp-rockers Barclay James Harvest, they can hardly by said to have influenced anybody; sole UK hit was top 10 single *Northern lights* '78. (Donald Clarke 21.5.88).

BACK HOME ONCE AGAIN
Tracks: / Back home once again.
7" Single: Released Sep '77, on Warner Bros., by WEA Records. Catalogue no: **K 17012**

BONJOUR SWANSONG
Tracks: / Bonjour swansong.
7" Single: Released Jan '82, on Illegal, by Faulty Products Records. Catalogue no: **ILS 0027**

FAIRIES LIVING AT THE BOTTOM OF MY....
Tracks: / Fairies living at the bottom of my... / Remember.
7" Single: Released Sep '81, on Illegal, by Faulty Products Records. Catalogue no: **ILS 0025**

NORTHERN LIGHTS
Tracks: / Northern lights.
7" Single: Released May '78, on Warner Bros., by WEA Records. Catalogue no: **K 17177**

Renaldo, Lee

FROM HERE TO ETERNITY
Tracks: / From here to eternity.
12" Single: Released Jul '87, on Blast First, by Blast First Records. Catalogue no: **BFFP 9T**

Renaldo & The Loaf

HAMBU HODO
Tracks: / He loves us all.
12" Single: Released Jan '87, on Some Bizzare, by Some Bizzare Records. Catalogue no: **RD 4**

Renate

NICOLEOS
Tracks: / Nicoleos.
7" Single: Released Oct '81, on Cambridge, by Cambridge Records. Deleted '83. Catalogue no: **ULT 100**

Renato

(SEE ALSO UNDER RENEE & RENATO)

FUNICULI FUNICULA
Tracks: / Funiculi funicula / He loves us all.
7" Single: Released Nov '86, on Hollywood, by Hollywood Records. Catalogue no: **HWD 018**
12" Single: Released Nov '86, on Hollywood, by Hollywood Records. Catalogue no: **HWD 12018**

SHE WEARS MY RING
Tracks: / She wears my ring.
7" Single: Released Jan '83, on Lifestyle, by Micrometro Ltd (Records). Catalogue no: **LIFE 2**

Rendell, Don

TIME PRESENCE
Tracks: / Time presence.
7" Single: Released May '89, on DR, Catalogue no: **DR 101**

Rendez Vous

YOU LOOK SO BEAUTIFUL TONIGHT
Tracks: / You look so beautiful tonight.
7" Single: Released May '85, on Red Diamond, by Red Diamond Records. Catalogue no: **RD VOUS 60**

Rene

WHEN I NEED LOVE
Tracks: / When I need love.
12" Single: on Burning Sounds, by Burning Sounds Records. Deleted May '88. Catalogue no: **BSD 030**

Rene & Angela

BANGING THE BOOGIE
Tracks: / Banging the boogie.
7" Single: Released May '83, on Capitol, by EMI Records. Deleted '88. Catalogue no: **CL 293**
12" Single: Released May '83, on Capitol, by EMI Records. Deleted '85. Catalogue no: **12 CL 293**

DO YOU REALLY LOVE ME
Tracks: / Do you really love me / Hotel California.
7" Single: Released May '80, on Capitol, by EMI Records. Deleted May '83. Catalogue no: **CL 16145**

FREE AND EASY
Tracks: / Free and easy / I don't know where love comes from / Hotel California.
7" EP: Released 20 Jun '80, on Capitol, by EMI Records. Deleted '83. Catalogue no: **CL 16155**

I'LL BE GOOD
Tracks: / I'll be good.
7" Single: Released Sep '85, on Club, by Phonogram Ltd. Deleted '88. Catalogue no: **JAB 18**

I'LL BE GOOD (OLD GOLD 12")
Tracks: / I'll be good / Save your love (for number 1).
12" Single: Released Nov '88, on Old Gold, by Old Gold Records. Catalogue no: **OG 4087**

SAVE YOUR LOVE (FOR NUMBER 1)
Tracks: / Save your love (for number 1).
7" Single: Released Jun '85, on Club, by Phonogram Ltd. Deleted '88. Catalogue no: **JAB 14**

SECRET RENDEZVOUS
Tracks: / Secret rendezvous.
7" Single: Released Oct '85, on Champion, by Champion Records. Catalogue no: **CHAMP 5**
12" Single: Released Oct '85, on Champion, by Champion Records. Catalogue no: **CHAMP 125**

YOUR SMILE
Tracks: / Your smile / Your smile (Inst.) / Secret rendezvous '86 (Available on 12" version only.).
7" Single: Released '86, on Club, by Phonogram Ltd. Catalogue no: **JAB 24**
12" Single: Released '86, on Club, by Phonogram Ltd. Catalogue no: **JABX 24**

Rene & Yvette

JE T'AIME (ALLO ALLO)
Tracks: / Rene DMC.
7" Single: Released Nov '86, on Sedition, by Sedition Records. Catalogue no: **EDIT 3319**
12" Single: Released Nov '86, on Sedition, by Sedition Records. Catalogue no: **EDITL 3319**

Renee & Renato

JESUS LOVES US ALL
Tracks: / Jesus loves us all / At the touch of your hand.
7" Single: Released Nov '83, on Hollywood, by Hollywood Records. Catalogue no: **HWD 012**

JUST ONE MORE KISS
Tracks: / Just one more kiss / It's a lovely day.
7" Single: Released Oct '85, on Hollywood, by Hollywood Records. Catalogue no: **HWD 006**

LITTLE BITTA ME, A
Tracks: / Little bitta me, A.
7" Single: Released Oct '83, on Hollywood, by Hollywood Records. Catalogue no: **HWD 009**

ONLY YOU
Tracks: / Only you.
7" Single: Released May '84, on Hollywood, by Hollywood Records. Catalogue no: **HWD 011**

SAVE YOUR LOVE
Tracks: / Save your love.
7" Single: Released Sep '82, on Hollywood, by Hollywood Records. Catalogue no: **HWD 003**

Renegade Soundwave

BITING MY NAILS
Tracks: / Biting my nails / Biting my nails (inst).
CD 5": Released Sep '88, on Mute, by Mute Records. Catalogue no: **CDMUTE 82**
7" Single: Released Sep '88, on Mute, by Mute Records. Catalogue no: **MUTE 82**
12" Single: Released Sep '88, on Mute, by Mute Records. Catalogue no: **12 MUTE 82**

COCAINE SEX
Tracks: / Cocaine sex.
7" Single: Released Jan '88, on Rhythm King, by Mute Records. Catalogue no: **LEFT 20**
12" Single: Released Jan '88, on Rhythm King, by Mute Records. Catalogue no: **LEFT 20T**

KRAY TWINS
Tracks: / Kray twins.
7" Single: Released May '87, on Rhythm King, by Mute Records. Catalogue no: **LEFT 8**
12" Single: Released May '87, on Rhythm King, by Mute Records. Catalogue no: **LEFT 8T**

PHANTOM
Tracks: / Phantom.
7" Single: Released Jun '89, on Mute, by Mute Records. Catalogue no: **MUTE 088**
12" Single: Released Jun '89, on Mute, by Mute Records. Catalogue no: **12MUTE 088**

SPACE GLADIATOR
Tracks: / Space gladiator.
7" Single: Released Oct '89, on Mute, by Mute Records. Catalogue no: **MUTE 104**
12" Single: Released Oct '89, on Mute, by Mute Records. Catalogue no: **12MUTE 104**

Reno, Johnny

BORN TO BLOW
Tracks: / Born to blow.
12" Single: Released '88, on Black Top (USA), by Rounder Records (USA). Catalogue no: **BT 1025**

Reno, Mike

ALMOST PARADISE
Tracks: / Almost paradise.
7" Single: Released Jun '84, on CBS, by CBS Records. Catalogue no: **A 4480**

Rent Boys

KICK DOWN THE BOY
Tracks: / Kick down the boy / Feeling ice.
7" Single: Released May '80, on WEA, by WEA Records. Deleted May '85. Catalogue no: **K 18230**

Rent Party

Biographical details: A UK jump band formed in 1982 at Southend. Lineup: Jackson Sloane, vocals; John Willmott, tenor sax; sister Chris Willmott, alto; Laurence Parry, trumpet; Steve Weston, piano; Andy Stevens, guitar; Tony Wilsonham, bass; Neil Robinson, drums; all b in '60's, all former students of blue-collar workers. A revivalist group searching behind disco for some good music, and doing it well with plenty of spitit; wearing zoot-suits with wide ties, they describe their stuff as '50's R&B/jazz dance music, influenced by Count Basie, Louis Jordan, Big Joe Turner. (Donald Clarke 21.5.88).

AIN'T MISBEHAVIN'
Tracks: / Ain't misbehavin' / Somebody turned the lights out / Liquor store (Available on 12" version only.) / Barking jump (Available on 12" version only.).
7" Single: Released '86, on Waterfront, by Waterfront Music. Catalogue no: **WFS 26**
12" Single: Released '86, on Waterfront, by Waterfront Music. Catalogue no: **WFT 26**

HONEY BEE
Tracks: / Honey bee / Take it like a man / High class woman.
7" Single: Released Feb '84, on Waterfront, by Waterfront Music. Catalogue no: **WFS 004**

RENT PARTY
Tracks: / Rent party / Letter of love.
7" Single: Released Sep '83, on Projection, Catalogue no: **WFSS 002**

Rental, Robert

DOUBLE HEART
Tracks: / Double heart.
7" Single: Released Oct '80, on Mute, by Mute Records. Catalogue no: **MUTE 10**

Rentals

I'VE GOT A CRUSH ON YOU
Tracks: / I've got a crush on you / New York.
7" Single: Released Jan '80, on Beggars Banquet, by Beggars Banquet Records. Deleted Jan '88. Catalogue no: **BEG 24**

Rentaracket

MANIAC
Tracks: / Maniac.
7" Single: Released '86, on Killing For Pleasure, Catalogue no: **RKT 1**

Rentzos, Emmanuel

TAMPI TAMPOCA

Tracks: / Tampi tampoca / Rock with you.
12" Single: Released Aug '80, on Afrodisc, by RCA Records. Deleted '83. Catalogue no: **ROK 12 14**

Renwick, Tim

DARK ISLAND
Tracks: / Dark Island / Lip service.
7" Single: Released May '80, on CBS, by CBS Records. Deleted May '83. Catalogue no: **CBS 8537**

PERFECT STRANGERS
Tracks: / Perfect strangers / Crazy for your love.
7" Single: Released Jan '80, on CBS, by CBS Records. Deleted Jan '83. Catalogue no: **CBS 8185**

REO Speedwagon

Biographical details: A USA rock group formed in 1967 in Champagne, Illinois, named after a make of fire engine. Founder members were University of Illinois students Alan Gratzer on drums, Neal Doughty on keyboards, plus gary Richrath on guitar. Terry Luttrell on vocals, Gregg Philbin on bass. After eponymous LP debut in 1971 Luttrell was replaced by Kevin Cronin, himself replaced after R.E.O. T.W.O by Mike Murphy. They played long tours on stadium circuit with Ted Nugent, Bob Seger, Kansas; seen as a bar band who might make it, wished well by critics; they make it eventually without getting better. Cronin returned in 1975 his country-tinged singing giving Richrath's songs a little more distinction. They struck it rich as USA radio became completely spineless, making major-label moneyspinners of faceless bands like REO, Kansas, Journey, Styx who could graft an occasional hook onto otherwise unmemorable songs. Later LP's were less frequent, but still sold well as mood music for grown-up baby-boomers. (Donald Clarke 21.5.88).

6 TRACK HITS
Tracks: / Only the strong survive / Meet me on the mountain / Shakin' it loose / In your letter / I need you tonight / Roll with the changes.
7" EP: Released Aug '84, on Scoop 33, by Pickwick Records. Catalogue no: **7SR 5049**

CAN'T FIGHT THIS FEELING
Tracks: / Can't fight this feeling / Keep on loving you / Rock 'n' roll star.
7" Single: Released Mar '85, on Epic, by CBS Records. Deleted '88. Catalogue no: **A 4880**

HERE WITH ME
Tracks: / Here with me / Wherever you're goin' (it's alright).
CD 5": Released Sep '88, on Epic, by CBS Records. Deleted 17 Apr '89. Catalogue no: **651646 2**
7" Single: Released Sep '88, on Epic, by CBS Records. Deleted 17 Apr '89. Catalogue no: **651646 7**
12" Single: Released Sep '88, on Epic, by CBS Records. Deleted 17 Apr '89. Catalogue no: **651646 6**

IN MY DREAMS
Tracks: / In my dreams / Over the edge.
7" Single: Released Nov '87, on Epic, by CBS Records. Deleted Jun '88. Catalogue no: **651040 7**

IN YOUR LETTER
Tracks: / In your letter / Shakin' it loose.
7" Single: Released Oct '81, on Epic, by CBS Records. Deleted Oct '84. Catalogue no: **EPCA 1562**

KEEP ON LOVING YOU
Tracks: / Keep on loving you / Time for me to fly.
7" Single: Released Apr '81, on Epic, by CBS Records. Deleted '84. Catalogue no: **EPC 9544**
CD 3": Released Aug '88, on Epic (USA), by CBS Records (USA). Catalogue no: **34K02153**

KEEP THE FIRE BURNING
Tracks: / Keep the fire burning / I'll follow you.
7" Single: Released Jul '82, on Epic, by CBS Records. Deleted Jul '85. Catalogue no: **EPCA 2495**

KEY, THE
Tracks: / Key, The / Let's beop.
7" Single: Released Oct '82, on Epic, by CBS Records. Catalogue no: **EPC A 2889**

SWEET TIME
Tracks: / Sweet time.
7" Single: Released Sep '82, on Epic, by CBS Records. Catalogue no: **EPC A 2715**

TAKE IT ON THE RUN
Tracks: / Take it on the run / Someone tonight.
7" Single: Released Jun '81, on Epic, by CBS Records. Deleted '84. Catalogue no: **EPC A 1207**

THAT AIN'T LOVE
Tracks: / That ain't love / Accidents can happen.
7" Single: Released Mar '87, on Epic, by CBS Records. Deleted Aug '87. Catalogue no: **650390 7**

Reparata

CAPTAIN OF YOUR SHIP
Tracks: / Captain of your ship.
7" Single: Released Mar '68, on Bell. Deleted '71. Catalogue no: **BELL 1002**

PANIC
Tracks: / Panic.
7" Single: Released Mar '83, on Neil Rushton, Catalogue no: **CC 3**

SHOES
Tracks: / Shoes.
7" Single: Released Oct '75, on Dart, by President Records. Deleted '78. Catalogue no: **2066 562**

Repitition

WILL TO WIN
Tracks: / Will to win.
12" Single: Released Dec '82, on Red Flame (1), by Red Flame Records. Catalogue no: **RF 1213**

Replacements

ALEX CHILTON
Tracks: / Alex Chilton / Election day / Nightclub jitters (Extra track on 12") / Route 66".
7" Single: Released Jun '87, on Sire (USA). Deleted Jul '88. Catalogue no: **W 8297**
12" Single: Released Jun '87, on Sire (USA), Catalogue no: **W 8297T**

KISS ME ON THE BUS
Tracks: / Kiss me on the bus / Little mascara.
7" Single: Released '86, on Sire (USA). Deleted Jun '87. Catalogue no: **W 8679**

SWINGIN' PARTY
Tracks: / Swingin' party.
7" Single: Released '86, on Warner Bros., by WEA Records. Deleted Jun '87. Catalogue no: **W 8727**

Replay

MICHAEL MANIA MEDLEY
Tracks: / Michael mania medley.
7" Single: Released Aug '89, on Radical, by Radical Records. Catalogue no: **RADICAL 6-7**
12" Single: Released Aug '89, on Radical, by Radical Records. Catalogue no: **RADICAL 6-12**

Repro

LETTERS HOME
Tracks: / Letters home.
7" Single: Released Sep '82, on Observation, by Observation Records. Catalogue no: **EYE 106**

REPRO 80
Tracks: / Repro 80.
7" Single: Released Oct '81, on Observation, by Observation Records. Catalogue no: **EYE 100**

Reprobates

SETTLEMENT
Tracks: / Settlement.
12" Single: Released Sep '84, on Fashion, by Fashion Records. Catalogue no: **Not known**

Reptiles

REPTILES FOR TEA EP
Tracks: / Reptiles for tea / Noises.
7" Single: Released Jul '83, on Volume (1), by Volume Records. Catalogue no: **VOL 4**

Reptiles At Dawn

AFTER THE PLAGUE
Tracks: / After the plague.
7" Set: Released 13 Jun '87, on New Rose (1), by New Rose Records. Catalogue no: **NEW 88**
7" Single: Released Mar '87, on New Rose (1), by New Rose Records. Catalogue no: **NEW 088**

Reptiles & Lesdemonds

NIGHT AFTER NIGHT
Tracks: / Night after night / Halfway to heaven.
7" Single: Released Jun '87, on Blue Hat, by Blue Hat Records. Catalogue no: **BHR 50**

Repton Boxing Club

JAB AND MOVE
Tracks: / Jab and move.
7" Single: Released Apr '80, on Bridgehouse, Deleted '88. Catalogue no: **BHS 9**

Republic

GOD IS ANGRY
Tracks: / God is angry.
12" Single: Released Sep '89, on Consortium, Catalogue no: **DEF CON 1**

MY SPIES
Tracks: / My spies.
12" Single: Released Apr '83, on Oval, by Oval Records. Catalogue no: **FLAG 24/12**

ONE CHANCE
Tracks: / One chance / Dance into the distance.
7" Single: Released Apr '84, on Oval, by Oval Records. Catalogue no: **OVAL 29**
12" Single: Released Mar '84, Catalogue no: **OVALT 29-12**

Republic Of Ireland

BOYS IN GREEN, THE
Tracks: / Boys in green, The / Molly Malone.
7" Single: Released 16 May '88, on Island, by Island Records. Deleted Apr '89. Catalogue no: **BUA 822**

R.E.Q.

CASA FORTE
Tracks: / Casa forte.
12" Single: Released Dec '84, on Passion, by Skratch Records. Catalogue no: **PASH 37(12)**

Rescuers

RESCUERS (SINGLE)
7" EP: Released Nov '88, on Disneyland, by Disneyland Records. Catalogue no: **D 367**

Reserve

TWO HEARTS BEAT IN A HOLE
Tracks: / Two hearts beat in a hole / Sun slid down behind the tower, The / Tender young believer / Perfect lie, A.
12" Single: Released 22 Aug '88, on Sombrero, by Sombrero Records. Catalogue no: **SOMBRERO 4**

Residents

AMBER
Tracks: / Amber / Red rider / Picnic boy / When we were young / Phantom / Moisture.
7" Single: Released Oct '80, on Pre, by Charisma Records. Deleted Oct '83. Catalogue no: **PRE 9**

HIT THE ROAD
Tracks: / Hit the road.
7" Single: Released 30 May '87, on Torso, by Torso Records. Catalogue no: **TORSO 70032**
12" Single: Released 30 May '87, on Torso, by Torso Records. Catalogue no: **TORSO 12032**

INTERMISSION-LIGHTS OUT
Tracks: / Intermission (lights out).
12" Single: Released Jun '83, on Ralph (USA), by Ralph Records (USA). Catalogue no: **RALPH 1**

KAW-LIGA
Tracks: / Kaw-Liga.
CD 5": Released Dec '88, on Torso, by Torso Records. Catalogue no: **CD 322**
7" Single: Released Dec '86, on Torso, by Torso Records. Catalogue no: **TORSO 70022**
12" Single: Released Mar '89, on Torso, by Torso Records. Catalogue no: **TORSO 12110**
12" Single: Released Dec '86, on Torso, by Torso Records. Catalogue no: **TORSO 12022**

Resistance

IS THIS WHAT ENGLAND IS?
Tracks: / Is this what England is?.
7" Single: Released 13 Jun '87, on Timebox, Catalogue no: **7 TARDIS 2**
12" Single: Released 13 Jun '87, on Timebox, Catalogue no: **TARDIS 2**

NOWHERE TO PLAY
Tracks: / Nowhere to play.
7" Single: Released Dec '82, on Riot City, by Riot City Records. Catalogue no: **RIOT 18**

SURVIVAL KIT
Tracks: / Survival kit / Big flame.
7" Single: Released May '81, on Fontana, by Phonogram Ltd. Deleted May '86. Catalogue no: **KIT 1**

VIVA LA RESISTANCE
Tracks: / Viva la resistance.
7" Single: Released Mar '84, on Red Rhino, by Red Rhino Records. Catalogue no: **ASS 6**

Resonators

SOMEBODY HELP ME
Tracks: / Somebody help me / Gonna get to you someday.
7" Single: Released Feb '81, on Stagecoach, Catalogue no: **BANG 1**

Rest

CARNIVAL
Tracks: / Carnival.
7" Single: Released Apr '80, on Shooting Star, Catalogue no: **SSR 1**

Restivo, Johnny

SHAPE I'M IN
Tracks: / Shape I'm in, The / Ya-ya.
7" Single: Released Aug '81, on RCA Golden Grooves, by BMG Records (UK). Catalogue no: **GOLD 525**

SHAPE I'M IN (OLD GOLD)
Tracks: / Shape I'm in, The / Makin' love.
7" Single: Released '86, on Old Gold, by Old Gold Records. Catalogue no: **OG 9623**

Restless

EDGE ON YOU
Tracks: / Edge on you.
7" Single: Released Oct '83, on Nervous, by Nervous Records. Catalogue no: **NER 006**

ICE COLD
Tracks: / Ice cold.
7" Single: Released Apr '87, on ABC (indie), Catalogue no: **ABCS 013**
12" Single: Released Apr '87, on ABC (indie), Catalogue no: **ABCS 013T**

JUST A FRIEND
Tracks: / Just a friend / Girl invisible, The.
7" Single: Released Aug '86, on ABC (indie), Catalogue no: **ABCS 012**

MR. BLUES
Tracks: / Mr. Blues / Fools gold.
7" Single: Released Jan '85, on Big Beat, by Ace Records. Deleted '88. Catalogue no: **NS 104**

NEUTRON DANCE
Tracks: / Neutron dance.
7" Single: Released Dec '88, on Madhouse, by Madhouse Records. Catalogue no: **DAFT 1**
12" Single: Released Dec '88, on Madhouse, by Madhouse Records. Catalogue no: **DAFT 1T**

SOMEBODY TOLD ME
Tracks: / Somebody told me / How can I find you / Deep The (Extra track on 12" version only.).
7" Single: Released May '86, on ABC (indie), Catalogue no: **ABCS 010**
12" Single: Released May '86, on ABC (indie), Catalogue no: **ABCS 010T**

VANISH WITHOUT A TRACE
7" Single: Released May '85, on ABC (indie), Catalogue no: **ABCS 005**
12" Single: Released May '85, on ABC (indie), Catalogue no: **ABCS 005T**

Restricted Code

LOVE TO MEET YOU
Tracks: / Love to meet you / Monkey monkey monkey.
7" Single: Released May '81, on Pop Aural, Catalogue no: **POP 009**

Restriction

ACTION EP
Tracks: / Action.
7" Single: Released May '84, on Restriction, Catalogue no: **RREST 1**

Reuben

DON'T RUSH ME
Tracks: / Don't rush me / Don't rush me (Dub rush).
12" Single: Released Jul '86, on Blakemix, Catalogue no: **BLK 01**

Reubens, Jack

BOXING
Tracks: / Boxing / Heavyweight champion.
12" Single: Released Aug '86, on Shuttle, Catalogue no: **SH 022**

Reunion

LIFE IS A ROCK (BUT THE RADIO ROLLED ME)
Tracks: / Life is a rock (but the radio rolled me).
7" Single: Released Sep '74, on RCA, by BMG Records (UK). Deleted '77. Catalogue no: **PB 10056**

Rev Revolution

MOTORBOYS UK
Tracks: / Motorboys UK.
12" Single: Released Oct '88, on Plastic Head, by Plastic Head Records. Catalogue no: **PLASPOP 1**

Revelation

CRAZY FOR YOU
Tracks: / Crazy for you.
12" Single: Released Aug '85, on Kingdom, by Kingdom Records. Deleted '87. Catalogue no: **KV 8033 12**

FEEL IT
Tracks: / Feel it / When I fall in love.

REVERB BROTHERS - YOU'RE THE ONLY ONE (Released on RCA)

7" Single: Released Apr '81, on Hansa, by Hansa Records. Deleted '85. Catalogue no: **HANDS 3**
12" Single: Released Apr '81, on Hansa, by Hansa Records. Deleted '85. Catalogue no: **HANDX 3**

THAT GIRL
Tracks: / That girl / Sunday morning.
7" Single: Released Jan '82, on Kingdom, by Kingdom Records. Deleted Jan '85. Catalogue no: **KV 8022**
12" Single: Released Dec '81, on Kingdom, by Kingdom Records. Deleted '82. Catalogue no: **KV 8022 12**

TONIGHT
Tracks: / Tonight / Fussin' and fightin'.
7" Single: Released Feb '81, on Kingdom, by Kingdom Records. Deleted '83. Catalogue no: **KV 8013**
12" Single: Released Feb '81, on Kingdom, by Kingdom Records. Deleted '82. Catalogue no: **KV 8013 12**

WHEN I FALL IN LOVE
Tracks: / When I fall in love / Feel it.
7" Single: Released Sep '80, on Handshake, Deleted '83. Catalogue no: **HANDS 1**

Reverb Brothers

AIN'T SO SORRY
Tracks: / Ain't so sorry / Another teenage bride.
7" Single: Released Jun '84, on Spectacle, Deleted '86. Catalogue no: **RNB 001**

SOMEONE'S SELLING OF THE COUNTRY
Tracks: / Someone's selling of the country / Big thing / Far away aint so sorry (Extra track on 12" version only.).
7" Single: Released Jul '86, on RCA, by BMG Records (UK). Catalogue no: **PB 40851**
12" Single: Released Jul '86, on RCA, by BMG Records (UK). Catalogue no: **PT 40852**

YOU'RE THE ONLY ONE (see panel above)
Tracks: / You're the only one / In the nightclub.
7" Single: Released Oct '85, on RCA, by BMG Records (UK). Catalogue no: **PB 40415**
12" Single: Released Oct '85, on RCA, by BMG Records (UK). Catalogue no: **PT 40415**

Reverend Sunshine

TONIGHT
Tracks: / Tonight.
12" Single: Released Oct '82, on DATC, Catalogue no: **DATC 014**

Revie, Kim

COMING ALIVE TONIGHT
Tracks: / Coming alive tonight.
7" Single: Released Jun '82, on Pavilion (USA), by CBS Records. Catalogue no: **PAV 401**

DREAMS IN THE NIGHT
Tracks: / Dreams in the night / It's never too late.
7" Single: Released Dec '83, on Mystery, Deleted '85. Catalogue no: **MIST 1**

Revillos

BITTEN BY A LOVE BUG
Tracks: / Bitten by a love bug.
7" Single: Released Oct '83, on EMI, by EMI Records. Catalogue no: **RVL 1**
12" Single: Released Oct '83, on EMI, by EMI Records. Catalogue no: **12 RVL 1**

BONGO BRAIN
Tracks: / Bongo brain / Hip City / You were meant for me.
7" Single: Released Feb '82, on Superville, Catalogue no: **SV 2001**

HUNGRY FOR LOVE
Tracks: / Hungry for love.
7" Single: Released Aug '80, on Dindisc, by Virgin Records. Catalogue no: **DIN Z 20**

MONSTER MAN
Tracks: / Monster man / Mindbending cutie doll.
7" Single: Released Aug '81, on Superville, Catalogue no: **SV 1001**

MOTORBIKE BEAT
Tracks: / Motorbike beat.
7" Single: Released Jan '80, on Dindisc, by Virgin Records. Deleted '89. Catalogue no: **DIN 5**

SCUBA SCUBA
Tracks: / Scuba scuba.
7" Single: Released Apr '80, on Dindisc, by Virgin Records. Catalogue no: **DIN Z 16**

TELL HIM
Tracks: / Tell him / Graveyard groove.
7" Single: Released Nov '82, on Aura Records, by Aura Records. Catalogue no: **AUS 135**

WHERE'S THE BOY FOR ME
Tracks: / Where's the boy for me.
7" Single: Released Sep '79, on Dindisc, by Virgin Records. Deleted '89. Catalogue no: **DIN 1**

Revolting Cocks

NO DEVOTION
Tracks: / No devotion / Attack ships / On Fire.
12" Single: Released Feb '86, on Wax Trax, by Wax Trax Records. Catalogue no: **WAXUK 011**

STAINLESS STEEL PROVIDERS
Tracks: / Stainless steel providers / At the top.
12" Single: Released Mar '89, on Wax Trax, by Wax Trax Records. Catalogue no: **WAX 042**

YOU OFTEN FORGET
12" Single: Released Feb '87, on Wax Trax, by Wax Trax Records. Catalogue no: **WAXUK 022**

Revolutionaries

CINDERELLA
Tracks: / Cinderella.
7" Single: Released Jul '83, on Dart, by President Records. Catalogue no: **DART 1**

Revolver

FIND ANOTHER LOVE
Tracks: / Find another love / Maybe you're too young to ever know.
7" Single: Released Nov '88, on PSL, by PSL Records. Catalogue no: **PSP 024**

ONE AND ONE IS TWO
Tracks: / One and one is two.
7" Single: Released Dec '79, on Rox, by Rox Records. Catalogue no: **ROX 010**

Revolving Paint Dream

FLOWERS ARE IN THE SKY
Tracks: / Flowers are in the sky / In the afternoon.
7" Single: Released Feb '84, on Creation, by Creation Records. Deleted Jul '88. Catalogue no: **CRE 002**

Revox Cadets

TONY GOES TO TOKYO
Tracks: / Tony goes to Tokyo / Airfields.
7" Single: Released Dec '81, on Cocteau, by Cocteau Records. Catalogue no: **COQ 4**

Revulsion

EVER GET THAT FEELING OF UTTER REVULSION
Tracks: / Ever get that feeling of utter revulsion.
12" Single: Released Apr '85, on Radical Change, by Backs Recording Co.. Catalogue no: **RC 12 007**

Reward

IT MUST BE LOVE
Tracks: / It must be love.
7" Single: Released Jul '84, on Impression, Catalogue no: **IMS 4**
12" Single: Released Jul '84, on Impression, Catalogue no: **IMST 4**

STRANGERS THIS TIME
Tracks: / Strangers this time.
7" Single: Released Jan '85, on Impression, Catalogue no: **IMS 7**
12" Single: Released Jan '85, on Impression, Catalogue no: **IMST 7**

REX

FAR CRY, A
Tracks: / Far cry / Too pretty too soon.
7" Single: Released Jul '89, on Chrysalis, by Chrysalis Records. Catalogue no: **CHS 3399**
12" Single: Released Jul '89, on Chrysalis, by Chrysalis Records. Catalogue no: **CHS 12 3399**

SLEEPWALKING
Tracks: / Sleepwalking / Thirteen frightened girls / Tears on a wheel (Only on 12" version).
7" Single: Released May '89, on Chrysalis, by Chrysalis Records. Catalogue no: **CHS 3373**
12" Single: Released May '89, on Chrysalis, by Chrysalis Records. Catalogue no: **CHS 123373**

Rey, David

WHAT DO YOU DO WITH YOUR LIFE
Tracks: / What do you do with your life / No one's hero.
7" Single: Released 30 May '87, on Absoloot, Catalogue no: **ABS 001**

Reyne, James

MOTOR'S TOO FAST
Tracks: / Motor's too fast / Counting on me / Motor's too fast (Album version) (12" only.) / Submarines (12" only.).
7" Single: Released Sep '88, on Capitol, by EMI Records. Deleted Jun '89. Catalogue no: **CL 508**
12" Single: Released Sep '88, on Capitol, by EMI Records. Deleted Jun '89. Catalogue no: **12CL 508**

Reynolds, Barry

I SCARE MYSELF
Tracks: / I scare myself / Till the doctor gets back.
7" Single: Released Aug '82, on Island, by Island Records. Catalogue no: **WIP 6812**

Reynolds, Debbie

TAMMY
Tracks: / Tammy.
7" Single: Released Aug '57, on Vogue, by Vogue Records. Deleted '60. Catalogue no: **Q 72274**

TAMMY (OLD GOLD)
Tracks: / Tammy.
7" Single: Released Jul '82, on Old Gold, by Old Gold Records. Catalogue no: **OG 9206**

Reynolds Girls

I'D RATHER JACK
Tracks: / I'd rather jack
12" Pic: Released Feb '89, on PWL, by PWL Records. Catalogue no: **PWLT 25 P**
7" Pic: Released Feb '89, on PWL, by PWL Records. Catalogue no: **PWL 25 P**
7" Single: Released Feb '89, on PWL, by PWL Records. Catalogue no: **PWL 25**
12" Single: Released Feb '89, on PWL, by PWL Records. Catalogue no: **PWLT 25**

Reynolds, Jody

ENDLESS SLEEP (OLD GOLD)
Tracks: / Endless sleep.
7" Single: Released Jul '82, on Old Gold, by Old Gold Records. Catalogue no: **OG 9015**

ENDLESS SLEEP (SINGLE)
Tracks: / Endless sleep.
7" Single: Released Apr '79, on Lightning, Deleted '82. Catalogue no: **LIG 9015**

Reynolds, L.J.

SPECIAL EFFECTS
Tracks: / Special effects / Key to the world.
7" Single: Released Aug '82, on Capitol, by EMI Records. Deleted Aug '85. Catalogue no: **CL 260**
12" Single: Released Aug '82, on Capitol, by EMI Records. Deleted Aug '85. Catalogue no: **12CL 260**

WEIGH ALL THE FACTS
Tracks: / Weigh all the facts.
7" Single: Released Jun '84, on Club, by Phonogram Ltd. Catalogue no: **JAB 5**
12" Single: Released Jun '84, on Club, by Phonogram Ltd. Catalogue no: **TABX 5**

Reynolds, Ray

SHANK
Tracks: / Shank.
12" Single: Released Sep '82, on Darace, Catalogue no: **DML 5387**

Rezillos

COLD WARS
Tracks: / Cold wars.
7" Single: Released Apr '79, on Sire (USA), Catalogue no: **SIR 4014**

DESTINATION VENUS
Tracks: / Destination Venus.
7" Single: Released '78, on Sire (USA), Catalogue no: **SIR 4008**

I CAN'T STAND MY BABY
Tracks: / I can't stand my baby.
7" Single: Released Jul '79, on Sensible, Deleted '80. Catalogue no: **FAB 1**

I WANNA BE YOUR MAN
Tracks: / I wanna be your man / I can't stand my baby.
7" Single: Released Aug '79, on Sensible, Deleted '82. Catalogue no: **SAB 1**

TOP OF THE POPS
Tracks: / Top of the pops / Destination Venus.
7" Single: Released Jul '78, on Sire (USA), Catalogue no: **SIR 4001**

Rheingold

FANFANFANATIC
Tracks: / Fanfanfanatic / River.
7" Single: Released Apr '82, on EMI, by EMI Records. Deleted Apr '85. Catalogue no: **EMI 5285**
12" Single: Released Apr '82, on EMI, by EMI Records. Deleted Apr '85. Catalogue no: **12EMI 5285**

LOOKS GOOD ON YOU
Tracks: / Looks good on you / Stahlherz.
7" Single: Released Aug '82, on EMI, by EMI Records. Deleted Aug '85. Catalogue no: **EMI 5329**
12" Single: Released Aug '82, on EMI, by EMI Records. Deleted Aug '85. Catalogue no: **12EMI 5329**

Rhine Heart

STUCK BETWEEN A ROCK
Tracks: / Stuck between a rock.
7" Single: Released Mar '85, on Brain Stir, Catalogue no: **BS 100**

Rhoda

BOILER, THE
Tracks: / Boiler, The / Boiler, Theme from.
7" Single: Released Jan '82, on Two-Tone, by Chrysalis Records. Catalogue no: **CHS TT 18**

Rhoden, Donna

DON'T YOU
Tracks: / Don't you.
12" Single: Released Oct '82, on Ital, by Ital Records. Catalogue no: **ITD 0014**

I'M FALLING IN LOVE
Tracks: / I'm falling in love.
12" Single: Released Mar '82, on Ital, by Ital

Records. Catalogue no: **ITD 0010**

SHY GIRL
Tracks: / Shy girl.
12" Single: Released Sep '81, on Solid Gold (1), by Creole Records. Deleted '86. Catalogue no: **SG 002**

WARM AND TENDER LOVE
Tracks: / Warm and tender love.
12" Single: Released Jan '84, on Ital, by Ital Records. Catalogue no: **ITD 0025**

WE ARE IN LOVE
Tracks: / We are in love.
12" Single: Released May '83, on Ital, by Ital Records. Catalogue no: **ITD 0019**

Rhoden, Pat

STOP
Tracks: / Stop / Sweet sunshine.
7" Single: Released Jul '82, on Jama, Catalogue no: **JA 0050**
12" Single: Released Jul '82, on Jama, Catalogue no: **JADC 0050**

Rhodes, Abigail

TOGETHER AGAIN
Tracks: / Together again.
7" Single: Released Oct '79, on Klub, by Klub Records. Catalogue no: **KLUB 10**

Rhon, Thomas

SCAR
Tracks: / Scar / Give me blood, give me soul.
7" Single: Released 29 Aug '88, on Breakin', by Breakin' Records. Catalogue no: **7 BRK 3**

Rhone, Joan

TRY ME
Tracks: / Try me.
12" Single: Released Aug '81, on Dancebeat, Catalogue no: **DBD 1308**

Rhyme Thyme

REASONS TO BELIEVE (BIG MAX MIX)
Tracks: / Reasons to believe (Big Max mix) / Reasons to believe (dub).
12" Single: Released Sep '89, on Debut, by Skratch Records. Catalogue no: **DEBTX 3074**

Rhythm Clicks

SHORT TIME
Tracks: / Short time.
7" Single: Released 26 Jun '85, on Red Rhino, by Red Rhino Records. Deleted '88. Catalogue no: **RED 006**

Rhythm & Faith

TIME TO RUN
Tracks: / Time to run.
12" Single: Released Nov '83, on Future, Catalogue no: **12 FS 8**

Rhythm From Zaire

AFRIKAN DREAM
Tracks: / Afrikan Dream.
12" Single: Released Jun '87, on BA, Deleted '88. Catalogue no: **BA 8702**

Rhythm Hawks

NO CHANCE
Tracks: / No chance / Clap your hands and dance.
7" Single: Released Apr '81, on Hot Rock, by Hot Rock Records. Catalogue no: **HR 45 009**

ZODIAC
Tracks: / Zodiac.
7" Single: Released Jul '80, on Hot Rock, by Hot Rock Records. Catalogue no: **HR 45 004**

Rhythm Is Rhythm

NUDE PHOTO
Tracks: / Nude photo.
12" Single: Released Oct '87, on Transmat (USA), Catalogue no: **MS 002**

STRINGS
Tracks: / Strings.
12" Single: Released Oct '87, on Transmat (USA), Catalogue no: **MS 004**

STRINGS OF LIFE
Tracks: / Strings of life / Off to battle / Kaos.
12" Single: Released 20 Feb '88, on Indigo (USA), Catalogue no: **12 JTRAX**

Rhythm Kings

A LA RECHERCHE
Tracks: / A la recherche.
12" Single: Released May '89, on Kaos, Catalogue no: **KAOS 017**
CD 5": Released May '89, on Kaos, Catalogue no: **KAOS 017 CD**

Rhythm Method

DIANA
Tracks: / Diana.
7" Single: Released Jul '81, on Watteau, by Armageddon Records. Catalogue no: **WATT 1**

Rhythm Mode D

FLEX WITH THE POSSE (REMIX)
Tracks: / Flex with the posse (remix).
12" Single: Released Mar '89, on Blue Chip, by Blue Chip Records. Catalogue no: **BLUE CHIP 18T**

GANGSTER BOOGIE
Tracks: / Gangster boogie / Can you feel it.
12" Single: Released Nov '88, on Blue Chip, by Blue Chip Records. Catalogue no: **BLUE-CHIP 7 T**

SO DAMN TOUGH
Tracks: / So damn tough.
12" Single: Released May '88, on Blue Chip, by Blue Chip Records. Catalogue no: **BLUERM 1**

SO DAMN TOUGH (REMIX)
Tracks: / So damn tough (remix).
12" Single: Released Jul '88, on Rhythm Mode D, Catalogue no: **RMDR 1**

Rhythm Of Life

SOON
Tracks: / Soon.
7" Single: Released Jan '82, on Rhythm of Life, Catalogue no: **RATE 6**
12" Single: Released Jan '82, on Rhythm of Life, Catalogue no: **RHYTHM 001**

UNCLE SAM
Tracks: / Uncle Sam.
7" Single: Released Apr '82, on Rational, Catalogue no: **RATE 7**

Rhythm On The Radio

WITCHES BREW
Tracks: / Witches brew / Party's over.
7" Single: Released Jan '80, on Oval, by Oval Records. Catalogue no: **OVAL 1015**

Rhythm Party

NOW I KNOW YOU'RE HERE
Tracks: / Now I know you're here.
7" Single: Released Sep '84, on Sly, Catalogue no: **SLY 1**

Rhythm Sisters

AMERICAN BOYS
Tracks: / American boys.
12" Single: Released 14 May '88, on Red Rhino, by Red Rhino Records. Catalogue no: **REDT 92**
7" Single: Released 14 May '88, on Red Rhino, by Red Rhino Records. Catalogue no: **RED 92**

Rhythm Slaves

ELECTRICITY
Tracks: / Electricity / Voices in the wind.
7" Single: Released May '81, on CBS, by CBS Records. Deleted May '84. Catalogue no: **CBS A 1109**

Rhythm Tendencies

COME BACK
Tracks: / Come back / Way of the world.
12" Single: Released Mar '83, on Dakota, Catalogue no: **RYTEN 121**
7" Single: Released Mar '83, on Dakota, Catalogue no: **RYTEN 1**

Ria

NICE GUYS
Tracks: / Nice guys / Walking in the cold.
7" Single: Released Jun '84, on Dead Dog, by Dead Dog Records. Deleted '86. Catalogue no: **DOG 3**

Ria, Nikki

JUST AS I THOUGHT
Tracks: / Just as I thought.
7" Single: Released May '83, on PRT, by Castle Communications Records. Catalogue no: **7P 273**

Ric Tic Live Revue

RIC TIC LIVE REVUE
12" Single: Released Mar '84, on Inferno (1), by Inferno Records. Catalogue no: **12 BURN 3**

Ricardo, Don

CAN YOU STAND THE RAIN
Tracks: / Can you stand the rain.
12" Single: Released May '89, on Progressive, Catalogue no: **PSP 003**

RIBBON IN THE SKY
Tracks: / Ribbon in the sky.
12" Single: Released Jan '89, on Progressive, Catalogue no: **PSP 001**

Riccs, Glen

KEEP ON SEARCHING
Tracks: / Keep on searching.
12" Single: Released Dec '84, on Jetstar, by Jetstar Records. Catalogue no: **INT 015**

LOVELY LADY
Tracks: / Lovely lady.
12" Single: Released Jul '83, on Diamond C, Catalogue no: **DC 001**

THIS CHRISTMAS
Tracks: / This Christmas.
12" Single: Released Dec '83, on Intense, by Intense Records. Catalogue no: **INT 012**

Riccs, Paul

NO REPLY
Tracks: / No reply / Losing you.
7" Single: Released Oct '89, on Axion, Catalogue no: **AXION 891**

Rich, Charlie

Biographical details: Rich, Charlie was born in 1932 in Arkansas. He is a country singer with pop crossover success, also called the Silver Fox (his hair turned prematurely white at age 23). A gifted keyboardist, he led a jazz-blues band in the USA; moved back to Arkansas and tried farming, but the pull of music was too strong. He worked as a session player at Sun Records in Memphis, began making his own records in 1958, had a hit with *Lonely weekends* in 1960; recorded for RCA subsidiary groove where he made two highly praised LP's in 1963-4; went to Mercury's Smash, had hit *Mohair Sam* in 1965; recorded for Memphis label 'Hi', then reunited with producer Billy Sherrill, whom he knew from Sun: wigned with Epic in Nashville and was groomed by Sherrill in the early days of countrypolitan, an easy listening country style that would appeal to the middle-of-the-road market: *Behind closed doors* was his first country number one (number 15 pop, won a grammy and three CMA awards in 1973 for Best Male Vocalist, Best Single and Best Album. *The most beautiful girl* same year was number one in both country and pop charts. Reached top 10 in UK. Groove tracks were re-issued by RCA and three of them became number one country hits. He slipped in the charts after turning up drunk to present the CMA Awards show in 1975, but soon bounced back withmore number ones. He switched to UA in 1978, and has had fewer hits since.

BEHIND CLOSED DOORS (SINGLE)
Tracks: / Behind closed doors.
7" Single: Released Apr '74, on Epic, by CBS Records. Deleted '77. Catalogue no: **EPC 1539**

MOST BEAUTIFUL GIRL IN THE WORLD, THE (OLD GOLD)
Tracks: / Most beautiful girl in the world, The.
7" Single: Released Jul '82, on Old Gold, by Old Gold Records. Catalogue no: **OG 9185**

MOST BEAUTIFUL GIRL IN THE WORLD, THE
7" Single: Released Jul '82, on Old Gold, by Old Gold Records. Catalogue no: **OG 9185**

WE LOVE EACH OTHER
Tracks: / We love each other.
7" Single: Released Feb '75, on Epic, by CBS Records. Deleted '78. Catalogue no: **EPC 2868**

Rich, Denise

SWEET PAIN OF LOVE (SINGLE)
Tracks: / Sweet pain of love.
12" Single: Released Feb '87, on Foundry, Deleted May '88. Catalogue no: **FOUND 412**
7" Single: Released Feb '87, on Foundry, Deleted May '88. Catalogue no: **FOUND 4**

WE WALKED AWAY FROM A LOVE AFFAIR
Tracks: / We walked away from a love affair / Win in my soul.
12" Single: Released May '86, on MCA, by MCA Records. Catalogue no: **MCAT 1039**
7" Single: Released May '86, on MCA, by MCA Records. Catalogue no: **MCA 1039**

Rich Fresh

TIME TO BUILD
Tracks: / Time to build / Party rocker.

7" Single: Released Nov '88, on Citybeat, by Beggars Banquet Records. Catalogue no: **CBE 732**
12" Single: Released Nov '88, on Citybeat, by Beggars Banquet Records. Catalogue no: **CBE 1232**

Rich Gypsy

TWIST AND SHOUT
Tracks: / Twist and shout / Nothing but a tease.
7" Single: Released Feb '81, on Splash, by Splash Records. Deleted Feb '84. Catalogue no: **SP 21**

Rich Kids

RICH KIDS
Tracks: / Rich kids.
7" Single: Released Jan '78, on EMI, by EMI Records. Deleted '81. Catalogue no: **EMI 2738**

Rich Mix

I'VE GOT THE LOVE
Tracks: / I've got the love.
12" Single: Released Aug '83, on Satril, by Satril Records. Catalogue no: **12 SAT 509**
7" Single: Released Aug '83, on Satril, by Satril Records. Catalogue no: **SAT 509**

Rich, Richie

CHECK IT OUT
Tracks: / Check it out / Scratch it out.
Note: G/Self-98 Fulham Place Road,London-01 741 0543.
12" Single: Released Jun '86, on Spin-Off's, Catalogue no: **12 OFF 1**

I CAN MAKE YOU DANCE (SINGLE)
Tracks: / I can make you dance.
7" Single: Released Jul '89, on Gee Street, by Gee Street Records. Catalogue no: **GEE 22**
12" Single: Released Jul '89, on Gee Street, by Gee Street Records. Catalogue no: **GEET 22**

MY DJ (PUMP IT UP SOME)
Tracks: / My DJ (pump it up some).
7" Single: Released Nov '88, on Gee Street, by Gee Street Records. Catalogue no: **GEE 007**
12" Single: Released Nov '88, on Gee Street, by Gee Street Records. Catalogue no: **GEE 12007**

MY DJ (PUMP IT UP SOME) (REMIX)
Tracks: / My DJ (pump it up some) / D.J. beats.
12" Single: Released Jan '89, on Gee Street, by Gee Street Records. Catalogue no: **GEET 7R**

ROCKING ON THE GO-GO SCENE
Tracks: / Rocking on the go-go scene.
7" Single: Released 27 Feb '89, on Gee Street, by Gee Street Records. Catalogue no: **GEE 012**
12" Single: Released 27 Feb '89, on Gee Street, by Gee Street Records. Catalogue no: **GEET 012**

SALSA HOUSE
Tracks: / Salsa house / Salsa house (dub zone) / Salsa house (silver on black remix) (Only on 12" single.) / Salsa house (original orbital mix) (Only on 12" single.).
7" Single: Released Aug '89, on ffrr, by London Records. Catalogue no: **F 113**
12" Single: Released Aug '89, on ffrr, by London Records. Catalogue no: **FX 223**

SOUL TRAIN
Tracks: / Soul train.
12" Single: Released 2 May '89, on Gee Street, by Gee Street Records. Catalogue no: **UNKNOWN**
7" Single: Released 2 May '89, on Gee Street, by Gee Street Records. Catalogue no: **UNKNOWN**

TURN IT UP
Tracks: / Turn it up.
Note: "Built on a totally infectious rhythm and put together in striking fashion despite the presence of some too-well samples, this bubbling dance track should pick up cross-over play." (Music Week, July 1988)
7" Single: Released Jun '88, on Phonogram, by Phonogram Ltd. Deleted 31 May '89. Catalogue no: **JAB 68**
12" Single: Released Jun '88, on Phonogram, by Phonogram Ltd. Deleted 31 May '89. Catalogue no: **JABX 68**

Richard, Cliff

Biographical details:
Richard, Cliff was born Harry Roger Webb in India in 1940. He is the most durable of UK pop stars.
He fomed the Drifters in 1958, played at the 2 I's coffee bar in Soho, cradle of UK rock 'n' roll; changed his name on the advice of an agent and signed to Columbia: first single was cover of Bobby Helms' *Schoolboy Crush*, flipped to reveal *Move it* the most exciting UK R&R disc until then, a number two hit.
Drifters renamed to avoid confusion with USA R&B group; new personnel recruited for tours turned out to be the Shadows
. Initially Richard was an Elvis Presley imitator, but clearly in a class above the others. He had 93 chart hits in UK 1958-86 not counting re-entries, and five number one albums.
He made family musical films which have not held up well; he ignored changes in pop during the '60's, perhaps because of his well-publicised conversion to Christianity; he disavowed a cover of *Honky Tonk Angel* when someone told him it was refering to a prositute.
A remake for charity of the hit *Living Doll*, with the comedy team the Young Ones in 1986

was a number one; duet *All I ask of you* with Sarah Brightman was top 3. He also made inspirational LP *Walking in the light* '85 for Word; recorded with Olivia Newton John, Phil Everly and Shadow star Hank Marvin; appeared in first stage musical **Time** 1985, had two hits from it, left in 1987. He is a hard working pro and his live shows are good value for fans. (Donald Clarke 21.5.88)
This British singer, guitarist and actor is the most popular homegrown artist in UK chart history. He was actually born in Lucknow, India, where his English father worked for a catering company, in 1940. The family moved back to Britain in 1948. After performing in a number of small-time rock'n'roll and skiffle groups, he changed his name from Harry Webb to Cliff Richard in early 1958. With his backing group, the 'Drifters' (who later changed their name to the 'Shadows' to avoid confusion with the black American vocal group), the singer signed with Columbia Records in August of that year and has remained on the EMI roster ever since. Things happened quickly for Cliff Richard in 1958. In September he made his first television appearance on ITV's Jack Good-produced pop show *Oh Boy!*; helped by this exposure, his debut single *Move It* entered the UK chart in the same month. In an era when British imitations of American rock'n'roll records were almost always inferior to the real US thing, *Move It* stood up as one of the few great UK rock'n'roll records. It climbed to No.2 on the UK charts, and Cliff Richard was hailed as Britain's first real challenge to Elvis Presley. Although he had to wait almost 20 years before enjoying substantial American success, Cliff Richard soon established himself as the hottest property in the British music business. The authentic rock'n'roll hits lasted for barely a year, and then Cliff adopted an out-and-out pop approach in the summer of 1959 with *Living Doll*; this record was his first No.1 hit, and marked the real beginning of his long-term career as Britain's most reliable purveyor of pleasant pop. *Living Doll* was followed by a second consecutive No.1 single, *Travellin' Light* (which topped the charts for the whole of November 1959). Richard was at the very peak of his UK commercial success during the early Sixties. Before the 'Beatles' and 'Merseybeat' sxploded in 1963, Cliff & the Shadows were easily the top act in the nation. Virtually every single he issued reached the Top 5; *Please Don't Tease, I Love You, The Young Ones* (the title song from one of his many movie vehicles), the double A sided single *The Next Time/Bachelor Boy* and *Summer Holiday* all climbed to No.1. He also chalked up three chart-topping albums during this period, and the 'Shadows' enjoyed five No.1 singles on their own.
Showing remarkable staying power, Cliff remained a regular visitor to the UK Top 10 throughout the 'Beatles' heyday of the Sixties, while many of his contemporaries were torpedoed out of the charts by the emphasis on groups. In April 1965 he proved that he was still capable of reaching the exalted No.1 spot, when *The Minute You're Gone* climbed to the very top; like almost all his chart-toppers it was produced by Norrie Paramor, the long-standing head of Columbia, who had nurtured his hitmaking career from the beginning. During the late Sixties and early Seventies Cliff was a less successful, but still consistent, chart force. He became less of a pop star, and more of an all-round showbusiness entertainer. This progression was fuelled by a number of factors, including his conversion to Christianity, his two appearances in the Eurovision Song Contest (with the No.1 hit *Congratulations* in 1968, and *Power To All Our Friends* in 1973), his partipation in pantomime, his showbizzy TV series and his choice of banal material like *Big Ship* and *Goodbye Sam Hello Samantha*. Cliff's credibility as a pop star was restored in 1976, with the release of the excellent album *I'm nearly famous*. This contained his best ever ballad *Miss You Nights* and the highly acclaimed *Devil Woman*, which harked back to his rock'n'roll roots and provided him with his first ever American smash. 1979 brought him his 10th British No.1 single, and his first for eleven years, with the ultra-catchy *We Don't Talk Anymore*. Then followed a string of further UK Top Tenners during the early Eighties, although consistent American success continued to elude him. In the mid-Eighties he embarked on his first ever stage musical, Dave Clark's *Time*. Cliff Richard is the perennially youthful Mr. Nice Guy of British pop, and has avoided the pitfalls and pressures and personal weaknesses that are often associated with the music business. He has chalked up more hits than anybody except Elvis Presley, and remains a highly approachable yet slightly enigmatic superstar. (Bob MacDonald, 10.3.86)..

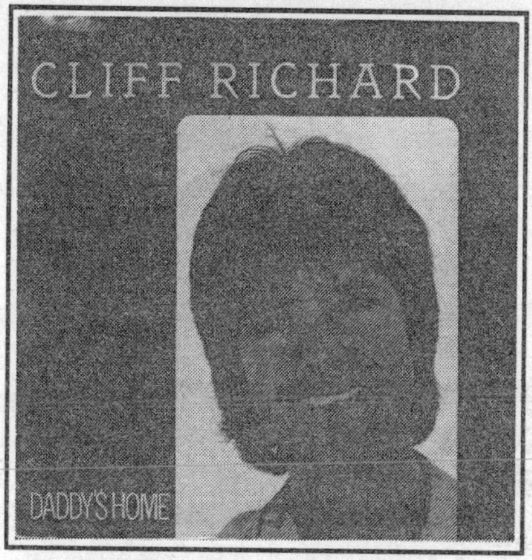

CLIFF RICHARD - DADDY'S HOME (Released On EMI)

ALL I ASK OF YOU
Tracks: / All I ask of you / Phantom of the opera overture (Act II) / Only you (Extra track on 12" version only.).
12" Single: Released Sep '86, on Polydor, by Polydor Ltd. Deleted Aug '87. Catalogue no: **POSPX 802**
7" Single: Released Sep '86, on Polydor, by Polydor Ltd. Deleted Mar '88. Catalogue no: **POSP 802**

ALL MY LOVE
Tracks: / All my love.
7" Single: Released Nov '67, on Columbia, by EMI Records. Deleted '70. Catalogue no: **DB 8293**

BABY YOU'RE DYNAMITE
Tracks: / Baby you're dynamite / Ocean deep.
7" Single: Released Mar '84, on EMI, by EMI Records. Deleted '87. Catalogue no: **EMI 5457**

BEST OF ME, THE
Tracks: / Best of me, The / Move it / Lindsay Jane / High class baby (CD single only.).
Cassingle: Released May '89, on EMI, by EMI Records. Catalogue no: **TCEM 92**
CD 5": Released May '89, on EMI, by EMI Records. Catalogue no: **CDEMS 92**
CD 5": Released May '89, on EMI, by EMI Records. Catalogue no: **CDEM 92**
Cassingle: Released May '89, on EMI, by EMI Records. Catalogue no: **203 383 4**
7" Single: Released May '89, on EMI, by EMI Records. Catalogue no: **EM 92**
7" Single: Released May '89, on EMI, by EMI Records. Catalogue no: **EMS 92**
12" Single: Released May '89, on EMI, by EMI Records. Catalogue no: **12EMS 92**
12" Single: Released May '89, on EMI, by EMI Records. Catalogue no: **12EM 92**

BIG SHIP
Tracks: / Big ship.
7" Single: Released May '69, on Columbia, by EMI Records. Deleted '72. Catalogue no: **DB 8581**

BLUE TURNS TO GREY
Tracks: / Blue turns to grey.
7" Single: Released Mar '66, on Columbia, by EMI Records. Deleted '69. Catalogue no: **DB 7866**

BORN TO ROCK 'N' ROLL
Tracks: / Born to rock 'n' roll / Law of the universe.
12" Single: Released May '86, on EMI, by EMI Records. Catalogue no: **12EMI 5545**
7" Single: Released May '86, on EMI, by EMI Records. Catalogue no: **EMI 5545**

CAROL SINGERS (EP)
Tracks: / God rest ye merry gentlemen / In the bleak mid winter / Unto us a child is born / While shepherds watched their flocks by night / O little town of Bethlehem.
12" Single: Released '83, on EMI (Holland), by EMI Records. Catalogue no: **K 062Z 07571**

CARRIE
Tracks: / Carrie / Moving in.
7" Single: Released Feb '80, on EMI, by EMI Records. Deleted '83. Catalogue no: **EMI 5006**
12" Single: Released '83, on EMI (Germany), by EMI Records. Catalogue no: **IC 052K 07188YZ**

CONGRATULATIONS
Tracks: / Congratulations / High 'n' dry.
7" Single: Released Mar '68, on Columbia, by EMI Records. Deleted '71. Catalogue no: **DB 8376**

CONSTANTLY
Tracks: / Constantly.
7" Single: Released Apr '64, on Columbia, by EMI Records. Deleted '67. Catalogue no: **DB 7272**

DADDY'S HOME (See panel above)
Tracks: / Daddy's home / Shakin' all over.
7" Single: Released Nov '81, on EMI, by EMI Records. Catalogue no: **EMI 5251**

DAY I MET MARIE, THE
Tracks: / Day I met Marie, The.
7" Single: Released Aug '67, on Columbia, by EMI Records. Deleted '70. Catalogue no: **DB 8245**

DEVIL WOMAN
Tracks: / Devil woman / Love on.
7" Single: Released May '76, on EMI, by EMI Records. Deleted '79. Catalogue no: **EMI 2458**

DON'T FORGET TO CATCH ME
Tracks: / Don't forget to catch me.
7" Single: Released Nov '68, on Columbia, by EMI Records. Deleted '71. Catalogue no: **DB 8503**

DON'T TALK TO HIM
Tracks: / Don't talk to him.
7" Single: Released Nov '63, on Columbia, by EMI Records. Deleted '66. Catalogue no: **DB 7150**

DREAM (EP)
Tracks: / Dream.
12" Single: Released '82, on EMI (Holland), by EMI Records. Catalogue no: **K 062Z 07614**

DREAMIN'
Tracks: / Dreamin' / Dynamite.
7" Single: Released Aug '80, on EMI, by EMI Records. Deleted '83. Catalogue no: **EMI 5095**

DRIFTING (EP)
Tracks: / Drifting.
7" Single: Released May '83, on DJM, Catalogue no: **SHEIL 1**
12" Single: Released May '83, on DJM, Catalogue no: **SHEIL 100**

DYNAMITE
Tracks: / Dynamite.
7" Single: Released Oct '59, on Columbia, by EMI Records. Deleted '62. Catalogue no: **DB 4351**

EXPRESSO BONGO (EP)
Tracks: / Love / Voice in the wilderness, A / Shrine on the second floor / Bongo blues.
12" Single: Released '83, on EMI (Holland), by EMI Records. Catalogue no: **K 052 07329**
7" Single: Released Jan '60, on Columbia, by EMI Records. Deleted '63. Catalogue no: **SEG 7971**

FALL IN LOVE WITH YOU
Tracks: / Fall in love with you.
7" Single: Released Mar '60, on Columbia, by EMI Records. Deleted '63. Catalogue no: **DB 4431**

FLYING MACHINE
Tracks: / Flying machine.
7" Single: Released Jul '71, on Columbia, by EMI Records. Deleted '73. Catalogue no: **DB 8797**

GEE WHIZ IT'S YOU
Tracks: / Gee whiz it's you.
7" Single: Released Mar '61, on Columbia, by EMI Records. Deleted '64. Catalogue no: **DC 756**

GIRL LIKE YOU, A
Tracks: / Girl like you, A.
7" Single: Released Jun '61, on Columbia, by EMI Records. Deleted '64. Catalogue no: **DB 4667**

GOOD TIMES (BETTER TIMES)
Tracks: / Good times (better times).
7" Single: Released Feb '69, on Columbia, by EMI Records. Deleted '72. Catalogue no: **DB 8548**

GOODBYE SAM HELLO SAMANTHA
Tracks: / Goodbye Sam hello Samantha.
7" Single: Released Jun '70, on Columbia, by EMI Records. Deleted '73. Catalogue no: **DB 8685**

GREEN LIGHT
Tracks: / Green light.
7" Single: Released Mar '79, on EMI, by EMI Records. Deleted '82. Catalogue no: **EMI 2920**

HEART USER
Tracks: / Heart user.
7" Single: Released Feb '85, on EMI, by EMI Records. Deleted '88. Catalogue no: **RICH 2**

HELP IT ALONG
Tracks: / Help it along / Tomorrow rising.
7" Single: Released Jun '73, on EMI, by EMI Records. Deleted '76. Catalogue no: **EMI 2022**

HEY MR DREAM MAKER
Tracks: / Hey Mr. Dream maker.
7" Single: Released Dec '76, on EMI, by EMI Records. Deleted '79. Catalogue no: **EMI 2559**

HIGH CLASS BABY
Tracks: / High class baby.
7" Single: Released '80, on Columbia, by EMI Records. Catalogue no: **LR 4642**
7" Single: Released Nov '58, on Columbia, by EMI Records. Deleted '61. Catalogue no: **DB 4203**

HOLIDAY CARNIVAL (EP)
Tracks: / Holiday carnival.
12" Single: Released '82, on EMI (Holland), by EMI Records. Catalogue no: **K 062Z 07616**

HOT SHOT
Tracks: / Hot shot.
7" Single: Released Nov '79, on EMI, by EMI Records. Deleted '82. Catalogue no: **EMI 5003**

I AIN'T GOT TIME ANYMORE
Tracks: / I ain't got time anymore.
7" Single: Released Sep '70, on Columbia, by EMI Records. Deleted '73. Catalogue no: **DB 8708**

I CAN'T ASK FOR ANYMORE THAN YOU
Tracks: / I can't ask for anymore than you.
7" Single: Released Aug '76, on EMI, by EMI Records. Deleted '79. Catalogue no: **EMI 2499**

I COULD EASILY FALL
Tracks: / I could easily fall in love with you.
7" Single: Released Dec '64, on Columbia, by EMI Records. Deleted '67. Catalogue no: **DB 7420**

I JUST DON'T HAVE THE HEART
Tracks: / I just don't have the heart / Wide open space / I just don't have the heart (inst.) (12" & CD single only.).
Note: Produced by Stock Aitken Waterman.
7" Single: Released Aug '89, on EMI, by EMI Records. Catalogue no: **EM 101**
CD 5": Released Aug '89, on EMI, by EMI Records. Catalogue no: **203 477 2**
CD 5": Released Aug '89, on EMI, by EMI Records. Catalogue no: **CDEM 101**
Cassingle: Released Aug '89, on EMI, by EMI Records. Catalogue no: **TCEM 101**
7" Single: Released Aug '89, on EMI, by EMI Records. Catalogue no: **203 477 7**
12" Single: Released Aug '89, on EMI, by EMI Records. Catalogue no: **203 477 6**
12" Single: Released Aug '89, on EMI, by EMI Records. Catalogue no: **203 538 6**
12" Single: Released Aug '89, on EMI, by EMI Records. Catalogue no: **12EM 101**
12" Single: Released Aug '89, on EMI, by EMI Records. Catalogue no: **12EMX 101**
Cassingle: Released Aug '89, on EMI, by EMI Records. Catalogue no: **203 477 4**
12" Single: Released Aug '89, on EMI, by

EMI Records. Catalogue no: **12EMP 101**
12" Single: Released Aug '89, on EMI, by EMI Records. Catalogue no: **203 477 8**

I LOVE YOU (SINGLE)
Tracks: / I love you.
7" Single: Released Dec '60, on Columbia, by EMI Records. Deleted '63. Catalogue no: **DB 4547**

I'LL COME RUNNING
Tracks: / I'll come running.
7" Single: Released Jun '67, on Columbia, by EMI Records. Deleted '70. Catalogue no: **DB 8210**

I'LL LOVE YOU FOREVER TODAY
Tracks: / I'll love you forever today.
7" Single: Released Jun '68, on Columbia, by EMI Records. Deleted '71. Catalogue no: **DB 8437**

I'M LOOKING OUT THE WINDOW
Tracks: / I'm looking out the window / Do you wanna dance.
7" Single: Released May '62, on Columbia, by EMI Records. Deleted '65. Catalogue no: **DB 4828**

I'M THE LONELY ONE
Tracks: / I'm the lonely one.
7" Single: Released Feb '64, on Columbia, by EMI Records. Deleted '67. Catalogue no: **DB 7203**

IN THE COUNTRY
Tracks: / In the country.
7" Single: Released Dec '66, on Columbia, by EMI Records. Deleted '69. Catalogue no: **DB 8094**

IT'LL BE ME
Tracks: / It'll be me.
7" Single: Released Sep '62, on Columbia, by EMI Records. Deleted '65. Catalogue no: **DB 4886**

IT'S ALL IN THE GAME
Tracks: / It's all in the game.
7" Single: Released Aug '63, on Columbia, by EMI Records. Deleted '66. Catalogue no: **DB 7089**

IT'S ALL OVER
Tracks: / It's all over.
7" Single: Released Mar '67, on Columbia, by EMI Records. Deleted '70. Catalogue no: **DB 8150**

IT'S IN EVERY ONE OF US
Tracks: / It's in everyone of us.
12" Single: Released Nov '85, on EMI, by EMI Records. Catalogue no: **12EMI 5537**
7" Single: Released Nov '85, on EMI, by EMI Records. Catalogue no: **EMI 5537**

JESUS
Tracks: / Jesus.
7" Single: Released Mar '72, on Columbia, by EMI Records. Deleted '75. Catalogue no: **DB 8864**

JOY OF LIVING
Tracks: / Joy of living.
7" Single: Released Feb '70, on Columbia, by EMI Records. Deleted '73. Catalogue no: **DB 8657**

LEAN ON YOU
Tracks: / Lean on you / Lean on you(ext. mix) (12" & CD single only.) / Hey Mister.
Cassingle: Released Oct '89, on EMI, by EMI Records. Catalogue no: **203 528 4**
CD 5": Released Oct '89, on EMI, by EMI Records. Catalogue no: **203 528 2**
7" Pic: Released Oct '89, on EMI, by EMI Records. Catalogue no: **EMPD 105**
7" Single: Released Oct '89, on EMI, by EMI Records. Catalogue no: **203 528 7**
12" Single: Released Oct '89, on EMI, by EMI Records. Catalogue no: **203 528 6**
7" Single: Released Oct '89, on EMI, by EMI Records. Catalogue no: **EM 105**
7" Pic: Released Oct '89, on EMI, by EMI Records. Catalogue no: **203 528 0**
Cassingle: Released Oct '89, on EMI, by EMI Records. Catalogue no: **TCEM 105**
12" Single: Released Oct '89, on EMI, by EMI Records. Catalogue no: **12EM 105**
CD 5": Released Oct '89, on EMI, by EMI Records. Catalogue no: **CDEM 105**

LITTLE IN LOVE, A
Tracks: / Little in love, A / Keep on looking.
7" Single: Released Jan '81, on EMI, by EMI Records. Deleted '84. Catalogue no: **EMI 5123**

LITTLE TOWN
Tracks: / Little town / Love and a helping hand.
7" Single: Released Nov '82, on EMI, by EMI Records. Catalogue no: **EMI 5348**

LIVIN' LOVIN' DOLL
Tracks: / Livin' lovin' doll.
7" Single: Released '80, on Columbia, by EMI Records. Catalogue no: **LR 4641**
7" Single: Released Jan '59, on Columbia, by EMI Records. Deleted '62. Catalogue no: **DB 4249**

LIVING DOLL
Tracks: / Living doll / (All the flowers are) Happy / Disco funk get up,get down (go to the lavatory mix) (Extra track on 12" version only.).
7" Single: Released Mar '86, on WEA, by WEA Records. Deleted Jan '88. Catalogue no: **YZ 65**
7" Single: Released Jul '59, on Columbia, by EMI Records. Catalogue no: **DB 4306**
12" Single: Released Mar '86, on WEA, by WEA Records. Deleted Jun '87. Catalogue no: **YZ 65T**

LIVING IN HARMONY
Tracks: / Living in harmony.
7" Single: Released Aug '72, on Columbia, by EMI Records. Deleted '75. Catalogue no: **DB 8917**

LUCKY LIPS
Tracks: / Lucky lips.
7" Single: Released May '63, on Columbia, by EMI Records. Deleted '66. Catalogue no: **DB 7034**

MARIANNE
Tracks: / Marianne.
7" Single: Released Sep '68, on Columbia, by EMI Records. Deleted '71. Catalogue no: **DB 8476**

MEAN STREAK
Tracks: / Mean streak.
7" Single: Released May '59, on Columbia, by EMI Records. Deleted '62. Catalogue no: **DB 4290**
7" Single: Released '80, on Columbia, by EMI Records. Catalogue no: **LR 4643**

MINUTE YOU'RE GONE, THE
Tracks: / Minute you're gone, The.
7" Single: Released Mar '65, on Columbia, by EMI Records. Deleted '68. Catalogue no: **DB 7496**

MISS YOU NIGHTS
Tracks: / Miss you nights / Love enough.
7" Single: Released Feb '76, on EMI, by EMI Records. Deleted Jun '89. Catalogue no: **EMI 2376**

MISTLETOE & WINE
Tracks: / Mistletoe & wine / Marmaduke (Tarney/Spencer) / Little town (12" & CD single only.) / La gonave (CD single only.) / True love ways (Limited edition 7" only.).
12" Single: Released Nov '88, on EMI, by EMI Records. Deleted Oct '89. Catalogue no: **12EM 78**
7" Single: Released Nov '88, on EMI, by EMI Records. Deleted Jan '89. Catalogue no: **EM 78**
12" Single: Released Nov '88, on EMI, by EMI Records. Deleted Aug '89. Catalogue no: **12EMX 78**
CD 5": Released Nov '88, on EMI, by EMI Records. Catalogue no: **CDEM 78**
7" Single: Released Dec '88, on EMI, by EMI Records. Catalogue no: **EMS 78**
7" Single: Released Nov '88, on EMI, by EMI Records. Deleted Aug '89. Catalogue no: **EMP 78**

MOVE IT
Tracks: / Move it / Schoolboy crush.
7" Single: Released Feb '82, on Columbia, by EMI Records. Catalogue no: **DB 4178**

MY KINDA LIFE
Tracks: / My kinda life.
7" Single: Released Mar '77, on EMI, by EMI Records. Deleted '80. Catalogue no: **EMI 2584**

MY PRETTY ONE
Tracks: / My pretty one / Love ya / Under the gun* (*Extra track on 12").
7" Single: Released Jun '87, on EMI, by EMI Records. Deleted Nov '88. Catalogue no: **EM 4**
12" Single: Released Jun '87, on EMI, by EMI Records. Deleted Apr '88. Catalogue no: **12EM 4**
7" Single: Released Jun '87, on EMI, by EMI Records. Deleted Oct '87. Catalogue no: **EMG 4**
12" Single: Released Jun '87, on EMI, by EMI Records. Catalogue no: **EMP 4**

NEVER MIND
Tracks: / Never mind.
7" Single: Released May '59, on Columbia, by EMI Records. Deleted '62. Catalogue no: **DB 4290**

NEVER SAY DIE (GIVE A LITTLE BIT MORE)
Tracks: / Never say die (give a little bit more).
7" Single: Released Sep '83, on EMI, by EMI Records. Deleted '86. Catalogue no: **EMI 5415**

NEXT TIME, THE
Tracks: / Next time, The / Bachelor boy.
7" Single: Released Dec '62, on Columbia, by EMI Records. Deleted Aug '89. Catalogue no: **DB 4950**

NINE TIMES OUT OF TEN
Tracks: / Nine times out of ten.
7" Single: Released Sep '60, on Columbia, by EMI Records. Deleted '63. Catalogue no: **DB 4506**

ON MY WORD
Tracks: / On my word.
7" Single: Released Jun '65, on Columbia, by EMI Records. Deleted '68. Catalogue no: **DB 7596**

ON THE BEACH
Tracks: / On the beach.
7" Single: Released Jul '64, on Columbia, by EMI Records. Deleted '67. Catalogue no: **DB 7305**

ONLY WAY OUT, THE
Tracks: / Only way out, The / Influence.
7" Single: Released Jul '82, on EMI, by EMI Records. Deleted '85. Catalogue no: **EMI 5318**

PLEASE DON'T FALL IN LOVE
Tracks: / Please don't fall in love / Too close to heaven.
7" Single: Released Nov '83, on EMI, by EMI Records. Deleted '86. Catalogue no: **EMI 5437**

PLEASE DON'T TEASE
Tracks: / Please don't tease / Where is my heart.
7" Single: Released Jun '60, on Columbia, by EMI Records. Deleted '63. Catalogue no: **DB 4479**

POWER TO ALL OUR FRIENDS
Tracks: / Power to all our friends.
7" Single: Released Mar '73, on EMI, by EMI Records. Deleted '76. Catalogue no: **EMI 2012**

REMEMBER ME
Tracks: / Brave new world / Remember me / Another Christmas day / Some people.
12" Single: Released Oct '87, on EMI, by EMI Records. Deleted Nov '88. Catalogue no: **12EM 31**
CD 5": Released Nov '87, on EMI, by EMI Records. Deleted Nov '88. Catalogue no: **CDEM 31**
7" Single: Released Oct '87, on EMI, by EMI Records. Deleted Jun '89. Catalogue no: **EM 31**
12" Single: Released Oct '87, on EMI, by EMI Records. Deleted Nov '88. Catalogue no: **12EMP 31**

SERIOUS CHARGE (EP)
Tracks: / Serious charge.
12" Single: Released '83, on EMI (Holland), by EMI Records. Catalogue no: **K 062Z 07528**

SHE'S SO BEAUTIFUL
Tracks: / She's so beautiful.
7" Single: Released Sep '85, on EMI, by EMI Records. Deleted '88. Catalogue no: **EMI 5531**

SHOOTING FROM THE HEART
Tracks: / Shooting from the heart.
7" Pic: Released Nov '84, on EMI, by EMI Records. Catalogue no: **RICHP 1**
7" Single: Released Nov '84, on EMI, by EMI Records. Deleted '87. Catalogue no: **RICH 1**

SILVERY RAIN
Tracks: / Silvery rain.
7" Single: Released Apr '71, on Columbia, by EMI Records. Deleted '74. Catalogue no: **DB 8774**

SING A SONG OF FREEDOM
Tracks: / Sing a song of freedom.
7" Single: Released Nov '71, on Columbia, by EMI Records. Deleted '74. Catalogue no: **DB 8836**

SOME PEOPLE
Tracks: / Some people / One time lover man.
12" Single: Released Aug '87, on EMI, by EMI Records. Deleted Nov '88. Catalogue no: **12EM 18**
7" Single: Released Aug '87, on EMI, by EMI Records. Deleted Oct '87. Catalogue no: **EMG 18**
Special: Released Aug '87, on EMI, by EMI Records. Deleted Jan '88. Catalogue no: **EMP 18**
7" Single: Released Aug '87, on EMI, by EMI Records. Deleted Jun '89. Catalogue no: **EM 18**

SUMMER HOLIDAY
Tracks: / Summer holiday / Dancing shoes.
7" Single: Released Feb '82, on Columbia, by EMI Records. Catalogue no: **DB 4977**

SUNNY HONEY GIRL
Tracks: / Sunny honey girl.
7" Single: Released Jan '71, on Columbia, by EMI Records. Deleted '74. Catalogue no: **DB 8747**

TAKE ME HIGH (SINGLE)
Tracks: / Take me high.
7" Single: Released Dec '73, on EMI, by EMI Records. Deleted '76. Catalogue no: **EMI 2088**

THEME FOR A DREAM
Tracks: / Theme for a dream.
7" Single: Released Mar '61, on Columbia, by EMI Records. Deleted '64. Catalogue no: **DB 4593**

THROW DOWN A LINE
Tracks: / Throw down a line.
7" Single: Released Sep '69, on Columbia, by EMI Records. Deleted '72. Catalogue no: **DB 8615**

THUNDERBIRDS (EP)
Tracks: / Thunderbird.
12" Single: Released '83, on EMI (Holland), by EMI Records. Catalogue no: **K 052Z 07330**

TIME DRAGS BY
Tracks: / Time drags by.
7" Single: Released Oct '66, on Columbia, by EMI Records. Deleted '69. Catalogue no: **DB 8017**

TIME IN BETWEEN, THE
Tracks: / Time in between, The.
7" Single: Released Aug '65, on Columbia, by EMI Records. Deleted '68. Catalogue no: **DB 7660**

TRAVELLIN' LIGHT
Tracks: / Travellin' light / Dynamite.
7" Single: Released Oct '59, on Columbia, by EMI Records. Catalogue no: **DB 4351**

TRUE LOVE WAYS
Tracks: / True love ways.
7" Single: Released Apr '83, on EMI, by EMI Records. Deleted '86. Catalogue no: **EMI 5385**

TWELFTH OF NEVER
Tracks: / Twelfth of never.
7" Single: Released Oct '64, on Columbia, by EMI Records. Deleted '67. Catalogue no: **DB 7372**

TWO HEARTS
Tracks: / Two hearts / Yesterday, today and forever / Two hearts (ext. version) (Extra track on CD single.) / Wild geese, The (Extra track on CD single.).
12" Single: Released Jan '88, on EMI, by EMI Records. Deleted Nov '88. Catalogue no: **12EMG 42**
12" Single: Released Jan '88, on EMI, by EMI Records. Deleted Nov '88. Catalogue no: **12EM 42**
7" Single: Released Feb '88, on EMI, by EMI Records. Deleted Jun '89. Catalogue no: **EM 42**
7" Single: Released Feb '88, on EMI, by EMI Records. Deleted Nov '88. Catalogue no: **EMP 42**
CD 5": Released Feb '88, on EMI, by EMI Records. Deleted 31 Jul '88. Catalogue no: **CDEM 42**

TWO TO THE POWER
Tracks: / Two to the power.
12" Single: Released Sep '84, on A&M, by A&M Records. Deleted '88. Catalogue no: **AMX 210**
7" Single: Released Sep '84, on A&M, by A&M Records. Deleted '88. Catalogue no: **AM 210**

VISIONS
Tracks: / Visions.
7" Single: Released Jul '66, on Columbia, by EMI Records. Deleted '69. Catalogue no: **DB 7968**

VOICE IN THE WILDERNESS
Tracks: / Voice in the wilderness, A.
7" Single: Released Jan '60, on Columbia, by EMI Records. Deleted '63. Catalogue no: **DB 4398**

WE DON'T TALK ANYMORE
Tracks: / We don't talk anymore / Count me out.
7" Single: Released Jul '79, on EMI, by EMI Records. Deleted '82. Catalogue no: **EMI 2975**
12" Single: Released '83, on EMI (Germany), by EMI Records. Catalogue no: **IC 052 07076YZ**

WHEN THE GIRL IN YOUR ARMS IS THE GIRL IN YOUR
Tracks: / When the girl in your arms is the girl in your.
7" Single: Released Oct '61, on Columbia, by EMI Records. Deleted '64. Catalogue no: **DB 4716**

WHEN TWO WORLDS DRIFT APART
Tracks: / When two worlds drift apart.
7" Single: Released Jul '77, on EMI, by EMI Records. Deleted '80. Catalogue no: **EMI 2633**

WHERE DO WE GO FROM HERE
Tracks: / Where do we go from here / Discovering.
7" Single: Released Sep '82, on EMI, by EMI Records. Deleted '85. Catalogue no: **EMI 5341**

WIND ME UP (LET ME GO)
Tracks: / Wind me up (let me go) / Night.
7" Single: Released Nov '65, on Columbia, by EMI Records. Deleted '68. Catalogue no:

DB 7745

WIRED FOR SOUND (SINGLE)
Tracks: / Wired for sound / Hold on.
7" Single: Released Aug '81, on EMI, by EMI Records. Deleted '86. Catalogue no: **EMI 5221**

WITH THE EYES OF A CHILD
Tracks: / With the eyes of a child.
7" Single: Released Dec '69, on Columbia, by EMI Records. Deleted '72. Catalogue no: **DB 8641**

YOU KEEP ME HANGIN' ON
Tracks: / You keep me hangin' on.
7" Single: Released May '74, on EMI, by EMI Records. Deleted '77. Catalogue no: **EMI 2150**

YOUNG ONES, THE
Tracks: / Young ones, The / We say yeah.
7" Single: Released Jan '62, on Columbia, by EMI Records. Deleted '65. Catalogue no: **DB 4761**

Richard, Wendy

COME OUTSIDE (see under Sarne, Mike)
Tracks: / Give it a try / Come outside.
7" Single: Released May '62, on Parlophone, by EMI Records. Deleted May '67. Catalogue no: **R 4902**

Richards, David

COLOUR OF THE RAINBOW
Tracks: / Colour of the rainbow.
12" Single: on Attack, Deleted '88. Catalogue no: **TACK 14**

Richards, Digby

BEAUTIFUL TO ME
Tracks: / Beautiful to me / Go for the doctor.
7" Single: Released Sep '81, on Peach River, Deleted '82. Catalogue no: **PRIVY 502**

CATHY COME HOME
Tracks: / Cathy come home / Typewriter.
7" Single: Released Jul '82, on Peach River, Deleted '83. Catalogue no: **BBPR 1**

STUCK BETWEEN THE LIVING AND THE LEAVING
Tracks: / Stuck between the living and the leaving / Falling out of love again.
7" Single: Released Feb '81, on Polydor, by Polydor Ltd. Deleted '84. Catalogue no: **POSP 227**

Richards, Errol

SUPER BAD
Tracks: / Super bad.
12" Single: Released Jul '83, on Sun Set (reggae), Catalogue no: **SSRD 001**

Richards, Keith

MAKE NO MISTAKE
Tracks: / Make no mistake / It means a lot.
7" Single: Released 24 Apr '89, on Virgin, by Virgin Records. Catalogue no: **VS 1179**
CD 5": Released Apr '89, on Virgin, by Virgin Records. Catalogue no: **VSCD 1179**
12" Single: Released 24 Apr '89, on Virgin, by Virgin Records. Catalogue no: **VST 1179**

TAKE IT SO HARD
Tracks: / Take it so hard / I could have stood you up / It means a lot (On CD & 12" only).
7" Single: Released 10 Oct '88, on Virgin, by Virgin Records. Catalogue no: **VS 1125**
12" Single: Released 10 Oct '88, on Virgin, by Virgin Records. Catalogue no: **VST 1125**
CD 3": Released '88, on Virgin, by Virgin Records. Catalogue no: **VSCD 1125**

Richards, Maxine

LOVE IS IN THE HOUSE
Tracks: / Love is in the house.
7" Single: Released Jul '88, on Blue Chip, by Blue Chip Records. Catalogue no: **BLUE-CHIP 1**
12" Single: Released Jul '88, on Blue Chip, by Blue Chip Records. Catalogue no: **BLUE-CHIP 1 T**

Richards, Nick

MUSIC TO WATCH GIRLS BY
Tracks: / Music to watch girls by.
7" Single: Released Nov '84, on Legacy, by Legacy Records. Catalogue no: **LGY 10**

Richards, Nikki

FACTORY GIRL
Tracks: / Factory girl / Back to school.
7" Single: Released Nov '80, on RCA, by BMG Records (UK). Deleted Nov '83. Catalogue no: **PB 5297**

HOT LOVE
Tracks: / Hot love / Zigeuner music.
7" Single: Released Jan '81, on RCA, by BMG Records (UK). Deleted Jan '84. Catalogue no: **RCA 27**

Richards, Regina

TON OF BRICKS
Tracks: / Ton of bricks / Not looking for love.
7" Single: Released Mar '81, on A&M, by A&M Records. Deleted Mar '84. Catalogue no: **AMS 8115**

TYGER
Tracks: / Tyger / Tug of war.
7" Single: Released Apr '80, on A&M, by A&M Records. Deleted Apr '83. Catalogue no: **AMS 7516**

Richards, Reuben

I FOUND LOVE
Tracks: / I found love(inst).
12" Single: Released Nov '86, on Orbitone, by Orbitone Records. Catalogue no: **OR 1219**

I'LL CHOOSE YOU
Tracks: / I'll choose you / Rolling on.
7" Single: Released 23 Apr '88, on Orbitone, by Orbitone Records. Catalogue no: **OR 726**

Richards, Roy

FREEDOM BLUE
Tracks: / Freedom blue.
7" Single: Released May '89, on Coxsone, Catalogue no: **UNKNOWN**

POWER OF LOVE
Tracks: / Power of love, The / Come boogie with me.
12" Single: Released Sep '82, on Salamo, Catalogue no: **S 003**

Richards, Turley

STAND BY ME
Tracks: / Stand by me / All over the world.
7" Single: Released 20 Jun '80, on Atlantic, by WEA Records. Deleted '83. Catalogue no: **K 11485**

YOU MIGHT NEED SOMEBODY
Tracks: / You might need somebody / Up to you.
7" Single: Released Feb '80, on Atlantic, by WEA Records. Deleted '83. Catalogue no: **K 11445**

Richardson, John

MAHATMA GANDHI KNEW
Tracks: / Mahatma Gandhi knew / B.P.U..
7" Pic: Released May '83, on Loose, by Loose Records. Catalogue no: **PLSE 1**
7" Single: Released May '83, on Loose, by Loose Records. Catalogue no: **SE 1**

Richenel

DANCE AROUND THE WORLD
Tracks: / Dance around the world.
7" Single: Released 13 Jun '87, on CBS, by CBS Records. Deleted Nov '87. Catalogue no: **650214 7**
12" Single: Released 13 Jun '87, on CBS, by CBS Records. Deleted Nov '87. Catalogue no: **650214 9**

L'ESCLAVE ENDORM
Tracks: / L'esclave endorm.
12" Single: Released Mar '86, on 4AD, by 4AD Records. Catalogue no: **BAD 601**

Richey Paul

DEVIL INSIDE (SINGLE)
Tracks: / Devil inside / Jedidiah Jones.
7" Single: Released Jul '83, on Pinnacle, by Pinnacle Records. Catalogue no: **DEVIL 1**

Richie

BE YOUR OWN WOMAN
Tracks: / Be your own woman.
12" Single: Released Aug '84, on Challenge, by Elite Records. Catalogue no: **TALL 9**

TRYING IT ON
Tracks: / Trying it on / Trying it on (hot and sticky mix).
12" Single: Released Dec '83, on Challenge, by Elite Records. Catalogue no: **TALL 5**

Richie, Lionel

Biographical details: Richie, Lionel was born in Alabama in 1950. He is a soul singer, songwriter and producer who began as a founder member of the Commodores, a vocal/instrumental act successful on Motown from 1974; he played tenor sax, then his lead vocals and songwriting made the group even bigger; he went solo in 1981 and became the biggest black crossover artist of the '80's with fine ballads and a smooth voice nine top 10 USA hits in 1982-5. His song *Three times a lady* (hit for the Commodores and nominated for a Grammy in 1978) won an ASCAP Nashville Country Songwriter Award making crossover success complete. (Donald Clarke 21.5.88).

ALL NIGHT LONG
Tracks: / All night long.
7" Single: Released Sep '83, on Motown, by BMG Records (UK). Catalogue no: **TMG 1319**

BALLERINA GIRL
Tracks: / Deep river woman / Dancing on the ceiling*.
7" Single: Released Dec '86, on Motown, by BMG Records (UK). Deleted '87. Catalogue no: **LIO 3**
12" Single: Released Dec '86, on Motown, by BMG Records (UK). Deleted '87. Catalogue no: **LOIT 3**

DANCING ON THE CEILING (SINGLE)
Tracks: / Dancing on the ceiling.
12" Single: Released Jul '86, on RCA, by BMG Records (UK). Catalogue no: **LIOT 1**
7" Single: Released Jul '86, on RCA, by BMG Records (UK). Catalogue no: **LIO 1**

ENDLESS LOVE
Tracks: / Endless love.
7" Single: Released Oct '81, on Motown, by BMG Records (UK). Catalogue no: **TMG 1240**

HELLO
Tracks: / Hello / All night long / Running with the night.
7" Single: Released Mar '84, on Motown, by BMG Records (UK). Catalogue no: **TMG 1330**
12" Single: Released Mar '84, on Motown, by BMG Records (UK). Catalogue no: **TMGT 1330**

LOVE WILL CONQUER ALL
Tracks: / Love will conquer all / Only one, The / Love will conquer all (remix) / Love will conquer all (ext remix) / Love will conquer all (radio edit) / Love will conquer all (inst).
12" Single: Released Sep '86, on Motown, by BMG Records (UK). Deleted '87. Catalogue no: **LIOT 2**
7" Single: Released Sep '86, on Motown, by BMG Records (UK). Deleted '87. Catalogue no: **LIO 2**
12" Single: Released Oct '86, on Motown, by BMG Records (UK). Deleted '87. Catalogue no: **LIOT 2R**

MY LOVE
Tracks: / My love / Round and round.
7" Single: Released Apr '83, on Motown, by BMG Records (UK). Deleted '85. Catalogue no: **TMG 1300**
12" Single: Released Apr '83, on Motown, by BMG Records (UK). Deleted '85. Catalogue no: **TMGT 1300**

PENNY LOVER
Tracks: / Penny lover.
7" Single: Released Oct '84, on Motown, by BMG Records (UK). Catalogue no: **TMG 1356**
12" Single: Released Oct '84, on Motown, by BMG Records (UK). Deleted '87. Catalogue no: **TMGT 1356**

RUNNING WITH THE NIGHT
Tracks: / Running with the night / All night long.
12" Single: Released Nov '83, on Motown, by BMG Records (UK). Deleted '87. Catalogue no: **TMGT 1324**
7" Single: Released Nov '83, on Motown, by BMG Records (UK). Catalogue no: **TMG 1324**

SAY YOU SAY ME
Tracks: / Say you, say me.
7" Single: Released Nov '85, on Motown, by BMG Records (UK). Catalogue no: **ZB 40421**
12" Single: Released Nov '85, on Motown, by BMG Records (UK). Catalogue no: **ZT 40421**

SELA
Tracks: / Sela / Serves you right.
CD 5": Released Jun '89, on Motown, by BMG Records (UK). Catalogue no: **LIOCD 4**
7" Single: Released Mar '87, on Motown, by BMG Records (UK). Catalogue no: **LIO 4**
12" Single: on Motown, by BMG Records (UK). Catalogue no: **LIOT 4**

STUCK ON YOU
Tracks: / Stuck on you / Round and round / Tell me.
7" Single: Released Jun '84, on Motown, by BMG Records (UK). Deleted '87. Catalogue no: **TMG 1341**

TRULY
Tracks: / Truly / Just put some love in your heart.
12" Single: Released Jan '83, on Motown, by BMG Records (UK). Catalogue no: **TMGT 1290**
7" Single: Released Jan '83, on Motown, by BMG Records (UK). Catalogue no: **TMG 1290**
7" Single: Released Nov '82, on Motown, by BMG Records (UK). Catalogue no: **TMG 1284**

YOU ARE
Tracks: / You are.
7" Single: Released Jan '83, on Motown, by BMG Records (UK). Deleted '86. Catalogue no: **TMG 1290**

Richie, Pearl

ONE DAY YOU'LL COME
Tracks: / One day you'll come / Radio show / Sloane Army;Kensington war cry.
Note: Distributor:Splinter Records,33 Regents Park Road London NW1 7TL.
7" Single: Released Mar '86, on Splinter, Catalogue no: **SPNT 2**

Richman, Jonathan

Biographical details: Richman, Jonathan was born in 1951 in Boston, Massachusetts; the singer and songwriter is leader of the Modern Lovers, a USA new wave act with a cult following, better known in UK than at home: he is described as a naive genius. He heard The Velvet Underground at 15 and it was said that he went to more of their gigs than they did. His demo records were unsuccessful in the heyday of more conventional singer/songwriters James Taylor and Joni Mitchell ; his dark and brooding rock was out of step; they are compiled in *The original Modern Lovers*. Early lineups included people who were later members of Talking Heads and The Cars. By the time he became more successful his style had become more twee. (Donald Clarke 4.2.88).

EGYPTIAN REGGAE
Tracks: / Egyptian reggae.
7" Single: Released Jul '82, on Old Gold, by Old Gold Records. Catalogue no: **OG 9112**

EGYPTIAN REGGAE (OLD GOLD)
Tracks: / Egyptian reggae / Morning of our lives, The.
7" Single: Released Jul '82, on Old Gold, by Old Gold Records. Catalogue no: **OG 9112**

I'M JUST BEGINNING TO LIVE
Tracks: / I'm just beginning to live.
7" Single: Released Aug '85, on Rough Trade, by Rough Trade Records. Catalogue no: **RT 154**
12" Single: Released Aug '85, on Rough Trade, by Rough Trade Records. Catalogue no: **RTT 154**

ROAD RUNNER ONCE
Tracks: / Road runner once / Road runner twice.
7" Single: Released Jul '82, on Old Gold, by Old Gold Records. Catalogue no: **OG 9113**

ROADRUNNER
Tracks: / Roadrunner.
7" Single: Released Jul '77, on Beserkley, by Beserkley Records (USA). Deleted '80. Catalogue no: **BZZ 1**

THAT SUMMER FEELING
Tracks: / That summer feeling.
7" Single: Released May '85, on Rough Trade, by Rough Trade Records. Catalogue no: **RT 152**
12" Single: Released May '85, on Rough Trade, by Rough Trade Records. Catalogue no: **RTT 152**

Rick And D.J. Jimmie

FUNKY RAPPIN'
Tracks: / Funky rappin'.
12" Single: Released Nov '87, on Pow Wow (USA), Catalogue no: **PW 427**

Rick & Lisa

WHEN YOU GONNA
Tracks: / When you gonna.
12" Single: Released May '87, on RCA, by BMG Records (UK). Deleted May '89. Catalogue no: **PT 41286**
7" Single: Released May '87, on RCA, by BMG Records (UK). Deleted '87. Catalogue no: **PB 41285**

Rickfors, Mikael

DANCING ON THE EDGE OF DANGER
Tracks: / Dancing on the edge of danger / Resistance.
7" Single: Released Jun '80, on Sonet, by Sonet Records. Deleted Jun '83. Catalogue no: **SON 2208**

Rickster

NIGHT MOVES
Tracks: / Night moves.
12" Single: Released '89, on Sure Delight, by Sure Delight Records. Catalogue no: **SDT 6**

Ricky

BANG BANG BANG
Tracks: / Bang Bang Bang / Bang Bang Bang (who's on the phone?).
7" Single: Released Jun '86, on A&M, by A&M Records. Deleted '88. Catalogue no: **AM 323**
12" Single: Released Jun '86, on A&M, by A&M Records. Deleted '88. Catalogue no: **AMY 323**

Ricky & The Mutations

THATCHER RAP
Tracks: / Thatcher rap / Crisis.
12" Single: Released Jul '83, on Cool Ghoul, by Cool Ghoul Records. Catalogue no: **COOL 3**

Rico

JUNGLE MUSIC
Tracks: / Jungle music / Rasta call you / Easter Island (Only on 12" version.).
7" Single: Released Feb '82, on Chrysalis, by Chrysalis Records. Deleted '87. Catalogue no: **CHS TT 19**
12" Single: Released '83, on Two-Tone, by Chrysalis Records. Deleted '87. Catalogue no: **CHS TT 1219**

MYSTERIES OF THE WORLD
Tracks: / Mysteries of the world / Cool river.
12" Single: Released Sep '89, on Debut, by Skratch Records. Catalogue no: **DEBTX 3078**

SEA CRUISE
Tracks: / Sea cruise / Carolina.
7" Single: Released '83, on Two-Tone, by Chrysalis Records. Deleted '87. Catalogue no: **CHS TT 15**

SPANISH HUSTLE Latin Jackin' mix
Tracks: / Spanish hustle / Spanish hustle (version).
12" Single: Released '88, on Debut, by Skratch Records. Catalogue no: **DEBTX 3040**

Rico, J.

TIME AFTER TIME
Tracks: / Time after time / Time after time (dub).
7" Single: Released 17 Oct '87, on Leopard Music, by Leopard Music. Catalogue no: **RJLM 1**
12" Single: Released 17 Oct '87, on Leopard Music, by Leopard Music. Catalogue no: **RJLMT 1**

Ricochets

IN CAR STEREO
Tracks: / In car stereo / What do you make of love.
7" Single: Released '82, on Arista, by BMG Records (UK). Deleted '87. Catalogue no: **BELL 1505**

Riddle, Nelson

Biographical details: Riddle, Nelson was born in 1921 in New Jersey; he died in 1985 in Los Angeles. He was an arranger, conductor and composer who began trombone and arranging for bandleaders Charlie Spivak in 1940, then Jerry Wald, Tommy Dorsey, Bob Crosby; from 1950 on Capitol Records he accompanied Judy Garland, Jimmy Wakely, Betty Hutton, Margaret Whiting, Ella Mae Morse, Dean Martin, Peggy Lee and others; he arranged the Nat Cole hits *Mona Lisa* and *Too young* in 1950-1, but became the best known arranger in Hollywood with Frank Sinatra from April 1953: he used first class sidemen such as Harry Edison, generating wit and swing by such devices as the use of a bass clarinet or trombone as springboard for rhythmic phrases, knowledge of precisely when to bring in rhythm section after introduction to song, when to allow an explosion of brass. He had his own hits: *Lisbon Antigua* was a number one USA instrumental in 1955; his many albums included a grammy-winner in 1958; *Cross country suite* on Dot, featuring clarinettist Buddy De Franco. He worked freelance with Oscar Peterson, Ella Fitzgerald, Sinatra Rosemary Clooney, Johnny Mathis, others; also did film and TV work. He was wasted in his last three albums with Linda Ronstadt: she is a fine singer but hopelessly unsuited to the classic American songs of Sinatra's type, but *What's new* in 1983 won another grammy for the arrangments): he also arranged *Blue Skies* in 1985 for opera singer Kiri Te Kanawa. (Donald Clarke 21.5.88).

BATMAN THEME
Tracks: / Batman theme / Batusi a-go go.
Note: The original television soundtrack theme to Batman. The real 'duh-na-na-na-na Batman' music. This original and recognizable soundtrack theme was written by Neal Hefti, and then orchestrated and conducted by Nelson Riddle. (Phonogram, July 1989)
7" Single: Released Jul '89, on Phonogram, by Phonogram Ltd. Catalogue no: **BATSP 1**
12" Single: Released Jul '89, on Phonogram, by Phonogram Ltd. Catalogue no: **BATSM 1**

Ride

HALF TIME CLOSING
Tracks: / Half time closing / Fairground.
7" Single: Released Sep '81, on Ride, Deleted Sep '84. Catalogue no: **RIDE 001**

Rider, Pablo

TOO RED EYE
Tracks: / Too red eye.
12" Single: Released Jan '89, on New Talents, Catalogue no: **NT 007**

Ridgway, Stan

BIG HEAT (SINGLE)
Tracks: / Big heat / Drive she said.
7" Single: Released Apr '85, on Illegal, by Faulty Products Records. Catalogue no: **STAN 1**
7" Single: Released Sep '86, on I.R.S, Catalogue no: **IRM 123**
12" Single: Released Apr '85, on Illegal, by Faulty Products Records. Catalogue no: **STAN 12**
12" Single: Released Sep '86, on I.R.S, Catalogue no: **IRMT 123**

CALLING OUT TO CAROL
Tracks: / Calling out to Carol / Can't stop the show / Drive she said (Not on 7".).
CD 5": Released May '89, on I.R.S, Catalogue no: **EIRSCD 106**
7" Single: Released May '89, on I.R.S, Catalogue no: **EIRS 106**
12" Single: Released May '89, on I.R.S, Catalogue no: **EIRST 106**

CAMOUFLAGE
Tracks: / Camouflage / Rio greyhound / Stormy side of town (Extra track on 12" version only.)
7" Single: Released Jun '86, on I.R.S, Catalogue no: **IRM 114**
12" Single: Released Jun '86, on I.R.S, Catalogue no: **IRMT 114**

GOING SOUTHBOUND
Tracks: / Going southbound.
7" Single: Released Sep '89, on I.R.S, Catalogue no: **EIRS 122**
12" Single: Released Sep '89, on I.R.S, Catalogue no: **EIRST 122**

WALKING HOME ALONE
Tracks: / Walking home alone.
7" Single: Released Feb '87, on I.R.S, Catalogue no: **IRM 130**
12" Single: Released Feb '87, on I.R.S, Catalogue no: **IRMT 130**

Rididi

SHAFT Featuring The Shadow Man
Tracks: / Shaft, Theme from / Rio bamba.
7" Single: Released Jul '88, on Tent, by BMG Records (UK). Catalogue no: **TENT 6**
12" Single: Released Jul '88, on Tent, by BMG Records (UK). Catalogue no: **TENTT 6**

Ridley, Emma

SCHOOL'S OUT
Tracks: / School's out.
7" Single: Released Jun '88, on Awesome Records, by Awesome Records. Catalogue no: **CRUNCH 1**
12" Single: Released Jun '88, on Awesome Records, by Awesome Records. Catalogue no: **CRUNCH 1T**

Riff, Eddie

MY BABY'S GONE AWAY
Tracks: / My baby's gone away / Ain't that loving you baby.
7" Single: Released Feb '88, on Fleetville, Catalogue no: **45-FV-301**

Riff Raff

YOU WANNA DANCE
Tracks: / You wanna dance.
12" Single: Released Sep '88, on 20/20, by 20/20 Records. Catalogue no: **TT 122020**

Rigg, Michael

ANGEL
Tracks: / Angel / Watcha gonna do now.
7" Single: Released Jul '83, on Rooster (Europe), by Rooster Records. Catalogue no: **ROO 103**

DON'T YOU BELIEVE IT
Tracks: / Don't you believe it / Hold on.
7" Single: Released Oct '83, on Rooster (Europe), by Rooster Records. Catalogue no: **ROO 105**

TONIGHT
Tracks: / Tonight / You light up my life.
7" Single: Released Jan '83, on Rooster (Europe), by Rooster Records. Catalogue no: **ROO 102**

Righeira

VAMOS A LA PLAYA
Tracks: / Vamos a la playa.
7" Single: Released Sep '83, on A&M, by A&M Records. Deleted '86. Catalogue no: **AM 137**

Right Stuff

SIMPLE
Tracks: / Simple.
7" Single: Released Sep '86, on Bodybeat, Deleted '88. Catalogue no: **BLU 001**

Righteous Brothers

Biographical details: A white soul duo formed in 1962; Bobby Harfield's soaring gospel-style voice with bass Bill Medley (both born in 1940). First called the Paramours, their sound dubbed 'blue-eyed soul' and 'righteous' by black fans; they had minor hits, were signed by Phil Spector to his Philles label in 1964 and had number one USA/UK with *You've lost that loving feeling*, co-written by Spector, Barry Mann and Cynthia Weill, one of the biggest, most fondly remembered hits of the era. They subsequently recorded mostly doo-wop standards, and had another number one in the USA with *You are my soul* and *Inspiration* on Verve. They split up in 1968; Hatfield recruited Jimmy Walker as a bogus brother for a Verve Lp and Medley went solo. They re-united in 1974-5 and had a surprise hit with *Rock and Roll Heaven* at number three USA. (Donald Clarke 21.5.88).

EBB TIDE
Tracks: / Ebb tide.
7" Single: Released Jan '66, on London-American, Deleted '69. Catalogue no: **HL 10011**

ISLAND IN THE SUN
Tracks: / Island in the sun.
7" Single: Released Dec '66, on Verve, Deleted '69. Catalogue no: **VS 547**

UNCHAINED MELODY
Tracks: / Unchained melody.
7" Single: Released Aug '65, on London Records, by London Records. Deleted '68. Catalogue no: **HL 9975**

WHITE CLIFFS OF DOVER
Tracks: / White cliffs of Dover, The.
7" Single: Released Nov '66, on London-American, Deleted '69. Catalogue no: **HL 10086**

(YOU'RE MY) SOUL AND INSPIRATION
Tracks: / (You're my) soul and inspiration.
7" Single: Released Apr '66, on Verve, Deleted '69. Catalogue no: **VS 535**

YOU'VE LOST THAT LOVIN' FEELING
Tracks: / You've lost that lovin' feeling.
7" Single: Released Feb '69, on London-American, Deleted '72. Catalogue no: **HL 10241**
7" Single: Released Jan '65, on London-American, Deleted '68. Catalogue no: **HLU 9943**
7" Single: Released Nov '77, on Phil Spector Int., by Chrysalis Records. Deleted '80. Catalogue no: **2010 022**

YOU'VE LOST THAT LOVIN' FEELING (OLD GOLD)
Tracks: / You've lost that lovin' feeling / Unchained melody.
7" Single: Released Jun '88, on Old Gold, by Old Gold Records. Catalogue no: **OG 9450**

Rikki

BAD MONEY
7" Single: Released Mar '85, on OK, by Klub Records. Catalogue no: **OK 008**
12" Single: Released Mar '85, on OK, by Klub Records. Catalogue no: **OKL 008**

HEAVEN AND HELL
Tracks: / Heaven and hell / Can't stop dancing.
7" Single: Released Nov '82, on OK, by Klub Records. Catalogue no: **OK 005**

ONLY THE LIGHT
Tracks: / Only the light / You came into my life.
Note: UK Eurovision entry
7" Single: Released Apr '87, on OK, by Klub Records. Catalogue no: **OK 010**
12" Single: Released Apr '87, on OK, by Klub Records. Catalogue no: **OKL 010**

SEVEN DAYS A WEEK
Tracks: / Seven days a week.
7" Single: Released Oct '85, on OK, by Klub Records. Catalogue no: **OK 009**
12" Single: Released Oct '85, on OK, by Klub Records. Catalogue no: **OKL 009**

SMILE FOR ME
Tracks: / Smile for me / Hanging on.
7" Single: Released Apr '84, on OK, by Klub Records. Catalogue no: **OK 006**

Riley, Billy Lee

Biographical details: Riley, Billy Lee was born around 1933 in Arkansas. The rockabilly singer played guitar, bass, harmonica and drums. First release on sun *Rock with me baby* was recorded by Jack Clement at WMPS Radio in Memphis, Riley's guitar, bass and drums overdubbed, one of the few Sun discs of the era that had so much production in it; it was Clement's entree to Sun as well as Riley's. He never had any big hits despite good looks and powerful rock 'n' roll, but his influence on the Sun sound was great: Lewis played piano on his regional hit *Flying saucers rock 'n' roll* in 1957; his band include the Sun house band. He added sax to rockabilly (Martin Willis, then Ace Cannon, who both also worked for Bill Black); he also recorded pop, soul, funky country. (Donald Clarke 21.5.88).

BLUE MONDAY
Tracks: / Blue Monday / Good old rock 'n' roll.
7" Single: Released Mar '79, on Rollercoaster, by Rollercoaster Records. Deleted Dec '88. Catalogue no: **SR 706**

Riley, Cheryl Pepsii

THANKS FOR MY CHILD
Tracks: / Thanks for my child / Child.
CD 5": Released Dec '88, on CBS, by CBS Records. Deleted 10 Jul '89. Catalogue no: **653 153-2**
7" Single: Released Dec '88, on CBS, by CBS Records. Deleted 10 Jul '89. Catalogue no: **653 153-7**
12" Single: Released Dec '88, on CBS, by CBS Records. Deleted 10 Jul '89. Catalogue no: **653 153-6**

Riley, Jeannie C.

Biographical details: Riley, Jeanne C. was born Jeannie Stephenson in Anson, Texas in 1945. She is a country singer who made one of the biggest hits of all time: her debut single of Tom T. Hall's *Harper Valley P.T.A* was number one on both country and pop charts in the USA and a worldwide hit. She was packaged with a sexy image (knee length boots, mini skirts), won a Grammy for Best Female Country Vocal Performance and had more hits on several label; top tens *The girl most likely, There never was a time, Country girl, Oh singer, Good enough to be your wife* all reached the pop charts as well. She also recorded gospel music. (Donald Clarke 21.5.88).

HARPER VALLEY PTA (SINGLE)
Tracks: / Harper Valley PTA.
7" Single: Released Oct '68, on Polydor, by Polydor Ltd. Deleted '71. Catalogue no: **56 148**

Riley, Jimmy

EVERYBODY NEEDS MONEY
Tracks: / Everybody needs money.
12" Single: Released Sep '84, on Full Moon (1), Catalogue no: **UNKNOWN**

EVERYTIME YOU GO AWAY
Tracks: / Everytime you go away.
12" Single: Released Nov '85, on Germain Revolutionary, Catalogue no: **DG 101985**

GIVE THANKS AND PRAISE
Tracks: / Give thanks and praise.
12" Single: on Attack, Deleted '88. Catalogue no: **TACK 1**

HEY LOVE
Tracks: / Hey love / Give me your love / Delicious.
10" single: Released Jul '82, on Taxi (2), by Island Records. Catalogue no: **10WIP 6796**

HOT SUMMER
Tracks: / Hot summer.
12" Single: Released Oct '84, on Blue Trac, by Blue Trac Records. Catalogue no: **BTR 001**

ONE NIGHT OF SIN
Tracks: / One night of sin.
12" Single: on Black Roots, Deleted May '88. Catalogue no: **BRD 022**

ROCKIN' DOLLY
Tracks: / Rockin' dolly.
12" Single: Released Apr '85, on Taxi (1), Catalogue no: **UNKNOWN**

SWEET FOR MY SWEET
Tracks: / Sweet for my sweet.
12" Single: Released Oct '88, on Moodies, Catalogue no: **RG 15**

Riley, Marc

BABY'S ON FIRE
Tracks: / Baby's on fire.
7" Single: Released Apr '86, on In Tape, by In Tape Records. Catalogue no: **IT 033**
12" Single: Released Apr '86, on In Tape, by In Tape Records. Catalogue no: **ITTI 033**

BARD OF WOKING

Tracks: / Bard of Woking.
7" Set: Released 29 Sep '85, on In Tape, by In Tape Records. Deleted '88. Catalogue no: **IT 025**

CREEPING AT MAIDA VALE (EP)
Tracks: / Creeping at Maida Vale.
7" Single: Released Feb '84, on In Tape, by In Tape Records. Deleted '88. Catalogue no: **IT 004**

FAVOURITE SISTER
Tracks: / Favourite sister.
7" Single: Released Jul '83, on In Tape, by In Tape Records. Catalogue no: **IT 001**

FOUR A'S AT MAIDA VALE
Tracks: / Four A's at Maida Vale.
7" Single: Released Oct '85, on In Tape, by In Tape Records. Catalogue no: **IT 025**
12" Single: Released Oct '85, on In Tape, by In Tape Records. Catalogue no: **ITT 025**

JUMPER CLOWN
Tracks: / Jumper clown.
7" Single: Released Oct '83, on In Tape, by In Tape Records. Catalogue no: **IT 002**

POLLYSTIFF
Tracks: / Pollystiff.
7" Single: Released May '84, on In Tape, by In Tape Records. Catalogue no: **IT 006**

SHADOW FIGURE
Tracks: / Shadow figure.
12" Single: Released Sep '84, on In Tape, by In Tape Records. Catalogue no: **IT 009**

WARTS AND ALL - LIVE IN AMSTERDAM
10" single: Released Nov '85, on In Tape, by In Tape Records. Catalogue no: **IT 026**

Riley, Teddy

MY FANTASY (IMPORT)
Tracks: / My fantasy.
12" Single: Released Jul '89, on Motown, by BMG Records (UK). Catalogue no: **MOT 4643**

Rimshots

7654321 (BLOW YOUR WHISTLE)
Tracks: / 7654321 (blow your whistle).
7" Single: Released Jan '83, on Flashback, by Mainline Records. Catalogue no: **FBS 24**
7" Single: Released Jul '75, on All Platinum, Deleted '78. Catalogue no: **6146 304**

AT NIGHT
Tracks: / At night.
7" Single: Released Oct '81, on Spectro, Deleted '86. Catalogue no: **SPEC 101**

I WAS WRONG
Tracks: / I was wrong / Stuck in a boat.
7" Single: Released Jul '80, on Shoc-Wave, Catalogue no: **SRP 0007**

Rin Tin Tin

SHAKE IT
Tracks: / Shake it.
12" Single: Released Oct '85, on Irrepressable, Catalogue no: **PRESIT 3**
7" Single: Released Oct '85, on Irrepressable, Catalogue no: **PRES 3**

Rinf

BANG BANG
Tracks: / Bang bang.
12" Single: Released 1 Jul '85, on Lacer, Catalogue no: **LACER 011**

RUBBER ON RIDER
Tracks: / Rubber on rider.
12" Single: Released Sep '88, on IDL, Catalogue no: **LACER 13**

Ring

IS THIS WHAT YOU CALL ROMANCE
Tracks: / Is this what you call romance / Is this what you call romance (version).
12" Single: Released Feb '89, on Survival (2), Catalogue no: **BOSS 1**

RECO
Tracks: / Reco / Make a buck and lose it.
7" Single: Released Mar '80, on Carrere, Deleted '83. Catalogue no: **CAR 136**

Ring O' Bells

NORTHERN LIGHTS
Tracks: / Northern lights / Greenland whale fisheries.
7" Single: Released Dec '88, on Beechwood, by Beechwood. Catalogue no: **BEE 005**

Ringer, Paul

SOMETHING TO LIVE FOR
Tracks: / Something to live for / Scarlet ribbons.
7" Single: Released Dec '80, on Evolution, by Evolution Records. Deleted Dec '85. Catalogue no: **EV 9**

Ringers

NO NO NO
Tracks: / No No No / What can I do?.
7" Single: Released Jun '81, on Magic Moon, Catalogue no: **MACH 7**

Ringing

CAPRICE
Tracks: / Caprice.
7" Single: Released Sep '84, on Pink Label, by Pink Label Records. Catalogue no: **PINKY 2**

Ringo

DUB AND LEF
Tracks: / Dub and lef.
12" Single: Released Aug '82, on Musical Ambassador, Catalogue no: **MAPE 002**

ONE O'CLOCK ROCK
Tracks: / One o'clock rock.
12" Single: Released Apr '83, on Black Roots, Catalogue no: **BRD 06**

VIDEO KILLED THE RADIO STAR
Tracks: / Video killed the radio star (french version) / Ne laissez pas mourier le rock.
7" Single: Released 20 Jun '80, on Carrere, Deleted '83. Catalogue no: **CAR 152**

Rings

LET ME GO
Tracks: / Let me go / Third generation.
7" Single: Released Mar '81, on MCA, by MCA Records. Deleted Mar '84. Catalogue no: **MCA 686**

Rio

ATLANTIC RADIO
Tracks: / Atlantic radio.
12" Single: Released Jul '86, on Music For Nations, by Music For Nations Records. Catalogue no: **12 KUT 123**
7" Single: Released Jul '86, on Music For Nations, by Music For Nations Records. Catalogue no: **KUT 123**

I DON'T WANNA BE THE FOOL
Tracks: / I don't wanna be the fool.
12" Single: Released Sep '85, on Music For Nations, by Music For Nations Records. Catalogue no: **12 KUT 118**
7" Single: Released Sep '85, on Music For Nations, by Music For Nations Records. Catalogue no: **KUT 118**

Rio, James

SKA REGGAE
Tracks: / Ska reggae.
7" Single: Released Sep '82, on Carib Jems, Catalogue no: **CGDD 17**

Rio & The Robots

FIND A GOAL
Tracks: / Find a goal.
7" Single: Released Nov '81, on Tuff, Catalogue no: **TUFF 1**

Rios, Miquel

SONG OF JOY
Tracks: / Song of joy.
7" Single: Released Jul '70, on A&M, by A&M Records. Deleted '73. Catalogue no: **AMS 790**

Riot

OUTLAW
Tracks: / Outlaw / Rock city.
7" Single: Released Oct '81, on Elektra, by Elektra Records (UK). Deleted Oct '84. Catalogue no: **K 12565**

Riot Clone

BLOOD ON YOUR HANDS
Tracks: / Blood on your hands.
7" EP: Released Dec '84, on Riot Clone, Catalogue no: **RCR 004**

DESTROY THE MYTH OF MUSICAL DESTRUCTION
Tracks: / Destroy the myth of musical destruction.
7" Single: Released Dec '82, on Riot Clone, Catalogue no: **RC 002**

THERE'S NO GOVT LIKE NO GOVT.
Tracks: / There's no govt like no govt...
7" Single: Released Apr '82, on Riot Clone, Catalogue no: **RC 001**

Riot Of Colour

SHOULD'VE LISTENED TO ME
Tracks: / Should've listened to me.
12" Single: Released Mar '88, on Play Room Discs, by Play Room Discs. Catalogue no: **PLAYD 004-12**

SIGN OF THE CROSS
Tracks: / Sign of the cross.
12" Single: Released Nov '88, on Play Room Discs, by Play Room Discs. Catalogue no: **PLAYD 004-12**

SKINK
Tracks: / Skink.
12" Single: Released Mar '87, on Dreamworld, by Dreamworld Records. Catalogue no: **DREAM 009T**

Riot Rockers

BRAND NEW CADILLAC
Tracks: / Brand new Cadillac / Please Mr.Mayor / Beetlebug-hop / Goodnight Irene.
7" Single: Released Jun '81, on Humber, by Humber Records. Catalogue no: **HREP 051**

GOODNIGHT IRENE
Tracks: / Goodnight Irene / Brand new cadillac.
7" Single: Released Jul '81, on Humber, by Humber Records. Deleted '84. Catalogue no: **HREP 051**

Riot Squad

DON'T BE DENIED (EP)
Tracks: / Don't be denied.
7" Single: Released Jun '83, on Rondelet Music, by Rondelet Music & Records. Catalogue no: **ASS 1**

FUCK THE TORIES
Tracks: / F**k the Tories.
7" Single: Released Aug '82, on Rondelet Music, by Rondelet Music & Records. Catalogue no: **ROUND 23**

I'M OK FUCK YOU
Tracks: / I'm OK fuck you.
7" Single: Released Sep '83, on Rot, by Rot Records. Catalogue no: **ASS 2**

RIOT IN THE CITY
Tracks: / Riot in the city.
7" Single: Released Sep '82, on Rondelet Music, by Rondelet Music & Records. Catalogue no: **ROUND 25**

THERE AIN'T NO SOLUTION
Tracks: / There ain't no solution.
7" Single: Released Jan '84, on Rot, by Rot Records. Catalogue no: **ASS 3**

TOTAL ONSLAUGHT
Tracks: / Total onslaught.
7" Single: Released Aug '82, on The, Catalogue no: **THE 001**

WHY DO YOU MAKE ME WAIT
Tracks: / Why do you make me wait.
12" Single: Released Mar '82, on Extinguish, Catalogue no: **EXT 004**

Rip Rig & Panic

BOB HOPE TAKES RISKS
Tracks: / Bob Hope takes risks.
7" Single: Released Nov '81, on Virgin, by Virgin Records. Deleted Nov '84. Catalogue no: **VS 468**
12" Single: Released Nov '81, on Virgin, by Virgin Records. Deleted Nov '84. Catalogue no: **VS 48612**

YOU'RE MY KIND OF CLIMATE
Tracks: / You're my kind of climate / She gets so hungry.
12" Single: Released Jun '82, on Virgin, by Virgin Records. Deleted '89. Catalogue no: **VS 507 12**
7" Single: Released Jun '82, on Virgin, by Virgin Records. Deleted '89. Catalogue no: **VS 507**

Riperton, Minnie

Biographical details: Riperton, Minnie was born in 1948 in Chicago; she died of cancer in Los Angeles in 1979. She was a soul singer with operatic training and a five-octave range whose life ended just as she was having the success she deserved. She joined girl-group **The Gems**, worked as receptionist at Chess; the group sang backup for Fontella Bass, Etta James, etc; she sang lead with the Canadian group Rotary Connection in 1968 recorded solo as Andrea Davis; toured with Roberta Flack, Quincy Jones etc; did studio work; solo albums began charting in 1974: hit single *Lovin' you* was co-written with her husband, Dicky Rudolph. (Donald Clarke 21.5.88).

ISLAND IN THE SUN
Tracks: / Island in the sun / Light my fire / Lover and friend (12" only).
7" Single: Released Apr '81, on Capitol, by EMI Records. Deleted '85. Catalogue no: **CL 16165**
12" Single: Released Apr '81, on Capitol, by EMI Records. Deleted '85. Catalogue no: **12CL 16165**

LOVING YOU
Tracks: / Loving you / Inside my love.
7" Single: Released Apr '75, on Polydor, by Polydor Ltd. Deleted '78. Catalogue no: **EPC 3121**
7" Single: Released '80, on Lightning, Catalogue no: **LR 1364**

LOVING YOU (OLD GOLD)
Tracks: / Loving you.
7" Single: Released Jun '88, on Old Gold, by Old Gold Records. Deleted Sep '89. Catalogue no: **OG 9725**

Ripley, Duane

REVENGE OF THE 50 FOOT KILLER GO GO GIRLS
Tracks: / Revenge of the 50 foot killer go go girls.
7" Single: Released Feb '86, on Barbarella, Catalogue no: **BAD 1**

Riprize

BEWITCHED
Tracks: / Bewitched / Faith.
7" Single: Released Jun '89, on Karbon, by Karbon Records. Catalogue no: **KAR 611**

Risaedlan

O
Tracks: / O.
12" Single: Released Jul '89, on One Little Indian, by One Little Indian Records. Catalogue no: **SM 017T**

Risan

EASTERN PALACE
Tracks: / Eastern palace.
12" Single: Released Nov '82, on Saffron, Catalogue no: **SAFT 1**
7" Single: Released Nov '82, on Saffron, Catalogue no: **SAF 1**

Rise

GIVING IN TO ANOTHER SIN
Tracks: / Giving in to another sin.
7" Single: Released Mar '89, on Allover London, Catalogue no: **AOL 001**

Rising Fire

YOU LIED
Tracks: / You lied.
12" Single: Released Jan.'82, on Cha-Cha, by Cha-Cha Records. Catalogue no: **CHAD 45**

Risk

STATE OF THE UNICORN
Tracks: / State of the unicorn.
12" Single: Released May '89, on Unicorn Records, by Unicorn Records. Catalogue no: **12PHZ 38**

STATE OF THE UNION
Tracks: / State of the union.
12" Single: Released Jul '89, on Unicorn Records, by Unicorn Records. Catalogue no: **12PHZ 42**

Risky Business

JAMMIN' TO NEW ORLEANS
Tracks: / Jammin' to New Orleans / Jammin' to New Orleans (club mix) / Jammin' to New Orleans (alternate mix) / Jammin' to New Orleans (radio edit).
12" Single: Released Apr '87, on Kool Kat, by Kool Kat Records. Catalogue no: **12 KAT 1**

Risse

HOUSE TRAIN
Tracks: / House train.
7" Single: Released Mar '88, on Jack Trax, Catalogue no: **7JTX 7**
12" Single: Released Mar '88, on Jack Trax, Catalogue no: **JTX 7**

Ritchie, Brian

SUN RA MAN FROM OUTER SPACE
Tracks: / Sun ra man from outer space.
12" Single: Released Jan '89, on SST (USA), by SST Records (USA). Catalogue no: **SST 227**
CD 5": Released Jan '89, on SST (USA), by SST Records (USA). Catalogue no: **SSTCD 227**

Ritchie & Cufflinks

SHE'S CRAZY
Tracks: / She's crazy / Starting line.
7" Single: Released Aug '80, on MCA, by MCA Records. Deleted '83. Catalogue no: **MCA 623**

Ritchie Family

AMERICAN GENERATION (SINGLE)
Tracks: / American generation.
7" Single: Released Feb '79, on Mercury, by Phonogram Ltd. Deleted '82. Catalogue no: **6007 199**

BEST DISCO IN TOWN (OLD GOLD)
Tracks: / Best disco in town, The / Brazil.
12" Single: Released 30 Jan '89, on Old Gold, by Old Gold Records. Catalogue no: **OG 4092**

BEST DISCO IN TOWN, THE
Tracks: / Best disco in town, The.
7" Single: Released Sep '76, on Polydor, by Polydor Ltd. Deleted '79. Catalogue no:

THE RITCHIE FAMILY - GIVE ME A BREAK (Released on Mercury)

2058 777

BRAZIL
Tracks: / Brazil.
7" Single: Released Aug '75, on Polydor, by Polydor Ltd. Deleted '78. Catalogue no: **2058 625**

GIVE ME A BREAK (See panel above)
Tracks: / Give me a break / Bad reputation.
7" Single: Released '80, on Mercury, by Phonogram Ltd. Catalogue no: **MER 17**

Ritchie & Houseowners

HAVE A NICE DAY
Tracks: / Have a nice day.
7" Single: Released Feb '82, on Fliptone. Deleted '83. Catalogue no: **FT 002**

Ritchie, Lynn

LOVE IS BAD FOR YOUR HEALTH
Tracks: / Love is bad for your health / They said.
7" Single: Released Apr '82, on Abstract, by Abstract Sounds. Catalogue no: **ABS 008**

NIGHT MOVES
Tracks: / Night moves / Night moves (Radio mix) / Night moves (House of trix mix).
12" Single: Released '88, on Sure Delight, by Sure Delight Records. Catalogue no: **SDT6**

Ritchie & The

HAVE A NICE DAY
Tracks: / Have a nice day.
7" Single: Released Sep '84, on Rosie, by Rosie Records. Catalogue no: **RR 006**

Rite, Sammy

IT'S NICE
Tracks: / It's nice / One summer.
7" Single: Released Jun '89, on World State. Deleted Sep '89. Catalogue no: **WRST 1**
12" Single: Released Jun '89, on World State. Deleted Sep '89. Catalogue no: **12WRST 1**

Ritenour, Lee

Biographical details: Guitarist Lee Ritenour, born in Hollywood in 1952, also plays banjo, mandolin and other instruments. He became an ace studio musician and seven of his easy-listening albums, fusing Latin, jazz and soul, charted in America between 1977 and 1984. (Donald Clarke, February 1988.).

IS IT YOU
Tracks: / Is it you.
7" Single: Released Jun '81, on Elektra Asylum, by Elektra Records (USA). Catalogue no: **K 12540**
12" Single: Released Jun '81, on Elektra Asylum, by Elektra Records (USA). Catalogue no: **K 12540T**

MR. BRIEFCASE
Tracks: / Mr. Briefcase / Sugarloaf Express.
12" Single: Released Apr '81, on Elektra Asylum, by Elektra Records (USA). Catalogue no: **K 12525T**
7" Single: Released Apr '81, on Elektra Asylum, by Elektra Records (USA). Catalogue no: **K 12525**

SUGARLOAF EXPRESS
Tracks: / Sugarloaf express / Gentle afternoon / Jennifer Anne's samba / Beginning song.
7" Single: Released Jul '84, on Elite Records, by Elite Records. Deleted '86. Catalogue no: **4PLAY 101**
12" Single: Released Oct '82, on Elite (Inner City). Catalogue no: **4PLAY 101**

Rites Of Spring

ALL THROUGH A LIFE
7" EP: on Dischord, by Dischord Records. Catalogue no: **DISCHORD 22**

Ritter, Tex

Biographical details: One of the great singing cowboys, Tex was born Woodward Maurice Ritter in Texas in 1905 and died in Nashville in 1974. He starred on the stage, on radio and in more than 50 films, and began recording in 1934. He was the first country singer to sign with Capitol in 1942. His hits included *High Noon* in 1952: the Oscar-winning theme from the Gary Cooper movie crossed over to the pop chart. Ritter helped to set up the County Music Foundation and Hall of Fame, and was elected to it in 1964. (Donald Clarke, February 1988.).

WAYWARD WIND
Tracks: / Wayward wind.
7" Single: Released Jun '56, on Capitol, by EMI Records. Deleted '59. Catalogue no: **CL 14581**

Ritual

KANGAROO COURT
Tracks: / Kangaroo court / Bridges.
12" Single: Released Mar '83, on Red Flame (1), by Red Flame Records. Catalogue no: **RF1217**

MIND DISEASE
Tracks: / Mind disease / Nine.
7" Single: Released Oct '82, on Red Flame (1), by Red Flame Records. Catalogue no: **RF 712**

OVERDOSE
Tracks: / Overdose.
12" Single: Released Mar '89, on Pure. Catalogue no: **PURET 33**

SORE LIP
Tracks: / Sore lip.
7" Single: Released 17 Oct '87, on Warrior, by Warrior Records. Catalogue no: **WR 12001**

Rivals

FUTURE RIGHTS
Tracks: / Future rights / Flowers.
7" Single: Released Feb '80, on Ace, by Ace Records. Deleted Jun '88. Catalogue no: **ACE 007**

HERE COMES THE NIGHT
Tracks: / Here comes the night.
7" Single: Released May '80, on Ace, by Ace Records. Deleted Jun '88. Catalogue no: **ACE 011**

River

JUBILEE
Tracks: / Jubilee / Reason to love.
7" Single: Released Jan '89, on Skysaw, by Skysaw Records. Catalogue no: **DSB 3**

River Boys

CADILLAC CAR EP
Tracks: / Cadillac car.
7" Single: Released Feb '88, on Wag. Catalogue no: **WAG 7**

KISS MY BABY GOODBYE (EP)
Tracks: / It could happen to you / Drives me wild / Claw of a tiger / I love her / If you wanna be loved / She's my girl / Danger zone / Bait ups boogie.
12" Single: Released Oct '87, on Wag. Catalogue no: **WAG 6**

River City People

SAY SOMETHING GOOD (SINGLE)
Tracks: / Say something good (Not on 12".) / Wasted / Say something good (ext. version) (Not on 7".) / No doubt (Demo) (CD single only.).
CD 5": Released Oct '89, on EMI, by EMI Records. Catalogue no: **CDEM 110**
7" Single: Released Oct '89, on EMI, by EMI Records. Catalogue no: **203 561 7**
CD 5": Released Oct '89, on EMI, by EMI Records. Catalogue no: **203 561 2**
12" Single: Released Oct '89, on EMI, by EMI Records. Catalogue no: **203 561 6**
12" Single: Released Oct '89, on EMI, by EMI Records. Catalogue no: **12EM 110**
7" Single: Released Oct '89, on EMI, by EMI Records. Catalogue no: **EM 110**

WHAT'S WRONG WITH DREAMING
Tracks: / What's wrong with dreaming / Huskisson Street / Find a reason (Not on 7".) / Seems like years (CD single only.).
CD 5": Released Jul '89, on EMI, by EMI Records. Catalogue no: **203 428 2**
7" Single: Released Jul '89, on EMI, by EMI Records. Catalogue no: **EM 95**
CD 5": Released Jul '89, on EMI, by EMI Records. Catalogue no: **CDEM 95**
12" Single: Released Jul '89, on EMI, by EMI Records. Catalogue no: **12EM 95**
12" Single: Released Jul '89, on EMI, by EMI Records. Catalogue no: **203 428 6**
7" Single: Released Jul '89, on EMI, by EMI Records. Catalogue no: **203 428 7**

River Detectives

CHAINS (See panel below)
Tracks: / Chains.
Cassingle: Released Jul '89, on WEA, by WEA Records. Catalogue no: **YZ 383 C**
7" Single: Released Jul '89, on WEA, by WEA Records. Catalogue no: **YZ 383**
CD 5": Released Jul '89, on WEA, by WEA Records. Catalogue no: **YZ 383 CD**
12" Single: Released Jul '89, on WEA, by WEA Records. Catalogue no: **YZ 383 T**

SATURDAY NIGHT SUNDAY MORNING (SINGLE)
Tracks: / Saturday night Sunday morning / He still needs you / You may be just the one.
CD 5": Released Sep '89, on WEA, by WEA Records. Catalogue no: **YZ 419 CD**
7" Single: Released Sep '89, on WEA, by WEA Records. Catalogue no: **YZ 419**
12" Single: Released Sep '89, on WEA, by WEA Records. Catalogue no: **YZ 419 T**
Cassingle: Released Sep '89, on WEA, by WEA Records. Catalogue no: **YZ 419 C**

Rivers, Danny

CAN'T YOU HEAR MY HEART
Tracks: / Can't you hear my heart.
7" Single: Released Jan '61, on Decca, by Decca Records. Deleted '64. Catalogue no: **F 11294**

Rivers Deke

RETURN TO SENDER (ELVIS MEDLEY)
Tracks: / Return to sender (Elvis medley) / Presley press conference.
7" Single: Released Sep '81, on Ace, by Ace Records. Deleted Jun '88. Catalogue no: **NS 71**

Riviera

NOTHING TO HIDE
Tracks: / Nothing to hide / Emotion.
7" Single: Released Jun '83, on UNKNOWN. Catalogue no: **S 1026**

WELL SEASONED
Tracks: / Well seasoned / Michigan lady.
7" Single: Released Aug '81, on Miracle, by Gull Records. Deleted Aug '84. Catalogue no: **M 25**

Rix, Karen

HUNGRY WATERS
Tracks: / Hungry waters / Stop the night.
7" Single: Released Sep '87, on Influx, by Influx Vinyls. Catalogue no: **INFV 1**
12" Single: Released Sep '87, on Influx, by Influx Vinyls. Catalogue no: **INFV 112**

Rizma

I'M ON MY WAY
Tracks: / I'm on my way / Going zero.
7" Single: Released Mar '84, on Zone To Zone, by Zone To Zone Records. Catalogue no: **ZON 08**

Rizzo, Linda Jo

PERFECT LOVE
Tracks: / Perfect love.
Note: Music class Hi-NRG.
7" Single: Released May '88, on Reflection, by Nightmare Records. Catalogue no: **7FLE 3**
12" Single: Released May '88, on Reflection, by Nightmare Records. Catalogue no: **FLE 3**

Ro Yeah Yeah

I HOPE AND PREY
Tracks: / I hope and prey.
12" Single: Released Aug '85, on Chrysalis, by Chrysalis Records. Catalogue no: **CHS 122910**
7" Single: Released Aug '85, on Chrysalis, by Chrysalis Records. Catalogue no: **CHS 2910**

Roach, Colin

DEBE DEBE SOUND
Tracks: / Debe debe sound / Debe debe sound.

RIVER DETECTIVES - CHAINS (Released on WEA)

ROACHFORD - KATHLEEN (Released on CBS)

7" Single: Released Jun '88, on Blue Trac, by Blue Trac Records. Catalogue no: **BTR 017**

LATELY
Tracks: / Lately.
7" Single: Released May '88, on Pioneer Muzik, Catalogue no: **PM 005**

Roachford

CUDDLY TOY
Tracks: / Cuddly toy / Lions den / Cuddly toy (live) (On 12" only) / Cuddly toy (the feel for me mix) (On CD only).
CD 5": Released Jan '89, on CBS, by CBS Records. Deleted 10 Jul '89. Catalogue no: **CD ROA 4**
CD 5": Released May '88, on CBS, by CBS Records. Catalogue no: **CDROA 2**
7" Single: Released Jan '89, on CBS, by CBS Records. Deleted 10 Jul '89. Catalogue no: **ROA 4**
7" Single: Released May '88, on CBS, by CBS Records. Deleted Jan '89. Catalogue no: **ROA 2**
7" Single: Released Jan '89, on CBS, by CBS Records. Deleted 10 Jul '89. Catalogue no: **ROA EP 4**
12" Single: Released May '88, on CBS, by CBS Records. Deleted Jan '89. Catalogue no: **ROAQT 2**
12" Single: Released Jan '89, on CBS, by CBS Records. Deleted 10 Jul '89. Catalogue no: **ROA T4**
12" Single: Released May '88, on CBS, by CBS Records. Deleted Jan '89. Catalogue no: **ROAT 2**
7" Single: Released May '88, on CBS, by CBS Records. Deleted Jan '89. Catalogue no: **ROAB 2**

CUDDLY TOY (X-RATED ACID TOY MIX)
Tracks: / Cuddly toy (x-rated acid toy mix).
12" Single: Released Jan '89, on CBS, by CBS Records. Deleted 10 Jul '89. Catalogue no: **ROA QT 4**
12" Single: Released 6 Jun '88, on CBS, by CBS Records. Catalogue no: **ROA QT2**

FAMILY MAN
Tracks: / Family man / Family man (extended version) / Give it up (ext. version).
CD 5": Released Feb '88, on CBS, by CBS Records. Deleted Oct '89. Catalogue no: **CDROA 1**
7" Single: Released Feb '88, on CBS, by CBS Records. Deleted Oct '89. Catalogue no: **ROA 1**
7" EP: Released Feb '88, on CBS, by CBS Records. Deleted Oct '89. Catalogue no: **ROA EP1**
12" Single: Released Feb '88, on CBS, by CBS Records. Deleted Oct '89. Catalogue no: **ROAT 1**

FAMILY MAN (RE-RELEASE)
Tracks: / Family man / Never / Family man (extended version) (Only on 12"s and CD single.) / Give it up (extended Saturday night special mix) (On both 12"s only) / Cuddly toy (extended version) (Only on 12" (gatefold sleeve)) / Gun crazy (Only on 7" Ep.) / Why (Only on 7" Ep.).
CD 5": Released 6 Mar '89, on CBS, by CBS Records. Catalogue no: **CDROA 5**
7" Single: Released 6 Mar '89, on CBS, by CBS Records. Catalogue no: **ROA 5**
7" EP: Released 13 Mar '89, on CBS, by CBS Records. Catalogue no: **ROAEP 5**
12" Single: Released 6 Mar '89, on CBS, by CBS Records. Catalogue no: **ROAGT 5**
12" Single: Released 6 Mar '89, on CBS, by CBS Records. Catalogue no: **ROAT 5**

FIND ME ANOTHER LOVE
Tracks: / Find me another love / Find me another love (ext.) (12" & CD single only.) / Ling again / Just can't go (12" only.) / Born again (DEAC EP 7 only.) / It's not funny anymore (DEAC EP 7 only.) / Real gone kid (ext.) (12" only.) / Find me another love ('psycho bump beat' mix) (CD single only.) / Lying again (CD single only.).
CD 5": Released Oct '88, on CBS, by CBS Records. Deleted 10 Jul '89. Catalogue no: **CD ROA 3**
7" Single: Released Oct '88, on CBS, by CBS Records. Deleted 10 Jul '89. Catalogue no: **ROA 3**
12" Single: Released Oct '88, on CBS, by CBS Records. Deleted 10 Jul '89. Catalogue no: **ROA T3**
12" Single: Released Oct '88, on CBS, by CBS Records. Deleted 10 Jul '89. Catalogue no: **ROA QT 3**

KATHLEEN (See panel above)
Tracks: / Kathleen (7" & CD only.) / Kathleen (extended) (12" & CD only.) / Just can't go / Kathy's house (12" & CD only.) / Lying again (live) (EP & cassette only.) / Beautiful morning (live) (EP & cassette only).
7" EP: Released Jun '89, on CBS, by CBS Records. Catalogue no: **ROA G6**
CD 5": Released Jun '89, on CBS, by CBS Records. Catalogue no: **CD ROA 6**
Cassingle: Released Jun '89, on CBS, by CBS Records. Catalogue no: **ROA C6**
7" Single: Released Jun '89, on CBS, by CBS Records. Catalogue no: **ROG 6**
7" Single: Released Jul '89, on CBS, by CBS Records. Catalogue no: **ROAF 6**
12" Single: Released Jun '89, on CBS, by CBS Records. Catalogue no: **ROA T6**
7" EP: Released Jun '89, on CBS, by CBS Records. Catalogue no: **ROA EP 6**

Road Runners

C.B. INDEPENDENT
Tracks: / C.B. independent / White line fever.
7" Single: Released Apr '81, on EMI, by EMI Records. Deleted '85. Catalogue no: **EMI 5115**

Roadholders

MOTORCYCLE GIRLS
Tracks: / Motorcycle girls.
7" Single: Released Jul '89, on Damaged Goods, Catalogue no: **YUBB 1**

Roar Sound

SHARE
Tracks: / Share.
7" Single: Released Jun '85, on Roar, Deleted '86. Catalogue no: **ROAR 1**
12" Single: Released Jun '85, on Roar, Deleted '86. Catalogue no: **ROART 1**

Roaring Jelly

CHRISTMAS IN AUSTRALIA
Tracks: / Christmas in Australia.
7" Single: Released Nov '80, on Ideal, by Topic Records. Catalogue no: **SPOT 4**

Robb, Natalie

GIRLS, GIRLS, GIRLS
Tracks: / Girls, girls, girls / It's obvious.
7" Single: Released May '88, on Rio Digital, by Rio Digital Records. Catalogue no: **7RDS 1**
12" Single: Released May '88, on Rio Digital, by Rio Digital Records. Catalogue no: **12RDS 1**

Robbie B

JAZZY J ON THE SCRATCH
Tracks: / Jazzy J on the scratch.
12" Single: Released Oct '87, on Schooly-D (USA), Catalogue no: **SD 119**

Robbie, Colonel

WICKED FELLA
Tracks: / Wicked fella.
12" Single: Released 24 Jul '89, on Sir George, Catalogue no: **SG 060**

Robbins, Kate

I WANT YOU BACK
Tracks: / I want you back / Anytime at all.
7" Single: Released Aug '81, on RCA, by BMG Records (UK). Deleted '84. Catalogue no: **RCA 108**

IF YOU WANNA HELP SOMEBODY
Tracks: / If you wanna help somebody / Say anything you want.
Note: Composed by Kate Robbins for TV am's Caring Christmas Campaign 1988, which is a charity for the elderly.
7" Single: Released Nov '88, on Bright, by Bright Records. Catalogue no: **BULB 11**

MORE THAN IN LOVE
Tracks: / More than in love.
7" Single: Released May '81, on RCA, by BMG Records (UK). Deleted '84. Catalogue no: **RCA 69**

REAL ME, THE
Tracks: / Real me, The / Photo fit.
7" Single: Released Jan '83, on RCA, by BMG Records (UK). Catalogue no: **RCA 309**

RUN WILD
Tracks: / Run wild / Cassie's song.
7" Single: Released Oct '81, on RCA, by BMG Records (UK). Deleted Oct '84. Catalogue no: **RCA 145**

THAT FIRST LOVE
Tracks: / That first love.
7" Single: Released Mar '84, on Bright, by Bright Records. Catalogue no: **BULB 6**

Robbins, Mark

LOVE ON A MONDAY
Tracks: / Love on a Monday / Fool.
7" Single: Released Mar '80, on Carrere, Deleted '83. Catalogue no: **CAR 137**

Robbins, Marty

BIG IRON
Tracks: / Big iron.
7" Single: Released May '60, on Fontana, by Phonogram Ltd. Deleted '63. Catalogue no: **H 229**

DEVIL WOMAN
Tracks: / Devil woman.
7" Single: Released Sep '62, on CBS, by CBS Records. Deleted '65. Catalogue no: **AAG 114**

DEVIL WOMAN (OLD GOLD)
Tracks: / Devil woman / El Paso.
7" Single: Released 27 Feb '89, on Old Gold, by Old Gold Records. Catalogue no: **OG 9866**

EL PASO (SINGLE)
Tracks: / El paso.
7" Single: Released Jan '60, on Fontana, by Phonogram Ltd. Deleted '63. Catalogue no: **H 233**

RUBY ANN
Tracks: / Ruby Ann.
7" Single: Released Jan '63, on CBS, by CBS Records. Deleted '66. Catalogue no: **AAG 128**

Robbins, Rockie

I'VE GOT YOUR NUMBER
Tracks: / I've got your number.
7" Single: Released Jul '85, on MCA, by MCA Records. Catalogue no: **MCA 975**
12" Single: Released Jul '85, on MCA, by MCA Records. Catalogue no: **MCAT 975**

SERIOUS
Tracks: / Serious.
12" Single: Released Aug '89, on Respect, Catalogue no: **PECT 1**
7" Single: Released Aug '89, on Respect, Catalogue no: **PEC 1**

WE BELONG TOGETHER
Tracks: / We belong together.
7" Single: Released Apr '85, on MCA, by MCA Records. Catalogue no: **MCA 950**
12" Single: Released Apr '85, on MCA, by MCA Records. Catalogue no: **MCAT 950**

Robe

I'LL BE THERE
Tracks: / I'll be there / Walk of fame.
CD 5": Released Jul '88, on 2000 AD, Catalogue no: **ROBECD 2**
7" Single: Released Jul '88, on 2000 AD, Catalogue no: **ROBE 2**
12" Single: Released Jul '88, on 2000 AD, Catalogue no: **ROBET 2**

TURN ON THE MOON
Tracks: / Turn on the Moon / I wanna get next to you.
7" Single: Released Feb '88, on 2000 AD, Catalogue no: **ROBE 1**
12" Single: Released Feb '88, on 2000 AD, Catalogue no: **ROBET 1**

Robert, Moja-Rappa

UPTOWN ROCK (GHETTO MAN SOUNDS)
Tracks: / Uptown rock (ghetto man sounds).
12" Single: Released Dec '83, on Ethnic, Catalogue no: **ETH 2243**

Robert, Rappa

BULLETIN ONE
Tracks: / Bulletin one.
7" Single: Released Nov '88, on Taurus, Catalogue no: **UNKNOWN**

Roberts, Al Jnr.

I WISH I WAS IN LA
Tracks: / I wish I was in LA.
7" Single: Released Feb '80, on Red Hot, by Beserkley Records (USA). Deleted '83. Catalogue no: **REP 1002**

Roberts, Austin

ROCKY
Tracks: / Rocky.
7" Single: Released Oct '75, on Private Stock, Deleted '78. Catalogue no: **PVT 33**

Roberts, Charlie

BLOWIN' MY MIND
Tracks: / Blowin' my mind / Blowin' my mind (inst).
7" Single: Released Jul '87, on Arista, by BMG Records (UK). Catalogue no: **RIS 25**
12" Single: Released Jul '87, on Arista, by BMG Records (UK). Catalogue no: **RIST 25**

BLOWIN' MY MIND WITH YOUR BODY
12" Single: Released Feb '87, on Affair, Catalogue no: **TART 4**
7" Single: Released Feb '87, on Affair, Catalogue no: **TARTS 4**

Roberts, David Thomas

BOYS IN AUTUMN
Tracks: / Boys in autumn.
7" Single: Released Mar '83, on WEA, by WEA Records. Catalogue no: **K 72021**

Roberts, Eric

NEXT IN LINE
Tracks: / Next in line.
12" Single: Released Jun '84, on Electricity, by Electricity Records. Deleted '88. Catalogue no: **TRICT 8**
7" Single: Released Jun '84, on Electricity, by Electricity Records. Deleted '88. Catalogue no: **TRIC 8**

Roberts, Isabel

I JUST FALL IN LOVE
Tracks: / Ijust fall in love / Ijust fall in love (version).
12" Single: Released Jun '87, on Hot Vinyl, Catalogue no: **HVT 36**

RHYTHM OF YOUR LOVE
Tracks: / Rhythm of your love / Rhythm of your love (Instrumental).
12" Single: Released Mar '86, on Hot Vinyl, Catalogue no: **HVT 18**

Roberts, Joy

LOVE ME INSIDE
Tracks: / Love me inside.
12" Single: Released Apr '82, on Love Linch, Catalogue no: **LL 21**

Roberts, Julie

AIN'T YOU HAD ENOUGH LOVE
Tracks: / Ain't you had enough love.
7" Single: Released Oct '85, on Bluebird (2), by BMG Records (UK). Catalogue no: **BR 19**
12" Single: Released Oct '85, on Bluebird (2), by BMG Records (UK). Catalogue no: **BR 19T**

I DON'T WANNA LOSE YOU
Tracks: / I don't wanna lose you / Since you've been gone.

MALCOLM ROBERTS - STAND BESIDE ME (Released on Major Minor)

ROBERTS PAUL - WORKING FOR THE GOODTIMES (Released on Sonet)

7" Single: Released Aug '84, on Bluebird (2), by BMG Records (UK). Catalogue no: **BR 7**
12" Single: Released Aug '84, on Bluebird (2), by BMG Records (UK). Catalogue no: **BRT 7**

IT'S BEEN A LONG LONG TIME
Tracks: / It's been a long long time.
12" Single: Released Jul '83, on Bluebird (2), by BMG Records (UK). Catalogue no: **BRT 3**
7" Single: Released Jul '83, on Bluebird (2), by BMG Records (UK). Catalogue no: **BR 3**

MORE THAN ONE NIGHT
Tracks: / More than one night / More than one night (instrumental).
7" Single: Released Jun '86, on Bluebird (2), by BMG Records (UK). Catalogue no: **BR 22**
12" Single: Released Jun '86, on Bluebird (2), by BMG Records (UK). Catalogue no: **BRT 22**

Roberts, Lloyd

BABY HANG UP THE PHONE
Tracks: / Baby hang up the phone.
12" Single: Released Jul '85, on Nice & Cool, Catalogue no: **NKRD 0029**

Roberts, Malcolm

EVERY SINGLE BEAT OF YOUR HEART
Tracks: / Every single beat of your heart / So wrong.
7" Single: Released Mar '81, on Cheapskate, Deleted Mar '84. Catalogue no: **CHEAP 18**

LOVE IS ALL
Tracks: / Love is all.
7" Single: Released Nov '69, on Major Minor, Deleted '72. Catalogue no: **MM 637**

MAY I HAVE THE NEXT DREAM WITH YOU
Tracks: / May I have the next dream with you.
7" Single: Released Oct '68, on Major Minor, Deleted '71. Catalogue no: **MM 581**

STAND BESIDE ME (See panel above)
Tracks: / Stand beside me / Dancing partner.
7" Single: Released '69, on Major Minor, Catalogue no: **MM 598**

TIME ALONE WILL TELL
Tracks: / Time alone will tell.
7" Single: Released May '67, on RCA, by BMG Records (UK). Deleted '70. Catalogue no: **RCA 1578**

WANDERER
Tracks: / Wanderer.
7" Single: Released Mar '83, on Dakota, Catalogue no: **DAK 8**

Roberts, Papa

GANJA TRAFFICKING
Tracks: / Ganja trafficking / Right track.
10" single: Released Sep '82, on Spiderman, Catalogue no: **SMD 1002**

Roberts, Paul

BACK TO ENGLAND
Tracks: / Back to England / Good life.
7" Single: Released Feb '86, on Sonet, by Sonet Records. Catalogue no: **SON 2297**

HAND OF FATE
Tracks: / Night starvation.
7" Single: Released Jan '87, on Sonet, by Sonet Records. Catalogue no: **SON 2315**

KING OF YOUR HEART
Tracks: / King of your heart / What love is.
7" Single: Released Jul '87, on Sonet, by Sonet Records. Catalogue no: **SON 230**

RAILROAD TO THE SEA
Tracks: / Railroad to the sea.
7" Single: Released Oct '85, on Sonet, by Sonet Records. Catalogue no: **SON 2290**

WORKING FOR THE GOODTIMES (See panel top right)
Tracks: / Working for the good times / Away too long.
7" Single: Released Aug '87, on Sonet, by Sonet Records. Catalogue no: **SON 2326**
12" Single: Released Aug '87, on Sonet, by Sonet Records. Catalogue no: **SONL 2326**

Roberts, Steve

AS TEARS GO BY
Tracks: / As tears go by / Yeah yeah.
7" Single: Released Jun '82, on Exploited, Catalogue no: **EXP 1004**

Roberts, Wendy

I WANT YOU BACK
Tracks: / I want you back.
7" Single: Released Aug '85, on PRT, by Castle Communications Records. Catalogue no: **7P 331**
12" Single: Released Aug '85, on PRT, by Castle Communications Records. Catalogue no: **12P 331**

Robertson, B.A.

BANG BANG (See panel opposite)
Tracks: / Bang bang / 2 (b) B side the C side.
7" Single: Released Jun '79, on Elektra Asylum, by Elektra Records (USA). Catalogue no: **K 13152**

CEUD MILE FAILTE (A HUNDRED THOUSAND WELCOMES)
Tracks: / Ceud mile failte (A hundred thousand welcomes) / BBC TR Commonwealth Games theme, The / See you in Auckland.
7" Single: Released Jul '86, on BBC, by BBC Records & Tapes. Deleted Sep '87. Catalogue no: **RESL 192**
12" Single: Released Jul '86, on BBC, by BBC Records & Tapes. Deleted Sep '87. Catalogue no: **12 RSL 192**

DOT DOT DOT
Tracks: / Dot dot dot.
7" Single: Released Jul '82, on Elektra Asylum, by Elektra Records (USA). Catalogue no: **K 13190**

FLIGHT 19
Tracks: / Flight 19 / Alright on the night.
7" Single: Released Oct '80, on Asylum, by WEA Records. Deleted Oct '83. Catalogue no: **K 12482**

HOLD ME (See panel on next page)
Tracks: / Hold me / Spring Greens.
7" Single: Released Oct '81, on Swansong, Deleted '84. Catalogue no: **BAM 1**

I AM A SEEKER
Tracks: / I am a seeker.
7" Single: Released Dec '83, on Epic, by CBS Records. Catalogue no: **A 3983**

KNOCKED IT OFF (See panel on next page)
Tracks: / Knocked it off / Sci-Fi.
7" Single: Released Oct '79, on Asylum, by WEA Records. Deleted '82. Catalogue no: **K 12396**

KOOL IN THE KAFTAN (See panel on next page")
Tracks: / Kool in the kaftan / Baby i'm a bat.
7" Single: Released Mar '80, on Asylum, by WEA Records. Deleted '83. Catalogue no: **K 12427**

NOW AND THEN
Tracks: / Now and then.
7" Single: Released Mar '83, on After Hours, Deleted '88. Catalogue no: **AFT 10**

ONE PLUS ONE
Tracks: / One plus one.
7" Single: Released Feb '82, on Asylum, by WEA Records. Catalogue no: **K 12595**

READY OR NOT
Tracks: / Ready or not / Les beans.
7" Single: Released Feb '82, on Elektra, by Elektra Records (UK). Deleted Feb '87. Catalogue no: **K 12602**

ST. SAENS
Tracks: / St. Saens / Gonzo for my girlfriend.
7" Single: Released Apr '81, on Asylum, by WEA Records. Deleted '85. Catalogue no: **K 12523**

TO BE OR NOT TO BE
Tracks: / To be or not to be.
7" Single: Released May '80, on Asylum, by WEA Records. Deleted '83. Catalogue no: **K 12449**

Robertson, Deby

SWEETA JAMAICA
Tracks: / Sweeta Jamaica.
12" Single: Released Nov '81, on Freedom, Catalogue no: **VG 107**

Robertson, Don

HAPPY WHISTLER, THE
Tracks: / Happy whistler, The.
7" Single: Released May '56, on Capitol, by EMI Records. Deleted '59. Catalogue no: **CL 14575**

Robertson, Jackie

PRETTY BLUE EYES
Tracks: / Pretty blue eyes.

B.A. ROBERTSON - BANG BANG (Released on Elektra)

12" Single: Released Jan '84, on Dancebeat, Catalogue no: **DBD 1302**

Robertson, Robbie

FALLEN ANGEL
Tracks: / Fallen angel / Hell's half acre / Testimony (Only on the 12" version.) / Somewhere down the crazy river.
7" Single: Released Sep '88, on Geffen, by Geffen Records (USA). Catalogue no: **GEF 46**
7" Single: Released 31 Oct '87, on Geffen, by Geffen Records (USA). Deleted Jul '88. Catalogue no: **GEF 32**
12" Single: Released Sep '88, on Geffen, by Geffen Records (USA). Catalogue no: **GEF 46 T**
12" Single: Released 31 Oct '87, on Geffen, by Geffen Records (USA). Deleted Jul '88. Catalogue no: **GEF 32 T**
CD 5": Released Sep '88, on Geffen, by Geffen Records (USA). Catalogue no: **GEF 46 CD**

SOMEWHERE DOWN THE CRAZY RIVER
Tracks: / Somewhere down the crazy river / Broken arrow / Tailgate.
7" Single: Released Jun '88, on Geffen, by Geffen Records (USA). Catalogue no: **GEF 40**
12" Single: Released Jun '88, on Geffen, by Geffen Records (USA). Catalogue no: **GEF 40T**

Robertson/Oliff

HOO HA RAH
Tracks: / Hoo ha rah / Gigalo.
7" Single: Released Mar '84, on Noga, Catalogue no: **PARA 001**

Robeson, Natty

LOVE AFRICA
Tracks: / Love Africa / Tema dub.
12" Single: Released Apr '88, on Legal Lights, by Legal Light Records. Catalogue no: **LLQ 29**

Robic, Ivo

MORGEN (SINGLE)
Tracks: / Morgen.
7" Single: Released Nov '59, on Polydor, by Polydor Ltd. Deleted '62. Catalogue no: **23 923**

Robin, Roger

DO RIGHT
Tracks: / Do right.
12" Single: Released Aug '88, on Saxon Studio, Catalogue no: **SHF 004**

Robin & The Mad

MYSTIC LOVING
Tracks: / Mystic loving.
12" Single: Released Jul '82, on Ariwa Sounds, by Ariwa Sounds. Catalogue no: **ARI 1006**

Robinson, Dave

GIVE THANKS
Tracks: / Give thanks.
12" Single: Released Jun '84, on Iyah Bingi, by Iyah Bingi Records. Catalogue no: **ND 003**

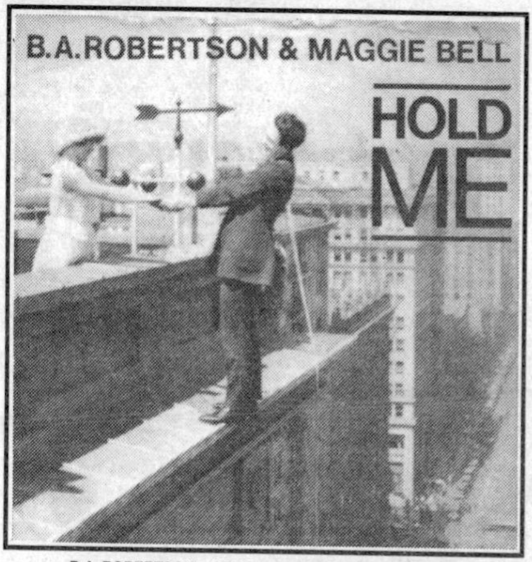

B.A. ROBERTSON - HOLD ME (Released on Swansong)

Robinson, Della

CHANCE FOR ROMANCE
Tracks: / Chance for romance.
12" Single: Released Nov '87, on Blue (USA), Catalogue no: **B 10018**

Robinson, Dutch

HAPPY
Tracks: / Happy.
7" Single: Released Feb '85, on Epic, by CBS Records. Catalogue no: **A 5021**

LOWDOWN
12" Single: Released Jun '88, on New York 42, by Satril Records. Catalogue no: **NYT 103**
7" Single: Released Jun '88, on New York 42, by Satril Records. Catalogue no: **NY 103**

Robinson, Floyd

MAKIN' LOVE
7" Single: Released Oct '59, on RCA, by BMG Records (UK). Deleted '62. Catalogue no: **RCA 1146**

MAKIN' LOVE (OLD GOLD)
Tracks: / Makin' love / Shape I'm in, The.

7" Single: Released Oct '86, on Old Gold, by Old Gold Records. Catalogue no: **OG 9623**

Robinson, Geoff

TAKE ME BACK
Tracks: / Take me back / Hot stuff.
7" Single: Released Jul '81, on PVK, by PVK Records. Catalogue no: **PV 110**

Robinson, Jackie

BODY MUSIC
Tracks: / Body music.
12" Single: Released May '88, on Body Music, by Nuclear Records. Catalogue no: **BZT 014**

SANTA ISN'T COMING TO BRIXTON TOWN
Tracks: / Santa isn't coming to Brixton town.
12" Single: Released Jan '86, on Reel Grande, Catalogue no: **71312**

Robinson, James

CAN WE DO IT AGAIN
Tracks: / Can we do it again / You're the one I've been dreaming of.
12" Single: Released Jul '87, on Tabu, Catalogue no: **650902 6**
7" Single: Released Jul '87, on Tabu, Catalogue no: **650902 7**

Robinson, Lloyd

CANDY GIRL
Tracks: / Candy girl.
10" single: Released Nov '82, on Pama, by Pama Records. Catalogue no: **PMD 3223**

HAPPY TO BE WITH YOU
Tracks: / Happy to be with you / Happy to be with you (Version).
12" Single: Released Feb '86, on Jah Tubbys, Catalogue no: **JT 016**

MIDAS TOUCH
Tracks: / Midas touch / Midas touchings.
12" Single: Released Apr '86, on Paradise, Catalogue no: **PPDIS 518**

Robinson, Mark

PRETTY JANE
Tracks: / Pretty Jane.
7" Single: Released Jan '85, on Bison Bop, by Bear Family Records (Germany). Catalogue no: **TG 104**

Robinson, Martell

I STILL LOVE YOU (SINGLE)
Tracks: / I still love you.
12" Single: Released Jun '88, on Orbitone, by Orbitone Records. Catalogue no: **OR 1230**

Robinson, Michael

DON'T GIRLS GET LONELY
Tracks: / Don't girls get lonely.
7" Single: Released Jul '84, on DJM, Catalogue no: **DJS 12**

Robinson, Paul

COME ON SISTER
Tracks: / Come on sister.
12" Single: Released May '82, on King & City, Catalogue no: **KHCBS 006**

Robinson, Ray

UNTIL THE NIGHT IS OVER
Tracks: / Until the night is over / Long way back to love.
7" Single: Released Apr '81, on WEA, by WEA Records. Deleted Apr '82. Catalogue no: **K 18434**

Robinson, Sandra

SENSI FOR SALE
Tracks: / Sensi for sale.
7" Single: Released Nov '85, on Trojan, by Trojan Records. Deleted May '88. Catalogue no: **TRO 9079**
12" Single: Released Nov '85, on Trojan, by Trojan Records. Deleted May '88. Catalogue no: **TROT 9079**

Robinson, Smokey

Biographical details: The singer, songwriter and producer Robinson was born in Detroit in 1940. The group that was to become the Miracles was formed in high school in 1955 and met up with independent songwriter-producer Berry Gordy a couple of years later. First Miracles single was *Got A Job*, followed by a minor hit, *Bad Girl*.
Then Robinson persuaded Gordy to form his own company: so began the story of Tamla Motown, the greatest record corporation in the history of black music. Tamla's first taste of major success was the Miracles' *Shop Around*, composed by Gordy and Robinson, which was a smash on both the rhythm-and-

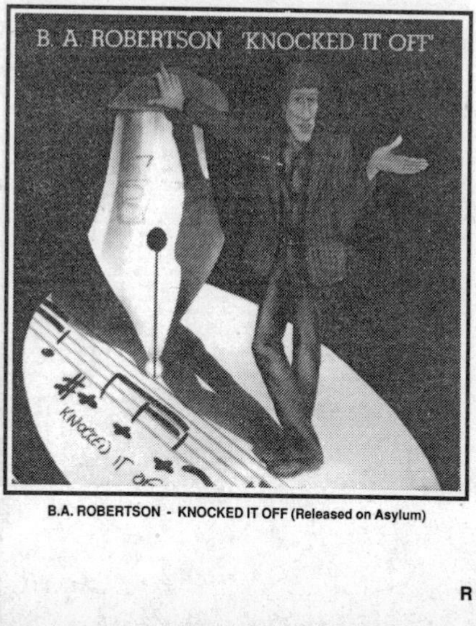

B.A. ROBERTSON - KNOCKED IT OFF (Released on Asylum)

B.A. ROBERTSON - KOOL IN THE KAFTAN (Released on Asylum)

blues and pop charts in America in early '61. Robinson consolidated this breakthrough during '62-'63 with a series of US Top Ten smashes.
He wrote and produced three Top Tenners for fellow Motown vocalist Mary Wells and the Miracles made the grade with *You Really Got A Hold On Me* and *Mickey's Monkey*.
Throughout the 60's Smokey Robinson was one of the greatest members of the Motown stable.
His high tenor voice was expressive, emotional and distinctive, whether on uptempo dance hits like *Going To A Go-Go* and *If You Can Want* or on slow, soulful ballads such as *The Tracks Of My Tears* and *My Girl Has Gone*. His dominant role in the Miracles was reflected by the fact that, from 1967, the group were billed as Smokey Robinson & The Miracles.
Though they did not reach the highest echelons of the charts as frequently as the Supremes or the Temptations they were forever on the US Top Forty throughout the 60's. Robinson's vocal prowess was matched only by his skills as a songwriter.
In addition to penning most of the Miracles' hits he provided songs for many other Motown acts. These included two "companion" records, *My Guy* and *My Girl*, US No 1 hits for Mary Wells and the Temptations respectively.
His other Temptations classics included *The Way You Do The Things You Do*, *Since I Lost My Baby* and *Get Ready*. He also wrote memorable hits for Marvin Gaye (*I'll Be Doggone* and *Ain't That Peculiar?*) and the Marvelettes (*Don't Mess With Bill* and *The Hunter Got Captured By The Game*). Robinson, who became a vice president of Motown, helped to shape the company's history. He firmly established himself as one of the greatest lyricists in soul and pop music: he nearly always stuck to pop's favourite subject, love, but found new ways to write about it. He was an adept phraseologist, ever witty but never scholarly.Smokey Robinson & The Miracles reached No 1 on both side of the Atlantic in 1970 with *Tears Of A Clown*, which had first appeared on a 1967 album. During the early 70's he wrote hits for the Four Tops and the Supremes.
He split from the Miracles at the end of '71 and became a less prolific figure. But throughout the 70's and 80's he has remained one of the most loyal and enthusiastic members of Berry Gordy's organisation and he still makes classic records from time to time, as shown by *Baby Come Close* (1974), *Cruisin'* (1980) and the seminal *Being With You*, a British No 1 and American No 2 smash in 1981. (Bob MacDonald 27.5.86)
Smokey Robinson was born William Robinson Jr in Detroit in 1940.He was a lead singer of the Miracles, a songwriter and producer and became vice-president of Motown in 1972. The group was called the Matadors in high school; other founder members were Ronnie White, Bobby Rogers, Pete Moore and Claudette Rogers (Barry's sister), all from Detroit. They knew Barry Gordy when he was writing songs for Jakie Wilson and hadn't formed his label yet; they were among the first signings when he did, although their first records appeared on other labels.
The Miracleshad 46 Hot 100 hits 1959-75, 29 in top 40, all but the first on Motown, all but the last four with Smokey, one of America's best loved vocal groups. Claudette and Smokey got married in 1959; after a while they stopped touring; the group was called Smokey Robinson And The Miricles from 1967. A great many of their hits were written and produced by Smokey; Holland-Dozier-Holland were his only rivalsfor total number of Motown hits: he is one of the few in the rock era to have hits in four decades: his memorable tunes, *Unique falsetto, Way with the metaphor* were probably helped by his strong marriage. Bob Dylan called him the greatest living poet in America. (Donald Clarke 4.2.88)
This American singer, songwriter and producer was born William Robinson in Detroit in 1940.
The group that was to become the 'Miracles' was formed in high school in Detroit in 1955, and met up with a local independent songwriter/producer called Berry Gordy a couple of years later. The 'Miracles' first single was called *Got a Job*, and the second single *Bad Girl* became the vocal group's first minor hit.

Then Smokey persuaded Berry Gordy to form his own record company; thus began the story of Tamla Motown, the greatest disc corporation in the history of black music. Tamla's first taste of major success was the 'Miracles' *Shop Around*, jointly composed by Gordy and Robinson. This was a smash on both R&B and pop charts in America in early 1961. Smokey consolidated upon this breakthrough during 1962-63 with a series of US Top 10 smashes: he wrote and produced three Top Tenners for fellow Motown vocalist Mary Wells, and the 'Miracles' made the grade with *You Really Got A Hold n Me* and *Mickey's Monkey*. Throughout the Sixties, Smokey Robinson was one of the greatest members of the Motown stable.
His high tenor voice was expressive, emotional and distinctive, whether on uptempo dance hits like *Going to a Go-Go* and *If you can want* or on slow soulful ballads such as *The tracks of my tears* and *My girl has gone*. His dominant role in the 'Miracles' was reflected by the fact that, from 1967, the group's records were billed as 'Smokey Robinson & The Miracles'. Though they did not reach the highest echelons of the charts as frequently as the 'Supremes' or the 'Temptations', they were forever on the US Top 40 throughout the Sixties.
Robinson's vocal prowess was upstaged only by his prolific skill as a songwriter. In addition to penning the lion's share of the'Miracles' hits, he provided compositions for many other Motown acts. These included two 'companion' records, *My Guy* and *My Girl*, which became US No.1 hits for Mary Wells and the 'Temptations' respectively. His other 'Temptations' classics included *The Way You Do The Things You Do*, *Since I Lost My Baby* and *Get Ready*.
Smokey also wrote memorable hits for Marvin Gaye (*I'll be doggone* and *Ain't that peculiar*) and the 'Marvelettes' (*Don't mess with Bill* and *The hunter gets captured by the game*). Robinson, who became a vice-president of Motown, helped to shape the company's history during the Sixties. He firmly established himself as one of the greatest lyricists in soul and pop music - he nearly always stuck to pop's favourite subject, love, but always found new ways to write about it. He was an adept phraseologist, ever witty but never scholarly. Smokey Robinson & the Miracles reached No.1 on both sides of the Atlantic in 1970 with *Tears of a clown*, a track that had first appeared on a 1967 album. During the early Seventies, Smokey wrote hits for the 'Four Tops' and the 'Supremes'. He split from the 'Miracles' at the end of 1971, and became a less prolific figure. But throughout the Seventies and Eighties, he has remained one of the most loyal and enthusiastic members of Berry Gordy's organisation; and he still makes classic records from time to time, as shown by *Baby come close* (1974), *Cruisin'* (1980) and the seminal *Being with you* (a British No.1 and American No.2 smash in 1981). (Bob MacDonald, 10.3.86)..

AND I DON'T LOVE YOU
Tracks: / And I don't love you / Dynamite.
12" Single: Released Jun '84, on Motown, by BMG Records (UK). Deleted '86. Catalogue no: **TMGT 1344**
7" Single: Released Jun '84, on Motown, by BMG Records (UK). Deleted '86. Catalogue no: **TMG 1344**

BEING WITH YOU (SINGLE)
Tracks: / Being with you / What's in your life for me.
7" Single: Released May '81, on Tamla Motown, by Motown Records (UK). Deleted '84. Catalogue no: **TMG 1223**

BLAME IT ON LOVE Greatest hits
Tracks: / Blame it on love / Being with you / Cruisin' / Just my soul responding.
7" Single: Released Aug '83, on Motown, by BMG Records (UK). Deleted '85. Catalogue no: **TMG 1313**

(COME 'ROUND HERE) I'M THE ONE YOU NEED (Robinson, Smokey & The Miracles)
Tracks: / (Come 'round here) I'm the one you need.
7" Single: Released Dec '66, on Tamla Motown, by Motown Records (UK). Deleted '69. Catalogue no: **TMG 584**
7" Single: Released Jan '71, on Tamla Motown, by Motown Records (UK). Deleted '74. Catalogue no: **TMG 761**

CRUISIN'
Tracks: / Only game in town, The / Cruisin' / Humming song.
7" Single: Released Aug '82, on Motown, by BMG Records (UK). Deleted '83. Catalogue no: **TMG 1274**
12" Single: Released Aug '82, on Motown, by BMG Records (UK). Catalogue no: **TMGT 1274**
7" Single: Released Feb '80, on Motown, by BMG Records (UK). Deleted Feb '85. Catalogue no: **TMG 1164**

GOING A GO GO (Robinson, Smokey & The Miracles)
Tracks: / Going a go go / Whole lot of shaking in my heart / Yester-love.
7" Single: Released Feb '66, on Tamla Motown, by Motown Records (UK). Deleted '69. Catalogue no: **TMG 547**
7" Single: Released Oct '81, on Motown, by BMG Records (UK). Catalogue no: **TMG 853**

HEAVY ON THE PRIDE(LIGHT OF LOVE)
Tracks: / Heavy on the pride (light of love).
7" Single: Released Oct '81, on Motown, by BMG Records (UK). Deleted '83. Catalogue no: **TMGT 1191**

HOLD ON TO YOUR LOVE
Tracks: / Hold on to your love / Train of thought.
12" Single: Released Jan '86, on Motown, by BMG Records (UK). Deleted '88. Catalogue no: **ZT 40554**
7" Single: Released Jan '86, on Motown, by BMG Records (UK). Deleted '88. Catalogue no: **ZB 40553**

I DON'T BLAME YOU AT ALL (Robinson, Smokey & The Miracles)
Tracks: / I don't blame you at all / Ooh baby baby.
7" Single: Released Jun '71, on Tamla Motown, by Motown Records (UK). Deleted '74. Catalogue no: **TMG 774**
7" Single: Released Mar '83, on Motown, by BMG Records (UK). Deleted '85. Catalogue no: **TMG 980**

I MADE LOVE TO YOU A THOUSAND TIMES
Tracks: / I made love to you a thousand times.
7" Single: Released Feb '83, on Motown, by BMG Records (UK). Deleted '85. Catalogue no: **TMG 1295**

I SECOND THAT EMOTION (Robinson, Smokey & The Miracles)
Tracks: / I second that emotion.
7" Single: Released Dec '67, on Tamla Motown, by Motown Records (UK). Deleted '70. Catalogue no: **TMG 631**

IF YOU CAN WANT (Robinson, Smokey & The Miracles)
Tracks: / If you can want.
7" Single: Released Apr '68, on Tamla Motown, by Motown Records (UK). Deleted '72. Catalogue no: **TMG 648**

I'M THE ONE
Tracks: / I'm the one.
7" Single: Released Oct '81, on Motown, by BMG Records (UK). Catalogue no: **TMG 957**

I'M THE ONE YOU NEED (Robinson, Smokey & The Miracles)
Tracks: / I'm the one you need / I second that emotion.
7" Single: Released Oct '80, on Motown, by BMG Records (UK). Deleted Oct '83. Catalogue no: **TMG 957**

JUST MY SOUL RESPONDING
Tracks: / Just my soul responding.
7" Single: Released Feb '74, on Tamla Motown, by Motown Records (UK). Deleted '77. Catalogue no: **TMG 883**

JUST TO SEE HER
Tracks: / Just to see her / I'm gonna love you like there's no tomorrow / You've really got a hold on me (Only available on 12" version.) / That's what love is made of (Only on 12" .) / Ooh baby baby (Only on 12").
12" Single: Released 13 Jun '87, on Motown, by BMG Records (UK). Catalogue no: **ZB 41148A**
12" Single: Released Feb '87, on Motown, by BMG Records (UK). Catalogue no: **ZT 41148**
7" Single: Released Feb '87, on Motown, by BMG Records (UK). Catalogue no: **ZB 41147**
7" Single: Released 13 Jun '87, on Motown, by BMG Records (UK). Catalogue no: **ZB 41147**

LET ME BE THE CLOCK
Tracks: / Let me be the clock / Travellin' through.
7" Single: Released Oct '81, on Motown, by BMG Records (UK). Deleted '82. Catalogue no: **TMG 1182**

LOVE DON'T GIVE NO REASON
Tracks: / Love don't give no reason / Love don't give no reason (dub mix) (on 12" only) / Love don't give no reason (dance mix) (CD Single only) / Going to a go-go (CD Single only) / You've really got a hold on me (CD Single only).
7" Single: Released Mar '88, on Motown, by BMG Records (UK). Catalogue no: **ZB 41783**
12" Single: Released Mar '88, on Motown, by BMG Records (UK). Catalogue no: **ZT 41784**
CD 5": Released Mar '88, on Motown, by BMG Records (UK). Catalogue no: **ZD 41784**

OLD FASHIONED LOVE
Tracks: / Old fashioned love / Destiny.
12" Single: Released May '82, on Motown, by BMG Records (UK). Catalogue no: **TMGT 1262**
7" Single: Released May '82, on Motown, by BMG Records (UK). Catalogue no: **TMG 1262**

ONE HEARTBEAT
Tracks: / It's time to stop shoppin' around / Why do happy memories hurt so bad / You don't know what it's like / What's too much / Love bought us here tonight / Love don't give no reason / Keep me / One heartbeat / Just to see her.
7" Single: Released Sep '87, on Motown, by BMG Records (UK). Catalogue no: **ZB 41525**
12" Single: Released Sep '87, on Motown, by BMG Records (UK). Catalogue no: **ZT 41526**

SLEEPLESS NIGHTS
Tracks: / Sleepless nights / Close encounters of the first kind / Mickey's monkey (Extra track on 12" version only.) / I got a dance to keep from crying (Extra track on 12" version only.) / Some people (will do anything for love).
7" Single: Released May '86, on Motown, by BMG Records (UK). Catalogue no: **ZB 40717**
12" Single: Released May '86, on Motown, by BMG Records (UK). Deleted '87. Catalogue no: **ZT 40718**

TEARS OF A CLOWN (Robinson, Smokey & The Miracles)
Tracks: / Tears of a clown / Tracks of my tears.
7" Single: Released Jun '83, on Motown, by BMG Records (UK). Catalogue no: **TMG 1048**
7" Single: Released Aug '70, on Tamla Motown, by Motown Records (UK). Deleted '73. Catalogue no: **TMG 745**

TELL ME TOMORROW
Tracks: / Tell me tomorrow / Tell me tomorrow (part 2) / Being with you / Aqui con tigo.
12" Single: Released Feb '82, on Motown, by BMG Records (UK). Deleted '83. Catalogue no: **TMGT 1255**
7" Single: Released Feb '82, on Motown, by BMG Records (UK). Deleted '83. Catalogue no: **TMG 1255**

TOUCH THE SKY (SINGLE)
Tracks: / Touch the sky / All my life's a lie.
7" Single: Released May '83, on Motown, by BMG Records (UK). Deleted '85. Catalogue no: **TMG 1307**

TRACKS OF MY TEARS (Robinson, Smokey & The Miracles)
Tracks: / Tracks of my tears / I second that emotion / Going to a go-go* / Shop around*.
7" Single: Released May '69, on Motown, by BMG Records (UK). Deleted '72. Catalogue no: **TMG 696**
7" Single: Released 23 May '87, on Motown, by BMG Records (UK). Catalogue no: **ZB 41373**
12" Single: Released 23 May '87, on Motown, by BMG Records (UK). Catalogue no: **ZB 41374**

YOU ARE FOREVER
Tracks: / You are forever / I hear the children singing.
7" Single: Released Oct '81, on Motown, by BMG Records (UK). Deleted '83. Catalogue no: **TMG 1237**

Robinson, Tom

Biographical details: Tom Robinson was born in Cambridge in 1950; he is a singer, songwriter, bandleader and gay activist. He studied oboe, clarinet and bass; with the guitarist Danny Kustow he formed cafe society in 1973, one of the first signings to the kinkslabel; their album sold about 600 copies and they left acrimoniously.
He formed the Tom Robinson Band with Kustow, drummer 'Dolphin' Taylor and keyboardist MarkAmbler; within months they were the talk of London: the comitted political activist Robinson was older and more articulate than most punks and was soon the darling of the critics *Power In The Darkness* in 1978 was an essential punk LP, like debuts of Clash and Sex Pistols, to understanding political/musical mood of UK late '70s. TRB live were good value, but TRB 2 in 1979 saw acute lyrics largely replaced by sloganeering; they split that year; Robinson collaborated on songs with Elton John (Tongue in-cheek gay single *'Never Gonna Fall in Love'*), Peter Gabriel; formed Sector 27 for a flaccid album in 1980; he moved to East Germany. Solo *North by northwest* in 1982 made in Hamburg was a return to form. *Tom Robinson Band* in 1981 was a definitive compilation.He returned to the UK in 1982, worked in cabaret and fringe theatre, continued recording. (Donald Clarke 4.2.88).

2.4.6.8. MOTORWAY (Live)
Tracks: / 2-4-6-8 motorway / Sing if you're glad to be gay.
7" Single: Released Sep '87, on EMI, by EMI Records. Deleted Nov '88. Catalogue

no: **EM 28**
7" Single: Released Oct '77, on EMI, by EMI Records. Catalogue no: **EMI 2715**
12" Single: Released Sep '87, on EMI, by EMI Records. Deleted Nov '88. Catalogue no: **12EM 28**

2.4.6.8 MOTORWAY (SINGLE)
Tracks: / 2.4.6.8 motorway / Don't take no for an answer.
7" Single: Released Oct '83, on Old Gold, by Old Gold Records. Deleted Jul '88. Catalogue no: **OG 9379**

ATMOSPHERICS (5 TRACK EP)
12" Single: Released Feb '83, on Panic, by Panic Records. Catalogue no: **NIC 212**

BACK IN THE OLD COUNTRY
Tracks: / Back in the old country.
12" Single: Released Jun '84, on Castaway, by BMG Records (UK). Catalogue no: **TRT 1**
7" Single: Released Jun '84, on Castaway, by BMG Records (UK). Catalogue no: **TR 1**

BULLY FOR YOU
Tracks: / Bully for you.
7" Single: Released Mar '79, on EMI, by EMI Records. Deleted '82. Catalogue no: **EMI 2916**

DON'T TAKE NO FOR AN ANSWER
Tracks: / Don't take no for an answer / Sing if you're glad to be gay / Martin / Right on sister.
7" Single: Released Feb '78, on EMI, by EMI Records. Deleted '81. Catalogue no: **EMI 2749**

FEELS SO GOOD
Tracks: / Northern rain / You tattooed me / Change.
7" Single: Released Jan '87, on Castaway, by BMG Records (UK). Catalogue no: **TR 5**

LISTEN TO THE RADIO:ATMOSPHERICS
7" Single: Released Nov '83, on Panic, by Panic Records. Catalogue no: **NIK 3**
12" Single: Released Nov '83, on Panic, by Panic Records. Catalogue no: **NIKT 3**

NOT READY
Tracks: / Not ready / Can't keep away.
7" Single: Released Jul '80, on Panic, by Panic Records. Deleted Jul '83. Catalogue no: **SEC 27**

NOW MARTIN'S GONE
Tracks: / Now Martin's gone / Atmospherics.
7" Single: Released Jul '82, on Panic, by Panic Records. Catalogue no: **NIC 1**
12" Single: Released Jul '82, on Panic, by Panic Records. Catalogue no: **NIC 212**

PRISON
Tracks: / Prison / More lives than one.
12" Single: Released May '85, on Castaway, by BMG Records (UK). Catalogue no: **ZT 40019**
7" Single: Released May '85, on Castaway, by BMG Records (UK). Catalogue no: **ZB 40019**

REAL THING, THE
Tracks: / Real thing, The / Wedding, The.
12" Single: Released Jun '86, on RCA, by BMG Records (UK). Catalogue no: **TRT 3**
7" Single: Released Jun '86, on RCA, by BMG Records (UK). Catalogue no: **TR 3**

RIKKI DON'T LOSE THAT NUMBER
Tracks: / Rikki don't lose that number / Cabin boy.
7" Single: Released Aug '84, on Castaway, by BMG Records (UK). Catalogue no: **TR 2**
12" Single: Released Aug '84, on Castaway, by BMG Records (UK). Catalogue no: **TRT 2**

SPAIN
Tracks: / Spain / Drive all night / Nothing like the real thing.
7" Single: Released May '87, on RCA, by BMG Records (UK). Catalogue no: **ZB 41333**
12" Single: Released May '87, on RCA, by BMG Records (UK). Catalogue no: **ZT 41334**

STILL LOVING YOU (SINGLE)
Tracks: / Still loving you / Saturday disco, The.
12" Single: Released Aug '86, on Castaway, by BMG Records (UK). Catalogue no: **TRT 4**
7" Single: Released Aug '86, on Castaway, by BMG Records (UK). Catalogue no: **TR 4**

TANGO AN DER WAND
Tracks: / Tango an der wand.
7" Single: Released Dec '81, on IMS, by Polydor Ltd. Catalogue no: **6005 183**

UP AGAINST THE WALL
Tracks: / Up against the wall.
7" Single: Released May '78, on EMI, by EMI Records. Deleted '81. Catalogue no: **EMI 2787**

WAR BABY
Tracks: / War baby / Hell yes / Martin gone.
7" Single: Released Jun '83, on Panic, by Panic Records. Catalogue no: **NIC 2**
12" Single: Released Jun '83, on Panic, by Panic Records. Catalogue no: **NICT 2**

Robinson, Vicki Sue

TURN THE BEAT AROUND (OLD GOLD)
Tracks: / Turn the beat around / Rock the boat.
7" Single: Released Nov '86, on Old Gold, by Old Gold Records. Catalogue no: **OG 9657**

Robotman & Friends

I WANNA BE YOUR ROBOTMAN
Tracks: / I wanna be your robotman / Hi tech heart touch.
7" Single: Released Feb '86, on Columbia, by EMI Records. Catalogue no: **DB 9126**

Robson, Nicky

STARS
Tracks: / Stars / Eye to eye.
12" Single: Released Oct '81, on Scratch, by Scratch Records. Deleted Oct '84. Catalogue no: **SCRT 006**

Rocca, John

EXTRA EXTRA
Tracks: / Extra extra / Move (rude boy mix).
12" Single: Released Nov '87, on Citybeat, by Beggars Banquet Records. Catalogue no: **CBE 1214**
7" Single: Released Nov '87, on Citybeat, by Beggars Banquet Records. Deleted Jan '88. Catalogue no: **CBE 714**

I WANT IT TO BE REAL
Tracks: / I want it to be real (12" version only.) / Club vocal mix (12" version only) / I want it to be real (club vocal) / Basement beats / Farley's hot house piano mix (12" version only.) / I want it to be real (Alternate dance mix) (12" version only.).
7" Single: Released Mar '87, on Citybeat, by Beggars Banquet Records. Deleted Jan '88. Catalogue no: **CBE 710**
12" Single: Released Mar '87, on Citybeat, by Beggars Banquet Records. Catalogue no: **CBE 1210**

I WANT YOU
Tracks: / I want you.
12" Single: on Beggars Banquet, by Beggars Banquet Records. Deleted Jun '87. Catalogue no: **BEG 138 T**

RIVER MUST FLOW, THE
Tracks: / River must flow, The / River must flow, The (Zulu dub).
12" Single: Released Mar '89, on Cobra, Catalogue no: **COBRA 1 T**

SOUTHERN FREEEZ PART II
Tracks: / Southern freeze part II / Rocca's revenge.
12" Single: Released Mar '89, on Cobra, Catalogue no: **COBRA 2 T**

TE QUIERO MI AMOUR
Tracks: / Te quiero mi amour.
12" Single: Released Oct '88, on Who'd She Coo, Catalogue no: **WSC 2T**

X.Y.Z.
Tracks: / X.Y.Z / Eezy dub / Groovin.
12" Single: Released Jul '89, on Cobra, Catalogue no: **COBRA 3T**

Roccotto

SHE'S A WOMAN
Tracks: / She's a woman.
7" Single: Released Nov '81, on State, by State Records. Deleted '84. Catalogue no: **STAT 110**

Rochdale Fairies

THREE GREEN BOTTLES
Tracks: / Three green bottles / Edelweiss.
7" Single: Released Dec '83, on SNT, Catalogue no: **SNT 116**

Rochee & The Sarnos

SARNO FEVER
Tracks: / Sarno fever.
7" Single: Released Mar '84, on Kay-Y, Catalogue no: **KY 701**

WHISTLE WRIGGLE
Tracks: / Whistle wriggle.
7" Single: Released Jun '85, on Nervous, by Nervous Records. Catalogue no: **NER 007-7**

Rochelle

MY MAGIC MAN
Tracks: / My magic man / Machine gun dub.
12" Single: Released Jan '86, on Warner Bros., by WEA Records. Catalogue no: **W 8838 T**
7" Single: Released Jan '86, on Warner Bros., by WEA Records. Catalogue no: **W 8838**

Roches

LOSING TRUE
Tracks: / Losing true / Scorpian lament.
7" Single: Released Nov '82, on Warner Bros., by WEA Records. Catalogue no: **K 929857 7**

Rock...

ROCK THE HOUSE, PART 1
Tracks: / Rock the house, part 1: *Various artists.*
12" Single: Released Nov '87, on TD (USA), Catalogue no: **TD 801**

Rock Candy

REMEMBER
Tracks: -/ Remember.
7" Single: Released Sep '71, on MCA, by MCA Records. Deleted '74. Catalogue no: **MK 5069**

Rock, Chubb

YA BAD CHUBBS
Tracks: / Ya bad chubbs / Love makes no promises (h).
7" Single: Released Sep '89, on Champion, by Champion Records. Catalogue no: **CHAMP 215**
7" Single: Released May '89, on Select (USA), Catalogue no: **FMS 62336**
12" Single: Released Sep '89, on Champion, by Champion Records. Catalogue no: **CHAMP 12215**

Rock, Dickie

BOP
Tracks: / Bop.
7" Single: Released '88, on I&B, by I & B Records. Catalogue no: **CAR 93**

Rock Goddess

HEAVY METAL ROCK'N'ROLL
Tracks: / Heavy metal rock'n'roll / Satisfied the crucified.
12" Single: Released Nov '82, on CBS, by CBS Records. Deleted Nov '85. Catalogue no: **AMSX 8263**

I DIDN'T KNOW I LOVED YOU TILL I SAW YOU ROCK
Tracks: / I didn't know I loved you till I saw you rock'n'roll / Hell hath no fury.
7" Single: Released Mar '84, on A&M, by A&M Records. Deleted '87. Catalogue no: **AMS 185**

MY ANGEL
Tracks: / My angel / In the heat of the night.
7" Single: Released Feb '83, on A&M, by A&M Records. Deleted '88. Catalogue no: **AMS 8311**
12" Single: Released Feb '83, on A&M, by A&M Records. Deleted '88. Catalogue no: **AMSX 8311**

Rock & Hyde

DIRTY WATER
Tracks: / Dirty water (single) / Dirty water (version 1) / Dirty water (dance version) / Middle of the night / Dirty water (version 2) / Dirty water (version 3).
7" Single: Released Mar '87, on EMI, by EMI Records. Catalogue no: **EMI 5598**
12" Single: Released Mar '87, on EMI, by EMI Records. Catalogue no: **12EMI 5598**
7" Set: Released Mar '87, on EMI, by EMI Records. Deleted Jul '87. Catalogue no: **12EMID 5598**

I WILL
Tracks: / I will / What children say.
7" Single: Released 21 Nov '87, on EMI, by EMI Records. Deleted 31 Jul '88. Catalogue no: **EM 13**
12" Single: Released 21 Nov '87, on EMI, by EMI Records. Deleted 31 Jul '88. Catalogue no: **12 EM 13**

Rock Island Line

GO 'WAY HOUND DOG
Tracks: / Go 'way hound dog / Maybe that's why I care.
7" Single: Released Oct '80, on RCA, by BMG Records (UK). Deleted Oct '83. Catalogue no: **PB 5283**

Rock Melons

NEW GROOVE
Tracks: / New groove / Dreams in the empty city.
7" Single: Released Jul '89, on Atlantic, by WEA Records. Catalogue no: **A 8908**
12" Single: Released Jul '89, on Atlantic, by WEA Records. Catalogue no: **A 8908T**

Rock Steady Crew

(HEY YOU) ROCKSTEADY CREW (OLD GOLD)
Tracks: / Hey you (the Rocksteady Crew) / Hey D.J..
12" Single: Released 27 Feb '89, on Old Gold, by Old Gold Records. Catalogue no: **OG 4102**

HEY YOU (THE ROCK STEADY CREW)
Tracks: / Hey you (the Rock Steady Crew).
7" Single: Released Sep '83, on Charisma, by Virgin Records. Deleted May '88. Catalogue no: **RSC 1**
12" Single: Released Sep '83, on Charisma, by Virgin Records. Deleted May '88. Catalogue no: **RSC 112**

UPROCK
Tracks: / Uprock.
7" Single: Released May '84, on Charisma, by Virgin Records. Deleted '87. Catalogue no: **RSC 2**

Rockabilly Rebs.

BOPPIN' BULLFROG
Tracks: / Boppin' bullfrog / Ragbones.
7" Single: Released May '83, on Small Run, Catalogue no: **RIDUP 001**

Rockaway Three

IT'S YOUR THING
Tracks: / It's your thing / Do your thing.
7" Single: Released 11 Jul '88, on Urban, by Polydor Ltd. Catalogue no: **URB 18**
12" Single: Released 11 Jul '88, on Urban, by Polydor Ltd. Catalogue no: **URBX 18**

Rockelodeon

MUSIC, MUSIC, MUSIC
Tracks: / Music, music, music / I got hitched.
7" Single: Released Jun '82, on Technical, by Technical Records. Deleted Jun '85. Catalogue no: **TECS 3**

Rocker's Express

PHOENIX CITY
Tracks: / Phoenix city / Chinese brush.
7" Single: Released Feb '80, on Korova, by WEA Records. Deleted Feb '83. Catalogue no: **KOW 2**

Rockers Galore

SGT. PEPPER
Tracks: / Sgt. Pepper.
7" Single: Released Jul '87, on Jive, by Zomba Records. Catalogue no: **JIVE 149**
12" Single: Released Jul '87, on Jive, by Zomba Records. Deleted Nov '87. Catalogue no: **JIVET 149**

Rockers Revenge

ACID MIND PARTIES
Tracks: / Acid mind parties.
12" Single: Released Jan '88, on R.A.R., Catalogue no: **RAR 001**

HARDER THEY COME
Tracks: / Harder they come, The.
7" Single: Released Jan '83, on London Records, by London Records. Catalogue no: **LON 18**
12" Single: Released Jan '83, on London Records, by London Records. Catalogue no: **LONX 18**

WALKIN' ON SUNSHINE
Tracks: / Walking on sunshine.
7" Single: Released Jul '82, on London Records, by London Records. Catalogue no: **LON 11**
12" Single: Released Jul '82, on London Records, by London Records. Catalogue no: **LONX 11**

Rocket

I WANT TO KNOW
Tracks: / I want to know / It keeps me....
7" Single: Released Nov '82, on Virgin, by Virgin Records. Deleted '89. Catalogue no: **VS 559**
12" Single: Released Nov '82, on Virgin, by Virgin Records. Deleted '89. Catalogue no: **VS 559-12**

Rockin' Berries

HE'S IN TOWN
Tracks: / He's in town / Poor man's son.
7" Single: Released Oct '64, on Piccadilly, Deleted '67. Catalogue no: **7 N 35203**
7" Single: Released Apr '79, on Flashback, by Mainline Records. Catalogue no: **FBS 8**

I DIDN'T MEAN TO HURT YOU
Tracks: / I didn't mean to hurt you.
7" Single: Released Oct '64, on Piccadilly, Deleted '67. Catalogue no: **7 N 35197**

PARTY 45
Tracks: / Party 45 / Give me some time (on

12" only).
12" Single: Released Nov '81, on DJM, Deleted Nov '84. Catalogue no: **DJR 10980**
7" Single: Released Nov '81, on DJM, Deleted Nov '84. Catalogue no: **DJS 10980**

POOR MAN'S SON
Tracks: / Poor man's son.
7" Single: Released May '65, on Piccadilly, Deleted '68. Catalogue no: **7 N 35236**

POOR MAN'S SON (OLD GOLD)
Tracks: / Poor man's son / He's in town.
7" Single: Released Jan '89, on Old Gold, by Old Gold Records. Catalogue no: **OG 9840**

WATER IS OVER MY HEAD, THE
Tracks: / Water is over my head, The.
7" Single: Released Jan '66, on Pye, Deleted '69. Catalogue no: **7 N 35270**

WHAT IN THE WORLD'S COME OVER YOU
Tracks: / What in the world's come over you.
7" Single: Released Jan '65, on Piccadilly, Deleted '68. Catalogue no: **7 N 35217**

YOU'RE MY GIRL
Tracks: / You're my girl.
7" Single: Released Aug '65, on Pye, Deleted '68. Catalogue no: **7 N 35254**

Rockin' Jimmy

ROCKIN' ALL NITE
Tracks: / Rockin' all nite.
7" Single: Released May '83, on Sonet, by Sonet Records. Catalogue no: **SON 2255**

Rockin' Johnny

ALL THE TIME EP
Tracks: / All the time.
7" Single: Released Apr '80, on Nervous, by Nervous Records. Catalogue no: **NEP 001**

Rockin' Renegades

TEENAGER IN LOVE
Tracks: / Teenager in love / Rockin' chair.
7" Single: Released Nov '83, on Zone To Zone, by Zone To Zone Records. Catalogue no: **ZON 06**

Rockin' Robin

PLAY THAT FUNKY MUSIC
Tracks: / Play that funky music.
12" Single: Released Apr '85, on Debut, by Skratch Records. Catalogue no: **DEBT 05(12)**

Rockin Roll

I JUST WANNA RAP
Tracks: / I just wanna rap (edit).
7" Single: Released Aug '87, on Magnetic Dance, by Magnet Records. Deleted Jun '88. Catalogue no: **MAGD 8**
12" Single: Released Aug '87, on Magnetic Dance, by Magnet Records. Deleted Jun '88. Catalogue no: **MAGDT 8**

Rockin' Sidney

LOUISIANA CREOLE MAN
Tracks: / Louisiana Creole man / Good time.
7" Single: Released Dec '82, on Bally Hoo (USA), Catalogue no: **BH 1013**

MY TOOT TOOT
Tracks: / My toot toot
7" Single: Released Sep '85, on Ace, by Ace Records. Deleted Jun '88. Catalogue no: **KID 001**

PLAY JOLI BLON FOR ME
Tracks: / Play Joli Blon for me / Go Lucy go.
7" Single: Released Nov '82, on Bally Hoo (USA), Catalogue no: **BH 1017**

SCOOP, THE
Tracks: / Scoop, The / I'm not gonna spend this Christmas alone.
7" Single: Released Dec '82, on Bally Hoo (USA), Catalogue no: **BH 1016**

SHOW ME WHERE IT ITCHES
Tracks: / Show me where it itches / Wet eyes , red nose and tonsils .
7" Single: Released Dec '82, on Bally Hoo (USA), Catalogue no: **BH 1014**

Rockit

RED CADILLAC & A BLACK MOUSTACHE
Tracks: / Red cadillac and a black moustache / That's alright mama.
7" Single: Released Jun '81, on Revolver, by FM-Revolver Records. Catalogue no: **REV 5**

Rockleodeon

MUSIC MUSIC MUSIC
Tracks: / Music music music / I got hitched.
7" Single: Released Jun '82, on Technical, by Technical Records. Catalogue no: **TECS 3**

ROCK'N'ROLL ORIGINALS CD EP
Tracks: / Ooby dooby: *Orbison, Roy* / Jungle rock: *Mizell, Hank* / Flyin' saucers rock 'n' roll: *Riley, Billy Lee* / Red cadillac and a black moustache: *Smith, Warren.*
CD 5": Released Feb '89, on Charly, by Charly Records. Catalogue no: **CDS 8**

Rock-olas

LANGUAGE OF LOVE
Tracks: / Language of love / Eyes of blue.
7" Single: Released Mar '82, on Rocket, by Rocket Records. Catalogue no: **XPRES 75**

LET'S DANCE
Tracks: / Let's dance / Big tears.
7" Single: Released Dec '82, on MCA, by MCA Records. Deleted Dec '87. Catalogue no: **LE 101**

Rockpile

TEACHER TEACHER
Tracks: / Teacher teacher / Fool too long.
7" Single: Released Dec '80, on F-Beat, by F-Beat Records. Deleted Dec '85. Catalogue no: **XX 11**

WRONG WAY
Tracks: / Wrong way / Now and always.
7" Single: Released Sep '80, on F-Beat, by F-Beat Records. Deleted '83. Catalogue no: **XX 9**

Rockwell

CARME
Tracks: / Carme / Carme (Inst.) / Somebody's watching me (Extra track on 12"version only.).
12" Single: Released Jul '86, on RCA, by BMG Records (UK). Deleted '87. Catalogue no: **ZT 40778**
7" Single: Released Jul '86, on RCA, by BMG Records (UK). Catalogue no: **ZB 40777**

HE'S A COBRA
Tracks: / He's a cobra / Change your ways.
12" Single: Released Mar '85, on Motown, by BMG Records (UK). Deleted '87. Catalogue no: **TMGT 1374**
7" Single: Released Mar '85, on Motown, by BMG Records (UK). Deleted '87. Catalogue no: **TMG 1374**

OBSCENE PHONE CALLER
Tracks: / Obscene phone caller.
7" Single: Released Mar '84, on Motown, by BMG Records (UK). Deleted '86. Catalogue no: **TMG 1336**
12" Single: Released Mar '84, on Motown, by BMG Records (UK). Deleted '86. Catalogue no: **TMGT 1336**

PEEPING TOM
Tracks: / Peeping Tom / Tokyo.
7" Single: Released May '85, on Gordy (USA), by BMG Records (UK). Catalogue no: **ZB 40099**

SOMEBODY'S WATCHING ME (SINGLE)
Tracks: / Somebody's watching me / Somebody's watching me (instrumental).
7" Single: Released Jan '84, on Motown, by BMG Records (UK). Catalogue no: **TMG 1331**
12" Single: Released Jan '84, on Motown, by BMG Records (UK). Catalogue no: **TMGT 1331**

TAXMAN
Tracks: / Taxman / Wasting away / Change your ways.
7" Single: Released Jul '84, on Motown, by BMG Records (UK). Deleted '86. Catalogue no: **TMG 1345**
12" Single: Released Jul '84, on Motown, by BMG Records (UK). Deleted '86. Catalogue no: **TMGT 1345**

Rocky Horror Show

ROCKY HORROR DISCO SHOW
12" Single: Released Nov '85, on ZYX (Germany), Catalogue no: **ZYX 5299**

Rocky M

DISCO LADY
Tracks: / Disco lady (special DJ mix) / Disco lady (inst.).
12" Single: Released May '86, on Conifer, Catalogue no: **ICK 052 1554776**

Rocky Sumeray

BACK TO SCHOOL AGAIN
Tracks: / Back to school again / Mothers eyes.
7" Single: Released Sep '81, on EMI, by EMI Records. Deleted Sep '84. Catalogue no: **EMI 5237**

Rocky Valley

FESTIVAL SONG
Tracks: / Festival song / National garden festival theme (Conducted by : Ted Gray) / Festival song (inst. version).
7" Single: Released Jun '86, on Valentine, by Valentine Records. Catalogue no: **VALS 125**

Roco

HELLO HELLO
Tracks: / Hello hello / Sara.
7" Single: Released Jul '83, on Straight 8, Deleted '86. Catalogue no: **ROCO 1**

Rococo

SNOWSCAPE
Tracks: / Snowscape / Amadeus.
7" Single: Released Jan '81, on Rialto (1), by Rialto Records. Deleted Jan '84. Catalogue no: **TREB 130**

Rocos, Cleo

LOVE DILEMMA
Tracks: / Love dilemma / It's Christmas.
Note: with Enrico Valdez Orchestra.
7" Single: Released Dec '87, on DK, Catalogue no: **DK 1**

Rod

JUST KEEP ON WALKING
Tracks: / Just keep on walking.
7" Single: Released Mar '83, on Creole, by Creole Records. Catalogue no: **CR 52**
12" Single: Released Mar '83, on Creole, by Creole Records. Catalogue no: **CR 1252**

Rod, Jane & Freddy

HAPPY CHRISTMAS
Tracks: / Happy Christmas.
7" Single: Released Dec '81, on Video, Deleted '82. Catalogue no: **VID 001**

Roden,Shirley

IS THIS GOODBYE
Tracks: / Is this goodbye / I think I'll disappear.
7" Single: Released Nov '83, on Nouveau Music, Catalogue no: **NMS 3**

Rodger, Mart

I BELIEVE IN RAINBOWS
Tracks: / I believe in rainbows / I'll be loving you always.
7" Single: Released Jun '88, on Bowstone, Catalogue no: **OWS 201**

Rodgers, Clodagh

BILJO
Tracks: / Biljo.
7" Single: Released Nov '69, on RCA, by BMG Records (UK). Deleted '72. Catalogue no: **RCA 1891**

CAN'T AFFORD THAT FEELING ANYMORE
Tracks: / Can't afford that feeling anymore / My simple heart.
7" Single: Released Sep '80, on Precision (1), Deleted '83. Catalogue no: **PAR 109**

COME BACK AND SHAKE ME
Tracks: / Come back and shake me.
7" Single: Released Jun '69, on RCA, by BMG Records (UK). Deleted '72. Catalogue no: **RCA 1792**

EVERYBODY GO HOME THE PARTY'S OVER
Tracks: / Everybody go home the party's over.
7" Single: Released Nov '69, on RCA, by BMG Records (UK). Deleted '72. Catalogue no: **RCA 1891**

GOODNIGHT MIDNIGHT
Tracks: / Goodnight midnight.
7" Single: Released Jun '69, on RCA, by BMG Records (UK). Deleted '72. Catalogue no: **RCA 1852**

JACK IN THE BOX
Tracks: / Jack in the box.
7" Single: Released Mar '71, on RCA, by BMG Records (UK). Deleted '74. Catalogue no: **RCA 2066**

LADY LOVE BUG
Tracks: / Lady love bug.
7" Single: Released Oct '71, on RCA, by BMG Records (UK). Deleted '74. Catalogue no: **RCA 2117**

PERSON TO PERSON
Tracks: / Person to person / My simple heart.
7" Single: Released May '81, on Precision (1), Deleted May '86. Catalogue no: **PAR 119**

Rodgers, Frank

CHILDHOOD HEROES
Tracks: / Childhood heroes / Rock'n'roll paradise.
7" Single: Released May '82, on Pulsar, by Lismor Records. Catalogue no: **PUS 104**

Rodgers, Jimmie (2)

Biographical details: Pop singer.

ENGLISH COUNTRY GARDEN
Tracks: / English country garden / Woman from Liberia.
7" Single: Released Jan '83, on Flashback, by Mainline Records. Catalogue no: **FBS 21**
7" Single: Released Jun '62, on Columbia, by EMI Records. Deleted '65. Catalogue no: **DB 4847**

HONEYCOMB
Tracks: / Honeycomb.
7" Single: Released Nov '57, on Columbia, by EMI Records. Deleted '60. Catalogue no: **DB 3986**

KISSES SWEETER THAN WINE (SINGLE)
Tracks: / Kisses sweeter than wine.
7" Single: Released Dec '57, on Columbia, by EMI Records. Deleted '60. Catalogue no: **DB 4052**

OH OH I'M FALLING IN LOVE AGAIN
Tracks: / Oh oh I'm falling in love again.
7" Single: Released Mar '58, on Columbia, by EMI Records. Deleted '61. Catalogue no: **DB 4078**

WOMAN FROM LIBERIA
Tracks: / Woman from Liberia.
7" Single: Released Dec '58, on Columbia, by EMI Records. Deleted '61. Catalogue no: **DB 4206**

Rodgers, Michael

I GOT LOVE (IMPORT)
Tracks: / I got love.
12" Single: Released Sep '89, on WTG, Catalogue no: **416 886 7**

Rodgers, Nile

LAND OF THE GOOD GROOVE
Tracks: / Land of the good groove.
7" Single: Released Apr '83, on Mirage (USA), Catalogue no: **B 6911**
12" Single: Released Apr '83, on Mirage (USA), Catalogue no: **B 9911T**

YUM YUM
Tracks: / Yum yum.
12" Single: Released May '83, on Mirage (USA), Catalogue no: **B 9918T**
7" Single: Released May '83, on Mirage (USA), Catalogue no: **B 9918**

Rodgers, Paul

CUT LOOSE(7")
Tracks: / Cut loose.
7" Single: Released Nov '84, on Atlantic, by WEA Records. Catalogue no: **A 9749**

Rodigan, Junior

WINDING DEGREE
Tracks: / Winding degree.
7" Single: Released Apr '89, on Gyas, Catalogue no: **GA 050**

Rodney, Frank

GOTTA GIVE IT UP
Tracks: / Gotta give it up.
7" Single: Released Feb '89, on RCA, by BMG Records (UK). Deleted Aug '89. Catalogue no: **PB 49475**

Rodriguez, Antonia

LA BAMBA
Tracks: / La Bamba / Sweet love.
7" Single: Released Sep '81, on Magnet, by WEA Records. Catalogue no: **MAG 149**
12" Single: Released Sep '81, on Magnet, by WEA Records. Catalogue no: **12 MAG 149**

Rodriguez, Johnny

LOVE LOOK AT US NOW
Tracks: / Love look at us now / Where did it go.
7" Single: Released Aug '80, on Epic, by CBS Records. Deleted '83. Catalogue no: **EPC 8769**

Rodriguez, Ivan 'Doc'

IN DOC WE TRUST
Tracks: / In Doc we trust.
12" Single: Released Feb '89, on Risin', by Risin' Records. Catalogue no: **RAHT 104**

Rods

POWER LOVER
Tracks: / Power lover / Nothing going on in the city.
12" Single: Released Feb '82, on Arista, by BMG Records (UK). Catalogue no: **ARIST 12457**
7" Single: Released Mar '82, on Arista, by BMG Records (UK). Catalogue no: **ARIST 457**

TOO HOT TO STOP
Tracks: / Too hot to stop / Power lover.

7" Single: Released '82, on Arista, by BMG Records (UK). Deleted '87. Catalogue no: **ARIST 484**
12" Single: Released '82, on Arista, by BMG Records (UK). Deleted '87. Catalogue no: **ARIST 12484**

YOU KEEP ME HANGING ON
Tracks: / You keep me hangin' on.
7" Pic: Released May '82, on Arista, by BMG Records (UK). Catalogue no: **ARIPD 467**
7" Single: Released '82, on Arista, by BMG Records (UK). Deleted '87. Catalogue no: **ARIST 467**

Rodway, Steve

KEEP ON WALKING
Tracks: / Keep on walking.
12" Single: Released Jun '85, on Record Shack, by Record Shack Records. Catalogue no: **SOHOT 44**
7" Single: Released Jun '85, on Record Shack, by Record Shack Records. Catalogue no: **SOHO 44**

SAY GOODBYE TO YOU
Tracks: / Say goodbye to you / Fallin' in without you.
7" Single: Released Mar '81, on Solid Gold (USA), by MCA Records (USA). Deleted Mar '84. Catalogue no: **SGR 106**

Roe, Tommy

Biographical details: Tommy Roe was born in Georgia in 1942. The pop singer had 22 USA Hot 100 entries 1962-73 including transatlantic hits. He became even more poppy, the oldest of the bubblegum blowers in the heyday of the Monkees and the Archies, had a transatlantic number one with the infuriating *Dizzy* in 1969. Like many bubblegum/pop contemporaries (Paul Revere's Mark Lindsay, etc) he turned to country music, occasionally toured as an oldie. (Donald Clarke 4.2.88)..

DIZZY
Tracks: / Dizzy.
7" Single: Released Apr '69, on Stateside, by EMI Records. Deleted '72. Catalogue no: **SS 2143**

EVERYBODY
Tracks: / Everybody.
7" Single: Released Sep '63, on H.M.V., by EMI Records. Deleted '66. Catalogue no: **POP 1207**

FOLK SINGER, THE
Tracks: / Folk singer, The.
7" Single: Released Mar '63, on H.M.V., by EMI Records. Deleted '66. Catalogue no: **POP 1138**

HEATHER HONEY
Tracks: / Heather honey.
7" Single: Released Jul '69, on Stateside, by EMI Records. Deleted '72. Catalogue no: **SS 2152**

SHEILA
Tracks: / Sheila.
7" Single: Released Jul '82, on Old Gold, by Old Gold Records. Catalogue no: **OG 9166**
7" Single: Released Sep '62, on H.M.V., by EMI Records. Deleted '65. Catalogue no: **POP 1060**

SUSIE DARLIN'
Tracks: / Susie darlin'.
7" Single: Released Dec '62, on H.M.V., by EMI Records. Deleted '65. Catalogue no: **POP 1092**

Roger

I HEARD IT THROUGH THE GRAPEVINE
Tracks: / I heard it through the grapevine / Chunk of sugar.
7" Single: Released Nov '81, on Warner Bros., by WEA Records. Deleted Nov '84. Catalogue no: **K 17865**

I WANT TO BE YOUR MAN
Tracks: / I want to be your man / I really want to be your man / Bedistgutarist-a-rown.
7" Single: Released Sep '87, on Warner Bros., by WEA Records. Catalogue no: **W 8229**
12" Single: Released Sep '87, on Warner Bros., by WEA Records. Catalogue no: **W 8229T**

Rogers, Cece

FOREVER
Tracks: / Forever / Someday.
7" Single: Released Aug '89, on Atlantic, by WEA Records. Catalogue no: **A 8852**
12" Single: Released Aug '89, on Atlantic, by WEA Records. Catalogue no: **A 8852T**

Rogers, Evan

PRIVATE JOY
Tracks: / Private joy.
12" Single: Released Jul '85, on RCA International, by BMG Records (UK). Catalogue no: **PT 49937**
7" Single: Released Jul '85, on RCA International, by BMG Records (UK). Catalogue no: **PB 49937**

SECRET LOVE
Tracks: / Secret love.
12" Single: Released Feb '84, on RCA, by BMG Records (UK). Catalogue no: **RCAT 392**

STAY HERE WITH ME
Tracks: / Stay here with me.
12" Single: Released May '84, on RCA, by BMG Records (UK). Catalogue no: **RCAT 416**
7" Single: Released May '84, on RCA, by BMG Records (UK). Catalogue no: **RCA 416**

Rogers, Helen

CANDIDATE FOR LOVE
Tracks: / Candidate for love.
12" Single: Released Sep '84, on Justice, Catalogue no: **JUS 004**

WHAT'S LOVE GOT TO DO WITH IT
Tracks: / What's love got to do with it / Beautiful weekend.
12" Single: Released Sep '84, on Hot Rod, Catalogue no: **HR 005**

Rogers, Julie

HAWAIIAN WEDDING SONG
Tracks: / Hawaiian wedding song.
7" Single: Released Mar '65, on Mercury, by Phonogram Ltd. Deleted '68. Catalogue no: **MF 849**

LIKE A CHILD
Tracks: / Like a child.
7" Single: Released Dec '64, on Mercury, by Phonogram Ltd. Deleted '67. Catalogue no: **MG 838**

WEDDING
Tracks: / Wedding / Love letters.
7" Single: Released Jun '81, on Mercury, by Phonogram Ltd. Deleted Jun '84. Catalogue no: **MER 67**

WEDDING, THE
Tracks: / Wedding, The.
7" Single: Released Aug '64, on Mercury, by Phonogram Ltd. Deleted '67. Catalogue no: **MF 820**

WEDDING, THE (OLD GOLD)
Tracks: / Wedding, The / Amanda.
7" Single: Released Jul '82, on Old Gold, by Old Gold Records. Catalogue no: **OG 9255**

Rogers, Kenny

ALL MY LIFE
Tracks: / All my life.
7" Single: Released Apr '83, on United Artists, by EMI Records. Catalogue no: **UP 659**

CHRISTMAS WITHOUT YOU See under Parton, Dolly
7" Single: Released Nov '84, on RCA, by BMG Records (UK). Catalogue no: **RCA 465**

COWARD OF THE COUNTY
Tracks: / Coward of the county / I want to make you smile.
7" Single: Released Sep '85, on United Artists, by EMI Records. Catalogue no: **UP 614**
7" Single: Released Sep '85, on Liberty, by EMI Records. Catalogue no: **BP 427**

DAYTIME FRIENDS
Tracks: / Daytime friends.
7" Single: Released Sep '77, on United Artists, by EMI Records. Deleted '80. Catalogue no: **UP 36289**

DON'T FALL IN LOVE WITH A DREAMER
Tracks: / Don't fall in love with a dreamer / Goin' home to the Rock/Gideon.
7" Single: Released Oct '85, on EMI-America, by EMI Records. Catalogue no: **EA 208**
7" Single: Released Jan '81, on United Artists, by EMI Records. Deleted Jan '84. Catalogue no: **UP 625**

EYES THAT SEE IN THE DARK (SINGLE)
Tracks: / Eyes that see in the dark.
7" Single: Released Sep '83, on RCA, by BMG Records (UK). Catalogue no: **RCA 358**

GAMBLER, THE
7" Single: Released Mar '85, on United Artists, by EMI Records. Catalogue no: **PB 425**

I DON'T NEED YOU
Tracks: / I don't need you / Without you in my life.
7" Single: Released Jul '81, on United Artists, by EMI Records. Deleted '84. Catalogue no: **UP 640**

ISLANDS IN THE STREAM
Tracks: / Islands in the stream.
7" Single: Released Nov '83, on RCA, by BMG Records (UK). Catalogue no: **RCA 378**

LADY (SINGLE)
Tracks: / Lady / Sweet music man.
7" Single: Released Nov '80, on United Artists, by EMI Records. Deleted '83. Catalogue no: **UP 635**

LONG ARM OF THE LAW
Tracks: / Long arm of the law / Make me wonderif i ever said goodbye.
7" Single: Released Feb '82, on United Artists, by EMI Records. Deleted '85. Catalogue no: **UP 650**

LOVE WILL TURN YOU AROUND (SINGLE)
Tracks: / Love will turn you around.
7" Single: Released Jul '82, on United Artists, by EMI Records. Catalogue no: **UP 654**

LUCILLE (SINGLE)
Tracks: / Lucille.
7" Single: Released Apr '77, on United Artists, by EMI Records. Catalogue no: **UP 36242**

MORNING DESIRE
Tracks: / Morning desire.
12" Single: Released Oct '85, on RCA, by BMG Records (UK). Catalogue no: **PT 49926**
7" Single: Released Oct '85, on RCA, by BMG Records (UK). Catalogue no: **PB 49925**

RUBY DON'T TAKE YOUR LOVE TO TOWN (SINGLE)
Tracks: / Ruby don't take your love to town / Lucille.
7" Single: Released Oct '69, on Reprise, by WEA Records. Deleted '72. Catalogue no: **RS 2089**
7" Single: Released Mar '84, on EMI Golden 45's, by EMI Records. Catalogue no: **G45 7**

SHE BELIEVES IN ME
Tracks: / She believes in me.
7" Single: Released Jun '79, on United Artists, by EMI Records. Deleted '82. Catalogue no: **UP 36533**

SO IN LOVE WITH YOU
Tracks: / So in love with you / Share your love with me.
7" Single: Released Oct '81, on United Artists, by EMI Records. Deleted Oct '84. Catalogue no: **UP 646**

SOMETHING'S BURNING
Tracks: / Something's burning / Ruby don't take your love to town.
7" Single: Released Feb '70, on Reprise, by WEA Records. Deleted '73. Catalogue no: **RS 20888**
7" Single: Released May '80, on Reprise (USA), Catalogue no: **K 14483**

THIS WOMAN
Tracks: / This woman / Hold me.
7" Single: Released Jan '84, on RCA, by BMG Records (UK). Catalogue no: **RCA 390**

WE'VE GOT TONIGHT (see under Easton, Sheena)

WHEN YOU PUT YOUR HEART IN IT
Tracks: / When you put your heart in it / So little love in the world / Vowels go broken, The (Only on 12").
7" Single: Released Sep '88, on Warner Bros., by WEA Records. Catalogue no: **W 7711**
12" Single: Released Sep '88, on Warner Bros., by WEA Records. Catalogue no: **W 7711T**

Rogers, Mark

LET'S GET TOGETHER
Tracks: / Let's get together / I promise.
12" Single: Released Mar '89, on Warriors Dance, by Warriors Dance Records. Catalogue no: **WAFT 009**
7" Single: Released Mar '89, on Warriors Dance, by Warriors Dance Records. Catalogue no: **WAF 009**

Rogers, Mick

BRING BACK THE NIGHT
Tracks: / Bring back the night / Too late.
7" Single: Released Feb '86, on Trojan, by Trojan Records. Deleted May '88. Catalogue no: **MR 1**

Rogers, Nick

RIVERS
Tracks: / Rivers.
7" Single: on Mooncrest, by Trojan Records. Deleted May '88. Catalogue no: **MOON 1001**

Rogers, Shorty

Biographical details: Shorty Rogers was born Milton Michael Rajonsky in 1924 in Massachusetts; the trumpeter, bandleader, arranger and composer was popular in the 1950's, and reissues show that his work hasn't dated: he is a swing era musician who was influenced in his writing by bop, and his all-star West-coast small-group sides from the early '50s, as well as the work on Atlantic c.1955 (the *Martians Go Home* period) still sounds very good indeed. His big-band work was directly influenced by Count Basie. He toured the UK in 1982 with National Youth Jazz Orchestra. (Donald Clarke 4.2.88)..

MARLON BRANDO: THE WILD ONE (EP) (film soundtrack)
Tracks: / Chino / Blues for Brando / Wild one / Windswept.
12" Single: Released 1 Jun '89, on Bear Family, by Bear Family Records (Germany). Catalogue no: **BFE 15349**

Rogers, Nile

STATE OF MIND
Tracks: / State of mind / Stayed out of light.
12" Single: Released Jan '86, on Warner Bros., by WEA Records. Deleted Sep '87. Catalogue no: **W 8921 T**

Rogue

BY THE DEVIL I WAS TEMPTED
Tracks: / By the devil I was tempted / My friend.
7" Single: Released May '80, on Ariola, by BMG Records (UK). Deleted May '83. Catalogue no: **ARO 226**

Rogue Male

ALL OVER YOU
Tracks: / All over you.
12" Single: Released May '85, on Music For Nations, by Music For Nations Records. Catalogue no: **12 KUT 114**

BELFAST
Tracks: / Belfast / Rough tough (pretty too) / Take no shit.
12" Single: Released Jul '86, on Music For Nations, by Music For Nations Records. Catalogue no: **12 KUT 122**

Rokko, Red

GUM GUM TREE, THE
Tracks: / Gum gum tree, The.
7" Single: Released Sep '84, on Frame Up, Catalogue no: **MSFU 1**

Rokoca

I'LL BE THERE
Tracks: / I'll be there / Echoes.
7" Single: Released Mar '85, on PRT, by Castle Communications Records. Catalogue no: **7P 322**

Rokotto

BOOGIE ON UP
Tracks: / Boogie on up.
7" Single: Released Oct '77, on State, by State Records. Deleted '80. Catalogue no: **STAT 62**

FUNK THEORY
Tracks: / Funk theory.
7" Single: Released Jun '78, on State, by State Records. Deleted '81. Catalogue no: **STAT 80**

IF I HAD YOU
Tracks: / If I had you / Six million dollar baby.
7" Single: Released Sep '81, on State, by State Records. Deleted '84. Catalogue no: **STAT 107**

Roland

PARADISE
Tracks: / Paradise.
7" Single: Released Sep '84, on Master Discs, by Master Discs. Catalogue no: **MD 01**

STORMY NIGHT
Tracks: / Stormy night.
12" Single: Released Jan '82, on Plantation, Catalogue no: **PL 002**

Roland, Paul

ALICE'S HOUSE
Tracks: / Alice's house.
12" Single: Released 20 Feb '88, on Bam Caruso, by Demon Records. Catalogue no: **PABL 094**

BEAU BRUMMEL
Tracks: / Beau Brummel / I can't control myself.
7" Single: Released Apr '89, on New Rose (1), by New Rose Records. Catalogue no: **FREE 14**

BLADES OF BATTENBURG
Tracks: / Blades of Battenburg.
12" Single: Released Aug '83, on Aftermath (1), by Aftermath Records. Catalogue no: **AEP 12011**

DEATH OF GLORY
Tracks: / Death or glory / Great Edwardian air raid, The / Beau Brummel / Curious case of Richard Fielding, The.
12" Single: Released Jul '86, on Aftermath (1), by Aftermath Records. Catalogue no: **AEP 12012**

DOCTOR STRANGE
Tracks: / Doctor Strange / Madeline.
7" Single: Released Jul '82, on Aristocrat, Catalogue no: **ARC 1398**

GABRIELLE
Tracks: / Gabrielle / Berlin / Sword and

sorcery.
7" EP: Released 23 May '87, on Aftermath (1), by Aftermath Records. Catalogue no: **AEP 12013**

MADAM GUILLOTINE
Note: Double 'A' side
7" Single: Released Apr '87, on Bam Caruso, by Demon Records. Catalogue no: **OPRA 081**

SWORD AND SORCERY
Tracks: / Sword and sorcery.
7" Single: Released '88, on Constrictor, by Constrictor Records (Germany). Catalogue no: **COLL 008**

Roland Rat

LIVING LEGEND
Tracks: / Living legend / Living legend.
12" Single: Released Sep '86, on Rodent, Deleted Jan '88. Catalogue no: **12 RAT 5**
7" Single: Released Sep '86, on Rodent, Deleted Jan '88. Catalogue no: **RAT 5**

LOVE ME TENDER
Tracks: / Love me tender / Pink bucket song.
7" Single: Released Mar '84, on Rodent, Deleted Jan '88. Catalogue no: **RAT 2**
12" Single: Released Mar '84, on Rodent, Catalogue no: **12 RAT 2**

NUMBER ONE RAT FAN
Tracks: / Number one Rat Fan.
7" Single: Released Jan '85, on Rodent, Deleted Jan '88. Catalogue no: **RAT 4**
12" Single: Released Jan '85, on Rodent, Deleted Jan '88. Catalogue no: **12 RAT 4**
7" Pic: Released Jan '85, on Rodent, Deleted Jan '88. Catalogue no: **RATP 4**

RAT RAPPING
Tracks: / Rat rapping.
7" Single: Released Nov '83, on Rodent, Deleted Jan '88. Catalogue no: **RAT 1**
12" Single: Released Nov '83, on Rodent, Catalogue no: **12 RAT 1**

Rolands

BELINDA
Tracks: / Belinda.
10" single: Released Aug '82, on Pama, by Pama Records. Catalogue no: **PMD 3216**

Role, Honor

TWIST, THE
Tracks: / Twist, The.
7" Single: Released Jun '88, on Homestead, Catalogue no: **HMS 101**

Rolfe, Kit

WIZARD
Tracks: / Wizard / Play another song.
7" Single: Released Mar '80, on DJM, Deleted Mar '83. Catalogue no: **DJS 10935**

Rolfe,Nigel

AFRICAN FLOWER
Tracks: / African flower / P.W. Botha's funeral march.
7" Single: Released Sep '86, on Reekus, by Reekus Records. Catalogue no: **RKS 019**
12" Single: Released Sep '86, on Reekus, by Reekus Records. Catalogue no: **RKST 019**

Roll Ups

BLACKMAIL
Tracks: / Blackmail.
7" Single: Released Jan '80, on Bridgehouse, Deleted '88. Catalogue no: **BHS 6**

Rollback

REMEMBER
Tracks: / Remember.
7" Single: Released Oct '81, on KRL, by Kaleidoscope Records (UK). Deleted Oct '84. Catalogue no: **KRLA 1652**

Rollens, Audley

ALL I WANT
Tracks: / All I want / Sounds cool killer.
12" Single: Released Dec '83, on Wackies, Catalogue no: **WACKIES 1990**

Rollercoaster

HIGHER GROUND
Tracks: / Higher ground / I wish.

7" Single: Released Jan '81, on Calibre, Deleted Jan '84. Catalogue no: **CAB 107**

Rollers

LIFE ON THE RADIO
Tracks: / Life on the radio / Ricochet.
7" Single: Released May '81, on Epic, by CBS Records. Deleted May '84. Catalogue no: **A 1225**

NO DOUBT ABOUT IT
Tracks: / No doubt about it / Set the fashion.

7" Single: Released Jul '81, on Epic, by CBS Records. Deleted '84. Catalogue no: **EPCA 1402**

Rolling Hits

MEDLEY
Tracks: / Medley / Gonna catch you.
7" Single: Released Oct '81, on Philips, by Phonogram Ltd. Deleted Oct '84. Catalogue no: **ROLL 7**
12" Single: Released Oct '81, on Philips, by Phonogram Ltd. Deleted Oct '84. Catalogue no: **ROLL 12**

Rolling Stones

Biographical details: The Rolling Stones are the second-greatest band in the history of rock, and the only group of the 60's to merit comparison with the Beatles. The Stones' line-up has always contained Mick Jagger, Keith Richards (the 's' of his surname was dropped for much of the band's career), Bill Wyman and Charlie Watts. Guitarist Brian Jones quit in June 1969 and died the following month, aged 27. Mick Taylor took over but was in turn replaced by ex-Faces guitar man Ron Wood in 1975. Keyboardist Ian Stewart was an unofficial "sixth Stone" from the group's formation until his death in December '85.
The Stones came together via a gradual sequence of events that took place on the London blues scene during 1962-63. The two most important outside figures during their early years were musician Alexis Korner, who was the catalyst who brought about their formation, and Andrew Loog Oldham, who became their manager and producer.
During '63-'64 the Stones chalked up their first five British hit singles, all drawn from other sources. They were Chuck Berry's *Come On*, Lennon and McCartney's *I Wanna Be Your Man*, the Crickets' *Not Fade Away*, the Valentinos' *It's All Over Now* and Willie Dixon's *Little Red Rooster*. The last two songs gave the band the first of their eight UK No 1 singles of the 60's: the other six chart-toppers were all written by the ace team of Jagger and Richard, who became the group's key creative forces and focal points on stage.
Unlike the Beatles, all four of whom were well known, the public profiles of vocalist Jagger and guitarist Richard tended to overshadow the others, particularly after Jones' death. The Rolling Stones were a world sensation during the 60's, many of their records becoming all-time classics. Satisfaction, *Get Off My Cloud*, *Paint It Black* and *Honky Tonk Woman* reached No 1 in both Britain and America. *The Last Time* and *Jumping Jack Flash* were also chart-toppers in the UK and *Ruby Tuesday* was a No 1 smash in the States.
Albums were also huge sellers, 1968's *Beggars' Banquet* being the best from an artistic standpoint. Oldham, whose association with the Stones lasted until '67, deliberately moulded the group as an antidote to the Beatles. While the Fab Four were lovable and acceptable to people of all generations, the Stones were utterly rebellious and emphasised their anti-establishment stance. The notorious Jagger was accused of having no morals. Several members were arrested for possession of drugs. Whereas the Beatles decided that the magic of the 60's could not be recreated in the 70's, the Stones rocked on and on into the 80's. In purely commercial terms, notably with tour grosses, the band became bigger and bigger, but as they grew older their social importance inevitably diminished and their rebellious impact lessened. They were now simply a rock band, sometimes great and sometimes complacent.
Among the best of their later singles were *Brown Sugar* ('71), *Angie* ('73) and *Miss You* ('78), all of which reached No 1 in the US and the Top Five in Britain. And their albums continued to sell in vast numbers, 1978's *Some Girls* being a particularly worthy item. In 1985 Jagger turned in one of his best latterday performances on the single and video of *Dancing In The Street*, his Live Aid collaboration with David Bowie.
In the following year the Stones went back to their R & B roots with *Harlem Shuffle*, a remake of Bob and Earl's 1963 oldie. (Bob MacDonald, March 1986.)
UK rock band, self-styled the greatest rock'n'roll band in the world: vocalist Mick Jagger (born in 1943 Dartford), guitarist Keith Richards (born 1943 Dartford); bassist Bill Wyman (born 1936 in Penge), drummer Charlie Watts (born in 1941 in Neasdon); plus Brian Jones on rhythm guitar, other instuments (born Lewis Brian Hopkins Jones in 1942 in Cheltenam; died in 1969), replaced by Mick Taylor (born 1940 Herts.) who was succeeded by ex-Faces Ron Wood (born in 1947 in Hillingdon, Middx.); and Ian Stewart on keyboards (born in 1938, died in 1985).
Jagger and Richards attended primary school together, met on a train as teenagers and discovered they were both R&B fans (with fame Keith dropped the 's' calling himself Richard, until reconciled with his father years later); Jones followed a similar enthusiasm a hundred miles away, travelled to landon to visit Korner's club, where Jagger was second string vocalist after Long John Baldry, and where he met Watts and Stewart; the nucleus of Jones, Jagger and Richards began to rehearse together.
Watts was persuaded to quit his advertising job in 1963. European blues enthusiast Giorgio Gomelsky booked them a weekly slot at the Railway Hotel in Richmond, Surrey, acted as unofficial manager until they attracted a following, when hustling publicist Andrew Loog Oldhan turned up, moulded them into a saleable commodity as a rebellious London answer to the relatively goody-goody Beatles; he demoted Stewart, who did not fit the image (Stewart became tour manager, trusted confidant, frequent keybaoard player on tours/records).
Contract with Decca was easily obtained as that label was kicking itself for turning down the beatles; the Stones' first record in 1963 was a cover of Chuck Berry's *Come On*, a minor UK hit. They toured the UK at the bottom of the bill with the Everly Brothers and Little Richard, and worked their way up. In America they sounded like Chuck Berry immitators and did not have a number one hit until *Satisfaction* in 1965.
They exploited their image, refusing to wave bye-bye on a UK pop TV programme; while the Beatles collected MBEs from the Queen, the Stones were arrested for urinating in a garage forecourt; but they thought they had to copy the Beatles' psycadelic *Sgt Pepper*: their album *Their Santanic Majesties Request* in 1967 was a dreadfull failure and their worst record, but they came back with their best. Meanwhile Jagger, Richards and Jones had been arrested on drug charges; prison terms were quashed after a famous *Times* leader asked, quoting William Blake, *Who Breaks A Butterfly Upon A Wheel?*. *Jumpin' Jack Flash* was classic, exciting rock'n'roll, dispelling notions of studio or electronic wizadary for the Stones: while the Beatles no longer toured at all, the Stones had to tour, because they really were the worlds greatest rock'n'roll band.
Beggars Banquet and *Let It Bleed* in 1968-9 were their first masterpieces. Jagger made film *Performance* in 1968, playing a jaded, faded rock star; Jagger's only song was *Memo from Turner*, one of his best tracks, recorded with members of Traffic including Steve Winwood. TV film *Rolling Stonees Rock and Roll Circus* was made in December, with the Who, Jethro Tull, John Lennon, Clapton, others, but never shown; Jagger thought he had been outdone by the Who. Brian Jones was far more than a rhythm guitarist; he had been the musical centre of the group many times, his slide guitar on *No Expectations* e.g. an attraction of *Beggars Banquet*.
They might not have accomplished anything without him, but he was now unreliable, drug-sodden and alcoholic; in May '69 he was eased out of the group; in July he drowned in his swimming pool. (His last project was issued in 1972 as *Brain Jones Presents The Pipes Of Pan In Joujouka*, Moroccan trad. music.)
A free concert in Hyde Park two days later with Mick Taylor (ex-John Mayall's Bluesbreakers) went on as scheduled; in tribute to Jones boxes of butterflies were released, many of them also dead; the band gave one of its worst performances ever. Jagger and Marianne Faithfull then flew to Australia; he played legendary outlaw in flop film *Ned Kelly*; she took an overdose of pills and Jagger saved her life, but the days of their affair were more numbered. *Honkey Tonk Woman* was number one in USA/UK mid-'69, one of their best and a different version from the track on *Let It Bleed* (video saw them in drag).
The flower-power era ended with another free concert at Altamont, a disused racetrack in California, in December 1969: bad organisation had 'security' provided by Hells Angels, who hacked and stomped to death Meredith Hunter, an 18-year-old black man foolishly waving a pistol, the killing captured in the film Gimme Shelter. *Get Your Ya-Yas Out* in 1970 was their best live LP, made during the USA tour; *Sticky Fingers* in 1971 included *Brown Sugar* (no.1 USA, 2 UK), *Wild Horses* and *Sister Morphine* (influenced by Gram Parsons, who fell out with Jagger over composer credits.) The double album *Exile On Main Street* in 1972 was their last undoubted masterpiece; since then they have gone up and down, but mostly immitated themselves.
Some Girls in 1978 was their best in years, perhaps pushed with competition with punk rock, including disco-ish *Miss You* (their last number one single); feminists were outraged by the title track, as though surprised by stone-age chauvinism. Jagger, Woods and Wyman have made solo albums, incl. Wyman's *Willie & The Poor Boys*. Always a jazz fan, Watts bankrolled the Charlie Watts Big Band, which played at Ronnie Scott's, toured the USA and made an album for CBS at Fulham Town Hall. (Donald Clarke 4.2.88).

This British rock band has always contained Mick Jagger, Keith Richards (the 's' of his surname was dropped for much of the group's career), Charlie Watts and Bill Wyman. Guitarist Brian Jones quit the band in June 1969, and died the following month at the age of 27; he was replaced by Ron Wood (ex-'Faces') in 1975. Keyboardist Ian Stewart was an unofficial 'sixth Stone' from the group's formation until his death in December 1985.
The Rolling Stones are the second greatest band in the history of rock, and were the only pop group of the ixties to merit comparison with the Beatles. The Stones were formed via a gradual sequence of events that took place on the London blues scene during 1962-3. The two most important outside figures during the group's early days were the legendary blues musician Alexis Korner, who was the catalyst who brought about their formation, and Andrew Loog Oldham, who became the Stones' manager and producer. During 1963-4 the Rolling Stones chalked up their first five British hit singles, all of which were drawn from other sources. These were Chuck Berry's *Come On*, Lennon & McCartney's *I wanna be your man*, the Crickets' *Not fade away*, the Valentinos' *It's*

ROLLING STONES - EMOTIONAL RESCUE (Released on Rolling Stones)

ROLLING STONES - MISS YOU (Released on EMI)

ROLLING STONES - RESPECTABLE (Released on EMI)

all over now and Willie Dixon's *Little red rooster*.
The latter two songs gave the group the first of their eight UK No.1 singles of the Sixties. The other six chart-toppers were all written by the ace team of Mick Jagger & Keith Richard, who became the group's key creative force and their focal point on stage. Unlike the Beatles, all four of whom were equally well known, the public profile of vocalist Mick and guitarist Keith tended to overshadow the other members.
The Rolling Stones were a world sensation during the Sixties, many of their records becoming all time classics. *(I can't get no) Satisfaction*, *Get off of my cloud*, *Paint it black* and *Honky tonk women* reached No.1 in both Britain and America. *The last time*. and *Jumping Jack Flash* were also chart-toppers in the UK, and *Ruby Tuesday* was a No.1 smash in the States. The Stones' albums were also huge sellers, 1968's *Beggars banquet* being the best from an artistic standpoint. Oldham, whose association with the Stones lasted until 1967, deliberately moulded the group as the antidote to the Beatles. While the Fab Four were lovable and acceptable to people of all generations, the Stones were utterly rebellious and emphasised their anti-establishment stance.
The notorious Jagger was accused of not having any morals. Several members were arrested for possession of drugs, but the ensuing jail sentences were thrown out when the group appealed. Whereas the Beatles decided that the magic of the Sixties could not be recreated in the Seventies, the Rolling Stones rocked on through the latter decade and even through the Eighties. In purely commercial terms, notably with tour grosses, the band became bigger and bigger; but as they grew older, their social importance inevitably diminished and their rebellious impact lessened.
They were now simply a rock band, sometimes great, sometimes complacent. Amongst the best of their later singles were *Brown sugar* (1971), *Angie* (1973) and *Miss you* (1978), all of which reached No.1 in America and the Top 5 in the UK. Their albums continued to sell in vast quantities, 1978's *Some girls* being a particularly worthy item.

In 1985 Jagger turned in one of his best latterday performances on the single and video of *Dancing in the street*, his Live Aid collaboration with David Bowie. In the following year, the Stones went back to their R&B roots with *Harlem Shuffle*, a remake of Bob & Earl's 1963 oldie. (Bob MacDonald, 10.3.86).

19TH NERVOUS BREAKDOWN
Tracks: / 19th nervous breakdown.
7" Single: Released Mar '82, on Decca, by Decca Records. Deleted '88. Catalogue no: **F 12331**
7" Single: Released Aug '80, on Decca, by Decca Records. Deleted '83. Catalogue no: **STONE 8**

ANGIE
Tracks: / Angie.
7" Single: Released Sep '73, on Rolling Stones (1), Catalogue no: **RS 19105**
7" Single: Released Apr '83, on EMI (France), by EMI Records. Catalogue no: **2C 008H 64734**

BROWN SUGAR
Tracks: / Brown sugar / Bitch / Let it rock.
7" Pic: Released Jul '84, on Rolling Stones (1), Catalogue no: **SUGARP 1**
7" Single: Released Jun '84, on Rolling Stones (1), Catalogue no: **SUGAR 1**
7" Single: Released Apr '71, on Rolling Stones (1), Catalogue no: **RS 19100**

COME ON
Tracks: / Come on / I wanna be your man.
7" Single: Released Aug '80, on Decca, by Decca Records. Deleted '83. Catalogue no: **STONE 1**
7" Single: Released Jul '63, on Decca, by Decca Records. Deleted '88. Catalogue no: **F 11675**

EMOTIONAL RESCUE (SINGLE)
Tracks: / Emotional rescue / Down in the hole.
7" Single: Released Jun '80, on Rolling Stones (1), Catalogue no: **RSR 105**

FOOL TO CRY
Tracks: / Fool to cry.
7" Single: Released May '76, on Rolling Stones (1), Catalogue no: **RS 19121**

GET OFF MY CLOUD
Tracks: / Get off my cloud.
7" Single: Released Oct '65, on Decca, by Decca Records. Deleted '88. Catalogue no: **F 12263**

GET OFF OF MY CLOUD
Tracks: / Get off of my cloud / Play with fire.
7" Single: Released Aug '80, on Decca, by Decca Records. Deleted '83. Catalogue no: **STONE 6**

GOING TO A GO-GO
Tracks: / Going to a go-go / Beast of burden.
7" Single: Released Jun '82, on Rolling Stones (1), Catalogue no: **RSR 110**

HARLEM SHUFFLE
Tracks: / Harlem shuffle / Had it with you / Harlem shuffle (New York Mix) (Extra track on 12" version only.) / Harlem shuffle (London Mix) (Extra track on 12" version only.).
7" Single: Released Mar '86, on CBS, by CBS Records. Catalogue no: **A 6864**
12" Single: Released Mar '86, on CBS, by CBS Records. Catalogue no: **QTA 6864**
12" Single: Released Mar '86, on CBS, by CBS Records. Catalogue no: **TA6864**

HAVE YOU SEEN YOUR MOTHER BABY
Tracks: / Have you seen your mother baby, standing in the shadow.
7" Single: Released Sep '66, on Decca, by Decca Records. Deleted '88. Catalogue no: **F 12497**

HONKY TONK WOMEN
Tracks: / Honky tonk women / You can't always get what you want.
7" Single: Released Jul '69, on Decca, by Decca Records. Deleted '88. Catalogue no: **F 12952**
7" Single: Released Aug '80, on Decca, by Decca Records. Deleted '83. Catalogue no: **STONE 10**

(I CAN'T GET NO) SATISFACTION
Tracks: / (I can't get no) satisfaction / Little by little.
7" Single: Released Aug '80, on Decca, by Decca Records. Deleted '83. Catalogue no: **STONE 3**
7" Single: Released Aug '65, on Decca, by Decca Records. Catalogue no: **F 12220**

I WANNA BE YOUR MAN
Tracks: / I wanna be your man.
7" Single: Released Nov '63, on Decca, by Decca Records. Deleted '88. Catalogue no: **F 11764**

IT'S ALL OVER NOW
Tracks: / It's all over now / I want to be loved.
7" Single: Released Aug '80, on Decca, by Decca Records. Deleted '83. Catalogue no: **STONE 2**
7" Single: Released Jul '64, on Decca, by Decca Records. Deleted '88. Catalogue no: **F 11934**

IT'S ONLY ROCK'N'ROLL (SINGLE)
Tracks: / It's only rock 'n' roll.
7" Single: Released '74, on Rolling Stones (1), Deleted '77. Catalogue no: **RS 19114**

JUMPIN' JACK FLASH
Tracks: / Jumpin' Jack Flash / As tears go by.
7" Single: Released Aug '80, on Decca, by Decca Records. Deleted '83. Catalogue no: **STONE 7**
7" Single: Released May '68, on Decca, by Decca Records. Deleted '88. Catalogue no: **F 12782**

JUMPING JACK FLASH
Tracks: / Jumpin' Jack Flash / Child of the man / Sympathy for the devil.
12" Single: Released May '87, on Decca, by Decca Records. Deleted Feb '89. Catalogue no: **FX 102**
7" Single: Released May '87, on Decca, by Decca Records. Catalogue no: **F 102**

LAST TIME
Tracks: / Last time / Paint it black.
7" Single: Released Aug '80, on Decca, by Decca Records. Deleted '83. Catalogue no: **STONE 5**
7" Single: Released Mar '65, on Decca, by Decca Records. Deleted '88. Catalogue no: **F 12104**

LET'S SPEND THE NIGHT TOGETHER
Tracks: / Let's spend the night together / Ruby Tuesday.
7" Single: Released Jan '67, on Decca, by Decca Records. Deleted '88. Catalogue no: **F 12546**
7" Single: Released May '83, on Rolling Stones (1), Catalogue no: **RSR 112**
7" Single: Released Aug '80, on Decca, by Decca Records. Deleted '83. Catalogue no: **STONE 9**

LITTLE RED ROOSTER
Tracks: / Little red rooster.
7" Single: Released Nov '64, on Decca, by Decca Records. Deleted '88. Catalogue no: **F 12014**

MISS YOU (See panel top left)
Tracks: / Miss you / Far away eyes.
7" Single: Released Jun '78, on Rolling Stones (1), Deleted '81. Catalogue no: **EMI 2802**
12" Single: Released Sep '84, on EMI (Europe), by EMI Records. Catalogue no: **1CK 052 61201**

MIXED EMOTIONS
Tracks: / Mixed emotions (Chris Kimsey's 12") (Only on 12" single.) / Mixed emotions / Fancyman blues / Tumbling dice (Only on CD single.) / Miss you (Onlyo n CD single.) / Shattered (Only on CD single (655214 2)) / Waiting on a friend (Only on CD single (655214 2)).
CD 5": Released 21 Aug '89, on CBS, by CBS Records. Catalogue no: **655193 5**
Cassingle: Released 21 Aug '89, on CBS, by CBS Records. Catalogue no: **655193 4**
CD 5": Released Sep '89, on CBS, by CBS Records. Catalogue no: **655214 2**
12" Single: Released 21 Aug '89, on CBS, by CBS Records. Catalogue no: **655193 6**
7" Single: Released 21 Aug '89, on CBS, by CBS Records. Catalogue no: **655193 7**

NINETEENTH NERVOUS BREAKDOWN
Tracks: / Nineteenth nervous breakdown.
7" Single: Released Feb '66, on Decca, by Decca Records. Deleted '69. Catalogue no: **F 12331**

NOT FADE AWAY
Tracks: / Not fade away / Little red rooster.
7" Single: Released Aug '80, on Decca, by Decca Records. Deleted '83. Catalogue no: **STONE 4**
7" Single: Released Feb '64, on Decca, by Decca Records. Deleted '88. Catalogue no: **F 11845**

ONE HIT TO THE BODY
Tracks: / One hit to the body / Fight.
12" Single: Released May '86, on Rolling Stones (1), Catalogue no: **TA 7160**
7" Single: Released May '86, on Rolling Stones (1), Catalogue no: **A 7160**

OUT OF TIME
Tracks: / Out of time.
7" Single: Released Sep '75, on Decca, by Decca Records. Deleted '78. Catalogue no: **F 13597**

PAINT IT BLACK
Tracks: / Paint it black.
7" Single: Released May '66, on Decca, by Decca Records. Deleted '88. Catalogue no: **F 12395**

RESPECTABLE (See panel above)
Tracks: / Respectable / When the whip comes down.
7" Single: Released Sep '78, on EMI, by EMI Records. Catalogue no: **EMI 2861**

ROLLING STONES (EP)
Tracks: / You better move on / Poison ivy / Bye bye Johnny / Money.
7" Single: Released Mar '82, on Decca, by Decca Records. Deleted '88. Catalogue no: **DFE 8560**
12" Single: Released Dec '83, on Decca, by Decca Records. Deleted '88. Catalogue no:

DFEX 8560

SHE WAS HOT
Tracks: / She was hot / I think I'm going mad.
7" Single: Released Jan '84, on Rolling Stones (1), Catalogue no: **RSR 114**
12" Single: Released Jan '84, on Rolling Stones (1), Catalogue no: **RSRP 114**

SHE'S SO COLD
Tracks: / She's so cold / Send it to me.
7" Single: Released Sep '80, on Rollin' Rock, Catalogue no: **RSR 106**

START ME UP
Tracks: / Start me up / No use in crying.
7" Single: Released Aug '81, on Rolling Stones (1), Catalogue no: **RSR 108**

STREET FIGHTING MAN
Tracks: / Street fighting man / Out of time.
7" Single: Released Aug '80, on Decca, by Decca Records. Deleted '83. Catalogue no: **STONE 11**
7" Single: Released Jul '71, on Decca, by Decca Records. Deleted '88. Catalogue no: **F 13195**

SYMPATHY FOR THE DEVIL
Tracks: / Sympathy for the devil / Gimme shelter.
7" Single: Released Aug '80, on Decca, by Decca Records. Deleted '83. Catalogue no: **STONE 12**

TIME IS ON MY SIDE
Tracks: / Time is on my side / 20 flight rock / Under my thumb (Only on 12" single.).
7" Single: Released Sep '82, on Rolling Stones (1), Catalogue no: **RSR 111**
12" Single: Released Sep '82, on Rolling Stones (1), Catalogue no: **12 RSR 111**

TUMBLING DICE
Tracks: / Tumbling dice.
7" Single: Released '80, on Rolling Stones(USA), by Atlantic Recording Corp.(USA). Catalogue no: **LR 0823**
7" Single: Released Apr '72, on Rolling Stones (1), Deleted '75. Catalogue no: **RS 19103**

UNDERCOVER OF THE NIGHT
Tracks: / Undercover of the night / All the way down / Feel on baby.
7" Single: Released Oct '83, on Rolling Stones (1), Catalogue no: **RSR 113**
12" Single: Released Oct '83, on Rolling Stones (1), Catalogue no: **12 RSR 113**

WAITING ON A FRIEND
Tracks: / Waiting on a friend / Little T and A.
7" Single: Released Nov '81, on Rolling Stones (1), Catalogue no: **RSR 109**

WE LOVE YOU
Tracks: / We love you / Dandelion.
7" Single: Released Aug '67, on Decca, by Decca Records. Deleted '88. Catalogue no: **F 12654**

Rollin' Thunder

TOO LOOSE
Tracks: / Too loose.
7" Single: Released 3 Jul '85, on Hell's Kitchen, Deleted '88. Catalogue no: **NICK 001**

Rollright, Craig

YOUNG GIRL WITH CHINESE EYES
Tracks: / Young girl with chinese eyes / Shadow, The.
7" Single: Released Jul '84, on A Record Company, Deleted '88. Catalogue no: **ARC 004**

Roly Poly

LUMPY LUMP LUMP
Tracks: / Lumpy lump lump.
7" Single: Released May '83, on Crash, by Satril Records. Deleted '85. Catalogue no: **CRA 508**

Roman Grey

LOOK ME IN THE EYES
Tracks: / Look me in the eyes.
7" Single: Released Apr '83, on Food For Thought, by Music For Nations Records. Catalogue no: **FMC 21**

SHAKEDOWN
Tracks: / Shakedown.
12" Single: Released Jun '84, on Food For Thought, by Music For Nations Records. Catalogue no: **YUMT 106**

Roman Ha

CASTLE IN THE AIR
Tracks: / Castle in the air.
12" Single: Released Nov '87, on KDF World Service, Catalogue no: **KDFOOL 1**

Roman Holiday

DON'T TRY TO STOP IT
Tracks: / Don't try to stop it.
7" Single: Released Jun '83, on Jive, by Zomba Records. Catalogue no: **JIVE 39**
12" Single: Released Jun '83, on Jive, by Zomba Records. Catalogue no: **JIVET 39**

FIRE ME UP
Tracks: / Fire me up.
7" Single: Released Aug '84, on Jive, by Zomba Records. Catalogue no: **JIVE 59**
12" Single: Released Aug '84, on Jive, by Zomba Records. Catalogue no: **JIVET 59**

MOTOR MANIA
Tracks: / Motor mania / Cookin' on the roof.
12" Single: Released Sep '83, on Jive, by Zomba Records. Catalogue no: **JIVET 49**
7" Single: Released Sep '83, on Jive, by Zomba Records. Catalogue no: **JIVE 49**

ONE FOOT BACK IN YOUR DOOR
Tracks: / One foot back in your door / I'll wait / Stand by (on 12" only) / Don't try to stop it (on 12" only).
7" Single: Released Feb '85, on Jive, by Zomba Records. Catalogue no: **JIVE 83**
12" Single: Released Feb '85, on Jive, by Zomba Records. Catalogue no: **JIVET 83**

STAND BY
Tracks: / Stand by / Round....
7" Set: Released Jan '83, on Jive, by Zomba Records. Catalogue no: **JIVEG 31**
7" Single: Released Mar '83, on Jive, by Zomba Records. Catalogue no: **JIVE 31**
12" Single: Released Mar '83, on Jive, by Zomba Records. Catalogue no: **JIVET 31**

TOUCH TOO MUCH
Tracks: / Touch too much / Runaway.
7" Single: Released May '85, on Jive, by Zomba Records. Catalogue no: **JIVE 91**
12" Single: Released May '85, on Jive, by Zomba Records. Catalogue no: **JIVET 91**

Roman, Johnny

BEST CHRISTMAS OF THEM ALL, THE
Tracks: / Best Christmas of them all, The / Blue Christmas.
7" Single: Released Nov '87, on Young Blood, by Young Blood Records. Catalogue no: **YBL 2**

BUONA SERA
Tracks: / Buona sera / I love you.
7" Single: Released Jul '83, on Crazy Viking, by Crazy Vikings Records. Catalogue no: **CV 005**

I LOVE YOU
Tracks: / I love you / I remember Elvis Presley / Sun days '54 (Elvis interview)* (Only on picture disc.).
7" Pic: Released Sep '87, on Young Blood, by Young Blood Records. Catalogue no: **WPB 1**
12" Single: Released Sep '87, on Young Blood, by Young Blood Records. Catalogue no: **WBLT 1**

KING OF ROCK 'N' ROLL
Tracks: / King of rock 'n' roll / I love you / I remember Elvis Presley (Extra track available on 12" picture bag only) / Sun Days 64 (Available on 12" Picture Bag only - Rare Elvis Interview).
7" Single: Released Aug '87, on Young Blood, by Young Blood Records. Catalogue no: **YBL 1**
12" Single: Released Aug '87, on Young Blood, by Young Blood Records. Catalogue no: **YBLT 1**

Roman, Lyn

I WANT YOU
Tracks: / I want you / Born to live.
12" Single: Released Jun '88, on Ichiban, by Ichiban Records (UK). Catalogue no: **ICHT 703**
7" Single: Released Jun '88, on Ichiban, by Ichiban Records (UK). Catalogue no: **ICHS 703**

LOVE SLAVE
Tracks: / Love slave.
12" Single: Released 21 Nov '87, on Ichiban, by Ichiban Records (UK). Catalogue no: **12PO 4**

Romana

COME SHOW YOUR LOVE
Tracks: / Come show your love.
12" Single: Released 6 Aug '88, on Metro Music International, Catalogue no: **12MMI2**
7" Single: Released 6 Aug '88, on Metro Music International, Catalogue no: **MMI2**

Romance

TIE ME DOWN
Tracks: / Tie me down.
12" Single: Released '88, on Passion, by Skratch Records. Catalogue no: **PASH 21(12)**

Romanelli

CONNECTING FLIGHT
Tracks: / Connecting flight / Chain reaction.
12" Single: Released Jul '82, on 21 Records, by Polydor Ltd. Catalogue no: **POSPX 484**
7" Single: Released Jul '82, on 21 Records, by Polydor Ltd. Catalogue no: **POSP 484**

Romanos, Carlos

TAKE MY HAT OFF
Tracks: / Take my hat off / All through the night.
7" Single: Released Feb '80, on PVK, by PVK Records. Deleted Feb '85. Catalogue no: **PV 35**

Romantics

TALKING IN YOUR SLEEP
Tracks: / Talking in your sleep / I'm hip.
12" Single: Released Jan '84, on Epic, by CBS Records. Catalogue no: **RTA 4118**

TOP OF THE WORLD
Tracks: / Top of the world / Ecstacy.
7" Single: Released Sep '82, on Towerbell, Catalogue no: **TOW 26**

WHAT I LIKE ABOUT YOU
Tracks: / What I like about you / First in line.
7" Single: Released Mar '80, on Epic, by CBS Records. Deleted '83. Catalogue no: **EPC 8248**

Rome

SYMPATHY
Tracks: / Sympathy / Listen to your heart.
7" Single: Released Oct '86, on Network, by CBS Records. Catalogue no: **PLOT 7003**

Rome, Toney

ROCK THIS WAY
Tracks: / Rock this way.
7" Single: Released Feb '87, on Rhythm King, by Mute Records. Catalogue no: **LEFT 4**
12" Single: Released Feb '87, on Rhythm King, by Mute Records. Catalogue no: **LEFT 4T**

Romeo And Juliet

LOVE THEME
Tracks: / Love theme / Bohemian rhapsody.
7" Single: Released Nov '85, on Stiff, by Stiff Records. Catalogue no: **BUY 231**

Romeo, Jennifer

I'M NOT GUILTY
Tracks: / I'm not guilty / Medley connection (Owen Grey).
12" Single: Released Oct '86, on Pioneer International, Catalogue no: **PI 4**

YOU CAN WAKE UP WITH ME
Tracks: / You can wake up with me / One life to live.
12" Single: Released Aug '86, on Pioneer International, Catalogue no: **PI 3**

Romeo, Max

KEEP ON MOVING
Tracks: / Keep on moving.
7" Single: Released Oct '88, on Wackies, Catalogue no: **NJ 24**

WET DREAM
Tracks: / Wet dream.
7" Single: Released May '69, on Unity, Deleted '72. Catalogue no: **UN 503**

WET DREAM (OLD GOLD)
Tracks: / Wet dream / She's but a little girl.
7" Single: Released Jul '82, on Old Gold, by Old Gold Records. Catalogue no: **OG 9100**

Romeo & Rose

EBONY AND IVORY
Tracks: / Ebony and ivory / Jamaican child.
12" Single: Released Apr '82, on Seara, Catalogue no: **SEA 3**

Romeo Street Gang

HEAVY HOUSE (MONEY TALKS)
Tracks: / Heavy house (money talks).
12" Single: Released Jan '88, on Jungle, by Jungle Records. Catalogue no: **JUNG 36T**

Romeo, Victor

I WANT YOUR LOVE
Tracks: / I want your love / Art of acid.
12" Single: Released 6 Aug '88, on Dance Mania, Catalogue no: **DM 013**

Romeo Void

GIRL IN TROUBLE (IS A TEMPORARY THING), A
Tracks: / Girl in trouble (is a temporary thing), A / Going to neon.
7" Single: Released Oct '84, on 415 Records, Catalogue no: **A 4756**

NEVER SAY NEVER
Tracks: / Never say never / Flashflood.
7" Single: Released Sep '82, on CBS, by CBS Records. Deleted Sep '85. Catalogue no: **A 2733**

SAY NO
Tracks: / Say no / Six days and one / Out on my own.
7" Single: Released Jan '85, on CBS, by CBS Records. Catalogue no: **A 5028**
12" Single: Released Jan '85, on CBS, by CBS Records. Catalogue no: **TA5028**

Romeo's Daughter

DON'T BREAK MY HEART
Tracks: / Don't break my heart.
7" Single: Released Oct '88, on Jive, by Zomba Records. Catalogue no: **JIVE 186**
12" Single: Released Oct '88, on Jive, by Zomba Records. Catalogue no: **JIVET 186**

I CRY MYSELF TO SLEEP
Tracks: / I cry myself to sleep at night.
CD 5": Released Feb '89, on Jive, by Zomba Records. Catalogue no: **JIVECD 194**
7" Single: Released Feb '89, on Jive, by Zomba Records. Catalogue no: **JIVE 194**
12" Single: Released Feb '89, on Jive, by Zomba Records. Catalogue no: **JIVET 194**

Romi & Jazz

LOVE CRIME
Tracks: / Love crime.
7" Single: Released Jul '89, on Chrysalis, by Chrysalis Records. Catalogue no: **CHS 3344**
12" Single: Released Jul '89, on Chrysalis, by Chrysalis Records. Catalogue no: **CHS 12 3344**

PEOPLE IN THE HOUSE
Tracks: / People in the house / Believe in love / People in the house (Bhangra beat mix) (12" & Cassingle only.).
7" Single: Released Sep '88, on Chrysalis, by Chrysalis Records. Catalogue no: **CHS 3304**
12" Single: Released Sep '88, on Chrysalis, by Chrysalis Records. Catalogue no: **CHS 123304**
Cassingle: Released Sep '88, on Chrysalis, by Chrysalis Records. Catalogue no: **SHSC 3304**

REACH OUT
Tracks: / Reach out / Reach out (version).
12" Single: Released 14 May '88, on Arishma, by Arishma Records. Catalogue no: **ARIS 2001**
7" Single: Released 14 May '88, on Arishma, by Arishma Records. Catalogue no: **ARIS 0201**

Rondelle, Gordon

AUTUMN LEAVES
Tracks: / Autumn leaves.
7" Single: Released Sep '85, on Igloo, Catalogue no: **IG 101**

Rondo, Jean

YOU WANT I TO BELIEVE A LIE
Tracks: / You want I to believe a lie / Just for you.
12" Single: Released Dec '82, on R & H, Catalogue no: **RH 11**
12" Single: Released Dec '82, on R & H, Deleted Dec '85. Catalogue no: **RH 1 12**

Rondo, Johnny

LAS BICICLETAS
Tracks: / Las bicicletas.
7" Single: Released '78, on Chiltern Sound, Catalogue no: **RONDO 1**

Rondo Rondo

HELLO WORDS
Tracks: / Hello words / Missing persons.
7" Single: Released Sep '81, on Scoff, Catalogue no: **DT 009**

Rondo Veneziano

LA SERENISSIMA
Tracks: / La serenissima.
7" Single: Released Jun '84, on Ferroway, Catalogue no: **7 RON 1**

NOT QUITE JERUSALEM LOVE THEME
Tracks: / Not quite Jerusalem love theme.
7" Single: Released Mar '85, on Fanfare, by Captain Billy's Music. Catalogue no: **RONS 4**

ODISSEA
Tracks: / Odissea.
7" Single: Released Oct '85, on Fanfare, by Captain Billy's Music. Catalogue no: **RONS 5**

SAN MARCO
Tracks: / San Marco.
7" Single: Released Oct '84, on Ferroway, Catalogue no: **RONS 3**

SINFONIA PER UN ADDIO
Tracks: / Sinfonia per un addio.
7" Single: Released Nov '83, on Ferroway, Catalogue no: **7 RON 1**
12" Single: Released Nov '83, on Ferroway, Catalogue no: **12 RON 1**

VENICE
Tracks: / Venice.
7" Single: Released Jan '84, on Ferroway, Catalogue no: **7 RON 2**

Ronettes

Biographical details: Girl vocal trio formed in NYC in 1959: sister Veronica and Estelle Bennett, cousin Nedra Talley. Signed by Phil

Spector in 1963: fist single and biggest hit *Be My Baby* was number 2 USA/ 4 UK, spector's everything-but-the-kitchen-sink production style including castanets, strings etc. They alternated between aching teen ballads and uptempo boomers like the first; they had eight hits in the Hot 100 '63-6. Ronnie was married to Spector 1968-74; she went solo, sang with *Southside Johnny* and the Asbury Jukes, Bruce Springsteen. The group's hits are still classics of their kind. (Donald Clarke 4.2.88)..

BABY I LOVE YOU
Tracks: / Baby I love you.
7" Single: Released Jan '64, on London-American, Deleted '67. Catalogue no: **HLU 9826**

BE MY BABY
Tracks: / Be my baby.
7" Single: Released '80, on Phil Spector Int., by Chrysalis Records. Catalogue no: **LR 8245**
7" Single: Released Oct '63, on London-American, Deleted '66. Catalogue no: **HLU 9793**

BEST PART OF BREAKING UP
Tracks: / Best part of breaking up.
7" Single: Released Aug '64, on London-American, Deleted '67. Catalogue no: **HLU 9905**

DO I LOVE YOU
Tracks: / Do I love you / Breaking up.
7" Single: Released Oct '64, on London-American, Deleted '67. Catalogue no: **HLU 9922**
7" Single: Released Oct '81, on Polydor, by Polydor Ltd. Deleted '85. Catalogue no: **POSP 377**

Roni

CLEAN UP
Tracks: / Clean up.
12" Single: Released Jul '85, on Love Shark, Catalogue no: **LS 02**

LOVERS AFFAIR
Tracks: / Lovers affair.
12" Single: Released May '89, on Briggie C, Catalogue no: **BC 006**

Ronnie Can You Hear

VROOM FOR ROMANCE
Tracks: / Vroom for romance.
7" Single: Released Jun '85, on Ronnie, Catalogue no: **SPOON 1**

Ronnie & The Raiders

MIDDLE OF THE HOUSE
Tracks: / Middle of the house / Eileen Eileen.
7" Single: Released Jun '85, on Da Doo Ron Ron, by Da Doo Ron Ron Records. Deleted '88. Catalogue no: **RON 002**

Ronnie & Yuri

SATELLITE ZAP
Tracks: / Satellite zap / Zap warp.
12" Single: Released Jun '85, on Zap International, by Zap International Records. Catalogue no: **ZAPX 2**

Ronny

COMPARE ME TO THE REST
Tracks: / Compare me to the rest.
7" Single: Released Sep '81, on Polydor, by Polydor Ltd. Deleted Sep '84. Catalogue no: **POSP 289**
12" Single: Released Sep '81, on Polydor, by Polydor Ltd. Deleted Sep '84. Catalogue no: **POSPX 289**

IF YOU WANT ME TO STAY
Tracks: / If you want me to stay.
12" Single: Released Apr '81, on Polydor, by Polydor Ltd. Deleted '85. Catalogue no: **POSPX 247**
7" Single: Released Apr '81, on Polydor, by Polydor Ltd. Deleted '85. Catalogue no: **POSP 247**

Ronson, Mick

BILLY PORTER
Tracks: / Billy Porter / Slaughter on 10th Avenue.
7" Single: Released May '82, on RCA Golden Grooves, by BMG Records (UK). Catalogue no: **GOLD 546**

Ronstadt, Linda

Biographical details: Linda Marie Ronstadt was born in 1946 in Tuscon, Arizona. She made three LPs on Capitol with the Stone Poneys (trio with two guitarists, backing musicians on disc) incl. top 20 hit *Different Drum*; her solo album on Capitol established her as a counry rock vocalist with a gorgeous gospel-influenced voice. *Linda Ronstadt* in 1972 included backing by all four original Eagles. She changed labels to Asylum with producer Pete Asher; *Don't Cry Now* '73 made top 50 LPs without a big hit single; *Heart Like A Wheel* appeared on Capitol, reached number one in 1974 with two big hit singles; *Prisoners In Disguise* and *Hasten Down The Wind* 1975-6 were top 5 albums; *Simple Dreams* and *Living In The USA* 1977-78 were number ones; *Mad Love* in 1980 was number three. *Get Closer* in 1982 slipped a bit. Three singles, five LPs were hit s in the UK. Her relationship with then-Govenor Jerry Brown of California was in the news late '70s. Her appearance on stage in Gilbert and Sullivan's Pirates Of Penzance was praised; she switched to songs by George Gershwin, Irving Berlin, Billy Stayhorn etc For *What's New, Lush Life, For Sentimental Reasons* 1983-86, with arrangements by Nelson Riddle; her style was hopelessly wrong for these kinds of songs, but the albums were all hits. She also sang on Philip Glass's LP *Songs From Liquid Days* '85 on CBS, joined Dolly Parton and Emmylou Harris in the long-awaited *Trio* album in 1987: singing lead on Linda Thompson's beautiful *Telling Me Lies* she was back where she belonged. (Donald Clarke 4.2.88)..

ALISON
Tracks: / Alison.
7" Single: Released May '79, on Asylum, by WEA Records. Deleted '82. Catalogue no: **K 13149**

BACK IN THE USA
Tracks: / Back in the USA.
7" Single: Released '79, on Atlantic, by WEA Records. Catalogue no: **K 13133**

BLUE BAYOU
Tracks: / Blue bayou.
7" Single: Released Jan '78, on Asylum, by WEA Records. Deleted '81. Catalogue no: **K 13106**

GET CLOSER (SINGLE)
Tracks: / Get closer / Sometimes you just can't win.
7" Single: Released Nov '82, on Asylum, by WEA Records. Catalogue no: **969 948 7**

HOW DO I MAKE YOU
Tracks: / How do I make you / Rambler gambler.
7" Single: Released Feb '80, on Elektra, by Elektra Records (UK). Deleted Feb '83. Catalogue no: **K 12419**

HURT SO BAD
Tracks: / Hurt so bad / Justine.
7" Single: Released Jun '80, on Elektra Asylum, by Elektra Records (USA). Deleted Jun '83. Catalogue no: **K 12444**

I KNEW YOU WHEN
Tracks: / I knew you when / Talk to me of Mendocino.
12" Single: Released Jan '83, on Elektra, by Elektra Records (UK). Catalogue no: **E 9853T**
7" Single: Released Jan '83, on Elektra, by Elektra Records (UK). Catalogue no: **E 9853**

SOMEWHERE OUT THERE (See also Ingram, Richard)
Tracks: / Somewhere out there (a) / Somewhere out there (b) / Somewhere out there (fievels version) (On Picture disc only.) / Somewhere out there (instrumental) (On Picture disc only.).
7" Single: Released Jun '87, on MCA, by MCA Records. Catalogue no: **MCA 1172**
12" Single: Released Jun '87, on MCA, by MCA Records. Catalogue no: **MCAS 1172**
7" Pic: Released Jun '87, on MCA, by MCA Records. Catalogue no: **MCAP 1132**

TELL HIM
Tracks: / Tell him.
12" Single: Released Apr '83, on Elektra, by Elektra Records (UK). Catalogue no: **E 9877T**
7" Single: Released Mar '83, on Elektra, by Elektra Records (UK). Catalogue no: **E 9877**

TRACKS OF MY TEARS
Tracks: / Tracks of my tears.
7" Single: Released May '76, on Asylum, by WEA Records. Deleted '79. Catalogue no: **K 13034**

Rooftop Singers

WALK RIGHT IN
Tracks: / Walk right in.
7" Single: Released Jan '63, on Fontana, by Phonogram Ltd. Deleted '66. Catalogue no: **TF 271700**

Room

100 YEARS
Tracks: / 100 years / Whole world sings.
7" Single: Released Dec '82, on Red Flame (1), by Red Flame Records. Catalogue no: **RF 715**

IN SICKNESS AND HEALTH
Tracks: / In sickness and in health.
7" Single: Released Jul '81, on Box, Catalogue no: **BOX 003**

JACKPOT JACK
Tracks: / Jackpot Jack.
12" Single: Released Mar '85, on Red Flame (1), by Red Flame Records. Catalogue no: **RF 1242**

NEW DREAMS FOR OLD
Tracks: / New dreams for old.
7" Single: Released Jun '84, on Red Flame (1), by Red Flame Records. Catalogue no: **RFB 40**
12" Single: Released Jun '84, on Red Flame (1), by Red Flame Records. Catalogue no: **RFB 4012**

PEEL SESSIONS:ROOM
12" Single: Released Nov '88, on Strange Fruit, by Strange Fruit Records. Catalogue no: **SFPS 062**

THINGS HAVE LEARNT TO WALK THAT SHOULD...
Tracks: / Things have learnt to walk that should... / Dreams of flying.
7" Single: Released May '82, on Red Flame (1), by Red Flame Records. Catalogue no: **RF 703**

Room 101

ONE BY ONE
Tracks: / One by one / Tokyo nights.
7" Single: Released May '85, on Red Bus, by Red Bus Records. Catalogue no: **RBUS 2200**
12" Single: Released May '85, on Red Bus, by Red Bus Records. Catalogue no: **RBUSL 2200**
7" Single: Released Nov '83, on Norwood, by Norwood Records. Catalogue no: **S101**

TOKYO NIGHTS
Tracks: / Tokyo nights / I'm not your kind.
7" Single: Released Mar '84, on Norwood, by Norwood Records. Catalogue no: **ERL 5102**

Roots Foundation

HERE COMES THE SUN
Tracks: / Here comes the sun.
7" Single: Released Aug '81, on Lagos International, by L.A. International Records Ltd.. Catalogue no: **LIP 2**

Roots, Junior

LOSING YOU
Tracks: / Losing you.
12" Single: Released Aug '82, on Exile, Catalogue no: **EX 006**

Roots, Levi

IT A FI BUM
Tracks: / It a fi bum.
7" Single: Released Nov '84, on Conqueror, Catalogue no: **CON 003**

SHOULDER MOVE
Tracks: / Shoulder move.
12" Single: Released Aug '84, on Scom, Catalogue no: **BD 006**

Roots, Peter

MAKE IT WITH YOU
Tracks: / Make it with you.
12" Single: Released Jul '88, on Charm, by Charm Records. Catalogue no: **CRT 20**

Roots, Puddy

KING DISCOTHEQUE
Tracks: / King discotheque.
12" Single: Released Nov '84, on Greensleeves, by Greensleeves Records. Catalogue no: **GRED 161**

Roots Radics

I'M NOT A KING
Tracks: / I'm not a king / Earsay.
7" Single: Released Feb '85, on Kingdom, by Kingdom Records. Deleted '86. Catalogue no: **KV 8032**

Roots Rebel

GIVE THANKS
Tracks: / Give thanks.
12" Single: Released Oct '82, on Off-Beat (1), Catalogue no: **OB 1**

Roots, Stevie

HOW COULD I LIVE
Tracks: / How could I live.
12" Single: Released May '89, on Right Vibes, Catalogue no: **RV 001**

Roots Uprising

BEAUTIFUL MUSIC
Tracks: / Beautiful music
7" Single: Released '87, on UNKNOWN, Deleted Jun '89. Catalogue no: **TRI 3421**

JAMMING MASTER BLASTER
Tracks: / Jamming master blaster.
7" Single: Released '87, on UNKNOWN, Deleted Jun '89. Catalogue no: **TRI 4010**

Rope, Harry

LAUGHING INSIDE
Tracks: / Laughing inside / Laughing inside (version).
7" Single: Released 27 Feb '88, on Regal, Catalogue no: **HR 1**

Ropejump, Vic

MCENROE
Tracks: / McEnroe.
7" Single: Released Jul '81, on Surrey Sound, Catalogue no: **HMS 7**

Rori

WILD GIRL
Tracks: / Wild girl.
7" Single: Released Dec '85, on WEA, by WEA Records. Catalogue no: **W 8978**

Rorschach

TWO BUSTED FLIPPERS
Tracks: / Two busted flippers.
7" Single: Released Apr '89, on Big Truck, Catalogue no: **TRUCK 1**

Ros, Patrick

SEND ME YOUR TEARS
Tracks: / Send me your tears / When you're lonely.
7" Single: Released Feb '84, on Magic (1), by Submarine Records. Catalogue no: **MAGIC 11**

SONG OF LOVE
Tracks: / Song of love / Only the heart.
7" Single: Released Sep '83, on Magic (1), by Submarine Records. Catalogue no: **MAGIC 7**

Rosanne

THIS IS THE NIGHT
Tracks: / This is the night / Dallas, Theme from.
12" Single: Released Sep '85, on ACA, Catalogue no: **ACA 001**
12" Single: Released Aug '85, on Futura (1), Catalogue no: **FUT 001**
7" Single: Released Aug '85, on Futura (1), Catalogue no: **FUT 7001**

Rosario, Ralphi

I WANT YOU
Tracks: / I want you / I want you (version).
12" Single: Released Jan '88, on Jack Trax, Catalogue no: **12JTRAX 9**

IN THE NIGHT
Tracks: / In the night.
7" Single: Released Oct '88, on Hotmix (USA), Catalogue no: **HMF 110**

Roscoe

THIS TIME
Tracks: / This time / Love on track.
7" Single: Released Jul '88, on Zebra Int., by Zebra International Records. Catalogue no: **ZBR 2**
12" Single: Released Jul '88, on Zebra Int., by Zebra International Records. Catalogue no: **ZBR 122**

Rose

KITES
Tracks: / Voodoo / Kites.
7" Single: Released Nov '86, on Ratpack, Catalogue no: **12 RPC 003**

Rose, Avis

WOMAN IN LOVE
Tracks: / Woman in love / Rankin' Bogart.
12" Single: Released Oct '82, on Real Wax, Catalogue no: **RW 102**

Rose Brothers

WALL TO WALL FREAKS
Tracks: / Wall to wall (inst).
12" Single: Released Nov '86, on Affair, Catalogue no: **TART 6**
7" Single: Released Nov '86, on Affair, Catalogue no: **TARTS 6**

Rose, David

Biographical details: David Rose was born in 1910 in London and went to he USA at age 4. He became one of the most successful studio musicians, a composer, arranger and conductor. He was married to Martha Raye, then Judy Garland. His instumental *Holiday For Strings* presaged the era of the 'popular instumental' of the early '50s: recorded earlier, it was a big hit in 1943, during a recording band caused by a musicians' strike against the record companies which helped destroy the Big Band Era. Lesser hits in the '50s on MGM (where he backed Connie Francis on her hits) including Andre Previn's *Like Young* in 1959 with Previn on piano; then he reached number one with *The Stripper* in 1962, a brilliant piece of work: it is now impossible to imagine strippers without it. (Donald Clarke 4.2.88)..

STRIPPER, THE (OLD GOLD)
Tracks: / Stripper, The / Every time we say goodbye.
7" Single: Released Jun '88, on Old Gold, by Old Gold Records. Catalogue no: **OG 9451**

Rose Marie

ALL THE LOVE (IN ALL THE WORLD)

Tracks: / All the love (in all the world) / When your old wedding ring was new.
12" Single: Released Dec '85, on A.1, by A.1 Records. Deleted Nov '88. Catalogue no: **12 A1 292**
7" Single: Released Oct '85, on A.1, by A.1 Records. Deleted Nov '88. Catalogue no: **A1 292**

IF I HAD MY LIFE TO LIVE OVER
Tracks: / If I had my life to live over.
7" Single: Released Apr '85, on A.1, by A.1 Records. Deleted Nov '88. Catalogue no: **A1 290**

I'M COMING HOME
Tracks: / I'm coming home.
12" Single: Released Nov '86, on A.1, by A.1 Records. Catalogue no: **12 A1 296**
7" Single: Released Nov '86, on A.1, by A.1 Records. Catalogue no: **A1 296**

LET THE REST OF THE WORLD GO BY
Tracks: / Let the rest of the world go by.
7" Single: Released Oct '84, on A.1, by A.1 Records. Catalogue no: **A1 289**

SO LUCKY (SINGLE)
Tracks: / Danny Boy.
7" Single: Released Mar '87, on A.1, by A.1 Records. Catalogue no: **A1 298**
7" Single: Released May '86, on A.1, by A.1 Records. Deleted Nov '88. Catalogue no: **A1 293**

WAY OLD FRIENDS DO
Tracks: / Way old friends do, The / Abide with me.
7" Single: Released Nov '88, on A.1, by A.1 Records. Catalogue no: **A1 309**

WHEN I LEAVE MY WORLD BEHIND
Tracks: / When I leave the world behind.
7" Single: Released Nov '83, on A.1, by A.1 Records. Deleted '86. Catalogue no: **284**

WHILE I WAS MAKING LOVE TO YOU (EP)
Tracks: / While I was making love to you.
7" Single: Released Apr '82, on Ritz, by Ritz Records. Catalogue no: **RITZ 014**

WHO'S SORRY NOW
Tracks: / Who's sorry now.
7" Single: Released Oct '87, on A.1, by A.1 Records. Catalogue no: **A1 301**

Rose, Michael

BOGUS BADGE
Tracks: / Bogus badge.
12" Single: Released Nov '85, on Germaine, Catalogue no: **DG 121985**

BORN FREE
Tracks: / Born free.
12" Single: on Attack, Deleted '88. Catalogue no: **TACK 7**

GUESS WHO'S COMING TO DINNER
Tracks: / Guess who's coming to dinner / Guess who's coming to dinner (dub version).
7" Single: Released May '82, on Oval, by Oval Records. Catalogue no: **OVAL 1008**

Rose, Mykal

DUMP THE LUMP
Tracks: / Dump the lump.
12" Single: Released Aug '89, on Final Vinyl, Catalogue no: **12FV 001**

Rose Of Avalanche

ALWAYS THERE
Tracks: / Always there / Waiting for the sun / Majesty / Mainline man (Only on 12" remix version.).
Note: Mainline man is an extra track only available on 12" remix limited edition.
7" Single: Released Feb '87, on Fire, by Fire Records. Catalogue no: **BLAZE 18**
12" Single: Released Feb '87, on Fire, by Fire Records. Catalogue no: **BLAZE 18T**

GODDESS
Tracks: / Goddess.
12" Single: Released Sep '85, on Leeds Independent (LIL), by Revolver Records. Catalogue no: **LIL 12002**

L.A. RAIN
Tracks: / L.A. rain / Rise to the groove / Conceal me.
7" Single: Released May '85, on Leeds Independent (LIL), by Revolver Records. Catalogue no: **LIL 1**
12" Single: Released May '85, on Leeds Independent (LIL), by Revolver Records. Catalogue no: **LIL 12001**

NEVER ANOTHER SUNSET (SINGLE)
Tracks: / Never another sunset.
7" Single: Released Feb '89, on Avalantic, Catalogue no: **AVE 002**
12" Single: Released Feb '89, on Avalantic, Catalogue no: **AVE 002T**

TOO MANY CASTLES IN THE SKY
Tracks: / Velveteen / Who cares / Just like yesterday / Too many castles in the sky / Assassin / Dizzy Miss Lizzy (Track on 12" version only.).
7" Single: Released May '86, on Fire, by Fire Records. Catalogue no: **BLAZE 9**
12" Single: Released May '86, on Fire, by Fire Records. Catalogue no: **BLAZE 9T**
7" EP: Released May '87, on Fire, by Fire Records. Catalogue no: **BLAZE 19 EP**

VELVETEEN
Tracks: / Velveteen / Who cares / Just like yesterday (Track on 12" version only.).
7" Single: Released Sep '86, on Fire, by Fire Records. Catalogue no: **BLAZE 14**

WORLD IS OURS, THE
Tracks: / World is ours, The.
7" Single: Released Dec '88, on Avalantic, Catalogue no: **AVE 001**
12" Single: Released Dec '88, on Avalantic, Catalogue no: **AVE 001T**

Rose Of Romance Orch

TARA'S THEME From Gone With The Wind
Tracks: / Tara's theme / Masquerade.
7" Single: Released Dec '81, on BBC, by BBC Records & Tapes. Deleted '87. Catalogue no: **RESL 108**

WHITER SHADE OF PALE
Tracks: / Whiter shade of pale, A / Keepsake.
7" Single: Released Sep '82, on Moon, by Moon Records (UK). Catalogue no: **LUNA 3**

Rose Of Victory

SUFFRAGETTE CITY
Tracks: / Suffragette city / Overdrive.
7" Single: Released Jul '83, on No Future, Deleted '87. Catalogue no: **01 24**

Rose, Patrick

I WANNA GET NEXT TO YOU
Tracks: / I wanna get next to you / I don't wanna be alone (Donovan Bramwell.).
12" Single: Released Aug '86, on Sea View, Catalogue no: **SV 12**

ROSES ARE RED
Tracks: / Roses are red.
12" Single: Released Aug '88, on Sea View, Catalogue no: **SV 16**

SPECIAL
Tracks: / Special.
7" Single: Released Jul '88, on Sea View, Catalogue no: **SV 14**

YOU ARE MY LADY
Tracks: / You are my lady / You are my lady (version).
12" Single: Released Dec '85, on Sea View, Catalogue no: **SVR 11**

Rose, Paul

SAY HELLO
Tracks: / Say hello.
12" Single: Released Dec '88, on 20/20, by 20/20 Records. Catalogue no: **TT 122021**

Rose Royce

BEST LOVE
Tracks: / Best love / Talk to me.
7" Single: Released Apr '82, on Epic, by CBS Records. Catalogue no: **EPC A 2238**

CAR WASH
Tracks: / Car wash / Is it love you're after?.
7" Single: Released May '88, on MCA, by MCA Records. Catalogue no: **MCA 1253**
12" Single: Released May '88, on MCA, by MCA Records. Catalogue no: **MCAT 1253**
7" Single: Released Dec '76, on MCA, by MCA Records. Deleted '79. Catalogue no: **MCA 267**

CARWASH (OLD GOLD)
Tracks: / Car wash / I wanna get next to you / Which way is up, Theme from.
12" Single: Released 30 May '89, on Old Gold, by Old Gold Records. Catalogue no: **OG 4117**
7" Single: Released Apr '83, on Old Gold, by Old Gold Records. Catalogue no: **OG 9322**

DO YOUR DANCE
Tracks: / Do your dance.
7" Single: Released Sep '77, on Whitfield (USA), by WEA Records. Deleted '80. Catalogue no: **K 17006**

GOLDEN TOUCH (SINGLE)
Tracks: / Golden touch / Help yourself.
12" Single: Released Feb '81, on Whitfield (USA), by WEA Records. Catalogue no: **K 17747T**
7" Single: Released Feb '81, on Whitfield (USA), by WEA Records. Catalogue no: **K 17747**

I WANNA GET NEXT TO YOU (SINGLE)
Tracks: / I wanna get next to you / Put your money where your mouth is / Car wash 88 mix (on 12" only.).
CD 5": Released Jul '88, on MCA, by MCA Records. Catalogue no: **DMCA 1274**
7" Single: Released Jul '88, on MCA, by MCA Records. Catalogue no: **MCA 1274**
12" Single: Released Jul '88, on MCA, by MCA Records. Catalogue no: **MCAT 1274**
7" Single: Released Mar '77, on MCA, by MCA Records. Deleted '80. Catalogue no: **MCA 278**

I WONDER WHERE YOU ARE TONIGHT
Tracks: / I wonder where you are tonight.
7" Single: Released Aug '79, on Whitfield (USA), by WEA Records. Catalogue no: **K 17463**

I'M IN LOVE
Tracks: / I'm in love.
7" Single: Released Jan '79, on Warner Bros., by WEA Records. Catalogue no: **K 17291**

IS IT LOVE YOU'RE AFTER (SINGLE)
Tracks: / Is it love you're after.
7" Single: Released Nov '79, on Whitfield (USA), by WEA Records. Deleted '82. Catalogue no: **K 17456**

IT MAKES YOU FEEL LIKE DANCIN'
Tracks: / It makes you feel like dancin'.
7" Single: Released May '78, on Warner Bros., by WEA Records. Deleted '81. Catalogue no: **K 17148**

JUST MY IMAGINATION
Tracks: / Just my imagination / You're my piece of mind.
7" Single: Released 20 Feb '88, on Carrere, Catalogue no: **CAR 423**
12" Single: Released 20 Feb '88, on Carrere, Catalogue no: **CART 423**

LONELY ROAD
Tracks: / Lonely road / Doesn't have to be this way.
12" Single: Released Aug '87, on Carrere, Catalogue no: **CART 417**
7" Single: Released Aug '87, on Carrere, Catalogue no: **CAR 417**

LOVE DON'T LIVE HERE ANYMORE
Tracks: / Love don't live here anymore.
7" Single: Released Sep '78, on Whitfield (USA), by WEA Records. Catalogue no: **K 17236**

LOVE ME RIGHT NOW
Tracks: / Love me right now.
7" Single: Released Apr '85, on Streetwave, Deleted '88. Catalogue no: **KHAN 39**

MAGIC TOUCH
Tracks: / Magic touch / Safe and warm.
7" Single: Released Sep '84, on Streetwave, Deleted '87. Catalogue no: **KHAN 21**

OOH BOY
Tracks: / Ooh boy / What you been waitin' for.
7" Single: Released Feb '80, on Whitfield (USA), by WEA Records. Catalogue no: **K 17575**

PERFECT LOVER (IMPORT SINGLE)
7" Single: Released Mar '89, on Omni (USA), by First String Records (USA). Catalogue no: **086 452**

POP YOU FINGERS
Tracks: / Pop you fingers / I wonder where you are tonight.
12" Single: Released Aug '80, on Warner Bros., by WEA Records. Deleted Aug '83. Catalogue no: **K 17674T**

PUT YOUR MONEY WHERE YOUR MOUTH IS
Tracks: / Put your money where your mouth is.
7" Single: Released Jan '77, on MCA, by MCA Records. Deleted '80. Catalogue no: **MCA 259**

ROSE ROYCE EXPRESS
Tracks: / Rose Royce express.
7" Single: Released Nov '81, on Warner Bros., by WEA Records. Deleted '84. Catalogue no: **K 17875**
12" Single: Released Nov '81, on Warner Bros., by WEA Records. Deleted '84. Catalogue no: **K 17875T**

WISHING ON A STAR
Tracks: / Wishing on a star / Love don't live here anymore.
7" Single: Released Jan '78, on Warner Bros., by WEA Records. Catalogue no: **K 17060**

WISHING ON A STAR (OLD GOLD)
Tracks: / Wishing on a star.
7" Single: Released Sep '85, on Old Gold, by Old Gold Records. Catalogue no: **OG 9517**

Rose, Samantha

GO AWAY LITTLE GIRL
Tracks: / Go away little girl / You'll never get....
12" Single: Released May '82, on Third World, Catalogue no: **TWDIS 500**

KISS YOU ALL OVER
Tracks: / Kiss you all over / Baby all is you.
7" Single: Released Apr '81, on Limo, Deleted Apr '84. Catalogue no: **LIMO 2**

Rose Tattoo

ASSAULT AND BATTERY (SINGLE)
Tracks: / Assault and battery / Astra wally.
7" Single: Released Dec '81, on Carrere, Deleted Dec '84. Catalogue no: **CAR 220**

BAD BOY FOR LOVE
Tracks: / Bad boy for love / Tramp.
7" Single: Released May '81, on Carrere, Deleted May '86. Catalogue no: **CAR 191**

IT'S GONNA WORK ITSELF OUT
Tracks: / It's gonna work itself out.
7" Single: Released Mar '83, on Carrere, Catalogue no: **CAR 263**

ROCK 'N' ROLL IS KING
Tracks: / Rock 'n' roll is king / If I had you first.
7" Single: Released Oct '81, on Carrere, Deleted Oct '84. Catalogue no: **CAR 210**

ROCK'N'ROLL OUTLAW (SINGLE)
Tracks: / Rock 'n' roll outlaw / Remedy.
7" Single: Released Jul '81, on Carrere, Deleted '84. Catalogue no: **CAR 200**

Rose-Capri

PASSION
Tracks: / Passion.
12" Single: Released Feb '89, on Silicon, by Silicon Records. Catalogue no: **SSM 005**

Rosehips

I SHOULDN'T HAVE TO SAY
Tracks: / I shouldn't have to say.
7" Single: Released Jul '87, on Subway, by Subway Records. Catalogue no: **SUBWAY 16**
12" Single: Released Jul '87, on Subway, by Subway Records. Catalogue no: **SUBWAY 16T**

ROOM IN YOUR HEART
Tracks: / Room in your heart.
7" Single: Released Mar '87, on Subway, by Subway Records. Catalogue no: **SUBWAY 10**
12" Single: Released Mar '87, on Subway, by Subway Records. Catalogue no: **SUBWAY 10T**

SYMPATHY FOR THE ROSEHIPS
Tracks: / Sympathy for the Rosehips.
12" Single: Released Feb '89, on Chaotic Brilliance, Catalogue no: **BRILL 1**

Roselli, Jimmy

SAY IT ISN'T SO
Tracks: / Addio amor.
7" Single: Released Nov '86, on First Night, by First Night Records. Catalogue no: **SCORE 5**

THERE, I'VE SAID IT AGAIN
Tracks: / There, I've said it again / Angelina.
7" Single: Released Sep '87, on First Night, by First Night Records. Catalogue no: **SCORE 11**

WHEN YOUR OLD WEDDING RING WAS NEW (SINGLE)
Tracks: / When your wedding ring was new / Say it isn't so / Addio amor.
12" Single: Released 23 May '87, on First Night, by First Night Records. Catalogue no: **SCOREC 9**
7" Single: Released Nov '82, on A.1, by A.1 Records. Deleted '87. Catalogue no: **A1 282**
7" Single: Released 23 May '87, on First Night, by First Night Records. Catalogue no: **SCORE 9**
Cassingle: Released 30 May '87, on First Night, by First Night Records. Catalogue no: **SCORE 9C**

Rosemary

SHOOBY DOOBY DOO
Tracks: / Shooby dooby doo.
12" Single: Released May '83, on M & R, Catalogue no: **DISO 1**

WISHING ON A STAR
Tracks: / Wishing on a star / Way we were, The.
12" Single: Released Feb '83, on Negus Roots, Catalogue no: **NERT 016**

Rosemary, Althea

MY BABY JUST CARES FOR ME
Tracks: / My baby just cares for me.
12" Single: Released Mar '82, on SS Music, Catalogue no: **SSMD 001**

TONIGHT IS THE NIGHT
Tracks: / Tonight is the night / You're unique.
7" Single: Released Jul '82, on SS Music, Deleted '85. Catalogue no: **ISB 017**
12" Single: Released Jul '82, on SS Music, Catalogue no: **SSMD 017**

Rosemary's children

SOUTHERN FIELDS
Tracks: / Southern fields / (Whatever happened to) Alice?.
7" Single: Released Jul '86, on El, by Cherry

Red Records. Catalogue no: **GPO 12**

Rosen, Michael

MINERS STRIKE RAP, THE
Tracks: / Miners' strike rap, The.
7" Single: Released Feb '85, on Pit, Catalogue no: **PIT 100**

Rosetta Stone

HIDING FROM LOVE
Tracks: / Hiding from love.
7" Single: Released Jan '81, on Limo, Deleted '83. Catalogue no: **LIMO 1**

STRAIGHT FROM THE HEART
Tracks: / Straight from the heart / Too bad.
7" Single: Released Nov '82, on Sire (USA), Catalogue no: **929935 7**

WATCH OUT I'M BACK
Tracks: / Watch out I'm back.
7" Single: Released Sep '81, on Limo, Deleted '83. Catalogue no: **LIMO 6**

Ross, Diana

Biographical details: Born Diane Earle in Detroit in 1944, Ross was 20 when she rose to superstardom as lead singer with the Supremes: with their 12 US No 1 singles the Motown vocal trio were America's hottest act of the 60's.
Halfway through their historic string of smashes the group's label billing became Diana Ross & The Supremes in recognition of Ross's dominant talent and charisma. At the beginning of 1970 Tamla Motown decided to begin the new decade by launching her as a solo artist. Ross's first single was *Reach Out And Touch (Somebody's Hand)*, which received a lukewarm response at the time although it later became a mini-classic. The second offering, however, was the stunning *Ain't No Mountain High Enough*, writted and produced by Ashford and Simpson, who had orginally given the song to Marvin Gaye and Tammi Terrell in 1967. Ross's dramatic rendition climbed to No 1 in America and No 6 in Britain.
I'm Still Waiting, a less epic and more sugary but equally moving ballad, became a UK No 1 smash in 1971. Two years later, through careful planning by Motown chief Berry Gordy, Ross was transformed from a pop and soul star to an actress. She played the part of the great jazz singer Billie Holiday in the film Lady Sings The Blues. Though her later movies -- Mahogany ('76) and The Wiz ('78) -- were given hostile critical receptions, Lady Sings The Blues was acclaimed by journalists and public alike and helped to broaden her into an all-round showbiz superstar. Also in 1973 she collected her second solo US No 1 single with *Touch Me In The Morning*. Mahogany was not liked by reviewers but its theme song, *Do You Know Where You're Going To?*, provided Ross with another chart-topper in 1976. Within months it was followed by her fourth American No 1: *Love Hangover* was a funky disco workout whose success paved the way for Donna Summer's *I Feel Love* and several other dancefloor classics.
Ross's fifth US No 1 was a similarly streetwise piece of funk, 1980's *Upside Down*, written and produced by Bernard Edwards and Nile Rodgers, of Chic fame, which gave her her biggest American hit since the Supremes' *Baby Love*. In 1981 Ross ended her 20-year association with Motown and linked up with RCA for North America and EMI/Capitol for the rest of the world. She quit Tamla in style with her duet with Lionel Richie, *Endless Love*, which logged nine weeks on top of the Billboard Hot Hundred and gave Gordy's company its biggest-ever US hit.
Her post-Motown career continued with an endless stream of hits and she worked with big-name writers and producers including Michael Jackson, Daryl Hall and the Bee Gees. In 1985 she was lifted out of a slight slump by two simultaneous hits. Her touching tribute to her old friend and Motown colleague, the late Marvin Gaye, reached the US Top Ten; penned and produced by Richie, it was entitled *Missing You*. At the same time she was one of many mega-stars who contributed her voice to USA For Africa's international chart-topper *We Are The World*. In Britain she became the first USA For Africa singer to return to the No 1 slot when *Chain Reaction* cruised to the top of the UK chart in March 1986. This was a cut from her *Eaten Alive* album, written and produced by the Gibb Brothers, and gave her her first British chart-topper since 1971's *I'm Still Waiting*. (Bob MacDonald, March 1986.)
Diana Ross is a pop/soul vocalist and superstar: famous as lead singer of the supremes, she became the centerpiece when the trio's name was changed to 'Diana Ross And The Supremes'; she went solo in 1970 and had 33 Hot 100 hits in the US through 1985; she had duet hits with Marvin Gaye, later Lionel Richie (*Endless Love* was number one for nine weeks in the USA in 1981).
She had always been the favorite of Motown's Berry Gordy, who saw her as the ultimate Motown superstar; he obtained her first film role for her in *Lady Sings The Blues* (1972): as a biopic of Billie Holiday it was planned, but commercially successful, with a number one soundtrack album. Ross was nominated for an oscar. Her second film *Mahogany* was not very well recieved in 1975; there was something sad about Gordy directing her in what amounted to an old-fashioned Joan Crawford sort of vehicle. She played the Dorothy character in The Wiz in 1978 (a black remake of Wizard Of Oz, with a pre-immortal Michael Jackson in the cast); Ross was obviously too old. Her records are uneven whenever she tries to step out of her style which made her famous, but the star quality that Gordy recognised 25 years ago is still there. One of her best albums was *The Boss* in 1979. She left Motown for RCA in 1981 (Capitol in UK). *Eaten Alive* in 1985 was co-produced and largely written by Bee Gee Barry Gibb: the title track had Jackson's backing vocal, *Missing you* was dedicated to Gaye and produced by Ritchie, *Chain Reaction* barely made the Hot 100 in the USA but was a huge hit in the UK: it could have been a supremes track. (Donald Clarke 4.2.88).

This American singer and actress was born Diane Earle in Detroit in 1944, and was 20 years old when she rose to superstardom as lead vocalist of the Supremes. With their 12 US No.1 singles, the Motown vocal trio were America's hottest act of the Sixties. Halfway through the threesome's historic string of smashes, the group's label billing became Diana Ross & the Supremes in recognition of Ross's dominant talent and charisma. At the beginning of 1970, Tamla Motown decided to begin the new decade by launching her as a solo artist. Ross's first single was *Reach out and touch (somebody's hand)*, which received a lukewarm response at the time although it later became a mini-classic. The second offering, however, was the stunning *Ain't no mountain high enough*, written and produced by Ashford & Simpson, who had originally given the song to Marvin Gaye & Tammi Terell in 1967, Diana's dramatic rendition climbed to No.1 in America and No.6 in Britain.
I'm still waiting, a less epic and more sugary but equally moving ballad, became a No.1 smash in 1971. In 1973, through careful planning by Motown chief Berry Gordy, Diana was transformed from a pop and soul star to an actress. She played the role of legendary blues vocalist Billie Holiday in the musical movie *Lady sings the blues*. Though Ross' later cinematic ventures, *Mahogany* (1976) and *The wiz* (1978), were given a hostile critical reception, *Lady sings the blues* was acclaimed by journalists and public alike and helped to broaden Ross into an all-round showbusiness superstar. Also in 1973, she collected her second solo US No.1 single with *Touch me in the morning*. *Mahogany* was not liked by reviewers, but its theme song *Do you know where you're going to?* provided the Motown star with another chart-topper in 1976. Within months it was followed by her fourth solo American No.1 - but whereas the first three were all ballads, *Love hangover* was a funky disco workout, whose success paved the way for Donna Summer's *I feel love* and several other dancefloor classics. Ross' fifth American No.1 was a similarly streetwise slice of funk: 1980's *Upside down* was written and produced by Bernard Edwards & Nile Rodgers of Chic fame, and gave Diana her biggest US hit since the Supremes' *Baby love*.

In 1981 Ross ended her 20-year association with Motown, and linked up with RCA for North America and EMI/Capitol for the rest of the world.
She quit Tamla in style with *Endless love* - by logging nine weeks on top of the Billboard Hot 100, this Diana Ross/Lionel Richie duet gave Berry Gordy's company its biggest ever US hit. Diana's post-Motown career continued to provide her with an endless stream of hits, and she carried on working with big-name writers and producers including Michael Jackson, Daryl Hall and the Bee Gees. In 1985 Diana was lifted out of a slight slump by two simultaneous hits. Her touching tribute to her old friend and colleague at Motown, the late Marvin Gaye, reached the US Top 10; penned and produced by Richie, it was entitled *Missing you*. At the same time, she was one of the many megastars who contributed her voice to USA For Africa's international chart-topper *We are the world*.

In Britain she became the first USA For Africa vocalist to return to the No.1 slot, when *Chain reaction* cruised to the top of the UK chart in March 1986. This was a cut from her *Eaten alive* album, written and produced by the Gibb brothers. Though by no means the best of her 36 solo UK hit singles, the catchy *Chain reaction* was the record which provided the singer with her first British chart-topper since 1971's *I'm still waiting*. At the age of 41, Diana Ross proved yet again that she was the world's most enduring and successful female vocalist. (Bob MacDonald, 11.3.86)..

AIN'T NO MOUNTAIN HIGH ENOUGH (SINGLE)
Tracks: / Ain't no mountain high enough / It's my house / Boss, The (Available on 12" single only) / Remember me (Available on 12" single only.).
12" Single: Released Jul '86, on Tamla Motown, by Motown Records (UK). Catalogue no: **ZT 40804**
7" Single: Released Jul '86, on Tamla Motown, by Motown Records (UK). Catalogue no: **AB 40803**
7" Single: Released Sep '70, on Tamla Motown, by Motown Records (UK). Catalogue no: **TMG 751**

ALL OF MY LIFE
Tracks: / All of my life / Simple thing like love, A.
7" Single: Released Oct '81, on Motown, by BMG Records (UK). Deleted '83. Catalogue no: **TMG 880**

ALL OF YOU
Tracks: / All of you.
7" Single: Released Jun '84, on CBS, by CBS Records. Catalogue no: **A 4522**

BABY LOVE
Tracks: / Baby love / Stop in the name of love.
7" Single: Released Oct '81, on Motown, by BMG Records (UK). Catalogue no: **TMG 1044**
7" Single: Released Aug '74, on Tamla Motown, by Motown Records (UK). Deleted '77. Catalogue no: **TMG 915**

BOSS, THE (SINGLE)
Tracks: / Boss, The.
7" Single: Released Oct '81, on Motown, by BMG Records (UK). Deleted '83. Catalogue no: **TMG 1150**

CHAIN REACTION
Tracks: / Chain reaction / More and more / Chain reaction (Special dance remix) / Chain reaction (single version).
12" Single: Released Jan '86, on Capitol, by EMI Records. Catalogue no: **12CL 386**
7" Single: Released Jan '86, on Capitol, by EMI Records. Catalogue no: **CL 386**

CRYIN' MY HEART OUT FOR YOU
Tracks: / Crying my heart out for you / To love again.
7" Single: Released Oct '81, on Motown, by BMG Records (UK). Deleted '83. Catalogue no: **TMG 1233**

DIRTY LOOKS
Tracks: / Dirty looks / So close.
7" Single: Released 23 May '87, on EMI, by EMI Records. Deleted Apr '88. Catalogue no: **EM 2**
12" Single: Released 23 May '87, on EMI, by EMI Records. Deleted Apr '88. Catalogue no: **12 EM 2**

DIRTY LOOKS (REMIX)
Tracks: / Dirty looks / Dirty looks (bonus beat) / Dirty looks (inst).
12" Single: Released Jun '87, on EMI, by EMI Records. Deleted Oct '87. Catalogue no: **12EMP 2**

DO YOU KNOW WHERE YOU'RE GOING TO?
Tracks: / Do you know where you're going to?.
7" Single: Released Oct '81, on Motown, by BMG Records (UK). Catalogue no: **TMG 1010**
7" Single: Released Apr '76, on Tamla Motown, by Motown Records (UK). Deleted '79. Catalogue no: **TMG 1010**

DOOBEDOOD'NDOOBEDOOBED OOD'NDOOBE
Tracks: / Doobedood'ndoobe, doobedood'ndoobe.
7" Single: Released May '72, on Tamla Motown, by Motown Records (UK). Deleted '75. Catalogue no: **TMG 812**

EATEN ALIVE (SINGLE)
Tracks: / Eaten alive.
12" Single: Released Sep '85, on Capitol, by EMI Records. Deleted '88. Catalogue no: **12CL 372**
7" Single: Released Sep '85, on Capitol, by EMI Records. Deleted '88. Catalogue no: **CL 372**

ENDLESS LOVE
Tracks: / Endless love.
7" Single: Released Oct '81, on Motown, by BMG Records (UK). Catalogue no: **TMG 1240**

EXPERIENCE
Tracks: / Experience / Oh teacher.
12" Single: Released Apr '86, on Capitol, by EMI Records. Deleted '88. Catalogue no: **12CL 400**
7" Single: Released Apr '86, on Capitol, by EMI Records. Deleted '88. Catalogue no: **CL 400**

FOREVER CAME TODAY
Tracks: / Forever came today.
7" Single: Released Apr '68, on Tamla Motown, by Motown Records (UK). Deleted '71. Catalogue no: **TMG 650**

GETTIN' READY FOR LOVE
Tracks: / Gettin' ready for love.
7" Single: Released Oct '81, on Motown, by BMG Records (UK). Deleted '83. Catalogue no: **TMG 1090**

I SECOND THAT EMOTION
Tracks: / I second that emotion.
7" Single: Released Sep '69, on Tamla Motown, by Motown Records (UK). Deleted '72. Catalogue no: **TMG 709**

I THOUGHT IT TOOK A LITTLE TIME
Tracks: / I thought it took a little time.
7" Single: Released Jul '76, on Tamla Motown, by Motown Records (UK). Deleted '79. Catalogue no: **TMG 1032**

I'M COMING OUT
Tracks: / I'm coming out / Give up.
7" Single: Released Oct '81, on Motown, by BMG Records (UK). Deleted '83. Catalogue no: **TMG 1210**
12" Single: Released Oct '81, on Motown, by BMG Records (UK). Deleted '83. Catalogue no: **TMGT 1210**

I'M GONNA MAKE YOU LOVE ME
Tracks: / I'm gonna make you love me.
12" Single: Released Apr '85, on Motown, by BMG Records (UK). Catalogue no: **TMGT 991**
7" Single: Released Jan '69, on Tamla Motown, by Motown Records (UK). Deleted '72. Catalogue no: **TMG 685**
7" Single: Released Apr '85, on Motown, by BMG Records (UK). Catalogue no: **TMG 991**
7" Single: Released Oct '81, on Motown, by BMG Records (UK). Catalogue no: **TMG 1045**

I'M LIVING IN SHAME
Tracks: / I'm living in shame.
7" Single: Released Apr '69, on Tamla Motown, by Motown Records (UK). Deleted '72. Catalogue no: **TMG 695**

I'M STILL WAITING (SINGLE)
Tracks: / I'm still waiting / Touch me in the morning.
7" Single: Released Mar '83, on Motown, by BMG Records (UK). Catalogue no: **TMG 1041**
7" Single: Released Jul '71, on Tamla Motown, by Motown Records (UK). Deleted '74. Catalogue no: **TMG 781**

IN AND OUT OF LOVE
Tracks: / In and out of love.
7" Single: Released Nov '67, on Tamla Motown, by Motown Records (UK). Deleted '70. Catalogue no: **TMG 632**

IT'S MY HOUSE
Tracks: / It's my house.
12" Single: Released Oct '81, on Motown, by BMG Records (UK). Catalogue no: **TMGT 1169**
7" Single: Released Oct '81, on Motown, by BMG Records (UK). Catalogue no: **TMG 1169**

IT'S MY TURN
Tracks: / It's my turn / Sleepin'.
7" Single: Released Oct '81, on Motown, by BMG Records (UK). Deleted '83. Catalogue no: **TMG 1217**

IT'S NEVER TOO LATE
Tracks: / It's never too late / Endless love / Sweet surrender.
12" Single: Released Jul '82, on Capitol, by EMI Records. Deleted '88. Catalogue no: **12Cl 256**
7" Single: Released Jul '82, on Capitol, by EMI Records. Deleted '88. Catalogue no: **CL 256**

LAST TIME I SAW HIM (SINGLE)
Tracks: / Last time I saw him.
7" Single: Released May '74, on Tamla Motown, by Motown Records (UK). Deleted '77. Catalogue no: **TMG 893**

LOVE CHILD (SINGLE)
Tracks: / Love child.
7" Single: Released Nov '68, on Tamla Motown, by Motown Records (UK). Deleted '71. Catalogue no: **TMG 677**

LOVE HANGOVER
Tracks: / Love hangover.
7" Single: Released Oct '81, on Motown, by BMG Records (UK). Deleted '88. Catalogue no: **TMG 1024**
7" Single: Released Apr '85, on Motown, by BMG Records (UK). Catalogue no: **TMG 1380**
12" Single: Released Apr '85, on Motown, by BMG Records (UK). Catalogue no: **TMGT 1380**

LOVE HANGOVER (RE-RELEASE)

DIANA ROSS - MY OLD PIANO (Released on Motown)

Tracks: / Love hangover / Love hangover (instrumental) / Love hangover (urban remix) (Only on 12" version ZT 42348.) / Love hangover (urban dub) (Only on 12" version ZT 42348.).
7" Single: Released Nov '88, on Motown, by BMG Records (UK). Catalogue no: **ZB 42307**
12" Single: Released Nov '88, on Motown, by BMG Records (UK). Catalogue no: **ZT 42308**
CD 5": Released 21 Nov '88, on Motown, by BMG Records (UK). Catalogue no: **ZD 42308**
12" Single: Released Dec '88, on Motown, by BMG Records (UK). Catalogue no: **ZT 42348**

LOVE IS HERE AND NOW YOU'RE GONE
Tracks: / Love is here and now you're gone / Back in my arms again.
7" Single: Released Mar '83, on Motown, by BMG Records (UK). Catalogue no: **TMG 981**
7" Single: Released Mar '67, on Tamla Motown, by Motown Records (UK). Deleted '70. Catalogue no: **TMG 597**

LOVE ME
Tracks: / Love me.
7" Single: Released Sep '74, on Tamla Motown, by Motown Records (UK). Deleted '77. Catalogue no: **TMG 917**

LOVIN' LIVIN' AND GIVIN'
Tracks: / Lovin', livin' and givin'.
7" Single: Released Jul '78, on Tamla Motown, by Motown Records (UK). Deleted '81. Catalogue no: **TMG 1112**

MIRROR MIRROR
Tracks: / Mirror mirror.
12" Single: Released Jan '82, on Capitol, by EMI Records. Deleted Jan '85. Catalogue no: **12 CL 234**
7" Single: Released Jan '82, on Capitol, by EMI Records. Deleted '85. Catalogue no: **CL 234**

MISSING YOU
Tracks: / Missing you.
7" Single: Released Dec '84, on Capitol, by EMI Records. Deleted '88. Catalogue no: **CL 348**
12" Single: Released Mar '85, on Capitol, by EMI Records. Deleted '88. Catalogue no: **12CL 348**

MR LEE
Tracks: / Mr. Lee (Swing mix) (12" & CD single only.) / Mr. Lee (Swing edit) (12EM 73 & 7" only.) / Mr. Lee (Album version) / Mr. Lee (Rare groove version) (12EMX & CD single only.).
CD 5": Released Sep '88, on EMI, by EMI Records. Deleted Aug '89. Catalogue no: **CDEM 73**
12" Single: Released Sep '88, on EMI, by EMI Records. Deleted Aug '89. Catalogue no: **12EMX 73**
12" Single: Released Sep '88, on EMI, by EMI Records. Deleted Aug '89. Catalogue no: **12EM 73**
7" Single: Released Sep '88, on EMI, by EMI Records. Deleted Aug '89. Catalogue no: **EM 73**

MUSCLES
Tracks: / Muscles / I am me.
12" Single: Released Oct '82, on Capitol, by EMI Records. Deleted '88. Catalogue no: **12CL 268**
7" Single: Released Oct '82, on Capitol, by EMI Records. Deleted '88. Catalogue no: **CL 268**

MY OLD PIANO (See panel above)
Tracks: / My old piano / Where did we go wrong.
7" Single: Released Oct '81, on Motown, by BMG Records (UK). Deleted '83. Catalogue no: **TMG 1202**
12" Single: Released Apr '85, on Motown, by BMG Records (UK). Catalogue no: **TMGT 1387**
7" Single: Released Apr '85, on Motown, by BMG Records (UK). Catalogue no: **TMG 1387**

NO MATTER WHAT SIGN YOU ARE
Tracks: / No matter what sign you are.
7" Single: Released Jul '69, on Tamla Motown, by Motown Records (UK). Deleted '72. Catalogue no: **TMG 704**

NO ONE GETS THE PRIZE
Tracks: / No one gets the prize.
7" Single: Released Oct '81, on Motown, by BMG Records (UK). Deleted '83. Catalogue no: **TMG 1160**

OLD FUNKY ROLLS
Tracks: / Old funky rolls / Boss.
12" Single: Released Aug '82, on Motown, by BMG Records (UK). Deleted '84. Catalogue no: **TMGT 1273**
7" Single: Released Aug '82, on Motown, by BMG Records (UK). Deleted '84. Catalogue no: **TMG 1273**

ONE MORE CHANCE
Tracks: / One more chance / Confide in me.
7" Single: Released Oct '81, on Motown, by BMG Records (UK). Deleted '82. Catalogue no: **TMG 1227**

PARADISE
Tracks: / Paradise (LP version) (7" & Cassingle only.) / We stand together (7" & Cassingle only.) / Paradise (exotic mix) (12" & CD single only.) / Paradise (desert island dub) (12" & CD single only.) / We stand together (edit) (12" & CD single only.) / Paradise (12" remix) (12EMX 94 only.).
CD 5": Released Jul '89, on EMI, by EMI Records. Catalogue no: **203 427 2**
7" Single: Released Jul '89, on EMI, by EMI Records. Catalogue no: **203 427 7**
7" Single: Released Jul '89, on EMI, by EMI Records. Catalogue no: **EM 94**
12" Single: Released Jul '89, on EMI, by EMI Records. Catalogue no: **12EMX 94**
12" Single: Released Jul '89, on EMI, by EMI Records. Catalogue no: **203 427 8**
Cassingle: Released Jul '89, on EMI, by EMI Records. Catalogue no: **TCEM 94**
12" Single: Released Jul '89, on EMI, by EMI Records. Catalogue no: **12EMP 94**
CD 5": Released Jul '89, on EMI, by EMI Records. Catalogue no: **CDEM 94**
12" Single: Released Jul '89, on EMI, by EMI Records. Catalogue no: **12EM 94**
Cassingle: Released Jul '89, on EMI, by EMI Records. Catalogue no: **203 427 4**
12" Single: Released Jul '89, on EMI, by EMI Records. Catalogue no: **203 427 0**
12" Single: Released Jul '89, on EMI, by EMI Records. Catalogue no: **203 427 6**

PIECES OF ICE
Tracks: / Pieces of ice.
7" Single: Released Jun '83, on Capitol, by EMI Records. Deleted '88. Catalogue no: **CL 298**
12" Single: Released Jun '83, on Capitol, by EMI Records. Deleted '88. Catalogue no: **12CL 298**

POPS, WE LOVE YOU
Tracks: / Pops, we love you.
7" Single: Released Feb '79, on Motown, by BMG Records (UK). Deleted '82. Catalogue no: **TMG 1136**

REACH OUT AND TOUCH
Tracks: / Reach out and touch (somebody's hand) / Surrender.
7" Single: Released Apr '88, on Motown, by BMG Records (UK). Catalogue no: **ZB 41923**
7" Single: Released Jul '70, on Tamla Motown, by Motown Records (UK). Deleted '73. Catalogue no: **TMG 743**

REACH OUT AND TOUCH (SOMEBODY'S HAND)
Tracks: / Reach out and touch (somebody's hand).
7" Single: Released Jul '84, on Motown, by BMG Records (UK). Catalogue no: **TMG 988**

REFLECTIONS (SINGLE)
Tracks: / Reflections / Love child.
7" Single: Released Oct '81, on Motown, by BMG Records (UK). Catalogue no: **TMG 960**

REMEMBER ME
Tracks: / Remember me / Surrender.
7" Single: Released Apr '71, on Tamla Motown, by Motown Records (UK). Deleted '74. Catalogue no: **TMG 768**
7" Single: Released Oct '81, on Motown, by BMG Records (UK). Deleted '83. Catalogue no: **TMG 970**

SHOCK WAVE
Tracks: / Shockwaves (12" remix) (on 12" only) / Shockwaves (7" remix) / Shockwaves (instrumental) / I am one.
Note: * Extra tracks on 12" version only.
7" Single: Released Sep '87, on EMI, by EMI Records. Deleted Apr '88. Catalogue no: **EM 22**
12" Single: Released Sep '87, on EMI, by EMI Records. Deleted Apr '88. Catalogue no: **12EM 22**

SO CLOSE
Tracks: / So close / Fool for your love.
7" Single: Released Jan '83, on Capitol, by EMI Records. Deleted '88. Catalogue no: **CL 277**
12" Single: Released Jan '83, on Capitol, by EMI Records. Deleted '88. Catalogue no: **12CL 277**

SOMEDAY WE'LL BE TOGETHER
Tracks: / Someday we'll be together.
7" Single: Released Oct '81, on Motown, by BMG Records (UK). Deleted '83. Catalogue no: **TMG 1080**
7" Single: Released Apr '88, on Motown, by BMG Records (UK). Catalogue no: **ZB 41925**
7" Single: Released Dec '69, on Tamla Motown, by Motown Records (UK). Deleted '72. Catalogue no: **TMG 721**

SORRY DOESN'T ALWAYS MAKE IT RIGHT
Tracks: / Sorry doesn't always make it right.
7" Single: Released Mar '75, on Tamla Motown, by Motown Records (UK). Deleted '78. Catalogue no: **TMG 941**

STOP IN THE NAME OF LOVE
Tracks: / Stop in the name of love / Automatically sunshine / Automatically sunshine (medley) (12" only).
7" Single: Released 6 Feb '89, on Motown, by BMG Records (UK). Catalogue no: **ZB 41963**
12" Single: Released 6 Feb '89, on Motown, by BMG Records (UK). Catalogue no: **ZT 41964**

STOP LOOK LISTEN TO YOUR HEART
Tracks: / Stop look listen to your heart.
7" Single: Released Oct '81, on Motown, by BMG Records (UK). Catalogue no: **TMG 906**

SUPREMES MEDLEY
Tracks: / Supremes medley.
12" Single: Released Oct '81, on Motown, by BMG Records (UK). Deleted '83. Catalogue no: **TMGT 1180**
7" Single: Released Oct '81, on Motown, by BMG Records (UK). Deleted '83. Catalogue no: **TMG 1180**

SURRENDER
Tracks: / Surrender.
7" Single: Released Oct '71, on Tamla Motown, by Motown Records (UK). Deleted '74. Catalogue no: **TMG 792**

TENDERNESS
Tracks: / Tenderness.
7" Single: Released Dec '81, on Motown, by BMG Records (UK). Catalogue no: **TMG 1248**
12" Single: Released Dec '81, on Motown, by BMG Records (UK). Catalogue no: **TMGT 1248**

THIS HOUSE
Tracks: / This house / Chain reaction (live).
12" Single: Released Nov '89, on EMI, by EMI Records. Catalogue no: **12EM 118**
7" Single: Released Nov '89, on EMI, by EMI Records. Catalogue no: **203 606 7**
Cassingle: Released Nov '89, on EMI, by EMI Records. Catalogue no: **203 606 4**
CD 5": Released Nov '89, on EMI, by EMI Records. Catalogue no: **203 606 2**
CD 5": Released Nov '89, on EMI, by EMI Records. Catalogue no: **CDEM 118**
Cassingle: Released Nov '89, on EMI, by EMI Records. Catalogue no: **TCEM 118**
7" Single: Released Nov '89, on EMI, by EMI Records. Catalogue no: **EM 118**
12" Single: Released Nov '89, on EMI, by EMI Records. Catalogue no: **203 606 6**

TOUCH BY TOUCH
Tracks: / Touch by touch.
7" Single: Released Sep '84, on Capitol, by EMI Records. Deleted '87. Catalogue no: **CL 357**

TOUCH ME IN THE MORNING (SINGLE)
Tracks: / Touch me in the morning.
7" Single: Released Oct '81, on Motown, by BMG Records (UK). Catalogue no: **TMG 861**

UP FRONT
Tracks: / Up front.
7" Single: Released Oct '83, on Capitol, by EMI Records. Deleted Jan '88. Catalogue no: **CL 306**
12" Single: Released Oct '83, on Capitol, by EMI Records. Deleted '88. Catalogue no: **12CL 306**

UPSIDE DOWN
Tracks: / Upside down.
7" Single: Released Jul '80, on Motown, by BMG Records (UK). Deleted '83. Catalogue no: **TMG 1195**

WHAT YOU GAVE ME
Tracks: / What you gave me.
7" Single: Released Oct '81, on Motown, by BMG Records (UK). Deleted '83. Catalogue no: **TMG 1135**

WHERE DID OUR LOVE GO (SINGLE) (Ross, Diana & The Supremes)
Tracks: / Where did our love go.
7" Single: Released Oct '81, on Motown, by BMG Records (UK). Catalogue no: **TMG 925**

WHY DO FOOLS FALL IN LOVE?
Tracks: / Why do fools fall in love?.
7" Single: Released Nov '81, on Capitol, by EMI Records. Deleted '84. Catalogue no: **CL 226**

WHY (MUST WE FALL IN LOVE)
Tracks: / Why (must we fall in love).
7" Single: Released Mar '70, on Tamla Motown, by Motown Records (UK). Deleted '73. Catalogue no: **TMG 730**

WORK THAT BODY
Tracks: / Work that body / Two can make it.
7" Single: Released May '82, on Capitol, by EMI Records. Deleted '85. Catalogue no: **CL 241**

WORKIN' OVERTIME (REMIX)
Tracks: / Workin' overtime (the boss mix) / Workin' overtime (the boss inst.) / Workin' overtime (the boss beat) / Workin' overtime (the bossapella).
12" Single: Released May '89, on EMI, by EMI Records. Catalogue no: **12EMX 91**

WORKIN' OVERTIME (SINGLE0
Tracks: / Workin' overtime / Workin' overtime (ext. version) (Not on 7".) / Workin' overtime (house mix) (12" only.) / Workin' overtime (Instrumental version) (7" only.) / Workin' overtime (club mix) (CD single only.).
12" Single: Released Apr '89, on EMI, by EMI Records. Catalogue no: **12EM 91**
CD 5": Released Apr '89, on EMI, by EMI Records. Catalogue no: **CDEM 91**
7" Single: Released Apr '89, on EMI, by EMI Records. Catalogue no: **EM 91**

YOU ARE EVERYTHING
Tracks: / You are everything.
12" Single: Released Apr '85, on Motown, by BMG Records (UK). Catalogue no: **TMGT 998**
7" Single: Released May '82, on Motown, by BMG Records (UK). Catalogue no: **TMG 890**
7" Single: Released Apr '85, on Motown, by BMG Records (UK). Catalogue no: **TMG 998**

YOU CAN'T HURRY LOVE
Tracks: / You can't hurry love.

7" Single: Released Oct '81, on Motown, by BMG Records (UK). Catalogue no: **TMG 956**

YOU KEEP ME HANGIN ON
Tracks: / You keep me hangin on / Come see about me / I hear a symphony / Your love is like an itching in my heart.
12" Single: Released Apr '86, on Motown, by BMG Records (UK). Deleted '87. Catalogue no: **ZT 40710**
7" Single: Released Apr '86, on Motown, by BMG Records (UK). Catalogue no: **ZB 40709**

Ross, Drew

BALLAD OF JR
Tracks: / Ballad of JR / Midnight in Dallas.
7" Single: Released Jun '80, on Hot Rod, Catalogue no: **HR 001**

Ross, Errol

ROUND IN CIRCLES
Tracks: / Round in circles / Reggae music of today.
7" Single: Released May '80, on Carrere, Deleted '83. Catalogue no: **CAR 149**

Ross, Jimmy

FIRST TRUE LOVE AFFAIR
Tracks: / First true love affair / First true love affair (pt 2).
7" Single: Released Aug '81, on Megafunk, Deleted Aug '84. Catalogue no: **MF1**
12" Single: Released Aug '81, on Megafunk, Deleted Aug '84. Catalogue no: **MFX 1**

NEW YORK TO MOSCOW
Tracks: / New York to Moscow.
7" Single: Released Sep '84, on Trance, Deleted '86. Catalogue no: **7 TRN 2001**
12" Single: Released Sep '84, on Trance, Deleted '86. Catalogue no: **12 TRN 2001**

Ross, Lian

FANTASSY
Tracks: / Fantassy.
12" Single: Released Nov '85, on ZYX (Germany), Catalogue no: **ZYX 5320**

FANTASY
Tracks: / Fantasy / Fantasy remix / Say you'll never / Saturday night.
12" Single: Released Nov '86, on Greyhound, by Greyhound Records. Catalogue no: **GRY 002**

IT'S UP TO YOU
Tracks: / It's up to you / Love call (mix).
12" Single: Released May '86, on Conifer, Catalogue no: **ICK 052 1554906**

SAY YOU'LL NEVER
Tracks: / Say you'll never / D.J. alternative mix.
12" Single: Released Dec '85, on ZYX (Germany), Catalogue no: **ZYX 5355**

Ross, Steven

THEN THERE WAS YOU
Tracks: / Then there was you.
7" Single: Released Jul '85, on Arista, by BMG Records (UK). Catalogue no: **ARIST 629**
12" Single: Released Jul '85, on Arista, by BMG Records (UK). Catalogue no: **ARIST 12629**

Ross, T.T.

HE IS MINE
Tracks: / He is mine / He is mine (Instrumental version).
12" Single: Released Apr '86, on Dione, Catalogue no: **DIO 004**

LAST DATE
Tracks: / Last date.
12" Single: Released Oct '84, on Cima, Catalogue no: **CR 002**

Rosselson, Leon

Biographical details: Leon Rosselson was born in 1934; a folk revivalist, he is one of the most important writers and singers of political, often polemical songs. He wrote for TV's **That Was The Week That Was** in the early '60s; was a member fo the Galliards and Three City Four on LPs '62-5; his first solo album was made in 1967. *Palaces Of Gold* (remakes of older songs) and *That's Not The Way It's Got To Be* have been reissued from 1975; the other albums on Fuse are more recent. *Ballad Of A Spycatcher* in 1987 on Upside Down Records, with Billy Bragg and the Oyster Band, is an example of trenchant topicality, adressing the governments's paranoia over a second-rate book and the issue of freedom of the press. (Donald Clarke 4.2.88)..

BALLAD OF A SPYCATCHER
Tracks: / Ballad of a spycatcher / Song of the free press.
7" Single: Released 17 Oct '87, on Upside Down, Catalogue no: **UPDO 007**

Rosser & Davis

FRIENDS
Tracks: / Friends.
12" Single: Released Aug '87, on Lifestyle, by Micrometro Ltd (Records). Catalogue no: **XYT 4**
7" Single: Released Aug '87, on Lifestyle, by Micrometro Ltd (Records). Deleted '88. Catalogue no: **XY 4**

SIMON SAYS
Tracks: / Simon says / Fiends / Party medley.
7" Single: Released Nov '87, on Lifestyle, by Micrometro Ltd (Records). Catalogue no: **XY5**
12" Single: Released Nov '87, on Lifestyle, by Micrometro Ltd (Records). Catalogue no: **XY T5**

Rossi, Francis

MODERN ROMANCE
Tracks: / Modern romance / Modern romance.
7" Single: Released Apr '85, on Vertigo, by Phonogram Ltd. Catalogue no: **VER 17**
7" Single: Released May '85, on Vertigo, by Phonogram Ltd. Deleted '88. Catalogue no: **FROS 1**

Rossington Collins

ONE GOOD MAN
Tracks: / One good man / Misery loves company.
7" Single: Released Oct '80, on MCA, by MCA Records. Deleted Oct '83. Catalogue no: **MCA 648**

Rossiter, Leonard

RISING DAMP
Tracks: / Rising damp / Damp disco.
7" Single: Released Jan '80, on Chips, Deleted '83. Catalogue no: **CHI 101**

Rosso, Nini

IL SILENZIO
Tracks: / Il silenzio.
7" Single: Released Aug '65, on Durium, Deleted '68. Catalogue no: **DRS 54000**
7" Single: Released Jul '82, on Old Gold, by Old Gold Records. Catalogue no: **OG 9055**

Rot, Jan

COUNTING SHEEP
Tracks: / Counting sheep / For Eliya.
7" Single: Released Sep '82, on WEA, by WEA Records. Catalogue no: **K 19160**

Rotation

ICE COLD EYES
Tracks: / Ice cold eyes / Highway robbery.
7" Single: Released Jul '80, on Happy Face, by Standard Sound Productions. Deleted Jul '83. Catalogue no: **MM 123**

Rote Kapelle

BIG SMELL DINOSAUR
Tracks: / Big smell dinosaur.
7" Single: Released '88, on Big Smell, Catalogue no: **SMELLY 001**

FIRE ESCAPE
Tracks: / Fire escape.
7" Single: Released Apr '88, on In Tape, by In Tape Records. Catalogue no: **IT 051**

IT MOVES...BUT DOES IT SWING?
Tracks: / Marathon man / Jellystone Park / Anna / Acid face baby / Sunday / you don't know.
Note: Recorded for BBC Radio One John Peel programme.
7" EP: Released Jul '87, on In Tape, by In Tape Records. Catalogue no: **IT 044**

SAN FRANCISCO AGAIN
Tracks: / San Francisco again.
12" Single: Released Jun '88, on In Tape, by In Tape Records. Catalogue no: **IT 054**

THESE ANIMALS ARE DANGEROUS
Tracks: / These animals are dangerous / Sunday.
7" Single: Released Sep '86, on In Tape, by In Tape Records. Catalogue no: **IT 037**

Roten Rosen

ITSY BITSY TEENIE WEENIE
Tracks: / Itsy bitsy teenie weenie / Agent X (This track is available on 12" single only.).
7" Single: Released 21 Nov '87, on Virgin, by Virgin Records. Deleted May '88. Catalogue no: **VS 1031**
12" Single: Released 21 Nov '87, on Virgin, by Virgin Records. Deleted May '88. Catalogue no: **VST 1031**

Roth, David Lee

CALIFORNIA GIRLS
Tracks: / California girls / Just a gigolo / I ain't got nobody / Yankie rose (12" & CD single only.).
7" Single: Released Feb '85, on Warner Bros., by WEA Records. Deleted '88. Catalogue no: **W 9102**
7" Single: Released Nov '88, on Warner Bros., by WEA Records. Catalogue no: **W 7650**
12" Single: Released Nov '88, on Warner Bros., by WEA Records. Catalogue no: **W 7650T**
CD 5": Released Nov '88, on Warner Bros., by WEA Records. Catalogue no: **W 7650 CD**

DAMN GOOD
Tracks: / Damn good / Stand up.
7" Single: Released 30 Aug '88, on Warner Bros., by WEA Records. Catalogue no: **W 7753**
12" Single: Released Sep '88, on Warner Bros., by WEA Records. Catalogue no: **W 7753 T**

JUST A GIGOLO (MEDLEY)
Tracks: / Just a gigolo.
7" Single: Released Apr '85, on Warner Bros., by WEA Records. Catalogue no: **W 9040**

YANKEE ROSE
Tracks: / Yankee rose / Shy boy / Easy Street (Extra track available on 12" version only.).
7" Single: Released Jul '86, on Warner Bros., by WEA Records. Deleted Jun '87. Catalogue no: **W 8656**
12" Single: Released Jul '86, on Warner Bros., by WEA Records. Deleted Jan '88. Catalogue no: **W 8656T**

Roth, Uli John

NIGHT THE MASTER COMES
Tracks: / Night the master comes.
7" Single: Released Jan '85, on EMI, by EMI Records. Catalogue no: **EMI 5511**

Rouen

HOLD ME
Tracks: / Hold me / Ne better place / Follow me (Extra track available on 12" version only.).
7" Single: Released Sep '86, on E.G., by E.G. Records. Deleted May '88. Catalogue no: **EGO 29**
12" Single: Released Sep '86, on E.G., by E.G. Records. Deleted May '88. Catalogue no: **EGOX 29**

LET IT ALL OUT
Tracks: / Too close to the edge / All the way back home.
12" Single: Released Jan '87, on E.G., by E.G. Records. Deleted May '88. Catalogue no: **EGOX 33**
7" Single: Released Jan '87, on E.G., by E.G. Records. Deleted May '88. Catalogue no: **EGO 33**

ORDINARY LIFE
Tracks: / Ordinary life.
12" Single: Released Jun '85, on Island, by Island Records. Deleted '87. Catalogue no: **12IS 189**
7" Single: Released Jun '85, on Island, by Island Records. Catalogue no: **IS 189**

YOUNG FOR A DAY (SINGLE)
Tracks: / Young for a day / Take me back home.
7" Single: Released Jun '86, on Kick, Catalogue no: **KIC 09**

Rough Club

BAD TIMES
Tracks: / Bad times.
7" Single: Released Feb '88, on Citybeat, by Beggars Banquet Records. Catalogue no: **CBE 1219**

BAD TIMES (REMIX)
Tracks: / Bad times (remix).
12" Single: Released May '88, on Citybeat, by Beggars Banquet Records. Catalogue no: **CBX 1219**

URBAN DECAY
Tracks: / Urban decay.
12" Single: Released Jun '88, on Citybeat, by Beggars Banquet Records. Catalogue no: **CBE 1223**

Rough Trade

CRIMES OF PASSION
Tracks: / Crimes of passion.
7" Single: Released Oct '85, on FM, by FM-Revolver Records. Catalogue no: **VHF 19**
12" Single: Released Oct '85, on FM, by FM-Revolver Records. Catalogue no: **12 VHF 19**

Roughneck

FORCE 10 FROM NAVARONE
Tracks: / Force 10 from Navarone / Jack off / Force 10 from Navarone (extended version) (Only on 12" version.).
7" Single: Released May '89, on Mango, by Island Records. Catalogue no: **MNG 709**
12" Single: Released May '89, on Mango, by Island Records. Catalogue no: **12 MNG 709**

Roulette

LOVERS AND GAMBLERS
Tracks: / Lovers and gamblers / Bankrupt.
12" Single: Released Jan '80, on Ariola, by BMG Records (UK). Deleted Jan '85. Catalogue no: **AROD 196**
7" Single: Released Jan '80, on Ariola, by BMG Records (UK). Deleted Jan '85. Catalogue no: **ARO 196**

Round Midnight

ROUND MIDNIGHT
Tracks: / Round midnight.
12" Single: Released Jul '87, on Music Of Life, by Music Of Life Records. Catalogue no: **NOTE 9**

Round-A-Way-Wrong

BOY
Tracks: / Boy.
7" Single: Released Dec '84, on Wrong, by Wrong Records. Catalogue no: **WRONG 001**

Roundtree

HIT ON YOU
Tracks: / Hit on you.
7" Single: Released Jun '82, on Virgin, by Virgin Records. Deleted Jun '85. Catalogue no: **VS 506**
12" Single: Released Jun '82, on Virgin, by Virgin Records. Deleted Jun '85. Catalogue no: **VS 506 12**

Rouska - Profane 9

10" SAMPLER
Tracks: / Rouska - Profane 9: *Various artists.*
10" single: Released '86, on Rouska, by Rouska Records. Catalogue no: **PROFANE 009**

Rousseau, Charles

I WANT YOUR LOVE RIGHT NOW
Tracks: / I want your love right now.
7" Single: Released May '83, on Dancefloor, Catalogue no: **DF 7002**
12" Single: Released May '83, on Dancefloor, Catalogue no: **DFT 7002**

Roussos, Demis

Biographical details: Demis Roussos was born in 1947 in Egypt. The Greek crooner was a member of the successful trio Aphrodite's Child; then went solo, singing in several languages with a high-pitched voice and considerable girth, who then lost considerable weight (perhaps tired of Ronnie Scott's jokes about him filling the club). He sold a lot of records in Europe in the mid'70s and no doubt still has fans. (Donald Clarke 4.2.88).
Demis Roussos was born at the end of the Second World war in Egypt to Greek parents living in a small orthodox christian community in a Moslem town. The family's Egyptian location meant that not only could Demis hear the rock'n'roll of Bill Haley or the big ballads of Italian music, which were in fashion at that time, but the local music, too, suffused him with its colour and vitality. The international radio broadcasts excited his imagination, but equally natural was his participation in the choir of the Byzantine Church. At eight his passion for singing had begun to surface and he entertained friends and family with impromtu little concerts. In his teens, he studied guitar and piano while continuing to develop his singing skills. He realised that by combining the energy and structure of Western pop with what he already knew, he could achieve a truly international style of his own, and he did it. The beginnings of his stardom were interstingly as a musician, not a singer. He toured with various bands to North Africa, Greece, Israel and Italy, and in each town left a devoted following in his wake. With a Greek friend he formed a band, and went to Paris in 1968 where, under the name Aphrodite's Child, they recorded *Rain and tears* for Phillips. With Demis singing, it was a smash and three more successful recordings followed. His personal music vision, the mixing of folk themes of his youth with modern rhythms, demanded fuller expression and he went out on his own. His first singe *We shall dance*, became one of the biggest European records of 1971, and his debut solo album, *Fire and ice*, made him an international star. In the last 10 years, Demis has travelled more than half a million miles all over the globe giving performances which have ranged from a tiny, intimate private audience of forty at a celebration party for the late Shah, to a gigantic concert with an audience of 150,000 at the Maracana Stadium in Brazil. The triumphs that followed - Japan, Australia and Canada - are almost too many enumerate, but it a measure of Demis' stature that when he played Los Angeles Greek Theatre the mayor of L.A. made him 'Man of the Day'. Within the last three years, Demis Roussos had undergone some major changes. His image has altered dramatically, some eight stone in weight have been reduced from his legendary figure, and much more time and care is taken over his recordings and his musical direction. (Polydor Records, May 1983).

BECAUSE
Tracks: / Because.
7" Single: Released Mar '77, on Philips, by Phonogram Ltd. Deleted '80. Catalogue no: **6042 245**

CAN'T SAY HOW MUCH I LOVE YOU
Tracks: / Can't say how much I love you.
7" Single: Released Feb '76, on Philips, by Phonogram Ltd. Deleted '79. Catalogue no: **6042 114**

FOLLOW ME
Tracks: / Follow me.
7" Single: Released Sep '82, on Polydor, by Polydor Ltd. Catalogue no: **DR 2**

HAPPY TO BE ON AN ISLAND IN THE SUN
Tracks: / Happy to be on an island in the sun.
7" Single: Released Nov '75, on Philips, by Phonogram Ltd. Deleted '78. Catalogue no: **6042 033**

I NEED YOU
Tracks: / I need you / No love today.
7" Single: Released Apr '81, on Mercury, by Phonogram Ltd. Deleted '85. Catalogue no: **MER 45**

JAY
Tracks: / Jay.
7" Single: Released Jun '83, on Polydor, by Polydor Ltd. Catalogue no: **DR 3**

KYRILA
Tracks: / Kyrila / I'm gonna fall in love / I dig you / Sister Emilyne.
7" Single: Released Jun '77, on Philips, by Phonogram Ltd. Deleted '80. Catalogue no: **DEMIS 002**

LAMENT
Tracks: / Lament / We're shining.
7" Single: Released Feb '82, on Polydor, by Polydor Ltd. Deleted Feb '87. Catalogue no: **DR 1**

LOST IN LOVE
Tracks: / Lost in love / Had to run.
7" Single: Released Mar '80, on Mercury, by Phonogram Ltd. Deleted Mar '83. Catalogue no: **MER 10**

LOVE ME TENDER
Tracks: / Love me tender.
7" Single: Released Nov '84, on Starblend, by Starblend Records. Catalogue no: **STAR 4**

RACE TO THE END
Tracks: / Race to the end / Eric's theme.
7" Single: Released Mar '81, on Polydor, by Polydor Ltd. Deleted Mar '84. Catalogue no: **POSP 238**

RAIN AND TEARS
Tracks: / Rain and tears / Summer wine.
7" Single: Released May '87, on Apollo Music Int., Deleted '88. Catalogue no: **ZONE 1**
12" Single: Released May '87, on Apollo Music Int., Deleted '88. Catalogue no: **12 ZONE 1**

ROUSSOS PHENOMENON, THE
Tracks: / Forever and ever / Sing an ode to love / So dreamy / My friend the wind.
7" EP: Released Jun '76, on Philips, by Phonogram Ltd. Deleted '79. Catalogue no: **DEMIS 001**

SUMMER IN HER EYES
Tracks: / Summer in her eyes / I miss you.
7" Single: Released Sep '86, on Jive, by Zomba Records. Deleted Jul '87. Catalogue no: **DEM 1**
12" Single: Released Sep '86, on Jive, by Zomba Records. Deleted Jul '87. Catalogue no: **DEMT 1**

WHEN FOREVER HAS GONE
Tracks: / When forever has gone.
7" Single: Released Oct '76, on Philips, by Phonogram Ltd. Deleted '79. Catalogue no: **6042 186**

Routers

LET'S GO
Tracks: / Let's go.
7" Single: Released Jul '81, on Warner Bros., by WEA Records. Catalogue no: **K 16156**

Rovers

WASN'T THAT A PARTY
Tracks: / Wasn't that a party / Matchstalk men and matchstalk cats and dogs.
7" Single: Released Jan '82, on Attica, by Attica Records. Deleted Jan '85. Catalogue no: **ATX 231**
7" Single: Released Mar '81, on Epic, by CBS Records. Deleted Mar '84. Catalogue no: **EPC A 1062**

Rowan, Peter

T FOR TEXAS
Cassingle: Released Jun '86, on Waterfront, by Waterfront Music. Catalogue no: **WFS 011 C**
12" Single: Released Apr '85, on Waterfront, by Waterfront Music. Catalogue no: **WFT 11**

Rowe, Gwen

WOMAN NEEDS TO BELONG TO A GOOD MAN, A
Tracks: / Woman needs to belong to a good man, A / Brown eyes blue.
12" Single: Released Jun '84, on WE, Catalogue no: **WE 1033**

Rowe, Keith

GROOVY SITUATION
Tracks: / Groovy situation.
12" Single: Released Jun '84, on Seven Leaves, Catalogue no: **SLD 02**

Rowe, Nick

AMRITA
Tracks: / Amrita / Fire and the moon, The.
7" Single: Released Feb '89, on White Mountain, Catalogue no: **WMR 45 01**

Rowe, Xenia

REACHING FOR THE BEST
Tracks: / Reaching for the best.
12" Single: Released Oct '84, on Crystal City, by Crystal City Records. Catalogue no: **CRITY 1**

Rowland, Kevin

WALK AWAY
Tracks: / Walk away / Even when I hold you / Way you look tonight (Track on 12" version only.) / Because of you (+ Track on CD version only.).
12" Single: Released Apr '88, on Mercury, by Phonogram Ltd. Deleted Oct '88. Catalogue no: **DEXYS 1412**
7" Single: Released Apr '88, on Mercury, by Phonogram Ltd. Deleted Oct '88. Catalogue no: **DEXYS 14**
12" Single: on Mercury, by Phonogram Ltd. Deleted Oct '88. Catalogue no: **DEXYB 1412**
CD 5": Released May '88, on Mercury, by Phonogram Ltd. Deleted Oct '88. Catalogue no: **DEXCD 14**

YOUNG MAN
Tracks: / Young man / Ticket to Palookahville / Jackie Wilson said (Only on 12" and CD single.) / Show me (Only on CD single.).
CD 5": Released Oct '88, on Mercury, by Phonogram Ltd. Catalogue no: **ROWCD 2**
7" Single: Released Oct '88, on Mercury, by Phonogram Ltd. Deleted 31 May '89. Catalogue no: **ROW 2**
12" Single: Released Oct '88, on Mercury, by Phonogram Ltd. Catalogue no: **ROWS 12**
12" Single: Released Oct '88, on Mercury, by Phonogram Ltd. Deleted 31 May '89. Catalogue no: **ROW 212**

Rowland, Kevin &

CELTIC SOUL BROTHERS
7" Single: Released Mar '83, on Mercury, by Phonogram Ltd. Deleted '87. Catalogue no: **DEXYS 12**
12" Single: Released Mar '83, on Mercury, by Phonogram Ltd. Catalogue no: **DEXYS 1212**

LET'S GET THIS STRAIGHT
Tracks: / Let's get this straight / Old.
7" Single: Released Nov '82, on Mercury, by Phonogram Ltd. Deleted '87. Catalogue no: **DEXYS 11**
12" Single: Released Nov '82, on Mercury, by Phonogram Ltd. Deleted '87. Catalogue no: **DEXYS 1112**

Rowles, John

HUSH NOT A WORD TO MARY
Tracks: / Hush not a word to Mary.
7" Single: Released Jun '68, on MCA, by MCA Records. Deleted '71. Catalogue no: **MU 1023**

IF I ONLY HAD TIME
Tracks: / If I only had time.
7" Single: Released Mar '68, on MCA, by MCA Records. Deleted '71. Catalogue no: **MU 1000**
7" Single: Released Jun '88, on Old Gold, by Old Gold Records. Catalogue no: **OG 9793**

Rox

DDDDDANCE
Tracks: / DDDDDance / You don't know what I caught.
7" Single: Released May '81, on Epic, by CBS Records. Deleted May '84. Catalogue no: **EPC A 1212**

HOT LOVE IN THE CITY
Tracks: / Hot love in the city.
7" Single: Released Aug '82, on Teentees, Deleted '83. Catalogue no: **ROX 100**

KRAZY KUTS
Tracks: / Krazy kuts.
12" Single: Released Sep '83, on Music For Nations, by Music For Nations Records. Catalogue no: **12 KUT 103**

Rox, Angie

ARE YOU WAITING
Tracks: / Are you waiting / Interacting heat.
7" Single: Released Dec '80, on Surrey Sound, Catalogue no: **HMS 4**

Roxanne

PLAY THAT FUNKY MUSIC
Tracks: / Play that funky music / Play that funky music / Over you.
7" Single: Released May '88, on Polydor, by Polydor Ltd. Catalogue no: **POSP 919**
12" Single: Released May '88, on Polydor, by Polydor Ltd. Catalogue no: **POSPX 919**

SINGLE GIRL
Tracks: / Single girl / Make the break.
7" Single: Released Feb '82, on RCA, by BMG Records (UK). Deleted Feb '87. Catalogue no: **RCA 184**

Roxette

DRESSED FOR SUCCESS
Tracks: / Dressed for success / Voice, The / Dressed for success (the remix) (12" & CD single only.) / Look, The (7" version) (CD single only.) / Look, The (big red mix) (12" only.).
Note: Produced by Clarence Ofwerman.
CD 5": Released Jul '89, on EMI, by EMI Records. Catalogue no: **CDEM 96**
Cassingle: Released Jul '89, on EMI, by EMI Records. Catalogue no: **TCEM 96**
7" Single: Released Jul '89, on EMI, by EMI Records. Catalogue no: **136 351 7**
7" Single: Released Jul '89, on EMI, by EMI Records. Catalogue no: **EM 96**
12" Single: Released Jul '89, on EMI, by EMI Records. Catalogue no: **136 354 6**
Cassingle: Released Jul '89, on EMI, by EMI Records. Catalogue no: **136 352 4**
7" Single: Released Jul '89, on EMI, by EMI Records. Catalogue no: **EMX 96**
7" Single: Released Jul '89, on EMI, by EMI Records. Catalogue no: **136 352 7**
12" Single: Released Jul '89, on EMI, by EMI Records. Catalogue no: **12EM 96**

LISTEN TO YOUR HEART
Tracks: / Listen to your heart (Swedish single mix) (Not on 12".) / (I could never) give you up / Listen to your heart (L.P. version) (12" only.) / Dressed for success (Success mix) (12" only.) / Dressed for success (New radio mix) (CD single.).
Cassingle: Released Oct '89, on EMI, by EMI Records. Catalogue no: **136 323 4**
7" Single: Released Oct '89, on EMI, by EMI Records. Catalogue no: **EM 108**
Cassingle: Released Oct '89, on EMI, by EMI Records. Catalogue no: **TCEM 108**
CD 5": Released Oct '89, on EMI, by EMI Records. Catalogue no: **CDEM 108**
CD 5": Released Oct '89, on EMI, by EMI Records. Catalogue no: **136 363 2**
7" Single: Released Oct '89, on EMI, by EMI Records. Catalogue no: **136 323 7**
12" Single: Released Oct '89, on EMI, by EMI Records. Catalogue no: **12EM 108**
12" Single: Released Oct '89, on EMI, by EMI Records. Catalogue no: **136 363 6**

LOOK, THE
Tracks: / Look, The / Look, The (heddrum mix) (12" only.) / Silver blue (demo).
CD 5": Released Mar '89, on EMI, by EMI Records. Catalogue no: **CDEM 87**
7" Single: Released Mar '89, on EMI, by EMI Records. Catalogue no: **EM 87**
12" Single: Released Mar '89, on EMI, by EMI Records. Catalogue no: **12EM 87**

Roxon Roadshow

MOTORWAY QUEEN
Tracks: / Motorway queen / Fiddlin' in fancy free.
7" Single: Released Apr '82, on Roxon, Catalogue no: **ROX 033**

Roxy Music

Biographical details: Bryan Ferry, Andy Mackay and Phil Manzanera are the three men who have been part of every successful line-up of this British rock band.
Many other notable musicians -- including Brian Eno, Paul Thompson, John Porter, Eddie Jobson, John Wetton and Gary Tibbs -- have been members at one time or another. Founded by singer/keyboards player/lyricist Ferry in late 1970, Roxy Music initially met with zero interest from record companies. But they built up a cult following, thanks to the support of journalist Richard Williams (Melody Maker) and disc jockey John Peel. Many others then started to take notice and Roxy Music had the good fortune to reach the UK Top Ten in 1972 with their first single and first album: the former was the stunningly original and extremely catchy *Virginia Plain* (No 4), the latter simply called *Roxy Music* (No 10). During their early days the band had the impressive ability to be avant-garde yet accessible to mainstream pop and rock fans -- they were both experimental and commercial.
They consolidated their initial success with a further British Top Ten single and LP, *Pyjamarama* and *For Your Pleasure*. In the summer of 1973 Ferry's role as leader was confirmed by the departure of synthesiser player Brian Eno, whose charismatic stage presence was stealing some of the spotlight from the singer. While Eno embarked on a series of esoteric and acclaimed projects, solo and with various collaborators, Roxy Music confirmed their status as one of Britain's most exciting and successful bands. The smooth, suave and sophisticated Ferry greatly enhanced his personal profile with a pair of highly successful solo albums and a run of hit singles. While his subsidiary solo career was generally a vehicle for imaginative reworkings of familiar pop and pre-pop standards, the best original numbers were saved for Roxy.
The group's third LP, *Stranded*, reached the UK No 1 slot in December 1973 and was followed by *Country Life* ('74) and *Siren* ('75). Hit singles included *Street Life* and the classic *Love Is The Drug*, which climbed to No 2 on the British chart in late 1975. Roxy Music disbanded in 1976 and Ferry's solo career began to yield strong new material as well as cover versions. Mackay co-wrote the well-received *Rock Follies* TV soundtrack while Manzanera was part of the short-lived band 801. A Roxy reformation took place in early 1979 and the band enjoyed even greater success than before (though the United States remained impervious). Their comeback album, *Manifesto*, spawned the UK No 2 single Dance Away and the equally danceable No 4, Angel Eyes. The following year's *Flesh And Blood* LP was a British chart topper and contained the Top Five singles *Over You* and *Oh Yeah* (On The Radio). Their records were no longer as innovative as they had once been but they continued to ooze class, sophistication and infectious melodic sensibility.
In March 1981, three months after the murder of John Lennon, Roxy achieved their first-ever British No 1 single with his Jealous Guy and 1982 brought the increasingly relaxed band another chart-topping album, *Avalon*, plus the big hit single *More Than This*. After 1982, however, the band released no further new material. An official split was not formally announced but it eventually became clear that the band were defunct. Ferry returned to the limelight in 1985 with his smash hit solo LP *Boys And Girls*. (Bob MacDonald, March 1986.)
A band of the 1970s that originated the genre of chic, lounge-lizard rock. The core of vocalist Bryan Ferry, who also wrote songs and played keyboards, Phil Manzanera on guitar (born Philip Targett-Adams in 1951 in London) and Andy Mackay on sax made their last album in 1983, long after they had suffered from fickle public taste. Their musical hybrid was beguiling when it was new; only David Bowie had anything like as much stylistic influence in the early 1970s. Brian Eno, who later became a synth wizard in avant-garde pop, was important on the band's first two albums; he left in 1973; *Stranded* that year introduced multi-instrumentalist Eddie Jobson and Ferry's parallel solo carreer began. Manzanera also did some interesting solo work. (Donald Clarke 4.2.88)
Bryan Ferry, Andy Mackay and Phil Manzanera are the three men who have been part of every successful line-up of this British rock band.
Many other musicians have been members at one time or another, the most notable being Brian Eno, Paul Thompson, John Porter, Eddie Jobson, John Wetton and Gary Tibbs. Founded by singer/keyboards player/lyricist Bryan Ferry in late 1970, Roxy Music initially met with zero interest from record companies; but they built up a cult following, thanks to the support of journalist Richard Williams (of Melody Maker) and disc jockey John Peel (of BBC Radio One). Many other people then started to take notice, and Roxy Music had the good fortune to reach the UK Top 10 with their first single and first album. The former was the stunningly original and extremely catchy *Virginia Plain* (No.4 in 1972), the latter was simply called *Roxy Music* (No.10 in 1972). During their early days, Roxy Music had the impressive ability to be avant-garde yet accessible to mainstream pop and rock fans.
They were experimental but commercial. The band consolidated their initial success with a further UK Top 10 single and LP, *Pyjamarama* and *For your pleasure*. In the summer of 1973 Ferry's role as leader was confirmed by the departure of synthesiser player Brian Eno, whose charismatic stage presence was stealing some of the spotlight from the singer. While Eno embarked upon a series of esoteric and acclaimed projects, solo and with various collaborators, Roxy Music confirmed their status as one of Britain's most exciting and successful bands. The smooth, suave and sophisticated Ferry

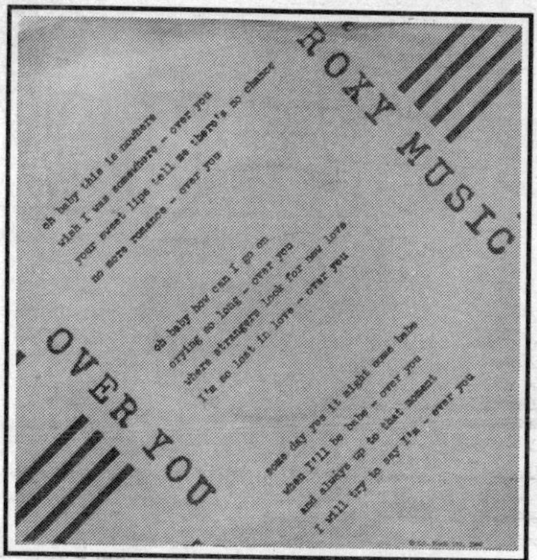

ROXY MUSIC - OVER YOU (Released on Polydor)

greatly enhanced his personal profile with a pair of highly successful solo albums and a run of hit singles.
While his subsidiary solo career was generally a vehicle for his imaginative reworkings of familiar pop and pre-pop standards, the best original numbers were saved for Roxy. The group's third LP *Stranded* reached the UK No.1 slot in December 1973, and was followed by *Country life* (1974) and *Siren* (1975). Their hit singles included *Street life* and the classic *Love is the drug*, which climbed to No.2 on the British chart in late 1975.
Roxy Music disbanded in 1976, and Ferry's solo career thus began to yield strong new material as well as cover versions. Mackay co-wrote the extraordinary well recieved *Rock follies* TV soundtrack, while Manzanera was part of the short lived band 801. A Roxy reformation took place in early 1979, and the band enjoyed even greater success than before (although the United States remained impervious to the band).
Their comeback album *Manifesto* spawned the UK No.2 single *Dance away* and the equally danceable No.4 smash *Angel eyes*. 1980's *Flesh and blood* LP was a British chart-topper, and contained the Top 5 singles *Over you* and *Oh yeah (on the radio*. Their records were no longer as innovative as they had once been, but they continued to ooze class, sophistication and infectious melodic sensibility. In March 1981, three months after the murder of John Lennon, Roxy achieved their first ever British No.1 single with their highly tasteful rendition of his *Jealous guy*. 1982 brought the increasingly relaxed band another chart-topping LP, *Avalon*, plus the big hit single *More than this*. After 1982, however, the band released no further new material. An official split was not formally announced, but it eventually became clear that the band were defunct. Ferry returned to the limelight in 1985 with his smash solo LP *Boys and girls*. (Bob MacDonald, 11th March 1986).

ALL I WANT IS YOU
Tracks: / All I want is you.
7" Single: Released Oct '74, on Island, by Island Records. Deleted '77. Catalogue no: **WIP 6208**

ANGEL EYES
Tracks: / Angel eyes.
7" Single: Released Aug '79, on Polydor, by Polydor Ltd. Deleted '82. Catalogue no: **POSP 67**

AVALON (SINGLE)
Tracks: / Avalon / Always unknowing.
7" Single: Released Jun '82, on E.G., by E.G. Records. Deleted '85. Catalogue no: **ROXY 4**

BOTH ENDS BURNING
Tracks: / Both ends burning.
7" Single: Released Mar '79, on Polydor, by Polydor Ltd. Deleted '82. Catalogue no: **POSP 32**

DANCE AWAY
Tracks: / Dance away.
7" Single: Released Apr '79, on Polydor, by Polydor Ltd. Deleted '82. Catalogue no: **POSP 44**

7" Single: Released '80, on Island, by Island Records. Catalogue no: **LR 5257**

DO THE STRAND
Tracks: / Do the Strand.
7" Single: Released Jan '78, on Polydor, by Polydor Ltd. Catalogue no: **2001 756**

JEALOUS GUY
Tracks: / Jealous guy / To turn you on.
7" Single: Released Feb '81, on E.G., by E.G. Records. Deleted '84. Catalogue no: **ROXY 2**

JEALOUS GUY (CD SINGLE)
Tracks: / Jealous guy / Lover / South downs.
CD 3": Released Jun '88, on Virgin, by Virgin Records. Catalogue no: **CDT 8**

LOVE IS THE DRUG
Tracks: / Love is the drug.
7" Single: Released Oct '75, on Island, by Island Records. Deleted '78. Catalogue no: **WIP 6248**

MORE THAN THIS
Tracks: / More than this / India.
7" Single: Released Mar '82, on E.G., by E.G. Records. Catalogue no: **ROXY 3**

OH YEAH
Tracks: / Oh yeah.
7" Single: Released Jul '80, on Polydor, by Polydor Ltd. Catalogue no: **2001 972**

OVER YOU (see panel above)
Tracks: / Over you / Manifesto.
7" Single: Released May '80, on Polydor, by Polydor Ltd. Catalogue no: **POSP 93**

PYJAMARAMA
Tracks: / Pyjamarama.
7" Single: Released Mar '73, on Island, by Island Records. Deleted '76. Catalogue no: **WIP 6159**

SAME OLD SCENE, THE
Tracks: / Same old scene / Lover.
7" Single: Released Nov '80, on Polydor, by Polydor Ltd. Deleted '83. Catalogue no: **ROXY 1**

STREET LIFE
Tracks: / Street life.
7" Single: Released Nov '73, on Island, by Island Records. Deleted '76. Catalogue no: **WIP 6173**

TAKE A CHANCE WITH ME
Tracks: / Take a chance with me.
7" Single: Released Sep '82, on E.G., by E.G. Records. Deleted '85. Catalogue no: **ROXY 5**

VIRGINIA PLAIN
Tracks: / Virginia plain.
7" Single: Released Aug '72, on Island, by Island Records. Deleted '75. Catalogue no: **WIP 6144**
7" Single: Released Oct '77, on Polydor, by Polydor Ltd. Catalogue no: **2001 739**

Roxy Rollers

DISCO SKATING
Tracks: / Disco skating.
7" Single: Released Nov '80, on Young Blood, by Young Blood Records. Deleted Nov '83. Catalogue no: **YB 99**

Roy, Barbara

GONNA PUT UP A FIGHT
Tracks: / Gonna put up a fight / Gotta see you tonight.
7" Single: Released Mar '87, on RCA, by BMG Records (UK). Deleted '87. Catalogue no: **PB 49733**
12" Single: Released Mar '87, on RCA, by BMG Records (UK). Deleted '87. Catalogue no: **PT 49734**

GOT TO SEE YOU TONIGHT
Tracks: / Got to see you tonight.
7" Single: Released Aug '86, on RCA, by BMG Records (UK). Deleted '87. Catalogue no: **PB 49803**
12" Single: Released Aug '86, on RCA, by BMG Records (UK). Deleted '87. Catalogue no: **PT 49804**

IF YOU WANT ME
Tracks: / If you want me / I've got you.
7" Single: Released Jul '81, on Excaliber, by Red Bus Records. Deleted '84. Catalogue no: **EXC 512**
12" Single: Released Jul '81, on Excaliber, by Red Bus Records. Deleted '84. Catalogue no: **EXCL 512**

WALKING TALKING DOLLY
Tracks: / Wild mountain / Walking talking dolly.
7" Single: Released Dec '86, on August (USA), by Rounder Records (USA). Catalogue no: **GBH 7S 407**

Roy C

SHOTGUN WEDDING
Tracks: / Monster mash / Shotgun wedding.
7" Single: Released Nov '72, on UK, by UK Records. Deleted '75. Catalogue no: **UK 19**
7" Single: Released Mar '82, on Decca, by Decca Records. Deleted '88. Catalogue no: **F 13902**
7" Single: Released Apr '66, on Island, by Island Records. Deleted '69. Catalogue no: **WI 273**

SHOTGUN WEDDING (OLD GOLD)
Tracks: / Shotgun wedding.
7" Single: Released Jul '88, on Old Gold, by Old Gold Records. Catalogue no: **OG 9345**

Royal...

HOMEWARD BOUND FOR CHRISTMAS
Tracks: / Homeward bound for Christmas / I couldn't live.
7" Single: Released Dec '85, on Empire Records, Catalogue no: **MSER 100**

HUCKLEBUCK, THE
Tracks: / Hucklebuck, The / I ran all the way home / Fun, fun, fun.
7" Single: Released Feb '81, on H.M.V., by EMI Records. Catalogue no: **POP 2023**

Royal Air Force

DAMBUSTERS MARCH, THE
Tracks: / Dambusters march.
7" Single: Released Oct '55, on H.M.V., by EMI Records. Deleted '58. Catalogue no: **B 10877**

Royal Assassins

OPEN UP THE RIVERS
Tracks: / Open up the rivers.
12" Single: Released May '88, on Fire, by Fire Records. Catalogue no: **BLAZE 26T**

Royal, Billy Joe

DOWN IN THE BOONDOCKS
Tracks: / Down in the boondocks.
7" Single: Released Oct '65, on CBS, by CBS Records. Deleted '68. Catalogue no: **CBS 201802**

HOW DO I LIKE TO DANCE SLOWLY
Tracks: / How do I like to dance slowly.
7" Single: Released Oct '80, on Mercury, by Phonogram Ltd. Deleted Oct '83. Catalogue no: **MER 36**

Royal Cash

RADIOACTIVITY
Tracks: / Radioactivity.
12" Single: Released Dec '83, on Buddah, by Buddah Records Inc.(USA). Catalogue no: **BDSL 503**

Royal Court Of China

Biographical details: This band come from Nashville, Tennessee but they play guitar-driven rock. Robert Logue is quoted as saying "We're just four guys who strap on our guitars and play."c.

IT'S ALL CHANGED (EP)
Tracks: / Last day, The / Forget it / Hope.
12" Single: Released Feb '88, on A&M, by A&M Records. Deleted Aug '88. Catalogue no: **AMY 424**

Royal Delite

FREAK 4 YOU
Tracks: / Freak 4 you.

12" Single: Released Oct '88, on Danceyard, by Danceyard Records. Catalogue no: **YARD T3**
7" Single: Released Oct '88, on Danceyard, by Danceyard Records. Catalogue no: **YARD 3**

Royal Family & The

DREAM DOMINION
Tracks: / Dream dominion / Art.
12" Single: Released Feb '82, on Factory (1), by Factory Records. Catalogue no: **FACT 43**

RESTRAINED IN A MOMENT
Tracks: / Restrained in a moment.
12" Single: Released Jan '88, on Gaia (UK), by Gaia Records (UK). Catalogue no: **PHASE 004**

WE LOVE THE MOON
Tracks: / We love the moon.
7" Single: Released Jan '86, on Factory (1), by Factory Records. Catalogue no: **FAC 139**

Royal Guardsmen

RETURN OF THE RED BARON
Tracks: / Return of the Red Baron.
7" Single: Released Apr '67, on Stateside, by EMI Records. Deleted '70. Catalogue no: **SS 2010**

SNOOPY V THE RED BARON
Tracks: / Snoopy v the Red Baron.
7" Single: Released Jan '67, on Stateside, by EMI Records. Deleted '70. Catalogue no: **SS 574**
7" Single: Released Oct '81, on RCA, by BMG Records (UK). Catalogue no: **GOLD 538**

SNOOPY V THE RED BARON (OLD GOLD)
Tracks: / Snoopy v the Red Baron / Pipkins, gimme dat ding / Snoopy v the Red Baron.
7" Single: Released 21 Nov '87, on Old Gold, by Old Gold Records. Catalogue no: **OG 9730**

Royal House

BETTER WAY, A
Tracks: / Better way, A.
12" Single: Released May '89, on Champion, by Champion Records. Catalogue no: **CHAMP 12201**
7" Single: Released May '89, on Champion, by Champion Records. Catalogue no: **CHAMP 201**

CAN YOU PARTY?
Tracks: / Can you party ? / Yeah buddy / Chase, The / Party people.
7" Single: Released May '88, on Champion, by Champion Records. Catalogue no: **CHAMP 79**
12" Single: Released May '88, on Champion, by Champion Records. Catalogue no: **CHAMP 1279**

GET FUNKY
Tracks: / Get funky / Get funky (version).
7" Single: Released Aug '89, on Champion, by Champion Records. Catalogue no: **CHAMP 218**
12" Single: Released Aug '89, on Champion, by Champion Records. Catalogue no: **CHAMP 12218**

PARTY PEOPLE
Tracks: / Party people.
7" Single: Released Jan '88, on Champion, by Champion Records. Catalogue no: **CHAMP 66**
12" Single: Released Jan '88, on Champion, by Champion Records. Catalogue no: **CHAMP 1266**

YEAH BUDDY
Tracks: / Yeah buddy / Chase, The.
12" Single: Released Nov '88, on Champion, by Champion Records. Catalogue no: **CHAMP 1291**
7" Single: Released Nov '88, on Champion, by Champion Records. Catalogue no: **CHAMP 91**

Royal Philharmonic

BEATLES MEDLEY
7" Single: Released Apr '83, on Evolution, by Evolution Records. Catalogue no: **RPO 20**

BEST OF BRITISH Love theme
Tracks: / Best of British (love theme) / Best of British (main theme).
7" Single: Released 13 Jun '87, on RCA, by BMG Records (UK). Catalogue no: **PB 41349**

CHAMPIONS THEME
Tracks: / Champions.
7" Single: Released Mar '84, on Safari, by Safari Records. Catalogue no: **SAFE 62**

CHRISTMAS CAROUSEL
Tracks: / Christmas carousel
7" Single: Released Dec '82, on PRT, by Castle Communications Records. Catalogue no: **7P 227**

12" Single: Released Dec '82, on PRT, by Castle Communications Records. Catalogue no: **12P 227**

FIESTA
Tracks: / Fiesta / Fiesta (part 2).
7" Single: Released Oct '82, on CBS, by CBS Records. Deleted Oct '85. Catalogue no: **CBS A 2471**

HAPPY VALLEY
Tracks: / Happy valley / Tempest.
7" Single: Released Jul '83, on Nouveau Music, Catalogue no: **NMS 1**
7" Single: Released Nov '82, on WEA, by WEA Records. Deleted Nov '85. Catalogue no: **SHELL 1**

HOOKED ON AMERICA
7" Single: Released Oct '82, on RCA, by BMG Records (UK). Catalogue no: **RCA 277**

HOOKED ON CAN CAN
Tracks: / Hooked on can can / Hooked on romance.
12" Single: Released Oct '81, on RCA, by BMG Records (UK). Catalogue no: **RCAT 151**
7" Single: Released Oct '81, on RCA, by BMG Records (UK). Catalogue no: **RCA 151**

HOOKED ON CHRISTMAS
7" Single: Released Dec '81, on PRT, by Castle Communications Records. Catalogue no: **7P 277**
7" Single: Released Dec '83, on K-Tel, by K-Tel Records. Catalogue no: **HOC 007**
12" Single: Released Dec '81, on PRT, by Castle Communications Records. Catalogue no: **12P 277**

HOOKED ON RODGERS & HAMMERSTEIN
7" Single: Released Aug '83, on K-Tel, by K-Tel Records. Catalogue no: **HOC 004**

HOOKED ON SCOTLAND THE BRAVE
7" Single: Released Apr '83, on K-Tel, by K-Tel Records. Catalogue no: **HOC 003**

IF YOU KNEW SOUSA
Tracks: / If you knew sousa (and friends) / Hooked on baroque.
12" Single: Released Jul '82, on RCA, by BMG Records (UK). Catalogue no: **RCAT 256**
7" Single: Released Jul '82, on RCA, by BMG Records (UK). Catalogue no: **RCA 256**

LOVE CAME FOR ME
Tracks: / Love came for me.
7" Single: Released Jun '84, on Cherry Lane, by Cherry Lane Productions. Deleted '86. Catalogue no: **PIP 710**

TEMPEST
Tracks: / Tempest.
7" Single: Released Jun '83, on Nouveau Music, Catalogue no: **NMS 1**

WALKING ON THE MOON
Tracks: / Walking on the moon / Arrested.
7" Single: Released Feb '83, on RCA, by BMG Records (UK). Catalogue no: **RCA 310**

WILTSHIRE RADIO ENTERTAINER
7" Single: Released Nov '82, on Wiltshire Radio, by Wiltshire Radio. Catalogue no: **WR 1**

WORLD CUP GRANDSTAND
Tracks: / World cup grandstand.
7" Single: Released Jun '82, on BBC, by BBC Records & Tapes. Deleted '87. Catalogue no: **RESL 116**

Royal Rasses

OLD TIME FRIENDS
Tracks: / Old time friends.
7" Single: Released Jan '81, on United Artists, by EMI Records. Deleted Jan '84. Catalogue no: **UP 63496**

WALL FLOWER
Tracks: / Wall flower.
7" Single: Released Nov '86, on Rhino, by Creole Records. Catalogue no: **RNO 6**

Royal Regiment Of

MOVIN' ON
Tracks: / Movin' on.
7" EP: Released May '88, on Mascot (2), Catalogue no: **RRW 05881**

Royal Scots Dragoon...

AMAZING GRACE
Tracks: / Amazing grace.
7" Single: Released Apr '72, on RCA, by BMG Records (UK). Deleted '75. Catalogue no: **RCA 2191**
7" Single: Released Oct '81, on RCA Golden Grooves, by BMG Records (UK). Catalogue no: **GOLD 532**

AMAZING GRACE (OLD GOLD)
Tracks: / Amazing grace / Little donkey.
7" Single: Released Nov '86, on Old Gold, by Old Gold Records. Catalogue no: **OG 9639**

HEYKENS SERENADE
Tracks: / Heykens serenade / Day is over, The.
7" Single: Released Aug '72, on RCA, by BMG Records (UK). Deleted '75. Catalogue no: **RCA 2251**

LITTLE DRUMMER BOY
Tracks: / Little drummer boy.
7" Single: Released Dec '72, on RCA, by BMG Records (UK). Deleted '75. Catalogue no: **RCA 2301**

Royal Tournament

CHARIOTS OF FIRE
Tracks: / Chariots of fire / Fanfare.
7" Single: Released Jun '82, on Polydor, by Polydor Ltd. Deleted Jun '85. Catalogue no: **POSP 460**

Royalle Delite

(I'LL BE A) FREAK FOR YOU
Tracks: / I'll be a freak for you.
7" Single: Released Sep '85, on Streetwave, Deleted '88. Catalogue no: **KHAN 51**

I'LL COME WHEN YOU CALL
Tracks: / I'll come when you call / Radio cut.
12" Single: Released Aug '86, on Streetwise, Catalogue no: **MKHAN 71**

SPEND A LITTLE TIME WITH ME
Tracks: / Send a little time with me.
7" Pic: Released Dec '85, on Streetwise, Catalogue no: **MKHPX 60**
7" Single: Released Dec '85, on Streetwise, Catalogue no: **KHAN 60**
12" Single: Released Dec '85, on Streetwise, Catalogue no: **MKHAN 60**

Royals

CHARLIE (WILL YOU MARRY ME)
Tracks: / Charlie (Will you marry me) / All the Queens men.
7" Single: Released Sep '80, on Monarch, by Monarch Records. Deleted '83. Catalogue no: **MON 17**

LADY DI
Tracks: / Lady Di / Lady Di theme.
7" Single: Released Jul '81, on Rimington, Deleted Jul '84. Catalogue no: **JPR 1**

MAN WHO WOULD BE KING
Tracks: / Man who would be king.
7" Single: Released Dec '84, on Dakota, Catalogue no: **DAK 20**

PICK UP THE PIECES (SINGLE)
Tracks: / Pick up the pieces.
7" Single: Released May '89, on Studio One, Catalogue no: **UNKNOWN**

STRANGE WORLD
Tracks: / Strange world / No one knows.
12" Single: Released Jun '81, on Kingdom, by Kingdom Records. Deleted '83. Catalogue no: **KV 8017 12**

Royalty Ladies

IT'S OUR TURN
Tracks: / It's our turn.
12" Single: Released Oct '87, on Sharpp (USA), Catalogue no: **SHR 2154**

Royston

LONG DISTANCE LOVE
Tracks: / Long distance love.
7" Single: Released Oct '83, on VM, by VM Records. Catalogue no: **VMS 002**

Roza, Lita

HEY THERE
Tracks: / Hey there.
7" Single: Released Oct '55, on Decca, by Decca Records. Deleted '58. Catalogue no: **F 10611**

HOW MUCH IS THAT DOGGIE IN THE WINDOW
Tracks: / How much is that doggie in the window.
7" Single: Released Mar '53, on Decca, by Decca Records. Deleted '56. Catalogue no: **F 10070**

JIMMY UNKNOWN
Tracks: / Jimmy unknown.
7" Single: Released Mar '56, on Decca, by Decca Records. Deleted '59. Catalogue no: **F 10679**

R.P.M.

LOST IN SPACE
Tracks: / Lost in space / Watch the world go round.
7" Single: Released Aug '81, on Ariola, by BMG Records (UK). Deleted Aug '84. Catalogue no: **ARO 267**

NOW THAT SUMMER'S HERE
Tracks: / Now that summer's here / I'm energy.

7" Single: Released Jul '81, on Ariola, by BMG Records (UK). Deleted '84. Catalogue no: **ARO 264**

RUBETTES - JUKEBOX JIVE (Released on Polydor)

R.S.W.

PROBABLY A ROBBERY
CD 5": Released Sep '89, on Mute, by Mute Records. Catalogue no: **UNKNOWN**
7" Single: Released Sep '89, on Mute, by Mute Records. Catalogue no: **UNKNOWN**
12" Single: Released Sep '89, on Mute, by Mute Records. Catalogue no: **UNKNOWN**

R-Tyme

ILLUSION
Tracks: / Illusion / R-theme.
12" Single: Released 3 Jul '89, on Kool Kat, by Kool Kat Records. Catalogue no: **KOOLR 500**
12" Single: Released 3 Jul '89, on Kool Kat, by Kool Kat Records. Catalogue no: **KOOLT 500**

Rubber Rodeo

ANYWHERE WITH YOU
Tracks: / Anywhere with you.
7" Single: Released Aug '84, on EAT, Catalogue no: **CHOMP 2**
12" Single: Released Aug '84, on EAT, Catalogue no: **CHOMP 212**

HARDEST THING
Tracks: / Hardest thing / Walking after midnight.
7" Single: Released Jun '84, on EAT, Catalogue no: **CHOMP 1**
12" Single: Released Jun '84, on EAT, Catalogue no: **CHOMP 112**

Rubber Yahoo

RUBBER YAHOO
Tracks: / Rubber Yahoo.
7" Single: Released Jul '85, on Off The Cuff, Catalogue no: **YAHOO 1**

Rubella Ballet

42% F
Tracks: / 42% F.
12" Single: on Jungle, by Jungle Records. Catalogue no: **JUNG 12**

ARCTIC FLOWERS
Tracks: / Arctic flowers.
7" Single: Released '86, on Dayglo, Catalogue no: **DAYGLO 3**
12" Single: Released 1 Sep '86, on Ubiquitous, by Ubiquitous Records. Catalogue no: **DAYGLO 003**

BALLET DANCE
Tracks: / Ballet dance.
7" Single: Released Sep '82, on Xntrix, Catalogue no: **XN 2005**

MONEY TALKS
Tracks: / Money talks.
12" Single: Released Mar '85, on Ubiquitous Dayglo, Catalogue no: **DAYGLO 1**

Rubettes

BABY I KNOW
Tracks: / Baby I know.
7" Single: Released Feb '77, on State, by State Records. Deleted '80. Catalogue no: **STAT 37**

DON'T COME CRYING
Tracks: / Don't come crying.
7" Single: Released Feb '82, on V-Tone, Catalogue no: **VTONE 004**

FOR DEE O DEE
Tracks: / For dee o dee.
7" Single: Released Jun '75, on State, by State Records. Deleted '78. Catalogue no: **STAT 7**

I CAN DO IT
Tracks: / I can do it.
7" Single: Released Mar '75, on State, by State Records. Deleted '78. Catalogue no: **STAT 1**

JUKE BOX JIVE (See panel above)
Tracks: / Jukebox jive / When you're falling in love.
7" Single: Released Nov '74, on Polydor, by Polydor Ltd. Deleted '77. Catalogue no: **2058 529**

LITTLE DARLING
Tracks: / Little darlin'.
7" Single: Released Nov '75, on State, by State Records. Deleted '78. Catalogue no: **STAT 13**

SUGAR BABY LOVE
Tracks: / Sugar baby love / Tonight / Little darlin' / I can do it / Juke box jive / Foe-deoh-dee.
7" EP: Released Aug '81, on Polydor, by Polydor Ltd. Catalogue no: **POSP 342**
7" Single: Released May '74, on Polydor, by Polydor Ltd. Deleted '77. Catalogue no: **2058 442**
7" Single: Released Jul '82, on Old Gold, by Old Gold Records. Catalogue no: **OG 9152**

TONIGHT
Tracks: / Tonight.
7" Single: Released Jul '74, on Polydor, by Polydor Ltd. Deleted '77. Catalogue no: **2058 499**

UNDER ONE ROOF
Tracks: / Under one roof.
7" Single: Released Sep '76, on State, by State Records. Deleted '79. Catalogue no: **STAT 27**

YOU'RE THE REASON WHY
Tracks: / You're the reason why.
7" Single: Released May '76, on State, by State Records. Deleted '79. Catalogue no: **STAT 20**

Rubey Forde

SPEED OF LIGHT
Tracks: / Speed of light.
12" Single: Released Aug '85, on Ram, by Ram Records. Catalogue no: **12CHP 7012**

Rubicon

I COULD SHOW YOU LOVE
Tracks: / I could show you love.
7" Single: Released Mar '88, on Preset, by Preset Records. Catalogue no: **PRES 200**
12" Single: Released Mar '88, on Preset, by Preset Records. Catalogue no: **12 PRES 200**

Rubinoos

I THINK WE'RE ALONE NOW
Tracks: / I think we're alone now.
7" Single: Released Jan '88, on Beserkley.

by Beserkley Records (USA). Catalogue no: **7BZ 1202**

Ruby Blue

BECAUSE
Tracks: / Because.
7" Single: Released Mar '88, on Red Flame (1), by Red Flame Records. Catalogue no: **RF 757**
12" Single: Released Mar '88, on Red Flame (1), by Red Flame Records. Catalogue no: **RF 1257**

BLOOMSBURY BLUE
Tracks: / Bloomsbury blue / Save me / Childs song (Only on 12" version.).
7" Single: Released Nov '88, on Red Flame (1), by Red Flame Records. Catalogue no: **RF 759**
12" Single: Released Nov '88, on Red Flame (1), by Red Flame Records. Catalogue no: **RF 1259**

SO UNLIKE ME
Tracks: / So unlike me / Life and time of the twentieth century.
7" Single: Released Sep '87, on Red Flame (1), by Red Flame Records. Catalogue no: **RF 756**
12" Single: Released Sep '87, on Red Flame (1), by Red Flame Records. Catalogue no: **RF 1256**

Ruby Desire

BAD GIRLS
Tracks: / Bad girls.
12" Single: Released 23 Nov '87, on Interior Music, by Interior Music Records. Catalogue no: **IM 002**

Ruby & The Romantics

OUR DAY WILL COME (SINGLE)
Tracks: / Our day will come.
7" Single: Released Mar '63, on London-American, Deleted '66. Catalogue no: **HLR 9679**

Rudder, David

Biographical details: David Rudder was born in 1953 in Trinidad. He has been a sensational success in the last few years in the island's annual Carnival, winning many titles as a calypso/soca artist, and controversial because he came from a soul/R&B direction and because he has not adopted a traditional calypso type of nom-de-plume (though Mighty Sparrow called him King David). Calypso purists are critical, but they forget that Soca itself was fueled by a new international consciousness and was criticised before becoming today's dominant calypso form. Rudder told David Heatherington in the Wire: 'When people hear soca they'll say , 'I'm hearing jazz in there, I'm hearing reggae, samba, blues. In fact...they're hearing Africa...the reason I've crossed over is because I've crossed back''. (Donald Clarke 4.2.88)..

BAHIA GIRL
Tracks: / Bahia girl / Outta hand.
7" Single: Released '86, on London Records, by London Records. Catalogue no: **LON 98**
12" Single: Released '86, on London Records, by London Records. Catalogue no: **LONX 98**

MADNESS
Tracks: / Madness.
12" Single: Released Oct '87, on London Records, by London Records. Catalogue no: **LONX 148**

THIS PARTY IS IT
Tracks: / This party is it / Bacchanel lady / Rally round the West Indies..
12" Single: Released Jul '88, on London Records, by London Records. Catalogue no: **LONX 189**
7" Single: Released Jul '88, on London Records, by London Records. Catalogue no: **LON 189**

Ruddock, Annie

MY HEART BELONGS TO YOU
Tracks: / My heart belongs to you / My heart belongs to you (Pop house) (7" & 12" only.) / My heart belongs to you (12" mix) (12" & CD single only.) / My heart belongs to you (dub) (12" only.) / My heart belongs to you (pop 12") (12" special only.) / My heart belongs to you (Pop dub) (12" special only.) / My heart belongs to you (pop radio mix) (12" special only.) / Mony mony (CD single only.).
Note: Arranger: Joe Cavanagh.
7" Single: Released Oct '88, on EMI, by EMI Records. Deleted Jun '89. Catalogue no: **EM 70**
CD 5": Released Oct '88, on EMI, by EMI Records. Deleted Jun '89. Catalogue no: **CDEM 70**
12" Single: Released Oct '88, on EMI, by EMI Records. Deleted Aug '89. Catalogue no: **12EM 70**
12" Single: Released Nov '88, on EMI, by EMI Records. Deleted Jun '89. Catalogue no: **12EMX 70**

Rude Boys

RUDE BOY SHUFFLE
Tracks: / Rude boy shuffle.
12" Single: Released Aug '89, on SKA, by SKA Records. Catalogue no: **SKAT 002**

Rudi

BIG TIME
Tracks: / Big time.
12" Single: Released Sep '79, on Good Vibration, by Good Vibrations Records. Catalogue no: **GOT 12**

CRIMSON
Tracks: / Crimson / 14 steps.
7" Single: Released Feb '82, on Jamming, Catalogue no: **CREATE 3**

I SPY
Tracks: / I spy.
7" Single: Released Aug '79, on Good Vibration, by Good Vibrations Records. Catalogue no: **GO 12**

WHEN I WAS DEAD
Tracks: / When I was dead / Beware wolf / Pressures on.
7" Single: Released Oct '81, on Jamming, Catalogue no: **CREATE 1**

Rudi Mental

PLAIN TALK
Tracks: / Plain talk.
7" Single: Released Dec '81, on Slime, Deleted '83. Catalogue no: **RIS 1**

Rudi & Mona

AEROBIC AFFAIR
Tracks: / Aerobic affair.
7" Single: Released Nov '83, on Cambra, by Cambra Records. Deleted '88. Catalogue no: **CMB 06**

Rudie, Jennifer

FOREVER LOVING YOU
Tracks: / Forever loving you / Nuff stylee.
12" Single: Released Mar '84, on Ruff Cut, Catalogue no: **RC 003**

Rudimentary Peni

FARCE
Tracks: / Farce.
7" Single: Released Jul '82, on Crass, by Crass Records. Catalogue no: **CRASS 211984/2**

FIRST EP
7" EP: on Himalayan, by Southern Studios Ltd.. Catalogue no: **BOOB 001**

RUDIMENTARY PENI
Tracks: / Rudimentary peni.
7" Single: Released Mar '82, on Outer Himalayen, Catalogue no: **29000**

Rudy & Rhonda

AEROBIC AFFAIR
Tracks: / Aerobic affair / Aerobic around the world.
7" Single: Released Mar '84, on Cambra, by Cambra Records. Deleted '88. Catalogue no: **CMB 08**

Rudy & Rialtos

CHRISTMAS TEARS WILL FALL
Tracks: / Chrismas tears will fall / Week of love.
7" Single: Released Dec '81, on Dakota, Deleted Dec '84. Catalogue no: **DAK 3**

Rudy & Sketto

EVERY NIGHT
Tracks: / Every night.
12" Single: Released Jan '84, on Pama, by Pama Records. Catalogue no: **PMD 3237**

Rudy & Valentinos

SWAMP STOMP
Tracks: / Swamp stomp.
7" Single: Released Jul '84, on Towerbell, Catalogue no: **TOW 57**
12" Single: Released Jul '84, on Towerbell, Catalogue no: **12TOW 57**

Rue De Remarx

ONE WAY TRIP
Tracks: / One way trip / Full circle.
7" Single: Released Jan '82, on Underground Music, Catalogue no: **UMA 003**

Ruefrex

CAPITAL LETTERS
Tracks: / Capital letters.
7" Single: Released Apr '83, on Kabuki, Catalogue no: **KAR 7**

IN THE TRAPS
Tracks: / In the traps / Leader of the last resort / In the tracks (instrumental) (Available on 12" version only).
7" Single: Released '86, on Kasper, Catalogue no: **KAS 3**
12" Single: Released '86, on Kasper, Catalogue no: **12KAS 3**

PAIN IN MIND
Tracks: / Pain in mind / Perfect crime.
7" Single: Released Aug '84, on One By One, by One By One Records. Catalogue no: **1 X 1**

WILD COLONIAL BOY
Tracks: / Wild colonial boy / Even in the dark hours.
7" Single: Released Aug '85, on Kasper, Catalogue no: **KAT 1**
7" Single: Released '86, on Kasper, Catalogue no: **KAS 2**
12" Single: Released '86, on Kasper, Catalogue no: **12KAS 2**

Ruffelle, Frances

HE'S MY HERO
Tracks: / He's my hero / Love's not for me.
7" Single: Released '86, on RCA, by BMG Records (UK). Catalogue no: **PB 40731**
12" Single: Released '86, on RCA, by BMG Records (UK). Catalogue no: **PT 40732**

ON MY OWN
Tracks: / On my own (Taken from 'Les Miserables'.) / Finale / Do you hear the people sing? / One day more (Available on cassette version only) / Prologue (Available on cassette version only).
7" Single: Released Sep '87, on RCA, by BMG Records (UK). Deleted May '89. Catalogue no: **PB 41529**
7" Single: Released '86, on First Night, by First Night Records. Catalogue no: **7 SCORE 2**
12" Single: Released Sep '87, on RCA, by BMG Records (UK). Deleted May '89. Catalogue no: **PT 41530**

Ruffin, Bruce

GET IT UP FOR LOVE
Tracks: / Get it up for love / Just got to see it through.
7" Single: Released Mar '81, on RCA, by BMG Records (UK). Deleted Mar '85. Catalogue no: **RCA 57**

JUST A PRECAUTION
Tracks: / Just a precaution.
12" Single: Released May '83, on Slick, by Slick Records. Catalogue no: **SR 001**

MAD ABOUT YOU
Tracks: / Mad about you.
7" Single: Released Jun '72, on Rhino, by Creole Records. Deleted '75. Catalogue no: **RNO 101**

MESSIN' AROUND
Tracks: / Messin' around / Was I just a fool.
7" Single: Released May '80, on WEA, by WEA Records. Deleted '85. Catalogue no: **PB 251**

RAIN
Tracks: / Rain.
7" Single: Released May '71, on Trojan, by Trojan Records. Deleted '74. Catalogue no: **TR 7814**

Ruffin, David

WALK AWAY FROM LOVE
Tracks: / Walk away from love / I'll say forever my love.
7" Single: Released Oct '81, on Motown, by BMG Records (UK). Catalogue no: **TMG 1017**
7" Single: Released Apr '88, on Motown, by BMG Records (UK). Catalogue no: **ZB 41927**

Ruffin, Jimmy

EASY JUST TO SAY (I LOVE YOU)
Tracks: / Easy to say I love you / You never have time (for me) / Easy just to say (I love you) / You never have time (for me) / Easy just to say (I love you) (Ext. club mix) / Easy just to say (I love you) (Eeesay mix).
7" Single: Released Jun '87, on Polydor, by Polydor Ltd. Catalogue no: **POSP 869**
12" Single: Released Jun '87, on Polydor, by Polydor Ltd. Deleted Jan '88. Catalogue no: **POSPX 869**

FAREWELL IS A LONELY SOUND
Tracks: / Farewell is a lonely sound.
7" Single: Released Feb '70, on Tamla Motown, by Motown Records (UK). Deleted '73. Catalogue no: **TMG 726**

FAREWELL IS A LONELY SOUND (SINGLE)
Tracks: / Farewell is a lonely sound.
7" Single: Released Feb '70, on Motown, by BMG Records (UK). Deleted '73. Catalogue no: **TMG 726**
7" Single: Released Oct '81, on Motown, by BMG Records (UK). Catalogue no: **TMG 922**

GONNA GIVE HER ALL THE LOVE I'VE GOT
Tracks: / Gonna give her all the love I've got.
7" Single: Released Apr '67, on Tamla Motown, by Motown Records (UK). Deleted '70. Catalogue no: **TMG 603**
7" Single: Released Apr '85, on Motown, by BMG Records (UK). Deleted '87. Catalogue no: **TMG 996**
12" Single: Released Apr '85, on Motown, by BMG Records (UK). Deleted '87. Catalogue no: **TMGT 996**

HOLD ON TO MY LOVE
Tracks: / Hold on to my love / Hold on to my love (part 2).
7" Single: Released May '80, on RSO, by Polydor Ltd. Deleted '83. Catalogue no: **RSO 57**

I'LL SAY FOREVER MY LOVE
Tracks: / I'll say forever my love / It's wonderful.
7" Single: Released Jul '70, on Tamla Motown, by Motown Records (UK). Deleted '73. Catalogue no: **TMG 740**
7" Single: Released Oct '81, on Motown, by BMG Records (UK). Deleted '83. Catalogue no: **TMG 961**

I'M GONNA LOVE YOU FOREVER
Tracks: / I'm gonna love you forever.
12" Single: Released Jun '84, on ERC, Catalogue no: **ERCRL 109**
7" Single: Released Jun '84, on ERC, Catalogue no: **ERCR 109**

IT'S WONDERFUL
Tracks: / It's wonderful.
7" Single: Released Oct '70, on Tamla Motown, by Motown Records (UK). Deleted '73. Catalogue no: **TMG 753**

I'VE PASSED THIS WAY BEFORE
Tracks: / I've passed this way before.
7" Single: Released Feb '67, on Tamla Motown, by Motown Records (UK). Deleted '70. Catalogue no: **TMG 593**
7" Single: Released Oct '81, on Motown, by BMG Records (UK). Deleted '83. Catalogue no: **TMG 934**
7" Single: Released Aug '69, on Tamla Motown, by Motown Records (UK). Deleted '72. Catalogue no: **TMG 703**

TELL ME WHAT YOU WANT
Tracks: / Tell me what you want.
7" Single: Released Nov '74, on Polydor, by Polydor Ltd. Deleted '77. Catalogue no: **2058 433**

THERE WILL NEVER BE ANOTHER YOU
Tracks: / There will never be another you.
7" Single: Released Jan '85, on EMI, by EMI Records. Deleted '88. Catalogue no: **EMI 5541**

WHAT BECOMES OF THE BROKEN-HEARTED
Tracks: / What becomes of the broken hearted?.
7" Single: Released Oct '81, on Motown, by BMG Records (UK). Catalogue no: **TMG 1052**
7" Single: Released Oct '66, on Tamla Motown, by Motown Records (UK). Deleted '69. Catalogue no: **TMG 577**
7" Single: Released Jul '74, on Tamla Motown, by Motown Records (UK). Deleted '77. Catalogue no: **TMG 911**

YOUNG HEART
Tracks: / Young heart.
12" Single: Released Mar '85, on ERC, Catalogue no: **ERCL 117**
7" Single: Released Mar '85, on ERC, Catalogue no: **ERC 117**

Ruffin & Kendricks

I COULDN'T BELIEVE IT
Tracks: / I couldn't believe it / Don't know why you're dreaming.
7" Single: Released Jan '88, on RCA, by BMG Records (UK). Deleted May '89. Catalogue no: **PB 49611**
12" Single: Released Jan '88, on RCA, by BMG Records (UK). Deleted May '89. Catalogue no: **PT 49612**

Rufus

AIN'T NOBODY
Tracks: / Stop on by / Ain't nobody / Don't go to strangers.
7" Single: Released Jun '89, on Warner Bros., by WEA Records. Catalogue no: **W 2880**
7" Single: Released Mar '84, on Warner Bros., by WEA Records. Catalogue no: **RCK 1**
12" Single: Released Jun '89, on Warner Bros., by WEA Records. Catalogue no: **W**

2880T
12" Single: Released Mar '84, on Warner Bros., by WEA Records. Catalogue no: **RCKT 1**
CD 5": Released Jun '89, on Warner Bros., by WEA Records. Catalogue no: **W 2880CD**
Cassingle: Released Jun '89, on Warner Bros., by WEA Records. Catalogue no: **W 2880C**

ANY LOVE
Tracks: / Any love / What am I missing?.
7" Single: Released Mar '80, on MCA, by MCA Records. Deleted '83. Catalogue no: **MCA 575**
12" Single: Released Mar '80, on MCA, by MCA Records. Deleted '83. Catalogue no: **MCAT 575**

DO YOU LOVE WHAT YOU FEEL
Tracks: / Do you love what you feel.
7" Single: Released Jun '84, on MCA, by MCA Records. Catalogue no: **MCA 892**
12" Single: Released Jun '84, on MCA, by MCA Records. Catalogue no: **MCAT 892**

TAKE IT TO THE TOP
Tracks: / Take it to the top / Distant lover.
7" Single: Released Mar '83, on Warner Bros., by WEA Records. Catalogue no: **W 9790**
12" Single: Released Mar '83, on Warner Bros., by WEA Records. Catalogue no: **W 9790 T**

TONIGHT WE LOVE
Tracks: / Tonight we love / Party til' you're broke.
7" Single: Released Mar '81, on MCA, by MCA Records. Deleted Mar '84. Catalogue no: **MCA 690**
12" Single: Released Mar '81, on MCA, by MCA Records. Deleted Mar '84. Catalogue no: **MCAT 690**

Rumba Tres

RUMBAMANIA
Tracks: / Rumbamania.
7" Single: Released Sep '88, on Red Bullet, Catalogue no: **KWEST 3**
12" Single: Released Sep '88, on Red Bullet, Catalogue no: **KWEST T3**

Rumblefish

DON'T LEAVE ME
Tracks: / Don't leave me.
12" Single: Released 27 Jun '88, on Summerhouse, by Summerhouse Records. Catalogue no: **SUMS 006**

MEDICINE
Tracks: / Medicine / Lodgers, The / Sing slim / So lightly.
12" Single: Released Jan '88, on Summerhouse, by Summerhouse Records. Catalogue no: **SUMS 5**

TUG BOAT LINE
Tracks: / Tug boat line.
7" Single: Released Mar '87, on Pink Label, by Pink Label Records. Catalogue no: **PINKY 16**
12" Single: Released Mar '87, on Pink Label, by Pink Label Records. Catalogue no: **PINKY 16T**

Rumour

I DON'T WANT THE NIGHT TO END
Tracks: / I don't want the night to end / Pyramids.
7" Single: Released Sep '80, on Stiff, by Stiff Records. Deleted '83. Catalogue no: **BUY 92**

Rumpf, Inga

IT'S ONLY LOVE
Tracks: / It's only love / Pain in my heart.
7" Single: Released Feb '80, on RCA, by BMG Records (UK). Deleted Feb '83. Catalogue no: **PB 1759**

Rumple-Stilts-Skin

I THINK I WANT TO DANCE WITH YOU
Tracks: / I think I want to dance with you.
7" Single: Released Sep '83, on Montage, by Polydor Ltd. Deleted '86. Catalogue no: **POSP 649**

Run D.M.C.

CHRISTMAS IN HOLLIS
Tracks: / Christmas in Hollis / Peter Piper / Walk this way (Available on 12" single only.) / My adidas (Available on 12" single only.) / King of rock (Available on 12" single only.).
7" Single: Released '88, on London Records, by London Records. Deleted Feb '89. Catalogue no: **LONG 163**
7" Single: Released 21 Nov '87, on London Records, by London Records. Catalogue no: **LON 163**
12" Single: Released 21 Nov '87, on London Records, by London Records. Deleted Feb '89. Catalogue no: **LONX 163**

GHOSTBUSTERS
Tracks: / Ghostbusters / Pause.
CD 5": Released Aug '89, on Profile (USA), by Profile Records (USA). Catalogue no: **PROCD 262**
Cassingle: Released Aug '89, on MCA, by MCA Records. Catalogue no: **MCAC 1360**
7" Single: Released Aug '89, on MCA, by MCA Records. Catalogue no: **MCA 1360**
12" Single: Released Aug '89, on Profile (USA), by Profile Records (USA). Catalogue no: **PROFT 262**

IT'S TRICKY (REMIX)
Tracks: / It's tricky (remix) / Proud to be black / Up tempo (extra track on 12" only) / It's tricky (scratchapella) (Extra track on 12" only) / Tricky (reprise) (Extra track on 12" only).
7" Single: Released May '87, on London Records, by London Records. Deleted Sep '87. Catalogue no: **LON 130**
12" Single: Released May '87, on London Records, by London Records. Deleted Feb '89. Catalogue no: **LONX 130**

KING OF ROCK (SINGLE)
Tracks: / King of rock / Jam master Jay / You talk too much (12" only) / King of rock (cut-up) (12 BRWX 56 only) / Jay's game (12 BRWX 56 only) / Rock box (12 BRWX 56 only).
12" Single: Released '86, on 4th & Broadway, by Island Records. Deleted Jul '87. Catalogue no: **12 BRWX 56**
7" Single: Released Mar '85, on 4th & Broadway, by Island Records. Catalogue no: **BRW 21**
7" Single: Released '86, on 4th & Broadway, by Island Records. Catalogue no: **BRW 56**
12" Single: Released Mar '85, on 4th & Broadway, by Island Records. Catalogue no: **12 BRW 21**
12" Single: Released '86, on 4th & Broadway, by Island Records. Deleted Jun '88. Catalogue no: **12 BRW 56**

MARY MARY
Tracks: / Mary Mary / Razing hell.
7" Single: Released Aug '88, on London Records, by London Records. Deleted Feb '89. Catalogue no: **LON 191**
12" Single: Released Aug '88, on London Records, by London Records. Deleted Feb '89. Catalogue no: **LONX 191**
Special: Released Aug '88, on London Records, by London Records. Deleted Feb '89. Catalogue no: **LONS 191**

MY ADIDAS
Tracks: / My Adidas / Peter Pan (Inst).
7" Single: Released '86, on London Records, by London Records. Deleted Oct '88. Catalogue no: **LON 101**
12" Single: Released '86, on London Records, by London Records. Deleted Oct '88. Catalogue no: **LONX 101**

PETER PIPER
Tracks: / Peter Piper / My adidas / Walk this way (12" only) / King of rock (12" only).
7" Single: Released Sep '87, on London Records, by London Records. Catalogue no: **LON 154**
12" Single: Released Sep '87, on London Records, by London Records. Catalogue no: **LONX 154**

ROCK BOX
Tracks: / Rock box.
7" Single: Released Jul '84, on 4th & Broadway, by Island Records. Catalogue no: **BRW 8**
12" Single: Released Jul '84, on 4th & Broadway, by Island Records. Deleted '87. Catalogue no: **12 BRW 8**

RUN'S HOUSE
Tracks: / Run's house / Beat to the rhyme / Run's house (instr) (Only available on 12" version) / Beats to the rhyme (instr) (Only available on 12" version).
CD 5": Released '88, on London Records, by London Records. Deleted Jul '89. Catalogue no: **LONCD 177**
7" Single: Released '88, on London Records, by London Records. Deleted Feb '89. Catalogue no: **LONP 177**
7" Single: Released Apr '88, on London Records, by London Records. Deleted Oct '88. Catalogue no: **LON 177**
12" Single: Released Apr '88, on London Records, by London Records. Deleted Oct '88. Catalogue no: **LONX 177**

WALK THIS WAY
Tracks: / Walk this way / Walk this way (Inst.) / My Adidas (Available on 12" version only).
7" Single: Released '86, on London Records, by London Records. Deleted Oct '88. Catalogue no: **LON 104**
12" Single: Released '86, on London Records, by London Records. Deleted Oct '88. Catalogue no: **LONX 104**

YOU BE ILLIN'
Tracks: / Hit it Run.
7" Single: Released Jan '87, on London Records, by London Records. Deleted Sep '87. Catalogue no: **LON 118**
12" Single: Released Jan '87, on London Records, by London Records. Deleted Feb '89. Catalogue no: **LONX 118**

YOU TALK TOO MUCH
Tracks: / You talk too much.
7" Single: Released Apr '85, on 4th & Broadway, by Island Records. Catalogue no: **BRW 25**
12" Single: Released Apr '85, on 4th & Broadway, by Island Records. Deleted Jul '87. Catalogue no: **12 BRW 25**

Run Rig

ALBA
Tracks: / Alba / Worker for the wind.
7" Single: Released Nov '87, on Ridle, Catalogue no: **RRS 007**

DANCE CALLED AMERICA
Tracks: / Dance called America / Na h-uain a's t-earrach.
7" Single: Released Aug '84, on Simple, Deleted '87. Catalogue no: **SIM 4**
12" Single: Released Aug '84, on Simple, Deleted '87. Catalogue no: **12 SIM 4**

LOCH LOMOND
Tracks: / Loch Lomond / Tuireadh.
7" Single: Released Dec '82, on Run Rig, Catalogue no: **RRS 103**

NEWS FROM HEAVEN
Tracks: / News from heaven / Small town / Chi min tir (Available on 12" format) / Times they are a changing (Available on 12" format).
12" Single: Released Sep '89, on Chrysalis, by Chrysalis Records. Catalogue no: **CHS 123404**
Cassingle: Released Sep '89, on Chrysalis, by Chrysalis Records. Catalogue no: **CHSMC 3404**
7" Single: Released Sep '89, on Chrysalis, by Chrysalis Records. Catalogue no: **CHS 3404**
CD 5": Released Sep '89, on Chrysalis, by Chrysalis Records. Catalogue no: **CHSCD 3404**

PROTECT AND SURVIVE
Tracks: / Protect and survive / Protect and survive (live) / Hearts of olden glory (live).
7" Single: Released 22 Aug '88, on Chrysalis, by Chrysalis Records. Catalogue no: **CHS 3284**
12" Single: Released 22 Aug '88, on Chrysalis, by Chrysalis Records. Catalogue no: **CHS 123284**

SKYE
Tracks: / Skye.
7" Single: Released Nov '84, on Simple, Deleted '87. Catalogue no: **SIM 8**

WORK SONG, THE
Tracks: / Work song.
7" Single: Released '88, on Ridge, Catalogue no: **RR 7006**

Rundgren, Todd

Biographical details: Todd Rundgren was born in 1948 in Philadelphia; he is a singer, songwriter, producer and multi-instumentalist. Inspired by the British Invasion and earlier groups like the Ventures, he acquired a guitar and soon formed the Nazz, named from a Lord Buckley routine; their three albums didn't sell very well at the time but are now regarded as classic US pop. While making these albums he was hooked on production and was hired by Albert Grossman as producer/engineer at his Bearsville studio near Woodstock, New York; his fame as a producer and as a performer since 1970 are about equal: his biggest commercial success as a producer is probably Meat Loaf's *Bat Out Of Hell*; on his own albums he has often played all the instruments himself, and they often suffer from too many ideas on one record. His work too fragmented to bring him superstar status, yet every album has charted in the USA; he is one of pop's enigmatic all-rounders. (Donald Clarke 27.5.87).

BANG THE DRUM ALL DAY
Tracks: / Bang the drum all day.
7" Single: Released Jun '83, on Lamborghini, by Lamborghini Records. Catalogue no: **LMG 1**

I SAW THE LIGHT
Tracks: / I saw the light.
7" Single: Released Jun '73, on Bearsville (USA), Deleted '76. Catalogue no: **K 15506**

MATED
Tracks: / Mated.
7" Single: Released Jun '85, on Food For Thought, by Music For Nations Records. Catalogue no: **YUM 107**

SOMETHING TO FALL BACK ON
Tracks: / Something to fall back on / Lock jaw / Something to fall back on (dance mix) (Available on 12" version only).
7" Single: Released '86, on Warner Bros., by WEA Records. Catalogue no: **W 8862**
12" Single: Released '86, on Warner Bros., by WEA Records. Catalogue no: **W 8862 T**

TIME HEALS
Tracks: / Time heals.
7" Single: Released Nov '82, on Bearsville (USA), Catalogue no: **AVAB 1**

TODD RUNDGREN
Tracks: / Bang the drum all day / I saw the light / Can we still be friends / All the children sing.
CD 3": Released '88, on Special Edition, by Castle Communications Records. Catalogue no: **CD3-6**

Runestaff

DO IT!
Tracks: / Do it!.
7" Single: Released Oct '85, on FM, by FM-Revolver Records. Catalogue no: **VHF 17**

ROAD TO RUIN
Tracks: / Road to ruin.
7" Single: Released Mar '85, on FM, by FM-Revolver Records. Catalogue no: **VHF 5**

Running Dogs

PRESENT TENSE
Tracks: / Present tense.
7" Single: Released Mar '80, on Shooting Star, Catalogue no: **SHOOT 1**

Running Wild

BAD TO THE BONE
Tracks: / Bad to the bone / Battle of Waterloo / March on (Not on 7".).
7" Single: Released Nov '89, on EMI (Noise), Catalogue no: **12EM 116**
7" Single: Released Nov '89, on EMI (Noise), Catalogue no: **203 555 7**
7" Single: Released Nov '89, on EMI (Noise), Catalogue no: **EM 116**
CD 5": Released Nov '89, on EMI (Noise), Catalogue no: **203 555 2**
CD 5": Released Nov '89, on EMI (Noise), Catalogue no: **CDEM 116**
7" Single: Released Nov '89, on EMI (Noise), Catalogue no: **203 555 6**

Runs

BUN IN THE OVEN
Tracks: / Bun in the oven.
7" Single: Released Feb '80, on Carrere, Deleted Feb '85. Catalogue no: **CAR 139**

Runswick, Daryl

MY FAMILY & OTHER ANIMALS
Tracks: / My family and other animals / Caterpillars and spiders.
7" Single: Released Oct '87, on BBC, by BBC Records & Tapes. Deleted Apr '89. Catalogue no: **RESL 220**
12" Single: Released Oct '87, on BBC, by BBC Records & Tapes. Deleted Apr '89. Catalogue no: **12RSL 220**

SKY CRYING RAIN
Tracks: / Sky crying rain.
7" Single: Released May '81, on BBC, by BBC Records & Tapes. Deleted '87. Catalogue no: **RESL 89**

WE THE ACCUSED
Tracks: / We the accused.
7" Single: Released Sep '80, on BBC, by BBC Records & Tapes. Deleted Sep '83. Catalogue no: **RESL 83**

Rupert Bear

RUPERT BEAR'S NEW ADVENTURES
Note: Four books & 1 long play cassette in presentation pack.
Special: Released Apr '88, on Tempo, by Warwick Records. Catalogue no: **00 104 132 0**

Rupert & Rupettes

SLOAN RAP
Tracks: / Sloan rap.
7" Single: Released May '83, on Works, by Works Records. Deleted '84. Catalogue no: **WK 1**

Rural Tension

WAITING ROOM
Tracks: / Waiting room / New confidence.
7" Single: Released Apr '82, on Rural Tension, Catalogue no: **ARTS 1**

Rush

Biographical details: Rush are a Canadian heavy metal trio formed in Ontario in 1969 by bassist/vocalist Geddy Lee and Guitarist Alex Lifeson (both born in 1953), with John Rutsey soon replaced by drummer/songwriter Neil Peart (born 1952). Their music has been the usual mythological crypto-Fascist stuff for the most part, with perhaps more ability to move with the times and write some occasionally intelligent lyrics than most such outfits. (Donald Clarke 27.5.87)..

BIG MONEY, THE
Tracks: / Big money, The.
7" Single: Released Oct '85, on Vertigo, by

JENIFER RUSH - THE POWER OF LOVE (REMIX) (Released on CBS)

Phonogram Ltd. Deleted '88. Catalogue no: **RUSH 12**

BODY ELECTRIC, THE
Tracks: / Body electric, The.
10" single: Released Apr '84, on Vertigo, by Phonogram Ltd. Catalogue no: **RUSH 1110**
7" Single: Released Apr '84, on Vertigo, by Phonogram Ltd. Catalogue no: **RUSH 11**

CLOSER TO THE HEART
Tracks: / Closer to the heart / Trees.
7" Single: Released Feb '78, on Mercury, by Phonogram Ltd. Deleted '81. Catalogue no: **RUSH 7**

COUNTDOWN
Tracks: / Countdown / New world man.
7" Single: Released May '83, on Mercury, by Phonogram Ltd. Deleted '86. Catalogue no: **RUSH 10**

MANHATTAN PROJECT
Tracks: / Manhattan project.
7" Single: Released Feb '86, on Vertigo, by Phonogram Ltd. Catalogue no: **RUSH 13**
12" Single: Released Feb '86, on Vertigo, by Phonogram Ltd. Catalogue no: **RUSH 13-12**

NEW WORLD MAN
Tracks: / New world man.
7" Pic: Released Jun '83, on Mercury, by Phonogram Ltd. Catalogue no: **RUSHP 10**
7" Single: Released Jun '83, on Mercury, by Phonogram Ltd. Catalogue no: **RUSH 10**
12" Single: Released Jun '83, on Mercury, by Phonogram Ltd. Catalogue no: **RUSH 1012**
7" Single: Released Sep '82, on Mercury, by Phonogram Ltd. Deleted '85. Catalogue no: **RUSH 8**

PRIME MOVER
Tracks: / Prime mover / Distant early warning / Distant early warning (live) (Track on Ltd. Ed. 12".) / New world man (Track on Ltd. Ed. 12".).
7" Single: Released Apr '88, on Vertigo, by Phonogram Ltd. Deleted Feb '89. Catalogue no: **RUSHR 14**
12" Single: Released Jul '88, on Vertigo (Germany), Catalogue no: **INT18701091**
7" Single: Released Apr '88, on Vertigo, by Phonogram Ltd. Deleted Oct '88. Catalogue no: **RUSH 14**
CD 5": Released Apr '88, on Vertigo, by Phonogram Ltd. Deleted Feb '89. Catalogue no: **RUSHCD 14**
12" Single: Released Apr '88, on Vertigo, by Phonogram Ltd. Deleted Oct '88. Catalogue no: **RUSH 1412**
12" Single: Released Apr '88, on Vertigo, by Phonogram Ltd. Deleted Oct '88. Catalogue no: **RUSHR 1412**

SPIRIT OF THE RADIO
Tracks: / Spirit of the radio / Trees / Working man (Only on 12" single.).
7" Single: Released Feb '80, on Mercury, by Phonogram Ltd. Deleted '83. Catalogue no: **RADIO 7**
12" Single: Released Feb '80, on Mercury, by Phonogram Ltd. Deleted '83. Catalogue no: **RADIO 12**

SPIRIT OF THE RADIO (OLD GOLD)
Tracks: / Spirit of the radio / Closer to the heart.
7" Single: Released Feb '88, on Old Gold, by Old Gold Records. Catalogue no: **OG 9767**

SUBDIVISIONS
Tracks: / Subdivisions.
7" Single: Released Oct '82, on Mercury, by Phonogram Ltd. Deleted '85. Catalogue no: **RUSH 9**

TIME STAND STILL
Tracks: / Time stands still / Force ten / Enemy within (live) (extra track on 12" only.) / Witchhunt (live) (Extra track on 12" only).
7" Pic: Released Oct '87, on Vertigo, by Phonogram Ltd. Deleted Oct '88. Catalogue no: **RUSHP 1312**
7" Single: Released Oct '87, on Vertigo, by Phonogram Ltd. Deleted Oct '88. Catalogue no: **RUSH 13**
12" Single: Released Oct '87, on Vertigo, by Phonogram Ltd. Deleted Oct '88. Catalogue no: **RUSH 1312**

TOM SAWYER (LIVE)
Tracks: / Tom Sawyer.
7" Single: Released Oct '81, on Mercury, by Phonogram Ltd. Catalogue no: **EXIT 7**
12" Single: Released Oct '81, on Mercury, by Phonogram Ltd. Catalogue no: **EXIT 12**

VITAL SIGNS
Tracks: / Vital signs / Passage to Bangkok, A.
7" Single: Released Mar '81, on Mercury, by Phonogram Ltd. Catalogue no: **VITAL 7**
12" Single: Released Mar '81, on Mercury, by Phonogram Ltd. Catalogue no: **VITAL 12**

Rush, Barbara

CRUISIN'
Tracks: / Cruisin'.
12" Single: Released May '82, on Phil Pratt, Catalogue no: **NT 1007**

MODERATION
Tracks: / Moderation.
12" Single: Released Mar '85, on Terminal, Catalogue no: **TM 18**

RIGHT TIME
Tracks: / Right time, The.
12" Single: Released Nov '84, on Phil Pratt, Catalogue no: **PP 287**

Rush, Donell

KNOCKIN' AT ME DOOR
Tracks: / Knockin' at me door.
12" Single: Released Oct '88, on Westside, by Westside Records. Catalogue no: **WSRT 11**
7" Single: Released Oct '88, on Westside, by Westside Records. Catalogue no: **WSR 11**
12" Single: Released Dec '88, on Trax, by Filmtrax Records. Catalogue no: **TAXT 1**
7" Single: Released Dec '88, on Trax, by Filmtrax Records. Catalogue no: **TAX 1**

Rush, Heather

SOMEBODY (IS TAKING YOUR LOVE AWAY)
Tracks: / Somebody (is taking your love away).
7" Single: Released Jun '85, on President, by President Records. Catalogue no: **PT 535**
12" Single: Released Jun '85, on President, by President Records. Catalogue no: **PT 12535**

Rush Hour

CUSTOM MADE LOVE
Tracks: / Custom made love.
12" Single: Released Nov '87, on Star Gaze (USA), Catalogue no: **RH 1010**

Rush, Jennifer

DESTINY
Tracks: / Destiny / Right time has come now.
7" Pic: Released Apr '86, on CBS, by CBS Records. Catalogue no: **WTA 6574**
7" Single: Released Apr '86, on CBS, by CBS Records. Catalogue no: **A 6574**
7" Single: Released Apr '86, on CBS, by CBS Records. Catalogue no: **QA 6574**
12" Single: Released Apr '86, on CBS, by CBS Records. Catalogue no: **TA 6574**

FLAMES OF PARADISE (See under John, Elton)
12" Single: Released Jun '87, on CBS, by CBS Records. Deleted Nov '87. Catalogue no: **650865 8**

I COME UNDONE
Tracks: / I come undone / Search for the sky.
7" Single: Released Feb '87, on CBS, by CBS Records. Catalogue no: **650 380 7**
12" Single: Released Feb '87, on CBS, by CBS Records. Catalogue no: **650 380 6**

KEEP ALL THE FIRES BURNING BRIGHT
Tracks: / Keep all the fires burning bright (ext.version) (On 12" only) / I come undone (ext.version) (On 12" only) / Keep all the fires burning bright (edit) (On 7" only) / You don't know what you've got / Keep all the fires burning bright (club mix) / Heart over mind.
CD 5": Released 20 Feb '89, on CBS, by CBS Records. Deleted 10 Jul '89. Catalogue no: **653 159-3**
7" Single: Released 9 Jan '89, on CBS, by CBS Records. Deleted 10 Jul '89. Catalogue no: **653 159-7**
12" Single: Released 9 Jan '89, on CBS, by CBS Records. Deleted 10 Jul '89. Catalogue no: **653 159-8**
12" Single: Released 20 Feb '89, on CBS, by CBS Records. Deleted 10 Jul '89. Catalogue no: **653 159-1**

MADONNA'S EYES
Tracks: / Madonna's eyes / Surrender.
7" Single: Released Feb '86, on CBS, by CBS Records. Catalogue no: **A 6910**
12" Single: Released Feb '86, on CBS, by CBS Records. Catalogue no: **TA 6910**

POWER OF LOVE (see panel top left)
Tracks: / Power of love, The / I see a shadow (not a fantasy).
12" Single: Released Nov '86, on CBS, by CBS Records. Catalogue no: **TX 5003**
7" Single: Released Nov '86, on CBS, by CBS Records. Catalogue no: **A 5003**

RING OF ICE
Tracks: / Ring of ice.
7" Single: Released Dec '85, on CBS, by CBS Records. Deleted '88. Catalogue no: **A 4745**

YOU'RE MY ONE AND ONLY
Tracks: / You're my one and only / Rain coming down on me / You're my one and only (extended version) (Only on 12" & CD single.) / Power of love (remix) (Only on 12" & CD single.) / You're my one and only (7" version) (Only on CD single.).
7" Single: Released Oct '88, on CBS, by CBS Records. Deleted 17 Apr '89. Catalogue no: **653043 7**
12" Single: Released Oct '88, on CBS, by CBS Records. Deleted 17 Apr '89. Catalogue no: **653043 8**
CD 5": Released Oct '88, on CBS, by CBS Records. Deleted 17 Apr '89. Catalogue no: **653043 2**

Rushen, Patrice

DON'T BLAME ME
Tracks: / Don't blame me / Time will tell.
7" Single: Released Jun '81, on Elektra, by Elektra Records (UK). Catalogue no: **K 12542**
12" Single: Released Jun '81, on Elektra, by Elektra Records (UK). Catalogue no: **K 12542T**

FEELS SO REAL (WON'T LET GO)
Tracks: / Feel so real (won't let go).
7" Single: Released Jun '84, on Elektra, by Elektra Records (UK). Deleted '87. Catalogue no: **E 9742**

FORGET ME NOT
Tracks: / Forget me not / Havent you heard.
7" Single: Released Apr '82, on Elektra, by Elektra Records (UK). Catalogue no: **K 13173**
12" Single: Released Apr '82, on Elektra, by Elektra Records (UK). Catalogue no: **K 13173T**

HAVEN'T YOU HEARD
Tracks: / Haven't you heard / Keepin' faith in love.
7" Single: Released Mar '80, on Elektra, by Elektra Records (UK). Deleted '83. Catalogue no: **K 12414**

I WAS TIRED OF BEING ALONE
Tracks: / I was tired of being alone / Number one.
7" Single: Released Jun '82, on Elektra, by Elektra Records (UK). Catalogue no: **K 13184**
12" Single: Released Jun '82, on Elektra, by Elektra Records (UK). Catalogue no: **K 13184T**

LOOK UP
Tracks: / Look up / Dream.
7" Single: Released Apr '81, on Elektra, by Elektra Records (UK). Catalogue no: **K 12506**
12" Single: Released Apr '81, on Elektra, by Elektra Records (UK). Catalogue no: **K 12506T**

NEVER GONNA GIVE YOU UP
Tracks: / Never gonna give you up / Don't blame me.
7" Single: Released Nov '80, on Elektra, by Elektra Records (UK). Catalogue no: **K 12494**
12" Single: Released Nov '80, on Elektra, by Elektra Records (UK). Catalogue no: **K 12494T**

WATCH OUT (OBSERVATION MIX)
Tracks: / Watch out (ext mix) / Watch out (observation mix) / Watch out (ext mix) / Over the phone.
12" Single: Released Apr '87, on Arista, by BMG Records (UK). Deleted '87. Catalogue no: **RIST 12R**

Russ, Eddie

ZAIUS
Tracks: / Zaius.
12" Single: Released Aug '82, on Impact, by Ace Records. Catalogue no: **IMP 5**

Russanti

CARRY THE CAN
Tracks: / Carry the can.
7" Single: Released Jun '83, on Mach 1, by Mach 1 Records. Catalogue no: **MAGIC 5**

IT HAPPENED THEN
Tracks: / It happened then.
7" Single: Released Jan '83, on Mach 1, by Mach 1 Records. Catalogue no: **MAGIC 3**

Russel, Jerome

GO FOR GOLD
Tracks: / Go for gold.
Note: The official olympic single
7" Single: Released Aug '88, on Sunnyside, by Sunnyside Recording. Catalogue no: **STYLE 2**

Russell, Arthur

LETS GO SWIMMING
Tracks: / Lets go swimming.
12" Single: Released Sep '86, on Rough Trade, by Rough Trade Records. Catalogue no: **RTT 184**

Russell, Big John

HOKIE POKIE
Tracks: / Hokie pokie / Point your finger.
7" Single: Released May '81, on Red Bus, by Red Bus Records. Deleted May '84. Catalogue no: **RBUS 60**
12" Single: Released May '81, on Red Bus, by Red Bus Records. Deleted May '84. Catalogue no: **RBUSL 60**

Russell, Brenda

GET HERE (SINGLE)
Tracks: / Get here / Le restaurant / Little bit of love, A (Only on 12") / So good, so right (Only on 12").
12" Single: Released Sep '88, on Breakout, by A&M Records. Catalogue no: **USAT 647**
7" Single: Released Sep '88, on Breakout, by A&M Records. Catalogue no: **USA 647**

GRAVITY
Tracks: / Gravity / If only for one night.
CD 5": Released May '88, on Breakout, by A&M Records. Deleted Feb '89. Catalogue

PATRICE RUSHEN - FORGET ME NOTS (Released on Elektra)

no: **USACD 627**
7" Single: Released Jun '88, on Breakout, by A&M Records. Deleted Feb '89. Catalogue no: **USA 630**
12" Single: Released Jun '88, on Breakout, by A&M Records. Deleted Feb '89. Catalogue no: **USAT 630**
CD 5": Released Jun '88, on Breakout, by A&M Records. Deleted Feb '89. Catalogue no: **USACD 630**

PIANO IN THE DARK
Tracks: / Piano in the dark / In the thick of it.
CD 5": Released Mar '88, on Breakout, by A&M Records. Deleted Feb '89. Catalogue no: **USACD 623**
12" Single: Released Feb '88, on Breakout, by A&M Records. Deleted Feb '89. Catalogue no: **USAT 623**
7" Single: Released Feb '88, on Breakout, by A&M Records. Deleted Feb '89. Catalogue no: **USA 623**

SO GOOD SO RIGHT
Tracks: / So good so right / In the thick of it.
7" Single: Released Apr '80, on A&M, by A&M Records. Deleted '83. Catalogue no: **AMS 7515**

TWO EYES
Tracks: / Two eyes.
7" Single: Released Jul '83, on Warner Bros., by WEA Records. Catalogue no: **W 9557**

Russell & Brown

CAN'T GET YOU OUT OF MY MIND
Tracks: / Can't get you out of my mind / Far away.
7" Single: Released Nov '83, on Creole, by Creole Records. Catalogue no: **CR 62**

Russell, Dan

TENNIS SHOES
Tracks: / Tennis shoes / Tennis shoes.
7" Single: Released Jun '85, on Tembo, by Tembo Records. Catalogue no: **TML 107**
12" Single: Released Jun '86, on Tembo, by Tembo Records. Catalogue no: **TMLX 107**

Russell, Devon

CARELESS WHISPER
Tracks: / Careless whisper / Careful whisper.
12" Single: Released Jun '86, on Uptempo, Deleted Jun '89. Catalogue no: **TEMP 004**

COME-A-ME GIRL
Tracks: / Come-a-me girl.
12" Single: Released Jul '83, on Ethnic, Catalogue no: **ETH 2237**

VISION OF LOVE
Tracks: / Vision of love.
12" Single: Released Feb '85, on Jedi, Catalogue no: **JJ 224**

Russell, Johnny

SONG OF THE SOUTH
Tracks: / Song of the south / I'm getting holes in my boots.

7" Single: Released Apr '81, on Mercury, by Phonogram Ltd. Deleted Apr '84. Catalogue no: **MER 68**

Russia

FIGHT BACK
Tracks: / Fight back / Nothing to say.
7" Single: Released Jul '80, on Warner Bros., by WEA Records. Deleted Jul '83. Catalogue no: **K 17623**

Russian...

COME INTO MY ROOM
Tracks: / Come into my room.
7" Single: Released Jan '84, on Red Bus, by Red Bus Records. Catalogue no: **RBUS 86**

Russian Orchestra

POPULAR RUSSIAN ORCHESTRA
Special: Released Sep '89, on Crystal, by President Records. Catalogue no: **11 0622 2011**

Rutherford, Mike

ACTING VERY STRANGE
Tracks: / Acting very strange / Couldn't get arrested.
7" Single: Released Oct '82, on WEA, by WEA Records. Catalogue no: **RUTH 1**
12" Single: Released Oct '82, on WEA, by WEA Records. Catalogue no: **RUTH 1T**

HALFWAY THERE
Tracks: / Halfway there / Day to remember.
7" Single: Released Aug '82, on WEA, by WEA Records. Catalogue no: **K 79331**

HIDEAWAY
Tracks: / Hideaway / Calypso.
7" Single: Released Jan '83, on WEA (International), by WEA Records. Catalogue no: **U 9967**

SATISFACTION
Tracks: / Satisfaction.
12" Single: Released Aug '82, on Rudy T, Catalogue no: **RT 02**

WORKING IN LINE
Tracks: / Working in line / Compression.
7" Single: Released Feb '80, on Charisma, by Virgin Records. Deleted Feb '83. Catalogue no: **CB 353**

Rutherford, Noel

TRADE WIND
Tracks: / Trade wind.
12" Single: Released 30 May '89, on Steely & Cleevie, Catalogue no: **VPRD 438**

Rutherford, Paul

GET REAL
Tracks: / Get real / Happy face / Get real (happy house mix) / Get real (Only on 12".) / Get real (Only on 12".) / Get real (radio) (Only on CD single.).
12" Single: Released Aug '88, on 4th & Broadway, by Island Records. Deleted Apr '89. Catalogue no: **12 BRW 113**
7" Single: Released Aug '88, on 4th & Broadway, by Island Records. Deleted Apr '89. Catalogue no: **BRW 113**
CD 5": Released Oct '88, on 4th & Broadway, by Island Records. Catalogue no: **BRCDP 113**

GET REAL (REMIX)
Tracks: / Get real (remix).
12" Single: Released '88, on 4th & Broadway, by Island Records. Deleted Apr '89. Catalogue no: **12 BRX 113**

I WANT YOUR LOVE
Tracks: / I want your love / Pushed away / I want your L.U.R.V.E..
7" Single: Released 27 Mar '89, on 4th & Broadway, by Island Records. Catalogue no: **BRW 124**
12" Single: Released 27 Mar '89, on 4th & Broadway, by Island Records. Catalogue no: **12 BRW 124**
12" Single: Released Apr '89, on 4th & Broadway, by Island Records. Catalogue no: **12 BRX 124**
CD 5": Released 27 Mar '89, on 4th & Broadway, by Island Records. Catalogue no: **BRCD 124**

OH WORLD (REMIX) (See panel below)
Tracks: / Oh world (universal mix) / Oh world (universal dub) (12" only) / Oh world (delirium dub) (12" only) / Seduction, The (12" only).

12" Single: Released Aug '89, on 4th & Broadway, by Island Records. Catalogue no: **12 BRX 136**

OH WORLD (SINGLE)
Tracks: / Oh world / Seduction, The / Oh world (instrumental) (Only on 12" and CD single.) / Oh world (extended remix) (Only on CD single.).
Cassingle: Released Jul '89, on 4th & Broadway, by Island Records. Catalogue no: **BRCA 136**
CD 5": Released Jul '89, on 4th & Broadway, by Island Records. Catalogue no: **BRCD 136**
7" Single: Released Jul '89, on 4th & Broadway, by Island Records. Catalogue no: **BRW 136**
12" Single: Released Jul '89, on 4th & Broadway, by Island Records. Catalogue no: **12 BRX 136**

Ruthjoy

DON'T PUSH IT
Tracks: / Don't push it.

12" Single: Released Aug '89, on MCA, by MCA Records. Catalogue no: **RJOY 1**
12" Single: Released Aug '89, on MCA, by MCA Records. Catalogue no: **RJOYX 1**
7" Single: Released Aug '89, on MCA, by MCA Records. Catalogue no: **MCA 1362**
12" Single: Released Aug '89, on MCA, by MCA Records. Catalogue no: **MCAT 1362**

Ruthless

METAL WITHOUT MERCY
7" EP: Released Jan '86, on Iron Works (USA), by Azra International (USA). Catalogue no: **IW 1004**

Rutles

I MUST BE IN LOVE
Tracks: / I must be in love.
7" Single: Released Apr '78, on Warner Bros., by WEA Records. Deleted '81. Catalogue no: **K 17125**

Ruts

BABYLON'S BURNING (7" SINGLE)
Tracks: / Babylon's burning / Society.
7" Single: Released '79, on Virgin, by Virgin Records. Catalogue no: **VS 271**

BABYLONS BURNING (12" SINGLE)
Tracks: / Babylon's burning / Something that I said / Staring at the rude boys / West one (shine on me).
12" Single: Released Apr '83, on Virgin, by Virgin Records. Catalogue no: **VS 583-12**

BABYLON'S BURNING (OLD GOLD)
Tracks: / Babylon's burning / Staring at the rude boys.
7" Single: Released Nov '88, on Old Gold, by Old Gold Records. Catalogue no: **OG 9829**

DIFFERENT VIEW
Tracks: / Different view / Formula boys.
7" Single: Released Feb '81, on Virgin, by Virgin Records. Deleted '84. Catalogue no: **VS 396**

IN A RUT
Tracks: / In a rut.
7" Single: Released Jun '79, on Spartan, Catalogue no: **RUT 1**

PEEL SESSIONS:RUTS 27.11.78
12" Single: Released Jun '87, on Strange Fruit, by Strange Fruit Records. Catalogue no: **SFPS 028**

PEEL SESSIONS:RUTS II 21.5.79
Cassingle: Released 30 May '87, on Strange Fruit, by Strange Fruit Records. Catalogue no: **SFPSC 011**
12" Single: Released Nov '86, on Strange Fruit, by Strange Fruit Records. Catalogue no: **SFPS 011**

SOMETHING THAT I SAID
Tracks: / Something that I said.
7" Single: Released Sep '79, on Virgin, by Virgin Records. Deleted '82. Catalogue no: **VS 285**

STARING AT THE RUDE BOYS
Tracks: / Staring at the rude boys / Love in vain.
7" Single: Released Apr '80, on Virgin, by Virgin Records. Deleted '83. Catalogue no: **VS 327**

WEAK HEART
Tracks: / Weak heart / Militant / Accusation.
12" Single: Released Mar '83, on Bohemian, Catalogue no: **12 BO 3**

WEST ONE (SHINE ON ME)
Tracks: / West one (shine on me).
7" Single: Released Aug '80, on Virgin, by Virgin Records. Deleted '83. Catalogue no: **VS 370**

Ruts D.C

STEPPING BONDAGE
Tracks: / Stepping bondage.
7" Single: Released Mar '83, on Bohemian, Catalogue no: **BO 4**

WHATEVER WE DO
Tracks: / Whatever we do.

PAUL RUTHERFORD - OH WORLD (Released 0n 4th & Broadway)

7" Single: Released Jul '82, on Bohemian, Catalogue no: **BO 2**

Ryan, Barry

CAN'T LET YOU GO
Tracks: / Can't let you go.
7" Single: Released Jan '72, on Polydor, by Polydor Ltd. Deleted '75. Catalogue no: **2001 256**

ELOISE
Tracks: / Eloise.
7" Single: Released Jul '84, on Old Gold, by Old Gold Records. Catalogue no: **OG 9440**

ELOISE (SINGLE)
Tracks: / Eloise.
7" Single: Released Oct '68, on MGM, by Polydor Ltd. Deleted '71. Catalogue no: **MGM 1442**

HUNT
Tracks: / Hunt, The.
7" Single: Released Oct '69, on Polydor, by Polydor Ltd. Deleted '72. Catalogue no: **56 348**

KITSCH
Tracks: / Kitsch.
7" Single: Released May '70, on Polydor, by Polydor Ltd. Deleted '73. Catalogue no: **2001 035**

LOVE IS LOVE
Tracks: / Love is love.
7" Single: Released Feb '69, on MGM, by Polydor Ltd. Deleted '72. Catalogue no: **MGM 1464**

MAGICAL SPIEL
Tracks: / Magical spiel.
7" Single: Released Feb '70, on Polydor, by Polydor Ltd. Deleted '73. Catalogue no: **56 370**

Ryan, Lloyd

JUNGLE ANTHEM
Tracks: / Jungle anthem.
7" Single: Released Nov '79, on Playback (USA), by Playback Records (USA). Catalogue no: **PBR 7001**

LET THERE BE DRUMS
Tracks: / Let there be drums.
7" Single: Released Jan '84, on Playback (USA), by Playback Records (USA). Catalogue no: **PBR 7003**

Ryan, Marion

LOVE ME FOREVER
Tracks: / Love me forever.
7" Single: Released Jan '58, on Pye Nixa, Deleted '61. Catalogue no: **N 15121**

Ryan, Paul & Barry

CLAIRE
Tracks: / Claire.
7" Single: Released Jun '67, on Decca, by Decca Records. Deleted '70. Catalogue no: **F 12633**

DON'T BRING ME YOUR HEARTACHES
Tracks: / Don't bring me your heartaches.
7" Single: Released Dec '65, on Decca, by Decca Records. Deleted '68. Catalogue no: **F 12260**

HAVE PITY ON THE BOY
Tracks: / Have pity on the boy.
7" Single: Released Feb '66, on Decca, by Decca Records. Deleted '69. Catalogue no: **F 12319**

HAVE YOU EVER LOVED SOMEBODY
Tracks: / Have you ever loved somebody.
7" Single: Released Sep '66, on Decca, by Decca Records. Deleted '69. Catalogue no: **F 12494**

I LOVE HER
Tracks: / I love her.
7" Single: Released May '66, on Decca, by Decca Records. Deleted '69. Catalogue no: **F 12391**

I LOVE HOW YOU LOVE ME
Tracks: / I love how you love me.
7" Single: Released Aug '66, on Decca, by Decca Records. Deleted '69. Catalogue no: **F 12445**

KEEP IT OUT OF SIGHT
Tracks: / Keep it out of sight.
7" Single: Released Mar '67, on Decca, by Decca Records. Deleted '70. Catalogue no: **F 12567**

MISSY MISSY
Tracks: / Missy missy.
7" Single: Released Dec '66, on Decca, by Decca Records. Deleted '69. Catalogue no: **F 12520**

Ryan, Ron

AH YOU GOT YOUR EARS ON
7" Single: Released Sep '82, on Buffalo (UK), by M.I.S.Records. Catalogue no: **BUFF 1004**

Ryan & The Texolets

JOE TEX
Tracks: / Joe Tex.
7" Single: Released Oct '82, on Prairie Dust (USA), by Prairie Dust Records (USA). Catalogue no: **PR 005**

Rydell, Bobby

Biographical details: Born Bobby Ridarelli in 1942, in Philadelphia, Bobby Rydell was one of the less objectionable teen idols in the US in the late 50's-early 60's. Unlike Frankie Avalon and Fabian he could actually sing. Encouraged by his parents he made it to TV with Paul Whiteman, at the age of nine. Later he turned to rock 'n' roll and had 26 hits on the Billboard Hot Hundred until '64, when he was washed away by the British Invasion. (Donald Clarke, February 1988.).

FORGET HIM
Tracks: / Forget him.
7" Single: Released May '63, on Cameo Parkway, by Pye Records. Deleted '66. Catalogue no: **C 108**

GOOD TIME BABY
Tracks: / Good time baby.
7" Single: Released Mar '61, on Columbia, by EMI Records. Deleted '64. Catalogue no: **DB 4600**

SWAY
Tracks: / Sway.
7" Single: Released Dec '60, on Columbia, by EMI Records. Deleted '63. Catalogue no: **DB 4545**

SWINGING SCHOOL
Tracks: / Swinging school.
7" Single: Released Jun '60, on Columbia, by EMI Records. Deleted '63. Catalogue no: **DB 4429**

VOLARE
Tracks: / Volare.
7" Single: Released Sep '60, on Columbia, by EMI Records. Deleted '63. Catalogue no: **DB 4495**

WILD ONE (SINGLE)
Tracks: / Wild one.
7" Single: Released Mar '60, on Columbia, by EMI Records. Deleted '63. Catalogue no: **DB 4429**

Rydell, Brian

PASSAGE, THE
Tracks: / Passage, The / Passage, The (instrumental).
7" Single: Released 17 Oct '87, on A.R.I.A., Catalogue no: **ARIA 3**

Ryder

RUNNER IN THE NIGHT
Tracks: / Runner in the night.
Note: Eurovision entry
7" Single: Released Apr '86, on 10 Records, by Virgin Records. Deleted '89. Catalogue no: **TEN 1**

Ryder, Kris

EVERYBODY KNOWS
Tracks: / Everybody knows / She's a romantic.
7" Single: Released Apr '82, on DJM, Deleted Apr '85. Catalogue no: **DJS 10986**

Ryder, Mark

WRAP MY ARMS AROUND YOU
Tracks: / Wrap my arms around you.
7" Single: Released Sep '85, on PRT, by Castle Communications Records. Catalogue no: **7P 332**

Ryder, Mitch

Biographical details: Mitch Ryder & The Detroit Wheels were an American pop group of the 1960's formed by Ryder -- born William Levise in Michigan in 1945 -- who had been brought up on black music in Detroit. Their hits made up in energy what they lacked in originality. They had seven hits from 1954-67 then he went solo and had four more. He came back to the Hot Hundred in 1983 with When You Were Mine, written by Prince and produced by John Cougar Mellencamp. (Donald Clarke, February 1988.).

JENNY TAKE A RIDE
Tracks: / Jenny take a ride.
7" Single: Released Feb '66, on Stateside, by EMI Records. Deleted '69. Catalogue no: **SS 481**

WHEN YOU WERE MINE
Tracks: / When you were mine / Come again.
7" Single: Released Nov '83, on Towerbell, Catalogue no: **TOW 44**

Ryder, Scobie

ZERO
Tracks: / Zero / Was that a take?.
7" Single: Released Mar '80, on EMI, by EMI Records. Deleted '83. Catalogue no: **EMI 5044**

Ryder-Desmond

VISIONS
Tracks: / Visions / Nobody's gonna get my girl.
7" Single: Released Jul '81, on DJM, Deleted '84. Catalogue no: **DJS 10972**

Rye & Quarterboys

FANTASY
Tracks: / Fantasy / Private number.
7" Single: Released Apr '82, on Replay, by Creole Records. Deleted Apr '85. Catalogue no: **REPLAY 001**

Ryshworth Middle

CHRISTMAS SONG
Tracks: / Christmas song, The.
7" Single: Released Dec '83, on Reindeer, Catalogue no: **JPR 2**

Ryvers, Debie

LET THE SUN SHINE
Tracks: / Let the sun shine in.
12" Single: Released Apr '85, on Tom Tom, Catalogue no: **TT 2**

S

The following information was taken from the Music Master database on 20th October, 1989

SA 55

COMPROMISE
Tracks: / Compromise / Love is blind.
7" Single: Released Jul '82, on 1966, Catalogue no: **EISP 9868**

SA 242

PRO PATRIA (SINGLE)
Tracks: / Pro patria.
CD 5": Released '89, on Licensed, Catalogue no: **LD 8928 CD**
12" Single: Released '89, on Licensed, Catalogue no: **LD 8928**

Saad, Sue

YOUNG GIRL
Tracks: / Young girl / Cold night train.
7" Single: Released May '80, on Electra, Deleted May '83. Catalogue no: **K 12425**

Saatchi, Phil

LITTLE IN LOVE
Tracks: / Little in love, A / When we dream.
7" Single: Released Apr '87, on A&M, by A&M Records. Deleted Mar '88. Catalogue no: **AM 389**
12" Single: Released Apr '87, on A&M, by A&M Records. Deleted Mar '88. Catalogue no: **AMY 389**

POOR MAN'S PARADISE
Tracks: / Poor man's paradise / You should be mine / Cancel my subscriptions (Track on 12" only).
7" Single: Released Mar '86, on A&M, by A&M Records. Deleted '88. Catalogue no: **AM 303**

THREE MIRACLES
Tracks: / Three miracles / Push a little harder.
12" Single: Released 27 Mar '89, on A&M, by A&M Records. Catalogue no: **AMY 498**
7" Single: Released 27 Mar '89, on A&M, by A&M Records. Catalogue no: **AM 498**

WHEEL OF FORTUNE
Tracks: / Wheel of fortune / You should have warned me / White (This track is on the 12" version only).
12" Single: Released Jan '87, on A&M, by A&M Records. Deleted Aug '88. Catalogue no: **AMY 327**
7" Single: Released Jan '87, on A&M, by A&M Records. Deleted Mar '88. Catalogue no: **AM 327**

Sebastian, John

IN A CARE BEAR FAMILY
Tracks: / In a care bear family.
7" Single: Released Jul '85, on Cherry Lane, by Cherry Lane Productions. Deleted '86. Catalogue no: **PIP 717**

Sebastians Men

HORIZON
Tracks: / Horizon.
7" Single: Released Aug '84, on Horizon 5, Catalogue no: **SEB 001**

Sabbah, Claude

HARD TIMES NEED THE KISS OF LIFE
Tracks: / Hard times need the kiss of life.
12" Single: Released Sep '88, on Serious, by Serious Records. Catalogue no: **FREN 1**
7" Single: Released Sep '88, on Serious, by Serious Records. Catalogue no: **7FREN 1**
7" Single: Released Feb '89, on PRT, by Castle Communications Records. Catalogue no: **PYS 21**
12" Single: Released Feb '89, on PRT, by Castle Communications Records. Catalogue no: **PYT 21**

Sabina

USE WHAT YOU GOT
Tracks: / Use what you got.

12" Single: Released Oct '89, on Punch Bag, Catalogue no: **RBBT 002**

Sabotage

SABOTAGE
Special: Released Jun '88, on Trans Euro, by Azra International (USA). Catalogue no: **TE 2002**

Sabre

HIDDEN VISIONS
7" EP: Released Jun '88, on Masque, by Azra International (USA). Catalogue no: **MSQ 8703**

MIRACLE MAN
Tracks: / On the loose / Miracle man.
7" Single: Released Jun '83, on Neat, by Neat Records. Catalogue no: **NEAT 23**

Sabrina

ALL OF ME
Tracks: / All of me.
12" Single: Released Oct '88, on PWL, by PWL Records. Catalogue no: **PWLT 19**
7" Single: Released Oct '88, on PWL, by PWL Records. Catalogue no: **PWL 19**

BOYS (SUMMERTIME LOVE)
Tracks: / Boys (summertime love) / Get ready (holiday rock).
7" Single: Released Jun '88, on Ibiza, by London Records. Deleted Feb '89. Catalogue no: **IBIZ 1**
CD 5": Released Jun '88, on Ibiza, by London Records. Deleted Feb '89. Catalogue no: **IBIZXR 1**
12" Single: Released Jun '88, on Ibiza, by London Records. Deleted Feb '89. Catalogue no: **IBIZX 1**

GRINGO
Tracks: / Gringo / Gringo (version).
12" Single: Released Sep '89, on RCA, by BMG Records (UK). Catalogue no: **PT 42116**
CD 5": Released Sep '89, on RCA, by BMG Records (UK). Catalogue no: **PD 42116**
7" Single: Released Sep '89, on RCA, by BMG Records (UK). Catalogue no: **PB 42115**
12" Single: Released Oct '89, on RCA, by BMG Records (UK). Catalogue no: **PT 43160**

LIKE A YO-YO
Tracks: / Like a yo-yo.
7" Single: Released Jul '89, on Videogram, Catalogue no: **DCUP 1**
12" Single: Released Jul '89, on Videogram, Catalogue no: **12 DCUP 1**

Sabu

ANGELINE
Tracks: / Angeline / Shake, rattle and roll.
7" Single: Released Oct '85, on FM, by FM-Revolver Records. Catalogue no: **VHF 25**

Sacchi, Robert

JUNGLE QUEEN
Tracks: / Jungle Queen / Casablanca.
12" Single: Released Oct '82, on Splash, by Splash Records. Catalogue no: **12SP 23**
7" Single: Released Oct '82, on Splash, by Splash Records. Catalogue no: **SP 23**

Sacha

LIES
Tracks: / Lies.
7" Single: Released Sep '89, on Sasha, Catalogue no: **SASHA 1**
12" Single: Released Sep '89, on Sasha, Catalogue no: **SASHA 1T**

Sacher Musak

VAN DEN BEAT
Tracks: / Van den beat.
12" Single: Released '89, on Sampler Et Sans Reproches, Catalogue no: **12 SSR 95**

Sachs Andrew

SHADDAP YOU FACE
Tracks: / Shaddap you face / Waiter there's a flea in my soup.
7" Single: Released Feb '81, on Rocket, by Rocket Records. Deleted '84. Catalogue no: **XPRES 47**

Sacred Alien

LEGENDS
Tracks: / Legends / Sittin' in the front row.
7" Single: Released Mar '84, on Neon, by Neon Records. Catalogue no: **SAD 001X**

Sacred Heart School

HURDY GURDY MAN
Tracks: / Hurdy gurdy man / Seth Davey.
7" Single: Released Jan '81, on Tin Pan Alley Music, Catalogue no: **TIN 001**

Sacred Reich

SURF NICARAGUA
Tracks: / Surf Nicaragua.
Note: Surf Nicaragua shows exactly how far this band has progressed in such a very short time.
12" Single: Released Dec '88, on Road Runner (1), by Road Runner Records. Catalogue no: **RR 9512 1**
CD 5": Released Dec '88, on Road Runner (1), by Road Runner Records. Catalogue no: **RR 9512 2**

Sacrifice

DREAMING OF YOUR LOVE
Tracks: / Dreaming of your love.
12" Single: Released Oct '81, on S & G (2), Catalogue no: **SG 9**

Sad Among Strangers

TAKING OFF THE BREAKS
Tracks: / Taking off the breaks / I Salamander.
12" Single: Released Oct '86, on Broken Hill, Catalogue no: **BHPT 002**
7" Single: Released Oct '86, on Broken Hill, Catalogue no: **BHP 002**

Sad Cafe

BLACK ROSE
Tracks: / Black rose / I beleive love will survive / Emptiness / Hungry eyes.
7" Single: Released Feb '81, on RCA, by BMG Records (UK). Deleted '84. Catalogue no: **RCAE 42**

EVERY DAY HURTS
Tracks: / Everyday hurts.
7" Single: Released Sep '79, on RCA, by BMG Records (UK). Deleted Jul '82. Catalogue no: **PB 5180**

EVERY DAY HURTS (SINGLE)
Tracks: / Everyday hurts / My oh my.
7" Single: Released Nov '86, on Old Gold, by Old Gold Records. Catalogue no: **OG 9644**

FOLLOW YOU ANYWHERE
Tracks: / Follow you anywhere / No.9.
7" Single: Released Feb '82, on Polydor, by Polydor Ltd. Catalogue no: **POSP 366**

I'M IN LOVE AGAIN
Tracks: / I'm in love again / Restless.
7" Single: Released Dec '80, on RCA, by BMG Records (UK). Deleted Dec '83. Catalogue no: **SAD 6**

LA DI DA
Tracks: / La di da.
7" Single: Released Sep '80, on RCA, by BMG Records (UK). Deleted Sep '83. Catalogue no: **SAD 5**

MISUNDERSTANDING
Tracks: / Misunderstanding.
7" Single: Released Sep '82, on Polydor, by Polydor Ltd. Catalogue no: **POSP 324**

MY OH MY
Tracks: / My oh my / Cottage love.
7" Single: Released Mar '80, on RCA, by BMG Records (UK). Deleted Mar '83. Catalogue no: **SAD 3**

NOTHING LEFT TOULOUSE
Tracks: / Nothing left Toulouse / On with the shadow.
7" Single: Released Jun '80, on RCA, by BMG Records (UK). Deleted Jun '83. Catalogue no: **SAD 4**

ONLY LOVE
Tracks: / Only love (special remix) / China seize.
7" Single: Released Jan '86, on Legacy, by Legacy Records. Catalogue no: **LGY 40**

REFUGEES
Tracks: / Refugees.
7" Single: Released Oct '85, on Legacy, by Legacy Records. Catalogue no: **LGY 29**
12" Single: Released Oct '85, on Legacy, by Legacy Records. Catalogue no: **LGYT 29**

STRANGE LITTLE GIRL
Tracks: / Strange little girl / Time is so hard to find.
7" Single: Released Jan '80, on RCA, by BMG Records (UK). Deleted Jan '85. Catalogue no: **PB 5202**

TAKE ME (HEART AND SOUL)
Tracks: / Take me (heart and soul).
7" Single: Released Mar '89, on Legacy, by Legacy Records. Catalogue no: **LGY 66**

Sad Lovers & Giants

COWBOYS
Tracks: / Cowboys.
12" Single: Released Mar '88, on Midnight Music, by Midnight Music Records. Catalogue no: **DONG 36**

LOST IN A MOMENT
Tracks: / Lost in a moment / Tightrope touch.
7" Single: Released Nov '82, on Midnight Music, by Midnight Music Records. Catalogue no: **DING 1**

MAN OF STRAW
Tracks: / Man of straw / Cowboys.
7" Single: Released Oct '83, on Midnight Music, by Midnight Music Records. Catalogue no: **DING 5**
12" Single: Released Oct '83, on Midnight Music, by Midnight Music Records. Catalogue no: **DONG 5**

WHITE RUSSIAN
Tracks: / White Russian.
7" Single: Released Jul '87, on Midnight Music, by Midnight Music Records. Catalogue no: **DONG 34**

Sad Society

CONTAMINATE
Tracks: / Contaminate.
7" Single: Released 30 May '87, on X-Cert, Catalogue no: **X-CERT 011**

Sad, Sue

GIVE ME LOVE, GIVE ME PAIN
Tracks: / Give me love, give me pain / It's gotcha.
7" Single: Released Feb '80, on Planet, Deleted Feb '83. Catalogue no: **K 12421**

Sadane

ONE WAY LOVE AFFAIR
Tracks: / One way love affair / You're the one for me / Fool in me / Never gonna stop this heart of mine / Standing in the shadows of love / Sit up / Girl come on / Love can't wait / Midnight love dance / Make up your mind.
12" Single: Released Jun '81, on Warner Bros., by WEA Records. Catalogue no: **K 17816 T**
7" Single: Released Jun '81, on Warner Bros., by WEA Records. Catalogue no: **K 17816**

Sadane, Mark

ONE MINUTE FROM LOVE
Tracks: / One minute from love.
12" Single: Released Oct '82, on Warner Bros., by WEA Records. Deleted Oct '85. Catalogue no: **K 17961 T**
7" Single: Released Oct '82, on Warner Bros., by WEA Records. Deleted Oct '85. Catalogue no: **K 17961**

Sade

Biographical details:
Sade's full name is Helen Folasade Adu; she was born 16 January 1960, in Ibada, Nigeria. Her mother was British and her father a Nigerian teacher at Ibadan University. She came to the UK in 1963. She was influenced by singers like Peggy Lee, Julie London and Astrud Gilberto; She studied fashion design but switched to music, joining a Latin-funk group called Ariva in 1981, which evolved into Pride and hired saxophonist Stuart Matthewman (born in 1961), who recruited bassist Paul Denman (born in 1959); Pride changed their name to Sade (name of both singer and group, pronounced Sha-day, abbreviation of Folasade), added pianist Andre Hale (born in 1963); other regulars include Matthewson's brother Gordon. When Epic signed her in January 1984 they wanted her solo, but she insisted that the band was included. She appeared on cover of trendy mag *The Face* April '84, was featured in *Vogue*, *Cosmopolitan*, *Elle*; by the time she made the cover of *Time* (6 April 1986) she was the queen of cool, and two albums of

SADE - YOUR LOVE IS KING (Released on Epic)

laid-back, jazz influenced cabaret-style vocals had sold 12 million copies worldwide. (Donald Clarke). [Donald Clarke, April 87].

IS IT A CRIME
Tracks: / Is it a crime / Punch drunk.
12" Single: Released Dec '85, on Epic, by CBS Records. Catalogue no: **TA 6742**
7" Single: Released Dec '85, on Epic, by CBS Records. Catalogue no: **A 6742**

LOVE IS STRONGER THAN PRIDE
Tracks: / Love is stronger than pride / Super bien total / Super bien total (extended mix).
7" Single: Released Mar '88, on Epic, by CBS Records. Deleted Aug '88. Catalogue no: **SADE 1**
CD 5": Released Mar '88, on Epic, by CBS Records. Deleted Jan '89. Catalogue no: **CD SADE 1**
7" Single: Released Mar '88, on Epic, by CBS Records. Deleted Aug '88. Catalogue no: **SADE P1**
12" Single: Released Mar '88, on Epic, by CBS Records. Deleted Aug '88. Catalogue no: **SADE T1**
Special: Released Mar '88, on Epic, by CBS Records. Deleted Aug '88. Catalogue no: **SADE QT 1**

NEVER AS GOOD AS THE FIRST TIME
Tracks: / Never as good as the first time.
12" Single: Released Mar '86, on Epic, by CBS Records. Catalogue no: **TA 7061**
7" Single: Released Mar '86, on Epic, by CBS Records. Catalogue no: **A 7061**

NOTHING CAN COME BETWEEN US
Tracks: / Nothing can come between us / Make some room / You're not the man (CD only).
CD 5": Released Aug '88, on Epic, by CBS Records. Deleted 17 Apr '89. Catalogue no: **CDSADE 3**
12" Single: Released Aug '88, on Epic, by CBS Records. Deleted 17 Apr '89. Catalogue no: **SADE T3**
12" Single: Released '88, on CBS, by CBS Records. Deleted 17 Apr '89. Catalogue no: **SADE QT3**
7" Single: Released Aug '88, on Epic, by CBS Records. Deleted 17 Apr '89. Catalogue no: **SADE 3**

PARADISE
Tracks: / Paradise (remix) (7") / Paradise (inst) (7" & CD single.) / Paradise (ext. remix) (12" & CD single.) / Paradise (ext. inst.) (12".) / Paradise (extra beats) (12".) / Hang on to your love (U.S. remix) (CD single.) / Keep hanging on (live) (CD single.).
7" Single: Released May '88, on Epic, by CBS Records. Deleted Jan '89. Catalogue no: **SADE 2**
12" Single: Released May '88, on Epic, by CBS Records. Deleted Jan '89. Catalogue no: **SADE QT2**
CD 5": Released Jun '88, on Epic, by CBS Records. Deleted Jan '89. Catalogue no: **651617 2**
12" Single: Released May '88, on Epic, by CBS Records. Deleted Jan '89. Catalogue no: **SADE T2**
CD 5": Released May '88, on Epic, by CBS Records. Deleted Jan '89. Catalogue no: **CD SADE 2**

SMOOTH OPERATOR
Tracks: / Smooth operator / Spirit / Red eyes (on 12" only).
7" Single: Released Sep '84, on Epic, by CBS Records. Deleted Sep '87. Catalogue no: **A 4655**

SWEETEST TABOO
Tracks: / Sweetest taboo, The.
7" Single: Released Oct '85, on Epic, by CBS Records. Deleted Oct '88. Catalogue no: **A 6609**

TURN MY BACK ON YOU
Tracks: / Turn my back on you (remix) / Turn my back on you (extended remix) (Not on 7".) / Turn my back on you (Heff's mix) (Not on 7".) / Keep looking.
CD 5": Released 21 Nov '88, on Epic, by CBS Records. Deleted 17 Apr '89. Catalogue no: **CD SADE 4**
7" Single: Released 21 Nov '88, on Epic, by CBS Records. Deleted 17 Apr '89. Catalogue no: **SADE 4**
12" Single: Released 21 Nov '88, on Epic, by CBS Records. Deleted 17 Apr '89. Catalogue no: **SADE T4**

WHEN AM I GOING TO MAKE A LIVING
Tracks: / When am I going to make a living / Should I love you / Why can't we live together (on 12" only).
7" Single: Released May '84, on Epic, by CBS Records. Catalogue no: **A 4437**
12" Single: Released May '84, on Epic, by CBS Records. Catalogue no: **TA 4437**

YOUR LOVE IS KING (See panel above)
Tracks: / Your love is king / Love affair with life (live).
7" Single: Released Feb '84, on Epic, by CBS Records. Deleted Feb '87. Catalogue no: **A 4137**

Sadie Nine

KISS ME NOT HIM
Tracks: / Kiss me not him / You take a morning.
7" Single: Released Jan '82, on Precious Organisation, by Precious Organisation. Catalogue no: **AVE 3**

Sadista Sisters

RAG DOLL DUCHESS
Tracks: / Rag doll Duchess / Foetus.
7" Single: Released May '82, on KD, Catalogue no: **KD 001**

Sadler, Sgt. Barry

BALLAD OF THE GREEN BERETS (SINGLE)
Tracks: / Ballad of the Green Berets.
7" Single: Released Mar '66, on RCA, by BMG Records (UK). Deleted Mar '69. Catalogue no: **RCA 1506**
7" Single: Released '80, on USA, by Charly Records. Catalogue no: **LR 1899**

Sadonians

DISAPPOINTMENTS (see also Clint Eastwood)
Tracks: / Disappointments.
12" Single: Released Aug '80, on Freedom, Catalogue no: **FSD 019**

GOODBYE MY LOVE
Tracks: / Goodbye my love / Good love.
12" Single: Released Feb '80, on Freedom, Catalogue no: **FSD 012**

Sae, Kelli

IT'S TOO LATE
Tracks: / It's too late.
12" Single: Released Sep '89, on Easy Street, Catalogue no: **12EASY 100**

Safari Party

HOPE IN HELL
Tracks: / Hope in hell.
7" Single: Released Jun '85, on Pure & Vain, Catalogue no: **PAV 1**

Safe

SKIN
Tracks: / Skin.
7" Single: Released Sep '89, on Body, Catalogue no: **BODY 001**

Saffrice

SUMMER DAYS
Tracks: / Summer days / Winter morning.
12" Single: Released Mar '82, on S & G (2), Catalogue no: **SG 8**

Saffrons

PHYSICAL CONTACT
Tracks: / Physical contact / Physical contact (instrumental).
7" Single: Released Mar '86, on Bolts, by Bolts Records. Catalogue no: **BOLTS 02/7**

THEN HE KISSED ME
Tracks: / Then he kissed me.
7" Single: Released Oct '88, on Westside, by Westside Records. Catalogue no: **WSR 9**
12" Single: Released Oct '88, on Westside, by Westside Records. Catalogue no: **WSRT 9**

Sa-Fire

GONNA MAKE IT
Tracks: / Gonna make it / Gonna make it (drum you like) / I wanna make you mine.
CD 5": Released 31 Jul '89, on Mercury, by Phonogram Ltd. Catalogue no: **MERCD 298**
12" Single: Released 31 Jul '89, on Mercury, by Phonogram Ltd. Catalogue no: **MERXZ 298**
7" Single: Released 31 Jul '89, on Mercury, by Phonogram Ltd. Catalogue no: **MER 298**
12" Single: Released 31 Jul '89, on Mercury, by Phonogram Ltd. Catalogue no: **MERXY 298**
Cassingle: Released 31 Jul '89, on Mercury, by Phonogram Ltd. Catalogue no: **MERMC 298**

THINKING OF YOU
Tracks: / Thinking of you / Let me be the one.
7" Single: Released May '89, on Mercury, by Phonogram Ltd. Catalogue no: **MER 283**

Saga

CAREFUL WHERE YOU STEP
Tracks: / Careful where you step / How long / Take it or leave it.
12" Single: Released Feb '81, on Polydor, by Polydor Ltd. Deleted Feb '84. Catalogue no: **POSPX 228**
7" Single: Released Feb '81, on Polydor, by Polydor Ltd. Deleted Feb '84. Catalogue no: **POSP 228**

IT'S TIME
Tracks: / It's time / Mouse in a maze.
7" Single: Released 20 Sep '80, on Polydor, by Polydor Ltd. Deleted '83. Catalogue no: **2095246**

ON THE LOOSE
Tracks: / On the loose / Framed.
7" Single: Released Jan '83, on Portrait, by CBS Records. Catalogue no: **PRT A 2958**

SCRATCHING THE SURFACE
Tracks: / Scratching the surface / Sound of strangers, The.
7" Single: Released Jan '84, on Portrait, by CBS Records. Catalogue no: **A 4067**
12" Single: Released Jan '84, on Portrait, by CBS Records. Catalogue no: **TA 4067**

TAKE A CHANCE
Tracks: / Take a chance / You and the night.
7" Single: Released Jan '86, on Portrait, by CBS Records. Catalogue no: **A 6840**
12" Single: Released Jan '86, on Portrait, by CBS Records. Catalogue no: **TX 6840**

WIND HIM UP
Tracks: / Wind him up.
7" Single: Released Mar '83, on Portrait, by CBS Records. Catalogue no: **PRT A 3053**

Sagar, Mike

DEEP FEELING
Tracks: / Deep feeling.
7" Single: Released Dec '60, on H.M.V., by EMI Records. Deleted Dec '63. Catalogue no: **POP 819**

Sager, Carole Bayer

Biographical details:
The wife of the legendary composer and arranger Burt Bacharach, this American singer and songwriter is best known in Britain for her 1977 Top 10 hit *You're Moving Out Today*, a tongue-in-cheek account of the breaking up of a relationship. Yet that jaunty number is quite untypical of her work. Sager's forte is the writing of Broadway musical-type emotional love lyrics, in the tradition of Cole Porter and Hal David. Hence she normally co-writes with composers. The biggest success of her career came in that same year of '77, when Leo Sayer took *When I Need You* to No. 1 on both sides of the Atlantic. Her partner on that song was Albert Hammond, but she has also teamed with the likes of Marvin Hamlisch and, of course, Bacharach. Indeed it was she who brought her husband back into the realms of success in the early Eighties - he had been creatively drained since the split with lyricist Hal David some ten years before. Among Carole Bayer Sager's list of mature ballad hits are Carly Simon's *Nobody Does It Better*, Diana Ross' *It's My Turn* and Christopher Cross' US No. 1 *Arthur's Theme (Best That You Can Do)*. In her own right as an artist, she has only cracked the US Top 40 once, with 1981's *Stronger Than Before*. Her talents are better utilised when her songs are recorded by name artists with stronger voices. Her consistently successful way with words means that many record collectors possess plenty of Sager's work, without realising it. Michael Jackson's multi-platinum *Off The Wall* LP, for example, includes Sager's *It's The Falling In Love*. (Bob MacDonald).
Sngerl/songwriter Carole Bayer Sager was born in New York in 1947, and began writing at 15. She signed as a writer with Don Kirshner's Screen Gems and her first demo, *Groovy Kind Of Love* (co-written with Tony Wein), was a no.2 hit in both the USA and UK by the Mindbenders in 1966; but her greatest success began in the 1970s. She was the youngest lyricist ever to write a Broadway musical, but *Georgy* flopped in 1970, but she has co-written dozens of hits with Melissa Manchester, Peter Allen, film composer Marvin Hamlisch (born in New York, 2 June 1944), others; she and Hamlisch wrote songs for Nil Simon's musical *They're Playing Our Song) in 1979, said to have been loosely based on their relationship; married Burt Bacharach in 1982. Her albums have always been critically praised; Bacharach collaborated on their album, Sometimes Late At Night* in 1981, the first to reach Billboard's album chart, including a Top 30 hit *Stronger Than Before.* (Donald Clarke)..

EASY TO LOVE AGAIN
Tracks: / Easy to love again / Wild again.
7" Single: Released Nov '81, on Epic, by CBS Records. Catalogue no: **EPC A 1717**

IT'S THE FALLING IN LOVE
Tracks: / It's the falling in love / There's something.
7" Single: Released Feb '80, on Electra, Deleted Feb '83. Catalogue no: **K 12314**

YOU'RE MOVING OUT TODAY
Tracks: / You're moving out today.
7" Single: Released May '77, on Elektra, by Elektra Records (UK). Deleted May '80. Catalogue no: **A 12257**

Sahara

LOVE SO FINE
Tracks: / Love so fine.
12" Single: Released May '85, on Elite Records, by Elite Records. Deleted '86. Catalogue no: **DAZZ 38**

Sahuleka, Daniel

VIVA LA LIBERTADE
Tracks: / Viva la libertade.
12" Single: Released Oct '82, on Polydor, by Polydor Ltd. Catalogue no: **POSPX 503**
7" Single: Released Oct '82, on Polydor, by Polydor Ltd. Catalogue no: **POSP 503**

Saigon

DIVING THROUGH SAND
Tracks: / Diving through sand / Which way to Paradise.
7" Single: Released Nov '81, on Ryme Time, by Lismor Records. Catalogue no: **WRS 805**

GOTHIC BOP (EP)
Tracks: / Gothic bop.
7" Single: Released May '84, on First Floor, Catalogue no: **FF 5**

GREEN CARNATION
Tracks: / Green carnation / Falls the shadow.
7" Single: Released Nov '81, on Ryme Time, by Lismor Records. Catalogue no:

WRS 804

WHERE ARE THE ROSES
Tracks: / Where are the roses? / Parallel.
7" Single: Released May '81, on Ryme Time, by Lismor Records. Catalogue no: **WRS 802**

Sailor

Biographical details:
Sailor was a keyboard-based pop quartet formed in 1974 by guitarist-vocalist George Kajanus (real name Georg Hultgren), a former member of Australian folk-rockers Eclection (which also included guitarist Trevor Lucas - later with Fairport Convention). Kajanus teamed with Phil Pickett for guitar-keyboard duo, but added Henry Marsh on keyboards, Grant Serpell on drums for unusual group with no bass or electric guitar (Kajanus played acoustic). After a lot of success with eclectic music, sometimes including accordian, etc. until punk took over. Pickett resurfaced as keyboardist and songwriter with Culture Club, co-wrote *Karma Chameleon*. (Donald Clarke, April 87)..

DANGER ON THE TITANIC
Tracks: / Danger on the Titanic / Starlight.
7" Single: Released Apr '81, on Caribou, by CBS Records. Deleted '85. Catalogue no: **CRB A 1110**

DON'T SEND FLOWERS
Tracks: / Don't send flowers / Don't look a gift horse.
7" Single: Released Jan '81, on Caribou, by CBS Records. Deleted Jan '84. Catalogue no: **CRB 9077**

GIRLS GIRLS GIRLS
Tracks: / Girls girls girls.
7" Single: Released Mar '76, on Epic, by CBS Records. Deleted Mar '79. Catalogue no: **EPC 3858**

GLASS OF CHAMPAGNE
Tracks: / Glass of champagne.
7" Single: Released Dec '75, on Epic, by CBS Records. Deleted Dec '78. Catalogue no: **EPC 3770**

GLASS OF CHAMPAGNE (OLD GOLD)
Tracks: / Glass of champagne / Girls girls girls.
7" Single: Released 27 Feb '89, on Old Gold, by Old Gold Records. Catalogue no: **OG 9863**

ONE DRINK TOO MANY
Tracks: / One drink too many.
7" Single: Released Feb '77, on Epic, by CBS Records. Deleted Feb '80. Catalogue no: **EPC 4804**

Sainte-Marie, Buffy

Biographical details: Singer, guitarist and songwriter Buffy Sainte-Marie was born in Canada in 1941. She was categorised as a folksinger but performed her own material from the beginning. She is part Red Indian and many of her songs reflect a wide-ranging interest in social issues. Six of her albums charted in the USA during the 1960's and most of them are still in print there, testifying to the loyalty of her fans and the lasting quality of her work. The PRT album in Britain is a "Best Of" from her classic Vanguard years. Her best-known song, Universal Soldier, was a hit for Donovan and has been covered many times. (Donald Clarke, March 1987.).

I'M GONNA BE A COUNTRY GIRL AGAIN
Tracks: / I'm gonna be a country girl again.
7" Single: Released Mar '72, on Vanguard, by Start Records Ltd.. Deleted Mar '75. Catalogue no: **VRS 35143**

SOLDIER BLUE
Tracks: / Soldier blue / I'm gonna be a country girl again.
7" Single: Released Jan '83, on Flashback, by Mainline Records. Catalogue no: **FBS 17**
7" Single: Released Jul '71, on RCA, by BMG Records (UK). Deleted Jul '74. Catalogue no: **RCA 2081**

Saints

ALWAYS
Tracks: / Always / In the mirror.
7" Single: Released Jun '82, on New Rose (1), by New Rose Records. Catalogue no: **NEW 3**

FOLLOW THE LEADER
Tracks: / Follow the leader.
7" Single: Released Feb '83, on Flicknife, by Flicknife Records. Catalogue no: **FLS 215**

GHOST SHIPS
Tracks: / Ghost ships.
7" Single: Released Mar '85, on New Rose (1), by New Rose Records. Catalogue no: **NEW 37**

IMAGINATION
Tracks: / Imagination.
7" Single: Released Dec '84, on New Rose (1), by New Rose Records. Catalogue no: **NEW 43**

JUST LIKE FIREWOULD
Tracks: / Just like firewould / East is east / Casablanca.
7" Single: Released Mar '87, on Polydor, by Polydor Ltd. Deleted Jan '88. Catalogue no: **POSP 848**
12" Single: Released Mar '87, on Polydor, by Polydor Ltd. Deleted Jan '88. Catalogue no: **POSPX 848**

PARALYTIC TONIGHT DUBLIN TOMORROW
Tracks: / Paralytic tonight Dublin tomorrow.
7" Single: Released Jun '82, on New Rose (1), by New Rose Records. Catalogue no: **NEW 1**

PRODICAL SON
Tracks: / Prodical son.
7" Single: Released Oct '89, on Blue Beat, Catalogue no: **MR 101**
12" Single: Released Oct '89, on Blue Beat, Catalogue no: **MR 101T**

TEMPLE OF THE LORD, THE
Tracks: / Temple of the Lord, The / Celtic ballad / How to avoid disaster (12" only.).
7" Single: Released Oct '86, on Polydor, by Polydor Ltd. Deleted Mar '87. Catalogue no: **POSP 825**
12" Single: Released Oct '86, on Polydor, by Polydor Ltd. Deleted Mar '87. Catalogue no: **POSPX 825**

THIS PERFECT DAY
Tracks: / This perfect day.
7" Single: Released Jul '77, on Harvest (1), by EMI Records. Deleted Jul '80. Catalogue no: **HAR 5130**

Sainty, Russ

50'S HITS RIGHT HERE ON 45
7" Single: Released Nov '83, on Russ, Deleted '85. Catalogue no: **RUSS 1**

Sakamoto, Kyu

SUKIYAKI
Tracks: / Sukiyaki.
7" Single: Released '80, on USA, by Charly Records. Catalogue no: **LR 1864**
7" Single: Released Jun '63, on H.M.V., by EMI Records. Deleted Jun '66. Catalogue no: **POP 1171**

Sakamoto, Ryuichi

FIELD WORK
Tracks: / Field work / Exhibition (12" only.).
7" Single: Released Jan '86, on 10 Records, by Virgin Records. Deleted '89. Catalogue no: **TEN 112**
12" Single: Released Jan '86, on 10 Records, by Virgin Records. Deleted '89. Catalogue no: **TEN 112-12**

LAST EMPEROR, THE (SINGLE)
Tracks: / Last Emperor, The (end title theme) / Last Emperor, The (front title theme).
7" Single: Released Jan '88, on Virgin, by Virgin Records. Catalogue no: **VS 1038**
12" Single: Released Jan '88, on Virgin, by Virgin Records. Catalogue no: **VST 1038**

MERRY CHRISTMAS MR. LAWRENCE (SINGLE)
Tracks: / Merry Christmas Mr. Lawrence / Sowing the seed.
7" Single: Released Sep '83, on Virgin, by Virgin Records. Catalogue no: **VS 627**

ONCE IN A LIFETIME
Tracks: / Once in a lifetime / Kachakuchanee.
7" Single: Released Oct '82, on Epic, by CBS Records. Catalogue no: **EPC A 2837**

RIOT IN LAGOS
Tracks: / Riot in Lagos / Iconic storage.
7" Single: Released May '81, on Island, by Island Records. Deleted May '84. Catalogue no: **IPR 2048**

RISKY
Tracks: / Risky / After all.
12" Single: Released Aug '87, on CBS, by CBS Records. Catalogue no: **651 017 6**
7" Single: Released Aug '87, on CBS, by CBS Records. Catalogue no: **651 017 7**

WARHEAD
Tracks: / Warhead.
12" Single: Released Aug '81, on Island, by Island Records. Catalogue no: **12WIP 6723**
7" Single: Released Aug '81, on Island, by Island Records. Catalogue no: **WIP 6723**

Sakhile

SAKHILE
Tracks: / Sakhile.
7" Single: Released Sep '83, on Jive, by Zomba Records. Catalogue no: **JIVE 48**
12" Single: Released Sep '83, on Jive, by Zomba Records. Catalogue no: **JIVET 48**

Sakkarin

SUGAR SUGAR (Jonathan King under a false name)
Tracks: / Sugar sugar.
7" Single: Released Apr '71, on RCA, by BMG Records (UK). Deleted Apr '74. Catalogue no: **RCA 2064**

PHILIP SALLON - SUMMER DREAM (Released on Parlophone)

Sal Paradise

MIRACLE
Tracks: / Miracle.
7" Single: Released Nov '84, on Audiotrax, Deleted '86. Catalogue no: **ATX 8**

Salant, Norman

SAX TALK
Tracks: / Sax talk.
12" Single: Released Feb '85, on C&D, Catalogue no: **CD 023**

Salazar

1-2-3
Tracks: / 1-2-3 / Let's hang on.
7" Single: Released Oct '82, on Cricket International, by Cricket International Records. Catalogue no: **LBW 003**
12" Single: Released Oct '82, on Cricket International, by Cricket International Records. Catalogue no: **HOWZAT 003**

Saleh, Kumbi

EKU EGHEMI
Tracks: / Eku eghemi.
7" Single: Released Aug '88, on Torso, by Torso Records. Catalogue no: **TORSO 70066**
12" Single: Released Aug '88, on Torso, by Torso Records. Catalogue no: **TORSO 12066**

Salem 66

ACROSS THE SEA
Tracks: / Across the sea.
7" Single: Released Feb '86, on Homestead, Catalogue no: **HMS 006**

Salem Foundation

SAY YOU'RE READY
Tracks: / Love games / Say you're ready.
12" Single: Released Sep '86, on Solid Music, Catalogue no: **SM 003**

Salesman, Leisa

BABY I AM YOURS
Tracks: / Baby I am yours.
12" Single: Released Jun '88, on Music House, Catalogue no: **MH 4**

Salford Jets

PAIN IN MY HEART
Tracks: / Pain in my heart.
7" Single: Released Mar '83, on KA, Catalogue no: **KA 17**
12" Single: Released Mar '83, on KA, Catalogue no: **KAT 17**

SOLDIERS OF FORTUNE
Tracks: / Soldiers of fortune / Young bugs.
7" Single: Released Mar '81, on Polydor, by Polydor Ltd. Deleted Mar '84. Catalogue no: **POSP 248**

WHO YOU LOOKING AT
Tracks: / Who you looking at / Don't start trouble.
7" Single: Released May '80, on RCA, by BMG Records (UK). Deleted May '83. Catalogue no: **PB 5239**

Sallon, Philip

SUMMER DREAM (See panel above)
Tracks: / Summer dream / Summer dream (mix).
7" Single: Released '84, on Parlophone, by EMI Records. Catalogue no: **R 6082**

Sally Cinnamon

ALL ACROSS THE SAND
Tracks: / All across the sand / Here it comes.
12" Single: Released '87, on Black (1), by FM-Revolver Records. Catalogue no: **12 REV 36**

Salon Music

HUNTING ON PARIS
Tracks: / Hunting on Paris / Lizard.
7" Single: Released Apr '82, on Mobile Suit Corporation, Catalogue no: **CORP 3**

Salsoul Orchestra

CHRISTMAS TIME
Tracks: / Christmas time / New York medley.
12" Single: Released Nov '81, on Epic, by CBS Records. Catalogue no: **EPC A 13 1883**
7" Single: Released Nov '81, on Epic, by CBS Records. Catalogue no: **EPC A 1883**

OOH I LOVE IT
Tracks: / Ooh I love it.
12" Single: Released Mar '83, on Salsoul, Catalogue no: **SALT 102**

Salt 'N' Pepa

I AM DOWN
Tracks: / I am down.
12" Single: Released Nov '87, on Next Plateau (USA), Catalogue no: **NP 50071**

I LIKE IT LIKE THAT
Tracks: / I like it like that / Push.
12" Single: Released Feb '89, on ffrr, by London Records. Catalogue no: **FFRX 20**
7" Single: Released Feb '89, on ffrr, by London Records. Catalogue no: **FFR 20**

MY MIKE SOUNDS NICE
Tracks: / My mike sounds nice.
7" Single: Released Feb '87, on Champion, by Champion Records. Catalogue no: **CHAMP 39**
12" Single: Released Apr '87, on Champion, by Champion Records. Catalogue no: **CHAMP 1239**

PUSH IT
Tracks: / Push it / Hit 'em with this (12" only.) / I am down / Push it (US remix) / I am down / Tramp / Push it (full length remix) (12" only.) / Push it (UK mix- the Shuv'd mix) (12" only.) / I am down (club mix) (12" only.).
7" Single: Released 20 Feb '88, on ffrr, by London Records. Deleted Feb '89. Catalogue no: **FFREE 2**
12" Single: Released 20 Feb '88, on ffrr, by London Records. Catalogue no: **FFRRX 2**
7" Single: Released 20 Feb '88, on ffrr, by London Records. Catalogue no: **FFRR 2**
7" Pic: Released 20 Feb '88, on ffrr, by London Records. Deleted Feb '89. Cata-

logue no: **FFRPD 2**
12" Single: Released Feb '88, on ffrr, by London Records. Deleted Feb '89. Catalogue no: **FFRRX 2**

PUSH IT (NOISE BOYZ REMIX)
Tracks: / Push it (Noise Boyz remix) / Tramp (Alan Coultard mix).
12" Single: Released Jul '88, on Champion, by Champion Records. Catalogue no: **CHAMPX 1251**

PUSH IT (US REMIX)
Tracks: / Push it.
12" Single: Released 13 Jun '88, on ffrr, by London Records. Catalogue no: **FFRX 2**
7" Single: Released 13 Jun '88, on ffrr, by London Records. Deleted May '89. Catalogue no: **FFR 2**

SHAKE YOUR THANG
Tracks: / Shake your thang / Spinderella's not a fella (but a girl, D.J.) / Shake your thang (club mix) (12" & CD single only.) / Shake your thang (instru-pella) (12" & CD single only.) / Spinderella's not a fella (but a girl, D.J.)(instru-pella) (12" & CD single only.).
12" Single: Released Aug '88, on ffrr, by London Records. Deleted May '89. Catalogue no: **FFRXR 11**
CD 5": Released Aug '88, on ffrr, by London Records. Catalogue no: **FFRCD 11**
7" Single: Released 22 Aug '88, on ffrr, by London Records. Deleted May '89. Catalogue no: **FFR 11**
12" Single: Released Aug '88, on ffrr, by London Records. Deleted May '89. Catalogue no: **FFRXP 11**
7" Single: Released Aug '88, on ffrr, by London Records. Catalogue no: **FFRG 11**
12" Single: Released 22 Aug '88, on ffrr, by London Records. Deleted May '89. Catalogue no: **FFRX 11**

TRAMP (REMIX)
Tracks: / Tramp (remix) / Push it / Idle chatter / I'll take your man (Only on picture bag.).
12" Single: Released Jul '87, on Champion, by Champion Records. Catalogue no: **CHAMP 1251**
CD 5": Released Jun '88, on Champion, by Champion Records. Catalogue no: **CHAMP CD 51**
7" Single: Released Jul '87, on Champion, by Champion Records. Catalogue no: **CHAMP 51**

TWIST & SHOUT
Tracks: / Twist and shout / Everybody get up.
12" Single: Released Oct '88, on ffrr, by London Records. Deleted May '89. Catalogue no: **FFRX 16**
7" Pic: Released Oct '88, on ffrr, by London Records. Deleted May '89. Catalogue no: **FFRB 16**
7" Single: Released Oct '88, on ffrr, by London Records. Deleted 26 Jun '89. Catalogue no: **FFR 16**
CD 5": Released Oct '88, on ffrr, by London Records. Catalogue no: **FFRCD 16**

Salty Dog

OLYMPIC CITY 1992
Tracks: / Olympic city 1992 / Long distance runner.
7" Single: Released May '86, on Sub-Zero Music, by Sub-Zero Music. Catalogue no: **SZM 6**

Salvation

ALL AND MORE
Tracks: / All and more / Happening, The / She's an island.
12" Single: Released May '89, on Karbon, by Karbon Records. Catalogue no: **KAR 612 T**

GIRLSCHOOL
Tracks: / Girl school.
7" Single: Released Sep '83, on Merciful Release, by Merciful Release. Catalogue no: **MR 25**
12" Single: Released Sep '83, on Merciful Release, by Merciful Release. Catalogue no: **MRX 25**

JESSICA'S CRIME
Tracks: / Jessica's crime.
12" Single: Released Feb '86, on Batfish, Catalogue no: **USS 104**
7" Single: Released Feb '86, on Batfish, Deleted Jun '88. Catalogue no: **BF 103**

SEEK
Tracks: / Seek.
12" Single: Released Nov '86, on Ediesta, Deleted '88. Catalogue no: **CALC 4T**
7" Single: Released Nov '86, on Ediesta, Deleted '88. Catalogue no: **CALC 4**

SUNSHINE SUPERMAN
Tracks: / Sunshine Superman.
7" Single: Released Jul '88, on Karbon, by Karbon Records. Catalogue no: **KAR 609**
12" Single: Released Jul '88, on Karbon, by Karbon Records. Catalogue no: **KAR 609 (T)**

Salvation Sunday

COLD GREY EYES
Tracks: / Cold grey eyes / Torn to pieces (* Track listed twice for 12" version only.) / Cold to the touch (Track appears on Double pack only.) / Measure of the man (Track appears on Double pack only.).
Note: Tracks vary between versions.
7" Single: Released Sep '86, on Polydor, by Polydor Ltd. Deleted Aug '87. Catalogue no: **SALY 1**
12" Single: Released Sep '86, on Polydor, by Polydor Ltd. Deleted Aug '87. Catalogue no: **SALYX 1**
7" Set: Released Sep '86, on Polydor, by Polydor Ltd. Catalogue no: **SALYG 1**

COME TO YOUR SENSES
Tracks: / Come to your senses.
7" Single: Released Aug '87, on Polydor, by Polydor Ltd. Catalogue no: **SALY 3**
12" Single: Released Aug '87, on Polydor, by Polydor Ltd. Catalogue no: **SALYX 3**

HEART IN MOTION
Tracks: / Heart in motion / Heartbreaking man (demo).
7" Single: Released May '87, on Polydor, by Polydor Ltd. Deleted Jan '88. Catalogue no: **SALY 2**

Salvatore Cutungo

INNAMORATI
Tracks: / Innamorata.
7" Single: Released Jun '82, on Sonet, by Sonet Records. Catalogue no: **SON 2244**

Salvetti, Tocko

ISLE OF CAPRI
Tracks: / Isle of Capri.
7" Single: Released Aug '84, on Young Blood, by Young Blood Records. Catalogue no: **BH H0086**

Salvo, Joe

LIFE COULD BE BETTER
Tracks: / Life could be better.
7" Single: Released Aug '84, on Towerbell, Catalogue no: **TOW 59**

Sam & Dave

Biographical details:
Soul vocal duo Sam & Dave were Sam Moore, born in 1935 in Miami, Florida, and Dave Prater, born in 1937 in Ocilla, Georgia. They got together onstage in Miami in 1958 and audience response persuaded them to team up, but they had no hits during a period on Roulette. They signed with Atlantic in 1965, Jerry Wexler sent them to Stax to record songs by Isaac Hayes and David Porter with the Memphis Horns, and some of the best loved hits of the soul era resulted. (Donald Clarke, April 1987.).

HOLD ON, I'M COMING (OLD GOLD)
Tracks: / Hold on, I'm coming.
7" Single: Released Jan '85, on Old Gold, by Old Gold Records. Catalogue no: **OG 9498**

HOLD ON, I'M COMING (SINGLE)
Tracks: / Hold on I'm coming / Soothe me soul sister.
7" Single: Released '80, on Atlantic, by WEA Records. Catalogue no: **LR 0836**
7" Single: Released Jan '81, on Atlantic, by WEA Records. Deleted Jan '84. Catalogue no: **K 11616**

I THANK YOU
Tracks: / I thank you.
7" Single: Released Mar '68, on Stax, by Fantasy Inc (USA). Deleted Mar '71. Catalogue no: **601 030**

SAM & DAVE MEDLEY-SOUL REVIEW
12" Single: Released Nov '85, on Polydor, by Polydor Ltd. Catalogue no: **POSPX 775**
7" Single: Released Nov '85, on Polydor, by Polydor Ltd. Catalogue no: **POSP 775**

SOOTHE ME
Tracks: / Soothe me.
7" Single: Released Mar '67, on Stax, by Fantasy Inc (USA). Deleted Mar '70. Catalogue no: **6C' 004**

SOUL MAN (SINGLE)
Tracks: / Soul man.
7" Single: Released Nov '67, on Stax, by Fantasy Inc (USA). Deleted Nov '70. Catalogue no: **601 023**
12" Single: Released May '87, on Perfect, Catalogue no: **PER 12 8604**

SOUL SISTER BROWN SUGAR
Tracks: / Soul sister brown sugar.
7" Single: Released Jan '69, on Atlantic, by WEA Records. Deleted Jan '72. Catalogue no: **584 237**

Sam & Galore

HEAVEN KNOWS
Tracks: / Heaven knows / Walk my way(live).
7" Single: Released Jul '88, on Fine Tune, by Fine Tune Records. Catalogue no: **FTR 701**
12" Single: Released Jul '88, on Fine Tune, by Fine Tune Records. Catalogue no: **12FTR 01**

Sam, Jeff

DON'T ROCK THE THING SO
Tracks: / Don't rock the thing so / Body beat (Peter King).
12" Single: Released Aug '86, on Blackbeat, Catalogue no: **BBD 181**

Sam & Kitty

I'VE GOT SOMETHING GOOD
Tracks: / I've got something good / Love is the greatest.
7" Single: Released May '80, on Grapevine (Northern Soul), by BMG Records (UK). Deleted May '83. Catalogue no: **GRP 132**

Sam The Ram

WOOLY BULLY
Tracks: / Salt and vinegar / Wooly bully.
7" Single: Released Dec '86, on Starblend, by Starblend Records. Catalogue no: **STAR 9**
12" Single: Released Dec '86, on Starblend, by Starblend Records. Catalogue no: **12STAR 9**

Sam The Sham

LIL RED RIDING HOOD
Tracks: / Lil' red riding hood.
7" Single: Released Aug '66, on MGM, by Polydor Ltd. Deleted Aug '69. Catalogue no: **MGM 1315**

WOOLY BULLY
Tracks: / Wooly bully.
7" Single: Released Jun '65, on MGM, by Polydor Ltd. Deleted Jun '68. Catalogue no: **MGM 1269**

WOOLY BULLY (OLD GOLD)
Tracks: / Wooly bully.
7" Single: Released Jul '84, on Old Gold, by Old Gold Records. Catalogue no: **OG 9447**

Samaria

TAKE BACK THE LOVE
Tracks: / Take back the love.
12" Single: Released Nov '87, on Next Plateau (USA), Catalogue no: **NP 50068**

Same

DOWNTOWN
Tracks: / Downtown.
7" Single: Released Sep '82, on Unlikely, by Unlikely Records. Catalogue no: **URS 49**

MOVEMENT
Tracks: / Movement / Wild about you.
7" Single: Released Feb '80, on Blue Print, Deleted '83. Catalogue no: **BLU 2008**

Sammes, Mike

ROYAL WEDDING WALTZ
Tracks: / Royal wedding waltz / Love is silver , love is gold.
7" Single: Released Apr '81, on President, by President Records. Catalogue no: **PT 494**

SOMEWHERE MY LOVE
Tracks: / Somewhere my love.
7" Single: Released Sep '66, on H.M.V., by EMI Records. Deleted Sep '69. Catalogue no: **POP 1546**

Sample, Joe

BURNIN' UP THE CARNIVAL
Tracks: / Burnin' up the carnival / Dream of dreams.
12" Single: Released Feb '81, on MCA, by MCA Records. Deleted '84. Catalogue no: **MCAT 671**
7" Single: Released Feb '81, on MCA, by MCA Records. Deleted '84. Catalogue no: **MCA 671**

Sample, Nick

MARVELLOUS CONCEPT
Tracks: / Marvellous concept.
12" Single: Released Dec '88, on Dance Stance, Catalogue no: **DS 12001**

Sample Syndicate

HIJACK (MACH II REMIX)
Tracks: / Hijack (Mac II remix).
12" Single: Released Feb '89, on Domino, by Domino Records. Catalogue no: **DOM T10**

Sampson, Dave

SWEET DREAMS
Tracks: / Sweet dreams.
7" Single: Released May '60, on Columbia, by EMI Records. Deleted May '63. Catalogue no: **DB 4449**

Sams Orchestra

DISCO PANTHER
Tracks: / Disco panther.
7" Single: Released Sep '83, on Loose, by Loose Records. Catalogue no: **LSE 3**
12" Single: Released Sep '83, on Loose, by Loose Records. Catalogue no: **LSET 3**

Samson

Biographical details: Paul Samson originally formed Samson in early '78 with Chris Aylmer on bass, Clive Burr on drums and Paul himself on guitar and vocals. At the end of that year, Clive left the band, later to join **Iron Maiden** and was replaced by the mysterious masked character, Thunderstick. A debut album *Survivors* was released in October '79. Deciding that more vocal power was needed, Paul enlisted young vocalist PaulDickinson, at the time a member of the London rock band **The Shots**. During the next couple of years, with the line-up of Dickinson, Samson, Aylmer and Thunderstick, the band were at the forefront of the so-called New Wave of British Heavy Metal, along with **Iron Maiden, Def Leppard** and **Saxon.** They toured extensively in Britain and Europe and released two albums during this period, *Head On* and *Shock Tactics*. Due to the demise of the record company involved, this material became unavailable by mid '82 and, following requests by fans of Dickinson and Samson, this album has now been made available. The group disbanded in 1984 and Paul Samson has recently completed his first solo album. The tracks on *Head Tactics* were selected from *Head On* and *Shock Tactics* and were remixed by Jo Julian and Paul Samson and the Music Works in London. An additional track *Losing My Grip* was included, this being the only version of the song with Bruce Dickinson on vocals. (EMI Records 3/88)e.

ARE YOU READY
Tracks: / Are you ready / Front page news / La Grange.
7" Pic: Released Feb '84, on Polydor, by Polydor Ltd. Catalogue no: **POPP 670**
7" Single: Released Feb '84, on Polydor, by Polydor Ltd. Catalogue no: **POSP 670**
12" Single: Released Feb '84, on Polydor, by Polydor Ltd. Catalogue no: **POSPX 670**

FIGHT GOES ON
Tracks: / Fight goes on / Riding with the angels / Vice versa (Available on 12" only).
7" Single: Released Apr '84, on Polydor, by Polydor Ltd. Catalogue no: **POSP 680**
12" Single: Released Apr '84, on Polydor, by Polydor Ltd. Catalogue no: **POSPX 680**

LIFE ON THE RUN
Tracks: / Life on the run.
7" Set: Released Oct '82, on Polydor, by Polydor Ltd. Catalogue no: **POSPG 519**
7" Single: Released Oct '82, on Polydor, by Polydor Ltd. Catalogue no: **POSP 519**

LOSING MY GRIP
Tracks: / Losing my grip.
7" Pic: Released Jun '82, on Polydor, by Polydor Ltd. Catalogue no: **POSPP 471**
12" Single: Released Jun '82, on Polydor, by Polydor Ltd. Catalogue no: **POSPX 471**

MR. ROCK 'N' ROLL
Tracks: / Mr. Rock & Roll / Primrose shuffle / Telephone / Leavin' you.
Note: Original two singles from one of the top heavy metal bands in the country. (Magnum Music May, 1988).
12" Single: Released Apr '84, on Thunderbolt, by Magnum Music Group. Catalogue no: **THBE 1.003**

RED SKIES
Tracks: / Red skies / Living, loving, lying.
7" Single: Released Mar '83, on Polydor, by Polydor Ltd. Deleted Mar '86. Catalogue no: **POSP 554**

RIDIN' WITH THE ANGELS
Tracks: / Ridin' with the angels / Little big man.
7" Single: Released May '81, on RCA, by BMG Records (UK). Catalogue no: **RCA 67**

VICE VERSA (SINGLE)
Tracks: / Vice versa / Losing my grip.
12" Single: Released Feb '86, on Capitol, by EMI Records. Deleted '88. Catalogue no: **12CL 395**
7" Single: Released Feb '86, on Capitol, by EMI Records. Deleted '88. Catalogue no: **CL 395**

VICE VERSA (SINGLE 2)
Tracks: / Vice versa / Hammer head.
7" Single: Released 20 Jun '80, on Gem, Deleted '83. Catalogue no: **GEMS 34**
7" Single: Released May '80, on EMI, by EMI Records. Deleted '85. Catalogue no: **EMI 5061**

Samuels, Michael

LET'S DO IT AGAIN
Tracks: / Let's do it again.
12" Single: Released Jan '89, on Clique, by

Clique Records. Catalogue no: **ML 002**

Samuels, Winston

I'LL BE HERE
Tracks: / I'll be here.
12" Single: Released May '84, on WE, Catalogue no: **WE 1032**

Samurai

FIRES OF HELL
Tracks: / Fires of hell / Dreams of the world.
7" Single: Released Dec '84, on Ebony (2), by Ebony Records. Catalogue no: **EBON 25**

San Jose

ARGENTINE MELODY (CANCION DE ARGENTINA)
Tracks: / Argentine melody (cancion de Argentina).
7" Single: Released Jun '78, on MCA, by MCA Records. Deleted Jun '81. Catalogue no: **MCA 369**

San, Papa

I WILL SURVIVE
Tracks: / I will survive.
7" Single: Released Jan '89, on Dallas Texas, Catalogue no: **Unknown**

LEGAL RIGHTS
Tracks: / Legal rights.
12" Single: Released Jun '89, on Techniques, Catalogue no: **WRT 46**

ME NO LIKE IT
Tracks: / Me no like it.
7" Single: Released May '89, on Music Master, Catalogue no: **UNKNOWN**

PASTOR FE STOP IT
Tracks: / Pastor fe stop it.
7" Single: Released May '89, on Music Master, Catalogue no: **UNKNOWN**

SHE GI MI PUDDING
Tracks: / She gi mi pudding.
12" Single: Released 30 May '89, on Black Scorpio, Catalogue no: **CDBS 12**

STYLE & FASHION
12" Single: Released Nov '88, on Black Scorpio, Catalogue no: **BS 019**

TALK BACKWAYS
Tracks: / Talk backaways.
12" Single: Released Jun '89, on Kaya, Catalogue no: **JLT 1001**

WATCH WATCH
Tracks: / Watch watch.
7" Single: Released May '89, on Jammy's, Catalogue no: **UNKNOWN**

San Raphael

SHINE THE LIGHTS (2 PARTS)
Tracks: / Shine the lights (part 1) / Shine the lights (part 2).
12" Single: Released Jun '83, on M & R, Catalogue no: **DIS 02**

San Remo Strings

FESTIVAL TIME
Tracks: / Festival time / All turned on.
7" Single: Released Oct '81, on Tamla Motown, by Motown Records (UK). Catalogue no: **TMG 795**

San Sabastian

SOPHIA NATIONAL
Tracks: / Sophia national / Exotic love.
7" Single: Released Jun '83, on Sonet, by Sonet Records. Catalogue no: **SON 2257**

Sanborn, David

Biographical details:
David Sanborn, born in 1945 in Tampa, Florida, plays alto sax and flute, and has been described as the white Junior Walker for his soulful sound. He played with Albert King and Little Milton at 14, with Paul Butterfield Blues Band on and off 1967-72, with Stevie Wonder, Gil Evans, David Bowie and Paul Simon in the early 1970s, began making successful solo albums. (Donald Clarke, 27.3.88)..

CHICAGO SONG
Tracks: / Chicago song / Imogene.
7" Single: Released May '87, on Warner Bros., by WEA Records. Deleted Jan '88. Catalogue no: **W 8392**
12" Single: Released May '87, on Warner Bros., by WEA Records. Deleted Jul '88. Catalogue no: **W 8392T**

DREAM, THE (REMIX)
Tracks: / Dream (remix),The / Imogene / Change of heart, A (Extra track on 12" only).
7" Single: Released Feb '87, on Warner Bros., by WEA Records. Deleted Jan '88. Catalogue no: **W 8414**
12" Single: Released Feb '87, on Warner Bros., by WEA Records. Deleted Jan '88. Catalogue no: **W 8414T**

LET'S JUST SAY GOODBYE
Tracks: / Let's just say goodbye / Seduction, The.
7" Single: Released Jul '81, on Warner Bros., by WEA Records. Catalogue no: **LV 46**

NEITHER ONE OF US
Tracks: / Neither one of us / Let's just say goodbye / Love is not enough.
7" Single: Released Jan '84, on Warner Bros., by WEA Records. Catalogue no: **W 9430**
12" Single: Released Jan '84, on Warner Bros., by WEA Records. Catalogue no: **W 9430T**

Sanchez

BABY CAN I HOLD YOU TONIGHT
Tracks: / Baby can I hold you tonight.
7" Single: Released Jul '89, on Charm, by Charm Records. Catalogue no: **CR 34**
12" Single: Released Jul '89, on Charm, by Charm Records. Catalogue no: **CRT 34**

COME TO RULE
Tracks: / Come to rule.
7" Single: Released Apr '89, on Sir Coxsone, Catalogue no: **BD 8908**

CROWN OF MY SOUND
Tracks: / Crown of my sound.
12" Single: Released Feb '89, on Dennis Star, Catalogue no: **DS 006**

END OF THE WORLD
Tracks: / Live and loud.
12" Single: Released Mar '89, on Live & Love, Catalogue no: **LLD 108**

FOR MY LOVER
Tracks: / For my lover.
7" Single: Released May '89, on Power House, Catalogue no: **UNKNOWN**

GREATEST LOVE, THE
Tracks: / Greatest love, The.
12" Single: Released Jun '88, on Flash, by Mainline Records. Catalogue no: **FID 04**

GREEN GREEN GRASS OF HOME
Tracks: / Green green grass of home.
7" Single: Released Jan '89, on Exterminator, Catalogue no: **Unknown**
12" Single: Released Jan '89, on Scom, Catalogue no: **BD 8803**

JUST MY IMAGINATION
Tracks: / Just my imagination / I want T be your man.
12" Single: Released Jul '89, on Greensleeves, by Greensleeves Records. Catalogue no: **GRED 249**

LADY IN RED
Tracks: / Lady in red.
12" Single: Released Aug '88, on Redman International, Catalogue no: **VPRED 106**

LET IT BE ME
Tracks: / Let it be me.
12" Single: Released Jun '89, on Sir Coxsone, Catalogue no: **BD 8912**

LET ME LOVE YOU NOW
Tracks: / Let me love you.
12" Single: Released Jul '88, on Charm, by Charm Records. Catalogue no: **CRT 18**

LONELINESS LEAVE ME ALONE
Tracks: / Loneliness leave me alone.
12" Single: Released Jun '88, on Techniques, Catalogue no: **WRT 36**

LONELY
Tracks: / Lonely.
12" Single: Released Jun '88, on Guiding Star, Catalogue no: **GS 004**

LOVE IS THE POWER
Tracks: / Love is the power.
12" Single: Released Sep '89, on White, Catalogue no: **PH 22**

MASH IT UP
Tracks: / Mash it up.
12" Single: Released Aug '89, on Mango, by Island Records. Catalogue no: **12 MNG 716**

MY GIRL
Tracks: / My girl.
7" Single: Released Dec '88, on BP International, Catalogue no: **BPKT 3**

OLD FRIEND
Tracks: / Old friend.
12" Single: Released Apr '88, on Redman International, Catalogue no: **RED 6**

OLD FRIENDS VERSION
Tracks: / Old friends (version).
7" Single: Released Jun '88, on Saxon Studio, Catalogue no: **SS 590**

ONE IN A MILLION
Tracks: / One in a million.
12" Single: Released Sep '88, on Germaine, Catalogue no: **DGT 42**

OUT OF MY MIND
Tracks: / Out of my mind.
12" Single: Released Jun '88, on Black Scorpio, Catalogue no: **BS 017**

SWEETEST SOUND
Tracks: / Sweetest sound.
12" Single: Released Jul '88, on Techniques, Catalogue no: **WRT 27**

TELL HIM I'M NOT HOME
Tracks: / Tell him I'm not home.
12" Single: Released Jan '89, on Jammy's, Catalogue no: **VPRD 379**
12" Single: Released Feb '89, on Live & Love, Catalogue no: **LLD 104**

WILD SANCHEZ (SINGLE)
Tracks: / Wild sanchez.
12" Single: Released 8 Aug '88, on Dennis Star, Catalogue no: **DSI 07**

Sanchez, Jackie

GUNFIGHTERS
Tracks: / Gunfighters / Get down.
7" Single: Released Mar '80, on RCA, by BMG Records (UK). Deleted Mar '83. Catalogue no: **PB 5231**

Sandee

YOU'RE THE ONE (MIAMI MIX)
Tracks: / You're the one (Miami mix).
12" Single: Released 30 May '87, on Atlantic, by WEA Records. Deleted 1 Jan '88. Catalogue no: **YZ 136 T**

Sanders, Robert

DOING BAD
Tracks: / Doing bad.
12" Single: Released Oct '86, on Flame (2), by Rhythm King Records. Catalogue no: **MELT 1T**

Sanderson, Richard

WHEN FORTUNE REIGNS
Tracks: / Puissance et loire / When fortune reigns.
7" Single: Released Feb '87, on Carrere, Catalogue no: **CAR 408**

Sandford, Chas

TEMPTATION
Tracks: / Temptation / Julie.
7" Single: Released Jul '82, on Elektra, by Elektra Records (UK). Catalogue no: **K 13188**

Sandford, Chris

NOT TOO LITTLE NOT TOO MUCH
Tracks: / Not too little not too much.
7" Single: Released Dec '63, on Decca, by Decca Records. Deleted Dec '66. Catalogue no: **F 11778**

Sandglow Marinas

GONE TO CHINA
Tracks: / Gone to China.
7" Single: Released Jun '84, on Spellbound, by Spellbound Records. Catalogue no: **SPELL 5**

Sandi & The Sunsetz

ALIVE
Tracks: / Alive / Heat scale.
7" Single: Released Mar '82, on Alfa, Catalogue no: **ALFA 2211**

DREAMS OF IMMIGRANTS
Tracks: / Dreams of immigrants / Mirrors of eyes / Chunk of funk / Jinjirogeh.
7" Single: Released Oct '82, on Warner Bros., by WEA Records. Catalogue no: **2599897**
7" Single: Released Oct '82, on Sire (USA), Catalogue no: **SAND 1**
12" Single: Released Oct '82, on Sire (USA), Catalogue no: **SAND 1T**
7" Pic: Released Oct '82, on Sire (USA), Catalogue no: **SAND 1P**

Sandkings

ALL'S WELL WITH THE WORLD
Tracks: / All's well with the world / Swing / Say goodbye to the railway side (Only on 12" single.) / Colour (Only on 12" single.).
7" Single: Released Aug '89, on Long Beach, by Long Beach Records. Catalogue no: **BEACH 3**
12" Single: Released Aug '89, on Long Beach, by Long Beach Records. Catalogue no: **BEACH 3T**

HOPE SPRINGS ETERNAL
Tracks: / Hope springs eternal.
12" Single: Released 13 Feb '89, on Long Beach, by Long Beach Records. Catalogue no: **BEACH 2 T**

RAIN
Tracks: / Rain.
7" Single: Released Jul '88, on Long Beach, by Long Beach Records. Catalogue no: **BEACH 1**
12" Single: Released Aug '88, on Long Beach, by Long Beach Records. Catalogue no: **BEACH 1 T**

Sandpipers

GUANTANAMERA (OLD GOLD)
Tracks: / Guantanamera / Oh Lori.
7" Single: Released Oct '88, on Old Gold, by Old Gold Records. Catalogue no: **OG 9815**

GUANTANAMERA (SINGLE)
Tracks: / Guantanamera.
7" Single: Released Sep '66, on Pye International, Deleted Sep '69. Catalogue no: **7N 25380**
7" Single: Released '80, on USA, by Charly Records. Catalogue no: **LR 1934**

HANG ON SLOOPY
Tracks: / Hang on sloopy.
7" Single: Released Nov '76, on Satril, by Satril Records. Deleted Nov '79. Catalogue no: **SAT 114**

KUMBAYA
Tracks: / Kumbaya.
7" Single: Released Mar '69, on A&M, by A&M Records. Deleted Mar '72. Catalogue no: **AMS 744**

MAN WITHOUT LOVE, A
Tracks: / Man without love, A.
7" Single: Released Jun '68, on A&M, by A&M Records. Deleted Jun '71. Catalogue no: **AMS 723**

Sandra

EVERLASTING LOVE (SINGLE)
Tracks: / Everlasting love / Stop for a minute (On all versions) / Everlasting love (remix) (On 12" & CD only) / Everlasting dub (On 12" only.) / I'll never be Maria Magdalena (On CD only).
12" Single: Released Jun '89, on Virgin (USA), by Virgin Records. Catalogue no: **UNKNOWN**
12" Single: Released Nov '88, on Siren, by Virgin Records. Catalogue no: **SRNT 85**
7" Single: Released Nov '88, on Siren, by Virgin Records. Catalogue no: **SRN 85**
CD 5": Released '88, on Siren, by Virgin Records. Catalogue no: **SRNCD 85**
7" Single: Released Jun '89, on Virgin (USA), by Virgin Records. Catalogue no: **UNKNOWN**

HEAVEN CAN WAIT
Tracks: / Heaven can wait / Heaven's theme.
CD 3": Released Feb '89, on Siren, by Virgin Records. Catalogue no: **SRNCD 104**
7" Single: Released Feb '89, on Siren, by Virgin Records. Catalogue no: **SRN 104**
12" Single: Released Feb '89, on Siren, by Virgin Records. Catalogue no: **SRNT 104**

(I'LL NEVER BE) MARIE MAGDALENA
Tracks: / I'll never be Maria Magdelena / Party games (instrumental) / Little girl (12" only) / I'll never be Maria Magdalena (12" version).
12" Single: Released Sep '85, on 10 Records, by Virgin Records. Catalogue no: **TEN 78-12**
7" Single: Released Sep '85, on 10 Records, by Virgin Records. Catalogue no: **TEN 78**

IN THE HEAT OF THE NIGHT
Tracks: / In the heat of the night / Heatwave (instrumental) / In the heat of the night (extended) (12" only).
7" Single: Released Jan '86, on 10 Records, by Virgin Records. Deleted '89. Catalogue no: **TEN 113**
12" Single: Released Jan '86, on 10 Records, by Virgin Records. Catalogue no: **TEN 113-12**

Sands, Jodie

SOMEDAY
Tracks: / Someday.
7" Single: Released Oct '58, on H.M.V., by EMI Records. Deleted Oct '61. Catalogue no: **POP 533**

Sands, Tommy

OLD OAKEN BUCKET
Tracks: / Old oaken bucket.
7" Single: Released Aug '60, on Capitol, by EMI Records. Deleted Aug '63. Catalogue no: **CL 15143**

Sandy Bay

FROZEN ORANGE JUICE
Tracks: / Frozen orange juice.
7" Single: Released Apr '83, on Peach River, Deleted '84. Catalogue no: **BBPR 3**

Sandy, Freddie

BICYCLE SONG
Tracks: / Bicycle song.
7" Single: Released Sep '83, on Mind, by Zella Records. Catalogue no: **ZELLA 406**

Sane Inmates

GIRL IS MINE
Tracks: / Girl is mine, The / Girl is mine, The.
10" single: Released Apr '83, on Holly Cone, by Ariwa Sounds. Catalogue no: **HC 104**

Sang, Samantha

EMOTIONS

Tracks: / Emotions.
7" Single: Released Feb '78, on Private Stock, Deleted Feb '81. Catalogue no: **PVT 128**

IN THE MIDNIGHT HOUR
Tracks: / In the midnight hour / It's the falling in love.
7" Single: Released Jan '80, on Liberty, by EMI Records. Deleted Jan '83. Catalogue no: **UP 612**

Sangria

PEOPLE FROM IBIZA
Tracks: / People from Ibiza.
7" Single: Released Nov '84, on Sangria, Catalogue no: **SANGRIA 1**
12" Single: Released Nov '84, on Sangria, Catalogue no: **SANGRIA 121**

Sanny X

GOLDEN RULES
Tracks: / Golden rules / She moves.
7" Single: Released Sep '86, on DMC, Catalogue no: **DECK 2**
12" Single: Released Sep '86, on DMC, Deleted '87. Catalogue no: **DECK 122**

SPLASH DOWN
Tracks: / Splash down.
12" Single: Released Jul '85, on DRC, Catalogue no: **DRC 001**

Sano, Motoharu

COMPLICATION SHAKEDOWN
Tracks: / Complication shakedown.
7" Single: Released Jan '85, on Epic, by CBS Records. Catalogue no: **A 4476**
12" Single: Released Jan '85, on Epic, by CBS Records. Catalogue no: **TA 4476**

Sans Harbour

SANS HARBOUR
Tracks: / Sans harbour / Lonely lovesick blues.
7" Single: Released Mar '82, on Pinnacle, by Pinnacle Records. Catalogue no: **PIN 512**

Santa B Boys

CANARIA CANARIA
Tracks: / Canaria Canaria.
12" Single: Released Jun '89, on Bbat, Catalogue no: **BBAT 003T**

Santa Claus

SINGALONG A SANTA
Tracks: / Singalong a Santa / Blues for father christmas.
7" Single: Released Dec '82, on Polydor, by Polydor Ltd. Deleted Dec '85. Catalogue no: **IVY 1**

SINGALONG A SANTA AGAIN
Tracks: / Singalong a Santa again / Goblin party / Jolly old Santa.
7" Single: Released Dec '83, on Polydor, by Polydor Ltd. Deleted Dec '86. Catalogue no: **IVY 2**

Santa Esmerelda

DON'T LET ME BE MISUNDERSTOOD
Tracks: / Don't let me be misunderstood.
7" Single: Released Nov '77, on Philips, by Phonogram Ltd. Deleted Nov '80. Catalogue no: **6042 325**

Santa, Tracy

HELL IN A HANDTRUCK
Tracks: / Hell in a handtruck.
7" Single: Released May '87, on Exile, Catalogue no: **EX 7005**

SIGNIFY YOUR MIND
Tracks: / Signify your mind.
10" single: Released 16 Sep '88, on Exile, Catalogue no: **EX 10EP 04**

Santana

ALL I EVER WANTED
Tracks: / All I ever wanted / Love.
7" Single: Released Mar '80, on CBS, by CBS Records. Deleted Mar '85. Catalogue no: **CBS 8160**

AQUA MARINE
Tracks: / Aqua marine / Stand up runnin'.
7" Single: Released 20 Jun '80, on CBS, by CBS Records. Deleted '83. Catalogue no: **CBS 8649**

BLACK MAGIC WOMAN
Tracks: / Black magic woman.
7" Single: Released '80, on CBS, by CBS Records. Catalogue no: **LR 0837**

HOLD ON
Tracks: / Hold on / Oxun.
7" Single: Released Aug '82, on CBS, by CBS Records. Deleted Aug '85. Catalogue no: **A 2582**

SAMBA PA TI (OLD GOLD)
Tracks: / Samba pa ti / She's not there.
12" Single: Released Feb '86, on Old Gold, by Old Gold Records. Catalogue no: **OG 4005**
7" Single: Released Jan '88, on Old Gold, by Old Gold Records. Catalogue no: **OG 9753**

SAMBA PA TI (SINGLE)
Tracks: / Samba pa ti.
7" Single: Released Sep '74, on CBS, by CBS Records. Deleted Sep '77. Catalogue no: **CBS 2561**

SENSITIVE KIND
Tracks: / Sensitive kind / American gypsy.
7" Single: Released Oct '81, on CBS, by CBS Records. Deleted Oct '84. Catalogue no: **CBSA 1556**

SHE'S NOT THERE
Tracks: / She's not there.
7" Single: Released Oct '77, on CBS, by CBS Records. Deleted Oct '80. Catalogue no: **CBS 5671**

VERA CRUZ
Tracks: / Vera cruz / Mandela.
7" Single: Released May '87, on CBS, by CBS Records. Deleted Nov '87. Catalogue no: **650417 7**
12" Single: Released May '87, on CBS, by CBS Records. Deleted Nov '87. Catalogue no: **650417 6**

WELL ALL RIGHT
Tracks: / Well all right.
7" Single: Released Nov '78, on CBS, by CBS Records. Deleted Nov '81. Catalogue no: **CBS 6755**

WINNING
Tracks: / Winning / Brightest star.
7" Single: Released Mar '81, on CBS, by CBS Records. Deleted Mar '84. Catalogue no: **A 1139**

Santana, Carlos

Biographical details: Guitarist Carlos Santana, born in Mexico in 1947, formed his influential Latin-rock group in 1969, first called Santana Bluesband. The band played at the Woodstock Festival in 1969; His first album *Santana* was a number 4 LP in the USA, the next two *Abraxas* and *Santana 3* were both number 1. Most of his subsequent albums have charted, but those big hits were the most influential. *Abraxas) included Black magic woman,* also a hit for Fleetwood Mac. (Donald Clarke)..

WATCH YOUR STEP
Tracks: / Watch your step / Lightning.
7" Single: Released Apr '83, on CBS, by CBS Records. Catalogue no: **A 3330**

Santiago

WALKING THE VOODOO NIGHTS
Tracks: / Walking the voodoo nights / Just another night flight.
7" Single: Released Nov '80, on Hertford, Deleted Nov '83. Catalogue no: **HER 1**
12" Single: Released Nov '80, on Hertford, Deleted Nov '83. Catalogue no: **HERL 1**

Santing, Mathilde

LOVE OF THE COMMON MAN
Tracks: / Love of the common man / One day as a lion.
7" Single: Released 23 May '87, on WEA (International), by WEA Records. Deleted 1 Jan '88. Catalogue no: **YZ 129**

YOU TOOK ADVANTAGE OF ME
Tracks: / You took advantage of me.
7" Single: Released Sep '82, on WEA, by WEA Records. Catalogue no: **K 19254**

Santo & Johnny

SLEEP WALK
7" Single: Released Oct '59, on Pye International, Deleted Oct '62. Catalogue no: **7N 25037**

SLEEP WALK (OLD GOLD)
Tracks: / Sleepwalk / Teardrop.
7" Single: Released Oct '86, on Old Gold, by Old Gold Records. Catalogue no: **OG 9636**

TEARDROP
Tracks: / Teardrop.
7" Single: Released Mar '60, on Parlophone, by EMI Records. Deleted Mar '65. Catalogue no: **R 4619**

Santrax

COME AND GET IT
Tracks: / Come and get it.
12" Single: Released Jul '83, on Hitman, Catalogue no: **HM 001**

S.A.O. Band

CHAMPS ELYSEE
Tracks: / Champs Elysee.
7" Single: Released Jun '88, on Antler, by Antler Records (Belgium). Catalogue no: **ANT 035**

Sapphire

BURNING
Tracks: / Burning / Burning(instrumental).
7" Single: Released '88, on Passion, by Skratch Records. Catalogue no: **PASH 54**
12" Single: Released Apr '86, on Passion, by Skratch Records. Catalogue no: **PASH 54(12)**

Sapphires

GONNA BE A BIG THING
Tracks: / Gonna be a big thing / Playin' hide and seek.
Note: Also features "Playin' hide and seek" by Eddie Regan.
7" Single: Released Jun '78, on ABC Records, by MCA Records. Catalogue no: **ABC 4221**

MY BABY MUST BE A MAGICIAN
Tracks: / My baby must be a magician / Whatever you want my love.
12" Single: Released Apr '83, on Stiff, by Stiff Records. Catalogue no: **BUYIT 179**
7" Single: Released Apr '83, on Stiff, by Stiff Records. Catalogue no: **BUY 179**

ROCK ME SLOWLY
Tracks: / Rock me slowly / Make love to the music.
12" Single: Released Jan '84, on Beckett, Deleted '85. Catalogue no: **BKSL 9**

Sara Goes Pop

SARA GOES POP
Tracks: / Sara goes pop.
7" Set: Released Nov '82, on It's War Boys, Deleted '86. Catalogue no: **POUND 4 A**

Saracen

NO MORE LONELY NIGHTS
Tracks: / No more lonely nights / Rock of ages.
7" Single: Released May '82, on Nucleus, by Decca Records. Catalogue no: **SARI 1**

WE HAVE ARRIVED
Tracks: / We have arrived / Face in the crowd.
7" Single: Released Aug '83, on Neat, by Neat Records. Catalogue no: **NEAT 30**

Sarah Goes Shopping

MONEY SPEAKS LOUDER THAN WORDS
Tracks: / Money speaks louder than words.
7" Single: Released Jul '85, on Crystal, by President Records. Catalogue no: **CC 1022**

Sarah & The Planes

TWO CAN HAVE A PARTY
Tracks: / Two can have a party.
7" Single: Released Apr '85, on Cloud International, by Creole Records. Deleted '86. Catalogue no: **CR 80**

Sarah's Kids

SHE'LL MAKE A LOVELY BRIDE
Tracks: / She'll make a lovely bride / Brothers & sisters.
7" Single: Released Jul '81, on Polydor, by Polydor Ltd. Deleted Jul '84. Catalogue no: **POSP 299**

Saraya

LOVE HAS TAKEN IT'S TOLL
Tracks: / Love has taken it's toll / Running out of time.
7" Single: Released Jul '89, on Polydor, by Polydor Ltd. Catalogue no: **889 292 7**
12" Single: Released Jul '89, on Polydor, by Polydor Ltd. Catalogue no: **889 293 1**

Sarbani

ISH KA DEH MARMALEH
Tracks: / Ish ka deh marmaleh / Experience / Ish ka deh marmaleh (extended version) (12" only) / Experience (extended version) (12" only).
Note: "Marmaleh is an acid house version of a 500 year old Indian song. It has already been a hit in the Bhangra charts" (Virgin Records, July 1988)
12" Single: Released Jul '88, on Virgin, by Virgin Records. Catalogue no: **VST 1110**
7" Single: Released Jul '88, on Virgin, by Virgin Records. Catalogue no: **VS 1110**

Sarean Quartar

PARIS NEED NOT BE WARM
Tracks: / Paris need not be warm.
7" Single: Released Nov '86, on Contempo, Catalogue no: **DUCA 107**

PRECIOUS
Tracks: / Precious.
12" Single: Released Jan '88, on Contempo, Catalogue no: **TEMPO 112**

Sargeant & Malone

LOVE MESSAGE
Tracks: / Love message / I know who you are.
12" Single: Released Sep '82, on Half Moon, by Rondelet Music & Records. Catalogue no: **12 ROUND 2001**
7" Single: Released Sep '82, on Half Moon, by Rondelet Music & Records. Catalogue no: **ROUND 2001**

MOVING UP
Tracks: / Moving up / Moving up (instrumental).
7" Single: Released Sep '82, on Half Moon, by Rondelet Music & Records. Catalogue no: **ROUND 2006**
12" Single: Released Sep '82, on Half Moon, by Rondelet Music & Records. Catalogue no: **12 ROUND 2006**

Sarne, Mike

CODE OF LOVE
Tracks: / Code of love.
7" Single: Released Mar '63, on Parlophone, by EMI Records. Deleted Mar '66. Catalogue no: **R 5010**

COME OUTSIDE
12" Single: Released Nov '86, on WEA, by WEA Records. Deleted Jan '88. Catalogue no: **YZ 91T**
7" Single: Released Nov '86, on WEA, by WEA Records. Deleted Jan '88. Catalogue no: **YZ 91**

JUST FOR KICKS
Tracks: / Just for kicks.
7" Single: Released Jan '63, on Parlophone, by EMI Records. Deleted Jan '66. Catalogue no: **R 4974**

WILL I WHAT
Tracks: / Will I what.
7" Single: Released Aug '62, on Parlophone, by EMI Records. Deleted Aug '65. Catalogue no: **R 4932**

Sarney, Joy

NAUGHTY NAUGHTY NAUGHTY
Tracks: / Naughty naughty naughty.
7" Single: Released May '77, on Alaska, Deleted May '80. Catalogue no: **ALA 2005**

Sarr Band

MAGIC MANDRAKE
Tracks: / Magic mandrake.
7" Single: Released Sep '78, on Calendar, Deleted Sep '81. Catalogue no: **DAY 115**

STRUT YOUR STUFF
Tracks: / Strut your stuff.
12" Single: Released Mar '80, on Calendar, Catalogue no: **DAY 12 127**
7" Single: Released Mar '80, on Calendar, Catalogue no: **DAY 127**

Sarstedt, Clive

LOVE CAN HURT
Tracks: / Love can hurt / Don't kick me again.
7" Single: Released Sep '81, on Spectra, by Spectra Records. Deleted '87. Catalogue no: **SPC 2**

SUPER LOVE
Tracks: / Super love.
7" Single: Released Nov '81, on Spectra, by Spectra Records. Deleted '87. Catalogue no: **SPC 4**

Sarsted, Peter

ENGLISH GIRLS
Tracks: / English girls / Where do you go to my lovely / Frozen orange juice.
7" Single: Released May '81, on Liberty, by EMI Records. Deleted May '84. Catalogue no: **BP 396**

FROZEN ORANGE JUICE
Tracks: / Frozen orange juice.
7" Single: Released Jun '69, on United Artists, by EMI Records. Deleted Jun '72. Catalogue no: **UP 35021**

HEMINGWAY
Tracks: / Hemingway / Don Quixote.
7" Single: Released Apr '86, on Filmtrax, by Filmtrax Records. Catalogue no: **FRAME 102**

LOVE AMONG THE RUINS
Tracks: / Love among the ruins / Don Quixote.
7" Single: Released Sep '82, on Peach River, Deleted '83. Catalogue no: **BBPR 2**

SUZANNE
Tracks: / Suzanne.
7" Single: Released Oct '87, on Filmtrax, by Filmtrax Records. Catalogue no: **PTS 01**

WHERE DO YOU GO TO MY LOVELY
Tracks: / Where do you go to my lovely / Morning mountain.
7" Single: Released Feb '69, on United Artists, by EMI Records. Deleted Feb '72. Catalogue no: **UP 2262**
7" Single: Released Aug '73, on United Artists, by EMI Records. Deleted Oct '89. Catalogue no: **UP 35580**

WHERE DO YOU GO TO, MY LOVELY? (OLD GOLD)
Tracks: / Where do you go to, my lovely? / Frozen orange juice.
7" Single: Released Jun '88, on Old Gold, by Old Gold Records. Deleted Sep '89. Cata-

logue no: **OG 9365**

Sarstedt, Robin

I WON'T DANCE
Tracks: / I won't dance / Prisoner of love.
7" Single: Released Sep '80, on Piccadilly, Deleted '83. Catalogue no: **7 P 206**

MY RESISTANCE IS LOW
Tracks: / My resistance is low.
7" Single: Released May '76, on Decca, by Decca Records. Deleted May '79. Catalogue no: **F 13624**

MY RESISTANCE IS LOW (OLD GOLD)
Tracks: / My resistance is low.
7" Single: Released Sep '85, on Old Gold, by Old Gold Records. Catalogue no: **OG 9539**

SOMEBODY LOVES ME
Tracks: / Somebody loves me / Got a date with an angel.
7" Single: Released Aug '80, on Piccadilly, Deleted '83. Catalogue no: **7P 193**

YOU'RE JUST IN LOVE
Tracks: / You're just in love / You can't have your cake and eat it.
7" Single: Released Nov '82, on RAK, by EMI Records. Deleted Nov '85. Catalogue no: **RAK 355**

S.A.S. Paratroopers

WINGED DAGGER
Tracks: / Winged dagger.
7" Single: Released Mar '83, on Bandleader, by Valentine Records. Deleted Dec '87. Catalogue no: **BNDS 14**

Sass

BABY TALK
Tracks: / Baby talk.
7" Single: Released Nov '85, on 10 Records, by Virgin Records. Deleted '86. Catalogue no: **TEN 85**
12" Single: Released Nov '85, on 10 Records, by Virgin Records. Deleted '89. Catalogue no: **TEN 85-12**

I DIDN'T MEAN IT ALL
Tracks: / I didn't mean it all.
12" Single: Released Jan '85, on 10 Records, by Virgin Records. Deleted '86. Catalogue no: **TEN 41-12**
7" Single: Released Jan '85, on 10 Records, by Virgin Records. Deleted '89. Catalogue no: **TEN 41**

Satalite

I WONDER WHY
Tracks: / I wonder why / Combination 2.
12" Single: Released Mar '82, on Star Track, Catalogue no: **ST 004**

NIGHTMARE, THE (EP)
Tracks: / Nightmare, The / New holy war / Dance macabre.
7" Single: Released Feb '83, on Kamera, Deleted '88. Catalogue no: **ERA 016**

URBAN GORILLA
Tracks: / Urban gorilla / High-rise hillbillies.
7" Single: Released Aug '80, on Rewind, Catalogue no: **REWIND 2**

VIETNAM
Tracks: / Vietnam / Lucy is a prostitute / I fell in love with a lesbian.
7" Single: Released Sep '83, on Brickyard, by Brickyard Records. Deleted Oct '85. Catalogue no: **EOR 1**

Satan

KISS OF DEATH
Tracks: / Kiss of death / Heads will roll.
7" Single: Released Sep '82, on Guardian, Catalogue no: **GRC 145**

Satan, Nick

WE WISH YOU A TEDDY CHRISTMAS
Tracks: / We wish you a teddy Christmas / Dance of the teddy boys.
7" Single: Released Nov '80, on Hot Rock, by Hot Rock Records. Catalogue no: **HR45 008**

Satanic Malfunctions

I'VE JUST HAD ABOUT...
Tracks: / I've just had about....
7" Single: Released Oct '87, on Loony Tunes, by Loony Tunes Records. Catalogue no: **TUNE 008**

WHO WANTS THE WORLD(EP)
Tracks: / Who wants the world.
7" EP: Released Oct '86, on Tea Core, Catalogue no: **TEACORE 001**

Satanic Rites

LIVE TO RIDE
Tracks: / Live to ride / Hit and run.
7" Single: Released Sep '81, on Heavy Metal, by FM-Revolver Records. Catalogue no: **HEAVY 8**

Satin, C.T.

FINALLY I FOUND A FRIEND
Tracks: / Finally I found a friend / Finally I found a friend (Garage mix).
7" Single: Released Mar '87, on Nine O Nine, by Creole Records. Catalogue no: **NINE 3**

Satriani, Joe

ALWAYS WITH YOU, ALWAYS WITH ME
Tracks: / Always with you, always with me.
7" Single: Released Jun '88, on Music For Nations, by Music For Nations Records. Catalogue no: **YUM 112**

DREAMING 11
Tracks: / Dreaming 11.
12" Single: Released Dec '88, on Food For Thought, by Music For Nations Records. Catalogue no: **12 YUM 114**

Saturday Night Band

COME ON DANCE DANCE
Tracks: / Come on dance dance.
7" Single: Released Jul '78, on CBS, by CBS Records. Deleted Jul '81. Catalogue no: **CBS 6367**

Saturnalia

GIRL ON THE EIGHTH FLOOR
Tracks: / Girl on the eigth floor / Cold night air / Inside the devil's circus / Promise, The.
7" Single: Released Jan '83, on Burning Words, Deleted '84. Catalogue no: **BW 002**

INSIDE THE DEVILS CIRCLE
Tracks: / Inside the devils circle / Promise, The.
7" Single: Released Jul '82, on Burning Words, Deleted '83. Catalogue no: **BW 001**

Saucerman

SCATTERBRAIN
Tracks: / Scatterbrain.
12" Single: Released Oct '88, on Fierce, Catalogue no: **FRIGHT 029**

Saucers

SPRING HAS SPRUNG
Tracks: / Spring has sprung / Major breakthrough.
7" Single: Released Apr '82, on BBC, by BBC Records & Tapes. Deleted '87. Catalogue no: **RESL 114**

Saulsberry, Rodney

I WONDER
Tracks: / I wonder.
7" Single: Released Nov '84, on Allegience, Catalogue no: **ALES 7**
12" Single: Released Nov '84, on Allegience, Catalogue no: **ALES 127**

Saunders, Ann Marie

WHEN YOU LOVE SOMEBODY
Tracks: / When you love somebody.
12" Single: Released Sep '89, on Jetstar, by Jetstar Records. Catalogue no: **RR 0001**

Saunders, Anthony

DANGER GIRL
Tracks: / Danger girl / Fuss fuss.
12" Single: Released May '84, on The Foundation, Catalogue no: **TF 015**

Saunders, Jesse

FUNK YOU UP
Tracks: / Funk you up.
12" Single: Released Jun '84, on Streetfire, Catalogue no: **84164**

Savage

ONLY YOU
Tracks: / Only you / Turn around.
12" Single: Released Nov '84, on Carrere, Catalogue no: **CART 350**
7" Single: Released Nov '84, on Carrere, Catalogue no: **CAR 350**

WE GOT THE EDGE
Tracks: / We got the edge.
12" Single: Released Nov '84, on Zebra (1), by Zebra Records (1). Catalogue no: **12 RA 4**

Savage Amusement

SAVAGE AMUSEMENT EP
Tracks: / Ride a white swan: *Captain Sensible* / Visit, The: *Asherton, John* / Mustang Ford: *Tigersharks* / Belfast gipsy: *Tigersharks*.
12" Single: Released Dec '87, on Barracuda, Catalogue no: **12 UTA 10**

Savage, Edna

ARRIVEDERCI DARLING
Tracks: / Arrivederci darling.
7" Single: Released Jan '56, on Parlophone, by EMI Records. Deleted Jan '59. Catalogue no: **R 4097**

Savage, Johnny

SAVAGE PROGRESS - BURNING BUSH (Released on 10 Records)

WINDS OF WARMTH
Tracks: / Winds of warmth.
7" Single: Released Aug '84, on Loco, by Loco Records. Catalogue no: **LOCO 1017**

Savage Progress

BURNING BUSH (see panel above)
Tracks: / Burning bush / Tears of love.
12" Single: Released Aug '84, on 10 Records, by Virgin Records. Deleted '89. Catalogue no: **TEN 27-12**
7" Single: Released Aug '84, on 10 Records, by Virgin Records. Deleted May '88. Catalogue no: **TEN 27**

HEART BEGIN TO BEAT
Tracks: / Heart begin to beat.
12" Single: Released Jun '84, on 10 Records, by Virgin Records. Deleted '86. Catalogue no: **TEN 22-12**
7" Single: Released Jun '84, on 10 Records, by Virgin Records. Deleted '86. Catalogue no: **TEN 22**

MY SOUL UNWRAPS TONIGHT
Tracks: / My soul unwraps tonight / Tin man.
12" Single: Released Mar '84, on 10 Records, by Virgin Records. Deleted '89. Catalogue no: **TEN 16-12**
7" Single: Released Mar '84, on 10 Records, by Virgin Records. Deleted '86. Catalogue no: **TEN 16**

Savalas, Telly

IF
Tracks: / If.
7" Single: Released Feb '75, on MCA, by MCA Records. Deleted Feb '78. Catalogue no: **MCA 174**

SOME BROKEN HEARTS NEVER MEND
Tracks: / Some broken hearts never mend / Look what you've done to me.
7" Single: Released Oct '80, on Satril, by Satril Records. Deleted Oct '83. Catalogue no: **HH 152**

YOU'VE LOST THAT LOVING FEELING
Tracks: / You've lost that lovin' feeling.
7" Single: Released May '75, on MCA, by MCA Records. Deleted May '78. Catalogue no: **MCA 189**

Savanna

I CAN'T TURN AWAY
Tracks: / I can't turn away.
7" Single: Released Sep '81, on Red Bus, by Red Bus Records. Catalogue no: **RBS 203**
12" Single: Released Sep '81, on Red Bus, by Red Bus Records. Catalogue no: **RBL 203**

NEVER LET YOU GO
Tracks: / Never let you go / Never let you go (version).
7" Single: Released Mar '82, on RCA, by BMG Records (UK). Catalogue no: **RBS 209**
12" Single: Released Mar '82, on RCA, by BMG Records (UK). Catalogue no: **RBL 209**

Save Sex

DON'T DO A THING
Tracks: / Don't do a thing.
12" Single: Released 10 Jul '87, on Sub Antler, by Sub Antler Records. Catalogue no: **SUBANT 001**

I DON'T DO A THING
Tracks: / I don't do a thing.
12" Single: Released '88, on Subway, by Subway Records. Catalogue no: **SUB 001**

Save The Children...

LITTLE STAR
Tracks: / Little star / Map of, A.
7" Single: Released Nov '81, on Stiff, by Stiff Records. Catalogue no: **SAVE 1**

Save Us

HISTORY TO THE WOMB
Tracks: / History to the womb / Man out of context.
7" Single: Released Jan '86, on Quiet, by Quiet Records. Catalogue no: **QS 010**

Savell, Heather

HOLIDAY
Tracks: / Holiday / Anticipation.
7" Single: Released Oct '81, on Polydor, by Polydor Ltd. Deleted '85. Catalogue no: **POSP 348**

Saville, Roland

LITTLE JIMMY BROWN
Tracks: / Little Jimmy Brown / Do you like it.
7" Single: Released Nov '80, on Precision (1), Deleted Nov '83. Catalogue no: **PAR 112**

Savoy

BROKEN DOWN TRANSISTOR RADIO
Tracks: / Broken down transistor radio / Human race are we.
7" Single: Released May '80, on EMI, by EMI Records. Deleted May '83. Catalogue no: **EMI 5068**

Saw, Tenor

DANCE HALL FEELING
Tracks: / Dance hall feeling.
7" Single: Released May '89, on Skengdon, Catalogue no: **UNKNOWN**

Sawyer, Nigel

LAST LOVE SONG
Tracks: / Last love song / To Kirkham & beyond.
7" Single: Released Sep '82, on RCA, by BMG Records (UK). Catalogue no: **RCA 272**

Sawyer, Roy

I DON'T FEEL MUCH LIKE SMILIN'
Tracks: / I don't feel much like smilin' / Drinking wine alone.
7" Single: Released Apr '80, on Capitol, by EMI Records. Deleted Apr '83. Catalogue no: **CL 16129**

I'M READY TO FALL IN LOVE AGAIN
Tracks: / I'm ready to fall in love again.
7" Single: Released Oct '85, on Premier, by Premier Records. Catalogue no: **PATCH 1**

Sax Happy

FACTORY SONG
Tracks: / Factory song.
7" Single: Released Feb '83, on Take A Hammer, Catalogue no: **TAH 001**

Sax Maniacs

NEVER GONNA LOSE ME
Tracks: / Never gonna lose me / Let's twist again.
7" Single: Released Mar '81, on Penthouse, by Penthouse Records. Catalogue no: **PEN 3**

ONE HUNDRED AND EIGHTY
Tracks: / One hundred and eighty / Somebody help me.
7" Single: Released Nov '81, on Penthouse, by Penthouse Records. Catalogue no: **PENT 10**

SARA SARA KI KI
Tracks: / Sara sara ki ki / Ansaphone.
7" Single: Released Jun '82, on Penthouse, by Penthouse Records. Catalogue no: **PENT 12**

Saxon

Biographical details:
Heavy metal band Saxon was formed in 1977in Yorkshire, England, by vocalist Peter 'Biff' Byford (born 5 January1951); Paul Quinn, Graham Oliver, guitars; Steve Dawson, bass; Pete Gill, drums. They showed some lyrical ability not restricted to the tired sex and sword-and-sorcery themes of some of the others. [Donald Clarke, April 87].

747 (STRANGERS IN THE NIGHT)
Tracks: / 747 (strangers in the night).
7" Single: Released Jun '80, on Carrere, Deleted Jun '83. Catalogue no: **CAR 151**

AND THE BANDS PLAYED ON
Tracks: / And the bands played on.
7" Single: Released Apr '81, on Carrere, Deleted Apr '84. Catalogue no: **CAR 180**

BACK ON THE STREETS
Tracks: / Back on the streets.
7" Single: Released Jul '85, on Parlophone, by EMI Records. Catalogue no: **R 6103**
12" Single: Released Jul '85, on Parlophone, by EMI Records. Catalogue no: **12R 6103**
12" Single: Released Aug '85, on Parlophone, by EMI Records. Catalogue no: **12RA 6103**

BACKS TO THE WALL
Tracks: / Backs to the wall.
7" Single: Released Jun '80, on Carrere, Deleted Jun '83. Catalogue no: **HM 6**
7" Single: Released Jul '80, on Carrere, Catalogue no: **CAR 129**

BIG TEASER
Tracks: / Big teaser / Rainbow theme.
7" Single: Released Jun '80, on Carrere, Deleted Jun '83. Catalogue no: **HM 5**

DO IT ALL FOR YOU
Tracks: / Do it all for you / Just let me rock.
7" Single: Released May '84, on Carrere, Catalogue no: **CAR 323**
12" Single: Released May '84, on Carrere, Catalogue no: **CART 323**

I CAN'T WAIT ANYMORE
Tracks: / I can't wait anymore / Broken heroes / Gonna shout.
12" Single: Released Apr '88, on EMI, by EMI Records. Deleted Jun '89. Catalogue no: **12EM 54**
7" Single: Released Apr '88, on EMI, by EMI Records. Deleted Aug '89. Catalogue no: **EMS 54**
7" Single: Released Apr '88, on EMI, by EMI Records. Deleted Jun '89. Catalogue no: **EM 54**

NEVER SURRENDER
Tracks: / Never surrender / 20.000 feet.
7" Single: Released Jul '81, on Carrere, Catalogue no: **CAR 204**

NIGHTMARE
Tracks: / Nightmare.
12" Single: Released Jul '83, on Carrere, Catalogue no: **CART 284**
7" Pic: Released Jul '83, on Carrere, Catalogue no: **CARP 284**
7" Single: Released Jul '83, on Carrere, Catalogue no: **CAR 284**

NORTHERN LADY
Tracks: / Everybody up (live in Madrid) / Dallas 1pm (live in Madrid) (12" only.).
12" Single: Released Jan '87, on EMI, by EMI Records. Catalogue no: **12EMI 5593**
7" Single: Released Jan '87, on EMI, by EMI Records. Catalogue no: **EMI 5593**

POWER AND THE GLORY (SINGLE)
Tracks: / Power and the glory.
12" Single: Released Apr '83, on Carrere, Catalogue no: **SAXONT 1**
7" Single: Released Apr '83, on Carrere, Catalogue no: **SAXON 1**
7" Pic: Released Apr '83, on Carrere, Catalogue no: **SAXON P 1**

PRINCESS OF THE NIGHT
Tracks: / Princess of the night / Fire in the sky.
7" Single: Released Oct '81, on Carrere, Catalogue no: **CAR 208**

RIDE LIKE THE WIND
Tracks: / Ride like the wind / Red alert / Rock the nations (Live at Hammersmith.) / Back on the streets (live).
CD 5": Released Feb '88, on EMI, by EMI Records. Deleted Jun '89. Catalogue no: **CDEM 43**
7" Single: Released Feb '88, on EMI, by EMI Records. Deleted Jun '89. Catalogue no: **EM 43**
12" Single: Released Feb '88, on EMI, by EMI Records. Deleted Jun '89. Catalogue no: **12EM 43**
7" Pic: Released Feb '88, on EMI, by EMI Records. Deleted Aug '89. Catalogue no: **EMP 43**

ROCK THE NATIONS (SINGLE)
Tracks: / Rock the nations.
12" Single: Released '86, on EMI, by EMI Records. Deleted Oct '87. Catalogue no: **12EMI 5587**
7" Single: Released '86, on EMI, by EMI Records. Deleted Oct '87. Catalogue no: **EMI 5587**
12" Pic: Released '86, on EMI, by EMI Records. Deleted Oct '87. Catalogue no: **12EMIP 5587**
7" Pic: Released '86, on EMI, by EMI Records. Deleted Oct '87. Catalogue no: **EMIP 5587**

ROCKIN' AGAIN
Tracks: / Rockin' again.
12" Single: Released Sep '85, on Parlophone, by EMI Records. Catalogue no: **12R 6112**
7" Single: Released Sep '85, on Parlophone, by EMI Records. Catalogue no: **R 6112**

ROCK'N'ROLL GYPSY
Tracks: / Rock 'n' roll gypsy / Krakatoa 1 / Krakatoa / Medley, The : Heavy metal thunder (Available on 12" version only) / Stand up and be counted (Available on 12" version only) / Taking your chances (Available on 12" version only) / Warrior (Available on 12" version only).
7" Single: Released '86, on Parlophone, by EMI Records. Catalogue no: **R 6112**
12" Single: Released '86, on Parlophone, by EMI Records. Catalogue no: **12R 6112**
7" Pic: Released '86, on Parlophone, by EMI Records. Deleted Jul '87. Catalogue no: **RP 6112**

SAILING TO AMERICA
Tracks: / Sailing to America / Little bit of what you fancy.
12" Single: Released Jan '84, on Carrere, Catalogue no: **CART 6301**
7" Single: Released Jan '84, on Carrere, Catalogue no: **CAR 301**

STRONG ARM OF THE LAW (SINGLE)
Tracks: / Strong arm of the law / Taking your chances.
7" Single: Released Nov '80, on Carrere, Catalogue no: **CAR 170**
12" Single: Released Nov '80, on Carrere, Catalogue no: **CAR 170T**

SUZY HOLD ON
Tracks: / Suzy hold on.
7" Single: Released Sep '80, on Carrere, Catalogue no: **CAR 165**
12" Single: Released Sep '80, on Carrere, Catalogue no: **CAR 165T**

WAITING FOR THE NIGHT
Tracks: / Waiting for the train (extended version) / Chase the fade.
12" Single: Released '86, on EMI, by EMI Records. Deleted Oct '87. Catalogue no: **12EMI 5575**
7" Single: Released '86, on EMI, by EMI Records. Deleted Oct '87. Catalogue no: **EMI 5575**

WHEELS OF STEEL (SINGLE)
Tracks: / Wheels of steel / Stand up and be counted (On CAR 143 only) / 747 (On SPC 8 only).
7" Single: Released Apr '81, on WEA, by WEA Records. Deleted Apr '84. Catalogue no: **SPC 8**
7" Single: Released Mar '80, on Carrere, Deleted Mar '83. Catalogue no: **CAR 143**

Saxon, Al

BLUE-EYED BOY
Tracks: / Blue-eyed boy.
7" Single: Released Dec '60, on Fontana, by Phonogram Ltd. Deleted Dec '65. Catalogue no: **H 278**

ONLY SIXTEEN
Tracks: / Only sixteen.
7" Single: Released Aug '59, on Fontana, by Phonogram Ltd. Deleted Aug '62. Catalogue no: **H 205**

LEO SAYER - LET IT BE (Released on Chrysalis)

THERE, I'VE SAID IT AGAIN
Tracks: / There, I've said it again.
7" Single: Released Sep '61, on Piccadilly, Deleted Sep '66. Catalogue no: **7N 35011**

YOU'RE THE TOP CHA
Tracks: / You're the top cha.
7" Single: Released Jan '59, on Fontana, by Phonogram Ltd. Deleted Jan '62. Catalogue no: **H 164**

Saxton, Tony

DESIRE
Tracks: / Desire.
12" Single: on Burning Sounds, by Burning Sounds Records. Deleted May '88. Catalogue no: **BSD 005**

Sayer, Leo

Biographical details:
Singer, songwriter Leo Sayer was born in Sussex on 21 May 1948. He went to art college, busked in London streets with Lol Coxhill, formed a writing partnership with David Courtney and had 15 hits in the UK in ten years from 1973, more than half in the top ten. He is still popular on TV variety shows. [Donald Clarke, April '87
Leo (whose real name is Gerald Hugh Sayer) was born on 21.5.48 in Shoreham by Sea, educated in Worthing and began his music career as a busker around the London clubs. His big break came when he applied for an audition at the Royal Pavilion Brighton, given by David Courtney and so discovered the first in a remarkably successful string of songwriting relationships. Sayer and Courtney spent hours sitting in an unfurnished Brighton flat creating the early batch of hit singles, including Roger Daltrey's success *Giving it all away.* Sayer's own singing career (now one of rock music's many legendary success stories) was launched in 1974 with the album *Silverbird* behind a clown like image typical of the rather precious fashion sense of the early 1970's. This image was thankfully dropped when the Sayer/Courtney partnership realised it could succeed on songwriting and singing talent alone. They proved it with Leo's second album *Just a boy* with it's hit single *Long tall glasses.* Since then, and through fresh songwriting collaborations with the likes of Barry Mann and Albert Hammond in America and Alan Tarney (with whom he is writing now) in Britain, the Leo Sayer catalogue has become prepared with hit records - and all this from a man who claims not to necessarily set out to write his own material. He also did a six week run on a TV show and launched himself into a series of unknown sporting adventures. Leo also used the British television series as an excuse to sing some of his favourite songs and invite guest artists on to the show who he particulary admired. He sang songs like *Dock of the bay* and Lennon's *Jealous guy,* he introduced such guest names as Randy Newman, Phil Collins and Linda Rondstadt and finished every programme with a live concert spot with Leo and the band playing their own concert material. (Chrysalis Records, October 1983).

BYE NOW MY SWEET LOVE
Tracks: / Bye now my sweet love / You win, I lose.
7" Single: Released Feb '81, on Polydor, by Polydor Ltd. Deleted Feb '84. Catalogue no: **CHS 2498**

HAVE YOU EVER BEEN IN LOVE (SINGLE)
Tracks: / Have you ever been in love / I don't need dreaming anymore.
7" Single: Released Mar '82, on Chrysalis, by Chrysalis Records. Deleted '87. Catalogue no: **CHS 2596**

HEART (STOP BEATING IN TIME)
Tracks: / Heart (stop beating in time) / End of the game, The.
7" Single: Released May '82, on Chrysalis, by Chrysalis Records. Deleted '87. Catalogue no: **CHS 2616**

HOW MUCH LOVE
Tracks: / How much love.
7" Single: Released Apr '77, on Chrysalis, by Chrysalis Records. Deleted Apr '80. Catalogue no: **CHS 2140**

I CAN'T STOP LOVING YOU
Tracks: / I can't stop loving you / No looking back.
7" Single: Released Sep '78, on Chrysalis, by Chrysalis Records. Deleted '83. Catalogue no: **CHS 2240**

LET IT BE
Tracks: / Let it be / Another year.
7" Single: Released '75, on Chrysalis, by Chrysalis Records. Catalogue no: **CHS 2080**

LIVING IN A FANTASY
Tracks: / Living in a fantasy / Millionaire.
7" Single: Released May '81, on Chrysalis, by Chrysalis Records. Deleted May '86. Catalogue no: **CHS 2513**

LONG TALL GLASSES
Tracks: / Long tall glasses.
7" Single: Released Sep '74, on Chrysalis, by Chrysalis Records. Deleted Sep '77. Catalogue no: **CHS 2052**

MOONLIGHTING (OLD GOLD)
Tracks: / Long tall glasses / Moonlighting.
7" Single: Released Feb '87, on Old Gold, by Old Gold Records. Catalogue no: **OG 9689**

MOONLIGHTING (SINGLE)
Tracks: / Moonlighting.
7" Single: Released Aug '75, on Chrysalis, by Chrysalis Records. Deleted Aug '78. Catalogue no: **CHS 2076**

MORE THAN I CAN SAY
Tracks: / More than I can say.
7" Single: Released Jun '80, on Chrysalis, by Chrysalis Records. Catalogue no: **CHS 2442**

ONCE IN A WHILE
Tracks: / Once in a while / Living in a fantasy.
7" Single: Released Sep '80, on Chrysalis, by Chrysalis Records. Deleted '83. Catalogue no: **CHS 2460**

ONE MAN BAND
Tracks: / One man band.

7" Single: Released Jun '74, on Chrysalis, by Chrysalis Records. Deleted Jun '77. Catalogue no: **CHS 2045**

ORCHARD ROAD
Tracks: / Orchard road / Gone solo.
7" Single: Released '83, on Chrysalis, by Chrysalis Records. Catalogue no: **CHS 2677**

RAINING IN MY HEART
Tracks: / Raining in my heart.
7" Single: Released Nov '78, on Chrysalis, by Chrysalis Records. Deleted Nov '81. Catalogue no: **CHS 2277**

REAL LIFE
Tracks: / Real life / Girl is with me, The.
7" Single: Released '86, on Chrysalis, by Chrysalis Records. Catalogue no: **LEO 4**

SEA OF HEARTBREAK
Tracks: / Sea of heartbreak.
7" Single: Released Jan '84, on Chrysalis, by Chrysalis Records. Catalogue no: **LEO 2**
12" Single: Released Jan '84, on Chrysalis, by Chrysalis Records. Catalogue no: **LEOX 2**

SHOW MUST GO ON, THE (OLD GOLD)
Tracks: / One man band / Show must go on.
7" Single: Released Feb '87, on Old Gold, by Old Gold Records. Catalogue no: **OG 9687**

SHOW MUST GO ON, THE (SINGLE)
Tracks: / Show must go on.
7" Single: Released Dec '73, on Chrysalis, by Chrysalis Records. Deleted Dec '76. Catalogue no: **CHS 2023**

SOLO
Tracks: / Solo / Passion.
7" Single: Released '86, on Chrysalis, by Chrysalis Records. Catalogue no: **LEO 5**

THUNDER IN MY HEART (SINGLE)
Tracks: / Thunder in my heart.
7" Single: Released Sep '77, on Chrysalis, by Chrysalis Records. Deleted Sep '80. Catalogue no: **CHS 2163**

TILL YOU COME BACK TO ME
Tracks: / Till you come back to me / Train.
7" Single: Released Oct '83, on Chrysalis, by Chrysalis Records. Deleted Oct '86. Catalogue no: **LEO 01**

UNCHAINED MELODY
Tracks: / Unchained melody / Heart for sale / How much love (Available on 12" only) / Orchard road (Available on 12" version only).
7" Single: Released '86, on Chrysalis, by Chrysalis Records. Catalogue no: **LEO 3**
12" Single: Released '86, on Chrysalis, by Chrysalis Records. Catalogue no: **LEOX 3**

WHEN I NEED YOU (OLD GOLD)
Tracks: / When I need you.
7" Single: Released Feb '87, on Old Gold, by Old Gold Records. Catalogue no: **OG 9691**

WHEN I NEED YOU (SINGLE)
Tracks: / When I need you / I think we fell in love too fast.
7" Single: Released Jan '77, on Chrysalis, by Chrysalis Records. Deleted '82. Catalogue no: **CHS 2127**

WHERE DID WE GO WRONG
Tracks: / Where did we go wrong / Millionaire.
7" Single: Released Oct '80, on Chrysalis, by Chrysalis Records. Deleted Oct '83. Catalogue no: **CHS 2469**

YOU MAKE ME FEEL LIKE DANCING
Tracks: / You make me feel like dancing / Magdelena.
7" Single: Released Oct '76, on Chrysalis, by Chrysalis Records. Deleted '81. Catalogue no: **CHS 2119**

Sayle, Alexei

Biographical details: Alexei Sayle was born in Liverpool. His parents - a Jewish Lithuanian mother and a Manx father - were both members of the Communist Party of Great Britain. His father, a railway guard, was active in the union and most of Alexei's childhood memories are of being taken on N.U.R. delegations to Eastern Europe, long summers spent watching folk dance exhibitions and visiting ball-bearing factories. Despite this his political views remain very firmly on the left. Alexei distinguished himself at school chiefly for having a beard when he was 14. Scraping through three '0' levels he managed to get himself to Southport Art College and then on to Chelsea School of Art where he was officially studying Fine Art but spent most of his time making home movies. After art school Alexei drifted into the obligatory series of odd jobs, including filing clerk, drama teacher, dinner lady and a stint as a labourer during which he built three inches of the Jubilee Line on the London Underground. A friend writing and producing a Brecht cabaret noticed Alexei's resemblance to Bertolt Brecht and asked him to take the title role. This accidental introduction to fringe theatre led him to writing and performing in a series of fringe theatre revues, initially as part of a double act and then solo.
In 1979 the Comedy Store, a club for aspiring comedians, opened in London's Soho. Alexei went to audition as a performer and was promptly signed up as the compere; his acidic tongue and aggressive bulk proving invaluable. After honing his wit on the Store's late night audiences, Alexei left after a year to become the co-founder and compere of The Comic Strip - a show featuring the best acts from The Comedy Store in a theatre within Raymond's Revue Bar in Soho. At the same time Alexei was a founder member of Alternative Cabaret, a collective of comics and musicians who gigged mostly in pubs in the London area performing innovative cabaret type shows. Alexei had rapidly established himself at the front of the so-called New Wave of young comics and as a result was asked to appear in The Secret Policeman's Other Ball - four shows for Amnesty International that were edited into a very successful film. Alexei's performance has generally been acknowledged as one of the show's highlights. He wrote two highly successful comedy serials for London's Capital Radio. The first one *Alexei Sayle Community Detective in Alexei Sayle and the Fish People* won the Pye Radio Award for 1982's best contribution to light entertainment. He has done several tours in Britian - firstly with the Comic Strip team and lately he has done two solo tours which included sell-out gigs at such venues as Birmingham Town Hall, London's Cambridge Theatre and Nottingham's Theatre Royal. He plans to tour in the spring of 1984. Alexei's television appearances have included presenting and co-writing the BBC Arena documentary on the Cortina car. He was also in three of the most talked about comedy shows of 1982. Alexei was a guest on ITV's O.T.T., a show that received more press coverage and flak than the Normandy Landings. He also had a cameo role as a KGB torturer in Whoops Apocalypse. Then Alexei appeared as the entire Balowski family in BBC's The Young Ones. Alexei also wrote his own half hour show for BBC's Commic Roots series, repeated within a month of its first transmission. Some of the flavour of Alexei's live act can be caught on his album *Cak* and his video *The Alexei Sayle Pirate Video.* His work as a solo stand up comedian is his major concern but he has begun to diversify into other fields. Alexei's first book *Train to Hell* was published by Methuen in February and he also appears in the movie, Gorky Park. Alexei's new album *The Fish People Tapes* is released by Island in March, 1984. (Island Records, 1984).

MEANWHILE
Tracks: / Meanwhile / Advertising.
7" Single: Released '86, on Epic, by CBS Records. Catalogue no: **A 6669**
12" Single: Released '86, on Epic, by CBS Records. Catalogue no: **TA 6669**

ULLO JOHN GOT A NEW MOTOR
Tracks: / Ullo John got a new motor.
7" Single: Released Feb '84, on Springtime, by Springtime Records. Catalogue no: **IS 162**

Sayzer, Michael

WHEN THE LIGHTS GO DOWN
Tracks: / When the lights go down.
7" Single: Released Oct '85, on Musik, Catalogue no: **NRMS 103**

Scab Aid

LET IT BE
Tracks: / Let it be.
7" Single: Released Jul '87, on Scum, Deleted '88. Catalogue no: **SCAB 1**

Scabs

CRYSTAL EYES
Tracks: / Crystal eyes.
7" Single: Released '89, on Play It Again Sam(Belgium), by Play It Again Sam (Belgium). Catalogue no: **BIAS 117**

HALFWAY HOME
Tracks: / Halfway home / Greater reward.
7" Single: Released Sep '88, on Play It Again Sam(Belgium), by Play It Again Sam (Belgium). Catalogue no: **BIAS 096**

PIMP, THE
Tracks: / Pimp, The.
12" Single: Released Dec '87, on Play It Again Sam(Belgium), by Play It Again Sam (Belgium). Catalogue no: **BIAS 082**

Scadding, Sue

SIMPLE LOVER
Tracks: / Simple lover.
7" Single: Released Aug '83, on Speed, Catalogue no: **FRIED 5**

Scaffold

DO YOU REMEMBER
Tracks: / Do you remember.
7" Single: Released Mar '68, on Parlophone, by EMI Records. Deleted Mar '71. Catalogue no: **R 5679**

GIN GAN GOOLIE
Tracks: / Gin gan goolie.
7" Single: Released Nov '69, on Parlophone, by EMI Records. Deleted Nov '72. Catalogue no: **R 5812**

LILY THE PINK
Tracks: / Lily the pink.
7" Single: Released Nov '68, on Parlophone, by EMI Records. Deleted Nov '71. Catalogue no: **R 5734**
7" Single: Released Oct '77, on EMI, by EMI Records. Catalogue no: **EMI 2690**

LIVERPOOL LOU
Tracks: / Liverpool Lou.
7" Single: Released Jun '74, on Warner Bros., by WEA Records. Deleted Jun '77. Catalogue no: **K 16400**

THANK U VERY MUCH
Tracks: / Thank u very much.
7" Single: Released Nov '67, on Parlophone, by EMI Records. Deleted Nov '70. Catalogue no: **R 5643**

Scaggs, Boz

Biographical details:
Rock singer, songwriter Boz Scaggs was born William Ross Scaggs, 8 June 1944, in Ohio. He grew up in Texas,he played in bands with schoolmate Steve Miller in Texas and in Madison, Wisconsin; later in San Francisco; he had gone to Europe with musicians who later bacame Mother Earth, he made his first solo album *Boz* for Polydor in Sweden in 1964, but his proper debut as a confident artist was in 1969 on Atlantic, with Diane Allman and Muscle Shoals Sideman; then on CBS. His albums have been selling strongly ever since, all still in print in the USA. [Donald Clarke, April 87].

BREAKDOWN DEAD AHEAD
Tracks: / Breakdown dead ahead / Isn't it time.
7" Single: Released Apr '80, on CBS, by CBS Records. Deleted Apr '83. Catalogue no: **CBS 8501**

HEART OF MINE
Tracks: / Heart of mine / You'll never know / Soul to soul (12" and CD single only.) / What can I say (12" and CD single only.) / We're all alone / Slow dancer.
12" Single: Released May '88, on CBS, by CBS Records. Deleted Jan '89. Catalogue no: **651 559 8**
CD 5": Released May '88, on CBS, by CBS Records. Deleted Jan '89. Catalogue no: **651 559 2**
7" Single: Released May '88, on CBS, by CBS Records. Deleted Jan '89. Catalogue no: **651 559 7**
12" Single: Released 13 Jun '88, on CBS, by CBS Records. Catalogue no: **651 559 6**

HOLLYWOOD
Tracks: / Hollywood.
7" Single: Released Dec '77, on CBS, by CBS Records. Deleted Dec '80. Catalogue no: **CBS 5836**

JO JO
Tracks: / Jo Jo / Do like you do in New York.
7" Single: Released 20 Jun '80, on CBS, by CBS Records. Deleted '83. Catalogue no: **CBS 8740**

LIDO SHUFFLE
Tracks: / Lido shuffle.
7" Single: Released May '77, on CBS, by CBS Records. Deleted May '80. Catalogue no: **CBS 5136**

LOOK WHAT YOU'VE DONE TO ME
Tracks: / Look what you've done to me / Just my imagination.
7" Single: Released Oct '80, on CBS, by CBS Records. Deleted Oct '83. Catalogue no: **CBS 9034**

LOWDOWN
Tracks: / Lowdown.
7" Single: Released Oct '76, on CBS, by CBS Records. Deleted Oct '79. Catalogue no: **CBS 4563**

MISS SUN
Tracks: / iMiss sun / Dinah Flo.
7" Single: Released Jan '81, on CBS, by CBS Records. Deleted Jan '84. Catalogue no: **CBS 9424**

WHAT CAN I SAY
Tracks: / What can I say.
7" Single: Released Jan '77, on CBS, by CBS Records. Deleted Jan '80. Catalogue no: **CBS 4869**

WHAT CAN I SAY (OLD GOLD)
Tracks: / What can I say / Lido shuffle.
7" Single: Released 27 Feb '89, on Old Gold, by Old Gold Records. Catalogue no: **OG 9862**

Scala

SECRET CEREMONY THEME FROM BROND Featuring Bill Nelson & Daryl Runswick
Tracks: / Secret ceremony / Wiping a tear from the all seeing eye.
12" Single: Released 23 May '87, on Cocteau, by Cocteau Records. Catalogue no: **COQ T 21**
CD 5": Released Jun '88, on Cocteau, by Cocteau Records. Catalogue no: **COQ CD 21**

Scala Timpani

WINDS OF CHANGE
Tracks: / Winds of change.
12" Single: Released Apr '85, on Fire, by Fire Records. Catalogue no: **FIRE 3**

Scales, Charles

INSIDE MY LOVE
Tracks: / Inside my love / Inside my love (version).
12" Single: Released Sep '88, on Expansion, Catalogue no: **EXPAND 14**

Scandal

GOODBYE TO YOU
Tracks: / Goodbye to you / All my life.
7" Single: Released Jan '83, on CBS, by CBS Records. Catalogue no: **A 3019**

HANDS TIED
Tracks: / Hands tied / Maybe you went too far.
7" Single: Released Jan '85, on CBS, by CBS Records. Catalogue no: **A 4893**

I WANNA DO IT
Tracks: / I wanna do it / Love either grows or goes.
7" Single: Released Jun '81, on Creole, by Creole Records. Catalogue no: **CR 10**
12" Single: Released Jun '81, on Creole, by Creole Records. Catalogue no: **CR 1210**

Scarab

ROCK NIGHT
Tracks: / Rock night / Wicked woman.
7" Single: Released Aug '80, on Inferno (1), by Inferno Records. Catalogue no: **HEADBANGER 1**

Scarbury, Joey

BELIEVE IT OR NOT
Tracks: / Believe it or not.
7" Single: Released Oct '81, on Elektra, by Elektra Records (UK). Catalogue no: **K 12547**

Scarecrows

DEEP END
Tracks: / Deep end.
7" Single: Released Aug '85, on Swordfish, by Swordfish Records. Catalogue no: **SWF 002**

NAPALM WITH SILVER
Tracks: / Napalm with silver.
12" Single: Released Jan '85, on Swordfish, by Swordfish Records. Catalogue no: **SWF 001**

Scarlet Alive

HEAT GOES UP
Tracks: / Heat goes up.
7" Single: Released Oct '82, on Jive Alive, by Zomba Records. Catalogue no: **JA 001**

ON EARTH AND IN HEAVEN
Tracks: / On earth and in heaven.
7" Single: Released Mar '83, on Small Run, Catalogue no: **SRR 0011**

Scarlet, Bobby

WHITE PEARL
Tracks: / White pearl / Mosquito / Jessica Jayne / I've been insulted by more Texans.. (Full title: I've been insulted by more Texans than anyone else in the wo).
12" Single: Released Nov '88, on LA-DI-DA, Catalogue no: **LA DI DA 002**

Scarlet Fantastic

FILM STAR KISS
Tracks: / Film star kiss / Film star kiss (stonkin' boogie mix) (12" only.) / Follow that star / Exterminating angel (12" only.).
7" Single: Released Apr '88, on Arista, by BMG Records (UK). Catalogue no: **109 882**
12" Single: Released Apr '88, on Arista, by BMG Records (UK). Deleted May '89. Catalogue no: **609 882**

NO MEMORY

SCARY THIEVES - DYING IN VAIN (Released on Parlophone)

Tracks: / No memory / No memory (no technology) / No memory (ecastasy mix).
12" Single: Released Sep '87, on Arista, by BMG Records (UK). Deleted May '89. Catalogue no: **RIST 36**
CD 5": Released Nov '87, on Arista, by BMG Records (UK). Deleted Jul '89. Catalogue no: **RISCD 36**
12" Single: Released Oct '87, on Arista, by BMG Records (UK). Catalogue no: **RISTX 36**
7" Single: Released Sep '87, on Arista, by BMG Records (UK). Catalogue no: **RIS 36**

PLUG ME IN (TO THE CENTRAL LOVE LINE)
Tracks: / Plug me in (to the central love line) / Plug me in (the French connection) (12" only.) / Plug me in (the Amsterdam connection) (Special limited edition scarlet vinyl with 6 free picture postcards.) / Plug me in (the F train connection) (Special limited edition scarlet vinyl with 6 free picture postcards.) / I blame thee not (Only on CD single.).
12" Single: Released Jan '88, on Arista, by BMG Records (UK). Deleted May '89. Catalogue no: **609 693**
7" Single: Released Jan '88, on Arista, by BMG Records (UK). Deleted May '89. Catalogue no: **109 693**
CD 5": Released Jan '88, on Arista, by BMG Records (UK). Catalogue no: **659 693**

STAY
Tracks: / Stay / Plug me in / Silver bullet (Available on 12" only).
12" Single: Released 23 Jul '88, on Arista, by BMG Records (UK). Catalogue no: **611626**
7" Single: Released 23 Jul '88, on Arista, by BMG Records (UK). Catalogue no: **111626**

Scarlet Party

101 DAMNATIONS
Tracks: / 101 dalmations / What is this thing?.
7" Single: Released Sep '82, on Parlophone, by EMI Records. Catalogue no: **R 6058**

EYES OF ICE
Tracks: / Eyes of ice / Another world.
7" Single: Released Feb '83, on Parlophone, by EMI Records. Catalogue no: **R 6060**

Scarlett

SAD SONGS ON THE RADIO
Tracks: / Sad songs on the radio.
7" Single: Released Aug '84, on Lamborghini, by Lamborghini Records. Catalogue no: **LMG 14**

SISTERS UNDER THE SKIN
Tracks: / Sisters under the skin.
7" Single: Released Mar '84, on Lamborghini, by Lamborghini Records. Catalogue no: **LMG 8**
12" Single: Released Mar '84, on Lamborghini, by Lamborghini Records. Catalogue no: **12LMG 8**
7" Single: Released Oct '84, on Lamborghini, by Lamborghini Records. Catalogue no: **LMG 17**

Scarlett & Black

LET YOURSELF GO-GO
Tracks: / Let yourself go-go (7" only) / Watcher, The / Let yourself go-go (dub) (12" only) / Let yourself go-go (12" mix).
Note: "Male/female duo Scarlett and Black (Robin Hild - keyboards and Sue West - vocals), are originally from London, but are now based in Los Angeles. They have taken influences from both cities to create a fast moving pop/dance record." (Virgin, July 1988)
12" Single: Released Jul '88, on Virgin, by Virgin Records. Catalogue no: **VST 1077**
7" Single: Released Jul '88, on Virgin, by Virgin Records. Catalogue no: **VS 1077**

YOU DON'T KNOW
Tracks: / You don't know (7" only) / You don't know (12" mix) / Japan / You don't know (remix) (12" only).
12" Single: Released Mar '88, on Virgin, by Virgin Records. Catalogue no: **VST 1061**
7" Single: Released Mar '88, on Virgin, by Virgin Records. Catalogue no: **VS 1061**

YOU NEVER UNDERSTOOD ME
Tracks: / You never understood me / Oliver (ext.mix).
12" Single: Released Sep '86, on MDM, by MDM Communications. Deleted May '88. Catalogue no: **MDM 13-12**
7" Single: Released Sep '86, on MDM, by MDM Communications. Deleted May '88. Catalogue no: **MDM 13**

Scars

ALL ABOUT YOU
Tracks: / All about you / Author, author.
7" Single: Released Mar '81, on Charisma, by Virgin Records. Deleted Mar '84. Catalogue no: **PRE 14**

THEY CAME AND TOOK HER
Tracks: / They came and took her / Romance by mail.
7" Single: Released Feb '80, on Charisma, by Virgin Records. Deleted Feb '85. Catalogue no: **PRE 002**

Scary Thieves

DYING IN VAIN
Tracks: / Dying in vain / Behind the lines.
7" Single: Released '85, on Parlophone, by EMI Records. Catalogue no: **R 6090**

Scattered Order

ESCAPE VIA CESSNOCK
Tracks: / Escape via Cessnock.
12" Single: Released Mar '86, on Ink, by Red Flame Records. Catalogue no: **INK 1217**

Sca-Ville Train

RETURN OF BLACK PANTHER
Tracks: / Return of black panther.
7" Single: Released Dec '87, on Top Beat, Catalogue no: **POTT 001**

Scawta Rocks

SUDDENLY
Tracks: / Suddenly.
12" Single: Released Apr '83, on Rite Sound, Catalogue no: **RTS 002**

Scene

GOOD LOVIN'
Tracks: / Good lovin'.
7" Single: Released Sep '85, on Diamond, by Revolver Records. Catalogue no: **DIA 007**
12" Single: Released Sep '85, on Diamond, by Revolver Records. Catalogue no: **DIAEL 007**

I'VE HAD ENOUGH
Tracks: / I've had enough.
7" Single: Released Jul '80, on Inferno (1), by Inferno Records. Catalogue no: **BEAT 2**

SOMETHING THAT YOU SAID
Tracks: / Something that you said.
7" Single: Released Jan '85, on Diamond, by Revolver Records. Catalogue no: **DIA 008**

Schenker, Michael

ARMED AND READY
Tracks: / Armed and ready / Bijou pleasurette.
7" Single: Released Aug '80, on Chrysalis, by Chrysalis Records. Catalogue no: **CHS 2455**

CRY FOR NATIONS
Tracks: / Cry for the nations / Armed & ready (live) / Into the arena (live).
7" Single: Released Nov '80, on Chrysalis, by Chrysalis Records. Deleted Nov '83. Catalogue no: **CHS 2471**
12" Single: Released Nov '80, on Chrysalis, by Chrysalis Records. Deleted '85. Catalogue no: **CHS 12 2471**

DANCER
Tracks: / Dancer / Girl from uptown.
7" Single: Released Aug '82, on Chrysalis, by Chrysalis Records. Catalogue no: **CHS 2636**
12" Single: Released Aug '82, on Chrysalis, by Chrysalis Records. Catalogue no: **CHS 12 2636**

READY TO ROCK
Tracks: / Ready to rock / Attack of the mad axeman.
7" Single: Released Sep '81, on Chrysalis, by Chrysalis Records. Deleted Sep '84. Catalogue no: **CHS 2541**

Schifrin, Lalo

JAWS
Tracks: / Jaws.
7" Single: Released Oct '76, on CTI (1), by Polydor Ltd. Deleted Oct '79. Catalogue no: **CTSP 005**

Schiksall

24 HOURS
Tracks: / 24 hours.
12" Single: Released '89, on Subway, by Subway Records. Catalogue no: **SUB 048**

Schiller, Nina

STAY THE NIGHT
Tracks: / Stay the night.
7" Single: Released Oct '83, on Ecstasy, by Creole Records. Catalogue no: **XTC 5**
12" Single: Released Oct '83, on Ecstasy, by Creole Records. Catalogue no: **XTCT 5**

Schilling, Peter

ALL THE LOVE I NEED
Tracks: / All the love I need / In my youth.
7" Single: Released Nov '86, on WEA (International), by WEA Records. Deleted Jun '87. Catalogue no: **X 8603**
12" Single: Released Nov '86, on WEA (International), by WEA Records. Deleted Jun '87. Catalogue no: **X 8603T**

DIFFERENT STORY, THE World of lust and crime
Tracks: / Different story, The.
12" Single: Released Jul '89, on WEA, by WEA Records. Catalogue no: **YZ 411 T**
CD 5": Released Jul '89, on WEA, by WEA Records. Catalogue no: **YZ 411 CD**
7" Single: Released Jul '89, on WEA, by WEA Records. Catalogue no: **YZ 411**

MAJOR TOM (COMING HOME)
12" Single: Released Sep '83, on WEA (International), by WEA Records. Catalogue no: **X 9665T**
7" Single: Released Mar '83, on WEA (International), by WEA Records. Catalogue no: **X 9967**
7" Single: Released Sep '83, on WEA (International), by WEA Records. Catalogue no: **X 9655**

MAJOR TOM (2 PARTS)
Tracks: / Major Tom (part 1) / Major Tom (part 2).
7" Single: Released May '83, on WEA, by WEA Records. Catalogue no: **X 9786**

MAJOR TOM (COMING HOME)
Tracks: / Major Tom (coming home) / Noah plan.
7" Single: Released May '84, on WEA, by WEA Records. Deleted May '87. Catalogue no: **X 9438**

Schlaflose Nachte

DRUM DANCE AND SONG
Tracks: / Drum dance and song.
12" Single: Released Jun '82, on Red Flame (1), by Red Flame Records. Catalogue no: **RF 1207**

FLUSTERN
Tracks: / Flustern / Move.
7" Single: Released Apr '82, on Armageddon, by Armageddon Records. Catalogue no: **AS 019**

Schleimer K

FOUR TRACK EP
12" Single: Released Jul '82, on Glass, by Glass Records. Deleted '83. Catalogue no: **GLASS 028**

Schloss, Cynthia

AM I LOSING YOU?
Tracks: / Am I losing you? / This song is just for you.
12" Single: Released 8 Aug '88, on Charm, by Charm Records. Catalogue no: **CRT 22**

AS IF I DIDN'T KNOW
Tracks: / As if I didn't know.
12" Single: Released Jan '85, on Revue, by Creole Records. Catalogue no: **REV 009T**

Schneider, Helen

HOT SUMMER NIGHTS
Tracks: / Hot summer nights / Shouts.
7" Single: Released Jul '82, on WEA, by WEA Records. Catalogue no: **K 19148**

ROCK AND ROLL GYPSY
Tracks: / Rock and roll gypsy / Don't let me be misunderstood.
7" Single: Released Mar '82, on WEA, by WEA Records. Catalogue no: **K 18830**

Schneider, John

IN THE DRIVER'S SEAT
Tracks: / In the drivers seat / Let me love you.
7" Single: Released Apr '82, on Scotti Bros (Germany), Deleted Apr '85. Catalogue no: **A 2231**

IT'S NOW OR NEVER
Tracks: / It's now or never / Stay.
7" Single: Released Oct '81, on Epic, by CBS Records. Deleted Oct '84. Catalogue no: **EPCA 1411**

WHAT'S A MEMORY LIKE YOU (DOIN' IN A LOVE LIKE THIS)
Tracks: / What's a memory like you (doin' in a love like this).
7" Single: Released Aug '87, on MCA, by MCA Records. Catalogue no: **MCA 1156**

Schoener, Eberhard

VIDEO-MAGIC
Tracks: / Video-magic / Code-word Elvis.
7" Single: Released Feb '80, on Harvest (1), by EMI Records. Deleted Feb '83. Catalogue no: **HAR 5196**

Schoenfeld, Philip

CHARLOTTE'S ROOM
Tracks: / Charlotte's room.
12" Single: Released Nov '88, on Cog Sinister, Catalogue no: **COGSIN 002**

School Band

TAKE THEM TO SCHOOL
Tracks: / Tonight / Take them to school.
7" Single: Released Feb '87, on Total Eclipse, by Total Eclipse Records. Catalogue no: **TECLR 3**

School Report

THIS SONG IS CRAZY
Tracks: / This song is crazy.
7" Single: Released Aug '85, on Mr.Sam, by Mr.Sam Music. Catalogue no: **SAS 103**

School Sinners

SCHOOL'S OUT
Tracks: / School's out / Detention.
7" Single: Released Jun '87, on MBS, by MBS Records. Catalogue no: **MBS 003**
12" Single: Released Jun '87, on MBS, by MBS Records. Catalogue no: **12MBS 003**

School Ties

HOUSE OF THE RISING SUN
Tracks: / House of the rising sun / Insanity.
7" Single: Released Dec '82, on Qwest (USA), by Qwest Records (USA). Catalogue no: **CUS 159**

Schoolboys

CALL ME
Tracks: / Call me.
12" Single: Released Mar '89, on Live & Love, Catalogue no: **LLD 112**

MISTER MOUTH
Tracks: / Mister mouth / While the others cry.

7" Single: Released Feb '83, on Avatar, by Avatar Record Corporation. Catalogue no: **AVAT 1**

Schoolly D

DEDICATION TO ALL B-BOYS
Tracks: / Dedication to all B-Boys / I don't like rock'n'roll radio / Maniac / Gangster boogie.
12" Single: Released Jul '87, on Mute, by Mute Records. Catalogue no: **MELT 6T**
7" Single: Released Jul '87, on Mute, by Mute Records. Catalogue no: **MELT 6**

LIVIN' IN A JUNGLE
Tracks: / Livin' in a jungle.
12" Single: Released Sep '89, on Jive, by Zomba Records. Catalogue no: **JIVET 228**

OPSTA NOW
Tracks: / Opsta now.
12" Single: Released Oct '87, on Schooly-D (USA), Catalogue no: **SD 118**

PARKSIDE 5-2
Tracks: / Parkside 5-2 / Saturday night.
12" Single: Released '88, Deleted '88. Catalogue no: **JIVET 158**
12" Single: Released Sep '87, on Jive (USA), by Zomba Records. Catalogue no: **10691 JD**

PUT YOUR FILAS ON
Tracks: / Put your filas on.
12" Single: Released Oct '86, on Flame (1), Catalogue no: **MELT 2T**

SATURDAY NIGHT
Tracks: / Saturday night / Do it do it.
Note: Double album.
12" Single: Released Feb '87, on Flame (1), Catalogue no: **MELT 4T**

SMOKE SOME KILL (SINGLE)
Tracks: / Smoke some kill.
12" Single: Released '88, on Jive, by Zomba Records. Deleted '88. Catalogue no: **JIVET 178**

Schroeder, Robert

SPACE DETECTIVE (DANCE MIX)
Tracks: / Space detective (dance mix) / Sky walker.
12" Single: Released Dec '83, on IC (Germany), Catalogue no: **KS 45/80029**

Schultz & Kurly Band

WEGGIS SONG
Tracks: / Weggis song / Am bachalpsee.
7" Single: Released Dec '81, on Square Peg, by Sonet Records. Catalogue no: **SON 2241**

Schuman, Mort

SORROW
Tracks: / Sorrow.
7" Single: Released Sep '86, on Sierra, by Sierra Records. Catalogue no: **FED 26**

Schuur, Diane

BY DESIGN See under Feliciano, Jose
Tracks: / By Design.
7" Single: Released Apr '86, on GRP (USA), by GRP Records (USA). Catalogue no: **GRP 5099**

Schwartz, Eddie

ALL OUR TOMORROWS
Tracks: / All our tomorrows / Tonight.
7" Single: Released Mar '82, on Atco, by Atlantic Recording Corp.(USA). Catalogue no: **K 11717**

Schwarzkopf, Elizabeth

BARCAROLLE
Tracks: / Barcarolle.
7" Single: Released Dec '85, on H.M.V., by EMI Records. Deleted Oct '88. Catalogue no: **CATNAP 1**

Schygulla, Hanna

LILI MARLENE
Tracks: / Lili marlene.
7" Single: Released Feb '82, on Island, by Island Records. Deleted Feb '87. Catalogue no: **WIP 6767**

Sci Fi Sex Stars

ROCKITT MISS USA
Tracks: / Rockitt Miss USA.
12" Single: Released Oct '86, on Sputnikco, Catalogue no: **WM 1001**

Science

TOKYO
Tracks: / Tokyo.
7" Single: Released Jan '81, on Rialto (1), by Rialto Records. Catalogue no: **TREB 124**

Science Fiction

SCIENCE FICTION SOUNDBOOK
Special: Released Sep '80, on Caedmon (USA), by Caedmon Records (USA). Catalogue no: **SBR 104**
Special: Released Sep '80, on Caedmon (USA), by Caedmon Records (USA). Catalogue no: **SBC 104**

Scientists

HAPPY HOUR
7" Single: Released Oct '83, on Au-Go-Go (Australia), by Au-Go-Go Records (Australia). Catalogue no: **ANDA 25**

WE HAD LOVE
Tracks: / We had love / Clear spot.
7" Single: Released Oct '83, on Au-Go-Go (Australia), by Au-Go-Go Records (Australia). Catalogue no: **ANDA 31**

YOU ONLY LIVE TWICE
Tracks: / You only live twice.
7" Single: Released Oct '85, on Karbon, by Karbon Records. Catalogue no: **KAR 007**

Scion Sashay Success

DANCE HALL QUEEN
Tracks: / Dancehall queen.
12" Single: Released Jun '84, on Jah Life, Catalogue no: **JL 003**

NO WORRY YOU MIND
Tracks: / No worry you mind.
12" Single: Released Jan '88, on Selectors Choice, Catalogue no: **SC 001**

NUFF A WE RUDE BOY
Tracks: / Nuff a we rude boy.
12" Single: Released Dec '88, on Eclipse, Catalogue no: **HCF 101612**

PAIN A BACK
Tracks: / Pain a back.
12" Single: Released Aug '84, on Greensleeves, by Greensleeves Records. Catalogue no: **GRED 151**

PUT IT ON
Tracks: / Put it on / Take it off.
12" Single: Released Mar '85, on Jah Life, Catalogue no: **JL 007**

YOUNG AFRICANS
Tracks: / Young Africans.
12" Single: Released Oct '85, on Jah Life, Catalogue no: **LM 003**

Scissor Fits

I DON'T WANT TO WORK FOR BRITISH AIRWAYS
Tracks: / I don't want to work for British airways.
7" Single: Released Oct '79, on Dubious, Deleted '82. Catalogue no: **DUB 1**

Scooby

NO MASH UP THE DANCE
Tracks: / No mash up the dance.
12" Single: Released Sep '88, on Digitec, Catalogue no: **DT 002**

Scoop

PANIC
Tracks: / Panic / Never dress right.
7" Single: Released Jan '82, on Towerbell, Catalogue no: **TOW 16**

Scorched Earth

I DON'T WANT TO FIGHT IN YOUR WARS
Tracks: / I don't want to fight in your wars / Blow yourself to bits.
7" Single: Released Mar '83, on Page One, by Page One Records. Catalogue no: **POR 101**

TOMORROW NEVER COMES
Tracks: / Tomorrow never comes / Questions.
12" Single: Released Feb '85, on Carrere, Catalogue no: **CART 342**

Scorcher, Erroll

ROACH IN THE CORNER
Tracks: / Roach in the corner.
7" Single: Released Apr '80, on D. Roy, Catalogue no: **DRDD 23**

RUDE BOY STEP
Tracks: / Rude boy step / Letting go.
12" Single: Released Apr '82, on Jux, Catalogue no: **DPY 2**

Scorpion

RIDE AND GO
Tracks: / Ride and go.
7" Single: Released May '89, on Park Heights, Catalogue no: **UNKNOWN**

Scorpions

Biographical details:
German heavy metal band the Scorpions were formed in Hanover in 1970 by guitarist brothers Michael and Rudolph Schenker with Klaus Meine (vocals), Lothar Heimberg (bass) and Wolfgang Dziony (drums). Their first album, *Lonesome Crow*, in 1972, sold well in Germany and led to film score work on *The Cold Paradise*, but Michael Schenker quit in 1973 to join UFO and Rudy re-formed with Meine and Ulrich Roth (guitar), Francis Buchholz (bass) and Jorgen Rosenthal (drums). They went from strength to strength, becoming a top attraction in Japan in the late 70's and having surprising success in America. (Donald Clarke, April 1987.).

BELIEVE IN LOVE
Tracks: / Believe in love / Love on the run / Believe in love (LP version) (On 12" only.).
7" Single: Released 22 Aug '88, on EMI, by EMI Records. Deleted Jun '89. Catalogue no: **HAR 5241**
12" Single: Released 22 Aug '88, on EMI, by EMI Records. Deleted Jun '89. Catalogue no: **12 HAR 5241**

CAN'T LIVE WITHOUT YOU
Tracks: / Can't live without you / Always somewhere.
7" Single: Released Jul '82, on Harvest (1), by EMI Records. Catalogue no: **HAR 5221**

IS THERE ANYBODY THERE
Tracks: / Is there anybody there? / Another piece of meat.
7" Single: Released May '79, on Harvest (1), by EMI Records. Deleted May '82. Catalogue no: **HAR 5185**

LOVEDRIVE (SINGLE)
Tracks: / Lovedrive.
7" Single: Released Aug '79, on Harvest (1), by EMI Records. Deleted Aug '82. Catalogue no: **HAR 5188**

MAKE IT REAL
Tracks: / Make it real / Don't make no promises.
7" Single: Released May '80, on Harvest (1), by EMI Records. Deleted May '83. Catalogue no: **HAR 5206**

NO ONE LIKE YOU
Tracks: / No one like you.
7" Single: Released Jun '85, on Harvest (1), by EMI Records. Catalogue no: **HAR 5237**
7" Single: Released Apr '82, on Harvest (1), by EMI Records. Deleted Apr '85. Catalogue no: **HAR 5219**

PASSION RULES THE GAME
Tracks: / Passion rules the game / Every minute everyday / Is there anybody there? (CD single & 12" only.).
CD 5": Released Jan '89, on Harvest (1), by EMI Records. Deleted Aug '89. Catalogue no: **CDHAR 5242**
7" Single: Released Jan '89, on Harvest (1), by EMI Records. Deleted Aug '89. Catalogue no: **HAR 5242**
7" Pic: Released Feb '89, on Harvest (1), by EMI Records. Catalogue no: **HARP 5242**
12" Single: Released Jan '89, on Harvest (1), by EMI Records. Deleted Aug '89. Catalogue no: **12HAR 5242**
12" Single: Released Feb '89, on Harvest (1), by EMI Records. Catalogue no: **12HARG 5242**
7" Single: Released Feb '89, on Harvest (1), by EMI Records. Deleted Aug '89. Catalogue no: **HARS 5242**

RHYTHM OF LOVE
Tracks: / Rhythm of love / We let it rock (you let it roll) / Love on the run (rough mix version) (Track on 12" version only).
12" Single: Released May '88, on Harvest (1), by EMI Records. Deleted Jun '89. Catalogue no: **12HAR 5240**
7" Pic: Released 23 May '88, on Harvest (1), by EMI Records. Deleted Nov '88. Catalogue no: **HARP 5240**
7" Single: Released May '88, on Harvest (1), by EMI Records. Deleted Jun '89. Catalogue no: **HAR 5240**
7" Set: Released 23 May '88, on Harvest (1), by EMI Records. Deleted Nov '88. Catalogue no: **HARX 5240**

ZOO, THE
Tracks: / Zoo, The / Holiday.
7" Single: Released Sep '80, on Harvest (1), by EMI Records. Deleted Sep '83. Catalogue no: **HAR 5212**

Scotch

DIACO BAND
Tracks: / Diaco band.
12" Single: Released Jun '85, on Red Bus, by Red Bus Records. Catalogue no: **RBUSL 2201**

Scotch Mist

HOOTS MON
Tracks: / Hoots mon / Red river valley.
7" Single: Released Nov '82, on Starblend, by Starblend Records. Catalogue no: **HOOT 1**

Scotland World Cup

BIG TRIP TO MEXICO
Tracks: / Big trip to Mexico / Carry the hopes of Scotland.
7" Single: Released Apr '86, on Columbia, by EMI Records. Catalogue no: **DB 9130**

EASY EASY
Tracks: / Easy easy.
7" Single: Released Jun '74, on Polydor, by Polydor Ltd. Deleted Jun '77. Catalogue no: **2058 452**

Scots Guards...

CRAGS OF TUMBLEDOWN MOUNTAIN
Tracks: / Crags of Tumbledown mountain / Dark island.
7" Single: Released Sep '82, on Ross, by Ross Records. Catalogue no: **SWGR 007**

Scott, Amanda

LIES
Tracks: / Experience / Lies.
7" Single: Released Feb '87, on Starblend, by Starblend Records. Catalogue no: **AMANDA 1**
12" Single: Released Feb '87, on Starblend, by Starblend Records. Catalogue no: **12AMAND 1**

Scott, Andy

INVISIBLE
Tracks: / Invisible.
7" Single: Released Apr '85, on Statik, Catalogue no: **TAK 31**
12" Single: Released Apr '85, on Statik, Catalogue no: **TAK 3112**

KRUGGERRANDS
Tracks: / Kruggerrands.
7" Single: Released Nov '83, on Statik, Catalogue no: **TAK 10**
12" Single: Released Nov '83, on Statik, Catalogue no: **TAK 10-12**

LET HER DANCE
Tracks: / Let her dance.
7" Single: Released Sep '84, on Statik, Catalogue no: **TAK 24**
12" Single: Released Sep '84, on Statik, Catalogue no: **TAK 24-12**

Scott, Audrey

GOODBYE MY LOVE
Tracks: / Goodbye my love.
7" Single: Released Apr '89, on Clarendon Sounds, Catalogue no: **CS 007**

Scott, Cynthia

JUGGLER OF HEARTS
Tracks: / Juggler of hearts.
7" Single: Released Jan '84, on Red Flame (1), by Red Flame Records. Catalogue no: **RSB 38**
12" Single: Released Jan '84, on Red Flame (1), by Red Flame Records. Catalogue no: **RSB 38-12**

X-BOY, THE
Tracks: / X-Boy, The.
7" Single: Released Aug '82, on Compact Organisation, Deleted '84. Catalogue no: **ACT 6**
12" Single: Released Aug '82, on Compact Organisation, Deleted '84. Catalogue no: **ACTX 6**

Scott, Dave

STROLLING ALONG
Tracks: / Strolling along / Hello rock 'n' roll.
7" Single: Released Sep '81, on Telscot, by Telscot Records. Catalogue no: **TEL 2**

Scott, Jack

Biographical details:
Rock'n'roller singer and songwriter turned country artist Jack Scott was born in 1936, grew up in Detroit listening to country music on the radio. His series of hit singles with a rocker on one side and a ballad on the other began with *Leroy/My True Love* in 1958, his deep voice combined with excellent recorded sound for the period. He had hits on Top Rank and Capitol, veered towards a country sound on the RCA subsidiary Groove in 1963 as the original pure rock'n'roll lost ground in the marketplace. (Donald Clarke).

BURNING BRIDGES (SINGLE)
Tracks: / Burning bridges.
7" Single: Released Jun '60, on Top Rank (1), Deleted Jun '63. Catalogue no: **JAR 375**

MY TRUE LOVE
Tracks: / My true love.
7" Single: Released Oct '58, on London-American, Deleted Oct '61. Catalogue no: **HLU 8626**

WAY I WALK, THE
Tracks: / Way I walk, The.
7" Single: Released Sep '59, on London-American, Deleted Sep '62. Catalogue no: **HLL 8912**

WHAT IN THE WORLD'S COME OVER YOU
Tracks: / What in the world's come over you.
7" Single: Released Mar '60, on Top Rank (1), Deleted Mar '63. Catalogue no: **JAR 280**

Scott, Jacqui

BABY HOLD ON
Tracks: / Baby hold on / I'll always love you.
7" Single: Released Sep '80, on CBS, by

CBS Records. Deleted '83. Catalogue no: **CBS 8973**

SYMPHONY FOR YOU
Tracks: / Symphony for you / Falling in love.
7" Single: Released Mar '80, on CBS, by CBS Records. Deleted Mar '83. Catalogue no: **CBS 8330**

Scott, Jeff

KEEP ON PROVING IT
Tracks: / Keep on proving it.
7" Single: Released Aug '80, on Surrey Sound, Catalogue no: **HMS 1**

Scott, Jimmy

HUNT, THE
Tracks: / Hunt (The) / Missing link The.
7" Single: Released May '86, on Move, Catalogue no: **MS 9**
12" Single: Released May '86, on Move, Catalogue no: **MSS 9**

Scott, L.B.

LONELY CHRISTMAS
Tracks: / Lonely Christmas.
12" Single: Released Dec '88, on Power Pakk, Catalogue no: **PP 3**

Scott, Linda

DON'T BET MONEY HONEY
Tracks: / Don't bet money honey.
7" Single: Released Sep '61, on Columbia, by EMI Records. Deleted Sep '64. Catalogue no: **DB 4692**

I'VE TOLD EVERY LITTLE STAR
Tracks: / I've told every little star.
7" Single: Released May '61, on Columbia, by EMI Records. Deleted May '64. Catalogue no: **DB 4638**

Scott, Maggie

DON'T FOOL AROUND WITH HIS FEELINGS
Tracks: / Don't fool around with his feelings.
7" Single: Released Oct '83, on Donut, Deleted '87. Catalogue no: **DON 001**

Scott, Mike

KIND OF LOVING, A
Tracks: / Kind of loving, A / Hey lady.
7" Single: Released Jun '86, on ESR, by ESR Records. Catalogue no: **ESR 0019**

Scott, Millie

AUTOMATIC
Tracks: / Automatic / Automatic(instrumental).
7" Single: Released Aug '86, on 4th & Broadway, by Island Records. Catalogue no: **BRW 51**
12" Single: Released Aug '86, on 4th & Broadway, by Island Records. Deleted Jul '87. Catalogue no: **12 BRW 51**

EV'RY LITTLE BIT (SINGLE)
Tracks: / Ev'ry little bit.
7" Single: Released Feb '87, on 4th & Broadway, by Island Records. Catalogue no: **BRW 58**
12" Single: Released Feb '87, on 4th & Broadway, by Island Records. Deleted Apr '88. Catalogue no: **12 BRW 58**

LET'S TALK IT OVER
Tracks: / Let's talk it over.
7" Single: Released Jun '87, on 4th & Broadway, by Island Records. Catalogue no: **BRW 68**
12" Single: Released Jun '87, on 4th & Broadway, by Island Records. Catalogue no: **12 BRW 68**

PRISONER OF LOVE
Tracks: / Prisoner of love / Prisoner of the groove.
7" Single: Released Mar '86, on 4th & Broadway, by Island Records. Catalogue no: **BRW 45**
12" Single: Released Mar '86, on 4th & Broadway, by Island Records. Catalogue no: **12 BRW 45**

TO THE LETTER
Tracks: / To the letter / It's my life / Keep it to yourself (Only on 12" single.).
7" Single: Released Aug '88, on 4th & Broadway, by Island Records. Deleted Apr '89. Catalogue no: **BRW 107**
12" Single: Released Aug '88, on 4th & Broadway, by Island Records. Deleted Apr '89. Catalogue no: **12 BRW 107**

Scott, Pete

BABY STAY
Tracks: / Baby stay.
7" Single: Released Jul '76, on Rubber, by Mawson & Wareham Music. Catalogue no: **ADUB 9**

Scott, Robin

EUREKA
Tracks: / Eureka.
7" Single: Released Oct '85, on Discovery (1), by Oryx Records. Catalogue no: **DIS 2**
12" Single: Released Oct '85, on Discovery (1), by Oryx Records. Catalogue no: **12DIS 2**

EUREKA KA KA
Tracks: / Eureka ka ka.
12" Single: Released Jun '83, on Albion, by Albion Records. Catalogue no: **12ION 1048**
7" Single: Released Jun '83, on Albion, by Albion Records. Catalogue no: **ION 1048**

Scott, Ronnie

Biographical details:
Tenor saxophonist and bandleader Ronnie Scott was born in London in 1927. He is best known as co-operator (with Peter King) of one of the most famous jazz clubs in the world for almost 30 years, also for his elderly and terrible jokes, but he is an underrated (even by himself) musician, having studied jazz in New York at the height of the bop era thanks to Geraldo's Navy (bandleader Geraldo hired musicians to work on the Queen Mary, back and forth across the Atlantic). Among his best-known albums include the *Battle Royal*, made in 1951 with two tenors, Victor Feldman on piano; *Serious Gold* was made in 1977 with John Taylor on keyboards (lately of Azimuth), Ron Matthewson on bass and Martin Drew on drums (who still play in the quintet at the club) and Louis Stewart on guitar. (Donald Clarke, April 87)..

BATTLE ROYAL
Tracks: / Battle royal
7" Single: Released May '81, on Esquire, by Titan Int. Prod.. Catalogue no: **ESQ 311**

MUSIC FROM RONNIE'S
Special: Released Sep '78, on Pye, Catalogue no: **11PP 603**

Scott, Sharon

OH WHAT A NIGHT FOR LOVE
Tracks: / Oh what a night for love / I like it.
12" Single: Released Jul '86, on Debut, by Skratch Records. Catalogue no: **DEBTX 3007**
7" Single: Released Jul '86, on Debut, by Skratch Records. Catalogue no: **DEBT 3007**

Scott, Simon

MOVE IT BABY
Tracks: / Move it baby.
7" Single: Released Aug '64, on Parlophone, by EMI Records. Deleted Aug '67. Catalogue no: **R 5164**

Scott, Steve

ALL THE SIGNS SAY CLOSED
Tracks: / All the signs say closed / Will / Party, The.
7" EP: Released Jun '88, on Gagged, by Gagged Records. Catalogue no: **GAG 1**

Scott, T T

LOVER GAME
Tracks: / Lover game / Children of Zion.
12" Single: Released Feb '86, on UNKNOWN, Catalogue no: **CD 007**

SCRATCHMO - PLAY THAT THING (Released on 4th & Broadway)

Scott, Tommy

GOING HOME
Tracks: / Going home.
7" Single: Released Sep '84, on August Records, by Scotdisc Records. Catalogue no: **ITVS 371**
7" Single: Released Aug '84, on Scotdisc, by Scotdisc Records. Catalogue no: **7S371**

'TIS A GIFT (TO BE SIMPLE)
Tracks: / 'Tis a gift (to be simple).
7" Single: Released Nov '85, on August (USA), by Rounder Records (USA). Catalogue no: **GBH 7S 403**

Scott, Toni

THAT'S HOW I'M LIVING
Tracks: / That's how I'm living.
7" Single: Released Mar '89, on Champion, by Champion Records. Deleted Aug '89. Catalogue no: **CHAMP 97**
12" Single: Released Jul '89, on Champion, by Champion Records. Deleted Aug '89. Catalogue no: **CHAMPX 1297**
12" Single: Released Mar '89, on Champion, by Champion Records. Deleted Aug '89. Catalogue no: **CHAMP 1297**

Scott-Heron, Gil

Biographical details:
Gil Scott-Heron was born in Chicago in 1949. He published novels *The Vulture*, *The Nigger Factory*, also poetry. He began collaborating with **Brian Robert Jackson** on music so as to get his social message across, half-spoken, half sung; he has a large cult audience. (Donald Clarke)..

BOTTLE, THE
Tracks: / Bottle, The.
12" Single: Released Jul '80, on Inferno (1), by Inferno Records. Catalogue no: **HEAT 23 12**
12" Single: Released Jan '81, on Champagne (DJM), Catalogue no: **VATS 302**
7" Single: Released Jul '80, on Inferno (1), by Inferno Records. Catalogue no: **HEAT 23**
7" Single: Released Jan '81, on Champagne (DJM), Catalogue no: **VAT 302**

BOTTLE, THE (OLD GOLD)
Tracks: / Bottle, The / Johannesburg / Winter in America.
12" Single: Released 28 Mar '88, on Old Gold, by Old Gold Records. Catalogue no: **OG 4054**

STORM MUSIC
Tracks: / Storm music / B movie.
7" Single: Released '82, on Arista, by BMG Records (UK). Deleted '87. Catalogue no: **ARIST 452**
12" Single: Released '82, on Arista, by BMG Records (UK). Deleted '87. Catalogue no: **ARIST 12452**

WINTER IN AMERICA
Tracks: / Winter in America.
7" Single: Released Nov '85, on Arista, by BMG Records (UK). Catalogue no: **ARIST 643**
10" single: Released Nov '85, on Arista, by BMG Records (UK). Catalogue no: **ARIST 10643**

Scottish World Cup...

WE HAVE A DREAM
Tracks: / We have a dream / Wrap up the cup.
7" Single: Released Apr '82, on WEA, by WEA Records. Catalogue no: **K 19145**

Scotty

CLOSE TO ME
Tracks: / Close to me.
12" Single: Released Mar '89, on Germaine, Catalogue no: **DGT 53**

Scotty & Shakademus

BRING IT TO ME
Tracks: / Bring it to me.
12" Single: Released Jul '89, on Penthouse, by Penthouse Records. Catalogue no: **PHT 11**

Scram

RUNNIN' AWAY
Tracks: / Runnin' away / Runnin' away (version).
7" Single: Released Nov '88, on Citybeat, by Beggars Banquet Records. Catalogue no: **CBE 729**
12" Single: Released Nov '88, on Citybeat, by Beggars Banquet Records. Catalogue no: **CBE 1229**

Scramble

DON'T THROW YOUR LOVE AWAY
Tracks: / Don't throw your love away / Only rock 'n' roll.
7" Single: Released Apr '80, on WEA, by WEA Records. Deleted Apr '83. Catalogue no: **K18206**

Scrambled Egos

CLOSE YOUR EYES
Tracks: / Close your eyes / Love is a four letter word.
7" Single: Released Mar '80, on Jet, by Jet Records. Deleted Mar '83. Catalogue no: **JET 173**

Scratch

KEEP ON SEARCHING FOR LOVE
Tracks: / Keep on searching for love / Eastern lady.
12" Single: Released Jun '84, on Master Funk, Catalogue no: **MF 007**

Scratchmo

PLAY THAT THING (see panel on previous page)
Tracks: / Play that thing / Play that thing (7" version) / Louis says b'doody (gunpowder mix).
Note: Produced by Baker/Rapoport/Taylor. Executive Producer: Alan Rapoport.
7" Single: Released Mar '88, on 4th & Broadway, by Island Records. Deleted Jun '88. Catalogue no: **BRW 91**
12" Single: Released Mar '88, on 4th & Broadway, by Island Records. Deleted Dec '88. Catalogue no: **12 BRW 91**

Scratsch Band

YOUR PLACE OR MINE
Tracks: / Your place or mine.
12" Single: Released Mar '81, on EMI, by EMI Records. Deleted Mar '84. Catalogue no: **12 EMI 5154**
7" Single: Released Mar '81, on EMI, by EMI Records. Deleted Mar '84. Catalogue no: **EMI 5154**

Scream

WALKING BY MYSELF
Tracks: / Walking by myself.
7" Single: Released Mar '87, on Jungle Hop, Catalogue no: **PIH 1**

Scream & Dance

IN RHYTHM
Tracks: / In rhythm / Giacometi.
12" Single: Released Apr '82, on Recreational, by Revolver Records. Catalogue no: **SPORT 7 12**
7" Single: Released Apr '82, on Recreational, by Revolver Records. Catalogue no: **SPORT 7**

Screaming Abdabs

STEP BY STEP
Tracks: / Step by step.
7" Single: Released Sep '87, on Tell Them To Stop, Catalogue no: **ABDAB 1**

Screaming Blue

BIKINI RED (SINGLE)
Tracks: / Bikini red / All shook down.
7" Single: Released 31 Oct '87, on WEA, by WEA Records. Deleted Jul '88. Catalogue no: **YZ 158**
12" Single: Released 31 Oct '87, on WEA, by WEA Records. Deleted Jul '88. Catalogue no: **YZ 158T**

I CAN SPEAK AMERICAN
Tracks: / I can speak American / Good and gone / Twin Cadillac valentine (Extra track on 12") / Valentine (Extra track on 12").
7" Single: Released Mar '88, on WEA, by WEA Records. Catalogue no: **YZ 176**
12" Single: Released Mar '88, on WEA, by WEA Records. Catalogue no: **YZ 176T**

I WANNA BE A FLINTSTONE
Tracks: / All shook down / I wanna be a flintstone / Jerry's electric church.
12" Single: Released Dec '87, on WEA, by WEA Records. Catalogue no: **YZ 166T**
7" Single: Released Dec '87, on WEA, by WEA Records. Catalogue no: **YZ 166**

PAINT IT BLACK
7" Single: Released Jan '84, on No Future, Catalogue no: **SKULL 2**

PEEL SESSIONS:SCREAMING BLUE MESSIAHS 24.7.84
Tracks: / Someone to talk to / Tracking the dog / Let's go down to the woods.
12" Single: Released 13 Jun '87, on Strange Fruit, by Strange Fruit Records. Catalogue no: **SFPS 003**
12" Single: Released Sep '86, on Strange Fruit, by Strange Fruit Records. Catalogue no: **SFPS 003**

SMASH THE MARKET PLACE
Tracks: / Smash the market place / Just for fun / Power glide, The (Extra track available on 12" version only).
12" Single: Released Apr '86, on WEA, by WEA Records. Deleted Jun '87. Catalogue no: **YZ 69T**
7" Single: Released Apr '86, on WEA, by WEA Records. Deleted Jun '87. Catalogue no: **YZ 69**

TWIN CADILLAC VALENTINE
Tracks: / Twin cadillac valentine.
12" Single: Released Oct '85, on WEA, by WEA Records. Catalogue no: **YZ 50T**
7" Single: Released Oct '85, on WEA, by WEA Records. Catalogue no: **YZ 50**

WILD BLUE YONDER
Tracks: / Wild blue yonder / Killer born man / I'm mad again (Extra track available on 12" version only.).
7" Single: Released Sep '86, on WEA, by WEA Records. Deleted Jun '87. Catalogue no: **YZ 73**
12" Single: Released Sep '86, on WEA, by WEA Records. Deleted Jun '87. Catalogue no: **YZ 73T**

Screaming Dead

CREATURES OF THE NIGHT
Tracks: / Creatures of the night.
12" Single: Released Jul '83, on No Future, Catalogue no: **12 01 25**

DANSE MACABRE COLLECTION
Tracks: / Danse macabre collection.
12" Single: Released Sep '84, on Angel (2), by Nine Mile. Catalogue no: **ANG 1**

DREAM OF YESTERDAY, A
Tracks: / Dream of yesterday, A.
12" Single: Released Feb '85, on Angel (2), by Nine Mile. Catalogue no: **ANG 002**

NECROMARIA
Tracks: / Necromaria.
12" Single: Released Aug '83, on No Future, Catalogue no: **12 01 125**

VALLEY OF THE DEAD
Tracks: / Valley of the dead / School girl....
7" Single: Released Sep '82, on Skull, Catalogue no: **EAD 1**

Screaming Marionettes

LIKE CHRISTABEL
Tracks: / Like Christabel / Screaming master.
12" Single: Released Aug '89, on Mandrake, by Mandrake Records. Catalogue no: **SMM 001T**
7" Single: Released Aug '89, on Mandrake, by Mandrake Records. Catalogue no: **SMM 001**

OBSESSION
Tracks: / Obsession / Play dead.
7" Single: Released Mar '88, on Lambs To The Slaughter, by Prism Records. Catalogue no: **LTS 25**
12" Single: Released Mar '88, on Lambs To The Slaughter, by Prism Records. Catalogue no: **LTST 25**

Screaming Nobodies

BURGER KING EP
Tracks: / Burger king EP / Big fat sucker.
12" Single: Released Feb '86, on Supreme Int.Editions, by Supreme Int.Records. Catalogue no: **EDITION 86-10**

Screaming Silence

SAME OLD STORY
Tracks: / Same old story.
7" Single: Released Sep '86, on Acrobat, by Acrobat Records. Deleted '88. Catalogue no: **AA 001**

Screaming Sirens

YOUR GOOD GIRL'S GOING BAD
Tracks: / Your good girl's going bad.
7" Single: Released Jul '85, on Beat Culture, Catalogue no: **1 BC**

Screaming Trees

ASYLUM
Tracks: / Asylum / Take it to the tree native.
12" Single: Released Jan '88, on Native (1), by Native Records. Catalogue no: **12 NTV 24**
7" Single: Released Jan '88, on Native (1), by Native Records. Catalogue no: **NTV 24**

BEATEN BY THE UGLY STICK
Tracks: / Beaten by the ugly stick.
12" Single: Released Feb '87, on Native (1), by Native Records. Catalogue no: **NTV 12010**

BIG HITTER
Tracks: / Big hitter.
7" Single: Released Jun '88, on Native (1), by Native Records. Catalogue no: **NTV 34**
12" Single: Released Jun '88, on Native (1), by Native Records. Catalogue no: **12 NTV 34**

HIT THE FLOOR
Tracks: / Hit the floor / Hit the floor (version).
7" Single: Released Oct '88, on Native (1), by Native Records. Catalogue no: **NTV 38**

IRON-GURU (4 track EP)
Tracks: / Iron-guru.
7" Single: Released Aug '88, on Native (1), by Native Records. Catalogue no: **NTV 23**
12" Single: Released Aug '88, on Native (1), by Native Records. Catalogue no: **12 NTV 23**

RELEASE
Tracks: / Release.
12" Single: Released Mar '86, on Native (1), by Native Records. Catalogue no: **NTV 6**

TANGIERS
Tracks: / Tangiers.
7" Single: Released 23 Jul '88, on Native (1), by Native Records. Catalogue no: **NTV 34**
12" Single: Released 23 Jul '88, on Native (1), by Native Records. Catalogue no: **12 NTV 34**

Screaming Tribesman

DATE WITH A VAMPYRE
Tracks: / Date with a vampyre.
12" Single: Released Nov '85, on What Goes On, by What Goes On Records. Catalogue no: **GOES ON 04T**

MOVE A LITTLE CLOSER
Tracks: / Move a little closer.
12" Single: Released Aug '85, on What Goes On, by What Goes On Records. Catalogue no: **GOES ON 02T**

Screecher Nice

HAVE TO GET A FLAT
Tracks: / Have to get a flat.
12" Single: Released Oct '84, on Jammy's, Catalogue no: **UNKNOWN**

Screechie, Delton

ANSWER MY QUESTION
Tracks: / Answer my question / Dub me the answer.
12" Single: Released Jun '83, on Peoples Choice, Catalogue no: **PC 001**

MOVING AWAY
Tracks: / Moving away / Moving away(version).
12" Single: Released Dec '83, on Peoples Choice, Catalogue no: **PC 002**

SWEET AFRICA
Tracks: / Sweet Africa.
10" single: Released Jul '82, on King Jam, Catalogue no: **KJ 064**

Screen Idols

SOMETHING'S GOTTEN HOLD OF MY HEART
Tracks: / Something's gotten hold of my heart / Runaway.
7" Single: Released Feb '80, on Parlophone, by EMI Records. Deleted '83. Catalogue no: **R 6032**

Screen Three

COME INTO MY JUNGLE
Tracks: / Dividing, The / Come into my jungle.
12" Single: Released Feb '83, on Epic, by CBS Records. Catalogue no: **EPC A 13 3130**
7" Single: Released Feb '83, on Epic, by CBS Records. Catalogue no: **EPC A 3130**

NEW BLOOD
Tracks: / New blood / European journey.
7" Single: Released Nov '81, on Romans In Britain, Deleted '83. Catalogue no: **NERO 3**

VISITOR, THE
Tracks: / Visitor, The.
12" Single: Released Mar '84, on Gross Product, Catalogue no: **OBCT 1**

Screwdriver

FAMILY COUNCILOR
Tracks: / Family councillor / Family councillor (version).
12" Single: Released Feb '87, on Revolutionary Sounds, Catalogue no: **RS 004**

SHARON PREGNANT AGAIN
Tracks: / Sharon pregnant again.
12" Single: Released Jan '89, on Top Rank (2), Catalogue no: **VPTRR 101**

Scritti Politti

ABSOLUTE
Tracks: / Absolute / Absolute (version) (12" only).
7" Pic: Released Jul '84, on Virgin, by Virgin Records. Deleted '89. Catalogue no: **VSY 680**
12" Single: Released '84, on Virgin, by Virgin Records. Catalogue no: **VS 680-12**

ASYLUMS IN JERUSALEM
Tracks: / Asylums in Jerusalem.
7" Pic: Released Jul '82, on Rough Trade, by Rough Trade Records. Catalogue no: **RT 111P**
12" Single: Released Jul '82, on Rough Trade, by Rough Trade Records. Catalogue no: **RT 111T**
7" Single: Released Jul '82, on Rough Trade, by Rough Trade Records. Catalogue no: **RT 111**

BOOM-THERE SHE WAS
Tracks: / Boom-there she was (US mix) (7" & CD only) / Philosophy now (On all versions) / Boom-there she was (sonic property mix) (12" & CD only) / Boom-there she was (dub) (12" only).
7" Single: Released '88, on Virgin, by Virgin Records. Catalogue no: **VS 1143**
Special: Released '88, on Virgin, by Virgin Records. Catalogue no: **VSTX 1143**
CD 3": Released '88, on Virgin, by Virgin Records. Catalogue no: **VSCD 1143**
12" Single: Released '88, on Virgin, by Virgin Records. Catalogue no: **VST 1143**

FAITHLESS
Tracks: / Faithless / Faithless (instrumental).
7" Single: Released Apr '82, on Rough Trade, by Rough Trade Records. Catalogue no: **RT 107**
12" Single: Released Apr '82, on Rough Trade, by Rough Trade Records. Catalogue no: **RT 107T**

FIRST BOY IN THIS TOWN
Tracks: / First boy in this town (lovesick) (On 7" & CD only) / World come back to life (On all versions) / First boy in this town (lovesick) (extended remix) (On 12" & CD) / First boy in this town (lovesick) (instrumental) (On 12" only).
CD 5": Released '88, on Virgin, by Virgin Records. Catalogue no: **VSCD 1082**
Special: Released '88, on Virgin, by Virgin Records. Catalogue no: **VSTX 1082**
7" Single: Released 25 Jul '88, on Virgin, by Virgin Records. Catalogue no: **VS 1082**
12" Single: Released 25 Jul '88, on Virgin, by Virgin Records. Catalogue no: **VST 1082**

HEGAMONY
Tracks: / Hegamony.
7" Single: Released Oct '79, on Rough Trade, by Rough Trade Records. Catalogue no: **RT 027**

HYPNOTISE
Tracks: / Hypnotise (long) / Hypnotise (short) / Hypnotise (version).
12" Single: Released Nov '84, on Virgin, by Virgin Records. Catalogue no: **VS 725-12**
7" Single: Released Nov '84, on Virgin, by Virgin Records. Deleted '89. Catalogue no: **VS 725**

OH PATTI (DON'T FEEL SORRY FOR LOVERBOY)
Tracks: / Oh Patti (don't feel sorry for loverboy) (On all versions) / Oh Patti (instrumental) (NOT on cassette) / Oh Patti (don't feel sorry for loverboy) (ext.) (NOT on 7") / Oh Patti (drumless mix) (Cassette only) / Best thing ever (CD & cassette only).
7" Single: Released Mar '88, on Virgin, by Virgin Records. Catalogue no: **VS 1006**
CD 5": Released Aug '88, on Virgin, by Virgin Records. Catalogue no: **CDEP 17**
Cassingle: Released '88, on Virgin, by Virgin Records. Catalogue no: **VSTC 1006**
12" Single: Released Mar '88, on Virgin, by Virgin Records. Catalogue no: **VST 1006**

PERFECT WAY
Tracks: / Perfect way (7" only) / Perfect way (version) (7" only) / Perfect way (extended mix) (12" only) / Perfect way (version-extended mix) (12" only).
12" Single: Released Aug '85, on Virgin, by Virgin Records. Catalogue no: **VS 780-12**
7" Single: Released Aug '85, on Virgin, by Virgin Records. Catalogue no: **VS 780**

SCRITLOCKS DOOR
Tracks: / Scritlocks door / Messthetics.
7" Single: Released Nov '79, on Rough Trade, by Rough Trade Records. Catalogue no: **RT 034**

SWEETEST GIRL
Tracks: / Sweetest girl, The / Lions after slumber.
12" Single: Released Oct '81, on Rough Trade, by Rough Trade Records. Catalogue no: **RT 091 T**
7" Single: Released Oct '81, on Rough Trade, by Rough Trade Records. Catalogue no: **RT 091**

WOOD BEEZ (PRAY LIKE ARETHA FRANKLIN)
Tracks: / Wood beez (Pray like Aretha Franklin) / Small talk (CD only) / Wood beez (version).
CD 3": Released '88, on Virgin, by Virgin Records. Catalogue no: **CDT 34**
12" Single: Released Mar '84, on Virgin, by Virgin Records. Catalogue no: **VS 657-12**
7" Single: Released Mar '84, on Virgin, by Virgin Records. Catalogue no: **VS 657**

WORD GIRL, THE
Tracks: / Word girl, The (On all versions) / Flesh and blood (On all versions) / Word girl, The (flesh and blood version) (On CD & VS

747-12 only) / Scritti Politti (Turntable mix by Mastermind) (On VS 747-13).
7" Single: Released Apr '85, on Virgin, by Virgin Records. Catalogue no: **VS 747**
CD 3": Released Jun '88, on Virgin, by Virgin Records. Catalogue no: **CDT 13**
12" Single: Released Apr '85, on Virgin, by Virgin Records. Catalogue no: **VS 747-12**
12" Single: Released '85, on Virgin, by Virgin Records. Catalogue no: **VS 747-13**

Scrubs

BATTLE
Tracks: / Battle / Battle narrative.
7" Single: Released Sep '86, on Anubis, Catalogue no: **ANU 003**

TIME FOR YOU
Tracks: / Time for you / Battle / Lorraine (Extra track on SSJT 200 only).
7" Single: Released May '87, on Flicknife, by Flicknife Records. Catalogue no: **FLSO 35**

Scruffy Gents

SCRUFFY GENTS
Tracks: / Scruffy gents / It takes too long.
7" Single: Released Jan '82, on MRS, Catalogue no: **MRS 007**

Scrunter

JUDIT
Tracks: / Judit / Oil in the coil.
12" Single: Released Jun '86, on Hot Vinyl, Catalogue no: **HVT 023**

Scullion

CAROL
Tracks: / Carol.
7" Single: Released Oct '88, on Grape-Vine, by Grapevine Records. Catalogue no: **GRAPE SC 703**

TENSION
Tracks: / Tension / Yellow train.
7" Single: Released Oct '80, on WEA, by WEA Records. Deleted Oct '83. Catalogue no: **K 18341**

Sea Breeze

BEND DOWN AND ROLL YOUR BELLY
Tracks: / Bend down and roll your belly / I don't mind.
12" Single: Released Aug '86, on Hot Vinyl, Catalogue no: **HVT 27**

Sea Hags

HALF THE WAY VALLEY
Tracks: / Half the valley.
7" Single: Released Jul '89, on Chrysalis, by Chrysalis Records. Catalogue no: **CHS 3396**
12" Single: Released Jul '89, on Chrysalis, by Chrysalis Records. Catalogue no: **CHS 12 3396**

Sea Level

FIFTY FOUR
Tracks: / Fifty four.
7" Single: Released Feb '79, on Capricorn, by Polydor Ltd. Deleted Feb '82. Catalogue no: **POSP 28**

Sea Stone

AGAINST THE TIDE
Tracks: / Against the tide.
7" EP: Released Oct '82, on Plankton, by Plankton Records. Catalogue no: **PLANK 002**

SUMMER FEVER
Tracks: / Summer fever.
7" Single: Released Oct '80, on Plankton, by Plankton Records. Catalogue no: **PLANK 001**

Sea Urchins

PRISTINE CHRISTINE
Tracks: / Pristine Christine.
7" Single: Released Jul '87, on Sarah, Catalogue no: **SARAH 001**

SOLACE
Tracks: / Solace / Please rain fall.
7" Single: Released Jun '88, on Sarah, Catalogue no: **SARAH 008**

Seagulls

GOLDSTONE RAP, THE
Tracks: / Goldstone rap, The / In Brighton.
7" Single: Released May '83, on Energy (UK), by Energy Records. Catalogue no: **NRG 11**
12" Single: Released May '83, on Energy (UK), by Energy Records. Catalogue no: **NRG 11T**

Seal

SEALED WITH A KISS
Tracks: / Sealed with a kiss.
12" Single: Released Sep '87, on Seal, by In-Market Ltd.. Catalogue no: **S 121**
7" Single: Released Sep '87, on Seal, by In-Market Ltd.. Catalogue no: **S 71**

YOU AND I
Tracks: / You and I / Pale girl of the neat white uniform.
7" Single: Released Jan '88, on Seal, by In-Market Ltd.. Catalogue no: **S 72**

Seal, Geof

WHAT I'M GONNA BE
Tracks: / What I"m gonna be / What I'm gonna be (Instrumental).
7" Single: Released Jul '86, on LBA, Catalogue no: **LBA 110**

Seals, Dan

ADDICTED
Tracks: / Addicted / Maybe I'm missing you now.
7" Single: Released Sep '88, on EMI, by EMI Records. Deleted Jun '89. Catalogue no: **CL 504**

BOP
Tracks: / Bop / In San Antone.
7" Single: Released Apr '86, on EMI-America, by EMI Records. Catalogue no: **EA 214**

Search

LIKE THE WAY YOU FUNK WITH ME
Tracks: / Like the way you funk with me / Like the way you funk with me (part 2).
12" Single: Released Mar '82, on Philly World (USA), by Philly World (USA). Catalogue no: **PWSL 101**
7" Single: Released Mar '82, on Philly World (USA), by Philly World (USA). Catalogue no: **PWS 101**

PEANUT BUTTER AND JAM
Tracks: / Peanut butter and jam / Song for Carrie.
7" Single: Released Jul '82, on Philly World (USA), by Philly World (USA). Catalogue no: **PWS 103**
12" Single: Released Jul '82, on Philly World (USA), by Philly World (USA). Catalogue no: **PWSL 103**

Search Party

ALL AROUND THE WORLD
Tracks: / All around the world / Lost paradise.
12" Single: Released Dec '83, on Magnet, by WEA Records. Catalogue no: **12 SP 1**
7" Single: Released Dec '83, on Magnet, by WEA Records. Catalogue no: **SP 1**

URBAN FOXES
Tracks: / Urban foxes / More.
12" Single: Released Mar '82, on Magnet, by WEA Records. Catalogue no: **12MAG 222**
7" Single: Released Mar '82, on Magnet, by WEA Records. Catalogue no: **MAG 222**

WALKING ON ICE
Tracks: / Walking on ice / Walking on ice (rub mix).
7" Single: Released Jul '87, on President, by President Records. Catalogue no: **PT 564**

Searchers

Biographical details:
The Searchers are still one of the best-loved pop quartets from the 1960s, as good as the Beatles at the start, though unlike the mop-tops they did not progress from there: lead guitarist John McNally was born 30 August 1941; rhythm guitarist Mike Pender on 3 March 1942; bassist Tony Jackson on 16 July 1940, drummer Chris Curtis (the only one not originally from Liverpool) on 16 August 1941 in Oldham. They named themselves after the John Wayne film (Wayne's catchphrase in the film *That'll be the day!* also providing the title of Buddy Holly's first hit). Their imaginitive harmonies and distinctive guitar sound influenced the Byrds; like the Beatles, they played at the Cavern and in Hamburg 1961-62; they had three never-to-be-forgotten no. one hits 1963-64 with *Sweets For My Sweet, Needles & Pins, Don't Throw Your Love Away* (last two were also top 20 USA).(Donald Clarke, April 87)..

ANOTHER NIGHT
Tracks: / Another night.
7" Single: Released Mar '81, on Sire (USA), Catalogue no: **SIR 4049H**

DON'T THROW YOUR LOVE AWAY
Tracks: / Don't throw your love away.
7" Single: Released Apr '64, on Pye, Deleted Apr '67. Catalogue no: **7N 15630**

GOODBYE MY LOVE
Tracks: / Goodbye my love.
7" Single: Released Mar '65, on Pye, Deleted Mar '68. Catalogue no: **7N 15794**

HAVE YOU EVER LOVED SOMEBODY
Tracks: / Have you ever loved somebody.
7" Single: Released Oct '66, on Pye, Deleted Oct '69. Catalogue no: **7N 17170**

HE'S GOT NO LOVE
Tracks: / He's got no love.
7" Single: Released Jul '65, on Pye, Deleted Jul '68. Catalogue no: **7N 15878**

I DON'T WANT TO BE THE ONE
Tracks: / I don't want to be the one / Hollywood.
7" Single: Released Nov '82, on PRT, by Castle Communications Records. Catalogue no: **7P 250**

IT'S TOO LATE
Tracks: / It's too late / This kind of love affair affair.
7" Single: Released Mar '80, on Sire, by Sire Records. Deleted '83. Catalogue no: **SIR 4036**

NEEDLES AND PINS (OLD GOLD)
Tracks: / Needles and pins / Don't throw your love away.
7" Single: Released Jul '82, on Old Gold, by Old Gold Records. Deleted '1. Catalogue no: **OG 9141**

NEEDLES AND PINS (OLD GOLD CD SINGLE)
Tracks: / Needles and pins / Sweets for my sweet / When you walk in the room.
CD 5": Released Nov '88, on Old Gold, by Old Gold Records. Catalogue no: **OG 6103**

NEEDLES AND PINS (SINGLE)
Tracks: / Needles and pins.
7" Single: Released Jan '64, on Pye, Deleted Jan '67. Catalogue no: **7N 15594**
7" Single: Released Apr '79, on Flashback, by Mainline Records. Catalogue no: **FBS 4**
7" Single: Released May '76, on PRT, by Castle Communications Records. Catalogue no: **7N 45598**

SEARCHERS EP
Tracks: / When you walk in the room / Someday we're gonna love again / Don't throw your love away / Take me for what I'm worth.
7" EP: Released 20 Jun '80, on Flashback, by Mainline Records. Deleted '83. Catalogue no: **FBEP 105**

SOMEDAY WE'RE GONNA LOVE AGAIN
Tracks: / Someday we're gonna love again.
7" Single: Released Jul '64, on Pye, Deleted Jul '67. Catalogue no: **7N 15670**

SUGAR AND SPICE (SINGLE)
Tracks: / Sugar and spice.
7" Single: Released Oct '63, on Pye, Deleted Oct '66. Catalogue no: **7N 15566**

SWEET NOTHINS
Tracks: / Sweet nothins.
7" Single: Released Oct '63, on Philips, by Phonogram Ltd. Deleted Oct '66. Catalogue no: **BF 1274**

SWEETS FOR MY SWEET (OLD GOLD)
Tracks: / Sweets for my sweet / When you walk in the room.
7" Single: Released Jul '84, on Old Gold, by Old Gold Records. Catalogue no: **OG 9409**

SWEETS FOR MY SWEET (SINGLE)
Tracks: / Sweets for my sweet.
7" Single: Released Jun '63, on Pye, Deleted Jun '66. Catalogue no: **7N 15533**

TAKE IT OR LEAVE IT
Tracks: / Take it or leave it.
7" Single: Released Apr '66, on Pye, Deleted Apr '69. Catalogue no: **7N 17094**

TAKE ME FOR WHAT I'M WORTH
Tracks: / Take me for what I'm worth.
7" Single: Released Dec '65, on Pye, Deleted Dec '68. Catalogue no: **7N 15992**

WHAT HAVE THEY DONE TO THE RAIN
Tracks: / What have they done to the rain.
7" Single: Released Dec '64, on Pye, Deleted Dec '67. Catalogue no: **7N 15739**

WHEN I GET HOME
Tracks: / When I get home.
7" Single: Released Oct '65, on Pye, Deleted Oct '68. Catalogue no: **7N 15950**

WHEN YOU WALK IN THE ROOM (SINGLE)
Tracks: / When you walk in the room.
7" Single: Released Jul '80, on Flashback, by Mainline Records. Catalogue no: **FBEP 105**
7" Single: Released Sep '64, on Pye, Deleted Sep '67. Catalogue no: **7N 15694**

Seary, Everton

POOR MAN A CRY
Tracks: / Poor man a cry.
12" Single: Released Oct '84, on Small Acts, Catalogue no: **UNKNOWN**

Seaton, B. B.

BORN FREE
Tracks: / Born free.
12" Single: Released Apr '87, on Jama, Catalogue no: **JADC 0028**

EVERYDAY PEOPLE (SINGLE)
Tracks: / Everyday people.
12" Single: Released Mar '85, on Revue, by Creole Records. Catalogue no: **REV 021T**

I'LL NEVER RUN AROUND
Tracks: / I"ll never run around / Bubbling around.
12" Single: Released Apr '86, on BI, Catalogue no: **BI 004**

IT'S DREAD
Tracks: / It's dread.
12" Single: Released Nov '85, on BI, Catalogue no: **BI 002**

JAH HELPS THOSE THAT HELP THEMSELVES
Tracks: / Jah helps those that help themselves.
12" Single: Released Apr '82, on Disco Rocker, Catalogue no: **DR 1001**

JUST A LITTLE MORE TIME
Tracks: / Just a little more time / Private lessons.
7" Single: Released May '85, on Rhino, by Creole Records. Catalogue no: **RNO 3**

LOVE IS TREASURE
Tracks: / Love is treasure.
12" Single: Released Aug '87, on Pioneer International, Catalogue no: **PI 44**

MEDLEY OF LOVE
Tracks: / Medley of love.
12" Single: Released Jun '85, on King 1, Catalogue no: **KSI DM 005**

PLEASURE AND PAIN
Tracks: / Pleasure and pain / Lovely lady.
12" Single: Released 27 Feb '88, on Challenge, by Elite Records. Catalogue no: **MBX 003**

TWO SIDES TO EACH STORY
Tracks: / Two sides to each story / You've got what I need.
12" Single: Released Oct '87, on MB Music, Catalogue no: **MBMPX 002**

Seaton, Dennis

I'M INTO SOMETHING GOOD
Tracks: / I'm into something good.
12" Single: Released Aug '87, on Creole, by Creole Records. Catalogue no: **CRT 106**
7" Single: Released Aug '87, on Creole, by Creole Records. Catalogue no: **CR 106**

WHAT YA TALKIN' 'BOUT
Tracks: / What ya talkin' bout.
CD 5": Released Jul '89, on Brouhaha, by Brouhaha Records. Catalogue no: **CDCUE 15**
12" Single: Released Jul '89, on Brouhaha, by Brouhaha Records. Catalogue no: **12 CUE 15**
7" Single: Released Jul '89, on Brouhaha, by Brouhaha Records. Catalogue no: **CUE 15**

Seaton, Johnny

UPTOWN (SINGLE)
Tracks: / Uptown / Don't play with me.
7" Single: Released Apr '84, on Rockhouse, by Rockhouse Records (Holland). Catalogue no: **SP 8209**

Seaview Singers

GINGER TOM
Tracks: / Ginger Tom / Looking for wiggywam.
7" Single: Released Apr '81, on Lancaster, by Lancaster Records. Deleted '85. Catalogue no: **LG 3**

Seawind

WHAT CHA DOIN'
Tracks: / What cha doin' / I need your love.
7" Single: Released Nov '80, on A&M, by A&M Records. Deleted Nov '83. Catalogue no: **AMS 7575**
12" Single: Released Nov '80, on A&M, by A&M Records. Deleted Nov '83. Catalogue no: **AMSX 7575**

Sebastian, David

SINCE YOU WENT AWAY
Tracks: / Since you went away.
12" Single: Released Sep '81, on Noel, Catalogue no: **DN 004**

Secession

BETRAYALS
Tracks: / Betrayals.
7" Single: Released Oct '82, on Garden, Catalogue no: **GAR 1**

FIRE ISLAND
Tracks: / Fire island.
12" Single: Released '88, on Beggars Banquet, by Beggars Banquet Records. Catalogue no: **BEG 112T**

MAGICIAN, THE
Tracks: / Magician, The / Killing season, The.
7" Single: Released Mar '87, on Siren, by Virgin Records. Deleted '89. Catalogue no: **SRN 31**
12" Single: Released Mar '87, on Siren, by Virgin Records. Deleted '89. Catalogue no:

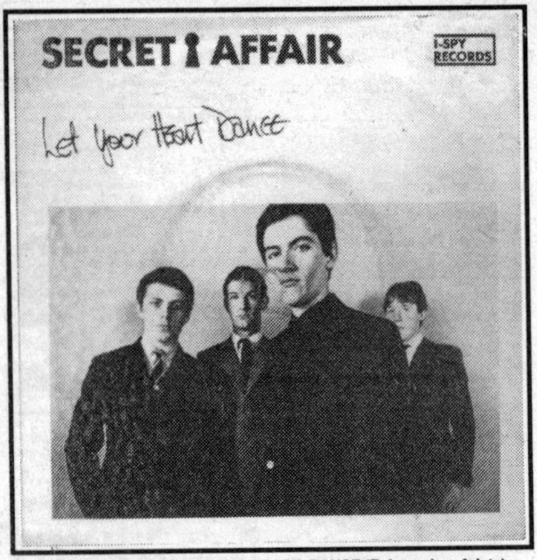

SECRET AFFAIR - LET YOUR HEART DANCE (Released on Arista)

SRN 31-12

PROMISE
Tracks: / Promise, The / Havoc.
7" Single: Released Jun '87, on Siren, by Virgin Records. Deleted May '88. Catalogue no: **SRN 48**
12" Single: Released Jun '87, on Siren, by Virgin Records. Deleted '89. Catalogue no: **SRN 48-12**

RADIOLAND
Tracks: / Radioland / Simon says.
12" Single: Released Sep '87, on Siren, by Virgin Records. Deleted '89. Catalogue no: **SRN 62-12**
7" Single: Released Sep '87, on Siren, by Virgin Records. Deleted May '88. Catalogue no: **SRN 62**

SNEAKYVILLE
Tracks: / Sneakyville (Not on CD) / Reflections (On all versions) / All the animals come out at night (CD & 12" only) / Sneakyville (extended mix) (12" only) / Sneakyville (remix) (CD only).
CD 5": Released 22 Aug '88, on Siren, by Virgin Records. Catalogue no: **SRNCD 77**
12" Single: Released 8 Aug '88, on Siren, by Virgin Records. Catalogue no: **SRNT 77**
7" Single: Released 8 Aug '88, on Siren, by Virgin Records. Catalogue no: **SRN 77**

TOUCH
Tracks: / Touch.
12" Single: Released '88, on Beggars Banquet, by Beggars Banquet Records. Catalogue no: **BEG 118T**

Secombe, Harry

IF I RULED THE WORLD (OLD GOLD)
Tracks: / If I ruled the world.
7" Single: Released Jul '82, on Old Gold, by Old Gold Records. Deleted Jul '88. Catalogue no: **OG 9253**

IF I RULED THE WORLD (SINGLE)
Tracks: / If I ruled the world.
7" Single: Released Oct '63, on Philips, by Phonogram Ltd. Deleted Oct '66. Catalogue no: **BF 1261**

ON WITH THE MOTLEY
Tracks: / On with the motley.
7" Single: Released Dec '55, on Philips, by Phonogram Ltd. Deleted Dec '58. Catalogue no: **PB 523**

THIS IS MY SONG
Tracks: / This is my song.
7" Single: Released Feb '67, on Philips, by Phonogram Ltd. Deleted Feb '70. Catalogue no: **BF 1539**

Second City Sound

DREAM OF OLWEN
Tracks: / Dream of Olwen.
7" Single: Released Apr '69, on Major Minor, Deleted Apr '72. Catalogue no: **MM 600**

TCHAIKOVSKY ONE
Tracks: / Tchaikovsky one.
7" Single: Released Jan '66, on Decca, by Decca Records. Deleted Jan '69. Catalogue no: **F 12310**

Second Coming

INCEST
Tracks: / Incest.
7" Single: Released Nov '84, on Torment, Catalogue no: **RV 666**

RETURN , THE
12" Single: Released May '85, on Torment, Catalogue no: **RSV 667**

Second Generation

PHASE III PROJECT (EP)
7" EP: Released Oct '87, on Unicorn-Kanchana, by Unicorn - Kanchana Records. Catalogue no: **PHZ 13**

Second Image

BETTER TAKE TIME
Tracks: / Better take time.
7" Single: Released Apr '83, on Polydor, by Polydor Ltd. Deleted Apr '87. Catalogue no: **POSP 565**

CAN'T KEEP HOLDING ON
Tracks: / Can't keep holding on / Images.
7" Single: Released Oct '81, on Polydor, by Polydor Ltd. Deleted '85. Catalogue no: **POSP 336**

DANCE DANCE DANCE
Tracks: / Dance dance dance / Jazzy dancer.
7" Single: Released Feb '81, on Polydor, by Polydor Ltd. Deleted '84. Catalogue no: **POSPX 224**

DON'T YOU
Tracks: / Don't you.
7" Single: Released Nov '83, on MCA, by MCA Records. Deleted Nov '86. Catalogue no: **MCA 848**

FALL IN LOVE
Tracks: / Fall in love / Take a trip.
12" Single: Released Feb '82, on Polydor, by Polydor Ltd. Deleted Feb '87. Catalogue no: **POSPX 395**
7" Single: Released Feb '82, on Polydor, by Polydor Ltd. Deleted Feb '87. Catalogue no: **POSP 395**

(GET YOUR FINGER OUT) PINPOINT THE FEELING
Tracks: / (Get your finger out) pinpoint the feeling / Cool breeze.
12" Single: Released May '81, on Polydor, by Polydor Ltd. Deleted May '84. Catalogue no: **POSPX 263**
7" Single: Released May '81, on Polydor, by Polydor Ltd. Deleted May '84. Catalogue no: **POSP 263**

SING AND SHOUT
Tracks: / Sing and shout.
7" Single: Released Aug '84, on MCA, by MCA Records. Deleted Aug '87. Catalogue no: **MCA 882**

STAR
Tracks: / Star / Sambolic.
12" Single: Released Jun '82, on Polydor, by Polydor Ltd. Catalogue no: **POSPX 457**
7" Single: Released Jun '82, on Polydor, by Polydor Ltd. Catalogue no: **POSP 457**

STARTING AGAIN
Tracks: / Starting again.
7" Single: Released Jan '85, on MCA, by MCA Records. Catalogue no: **MCA 936**
12" Single: Released Jan '85, on MCA, by MCA Records. Catalogue no: **MCAT 936**

THERE SHE GOES
Tracks: / There she goes.
7" Single: Released Jan '84, on MCA, by MCA Records. Catalogue no: **MCA 863**
12" Single: Released Jan '84, on MCA, by MCA Records. Catalogue no: **MCAT 863**

WHAT'S HAPPENING
Tracks: / What's happening.
12" Single: Released Sep '82, on Polydor, by Polydor Ltd. Catalogue no: **POSPX 512**
7" Single: Released Sep '82, on Polydor, by Polydor Ltd. Catalogue no: **POSP 512**

Seconds Of Pleasure

PULL ME UP
Tracks: / Pull me up.
7" Single: Released Apr '85, on Paladin, Catalogue no: **PALS 102**
12" Single: Released Apr '85, on Paladin, Catalogue no: **PALS 102 12**

Secret Act

FRED FLINTSTONE WHERE ARE YOU?
Tracks: / Fred Flintsone where are you? / Heaven.
7" Single: Released Aug '86, on Lifeline, Catalogue no: **LINE 1**

Secret Affair

DO YOU KNOW
Tracks: / Do you know / Dance master.
7" Single: Released Oct '81, on I-Spy, Deleted Oct '84. Catalogue no: **SEE 10**

LET YOUR HEART DANCE (see panel at top left)
Tracks: / Let your heart dance / Sorry wrong number.
7" Single: Released '82, on Arista, by BMG Records (UK). Deleted '87. Catalogue no: **SEE 3**

LOST IN THE NIGHT (MAC THE KNIFE)
Tracks: / Lost in the night / Big beat.
7" Single: Released '82, on Arista, by BMG Records (UK). Deleted '87. Catalogue no: **SEE 11**

MY WORLD
Tracks: / My world.
7" Single: Released Feb '80, on I-Spy, Catalogue no: **SEE 5**

SOUNDS OF CONFUSION
Tracks: / Sounds of confusion / Take it or leave it.
7" Single: Released Aug '80, on I-Spy, Deleted '83. Catalogue no: **SEE 8**

TIME FOR ACTION
Tracks: / Time for action.
7" Single: Released Aug '79, on I-Spy, Catalogue no: **SEE 1**

Secret Harts

DANCE LIKE BOY DANCE LIKE GIRL
Tracks: / Dance like boy dance like girl.
12" Single: Released Jul '83, on WEA (International), by WEA Records. Catalogue no: **X 9731T**
7" Single: Released Jul '83, on WEA (International), by WEA Records. Catalogue no: **X 9731**

Secret People

CHINA
Tracks: / China / Evergreen.
7" Single: Released Dec '87, on Jive, by Zomba Records. Deleted '88. Catalogue no: **JIVE 162**
7" Single: Released 11 May '87, on Two Bad, Catalogue no: **TWOB 002**
12" Single: Released Dec '87, on Jive, by Zomba Records. Catalogue no: **JIVET 162**

Secret Service

FLASH IN THE NIGHT
Tracks: / Flash in the night.
7" Single: Released Jan '82, on Sonet, by Sonet Records. Catalogue no: **SON 2238**

HOW I WANT YOU
Tracks: / How I want you / Eyes are talking.
7" Single: Released Dec '84, on Sonet, by Sonet Records. Catalogue no: **SON 2275**

LA GOODBYE
Tracks: / La goodbye.
7" Single: Released Sep '81, on Sonet, by Sonet Records. Catalogue no: **SON 2228**

OVER TOWN
Tracks: / Over town / If I try.
7" Single: Released Feb '83, on Sonet, by Sonet Records. Catalogue no: **SON 2252**

WHEN THE NIGHT CLOSES IN
Tracks: / When the night closes in / Let us dance a little bit more.
12" Single: Released Jun '86, on Sonet, by Sonet Records. Catalogue no: **SONL 2299**
7" Single: Released Jun '86, on Sonet, by Sonet Records. Catalogue no: **SON 2299**

Secret Seven

EINS ZWEI DREI
Tracks: / Eins zwei drei / Holiday in Berlin.
7" Single: Released Jun '87, on GTF Records, by GTF Records. Catalogue no: **GTF 7**

HOLD ON TO LOVE
Tracks: / Hold on to love.
7" Single: Released Apr '83, on Bronze, by Bronze Records. Catalogue no: **BRO 164**
12" Single: Released Apr '83, on Bronze, by Bronze Records. Catalogue no: **BROX 164**

Secret Troup

JUNCTION 16 - WAITING FOR A CALL
Tracks: / Junction 16 - waiting for a call / Concrete garden.
12" Single: Released Dec '85, on RS, Catalogue no: **RSAT 1**

Secretaries From

ART INTERFACE
Tracks: / Art interface.
7" Single: Released Jun '83, on Interface, Catalogue no: **IF 2**

Secrets Of China

CHINESE WAYS
Tracks: / Chinese ways.
12" Single: Released May '88, on Subway, by Subway Records. Catalogue no: **SUB 022**

Sect

FREE ENGLAND
Tracks: / Free England.
7" Single: Released Oct '86, on Insect, Catalogue no: **NASTY 1**

SUMMER GIRL
Tracks: / Summer girl.
12" Single: Released Apr '89, on Damaged Goods, Catalogue no: **YUBB 2**

Section 25

BACK TO WONDER
Tracks: / Back to wonder.
7" Single: Released Jun '83, on Factory (1), by Factory Records. Catalogue no: **FAC 68**

BAD NEWS WEEK
Tracks: / Bad news week.
12" Single: Released Dec '86, on Factory (1), by Factory Records. Catalogue no: **FAC 157**

BEAST, THE
Tracks: / Beast, The / Sakura / Trident.
12" Single: Released Jul '82, on Factory (1), by Factory Records. Catalogue no: **FAC 6612**

CRAZY WISDOM
Tracks: / Crazy wisdom.
7" Single: Released Sep '85, on Factory Benelux, by Rough Trade Records. Catalogue no: **FBN 45**

GIRLS DON'T COUNT
Tracks: / Girls don't count.
12" Single: Released Jul '80, on Factory (1), by Factory Records. Catalogue no: **FAC 1812**

LOOKING FROM A HILLTOP
Tracks: / Looking from a hilltop.
7" Single: Released Jun '84, on Factory (1), by Factory Records. Catalogue no: **FAC 108**
12" Single: Released Jun '84, on Factory (1), by Factory Records. Catalogue no: **FAC 10812**

Section A

STILETTO
Tracks: / Stiletto / Call my name.
7" Single: Released Apr '85, on LBA, Catalogue no: **LBA 107**

TIME STANDS STILL
Tracks: / Time stands still.
7" Single: Released Jul '82, on Subversive, Catalogue no: **SUB 005**

Sector 27

EXCALIBUR
Tracks: / Excalibur.
12" Single: Released May '84, on Rocket, by Rocket Records. Catalogue no: **ESP 512**
7" Single: Released May '84, on Rocket, by Rocket Records. Catalogue no: **ESP 5**

INVITATION
Tracks: / Invitation / What have we to lose /

SECTOR 27 - MARTINS GONE (Released on Panic)

Dungannon.
7" Single: Released Oct '80, on Panic, by Panic Records. Deleted Oct '83. Catalogue no: **SEC 28**

MARTIN'S GONE (see panel above)
Tracks: / Martin's gone / Christopher calling.
7" Single: Released '81, on Panic, by Panic Records. Catalogue no: **SEC 30**

TOTAL RECALL
Tracks: / Total recall / Stornaway.
7" Single: Released Jan '81, on Fontana, by Phonogram Ltd. Deleted Jan '84. Catalogue no: **SEC 29**

Security Leak

KEEP THE TEARS
Tracks: / Keep the tears.
7" Single: Released Jun '84, on Audiotrax. Deleted '86. Catalogue no: **ATX 2**

Sedaka, Dara & Neil

YOUR PRECIOUS LOVE
Tracks: / Your precious love / Searchin'.
7" Single: Released Feb '84, on MCA, by MCA Records. Catalogue no: **MCA 860**

Sedaka, Neil

Biographical details:
Neil Sedaka, born in New York in 1939, is a singer-songwriter who had early success in the late 1950's-early 1960's and who turned out to have the talent to stick around. From a piano-playing family, he is a fine pianist himself; writing with Howard Greenfield, his success with teen pop was so great from 1959 to 1963 that only Elvis Presley outsold him. He switched to MOR during the progressive rock era of the late 60's, and came back mid-70's with quality pop: a Tin Pan Alley trouper. (Donald Clarke, April 1987.).

BEAUTIFUL YOU
Tracks: / Beautiful you.
7" Single: Released Nov '72, on RCA, by BMG Records (UK). Deleted Nov '75. Catalogue no: **RCA 2269**

BREAKING UP IS HARD TO DO (OLD GOLD)
Tracks: / Breaking up is hard to do / I go ape.
7" Single: Released Nov '86, on Old Gold, by Old Gold Records. Catalogue no: **OG 9654**

BREAKING UP IS HARD TO DO (SINGLE)
Tracks: / Breaking up is hard to do.
7" Single: Released Jan '80, on RCA, by BMG Records (UK). Deleted '83. Catalogue no: **LR 8068**
7" Single: Released Jul '62, on RCA, by BMG Records (UK). Deleted Jul '65. Catalogue no: **RCA 1298**

CALENDAR GIRL
Tracks: / Calendar girl.
7" Single: Released Feb '61, on RCA, by BMG Records (UK). Deleted Feb '64. Catalogue no: **RCA 1220**

GOOD TIMES, THE (SINGLE)
Tracks: / Good times, The.
7" Single: Released Apr '86, on PRT, by Castle Communications Records. Catalogue no: **7P 341**

HAPPY BIRTHDAY SWEET SIXTEEN
Tracks: / Happy birthday sweet sixteen.
7" Single: Released Jul '81, on RCA Golden Grooves, by BMG Records (UK). Deleted May '89. Catalogue no: **GOLD 519**
7" Single: Released Dec '61, on RCA, by BMG Records (UK). Deleted Dec '63. Catalogue no: **RCA 1266**
7" Single: Released Jan '80, on RCA, by BMG Records (UK). Catalogue no: **LR 8181**

HAPPY BIRTHDAY SWEET SIXTEEN (OLD GOLD)
Tracks: / Happy Birthday Sweet Sixteen / Calendar girl.
7" Single: Released Oct '86, on Old Gold, by Old Gold Records. Catalogue no: **OG 9613**

I GO APE
Tracks: / I go ape.
7" Single: Released Apr '59, on RCA, by BMG Records (UK). Deleted Apr '62. Catalogue no: **RCA 1115**

KING OF CLOWNS
Tracks: / King of clowns.
7" Single: Released Apr '62, on RCA, by BMG Records (UK). Deleted Apr '65. Catalogue no: **RCA 1282**

LAUGHTER IN THE RAIN (OLD GOLD)
Tracks: / Laughter in the rain / Out last song together.
7" Single: Released Jul '84, on Old Gold, by Old Gold Records. Deleted Dec '88. Catalogue no: **OG 9433**

LAUGHTER IN THE RAIN (SINGLE)
Tracks: / Laughter in the rain.
7" Single: Released Jun '74, on Polydor, by Polydor Ltd. Deleted Jun '77. Catalogue no: **2058 494**

LET'S GO STEADY AGAIN
Tracks: / Let's go steady again.
7" Single: Released May '63, on RCA, by BMG Records (UK). Deleted May '67. Catalogue no: **RCA 1343**

LETTING GO
Tracks: / Letting go / Your so good for me.
7" Single: Released May '80, on Polydor, by Polydor Ltd. Deleted May '83. Catalogue no: **205924-8**

LITTLE DEVIL
Tracks: / Little devil.
7" Single: Released May '61, on RCA, by BMG Records (UK). Deleted May '64. Catalogue no: **RCA 1236**

LITTLE LOVIN', A
Tracks: / Little loving, A.
7" Single: Released Feb '74, on Polydor, by Polydor Ltd. Deleted Feb '77. Catalogue no: **2058 434**

LOSING YOU
Tracks: / Losing you / On the road again.
7" Single: Released Apr '81, on Polydor, by Polydor Ltd. Deleted Apr '84. Catalogue no: **POSP 245**

NEXT DOOR TO AN ANGEL
Tracks: / Next door to an angel.
7" Single: Released Nov '62, on RCA, by BMG Records (UK). Deleted Nov '65. Catalogue no: **RCA 1319**

OH CAROL (EP)
Tracks: / Oh Carol / Breaking up is hard to do / Little devil.
7" EP: Released Oct '72, on RCA, by BMG Records (UK). Deleted Oct '75. Catalogue no: **RCA 2259**

OH CAROL (OLD GOLD)
Tracks: / Oh Carol.
7" Single: Released Oct '86, on Old Gold, by Old Gold Records. Catalogue no: **OG 9615**

OH CAROL (SINGLE)
Tracks: / Oh Carol / Calendar girl.
7" Single: Released May '82, on Golden Grooves, by BMG Records (UK). Deleted May '89. Catalogue no: **GOLD 542**
7" Single: Released Nov '59, on RCA, by BMG Records (UK). Deleted Nov '62. Catalogue no: **RCA 1152**

OUR LAST SONG TOGETHER
Tracks: / Our last song together.
7" Single: Released Aug '73, on MGM, by Polydor Ltd. Deleted Aug '76. Catalogue no: **2006 307**

QUEEN OF 1964, THE
Tracks: / Queen of 1964.
7" Single: Released Mar '75, on Polydor, by Polydor Ltd. Deleted Mar '78. Catalogue no: **2058 546**

SHOULD'VE NEVER LET YOU GO
Tracks: / Should've never let you go / What a difference a day made.
7" Single: Released Aug '80, on Polydor, by Polydor Ltd. Deleted '83. Catalogue no: **POSP 153**

STAIRWAY TO HEAVEN (SINGLE)
Tracks: / Stairway to heaven.
7" Single: Released Apr '60, on RCA, by BMG Records (UK). Deleted Apr '63. Catalogue no: **RCA 1178**

STANDING ON THE INSIDE
Tracks: / Standing on the inside.
7" Single: Released Jun '73, on MGM, by Polydor Ltd. Deleted Jun '76. Catalogue no: **2006 267**

THAT'S WHEN THE MUSIC TAKES ME
Tracks: / That's when the music takes me.
7" Single: Released Feb '73, on RCA, by BMG Records (UK). Deleted Feb '76. Catalogue no: **RCA 2310**

YOU MEAN EVERYTHING TO ME
Tracks: / You mean everything to me.
7" Single: Released Sep '60, on RCA, by BMG Records (UK). Deleted Sep '63. Catalogue no: **RCA 1198**

Sedition

MIGHTY DEVICE, THE
Tracks: / Mighty device, The.
12" Single: Released Sep '86, on Fun, Catalogue no: **SED 2**

Seducer

INDECENT EXPOSURE
Tracks: / Indecent exposure / Down, down / No no / D.T.'s / Wild joker.
Note: Top southern heavy rock 'biker' band. (Magnum Music May, 1988).
12" Single: Released Nov '84, on Thunderbolt, by Magnum Music Group. Catalogue no: **THBE 1.007**

Seduction

ELECTRICITY
Tracks: / Electricity.
12" Single: Released Feb '85, on Challenge, by Elite Records. Catalogue no: **TALL 14**

SEDUCTION
Tracks: / Seduction (radio edit) / Seduction (hot mix).
12" Single: Released 6 Feb '89, on A&M, by A&M Records. Catalogue no: **USAT 651**
7" Single: Released 6 Feb '89, on A&M, by A&M Records. Catalogue no: **USA 651**

YOU'RE MY ONE AND ONLY TRUE LOVE
Tracks: / You're my one and only true love / You're my one and only true love (rap version).
7" Single: Released Sep '89, on Breakout, by A&M Records. Catalogue no: **USA 671**
12" Single: Released Sep '89, on Breakout, by A&M Records. Catalogue no: **USAT 671**

See You In Vegas

WORK
Tracks: / Work.
7" Single: Released Aug '83, on Red Rhino, by Red Rhino Records. Catalogue no: **RED 30**

Seeds (Group)

PUSHING TOO HARD
Tracks: / Pushing too hard / Greener day.
7" Single: Released 23 Apr '88, on Bam Caruso, by Demon Records. Catalogue no: **OPRA 091**

Seek, Sue

AMERICAN MAN, AMERICAN LOVER
Tracks: / American man, American lover / DC shadow of the white moon / Calling UFO beta.
7" Single: Released Jun '85, on Red Ruby, by Red Ruby Records. Catalogue no: **RY 002**

SHADOW OF MY MIND
Tracks: / Shadow of my mind / Calling.
7" Single: Released Jun '87, on Red Ruby, by Red Ruby Records. Catalogue no: **RY 001**

Seekers

Biographical details: The Seekers were a vocal-instrumental folk/pop group formed in Australia by guitarist **Keith Potger** (born 2 March 1941, Ceylon), lead singer **Judith Durham** (born 7 July 1943) and two others; they came to London and gigged at the Palladium in 1964 with **Dusty Springfield**, who wrote their no.1 hit **"I'll Never Find Another You"** (1965). Other hits include **"A World Of Our Own"**, film theme **"Georgy Girl"**; they split up in 1968, but Potger formed the sextet **New Seekers** the next year, with lead singer **Eve Graham** (born 13 April 1943, Perth, Scotland) this group had hits in 1970-73 including Delaney Bramlett's **"Never Ending Story Of Love"** (no.2 UK), **"Look What They've Done To My Song, Ma'"** written by Melanie Safka (top 50 UK, top 20 USA), **"I'd Like To Teach The World To Sing (In Perfect Harmony)'** no.1 UK/7 USA (a Roger Cook/Roger Greenway song), medley **"Pinball Wizard/See Me Feel Me"** from the Who's **Tommy**, British hits continuing to 1978. [Donald Clarke, April 87].

CARNIVAL IS OVER, THE (OLD GOLD)
Tracks: / Carnival is over, The.
7" Single: Released Oct '79, on Old Gold, by Old Gold Records. Deleted Jul '88. Catalogue no: **OG 9041**

CARNIVAL IS OVER, THE (SINGLE)
Tracks: / Carnival is over, The.
7" Single: Released Jul '84, on EMI (Holland), by EMI Records. Catalogue no: **1A 006 05824**
7" Single: Released Oct '65, on Columbia, by EMI Records. Deleted Oct '68. Catalogue no: **DB 7711**

EMERALD CITY
Tracks: / Emerald city.
7" Single: Released Dec '67, on Columbia, by EMI Records. Deleted Dec '70. Catalogue no: **DB 8313**

GEORGY GIRL
Tracks: / Georgy girl.
7" Single: Released Feb '67, on Columbia, by EMI Records. Catalogue no: **DB 8134**

I'LL NEVER FIND ANOTHER YOU
Tracks: / I'll never find another you.
7" Single: Released Jan '65, on Columbia, by EMI Records. Deleted Jan '68. Catalogue no: **DB 7431**
7" Single: Released '80, on IMS, by Polydor Ltd. Catalogue no: **LR 1866**

MORNINGTOWN RIDE
Tracks: / Morningtown ride.
7" Single: Released Nov '66, on Columbia, by EMI Records. Catalogue no: **DB 8060**

SOME DAY ONE DAY
Tracks: / Some day one day.
7" Single: Released Mar '66, on Columbia, by EMI Records. Deleted Mar '69. Catalogue no: **DB 7867**

WALK WITH ME
Tracks: / Walk with me.
7" Single: Released Sep '66, on Columbia, by EMI Records. Deleted Sep '69. Catalogue no: **DB 8000**

WHEN WILL THE GOOD APPLES FALL
Tracks: / When will the good apples fall.
7" Single: Released Sep '67, on Columbia, by EMI Records. Deleted Sep '70. Catalogue no: **DB 8273**

WORLD OF OUR OWN, A (SINGLE)
Tracks: / World of our own, A.
7" Single: Released Apr '65, on Columbia, by EMI Records. Deleted Apr '68. Catalogue no: **DB 7532**

Seeley, Leonard K

TRADITION
Tracks: / Tradition.
12" Single: Released Sep '83, on Ram, by Ram Records. Catalogue no: **RAMT 004**
7" Single: Released Sep '83, on Ram, by Ram Records. Catalogue no: **RAM 7004**

Seers

FREEDOM TRIPS
Tracks: / Freedom trips.
7" Single: Released Sep '88, on Skull, Catalogue no: **SKULL 1**
12" Single: Released Sep '88, on Skull, Catalogue no: **SKULL 1T**

LIGHTNING STRIKES
Tracks: / Lightning strikes.
12" Single: Released 27 Feb '88, on Rough Trade, by Rough Trade Records. Catalogue no: **RTT 182**
7" Single: Released 27 Feb '88, on Rough Trade, by Rough Trade Records. Catalogue no: **RT 182**

SUN IS IN THE SKY
Tracks: / Sun is in the sky / Magic potion / Sun is in the sky (version) (12" only).
7" Single: Released Feb '89, on Virgin, by Virgin Records. Catalogue no: **HEDD 5**
12" Single: Released Feb '89, on Virgin, by Virgin Records. Catalogue no: **HEDD 512**

Seething Wells

RISING SUN OF RANTING VERSE
Tracks: / Rising sun of ranting verse.
7" Single: Released Dec '82, on Radical Wallpaper, Catalogue no: **RADWAL 004**

Segarini, Bob

PLEASE, PLEASE, PLEASE
Tracks: / Please, please, please / Don't believe a word I say.
7" Single: Released Mar '80, on Epic, by CBS Records. Deleted Mar '83. Catalogue no: **EPC 8223**

Seger, Bob

Biographical details: Rock singer/songwriter **Bob Seger** was born 6 May 1945 in Ann Arbor, Michigan. He began performing in 1961 and became a local hero who took some years to make an international breakthrough: he formed his first band **Last Heard** in 1964; their single **'Heavy Music'** on the Cameo-Parkway label almost reached the USA national top 100 '67, but the label folded. **'Ramblin' Gamblin' Man'** '68 made the top 20 on Capitol, but he made eight albums before the live two-record set **Silver Bullet** reached the top 40 LPs in the USA, staying in the charts for 140 weeks; since then all his LPs have gone platinum. He had 13 top 40 singles in the USA 1977-83, many ballads and almost all his own compositions; none were hits in Britain, although some of his albums have charted. His music is considered to be unpretentious 'working class rock' and his following is similar to that of Bruce Springsteen in terms of audience identification. [Donald Clarke, April 87].

AGAINST THE WIND (EP)
Tracks: / Against the wind / Get out of Denver / Nutbush City limits.
7" EP: Released Nov '80, on Capitol, by EMI Records. Deleted Nov '83. Catalogue no: **CL 16174**

AGAINST THE WIND (SINGLE)
Tracks: / Against the wind / No man's land.
7" Single: Released May '80, on Capitol, by EMI Records. Deleted May '83. Catalogue no: **CL 16143**

AMERICAN STORM
Tracks: / American Storm / Fortunate son / Hollywood nights (Track available on 7" Double pack only.) / Live (version) (Available on 7" Double pack Only).
7" Single: Released Mar '86, on Capitol, by EMI Records. Deleted '88. Catalogue no: **CL 396**
7" Single: Released Mar '86, on Capitol, by EMI Records. Catalogue no: **CLD 396**

EVEN NOW
Tracks: / Even now.
7" Single: Released Mar '83, on Capitol, by EMI Records. Deleted '88. Catalogue no: **CL 284**

HOLLYWOOD NIGHTS
Tracks: / Hollywood nights.
7" Single: Released Oct '81, on Capitol, by EMI Records. Deleted '88. Catalogue no: **CL 223**
7" Single: Released Sep '78, on Capitol, by EMI Records. Deleted Sep '81. Catalogue no: **CL 16004**
12" Single: Released Oct '81, on Capitol, by EMI Records. Deleted '88. Catalogue no: **12CL 223**

LIKE A ROCK (SINGLE)
Tracks: / Like a rock.
12" Single: Released Jun '86, on Capitol, by EMI Records. Deleted '88. Catalogue no: **12CL 408**
7" Single: Released Jun '86, on Capitol, by EMI Records. Deleted '88. Catalogue no: **CL 408**

ROLL ME AWAY
Tracks: / Roll me away.
7" Single: Released Jul '83, on Capitol, by EMI Records. Deleted '88. Catalogue no: **CL 297**

SHAKEDOWN
Tracks: / Shakedown / Aftermath.
Note: Shakedolwn is taken from the forthcoming Beverly Hills Cop II film soundtrack.
12" Single: Released Jun '87, on MCA, by MCA Records. Catalogue no: **MCAS 1172**
12" Single: Released Oct '87, on MCA, by MCA Records. Catalogue no: **MCAT 1172**
7" Single: Released Jun '87, on MCA, by MCA Records. Catalogue no: **MCA 1172**

SHAME ON THE MOON
Tracks: / Shame on the moon / House behind a house.
7" Single: Released Jan '83, on Capitol, by EMI Records. Deleted '88. Catalogue no: **CL 275**

WE'VE GOT TONITE
Tracks: / We've got tonite.
7" Single: Released Feb '79, on Capitol, by EMI Records. Deleted Feb '82. Catalogue no: **CL 16028**

WE'VE GOT TONITE (RE-ISSUE)
Tracks: / We've got tonite (re-issue) / Brave strangers / Feel like a number.
7" Single: Released Feb '82, on Capitol, by EMI Records. Deleted Feb '85. Catalogue no: **CL 235**
12" Single: Released Jan '82, on Capitol, by EMI Records. Deleted Jan '85. Catalogue no: **12 CL 235**

Seger, Bob & The

FIRE LAKE
Tracks: / Fire lake / Long twin silver line.
7" Single: Released Feb '80, on Capitol, by EMI Records. Deleted Feb '85. Catalogue no: **CL 16130**

Segue

THREE ON THE TROT
Tracks: / Three on the trot.
7" Single: Released Aug '83, on Tart'n, Catalogue no: **STORM 1**

VISION OF THE FUTURE
Tracks: / Vision of the future.
12" Single: Released May '85, on Amazing (USA), by Amazing Records (USA). Catalogue no: **AMAZE 2**

Seidel, Jan

ON THE FARM
Tracks: / On the farm / Cow polka, The.
7" Single: Released Feb '82, on RCA, by BMG Records (UK). Catalogue no: **PB 4576**

Seize

EVERYBODY DOES (EP)
Tracks: / Everybody does.
7" EP: Released Sep '82, on Whynot (Japan), Deleted '83. Catalogue no: **NOT 002**

Sektion II

TWO OF US
Tracks: / Two of us, The.
7" Single: Released Aug '84, on National Health, Deleted '87. Catalogue no: **SCRIT 001**

Selecter

CELEBRATING THE BULLET (SINGLE)
Tracks: / Celebrating the bullet / Last tango in dub.
7" Single: Released Feb '81, on Chrysalis, by Chrysalis Records. Deleted Feb '84. Catalogue no: **CHS 2484**

MISSING WORDS
Tracks: / Missing words / Carry go bring come.
7" Single: Released Mar '80, on Two-Tone, by Chrysalis Records. Catalogue no: **CHS TT 10**

ON MY RADIO (OLD GOLD)
Tracks: / Three minute hero / On my radio / Too much pressure.
7" Single: Released Feb '87, on Old Gold, by Old Gold Records. Catalogue no: **OG 9681**
12" Single: Released Jan '87, on Old Gold, by Old Gold Records. Catalogue no: **OG 4071**

ON MY RADIO (SINGLE)
Tracks: / On my radio / Too much pressure.
7" Single: Released Oct '79, on Two-Tone, by Chrysalis Records. Catalogue no: **CHS TT 4**

THREE MINUTE HERO
Tracks: / Three minute hero / James Bond.
7" Single: Released Jan '80, on Two-Tone, by Chrysalis Records. Catalogue no: **CHS TT 8**

WHISPER, THE
Tracks: / Whisper / Train to skaville.
7" Single: Released Aug '80, on Chrysalis, by Chrysalis Records. Deleted Aug '83. Catalogue no: **CHSS 1**

PETER SELLERS - A HARD DAYS NIGHT (Released on Parlophone)

Selectors

JENNY JENNY
Tracks: / Jenny Jenny.
7" Single: Released Nov '84, on Ethnic, Catalogue no: **ETH 2254**

Selena

SHOTGUN
Tracks: / Shotgun / Shotgun (inst).
7" Single: Released Aug '88, on Columbia, by EMI Records. Deleted Nov '88. Catalogue no: **DB 9171**
12" Single: Released Aug '88, on Columbia, by EMI Records. Deleted Nov '88. Catalogue no: **12DB 9171**

Self Abuse

SOLDIER, THE (EP)
Tracks: / Soldier, The.
7" EP: Released Mar '84, on Radical Change, by Backs Recording Co.. Catalogue no: **RC 5**

Self Destructors

MISSION IMPOSSIBLE '88
Tracks: / Mission impossible '88 / Breaking loose.
CD 5": Released Oct '88, on Nowyertalkin', by Nowyertalikin' Records. Catalogue no: **CD TALK 3**
7" Single: Released Oct '88, on Nowyertalkin', by Nowyertalikin' Records. Catalogue no: **7 TALK 3**
12" Single: Released Oct '88, on Nowyertalkin', by Nowyertalikin' Records. Catalogue no: **12 TALK 3**

Self Service

HEAVEN'S ABOVE
Tracks: / Heaven's above.
7" Single: Released May '83, on Racket Manufacture, Catalogue no: **RR 001**

Sellers, Peter

ANY OLD IRON
Tracks: / Any old iron.
7" Single: Released Aug '57, on Parlophone, by EMI Records. Catalogue no: **R 4337**

BANGERS AND MASH
Tracks: / Bangers and mash.
7" Single: Released Jan '61, on Parlophone, by EMI Records. Deleted Jan '64. Catalogue no: **R 4724**

GOODNESS GRACIOUS ME
Tracks: / Goodness gracious me.
7" Single: Released Sep '80, on H.M.V., by EMI Records. Deleted '83. Catalogue no: **POP 2018**
7" Single: Released Nov '60, on Parlophone, by EMI Records. Deleted Nov '63. Catalogue no: **R 4702**

HARD DAY'S NIGHT, A (see panel above)
Tracks: / Hard day's night, A / Help.
7" Single: Released Dec '65, on Parlophone, by EMI Records. Deleted Dec '68. Catalogue no: **R 5393**
7" Single: Released Sep '80, on H.M.V., by EMI Records. Deleted '83. Catalogue no: **POP 2012**

SHE LOVES YOU
Tracks: / She loves you.
7" Single: Released Jan '81, on Parlophone, by EMI Records. Catalogue no: **R 6043**

THEY'RE PARKING CAMELS WHERE TAXIS USED TO BE
Tracks: / They're parking camels where taxis used to be / Night and day.
7" Single: Released Apr '80, on Liberty, by EMI Records. Deleted '83. Catalogue no: **BP 335**

Selvester, Cathryn

IF YOU'RE NOT HERE
12" Single: Released Sep '84, on Capo, by Capo Records. Catalogue no: **TSMP 769**

Sembello, Michael

MANIAC
Tracks: / Maniac.
7" Single: Released Aug '85, on Casablanca, by PolyGram UK Ltd. Deleted '87. Catalogue no: **CAN 1017**

Semprini

EXODUS (THEME FROM)
Tracks: / Exodus.
7" Single: Released Mar '61, on H.M.V., by EMI Records. Deleted Mar '64. Catalogue no: **POP 842**

Senate

ORIGINAL SIN, (THE)
Tracks: / Original sin, The.
12" Single: Released Jul '84, on W.A.R., by W.A.R. Records. Catalogue no: **12 WAR 1**
7" Single: Released Jul '84, on W.A.R., by W.A.R. Records. Catalogue no: **WAR 1**

Senator, Asher

ABBREVIATION QUALIFICATION
Tracks: / Abbreviation qualification / Fast style origination.
12" Single: Released Aug '84, on Fashion, by Fashion Records. Catalogue no: **FAD 023**

BIG MATCH, THE
Tracks: / Big match, The.
12" Single: Released Nov '85, on Fashion, by Fashion Records. Catalogue no: **FAD 031**
7" Single: Released Nov '85, on Fashion, by Fashion Records. Catalogue no: **FAD 7031**

BUBBLE WITH I
Tracks: / Bubble with I.
12" Single: Released Mar '86, on Fashion, by Fashion Records. Catalogue no: **FAD 044**

COWBOY DANCE
Tracks: / Cowboy dance.
12" Single: Released Apr '88, on Senator, Catalogue no: **ZZ 003**

Senators

I DON'T CARE ABOUT THE PAST
Tracks: / I don't care about the past / Tom

in two / So far away (On 12" & CD only) / I have no right (Only on 12") / Don't fall in love (On CD only).
CD 5": Released '88, on Virgin, by Virgin Records. Catalogue no: **VSCD 1126**
12" Single: Released 26 Sep '88, on Virgin, by Virgin Records. Catalogue no: **VST 1126**
7" Single: Released 26 Sep '88, on Virgin, by Virgin Records. Catalogue no: **VS 1126**

MAN NO MORE
Tracks: / Man no more / Quiet life / Hey girl don't bother me.
7" Single: Released Feb '89, on Virgin, by Virgin Records. Catalogue no: **VS 1170**
12" Single: Released Feb '89, on Virgin, by Virgin Records. Catalogue no: **VST 1170**
CD 5": Released Feb '89, on Virgin, by Virgin Records. Catalogue no: **VSCD 1170**

ONE MORE CHANCE
Tracks: / One more chance / Strange / Little Italy (on 12' & CD only) / My little heart (on CD only).
12" Single: Released Dec '88, on Virgin, by Virgin Records. Catalogue no: **VST 1146**
CD 3": Released '88, on Virgin, by Virgin Records. Catalogue no: **VSCD 1146**
7" Single: Released Dec '88, on Virgin, by Virgin Records. Catalogue no: **VS 1146**

Send No Flowers

PLAYING FOR TIME
Tracks: / Playing for time.
7" Single: Released Aug '82, on Praxis (1), Catalogue no: **TM 1**

Sensations

BABY LOVE
Tracks: / Baby love.
12" Single: Released Sep '83, on Treasure Isle, Catalogue no: **TKE 007**

Sense

HOLDING ON
Tracks: / Holding on / Life's too hard.
7" Single: Released Nov '83, on Carrere, Catalogue no: **CAR 295**

JAMIE
Tracks: / Jamie.
12" Single: Released Jul '85, on W.A.R., by W.A.R. Records. Catalogue no: **12 WAR 3001**
7" Single: Released Jul '85, on W.A.R., by W.A.R. Records. Catalogue no: **WAR 3001**

THREE MINUTES LATE
Tracks: / Three minutes late.
7" Single: Released Jul '83, on Carrere, Catalogue no: **CAR 275**
12" Single: Released Jul '83, on Carrere, Catalogue no: **CART 275**

YOU CRY
Tracks: / You cry.
12" Single: Released Sep '84, on W.A.R., by W.A.R. Records. Catalogue no: **12 WAR 2**

Sense of Vision

DREAM
Tracks: / Dream.
7" Single: Released Jan '84, on Clean, by Clean Records. Catalogue no: **WIPE 2**

Senseless Things

GIRLFRIEND
Tracks: / Girlfriend.
7" Single: Released Mar '89, on Way Cool, Catalogue no: **WC 001**

UP AND COMING
Tracks: / Up and coming / Where the secret lies.
7" Single: Released Dec '88, on R.E.D., Catalogue no: **RED 001**
12" Single: Released Dec '88, on R.E.D., Catalogue no: **RED 001T**

Senses

IF YOU CAN COUNT
Tracks: / If you can count.
7" Single: Released Feb '84, on West End, Catalogue no: **WEND 5**
12" Single: Released Feb '84, on West End, Catalogue no: **WEND 125**

Sensible Jerseys

RIGHT AND WRONG
Tracks: / Right and wrong.
7" Single: Released Jun '85, on Virgin, by Virgin Records. Deleted '86. Catalogue no: **VS 792**

TWO WAY RADIO
Tracks: / Two way radio.
7" Single: Released Sep '85, on Virgin, by Virgin Records. Deleted '86. Catalogue no: **VS 813**
12" Single: Released Sep '85, on Virgin, by Virgin Records. Deleted '86. Catalogue no: **VS 813-12**

Sensible Shoes

BUILD ME AN EMPIRE
Tracks: / Build me an empire / Build me an empire (Version).
7" Single: Released Jul '86, on Lambs To The Slaughter, by Prism Records. Catalogue no: **LTS 14**

GAME
Tracks: / Game.
7" Single: Released Jan '85, on Instep, Catalogue no: **PL 0029**

LONE STAR HERO
Tracks: / Lone star hero.
7" Single: Released Mar '87, on Lambs To The Slaughter, by Prism Records. Catalogue no: **LTS 20**

Senyah, Jimmy

WEAKNESS FOR YOUR SWEETNESS
Tracks: / Weakness for your sweetness / Weakness for your sweetness (part 2).
7" Single: Released Aug '80, on Afrodisc, by RCA Records. Deleted '83. Catalogue no: **ROK 12 13**

Seona Dancing

BITTER HEART
Tracks: / Bitter heart.
12" Single: Released Sep '83, on London Records, by London Records. Catalogue no: **LONX 32**
7" Single: Released Sep '83, on London Records, by London Records. Catalogue no: **LON 32**

MORE TO LOSE
Tracks: / More to lose.
12" Single: Released May '83, on London Records, by London Records. Catalogue no: **LONX 22**
7" Single: Released May '83, on London Records, by London Records. Catalogue no: **LON 22**

Separate Minds

CAN YOU FEEL THE DIFFERENCE
Tracks: / Can you feel the difference.
12" Single: Released Nov '88, on 1st Bass, Catalogue no: **EXP 014**

September

LOVER IN ME, THE
Tracks: / Lover in me, The.
7" Single: Released Jun '85, on 10 Records, by Virgin Records. Deleted '89. Catalogue no: **TEN 62**

SLOWLY
Tracks: / Slowly / Lover is me, The.
7" Single: Released Mar '86, on 10 Records, by Virgin Records. Deleted '89. Catalogue no: **TEN 68**
12" Single: Released Mar '86, on 10 Records, by Virgin Records. Deleted '89. Catalogue no: **TEN 68-12**

Septic Death

KICHIGAI
Tracks: / Kichigai.
7" Single: Released Dec '88, on Pusmort, by Pusmort Records. Catalogue no: **PUS 007-03**

Sequal

I'M OVER YOU
Tracks: / I'm over you (island edit) / I'm over you (over easy dub) / I'm over you (Long Island mix) (12" only.) / I'm over you (overdub) (12" only.) / I'm over you (bonus beats) (12" only.) / I'm over you (Miami sound mix) (12CLX 512 only.) / I'm over you (Miami sound dub) (12CLX 512 only.) / I'm over you (Miami radio edit) (12CLX 512 only.).
12" Single: Released Jan '89, on Capitol, by EMI Records. Deleted Aug '89. Catalogue no: **12CLX 512**
12" Single: Released Jan '89, on Capitol, by EMI Records. Deleted Aug '89. Catalogue no: **12CL 512**
7" Single: Released Jan '89, on Capitol, by EMI Records. Deleted Aug '89. Catalogue no: **CL 512**

TELL HIM I CALLED
Tracks: / Tell him I called (7" watermix) (7" only.) / Tell him I called (12" watermix) (12" only.) / Tell him I called (dub) (12" only.) / Tell him I called (obo mix).
7" Single: Released Jun '89, on Capitol, by EMI Records. Catalogue no: **CL 528**
7" Single: Released Jun '89, on Capitol, by EMI Records. Catalogue no: **203 380 7**
12" Single: Released Jun '89, on Capitol, by EMI Records. Catalogue no: **12CL 528**
12" Single: Released Jun '89, on Capitol, by EMI Records. Catalogue no: **203 380 6**

Seram

I NEED YOUR LOVIN'
Tracks: / I need your lovin' / Come to me.
7" Single: Released Sep '89, on Citybeat, by Beggars Banquet Records. Catalogue no: **CBE 743**
12" Single: Released Sep '89, on Citybeat, by Beggars Banquet Records. Catalogue no: **CBE 1243**

Seratt, Kenny

DIESEL DEVIL
Tracks: / Diesel devil / Queen of the road.
7" Single: Released Dec '81, on Big R, by Big R Records. Catalogue no: **BRS 06**

SATURDAY NIGHT IN DALLAS (SINGLE)
Tracks: / Saturday night in Dallas / Bitter end.
7" Single: Released Nov '80, on Big R, by Big R Records. Catalogue no: **BRS 02**

Serenaders

MARIAN
Tracks: / Marian / Rice and peas.
12" Single: Released Jul '83, on Brown, Catalogue no: **BR 002**

SWEET LOVING
Tracks: / Sweet loving / Sweet loving (Version).
12" Single: Released Apr '86, on Brown, Catalogue no: **BR 007**

VELVET MORDE
Tracks: / Velvet morde / Velvet morde (Version).
12" Single: Released Sep '86, on Jetstar, by Jetstar Records. Catalogue no: **BRO 008**

Sergeant, Will

FAVOURITE BRANCHES
Tracks: / Favourite branches.
7" Single: Released Jul '82, on WEA, by WEA Records. Catalogue no: **K 19238**

Sergion & Herbtree

EASTENDAH
Tracks: / Eastendah / Eastendah (Dub).
7" Single: Released May '86, on Yellow Balloon, Deleted Sep '87. Catalogue no: **NDAH 1**

RIGHT TO FUNK
Tracks: / Right to funk / Right to funk (version).
12" Single: Released 23 May '87, on Safe House, Catalogue no: **SASHT 1**

Serious Drinking

COUNTRY GIRL (BECOMES DRUGS & SEX PUNK)
Tracks: / Country girl (becomes drugs & sex punk) / Go for the burn.
7" Single: Released May '84, on Upright, by Upright Records. Catalogue no: **UP 8**

HANGOVER
Tracks: / Hangover.
7" Single: Released Mar '83, on Upright, Catalogue no: **UP 5**

LOVE ON THE TERRACES (EP)
Tracks: / Love on the terraces / Hypocrite / Bobby Moore was innocent / Nobody likes him.
7" EP: Released Sep '82, on Upright, by Upright Records. Catalogue no: **UP 4**

Serious House Mixer

TELL ME (THAT YOU WANT ME)
Tracks: / Tell me (that you want me).
12" Single: Released Nov '87, on Play House (USA), Catalogue no: **PHR 624**

Serious Intention

SERIOUS
Tracks: / Serious / Serious (Dub).
12" Single: Released Mar '86, on London Records, by London Records. Catalogue no: **LONX 93**
7" Single: Released Mar '86, on London Records, by London Records. Catalogue no: **LON 93**

YOU DON'T KNOW
Tracks: / You don't know.
12" Single: Released Oct '85, on Important, Catalogue no: **TANT 8**
7" Single: Released Oct '85, on Important, Catalogue no: **TAN 8**

Serious Posse

I DON'T BELIEVE
Tracks: / I don't believe.
7" Single: Released Jul '84, on Eyes, Catalogue no: **EYES 5**
12" Single: Released Jul '84, on Eyes, Catalogue no: **EYET 5**

Seris, Jaques

FREE TO LOVE-OID
Tracks: / Free to love-oid.
7" Single: Released Jun '80, on JSO, Deleted '83. Catalogue no: **EAT 2**

Sern, Lou

SWISS BOY
Tracks: / Cuckoo clock (inst.).
12" Single: Released Nov '86, on Greyhound, by Greyhound Records. Catalogue no: **GRY 004**

Servant

SHE'S ALWAYS HIDING
Tracks: / She's always hiding / Transpired.
7" Single: Released Mar '86, on Head, Catalogue no: **HEAD 1**

SUN, A SMALL STAR, THE
Tracks: / Sun, a small star, The.
12" Single: Released Oct '86, on Head, Catalogue no: **HEAD 3**

Servants

IT'S MY TURN
Tracks: / It's my turn.
12" Single: Released Sep '89, on Glass, by Glass Records. Catalogue no: **GLASS 12 056**
7" Single: Released Sep '89, on Glass, by Glass Records. Catalogue no: **GLASS 056**

Session

BRIDGE OVER TROUBLED WATER
Tracks: / Bridge over troubled water.
Note: Proceeds to Hungerford fund.
7" Pic: Released Sep '87, on PRT, by Castle Communications Records. Catalogue no: **HTF 1**

Sesto, Camilo

SHOULDER TO SHOULDER
Tracks: / Shoulder to shoulder.
7" Single: Released Feb '83, on Ariola, by BMG Records (UK). Catalogue no: **ARO 296**

Set

NOTHING TO LOSE
Tracks: / Nothing to lose / If I had the chance.
7" Single: Released Apr '82, on Dakota, Deleted Apr '85. Catalogue no: **DAK 5**
12" Single: Released Apr '82, on Dakota, Deleted Apr '85. Catalogue no: **12DAK 5**

Set The Tone

DANCE SUCKER
Tracks: / Dance sucker / Let loose.
12" Single: Released Jan '83, on Island, by Island Records. Deleted Jan '86. Catalogue no: **12WIP 6836**
7" Single: Released Jan '83, on Island, by Island Records. Deleted Jan '86. Catalogue no: **WIP 6836**

RAP YOUR LOVE
Tracks: / Rap your love / Suprise.
7" Single: Released Mar '83, on Island, by Island Records. Deleted Mar '86. Catalogue no: **IS 110**

Settlers

LIGHTNING TREE
Tracks: / Lightning tree.
7" Single: Released Oct '71, on York, Deleted Oct '74. Catalogue no: **SYK 505**

Setzer, Brian

KNIFE FEELS LIKE JUSTICE, THE (SINGLE)
Tracks: / Knife feels like justice, The.
7" Single: Released Apr '86, on EMI-America, by EMI Records. Catalogue no: **EA 213**

WHEN THE SKY COMES TUMBLIN' DOWN
Tracks: / When the sky comes tumblin' down / Cross of love / When the sky comes tumblin' down (ext. version) (Extra track on 12" only.).
7" Single: Released 6 Jun '88, on EMI-Manhattan, by EMI Records. Deleted Jun '89. Catalogue no: **MT 45**
12" Single: Released 6 Jun '88, on EMI-Manhattan, by EMI Records. Deleted Jun '89. Catalogue no: **12 MT 45**

Sevelle, Taja

LOVE IS CONTAGIOUS
Tracks: / Love is contagious / Mama.
7" Single: Released Feb '88, on Warner Bros., by WEA Records. Catalogue no: **W 8257**
12" Single: Released Feb '88, on Warner Bros., by WEA Records. Catalogue no: **W 8257T**

WOULDN'T YOU LOVE TO LOVE ME
Tracks: / Wouldn't you love to love me / Baby's got a lover / Love is contagious (Extra track available on CD format only.).
7" Single: Released Apr '88, on Paisley Park (USA), by WEA Records. Catalogue no: **W 8127**
12" Single: Released Apr '88, on Paisley Park (USA), by WEA Records. Catalogue no: **W 8127T**
CD 5": Released Apr '88, on Paisley Park (USA), by WEA Records. Catalogue no: **W 8127CD**

Seven

STRANGER THAN FICTION
Tracks: / Stranger than fiction.

12" Single: Released Oct '84, on Polydor, by Polydor Ltd. Catalogue no: **SVNX 1**
7" Single: Released Oct '84, on Polydor, by Polydor Ltd. Catalogue no: **SVN 1**

Seven Dwarfs & ...

SEVEN DWARFS & THEIR DIAMOND MINE
7" EP: Released Apr '81, on Disneyland, by Disneyland Records. Catalogue no: **D 314**

Seven Four Seven

SLIPWAY
Tracks: / Slipway.
7" Single: Released Jun '85, on Floating World, by Floating World Records. Catalogue no: **FLOAT 06**

Seven West

WHEN THE COLOUR STARTS TO FADE
Tracks: / When the colour starts to fade / Nothing changes.
7" Single: Released Feb '86, on UNKNOWN, Catalogue no: **BEL 001**

Seventeen

DON'T LET GO
Tracks: / Don't let go / Bank holiday weekend.
7" Single: Released Mar '80, on Vendetta, Catalogue no: **VD 001**

Seventh Avenue

ARMED ROBBERY
Tracks: / Armed robbery / Armed robbery (inst).
7" Single: Released Jun '87, on Columbia, by EMI Records. Deleted Oct '87. Catalogue no: **DB 9148**
12" Single: Released Jun '87, on Nightmare, by Nightmare Records. Catalogue no: **MARE 25**
7" Single: Released Jun '87, on Nightmare, by Nightmare Records. Catalogue no: **MARES 25**

ENDING UP ON A HIGH
Tracks: / Ending up on a high.
12" Single: Released May '85, on Record Shack, by Record Shack Records. Catalogue no: **SOHOT 42**
7" Single: Released May '85, on Record Shack, by Record Shack Records. Catalogue no: **SOHO 42**

I HEAR THUNDER
Tracks: / I hear thunder.
12" Single: Released Jun '84, on Record Shack, by Record Shack Records. Catalogue no: **SOHOT 22**
7" Single: Released Jun '84, on Record Shack, by Record Shack Records. Catalogue no: **SOHO 22**

LOVE I LOST, THE
Tracks: / Love I lost, The / Right combination, The.
7" Single: Released Jul '88, on Nightmare, by Nightmare Records. Catalogue no: **MARES 56**
12" Single: Released Jul '88, on Nightmare, by Nightmare Records. Catalogue no: **MARE 56**

LOVE'S GONE MAD
Tracks: / Love's gone mad / Love's gone mad (instrumental) / Love's gone mad / Love's gone mad (hot mix).
12" Single: Released Feb '86, on Record Shack, by Record Shack Records. Catalogue no: **SOHO 56 T**
12" Single: Released Feb '88, on Record Shack, by Record Shack Records. Catalogue no: **SOHOB 5**
7" Single: Released Oct '86, on Tangerine, Deleted '88. Catalogue no: **SEG 1**
7" Single: Released Feb '86, on Record Shack, by Record Shack Records. Catalogue no: **SOHO 56**
12" Single: Released Oct '86, on Tangerine, Deleted '88. Catalogue no: **SEG 1T**

NO MAN'S LAND
Tracks: / No man's land / Ending up on a high / Love's gone mad / No man's land instrumental.
12" Single: Released Aug '86, on Record Shack, by Record Shack Records. Catalogue no: **SOHOT 67**
7" Single: Released Aug '86, on Record Shack, by Record Shack Records. Catalogue no: **SOHO 67 D**
7" Single: Released Aug '86, on Record Shack, by Record Shack Records. Catalogue no: **SOHO 67**

RIGHT COMBINATION
Tracks: / Right combination, The / Right combination, The (dub mix).
12" Single: Released Jan '88, on Nightmare, by Nightmare Records. Catalogue no: **MARE 47**
7" Single: Released Jan '88, on Nightmare, by Nightmare Records. Catalogue no: **MARES 47**

Seventh Extension

LIKE AN OPEN DOOR
Tracks: / Like an open door.
12" Single: Released Apr '82, on Dancebeat, Catalogue no: **DBD 1315**

Seventh Heaven

HANKY PANKY
Tracks: / Hanky panky / Gemini logic.
12" Single: Released May '87, on Mercury, by Phonogram Ltd. Deleted Dec '87. Catalogue no: **MERX 245**
7" Single: Released May '87, on Mercury, by Phonogram Ltd. Deleted Dec '87. Catalogue no: **MER 245**

HOT SUN
Tracks: / Hot sun.
7" Single: Released Aug '85, on Mercury, by Phonogram Ltd. Catalogue no: **MER 199**
12" Single: Released Aug '85, on Mercury, by Phonogram Ltd. Catalogue no: **MERX 199**

LITTLE GIRLS IN BIG CARS
Tracks: / Hanky panky / Little girls in big cars.
7" Single: Released Aug '87, on Epic, by CBS Records. Catalogue no: **HONK 1**
12" Single: Released Aug '87, on Epic, by CBS Records. Catalogue no: **HONK T1 1**

LITTLE PRINCESS
Tracks: / Little princess (nasty version) / Shake it / Little princess (12" version).
12" Single: Released 1 Feb '88, on Epic, by CBS Records. Deleted Aug '88. Catalogue no: **HONK QT2**
12" Single: Released Jan '88, on Epic, by CBS Records. Deleted Aug '88. Catalogue no: **HONK T2**
7" Single: Released Jan '88, on Epic, by CBS Records. Deleted Aug '88. Catalogue no: **HONK 2**

Seventh Seance

ANOTHER EMPTY FACE
Tracks: / Another empty face.
12" Single: Released May '84, on Icon, Catalogue no: **IC 003**

INTO THE OUTSIDE
Tracks: / Into the outside.
7" Single: Released Aug '84, on Icon, Catalogue no: **ICS 001**

Seventh Wonder

CAPTAIN OF MY SHIP
Tracks: / Captain of my ship / Pharoah.
7" Single: Released Feb '80, on Grapevine (Northern Soul), by BMG Records (UK). Deleted Feb '83. Catalogue no: **GRP 130**

Severed Heads

20 DEADLY DISEASES
Tracks: / Twenty deadly kisses.
12" Single: Released Sep '87, on Nettwerk, by Nettwerk Records. Catalogue no: **NT 12 3003**

ALL SAINTS DAY
Tracks: / All Saints Day.
12" Single: Released Oct '89, on Nettwerk, by Nettwerk Records. Catalogue no: **NET 012**

BAD MOOD GUY (SINGLE)
12" Single: Released Dec '87, on Nettwerk, by Nettwerk Records. Catalogue no: **NET 001**

DEAD EYES OPENED
Tracks: / Dead eyes opened / Bullet.
12" Single: Released '89, on Nettwerk, by Nettwerk Records. Catalogue no: **NET 011**
12" Single: Released '88, on Nettwerk, by Nettwerk Records. Catalogue no: **NTM 6303**
Cassingle: Released '88, on Nettwerk, by Nettwerk Records. Catalogue no: **NTMC 6303**
12" Single: Released Mar '84, on Rough Trade, by Rough Trade Records. Catalogue no: **INK 122**

GOODBYE TONSILS
Tracks: / Goodbye tonsils.
7" Single: Released Feb '85, on Ink, by Red Flame Records. Catalogue no: **INK 129**

GREATER REWARD
Tracks: / Greater reward / Nation.
12" Single: Released Sep '88, on Network, by CBS Records. Catalogue no: **NET 004**
12" Single: Released Aug '88, on Nettwerk, by Nettwerk Records. Catalogue no: **NT 12 3019**

HEAT SEEKING SUSAN
Tracks: / Heat seeking Susan.
12" Single: Released Sep '85, on Ink, by Red Flame Records. Catalogue no: **INK 1214**

HEAVY METAL
Tracks: / Heavy metal.
7" Single: Released Apr '83, on Plastic Canvas, Catalogue no: **PC 002**

HOT WITH FLEAS
Tracks: / Hot with fleas.
12" Single: Released 23 Oct '87, on Nettwerk, by Nettwerk Records. Catalogue no: **NT12-3011**

PROPELLOR
Tracks: / Propellor / Harold and Cindy hospital.
12" Single: Released Jul '86, on Ink, by Red Flame Records. Catalogue no: **INK 1222**

Severine

UN BANC, UN ARBRE, UNE RUE
Tracks: / Un banc, un arbre, une rue.
7" Single: Released Apr '71, on Philips, by Phonogram Ltd. Deleted Apr '74. Catalogue no: **6009 135**

Seville

TAKE A WALK
Tracks: / Take a walk.
12" Single: Released Sep '87, on Cutting (USA), Catalogue no: **CR 213**

Seville, David

Biographical details: David Seville was a pseudonym for actor/songwriter **Ross Bagdasarian**, who was born in 1919 in Frenso, California; he was a cousin of the playright **William Saroyan** and acted in his hit play **The Time Of Your Life**. They co-wrote **'Come On-A My House'** in 1939; it was a big hit by Rosemary Clooney in 1951. He played bit roles in films, then went to Liberty Records as David Seville, writing instrumental/novelty hits **'Armen's Theme'**, **'Witch Doctor'** 1966-58; the lattera no.1 '58, created by recording at half speed and playing the tape back at full speed. Next he did the same thing with voices, creating a trio of chipmunks: Alvin, Simon and Theodore were named after the bosses at Liberty, and their Christmas novelty **'Th Chipmunk Song'** sold 3.5 million copies in five weeks in 1958, followed by more hits, mostly seasonal. He died in Beverly Hills in 1972; his son revived the chipmunks for more hits in the early 1980's. [Donald Clarke, April 87].

WITCH DOCTOR
Tracks: / Witch doctor.
7" Single: Released May '58, on London-American, Deleted May '61. Catalogue no: **HLU 8619**

Sevillia

CAVATINA
Tracks: / Cavatina.
7" Single: Released Mar '79, on Polydor, by Polydor Ltd. Catalogue no: **POSP 41**

Sex Aids

BACK ON THE PISS AGAIN
Tracks: / Back on the piss again.
7" Single: Released Sep '83, on Riot City, by Riot City Records. Catalogue no: **RIOT 23**

Sex Beat

PUMP
Tracks: / Pump.
7" Single: Released Apr '84, on ABC (indie), Catalogue no: **ABCS 002**
12" Single: Released Apr '84, on ABC (indie), Catalogue no: **ABCS 002T**

Sex Gang Children

BEASTS
Tracks: / Beasts / Cannibal queen / Who on earth can that be / Sense of elation / Into the abyss / Dieche / Salvation / Mocnoglia / Times of our lives.
12" Single: Released Feb '85, on Illuminated, Catalogue no: **ILL 1112**

DEICHE
Tracks: / Deiche.
12" Single: Released Feb '85, on Illuminated, Catalogue no: **ILL 3912**
12" Single: Released Sep '85, on Saderal, by Saderal Records. Catalogue no: **SLS 12001**

INTO THE ABYSS
Tracks: / Into the abyss / Dieche.
7" Single: Released Feb '85, on Illuminated, Catalogue no: **ILL 15**

MAURITIA MAYER
Tracks: / Mauritia Mayer.
12" Single: Released Sep '83, on Clay, by Clay Records. Deleted '88. Catalogue no: **12 CLAY 27**
7" Single: Released Sep '83, on Clay, by Clay Records. Deleted '88. Catalogue no: **CLAY 27**

SEBASTIANE
Tracks: / Sebastiane / Mongolia / Who on earth can that be.
12" Single: Released Mar '85, on Illuminated, Catalogue no: **ILL 2212**

SONG AND LEGEND (SINGLE)
Tracks: / Song and legend.
7" Single: Released Mar '83, on Illuminated, Catalogue no: **ILL 20**

Sex, John

BUMP GRIND IT
Tracks: / Bump, grind it.
12" Single: Released Feb '87, on Southern Studios, Catalogue no: **V 121**

Sex Pistols

Biographical details:
The best-known of all the punk bands of the late 1970's, the Sex Pistols were formed in 1975 by vocalist Johnny Rotten (born John Lydon, 31 January 1956), guitarist Steve Jones (born 3 May 1955), bassist Glen Matlock (born 27 August 1956), drummer Paul Cook (born 27 July 1956). Matlock was replaced in 1977 by Sid Vicious (born John Simon Ritchie, 10 May 1957; died 2 February 1979 in NYC of a heroin overdose while under indictment for killing his girlfriend Nancy Spungeon). They were encouraged by boutique owner/entrepreneur Malcolm McLaren, who in turn had been inspired by briefly managing the New York Dolls, their American rquivalent. Cook, Matlock and Jones had formed the Swankers, then recruited Rotten. They bragged that they had no abilty to play or sing; their object was to make rock and roll exciting and to put superstars out of business. Their EMI single *Anarchy In The UK* was a hit in late 1976 but their contract was cancelled due to obnoxious behaviour in public and on TV amid a media circus. A & M sugned them but also cancelled; *God Save The Queen* was released on Virgin during Queen Elizabeth II's Silver Jubilee in June 1977 and was banned by the BBC but became a no.2 hit. Six more singles were top 10 and their debut album *Never Mind The Bollocks - Here's The Sex Pistols* was no.1 in 1977. Their film *The Great Rock'n'Roll Swindle* is a record of McLaren at work and a pop artifact. Rotten quit in 1978, changed his name back to Lydon and formed Public Image Ltd; the remaining trio completed the film, recorded new material with Vicious singing (*My Way, 'C'mon Everybody, Something Else* - all UK top 10 hits), also recorded a track and additional film footage with train robber Ronnie Biggs. They tried new singers including Jimmy Pursey and Tenpole Tudor (who appeared in the film). The most notorious of the punks, but outlasted by The Clash and The Damned. (Donald Clarke, April 87).

ANARCHY IN THE UK
Tracks: / Anarchy in the UK / No fun / EMI (On CD & 12" only).
CD 3": Released Jun '88, on Virgin, by Virgin Records. Catalogue no: **CDT 3**
7" Single: Released '83, on Virgin, by Virgin Records. Catalogue no: **VS 609**
12" Single: Released '83, on Virgin, by Virgin Records. Catalogue no: **VS 609-12**

ANARCHY IN THE UK (LIVE VERSION)
Tracks: / Anarchy in the UK (live version) / Flogging a dead horse.
12" Single: Released Apr '86, on McDonald Brothers, Catalogue no: **JOCK 1201**

ANARCHY IN THE UK (SINGLE)
Tracks: / Anarchy in the UK.
7" Single: Released '80, on EMI (Europe), by EMI Records. Catalogue no: **LR 8000**
7" Single: Released Dec '76, on EMI (Europe), by EMI Records. Deleted Dec '79. Catalogue no: **EMI 2566**

C'MON EVERYBODY
Tracks: / C'mon everybody / God save the Queen (symphony) / Watcha gonna do about it.
7" Single: Released '79, on Virgin, by Virgin Records. Catalogue no: **VS 272**

GOD SAVE THE QUEEN
Tracks: / God save the Queen / Did you no wrong / Don't give me no lip child (CD only).
CD 3": Released '88, on Virgin, by Virgin Records. Catalogue no: **CDT 37**
7" Single: Released May '77, on Virgin, by Virgin Records. Catalogue no: **VS 181**

GREAT ROCK'N'ROLL SWINDLE, THE (SINGLE)
Tracks: / Great rock'n'roll swindle, The / Rock around the clock.
7" Single: Released '80, on Virgin, by Virgin Records. Catalogue no: **VS 290**

HOLIDAYS IN THE SUN
Tracks: / Holidays in the sun / Satellite.
7" Single: Released Oct '77, on Virgin, by Virgin Records. Catalogue no: **VS 191**

I'M NOT YOUR STEPPING STONE
Tracks: / I'm not your stepping stone / Pistols propaganda.
7" Single: Released Jun '80, on Virgin, by Virgin Records. Catalogue no: **VS 339**

NO ONE IS INNOCENT (A punk prayer by Ronald Biggs)
Tracks: / My way / No one is innocent (7" only) / Biggest blow, The (12" only).
7" Single: Released Jun '78, on Virgin, by Virgin Records. Catalogue no: **VS 220**

12" Single: Released Apr '83, on Virgin, by Virgin Records. Catalogue no: **VS 220-12**

ORIGINAL PISTOLS (CD)
CD 5": Released Nov '88, on Counterpoint, Catalogue no: **CDEP 13 C**

PRETTY VACANT
Tracks: / Pretty vacant / No fun.
7" Single: Released Jul '77, on Virgin, by Virgin Records. Catalogue no: **VS 184**

SEX PISTOLS LIVE
Tracks: / Anarchy in the UK / I'm a lazy sod / Pretty vacant / Substitute.
CD 5": Released Aug '89, on MFP, by EMI Records. Catalogue no: **CDFA 3149**
12" Single: Released Aug '86, on Archive 4, by Castle Communications Records. Catalogue no: **TOF 104**

SILLY THING
Tracks: / Silly thing / Who killed Bambi.
7" Single: Released Mar '79, on Virgin, by Virgin Records. Catalogue no: **VS 256**

SOMETHING ELSE
Tracks: / Something else / Friggin' in the riggin'.
7" Single: Released Feb '79, on Virgin, by Virgin Records. Catalogue no: **VS 240**

SUBMISSION
Tracks: / Submission / No feelings.
7" Single: Released Mar '87, on Chaos, by Backs Recording Co.. Catalogue no: **DICK 1**

WHO KILLED BAMBI
Tracks: / Who killed Bambi.
7" Single: Released Sep '81, on Virgin, by Virgin Records. Deleted '89. Catalogue no: **VS 443**

Sexgang, Andi

ASSASSIN YEARS
Tracks: / Assassin years.
7" Single: Released Mar '89, on Jungle, by Jungle Records. Catalogue no: **JUNG 48**
12" Single: Released Mar '89, on Jungle, by Jungle Records. Catalogue no: **JUNG 48 T**

S.Express

HEY MUSIC LOVER
Tracks: / Hey music lover.
12" Single: Released Nov '88, on Rhythm King, by Mute Records. Catalogue no: **LEFT 030T**
7" Single: Released Nov '88, on Rhythm King, by Mute Records. Catalogue no: **LEFT 030**

MANTRA FOR A STATE OF MIND
Tracks: / Mantra for the state of mind.
CD 3": Released Oct '89, on Rhythm King, by Mute Records. Catalogue no: **LEFT 035CD**
12" Single: Released May '89, on Rhythm King, by Mute Records. Catalogue no: **LEFT 035T**
7" Single: Released May '89, on Rhythm King, by Mute Records. Catalogue no: **LEFT 035**

SUPERFLY GUY
Tracks: / Superfly guy.
12" Single: Released Jul '88, on Rhythm King, by Mute Records. Catalogue no: **LEFT 28 T**
7" Single: Released Jul '88, on Rhythm King, by Mute Records. Catalogue no: **LEFT 28**

SUPERFLY GUY (FLUFFY BAGEL MIX)
Tracks: / Lollipop / Funky killer / Superfly guy (fluffy bagel mix).
CD 5": Released Aug '88, on Rhythm King, by Mute Records. Catalogue no: **LEFTCD 28**
12" Single: Released Aug '88, on Rhythm King, by Mute Records. Catalogue no: **LEFT R 28T**

THEME FROM S.EXPRESS
Tracks: / Theme from S.Express.
12" Single: Released 5 Mar '88, on Rhythm King, by Mute Records. Catalogue no: **LEFT 21T**
7" Single: Released Apr '88, on Rhythm King, by Mute Records. Catalogue no: **LEFT 21**

Sexton, Ann

YOU'VE BEEN GONE TOO LONG
Tracks: / You've been gone too long.
7" Single: Released Jul '80, on Inferno (1), by Inferno Records. Catalogue no: **HEAT 21**

Sexton, Charlie

Biographical details:
Guitarist Charlie Sexton was born in 1968 in San Antonio, Texas; a guitar prodigy, he was playing in public at the age of 11, in Texas singer/songwriter Joe Ely's band at 13, then recording with Bob Dylan, others incl. Rolling Stones Keith Richard and Ron Wood in a film soundtrack *Easy Street*. His first album, *Pictures For Pleasure* was a top 20 USA hit in 1986. (Donald Clarke)..

BEATS SO LONELY
Tracks: / Beats so lonely / Attraction / Hold me / Beats so lonely.
7" Single: Released Mar '86, on MCA, by MCA Records. Catalogue no: **MCA 1026**
12" Single: Released Mar '86, on MCA, by MCA Records. Catalogue no: **MCAT 1026**
7" Pic: Released Mar '86, on MCA, by MCA Records. Catalogue no: **MCAP 1026**

HOLD ME
Tracks: / Beats so lonely / Control me.
12" Single: Released Jan '87, on MCA, by MCA Records. Catalogue no: **MCAT 1081**
7" Single: Released Jan '87, on MCA, by MCA Records. Catalogue no: **MCA 1081**

Sexual Harassment

I NEED A FREAK
Tracks: / I need a freak.
12" Single: Released Sep '83, on Elite Records, by Elite Records. Deleted '84. Catalogue no: **USDAZZ 27**

Sexx

SEXX
7" EP: Released May '87, on Iron Works (USA), by Azra International (USA). Catalogue no: **IW 1011**

Seymour, Phil

LET HER DANCE
Tracks: / Let her dance / I'm totally yours.
7" Single: Released Jul '81, on Epic, by CBS Records. Deleted '84. Catalogue no: **EPCA 1402**

PRECIOUS TO ME
Tracks: / Precious to me / Suzie Glider.
7" Single: Released May '81, on Epic, by CBS Records. Deleted May '84. Catalogue no: **EPC A 1154**

Seyton, Denny

WAY YOU LOOK TONIGHT, THE
Tracks: / Way you look tonight.
7" Single: Released Sep '64, on Mercury, by Phonogram Ltd. Deleted Sep '67. Catalogue no: **MF 824**

SFX

ROCKIN' WITH MY RADIO
Tracks: / Rockin' with my radio.
7" Single: Released Oct '83, on Lamborghini, by Lamborghini Records. Catalogue no: **LMG 4**

SGB

C'EST LA VIE
Tracks: / C'est la vie / I love the way you're dancing.
7" Single: Released Mar '86, on Trojan, by Trojan Records. Deleted May '88. Catalogue no: **SGB 2**

INFATUATION
Tracks: / Infatuation / All kinds of people.
7" Single: Released Nov '85, on Trojan, by Trojan Records. Deleted May '88. Catalogue no: **SGB 1**
7" Single: on Mooncrest, by Trojan Records. Deleted May '88. Catalogue no: **MOON 1003**

RUN FOR YOUR LIFE
Tracks: / Run for your life.
7" Single: on Trojan, by Trojan Records. Deleted May '88. Catalogue no: **SGB 1000**

Sgt. Frog

BUTTERFLY BALL (LOVE IS ALL)
Tracks: / Butterfly ball (love is all) / Profile dance.
7" Single: Released Oct '82, on Safari, by Safari Records. Catalogue no: **SAFE 51**

Sgt. Pepper

DANCING TO REGGAE MUSIC
Tracks: / Dancing to reggae music / Cry over me.
12" Single: Released Sep '83, on Ariwa Sounds, by Ariwa Sounds. Catalogue no: **ARI 1026**

ONE FAMILY
Tracks: / One family / Rasta man.
12" Single: Released Mar '84, on Jah Shaka, Catalogue no: **SHAKA 843**

TIME TO GO DREAD
Tracks: / Time to go dread / Time to go dread (bengali dub).
12" Single: Released Apr '83, on Ariwa Sounds, by Ariwa Sounds. Catalogue no: **HARI 1017**

Sha Sha

LIES
Tracks: / Lies.
12" Single: Released May '89, on White label (2), Catalogue no: **NST 1**

LIES (REMIX)
Tracks: / Lies (remix).
7" Single: Released Jul '89, on White Label (1), Catalogue no: **SHASHA 1**

12" Single: Released Jul '89, on White Label (1), Catalogue no: **SHASHA 1T**

Shabazz

TAKES ME HIGHER
Tracks: / Takes me higher.
12" Single: Released Sep '87, on Coslit (USA), Catalogue no: **CR 10002**

Shabazz, Lakim

PURE RIGHTEOUSNESS (SINGLE)
Tracks: / Pure righteousness.
12" Single: Released 20 Mar '89, on White Label (1), Catalogue no: **SDT 8**

Shack

EMERGENCY
Tracks: / Emergency / Liberation / Faith (Only on 12" single.) / What's it like (Only on CD single.).
7" Single: Released Mar '88, on Ghetto, by CBS Records. Deleted Aug '88. Catalogue no: **GTG 1**
12" Single: Released Mar '88, on Ghetto, by CBS Records. Deleted Aug '88. Catalogue no: **GTG T1**
CD 5": Released Mar '88, on Ghetto, by CBS Records. Deleted Jan '89. Catalogue no: **CD GTG 1**
Special: Released Apr '88, on Ghetto, by CBS Records. Catalogue no: **GTG B1**

HIGH RISE LOW LIFE
Tracks: / High rise low life / Who killed Clayton Square? / High rise low life (Bert Hardy mix) (Only on 12" single.).
CD 5": Released 13 Jun '88, on Ghetto, by CBS Records. Deleted Jan '89. Catalogue no: **CD GTG 2**
7" Single: Released 6 Jun '88, on Ghetto, by CBS Records. Deleted Jan '89. Catalogue no: **GTG 2**
12" Single: Released 13 Jun '88, on Ghetto, by CBS Records. Deleted Jan '89. Catalogue no: **GTGT 2**

Shade Adejumo

SUMMER DAYS
Tracks: / Summer days.
12" Single: Released Mar '82, on Solid Groove, Catalogue no: **SG 8**

Shades

I NEVER KNEW
Tracks: / I never knew.
7" Single: Released 12 May '89, on Jetstar, by Jetstar Records. Catalogue no: **TC 101**

LIVE AT CAISTER
7" Single: Released Apr '81, on Magnum Force, by Magnum Music Group. Catalogue no: **MFEP 002**

RUNNING WILD
Tracks: / Running wild (Theme from the LWT TV Series.) / Running wild vocal version.
Note: Running Wild is the theme from the LWT TV Series.
7" Single: Released Mar '87, on Sierra, by Sierra Records. Catalogue no: **FED 34**

Shades Of Rhythm

JUST FEEL IT
Tracks: / Just feel it / J.S.J. & feel this way.
12" Single: Released Feb '89, on Beat Box, by Beat Box Records. Catalogue no: **BBOX T4**

Shadow

AH COME OUT TO PARTY
Tracks: / Ah come out to party.
12" Single: Released Jun '85, on Hot Vinyl, Catalogue no: **HVD 001**

STORM, THE
Tracks: / Storm, The.
12" Single: Released Mar '83, on Sunburn, by Orbitone Records. Catalogue no: **SBD 29**

WALK AND WINCE
Tracks: / Walk and wince / We gonna jam / Bend down and roll your belly.
12" Single: Released Jun '82, on Seara, Catalogue no: **SEA 2**

Shadow Talk

PEOPLE WATCHING PEOPLE
Tracks: / People watching people / Heaven up here / Touch of luck (Available on 12" only.).
7" Single: Released May '84, on Magnet, by WEA Records. Catalogue no: **MAG 257**
12" Single: Released May '84, on Magnet, by WEA Records. Catalogue no: **MAGT 257**

YOU COULD BE MINE
Tracks: / You could be mine.
7" Single: Released Sep '84, on Magnet, by WEA Records. Catalogue no: **MAG 265**

Shadowboys

WAITING FOR TOMORROW
Tracks: / Waiting for tomorrow.
7" Single: Released Jan '84, on Pete-Nik, Catalogue no: **DNF 01**

Shadowdance Theatre

COLOUR OF MIDNIGHT
Tracks: / Colour of midnight.
7" Single: Released Nov '83, on Ariel(Canada), by Ariel (Canada). Catalogue no: **AR 123**

Shadows

Biographical details: The original line-up of this British combo was Jet Harris, Hank Marvin, Tony Meehan and Bruce Welch. They were initially called the Drifters, but changed their name when the black American vocal group threatened legal action. Lead guitarist Marvin and rhythm guitarist Welch have been the two perennial members of the Shadows; bass guitarist was occupied by Brian 'Licorice' Locking followed by John Rostill; drummer Meehan was replaced by Brian Bennett. After more than a year of fame as Cliff Richard's backing group, the Shadows' own subsidiary career took off in August 1960 when their fourth single *Apache* reached the No.1 spot. Written by Jerry Lordan, who was also responsible for their other biggest hit *Wonderful land*, the memorable *Apache* logged five weeks at the top and set the standard for a long series of Shadows instrumentals. While continuing to back Richard on his many smash hits during the early Sixties, the Shadows themselves were never far from the UK Top 10 from 1960 till 1963. Their five No.1 singles were *Apache*, *Kon-Tiki*, *Wonderful land* (which stayed at the summit for eight weeks in 1962), *Dance on!* and *Foot tapper*, they reached No.1 on the UK album listings with *The Shadows* (1961) and *Out of the Shadows* (1962).
Cliff and the Shads were easily the biggest phenomenon in the British pop business prior to the arrival of the Beatles. Hank Marvin inspired an entire generation of budding guitarists. Many of the most famous axemen in British rock during the Sixties and Seventies cited Marvin as their most important early hero. When Dire Straits were named Best British Band at the BPI Awards in Feb 1986, Mark Knopfler asked Marvin to accept the trophy on the group's behalf. Though the Shadows' music and image were crisp, uniformed and efficient, their apparent tameness was counterbalanced by an innate feeling for what the teenage fans wanted. Smashes like *Frightened city* and *Atlantis* were amongst the finest pop singles of the era. Like Cliff Richard, however, the group did not catch on in America. Shortly after leaving the Shadows, Jet Harris and Tony Meehan formed a duo and enjoyed their own run of hits in 1963. Meanwhile, Hank and Bruce's group survived the Merseybeat onslaught surprisingly well and remained a regular albeit lesser chart force until 1967. A few of their later hits were conventional vocal singles rather than instrumentals. The group called it a day in 1969, but reformed to participate in the 1975 Eurovision Contest; their entry was the mediocre *Let me be the one*, which managed to be placed second in the Contest and returned the group to the British Top 20 for the first time in a decade. After hitting the UK No.1 slot with the TV advertised 1977 compilation album *20 golden greats*, they went back to their classic instrumental style for the 1979 Top 10 singles *Don't cry for me Argentina* and *Cavatina (theme from 'The Deer Hunter'). In March 1980 the Shadows topped the UK LP chart with String of hits*. The group celebrated their 25th anniversary in 1983, by which time they were regarded with respect and affection as founding fathers of UK pop. Bruce Welch had a hand in writing several of Cliff's early smashes including the No.1 hits, *Please don't tease*, *I love you*, *Bachelor boy* and *Summer holiday*. When he took over as Richard's producer in the mid-Seventies, he completely revitalised the singer's somewhat stale career; the Welch injection culminated in his production of Cliff's classic 1979 chart-topper *We don't talk anymore*. (Bob MacDonald, 11th March 1986).

The Shadows were the most influential instrumental rock'n'roll group in Britain, with 24 Top 40 hits 1960-66 (more than half in the Top 10) beginning with *Apache* at no.1. The original lineup was Hank Marvin, lead guitar; Bruce Welch, rhythm guitar; Jet Harris, bass; Tony Meehan, drums. They came together to back Cliff Richard on his first tour, calling themselves the Drifters in 1958, changing their name mid-1959 to avoid confusion with the black American vocal group. Their trademarks were gleaming red Fender Stratocaster guitars and the 'Shadows Step', a three-step onstage movement. They played on all of Richard's hits from '58 to 1961, and many more through 1968, when they split up; they re-formed in the early '70s, delighted old fans on tours and sold hit albums and singles well into the 1980s. (Donald Clarke)..

49ERS
Tracks: / 49ers.

SHADOWS - MOUNTAINS OF THE MOON (Released on Polydor)

12" Single: Released Sep '89, on Music Man, Catalogue no: **MMPT 12010**
7" Single: Released Sep '89, on Music Man, Catalogue no: **MMPS 7010**

APACHE (SINGLE)
Tracks: / Apache.
7" Single: Released '83, on EMI (France), by EMI Records. Catalogue no: **2C 008 04700**
7" Single: Released Jan '77, on EMI, by EMI Records. Catalogue no: **EMI 2573**
7" Single: Released Jul '60, on Columbia, by EMI Records. Deleted Jul '63. Catalogue no: **DB 4484**

ATLANTIS
Tracks: / Atlantis.
7" Single: Released Jun '63, on Columbia, by EMI Records. Deleted Jun '66. Catalogue no: **DB 7047**

BOYS,THE
Tracks: / Boys, The.
12" Single: Released '82, on EMI (Holland), by EMI Records. Catalogue no: **K 062Z 07615**

DANCE ON
Tracks: / Dance on.
7" Single: Released Dec '62, on Columbia, by EMI Records. Deleted Dec '65. Catalogue no: **DB 4948**

DANCING IN THE DARK
Tracks: / Dancing in the dark / Turning point.
12" Single: Released Aug '86, on Polydor, by Polydor Ltd. Deleted Mar '87. Catalogue no: **POSPX 808**
7" Single: Released Aug '86, on Polydor, by Polydor Ltd. Deleted Mar '87. Catalogue no: **POSP 808**

DEER HUNTER (CAVATINA), THEME FROM
Tracks: / Deer Hunter (Cavatina), Theme from.
7" Single: Released Apr '79, on EMI, by EMI Records. Catalogue no: **EMI 2939**

DON'T CRY FOR ME ARGENTINA (SINGLE)
Tracks: / Don't cry for me Argentina.
7" Single: Released '80, on EMI, by EMI Records. Catalogue no: **LR 4978**
7" Single: Released Dec '78, on EMI, by EMI Records. Deleted Dec '81. Catalogue no: **EMI 2890**

DON'T MAKE MY BABY BLUE
Tracks: / Don't make my baby blue.
7" Single: Released Aug '65, on Columbia, by EMI Records. Deleted Aug '68. Catalogue no: **DB 7650**

DREAMS I DREAM, THE
Tracks: / Dreams I dream, The.
7" Single: Released Nov '66, on Columbia, by EMI Records. Deleted Nov '69. Catalogue no: **DB 8034**

EASTENDERS & HOWARDS WAY, THEME FROM
Tracks: / No dancing / Eastenders (theme from) / Howards Way (theme from).
7" Single: Released Nov '86, on Polydor, by Polydor Ltd. Deleted Jan '88. Catalogue no: **POSP 847**

EQUINOXE
Tracks: / Equinoxe / Fender bender.
7" Single: Released Aug '80, on Polydor, by Polydor Ltd. Deleted '83. Catalogue no: **POSP 148**

F.B.I.
Tracks: / F.B.I..
7" Single: Released Feb '61, on Columbia, by EMI Records. Deleted Feb '64. Catalogue no: **DB 4580**

FOOT TAPPER
Tracks: / Foot tapper.
7" Single: Released Mar '63, on Columbia, by EMI Records. Deleted Mar '66. Catalogue no: **DB 4984**

FRIGHTENED CITY
Tracks: / Frightened city.
7" Single: Released May '61, on Columbia, by EMI Records. Deleted May '64. Catalogue no: **DB 4637**

GENIE WITH THE LIGHT BROWN LAMP
Tracks: / Genie with the light brown lamp.
7" Single: Released Dec '64, on Columbia, by EMI Records. Deleted Dec '67. Catalogue no: **DB 7416**

GERONIMO
Tracks: / Geronimo.
7" Single: Released Dec '63, on Columbia, by EMI Records. Deleted Dec '66. Catalogue no: **DB 7163**

GUITAR TANGO
Tracks: / Guitar tango.
7" Single: Released Aug '62, on Columbia, by EMI Records. Deleted Aug '65. Catalogue no: **DB 4870**

HEART OF GLASS
Tracks: / Heart of glass / Return to the Alamo.
7" Single: Released Jun '80, on EMI, by EMI Records. Deleted '83. Catalogue no: **EMI 5083**

I MET A GIRL
Tracks: / I met a girl.
7" Single: Released Mar '66, on Columbia, by EMI Records. Deleted Mar '69. Catalogue no: **DB 7853**

IMAGINE/WOMAN
Tracks: / Imagine/woman / Hats off the wally.
7" Single: Released Oct '81, on Polydor, by Polydor Ltd. Deleted '85. Catalogue no: **POSP 376**

KON-TIKI
Tracks: / Kon-tiki.
7" Single: Released Sep '61, on Columbia, by EMI Records. Deleted Sep '64. Catalogue no: **DB 4698**

LET ME BE THE ONE
Tracks: / Let me be the one.
7" Single: Released Mar '75, on EMI, by EMI Records. Deleted Mar '78. Catalogue no: **EMI 2269**

MAN OF MYSTERY (SINGLE)
Tracks: / Man of mystery / Stranger, The.
7" Single: Released Nov '60, on Columbia, by EMI Records. Deleted Nov '63. Catalogue no: **DB 4530**

MAROC 7
Tracks: / Maroc 7.
7" Single: Released Apr '67, on Columbia, by EMI Records. Deleted Apr '70. Catalogue no: **DB 8170**

MARY ANNE
Tracks: / Mary Anne.
7" Single: Released Feb '65, on Columbia, by EMI Records. Deleted Feb '68. Catalogue no: **DB 7476**

MISSING
Tracks: / Missing.
7" Single: Released Jul '82, on Polydor, by Polydor Ltd. Catalogue no: **POSP 485**

MOONLIGHT SHADOW (SINGLE)
Tracks: / Moonlight shadow / Johnny Staccato.
7" Single: Released Apr '86, on Polydor, by Polydor Ltd. Catalogue no: **POSP 792**

MOUNTAINS OF THE MOON (see panel on left)
Tracks: / Mountains of the moon / Stack-it.
7" Single: Released Apr '89, on Polydor, by Polydor Ltd. Deleted Oct '89. Catalogue no: **PO 47**
CD 5": Released Apr '89, on Polydor, by Polydor Ltd. Catalogue no: **PZCD 47**

MOZART FORTE
Tracks: / Mozart forte / Midnight creepin'.
7" Single: Released Oct '80, on Polydor, by Polydor Ltd. Deleted Oct '83. Catalogue no: **POSP 187**

MUSTANG
Tracks: / Mustang.
7" Single: Released Sep '82, on EMI (Europe), by EMI Records. Catalogue no: **K 062Z 07613**
12" Single: Released '82, on EMI (Holland), by EMI Records. Catalogue no: **K 062Z 07613**

ON A NIGHT LIKE THIS
Tracks: / On a night like this.
7" Single: Released Aug '84, on Polydor, by Polydor Ltd. Catalogue no: **POSP 694**

PLACE IN THE SUN, A
Tracks: / Place in the sun, A.
7" Single: Released Jul '66, on Columbia, by EMI Records. Deleted Jul '69. Catalogue no: **DB 7952**

PULASKI
Tracks: / Pulaski.
7" Single: Released Oct '87, on Polydor, by Polydor Ltd. Catalogue no: **POSP 886**

RHYTHM & GREENS
Tracks: / Rhythm & greens.
12" Single: Released '82, on EMI (Europe), by EMI Records. Catalogue no: **K 062Z 07527**
7" Single: Released Sep '64, on Columbia, by EMI Records. Deleted Sep '67. Catalogue no: **DB 7342**

RIDERS IN THE SKY
Tracks: / Riders in the sky / Rusk.
7" Single: Released Jan '80, on EMI, by EMI Records. Deleted Jan '83. Catalogue no: **EMI 5027**

RISE AND FALL OF FLINGEL BUNT, THE
Tracks: / Rise and fall of Flingel Bunt, The.
7" Single: Released May '64, on Columbia, by EMI Records. Deleted May '67. Catalogue no: **DB 7261**

SAVAGE, THE
Tracks: / Savage, The.
7" Single: Released Nov '61, on Columbia, by EMI Records. Deleted Nov '64. Catalogue no: **DB 4726**

SHADOWS IN JAPAN
12" Single: Released '83, on EMI (Holland), by EMI Records. Catalogue no: **1A 062Z 07491**

SHINDIG
Tracks: / Shindig.
7" Single: Released Sep '63, on Columbia, by EMI Records. Deleted Sep '66. Catalogue no: **DB 7106**

SNOWMAN, THE (THEME FROM)
Tracks: / Snowman, The (theme from) / Outigo.
7" Single: Released Jul '87, on Polydor, by Polydor Ltd. Catalogue no: **POSP 898**

STINGRAY
Tracks: / Stingray.
7" Single: Released Jun '65, on Columbia, by EMI Records. Deleted Jun '68. Catalogue no: **DB 7588**

TELSTAR
Tracks: / Telstar / Summer love '59.
7" Single: Released Aug '81, on Polydor, by Polydor Ltd. Deleted Aug '84. Catalogue no: **POSP 316**

THEME FOR YOUNG LOVERS
Tracks: / Theme for young lovers.
7" Single: Released Mar '64, on Columbia, by EMI Records. Deleted Mar '67. Catalogue no: **DB 7231**

THEME FROM THE DEER HUNTER (CAVATINA)
Tracks: / Deer hunter, Theme from the (cavatina).
7" Single: Released Apr '79, on EMI, by EMI Records. Deleted Apr '82. Catalogue no: **EMI 2939**

THIRD MAN, THE
Tracks: / Third man, Theme from / Fourth man, The.
7" Single: Released May '81, on Polydor, by Polydor Ltd. Deleted May '84. Catalogue no: **POSP 255**

TREAT ME NICE
Tracks: / Treat me nice / Spot the ball.
7" Single: Released May '82, on Polydor, by Polydor Ltd. Deleted '85. Catalogue no: **POSP 439**

WAR LORD
Tracks: / War lord.
7" Single: Released Nov '65, on Columbia, by EMI Records. Deleted Nov '68. Catalogue no: **DB 7769**

WONDERFUL LAND
Tracks: / Wonderful land.
7" Single: Released Mar '62, on Columbia, by EMI Records. Deleted Mar '65. Catalogue no: **DB 4790**

Shadowshow

ECHOES
Tracks: / Echoes.
7" Single: Released Mar '84, on Original, Catalogue no: **7 TM 4**

SECURE IN YOU
Tracks: / Secure in you / Noonday kisses.
7" Single: Released Oct '83, on Original, Catalogue no: **7 TM 2**

Shadraak

SEND MY LOVE TO THE USA
Tracks: / Send my love to the USA.
7" Single: Released 23 Apr '88, on Aromi, Catalogue no: **001**

Shady

GET RIGHT NEXT TO YOU
Tracks: / Get right next to you.
12" Single: Released May '86, on Funkin' Marvellous, by Steinar Records (UK). Catalogue no: **12MARV 2**
7" Single: Released May '86, on Funkin' Marvellous, by Steinar Records (UK). Catalogue no: **7MARV 2**

Shaffer, Doreen

BABY LAY DOWN
Tracks: / Baby lay down.
7" Single: Released Jun '85, on Revue, by Creole Records. Catalogue no: **REV 024**

Shag

LOOP DI LOVE (OLD GOLD) (alias Jonathan King)
Tracks: / Loop di love / Lay it down.
7" Single: Released Jul '82, on Old Gold, by Old Gold Records. Deleted Jul '88. Catalogue no: **OG 9098**

LOOP DI LOVE (SINGLE) (alias Jonathan King)
Tracks: / Loop di love.
7" Single: Released Oct '72, on UK, by UK Records. Deleted Oct '75. Catalogue no: **UK 7**

Shaka, Jah

GIVER OF LIFE
Tracks: / Giver of life.
12" Single: Released Oct '87, on Jah Shaka, Catalogue no: **SHAKA 865**

Shakademus

REALITY
Tracks: / Reality.
12" Single: Released Feb '89, on Blue Mountain, Catalogue no: **BMD 048**

YOUNG GAL BUSINESS
Tracks: / Young gal business.
12" Single: Released May '88, on Skengdon, Catalogue no: **SKD 060**

Shakatak

BRAZILIAN DAWN
Tracks: / Brazilian dawn / You'll never know
12" Single: Released Jul '81, on Polydor, by Polydor Ltd. Deleted Jul '84. Catalogue no: **POSPX 282**
7" Single: Released Jul '81, on Polydor, by Polydor Ltd. Deleted Jul '84. Catalogue no

SHAKESPEAR'S SISTER - YOU'RE HISTORY (Released on Ffrr)

POSP 282

CITY RHYTHM
Tracks: / City rhythm.
12" Single: Released Aug '85, on Polydor, by Polydor Ltd. Catalogue no: **POSPX 754**
7" Single: Released Aug '85, on Polydor, by Polydor Ltd. Catalogue no: **POSP 754**

DARK IS THE NIGHT
Tracks: / Dark is the night.
7" Single: Released Jun '83, on Polydor, by Polydor Ltd. Deleted Jun '86. Catalogue no: **POSP 595**

DAY BY DAY (SINGLE)
Tracks: / Day by day.
12" Single: Released '85, on Polydor, by Polydor Ltd. Deleted Mar '87. Catalogue no: **POSPX 770**
7" Single: Released Nov '85, on Polydor, by Polydor Ltd. Deleted Nov '88. Catalogue no: **POSP 770**

DOCTOR DOCTOR
Tracks: / Doctor Doctor / Doctor Doctor (Critical mix) / Doctor Doctor (sulphuric mix).
12" Single: Released Apr '88, on Polydor, by Polydor Ltd. Catalogue no: **DTRX 1**
7" Single: Released Apr '88, on Polydor, by Polydor Ltd. Catalogue no: **DTR 1**

DON'T BLAME IT ON LOVE
Tracks: / Don't blame it on love.
7" Single: Released Sep '84, on Polydor, by Polydor Ltd. Deleted Sep '87. Catalogue no: **POSP 699**

DOWN ON THE STREET (SINGLE)
Tracks: / Down on the street / Holding on.
7" Single: Released Jul '84, on Polydor, by Polydor Ltd. Deleted Jul '87. Catalogue no: **POSP 688**

EASIER SAID THAN DONE
Tracks: / Easier said than done / Continental shelf.
7" Single: Released Nov '81, on Polydor, by Polydor Ltd. Deleted Nov '84. Catalogue no: **POSP 375**
12" Single: Released Nov '81, on Polydor, by Polydor Ltd. Deleted Nov '84. Catalogue no: **POSPX 375**

EASIER SAID THAN DONE (OLD GOLD)
Tracks: / Easier said than done / Nightbirds.
12" Single: Released Oct '88, on Old Gold, by Old Gold Records. Catalogue no: **OG 4079**

FEELS LIKE THE RIGHT TIME
Tracks: / Feels like the right time.
7" Single: Released Nov '80, on Polydor, by Polydor Ltd. Deleted Nov '83. Catalogue no: **POSP 188**

IF YOU COULD SEE ME NOW
Tracks: / If you could see me now.
7" Single: Released Aug '83, on Polydor, by Polydor Ltd. Deleted Aug '86. Catalogue no: **POSP 635**

INVITATIONS (SINGLE)
Tracks: / Invitations / In the shadows.
7" Single: Released Sep '82, on Polydor, by Polydor Ltd. Deleted Sep '85. Catalogue no: **POSP 502**
12" Single: Released Sep '82, on Polydor, by Polydor Ltd. Deleted Sep '85. Catalogue no: **POSPX 502**

LIVING IN THE UK
Tracks: / Living in the UK / Esperito.
12" Single: Released Mar '81, on Polydor, by Polydor Ltd. Deleted Mar '84. Catalogue no: **POSPX 230**
7" Single: Released Mar '81, on Polydor, by Polydor Ltd. Deleted Mar '84. Catalogue no: **POSP 230**

MR. MANIC & SISTER COOL
Tracks: / Mr. Manic & Sister Cool / One for Cara / Mr. Manic & Sister Cool(remix) / Mr. Manic & Sister Cool (alternative cool mix) (Only on 12" single).
12" Single: Released Sep '87, on Polydor, by Polydor Ltd. Catalogue no: **MANIX 1**
7" Single: Released Sep '87, on Polydor, by Polydor Ltd. Catalogue no: **MANIC 1**

NIGHT BIRDS (SINGLE)
Tracks: / Night birds / Rio nights.
7" Single: Released Apr '82, on Polydor, by Polydor Ltd. Deleted Apr '85. Catalogue no: **POSP 407**

SOMETHING SPECIAL
Tracks: / Something special / Cavalcante.
12" Single: Released 30 May '87, on Polydor, by Polydor Ltd. Deleted Jan '88. Catalogue no: **POSPX 863**
7" Single: Released 30 May '87, on Polydor, by Polydor Ltd. Deleted Jan '88. Catalogue no: **POSP 863**

STEPPIN'
Tracks: / Steppin' / Killing time.
7" Single: Released Aug '80, on Polydor, by Polydor Ltd. Deleted '83. Catalogue no: **POSP 163**
12" Single: Released Aug '80, on Polydor, by Polydor Ltd. Deleted '83. Catalogue no: **POSPX 163**

STRANGER
Tracks: / Stranger / Sol Fuego.
12" Single: Released Nov '82, on Polydor, by Polydor Ltd. Catalogue no: **POSPX 530**
7" Single: Released Nov '82, on Polydor, by Polydor Ltd. Catalogue no: **POSP 530**

STREETWALKIN'
Tracks: / Streetwalkin' / Go for it.
7" Single: Released Jun '82, on Polydor, by Polydor Ltd. Catalogue no: **POSP 452**
12" Single: Released Jun '82, on Polydor, by Polydor Ltd. Catalogue no: **POSPX 452**

TURN THE MUSIC UP
Tracks: / Turn the music up / Be bop.
7" Single: Released Jul '89, on Polydor, by Polydor Ltd. Catalogue no: **PO 49**
12" Single: Released Jul '89, on Polydor, by Polydor Ltd. Catalogue no: **PZ 49**
CD 5": Released Jul '89, on Polydor, by Polydor Ltd. Catalogue no: **PZCD 49**

Shake

INVASION OF THE GAMMA MEN
Tracks: / Invasion of the gamma men / Night by night.
7" Single: Released Feb '80, on Sire, by Sire Records. Deleted '83. Catalogue no: **SIR 4035**

Shake Appeal

GIMME FEVER
Tracks: / Gimme fever.
7" Single: Released '88, on Notown, Catalogue no: **NO 002**

MY OWN WAY
Tracks: / My own way / Not interested.
7" Single: Released May '90, on Rockburgh, Deleted '85. Catalogue no: **ROCS 223**

Shakers

MISSING LINK EP
Cassingle: Released '87, on Waterfront, by Waterfront Music. Catalogue no: **WFT 25C**
12" Single: Released '87, on Waterfront, by Waterfront Music. Catalogue no: **WFT 25**

TEMPTATION WALK
Tracks: / Temptation walk / Catch on / Respect.
7" Single: Released Feb '84, on Waterfront, by Waterfront Music. Catalogue no: **WFSS 003**

Shakespeare, Maria

JOEY'S SONGBOOK
Tracks: / Joey's songbook / Joey's songbook (dub).
12" Single: Released Jun '86, on Dean's, Catalogue no: **MEI 0001**

Shakespear's Sister

BREAK MY HEART
Tracks: / Break my heart (you really) / Break my heart (you really) (extended version) (Only on the 12" single and CD single.) / Break my heart (you really) (acidic mix).
12" Single: Released Oct '88, on London Records, by London Records. Deleted May '89. Catalogue no: **LONXR 200**
CD 5": Released Oct '88, on London Records, by London Records. Catalogue no: **LONCD 200**
7" Single: Released Oct '88, on London Records, by London Records. Deleted May '89. Catalogue no: **LON 200**
12" Single: Released Oct '88, on London Records, by London Records. Deleted May '89. Catalogue no: **LONX 200**

RUN SILENT
Tracks: / Run silent / Mr. Wrong / Run silent (deep mix) (On 12" and CD only).
7" Single: Released Sep '89, on ffrr, by London Records. Catalogue no: **F 119**
Cassingle: Released Sep '89, on ffrr, by London Records. Catalogue no: **FCS 119**
12" Single: Released Sep '89, on ffrr, by London Records. Catalogue no: **FX 119**
CD 5": Released Sep '89, on ffrr, by London Records. Catalogue no: **FCD 119**

YOU'RE HISTORY (see panel top left)
Tracks: / You're history / Dirty mind / Herione.
CD 5": Released 17 Jul '89, on ffrr, by London Records. Catalogue no: **FCD 112**
12" Single: Released 17 Jul '89, on ffrr, by London Records. Catalogue no: **FX 112**
Cassingle: Released 17 Jul '89, on ffrr, by London Records. Catalogue no: **FCS 112**
7" Single: Released 17 Jul '89, on ffrr, by London Records. Catalogue no: **F 112**

Shakin' Pyramids

CUMBERLAND GAP
Tracks: / Cumberland gap / Wabash cannonball / Don't you rock me daddy-o / Only my pillow.
7" EP: Released Nov '81, on Virgin, by Virgin Records. Deleted '89. Catalogue no: **VS 460**

JUST A MEMORY
Tracks: / Just a memory / Who cares.
7" Single: Released Jun '82, on Virgin, by Virgin Records. Deleted '89. Catalogue no: **VS 505**

PHAROAH'S CHANT
Tracks: / Pharoah's chant / Just one time.
7" Single: Released Mar '82, on Virgin, by Virgin Records. Deleted '85. Catalogue no: **VS 461**

TAKE A TRIP
Tracks: / Take a trip / Hellbent on rockin' / Wake up little Susie / Reeferbilly boogie.
7" EP: Released Mar '81, on Cuba Libre, by Virgin Records. Deleted '89. Catalogue no: **VS 404**

TENNESSEE ROCK 'N' ROLL
Tracks: / Tennessee rock'n'roll.
7" Single: Released May '81, on Virgin, by Virgin Records. Deleted '89. Catalogue no: **VS 415**

Shakin' Street

SUSIE WONG
Tracks: / Susie Wong / Every man, every woman is a star.
7" Single: Released Apr '80, on CBS, by CBS Records. Deleted Apr '83. Catalogue no: **CBS 8512**

Shakti

FORBIDDEN DREAMS
Tracks: / Forbidden dreams.
12" Single: Released Apr '88, on Subway, by Subway Records. Catalogue no: **SUB 006**

Shaky & Bonnie

ROCKIN' GOOD WAY
Tracks: / Rockin' good way, A.
7" Pic: Released Jan '84, on Epic, by CBS Records. Catalogue no: **WA 4071**
12" Single: Released Jan '84, on Epic, by CBS Records. Catalogue no: **TA 4071**
7" Single: Released Jan '84, on Epic, by CBS Records. Catalogue no: **A 4071**

Shalamar

CIRCUMSTANTIAL EVIDENCE (SINGLE)
Tracks: / Circumstantial evidence.
7" Single: Released Aug '87, on MCA, by MCA Records. Catalogue no: **SHAL 6**
12" Single: Released Aug '87, on MCA, by MCA Records. Catalogue no: **SHALT 6**

DANCING IN THE STREETS
Tracks: / Dancing in the streets.

SHALAMAR - DEAD GIVE AWAY (Released on Solar)

12" Single: Released Jun '84, on CBS, by CBS Records. Catalogue no: **TA 4171**
7" Single: Released Jun '84, on CBS, by CBS Records. Catalogue no: **A 4171**

DEAD GIVEAWAY
Tracks: / Dead giveaway / I don't wanna be the last to know.
7" Single: Released Jun '83, on Solar Records, Deleted Jun '86. Catalogue no: **E 9818**

DEADLINE USA
Tracks: / Deadline USA / Knock me off my feet.
7" Single: Released Mar '84, on MCA, by MCA Records. Catalogue no: **MCA 866**
12" Single: Released Mar '84, on MCA, by MCA Records. Catalogue no: **MCAT 866**

DISAPPEARING ACT
Tracks: / Disappearing act.
7" Single: Released Aug '83, on Solar Records, Deleted Aug '86. Catalogue no: **E 9807**

FRIENDS (SINGLE)
Tracks: / Friends / I just stopped because I had to.
7" Single: Released Nov '82, on Solar Records, Deleted Nov '85. Catalogue no: **CHUM 1**

I CAN MAKE YOU FEEL GOOD
Tracks: / I can make you feel good / Help me.
7" Single: Released Mar '82, on Solar Records, Deleted Feb '85. Catalogue no: **K 12599**

I OWE YOU ONE
Tracks: / I owe you one / Right time for us.
7" Single: Released Aug '80, on Solar Records, Deleted Aug '83. Catalogue no: **SO 11**

MAKE THAT MOVE
Tracks: / Make that move / Pop along kid.
7" Single: Released Mar '81, on Solar Records, Deleted Mar '84. Catalogue no: **SO 17**
12" Single: Released Mar '81, on Solar Records, Deleted Mar '84. Catalogue no: **SOT 17**

MY GIRL LOVES ME
Tracks: / My girl loves me.
7" Single: Released Jan '85, on MCA, by MCA Records. Catalogue no: **SHAL 2**
12" Single: Released Jan '85, on MCA, by MCA Records. Catalogue no: **SHALT 2**

NIGHT TO REMEMBER
Tracks: / Night to remember / Take that to the bank / Uptown festival / I can make you feel good.
7" Single: Released Jun '82, on Solar Records, Deleted Jun '85. Catalogue no: **K 13162**
12" Single: Released 30 May '87, on I.R.S, Catalogue no: **SHALT 5**
7" Single: Released 30 May '87, on I.R.S, Catalogue no: **SHAL 5**

NIGHT TO REMEMBER,A (RE-MIX)
Tracks: / Night to remember (re-mix).
7" Single: Released Apr '86, on MCA, by MCA Records. Catalogue no: **SHAL 3**

NIGHT TO REMEMBER (OLD GOLD)
Tracks: / Night to remember.
12" Single: Released Jul '89, on Old Gold, by Old Gold Records. Catalogue no: **OG 4059**

OVER AND OVER
Tracks: / Over and over.
7" Single: Released Oct '83, on Solar Records, Deleted Oct '86. Catalogue no: **E 9792**

RIGHT IN THE SOCKET
Tracks: / Right in the socket / Right time for us.
7" Single: Released Feb '80, on Solar Records, Deleted Feb '83. Catalogue no: **SO 2**
12" Single: Released Feb '80, on Solar Records, Deleted Feb '83. Catalogue no: **SO 12 2**

SECOND TIME AROUND, THE
Tracks: / Second time around.
7" Single: Released Nov '79, on Solar Records, Deleted Nov '82. Catalogue no: **FB 1709**

SWEETER AS THE DAYS GO BY
Tracks: / Sweeter as the days go by / Final analysis.
12" Single: Released Oct '81, on Solar (USA), by MCA Records. Catalogue no: **SOT 23**
7" Single: Released Nov '81, on Solar (USA), by MCA Records. Catalogue no: **SO 23**

TAKE THAT TO THE BANK
Tracks: / Take that to the bank (M & M Mix) / Right in the socket / Right in the socket (Original US 12") (On 12" version only.) / Take that to the band (Original US 12") (On 12" version only.).
7" Single: Released Aug '86, on MCA, by MCA Records. Catalogue no: **SHAL 4**
7" Single: Released Dec '78, on RCA, by BMG Records (UK). Deleted Dec '81. Catalogue no: **FB 1379**
12" Single: Released Aug '86, on MCA, by MCA Records. Catalogue no: **SHALT 4**

TAKE THAT TO THE BANK (OLD GOLD)
Tracks: / Take that to the bank / I owe you one.
12" Single: Released 30 May '89, on Old Gold, by Old Gold Records. Catalogue no: **OG 4115**

TALK TO ME
Tracks: / Talk to me / Appeal.
12" Single: Released Jan '82, on Solar (USA), by MCA Records. Catalogue no: **SOT 24**
7" Single: Released Jan '82, on Solar (USA), by MCA Records. Deleted Feb '87. Catalogue no: **SO 24**

THERE IT IS
Tracks: / There it is / I don't wanna be the last to know.
7" Single: Released Sep '82, on Solar Records, Deleted Sep '85. Catalogue no: **K 13194**

THERE IT IS (OLD GOLD)
Tracks: / There it is / Friends.
12" Single: Released May '88, on Old Gold, by Old Gold Records. Catalogue no: **OG 4066**

UPTOWN FESTIVAL
Tracks: / Uptown festival / Take that to the bank.
12" Single: Released Jun '81, on Solar (USA), by MCA Records. Catalogue no: **GOLDT 515**
7" Single: Released May '77, on Soul Train, Deleted May '80. Catalogue no: **FB 0885**
7" Single: Released Jul '81, on Solar (USA), by MCA Records. Catalogue no: **GOLD 515**

WORK IT OUT
Tracks: / Work it out / Somewhere there's a love.
12" Single: Released May '82, on Solar (USA), by MCA Records. Catalogue no: **SOT 21**
7" Single: Released May '82, on Solar (USA), by MCA Records. Catalogue no: **SO 21**

Shalobberdop Twins

FAMOUS MAN
Tracks: / Famous man.
7" Single: Released Nov '84, on Riviera (1), Catalogue no: **SEA 3**

Sha-Lor

SO IN LOVE
Tracks: / So in love.
7" Single: Released Jul '89, on RCA, by BMG Records (UK). Catalogue no: **ZB 42891**
12" Single: Released Jul '89, on RCA, by BMG Records (UK). Catalogue no: **ZT 42892**

Sham 69

ANGELS WITH DIRTY FACES (SINGLE)
Tracks: / Angels with dirty faces / Borstal breakout.
7" Single: Released May '78, on Polydor, by Polydor Ltd. Deleted May '81. Catalogue no: **2059 023**
12" Single: Released Nov '82, on Polydor, by Polydor Ltd. Deleted Nov '85. Catalogue no: **POSPX 602**

HERSHAM BOYS
Tracks: / Hersham boys.
7" Single: Released Aug '79, on Polydor, by Polydor Ltd. Deleted Aug '82. Catalogue no: **POSP 64**

HURRY UP HARRY
Tracks: / Hurry up Harry.
7" Single: Released Oct '78, on Polydor, by Polydor Ltd. Deleted Oct '81. Catalogue no: **POSP 7**

I DON'T WANNA
Tracks: / I don't wanna.
7" Single: Released Oct '79, on Step Forward, by Faulty Products Records. Catalogue no: **SF 4**
12" Single: Released Oct '77, on Step Forward, by Faulty Products Records. Catalogue no: **SF 412**

IF THE KIDS ARE UNITED
Tracks: / If the kids are united.
7" Single: Released Jul '78, on Polydor, by Polydor Ltd. Deleted Jul '81. Catalogue no: **2059 050**

OUTSIDE THE WAREHOUSE
Tracks: / Outside the warehouse / Outside the warehouse (version) / How the west was one (Extra track on 12").
7" Single: Released Feb '88, on Legacy, by Legacy Records. Catalogue no: **LGY 71**
12" Single: Released Feb '88, on Legacy, by Legacy Records. Catalogue no: **LGYT 71**

QUESTIONS AND ANSWERS
Tracks: / Questions and answers.
7" Single: Released Mar '79, on Polydor, by Polydor Ltd. Deleted Mar '82. Catalogue no: **POSP 27**

RIP AND TEAR
Tracks: / Rip and tear.
7" Single: Released Aug '87, on Legacy, by Legacy Records. Catalogue no: **LGY 69**

TELL THE CHILDREN
Tracks: / Tell the children / Jack.
7" Single: Released Mar '80, on Polydor, by Polydor Ltd. Catalogue no: **POSP 136**

YOU'RE A BETTER MAN THAN I
Tracks: / You're a better man than I.
7" Single: Released Oct '79, on Polydor, by Polydor Ltd. Deleted Oct '82. Catalogue no: **POSP 82**

Shambeko Say Wah!

REMEMBER (A CRACK IS A CRACK)
Tracks: / Remember (a crack is a crack).
7" Single: Released Apr '82, on Eternal, by Eternal Records. Catalogue no: **ZAZU 1**
12" Single: Released Apr '82, on Eternal, by Eternal Records. Catalogue no: **ZAZU 1T**

Shame

SHAME, THE
Tracks: / Shame, The (EP).
12" Single: Released Jul '86, on Shake The Label, Catalogue no: **SIW 001**

Shamen

CHRISTOPHER MAYHEW SAYS
Tracks: / Christopher Mayhew says / Shitting on Britain / Fire engine.
7" Single: Released Sep '87, on Moksha, by Moksha Records. Catalogue no: **SOMA 3**
12" Single: Released Sep '87, on Moksha, by Moksha Records. Catalogue no: **SOMA 3T**

JESUS LOVES AMERIKA
Tracks: / Jesus loves Amerika.
CD 5": Released Jun '88, on Ediesta, Catalogue no: **CALC 069CD**
12" Single: Released '88, on Ediesta, Catalogue no: **CALC 069T**
7" Single: Released '88, on Ediesta, Catalogue no: **CALC 069**

NATURE OF A GIRL
Tracks: / Nature of a girl.
12" Single: Released 20 Feb '88, on Moksha, by Moksha Records. Catalogue no: **SOMA 4T**
7" Single: Released 20 Feb '88, on Moksha, by Moksha Records. Catalogue no: **SOMA 4**

OMEGA AMIGO
Tracks: / Omega amigo.
12" Single: Released Oct '89, on One Little Indian, by One Little Indian Records. Catalogue no: **TP 12030**
CD 5": Released Oct '89, on One Little Indian, by One Little Indian Records. Catalogue no: **TP 7030CD**

SOMETHING ABOUT YOU
Tracks: / Something about you.
7" Single: Released 23 May '87, on Moksha, by Moksha Records. Catalogue no: **SOMA 2**
12" Single: Released 23 May '87, on Moksha, by Moksha Records. Catalogue no: **SOMA 2T**

THEY MAY BE RIGHT
Tracks: / They may be right.
12" Single: Released Apr '86, on One Big Guitar, by One Big Guitar Records. Catalogue no: **OBG 003 T**

TRANSCENDENTAL
Tracks: / Transcendental / Transcendental (house mix).
12" Single: Released Nov '88, on Desire, by Desire Records. Catalogue no: **WANTX 10**

YOU, ME AND EVERYTHING
Tracks: / You, me and everything.
CD 5": Released 28 Mar '89, on Moksha, by Moksha Records. Catalogue no: **SOMA 6 CD**
7" Single: Released 28 Mar '89, on Moksha, by Moksha Records. Catalogue no: **SOMA 6**
12" Single: Released 28 Mar '89, on Moksha, by Moksha Records. Catalogue no: **SOMA 6 T**

YOUNG 'TIL YESTERDAY
Tracks: / Young 'til yesterday / World theatre / Golden hair / Strange day dream / It's all around.
7" Single: Released Nov '86, on Moksha, by Moksha Records. Catalogue no: **SOMA 1**
12" Single: Released Nov '86, on Moksha, by Moksha Records. Catalogue no: **SOMA 1T**

Shampoo

EVERLASTING (2 PARTS)
Tracks: / Everlasting (part 1) / Everlasting (part 2).
7" Single: Released Aug '81, on Arrival, by Blaylock Management Ltd.. Deleted '86. Catalogue no: **PIK 5**
12" Single: Released Aug '81, on Arrival, by Blaylock Management Ltd.. Deleted '86. Catalogue no: **12PIK 5**

Shan, M.C.

I PIONEERED THIS
Tracks: / I pioneered this.
7" Single: Released Oct '88, on Cold Chillin', by Cold Chillin' Records. Catalogue no: **0-21079**

Shand, Jimmy

BLUEBELL POLKA
Tracks: / Bluebell polka.
7" Single: Released Dec '55, on Parlophone, by EMI Records. Deleted Dec '58. Catalogue no: **F 3436**

Shandi

NOBODY LOVES YOU BETTER
Tracks: / Nobody loves you better / Mine.
7" Single: Released Aug '80, on Dreamland, Deleted '83. Catalogue no: **DLSP 2**

Shandileer

HAPPY
Tracks: / Happy.
12" Single: Released May '88, on Hot Vinyl, Catalogue no: **HVT 51**

Shane, Paul

HI DE HI
Tracks: / Hi de hi / Holiday rock / Juke box / Saturday night.
7" EP: Released Dec '81, on BBC, by BBC Records & Tapes. Deleted Dec '84. Catalogue no: **RESL 103**

HI DE HI (HOLIDAY ROCK)
Tracks: / Hi de hi (holiday rock) / Juke box saturday night.
7" Single: Released May '81, on Parlophone, by EMI Records. Deleted May '84. Catalogue no: **F 3436**
7" Single: Released May '81, on EMI, by EMI Records. Deleted May '84. Catalogue no: **EMI 5180**

Shanghai Syncopated...

SHANGHAI
Tracks: / Shanghai / Vo-do-do-de-o.
7" Single: Released Dec '82, on Playfar, by Playfar Records. Deleted Dec '85. Catalogue no: **GSM 108202**

Shango

SHANGO MESSAGE
Tracks: / Shango message / Thank you.
12" Single: Released Aug '84, on Carrere, Catalogue no: **CART 341**

Shangri-Las

Biographical details:
The Shangri-Las were an influential girl group with 11 USA hits '64-6, a milestone in pop both for the records and for their live act: lead vocalist Betty Weiss, sister Mbary Weiss, twins Marge and Mary Ann Ganser had an image that was a cross between cheerleaders and biker's molls, a not-so-virgin queen with streetwise ladies-in-waiting, and their vocal style is still being parodied. Their hits were produced by George 'Shadow' Morton, the biggest being *Leader Of The Pack* at no.1, with revving motorcycles dubbed in and a horrific crash at the end: it inspired a Top 20 send-up in *Leader Of The Laundramat* by the Detergents. (Donald Clarke)..

LEADER OF THE PACK
Tracks: / Leader of the pack / Give him a great big kiss.
7" Single: Released Jun '76, on Contempo, Deleted Jun '79. Catalogue no: **CS 9032**
7" Single: Released Jan '65, on Red Bird, by Charly Records. Deleted Jan '68. Catalogue no: **RB 10014**
7" Single: Released Oct '80, on Phonogram, by Phonogram Ltd. Deleted Oct '83. Catalogue no: **CUT 112**
7" Single: Released '80, on Charly, by Charly Records. Deleted '88. Catalogue no: **CYS 1009**
7" Single: Released Oct '72, on Kama Sutra, by Buddah Records Inc.(USA). Deleted Oct '75. Catalogue no: **2013 024**

LEADER OF THE PACK (OLD GOLD)
Tracks: / Leader of the pack / Remember (walking in the sand) / Chapel of love.
CD 5": Released 27 Feb '89, on Old Gold, by Old Gold Records. Catalogue no: **OG 6114**
7" Single: Released Jun '88, on Old Gold, by Old Gold Records. Catalogue no: **OG 9085**

REMEMBER (WALKING IN THE SAND) (CD EP)
Tracks: / Remember (walking in the sand) /

Leader of the pack / Give him a great big kiss / Past, present and future.
CD 5": Released Feb '89, on Charly, by Charly Records. Catalogue no: **CDS 3**

REMEMBER (WALKING IN THE SAND) (SINGLE)
Tracks: / Remember (walking in the sand).
7" Single: Released Oct '64, on Red Bird, by Charly Records. Deleted Oct '67. Catalogue no: **RB 10008**

Shani

LOVING THAT YOU WANT
Tracks: / Loving that you want.
12" Single: Released Jul '88, on Gyas, Catalogue no: **GA 021**

Shankar, Ravi

Biographical details:
Virtuoso sitar player Ravi Shankar was born in 1920 in Benares, India. He worked in Indian radio 1949-56, went to the USA and lectured in the mid-1960s at universities there; when Beatle George Harrison played sitar on *Norwegian Wood* '65, his teacher had been Shankar. The sitar became a fad in rock; Shankar played at the Woodstock Festival 1969 and in George Harrison's *Concert For Bangla Desh* 1971; as the sitar in rock became associated with drugs in the public mind, Shankar gracefully withdreww from the scene. He is a best-selling classical artist in India; there is a two-disc set of ragas on Fantasy USA. (Donald Clarke)..

HIMALAYA
Tracks: / Himalaya.
7" Single: Released Jul '82, on WEA, by WEA Records. Catalogue no: **K 19238**

Shannon

DANCIN'
Tracks: / Dancin' / Faces in the crowd.
12" Single: Released Apr '87, on Club, by Phonogram Ltd. Deleted Dec '87. Catalogue no: **JABX 50**
7" Single: Released Apr '87, on Club, by Phonogram Ltd. Deleted Dec '87. Catalogue no: **JAB 50**

GIVE ME TONIGHT
Tracks: / Give me tonight.
7" Single: Released Apr '84, on Club, by Phonogram Ltd. Deleted Apr '87. Catalogue no: **JAB 1**

LET THE MUSIC PLAY
Tracks: / Let the music play.
7" Single: Released Jan '84, on Club, by Phonogram Ltd. Deleted Jan '87. Catalogue no: **LET 112**
7" Single: Released Nov '83, on Club, by Phonogram Ltd. Deleted Nov '86. Catalogue no: **LET 1**

LET THE MUSIC PLAY (OLD GOLD)
Tracks: / Let the music play / Give me tonight.
12" Single: Released Feb '88, on Old Gold, by Old Gold Records. Catalogue no: **OG 4048**

STRONGER TOGETHER
Tracks: / Stronger together.
7" Single: Released Jul '85, on Club, by Phonogram Ltd. Deleted Jul '88. Catalogue no: **JAB 15**

SWEET SOMEBODY
Tracks: / Sweet somebody.
7" Single: Released Jun '84, on Club, by Phonogram Ltd. Deleted Jun '87. Catalogue no: **JAB 3**

Shannon, Del

Biographical details:
Rock'n'roll singer and songwriter Del Shannon was born 30 December 1939 in Michigan. Like most of the best singer/songwriters in rock'n'roll, he was influenced by country music, especially Hank Williams. His first hit was *Runaway*, no.1 in the USA in 1961, notable for one of the early uses of the musitron, and early synthesier. He had 15 more hits through 1966 and was popular in the UK, where he had eight top 10 hits; he was also the first artist to cover a Beatles song (*From Me T You*). His falsetto and his songwriting were influential; he was one of the first to write his own hits. He later worked with Dave Edmunds and Nick Lowe, among others. [Donald Clarke, April 87].

CHEAP LOVE
Tracks: / Cheap love.
7" Single: Released May '83, on Demon, by Demon Records. Catalogue no: **D 1017**

CRY MYSELF TO SLEEP
Tracks: / Cry myself to sleep.
7" Single: Released Sep '62, on London-American, Deleted Sep '65. Catalogue no: **HLX 9587**

HANDYMAN
Tracks: / Handyman.
7" Single: Released Jul '64, on Stateside, by EMI Records. Deleted Jul '67. Catalogue no: **SS 317**

HATS OFF TO LARRY
Tracks: / Hats off to Larry.
7" Single: Released Sep '61, on London-American, Deleted Sep '64. Catalogue no: **HLX 9402**

HATS OFF TO LARRY (OLD GOLD)
Tracks: / Hats off to Larry / Hey little girl.
7" Single: Released '88, on Old Gold, by Old Gold Records. Catalogue no: **OG 7257**

HATS OFF TO LARRY (RE-RELEASE)
Tracks: / Hats off to Larry / Little town flirt.
7" Single: Released Mar '82, on Juke Box (Re-issue), Deleted '85. Catalogue no: **JB 05**

HEY LITTLE GIRL
Tracks: / Hey little girl.
7" Single: Released Mar '62, on London-American, Deleted Mar '65. Catalogue no: **HLX 9515**

KEEP SEARCHIN' (OLD GOLD)
Tracks: / Keep searchin'.
7" Single: Released Apr '83, on Old Gold, by Old Gold Records. Catalogue no: **OG 9260**

KEEP SEARCHIN' (WE'LL FOLLOW THE SUN)
Tracks: / Keep searchin'.
7" Single: Released Jan '65, on Stateside, by EMI Records. Deleted Jan '68. Catalogue no: **SS 368**

LITTLE TOWN FLIRT (OLD GOLD)
Tracks: / Little town flirt.
7" Single: Released Apr '83, on Old Gold, by Old Gold Records. Deleted Jul '88. Catalogue no: **OG 9259**

LITTLE TOWN FLIRT (SINGLE)
Tracks: / Little town flirt.
7" Single: Released Jan '63, on London-American, Deleted Jan '66. Catalogue no: **HLX 9653**

MARY JANE
Tracks: / Mary Jane.
7" Single: Released Mar '64, on Stateside, by EMI Records. Deleted Mar '67. Catalogue no: **SS 269**

RUNAWAY (OLD GOLD)
Tracks: / Runaway / Hats off to Larry / Keep searchin' (Available on CD single only.) / Rubber ball.
7" Single: Released Jun '88, on Old Gold, by Old Gold Records. Catalogue no: **OG 9256**
CD 5": Released 27 Feb '89, on Old Gold, by Old Gold Records. Catalogue no: **OG 6113**

RUNAWAY (SINGLE)
Tracks: / Runaway / Jody / Hats off to Larry / Rubber ball..
7" Single: Released Aug '82, on Blast From The Past, by Creole Records. Catalogue no: **CR 196**
7" Single: Released Mar '81, on London-American, Catalogue no: **HL 10580**
7" Single: Released Apr '61, on London-American, Deleted Apr '64. Catalogue no: **HLX 9317**
7" Single: Released Jun '80, on JB, Deleted '84. Catalogue no: **JB 01**

SEA OF LOVE
Tracks: / Sea of love.
7" Single: Released Nov '83, on Demon, by Demon Records. Catalogue no: **D 1019**

SO LONG BABY
Tracks: / So long baby.
7" Single: Released Dec '61, on London-American, Deleted Dec '64. Catalogue no: **HLX 9462**

STRANGER IN TOWN
Tracks: / Stranger in town.
7" Single: Released Mar '65, on Stateside, by EMI Records. Deleted Mar '68. Catalogue no: **SS 395**

SUE'S GOTTA BE MINE
Tracks: / Sue's gotta be mine.
7" Single: Released Oct '63, on London-American, Deleted Oct '66. Catalogue no: **HLU 9800**

SWISS MAID (OLD GOLD)
Tracks: / Swiss maid.
7" Single: Released Apr '83, on Old Gold, by Old Gold Records. Catalogue no: **OG 9258**

SWISS MAID (SINGLE)
Tracks: / Swiss maid.
7" Single: Released Oct '62, on London-American, Deleted Oct '65. Catalogue no: **HLX 9609**

TWO KINDS OF TEARDROPS (SINGLE)
Tracks: / Two kinds of teardrops.
7" Single: Released Apr '63, on London-American, Deleted Apr '66. Catalogue no: **HLX 9710**

TWO SILHOUETTES (SINGLE)
Tracks: / Two silhouettes.
7" Single: Released Aug '63, on London-American, Deleted Aug '66. Catalogue no: **HLX 9761**

Shante, Roxanne

BITE THIS
Tracks: / Bite this.
7" Single: Released Nov '85, on 10 Records, by Virgin Records. Deleted '89. Catalogue no: **TEN 88**

GO ON GIRL
Tracks: / Go on girl / Have a nice day.
7" Single: Released Jun '88, on Breakout, by A&M Records. Catalogue no: **USA 633**
12" Single: Released Jun '88, on Breakout, by A&M Records. Deleted Feb '89. Catalogue no: **USAF 633**
12" Single: Released Jun '88, on Breakout, by A&M Records. Deleted Feb '89. Catalogue no: **USAT 633**

HAVE A NICE DAY
Tracks: / Have a nice day / Have a nice day (inst).
7" Single: Released Jul '87, on Breakout, by A&M Records. Deleted Feb '89. Catalogue no: **USA 612**
12" Single: Released Jul '87, on Breakout, by A&M Records. Deleted Feb '89. Catalogue no: **USAT 612**

LIVE ON STAGE
Tracks: / Live on stage.
12" Single: Released Sep '89, on A&M, by A&M Records. Catalogue no: **USAT 669**
7" Single: Released Sep '89, on A&M, by A&M Records. Catalogue no: **USA 669**

Shapiro, Helen

Biographical details:
Helen Shapiro was born in Bethnal Green in 1946 and had her first hit at the age of 13, becoming one of the biggest pop stars of the immediately pre-Beatle era. She had eleven hits between 1961 and 1964, including two chart toppers, and starred in films *It's Trad, Dad* (directed by Richard Lester) and *Play It Cool* (by Michael Winner), both in 1962. She was succesful in clubs, then turned to the stage, including a revival of Lionel Bart's *Oliver!*; more recently she has gigged with Humphrey Lyttleton and George Melley. (Donald Clarke)..

BRICKYARD BLUES
Tracks: / Brickyard blues.
7" Single: Released Jan '84, on Oval, by Oval Records. Catalogue no: **OVAL 26**

CRY ME A RIVER
Tracks: / Cry me a river.
10" single: Released Apr '83, on Oval, by Oval Records. Catalogue no: **HELEN 25/10**

DON'T TREAT ME LIKE A CHILD
Tracks: / Don't treat me like a child.
7" Single: Released Mar '61, on Columbia, by EMI Records. Deleted Mar '64. Catalogue no: **DB 4589**

FEVER
Tracks: / Fever.
7" Single: Released Jan '64, on Columbia, by EMI Records. Deleted Jan '67. Catalogue no: **DB 7190**

KEEP AWAY FROM OTHER GIRLS
Tracks: / Keep away from other girls.
7" Single: Released Oct '62, on Columbia, by EMI Records. Deleted Oct '65. Catalogue no: **DB 4908**

LET YOURSELF GO
Tracks: / Let yourself go.
7" Single: Released Apr '83, on Oval, by Oval Records. Catalogue no: **HELEN 25**

LET'S TALK ABOUT LOVE
Tracks: / Let's talk about love.
7" Single: Released May '62, on Columbia, by EMI Records. Deleted May '65. Catalogue no: **DB 4824**

LITTLE MISS LONELY
Tracks: / Little miss lonely.
7" Single: Released Jul '62, on Columbia, by EMI Records. Deleted Jul '65. Catalogue no: **DB 4869**

LOOK WHO IT IS
Tracks: / Look who it is.
7" Single: Released Oct '63, on Columbia, by EMI Records. Deleted Oct '66. Catalogue no: **DB 7130**

QUEEN FOR TONIGHT
Tracks: / Queen for tonight.
7" Single: Released Feb '63, on Columbia, by EMI Records. Deleted Feb '66. Catalogue no: **DB 4966**

TELL ME WHAT HE SAID
Tracks: / Tell me what he said.
7" Single: Released Feb '62, on Columbia, by EMI Records. Deleted Feb '65. Catalogue no: **DB 4782**

WALKING BACK TO HAPPINESS
Tracks: / Walkin' back to happiness.
7" Single: Released Jul '84, on EMI (Holland), by EMI Records. Catalogue no: **1A 006 05198**
7" Single: Released Sep '61, on Columbia, by EMI Records. Deleted Sep '64. Catalogue no: **DB 4715**

WALKING BACK TO HAPPINESS (2)
Tracks: / Walking back to happiness / Let's talk about love.
7" Single: Released Sep '89, on Calligraph, Catalogue no: **CLGS 702**

WOE IS ME
Tracks: / Woe is me.
7" Single: Released Apr '63, on Columbia, by EMI Records. Deleted Apr '66. Catalogue no: **DB 7026**

YOU DON'T KNOW
Tracks: / You don't know.
7" Single: Released Jun '61, on Columbia, by EMI Records. Deleted Jun '64. Catalogue no: **DB 4670**

YOU DON'T KNOW (OLD GOLD)
Tracks: / You don't know.
7" Single: Released Oct '83, on Old Gold, by Old Gold Records. Deleted Sep '89. Catalogue no: **OG 9370**

Shapiros

ISOLADE
Tracks: / Isolade.
7" Single: Released Nov '79, on North Of Watford, by North Of Watford Records. Catalogue no: **N 702**

PERISHED LEATHER
Tracks: / Perished leather.
12" Single: Released Mar '85, on Swim, Catalogue no: **MAQB 001**

Shar

JUNIOR JACKIN'
Tracks: / Junior jackin' / Junior jackin' (dub mix).
12" Single: Released Mar '87, on Debut, by Skratch Records. Catalogue no: **DEBTX 3016**

Shara

CAN'T GET OVER YOU
Tracks: / Can't get over you.
7" Single: Released Mar '86, on Unit 7, by Greensleeves Records. Catalogue no: **UNST 1**

Sharazade

REFLECTIONS
Tracks: / Reflections / Move your seat.
12" Single: Released Mar '83, on Code, by Code Records. Catalogue no: **12COD 006**
7" Single: Released Mar '83, on Code, by Code Records. Catalogue no: **COD 006**

Sharing The House..

STAR WARS
Tracks: / Star Wars.
12" Single: Released Jul '86, on Adventures In Clubland, Catalogue no: **AICT 1**

Shark Taboo

BIG SELL, THE
Tracks: / Big sell, The.
7" Single: Released Oct '85, on Crisis, by Prism Records. Deleted '88. Catalogue no: **CSS 2**

CAGE (EP)
Tracks: / Cage / Pulse in time / Scrap heap.
7" Single: Released May '85, on Lambs To The Slaughter, by Prism Records. Catalogue no: **LTS 3**

COME IN FROM THE COLD
Tracks: / Come in from the cold.
12" Single: Released Feb '89, on Plastic Head, by Plastic Head Records. Catalogue no: **PLASS 009**

SEEDS OF A LUNATIC
Tracks: / Seeds of a lunatic.
7" Single: Released Nov '85, on Crisis, by Prism Records. Deleted '88. Catalogue no: **CSS 3**

TROINEANN - SIAD
Tracks: / Troineann - siad.
7" Single: Released Nov '84, on Lambs To The Slaughter, by Prism Records. Catalogue no: **TEETH 4U**

Shark Vegas

YOU HURT ME (SINGLE)
Tracks: / You hurt me.
12" Single: Released Sep '85, on Factory (1), by Factory Records. Catalogue no: **FAC 111**

Sharkey, Feargal

Biographical details: Sharkey is a rock singer who was born in '58 in Londonderry,

Northern Ireland. He began with the Undertones, formed in Derry '77 with John and Damian O'Neill on guitars, Michael Bradley on bass, drummer Billy Doherty; John Peel championed them on the radio and *Teenage Kicks* was a minor hit in 1978: their appeal was that they were a quintessential pop band during the earnest trashiness of the punk era. The O'Neills were good songwriters; the band's biggest hit was *My Perfect Cousin*(Top 10), but fans and critics wouldn't let them grow up and they split in 1983. (The O'Neills formed That Petrol Emotion, made singles *Keen* and *V2* in 1985, well-received album *Manic Pop Thrill* in 1986.) Sharkey worked with Vince Clarke in Assembly (had top 5 hit in 1983 with *Never Never*), had solo top 30 hit in 1984 with funky *Listen To Your Father*, his debut solo LP *Feargal Sharkey* in 1985 sold two million copies around the world (compared to total Undertones sales of perhaps 250,000), including no. 1 hit in UK with *Lone Justice* song *A Good Heart*. He worked with Dave Stewart of the Eurhythmics, appeared in Bob Dylans videos in 1985; he has one of rock's identifiable voices: his second LP *Wish* (made in 1987) includes singles *More Love* with guest Keith Richards on guitar. (Donald Clarke 1.88).

GOOD HEART, A
Tracks: / Good heart, A / Anger is holy / Ghost train (12" only).
7" Single: Released Sep '85, on Virgin, by Virgin Records. Catalogue no: **VS 808**
12" Single: Released Sep '85, on Virgin, by Virgin Records. Catalogue no: **VS 808-12**

LISTEN TO YOUR FATHER
Tracks: / Listen to your father.
7" Single: Released Sep '84, on Charisma, by Virgin Records. Deleted May '88. Catalogue no: **JAZZ 1**
12" Single: Released Sep '84, on Charisma, by Virgin Records. Deleted May '88. Catalogue no: **JAZZ 112**

LOVING YOU
Tracks: / Loving you / Is this an explanation.
7" Single: Released Jun '85, on Virgin, by Virgin Records. Deleted May '88. Catalogue no: **VS 770**
12" Single: Released Jun '85, on Virgin, by Virgin Records. Catalogue no: **VS 770-12**

MORE LOVE
Tracks: / More love / Breath of scandal, A / More love (piano version) (CD & 12" only) / Good heart, A (original version) (CD only).
12" Single: Released Jan '88, on Virgin, by Virgin Records. Catalogue no: **VS 992-12**
CD 5": Released Aug '88, on Virgin, by Virgin Records. Catalogue no: **CDEP 18**
7" Single: Released Jan '88, on Virgin, by Virgin Records. Catalogue no: **VS 992**

OUT OF MY SYSTEM
Tracks: / Out of my system (7" version also on CD) / Touch of blue, A (On all versions) / Out of my system (The Popstand Delmonte mix) (CD & 12" only) / Out of my system (The Delmonte dub) (12" only) / Blue days (CD only).
7" Single: Released 7 Mar '88, on Virgin, by Virgin Records. Catalogue no: **VS 1051**
CD 5": Released Aug '88, on Virgin, by Virgin Records. Catalogue no: **VSCD 1051**
12" Single: Released 7 Mar '88, on Virgin, by Virgin Records. Catalogue no: **VST 1051**

SOMEONE TO SOMEBODY
Tracks: / Someone to somebody / Cold water.
12" Single: Released Mar '86, on Virgin, by Virgin Records. Deleted '89. Catalogue no: **VS 828-12**
7" Single: Released Mar '86, on Virgin, by Virgin Records. Deleted '89. Catalogue no: **VS 828**

YOU LITTLE THIEF
Tracks: / You little thief / Living actor, The (Not on CD) / Listen to your father (CD only) / More love (CD only).
CD 3": Released '88, on Virgin, by Virgin Records. Catalogue no: **CDT 36**
12" Single: Released Dec '85, on Virgin, by Virgin Records. Catalogue no: **VS 840-12**
7" Single: Released Dec '85, on Virgin, by Virgin Records. Deleted May '88. Catalogue no: **VS 840**

Sharks In Italy

PRECIOUS
Tracks: / Precious.
7" Single: Released Oct '85, on Clay, by Clay Records. Deleted '88. Catalogue no: **CLAY 46**

TIME
Tracks: / Time.
7" Single: Released Nov '84, on Clay, by Clay Records. Deleted '88. Catalogue no: **CLAY 38**

TIME IS OURS
Tracks: / Time is ours / Pressure.
12" Single: Released Oct '86, on Bonaire, by Bonaire Records. Deleted '88. Catalogue no: **BON 124**
7" Single: Released Sep '86, on Bonaire, by Bonaire Records. Deleted '88. Catalogue no: **BON 4**

Sharon & Tracey

DO THE BELLY DANCE
Tracks: / Do the belly dance.
7" Single: Released Sep '89, on MIL, by MIL Records. Catalogue no: **MILS 002**

Sharone

PLAY TO WIN
Tracks: / Play to win.
12" Single: Released Sep '89, on Republic, by Code Records. Catalogue no: **UNKNOWN**
7" Single: Released Mar '89, on Republic, by Code Records. Catalogue no: **LICT 023**

Sharonettes

GOING TO A GO-GO
Tracks: / Going to a go-go.
7" Single: Released Jul '75, on Black Magic, by Topic Records. Deleted Jul '78. Catalogue no: **BM 104**

PAPA OOM MOW MOW
Tracks: / Papa oom mow mow / Papa oom mow mow.
7" Single: Released Apr '75, on Black Magic, by Topic Records. Deleted Apr '78. Catalogue no: **BM 102**

Sharp

ENTERTAIN ME
Tracks: / So say harrah.
7" Single: Released Nov '86, on Unicorn-Kanchana, by Unicorn - Kanchana Records. Catalogue no: **PHZ 5**
12" Single: Released Nov '86, on Unicorn-Kanchana, by Unicorn - Kanchana Records. Catalogue no: **12PHZ 5**

Sharp, Al

POKE, THE
Tracks: / Poke, The / Keep in pokin'.
12" Single: Released Jul '82, on Solid, by Solid Records. Catalogue no: **12 STOP 001**
7" Single: Released Jul '82, on Solid, by Solid Records. Catalogue no: **STOP 001**

SAVE YOUR LOVE FOR ME
Tracks: / Save your love for me.
7" Single: Released Aug '83, on Solid, by Solid Records. Catalogue no: **STOP 008**

Sharp, Debbie

RISING STAT (ALT MIX)
Tracks: / Rising stat (alt mix).
12" Single: Released May '87, on Debut, by Skratch Records. Catalogue no: **DEBTX 3025**
7" Single: Released May '87, on Debut, by Skratch Records. Catalogue no: **DEBT 3025**

Sharp, Dee

IT'S ALL IN THE GAME
Tracks: / It's all in the game / It's all in the dub.
7" Single: Released Dec '87, on D.E.M., Deleted '88. Catalogue no: **DEM 001**

MAGICIAN
Tracks: / Magician.
12" Single: Released May '83, on RCA, by BMG Records (UK). Catalogue no: **RCAT 339**
7" Single: Released May '83, on RCA, by BMG Records (UK). Catalogue no: **RCA 339**

MOONDANCE
Tracks: / Moondance / Love me / Moondance (instrumental) (Only on 12".).
12" Single: Released Jan '88, on EMI, by EMI Records. Deleted 31 Jul '88. Catalogue no: **12SY 9**
7" Single: Released Jan '88, on Syncopate, by EMI Records. Deleted 31 Jul '88. Catalogue no: **SY 9**

RISING TO THE TOP
Tracks: / Rising to the top.
12" Single: Released Jul '83, on Fashion, by Fashion Records. Catalogue no: **FAD 015**

Sharp, Emma

I'M A MILLIONAIRE
Tracks: / I'm a millionaire / Wonderland.
7" Single: Released Dec '81, on Mean, by Mean Records. Catalogue no: **MEAN 4**

REMEMBER MY JEALOUSY
Tracks: / Remember my jealousy.
7" Single: Released Jul '83, on EMI, by EMI Records. Catalogue no: **EMI 5395**

Sharp, Rebby

GREEN STREET
Tracks: / Green street.
7" Single: Released Aug '82, on Zensor (Germany), Catalogue no: **ZENSOR 003**

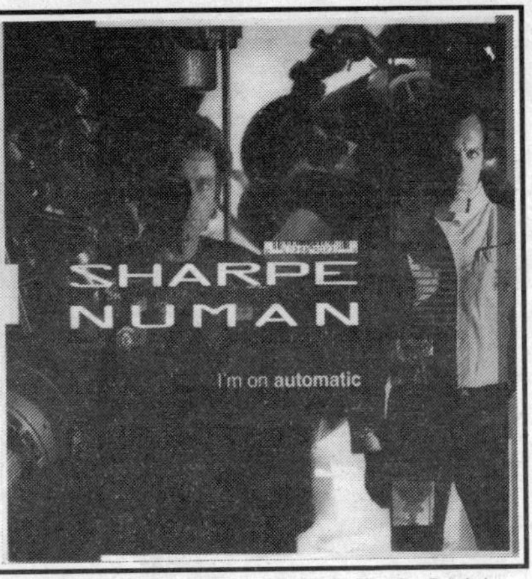

SHARPE & NUMAN - I'M ON AUTOMATIC (Released on Polydor)

Sharpe, Dee Dee

DO THE BIRD
Tracks: / Do the bird.
7" Single: Released Apr '63, on Cameo Parkway, by Pye Records. Deleted Apr '66. Catalogue no: **C 244**

Sharpe & Numan

CHANGE YOUR MIND
Tracks: / Change your mind.
12" Single: Released Jan '85, on Polydor, by Polydor Ltd. Catalogue no: **POSPX 722**
7" Single: Released Jan '85, on Polydor, by Polydor Ltd. Catalogue no: **POSP 722**

I'M ON AUTOMATIC (see panel above)
Tracks: / I'm on automatic / Love like a ghost.
12" Pic: Released 22 May '89, on Polydor, by Polydor Ltd. Catalogue no: **POPZ 43**
CD 5": Released 22 May '89, on Polydor, by Polydor Ltd. Catalogue no: **PZCD 43**
7" Pic: Released 22 May '89, on Polydor, by Polydor Ltd. Catalogue no: **POPD 43**
12" Single: Released 22 May '89, on Polydor, by Polydor Ltd. Catalogue no: **PZ 43**
Special: Released 22 May '89, on Polydor, by Polydor Ltd. Catalogue no: **POPB 43**
7" Single: Released 22 May '89, on Polydor, by Polydor Ltd. Catalogue no: **PO 43**

NEW THING FROM LONDON TOWN
Tracks: / New thing from London town / Time to die.
7" Pic: Released May '86, on Numa, by Numa Records. Catalogue no: **NUP 19**
7" Single: Released Sep '86, on Numa, by Numa Records. Catalogue no: **NU 19**
12" Single: Released Sep '86, on Numa, by Numa Records. Catalogue no: **NUM 19**
7" Pic: Released May '86, on Numa, by Numa Records. Catalogue no: **NUMP 19**

NO MORE LIES
Tracks: / No more lies / Voices.
Note: Bill Sharpe & Gary Numan.
12" Single: Released '88, on Polydor, by Polydor Ltd. Deleted 30 May '89. Catalogue no: **POSPT 894**
7" Pic: Released Jan '88, on Polydor, by Polydor Ltd. Catalogue no: **POSPP 894**
7" Single: Released Jan '88, on Polydor, by Polydor Ltd. Catalogue no: **POSP 894**
12" Pic: Released Jan '88, on Polydor, by Polydor Ltd. Catalogue no: **POPX 894**
12" Single: Released Jan '88, on Polydor, by Polydor Ltd. Catalogue no: **POSPX 894**
CD 5": Released Jan '88, on Polydor, by Polydor Ltd. Catalogue no: **POCD 894**

Sharpe, Rocky

CLAP YOUR HANDS
Tracks: / Clap your hands / 20-4 hours.
7" Single: Released Aug '82, on RAK, by EMI Records. Deleted Aug '85. Catalogue no: **RAK 345**

COME ON LET'S GO
Tracks: / Come on let's go / Please don't say goodbye.
7" Single: Released Sep '81, on Chiswick Records, Catalogue no: **CHIS 152**

HEART
Tracks: / Heart / Mary, won't you marry me.
7" Single: Released Jun '82, on Chiswick Records, Catalogue no: **DICE 9**

IF YOU WANNA BE HAPPY
Tracks: / If you wanna be happy / If you know how to rock and roll.
7" Single: Released Feb '83, on Polydor, by Polydor Ltd. Catalogue no: **POSP 560**

IMAGINATION
Tracks: / Imagination.
7" Single: Released Mar '79, on Chiswick Records, Deleted Mar '82. Catalogue no: **CHIS 110**

LOVE WILL MAKE YOU FAIL IN SCHOOL
Tracks: / Love will make you fail in school.
7" Single: Released Aug '79, on Chiswick Records, Deleted Aug '82. Catalogue no: **CHIS 114**

MARTIAN HOP
Tracks: / Martian hop / Fool in love with you.
7" Single: Released Feb '80, on Chiswick Records, Deleted Feb '83. Catalogue no: **CHIS 121**

NEVER BE ANYONE ELSE BUT YOU
Tracks: / Never be anyone else but you / Paradise lost.
7" Single: Released Apr '81, on Chiswick Records, Deleted Apr '84. Catalogue no: **CHIS 145**

RAMA LAMA DING DONG
Tracks: / Rama lama ding dong.
7" Single: Released Dec '78, on Chiswick Records, Deleted Dec '81. Catalogue no: **CHIS 104**

SHOUT SHOUT (KNOCK YOURSELF OUT) (SINGLE)
Tracks: / Shout shout (knock yourself out) / Hey hey good lookin'.
7" Single: Released Apr '82, on Chiswick Records, Deleted Apr '85. Catalogue no: **DKE 3**

SHOUT SHOUT (SINGLE)
Tracks: / Shout shout / Hey good looking.
7" Single: Released Mar '82, on Chiswick Records, Deleted '85. Catalogue no: **DICE 3**

STOP PLEASE STOP
Tracks: / Stop, please stop.
7" Single: Released Jun '83, on Polydor, by Polydor Ltd. Catalogue no: **POSP 579**

TEENAGER IN LOVE
Tracks: / Teenager in love / You've gone away.
7" Single: Released Apr '80, on Chiswick Records, Deleted Apr '83. Catalogue no: **CHIS 128**

WHITE CHRISTMAS
Tracks: / White Christmas / Christmas tears will fall / Have a good New Year / Happy New Year.
7" Single: Released Nov '80, on Chiswick Records, Deleted Nov '83. Catalogue no: **CHIS 138**

YOU'RE THE ONE
Tracks: / You're the one.

7" Single: Released Sep '80, on Chiswick Records, Catalogue no: **CHIS 134**

Sharpe, Stevie

WE ARE THE MODS
Tracks: / We are the mods / He wants to be a mod.
7" Single: Released 20 Jun '80, on Happy Face, by Standard Sound Productions. Deleted '83. Catalogue no: **MM 122**

Sharpees

BACK TO ZERO
Tracks: / Back to zero / Horoscope.
7" Single: Released May '82, on Moonlight, by Lithon Recording & Music Publishing. Catalogue no: **MNS 002**

Sharper Image

DRESS TO KILL
Tracks: / Dress to kill.
12" Single: Released Sep '87, on Hitz Squad (USA), Catalogue no: **HSM 618**

Shaskeen

ATLANTIC BREEZE
Tracks: / Atlantic breeze.
7" Single: Released '88, on I&B, by I & B Records. Catalogue no: **CFA 3505**

S-Haters

SOLITARY HABIT
Tracks: / Solitary habit / In death / Necromancer.
12" Single: Released May '84, on Midnight Music, by Midnight Music Records. Catalogue no: **DONG 6**
7" Single: Released May '84, on Midnight Music, by Midnight Music Records. Catalogue no: **DING 6**

STRANGE GIRL
Tracks: / Strange girl / Bishop of the diocese.
7" Single: Released Mar '85, on Midnight Music, by Midnight Music Records. Catalogue no: **DONG 10**

Shattered Dreams

NOTHING VENTURED NOTHING GAINED
Tracks: / Nothing ventured nothing gained / Feel it from here / War.
7" Single: Released Mar '84, on Epigram, by Epigram Records. Catalogue no: **EPIGRAM 003**

Shaun & The Sounds

YOU ANGEL YOU
Tracks: / You angel you.
7" Single: Released Jul '83, on Quazar, Catalogue no: **A 007**

Shaw, Francis

MARY'S THEME (FROM JAMAICA INN)
Tracks: / Mary's theme (from Jamaica Inn).
7" Single: Released Apr '83, on Peach River, Deleted '84. Catalogue no: **BBPR 4**

Shaw, Marlena

YUMA
Tracks: / Yuma / Go away little boy / New York, New York.
12" Single: Released Sep '88, on Old Gold, by Old Gold Records. Catalogue no: **OG 4506**

Shaw, Martin

CROSS MY HEART
Tracks: / Cross my heart.
7" Single: Released Jan '84, on Nouveau Music, Catalogue no: **NMS 4**

Shaw, Nina

I BELIEVED IN YOU
Tracks: / I believed in you.
7" Single: Released Feb '83, on Creole, by Creole Records. Catalogue no: **CR 47**
12" Single: Released Feb '83, on Creole, by Creole Records. Catalogue no: **CR 12 47**

LOOK AT ME NOW
Tracks: / Look at me now / Turkish delight.
7" Single: Released Apr '84, on Red Bus, by Red Bus Records. Catalogue no: **RBUS 90**

STOP IF YOU LOVE ME
7" Single: Released Sep '83, on Ecstasy, by Creole Records. Catalogue no: **XTC 3**
12" Single: Released Sep '83, on Ecstasy, by Creole Records. Catalogue no: **XTCT 3**

Shaw, Sandie

Biographical details:
Sandie Shaw's real name is Sandra Goodrich. She was born in 1947 in Dagenham. Helped by Adam Faith and then the songs of Chris Andrews, she became a pop star in the mid-60's, winning the Eurovision Song Contest in 1967 with *Puppet On A String*, in a bouncy style which was widely imitated. She guested on Heaven 17's album *Music of Quality & Distinction* in '81, had a couple of minor hits and played succesful concerts in London in 1986. (Donald Clarke)..

ALWAYS SOMETHING THERE TO REMIND ME
Tracks: / Always something there to remind me.
7" Single: Released Oct '64, on Pye, Deleted Oct '67. Catalogue no: **7N 15704**
7" Single: Released Apr '89, on PRT, by Castle Communications Records. Catalogue no: **PYS 25**
12" Single: Released Apr '89, on PRT, by Castle Communications Records. Catalogue no: **PYT 25**
7" Single: Released Jul '82, on Old Gold, by Old Gold Records. Catalogue no: **OG 9144**

ANYONE WHO HAD A HEART
Tracks: / Anyone who had a heart.
7" Single: Released Apr '82, on Virgin, by Virgin Records. Deleted Apr '85. Catalogue no: **VS 484**

ARE YOU READY TO BE HEARTBROKEN?
Tracks: / Are you ready to be heartbroken? / Steven (you don't eat meat) / Hand in glove (* Track on 12" version only.).
7" Single: Released May '86, on Polydor, by Polydor Ltd. Catalogue no: **POSP 793**
12" Single: Released May '86, on Polydor, by Polydor Ltd. Catalogue no: **POSPX 793**

FREDERICK
Tracks: / Frederick / Go Johnny go / Girl don't come (Track on 12" version only).
7" Single: Released Jul '86, on Polydor, by Polydor Ltd. Deleted Mar '87. Catalogue no: **POSP 811**
12" Single: Released Jul '86, on Polydor, by Polydor Ltd. Deleted Mar '87. Catalogue no: **POSPX 811**

GIRL DON'T COME
Tracks: / Girl don't come.
7" Single: Released Dec '64, on Pye, Deleted Dec '67. Catalogue no: **7N 15743**

HAND IN GLOVE
Tracks: / Hand in glove / I don't owe you anything / Jeanne (Available on 12" only.).
7" Single: Released May '84, on Rough Trade, by Rough Trade Records. Catalogue no: **RT 130**
12" Single: Released May '84, on Rough Trade, by Rough Trade Records. Catalogue no: **RTT 130**

HOW CAN YOU TELL
Tracks: / How can you tell.
7" Single: Released Nov '65, on Pye, Deleted Nov '68. Catalogue no: **7N 15987**

I DON'T NEED ANYTHING
Tracks: / I don't need anything.
7" Single: Released Jan '67, on Pye, Deleted Jan '70. Catalogue no: **7N 17239**

I'LL STOP AT NOTHING
Tracks: / I'll stop at nothing.
7" Single: Released Feb '65, on Pye, Deleted Feb '68. Catalogue no: **7N 15783**

JANICE LONG SESSION: SANDIE SHAW
12" Single: Released Jul '87, on Night Tracks, by Pinnacle Records. Catalogue no: **SFNT 002**

LONG LIVE LOVE
Tracks: / Long live love.
7" Single: Released May '65, on Pye, Deleted May '68. Catalogue no: **7N 15841**

MESSAGE UNDERSTOOD
Tracks: / Message understood.
7" Single: Released Sep '65, on Pye, Deleted Sep '68. Catalogue no: **7N 15940**

MONSIEUR DUPONT
Tracks: / Monsieur Dupont.
7" Single: Released Feb '69, on Pye, Deleted Feb '72. Catalogue no: **7N 17615**

NOTHING COMES EASY
Tracks: / Nothing comes easy.
7" Single: Released May '66, on Pye, Deleted May '69. Catalogue no: **7N 17086**

NOTHING LESS THAN BRILLIANT
Tracks: / Nothing less than brilliant / Love peace.
7" Single: Released Nov '88, on Rough Trade, by Rough Trade Records. Catalogue no: **RT 230**
CD 5": Released Nov '88, on Rough Trade, by Rough Trade Records. Catalogue no: **CDRT 230**
12" Single: Released Nov '88, on Rough Trade, by Rough Trade Records. Catalogue no: **RTT 230**

PLEASE HELP THE CAUSE AGAINST LONELINESS
Tracks: / Please help the cause against loneliness.
7" Single: Released Sep '88, on Rough Trade, by Rough Trade Records. Catalogue no: **RT 220**
12" Single: Released Sep '88, on Rough Trade, by Rough Trade Records. Catalogue no: **RTT 220**

PUPPET ON A STRING
Tracks: / Puppet on a string / Long live love.
7" Single: Released Jul '82, on Old Gold, by Old Gold Records. Catalogue no: **OG 9133**

PUPPET ON A STRING (SINGLE)
Tracks: / Puppet on a string.
7" Single: Released Jul '80, on Flashback, by Mainline Records. Catalogue no: **FBEP 109**
7" Single: Released Mar '67, on Pye, Deleted Mar '70. Catalogue no: **7N 17272**

RUN
Tracks: / Run.
7" Single: Released Sep '66, on Pye, Deleted Sep '69. Catalogue no: **7N 17163**

THINK IT ALL OVER
Tracks: / Think it all over.
7" Single: Released May '69, on Pye, Deleted May '72. Catalogue no: **7N 17726**

THINK SOMETIMES ABOUT ME
Tracks: / Think sometimes about me.
7" Single: Released Nov '66, on Pye, Deleted Nov '69. Catalogue no: **7N 17212**

TODAY
Tracks: / Today.
7" Single: Released Feb '68, on Pye, Deleted Feb '71. Catalogue no: **7N 17441**

TOMORROW
Tracks: / Tomorrow.
7" Single: Released Jan '66, on Pye, Deleted Jan '69. Catalogue no: **7N 17036**

TONIGHT IN TOKYO
Tracks: / Tonight in Tokyo.
7" Single: Released Jul '67, on Pye, Deleted Jul '70. Catalogue no: **7N 17346**

WISH I WAS
Tracks: / Wish I was.
7" Single: Released May '83, on Palace, by Virgin Records. Catalogue no: **PS 3**

YOU'VE NOT CHANGED
Tracks: / You've not changed.
7" Single: Released Oct '67, on Pye, Deleted Oct '70. Catalogue no: **7N 17378**

Shaw, Tina

SEXUAL ATTRACTION
Tracks: / Sexual attraction.
7" Single: Released Mar '85, on Creole, by Creole Records. Catalogue no: **CR 79**

Shaw, Tommy

EVER SINCE THE WORLD BEGAN
Tracks: / Ever since the world began / Outsider, The / No such thing (on 12" version only.).
12" Single: Released May '88, on Atlantic, by WEA Records. Catalogue no: **A 9138 T**
7" Single: Released May '88, on Atlantic, by WEA Records. Catalogue no: **A 9138**

Shaw, Winifred

LULLABY OF BROADWAY
Tracks: / Lullaby of broadway.
7" Single: Released Aug '76, on United Artists, by EMI Records. Deleted Aug '79. Catalogue no: **UP 36131**

JULES SHEAR - STEADY (Released on EMI)

Shaw, Woody

Biographical details:
American jazzman Woody Shaw was born in 1944 in North Carolina. He plays trumpet and flugelhorn and has become a highly regarded composer. He gigged with Chick Corea, Eric Dolphy, Art Blakey and many others. He has become a highly regarded composer and bandleader since finding his own voice in the 1970's. (Donald Clarke)..

LONELY SCHOOL
Tracks: / Lonely school.
12" Single: Released Jan '85, on A&M, by A&M Records. Deleted '88. Catalogue no: **AMY 231**
7" Single: Released Jan '85, on A&M, by A&M Records. Deleted '88. Catalogue no: **AM 231**

Shawnie, G

MISSION IMPOSSIBLE
Tracks: / Mission impossible.
7" Single: Released Jul '87, on Mute, by Mute Records. Catalogue no: **LEFT 13**
12" Single: Released Jul '87, on Rhythm King, by Mute Records. Catalogue no: **LEFT 13T**

Shazam

LOGAN'S RUN
Tracks: / Logan's run.
7" Single: Released '78, on UNKNOWN, Catalogue no: **BD 14**

She

NEVER SURRENDER
Tracks: / Breaking away / I'm on my way / Never surrender.
7" Single: Released May '85, on Neat, by Neat Records. Catalogue no: **NEAT 50**
12" Single: Released May '85, on Neat, by Neat Records. Catalogue no: **NEAT 50 12**

She Captured

NEW START
Tracks: / New start.
7" Single: Released Mar '86, on Eve, Catalogue no: **SHE 001**

She Rockers

GIVE IT A REST
Tracks: / Give it a rest.
12" Single: Released Mar '88, on Music Of Life, by Music Of Life Records. Catalogue no: **NOTE 14**

ON STAGE
Tracks: / On stage / Get up on this.
12" Single: Released Feb '89, on Jive, by Zomba Records. Catalogue no: **JIVET 195**
7" Single: Released Feb '89, on Jive, by Zomba Records. Catalogue no: **JIVE 195**

She Sherriff

I FORGOT MORE THAN YOU'LL EVER KNOW
Tracks: / I forgot more than you'll ever know.
7" Single: Released Mar '82, on Charisma, by Virgin Records. Deleted '89. Catalogue no: **CB 394**

Shear, Jules

STEADY (see panel on previous page)
Tracks: / Steady / Still I see you.
7" Single: Released '85, on EMI, by EMI Records. Catalogue no: **EA 196**

WHISPERING YOUR NAME
Tracks: / Whispering your name.
7" Single: Released May '83, on EMI-America, by EMI Records. Catalogue no: **EA 153**

Shearing, George

Biographical details:
Pianist George Shearing was born blind in London in 1919. He was already a highly regarded jazz musician when he went to the USA in 1947, sponsored by British-born critic/composer/producer Leonard Feather; in 1949 he invented a much imitated style with his quintet of piano, guitar, vibes, bass and drums, playing in the bop-flavoured 'locked hands' chordal style. He has been one of the mmost popular jazz musicians in the world ever since. (Donald Clarke)..

BAUBLES,BANGLES & BEADS
Tracks: / Baubles, bangles and beads.
7" Single: Released Oct '62, on Capitol, by EMI Records. Deleted Oct '65. Catalogue no: **CL 15269**

Shearston, Gary

I GET A KICK OUT OF YOU (OLD GOLD)
Tracks: / I get a kick out of you.
7" Single: Released Jul '82, on Old Gold, by Old Gold Records. Deleted Jul '88. Catalogue no: **OG 9009**

I GET A KICK OUT OF YOU (SINGLE)
Tracks: / I get a kick out of you.
7" Single: Released Oct '74, on Charisma, by Virgin Records. Deleted Oct '77. Catalogue no: **CB 234**

Sheba Sound

GIG EN RONDEAU
Tracks: / Gig en rondeau / Cuckoo.
7" Single: Released Feb '80, on Pye, Deleted Feb '83. Catalogue no: **7P 160**

Sheean

I WILL PROTECT YOU
Tracks: / I will protect you / I will protect you (instrumental).
7" Single: Released Nov '88, on Supertrack, Catalogue no: **RES 012**

Sheeba

HEY EVERYBODY
Tracks: / Hey everybody.
7" Single: Released Dec '81, on Multitone, by Multitone Records/Savera. Catalogue no: **MUL 1001**

HOROSCOPES
Tracks: / Horoscope / You came through love with me.
7" Single: Released Apr '81, on Ritz, by Ritz Records. Deleted '85. Catalogue no: **RITZ 007**
7" Single: Released Apr '81, on Ritz, by Ritz Records. Catalogue no: **RITZ 006**

NEXT NIGHT
Tracks: / Next night.
7" Single: Released Aug '81, on Ritz, by Ritz Records. Catalogue no: **RITZ 002**

WOMAN WITHOUT LOVE
Tracks: / Woman without love / Like a falling star.
7" Single: Released Sep '80, on Gem, Deleted Sep '83. Catalogue no: **GEMS 21**

Sheehan, Henry

FADE
Tracks: / Fade.
7" Single: Released Feb '82, on Big H, Deleted '86. Catalogue no: **HBS 001**

Sheer Elegance

IT'S TEMPTATION
Tracks: / It's temptation.
7" Single: Released Jul '76, on Pye International, Deleted Jul '79. Catalogue no: **7N 25715**

LIFE IS TOO SHORT, GIRL (OLD GOLD)
Tracks: / Life is too short, girl.
7" Single: Released Jan '85, on Old Gold, by Old Gold Records. Deleted Jul '88. Catalogue no: **OG 9471**

LIFE IS TOO SHORT, GIRL (SINGLE)
Tracks: / Life is too short, girl.
7" Single: Released Apr '76, on Pye International, Deleted Apr '79. Catalogue no: **7N 25703**

MILKY WAY
Tracks: / Milky way.
7" Single: Released Dec '75, on Pye International, Deleted Dec '78. Catalogue no: **7N 25697**

Sheer Gold

NO MORE WILL I ROAM
Tracks: / No more will I roam.
12" Single: Released Dec '84, on Negro, Catalogue no: **NEG 003**

Sheik Fawaz

MOHAMED'S HOUSE
Tracks: / Mohamed's house (live at the harem) (On YRT 10 only) / Fawaz's groove (On YRT 10 only) / Salaam aleikum (house version) (7" only) / Mohamed's house (7" only) / Salaam aleikum (On YRT 10 only) / Mohamed's house (Arabic acid remix) (On YRTX 10 only) / Mohamed's house (Islamic fundamental mix) (On YRTX 10 only).
12" Single: on Circa, by Virgin Records. Catalogue no: **YRTX 10**
12" Single: Released 7 Mar '88, on Virgin, by Virgin Records. Catalogue no: **YRT 10**
7" Single: Released 7 Mar '88, on Virgin, by Virgin Records. Catalogue no: **YR 10**

Sheila E

BELLE OF ST. MARK, THE
Tracks: / Belle of St Mark, The.
7" Single: Released Jan '85, on Warner Bros., by WEA Records. Catalogue no: **W 1980**

HOLD ME
Tracks: / Hold me / World is high, The.
7" Single: Released Feb '87, on Paisley Park (USA), by WEA Records. Deleted Jan '88. Catalogue no: **W 8580**
12" Single: Released Feb '87, on Paisley Park (USA), by WEA Records. Deleted Jan '88. Catalogue no: **W 8580T**

KOO KOO
Tracks: / Koo koo / Paradise garden.
7" Single: Released Jun '87, on Warner Bros., by WEA Records. Deleted Jul '88. Catalogue no: **W 8348**
12" Single: Released Jun '87, on Warner Bros., by WEA Records. Deleted Jul '88. Catalogue no: **W 8348T**

LOVE BIZARRE, A
Tracks: / Love bizarre, A / Love bizarre, A (part 2) / Save the people (on 12" only).
12" Single: Released Jan '86, on Paisley Park (USA), by WEA Records. Catalogue no: **W 8890T**
7" Single: Released Jan '86, on Paisley Park (USA), by WEA Records. Deleted Jun '87. Catalogue no: **W 8890**

Sheldon, Doug

I SAW LINDA YESTERDAY
Tracks: / I saw Linda yesterday.
7" Single: Released Feb '63, on London-American, Deleted Feb '66. Catalogue no: **F 11564**

RUNAROUND SUE
Tracks: / Runaround Sue.
7" Single: Released Nov '61, on London-American, Deleted Nov '64. Catalogue no: **F 11398**

YOUR MA SAID YOU CRIED IN YOUR SLEEP LAST NIGHT
Tracks: / Your ma said you cried in your sleep.
7" Single: Released Jan '62, on London-American, Deleted Jan '65. Catalogue no: **F 11416**

Shell, Ray

EVERYDAY PEOPLE
Tracks: / Everyday people / Street angel.
12" Single: Released Feb '82, on Record Shack, by Record Shack Records. Catalogue no: **SFM 1**

THEM HEAVY PEOPLE
Tracks: / Them heavy people.
7" Single: Released Feb '81, on EMI, by EMI Records. Deleted '84. Catalogue no: **EMI 5142**

Shelley

POETRY IN MOTION
Tracks: / Poetry in motion / Savoir-faire.
7" Single: Released Sep '82, on Impact, by Ace Records. Catalogue no: **ACT 4**

Shelley, Pete

Biographical details: For three years Pete Shelley was the driving force behind the Buzzcocks (the Manchester band that emerged from the heady punk scene of '77 to become one of Britain's major league groups).
In early 1981 Shelley quit the band. The confines of the group format were imposing severe limitations on his creativity, besides which, the Buzzcocks were beginning to lose their impetus. Immediately after the dissolution of the Buzzcocks Shelley started work on his first solo album *Homosapien* recorded at Genetic Sound studios with Martin Rushent producing. The title track itself scored noteable worldwide success. In Australia, for instance, it was a number one record whilst the album accrued gold status. All over America *Homosapien* was one of, if not, THE club hit of the year, paving the way for Shelley's tour in 1982 - the Man and Machines tour - his first solo outing (although he was backed by both a drummer and bass player). The tour played to packed houses throughout Britain. *Homosapien* the album, cracked the US top 100 whilst *Homosapien* the single made inroads on their disco charts.
In February 1983 Pete Shelley returned to Genetic Sound studios to start work on his second solo album, again with Martin Rushent producing. Early indications of the vinyl quality can be found on his single *Telephone Operator*. (Cosmopolitan, 1982).

BLUE EYES
Tracks: / Blue eyes / Nelson's riddle.
7" Single: Released Jul '86, on Mercury, by Phonogram Ltd. Catalogue no: **MER 225**
12" Single: Released Jul '86, on Mercury, by Phonogram Ltd. Catalogue no: **MERX 225**

HOMOSAPIEN (SINGLE)
Tracks: / Homosapien / Homosapien II (icon mix) (Only on CD single.) / Homosapien II (radio mix) (Only on CD single.) / Homosapien II (shower mix) (Only on CD single.).
7" Single: Released Apr '89, on Immaculate, by Immaculate Records. Catalogue no: **IMMAC 11**
12" Single: Released Apr '89, on Immaculate, by Immaculate Records. Catalogue no: **12IMMAC 11**
CD 3": Released Apr '89, on Immaculate, by Immaculate Records. Catalogue no: **IMMACD 11**
12" Single: Released Sep '81, on Genetic, by Island Records. Deleted Sep '84. Catalogue no: **12WIP 6720**
7" Single: Released Sep '81, on Genetic, by Island Records. Deleted Sep '84. Catalogue no: **WIP 6720**

I SURRENDER
Tracks: / I surrender / I need a minit.
7" Single: Released Nov '86, on Mercury, by Phonogram Ltd. Catalogue no: **MER 234**
12" Single: Released Nov '86, on Mercury, by Phonogram Ltd. Catalogue no: **MERX 234**

NEVER AGAIN
Tracks: / Never again / Give it to me.
7" Single: Released Nov '84, on Immaculate, by Immaculate Records. Deleted '89. Catalogue no: **IMMAC 1**
12" Single: Released Nov '84, on Immaculate, by Immaculate Records. Catalogue no: **12IMMAC 1**

ON YOUR OWN
Tracks: / On your own / Please forgive me...but I cannot endure it any longer.
7" Single: Released May '86, on Mercury, by Phonogram Ltd. Catalogue no: **MER 221**
12" Single: Released May '86, on Mercury, by Phonogram Ltd. Catalogue no: **MERX 221**

TELEPHONE OPERATOR
Tracks: / Telephone operator.
7" Single: Released Mar '83, on Genetic, by Island Records. Deleted Mar '86. Catalogue no: **XX 1**

WAITING FOR LOVE
Tracks: / Waiting for love / Designer lamps.
12" Single: Released Feb '86, on Mercury, by Phonogram Ltd. Catalogue no: **MERX 215**
7" Single: Released Feb '86, on Mercury, by Phonogram Ltd. Catalogue no: **MER 215**
12" Single: Released '88, on Immaculate, by Immaculate Records. Catalogue no: **12 IMMAC 4**

Shelley, Peter

GEE BABY
Tracks: / Gee baby / Love me, love my dog.
7" Single: Released Aug '81, on Magnet, by WEA Records. Catalogue no: **MAG 302**
7" Single: Released Sep '74, on Magnet, by WEA Records. Deleted Sep '77. Catalogue no: **MAG 12**

LOVE ME LOVE MY DOG (OLD GOLD)
Tracks: / Gee baby.
7" Single: Released Jan '87, on Old Gold, by Old Gold Records. Catalogue no: **OG 9671**

LOVE ME LOVE MY DOG (SINGLE)
Tracks: / Love me love my dog.
7" Single: Released Mar '75, on Magnet, by WEA Records. Deleted Mar '78. Catalogue no: **MAG 22**

Shelleyan Orphan

ANATOMY OF LOVE
Tracks: / Anatomy of love.
7" Single: Released Apr '87, on Rough Trade, by Rough Trade Records. Catalogue no: **RT 207**
12" Single: Released Apr '87, on Rough Trade, by Rough Trade Records. Catalogue no: **RTT 207**

CAVALRY OF CLOUD
Tracks: / Cavalry of the clouds.
7" Single: Released Sep '86, on Rough Trade, by Rough Trade Records. Catalogue no: **RT 170**
12" Single: Released Sep '86, on Rough Trade, by Rough Trade Records. Catalogue no: **RTT 170**

SHATTER
Tracks: / Shatter / Tar baby (live) / Amanita Muscario (12" only) / Timeblind (12" only).
7" Single: Released Jul '89, on Rough Trade, by Rough Trade Records. Catalogue no: **RT 217**
12" Single: Released Jul '89, on Rough Trade, by Rough Trade Records. Catalogue no: **RTT 217**

Shelto, Steve

DON'T GIVE YOUR LOVE AWAY
Tracks: / Don't give your love away.
7" Single: Released Mar '83, on Epic, by CBS Records. Catalogue no: **EPC A 3277**
12" Single: Released Mar '83, on Epic, by CBS Records. Catalogue no: **EPC A 13 3277**

Shelton, Anne

Biographical details:
Singer Ann Shelton was born in Dulwich in 1927, and performed on the BBC at age 12. She went to work for bandleader Ambrose rather than be evacuated from WWII London. She was under contract to Ambrose for years, but also worked with Glen Miller and Bing Crosby during the war at their request. She had many hit records before UK charts began (she was the first to sing *Lili Marlene* in English) and continued into the 1950's. With Vera Lynn one of the country's best loved artists from that era, she was also succesful in the USA. She sang *You'll never Know* for the Queen Mother on her 80th birthday, and sang on UK TV with a Glen Miller ghost band in 1984 during celebrations for the 4oth anniversary of D-Day. (Donald Clarke)..

ARRIVEDERCI DARLING
Tracks: / Arrivederci darling.
7" Single: Released Dec '55, on H.M.V., by EMI Records. Deleted Dec '58. Catalogue no: **POP 146**

CRAZY
Tracks: / Crazy.
7" Single: Released Sep '82, on President, by President Records. Catalogue no: **PT 510**

LAY DOWN YOUR ARMS
Tracks: / Lay down your arms.
7" Single: Released Aug '56, on Philips, by Phonogram Ltd. Deleted Aug '59. Catalogue no: **PB 616**

SAILOR
Tracks: / Sailor.
7" Single: Released Jan '61, on Philips, by Phonogram Ltd. Deleted Jan '64. Catalogue no: **PB 1096**

SEVEN DAYS
Tracks: / Seven days.
7" Single: Released Apr '56, on Philips, by Phonogram Ltd. Deleted Apr '59. Catalogue no: **PB 567**

VILLAGE OF ST. BERNADETTE
Tracks: / Village of St. Bernadette.
7" Single: Released Nov '59, on Philips, by Phonogram Ltd. Deleted Nov '62. Catalogue no: **PB 969**

Shenhai

FOLLOW ME
Tracks: / Follow me.
7" Single: Released Jan '88, on Deep, Catalogue no: **DP 5919**

Shenton, Robb

LONELY JOE
Tracks: / Lonely Joe / Is that all there is.
7" Single: Released Sep '82, on Sterling, Catalogue no: **STG 1**

Sheperet, David

PRETTY LOOKS
Tracks: / Pretty looks / Marjorie.
12" Single: Released Jan '83, on Rusty International, Catalogue no: **RI 004**

Shepherd, Cybill

BLUE MOON
Tracks: / Blue moon / I told you I loved you so get out.
12" Single: Released Nov '87, on MCA, by MCA Records. Catalogue no: **MCAS 1218**
7" Single: Released Oct '87, on MCA, by MCA Records. Catalogue no: **MCA 1218**

Shepherd, Robbie

UP THE DONS
Tracks: / Up the dons.
7" Single: Released May '83, on Ross, by

Ross Records. Catalogue no: **SWGR 008**

Shepherd Sisters

ALONE
Tracks: / Alone.
7" Single: Released Nov '57, on H.M.V., by EMI Records. Deleted Nov '60. Catalogue no: **POP 411**

Sheppard, Andy

JAVA JIVE
Tracks: / Java jive / Sol.
Note: Saxophonist, composer and bandleader. He also won the Newcomer of the year in the 1988 Jazz awards.
7" Single: Released Jun '88, on Antilles/New Directions, by Island Records. Catalogue no: **ANN 5**

Sheppard, David

IT'S HARD FOR A WOMAN
Tracks: / It's hard for a woman.
12" Single: Released Jun '85, on Red Sea, Catalogue no: **RSC 001**

Sheppard, Doug

ELEANOR RIGBY
Tracks: / Eleanor Rigby / Fight back.
7" Single: Released Mar '80, on EMI, by EMI Records. Deleted '83. Catalogue no: **EMI 5041**

Sheppard, T.G.

Biographical details: T.G.Sheppard is a country singer/songwriter with an intimate style that appeals to female fans. He was born **William Bowder** in Tennessee on 20 July 1944. He recorded for Atlantic as **Bryan Stacy** in 1962, but had quit performing to do promotional work in Memphis when he couldn't get anyone to record **The Devil In A Bottle**, a song by **Bobby David** that he believed in, so he recorded it himself and had a no.1 country hit in 1975; he's been a star ever since. Among his many hits was **Make My Day**, a duet with actor **Clint Eastwood.** Hits that crossed over to the pop chart include **I Loved Them Every One.**.

FINALLY (SINGLE)
Tracks: / Finally.
7" Single: Released May '82, on Warner Bros., by WEA Records. Catalogue no: **K 17944**

I LOVED 'EM EVERY ONE
Tracks: / I loved 'em every one / I could never dream the way you feel.
7" Single: Released Jun '81, on Curb, by BMG Records (UK). Catalogue no: **K 17792**

MAKE MY DAY
Tracks: / Make my day / How lucky we are.
7" Single: Released Feb '84, on Warner Bros., by WEA Records. Catalogue no: **W 9343**

ONLY ONE YOU
Tracks: / Only one you / We belong in love tonight.
7" Single: Released Apr '82, on Warner Bros., by WEA Records. Catalogue no: **K 17923**

PARTY TIME
Tracks: / Party time / You walzed yourself into my life.
7" Single: Released Dec '81, on Curb, by BMG Records (UK). Catalogue no: **K 17884**

STRONG HEART
Tracks: / What you gonna do about her / Strong heart.
7" Single: Released Nov '86, on CBS, by CBS Records. Catalogue no: **650274 7**

Sheppard, Towanna

STRONGER THE LOVE, THE
Tracks: / Stronger the love, The.
7" Single: Released Mar '89, on Renown, Catalogue no: **K 3601**

Sherbet

HOWZAT
Tracks: / Howzat.
7" Single: Released Sep '76, on Epic, by CBS Records. Deleted Sep '79. Catalogue no: **EPC 4574**

Sherbourne, Janet

NOBODY BUT YOU
Tracks: / Nobody but you / Everyday / Ivory.
7" Single: Released '81, on Practical Music, by Practical Music. Catalogue no: **PR 1**

Sherbs

I HAVE THE SKILL
Tracks: / I have the skill / Into the heart.
7" Single: Released Apr '81, on Atlantic, by WEA Records. Deleted Apr '84. Catalogue no: **K 11567**

Sheri & Son

LIES
Tracks: / Lies.
7" Single: Released Sep '81, on Precious Organisation, by Precious Organisation. Catalogue no: **AVE 2**

Sheridan, Mike

DONNA
Tracks: / Donna / Moonshine.
7" Single: Released '67, on Swoop, Catalogue no: **RTLS 007**
7" Single: Released Feb '82, on Swoop, Catalogue no: **RHTLS 007**

Sheridan, Nicki

FEEL THE RHYTHM
Tracks: / Feel the rhythm.
7" Single: Released Jun '89, on GML, Catalogue no: **GEMS 1**

Sheridan, Tony

MY BONNIE
Tracks: / My bonnie.
7" Single: Released Jun '63, on Polydor, by Polydor Ltd. Deleted Jun '66. Catalogue no: **NH 66833**

Sheriff

WHEN I'M WITH YOU
Tracks: / When I'm with you / Give me rock 'n' roll / California (12" only.).
7" Single: Released Feb '89, on Capitol, by EMI Records. Deleted Aug '89. Catalogue no: **CL 524**
12" Single: Released Feb '89, on Capitol, by EMI Records. Deleted Aug '89. Catalogue no: **12CL 524**

Sheriff, Dave

I'LL BE ALONE TONIGHT
Tracks: / I'll be alone tonight.
7" Single: Released Dec '77, on Tank, Catalogue no: **BSS 201**

Sheriff, Jack

LET'S BE NONCHALANT EP:BUY EVERYBODY A CAKE
Tracks: / We're gonna be in love / Whatcha gonna do? / Buttered slice of democracy.
7" EP: Released Feb '86, on Midnight Music, by Midnight Music Records. Catalogue no: **DONG 20**

Sheriff, Jamie

NO HERO
Tracks: / No hero / Sexy thing.
7" Single: Released Apr '81, on Polydor, by Polydor Ltd. Deleted '85. Catalogue no: **POSP 172**

Sheriff, Nick

FOURTH OF JULY
Tracks: / Fourth of July / I like girls.
7" Single: Released 20 Jun '80, on Charisma, by Virgin Records. Deleted '83. Catalogue no: **CB 367**

GIRLS OUT TONIGHT
Tracks: / Girls out tonight / At midnight.
7" Single: Released Oct '80, on Charisma, by Virgin Records. Deleted Oct '83. Catalogue no: **CB 375**

Sherman, Allan

HELLO MUDDAH HELLO FADDAH
Tracks: / Hello muddah hello faddah.
7" Single: Released Sep '63, on Warner Bros., by WEA Records. Deleted Sep '66. Catalogue no: **WB 106**
7" Single: Released Jul '81, on Warner Bros., by WEA Records. Catalogue no: **K 16691**

Sherman, Bim

HAPPINESS
Tracks: / Happiness / Exile dub.
12" Single: Released Dec '82, on Jah Shaka, Catalogue no: **SHAKA 830**

KEEP YOU DANCING
Tracks: / Keep you dancing / Can't stop jumping.
10" single: Released Dec '83, on On-U-Sound, by On-U-Sound Records. Catalogue no: **ONUDP 10**

LIGHTNING AND THUNDER
Tracks: / Lightning and thunder.
12" Single: on Attack, Deleted '88. Catalogue no: **TACK 9**

POWER, THE
Tracks: / Power.
7" Single: Released Apr '89, on Jetstar, by Jetstar Records. Catalogue no: **DISC 01**

REVOLUTION
Tracks: / Revolution / Too much work load.
10" single: Released Apr '82, on On-U-Sound, by On-U-Sound Records. Catalogue no: **DP 2**

STOP THAT TRAIN
Tracks: / Stop that train.
12" Single: Released Aug '88, on On-U-Sound, by On-U-Sound Records. Catalogue no: **ONUDP 14**

Sherman, Morton

IN ACTION
Tracks: / In action.
12" Single: Released Apr '89, on Subway, by Subway Records. Catalogue no: **SUB 053**

Sherman, Morton &

SOUNDSYSTEM
Tracks: / Soundsystem.
12" Single: Released Aug '88, on Subway, by Subway Records. Catalogue no: **SUB 032**

Sherman, Tony

ELLOVEE-EE
Tracks: / Ellovee-ee.
7" Single: Released Oct '82, on Polydor, by Polydor Ltd. Catalogue no: **POSP 517**
12" Single: Released Oct '82, on Polydor, by Polydor Ltd. Catalogue no: **POSPX 517**

Sherrick

BABY I'M FOR REAL
Tracks: / Baby I'm for real / Send for me.
7" Single: Released Apr '88, on Warner Bros., by WEA Records. Catalogue no: **W 7942**
12" Single: Released Apr '88, on Warner Bros., by WEA Records. Catalogue no: **W 7942 T**

JUST CALL
Tracks: / Just call / I'm scared of you.
7" Single: Released Jul '87, on Warner Bros., by WEA Records. Deleted Jul '88. Catalogue no: **W 8380**
12" Single: Released Jul '87, on Warner Bros., by WEA Records. Deleted Jul '88. Catalogue no: **W 8380T**

LET'S BE LOVERS TONIGHT
Tracks: / Let's be lovers tonight / I told you I loved you so get out.
12" Single: Released 31 Oct '87, on Warner Bros., by WEA Records. Catalogue no: **W 8146 T**
7" Single: Released 31 Oct '87, on Warner Bros., by WEA Records. Deleted Jul '88. Catalogue no: **W 8146**

Sherriff, Dave

DON'T TELL ME LIES
Tracks: / Don't tell me lies / Woman's touch.
7" Single: Released Apr '84, on Dapa, Deleted '87. Catalogue no: **CEN 383**

Shertz

YOU'VE GOT YOUR TROUBLES
Tracks: / You've got your troubles / Over the eight.
7" Single: Released Feb '83, on Wat, Deleted '86. Catalogue no: **MAB 101**

Shervington, Pluto

DAT
Tracks: / Dat.
7" Single: Released Feb '76, on Opal, Deleted Feb '79. Catalogue no: **PAL 5**

RAM GOAT LIVER
Tracks: / Ram goat liver.
12" Single: Released Apr '82, on Trojan, by Trojan Records. Catalogue no: **TROT 9066**
7" Single: Released Apr '82, on Trojan, by Trojan Records. Catalogue no: **TRO 9066**
7" Single: Released Apr '76, on Trojan, by Trojan Records. Deleted Apr '79. Catalogue no: **TR 7978**

Sherwood, Holly

DAY BY DAY
Tracks: / Day by day.
7" Single: Released Feb '72, on Bell, Deleted Feb '75. Catalogue no: **BELL 1182**

Sheryll, Alison

BLUE TRAIN, THE
Tracks: / Blue train, The.
7" Single: Released Oct '88, on Sierra, by Sierra Records. Catalogue no: **FED 51**

YOU'RE NOT ALONE
Tracks: / You're not alone / Worlds apart.
7" Single: Released 20 Feb '88, on Sierra, by Sierra Records. Catalogue no: **FED 44**

Sheveton, Tony

MILLION DRUMS
Tracks: / Million drums.
7" Single: Released Feb '64, on Oriole, Deleted Feb '67. Catalogue no: **CB 1895**

Shiek

FINDERS KEEPERS
Tracks: / Finders keepers.
12" Single: Released Sep '87, on Zone (USA), Deleted Oct '87. Catalogue no: **Z 1001**

Shields, Duncan

STAY TOGETHER
Tracks: / Stay together.
7" Single: Released May '85, on Markar, Catalogue no: **JUNE 1**

Shikane

CHANGE YOUR MIND
Tracks: / Change your mind / Burning passion.
7" Single: Released Feb '84, on Red Bus, by Red Bus Records. Catalogue no: **RBUS 87**
12" Single: Released Feb '84, on Red Bus, by Red Bus Records. Catalogue no: **RBUSL 87**

Shillelagh Sisters

GIVE ME MY FREEDOM
Tracks: / Give me my freedom / Cheatin' teasin' man.
7" Single: Released Aug '87, on CBS, by CBS Records. Catalogue no: **A 4217**
7" Pic: Released Apr '84, on CBS, by CBS Records. Catalogue no: **WA 4217**
12" Single: on CBS, by CBS Records. Catalogue no: **TA 4217**

PASSION FRUIT
Tracks: / Passion fruit.
12" Single: Released Aug '84, on CBS, by CBS Records. Catalogue no: **TA 4684**
7" Single: Released Aug '84, on CBS, by CBS Records. Catalogue no: **A 4684**

Shine

I DREAM IN BLUE
Tracks: / Last time round / I dream in blue.
7" Single: Released Apr '86, on China, by Polydor Ltd. Catalogue no: **WOK 8**
12" Single: Released Apr '86, on China, by Polydor Ltd. Catalogue no: **WOKX 8**

Shine, Brendan

BIDDY FROM GLENROE
Tracks: / Biddy from Glenroe.
7" Single: Released '88, on Play (Ireland), Catalogue no: **PLAY 176**

BUNCH OF VIOLETS BLUE
Tracks: / Bunch of violets blue.
7" Single: Released Sep '84, on Play (Ireland), Catalogue no: **PLAY 153**
7" Single: Released '88, on Homespun (Ireland), by Outlet Records. Catalogue no: **HIS 19**

CAN'T HOLD BACK THE YEARS
Tracks: / Can't hold back the years.
7" Single: Released '88, on Play (Ireland), Catalogue no: **PLAY 155**

CARROTS
Tracks: / Carrots.
7" Single: Released Sep '80, on Play (Ireland), Catalogue no: **PLAY 140**

CATCH ME IF YOU CAN
Tracks: / Catch me if you can.
7" Single: Released '88, on Play (Ireland), Catalogue no: **PLAY 135**

CHRISTMAS TIME IN IRELAND
Tracks: / Christmas time in Ireland.
7" Single: Released Oct '76, on Play (Ireland), Catalogue no: **PLAY 81**

COUNTY DOWN
Tracks: / County down.
7" Single: Released Aug '83, on Play (Ireland), Catalogue no: **PLAY 149**

DO YOU WANT YOUR OLD LOBBY WASHED
Tracks: / Do you want yer oul lobby washed down.
7" Single: Released Sep '79, on Play (Ireland), Catalogue no: **PLAY 122**
7" Single: Released Sep '87, on Play, by Play Records. Catalogue no: **PLAY 223**

DOOGEENS
Tracks: / Doogeens.
7" Single: Released May '81, on Play (Ireland), Catalogue no: **PLAY 141**

FOUR GREAT TRACKS
7" EP: Released Jul '81, on Play (Ireland), Catalogue no: **PLAYS1**

HEY LOUISE
Tracks: / Hey Louise / Got a honey of a deal.
7" Single: Released Apr '82, on Play (Ireland), Catalogue no: **PLAY 144**

LONELINESS
Tracks: / Accordion (inst) / These are the sounds I love / My son / Loneliness.
7" Single: Released Feb '86, on Play, by Play Records. Catalogue no: **PLAY 206**
12" Single: Released May '86, on Play, by Play Records. Catalogue no: **PLAY 206 T**

ME OLD BONESHAKER
Tracks: / Me old boneshaker / Promise and the dream.
7" Single: Released Nov '82, on Play (Ireland), Catalogue no: **PLAY 146**

ME UNCLE MIKE
Tracks: / Me Uncle Mike / Me Mother from County Mayo.
7" Single: Released Jun '88, on Play, by Play Records. Catalogue no: **PLAY 228**

MELODY

Tracks: / Melody.
7" Single: Released Jul '85, on Play (Ireland), Catalogue no: **PLAY 203**

MOONSHINE
Tracks: / Moonshine / Girl from Clare, The.
7" Single: Released Mar '87, on Play, by Play Records. Catalogue no: **PLAY 214**

MY OLD COUNTRY HOME (SINGLE)
Tracks: / My old country home.
7" Single: Released Jan '83, on Play (Ireland), Catalogue no: **PLAY 147**

MY SON
Tracks: / My son / Did you kiss me.
7" Single: Released Jan '86, on Play, by Play Records. Catalogue no: **PLAY 207**

NOW I'M EASY(COCK FARMER)
Tracks: / Now I'm easy (cock farmer).
7" Single: Released May '84, on Play (Ireland), Catalogue no: **PLAY 152**

OLD RUGGED CROSS
Tracks: / Old rugged cross, The.
7" Single: Released Jun '82, on Play (Ireland), Catalogue no: **PLAY 145**

PUB CRAWL
Tracks: / Pub crawl.
7" Single: Released Nov '81, on Play (Ireland), Catalogue no: **PLAY 143**

THANK GOD FOR KIDS
Tracks: / Thank God for kids.
7" Single: Released Dec '83, on Play (Ireland), Catalogue no: **PLAY 150**

VILLAGE WHERE I WENT TO SCHOOL
Tracks: / Village where I went to school.
7" Single: Released May '83, on Play (Ireland), Catalogue no: **PLAY 148**

YOU'LL NEVER GO BACK
Tracks: / You'll never go back / Biddy from Glenroe.
7" Single: Released Oct '86, on Play, by Play Records. Catalogue no: **PLAY 212**

Shinehead

BILLIE JEAN
Tracks: / Billie Jean.
12" Single: Released Sep '84, on Hawkeye, by Hawkeye Records. Catalogue no: **HD 58**

CHAIN GANG RAP
Tracks: / Chain gang rap / Chain gang rap (version).
12" Single: Released Oct '88, on Elektra, by Elektra Records (UK). Catalogue no: **EKR 81 T**
7" Single: Released Oct '88, on Elektra, by Elektra Records (UK). Catalogue no: **EKR 81**

WHO THE CAP FIT
Tracks: / Who the cap fits / Billie Jean/Mama used to say.
12" Single: Released Nov '86, on Virgin, by Virgin Records. Catalogue no: **VS 917-12**
7" Single: Released Nov '86, on Virgin, by Virgin Records. Deleted May '88. Catalogue no: **VS 917**

Shining

WORKING CLASS HERO
Tracks: / Working class hero.
12" Single: Released Jun '83, on Turbo, Catalogue no: **BRAKE 01-02**

Shiny To Shiny

WAITING FOR US
Tracks: / Waiting for us.
7" Single: Released Nov '83, on Red Flame 10, by Virgin Records. Catalogue no: **RFB 29**
12" Single: Released Nov '83, on Red Flame 10, by Virgin Records. Catalogue no: **RFB 2912**

Shirelles

Biographical details: The Shirelles were the first and are probably still the best loved (except perhaps for the **Supremes**) of all the girl groups. The began in Passaic, New Jersey in 1958. The original members, all born 1940-41, were lead singer **Shirley Owens** (later a succesful solo artist as **Shirley Alston**), **Addie 'Mickey' Harris, Beverley Lee and Doris Kenner.** A schoolmate's mother, **Florence Greenberg**, signed the group to her tiny Tiara label and recorded **I Met Him On A Sunday**, which they'd written themselves. Distributed by US Decca (now MCA) it reached the US top 50 in 1958. Greenberg formed the new Scepter label just for them, and **Dedicated To The One I Love** (written in 1957 by **Lowman Pauling** of the **Five Royals**, revived in 1967 by the **Mamas & The Papas**) made the Billboard chart in 1959, a considerable feat then for a record by a black group on a small label. Their other big hits included a no.1 with **Gerry Goffin & Carole King's Will You Love Me Tomorrow**in 1960 (also a UK no.4 hit). **Dedicated** was then reiisued and this time made no.3. **Boys** (written for them by Luthor Dixon) and **Baby It's You** were covered by the **Beatles** on their first album. They had hits until 1967 and are still loved around the world. [Donald Clarke, April 87].

FOOLISH LITTLE GIRL
Tracks: / Foolish little girl.
7" Single: Released May '63, on Stateside, by EMI Records. Deleted May '66. Catalogue no: **SS 181**

SOLDIER BOY
Tracks: / Soldier boy.
7" Single: Released May '62, on H.M.V., by EMI Records. Deleted May '65. Catalogue no: **POP 1019**

WILL YOU LOVE ME TOMORROW
Tracks: / Will you love me tomorrow.
12" Single: Released Dec '88, on Charly, by Charly Records. Catalogue no: **CYZ 130**
7" Single: Released Aug '82, on Dakota, Catalogue no: **BAK 12**
7" Single: Released Dec '88, on Charly, by Charly Records. Catalogue no: **CYZ 7 130**
CD 5": Released Dec '88, on Charly, by Charly Records. Catalogue no: **CDS 12**
7" Single: Released Feb '61, on Top Rank (1), Deleted Feb '64. Catalogue no: **JAR 540**

WILL YOU LOVE ME TOMORROW (OLD GOLD)
Tracks: / Will you love me tomorrow / Soldier boy / Mama said (CD single only.).
CD 5": Released Nov '88, on Old Gold, by Old Gold Records. Catalogue no: **OG 6105**
7" Single: Released Apr '83, on Old Gold, by Old Gold Records. Catalogue no: **OG 9286**

Shirleene

SPARROW SONG
Tracks: / Sparrow song / Ballad of J.R..
7" Single: Released Dec '81, on Pith, Deleted Dec '84. Catalogue no: **PITH 2T**

Shirley & Company

SHAME SHAME SHAME
Tracks: / Shame shame shame.
7" Single: Released Jul '84, on Old Gold, by Old Gold Records. Deleted Jul '88. Catalogue no: **OG 9414**

SHAME SHAME SHAME (2)
Tracks: / Shame shame shame / Rimshots.
7" Single: Released Feb '75, on All Platinum, Deleted Feb '78. Catalogue no: **6146 301**
7" Single: Released Jan '83, on Flashback, by Mainline Records. Catalogue no: **FBS 24**

Shirley Junior Choir

HOMEWARD BOUND
Tracks: / Homeward bound / Twentieth century carol.
7" Single: Released Nov '82, on Thunderbay, Catalogue no: **TBR 001**

Shirley & Lee

Biographical details: Shirley & Lee were Shirley Pixley Goodman,born in 1937,and Leonard Lee,born in 1935;their r&b hits began in 1952 on the Alladin label,and included one of the all-time great party records for teenagers of all ages,*Let the Good Times Roll*which crossed over to top 20 pop in 1956.Their style was based on the contrast between his big voice & her little one.See also **Shirley & Co.**:Shirley had one of the first disco hits in 1976,*Shame Shame Shame*,produced & written by **Sylvia Robinson (of Mickey & Sylvia).** (Donald Clarke)..

LET THE GOOD TIMES ROLL
Tracks: / Let the good times roll.
7" Single: Released Aug '84, on Creole (Replay), by Creole Records. Catalogue no: **CR 218**

Shirley, Roy

FOR EVERYONE
Tracks: / For everyone.
7" Single: Released Jan '85, on Shirley, Catalogue no: **SHIRLEY 1**

Shirts

LAUGH AND WALK AWAY
Tracks: / Laugh and walk away / Triangulum.
7" Single: Released Feb '80, on Harvest (1), by EMI Records. Deleted '83. Catalogue no: **HAR 5195**

ONE LAST CHANCE
Tracks: / One last chance / Too much trouble.
7" Single: Released Aug '80, on Capitol, by EMI Records. Deleted '83. Catalogue no: **CL 16161**

Shiva

ANGEL OF MONZ
Tracks: / Angel of monz.
7" Single: Released Nov '82, on Heavy Metal, by FM-Revolver Records. Catalogue no: **HEAVY 16**

ROCK LIFE ON
Tracks: / Rock life on / Sympathy for the devil.
7" Single: Released Feb '82, on Heavy Metal, by FM-Revolver Records. Deleted Feb '87. Catalogue no: **HEAVY 13**

Sho Nuff

SHAME SHAME SHAME
Tracks: / Shame shame shame.
7" Single: Released May '80, on Ensign, by Ensign Records. Deleted May '83. Catalogue no: **ENY 37**

Shoc Corridor

BLIND SIGN
Tracks: / Blind sign.
7" Single: Released Oct '82, on Shout, by Shout Records. Catalogue no: **XW 1203**

FEVER
Tracks: / Fever.
12" Single: Released Nov '84, on Quiet, by Quiet Records. Catalogue no: **QST 005**

HOLDING TREASURE
Tracks: / Holding treasure / Almost in walking distance.
7" Single: Released Jun '84, on Shout, by Shout Records. Catalogue no: **XS 009**

Shock

ANGEL FACE
Tracks: / Angel face / R.E.R.B..
7" Single: Released Sep '80, on RCA, by BMG Records (UK). Deleted '83. Catalogue no: **RCA 14**

DYNAMO BEAT
Tracks: / Dynamo beat / Dream games.
7" Single: Released Oct '81, on RCA, by BMG Records (UK). Catalogue no: **RCA 133**
12" Single: Released Oct '81, on RCA, by BMG Records (UK). Catalogue no: **RCAT 133**

Shock Headed Peters

FIRE EXTINGUISHER
Tracks: / Fire extinguisher.
12" Single: Released '87, on Beach Culture, Catalogue no: **BC 003**

I BLOODBROTHER BE
Tracks: / I bloodbrother be.
7" Single: Released Nov '84, on Island, by Island Records. Catalogue no: **IS 213**
12" Single: Released Nov '84, on Island, by Island Records. Catalogue no: **12IS 213**
12" Single: Released Sep '84, on El, by Cherry Red Records. Catalogue no: **EL 1 T**
7" Single: Released Sep '84, on El, by Cherry Red Records. Catalogue no: **EL 1**

Shock Taktix

MOROCKO
Tracks: / Morocko / This is not / Morocko (Mad house mix).
12" Single: Released 13 Jun '87, on RCA, by BMG Records (UK). Deleted May '89. Catalogue no: **PT 41356**
7" Single: Released 13 Jun '87, on RCA, by BMG Records (UK). Catalogue no: **PB 41355**

TIME IS NOT JAZZ
Tracks: / Time is not jazz / Time eat time.
7" Single: Released Apr '88, on RCA, by BMG Records (UK). Deleted May '89. Catalogue no: **PB 41877**
12" Single: Released Apr '88, on RCA, by BMG Records (UK). Deleted May '89. Catalogue no: **PT 41878**

Shock USA

THAT'S A LADY
Tracks: / That's a lady / Electrophonic funk.
7" Single: Released Aug '82, on Fantasy (1), by BMG Records (UK). Catalogue no: **FTC 200**
12" Single: Released Jul '82, on Fantasy (1), by BMG Records (UK). Catalogue no: **FTCT 200**

Shockabilly

19TH NERVOUS BREAKDOWN
Tracks: / 19th nervous breakdown.
7" Single: Released Mar '83, on Rough Trade, by Rough Trade Records. Catalogue no: **RT 127**

DAWN OF SHOCKABILLY
Tracks: / Dawn of shockabilly.
12" Single: Released Nov '82, on Rough Trade, by Rough Trade Records. Catalogue no: **RT 120T**

Shocked, Michelle

ANCHORAGE
Tracks: / Anchorage / Frog town / Strawberry jam (live) (Only on 12") / Penny Evans (live) (Only on 12").
CD 5": Released 16 Sep '88, on London Records, by London Records. Catalogue no: **LONCD 193**
7" Single: Released 16 Sep '88, on London Records, by London Records. Deleted May '89. Catalogue no: **LON 193**
12" Single: Released 16 Sep '88, on London Records, by London Records. Deleted May '89. Catalogue no: **LONX 193**
10" single: Released 16 Sep '88, on London Records, by London Records. Deleted May '89. Catalogue no: **LONT 193**

DISORIENTED
Tracks: / Disoriented / If love was a train / Chainsmoker (*Extra track on 12") / Stranded in a limousine (Extra track on 12") / Goodnight Irene (*Extra track on 12").
12" Single: Released Jun '87, on Cooking Vinyl, by Cooking Vinyl Records. Catalogue no: **FRY 002T**
7" Single: Released Jun '87, on Cooking Vinyl, by Cooking Vinyl Records. Catalogue no: **FRY 002**

IF LOVE WAS A TRAIN
Tracks: / If love was a train / Memories of East Texas / Graffiti limbo (live) (Available on 12" format only.) / VFD (Avaliable on CD single format only.) / Jamboree queen (Avaliable on CD single format only.).
CD 5": Released Jan '89, on London Records, by London Records. Catalogue no: **LONCD 212**
12" Single: Released Jan '89, on London Records, by London Records. Deleted 26 Jun '89. Catalogue no: **LONX 212**
7" Single: Released Jan '89, on London Records, by London Records. Deleted 26 Jun '89. Catalogue no: **LON 212**

WHEN I GROW UP
Tracks: / When I grow up / 5am in Amsterdam / Goodnight Irene (12" only.) / Campfire crusade (CD single only.).
7" Single: Released Feb '89, on London Records, by London Records. Deleted Jul '89. Catalogue no: **LON 219**
12" Single: Released Feb '89, on London Records, by London Records. Deleted Jul '89. Catalogue no: **LONX 219**
CD 5": Released Feb '89, on London Records, by London Records. Catalogue no: **LONCD 219**

Shocking Blue

MIGHTY JOE
Tracks: / Mighty Joe.
7" Single: Released Apr '70, on Penny Farthing, by Penny Farthing Records. Deleted Apr '73. Catalogue no: **PEN 713**

VENUS
Tracks: / Venus.
7" Single: Released Jan '70, on Penny Farthing, by Penny Farthing Records. Deleted Jan '73. Catalogue no: **PEN 702**

VENUS (OLD GOLD)
Tracks: / Venus / Dancing on a Saturday night / Beautiful Sunday.
CD 5": Released 28 Mar '89, on Old Gold, by Old Gold Records. Catalogue no: **OG 6122**
7" Single: on Old Gold, by Old Gold Records. Deleted Jul '88. Catalogue no: **OG 9006**
7" Single: Released 21 Nov '87, on Old Gold, by Old Gold Records. Catalogue no: **OG 9736**

Shocking Stockings

RED CHINA
Tracks: / Red China / You move the movement.
7" Single: Released May '80, on Carrere, Deleted '83. Catalogue no: **CAR 147**

Shoe People

SHOE PEOPLE
Tracks: / Shoe people / Welcome to the world of the Shoe People.
7" Single: Released 14 May '88, on Bright, by Bright Records. Catalogue no: **BULB 10**

Shoehorn

DO THE BEST I CAN
Tracks: / Do the best I can / Don't blame me.
7" Single: Released Sep '81, on Monarch, by Monarch Records. Catalogue no: **MON 027**

Shoes

YOUR IMAGINATION
Tracks: / Your imagination / Things you do.
7" Single: Released Apr '81, on Elektra, by Elektra Records (UK). Deleted Apr '84. Catalogue no: **K 12520**

Shoes For Industry

I CAN'T HELP IT
Tracks: / I can't help it.
7" Single: Released Jul '81, on Fried Egg, by Fried Egg Records. Deleted '87. Catalogue no: **EGG 1**

SPEND
Tracks: / Spend.

7" Single: Released Jul '81, on Fried Egg, by Fried Egg Records. Deleted '87. Catalogue no: **EGG 4**

Shoes (Group)

TOO LATE
Tracks: / Too late / Now and then.
7" Single: Released Feb '80, on Elektra Asylum, by Elektra Records (USA). Deleted Feb '83. Catalogue no: **K 12404**

WHEN PUSH COMES TO SHOVE
Tracks: / When push comes to shove.
7" Single: Released Jan '85, on Demon, by Demon Records. Catalogue no: **D 1029**

Shogun

CLOAK AND DAGGER
Tracks: / Cloak and dagger / Too late for the hunter / Tokyo girl (Only on 12" single.).
7" Single: Released Sep '87, on Jet, by Jet Records. Catalogue no: **JET 7049**
12" Single: Released Sep '87, on Jet, by Jet Records. Catalogue no: **JET 12049**

VOICES FROM THE HEART
Tracks: / Voices from the heart / Cold truth / Time will tell (Track on 12".).
12" Single: Released Mar '88, on Jet, by Jet Records. Deleted Aug '88. Catalogue no: **651 472-6**
7" Single: Released Mar '88, on Jet, by Jet Records. Deleted Aug '88. Catalogue no: **651 472-7**

Shogun MC

READY FOR ACTION
Tracks: / Ready for action.
12" Single: Released Aug '89, on Blue Chip, by Blue Chip Records. Catalogue no: **BLUEC 22**

Shokk

AMAZIN
Tracks: / Amazin / Stay.
12" Single: Released Jan '88, on Raka, Catalogue no: **ROX AT001**
7" Single: Released Jan '88, on Raka, Catalogue no: **ROX A001**

LOCK ME OUT
Tracks: / Lock me out.
7" Single: Released Mar '87, on Polydor, by Polydor Ltd. Catalogue no: **POSP 851**
12" Single: Released Mar '87, on Polydor, by Polydor Ltd. Catalogue no: **POSPX 851**

Shondell, Troy

THIS TIME
Tracks: / This time.
7" Single: Released Nov '61, on London-American, Deleted Nov '64. Catalogue no: **HLG 9432**

Shoot

WORK AND WIT
Tracks: / Work and wit.
7" Single: Released '88, on Dayjob, Catalogue no: **JOB 001**

Shoot Dispute

GAT GUN
Tracks: / Gat gun.
7" Single: Released Jul '85, on Zanzibar, Catalogue no: **ZAN 001**

Shoot To Thrill

CINCO DE MAYO
Tracks: / Cinco de mayo.
CD 5": Released Dec '88, on Doctor Beat, by Doctor Beat Records. Catalogue no: **DRXCD 7**
12" Single: Released Dec '88, on Doctor Beat, by Doctor Beat Records. Catalogue no: **DRX 712**
7" Single: Released Dec '88, on Doctor Beat, by Doctor Beat Records. Deleted Sep '89. Catalogue no: **DRX 7**

Shooting Party

I GO TO PIECES
Tracks: / I go to pieces.
7" Single: Released Aug '89, on Lisson, by PWL Records. Catalogue no: **DOLE 11**
12" Single: Released Aug '89, on Lisson, by PWL Records. Catalogue no: **DOLEQ 11**

I KNOW THAT MOOD
Tracks: / I know that mood / One shot.
12" Single: Released Jan '86, on Siren, by Virgin Records. Deleted '89. Catalogue no: **SIREN 12-12**
7" Single: Released Jan '86, on Siren, by Virgin Records. Deleted '89. Catalogue no: **SIREN 12**

SAFE IN THE ARMS OF LOVE
Tracks: / Safe in the arms of love / Safe in the arms of love (instrumental).
7" Single: Released 14 May '88, on Lisson, by PWL Records. Catalogue no: **DOLE 9**
12" Single: Released 14 May '88, on Lisson, by PWL Records. Catalogue no: **DOLEQ 9**

Showaddywaddy - Always and Ever (Released on Arista)

TRICK OF THE LIGHT
Tracks: / Trick of the light / Hold that emotion.
7" Single: Released Sep '85, on Siren, by Virgin Records. Deleted '86. Catalogue no: **SIREN 7**
12" Single: Released Sep '85, on Siren, by Virgin Records. Deleted '86. Catalogue no: **SIREN 7-12**
12" Single: Released Jun '86, on Towerbell, Catalogue no: **TOWT 91**
7" Single: Released Jun '86, on Towerbell, Catalogue no: **TOW 91**

Shooting Star

FLESH AND BLOOD
Tracks: / Flesh and blood.
7" Single: Released Jan '82, on Virgin, by Virgin Records. Deleted '89. Catalogue no: **VS 469**

SUMMER SUN
Tracks: / Summer sun.
12" Single: Released Jul '85, on Virgin, by Virgin Records. Deleted '86. Catalogue no: **VS 794-12**
7" Single: Released Jul '85, on Virgin, by Virgin Records. Deleted '89. Catalogue no: **VS 794**

YOU'VE GOT WHAT I NEED
Tracks: / You've got what I need / Wild in the streets.
7" Single: Released Feb '80, on Virgin, by Virgin Records. Deleted '89. Catalogue no: **VS 291**

Shop Assistants

ALL DAY LONG
Tracks: / All day long.
7" Single: Released Jun '85, on Subway Organisation, Catalogue no: **SUBWAY 1**

I DON'T WANNA BE FRIENDS WITH YOU
Tracks: / I don't wanna be friends with you / Look back.
7" Single: Released Sep '86, on Blue Guitar, by Blue Guitar Records. Catalogue no: **AZUR 2**
12" Single: Released Sep '86, on Blue Guitar, by Blue Guitar Records. Catalogue no: **AZURX 2**

SOMEWHERE IN CHINA
Tracks: / Somewhere in China / Almost made it.
12" Single: Released Feb '86, on 53rd & 3rd, by 53rd & 3rd Records. Catalogue no: **AGARR 112**
7" Single: Released Feb '86, on 53rd & 3rd, by 53rd & 3rd Records. Catalogue no: **AGARR 1**

Shopping For Girls

JEALOUSY
Tracks: / Jealousy / Baby.
7" Single: Released Mar '82, on Bridgehouse, Deleted '85. Catalogue no: **BHS 5**

SORRY WRONG ONE
Tracks: / Sorry wrong one.
7" Single: Released Jan '82, on Triangle, by Triangle Records. Catalogue no: **TRANG 1**

Short People

WHY'D YOU PUT IT TO ME BABY
Tracks: / Why'd you put it to me baby.
7" Single: Released Sep '79, on Inferno (1), by Inferno Records. Catalogue no: **HEAT 22**

Shorts

COMMENT CA VA
Tracks: / Comment ca va.
7" Single: Released Jul '83, on EMI, by EMI Records. Catalogue no: **EMI 5406**

Shot

MAIN THING
Tracks: / Main thing / Main dub.
Note: Featuring Kim Marsh
12" Single: Released Sep '86, on Affair, Catalogue no: **FAIR 2**

Shot In The Dark

PLAYING WITH LIGHTNING
Tracks: / Playing with lightning / Speak your language.
7" Single: Released Aug '81, on RSO, by Polydor Ltd. Deleted '84. Catalogue no: **RSO 79**

Shotgun

GREY COAT BOY(EP)
Tracks: / Grey coat boy.
7" Single: Released Apr '79, on Billy Goat, by Chick-A-Boom Records. Catalogue no: **HEP 501**

HAPPY FEELIN'
Tracks: / Happy feelin' / You just wanna dance.
7" Single: Released Mar '80, on MCA, by MCA Records. Deleted Mar '83. Catalogue no: **MCA 578**
12" Single: Released Mar '80, on MCA, by MCA Records. Deleted Mar '83. Catalogue no: **MCAT 578**

Shotgun Brides

RESTLESS
Tracks: / Restless.
7" Single: Released Apr '87, on Neat, by Neat Records. Catalogue no: **NEAT 57**

Shotgun Express

I COULD FEEL THE WHOLE WORLD TURN AROUND
Tracks: / I could feel the whole world turn round / Curtains / Funny 'cos neither could I / Indian thing.
10" single: Released Jun '83, on See For Miles, by See For Miles Records. Catalogue no: **CYM 2**

Shout

STARTING LINE
Tracks: / Starting line.
7" Single: Released Apr '82, on Mercury, by Phonogram Ltd. Catalogue no: **SHOUT 1**

SUSPICION
Tracks: / Suspicion.
12" Single: Released Jan '85, on Passion, by Skratch Records. Catalogue no: **PASH 39(12)**

THEY'VE GOT YOU WHERE THEY WANT YOU
12" Single: on Lost Moments, Catalogue no: **LM 12 033**

TRIBAL
Tracks: / Tribal.
7" Single: Released Feb '85, on Lost Moments, Catalogue no: **LM 015**

Shout Bamalam

AMBITION, THE GROOVE AND
Tracks: / Ambition, the groove and.
12" Single: Released May '88, on Flexible Bullets, Catalogue no: **FBL 001**

RESPONSIBILITY
Tracks: / Responsibility.
12" Single: Released Feb '88, on Flexible Bullets, Catalogue no: **FBL 1**

Shout-A-Loud

4 MINUTE WARNING
Tracks: / 4 minute warning.
7" Single: Released Mar '83, on Vroom, Catalogue no: **DEAD 1**

Showaddywaddy

Biographical details: Showaddywaddy are a UK rock'n'roll revival group formed in 1973 and still popular in cabaret: members have included vocalists Dave Bartram and Buddy Gask, Russ Field and Trevor Oakes on guitars; Al James and Rod Deas on bass; Malcolm Allured and Romeo Challenger on drums.
They had 22 top 40 singles '74-81, mostly covers after *Hey Rock And Roll* in 1974. Last top 40 hit was *Who Put The Bomp (In The Bomp-Bomp-Bomp)* in 1982.
(Donald Clarke 27.5.87)..

ALWAYS AND EVER (see adjacent panel)
Tracks: / Always and ever / Cool cool cat.
7" Single: Released '80, on Arista, by BMG Records (UK). Catalogue no: **ARIST 339**

BLUE MOON
Tracks: / Blue moon / Really goin' out of my mind.
7" Single: Released Nov '80, on Arista, by BMG Records (UK). Deleted Nov '83. Catalogue no: **ARIST 379**

DANCIN' PARTY
Tracks: / Dancin' party.
7" Single: Released Nov '77, on Arista, by BMG Records (UK). Deleted Nov '80. Catalogue no: **ARISTA 149**

DO WAH DIDDY
Tracks: / Do wah diddy / You are love.
7" Single: Released Feb '81, on Arista, by BMG Records (UK). Deleted Feb '84. Catalogue no: **ARIST 393**

FOOTSTEPS
Tracks: / Footsteps / Tribute.
7" Single: Released Nov '81, on Bell, Deleted Nov '84. Catalogue no: **BELL 1499**

GOOD TIMING
Tracks: / Good timin'.
7" Single: Released Feb '82, on Bell, Catalogue no: **BELL 1502**

GOODY GOODY
Tracks: / Goody goody / I want you to be my girl.
7" Single: Released Nov '82, on RCA, by BMG Records (UK). Catalogue no: **RCA 293**

HEARTBEAT
Tracks: / Heartbeat.
7" Single: Released Sep '75, on Bell, Deleted Sep '78. Catalogue no: **BELL 1450**

HEAVENLY
Tracks: / Heavenly.
7" Single: Released Nov '75, on Bell, Deleted Nov '78. Catalogue no: **BELL 1460**

HEY MR CHRISTMAS
Tracks: / Hey Mr. Christmas.
7" Single: Released Nov '74, on Bell, Deleted Nov '77. Catalogue no: **BELL 1387**

HEY ROCK AND ROLL
Tracks: / Hey rock and roll.
7" Single: Released May '74, on Bell, Deleted May '77. Catalogue no: **BELL 1357**

I WONDER WHY
Tracks: / I wonder why.
7" Single: Released Mar '78, on Arista, by BMG Records (UK). Deleted Mar '81. Catalogue no: **ARISTA 174**

LITTLE BIT OF SOAP, A
Tracks: / Little bit of soap, A.
7" Single: Released Jun '78, on Arista, by BMG Records (UK). Deleted Jun '81. Catalogue no: **ARISTA 191**

MULTIPLICATION
Tracks: / Multiplication / I wish.
7" Single: Released Jun '81, on Arista, by BMG Records (UK). Deleted Jun '84. Catalogue no: **ARIST 416**

Showaddywaddy - A Night at Daddy Gee's (Released on Arista)

NIGHT AT DADDY GEE'S, A (see panel above)
Tracks: / Night at daddy gee's, A / I appreciate the job.
7" Single: Released Nov '79, on Arista, by BMG Records (UK). Deleted Nov '82. Catalogue no: **ARISTA 314**

PRETTY LITTLE ANGEL EYES
Tracks: / Pretty little angel eyes.
7" Single: Released Nov '78, on Arista, by BMG Records (UK). Deleted Nov '81. Catalogue no: **ARIST 222**

REMEMBER THEN
Tracks: / Remember then.
7" Single: Released Mar '79, on Arista, by BMG Records (UK). Deleted Mar '82. Catalogue no: **ARISTA 247**

ROCK 'N' ROLL LADY
Tracks: / Rock and roll lady.
7" Single: Released Aug '74, on Bell. Deleted Aug '77. Catalogue no: **BELL 1374**

SOUL & INSPIRATION
Tracks: / Soul & inspiration / Run for your life.
7" Single: Released Jan '83, on RCA, by BMG Records (UK). Catalogue no: **RCA 312**

SWEET LITTLE ROCK 'N' ROLLER
Tracks: / Sweet little rock 'n' roller.
7" Single: Released Jul '79, on Arista, by BMG Records (UK). Deleted Jul '82. Catalogue no: **ARISTA 278**

SWEET MUSIC
Tracks: / Sweet music.
7" Single: Released Feb '75, on Bell. Deleted Feb '78. Catalogue no: **BELL 1403**

THREE STEPS TO HEAVEN
Tracks: / Three steps to heaven.
7" Single: Released May '75, on Bell. Deleted May '78. Catalogue no: **BELL 1426**

TROCADERO (SINGLE)
Tracks: / Trocadero.
7" Single: Released May '76, on Bell. Deleted May '79. Catalogue no: **BELL 1476**

UNDER THE MOON OF LOVE(SINGLE)
Tracks: / Under the moon of love.
7" Single: Released Nov '76, on Bell. Deleted Nov '79. Catalogue no: **BELL 1495**
7" Single: Released Aug '86, on Genie. Catalogue no: **GEN 7**
12" Single: Released Aug '86, on Genie. Catalogue no: **12 GEN 7**

WHEN
Tracks: / When.
7" Single: Released Mar '77, on Arista, by BMG Records (UK). Deleted Mar '80. Catalogue no: **ARISTA 91**

WHO PUT THE BOMP
Tracks: / Who put the bomp / Do it again.
7" Single: Released Aug '82, on RCA, by BMG Records (UK). Catalogue no: **RCA 236**

WHY?
Tracks: / Why? / Out on the town / Three steps to heaven.
Note: * extra track on 12" version.
12" Single: Released Sep '87, on Tiger, by Legend Music Group. Catalogue no: **SHOW T1**
7" Single: Released Sep '87, on Tiger, by Legend Music Group. Catalogue no: **SHOW 1**

WHY DO LOVERS BREAK EACH OTHER'S HEARTS
Tracks: / Why do lovers break each other's hearts / Don't like rock 'n' roll anymore.
7" Single: Released Sep '80, on Arista, by BMG Records (UK). Deleted Sep '83. Catalogue no: **ARIST 359**

YOU GOT WHAT IT TAKES
Tracks: / You got what it takes.
7" Single: Released Jul '77, on Arista, by BMG Records (UK). Deleted Jul '80. Catalogue no: **ARISTA 126**

Showbiz Club Of

MEXICO HERE WE GO
Tracks: / Mexico here we go / Northern Ireland.
7" Single: Released Mar '86, on Mint, by Emerald Records. Deleted '88. Catalogue no: **CHEW 105**

Showdown

KEEP DOIN' IT
Tracks: / Keep doin' it.
7" Single: Released Dec '77, on State, by State Records. Deleted Dec '80. Catalogue no: **STAT 63**

Showmen

IT WILL STAND
Tracks: / It will stand / 39-21-40 shape / Let her feel it in your kiss (On 12" version only.).
12" Single: Released Nov '88, on Charly R&B, by Charly Records. Catalogue no: **CYZ 128**
7" Single: Released Nov '88, on Charly R&B, by Charly Records. Catalogue no: **CYZ 7 128**

Showstoppers

AIN'T NOTHING BUT A HOUSE PARTY
Tracks: / Ain't nothing but a house party.
7" Single: Released Jan '71, on Beacon. Deleted Jan '74. Catalogue no: **BEA 100**
7" Single: Released Mar '68, on Beacon. Deleted Mar '71. Catalogue no: **BEACON 3 100**
7" Single: Released Sep '79, on Inferno (1), by Inferno Records. Catalogue no: **HEAT 12**
7" Single: Released '80, on USA, by Charly Records. Catalogue no: **LR 2778**
12" Single: Released Apr '83, on Inferno (1), by Inferno Records. Catalogue no: **10 BURN 1**
7" Single: Released Apr '83, on Inferno (1), by Inferno Records. Catalogue no: **BURN 1**

EENY MEENY
Tracks: / Eeny meeny.
7" Single: Released Nov '68, on MGM, by Polydor Ltd. Deleted Nov '71. Catalogue no: **MGM 1346**

Showstoppers 81

DISCO SOUND OF MUSIC
Tracks: / Disco sound of music / Sound rapping.
12" Single: Released Sep '81, on Whisper, by Whisper Records. Catalogue no: **12WSP 105**
7" Single: Released Sep '81, on Whisper, by Whisper Records. Catalogue no: **WSP 105**

Shox

NO TURNING BACK
Tracks: / No turning back / Lying here.
7" Single: Released Feb '80, on Beggars Banquet, by Beggars Banquet Records. Deleted Feb '85. Catalogue no: **BEG 33**

Shreeve, Mark

LEGION (SINGLE)
Tracks: / Legion.
12" Single: Released Aug '85, on Jive Electro, by Zomba Records. Catalogue no: **JIVET 102**
7" Single: Released Aug '85, on Jive Electro, by Zomba Records. Catalogue no: **JIVE 102**

Shrew Kings

GREEN EYED KID
Tracks: / Green eyed kid / One day in hell / This is the land / Mac the knife (radio version) / Alabama song.
12" Single: Released Feb '87, on Thin Sliced, by Thin Sliced Records. Catalogue no: **TSR 12T**

PLAY BRECHT
Tracks: / Play Brecht.
7" Single: Released Jun '85, on Thin Sliced, by Thin Sliced Records. Catalogue no: **TSR 6**

Shriekback

Biographical details:
Shriekback refers primarily to the three-man nucleus at the centre of the group's activities - Dave Allen, Barry Andrews and myself, Carl Marsh.

We met when Dave decided to start playing again after leaving the **Gang of Four** in summer 1981; he had met Barry before when the **Gang's** path had crossed the **League of Gentlemen's** and I introduced myself after Nick Launay, a mutual friend and producer, had suggested compatibility. Initially, there was no strong commitment; Dave had the idea of a short term, possibly one-off project; Barry had not yet folded his own group, **Restaurant for Dogs** and saw **Shriekback** as an interesting sideline and I wanted a loose set-up after the demise of my previous group **Out On Blue Six**.
A new album *Jam Science* is to be released in January 1984 to be followed by live dates in February and beyond.
(Carl Marsh, 1984).

ACCRETIONS Monstrous dance mix
Tracks: / Accretions.
12" Single: Released Aug '83, on Y. Catalogue no: **YT 106**

FISH BELOW THE ICE
Tracks: / Fish below the ice.
12" Single: Released Sep '85, on Arista, by BMG Records (UK). Catalogue no: **SHRK 124**

GET DOWN TONIGHT
Tracks: / Get down tonight / Big fun / Big fun (acid house remix) (Only on 12" version.).
12" Single: Released Jul '88, on Island, by Island Records. Deleted Apr '89. Catalogue no: **12IS 343**
7" Single: Released Jul '88, on Island, by Island Records. Deleted Apr '89. Catalogue no: **IS 343**

GUNNING FOR BUDDHA
Tracks: / Bludgeoned / Black light trap (Only on 12" single.).
7" Single: Released Dec '86, on Island, by Island Records. Catalogue no: **IS 314**
12" Single: Released Dec '86, on Island, by Island Records. Deleted Jul '87. Catalogue no: **12IS 314**

HAND ON MY HEART
Tracks: / Hand on my heart / Nerve.
7" Pic: Released Aug '84, on Arista, by BMG Records (UK). Catalogue no: **SHRPD 1**
12" Single: Released Jun '84, on Arista, by BMG Records (UK). Catalogue no: **SHRK 121**
7" Single: Released Jun '84, on Arista, by BMG Records (UK). Catalogue no: **SHRK 1**

LINED UP
Tracks: / Lined up / Lepax legomena.
7" Single: Released Feb '83, on Y. Catalogue no: **Y 102**
12" Single: Released Feb '83, on Y. Catalogue no: **YT 102**

LINED UP (REMIX)
Tracks: / Lined up.
7" Single: Released Aug '83, on Y. Catalogue no: **Y 106**

MERCY DASH
Tracks: / Mercy dash.
7" Pic: Released Nov '84, on Arista, by BMG Records (UK). Catalogue no: **SHRPD 122**
12" Single: Released Nov '84, on Arista, by BMG Records (UK). Catalogue no: **SHRK 122**

MY SPINE IS THE BASS LINE
Tracks: / My spine is the bass line.
12" Single: Released Sep '82, on Y. Catalogue no: **Y 27T**
7" Single: Released Sep '82, on Y. Catalogue no: **Y 27**

NEMESIS
Tracks: / Nemesis / Suck.
7" Single: Released May '85, on Arista, by BMG Records (UK). Catalogue no: **SHRK 3**
12" Single: Released May '85, on Arista, by BMG Records (UK). Catalogue no: **SHRK 123**

SEXTHINKONE
Tracks: / Sexthinkone / Here comes my handclap.
7" Single: Released Jun '82, on Y. Catalogue no: **Y 22**

TENCH
Tracks: / Tench.
7" EP: Released Jun '82, on Y. Catalogue no: **Y 21**
12" Single: Released Jun '82, on Y. Catalogue no: **Y 21T**

WORKING ON THE GROUND
Tracks: / Working on the ground.
7" Single: Released Jun '83, on Y. Catalogue no: **Y 104**
12" Single: Released Jun '83, on Y. Catalogue no: **YT 104**

Shrine Of Eight

PERFECT CRIME (WE ALL HURT INSIDE)
Tracks: / Perfect crime (we all hurt inside).
7" Single: Released May '89, on Moles. Deleted Sep '89. Catalogue no: **MRCL 1**
12" Single: Released May '89, on Moles. Deleted Sep '89. Catalogue no: **12MRCL 1**
CD 5": Released May '89, on Moles. Deleted Sep '89. Catalogue no: **MRCLCDS 1**

Shrink

WIBBLE WOBBLE
Tracks: / Wibble wobble / Prisoner.
7" Single: Released May '81, on RCA, by BMG Records (UK). Deleted May '84. Catalogue no: **RCA 70**

Shrinking Men

HAZARDS IN THE HOME
Tracks: / Hazards in the home / Zambesi Mission.
7" EP: Released Feb '82, on Pop, by Magnet Records. Catalogue no: **POP 999**

Shrubs

ANOTHER AGE
Tracks: / Another age.
12" Single: Released Sep '88, on Public Domain. Catalogue no: **DOM 001**

Shrug

NEVIL WANLESS EP, THE
12" Single: Released Jul '88, on Our Mam's Records, by Our Mam's Records. Catalogue no: **MAM 001**

Shusha

HERE I LOVE YOU (SINGLE)
Tracks: / Here I love you / You can always feel it.
7" Single: Released Nov '80, on President, by President Records. Deleted Nov '83. Catalogue no: **PT 487**
7" Single: Released Oct '80, on President, by President Records. Catalogue no: **PHT 487**

Shuttleworth, John

SWIMMING WITH SHARON
Tracks: / Swimming with Sharon.
12" Single: Released Jun '87, on Idea, by Idea Records. Catalogue no: **IDEAT 005**
7" Single: Released Jun '87, on Idea, by Idea Records. Catalogue no: **IDEA 005**

Shy

GIRL
Tracks: / Girl / Hey you.
7" Single: Released Mar '80, on Gallery. Deleted '83. Catalogue no: **GA 1**

GIVE IT ALL YOU'VE GOT
Tracks: / Give it all you've got / She's got what it takes.
CD 5": Released Oct '89, on MCA, by MCA Records. Catalogue no: **DMCAT 1369**
7" Single: Released Oct '89, on MCA, by MCA Records. Catalogue no: **MCA 1369**
12" Single: Released Oct '89, on MCA, by MCA Records. Catalogue no: **MCAT 1369**

Shy - Under Fire (Released on RCA)

12" Single: Released Oct '89, on MCA, by MCA Records. Catalogue no: **MCATT 1369**

HOLD ON(TO YOUR LOVE)
Tracks: / Hold on (to your love).
7" Single: Released Mar '85, on RCA, by BMG Records (UK). Catalogue no: **PB 40053**
12" Single: Released Mar '85, on RCA, by BMG Records (UK). Catalogue no: **PT 40054**

JUST LOVE ME
Tracks: / Just love me / Deep water / Hold on to your love / Break down the walls.
12" Single: Released Feb '88, on FM, by FM-Revolver Records. Catalogue no: **12 VHF 43**

REFLECTIONS
Tracks: / Reflections / Hunter / Deep water (on 12" only).
7" Single: Released May '85, on RCA, by BMG Records (UK). Catalogue no: **PB 40229**
12" Single: Released May '85, on RCA, by BMG Records (UK). Catalogue no: **PT 40230**

UNDER FIRE (sampler)
Tracks: / Under fire / Young heart / Break down the walls.
7" Single: Released '87, on RCA, by BMG Records (UK). Catalogue no: **SHY 100**

YOUNG HEART
Tracks: / Young heart / Run for cover / Don't want to lose your love (Available on 12" only.).
7" Single: Released Apr '87, on RCA, by BMG Records (UK). Deleted '87. Catalogue no: **PB 41295**
12" Single: Released Apr '87, on RCA, by BMG Records (UK). Deleted '87. Catalogue no: **PT 41296**

Shy Reptiles

HIGH DESIRE
Tracks: / High desire / Untitled / Landslide (Available on 12" format).
CD 5": Released Sep '89, on Fontana, by Phonogram Ltd. Catalogue no: **TILCD 2**
7" Single: Released Sep '89, on Fontana, by Phonogram Ltd. Catalogue no: **TILE 2**
12" Single: Released Sep '89, on Fontana, by Phonogram Ltd. Catalogue no: **TILE 212**

TRAIL BLAZE
Tracks: / Trail blaze / Overnight.
12" Single: Released May '89, on Fontana, by Phonogram Ltd. Deleted Oct '89. Catalogue no: **TILE 112**

Shygula

IT'S MUCH BETTER NOW
Tracks: / It's much better now.
7" Single: Released Sep '83, on Proto, by Proto Records. Catalogue no: **ENA 110**

Siam - Too Much Aggravation (Released on Ashanti)

Siam

CATRIX
Tracks: / Catrix / Lovers.
7" Single: Released Jan '81, on A&M, by A&M Records. Deleted Nov '84. Catalogue no: **AMS 8177**

DEJA VU
Tracks: / Deja vu / Overdrive.
7" Single: Released Mar '81, on A&M, by A&M Records. Deleted Mar '84. Catalogue no: **AMS 8113**

DON'T LOOK BACK
Tracks: / Don't look back / Sitting pretty.
7" Single: Released May '81, on A&M, by A&M Records. Deleted May '84. Catalogue no: **AMS 8134**

TOO MUCH AGGRAVATION
Tracks: / Too much aggravation / On the street tonight.
7" Single: Released '82, on Ashanti, Catalogue no: **ACE 42**

Sian

FIGHT THE DRAGON
Tracks: / Fight the dragon.
7" Single: Released Jul '85, on Big Ben, by Big Ben Records. Catalogue no: **MSBB 1**

Sibbles, Leroy

DANCE HALL STYLE
Tracks: / Dancehall style.
12" Single: Released Jun '85, on Ranking Joe Universal, Catalogue no: **RHJ 009**

I DON'T KNOW
Tracks: / I don't know / Your love is real.
12" Single: Released Apr '86, on Ranking Joe Universal, Catalogue no: **RJ 0011**

LOVE WON'T COME EASY
Tracks: / Keep on knocking / Love won't come easy.
12" Single: Released Jan '87, on Greensleeves, by Greensleeves Records. Catalogue no: **GRED 209**

NEED YOU BESIDE ME
Tracks: / Need you beside me.
12" Single: Released Feb '88, on Live & Love, Catalogue no: **LLD 63**

NEVER GONNA GIVE YOU UP
Tracks: / Never gonna give you up.
12" Single: Released Apr '86, on Rhythms, Catalogue no: **LS 005**

ONLY WITH YOU
Tracks: / Only with you / Dubbin' with you.
12" Single: Released Dec '83, on Micron, Catalogue no: **MICCAN 0049**

ROCK & COME ON
Tracks: / Rock & come on.
12" Single: Released Jul '83, on Micron, Catalogue no: **MICCAN 0046**

Sibley, Don E

PUNK BASHING BOOGIE
Tracks: / Punk bashing boogie.
7" Single: Released Jan '80, on Hot Rock, by Hot Rock Records. Catalogue no: **HR 45002**

Sick Things

LEGENDARY SICK THINGS (EP)
Tracks: / Legendary sick things.
7" Single: Released Jan '84, on Chaos, by Backs Recording Co.. Catalogue no: **CHS 3**

Sickidz

I COULD GO TO HELL FOR YOU (EP)
Tracks: / I could go to hell for you.
12" Single: Released Jun '84, on Big Beat, by Ace Records. Deleted '88. Catalogue no: **SWT 97**

Sidden, Gilroy

NEVER GONNA GET TO KNOW
Tracks: / Never gonna get to know.
12" Single: Released Sep '88, on Slick, by Slick Records. Catalogue no: **SR 002**

Siddleys

SUNSHINE THUGGERY
Tracks: / Sunshine thuggery / Are you still evil when you're sleeping? / Falling off my feet again / Bible bruising.
12" Single: Released 22 Aug '88, on Sombrero, by Sombrero Records. Catalogue no: **SOMBRERO 3**

WHAT WENT WRONG THIS TIME?
Tracks: / What went wrong this time.
7" Single: Released Aug '87, on Medium Cool, by Medium Cool Records. Catalogue no: **MC 005**

Side Effect

ALWAYS THERE
Tracks: / Always there.
12" Single: Released Dec '85, on Streetwave, Catalogue no: **SWAVE 4**

Side On

MAGIC
Tracks: / Magic.
7" Single: Released Feb '82, on Beggars Banquet, by Beggars Banquet Records. Deleted Jan '88. Catalogue no: **BEG 71**
12" Single: Released Feb '82, on Beggars Banquet, by Beggars Banquet Records. Deleted Jan '88. Catalogue no: **BEG 71T**

Sideboard, Sid

BUCKET & SPADES
Tracks: / Bucket and spades.
7" Single: Released Jul '82, on PRT, by Castle Communications Records. Catalogue no: **7P 244**

Sidebottom, Frank

CHRISTMAS IS REALLY FANTASTIC
Tracks: / Christmas is really fantastic.
7" Single: Released Dec '86, on In Tape, by In Tape Records. Catalogue no: **IT 041**
12" Single: Released Dec '86, on In Tape, by In Tape Records. Catalogue no: **ITTI 041**

FRANK SINGS THE MAGIC OF FREDDIE MERCURY &...
Tracks: / I should be so lucky / Love poem for Kylie / Radio ga ga / Save me / We will rock you / Frank Gordon / Queen (hip hop disco mix) / Everybody sings Queen / I am the champion.
Note: The full title is Frank sings the magic of Freddie Mercury & Queen & Kylie Minogue.
12" Single: Released '88, on In Tape, by In Tape Records. Catalogue no: **ITTI 045**

I'M THE URBAN SPACEMAN
Tracks: / I'm the urban spaceman / Oh supermum / Sci-fi medley / Space is ace / Robot Frank / Fireball XL5 (Extra track available on 12" version only.) / Life on Mars (Extra track available on 12" version only.) / Close encounters of the third kind (Extra track available on 12" version only.).
7" Pic: Released Jul '86, on Zonophone, by EMI Records. Catalogue no: **ZP 41**
7" Single: Released Jul '86, on Regal Zonophone, by EMI Records. Catalogue no: **Z 41**
12" Single: Released Jul '86, on Regal Zonophone, by EMI Records. Catalogue no: **12 Z 41**

OH BLIMEY IT'S CHRISTMAS
Tracks: / Oh blimey it's Christmas / Oliver's army / Christmas in Australia / In the summertime / Old lang zine / Life in a northern town / Greengrocer on the corner ('Greengrocer on the corner' on 12" only.).
7" Single: Released Nov '85, on Regal Zonophone, by EMI Records. Catalogue no: **Z 40**
12" Single: Released Nov '85, on Regal Zonophone, by EMI Records. Catalogue no: **12Z 40**

POPULAR MEDLEY
Tracks: / Bohemian rhapsody / Anarchy in the U.K. / Every breath you take / Material boy / God save the queen.
7" Single: Released Aug '85, on Regal Zonophone, by EMI Records. Catalogue no: **Z 39**

TIMPERLEY SUNSET
Tracks: / Timperley sunset.
7" Single: Released Nov '87, on In Tape, by In Tape Records. Catalogue no: **IT 048**
12" Single: Released Nov '87, on In Tape, by In Tape Records. Catalogue no: **ITTI 048**

Sidewalk

Biographical details: Sidewalk are Paul Mark Tams and John Springate. Paul's work with Bucks Fizz, Matt Bianco and disco supremo Ian Levine has given him a perfect grounding for knowing what kind of music people ask for a clubs and parties. John was a member of the brilliant Glitter Band in the 70's and has since moved into production working with Shakin' Stevens and other top names. (Pickwick, July 1989).

TAKE AWAY THE RAIN
Tracks: / Take away the rain / Take away the rain (version).
7" Single: Released Apr '88, on Reflection, by Nightmare Records. Catalogue no: **7 FLE2**
12" Single: Released Apr '88, on Reflection, by Nightmare Records. Catalogue no: **FLE 2**

Sidewinder

BASIL HEARD
Tracks: / Basil heard / Game, The.
7" Single: Released Dec '83, on Pope Creation, Catalogue no: **PCL 1**

Siegel, Janis

BACK TO THE ISLAND
Tracks: / Back to the island / Don't get scared.
7" Single: Released Oct '82, on Atlantic, by WEA Records. Catalogue no: **K 11766**

CHRIS SIEVEY - CAMOFLAGE (Released on EMI)

Sievey, Chris

BAISER
Tracks: / Baiser / Last.
7" Single: Released Sep '82, on Rabid, by Rabid Records. Catalogue no: **TOSH 109**

CAMOFLAGE (see panel above)
Tracks: / Camoflage / Flying train / FT.
7" Single: Released Jun '83, on EMI, by EMI Records. Catalogue no: **EMI 5398**
Cassingle: Released Jun '83, on EMI, by EMI Records. Catalogue no: **TC EMI 5398**

RED INDIAN MUSIC
Tracks: / Red Indian music.
7" Single: Released Sep '82, on Razz, by Razz Records. Catalogue no: **RAZZ 8**

WE'RE LIKE YOU
Tracks: / We're like you.
7" Single: Released Sep '81, on Razz, by Razz Records. Catalogue no: **RAZZ 5**

Siffre, Labi

CRYING, LAUGHING, LOVING, LYING (SINGLE)
Tracks: / Crying, laughing, loving, lying.
7" Single: Released Mar '72, on Pye International, Deleted Mar '75. Catalogue no: **7N 25576**

I WILL ALWAYS LOVE YOU
Tracks: / I will always love you / Tragical history tour / Listen to the voices (On 12" as extra track).
CD 5": Released Dec '88, on China, by Polydor Ltd. Catalogue no: **CHICD 12**
12" Single: Released Dec '88, on China, by Polydor Ltd. Deleted 30 Jun '89. Catalogue no: **CHINX 12**
7" Single: Released Dec '88, on China, by Polydor Ltd. Deleted 30 Jun '89. Catalogue no: **CHINA 12**

IT MUST BE LOVE
Tracks: / It must be love / Crying, laughing, loving, lying.
7" Single: Released Oct '86, on Old Gold, by Old Gold Records. Catalogue no: **OG 9637**

IT MUST BE LOVE (SINGLE)
Tracks: / It must be love.
7" Single: Released Nov '71, on Pye International, Deleted Nov '74. Catalogue no: **7N 25572**

LISTEN TO THE VOICE
Tracks: / Listen to the voices / Never let you down / So strong (Only on 12").
CD 5": Released Sep '88, on China, by Polydor Ltd. Catalogue no: **CHICD 9**
7" Single: Released Sep '88, on China, by Polydor Ltd. Catalogue no: **CHINA 9**
12" Single: Released Sep '88, on China, by Polydor Ltd. Catalogue no: **CHINX 9**

NOTHIN'S GONNA CHANGE
Tracks: / Nothin's gonna change / Secret, The.
12" Single: Released Nov '87, on Chrysalis, by Chrysalis Records. Catalogue no: **WOKX 16**
7" Single: Released Nov '87, on Chrysalis, by Chrysalis Records. Catalogue no: **WOK 16**

RUN TO HIM
Tracks: / Run to him / Love thing.
7" Single: Released Jan '81, on Polydor, by Polydor Ltd. Deleted Jan '84. Catalogue no: **POSP 215**

(SOMETHING INSIDE) SO STRONG
Tracks: / Something inside.
12" Single: Released Feb '87, on China, by Polydor Ltd. Catalogue no: **WOKX 12**
7" Single: Released Feb '87, on China, by Polydor Ltd. Catalogue no: **WOK 12**

WATCH ME
Tracks: / Watch me.
7" Single: Released Jul '72, on Pye International, Deleted Jul '75. Catalogue no: **7N 25586**

Sigerson, Davitt

I NEVER FALL IN LOVE
Tracks: / I never fall in love / Break my heart.
7" Single: Released Jul '80, on Island, by Island Records. Deleted Jul '83. Catalogue no: **WIP 6564**

TWIST
Tracks: / Twist / Mood piece.
7" Single: Released Sep '80, on Island, by Island Records. Deleted '83. Catalogue no: **WIP 6643**

Siglo XX

ART OF WAR
Tracks: / Art of war.
12" Single: Released May '82, on Antler, by Antler Records (Belgium). Deleted '88. Catalogue no: **ANT 002**

DREAMS OF PLEASURE
Tracks: / Dreams of pleasure / In the garden / Silent house.
12" Single: Released Dec '83, on Antler, by Antler Records (Belgium). Deleted '88. Catalogue no: **ANT 020**

END OF THE NIGHT, THE
Tracks: / End of the night.
12" Single: Released 26 Jan '87, on Play It Again Sam(Belgium), by Play It Again Sam (Belgium). Catalogue no: **BIAS 046**

FEAR & DESIRE (SINGLE)
Tracks: / Fear and desire.
7" Single: Released Mar '88, on Play It Again Sam(Belgium), by Play It Again Sam (Belgium). Catalogue no: **BIAS 87**

IN THE GARDEN
Tracks: / In the garden.
7" Single: Released 14 Jun '85, on Paragon, Catalogue no: **VIRTUE 004**

IN THE GARDENS
Tracks: / In the gardens.
7" Single: Released May '84, on Paragon, Catalogue no: **VIRTUE 6**

IT'S ALL OVER NOW
Tracks: / It's all over now.
12" Single: Released Jun '88, on Antler, by Antler Records (Belgium). Deleted '88. Catalogue no: **ANT 042**

SUMMERS DIE
Tracks: / Summers die.
12" Single: Released 1 Aug '89, on Play It Again Sam(Belgium), by Play It Again Sam (Belgium). Catalogue no: **BIAS 114**
CD 5": Released 1 Aug '89, on Play It Again Sam(Belgium), by Play It Again Sam (Belgium). Catalogue no: **BIAS 114CD**

VIEW OF THE WIERD
Tracks: / View of the wierd.
12" Single: Released Sep '87, on Play It Again Sam(Belgium), by Play It Again Sam (Belgium). Catalogue no: **BIAS 073**

Sigmund...

GLORY TO THE NEW BORN KING
Tracks: / Glory to the new born king.
12" Single: Released Dec '88, on Antler, by Antler Records (Belgium). Catalogue no: **ANT 097**

SACRED
Tracks: / Sacred / Sacred.
12" Single: Released Jun '88, on Antler, by Antler Records (Belgium). Catalogue no: **ANT 064**

SECRET
Tracks: / Secret.
12" Single: Released Jun '88, on Antler, by Antler Records (Belgium). Catalogue no: **ANT 063**

Sign Language

BELIEF AND OTHER CAUSES
Tracks: / Belief and other causes.
12" Single: Released Mar '86, on Fire, by Fire Records. Catalogue no: **FIRE 6**

Signal Aout 42

CARNAVAL
Tracks: / Carnaval.
CD 5": Released 1 Aug '89, on Play It Again Sam(Belgium), by Play It Again Sam (Belgium). Catalogue no: **LDCD 8822**
12" Single: Released 1 Aug '89, on Play It Again Sam(Belgium), by Play It Again Sam (Belgium). Catalogue no: **LD 8822**

GIRLS OF "VLAANDEREN"
Tracks: / Girls of "Vlaanderen".
12" Single: Released 1 Jan '87, on Disco Smash, Catalogue no: **SA 042**

PLEASURE & CRIME (REMIX)
Tracks: / Pleasure & crime (remix).
12" Single: Released '88, on Licensed, Catalogue no: **LD 8817**

Sigue Sigue Sputnik

21ST CENTURY BOY
Tracks: / 21st century boy / Buy.
7" Single: Released May '86, on EMI, by EMI Records. Deleted Oct '87. Catalogue no: **SSS 2**
12" Single: Released May '86, on EMI, by EMI Records. Deleted Oct '87. Catalogue no: **12SSS 2**

ALBINONI VS. STAR WARS
Tracks: / Albino vs. Star Wars (Pt. 1) (Not on 12".) / Albino vs. Star Wars (Pt. 1&2) (Not on 12".) / Albino vs. Star Wars (Pt. 1ext.) (not on 7".) / Albino vs. Star Wars (Pt. 2ext.) (not on 7".).
CD 5": Released May '89, on Parlophone, by EMI Records. Deleted Aug '89. Catalogue no: **CDSSS 4**
CD 5": Released May '89, on Parlophone, by EMI Records. Deleted Aug '89. Catalogue no: **203 233 2**
7" Single: Released May '89, on Parlophone, by EMI Records. Deleted Oct '89. Catalogue no: **203 233 7**
12" Single: Released May '89, on Parlophone, by EMI Records. Deleted Oct '89. Catalogue no: **12SSS 4**
12" Single: Released May '89, on Parlophone, by EMI Records. Deleted Oct '89. Catalogue no: **203 233 6**
7" Single: Released May '89, on Parlophone, by EMI Records. Deleted Oct '89. Catalogue no: **SSS 4**

DANCERAMA
Tracks: / Dancerama (Not on 12SSSX 5.) / Barbarandroid (Not on CD 5".) / Dancerama (12" ext.) (12SSS 5 & CD 5" only.) / Dancerama (kashmire remix) (12SSSX 5 only.) / Dancerama (saxy remix) (12SSSX 5 only.) / Dancerama club (introduction) (12SSSPD 5 only.) / Dancerama (album mix ext.) (12SSSPD 5 & CD 5" only.).
CD 5": Released Mar '89, on Parlophone, by EMI Records. Catalogue no: **CDSSS 5**
CD 5": Released Mar '89, on Parlophone, by EMI Records. Catalogue no: **203 291 2**
7" Single: Released Mar '89, on Parlophone, by EMI Records. Deleted Aug '89. Catalogue no: **SSS 5**
12" Single: Released Mar '89, on Parlophone, by EMI Records. Deleted Aug '89. Catalogue no: **203 291 6**
12" Single: Released Mar '89, on Parlophone, by EMI Records. Deleted Aug '89. Catalogue no: **203 298 0**
12" Single: Released Mar '89, on Parlophone, by EMI Records. Deleted Aug '89. Catalogue no: **12SSSX 5**
12" Single: Released Mar '89, on Parlophone, by EMI Records. Deleted Aug '89. Catalogue no: **12SSS 5**
12" Single: Released Mar '89, on Parlophone, by EMI Records. Deleted Aug '89. Catalogue no: **12SSSPD 5**
12" Single: Released Mar '89, on Parlophone, by EMI Records. Deleted Aug '89. Catalogue no: **203 298 6**
7" Single: Released Mar '89, on Parlophone, by EMI Records. Deleted Aug '89. Catalogue no: **203 291 7**

LOVE MISSILE F1-11
Tracks: / Love missile F1-11 / Hack attack / Love missile (dance mix) (Extra track on 12" only).
Note: Extra track on 12" only
7" Single: Released Feb '86, on Parlophone, by EMI Records. Catalogue no: **R 5551**
12" Single: Released Feb '86, on Parlophone, by EMI Records. Catalogue no: **12R 5551**

LOVE MISSILE F1-11(2)
Tracks: / Love missile F1-11(trailer video mix) / Love missile F1-11 / And actuality sound / Hack attack.
7" Single: Released Mar '86, on Parlophone, by EMI Records. Deleted Mar '89. Catalogue no: **SSS 1**
12" Single: Released Mar '86, on EMI, by EMI Records. Catalogue no: **12 SSSX 1**

RIO ROCKS
Tracks: / Rio rocks (7" & CD single only.) / Aliens (7" only.) / Rio rocks (ext.) (12" & CD single only.) / Rio rocks (samba) (CD single & Special only.) / Rio rocks (7" samba) (Special Product only.) / Rio rocks (acid) (Special Product only.).
CD 5": Released Jul '89, on Parlophone, by EMI Records. Catalogue no: **203 452 2**
7" Single: Released Jul '89, on Parlophone, by EMI Records. Catalogue no: **203 452 7**
7" Single: Released Jul '89, on Parlophone, by EMI Records. Catalogue no: **SSS 6**
12" Single: Released Jul '89, on Parlophone, by EMI Records. Catalogue no: **12SSS 6**
12" Single: Released Jul '89, on Parlophone, by EMI Records. Catalogue no: **203 452 6**
Special: Released Jul '89, on Parlophone, by EMI Records. Catalogue no: **203 452 0**
Special: Released Jul '89, on Parlophone, by EMI Records. Catalogue no: **12SSSX 6**
CD 5": Released Jul '89, on Parlophone, by EMI Records. Catalogue no: **CDSSS 6**

SUCCESS
Tracks: / Success / Frankenstein cha cha cha / Success (ext) (12" only.) / Frankenstein cha cha cha (ext.) (12" only.) / Nightmare of Neal X (Pic disc only.) / Success Sputnik style (Pic disc only.) / Success (acid mix #1) / Success (Acid Mix #2) / Frankenstein cha cha cha (7" mix) (12SSSX only.) / Success (Balaeracidic 12") (12SSSX & CD single only.).
CD 5": Released Nov '88, on Parlophone, by EMI Records. Catalogue no: **CDSSS 3**
7" Single: Released Nov '88, on Parlophone, by EMI Records. Deleted Aug '89. Catalogue no: **SSS 3**
12" Single: Released Nov '88, on Parlophone, by EMI Records. Deleted Aug '89. Catalogue no: **12 R 6196**
12" Single: Released Nov '88, on Parlophone, by EMI Records. Deleted Aug '89. Catalogue no: **12SSSW 3**
12" Single: Released Nov '88, on Parlophone, by EMI Records. Deleted Aug '89. Catalogue no: **12SSS 3**
12" Single: Released Nov '88, on Parlophone, by EMI Records. Deleted Aug '89. Catalogue no: **12SSSX 3**
12" Pic: Released Nov '88, on Parlophone, by EMI Records. Deleted Aug '89. Catalogue no: **12SSSP 3**

Silence & The Beat

FREEZING POINT
Tracks: / Freezing point (remix) / Freezing point (Inst).
12" Single: Released Nov '86, on Silver Lining, Deleted '87. Catalogue no: **SLVRT 22**
7" Single: Released Oct '86, on Silver Lining, Deleted '87. Catalogue no: **SLVR 22**

Silencers

ANSWER ME
Tracks: / Answer me / My love is like a wave / Razor blade reprise / Not quite the blues (Only on 12" and CD single.) / Overboard (Only on 12" version.) / Blues for buddah, A (Only on the CD single.).
CD 5": Released Oct '88, on RCA, by BMG Records (UK). Deleted Jul '89. Catalogue no: **PD 42284**
12" Single: Released Oct '88, on RCA, by BMG Records (UK). Deleted Aug '89. Catalogue no: **PT 42284**
7" Single: Released Oct '88, on RCA, by BMG Records (UK). Deleted May '89. Catalogue no: **PB 42283**

I CAN'T CRY
Tracks: / I can't cry / Crucify me / Blue desire

SILICON TEENS - MEMPHIS TENNESSEE (Released on Mute)

(Extra track on 12").
7" Single: Released Jul '87, on RCA, by BMG Records (UK). Deleted '87. Catalogue no: **HUSH 1**
12" Single: Released Jul '87, on RCA, by BMG Records (UK). Catalogue no: **HUSHT 1**

I SEE RED
Tracks: / I see red / Return to centre.
CD 5": Released Jun '89, on RCA, by BMG Records (UK). Deleted Jul '89. Catalogue no: **PD 41708**
7" Single: Released Jan '88, on RCA, by BMG Records (UK). Deleted May '89. Catalogue no: **PB 41707**
12" Single: Released Jan '88, on RCA, by BMG Records (UK). Deleted May '89. Catalogue no: **PT 41708**

PAINTED MOON
Tracks: / Painted moon / Here comes the train / Taxi to Disneyland.
Note: "All tracks on both the 7" and 12" were produced by Dave Bascombe who is already well-known for his work with Tears For Fears and Peter Gabriel". (RCA Records, May 1988).
CD 5": Released Jun '89, on RCA, by BMG Records (UK). Deleted Jul '89. Catalogue no: **HUSHC 1**
7" Single: Released May '88, on RCA, by BMG Records (UK). Catalogue no: **HUSH 1**
12" Single: Released May '88, on RCA, by BMG Records (UK). Catalogue no: **HUSH T 1**

REAL MCCOY, THE
Tracks: / Real McCoy, The / White carnation.
CD 5": Released Aug '89, on RCA, by BMG Records (UK). Catalogue no: **PD 42586**
7" Single: Released Jan '88, on RCA, by BMG Records (UK). Catalogue no: **PB 42585**
12" Single: Released Jan '88, on RCA, by BMG Records (UK). Catalogue no: **PT 42586**
12" Single: Released Sep '89, on RCA, by BMG Records (UK). Catalogue no: **PT 43158**

SCOTTISH RAIN
Tracks: / Scottish rain / Blues for buddah, A / Gimme shelter.
CD 5": Released 15 May '89, on RCA, by BMG Records (UK). Catalogue no: **PD 42702**
7" Single: Released May '89, on RCA, by BMG Records (UK). Catalogue no: **PB 42701**
12" Single: Released May '89, on RCA, by BMG Records (UK). Catalogue no: **PT 42702**
Cassingle: Released Jun '89, on RCA, by BMG Records (UK). Catalogue no: **PK 42701**

Silent, B. C.

TAKE IT OR LEAVE IT
Tracks: / Consequences / Take it or leave it.
7" Single: Released Jan '87, on Sonet, by Sonet Records. Catalogue no: **SON 2316**

Silent Guests

HOUSE OF WAX
Tracks: / House of wax / Guillotine.
7" Single: Released Jun '82, on Third World, Catalogue no: **HIT 104**

Silent Rage

OH BABY
Tracks: /.Oh baby.
7" Single: Released May '85, on Lost Moments, Catalogue no: **LM 025**

REBEL WITH A CAUSE
Tracks: / Rebel with a cause.
12" Single: Released 16 Sep '88, on Chameleon (USA), by Chameleon Music Group (USA). Catalogue no: **CH 12006**

Silent Rite

GREATEST SHOW
Tracks: / Greatest show, The.
7" Single: Released Sep '83, on 46 Records (Germany), Catalogue no: **5102**

Silent Running

EMOTIONAL WARFARE
Tracks: / Emotional warfare / Speed of life.
12" Single: Released Mar '84, on EMI, by EMI Records. Catalogue no: **12R 6066**
7" Single: Released Mar '84, on EMI, by EMI Records. Catalogue no: **R 6066**

HEARTLAND
Tracks: / Heartland / Winds of war.
7" Single: Released Apr '88, on Atlantic, by WEA Records. Catalogue no: **A 9103**
12" Single: Released Apr '88, on Atlantic, by WEA Records. Catalogue no: **A 9103 T**

NO FAITH IS BLIND
Tracks: / No faith is blind.
12" Single: Released Oct '85, on Parlophone, by EMI Records. Catalogue no: **12RA 6104**

SANCTUARY
Tracks: / Sanctuary / Under your skin.
12" Single: Released Sep '87, on Atlantic, by WEA Records. Deleted Jul '88. Catalogue no: **A 9186 T**
7" Single: Released Sep '87, on Atlantic, by WEA Records. Deleted Jul '88. Catalogue no: **A 9186**

WHEN THE 12TH OF NEVER COMES
Tracks: / When the 12th of never comes.
7" Single: Released Jun '83, on EMI, by EMI Records. Catalogue no: **EMI 5400**

Silent Screen

HANDSTANDS
Tracks: / Handstands.
7" Single: Released May '84, on TMI, Catalogue no: **TMI 001**

Silhouette

CLOWN
Tracks: / Clown.
7" Single: Released Apr '83, on Thunderbay, Catalogue no: **TBR 022**

I CAN TAKE A HINT
Tracks: / I can take a hint.
7" Single: Released Jun '84, on Spirit (1), by Spirit Records. Catalogue no: **FIRE 3**

MAKE THE MOST OF IT
Tracks: / Make the most of it.
7" Single: Released Sep '85, on Spirit (1), by Spirit Records. Catalogue no: **FIRE 7**

NO GOOD SAYING NO GOOD
Tracks: / No good saying no good.
7" Single: Released Apr '83, on Thunderbay, Catalogue no: **TBR 23**

Silhouettes

Biographical details: The Silhouettes are a vocal quartet who got together in 1955 in Philadelphia as a gospel group; they sang R&B as the Thunderbirds, then became the Silhouettes, with lead singer Billy Horton (born in 1929), tenor Richard Lewis (born in 1933), baritone Earl Beal (born in 1924), bass Raymond Edwards (born 1922). They had only one big hit but it was a monster: *Get A Job* was no.1 in both R&B and pop charts '58, co-written by Lewis with arranger Howard Biggs; its influential doo-wop lyric provided the name for the rock'n'roll revival group Sha Na Na in the 1970s. They have reunited for oldies shows. (Donald Clarke 27.5.87)..

GET A JOB
Tracks: / Get a job / Stagger Lee / Ten commandments of love.
7" Single: Released Jul '82, on Old Gold, by Old Gold Records. Deleted Jul '88. Catalogue no: **OG 9093**
7" Single: Released 23 May '87, on Stateside, by EMI Records. Deleted Apr '88. Catalogue no: **STATES 2**
12" Single: Released 23 May '87, on Stateside, by EMI Records. Deleted Apr '88. Catalogue no: **12 STATES 2**

Silicon Chip

STAY
Tracks: / Stay / Stay (remix) (On BP 12006R only.).
12" Single: Released May '89, on BPM, Catalogue no: **BP 12006R**
12" Single: Released Nov '88, on BPM, Catalogue no: **BP 12006**

Silicon Teens

JUDY IN DISGUISE (see panel below)
Tracks: / Judy in disguise / Chip 'n' roll.
7" Single: Released Jan '80, on Mute, by Mute Records. Catalogue no: **MUTE 4**

JUST LIKE EDDIE
Tracks: / Just like Eddie.
7" Single: Released Jul '80, on Mute, by Mute Records. Catalogue no: **MUTE 8**

MEMPHIS TENNESSEE (see panel above)
Tracks: / Memphis Tennessee / Let's dance.
7" Single: Released Aug '79, on Mute, by Mute Records. Catalogue no: **MUTE 003**

RED RIVER ROCK
Tracks: / Red river rock / Chip 'n' roll.
12" Single: Released Sep '88, on Mute, by Mute Records. Catalogue no: **SILI T1**
7" Single: Released Aug '88, on Mute, by Mute Records. Catalogue no: **SILI 1**

Silicone Fish

HEARTBURN
Tracks: / Heartburn / Watch out for yourself.
7" Single: Released Mar '80, on White Dove, by White Dove Records. Deleted '83. Catalogue no: **WD 104**

Silk

FLY AWAY
Tracks: / Fly away / Nancy O.
7" Single: Released Apr '84, on Stage One, Catalogue no: **ARL 101**

Silk, J.M.

I CAN'T TURN AROUND
Tracks: / I can't turn around.
7" Single: Released Oct '86, on RCA, by BMG Records (UK). Catalogue no: **PB 49793**
12" Single: Released Oct '86, on RCA, by BMG Records (UK). Deleted May '89. Catalogue no: **PT 49794**

LET THE MUSIC TAKE CONTROL
Tracks: / Insane (apella mix).
12" Single: Released Feb '87, on RCA, by BMG Records (UK). Deleted May '89. Catalogue no: **PT 49768**
7" Single: Released Feb '87, on RCA, by BMG Records (UK). Deleted '87. Catalogue no: **PB 49767**

SHE'S SO FAR AWAY
Tracks: / She's so far away / Jack your body / House in Eb minor (Extra track on 12") / I can't turn around* (*Extra track on 12").
7" Single: Released 13 Jun '87, on RCA, by BMG Records (UK). Catalogue no: **PB 49713**
12" Single: Released 13 Jun '87, on RCA, by BMG Records (UK). Deleted May '89. Catalogue no: **PT 49714**

Silk & Steele

DOCTOR'S ORDERS
Tracks: / Doctor's orders / Emotions in motion.
7" Single: Released Jul '88, on Strike (2), Catalogue no: **STRK 4**
12" Single: Released Jul '88, on Strike (2), Catalogue no: **12 STRK 4**

DON'T TALK TO STRANGERS
Tracks: / Don't talk to strangers / Emotions in motion.
12" Single: Released Dec '88, on Strike (2), Catalogue no: **12 STRK 6**
7" Single: Released Dec '88, on Strike (2), Catalogue no: **STRK 6**

Silkie

YOU'VE GOT TO HIDE YOUR LOVE AWAY
Tracks: / You've got to hide your love away.
7" Single: Released Sep '65, on Fontana, by Phonogram Ltd. Deleted Sep '68. Catalogue no: **TF 603**

Silky

LEFT RIGHT CENTRE
Tracks: / Left right centre.
7" Single: Released Sep '84, on Panther, by MCA Records. Catalogue no: **PAN 7**
12" Single: Released Sep '84, on Panther, by MCA Records. Catalogue no: **PANT 7**

Silly Wizzard •

TAKE THE HIGH ROAD
Tracks: / Take the high road.

SILICON TEENS - JUDY IN DISGUISE (Released on Mute)

7" Single: Released Oct '80, on Highway, by Highway Records. Catalogue no: **SHY 100**

Silsoe

AZTEC GOLD The official ITV theme(World Cup)
Tracks: / Aztec gold / On wings of the wind.
7" Single: Released May '86, on CBS, by CBS Records. Catalogue no: **A 7231**

TWO OF US, THE
Tracks: / Genesis-A.O.N.
7" Single: Released Dec '86, on Sierra, by Sierra Records. Catalogue no: **FED 30**

Silva, Victy

I THINK I'LL ALWAYS LOVE YOU
Tracks: / I think I'll always love you / Sea of love.
7" Single: Released Jun '80, on Mercury, by Phonogram Ltd. Deleted Jun '83. Catalogue no: **MER 20**

Silver Bullet

BRING FORTH THE GUILLOTINE
Tracks: / Bring forth the guillotine.
7" Single: Released May '89, on Tom Tom, Catalogue no: **TTT 008**

BRING FORTH THE GUILLOTINE (REMIX)
Tracks: / Bring forth the guillotine (remix).
12" Single: Released Sep '89, on Tam Tam, Catalogue no: **TTT 013**

Silver Chapter

DEBBIE
Tracks: / Debbie / Neon Queen.
12" Single: Released Aug '87, on Anagram, by Cherry Red Records. Catalogue no: **12 ANA 37**

Silver Convention

EVERYBODY'S TALKIN' 'BOUT LOVE
Tracks: / Everybody's talkin' 'bout love.
7" Single: Released Jan '77, on Magnet, by WEA Records. Deleted Jan '80. Catalogue no: **MAG 81**

FLY ROBIN FLY
Tracks: / Fly robin fly / Get up & boogie.
7" Single: Released Sep '81, on Magnet, by WEA Records. Catalogue no: **MAG 304**
7" Single: Released Nov '75, on Magnet, by WEA Records. Deleted Nov '78. Catalogue no: **MAG 43**

GET UP AND BOOGIE (OLD GOLD)
Tracks: / Fly Robin fly / Save me* / Everybody's talking 'bout love (Available on 12" only) / Get up and boogie.
7" Single: Released Jan '87, on Old Gold, by Old Gold Records. Catalogue no: **OG 9669**
12" Single: Released Jan '87, on Old Gold, by Old Gold Records. Catalogue no: **OG 4015**

GET UP AND BOOGIE (SINGLE)
Tracks: / Get up and boogie.
7" Single: Released Mar '76, on Magnet, by WEA Records. Catalogue no: **MAG 55**

SAVE ME
Tracks: / Save me.
7" Single: Released Apr '75, on Magnet, by WEA Records. Deleted Apr '78. Catalogue no: **MAG 26**

TIGER BABY/NO NO JOE
Tracks: / Tiger baby / No no Joe.
7" Single: Released Jun '76, on Magnet, by WEA Records. Deleted Jun '79. Catalogue no: **MAG 69**

Silver, Damion

PUT YOUR HEAD ON MY SHOULDER
Tracks: / Put your head on my shoulder.
7" Single: Released Jul '84, on AWA, Catalogue no: **SAW 009**

Silver, Dave

GYM-PANIC
Tracks: / Gym-panic.
12" Single: Released Jun '83, on UN-KNOWN, Catalogue no: **45058**

Silver, Jimmy

SKIN TALK & BODY TALK
Tracks: / Skin talk & body talk / Tune me in.
7" Single: Released Jan '80, on Gem, Deleted '85. Catalogue no: **GEMS 15**

Silver, Karen

I DON'T WANNA FALL IN LOVE AGAIN
Tracks: / I don't wanna fall in love again.
12" Single: Released Apr '85, on Ecstasy, by Creole Records. Catalogue no: **XTCT 14**

Silver, Maxwell

17 AND READY
Tracks: / 17 and ready.
7" Single: Released Mar '85, on BM, by BM Records. Deleted '88. Catalogue no: **BMR 001**

MORE I LOOK, THE
Tracks: / More I look, The.
7" Single: Released Jul '85, on BM, by BM Records. Deleted '88. Catalogue no: **BMR 2**

Silver, Mick

EVERYTHING YOU NEED
Tracks: / Everything you need.
7" Single: Released Apr '85, on Legacy, by Legacy Records. Catalogue no: **LGY 23**
12" Single: Released Apr '85, on Legacy, by Legacy Records. Catalogue no: **LGYT 23**

IT'S TRUE
Tracks: / It's true / Life in the shade.
12" Single: Released Apr '86, on Legacy, by Legacy Records. Catalogue no: **LGYT 41**
7" Single: Released Apr '86, on Legacy, by Legacy Records. Catalogue no: **LGY 41**

LAST SONG, THE
Tracks: / Last song, The / Home again.
7" Single: Released Oct '86, on Carrere, Catalogue no: **CAR 402**
12" Single: Released Oct '86, on Carrere, Catalogue no: **CART 402**

Silver Pozzoli

AROUND MY DREAM
Tracks: / Around my dream.
7" Single: Released Jul '85, on Sierra, by Sierra Records. Catalogue no: **FED 15**
12" Single: Released Jul '85, on Sierra, by Sierra Records. Catalogue no: **FED 15T**

Silvera, Carmen

ALLO 'ALLO
Tracks: / Under the bridges of Paris / Allo allo.
7" Single: Released Nov '86, on First Night, by First Night Records. Catalogue no: **SCORE 4**

Silverfish

SILVERFISH (EP)
Tracks: / Silverfish.
12" Single: Released 31 Jul '89, on Wiiija, Catalogue no: **WIIJI T4**

Silvers, Colonel Jim

CRYING MY HEART OUT OVER YOU
Tracks: / Crying my heart out over you / Blue night.
7" Single: Released Oct '81, on Rondelet Music, by Rondelet Music & Records. Catalogue no: **ROUND 1006**

Silverspoon, Dooley

LET ME BE THE NUMBER ONE
Tracks: / Let me be the number one.
7" Single: Released Jan '76, on Seville, by President Records. Deleted Jan '79. Catalogue no: **SEV 1020**

Silverwing

SITTING PRETTY
Tracks: / Sitting pretty / Teenage love / Flashbomb fever (Only on 12" single.) / Rock'n'roll mayhem (Only on 12" single.).
7" Single: Released Apr '82, on Neon Music, Catalogue no: **SILV 002**
12" Single: Released Apr '82, on Neon Music, Catalogue no: **SILV 00212**

THAT'S ENTERTAINMENT
Tracks: / That's entertainment / Flashborne fever.
7" Single: Released Nov '82, on Mayhem, by International Records & Tapes. Catalogue no: **SILV 3**

Simcess

LIFE OF BEAUTY
Tracks: / Life of beauty.
7" Single: Released Apr '89, on Access All Areas Music, Catalogue no: **7013**
12" Single: Released Apr '89, on Access All Areas Music, Catalogue no: **8013**

Simeon Andre

SWEET TALKING
Tracks: / Sweet talking / Hey fatman.
7" Single: Released Jan '82, on Get Set Sounds, Deleted Jan '85. Catalogue no: **GS 0017**

Simeone, Harry

LITTLE DRUMMER BOY
Tracks: / Little drummer boy.
7" Single: Released Feb '59, on Top Rank (1), Deleted Feb '62. Catalogue no: **JAR 101**

ONWARD CHRISTIAN SOLDIERS
Tracks: / Onward christian soldiers.
7" Single: Released Dec '60, on ember, Deleted Dec '64. Catalogue no: **EMBS 118**
7" Single: Released Dec '62, on ember, Deleted Dec '65. Catalogue no: **EMBS 144**

Simeone, Harry Chorale

LITTLE DRUMMER BOY THE
Tracks: / Little drummer boy / O bambino.
7" Single: Released Dec '82, on MCA, by MCA Records. Deleted Dec '87. Catalogue no: **MCA 806**

Simien, Sidney

ZYDECO LUCY GO
Tracks: / Zydeco Lucy go / Jo pete is in the bed.
7" Single: Released Dec '82, on Bally Hoo (USA), Catalogue no: **BH 1018**

Simion, Lascell

ALL CREATURES GREAT AND SMALL
Tracks: / All creatures great and small.
12" Single: Released Apr '82, on Clarendon Sounds, Catalogue no: **CS 002**

Simmonds, Leroy

I JUST WANT TO LOVE YOU
Tracks: / I just want to love you.
12" Single: Released 5 Mar '88, on Ariwa Sounds, by Ariwa Sounds. Catalogue no: **ARI 72**

Simmons, Carl

RED LIGHT RUBY
Tracks: / Red light Ruby / Ruby hold on.
7" Single: Released Jun '81, on Polydor, by Polydor Ltd. Deleted Jun '84. Catalogue no: **POSP 281**

Simmons, Chandra

NEVER GONNA LET YOU GO
Tracks: / Never gonna let you go.
12" Single: Released Aug '87, on Fresh (USA), Catalogue no: **FRE 13**

Simmons, Gene

RADIOACTIVE
Tracks: / Radioactive.
7" Single: Released Jan '79, on Casablanca, by PolyGram UK Ltd. Deleted Jan '82. Catalogue no: **CAN 134**

Simmons, Leroy

LOVE THAT YOU'RE LOOKING FOR
Tracks: / Love that you're looking for.
12" Single: Released Oct '89, on Ariwa Sounds, by Ariwa Sounds. Catalogue no: **ARI 096**

Simmons, Patrick

SO WRONG
Tracks: / So wrong.
7" Single: Released May '83, on Elektra, by Elektra Records (UK). Catalogue no: **E 9839**
12" Single: Released May '83, on Elektra, by Elektra Records (UK). Catalogue no: **E 9839T**

Simms Brothers

TAKE ME AS I AM
Tracks: / Take me as I am / You've got style.
7" Single: Released Jan '80, on Elektra, by Elektra Records (UK). Catalogue no: **K 12417**

Simms, Claudette

LOVERBOY
Tracks: / Loverboy / Loverboy (version).
12" Single: Released Jul '86, on Speciality (reggae), Catalogue no: **SP 001**

YOU'RE MY NATTY DREAD
Tracks: / You're my natty dread.
12" Single: Released Jan '85, on Code, by Code Records. Catalogue no: **12 LOB 019**

Simon, Carly

Biographical details: Carly Simon is a singer/songwriter born 25 June 1945 in New York. The Simon Sisters (with sister Lucy) had a minor hit in 1964 with *Winken, Blinken And Nod*; her solo debut *Carly Simon* on Electra in 1971 was co-written with film critic Jacob Brackman, and was somewhat more mature than most in singer/songwriter genre. Hit singles have included *That's The Way I've Always Heard It Should Be* (top 10 in USA 1971) and *You're So Vain* in 1972 was a bit hit in the UK and the USA. She was married to James Taylor, then to Weat Coast session drummer Russ Kunkel. USA hit *Coming Round Again* in 1986 is the theme from her score for the film Heartburn, based on Nora Ephron novel; she said she was writing a novel of her own.
(Donald Clarke 27.5.87)..

ALL I WANT IS YOU
Tracks: / All I want is you / You have to hurt.
7" Single: Released Nov '87, on Arista, by BMG Records (UK). Deleted May '89. Catalogue no: **RIS 47**

COME UPSTAIRS (SINGLE)
Tracks: / Come upstairs / Jesse.
7" Single: Released Dec '82, on Mirage (USA), Catalogue no: **CARLY 1**
12" Single: Released Dec '82, on Mirage (USA), Catalogue no: **CARLY 1T**

COMING AROUND AGAIN (SINGLE)
Tracks: / Coming around again.
CD 5": Released Feb '87, on Arista, by BMG Records (UK). Catalogue no: **ARIST CD 687**
7" Single: Released Jan '87, on Arista, by BMG Records (UK). Catalogue no: **ARIST 687**
12" Single: Released Jan '87, on Arista, by BMG Records (UK). Catalogue no: **ARIST 12687**

GIVE ME ALL NIGHT
Tracks: / Give me all night / Two hot girls / Hold what you've got.
7" Single: Released Apr '87, on Arista, by BMG Records (UK). Catalogue no: **RIS 8**
12" Single: Released Apr '87, on Arista, by BMG Records (UK). Catalogue no: **RIST 8**

HURT
Tracks: / Hurt / From the heart.
7" Single: Released Jan '82, on Warner Bros., by WEA Records. Catalogue no: **K 17898**

IT'S HARD TO BE TENDER
Tracks: / It's hard to be tender / Face to face with the mirror.
7" Single: Released Sep '87, on Philips, by Phonogram Ltd. Catalogue no: **SINS 1**

JESSE
Tracks: / Jesse / Stardust.
7" Single: Released Nov '80, on Warner Bros., by WEA Records. Catalogue no: **K 17689**

LET THE RIVER RUN
Tracks: / Let the river run / Carlotta's heart.
7" Single: Released Feb '89, on Arista, by BMG Records (UK). Catalogue no: **112 124**
12" Single: Released Feb '89, on Arista, by BMG Records (UK). Catalogue no: **612 124**
CD 5": Released Feb '89, on Arista, by BMG Records (UK). Catalogue no: **162 124**

MOCKINGBIRD
Tracks: / Mockingbird.
7" Single: Released Mar '74, on Elektra, by Elektra Records (UK). Deleted Mar '77. Catalogue no: **K 12134**

NOBODY DOES IT BETTER
Tracks: / Nobody does it better.
7" Single: Released Mar '82, on Elektra, by Elektra Records (UK). Catalogue no: **K 12261**

NOBODY DOES IT BETTER (LIVE)
Tracks: / Nobody does it better (Live) / All I want is you / Never been gone.
CD 5": Released Oct '88, on Arista, by BMG Records (UK). Catalogue no: **661807**
12" Single: Released Oct '88, on Arista, by BMG Records (UK). Catalogue no: **611 807**

RIGHT THING TO DO, THE
Tracks: / Right thing to do.
7" Single: Released Mar '73, on Elektra, by Elektra Records (UK). Deleted Mar '76. Catalogue no: **K 12095**

STUFF THAT DREAMS ARE MADE OF, THE
Tracks: / As time goes by / Sleight of hand / Stuff that dreams are made of.
7" Single: Released Aug '87, on Arista, by BMG Records (UK). Catalogue no: **RIS 33**
12" Single: Released Aug '87, on Arista, by BMG Records (UK). Catalogue no: **RIST 33**

TIRED OF BEING BLONDE
Tracks: / Tired of being blonde.
12" Single: Released Jul '85, on Epic, by CBS Records. Catalogue no: **TA 6388**
7" Single: Released Jul '85, on Epic, by CBS Records. Catalogue no: **A 6388**

WHY?
Tracks: / Why / Inst - CHIC.
7" Single: Released Jun '89, on WEA, by WEA Records. Catalogue no: **U 7501**
7" Single: Released Jul '82, on Elektra, by Elektra Records (UK). Catalogue no: **K 79300**
12" Single: Released Jul '82, on Elektra, by Elektra Records (UK). Catalogue no: **K 79300T**
12" Single: Released Jun '89, on WEA, by WEA Records. Catalogue no: **U 7501T**

YOU'RE SO VAIN (SINGLE)
Tracks: / You're so vain / Do the walls come down / Coming around again* / Itsy bitsy spider*.
Note: * extra tracks on 12 inch only

7" Single: Released Dec '72, on Elektra, by Elektra Records (UK). Deleted Dec '75. Catalogue no: **K 12077**
7" Single: Released Aug '88, on Arista, by BMG Records (UK). Catalogue no: **11701**

7" Single: Released Sep '85, on Old Gold, by Old Gold Records. Catalogue no: **OG 9521**
12" Single: Released Aug '88, on Arista, by BMG Records (UK). Catalogue no: **611701**
7" Single: Released Sep '76, on Elektra, by Elektra Records (UK). Deleted Jun '87. Catalogue no: **K 12233**

Simon & Garfunkel

Biographical details: Simon & Garfunkel were a vocl duo, among the biggest stars of the 1960s. Songwriters Paul Simon and Art Garfunkel were born in 1941 and were fast friends from childhood in New York City; as Tom & Jerry they had a USA hit in 1957 with *Hey Schoolgirl*. Strongly influenced by the Everly Brothers, they made their first album, *Wednesday Morning 3 AM* in 1964; not much happened at first, but then CBS producer Tom Wilson put a rock-style backing track on *The Sound Of Silence*; released as a single, it was a no.1 hit in the USA in 1965 (while Simon was touring the UK as a solo folk artist). *The Graduate* was directed by Mike Nichols in 1967; it made a star of Dustin Hoffman and was the first major film to have a rock soundtrack. Their last album as a duo, *Bridge Over Troubled Water* was one of the biggest sellers of all time. Simon continued with his perfectionist songwriting and recording; Garfunkel has had a successful acting career, also making solo albums. They reunited for *The Concert In Central Park* in 1982. (Donald Clarke 27.5.87)
Paul Simon and Art Garfunkel were just 15 years old when they scored a minor US hit in late 1957 under the pseudonym Tom & Jerry - *Heyschoolgirl* peaked at No.59 on the Billboard Top 100. Nothing more was heard from Tom & Jerry but, of all time. During the late Fifties and early Sixties, the two young men went their separate ways. They recorded an unsuccessful album together in 1964, then parted again. Paul Simon struggled hard to gain a reputation as a solo artist during these early years; of the two, he has always had the greater commitment to the music business. The 1964 LP, titled *Wednesday morning 3 am*, suddenly became successful in early 1966 when the track called *The sound of silence* zoomed to No.1 on the American singles chart. Its unexpected lease of life was prompted by producer Tom Wilson, who added a rock backing track to the original folk sound and thus made it part of the folk sound and thus made it part of the folk-rock boom that Bob Dylan and the Byrds had pioneered in 1965. *The sound of silence* turned Simon & Garfunkel into stars, and was quickly followed by two further US Top 5 hits: *Homeward bound* and *I am a rock*.
The duo's career reahced even greater heights in 1968, when the exuberantly catchy *Mrs Robinson* became their second US No.1 single and their first UK Top 5 hit. It was taken from the movie soundtrack *The graduate*, which gave them a smash album; in that same year, the *Bookends* LP reached No.1 in Britain. Simon & Garfunkel became firm favourites with the increasingly important student market on both sides of the Atlnatic. Simon's lyrics and stance captured the restless mood of the campuses, and his strong melodies appealed to abroad pop audience. Because Paul was the main source of material, many people came to regard him as the duo's principal talent; but Arthur's angelic voice and good looks were a vital part of the S & G success story. When the two men harmonised, they sounded like the Everly Brothers, whose debt they acknowledged when they released a cover version of *Bye bye love* on the 1970 set *Bridge over troubled water*. The *Bridge* LP and single represented the commercial and artistic peak of Simon & Garfunkel's career. The album became the world's biggest seller to that date, shifting nine million copies; it was Britain's No.1 album of the Seventies, logging 303 weeks on the charts. The title single, written by Simon and given a stunning solo vocal performance by Garfunkel, was a giant No.1 hit in the US and UK; it was a big ballad of epic proportions, and has subsequently become one of the half-dozen greatest classics of the rock era. Despite the massive success of *Bridge over troubled water*, the duo parted company soon afterwards. While a *Greatest hits* album was released to massive sales, they pursued separate careers. Simon's was, predictably more interesting from a musical standpoint. Garfunkel became more interested in movie acting, although his musical activities yielded British No.1 singles with *I only have eyes for you* (1975) and *Bright eyes* (1979). The pair reunitied for the US Top 10 single *My little town* (1975) and the massively successful reunion concert in New York's Central Park in 1981).

AMERICA
Tracks: / America.
7" Single: Released Oct '72, on CBS, by CBS Records. Deleted Oct '75. Catalogue no: **CBS 8336**

BOXER, THE
Tracks: / Boxer, The.
7" Single: Released Apr '69, on CBS, by CBS Records. Deleted Apr '72. Catalogue no: **CBS 4162**

BRIDGE OVER TROUBLED WATER (SINGLE)
Tracks: / Bridge over troubled water / Cecilia.
7" Single: Released Feb '70, on CBS, by CBS Records. Deleted Feb '73. Catalogue no: **CBS 4790**
CD 3": Released Aug '88, on Columbia (USA), by CBS Records (USA). Catalogue no: **38K33187**

HOMEWARD BOUND
Tracks: / Homeward bound / 59th Street bridge song.
7" Single: Released Mar '66, on CBS, by CBS Records. Deleted Mar '69. Catalogue no: **CBS 202045**
7" Single: Released Jan '82, on CBS, by CBS Records. Deleted Jan '85. Catalogue no: **A 1938**

I AM A ROCK
Tracks: / I am a rock.
7" Single: Released Jun '66, on CBS, by CBS Records. Deleted Jun '69. Catalogue no: **CBS 202303**

MRS ROBINSON
Tracks: / Mrs. Robinson / Bridge over troubled water.
7" Single: Released Jul '82, on Geffen, by Geffen Records (USA). Catalogue no: **GEFA 2221**
7" Single: Released '80, on CBS, by CBS Records. Catalogue no: **LR 0905**
7" Single: Released Jul '68, on CBS, by CBS Records. Deleted Jul '71. Catalogue no: **CBS 3443**

MRS ROBINSON (EP)
Tracks: / Mrs. Robinson.
7" Single: Released Jan '69, on CBS, by CBS Records. Deleted Jan '72. Catalogue no: **CBS EP 6400**

SOUNDS OF SILENCE (SINGLE)
Tracks: / Sound of silence.
7" Single: Released '80, on CBS, by CBS Records. Catalogue no: **LR 0903**

WAKE UP LITTLE SUSIE
Tracks: / Wake up little Susie / Boxer, The.
7" Single: Released Apr '82, on Geffen, by Geffen Records (USA). Deleted Apr '85. Catalogue no: **GEFA 2287**

Simon, Jo

ONE LAST LOOK
Tracks: / One last look / One last look (extended) / Always on my mind.
12" Single: Released Feb '86, on Compleat (USA), by Compleat Entertainment Corp.(USA). Deleted '87. Catalogue no: **12CLP 2800**

Simon, Joe

BRING IT ON HOME TO ME
Tracks: / Bring it on home to me.
7" Single: Released '80, on Charly, by Charly Records. Deleted '87. Catalogue no: **CTD 109**

STEP BY STEP
Tracks: / Step by step.
7" Single: Released Jun '73, on Mojo, Deleted Jun '76. Catalogue no: **2093 030**

Simon, Paul

Biographical details: Paul Simon is a singer, songwriter and guitarist; half of Simon & Garfunkel. He had minor USA solo hits in 1962-63 as Tico & The Triumphs and Jerry Landis; his debut solo album *The Paul Simon Song Book* was made in 1965, just before the duo became the biggest stars of the decade. He wrote virtually all of their material and remains one of the most important of contemporary songwriters, though his perfectionism means that new albums are few and far between. His Greatest Hits album includes otherwise unavailable singles; in the film One Trick Pony he played a fading rock star; the album *Hearts and Bones* began as a studio reunion for the duo, but that idea was scrapped; *Graceland* was one of the biggest hits of 1986. (Donald Clarke 27.5.87).

50 WAYS TO LEAVE YOUR LOVER
Tracks: / 50 ways to leave your lover.
7" Single: Released Jan '76, on CBS, by CBS Records. Deleted Jan '79. Catalogue no: **CBS 3887**

ALLERGIES
Tracks: / Allergies.
7" Single: Released Nov '83, on Warner Bros., by WEA Records. Catalogue no: **W 9453**

BOY IN THE BUBBLE
Tracks: / Boy in the bubble (remix) / Hearts and bones (Available on 12" only).
7" Single: Released Nov '86, on Warner Bros., by WEA Records. Deleted Jan '88. Catalogue no: **W 8509**
12" Single: Released Nov '86, on Warner Bros., by WEA Records. Deleted Jan '88. Catalogue no: **W 8509T**

DIAMONDS ON THE SOLES OF HER SHOES
Tracks: / All around the world or the myth of fingerprints.
12" Single: Released Feb '87, on Warner Bros., by WEA Records. Deleted Jan '88. Catalogue no: **W 8404T**
7" Single: Released Feb '87, on Warner Bros., by WEA Records. Deleted Jan '88. Catalogue no: **W 8404**

GRACELAND (SINGLE)
Tracks: / Graceland / Crazy Love vol.2 / Late great Johnny Ace, The (on 12" only.).
7" Single: Released Apr '87, on Warner Bros., by WEA Records. Deleted Jan '88. Catalogue no: **W 8349**
12" Single: Released Apr '87, on Warner Bros., by WEA Records. Deleted Jan '88. Catalogue no: **W 8349T**

LATE IN THE EVENING
Tracks: / Late in the evening.
7" Single: Released Aug '80, on Warner Bros., by WEA Records. Catalogue no: **K 17666**

LOVES ME LIKE A ROCK
Tracks: / Loves me like a rock.
7" Single: Released Sep '73, on CBS, by CBS Records. Deleted Sep '76. Catalogue no: **CBS 1700**

ME AND JULIO DOWN BY THE SCHOOLYARD
Tracks: / Me and Julio down by the schoolyard.
7" Single: Released Apr '72, on CBS, by CBS Records. Deleted Apr '75. Catalogue no: **CBS 7964**

MOTHER AND CHILD REUNION
Tracks: / Mother and child reunion.
7" Single: Released '74, on CBS, by CBS Records. Catalogue no: **CBS 7793**

MOTHER AND CHILD REUNION (RE-RELEASE)
Tracks: / Mother and child reunion / Train in the distance / Boy in the bubble, The (On 12" version only.).
CD 5": Released Nov '88, on Warner Bros., by WEA Records. Catalogue no: **W 7655 CD**
12" Single: Released Nov '88, on Warner Bros., by WEA Records. Catalogue no: **W 7655 T**
7" Single: Released Nov '88, on Warner Bros., by WEA Records. Catalogue no: **W 7655**

OH MARION
Tracks: / Oh Marion / God bless the absentee.
7" Single: Released Jan '81, on Warner Bros., by WEA Records. Catalogue no: **K 17745**

ONE-TRICK PONY (SINGLE)
Tracks: / One-trick pony / Long long day.
7" Single: Released Nov '80, on Warner Bros., by WEA Records. Deleted Nov '83. Catalogue no: **K 17715**

SLIP SLIDIN' AWAY
Tracks: / Slip slidin' away.
7" Single: Released Dec '77, on CBS, by CBS Records. Deleted Dec '80. Catalogue no: **CBS 5770**

TAKE ME TO THE MARDI GRAS
Tracks: / Take me to the mardi gras.
7" Single: Released Jun '73, on CBS, by CBS Records. Deleted Jun '76. Catalogue no: **CBS 1578**

UNDER AFRICAN SKIES
Tracks: / I know what I know / Homeless (Available on 12" only.).
7" Single: Released Aug '87, on Warner Bros., by WEA Records. Deleted Jul '88. Catalogue no: **W 8221**
12" Single: Released Aug '87, on Warner Bros., by WEA Records. Deleted Jul '88. Catalogue no: **W 8221 T**

YOU CAN CALL ME AL
Tracks: / You can call me Al / Gumboots.
7" Single: Released Aug '86, on Warner Bros., by WEA Records. Deleted Jan '88. Catalogue no: **W 8667**
12" Single: Released Aug '86, on Warner Bros., by WEA Records. Deleted Jan '88. Catalogue no: **W 8667T**

Simon, Tito

CAN'T STOP LOVING YOU
Tracks: / Can't stop loving you.
12" Single: Released May '83, on Pama, by Pama Records. Catalogue no: **PMD 3233**

DARLING (YOU'RE ALL I NEED TO GET BY)
Tracks: / Darling (you're all I need to get by).
12" Single: Released Jan '84, on Studio 80, Catalogue no: **ST 80 001**

OH PATRICIA
Tracks: / Oh Patricia / What a party.
7" Single: Released Apr '80, on Splash, by Splash Records. Deleted '83. Catalogue no: **SP 011**

REGGAE MUSIC COME FROM JAMAICA
Tracks: / Reggae music come from Jamaica / This magic moment.
12" Single: Released Feb '84, on Pama, by Pama Records. Catalogue no: **PMD 3241**

SAD AFFAIR (YOU DON'T LOVE ME AT ALL)
Tracks: / Sad affair.
12" Single: Released Nov '84, on TTT, Catalogue no: **TID 007**

THIS MONDAY MORNING FEELING
Tracks: / This Monday morning feeling / Feel the rhythm.
12" Single: Released Jul '86, on Body Music, by Nuclear Records. Catalogue no: **BMDIS 012**
7" Single: Released Feb '75, on Horse, by Trojan Records. Deleted Feb '78. Catalogue no: **HOSS 57**

Simon, Vincent

I'VE GOT SOMETHING TO SAY
Tracks: / I've got something to say.
12" Single: Released Dec '83, on Crucial Roots, Catalogue no: **CR 001**

Simone

HIM
Tracks: / Him.
7" Single: Released Aug '84, on Electricity, by Electricity Records. Deleted '88. Catalogue no: **TRIC 9**
12" Single: Released Aug '84, on Electricity, by Electricity Records. Deleted '88. Catalogue no: **TRICT 9**
7" Pic: Released Aug '84, on Electricity, by Electricity Records. Deleted '88. Catalogue no: **PTRIC 9**

IT'S TOO LATE
Tracks: / It's too late.
7" Single: Released Nov '83, on KRP, Catalogue no: **KRP 102**
12" Single: Released Nov '83, on KRP, Catalogue no: **KRPT 102**
7" Single: Released Mar '84, on Electricity, by Electricity Records. Deleted '88. Catalogue no: **TRIC 6**
12" Single: Released Mar '84, on Electricity, by Electricity Records. Deleted '88. Catalogue no: **TRICT 6**
12" Single: Released 23 May '87, on Electricity, by Electricity Records. Deleted '88. Catalogue no: **TRICT 102**

RED LIGHT SPELLS DANGER
7" Single: Released '85, on Spirit (1), by Spirit Records. Catalogue no: **FIRE 8**
12" Single: Released '85, on Spirit (1), by Spirit Records. Catalogue no: **FIRET 8**

Simone, Nina

Biographical details: Nina Simone was born Eunice Waymon on 21 Feb 1933 in North Carolina. As pianist, singer and songwriter, she is one of the all-time great cabaret artists, though unpredictable: sometimes she doesn't show up. Her first album, on Bethlehem in the USA in 1959, included top 20 singles *I Loves You Porgy*; the album is now called *My Baby Just Cares For Me* on Charly in the UK. (Donald Clarke 27.5.87).

AIN'T GOT NO....I GOT LIFE
Tracks: / Ain't got no....I got life / To love somebody.
7" Single: Released Oct '86, on Old Gold, by Old Gold Records. Catalogue no: **OG 9609**

AIN'T GOT NO....I GOT LIFE (SINGLE)
Tracks: / Ain't got no....I got life / Do what you gotta do.
7" Single: Released Oct '68, on RCA, by BMG Records (UK). Deleted Oct '71. Catalogue no: **RCA 1743**

I PUT A SPELL ON YOU (SINGLE)
Tracks: / I put a spell on you.
7" Single: Released Aug '65, on Philips, by Phonogram Ltd. Deleted Aug '68. Catalogue no: **BF 1415**

IT'S COLD OUT HERE
Tracks: / It's cold out here / I sing just to know that i'm alive / Mississippi Goddamn (live) / My baby.
CD 5": Released 22 May '89, on Jungle, by Jungle Records. Catalogue no: **JUNG 051 CD**
7" Single: Released 22 May '89, on Jungle, by Jungle Records. Catalogue no: **JUNG 051**
12" Single: Released 22 May '89, on Jungle, by Jungle Records. Catalogue no: **JUNG 051 T**
Cassingle: Released Jun '89, on Jungle, by Jungle Records. Catalogue no: **JUNG 051 C**

SIMPLE MINDS - THIS IS YOUR LAND (Released on Virgin)

LITTLE GIRL BLUE
Tracks: / Little girl blue / I loves you, Porgy / For all we know (12" only).
12" Single: Released Dec '87, on Charly, by Charly Records. Catalogue no: **CYZ 123**
7" Single: Released Dec '87, on Charly, by Charly Records. Catalogue no: **CYZ 7 123**

MISTER BOJANGLES
Tracks: / Mister bojangles / Turn me on / Ain't got no....I got life (Extra track on 12") / Ozy Mandras (Extra track on Cassingle and C.D.single.).
7" Single: Released Feb '88, on Enterprizes, Deleted May '89. Catalogue no: **PB 41775**
12" Single: Released Feb '88, on Enterprizes, Deleted May '89. Catalogue no: **PT 41776**

MY BABY JUST CARES FOR ME
Tracks: / My baby just cares for me / Little girl blue / I loves you Porgy (Only on 10" single.) / Love me or leave me (Only on 10" single.).
7" Single: Released May '82, on Charly, by Charly Records. Deleted '85. Catalogue no: **7 CYX 201**
10" single: Released May '82, on Charly, by Charly Records. Deleted '85. Catalogue no: **CYX 201**

MY BABY JUST CARES FOR ME (SINGLE)
Tracks: / My baby just cares for me / Love me or leave me / Little girl blue (Extra track on 12" only).
CD 5": Released Nov '87, on Charly, by Charly Records. Catalogue no: **CDS 1**
12" Single: Released Oct '87, on Charly, by Charly Records. Catalogue no: **CYZ 112**
7" Single: Released Apr '85, on Charly, by Charly Records. Deleted '87. Catalogue no: **CYZ 7 112**

TO LOVE SOMEBODY
Tracks: / To love somebody.
7" Single: Released Jan '69, on RCA, by BMG Records (UK). Deleted Jan '72. Catalogue no: **RCA 1779**

Simonics

IN THIS HEAT
Tracks: / In this heat.
7" Single: Released Nov '85, on Thin Sliced, by Thin Sliced Records. Catalogue no: **TSR 7**
12" Single: Released Nov '85, on Thin Sliced, by Thin Sliced Records. Catalogue no: **TSR 7T**

UNDER A GLASS BELL
Tracks: / Under a glass bell.
12" Single: Released Aug '86, on Temple Records, by Temple Records (2). Catalogue no: **SLUG 12**
7" Single: Released Aug '86, on Temple Records, by Temple Records (2). Catalogue no: **SLUG 2**

Simons, Leroy

AT THE DANCE
Tracks: / At the dance.
12" Single: Released 20 Mar '89, on Ariwa Sounds, by Ariwa Sounds. Catalogue no: **ARI 88**
12" Single: Released Sep '82, on Neville King, by Neville King Records. Deleted '88. Catalogue no: **NKRD 009**

Simper, Nick Fandango

JUST ANOTHER DAY IN THE LIFE OF A FOOL
Tracks: / Just another day in the life of a fool / I wish I'd never woken up.
7" Single: Released Feb '83, on Paro, by Paro Records. Catalogue no: **PARO S4**

Simple, Lee J.

PHANTOM OF THE SOAP OPERA
Tracks: / Phantom of the soap opera.
7" Single: Released 31 Jul '89, on Silverword, by Silverword Records. Catalogue no: **RIV 89001**

Simple Minds

Biographical details: Simple Minds are a Scottish new wave band formed in 1977 as punk outfit Johnny And The Self Abusers, who released a single *Saints And Sinners* on Chiswick, split on the day of its issue. Vocalist Jim Kerr, Guitarist Charlie Burchill, Brian McGee on drums re-formed in 1978 with bassist Derek Forbes, Mick McNeill on keyboards; their first album made the top 30 in the UK. They refined their style until their appeal as a guitar band became broad enough to conquer the USA, and are still going strong. (Donald Clarke 27.5.87)..

ALIVE AND KICKING
Tracks: / Alive and kicking / Alive and kicking (instrumental).
12" Single: Released Sep '85, on Virgin, by Virgin Records. Catalogue no: **VS 817-13**
7" Single: Released Sep '85, on Virgin, by Virgin Records. Catalogue no: **VS 817**

ALIVE & KICKING AUSTRALIAN TOUR E.P.
Tracks: / Alive and kicking / Sanctify yourself / All the things / Up on the catwalk.
7" EP: Released Sep '87, on Virgin (Australia), by Virgin Records. Catalogue no: **SMVOZO 1**

ALL THE THINGS SHE SAID
Tracks: / All the things she said (7" only) / Don't you (forget about me) / Promised you a miracle (US remix) (12" only) / All the things she said (extended version) (12" only).
12" Single: Released '85, on Virgin, by Virgin Records. Catalogue no: **VS 860-12**
7" Single: Released Mar '86, on Virgin, by Virgin Records. Catalogue no: **VS 860**

AMERICAN, THE
Tracks: / American, The / League of nations.
7" Single: Released '81, on Virgin, by Virgin Records. Catalogue no: **VS 410**
12" Single: Released '81, on Virgin, by Virgin Records. Catalogue no: **VS 410-12**

BELFAST CHILD
Tracks: / Belfast child / Mandela day / Biko.
7" EP: Released Feb '89, on Virgin, by Virgin Records. Catalogue no: **SMX 3**
CD 5": Released Feb '89, on Virgin, by Virgin Records. Catalogue no: **SMXCD 3**
12" Single: Released Feb '89, on Virgin, by Virgin Records. Catalogue no: **SMXB 3**
12" Single: Released Feb '89, on Virgin, by Virgin Records. Catalogue no: **SMXT 3**
Cassingle: Released Feb '89, on Virgin, by Virgin Records. Catalogue no: **SMXC 3**

CELEBRATE
Tracks: / Celebrate / Changeling / I travel.
12" Single: Released Feb '81, on Arista, by BMG Records (UK). Deleted Feb '84. Catalogue no: **ARIST 12394**
7" Single: Released Feb '81, on Arista, by BMG Records (UK). Deleted Feb '84. Catalogue no: **ARIST 394**

CHANGELING
Tracks: / Changeling / Premonition.
7" Single: Released Jan '80, on Arista, by BMG Records (UK). Deleted Jan '83. Catalogue no: **ARIST 325**

DON'T YOU (FORGET ABOUT ME)
Tracks: / Don't you (forget about me) / Brass band in African chimes, A.
12" Single: Released Apr '85, on Virgin, by Virgin Records. Catalogue no: **VS 749-12**
CD 3": Released '88, on Virgin, by Virgin Records. Catalogue no: **CDT 2**
7" Single: Released Apr '85, on Virgin, by Virgin Records. Catalogue no: **VS 749**

GHOSTDANCING
Tracks: / Jungleland (extended) (12" only) / Ghostdancing (7" only) / Jungleland (instrumental) (On all versions) / Ghostdancing (extended) (12" only) / Ghostdancing (instrumental) (CD & 12" only) / Ghostdancing (special extended 12" remix) (CD only) / Jungleland (special extended 12" remix) (CD only).
7" Single: Released Nov '86, on Virgin, by Virgin Records. Catalogue no: **VS 907**
12" Single: Released Nov '86, on Virgin, by Virgin Records. Catalogue no: **VS 907-12**
CD 5": Released Nov '86, on Virgin, by Virgin Records. Catalogue no: **MIKE 90712**

GLITTERING PRIZE
Tracks: / Glittering prize (7" only) / Glittering prize (theme) / Glittering prize (club mix) (12" only).
12" Single: Released Aug '82, on Virgin, by Virgin Records. Catalogue no: **VS 511-12**
7" Single: Released Aug '82, on Virgin, by Virgin Records. Catalogue no: **VS 511**

I TRAVEL
Tracks: / I travel / Film theme / Thirty frames a second.
7" Single: Released Oct '80, on Arista, by BMG Records (UK). Deleted Oct '83. Catalogue no: **ARIST 372**
12" Single: Released Feb '82, on Arista, by BMG Records (UK). Deleted Feb '87. Catalogue no: **ARIST 12448**
12" Single: Released Apr '83, on Virgin, by Virgin Records. Catalogue no: **VS 578-12**
7" Single: Released Feb '82, on Arista, by BMG Records (UK). Deleted Feb '87. Catalogue no: **ARIST 448**

I TRAVEL (2)
Tracks: / I travel / Thirty frames a second.
12" Single: Released Jan '82, on Arista, by BMG Records (UK). Catalogue no: **ARIST 12448**
7" Single: Released Jan '82, on Arista, by BMG Records (UK). Catalogue no: **ARIST 448**

KICK IT IN (see panel below)
Tracks: / Kick it in / Waterfront (89 remix) / Big Sleep (live) (12" only).
CD 5": Released 24 Jul '89, on Virgin, by Virgin Records. Catalogue no: **SMXCD 5**
7" Single: Released 24 Jul '89, on Virgin, by Virgin Records. Catalogue no: **SMX 5**
12" Single: Released 24 Jul '89, on Virgin, by Virgin Records. Catalogue no: **SMXT 5**
Cassingle: Released 24 Jul '89, on Virgin, by Virgin Records. Catalogue no: **SMXC 5**

LIFE IN A DAY
Tracks: / Life in a day.
7" Single: Released May '79, on zoom, Deleted May '82. Catalogue no: **ZUM 10**

LOVE SONG
Tracks: / Love song / Earth that you walk upon, The.
7" Single: Released Aug '81, on Virgin, by Virgin Records. Catalogue no: **VS 434**
12" Single: Released Aug '81, on Virgin, by Virgin Records. Catalogue no: **VS 434-12**

PROMISED YOU A MIRACLE (see panel on next page)
Tracks: / Promised you a miracle / Theme for great cities / Seeing out the angel (12" only).
7" Single: Released Mar '82, on Virgin, by Virgin Records. Catalogue no: **VS 488**
12" Single: Released Mar '82, on Virgin, by Virgin Records. Catalogue no: **VS 488-12**

PROMISED YOU A MIRACLE (LIVE)
Tracks: / Promised you a miracle (live) / Book of brilliant things (live) / Glittering prize (live) / Celebration (live).
Cassingle: Released 20 Jun '87, on Virgin, by Virgin Records. Deleted '89. Catalogue no: **MSC 212**

PROMISED YOU A MIRACLE (RE-RELEASE)
Tracks: / Promised you a miracle (On all versions) / Book of brilliant things (On all versions) / Glittering prize (12" only) / Celebrate (12" only).
10" single: Released Jun '87, on Virgin, by Virgin Records. Catalogue no: **SM 210**
7" Single: Released Jun '87, on Virgin, by Virgin Records. Catalogue no: **SM 2**
12" Single: Released 13 Jun '87, on Virgin, by Virgin Records. Catalogue no: **SM 212**

SANCTIFY YOURSELF
Tracks: / Sanctify yourself / Sanctify yourself (extended mix) / Sanctify yourself (dub).
7" Single: Released Jan '86, on Virgin, by Virgin Records. Deleted May '88. Catalogue no: **SM 1**
12" Single: Released Jan '86, on Virgin, by Virgin Records. Catalogue no: **SM 112**

SOMEONE SOMEWHERE (IN SUMMERTIME)
Tracks: / Someone, somewhere in summertime / King is white and in the crowd / Soundtrack for every heaven (12" only).
12" Single: Released Nov '82, on Virgin, by Virgin Records. Catalogue no: **VS 538-12**
7" Single: Released Nov '82, on Virgin, by Virgin Records. Deleted '89. Catalogue no: **VS 538**

SPEED YOUR LOVE TO ME
Tracks: / Speed your love to me / Bass line

SIMPLE MINDS - KICK IT IN (Released on Virgin)

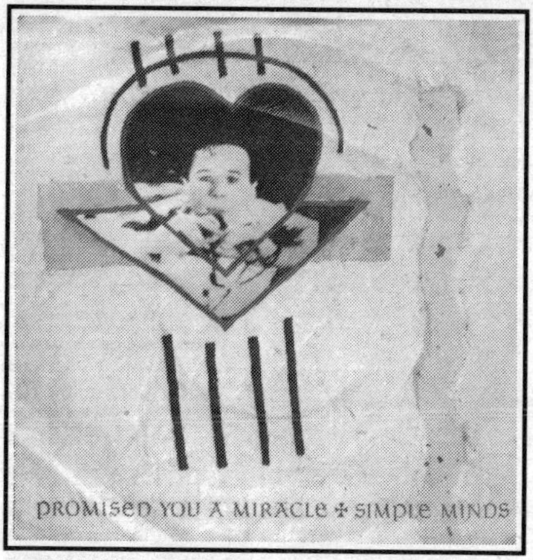

SIMPLE MINDS - PROMISED YOU A MIRACLE (Released on Virgin)

/ Speed your love to me (extended mix) (On 12" only).
7" Single: Released '84, on Virgin, by Virgin Records. Catalogue no: **VS 649**
12" Single: Released '84, on Virgin, by Virgin Records. Catalogue no: **VS 649-12**

SWEAT IN BULLET
Tracks: / Sweat in bullet / 20th century promised land / League of nations / In trance as mission.
12" Single: Released Nov '81, on Virgin, by Virgin Records. Catalogue no: **VS 451-12**
7" Single: Released Oct '81, on Virgin, by Virgin Records. Deleted '89. Catalogue no: **VS 451**

THIS IS YOUR LAND (see panel on previous page)
Tracks: / This is your land / Saturday girl / Year of the dragon (12" only).
Cassingle: Released 10 Apr '89, on Virgin, by Virgin Records. Catalogue no: **SMXC 4**
12" Single: Released 10 Apr '89, on Virgin, by Virgin Records. Catalogue no: **SMXT 4**
CD 3": Released 10 Apr '89, on Virgin, by Virgin Records. Catalogue no: **SMXCD 4**
7" Single: Released 10 Apr '89, on Virgin, by Virgin Records. Catalogue no: **SMX 4**

UP ON THE CATWALK
Tracks: / Up on the catwalk / Brass band in Africa, A.
7" Single: Released '84, on Virgin, by Virgin Records. Catalogue no: **VS 661**

WATERFRONT
Tracks: / Waterfront / Hunter and the hunted.
7" Single: Released Nov '83, on Virgin, by Virgin Records. Catalogue no: **VS 636**
12" Single: Released Nov '83, on Virgin, by Virgin Records. Catalogue no: **VS 636-12**

Simple Simon

FOREIGN MINDS
Tracks: / Foreign minds.
12" Single: Released Sep '84, on Rosie Uprising, Catalogue no: **Unknown**

LIFE IN THE GHETTO
Tracks: / Life in the ghetto.
12" Single: Released Oct '82, on Greensleeves, by Greensleeves Records. Catalogue no: **GRED 95**

Simplicious

LET HER FEEL IT
Tracks: / Let her feel it.
7" Single: Released Sep '84, on 4th & Broadway, by Island Records. Catalogue no: **BRW 13**
12" Single: Released Sep '84, on 4th & Broadway, by Island Records. Deleted Jul '87. Catalogue no: **12 BRW 13**

Simplicity

BLACK IS OUR COLOUR
Tracks: / Black is our colour.
12" Single: Released Oct '81, on King & City, Catalogue no: **KCD 004**

FOR THE LOVE OF YOU
Tracks: / For the love of you.
12" Single: Released Nov '88, on Production House (2), Catalogue no: **PH 001**

LET'S ROCK
Tracks: / Let's rock.
12" Single: Released Jul '83, on S & G (1), Catalogue no: **SG 30**

LOVIN' KIND
Tracks: / Lovin' king.
12" Single: Released Dec '86, on King's Records, Catalogue no: **KRD 003**

THIS LOVE IS REAL
Tracks: / This love is real.
12" Single: Released Jul '82, on S & G (1), Catalogue no: **SG 19**

WAITING
Tracks: / Waiting.
12" Single: Released Oct '81, on King & City, Catalogue no: **KCD 003**

Simply Red

COME TO MY AID
Tracks: / Come to my aid.
12" Single: Released Aug '85, on Elektra, by Elektra Records (UK). Catalogue no: **EKR 19T**
7" Single: Released Aug '85, on Elektra, by Elektra Records (UK). Catalogue no: **EKR 19**

EV'RY TIME WE SAY GOODBYE
Tracks: / Every time we say goodbye / Love for sale.
7" Single: Released Jul '87, on WEA, by WEA Records. Deleted Jul '88. Catalogue no: **YZ 161**
CD 5": Released Jul '87, on WEA, by WEA Records. Deleted Jul '88. Catalogue no: **YZ 161CD**
12" Single: Released Jul '87, on WEA, by WEA Records. Deleted Jul '88. Catalogue no: **YZ 161TE**

HOLDING BACK THE YEARS
Tracks: / Holding back the years / Drowning in my own tears / Picture book (Track on 12" version only).
7" Pic: Released Nov '85, on Elektra, by Elektra Records (UK). Catalogue no: **EKR 29P**
7" Single: Released Nov '85, on Elektra, by Elektra Records (UK). Catalogue no: **EKR 29F**
7" Single: Released May '86, on WEA, by WEA Records. Catalogue no: **YZ 70**
7" Single: Released Nov '85, on Elektra, by Elektra Records (UK). Catalogue no: **EKR 29**
12" Single: Released Nov '85, on Elektra, by Elektra Records (UK). Catalogue no: **EKR 29T**
12" Single: Released May '86, on WEA, by WEA Records. Catalogue no: **YZ 70 T**

I WON'T FEEL BAD
Tracks: / I won't feel bad / Lady Godiva's room.
CD 5": Released 20 Feb '88, on WEA, by WEA Records. Catalogue no: **YZ 172 CD**
7" Single: Released Jan '88, on WEA, by WEA Records. Catalogue no: **YZ 172**
12" Single: Released Jan '88, on WEA, by WEA Records. Catalogue no: **YZ 172T**

IF YOU DON'T KNOW ME BY NOW
Tracks: / If you don't know me by now.
CD 5": Released Apr '89, on Elektra, by Elektra Records (UK). Catalogue no: **YZ 377 CDX**
CD 5": Released Mar '89, on Elektra, by Elektra Records (UK). Catalogue no: **YZ 377 CD**
10" single: Released Apr '89, on Elektra, by Elektra Records (UK). Catalogue no: **YZ 377 TE**
7" Single: Released Mar '89, on Elektra, by Elektra Records (UK). Catalogue no: **YZ 377**
12" Single: Released Mar '89, on Elektra, by Elektra Records (UK). Catalogue no: **YZ 377 T**

INFIDELITY
Tracks: / Infidelity / Lady Godiva's room.
7" Single: Released May '87, on WEA, by WEA Records. Deleted Jul '88. Catalogue no: **YZ 114**
12" Single: Released May '87, on WEA, by WEA Records. Deleted Jul '88. Catalogue no: **YZ 114T**

IT'S ONLY LOVE
Tracks: / It's only love / Turn it up.
7" Single: Released Jan '89, on WEA, by WEA Records. Catalogue no: **YZ 349**
12" Single: Released Jan '89, on WEA, by WEA Records. Catalogue no: **YZ 349 T**

JERICO
Tracks: / Jericho / Jericho (The musical) / Money's too tight to mention (live) (Track on 12" version only) / Heaven (live) (Track on 12" version only).
7" Single: Released Feb '86, on WEA, by WEA Records. Catalogue no: **YZ 63**
12" Single: Released Feb '86, on WEA, by WEA Records. Deleted Jan '88. Catalogue no: **YZ 63T**

MAYBE SOMEDAY
Tracks: / Maybe someday / Let me have it all.
7" Single: Released Jul '87, on Elektra, by Elektra Records (UK). Deleted Jul '88. Catalogue no: **YZ 141**
12" Single: Released Jul '87, on Elektra, by Elektra Records (UK). Deleted Jul '88. Catalogue no: **YZ 141T**

MONEYS TOO TIGHT(TO MENTION)
Tracks: / Money's too tight (to mention).
7" Single: Released Jun '85, on Elektra, by Elektra Records (UK). Deleted Jan '88. Catalogue no: **EKR 9**
12" Single: Released Jun '85, on Elektra, by Elektra Records (UK). Catalogue no: **EKR 9T**
Special: Released Jun '85, on Elektra, by Elektra Records (UK). Deleted Jun '87. Catalogue no: **EKR 9TX**
7" Pic: Released Jun '85, on Elektra, by Elektra Records (UK). Catalogue no: **EKR 9P**

NEW FLAME, A (SINGLE)
Tracks: / New flame, A.
10" single: Released Jun '89, on WEA, by WEA Records. Catalogue no: **YZ 404TE**
Cassingle: Released Jun '89, on WEA, by WEA Records. Catalogue no: **YZ 404C**
CD 5": Released Jun '89, on WEA, by WEA Records. Catalogue no: **YZ 404CD**
12" Single: Released Jun '89, on WEA, by WEA Records. Catalogue no: **YZ 404T**
7" Single: Released Jun '89, on WEA, by WEA Records. Catalogue no: **YZ 404**

OPEN UP THE RED BOX
Tracks: / Open up the red box / Look at you now / Heaven (Track on 12" version only.).
7" Single: Released Jul '86, on WEA, by WEA Records. Deleted Jun '87. Catalogue no: **YZ 75**
12" Single: Released Jul '86, on WEA, by WEA Records. Deleted Jun '87. Catalogue no: **YZ 75T**

RIGHT THING, THE
Tracks: / There's a light / Every time we say goodbye / Right thing, The.
7" Single: Released Jan '87, on WEA, by WEA Records. Deleted Jul '88. Catalogue no: **YZ 103**
12" Single: Released Jan '87, on WEA, by WEA Records. Catalogue no: **YZ 103T**

Simpson, Chris

LIVING WITH A WOMAN LIKE YOU
Tracks: / Living with a woman like you.
7" Single: Released Jul '83, on Speed, Catalogue no: **NICK 1**

STING OF THE GIN
Tracks: / Sting of the gin / I'll walk mine.
7" Single: Released Dec '82, on Juice, by Juice Records. Deleted '88. Catalogue no: **JU 102**

Simpson, Mickey

GOOD GOOD LOVING
Tracks: / Good good lovin' / Honey it's you.
12" Single: Released May '84, on Sanity, Catalogue no: **STY 12010**

STUMBLING BLOCK
Tracks: / Stumbling block / Hurtin thing.
12" Single: Released Nov '83, on Mandingo, Catalogue no: **MAEX 002**

Simpson, Paul

CAN'T GET OVER YOUR LOVE
Tracks: / Can't get over your love.
12" Single: Released Jul '89, on Republic, by Code Records. Catalogue no: **LICT 028**
7" Single: Released Jul '89, on Republic, by Code Records. Catalogue no: **LIC 028**

EVERYBODY'S A STAR
Tracks: / Everybody's a star / Everybody's a star (version).
CD 5": Released Sep '89, on Cool Tempo, by Chrysalis Records. Catalogue no: **COOLCD 190**
12" Single: Released Sep '89, on Cool Tempo, by Chrysalis Records. Catalogue no: **COOLX 190**
7" Single: Released Sep '89, on Cool Tempo, by Chrysalis Records. Catalogue no: **COOL 190**

MUSICAL FREEDOM
Tracks: / Musical freedom / Jam up de music.
7" Single: Released 14 May '88, on Cool Tempo, by Chrysalis Records. Catalogue no: **COOL 165**
7" Single: Released 21 Apr '89, on Cool Tempo, by Chrysalis Records. Catalogue no: **COOLXR 182**
12" Single: Released 14 May '88, on Cool Tempo, by Chrysalis Records. Catalogue

JOYCE SIMS - LOOKING FOR LOVE (Released on London)

Frank Sinatra - Come Fly With me (Released on Capitol)

no: **COOLX 165**

MUSICAL FREEDOM (RE-RELEASE)
Tracks: / Musical freedom.
7" Single: Released Mar '89, on Cool Tempo, by Chrysalis Records. Catalogue no: **COOL 182**
12" Single: Released Mar '89, on Cool Tempo, by Chrysalis Records. Catalogue no: **COOLX 182**

Simpson, Ray

PLEASE DON'T WALK AWAY
Tracks: / Please don't walk away.
12" Single: Released Feb '82, on Big Youth, Catalogue no: **BY 004**

Simpson, Raymond

DREAM GIRL
Tracks: / Dream girl.
12" Single: Released Jan '84, on Vibes Corner, Catalogue no: **VI 001**

IS IT ALWAYS GONNA BE LIKE THIS?
Tracks: / Is it always gonna be like this? / Paradise in your eyes.
7" Single: Released Dec '82, on JB Music, Deleted Dec '85. Catalogue no: **JBD 043**

TURN YOUR LOVE AROUND
Tracks: / Turn your love around.
12" Single: Released Feb '82, on JBM, by Jason Black Music. Catalogue no: **JBD 037**

Simpson, Sandra

YOU'RE MY EVERYTHING
Tracks: / You're my everything / Can't you love me.
12" Single: Released Apr '85, on Innovation (1), Catalogue no: **INZ 001**

Simpson, Steve

JIVING
Tracks: / Jiving / Battle of New Orleans.
7" Single: Released Oct '81, on Roxon, Catalogue no: **ROX H024**

Sims, Joyce

ALL AND ALL
Tracks: / All and all / All and all (Dub).
12" Single: Released Nov '87, on Sleeping Bag, by Sleeping Bag Records. Catalogue no: **SLX 0017**
12" Single: Released Apr '86, on London Records, by London Records. Catalogue no: **LONX 94**
7" Single: Released Apr '86, on London Records, by London Records. Catalogue no: **LON 94**

COME INTO MY LIFE (SINGLE)
Tracks: / Come into my life.
12" Single: Released Dec '87, on London Records, by London Records. Deleted Oct '88. Catalogue no: **LONX 161**
12" Single: Released Oct '87, on Sleeping Bag, by Sleeping Bag Records. Catalogue no: **SLX 28**
7" Single: Released Dec '87, on London Records, by London Records. Deleted Oct '88. Catalogue no: **LON 161**

LIFETIME LOVE
Tracks: / Lifetime love (jazzy edit) / Lifetime love (def edit).
12" Single: Released Nov '87, on Sleeping Bag, by Sleeping Bag Records. Catalogue no: **SLX 24**
12" Single: Released 30 May '87, on London Records, by London Records. Catalogue no: **LONX 137**
7" Single: Released 30 May '87, on London Records, by London Records. Deleted Oct '88. Catalogue no: **LON 137**

LOOKING FOR A LOVE
Tracks: / Looking for a love / Looking for a love (instrumental) / Looking for a love (club mix) (Only on 12" and CD single.) / Come into my life (Only on CD single.).
Cassingle: Released Jun '89, on London Records, by London Records. Catalogue no: **FCS 109**
7" Single: Released Jun '89, on London Records, by London Records. Catalogue no: **F 109**
CD 5": Released Jun '89, on London Records, by London Records. Catalogue no: **FCD 109**
12" Single: Released Jun '89, on London Records, by London Records. Catalogue no: **FX 109**

LOVE MAKES A WOMAN
Tracks: / Love makes a woman.
CD 5": Released 1 Aug '88, on London Records, by London Records. Catalogue no: **LONCD 183**
7" Single: Released Jul '88, on London Records, by London Records. Deleted Feb '89. Catalogue no: **LON 183**
12" Single: Released Jul '88, on London Records, by London Records. Deleted Feb '89. Catalogue no: **LONX 183**

TAKE CAUTION WITH MY HEART
Tracks: / Take caution with my heart (On 7", 12" and MC only) / Take caution with my heart (take precaution edit) (On 7" and CD only) / Take caution with my heart (take precaution 12") (On 12", CD and MC only) / Take caution with my heart (dub) (On 12" and MC only) / Take caution with my heart (Justin's house mix) (On CD only).
CD 5": Released Sep '89, on London Records, by London Records. Catalogue no: **FCD 118**
Cassingle: Released Sep '89, on London Records, by London Records. Catalogue no: **FCS 118**
12" Single: Released Sep '89, on London Records, by London Records. Catalogue no: **FX 118**
7" Single: Released Sep '89, on London Records, by London Records. Catalogue no: **F 118**

WALK AWAY
Tracks: / Walk away (remix) / Walk away (hip hop dub) / Walk away (12" club mix - hip hop style) (On 12" only) / Walk away (12" house mix) (On 12" only).
Note: Remixed by Robert Clivilles and David Cole
12" Single: Released '88, on London Records, by London Records. Deleted Feb '89. Catalogue no: **LONXR 176**
12" Single: Released Apr '88, on Sleeping Bag, by Sleeping Bag Records. Deleted Oct '88. Catalogue no: **LONX 176**
7" Single: Released Apr '88, on Sleeping Bag, by Sleeping Bag Records. Deleted Oct '88. Catalogue no: **LON 176**

Sims, Zoot

Biographical details: Zoot Sims was born John Haley Sims on 29 October 1925 in Inglewood, California; he died on 22 March 1985. He first came to fame as one of the famous Four Brothers reed section in Woody Herman's legendary band of 1947-49, and continued with his warm, personal style as one of the best loved tenor sax players of his generation. He later also played some soprano sax; his albums with trombonist Bobby Brookmeyer and saxist Al Cohn are especially well regarded. (Donald Clarke 27.5.87)..

AFRICAN CHALLENGE
Tracks: / African challenge.
12" Single: Released Sep '84, on Studio One, Catalogue no: **Unknown**

Simson, Paul

TREAT HER SWEETER
Tracks: / Treat her sweeter.
7" Single: Released Jun '85, on 10 Records, by Virgin Records. Catalogue no: **TEN 59**
12" Single: Released Jun '85, on 10 Records, by Virgin Records. Catalogue no: **TEN 59-12**

Sinatra, Frank

Biographical details: Francis Albert Sinatra was born on 12 December 1915 in Hoboken, New Jersey, the son of Italian immigrants. His father, Anthony Sinatra, of Sicilian origin, was an ex-professional boxer who tried various jobs before joining the fire brigade and making the grade as captain. His mother, Natalia Gavaranti, known as Dolly, was from Genoa. She was an energetic woman who became politically active in the local Democratic Party. Sinatra, a slight, only child, had to learn to defend himself in the rough neighbourhood where he grew up. At home his family was, by tradition, musically minded. At 18, against his family's wishes, Sinatra decided to make music his career. Dolly, resigned to this, helped him to start out. He formed a vocal quartet, the Hoboken Four, touring the roadhouses, but it soon broke up as Sinatra gained attention as a solo singer. In February 1939 he married Nancy. He continued to work in the New York area and while at the Rustic Cabin Roadhouse met Harry James (former trumpet player with Benny Goodman), whose band he joined as a vocalist. In 1939, Sinatra began touring with the Tommy Dorsey band and made his first recording, The Sky Fell Down. Up to 1942 he and Dorsey recorded 80 songs together. Sinatra rapidly gained stardom and became known as "The Voice". He topped the hit parades and was the first singer to evoke hysteria among his audience, capturing the hearts of millions of women. In 1944, he was called up by the army but was exonerated. Nonetheless he contributed to the war effort with the special broadcasts and concerts which he gave for the American forces in Europe and North Africa. This enabled him to aquire fame outside the United States. Alongside his singing career Sinatra was also becoming well known as an actor, making many excellent films. Meanwhile he also had a reputation as a womanizer: having a succession of love affairs which, however, did not affect the stability of his marriage with Nancy until he fell passionately in love with Ava Gardner. This completely disrupted his public image. He divorced Nancy to marry Ava and rapidly lost popularity as a singer while his acting career came to a standstill. The Frank-Ava relationship was passionate and stormy and eventually ended in divorce in 1957. Sinatra, who had recorded in the 'forties with RCA and then Columbia -- which refused to renew his contract in 1952 -- signed with Capitol in 1953, when he asked for the star role in the film From Here To Eternity. This film earned him an Academy Award and marked a turning point. He developed a more mature, sophisticated style as a singer while exploiting his business capacities in other fields. In 1961, he founded his own record company Reprise. He was briefly married to actress Mia Farrow, and is now married to Barbara, former wife of Zeppo, one of the famous Marx Brothers. In the early 'seventies, Sinatra announced his retirement but has continued to record and to make personal appearances.
Frank Sinatra is one of the all-time biggest stars in popular music. He was born Francis Albert Sinatra, 12 December 1915 in Hoboken, New Jersey. After his idol Bing Crosby, he becames the most innovative and influential of all male singers, perhaps the best interpreter of the finest American songs; though not regarded as a jazz singer, the combination of his attractive baritone and his phrasing gave the impression that he was singing directly to each listener, and appealed accross the board to critics, listeners and fans in both jazz and pop categories. He began in Hoboken clubs, singing for anyone who would have him, often for free; bandleader Harry James hired him in 1939 to sing with his new band, and later the same year he moved to Tommy Dorsey's band, singing solo and with the Pied Pipers, who also included Jo Stafford; he went solo in 1942 (taking arranger Axel Stordahl with him from Dorsey) and had about 90 hit records in ten years (not counting those with Dorsey). He caused the first pop hysteria and was called 'The Sultan Of Swoon' and 'The Voice'. His films in the 1940s included three classics with Gene Kelly: **Anchors Aweigh** in 1945, **Take Me Out To The Ball Game** and **On The Town** in 1949; he recieved a special Oscar in 1946 for the short film **The House I Live In**, a plea for racial and religious tolerance. He had married his sweetheart Nancy; then married actress Ava Gardener in 1950; the relationship was stormy and he co-wrote and recorded *I'm A Fool To Want You* at the time. An outspoken man who had been at the top for a long time, his passionate private life was public gossip and Columbia USA (CBS) shoved songs at him that were not suitable: the press turned against him and his career seemed a shambles. Then he played Maggio in **From Here To Etenity** (won an Oscar in 1954) and switched to Capitol Records, where his series of classic albums, mostly with arranger-conductor Nelson Riddle, put him back at the top where he has stayed ever since. He formed his own Reprise label in 1961, merged it with Warner Bros. in 1963 in a deal that made him very rich. He had more than 60 hit albums, made with Duke Ellington, Count Basie, Gordon Jenkins and many others as well as Riddle; he also had more than 30 hit singles and nearly 40 hit albums in the UK. He made over 40 more films, not all masterpieces; among the best were musicals **Guys And Dolls** (songs by Frank Losser), **High Society** (Cole Porter), and **Pal Joey** (Rodgers and Hart), all in the mid-1950s. Hit songs written for Sinatra films by ace songwriters Sammy Cahn and Jimmy Van Heusen incl. *The Tender Trap, Love And Marriage, High Hopes* and *Come Blow Your Horn*. It is unfortunate that he is best known among young people today for *Strangers In The Night*, a song not up to his old standard; in 1980 thousands of his fans voted Porter's *I've Got You Under My Skin* as their all time favorite Sinatra record (from *Songs For Swingin' Lovers*, 1956); *In the Wee Small Hours* (1955) is often called the first concept album. All of the Capitol albums were recently digitally remastered and reissued by EMI. He was once engaged to dancer Juliet Prowse; then married to actress Mia Farrow, now to Barbara Marx, widow of Zeppo, one of the original Marx Brothers. His son Frank Sinatra Jr. (born 10 Jan 1944) and daughter Nancy (born 7 June 1940) both had successful careers as vocalists, Nancy helped by producer Lee Hazlewood. (Donald Clarke 27.5.87)..

BANG BANG
Tracks: / Bang bang / It was a very good year.
7" Single: Released Dec '81, on Reprise (USA), Catalogue no: **K 14515**

CHICAGO
Tracks: / Chicag / All the way.
7" Single: Released Nov '57, on Capitol, by EMI Records. Deleted Nov '60. Catalogue no: **CL 14800**

COFFEE SONG, THE
Tracks: / Coffee song, The.
7" Single: Released Nov '61, on Reprise, by WEA Records. Deleted Nov '64. Catalogue no: **R 20035**

COME FLY WITH ME (SINGLE) (see panel above)
Tracks: / It happened in Monterry / Blue Hawaii / Brazil.
7" Single: Released '59, on Capitol, by EMI Records. Catalogue no: **EAP 4920**

DOOBE DOOBE DOO STRANGERS IN THE NIGHT
Tracks: / Doobe doobe doo strangers in the night / In the wee small hours of the morning / Last night when we were young (Track on 12" version only.).
12" Single: Released Apr '86, on Reprise (USA), Catalogue no: **W 8699T**
7" Single: Released Apr '86, on Reprise (USA), Deleted Jun '87. Catalogue no: **W 8699**

EVERYBODY'S TWISTING
Tracks: / Everybody's twisting.
7" Single: Released Apr '62, on Reprise, by WEA Records. Deleted Apr '65. Catalogue no: **R 20063**

FRENCH FOREIGN LEGION
Tracks: / French foreign legion.
7" Single: Released Apr '59, on Capitol, by EMI Records. Deleted Apr '62. Catalogue no: **CL 14997**

GRANADA
Tracks: / Granada.
7" Single: Released Sep '61, on Reprise, by WEA Records. Deleted Sep '64. Catalogue no: **R 20010**

HELLO DOLLY
Tracks: / Hello Dolly.
7" Single: Released Sep '64, on Reprise, by WEA Records. Deleted Sep '67. Catalogue no: **R 20351**

HIGH HOPES
Tracks: / High hopes.
7" Single: Released Aug '59, on Capitol, by EMI Records. Deleted Aug '62. Catalogue no: **CL 15052**

I BELIEVE I'M GONNA LOVE YOU
Tracks: / I believe I'm gonna love you.
7" Single: Released Dec '75, on Reprise (USA), Deleted Dec '78. Catalogue no: **K 14400**

I WILL DRINK THE WINE
Tracks: / I will drink the wine.
7" Single: Released Mar '71, on Reprise (USA), Deleted Mar '74. Catalogue no: **RS 23487**

IT'S NICE TO GO TRAV'LING
Tracks: / It's nice to go travellin'.
7" Single: Released Apr '60, on Capitol, by EMI Records. Deleted Apr '63. Catalogue no: **CL 15116**

LEARNIN' THE BLUES
Tracks: / Learnin' the blues.
7" Single: Released Aug '55, on Capitol, by EMI Records. Deleted Aug '58. Catalogue no: **CL 14296**

LOVE AND MARRIAGE
Tracks: / Love and marriage.
7" Single: Released Jan '56, on Capitol, by EMI Records. Deleted Jan '59. Catalogue no: **CL 14503**

LOVE & MARRIAGE
Tracks: / Love & marriage / Love & marriage.
7" Single: Released Mar '84, on EMI Golden 45's, by EMI Records. Catalogue no: **G45 9**

LOVE'S BEEN GOOD TO ME
Tracks: / Love's been good to me.
7" Single: Released Oct '69, on Reprise (USA), Deleted Oct '72. Catalogue no: **RS 20852**

ME AND MY SHADOW
Tracks: / Me and my shadow.
7" Single: Released Dec '62, on Reprise (USA), Deleted Dec '66. Catalogue no: **R 20128**

MR SUCCESS
Tracks: / Mr. Success.
7" Single: Released Nov '58, on Capitol, by EMI Records. Deleted Nov '62. Catalogue no: **CL 14956**

MY BLUE HEAVEN
Tracks: / My blue Heaven.
7" Single: Released Apr '61, on Capitol, by EMI Records. Deleted Apr '64. Catalogue no: **CL 15193**

MY KIND OF GIRL
Tracks: / My kind of girl.
7" Single: Released Mar '63, on Reprise, by WEA Records. Deleted Mar '66. Catalogue no: **R 20148**

MY WAY (SINGLE)
Tracks: / My way.
7" Single: Released Jul '81, on Reprise (USA), Deleted Jun '87. Catalogue no: **K 14008**
7" Single: Released '80, on Reprise (USA), Catalogue no: **K 14474**
7" Single: Released Apr '69, on Reprise (USA), Deleted Jan '75. Catalogue no: **RS 20817**

NEW YORK, NEW YORK
Tracks: / New York, New York / My kind of town (Track on 12" version only) / LA is my lady (Track on 12" version only).
7" Single: Released Feb '86, on Warner Bros., by WEA Records. Catalogue no: **K 14502**
12" Single: Released Feb '86, on Warner Bros., by WEA Records. Deleted Jan '88. Catalogue no: **K 14502T**

NICE AND EASY
Tracks: / Nice and easy / Come fly with me / One for my baby (Extra track included on 12" version).
7" Single: Released Sep '86, on Capitol, by EMI Records. Deleted Oct '87. Catalogue no: **CL 426**
12" Single: Released Sep '86, on Capitol, by EMI Records. Deleted '88. Catalogue no: **12CL 426**

NICE 'N' EASY
Tracks: / Nice 'n' easy.
7" Single: Released Sep '60, on Capitol, by EMI Records. Deleted Sep '63. Catalogue no: **CL 15150**

NOT AS A STRANGER
Tracks: / Not as a stranger.
7" Single: Released Sep '55, on Capitol, by EMI Records. Deleted Sep '58. Catalogue no: **CL 14326**

OL' MACDONALD
Tracks: / Ol' MacDonald.
7" Single: Released Nov '60, on Capitol, by EMI Records. Deleted Nov '63. Catalogue no: **CL 15168**

RIVER STAY 'WAY FROM MY DOOR
Tracks: / River stay 'way from my door.
7" Single: Released Jun '60, on Capitol, by EMI Records. Deleted Jun '63. Catalogue no: **CL 15135**

SAY HELLO
Tracks: / Say hello / Good thing going.
7" Single: Released Nov '81, on Reprise (USA), Catalogue no: **K 14513**

STRANGERS IN THE NIGHT (SINGLE)
Tracks: / Strangers in the night.
7" Single: Released May '66, on Reprise (USA), Deleted May '69. Catalogue no: **R 23052**
7" Single: Released '80, on Reprise (USA), Deleted Sep '87. Catalogue no: **K 14043**

SUMMER WIND
Tracks: / Summer wind.
7" Single: Released Sep '66, on Reprise, by WEA Records. Deleted Sep '69. Catalogue no: **RS 20509**

TENDER TRAP, THE
Tracks: / Tender trap, The.
7" Single: Released Jan '56, on Capitol, by EMI Records. Deleted Jan '59. Catalogue no: **CL 14511**

THAT'S LIFE
Tracks: / That's life.
7" Single: Released Dec '66, on Reprise (USA), Deleted Dec '69. Catalogue no: **RS 20531**

THREE COINS IN THE FOUNTAIN
Tracks: / Three coins in the fountain.
7" Single: Released Jul '54, on Capitol, by EMI Records. Deleted Jul '57. Catalogue no: **CL 14120**

TO LOVE A CHILD
Tracks: / To love a child / That's what god looks like to me.
7" Single: Released Dec '82, on Reprise (USA), Catalogue no: **W 9903**

WITCHCRAFT
Tracks: / Witchcraft.
7" Single: Released Feb '58, on Capitol, by EMI Records. Deleted Feb '61. Catalogue no: **CL 14819**

WORLD WE KNEW, THE
Tracks: / World we knew, The.
7" Single: Released Aug '67, on Reprise (USA), Deleted Aug '70. Catalogue no: **RS 20610**

YOU MY LOVE
Tracks: / You my love.
7" Single: Released Jun '55, on Capitol, by EMI Records. Deleted Jun '58. Catalogue no: **CL 14240**

YOUNG AT HEART
Tracks: / Young at heart.
7" Single: Released Jul '54, on Capitol, by EMI Records. Deleted Jul '57. Catalogue no: **CL 14064**

Sinatra, Nancy

HIGHWAY SONG
Tracks: / Highway song.
7" Single: Released Nov '69, on Reprise, by WEA Records. Deleted Nov '72. Catalogue no: **RS 20869**

HOW DOES THAT GRAB YOU DARLIN' (SINGLE)
Tracks: / How does that grab you darlin'.
7" Single: Released Apr '66, on Reprise (USA), Deleted Apr '69. Catalogue no: **R 20461**

LADYBIRD
Tracks: / Ladybird.
7" Single: Released Nov '67, on Reprise (USA), Deleted Nov '70. Catalogue no: **RS 20629**

SOMETHIN' STUPID
Tracks: / Something stupid.
7" Single: Released Mar '67, on Reprise (USA), Deleted Mar '70. Catalogue no: **RS 23166**

SUGAR TOWN
Tracks: / Sugar town.
7" Single: Released Jan '67, on Reprise (USA), Deleted Jan '70. Catalogue no: **RS 20527**

THESE BOOTS ARE MADE FOR WALKING
Tracks: / These boots are made for walking.
7" Single: Released Jan '66, on Reprise (USA), Deleted Jan '69. Catalogue no: **R 20432**

YOU ONLY LIVE TWICE
Tracks: / You only live twice / Jackson.
7" Single: Released Jul '67, on Reprise (USA), Deleted Jul '70. Catalogue no: **RS 20595**

Sinatras

HAPPY FEELING
Tracks: / Happy feeling.
7" Single: Released Jun '81, on Dining Out, by Dining Out Records. Catalogue no: **TUX 6**

I'M LONELY
Tracks: / I'm lonely.
7" Single: Released Sep '85, on Shriekback, Catalogue no: **SBR 5**
12" Single: Released Sep '85, on Shriekback, Catalogue no: **SBR 5T**

SEEING COMES BEFORE WORDS
Tracks: / Seeing comes before words / That shape.
7" Single: Released Nov '81, on Dining Out, by Dining Out Records. Catalogue no: **TUX 16**

SWEAT
Tracks: / Sweat.
7" Single: Released Sep '82, on Empire Records, Catalogue no: **HAM 4**
12" Single: Released Sep '82, on Empire Records, Catalogue no: **HAM 4T**

YOU MAKE ME FEEL...
Tracks: / You make me feel....
7" Single: Released Mar '82, on Transmanor, Catalogue no: **CBV 001**

YOU MAKE ME FEEL LIKE I'M WEARING NEW...
Tracks: / You make me feel like I'm wearing new... / Finding your own level.
7" Single: Released Apr '82, on Empire Records, Catalogue no: **HAM 1**

Sinceros

DISAPPEARING
Tracks: / Disappearing / I can't stop.
7" Single: Released Mar '81, on Epic, by CBS Records. Deleted Mar '84. Catalogue no: **EPC 1084**
7" Single: Released Sep '80, on Epic, by CBS Records. Deleted '83. Catalogue no: **EPC 8943**

MEMORY LANE
Tracks: / Memory lane / Beady eyes.
7" Single: Released Jun '81, on Epic, by CBS Records. Deleted Jun '84. Catalogue no: **EPCA 1321**

SOCIALLY
Tracks: / Socially / Beady eyes.
7" Single: Released Oct '80, on Epic, by CBS Records. Deleted Oct '83. Catalogue no: **EPC 9306**

Sinclair

THAT GIRL
Tracks: / That girl.
12" Single: Released 6 Feb '89, on Criminal (1), by Criminal Records. Catalogue no: **BUST 010**

Sinclair, Belinda

WHITE HORSES
Tracks: / White horses / Lovers and dreamers.
7" Single: Released Jun '81, on Applause, by Riva Records. Catalogue no: **CLAP 4**

Sinclair, Evlyn

BABY YOU GET TO ME
Tracks: / Baby you get to me / Baby you get to me (version).
12" Single: Released Dec '88, on Hot Melt, by Hot Melt Records. Catalogue no: **12TCT 20**
7" Single: Released Dec '88, on Hot Melt, by Hot Melt Records. Catalogue no: **7TC 20**

Sinclair, Jimmy

RIVER LOVE SONG
Tracks: / River love song / River love song (part 2).
12" Single: Released Nov '83, on Thunderbolt, by Magnum Music Group. Deleted '89. Catalogue no: **TBD 05**

Sinclair, John

NAZ, THE
Tracks: / Naz, The / Straight from the heart.
7" Single: Released Nov '82, on Charisma, by Virgin Records. Deleted '89. Catalogue no: **CB 404**

Sinclair, Loretta

EVERYTIME WE TOUCH
Tracks: / Everytime we touch / Everytime we touch (instrumental - rhythm mix).
12" Single: Released Sep '86, on Citybeat, by Beggars Banquet Records. Catalogue no: **CBE 1206**
7" Single: Released Sep '86, on Citybeat, by Beggars Banquet Records. Deleted Jun '87. Catalogue no: **CBE 706**

Sindecut Kicking

SINDECUT KICKING
Tracks: / Sindecut kicking: *Sindecut* / Page sixty seven: *Myster E* / Cuban jacking: *Rio Rhythm Band* / Y'ready: *Noise Inc.*
12" Single: Released Jan '88, on Baad, by Baad Records. Catalogue no: **BD 666**

Sindicate

I AIN'T STOPPING
Tracks: / I ain't stopping.
12" Single: Released Jun '88, on Baad, by Baad Records. Catalogue no: **BD 777**

Sindy & The Action Men

WHO'S SHE
Tracks: / Who's she / Sleeping.
12" Single: Released Feb '84, on Wimp, by Wimp Records. Catalogue no: **WIMP 009**
7" Single: Released Feb '84, on Wimp, by Wimp Records. Catalogue no: **WIMP 008**

YOU'RE LUCKY
Tracks: / You're lucky / Pinned against the wall.
7" Single: Released Dec '82, on Wimp, by Wimp Records. Catalogue no: **WIMP 002**

Sine

JUST LET ME DO MY THING
Tracks: / Just let me do my thing.
7" Single: Released Jun '78, on CBS, by CBS Records. Deleted Jun '81. Catalogue no: **CBS 6351**

Sineni, Tony

RHYTHM OF THE BEAT
Tracks: / Rhythm of the beat.
12" Single: Released Nov '87, on Hotmix (USA), Catalogue no: **HMF 105**

Sing Market

VIA TV
Tracks: / Via TV.
12" Single: Released Aug '86, on Dark Network, by Dance Network Records. Catalogue no: **DARK 001**

Sing Sing & The Crime

LITTLE MAN
Tracks: / Little man / Leave the cold behind / Happy for a moment.
12" Single: Released Mar '87, on Wire, by Wire Records. Catalogue no: **WRMS 015**
7" Single: Released 23 May '87, on Wire, by Wire Records. Catalogue no: **WRS 015**

Singelton, Maxine

DON'T YOU LOVE IT
Tracks: / Don't you love it / Don't you love it (part 2).
7" Single: Released Jan '82, on System, Catalogue no: **STEM 1**
12" Single: Released Jan '82, on System, Catalogue no: **12STEM 1**

YOU CAN'T RUN AWAY FROM LOVE
Tracks: / You can't run away from love.
12" Single: Released Feb '83, on Creole, by Creole Records. Catalogue no: **CR 1250**
7" Single: Released Feb '83, on Creole, by Creole Records. Catalogue no: **CR 50**

Singer, James

AFRICA
Tracks: / Africa / Jah bless the children.
12" Single: Released Oct '82, on PC, Catalogue no: **PC 002**

LEVEL VIBES
Tracks: / Level vibes.
12" Single: Released Jun '84, on BWB, Catalogue no: **BWB 001**

WORLD SMILING WITH YOU
Tracks: / World smiling with you.
12" Single: Released Dec '84, on BWB, Catalogue no: **BWB 004**

Singers & Players

REVOLUTION
Tracks: / Revolution / Too much workload.
10" single: Released Apr '82, on On-U-Sound, by On-U-Sound Records. Catalogue no: **1P 2**

Singh, Peter

ELVIS I'M ON THE PHONE
Tracks: / Elvis I'm on the phone.
7" Single: Released Apr '82, on Screaming Out For Red, Deleted '83. Catalogue no: **RED 1**

Singh, Romie

DANCING TO FORGET

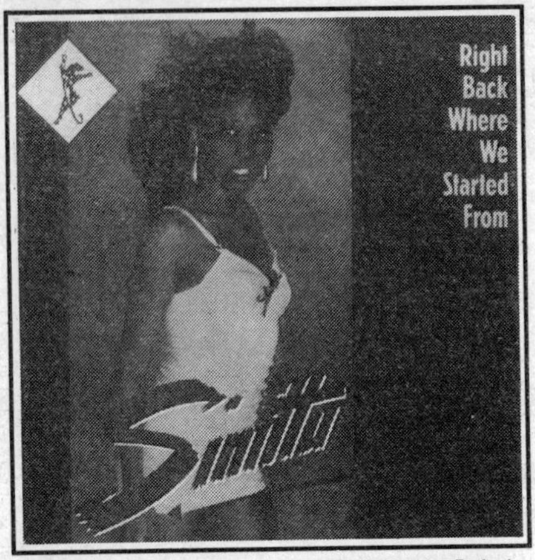

SINITTA - RIGHT BACK WHERE WE STARTED (Released on Fanfare)

Tracks: / Peeping Tom / Dancing to forget.
12" Single: Released Feb '87, on Portrait, by CBS Records. Deleted Aug '87. Catalogue no: **650074 6**
7" Single: Released Feb '87, on Portrait, by CBS Records. Deleted Aug '87. Catalogue no: **650074 7**

Single, Singe

LEAVES BADNESS ALONE
Tracks: / Leaves badness alone.
12" Single: Released Jan '85, on Vibes, by Vibes Records. Catalogue no: **VV 005**

SHOULDER MOVE
Tracks: / Shoulder move.
12" Single: Released Sep '83, on Tads, Catalogue no: **TRD 1983**

YES SHE GONE
Tracks: / Yes she gone.
12" Single: Released Jul '85, on Blue Mountain, Catalogue no: **BTR 20**

Singing Dogs

SINGING DOGS (MEDLEY)
Tracks: / Pat-a-cake / Three blind mice / Jingle bells / Oh Susannah.
7" Single: Released Nov '55, on Nixa, by Pye Records. Deleted Nov '58. Catalogue no: **N 15009**

Singing Fireman

WELLEPHANT
Tracks: / Wellephant / What do you do.
7" Single: Released Oct '86, on Island, by Island Records. Catalogue no: **BSAFE 1**

Singing Melody

CHAMPION SOUND
Tracks: / Champion sound.
7" Single: Released Nov '88, on Parish, Catalogue no: **UNKNOWN**

SAY YOU LOVE ME BABY
Tracks: / Say you love me baby.
12" Single: Released May '89, on Live & Love, Catalogue no: **LLD 118**

Singing Nun

DOMINIQUE
Tracks: / Dominique.
7" Single: Released Jan '80, on Philips, by Phonogram Ltd. Catalogue no: **LR 0920**
7" Single: Released Dec '63, on Philips, by Phonogram Ltd. Deleted Dec '66. Catalogue no: **BF 1293**

Singing Ringing Tree

GOOD DAY GOOD
Tracks: / Good day good / Generally dancing.
7" Single: Released Aug '87, on Sample, Catalogue no: **SAMPLE 1**

HANGING TREE, THE
Tracks: / Hanging tree, The.
7" Single: Released '88, on UNKNOWN, Catalogue no: **SRT 001**

Singing Sheep

BAA BAA BLACK SHEEP
Tracks: / Baa baa black sheep / Flock around the clock.
7" Single: Released Dec '82, on Sheep, by Virgin Records. Catalogue no: **BAA 1**

Single English

HEAVEN GONE WRONG
Tracks: / Heaven gone wrong.
7" Single: Released Aug '84, on Rebound, Catalogue no: **BOUNCE 4**

Single File

OUT IN THE TRAFFIC
Tracks: / Out in the traffic.
7" Single: Released May '86, on Mainline (1), Catalogue no: **MLR 005**

Single Gun Theory

EXORCISE THIS WASTELAND (SINGLE)
Tracks: / Exorcise this wasteland.
CD 5": Released '88, on Nettwerk, by Nettwerk Records. Catalogue no: **NTC 0039**
12" Single: Released Oct '87, on Nettwerk, by Nettwerk Records. Catalogue no: **NT 12 3009**

OPEN SKIES (REMIX)
Tracks: / Open skies (remix).
12" Single: Released Apr '88, on Nettwerk, by Nettwerk Records. Catalogue no: **NT 12 3018**

Singles

EASY TO DO
Tracks: / Easy to do.
7" Single: Released '88, on Antler, by Antler Records (Belgium). Catalogue no: **ANT 003**

ON THE LINE
Tracks: / On the line / Fools party.
7" Single: Released Aug '83, on Posh, by Posh Records. Catalogue no: **POSH 005006**

T.V DETECTIVES
Tracks: / T.V. detectives / Send for sorrow.
7" Single: Released Nov '81, on Mint, by Emerald Records. Deleted '88. Catalogue no: **CHEW 53**

Singleton, Charlie

NOTHING VENTURED NOTHING GAINED(SINGLE)
Tracks: / Nothing ventured nothing gained.
12" Single: Released Nov '87, on Epic, by CBS Records. Deleted Jun '88. Catalogue no: **NVT 1**

Sinister Cleaners

GNOMES OF ZURICH
Tracks: / Gnomes of Zurich.
7" Single: Released Feb '85, on AAZ, by AAZ Records. Catalogue no: **AAZ 2**

GOODBYE MS JONES
Tracks: / Goodbye Ms. Jones / I'll never forget this / Bastards / Wild flower.
12" Single: Released Nov '86, on AAZ, by AAZ Records. Deleted '88. Catalogue no: **AAZ 6**

LEMON MERINGUE BEDSIT
Tracks: / Lemon meringue bedsit.
12" Single: Released Jun '86, on AAZ, by AAZ Records. Deleted '88. Catalogue no: **AAZ 5**

LONGING FOR NEXT YEAR
Tracks: / Longing for next year / Bleed / Monkey & the typewriter / Goodbye Ms. Jones / Complication day.
Note: Contact AAZ Records, 47 Brudenell Mount, Leeds LS6 1HS Tel: 0532 780855.
12" Single: Released Jun '87, on AAZ, by AAZ Records. Deleted '88. Catalogue no: **AAZ 7**

Sinitta

CROSS MY BROKEN HEART (REMIX)
Tracks: / Cross my broken heart (remix) / Toy boy (remix).
12" Pic: Released 5 Mar '88, on Fanfare, by Captain Billy's Music. Catalogue no: **12 FAN 15**
7" Single: Released 5 Mar '88, on Fanfare, by Captain Billy's Music. Catalogue no: **FAN 15**
7" Pic: Released 5 Mar '88, on Fanfare, by Captain Billy's Music. Catalogue no: **FAN PIC 15**

CRUISING
Tracks: / Cruisin'.
7" Single: Released Feb '85, on Fanfare, by Captain Billy's Music. Catalogue no: **FAN 2**
12" Single: Released Feb '85, on Fanfare, by Captain Billy's Music. Catalogue no: **12 FAN 2**

FEELS LIKE THE FIRST TIME
Tracks: / Feels like the first time / Feels like the first time (dub mix).
7" Single: Released Oct '86, on Fanfare, by Captain Billy's Music. Catalogue no: **FAN 8**
12" Single: Released Oct '86, on Fanfare, by Captain Billy's Music. Catalogue no: **12 FAN 8**
12" Single: Released Oct '86, on Fanfare, by Captain Billy's Music. Catalogue no: **12 FANX 8**
7" Single: Released Oct '86, on Fanfare, by Captain Billy's Music. Catalogue no: **FAN X 8**

GTO
Tracks: / GTO / GTO (instrumental).
12" Single: Released Nov '87, on Fanfare, by Captain Billy's Music. Catalogue no: **12 FAN 14**
7" Single: Released Nov '87, on Fanfare, by Captain Billy's Music. Catalogue no: **FAN 14**

I COULD BE
Tracks: / I could be.
7" Single: Released Nov '83, on Midas, by Magnet Records. Catalogue no: **MID 4**
12" Single: Released Nov '83, on Midas, by Magnet Records. Catalogue no: **12 MID 4**

I DON'T BELIEVE IN MIRACLES
Tracks: / I don't believe in miracles / I don't believe in miracles (inst).
CD 5": Released Sep '88, on Fanfare, by Captain Billy's Music. Catalogue no: **CDFAN 16**
7" Single: Released Sep '88, on Fanfare, by Captain Billy's Music. Catalogue no: **FAN 16**
12" Single: Released Sep '88, on Fanfare, by Captain Billy's Music. Catalogue no: **12 FAN 16**

LOVE ON A MOUNTAIN TOP
Tracks: / Love on a mountain top.
7" Single: Released Oct '89, on Fanfare, by Captain Billy's Music. Catalogue no: **FAN 21**
12" Single: Released Oct '89, on Fanfare, by Captain Billy's Music. Catalogue no: **12 FAN 21**

NEVER TOO LATE
Tracks: / Never too late.
12" Single: Released Sep '83, on Midas, by Magnet Records. Catalogue no: **12MID 3**
7" Single: Released Sep '83, on Midas, by Magnet Records. Catalogue no: **MID 3**

RIGHT BACK WHERE WE STARTED FROM (see panel above)
Tracks: / Right back where we started from / Right back where we started from(version) / I just can't help it.
CD 5": Released Jun '89, on Fanfare, by Captain Billy's Music. Catalogue no: **FANCD 18**
7" Pic: Released Jun '89, on Fanfare, by Captain Billy's Music. Catalogue no: **FANPIC 18**
12" Single: Released Jun '89, on Fanfare, by Captain Billy's Music. Catalogue no: **12 FAN 18**
7" Single: Released Jun '89, on Fanfare, by Captain Billy's Music. Catalogue no: **FAN 18**

SO MACHO
Tracks: / So macho / Cruisin' (remix).
7" Single: Released Jul '85, on Fanfare, by Captain Billy's Music. Catalogue no: **FAN 5**
12" Single: Released Jul '85, on Fanfare, by Captain Billy's Music. Catalogue no: **12 FAN 5**
12" Single: Released Feb '86, on Fanfare, by Captain Billy's Music. Catalogue no: **12 FAN 7**
7" Single: Released Feb '86, on Fanfare, by Captain Billy's Music. Catalogue no: **FAN 7**

TOY BOY
Tracks: / Toy boy / Toy boy (inst).
Note: Cassette single contains 4 mixes.
7" Single: Released Jul '87, on Fanfare, by Captain Billy's Music. Catalogue no: **FAN 12**
12" Single: Released Jul '87, on Fanfare, by Captain Billy's Music. Catalogue no: **12 FAB 12**
Cassingle: Released Aug '87, on Funkin' Marvellous, by Steinar Records (UK). Deleted Jan '88. Catalogue no: **FANC 12**

Sink

ON THE TRACKS
Tracks: / On the tracks.
7" Single: Released Jun '89, on Poontang, by Poontang Records. Catalogue no: **POON 2**

Sinking Ships

CINEMA CLOCK
Tracks: / Cinema clock / Strangers.
12" Single: Released Dec '80, on Dead Good, Deleted '81. Catalogue no: **DEAD 14**

Sinnamon

HE'S GONNA TAKE YOU HOME TO HIS HOUSE
Tracks: / He's gonna take you home to his house.
12" Single: Released Jan '83, on Beckett, Deleted '85. Catalogue no: **BKSL 7**

THANKS TO YOU
Tracks: / Thanks to you / Thanks to you (house mix) (Only on 12" version.) / Thanks to you (deep house mix) (Only on 12" version.) / Thanks to you (original Shep Pettibone mix) (Only on 12" version.) / Thanks to you (accapella mix) (Only on 7" version.).
7" Single: Released Mar '89, on Living Beat, by Living Beat Records. Catalogue no: **7 SMASH 3**
12" Single: Released Mar '89, on Living Beat, by Living Beat Records. Catalogue no: **SMASH 3**
12" Single: Released Jun '82, on Beckett, Deleted '84. Catalogue no: **BKSL 3**
7" Single: Released Jun '82, on Beckett, Deleted '84. Catalogue no: **BKS 3**

Sins Of The Flesh

FLESH & BLOOD
Tracks: / Flesh and blood.
12" Single: Released Apr '89, on Plastic Head, by Plastic Head Records. Catalogue no: **PLASS 011**

IN THE IMAGE OF TORTURE
Tracks: / In the image of torture / Our lady of pain / Crowned with thorns.
12" Single: Released Oct '12, on Plastic Head, by Plastic Head Records. Catalogue no: **PLASS 014**

Sinster Ducks

MARCH OF THE SINSTER DUCKS
Tracks: / March of the Sinster Ducks.
7" Single: Released Aug '83, on Situation 2, by Beggars Banquet Records. Catalogue no: **SIT 25**

Sinyx

BLACK DEATH (EP)
Tracks: / Black death.
7" Single: Released Mar '82, on Reality Attack, Catalogue no: **EJSP 9815**

Siouxsie & Banshees

ARABIAN KNIGHTS
Tracks: / Arabian knights.
7" Single: Released Aug '81, on Polydor, by Polydor Ltd. Deleted Aug '84. Catalogue no: **POSP 309**

CANDYMAN
Tracks: / Candyman / Lullaby / Umbrella (Track on 12" version only).
7" Single: Released Feb '86, on Wonderland (1), by Polydor Ltd. Catalogue no: **SHE 10**
12" Single: Released Feb '86, on Wonderland (1), by Polydor Ltd. Catalogue no: **SHEX10**

CHRISTINE
Tracks: / Christine / Eve white, Eve black.
7" Single: Released Jun '80, on Polydor, by Polydor Ltd. Deleted Jun '83. Catalogue no: **2059 249**

CITIES IN DUST
Tracks: / Cities in dust.
7" Single: Released Oct '85, on Wonderland (1), by Polydor Ltd. Deleted Oct '88. Catalogue no: **SHE 9**

DAZZLE
Tracks: / Dazzle.
7" Single: Released Jun '84, on Wonderland (1), by Polydor Ltd. Catalogue no: **SHE 7**
12" Single: Released Jun '84, on Wonderland (1), by Polydor Ltd. Catalogue no: **SHEX 7**

DEAR PRUDENCE
Tracks: / Dear Prudence.
7" Single: Released Oct '83, on Wonderland (1), by Polydor Ltd. Deleted Oct '86. Catalogue no: **SHE 4**

FIRE WORKS
Tracks: / Fire works / Coal mind / We fall.
7" Single: Released May '82, on Polydor, by Polydor Ltd. Deleted May '85. Catalogue no: **POSPG 450**
12" Single: Released May '82, on Polydor, by Polydor Ltd. Deleted May '85. Catalogue no: **POSPX 450**

HAPPY HOUSE
Tracks: / Happy house / Drop dead.
7" Single: Released Mar '80, on Polydor, by Polydor Ltd. Deleted Mar '83. Catalogue no: **POSP 117**

HONG KONG GARDEN
Tracks: / Hong Kong garden.
7" Single: Released Aug '78, on Polydor, by Polydor Ltd. Deleted Aug '81. Catalogue no: **2059 052**

ISRAEL
Tracks: / Israel / Red over white.
7" Single: Released Dec '80, on Polydor, by Polydor Ltd. Deleted Dec '83. Catalogue no: **POSP 205**
12" Single: Released Jan '81, on Polydor, by Polydor Ltd. Deleted Jan '84. Catalogue no: **POSPX 205**

KILLING JAR
Tracks: / Killing jar / Something wicked (this way comes) / Are you still dying, darling (Only on 12").

CD 5": Released Sep '88, on Wonderland (1), by Polydor Ltd. Catalogue no: **SHECD 15**
7" Pic: Released Sep '88, on Wonderland (1), by Polydor Ltd. Deleted 30 May '89. Catalogue no: **SHEP 15**
7" Single: Released Sep '88, on Wonderland (1), by Polydor Ltd. Deleted 30 May '89. Catalogue no: **SHEG 15**
12" Single: Released Sep '88, on Wonderland (1), by Polydor Ltd. Catalogue no: **SHEX 15**
7" Single: Released Sep '88, on Wonderland (1), by Polydor Ltd. Deleted 30 May '89. Catalogue no: **SHE 15**

LAST BEAT OF MY HEART, THE
Tracks: / Last beat of my heart / El dia de los muertos / Sunless (On 12" & CD only.) / El dia de los muertos (Espiritu mix) (On CD only.).
CD 5": Released 21 Nov '88, on Polydor, by Polydor Ltd. Catalogue no: **SHECD 16**
7" Single: Released Nov '88, on Wonderland (1), by Polydor Ltd. Deleted 30 May '89. Catalogue no: **SHEG 16**
12" Single: Released Nov '88, on Wonderland (1), by Polydor Ltd. Catalogue no: **SHEXG 16**
7" Single: Released 21 Nov '88, on Polydor, by Polydor Ltd. Deleted 30 May '89. Catalogue no: **SHE 16**
12" Single: Released 21 Nov '88, on Polydor, by Polydor Ltd. Catalogue no: **SHEX 16**

MELT/IL EST NE LE DIVIN ENFANT
Tracks: / Melt / Il est ne le divin enfant.
7" Single: Released Dec '82, on Polydor, by Polydor Ltd. Deleted Dec '85. Catalogue no: **POSP 539**

MITTAGEISEN (METAL POSTCARD)
Tracks: / Mittageisen (metal postcard).
7" Single: Released Sep '79, on Polydor, by Polydor Ltd. Deleted Sep '82. Catalogue no: **2059 151**

PASSENGER, THE
Tracks: / Passenger (The) / She's cuckoo / Something blue (extra track on 12" only).
12" Single: Released Mar '87, on Wonderland (1), by Polydor Ltd. Deleted Aug '87. Catalogue no: **SHEG 12**
12" Single: Released Mar '87, on Wonderland (1), by Polydor Ltd. Deleted Jan '88. Catalogue no: **SHEX 12**
7" Single: Released Mar '87, on Wonderland (1), by Polydor Ltd. Deleted Jan '88. Catalogue no: **SHE 12**

PEEK-A-BOO
Tracks: / Peek-a-boo / False face / Catwalk (12" only) / Peek-a-boo (Silver Dollar Mix) (Extra track available on 12".) / Peek-a-boo (Stockhausen & Waterphone Mix) (Extra track availble on 12".).

Cassingle: Released Jul '88, on Wonderland (1), by Polydor Ltd. Deleted Oct '89. Catalogue no: **SHECS 14**
7" Single: Released Jul '88, on Wonderland (1), by Polydor Ltd. Catalogue no: **SHEG 14**
7" Single: Released Jul '88, on Wonderland (1), by Polydor Ltd. Deleted 30 May '89. Catalogue no: **SHE 14**
12" Single: Released Jul '88, on Wonderland (1), by Polydor Ltd. Deleted 30 May '89. Catalogue no: **SHEXR 14**
12" Single: Released Jul '88, on Wonderland (1), by Polydor Ltd. Catalogue no: **SHEX 14**
CD 5": Released 18 Jul '88, on Wonderland (1), by Polydor Ltd. Deleted Oct '89. Catalogue no: **SHECD 14**

PEEL SESSIONS:SIOUXSIE & THE BANSHEES II
CD 5": Released Feb '89, on Strange Fruit, by Strange Fruit Records. Catalogue no: **SFPSCD 066**
CD 5": Released Aug '88, on Strange Fruit, by Strange Fruit Records. Catalogue no: **SFPSCD 012**
12" Single: Released Feb '89, on Strange Fruit, by Strange Fruit Records. Catalogue no: **SFPS 066**
12" Single: Released Feb '87, on Strange Fruit, by Strange Fruit Records. Catalogue no: **SFPS 012**
Cassingle: Released 13 Jun '87, on Strange Fruit, by Strange Fruit Records. Catalogue no: **SFPSC 012**

PLAYGROUND TWIST
Tracks: / Playground twist.
7" Single: Released Jul '79, on Polydor, by Polydor Ltd. Deleted Jul '82. Catalogue no: **POSP 59**

SLOWDIVE
Tracks: / Slowdive.
7" Single: Released Oct '82, on Polydor, by Polydor Ltd. Deleted Oct '85. Catalogue no: **POSP 510**
12" Single: Released Oct '82, on Polydor, by Polydor Ltd. Deleted Oct '85. Catalogue no: **POSPX 510**

SONG FROM THE EDGE OF THE WORLD
Tracks: / Song from the edge of the world / Whole price of blood, The / Mechanical eyes (Extra track on 12").
7" Single: Released Jul '87, on Wonderland (1), by Polydor Ltd. Catalogue no: **SHE 13**
12" Single: Released Jul '87, on Wonderland (1), by Polydor Ltd. Catalogue no: **SHEX 13**
Cassingle: Released Jul '87, on Wonderland (1), by Polydor Ltd. Deleted 30 Jun '89. Catalogue no: **SHEPC 13**

SPELLBOUND
Tracks: / Spellbound / Follow the sun / Slap dash snap (on 12" only).
7" Single: Released May '81, on Polydor, by Polydor Ltd. Deleted May '84. Catalogue no: **POSP 273**
12" Single: Released May '81, on Polydor, by Polydor Ltd. Deleted May '84. Catalogue no: **POSPX 273**

STAIRCASE (MYSTERY), THE
Tracks: / Staircase (mystery), The.
7" Single: Released Mar '79, on Polydor, by Polydor Ltd. Deleted Mar '79. Catalogue no: **POSP 9**

SWIMMING HORSES
Tracks: / Swimming horses / Let go.

7" Single: Released Mar '84, on Polydor, by Polydor Ltd. Catalogue no: **SHE 6**
12" Single: Released Mar '84, on Polydor, by Polydor Ltd. Catalogue no: **SHX 6**

THIS WHEEL'S ON FIRE
Tracks: / Shooting sun / Sleepwalking (on the high wire).
7" Single: Released Jan '87, on Wonderland (1), by Polydor Ltd. Deleted Aug '87. Catalogue no: **SHE 11**
12" Single: Released Jan '87, on Wonderland (1), by Polydor Ltd. Deleted Aug '87. Catalogue no: **SHEG 11**
12" Single: Released Jan '87, on Wonderland (1), by Polydor Ltd. Deleted Aug '87. Catalogue no: **SHEX 11**

THORN, THE
Tracks: / Thorn, The / Voices.
7" Single: Released Oct '84, on Wonderland (1), by Polydor Ltd. Deleted Oct '87. Catalogue no: **SHEEP 8**

Sipho Mabuse

CHANT OF THE MARCHING (SINGLE)
Tracks: / Chant of the marching / Taxi driver.

7" Single: Released '88, on Virgin, by Virgin Records. Catalogue no: **VS 1160**
12" Single: Released '88, on Virgin, by Virgin Records. Catalogue no: **VST 1160**

Sir Alick

IN SEARCH OF THE PERFECT BABY
Tracks: / In search of the perfect baby.
7" Single: Released Mar '82, on Recommended, by Recommended Records. Catalogue no: **7NO 5**

Sir Bromwell

SEXY LADY
Tracks: / Sexy lady.
12" Single: Released Jun '84, on Three Kings, Catalogue no: **TK 010**

Sir Douglas Quintet

EVERY BREATH YOU TAKE
Tracks: / Every breath you take.
7" Single: Released Jul '84, on Sonet, by Sonet Records. Catalogue no: **SON 2266**

SHE'S ABOUT A MOVER
Tracks: / She's about a mover.
7" Single: Released Jun '65, on London-American, Deleted Jun '68. Catalogue no: **HLU 9964**
7" Single: Released '80, on USA, by Charly Records. Catalogue no: **LR 8150**

WHO WERE YOU THINKING OF
Tracks: / Who were you thinking of.
7" Single: Released Jun '82, on Sonet, by Sonet Records. Catalogue no: **SON 2243**

Sir Horatio

ABRACADABRA
Tracks: / Abracadabra.
12" Single: Released Sep '82, on Rock Steady, by Rock Steady Records. Catalogue no: **MIX 1T**

Sir Mix A Lot

IRON MAN
Tracks: / Iron man.
12" Single: Released Jun '89, on Tam Tam, Catalogue no: **TTT 121**
7" Single: Released Jun '89, on Tam Tam, Catalogue no: **TTT 009**

Sir Mix-a-Lot

SQUARE DANCE RAP
Tracks: / Square dance rap (version) / Square dance rap.
12" Single: Released Jun '86, on Streetwave, Catalogue no: **MKHAN 69**
7" Single: Released Jun '86, on Streetwave, Catalogue no: **KHAN 69**

Sir Stephen

TURNTABLE TERROR TRAX VOL.2
Tracks: / Stephen's overture / Let's begin / In the bass / Rock the bass / Vox.
12" Single: Released 13 Jun '87, on Bluebird (2), by BMG Records (UK). Catalogue no: **BRT 42**

Siren

AMERICAN GIRL
Tracks: / American girl.
7" Single: Released Aug '84, on Distant Cousins, Catalogue no: **DC 4R**

Sirens

IT DOESN'T REALLY MATTER
Tracks: / It doesn't really matter / Rock 'n' roll disaster.
7" Single: Released Sep '80, on Liberty (USA), by EMI Records. Deleted '83. Catalogue no: **STP 4**

Sirens Of 7th Avenue

HERE TO GO
Tracks: / Here to go.
12" Single: Released 31 Oct '87, on New Rose (1), by New Rose Records. Catalogue no: **NEW 95**

SHINE ON
Tracks: / Shine on.
12" Single: Released 13 Jun '87, on New Rose (1), by New Rose Records. Catalogue no: **NEW 85**

Sirrs, Ed

I THINK I THINK TOO MUCH
Tracks: / I think I think too much.
7" Single: Released May '82, on Oval, by Oval Records. Catalogue no: **OVAL 1014**

Sissi

I'VE GOT A CRUSH ON YOU
Tracks: / I've got a crush on you.
12" Single: Released Jul '89, on Who's That Beat, by Play It Again Sam (Belgium). Catalogue no: **WHOS 20**

Sister Annuniciata

HEY FATHER CHRISTMAS
Tracks: / Hey Father Christmas / Peace on earth (silent night).
7" Single: Released Dec '81, on Mayfield, Catalogue no: **MA 102**

Sister Audrey

DAYLIGHT AND DARKNESS
Tracks: / Daylight and darkness.
12" Single: Released Oct '88, on Ariwa Sounds, by Ariwa Sounds. Catalogue no: **ARI 71**

HAPPINESS
Tracks: / Children of the ghetto / Happiness.
12" Single: Released Nov '86, on Ariwa Sounds, by Ariwa Sounds. Catalogue no: **ARI 54**

I LOVE YOU
Tracks: / I love you.
12" Single: Released Jul '85, on Ariwa Sounds, by Ariwa Sounds. Catalogue no: **ARI 40**

Sister B

SLIM IN A BODY
Tracks: / Slim in a body.
12" Single: Released Jul '88, on Vibes, by Vibes Records. Catalogue no: **VIBES 027**

Sister Candy

KEEP BUBBLING
Tracks: / Keep bubbling.
7" Single: Released Nov '84, on Raiders, Catalogue no: **LGR 7006**
12" Single: Released Nov '84, on Raiders, Catalogue no: **LGR 006**

Sister Carol

INTERNATIONAL STYLE
Tracks: / International style / Down in the ghetto.
12" Single: Released May '84, on Jah Life, Catalogue no: **JL 002**

Sister Charmaine

BODY, THE
Tracks: / Body, The.
12" Single: Released Apr '88, on Techniques, Catalogue no: **WRT 30**

DREAM LOVE
Tracks: / Dream love.
12" Single: Released Oct '88, on Rock Star (2), Catalogue no: **RSD 002**

HOLAREST
Tracks: / Holarest.
12" Single: Released Aug '87, on Technics, Catalogue no: **WRT 02**

IF YOU SHOULD LOOSE
Tracks: / If you should loose.
12" Single: Released 8 Aug '88, on Redman International, Catalogue no: **VPRED 111**

WATCH THE MATIE
Tracks: / Watch the matie.
12" Single: Released Nov '88, on Steely & Cleevie, Catalogue no: **VPRD 351**

Sister Love

DON'T TELL HIM
Tracks: / Don't tell him.
12" Single: Released Feb '82, on Future, Catalogue no: **FT 0018**

HE IS LEAVING YOU
Tracks: / He is leaving you.
12" Single: Released Jul '82, on Loving Times, Catalogue no: **LTD 001**

Sister Nancy

ONE TWO
Tracks: / One two.
12" Single: Released Jul '82, on Black Music, Catalogue no: **BM 708**

Sister Nyah

JAH JAH WAY
Tracks: / Jah jah way.
12" Single: Released Oct '87, on Jah Shaka, Catalogue no: **SHAKA 864**

Sister Orli

D.J.QUEEN
Tracks: / D.J. Queen.
12" Single: Released May '84, on Lost Tribes, Catalogue no: **LT 1**

Sister Scene

HOLD BACK YOUR LOVE
Tracks: / Hold back your love.
7" Single: Released Nov '84, on Magnet, by WEA Records. Catalogue no: **MAG 263**

Sister Sledge

ALL AMERICAN GIRLS
Tracks: / All American girls / Happy feeling.
7" Single: Released Mar '81, on Atlantic, by WEA Records. Catalogue no: **K 11656**
12" Single: Released Mar '81, on Atlantic, by WEA Records. Catalogue no: **K 11656 T**

DANCING ON THE JAGGED EDGE
Tracks: / Dancing on the jagged edge.
7" Single: Released Aug '85, on Atlantic, by WEA Records. Deleted Aug '88. Catalogue no: **A 9520**

EASY STREET
Tracks: / Easy street / How to love.
7" Single: Released Mar '80, on Atlantic, by WEA Records. Deleted '83. Catalogue no: **K 11455**

FRANKIE
Tracks: / Frankie / Hold out puppy.
7" Single: Deleted Jun '87. Catalogue no: **A 9547**

GOT TO LOVE SOMEBODY
Tracks: / Got to love somebody / Good girl now.
7" Single: Released Jan '80, on Atlantic, by WEA Records. Deleted Jan '83. Catalogue no: **K 11404**

HERE TO STAY
Tracks: / Make a wish / Here to stay*.
7" Single: Released Jan '87, on Parlophone, by EMI Records. Deleted Oct '87. Catalogue no: **R 6141**
12" Single: Released Jan '87, on Parlophone, by EMI Records. Deleted Oct '87. Catalogue no: **12 R6141**

HE'S JUST A RUNAWAY
Tracks: / He's just a runaway.
7" Single: Released Aug '81, on Cotillion (Import), by WEA Records. Catalogue no: **K 11676**
12" Single: Released Aug '81, on Cotillion (Import), by WEA Records. Catalogue no: **K 11676T**

HE'S THE GREATEST DANCER
Tracks: / He's the greatest dancer.
7" Single: Released Mar '79, on Atlantic, by WEA Records. Deleted Mar '82. Catalogue no: **K 11257**

IF YOU REALLY WANT ME
Tracks: / If you really want me to, I'll go / Make a move.
7" Single: Released May '81, on Atlantic, by WEA Records. Catalogue no: **K 11591**
12" Single: Released May '81, on Atlantic, by WEA Records. Catalogue no: **K 115916 T**

LOST IN MUSIC
Tracks: / Lost in music.
7" Single: Released Aug '79, on Atlantic, by WEA Records. Deleted Aug '82. Catalogue no: **K 11337**
7" Single: Released Aug '84, on Cotillion (Import), by WEA Records. Catalogue no: **B 9718**
12" Single: Released Aug '84, on Cotillion (Import), by WEA Records. Catalogue no: **B 9718T**

MAMA NEVER TOLD ME
Tracks: / Mama never told me.
7" Single: Released Jun '75, on Atlantic, by WEA Records. Deleted Jun '78. Catalogue no: **K 10619**

MY GUY
Tracks: / My guy.
7" Single: Released Feb '82, on Cotillion (Import), by WEA Records. Catalogue no: **K 11710**

REACH YOUR PEAK
Tracks: / Reach your peak / You fooled around.
7" Single: Released May '80, on Atlantic, by WEA Records. Deleted May '83. Catalogue no: **K 11477**

THINKING OF YOU
Tracks: / Thinking of you / We are family / Greatest dancer.

7" Single: Released May '84, on Cotillion (Import), by WEA Records. Deleted Jun '87. Catalogue no: **B 9744**
12" Single: Released May '84, on Cotillion (Import), by WEA Records. Deleted Jan '88. Catalogue no: **B 9744T**

WE ARE FAMILY (SINGLE)
Tracks: / We are family.
7" Single: Released Nov '84, on Cotillion (Import), by WEA Records. Catalogue no: **B 6992**
7" Single: Released May '79, on Atlantic, by WEA Records. Catalogue no: **K 11293**

WHEN THE BOYS MEET THE GIRLS (SINGLE)
Tracks: / When the boys meet the girls.

7" Single: Released Feb '86, on Atlantic, by WEA Records. Catalogue no: **A 9486**
12" Single: Released Feb '86, on Atlantic, by WEA Records. Catalogue no: **A 9486 T**

Sister Sonie

FEEL LIKE JUMPING
Tracks: / Feel like jumping.
12" Single: Released Nov '84, on Chartbound, Catalogue no: **UNKNOWN**

Sister Verna

UP FRONT LOVER
Tracks: / Up front lover / Up front lover (dub version).
12" Single: Released Apr '86, on Photographer, Catalogue no: **P 001**

Sisterhood

GIVING GROUND
Tracks: / Giving ground.
7" Single: Released Jan '86, on Merciful Release, by Merciful Release. Catalogue no: **SIS 010**

Sisters Of Mercy

ALICE
Tracks: / Alice / Floorshow / 1969 / Phantom.
12" Single: Released 14 Jun '85, on Merciful Release, by Merciful Release. Catalogue no: **MR 021**
7" Single: Released Nov '82, on Merciful Release, by Merciful Release. Catalogue no: **MR 15**

ANACONDA
Tracks: / Anaconda.
7" Single: Released Mar '83, on Merciful Release, by Merciful Release. Catalogue no: **MR 19**

BODY AND SOUL
Tracks: / Body and soul / Body electric / Afterhours / Train.

12" Single: Released Jun '84, on Merciful Release, by Merciful Release. Deleted Jun '87. Catalogue no: **MR 29T**
7" Single: Released Jun '84, on Merciful Release, by Merciful Release. Catalogue no: **MR 29**

BODY ELECTRIC
Tracks: / Body electric / Adrenachrome.
7" Single: Released Apr '82, on CNT, Deleted '83. Catalogue no: **CNT 002**

BODY & SOUL
Tracks: / Now's The Time / Filthy McNasty / Oh gee.
Note: 4 track 12" featuring "Body Electric", "Train", "Afterhours" and the title track. Comes in picture cover (no longer available on the U.K. version).

12" Single: Released Nov '87, on Merciful Release (Germany), Catalogue no: **2493620**

DAMAGE DONE
Tracks: / Damage done.
7" Single: Released Feb '83, on Merciful Release, by Merciful Release. Deleted '85. Catalogue no: **MR 7**

DOMINION
Tracks: / Dominion / Neverland.
CD 5": Released Feb '88, on Merciful Release, by Merciful Release. Deleted Jul '88. Catalogue no: **MR 43CD**
7" Single: Released Jan '88, on Merciful Release, by Merciful Release. Catalogue no: **MR 43**
12" Single: Released Jan '88, on Merciful Release, by Merciful Release. Deleted Jul '88. Catalogue no: **MR 43T**
Cassingle: Released Feb '88, on Merciful Release, by Merciful Release. Deleted Jul '88. Catalogue no: **MR 43C**

LIFE
Tracks: / Life.
Special: Released Feb '89, on Stampa Alternative (Italy), Catalogue no: **SCONC 007**

LUCRETIA MY REFLECTION
Tracks: / Lucretia my reflection / Long train.
7" Single: Released May '88, on Merciful Release, by Merciful Release. Catalogue no: **MR 45**
12" Single: Released May '88, on Merciful Release, by Merciful Release. Catalogue no: **MR 45T**

NO TIME TO CRY
Tracks: / No time to cry / Blood money / Bury me deep (on 12" only).
12" Single: Released Feb '85, on Merciful Release, by Merciful Release. Catalogue no: **MR 335T**

REPTILE HOUSE
Tracks: / Reptile house.
12" Single: Released May '83, on Merciful Release, by Merciful Release. Catalogue no: **MR 22**
12" Single: Released 14 Jun '85, on Merciful Release, by Merciful Release. Catalogue no: **MR 023**

SISTERS OF MERCY INTERVIEW (2)
7" Pic: Released '89, on Wax, by Wax Records. Catalogue no: **MERCY 7**

SISTERS OF MERCY: INTERVIEW PICTURE DISC Collection
7" Set: Released Apr '88, on Baktabak, by Baktabak Records. Catalogue no: **BAKPAK 1009**

TEMPLE OF LOVE
Tracks: / Temple of love.
7" Single: Released Oct '83, on Merciful Release, by Merciful Release. Catalogue no: **MR 27**
12" Single: Released Oct '83, on Merciful Release, by Merciful Release. Catalogue no: **MRX 27**

THIS CORROSION
Tracks: / This corrosion / Torch / Colours.
CD 5": Released Sep '87, on Merciful Release, by Merciful Release. Catalogue no: **MR 39CD**
Cassingle: Released Sep '87, on Merciful Release, by Merciful Release. Catalogue no: **MR 39C**
7" Single: Released Sep '87, on Merciful Release, by Merciful Release. Catalogue no: **MR 39**
12" Single: Released Sep '87, on Merciful Release, by Merciful Release. Catalogue no: **MR 39T**
CD 5": Released Nov '87, on Merciful Release (Germany), Catalogue no: **248 214 2**

WALK AWAY
Tracks: / Walk away / Poison door / On the wire.
12" Single: on Merciful Release, by Merciful Release. Deleted Jun '87. Catalogue no: **MR 33T**

Situation

FUN
Tracks: / Fun / I don't know what day it is / Here she comes.
7" Single: Released Apr '84, on President, by President Records. Catalogue no: **PT 525**
12" Single: Released Apr '84, on President, by President Records. Catalogue no: **PT 12 525**

Sivuca

AIN'T NO SUNSHINE
Tracks: / Ain't no sunshine.
12" Single: Released Jul '84, on London Records, by London Records. Catalogue no: **LONX 51**
7" Single: Released Jul '84, on London Records, by London Records. Catalogue no: **LON 51**

Six...

SIX COUNTRY HITS Various artists
7" EP: Released Jun '84, on Scoop 33, by Pickwick Records. Catalogue no: **7SR 5041**

SIX NUMBER ONES Various artists
Tracks: / I love to love: *Charles, Tina* / When will I see you again?: *Three Degrees* / San Francisco: *McKenzie, Scott* / What's another year?: *Logan, Johnny* / Ob la di ob la da: *Marmalade* / Yellow river: *Christine*.

7" EP: Released Oct '84, on Scoop 33, by Pickwick Records. Catalogue no: **7SR 5052**

Six Billion Monkeys

SWAYING TO THE BEAT
Tracks: / Swaying to the beat / Six billion monkeys.

12" Single: Released 23 Apr '88, on Moogungwha, Catalogue no: **MGW 0000000 1**

SWING TO THE BEAT
Tracks: / Swing to the beat.
12" Single: Released '88, on Moogungwha, Catalogue no: **MGWOO 002**

Six Minute War

MORE SHORT SONGS
Tracks: / More short songs.
7" EP: Released Jul '82, on Six Minute War, Catalogue no: **SMW 1**

SIX MINUTE WAR, THE
Tracks: / Six minute war, The.
7" Single: Released Jun '82, on S & G (2), Catalogue no: **SGS 113**

SLIGHTLY LONGER SONGS
Tracks: / Slightly longer songs.
7" Single: Released Oct '82, on Six Minute War, Catalogue no: **SMW 003**

Six Pack

SIX PACK COUNTRY MUSIC (EP)
Tracks: / Six pack country music.
12" Single: Released 24 Jul '89, on Silver Heart, by Silver Heart Records. Catalogue no: **CUFF 1AA**

Six Three Eight..

ATAVISTIC VIEW OF YOU
Tracks: / Atavistic view of you.
7" Single: Released Oct '87, on Ediesta, Catalogue no: **CALC 034**

Six-One-X

WORKING MAN
Tracks: / Working man / Sun says.
7" Single: Released Apr '84, on President, by President Records. Catalogue no: **PT 526**

Sixteen Dance Party

16 DANCE PARTY HITS
7" Single: Released Aug '86, on Recommended, by Recommended Records. Catalogue no: **RE 007AN**

Sixteen, Earl

BABY BABY
Tracks: / Baby baby.
12" Single: Released Jan '88, on Sure Spin, Catalogue no: **SPN 004**

BAD COMPANY
Tracks: / Bad company / Hey girl.
7" Single: Released Jun '82, on Teletec, Deleted Jun '85. Catalogue no: **AH 104**
12" Single: Released Apr '83, on Clair, Catalogue no: **C 005**

DANCE HALL QUEEN
Tracks: / Dancehall queen.
12" Single: Released Sep '85, on Now Generation, Catalogue no: **NG 001**

GIVE JAH PRAISE
Tracks: / Give Jah praise.
12" Single: Released May '82, on Teletec, Catalogue no: **AH 103**

GIVE ME THE REASON
Tracks: / Give me the reason.
12" Single: Released 20 Mar '89, on Rock Star (2), Catalogue no: **RS 004**

GIVE YOUR LOVE
Tracks: / Give your love.
12" Single: Released Jan '86, on Conqueror, Catalogue no: **COND 007**

HOLDING BACK THE YEARS
Tracks: / Holding back the years.
12" Single: Released Oct '88, on Rock Star (2), Catalogue no: **RS 001**

IF WE GET TOGETHER
Tracks: / If we get together.
12" Single: Released Nov '88, on Thameside (2), Catalogue no: **TRR 1616**

LEGGO GIRL
Tracks: / Leggo girl.
12" Single: Released Mar '84, on Cyprian, Catalogue no: **CYP 005**

MINE TO LOVE
Tracks: / Mine to love.
12" Single: Released Mar '86, on DATC, Catalogue no: **DACTD 019**

NIGHT AND DAY
Tracks: / Night and day / Changing world.
12" Single: Released Dec '85, on New Generation, Catalogue no: **NG 004**

NO MASH UP THE DANCE
Tracks: / No mash up the dance.
12" Single: Released Sep '84, on Studio One, Catalogue no: **UNKNOWN**

PEEK-A-BOO
Tracks: / Peek-a-boo / Julia.
12" Single: Released Jan '84, on CSA, by CSA Records. Deleted '88. Catalogue no: **SPCSA 12007**

PROBLEMS
Tracks: / Problems.
12" Single: Released Aug '85, on Reggae City, Catalogue no: **RC 002**

RUB UPON ME
Tracks: / Rub upon me.
12" Single: Released Nov '84, on Fatman Studio, Catalogue no: **FS 001**

WARNING
Tracks: / Warning.
12" Single: Released Jul '84, on Time, Catalogue no: **TR 004**

WISH IT WAS LOVE
Tracks: / Wish it was love / You're my love.
12" Single: Released May '86, on Original, Catalogue no: **OS 005**

Sixteen Tambourines

IF I SHOULD STAY
Tracks: / If I should stay / Same old story / Pokey town.
7" Single: Released Sep '89, on Arista, by BMG Records (UK). Catalogue no: **111816**
12" Single: Released Sep '89, on Arista, by BMG Records (UK). Catalogue no: **611816**
CD 5": Released Sep '89, on Arista, by BMG Records (UK). Catalogue no: **661816**

Sixth Comm

TASTE FOR FLESH, THE
Tracks: / Taste for flesh, The.
12" Single: Released Dec '87, on Eyas Media, by Eyas Media. Catalogue no: **EYAS 005**

Sixties

POWER TO ALL OUR FRIENDS
Tracks: / Power to all our friends / You are always on my mind.
7" Single: Released Nov '81, on Telefunken (Germany), Deleted '84. Catalogue no: **CLIFF 1**

Sixty Six Squad

WORLD IS YOURS, THE
Tracks: / World is yours, The.
12" Single: Released Jul '89, on Institute, Catalogue no: **12 INS 001**

Sixy

LOVE ME SOME MORE
Tracks: / Love me some more.
12" Single: Released 20 Mar '89, on Blue Mountain, Catalogue no: **BMD 038**

Siy Lion

WITHIN
Tracks: / Within / You are love.
Note: Irish Eurovision entry
7" Single: Released Apr '87, on Silent (1), by Silent Records. Deleted Nov '87. Catalogue no: **SIL 2**

Ska Boom

PLAN, THE
Tracks: / Plan, The / Long shot kick the bucket.
12" Single: Released Jul '89, on Staccato, Catalogue no: **12RUDE 4**

ROMEO
Tracks: / Romeo / Ska summer.
12" Single: Released Oct '89, on Rimshot, Catalogue no: **RIMSHOT 0022**

Ska City Rockers

TIME IS TIGHT
Tracks: / Time is tight / You don't know like I know / Road runner.
7" Single: Released Feb '80, on Inferno (1), by Inferno Records. Catalogue no: **BEAT 1**

Ska, Donny

UNITED AFRICA
Tracks: / United Africa / Dub it in Africa.
12" Single: Released Aug '86, on Solomonic (1), by Solomonic Records. Catalogue no: **SM 12025**

SKA Flames

SKA FEVER
Tracks: / Ska fever / Osaka ska.
7" Single: Released Nov '88, on Gaz's, Catalogue no: **GAZ 009**

Ska-Dows

APACHE
Tracks: / Apache / Tune that time forgot.
7" Single: Released Jun '80, on Cheapskate, Deleted Jun '83. Catalogue no: **CHEAP 1**

SKAS ON 45
Tracks: / Skas on 45 / Rhapsody in buh.
7" Single: Released Sep '81, on Penthouse, by Penthouse Records. Catalogue no: **PENT 7**
12" Single: Released Sep '81, on Penthouse, by Penthouse Records. Deleted Sep '84. Catalogue no: **PENT 12 7**
12" Single: Released Jan '85, on Penthouse, by Penthouse Records. Catalogue no: **PENT 127**
12" Single: Released Oct '81, on Cheapskate, Catalogue no: **CHEAPT 36**
7" Single: Released Oct '81, on Cheapskate, Catalogue no: **CHEAP 36**

TELSTAR
Tracks: / Telstar / Yes yes yes.
7" Single: Released Apr '81, on Cheapskate, Deleted '85. Catalogue no: **CHEAP 4**

WE GOTTA GET OUT OF THIS PLACE
Tracks: / We gotta get out of this place.
7" Single: Released Apr '82, on Cheapskate, Catalogue no: **CHEAP 41**

YES YES YES
Tracks: / Yes yes yes / Twice.
7" Single: Released Jun '81, on Cheapskate, Deleted Jun '84. Catalogue no: **CHEAP 25**

Skafish

OBSESSIONS OF YOU
Tracks: / Obsessions of you.
7" Single: Released Jul '80, on Illegal, by Faulty Products Records. Catalogue no: **ILS 0020**

Skaggs, Ricky

Biographical details: Ricky Scaggs is a country singer and musician, born 18th July 1954 in Cordell, Kentucky, who has dominated the USA charts in the 1980's with his neo- traditional style. He plays mandolin and fiddle as well as guitar. He worked in bluegrass groups and with **Emmylou Harris's Hot Band** 1977-80 (wrote arrangements for her *Roses In The Snow* album) before going solo with an album on the small Sugar Hill label, then switching to Epic. He is married to Sharon White and also produces albums by **The Whites**. [Donald Clarke, April 1987]..

ARTIFICIAL HEART
Tracks: / Artificial heart / Whell hoss.
7" Single: Released Sep '86, on Epic, by CBS Records. Catalogue no: **650100 7**

CAJUN MOON
Tracks: / Cajun Moon / Rockin'the boat.
7" Single: Released May '86, on Epic, by CBS Records. Catalogue no: **A 7222**

HEARTBROKE
Tracks: / Heartbroke.
7" Single: Released Sep '83, on Epic, by CBS Records. Catalogue no: **A 3791**

HONEY (OPEN THAT DOOR)
Tracks: / Honey (open that door).
7" Single: Released Jul '84, on Epic, by CBS Records. Catalogue no: **A 4604**

NEW STAR SHINING
Tracks: / Walking in Jerusalem / New star shining.
7" Single: Released Nov '86, on Epic, by CBS Records. Catalogue no: **650250 7**

Skanga

HEY FRED You need a sunbed
Tracks: / Hey Fred / Feeling inside.
7" Single: Released Jun '87, on CSA, by CSA Records. Catalogue no: **CSA 511**
12" Single: Released Jun '87, on CSA, by CSA Records. Deleted '88. Catalogue no: **12CSA 511**

Skank Orchestra

WE ARE THE PEOPLE
Tracks: / We are the people.
12" Single: Released Sep '81, on Scorpio, by Scorpio Records. Catalogue no: **12 STING 1**
7" Single: Released Sep '81, on Scorpio, by Scorpio Records. Catalogue no: **STING 1**

Skat

FEMME FATALE
Tracks: / Femme fatale / One fine day.
7" Single: on Graduate, by Graduate Records. Deleted Jan '87. Catalogue no: **GRAD 14**

Skatalites

GUNS OF NAVARONE
Tracks: / Guns of Navarone / Marcus Garvey.
7" Single: Released Jan '80, on Island, by Island Records. Catalogue no: **WIP 6571**
7" Single: Released Apr '67, on Island, by Island Records. Deleted Apr '70. Catalogue no: **WI 168**

Skaville Train

COOL IT OUT
Tracks: / Cool it out.
12" Single: Released Apr '89, on Top Beat, Catalogue no: **TBUK 002**

TAKE OVER
Tracks: / Take over.
Note: Also released as Take Over Ska by Anarchy Sax (10/89)
12" Single: Released Aug '89, on JJB, Catalogue no: **JJB 001**

Skeete, Beverley

IF THE FEELING IS RIGHT
Tracks: / If the feeling is right / Keep on running.
12" Single: Released Sep '83, on Elite Records, by Elite Records. Deleted '85. Catalogue no: **DAZZ 21**

WARM
Tracks: / Warm / Blowing warmer.
7" Single: Released Feb '85, on Elite Records, by Elite Records. Deleted '86. Catalogue no: **DAZZ 36**

YOU CAN'T SAY NO
Tracks: / You can't say no.
12" Single: Released Jun '85, on Elite Records, by Elite Records. Deleted '86. Catalogue no: **DAZZ 39**
7" Single: Released Jun '85, on Elite Records, by Elite Records. Deleted '86. Catalogue no: **DAZZ 339**

Skeletal Family

ALONE SHE CRIES
Tracks: / Alone she cries.
7" Single: Released Jan '84, on Red Rhino, by Red Rhino Records. Deleted '88. Catalogue no: **RED 041**
12" Single: Released Jan '84, on Red Rhino, by Red Rhino Records. Deleted '88. Catalogue no: **REDT 041**

JUST A FRIEND
Tracks: / Just a friend.
7" Single: Released Mar '83, on Luggage, by Multicord Records. Catalogue no: **RRP 0724**

JUST A MINUTE
Tracks: / Just a minute / Big love.
7" Single: Released Aug '86, on Chrysalis, by Chrysalis Records. Catalogue no: **CHS 3015**
12" Single: Released Aug '86, on Chrysalis, by Chrysalis Records. Catalogue no: **CHS12 3015**

NIGHT, THE
Tracks: / Night, The.
7" Single: Released Oct '88, on Red Rhino, by Red Rhino Records. Catalogue no: **RED 36**

PROMISED LAND
Tracks: / Promised land.
7" Single: Released Feb '85, on Red Rhino, by Red Rhino Records. Catalogue no: **RED 54**
12" Single: Released Feb '85, on Red Rhino, by Red Rhino Records. Catalogue no: **REDT 54**

RECOLLECT
Tracks: / Recollect.
12" Single: Released 27 Jun '85, on Red Rhino, by Red Rhino Records. Catalogue no: **REDT 042**

RECOLLECTS
7" Single: Released May '84, on R.E.D., Catalogue no: **T 42**

RESTLESS
Tracks: / Restless / What goes up.
12" Single: Released Mar '86, on Chrysalis, by Chrysalis Records. Catalogue no: **CHS12 2970**
7" Single: Released Mar '86, on Chrysalis, by Chrysalis Records. Catalogue no: **CHS 2970**

SO SURE
Tracks: / So sure.
7" Single: Released Jun '84, on Red Rhino, by Red Rhino Records. Catalogue no: **RED 43**
12" Single: Released Jun '84, on Red Rhino, by Red Rhino Records. Catalogue no: **REDT 43**

Skellern, Peter

BUSY LINE
Tracks: / Busy line / Tell me that ain't wrong.
7" Single: Released Feb '83, on Mercury, by Phonogram Ltd. Catalogue no: **MER 137**

CHRISTMAS SONG, A
Tracks: / Christmas song, The / When you wish upon a star.
7" Single: Released Dec '87, on Alligator, by Alligator Records (USA). Catalogue no: **SON 2334**

DREAMING
Tracks: / Dreaming / Still magic.
7" Single: Released Oct '81, on Mercury, by Phonogram Ltd. Deleted Oct '84. Catalogue no: **MER 83**

HOLD ON TO LOVE
Tracks: / Hold on to love.
7" Single: Released Mar '75, on London-American, Deleted Mar '78. Catalogue no: **F 13568**

HOW LOVED YOU ARE
Tracks: / How loved you are / Freewheelin'.
7" Single: Released Jul '87, on Sonet, by Sonet Records. Catalogue no: **SON 2327**

I'LL STRING ALONG WITH YOU
Tracks: / I'll string along with you / Still magic.
7" Single: Released Nov '82, on Mercury, by Phonogram Ltd. Deleted Nov '85. Catalogue no: **MER 130**

ISN'T THIS A LOVELY DAY
Tracks: / You can't take that away from me / Isn't this a lovely day.
7" Single: Released Aug '87, on Mercury, by Phonogram Ltd. Catalogue no: **MER 256**

LOVE IS THE SWEETEST THING
Tracks: / Love is the sweetest thing.
7" Single: Released Oct '78, on Mercury, by Phonogram Ltd. Deleted Oct '81. Catalogue no: **6008 603**

ME AND MY GIRL
Tracks: / Me and my girl.
7" Single: Released Sep '84, on Sierra, by Sierra Records. Catalogue no: **FED 1**

PUTTING ON THE RITZ
Tracks: / Putting on the ritz / Top hat, white tie and tails.
7" Single: Released Feb '80, on Mercury, by Phonogram Ltd. Deleted Feb '83. Catalogue no: **600 860 6**

SOMEDAY SOON
Tracks: / Someday soon / Lancashire lullaby.
7" Single: Released Dec '81, on BBC, by BBC Records & Tapes. Deleted Dec '84. Catalogue no: **RESL 105**

TOO MUCH I'M IN LOVE
Tracks: / Too much I'm in love / Oh what a night for love.
7" Single: Released Jan '81, on Mercury, by Phonogram Ltd. Deleted Jan '84. Catalogue no: **MER 49**

WHEN YOU WISH UPON A STAR
Tracks: / When you wish upon a star / Christmas song, The.
CD 5": Released Dec '87, on Sonet, by Sonet Records. Catalogue no: **SONCD 2334**
7" Single: Released 21 Nov '87, on Sonet, by Sonet Records. Catalogue no: **SON 2334**

YOU'RE A LADY (SINGLE)
Tracks: / You're a lady.
7" Single: Released Mar '82, on Decca, by Decca Records. Deleted '88. Catalogue no: **F 13333**
7" Single: Released Oct '83, on Old Gold, by Old Gold Records. Catalogue no: **OG 9350**

Skeng, Bob

I'M NOT A KING
Tracks: / I'm not a king.
12" Single: Released Sep '89, on First Dan, Catalogue no: **FD 001**

Skens, Bob

PREACHER BOY
Tracks: / Preacher boy.
7" Single: Released Oct '88, on BP International, Catalogue no: **BP 24**

Skeptix

RETURN TO HELL
Tracks: / Return to hell / Another day.
7" Single: Released May '84, on Zenon, Catalogue no: **SKEP 003**

ROUTINE MACHINE
Tracks: / Routine machine / Curfew.
7" Single: Released Oct '82, on Zenon, Catalogue no: **SKEP 001**

SCARRED FOR LIFE
Tracks: / Scarred for life.
7" Single: Released Aug '83, on Neon, by Neon Records. Catalogue no: **SKEP 002**

VENDETTA
Tracks: / Vendetta / Berlin wall.
7" Single: Released Feb '84, on White Rose, by White Rose Records. Deleted '86. Catalogue no: **BD 1**

Sketch

CRAZY SUNDAY
Tracks: / Crazy Sunday.
12" Single: Released Jul '87, on Sketch, by Sketch Records. Catalogue no: **ZAT 4**

Ski Patrol

BRIGHT SHINY THINGS
Tracks: / Bright shiny things / Electric bill girls.
7" Single: Released Sep '82, on Clever Metal, Catalogue no: **VIM 002**

FAITH IN TRANSITION
Tracks: / Faith in transition.
7" Single: Released Jul '81, on Malicious Damage, Catalogue no: **MD 3 45**

Skids

Biographical details:
The Skids were an innovative Scottish new wave band formed in 1977 by guitarist Stuart Adamson and bassist Bill Simpson with drummer Tom Kellichan and vocalist Richard Jobson. On their third album, *The Absolute Game*, in 1980, Russell Webb and Mike Baillie replaced Simpson and Kellichan, then Kenny Hyslop replaced Baillie on some singles. Adamson left to form Big Country, further developing his guitar concept. Webb and Jobson made Joy, but it was the combination of Adamson's guitar and Jobson's lyrics that had made the Skids a success. (Donald Clarke, March 1987.).

ANIMATION
Tracks: / Animation / Pros and cons.
7" Single: Released Mar '80, on Virgin, by Virgin Records. Deleted Mar '83. Catalogue no: **VS 323**

CHARADE
Tracks: / Charade.
7" Single: Released Sep '79, on Virgin, by Virgin Records. Deleted Sep '82. Catalogue no: **VS 288**

CHARLES
Tracks: / Charles.
7" Single: Released Apr '78, on No Bad, Catalogue no: **NB 1**

CIRCUS GAMES
Tracks: / Circus games.
7" Single: Released Aug '80, on Virgin, by Virgin Records. Deleted Aug '83. Catalogue no: **VS 359**

GOODBYE CIVILIAN
Tracks: / Goodbye civilian / Monkey McGuire meets Specky Potter.
7" Single: Released Oct '80, on Virgin, by Virgin Records. Deleted Oct '83. Catalogue no: **VS 373**

INTO THE VALLEY
Tracks: / Into the valley / T.V. stars.
12" Single: Released May '83, on Virgin, by Virgin Records. Deleted May '88. Catalogue no: **VS 591-12**
7" Single: Released Feb '79, on Virgin, by Virgin Records. Catalogue no: **VS 241**

Skids - Iona (Released on Virgin)

Skipworth & Turner - Cash (Released on 4th & Broadway)

IONA (see panel above)
Tracks: / Iona / Blood and soil.
7" Single: Released '81, on Virgin, by Virgin Records. Catalogue no: **VS 449**

MASQUERADE
Tracks: / Masquerade.
7" Single: Released May '79, on Virgin, by Virgin Records. Deleted May '82. Catalogue no: **VS 262**

SAINTS ARE COMING, THE
Tracks: / Saints are coming, The.
7" Single: Released Nov '78, on Virgin, by Virgin Records. Deleted Nov '81. Catalogue no: **VS 232**

SWEET SUBURBIA
Tracks: / Sweet suburbia.
7" Single: Released Sep '78, on Virgin, by Virgin Records. Deleted '89. Catalogue no: **VS 227**

WOMAN IN WINTER
Tracks: / Woman in winter, A / Working for the yankee dollar.
7" Single: Released Dec '80, on Virgin, by Virgin Records. Deleted Dec '83. Catalogue no: **VSK 101**

WORKING FOR THE YANKEE DOLLAR
Tracks: / Working for the yankee dollar.
7" Single: Released Nov '79, on Virgin, by Virgin Records. Deleted Nov '82. Catalogue no: **VS 306**

Skiff Skats

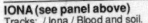

CRIPPLE CREEK
Tracks: / Cripple creek.
7" Single: Released Jan '85, on Doggo, Catalogue no: **DOG 1**

Skifs, Bjorn

ARBITER
Tracks: / Arbiter, The.
12" Single: Released Apr '85, on RCA, by BMG Records (UK). Catalogue no: **CHEST 4**
7" Single: Released Apr '85, on RCA, by BMG Records (UK). Catalogue no: **CHESS 4**

HAUNTED BY A DREAM
Tracks: / Haunted by a dream / Fangad i en drom.
7" Single: Released Apr '81, on EMI, by EMI Records. Deleted Apr '84. Catalogue no: **EMI 5172**

Skilts

LIVING WITHOUT YOUR LOVE
Tracks: / Living without your love / Was I dreaming.
7" Single: Released Apr '82, on Roller, by Roller Records. Deleted Apr '85. Catalogue no: **ROL 001**

Skin

1000 YEARS
Tracks: / 1000 years / My own hands.
7" Single: Released Mar '87, on Product Inc., Catalogue no: **7 PROD 3**
12" Single: Released Mar '87, on Product Inc., Catalogue no: **12PROD 3**

GIRL COME OUT
Tracks: / Girl come out / Girl come out (dub).
12" Single: Released Jul '87, on Product Inc., Catalogue no: **12PROD 6**
7" Single: Released Jul '87, on Product Inc., Catalogue no: **PROD 6**

THOUSAND YEARS
Tracks: / Thousand years, A.
7" Single: Released Mar '87, on Product Inc., Catalogue no: **7 PROD 3**
12" Single: Released Mar '87, on Product Inc., Catalogue no: **12PROD 3**

Skin & Fingers

BABY'S BACK
Tracks: / Baby's back / Talking in my sleep.
7" Single: Released May '82, on Ensign, by Ensign Records. Deleted '83. Catalogue no: **ENY 225**

Skin Flicks

IN THE HEAT
Tracks: / In the heat.
7" Single: Released Jan '85, on Lost Moments, Catalogue no: **LM 014**
12" Single: Released Jan '85, on Lost Moments, Catalogue no: **LM 12 014**

Skin Games

BRILLIANT SHINING
Tracks: / Brilliant shining / Hold the mirror / Brilliant shining (ext.) (12" only.) / Seasong (12" & CD single only.) / Blanche (CD single only.) / Money talks (Only on 12".).
CD 5": Released Oct '88, on Epic, by CBS Records. Deleted 17 Apr '89. Catalogue no: **CD SGA 3**
7" Single: Released Oct '88, on Epic, by CBS Records. Deleted 17 Apr '89. Catalogue no: **SGAG 3**
12" Single: Released Oct '88, on Epic, by CBS Records. Deleted 17 Apr '89. Catalogue no: **SGAT 3**
7" Single: Released Oct '88, on Epic, by CBS Records. Deleted 17 Apr '89. Catalogue no: **SGA 3**

COWBOY JOE
Tracks: / Cowboy Joe / Blanche.
7" Single: Released Jul '87, on Epic, by CBS Records. Catalogue no: **SGA 1**
12" Single: Released Jul '87, on Epic, by CBS Records. Catalogue no: **SGAT 1**

NO CRIMINAL MIND
Tracks: / No criminal mind / Seasong.
7" Single: Released 31 Oct '87, on Epic, by CBS Records. Deleted Jun '88. Catalogue no: **SGA 2**
12" Single: Released 31 Oct '87, on Epic, by CBS Records. Deleted Jun '88. Catalogue no: **SGAT 2**

TIRADE (EVERYTHING MUST CHANGE)
Tracks: / Tirade (everything must change) / Fiction / Anna's field (Only on 12" single.) / Tirade (everything must change) (full version).
CD 5": Released Jul '89, on Epic, by CBS Records. Catalogue no: **CDSGA 5**
7" Single: Released Jul '89, on Epic, by CBS Records. Catalogue no: **SGA 5**
12" Single: Released Jul '89, on Epic, by CBS Records. Catalogue no: **SGAT 5**

YOUR LUCK'S CHANGED
Tracks: / Your luck's changed / Arabesque / It's natural / Mother pearl
CD 5": Released 8 May '89, on Epic, by CBS Records. Catalogue no: **CD SGA 4**
7" Set: Released 15 May '89, on Epic, by CBS Records. Deleted Oct '89. Catalogue no: **SGA B4**
12" Single: Released 8 May '89, on Epic, by CBS Records. Deleted Oct '89. Catalogue no: **SGA T4**
Special: Released 15 May '89, on Epic, by CBS Records. Catalogue no: **SGA E4**
7" Single: Released 8 May '89, on Epic, by CBS Records. Deleted Oct '89. Catalogue no: **SGA 4**

Skin Side Out

TO HELL WITH CARNIVAL
Tracks: / To hell with carnival
12" Single: Released Feb '87, on Lost Moments, Catalogue no: **LM 12 041**

VIPER PANG
Tracks: / Viper pang.
12" Single: Released Nov '85, on Lost Moments, Catalogue no: **LM 12 035**
7" Single: Released Nov '85, on Lost Moments, Catalogue no: **LM 035**

Skinhead Classics

SKINHEAD CLASSICS VOL.1
Tracks: / Train to Skaville: *Ethiopians* / Monkey man: *Maytals* / Return of Djanjo: *Upsetters* / Phoenix City: *Alphonso, Roland*
7" EP: Released '83, on Trojan, by Trojan Records. Deleted May '88. Catalogue no: **TMX 4009**

SKINHEAD CLASSICS VOL.2
Tracks: / Barbwire: *Various artists* / Wreck a buddy: *Various artists* / Skinhead moonstomp: *Various artists* / 54-56 was my number: *Various artists*.
7" EP: Released '83, on Trojan, by Trojan Records. Deleted May '88. Catalogue no: **TMX 4013**

Skinner, Julian

BLESSED BY YOU
Tracks: / Blessed by you.
12" Single: Released Oct '85, on Jungle Rhythm, Catalogue no: **SWET 6**

Skinny Boys

GET PEPPED
Tracks: / Get pepped.
12" Single: Released Jun '88, on Jive, by Zomba Records. Deleted '88. Catalogue no: **JIVET 177**

SET THE PACE
Tracks: / Set the pace / Stylin'.
7" Single: Released Nov '88, on Jive, by Zomba Records. Catalogue no: **JIVE 191**
12" Single: Released Nov '88, on Jive, by Zomba Records. Catalogue no: **JIVET 191**

Skinny Kid Band

MORNING STAR
Tracks: / Morning star / Dreams are forever.
7" Single: Released Jan '80, on PVK, by PVK Records. Deleted Jan '83. Catalogue no: **PV 33**

Skinny Puppy

ADDICTION
Tracks: / Addiction.
12" Single: Released Oct '87, on Nettwerk, by Nettwerk Records. Catalogue no: **NT 12 3010**

CENSOR
Tracks: / Censor (ext. mix) / Punk in park zoo's / Ys he ran / Censor.
12" Single: Released Nov '88, on Capitol, by EMI Records. Deleted Aug '89. Catalogue no: **12CL 517**
7" Single: Released Dec '88, on Nettwerk, by Nettwerk Records. Catalogue no: **CL 517**

CHAINSAW
Tracks: / Chainsaw.
12" Single: Released 15 May '87, on Nettwerk, by Nettwerk Records. Catalogue no: **NTM 6305**

DIG IT
Tracks: / Digit.
12" Single: Released Nov '86, on Play It Again Sam(Belgium), by Play It Again Sam (Belgium). Catalogue no: **BIAS 037**

Skint Video

COPS ON 45
Tracks: / Cops on 45 / Rogues.
7" Single: Released 4 Dec '86, on Off The Kerb, Catalogue no: **COP 001**

Skipworth & Turner

CASH
Tracks: / Cash / Cash (inst.) / Cash (message for carmen mix) (Available on 12" only) / Cash (God bless the money mix) (Available on 12" only).
12" Single: Released Jul '89, on 4th & Broadway, by Island Records. Catalogue no: **12 BRW 135**
7" Single: Released Jul '89, on 4th & Broadway, by Island Records. Catalogue no: **BRW 135**

HOT PURSUIT
Tracks: / Hot pursuit.
12" Single: Released Sep '85, on 4th & Broadway, by Island Records. Catalogue no: **12 BRW 33**

I MISS IT
Tracks: / I miss it / I miss it (instrumental) (On 7" only) / I miss it (album mix) (On 12" only) / I miss it (Paul Simpson remix) (On 12" only) / I miss it (I missed a beat mix) (On 12" only)
7" Single: Released Sep '89, on 4th & Broadway, by Island Records. Catalogue no: **BRW 151**
12" Single: Released Sep '89, on 4th & Broadway, by Island Records. Catalogue no: **12 BRW 151**

MAKE IT LAST
Tracks: / Make it last / Make it last (alternative) / Make it last (instrumental) (Only on 12".).
7" Single: Released Jan '89, on 4th &

Broadway, by Island Records. Catalogue no: **BRW 118**
12" Single: Released Jan '89, on 4th & Broadway, by Island Records. Catalogue no: **12 BRW 118**

THINKING ABOUT YOUR LOVE
Tracks: / Thinking about your love.
12" Single: Released Jun '85, on 4th & Broadway, by Island Records. Catalogue no: **12 BRWX 23**
12" Single: Released Apr '85, on 4th & Broadway, by Island Records. Deleted Jul '87. Catalogue no: **12 BRW 23**
7" Single: Released Apr '85, on 4th & Broadway, by Island Records. Deleted Apr '88. Catalogue no: **BRW 23**

Skirted Issue

RUM AND COCA COLA
Tracks: / Rum and coca cola / Leader of the pack.
7" Single: Released Apr '82, on T. E. R., by That's Entertainment Records. Catalogue no: **TER 001**

Skitts

LIVING WITHOUT YOU
Tracks: / Living without you.
7" Single: Released Apr '82, on Will, Catalogue no: **SKITT 001**

Skool Boyz

SLIP AWAY
Tracks: / Slip away.
7" Single: Released Sep '84, on CBS, by CBS Records. Catalogue no: **A 4568**

Skrewdriver

BACK WITH A BANG
Tracks: / Back with a bang.
7" Single: Released Sep '82, on Skrewdriver, Catalogue no: **SKREW 1**
12" Single: Released Sep '82, on Skrewdriver, Catalogue no: **SKREW 1T**

Skroteez

NEW TOWN
Tracks: / New town / Who's law / Livi punkz.
7" Single: Released May '82, on Overspill, Deleted '83. Catalogue no: **SPILL 1**

SKT

YOUR LOVE IS ALRIGHT
Tracks: / Your love is alright / Spinn on warning.
7" Single: Released Jun '84, on RCA, by BMG Records (UK). Catalogue no: **RCA 423**
12" Single: Released Jun '84, on RCA, by BMG Records (UK). Catalogue no: **RCAT 423**

Skull

LIVING
Tracks: / Living.
12" Single: Released Feb '87, on One Little Indian, by One Little Indian Records. Catalogue no: **12TP 5**

Skullflower

BIRTH, DEATH
Tracks: / Birth, death / Grub song / Time bomb / Blood harvest.
12" Single: Released Jan '89, on Broken Flag, Catalogue no: **BFV 9**

Skulls

GRAVEYARD SIGNAL
Tracks: / Graveyard signal.
7" Single: Released 31 Jul '89, on Snakeskin, Catalogue no: **SS001**

Sky

Biographical details: In early December 1978, John Williams, Herbie Flowers, Francis Monkman, Kevin Peek and Tristan Fry went into Abbey Road studios to cut their self titled debut album. Self produced with the help of two house engineers, Tony Clark and Haydn Bendall, the album showed a variance and precision rare of it's type, avoiding the usual pitfalls of classic/rock influenced instrumental works. The album was released on the Ariola Records label in April, 1979 and did not take long to gain a position within the Top 10 and achieve a double gold status. In May 1979, Sky embarked on its first UK tour - culminating with their debut at London's Royal Albert Hall. Their autumn tour of the same year put Sky in the top league with sell out concerts at all venues culminating in five successive nights at the Dominion Theatre in London. The tour also gave the band the first opportunity to try some un-tested material on it's audience, much of which formed the second album, *Sky 2* on which work began, once again at Abbey Road in Jan. 1980 with the same production crew at the helm. If Sky's audience was surprised with its adventurous spirit in the past, this double album, comprising nearly 80 minutes music, went far beyond that. On completion of the album, the band made it's first overseas tour. The response echoed that which had gone before in the UK. *Sky 2* topped the charts in it's second week of release and was certified gold that August. The band's third album *Sky 3*, was released in Feb. '81 and quickly found its way to the top of the album charts in Britain and around the world. A 20 date UK tour in June gave Sky's fans a chance to appreciae its newest recruit, Steve Gray who took over the keyboardists stool from Francis Monkman. Gray had already toured with the band in Dec.'80 and his writing and playing on *Sky 3* illustrated the added compatability of his style to that of the band. In Feb. '81, Sky broke new ground with a concert at Westminster Abbey which was later transmitted as a special on BBC TV. This was followe with an extensive tour of the UK and Europe, selling out venues. 1982 saw the release of a box-set of Sky's first three albums as well as *Sky 4 Forthcoming* in March. Sky achieved overwhelming success on their 1982 Australian tour during which time they recorded their fifth album entitled *Sky 5 - Live*. 1983 also saw tours of Japan and Australia and another European and UK tour. After their sixth album *Cadmium* and the single *Troika* that John Williams announced his departure from the group. (Ariola Records, April 1984).

ANIMALS, THE (PART 1)
Tracks: / Animals, The (part 1) / KP 11.
7" Single: Released Jan '83, on Ariola, by BMG Records (UK). Catalogue no: **ARO 292**

FOOL ON THE HILL
Tracks: / Fool on the hill / Spirits.
7" Single: Released Apr '81, on Ariola, by BMG Records (UK). Catalogue no: **ARO 311**

MASQUERADE
Tracks: / Masquerade / Fantasy.
7" Single: Released Mar '82, on Ariola, by BMG Records (UK). Deleted '85. Catalogue no: **ARO 276**

MY GISELLE
Tracks: / My Giselle / Fantasia.
7" Single: Released Jun '82, on Ariola, by BMG Records (UK). Deleted Jun '85. Catalogue no: **ARO 278**

TOCCATA
Tracks: / Toccata / Vivaldi.
7" Single: Released Sep '82, on Ariola, by BMG Records (UK). Catalogue no: **ARO 300**

Sky City Rockers

NICE AND SLOW
Tracks: / Nice and slow.
7" Single: Released Aug '87, on Sedition, by Sedition Records. Catalogue no: **EDIT 3326**
12" Single: Released Aug '87, on Sedition, by Sedition Records. Catalogue no: **EDITL 3326**

Skyers,Nathan

OH LOVE
Tracks: / Oh love / Leave bad company.
12" Single: Released Apr '86, on Mandingo, Catalogue no: **MAH 022**

Skyhooks

WOMEN IN UNIFORM
Tracks: / Women in uniform.
7" Single: Released Jun '79, on United Artists, by EMI Records. Deleted Jun '82. Catalogue no: **UP 36508**

Skynard, Lynard

I'VE NEVER BEEN YOUR FOOL
Tracks: / I've never been your fool / Gotta go.
12" Single: Released Nov '82, on MCA, by MCA Records. Deleted Nov '85. Catalogue no: **MCAT 799**
7" Single: Released Nov '82, on MCA, by MCA Records. Deleted Nov '85. Catalogue no: **MCA 799**

Skyriders

SNOOPY V THE RED BARON
Tracks: / Snoopy v the Red Baron / Lollipop love.
7" Single: Released Mar '85, on Airport, Catalogue no: **AIRP 747**

Skyscrapers

CHIFFON CHIFFON
Tracks: / Chiffon chiffon / Jenny.
7" Single: Released Nov '81, on Zilch, by Zilch Records. Catalogue no: **ZILCH 12**

HOTLINE FROM WASHINGTON
Tracks: / Hotline from Washington.
7" Single: Released Apr '81, on Zilch, by Zilch Records. Catalogue no: **ZILCH 2**

WAITING FOR THIS MOMENT ALL NIGHT
Tracks: / Waiting for this moment all night / BB air.
7" Single: Released May '82, on Zilch, by Zilch Records. Catalogue no: **ZILCH 19**

Skytrain

FOX ON THE RUN
Tracks: / Fox on the run.
12" Single: Released Jun '83, on Half Moon, by Rondelet Music & Records. Catalogue no: **HMB 1128T**
7" Single: Released Jun '83, on Half Moon, by Rondelet Music & Records. Catalogue no: **HM 1128**

Slab

CANCER BEACH
Tracks: / Cancer beach.
12" Single: Released 16 Jan '89, on Ink, by Red Flame Records. Catalogue no: **INK 12040**

DEATH'S HEAD SOUP
Tracks: / Death's head soup.
7" Single: Released May '89, on Ink, by Red Flame Records. Catalogue no: **INK 740**
12" Single: Released Apr '89, on Ink, by Red Flame Records. Catalogue no: **INK 1240**

PARALAX AVENUE
Tracks: / Yukou / Flirt / Paralax Avenue.
12" Single: Released Feb '87, on Ink, by Red Flame Records. Catalogue no: **INK 1226**

PEOPLE PIE
Tracks: / People pie / Railroad.
12" Single: Released Jun '88, on Ink, by Red Flame Records. Catalogue no: **INK 1234**

SMOKE RINGS
Tracks: / Smoke rings / Abbasloth (Double A side).
12" Single: Released Jun '87, on Ink, by Red Flame Records. Catalogue no: **INK 1229**
7" Single: Released Jun '87, on Ink, by Red Flame Records. Catalogue no: **INK 729**

Slade

ALL JOIN HANDS
Tracks: / All join hands.
7" Single: Released Nov '84, on RCA, by BMG Records (UK). Catalogue no: **RCA 455**
12" Single: Released Nov '84, on RCA, by BMG Records (UK). Catalogue no: **RCAT 455**

AND NOW THE WALTZ,C'EST LAVIE
Tracks: / And now the waltz, c'est lavie / Merry Christmas everybody.
7" Single: Released Nov '82, on RCA, by BMG Records (UK). Catalogue no: **RCA 291**

BANGIN' MAN
Tracks: / Bangin' man.
7" Single: Released Jul '74, on Polydor, by Polydor Ltd. Deleted Jul '77. Catalogue no: **2058 492**

COZ I LUV YOU (SINGLE)
Tracks: / Coz I luv you.
7" Single: Released Oct '71, on Polydor, by Polydor Ltd. Deleted Oct '74. Catalogue no: **2058 155**

CUM ON FEEL THE NOIZE
Tracks: / Cum on feel the noize / Cos I love you / Take me back 'ome / Goodbye to Jane.
7" Single: Released Mar '73, on Polydor, by Polydor Ltd. Deleted Mar '76. Catalogue no: **2058 339**
12" Single: Released Dec '81, on Polydor, by Polydor Ltd. Deleted Dec '84. Catalogue no: **POSPX 399**

DO YOU BELIEVE IN MIRACLES
Tracks: / Do you believe in miracles.
12" Single: Released Nov '85, on RCA, by BMG Records (UK). Catalogue no: **PT 40450**
7" Single: Released Nov '85, on RCA, by BMG Records (UK). Catalogue no: **PB 40449**

EVERYDAY
Tracks: / Everyday.
7" Single: Released Apr '74, on Polydor, by Polydor Ltd. Deleted Apr '77. Catalogue no: **2058 453**

FAR FAR AWAY
Tracks: / Far far away.
7" Single: Released Oct '74, on Polydor, by Polydor Ltd. Deleted Oct '77. Catalogue no: **2058 522**

GET DOWN AND GET WITH IT
Tracks: / Get down and get with it.
7" Single: Released Jun '71, on Polydor, by Polydor Ltd. Deleted Jun '74. Catalogue no: **2058 112**

GUDBUY T'JANE
Tracks: / Gudbuy t'Jane.
7" Single: Released Nov '72, on Polydor, by Polydor Ltd. Deleted Nov '75. Catalogue no: **2058 312**

GYPSY ROAD HOG
Tracks: / Gypsy road hog.
7" Single: Released Feb '77, on Barn, by Barn Records. Deleted Feb '80. Catalogue no: **2014 105**

HOKEY COKEY
Tracks: / Hokey cokey / Get down and get with it.
7" Single: Released Dec '82, on Speed, Deleted '85. Catalogue no: **SPEED 201**

HOW DOES IT FEEL
Tracks: / How does it feel.
7" Single: Released Feb '75, on Polydor, by Polydor Ltd. Deleted Feb '78. Catalogue no: **2058 547**

IN FOR A PENNY
Tracks: / In for a penny.
7" Single: Released Nov '75, on Polydor, by Polydor Ltd. Deleted Nov '78. Catalogue no: **2058 663**

KNUCKLE SANDWICH NANCY
Tracks: / Knuckle sandwich Nancy / I'm mad.
7" Single: Released May '81, on Cheapskate, Catalogue no: **CHEAP 24**

LET'S CALL IT QUITS
Tracks: / Let's call it quits.
7" Single: Released Feb '76, on Polydor, by Polydor Ltd. Deleted Feb '79. Catalogue no: **2058 690**

LET'S DANCE (REMIX 1988)
Tracks: / Let's dance (remix 1988) / Standing in the corner.
7" Single: Released Dec '88, on Cheapskate, Catalogue no: **BOYZ 3**

LOCK UP YOUR DAUGHTERS
Tracks: / Lock up your daughters.
7" Single: Released Sep '81, on RCA, by BMG Records (UK). Catalogue no: **RCA 124**

LOOK WOT YOU DUN
Tracks: / Look wot you dun.
7" Single: Released Feb '72, on Polydor, by Polydor Ltd. Deleted Feb '75. Catalogue no: **2058 195**

MAMA WEER ALL CRAZEE NOW
Tracks: / Mama weer all crazee now.
7" Single: Released Sep '72, on Polydor, by Polydor Ltd. Deleted Sep '75. Catalogue no: **2058 274**

MERRY XMAS EVERYBODY
Tracks: / Merry Xmas everybody / Hokey cokey.
7" Single: Released Nov '80, on Cheapskate, Deleted '83. Catalogue no: **CHEAP 11**
7" Single: Released Nov '86, on Polydor, by Polydor Ltd. Deleted 30 Jun '89. Catalogue no: **POSP 780**
12" Single: Released Nov '86, on Polydor, by Polydor Ltd. Deleted 31 May '89. Catalogue no: **POSPX 780**
7" Single: Released Dec '73, on Polydor, by Polydor Ltd. Deleted Dec '87. Catalogue no: **2058 422**

MY BABY LEFT ME-THAT'S ALL RIGHT (MEDLEY)
Tracks: / My baby left me - that's all right.
7" Single: Released Oct '77, on Barn, by Barn Records. Deleted Oct '80. Catalogue no: **2014 114**

MY FRIEND STAN
Tracks: / My friend Stan.
7" Single: Released Oct '73, on Polydor, by Polydor Ltd. Deleted Oct '76. Catalogue no: **2058 407**

MY OH MY
Tracks: / My oh my.
7" Single: Released Nov '83, on RCA, by BMG Records (UK). Deleted Nov '86. Catalogue no: **RCA 373**

MYZSTERIOUS MIZSTER JONES
Tracks: / Myzsterious Mizster Jones / Mama nature is a rocker / My oh my.
7" Single: Released Mar '85, on RCA, by BMG Records (UK). Catalogue no: **PB 40027**
12" Single: Released Mar '85, on RCA, by BMG Records (UK). Catalogue no: **PB 40028**

NIGHT STARVATION
Tracks: / Night starvation / When I'm dancin', I'm not fightin' / I'm a rocker / Don't waste your time / Wheels ain't coming down / Nine to five.
7" EP: Released Jun '80, on RCA (USA), Deleted Jun '83. Catalogue no: **45-3**

OKEY COKEY
Tracks: / Okey Cokey.
7" Pic: Released Dec '82, on Speed, Deleted May '85. Catalogue no: **SPEEDP 201**
7" Single: Released Dec '86, on Receiver, by Trojan Records. Deleted May '85. Catalogue no: **SPEED 201**

RUBY RED
Tracks: / Ruby red.
7" Single: Released Mar '82, on RCA, by BMG Records (UK). Catalogue no: **RCA 191**

RUN RUN AWAY
Tracks: / Run runaway.

7" Single: Released Feb '84, on RCA, by BMG Records (UK). Deleted Feb '87. Catalogue no: **RCA 385**

SEVEN YEAR (B)ITCH, THE (SINGLE)
Tracks: / Seven year (B)itch, The.
7" Single: Released Jan '85, on RCA, by BMG Records (UK). Catalogue no: **RCA 475**
12" Single: Released Jan '85, on RCA, by BMG Records (UK). Catalogue no: **RCAT 475**

SKWEEZE ME PLEEZE ME
Tracks: / Skweeze me pleeze me.
7" Single: Released Jun '73, on Polydor, by Polydor Ltd. Deleted Jun '76. Catalogue no: **2058 377**

SLADE ALIVE AT READING '80 (EP)
Tracks: / When I'm dancin' I ain't fighting / Born to be wild / Something else / Pistol packin' mama / Keep a rollin'.
7" EP: Released Oct '80, on Cheapskate, Deleted Oct '83. Catalogue no: **CHEAP 5**

STILL THE SAME
Tracks: / Gotta go home / Still the same.
7" Single: Released Jan '87, on RCA, by BMG Records (UK). Catalogue no: **PB 41137**

STILL THE SAME (EXT)
Tracks: / Gotta go home / Still the same.
12" Single: Released Feb '87, on RCA, by BMG Records (UK). Deleted '87. Catalogue no: **PT 41138**

TAKE ME BAK 'OME
Tracks: / Take me bak 'ome.
7" Single: Released Jun '72, on Polydor, by Polydor Ltd. Deleted Jun '75. Catalogue no: **2058 231**

THANKS FOR THE MEMORY (WHAM BAM THANK YOU MAM)
Tracks: / Thanks for the memory.
7" Single: Released May '75, on Polydor, by Polydor Ltd. Deleted May '78. Catalogue no: **2058 585**

THAT'S WHAT FRIENDS ARE FOR
Tracks: / That's what friends are for / Wild party.
7" Single: Released Apr '87, on RCA, by BMG Records (UK). Catalogue no: **PB 41271**
12" Single: Released Apr '87, on RCA, by BMG Records (UK). Catalogue no: **PT 41272**

WE WON'T GIVE IN
Tracks: / We won't give in.
7" Single: on Cheapskate, Catalogue no: **BOYZ 2**

WE'LL BRING THE HOUSE DOWN (SINGLE)
Tracks: / We'll bring the house down / Hold on to your hats.
7" Single: Released Jan '81, on Cheapskate, Catalogue no: **CHEAP 16**

WHEELS AIN'T COMING DOWN
Tracks: / Wheels ain't coming down.
7" Single: Released Apr '81, on Cheapskate, Deleted Apr '84. Catalogue no: **CHEAP 21**

WIZZARD/SLADE
CD 5": Released Nov '88, on Counterpoint, Catalogue no: **CDEP 12 C**

YOU BOYZ MAKE BIG NOIZE (SINGLE)
Tracks: / You boyz make big noize.
12" Single: Released Jul '87, on Cheapskate, Catalogue no: **TBOYZ 1**
7" Single: Released Jul '87, on Cheapskate, Catalogue no: **BOYZ 1**

Slainte

AS TEARS GO BY
Tracks: / As tears go by.
7" Single: Released Oct '82, on Mint, by Emerald Records. Deleted '88. Catalogue no: **CHEW 70**

WHEN I GROW TOO OLD TO DREAM
Tracks: / When I grow too old to dream.
7" Single: Released Apr '82, on Mint, by Emerald Records. Deleted '88. Catalogue no: **CHEW 62**

Slam Slam

MOVE (DANCE ALL NIGHT)
Tracks: / Move (dance all night) / Smooth.
Cassingle: Released 31 Jul '89, on MCA, by MCA Records. Catalogue no: **MCAC 1346**
7" Single: Released 31 Jul '89, on MCA, by MCA Records. Catalogue no: **MCA 1346**
12" Single: Released 31 Jul '89, on MCA, by MCA Records. Catalogue no: **MCAT 1346**
CD 5": Released 31 Jul '89, on MCA, by MCA Records. Catalogue no: **DMCA 1346**

Slanted View

WHITE PAPER
Tracks: / White paper.
12" Single: Released Aug '85, on Tite, Catalogue no: **TITE 1**

Slapp Happy

EVERYBODY'S SLIMMIN
Tracks: / Everybody's slimmin'.
7" Single: Released Jun '83, on Half Cat, Catalogue no: **HC 001**

Slater, Roy, L.

WONDER
Tracks: / Wonder.
7" Single: Released Apr '79, on Jama, Catalogue no: **JA 24**

Slater, Stuart

ALL AROUND THE WORLD
Tracks: / All around the world.
7" Single: Released Apr '83, on Chrysalis, by Chrysalis Records. Catalogue no: **RAT 1**

Slaughter

EAST SIDE OF TOWN
Tracks: / East side of town / One by one.
7" Single: Released Mar '80, on DJM, Deleted '83. Catalogue no: **DJS 10936**

Slaughter, Joe

I'LL FOLLOW YOU DOWN
Tracks: / I'll follow you down / Napalm girl / Surely some of Slaughter's blues / Fall apart.
12" Single: Released Nov '85, on Creation, by Creation Records. Deleted Jul '88. Catalogue no: **CRE 019T**
7" Single: Released Nov '85, on Creation, by Creation Records. Deleted Jul '88. Catalogue no: **CRE 019**

SHE'S SO OUT OF TOUCH
Tracks: / She's so out of touch / I know you rider / Lonesome death of Thurston Moore,The (Extra track on 12" version only.).
7" Single: Released Nov '86, on Creation, by Creation Records. Catalogue no: **CRE 035**
12" Single: Released Nov '86, on Creation, by Creation Records. Catalogue no: **CRE 035T**

Slaughter & the Dogs

I'M THE ONE
Tracks: / I'm the one.
7" Single: Released Jun '80, on DJM, Catalogue no: **DJS 10945**

TWIST AND TURN
Tracks: / Twist and turn / Cranked up really high / Where have all the boot boys gone.
12" Single: Released Feb '83, on Thrush, by Thrush Records. Catalogue no: **THRUSH 1**

WHERE HAVE ALL THE BOOT BOYS GONE
Tracks: / Where have all the boot boys gone / You're a bore.
7" Single: Released Mar '81, on Decca, by Decca Records. Deleted '88. Catalogue no: **F 13723**
7" Single: Released Nov '88, on Damaged Goods, Catalogue no: **FNAAR 1**

YOU'RE READY NOW
Tracks: / You're ready now.
7" Single: Released Nov '79, on DJM, Catalogue no: **DJS 10927**

Slave

ARE YOU READY FOR LOVE?
Tracks: / Are you ready for love? / Foxy lady.
7" Single: Released Jun '80, on Atlantic, by WEA Records. Deleted Jun '83. Catalogue no: **K 11482**

BARBARA JEAN BLVD
Tracks: / Barbara Jean Blvd / Dangerous.
12" Single: Released 13 Mar '89, on Ichiban, by Ichiban Records (UK). Catalogue no: **12PO 20**

DO YOU LIKE IT GIRL
Tracks: / Do you like it girl / You and me.
7" Single: Released Mar '83, on Cotillion, by WEA Records. Catalogue no: **B 9912**
12" Single: Released Mar '83, on Cotillion, by WEA Records. Catalogue no: **B 9962 T**

DONT WASTE MY TIME
Tracks: / Don't waste my time.
7" Single: Released Oct '85, on Certain, by Certain Records. Catalogue no: **ACERT 2**
12" Single: Released Oct '85, on Certain, by Certain Records. Catalogue no: **12 ACERT 2**

FEEL MY LOVE
Tracks: / Stone jam / Feel my love.
7" Single: Released Jan '81, on Cotillion, by WEA Records. Deleted Jan '84. Catalogue no: **K 11633**

JUICY-O
Tracks: / I like your style / Juicy o.
12" Single: Released Jul '87, on Ichiban, by Ichiban Records (UK). Catalogue no: **12PO 2**

JUST A TOUCH OF LOVE
Tracks: / Just a touch of love / Wait for me.
7" Single: Released May '84, on Cotillion, by WEA Records. Catalogue no: **B 6955**
12" Single: Released May '84, on Cotillion, by WEA Records. Catalogue no: **B 6955T**
7" Single: Released Mar '80, on Atlantic, by WEA Records. Deleted Mar '83. Catalogue no: **K 11442**

SLIDE '88
Tracks: / Slide '88 / You take my breath away / Holiday.
12" Single: Released Mar '88, on Ichiban, by Ichiban Records (UK). Catalogue no: **ICHT 702**

STEPPIN' OUT
Tracks: / Steppin' out.
12" Single: Released Nov '83, on Cotillion, by WEA Records. Catalogue no: **SLAVE 1T**

THRILL ME
Tracks: / Thrill me / Jazzy lady / Unchained at last.
12" Single: Released Feb '86, on Certain, by Certain Records. Catalogue no: **12 ACERT 6**

WAIT FOR ME
Tracks: / Wait for me.
12" Single: Released Jan '82, on Cotillion, by WEA Records. Catalogue no: **K 11702T**
7" Single: Released Jan '82, on Cotillion, by WEA Records. Catalogue no: **K 11702**

WATCHING YOU
Tracks: / Watching you / Dreamin'.
7" Single: Released Feb '81, on Cotillion, by WEA Records. Deleted Feb '84. Catalogue no: **K 11645**

Slave Raider

YOUNG BLOOD
Tracks: / Young blood.
7" Single: Released Apr '89, on Jive, by Zomba Records. Catalogue no: **JIVE 198**
12" Single: Released Apr '89, on Jive, by Zomba Records. Catalogue no: **JIVET 198**

Slayer

CRIMINALLY INSANE
Tracks: / Criminally insane (remix) / Aggressive perfector / Post mortem*.
12" Single: Released 23 May '87, on London Records, by London Records. Catalogue no: **LONX 133**
7" Single: Released 23 May '87, on London Records, by London Records. Deleted Sep '87. Catalogue no: **LON 133**

HAUNTING THE CHAPEL
Tracks: / Haunting the chapel / Chemical warfare / Captor of sin.
12" Single: Released Oct '84, on Roadrunner (Germany), Catalogue no: **RR 125508**

SOUTH OF HEAVEN (SINGLE)
Tracks: / South of heaven.
12" Single: Released 16 Sep '88, on London Records, by London Records. Catalogue no: **LONX 201**

Sleazee

GIRL ARE OUT
Tracks: / Girl are out.
7" Single: Released Nov '83, on Calibre, Deleted '85. Catalogue no: **CAB 119**
12" Single: Released Nov '83, on Calibre, Deleted '85. Catalogue no: **CABT 119**

Sledge, Percy

Biographical details:
Percy Sledge was born in Alabama in 1941. His first single on Atlantic, *When A Man Loves A Woman*, in 1966, was No 1 on both pop and soul charts in America and No 5 in Britain, making him one of the biggest stars of the soul era. His hits are compiled on Charly as well as Atlantic. *When A Man Loves A Woman* was used in a TV advertisement in early '87 and became a hit all over again. (Donald Clarke, March 1987.).

COVER ME
Tracks: / Cover me / It tears me apart
12" Single: Released 23 May '87, on Atlantic, by WEA Records. Deleted Jul '88. Catalogue no: **YZ 199 T**
7" Single: Released 23 May '87, on Atlantic, by WEA Records. Deleted Jul '88. Catalogue no: **YZ 199**

JUST CAN'T STOP
Tracks: / Just can't stop.
7" Single: Released Feb '88, on Sonet, by Sonet Records. Catalogue no: **SON 2335**

WARM AND TENDER LOVE (SINGLE)
Tracks: / Warm and tender love.
7" Single: Released Aug '66, on Atlantic, by WEA Records. Deleted Aug '69. Catalogue no: **584 034**

WHEN A MAN LOVES A WOMAN (EP)
Tracks: / When a man loves a woman / Warm and tender love / What is soul / Stand by me.
7" EP: Released Apr '80, on Atlantic, by WEA Records. Deleted '83. Catalogue no: **ATM 3**

WHEN A MAN LOVES A WOMAN (OLD GOLD)
Tracks: / When a man loves a woman.
7" Single: Released Jan '85, on Old Gold, by Old Gold Records. Catalogue no: **OG 9496**

WHEN A MAN LOVES A WOMAN (SINGLE)
Tracks: / When a man loves a woman.
7" Single: Released May '66, on Atlantic, by WEA Records. Deleted May '69. Catalogue no: **584 001**
7" Single: Released '74, on Atlantic, by WEA Records. Catalogue no: **K 10104**
7" Single: Released Jan '87, on Atlantic, by WEA Records. Catalogue no: **TZ 96**
12" Single: Released Jan '87, on Atlantic, by WEA Records. Catalogue no: **YZ 96T**
CD 5": Released Jul '87, on Intertape, Deleted '88. Catalogue no: **500 068**

Sledgehammer

IN THE QUEUE
Tracks: / In the queue / Oxford City.
7" Pic: Released Mar '85, on Illuminated, Catalogue no: **ILL 333**

LIVING IN DREAMS
Tracks: / Living in dreams / Fantasia.
7" Single: Released Jan '81, on Slammer, Deleted Jan '84. Catalogue no: **CELL 2**

Sleepers

ISLAND OF DREAMS
Tracks: / Island of dreams.
7" Single: Released Mar '83, on SMC, Deleted '85. Catalogue no: **RAM 523**

Sleeping Dogs

BEWARE
Tracks: / Beware.
7" Single: Released Jun '83, on Crass, by Crass Records. Catalogue no: **CRASS 221984/11**

Sleeping Dogs Wake

CONFINED TO MEMORY
Tracks: / Confined to memory.
12" Single: Released '88, on One Little Indian, by One Little Indian Records. Catalogue no: **14TP 12**

TOYS FOR ALICE
Tracks: / Toys for Alice.
12" Single: Released Oct '88, on One Little Indian, by One Little Indian Records. Catalogue no: **12TP 014**

Sleeping Lions

CELEBRATION
Tracks: / Celebration / Wake up.
7" Single: Released Feb '83, on CBS, by CBS Records. Catalogue no: **LION 1**

WONDERFUL YOU ARE
Tracks: / Wonderful you are / Out of the darkness into the sun
7" Single: Released Nov '82, on CBS, by CBS Records. Deleted Nov '85. Catalogue no: **A 2815**

Sleeping Pictures

POSSESSION
Tracks: / Possession.
7" Single: Released May '85, on Lost Moments, Catalogue no: **LM 023**

Sleepy Wonder

FADE AWAY
Tracks: / Fade away.
12" Single: Released Nov '88, on Park Heights, Catalogue no: **PHD 0060**

Sleeque

ONE FOR THE MONEY
Tracks: / One for the money / One for the (dub).
12" Single: Released Jun '86, on Malaco, by Malaco Records (UK). Deleted '88. Catalogue no: **MAL 12 033**

Sleigh, Bob

I WANNA BE THE FAIRY ON THE XMAS TREE
Tracks: / I wanna be the fairy on the Xmas tree / Christmas day
7" Single: Released Nov '83, on Bulrush, by Bulrush Records. Catalogue no: **BULA 2**

Sleigh, Robert

FIRST SNOW
Tracks: / First snow / Snow bike.
7" Single: Released Nov '83, on Stiff, by Stiff Records. Catalogue no: **BUY 194**

Slick

FORGET YOU (IT'S TOO LATE)
Tracks: / Forget you (it's too late) / Betcha bottom dollar.

12" Single: Released Nov '80, on Fantasy (1), by BMG Records (UK). Deleted Nov '83. Catalogue no: **FTCT 193**
7" Single: Released Nov '80, on Fantasy (1), by BMG Records (UK). Deleted Nov '83. Catalogue no: **FTC 193**

SEXY CREAM
Tracks: / Sexy cream.
7" Single: Released Sep '79, on Fantasy (USA), by Fantasy Inc (USA). Deleted Sep '82. Catalogue no: **FTC 182**

SPACE BASS
Tracks: / Space bass.
7" Single: Released Jun '79, on Fantasy (USA), by Fantasy Inc (USA). Deleted Jun '82. Catalogue no: **FTC 176**
12" Single: Released Nov '85, on Streetwave, Catalogue no: **SWAVE 5**

Slick, Grace

Biographical details: Grace Slick hates to be called the first lady of rock'n'roll, but she is. The voice that launched a thousand trips first rocketed to the general attention of music fans in 1966 when from the remarkably successful LP *Surrealistic pillow* came the hit *White rabbit*. The song with Slick's lyrics brought 'sex, drugs and rock'n'roll full force to the music scene. This was the San Francisco sound and the outragiousness of the times found a female voice in Grace, a former model turned vocalist, initially for Great Society and later Jefferson Airplane. (RCA Records, February 1984).

DREAMS (SINGLE)
Tracks: / Dreams / Angel of night.
7" Single: Released May '80, on RCA, by BMG Records (UK). Deleted May '83. Catalogue no: **PB 9534**
7" Single: Released May '80, on RCA, by BMG Records (UK). Deleted May '83. Catalogue no: **PB 9534**

MISTREATER
Tracks: / Mistreater / Full moon man.
7" Single: Released Feb '81, on RCA, by BMG Records (UK). Deleted Feb '84. Catalogue no: **RCA 33**

Slick Rick

TEENAGE LOVE
Tracks: / Teenage love / Teenage love (dub) / Treat her like a prostitute (album version) (Only on 12" version.) / Treat her like a prostitute (movie version).
7" Single: Released Dec '88, on Def Jam, Deleted 10 Jul '89. Catalogue no: **653 167-7**
12" Single: Released Dec '88, on Def Jam, Deleted 10 Jul '89. Catalogue no: **653 167-8**

Slickee Boys

THIS PARTY SUCKS
Tracks: / This party sucks.
7" Single: Released Jul '88, on New Rose (1), by New Rose Records. Catalogue no: **NEW 112**

WHEN I GO TO THE BEACH
Tracks: / When I go to the beach / You've got what it takes.
7" Single: Released Aug '84, on New Rose (1), by New Rose Records. Catalogue no: **NEW 41**

YOUR AUTUMN EYES
Tracks: / Your autumn eyes.
7" Single: Released Dec '87, on New Rose (1), by New Rose Records. Catalogue no: **NEW 98**

Slide

SUPERMAN'S SHOES
Tracks: / Superman's shoes / Meet your new neighbour.
7" Single: Released Oct '80, on Crash, by Satril Records. Deleted Oct '83. Catalogue no: **POW 4**

WHY IS IT A CRIME?
Tracks: / Why is it a crime? / Never ever / Leave your love (Only on 12" and CD single.).
CD 5": Released Aug '89, on Mercury, by Phonogram Ltd. Catalogue no: **MERCD 292**
12" Single: Released Aug '89, on Mercury, by Phonogram Ltd. Catalogue no: **MERX 292**
7" Single: Released Aug '89, on Mercury, by Phonogram Ltd. Catalogue no: **MER 292**

S.L.I

DO THAT DANCE
Tracks: / Do that dance / It ain't nothing.
12" Single: Released Jan '89, on B-Ware, by B/Ware Records. Catalogue no: **UM 006**

Slik

FOREVER AND EVER
Tracks: / Forever and ever.
7" Single: Released Jan '76, on Bell, Deleted Jan '79. Catalogue no: **BELL 1464**

REQUIEM
Tracks: / Requiem.
7" Single: Released May '76, on Bell, Deleted May '79. Catalogue no: **BELL 1478**

Slim

IT'S IN THE MIX
Tracks: / It's in the mix.
12" Single: Released Jul '83, on Greyhound, by Greyhound Records. Catalogue no: **GRPT 104**

Slim, Tarheel

NUMBER 9 TRAIN
Tracks: / Number 9 train.
7" Single: Released Jul '82, on Charly, by Charly Records. Deleted '87. Catalogue no: **CTD 125**

WILDCAT TAMER
Tracks: / Wildcat tamer.
7" Single: Released '82, on Charly, by Charly Records. Catalogue no: **CTD 127**

Slimline

IF YOU CAN DANCE TO IT
Tracks: / If you can dance to it / If you can dance to it (part 2).
7" Single: Released Apr '82, on Channel, by Channel Records. Catalogue no: **CHAN 001**
12" Single: Released Apr '82, on Channel, by Channel Records. Catalogue no: **CHAN 001 T**

Slipperman

DANCE YOUR BODY DOWN
Tracks: / Dance your body / Kiss.
12" Single: Released May '88, on Rio Digital, by Rio Digital Records. Catalogue no: **12RDS 2**
7" Single: Released May '88, on Rio Digital, by Rio Digital Records. Catalogue no: **7RDS 2**

Slique

NEVER GIVE UP
Tracks: / Never give up / Cheating.
7" Single: Released Oct '89, on Champion, by Champion Records. Catalogue no: **CHAMP 212**
12" Single: Released Oct '89, on Champion, by Champion Records. Catalogue no: **CHAMP 12212**

Slits

ANIMAL SPACE
Tracks: / Animal space / Animal spacier.
7" Single: Released Jul '81, on Human (2), Deleted '82. Catalogue no: **HUM 4**

EARTHBEAT
Tracks: / Earthbeat / Begin again rhythm.
7" Single: Released Oct '81, on CBS, by CBS Records. Deleted '85. Catalogue no: **A 1498**

IN THE BEGINNING
Tracks: / In the beginning / Where there's a will.
7" Single: Released Mar '80, on Rough Trade, by Rough Trade Records. Catalogue no: **RT 039**

PEEL SESSIONS:SLITS 19.9.77
12" Single: Released Jan '87, on Strange Fruit, by Strange Fruit Records. Catalogue no: **SFPS 021**

TYPICAL GIRLS/I HEARD IT THROUGH THE GRAPEVINE
Tracks: / Typical girls / I heard it through the grapevine.
7" Single: Released Oct '79, on Island, by Island Records. Deleted Oct '82. Catalogue no: **WIP 6505**

Sloan, P.F.

SINS OF THE FAMILY
Tracks: / Sins of the family, The.
7" Single: Released Nov '65, on RCA, by BMG Records (UK). Deleted Nov '68. Catalogue no: **RCA 1482**

Sloane

ENTERTAINING MR SLOANE
Tracks: / Entertaining mr sloane / Get it while you're young.
7" Single: Released Feb '80, on Pye, Deleted Feb '85. Catalogue no: **7P159**

SO IN LOVE
Tracks: / So in love / Teller of tales.
7" Single: Released Sep '80, on Bitch, Deleted '83. Catalogue no: **BIT 09**

Sloley, Andrew

SUPERSTAR
Tracks: / Superstar / My baby.
12" Single: Released Apr '86, on Moove, Catalogue no: **SME 001**

Sloley, Glen

DON'T PLAY WITH LOVE
Tracks: / Don't play with love.
12" Single: Released Nov '84, on Star Disc, Catalogue no: **SDD 001**

Sloman, John

PERFECT STRANGERS
Tracks: / Perfect strangers.
7" Single: Released Aug '88, on FM, by FM-Revolver Records. Catalogue no: **VHF 49**

Slow

TONIGHT I'M IN THE MOOD FOR LOVE
Tracks: / Tonight I'm in the mood for love.
7" Single: Released May '83, on Island, by Island Records. Catalogue no: **IS 114**

Slow Children

PRESIDENT AM I (HARD TIME)
Tracks: / President am I (hard time) / Brazilian magazines.
7" Single: Released Jun '81, on Ensign, by Ensign Records. Deleted '82. Catalogue no: **ENY 212**

SPRING IN FIALTA
Tracks: / Spring in Fialta.
7" Single: Released Sep '81, on Ensign, by Ensign Records. Deleted '82. Catalogue no: **ENY 220**
12" Single: Released Sep '81, on Ensign, by Ensign Records. Deleted '83. Catalogue no: **ENYT 220**

TALK ABOUT HORSES
Tracks: / Talk about horses / Ticket to France.
7" Single: Released Mar '81, on Ensign, by Ensign Records. Deleted Mar '84. Catalogue no: **ENY 206**

Slow Motion

CHRISTMAS CHARADE Featuring White Christmas & Good King Wenceslas
Tracks: / Christmas charade.
7" Single: Released Nov '79, on RK, by RK Records. Deleted '81. Catalogue no: **RK 1024**

Slow Twitch Fibres

THIS IS YOUR LUNCH
Tracks: / This is your lunch / Illicit sects.
12" Single: Released Oct '81, on Rialto (1), by Rialto Records. Catalogue no: **12 RIA 1**
7" Single: Released Oct '81, on Rialto (1), by Rialto Records. Catalogue no: **RIA 1**

Slowfade

RUNNING AWAY
Tracks: / Running away / Surfin' in Kilburn.
7" Single: Released Jul '82, on Third World, Catalogue no: **HIT 109**

SOUND OF A BREAKING HEART
Tracks: / Sound of a breaking heart.
7" Single: Released Feb '83, on T.W., by T.W. Records. Catalogue no: **HIT 111**

Sluggy

GIMME MI LOVER
Tracks: / Gimme mi lover.
7" Single: Released Jun '88, on Witty, Catalogue no: **MMD 128**

ORIGINAL
Tracks: / Original.
7" Single: Released May '89, on Music Master, Catalogue no: **UNKNOWN**

STAMMA STYLE
Tracks: / Stamma style.
12" Single: Released Jul '88, on Blue Trac, by Blue Trac Records. Catalogue no: **PHD 050**

YOUNGER GENERATION
Tracks: / Younger generation.
7" Single: Released 4 Feb '89, on Blue Mountain, Catalogue no: **BMD 045**

Slum Turkeys

NO AXE TO GRIND
Tracks: / No axe to grind.
12" Single: Released Jul '89, on Crack, Catalogue no: **SLUM 001**

Slutz

NOVA THE NERVO
Tracks: / Nova the nervo / Lord of the flies.
7" Single: Released Mar '82, on Sky-Hi, Catalogue no: **SKY 780**

Sly Flack

DELINQUENT FUNK
Tracks: / Delinquent funk.
7" Single: Released Nov '84, on Ecstasy, by Creole Records. Catalogue no: **XTC 10**
12" Single: Released Nov '84, on Ecstasy, by Creole Records. Catalogue no: **XTCT 10**

Sly Fox

IF PUSH COMES TO SHOVE
Tracks: / If push comes to a shove / Stay true.
7" Single: Released Aug '86, on Capitol, by EMI Records. Deleted '88. Catalogue no: **CL 423**

LET'S GO ALL THE WAY (SINGLE)
Tracks: / Let's go all the way.
12" Single: Released Jun '86, on Capitol, by EMI Records. Catalogue no: **12 CLX 403**
12" Single: Released Apr '86, on Capitol, by EMI Records. Catalogue no: **12 CL 403**
7" Single: Released Apr '86, on Capitol, by EMI Records. Deleted Oct '87. Catalogue no: **CL 403**

Sly & Robbie

BOOPS (HERE TO GO)
Tracks: / Boops (here to go) / Don't stop the music.
7" Single: Released Mar '87, on 4th & Broadway, by Island Records. Deleted Apr '88. Catalogue no: **BRW 61**
12" Single: Released Mar '87, on 4th & Broadway, by Island Records. Deleted Apr '88. Catalogue no: **12 BRW 61**
12" Single: Released Apr '87, on 4th & Broadway, by Island Records. Catalogue no: **12 BRWX 61**

DANCING DIRTY
Tracks: / Dancing dirty / Rass brass.
12" Single: Released 28 Apr '89, on Taxi (1), Catalogue no: **TAXT 21**

DON'T STOP THE MUSIC
Tracks: / Don't stop the music / Stampede / El pussy catska (12" only).
7" Single: Released Dec '81, on Island, by Island Records. Catalogue no: **WIP 6717**
12" Single: Released Dec '81, on Island, by Island Records. Catalogue no: **12WIP 6717**

FIRE
Tracks: / Fire / Ticket to ride / Miles.
Cassingle: Released Jul '87, on 4th & Broadway, by Island Records. Deleted Apr '89. Catalogue no: **BRWC 71**
7" Single: Released Jul '87, on 4th & Broadway, by Island Records. Deleted Jun '88. Catalogue no: **BRW 71**
12" Single: Released Jul '87, on 4th & Broadway, by Island Records. Deleted Apr '88. Catalogue no: **12 BRW 71**

GET TO THIS, GET TO THAT
Tracks: / Get to this, get to that.
7" Single: Released Jul '85, on Island, by Island Records. Catalogue no: **IS 238**

IATOLA
Tracks: / Iatola.
7" Single: Released Oct '83, on Taxi (2), by Island Records. Catalogue no: **DSR 0513**

INSIDE OUTSIDE
Tracks: / Inside outside.
7" Single: Released Oct '83, on Taxi (1), Catalogue no: **DSRC 054**

MAKE 'EM MOVE
Tracks: / Make 'em move.
7" Single: Released Nov '85, on Island, by Island Records. Catalogue no: **IS 251**
12" Single: Released Nov '85, on Island, by Island Records. Deleted Jul '87. Catalogue no: **12IS 251**

RIVER NIGGER
Tracks: / River nigger.
7" Single: Released Oct '83, on Taxi (1), Catalogue no: **DSR 0511**

SEXUAL HEALING
Tracks: / Sexual healing / Search & destroy.
12" Single: Released Dec '82, on Taxi (2), by Island Records. Catalogue no: **IPR 2057**

TRIPLET
Tracks: / Triplet / Waterbed.
12" Single: Released Dec '83, on Taxi (2), by Island Records. Catalogue no: **IPR 2069**

Sly & The Family Stone

Biographical details:
The most original, innovative and influential American group of their era, sexually, racially and musically mixed, Sly & The Family Stone exploded from San Francisco with a fusion of pop, rock, soul, psychedelia and jazz-oriented horns to make first-class dance music with a social message. Lead singer, organist and guitarist Sly Stone was born Sylvester Stewart in Dallas, Texas, in 1944, and moved to the San Francisco area as a child. He formed groups, worked as a disc jockey and produced records on the legendary Autumn label. He formed the group in 1966 with brother Fred (guitar and vocals), Larry Graham (bass), Cynthia Robinson (trumpet), Rosie Stone (piano), Jerry Martini (sax) and Greg Errico (drums). Stone was one of the first to use a drum machine -- on *Family Affair*, 1971 -- and that innovation and Graham's sharp-edged, popping bass lines were widely imitated subsequently by lesser talents. Their time at the top was brief because of Sly's unreliability, related to drugs. His comeback albums on Warner Brothers were less successful. Graham later formed Graham Central Station. (Donald Clarke, March 1987.).

DANCE TO THE MUSIC (SINGLE)
Tracks: / Dance to the music.
7" Single: Released Jul '68, on Direction, Deleted Jul '71. Catalogue no: **58 3568**

7" Single: Released Jul '82, on Old Gold, by Old Gold Records. Catalogue no: **OG 9188**
12" Single: Released Sep '87, on Portrait, by CBS Records. Catalogue no: **SLY T1**
7" Single: Released Sep '87, on Portrait, by CBS Records. Catalogue no: **SLY 1**

EVERYDAY PEOPLE
Tracks: / Everyday people.
7" Single: Released Mar '69, on Direction, Deleted Mar '72. Catalogue no: **58 3938**

FAMILY AFFAIR
Tracks: / Family affair.
7" Single: Released Jan '72, on Epic, by CBS Records. Deleted Jan '75. Catalogue no: **EPC 7632**

M'LADY
Tracks: / M'lady.
7" Single: Released Oct '68, on Direction, Deleted Oct '71. Catalogue no: **58 3707**

RUNNIN' AWAY
Tracks: / Runnin' away.
7" Single: Released Apr '72, on Epic, by CBS Records. Deleted Apr '75. Catalogue no: **EPC 7810**

SM

SM
Tracks: / SM.
12" Single: Released '88, on Subway, by Subway Records. Catalogue no: **SUB 011**

Smack

LOVERS CONCERTO
Tracks: / Lover's concerto / Deep breathing.
7" Single: Released Jun '82, on Jive, by Zomba Records. Catalogue no: **JIVE 18**
12" Single: Released Jun '82, on Jive, by Zomba Records. Catalogue no: **JIVET 18**

Small Ads

FRIDAY NITE COWBOY
Tracks: / Friday nite cowboy.
7" Single: Released Nov '81, on Bronze, by Bronze Records. Catalogue no: **BRO 135**

HP MAN
Tracks: / HP man / Radio love.
7" Single: Released Jun '81, on Bronze, by Bronze Records. Deleted Jun '84. Catalogue no: **BRO 125**

SMALL ADS
Tracks: / Small ads / Motorway madness.
7" Single: Released Apr '81, on Bronze, by Bronze Records. Deleted Apr '84. Catalogue no: **BRO 115**

Small Brothers

GOT THE HURT
Tracks: / Got the hurt / Love and murder / Baby mine.
7" Single: Released Oct '80, on Albion, by Albion Records. Deleted Oct '83. Catalogue no: **ION 1003**

Small Chimes

EYES OF CHRISTMAS
Tracks: / Eyes of Christmas / Santa.
7" Single: Released Dec '83, on Cavendish, Catalogue no: **CAV 001**

Small Faces

Biographical details:
One of the best-loved pop groups of 1965-68, the Small Faces, all from London's East End, were Stevie Marriott on guitar and vocals, Ronnie Lane on bass and vocals, Ian McLagen on keyboards and Kenny Jones on drums. Like Phil Collins, Marriott had played the Artful Dodger in Lionel Bart's musical *Oliver!* He and Lane wrote many of the group's hits. They developed into psychedelia, recording for Andrew Loog Oldham's Immediate label. Their *Itchycoo Park* was notable for innovative use of electronic phasing. *Ogden's Nut Gone Flake* in 1968 was a No 1 album in Britain, with a round sleeve which was a landmark in the period's artwork. Marriott left to form Humble Pie and he still gigs in London with Packet of Three. Lane formed Faces with Rod Stewart and later fell victim to multiple sclerosis: in 1983 the Rolling Stones, Jimmy Page, Steve Winwood and Eric Clapton played MS benefits on his behalf in America and Britain. (Donald Clarke, March 1987.)

AFTERGLOW OF YOUR LOVE
Tracks: / Afterglow of your love.
7" Single: Released Mar '69, on Immediate, Deleted Mar '72. Catalogue no: **IM 077**

ALL OR NOTHING
Tracks: / All or nothing / My mind's eye.
7" Single: Released Oct '83, on Old Gold, by Old Gold Records. Catalogue no: **OG 9343**
7" Single: Released Aug '66, on Decca, by Decca Records. Deleted '88. Catalogue no: **F 12470**

HERE COMES THE NICE
Tracks: / Here comes the nice.
7" Single: Released Jun '67, on Immediate, Deleted Jun '70. Catalogue no: **IM 050**

HEY GIRL
Tracks: / Hey girl.
7" Single: Released May '66, on London-American, Deleted May '69. Catalogue no: **F 12393**

I CAN'T MAKE IT
Tracks: / I can't make it.
7" Single: Released Mar '67, on London-American, Deleted Mar '70. Catalogue no: **F 12565**

ITCHYCOO PARK
Tracks: / Itchycoo Park.
7" Single: Released Dec '75, on Immediate, Deleted Dec '78. Catalogue no: **IMS 102**
7" Single: Released '80, on EMI (Europe), by EMI Records. Deleted '84. Catalogue no: **LR 8042**
7" Single: Released Aug '67, on Immediate, Deleted Aug '70. Catalogue no: **IM 057**

ITCHYCOO PARK(12")
Tracks: / Itchycoo Park / Lazy Sunday / Sha-la-la-la-lee / Here comes the nice.
Note: Limited edition 12" single. All tracks licensed from Interworld Communications.
12" Single: Released Aug '86, on Archive 4, by Castle Communications Records. Catalogue no: **TOF 103**

ITCHYCOO PARK (OLD GOLD)
Tracks: / Itchycoo park / Lazy Sunday / Tin soldier.
7" Single: Released Jan '85, on Old Gold, by Old Gold Records. Catalogue no: **OG 9466**
12" Single: Released 27 Feb '89, on Old Gold, by Old Gold Records. Catalogue no: **OG 6119**

LAZY SUNDAY
Tracks: / Lazy Sunday / Rollin' over.
7" Single: Released Oct '82, on Immediate, Deleted Oct '85. Catalogue no: **IM 064**
Tracks: / Lazy Sunday / Autumn stone.
7" Single: Released Mar '76, on Immediate, Deleted Mar '79. Catalogue no: **IMS 106**
7" Single: Released Sep '81, on Immediate, Catalogue no: **IMS 701**

LAZY SUNDAY (OLD GOLD)
Tracks: / Lazy Sunday.
7" Single: Released Jan '85, on Old Gold, by Old Gold Records. Catalogue no: **OG 9465**

LONDON BOYS
Tracks: / London boys.
7" Single: Released Sep '79, on Decca, by Decca Records. Deleted '88. Catalogue no: **FR 13864**

MY MIND'S EYE
Tracks: / My mind's eye.
7" Single: Released Nov '66, on London-American, Deleted Nov '69. Catalogue no: **F 12500**

SHA LA LA LA LEE
Tracks: / Sha-la-la-la-lee.
7" Single: Released Feb '66, on Decca, by Decca Records. Deleted Feb '69. Catalogue no: **F 12317**
7" EP: Released Mar '81, on Decca, by Decca Records. Deleted Mar '84. Catalogue no: **F 13727**

SHA LA LA LA LEE (Old Gold).
Tracks: / Sha-la-la-la-lee / Whatcha gonna do about it.
7" Single: Released Oct '83, on Old Gold, by Old Gold Records. Catalogue no: **OG 9344**

SMALL FACES, THE (EP)
Tracks: / Itchycoo park / Lazy Sunday / All or nothing / Autumn stone.
CD 3": Released '88, on Special Edition, by Castle Communications Records. Catalogue no: **CD3-9**

TIN SOLDIER
Tracks: / Tin soldier.
7" Single: Released Dec '67, on Immediate, Deleted Dec '70. Catalogue no: **IM 062**

UNIVERSAL
Tracks: / Universal.
7" Single: Released Jul '68, on Immediate, Deleted Jul '71. Catalogue no: **IM 069**

WHATCHA GONNA DO ABOUT IT
Tracks: / Whatcha gonna do about it.
7" Single: Released Sep '65, on London-American, Deleted Sep '68. Catalogue no: **F 12208**

Small Hours

KID
Tracks: / Kid / Business in town.
7" Single: Released Nov '80, on Automatic, by Automatic Records. Deleted Nov '83. Catalogue no: **K 17708**

Small In A Big Way

KATIE'S LIPS
Tracks: / Katie's lips / Back to zero.
7" Single: Released Apr '84, on Bedlam, Catalogue no: **FLM 003**

Small Print

I DON'T LIKE IT
Tracks: / I don't like it / Urban realities.

7" Single: Released Apr '81, on Edge, Deleted '85. Catalogue no: **EDGE 12**
7" Single: Released Jul '81, on Arista, by BMG Records (UK). Deleted Jul '84. Catalogue no: **ARIST 421**

Small Talk

STOP IN THE NAME OF LOVE
Tracks: / Stop in the name of love / Ten minutes.
7" Single: Released Mar '81, on MCA, by MCA Records. Deleted Mar '84. Catalogue no: **MCA 687**

Small World

LOVE IS DEAD
Tracks: / Love is dead.
7" Single: Released May '82, on Whaam, Catalogue no: **WHAAM 03**

Smalling, Milton

FIGHTING SPIRIT
Tracks: / Fighting spirit.
12" Single: Released Jul '85, on CSA, by CSA Records. Deleted '88. Catalogue no: **12CSA 506**

Smalltime Hero

SORRY
Tracks: / Sorry / Only way, The.

7" Single: Released Aug '89, on UNKNOWN, Catalogue no: **FX 20/S**

Smalltown Boys

BEATSKI MIX
Tracks: / Beatski mix / Beatski mix (version) / Is it love I feel.
CD 5": Released Apr '89, on K-Tel, by K-Tel Records. Catalogue no: **ONE 6906**
7" Single: Released Apr '89, on K-Tel, by K-Tel Records. Catalogue no: **ONE 6106**
12" Single: Released Apr '89, on K-Tel, by K-Tel Records. Catalogue no: **ONE 6606**

Smalltown Elephants

WALKING ON ICE
Tracks: / Walking on ice / Walking on ice (Ext.) (Track on 12" version only.) / All for you (*Track on 12" version only.) / Inside out.
7" Single: Released Jul '87, on Polydor, by Polydor Ltd. Deleted Mar '88. Catalogue no: **POSP 873**
12" Single: Released Jul '87, on Polydor, by Polydor Ltd. Deleted Mar '88. Catalogue no: **POSPX 873**

Smart Alec

SCOOTER BOYS
Tracks: / Scooter boys / Soho.
7" Single: Released '87, on B & C, by Trojan Records. Deleted May '88. Catalogue no: **BCS 20**

Smart (group)

THIS TIME
Tracks: / This time / Mr. Right.
7" Single: Released Oct '82, on Complex (R.A.P.), Catalogue no: **CPX 1**

Smart, Leroy

CAUGHT UP IN LOVE
Tracks: / Caught up in love.
7" Single: Released 21 Apr '89, on Supertone, Catalogue no: **SR 08**

DADDY'S HOME
Tracks: / Daddy's home.
12" Single: Released Jun '88, on BP International, Catalogue no: **BP 20**

DEDICATE MY LOVE
Tracks: / Dedicate my love.
12" Single: Released 8 Aug '88, on BB, Catalogue no: **BP 19**

DON IN A THE PARTY
Tracks: / Don in a the party.
7" Single: Released May '89, on Fameous, Catalogue no: **UNKNOWN**

DON, THE
Tracks: / Don, The.
12" Single: Released Aug '85, on Kaya, Catalogue no: **KA 008**

GIRL YOU A FRAUD
Tracks: / Girl you a fraud.
7" Single: Released Nov '84, on Bromac, Catalogue no: **NOT KNOWN**

JUST THE WAY YOU ARE
Tracks: / Just the way you are.
12" Single: Released Sep '89, on Techniques, Catalogue no: **WRT 57**

LIT OFF SUP'M
Tracks: / Jack Slick / Lit off sup'm

12" Single: Released Dec '86, on Live & Love, Catalogue no: **LLDIS 0024**

LIVE UP ROOTS CHILDREN (SINGLE)
Tracks: / Live up roots children.
12" Single: Released Jun '85, on Striker Lee, Catalogue no: **BL 24**

LOVE JAH FOREVER
Tracks: / Love Jah forever.
12" Single: Released Jun '83, on Get Set Sounds, Catalogue no: **GT 118**

LOVE ME TONIGHT
Tracks: / Love me tonight.
12" Single: Released Aug '87, on Greensleeves, by Greensleeves Records. Catalogue no: **GRED 213**

MAKE THIS LOVE BE TRUE
Tracks: / Make this love be true.
7" Single: Released Jun '85, on Ranking Joe Universal, Catalogue no: **RJ 0010**

MANKIND IS SO UNJUST
Tracks: / Mankind is so unjust.
12" Single: Released Dec '82, on Music Works, Catalogue no: **MWRT 1296**

MONEY IS COMFORT
Tracks: / Money is comfort / If I give my love.

12" Single: Released Jul '86, on Time One, Catalogue no: **TR 016**

MOTHER LANCHIE
Tracks: / Mother Lanchie.
12" Single: Released Mar '83, on Guidance, Catalogue no: **VPRD 120**

NO ONE REMEMBER ME
Tracks: / No one remember me.
12" Single: on Burning Sounds, by Burning Sounds Records. Deleted May '88. Catalogue no: **BSD 011**

PRETTY LOOKS
Tracks: / Pretty looks.
12" Single: Released Dec '83, on Foundation, Catalogue no: **TF 113**

PROPHECY
Tracks: / Prophecy.
12" Single: Released Oct '86, on Techniques, Catalogue no: **WRT 09**

READY TO GIVE LOVING
Tracks: / Ready to give loving.
12" Single: Released Jan '89, on Ricky Ticky Music, Catalogue no: **LLR 002**

SET IT
Tracks: / Set it.
12" Single: Released Mar '86, on Java, Catalogue no: **JR 001**

SHE JUST A DRAW CARD (SINGLE)
Tracks: / She just a draw card.
12" Single: Released Jul '84, on Tads, Catalogue no: **TRD 91684**

SWEET LADY
Tracks: / Sweet lady.
12" Single: Released Aug '82, on Music Works, Catalogue no: **MW 011**

TALK OF THE TOWN
Tracks: / Talk of dub / Talk of the town.
12" Single: Released Dec '86, on Revue, by Creole Records. Catalogue no: **REV 042T**

THIS IS THE TIME
Tracks: / This is the time.
10" single: Released Oct '82, on Reggae, Catalogue no: **REG 007**

TURN OFF THE LIGHTS
Tracks: / Turn off the lights.
12" Single: Released Aug '85, on Time, Catalogue no: **TR 011**

WE RULE
Tracks: / We rule.
12" Single: Released Jun '85, on Unity Sound, Catalogue no: **UN 004**

Smash Palace

LIVING ON THE BORDER LINE
Tracks: / Living on the borderline / Night of a thousand faces

7" Single: Released Feb '86, on Epic, by CBS Records. Catalogue no: **A 6788**

Smashed Gladys

17 GOIN' ON CRAZY
Tracks: / 17 goin' on crazy.

7" Single: Released Oct '85, on FM, by FM-Revolver Records. Catalogue no: **VHF 22**

Smiley Culture

SCHOOL TIME CHRONICLE
Tracks: / School time chronicle / So what.
7" Single: Released Aug '86, on Polydor, by Polydor Ltd. Deleted Mar '87. Catalogue no: **POSP 815**
12" Single: Released Aug '86, on Polydor, by Polydor Ltd. Deleted Mar '87. Catalogue no: **POSPX 815**
7" Set: on Polydor, by Polydor Ltd. Deleted Mar '87. Catalogue no: **POSPD 815**

Smiley People

IT MAKES ME HAAAPY
Tracks: / It makes me haaapy.
12" Single: Released Nov '88, on Blue Chip, by Blue Chip Records. Catalogue no: **BLUE-CHIP 10 T**
12" Single: Released Jan '89, on Blue Chip, by Blue Chip Records. Catalogue no: **BLUE-CHIP 10 R**

Smiley, Red

TAKE A RIDE
Tracks: / Take a ride.
7" Single: Released Oct '79, on Jin, by Flat Town Music Co.(USA). Catalogue no: **JIN 107**

Smith

HERE COME'S MY BABY
Tracks: / Here come's my baby / Just another line / Too late.
7" EP: Released Nov '81, on Rarn, Catalogue no: **RARN 15**

Smith, Arthur

Biographical details:
Country guitarist, bandleader and composer Smith was born in 1921 in South Carolina and formed the Crackerjacks in 1938. *Guitar Boogie* was a million-selling international hit, recorded for Super-Disc probably in 1946 and picked up by MGM: it was a mystery later because there was no trace of it on any charts at the time, perhaps because it sold slowly for years. A jaunty country instrumental with excellent guitar work, it is often cited as an influence on rock 'n' roll. Smith co-wrote *Beautiful Brown Eyes*, a 1951 American hit for Rosemary Clooney, and composed *Duelling Banjoes*, a No 2 US hit in '72 from the film Deliverance, played by Eric Weissberg and Steve Mandel. He recorded for MGM for years, had his own TV series and also wrote gospel songs. (Donald Clarke, March 1987.).

GUITAR BOOGIE
Tracks: / Guitar boogie.
7" Single: Released '80, on USA, by Charly Records. Catalogue no: **LR 4212**

Smith, Carlton

EXCITE ME
Tracks: / Excite me.
7" Single: Released Oct '86, on Citybeat, by Beggars Banquet Records. Deleted Jun '87. Catalogue no: **CBE 708**
12" Single: Released Oct '86, on Citybeat, by Beggars Banquet Records. Deleted Jul '88. Catalogue no: **CBE 1208**

Smith, Charlie Boy

WEDDING OF THE YEAR
Tracks: / Wedding of the year.
7" Single: Released Jul '81, on Cool King, Catalogue no: **CK 003**

Smith, Conroy

GHETTO GIRL
Tracks: / Ghetto girl.
7" Single: Released May '89, on Power House, Catalogue no: **UNKNOWN**

MODEL PON ME
Tracks: / Model pon me.
12" Single: Released Jul '88, on Redman International, Catalogue no: **VPRD 102**

MR BIG STUFF
Tracks: / Mr. Big Stuff.
7" Single: Released Jan '89, on Blue Mountain, Catalogue no: **BMD 036**

RUN DOWN GIRLS
Tracks: / Run down girls / Yard man tune.
12" Single: Released May '89, on Greensleeves, by Greensleeves Records. Catalogue no: **GRED 242**

Smith, Dick

WAY OF THE WORLD
Tracks: / Way of the world / Giving the game away.
7" Single: Released Jan '81, on Hologram, by Aardvark Records. Catalogue no: **HOL 001**

Smith, Donovan

MR. WALKER
Tracks: / Mr. Walker.
12" Single: Released Feb '82, on Love Linch, Catalogue no: **LL 023**

Smith, Ernie

BEND DOWN LOW
Tracks: / Bend down low.
7" Single: Released Sep '81, on KR, Catalogue no: **KR 1**
12" Single: Released Sep '81, on KR, Catalogue no: **KRT 1**

Smith, Eugene

ROCK BY DAY, ROLL BY NIGHT
Tracks: / Rock by day, roll by night / Streetwise.
7" Single: Released Jul '86, on Tembo, by Tembo Records. Catalogue no: **TML 121**

Smith, Ezra

LOVE OF THE COMMON PEOPLE
Tracks: / Love of the common people.
12" Single: Released Feb '89, on Freedom Cry, Catalogue no: **FC 004**

SEND A LETTER
Tracks: / Send a letter.
12" Single: Released Jun '89, on Strike Force, Catalogue no: **SFD 001**

Smith, Fenton

BOOM IT UP
Tracks: / Boom it up.
12" Single: Released May '84, on Fashion, by Fashion Records. Catalogue no: **FAD 022**

GIRLS
Tracks: / Girls.
12" Single: Released Nov '84, on Fashion, by Fashion Records. Catalogue no: **FAD 024**

I LOST MY GIRL
Tracks: / I lost my girl.
12" Single: Released Mar '84, on Ital, by Ital Records. Catalogue no: **ITD 0026**

INTENTION ARE BIG
Tracks: / Intention are big / Got to get you baby.
12" Single: Released Jun '86, on Style, Catalogue no: **STY 001**

REGGAE PARTY
Tracks: / Reggae party.
7" Single: Released Feb '82, on Love Birds, Catalogue no: **LB 002**
12" Single: Released Feb '82, on Love Birds, Catalogue no: **LB 002 12**

SUGAR SUGAR
Tracks: / Can't romp with me / Sugar sugar.
12" Single: Released Jan '87, on Live, Catalogue no: **ALIVE 1**

WOMAN AS NICE, A
12" Single: Released Mar '83, on S & G (1), Catalogue no: **SG 26**

Smith, Frankie

DOUBLE DUTCH BUS
Tracks: / Double Dutch bus.
7" Single: Released Nov '80, on W.M.O.T.(USA), by Virgin Records. Deleted Nov '83. Catalogue no: **WMT 102**
12" Single: Released Feb '82, on Virgin, by Virgin Records. Deleted '89. Catalogue no: **VS 485-12**
7" Single: Released Feb '82, on Virgin, by Virgin Records. Deleted '89. Catalogue no: **VS 485**

Smith, G.E.

HEART FROZEN UP
Tracks: / Heart frozen up / Sad about girls.
7" Single: Released Jul '81, on Mirage (USA), Catalogue no: **K 11671**

Smith, Hettie

SITTING IN THE CAFE
Tracks: / Sitting in the cafe / Tell me how.
7" Single: Released Oct '80, on Rialto (1), by Rialto Records. Deleted Oct '83. Catalogue no: **TREB 128**

Smith, Huey

Biographical details: Huey Smith 'Piano' was born in New Orleans in 1934, his piano style influenced by Professor Longhair and infentail in its turn. He played on records with Guitar Slim, Earl King, Siley Lewis (*I Hear You Knockin'*), Lloyd Price and Little Richard; his own hits on Ace '57-8 with the Clowns include Bobby Marchan, lead singer; Charles illiams, drums; both Lee Allen and Red Taylor on saxes: *Rocking Pneumonia* and *Don't You Just Know It* are among the most rollicking, danceable nonsense of the whole period and crossed over to the pop chart in the USA. He switched to the Imperial label (with Gerri Hall and Curley Moore replacing Marchan) went back to Ace for albums *Somewhere There's Honey Fat For The Grizzly Bear* and *Twas The Night Before Christmas* '62: the latter album was withdrawn because of the adverse public reaction to R&B versions of the song like *Jingle Bells* and *White Christmas*, but has become something of a classic: as one New Orleans veteran remarked, "you have to hear it to believe it." as success declined, Huey became a Jehovah's Witness. (Donald Clarke).

DON'T YOU JUST KNOW IT
Tracks: / Don't you just know it.
7" Single: Released Aug '83, on Kent, by Ace Records. Catalogue no: **TOWN 502**

Smith, Hurricane

DON'T LET IT DIE
Tracks: / Don't let it die.
7" Single: Released Jun '71, on Columbia, by EMI Records. Deleted Jun '74. Catalogue no: **DB 8785**

DON'T LET IT DIE (OLD GOLD)
Tracks: / Don't let it die.
7" Single: Released Oct '83, on Old Gold, by Old Gold Records. Deleted Jul '88. Catalogue no: **OG 9371**

OH BABE WHAT WOULD YOU SAY
Tracks: / Oh babe what would you say.
7" Single: Released Apr '72, on Columbia, by EMI Records. Deleted Apr '75. Catalogue no: **DB 8878**

WHO WAS IT
Tracks: / Who was it.
7" Single: Released Sep '72, on Columbia, by EMI Records. Deleted Sep '75. Catalogue no: **DB 8916**

Smith, Jimmy (USA)

Biographical details:
Jimmy Smith, born in Norristown, Pennsylvania in 1925, became the most popular and influential jazz organist of all, his trio format widely imitated. About 20 albums for Blue Note, 1956-63, were issued, followed by Verve singles and albums, 1962-70, which crossed over to the American pop chart. (Donald Clarke, March 1987.).

GOT MY MOJO WORKING
Tracks: / Got my mojo working.
7" Single: Released Apr '66, on Verve, Deleted May '69. Catalogue no: **VS 536**

Smith, K.

DEATH IS ON THAT ROAD
Tracks: / Death is on that road.
12" Single: Released Mar '89, on Wing An' A Prayer, Catalogue no: **WAP 001**

Smith, Keely

YOU'RE BREAKIN' MY HEART
Tracks: / You're breaking my heart.
7" Single: Released Mar '65, on Reprise, by WEA Records. Deleted Mar '68. Catalogue no: **R 20346**

Smith, Kendra

FELL FROM THE SUN
Tracks: / Fell from the sun.
12" Single: Released Jan '85, on Rough Trade, by Rough Trade Records. Catalogue no: **RTT 129**

Smith, Lonnie Liston

Biographical details:
Keyboardist, composer and bandleader Smith, who was born in Richmond, Virginia, in 1940, has had most of his albums produced by Bob Theile, producer of John Coltrane's LPs on Impulse, since Smith recorded for Impulse with Pharoah Sanders. Smith, who also plays trumpet and tuba, wrote the Sanders album *Jewel Of Thought* and in 1973-74 he played with Miles Davis, at whose suggestion three CBS albums were made. (Donald Clarke, March 1987.).

EXPANSIONS
Tracks: / Expansions.
12" Single: Released Nov '83, on Bluebird (2), by BMG Records (UK). Catalogue no: **BRT 4**

GIVE PEACE A CHANCE
Tracks: / Give peace a chance / Sunburst.
12" Single: Released Jun '80, on CBS, by CBS Records. Deleted '83. Catalogue no: **13 8660**

IF YOU TAKE CARE OF ME
Tracks: / If you take care of me I'll take care of you.
7" Single: Released Feb '85, on Doctor Jazz (USA), by CBS Records (USA). Catalogue no: **7AS 3500**

Smith, Ludwig

LOVING NONSTOP
Tracks: / Loving nonstop.
12" Single: Released Jul '85, on Negus Roots, Catalogue no: **NERT 028**

Smith, Mandy

DON'T YOU WANT ME BABY
Tracks: / Don't you want me baby.
7" Single: Released Apr '89, on PWL, by PWL Records. Catalogue no: **PWL 37**
12" Single: Released Apr '89, on PWL, by PWL Records. Catalogue no: **PWLT 37**

I JUST CAN'T WAIT
Tracks: / You're never alone / Positive reaction / I just can't wait.
7" Single: Released Jan '87, on PWL, by PWL Records. Catalogue no: **PWL 1**
12" Single: Released Mar '88, on PWL, by PWL Records. Catalogue no: **PWLT 1**

POSITIVE REACTION
Tracks: / Positive reaction.
12" Single: Released Oct '87, on PWL, by PWL Records. Catalogue no: **PWLT 4**
7" Single: Released Oct '87, on PWL, by PWL Records. Catalogue no: **PWL 4**

VICTIM OF PLEASURE
Tracks: / Victim of pleasure, A.
7" Single: Released Nov '88, on PWL, by PWL Records. Catalogue no: **PWL 18**
12" Single: Released Nov '88, on PWL, by PWL Records. Catalogue no: **PWLT 18**

Smith, Mel

MEL SMITH'S GREATEST HITS
Tracks: / Mel Smith's greatest hits / Richard and Joey.
7" Single: Released Nov '81, on Mercury, by Phonogram Ltd. Deleted Nov '84. Catalogue no: **MEL 1**

ROCKIN' AROUND THE CHRISTMAS TREE
Tracks: / Rockin' around the Christmas tree (7" only) / Deck the blooming halls (The Mel Smith Yuletide choir) / Rockin' around the Christmas tree (the ultra merry magimix) (12" only).
7" Single: Released Dec '88, on 10 Records, by Virgin Records. Catalogue no: **TEN 2**
12" Single: Released Nov '88, on 10 Records, by Virgin Records. Catalogue no: **TEN 2-12**

TREMBLING
Tracks: / Tremblin' (From the film 'Knight & Emeralds') / Easy.
7" Single: Released '86, on 10 Records, by Virgin Records. Deleted '89. Catalogue no: **TEN 128**

Smith & Mighty

ANYONE
Tracks: / Anyone / Dark, The.
7" Single: Released Jun '88, on Beatmaster, by Beatmaster Records. Catalogue no: **BEATM 2**
12" Single: Released Jun '88, on Beatmaster, by Beatmaster Records. Catalogue no: **BEATM 212**
12" Single: Released Feb '88, on Three Stripe, Catalogue no: **SAM 111**

ANYONE(REMIX)
Tracks: / Anyone (remix).
12" Single: Released Feb '89, on Three Stripe, Catalogue no: **SAM 111R**

WALK ON BY
Tracks: / Walk on by / Travellin'.
12" Single: Released Nov '88, on Three Stripe, Catalogue no: **SAM 1114**
7" Single: Released Nov '88, on Three Stripe, Catalogue no: **7 SAM 1114**

WALK ON BY (REMIX)
Tracks: / Walk on by (remix) / Walk on by (version).
12" Single: Released Jan '89, on Three Stripe, Catalogue no: **SAM 114R**

Smith, Mike

GLAD ALL OVER
Tracks: / Glad all over.
7" Single: Released Aug '85, on Proto, by Proto Records. Catalogue no: **ENA 130**
12" Single: Released Aug '85, on Proto, by Proto Records. Catalogue no: **ENA 130T**

Smith, Muriel

HOLD ME THRILL ME KISS ME
Tracks: / Hold me thrill me kiss me.
7" Single: Released May '53, on Philips, by Phonogram Ltd. Deleted May '56. Catalogue no: **PB 122**

Smith, O.C

Biographical details:
Born Ocie Lee Smith in Mansfield, Louisiana, in 1932, pop and soul singer Smith recorded rockaballads for Cadence (the Everly Brothers' label) in the late 50's then succeeded Joe Williams in Count Basie's band. He achieved chart successes from 1968 to 1974, with 10 hits in the pop/soul charts, including a No 2 hit in '68 with Bobby Russell's Grammy-winning *Little Green Apples* and, the same year, a Top Forty version of Dallas Frazier's *Son Of Hickory Holler's Tramp* which was also a hit in Britain. Four LPs, plus a *Greatest Hits* compilation, made the US charts. (Donald Clarke, March 1987.).

SON OF HICKORY HOLLER'S TRAMP
Tracks: / Son of Hickory Holler's tramp, The.
7" Single: Released Jul '82, on Old Gold, by Old Gold Records. Catalogue no: **OG 9179**
7" Single: Released May '68, on CBS, by CBS Records. Deleted May '71. Catalogue no: **CBS 3343**

TOGETHER
Tracks: / Together.
7" Single: Released Mar '77, on Caribou, by CBS Records. Deleted Mar '80. Catalogue no: **CRB 4910**

Smith, Orville

GOTTA HOLD ON TO THIS FEELING
Tracks: / Gotta hold on to this feeling / Gotta hold on to this feeling (reggae version).
7" Single: Released '86, on Greensleeves, by Greensleeves Records. Deleted '87. Catalogue no: **GRE 204**
12" Single: Released '86, on Greensleeves, by Greensleeves Records. Catalogue no: **GRED 204**

Smith, Patti

Biographical details:
A poet who also found success as a new wave vocalist, Smith was born in Chicago in 1946. With actor-playwright Sam Shepard, she wrote a play, *Cowboy Mouth*, in '71, read poetry to guitar accompaniment, wrote for magazines *Creem* and *Rolling Stone*, published volumes of poetry and penned lyrics for Blue Oyster Cult. Her single *Piss Factory* ('74) and album *Horses* ('76) remain influential, especially on women in rock. She also co-wrote *Because The Night* with Bruce Springsteen. (Donald Clarke, March 1987.).

BECAUSE THE NIGHT
Tracks: / Because the night / Redondo beach / Dancing barefoot / Free money.
7" Single: Released Apr '78, on Arista, by BMG Records (UK). Deleted Apr '81. Catalogue no: **ARISTA 181**
7" Single: Released Apr '83, on Arista, by BMG Records (UK). Catalogue no: **ARIST 513**
12" Single: Released Apr '83, on Arista, by BMG Records (UK). Catalogue no: **ARIST 12513**

BECAUSE THE NIGHT (OLD GOLD)
Tracks: / Because the night / Gloria.
7" Single: Released Jul '84, on Old Gold, by Old Gold Records. Catalogue no: **OG 9458**

FREDERICK
Tracks: / Frederick.
7" Single: Released Jun '79, on Arista, by BMG Records (UK). Deleted Jun '82. Catalogue no: **ARISTA 264**

GLORIA
Tracks: / Gloria / My generation.
7" Single: Released Sep '77, on Arista, by BMG Records (UK). Catalogue no: **ARIST 135**

PEOPLE HAVE THE POWER
Tracks: / People have the power / Wild leaves / Where duty calls.
Note: * Only available on the 12" picture bag version.
7" Single: Released Jun '88, on Arista, by BMG Records (UK). Catalogue no: **109877**
12" Single: Released Jun '88, on Arista, by BMG Records (UK). Catalogue no: **609877**
CD 5": Released Jun '88, on Arista, by BMG Records (UK). Catalogue no: **659877**

PRIVILEGE (SET ME FREE)
Tracks: / Privilege.
7" Single: Released Aug '78, on Arista, by BMG Records (UK). Deleted Aug '81. Catalogue no: **ARISTA 197**

Smith, Ray

ROOM FULL OF ROSES
Tracks: / Room full of roses.
7" Single: Released Jan '80, on Wix (USA), Deleted '81. Catalogue no: **WIX 101**

Smith, Rex

EVERLASTING LOVE (SINGLE)
Tracks: / Everlasting love / Still thinking of you Billy.
7" Single: Released Aug '81, on CBS, by CBS Records. Deleted Aug '84. Catalogue no: **A 1405**

LOVE WILL ALWAYS MAKE YOU CRY
Tracks: / Love will always make you cry / Still thinking of you.
7" Single: Released Oct '81, on CBS, by CBS Records. Deleted '85. Catalogue no: **A 1682**

NEVER GONNA GIVE YOU UP
Tracks: / Never gonna give you up / Sooner or later.
7" Single: Released Jan '80, on CBS, by CBS Records. Deleted Jan '83. Catalogue no: **CBS 8100**

Smith, Richard Jon

ABC OF KISSING
Tracks: / ABC of kissing / Jessica.
7" Single: Released Mar '85, on Jive, by Zomba Records. Catalogue no: **JIVE 85**
12" Single: Released Mar '85, on Jive, by Zomba Records. Catalogue no: **JIVET 85**
7" Pic: Released May '85, on Jive, by Zomba Records. Catalogue no: **JIVEP 95**

BABY'S GOT ANOTHER
Tracks: / Baby's got another / This is the moment.
12" Single: Released Mar '83, on Jive, by Zomba Records. Catalogue no: **JIVET 29**
7" Single: Released Mar '83, on Jive, by Zomba Records. Catalogue no: **JIVE 29**

DANCE WITH ME
Tracks: / Dance with me.
7" Single: Released Jul '84, on Jive, by Zomba Records. Catalogue no: **JIVE 69**
12" Single: Released Jul '84, on Jive, by Zomba Records. Catalogue no: **JIVET 69**

DANCIN' IN AFRICA
Tracks: / Dancin' in Africa (african extasy mix) / (My home town) Meadowlands (Indian summer mix).
7" Single: Released Sep '88, on Charly Groove, by Charly Records. Catalogue no: **CYZ 7 129**
12" Single: Released Sep '88, on Charly Groove, by Charly Records. Catalogue no: **CYZ 129**

DON'T GO WALKING OUT THAT DOOR
Tracks: / Don't go walking out that door.
12" Single: Released Aug '82, on Jive, by Zomba Records. Catalogue no: **JIVET 19**
7" Single: Released Aug '82, on Jive, by Zomba Records. Catalogue no: **JIVE 19**

HOLD ON
Tracks: / Hold on.
7" Single: Released Sep '85, on Jive, by Zomba Records. Catalogue no: **JIVE 104**
12" Single: Released Sep '85, on Jive, by Zomba Records. Catalogue no: **JIVET 104**

IN THE NIGHT
Tracks: / In the night / Dun version.
7" Single: Released Jan '84, on Jive, by Zomba Records. Catalogue no: **JIVE 53**
12" Single: Released Jan '84, on Jive, by Zomba Records. Catalogue no: **JIVET 53**

(MY HOME TOWN) MEADOWLANDS
Tracks: / (My home town) Meadowlands / Shout it out.
12" Single: Released Jun '88, on Charly Groove, by Charly Records. Catalogue no: **CYZ 126**
7" Single: Released Jun '88, on Charly Groove, by Charly Records. Catalogue no: **CYZ 7 126**

SHE'S THE MASTER OF THE GAME
Tracks: / She's the master of the game / Love is what I'm after.
7" Single: Released Jul '83, on Jive, by Zomba Records. Catalogue no: **JIVE 38**
12" Single: Released Jul '83, on Jive, by Zomba Records. Catalogue no: **JIVET 38**

STAY WITH ME TONIGHT
Tracks: / Stay with me tonight.
7" Single: Released Feb '82, on Jive, by Zomba Records. Catalogue no: **JIVE 10**
12" Single: Released Feb '82, on Jive, by Zomba Records. Catalogue no: **JIVET 10**

Smith, Slim

BLESSED ARE THE POOR
Tracks: / Blessed are the poor / Promise to be true.
12" Single: Released '86, on Third World, Catalogue no: **TWDIS 3031**

EVERYBODY NEEDS LOVE
Tracks: / Everybody needs love.
10" single: Released Jul '82, on Pama Oldies, by Pama Records. Catalogue no: **PTP 1030**

LOVE AND DEVOTION
Tracks: / Love and devotion.
12" Single: Released Sep '84, on Rosie Uprising, Catalogue no: **UNKNOWN**

Smith, Stention

SUGAR & SPICE
Tracks: / Sugar & spice.
12" Single: Released Aug '84, on Clair, Catalogue no: **CM 13**

Smith, T

SHOW ME, SHOW ME
Tracks: / Show me, show me / Wantin' you, needin' you.
7" Single: Released Jan '82, on BBC, by BBC Records & Tapes. Deleted Jan '85. Catalogue no: **RESL 119**

Smith, Tommy

ALLY THE WALLYGATOR (Promo only)
Tracks: / Ally the wallygator / Pillow talk / Ever never land.
Note: Both tracks taken from album Step By Step.
12" Single: on Blue Note Int., by EMI Records. Catalogue no: **12BLTP 1**

Smith , Toni

OOH I LIKE THE WAY IT FEELS
Tracks: / Ooh, I like the way it feels / Ooh, I like the way it feels(dub).
7" Single: Released Jan '84, on Malaco, by Malaco Records (UK). Deleted '88. Catalogue no: **MAL 013**
12" Single: Released Jan '84, on Malaco, by Malaco Records (UK). Deleted '88. Catalogue no: **MAL 12 013**

Smith, T.V.

SERVANT
Tracks: / Servant / Looking down in London.
7" Single: Released Apr '81, on Kaleidoscope Sound, by Kaleidoscope Sound Records. Deleted '85. Catalogue no: **KRL 1162**

TOMAHAWK CRUISE
Tracks: / Tomahawk cruise / See Europe.
7" Single: Released Dec '80, on Big Beat, by Ace Records. Deleted Dec '85. Catalogue no: **NS 64**
7" Single: Released Jan '81, on Chiswick Records, Deleted Jan '84. Catalogue no: **CHIS 140**

WAR FEVER
Tracks: / War fever / Lies.
7" Single: Released Apr '83, on Expulsion, by Expulsion Records. Deleted '87. Catalogue no: **OUT 2**

Smith, Wayne

COME ALONG
Tracks: / Come along.
12" Single: Released Nov '84, on Greensleeves, by Greensleeves Records. Catalogue no: **GRED 162**

DANCING MACHINE
Tracks: / Dancing machine.
12" Single: Released Jul '85, on Tonos, Catalogue no: **TON 006**

ICKY ALL OVER
Tracks: / Icky all over.
12" Single: Released Jul '85, on Greensleeves, by Greensleeves Records. Catalogue no: **GRED 183**

LIFE IS A MOMENT IN SPACE
Tracks: / Life is a moment in space.
12" Single: Released Dec '82, on Black Joy, Catalogue no: **BH 815**

NO PUPPY LOVE
Tracks: / No puppy love / Teach me to dance.
12" Single: Released '86, on RAS (Real Authentic Sound), by Greensleeves Records. Catalogue no: **RAST 7021**

SLENG TENG MIXDOWN (REMIX)
Tracks: / Sleng teng mixdown.
12" Single: Released Apr '85, on Greensleeves, by Greensleeves Records. Catalogue no: **GRED 177**

SMOKER SUPPER
Tracks: / Smoker supper / When you're young.
12" Single: Released Dec '83, on Chartbound, Catalogue no: **CB 002**

TRY MY LOVE
Tracks: / Try my love / Murder commit.
12" Single: Released '86, on Unity, Catalogue no: **UN 109**

UNDER ME SLENG TENG
Tracks: / Under me sleng teng.
12" Single: Released Feb '85, on Greensleeves, by Greensleeves Records. Catalogue no: **GRED 169**

Smith, Whistling Jack

Biographical details: This British "artist" had a one-off 1967 hit with I Was Kaiser Bill's Batman. The catchy novelty tune was written by Roger Cook and Roger Greenaway, who had enjoyed a pair of UK hits the previous years under the David & Jonathan pseudonym. Kaiser Bill reached No 5 in the UK and No 20 in the States. It was not surprising that Whistling Jack Smith made a rapid disappearance from the scene: he never really existed. The whistling on the record was performed by the Mike Sammes Singers, a popular television vocal group. When the single became a hit a singer called Billy Moeller was given the Smith monicker for promotional purposes on TV and on tour. (Bob MacDonald, May 1985.).

I WAS KAISER BILL'S BATMAN
Tracks: / I was Kaiser Bill's batman / British grin and bear it.
7" Single: Released Mar '67, on Deram, by London Records. Deleted Mar '70. Catalogue no: **DM 112**
7" Single: Released Jan '80, on Deram, by London Records. Catalogue no: **LR 1425**
7" Single: Released May '82, on Decca, by Decca Records. Deleted '88. Catalogue no: **F 13922**

Smithereens

HOUSE WE USED TO LIVE IN
Tracks: / House we used to live in / Ruler of my heart / Blood and roses (live) (CD & 12" only) / House we used to live in (live) (CD only).
7" Single: Released 3 Oct '88, on Enigma, by Enigma Records (USA). Catalogue no: **ENV 2**
CD 3": Released '88, on Enigma, by Enigma Records (USA). Catalogue no: **ENVCD 2**
12" Single: Released 3 Oct '88, on Enigma, by Enigma Records (USA). Catalogue no: **ENVT 2**

IN A LONELY PLACE
Tracks: / Beauty and sadness / Blood and roses / Mr. Eliminator.
Note: Extra tracks on 12" only
7" Single: Released Feb '87, on Enigma, by Enigma Records (USA). Catalogue no: **ENIG 1**
7" Single: Released Dec '86, on Enigma, by Enigma Records (USA). Catalogue no: **ENIGMA 5003 2**
12" Single: Released Feb '87, on Enigma, by Enigma Records (USA). Catalogue no: **ENIG T1**

ONLY A MEMORY
Tracks: / Only a memory / Lust for life / Something new.
12" Single: Released Mar '88, on Enigma, by Enigma Records (USA). Catalogue no: **SMITT 1**
7" Single: Released Mar '88, on Enigma, by Enigma Records (USA). Catalogue no: **SMIT 1**

STRANGERS WHEN WE MEET
Tracks: / Strangers when we meet.
12" Single: Released Aug '87, on Enigma, by Enigma Records (USA). Catalogue no: **ENIG 3T**
7" Single: Released Aug '87, on MCA, by MCA Records. Catalogue no: **MCA 1166**
7" Single: Released Aug '87, on Enigma, by Enigma Records (USA). Catalogue no: **ENIG 3**

YOU IS A GUARANTEE OF LOVE
Tracks: / You is a guarantee for love / Promiscuous / Ask / Cemetery gates.
7" Single: Released '86, on WEA (International), by WEA Records. Catalogue no: **248934 7**

Smiths

Biographical details:
The Smiths, who split up early in 1988, were a vocal/instrumental quartet formed in their native Manchester in 1982 by singer Morrisey (born Steven Morrisey) and guitarist Johnny Marr. Morrisey's enigmatic lyrics and Marr's guitar kept them in the British charts and brought them a cult following in America. Their integrity was reflected by the fact that they stayed with their independent label despite offers from majors and they didn't bother to make videos. (Donald Clarke, March 1987.).

ASK
Tracks: / Ask.
7" Single: Released '86, on Rough Trade, by Rough Trade Records. Catalogue no: **RT 194**
12" Single: Released '86, on Rough Trade, by Rough Trade Records. Catalogue no: **RTT 194**

ASK (IMPORT)
Tracks: / Ask.
7" Single: Released Nov '87, on Rough Trade (Australia), Catalogue no: **RTANZ 019**
12" Single: Released Sep '88, on Megadisc (Holland), Catalogue no: **MD 125282**
12" Single: Released Nov '87, on Teldec (Germany), by ASV (Academy Sound & Vision). Catalogue no: **6 20676**

BARBARISM BEGINS AT HOME
Tracks: / Barbarism begins at home.
Note: Never released as a single in the U.K. Viv Nicholson sleeve. 'Shakespeare's Sister' on B-side, with extra track 'Stretch Out And Wait' on the 12".
CD 5": Released Nov '88, on Rough Trade, by Rough Trade Records. Catalogue no: **RTT 171CD**
7" Single: Released Nov '87, on Rough Trade (Germany), Catalogue no: **RTD 021**
12" Single: Released Nov '87, on Rough Trade (Germany), Catalogue no: **RTD 021T**

BIGMOUTH STRIKES AGAIN (SINGLE)
Tracks: / Big mouth strikes again / Money changes everything / Unloveable (Available on 12" verson only).
12" Single: Released '86, on Rough Trade, by Rough Trade Records. Catalogue no: **RTT 192**
7" Single: Released '86, on Rough Trade, by Rough Trade Records. Catalogue no: **RT**

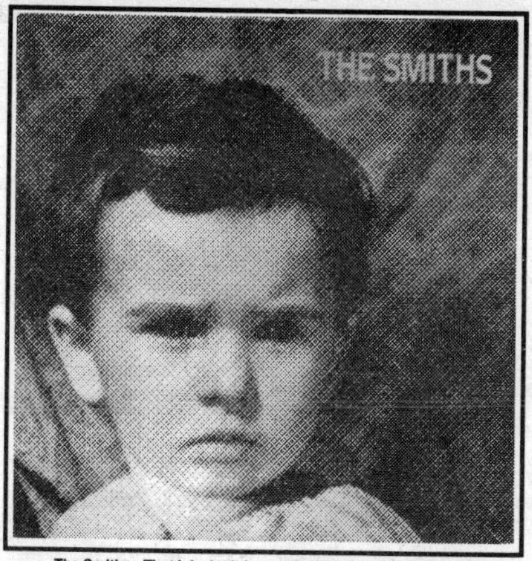

The Smiths - That joke isn't funny (Released on Rough Trade)

192

BOY WITH THE THORN IN HIS SIDE, THE
Tracks: / Boy with the thorn in his side The.
CD 5": Released Nov '88, on Rough Trade, by Rough Trade Records. Catalogue no: **RTT 191CD**
12" Single: Released Sep '85, on Rough Trade, by Rough Trade Records. Catalogue no: **RTT 191**
7" Single: Released Sep '85, on Rough Trade, by Rough Trade Records. Catalogue no: **RT 191**

GIRLFRIEND IN A COMA
Tracks: / Girlfriend in a coma.
7" Single: Released Aug '87, on Rough Trade, by Rough Trade Records. Catalogue no: **RT 197**
12" Single: Released Aug '87, on Rough Trade, by Rough Trade Records. Catalogue no: **RTT 197**

HAND IN GLOVE
Tracks: / Hand in glove.
7" Single: Released May '83, on Rough Trade, by Rough Trade Records. Catalogue no: **RT 131**

HEADMASTER RITUAL, THE
Tracks: / Headmaster ritual, The.
CD 5": Released Nov '88, on Rough Trade, by Rough Trade Records. Catalogue no: **RTT 215CD**
12" Single: Released Jul '85, on Pinnacle (Imports), by Pinnacle Records. Catalogue no: **UNKNOWN**

HEAVEN KNOWS I'M MISERABLE NOW
Tracks: / Heaven knows I'm miserable now.
7" Single: Released Sep '84, on Rough Trade, by Rough Trade Records. Catalogue no: **RT 156**
12" Single: Released Sep '84, on Rough Trade, by Rough Trade Records. Catalogue no: **RTT 156**
CD 5": Released Nov '88, on Rough Trade, by Rough Trade Records. Catalogue no: **RTT 156CD**

HOW SOON IS NOW
Tracks: / How soon is now.
12" Single: Released Feb '85, on Rough Trade, by Rough Trade Records. Catalogue no: **RTT 176**
7" Single: Released Feb '85, on Rough Trade, by Rough Trade Records. Catalogue no: **RT 176**

I STARTED SOMETHING I COULDN'T FINISH
Tracks: / I started something I couldn't finish / Pretty girls make graves.
7" Single: Released Jul '87, on Rough Trade, by Rough Trade Records. Catalogue no: **RT 198**
12" Single: Released Jul '87, on Rough Trade, by Rough Trade Records. Catalogue no: **RTT 198**

LAST NIGHT I DREAMED SOMEBODY LOVED ME
Tracks: / Last night.
12" Single: Released Dec '87, on Rough Trade, by Rough Trade Records. Catalogue no: **RTT 200**
7" Single: Released Dec '87, on Rough Trade, by Rough Trade Records. Catalogue no: **RT 200**

PANIC
Tracks: / Panic / Vicar in a tutu / Draize train The (Available on 12" version only).
Note: (Cat. No. 620648 - Limited edition on clear blue vinyl. Different B-side tracks to U.K. version).
7" Single: Released '86, on Rough Trade, by Rough Trade Records. Catalogue no: **RT 193**
12" Single: Released Nov '87, on Teldec (Germany), by ASV (Academy Sound & Vision). Catalogue no: **6 20648**
12" Single: Released '86, on Rough Trade, by Rough Trade Records. Catalogue no: **RTT 193**

PEEL SESSIONS:SMITHS
Tracks: / What difference does it make / Miserable lie / Reel around the fountain / Handsome devil.
CD 5": Released Oct '88, on Strange Fruit, by Strange Fruit Records. Catalogue no: **SFPSCD 055**
12" Single: Released Oct '88, on Strange Fruit, by Strange Fruit Records. Catalogue no: **SFPS 055**

SHAKESPEARE'S SISTER
Tracks: / Shakespeare's sister / What she said.
12" Single: Released Mar '85, on Rough Trade, by Rough Trade Records. Càtalogue no: **RTT 181**
7" Single: Released Mar '85, on Rough Trade, by Rough Trade Records. Catalogue no: **RT 181**

SHEILA TAKE A BOW
Tracks: / Sheila take a bow / Is it really so strange? / Sweet and tender hooligan*.
Note: *Extra track on 12" only
7" Single: Released Apr '87, on Rough Trade, by Rough Trade Records. Catalogue no: **RT 196**
12" Single: Released Apr '87, on Rough Trade, by Rough Trade Records. Catalogue no: **RTT 196**
12" Single: Released Oct '87, on Line (W.Germany), Catalogue no: **LIEP 300011**

SHOPLIFTERS OF THE WORLD
Tracks: / Unite / Half A Person / London (This track 12 inch version only) / Shoplifters of the world unite.
7" Single: Released '88, on Line (W.Germany), Catalogue no: **LIS 100020 B**
12" Single: Released '88, on Line (W.Germany), Catalogue no: **LIEP 30000 9E**
12" Single: Released Jan '87, on Rough Trade, by Rough Trade Records. Catalogue no: **RTT 195**
7" Single: Released Jan '87, on Rough Trade, by Rough Trade Records. Catalogue no: **RT 195**

SOME GIRLS ARE BIGGER THAN OTHERS
Tracks: / Some girls are bigger than others.
Note: German only single release, in picture cover. B-side tracks "Frankly, Mr.Shankly" & "The Draize Train".
12" Single: Released Nov '87, on Teldec (Germany), by ASV (Academy Sound & Vision). Catalogue no: **6 20628**

THAT JOKE ISN'T FUNNY ANYMORE
Tracks: / That joke isn't funny anymore / Meat is murder
12" Single: Released Jun '85, on Rough Trade, by Rough Trade Records. Catalogue no: **RTT 186**
7" Single: Released Jun '85, on Rough Trade, by Rough Trade Records. Catalogue no: **RT 186**

THIS CHARMING MAN
Tracks: / This charming man / Jeanne.
7" Single: Released Nov '83, on Rough Trade, by Rough Trade Records. Catalogue no: **RT 136**
12" Single: Released Nov '83, on Rough Trade, by Rough Trade Records. Catalogue no: **RTT 136**

THIS CHARMING MAN (IMPORT)
Tracks: / This charming man.
12" Single: Released Dec '88, on Rough Trade (Germany), Catalogue no: **RTD 010T**

WHAT DIFFERENCE DOES IT MAKE
Tracks: / What difference does it make / Back to the old house
7" Single: Released Jan '84, on Rough Trade, by Rough Trade Records. Catalogue no: **RT 146**
12" Single: Released Jan '84, on Rough Trade, by Rough Trade Records. Catalogue no: **RTT 146**

WILLIAM IT WAS REALLY NOTHING
Tracks: / William it was really nothing.
7" Single: Released Aug '84, on Rough Trade, by Rough Trade Records. Catalogue no: **RT 166**
12" Single: Released Aug '84, on Rough Trade, by Rough Trade Records. Catalogue no: **RTT 166**

Smith,Tono

CAN'T STOP
Tracks: / Can't stop / Can't stop(Dub mix).
12" Single: Released '86, on Lisson, by PWL Records. Catalogue no: **DOLEQ 4**
7" Single: Released '86, on Lisson, by PWL Records. Catalogue no: **DOLE 4**

Smoke

MY FRIEND JACK (SINGLE)
Tracks: / My friend Jack.
7" Single: Released Mar '67, on Columbia, by EMI Records. Deleted Mar '70. Catalogue no: **DB 8115**

Smoken, Lauren

SMILE
Tracks: / Smile.
12" Single: Released Aug '88, on Loop, by Loop Records. Catalogue no: **12 LOOP 101**
7" Single: Released Aug '88, on Loop, by Loop Records. Catalogue no: **LOOP 101**

Smokey

DON'T PLAY YOUR ROCK 'N' ROLL TO ME
Tracks: / Don't play your rock 'n' roll to me.
7" Single: Released Oct '75, on RAK, by EMI Records. Deleted Oct '78. Catalogue no: **RAK 217**

IF YOU THINK YOU KNOW HOW TO LOVE ME
Tracks: / If you think you know how to love me.
7" Single: Released Jul '75, on RAK, by EMI Records. Deleted Jul '78. Catalogue no: **RAK 206**

Smokie

Biographical details:
Smokie were a British pop group of the 1970's, originally called Kindness, then Smokey, finally changing the spelling to avoid confusion with Smokey Robinson. Line-up was Chris Norman (vocals, guitar, keyboards), Alan Silson (lead guitar), Peter Spencer (sax, drums) and Terry Uttley (bass).

Signed to UK bubblegum label Rak, they affected notions of progressive rock but soon emerged as a singles act and turned out to be class popsters. They had their greatest success with songs by Nicky Chinn and Mike Chapman, running out of steam when they tried to break away from the formula.
(Donald Clarke, March 1987.).

CRY IN THE NIGHT
Tracks: / Cry in the night / Working for the weekend.
7" Single: Released Sep '87, on Wag, Catalogue no: **WAG 4**

FOR A FEW DOLLARS MORE
Tracks: / For a few dollars more.
7" Single: Released Jan '78, on RAK, by EMI Records. Deleted Jan '81. Catalogue no: **RAK 267**

I'LL MEET YOU AT MIDNIGHT
Tracks: / I'll meet you at midnight.
7" Single: Released Sep '76, on RAK, by EMI Records. Deleted Sep '79. Catalogue no: **RAK 241**

IT'S YOUR LIFE
Tracks: / It's your life.
7" Single: Released Jul '77, on RAK, by EMI Records. Deleted Jul '80. Catalogue no: **RAK 260**

LAY BACK IN THE ARMS OF SOMEONE
Tracks: / Lay back in the arms of someone
7" Single: Released Mar '77, on RAK, by EMI Records. Deleted Mar '80. Catalogue no: **RAK 251**

LIVING NEXT DOOR TO ALICE
Tracks: / Living next door to Alice.
7" Single: Released Dec '76, on RAK, by EMI Records. Deleted Dec '79. Catalogue no: **RAK 244**

LOOKING DANCERS
Tracks: / Looking dancers / Hiding from the night.
7" Single: Released Nov '82, on Mean, by Mean Records. Catalogue no: **MEAN 101**

MEXICAN GIRL
Tracks: / Mexican girl.
7" Single: Released Sep '78, on RAK, by EMI Records. Deleted Sep '81. Catalogue no: **RAK 283**

MY HEART IS TRUE
Tracks: / My heart is true / My heart is true (version).
7" Single: Released Apr '88, on Priority, by Priority Records. Catalogue no: **WAG 5**

NEEDLES AND PINS
Tracks: / Needles and pins.
7" Single: Released Oct '77, on RAK, by EMI Records. Deleted Oct '80. Catalogue no: **RAK 263**

OH CAROL
7" Single: Released May '78, on RAK, by EMI Records. Deleted May '81. Catalogue no: **RAK 276**

RUN TO ME
Tracks: / Run to me / Look what you're doin'.
7" Single: Released Sep '80, on RAK, by EMI Records. Deleted '83. Catalogue no: **RAK 321**

SOMETHING'S BEEN MAKING ME BLUE
Tracks: / Something's been making me blue.
7" Single: Released Jan '76, on RAK, by EMI Records. Deleted Jan '79. Catalogue no: **RAK 227**

TAKE GOOD CARE OF MY BABY
Tracks: / Take good care of my baby / I wanna kiss your lips.
7" Single: Released Apr '80, on RAK, by EMI Records. Deleted Apr '83. Catalogue no: **RAK 309**

Smokin

MIDNIGHT
Tracks: / Midnight.
7" Single: Released Jan '83, on Zone To Zone, by Zone To Zone Records. Catalogue no: **ZON 03**

Smokin' Gang

JUST ROCK
Tracks: / Just rock.
12" Single: Released 14 Aug '89, on Kool Kat, by Kool Kat Records. Catalogue no: **KOOLT 506**

Smoking Hinchcliffes

SITTING PRETTY
Tracks: / Sitting pretty / Mary.
7" Single: Released Feb '89, on No, Catalogue no: **NOS 41**

Smoking Mirror

SIREN GIRL
Tracks: / Siren girl.
12" Single: Released Feb '89, on Sonic Death, Catalogue no: **SONIC 001T**

Smooth, Joe

CAN'T FAKE THE FEELING
Tracks: / Can't fake the feeling/I'll be there/Radical.
7" Single: Released May '89, on DJ International, by Westside Records. Catalogue no: **DJIN 13**
12" Single: Released May '89, on DJ International, by Westside Records. Catalogue no: **DJINT 13**
CD 5": Released May '89, on DJ International, by Westside Records. Catalogue no: **CDDJIN 13**

PROMISED LAND (SINGLE)

Sniff'n'The Tears - One Love (Released on Chiswick)

Tracks: / Promised land.
7" Single: Released Jan '89, on DJ International, by Westside Records. Catalogue no: **DJIN 6**
12" Single: Released Jan '89, on DJ International, by Westside Records. Catalogue no: **DJINT 6**

Smurfs

CLAPPING AND JUMPING SHOW
Tracks: / Clapping and jumping show / Welcome to Smurfland / Rockin' smurfs.
7" Single: Released Nov '81, on Creole, by Creole Records. Catalogue no: **CR 7**

JOKING SMURF
Tracks: / Joking smurf / Smurfing school.
7" Single: Released Mar '84, on Dureco (Holland), Catalogue no: **DUS 1**

SMURF FOR ALL IT'S WORTH IT
Tracks: / Smurf for all it's worth it / Smurf for all it's worth it (instr).
12" Single: Released May '83, on Celluloid (USA), by Celluloid Records (USA). Catalogue no: **CYZ 103**

Snake Corps

CALLING YOU
Tracks: / Calling you.
7" Single: Released 28 Mar '89, on Midnight, Catalogue no: **DING 050**
12" Single: Released 28 Mar '89, on Midnight, Catalogue no: **DONG 050**

PARTY'S OVER
Tracks: / Party's over, The.
12" Single: Released Aug '85, on Midnight, Catalogue no: **DONG 13**

SCIENCE KILLS
Tracks: / Science kills.
12" Single: Released Sep '85, on Midnight, Catalogue no: **DONG 13**

VICTORY PARADE
Tracks: / Victory parade / Always be the same / Painted ocean.
12" Single: Released '86, on Midnight Chime, Catalogue no: **DONG 19**

Snakepit

WAIT
Tracks: / Wait.
7" Single: Released '88, on Dunghill, Catalogue no: **DUNG 001**

Snakes Of Shake

SOUTHERN CROSS
Tracks: / Southern cross / You walk / Southern cross (Part 2) (Available on 12" version only).
7" Single: Released '86, on Making Waves, by Celtic Music. Deleted Nov '87. Catalogue no: **SURF 116**
12" Single: Released '86, on Making Waves, by Celtic Music. Deleted Nov '87. Catalogue no: **SURFT 116**

SOUTHERN CROSS (PT 3)
Tracks: / Southern cross (Pt 3).
12" Single: Released Aug '85, on Tense But Confident, Catalogue no: **GOBS 121**

Snap Shot

HALFWAY TO PARADISE
Tracks: / Halfway to paradise / Fly in my face.
7" Single: Released Jun '83, on Jammy, by Jammy Records. Catalogue no: **JRS 831**

Snapdragons

DOLE BOYS ON FUTONS
Tracks: / Dole boys on futons / lies / Fruits of the earth.
CD 5": Released Jun '89, on Native (1), by Native Records. Catalogue no: **CD NTV 41**
12" Single: Released Jun '89, on Native (1), by Native Records. Catalogue no: **12 NTV 41**

THINGS YOU WANT
Tracks: / Things you want / Silent world, The / Man of the dreams, The (Only on 12".).
7" Single: Released Oct '88, on Native (1), by Native Records. Catalogue no: **NTV 37**
12" Single: Released Oct '88, on Native (1), by Native Records. Catalogue no: **12 NTV 37**

Snapes

EYE TO EYE
Tracks: / Eye to eye / Missing from home / Digging up the dirt / Vision on.
Note: 4 track EP.
7" Single: Released Oct '89, on Regal Zonophone, by EMI Records. Catalogue no: **RZ 1**
7" Single: Released Oct '89, on Regal Zonophone, by EMI Records. Catalogue no: **203 588 7**

Snatch

SHOPPING FOR CLOTHES
Tracks: / Shopping for clothes / Joey.
12" Single: Released May '81, on Fetish, Catalogue no: **FET 004**

Sneakers

MORE THAN JUST THE TWO OF US
Tracks: / More than just the two of us / In time.
7" Single: Released Feb '82, on Ariola, by BMG Records (UK). Deleted Feb '87. Catalogue no: **HANDS 4**

Sneaky Pierre

ANOTHER STRING TO MY BOW
Tracks: / Another string to my bow / Doing the best I can.
7" Single: Released Jul '81, on Tigma, Deleted Jul '84. Catalogue no: **TIG 1**

Sneetches

ONLY FOR A MOMENT
Tracks: / Only for a moment.
12" Single: Released Apr '88, on Kaleidoscope Sound, by Kaleidoscope Sound Records. Catalogue no: **KS 106**

Sniff 'n' The Tears

DRIVERS SEAT
Tracks: / Driver's seat / Nightlife / Put your money where your mouth is / Slide away.
12" Single: Released Jun '83, on Chiswick Records, Catalogue no: **DICE 12 11**
7" Single: Released Jun '79, on Chiswick Records, Deleted Jun '82. Catalogue no: **CHIS 105**

HUNGRY EYES
Tracks: / Hungry eyes / Bagatelle.
7" Single: Released Jul '82, on Chiswick Records, Catalogue no: **DICE 10**

ONE LOVE
Tracks: / One love / 5 & Zero.
7" Single: Released '80, on Chiswick Records, Catalogue no: **CHIS 129**

POISEN PEN MAIL
Tracks: / Poisen pen mail / What can Daddy do?.
7" Single: Released Sep '80, on Chiswick Records, Deleted '83. Catalogue no: **CHIS 131**

THAT FINAL LOVE
Tracks: / That final love / Like my fantasy.
7" Single: Released May '81, on Chiswick Records, Deleted May '84. Catalogue no: **CHIS 146**

Snipers

THREE PEACE SUITE (EP)
Tracks: / Three peace suite.
7" Single: Released Dec '81, on Crass, by Crass Records. Catalogue no: **321984/4**

Snips

NINE O'CLOCK
Tracks: / Nine o'clock / What's your number.
7" Single: Released Feb '81, on EMI, by EMI Records. Deleted Feb '84. Catalogue no: **EMI 5040**

TIGHT SHOES
Tracks: / Tight shoes / Noise.
7" Single: Released Jan '81, on EMI, by EMI Records. Deleted Jan '84. Catalogue no: **EMI 5138**

YOU'RE A WONDERFUL ONE
Tracks: / You're a wonderful one / Mr. Dillinger.
7" Single: Released May '80, on EMI, by EMI Records. Deleted '83. Catalogue no: **EMI 5071**

Snivelling Shits

I CAN'T COME
Tracks: / I can't come/Terminal stupid.
7"Single Released on 16 Jan '89, on Damaged Goods, Catalogue no: **FNARR 3**

IS GOD A MAN
Tracks: / Is God a man.
7" Single: Released Jul '89, on Damaged Goods, Catalogue no: **FNARR 84**

Snow, Hank

Biographical details:
Hank Snow was born Clarence Eugene Snow, 9 May 1914, in Liverpool, Nova Scotia, Canada.
One of the biggest post-war country stars, singer, guitarist and songwriter Hank Snow had a record-breaking 45-year association with the same record company, RCA. He ran away to sea from a poverty-stricken background and began singing and playing on Canadian radio as *Clarence Snow & His Guitar*. RCA signed him in 1934 and within 10 years he was Canada's greatest country star.
After several false starts he made the breakthrough in the USA in 1949, with *Marriage Vow*. *I'm Moving On* ('50) was nearly a year on Billboard's country chart, 18 weeks at No 1, and crossed over to pop sales as well. His next 26 hits up to '57 were almost all Top Ten entrants, including *Golden Rocket*, *Rhumba Boogie and I Don't Hurt Anymore* at No 1. He made the country charts every year to '79, the year he was elected to the Country Music Hall of Fame. (Donald Clarke, March 1987.)
One has to count Hank Snow as one of the all time modern country artists - he sure has his place in the circle of the Top Ten artists of this kind of American music. Hank Snow started his career in 1936 in Canada. When he came to the States he was already well-known in his homecountry.
During the 50's he rose t0o stardom in the USA, and over the decades, Hank Snow's album output was among the most prolific of any country artist.
He still is a regular member of the Grand Ole Opry. In 1979 he was elected into the Country Music Hall of Fame.
(Bear Family, 1988)..

I'M MOVING ON
Tracks: / I'm movin' on.
7" Single: Released Jan '80, on RCA, by BMG Records (UK). Catalogue no: **LR 1132**

Snow, Phoebe

Biographical details:
Born in 1952 in Teaneck, New Jersey, Snow is a jazz-influenced singer, guitarist and songwriter. She began writing poems and setting them to music. Her first album was on Leon Russell's Shelter label: *Phoebe Snow* (1974) included *Poetry Man*, a Top Five hit in America. Backing on various tracks has included musicians of the calibre of Stan Getz, Teddy Wilson and Ron Carter. All Snow's albums have charted in the US and are still available there. (Donald Clarke, March 1987.).

EVERY NIGHT
Tracks: / Every night.
7" Single: Released Jan '79, on CBS, by CBS Records. Deleted Jan '82. Catalogue no: **CBS 6842**

GAMES
Tracks: / Games / Down in the basement.
7" Single: Released Apr '81, on Atlantic, by WEA Records. Catalogue no: **K 11566**

GASOLINE ALLEY
Tracks: / Gasoline Alley / I believe in you.
7" Single: Released Jun '81, on Mirage (USA), Catalogue no: **K 11663**

IF I CAN JUST GET THROUGH THE NIGHT
Tracks: / If I can just get through the night / Soothin' / Our love is insane.
7" Single: Released Apr '89, on Elektra, by Elektra Records (UK). Catalogue no: **EKR 91**
12" Single: Released Apr '89, on Elektra, by Elektra Records (UK). Catalogue no: **EKR 91T**
CD 5": Released Apr '89, on Elektra, by Elektra Records (UK). Catalogue no: **EKR 91CD**

Snow, Tom

SOMEWHERE DOWN THE ROAD
Tracks: / Somewhere down the road / Soon.
7" Single: Released Jan '83, on Arista, by BMG Records (UK). Catalogue no: **ARIST 505**

Snow White

SNOW WHITE AND THE SEVEN DWARFS (well loved tales age up to 9)
Tracks: / Snow White and the seven dwarfs / Water of life, The / Little people / Goose girl, The / King wren.
Note: (Book & cassette)
7" EP: Released Dec '82, on Disneyland, by Disneyland Records. Catalogue no: **D 310**

Snowboy

BRING ON THE BEAT
Tracks: / Bring on the beat.
12" Single: Released '85, on Arc, Catalogue no: **CRAX 001**

MAMBO TERESA
Tracks: / Mambo teresa / Wild spirit.
12" Single: Released '86, on Waterfront, by Waterfront Music. Catalogue no: **WFT 30**

NIGHT IN TUNISIA, A
Tracks: / waterfront.
12" Single: Released Jan '88, on Waterfront, by Waterfront Music. Catalogue no: **WFT 38**

RITMO SNOWBOY
Tracks: / Ritmo snowboy / Night in Tunisia.
12" Single: Released Mar '88, on Waterfront, by Waterfront Music. Catalogue no: **BGPT 002**

Snowmen

HOKEY COKEY
Tracks: / Hokey cokey / Don't go short.
7" Single: Released Nov '81, on Slack, by Stiff Records. Catalogue no: **OBD 1**

NIK NAK PADDY WAK
Tracks: / Nik nak paddy wak / Snowmen rappin' / Hokey cokey / Auld lang syne (Medley).
12" Single: Released '86, on Priority, by Priority Records. Catalogue no: **12 NAK 1**
7" Single: Released '86, on Priority, by Priority Records. Catalogue no: **NAK 1**

XMAS PARTY
Tracks: / Xmas party / Dance of the Snowmen.
7" Single: Released Dec '83, on Solid, by Solid Records. Catalogue no: **STOP 006**

Snowy Red

I'M ALRIGHT
Tracks: / I'm alright.
12" Single: Released Sep '88, on Antler, by Antler Records (Belgium). Catalogue no: **ANT 083**

I'M RED
Tracks: / I'm red / Megadeath.
7" Single: Released Apr '82, on Dirty Dance, Catalogue no: **DD 7002**

LOVE MACHINE
Tracks: / Love machine.
12" Single: Released Dec '88, on Subway, by Subway Records. Catalogue no: **SUB 051**

TREAT ME
Tracks: / Treat me.

12" Single: Released May '88, on Antler, by Antler Records (Belgium). Catalogue no: **ANT 080**

Snuff

NOT LISTENING
Tracks: / Not listening.
7" Single: Released Apr '89, on Workers Playtime, by Upright Records. Catalogue no: **PLAY 008**

Snuky Tate

HE'S THE GROOVE
Tracks: / He's the groove.
7" Single: Released Jun '82, on Island, by Island Records. Deleted Jun '85. Catalogue no: **WIP 6785**
12" Single: Released Jun '82, on Island, by Island Records. Deleted Jun '85. Catalogue no: **12WIP 6785**

So

ARE YOU SURE
Tracks: / Are you sure / Don't look back / Are you sure (12" mix)*.
Note: * extra tracks on 12" and CD single.
CD 5": Released Jan '88, on EMI, by EMI Records. Deleted 31 Jul '88. Catalogue no: **CDR 6173**
Cassingle: Released Feb '88, on EMI, by EMI Records. Deleted Nov '88. Catalogue no: **TCR 6173**
12" Single: Released Jan '88, on EMI, by EMI Records. Deleted Nov '88. Catalogue no: **12R 6173**
12" Single: Released Feb '88, on Parlophone, by EMI Records. Deleted Nov '88. Catalogue no: **12RX 6173**
7" Single: Released Jan '88, on EMI, by EMI Records. Deleted Nov '88. Catalogue no: **R 6173**

BURNING BUSH
Tracks: / Burning bush / Dreaming (cocktail mix) / Burning bush (extended mix)* / Burning bush (7" version)*.
Note: *Tracks on 12" version.
CD 5": Released Sep '88, on Parlophone, by EMI Records. Deleted Jun '89. Catalogue no: **CDR 6182**
12" Single: Released Sep '88, on Parlophone, by EMI Records. Deleted Jun '89. Catalogue no: **12R 6182**
7" Single: Released Sep '88, on Parlophone, by EMI Records. Deleted Jun '89. Catalogue no: **R 6182**

WOULD YOU DIE FOR ME
Tracks: / Would you die for me (7" only.) / Spies at home / Would you die for me (LP version) (Not on 7".) / Are you sure (Francois Kevorkian mix) (Gatefold & CD single only.) / Capitol Hill (John Luongo mix) (12" only.).
CD 5": Released Jan '89, on Parlophone, by EMI Records. Deleted Aug '89. Catalogue no: **CDR 6200**
12" Single: Released Jan '89, on Parlophone, by EMI Records. Deleted Aug '89. Catalogue no: **12R 6200**
12" Single: Released Jan '89, on Parlophone, by EMI Records. Deleted Aug '89. Catalogue no: **12RG 6200**
7" Single: Released Jan '89, on Parlophone, by EMI Records. Deleted Aug '89. Catalogue no: **R 6200**

So Few

GET INSIDE
Tracks: / Get inside / I'm not automatic.
7" Single: Released Nov '82, on All For One, Catalogue no: **AFO 073**

So Feww

SPIRITS HIGH
Tracks: / Spirits high / Rainmaker & his son.
7" Single: Released Jun '82, on All For One, Catalogue no: **PPC 118**

So You Think..

DON'T NEED YOU
Tracks: / Don't need you.
7" Single: Released Jun '84, on Cheatin'Heart, Catalogue no: **AA 01**

Soapy

TOP OF THE BOX
Tracks: / Top of the box.
12" Single: Released Nov '86, on BBC, by BBC Records & Tapes. Deleted 31 Aug '88. Catalogue no: **12 RSL 206**
7" Single: Released Nov '86, on BBC, by BBC Records & Tapes. Deleted 31 Aug '88. Catalogue no: **RESL 206**

S.O.B.

YOU MAKE ME WONDER
Tracks: / Make me wonder / Corporation buzz.
7" Single: Released Sep '89, on Rough Trade, by Rough Trade Records. Catalogue no: **RT 219**
12" Single: Released Sep '89, on Rough Trade, by Rough Trade Records. Catalogue no: **RTT 219**

Soca Syndicate

BOY LIKE YOU
Tracks: / Boy like you / Boy like you (version).
12" Single: Released Dec '83, on Sunburn, by Orbitone Records. Catalogue no: **SBD 42**

Soccio, Gino

DANCER
Tracks: / Dancer.
7" Single: Released Apr '79, on Warner Bros., by WEA Records. Deleted Apr '82. Catalogue no: **K 17357**

HUMAN NATURE
Tracks: / Human nature.
12" Single: Released Oct '85, on Noir, by Noir Records. Catalogue no: **12 CHALD 101**

TODAY
Tracks: / Today / Bully boys / World at ransom.
7" Single: Released Mar '83, on Karnage, Catalogue no: **KILL 18**

TRY IT OUT
Tracks: / Try it out / Closer.
7" Single: Released Jun '81, on Atlantic, by WEA Records. Catalogue no: **K 11594**
12" Single: Released Jun '81, on Atlantic, by WEA Records. Catalogue no: **K 11594 T**

Social Illness

FRESH ENUFF
Tracks: / Fresh enuff.
12" Single: Released Aug '87, on Music Of Life, by Music Of Life Records. Catalogue no: **NOTE 8**

Society

LOVE IT
Tracks: / Love it.
12" Single: Released 21 Nov '87, on Ahead Of Our Time, by Ahead of Our Time. Catalogue no: **BLR 1TCC**

SATURN GIRL
Tracks: / Saturn girl / Love it.
12" Single: Released Aug '87, on Big Life, by Big Life Records. Catalogue no: **BLR 001T**
7" Single: Released Aug '87, on Big Life, by Big Life Records. Catalogue no: **BLR 001**

Society Highes

BOOTS
Tracks: / Boots / Walkout.
7" Single: Released May '83, on Out To Lunch, by Out To Lunch Records. Catalogue no: **OTL 001**
12" Single: Released Jun '83, on Out To Lunch, by Out To Lunch Records. Catalogue no: **12 OTL 1**

Sockit

SWING ON A STAR
Tracks: / Swing on a star.
7" Single: Released Sep '85, on UNKNOWN, Catalogue no: **KIS 2**
12" Single: Released Sep '85, on UNKNOWN, Catalogue no: **12 KIS 2**

Soda, Frank

OVERSEXED & UNDERFED
Tracks: / Oversexed & underfed / Crazy girls.
7" Single: Released Jun '81, on Carrere, Catalogue no: **CAR 184**

Sodom

EXPOSURE OF SODOMY
Tracks: / Exposure of sodom.
12" Single: Released Aug '89, on S.P.V., Catalogue no: **502123**

Soft As Ghosts

MYSTIFIED
Tracks: / Mystified / Facets of love.
7" Single: Released Sep '83, on Rondelet Music, by Rondelet Music & Records. Catalogue no: **ROUND 31**

Soft Boys

HE'S A REPTILE
Tracks: / He's a reptile / Song no.4.
7" Single: Released Apr '83, on Midnight, Catalogue no: **DING 4**

I WANNA DESTROY YOU
Tracks: / I wanna destroy you.
7" Single: Released Jul '81, on Armageddon, by Armageddon Records. Catalogue no: **AS 005**

KINGDOM OF LOVE
Tracks: / Kingdom of love / Vegetable man.
7" Single: Released Jul '82, on Armageddon, by Armageddon Records. Catalogue no: **AEP 002**

ONLY THE STONE REMAINS
Tracks: / Only the stones remain.
7" Single: Released Oct '81, on Armageddon, by Armageddon Records. Catalogue no: **AS 029**

Soft Cell

Biographical details:
Soft Cell was an influential British duo -- singer-songwriter Marc Almond and David Ball on synthesisers -- between 1979 and 1983. Their New Romantic material was accompanied by strange, clever, tongue-in-cheek videos. They had five Top Five hits in the UK before splitting up. Ball made a solo album in 1983 and Almond has had further success with Marc & The Mambas and as a solo artist. (Donald Clarke, March 1988.).

12" SINGLES, THE
Tracks: / Tainted love / Memorabilia / Torch / Bedsitter / Say hello, wave goodbye / What.
Special: Released Nov '82, on Some Bizzare, by Some Bizzare Records. Deleted '83. Catalogue no: **CELBX 1**

BED SITTER
Tracks: / Bed sitter / Facility girls.
7" Single: Released Nov '81, on Some Bizzare, by Some Bizzare Records. Deleted Nov '84. Catalogue no: **BZS 6**
12" Single: Released Nov '81, on Some Bizzare, by Some Bizzare Records. Deleted Nov '84. Catalogue no: **BZS 6 12**

DOWN IN THE SUBWAY
Tracks: / Down in the subway / Disease and despaire.
7" Single: Released Feb '84, on Some Bizzare, by Some Bizzare Records. Deleted Feb '87. Catalogue no: **BZS 22**

MEMORABILIA
Tracks: / Memorabilia / Persuasion.
7" Single: Released Mar '81, on Some Bizzare, by Some Bizzare Records. Deleted Mar '84. Catalogue no: **HARD 12**

NUMBERS
Tracks: / Numbers / Barriers.
7" Single: Released Mar '83, on Some Bizzare, by Some Bizzare Records. Deleted Mar '86. Catalogue no: **BZS 17**

SAY HELLO WAVE GOODBYE
Tracks: / Say hello, wave goodbye / Fun city.
7" Single: Released Feb '82, on Some Bizzare, by Some Bizzare Records. Deleted Feb '85. Catalogue no: **BZS 7**
12" Single: Released Feb '82, on Some Bizzare, by Some Bizzare Records. Deleted Feb '85. Catalogue no: **BZS7 12**

SOFT CELL/MARC ALMOND - STAMPA ALTERNATIVA Lyric book & flexi
Special: Released 1 Nov '87, on Stampa Alternative (Italy), Catalogue no: **MA 001**

SOUL INSIDE
Tracks: / Soul inside / You only live twice / Loving you hating me (on 12" only) / 007 theme (on 12" only).
7" Single: Released Sep '83, on Some Bizzare, by Some Bizzare Records. Deleted Sep '86. Catalogue no: **BZS 20**

SOUL INSIDE (IMPORT)
Tracks: / Soul inside (12" mix) / You only live twice(12" mix) / Torch (12" mix) / Her imagination / Hendrix medley, The.
12" Single: Released Oct '88, on Vertigo (Canada), Catalogue no: **VEP 322**

TAINTED LOVE
Tracks: / Tainted love / Where did our love go.
12" Single: Released Feb '85, on Some Bizzare, by Some Bizzare Records. Deleted 31 May '89. Catalogue no: **BZS 212**
7" Single: Released Feb '85, on Some Bizzare, by Some Bizzare Records. Deleted 31 May '89. Catalogue no: **BZS 2**

TAINTED LOVE (IMPORT)
Tracks: / Torch / Say hello, wave goodbye.
Note: This recording includes a medley of "Tainted love" and "Where did our love go".
CD 5": Released Oct '88, on Vertigo (Germany), Catalogue no: **8886172**

TORCH
Tracks: / Torch.
7" Single: Released May '82, on Some Bizzare, by Some Bizzare Records. Deleted May '85. Catalogue no: **BZS 9**

WHAT
Tracks: / What.
7" Single: Released Aug '82, on Some Bizzare, by Some Bizzare Records. Deleted Aug '85. Catalogue no: **BZS 11**
12" Single: Released Jan '82, on Some Bizzare, by Some Bizzare Records. Deleted Jan '85. Catalogue no: **BZS 112**

WHERE THE HEART IS
Tracks: / Where the heart is / It's a mug's game.
7" Single: Released Dec '82, on Some Bizzare, by Some Bizzare Records. Deleted Dec '85. Catalogue no: **BZS 16**
12" Single: Released Dec '82, on Some Bizzare, by Some Bizzare Records. Deleted Dec '85. Catalogue no: **BZS 16 12**

Soft Drinks

CINZANO WET DREAM
Tracks: / Cinzano wet dream / Pop stars.
7" Single: Released Apr '82, on Outer Himalayen, Catalogue no: **OH 004**

Soft Shoe

KOJO
Tracks: / Kojo / Fear of flying.
7" Single: Released Aug '84, on IDM, Catalogue no: **IDM 70**

Soft Touch

IT'S MY LIFE
Tracks: / It's my life / Sus song, The.
7" Single: Released Nov '80, on Nems, by Castle Communications Records. Catalogue no: **BSS 103**

Soft Verdict

AT HOME
Tracks: / At Home / Not at home.
7" Single: Released Feb '82, on Les Disques Du Crepuscule(Belgium), by Les Disques Du Crepuscule(Belgium). Catalogue no: **7TWI 047**
12" Single: Released Aug '87, on Les Disques Du Crepuscule(Belgium), by Les Disques Du Crepuscule(Belgium). Catalogue no: **TWI 047**

CLOSER COVER
Tracks: / Closer cover.
7" Single: Released Nov '83, on Les Disques Du Crepuscule(Belgium), by Les Disques Du Crepuscule(Belgium). Catalogue no: **7TWI 154**

SOHO - REMEMBER MY NAME (Released on EMI)

Soho

CHILDREN OF THE NIGHT
Tracks: / Children of the night / Save your love for me.
7" Single: Released Jun '80, on Chopper, Deleted '83. Catalogue no: **CHOP 102**

MESSAGE FROM MY BABY
Tracks: / Message from my baby / Be my love / Turn it on (12" only).
7" Single: Released Feb '89, on Virgin, by Virgin Records. Catalogue no: **HEDD 4**
12" Single: Released Feb '89, on Virgin, by Virgin Records. Catalogue no: **HEDD 412**
CD 5": Released Feb '89, on Virgin, by Virgin Records. Catalogue no: **HEDCD 4**

PIECE OF YOU
Tracks: / Piece of you (NOT on 12") / Blonde on black (NOT on HEDD 113) / Piece of you (arcade extended mix) (On 12" only) / Piece of you (stomp mix) (On 12" & cassette only) / Little girl (On cassette only).
Cassingle: Released '88, on Virgin, by Virgin Records. Catalogue no: **HEDDC 112**
12" Single: Released '88, on Virgin, by Virgin Records. Catalogue no: **HEDD 113**
12" Single: Released Feb '88, on Virgin, by Virgin Records. Catalogue no: **HEDD 112**
7" Single: Released Feb '88, on Virgin, by Virgin Records. Catalogue no: **HEDD 1**

REMEMBER MY NAME (see panel on previous page)
Tracks: / Remember my name / Looking for you.
7" Single: Released '83, on EMI, by EMI Records. Catalogue no: **EMI 5408**

WALKING IN THE SAND
Tracks: / Walking in the sand / Rock solid lover / What is it like to be a girl (Available on 12" version only).
7" Single: Released '86, on Big Red Group, by Big Red Group Records. Catalogue no: **BED 1**
12" Single: Released '86, on Big Red Group, by Big Red Group Records. Catalogue no: **12 BED 1**

YOU WON'T HOLD ME DOWN
Tracks: / You won't hold me down (Not on 12") / More of a man / We came to rock (12" only) / You won't hold me down (Harley Davidson mix) (CD & 12" only) / Piece of you (CD only).
12" Single: Released Sep '88, on Virgin, by Virgin Records. Catalogue no: **HEDD 312**
CD 3": Released '88, on Virgin, by Virgin Records. Catalogue no: **HEDDCD 3**
7" Single: Released Sep '88, on Virgin, by Virgin Records. Catalogue no: **HEDD 3**

Soho Roses

SO ALONE
Tracks: / So alone / Yesterday's girl.
7" Single: Released Sep '88, on Trashcan, by Trashcan Records. Catalogue no: **TWAT 002**
12" Single: Released Sep '88, on Trashcan, by Trashcan Records. Catalogue no: **TWAT 00212**

Sola

YEAR OF THE SNAKE
Tracks: / Year of the snake.
12" Single: Released 6 Feb '89, on Criminal (1), by Criminal Records. Catalogue no: **BUST 016**

Soldier

SHERLEE
Tracks: / Sherlee / Force.
12" Single: Released Feb '82, on Heavy Metal, by FM-Revolver Records. Catalogue no: **HEAVY 12**

Soldier Dolls

TASTE OF BLOOD A
Tracks: / Taste of blood, A.
7" Single: Released Feb '85, on Scream, by Revolver Records. Catalogue no: **SCREAM 002**

WHAT DO THEY KNOW
Tracks: / What do they know.
7" Single: Released Mar '84, on UNKNOWN, Catalogue no: **SCREAM 1**

Soldiers Of Fortune

STARS
Tracks: / Stars / Autonmia.
7" Single: Released May '83, on Total Darkness, by Rough Trade Records. Catalogue no: **TD 1**

Solen, Andrzej

SOLIDARITY DEFIANT
Tracks: / Solidarity defiant / General feelings.
7" Single: Released Jul '82, on Solidarity, Deleted '83. Catalogue no: **7SUS 101**

Solitaire

BABY BLUE
Tracks: / Baby blue / Baby blue (clarinet instrumental).
7" Single: Released '86, on Plaza, by Plaza Records. Catalogue no: **PLAZA 020**

I DON'T WANT TO FALL IN LOVE
Tracks: / I don't want to fall in love / I don't want to fall in love (inst).
7" Single: Released 23 Apr '88, on Plaza, by Plaza Records. Catalogue no: **PZA 032**

IN LONDON
Tracks: / In London / Baby blue / Woman in me, The.
12" Single: Released Jul '87, on Plaza, by Plaza Records. Catalogue no: **PZA 028T**
7" Single: Released Jul '87, on Plaza, by Plaza Records. Catalogue no: **PZA 028**

MY MAN
Tracks: / My man.
7" Single: Released Jan '87, on Plaza, by Plaza Records. Catalogue no: **PLAZA 023**

WOMAN IN ME, THE
Tracks: / Woman in me, The / Woman in me, The (inst).
7" Single: Released Jul '87, on Plaza, by Plaza Records. Catalogue no: **PLAZA 025**
12" Single: Released Jul '87, on Plaza, by Plaza Records. Catalogue no: **PLAZA 025T**

Solo

SOLO
Tracks: / Solo / Right stuff, The.
7" Single: Released '85, on PRT, by Castle Communications Records. Catalogue no: **7P 335**

Solo, Sal

ADORAMUS TE
Tracks: / Adoramus Te / Panis Angelicas Frank / Adoramus Te (meditation version) / Need me (on 12" only.).
Note: *Adoramus Te (meditation version)* on 12" only. Producers: Sal Solo/Mel Simpson.
12" Single: Released Nov '87, on Magnet, by WEA Records. Deleted Jun '88. Catalogue no: **DECT 25**
7" Single: Released Nov '87, on Magnet, by WEA Records. Deleted Jun '88. Catalogue no: **DEC 25**

HOW WAS I TO KNOW
Tracks: / How was I to know / In innocence.
7" Single: Released Feb '87, on Awesome Records, by Awesome Records. Catalogue no: **AOR 8**

MUSIC AND YOU
Tracks: / Music and you.
7" Single: Released Apr '85, on MCA, by MCA Records. Deleted Apr '88. Catalogue no: **MCA 946**

SAN DAMIANO (HEART AND SOUL)
Tracks: / San Damiano (heart and soul).
7" Single: Released Dec '84, on MCA, by MCA Records. Deleted Dec '87. Catalogue no: **MCA 930**

Solo Teknik

WAIT A MINUTE
Tracks: / Wait a minute / Wait a minute (version).
12" Single: Released Sep '89, on Debut, by Skratch Records. Catalogue no: **DEBTX 3076**

Soloman, Gary

SEALED WITH A KISS
Tracks: / Sealed with a kiss.
12" Single: Released May '89, on Pyramid, by Pyramid Records. Catalogue no: **12PYR 8**
7" Single: Released May '89, on Pyramid, by Pyramid Records. Catalogue no: **PYR 8**

Soloman, Roger

IN THE GROOVE
Tracks: / In the groove.
12" Single: Released May '85, on Raiders, Catalogue no: **LGR 008**

Solomon, Diane

DREAM'S NOT A DREAM, A
Tracks: / Dream's not a dream, A / When the goin' gets rough.
7" Single: Released Jan '89, on Fly, by Fly Records. Catalogue no: **EAGLE 10**

WHEN THE LIGHTS GO OUT TONIGHT
Tracks: / When the lights go out tonight / Bluer than blue.
7" Single: Released Jul '80, on Lordell, Deleted Jul '83. Catalogue no: **LORD 1**

Solo's

TALKING PICTURES
Tracks: / Talking pictures / One way love / Psychic Eric.
7" Single: Released Feb '80, on Cobra, Deleted Feb '83. Catalogue no: **COB 8**

Some, Belouis

ANIMAL MAGIC
Tracks: / Animal magic / Aware of you.
Note: * 12" remix.
12" Single: Released Aug '87, on Parlophone, by EMI Records. Deleted Apr '88. Catalogue no: **12R 6161**
12" Single: Released Sep '87, on Parlophone, by EMI Records. Deleted Apr '88. Catalogue no: **12RX 6161**

IMAGINATION
Tracks: / Imagination / Have you ever been in love? / Target practice (Available on Doublepack edition).
7" Set: Released '86, on Parlophone, by EMI Records. Deleted '88. Catalogue no: **RD 1986**
7" Single: Released Mar '85, on Parlophone, by EMI Records. Deleted '86. Catalogue no: **R 6092**
7" Single: Released '86, on Parlophone, by EMI Records. Deleted Jul '87. Catalogue no: **R 1986**
7" Single: Released Apr '85, on Parlophone, by EMI Records. Deleted Apr '88. Catalogue no: **R 6097**
12" Single: Released Jan '86, on Parlophone, by EMI Records. Deleted Aug '89. Catalogue no: **12R 1986**
12" Single: Released Mar '85, on Parlophone, by EMI Records. Deleted '86. Catalogue no: **12R 6092**

JERUSALEM
Tracks: / Jerusalem / Target practice / Round round (Available on doublepack only.) / Stand down (Available on doublepack only.).
7" Single: Released '86, on Parlophone, by EMI Records. Catalogue no: **RD 6134**
7" Single: Released '86, on Parlophone, by EMI Records. Catalogue no: **R 6134**
12" Single: Released '86, on Parlophone, by EMI Records. Catalogue no: **12R 6134**

LET IT BE WITH YOU
Tracks: / Let it be with you / Wind of change / Let it be with you (ext dance mix) / Imagination (dance mix) / Some people.
CD 5": Released May '87, on Parlophone, by EMI Records. Deleted Apr '88. Catalogue no: **CDR 6154**
7" Single: Released Apr '87, on Parlophone, by EMI Records. Deleted Oct '87. Catalogue no: **RT 6154**
12" Single: Released Apr '87, on Parlophone, by EMI Records. Deleted Oct '87. Catalogue no: **12R 6154**
7" Single: Released Apr '87, on Parlophone, by EMI Records. Deleted Oct '87. Catalogue no: **R 6154**

LET IT BE WITH YOU (REMIX)
Tracks: / Let it be with you (remix) / Let it be with you (dub) / Wind of change.
12" Single: Released May '87, on EMI, by EMI Records. Deleted Oct '87. Catalogue no: **12 RX 6154**

SOME GIRLS
Tracks: / Some girls / Some girls (extended version) / Some girls (dub) / Imagination / Imagination (can u dig this mix).
7" Single: Released Feb '88, on EMI, by EMI Records. Deleted 31 Jul '88. Catalogue no: **R 6176**
12" Single: Released Feb '88, on EMI, by EMI Records. Deleted Nov '88. Catalogue no: **12R 6176**
CD 5": Released Feb '88, on EMI, by EMI Records. Deleted Nov '88. Catalogue no: **CDR 6176**

SOME PEOPLE (REMIX)
Tracks: / Some people / Walk way.
7" Pic: Released '86, on Parlophone, by EMI Records. Catalogue no: **RP 6130**
7" Single: Released '86, on Parlophone, by EMI Records. Catalogue no: **RX 6130**

SOME PEOPLE (SINGLE)
Tracks: / Some way / Walk away / Have you ever been in love (Live. Available on Double Pack editions only.) / Jerusalem (Live. Available on doublepack only.).
7" Set: Released Jul '85, on Parlophone, by EMI Records. Catalogue no: **12RD 6099**
7" Set: Released '86, on Parlophone, by EMI Records. Catalogue no: **RD 6130**
7" Single: Released '86, on Parlophone, by EMI Records. Catalogue no: **R 6130**
12" Single: Released Jul '85, on Parlophone, by EMI Records. Catalogue no: **12R 6099**
12" Single: Released '86, on Parlophone, by EMI Records. Catalogue no: **12R 6130**
7" Single: Released Jun '85, on Parlophone, by EMI Records. Catalogue no: **R 6099**

TARGET PRACTICE
Tracks: / Target practice.
7" Single: Released Jun '84, on EMI, by EMI Records. Catalogue no: **EMI 5462**
12" Single: Released Jun '84, on EMI, by EMI Records. Deleted '86. Catalogue no: **12EMI 5462**

Some Day Blue

DARK ROOM
Tracks: / Dark room.
7" Single: Released Nov '83, on Raucous, Catalogue no: **RAU 001**

Some Detergents

MODERN PROBLEMS
Tracks: / Modern problems.
7" Single: Released Jun '82, on Out Of Town, Catalogue no: **WIPE 1**

Some Kind Of Wonderful

D'YOU READ MY LETTER
Tracks: / D'you read my letter.
7" Single: Released Sep '82, on Reekus, by Reekus Records. Catalogue no: **RKS 006**

Some Now Are

TRUTH TO TELL
Tracks: / Truth to tell.
7" Single: Released Jan '84, on Interior Music, by Interior Music Records. Catalogue no: **INDEX 3**

Some People

BLUE HEAVEN
Tracks: / Blue heaven / Like the stranger.
7" Single: Released Nov '88, on Breakin', by Breakin' Records. Catalogue no: **7 BRK 6**

Someloves

KNOW YOU NOW
Tracks: / Know you now.
7" Single: Released Feb '89, on WEA (Australia), by WEA Records. Catalogue no: **K 596**

Someone Else

BE MY BABY
Tracks: / Be my baby / I need your love.
7" Single: Released Sep '83, on Stagmanor, by Stagmanor Records. Catalogue no: **STAG 002**

Somerset, Arthur

OK YA
Tracks: / Ok ya.
7" Single: Released Mar '84, on Loose End, by MCA Records. Catalogue no: **LE 111**

Something Blue

WHEN YOU SMILE YOU'RE A DIFFERENT GIRL
Tracks: / When you smile you're a different girl / Shame.
12" Single: Released Oct '88, on Fun After All, by Music For Nations Records. Catalogue no: **12 FAA 112**
7" Single: Released Oct '88, on Fun After All, by Music For Nations Records. Catalogue no: **FAA 112**

Something Happens

BEACH
Tracks: / Beach / Nothing more / Bag of bones (Only on 12").
7" Single: Released 3 Oct '88, on Virgin, by Virgin Records. Catalogue no: **VS 1075**
12" Single: Released 3 Oct '88, on Virgin, by Virgin Records. Deleted '89. Catalogue no: **VST 1075**

BURN CLEAR
Tracks: / Burn clear / Home / Borderline (12" only) / Burn clear (extended version) (12" only).
7" Single: Released Feb '88, on Virgin, by Virgin Records. Catalogue no: **VS 1058**
12" Single: Released Feb '88, on Virgin, by Virgin Records. Catalogue no: **VST 1058**

BURN CLEAR E.P.
Tracks: / Burn clear / Two chances.
7" EP: Released Sep '88, on Cooking Vinyl, by Cooking Vinyl Records. Catalogue no: **WILD 001**

Something Pretty

FREEFALL
Tracks: / Freefall.
12" Single: Released 16 Oct '89, on Creation, by Creation Records. Catalogue no: **CRE 066T**

Son, Joe

DARK SIDE OF TOWN
Tracks: / Dark side of town.
7" Single: Released Oct '84, on Sonet, by Sonet Records. Catalogue no: **SON 2272**

Son Of John

PEOPLE SHOUTING
Tracks: / People shouting / Your interpretation.
7" Single: Released Jul '86, on Individual, by Individual Records. Catalogue no: **AIRS 104**

Son Of Sam

1000 BEATS PER MINUTE
Tracks: / 1000 beats per minute.
12" Single: Released '87, on Rouska, by Rouska Records. Catalogue no: **PROFANE 027**

SONIA - YOU'LL NEVER STOP ME LOVING YOU (Released on Chrysalis)

DANGEROUS AGE FOR A WOMAN, A
Tracks: / Dangerous age for a woman, A / Cain / Fat walks the earth / Woman power.
12" Single: Released Sep '87, on Rouska, by Rouska Records. Catalogue no: **PROFANE 54**

HALLELUJAH GERONIMO
Tracks: / Hallelujah geronimo.
12" Single: Released '88, on Rouska, by Rouska Records. Catalogue no: **PROFANE 72**

Soni

AIN'T HAD ENOUGH LOVE
Tracks: / Ain't had enough Love / Reggae sensation.
12" Single: Released Aug '86, on Chartbound, Catalogue no: **CB 007**

Sonia

HARD TIMES
12" Single: Released Apr '80, on D. Roy, Catalogue no: **DRDD 17**

I CAN'T FORGET YOU
Tracks: / I can't forget you / I can't forget you (instrumental).
12" Single: Released Sep '89, on Chrysalis, by Chrysalis Records. Catalogue no: **CHS 123419**
7" Single: Released Sep '89, on Chrysalis, by Chrysalis Records. Catalogue no: **CHS 3419**

YOU'LL NEVER STOP ME FROM LOVING YOU (see panel above)
Tracks: / You'll never stop me from loving you / You'll never stop me from loving you (version).
Cassingle: Released Jul '89, on Chrysalis, by Chrysalis Records. Catalogue no: **CHSMC 3385**
12" Single: Released Jun '89, on Chrysalis, by Chrysalis Records. Catalogue no: **CHS 123385**
7" Single: Released Jun '89, on Chrysalis, by Chrysalis Records. Catalogue no: **CHS 3385**

Sonic Boom

ANGEL
Tracks: / Angel / Angel (version) / Help me please.
12" Single: Released Oct '89, on Silvertone, Catalogue no: **ORET 11**
CD 5": Released Oct '89, on Silvertone, Catalogue no: **ORECD 11**

Sonic Youth

DEATH VALLEY 69
Tracks: / Death valley 69.
12" Single: Released Jun '85, on Blast First, by Blast First Records. Catalogue no: **BFFP 2**

FLOWER
Tracks: / Flower.
Note: Only Coloured Vinyl
12" Single: Released Jan '86, on Blast First, by Blast First Records. Catalogue no: **BFFP 3**

HALLOWEEN 2 ENGRAVED
Tracks: / Halloween 2 engraved (Limited edition).
12" Single: Released Jul '86, on Blast First, by Blast First Records. Catalogue no: **BFFP 3P**

MASTER DIK
Tracks: / Beat on the brat / Master Dik.
12" Single: on Blast First, by Blast First Records. Catalogue no: **BFFP 12T**

STARPOWER
Tracks: / Starpower / Bubblegum / To your soul (Available on 12" version only).
7" Single: Released Oct '86, on Blast First, by Blast First Records. Catalogue no: **BFFP 7**
12" Single: Released Oct '86, on Blast First, by Blast First Records. Catalogue no: **BFFP 7T**

TOUCH ME I'M SICK
Tracks: / Touch me I'm sick / Halloween.
12" Single: Released 30 Jan '89, on Blast First, by Blast First Records. Catalogue no: **BFFP 46**

Sonny

DON'T STOP
Tracks: / Don't stop.
12" Single: Released May '87, on Chartbound, Catalogue no: **CB 008**

LAUGH AT ME
Tracks: / Laugh at me.
7" Single: Released Aug '65, on Atlantic, by WEA Records. Deleted Aug '68. Catalogue no: **AT 4038**

Sonny & Cher

Biographical details:
Sonny & Cher were a vocal duo -- also man and wife -- who had some of the biggest hits of the mid-60's in America, including the unforgettable *I Got You Babe*, which was No 1 in both America and Britain in 1965. Sonny was born Salvatore Bono in Detroit in 1935; Cher was born Cherylyn La Pierre in 1946 in California. Sonny worked as a producer for R & B labels like Speciality, wrote songs for Larry illiams and others -- he co-wrote the Searchers' big hit *Needles And Pins* with Jack Nitzsche -- and later worked with Phil Spector. Sonny and Cher met in a restaurant and he got her work singing back-up for Spector. The duo, with their hippie image, faded with the advent of progressive rock. Cher went on to success as a solo artist, TV star and highly-praised, Oscar-winning actress. She was briefly married to Gregg Allman. Sonny is now mayor of Palm Springs, California. (Donald Clarke, March 1987.).

ALL I EVER NEED IS YOU
Tracks: / All I ever need is you.
7" Single: Released Jan '72, on MCA, by MCA Records. Deleted Jan '75. Catalogue no: **MU 1145**

BABY DON'T GO
Tracks: / Baby don't go.
7" Single: Released Sep '65, on Reprise, by WEA Records. Deleted Sep '68. Catalogue no: **R 20309**

BEAT GOES ON, THE
Tracks: / Beat goes on, The.
7" Single: Released Feb '67, on Atlantic, by WEA Records. Deleted Feb '70. Catalogue no: **584 078**

BUT YOU'RE MINE
Tracks: / But you're mine.
7" Single: Released Oct '65, on Atlantic, by WEA Records. Deleted Oct '68. Catalogue no: **AT 4047**

HAVE I STAYED TOO LONG
Tracks: / Have I stayed too long.
7" Single: Released Jun '66, on Atlantic, by WEA Records. Deleted Jun '69. Catalogue no: **584 018**

I GOT YOU BABE
Tracks: / I got you babe / What now my love.
7" Single: Released Aug '65, on Atlantic, by WEA Records. Deleted '68. Catalogue no: **AT 4035**

7" Single: Released '80, on Atlantic (Import), by WEA Records. Catalogue no: **LR 8030**
7" Single: Released Sep '85, on Old Gold, by Old Gold Records. Catalogue no: **OG 9523**
7" Single: Released Jul '81, on Atlantic, by WEA Records. Catalogue no: **K 10200**

LITTLE MAN
Tracks: / Little man.
7" Single: Released Sep '66, on Atlantic, by WEA Records. Deleted Sep '69. Catalogue no: **584 040**

LIVING FOR YOU
Tracks: / Living for you.
7" Single: Released Nov '66, on Atlantic, by WEA Records. Deleted Nov '69. Catalogue no: **584 057**

WHAT NOW MY LOVE
Tracks: / What now my love.
7" Single: Released Feb '66, on Atlantic, by WEA Records. Deleted Feb '69. Catalogue no: **AT 4069**

Sons Of Cain

END OF SOMETHING
Tracks: / End of something / Kennedy waltz.
7" Single: Released Jan '82, on Loppylugs, Deleted '87. Catalogue no: **LOPPY 1**

Sons Of Jah

JOHNNY TOO LATE
Tracks: / Johnny too late.
12" Single: Released Nov '82, on Natty Congo, Catalogue no: **NCDM 017**

SAME OLD SONG
Tracks: / Same old song.
12" Single: Released Nov '88, on Natty Congo, Catalogue no: **NCDM 044**

SOMMER LOVE
Tracks: / Sommer love.
12" Single: Released Sep '85, on Natty Congo, Catalogue no: **NCDM 027**

Sons Of Man

IRON LADY
Tracks: / Iron lady.
7" Single: Released Nov '81, on Croydon Music, Catalogue no: **CMCP 01**

Sons Of Shane

FLY
Tracks: / Fly / All I had.
7" Single: Released Jul '87, on Whippet, Catalogue no: **WHIP 1**

Sons Of Valentino

JUST DREAMIN'
Tracks: / Just dreamin' / It's gotta be you / Something about the way

12" Single: Released Oct '89, on One Big Guitar, by One Big Guitar Records. Catalogue no: **OBG 007T**

Sons Of Wonder

FIRE ON ME
Tracks: / Fire on me.
12" Single: Released Oct '84, on Home Boy, Catalogue no: **HOBOT 1**

Soolaimon

RAMAYA
Tracks: / Ramaya / So much more than love.
7" Single: Released Aug '82, on Flair, by Flair Records. Catalogue no: **FLA 103**

Soprano Mystics

TELL ME WHY
Tracks: / Tell me why.
12" Single: Released Jul '83, on Horsemouth, Catalogue no: **HM 003**

Sore Throat

DIGGIN' A DREAM
Tracks: / Diggin' a dream / Stocker stomp.
7" Single: Released Apr '80, on Hurricane (2), Deleted Apr '83. Catalogue no: **FIRE 13**

Sorrows

TAKE A HEART
Tracks: / Take a heart.
7" Single: Released Sep '65, on Piccadilly, Deleted Sep '68. Catalogue no: **7N 35260**

Sorsa, Riki

REGGAE OK
Tracks: / Reggae OK / Autograph.
7" Single: Released Apr '81, on Epic, by CBS Records. Deleted Apr '84. Catalogue no: **EPC A1104**

S.O.S. Band

BORROWED LOVE
Tracks: / Borrowed Love / Do you still want to.
12" Single: Released Jun '86, on Tabu, Catalogue no: **TA 7241**
7" Single: Released Jun '86, on Tabu, Catalogue no: **A 7241**

EVEN WHEN YOU SLEEP
Tracks: / Even when you sleep.
12" Single: Released Nov '86, on Tabu, Catalogue no: **650128 6**

FINEST, THE
Tracks: / Finest, The / I don't want nobody else.
12" Single: Released Mar '86, on Tabu, Catalogue no: **TA 6997**
7" Single: Released Mar '86, on Tabu, Catalogue no: **A 6997**

GROOVIN (THAT'S WHAT WE'RE DOING)
Tracks: / Groovin' (that's what we're doin').
7" Single: Released Feb '83, on Tabu, Catalogue no: **A 3120**
12" Single: Released Feb '83, on Tabu, Catalogue no: **TA 3120**

HIGH HOPES
Tracks: / High hopes / Good and plenty.
7" Single: Released Nov '82, on Tabu, Deleted Nov '85. Catalogue no: **TBU A2936**
12" Single: Released Nov '82, on Tabu, Deleted Nov '85. Catalogue no: **TBU A132936**

JUST BE GOOD TO ME
Tracks: / Just be good to me.
7" Single: Released Apr '84, on Tabu, Deleted Apr '87. Catalogue no: **A 3626**

JUST THE WAY YOU LIKE IT (SINGLE)
Tracks: / Just the way you like it.
7" Set: Released Sep '84, on Tabu, Catalogue no: **DA 4621**
7" Single: Released Aug '84, on Tabu, Catalogue no: **A 4621**
12" Single: Released Aug '84, on Tabu, Catalogue no: **TA 4621**

NO LIES
Tracks: / No lies / Even when you sleep.
7" Single: Released Mar '87, on Tabu, Deleted Aug '87. Catalogue no: **650444 7**

TAKE YOUR TIME (DO IT RIGHT)
Tracks: / Take your time (do it right) / Take your time (do it right) (part 2).
7" Single: Released Jul '80, on Tabu, Deleted Jul '83. Catalogue no: **TBU 8564**

TELL ME YOU STILL CARE
Tracks: / Tell me you still care.
12" Single: Released Jun '84, on Tabu, Catalogue no: **TA 3927**
7" Single: Released Jun '84, on Tabu, Catalogue no: **A 3927**

WEEKEND GIRL
Tracks: / Weekend girl.
7" Single: Released Oct '84, on Tabu, Deleted Oct '87. Catalogue no: **A 4785**

Soskin, Mark

WALK TALL
Tracks: / Walk tall / Colossus.
12" Single: Released Jun '80, on Prestige, Deleted Jun '83. Catalogue no: **PRC 105**

Soso, Winston

I DON'T MIND
Tracks: / I don't mind / Dancing spell.
12" Single: Released Jul '86, on Strayco, Catalogue no: **GS 2774**

Soul

TRIBES
Tracks: / Tribes / Love.
7" Single: Released Jul '81, on Cherry Red, by Cherry Red Records. Deleted '87. Catalogue no: **CHERRY 27**

Soul Affair

ABC
Tracks: / ABC / Sugar daddy.
7" Single: Released Mar '84, on Rooster (Europe), by Rooster Records. Catalogue no: **ROO 106**
12" Single: Released Mar '84, on Rooster (Europe), by Rooster Records. Catalogue no: **12ROO 106**

Soul Asylum

CARTOON
Tracks: / Cartoon / Twiddly dee / Standing in the doorway (Only on the 12" version.).
7" Single: Released Aug '88, on A&M, by A&M Records. Deleted Feb '89. Catalogue no: **AM 463**
12" Single: Released Aug '88, on A&M, by A&M Records. Deleted Feb '89. Catalogue no: **AMY 463**

SOMETIME TO RETURN
Tracks: / Sometime to return / Put the bone in.
Note: "Minneapolis four-piece band Soul Asylum release their debut single "Sometime To Return", taken from their new A&M album "Hang Time"." (A&M Records, June 1988).
12" Single: Released 27 Jun '88, on A&M, by A&M Records. Deleted Feb '89. Catalogue no: **AMY 447**
7" Single: Released 27 Jun '88, on A&M, by A&M Records. Deleted Feb '89. Catalogue no: **AM 447**

Soul Brother Inc.

SKA-SOUL
Tracks: / Ska-soul / Ska-soul (versions).
12" Single: Released Jun '89, on Blue Chip, by Blue Chip Records. Catalogue no: **BLUEC 19**

Soul Brothers

I KEEP RINGING MY BABY
Tracks: / I keep ringing my baby.
7" Single: Released Apr '65, on London-American, Deleted Apr '68. Catalogue no: **F 12116**

Soul Club

I WANT YOUR GUY
Tracks: / I want your guy / I want your guy (dub).
7" Single: Released Feb '87, on Cool Tempo, by Chrysalis Records. Catalogue no: **COOL 135**
12" Single: Released Feb '87, on Cool Tempo, by Chrysalis Records. Catalogue no: **COOLX 135**

Soul Collection

SOUL COLLECTION (EP) Various artists
Tracks: / Oh girl: *Jones, Glenn* / Let me show you: *Jackson, Millie* / Love zone: *Ocean, Billy* / You bring out the best in me: *Armstrong, Vanessa*.
12" Single: Released Mar '88, on Jive, by Zomba Records. Deleted '88. Catalogue no: **JSOUL 2**

Soul, David

DON'T GIVE UP ON US
Tracks: / Don't give up on us.
7" Single: Released Dec '76, on Private Stock, Deleted Dec '79. Catalogue no: **PVT 84**

FOOL FOR LOVE
Tracks: / Fool for love / You're a woman.
7" Single: Released Feb '81, on Energy (USA), by Bulldog Records (USA). Catalogue no: **NRG 004**

GOING IN WITH MY EYES OPEN
Tracks: / Going in with my eyes open.
7" Single: Released Mar '77, on Private Stock, Deleted Mar '80. Catalogue no: **PVT 99**

HOW CAN YOU TELL YOU GOT IT
Tracks: / How can you tell you got it / Simple man.
7" Single: Released May '82, on Energy (USA), by Bulldog Records (USA). Catalogue no: **NRG 005**

I CAN'T AFFORD THAT FEELING ANYMORE
Tracks: / I can't afford that feeling anymore / How can you tell you got it.
7" Single: Released Dec '81, on Philips, by Phonogram Ltd. Catalogue no: **6017 226**

IT SURE BRINGS OUT THE LOVE IN YOUR EYES
Tracks: / It sure brings out the love in your eyes.
7" Single: Released May '78, on Private Stock, Deleted May '81. Catalogue no: **PVT 137**

LET'S HAVE A QUIET NIGHT IN
Tracks: / Let's have a quiet night in.
7" Single: Released Dec '77, on Private Stock, Deleted Dec '80. Catalogue no: **PVT 130**

SILVER LADY
Tracks: / Silver lady.
7" Single: Released Aug '77, on Private Stock, Deleted Aug '80. Catalogue no: **PVT 115**

SURRENDER TO ME
Tracks: / Surrender to me / Piper.
7" Single: Released Mar '80, on Energy (USA), by Bulldog Records (USA). Catalogue no: **NRG 001**

Soul Doctor

SOUL DOCTOR
Tracks: / Soul doctor / Nevermore.
7" Single: Released Jul '87, on Sticky Music, Catalogue no: **GUM 14**

Soul Hunter

MAELSTROM
Tracks: / Maelstrom.
12" Single: Released Mar '87, on Contempo, Catalogue no: **TEMPO 109**

Soul II Soul

BACK TO LIFE
Tracks: / Back to life / Back to the beats / Back to life (version) (Only on 12" version.).
Cassingle: Released 22 May '89, on 10 Records, by Virgin Records. Catalogue no: **TENW 265**
7" Single: Released 22 May '89, on 10 Records, by Virgin Records. Catalogue no: **TEN 265**
12" Single: Released 22 May '89, on 10 Records, by Virgin Records. Catalogue no: **TENX 265**
CD 3": Released 22 May '89, on 10 Records, by Virgin Records. Catalogue no: **TENCD 265**
Cassingle: Released 22 May '89, on 10 Records, by Virgin Records. Catalogue no: **TENC 265**

BACK TO LIFE (IMPORT)
Tracks: / Back to life.
12" Single: Released Oct '89, on Virgin, by Virgin Records. Catalogue no: **965 370**

FAIRPLAY
Tracks: / Fairplay (On TENX 228) / Fairplay (radio mix) (On all versions) / Fairplay (bonus beats) (NOT on TENR 228) / Fairplay (freestyle horns) (On TENR 228 only) / Ambition (rap) (On TENR 228).
12" Single: on 10 Records, by Virgin Records. Catalogue no: **TENR 228**
12" Single: Released May '88, on 10 Records, by Virgin Records. Catalogue no: **TENX 228**
7" Single: Released May '88, on 10 Records, by Virgin Records. Catalogue no: **TEN 228**

FEEL FREE Featuring Do'reen
Tracks: / Feel free (7" version also on CD) / Fairplay (On all versions) / Feel free (extended version) (On CD & 12" only) / Feel free (instrumental) (On CD & 12" only).
12" Single: Released Sep '88, on 10 Records, by Virgin Records. Catalogue no: **TENX 239**
7" Single: Released Sep '88, on 10 Records, by Virgin Records. Catalogue no: **TEN 239**
CD 5": Released '88, on 10 Records, by Virgin Records. Catalogue no: **TENCD 239**

KEEP ON MOVING
Tracks: / Keep on moving.
12" Single: Released 27 Feb '89, on 10 Records, by Virgin Records. Catalogue no: **TENX 263**
CD 3": Released May '89, on 10 Records, by Virgin Records. Catalogue no: **TENRCD 263**
CD 3": Released May '89, on 10 Records, by Virgin Records. Catalogue no: **TENCD 263**
7" Single: Released May '89, on 10 Records, by Virgin Records. Catalogue no: **796 556 0**
7" Single: Released 27 Feb '89, on 10 Records, by Virgin Records. Catalogue no: **TEN 263**
12" Single: Released May '89, on 10 Records, by Virgin Records. Catalogue no: **TENR 263**

Soul, Jimmy

IF YOU WANNA BE HAPPY
Tracks: / If you wanna be happy.
7" Single: Released Jul '63, on Stateside, by EMI Records. Deleted Jul '66. Catalogue no: **SS 178**

Soul, Junior

JOSEPHINE
Tracks: / Josephine.
12" Single: Released Nov '88, on 2M, Catalogue no: **J 6**

MESSAGE FROM MARIA
Tracks: / Message from Maria / Message from Maria (version).
12" Single: Released Jun '87, on Creole, by Creole Records. Catalogue no: **CRT 104**

STORY BOOK CHILDREN
Tracks: / Story book children / Story book children (version).
7" Single: Released Jun '87, on Creole, by Creole Records. Catalogue no: **CR 103**
12" Single: Released Jun '87, on Creole, by Creole Records. Catalogue no: **CRT 103**

Soul Kings

KING OF SOUL
Tracks: / King of soul.
12" Single: Released Apr '84, on Red Rooster, Catalogue no: **HEN 4T**

Soul On Ice

UNDERWATER
Tracks: / Underwater / Splintered lens.
7" Single: Released Jan '82, on Red Rhino, by Red Rhino Records. Deleted '88. Catalogue no: **RED 010**
12" Single: Released Jan '82, on Red Rhino, by Red Rhino Records. Deleted '88. Catalogue no: **REDT 010**

WINDSCREEN
Tracks: / Windscreen / Voice.
7" Single: Released 26 Jun '85, on Red Rhino, by Red Rhino Records. Deleted '88. Catalogue no: **RED 024**

Soul Sisters

SOUL SISTERS EP
7" Single: Released Jul '85, on Chess (PRT), Deleted '88. Catalogue no: **CHES 4009**

Soul Sonic Force

PLANET ROCK
Tracks: / Planet rock.
7" Single: Released Aug '82, on 21 Records, by Polydor Ltd. Catalogue no: **POSP 497**
12" Single: Released Aug '82, on 21 Records, by Polydor Ltd. Catalogue no: **POSPX 497**

Soulside

BASS
Tracks: / Bass / 103.
7" Single: Released Jun '89, on Dischord, by Dischord Records. Catalogue no: **DISCHORD 34**

Soulsister

WAY TO YOUR HEART, THE
Tracks: / Way to your heart (UK version) / Bye bye (7" only.) / Way to your heart (long version) (12" only.) / Way to your heart (instrumental) (12" only.).
CD 5": Released Jul '89, on Columbia, by EMI Records. Catalogue no: **119 239 2**
CD 5": Released Jul '89, on Columbia, by EMI Records. Catalogue no: **CDDB 9175**
7" Single: Released Apr '89, on Columbia, by EMI Records. Catalogue no: **DB 9175**
12" Single: Released Apr '89, on Columbia, by EMI Records. Catalogue no: **12DB 9175**

Sound 9418

IN THE MOOD
Tracks: / In the mood.
7" Single: Released Feb '76, on UK, by UK Records. Deleted Feb '79. Catalogue no: **UK 121**

Sound Asleep

I'M COLD OUTSIDE
Tracks: / I'm cold outside / Kings of the clover green.
7" Single: Released Oct '86, on Vinyl Solution, by Vinyl Solution Records. Catalogue no: **VS 1**

Sound Assassins

GET OUT OF MY HOUSE
Tracks: / Get out of my house.
7" Single: Released Aug '88, on Cool Tempo, by Chrysalis Records. Catalogue no: **COOL 173**
12" Single: Released Aug '88, on Cool Tempo, by Chrysalis Records. Catalogue no: **COOLX 173**

LET ME HEAR YOU SAY PAARTY
Tracks: / Let me hear you say party.
12" Single: Released Mar '89, on Anxious, by Anxious Records. Catalogue no: **NERVT 002**

PAARTY (MAYHEM)
Tracks: / Paarty (mayhem) / Paarty (mayhem) (version).
12" Single: Released Feb '89, on Anxious, by Anxious Records. Catalogue no: **NERVT 2**

Sound (band)

COUNTING THE DAYS (SINGLE)
Tracks: / Counting the days / Dreams then plans.
7" Single: Released May '84, on Statik, Catalogue no: **TAK 16**

HAND OF LOVE
Tracks: / Hand of love.
7" Single: Released 30 May '87, on Play It Again Sam(Belgium), by Play It Again Sam (Belgium). Catalogue no: **BIAS 063**
12" Single: Released 30 May '87, on Play It Again Sam(Belgium), by Play It Again Sam (Belgium). Catalogue no: **BIAS 063T**

HEYDAY
Tracks: / Heyday.
7" Single: Released Sep '80, on Korova, by WEA Records. Catalogue no: **KOW 10**

HOT HOUSE
Tracks: / Hot house / New dark age.
7" Single: Released May '82, on Korova, by WEA Records. Catalogue no: **KOW 23**

IRON YEARS
Tracks: / Iron years.
7" Single: Released 31 Oct '87, on Play It Again Sam(Belgium), by Play It Again Sam (Belgium). Catalogue no: **BIAS 49**
12" Single: Released 31 Oct '87, on Play It Again Sam(Belgium), by Play It Again Sam (Belgium). Catalogue no: **BIAS 49T**

ONE THOUSAND REASONS
Tracks: / One thousand reasons.
7" Single: Released Nov '84, on Statik, Catalogue no: **TAK 28**
12" Single: Released Nov '84, on Statik, Catalogue no: **TAK 28-12**

TEMPERATURE DROP
Tracks: / Temperature drop.
7" Single: Released Jun '85, on Statik, Catalogue no: **TAK H34**

Sound Barrier

FASTEN YOUR SEAT BELT
Tracks: / Fasten your seat belts / Fasten your seat belt.
12" Single: Released Jul '85, on Compact Organisation, Deleted '86. Catalogue no: **ACTX 17**

MORNINGTON CRESCENT
Tracks: / Mornington crescent / Bank holiday.
7" Single: Released Jun '84, on Compact Organisation, Deleted '86. Catalogue no: **ACT 11**

Sound Ceremony

YOU'RE BREAKING MY HEART
Tracks: / You're breaking my heart / Dancing with my shadow.
7" Single: Released Feb '89, on Sound Ceremony, by Sound Ceremony Records. Catalogue no: **SRT 8KF**

Sound Garden

FLOWER
Tracks: / Flower.
CD 5": Released May '89, on SST (USA), by SST Records (USA). Catalogue no: **SSTCD 231**
Cassingle: Released Jul '89, on SST (USA), by SST Records (USA). Catalogue no: **SSTC 231**
12" Single: Released May '89, on SST (USA), by SST Records (USA). Catalogue no: **SST 231**

Sound Iration

KING OF KINGS
Tracks: / King of kings / King of kings (part 2) / Give thanks & praise.
12" Single: Released Sep '89, on Mr.Modo, Catalogue no: **MWS 015T**

SOUND IRATION IN DUB
12" Single: Released Jun '89, on Wau, Catalogue no: **MOWLP 001**

Sound & Motion

SHIPWRECKED
Tracks: / Shipwrecked.
7" Single: Released Oct '86, on GC, Catalogue no: **GC 03**
7" Single: Released Aug '86, on KR, Catalogue no: **KR 2**
12" Single: Released Aug '86, on KR, Catalogue no: **KRT 2**
12" Single: Released Oct '86, on GC, Catalogue no: **GCT 03**

Soundememsion

REAL ROCK
Tracks: / Real rock.
7" Single: Released May '89, on Studio One, Catalogue no: **UNKNOWN**

Sounds Incorporated

SPANISH HARLEM
Tracks: / Spanish harlem.
7" Single: Released Jul '64, on Columbia, by EMI Records. Deleted Jul '67. Catalogue no: **DB 7321**

SPARTANS, THE
Tracks: / Spartans, The.
7" Single: Released Apr '64, on Columbia, by EMI Records. Deleted Apr '67. Catalogue no: **DB 7239**

Sounds Magic

JUST TIME
Tracks: / Just time.
7" Single: Released Sep '83, on Genie, Catalogue no: **GNS 1**

Sounds Nice

LOVE AT FIRST SIGHT (JE T'AIME-MOI NON PLUS)

Tracks: / Love at first sight.
7" Single: Released Sep '69, on Parlophone, by EMI Records. Deleted Sep '72. Catalogue no: **R 5797**

Sounds Orchestral

CAST YOUR FATE TO THE WIND (OLD GOLD)
Tracks: / Cast your fate to the wind.
7" Single: Released Jul '82, on Old Gold, by Old Gold Records. Deleted Jul '88. Catalogue no: **OG 9087**

CAST YOUR FATE TO THE WIND (SINGLE)
Tracks: / Cast your fate to the wind.
7" Single: Released Dec '64, on Piccadilly, Deleted Dec '67. Catalogue no: **7N 35206**

MOONGLOW
Tracks: / Moonglow.
7" Single: Released Jul '65, on Piccadilly, Deleted Jul '68. Catalogue no: **7N 35248**

Soundtrack

CRAZY
Tracks: / Crazy / Freeze frame.
7" Single: Released Jun '82, on Rialto (1), by Rialto Records. Catalogue no: **RIA 9**

GHOST OF LOVE
Tracks: / Ghost of love / Mood I'm in.
7" Single: Released Apr '82, on Rialto (1), by Rialto Records. Catalogue no: **RIA 6**

Soundtracks & Head

RAIN RAIN RAIN
Tracks: / Rain, rain, rain.
12" Single: Released Jun '82, on Rough Trade, by Rough Trade Records. Catalogue no: **RT 104 12**

Soup Dragons

BACKWARDS DOG
Tracks: / Backwards dog.
7" Single: Released Jul '89, on Raw TV Products, Catalogue no: **RTV 006**
12" Single: Released Jul '89, on Raw TV Products, Catalogue no: **RTV 12006**

CAN'T TAKE NO MORE
Tracks: / Can't take no more / Whitewash / Aha experience (*Extra track on 12").
Note: *Aha experience* on 12" only.N
7" Single: Released Jun '87, on Raw TV Products, Catalogue no: **RTV 3**
12" Single: Released Jun '87, on Raw TV Products, Catalogue no: **RTV 123**

HANG-TEN!
Tracks: / Just mind your step girl / Slow things down (Extra track on 12" version only) / Man about town with chairs (Extra track on 12" version only).
7" Single: Released Oct '86, on Raw TV Products, Catalogue no: **RTV 1**
12" Single: Released Oct '86, on Raw TV Products, Catalogue no: **RTV 121**

HEAD GONE ASTRAY
Tracks: / Girl in the world / So sad I feel.
7" Single: Released Jan '87, on Raw TV Products, Catalogue no: **RTV 2**
12" Single: Released Jan '87, on Raw TV Products, Catalogue no: **RTV 122**

KINGDOM CHAIRS
Tracks: / Kingdom chairs / White cruising(live) / Family ways (on 12" only.) / King of the castle(live) (Only on 10" single.) / I am not your stepping stone / All because of you.
10" single: Released Jun '88, on Sire, by Sire Records. Catalogue no: **W 7820 TE**
7" Single: Released Jun '88, on Sire, by Sire Records. Catalogue no: **W 7820**
12" Single: Released Jun '88, on Sire, by Sire Records. Catalogue no: **W 7820 T**

MAJESTIC HEAD
Tracks: / Majestic head.
7" Pic: Released 5 Mar '88, on Raw, Catalogue no: **RTV 5P**
7" Single: Released 5 Mar '88, on Raw, Catalogue no: **RTV 5**
12" Single: Released 5 Mar '88, on Raw, Catalogue no: **RTV 125**

MOTHER UNIVERSE
Tracks: / Mother Universe / Backwards dog / Crotch deep trash.
7" Single: Released Jul '89, on Raw TV Products, Catalogue no: **RTV 007**
12" Single: Released Jul '89, on Raw TV Products, Catalogue no: **RTV 12 007R**
12" Single: Released Jul '89, on Raw TV Products, Catalogue no: **RTV 12 007**

SOFT AS YOUR FACE
Tracks: / Soft as your face / It's always autumn.
Note: 12" includes * limited edition double groove incl Can't Take No More/Whole Wide World (live)
7" Single: Released Aug '87, on Raw TV Products, Catalogue no: **RTV 4**
12" Single: Released Aug '87, on Raw TV Products, Catalogue no: **RTV 124**
12" Single: Released Aug '87, on Raw TV Products, Catalogue no: **RTV 124D***

SUN IS IN THE SKY EP
Tracks: / Sun is in the sky.
7" Single: Released Feb '86, on Subway, by Subway Records. Catalogue no: **SUBWAY 2**

WHOLE WIDE WORLD
Tracks: / I know everything / Pleasantly surprised / Whole wide world.
7" Single: Released May '86, on Subway Organisation, Catalogue no: **SUBWAY 004**
12" Single: Released May '86, on Subway Organisation, Catalogue no: **SUBWAY 004T**

South, April

CHAINS THAT BIND ME
Tracks: / Chains that bind me / You want to rock.
7" Single: Released Jan '83, on President, by President Records. Catalogue no: **PT 513**

HEROES OF THE NIGHT
Tracks: / Heroes of the night / Boys are out....
7" Single: Released Apr '82, on President, by President Records. Catalogue no: **PT 501**

South Bank Orchestra

DEMPSEY & MAKEPEACE
Tracks: / Dempsey & Makepeace.
7" Single: Released Jan '85, on Sierra, by Sierra Records. Catalogue no: **FED 9**

South Coast Ska Stars

SOUTH COAST RUMBLE
Tracks: / South coast rumble / Head on.
7" Single: Released Apr '80, on Safari, by Safari Records. Catalogue no: **SAFE 27**

South, Joe

GAMES PEOPLE PLAY (OLD GOLD)
Tracks: / Games people play / Rock me gently.
Note: Also contains:"Rock me gently" by Andy Kim
7" Single: Released Apr '87, on Old Gold, by Old Gold Records. Deleted Sep '89. Catalogue no: **OG 9717**

GAMES PEOPLE PLAY (SINGLE)
Tracks: / Games people play.
7" Single: Released Mar '69, on Capitol, by EMI Records. Deleted Mar '72. Catalogue no: **CL 15579**

South Rebels

ROCKIN' DADDY EP
7" Single: Released Feb '80, on Red Hot, by Beserkley Records (USA). Deleted '83. Catalogue no: **REP 1003**

Southern Death Cult

FAT MAN
Tracks: / Fat man / Moya.
7" Single: Released Dec '82, on Situation 2, by Beggars Banquet Records. Catalogue no: **SIT 19**
12" Single: Released Dec '82, on Situation 2, by Beggars Banquet Records. Catalogue no: **SIT 19T**

Southern, Jeri

Biographical details: Born Genevieve Hering in Nebraska in 1926, Southern was an exceptionally fine cabaret singer even more popular in Britain than America: her 1952 version of *When I Fall In Love* sold better here than the huge US Doris Day hit. Southern quit in the early 60's to teach singing. (Donald Clarke, March 1987.).

FIRE DOWN BELOW
Tracks: / Fire down below.
7" Single: Released Jun '57, on Brunswick, by Decca Records. Deleted Jun '60. Catalogue no: **05665**

Southern, Sheila

WHITE WEDDING Sheila Southern with various artists
Tracks: / White wedding / Good luck, good health, God bless you.
7" Single: Released May '81, on EMI, by EMI Records. Catalogue no: **MIEP 4001**

Southforks

NOBODY EVER DIES IN DALLAS
Tracks: / I'm sorry now / Nobody ever dies in Dallas.
7" Single: Released Dec '86, on Keyhole, by Orbitone Records. Catalogue no: **KOLE 001**

Southlanders

ALONE
Tracks: / Alone.
7" Single: Released Nov '57, on London-American, Deleted Nov '60. Catalogue no: **F 10946**

Southroad Connection

TAKE ME BACK FOR MORE
Tracks: / Take me back for more / I need to love you.
7" Single: Released Apr '80, on Liberty (USA), by EMI Records. Deleted Apr '83. Catalogue no: **12 UP 623**

Southside Johnny

AIN'T THAT PECULIAR
Tracks: / Ain't that peculiar / Act of love / Take my love (Only on CD single.) / On the air tonight (Only on CD single.).
CD 5": Released 22 May '89, on RCA, by BMG Records (UK). Catalogue no: **PD 42844**
7" Single: Released 15 May '89, on RCA, by BMG Records (UK). Catalogue no: **PB 42843**
12" Single: Released 15 May '89, on RCA, by BMG Records (UK). Catalogue no: **PT 42844**

ALL I WANT IS EVERYTHING
Tracks: / All I want is everything.
7" Single: Released Jul '81, on Mercury (USA), by PolyGram Rec.Inc.(USA). Catalogue no: **6170 147**

EXPRESSWAY TO YOUR HEART
Tracks: / Expressway to your heart / Evil.
7" Single: Released Feb '88, on Sonet, by Sonet Records. Catalogue no: **SON 2336**

HARD TO FIND
Tracks: / You can count on me / I should have said I loved you / Hard to find.
12" Single: Released Jan '87, on RCA, by BMG Records (UK). Catalogue no: **SSJT 100**

ON THE AIR TONIGHT
Tracks: / On the air tonight / Walking through midnight / Tell me (Only on CD single and 12".).
CD 5": Released Feb '89, on RCA, by BMG Records (UK). Deleted Jul '89. Catalogue no: **PD 42618**
7" Single: Released Feb '89, on RCA, by BMG Records (UK). Catalogue no: **PB 42617**
12" Single: Released Feb '89, on RCA, by BMG Records (UK). Catalogue no: **PT 42618**

TELL ME That our love's still strong
Tracks: / Tell me / I only want to be with you.
7" Single: Released May '87, on RCA, by BMG Records (UK). Deleted '87. Catalogue no: **SSJ 200**
7" Single: on RCA, by BMG Records (UK). Deleted '87. Catalogue no: **SSJT 200**

WALK AWAY RENEE
Tracks: / I can't wait / Walk away Renee.
12" Single: Released Jun '86, on RCA, by BMG Records (UK). Catalogue no: **PT 40766**
7" Single: Released Jun '86, on RCA, by BMG Records (UK). Catalogue no: **PB 40765**

YOU CAN COUNT ON ME
Tracks: / Till the end of the night / I should have said I love you (Extra track on 12" version only) / You can count on me.
7" Single: Released Oct '86, on RCA, by BMG Records (UK). Catalogue no: **PB 40915**
12" Single: Released Oct '86, on RCA, by BMG Records (UK). Catalogue no: **PT 40915**

Sovereign

ALIENS
Tracks: / Aliens / Time out.
7" Single: Released Nov '88, on Tabitha, by Tabitha Records. Catalogue no: **TAB 7**

Sovereign Collection

MOZART 40
Tracks: / Mozart 40.
7" Single: Released Apr '71, on Capitol, by EMI Records. Deleted Apr '74. Catalogue no: **CL 15676**

Soviet France

O.K. BOYS
Tracks: / O.K. boys.
12" Single: Released 27 Jun '85, on Red Rhino, by Red Rhino Records. Catalogue no: **REDT 012**

RITUAL
Tracks: / Ritual / Mudbast boys / Sem boys / Bring Hessa / Mounw.
12" Single: Released '82, on Red Rhino, by Red Rhino Records. Catalogue no: **RED 12**

Sovine, Red

Biographical details: Country singer Sovine was born Woodrow Wilson Sovine in 1918 and died in 1980. He was a popular regular on the *Grand Ole Opry* for many years before hitting stardom with truck-driving songs, beginning with *Giddyup Go* in '63. *Phantom 309* is the ultimate truck-drivin' ghost story and *Teddy Bear* scored in country, pop and British charts. (Donald Clarke, March 1987.).

GIDDY UP GO (SINGLE)
Tracks: / Giddy up go.
7" Single: Released Sep '81, on Starday (USA), by Gusto Records (USA). Catalogue no: **SD 177**

TEDDY BEAR
Tracks: / Teddy bear.
7" Single: Released Jun '81, on Starday (USA), by Gusto Records (USA). Deleted Jun '84. Catalogue no: **SD 142**

Sowell Radics

CAUTION
Tracks: / Caution / Bali-hi special.
12" Single: Released Jan '81, on Attack, Deleted '88. Catalogue no: **TACK 24**

FIGHT, FIGHT, FIGHT
Tracks: / Fight, fight, fight / Aces rock.
12" Single: Released Apr '81, on Attack, Deleted '88. Catalogue no: **TACK 27**

GIVE ME YOUR LOVE
Tracks: / Give me your love.
12" Single: Released Oct '82, on DATC, Catalogue no: **DATC 011**

LOVE IS WHAT SHE WANTS
Tracks: / Love is what she wants.
12" Single: Released Apr '82, on Big Youth, Catalogue no: **BYD 001**

WHEEL O MITILDA
Tracks: / Wheel o'Mitilda / Rub this ya one ya.
12" Single: Released Dec '81, on Solid Groove, Catalogue no: **SG 15**

WILD STYLE
Tracks: / Wild style.
12" Single: Released Jul '82, on Regal, Catalogue no: **RD 004**

Soxx, Bob B.

ZIP A DEE DOO DAH
Tracks: / Zip a dee doo dah.
7" Single: Released Jan '63, on London-American, Deleted Jan '66. Catalogue no: **HLU 9646**

SP Band

DON'T SAY IT
Tracks: / Because of heaven / Don't say it.
7" Single: Released Mar '86, on Bond, Catalogue no: **STAGE 1**

Space

FRAULEIN
Tracks: / Fraulein / Blueberry blue.
7" Single: Released Oct '80, on Young Blood, by Young Blood Records. Deleted Oct '83. Catalogue no: **YB 100**

MAGIC FLY
Tracks: / Magic fly.
7" Single: Released Aug '77, on Pye International, Deleted Aug '80. Catalogue no: **7N 25746**
7" Single: Released Feb '85, on Record Shack, by Record Shack Records. Catalogue no: **RMX 1**
12" Single: Released Feb '85, on Record Shack, by Record Shack Records. Catalogue no: **REMIX 1**

ON THE AIR
Tracks: / On the air
7" Single: Released Apr '80, on Pye, Deleted Apr '83. Catalogue no: **7P5015**

TENDER FORCE
Tracks: / Tender force / Robots.
7" Single: Released Apr '8, on Piccadilly, Deleted '85. Catalogue no: **7P 5018**

Space Children

LET'S GO DISCO
Tracks: / Let's go disco.
12" Single: Released Oct '88, on Sweatbox, by Sweatbox Records. Catalogue no: **SOX 038**

Space Monkey

CAN'T STOP RUNNING
Tracks: / Can't stop running.
7" Single: Released Sep '83, on Inner Vision, Catalogue no: **A 3742**
12" Single: Released Sep '83, on Inner Vision, Catalogue no: **TA 3742**

COME WITH ME
Tracks: / Come with me.
7" Single: Released Sep '84, on Inner Vision, Deleted '86. Catalogue no: **IVS 5**
12" Single: Released Sep '84, on Inner Vision, Deleted '86. Catalogue no: **IVST 5**

ONE MORE SHOT
Tracks: / One more shot.
7" Single: Released Aug '85, on Inner Vision, Catalogue no: **IVS 7**
12" Single: Released Aug '85, on Inner Vision, Catalogue no: **IVST 7**

Spacek, Sissy

COAL MINER'S DAUGHTER
Tracks: / Coal miner's daughter / I'm a honky tonk girl.
7" Single: Released Feb '81, on MCA, by MCA Records. Deleted Feb '84. Catalogue no: **MCA 674**

Spacelings

GROUNDED (SINGLE)
Tracks: / Grounded.
12" Single: Released Apr '89, on Medicine, Catalogue no: **MED 007**

LAST NIGHT I HAD THE STRANGEST DREAM
Tracks: / Last night I had the strangest dream.
7" Single: Released Nov '85, on Wise-Z, Deleted Nov '87. Catalogue no: **SPACE 1**

Spacemen 3

HYPNOTIZED
Tracks: / Hypnotized / Just to see you smile honey (part 2).
CD 5": Released Jul '89, on Fire, by Fire Records. Catalogue no: **BLAZE 36CD**
7" Single: Released Jul '89, on Fire, by Fire Records. Catalogue no: **BLAZE 36**
12" Single: Released Jul '89, on Fire, by Fire Records. Catalogue no: **BLAZE 36T**

REVOLUTION
Tracks: / Revolution.
CD 5": Released Nov '88, on Fire, by Fire Records. Catalogue no: **BLAZE 29CD**
7" Single: Released Nov '88, on Fire, by Fire Records. Catalogue no: **BLAZE 29T**
12" Single: Released Nov '88, on Fire, by Fire Records. Catalogue no: **BLAZE 29**

TAKE ME TO THE OTHER SIDE
Tracks: / Take me to the other side.
7" Single: Released Nov '87, on Glass, by Glass Records. Catalogue no: **GLASS 054**
12" Single: Released Nov '87, Deleted '88. Catalogue no: **GLASS 12054**

WALKING WITH JESUS
Tracks: / Walking with Jesus.
12" Single: Released Jul '87, on Glass, by Glass Records. Deleted Jan '89. Catalogue no: **GLAEP 105**

Spacewalkers

CAPTAIN ZEP
Tracks: / Captain Zep / Race against time.
7" Single: Released Jan '83, on BBC, by BBC Records & Tapes. Deleted '87. Catalogue no: **RESL 127**

Spagna

CALL ME
Tracks: / Call me / Girl , it's not the end of the world / Easy lady (Extra track on 12").
7" Single: Released May '87, on CBS, by CBS Records. Catalogue no: **650279 7**
12" Single: Released May '87, on CBS, by CBS Records. Catalogue no: **650279 6**

CALL ME (VIVA MIX)
Tracks: / Call me (viva mix).
12" Single: Released Aug '87, on CBS, by CBS Records. Catalogue no: **650279 8**

EASY LADY

SPANDAU BALLET - MUSCLE BOUND (Released on Chrysalis)

Tracks: / Jealousy / Easy lady / Dance, dance, dance / Jealousy.
7" Single: Released Sep '87, on CBS, by CBS Records. Catalogue no: **651169 7**
7" Single: Released Oct '86, on CBS, by CBS Records. Catalogue no: **A 7019**
12" Single: Released Oct '87, on CBS, by CBS Records. Catalogue no: **651169 6**
12" Single: Released Oct '86, on CBS, by CBS Records. Catalogue no: **TA 7019**

EVERY GIRL AND BOY
Tracks: / Every girl and boy.
Note: * Only available on the 12" version.
7" Single: Released Aug '88, on CBS, by CBS Records. Deleted 17 Apr '89. Catalogue no: **SPAG 1**
12" Single: Released Aug '88, on CBS, by CBS Records. Deleted 17 Apr '89. Catalogue no: **SPAGT 1**

EVERY GIRL AND BOY (SPECIAL BANGBANG REMIX)
Tracks: / Every girl and boy (special bangbang remix) / Every girl and boy / Don't call it love.
7" Single: Released 22 Aug '88, on CBS, by CBS Records. Deleted 17 Apr '89. Catalogue no: **SPAG QT1**

I WANNA BE YOUR WIFE
Tracks: / I want to be your wife / Woman in love / Sarah (Only on 12".) / I want to be your wife (extended version) (Only on CD single and 10" version.) / Every girl and boy (special bangbang remix) (Only on 10" version.) / So easy (Only on 10" version.).
CD 5": Released Oct '88, on CBS, by CBS Records. Deleted 10 Jul '89. Catalogue no: **CD SPAG 2**
10" single: Released Nov '88, on CBS, by CBS Records. Catalogue no: **SPAGQT 2**
7" Single: Released Oct '88, on CBS, by CBS Records. Deleted 10 Jul '89. Catalogue no: **SPAG 2**
12" Single: on CBS, by CBS Records. Deleted 10 Jul '89. Catalogue no: **SPAG Q2**
12" Single: Released Oct '88, on CBS, by CBS Records. Deleted 10 Jul '89. Catalogue no: **SPAG T2**

Spana Bana

LIFE GOES ON
Tracks: / Life goes on.
12" Single: Released Oct '89, on Techniques, Catalogue no: **WRT 58**

Spandau Ballet

Biographical details: British pop group Spandau Ballet were formed in 1979 by guitarist-songwriter Gary Kemp, with singer Tony Hadley, Steve Norman on rhythm guitar, Kemp's brother Martin on bass and drummer John Keeble. They signed with Chrysalis who gave them their own Reformation label. Their early hits were electro-funk experiments and they pioneered different mixes for 7in and 12in singles, a practice taken from black music. Later they turned to more commercial pop. (Donald Clarke, March 1987.)
Spandau Ballet made their first live performance in London in November 1979 in a private rehearsal room on a Saturday morning in front of an audience of the group's friends, young musicians and scenemakers.

SPANDAU BALLET - TRUE (Released on Chrysalis)

The nucleus of a new explosion of pop culture which came from the scene originally centred on Soho's fashion concious clubs, Blitz, Billy's, Hell and St Moritz. Here the customers expressed themselves by their clothes which changed exotically week by week, and danced to a selection of obscure imports and old records which fitted the musical requirements of a soundtrack to a scene which shone out in the drab world of post-punk. Spandau Ballet were the first group formed to make music specifically for the scene, as their five young members from central London were part of it, and reflected their audience like a mirror in their attitude and appearance. They went on to make appearances at events organised outside of the mainstream rock circuit, including the first appearance the group made at Steve Strange's Blitz club and to all of which increasing amounts of like minded people were attracted by word of mouth. Media interest in the group and the sub-culture surrounding them grew, and a late night performance at the scala cinema was filmed as part of a TV documentary on the whole scene. This interest in the group climaxed reaching the national press, with a performace on HMS Belfast, a battle ship moored on the thames opposite the Tower Of London, which was very much inkeeping with the groups developing policy of making every appearance an event, rather than just another boring rock gig. A major recording and label deal followed for the group's own Reformation label, with Chrysalis Records. Their first single *To cut a long story short* was a large and immediate hit, proving there was a nationwide demand for a group like Spandau. Also both *To cut a long story short* and *The freeze*, the groups second single, were available in highly successful extended remixed versions, specially for the dance floor, an innovation for a white group at the time. At the same time, the whole scene surrounding the group exploded - it's visuals to influence mainstream fashion, it's club format to be duplicated country wide into hundreds of style concious modern dance clubs, and countless groups of similar like inspired to make their own versions of the 'new dance music'. The group's first album *Journey's to glory* was released and went gold and top five in the UK very fast. The next single, a European folk chant *Musclebound* was backed with a fast funk song *Glow*, which was the first radical change of direction by the group into a more funk based feel on their dance numbers. This was to be fully realised in the summer of 1981 by the recording, release and subsequent number one status of *Chant No. 1*. On this number the group enlisted the help of a young black London horn section, Beggar and Co, to produce a funk hybrid which has since been repeated extensively by dozens of groups, and a single which was a club hit all over the world. In the USA *Chant No.1* was the first British record to be played widely on previously black dance radio. The group's live stateside debut in New York's Underground club combined uniquely with a fashion show by Axiom, a group of young London clothes designers, attracted a huge media response. During this period, as well as changing musically, Spandau Ballet were continually changing visually. The group's second album *Diamond* certainly confused the critics, and was itself split into two distinctive parts. The first side opened with *Chant No. 1* and continued in the same vein of funky hybrid of synthesisers and horns and was very much the side to dance to. The second side saw the group experiment with a variety of oriental instruments like chengs and tablas on four songs, more for listening than dancing to. Then *True*, recorded in Autumn '82 at the Compass Point studios in Nassau with the title track topping the British charts for four weeks and appearances at three of London's prestigious venues. Spandau Ballet consist of Tony Hadley (lead vocals), Gary Kemp (guitar and backing vocals), Martin Kemp (bass), Steve Norman (sax and percussion) and John Keeble (drums). (February 1984).

BE FREE WITH YOUR LOVE
Tracks: / Be free with your love / Be free with your love (dance mix edit) (On 7" & CD single.) / Be free with your love (extended dance mix) (On 12" only.) / Be free with your love (dub mix) (On 12" only.) / Be free with your love (extended 12" mix) (On CD single.) / Through the barricades (On pic CD single only.).
CD 5": Released 14 Aug '89, on CBS, by CBS Records. Catalogue no: **SPANS C4**
CD 5": Released 21 Aug '89, on CBS, by CBS Records. Catalogue no: **SPANS P4**
Cassingle: Released 21 Aug '89, on CBS, by CBS Records. Catalogue no: **SPANS M4**
7" Single: Released 14 Aug '89, on CBS, by CBS Records. Catalogue no: **SPANS 4**
12" Single: Released 14 Aug '89, on CBS, by CBS Records. Catalogue no: **SPANS T4**

CHANT NO.1 (I DON'T NEED THIS PRESSURE) (see panel on next page)
Tracks: / Chant no.1 (I don't need this pressure) / Feel the chant.
7" Single: Released Jul '81, on Reformation, by Chrysalis Records. Catalogue no: **CHS 2528**
12" Single: Released Jul '81, on Reformation, by Chrysalis Records. Catalogue no: **CHS 12 2528**

COMMUNICATION
Tracks: / Communication / Lifeline (B side of 12") / Communication (edited club mix) (B side of 7") / Communication (club mix) (Only on the 12" version.).
7" Single: Released '83, on Chrysalis, by Chrysalis Records. Catalogue no: **CHS 2668**
12" Single: Released '83, on Chrysalis, by Chrysalis Records. Catalogue no: **CHS 12 2668**

COMMUNICATION (OLD GOLD)
Tracks: / Communication.
12" Single: Released Jan '88, on Old Gold, by Old Gold Records. Catalogue no: **OG 4037**

FIGHT FOR OURSELVES
Tracks: / Fight for ourselves / Fight for the heartache.
7" Single: Released Jul '86, on CBS, by CBS Records. Catalogue no: **QTA 7264**

SPANDAU BALLET - CHANT No. 1 (Released on Chrysalis)

12" Single: Released Jul '86, on CBS, by CBS Records. Catalogue no: **QA 7264**

FREEZE, THE
Tracks: / Freeze, The / Freeze, The (version) / Freeze, The (special mix) (Only on 12" version.).
7" Single: Released Jan '81, on Chrysalis, by Chrysalis Records. Deleted '86. Catalogue no: **CHS 2486**
12" Single: Released '80, on Chrysalis, by Chrysalis Records. Catalogue no: **CHS 12 2486**

GLOW
Tracks: / Glow / To cut a long story short / Freeze.
7" EP: Released May '81, on Chrysalis, by Chrysalis Records. Deleted May '84. Catalogue no: **ZCHS 2509**

GOLD
Tracks: / Gold / Gold (instrumental).
7" Single: Released Aug '83, on Chrysalis, by Chrysalis Records. Catalogue no: **SPAN 2**
12" Single: Released Aug '83, on Chrysalis, by Chrysalis Records. Catalogue no: **SPANX 2**

HIGHLY STRUNG
Tracks: / Highly strung.
7" Single: Released Oct '84, on Reformation, by Chrysalis Records. Deleted Oct '87. Catalogue no: **SPAN 5**

HOW MANY LIES?
Tracks: / How many lies.
7" Single: Released Jan '87, on Reformation, by Chrysalis Records. Deleted Aug '87. Catalogue no: **SPANDS 2**
12" Single: Released Jan '87, on Reformation, by Chrysalis Records. Deleted Aug '87. Catalogue no: **SPANDS T2**

I'LL FLY FOR YOU
Tracks: / I'll fly for you / To cut a long story short.
7" Single: Released Aug '84, on Reformation, by Chrysalis Records. Catalogue no: **SPAN 4**
12" Single: Released Aug '84, on Reformation, by Chrysalis Records. Catalogue no: **SPANX 4**

INSTINCTION
Tracks: / Instinction / Gently / Chant no.1 (I don't need this pressure) (remix) (Only on 12" version.).
7" Single: Released Apr '82, on Chrysalis, by Chrysalis Records. Catalogue no: **CHS 2602**
12" Single: Released Apr '82, on Chrysalis, by Chrysalis Records. Catalogue no: **CHS 12 2602**

LIFELINE
Tracks: / Lifeline.
7" Single: Released '83, on Chrysalis, by Chrysalis Records. Catalogue no: **CHS 2642**
12" Single: Released '83, on Chrysalis, by Chrysalis Records. Catalogue no: **CHS 12 2642**

MUSCLEBOUND (see panel on previous page)
Tracks: / Musclebound / Glow.
7" Single: Released Apr '81, on Chrysalis, by Chrysalis Records. Deleted '86. Catalogue no: **CHS 2509**
12" Single: Released '81, on Chrysalis, by Chrysalis Records. Catalogue no: **CHS 12 2509**

ONLY WHEN YOU LEAVE
Tracks: / Only when you leave.
7" Single: Released Jun '84, on Reformation, by Chrysalis Records. Deleted Jun '87. Catalogue no: **SPAN 3**
12" Single: Released '83, on Chrysalis, by Chrysalis Records. Catalogue no: **SPANX 3**

PAINT ME DOWN
Tracks: / Paint me down / Man with guitar / Repaint (Only on 12" version.).
7" Single: Released Nov '81, on Chrysalis, by Chrysalis Records. Catalogue no: **CHS 2560**
12" Single: Released Nov '81, on Chrysalis, by Chrysalis Records. Catalogue no: **CHS 12 2560**

RAW
Tracks: / Raw / Raw (flip) / Raw (extended mix) (12" & CD only) / Raw (amnesia mix) (pic CD only).
CD 5": Released Aug '88, on CBS, by CBS Records. Deleted 17 Apr '89. Catalogue no: **SPANS D3**
CD 5": Released 22 Aug '88, on CBS, by CBS Records. Deleted 17 Apr '89. Catalogue no: **SPANS C3**
7" Single: Released 22 Aug '88, on CBS, by CBS Records. Deleted 17 Apr '89. Catalogue no: **SPANS 3**
7" Single: Released Aug '88, on CBS, by CBS Records. Deleted 17 Apr '89. Catalogue no: **SPANS P3**
12" Single: Released 22 Aug '88, on CBS, by CBS Records. Deleted 17 Apr '89. Catalogue no: **SPANS T3**
12" Single: Released Aug '88, on CBS, by CBS Records. Deleted 17 Apr '89. Catalogue no: **SPANS Q3**

ROUND AND ROUND
Tracks: / Round and round.
7" Single: Released Dec '84, on Reformation, by Chrysalis Records. Deleted Dec '87. Catalogue no: **SPAN 6**

SHE LOVED LIKE DIAMOND
Tracks: / She loved like diamond / She loved like diamond (instrumental).
7" Single: Released Jan '82, on Chrysalis, by Chrysalis Records. Deleted '87. Catalogue no: **CHS 2585**
12" Single: Released '82, on Chrysalis, by Chrysalis Records. Catalogue no: **CHS 12 2585**

THROUGH THE BARRICADES (SINGLE)
Tracks: / Through the barricades.
7" Single: Released Oct '86, on Reformation, by Chrysalis Records. Catalogue no: **SPANDS 1**
12" Single: Released Oct '86, on Reformation, by Chrysalis Records. Catalogue no: **SPANDS T1**

TO CUT A LONG STORY SHORT (see panel)
Tracks: / To cut a long story short / To cut a long story short (inst).
7" Single: Released Nov '80, on Chrysalis, by Chrysalis Records. Catalogue no: **CHS 2473**
12" Single: Released Dec '81, on Chrysalis, by Chrysalis Records. Catalogue no: **CHS 12 2473**

TO CUT A LONG STORY SHORT (OLD GOLD)
Tracks: / Chant no.1 (I don't need this pressure on) / To cut a long story short.
7" Single: Released Feb '87, on Chrysalis, by Chrysalis Records. Catalogue no: **OG 9677**

TRUE (OLD GOLD)
Tracks: / True / Gold.
7" Single: Released Feb '87, on Old Gold, by Old Gold Records. Catalogue no: **OG 9679**

TRUE (SINGLE) (see panel on previous page)
Tracks: / True / Lifeline (remix).
7" Single: Released '83, on Reformation, by Chrysalis Records. Catalogue no: **SPAN 1**
12" Single: Released '83, on Chrysalis, by Chrysalis Records. Catalogue no: **SPANX 1**

Spangs

FRIGHTENED OF THE NIGHT
Tracks: / Frightened of the night / Safe in my room.
7" Single: Released Mar '81, on RCA, by BMG Records (UK). Deleted Mar '84. Catalogue no: **RCA 47**

WHO INVITED YOU ANYWAY
Tracks: / Who invited you anyway / Duo tones.
7" Single: Released Jun '81, on RCA, by BMG Records (UK). Deleted Jun '84. Catalogue no: **RCA 90**

Spanish Prince

MARIA
Tracks: / Maria / Dance everybody dance.
7" Single: Released Oct '87, on 4th & Broadway, by Island Records. Deleted Apr '88. Catalogue no: **BRW 75**
12" Single: Released Oct '87, on 4th & Broadway, by Island Records. Deleted Jun '88. Catalogue no: **12 BRW 75**

Spank

OH BABY
7" Single: Released Apr '85, on Champion, by Champion Records. Deleted Jul '89. Catalogue no: **CHAMP 1**
12" Single: Released Apr '85, on Champion, by Champion Records. Deleted Aug '89. Catalogue no: **CHAMP 121**

Spanner, Mr.

WORLD CUP FOOTBALL
Tracks: / World cup football.
12" Single: Released Feb '88, on Uptempo, Catalogue no: **TEMP 021**

Spanner, Ranking

SOME SEE THE THRILL
Tracks: / Some see the thrill (Inst).
12" Single: Released Nov '86, on Stop'n'Rock, Catalogue no: **SNRIT 002**

Spanos, Danny

EXCUSE ME
Tracks: / Excuse me.
7" Single: Released Jan '84, on Epic, by CBS Records. Catalogue no: **A 3770**
12" Single: Released Jan '84, on Epic, by CBS Records. Catalogue no: **TA 3770**

Spargo

YOU AND ME
Tracks: / You and me / Worry.
7" Single: Released May '90, on Pye, Deleted '85. Catalogue no: **7P 5017**
7" Single: Released Jun '81, on Champagne (DJM), Catalogue no: **FIZZ 101**
12" Single: Released Jun '81, on Champagne (DJM), Catalogue no: **FIZY 1001**

Sparkes, Trevor

ROSES ARE RED
Tracks: / Roses are red.
12" Single: Released Jan '89, on Blue Trac, by Blue Trac Records. Catalogue no: **BTRD 030**

Sparkle

SO INSPIRED
Tracks: / So inspired.
7" Single: Released Oct '88, on Total Experience, Catalogue no: **TOTE 2**
12" Single: Released Oct '88, on Total Experience, Catalogue no: **TOTEX 2**

Sparklers

MERRY GO ROUND
Tracks: / Merry go round.
7" Single: Released Nov '88, on Mighty Boy, by Mighty Boy Records. Catalogue no: **MB 20057**

Sparks

AMATEUR HOUR
Tracks: / Amateur hour.
7" Single: Released Jul '74, on Island, by Island Records. Deleted Jul '77. Catalogue no: **WIP 6203**

BEAT THE CLOCK
Tracks: / Beat the clock.
7" Single: Released Jul '79, on Virgin, by Virgin Records. Deleted Jul '82. Catalogue no: **VS 270**

CHANGE
Tracks: / Change.
7" Single: Released Jul '85, on London Records, by London Records. Catalogue no: **LON 69**
12" Single: Released Jul '85, on London Records, by London Records. Catalogue no: **LONX 69**

COOL PLACES
Tracks: / Cool places / Sports.
7" Single: Released Jun '83, on Atlantic, by WEA Records. Catalogue no: **A 9866**

FUNNY FACES
Tracks: / Funny faces.
7" Single: Released Sep '81, on Why-Fi, by Why-Fi Records. Catalogue no: **WHY 4**

GET IN THE SWING
Tracks: / Get in the swing.

SPANDAU BALLET - TO CUT A LONG STORY (Released on Chrysalis)

7" Single: Released Jul '75, on Island, by Island Records. Deleted Jul '78. Catalogue no: **WIP 6236**

I PREDICT
Tracks: / I predict / Moustache.
7" Single: Released Jun '82, on Atlantic, by WEA Records. Catalogue no: **K 11740**

LOOKS LOOKS LOOKS
Tracks: / Looks looks looks.
7" Single: Released Oct '75, on Island, by Island Records. Deleted Oct '78. Catalogue no: **WIP 6249**

MUSIC THAT YOU CAN DANCE TO
7" Single: Released Nov '86, on Consolidated Allied, Catalogue no: **TOON 2**
12" Single: Released Nov '86, on Consolidated Allied, Catalogue no: **TOONT 2**

NEVER TURN YOUR BACK ON MOTHER
Tracks: / Never turn your back on Mother Earth.
7" Single: Released Oct '74, on Island, by Island Records. Deleted Oct '77. Catalogue no: **WIP 6211**

NUMBER ONE SONG IN HEAVEN
Tracks: / Number one song in heaven, The.
7" Single: Released Apr '79, on Virgin, by Virgin Records. Deleted Apr '82. Catalogue no: **VS 244**
12" Single: Released May '83, on Virgin, by Virgin Records. Deleted May '88. Catalogue no: **VS 590-12**

ROSEBUD
Tracks: / Rosebud.
7" Single: Released Feb '87, on Consolidated Allied, Catalogue no: **TOON 4**
12" Single: Released Feb '87, on Consolidated Allied, Catalogue no: **TOONT 4**

SO IMPORTANT
Tracks: / So important / Big brass ring.
7" Single: Released Jul '88, on Carrere, Catalogue no: **CAR 427**
12" Single: Released Jul '88, on Carrere, Catalogue no: **CART 427**

SO IMPORTANT (VERSION)
Tracks: / So important (version) / Just got back from heaven.
12" Single: Released Aug '89, on Carrere, Catalogue no: **CART 431**

SOMETHING FOR THE GIRL WITH EVERYTHING
Tracks: / Something for the girl with everything.
7" Single: Released Jan '75, on Island, by Island Records. Deleted Jan '78. Catalogue no: **WIP 6221**

THIS TOWN AIN'T BIG ENOUGH FOR BOTH OF US
Tracks: / This town ain't big enough for the both of us.
7" Single: Released May '74, on Island, by Island Records. Deleted May '77. Catalogue no: **WIP 6193**

TIPS FOR TEENS
Tracks: / Tips for teens / Don't shock me.
7" Single: Released Apr '81, on Why-Fi, by Why-Fi Records. Deleted '85. Catalogue no: **WHY 1**
12" Single: Released Apr '81, on Why-Fi, by Why-Fi Records. Deleted '85. Catalogue no: **WHYT 1**

TRYOUTS FOR THE HUMAN RACE
Tracks: / Tryouts for the human race.
7" Single: Released Oct '79, on Virgin, by Virgin Records. Deleted Oct '82. Catalogue no: **VS 289**

WHEN I'M WITH YOU
Tracks: / When I'm with you / When I'm with you (part 2).
7" Single: Released Feb '80, on Virgin, by Virgin Records. Deleted '83. Catalogue no: **VS 319**

YOUNG GIRLS
Tracks: / Young girls / Just because you love me.
7" Single: Released Apr '80, on Virgin, by Virgin Records. Deleted Apr '83. Catalogue no: **VS 343**
12" Single: Released Apr '80, on Virgin, by Virgin Records. Deleted Apr '83. Catalogue no: **VS 343 12**

Sparks, J.J.

I AM DREAMING
Tracks: / I am dreaming.
7" Single: Released Sep '82, on Ixia, Deleted '87. Catalogue no: **12MID 1**
12" Single: Released Sep '82, on Ixia, Catalogue no: **MID 1**

LET IT BE ME
Tracks: / Let it be me.
12" Single: Released Mar '82, on Echo, by Echo Records. Catalogue no: **12 ECHO 003**

Sparks, Trevor

ALL NIGHT
Tracks: / All night.
12" Single: Released Jul '88, on Gyas, Catalogue no: **GA 029**

BYE BYE LOVE
Tracks: / Bye bye love.
12" Single: Released Jun '88, on Live & Love, Catalogue no: **LLD 75**

DEVOTED TO YOU
Tracks: / Devoted to you.
7" Single: Released May '89, on Music Master, Catalogue no: **UNKNOWN**
12" Single: Released May '89, on Blue Trac, by Blue Trac Records. Catalogue no: **BTRD 40**

KEEP IT UP
Tracks: / Keep it up / Wings of love.
12" Single: Released 27 Feb '88, on Blue Trac, by Blue Trac Records. Catalogue no: **MMD 123**

MAKE UP YOUR MIND
Tracks: / Make up your mind.
12" Single: Released Mar '89, on Blue Trac, by Blue Trac Records. Catalogue no: **BTRD 034**

SLEEPLESS WEEKEND
Tracks: / Sleepless weekend.
7" Single: Released Dec '88, on Blue Trac, by Blue Trac Records. Catalogue no: **BTRD 031**

Sparling, Steve

MERCY MERCY ME
Tracks: / Mercy mercy me / Mercy mercy me (instrumental).
7" Single: Released Aug '86, on Important, Catalogue no: **TAN 5**
12" Single: Released Aug '86, on Important, Catalogue no: **TANT 5**

Sparta

ANGEL OF DEATH
Tracks: / Angel of death / Tonight.
7" Single: Released Oct '81, on Suspect, Catalogue no: **SUS 2**

Spartacus

TERMINAL LOVE
Tracks: / Terminal love / Terminal love too.
7" Single: Released Oct '81, on Carrere, Catalogue no: **CAR 214**

Spartacus R

WOZA MALCOLM
Tracks: / Woza Malcolm.
12" Single: Released May '87, on Zara, Catalogue no: **ZMRD 7**

Spear Of Destiny

ALL MY LOVE (ASK NOTHING)
Tracks: / All my love / Last card / Walk in my shadow (on 2" only).
7" Single: Released Jun '85, on Epic, by CBS Records. Deleted Jun '88. Catalogue no: **A 6333**
12" Single: Released Jun '85, on Burning Rome, Catalogue no: **QTA 6333**

COME BACK
Tracks: / Come back.
7" Single: Released Aug '85, on Epic, by CBS Records. Deleted Aug '88. Catalogue no: **A 6445**

FLYING SCOTSMAN
Tracks: / Flying Scotsman / Africa the man who tunes the drums.
7" Single: Released Feb '83, on Epic, by CBS Records. Catalogue no: **SPEAR 1**
12" Single: Released Feb '83, on Epic, by CBS Records. Catalogue no: **SPEAR 13 1**

LIBERATOR
Tracks: / Liberator / Forbidden planet.
7" Single: Released Apr '84, on Burning Rome, Deleted Apr '87. Catalogue no: **A 4310**

NEVER TAKE ME ALIVE
Tracks: / Never take me alive (7" only) / Land of shame (Not on CD) / Never take me alive (extended version) (CD & 12" only) / Land of shame (extended version) (CD & 12" only) / Jack Straw (CD only).
7" Single: Released Mar '87, on 10 Records, by Virgin Records. Catalogue no: **TEN 162**
12" Single: Released Mar '87, on 10 Records, by Virgin Records. Catalogue no: **TENT 162**

PRISONER OF LOVE
Tracks: / Prisoner of love / Rosie / Grapes of wrath / Rainmaker.
7" Set: Released Jan '84, on Epic, by CBS Records. Catalogue no: **DA 4068**
7" Single: Released Jan '84, on Epic, by CBS Records. Catalogue no: **A 4068**
12" Single: Released Jan '84, on Epic, by CBS Records. Catalogue no: **TA 4068**

RADIO RADIO
Tracks: / Radio radio / Life goes on / Radio radio (extended version) (Only on 12" & CD) / Spirits (Only on 12" & CD) / Made in London (only on CD & 10").
10" single: Released '88, on Virgin, by Virgin Records. Catalogue no: **VSA 1144**
7" Single: Released Nov '88, on Virgin, by Virgin Records. Catalogue no: **VS 1144**
12" Single: Released Nov '88, on Virgin, by Virgin Records. Catalogue no: **VST 1144**
CD 3": Released '88, on Virgin, by Virgin Records. Catalogue no: **VSCD 1144**

SO IN LOVE WITH YOU
Tracks: / So in love with you / March or die / So in love with you (extended) (On 12' only) / Junkman (On CD only) / Jungle (On 10" only).
CD 5": Released Sep '88, on Virgin, by Virgin Records. Catalogue no: **VSCD 1123**
10" single: Released Sep '88, on Virgin, by Virgin Records. Catalogue no: **VSA 1123**
7" Single: Released Sep '88, on Virgin, by Virgin Records. Catalogue no: **VS 1123**
12" Single: Released Sep '88, on Virgin, by Virgin Records. Catalogue no: **VST 1123**

STRANGERS IN OUR TOWN
Tracks: / Somewhere out there (On all versions) / Time of our lives (original version) (On 12" only) / Strangers in our town (On 7" only) / Strangers in our town (extended version) (On 12" only) / Strangers in our town (alternative version) (On TENX 148 only) / Time of our lives (dub version) (On TENX 148 only).
7" Single: Released Jan '87, on 10 Records, by Virgin Records. Catalogue no: **TEN 148**
12" Single: Released Jan '87, on 10 Records, by Virgin Records. Catalogue no: **TENT 148**
Special: on 10 Records, by Virgin Records. Catalogue no: **TENX 148**

TRAVELLER, THE
Tracks: / Traveller, The / Late night psycho.
7" Single: on 10 Records, by Virgin Records. Catalogue no: **TEN 189**

WAS THAT YOU?
Tracks: / Was that you? (On 7" only) / Was that you? (live version) (On all versions) / Miami Vice (live) (On TENT 173 only) / Outlands (live) (On TENT 173 only) / Was that you? (extended remix) (On TENT 173) / Was that you? (psychological mix) (On TENR 173 only) / Jack straw (live) (On TENR 173 only) / Land of shame (live) (On TENR 173 only).
7" Single: Released Jul '87, on 10 Records, by Virgin Records. Catalogue no: **TEN 173**
12" Single: on 10 Records, by Virgin Records. Catalogue no: **TENR 173**
12" Single: Released Jul '87, on 10 Records, by Virgin Records. Catalogue no: **TENT 173**

WHEEL, THE
Tracks: / Wheel, The / Hop, The.
7" Single: Released Jun '83, on Epic, by CBS Records. Catalogue no: **A 3372**
12" Single: Released May '83, on Epic, by CBS Records. Catalogue no: **TA 3372**
12" Single: Released Jun '83, on Epic, by CBS Records. Catalogue no: **WA 3372**

WHEEL, THE (OLD GOLD)
Tracks: / Wheel, The / Flying Scotsman / Prisoner of love / Liberator.
12" Single: Released Feb '86, on Old Gold, by Old Gold Records. Catalogue no: **OG 4007**

WORLD SERVICE (SINGLE)
Tracks: / World service.
12" Single: Released Aug '85, on Epic, by CBS Records. Catalogue no: **40 26514**

Spears, Billie Jo

Biographical details: A country singer with a bluesy voice and downhome personality, Billie Jo Spears, born in Texas in 1937, is especially popular in Britain. A child prodigy, she appeared on the Louisiana Hayride in 1951 and '52 and the following year she recorded Too Old For Toys, Too Young For Boys on Abbot. She had her first real hit on Capitol in 1968 and her '75 smash, Blanket On The Ground, was a No 1 country hit in America and reached No 6 in the UK pop chart. In recent years she has not had a contract with a major label in the US but all her albums have done well in Britain. (Donald Clarke, March 1987.).

APOLOGISING ROSE
Tracks: / Apologising Rose.
7" Single: Released Aug '82, on Ritz, by Ritz Records. Catalogue no: **RITZ 027**

BLANKET ON THE GROUND (SINGLE)
Tracks: / Blanket on the ground.
7" Single: Released Apr '75, on United Artists, by EMI Records. Catalogue no: **UP 35805**

I CAN HEAR KENTUCKY CALLING ME
Tracks: / I can hear Kentucky calling me.
7" Single: Released Apr '83, on Ritz, by Ritz Records. Catalogue no: **RITZ 042**

I WILL SURVIVE
Tracks: / I will survive.
7" Single: Released Jul '79, on United Artists, by EMI Records. Deleted Jul '82. Catalogue no: **UP 601**

IF YOU WANT ME
Tracks: / If you want me / Here comes those lies again.
7" Single: Released Mar '77, on United Artists, by EMI Records. Catalogue no: **UP 36236**

MIDNIGHT BLUE
Tracks: / Midnight blue.
7" Single: Released Jul '85, on Premier, by Premier Records. Catalogue no: **PS 1004**

SING ME AN OLD FASHIONED SONG
Tracks: / Sing me an old fashioned song.
7" Single: Released Dec '76, on United Artists, by EMI Records. Deleted Dec '79. Catalogue no: **UP 36179**

SWINGIN
Tracks: / Swingin' / I can hear Kentucky calling me.
7" Single: Released May '83, on Ritz, by Ritz Records. Catalogue no: **RITZ 046**

WHAT I'VE GOT IN MIND
Tracks: / What I've got in mind.
7" Single: Released Sep '85, on Liberty, by EMI Records. Deleted Aug '89. Catalogue no: **UP 36118**
7" Single: Released Sep '85, on Liberty, by EMI Records. Catalogue no: **BP 428**

YOUR GOOD GIRL'S GONNA GO BAD
Tracks: / Your good girl's gonna go bad / Heartbreak Hotel.
7" Single: Released Nov '80, on United Artists, by EMI Records. Deleted Nov '83. Catalogue no: **UP 636**

Special AKA

Biographical details: Special AKA was formed by Jerry Dammers and John Bradbury from the ashes of the Specials. At first the new band's songs were too overtly political and flopped commercially, but Nelson Mandela was a Top Twenty hit in 1983 and it became the anthem of the anti-apartheid movement. (Donald Clarke, March 1987.).

FREE NELSON MANDELA Special 70th birthday remake
Tracks: / Free Nelson Mandela / Free Nelson Mandela.
Note: Produced by Jerry Dammers & Tom Frederickese.
7" Single: Released Jun '88, on Chrysalis, by Chrysalis Records. Catalogue no: **CHS 3276**
12" Single: Released Aug '88, on Chrysalis, by Chrysalis Records. Catalogue no: **FNMX 1**
12" Single: Released Jun '88, on Chrysalis, by Chrysalis Records. Catalogue no: **CHS 123276**

GANGSTERS
Tracks: / Gangsters / Selecter, The.
7" Single: Released Jul '79, on Two-Tone, by Chrysalis Records. Catalogue no: **TT1**

GIRLFRIEND
Tracks: / Girlfriend.
7" Single: Released Aug '84, on Two-Tone, by Chrysalis Records. Catalogue no: **TT 27**

NELSON MANDELA
Tracks: / Nelson Mandela / Break down the door.
12" Single: Released Mar '84, on Two-Tone, by Chrysalis Records. Catalogue no: **CHSTT 1226**
7" Single: Released Mar '84, on Two-Tone, by Chrysalis Records. Catalogue no: **CHSTT 26**

RACIST FRIEND
Tracks: / Racist friend / Bright lights / Racist friend (instrumental version) (Only on 12" version.) / Bright lights (instrumental version) (Only on 12" version.).
7" Single: Released '83, on Chrysalis, by Chrysalis Records. Deleted '87. Catalogue no: **CHS TT 25**
12" Single: Released '83, on Two-Tone, by Chrysalis Records. Deleted '87. Catalogue no: **CHS TT 1225**

ROCKIN' INTO THE NIGHT
Tracks: / Rockin' into the night / Robin Hood.
7" Single: Released Apr '80, on A&M, by A&M Records. Deleted Apr '83. Catalogue no: **AMS 7517**

WAR CRIMES
Tracks: / War crimes / War crimes (version).
7" Single: Released '83, on Chrysalis, by Chrysalis Records. Deleted '87. Catalogue no: **CHS TT 23**
12" Single: Released '83, on Chrysalis, by Chrysalis Records. Deleted '87. Catalogue no: **CHS TT 1023**

THE SPECIALS - GHOST TOWN (Released on Two-Tone)

WHAT I LIKE MOST ABOUT YOU IS YOUR GIRLFRIEND
Tracks: / What I like most about you is your girlfriend / Can't get a break.
7" Single: Released Sep '84, on Two-Tone, by Chrysalis Records. Deleted Sep '87. Catalogue no: **CHSTT 27**

Special Duties

BULLSHIT CRASS
Tracks: / Bullshit crass.
7" Single: Released Nov '82, on Rondelet Music, by Rondelet Music & Records. Catalogue no: **ROUND 24**

POLICE STATE
Tracks: / Police state / We gotta fight / Just ain't me / Special duties.
7" Single: Released May '82, on Rondelet Music, by Rondelet Music & Records. Catalogue no: **ROUND 20**

PUNK ROCKER
Tracks: / Punk rocker.
7" Single: Released May '83, on Expulsion, by Expulsion Records. Deleted '87. Catalogue no: **OUT 1**

VIOLENT SOCIETY
Tracks: / Violent society.
7" Single: Released Jan '82, on Rondelet Music, by Rondelet Music & Records. Catalogue no: **ROUND 15**

Special Ed

CLUB SCENE
Tracks: / Club scene.
7" Single: Released Oct '89, on Profile (USA), by Profile Records (USA). Catalogue no: **PROF 265**
12" Single: Released Sep '89, on Profile (USA), by Profile Records (USA). Catalogue no: **PROFT 265**

Special K

IS GOOD
Tracks: / Is good.
12" Single: Released Sep '87, on Public (USA), Catalogue no: **PAO 13**

Special Occasion

FLYING TO SANTA BARBARA
Tracks: / Flying to Santa Barbara.
12" Single: Released Nov '84, on Nunk, Catalogue no: **NUNK 1010**

Special Project

GREEN ONIONS
Tracks: / Green onions / Elephant man / Nightmare / Nightmare (skratch mix).
12" Single: Released Jul '87, on White Label (1), Catalogue no: **TWD 1954**

Special Request

TAKE IT TO THE MAX
Tracks: / Take it to the max.
7" Single: Released Aug '84, on Island, by Island Records. Catalogue no: **IS 194**
12" Single: Released Aug '84, on Island, by Island Records. Deleted Jul '87. Catalogue no: **12IS 194**

Specials

Biographical details: The Specials inaugurated the 2-Tone label and movement in pop in Britain after getting together in Coventry in 1977. They were Jerry Dammers, keyboards and songwriter, singer Terry Hall, Lynval Golding on rhythm guitar, all from Coventry, plus vocalist Neville Staples, guitarist Roddy Radiation, bassist Sir Horace Gentleman and drummer John Bradbury. The movement re-popularised ska and fought against racial preejudice in the UK. It was the most potent contribution to the post-punk music scene in Britain and was documented in a belated film, Dance Craze, in 1981. They were championed by the Clash and Elvis Costello, who produced their debut album. Dammers was the force behind the group as well as writer and when the band split up he and Bradbury carried on as the Special AKA. (Donald Clarke, March 1987.).

DO NOTHING
Tracks: / Do nothing / Maggie's farm.
7" Single: Released Dec '80, on Two-Tone, by Chrysalis Records. Catalogue no: **CHS TT 16**

GANGSTERS
Tracks: / Gangsters.
7" Single: Released Jul '79, on Two-Tone, by Chrysalis Records. Catalogue no: **TT 1**

GHOST TOWN (see panel above)
Tracks: / Ghost town / Why / Friday-night, saturday morning.
7" EP: Released Jun '81, on Two-Tone, by Chrysalis Records. Deleted '86. Catalogue no: **CHS TT 17**
12" Single: Released Jun '81, on Two-Tone, by Chrysalis Records. Deleted '86. Catalogue no: **CHS TT 1217**

GHOST TOWN (OLD GOLD)
Tracks: / Rat race / Ghost town.
7" Single: Released Feb '87, on Old Gold, by Old Gold Records. Catalogue no: **OG 9686**

MESSAGE TO YOU RUDY, A
Tracks: / Message to you Rudy, A / Nite klub.
7" Single: Released Oct '79, on Two-Tone, by Chrysalis Records. Catalogue no: **CHS TT 5**

PEEL SESSIONS:SPECIALS 29.5.79
12" Single: Released Jan '87, on Strange Fruit, by Strange Fruit Records. Catalogue no: **SFPS 018**

RAT RACE
Tracks: / Rat race / Rude boys outa jail.
7" Single: Released May '80, on Two-Tone, by Chrysalis Records. Catalogue no: **CHSTT 11**

STEREOTYPE
Tracks: / Stereotype / International jet set.
7" Single: Released Sep '80, on Two-Tone, by Chrysalis Records. Catalogue no: **CHS TT 13**

TOO MUCH TOO YOUNG
Tracks: / Too much too young / Guns of navarone / Long shot kick de bucket / Liquidator / Skinhead moonstomp.
7" Single: Released Jan '80, on Two-Tone, by Chrysalis Records. Deleted '83. Catalogue no: **CHS TT 7**

TOO MUCH TOO YOUNG (OLD GOLD)
Tracks: / Too much too young / Gangsters.
7" Single: Released Feb '87, on Old Gold, by Old Gold Records. Catalogue no: **OG 9683**

Specific Oceans

DO YOU?
Tracks: / Do you.
7" Single: Released Jun '84, on Ugly, by Ugly Records. Catalogue no: **TE 001**

Specimen

BEAUTY OF POISON
Tracks: / Beauty of poison / Returning from a journey / Kiss kiss bang bang.
7" Single; Released Nov '83, on London Records, by London Records. Catalogue no: **LON 40**
12" Single: Released Nov '83, on London Records, by London Records. Catalogue no: **LONX 40**

RETURNING FROM A JOURNEY
Tracks: / Return from a journey.
7" Pic: Released Jun '83, on London Records, by London Records. Catalogue no: **LONPD 24**
7" Single: Released May '83, on London Records, by London Records. Catalogue no: **LON 24**
12" Single: Released May '83, on London Records, by London Records. Catalogue no: **LONX 24**

SHARP TEETH PRETTY TEETH
Tracks: / Sharp teeth pretty teeth.
7" Single: Released Mar '85, on Truth (2), Catalogue no: **TRUE 001**
12" Single: Released Mar '85, on Truth (2), Catalogue no: **TRUET 001**

Spector, Phil

Biographical details: The most successful American producer of pop records between the advent of Elvis Presley and the arrival of the Beatles was born in the Bronx, New York, in 1940, moving to the West Coast as a child. Spector invented the famous "wall of sound" technique by packing musicians into small studios and using echo, tape loops etc. In high school he formed a vocal group, the Teddy Bears, and had a smash hit in 1958 with his own song, To Know Him Is To Love Him, inspired by his late father. He worked with Lee Hazlewood and Lester Sill in Phoenix, Arizona, then with Leiber and Stoller in New York (co-writing Ben E. King's hit, Spanish Harlem, with Leiber), formed the Philles label with Sill in 1961 and soon bought him out, becoming a millionaire "Tycoon of Teen" at 21 and producing hit after hit by Darlene Love, Bob B. Soxx and the Bluejeans, the Ronettes, The Crystals, the Righteous Brothers and others. Ike & Tina Turner's River Deep, Mountain High was a flop in the US in '66 but has charted twice in Britain. He was disgusted by what he saw as industry jealousy and retired for some years. He took a cameo part in the film Easy Rider ('69), produced John Lennon's Instant Karma and doctored tapes of the final Beatles album, Let It Be, in '70. He also produced albums for Lennon and Yoko Ono, George Harrison, Cher and others. (Donald Clarke, March 1987.).

CHRISTMAS SINGLE, THE (EP)
Tracks: / White Christmas / Frosty the snowman / Santa claus is coming.
7" Single: Released Nov '82, on Phil Spector Int., by Chrysalis Records. Catalogue no: **2010 010**

PHIL SPECTOR CHRISTMAS MIX, THE
Tracks: / Phil Spector christmas mix, The / Christmas baby please come home.
7" Single: Released Nov '87, on Chrysalis, by Chrysalis Records. Catalogue no: **CHS 3202**

Spector, Ronnie

DARLIN'
Tracks: / Darlin / Settin' the woods on fire.
7" Single: Released Jan '81, on Red Shadow, Catalogue no: **REDS 008**

HERE TODAY GONE TOMORROW
Tracks: / Here today and gone tomorrow.
7" Single: Released Mar '81, on Red Shadow, Catalogue no: **REDS 011**

WHO CAN SLEEP
Tracks: / Who can sleep / When we danced.
7" Single: Released 13 Jun '87, on CBS, by CBS Records. Catalogue no: **650823 7**
12" Single: Released 13 Jun '87, on CBS, by CBS Records. Catalogue no: **650823 6**

Spectra

DIGITAL LOVE
Tracks: / Digital love.
7" Single: Released May '86, on Certain, by Certain Records. Catalogue no: **ACERT 10**
12" Single: Released May '86, on Certain, by Certain Records. Catalogue no: **12 ACERT 10**

Spectral Display

IT TAKES A MUSCLE TO FALL IN LOVE
Tracks: / It takes a muscle to fall in love / Tango.
7" Single: Released Feb '83, on EMI, by EMI Records. Catalogue no: **EMI 5369**

Spectres

STORIES
Tracks: / Stories.
7" Single: Released Feb '81, on Demon, by Demon Records. Deleted '88. Catalogue no: **D 1002**

STRANGE EFFECT
Tracks: / Strange effect / Getting away from you.
7" Single: Released Jul '80, on Direct Hit, Catalogue no: **DH 1**

Spectrum

ALL OR NOTHING
Tracks: / All or nothing.
7" Single: Released Oct '85, on Phoenix (3), by Stiff Records. Deleted '86. Catalogue no: **7 THE 1**
12" Single: Released Nov '87, on Unicorn-Kanchana, by Unicorn - Kanchana Records. Catalogue no: **THE 001**
12" Single: Released Oct '85, on Phoenix (3), by Stiff Records. Deleted '86. Catalogue no: **THE 1**

HAVING A GOOD TIME
Tracks: / Having a good time / Shake it up.
12" Single: Released Jun '82, on Smokey, Catalogue no: **SMJD 006**

Spedding, Chris

CRYING GAME, THE
Tracks: / Crying game, The / Counterfeit.
7" Single: Released Oct '80, on RAK, by EMI Records. Catalogue no: **RAK 323**

I'M NOT LIKE EVERYBODY ELSE (SINGLE)
Tracks: / I'm not like everybody else / Contract.
7" Single: Released Jan '81, on RAK, by EMI Records. Deleted Jan '84. Catalogue no: **RAK 326**

MOTOR BIKING
Tracks: / Motor biking.
7" Single: Released Aug '75, on RAK, by EMI Records. Deleted Aug '78. Catalogue no: **RAK 210**

Speed, Bobby

BOBBY SPEED & AMENDERS
Special: Released Jun '88, on Azra (USA), by Azra International (USA). Catalogue no: **A 32**

Speed Emperors

LOSE CONTROL AND DO THE STOMP
Tracks: / Lose control and do the stomp / Lose control and do the stomp (version).
12" Single: Released 31 Jul '89, on Street Dance, Catalogue no: **STREET 2002**

NEW VIBRATION BEAT
Tracks: / New vibration beat.
12" Single: Released Apr '89, on Various, Catalogue no: **SD 2001**

Speedball

IS SOMEBODY THERE
Tracks: / Is somebody there / No survivors.
7" Single: Released Mar '80, on No-Pap, Deleted '83. Catalogue no: **DD 1**

Speirs, Sam

TALK TO ME
Tracks: / Talk to me / Shuffling.
7" Single: Released Oct '83, on Holyrood, by REL Records. Deleted '87. Catalogue no: **HOLLY 006**

Spellbound

ABCDEFGHIJKL.O.V.E I LOVE YOU
Tracks: / ABCDEFGHIJKL.O.V.E I love you / Don't ya do me that way.
7" Single: Released Jun '83, on Chrysalis, by Chrysalis Records. Catalogue no: **SPELL 1**
12" Single: Released Jun '83, on Chrysalis, by Chrysalis Records. Catalogue no: **SPELX 1**

MY KINDA GIRL
Tracks: / My kinda girl / Gone rockin'.
7" Single: Released May '86, on Sonet, by Sonet Records. Catalogue no: **SON 2294**

ROCKIN' RECKLESS
Tracks: / Rockin' reckless.
7" Single: Released Sep '86, on Sonet, by Sonet Records. Catalogue no: **SON 2306**

Speller, Jenny

RIDING ON A RAINBOW
Tracks: / Riding on a rainbow.
7" Single: Released Apr '81, on Roxon, Catalogue no: **ROX 015**

Spelling Misteaks

RUBBER DUCK POP STAR
Tracks: / Rubber duck pop star.
7" Single: Released Nov '79, on Stortbeat, by Stortbeat Records. Catalogue no: **BEAT 7**

Spellman, Benny

FORTUNE TELLER
Tracks: / Fortune teller / Lipstick traces (on a cigarette).
7" Single: Released Mar '83, on Bandy (USA), Catalogue no: **BANDY 1492**

Spence, Brian

CITY OF SHADOWS
Tracks: / City of shadows / Wondering how to cry / Love is the glory.
7" Single: Released Oct '87, on Polydor, by Polydor Ltd. Deleted Mar '88. Catalogue no: **POSP 876**
12" Single: Released Oct '87, on Polydor, by Polydor Ltd. Deleted Mar '88. Catalogue no: **POSPX 876**

COME BACK HOME
Tracks: / Come back home / Will she be home again / I will call you family (Only on 12" and CD single.) / Ghandi (we will write) (Only available on CD single.).
CD 5": Released Jul '88, on Polydor, by Polydor Ltd. Catalogue no: **PZCD 12**
7" Single: Released Jul '88, on Polydor, by Polydor Ltd. Catalogue no: **PO 12**
12" Single: Released Jul '88, on Polydor, by Polydor Ltd. Catalogue no: **PZ 12**

HEAR IT FROM THE HEART
Tracks: / Hear it from the heart / I will call you family.
7" Single: Released Aug '86, on Polydor, by Polydor Ltd. Deleted Mar '87. Catalogue no: **POSP 816**
12" Single: Released Aug '86, on Polydor, by Polydor Ltd. Deleted Mar '87. Catalogue no: **POSPX 816**

REPUTATION (SINGLE)
Tracks: / Reputation / Sliding down / Reputation (long version) / I still don't know*.
Note: * extra track on 12" & CD Single.
CD 5": Released Apr '88, on Polydor, by Polydor Ltd. Catalogue no: **POCD 916**
7" Single: Released Apr '88, on Polydor, by Polydor Ltd. Catalogue no: **POSP 916**
12" Single: Released Apr '88, on Polydor, by Polydor Ltd. Catalogue no: **POSPX 916**

WITHOUT YOUR LOVE
Tracks: / Without your love / There you go / When she runs (On 12" version only.).
7" Single: Released Oct '88, on Polydor, by Polydor Ltd. Deleted 30 May '89. Catalogue no: **PO 22**
12" Single: Released Oct '88, on Polydor, by Polydor Ltd. Deleted Oct '89. Catalogue no: **PZ 22**

Spence, Derek

SEE A BLACK MAN CRY
Tracks: / See a black man cry / Trilogy.
12" Single: Released Feb '82, on Cha-Cha, by Cha-Cha Records. Catalogue no: **CHAD 47**

Spence, Johnny

THEME FROM DR KILDARE
Tracks: / Dr Kildare, Theme from.
7" Single: Released Mar '62, on Parlophone, by EMI Records. Deleted Mar '65. Catalogue no: **R 4872**

Spence, Judson

IF YOU DON'T LIKE IT
Tracks: / If you don't like it / Everything she do.
CD 5": Released Apr '89, on WEA, by WEA Records. Catalogue no: **A 8950CD**
7" Single: Released Feb '89, on WEA, by WEA Records. Catalogue no: **A 8950**
12" Single: Released Feb '89, on WEA, by WEA Records. Catalogue no: **A 8950 T**

YEAH YEAH YEAH
Tracks: / Yeah yeah yeah / Dance with me.
7" Single: Released Nov '88, on Atlantic, by WEA Records. Catalogue no: **A 899**
12" Single: Released Nov '88, on Atlantic, by WEA Records. Catalogue no: **A 8999 T**

Spence, Peter

CRAZY FEELING
Tracks: / Crazy feeling.
7" Single: Released Apr '89, on Fine Style, by Fashion Records. Catalogue no: **FS 022**

DON'T LEAVE ME LONELY
Tracks: / Lonely (Inst) / Don't leave me lonely (P.A.Mix).
12" Single: Released Jan '87, on Greensleeves, by Greensleeves Records. Catalogue no: **UKMC 21**

FRIVOLOUS WOMAN
Tracks: / Frivolous woman / Frivolous woman (Dub Mix).
12" Single: Released Oct '86, on Movin' Music, Catalogue no: **MMD 001**

Spence, Sonia

JAMAICAN JUMP
Tracks: / Jamaican jump.
12" Single: Released Dec '84, on Cima, Catalogue no: **CR 003**

Spencer, Bill

GET ON UP
Tracks: / Get on up / African girl.
7" Single: Released Dec '82, on Olympic (2), Catalogue no: **PIC 003**
12" Single: Released Dec '82, on Olympic (2), Catalogue no: **PIC 003 12**

IMAGINE
Tracks: / Imagine / Do you really love me.
12" Single: Released Sep '82, on Olympic (2), Catalogue no: **PIC 002**

Spencer, Don

FIREBALL
Tracks: / Fireball.
7" Single: Released Mar '63, on H.M.V., by EMI Records. Deleted Mar '66. Catalogue no: **POP 1087**

Spencer, John

NATURAL MAN
Tracks: / Natural man / Crazy for my lady.
7" Single: Released Mar '80, on Beggars Banquet, by Beggars Banquet Records. Deleted '83. Catalogue no: **BEG 34**

Spencer, Johnny

STRIKE SONG, THE
Tracks: / Strike song, The.
7" Single: Released Oct '84, on Pastafont, by Pastafont Music. Catalogue no: **PF 3011**

Spencer, Juan

I'M ON MY WAY
Tracks: / I'm on my way / Recreation.
7" Single: on Soul Stop, by Dawn Promotions. Catalogue no: **SS 3009**

Spencer, Mike

OH MY PAPA
Tracks: / Oh my papa / Anyone for tennis.
7" Single: Released Nov '82, on Service, Catalogue no: **ALL 41**

Spencer, Tracie

SYMPTOMS OF TRUE LOVE
Tracks: / Symptoms of true love (symptomatic dance mix) / Symptoms of true love (mercyful energy mix) / Symptoms of true love (percussapella) / Symptoms of true love (edit) / Symptoms of true love (cappella).
7" Single: Released Jan '89, on Capitol, by EMI Records. Deleted Aug '89. Catalogue no: **CL 490**
12" Single: Released Jul '88, on Capitol, by EMI Records. Deleted Aug '89. Catalogue no: **12CLX 490**
12" Single: Released Jan '89, on Capitol, by EMI Records. Deleted Aug '89. Catalogue no: **12CL 490**

Spencer, Tracy

RUN TO ME
Tracks: / Run to Me / Mama run.
7" Single: Released Aug '86, on CBS, by CBS Records. Catalogue no: **A 7007**
12" Single: Released Aug '86, on CBS, by CBS Records. Catalogue no: **TA 7007**

Spencer's Alternative

MUMBO JUMBO
Tracks: / Mumbo jumbo / He's on fire / Old friend / Mumbo disco (Only on 12" single).
7" Single: Released May '80, on Bronze, by Bronze Records. Deleted '83. Catalogue no: **BRO 94**
12" Single: Released May '80, on Bronze, by Bronze Records. Deleted '83. Catalogue no: **BROX 94**

Spense, Barrington

FALLING IN LOVE FOR THE FIRST TIME
Tracks: / Falling in love for the first time.
12" Single: Released Feb '82, on Exclusive, Catalogue no: **EXC 601120**

Sperm Wails

BOY HAIRDRESSER
Tracks: / Boy hairdresser.
7" Single: Released Jun '88, on Spurt, Catalogue no: **SPURT 2**

GOLDEN AGE OF THE CARRY ON, THE
Tracks: / Golden age of the carry on, The.
7" Single: Released Oct '88, on Spurt, Catalogue no: **SPURT 003**

Spice

YOU'RE ALWAYS THERE
Tracks: / You're always there / Your always there (Dub Version).
12" Single: Released May '86, on Noir, by Noir Records. Catalogue no: **13 CHALK 102**

YOU'RE SO NICE
Tracks: / You're so nice.
7" Single: Released Jul '83, on Jive, by Zomba Records. Catalogue no: **JIVE 44**
12" Single: Released Jul '83, on Jive, by Zomba Records. Catalogue no: **JIVET 44**

Spiceland, Emmet

MARY FROM DUNGLOE
Tracks: / Mary from Dungloe.
7" Single: Released '88, on Homespun (Ireland), by Outlet Records. Catalogue no: **HIS 25**

Spicer, Jimmy

MONEY (DOLLAR BILL Y'ALL)
Tracks: / Money (dollar bill y'all) / Money (dollar bill y'all) (rap vocal).
12" Single: Released Sep '87, on Wax, by Wax Records. Catalogue no: **DOLLAR 12**

Spicer, Terry

GOING TO BRIGHTON
Tracks: / Going to Brighton / Persistently raining.
7" Single: Released Jul '82, on After Hours, Deleted '88. Catalogue no: **AFT 05**

Spider

ALL THE TIME
Tracks: / All the time.
7" Single: Released '81, on City, by City Records. Catalogue no: **NIK 7**

BETTER BE GOOD TO ME
Tracks: / Better be good to me / Our love.
7" Single: Released May '81, on Dreamland, Deleted May '84. Catalogue no: **DLSP 11**

BREAKAWAY
Tracks: / Breakaway.
7" Single: Released Jul '84, on A&M, by A&M Records. Deleted '88. Catalogue no: **AM 204**
12" Single: Released Jul '84, on A&M, by A&M Records. Deleted '88. Catalogue no: **AMX 204**

COLLEGE LUV
Tracks: / College luv / Born to be wild.
7" Single: Released Oct '80, on Alien, Deleted Oct '83. Catalogue no: **ALIEN 16**

GIMME GIMME IT ALL
Tracks: / Gimme gimme it all / Rock tonight / Live recording from the Kerrang concert (This track on double pack single) / Gimme gimme it all (extended version:see notes) (12" Version only) / Did ya like it baby (12" Version only).
7" Single: Released Mar '86, on PRT, by Castle Communications Records. Catalogue no: **7P 344**
12" Single: Released Mar '86, on PRT, by Castle Communications Records. Catalogue no: **12P 344**
Special: Released Mar '86, on PRT, by Castle Communications Records. Catalogue no: **7PX 344**

GUILTY
Tracks: / Guilty / Guilty (version).
7" Single: Released Jul '88, on Dove, Catalogue no: **JO 127**
12" Single: Released Jul '88, on Dove, Catalogue no: **JO 12127**

HERE WE GO ROCK 'N' ROLL
Tracks: / Here we go rock 'n' roll / Death row / I just wanna make love to you (on 12" only).
7" Pic: Released Mar '84, on A&M, by A&M Records. Deleted '88. Catalogue no: **AMP 180**
7" Single: Released Mar '84, on A&M, by A&M Records. Deleted Mar '87. Catalogue no: **AM 180**

NEW ROMANCE
Tracks: / New romance / Cross fire.
7" Single: Released May '80, on RSO, by Polydor Ltd. Deleted May '83. Catalogue no: **209044-1**

ROCK'N'ROLL FOREVER WILL LAST
Tracks: / Rock 'n' roll forever will last / Did ya like it baby.
7" Single: Released Aug '82, on RCA, by BMG Records (UK). Catalogue no: **RCA 268**

TALKIN' 'BOUT ROCK 'N' ROLL
Tracks: / Talkin' 'bout rock'n'roll / 'Til I'm certain.
7" Single: Released Mar '82, on Creole, by Creole Records. Deleted '85. Catalogue no: **CR 30**
7" Single: Released Nov '82, on RCA, by BMG Records (UK). Catalogue no: **RCA 294**

WHY D'YA LIE TO ME
Tracks: / Why d'ya lie to me / Footloose / 9 to 5.
7" Single: Released Feb '83, on RCA, by BMG Records (UK). Catalogue no: **RCA 313**
12" Single: Released Feb '83, on RCA, by BMG Records (UK). Catalogue no: **RCAT 313**

Spiders

MONY MONY
Tracks: / Mony Mony / Who's the other one.
7" Single: Released Apr '80, on R.E.D., Deleted Apr '83. Catalogue no: **REDS 004**

Spiking

BREAKTHROUGH
Tracks: / Breakthrough.
12" Single: Released May '82, on Splendid, by Orbitone Records. Catalogue no: **DSSP 07**

LOCAL DISH
Tracks: / Local dish.
12" Single: Released May '82, on Sunburn, by Orbitone Records. Catalogue no: **SBD 03**

MY MUSIC
Tracks: / My music / Ride no. 1.
12" Single: Released Dec '83, on Sunburn, by Orbitone Records. Catalogue no: **SBD 41**

PRIED UNE JEUNE FEMME
Tracks: / Pried une jeune femme.
12" Single: Released May '82, on Splendid, by Orbitone Records. Catalogue no: **DSSP 02**

WIND WITH MISS CARNIVAL
Tracks: / Wind with Miss Carnival.
12" Single: Released May '82, on Sunburn, by Orbitone Records. Catalogue no: **SBD 01**

Spinner Youth

LOVE IS HERE TO STAY
Tracks: / Love is here to stay.
12" Single: Released Aug '88, Catalogue no: **TM 1202**

Spinners

LIVERPOOL LOU
Tracks: / Liverpool lou / Going to the Zoo / Island in the sun.
7" Single: Released May '86, on PRT, by Castle Communications Records. Catalogue no: **7P 353**

WIND IS BLOWING, THE
Tracks: / Wind is blowing, The.
7" Single: Released Nov '85, on PRT, by Castle Communications Records. Catalogue no: **7P 316**

Spinstar

NO I CAN'T STAND IT
Tracks: / No I can't stand it / Peace and love / Suffering still.
7" Single: Released Sep '82, on KR, Catalogue no: **KR 12**
12" Single: Released Sep '82, on KR, Catalogue no: **KRT 12**

Spirit

1984
Tracks: / 1984.
7" Single: Released Jan '84, on Mercury, by Phonogram Ltd. Catalogue no: **MER 151**
12" Single: Released Jan '84, on Mercury, by Phonogram Ltd. Catalogue no: **MERX 151**

HARD LOVE
Tracks: / Hard love.
7" Single: Released Jun '89, on I.R.S, Catalogue no: **EIRS 117**
12" Single: Released Jun '89, on I.R.S, Catalogue no: **EIRST 117**

MR SKIN
Tracks: / Mr. Skin / Fresh garbage.
7" Single: Released Apr '84, on Mercury, by Phonogram Ltd. Catalogue no: **MER 162**
7" Single: Released Apr '84, on Mercury, by Phonogram Ltd. Catalogue no: **MER 1626**

TURN TO THE RIGHT
Tracks: / Turn to the right / Potatoland theme.
7" Single: Released Jun '81, on Beggars Banquet, by Beggars Banquet Records. Deleted Jan '88. Catalogue no: **BEG 56**

WE'VE GOT A LOT TO LEARN
Tracks: / We've got a lot to learn / Fish fry road.
7" Single: Released May '81, on Beggars Banquet, by Beggars Banquet Records. Deleted May '86. Catalogue no: **BEG 45**

Spirit Level

ALONE & HAPPY
Tracks: / Alone & happy.
7" Single: Released Jan '85, on Blue Waters, Catalogue no: **MSBW 1**

GIVE A LITTLE
Tracks: / Give a little.
7" Single: Released Feb '84, on Ram, by Ram Records. Catalogue no: **RAM 6001**

Spirit Of The Forest

SPIRIT OF THE FOREST
Tracks: / Spirit of the forest.
7" Single: Released 5 Jun '89, on Virgin, by Virgin Records. Catalogue no: **VS 1191**

Spiritborn

PITY THE UNBORN CHILD
Tracks: / Pity the unborn child.
7" Single: Released Sep '84, on Spearhead, Catalogue no: **SBSH 1**

Spiro, Simon

I FOUND A LOVE
Tracks: / I found a love / Could it be.
7" Single: Released Sep '81, on Bulldog Records, by President Records. Deleted Sep '84. Catalogue no: **BD 23**

Spit Like Paint

FOR THE LIFE OF ME
Tracks: / For the life of me / I have / 30 purple birds / I can't remember.
12" Single: Released Jul '82, on Dining Out, by Dining Out Records. Catalogue no: **TUX 24**

TIGHT AS OUR SOULS
Tracks: / Tight as our souls.
12" Single: Released Nov '87, on Hollow Planet, Catalogue no: **HOP 002**

Spitfire

SO YOU WANT TO BE A ROCK 'N' ROLL STAR
Tracks: / So you want to be a rock 'n' roll star.
7" Single: Released Sep '82, on Carrere America (USA), by PolyGram Rec.Inc.(USA). Catalogue no: **CAR 253**

WIND UP GIRL
Tracks: / Wind up girl / Swallowed up the sun.
7" Single: Released Apr '80, on Gun, Deleted '82. Catalogue no: **AIM 001**

Spitfires

FRIDAY ON MY MIND
Tracks: / Friday on my mind / I can't get you off my mind.
7" Single: Released Apr '80, on RCA, by BMG Records (UK). Deleted '82. Catalogue no: **PB 5248**

Spitting Image

CHICKEN SONG, THE
Tracks: / Chicken song, The / I've never met a nice South African / Hello, you must be going (12" only) / We're scared of Bob (12"only).
7" Single: Released Apr '86, on Virgin, by Virgin Records. Catalogue no: **SPIT 1**
12" Single: Released May '86, on Virgin, by Virgin Records. Deleted '89. Catalogue no: **SPIT 12**

SANTA CLAUS IS ON THE DOLE
Tracks: / First athiest / Tabernacle choir / Santa Claus is on the dole.
7" Single: Released Nov '86, on Virgin, by Virgin Records. Deleted May '88. Catalogue no: **VS 921**
12" Single: Released Nov '86, on Virgin, by Virgin Records. Deleted May '88. Catalogue no: **VS 921-12**

Spizz

6000 CRAZY
Tracks: / 6000 crazy.
7" Single: Released Jan '79, on Rough Trade, by Rough Trade Records. Catalogue no: **RTS 01**

COLD CITY
Tracks: / Cold city.
7" Single: Released Jan '79, on Rough Trade, by Rough Trade Records. Catalogue no: **RTS 02**

JUNGLE FEVER
Tracks: / Jungle fever / Meaning.
7" Single: Released Jul '82, on Rough Trade, by Rough Trade Records. Catalogue no: **RT 108**

PEEL SESSIONS:SPIZZ 7/8/78
Tracks: / Cold city / 6000 crazy / Pure noise / Alien language / Protect from heat / Platform 3 / Switched off.
12" Single: Released Feb '87, on Strange Fruit, by Strange Fruit Records. Catalogue no: **SFPS 022**

SOLDIER SOLDIER
Tracks: / Soldier soldier.
7" Single: Released Sep '79, on Rough Trade, by Rough Trade Records. Catalogue no: **RTS 03**

WHERE'S CAPTAIN KIRK (Original version)
Tracks: / Where's Captain Kirk.
7" Single: Released '79, on Rough Trade, by Rough Trade Records. Catalogue no: **RTS 04**
7" Single: Released Sep '87, on Hobo Railways, Catalogue no: **HOBO 001**
12" Single: Released Sep '87, on Hobo Railways, Catalogue no: **HOBO 12001**

WORK
Tracks: / Work.
7" Single: Released Feb '82, on Rough Trade, by Rough Trade Records. Catalogue no: **RT 096**

Spizz Orbit

LOVE ME LIKE A ROCKET
Tracks: / Love me like a rocket.
12" Single: Released 22 Aug '88, on Plastic Head, by Plastic Head Records. Catalogue no: **PLAS POP 2**

Spizzles

DANGERS OF LIVING
Tracks: / Dangers of living / Scared.
7" Single: Released Apr '81, on A&M, by A&M Records. Deleted Apr '84. Catalogue no: **AMS 8124**

RISK
Tracks: / Risk / Melancholy.
7" Single: Released Feb '81, on A&M, by A&M Records. Deleted Feb '84. Catalogue no: **AMS 8107**

SPK

BREATHLESS
Tracks: / Breathless.
12" Single: Released 14 May '88, on Nettwerk, by Nettwerk Records. Catalogue no: **NET 002**
12" Single: Released 1 Feb '88, on Nettwerk, by Nettwerk Records. Catalogue no: **NT12-3016**

DEKOMPOSITIONES
Tracks: / Dekompositiones.
12" Single: Released May '83, on Side Effects, Catalogue no: **SER 003**

IN FLAGRANTE DELICTO
Tracks: / In flagrante Delicto.
12" Single: Released May '86, on Side Effects, Catalogue no: **SFX 01**

METAL DANCE
Tracks: / Metal dance.
12" Single: Released Apr '85, on Desire, by Desire Records. Deleted '89. Catalogue no: **WANTX 1**

OFF THE DEEP END
Tracks: / Off the deep end.
12" Single: Released Sep '87, on Nettwerk, by Nettwerk Records. Catalogue no: **NT12-3008**

Splash

EUROPEAN BOY
Tracks: / European boy.
7" Single: Released Aug '87, on Rocket, by Rocket Records. Deleted Mar '88. Catalogue no: **BLAST 6**
12" Single: Released Aug '87, on Rocket, by Rocket Records. Deleted Mar '88. Catalogue no: **BLAST 612**

FEAR NO EVIL
Tracks: / Fear no evil / Gimme your body.
7" Single: Released Jul '81, on Ramkup, Deleted '85. Catalogue no: **CAP 004**
7" Single: Released Jul '81, on Ramkup, Catalogue no: **CAC 004**

MODERN WOMEN
Tracks: / Modern women / Hypnotised.
7" Single: Released Jan '82, on Ramkup, Catalogue no: **CAC 010**

Q'EST CE QUE C'EST
Tracks: / Q'est ce que c'est / Dont look back / Ce soir (on 12" only.).
7" Single: Released Aug '86, on Rocket, by Rocket Records. Catalogue no: **BLAST 1**
12" Single: Released Aug '86, on Rocket, by Rocket Records. Catalogue no: **BLAST 112**

Splash SF

CHANGE IS GONNA COME, A
Tracks: / Change is gonna come, A / Sweet dreaming.
7" Single: Released Sep '84, on Sucsa, Catalogue no: **SUC 1**

Splashdown

BUILD IT UP
Tracks: / Build it up.
7" Single: Released Jun '84, on Old Convent, by Old Convent Records. Catalogue no: **OCR 7S-001**

IT'S A BRAND NEW DAY
Tracks: / It's a brand new day.
7" Single: Released Jul '82, on Red Bus, by Red Bus Records. Catalogue no: **SHA 4**
12" Single: Released Jul '82, on Red Bus, by Red Bus Records. Catalogue no: **SHAL 4**

TO YOUR HEART
Tracks: / To your heart / Actions speak louder than words.
12" Single: Released Feb '83, on Shack, Deleted '85. Catalogue no: **SHAL 5**
7" Single: Released Feb '83, on Shack, Deleted '85. Catalogue no: **SHA 5**

Splat

JAZZIN' UP
Tracks: / Jazzin' up.
7" Single: Released Aug '88, on Sophisticated Noise, by Sophisticated Noise Records. Catalogue no: **SN1**
12" Single: Released Aug '88, on Sophisticated Noise, by Sophisticated Noise Records. Catalogue no: **12SN1**

TAXI
Tracks: / Taxi.
7" Single: Released Jul '84, on Ron Johnson, by Ron Johnson Records. Catalogue no: **RON 2**

YEAH THE DUM DUM
Tracks: / Yeah the dum dum.
7" Single: Released Aug '83, on Ron Johnson, by Ron Johnson Records. Catalogue no: **RON 1**

Spliff

CARBONARA
Tracks: / Carbonara.
7" Single: Released Jan '83, on CBS, by CBS Records. Catalogue no: **A 2722**

ROCK 'N' ROLL REFUGEE
Tracks: / Rock 'n' roll refugee / Gravy.
7" Single: Released Mar '81, on CBS, by CBS Records. Deleted Mar '84. Catalogue no: **A 1005**

Spliff Riff

MORE TODAY THAN YESTERDAY
Tracks: / More today than yesterday / You shook up my world.
7" Single: Released Feb '86, on JKO, Catalogue no: **JKO 111**
12" Single: Released Feb '86, on JKO, Catalogue no: **12JKO 111**

Splinter

COSTAFINE TOWN
Tracks: / Costafine town.
7" Single: Released Nov '74, on Dark Horse, by Dark Horse Records. Deleted Nov '77. Catalogue no: **AMS 7135**

DANGER ZONE
Tracks: / Danger zone.
7" Single: Released Jun '79, on Barn, by Barn Records. Catalogue no: **BARN 004**

INNOCENT
Tracks: / Innocent / All that love.
7" Single: Released Nov '80, on Bellaphon, Deleted Nov '83. Catalogue no: **BPS 009**

Split Beaver

SAVAGE
Tracks: / Savage / Hound of hell.
7" Single: Released Sep '81, on Heavy Metal, by FM-Revolver Records. Catalogue no: **HEAVY 7**

Split Cane

SAMBA SANDINISTA
Tracks: / Samba Sandinista.
7" Single: Released Jul '88, on Big Life, by Big Life Records. Catalogue no: **BLR 003**
12" Single: Released Jun '88, on Big Life, by Big Life Records. Catalogue no: **BLR 003T**

Split Enz

HISTORY NEVER REPEATS
Tracks: / History never repeats / Shark attack / What's the matter with you.
7" EP: Released May '81, on A&M, by A&M Records. Deleted May '84. Catalogue no: **AMS 8128**

I GOT YOU (see panel below)
Tracks: / I got you / Double happy.
7" Single: Released Aug '80, on A&M, by A&M Records. Deleted Aug '83. Catalogue no: **AMS 7546**

I SEE RED
Tracks: / I see red.
7" Single: Released Nov '79, on Illegal, by Faulty Products Records. Catalogue no: **ILS 1109**

NOBODY TAKES ME SERIOUSLY
Tracks: / Nobody takes me seriously / Choral sea.
7" Single: Released Nov '80, on A&M, by A&M Records. Deleted Nov '83. Catalogue no: **AMS 7574**

SIX MONTHS IN A LEAKY BOAT
Tracks: / Six months in a leaky boat / Make sense of it.
7" Single: Released Apr '82, on A&M, by A&M Records. Deleted Apr '85. Catalogue no: **AMS 8216**

Split Knee Loons

SPLIT KNEE LOONS
Tracks: / Split knee loons.
7" Single: Released Jul '81, on Avatar, by Avatar Record Corporation. Catalogue no: **AAA 111**

Split Level

GIRL
Tracks: / Girl / In the future.
7" Single: Released Apr '84, on Climate, Catalogue no: **CRBSL 724**

SATISFYIN' FEELING
Tracks: / Satisfyin' feeling / Further away it is.
7" Single: Released Mar '81, on Carve Up,

SPLIT ENZ - I GOT YOU (Released on A & M)

SPLODGENESSA BOUNDS - TWO LITTLE BOYS (Released on Deram)

THE SPORTS - WHO LISTENS TO THE RADIO (Released on Stiff)

by Red Lightning Records. Catalogue no: **CU 2**

Split Rivitt

SOUL LIMBO
Tracks: / Soul limbo / Safe from you / Can't be still.
7" Single: Released Sep '82, on Red Lightnin', by Red Lightning Records. Deleted Jun '89. Catalogue no: **RL 450032**

Split Second

BODY CHECK
Tracks: / Body check / Burnout / On command / Flesh.
12" Single: Released Nov '86, on Antler, by Antler Records (Belgium). Catalogue no: **ANT 046**

COLOSSEUM CRASH
Tracks: / Colosseum crash / Muscla machine.
12" Single: Released Apr '89, on Antler, by Antler Records (Belgium). Catalogue no: **ANT 100**
CD 5": Released Apr '89, on Antler, by Antler Records (Belgium). Catalogue no: **ANT 100CD**

FLESH
Tracks: / Flesh (remix) / Flesh (original version).
12" Single: Released Mar '89, on ffrr, by London Records. Deleted Jul '89. Catalogue no: **FFRX 23**
7" Single: Released Mar '89, on ffrr, by London Records. Deleted Jul '89. Catalogue no: **FFR 23**
CD 5": Released Dec '88, on Antler, by Antler Records (Belgium). Catalogue no: **ANT 090CD**

MAMBOWITCH
Tracks: / Mambowitch.
12" Single: Released Oct '88, on Antler, by Antler Records (Belgium). Catalogue no: **ANT 088-12**
7" Single: Released Oct '88, on Antler, by Antler Records (Belgium). Catalogue no: **ANT 088**

RIGOR MORTIS
Tracks: / Rigor Mortis / Flesh / Burn out.
12" Single: Released Jun '88, on Antler, by Antler Records (Belgium). Catalogue no: **ANT 061**
7" Single: Released Jun '88, on Antler, by Antler Records (Belgium). Catalogue no: **ANT 060**

SMELL OF BUDDHA, A
Tracks: / Smell of buddha, A.
12" Single: Released 31 Oct '87, on Antler, by Antler Records (Belgium). Catalogue no: **ANT 068**

Splitt

ALL I EVER WANTED
Tracks: / All I ever wanted / No great adventure.
12" Single: Released Oct '86, on Legend (1), by Legend Records (UK). Catalogue no: **12LM 2**
7" Single: Released Oct '86, on Legend (1), by Legend Records (UK). Catalogue no: **LM 2**

Splitz

TELEPATHY
Tracks: / Telpathy / Lolita.
7" Single: Released Apr '81, on EMI, by EMI Records. Deleted '85. Catalogue no: **EMI 5107**

Splodge

MOUTH AND TROUSERS
Tracks: / Mouth and trousers / In search of the seven golden duffets.
7" Single: Released Nov '82, on Razor, by Razor Records. Catalogue no: **RZS 102**

Splodge, Max

BICYCLE SEAT
Tracks: / Bicycle seat.
7" Single: Released Jan '81, on Deram, by London Records. Deleted Jan '84. Catalogue no: **BUM 2**

PHUT, PHUT, SPLODGENIK
Tracks: / 86 - The year of the bean / Phut phut splodgenik.
7" Single: Released Jan '87, on Completely Different, by Neat Records. Catalogue no: **MAD 003**

Splodgenessabounds

COWPUNK MEDLUM
Tracks: / Cowpunk medium / Brown paper / Have you got a light boy / Morning milky.
7" Single: Released Jun '81, on Deram, by London Records. Deleted Jun '84. Catalogue no: **BUM 3**

SIMON TEMPLAR
Tracks: / Simon Templar / 2 pints of lager and a packet of crisps please.
7" Single: Released Jun '80, on Deram, by London Records. Deleted Jun '83. Catalogue no: **BUM 1**

TWO LITTLE BOYS (see panel above)
Tracks: / Two little boys / Horse / Sex / Butterfly.
12" Single: Released Sep '80, on Deram, by London Records. Deleted Sep '83. Catalogue no: **ROLF 12**
7" Single: Released Sep '80, on Deram, by London Records. Deleted Sep '83. Catalogue no: **ROLF 1**

Spoilers

SHY GIRL
Tracks: / Shy girl / Cross fire.
7" Single: Released May '80, on Warner Bros., by WEA Records. Deleted May '83. Catalogue no: **K 18225**

STANDING IN A LINE
Tracks: / Standing in a line / Motorway.
7" Single: Released Feb '80, on WEA, by WEA Records. Deleted Feb '83. Catalogue no: **K 18144**

Spooky

ON THE ROCKS
Tracks: / On the rocks / Friends.
12" Single: Released May '81, on Satril, by Satril Records. Deleted May '86. Catalogue no: **12HH 153**
7" Single: Released May '81, on Satril, by Satril Records. Deleted May '86. Catalogue no: **HH 153**

Spoon Fazer

SUNSET
Tracks: / Sunset / Ballad of insectman / Flying bodies / Fly on the wall.
12" Single: Released Jul '82, on Illuminated, Deleted Jul '85. Catalogue no: **ILL 9 12**

Spoonie Gee

GODFATHER, THE
Tracks: / Godfather, The / Godfather, The (version).
12" Single: Released Aug '87, on Tuff City (USA), Catalogue no: **TUF 128019**

Spoons

NOVA HEART
Tracks: / Nova heart / Symmetry.
7" Single: Released Oct '82, on A&M, by A&M Records. Deleted Oct '85. Catalogue no: **AMS 8260**
12" Single: Released Oct '82, on A&M, by A&M Records. Deleted Oct '85. Catalogue no: **AMSX 8260**

Sport

MOVE TO THE MUSIC
Tracks: / Move to the music.
7" Single: Released Jul '84, on Baskerville, Catalogue no: **BAS 5**

THIS WHEEL'S ON FIRE
Tracks: / This wheel's on fire.
7" Single: Released Oct '83, on Chevy, by Chevy Records. Catalogue no: **CHEVY 002**
12" Single: Released Oct '83, on Chevy, by Chevy Records. Catalogue no: **CHEVY 003**

Sporting Life

HELP THE CHILDREN
Tracks: / Help the children.
12" Single: Released Oct '82, on Crash, by Satril Records. Deleted '84. Catalogue no: **12 CRA 501**
7" Single: Released Oct '82, on Crash, by Satril Records. Deleted '84. Catalogue no: **CRA 501**

Sports

DON'T THROW STONES (SINGLE)
Tracks: / Don't throw stones / Worst kind.
7" Single: Released Apr '80, on Sire, by Sire Records. Deleted '83. Catalogue no: **SIR 6002**

WHO LISTENS TO THE RADIO (see panel above)
Tracks: / Who listens to the radio / Step by step / So obvious / Suspicious minds.
7" EP: Released '79, on Stiff, by Stiff Records. Catalogue no: **LAST 5**

Spot The Dog

TOY
Tracks: / Toy.
7" Single: Released Sep '82, on Diatribe, Catalogue no: **DIAT 18**

Spotnicks

HAVA NAGILA
Tracks: / Hava nagila.
7" Single: Released Jan '63, on Oriole, Deleted Jan '66. Catalogue no: **CB 1790**

JUST LISTEN TO MY HEART
Tracks: / Just listen to my heart.
7" Single: Released Apr '63, on Oriole, Deleted Apr '66. Catalogue no: **CB 1818**

ORANGE BLOSSOM SPECIAL
Tracks: / Orange blossom special.
7" Single: Released Jun '62, on Oriole, Deleted Jun '65. Catalogue no: **CB 1724**

ROCKET MAN
Tracks: / Rocket man.
7" Single: Released Sep '62, on Oriole, Deleted Sep '65. Catalogue no: **CB 1755**

Springate, John

MY LIFE
Tracks: / My life.
7" Single: Released Feb '85, on Towerbell, Catalogue no: **TOW 67**

SONG FOR CHRISTMAS
Tracks: / Song for Christmas / So long ago.
7" Single: Released Dec '83, on Terrific, by Creole Records. Catalogue no: **TRIF 008**
7" Single: Released Nov '85, on Sedition, by Sedition Records. Catalogue no: **EDIT 3309**

TO BE A MATADOR
Tracks: / To be a matador / Wake up Madrid.
7" Single: Released Jul '87, on Epic, by CBS Records. Catalogue no: **OLE G2**
7" Single: Released Jul '87, on Epic, by CBS Records. Catalogue no: **OLE 2**

Springer Brothers

WHAT'S A NICE GIRL LIKE YOU DOING IN A LOVE LIKE
Tracks: / What's a nice girl like you doing ... / Twice as strong.
7" Single: Released Feb '80, on Elektra, by Elektra Records (UK). Deleted '83. Catalogue no: **K 12426**

Springer, Marvin

MERRY CHRISTMAS....
Tracks: / Merry Christmas....
7" Single: Released Dec '86, on Sold, Catalogue no: **S 110**

WHERE'S MY LOVE GONE
Tracks: / Where's my love gone.
7" Single: Released Nov '87, on Circle City, Catalogue no: **CC2**
12" Single: Released Nov '87, on Circle City, Catalogue no: **CCYT 2**

Springfield, Dusty

Biographical details: Dusty Springfield was born Mary O'Brien, 16 April 1939 in Hamstead, London. She is still reckoned one of the best British female singers of her generation. She sang in the Lana Sisters, then joined her brother Tom in folk trio the Springfields in the early 1960s; as a solo she had her own uniquely mature style infulenced by Motown, and exercised good choice of material, while other UK girl singers were content with production-line songs. *Wishin' And Hopin'* was No.6 hit in the USA in 1964, but did not chart in the UK; her biggest hit was *You Don't Have To Say You Love Me* 1966 (No.1 in the UK, 4 in the USA); *Son Of A Preacher Man* was top 10 in both countries 1968; her original version of Goffin & King's *Goin' Back* was top 10 UK 1966, the song later widely covered. She switched from Philips to Atlantic for *Dusty In Memphis* '69, probably her best, produced by Jerry Wexler (including *Preacher Man*); she moved to the USA in the early 1970s, her career there not a success; comebacks have not been successfull, but fans still hope she will find a sympathetic producer and the right songs. (Donald Clarke 27.5.87).

ALL I SEE IS YOU
Tracks: / All I see is you.
7" Single: Released Sep '66, on Philips, by Phonogram Ltd. Deleted Sep '69. Catalogue no: **BF 1510**

AM I THE SAME GIRL
Tracks: / Am I the same girl.
7" Single: Released Sep '69, on Philips, by Phonogram Ltd. Deleted Sep '72. Catalogue no: **BF 1811**

BABY BLUE
Tracks: / Baby blue.
7" Single: Released Oct '79, on Mercury, by Phonogram Ltd. Deleted Oct '82. Catalogue no: **DUSTY 4**

GIVE ME TIME
Tracks: / Give me time.
7" Single: Released May '67, on Philips, by Phonogram Ltd. Deleted May '70. Catalogue no: **BF 1577**

GOING BACK
Tracks: / Going back.
7" Single: Released Jul '66, on Philips, by Phonogram Ltd. Deleted Jul '69. Catalogue no: **BF 1502**

HOW CAN I BE SURE
Tracks: / How can I be sure.
7" Single: Released Sep '70, on Philips, by Phonogram Ltd. Deleted Sep '73. Catalogue no: **6006 045**

I CLOSE MY EYES AND COUNT TO TEN
Tracks: / I close my eyes and count to ten.
7" Single: Released Jul '68, on Philips, by Phonogram Ltd. Deleted Jul '71. Catalogue no: **BF 1682**

I JUST DON'T KNOW WHAT TO DO WITH MYSELF
Tracks: / I just don't know what to do with myself.
7" Single: Released Jul '64, on Philips, by Phonogram Ltd. Deleted Jul '67. Catalogue no: **BF 1348**
7" Single: Released Feb '88, on Old Gold, by Old Gold Records. Catalogue no: **OG 9763**

I ONLY WANT TO BE WITH YOU (OLD GOLD)
Tracks: / I only want to be with you.
7" Single: Released Jul '82, on Old Gold, by Old Gold Records. Catalogue no: **OG 9242**

I ONLY WANT TO BE WITH YOU (SINGLE)
Tracks: / I only want to be with you.
7" Single: on Phonogram, by Phonogram Ltd. Deleted Oct '88. Catalogue no: **BRITV 5**
7" Single: Released Oct '80, on Phonogram, by Phonogram Ltd. Deleted Oct '83. Catalogue no: **CUT 111**
12" Single: on Phonogram, by Phonogram Ltd. Deleted Oct '88. Catalogue no: **BRITV 55**
7" Single: Released Nov '63, on Philips, by Phonogram Ltd. Deleted Nov '66. Catalogue no: **BF 1292**

I WISH THAT LOVE WOULD LAST
Tracks: / I wish that love would last / It goes like it goes.
7" Single: Released Oct '80, on 20th Century, by 20th Century Records. Deleted Oct '83. Catalogue no: **TC 2457**

I'LL TRY ANYTHING
Tracks: / I'll try anything.
7" Single: Released Feb '67, on Philips, by Phonogram Ltd. Deleted Feb '70. Catalogue no: **BF 1553**

IN THE MIDDLE OF NOWHERE
Tracks: / In the middle of nowhere.
7" Single: Released Jul '65, on Philips, by Phonogram Ltd. Deleted Jul '68. Catalogue no: **BF 1418**

LITTLE BY LITTLE
Tracks: / Little by little.
7" Single: Released Jan '66, on Philips, by Phonogram Ltd. Deleted Jan '69. Catalogue no: **BF 1466**

LOSING YOU
Tracks: / Losing you.
7" Single: Released Oct '64, on Philips, by Phonogram Ltd. Deleted Oct '67. Catalogue no: **BF 1369**

NOTHING HAS BEEN PROVED
Tracks: / Nothing has been proved / Nothing has been proved (Inst.) / Nothing has been proved (Dance mix) (12" & CD Single only.). Note: Orchestra arranged and conducted by Angelo Badalamenti. Saxophone solo Courtney Pine.a
12" Single: Released Feb '89, on Parlophone, by EMI Records. Catalogue no: **12R 6207**
7" Single: Released Feb '89, on Parlophone, by EMI Records. Deleted Oct '89. Catalogue no: **R 6207**
CD 5": Released Feb '89, on Parlophone, by EMI Records. Catalogue no: **CDR 6207**
7" Single: Released Feb '89, on Parlophone, by EMI Records. Deleted Aug '89. Catalogue no: **RG 6207**
12" Single: Released Feb '89, on Parlophone, by EMI Records. Catalogue no: **12RG 6207**

PRIVATE NUMBER
Tracks: / Private number.
7" Single: Released Mar '84, on Allegience, Catalogue no: **ALES 3**

SOME OF YOUR LOVIN'
Tracks: / Some of your lovin'.
7" Single: Released Sep '65, on Philips, by Phonogram Ltd. Deleted Sep '68. Catalogue no: **BF 1430**

SOMETHING IN YOUR EYES
Tracks: / Something in your eyes / Time / Say yeah.
7" Single: Released Sep '87, on A&M, by A&M Records. Deleted '88. Catalogue no: **AM 406**
12" Single: Released Sep '87, on A&M, by A&M Records. Deleted 1 Aug '88. Catalogue no: **AMY 406**

SOMETIMES LIKE BUTTERFLIES
Tracks: / Sometimes like butterflies.
7" Single: Released Aug '85, on Hippodrome, by Hippodrome Records. Catalogue no: **HIPPO 103**
12" Single: Released Aug '85, on Hippodrome, by Hippodrome Records. Catalogue no: **12 HIPPO 103**

SON OF A PREACHER MAN
Tracks: / Son of a preacher man.
7" Single: Released Dec '68, on Philips, by Phonogram Ltd. Deleted Dec '71. Catalogue no: **BF 1730**

STAY AWHILE
Tracks: / Stay awhile.
7" Single: Released Feb '64, on Philips, by Phonogram Ltd. Deleted Feb '67. Catalogue no: **BF 1311**

YOU DON'T HAVE TO SAY YOU LOVE ME
Tracks: / You don't have to say you love me.
7" Single: Released Mar '66, on Philips, by Phonogram Ltd. Deleted Mar '69. Catalogue no: **BF 1482**
7" Single: Released '80, on Philips, by Phonogram Ltd. Catalogue no: **LR 1962**

YOUR HURTIN' KIND OF LOVE
Tracks: / Your hurtin' kind of love.
7" Single: Released Feb '65, on Philips, by Phonogram Ltd. Deleted Feb '68. Catalogue no: **BF 1396**

YOUR LOVE STILL BRINGS ME TO MY KNEES
Tracks: / Your love still brings me to my knees.
7" Single: Released Jan '80, on Mercury, by Phonogram Ltd. Catalogue no: **DUSTY 5**

Springfield, Rick

Biographical details: Rick Springfield is an Australian actor/singer based in the USA; he was born in Sydney on 23 August 1949. His band Rock House played covers to troops in Vietnam.His first albums on Capitol in 1972, CBS in 1974 were promising but he had work permit problems and he studied acting, landed parts in USA TV shows Wonder Woman, The Incredible Hulk etc; came back to music in 1980 with *Working Class Dog* on RCA, including No.1 USA hit with a hard-rocker, *Jessie's Girl.* More hits have been helped by this role in TV soap opera General Hospital, film Hard To Hold in 1984, videos on MTV. (Donald Clarke 27.5.87).

CELEBRATE YOUTH
Tracks: / Celebrate youth.
12" Single: Released Apr '85, on RCA, by BMG Records (UK). Catalogue no: **PT 49988**
7" Single: Released Apr '85, on RCA, by BMG Records (UK). Catalogue no: **PB 49987**

DON'T TALK TO STRANGERS
Tracks: / Don't talk to strangers / Tonight.
7" Single: Released Apr '82, on RCA, by BMG Records (UK). Catalogue no: **RCA 216**

HUMAN TOUCH
Tracks: / Human touch / Souls.
7" Single: Released Jun '83, on RCA, by BMG Records (UK). Catalogue no: **RCA 341**
7" Single: Released Jan '84, on RCA, by BMG Records (UK). Deleted Jan '87. Catalogue no: **RICK 1**
12" Single: Released Jun '83, on RCA, by BMG Records (UK). Catalogue no: **RCAT 341**

I'VE DONE ANYTHING FOR YOU
Tracks: / I've done anything for you / Jessie's girl.
7" Single: Released Nov '81, on RCA, by BMG Records (UK). Catalogue no: **RCA 158**

JESSIE'S GIRL (SINGLE)
Tracks: / Jessie's girl / Carry me away.
7" Single: Released Mar '84, on RCA, by BMG Records (UK). Catalogue no: **RICK 2**
10" single: Released Mar '84, on RCA, by BMG Records (UK). Catalogue no: **RICKP 2**
7" Single: Released May '81, on RCA, by BMG Records (UK). Catalogue no: **RCA 76**

LOVE SOMEBODY
Tracks: / Love somebody / Great art of conversation.
7" Single: Released May '84, on RCA, by BMG Records (UK). Catalogue no: **RICK 3**
12" Single: Released May '84, on RCA, by BMG Records (UK). Catalogue no: **RICKT 3**

ROCK OF LIFE (SINGLE)
Tracks: / Rock of life.
CD 5": Released Jun '89, on RCA, by BMG Records (UK). Deleted Jul '89. Catalogue no: **PD 49606**
7" Single: Released Feb '88, on RCA, by BMG Records (UK). Deleted May '89. Catalogue no: **PB 49605**
12" Single: Released Feb '88, on RCA, by BMG Records (UK). Deleted May '89. Catalogue no: **PT 49606**

STATE OF THE HEART
Tracks: / State of the heart.
7" Single: Released Aug '85, on RCA, by BMG Records (UK). Catalogue no: **PB 49959**
12" Single: Released Aug '85, on RCA, by BMG Records (UK). Catalogue no: **PT 49960**

WHAT KIND OF FOOL AM I
Tracks: / What kind of fool am I.
7" Single: Released Sep '82, on RCA, by BMG Records (UK). Catalogue no: **RCA 265**

Springfields

BAMBINO
Tracks: / Bambino.
7" Single: Released Nov '61, on Philips, by Phonogram Ltd. Deleted Nov '64. Catalogue no: **BF 1178**

BREAKAWAY
Tracks: / Breakaway.
7" Single: Released Aug '61, on Philips, by Phonogram Ltd. Deleted Aug '64. Catalogue no: **BF 1168**

COME ON HOME
Tracks: / Come on home.
7" Single: Released Jul '63, on Philips, by Phonogram Ltd. Deleted Jul '66. Catalogue no: **BF 1263**

ISLAND OF DREAMS (OLD GOLD)
Tracks: / Island of dreams.
7" Single: Released Jul '82, on Old Gold, by Old Gold Records. Deleted Jul '88. Catalogue no: **OG 9240**

ISLAND OF DREAMS (SINGLE)
Tracks: / Island of dreams.
7" Single: Released Dec '62, on Philips, by Phonogram Ltd. Deleted Dec '65. Catalogue no: **326557 BF**

SAY I WON'T BE THERE
Tracks: / Say I won't be there.
7" Single: Released Mar '63, on Philips, by Phonogram Ltd. Deleted Mar '66. Catalogue no: **326577 BF**

SUNFLOWER
Tracks: / Sunflower.
7" Single: Released Jun '88, on Sarah, Catalogue no: **SARAH 010**

Spring,Jane

LOVE BITES BACK
Tracks: / Love bites back.
12" Single: Released Oct '85, on Carrere, Catalogue no: **CART 374**

Springs, Helena

MIDNIGHT LADY
Tracks: / Midnight lady / Love satisfaction.
7" Single: Released Jul '87, on Arista, by BMG Records (UK). Catalogue no: **RIS 29**
12" Single: Released Jul '87, on Arista, by BMG Records (UK). Catalogue no: **RIST 29**

PAPER MONEY
Tracks: / Paper money / Go all the way.
12" Single: Released 23 May '87, on Arista, by BMG Records (UK). Catalogue no: **RIST 19**
7" Single: Released 23 May '87, on Arista, by BMG Records (UK). Catalogue no: **RIS 19**

Springsteen, Bruce

Biographical details: Bruce Springsteen was born Bruce Frederick Joseph Springsteen on 23 September 1949 in Freehold, New Jersey; a rock singer, guitarist, songwriter and bandleader, he is one of the biggest stars on the planet, aka 'The Boss'. He worked in a number of local bands, struck up firm relationship 1969-71 with guitarist 'Miami' Steve Van Zandt, had put together his E Street band by 1972 and was signed to CBS by John Hammond; his first two albums would have attracted attention by themselves, but he had to endure the press's attempts to name him the new Bob Dylan, and critic Jon Landau's describing him as the future of rock'n'roll. Then he had management problems which kept him out of the studio for several years; hard touring and marathon live sets meant that he became the most widely bootlegged recording artist since Dylan. He survived all this precisely because his appeal to his audience is the antithesis of hype. He knows the things that his audience knows: that most people's lives are ordinary lives and require the unromantic shouldering of responsibilities; he is a patriot too, but unlike president Reagen (who quoted some of Springsteen's lyrics during his last presidential campaign) he knows that loving one's country is not an uncomplicated act. With scrupulous attention to recording and generous, marathon live sets, all this means that even as a superstar his reciprocal identification with his audience is complete. Many of his songs are the only classic rock songs of recent years; he may in fact be the last rock star. (Donald Clarke 27.5.87)..

ATLANTIC CITY
Tracks: / Atlantic City / Mansion on the hill.
7" Single: Released Oct '82, on CBS, by CBS Records. Deleted Oct '85. Catalogue no: **A 2794**

BORN IN THE U.S.A. (SINGLE)
Tracks: / Born in the U.S.A. / Shut out the light.
12" Single: Released May '88, on Columbia (USA), by CBS Records (USA). Catalogue no: **4405147**
CD 3": Released Aug '88, on Columbia (USA), by CBS Records (USA). Catalogue no: **38K04680**

BORN TO RUN (SINGLE)
Tracks: / Born to run / Seeds (On 12").
CD 5": Released May '87, on CBS, by CBS Records. Deleted Nov '87. Catalogue no: **BRUCE C1**
7" Single: Released May '87, on CBS, by CBS Records. Deleted Nov '87. Catalogue no: **BRUCE 2**
12" Single: Released May '87, on CBS, by CBS Records. Deleted Nov '87. Catalogue no: **BRUCE T2**

BRILLIANT DISGUISE
Tracks: / Brilliant disguise / Lucky man. Note: Picture bag.
12" Single: Released Sep '87, on CBS, by CBS Records. Catalogue no: **651 141 6**
7" Single: Released Sep '87, on CBS, by CBS Records. Catalogue no: **651 141 7**
12" Single: Released Sep '87, on CBS, by CBS Records. Catalogue no: **651 141 0**

CADILLAC RANCH
Tracks: / Cadillac ranch / Wreck on the highway.
7" Single: Released Sep '81, on CBS, by CBS Records. Deleted '84. Catalogue no: **A 1557**

CHIMES OF FREEDOM
Tracks: / Chimes of freedom (live) / Be true (live) / Tougher than the rest (live) / Born to run (accoustic) (live).
CD 3": Released Sep '88, on Columbia (USA), by CBS Records (USA). Catalogue no: **44K44445**
12" Single: Released Sep '88, on Columbia (USA), by CBS Records (USA). Catalogue no: **4C44445**

COVER ME
Tracks: / Cover me / Jersey girl / Shut out the light (on 12" only) / Dancing in the dark (on 12" only).
7" Set: Released Sep '84, on CBS, by CBS Records. Catalogue no: **DA 4622**
7" Single: Released Oct '84, on CBS, by CBS Records. Deleted Oct '87. Catalogue no: **A 4662**

SPROUTHEAD UPRISING - THROW SOME WATER IN (Released on Stiff)

12" Single: Released May '88, on Columbia (USA), by CBS Records (USA). Catalogue no: **4405087**

DANCING IN THE DARK
Tracks: / Dancing in the dark / Pink cadillac.
7" Single: Released May '84, on CBS, by CBS Records. Deleted May '87. Catalogue no: **A 4436**

FIRE
Tracks: / Fire.
12" Single: Released Jan '87, on CBS, by CBS Records. Deleted Aug '87. Catalogue no: **650 381 6**
7" Single: Released Jan '87, on CBS, by CBS Records. Deleted Aug '87. Catalogue no: **650 381 7**

GLORY DAYS
Tracks: / Glory days.
7" Single: Released Aug '85, on CBS, by CBS Records. Deleted Aug '88. Catalogue no: **A 6375**

HUNGRY HEART
Tracks: / Hungry heart / Held up without a gun.
7" Single: Released Nov '80, on CBS, by CBS Records. Deleted Nov '83. Catalogue no: **CBS 9309**

I'M ON FIRE
7" Single: Released Jun '85, on CBS, by CBS Records. Deleted Jun '88. Catalogue no: **A 6342**

ONE STEP UP
Tracks: / One step up.
CD 5": Released May '88, on CBS (Holland), by CBS Records. Catalogue no: **6514422**

OPEN ALL NIGHT
Tracks: / Open all night / Big pay back.
7" Single: Released Nov '82, on CBS, by CBS Records. Catalogue no: **A 2926**

RIVER, THE (SINGLE)
Tracks: / River, The.
7" Single: Released Jun '81, on CBS, by CBS Records. Deleted Jun '84. Catalogue no: **A 1179**

SANTA CLAUS IS COMING TO TOWN
Tracks: / Santa Claus is coming to town / My hometown.
7" Single: Released Dec '85, on Epic, by CBS Records. Deleted Dec '88. Catalogue no: **A 6773**

SHERRY DARLING
Tracks: / Sherry darling / To be true.
7" Single: Released Feb '81, on CBS, by CBS Records. Deleted Feb '84. Catalogue no: **CBS 9568**

SPARE PARTS
Tracks: / Spare parts / Pink cadillac / Spare parts (live) / Chimes of freedom.
12" Single: Released 19 Sep '88, on CBS, by CBS Records. Deleted 17 Apr '89. Catalogue no: **BRUCE Q4**
12" Single: Released 16 Sep '88, on CBS, by CBS Records. Deleted 17 Apr '89. Catalogue no: **BRUCE T4**
CD 5": Released Sep '88, on CBS, by CBS Records. Deleted 17 Apr '89. Catalogue no: **BRUCE B4**
CD 5": Released 16 Sep '88, on CBS, by CBS Records. Deleted 17 Apr '89. Catalogue no: **BRUCE C4**
7" Single: Released 16 Sep '88, on CBS, by CBS Records. Deleted 17 Apr '89. Catalogue no: **BRUCE 4**

TOUGHER THAN THE REST
Tracks: / Tougher than the rest / Tougher than the rest (live) / Roulette / Be true (live) / Born to run (new live).
12" Single: Released 6 Jun '88, on CBS, by CBS Records. Deleted Jan '89. Catalogue no: **BRUCE T3**
7" Single: Released 6 Jun '88, on CBS, by CBS Records. Deleted Jan '89. Catalogue no: **BRUCE 3**
CD 5": Released 6 Jun '88, on CBS, by CBS Records. Deleted Jan '89. Catalogue no: **BRUCE C3**
12" Single: Released 13 Jun '88, on CBS, by CBS Records. Deleted Jan '89. Catalogue no: **BRUCE Q3**
7" Single: Released 13 Jun '88, on CBS, by CBS Records. Deleted Jan '89. Catalogue no: **BRUCE B3**

TUNNEL OF LOVE I
CD 3": Released '88, on CBS/Sony (Japan), by CBS Records. Catalogue no: **15 EP 8009**

TUNNEL OF LOVE II
CD 3": Released '88, on CBS/Sony (Japan), by CBS Records. Catalogue no: **15 EP 8010**

TUNNEL OF LOVE (SINGLE)
Tracks: / Tunnel of love / Two for the road / Brilliant disguise (Only on 3"CD single.).
CD 5": Released Dec '87, on CBS, by CBS Records. Deleted Jan '89. Catalogue no: **651 295 2**
12" Single: Released Nov '87, on CBS, by CBS Records. Deleted Jan '89. Catalogue no: **651 295-8**
12" Single: Released Nov '87, on CBS, by CBS Records. Deleted Jan '89. Catalogue no: **651 295 6**
7" Single: Released Nov '87, on CBS, by CBS Records. Deleted Jan '89. Catalogue no: **651 295 7**
CD 3": Released Sep '88, on CBS/Sony (Japan), by CBS Records. Catalogue no: **10EP3001**

WAR
Tracks: / Merry Xmas baby / Incident of 5th street / War.
7" Single: Released Nov '86, on CBS, by CBS Records. Catalogue no: **650193 7**
12" Single: Released Nov '86, on CBS, by CBS Records. Catalogue no: **650193 6**

Springstone, Bruce

TAKE ME OUT TO THE BALLPARK
Tracks: / Take me out to the ballpark.
7" Single: Released Jul '85, on Food For Thought, by Music For Nations Records. Catalogue no: **YUM 104**

Springwater

FIRST TIME
Tracks: / First time.
7" Single: Released Nov '82, on Flying, by Flying Records. Catalogue no: **FLY 103**

HARBOUR LIGHTS
Tracks: / Harbour lights / I will return.
7" Single: Released Jul '80, on Fabulous. Deleted Jul '83. Catalogue no: **FABS 103**

I WILL RETURN
Tracks: / I will return.
7" Single: Released Oct '71, on Polydor, by Polydor Ltd. Deleted Oct '74. Catalogue no: **2058 141**
7" Single: Released Jul '84, on Old Gold, by Old Gold Records. Catalogue no: **OG 9434**

Sprout Head Uprising

I WISH, I WISH
Tracks: / I wish I wish.
7" Single: Released Sep '82, on Rock Steady, by Rock Steady Records. Catalogue no: **MICK 011**

THROW SOME WATER IN (see panel)
Tracks: / Throw some water in / Nothing to sing.
7" Single: Released Jul '82, on Stiff, by Stiff Records. Catalogue no: **BUY 121**

Sprung Aus Dem Wolkum

PAS ATTENDRE
Tracks: / Pas Attendre.
12" Single: Released Feb '86, on Les Disques Du Soleil et De L'acier, by Red Rhino Records. Catalogue no: **DSA 54505**

Spurling, Johnny

TIMEWASTER
Tracks: / Timewaster.
CD 5": Released Jun '89, on Nightingale, Deleted Sep '89. Catalogue no: **CDNTG 1**
12" Single: Released Jun '89, on Nightingale, Deleted Sep '89. Catalogue no: **12NTG 1**
7" Single: Released Jun '89, on Nightingale, Catalogue no: **NTG 1**

Sputniks

SIX BY THE SPUTNIKS
12" Single: Released '87, on Wooley, Catalogue no: **SPUT 1001**

Spy

WHOLE LOTTA WAYS (TO CATCH A FISH)
Tracks: / Whole lotta ways (to catch a fish) / Gone fishing.
7" Single: Released Jun '84, on Mission Discs, by Mission Discs Records. Catalogue no: **BD 95**

Spyder D

HOW YA LIKE ME NOW
Tracks: / How ya like me now.
12" Single: Released Sep '87, on Profile (USA), by Profile Records (USA). Catalogue no: **PRO 7158**

I CAN'T WAIT (To rock the mike)
Tracks: / I can't wait.
7" Single: Released Jun '86, on Champion, by Champion Records. Catalogue no: **CHAMP 14**
12" Single: Released Jun '86, on Champion, by Champion Records. Deleted Aug '89. Catalogue no: **CHAMP 1214**

Spyro Gyra

CATCHING THE SUN (SINGLE)
Tracks: / Catching the sun / Percoloator / Cockatoo.
7" Single: Released Feb '80, on MCA, by MCA Records. Deleted Feb '83. Catalogue no: **MCA 568**

FREETIME (SINGLE)
Tracks: / Freetime / String soup.
7" Single: Released Nov '81, on MCA, by MCA Records. Deleted Nov '84. Catalogue no: **MCA 746**
12" Single: Released Nov '81, on MCA, by MCA Records. Deleted Nov '84. Catalogue no: **MCAT 746**

MORNING DANCE (SINGLE)
Tracks: / Morning dance.
7" Single: Released Jul '79, on Infinity, by MCA Records (USA). Deleted Jul '82. Catalogue no: **INF 111**

Squad

WHY DO YOU MAKE ME WAIT?
Tracks: / Why do you make me wait.
12" Single: Released May '82, on Sparkside, Deleted '86. Catalogue no: **EXT 004**

Square Department

LOVE ME
Tracks: / Love me.
7" Single: Released Aug '83, on Record Shack, by Record Shack Records. Catalogue no: **SOHO 7**

Square Peg

CAN'T SAY NO
Tracks: / Can't say no.
7" Single: Released Apr '89, on Stranded, by Stranded Records. Catalogue no: **XLNT 003**

ECHOES OF WAR
Tracks: / Echoes of war.
7" Single: Released Jun '84, on Stranded, by Stranded Records. Catalogue no: **XLNT 1**

Squeeze

Biographical details: Squeeze is a UK pop group formed in 1975 in Deptford, London by guitarists/vocalists/songwriters Glenn Tillbrook (born 31st August 1957) and Chris Difford (born april 1951 in Sheffield) with Jools Holland (born 24 January 1958) on keyboards, replaced by Paul Carrack (born april 1951 in Sheffield); John Bently an bass (born 16 April 1951) and Gilson Lavis on drums (born 27 june 1951). Difford and Tillbrook are the writers; critics compared them to Lennon & McCartney, though they were closer in style to the Kinks' Ray Davies. After *Argybargy* in 1980 Holland quit, released boogie album *Jools Holland And The Millionaires* 1981; fronted pop show The Tube on UK TV; his replacement Carrack quit in 1981, Worked with Nick Lowe and Carlene Carter and made solo albums. Squeeze split in 1982; Difford and Tilbrook wrote musical *Labelled With Love*, produced in Deptford in 1983, then album *Difford & Tillbrook* 1984. Squeze reunited for *Cosi Fan Titti Frutti* in 1985 and it was generally agreed that their charm was intact. (Donald Clarke 27.5.87).

853-5937

SQUEEZE - ANOTHER NAIL IN MY HEART (Released on A&M)

Tracks: / 853-5937 / Tough love.
12" Single: Released Jan '88, on A&M, by A&M Records. Deleted 1 Aug '88. Catalogue no: **AMY 426**
7" Single: Released Jan '88, on A&M, by A&M Records. Deleted 1 Aug '88. Catalogue no: **AM 426**

ANNIE GET YOUR GUN
Tracks: / Annie get your gun.
7" Single: Released Oct '82, on A&M, by A&M Records. Deleted Oct '85. Catalogue no: **AMS 8259**

ANOTHER NAIL IN THE HEART (see panel on previous page)
Tracks: / Another nail in my heart / Pretty thing.
7" Single: Released Mar '80, on A&M, by A&M Records. Deleted Mar '83. Catalogue no: **AMS 7507**

BANG BANG
Tracks: / Bang bang.
7" Single: Released Jun '78, on A&M, by A&M Records. Deleted Jun '81. Catalogue no: **AMS 7360**

BLACK COFFEE IN BED
Tracks: / Black coffee in bed / Hunt.
7" Single: Released Apr '82, on A&M, by A&M Records. Deleted '88. Catalogue no: **AMS 8219**

CHRISTMAS DAY
Tracks: / Christmas day / Going crazy.
7" Single: Released Nov '80, on A&M, by A&M Records. Deleted Nov '83. Catalogue no: **AMS 7495**

COOL FOR CATS (OLD GOLD)
Tracks: / Cool for cats.
7" Single: Released Sep '85, on Old Gold, by Old Gold Records. Catalogue no: **OG 9546**

COOL FOR CATS (SINGLE)
Tracks: / Cool for cats.
7" Single: Released Mar '79, on A&M, by A&M Records. Deleted Mar '82. Catalogue no: **AMS 7426**

FOOTPRINTS
Tracks: / Footprints / Striking matches (instant buff).
Note: "To tie in with their U.K. tour, Squeeze release a new single "Footprints". The Difford/Tilbrook composition, taken from the "Babylon And On" album, is available both on 7" and extended 12"." (A&M Records, June 1988).
12" Single: Released 27 Jun '88, on A&M, by A&M Records. Deleted Feb '89. Catalogue no: **AMY 450**
7" Single: Released 27 Jun '88, on A&M, by A&M Records. Deleted Feb '89. Catalogue no: **AM 450**

GOODBYE GIRL
Tracks: / Goodbye girl.
7" Single: Released Nov '78, on A&M, by A&M Records. Deleted Nov '81. Catalogue no: **AMS 7398**

HOUR GLASS
Tracks: / Hour glass / Wedding bells / Splitting into three* (*Extra track on 12").
12" Single: Released Jul '87, on A&M, by A&M Records. Deleted 1 Aug '88. Catalogue no: **AMY 400**
7" Single: Released Jul '87, on A&M, by A&M Records. Deleted 1 Aug '88. Catalogue no: **AM 400**

IF IT'S LOVE
Tracks: / If it's love / Franks bag.
12" Single: Released Sep '89, on A&M, by A&M Records. Catalogue no: **AMY 530**
7" Single: Released Sep '89, on A&M, by A&M Records. Catalogue no: **AM 530**
CD 5": Released Sep '89, on A&M, by A&M Records. Catalogue no: **CDEE 530**

IS THAT LOVE
Tracks: / Is that love / Trust.
7" Single: Released May '81, on A&M, by A&M Records. Deleted May '84. Catalogue no: **AMS 8129**

KING GEORGE STREET
Tracks: / King George Street / Love's crashing ways (live) / Up the junction (live) (on 12" only).
12" Single: Released Apr '86, on A&M, by A&M Records. Deleted '88. Catalogue no: **AMY 306**
7" Single: Released Apr '86, on A&M, by A&M Records. Deleted '88. Catalogue no: **AM 306**

LABELLED WITH LOVE
Tracks: / Labelled with love / Squabs on forty fab.
7" Single: Released Sep '81, on A&M, by A&M Records. Catalogue no: **AMS 8166**

LAST TIME FOREVER
Tracks: / Last time forever.
7" Single: Released Jun '85, on A&M, by A&M Records. Deleted Jun '88. Catalogue no: **AM 255**

PULLING MUSSELS (FROM THE SHELL)
Tracks: / Pulling mussels (from the shell) / What the butler saw.
7" Single: Released May '80, on A&M, by A&M Records. Deleted May '83. Catalogue no: **AMS 7523**

SLAP AND TICKLE
Tracks: / Slap and tickle.
7" Single: Released Sep '79, on A&M, by A&M Records. Deleted Sep '82. Catalogue no: **AMS 7466**

TAKE ME I'M YOURS (OLD GOLD)
Tracks: / Take me I'm yours.
7" Single: Released Oct '83, on Old Gold, by Old Gold Records. Catalogue no: **OG 9364**

TAKE ME I'M YOURS (SINGLE)
Tracks: / Take me I'm yours.
7" Single: Released Apr '78, on A&M, by A&M Records. Deleted Apr '81. Catalogue no: **AMS 7335**

TEMPTED
Tracks: / Tempted / Yap, yap, yap.
7" Single: Released Jul '81, on A&M, by A&M Records. Deleted Jul '84. Catalogue no: **AMS 8147**

TRUST ME TO OPEN MY MOUTH
Tracks: / Trust me to open my mouth / Take me I'm yours (live) / Black coffee in bed (live) (Only on 12" single.).
12" Single: Released Sep '87, on A&M, by A&M Records. Deleted 1 Aug '88. Catalogue no: **AMY 412**
7" Single: Released Sep '87, on A&M, by A&M Records. Deleted 1 Aug '88. Catalogue no: **AM 412**

UP THE JUNCTION
Tracks: / Up the junction.
7" Single: Released Jun '79, on A&M, by A&M Records. Deleted Jun '82. Catalogue no: **AMS 7444**

WAITING GAME, THE
Tracks: / Waiting game, The / Last time forever / Prisoner, The (on 12" only.).
12" Single: Released Nov '87, on A&M, by A&M Records. Deleted 1 Aug '88. Catalogue no: **AMY 420**
7" Single: Released Nov '87, on A&M, by A&M Records. Deleted 1 Aug '88. Catalogue no: **AM 420**

WHEN THE HANGOVER STRIKES
Tracks: / When the hangover strikes / Elephant girl.
7" Single: Released Jul '82, on A&M, by A&M Records. Deleted Jul '85. Catalogue no: **AMS 8237**

Squeezebrain...

LOVEGROOVE
Tracks: / Lovegroove / Slowly true is the love that grooves / Lustgroove / More love, more groove.
CD 5": Released 16 Jan '89, on Club, by Phonogram Ltd. Catalogue no: **JABCD 76**
12" Single: Released 16 Jan '89, on Club, by Phonogram Ltd. Deleted 31 Jul '89. Catalogue no: **JABX 76**
7" Single: Released 16 Jan '89, on Club, by Phonogram Ltd. Deleted 31 Jul '89. Catalogue no: **JAB 76**

Squibley, Steve

BAD MAN
Tracks: / Bad man.
12" Single: Released Nov '84, on White label (2), Catalogue no: **Unknown**

Squibs

ON THE LINE
Tracks: / On the line.
7" Single: Released Jul '81, on Oily, by Oily Records. Catalogue no: **SLICK 1**

PARADES
Tracks: / Parades / Out on the town.
7" Single: Released Jul '81, on Oily, by Oily Records. Catalogue no: **SLICK 3**

Squier, Billy

Biographical details: Billy Squier was born 12 May 1950 in Wellesey Hills, Massachusetts. He is a heavy metal singer/guitarist. Formed Sidewinders while still at school; then Piper (two albums c. 1977), went solo. His second album *Don't Say No* in 1981 yielded three USA hit singles. Despite his Anglophile leanings he has not done as well in the UK and so followed a more American trail, contributing to soundtrack of *Fast Times At Ridgemont High* in 1983. (Donald Clarke 27.5.88).

EMOTIONS IN MOTION (SINGLE)
Tracks: / Emotions in motion / Catch 22.
7" Single: Released Sep '82, on Capitol, by EMI Records. Deleted '88. Catalogue no: **CL 261**

EVERYBODY WANTS YOU
Tracks: / Everybody wants you / Keep me satisfied.
7" Single: Released Jan '83, on Capitol, by EMI Records. Deleted '88. Catalogue no: **CL 273**

IN THE DARK
Tracks: / In the dark / Rich kid.
7" Single: Released Jun '81, on Capitol, by EMI Records. Deleted Jun '84. Catalogue no: **CL 206**

LOVE IS THE HERO
Tracks: / Learn how to live (live).
7" Single: Released Jan '87, on Capitol, by EMI Records. Deleted '88. Catalogue no: **CL 433**
12" Single: Released Jan '87, on Capitol, by EMI Records. Deleted '88. Catalogue no: **12CL 433**

ROCK ME TONITE
Tracks: / Rock me tonite.
7" Single: Released Aug '84, on Capitol, by EMI Records. Catalogue no: **SQD 1**

STROKE, THE
Tracks: / Stroke, The / My kinda lover.
7" Single: Released Oct '81, on Capitol, by EMI Records. Deleted Oct '84. Catalogue no: **CL 214**

TOO DAZE GONE
Tracks: / Too daze gone / Whadda you want from me.
7" Single: Released Feb '82, on Capitol, by EMI Records. Deleted '88. Catalogue no: **CL 231**

YOU SHOULD BE HIGH LOVE
Tracks: / You should be high love / Music's all right.
7" Single: Released Aug '80, on Capitol, by EMI Records. Deleted '83. Catalogue no: **CL 16160**

Squire

EVERY TRICK IN THE BOOK OF LOVE
Tracks: / Every trick in the book of love.
12" Single: Released Oct '83, on C. More Tone, by Backs Recording Co.. Catalogue no: **HIT 003**

GIRL ON A TRAIN
Tracks: / Girl on a train.
7" Single: Released Jul '82, on Hi-Lo, by Hi-Lo Records & Tapes. Catalogue no: **HI 002**

JASAMINE
Tracks: / Jasamine.
7" Single: Released Sep '83, on Hi-Lo, by Hi-Lo Records & Tapes. Catalogue no: **HI 004**

NO TIME TOMORROW
Tracks: / No time tomorrow.
7" Single: Released Apr '82, on Hi-Lo, by Hi-Lo Records & Tapes. Catalogue no: **HI 001**

YOUNG IDEA, THE
Tracks: / Young idea, The.
7" Single: Released Jun '84, on Squire Fan Club, by Hi-Lo Records & Tapes. Catalogue no: **SFC 2**

Squire, Chris

RUN WITH THE FOX
Tracks: / Run with the fox / Return of the fox.
7" Single: Released Dec '82, on Atlantic, by WEA Records. Catalogue no: **K 11695**

Squire, Paul

RAINBOWS END
Tracks: / Rainbows end / Nicles and dimes.
7" Single: Released Oct '81, on Roxon, Catalogue no: **ROX 027**

Squires, Audrey

SILENT CHRISTMAS
Tracks: / Silent Christmas / Ding dong on Christmas night.
Note: All profits to st Raphaels hospice.
7" Single: Released Nov '86, on Lakeside, by Lakeside Records. Catalogue no: **LM 104**

Squires, Dorothy

FOR ONCE IN MY LIFE
Tracks: / For once in my life.
7" Single: Released Sep '69, on President, by President Records. Deleted Sep '73. Catalogue no: **PT 267**

I'M WALKING BEHIND YOU
Tracks: / I'm walking behind you.
7" Single: Released Jun '53, on Polygon, Deleted Jun '56. Catalogue no: **P 1068**

MY WAY
Tracks: / My way.
7" Single: Released Aug '70, on President, by President Records. Deleted Aug '73. Catalogue no: **PT 305**

SAY IT WITH FLOWERS (SINGLE)
Tracks: / Say it with flowers / And so to sleep again.
7" Single: Released Aug '61, on Columbia, by EMI Records. Deleted Aug '64. Catalogue no: **DB 4665**

TILL
Tracks: / Till.
7" Single: Released Feb '70, on President, by President Records. Deleted Feb '73. Catalogue no: **PT 281**

WE CLOWNS (SINGLE)
Tracks: / We clowns / I'm glad there is you.
7" Single: Released Mar '81, on President, by President Records. Deleted Mar '84. Catalogue no: **PT 490**

WINE IS THERE,THE
Tracks: / Try a little tenderness / Wine is there, The.
7" Single: Released Feb '87, on Esban, Catalogue no: **ES 14**

YOU'LL NEVER WALK ALONE
Tracks: / You'll never walk alone.
7" Single: Released Jul '85, on Esban, Catalogue no: **ES 10**

Squirrel Bait

KID DYNAMITE
Tracks: / Kid dynamite / Slake train coming.
7" Single: Released '86, on Homestead, Catalogue no: **HMS 061**

St. Andrew

PINBALL WIZARD
Tracks: / Pinball wizard / Skye boat song.
7" Single: Released Jul '86, on Dark Side Of The Haggis, Catalogue no: **DSH 001**

St. Andrews...

THANKS
Tracks: / Thanks / Black diamonds and green valleys.
Note: All proceeds to Aid International Foundation Charity
7" Single: Released Apr '86, on E.C.B.P., Deleted '87. Catalogue no: **ECBP 1**

St. Andrews Chorale

CLOUD 99
7" Single: Released Feb '76, on Decca, by Decca Records. Deleted Feb '79. Catalogue no: **F 13617**

St. Augustines...

BRAND NEW SHIRT & TIE
Tracks: / Brand new shirt & tie.
7" Single: Released Apr '81, on Stage One, Catalogue no: **STS 003**

St. Benedicts...

CHILDREN OF THE WORLD
Tracks: / Children of the world.
7" Single: Released Jan '87, on Twink, by Twink Records. Catalogue no: **TWK 47**

St. Cecilia

LEAP UP AND DOWN (WAVE YOUR KNICKERS IN THE AIR)
Tracks: / Leap up and down (wave your knickers in the air).
7" Single: Released Jun '71, on Polydor, by Polydor Ltd. Deleted Jun '74. Catalogue no: **2058 104**

St. Che

BE MY....
Tracks: / Be my.... / Exquisite.
12" Single: Released Oct '86, on Siren, by Virgin Records. Deleted May '88. Catalogue no: **SIREN 6-12**
7" Single: Released Oct '86, on Siren, by Virgin Records. Deleted May '88. Catalogue no: **SIREN 6**

St. Christopher

ALL OF A TREMBLE
Tracks: / All of a tremble.
7" Single: Released 24 Jul '89, on Sarah, Catalogue no: **SARAH 020**

CRYSTAL CLEAR
Tracks: / Crystal clear.
7" Single: Released Mar '84, on Red Rhino, by Red Rhino Records. Catalogue no: **GM 001**

GO AHEAD, CRY....
Tracks: / Go ahead and cry.
7" Single: Released Nov '86, on G & M, by G&M Tapes & Records. Catalogue no: **GM 003**

YOU DESERVE MORE
Tracks: / You deserve more.
7" Single: Released Feb '89, on Sarah, Catalogue no: **SARAH 15**

St. Clair, Carl

I PRETEND
Tracks: / I pretend.
7" Single: Released Jun '88, on Kalabash, Catalogue no: **KAL 007**

IT MUST BE YOU
Tracks: / It must be you.
7" Single: Released 21 Apr '89, on Kalabash, Catalogue no: **KAL 008**

St. Clair, Mick

DEEP HOUSE XTC
Tracks: / Deep house XTC / Deep house XTC (bhangra version) / Ishq dic gaddi.
12" Single: Released Apr '89, on Star, Catalogue no: **SRL PW01**
7" Single: Released Apr '89, on Star, Deleted Aug '89. Catalogue no: **ST 1**

FOR BRITANNIA
Tracks: / For Britannia / Love comes along.
7" Single: Released Apr '81, on Britannia Records, Deleted '85. Catalogue no: **BRIT 001**

St. James, Michael

FEEL MY LOVE
Tracks: / Feel my love / Sad song.
7" Single: Released Jan '86, on WEA, by WEA Records. Catalogue no: **YZ 58**
12" Single: Released Jan '86, on WEA, by WEA Records. Catalogue no: **YZ 58T**

GIFT FROM THE HEART
Tracks: / Gift from the heart, A (St James/Wherry.) / Holding back (St James/Hiller.) / Shine a light (12" only.).
12" Single: Released Mar '89, on Hit Or Miss, Deleted Aug '89. Catalogue no: **12HOM 5**
7" Single: Released Mar '89, on Hit Or Miss, Deleted Aug '89. Catalogue no: **HOM 5**

NOBODY WANTS TO LOVE ME
Tracks: / Nobody wants to love me / Shine a light.
7" Single: Released Sep '87, on Hit Or Miss, Deleted Jan '88. Catalogue no: **HOM 3**
12" Single: Released Sep '87, on Hit Or Miss, Deleted Jan '88. Catalogue no: **12HOM 3**

THERE IS ONLY ONE LOVE
Tracks: / There is only one love.
7" Single: Released Jul '85, on WEA, by WEA Records. Catalogue no: **YZ 44**

St. James, Phyllis

CANDLELIGHT AFTERNOON
Tracks: / Candlelight afternoon.
7" Single: Released Sep '84, on Motown, by BMG Records (UK). Catalogue no: **TMG 1358**

St. John, Barry

COME AWAY MELINDA
Tracks: / Come away Melinda.
7" Single: Released Dec '65, on Columbia, by EMI Records. Deleted Dec '68. Catalogue no: **DB 7783**

St. John, Vince

THREE R BOOGIE
Tracks: / Three r boogie / Alone in a room full of people / I'm in trouble over you / Tribute to Jerry Lee.
7" EP: on Magnum Force, by Magnum Music Group. Catalogue no: **MFEP 008**

St. Johns...

ONE STAR
Tracks: / One star / Star of Bethlehem.
7" Single: Released Dec '83, on Rebound, Catalogue no: **BOUNCE 2**

QUEEN'S BIRTHDAY, THE
Tracks: / Queen's birthday, The / Sparkling.
7" Single: Released Apr '86, on Columbia, by EMI Records. Catalogue no: **Q1**

St. Joseph's...

MY BEST FRIEND
7" Single: Released Nov '85, on Weasel, by Weasel Records. Catalogue no: **WR 4011**

St. Louis Union

GIRL
Tracks: / Girl.
7" Single: Released Jan '66, on Decca, by Decca Records. Deleted Jan '69. Catalogue no: **F 12318**

St. Paul

INTIMACY
Tracks: / Intimacy / Intimacy (instrumental) / Intimacy (extended) (Featured on 12" version only.) / Intimacy (bonus beats) (Featured on 12" version only.).
12" Single: Released 25 Apr '88, on MCA, by MCA Records. Catalogue no: **MCAT 1245**
7" Single: Released 25 Apr '88, on MCA, by MCA Records. Catalogue no: **MCA 1245**

St. Paul's...

MORNING HAS BROKEN
Tracks: / Morning has broken / Nunc dimittis.
7" Single: Released Dec '80, on Charisma, by Virgin Records. Deleted Dec '85. Catalogue no: **CB 376**

NYMPHS AND SHEPHERDS
Tracks: / Nymphs and shepherds / O for the wings of a dove.
7" Single: Released Nov '82, on Pip, by Pip Records. Catalogue no: **PIP 8201**

SILENT NIGHT
Tracks: / Silent night.
7" Single: Released Nov '80, on Charisma, by Virgin Records. Deleted '89. Catalogue no: **CB 376**

St Peters, Crispian

CHANGES
Tracks: / Changes.
7" Single: Released Sep '66, on Decca, by Decca Records. Deleted Sep '69. Catalogue no: **F 12480**

PIED PIPER
Tracks: / Pied piper.
7" Single: Released Mar '66, on Decca, by Decca Records. Deleted Mar '69. Catalogue no: **F 12359**

YOU WERE ON MY MIND
Tracks: / You were on my mind.
7" Single: Released Jan '66, on Decca, by Decca Records. Deleted Jan '69. Catalogue no: **F 12287**
CD 5": Released 24 Apr '89, on Old Gold, by Old Gold Records. Catalogue no: **OG 6137**
7" Single: Released Apr '80, on Virgin, by Virgin Records. Deleted Apr '83. Catalogue no: **VS 342**

St Philips Choir

ADORAMUS Featuring Jaymi Bandtock
Tracks: / Adoramus / San Damiano.
7" Single: Released Dec '88, on BBC, by BBC Records & Tapes. Catalogue no: **RESL 230**

SING FOREVER (SINGLE)
Tracks: / Sing forever / Light the candles.
7" Single: Released Jul '87, on BBC, by BBC Records & Tapes. Deleted 31 Aug '88. Catalogue no: **RESL 222**

St. Vitus

THIRSTY AND MISERABLE
Tracks: / Thirsty and miserable.
7" EP: Released Jul '87, on SST (USA), by SST Records (USA). Catalogue no: **SST 119**

WALKING DEAD, THE
Tracks: / Walking dead, The.
12" Single: Released Nov '85, on SST (USA), by SST Records (USA). Catalogue no: **SST 042**

St. Winifred's...

NO ONE QUITE LIKE GRANDMA
Tracks: / No one quite like grandma / Grandad.
7" Single: Released Nov '80, on MFP, by EMI Records. Deleted Nov '83. Catalogue no: **FP 900**
7" Single: Released Nov '88, on Columbia, by EMI Records. Deleted Oct '89. Catalogue no: **DB 9172**

WELCOME JOHN PAUL
Tracks: / Welcome John Paul / I can hear his voice.
7" Single: Released Apr '82, on Columbia, by EMI Records. Deleted Apr '85. Catalogue no: **DB 9094**

Staa Marx

CRAZY WEEKEND
Tracks: / Crazy weekend.
7" Single: Released Feb '79, on Cherry Red, by Cherry Red Records. Deleted '87. Catalogue no: **CHERRY 4**

Stabilizers

TYRANNY (SINGLE)
Tracks: / Tyranny.
7" Single: Released Aug '86, on CBS, by CBS Records. Catalogue no: **A 7187**
12" Single: Released Aug '86, on CBS, by CBS Records. Catalogue no: **TA 7187**

Stacey, Mike

I WANT YOU
Tracks: / I want you / Everything I am.
7" Single: Released May '87, on Sierra, by Sierra Records. Catalogue no: **FED 35**

Stacks

YOU'RE ON MY MIND
Tracks: / You're on my mind / Maybe monday.
7" Single: Released Mar '84, on Brand New, by Brand New Records. Deleted '88. Catalogue no: **BN 452**

Staddon, James

COMING HOME TO YOU
Tracks: / Coming home to you / I see a change in you.
7" Single: Released Mar '88, on Sagittarius, by Sagittarius Records. Catalogue no: **SAG/SRL/2**

Staff

TCHA TCHA TCHINA
Tracks: / Tcha Tcha Tchina / Secrets.
7" Single: Released Feb '82, on PRT, by Castle Communications Records. Catalogue no: **7P 231**

Staff, Kathy

BENNY
Tracks: / Benny.
7" Single: Released Mar '83, on Monarch, by Monarch Records. Catalogue no: **MON 039**

Stafford, Jim

LITTLE BITS AND PIECES
Tracks: / Little bits and pieces / Banjo Billy.
7" Single: Released Nov '84, on CBS, by CBS Records. Catalogue no: **A 4235**

MY GIRL BILL
Tracks: / My girl Bill.
7" Single: Released Jul '74, on MGM, by Polydor Ltd. Deleted Jul '77. Catalogue no: **2006 423**

SPIDERS AND SNAKES
Tracks: / Spiders and snakes.
7" Single: Released Jul '84, on Old Gold, by Old Gold Records. Catalogue no: **OG 9440**
7" Single: Released Apr '74, on MGM, by Polydor Ltd. Deleted Apr '78. Catalogue no: **2006 374**

Stafford, Jo

Biographical details: Jo Stafford was born on 12th november, 1920 in California; she is one of the most highly regarded of pop singers by public, critics and musicians alike. She joined the vocal group the Pied Pipers; they joined Tommy Dorsey in 1940 (Frank Sinatra was a member for a while), left Dorsey in 1942; she went solo in 1944 with her husband, arranger Paul Weston: she had nearly 50 hits on Capitol 1944-50 and about 30 more on USA Columbia 1950-57. She and Weston (as Jonathan and Darlene Edwards) did a comedy act of slightly wrong notes, hilarious and requiring great skill. Her original hit singles and albums are now available on the California Corinthian label. (Donald Clarke 27.3.88).

JAMBALAYA
Tracks: / Jambalaya.
7" Single: Released Dec '52, on Columbia, by EMI Records. Deleted Dec '55. Catalogue no: **DB 3169**

MAKE LOVE TO ME
Tracks: / Make love to me.
7" Single: Released May '54, on Philips, by Phonogram Ltd. Deleted May '57. Catalogue no: **PB 233**

SUDDENLY THERE'S A VALLEY
Tracks: / Suddenly there's a valley.
7" Single: Released Dec '55, on Philips, by Phonogram Ltd. Deleted Dec '59. Catalogue no: **PB 509**

YOU BELONG TO ME
Tracks: / You belong to me.
7" Single: Released Nov '52, on Columbia, by EMI Records. Deleted Nov '55. Catalogue no: **DB 3152**

Stafford, Terry

SUSPICION
Tracks: / Suspicion.
7" Single: Released May '64, on London-American, Deleted May '67. Catalogue no: **HLU 9871**

Stag Marks Gang

AIN'T NO FUN ON THE DOLE
Tracks: / Ain't no fun on the dole.
7" Single: Released Jul '82, on Double Image, by Double Image Records. Catalogue no: **DI 1**

Stage

DANCING DAYS
Tracks: / Dancing days / Too close for comfort.
12" Single: Released Sep '86, on I.R.S, Catalogue no: **IRMT 122**
7" Single: Released Sep '86, on I.R.S, Catalogue no: **IRM 122**

NOTHING STRANGER THAN TODAY
Tracks: / Kissing at the station / Stop the time.
Note: Extra track on 12" only
7" Single: Released Feb '87, on I.R.S, Catalogue no: **IRM 129**

Stage B

RECALL TO LIFE
Tracks: / Recall to life / Light on the hillside.
7" Single: Released Feb '80, on Shock Rock (Ireland), by Outlet Records. Catalogue no: **SRS 502**

Stagefright

STRANGER IN THE NIGHT
Tracks: / Stranger in the night.
7" Single: Released Jan '85, on S.T.N., Catalogue no: **STN 1**

Staiffi

MUSTAFA
Tracks: / Mustafa.
7" Single: Released Jul '60, on Pye International, Deleted Jul '63. Catalogue no: **7N 25057**

Stakker Humanoid

HUMANOID
Tracks: / Humanoid.
12" Single: Released Oct '88, on Westside, by Westside Records. Catalogue no: **WSR T 12**
7" Single: Released Oct '88, on Westside, by Westside Records. Catalogue no: **WSR 12**

Stalactite

SHAS
Tracks: / Shas.
7" Single: Released Jan '85, on Albatross (USA), by Albatross Records (USA). Catalogue no: **OSS 1**

Stalag 17

TRUTH WILL BE HEARD From Belfast with...
Tracks: / Truth will be heard.
12" Single: Released Sep '85, on Mortarhate, by Mortarhate Records. Catalogue no: **MORT 14**

Stallion

STALLION
Tracks: / Stallion / Doom watch.
12" Single: Released Sep '83, on Sunsplash, by Sunsplash Records. Deleted '87. Catalogue no: **SNS 05**

Stallone, Frank

CASE OF YOU
Tracks: / Case of you / Sea song.
7" Single: Released Oct '80, on Scotti Bros (Germany), Deleted Oct '83. Catalogue no: **K 11613**

FAR FROM OVER
Tracks: / Far from over.
7" Single: Released Oct '83, on RSO, by Polydor Ltd. Deleted Oct '86. Catalogue no: **RSO 95**

Stamey, Chris

IN THE WINTER OF LOVE
Tracks: / In the winter of love / It's a wonderful life.
12" Single: Released Jun '83, on Albion, by Albion Records. Catalogue no: **12ION 1045**

Stamford Bridge

CHELSEA
Tracks: / Chelsea.
7" Single: Released May '70, on Penny Farthing, by Penny Farthing Records. Deleted May '73. Catalogue no: **PEN 715**

Stampede

DAYS OF WINE AND ROSES
Tracks: / Days of wine and roses / Photographs.
7" Single: Released Sep '82, on Polydor, by Polydor Ltd. Catalogue no: **POSP 507**
12" Single: Released Sep '82, on Polydor, by Polydor Ltd. Catalogue no: **POSPX 507**

OTHER SIDE
Tracks: / Other side, The / Runner, The.
7" Single: Released May '83, on Polydor, by Polydor Ltd. Catalogue no: **POSP 592**

Stan & The Gang

GRANDADS MOTTO
Tracks: / Grandad's motto.
7" Single: Released Nov '81, on Spy 80, Deleted '86. Catalogue no: **S 1000**

Standing 4

ICE EMOTION
Tracks: / Ice emotion / Nightmare.
7" Single: Released Sep '87, on Four Records, by Four Records. Catalogue no: **FC 87001**

NIGHTMARE
Tracks: / Standing still / Nightmare / Ice emotion.
Cassingle: Released Sep '87, on Four Rec-

ords, by Four Records. Catalogue no: **FC 87002**

Standing Ovation

TIMES OF FUN
Tracks: / Times of fun / What meaning.
Cassingle: Released Dec '83, on Falling A, Catalogue no: **FAC 121**

Stanford - Le - Hope

RED RED WINE
Tracks: / Red red wine.
12" Single: Released Oct '83, on ABL, by ABL Records. Catalogue no: **ABL 002**

Stanger & Nelson

I'M DOING FINE NOW
Tracks: / I'm doing fine now.
12" Single: Released Oct '83, on Excaliber, by Red Bus Records. Deleted '88. Catalogue no: **EXCL 536**
7" Single: Released Oct '83, on Excaliber, by Red Bus Records. Deleted '88. Catalogue no: **EXC 536**

Stanisclaus, Olga J

DARLING COOL IT
Tracks: / Darling cool it / Jam something.
12" Single: Released Mar '83, on Sunburn, by Orbitone Records. Catalogue no: **SBD 26**

OLGA (2 PARTS)
Tracks: / Olga (part 1) / Olga (part 2).
12" Single: Released Mar '83, on Sunburn, by Orbitone Records. Catalogue no: **SBD 27**

Stanley, Michael

HE CAN'T LOVE YOU
Tracks: / He can't love you / Heart's on fire.
7" Single: Released Jan '81, on EMI-America, by EMI Records. Deleted Jan '84. Catalogue no: **EA 112**

Stanley, Pamela

COMING OUT OF HIDING
Tracks: / Coming out of hiding.
12" Single: Released Jun '84, on Casablanca, by PolyGram UK Ltd. Catalogue no: **CANX 1020**
7" Single: Released Jun '84, on Casablanca, by PolyGram UK Ltd. Catalogue no: **CAN 1020**

Stanley,Chuck

DAY BY DAY
Tracks: / Day by day / Finer things in life, The.
7" Single: Released Apr '87, on Def Jam, Deleted Nov '87. Catalogue no: **650499 7**
12" Single: Released Apr '87, on Def Jam, Catalogue no: **650499 6**

Stano

ROOM, THE
Tracks: / Room, The.
7" Single: Released Apr '82, on Vox Enterprise, Deleted '83. Catalogue no: **VE 1**

Stansfield, Lisa

ALL AROUND THE WORLD
Tracks: / All around the world.
7" Single: Released Oct '89, on Arista, by BMG Records (UK). Catalogue no: **112 693**
12" Single: Released Oct '89, on Arista, by BMG Records (UK). Catalogue no: **612 693**

I GOT A FEELING
Tracks: / I got a feeling / Red lights.
7" Single: Released Oct '83, on Polydor, by Polydor Ltd. Catalogue no: **POSP 651**

ONLY WAY
Tracks: / Only way, The / Only love.
7" Single: Released Oct '82, on Polydor, by Polydor Ltd. Catalogue no: **POSP 521**

THIS IS THE RIGHT TIME
Tracks: / This is the right time / Affection.
7" Single: Released Aug '89, on Arista, by BMG Records (UK). Catalogue no: **112 512**
Cassingle: Released 14 Aug '89, on Arista, by BMG Records (UK). Catalogue no: **409517**
CD 5": Released Aug '89, on Arista, by BMG Records (UK). Catalogue no: **662 512**
12" Single: Released Aug '89, on Arista, by BMG Records (UK). Deleted Sep '89. Catalogue no: **612 517**

THIS IS THE RIGHT TIME (REMIX)
Tracks: / This is the right time / Affection.
12" Single: Released Aug '89, on Arista, by BMG Records (UK). Catalogue no: **612512**

YOUR ALIBIS
Tracks: / Your alibis / Thought police.
7" Single: Released Mar '82, on Devil, by Devil Records. Catalogue no: **DEV 2**

Stanshall, Vivian

TERRY KEEPS HIS CLIPS ON
Tracks: / Terry keeps his clips on / King Kripple.
7" Single: Released Sep '80, on Charisma, by Virgin Records. Deleted Sep '83. Catalogue no: **CB 373**

Stanton, Eddie

LUCIFER WANTS ME FOR A SUNBEAM
Tracks: / Lucifer wants me for a sunbeam.
7" Single: Released May '81, on Black Eyes, Catalogue no: **DARK 1**

MILTON KEYNES WE LOVE YOU
Tracks: / Milton Keynes we love you.
7" Single: Released May '81, on Black Eyes, Catalogue no: **DARK 2**

TALES FROM THE RAJ
Tracks: / Tales from the raj / Desolation.
7" Single: Released Oct '82, on Polydor, by Polydor Ltd. Catalogue no: **POSP 520**

YOUNG AND THE FREE
Tracks: / Young and the free / Madonna and child.
7" Single: Released Jun '82, on Polydor, by Polydor Ltd. Deleted Jun '85. Catalogue no: **POSP 456**

Staples Singers

Biographical details: The Staple Singers are a family gospel group who later had on Epic and Stax, mostly with message songs. Roebuck 'Pops' Staples was born on 28th December, 1915 in Winona, Mississippi; he learned blues guitar, was converted to gospel at the age of 15, later settled in Chicago. Pops, son Pervis, daughters Cleo, Mavis and vonne made classic gospel discs on Vee-Jay in the 1950's (now on Charley). *This May Be The Last Time* was adapted by the Rolling Stones. Stax hits reached both pop and soul charts in the USA; Pops and Mavis appeared in the Band's film/concert/album *The Last Waltz* in 1978. (Donald Clarke 27.3.88).

IF YOU'RE READY (COME GO WITH ME)
Tracks: / If you're ready (come go with me).
7" Single: Released Jun '74, on Stax, by Fantasy Inc (USA). Deleted Jun '77. Catalogue no: **2025 224**

I'LL TAKE YOU THERE
Tracks: / I'll take you there / I'm just another soldier.
7" Single: Released Mar '82, on Stax, by Fantasy Inc (USA). Catalogue no: **STAX 1002**
7" Single: Released Sep '87, on Stax, by Fantasy Inc (USA). Catalogue no: **STAX 815**
7" Single: Released Jun '72, on Stax, by Fantasy Inc (USA). Deleted Jun '75. Catalogue no: **2025 110**

LONG WALK TO DC
Tracks: / Long walk to D.C..
7" Single: Released Oct '87, on Stax, by Fantasy Inc (USA). Catalogue no: **STAX 817**

RESPECT YOURSELF (SINGLE)
Tracks: / Respect yourself / This world / Heavy makes you happy / Long walk to DC.
7" Single: Released 13 Jun '87, on Stax, by Fantasy Inc (USA). Catalogue no: **STAX 805**
12" Single: Released Nov '87, on Stax, by Fantasy Inc (USA). Catalogue no: **STAT 805**

SLIPPERY PEOPLE
Tracks: / Slippery people.
7" Single: Released Sep '84, on Epic, by CBS Records. Catalogue no: **A 4784**
12" Single: Released Sep '84, on Epic, by CBS Records. Catalogue no: **TA 4784**

THIS IS OUR NIGHT
Tracks: / This is our night / Turning point.
7" Single: Released Jan '85, on Epic, by CBS Records. Catalogue no: **A 5008**
12" Single: Released Jan '85, on Epic, by CBS Records. Catalogue no: **TA 5008**

Stapleton, Cyril

BLUE STAR
Tracks: / Blue star.
7" Single: Released Sep '55, on London-American, Deleted Sep '58. Catalogue no: **F 10559**

ELEPHANT TANGO
Tracks: / Elephant tango.
7" Single: Released May '55, on London-American, Deleted May '58. Catalogue no: **F 10488**

FORGOTTEN DREAMS
Tracks: / Forgotten dreams.
7" Single: Released Jul '57, on London-American, Deleted Jul '60. Catalogue no: **F 10912**

HAPPY WHISTLER, THE
Tracks: / Happy whistler, The.
7" Single: Released Jun '56, on London-American, Deleted Jun '59. Catalogue no: **F 10735**

ITALIAN THEME, THE
Tracks: / Italian theme, The.
7" Single: Released Apr '56, on London-American, Deleted Apr '59. Catalogue no: **F 10703**

Star, Bonito

SAVE ALL YOUR LOVE
Tracks: / Save all your love.
12" Single: Released Nov '88, on Realistic, Catalogue no: **RR 013**

Star Sisters

DANGER
Tracks: / Danger / You're my first, you're my last.
12" Single: Released Jan '86, on Carrere, Catalogue no: **CART 379**
7" Single: Released Jan '86, on Carrere, Catalogue no: **CAR 379**

HE'S THE 1 (I LOVE)
Tracks: / He's the 1 (I love).
7" Single: Released Sep '85, on Carrere America (USA), by PolyGram Rec.Inc.(USA). Catalogue no: **CAR 373**
12" Single: Released Sep '85, on Carrere, Catalogue no: **CART 373**

Star Star

HOLD BACK THE NIGHT
Tracks: / Hold back the night.
12" Single: Released Jun '88, on Polydor, by Polydor Ltd. Catalogue no: **PZ 7**
7" Single: Released Jun '88, on Polydor, by Polydor Ltd. Catalogue no: **PO 7**

Star Trek

SEARCH FOR SPOCK
Tracks: / Search for Spock.
12" Single: Released Oct '84, on Walt Disney, Catalogue no: **RESLD 2**

Star Turn

CHRISTMAS PARTY (FLACCID MIX)
Tracks: / Christmas party (flaccid mix) / Old lag signed.
12" Single: Released Dec '88, on Pacific, by Pacific Records. Catalogue no: **DRINK 3 T**
7" Single: Released Dec '88, on Pacific, by Pacific Records. Deleted '89. Catalogue no: **DRINK 3**

GIVE IT LOCK, STOCK & BARREL
Tracks: / Give it lock, stock & barrel / House called.
12" Single: Released Jul '88, on Pacific, by Pacific Records. Catalogue no: **DRINK2T**
7" Single: Released Jul '88, on Pacific, by Pacific Records. Deleted '89. Catalogue no: **DRINK2**

PUMP UP THE BITTER
Tracks: / Pump up the bitter / Are you affiliated ?.
7" Single: Released Jun '88, on Pacific, by Pacific Records. Deleted '89. Catalogue no: **DRINK 1**
12" Single: Released '88, on Pacific, by Pacific Records. Catalogue no: **DRINK 1T**

STAR TURN FOR EUROPE
Tracks: / Star Turn for Europe / Ding dong ding dong.
7" Single: Released Mar '82, on V-Tone, Deleted '85. Catalogue no: **VTONE 005**
7" Single: Released Apr '86, on Star Turn, Deleted '87. Catalogue no: **UEZS 6001**

STAR TURN ON 45(PINTS)(see panel below)
Tracks: / Startum on 45 pints / D.I.Y..
7" Single: Released Sep '81, on V-Tone, Catalogue no: **VTONE 003**

Star Wars

STAR WARS
7" EP: Released Dec '82, on Disneyland, by Disneyland Records. Catalogue no: **D 450**

WHAT DO YOU GIVE A WOOKIE FOR CHRISTMAS
Tracks: / What do you give a wookie for Christmas / We wish you a merry Christmas.
7" Single: Released Jan '81, on RSO, by Polydor Ltd. Deleted Jan '84. Catalogue no: **RSO 72**

Stardust

ARIANA
Tracks: / Ariana.
7" Single: Released Oct '77, on Satril, by Satril Records. Deleted Oct '80. Catalogue no: **SAT 120**

BLAZIN'
Tracks: / Blazin'.
12" Single: Released Sep '89, on Republic, by Code Records. Catalogue no: **LICT 029**

Stardust, Alvin

Biographical details: Alvin Stardust was born Benard William Jewry on 27 September 1942 in Muswell Hill, London. He was road manager and occasional singer with Johnny Theakston and the Tremeloes; they submitted a tape to the BBC as Shane Fenton & the Fentones; Theakston died and Jewry became Fenton, with Top.40 hits 1961-62. He quit recording in 1964 to work in management, but came back in 1973 as Alvin Stardust, with new black leather image and many hit singles and albums; he was often seen on TV and made another chart comeback in the early 1980s, including 'I feel like Buddy Holly', written by Mike Batt. (Donald Clarke 27.3.87)
This British singer's real name was Bernard Jewry. He changed his name in the early Sixties, when he became the vocalist with an up-and-coming group called the Fentones. Having stepped into the breach following the death of the original singer, he stayed with them on a full-time basis and sang on the combo's first hit *I'm a moody guy* reached the UK No.22 position in late 1961. 1962 brought three moderate chart successes for Shane Fenton & The Fentones. *Walk away* peaked at No.38 on the British listings; *It's all over now* (nothing to do with the Rolling Stones' later hit) reached No.29; and Fenton's best remembered record *Cindy's birthday* climbed to No.19 - this was a rapid and opportunistic cover version of Johnny Crawford's US Top Tenner. In the same year, the nifty Fentones managed a couple of minor hits on their own, with their instrumental discs *The Mexican* and *The breeze and I.* Just when it seemed that Fenton and his group were poised to become major pop stars, they were torpedoed into obscurity by the Beatles and the whole Merseybeat revolution. Films and package tours could not rescue the singer's career, and he could only take comfort from the fact that many of his early Sixties peers were similarly stymied by the Liverpool explosion. Fenton moved into

STAR TURN - STAR TURN ON 45 PINTS (Released on Pacific)

ALVIN STARDUST - WEEK END (Released on Stiff)

the field of artist management, but made an amazing chart comeback in 1973. Although he was turning 30, he became a teen ido as the leather clad 'Alvin Stardust', and enjoyed greater success than he had ever known as Shane Fenton. Sticking with the Stardust moniker but dropping the leather he was something of a British showbusiness institution by the mid-Eighties. (Bob MacDonald, 23rd August 1985).

ALVIN STARDUST (6 TRACK HITS)
Tracks: / My coo ca choo / Guitar star / Red dress / You, you, you / Dreambreaker / You're my everything.
7" EP: Released Sep '83, on Scoop 33, by Pickwick Records. Catalogue no: **7SR 5030**

CLOCK ON THE WALL
Tracks: / Clock on the wall.
7" Single: Released Apr '85, on Chrysalis, by Chrysalis Records. Catalogue no: **ALVIN 1**
12" Single: Released Apr '85, on Chrysalis, by Chrysalis Records. Catalogue no: **ALVINX 1**

GOOD LOVE CAN NEVER DIE
Tracks: / Good love can never die.
7" Single: Released Feb '75, on Magnet, by WEA Records. Deleted Feb '78. Catalogue no: **MAG 21**

GOT A LITTLE HEARTACHE
Tracks: / Got a little heartache / Again / Hurt by love (on 12" only).
7" Single: Released Mar '85, on Chrysalis, by Chrysalis Records. Deleted Mar '88. Catalogue no: **CHS 2856**

I FEEL LIKE BUDDY HOLLY
Tracks: / I feel like Buddy Holly / Luxury.
7" Single: Released Apr '84, on Chrysalis, by Chrysalis Records. Catalogue no: **CHS 2784**
12" Single: Released Jun '84, on Chrysalis, by Chrysalis Records. Catalogue no: **CHS 122784**

I HOPE AND I PRAY
Tracks: / I hope and I pray / Speak of love.
12" Single: Released Mar '86, on Chrysalis, by Chrysalis Records. Catalogue no: **ALVX 4**
7" Single: Released Mar '86, on Chrysalis, by Chrysalis Records. Catalogue no: **ALV 4**

I WANT YOU BACK IN MY LIFE AGAIN
7" Pic: Released Jul '82, on Stiff, by Stiff Records. Catalogue no: **PBUY 152**
7" Single: Released Jul '82, on Stiff, by Stiff Records. Catalogue no: **BUY 152**

I WON'T RUN AWAY
Tracks: / I won't run away.
7" Single: Released Oct '84, on Chrysalis, by Chrysalis Records. Deleted Oct '87. Catalogue no: **CHS 2829**

JAILHOUSE ROCK
Tracks: / Jailhouse rock / Love is real / My coo ca choo (12" only).
7" Single: Released Oct '86, on Magnet, by WEA Records. Deleted '87. Catalogue no: **DUST 1**
12" Single: Released Oct '86, on Magnet, by WEA Records. Deleted '87. Catalogue no: **12 DUST 1**

JEALOUS MIND
Tracks: / Jealous mind.
7" Single: Released Feb '74, on Magnet, by WEA Records. Deleted Feb '77. Catalogue no: **MAG 5**

MY COO CA CHOO
Tracks: / My coo ca choo / Jealous mind.
7" Single: Released Sep '81, on Magnet, by WEA Records. Catalogue no: **MAG 301**
7" Single: Released Nov '73, on Magnet, by WEA Records. Catalogue no: **MAG 1**

PICTURE OF YOU
Tracks: / Picture of you / Hold tight.
7" Single: Released Nov '82, on Stiff, by Stiff Records. Catalogue no: **BUY 160**

PRETEND (see panel below)
Tracks: / Pretend / Goose bumps.
7" Single: Released Aug '81, on Stiff, by Stiff Records. Catalogue no: **BUY 124**

RED DRESS
Tracks: / Red dress.
7" Single: Released Apr '74, on Magnet, by WEA Records. Catalogue no: **MAG 8**

SLEEPLESS NIGHTS
Tracks: / Sleepless nights.
7" Single: Released Jun '85, on Chrysalis, by Chrysalis Records. Catalogue no: **AL 2**
12" Single: Released Jun '85, on Chrysalis, by Chrysalis Records. Catalogue no: **ALX 2**

SO NEAR TO CHRISTMAS
Tracks: / So near to Christmas.
7" Single: Released Dec '84, on Chrysalis, by Chrysalis Records. Deleted Dec '87. Catalogue no: **CHS 2835**

SWEET CHEATIN' RITA
Tracks: / Sweet cheatin' Rita.
7" Single: Released Jul '75, on Magnet, by WEA Records. Deleted Jul '78. Catalogue no: **MAG 32**

TELL ME WHY
Tracks: / Tell me why.
7" Single: Released Nov '74, on Magnet, by WEA Records. Deleted Nov '77. Catalogue no: **MAG 19**

WALK AWAY RENEE
Tracks: / Walk away Renee.
7" Single: Released Apr '83, on Stiff, by Stiff Records. Catalogue no: **BUY 182**

WEEKEND (see panel above)
Tracks: / Weekend / Butterflies.
7" Single: Released Apr '82, on Stiff, by Stiff Records. Catalogue no: **BUY 142**

WONDERFUL TIME UP THERE
Tracks: / Wonderful time up there, A / Love you so much.
7" Single: Released Nov '81, on Stiff, by Stiff Records. Catalogue no: **BUY 132**

YOU YOU YOU
Tracks: / You you you.
7" Single: Released Aug '74, on Magnet, by WEA Records. Deleted Aug '77. Catalogue no: **MAG 13**

Starfighters

ALLEY CAT BLUES
Tracks: / Alley cat blues / Don't touch me / Rock 'em dead (Only on 12" single.).
12" Single: Released Aug '81, on Jive, by Zomba Records. Catalogue no: **JIVET 3**
7" Single: Released Aug '81, on Jive, by Zomba Records. Catalogue no: **JIVE 3**

POWER CRAZY (SINGLE)
Tracks: / Power crazy / I want you / Get out while you can (12" only).
12" Single: Released Oct '81, on Jive, by Zomba Records. Catalogue no: **JIVET 6**
7" Single: Released Oct '81, on Jive, by Zomba Records. Catalogue no: **JIVE 6**

Stargard

LOVE IS SO EASY
Tracks: / Love is so easy.
7" Single: Released Apr '78, on MCA, by MCA Records. Deleted Apr '81. Catalogue no: **MCA 354**

THEME FROM 'WHICH WAY IS UP'
Tracks: / Which way is up, Theme from.
7" Single: Released Jan '78, on MCA, by MCA Records. Deleted Jan '81. Catalogue no: **MCA 346**

WEAR IT OUT
Tracks: / Wear it out.
7" Single: Released Jan '80, on Warner Bros., by WEA Records. Catalogue no: **K 17475**

WHAT YOU WAITING FOR
Tracks: / What you waiting for.
7" Single: Released Sep '78, on MCA, by MCA Records. Deleted Sep '81. Catalogue no: **MCA 382**

Stargazers

AIN'T NOBODY HERE BUT US CHICKENS
Tracks: / Ain't nobody here but us chickens / Rocket ship to the moon.
7" Single: Released Jan '83, on Epic, by CBS Records. Catalogue no: **EPC A 3013**

BROKEN WINGS
Tracks: / Broken wings.
7" Single: Released Feb '53, on London-American, Deleted Feb '56. Catalogue no: **F 10047**

CLOSE THE DOOR
Tracks: / Close the door.
7" Single: Released Sep '55, on London-American, Deleted Sep '58. Catalogue no: **F 10594**

CRAZY OTTO RAG
Tracks: / Crazy otto rag.
7" Single: Released Jun '55, on London-American, Deleted Jun '58. Catalogue no: **F 10523**

GROOVE BABY GROOVE (EP)
Tracks: / Groove baby groove / Jump around / La rock'n'roll (quelques uns a la lune) / Red light green light.
7" EP: Released Feb '82, on Epic, by CBS Records. Deleted Feb '85. Catalogue no: **EPC A 1924**

HAPPY WANDERER
Tracks: / Happy wanderer, The.
7" Single: Released Apr '54, on London-American, Deleted Apr '57. Catalogue no: **F 10259**

HEY MARIE
Tracks: / Hey Marie / Scat the riff / Go honey.
12" Single: Released Jun '82, on Epic, by CBS Records. Deleted Jun '85. Catalogue no: **EPCA 132422**

HOT DIGGITY
Tracks: / Hot diggity.
7" Single: Released Jun '56, on London-American, Deleted Jun '59. Catalogue no: **F 10731**

I SEE THE MOON
Tracks: / I see the moon.
7" Single: Released Feb '54, on London-American, Deleted Feb '57. Catalogue no: **F 10213**

SOMEBODY
Tracks: / Somebody.
7" Single: Released Mar '55, on London-American, Deleted Mar '58. Catalogue no: **F 10437**

TOSSING AND TURNING
Tracks: / Tossing and turning / Pretty senorita.
7" Single: Released Oct '82, on Epic, by CBS Records. Deleted Oct '85. Catalogue no: **EPCA 2843**

TWENTY TINY FINGERS
Tracks: / Twenty tiny fingers.
7" Single: Released Nov '55, on London-American, Deleted Nov '58. Catalogue no: **F 10626**

Starjets

SHIRALEO
Tracks: / Shiraleo / Stand by nineteen.
7" Single: Released Jun '80, on Epic, by CBS Records. Deleted Jun '83. Catalogue no: **EPC 8276**

WAR STORIES
Tracks: / War stories.
7" Single: Released Sep '79, on Epic, by CBS Records. Deleted Sep '82. Catalogue no: **EPC 7770**

Starland Vocal Band

AFTERNOON DELIGHT
Tracks: / Afternoon delight.
7" Single: Released Aug '76, on RCA, by BMG Records (UK). Deleted Aug '79. Catalogue no: **RCA 2716**

Starlight

DREAM OF ME
Tracks: / Dream of me.
12" Single: Released Jul '84, on BB, Catalogue no: **GG 112**

IF I HAD MONEY
Tracks: / If I had money / If I had money (inst).
7" Single: Released Aug '86, on Record Shack, by Record Shack Records. Catalogue no: **SOHO 68**
12" Single: Released Aug '86, on Record Shack, by Record Shack Records. Catalogue no: **SOHOT 68**

NUMERO UNO

ALVIN STARDUST - PRETEND (Released on Stiff)

Tracks: / Numero uno.
12" Single: Released Aug '89, on Citybeat, by Beggars Banquet Records. Catalogue no: **CBE 1242**
7" Single: Released Aug '89, on Citybeat, by Beggars Banquet Records. Catalogue no: **CBE 742**

Starlite

GENTLE PEOPLE
Tracks: / Gentle people / Carribean Christmas.
7" Single: Released Dec '81, on Solid Gold (1), by Creole Records. Deleted '86. Catalogue no: **SGR 111**

Starpoint

BRING YOUR SWEET LOVIN' BACK
Tracks: / Bring your sweet lovin' back / I want you closer.
12" Single: Released Jan '82, on Casablanca, by PolyGram UK Ltd. Deleted Jan '85. Catalogue no: **CANX 1013**
7" Single: Released Jan '82, on Casablanca, by PolyGram UK Ltd. Deleted Jan '85. Catalogue no: **CAN 1013**

HE WANTS MY BODY
Tracks: / He wants my boys / Satisfy me love.
7" Single: Released Apr '87, on Elektra (USA), by Elektra Records (USA). Deleted Jan '88. Catalogue no: **EKR 55**
12" Single: Released Apr '87, on Elektra (USA), by Elektra Records (USA). Deleted Jan '88. Catalogue no: **EKR 55 T**

I JUST WANT TO BE YOUR LOVER
Tracks: / I just want to be your lover / Keep it on.
12" Single: Released May '81, on Casablanca, by PolyGram UK Ltd. Deleted May '84. Catalogue no: **CANX 1001**
7" Single: Released May '81, on Casablanca, by PolyGram UK Ltd. Deleted May '84. Catalogue no: **CAN 1001**

IT'S ALL YOURS
Tracks: / It's all yours.
7" Single: Released May '84, on Elektra, by Elektra Records (UK). Catalogue no: **E 6964**

OBJECT OF MY DESIRE
Tracks: / Object of my desire / Am I still the one.
7" Single: Released Jan '86, on Elektra (USA), by Elektra Records (USA). Catalogue no: **EKR 26**
12" Single: Released Jan '86, on Elektra (USA), by Elektra Records (USA). Catalogue no: **EKR 26 T**

Starr, Andy

SQUEAKY SHOES
Tracks: / Squeaky shoes.
7" Single: Released Jun '80, on Rollin' Rock. Catalogue no: **45 042**

Starr, Bonito

ELECTRIC
Tracks: / Electric / Shock.
12" Single: Released Jun '86, on New Generation. Catalogue no: **NG 008**

Starr, Brenda.K.

WHAT YOU SEE IS WHAT YOU GET
Tracks: / What you see is what you get.
12" Single: Released 16 Sep '88, on MCA, by MCA Records. Catalogue no: **MCAT 1279**
7" Single: Released 16 Sep '88, on MCA, by MCA Records. Catalogue no: **MCA 1279**

Starr, Edwin

AGENT DOUBLE O SOUL
Tracks: / Agent double o soul.
7" Single: Released Oct '81, on Motown, by BMG Records (UK). Catalogue no: **TMG 790**

CONTACT
Tracks: / Contact.
7" Single: Released Jan '79, on 20th Century, by 20th Century Records. Deleted Jan '82. Catalogue no: **BTC 2396**

CONTACT (OLD GOLD)
Tracks: / Contact / Get down.
7" Single: Released Jun '88, on Old Gold, by Old Gold Records. Catalogue no: **OG 9487**

GRAPEVINE
Tracks: / Grapevine / I need your love / Grapevine (parts 1 & 2) ('Grapevine (parts 1 & 2)' on 12" only.).
7" Single: Released Mar '86, on Hippodrome, by Hippodrome Records. Catalogue no: **HIPPO 107**
12" Single: Released Mar '86, on Hippodrome, by Hippodrome Records. Catalogue no: **12 HIPPO 107**

H.A.P.P.Y. RADIO
Tracks: / H.A.P.P.Y. radio.
7" Single: Released May '79, on RCA, by BMG Records (UK). Deleted May '82. Catalogue no: **TC 2408**

HEADLINE NEWS
Tracks: / Headline news.
7" Single: Released Aug '66, on Polydor, by Polydor Ltd. Deleted Aug '69. Catalogue no: **56 717**

I WANNA TAKE YOU HOME
Tracks: / I wanna take you home / Hit the nail on your head.
12" Single: Released Jan '83, on Avatar, by Avatar Record Corporation. Catalogue no: **AVATX 2**
7" Single: Released Jan '83, on Avatar, by Avatar Record Corporation. Catalogue no: **AVAT 2**

IT AIN'T FAIR
Tracks: / It ain't fair.
7" Single: Released May '85, on Hippodrome, by Hippodrome Records. Catalogue no: **HIP 101**
12" Single: Released May '85, on Hippodrome, by Hippodrome Records. Catalogue no: **12 HIP 101**

MISSILES(WE DONT WANT TO DIE)
Tracks: / Missiles (we don't want to die).
12" Single: Released Oct '85, on Hippodrome, by Hippodrome Records. Catalogue no: **12HIPPO 105**
7" Single: Released Oct '85, on Hippodrome, by Hippodrome Records. Catalogue no: **HIPPO 105**

SMOOTH
Tracks: / Smooth.
7" Single: Released Aug '83, on Calibre, Deleted '85. Catalogue no: **CAB 114**
12" Single: Released Aug '83, on Calibre, Deleted '84. Catalogue no: **CABL 114**

SOUL SINGER
Tracks: / Soul singer / Eye to eye contact (remake).
7" Single: Released Jul '86, on Hippodrome, by Hippodrome Records. Catalogue no: **HIPPO 108**
12" Single: Released Jul '86, on Hippodrome, by Hippodrome Records. Catalogue no: **12 HIPPO 108**

STOP HER ON SIGHT (SOS)
Tracks: / Stop her on sight (SOS) / Headline news.
7" Single: Released Oct '81, on Tamla Motown, by Motown Records (UK). Catalogue no: **TMG 905**
7" Single: Released May '66, on Polydor, by Polydor Ltd. Deleted May '69. Catalogue no: **BM 56 702**
7" Single: Released Dec '68, on Polydor, by Polydor Ltd. Deleted Dec '71. Catalogue no: **56 153**

STOP THE WAR NOW
Tracks: / Stop the war now.
7" Single: Released Feb '71, on Tamla Motown, by Motown Records (UK). Deleted Feb '74. Catalogue no: **TMG 764**

TELESTAR
Tracks: / Telestar / Bop bop song.
7" Single: Released May '90, on 20th Century, by 20th Century Records. Deleted '85. Catalogue no: **TC 2450**

TWENTY FIVE MILES
Tracks: / Twenty five miles / Never turn my back on you.
12" Single: Released Jan '81, on 20th Century, by 20th Century Records. Deleted Jan '84. Catalogue no: **TCD 2477**
7" Single: Released Oct '81, on Motown, by BMG Records (UK). Deleted '83. Catalogue no: **TMG 672**

TWENTY FIVE MILES ('89 REMIX)
Tracks: / Twenty five miles ('89 remix) / Twenty five miles (original instrumental) / Twenty five miles (12" dub) (Only on 12" single.).
7" Single: Released Jul '89, on Motown, by BMG Records (UK). Catalogue no: **ZB 41965**
12" Single: Released Jul '89, on Motown, by BMG Records (UK). Catalogue no: **ZT 41966**

WAR
Tracks: / War.
7" Single: Released Oct '80, on Tamla Motown, by Motown Records (UK). Deleted Oct '83. Catalogue no: **TMG 968**
7" Single: Released Oct '70, on Tamla Motown, by Motown Records (UK). Deleted Oct '73. Catalogue no: **TMG 754**
7" Single: Released Oct '81, on Tamla Motown, by Motown Records (UK). Catalogue no: **TMG 984**

WHATEVER MAKES OUR LOVE GROW
Tracks: / Whatever makes our love grow / Whatever makes our love grow (instrumental).
7" Single: Released Sep '87, on 10 Records, by Virgin Records. Catalogue no: **TEN 199**
12" Single: Released Sep '87, on 10 Records, by Virgin Records. Deleted '89. Catalogue no: **TENT 199**

Starr, Emily

SAMSON
Tracks: / Samson (part 1) / Samson (part 1).
7" Single: Released Apr '81, on Ariola, by BMG Records (UK). Deleted Apr '84. Catalogue no: **ARO 260**

Starr, Freddie

CRYING GAME
Tracks: / Crying game, The / Spacerama.
7" Single: Released Feb '82, on Towerbell, Catalogue no: **TOW 19**

GREAT PRETENDER
Tracks: / Great pretender, The / Spacerama.
7" Single: Released Jul '82, on Towerbell, Catalogue no: **TOW 24**

HOLLYWOOD
Tracks: / Hollywood.
7" Single: Released Aug '83, on Savoir Faire, Catalogue no: **FAIS 003**

IT'S YOU
Tracks: / It's you.
7" Single: Released Feb '74, on Tiffany, by Tiffany Records. Deleted Feb '77. Catalogue no: **6121 501**

WHITE CHRISTMAS
Tracks: / White Christmas.
7" Single: Released Dec '75, on Thunderbird, by President Records. Deleted Dec '78. Catalogue no: **THE 102**

WILL YOU STILL LOVE ME TOMORROW
Tracks: / Will you still love me tomorrow / It's all over now.
7" Single: Released Jun '80, on WEA, by WEA Records. Deleted Jun '83. Catalogue no: **WEA 18262**

Starr, Kay

Biographical details: Kay Starr was born in 1922 in Oklahoma; she sang with the bands of Bob Crosby and Charlie Barnet, then was one of the biggest USA pop stars from 1948 on Capitol with her big voice, distinctive vocal colour; *Wheel Of Fortune* was No. 1 for ten weeks in 1952; she was double-tracked for duets with herself, unusual then and particularly effective on *Side By Side*. She switched to RCA and *Rock 'n' Roll Waltz* was No. 1 for six weeks in 1955; then she went back to Capitol. (Donald Clarke 27.3.87).

AM I A TOY OR A TREASURE
Tracks: / Am I a toy or a treasure.
7" Single: Released Oct '54, on Capitol, by EMI Records. Deleted Oct '57. Catalogue no: **CL 14151**

CHANGING PARTNERS
Tracks: / Changing partners.
7" Single: Released Mar '54, on Capitol, by EMI Records. Deleted Mar '57. Catalogue no: **CL 14050**

COMES A-LONG A-LOVE
Tracks: / Comes a-long a-love.
7" Single: Released Dec '52, on Capitol, by EMI Records. Deleted Dec '55. Catalogue no: **CL 13808**

ROCK AND ROLL WALTZ
Tracks: / Rock and roll waltz.
7" Single: Released Feb '56, on H.M.V., by EMI Records. Deleted Feb '59. Catalogue no: **POP 168**

ROCK AND ROLL WALTZ (OLD GOLD)
Tracks: / Rock and roll waltz / Wheel of fortune.
7" Single: Released Apr '87, on Old Gold, by Old Gold Records. Deleted Sep '89. Catalogue no: **OG 9724**

SIDE BY SIDE
Tracks: / Side by side.
7" Single: Released Apr '53, on Capitol, by EMI Records. Deleted Apr '56. Catalogue no: **CL 13871**

WHEEL OF FORTUNE
Tracks: / Wheel of fortune.
7" Single: Released '80, on Capitol, by EMI Records. Catalogue no: **LR 1870**

Starr, Ringo

Biographical details: Born Richard Starkey in July 1940, Ringo Starr drummed with Liverpool's Rory Storme & The Hurricanes, was picked to replace Pete Best in the Beatles and became world-famous. His post-Beatles solo career has not been spectacular but worldwide affection for him is always strong. For *Ringo*, in 1973, producer Richard Perry brought together Marc Bolan, Billy Preston, Harry Nillson and the other three Beatles on various tracks -- the closest they have ever come to a reunion. The album had three hit singles and was Starr's best. He made many films, co-starring with David Essex in *That'll Be The Day* (1973) and *Stardust* (1975), and he produced and directed the Bolan biopic *Born To Boogie*. He is now a bowbiz businessman. His son Zak is a rock drummer who played with Ringo on the Sun City anti-apartheid single and with Roger Daltrey on the Keith Moon tribute, *Under A Raging Moon*, in 1985. (Donald Clarke, March 1987.).

BACK OFF BOOGALOO
Tracks: / Back off boogaloo.
7" Single: Released Apr '72, on Apple, by Apple Records. Deleted Apr '75. Catalogue no: **R 5944**

IT DON'T COME EASY
Tracks: / It don't come easy.
7" Single: Released May '84, on EMI Golden 45's, by EMI Records. Deleted Oct '87. Catalogue no: **G45 13**
7" Single: Released Apr '71, on Apple, by Apple Records. Deleted Apr '74. Catalogue no: **R 5898**

ONLY YOU
Tracks: / Only you.
7" Single: Released Nov '74, on Apple, by Apple Records. Deleted Nov '77. Catalogue no: **R 6000**

PHOTOGRAPH
Tracks: / Photograph.
7" Single: Released Oct '73, on Apple, by Apple Records. Deleted Oct '76. Catalogue no: **R 5992**

WRACK MY BRAIN
Tracks: / Wrack my brain / Drumming in my madness.
7" Single: Released Nov '81, on RCA, by BMG Records (UK). Catalogue no: **RCA 166**

YOU'RE SIXTEEN
Tracks: / You're sixteen.
7" Single: Released Feb '74, on Parlophone, by EMI Records. Deleted Jun '89. Catalogue no: **R 5995**

Stars Of Heaven

CLOTHES OF PRIDE
Tracks: / Clothes of pride.
7" Single: Released Jan '86, on Hotwire, by Crashed Records. Catalogue no: **HWS 853**

HOLYHEAD
Tracks: / Holyhead.
12" Single: Released Mar '87, on Rough Trade, by Rough Trade Records. Catalogue no: **RTT 203**
7" Single: Released Mar '87, on Rough Trade, by Rough Trade Records. Catalogue no: **RT 203**

Starship

BEAT PATROL
Tracks: / Beat patrol / Girls like you / Beat patrol (ext.) (on 12" only.) / Beat patrol (dub) (on 12" only.).
7" Single: Released Nov '87, on RCA, by BMG Records (UK). Deleted May '89. Catalogue no: **RCA 5002**
12" Single: Released Nov '87, on RCA, by BMG Records (UK). Deleted May '89. Catalogue no: **RCAT 5002**

IT'S NOT ENOUGH
Tracks: / It's not enough / Love among the cannibals.
Cassingle: Released Aug '89, on RCA, by BMG Records (UK). Catalogue no: **PK 49357**
CD 5": Released Aug '89, on RCA, by BMG Records (UK). Catalogue no: **PD 49356**
7" Single: Released Aug '89, on RCA, by BMG Records (UK). Catalogue no: **PB 49357**
12" Single: Released Aug '89, on RCA, by BMG Records (UK). Catalogue no: **PT 49358**

IT'S NOT OVER ('TIL IT'S OVER)
Tracks: / It's not over ('til it's over).
12" Single: Released Aug '87, on RCA, by BMG Records (UK). Deleted May '89. Catalogue no: **RCAT 5002**
7" Single: Released Aug '87, on RCA, by BMG Records (UK). Catalogue no: **RCA 5001**

NOTHING'S GONNA STOP US NOW
Tracks: / Nothing's gonna stop us now / Laying it on the line / We built this city (Extra track on 12" only) / Tomorrow doesn't matter tonight (Extra track on 12" only).
7" Single: Released Mar '87, on RCA, by BMG Records (UK). Catalogue no: **FB 49757**
CD 5": Released Jun '89, on RCA, by BMG Records (UK). Catalogue no: **PD 49451**
12" Single: Released Mar '87, on RCA, by BMG Records (UK). Catalogue no: **FT 49758**

SARA
Tracks: / Sara / Hearts of the world will understand / Jane (Extra track on 12" version only.).
7" Single: Released Jan '86, on RCA, by BMG Records (UK). Catalogue no: **FB 49893**
12" Single: Released Jan '86, on RCA, by

BMG Records (UK). Catalogue no: **FT 49894**

TOMORROW DOESN'T MATTER TONIGHT
Tracks: / Tomorrow doesn't matter tonight / Love rusts / No way out (Extra tack on 12" version only) / Love rusts (version) (Extra tack on 12" version only) / Laying it on the line (extra tack on 12" version only).
12" Single: Released May '86, on RCA, by BMG Records (UK). Catalogue no: **FT 49856**
7" Single: Released May '86, on RCA, by BMG Records (UK). Catalogue no: **FB 49855**

WE BUILT THIS CITY
Tracks: / We built this city.
7" Single: Released Oct '85, on RCA, by BMG Records (UK). Catalogue no: **FB 49929**
12" Single: Released Oct '85, on RCA, by BMG Records (UK). Catalogue no: **FT 49930**

WILD AGAIN
Tracks: / Wild again / Laying it on the line / Tutti frutti (Only on 12" version.).
7" Single: Released Jan '89, on Elektra, by Elektra Records (UK). Catalogue no: **EKR 88**
12" Single: Released Jan '89, on Elektra, by Elektra Records (UK). Catalogue no: **EKR 88T**

Starship Orchestra

YOU'RE A STAR
Tracks: / You're a star / Celestial sky.
12" Single: Released Aug '80, on CBS, by CBS Records. Deleted '83. Catalogue no: **CBS 13-8898**
7" Single: Released Aug '80, on CBS, by CBS Records. Deleted '83. Catalogue no: **CBS 8898**

Starsound

GREATEST ROCK AND ROLL BAND IN THE WORLD
Tracks: / Greatest rock and roll band in the world / Beatles medley / Don't give up.
7" Single: Released Nov '82, on CBS, by CBS Records. Deleted Nov '85. Catalogue no: **A2269**
12" Single: Released Nov '82, on CBS, by CBS Records. Deleted Nov '85. Catalogue no: **A13 2269**

STARS ON 45 (SINGLE)
Tracks: / Stars on 45: *Various artists.*
12" Single: Released Apr '81, on CBS, by CBS Records. Deleted Apr '84. Catalogue no: **CBS A 13 1102**
7" Single: Released Apr '81, on CBS, by CBS Records. Deleted Apr '84. Catalogue no: **CBS A 1102**
Cassingle: Released Apr '81, on CBS, by CBS Records. Deleted Apr '84. Catalogue no: **CBS A 40 1102**

STARS ON 45 (SINGLE/OLD GOLD)
Tracks: / Stars on 45.
12" Single: Released 21 Nov '87, on Old Gold, by Old Gold Records. Catalogue no: **OG 4036**
7" Single: Released 21 Nov '87, on Old Gold, by Old Gold Records. Catalogue no: **OG 9738**

STARS ON 45, VOLUME 2
Tracks: / Stars on 45, volume 2: *Various artists.*
7" Single: Released Jul '81, on CBS, by CBS Records. Deleted Jul '84. Catalogue no: **A 1407**

STARS ON 45, VOLUME 3
Tracks: / Stars on 45, volume 3: *Various artists.*
7" Single: Released Sep '81, on CBS, by CBS Records. Deleted Sep '84. Catalogue no: **A 1521**
12" Single: Released Sep '81, on CBS, by CBS Records. Deleted Sep '84. Catalogue no: **A13 1521**

STARS ON STEVIE
Tracks: / Stars on Stevie / It's not a wonder it's a miracle.
7" Single: Released Feb '82, on CBS, by CBS Records. Catalogue no: **A 2041**
12" Single: Released Feb '82, on CBS, by CBS Records. Catalogue no: **A 13 2041**

Start

HEY YOU
Tracks: / Hey you / Gotta have love.
7" Single: Released Jan '81, on EMI, by EMI Records. Deleted Jan '84. Catalogue no: **START 1**

Startled Insects

UNDERWORLD
Tracks: / Underworld.
12" Single: Released May '85, on Antenna, Catalogue no: **BUTT 1**

Startrax

REGGAES GREATEST HITS MEDLEY (SINGLE)
Tracks: / Reggaes greatest hits medley.
12" Single: Released Nov '81, on Picksy, by Pickwick Records. Deleted Nov '84. Catalogue no: **KSYX 1005**
7" Single: Released Nov '81, on Picksy, by Pickwick Records. Deleted Nov '84. Catalogue no: **KSY 1005**

STARTRAX CLUB DISCO (SINGLE)
Tracks: / Startrax club disco.
7" Single: Released Aug '81, on Picksy, by Pickwick Records. Deleted '84. Catalogue no: **KSY 1001**

Starvation

STARVATION
Tracks: / Starvation / Tam - Tam pour l'Ethiopie.
12" Single: Released Feb '85, on Zarjazz, by Zarjazz Records. Deleted May '88. Catalogue no: **JAZZ 3-12**
7" Single: Released Feb '85, on Zarjazz, by Zarjazz Records. Deleted May '88. Catalogue no: **JAZZ 3**

Starz

SO YOUNG, SO BAD
Tracks: / So young, so bad.
7" Single: Released May '85, on Heavy Metal America, by FM-Revolver Records. Catalogue no: **VHF 6**

Statchil

SING CHILDREN SING
Tracks: / Sing children sing.
7" Single: Released Jun '81, on CBS, by CBS Records. Deleted Jun '84. Catalogue no: **A 1275**

State Of Emergency

MEN OF ACTION
Tracks: / Men of action.
7" Single: Released Jul '83, on Northeast Music, by Northeast Music Records. Catalogue no: **PMC 1**

State Of Grace

HELLO WINTERTIME
Tracks: / Hello wintertime.
12" Single: Released Jan '84, on PRT, by Castle Communications Records. Catalogue no: **12P 295**
7" Single: Released Jan '84, on PRT, by Castle Communications Records. Catalogue no: **7P 295**

THAT'S WHEN WE'LL BE FREE
Tracks: / That's when we'll be free.
12" Single: Released Nov '82, on PRT, by Castle Communications Records. Deleted Nov '85. Catalogue no: **12P252**
7" Single: Released Nov '82, on PRT, by Castle Communications Records. Deleted Nov '85. Catalogue no: **7P252**

WALKING RHYTHM
Tracks: / Walking rhythm / Walking.
7" Single: Released Nov '81, on Flamingo, by Airwave Records (USA). Catalogue no: **FM 18**

State Of Mind

GOD ONLY KNOWS
Tracks: / God only knows.
12" Single: Released May '89, on Big Life, by Big Life Records. Catalogue no: **BLR 009T**
CD 5": Released Jul '89, on Big Life, by Big Life Records. Catalogue no: **BLR 009 CD**
7" Single: Released May '89, on Big Life, by Big Life Records. Catalogue no: **BLR 009**

State Of Play

NATURAL COLOURS
Tracks: / Natural colours / Lost souls.
7" Single: Released Apr '86, on Virgin, by Virgin Records. Deleted '89. Catalogue no: **VS 850**
12" Single: Released Apr '86, on Virgin, by Virgin Records. Deleted '89. Catalogue no: **VS 850-12**

ROCK A BYE BABY
Tracks: / Rockabye baby / Metropolis.
12" Single: Released Jun '86, on Virgin, by Virgin Records. Deleted '89. Catalogue no: **VS 873-12**
7" Single: Released Jun '86, on Virgin, by Virgin Records. Deleted May '88. Catalogue no: **VS 873**

State Of The Art

INSTINCT
Tracks: / Instinct.
7" Single: Released 20 Jun '87, on Big Freeze, Catalogue no: **BFR 1**

State Project

EMPIRE STATE (SINGLE) Original soundtrack
Tracks: / Empire State / Money.
12" Single: Released 20 Jun '87, on Priority, by Priority Records. Deleted 11 Jan '88. Catalogue no: **12 EMPIRE 1**
7" Single: Released 20 Jun '87, on Priority, by Priority Records. Deleted Jan '88. Catalogue no: **EMPIRE 1**

Statetrooper

SHE GOT THE LOOK
Tracks: / Veni, vidi, vici / Set fire to the night / She got the look.
7" Single: Released '88, on Neat, by Neat Records. Catalogue no: **NEAT 52**
12" Single: Released '88, on Neat, by Neat Records. Catalogue no: **NEAT 52 12**

Static Activity

EPICALLY BLAZING ADVENTURES of static activity in the land of Zing
Tracks: / Epically blazing adventures.
7" Single: Released Aug '83, on Rapp, Catalogue no: **RAPP 34567**

Statics

TURN THE RADIO ON
Tracks: / Turn the radio on / Last night in chinatown / Over now.
7" Single: Released Sep '80, on Mercury, by Phonogram Ltd. Deleted '83. Catalogue no: **MER 41**
7" Single: Released May '81, on Carrere, Deleted May '86. Catalogue no: **CAR 186**

Statler Brothers

FLOWERS ON THE WALL
Tracks: / Flowers on the wall.
7" Single: Released Feb '66, on CBS, by CBS Records. Deleted '69. Catalogue no: **CBS 201976**

TOO MUCH OF MY HEART
Tracks: / Too much of my heart / Hello Mary Lou.
7" Single: Released Jan '86, on Mercury, by Phonogram Ltd. Catalogue no: **MER 209**

Staton, Candi

COUNT ON ME
Tracks: / Count on me.
12" Single: Released Jul '82, on Sugarhill (USA), Catalogue no: **SHL 115**
7" Single: Released Jul '82, on Sugarhill (USA), Deleted '88. Catalogue no: **SH 115**

DESTINY
Tracks: / Destiny.
7" Single: Released Sep '76, on Warner Bros., by WEA Records. Deleted '79. Catalogue no: **K 16806**

HONEST I DO LOVE YOU
Tracks: / Honest I do love you.
7" Single: Released Jun '78, on Warner Bros., by WEA Records. Deleted '81. Catalogue no: **K 17164**

NIGHTS ON BROADWAY
Tracks: / Nights on Broadway.
7" Single: Released Jul '77, on Warner Bros., by WEA Records. Deleted '80. Catalogue no: **K 16972**

SUSPICIOUS MINDS (OLD GOLD)
Tracks: / Suspicious minds.
7" Single: Released Sep '85, on Old Gold, by Old Gold Records. Catalogue no: **OG 9518**

SUSPICIOUS MINDS (SINGLE)
Tracks: / Suspicious minds / Nights on Broadway.
12" Single: Released Mar '82, on Sugarhill (USA), Catalogue no: **SHL 112**
7" Single: Released Mar '82, on Sugarhill (USA), Catalogue no: **SH 112**

YOUNG HEARTS RUN FREE (REMIX)
Tracks: / Young hearts run free / Young hearts run free (M & M ' 86 remix).
12" Single: Released May '86, on Warner Bros., by WEA Records. Deleted Jan '88. Catalogue no: **W 8680T**
7" Single: Released May '86, on Warner Bros., by WEA Records. Deleted Jan '88. Catalogue no: **W 8680**

YOUNG HEARTS RUN FREE (SINGLE)
Tracks: / Young hearts run free.
7" Single: Released May '76, on Warner Bros., by WEA Records. Deleted '79. Catalogue no: **K 16730**

YOU'VE GOT THE LOVE
Tracks: / You've got the love (mix).
7" Single: Released Nov '86, on DM Streetsounds, Catalogue no: **KHAN 78**
12" Single: Released Nov '86, on DM Streetsounds, Catalogue no: **MKHAN 78**

Status IV

LOVIN' YOU
Tracks: / Loving you.
7" Single: Released Mar '84, on Design Communications, Catalogue no: **DES 8**
12" Single: Released Mar '84, on Design Communications, Catalogue no: **DEST 8**

YOU AIN'T REALLY DOWN
Tracks: / You ain't really down.
12" Single: Released Jul '83, on T.M.T., by T.M.T. Productions. Deleted '87. Catalogue no: **TMTT 4**
7" Single: Released Jul '83, on T.M.T., by T.M.T. Productions. Deleted '87. Catalogue no: **TMT 4**
12" Single: Released May '85, on Domino, by Domino Records. Deleted Jan '88. Catalogue no: **DOM 1T**

Status Quo

Biographical details: Status Quo is a UK rock group formed in 1962 and still going. Lineup: Francis Rossi (born 29 April 1949) and Richard Parfitt (born 12 October 1948), guitars and vocals; Alan Lancaster (born 7 February 1949) on bass. John Coghlan (born 19 September 1946) on drums, all Londoners. They began as the Spectres in school, made singles; then as Traffic Jam made more singles; then abandoned harmony pop and boogied into the charts as Status Quo; they have toured USA but are far more successful at home. They have had more than 30 single hits in the UK, over half in top the 10, and about 30 albums of which the first was *Picturesque matchstickable* '68; first to chart was *Piledriver* '73 (at No. 5); *Hello* '73, *On the level* '75, *Blue for you* '76, *1982* were all No. 1 albums. (Donald Clarke 21.5.88).

ACCIDENT PRONE
Tracks: / Accident prone.
7" Single: Released Nov '78, on Vertigo, by Phonogram Ltd. Deleted '81. Catalogue no: **QUO 2**

AGAIN AND AGAIN
Tracks: / Again and again.
7" Single: Released Sep '78, on Vertigo, by Phonogram Ltd. Deleted '81. Catalogue no: **QUO 1**

AIN'T COMPLAINING (SINGLE)
Tracks: / Ain't complaining / That's alright / Ain't complaining (extended) / Lean machine (on 12" only.) / In the army now (remix) (on CD version.).
Note: *Ain't complaining (extended)* on 12" only.u
7" Single: Released 14 Mar '88, on Vertigo, by Phonogram Ltd. Deleted Oct '88. Catalogue no: **QUO 22**
7" Single: Released Mar '88, on Vertigo, by Phonogram Ltd. Deleted Oct '88. Catalogue no: **QUOH 22**
CD 5": Released 14 Mar '88, on Vertigo, by Phonogram Ltd. Deleted Oct '88. Catalogue no: **QUOCD 22**
12" Single: Released 14 Mar '88, on Vertigo, by Phonogram Ltd. Deleted Oct '88. Catalogue no: **QUO 2212**

ARE YOU GROWING TIRED OF MY LOVE
Tracks: / Are you growing tired of my love.
7" Single: Released May '69, on Pye, Deleted '72. Catalogue no: **7 N 17728**

BREAK THE RULES
Tracks: / Break the rules.
7" Single: Released May '74, on Vertigo, by Phonogram Ltd. Deleted '77. Catalogue no: **6059 101**

BURNING BRIDGES (ON AND OFF AND ON AGAIN)
Tracks: / Burning bridges (on and off and on again) / What ever you want / Marguerita time (Only on 12" version and CD single.) / Burning bridges (on and off and on again)(extended) (Only on 12" version and CD single.).
12" Single: Released Nov '88, on Vertigo, by Phonogram Ltd. Deleted 31 Jul '89. Catalogue no: **QUO 2512**
7" Single: Released Nov '88, on Vertigo, by Phonogram Ltd. Deleted 31 Jul '89. Catalogue no: **QUO 25**
CD 5": Released Nov '88, on Vertigo, by Phonogram Ltd. Catalogue no: **QUOCD 25**

CAROLINE
Tracks: / Caroline.
7" Single: Released Sep '73, on Vertigo, by Phonogram Ltd. Deleted '76. Catalogue no: **6059 085**

CAROLINE (LIVE AT THE NEC)
Tracks: / Caroline.
7" Single: Released Oct '82, on Vertigo, by Phonogram Ltd. Deleted '87. Catalogue no: **QUO 10**

CAROLINE (OLD GOLD)
Tracks: / Caroline.
7" Single: Released Sep '85, on Old Gold, by Old Gold Records. Catalogue no: **OG 9566**

DEAR JOHN
Tracks: / Dear John.
7" Single: Released Mar '82, on Vertigo, by Phonogram Ltd. Catalogue no: **QUO 7**

DOWN DOWN
Tracks: / Down down.
7" Single: Released Dec '74, on Vertigo, by Phonogram Ltd. Deleted '77. Catalogue no:

STATUS QUO - OL' RAG BLUES (Released on Vertigo)

6059 114

DOWN THE DUSTPIPE (SINGLE)
Tracks: / Down the dustpipe.
7" Single: Released '74, on PRT, by Castle Communications Records. Catalogue no: **7N 17907**
12" Single: Released Jun '77, on Big Deal, Deleted '80. Catalogue no: **BD 103**

DREAMIN'
Tracks: / Dreamin' / Long legged girl with the short dress on / Quo Christmas cake mix, The (On 12" only).
7" Single: Released Nov '86, on Vertigo, by Phonogram Ltd. Deleted Jul '87. Catalogue no: **QUO 21**
12" Single: on Vertigo, by Phonogram Ltd. Deleted Jul '87. Catalogue no: **QUO 2112**

GERDUNDULA
Tracks: / Gerdundula.
7" Single: Released Jun '73, on PRT, by Castle Communications Records. Catalogue no: **7N 45253**

GOING DOWN TOWN TONIGHT
Tracks: / Going down town tonight / To close to the ground.
7" Single: Released Apr '84, on Vertigo, by Phonogram Ltd. Catalogue no: **QUO 15**

ICE IN THE SUN
Tracks: / Ice in the sun.
7" Single: Released Aug '68, on Pye, Deleted '71. Catalogue no: **7 N 17581**
7" Single: Released '80, on Mercury, by Phonogram Ltd. Catalogue no: **LR 8244**

IN MY CHAIR
Tracks: / In my chair.
7" Single: Released Nov '70, on Pye, Deleted '73. Catalogue no: **7 N 17998**
7" Single: Released Jun '79, on PRT, by Castle Communications Records. Catalogue no: **7P 103**

IN THE ARMY NOW (SINGLE)
Tracks: / In the army now / Heartburn / Late last night.
7" Single: Released Sep '86, on Vertigo, by Phonogram Ltd. Catalogue no: **QUO 20**
12" Single: Released Sep '86, on Vertigo, by Phonogram Ltd. Catalogue no: **QUO 2012**

LIES
Tracks: / Lies / Don't drive my car.
7" Single: Released Dec '80, on Vertigo, by Phonogram Ltd. Deleted '83. Catalogue no: **QUO 4**

LIVING ON AN ISLAND
Tracks: / Living on an island.
7" Single: Released Nov '79, on Vertigo, by Phonogram Ltd. Deleted '82. Catalogue no: **6059 248**

MARGUERITA TIME
Tracks: / Marguerita time / Resurrection.
7" Single: Released Dec '83, on Vertigo, by Phonogram Ltd. Deleted '86. Catalogue no: **QUO 14**

MEAN GIRL
Tracks: / Mean girl.
7" Single: Released Apr '73, on Pye, Deleted '76. Catalogue no: **7 N 45229**
7" Single: Released Jul '78, on PRT, by Castle Communications Records. Catalogue no: **7N 46095**
7" Single: Released Jul '82, on Old Gold, by Old Gold Records. Deleted Jul '88. Catalogue no: **OG 9142**

MESS OF THE BLUES, A
Tracks: / Mess of the blues.
7" Single: Released Nov '83, on Vertigo, by Phonogram Ltd. Deleted '86. Catalogue no: **QUO 12**

MYSTERY SONG
Tracks: / Mystery song.
7" Single: Released Jul '76, on Vertigo, by Phonogram Ltd. Deleted '79. Catalogue no: **6059 146**

NAUGHTY GIRL
Tracks: / Naughty girl.
12" Single: on Phonogram, by Phonogram Ltd. Deleted 31 May '89. Catalogue no: **QUO 1712**

OL' RAG BLUES (see panel above)
Tracks: / Ol' rag blues / Stay the night.
7" Single: Released Sep '83, on Vertigo, by Phonogram Ltd. Deleted '86. Catalogue no: **QUO 11**

PAPER PLANE
Tracks: / Paper plane.
7" Single: Released Jan '73, on Vertigo, by Phonogram Ltd. Deleted '76. Catalogue no: **6059 071**

PICTURES OF MATCHSTICK MEN
Tracks: / Pictures of matchstick men.
7" Single: Released Jan '68, on Pye, Deleted '71. Catalogue no: **7 N 17449**
7" Single: Released Apr '79, on Flashback, by Mainline Records. Catalogue no: **FBS 2**

PICTURES OF MATCHSTICK MEN (OLD GOLD)
Tracks: / Pictures of matchstick men.
7" Single: Released Apr '83, on Old Gold, by Old Gold Records. Catalogue no: **OG 9298**

RAIN
Tracks: / Rain.
7" Single: Released Feb '76, on Vertigo, by Phonogram Ltd. Deleted '79. Catalogue no: **6059 133**

RED SKY
Tracks: / Red sky / Don't give it up / Milton Keynes medley (Extra track on 12" version only.).
7" Single: Released Jul '86, on Vertigo, by Phonogram Ltd. Catalogue no: **QUO 19**
12" Single: Released Jul '86, on Vertigo, by Phonogram Ltd. Catalogue no: **QUO 1912**

ROCKIN' ALL OVER THE WORLD (OLD GOLD)
Tracks: / Rockin' all over the world.
7" Single: Released Nov '85, on Old Gold, by Old Gold Records. Catalogue no: **OG 9567**

ROCKIN' ALL OVER THE WORLD (SINGLE)
Tracks: / Rockin' all over the world.
7" Single: Released Oct '77, on Vertigo, by Phonogram Ltd. Deleted '80. Catalogue no: **6059 184**

ROCK'N'ROLL
Tracks: / Rock and roll / Hold you back.
7" Single: Released Nov '81, on Vertigo, by Phonogram Ltd. Deleted '84. Catalogue no: **QUO 6**

ROLL OVER LAY DOWN
Tracks: / Roll over lay down.
7" Single: Released May '75, on Vertigo, by Phonogram Ltd. Catalogue no: **QUO 13**

ROLLIN' HOME
Tracks: / Rollin' home / Lonely / Keep me guessing (12" vesion only).
12" Single: Released Apr '86, on Vertigo, by Phonogram Ltd. Catalogue no: **QUO 1812**
7" Single: Released Apr '86, on Vertigo, by Phonogram Ltd. Catalogue no: **QUO 18**

RUNNING ALL OVER THE WORLD
Tracks: / Running all over the world / Magic / Whatever you want.
Note: "This classic song which opened Live Aid in 1986 has been specially re-recorded for Sport Aid 88 and the Race Against Time. All profits from it's sales will go to build a better future for children throughout the world and to combat the hunger, poverty and disease which kills nearly 15 million children every year." (August 1988)
CD 5": Released 8 Aug '88, on Vertigo, by Phonogram Ltd. Catalogue no: **QUACD 1**
12" Single: Released 8 Aug '88, on Vertigo, by Phonogram Ltd. Deleted 31 May '89. Catalogue no: **QUAID 112**
7" Single: Released 8 Aug '88, on Vertigo, by Phonogram Ltd. Deleted 31 May '89. Catalogue no: **QUAID 1**

SHE DON'T FOOL ME
Tracks: / She don't fool me / Never too late.
7" Single: Released Jun '82, on Vertigo, by Phonogram Ltd. Catalogue no: **QUO 8**

SOMETHING 'BOUT YOU BABY I LIKE
Tracks: / Something 'bout you baby I like / Enough is enough.
7" Single: Released Feb '81, on Vertigo, by Phonogram Ltd. Deleted '84. Catalogue no: **QUO 5**

WANDERER, THE
Tracks: / Wanderer.
7" Single: Released Oct '84, on Vertigo, by Phonogram Ltd. Deleted '87. Catalogue no: **QUO 16**

WHAT YOU'RE PROPOSING
Tracks: / What you're proposing / AB blues.
7" Single: Released Oct '80, on Vertigo, by Phonogram Ltd. Deleted '83. Catalogue no: **QUO 3**

WHATEVER YOU WANT (SINGLE)
Tracks: / Whatever you want.
7" Single: Released Sep '79, on Vertigo, by Phonogram Ltd. Deleted '82. Catalogue no: **6059 242**

WHO GETS THE LOVE
Tracks: / Who gets the love / Wanderer.
Note: * extra track on CD Single.
7" Single: Released May '88, on Vertigo, by Phonogram Ltd. Deleted Oct '88. Catalogue no: **QUO 23**
7" Single: Released May '88, on Vertigo, by Phonogram Ltd. Deleted Oct '88. Catalogue no: **QUOH 23**
12" Single: Released May '88, on Vertigo, by Phonogram Ltd. Deleted Oct '88. Catalogue no: **QUO 2312**
CD 5": Released May '88, on Vertigo, by Phonogram Ltd. Deleted Oct '88. Catalogue no: **QUOCD 23**

WILD SIDE OF LIFE
Tracks: / Wild side of life.
7" Single: Released Dec '76, on Vertigo, by Phonogram Ltd. Deleted '79. Catalogue no: **6059 153**

Stavely Makepeace

JUST TELL HER FRED SAID GOODBYE
Tracks: / Just tell her Fred said goodbye.
7" Single: Released Nov '83, on Sma, Deleted '85. Catalogue no: **SMA 1502**

SONGS OF YESTERDAY
Tracks: / Songs of yesterday.
7" Single: Released Apr '80, on Scratch, by Scratch Records. Deleted '82. Catalogue no: **HS 404**

Stavin, Mary

ONLY YES WILL DO
Tracks: / Only yes will do / Teacher.
7" Single: Released May '90, on Ariola, by BMG Records (UK). Deleted '85. Catalogue no: **ARO 215**

Stax...

STAX (BOXED SET) 811-820
Note: Boxed set of ten 7" singles.
Special: Released Nov '87, on Stax, by Fantasy Inc (USA). Catalogue no: **STAX-BOX 2**

STAX ON 45 (MEDLEY)
Tracks: / Stax on 45 (Medley).
7" Single: Released Feb '82, on Stax, by Fantasy Inc (USA). Deleted Feb '87. Catalogue no: **STAX 2000**
12" Single: Released Feb '82, on Stax, by Fantasy Inc (USA). Deleted Feb '87. Catalogue no: **STAXT 2000**

Stax, John

DANCE FOR MY LOVE
Tracks: / Dance for my love.
7" Single: Released Oct '84, on Lamborghini, by Lamborghini Records. Catalogue no: **LMG 18**
12" Single: Released Oct '84, on Lamborghini, by Lamborghini Records. Catalogue no: **12LMG 18**

INFATUATION
Tracks: / Infatuation / Through silence.
7" Single: Released Mar '85, on Lamborghini, by Lamborghini Records. Catalogue no: **LMG 20**

WAITING IN THE MIDDLE OF THE NIGHT
Tracks: / Waiting in the middle of the night.
7" Single: Released Jan '84, on Lamborghini, by Lamborghini Records. Catalogue no: **LMG 7**
12" Single: Released Jan '84, on Lamborghini, by Lamborghini Records. Catalogue no: **12LMG 7**

Stay Prest

SCHOOL DAYS
Tracks: / School days / Tomorrow.
7" Single: Released '82, on Avatar, by Avatar Record Corporation. Catalogue no: **AAA 103**

St.Clair, Isla

CHRISTMAS DREAMS
Tracks: / Christmas dreams / Way it used to be.
7" Single: Released Dec '81, on Deauville, by Stiletto Records. Catalogue no: **STL 4**

ISLAND OF DREAMS
Tracks: / Island of dreams / My generation.
7" Single: Released Mar '82, on Deauville, by Stiletto Records. Catalogue no: **STL 5**

SONG BIRD
Tracks: / Song bird / Yuri.
7" Single: Released Oct '80, on Ariola-Hansa, by Hansa Records. Deleted Oct '83. Catalogue no: **AHA 566**

STILL NO SIGN OF THE LIFEBOATS
Tracks: / Still no sign of the lifeboats.
7" Single: Released Aug '83, on Dingle's, by Dingle's Records. Catalogue no: **SID 236**

Steady B

CHEATIN' GIRL
Tracks: / Bring the beat back / Cheatin' girl.
12" Single: Released Jan '87, on Jive, by Zomba Records. Deleted Jul '87. Catalogue no: **JIVET138**
7" Single: Released Jan '87, on Jive, by Zomba Records. Catalogue no: **JIVE 138**

LET THE HUSTLERS PLAY
Tracks: / Let the hustlers play.
12" Single: Released Oct '88, on Jive, by Zomba Records. Catalogue no: **JIVET 188**

NASTY GIRLS
Tracks: / Nasty girls.
7" Single: Released Jun '89, on Jive, by Zomba Records. Catalogue no: **JIVE 205**
12" Single: Released Jun '89, on Jive, by Zomba Records. Catalogue no: **JIVE T205**

SERIOUS
Tracks: / Serious / Miss Melody.
12" Single: Released Feb '89, on Jive, by Zomba Records. Catalogue no: **1167 1JD**
12" Single: Released Mar '89, on Jive, by Zomba Records. Catalogue no: **JIVET 199**
7" Single: Released May '89, on Jive, by Zomba Records. Catalogue no: **JIVE 199**

WHAT'S MY NAME (SINGLE)
Tracks: / What's my name / Don't disturb the groove.
12" Single: Released Sep '87, on Jive, by Zomba Records. Catalogue no: **10651 JD**

TEEL PULSE - PREDICTION (Released on Island)

Stealers Wheel

EVERYTHING'L TURN OUT FINE
Tracks: / Everything'l turn out fine.
7" Single: Released Sep '73, on A&M, by A&M Records. Deleted '76. Catalogue no: **AMS 7079**

STAR
Tracks: / Star.
7" Single: Released Jan '74, on A&M, by A&M Records. Deleted '77. Catalogue no: **AMS 7094**

STUCK IN THE MIDDLE
Tracks: / Stuck in the middle.
7" Single: Released May '73, on A&M, by A&M Records. Deleted '76. Catalogue no: **AMS 7036**

STUCK IN THE MIDDLE (OLD GOLD)
Tracks: / Stuck in the middle / Star.
7" Single: Released Jul '82, on Old Gold, by Old Gold Records. Catalogue no: **OG 9148**

Steam (group)

NA NA HEY HEY KISS HIM GOOD-BYE
Tracks: / Na na hey hey (kiss him goodbye).
7" Single: Released Jan '70, on Fontana, by Phonogram Ltd. Deleted '73. Catalogue no: **TF 1058**

NA NA HEY HEY KISS HIM GOOD-BYE (OLD GOLD)
Tracks: / Na na hey hey kiss him goodbye.
7" Single: Released Jan '85, on Old Gold, by Old Gold Records. Catalogue no: **OG 9491**

Steaming Towards Oslo

OFF THE HOOK
Tracks: / Off the hook.
7" Single: Released Jun '83, on Deptfor-discs, Catalogue no: **OSLO 1**

Steding, Walter

SECRET SPY
Tracks: / Secret spy / My room.
7" Single: Released Aug '82, on Animal, by Chrysalis Records. Catalogue no: **CHDOG 2633**

Steel

ROCK OUT
Tracks: / All systems go / Rock out.
7" Single: Released Nov '81, on Neat, by Neat Records. Catalogue no: **NEAT 14**

Steel, Anthony

WEST OF ZANZIBAR
Tracks: / West of Zanzibar.
7" Single: Released Sep '54, on Polygon, Deleted '57. Catalogue no: **P 1114**

Steel Breeze

DREAMIN' IS EASY
Tracks: / Dreamin' is easy.
7" Single: Released Apr '83, on RCA, by BMG Records (UK). Catalogue no: **RCA 302**

YOU DON'T WANT ME ANYMORE
Tracks: / You don't want me anymore / Who's gonna love you tonight.
7" Single: Released Oct '82, on RCA, by BMG Records (UK). Catalogue no: **RCA 283**

Steel Chain

RESTLESS (EP)
Tracks: / Restless.
12" Single: Released Oct '88, on Nightshift, by Nightshift Records. Catalogue no: **NISHI 207T**

Steel, Coco

CRUCIFIXION OF DONNY - LOVE PUPPY
Tracks: / Crucifixion of Donny - love puppy / Yuppie love (totally cut up).
12" Single: Released Sep '87, on Instant (1), by Instant Records. Catalogue no: **INST 7**

FRENZY
Tracks: / Frenzy.
CD 5": Released 5 Jun '89, on Sweatbox, by Sweatbox Records. Catalogue no: **SOX 043 CD**
12" Single: Released Nov '88, on Audio Instant, by Audio Instant Records. Catalogue no: **INST 010**
12" Single: Released 5 Jun '89, on Sweatbox, by Sweatbox Records. Catalogue no: **SOX 043**

SOUND OF EUROPE, THE
Tracks: / Sound of Europe, The / Sound of Europe, The (version).
12" Single: Released '88, on Audio Instant, by Audio Instant Records. Catalogue no: **INST 008**

Steel Locks

LET'S GET TOGETHER
Tracks: / Let's get together / 1980.
7" Single: Released Feb '80, on Voyage International, by Code Records. Deleted Feb '83. Catalogue no: **VOY 0013**

Steel Pulse

CAUGHT YOU DANCING
Tracks: / Caught you dancing / Caught.
12" Single: Released May '80, on Island, by Island Records. Deleted May '83. Catalogue no: **12WIP 6589**
7" Single: Released May '80, on Island, by Island Records. Deleted May '83. Catalogue no: **WIP 6589**

DON'T GIVE IN
Tracks: / Don't give in / Don't.
7" Single: Released Mar '80, on Island, by Island Records. Deleted '83. Catalogue no: **WIP 6562**

KU KLUX KLAN
Tracks: / Ku klux klan.
7" Single: Released Apr '78, on Island, by Island Records. Deleted '81. Catalogue no: **WIP 6428**

LOVE WALKS OUT
Tracks: / Love walks out / Kick that habit / Save black music (Extra track on 12" version only).
7" Single: Released Feb '86, on Elektra (USA), by Elektra Records (USA). Catalogue no: **EKR 34**
12" Single: Released Feb '86, on Elektra (USA), by Elektra Records (USA). Catalogue no: **EKR 34 T**

PREDICTION (see panel)
Tracks: / Prediction / Revolution (dub).
7" Single: Released '78, on Island, by Island Records. Catalogue no: **WIP 6461**

PRODIGAL SON
Tracks: / Prodigal son.
7" Single: Released Jul '78, on Island, by Island Records. Deleted '81. Catalogue no: **WIP 6449**

RAVERS
Tracks: / Ravers, The.
12" Single: Released Apr '82, on Wise Man Doctrine, Catalogue no: **12 WMDS 001**
7" Single: Released Apr '82, on Wise Man Doctrine, Catalogue no: **7 WMDS 001**

REACHING OUT
Tracks: / Reaching out.
7" Single: Released Oct '88, on MCA, by MCA Records. Catalogue no: **MCA 1283**
12" Single: Released Oct '88, on MCA, by MCA Records. Catalogue no: **MCAT 1283**

SOUND SYSTEM
Tracks: / Sound system.
7" Single: Released Jun '79, on Island, by Island Records. Deleted '82. Catalogue no: **WIP 6490**

STEPPIN' OUT
Tracks: / Steppin' out / Bodyguard.
12" Single: Released Mar '84, on Wise Man Doctrine, Deleted Mar '87. Catalogue no: **12 WMDS 003**

YOUR HOUSE
Tracks: / Your house / Blues dance rate.
12" Single: Released Jan '83, on Wise Man Doctrine, Catalogue no: **12 WMDS 002**

Steele, Jvetta

CALLING YOU
Tracks: / Calling you / Calling you (inst) / Zweisach.
7" Single: Released Mar '89, on Island, by Island Records. Catalogue no: **IS 385**
CD 5": Released 10 Apr '89, on Island, by Island Records. Catalogue no: **CID 385**

Steele, Maureen

BOYS WILL BE BOYS
Tracks: / Boys will be boys.
7" Single: Released Sep '85, on RCA, by BMG Records (UK). Catalogue no: **ZB 40343**
12" Single: Released Sep '85, on RCA, by BMG Records (UK). Catalogue no: **ZT 40344**

SAVE THE NIGHT FOR ME
Tracks: / Save the night for me / Rock my heart.
12" Single: Released Jun '85, on Motown, by BMG Records (UK). Catalogue no: **ZT 40160**
7" Single: Released Jun '85, on Motown, by BMG Records (UK). Catalogue no: **ZB 40159**

Steele, Sandra

I'M HUNG UP ON YOU
Tracks: / I'm hung up on you / Half the way.
7" Single: Released Apr '80, on Liberty (USA), by EMI Records. Deleted Apr '83. Catalogue no: **UP 620**

YOU MAKE IT SOUND SO EASY
Tracks: / You make it sound so easy.
7" Single: Released Mar '81, on Precision (1), Deleted '83. Catalogue no: **PAR 116**

Steele, Tommy

Biographical details: Steele, Tommy was born Thomas Hicks on 17 December 1936 in London. He was once touted as the British Elvis Presley, but turned out to be an all-round entertainer with roots in music hall. He was one of those discovered in the famours 2 I's coffee ship in Soho; his first release *Rock with the caveman* went top 20 in 1956: the following month his *Singin' the blues* replaced Guy Mitchell's at No. 1. He had 18 hits through 1961; he was washed away by the Merseybeat, but meanwhile played Tony Lumkin in Oliver Goldsmith's 18th century comedy *She stoops to conquer* in 1962 at the Old Vic, then the musical *Half a sixpence* in 1963, filmed in 1967 (based on the H.G. Wells novel Kipps), which was filmed in 1967; then played a leprechaun in a film of the 1947 Broadway hit *Finians Rainbow* in 1968, with Fred Astaire and Petula Clark; after Frank Loesser's musical *Hans Christian Anderson* at the London Palladium he had a record-breaking 60-week run in a one-man show at the Prince of Wales in 1979, then starred in and directed stage version of classic film *Singing in the rain* 1983-5. A natural performer, still with a permanent grin, he was awarded an OBE in 1979. (Donald Clarke 21.5.88).

BUTTERFINGERS
Tracks: / Butterfingers.
7" Single: Released May '57, on Decca, by Decca Records. Deleted '60. Catalogue no: **F 10877**

COME ON LET'S GO
Tracks: / Come on let's go.
7" Single: Released Nov '58, on Decca, by Decca Records. Deleted '61. Catalogue no: **F 11072**

GIVE GIVE GIVE
Tracks: / Give give give.
7" Single: Released Aug '59, on Decca, by Decca Records. Deleted '62. Catalogue no: **F 11152**

HAPPY GUITAR
Tracks: / Happy guitar.
7" Single: Released Apr '58, on Decca, by Decca Records. Deleted '61. Catalogue no: **F 10976**

HEY YOU
Tracks: / Hey you.
7" Single: Released Nov '57, on Decca, by Decca Records. Deleted '60. Catalogue no: **F 10941**

KNEE DEEP IN THE BLUES
Tracks: / Knee deep in the blues.
7" Single: Released Feb '57, on Decca, by Decca Records. Deleted '60. Catalogue no: **F 10849**

LITTLE WHITE BULL
Tracks: / Little white bull.
7" Single: Released '59, on Decca, by Decca Records. Deleted '88. Catalogue no: **F 11177**

MUST BE SANTA
Tracks: / Must be Santa.
7" Single: Released Dec '60, on Decca, by Decca Records. Deleted '63. Catalogue no: **F 11299**

NAIROBI
Tracks: / Nairobi.
7" Single: Released Mar '58, on Decca, by Decca Records. Deleted '61. Catalogue no: **F 10991**

ONLY MAN ON THE ISLAND, THE
Tracks: / Only man on the island, The.
7" Single: Released Jul '58, on Decca, by Decca Records. Deleted '61. Catalogue no: **F 11041**

ROCK WITH THE CAVEMAN
Tracks: / Rock with the caveman / Elevator rock.
7" Single: Released Oct '56, on Decca, by Decca Records. Deleted '59. Catalogue no: **F 10795**
7" Single: Released Mar '82, on Decca, by Decca Records. Deleted '88. Catalogue no: **F 13813**

SHIRALEE
Tracks: / Shiralee.
7" Single: Released Aug '57, on Decca, by Decca Records. Deleted '60. Catalogue no: **F 10896**

SINGING IN THE RAIN
Tracks: / Singing in the rain.
7" Single: Released Aug '87, on Safari, by Safari Records. Catalogue no: **SAFE 61**

SINGING THE BLUES
Tracks: / Singing the blues.
7" Single: Released Dec '56, on Decca, by Decca Records. Deleted '59. Catalogue no: **F 10819**
7" Single: Released '80, on Decca, by Decca Records. Deleted '88. Catalogue no: **LR 4683**

SINGING THE BLUES (OLD GOLD)
Tracks: / Singing the blues.
7" Single: Released Sep '85, on Old Gold, by Old Gold Records. Catalogue no: **OG 9536**

TALLAHASSEE LASSIE
Tracks: / Tallahassee Lassie.
7" Single: Released Aug '59, on Decca, by Decca Records. Deleted '62. Catalogue no: **F 11152**

WATER WATER
Tracks: / Water water / Handful of songs.
7" Single: Released Aug '57, on Decca, by Decca Records. Deleted '60. Catalogue no: **F 10923**

WHAT A MOUTH
Tracks: / What a mouth.
7" Single: Released Jun '60, on Decca, by Decca Records. Deleted '63. Catalogue no: **F 11245**

WRITING ON THE WALL
Tracks: / Writing on the wall.
7" Single: Released Aug '61, on Decca, by Decca Records. Deleted '64. Catalogue no: **F 11372**

Steeleye Span

ALL AROUND MY HAT (SINGLE)
Tracks: / Gaudete / All around my hat / Fighting for strangers / Boars head carol.
7" Single: Released Nov '82, on Chrysalis, by Chrysalis Records. Catalogue no: **CHS 2658**

ALL AROUND MY HAT (OLD GOLD)
Tracks: / ll around my hat.
7" Single: Released Feb '87, on Old Gold, by Old Gold Records. Catalogue no: **OG 9690**

BOAR'S HEAD CAROL, THE
Tracks: / Boar's head carol / Gaudete / Some rival.
7" Single: Released '83, on Chrysalis, by Chrysalis Records. Deleted '87. Catalogue no: **CHS 2192**

FOLLOWING ME
Tracks: / Following me.
7" Single: Released Sep '89, on Dover, by Chrysalis Records. Catalogue no: **SLUT 4**

GAUDETE
Tracks: / Gaudete / Holly and the ivy, The.
7" Single: Released Dec '73, on Chrysalis, by Chrysalis Records. Deleted '78. Catalogue no: **CHS 2007**

GONE TO AMERICA
Tracks: / Gone to America / Let her go down.
7" Single: Released Mar '81, on Chrysalis, by Chrysalis Records. Deleted Mar '84. Catalogue no: **CHS 2503**

PADSTOW
Tracks: / Padstow.
7" Single: Released Apr '89, on Supertrack, Catalogue no: **FLUT 3**

SAILS OF SILVER
Tracks: / Sails of silver / Senior service.
7" Single: Released Dec '80, on Chrysalis, by Chrysalis Records. Deleted Dec '85. Catalogue no: **CHS 2479**

SOMEWHERE IN LONDON
Tracks: / Somewhere in London.
7" Single: Released Nov '85, on Butterfly, by Priority Records. Catalogue no: **FLUT 1**

Steely Dan

Biographical details: Steely Dan was a USA jazz-influence band, renowned for meticulous production on records and cryptic lyrics, named after a dildo in William Burroughs' **Naked Lunch**. Basically a duo of songwriters/vocalists Walter Becker (bass, guitar) and Donald Fagen (keyboards; both born c.'50-1) who met at college in New York State; they wrote the soundtrack for the film **You gotta walk it like you talk it** in 1971, produced by Kenny Vance of Jay & The Americans (whose backing group they played in). They went with producer Gary Katz to ABC records as songwriters, began making their own albums. *Can't buy a thrill* in 1972 featured vocalist David Palmer; *Aja* in 1977 had Ry Cooder's drummer Jim Keltner; *Gaucho* in 1980 included Patti Austin, Mark Knopfler, the Brecker Brothers and david Sanborn. *Aja* and *Gaucho* both won Grammies for engineering. All LP's charted in USA, *Aja* at number 3. Guitarist Denny Dias played on all albums, Victor Feldman on most; sidemen on various tracks/albums including Wilton Felder, Larry Carlton, Phil Woods, Plas Johnson. Compilations etc. including Fagan and Becker's *The early years*. Fagen made solo album *The Nightfly* in 1982. (Donald Clarke 21.5.88).

BABYLON SISTERS
Tracks: / Babylon sisters / Time out of mind.
7" Single: Released Feb '81, on MCA, by MCA Records. Deleted Feb '84. Catalogue no: **MCA 680**

DO IT AGAIN
Tracks: / Do it again.
7" Single: Released Aug '75, on ABC Records, by MCA Records. Deleted '78. Catalogue no: **ABC 4075**

DO IT AGAIN (OLD GOLD)
Tracks: / Do it again.
7" Single: Released Apr '83, on Old Gold, by Old Gold Records. Catalogue no: **OG 9321**

FM (NO STATIC AT ALL)
Tracks: / FM (no static at all).
7" Single: Released Jul '78, on MCA, by MCA Records. Deleted '81. Catalogue no: **MCA 374**

HAITIAN DIVORCE
Tracks: / Haitian divorce.
7" Single: Released Oct '76, on ABC Records, by MCA Records. Deleted '79. Catalogue no: **ABC 4152**

HEY NINETEEN
Tracks: / Hey nineteen / Bodhisattva.
7" Single: Released Jan '81, on MCA, by MCA Records. Deleted Jan '84. Catalogue no: **MCA 659**

REELIN' IN THE YEARS (SINGLE)
Tracks: / Reelin' in the years.
7" Single: Released Nov '85, on MCA, by MCA Records. Catalogue no: **MSAM 32**
: by MCA Records.
7" Single: Released '80, on ABC Records, by MCA Records. Catalogue no: **LR 1120**

RIKKI DON'T LOSE THAT NUMBER (see panel below)
Tracks: / Rikki don't lose that number / Do it again.
7" Single: Released Oct '87, on MCA, by MCA Records. Catalogue no: **MCA 1214**
7" Single: Released Mar '79, on ABC Records, by MCA Records. Deleted '82. Catalogue no: **ABC 4241**

Steinman, Jim

DANCE IN MY PANTS
Tracks: / Dance in my pants / Left in the dark.
7" Single: Released Oct '81, on Epic, by CBS Records. Deleted '85. Catalogue no: **EPC A 1707**

LOST BOYS AND THE GOLDEN GIRLS
Tracks: / Lost boys and the golden girls / Left in the dark.
7" Single: Released Sep '81, on Epic, by CBS Records. Deleted '84. Catalogue no: **EPA A 1561**

ROCK'N'ROLL DREAMS COME THROUGH
Tracks: / Rock 'n' roll dreams come through / Life and death of an American guitar.
7" Single: Released Jul '81, on Epic, by CBS Records. Deleted '84. Catalogue no: **A 1236**

TONIGHT IS WHAT IT MEANS TO BE YOUNG
Tracks: / Tonight is what it means to be young / Hold that snake.
12" Single: Released May '84, on MCA, by MCA Records. Catalogue no: **MCAT 889**
7" Single: Released May '84, on MCA, by MCA Records. Catalogue no: **MCA 889**

STEELY DAN - RIKKI DON'T LOSE THAT NUMBER (Released on MCA)

Steinman, Lydia

TAKE ME TO THE FOREVER
Tracks: / Take me to the forever.
12" Single: Released Jun '85, on Long Island Sound, Catalogue no: **XSN 1002**

TOUCH ME IN THE MORNING (SINGLE)
Tracks: / Touch me in the morning.
12" Single: Released Feb '85, on Long Island Sound, Catalogue no: **XSN 1001**

Steinski

LET'S PLAY IT COOL
Tracks: / Let's play it cool / Let's play it cool (instrumental) (Track available on 12" version only.) / Let's play it cool (hippy boys jungle mix) (Track available on 12" version only.) / Let's play it cool (acapella) (Track available on 12" only.).
12" Single: Released 24 May '88, on 4th & Broadway, by Island Records. Catalogue no: **12 BRW 84**
7" Single: Released 24 May '88, on 4th & Broadway, by Island Records. Deleted Dec '88. Catalogue no: **BRW 84**

WE'LL BE RIGHT BACK
Tracks: / Bonus beats / We'll be right back.
7" Single: Released Jan '87, on 4th & Broadway, by Island Records. Deleted Jun '88. Catalogue no: **BRW 59**
12" Single: Released Feb '87, on 4th & Broadway, by Island Records. Deleted Jul '87. Catalogue no: **12 BRWX 59**
12" Single: Released Jan '87, on 4th & Broadway, by Island Records. Deleted Jun '88. Catalogue no: **12 BRW 59**

Stella

SI TU AIMES MA MUSIQUE
Tracks: / Si tu aimes ma musique / If you do like my music.
7" Single: Released Apr '82, on President, by President Records. Catalogue no: **PT 504**

Stems

SAD GIRL
Tracks: / Sad girl.
Note: Limited-edition blue vinyl version of the new single, taken from the album At First Sight.
7" Single: Released Oct '87, on White Label (Australia), Catalogue no: **K 408**

Stenberg, Berdien

RONDO RUSSO (SINGLE)
Tracks: / Rondo russo / Fire dance / Ecstacy.
7" Single: Released Jul '86, on Starblend, by Starblend Records. Catalogue no: **STAR 8**
7" Single: Released Nov '83, on Lifestyle, by Micrometro Ltd (Records). Catalogue no: **LIFE 5**

Stench

RASPBERY CRIPPLE
Tracks: / Raspbery cripple / Adoption and nonces.
7" Single: Released Mar '83, on Sticky, Catalogue no: **PEELOFF 5**

Step

CHAIN GANG
Tracks: / Chain gang / In the house.
7" Single: Released Jun '81, on Epic, by CBS Records. Deleted Jun '84. Catalogue no: **EPCA 1291**

LET ME BE THE ONE
Tracks: / Let me be the one / 6345789.
7" Single: Released Sep '80, on Direction, Deleted Sep '83. Catalogue no: **DIR 8944**

MODEL SOLDIERS
Tracks: / Model soldiers / Hightime Havana.
7" Single: Released Jul '81, on Epic, by CBS Records. Deleted '85. Catalogue no: **EPC A 1412**

TEARS THAT I CRY
Tracks: / Tears that I cry / Shake.
7" Single: Released Nov '80, on Direction, Deleted Nov '83. Catalogue no: **DIR 9311**

Step By Step

THERE SHE GOES
Tracks: / There she goes / There she goes (instrumental) / There she goes (radio mix).
7" Single: Released 22 Aug '88, on Splash, by Splash Records. Catalogue no: **CPS 1013**
12" Single: Released 22 Aug '88, on Splash, by Splash Records. Catalogue no: **CPST 1013**

Stepaside

SIT DOWN AND RELAPSE
Tracks: / Sit down and relapse.
7" Single: Released Apr '80, on Gale, Catalogue no: **GALE 2**

Steph Means Justice

PRICE YOU PAY (THE)
Tracks: / Price you pay, The.
7" Single: Released May '87, on Exile, Catalogue no: **EX 7008**

Stephanie

IRRESISTIBLE
Tracks: / Irresistible / Ouragan / Irresistible (version) (Extra track on 12" version only.) / Ouragan (version) (Extra track on 12" version only.).
12" Single: Released Mar '86, on Carrere, Catalogue no: **CARP 388**
12" Single: Released Mar '86, on Carrere, Catalogue no: **CART 388**
7" Single: Released Mar '86, on Carrere, Catalogue no: **CAR 388**

LIVE YOUR LIFE (SINGLE)
Tracks: / Les sega Mauricien / Live your life.
7" Single: Released Jan '87, on Carrere, Catalogue no: **CAR 407**
12" Single: Released Jan '87, on Carrere, Catalogue no: **CART 407**

SHAME
Tracks: / Shame.
12" Single: Released Feb '84, on Banana, Catalogue no: **FRUIT 7T**
7" Single: Released Feb '84, on Banana, Catalogue no: **FRUIT 7**

Stephens, Sam

DON'T DILLY DALLY
Tracks: / Don't dilly dally.
7" Single: Released Aug '83, on Dingle's, by Dingle's Records. Catalogue no: **SID 229**

Stephenson, Craig

TOUCH
Tracks: / Touch.
7" Single: Released Sep '86, on Arista, by BMG Records (UK). Catalogue no: **ARIST 676**
12" Single: Released Sep '86, on Arista, by BMG Records (UK). Catalogue no: **ARIST 12 676**

Stephenson, Kayly

I WANNA BE CLOSE TO YOU
Tracks: / I wanna be close to you.
12" Single: Released Jun '86, on Cassia Music, Catalogue no: **CAS 004**

Stephenson, Martin

BOAT TO BOLIVIA (SINGLE)
Tracks: / Boat to Bolivia.
12" Single: Released Oct '86, on Kitchenware, by Kitchenware Records. Deleted Feb '89. Catalogue no: **SKX 27**
7" Single: Released Oct '86, on Kitchenware, by Kitchenware Records. Catalogue no: **SK 27**

CROCODILE CRIER
Tracks: / Crocodile crier / Louis.
7" Single: Released Jun '86, on Kitchenware, by Kitchenware Records. Catalogue no: **SK 25**
12" Single: Released Jun '86, on Kitchenware, by Kitchenware Records. Deleted Feb '89. Catalogue no: **SKX 25**

SLOW LOVIN'
Tracks: / Slow lovin' / Tribute to the late Rev Gary Davis.
7" Single: Released Aug '86, on Kitchenware, by Kitchenware Records. Catalogue no: **SK 26**

THERE COMES A TIME
Tracks: / There comes a time / Running water / Little red bottle (Avaliable on 12" format only.) / Colleen (live) (Avaliable on 12" format only.).
12" Single: Released Oct '88, on Kitchenware, by Kitchenware Records. Deleted May '89. Catalogue no: **SKX 34**
7" Single: Released Oct '88, on Kitchenware, by Kitchenware Records. Catalogue no: **SK 4**

WHOLLY HUMBLE HEART
Tracks: / Wholly humble heart / Get, get gone / Come back to me (Extra track on 12") / I can see / Slow lovin'.
12" Single: Released Jul '88, on Kitchenware, by Kitchenware Records. Deleted Feb '89. Catalogue no: **SKX 36**
12" Single: Released '88, on Kitchehware, by Kitchenware Records. Deleted Feb '89. Catalogue no: **SKXR 36**
7" Single: Released Jul '88, on Kitchenware, by Kitchenware Records. Deleted Feb '89. Catalogue no: **SK 36**

Stephenson, Pamela

MR WRONG
Tracks: / Mr. Wrong / Music bitch weekly / Italian shoes / Pretty boys.
Special: Released Jan '82, on Mercury, by Phonogram Ltd. Catalogue no: **PAM 2**

Stephenson, Van

MODERN DAY DELILAH
Tracks: / Modern day Delilah / Don't do that.
7" Single: Released Jun '84, on MCA, by MCA Records. Catalogue no: **MCA 891**

WE'RE DOIN' ALRIGHT
Tracks: / We're doin' alright / Suspicious heart / What the big girls do (Extra track on 12" version only) / Modern day Delilah (Extra track on 12" version only).
7" Single: Released Sep '86, on MCA, by MCA Records. Catalogue no: **MCA 1082**
12" Single: Released Sep '86, on MCA, by MCA Records. Catalogue no: **MCAT 1082**

Stepp, Richard

HOLIDAY IN HOLLYWOOD
Tracks: / Holiday in Hollywood / Good to have you.
7" Single: Released May '80, on Harbour, by Harbour Records. Deleted '83. Catalogue no: **HRB 2**

Steppa

IT MEK
Tracks: / It mek / It mek.
12" Single: Released Dec '83, on Easy Street, Catalogue no: **ES 004**

Steppenwolf

Biographical details: Heavy metal band Steppenwolf -- named after Herman Hesse's novel -- were formed in California in 1967 with guitarist-vocalist John Kay, Goldy McJohn on keyboards and drummer Jerry Edmunton, who had all played with the Canadian group Sparrow. They recruited various rhythm sections for the new outfit. Their hits became rock anthems, especially the bikers' hymn *Born To Be Wild*, a transAtlantic hit in 1968-69. (Donald Clarke, March 1987.).

BORN TO BE WILD
Tracks: / Born to be wild / Pusher, The.
7" Single: Released Jun '69, on Stateside, by EMI Records. Deleted '72. Catalogue no: **SS 8017**

BORN TO BE WILD (OLD GOLD)
Tracks: / Born to be wild.
7" Single: Released Apr '83, on Old Gold, by Old Gold Records. Catalogue no: **OG 9323**

Stepper

OH LOVING SAVIOUR
Tracks: / Oh loving saviour.
12" Single: Released May '83, on Melody, Catalogue no: **M 001**

Stepper, Reggie

WINNING SKILL
Tracks: / Winning skill.
12" Single: Released Jul '89, on Mona Lisa, Catalogue no: **ML 0010**

Stepping Razor

LATIN TEARS
Tracks: / Latin tears.
12" Single: Released Sep '87, on Rough Trade, by Rough Trade Records. Catalogue no: **RTT 208**
7" Single: Released Sep '87, on Rough Trade, by Rough Trade Records. Catalogue no: **RT 208**

Steps Ahead

WELL IN THAT CASE...
Tracks: / Well in that case... / N.Y.C..
12" Single: Released Nov '89, on Intuition, Catalogue no: **203 594 6**
12" Single: Released Nov '89, on Intuition, Catalogue no: **12INTS 1**

Stepsisters

LUCKY NUMBER
Tracks: / Lucky number / Lucky number (version).
12" Single: Released Oct '88, on Debut, by Skratch Records. Catalogue no: **DEBTX 3057**
7" Single: Released Oct '88, on Debut, by Skratch Records. Catalogue no: **DEBT 3057**

Stereo Fun Inc.

GOT YOU WHERE I WANT YOU BABE
Tracks: / Got you where I want you babe.
12" Single: Released May '83, on Ecstasy, by Creole Records. Catalogue no: **XTCT 1**
7" Single: Released May '83, on Ecstasy, by Creole Records. Catalogue no: **XTC 1**

Stereo MC's

LYRICAL MACHINE
Tracks: / Lyrical machine / On the mike / Mechanical (12" only) / Bring it on (12" only).
7" Single: Released Aug '89, on 4th & Broadway, by Island Records. Catalogue no: **BRW 148**
12" Single: Released Aug '89, on 4th & Broadway, by Island Records. Catalogue no: **12 BRW 148**

MOVE IT
Tracks: / Move it / Feel so good.
7" Single: Released Mar '88, on 4th & Broadway, by Island Records. Deleted Jun '88. Catalogue no: **BRW 94**
12" Single: Released Mar '88, on 4th & Broadway, by Island Records. Deleted Dec '88. Catalogue no: **12 BRW 94**

ON 33
Tracks: / On 33 / Gee Street / Non stop (Only on 10".) / On 33 (A to B remix) (Only on 12".).
Cassingle: Released Jun '89, on 4th & Broadway, by Island Records. Catalogue no: **BRCA 134**
10" single: Released Jun '89, on 4th & Broadway, by Island Records. Catalogue no: **10BRW 134**
7" Single: Released Jun '89, on 4th & Broadway, by Island Records. Catalogue no: **BRW 134**
12" Single: Released Jun '89, on 4th & Broadway, by Island Records. Catalogue no: **12BRW 134**

WHAT IS SOUL
Tracks: / What is soul / What is soul (the good, the bad, and the Rob B. mix) / What is soul (vocal) (Only on 12") / What is soul (inst) (Only on 12") / What is soul (accapella) (Only on 12").
7" Single: Released Oct '88, on 4th & Broadway, by Island Records. Catalogue no: **BRW 119**
12" Single: Released Oct '88, on 4th & Broadway, by Island Records. Catalogue no: **12 BRW 119**

Stereo, Ricky

JEALOUS LOVER
Tracks: / Jealous lover.
12" Single: Released Jul '89, on Living Room, Catalogue no: **OH 16**

Stereotype

FREESTYLE
Tracks: / Freestyle.
12" Single: Released 20 Mar '89, on Big Buzz, Catalogue no: **STING 1**

Sterling, Lon

KEEP KNOCKING
Tracks: / Keep knocking.
7" Single: Released Jan '89, on Madcap, Catalogue no: **MAD 9 6**
12" Single: Released Jan '89, on Madcap, Catalogue no: **MAD 9**

OTHER SIDE OF TOWN, THE
Tracks: / Other side of town, The.
7" Single: Released Feb '89, on Madcat, by Revolver. Catalogue no: **MAD 146**
CD 5": Released Feb '89, on Madcat, by Revolver. Catalogue no: **MAD 143**
12" Single: Released Feb '89, on Madcat, by Revolver. Catalogue no: **MAD 145**

Sterling, Pam

IF YOU'RE NOT HERE
Tracks: / If you're not here / Vision.
12" Single: Released May '85, on Kufe, Catalogue no: **EB 005**

Sterling Void

RUNAWAY GIRL
Tracks: / Runaway girl / It's alright.
7" Single: Released Jan '89, on ffrr, by London Records. Deleted 26 Jun '89. Catalogue no: **FFR 21**
12" Single: Released Nov '88, on DJ International, by Westside Records. Catalogue no: **DJ 956**
12" Single: Released Jan '89, on ffrr, by London Records. Catalogue no: **FFRX 21**

Stetsasonic

FLOAT ON
Tracks: / Float on / Showtime.
7" Single: Released 28 Nov '88, on Breakout, by A&M Records. Catalogue no: **USA 649**
12" Single: Released 28 Nov '88, on Breakout, by A&M Records. Catalogue no: **USAT 649**

GO STETSA I
Tracks: / Go stetsa I / On fire.
7" Single: Released Mar '87, on Tommy Boy, by Polydor Ltd. Deleted Jan '88. Catalogue no: **U 8375**
12" Single: Released Mar '87, on Tommy Boy, by Polydor Ltd. Deleted Jan '88. Catalogue no: **U 8375T**

SALLY
Tracks: / Sally / D.B.C. Let the music play.
12" Single: Released 4 Jul '88, on Breakout, by A&M Records. Deleted Feb '89. Catalogue no: **USAT 638**
7" Single: Released 4 Jul '88, on Breakout, by A&M Records. Deleted Feb '89. Catalogue no: **USA 638**

TALKIN' ALL THAT JAZZ
Tracks: / Talkin' all that jazz / Talkin' all that jazz (Dominoes version).
7" Single: Released Sep '88, on Breakout, by A&M Records. Catalogue no: **USAF 640**
7" Single: Released 5 Sep '88, on Breakout, by A&M Records. Catalogue no: **USA 640**
12" Single: Released 5 Sep '88, on Breakout, by A&M Records. Catalogue no: **USAT 640**

Steve & Bonnie

ONCE IN ROYAL DAVID'S CITY
Tracks: / Once in Royal David's city.
7" Single: Released Dec '83, on Jeeves, Deleted '85. Catalogue no: **JSB 1**

Stevens, April

ONCE UPON A VERY SPECIAL TIME
Tracks: / Once upon a very special time.
7" Single: Released May '85, on Mr.Sam, by Mr.Sam Music. Catalogue no: **SAS 101**

Stevens, Billy

EXPLORATION
Tracks: / Exploration.
7" Single: Released '88, on IMI, Catalogue no: **IMI 2004**

Stevens, Cat

Biographical details: Cat Stevens was born Steven Demitri Georgiou on 21st July 1948 in London. He was one of the most popular singer/songwriters of the early 1970s. *Matthew & Son* and *New Masters* were above-average pop albums in 1967-68; he was ill with TB for a while but came back in 1970 with *Mona Bona Jakon*, first of a series of albums that established him as a top artist in both the UK and the USA. His biggest hits were *Tea For The Tillerman*, *Teaser And The Firecat*, *Catch Bull At Four* and *Buddah And The Chocolate Box* in 1971-74; later albums reflected disenchantment with the music business; by 1979 he had converted to Islam and is now a teacher in the London Muslim community. (Donald Clarke)..

ANOTHER SATURDAY NIGHT
Tracks: / Another Saturday night.
7" Single: Released Aug '74, on Island, by Island Records. Deleted '77. Catalogue no: **WIP 6206**

BAD NIGHT, A
Tracks: / Bad night, A.
7" Single: Released Aug '67, on Deram, by London Records. Deleted '70. Catalogue no: **DM 140**

CAN'T KEEP IT IN
Tracks: / Can't keep it in.
7" Single: Released Dec '72, on Island, by Island Records. Deleted '75. Catalogue no: **WIP 6152**

I LOVE MY DOG
Tracks: / I love my dog.
7" Single: Released Oct '66, on Deram, by London Records. Deleted '69. Catalogue no: **DM 102**

I'M GONNA GET ME A GUN
Tracks: / I'm gonna get me a gun.
7" Single: Released Mar '67, on Deram, by London Records. Deleted '70. Catalogue no: **DM 118**

KITTY
Tracks: / Kitty.
7" Single: Released Dec '67, on Deram, by London Records. Deleted '70. Catalogue no: **DM 156**

LADY D'ARBANVILLE
Tracks: / Lady D'Arbanville.
7" Single: Released Jun '70, on Island, by Island Records. Deleted '73. Catalogue no: **WIP 6086**

MATTHEW & SON (OLD GOLD)
Tracks: / Matthew & son.
7" Single: Released Oct '83, on Old Gold, by Old Gold Records. Deleted Sep '89. Catalogue no: **OG 9336**

MATTHEW & SON (SINGLE)
Tracks: / Matthew & son / Granny.
7" Single: Released Mar '82, on Decca, by Decca Records. Deleted '88. Catalogue no: **F 13909**
7" Single: Released Jul '80, on Deram, by London Records. Catalogue no: **DM 435**
7" Single: Released Jan '67, on Deram, by London Records. Deleted '70. Catalogue no: **DM 110**

MOON SHADOW
Tracks: / Moon shadow.
7" Single: Released Aug '71, on Island, by Island Records. Deleted '74. Catalogue no: **WIP 6092**

MORNING HAS BROKEN
Tracks: / Morning has broken.
7" Single: Released Jan '72, on Island, by Island Records. Deleted '75. Catalogue no: **WIP 6121**
7" Single: Released Nov '83, on Island, by Island Records. Catalogue no: **IS 123**
7" Single: Released '80, on Island, by Island Records. Catalogue no: **LR 0933**

REMEMBER THE DAYS OF THE OLD SCHOOL YARD
Tracks: / Remember the days of the old school yard.
7" Single: Released Aug '77, on Island, by Island Records. Deleted '80. Catalogue no: **WIP 6387**

Stevens, Connie

SIXTEEN REASONS
Tracks: / Sixteen reasons.
7" Single: Released May '60, on Warner Bros., by WEA Records. Deleted '63. Catalogue no: **WB 3**

Stevens, Flo

ROCK'N'ROLL WALTZ
Cassingle: Released Jul '82, on Country House, by Scotdisc Records. Catalogue no: **BGC 309**

Stevens, Jonathan

JEZEBEL
Tracks: / Jezebel / Honeymoon is over.
7" Single: Released May '80, on CBS, by CBS Records. Deleted '83. Catalogue no: **CBS 8302**

Stevens, Kenni

24-7-365
Tracks: / 24-7-365 / 24-7-365 (remix) (Only on 12" single.) / Who's been loving you.
7" Single: Released Jun '88, on Debut, by Skratch Records. Catalogue no: **DEBT 3051**
12" Single: Released Jun '88, on Debut, by Skratch Records. Catalogue no: **DEBTX 3051**

ALL DAY ALL NIGHT
Tracks: / All day all night / All day all night (keep on loving mix) / All day all night (jazz mix) / All day all night (funk mix).
12" Single: Released Feb '86, on Elite Records, by Elite Records. Deleted '88. Catalogue no: **DAZZ 50**

CANNOT LIVE WITHOUT YOUR LOVE (AT LAST THE DANCE MIX)
Tracks: / Cannot live without your love (dance mix) / Passionate (jam today remix).
7" Single: Released Jul '87, on Elite Records, by Elite Records. Deleted '88. Catalogue no: **KST 1**
12" Single: Released Jul '87, on Elite Records, by Elite Records. Deleted '88. Catalogue no: **12 KST 1**

NIGHT MOVIES
Tracks: / Night movies.
12" Single: Released Jul '85, on Elite Records, by Elite Records. Deleted '86. Catalogue no: **DAZZ 4112**
7" Single: Released Jul '85, on Elite Records, by Elite Records. Deleted '86. Catalogue no: **DAZZ 417**

SAILING
Tracks: / Sailing.
7" Single: Released Mar '89, on Debut, by Skratch Records. Catalogue no: **DEBT 3066**
12" Single: Released Mar '89, on Debut, by Skratch Records. Catalogue no: **DEBTX 3066**

TOO MUCH TOO SOON
Tracks: / Too much too soon / Night moves (ultra-sensual remix) / Too much too soon (Inst).
12" Single: Released Oct '86, on Elite Records, by Elite Records. Deleted '88. Catalogue no: **DAZZ 59**

Stevens, Mackenzie

LET IT PLAY
Tracks: / Let it play / Rastafari.
12" Single: Released Apr '86, on Trojan, by Trojan Records. Deleted May '88. Catalogue no: **TROT 9081**

Stevens, Mike

C'EST L'AFFAIRE
Tracks: / C'est l'affaire / C'est l'affair (pure sax mix) / C'est l'affaire (sax maniax mix) (extra track on 12") / C'est l'affaire (no sax please...) (extra track on 12").
7" Single: Released Feb '88, on RCA, by BMG Records (UK). Deleted May '89. Catalogue no: **PB 41751**
12" Single: Released Feb '88, on RCA, by BMG Records (UK). Deleted May '89. Catalogue no: **PT 41752**

Stevens, Ray

Biographical details: Ray Stevens was born on 24th January 1941 in Clarkdale, Georgia. He began as a disc jockey at the age of 15, then had a smash novelty hit in the USA *Ahab The Arab* in 1962 but turned out to have more staying power than the usual one-hit wonder: in 1969 he made it back into the USA album chart, in 1970 he first charted in the UK; since then albums and singles have made regular appearances. A popular all-round entertainer. (Donald Clarke)..

6 TRACK HITS
Tracks: / Misty / Everything is beautiful / Streak, The / Bridget the midget / Along came Jones / Ahab the Arab.
7" EP: Released Sep '83, on Scoop 33, by Pickwick Records. Catalogue no: **7SR 5008**

BRIDGET THE MIDGET
Tracks: / Bridget the midget.
7" Single: Released Mar '71, on CBS, by CBS Records. Deleted '74. Catalogue no: **CBS 7070**

BRIDGET THE MIDGET (OLD GOLD)
Tracks: / Bridget the midget.
7" Single: Released Jul '82, on Old Gold, by Old Gold Records. Catalogue no: **OG 9036**

EVERYTHING IS BEAUTIFUL (SINGLE)
Tracks: / Everything is beautiful.
7" Single: Released May '70, on CBS, by CBS Records. Deleted '73. Catalogue no: **CBS 4953**

HEY THERE
Tracks: / Hey there / You're never goin' to tamper with me.
7" Single: Released May '80, on RCA, by BMG Records (UK). Deleted May '83. Catalogue no: **PB 9525**

IN THE MOOD
Tracks: / In the mood.
7" Single: Released Mar '77, on Warner Bros., by WEA Records. Deleted '80. Catalogue no: **K 16875**

INDIAN LOVE CALL
Tracks: / Indian love call.
7" Single: Released Sep '75, on Janus. Deleted '78. Catalogue no: **6146 205**

MISSISSIPPI SQUIRREL REVIVAL
Tracks: / Mississippi squirel revival.
7" Single: Released Apr '85, on MCA, by MCA Records. Catalogue no: **MCA 954**
12" Single: Released Apr '85, on MCA, by MCA Records. Catalogue no: **MCAT 954**

MISTY (OLD GOLD CD SINGLE)
Tracks: / Misty / Bridget the midget / Everything is beautiful.
CD 5": Released 28 Mar '89, on Old Gold, by Old Gold Records. Catalogue no: **OG 6124**

MISTY (SINGLE)
Tracks: / Misty.
7" Single: Released Jun '75, on Janus. Deleted '78. Catalogue no: **6146 204**

STREAK, THE
Tracks: / Streak, The.
7" Single: Released May '74, on Janus. Deleted '77. Catalogue no: **6146 201**

STREAK, THE (OLD GOLD)
Tracks: / Streak, The / Misty.
7" Single: Released Jul '82, on Old Gold, by Old Gold Records. Catalogue no: **OG 9023**

TURN YOUR RADIO ON
Tracks: / Turn your radio on.
7" Single: Released Mar '72, on CBS, by CBS Records. Deleted '75. Catalogue no: **CBS 7634**

Stevens, Ricky

I CRIED FOR YOU
Tracks: / I cried for you.
7" Single: Released Dec '61, on Columbia, by EMI Records. Deleted '64. Catalogue no: **DB 4739**

Stevens, Sandy

J'AI FAIM DE TOI
Tracks: / J'ai faim de toi.
7" Single: Released Aug '88, on Carrere. Catalogue no: **CAR 430**

Stevens, Scott

DREAMIN' COUNTRY
Tracks: / Dreamin' country.
7" Single: Released Aug '78, on Klub, by Klub Records. Catalogue no: **KLUB 04**

Stevens, Shakin'

Biographical details:
Shakin' Stevens was born Michael Barratt, 4 March 1948 in Ely, Wales; he is a rock'n'roll revivalist with the style down pat. He began as a frontman with The Sunsets, a revival band formed in '69 who were a big live attraction; *A Legend* was originally released in 1970, produced by Dave Edmunds, the first of a series by the sunsets. Stevens won a role in the London musical *Elvis*, starring P.J. Proby; he starred in the hit TV revival of Jack Good's *Oh Boy* programme; his solo hits and albums began in 1980, produced first by Stuart Coleman, later by Edmunds; his first hit was *Hot Dog* (no.24 in 1980); *Marie Marie* (top 20 same year) was written by the then-unknown Dave Alvin of the Blasters; he had no.1 hits 1981-1982 with *This Ole House* (1954 American hit by Rosemary Clooney), *Green Door* (American no.1 by deejay Jim Lowe in 1956), *Oh Julie* (USA hit by the Crescendos, 1957). [Donald Clarke, April 87].

BECAUSE I LOVE YOU
Tracks: / Tell me one more time / Because I love you.
7" Single: Released Oct '86, on Epic, by CBS Records. Catalogue no: **SHAKY 2**
12" Single: Released Oct '86, on Epic, by CBS Records. Catalogue no: **SHAKY T2**

BREAKING UP MY HEART
Tracks: / Breaking up my heart.
7" Single: Released Mar '85, on Epic, by CBS Records. Deleted '88. Catalogue no: **A 6072**

COME SEE ABOUT ME
Tracks: / Come see about me / Boppity bop.
7" Single: Released Sep '87, on Epic, by CBS Records. Catalogue no: **SHAKY 4**
12" Single: Released Sep '87, on Epic, by CBS Records. Catalogue no: **SHAKY T4**

CRY JUST A LITTLE BIT
Tracks: / Cry just a little bit / Love me tonight.
7" Single: Released Nov '83, on Epic, by CBS Records. Deleted '86. Catalogue no: **A 3774**

ENDLESS SLEEP
Tracks: / Endless sleep.
7" Single: Released Apr '82, on Epic, by CBS Records. Catalogue no: **CBS 6845**

FEEL THE NEED IN ME
Tracks: / Feel the need in me / If I can't have you / Feel the need in me (dance mix) (CD version only).
7" Single: Released 27 Jun '88, on Epic, by CBS Records. Deleted Jan '89. Catalogue no: **SHAKY 6**
CD 5": Released 27 Jun '88, on Epic, by CBS Records. Deleted Jan '89. Catalogue no: **SHAKY C6**
12" Single: Released 27 Jun '88, on Epic, by CBS Records. Deleted Jan '89. Catalogue no: **SHAKY T6**
7" Single: Released Jul '88, on Epic, by CBS Records. Deleted Jan '89. Catalogue no: **SHAKY Q6**

FRANTIC
Tracks: / Frantic / Ready Teddy / Monkey's uncle / Tear it up.
7" EP: Released Feb '82, on Magnum Force, by Magnum Music Group. Catalogue no: **MFEP 007**

GIVE ME YOUR HEART TONIGHT
Tracks: / Give me your heart tonight / Thinkin' of you.
7" Single: Released Aug '82, on Epic, by CBS Records. Deleted '85. Catalogue no: **EPC A 2656**

GREATEST ORIGINAL HITS
Tracks: / This ole house / You drive me crazy / Green door / Oh Julie.
7" EP: Released Mar '83, on Epic, by CBS Records. Catalogue no: **EPC A 2620**

GREEN DOOR
Tracks: / Green door / Don't turn your back.
7" Single: Released Jul '81, on Epic, by CBS Records. Catalogue no: **EPC A 1354**

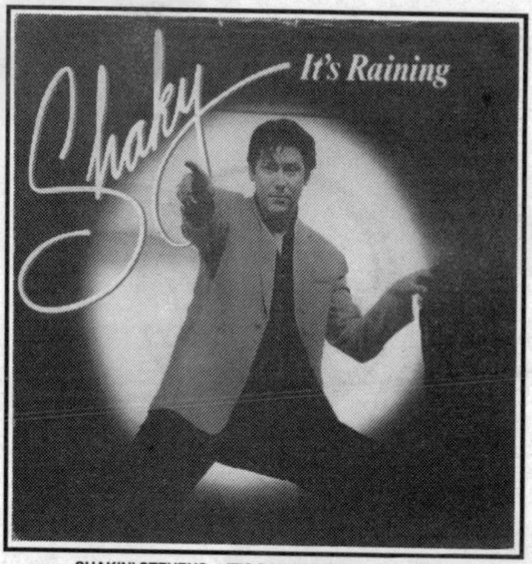

SHAKIN' STEVENS - IT'S RAINING (Released on Epic)

HEY MAE
Tracks: / Hey Mae / I guess I was a fool.
7" Single: Released Apr '82, on Epic, by CBS Records. Catalogue no: **CBS 8573**

HOT DOG (SINGLE)
Tracks: / Hot dog / Apron strings.
7" Single: Released Apr '82, on Epic, by CBS Records. Catalogue no: **EPC 8090**

HOW MANY TEARS CAN YOU HIDE
Tracks: / How many tears can you hide / If I really knew / How many tears can you hide (dance mix) (12" & CD single only.).
7" Single: Released Oct '88, on CBS, by CBS Records. Deleted 17 Apr '89. Catalogue no: **SHAKY Q7**
CD 5": Released Oct '88, on Epic, by CBS Records. Deleted 17 Apr '89. Catalogue no: **SHAKY C7**
7" Single: Released Oct '88, on Chrysalis, by Chrysalis Records. Deleted 17 Apr '89. Catalogue no: **SHAKY 7**
12" Single: Released Oct '88, on Chrysalis, by Chrysalis Records. Deleted 17 Apr '89. Catalogue no: **SHAKY T7**

I'LL BE SATISFIED
Tracks: / I'll be satisfied / Don't be late (Miss Kate).
7" Single: Released Oct '82, on Epic, by CBS Records. Deleted '85. Catalogue no: **EPC A 2846**

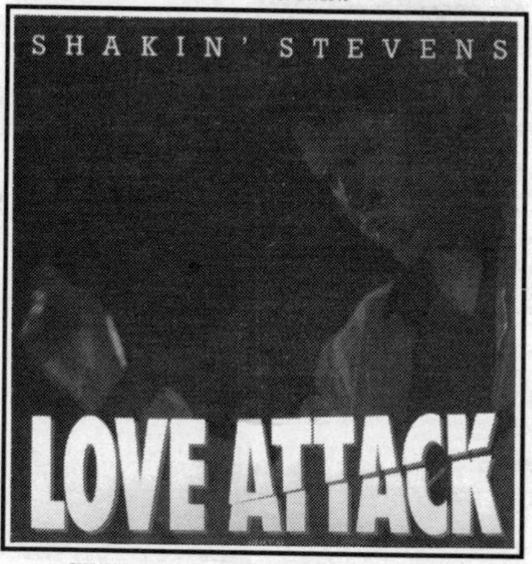

SHAKIN' STEVENS - LOVE ATTACK (Released on Epic)

IT'S LATE
Tracks: / It's late.
7" Single: Released Jul '83, on Epic, by CBS Records. Deleted '86. Catalogue no: **A 3565**

IT'S RAINING (see panel above)
Tracks: / It's raining / You and i were meant to be.
7" Single: Released Oct '81, on Epic, by CBS Records. Deleted '84. Catalogue no: **A 1643**

JEZEBEL
Tracks: / Jezebel / As long as I have you (live) / Jezebel (extended version) (On 12" & CD only.).
Special: Released Feb '89, on Epic, by CBS Records. Deleted 10 Jul '89. Catalogue no: **SHAKY P9**
7" Single: Released 6 Feb '89, on Epic, by CBS Records. Deleted 10 Jul '89. Catalogue no: **SHAKY 9**
CD 5": Released 6 Feb '89, on Epic, by CBS Records. Deleted 10 Jul '89. Catalogue no: **SHAKY C9**
12" Single: Released 6 Feb '89, on Epic, by CBS Records. Deleted 10 Jul '89. Catalogue no: **SHAKY T9**
7" Single: on Epic, by CBS Records. Deleted 10 Jul '89. Catalogue no: **SHAKY Q9**

JUNGLE ROCK
Tracks: / Jungle rock / Girl in red.
7" Single: Released Apr '81, on Battle Of The Bands. Catalogue no: **BOB 2**

JUSTINE
Tracks: / Justine / Jungle rock / Story of the rockers / My baby died.
7" EP: Released Feb '83, on Magnum Force, by Magnum Music Group. Catalogue no: **MFEP 010**

LETTER TO YOU, A
Tracks: / Letter to you, A / Come back and love me.
7" Single: Released Sep '84, on Epic, by CBS Records. Deleted '87. Catalogue no: **A 4677**

LIPSTICK, POWDER AND PAINT (SINGLE)
Tracks: / Lipstick, powder and paint.
7" Single: Released Oct '85, on Epic, by CBS Records. Deleted '88. Catalogue no: **A 6610**

LITTLE BOOGIE WOOGIE, A
Tracks: / Little boogie woogie, A
12" Single: Released 13 Jun '87, on Epic, by CBS Records. Deleted Nov '87. Catalogue no: **SHAKY T3**
Cassingle: Released 27 Jun '87, on Epic, by CBS Records. Deleted Nov '87. Catalogue no: **SHAKY C3**
7" Single: Released 13 Jun '87, on Epic, by CBS Records. Deleted Nov '87. Catalogue no: **SHAKY 3**

LOVE ATTACK (see panel left)
Tracks: / Love attack / As long as I have you / Love attack (extended version).
CD 5": Released 2 May '89, on Epic, by CBS

SHAKIN' STEVENS - GREEN DOOR (Released on Epic)

Records. Deleted Oct '89. Catalogue no: **SHAKYC 10**
Cassingle: Released 2 May '89, on Epic, by CBS Records. Deleted Oct '89. Catalogue no: **SHAKYM 10**
7" Single: Released 2 May '89, on Epic, by CBS Records. Deleted Oct '89. Catalogue no: **SHAKY 10**
12" Single: Released 2 May '89, on Epic, by CBS Records. Deleted Oct '89. Catalogue no: **SHAKYT 10**

LOVE WORTH WAITING FOR, A
Tracks: / Love worth waiting for, A / As long as i live.
7" Single: Released Mar '84, on Epic, by CBS Records. Deleted '87. Catalogue no: **A 4291**

MARIE MARIE
Tracks: / Marie Marie.
7" Single: Released Aug '80, on Epic, by CBS Records. Deleted '83. Catalogue no: **EPC 8725**

MEMPHIS EARTHQUAKE
Tracks: / You mostest girl / Evil hearted / My bucket's got a hole in it / Memphis earthquake.
7" EP: Released Apr '81, on Magnum Force, by Magnum Music Group. Catalogue no: **MFEP 001**

MERRY CHRISTMAS EVERYONE
Tracks: / Merry Christmas everyone.
7" Single: Released Nov '86, on Epic, by CBS Records. Catalogue no: **GA 6769**
12" Single: Released Nov '85, on Epic, by CBS Records. Catalogue no: **TA 6769**
7" Single: Released Nov '85, on Epic, by CBS Records. Catalogue no: **A 6769**

NO OTHER BABY
Tracks: / No other baby.
7" Single: Released Aug '81, on Mint, by Emerald Records. Deleted '88. Catalogue no: **CHEW 51**

OH JULIE
Tracks: / Oh Julie / I'm knocking.
7" Single: Released Jan '82, on Epic, by CBS Records. Deleted '85. Catalogue no: **EPC A 1742**

SHAKIN' STEVENS EP
Tracks: / Blue Christmas / Que sera sera / Josephine / Lawdy Miss Clawdy.
7" EP: Released Dec '82, on Epic, by CBS Records. Deleted '85. Catalogue no: **SHAKY 1**

SHAKY SINGS ELVIS
7" Single: Released Sep '81, on Solid Gold (1), by Creole Records. Deleted '86. Catalogue no: **SGR 107**

SHATTERED GLASS
Tracks: / Shattered glass / Rock 'n' roll winter.
7" Single: Released Dec '85, on Recoil, by Prism Records. Catalogue no: **RCL 4**

SHIRLEY
Tracks: / Shirley.
7" Single: Released Apr '82, on Epic, by CBS Records. Deleted '85. Catalogue no: **EPC A 2087**

SHOOTING GALLERY
Tracks: / Shooting gallery / Make it right tonight.
7" Single: Released Oct '80, on Epic, by CBS Records. Deleted Oct '83. Catalogue no: **EPC 9064**

SPOOKEY
Tracks: / Spookey / I don't want to.
7" Single: Released Apr '82, on Epic, by CBS Records. Catalogue no: **CBS 7325**

TEARDROPS
Tracks: / Teardrops / You shake me up.
7" Single: Released Dec '84, on Epic, by CBS Records. Catalogue no: **A 4882**

THIS OLE HOUSE (see panel below)
Tracks: / This ole house / Let me show you how.
7" Single: Released Feb '82, on Epic, by CBS Records. Deleted '86. Catalogue no: **EPC 9555**

TIGER (SINGLE)
Tracks: / Tiger.
7" Single: Released Oct '82, on Everest(Premier), by Everest Records. Catalogue no: **RAY 1**
7" Single: Released Jan '83, on Everest(Premier), by Everest Records. Catalogue no: **EV 10000**

TRUE LOVE
Tracks: / True love / Come on little girl / Merry christmas everyone (extended version) (On 12" & CD only.) / Blue christmas (On 12" & CD only.).
CD 5": Released 28 Nov '88, on Epic, by CBS Records. Deleted 17 Apr '89. Catalogue no: **SHAKY C8**
7" Single: Released Dec '88, on Epic, by CBS Records. Deleted 10 Jul '89. Catalogue no: **SHAKY Q8**
7" Single: Released 28 Nov '88, on Epic, by CBS Records. Deleted 17 Apr '89. Catalogue no: **SHAKY 8**
12" Single: Released 28 Nov '88, on Epic, by CBS Records. Deleted 17 Apr '89. Catalogue no: **SHAKY T8**

TURNING AWAY
Tracks: / Turning away / Diddle I.
7" Single: Released Jan '86, on Epic, by CBS Records. Catalogue no: **A 6819**
12" Single: Released Jan '86, on Epic, by CBS Records. Catalogue no: **TA 6810**

WHAT DO YOU WANT TO MAKE THOSE EYES AT ME FOR
Tracks: / What do you want to make those eyes at me for / Yeah you're evil / Merry Christmas (Extra track on SHAKY G5) / Blue Christmas (Extra track on SHAKY G5).
7" Single: Released Nov '87, on Epic, by CBS Records. Deleted Jun '88. Catalogue no: **SHAKY G5**
7" Single: Released Nov '87, on Epic, by CBS Records. Deleted Jun '88. Catalogue no: **SHAKY 5**

YOU DRIVE ME CRAZY
Tracks: / You drive me crazy.
7" Single: Released May '81, on Epic, by CBS Records. Deleted '84. Catalogue no: **A 1165**

Stevens, Shelly

SECRET LOVE
Tracks: / Secret love / Love me like you used to.
7" Single: Released Oct '80, on Rialto (1), by Rialto Records. Catalogue no: **TREB 125**

Stevens, Stu

ALBERT AND MARY
Tracks: / Albert and Mary / Superman.
7" Single: Released Jan '84, on Young Blood, by Young Blood Records. Catalogue no: **YB 0831**

COWBOY IN PARIS (SINGLE)
Tracks: / Cowboy in Paris.
12" Single: Released Sep '82, on Crazy Viking, by Crazy Vikings Records. Catalogue no: **STUT 001**
7" Single: Released Sep '82, on Crazy Viking, by Crazy Vikings Records. Catalogue no: **STU 001**

DREAM IT BACK
Tracks: / Dream it back / Cherokee mountain.
Note: Distributed by Ash Records Ltd, Cropwell House, Salmon Lane, Kirkby-in-Ashfield,Nottingham, NGH17 9HB. Tel: 0623 752448
7" Single: Released May '86, on Ash, by Ash Records. Catalogue no: **ASH 021**

EYES OF MY CHILD
Tracks: / Eyes of my child / Sunday comes quickly.
7" Single: Released Nov '82, on Ash, by Ash Records. Catalogue no: **ASH 015**

FOREVER
Tracks: / Forever.
7" Single: Released Jul '83, on Crazy Viking, by Crazy Vikings Records. Catalogue no: **CV 004**

HELLO PRETTY LADY
Tracks: / Hello pretty lady / Oldest rock 'n' roller.
7" Single: Released Feb '80, on MCA, by MCA Records. Deleted Feb '83. Catalogue no: **MCA 563**

MAN FROM OUTER SPACE
Tracks: / Streets I have walked / Man from outer space.
7" Single: Released May '88, on Ash, by Ash Records. Catalogue no: **ASH 004**
7" Single: Released '81, on Eagle (London), by Eagle (London) Records. Deleted '88. Catalogue no: **EGL 004**

REMEMBER ME AT SUNRISE
Tracks: / Remember me at sunrise / Winter world away.
7" Single: Released Sep '81, on Young Blood, by Young Blood Records. Catalogue no: **YB 0123**

SAD OLD SPANISH GUITAR
Tracks: / Sad old Spanish guitar / Square dance.
7" Single: Released Aug '84, on Young Blood, by Young Blood Records. Catalogue no: **YB 0084**

WAY LOVE'S SUPPOSED TO BE, THE
Tracks: / Way love's supposed to be, The.
7" Single: Released Aug '85, on Ritz, by Ritz Records. Catalogue no: **RITZ 083**

WHEN I DREAM
Tracks: / When I dream / Mind painter.
7" Single: Released Apr '81, on Eagle (London), by Eagle (London) Records. Deleted '82. Catalogue no: **EGL 014**

Stevens, Tony

TILL WE MEET AGAIN
Tracks: / Till we meet again / If I can forget her.
7" Single: Released '86, on Ritz, by Ritz Records. Catalogue no: **RITZ 152**

Stevenson, N.A.

BOOGIE WOOGIE COUNTRY GIRL
Tracks: / Boogie woogie country girl.
7" Single: Released May '83, on Spade, by Rollercoaster Records. Catalogue no: **SP 501**

Stevenson's Rocket

ALRIGHT BABY
Tracks: / Alright baby.
7" Single: Released Nov '75, on Magnet, by WEA Records. Deleted '78. Catalogue no: **MAG 47**

Stewart, Al

Biographical details: Al Stewart is a folk-rock singer/songwriter born in Glasgow on 5th September 1945. His first five albums included *Love Chronicles* in 1969 (with Jimmy Page and other guests), voted folk album of the year in the UK and his first USA release; it was remarkable at the time for the first use of the word 'fucked' on a record, being in the confessional style. He later switched to historical rather than personal epics. (Donald Clarke)..

INDIAN SUMMER (SINGLE)
Tracks: / Indian summer / Pandora.
7" Single: Released Oct '81, on RCA, by BMG Records (UK). Deleted Oct '84. Catalogue no: **RCA 149**

KING OF PORTUGAL
Tracks: / King of Portugal / Josephine Baker / Bad reputation (CD & 12" only) / King of Portugal (rock mix) (CD only).
Note: Return of Al Stewart with a new single taken from the album "Last Days of the Century".
7" Single: Released 17 Oct '88, on Enigma, by Enigma Records (USA). Catalogue no: **ENV 4**
12" Single: Released 17 Oct '88, on Enigma, by Enigma Records (USA). Catalogue no: **ENVT 4**
CD 3": Released '88, on Enigma, by Enigma Records (USA). Catalogue no: **ENVCD 4**

LORI DON'T GO RIGHT NOW
Tracks: / Lori don't go right now / Accident on 3rd Street.
7" Single: Released Jun '84, on RCA, by BMG Records (UK). Catalogue no: **RCA 414**

MONDO SINISTRO
Tracks: / Mondo sinistro / Merlin's time.
7" Single: Released Sep '80, on RCA, by BMG Records (UK). Deleted '83. Catalogue no: **RCA 2**

PAINT BY NUMBERS

SHAKIN' STEVENS - THIS OLE HOUSE (Released on Epic)

Tracks: / Paint by numbers / Optical illusion.
7" Single: Released Nov '80, on RCA, by BMG Records (UK). Deleted Nov '83. Catalogue no: **RCA 17**

YEAR OF THE CAT (OLD GOLD)
Tracks: / Year of the cat.
7" Single: Released Nov '86, on Old Gold, by Old Gold Records. Catalogue no: **OG 9642**

YEAR OF THE CAT (SINGLE)
Tracks: / Year of the cat.
7" Single: Released Jan '77, on RCA, by BMG Records (UK). Deleted '80. Catalogue no: **RCA 2771**

Stewart, Amii

ASH 48
Tracks: / Ash 48.
12" Single: Released Oct '85, on Sedition, by Sedition Records. Catalogue no: **EDITL 3306**

FRIENDS
Tracks: / Friends / Picture.
7" Single: Released Jan '85, on RCA, by BMG Records (UK). Catalogue no: **RCA 471**

JEALOUSY
Tracks: / Jealousy.
7" Single: Released Nov '79, on Atlantic, by WEA Records. Deleted '82. Catalogue no: **K 11386**

KNOCK ON WOOD
Tracks: / Knock on wood.
7" Single: Released Jul '85, on Sedition, by Sedition Records. Catalogue no: **EDIT 3303**
12" Single: Released Jul '85, on Sedition, by Sedition Records. Catalogue no: **EDITL 3303**
7" Single: Released '78, on Atlantic, by WEA Records. Catalogue no: **K 11214**

KNOCK ON WOOD (1985 REMIX)
Tracks: / Knock on wood (1985 remix) / Light my fire (1985 remix).
12" Single: Released 30 May '89, on Old Gold, by Old Gold Records. Catalogue no: **OG 4120**

LIGHT MY FIRE
Tracks: / Light my fire.
7" Single: Released Jun '79, on Atlantic, by WEA Records. Catalogue no: **K 11278**
12" Single: Released Aug '85, on Sedition, by Sedition Records. Catalogue no: **EDITX 3303**

LOVE AIN'T NO TOY
Tracks: / Lover to lover / Friends (Available on 12" version).
7" Single: Released Feb '87, on RCA, by BMG Records (UK). Deleted '87. Catalogue no: **PB 41105**
12" Single: Released Feb '87, on RCA, by BMG Records (UK). Deleted '87. Catalogue no: **PT 41106**

MY GUY, MY GIRL
Tracks: / My guy, my girl / Bring it on back to me / Knock on wood (Track included in double pack) / Light my fire (Track included in double pack).
12" Single: Released Jan '86, on Sedition, by Sedition Records. Catalogue no: **EDITX 3310**
7" Single: Released Nov '85, on Sedition, by Sedition Records. Catalogue no: **EDIT 3310**
7" Single: Released Jul '80, on Atlantic, by WEA Records. Deleted '83. Catalogue no: **K 11550**
12" Single: Released Nov '85, on Sedition, by Sedition Records. Catalogue no: **EDITL 3310**

PARADISE BIRD (SINGLE)
Tracks: / Paradise bird / Letter, The.
7" Single: Released Jan '80, on Atlantic, by WEA Records. Deleted '83. Catalogue no: **K 11424**

THAT LOVING FEELING
Tracks: / That loving feeling / Fever line.
7" Single: Released Mar '85, on RCA, by BMG Records (UK). Catalogue no: **PB 40017**
12" Single: Released Mar '85, on RCA, by BMG Records (UK). Catalogue no: **PT 40018**

WHERE DID OUR LOVE GO
Tracks: / Where did our love go / Premiere.
7" Single: Released Apr '81, on Atlantic, by WEA Records. Catalogue no: **K 11580**
12" Single: Released Apr '81, on Atlantic, by WEA Records. Catalogue no: **K 11580 T**

YOU REALLY TOUCH MY HEART
Tracks: / You really touch my heart.
7" Set: Released Nov '85, on Sedition, by Sedition Records. Catalogue no: **EDITP 3307**
7" Single: Released Oct '85, on Sedition, by Sedition Records. Catalogue no: **EDIT 3307**
12" Single: Released Oct '85, on Sedition, by Sedition Records. Catalogue no: **EDITL 3307**

Stewart, Andy

BATTLES O'ER, THE
Tracks: / Battles o'er, The.
7" Single: Released Jun '61, on Top Rank (1), Deleted '64. Catalogue no: **JAR 565**

DOCTOR FINLAY
Tracks: / Doctor Finlay.
7" Single: Released Aug '65, on H.M.V., by EMI Records. Deleted '68. Catalogue no: **POP 1454**

DONALD WHERE'S YOUR TROOSERS
Tracks: / Donald, where's yer troosers.
7" Single: Released Dec '60, on Top Rank (1), Deleted '63. Catalogue no: **JAR 427**

SCOTTISH SOLDIER, A
Tracks: / Scottish soldier, A.
7" Single: Released Jan '61, on Top Rank (1), Deleted '64. Catalogue no: **JAR 512**

Stewart, Angela

BREAKFAST IN BED
Tracks: / Breakfast in bed.
7" Single: Released Jun '88, on Brotherhood Music, Catalogue no: **BH 001**

COULD I HAVE THIS DANCE
Tracks: / Could I have this dance / Could I have this dance (instrumental).
12" Single: Released Nov '83, on Thunderbolt, by Thunderbolt Records. Deleted '89. Catalogue no: **TBD 07**

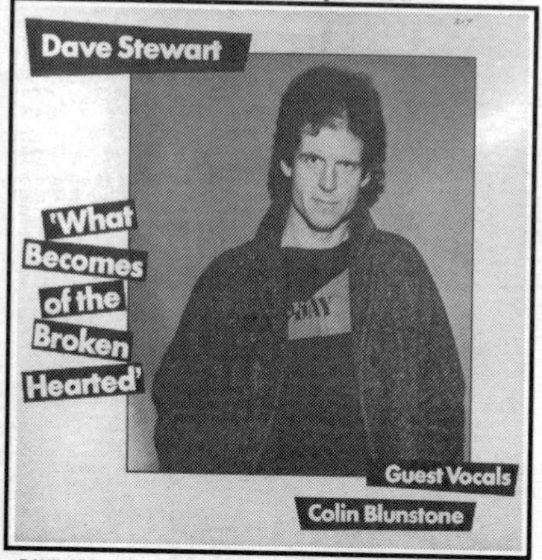

DAVE STEWART - WHAT BECOMES OF THE BROKEN HEARTED (Released on Broken)

DAVE STEWART & BARBARA GASKIN - IT'S MY PARTY (Released on Broken)

FEEL LIKE DANCING
Tracks: / Feel like dancing.
7" Single: Released Oct '83, on Nura, Catalogue no: **N 42**

MOONLIGHT LOVER
Tracks: / Moonlight lover.
12" Single: Released Jun '84, on Kingdom, by Kingdom Records. Catalogue no: **KV 8031 12**

WHEN LOVES COME KNOCKING
Tracks: / When loves come knocking / Love come knocking.
12" Single: Released Jun '82, on Dynamic, Catalogue no: **DYN 1211**
7" Single: Released Jun '82, on Dynamic, Deleted Jun '85. Catalogue no: **DYN 11**

Stewart, Babs

EASY WAY OUT
Tracks: / Easy way out.
12" Single: Released Oct '84, on Private Eye, Catalogue no: **PE 105**

IT HURTS SO GOOD
Tracks: / It hurts so good.
12" Single: Released Jul '83, on Sunburn, by Orbitone Records. Catalogue no: **SBD 34**

Stewart, Billy

SUMMERTIME
Tracks: / Summertime.
7" Single: Released Sep '66, on Chess, by Vogue Records. Deleted '69. Catalogue no: **CRS 8040**
7" Single: Released Jul '85, on Chess (PRT), Deleted '88. Catalogue no: **CHES 4007**

Stewart Brothers

NUMBER ONE SONG (RUB A DUB)
Tracks: / Number one song (rub a dub).
7" Single: Released Mar '85, on Vista Sounds, by Vista Sounds Records. Catalogue no: **VISTA 02**

Stewart, Caroline

DO YOU KNOW WHAT YOU WANT
Tracks: / Do you know what you want.
7" Single: Released Jul '88, on Soundisc, Catalogue no: **DS 1**
12" Single: Released Jul '88, on Soundisc, Catalogue no: **12DS 1**

Stewart, Dave

BUSY DOIN' NOTHING
Tracks: / Busy doin' nothing / World, The.
Note: Available from this address only. Broken Records (Mail Order), 18 Yeomen Way, Hainault, Ilford, Essex.
7" Pic: Released Aug '83, on Broken, by Broken Records. Catalogue no: **BRKP 5**
7" Single: Released Aug '83, on Broken, by Broken Records. Catalogue no: **BROKEN 5**

I'M IN A DIFFERENT WORLD
Tracks: / I'm in a different world.
7" Single: Released Jun '84, on Broken, by Broken Records. Catalogue no: **BROKEN 7**

IT'S MY PARTY (see panel above)
Tracks: / It's my party / Waiting in the wings.
7" Single: Released Aug '81, on Broken, by Broken Records. Catalogue no: **BROKEN 2**

JOHNNY ROCCO
Tracks: / Johnny Rocco / Hamburger song.
7" Single: Released Nov '82, on Broken, by Broken Records. Catalogue no: **BROKEN 3**

LEIPZIG
Tracks: / Leipzig / Rich for a day.
Note: Available from this address only. Broken Records (Mail Order), 18 Yeomen Way, Hainault, Ilford, Essex.
7" Single: Released Jan '84, on Broken, by Broken Records. Catalogue no: **BROKEN 6**

LOCOMOTION, THE
Tracks: / Locomotion, The / Make me promises.
7" Single: Released May '86, on Broken, by Broken Records. Catalogue no: **BROKEN 8**
12" Single: Released May '86, on Broken, by Broken Records. Catalogue no: **BROKIT 8**

SIAMESE CAT SONG
Tracks: / Siamese cat song / Emperors guitar.
Note: Available from this address only. Broken Records (Mail Order), 18 Yeomen Way, Hainault, Ilford, Essex.
7" Single: Released Feb '83, on Broken, by Broken Records. Catalogue no: **BROKEN 4**

WHAT BECOMES OF THE BROKEN HEARTED (see panel bottom left)
Tracks: / What becomes of the broken hearted? / There is no reward.
7" Single: Released Feb '81, on Broken, by Broken Records. Catalogue no: **BROKEN 1**

Stewart, Eric

GIRLS (SINGLE)
Tracks: / Girls / Discollapse.
7" Single: Released Feb '80, on Polydor, by Polydor Ltd. Deleted '83. Catalogue no: **POSP 123**

Stewart, Jermaine

DON'T EVER LEAVE ME
Tracks: / Give your love to me / Don't ever leave me.
7" Single: Released Jan '87, on 10 Records, by Virgin Records. Deleted May '88. Catalogue no: **TEN 157**
12" Single: Released Jan '87, on 10 Records, by Virgin Records. Deleted May '88. Catalogue no: **TENT 157**

DON'T TALK DIRTY TO ME
Tracks: / Don't talk dirty to me (7" only) / Places / Don't talk dirty to me (radio edit) (On CD only) / Don't talk dirty to me (edited remix) (On CD only) / Get lucky (New York mix) (On CD only).
7" Pic: Released '88, on Siren, by Virgin Records. Catalogue no: **SRNY 86**
7" Single: Released Sep '88, on Siren, by Virgin Records. Deleted '89. Catalogue no: **SRN 86**
CD 5": Released '88, on Siren, by Virgin Records. Catalogue no: **SRNCD 86**
7" Single: Released Sep '88, on Siren, by Virgin Records. Deleted '89. Catalogue no: **SRNP 86**
12" Single: Released Sep '88, on Siren, by

Virgin Records. Deleted '89. Catalogue no: **SRNT 86**

GET LUCKY
Tracks: / Get lucky (NOT on 12") / Get lucky (extended remix) (NOT on 7") / Imagine (On all versions) / Say it again (remix) (CD & Cassette only) / Get lucky (dub) (12" only).
Cassingle: Released '88, on Siren, by Virgin Records. Catalogue no: **SRNC 82**
12" Single: Released Mar '88, on Siren, by Virgin Records. Catalogue no: **SRNT 82**
7" Single: Released Mar '88, on Siren, by Virgin Records. Catalogue no: **SRN 82**
CD 5": Released Aug '88, on Siren, by Virgin Records. Catalogue no: **SRNCD 82**

GET OVER IT
Tracks: / Get over it.
7" Single: Released Jun '84, on 10 Records, by Virgin Records. Deleted May '88. Catalogue no: **TEN 23**
12" Single: Released Jun '84, on 10 Records, by Virgin Records. Deleted May '88. Catalogue no: **TEN 23-12**

I LIKE IT
Tracks: / I like it / Month of Mondays.
12" Single: Released May '85, on 10 Records, by Virgin Records. Deleted '86. Catalogue no: **TEN 50-12**
7" Single: Released May '85, on 10 Records, by Virgin Records. Deleted '86. Catalogue no: **TEN 50**

JODY
Tracks: / Jody / Dance floor.
7" Single: Released Oct '86, on 10 Records, by Virgin Records. Deleted May '88. Catalogue no: **TEN 143**
12" Single: Released Oct '86, on 10 Records, by Virgin Records. Deleted May '88. Catalogue no: **TENT 143**

SAY IT AGAIN (SINGLE)
Tracks: / Say it again (On all versions) / You promise (On all versions) / Say it again (extended remix) (On 12" only) / We don't have to take our clothes off (On CD only) / Dress it up (On CD only).
7" Single: Released Oct '87, on 10 Records, by Virgin Records. Catalogue no: **TENM 188**
CD 5": Released Oct '87, on 10 Records, by Virgin Records. Catalogue no: **SAYCD 188**
7" Single: Released Oct '87, on 10 Records, by Virgin Records. Catalogue no: **TEN 188**
12" Single: Released Oct '87, on 10 Records, by Virgin Records. Catalogue no: **TENT 188**

WE DON'T HAVE TO TAKE OUR CLOTHES OFF
Tracks: / We don't have to take our clothes off / Brilliance / We don't have to take our clothes off (extended0 (12" only).
7" Single: Released Feb '86, on 10 Records, by Virgin Records. Catalogue no: **TEN 96**
12" Single: Released Feb '86, on 10 Records, by Virgin Records. Catalogue no: **TEN 96-12**

WORD IS OUT (SINGLE)
Tracks: / Word is out, The / Word is out, The (instrumental).
12" Single: Released Mar '84, on 10 Records, by Virgin Records. Deleted May '88. Catalogue no: **TEN 10-12**
7" Single: Released Mar '84, on 10 Records, by Virgin Records. Catalogue no: **TEN 10**

Stewart, John

Biographical details: John Stewart is unclassifiable, a folk/rock/country singer/songwriter who has made 16 albums on seven labels and has a cult following all over the English speaking world. He was born on 5th September 1939 in the USA and was a member of the Kingston Trio 1961-67 (he also wrote *Daydream Believer* for the Monkees) but had started his solo career before that. Evidence of his loyal following is that his albums do not stay out of print; *California Bloodlines* (originally 1969) and *The Lonesome Picker Rides Again* (1971) have been underground classics for years. (Donald Clarke)..

DAYDREAM BELIEVER
Tracks: / Daydream believer / Just an old love song.
7" Single: Released Mar '80, on Warner Bros., by WEA Records. Deleted '83. Catalogue no: **K 17583**

GOLD
Tracks: / Gold.
7" Single: Released Jun '79, on RSO, by Polydor Ltd. Deleted '82. Catalogue no: **RSO 35**

NIGHT MAN
Tracks: / Night man / Love has tied my wings.
7" Single: Released May '80, on RSO, by Polydor Ltd. Deleted May '83. Catalogue no: **RSO 61**

ROD STEWART - SOME GUYS HAVE ALL THE LUCK (Released on Warner Bros.)

Stewart, Mark

HIGH IDEALS AND CRAZY DREAMS
Tracks: / High ideals and crazy dreams / Jerusalem.
12" Single: Released Oct '82, on On-U-Sound, by On-U-Sound Records. Catalogue no: **DP 5**

HYPNOTISED
Tracks: / Hypnotised.
7" Single: Released May '85, on Mute, by Mute Records. Catalogue no: **7 MUTE 37**
12" Single: Released May '85, on Mute, by Mute Records. Catalogue no: **12 MUTE 37**

STRANGER THAN LOVE
Tracks: / Stranger than love / Stranger than love (dub) / Anger is holy.
7" Single: Released Sep '87, on Mute, by Mute Records. Catalogue no: **MUTE 59**
12" Single: Released Sep '87, on Mute, by Mute Records. Catalogue no: **12 MUTE 59**

Stewart, Rod

Biographical details: Rod Stewart was born on 10th January 1945 in London and became a superstar in the 1970s, his gravelly voice and idiosyncratic, soulful delivery influenced by Sam Cooke. He worked with Long John Baldry, Brian Auger and Julie Driscoll in Steampacket, with Jeff Beck, then joined Faces 1971-5 and also launches a parallel solo career. *Every Picture Tells A Story* (1971) included *Maggie May*; both album and single were simultaneous number one hits in both USA and UK, the first of six number one albums in a row in the UK; his romance with Britt Eckland kept him in the gossip columns; by the time of *Blondes Have More Fun* in 1978 (including *Do Ya Think I'm Sexy?*, both album and single number one in USA) his jet-seeting had begun to tell, yet his work continues to chart well and his London concerts in 1983 were a huge success: maybe it's not his Jack-The-Lad image that's changed, or his audience, but the critics. (Donald Clarke)..

AIN'T LOVE A BITCH
Tracks: / Ain't love a bitch.
7" Single: Released Feb '79, on Riva, by Riva Records. Deleted '82. Catalogue no: **RIVA 16**

ANGEL
Tracks: / Angel / What made Milwaukee famous (has made a loser).
7" Single: Released Nov '72, on Mercury, by Phonogram Ltd. Deleted '75. Catalogue no: **6052 198**

ANOTHER HEARTACHE
Tracks: / Another heartache / You're in my heart.
7" Single: Released Aug '86, on Warner Bros., by WEA Records. Deleted Jun '87. Catalogue no: **W 8631**
12" Single: Released Aug '86, on Warner Bros., by WEA Records. Deleted Jun '87. Catalogue no: **W 8631T**

BABY JANE
Tracks: / Baby Jane / Ready now / If loving you is wrong I don't want to be right.
7" Single: Released Jun '83, on Warner Bros., by WEA Records. Deleted Jan '88. Catalogue no: **W 9608**
12" Single: Released Jun '83, on Warner Bros., by WEA Records. Catalogue no: **W 9608T**

BLONDES HAVE MORE FUN (SINGLE)
Tracks: / Blondes have more fun.
7" Single: Released May '79, on Riva, by Riva Records. Deleted '82. Catalogue no: **RIVA 19**

DO YA THINK I'M SEXY
Tracks: / Do ya think I'm sexy.
7" Single: Released Nov '78, on Riva, by Riva Records. Deleted '81. Catalogue no: **RIVA 17**

EVERY BEAT OF MY HEART (SINGLE)
Tracks: / Every beat of my heart.
12" Pic: Released Jun '86, on Warner Bros., by WEA Records. Deleted Jun '87. Catalogue no: **W 8625 TP**
12" Single: Released Jun '86, on Warner Bros., by WEA Records. Deleted Jan '88. Catalogue no: **W 8625 T**
7" Single: Released Jun '86, on Warner Bros., by WEA Records. Deleted Jan '88. Catalogue no: **W 8625**

FAREWELL
Tracks: / Farewell / Bring it on home to me / You send me.
7" Single: Released Oct '74, on Mercury, by Phonogram Ltd. Deleted '77. Catalogue no: **6167 033**

FOREVER YOUNG
Tracks: / Forever young.
12" Single: Released Jul '88, on Warner Bros., by WEA Records. Catalogue no: **W 7796 T**
CD 3": Released Jul '88, on Warner Bros., by WEA Records. Catalogue no: **W 7796 CD**
7" Single: Released Jul '88, on Warner Bros., by WEA Records. Catalogue no: **W 7796**

GET BACK
Tracks: / Get back.
7" Single: Released Nov '76, on Riva, by Riva Records. Deleted '79. Catalogue no: **RIVA 6**

GOOD MORNING SCHOOLGIRL
Tracks: / Good morning schoolgirl / I'm gonna move to the outsirts of town.
7" Single: Released Feb '82, on Decca, by Decca Records. Deleted Feb '87. Catalogue no: **F11996**

HOTLEGS
Tracks: / Hotlegs / I was only joking.
7" Single: Released Jan '78, on Riva, by Riva Records. Deleted '81. Catalogue no: **RIVA 10**

HOW LONG
Tracks: / How long / Jealous.
7" Single: Released Feb '82, on Riva, by Riva Records. Deleted '85. Catalogue no: **RIVA 35**

I DON'T WANT TO TALK ABOUT IT
Tracks: / I don't want to talk about it / First cut is the deepest.
7" Single: Released Apr '77, on Riva, by Riva Records. Deleted '80. Catalogue no: **RIVA 7**

I WAS ONLY JOKING
Tracks: / I was only joking / Hot legs.
7" Single: Released Jan '80, on Riva, by Riva Records. Catalogue no: **LR 4464**

IF LOVING YOU IS WRONG I DON'T WANT TO BE RIGHT
Tracks: / If loving you is wrong I don't want to be right / Last summer..
7" Single: Released May '80, on Riva, by Riva Records. Deleted '83. Catalogue no: **RIVA 23**

IN MY LIFE
Tracks: / In my own crazy way / Tonights the night (live version).
7" Single: Released Nov '86, on Warner Bros., by WEA Records. Deleted Jan '88. Catalogue no: **W 8489**
12" Single: Released Nov '86, on Warner Bros., by WEA Records. Deleted Jan '88. Catalogue no: **W 8489T**

INFATUATION
Tracks: / Infatuation / Three time loser / Tonight's the night (on 12" only).
7" Single: Released May '84, on Warner Bros., by WEA Records. Deleted '87. Catalogue no: **W 9256**

KILLING OF GEORGIE, THE
Tracks: / Killing of Georgia, The.
7" Single: Released Aug '76, on Riva, by Riva Records. Deleted '79. Catalogue no: **RIVA 4**

LITTLE MISS UNDERSTOOD
Tracks: / Little Miss Understood / So much to say.
7" Single: Released Feb '83, on Immediate, Catalogue no: **IM 060**
7" Single: Released Sep '80, on Immediate, Deleted '83. Catalogue no: **VS 366**

LOST IN YOU
Tracks: / Lost in you / Almost illegal / Baby Jane (Only on CD single.) / Every beat of my heart (Only on CD single.).
7" Single: Released May '88, on Warner Bros., by WEA Records. Catalogue no: **W 7927**
CD 5": Released May '88, on Warner Bros., by WEA Records. Catalogue no: **W 7927CD**
12" Single: Released May '88, on Warner Bros., by WEA Records. Catalogue no: **W 7927T**

LOVE TOUCH
Tracks: / Love touch / Heart is on the line / Hard lesson to learn (Extra track on 12" version only.).
12" Pic: Released May '86, on Warner Bros., by WEA Records. Deleted Jun '87. Catalogue no: **W 8668 TP**
7" Single: Released May '86, on Warner Bros., by WEA Records. Deleted Jun '87. Catalogue no: **W 8668**
12" Single: Released May '86, on Warner Bros., by WEA Records. Deleted Jun '87. Catalogue no: **W 8668 T**

MAGGIE MAY (OLD GOLD)
Tracks: / Maggie May.
7" Single: Released Feb '88, on Old Gold, by Old Gold Records. Catalogue no: **OG 9765**

MAGGIE MAY (SINGLE)
Tracks: / Maggie May.
7" Single: Released Sep '71, on Mercury, by Phonogram Ltd. Deleted '74. Catalogue no: **6052 097**
7" Single: Released Dec '76, on Mercury, by Phonogram Ltd. Deleted '79. Catalogue no: **6160 006**
7" Single: Released Oct '84, on Mercury, by Phonogram Ltd. Deleted Mar '88. Catalogue no: **CUT 201**

MY GIRL
Tracks: / My girl / She won't dance with me.
7" Single: Released Dec '80, on Riva, by Riva Records. Catalogue no: **RIVA 28**

MY HEART CAN'T TELL YOU NO
Tracks: / My heart can't tell you no / Wild horse, The.
7" Single: Released Apr '89, on Warner Bros., by WEA Records. Catalogue no: **W 7729**
12" Single: Released Apr '89, on Warner Bros., by WEA Records. Catalogue no: **W 7729T**
CD 5": Released Apr '89, on Warner Bros., by WEA Records. Catalogue no: **W 7729CD**

OH GOD I WISH I WAS HOME
Tracks: / Oh God I wish I was home / Somebody special.
7" Single: Released Mar '81, on Riva, by Riva Records. Catalogue no: **RIVA 29**
Cassingle: Released Mar '81, on Riva, by Riva Records. Deleted Mar '84. Catalogue no: **RIVA 29M**

OH NO NOT MY BABY
Tracks: / Oh no not my baby.
7" Single: Released Sep '73, on Mercury, by Phonogram Ltd. Deleted '76. Catalogue no: **6052 371**

OLE OLA (MUHLER BRASILEIRA)
Tracks: / Ole ola (muhler brasileira).
7" Single: Released May '78, on Riva, by Riva Records. Deleted '81. Catalogue no: **RIVA 15**

PASSION
Tracks: / Passion / Better off dead.
7" Single: Released Oct '80, on Riva, by Riva Records. Catalogue no: **RIVA 26**
12" Single: Released Oct '80, on Riva, by Riva Records. Catalogue no: **RIVA 26T**

PEOPLE GET READY
Tracks: / People get ready / Back on the street.
7" Single: Released Dec '85, on Epic, by CBS Records. Catalogue no: **A 6387**

REASON TO BELIEVE
Tracks: / Reason to believe.
7" Single: Released Sep '71, on Mercury, by Phonogram Ltd. Deleted '74. Catalogue no: **6052 097**

SAILING
Tracks: / Sailing / Stone cold sober.
7" Single: Released Jun '77, on Riva, by Riva Records. Catalogue no: **RIVA 9**
7" Single: Released Mar '87, on Warner Bros., by WEA Records. Catalogue no: **K 16600**

SOME GUYS HAVE ALL THE LUCK
Tracks: / Some guys have all the luck / I was only joking.
7" Single: Released Jul '84, on Warner Bros., by WEA Records. Deleted '87. Catalogue no: **W 9204**

SWEET SURRENDER
Tracks: / Sweet surrender / Ghetto blaster / God I wish I was home tonight.
7" Single: Released Nov '83, on Warner Bros., by WEA Records. Catalogue no: **W 9440**
12" Single: Released Nov '83, on Warner Bros., by WEA Records. Catalogue no: **W 9440T**

THIS OLD HEART OF MINE
Tracks: / This old heart of mine.
7" Single: Released Nov '75, on Riva, by Riva Records. Deleted '78. Catalogue no: **RIVA 1**

TONIGHT I'M YOURS (SINGLE)
Tracks: / Tonight I'm yours (don't hurt me).
7" Single: Released Oct '81, on Riva, by Riva Records. Deleted '84. Catalogue no: **RIVA 33**

TONIGHTS THE NIGHT
Tracks: / Tonights the night.
7" Single: Released Jul '76, on Riva, by Riva Records. Deleted '79. Catalogue no: **RIVA 3**
7" Single: Released Jan '80, on Riva, by Riva Records. Catalogue no: **LR 3930**

TRY A LITTLE TENDERNESS
Tracks: / Try a little tenderness / My heart can't tell you no / Passion (On 12" version only.).
7" Single: Released Jan '89, on Warner Bros., by WEA Records. Catalogue no: **W 7629**
12" Single: Released Jan '89, on Warner Bros., by WEA Records. Catalogue no: **W 7629 T**

TWISTIN' THE NIGHT AWAY
Tracks: / Twistin' the night away / Let's get small.
7" Single: Released Oct '87, on CBS, by CBS Records. Deleted Jun '88. Catalogue no: **RODS 1**

WHAT AM I GONNA DO
Tracks: / What am I gonna do.
7" Single: Released Aug '83, on Warner Bros., by WEA Records. Deleted '86. Catalogue no: **W 9564**

YOU WEAR IT WELL
Tracks: / You wear it well.
7" Single: Released Aug '72, on Mercury, by Phonogram Ltd. Deleted '75. Catalogue no: **6052 171**
7" Single: Released Jan '80, on Philips (Import), by PolyGram UK Ltd. Catalogue no: **LR 8209**

YOUNG TURKS
Tracks: / Young turks / Tora tora tora.
7" Single: Released Dec '81, on Riva, by Riva Records. Deleted '84. Catalogue no: **RIVA 34**

YOU'RE IN MY HEART
Tracks: / You're in my heart.
7" Single: Released Oct '77, on Riva, by Riva Records. Deleted '80. Catalogue no: **RIVA 11**

Stewart, Roman

LEFT WITH A BROKEN HEART
Tracks: / Left with a broken heart.
12" Single: Released May '89, on Living Room, Catalogue no: **LM 024**

ROMAN'S MEDLEY
Tracks: / Roman's medley.
12" Single: Released Oct '89, on FM Force, Catalogue no: **FM 010**

TODAY
Tracks: / Today / Listen to mummy and daddy.
12" Single: Released Dec '82, on S & G (1), Catalogue no: **SG 22**

WHAT YOU WANNA DO
Tracks: / What you wanna do.
12" Single: Released Apr '80, on D. Roy, Catalogue no: **DRDD 25**

Stewart, Sandy

IF YOU'RE NOT HERE
Tracks: / If you're not here.
7" Single: Released Mar '85, on Vista Sounds, by Vista Sounds Records. Catalogue no: **VISTA 01**

Stewart, Sheila

IT'S YOU
Tracks: / It's you / It's you (version) / It's you (remix).
7" Single: Released Mar '89, on Loading Bay, Catalogue no: **LBAY 1**

Stewart, Shirley

OUT OF BABYLON
Tracks: / Out of Babylon.
12" Single: Released Feb '89, on Charlie's, Catalogue no: **WAL 001**

Stewart & Stax

I GOT FAITH IN YOU
Tracks: / Rita's baby (Inst) / I got faith in you.
7" Single: Released Jan '87, on Rainbow, by Rainbow Records. Catalogue no: **RBR 10**

Stewart, Tiger & Tinga

ON THE ROOF
Tracks: / On the roof.
12" Single: Released May '89, on Power House, Catalogue no: **PHT 23**

Stewart, Tinga

BABY DON'T YOU GO
Tracks: / Baby don't you go.
12" Single: Released Mar '89, on Pickout, Catalogue no: **PICK 21**

COVER ME
Tracks: / Cover me.
12" Single: Released Sep '88, on Pickout, Catalogue no: **PICK 09**

DIDN'T I
Tracks: / Didn't I.
12" Single: Released Nov '88, on Park Heights, Catalogue no: **PHD 0061**

DO I WORRY
Tracks: / Do I worry?.
12" Single: Released Nov '88, on Steely & Cleevie, Catalogue no: **VPRD 356**

DREAM LOVER
Tracks: / Dream lover.
12" Single: Released Oct '89, on Pickout, Catalogue no: **PICK 26**

GONE AGAIN
Tracks: / Gone again.
12" Single: Released Nov '84, on Jedi, Catalogue no: **JJ 208**

GYPSY RASTAS
Tracks: / Gypsy rastas.
12" Single: Released Apr '83, on Gog, Catalogue no: **GOG 002**

HANG ON BABY
Tracks: / Hang on baby.
12" Single: Released Sep '88, on Realistic, Catalogue no: **RR 12**

I WANNA TAKE YOU HOME
Tracks: / I wanna take you home.
12" Single: Released Dec '88, on M.R.C. Productions, Catalogue no: **MRC 002**

I'M YOUR PUPPET
Tracks: / I'm your puppet.
12" Single: Released Feb '89, on Techniques, Catalogue no: **WRT 902**
12" Single: Released Mar '89, on Techniques, Catalogue no: **WRT 44**

IN THE MOOD
Tracks: / In the mood.
12" Single: Released Oct '89, on Rose Of Sharon, Catalogue no: **SW 729**

KEY TO YOUR HEART
Tracks: / Key to your heart / Key to your heart (instrumental).
12" Single: Released Aug '83, on Calabash, Catalogue no: **C 007**

RAM GOAT LIVER
Tracks: / Ram goat liver.
12" Single: Released Jul '89, on Now Generation, Catalogue no: **NGO 17**

RED RED WINE
Tracks: / Red red wine / You should never do that.
12" Single: Released Sep '83, on Jama, Catalogue no: **JADC 0021**

SAVE THE LAST DANCE FOR ME
Tracks: / Save the last dance for me.
12" Single: Released Dec '88, on Pickout, Catalogue no: **PICD 12**

TAKE TIME TO KNOW HER
Tracks: / Take time to know her.
12" Single: Released Jul '88, on Hawkeye, by Hawkeye Records. Catalogue no: **HD 88**

TAKE YOU TO THE DANCE
Tracks: / Take you to the dance / She pan wee mine.
12" Single: Released Aug '86, on Twin Explosion, Catalogue no: **TE 105**

TRUST ME
Tracks: / Trust me.
7" Single: Released Dec '88, on Pickout, Catalogue no: **PICK 08**

YOUR LOVE IS THE REMEDY
Tracks: / Your love is the remedy.
12" Single: Released Jun '88, on BP International, Catalogue no: **BP 16**

Stewart, Tinker

DRY UP YOUR TEARS
Tracks: / Dry up your tears.
12" Single: Released Feb '85, on White label (2), Catalogue no: **Unknown**

Stex

BLACK AND WHITE
Tracks: / Black and white.
7" Single: Released Jun '88, on Arista, by BMG Records (UK). Catalogue no: **111612**
12" Single: Released Jun '88, on Arista, by BMG Records (UK). Catalogue no: **611612**
12" Single: Released Jun '88, on Arista, by BMG Records (UK). Catalogue no: **STEX 1**

BOYS ARE VAIN
Tracks: / Boys are vain / Baby bomb.
7" Single: Released Nov '87, on Arista, by BMG Records (UK). Deleted May '89. Catalogue no: **RIS 24**
12" Single: Released Nov '87, on Arista, by BMG Records (UK). Deleted May '89. Catalogue no: **RIST 24**

Stezo

FREAK THE FUNK
Tracks: / Freak the funk.
12" Single: Released Oct '89, on Sleeping Bag, by Sleeping Bag Records. Catalogue no: **UNKNOWN**

TO THE MAX
Tracks: / To the max.
7" Single: Released Mar '89, on Sleeping Bag, by Sleeping Bag Records. Catalogue no: **SBUK 008**
12" Single: Released 27 Feb '89, on Sleeping Bag, by Sleeping Bag Records. Catalogue no: **SBUK 008 T**

Stickshifts

AUTOMOBILE
Tracks: / Automobile / Parramatta road.
7" Single: Released Jan '80, on Chiswick Records. Deleted '85. Catalogue no: **CHIS 118**

Sticky Wicket

TALKING CRICKET
Tracks: / Talking cricket / Cricket dub.
12" Single: Released Jul '84, on CSA, by CSA Records. Deleted '88. Catalogue no: **12CSA 503**
7" Single: Released Jun '84, on CSA, by CSA Records. Deleted '88. Catalogue no: **CSA 503**

Stiff All-Stars

MAYBE TONIGHT
Tracks: / Maybe tonight / It'll be me.
7" Single: Released Feb '80, on Chiswick-Ace, by Ace Records. Deleted Feb '85. Catalogue no: **CHIS 123**

YOU TELL ME LIES
Tracks: / You tell me lies / Voodoo.
7" Single: Released Oct '81, on Nancy Boys Music. Deleted Oct '84. Catalogue no: **NBM 1**

Stiff Kittens

CONTEMPT
Tracks: / Contempt / Light.
7" Single: Released May '86, on Chris. Deleted '88. Catalogue no: **CSS 4**

ETERNAL BLUE
Tracks: / Eternal blue.
12" Single: Released 20 Jun '87, on Crisis, by Prism Records. Deleted '88. Catalogue no: **CSS 6T**
7" Single: Released 20 Jun '87, on Crisis, by Prism Records. Deleted '88. Catalogue no: **CSS 6**

HAPPY NOW
Tracks: / Happy now.
12" Single: Released Aug '86, on Crisis, by Prism Records. Deleted '88. Catalogue no: **CSS 5T**
7" Single: Released Aug '86, on Crisis, by Prism Records. Deleted '88. Catalogue no: **CSS 5**

Stiff Little Fingers

ALTERNATIVE ULSTER
Tracks: / Alternative Ulster.
7" Single: Released Jan '79, on Rough Trade, by Rough Trade Records. Catalogue no: **RT 004**

AT THE EDGE
Tracks: / At the edge / Running bear / White Christmas.
7" Single: Released Feb '80, on Chrysalis, by Chrysalis Records. Catalogue no: **CHS 2406**

BACK TO FRONT
Tracks: / Back to front / Mr. Fire coal man.
7" Single: Released Aug '80, on Chrysalis, by Chrysalis Records. Deleted '85. Catalogue no: **CHS 2447**

BITS OF KIDS
Tracks: / Bits of kids / Stands to reason.
12" Single: Released Aug '82, on Chrysalis, by Chrysalis Records. Catalogue no: **CHS12 2637**
7" Single: Released Aug '82, on Chrysalis, by Chrysalis Records. Catalogue no: **CHS 2637**

GOTTA GETTAWAY
Tracks: / Gotta getaway.
7" Single: Released May '79, on Rough Trade, by Rough Trade Records. Catalogue no: **RT 015**

JOHNNY WAS
Tracks: / Johnny was / Law and order / Barbed wire love / Suspect device.
CD 5": Released Jul '88, on Strange Fruit, by Strange Fruit Records. Catalogue no: **SFPSCD 004**

JUST FADE AWAY
Tracks: / Just fade away / Go for it / Doesn't make it alright (live).
7" Single: Released Mar '81, on Chrysalis, by Chrysalis Records. Catalogue no: **CHS 2510**

LISTEN
Tracks: / Listen / Sad eyed people / That's when your blood bumps / Two guitars clash.
7" Single: Released Jan '82, on Chrysalis, by Chrysalis Records. Catalogue no: **CHS 2580**

NO SLEEP TIL BELFAST (SINGLE)
Tracks: / No sleep til Belfast.
12" Single: Released '88, on Skunx, Catalogue no: **SLFX 001**

NOBODY'S HERO (SINGLE)
Tracks: / Nobody's hero / Tin soldiers.
7" Single: Released May '80, on Chrysalis, by Chrysalis Records. Catalogue no: **CHS 2424**

PEEL SESSIONS:STIFF LITTLE FINGERS 12.9.78
Tracks: / Johnny was / Law and orde. / Barbed wire love / Suspect device.
CD 5": Released Jul '88, on Strange Fruit, by Strange Fruit Records. Catalogue no: **SFPSCD 004**
Cassingle: Released 30 May '87, on Strange Fruit, by Strange Fruit Records. Catalogue no: **SFPSC 004**
12" Single: Released Sep '86, on Strange Fruit, by Strange Fruit Records. Catalogue no: **SFPS 004**

PRICE OF ADMISSION, THE
Tracks: / Price of admission, The / Touch and go.
7" Single: Released '83, on Chrysalis, by Chrysalis Records. Catalogue no: **CHS 2671**

SILVERLINING
Tracks: / Silver lining / Safe as houses.
7" Single: Released May '81, on Chrysalis, by Chrysalis Records. Catalogue no: **CHS 2517**

ST PATRIX
Tracks: / St. Patrix.
CD 3": Released 6 Mar '89, on Virgin, by Virgin Records. Catalogue no: **SLFCD 1**
12" Single: Released 6 Mar '89, on Virgin, by Virgin Records. Catalogue no: **SLF 1**

STRAW DOGS
Tracks: / Straw dogs / You can't say crap on the radio.
7" Single: Released Sep '79, on Chrysalis, by Chrysalis Records. Deleted '84. Catalogue no: **CHS 2368**

SUSPECT DEVICE

THE STIFFS - GOODBYE MY LOVE (Released on Stiff)

Tracks: / Suspect device.
7" Single: Released Jan '79, on Rough Trade, by Rough Trade Records. Catalogue no: **RT 006**
7" Single: Released Jun '78, on Rigid Digits, by Survival Records. Catalogue no: **SRD 1**

TALK BACK
Tracks: / Talkback / Good for nothing / Talk back.
7" Single: Released Apr '82, on Chrysalis, by Chrysalis Records. Catalogue no: **CHS 2601**

Stiff, Lloyd

CONDOM
Tracks: / Condom.
7" Single: Released Apr '89, on Gyas, Catalogue no: **GA 044**

Stiffs

GOODBYE MY LOVE (see panel above)
Tracks: / Goodbye my love / Magic roundabout.
7" Single: Released Feb '81, on Stiff, by Stiff Records. Catalogue no: **BUY 86**

INSIDE OUT
Tracks: / Inside Out / Kids on the street.
7" Single: Released Dec '79, on Dork, by Dork Records. Deleted '88. Catalogue no: **UR-2**
12" Single: Released Apr '80, on Zonophone, by EMI Records. Deleted Apr '83. Catalogue no: **Z3**

STANDARD ENGLISH
Tracks: / Standard English / DC rip / Brookside riot squad.
7" Single: Released Mar '79, on Dork, by Dork Records. Catalogue no: **UR-1**

VOLUME CONTROL
Tracks: / Volume control / Nothing to lose.
7" Single: Released Sep '80, on Zonophone, by EMI Records. Deleted '83. Catalogue no: **Z 14**

Stiffs '85

YOUNG GUITARS, THE
Tracks: / Young guitars, The.
12" Single: Released Jun '85, on Dork, by Dork Records. Catalogue no: **UR-7**

Stiffy Dread

JAH DREADFUL (2 parts)
Tracks: / Jah dreadful.
12" Single: Released Sep '83, on Twinkle, by Twinkle Records. Catalogue no: **NG 201**

Stigma

REMEMBER
Tracks: / Remember.
12" Single: Released Sep '81, on Stigmatic Sound, Catalogue no: **STIG 1**

Stikki Stuff

SCHOOL
Tracks: / School / Wiggle.
7" Single: Released Aug '81, on Carrere, Deleted Aug '83. Catalogue no: **CAR 206**

YO YO
Tracks: / Yo yo / For all those who sail with us.
7" Single: Released Oct '86, on Total Eclipse, by Total Eclipse Records. Catalogue no: **TECLR 1**

Stiletto

SOMEONE LIKE YOU
Tracks: / Someone like you / Secret world.
7" Single: Released Sep '80, on Mercury, by Phonogram Ltd. Deleted '83. Catalogue no: **MER 34**

VIDEO
Tracks: / Video.
7" Single: Released Aug '81, on Wonderful, Deleted '83. Catalogue no: **WON 3**

Stiletto Rox

TAKE ME WHEN YOU GO
Tracks: / Take me when you go / Shouting out a reason.
7" Single: Released Oct '86, on Slik, Deleted '87. Catalogue no: **SLIK 1002**

Stilettos

THIS IS THE WAY
Tracks: / This is the way / Who can it be.
7" Single: Released Jan '80, on Ariola, by BMG Records (UK). Deleted Jan '85. Catalogue no: **ARO 200**

Still

CHORUS OF BLOWS
Tracks: / Chorus of blows.
7" EP: Released Aug '82, on Open Door, by Open Door Records. Catalogue no: **OD 002**

Still Life

AWAY FROM THIS TOWN
Tracks: / Away from this town / Teenage fun.
7" Single: Released Sep '82, on Regard, Catalogue no: **RG 102**

PASSION PLAY
Tracks: / Passion play.
7" Single: Released Aug '83, on Funzone, Catalogue no: **FUN 2**

Still Thinking

FIRST ROMANCE
Tracks: / First romance.
7" Single: Released Apr '83, on Last Minute, Catalogue no: **LIMP 1**

Stills, Stephen

Biographical details:
Stephen Stills was born on 3 January 1945 in Dallas, Texas; a singer, guitarist and songwriter who worked in Buffalo Springfield, auditioned to be a Monkee, then became a superstar with Crosby, Stills, Nash & Young. He wrote many of Buffalo's songs and has been doing it ever since; also played on Supersession in 1968 with Al Kooper and Mike Bloomfield; his first solo album Stephen Stills in 1970 was a smash hit and is still selling, with hit song *Love The One You're With*. (Donald Clarke)..

LOVE THE ONE YOU'RE WITH
Tracks: / Love the one you're with.
7" Single: Released Mar '71, on Atlantic, by WEA Records. Deleted '74. Catalogue no: **2091 046**
7" Single: Released '75, on Atlantic, by WEA Records. Catalogue no: **LR 3192**

Stilts

WAITING FOR A MIRACLE
Tracks: / Waiting for a miracle / People and buildings.
7" Single: Released Dec '81, on Rondelet Music, by Rondelet Music & Records. Catalogue no: **ROUND 12**

Sting

BE STILL MY BEATING HEART
Tracks: / Be still my beating heart.
12" Single: Released Sep '88, on A&M, by A&M Records. Deleted Feb '89. Catalogue no: **AMY 423**

COMPACT HITS: STING
Tracks: / Someone to watch over me / Englishman in New York / If you love somebody set them free / Spread a little happiness.
CD 5": Released Jul '88, on A&M, by A&M Records. Catalogue no: **AMCD 911**

ENGLISHMAN IN NEW YORK
Tracks: / Englishman in New York / Ghost in the strand / Bring on the night (live) / When the world is running down (live).
12" Single: Released Jan '88, on A&M, by A&M Records. Deleted Feb '89. Catalogue no: **AMY 431**
CD 5": Released Jan '88, on A&M, by A&M Records. Deleted Feb '89. Catalogue no: **AMCD 431**
7" Single: Released Jan '88, on A&M, by A&M Records. Deleted Feb '89. Catalogue no: **AM 431**

FORTRESS
Tracks: / Fortress.
7" Single: Released Sep '85, on A&M, by A&M Records. Deleted '88. Catalogue no: **AM 286**
12" Single: Released Sep '85, on A&M, by A&M Records. Deleted '88. Catalogue no: **AMY 286**

FRAGILE
Tracks: / Fragile.
Note: 7" with special limited edition fold-out poster, special 4-track 12" and CD single both include the Portuguese and Spanish versions.
CD 5": Released Mar '88, on A&M, by A&M Records. Catalogue no: **AMCD 439**
12" Single: Released Mar '88, on A&M, by A&M Records. Deleted Feb '89. Catalogue no: **AMY 439**
7" Single: Released Mar '88, on A&M, by A&M Records. Deleted Feb '89. Catalogue no: **AM 439**

IF YOU LOVE SOMEBODY SET THEM FREE
Tracks: / If you love somebody set them free / Another day.
7" Single: Released May '85, on A&M, by A&M Records. Deleted '88. Catalogue no: **AM 258**

LOVE IS THE SEVENTH WAVE
Tracks: / Love is the seventh wave.
7" Single: Released Aug '85, on A&M, by A&M Records. Deleted '88. Catalogue no: **AM 272**

MOON OVER BOURBON STREET
Tracks: / Moon over bourbon street / Mack the knife / Fortress around your heart (Extra track on 12"version only.).
7" Single: Released Feb '86, on A&M, by A&M Records. Deleted '88. Catalogue no: **AM 305**
12" Single: Released Feb '86, on A&M, by A&M Records. Deleted '88. Catalogue no: **AMY 305**

RUSSIANS
Tracks: / Russians.
12" Single: Released Nov '85, on A&M, by A&M Records. Deleted '88. Catalogue no: **AMY 292**
7" Single: Released Nov '85, on A&M, by A&M Records. Deleted '88. Catalogue no: **AM 292**

SEVENTH WAVE
Tracks: / Seventh wave.
12" Single: Released Aug '85, on A&M, by A&M Records. Deleted '88. Catalogue no: **AMY 272**
7" Single: Released Aug '85, on A&M, by A&M Records. Deleted '88. Catalogue no: **AM 272**

SOMEONE TO WATCH OVER ME
Tracks: / Englishman in New York / If you love somebody set them free / Spread a little happiness.
CD 5": Released Aug '88, on A&M, by A&M Records. Catalogue no: **AMC 911**

SPREAD A LITTLE HAPPINESS
Tracks: / Spread a little happiness / Only you.
7" Single: Released Aug '82, on A&M, by A&M Records. Deleted '85. Catalogue no: **AMS 8217**

THEY DANCE ALONE
Tracks: / They dance alone / Ellas danzan solas (cueco sola) / Si estamos juntos (Only on the 12" version.).
7" Single: Released Aug '88, on A&M, by A&M Records. Catalogue no: **AM 458**
12" Single: Released Aug '88, on A&M, by A&M Records. Catalogue no: **AMY 458**
CD 5": Released Aug '88, on A&M, by A&M Records. Catalogue no: **AMCD 458**

WE'LL BE TOGETHER
Tracks: / We'll be together / Conversation with a dog.
7" Single: Released Oct '87, on A&M, by A&M Records. Deleted 1 Aug '88. Catalogue no: **AM 410**
12" Single: Released Oct '87, on A&M, by A&M Records. Deleted 1 Aug '88. Catalogue no: **AMY 410**
CD 5": Released Oct '87, on A&M, by A&M Records. Deleted Oct '87. Catalogue no: **AMCD 410**

Stingray

MAN IN MY SHOES
Tracks: / Man in my shoes / Whole lot of fire.
7" Single: Released Mar '80, on Carrere, Deleted Mar '83. Catalogue no: **CAR 140**

Stingrays

BEHIND THE BEYOND
Tracks: / Behind the beyond.
7" Single: Released Nov '86, on Kaleidoscope Sound, by Kaleidoscope Sound Records. Catalogue no: **KS 702**
12" Single: Released Nov '86, on Kaleidoscope Sound, by Kaleidoscope Sound Records. Catalogue no: **KS 102**

COUNTDOWN
Tracks: / Countdown.
7" Single: Released Jul '81, on Fried Egg, by Fried Egg Records. Deleted '87. Catalogue no: **EGG 6**

DON'T BREAK DOWN
Tracks: / Don't break down.
7" Single: Released Aug '85, on Big Beat, by Ace Records. Deleted '88. Catalogue no: **NS 109**
12" Single: Released Aug '85, on Big Beat, by Ace Records. Deleted '88. Catalogue no: **NST 109**

ESCALATOR
Tracks: / Escalator / Loose lip sync ship.
7" Single: Released Mar '84, on Ace, by Ace Records. Catalogue no: **NS 95**

JUNE RHYME
Tracks: / June rhyme / Wedding ring / Militant tendency.
12" Single: Released Apr '86, on ABC (indie), Catalogue no: **ABCS 009T**

KISS THE BUTTERFLY
Tracks: / Kiss the butterfly / Only ashes remain.
7" Single: Released Nov '88, on PSL, by PSL Records. Catalogue no: **PSP 025**

NEVER DO
Tracks: / Never do / Satellite.
7" Single: Released Apr '81, on Circus, by Circus Records. Catalogue no: **CIRC 003**

RADIATOR ROCK
Tracks: / Radiator rock / Slap bass boogie.
7" Single: Released Apr '82, on Rocket, by Rocket Records. Catalogue no: **XPRES 78**

Stingrites

BABY'S GOT A BRAND NEW BRAIN
Tracks: / Baby's got a brand new brain.
7" Single: Released Feb '86, on Snaffle, Catalogue no: **RITE 1**

Stir

CHEEKY MONKEY
Tracks: / Cheeky monkey.
12" Single: Released '88, on Spoonin' Records, Catalogue no: **SPOON 001**

Stirling, Lee

EARTHQUAKE, LANDSLIDE, HURRICANE
Tracks: / Earthquake, landslide, hurricane / Soul music.
7" Single: Released Apr '80, on Charisma, by Virgin Records. Deleted '83. Catalogue no: **CB 358**

DELIGHTFUL DOLORES
Tracks: / Delightful Delores.
7" Single: Released Apr '79, on Wikk, by Jels Records. Catalogue no: **WKR 101**

Stitch

BIG MESS
Tracks: / Big mess.
12" Single: Released May '89, on In Tape, by In Tape Records. Catalogue no: **IT 063**

Stitched Back Foot

COSTA DEL SOL
Tracks: / Costa del Sol.
12" Single: Released Jun '88, on In Tape, by In Tape Records. Catalogue no: **ITTI 052**
7" Single: Released Jun '88, on In Tape, by In Tape Records. Catalogue no: **IT 052**

SHAKE UP
Tracks: / Shake up.
12" Single: Released Dec '87, on In Tape, by In Tape Records. Catalogue no: **IT 049**

WOULDN'T YOU LIKE TO KNOW
Tracks: / Wouldn't you like to know.
7" Single: Released Feb '87, on Very Mouth, Catalogue no: **EAT 10**

Stock, Catherine

TO HAVE AND TO HOLD
Tracks: / To have and to hold / Don't be afraid.
7" Single: Released Oct '86, on Sierra, by Sierra Records. Catalogue no: **FED 29**

Stock/Aitken/Waterman

PACKJAMMED (WITH THE PARTY POSSE)
Tracks: / Packjammed (with the party posse) / Packjammed (with the party posse) (writ mix).
Note: "Packjammed (with the party posse)" is the follow-up to the top 20 smash, "Roadblock", and promises to continue the Stock/ Aitken/ Waterman success story.
12" Single: Released 4 Dec '87, on Breakout, by A&M Records. Catalogue no: **USAT 620**
7" Single: Released 4 Dec '87, on Breakout, by A&M Records. Catalogue no: **USA 620**

ROADBLOCK
Tracks: / Roadblock / Roadblock (horn jammin' dub) / Roadblock (edit) / Roadblock (rare dub) (Available on USR 611 only).
7" Single: Released '87, on Breakout, by A&M Records. Catalogue no: **USR 611**
12" Single: Released Jul '87, on Breakout, by A&M Records. Catalogue no: **USAF 611**
7" Single: Released Jul '87, on Breakout, by A&M Records. Catalogue no: **USA 611**

S.S. PAPARAZZI
Tracks: / S.S. Paparazzi.
12" Single: Released Dec '88, on PWL, by PWL Records. Catalogue no: **PWLT 22**
7" Single: Released Dec '88, on PWL, by PWL Records. Catalogue no: **PWL 22**

Stockholm Monsters

ALL AT ONCE
Tracks: / All at once.
7" Single: Released Jun '84, on Factory (1), by Factory Records. Catalogue no: **FAC 107**

FAIRY TALES
Tracks: / Fairytales / Death is slowly.
7" Single: Released Jan '82, on Factory (1), by Factory Records. Catalogue no: **FAC 41**

GREETINGS TWO
Tracks: / Greetings two.
12" Single: Released 16 Mar '87, on Greetings, by Greetings Records. Catalogue no: **MASO 70002**

HAPPY EVER AFTER
Tracks: / Happy ever after.
7" Single: Released Aug '82, on Factory (1), by Factory Records. Catalogue no: **FAC 58**

Stockingcap

WAVE CRAZE
Tracks: / Wave craze.
12" Single: Released Mar '84, on GRP, by GRP Records (USA). Catalogue no: **GRPT 108**

Stockley, Eddie

I WILL ALWAYS LOVE YOU
Tracks: / I will always love you / I will always love you (fly guy house dub) / I will always love you (Tee Scott mix) (Only on 12" single.).
12" Single: Released Aug '88, on Mango Street, by Island Records. Deleted Apr '89. Catalogue no: **12 IS 344**
7" Single: Released Aug '88, on Mango Street, by Island Records. Deleted Apr '89. Catalogue no: **IS 344**

Stockton's Wing

Biographical details: Stockton's Wing are currently Ireland's no.1 band. Fusing traditional Irish Folk with Contemporary Rock and Pop idioms they have created a huge following throughout the Republic and Northern Ireland. This new album has just been released in Ireland and is currently riding high in the charts. *Full Flight* features the bands' last four hit singles, *So many miles, Why wait until tomorrow* and *Avondale*..

BEAUTIFUL AFFAIR
Tracks: / Beautiful affair / Ceili swing.
7" Single: Released Jan '82, on DJM, Catalogue no: **DJS 10983**

BEAUTIFUL WING
Tracks: / Beautiful wing.
7" Single: Released Apr '83, on Ritz, by Ritz Records. Catalogue no: **RITZ 044**

IN OUR WORLD
Tracks: / In our world.
7" Single: Released Oct '83, on Revolving, Catalogue no: **REV 001**

Stokes, Loretta

MY CONSCIENCE WON'T LET ME
Tracks: / My conscience won't let me.
12" Single: Released Feb '87, on Nightmare Gold, Catalogue no: **NRG 23**

Stokes, Val

LEAVING
Tracks: / Leaving.
7" Single: Released Jun '84, on BBC, by BBC Records & Tapes. Deleted '87. Catalogue no: **RESL 147**

Stolen Pets

CHANGES
Tracks: / Changes / No time for falling.
12" Single: Released Jun '82, on Carrere, Catalogue no: **CART 243**
7" Single: Released Jun '82, on Carrere, Catalogue no: **CAR 243**

Stolen Power

WHEELS STILL TURNING (EP)
Tracks: / Wheels still turning.
7" Single: Released Mar '82, on Hornsea Rising, Catalogue no: **SPEP 1**

Stoller, Rhet

CHARIOT
Tracks: / Chariot.
7" Single: Released Jan '61, on Decca, by Decca Records. Deleted '64. Catalogue no: **F 11302**

Stoloff, Morris

MOONGLOW & THEME FROM 'PICNIC'
Tracks: / Moonglow & theme from 'Picnic'.
7" Single: Released Jun '56, on Brunswick, by Decca Records. Deleted '59. Catalogue no: **05553**

Stone

CRAZY
Tracks: / Crazy.
7" Single: Released Jul '83, on Sound Of New York (USA), by Sound Of New York Records(USA). Catalogue no: **SYN 4**

GIRL I LIKE THE WAY YOU MOVE
Tracks: / Girl I like the way you move.
12" Single: Released Jan '83, on Carrere, Catalogue no: **CART 261**
7" Single: Released Jan '83, on Carrere, Catalogue no: **CAR 261**

TIME
Tracks: / Time.
7" Single: Released Apr '82, on Carrere, Catalogue no: **CAR 236**
12" Single: Released Apr '82, on Carrere, Catalogue no: **CART 236**
12" Single: Released Nov '87, on BCM (Germany), Catalogue no: **BC 12205640**

Stone City Band

ALL DAY AND ALL OF THE NIGHT
Tracks: / All day and all of the night.
7" Single: Released Oct '81, on Motown, by BMG Records (UK). Catalogue no: **TMG 1221**
12" Single: Released Oct '81, on Motown, by BMG Records (UK). Catalogue no: **TMGT 1221**

LADIES CHOICE
Tracks: / Ladies choice.
7" Single: Released Sep '83, on Motown, by BMG Records (UK). Catalogue no: **TMG 1316**
7" Single: Released Oct '81, on Motown, by BMG Records (UK). Catalogue no: **TMG 1239**
12" Single: Released Sep '83, on Motown, by BMG Records (UK). Catalogue no: **TMGT 1316**

STRUT YOUR STUFF
Tracks: / Strut your stuff / F.I.M.A..
7" Single: Released Oct '81, on Motown, by BMG Records (UK). Catalogue no: **TMG 1181**

Stone, Cyssy

SHOULD'VE BEEN ME
Tracks: / Should've been me / Part of the band.
7" Single: Released Jun '89, on Fifth Avenue, Catalogue no: **CYSSY 3**

Stone, Davina

FOR THE LOVE OF YOU
Tracks: / For the love of you.
12" Single: Released Oct '82, on Ariwa Sounds, by Ariwa Sounds. Catalogue no: **ARI 1009**

LOVE POWER
Tracks: / Love power.
7" Single: Released Feb '82, on Ariwa Sounds, by Ariwa Sounds. Catalogue no: **ARI 1004**

Stone, Dean

FOREVER YOUNG
Tracks: / Forever young.
7" Single: Released Jun '89, on Quartz, by Quartz Records. Catalogue no: **QUARTZ 003**

Stone, R & J

WE DO IT
Tracks: / We do it (B-side by Kandidate) / Jay cee peaes (we've gone and done it now).
7" Single: Released Jan '76, on RCA, by BMG Records (UK). Deleted '79. Catalogue no: **RCA 2616**
7" Single: Released Mar '87, on Old Gold, by Old Gold Records. Deleted Sep '89. Catalogue no: **OG 9684**
12" Single: Released Nov '87, on Soul Sity, Catalogue no: **SITYT 3**

Stone, Ricky

JENNY PLEASE
Tracks: / Jenny please.
7" Single: Released Feb '85, on Magnet, by WEA Records. Catalogue no: **MAG 273**

SOMETHING'S COOKING (Theme from Crazy Kitchen)
Tracks: / Something's cooking.
7" Single: Released Nov '85, on Magnet, by WEA Records. Deleted '87. Catalogue no: **MAG 287**

Stone Roses

ELEPHANT STONE
Tracks: / Elephant stone / Hardest thing in the world, The.
12" Single: Released Oct '88, on Silvertone, Catalogue no: **ORET 1**
7" Single: Released Oct '88, on Silvertone, Catalogue no: **ORE 1**

MADE OF STONE
Tracks: / Made of stone.
12" Single: Released Feb '89, on Silvertone, Catalogue no: **ORE T2**
7" Single: Released Feb '89, on Silvertone, Catalogue no: **ORE 2**

SALLY CINAMMON
Tracks: / Sally cinammon / Here it comes / All across the sands.
12" Single: Released May '87, on Black (1), by FM-Revolver Records. Catalogue no: **12 REV 36**

SHE BANGS THE DRUM
Tracks: / She bangs the drum / Standing here.
CD 5": Released May '89, on Silvertone, Catalogue no: **ORECD 6**
7" Single: Released May '89, on Silvertone, Catalogue no: **ORE 6**
12" Single: Released Jul '89, on Silvertone, Catalogue no: **OREZ 6**
12" Single: Released May '89, on Silvertone, Catalogue no: **ORET 6**
Cassingle: Released Jul '89, on Silvertone, Catalogue no: **ORE C6**
7" Single: Released Jul '89, on Silvertone, Catalogue no: **OREX 6**

SO YOUNG
Tracks: / So young.
12" Single: Released Sep '85, on Thin Line, by Thin Line Records. Catalogue no: **THIN 1**

Stone, Rosetta

IF YOU COULD SEE ME NOW
Tracks: / If you could see me now / Lovin' arms / Boys in action / It's been done before.
7" Single: Released Jan '80, on Ariola, by BMG Records (UK). Deleted Jan '85. Catalogue no: **ARO 203**

REMEMBER
Tracks: / Remember / London girls.
7" Single: Released May '81, on Limo, Deleted '83. Catalogue no: **LIMO 5**

Stone, Tony

INSTANT LOVE
Tracks: / Instant love / I don't want to be lonely.
7" Single: Released Nov '87, on Ensign, by Ensign Records. Catalogue no: **ENY 609**
12" Single: Released Nov '87, on Ensign, by Ensign Records. Catalogue no: **ENYX 609**

LOVE DON'T COME NO STRONGER
Tracks: / Love don't come no stronger / No more those lies.
7" Single: Released Oct '88, on Ensign, by Ensign Records. Catalogue no: **ENY 617**

THIS IS SERIOUS
Tracks: / This is serious / Fooling around and having fun / Leaving on a night train (Only on CD.) / Can't say bye (Only on CD.).
7" Single: Released Jun '88, on Ensign, by Ensign Records. Catalogue no: **ENY 615**
12" Single: Released Jun '88, on Ensign, by Ensign Records. Catalogue no: **ENYX 615**

Stonebolt

DON'T YOU HIDE IT
Tracks: / Don't you hide it / Love struck.
7" Single: Released May '80, on RCA, by BMG Records (UK). Deleted '83. Catalogue no: **PB 1910**

Stonebridge McGuinness

OOH EEH BABY
Tracks: / Ooh eeh baby.
7" Single: Released Aug '79, on RCA, by BMG Records (UK). Deleted '82. Catalogue no: **PB 5163**

Stoned Aid

ARE YOU GOING TO STONEHENGE?
Tracks: / Are you going to Stonehenge?.
7" Single: Released Jun '86, on Hit (UK), Catalogue no: **STONE 1**

Stonefree

CAN'T SAY BYE
Tracks: / Can't say bye / Night train.
7" Single: Released Mar '89, on Ensign, by Ensign Records. Catalogue no: **ENY 622**
7" Single: Released Apr '87, on Ensign, by Ensign Records. Catalogue no: **ENY 607**
12" Single: Released Mar '89, on Ensign, by Ensign Records. Catalogue no: **ENYX 622**
12" Single: Released Apr '87, on Ensign, by Ensign Records. Catalogue no: **ENYX 607**

Stonehenge

LEAVE IT UP TO ME
Tracks: / Leave it up to me.
7" Single: Released Nov '81, on Jet, by Jet Records. Catalogue no: **JET 7008**

Stonier, Nigel Band

STILL NOT OVER YOU
Tracks: / Still not over you.
7" Single: Released Jul '81, on Cargo, Catalogue no: **CRS 013**

Stooges

STOOGES, THE
Tracks: / What you gonna do (live cut '68) (Previously unreleased.) / Gimme danger (live 73) / Ron Asheton interview.
12" Single: Released Dec '88, on Revenge (France), Catalogue no: **CAXBOX 1**

Stop

I CAN'T FEEL IT
Tracks: / I can't feel it / Iauwata.
7" Single: Released Feb '80, on Calibre, Deleted Feb '83. Catalogue no: **CAB 101**

Stop The Violence...

SELF DESTRUCTION
Tracks: / Self destruction.
12" Single: Released Feb '89, on Jive, by Zomba Records. Catalogue no: **BDPS T1**

Stop The World

DON'T STOP THE MUSIC
Tracks: / Don't stop the music / Don't stop the music (version).
12" Pic: Released 27 Jun '88, on PRT, by Castle Communications Records. Catalogue no: **PYT 12**
7" Pic: Released 27 Jun '88, on PRT, by Castle Communications Records. Catalogue no: **PYS 12**

WORK
Tracks: / Work.
7" Single: Released Jan '85, on Juice, by Juice Records. Deleted '88. Catalogue no: **AA 1**
12" Single: Released Jan '85, on Juice, by Juice Records. Deleted '88. Catalogue no: **12 AA 1**

Storm

IT'S MY HOUSE
Tracks: / It's my house.
7" Single: Released Nov '79, on Scope, Deleted '82. Catalogue no: **SC 10**

LOVE LOVE LOVE
Tracks: / Love love love.
12" Single: Released Nov '84, on 4 Way, Catalogue no: **1 WAY**

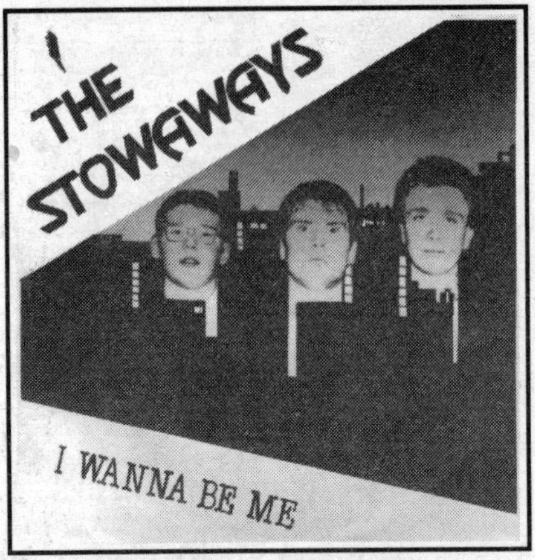

STOWAWAYS - I WANNA BE ME (Released on Supermusic)

MALICE IN WONDERLAND
Tracks: / Malice in wonderland / Malice in Wonderland (Dub Mix) / Doctor Storm.
12" Single: Released Mar '86, on Silent Record Company, by Silent Record Company. Catalogue no: **SILENT 1**

Storm, Danny

HONEST I DO
Tracks: / Honest I do.
7" Single: Released Apr '62, on Pye. Deleted '65. Catalogue no: **7 N 35025**

Storm, Johnny

FAST EDDIE
Tracks: / Fast Eddie / Forgive me.
7" Single: Released May '81, on Magnum Force, by Magnum Music Group. Catalogue no: **MFS 001**

Storm, Rebecca

MR. LOVE
Tracks: / Mr. Love / Mr. King.
7" Single: Released Feb '86, on Columbia, by EMI Records. Catalogue no: **DB 9124**

SHOW, THE (Theme from Connie)
Tracks: / Show, The.
12" Single: Released Jul '85, on Telebell, Catalogue no: **TVEP 3**
12" Single: Released Jul '85, on Telebell, Catalogue no: **ZCTVP 3**

WRONG GIRL, THE
Tracks: / Wrong girl, The / Swansong.
7" Single: Released Jul '86, on Spirit (1), by Spirit Records. Catalogue no: **FIRE 2**

Stormboys

DONNA
Tracks: / Donna.
7" Single: Released Dec '87, on Que, Catalogue no: **QU1**
12" Single: Released Dec '87, on Que, Catalogue no: **12QUI**

Stormed

BEAU-TERRY
Tracks: / Beau-Terry.
12" Single: Released '87, on Stormed, Catalogue no: **MRC 002**

Stormtrooper

ARMIES OF THE NIGHT
Tracks: / Armies of the night.
7" EP: Released Jan '87, on Iron Works (USA), by Azra International (USA). Catalogue no: **IW 1005**

Stout

IT'S HARD TO BE HUMBLE
Tracks: / It's hard to be humble / Reels and jigs.
7" Single: Released Oct '80, on Mint, by Emerald Records. Deleted '88. Catalogue no: **CHEW 39**

SANDCASTLE SAM
Tracks: / Sandcastle Sam / Kerry polkas.
7" Single: Released Mar '81, on Mint, by Emerald Records. Deleted '88. Catalogue no: **CHEW 48**

Stowaways

I WANNA BE ME (see panel above)
Tracks: / I wanna be me / My friends / You'll tie me down.
7" Single: Released Jul '84, on Supermusic, Catalogue no: **SUP 27**

STP023

LET JIMI TAKE OVER
Tracks: / Let Jimi take over / Let Jimi take over (remix).
12" Single: Released Apr '89, on Mr.Modo, Catalogue no: **WMS 001R**

Strafe

OUTLAW
Tracks: / Outlaw (Les Adams remix) / Strafe's groove (US edit).
7" Single: Released 30 May '87, on Breakout, by A&M Records. Deleted Mar '88. Catalogue no: **USA 606**
12" Single: Released 30 May '87, on Breakout, by A&M Records. Deleted Mar '88. Catalogue no: **USAT 606**

SET IT OFF
Tracks: / Set it off.
12" Single: Released Sep '87, on Jus Born (USA), Deleted Oct '87. Catalogue no: **JB 006**

Straight Eight

DESPERATION
Tracks: / Desperation / You are what you are.
7" Single: Released Jan '82, on Logo, by Logo Records. Catalogue no: **GO 406**

I'M SORRY
Tracks: / I'm sorry / Satisfy.
7" Single: Released Sep '80, on Logo, by Logo Records. Deleted Sep '83. Catalogue no: **DEAL 1**

TOMBSTONE
Tracks: / Tombstone.
7" Single: Released Sep '80, on Logo, by Logo Records. Deleted '83. Catalogue no: **DEAL 2**

TOMORROW
Tracks: / Tomorrow / Faded stars.
7" Single: Released Jun '82, on Logo, by Logo Records. Catalogue no: **GO 416**

Straightjacket Fits

LIFE IN ONE CHORD
Tracks: / Life in one chord.
12" Single: Released Nov '88, on Flying Nun, Catalogue no: **FNE 25**

Strait, George

BLAME IT ON MEXICO
Tracks: / Blame it on Mexico / Friday night fever.
7" Single: Released Apr '82, on MCA, by MCA Records. Catalogue no: **MCA 774**

CHAIR
Tracks: / In too deep / Chair.
7" Single: Released Mar '86, on MCA, by MCA Records. Catalogue no: **MCA 1036**

Straker, Nick

AGAINST THE WALL
Tracks: / Against the wall.
12" Single: Released Nov '83, on Tycho, Catalogue no: **FLAME 44T**

IT ONLY TAKES A MINUTE
Tracks: / It only takes a minute / Must you dance.
12" Single: Released Mar '85, on Touch, by Touch Records. Catalogue no: **12TOU 09**

LAST GOODBYE
Tracks: / Last goodbye / Little bit of Jazz.
7" Single: Released Feb '81, on CBS, by CBS Records. Deleted '84. Catalogue no: **CBS 9519**
12" Single: Released Feb '81, on CBS, by CBS Records. Deleted '84. Catalogue no: **13-9519**

LEAVING ON THE MIDNIGHT TRAIN
Tracks: / Leaving on the midnight train / Play the fool.
7" Single: Released Nov '80, on CBS, by CBS Records. Deleted '83. Catalogue no: **CBS 9088**

MUST YOU DANCE
Tracks: / Must you dance.
12" Single: Released Nov '84, on Touch, by Touch Records. Catalogue no: **12TOU 10**

STRAIGHT AHEAD
Tracks: / Straight ahead / Firebird.
7" Single: Released Oct '82, on Firebird, by Pinnacle Records. Catalogue no: **FLAME 33**
12" Single: Released Nov '82, on Firebird, by Pinnacle Records. Deleted Nov '85. Catalogue no: **12FLAME 33**

TURN ME DOWN
Tracks: / Turn me down / We can still be friends.
12" Single: Released Apr '84, on Pinnacle, by Pinnacle Records. Catalogue no: **PIN 100T**

WALK IN THE PARK
Tracks: / Way of life / Walk in the park, A.
7" Single: Released Aug '87, on Sedition, by Sedition Records. Catalogue no: **EDIT 3333**
12" Single: Released Aug '87, on Sedition, by Sedition Records. Catalogue no: **EDITL 3333**

WALK IN THE PARK, A (SINGLE)
Tracks: / Walk in the park, A.
7" Single: Released Aug '80, on CBS, by CBS Records. Deleted '83. Catalogue no: **CBS 8525**

WAY OF LIFE
Tracks: / Way of life / Airwaves.
7" Single: Released Jul '82, on Firebird, by Pinnacle Records. Catalogue no: **FLAME 3**
12" Single: Released Jul '82, on Firebird, by Pinnacle Records. Catalogue no: **FLAME 312**

YOU KNOW I LIKE IT
Tracks: / You know I like it.
7" Single: Released May '83, on Firebird, by Pinnacle Records. Catalogue no: **FLAME 43**
12" Single: Released May '83, on Firebird, by Pinnacle Records. Catalogue no: **FLAME 43T**

Straker, Peter

LATE NIGHT TAXI DRIVER
Tracks: / Late night taxi driver / Real natural man.
7" Single: Released Jul '80, on Rocket, by Rocket Records. Deleted Jul '83. Catalogue no: **XPRES 35**

SPIRIT IS WILLING, THE
Tracks: / Spirit is willing, The.
7" Single: Released Feb '72, on RCA, by BMG Records (UK). Deleted '75. Catalogue no: **RCA 2163**

ZOO NEW
Tracks: / Zoo new / I can't help it.
7" Single: Released Sep '82, on Rockers Forever, Catalogue no: **XPRES 84**

Strand

CAN'T LOOK BACK
Tracks: / Can't look back / Prisoner in paradise.
7" Single: Released Aug '80, on Island, by Island Records. Deleted '83. Catalogue no: **WIP 6631**

YOU SAW ME SWIMMING
Tracks: / You saw me swimming.
7" Single: Released May '83, on Albion, by Albion Records. Catalogue no: **ION 1042**
12" Single: Released May '83, on Albion, by Albion Records. Catalogue no: **12ION 1042**

Strands

AFRICAN LOVE DANCE
Tracks: / African love dance.
7" Single: Released Aug '85, on Tidalwave, Catalogue no: **TW 005**

DRUM MAJORETTE
Tracks: / Drum majorette.
7" Single: Released Jun '85, on Tidalwave, Catalogue no: **TW 003**

ONLY FOOLS LET TRUE LOVE DIE
Tracks: / Only fools let true love die / Flower song / Bookworm / Legend of Jesse James, The.
7" Single: Released Apr '86, on Tidalwave, Catalogue no: **TW 007**

PAPER SUN
Tracks: / Paper Sun / Supergirl.
7" Single: Released Aug '86, on Tidalwave, Catalogue no: **TW 008**

Strange Advance

LOVE GAMES
Tracks: / Love games / Kiss in the dark.
7" Single: Released Nov '82, on Capitol, by EMI Records. Deleted Nov '85. Catalogue no: **CL 270**
12" Single: Released Nov '82, on Capitol, by EMI Records. Deleted Nov '85. Catalogue no: **12CL 270**

SHE CONTROLS ME
Tracks: / She controls me.
7" Single: Released Jun '83, on Capitol, by EMI Records. Deleted '88. Catalogue no: **CL 289**

'TIL THE STARS FALL
Tracks: / Till the stars fall / Wild blue.
Note: Taken from the album The distance between on President Records – PTLS 1094.
7" Single: Released Aug '88, on President, by President Records. Catalogue no: **PT 576**

Strange Arrangement

INTO THE LIGHT
Tracks: / Into the light / Shoot them down.
7" Single: Released Mar '84, on Disc Noir, Deleted '87. Catalogue no: **DN 1001**
12" Single: Released Mar '84, on Disc Noir, Deleted '87. Catalogue no: **DNX 1001**

Strange Cargo

HAVE A NICE DAY
Tracks: / Have a nice day / Palais de danse.
7" Single: Released Apr '82, on 101, Catalogue no: **ICUR 4**

Strange Cruise

BEAT GOES ON
Tracks: / Beat goes on, The / Silver screen queen.
7" Single: Released May '86, on EMI, by EMI Records. Catalogue no: **EMI 5564**

REBEL BLUE ROCKER
Tracks: / Rebel blue rocker / Love addiction.
7" Single: Released Feb '86, on EMI, by EMI Records. Catalogue no: **EMI 5549**
12" Single: Released Feb '86, on EMI, by EMI Records. Catalogue no: **12EMI 5549**

Strange Days

WITHIN THESE WALLS
Tracks: / Within these walls.
7" Single: Released Oct '83, on Powerstation, by Powerstation Records. Catalogue no: **OHM 1**

Strange Daze

THROUGH THE DOORS
Tracks: / Through the doors.
7" Single: Released Jan '84, on Aura Records, by Aura Records. Deleted '88. Catalogue no: **AUS 141**

Strange Fruit

NIGHT TIME
Tracks: / Night time / Fun bags.
7" Single: Released Jul '82, on President, by President Records. Catalogue no: **PT 506**

Strange Meetings

ALIEN PARTY
Tracks: / Alien party.
7" Single: Released Sep '84, on Blue Waters, Catalogue no: **MSW 100**

Strange Relations

PARTY
Tracks: / Party / Same thing.
7" Single: Released Feb '84, on Rocket, by Rocket Records. Catalogue no: **ESP 3**

Strange, Richard

DAMASCUS
Tracks: / Damascus.
12" Single: Released Dec '88, on Nightshift, by Nightshift Records. Catalogue no: **NISHI 206 T**

INTERNATIONAL LANGUAGE
Tracks: / International language / Kiss goodbye tomorrow / God is science.
7" Single: Released Jan '80, on Cherry Red, by Cherry Red Records. Deleted '87. Catalogue no: **CHERRY 10**
7" Single: Released Jan '80, on Virgin, by Virgin Records. Deleted '87. Catalogue no: **VS 419**

NEXT
Tracks: / Next.
12" Single: Released May '83, on Albion, by Albion Records. Catalogue no: **SLAM 1**

Strange, Steve

IN THE YEAR 2525
Tracks: / In the year 2525 / Strange connections.
7" Single: Released Jun '82, on Stiff, by Stiff Records. Catalogue no: **PALACE 1**

Stranger Comforts

NEW YEAR
Tracks: / New year / Raincoats.
7" Single: Released Dec '83, on SCC, Catalogue no: **CCS 002**

WALKING ON AIR (2 PARTS)
7" Single: Released Apr '83, on SCC, Catalogue no: **CCS 001**

Stranger Still

SOLITUDE
Tracks: / Solitude / Survivor.
7" Single: Released Apr '82, on Exit, Catalogue no: **EXIT 001**

Stranger Than Fiction

PRELUDE
Tracks: / Prelude.
12" Single: Released Jul '87, on Constitution, Catalogue no: **CON 3T**

Strangers & Brothers

Biographical details: Jack and Charles Reilly, the fraternal fulcrum of Strangers & Brothers, had gone their own individual ways before a breath of mutual purpose brought them together in a musical sense some 18 months ago. Lyricist and lead singer Jack had been involved in various projects, including one with Creation Records supremo Alan McGhee, while brother Charles dabbled in a number of bands, the French Impressionists and an early manifestation of Lloyd Cole and the Commotions among them. But the dabbling stopped when the brothers Reilly struck up their songwriting partnership, added some ancillary musicians and found themselves in a band. Strangers & Brothers had begun. The band's potential were recognised early on, when they signed a major publishing deal on the basis of their very first gig. A brief hiatus ended when management problems were sorted out and a regular round of concerts began on the Scottish club and university circuit. It was at this point that the true Strangers & Brothers' identity began to emerge. Jack's darting, eccentric stage presence started to create a genuine sense of excitement at gigs, while the musical coherence of the band improved by leaps and bounds. Anchored on the superb, somewhat Knopflerish guitar playing of Charles the band sound developed out of an effective personal and musical chemistry. Bassist Brendan Moon, formerly of The Kissing Bandits and The Revillos, and ex-Altered Images drummer John Wilson provided the kind of rhythm section the band's music demanded - tight, solid, yet creative. The songs - a compelling combination of melodic appeal, crafted lyricism and rhythmic thrust - allowed the sometimes whispered, sometimes fiery vocals to cut, caress and cajole with all Jack's fractured, slightly manic passion. And so to a record deal. Several demos of high quality were recorded before Magnet Records stepped in with an offer which capped the intense interest the group had aroused within the business. Since then Strangers & Brothers have gone from strength to strength and have recorded their first two singles in Scotland's Highland Studios. (Tom Morton, 1984).

CANDI TRAIN
Tracks: / Candi train / In the heat of the night / What did we do? (Extra track on 12"version only.).
7" Single: Released Sep '86, on Magnet, by WEA Records. Deleted Jan '88. Catalogue no: **KILT 2**
12" Single: Released Sep '86, on Magnet, by WEA Records. Deleted Jan '88. Catalogue no: **12 KILT 2**

SENSATIONAL
Tracks: / Sensational.
7" Single: Released Mar '86, on Magnet, by WEA Records. Deleted Jan '88. Catalogue no: **KILT 1**
12" Single: Released Mar '86, on Magnet, by WEA Records. Deleted Jan '88. Catalogue no: **12 KILT 1**

Strangers In Rome

FURTHER ROOM
Tracks: / Further room / Psychedelia.
7" Single: Released Feb '83, on AFR, by AFR Records. Catalogue no: **AFR 001**

Strangeways

STRANGLERS - PARADISE (Released on Epic)

CLOSE TO THE EDGE
Tracks: / Close to the edge / Hold back your love / Heartbeat zone (Extra track on 12" version only.).
7" Single: Released Mar '86, on Bonaire, by Bonaire Records. Deleted '88. Catalogue no: **108 104**
12" Single: Released Mar '86, on Bonaire, by Bonaire Records. Deleted '88. Catalogue no: **608 104**

ONLY A FOOL
Tracks: / Only a fool / Empty street / Stand up & shout (live) (Extra track on 12" only) / Breaking down the barriers(live) (Extra track on 12" only).
7" Single: Released Nov '87, on Bonaire, by Bonaire Records. Deleted May '89. Catalogue no: **BON 6**
12" Single: Released Nov '87, on Bonaire, by Bonaire Records. Deleted May '89. Catalogue no: **BON 126**

Stranglers

Biographical details: Jet Black, drums and percussion; J.J.Burnell, bass and vocals; Hugh Cornwell, guitars and vocal; Dave Greenfield, keyboards and backing vocals..

5 MINUTES
Tracks: / 5 minutes.
7" Single: Released Jan '78, on United Artists, by EMI Records. Catalogue no: **UP 36350**

ALL DAY AND ALL OF THE NIGHT
Tracks: / All day and all of the night / Viva vlad / All day and all of the night (Jeff remix) (Only on 12" and CD single.) / Who wants the world (live) (Only on 12" and CD single.) / Strange little girl (live) (Only on CD single.).
CD 5": Released Dec '87, on Epic, by CBS Records. Deleted Jan '89. Catalogue no: **CD VICE 1**
7" Pic: Released Jan '88, on Epic, by CBS Records. Deleted Aug '88. Catalogue no: **VICE P1**
7" Single: Released Dec '87, on Epic, by CBS Records. Deleted Aug '88. Catalogue no: **VICE 1**
12" Single: Released Dec '87, on Epic, by CBS Records. Deleted Jun '88. Catalogue no: **VICE QT 1**
12" Single: Released Dec '87, on Epic, by CBS Records. Deleted Aug '88. Catalogue no: **VICE T1**

ALWAYS THE SUN
Tracks: / Always the sun / Normal normal.
7" Single: Released Oct '86, on Epic, by CBS Records. Catalogue no: **SOLAR 1**
12" Single: Released Oct '86, on Epic, by CBS Records. Catalogue no: **SOLART 1**

BEAR CAGE
Tracks: / Bear cage / Shah shah a go go.
7" Single: Released Mar '80, on United Artists, by EMI Records. Deleted '83. Catalogue no: **BP 344**

BIG IN AMERICA
Tracks: / Big in America.
7" Single: Released Nov '86, on Epic, by CBS Records. Catalogue no: **HUGH 1**
7" Single: Released Nov '86, on Epic, by CBS Records. Catalogue no: **650249 6**
12" Single: Released Nov '86, on Epic, by CBS Records. Catalogue no: **HUGH 1T**

CHOOSEY SUSIE
Tracks: / Choosey Susie / Mean to me.
7" Single: Released Apr '79, on King (USA), Catalogue no: **KING 17 F**

DON'T BRING HARRY
Tracks: / Don't bring Harry / Wired / Crabs (live) / In the shadows (live).
7" EP: Released Dec '79, on United Artists, by EMI Records. Deleted '82. Catalogue no: **STR 1**

DON'T BRING HARRY (FRENCH VERSION)
Tracks: / Don't bring Harry (French version).
12" Single: Released 30 May '87, on New Rose (1), by New Rose Records. Catalogue no: **HARRY 1**

DUCHESS
Tracks: / Duchess / Fools rush out.
7" Single: Released Aug '79, on United Artists, by EMI Records. Catalogue no: **BP 308**

EUROPEAN FEMALE
Tracks: / European female / Savage breast.
7" Single: Released Jan '83, on Epic, by CBS Records. Deleted '86. Catalogue no: **EPC A 2893**

EVENING SHOW SESSIONS, THE
CD 5": Released Jul '89, on Strange Fruit, by Strange Fruit Records. Catalogue no: **SFNTCD 020**
7" Single: Released Jul '89, on Strange Fruit, by Strange Fruit Records. Catalogue no: **SFNT 020**

FIVE MINUTES
Tracks: / Five minutes.
7" Single: Released Feb '78, on United Artists, by EMI Records. Deleted '81. Catalogue no: **UP 36350**

(GET A) GRIP (ON YOURSELF)
Tracks: / (Get a) grip (on yourself).
7" Single: Released Feb '77, on United Artists, by EMI Records. Deleted '80. Catalogue no: **UP 36211**

GOLDEN BROWN
Tracks: / Golden brown / Love 30.
7" Single: Released Mar '84, on EMI Golden 45's, by EMI Records. Catalogue no: **G45 6**
7" Single: Released Jan '82, on Liberty, by EMI Records. Catalogue no: **BP 407**
12" Single: Released May '88, on Liberty (Germany), by EMI Records. Catalogue no: **2013286**
12" Single: Released May '84, on EMI (Germany), by EMI Records. Catalogue no: **1 C KH 052 Z 83255**

GRIP '89
Tracks: / Grip '89 (get a grip on yourself) / Grip '89 (Grippin stuff mix) (12" only.) / Waltzinblack / Tomorrow was the hereafter (12" only.).
CD 5": Released Feb '89, on EMI, by EMI Records. Deleted Aug '89. Catalogue no: **CDEM 84**
7" Single: Released Jan '89, on Liberty, by EMI Records. Catalogue no: **EM 84**
12" Single: Released Jan '89, on Liberty, by EMI Records. Catalogue no: **12EM 84**
Special: Released Jan '89, on EMI, by EMI Records. Catalogue no: **EMR 84**

HANGING AROUND
Tracks: / Hanging around.
7" Single: Released '80, on United Artists, by EMI Records. Catalogue no: **LR 4432**

JUST LIKE NOTHING ON EARTH (SINGLE)
Tracks: / Just like nothing on earth / Man in white.
7" Single: Released Mar '81, on Liberty, by EMI Records. Deleted Mar '84. Catalogue no: **BP 393**

LA FOLIE (SINGLE)
Tracks: / La folie / Waltzinblack.
7" Single: Released Apr '82, on Liberty, by EMI Records. Deleted '85. Catalogue no: **BP 410**

LET ME DOWN EASY
Tracks: / Let me down easy.
7" Single: Released Feb '85, on Epic, by CBS Records. Deleted '88. Catalogue no: **A 6045**

LET ME INTRODUCE YOU TO THE FAMILY
Tracks: / Let me introduce you to the family / Vietnamerica.
7" Single: Released Nov '81, on United Artists, by EMI Records. Deleted '84. Catalogue no: **BP 405**

MIDNIGHT SUMMER DREAM
Tracks: / Midnight summer dream / Strange circumstance.
7" Single: Released Feb '83, on Epic, by CBS Records. Catalogue no: **EPC A 3167**
12" Single: Released Feb '83, on Epic, by CBS Records. Catalogue no: **EPC A 13 3167**

NICE IN NICE
Tracks: / Nice in Nice / Since you went away.
7" Single: Released Aug '86, on Epic, by CBS Records. Catalogue no: **650055 7**
12" Single: Released Aug '86, on Epic, by CBS Records. Catalogue no: **650055 6**

NICE 'N' SLEAZY
Tracks: / Nice 'n' sleazy.
7" Single: Released May '78, on United Artists, by EMI Records. Deleted '81. Catalogue no: **UP 36379**

NIGHT TRACKS EP
CD 5": Released Apr '89, on Night Tracks, by Pinnacle Records. Catalogue no: **SFNTCD 020**
12" Single: Released Apr '89, on Night Tracks, by Pinnacle Records. Catalogue no: **SFNT 020**

NO MERCY
Tracks: / No mercy.
7" Single: Released Dec '84, on Epic, by CBS Records. Deleted '87. Catalogue no: **A 4921**

NO MORE HEROES (SINGLE)
Tracks: / No more heroes.
7" Single: Released Sep '77, on United Artists, by EMI Records. Deleted Nov '88. Catalogue no: **UP 36300**

NUCLEAR DEVICE (THE WIZARD OF AUS)
Tracks: / Nuclear device (the wizard of Aus).
7" Single: Released Oct '79, on United Artists, by EMI Records. Deleted '82. Catalogue no: **BP 318**

PARADISE (see panel above)
Tracks: / Paradise / Pawsher.
7" Single: Released Aug '83, on Epic, by CBS Records. Deleted '86. Catalogue no: **A 3387**

PEACHES
Tracks: / Peaches / Go buddy go.
7" Single: Released Apr '79, on United Artists, by EMI Records. Deleted Aug '89. Catalogue no: **UP 36248**

SHAKIN' LIKE A LEAF
Tracks: / Shakin' like a leaf.
Note: Was it you?-on 12" only
7" Single: Released Feb '87, on Epic, by CBS Records. Deleted Aug '87. Catalogue no: **SHEIK 1**
12" Single: Released Feb '87, on Epic, by CBS Records. Deleted Aug '87. Catalogue no: **SHEIKQ 1**
12" Single: Released Feb '87, on Epic, by CBS Records. Deleted Aug '87. Catalogue no: **SHEIKT 1**

SKIN DEEP
Tracks: / Skin deep.
7" Single: Released Oct '84, on Epic, by CBS Records. Deleted '87. Catalogue no: **A 4738**

SOMETHING BETTER CHANGE
Tracks: / Something better change / Straighten out.
7" Single: Released Aug '77, on United Artists, by EMI Records. Deleted '80. Catalogue no: **UP 36277**

STRANGE LITTLE GIRL

Tracks: / Strange little girl / Cruel garden.
7" Single: Released Jul '82, on Liberty, by EMI Records. Catalogue no: **BP 412**

THROWN AWAY
Tracks: / Thrown away / Top secret.
7" Single: Released Jan '81, on United Artists, by EMI Records. Deleted '84. Catalogue no: **BP 383**

WALK ON BY
Tracks: / Walk on by.
7" Single: Released Jul '78, on United Artists, by EMI Records. Deleted Oct '87. Catalogue no: **UP 36429**

WHO WANTS THE WORLD
Tracks: / Who wants the world / Meninblack.
7" Single: Released Jun '80, on United Artists, by EMI Records. Deleted '83. Catalogue no: **BPX 355**

Straps

BRIXTON
Tracks: / Brixton / No liquor.
7" Single: Released Jul '82, on Donut, Deleted '87. Catalogue no: **DONUT 3**

Strasse

STAIRWAY TO YOU
Tracks: / Stairway to you.
7" Single: Released May '83, on RCA, by BMG Records (UK). Catalogue no: **RCA 316**
12" Single: Released May '83, on RCA, by BMG Records (UK). Catalogue no: **RCAT 316**

Strategy

DON'T EVER TRUST YOUR HEART
Tracks: / Don't ever trust your heart / I don't need you.
7" Single: Released Mar '81, on Ocean (1), by Ocean Records. Catalogue no: **OR 1**

Straw, Syd

FUTURE 40'S
Tracks: / Future 40's / Taken / Learning the game.
7" Single: Released Sep '89, on Virgin America, by Virgin Records. Catalogue no: **VUS 6**
12" Single: Released Sep '89, on Virgin America, by Virgin Records. Catalogue no: **VUST 6**

Strawberry Park

SUMMER IS COMING
Tracks: / Summer is coming / Beach party.
7" Single: Released Jun '82, on Sonet, by Sonet Records. Catalogue no: **SON 2245**

Strawberry Switchblade

JOLENE
Tracks: / Jolene.
7" Single: Released Aug '85, on Korova, by WEA Records. Catalogue no: **KOW 42**
12" Single: Released Aug '85, on Korova, by WEA Records. Deleted Jan '88. Catalogue no: **KOW 42T**

LET HER GO
Tracks: / Let her go / Beautiful end / Michael walks by night.
7" Single: Released Mar '85, on Korova, by WEA Records. Deleted '88. Catalogue no: **KOW 39**

SINCE YESTERDAY
Tracks: / Since yesterday.
7" Single: Released Nov '84, on Korova, by WEA Records. Deleted '87. Catalogue no: **KOW 38**
12" Single: on Korova, by WEA Records. Deleted Jun '87. Catalogue no: **KOW 38T**

TREES AND FLOWERS
Tracks: / Trees and flowers / Go away.
7" Single: Released Jul '83, on 92 Happy Customers, Catalogue no: **HAP 001**
12" Single: Released Jul '83, on 92 Happy Customers, Catalogue no: **HAPT 001**

Strawbs

LAY DOWN
Tracks: / Lay down.
7" Single: Released Oct '72, on A&M, by A&M Records. Deleted '75. Catalogue no: **AMS 7035**

LET IT RAIN
Tracks: / Let it rain.
7" Single: Released Nov '88, on Chord, by Chord Records. Catalogue no: **STRAWBS 101**

PART OF THE UNION
Tracks: / Part of the union / Go away.
7" Single: Released Jan '73, on A&M, by A&M Records. Deleted '76. Catalogue no: **AMS 7047**

PART OF THE UNION (OLD GOLD)
Tracks: / Part of the union / Lay down.
7" Single: Released Jul '82, on Old Gold, by Old Gold Records. Catalogue no: **OG 9149**

SHINE ON SILVER SUN
Tracks: / Shine on silver sun.
7" Single: Released Oct '73, on A&M, by A&M Records. Deleted '76. Catalogue no: **AMS 7082**

Stray Cats

Biographical details: It seems like only yesterday that the world first heard The Stray Cats. In fact, it practically was. Long Islanders Brian Setzer, Slim Jim Phanton and Lee Rocker, invaded England in 1980, looking to develop their music amidst sympathetic ears. Before you could say "tutti frutti", the Cats were on the move, racking up hit singles, and albums in the UK and Europe like nobody's business. And no wonder, with their snazzy look and swingin' blend of rockabilly, blues, honky tonk and even jazz. The Stray Cats had a winning combination of classic styles and modern-day energy that no true fan of real rock 'n' roll could resist. Following their self-titled UK debut LP and *Gonna Ball* not to mention a string of smokin' hit singles, The Stray Cats decided it was time to go back to the States and strut their stuff for the home folks. The band signed with EMI America Records in 1982 and compiled *Built For Speed* their US debut LP, from the best of their two UK albums, plus the brand new title track. At the time nobody knew if America would give The Stray Cats a home. After all, their kind of good-humoured, no-nonsense rock 'n' roll hadn't had much attention there since its first golden era over two decades ago. Of course, rock 'n' roll fanatics hadn't had much to listen to since then, apart from warmed-over nostalgia, and The Stray Cats weren't a revival band, they were the real thing. Quick as a flash The Stray Cats leapt to the top of the US charts. First *Rock This Town* shook up Top 40 then *Built For Speed* raced to platinum. Next the sultry *Stray Cats Strut* confirmed the rumours: all America wanted to go steady with The Stray Cats.
Which brings us to the present. Will success spoil Brian, Slim Jim and Lee? Absolutely not. *Rant 'n' Rave* makes good on the promise of *Built For Speed* and then some. The boys have reunited with kindred spirit Dave Edmunds, producer of their previous hit 45's, and if possible they are sharper and wilder than ever. Check out the LP's first single *She's sexy & 17* or go ahead and *Take A Look At That Cadillac*. After a spin of *Rant 'n' Rave* you'll be tempted to say you're *Too hip, gotta go* especially if you're *18 miles from Memphis*. On the other hand you might ask *How Long You Wanna Live, Anyway* or declare *I won't stand in your way*. (Arista Press Office, November 1983).

BRING IT BACK AGAIN
Tracks: / Bring it back again / Runaway boys (live) / I fought the law (12" & CD only.).
7" Single: Released Jan '89, on EMI-Manhattan, by EMI Records. Deleted Aug '89. Catalogue no: **MT 62**
CD 5": Released Jan '89, on EMI-Manhattan, by EMI Records. Deleted Aug '89. Catalogue no: **CDMT 62**
Special: Released Jan '89, on EMI-Manhattan, by EMI Records. Deleted Aug '89. Catalogue no: **MTS 62**
12" Single: Released Jan '89, on EMI-Manhattan, by EMI Records. Deleted Aug '89. Catalogue no: **12MT 62**

GINA
Tracks: / Gina / Two of a kind / Stray Cat strut (live version).
12" Single: Released Jun '89, on EMI-Manhattan, by EMI Records. Deleted Oct '89. Catalogue no: **12MT 67**
7" Single: Released Jun '89, on EMI-Manhattan, by EMI Records. Deleted Oct '89. Catalogue no: **203 403 7**
CD 5": Released Jun '89, on EMI-Manhattan, by EMI Records. Deleted Oct '89. Catalogue no: **203 403 2**
CD 5": Released Jun '89, on EMI-Manhattan, by EMI Records. Deleted Oct '89. Catalogue no: **CDMT 67**
12" Single: Released Jun '89, on EMI-Manhattan, by EMI Records. Deleted Oct '89. Catalogue no: **203 403 6**
7" Single: Released Jun '89, on EMI-Manhattan, by EMI Records. Deleted Oct '89. Catalogue no: **MT 67**
12" Single: Released Jun '89, on EMI-Manhattan, by EMI Records. Deleted Oct '89. Catalogue no: **203 403 8**
12" Single: Released Jun '89, on EMI-Manhattan, by EMI Records. Deleted Oct '89. Catalogue no: **12MTP 67**

LITTLE MISS PRISSY
Tracks: / Little Miss Prissy.
7" Single: Released '82, on Arista, by BMG Records (UK). Deleted '87. Catalogue no: **SCAT 5**

REBELS RULE
Tracks: / Rebels rule.
12" Single: Released '83, on Arista, by BMG Records (UK). Deleted '87. Catalogue no: **SCAT 127**
7" Single: Released '83, on Arista, by BMG Records (UK). Deleted '86. Catalogue no: **SCAT 7**

ROCK THIS TOWN
Tracks: / Rock this town / Can't hurry love.
7" Single: Released Jan '81, on Arista, by BMG Records (UK). Catalogue no: **SCAT 2**

RUNAWAY BOYS
Tracks: / Runaway boys / My one desire.
7" Single: Released Nov '80, on Arista, by BMG Records (UK). Deleted '83. Catalogue no: **SCAT 1**

(SHE'S) SEXY AND 17
Tracks: / (She's) sexy and 17.
7" Single: Released '83, on Arista, by BMG Records (UK). Deleted '86. Catalogue no: **SCAT 6**
12" Single: Released '83, on Arista, by BMG Records (UK). Deleted '86. Catalogue no: **SCAT 126**

STRAY CAT STRUT
Tracks: / Stray cat strut / Drink that bottle down.
12" Single: Released Apr '81, on Arista, by BMG Records (UK). Deleted '85. Catalogue no: **SCAT 123**
7" Single: Released Apr '81, on Arista, by BMG Records (UK). Deleted '84. Catalogue no: **SCAT 3**

YOU DON'T BELIEVE ME
Tracks: / You don't believe me / Cross that bridge.
7" Single: Released '82, on Arista, by BMG Records (UK). Deleted '87. Catalogue no: **SCAT 4**

Streep, Meryl

AMAZING GRACE
Tracks: / Amazing grace.
7" Single: Released May '84, on PRT, by Castle Communications Records. Catalogue no: **7P 309**

Street Angel

DRESSING UP
Tracks: / Dressing up.
7" Single: Released Nov '83, on Street Beat (USA), Catalogue no: **STB 100**
12" Single: Released Nov '83, on Street Beat (USA), Catalogue no: **STBX 100**

ONE BITE
Tracks: / One bite.
12" Single: Released Oct '85, on Calibre, Deleted '86. Catalogue no: **CABL 207**
7" Single: Released Oct '85, on Calibre, Deleted '86. Catalogue no: **CAB 207**

Street Bizarre

NORMAL LIFE
Tracks: / Normal life / Nervous exhaustion.
7" Single: Released Jan '80, on Monarch, by Monarch Records. Deleted Jan '83. Catalogue no: **MON 05**

Street, Danny

RISE AND SHINE
Tracks: / Rise and shine.
7" Single: Released '89, on Redrock, by Redrock Records. Catalogue no: **RKA 9**

Street Ducks

AFFECTION TRAINED
Tracks: / Affection trained.
12" Single: Released Dec '88, on Anything But, Catalogue no: **ABR 021**

DUCK AND COVER
Tracks: / Duck and cover.
12" Single: Released 1 May '87, on Smash, Catalogue no: **SMASH 004**

Street Funk Level

SHOW ME WHAT YOU GOT
Tracks: / Show me what you got.
7" Single: Released Nov '88, on Warriors Dance, by Warriors Dance Records. Catalogue no: **WAF 5**
12" Single: Released Oct '88, on Warriors Dance, by Warriors Dance Records. Catalogue no: **WAAF 5T**

Street, Judy

WHAT
Tracks: / What.
Note: You've heard the succesful cover version by Soft Cell, now hear the original version, as recorded for the U.S. Strider label circa 1967.
7" Single: Released Aug '82, on Soul Stop, by Dawn Promotions. Catalogue no: **SS 3003**

Street Level

NEVER KNEW
Tracks: / Never knew.
7" Single: Released Dec '84, on Embryo Arts (Belgium), Catalogue no: **EAS 002**

Street System

DELIRIOUS (IN A TRANCE)
Tracks: / Delirious (in a trance) / Scratch and break.
7" Single: Released May '84, on Vogue, by Vogue Records. Catalogue no: **VOG 3**
12" Single: Released May '84, on Vogue, by Vogue Records. Catalogue no: **VOGL 3**

Streetband

TOAST
Tracks: / Toast / Hold on.
7" Single: Released Nov '78, on Logo, by Logo Records. Deleted '81. Catalogue no: **GO 325**

Streetbeat

IN LOVE
Tracks: / In love.
7" Single: Released Sep '85, on Steinar, by Steinar Records (UK). Catalogue no: **STE 770**
7" Single: Released Sep '85, on Steinar, by Steinar Records (UK). Catalogue no: **STE 770**

RAP 'N' SCRATCH
Tracks: / Rap 'n' scratch / Mama loves you.
12" Single: Released Dec '84, on Steinar, by Steinar Records (UK). Catalogue no: **STE 1240**
7" Single: Released Dec '84, on Steinar, by Steinar Records (UK). Catalogue no: **STE 740**

Streetheart

SNOW WHITE
Tracks: / Snow white.
7" Single: Released Nov '84, on President, by President Records. Catalogue no: **PT 531**

Streetlife

ACT ON INSTINCT
Tracks: / Act on instinct.
12" Single: Released Feb '84, on Factory (1), by Factory Records. Catalogue no: **FAC 97T**

LOVE ME LIKE A LOVER
Tracks: / Love me like a lover / True love.
7" Single: Released Oct '80, on WEA, by WEA Records. Deleted Oct '83. Catalogue no: **K 18350**

SILENCE
Tracks: / Silence.
12" Single: Released Apr '85, on Factory (1), by Factory Records. Catalogue no: **FAC 124T**

Streetlife Fantasy

GOTTA STOP IT Nuclear war
Tracks: / Gotta stop it / We're in this together (club mix).
7" Single: Released 20 Jun '87, on Tidalwave, Catalogue no: **TW 010**

Streetrods

ROCK ROCK ROCK
Tracks: / Rock rock rock.
7" Single: Released Sep '83, on Rock Shop, Catalogue no: **RSR 001**

Streets Ahead

BACK TO MONO (EP)
Tracks: / Back to mono.
7" Single: Released Feb '82, on Dead Duck, Catalogue no: **DUCK 2**

Streisand, Barbra

ALL I ASK OF YOU
Tracks: / All I ask of you / Somewhere / Memory / Send in the clowns.
12" Single: Released Dec '88, on CBS, by CBS Records. Deleted 10 Jul '89. Catalogue no: **BARB T3**
7" EP: Released 30 Jan '89, on CBS, by CBS Records. Deleted 10 Jul '89. Catalogue no: **BARBEP 3**
Special: Released Feb '89, on CBS, by CBS Records. Deleted 10 Jul '89. Catalogue no: **BARB QT3**
Special: Released 6 Feb '89, on CBS, by CBS Records. Deleted 10 Jul '89. Catalogue no: **CP BARB 3**
7" Single: Released Dec '88, on CBS, by CBS Records. Deleted 10 Jul '89. Catalogue no: **BARB 3**
CD 5": Released Dec '88, on CBS, by CBS Records. Deleted 10 Jul '89. Catalogue no: **CDBARB 3**

COMIN' IN AND OUT OF YOUR LIFE
Tracks: / Comin' in and out of your life.
7" Single: Released Jan '82, on CBS, by CBS Records. Deleted '85. Catalogue no: **A 1789**

GUILTY (SINGLE)
Tracks: / Guilty / Life story.
7" Single: Released Dec '80, on CBS, by CBS Records. Deleted '83. Catalogue no:

CBS 9315

I AIN'T GONNA CRY TONIGHT
Tracks: / I ain't gonna cry tonight / I found you love.
7" Single: Released Feb '80, on CBS, by CBS Records. Deleted '83. Catalogue no: **CBS 8138**

KISS ME IN THE RAIN
Tracks: / Kiss me in the rain / Love break-down.
7" Single: Released Mar '80, on CBS, by CBS Records. Deleted Mar '83. Catalogue no: **CBS 8352**

LOVE INSIDE
Tracks: / Love inside / Never give up.
7" Single: Released Nov '81, on CBS, by CBS Records. Deleted Nov '84. Catalogue no: **CBS A 1660**

MAKE NO MISTAKE, HE'S MINE
Tracks: / Make no mistake, he's mine / Clear sailing.
7" Single: Released Jan '85, on CBS, by CBS Records. Catalogue no: **A 4994**

MEMORY
Tracks: / Memory / Evergreen.
7" Single: Released Feb '83, on CBS, by CBS Records. Catalogue no: **BARB 1**
7" Single: Released Mar '82, on CBS, by CBS Records. Deleted '85. Catalogue no: **A 1903**

NO MATTER WHAT HAPPENS
Tracks: / No matter what happens.
7" Single: Released Jan '84, on CBS, by CBS Records. Catalogue no: **A 4125**

NUTS
Tracks: / Nuts.
12" Single: Released Mar '88, on CBS, by CBS Records. Deleted 17 Apr '89. Catalogue no: **651379 6**

OVER THE RAINBOW
Tracks: / Over the rainbow / Guilty.
7" Single: Released 30 May '87, on CBS, by CBS Records. Catalogue no: **650920 7**

PEOPLE
Tracks: / People.
7" Single: Released '80, on CBS, by CBS Records. Catalogue no: **LR 0937**

PROMISES
Tracks: / Promises / Never give up.
7" Single: Released May '81, on CBS, by CBS Records. Deleted May '84. Catalogue no: **CBS A 1203**

SECOND HAND ROSE
Tracks: / Second hand Rose.
7" Single: Released Jan '66, on CBS, by CBS Records. Deleted '69. Catalogue no: **CBS 202025**

SEND IN THE CLOWNS
Tracks: / Send in the clowns / Being alive / Somewhere (Track in Double Pack only.).
7" Single: Released Mar '86, on CBS, by CBS Records. Catalogue no: **A 6988**
7" Set: Released Mar '86, on CBS, by CBS Records. Catalogue no: **DA 6988**

SOMEWHERE
Tracks: / Somewhere / Not while I'm around.
7" Single: Released Dec '85, on CBS, by CBS Records. Catalogue no: **A 6707**

STAR IS BORN LOVE THEME, A
Tracks: / Star is born love theme.
7" Single: Released Apr '77, on CBS, by CBS Records. Deleted '80. Catalogue no: **CBS 4855**

STONEY END (SINGLE)
Tracks: / Stoney end.
7" Single: Released Jan '71, on CBS, by CBS Records. Deleted '74. Catalogue no: **CBS 5321**

TILL I LOVED YOU (SINGLE)
Tracks: / Till I loved you / Two people / Guilty (Only on 12" & CD single.) / Left in the dark (Only on 12" & CD single.) / You don't bring me flowers (Only on 12" EP.) / What kind of fool.
CD 5": Released Oct '88, on CBS, by CBS Records. Deleted 17 Apr '89. Catalogue no: **CDBARB 2**
7" Single: Released Oct '88, on CBS, by CBS Records. Deleted 17 Apr '89. Catalogue no: **BARB 2**
12" Single: Released Oct '88, on CBS, by CBS Records. Deleted 17 Apr '89. Catalogue no: **BARB EP 2**
12" Single: Released Oct '88, on CBS, by CBS Records. Deleted 17 Apr '89. Catalogue no: **BARB T2**

WAY WE WERE, THE (SINGLE)
Tracks: / Way we were, The.
7" Single: Released Mar '74, on CBS, by CBS Records. Deleted '77. Catalogue no: **CBS 1915**

WAY YOU MAKE ME FEEL
Tracks: / Way you make me feel, The (Available on 12" only).
7" Single: Released Nov '83, on CBS, by CBS Records. Catalogue no: **A 3888**

WE'RE NOT MAKING LOVE ANY-MORE
Tracks: / We're not making love anymore / Here we are at last / Wet / No more tears (Enough is enough).
12" Single: Released Oct '89, on CBS, by CBS Records. Catalogue no: **BARB T4**
7" Single: Released Oct '89, on CBS, by CBS Records. Catalogue no: **BARB 4**
Cassingle: Released Oct '89, on CBS, by CBS Records. Catalogue no: **BARB QT4**
CD 5": Released Oct '89, on CBS, by CBS Records. Catalogue no: **CD BARB 4**

WHAT KIND OF FOOL
Tracks: / What kind of fool / Make it like a memory.
7" Single: Released Feb '81, on CBS, by CBS Records. Deleted Feb '84. Catalogue no: **CBS 9517**

WOMAN IN LOVE
Tracks: / Woman in love / Run wild.
7" Single: Released Apr '82, on CBS, by CBS Records. Catalogue no: **CBS 8966**

Strength

BREAKING HEARTS
Tracks: / Breaking hearts / Heartbeat / Girl for me, The / Breaking hearts (remix) (Only on 12" (612161).).
CD 5": Released Jun '89, on Arista, by BMG Records (UK). Catalogue no: **UNKNOWN**
7" Set: Released Jun '89, on Arista, by BMG Records (UK). Catalogue no: **112085**
7" Single: Released Jun '89, on Arista, by BMG Records (UK). Catalogue no: **112161**
12" Single: Released Jun '89, on Arista, by BMG Records (UK). Catalogue no: **612085**
7" Single: Released Jul '89, on Arista, by BMG Records (UK). Catalogue no: **112532**
12" Single: Released Jul '89, on Arista, by BMG Records (UK). Catalogue no: **612161**
Cassingle: Released Jun '89, on Arista, by BMG Records (UK). Catalogue no: **410085**

GIRL FOR ME, THE
Tracks: / Girl for me, The / Bad bad boy (sophisticated version) (Only on 7" single.) / Girl for me (version) (Only on the 12" version.) / Joy, peace and happiness (Only on the CD single.).
12" Single: Released Oct '88, on Arista, by BMG Records (UK). Catalogue no: **611648**
CD 5": Released Oct '88, on Arista, by BMG Records (UK). Catalogue no: **661648**
7" Single: Released Oct '88, on Arista, by BMG Records (UK). Catalogue no: **111648**

GOTTA BE STRONG
Tracks: / Gotta be strong / Gotta be funky / Gotta be strong (Gospel).
12" Single: Released Sep '89, on Arista, by BMG Records (UK). Catalogue no: **612 646**
CD 5": Released Sep '89, on Arista, by BMG Records (UK). Catalogue no: **662 646**
7" Single: Released Sep '89, on Arista, by BMG Records (UK). Catalogue no: **112 646**

UNDERSTANDING YOU
Tracks: / Understanding you / Severance.
7" Single: Released Mar '85, on Big A, Catalogue no: **BIG 001**

Stress

PLAYING GAMES
Tracks: / Playing games / Standing in a room.
7" Single: Released Jun '82, on Out Of Town, Catalogue no: **HOOT 1**

Stretch

WHY DID YOU DO IT
Tracks: / Why did you do it.
7" Single: Released Nov '75, on Anchor (1), by Anchor Records. Deleted '78. Catalogue no: **ANC 1021**

WHY DID YOU DO IT (OLD GOLD)
Tracks: / Why did you do it / How long.
7" Single: Released Jun '84, on Old Gold, by Old Gold Records. Deleted Dec '88. Catalogue no: **OG 9392**

Stretcheads

BROS ARE PISH
Tracks: / Bros are pish / I should be so lucky / Confront / Headache / Everything's going to break in a minute / Worry.
7" Pic: Released Nov '88, on Moksha, by Moksha Records. Catalogue no: **SOMA 5**

Strike 1

CAN'T TOUCH ME ANYMORE
Tracks: / Can't touch me anymore / Don't mix me any more.
12" Single: Released Jun '83, on Elite Records, by Elite Records. Deleted '86. Catalogue no: **DAZZ 22**

Strikers

BODY MUSIC
Tracks: / Body music.
7" Single: Released Jun '81, on Epic, by CBS Records. Deleted '84. Catalogue no: **EPC A 1290**
12" Single: Released Jun '81, on Epic, by CBS Records. Deleted '84. Catalogue no: **EPC A13 1290**

CONTAGIOUS
Tracks: / Contagious.
7" Single: Released Nov '82, on Prelude, Deleted Nov '85. Catalogue no: **PRLA 2970**
12" Single: Released Nov '82, on Prelude, Deleted Nov '85. Catalogue no: **PRLA 122970**

INCH BY INCH
Tracks: / Inch by inch.
7" Single: Released Oct '81, on Epic, by CBS Records. Deleted Oct '84. Catalogue no: **EPCA 1628**
12" Single: Released Oct '81, on Epic, by CBS Records. Deleted Oct '84. Catalogue no: **EPCA 131628**

String A Longs

WHEELS
Tracks: / Wheels.
7" Single: Released Feb '61, on London-American, Deleted '64. Catalogue no: **HLU 9278**

Stringer

THAT'S WHEN THE CRYING STARTS
Tracks: / That's when the crying starts.
7" Single: Released Oct '82, on Arrival, by Blaylock Management Ltd.. Deleted '86. Catalogue no: **PIK 9**

Strings

YUM YUM
Tracks: / Yum yum.
7" EP: Released Dec '82, on Parsley (Belgium), Catalogue no: **PP 023**

Striplin, Sylvia

GIVE ME YOUR LOVE
Tracks: / Give me your love / Give me your love (alternative mix) / You can't turn me away.
12" Single: Released Oct '86, on Music Of Love, Catalogue no: **MOLS 8**
12" Single: Released Feb '81, on Champagne (USA), by Goldbond Recording (USA). Deleted Feb '84. Catalogue no: **FIZY 504**
7" Single: Released Feb '81, on Champagne (USA), by Goldbond Recording (USA). Deleted Feb '84. Catalogue no: **FIZZ 504**

GOING HOME
Tracks: / Going home.
7" Single: Released May '89, on Dancefloor, Catalogue no: **DFT 1211**

YOU CAN'T TURN ME AWAY
Tracks: / You can't turn me away.
12" Single: Released Nov '87, on UMD (USA), Catalogue no: **UMD 7001**

Strizzi Rizzi

DRESSED UP LIKE ANIMALS
Tracks: / Dressed up like animals.
12" Single: Released Dec '85, on Organik, Catalogue no: **ORG 85/2**

Stroke

REVENGE
Tracks: / Revenge / Steven Steven.
7" Single: Released Oct '80, on CBS, by CBS Records. Deleted Oct '83. Catalogue no: **CBS 9018**

SILLY MISTAKES
Tracks: / Silly mistakes / Ina small cafe.
7" Single: Released Apr '81, on CBS, by CBS Records. Deleted '85. Catalogue no: **A 1058**

Strollers

WE SAY YEAH
Tracks: / We say yeah! / Please baby please.
7" Single: Released Aug '82, on Magnum Force, by Magnum Music Group. Catalogue no: **MFS 003**

Strong, John

LOVER IN DISGRACE
Tracks: / Lover in disgrace.
7" Single: Released May '85, on Flying, by Flying Records. Catalogue no: **FLY 11**

Strong, Rob

FAREWELL TO HARLEM
Tracks: / Farewell to Harlem.
7" Single: Released Sep '81, on Strong, Catalogue no: **WR 2**

Strongman, Jay

EAST WEST
7" Single: Released Oct '88, on Rhythm King, by Mute Records. Catalogue no: **LEFT 029**
12" Single: Released 16 Jan '89, on Rhythm King, by Mute Records. Catalogue no: **LEFTL 029**
12" Single: Released Oct '88, on Rhythm King, by Mute Records. Catalogue no: **LEFT 029T**

Strontium 90

ON THE MOVE
Tracks: / On the move.
12" Single: Released Jan '89, on G-Force, Catalogue no: **T 100T**

Struggle

NO STRONGER MUSIC
Tracks: / No stronger music.
12" Single: Released Jul '82, on Regal, Catalogue no: **RD 013**

ROCKY MUSIC (Sly & Robbie)
Tracks: / Rocky music.
12" Single: Released Oct '83, on Taxi (2), by Island Records. Catalogue no: **IPR 2063**

SILENT BASHERS
Tracks: / Silent bashers.
7" Single: Released Oct '83, on Volcana, Catalogue no: **DSR 0305**

Strummer, Joe

GANGSTERVILLE
Tracks: / Gangsterville / Jewellers and bums (On all versions.) / Punk rock blues / Don't tango with Django (On CD single only.) / Passport to Detroit (On gatefold EP only.).
12" Single: Released 14 Aug '89, on Epic, by CBS Records. Catalogue no: **STRUM T1**
CD 5": Released 14 Aug '89, on Epic, by CBS Records. Catalogue no: **STRUM C1**
Cassingle: Released 21 Aug '89, on Epic, by CBS Records. Catalogue no: **STRUM M1**
7" Single: Released 14 Aug '89, on Epic, by CBS Records. Catalogue no: **STRUM 1**
7" EP: Released 21 Aug '89, on Epic, by CBS Records. Catalogue no: **STRUM G1**

ISLAND HOPPING
Tracks: / Island hopping / Cholo vest / Mango street / Baby O'Boogie.
7" Single: Released Oct '89, on Epic, by CBS Records. Catalogue no: **STRUM 2**
CD 5": Released Oct '89, on Epic, by CBS Records. Catalogue no: **STRUM C2**
12" Single: Released Oct '89, on Epic, by CBS Records. Catalogue no: **STRUM T2**

LOVE KILLS
Tracks: / Love kills / Dum dum club.
7" Single: Released Jul '86, on CBS, by CBS Records. Catalogue no: **A 7244**
12" Single: Released Jul '86, on CBS, by CBS Records. Catalogue no: **TA 7244**

TRASH CITY
Tracks: / Trash city / Permanent record, Theme from / Nefertiti rock.
CD 5": Released 6 Jun '88, on Epic, by CBS Records. Deleted Jan '89. Catalogue no: **TRASH C1**
7" Single: Released 20 Jun '88, on Epic, by CBS Records. Deleted Jan '89. Catalogue no: **TRASH P1**
7" Single: Released 6 Jun '88, on Epic, by CBS Records. Deleted Jan '89. Catalogue no: **TRASH 1**
12" Single: Released 6 Jun '88, on Epic, by CBS Records. Deleted Jan '89. Catalogue no: **TRASH T1**

Strutz

START
Tracks: / Start.
7" Single: Released Feb '82, on Fast Products, by Fast Product Records. Deleted '87. Catalogue no: **BRAW 1**

Stryker, Scott

LESS THAN LOVERS, MORE THAN FRIENDS
Tracks: / Less than lovers... / Less than lovers... (inst).
12" Single: Released 23 May '87, on Nightmare, by Nightmare Records. Catalogue no: **MARE 24**
7" Single: Released 23 May '87, on Nightmare, by Nightmare Records. Catalogue no: **MARES 24**

Stryper

ALWAYS THERE FOR YOU
Tracks: / Always there for you (on all versions) / In God we trust (NOT on CD) / Soldiers under command (On 12" only) / Reign, The (On CD only) / Soldiers under command (live) (On CD only) / Robert Sweet interview-part one (On CD only).
CD 5": Released '88, on Enigma, by Enigma Records (USA). Catalogue no: **ENVCD 1**
7" Pic: Released Sep '88, on Enigma, by Enigma Records (USA). Deleted '89. Catalogue no: **ENCS 1**
7" Single: Released '88, on Enigma, by Enigma Records (USA). Catalogue no: **ENVS 1**
7" Single: Released 22 Aug '88, on Enigma, by Enigma Records (USA). Catalogue no: **ENV 1**
12" Single: Released 22 Aug '88, on Enigma, by Enigma Records (USA). Catalogue

no: **ENVT 1**

ALWAYS THERE FOR YOU (IMPORT)
Tracks: / Always there for you / In God we trust / Soldiers under command (live).
12" Single: Released Oct '88, on Enigma, by Enigma Records (USA). Catalogue no: **V 75509**

CALLING ON YOU
Tracks: / Calling on you.
7" Single: Released Apr '87, on Music For Nations, by Music For Nations Records. Catalogue no: **KUT 126**
12" Single: Released Apr '87, on Music For Nations, by Music For Nations Records. Catalogue no: **12 KUT 126**

WINTER WONDERLAND
Tracks: / Winter wonderland.
7" Single: Released Nov '85, on Enigma, by Enigma Records (USA). Catalogue no: **STRY 1**

Stuart, Bridgette

KEEP AN EYE ON YOU
Tracks: / Keep an eye on you.
12" Single: Released Apr '82, on SS Music, Catalogue no: **SSMD 021**

Stuart, Chad

YESTERDAY'S GONE
Tracks: / Yesterday's gone.
7" Single: Released Nov '63, on ember, Deleted '66. Catalogue no: **EMBS 180**

Stuart, Gene

FORTY AND FADING
Tracks: / Forty and fading.
7" Single: Released '88, on Ritz, by Ritz Records. Catalogue no: **RITZ 136**

Stuart, John

SUMMER BREEZE
Tracks: / Summer breeze / Black and blue.
12" Single: Released Aug '87, on Fon, by FON Records. Catalogue no: **FON 11T**
7" Single: Released Jul '87, on Fon, by FON Records. Catalogue no: **FON 11**

Stud Puppet

JOY (SO KEEP IT UP)
Tracks: / Joy (so keep it up).
12" Single: Released Apr '89, on Anagram, by Cherry Red Records. Catalogue no: **12 ANAD 47**

Student Fashion

BOYS & GIRLS AT THE UNIVERSITY
Tracks: / Boys & girls at the university.
7" Single: Released Oct '88, on Subway, by Subway Records. Catalogue no: **SUB 040-7**
12" Single: Released Oct '88, on Subway, by Subway Records. Catalogue no: **SUB 040**

Studio Two

DEVEL AND DEVIL BLUE SEA
Tracks: / Devel and devil blue sea.
7" Single: Released Jul '82, on Albion, by Albion Records. Catalogue no: **ION 1035**

Studioz

I SAW HER STANDING THERE
Tracks: / I saw her standing there.
7" Single: Released '82, on Warm, by Warm Records. Catalogue no: **AWWR 2019**

Stuff The Neighbours

STUFF THE NEIGHBOURS, PLAY IT LOUD
7" Single: Released Sep '84, on Cause For Concern, Catalogue no: **CFCEP 1**

Stump

BUFFALO
Tracks: / Buffalo / Song remains, The.
12" Single: Released Nov '88, on Ensign, by Ensign Records. Catalogue no: **ENYX 619**
7" Single: Released Nov '88, on Ensign, by Ensign Records. Catalogue no: **ENY 619**

CHAOS
Tracks: / Chaos / Ice the levant / Safe sex (track on 12" only.).
7" Single: Released Feb '88, on Ensign, by Ensign Records. Catalogue no: **ENY 612**
12" Single: Released Feb '88, on Ensign, by Ensign Records. Catalogue no: **ENYX 612**

CHARLTON HESTON
Tracks: / Charlton Heston.
7" Single: Released Jun '88, on Ensign, by Ensign Records. Catalogue no: **ENY 614**
12" Single: Released Jun '88, on Ensign, by Ensign Records. Catalogue no: **ENYX 614**

GRAB HANDS EP
12" Single: Released Mar '86, on Ron Johnson, by Ron Johnson Records. Catalogue no: **ZRON 6**

PEEL SESSIONS:STUMP 5.2.86
12" Single: Released Jan '87, on Strange Fruit, by Strange Fruit Records. Catalogue no: **SFPS 019**

Stunt Kites

HAIL TO THE ROOTS
Tracks: / Hail to the roots.
7" Single: Released Oct '83, on Criminal Damage, Catalogue no: **CRI 102**

LEBENSTRAUM
Tracks: / Lebenstraum.
7" Single: Released Nov '81, on Pax, by Pax Records. Catalogue no: **PAX 3**

LEONARA
Tracks: / Leonara / Hail.
7" Single: Released Feb '83, on Criminal Damage, Catalogue no: **CRL 101**

Stupids

FRANKFURTER
Tracks: / Frankfurter.
12" Single: Released Aug '87, on Vinyl Solution, by Vinyl Solution Records. Catalogue no: **FART 1**

PEEL SESSIONS:STUPIDS
12" Single: Released Sep '88, on Strange Fruit, by Strange Fruit Records. Catalogue no: **SFPS 054**

VAN STUPID
Special: Released May '87, on Vinyl Solution, by Vinyl Solution Records. Catalogue no: **SOL 2**

VIOLENT NUN
Tracks: / Violent nun.
7" Single: Released Mar '85, on Children Of The Revolution, by Revolver Records. Catalogue no: **COR 3**

Sturm Und Drang

RIVER
Tracks: / River.
12" Single: Released Mar '86, on Torso, by Torso Records. Catalogue no: **TORSO 12012**

Stutter, Marvin

GOING SOFA
Tracks: / Going sofa.
7" Single: Released Feb '87, on Ritz, by Ritz Records. Catalogue no: **RITZ 170**

Stutz Bear Cats

2 4 6 8 99
Tracks: / 2 4 6 8 99.
7" Single: Released Jun '84, on PRT, by Castle Communications Records. Catalogue no: **7P 311**

RUNNING IN THE NIGHT
Tracks: / Running in the night / Love situation.
7" Single: Released May '85, on PRT, by Castle Communications Records. Catalogue no: **7P 327**
12" Single: Released May '85, on PRT, by Castle Communications Records. Catalogue no: **12P 327**

SONG THAT I SING (SINGLE)
Tracks: / Song that I sing, The.
7" Single: Released Aug '87, on Multi-Media, Catalogue no: **MMT 112**
7" Single: Released Apr '82, on Multi-Media, Deleted '85. Catalogue no: **MMT 6**

Style

BUBBLE
Tracks: / Bubble / One one team in London.
7" Single: Released Dec '81, on West Ham FC, Catalogue no: **WHUFC 001**

IT'S A SECRET
Tracks: / New world / It's a secret / Te quiero.
7" Single: Released 20 Feb '89, on Epic, by CBS Records. Deleted 10 Jul '89. Catalogue no: **653 058-7**
12" Single: Released 20 Feb '89, on Epic, by CBS Records. Deleted 10 Jul '89. Catalogue no: **653 058-8**

WE'LL MEET AGAIN
Tracks: / We'll meet again.
7" Single: Released Oct '82, on Fatal, by White Bell Records. Catalogue no: **FATAL 1**

Style Council

AGENT 88 (EP)
Tracks: / Mick's up / Party chambers / Mick's blessings / Mick's company.
CD 5": Released Dec '87, on Polydor, by Polydor Ltd. Catalogue no: **TSCCD 103**
7" EP: Released Dec '87, on Polydor, by Polydor Ltd. Catalogue no: **TSCEP 3**

BIRDS & THE B'S, THE (EP)
Tracks: / Piccadilly trail / It just came to pieces in my hands / Spin drifting / Spring Summer Autumn.
7" EP: Released Dec '87, on Polydor, by Polydor Ltd. Catalogue no: **TSCEP 2**
CD 5": Released Dec '87, on Polydor, by Polydor Ltd. Catalogue no: **TSCCD 102**

CAFE BLEU (EP)
Tracks: / Headstart for happiness / Here's one that got away / Blue cafe / Strength of your nature.
CD 5": Released Dec '87, on Polydor, by Polydor Ltd. Catalogue no: **TSCCD 101**
7" EP: Released Dec '87, on Polydor, by Polydor Ltd. Deleted 30 May '89. Catalogue no: **TSCEP 1**

COME TO MILTON KEYNES
Tracks: / Come to Milton Keynes.
7" Single: Released Jun '85, on Polydor, by Polydor Ltd. Catalogue no: **TSC 9**
7" Set: Released Jun '85, on Polydor, by Polydor Ltd. Deleted Mar '87. Catalogue no: **TSCG 9**
12" Single: Released Jun '85, on Polydor, by Polydor Ltd. Catalogue no: **TSCX 9**

GROOVIN' (YOU'RE THE BEST THING)
Tracks: / Groovin'.
7" Single: Released May '84, on Polydor, by Polydor Ltd. Deleted '87. Catalogue no: **TSC 6**

HAVE YOU EVER HAD IT BLUE
Tracks: / Have you ever had it blue.
12" Single: Released Mar '86, on Polydor, by Polydor Ltd. Deleted Aug '87. Catalogue no: **CINEX 112**
Cassingle: on Polydor, by Polydor Ltd. Deleted Aug '87. Catalogue no: **CINEC 1**
7" Single: Released Mar '86, on Polydor, by Polydor Ltd. Deleted Mar '87. Catalogue no: **CINE 1**

HOW SHE THREW IT ALL AWAY
Tracks: / How she threw it all away / In love for the first time / Long hot summer (Available on 12" and CD only) / I do like to B side the A side (Available on 12" and CD only).
12" Single: Released 11 Jul '88, on Polydor, by Polydor Ltd. Catalogue no: **TSCX 16**
7" Single: Released 11 Jul '88, on Polydor, by Polydor Ltd. Deleted 30 May '89. Catalogue no: **TSC 16**
CD 5": Released 11 Jul '88, on Polydor, by Polydor Ltd. Catalogue no: **TSCCD 16**

IT DIDN'T MATTER
Tracks: / All year round / It didn't matter.
12" Single: Released Jan '87, on Polydor, by Polydor Ltd. Deleted Aug '87. Catalogue no: **TSCX 12**
7" Single: Released Jan '87, on Polydor, by Polydor Ltd. Deleted Aug '87. Catalogue no: **TSC 12**

LIFE AT A TOP PEOPLES HEALTH FARM
Tracks: / Sweet loving ways / Spank (Live at a top peoples health club) (Available on only 12" version and C.D. single) / Life at a top peoples health farm / Life at a top peoples health farm (Um & Argh Mix) (Only available on 12" version and C.D single).
Note: "The all new single from The Style Council, 'Health farm' marks the first instalment of the 88 campaign - 'Confessions of a Pop Group'. Life at a top peoples health farm comes in three formats complete with alternative mixes of the lead track, all dressed in deluxe packaging. Sweet Loving Ways will not be on the forthcoming album.
CD 5": Released May '88, on Polydor, by Polydor Ltd. Catalogue no: **TSCCD 15**
7" Single: Released May '88, on Polydor, by Polydor Ltd. Deleted 30 May '89. Catalogue no: **TSC 15**
12" Single: Released May '88, on Polydor, by Polydor Ltd. Deleted 30 May '89. Catalogue no: **TSCX 15**

LODGERS, THE
Tracks: / Lodgers, The.
12" Single: Released Sep '85, on Polydor, by Polydor Ltd. Deleted Mar '87. Catalogue no: **TSCX 10**
7" Single: Released Sep '85, on Polydor, by Polydor Ltd. Catalogue no: **TSC 10**
7" Set: Released Sep '85, on Polydor, by Polydor Ltd. Deleted Aug '87. Catalogue no: **TSCDP 10**

LONG HOT SUMMER
Tracks: / Long hot summer.
12" Single: Released Aug '83, on Polydor, by Polydor Ltd. Catalogue no: **TSCX 3**
7" Single: Released Aug '83, on Polydor, by Polydor Ltd. Catalogue no: **TSC 3**

LONG, HOT SUMMER - '89 REMIX
Tracks: / Long hot summer - '89 remix.
7" Single: Released 22 May '89, on Polydor, by Polydor Ltd. Catalogue no: **LHS 1**
12" Single: Released 22 May '89, on Polydor, by Polydor Ltd. Catalogue no: **LHSX 1**
CD 5": Released 22 May '89, on Polydor, by Polydor Ltd. Catalogue no: **LHSCD 1**

MONEY GO ROUND
Tracks: / Money go round.
12" Single: Released May '83, on Polydor, by Polydor Ltd. Catalogue no: **TSCX 2**
7" Single: Released May '83, on Polydor, by Polydor Ltd. Catalogue no: **TSC 2**

MY EVER CHANGING MOODS
Tracks: / Ever changing moods.
12" Single: Released Feb '84, on Polydor, by Polydor Ltd. Catalogue no: **TSCX 5**
7" Single: Released Feb '84, on Polydor, by Polydor Ltd. Deleted 30 May '89. Catalogue no: **TSC 5**

PROMISED LAND
Tracks: / Promised land / Can you still love me.
12" Single: Released 20 Feb '89, on Polydor, by Polydor Ltd. Deleted Oct '89. Catalogue no: **TSCXS 17**
7" Single: Released 6 Feb '89, on Polydor, by Polydor Ltd. Deleted Oct '89. Catalogue no: **TSC 17**
7" Single: Released 13 Feb '89, on Polydor, by Polydor Ltd. Deleted Oct '89. Catalogue no: **TSCB 17**
CD 5": Released 6 Feb '89, on Polydor, by Polydor Ltd. Catalogue no: **TSCCD 17**
12" Single: Released 6 Feb '89, on Polydor, by Polydor Ltd. Catalogue no: **TSCX 17**

SHOUT TO THE TOP
Tracks: / Shout to the top.
7" Single: Released Sep '84, on Polydor, by Polydor Ltd. Deleted 30 May '89. Catalogue no: **TSC 7**

SOLID BOND IN YOUR HEART
Tracks: / Solid bond in your heart, A.
7" Single: Released Nov '83, on Polydor, by Polydor Ltd. Deleted '86. Catalogue no: **TSC 4**

SPEAK LIKE A CHILD
Tracks: / Speak like a child.
7" Single: Released Mar '83, on Polydor, by Polydor Ltd. Deleted Aug '87. Catalogue no: **TSC 1**

WAITING
Tracks: / Waiting / Francoise / Jerusalem, Theme from (extra track on 12" only).
12" Single: Released Feb '87, on Polydor, by Polydor Ltd. Deleted Aug '87. Catalogue no: **TSCX 13**
7" Single: Released Feb '87, on Polydor, by Polydor Ltd. Deleted Aug '87. Catalogue no: **TSC 13**

WALLS COME TUMBLING DOWN
Tracks: / Walls come tumbling down.
7" Single: Released Apr '85, on Polydor, by Polydor Ltd. Catalogue no: **TSC 8**
12" Single: Released Apr '85, on Polydor, by Polydor Ltd. Catalogue no: **TSCX 8**

WANTED
Tracks: / Wanted / Cost of loving, The.
Cassingle: Released Oct '87, on Polydor, by Polydor Ltd. Catalogue no: **TSCCS 14**
7" Single: Released Oct '87, on Polydor, by Polydor Ltd. Deleted 30 May '89. Catalogue no: **TSC 14**
12" Single: Released Oct '87, on Polydor, by Polydor Ltd. Deleted 30 May '89. Catalogue no: **TSCX 14**

YOU'RE THE BEST THING
Tracks: / You're the best thing / Big boss groove.
7" Single: Released May '84, on Polydor, by Polydor Ltd. Deleted 30 May '89. Catalogue no: **TSC 6**
12" Single: Released May '84, on Polydor, by Polydor Ltd. Catalogue no: **TSCX 6**

Style X

NO SECRET AFFAIR
Tracks: / No secret affair / No secret affair (part 2).
12" Single: Released Oct '81, on Rygel, Catalogue no: **RYG 1**

Styler

OB LA DI OB LA DA
Tracks: / Ob la di ob la da / Ob la di ob la da (away version).
7" Single: Released Nov '86, on Seara, Catalogue no: **SEA 007**

Stylistics

16 BARS
Tracks: / 16 bars.
7" Single: Released Aug '76, on H & L (USA), by Amherst Records Inc (USA). Deleted '79. Catalogue no: **6105 059**

7000 DOLLARS AND YOU
Tracks: / 7000 dollars and you.
7" Single: Released Mar '77, on H & L (USA), by Amherst Records Inc (USA). Deleted '80. Catalogue no: **6105 073**

BETCHA BY GOLLY WOW
Tracks: / Betcha by golly wow.
7" Single: Released Jun '72, on Avco-Embassy, Deleted '75. Catalogue no: **6105 011**

BREAK UP TO MAKE UP
Tracks: / Break up to make up.
7" Single: Released Mar '73, on Avco-Embassy, Deleted '76. Catalogue no: **6105 020**

CAN'T GIVE YOU ANYTHING (BUT MY LOVE)
Tracks: / Can't give you anything (but my love).
7" Single: Released Jul '75, on Avco-Embassy, Deleted '78. Catalogue no: **6105 039**

CAN'T HELP FALLING IN LOVE
Tracks: / Can't help falling in love.
7" Single: Released Apr '76, on Avco-Embassy, Deleted '79. Catalogue no: **6105 050**

FUNKY WEEKEND
Tracks: / Funky weekend.
7" Single: Released Feb '76, on Avco-Embassy, Deleted '79. Catalogue no: **6105 044**

HURRY UP THIS WAY AGAIN (SINGLE)
Tracks: / Hurry up this way again / It started out.
7" Single: Released Sep '80, on Philadelphia Int., by EMI Records. Deleted '83. Catalogue no: **PIR 8907**

I'M STONE IN LOVE WITH YOU
Tracks: / I'm stone in love with you.
7" Single: Released Nov '72, on Avco-Embassy, Deleted '75. Catalogue no: **6105 015**

I'M STONE IN LOVE WITH YOU (OLD GOLD)
Tracks: / I'm still in love with you.
7" Single: Released Sep '85, on Old Gold, by Old Gold Records. Catalogue no: **OG 9568**

LET'S PUT IT ALL TOGETHER (SINGLE)
Tracks: / Let's put it all together.
7" Single: Released Oct '74, on Avco-Embassy, Deleted '77. Catalogue no: **6105 032**

LOVE IS NOT THE ANSWER
Tracks: / Love is not the answer.
7" Single: Released Jul '85, on Virgin, by Virgin Records. Deleted '89. Catalogue no: **VS 793**
12" Single: Released Jul '85, on Virgin, by Virgin Records. Deleted '89. Catalogue no: **VS 793-12**

NA NA IS THE SADDEST WORD
Tracks: / Na na is the saddest word.
7" Single: Released Nov '75, on Avco-Embassy, Deleted '78. Catalogue no: **6105 041**

PEEK A BOO
Tracks: / Peek-a-boo.
7" Single: Released Jun '73, on Avco-Embassy, Deleted '76. Catalogue no: **6105 023**

ROCKIN' ROLL BABY (SINGLE)
Tracks: / Rockin' roll baby.
7" Single: Released Jan '74, on Avco-Embassy, Deleted '77. Catalogue no: **6105 026**

SING BABY SING
Tracks: / Sing baby sing.
7" Single: Released May '75, on Avco-Embassy, Deleted '78. Catalogue no: **6105 036**

STAR ON A TV SHOW
Tracks: / Star on a TV show.
7" Single: Released Jan '75, on Avco-Embassy, Deleted '78. Catalogue no: **6105 035**

YOU MAKE ME FEEL BRAND NEW
Tracks: / You make me feel brand new.
7" Single: Released Jul '74, on Avco-Embassy, Deleted '77. Catalogue no: **6105 028**

YOU MAKE ME FEEL BRAND NEW (OLD GOLD)
Tracks: / You make me feel brand new.
7" Single: Released Jul '82, on Old Gold, by Old Gold Records. Catalogue no: **OG 9248**

YOU'LL NEVER GET TO HEAVEN
Tracks: / You'll never get to heaven / Country living / You are beautiful / Miracle, The.
7" EP: Released Nov '76, on H & L (USA), by Amherst Records Inc (USA). Deleted '79. Catalogue no: **STYL 001**

Styngrites

NIGHT CRUISING
Tracks: / Night cruising.
12" Single: Released Jul '88, on DDT, by D.D.T.Records. Catalogue no: **DISP 16T**

Styrene, Poly

GODS & GODESSES
Tracks: / Gods and godesses.
7" Single: Released Aug '86, on Awesome Records, by Awesome Records. Catalogue no: **AOR 7**
12" Single: Released Aug '86, on Awesome Records, by Awesome Records. Catalogue no: **AOR 7T**

Styx

BABE
7" Single: Released Jan '80, on A&M, by A&M Records. Deleted '83. Catalogue no: **AMS 7489**
7" Single: Released Sep '85, on Old Gold, by Old Gold Records. Catalogue no: **OG 9545**
12" Single: Released Jan '87, on Old Gold, by Old Gold Records. Catalogue no: **OG 4013**

BEST OF TIMES, THE
Tracks: / Best of times, The / Lights.
7" Single: Released Jan '81, on A&M, by

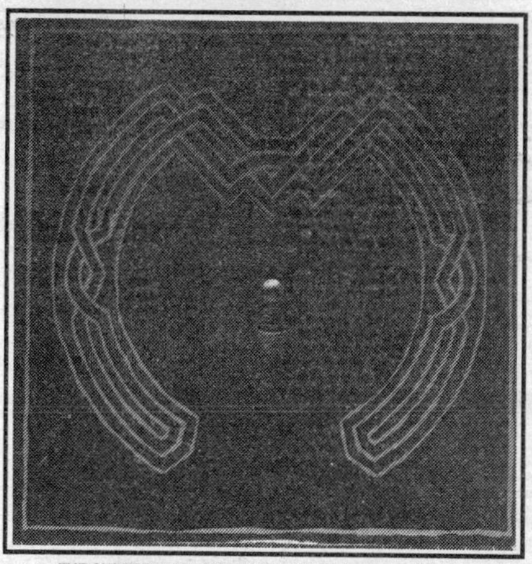

THE SUBTERRANEANS - MAXI JOY (Released on Mother)

A&M Records. Deleted '84. Catalogue no: **AMS 8102**

COMPACT HITS: STYX
Tracks: / Babe / Come sail away / Rockin' the paradise / Best of times, The.
CD 5": Released Apr '88, on A&M, by A&M Records. Deleted Feb '89. Catalogue no: **AMCD 904**

DON'T LET IT END
Tracks: / Don't let it end.
7" Single: Released Jun '83, on A&M, by A&M Records. Deleted '86. Catalogue no: **AM 120**

LIGHTS
Tracks: / Lights / Renegade / Light up (on 12" only).
7" Single: Released Jun '80, on A&M, by A&M Records. Deleted Jun '83. Catalogue no: **AMS 7528**
12" Single: Released Jun '80, on A&M, by A&M Records. Deleted Jun '83. Catalogue no: **AMSP 7528**

ROCKIN' THE PARADISE
Tracks: / Rockin' the paradise / Snow blind.
7" Single: Released Nov '81, on A&M, by A&M Records. Deleted Nov '84. Catalogue no: **AMS 8175**

TOO MUCH TIME ON MY HANDS
Tracks: / Too much time on my hands / Queen of spades.
7" Single: Released Mar '81, on A&M, by A&M Records. Deleted Mar '84. Catalogue no: **AMS 8118**

Suave

MY GIRL
Tracks: / My girl (club mix) (12" only) / My girl (edit) / My girl (a capella).
7" Single: Released 16 May '88, on Capitol, by EMI Records. Deleted Nov '88. Catalogue no: **CL 491**
12" Single: Released 16 May '88, on Capitol, by EMI Records. Deleted Nov '88. Catalogue no: **12CLX 491**
12" Single: Released 16 May '88, on Capitol, by EMI Records. Deleted Nov '88. Catalogue no: **12CL 491**

Sub Culture

LOUD AND CLEAR
Tracks: / Loud and clear / Rogue trooper / University city.
7" Single: Released Dec '83, on Essential, Catalogue no: **ESS 002**

Sub Muris

HONESTY
Tracks: / Honesty / Open doors.
7" Single: Released Dec '83, on Dog Rock, by Dog Rock Records. Catalogue no: **SD 104**

Sub Zero

OUT OF THE BLUE
Tracks: / Out of the blue / Too many nine to fives.
7" Single: Released Apr '84, on Sub-Zero Music, by Sub-Zero Music. Catalogue no: **SZM 02**

Subhumans

DEMOLITION WAR
Tracks: / Demolition war.
7" Single: Released Nov '81, on Spiderleg, Catalogue no: **SOB 1**
7" Single: on Bluurg, by Southern Studios Ltd.. Catalogue no: **XEP 1**

EVOLUTION
Tracks: / Evolution.
7" Single: Released Jun '83, on Bluurg, by Southern Studios Ltd.. Catalogue no: **FISH 2**

RATS
Tracks: / Rats.
7" Single: Released Dec '84, on Bluurg, by Southern Studios Ltd.. Catalogue no: **FISH 10**

REASONS FOR EXISTANCE
Tracks: / Reasons for existance.
7" Single: on Bluurg, by Southern Studios Ltd.. Catalogue no: **XEP 2**
7" Single: Released Apr '82, on Spiderleg, Catalogue no: **SDL 5**

RELIGIOUS WARS
Tracks: / Religious wars.
7" Single: Released Aug '82, on Spiderleg, Catalogue no: **SDL 7**
7" Single: on Bluurg, by Southern Studios Ltd.. Catalogue no: **XEP 3**

TIME FLIES BUT AEROPLANES CRASH
Tracks: / Time flies but aeroplanes crash.
7" Single: Released Nov '83, on Bluurg, by Southern Studios Ltd.. Catalogue no: **FISH 5**

Submarines

GREY SKIES BLUES
Tracks: / Grey skies blues.
7" Single: Released Jan '87, on Head, Catalogue no: **HEAD 4**

Subterraneans

MAXI JOY (see panel above)
Tracks: / Maxi joy / Slumb / Heading for the light (Available on 12" only).
12" Single: Released Nov '87, on Mother, by Mother Records. Catalogue no: **12 MUM 8**
7" Single: Released Nov '87, on Mother, by Mother Records. Catalogue no: **MUM 8**

MY FLAMINGO
Tracks: / My flamingo.
7" Single: Released Feb '81, on Demon, by Demon Records. Deleted '88. Catalogue no: **D 1001**

SLUM
Tracks: / Slum / Maxi joy / Heading for the light (Available on 12" only).
Note: * = Extra track on 12" only
7" Single: Released Apr '87, on Mother, by Mother Records. Catalogue no: **MUM 6**
12" Single: Released Apr '87, on Mother, by Mother Records. Catalogue no: **12 MUM 6**

Subtonics

TAKE IT EASY FLORENCE
Tracks: / Take it easy Florence / Nothing to lose.
7" Single: Released Jul '87, on Life of Man, Catalogue no: **LOM 001**

Suburban Boys

COMMUMIX
Tracks: / Commumix.
7" Single: Released Apr '88, on Extra, Catalogue no: **XTRA 8**
12" Single: Released Apr '88, on Extra, Catalogue no: **12XTRA 8**

Suburban Knight

GROOVE, THE
Tracks: / Groove.
12" Single: Released Oct '87, on Transmat (USA), Catalogue no: **MS 003**

Subway Sect

AMBITION
Tracks: / Ambition.
7" Single: Released Jan '79, on Rough Trade, by Rough Trade Records. Catalogue no: **RT 007**

Success Allstars

CHRISTMAS RUSH
Tracks: / Christmas rush.
12" Single: Released Dec '83, on Success (2), Catalogue no: **SSCD 175**

Suck

BILLION DOLLARS
Tracks: / Billion dollars.
12" Single: Released Oct '89, on Attica, by Attica Records. Catalogue no: **ATT 008**

SUCK Various artists
12" Single: Released Oct '88, on Attica, by Attica Records. Catalogue no: **ATT 005**

Sudatan Creche

KINDERGARTEN
Tracks: / Kindergarten.
12" Single: Released Jul '83, on Illuminated, Catalogue no: **ILL 1712**

Sudden Afternoon

ACID RAIN
Tracks: / Acid Rain / Red sun / City of night dreams / Die neue ahnung.
12" Single: Released Oct '86, on Midnight Music, by Midnight Music Records. Catalogue no: **DONG 27**

DANCING SHADOWS
Tracks: / Dancing shadows.
12" Single: Released Nov '85, on Midnight Music, by Midnight Music Records. Catalogue no: **CHIME 016**

INDUSTY & NATURE
Tracks: / Industry and nature.
12" Single: Released Sep '85, on Midnight Music, by Midnight Music Records. Catalogue no: **DONG 16**

Sudden, Nikki

BACK TO THE START
Tracks: / Back to the start.
7" Single: Released Jun '81, on Rather, by Rather Records. Catalogue no: **EAR 11**

CHANNEL STEAMER
Tracks: / Channel steamer / Chelsea embankment.
7" Single: Released Apr '82, on Abstract, by Abstract Sounds. Catalogue no: **ABS 009**

LAST BANDIT, THE
Tracks: / Last bandit.
7" Single: Released Sep '86, on Creation, by Creation Records. Deleted Jul '88. Catalogue no: **CRE 033**
12" Single: Released Sep '86, on Creation, by Creation Records. Deleted Jul '88. Catalogue no: **CRE 033T**

LUNACY IS LEGEND EP
12" Single: Released Jun '87, on Barracuda, Catalogue no: **12 UTA 9**

SHAME OF THE ANGELS, THE
Tracks: / Shame of the angels, The.
7" Single: Released Sep '84, on Pawnhearts, Catalogue no: **1747 01**

WEDDING HOTEL
Tracks: / Wedding hotel.
12" Single: Released Aug '87, on Creation, by Creation Records. Catalogue no: **CRE 040T**
7" Single: Released Aug '87, on Creation, by Creation Records. Catalogue no: **CRE 040**

Sudden Sway

JOB LOT OFFER
Tracks: / Job lot offer.
7" Single: Released Jan '87, on Rough Trade, by Rough Trade Records. Catalogue no: **RT 183**

PEEL SESSIONS: SUDDEN SWAY

12" Single: Released Sep '86, on Strange Fruit, by Strange Fruit Records. Catalogue no: **SFPS 005**
Cassingle: Released 13 Jun '87, on Strange Fruit, by Strange Fruit Records. Catalogue no: **SFPSC 005**

SAT'DAY MORNIN' EPISODE
Tracks: / Sat'day mornin' episode.
12" Single: Released Jul '87, on Rough Trade, by Rough Trade Records. Catalogue no: **RTT 213**

SINGASONG
Tracks: / Singasong.
12" Single: Released Apr '86, on Blanco Y Negro, by Blanco Y Negro Records. Catalogue no: **NEG 18V5**
7" Single: Released Apr '86, on Blanco Y Negro, by Blanco Y Negro Records. Catalogue no: **NEG 18V1**

TO YOU WITH REGARD
Tracks: / To you with regard.
7" Single: Released Aug '81, on Chant, Catalogue no: **TAKE 3**

Sue Ann

PLEASURE
Tracks: / Pleasure.
7" Single: Released May '89, on MCA, by MCA Records. Catalogue no: **MCA 23946**

Sue Instrumentals

SUE INSTRUMENTALS
7" EP: Released Oct '83, on Ensign, by Ensign Records. Deleted '84. Catalogue no: **ENS 6**

Suede Crocodiles

STOP THAT TRAIN
Tracks: / Stop that train.
7" Single: Released Aug '83, on No Strings, Catalogue no: **NOSP 2**

Sueno Latino

SUENO LATINO
Tracks: / Sueno latino.
CD 5": Released Sep '89, on BCM Records, Catalogue no: **BCM 323 CD**
12" Single: Released Sep '89, on BCM Records, Catalogue no: **BCM 323 X**
7" Single: Released Sep '89, on BCM Records, Catalogue no: **BCM 323**

Sugar Bear

DON'T SCANDALIZE MINE
Tracks: / Don't scandalize mine.
7" Single: Released Oct '88, on Champion, by Champion Records. Deleted Aug '89. Catalogue no: **CHAMP 92**
12" Single: Released Oct '88, on Champion, by Champion Records. Deleted Aug '89. Catalogue no: **CHAMP 12 92**

DON'T SCANDALIZE MINE (IMPORT)
Tracks: / Don't scandalize mine.
7" Single: Released Nov '88, on Coslit (USA), Catalogue no: **CR 1004**

Sugar Blue

PONTIAC
Tracks: / Pontiac.
7" Single: Released Oct '80, on Blue Sound, Deleted '85. Catalogue no: **BS 3501**

Sugar Bobby

SEASONS CHANGE
Tracks: / Seasons change.
12" Single: Released Sep '89, on Kaya, Catalogue no: **DA 104**

Sugar Cane

MONTEGO BAY
Tracks: / Montego bay.
7" Single: Released Sep '78, on Ariola-Hansa, by Hansa Records. Deleted '81. Catalogue no: **AHA 524**

Sugar Cubes

BIRTHDAY
Tracks: / Birthday / Cat / Motor crash.
CD 5": Released Nov '87, on One Little Indian, by One Little Indian Records. Catalogue no: **7TP 7CD**
12" Single: Released Jul '87, on One Little Indian, by One Little Indian Records. Catalogue no: **12TP 7**

BIRTHDAY: CHRISTMAS EVE, CHRISTMAS DAY
Tracks: / Birthday: Christmas eve, Christmas day / Christmas present / Petrol (live).
12" Single: Released Aug '88, on One Little Indian, by One Little Indian Records. Catalogue no: **12TP 11 L**
7" Single: Released Aug '88, on One Little Indian, by One Little Indian Records. Catalogue no: **TP 11**

COLD SWEAT
Tracks: / Cold sweat / Dragon / Traitor (on 12" only.) / Revolution (On CD only.).
12" Single: Released Jan '88, on One Little Indian, by One Little Indian Records. Catalogue no: **12TP 9**
CD 5": Released Jan '88, on One Little Indian, by One Little Indian Records. Catalogue no: **7TP 9 CD**
7" Single: Released Jan '88, on One Little Indian, by One Little Indian Records. Catalogue no: **7TP 9**

COLD SWEAT (SINGLE)
Tracks: / Cold sweat (meat mix) / Cold sweat (inst) / Birthday (Icelandic mix) / Delicious demon.
12" Single: Released Sep '88, on Elektra (USA), by Elektra Records (USA). Catalogue no: **066746**

DEUS
Tracks: / Deus / Lugtfitar / Steel of lift (Extra track on 12") / Organic prankster (Extra track on CD single.).
7" Single: Released Apr '88, on One Little Indian, by One Little Indian Records. Catalogue no: **7TP 10**
12" Single: Released Apr '88, on One Little Indian, by One Little Indian Records. Catalogue no: **12TP 10**
CD 5": Released Apr '88, on One Little Indian, by One Little Indian Records. Catalogue no: **7TP 10CD**

MOTORCRASH
Tracks: / Motorcrash / Motorcrash (live) / Polo / Blue eyed pop.
7" EP: Released Dec '88, on Elektra (USA), by Elektra Records (USA). Catalogue no: **066 726**
CD 3": Released Dec '88, on Elektra (USA), by Elektra Records (USA). Catalogue no: **667 262**

REGINA
Tracks: / Regina.
12" Single: Released Jul '89, on One Little Indian, by One Little Indian Records. Catalogue no: **TP7 12 26**
CD 5": Released Jul '89, on One Little Indian, by One Little Indian Records. Catalogue no: **TP7 26 CD**
Cassingle: Released Jul '89, on One Little Indian, by One Little Indian Records. Catalogue no: **TP7 26 C**
7" Single: Released Jul '89, on One Little Indian, by One Little Indian Records. Catalogue no: **TP7 26**

Sugar D

BUBBLE TO ROOTS ROCK REGGAE
Tracks: / Bubble to roots rock reggae.
12" Single: Released Jul '87, on Y & D, Catalogue no: **YDDO 109**

Sugar Dog Crew

GROOVE TO GET DOWN
Tracks: / Groove to get down.
12" Single: Released Feb '89, on Temple Records, by Temple Records (2). Catalogue no: **TOPY 43**

Sugar Ray Dinkie

CABRINI GREEN RAP
Tracks: / Cabrini green rap.
12" Single: Released May '87, on Flame (1), Catalogue no: **MELT 3T**
7" Single: Released May '87, on Flame (1), Catalogue no: **MELT 3**

Sugar & Spice

DOWNTOWN
Tracks: / Downtown.
7" Single: Released Jul '88, on Hot Melt, by Hot Melt Records. Catalogue no: **7 TC 17**
12" Single: Released Jul '88, on Hot Melt, by Hot Melt Records. Catalogue no: **12 TCT 17**
12" Single: Released 8 Aug '88, on Hot Melt, by Hot Melt Records. Catalogue no: **TCT 17**

SWEET LOVING
Tracks: / Sweet loving / Lovers mood.
12" Single: Released Oct '82, on Salamo, Catalogue no: **S 001**

Sugar Star

NINE O NINE (THE BEAT IS MINE)
Tracks: / Nine o nine (The beat is mine) / Nine o nine (The beat is mine) (Version).
12" Single: Released Mar '87, on Nine O Nine, by Creole Records. Catalogue no: **NINE 1**

Sugarhill Gang

8TH WONDER
Tracks: / Funk box / On the money / 8th wonder / Showdown / Giggalo / Hot hot summer day.
7" Single: Released Apr '81, on Sugarhill (USA), Catalogue no: **SH 553**

APACHE
Tracks: / Apache.
7" Single: Released Feb '82, on Sugarhill (USA), Deleted '88. Catalogue no: **SH 109**
12" Single: Released Feb '82, on Sugarhill (USA), Catalogue no: **SHL 109**

BAD NEWS DON'T BOTHER ME
Tracks: / Bad news don't bother me / Sugarhill groove.
7" Single: Released Feb '80, on Sugarhill (USA), Deleted '88. Catalogue no: **SH 103**
12" Single: Released Feb '80, on Sugarhill (USA), Catalogue no: **SHL 103**

BE A WINNER
Tracks: / Be a winner.
12" Single: Released Apr '83, on Sugarhill (USA), Catalogue no: **SHL 124**
7" Single: Released Apr '83, on Sugarhill (USA), Deleted '88. Catalogue no: **SH 124**

HOT HOT SUMMER DAY
Tracks: / Hot hot summer day / Hot hot summer day (part 2).
7" Single: Released Aug '80, on Sugarhill (USA), Deleted '88. Catalogue no: **SH 104**
12" Single: Released Aug '80, on Sugarhill (USA), Catalogue no: **SHL 104**

KICK IT LIVE FROM 9 TILL 5
Tracks: / Kick it live from 9 till 5.
12" Single: Released Oct '83, on Sugarhill (USA), Catalogue no: **SHL 129**

LIVIN' IN THE FAST LANE
Tracks: / Living in the fast lane.
12" Single: Released Jun '84, on Sugarhill (USA), Catalogue no: **SHL 134**

LOVER IN YOU
Tracks: / Lover on you.
7" Single: Released Jul '82, on Sugarhill (USA), Deleted '88. Catalogue no: **SH 116**
12" Single: Released Jul '82, on Sugarhill (USA), Catalogue no: **SHL 116**

RAPPERS DELIGHT
Tracks: / Rappers delight / Apache.
CD 3": Released '88, on Special Edition, by Castle Communications Records. Catalogue no: **CD3-3**
7" Single: Released Dec '79, on Sugarhill (USA), Deleted '82. Catalogue no: **SHL 101**

WORK WORK THE BODY
Tracks: / Work work the body.
12" Single: Released Mar '85, on Sugarhill (USA), Catalogue no: **SHL 142**

Suggestive Motion

LOVING YOU
Tracks: / Loving you.
7" Single: Released Oct '83, on Bodie, by Bodie Records. Deleted '86. Catalogue no: **BR 101**

Suicidal Tendencies

INSTITUTIONALISED
Tracks: / Institutionalised / War inside my head / Cyco.
12" Single: Released Feb '88, on Virgin, by Virgin Records. Catalogue no: **VST 1039**

POSSESSED TO SKATE
Tracks: / Possessed to skate / Human guinea pig / Two wrongs don't make a right (but they make me feel better) (12" only).
7" Single: Released May '87, on Virgin, by Virgin Records. Catalogue no: **VS 967**
12" Single: Released May '87, on Virgin, by Virgin Records. Catalogue no: **VS 967-12**

TRIP AT THE BRAIN
Tracks: / Trip at the brain / Suicyco mania.
12" Single: Released 22 Aug '88, on Virgin, by Virgin Records. Catalogue no: **VST 1127**

Suicide

CHEREE (SINGLE)
Tracks: / Cheree / I remember.
12" Single: Released Nov '86, on Demon, by Demon Records. Catalogue no: **D 1046 T**

RAIN OF RUIN
Tracks: / Rain of ruin / Surrender.
12" Single: Released Feb '89, on Chapter 22, by Chapter 22 Records. Catalogue no: **12CHAP 36**

SUICIDE (SINGLE)
Tracks: / Suicide.
12" Single: Released 30 May '89, on Chapter 22, by Chapter 22 Records. Catalogue no: **12 CHAP 42**

Suicide Highlife

MCARTHYVILLE
Tracks: / McArthyville.
12" Single: Released Nov '88, on F.O.A.D., Catalogue no: **FOADM 1**

Sullivan, Flo

HIGHER
Tracks: / Higher.
12" Single: Released Jun '85, on Red Flame (1), by Red Flame Records. Catalogue no: **RF 1243**

Sullivan, Norman

JOY BELLS RINGING
Tracks: / Joy bells ringing.
12" Single: Released '82, on Black Joy, Catalogue no: **BEH 816**

Sullivan, Rocky

BRING BACK THE NIGHT
Tracks: / Bring back the night / Who's kiddin' who.
7" Single: Released Mar '81, on Rag Baby, Catalogue no: **BRAG 103**

Summer, Donna

ALL SYSTEMS GO (SINGLE)
Tracks: / All systems go / Bad reputation.
7" Single: Released Jan '88, on Warner Bros., by WEA Records. Catalogue no: **U 8122**
12" Single: Released Jan '88, on Warner Bros., by WEA Records. Catalogue no: **U 8122 T**

BACK IN LOVE AGAIN
Tracks: / Back in love again.
7" Single: Released Apr '78, on GTO, Deleted '81. Catalogue no: **GT 117**

BAD GIRLS (SINGLE)
Tracks: / Bad girls / On my honour.
7" Single: Released Jul '79, on Casablanca, by PolyGram UK Ltd. Deleted '82. Catalogue no: **CAN 155**

COLD LOVE (SINGLE)
Tracks: / Cold love / Grand illusion.
7" Single: Released Dec '80, on Warner Bros., by WEA Records. Catalogue no: **K 79193**

COULD IT BE MAGIC
Tracks: / Could it be magic.
7" Single: Released May '76, on GTO, Deleted '79. Catalogue no: **GT 60**

DIM ALL THE LIGHTS
Tracks: / Dim all the lights.
7" Single: Released Sep '79, on Casablanca, by PolyGram UK Ltd. Deleted '82. Catalogue no: **CAN 162**

DINNER WITH GERSHWIN
Tracks: / Dinner with Gershwin / Tearing down the walls (Available on 12" only).
12" Single: Released Sep '87, on Warner Bros., by WEA Records. Catalogue no: **U 8237T**
7" Single: Released Sep '87, on Warner Bros., by WEA Records. Catalogue no: **U 8237**

DOWN DEEP INSIDE
Tracks: / Down deep inside.
7" Single: Released Aug '77, on Casablanca, by PolyGram UK Ltd. Deleted '80. Catalogue no: **CAN 111**

HEAVEN KNOWS
Tracks: / Heaven knows.
7" Single: Released Feb '79, on Casablanca, by PolyGram UK Ltd. Deleted '82. Catalogue no: **CAN 141**

HOT STUFF
Tracks: / Hot stuff.
7" Single: Released May '79, on Casablanca, by PolyGram UK Ltd. Deleted '82. Catalogue no: **CAN 151**

I DON'T WANNA GET HURT
Tracks: / I don't wanna get hurt / Dinner with Gershwin.
12" Single: Released May '89, on WEA, by WEA Records. Catalogue no: **U 7567T**
Cassingle: Released May '89, on WEA, by WEA Records. Catalogue no: **U 7567C**
7" Single: Released May '89, on WEA, by WEA Records. Catalogue no: **U 7567**
CD 5": Released May '89, on WEA, by WEA Records. Catalogue no: **U 7567CD**

I FEEL LOVE
Tracks: / I feel love / Can't we just sit down
7" Single: Released Oct '84, on Casablanca, by PolyGram UK Ltd. Deleted 31 Jul '89. Catalogue no: **FEEL 7**
7" Single: Released Jul '77, on GTO, Deleted '80. Catalogue no: **GT 100**
12" Single: Released Oct '84, on Casablanca, by PolyGram UK Ltd. Deleted 31 Jul '89. Catalogue no: **FEEL 12**

I FEEL LOVE (OLD GOLD)
Tracks: / Love to love you baby / I feel love
7" Single: Released Feb '88, on Old Gold, by Old Gold Records. Catalogue no: **O 9771**

I LOVE YOU
Tracks: / I love you.
7" Single: Released Dec '77, on Casablanca, by PolyGram UK Ltd. Deleted '80. Catalogue no: **CAN 114**

I REMEMBER YESTERDA (SINGLE)
Tracks: / I remember yesterday.
7" Single: Released Sep '77, on GTO, Deleted '80. Catalogue no: **GT 107**

LAST DANCE
Tracks: / Last dance.
7" Single: Released Jun '78, on Casabl

nca, by PolyGram UK Ltd. Deleted '81. Catalogue no: **TGIF 2**

LOVE IS IN CONTROL
Tracks: / Love is in control / Sometimes.
12" Single: Released Jun '82, on Warner Bros., by WEA Records. Catalogue no: **K 79302 T**
7" Single: Released Jun '82, on Warner Bros., by WEA Records. Catalogue no: **K 79302**

LOVE TO LOVE YOU
Tracks: / Love to love you.
12" Single: on Phonogram, by Phonogram Ltd. Deleted 31 May '89. Catalogue no: **CANX 1014**

LOVE TO LOVE YOU BABY
Tracks: / Love to love you baby.
7" Single: Released Jan '76, on GTO, Deleted '79. Catalogue no: **GT 17**

LOVE'S ABOUT TO CHANGE MY HEART
Tracks: / Love's about to change my heart / Love's about to change my heart (Inst.).
12" Single: Released Aug '89, on Warner Bros., by WEA Records. Catalogue no: **U 7494 T**
7" Single: Released Aug '89, on Warner Bros., by WEA Records. Catalogue no: **U 7494**

LOVE'S UNKIND
Tracks: / Love's unkind.
7" Single: Released Dec '77, on GTO, Deleted '80. Catalogue no: **GT 113**

LOVE'S UNKIND (OLD GOLD)
Tracks: / Love's unkind.
7" Single: on Old Gold, by Old Gold Records. Deleted Sep '85. Catalogue no: **OG 9565**

MACARTHUR PARK
Tracks: / Macarthur Park.
7" Single: Released Oct '78, on Casablanca, by PolyGram UK Ltd. Deleted '81. Catalogue no: **CAN 131**

NEVER LOSE YOUR SENSE OF HUMOUR
Tracks: / Never lose your sense of humour / Just you and me.
7" Single: Released Mar '80, on Casablanca, by PolyGram UK Ltd. Deleted Mar '83. Catalogue no: **NB 1002**
12" Single: Released Mar '80, on Casablanca, by PolyGram UK Ltd. Deleted Mar '83. Catalogue no: **NBL 1002**

NO MORE TEARS
Tracks: / No more tears.
12" Single: Released Nov '79, on Casablanca, by PolyGram UK Ltd. Deleted '82. Catalogue no: **CBS 8000**
7" Single: Released Nov '79, on Casablanca, by PolyGram UK Ltd. Deleted '82. Catalogue no: **CAN 174**

ON THE RADIO (SINGLE)
Tracks: / On the radio / There will always be a you.
7" Single: Released Feb '80, on Casablanca, by PolyGram UK Ltd. Deleted '83. Catalogue no: **NB 2236**

RUMOUR HAS IT
Tracks: / Rumour has it.
7" Single: Released Feb '78, on Casablanca, by PolyGram UK Ltd. Deleted '81. Catalogue no: **CAN 122**

SHE WORKS HARD FOR THE MONEY (SINGLE)
Tracks: / She works hard for the money.
7" Single: Released Jun '83, on Mercury, by Phonogram Ltd. Deleted '86. Catalogue no: **DONNA 1**

STATE OF INDEPENDENCE
Tracks: / State of independence / Love is just a breath away.
12" Single: Released Nov '82, on Warner Bros., by WEA Records. Deleted Sep '87. Catalogue no: **K 79344T**
7" Single: Released Nov '82, on Warner Bros., by WEA Records. Catalogue no: **K 79344**

STOP LOOK AND LISTEN
Tracks: / Stop look and listen.
7" Single: Released Jan '84, on Mercury, by Phonogram Ltd. Deleted '87. Catalogue no: **DONNA 3**

SUNSET PEOPLE
Tracks: / Sunset people / Our love.
12" Single: Released Jun '80, on Casablanca, by PolyGram UK Ltd. Deleted '83. Catalogue no: **CANL 198**
7" Single: Released Jun '80, on Casablanca, by PolyGram UK Ltd. Deleted '83. Catalogue no: **CAN 198**

THIS TIME I KNOW IT'S FOR REAL
Tracks: / This time I know it's for real / Whatever your heart desires.
7" Single: Released Jan '89, on Atlantic, by WEA Records. Catalogue no: **U 7780**
CD 5": Released Jan '89, on Atlantic, by WEA Records. Catalogue no: **U 7780 CD**
12" Single: Released Jan '89, on Atlantic, by WEA Records. Catalogue no: **U 7780 T**

UNCONDITIONAL LOVE
Tracks: / Unconditional love / Woman.
7" Single: Released Sep '83, on Mercury, by Phonogram Ltd. Deleted '86. Catalogue no: **DONNA 2**

WALK AWAY
Tracks: / Walk away / Could it be magic.
7" Single: Released Oct '80, on Casablanca, by PolyGram UK Ltd. Deleted Oct '83. Catalogue no: **CAN 211**

WANDERER, THE (SINGLE)
Tracks: / Wanderer.
7" Single: Released Sep '80, on Warner Bros., by WEA Records. Deleted '83. Catalogue no: **K 79180**

WHEN LOVE TAKES OVER YOU
Tracks: / When love takes over you / Whatever your heart desires.
12" Single: Released Nov '88, on WEA (International), by WEA Records. Catalogue no: **U 7780T**
7" Single: Released Nov '88, on WEA (International), by WEA Records. Catalogue no: **U 7780**

WHO DO YOU THINK YOUR FOOLING
Tracks: / Who do you think you're foolin'.
7" Single: Released Mar '81, on Geffen, by Geffen Records (USA). Catalogue no: **K 79201**

WINTER MELODY
Tracks: / Winter melody, A.
7" Single: Released Dec '76, on GTO, Deleted '79. Catalogue no: **GT 76**

WOMAN IN ME
Tracks: / Woman in me, The / Living in America.
7" Single: Released Nov '83, on Warner Bros., by WEA Records. Catalogue no: **W 9983**
12" Single: Released Nov '83, on Warner Bros., by WEA Records. Catalogue no: **W 69983 T**

Summer, Henry Lee

HEY BABY
Tracks: / Hey baby / Something is missing.
CD 5": Released Sep '89, on Epic, by CBS Records. Catalogue no: **655 018 2**
7" Single: Released Sep '89, on Epic, by CBS Records. Catalogue no: **655 018 7**
12" Single: Released Sep '89, on Epic, by CBS Records. Catalogue no: **655 018 8**

I WISH I HAD A GIRL
Tracks: / I wish I had a girl / Wing tip shoes / I know how you feel (Available on 12" only).
CD 5": Released 6 Jun '88, on Epic, by CBS Records. Deleted Jan '89. Catalogue no: **651484 2**
7" Single: Released May '88, on Epic, by CBS Records. Deleted Jan '89. Catalogue no: **651484 7**
12" Single: Released May '88, on Epic, by CBS Records. Deleted Jan '89. Catalogue no: **651458 6**

Summers, Andy

LOVE IS THE STRANGEST WAY
Tracks: / Love is the strangest way / XYZ.
7" Single: Released Jul '87, on MCA, by MCA Records. Catalogue no: **MCA 1167**
12" Single: Released Jul '87, on MCA, by MCA Records. Catalogue no: **MCAT 1167**

Summers, Bill

CALL IT WHAT YOU WANT
Tracks: / Call it what you want / Your style ain't that way.
7" Single: Released Mar '81, on MCA, by MCA Records. Deleted Mar '84. Catalogue no: **MCA 689**
12" Single: Released Mar '81, on MCA, by MCA Records. Deleted Mar '84. Catalogue no: **MCAT 689**

Summers, Dee J

MY BEST FRIEND TOLD ME
Tracks: / My best friend told me.
7" Single: Released Aug '87, on Creole, by Creole Records. Catalogue no: **CR 107**
12" Single: Released Aug '87, on Creole, by Creole Records. Catalogue no: **CRT 107**

Summers, Lorraine

LAY DOWN BESIDE ME
Tracks: / Lay down beside me / Come to me.
7" Single: Released May '81, on Klub, by Klub Records. Catalogue no: **KLUB 20**

Summers & Sanders

PHD GIRL
Tracks: / PHD girl.
7" Single: Released Aug '84, on Dawn Break, Catalogue no: **DBKS 1**

Sumner, J.D

EASY TO LOVE YOU
Tracks: / Easy to love you / Love on / Time is a thief / Glad I don't have a heartache.
7" Single: Released Feb '80, on Bulldog (USA), by Bulldog Records (USA). Deleted Feb '83. Catalogue no: **BDE 18**

Sumo Giants

TOWER OF BABEL
Tracks: / Tower of Babel.
7" Single: Released Mar '88, on Metro, by Hit Records. Catalogue no: **ELECS 1**
12" Single: Released Mar '88, on Metro, by Hit Records. Catalogue no: **ELECT 1**

Sumrall, David

IT'S A SHAME
Tracks: / It's a shame / Crying tears for you.
7" Single: Released Jan '80, on Pye, Deleted Jan '85. Catalogue no: **7P 154**

Sun

DANCE
Tracks: / Dance.
7" Single: Released Mar '85, on Air, by Chrysalis Records. Catalogue no: **AIR 3701 7**
12" Single: Released Mar '85, on Air, by Chrysalis Records. Catalogue no: **AIR 3701 12**

LEGS
Tracks: / Legs / Heartbreak hideaway.
7" Single: Released Dec '85, on Air City, Catalogue no: **7 AIR 3704**
12" Single: Released Dec '85, on Air City, Catalogue no: **12 AIR 3704**

START THE COUNTDOWN
Tracks: / Start the countdown / X factor, The.
7" Single: Released Sep '83, on Chevy, by Chevy Records. Catalogue no: **CHEVY 001**

Sun, Joe

SHOTGUN RIDER
Tracks: / Shotgun rider / I came on business for the king.
7" Single: Released Apr '80, on Ovation, by Gull Records. Deleted '83. Catalogue no: **OV 1201**

Sun, Nicci

WHO SAVED WHO?
Tracks: / Who saved who?.
7" Single: Released Sep '82, on RAK, by EMI Records. Catalogue no: **RAK 351**

Sun Palace

WINNING
Tracks: / Winning.
7" Single: Released Nov '83, on Passion, by Skratch Records. Catalogue no: **PASH 08**
12" Single: Released Nov '83, on Passion, by Skratch Records. Catalogue no: **PASH 08(12)**

WINNING (X-MIX)
Tracks: / Winning (x-mix) / Winning / Rude movements.
12" Single: Released 21 Mar '88, on Debut, by Skratch Records. Catalogue no: **DEBTX 3045**

Sun & The Moon

ALIVE NOT DEAD
Tracks: / Alive not dead.
12" Single: Released 30 Jan '89, on Midnight, Catalogue no: **DONG 44**
12" Single: Released Nov '88, on Glass Pyramid, Catalogue no: **12CDMC 001**
7" Single: Released Nov '88, on Glass Pyramid, Catalogue no: **7CDMC 001**
CD 5": Released 30 Jan '89, on Midnight, Catalogue no: **DONG 44 CD**
CD 5": Released Nov '88, on Glass Pyramid, Catalogue no: **CDMC 001**

SPEED OF LIFE, THE
Tracks: / Speed of life / Death of imagination / Boy who sees everything, The (Available on 12") / I love you, you bastard (Available on 12" only).
12" Single: Released Jul '88, on WEA, by WEA Records. Catalogue no: **GEF 39T**
7" Single: Released Jul '88, on WEA, by WEA Records. Catalogue no: **GEF 39**

Sun Yama

SUBTERRANEAN HOMESICK BLUES
Tracks: / Subterranean homesick blues / More Cane than Abel.
7" Single: Released Jul '82, on Trans, Deleted '87. Catalogue no: **TRANS 1**

Sundance

MONTEGO BAY
Tracks: / Montego Bay.
12" Single: Released Jun '84, on Passion, by Skratch Records. Catalogue no: **PASH 31(12)**
7" Single: Released Jun '84, on Passion, by Skratch Records. Catalogue no: **PASH 31**

WALK RIGHT IN
Tracks: / Walk right in / Jealousy.
7" Single: Released Jun '82, on Bronze, by Bronze Records. Deleted Jun '85. Catalogue no: **BRO 147**

WHAT'S LOVE?
Tracks: / What's love? / Song.
7" Single: Released Oct '81, on Bronze, by Bronze Records. Catalogue no: **BRO 132**

Sundays

CAN'T BE SURE
Tracks: / Can't be sure.
CD 5": Released 30 Jan '89, on Rough Trade, by Rough Trade Records. Catalogue no: **RT 218 CD**
7" Single: Released 30 Jan '89, on Rough Trade, by Rough Trade Records. Catalogue no: **RT 218**
12" Single: Released 30 Jan '89, on Rough Trade, by Rough Trade Records. Catalogue no: **RT T218**

Sundholm, Roy

BRIDGE ACROSS THE RIVER
Tracks: / Bridge across the river / Me and my mercedes.
7" Single: Released Apr '81, on Ensign, by Ensign Records. Deleted Apr '84. Catalogue no: **ENY 208**

GOOD GIRLS DON'T WEAR WHITE
Tracks: / Good girls don't wear white / My heart's on fire.
7" Single: Released Jul '81, on Ensign, by Ensign Records. Deleted '82. Catalogue no: **ENY 213**

Sundragon

GREEN TAMBOURINE
Tracks: / Green tambourine.
7" Single: Released Feb '68, on MGM, by Polydor Ltd. Deleted '71. Catalogue no: **MGM 1380**

Sunfire

STEP IN THE NIGHT
Tracks: / Step in the night.
7" Single: Released May '83, on Warner Bros., by WEA Records. Catalogue no: **W 9642**
12" Single: Released May '83, on Warner Bros., by WEA Records. Catalogue no: **W 9642 T**

YOUNG FREE AND SINGLE
Tracks: / Young free and single.
7" Single: Released Mar '83, on Warner Bros., by WEA Records. Deleted '86. Catalogue no: **W 9897**

Sunglasses After Dark

MORBID SILENCE
Tracks: / Morbid silence.
7" Single: Released Mar '84, on Anagram, by Cherry Red Records. Deleted '88. Catalogue no: **ANA 20**
12" Single: Released Mar '84, on Anagram, by Cherry Red Records. Deleted '88. Catalogue no: **12 ANA 20**

Sunny

DOCTOR'S ORDERS
Tracks: / Doctor's orders.
7" Single: Released Mar '74, on CBS, by CBS Records. Deleted '77. Catalogue no: **CBS 2068**

Suns Of Arqa

GET DOWN MAGIC
Tracks: / Get down magic.
12" Single: Released Sep '83, on Rock Steady, by Rock Steady Records. Catalogue no: **MIAXA A3T**

GOVINDA'S HOUSE
Tracks: / Govinda's house.
12" Single: Released Dec '88, on Antler, by Antler Records (Belgium). Catalogue no: **ANT 094**

REVENGE OF THE MOZABITES (SINGLE)
Tracks: / Revenge of the mozabites.
12" Single: Released Oct '83, on Rock Steady, by Rock Steady Records. Catalogue no: **ANT 018**

SOUL TO SAVE
Tracks: / Soul to save / Anata snake dance.
7" Single: Released '81, on Rock Steady, by Rock Steady Records. Catalogue no: **MICK 010**

Sunset Searchers

SECOND TIME AROUND
Tracks: / Second time around.
Note: Debut single from the Sunset Searchers.
7" Single: Released Oct '88, on After Sunset, by After Sunset Music Promotions. Catalogue no: **ASMP 002**
12" Single: Released Oct '88, on After Sun-

set, by After Sunset Music Promotions. Catalogue no: **ASMP 002-12**

Sunshine In ...

VISIONS IN GLASS
Tracks: / Visions in glass.
7" Single: Released Oct '88, on Mystic, Catalogue no: **XDM 1**

Sunshine & The Radics

MOUNT ZION
Tracks: / Mount Zion.
12" Single: Released Mar '83, on DATC, Catalogue no: **DATCD 012**

Supa Frutas

WE WANT TO GROW LIKE JESUS
Tracks: / We want to grow like Jesus.
7" Pic: Released Nov '87, on PRT, by Castle Communications Records. Catalogue no: **PYS 3**

Supastreak

TO BE OR NOT TO BE
Tracks: / To be or not to be / Love games.
7" Single: Released Jul '80, on Splash, by Splash Records. Deleted Jul '83. Catalogue no: **SP 014**

Super Beagle

LOT OF SOUND BOY A FI HIDE, A
Tracks: / Lot of sound boy a fi hide, A.
12" Single: Released Sep '89, on Techniques, Catalogue no: **WRT 53**

Super Black

BAD BOY GONE A SAIL
Tracks: / One time girl friend / Bad boy gone a sail.
12" Single: Released Jan '87, on Jammy's, Catalogue no: **JAM 005**

BUBBLING TIME
Tracks: / Take life easy / Bubbling time.
7" Single: Released Mar '86, on United Sound, Catalogue no: **UNO 14**

LOVESICK
Tracks: / Boom shakatak / Lovesick.
12" Single: Released Apr '86, on Unity, Catalogue no: **UN 016**

OLD TIME PEOPLE
Tracks: / Old time people / Dancehall night.
12" Single: Released Nov '86, on Live & Love, Catalogue no: **LLDIS 0018**

RAMBO
Tracks: / Rambo / Can't conquer me.
12" Single: Released Oct '86, on Live & Love, Catalogue no: **LLDIS 0017**

Super Cat

MUD UP
Tracks: / Mud up.
12" Single: Released May '88, on Skengdon, Catalogue no: **SKD 071**

NUFF DON DEA YA
Tracks: / Nuff don dea ya.
12" Single: Released Oct '88, on Blue Trac, by Blue Trac Records. Catalogue no: **BTRD 020**

SANDOCHAN
Tracks: / Sandochan.
12" Single: Released Sep '88, on Roots Rockers, Catalogue no: **RRD 006**

SWEET FOR MY SWEET
Tracks: / Sweet for my sweet.
12" Single: Released Aug '88, on Skengdon, Catalogue no: **SKDL 077**

Super Enigmatix

TOUCH THE BEAT
Tracks: / Touch the beat.
7" Single: Released Mar '87, on MDM, by MDM Communications. Deleted May '88. Catalogue no: **MDM 18**
12" Single: Released Mar '87, on MDM, by MDM Communications. Deleted May '88. Catalogue no: **MDM 18-12**

Super Lover...

DO THE JAMES
Tracks: / Do the James.
12" Single: Released 28 Sep '87, on DNA (USA), by DNA International Records (USA). Catalogue no: **DNA 1001**

Super Mazembe

SHAURI YAKO
Tracks: / Shauri Yako.
12" Single: Released Jan '84, on Earthworks, by Earthworks Records. Deleted '88. Catalogue no: **ET 001**

Super Nova

B.C.L.D.
Tracks: / B.C.L.D..
12" Single: Released '89, on Antler, by Antler Records (Belgium). Catalogue no: **SUB 056**

Supercats

BOOPS
Tracks: / Boops / Cry for the youth.
7" Single: Released Jun '86, on Techniques, Catalogue no: **WR 02**
12" Single: Released Jun '86, on Techniques, Catalogue no: **WRT 02**

Supercharge

PEACHES 'N' CREAM
Tracks: / Peaches 'n' cream.
7" Single: Released Oct '80, on Criminal (1), by Criminal Records. Catalogue no: **SWAG 20**

Supergroove

YAWNS ON 45
Tracks: / Yawns on 45.
7" Single: Released Aug '81, on Swamp, by Swamp Records. Deleted '87. Catalogue no: **WAM 115**

Superharps

SUPERHARPS EP
Tracks: / Superharps EP: *Various artists*.
7" Single: Released Dec '88, on Red Lightnin', by Red Lightning Records. Catalogue no: **RL 027**

Superiors

BE MY GIRL
Tracks: / Be my girl.
7" Single: Released May '84, on Polo, by Polo Records. Deleted '88. Catalogue no: **POLO 32**

Superman

SUPERMAN MARCH
Tracks: / Superman march / Lex escapes.
7" Single: Released Apr '81, on Warner Bros., by WEA Records. Deleted '85. Catalogue no: **K 17778**

Supermax

LOVE MACHINE
Tracks: / Love machine / Dance dance dance.
7" Single: Released Feb '80, on Carrere, Deleted Feb '85. Catalogue no: **CAR 132**

Supersonic Syd

KEEP THAT BOOTY CLEAN (SCRUB THAT BUTT)
Tracks: / Keep that booty clean (scrub that butt) / Keep that booty clean (scrub that butt)(Inst.).
12" Single: Released Sep '89, on Wrap, Catalogue no: **12 PO 21**

Superstar Mix Up

SUPERSTAR MIX UP
12" Single: Released Dec '84, on Greensleeves, by Greensleeves Records. Catalogue no: **GRED 164**

Superted

SUPERTED THEME AND OVERTURE
Tracks: / Superted theme / Spotty man song.
7" Single: Released Jan '84, on Rainbow Communication, Catalogue no: **TED 1**

Supertramp

BREAKFAST IN AMERICA (SINGLE)
Tracks: / Breakfast in America.
7" Single: Released Jun '79, on A&M, by A&M Records. Deleted '82. Catalogue no: **AMS 7451**

CANNONBALL
Tracks: / Every open door / Cannonball.
12" Single: Released Feb '86, on A&M, by A&M Records. Deleted '88. Catalogue no: **AMY 248**
7" Single: Released Feb '86, on A&M, by A&M Records. Deleted '88. Catalogue no: **AM 248**

COMPACT HITS: SUPERTRAMP
Tracks: / Goodbye stranger / Logical song, The / Breakfast in America / Bloody well right.
CD 5": Released Aug '88, on A&M, by A&M Records. Catalogue no: **AMCD 914**

DREAMER
Tracks: / Dreamer / You started laughing.
7" Single: Released Nov '80, on A&M, by A&M Records. Deleted Nov '83. Catalogue no: **AMS 7576**
7" Single: Released Feb '75, on A&M, by A&M Records. Deleted '78. Catalogue no: **AMS 7152**

DREAMER (OLD GOLD)
Tracks: / Dreamer.
7" Single: Released Sep '85, on Old Gold, by Old Gold Records. Catalogue no: **OG 9542**

FREE AS A BIRD (SINGLE)
Tracks: / Free as a bird.
7" Single: Released Feb '88, on A&M, by A&M Records. Deleted 1 Aug '88. Catalogue no: **AM 430**
12" Single: Released Feb '88, on A&M, by A&M Records. Deleted 1 Aug '88. Catalogue no: **AMY 430**

GIVE A LITTLE BIT
Tracks: / Give a little bit.
7" Single: Released Jun '77, on A&M, by A&M Records. Deleted '80. Catalogue no: **AMS 7293**

GOODBYE STRANGER
Tracks: / Goodbye stranger.
CD 5": Released Aug '88, on A&M, by A&M Records. Catalogue no: **AMC 914**
7" Single: Released Oct '79, on A&M, by A&M Records. Deleted '82. Catalogue no: **AMS 7481**

I'M BEGGING YOU
Tracks: / I'm begging you / No inbetween.
7" Single: Released Oct '87, on A&M, by A&M Records. Deleted 1 Aug '88. Catalogue no: **AM 415**
12" Single: Released Oct '87, on A&M, by A&M Records. Deleted 1 Aug '88. Catalogue no: **AMY 415**

IT'S RAINING AGAIN
Tracks: / It's raining again.
7" Single: Released Oct '82, on A&M, by A&M Records. Deleted '85. Catalogue no: **AMS 8255**

LOGICAL SONG
Tracks: / Goodbye stranger / Logical song.
7" Single: Released Mar '79, on A&M, by A&M Records. Deleted '82. Catalogue no: **AMS 7427**
7" Single: Released Sep '86, on A&M, by A&M Records. Deleted '88. Catalogue no: **AM 357**

MY KIND OF LADY
Tracks: / My kind of lady / Know who you are.
7" Single: Released Jan '83, on A&M, by A&M Records. Deleted '88. Catalogue no: **AMS 8301**

TAKE THE LONG WAY HOME
Tracks: / Take the long way home / From now on.
7" Single: Released Apr '81, on A&M, by A&M Records. Deleted '85. Catalogue no: **AMS 7560**

Support Band

HIGH HEEL SNEAKERS
Tracks: / High heel sneakers / Long legged lady.
7" Single: Released Mar '64, on Pye International, Deleted '67. Catalogue no: **7N 25238**
7" Single: Released Feb '87, on School, Deleted Nov '87. Catalogue no: **LITE 1**

Supporters

PLAY THE GAME (THE ANTHEM)
Tracks: / Play the game.
7" Single: Released Oct '85, on Sonic Communications, by Priority Records. Deleted Nov '87. Catalogue no: **JIMMY 1**

Supremes

AUTOMATICALLY SUNSHINE
Tracks: / Automatically sunshine.
7" Single: Released Jul '72, on Tamla Motown, by Motown Records (UK). Deleted '75. Catalogue no: **TMG 821**

BABY LOVE
Tracks: / Baby love.
7" Single: Released Oct '64, on Stateside, by EMI Records. Deleted '67. Catalogue no: **SS 350**

BACK IN MY ARMS AGAIN
Tracks: / Back in my arms again.
7" Single: Released '80, on Lightning, Catalogue no: **LR 3193**
7" Single: Released Jun '65, on Tamla Motown, by Motown Records (UK). Deleted '68. Catalogue no: **TMG 516**

BAD WEATHER
Tracks: / Bad weather.
7" Single: Released Apr '73, on Tamla Motown, by Motown Records (UK). Deleted '76. Catalogue no: **TMG 847**

COME SEE ABOUT ME
Tracks: / Come see about me.
7" Single: Released Jan '65, on Stateside, by EMI Records. Deleted '68. Catalogue no: **SS 376**

FLOY JOY
Tracks: / Floy joy / Bad weather.
7" Single: Released Oct '81, on Motown, by BMG Records (UK). Deleted '83. Catalogue no: **TMG 974**

HAPPENING, THE
Tracks: / Happening, The.
7" Single: Released May '67, on Tamla Motown, by Motown Records (UK). Deleted '70. Catalogue no: **TMG 607**

I HEAR A SYMPHONY (SINGLE)
Tracks: / I hear a symphony.
7" Single: Released Dec '65, on Tamla Motown, by Motown Records (UK). Deleted '68. Catalogue no: **TMG 543**

NATHAN JONES
Tracks: / Nathan Jones.
7" Single: Released Aug '71, on Tamla Motown, by Motown Records (UK). Deleted '74. Catalogue no: **TMG 782**

REACH OUT AND TOUCH
Tracks: / Reach out and touch (somebody's hand).
7" Single: Released Oct '81, on Motown, by BMG Records (UK). Deleted '83. Catalogue no: **TMG 836**

REFLECTIONS
Tracks: / Reflections / Happening, The.
7" Single: Released '80, on Lightning, Catalogue no: **LR 3188**
7" Single: Released Aug '67, on Tamla Motown, by Motown Records (UK). Deleted '70. Catalogue no: **TMG 616**

RIVER DEEP MOUNTAIN HIGH
Tracks: / River deep, mountain high / You gotta have more love in your heart.
7" Single: Released Oct '81, on Motown, by BMG Records (UK). Deleted '83. Catalogue no: **TMG 971**
7" Single: Released Jun '71, on Tamla Motown, by Motown Records (UK). Deleted '74. Catalogue no: **TMG 777**

SOME THINGS YOU NEVER GET USED TO
Tracks: / Some things you never get used to.
7" Single: Released Jul '68, on Tamla Motown, by Motown Records (UK). Deleted '71. Catalogue no: **TMG 662**

SOMEDAY WE'LL BE TOGETHER
Tracks: / My world is empty without you / Someday we'll be together.
7" Single: Released '80, on Motown, by BMG Records (UK). Catalogue no: **TMG 1080**

STONED LOVE
Tracks: / Stoned love.
7" Single: Released '80, on Motown, by BMG Records (UK). Catalogue no: **LR 0679**
7" Single: Released Jan '71, on Tamla Motown, by Motown Records (UK). Deleted '74. Catalogue no: **TMG 760**
7" Single: Released Oct '81, on Motown, by BMG Records (UK). Catalogue no: **TMG 1046**

STOP IN THE NAME OF LOVE
Tracks: / Stop in the name of love.
7" Single: Released Mar '65, on Tamla Motown, by Motown Records (UK). Deleted '68. Catalogue no: **TMG 501**
7" Single: Released '80, on Motown, by BMG Records (UK). Catalogue no: **LR 3193**

UP THE LADDER TO THE ROOF
Tracks: / Up the ladder to the roof.
7" Single: Released Apr '88, on Motown, by BMG Records (UK). Catalogue no: **ZB 41931**
7" Single: Released Oct '81, on Motown, by BMG Records (UK). Deleted '83. Catalogue no: **TMG 964**
7" Single: Released May '70, on Tamla Motown, by Motown Records (UK). Deleted '73. Catalogue no: **TMG 735**

WHERE DID OUR LOVE GO
Tracks: / Where did our love go.
CD 5": Released Jun '89, on Motown, by BMG Records (UK). Catalogue no: **ZD 41957**
7" Single: Released Sep '64, on Stateside, by EMI Records. Deleted '67. Catalogue no: **SS 327**

YOU CAN'T HURRY LOVE
Tracks: / You can't hurry love.
7" Single: Released '80, on Motown, by BMG Records (UK). Catalogue no: **TMG 956**
7" Single: Released Sep '66, on Tamla Motown, by Motown Records (UK). Deleted '69. Catalogue no: **TMG 575**

YOU GOTTA HAVE LOVE IN YOUR HEART
Tracks: / You gotta have love in your heart.
7" Single: Released Nov '71, on Tamla Motown, by Motown Records (UK). Deleted '74. Catalogue no: **TMG 793**

YOU KEEP ME HANGIN' ON
Tracks: / You keep me hangin' on.
7" Single: Released Dec '66, on Tamla Motown, by Motown Records (UK). Deleted '69. Catalogue no: **TMG 585**
7" Single: Released '80, on Motown, by BMG Records (UK). Catalogue no: **TMG 1080**
7" Single: Released Apr '85, on Motown, by BMG Records (UK). Catalogue no: **TMG 992**
12" Single: Released Apr '85, on Motown, by BMG Records (UK). Catalogue no: **TMGT 992**

Sure, Al B.

IF I'M NOT YOUR LOVER
Tracks: / If I'm not your lover / Noche y dia.
Cassingle: Released Jun '89, on Warner Bros., by WEA Records. Catalogue no: **W 2908 C**
7" Single: Released Jun '89, on Warner Bros., by WEA Records. Catalogue no: **W 2908**
12" Single: Released Jun '89, on Warner Bros., by WEA Records. Catalogue no: **W 2908 T**

NITE & DAY
Tracks: / Nite & day / Nuit et jour.
7" Single: Released Mar '88, on Warner Bros., by WEA Records. Catalogue no: **W 8192**
12" Single: Released Mar '88, on Warner Bros., by WEA Records. Catalogue no: **W 8192T**

OFF ON YOUR OWN
Tracks: / Off on your own.
7" Single: Released Jul '88, on WEA, by WEA Records. Catalogue no: **W 7870**
12" Single: Released Jul '88, on WEA, by WEA Records. Catalogue no: **W 7870 T**

RESCUE ME (I'M NOT MAD)
Tracks: / Rescue me (I'm not mad).
7" Single: Released Oct '88, on Uptown Records, by Uptown Records. Catalogue no: **0-21038**

Surf Drums

BLACK TAMBOURINE
Tracks: / Black tambourine.
7" Single: Released 31 Oct '87, on Kaleidoscope Sound, by Kaleidoscope Sound Records. Catalogue no: **KS 705**
12" Single: Released 31 Oct '87, on Kaleidoscope Sound, by Kaleidoscope Sound Records. Catalogue no: **KS 105**

THESE 7 YEARS
Tracks: / These 7 years.
12" Single: Released Sep '85, on Swordfish, by Swordfish Records. Catalogue no: **SWF 003**

WALK AWAY
Tracks: / Walk away.
7" Single: Released Mar '87, on Kaleidoscope Sound, by Kaleidoscope Sound Records. Catalogue no: **KS 703**
12" Single: Released Mar '87, on Kaleidoscope Sound, by Kaleidoscope Sound Records. Catalogue no: **KS 103**

Surface

FALLING IN LOVE
Tracks: / Falling in love.
7" Single: Released Jun '83, on Salsoul, Catalogue no: **SAL 104**
12" Single: Released Jun '83, on Salsoul, Catalogue no: **SALT 104**

HAPPY
Tracks: / Let's try again / Happy.
CD 5": Released Mar '87, on Scotti Bros (USA), Catalogue no: **450 136 2**
7" Single: Released Feb '87, on CBS, by CBS Records. Catalogue no: **650 393 7**
12" Single: Released Aug '87, on CBS, by CBS Records. Deleted Nov '87. Catalogue no: **650 393 6**

I MISSED
Tracks: / I missed (7" edit) (Only on 7" version.) / I missed (Only on 7" version.) / I missed (12" version) (Only on 12" version.) / I missed (dub version) (Only on 12" version.) / I missed (acappella) (Only on 12" version.).
7" Single: Released Nov '88, on CBS, by CBS Records. Deleted 17 Apr '89. Catalogue no: **653009 7**
12" Single: Released 21 Nov '88, on CBS, by CBS Records. Deleted 17 Apr '89. Catalogue no: **653009 1**
12" Single: Released Nov '88, on CBS, by CBS Records. Deleted 17 Apr '89. Catalogue no: **653009 8**

SHOWER ME WITH YOUR LOVE
Tracks: / Shower me with your love / Shower me with your love (instrumental) / Shower me with your love (LP version) (Only on 12" and CD single) / Happy (remix) (Only on 12" and CD single).
CD 5": Released Aug '89, on CBS, by CBS Records. Catalogue no: **655 245 2**
7" Single: Released Aug '89, on CBS, by CBS Records. Catalogue no: **655 245 0**
7" Single: Released Aug '89, on CBS, by CBS Records. Catalogue no: **655 245 7**
12" Single: Released Aug '89, on CBS, by CBS Records. Catalogue no: **655 245 6**

WHEN YOUR EX WANTS YOU BACK
Tracks: / When your ex wants you back.
7" Single: Released Jun '84, on Salsoul, Deleted '87. Catalogue no: **SAL 106**

Surface Band

JAH BIBLE
Tracks: / Jah Bible / New style.
12" Single: Released Aug '83, on Surface, Catalogue no: **SCL 001**

SHE HAS GONE AWAY
Tracks: / She has gone away / Warm and tender love.
12" Single: Released Dec '83, on Lucky Dice, Catalogue no: **LD 002**

Surface Mutants

ANAESTHETIC (EP)
Tracks: / Anaesthetic.
7" Single: Released Sep '82, on Clone, Catalogue no: **CLONIC 1**

TRAIN
Tracks: / Train / Somewhere strange / Help.
12" Single: Released Sep '82, on Rock Steady, by Rock Steady Records. Catalogue no: **MIX 2T**

Surface Noise

DANCIN' ON A WIRE
Tracks: / Dancin' on a wire.
7" Single: Released Aug '80, on Groove (USA), by Extra Sensory Productions (USA). Deleted '83. Catalogue no: **GP 102**

RIGHT BETWEEN THE EYES
Tracks: / Right between the eyes / Zero one.
7" Single: Released Jan '81, on WEA, by WEA Records. Deleted Jan '84. Catalogue no: **K 18396**

SCRATCH, THE
Tracks: / Scratch, The.
7" Single: Released May '80, on WEA, by WEA Records. Deleted '83. Catalogue no: **K 18291**

Surfadelics

TOO GOOD TO BE TRUE
Tracks: / Too good to be true.
7" Single: Released Nov '85, on Armchair, Deleted '87. Catalogue no: **ARLP 003**

Surfaris

WIPE OUT
Tracks: / Wipe out.
7" Single: Released Jul '63, on London-American, Deleted '66. Catalogue no: **HLD 9751**
7" Single: Released Sep '87, on MCA, by MCA Records. Catalogue no: **MCA 1170**

Surfin' Dave

STATESIDE CENTRE
Tracks: / Stateside centre.
7" Single: Released Sep '85, on Nine Mile, Catalogue no: **NM 1**

Surfin' Lungs

MICKEY'S CAR
Tracks: / Mickey's car.
7" Single: Released Mar '84, on Lovers Leap, by Backs Dist.. Catalogue no: **LEAP 1**

PRAY FOR SUN
Tracks: / Pray for sun / Surfing Chinese.
7" Single: Released Mar '85, on Lovers Leap, by Backs Dist.. Catalogue no: **LEAP 2**

SURF JET GIRL
Tracks: / Surf-jet girl / Girls are feelin' alright / Big man on campus.
7" Single: Released Jun '86, on Big Beat, by Ace Records. Deleted '88. Catalogue no: **SW 118**

Surkamp, David

LONIE
Tracks: / Lonie.
7" Single: Released Aug '86, on Shanghai, by Shanghai Records. Catalogue no: **MGLS 3**

LOUIE, LOUIE
Tracks: / Louie, Louie.
7" Single: Released Jan '88, on Butt, by Butt Records. Catalogue no: **MGLS 3**

Surprise Sisters

LA BOOGA ROOGA
Tracks: / La booga rooga.
7" Single: Released Mar '76, on Good Earth, Deleted '79. Catalogue no: **GD 1**

Surreal Estate

CURTAIN CALL
Tracks: / Curtain call.
12" Single: Released Nov '86, on Letharge, Catalogue no: **ARGE 10**

MIDAS TOUGH
Tracks: / Midas tough.
12" Single: Released Jul '85, on Probe Plus, by Probe Plus Records. Catalogue no: **PP 12**

Survival

WRITE TO ME
Tracks: / Write to me.
12" Single: Released Feb '82, on Riff-Raff, Catalogue no: **RFDC 790**

Survival Dance Report

SURVIVAL DANCE REPORT
7" Set: Released Nov '83, on Survival (1), by Survival Records. Catalogue no: **RE-PORT 3**
Special: Released Nov '83, on Survival (1), by Survival Records. Catalogue no: **RE-PORT 5**

Survival Singles

SURVIVAL SINGLES COLLECTION
7" Set: Released Jan '84, on Survival (1), by Survival Records. Catalogue no: **SURPACK 1**

Survivor

AMERICAN HEARTBEAT
Tracks: / American heartbeat / Silver girl.
7" Single: Released Oct '82, on Scotti Bros (USA), Deleted Oct '85. Catalogue no: **SCTA 2813**

BURNING HEART
Tracks: / Feels like love / Burning heart.
7" Single: Released Feb '86, on Scotti Bros (USA), Deleted '87. Catalogue no: **A 6708**
12" Single: Released Feb '86, on Scotti Bros (USA), Deleted '87. Catalogue no: **TX 6708**
7" Pic: Released Feb '86, on Scotti Bros (USA), Catalogue no: **WA 6708**
7" Set: Released Feb '86, on Scotti Bros (USA), Catalogue no: **DA 6708**

EYE OF THE TIGER
Tracks: / Eye of the tiger / Take you on a saturday.
7" Single: Released Jan '84, on Scotti Bros (USA), Catalogue no: **A 2411**
12" Single: Released Jan '84, on Scotti Bros (USA), Catalogue no: **TA 2411**

HIGH ON YOU
Tracks: / High on you.
7" Single: Released Jan '85, on Scotti Bros (USA), Catalogue no: **A 4946**

I CAN'T HOLD BACK
Tracks: / I can't hold back.
7" Single: Released Mar '86, on Scotti Bros (USA), Catalogue no: **A 6989**
12" Single: Released Mar '86, on Scotti Bros (USA), Catalogue no: **TA 6989**

IS THIS LOVE
Tracks: / Can't let you go / Is this love.
7" Single: Released Nov '86, on Scotti Bros (USA), Catalogue no: **650195-7**
12" Single: Released Nov '86, on Scotti Bros (USA), Catalogue no: **650195-6**

MOMENT OF TRUTH
Tracks: / Moment of truth.
7" Single: Released Aug '84, on Casablanca, by PolyGram UK Ltd. Catalogue no: **CAN 1021**

ONE THAT REALLY MATTERS
Tracks: / One that really matters / Hesitation dance.
7" Single: Released Jan '83, on Scotti Bros (USA), Catalogue no: **SCT A 3038**

POOR MAN'S SON
Tracks: / Poor man's son / Love is on my side.
7" Single: Released Feb '82, on CBS, by CBS Records. Deleted '85. Catalogue no: **SCTA 1903**

SEARCH IS OVER, THE
Tracks: / Search is over, The / It's the singer not the song.
7" Single: Released May '86, on Scotti Bros (USA), Deleted '87. Catalogue no: **A 6344**
12" Single: Released May '86, on Scotti Bros (USA), Catalogue no: **TA 6344**

SOMEWHERE IN AMERICA
Tracks: / Somewhere in America / Freelance.
7" Single: Released Mar '80, on Scotti Bros (USA), Deleted '83. Catalogue no: **K 11453**

Survivors

HANDS OFF
Tracks: / Hands off / Never too late.
7" Single: Released May '80, on Ariola-Hansa, by Hansa Records. Deleted '83. Catalogue no: **AHA 563**

Sus

YEARNING FOR YOUR LOVE
Tracks: / Yearning for your love / Sentimental reason.
12" Single: Released Jun '84, on Tit, Deleted '85. Catalogue no: **TID 005**

S.U.S. Band

LOVE IS HERE TO STAY
Tracks: / Love is here to stay.
12" Single: Released Apr '88, on Lucky, by Lucky Records. Catalogue no: **13 LTR 00212**

Susan

DREAM OF YOU
Tracks: / Dream of you / Freezing fish under the moonlight.
7" Single: Released Jul '81, on Epic, by CBS Records. Deleted '85. Catalogue no: **EPC A 1404**

I ONLY COME OUT AT NIGHT
Tracks: / I only come out at night / Blow out.
7" Single: Released Feb '82, on Epic, by CBS Records. Deleted Feb '87. Catalogue no: **EPC A2004**

Suspicions

LAUGHING POLICEMAN
Tracks: / Laughing policeman / Suspicions.
7" Single: Released Jul '80, on Arista, by BMG Records (UK). Deleted Jul '83. Catalogue no: **ARIST 361**

OUR LOVE IS IN THE POCKET
Tracks: / Our love is in the pocket.
7" Single: Released Apr '84, on Inferno (1), by Inferno Records. Catalogue no: **BURN 8**

Sussed

I'VE GOT ME PARKA
Tracks: / I've got me parka / Myself, myself and I repeated.
7" Single: Released Jul '80, on Graduate, by Graduate Records. Deleted Jan '87. Catalogue no: **GRAD 7**

Sussex

WITH A GIRL LIKE YOU
Tracks: / With a girl like you / What can I say.
7" Single: Released Oct '80, on Mercury, by Phonogram Ltd. Deleted Oct '83. Catalogue no: **SUSS 1**

Sutch, Screaming Lord

ALL BLACK AND HAIRY
Tracks: / All black and hairy / Jack the ripper / London rocker / Oh well.
7" Single: Released Jun '81, on Ace, by Ace Records. Deleted Jun '88. Catalogue no: **SW 70**

JACK THE RIPPER
Tracks: / Jack the Ripper / I'm a hog.
7" Single: Released May '82, on Decca, by Decca Records. Deleted '88. Catalogue no: **F 13697**

ROCK'N'ROLL MADMAN (EP)
Tracks: / Rock 'n' roll madman.
7" EP: Released May '82, on Magnum Force, by Magnum Music Group. Catalogue no: **MFEP 010**

Sutcliff, Bobby

ANOTHER JANGLY MESS EP
Tracks: / Another jangly mess.
7" Single: Released Mar '87, on Tambourine, by Tambourine Records. Catalogue no: **URINE 2**

Sutherland Brothers

ARMS OF MARY
Tracks: / Arms of Mary.
7" Single: Released Apr '76, on CBS, by CBS Records. Deleted '79. Catalogue no: **CBS 4001**

ARMS OF MARY (OLD GOLD)
Tracks: / Secrets / Arms of Mary.
7" Single: Released Jan '87, on Old Gold, by Old Gold Records. Catalogue no: **OG 9402**

EASY COME EASY GO
Tracks: / Easy come easy go.
7" Single: Released Jun '79, on CBS, by CBS Records. Deleted '82. Catalogue no: **CBS 7121**

SECRETS
Tracks: / Secrets.
7" Single: Released Nov '76, on CBS, by CBS Records. Deleted '79. Catalogue no: **CBS 4668**

WHEN WILL I BE LOVED
Tracks: / When will I be loved / Love sick.
7" Single: Released Oct '81, on RCA, by BMG Records (UK). Deleted Oct '84. Catalogue no: **RCA 110**

Sutherland, Iain

IT COULDA BEEN BUDDY HOLLY
Tracks: / It coulda been Buddy Holly.
7" Single: Released Sep '83, on Avatar, by Avatar Record Corporation. Catalogue no: **AVAT 5**

WHEEL, THE (FAITES VOS JEUX)
Tracks: / Wheel, The.
7" Single: Released Feb '84, on Avatar, by Avatar Record Corporation. Catalogue no: **AVAT 9**

Sutherland, Nadine

JUST YOU & ME TONIGHT
Tracks: / Just you & me tonight.
12" Single: Released Aug '88, on Greensleeves, by Greensleeves Records. Cata-

logue no: **GRED 228**

Sutton, Chris

DON'T GET ME WRONG
Tracks: / Don't get me wrong / Love is the reason.
12" Single: Released Jul '86, on Polydor, by Polydor Ltd. Deleted Mar '87. Catalogue no: **POSPX 799**
7" Single: Released Jul '86, on Polydor, by Polydor Ltd. Deleted Mar '87. Catalogue no: **POSP 799**

PRINCE OF JUSTICE
Tracks: / Prince of justice / Money ain't worth it.
12" Single: Released Apr '86, on Polydor, by Polydor Ltd. Catalogue no: **POSPX 785**
7" Single: Released Apr '86, on Polydor, by Polydor Ltd. Catalogue no: **POSP 785**

YOU WORRY ME
Tracks: / You worry me / All of my life (Live recording.) / Know it all (Extra track available on 12" version only.).
12" Single: Released Oct '86, on Boiling Point, by Polydor Ltd. Deleted Mar '87. Catalogue no: **POSPX 824**
7" Single: Released Oct '86, on Boiling Point, by Polydor Ltd. Deleted Mar '87. Catalogue no: **POSP 824**

Sutton, Mike & Brenda

DON'T LET GO OF ME
Tracks: / Don't let go of me.
12" Single: Released Nov '82, on Silvertown, by Silvertown Records. Catalogue no: **STST 1**
7" Single: Released Nov '82, on Silvertown, by Silvertown Records. Catalogue no: **STS 1**

WE'LL MAKE IT
Tracks: / We'll make it.
7" Single: Released Feb '82, on Virgin, by Virgin Records. Deleted '89. Catalogue no: **VS 480**
12" Single: Released Feb '82, on Virgin, by Virgin Records. Deleted '89. Catalogue no: **VS 480-12**

Suuka

C'EST LA VIE
Tracks: / C'est la vie / Don't cry for me.
12" Single: Released Nov '83, on Paro, by Paro Records. Catalogue no: **12 PARO 008**
7" Single: Released Nov '83, on Paro, by Paro Records. Catalogue no: **PARO 008**

Suxy May

CRAZY HOUND DOG
Tracks: / Crazy hound dog.
7" Single: Released Jul '82, on Sheet, Catalogue no: **BULL 4**

Suzan

GIRLS CAN JACK TOO
Tracks: / Girls can jack too.
7" Single: Released Nov '87, on Supreme, by Supreme Records. Catalogue no: **ZAN 1**

Suzie

DANCE
Tracks: / Dance / Midas majestic.
7" Single: Released Nov '82, on Speed, Catalogue no: **SPEED 2**

I FEEL IT (CONSTRUCTION MIX) (Suzie & The Cubans)
Tracks: / I feel it (construction mix) / I feel it (construction mix).
7" Single: Released Mar '88, on Champion, by Champion Records. Catalogue no: **CHAMP 70**
12" Single: Released Mar '88, on Champion, by Champion Records. Deleted Aug '89. Catalogue no: **CHAMP 1270**

Suzuki, Pat

I ENJOY BEING A GIRL
Tracks: / I enjoy being a girl.
7" Single: Released Apr '60, on RCA, by BMG Records (UK). Deleted '63. Catalogue no: **RCA 1171**

Suzy & The Red Stripes

SEASIDE WOMAN
Tracks: / Seaside woman / B-side to seaside.
7" Single: Released Jul '86, on EMI, by EMI Records. Catalogue no: **EMI 5572**
12" Single: Released Jul '86, on EMI, by EMI Records. Catalogue no: **12 EMI 5572**

Swaffield Junior

YULE CHANT
Tracks: / Yule chant / Get down yule.
7" Single: Released Dec '81, on Spectra, by Spectra Records. Deleted '87. Catalogue no: **SPC 5**
12" Single: Released Nov '81, on Spectra, by Spectra Records. Deleted '87. Catalogue no: **SPT 5**

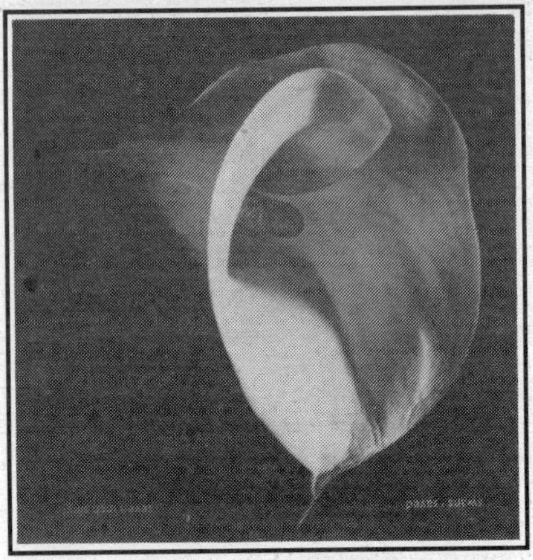

SWANS - SAVED (Released on MCA)

Swallow Tongue

GOT TO BE THERE
Tracks: / Got to be there / Hitch up honey.
7" Single: Released Sep '83, on Cherry Red, by Cherry Red Records. Deleted '87. Catalogue no: **CHERRY 68**
12" Single: Released Sep '83, on Cherry Red, by Cherry Red Records. Deleted '87. Catalogue no: **12 CHERRY 68**

Swamp Children

LITTLE VOICES
Tracks: / Little voices / Call me honey.
12" Single: Released Oct '81, on Factory (1), by Factory Records. Catalogue no: **FAC 49**

Swamp Terrorists

HE'S GUILTY
Tracks: / He's guilty.
12" Single: Released Jul '89, on BPM, Catalogue no: **19303 BPM**

Swamptrash

BONE EP, THE
12" Single: Released Oct '88, on DDT, by D.D.T.Records. Catalogue no: **DDT EP 002**

Swan, Billy

DON'T BE CRUEL
Tracks: / Don't be cruel.
7" Single: Released May '75, on Monument, Deleted '78. Catalogue no: **MNT 3244**

I CAN HELP
Tracks: / I can help.
7" Single: Released Dec '74, on Monument, Deleted '77. Catalogue no: **MNT 2752**
7" Single: Released '80, on Monument, Catalogue no: **LR 2528**

Swan, John

TEMPORARY HEARTACHE
Tracks: / Temporary heartache / I'll come home.
7" Single: Released Dec '82, on WEA, by WEA Records. Catalogue no: **K 70031**

Swan Lake (Group)

IN THE NAME OF LOVE
Tracks: / In the name of love / Dream, The.
CD 5": Released 22 Aug '88, on Champion, by Champion Records. Catalogue no: **CHAMP CD 86**
7" Single: Released 22 Aug '88, on Champion, by Champion Records. Catalogue no: **CHAMP 86**
12" Single: Released 22 Aug '88, on Champion, by Champion Records. Catalogue no: **CHAMP 1286**

Swanhunters

BLOODSPORT
Tracks: / Bloodsport.
12" Single: Released Nov '86, on Fon, by FON Records. Catalogue no: **SWAN 3**

Swans

CAN'T FIND MY WAY HOME
Tracks: / Can't find my way home / Universal emptiness.
7" Single: Released Aug '89, on MCA, by MCA Records. Catalogue no: **MCA 1347**
12" Single: Released Aug '89, on MCA, by MCA Records. Catalogue no: **MCATG 1347**
12" Single: Released Aug '89, on MCA, by MCA Records. Catalogue no: **MCAT 1347**

LOVE WILL TEAR US APART
Tracks: / Love will tear us apart.
12" Single: Released Jun '88, on Sleeping Bag, by Sleeping Bag Records. Catalogue no: **PROD 23 T**
7" Single: Released Jun '88, on Product Inc., Catalogue no: **PROD 23**
12" Single: Released Jun '88, on Product Inc., Catalogue no: **PROD 23B**
CD 5": Released Jun '88, on Product Inc., Catalogue no: **PROD 23CD**

NEWMIND
Tracks: / Newmind.
7" Single: Released Aug '87, on Product Inc., Catalogue no: **PROD 16**
12" Single: Released Aug '87, on Product Inc., Catalogue no: **12PROD 16**

RAPING A SLAVE EP
Tracks: / Raping a slave.
12" Single: Released Mar '85, on K 422, by K 422 Records. Catalogue no: **KDE 112**

SAVED (see panel above)
Tracks: / Saved / No cruel angel.
CD 5": Released 10 Apr '89, on MCA, by MCA Records. Catalogue no: **DMCAT 1332**
7" Single: Released 10 Apr '89, on MCA, by MCA Records. Catalogue no: **MCA 1332**
12" Single: Released 10 Apr '89, on MCA, by MCA Records. Catalogue no: **MCAT 1332**

SCREW, A
Tracks: / Screw, A.
12" Single: Released Sep '86, on K 422, by K 422 Records. Catalogue no: **KDE 312**

TIME IS MONEY (BASTARD)
Tracks: / Time is money (bastard) / Sealed in skin / Time is money (mix).
12" Single: Released Jan '86, on K 422, by K 422 Records. Catalogue no: **KDE 212**

Swansway

BALCONY THEME
Tracks: / Balcony theme / Vibration hoist.
7" Single: Released Aug '82, on Exit International, Catalogue no: **7EXIT 2**
12" Single: Released Aug '82, on Exit International, Catalogue no: **12EXIT 2**

ILLUMINATIONS
Tracks: / Illuminations.
7" Single: Released May '84, on Balgier, Deleted '87. Catalogue no: **PH 5**

SOUL TRAIN
Tracks: / Soul train.
7" Single: Released Feb '84, on Exit, Deleted '87. Catalogue no: **EXT 3**

Swat Band

DANIEL
Tracks: / Daniel.
12" Single: Released 8 Aug '88, on EAB, Catalogue no: **EA 002**

DEVIL WOMAN
Tracks: / Devil woman.
12" Single: Released May '85, on Rockas, Catalogue no: **R 003**

Swatch

SWATCH MEGA MIX (see panel below)
Tracks: / Jingo: *Jellybean* / Tramp: *Salt 'N' Pepa* / I know you got soul: *B, Eric & Rakim* / Time has a way: *Keller, Jerry.*
7" Pic: Released '88, on UNKNOWN, Catalogue no: **SW 191**

Sway

HANDS UP (GIVE ME YOUR HEART)
Tracks: / Hands up (7" only) / Hands up (7" only) / Hands up (give me your heart) (Penthouse mix) (12" only) / Hands up (give me your heart) (Powerhouse mix) (12" only).
Note: "The essential summer party record. This version of the Ottawan disco classic topped the Canadian dance chart for six weeks and spent sixteen weeks in the Canadian top forty, peaking at number 7." (Virgin, July 1988)
12" Single: Released Jul '88, on Virgin, by Virgin Records. Catalogue no: **VST 1104**
7" Single: Released Jul '88, on Virgin, by Virgin Records. Catalogue no: **VS 1104**

Swaye

COLD OPEN DOOR
Tracks: / Cold open door.
12" Single: Released Jan '85, on Kalabash,

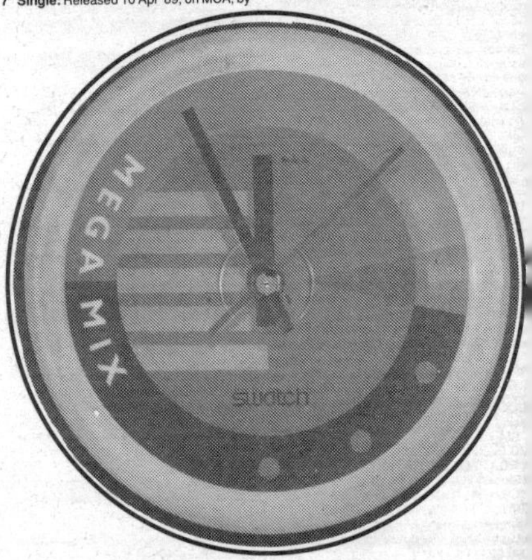

SWATCH - SWATCH MEGA MIX

Catalogue no: **KAL 1**

Swaysland

NO MONEY NO LOVE
Tracks: / No money no love.
7" Single: Released Aug '85, on Hemiola, by Hemiola Records. Catalogue no: **HEMD 1A**

Swayze, Patrick

SHE'S LIKE THE WIND
Tracks: / She's like the wind / Stay / I had the time of my life (Only avaliable on 12" format.).
7" Single: Released Mar '88, on RCA, by BMG Records (UK). Catalogue no: **PB 49565**
12" Single: Released Mar '88, on RCA, by BMG Records (UK). Deleted Aug '89. Catalogue no: **PT 49566**

Sweat

I MUST BE CRAZY
Tracks: / I must be crazy / Ginny don't cry.
7" Single: Released Oct '80, on Double Dee. Deleted Oct '83. Catalogue no: **DD 7**

Sweat, Keith

DON'T STOP YOUR LOVE
Tracks: / Don't stop your love / Don't stop your love (version).
7" Single: Released Nov '88, on Elektra, by Elektra Records (UK). Catalogue no: **EKR 84**
12" Single: Released Nov '88, on Elektra, by Elektra Records (UK). Catalogue no: **EKR 84 T**

I WANT HER
Tracks: / I want her.
7" Single: Released Feb '88, on Elektra, by Elektra Records (UK). Catalogue no: **EKR 68**
12" Single: Released Feb '88, on Elektra, by Elektra Records (UK). Catalogue no: **EKR 68T**

SOMETHING JUST AIN'T RIGHT
Tracks: / Something just ain't right.
CD 5": Released Apr '88, on Elektra, by Elektra Records (UK). Catalogue no: **EKR 72 CD**
7" Single: Released Mar '88, on Elektra, by Elektra Records (UK). Catalogue no: **EKR 72**
12" Single: Released Mar '88, on Elektra, by Elektra Records (UK). Catalogue no: **EKR 72T**

Sweden Through The

IT HELPS TO CRY
Tracks: / It helps to cry.
12" Single: Released Feb '86, on Snappy. Catalogue no: **SW 001**

Sweeney

I'VE BEEN MEANING TO SAY
Tracks: / I've been meaning to say / Take a little time / Las Vegas blues.
7" Single: Released Feb '83, on Small Run. Catalogue no: **SRR 0007**

Sweep, Jimmy

LONDON TOWN
Tracks: / London town / Bridgetown girls.
7" Single: Released Nov '81, on Tamarin. Deleted Nov '84. Catalogue no: **TAM 3**
7" Single: Released Feb '82, on PRT, by Castle Communications Records. Catalogue no: **7P 233**

Sweet

ACTION
Tracks: / Action.
7" Single: Released Jul '75, on RCA, by BMG Records (UK). Deleted '78. Catalogue no: **RCA 2578**

ALEXANDER GRAHAM BELL
Tracks: / Alexander Graham Bell.
7" Single: Released Oct '71, on RCA, by BMG Records (UK). Deleted '74. Catalogue no: **RCA 2121**

BALLROOM BLITZ
Tracks: / Ballroom blitz.
7" Single: Released Sep '73, on RCA, by BMG Records (UK). Deleted '76. Catalogue no: **RCA 2403**
7" Single: Released May '82, on Golden Grooves, by BMG Records (UK). Catalogue no: **GOLD 551**

BLOCKBUSTER
Tracks: / Blockbuster / Hellraiser.
7" Single: Released Jan '73, on RCA, by BMG Records (UK). Deleted '76. Catalogue no: **RCA 2305**
7" Single: Released Apr '87, on Old Gold, by Old Gold Records. Catalogue no: **OG 9707**
7" Single: Released Aug '81, on RCA Golden Grooves, by BMG Records (UK). Catalogue no: **GOLD 524**

CO CO
Tracks: / Co co.
7" Single: Released Jun '71, on RCA, by BMG Records (UK). Deleted '74. Catalogue no: **RCA 2087**

FOX ON THE RUN
Tracks: / Fox on the run / Hellraiser / Ballroom blitz / Blockbuster.
7" Single: Released Mar '75, on RCA, by BMG Records (UK). Deleted '78. Catalogue no: **RCA 2524**
7" Single: Released Jul '80, on RCA, by BMG Records (UK). Deleted Jul '83. Catalogue no: **PE 5226**

FOX ON THE RUN (OLD GOLD)
Tracks: / Fox on the run / Ballroom blitz.
7" Single: Released Apr '87, on Old Gold, by Old Gold Records. Catalogue no: **OG 9709**

FUNNY FUNNY
Tracks: / Funny funny.
7" Single: Released Mar '71, on RCA, by BMG Records (UK). Deleted '74. Catalogue no: **RCA 2051**

GIVE THE LADY SOME RESPECT
Tracks: / Give the lady some respect / Tall girls.
7" Single: Released Apr '80, on Polydor, by Polydor Ltd. Deleted Apr '83. Catalogue no: **2001946**

HELL RAISER
Tracks: / Hell raiser.
7" Single: Released May '73, on RCA, by BMG Records (UK). Deleted '76. Catalogue no: **RCA 2357**

IT'S THE SWEET MIX
12" Single: Released Dec '84, on Anagram, by Cherry Red Records. Deleted '88. Catalogue no: **12 ANA 28**
7" Single: Released Dec '84, on Anagram, by Cherry Red Records. Deleted '88. Catalogue no: **ANA 28**

LIES IN YOUR EYES
Tracks: / Lies in your eyes.
7" Single: Released Jan '76, on RCA, by BMG Records (UK). Deleted '79. Catalogue no: **RCA 2641**

LITTLE WILLY
Tracks: / Little Willy.
7" Single: Released Jun '72, on RCA, by BMG Records (UK). Deleted '75. Catalogue no: **RCA 2225**

LOVE IS LIKE OXYGEN
Tracks: / Love is like oxygen / Cover girl.
7" Single: Released Jan '78, on Polydor, by Polydor Ltd. Deleted '81. Catalogue no: **POSP 1**

POPPA JOE
Tracks: / Poppa Joe.
7" Single: Released Feb '72, on RCA, by BMG Records (UK). Deleted '75. Catalogue no: **RCA 2164**

SIX TEENS, THE
Tracks: / Six teens, The.
12" Single: Released Sep '84, on Anagram, by Cherry Red Records. Deleted '88. Catalogue no: **12 ANA 27**
7" Single: Released Sep '84, on Anagram, by Cherry Red Records. Catalogue no: **ANA 27**
7" Single: Released Jul '74, on RCA, by BMG Records (UK). Deleted '77. Catalogue no: **LPBO 5037**

SIXTIES MAN
Tracks: / Sixties man / Oh yeah.
7" Single: Released Sep '80, on Polydor, by Polydor Ltd. Deleted Sep '83. Catalogue no: **POSP 160**

SWEET SIXTEEN (SINGLE)
Tracks: / Sweet sixteen.
7" Pic: Released Aug '84, on Anagram, by Cherry Red Records. Deleted '88. Catalogue no: **PGRAM 16**

TEENAGE RAMPAGE
Tracks: / Teenage rampage.
7" Single: Released Jan '74, on RCA, by BMG Records (UK). Deleted '77. Catalogue no: **LPBO 5004**

TEENAGE RAMPAGE (OLD GOLD)
Tracks: / Teenage rampage / Hell raiser.
7" Single: Released Jan '88, on Old Gold, by Old Gold Records. Catalogue no: **OG 9762**

TURN IT DOWN
Tracks: / Turn it down.
7" Single: Released Nov '74, on RCA, by BMG Records (UK). Deleted '77. Catalogue no: **RCA 2480**

WIG WAM BAM
Tracks: / Wig wam bam.
7" Single: Released Sep '72, on RCA, by BMG Records (UK). Deleted '75. Catalogue no: **RCA 2260**

WIG WAM BAM (OLD GOLD)
Tracks: / Wig wam bam / Co co.
7" Single: Released Jan '88, on Old Gold, by Old Gold Records. Catalogue no: **OG 9760**

RACHEL SWEET - I GO TO PIECES (Released on Stiff)

Sweet Charles

YES IT'S YOU
Tracks: / Yes it's you / Rock me again & again & again...... /-Think about it (Extra track on 12".).
7" Single: Released Mar '88, on Urban, by Polydor Ltd. Catalogue no: **URB 15**
12" Single: Released Mar '88, on Urban, by Polydor Ltd. Deleted 31 May '89. Catalogue no: **URBX 15**

Sweet Dreams

HONEY HONEY
Tracks: / Honey honey.
7" Single: Released Jul '74, on Bradley's. Deleted '77. Catalogue no: **BRAD 7408**

I'M NEVER GIVING UP
Tracks: / I'm never giving up.
7" Single: Released '83, on Ariola, by BMG Records (UK). Deleted '86. Catalogue no: **ARO 333**

Sweet Ecstacy

PULL OUR LOVE TOGETHER
Tracks: / Pull our love together / Jam party.
12" Single: Released Apr '83, on Excaliber, by Red Bus Records. Deleted '88. Catalogue no: **EXCL 531**

Sweet Heat

THIS IS THE NIGHT
Tracks: / This is the night / This is the night (inst) / This is the night (dub).
12" Single: Released 30 May '87, on Champion, by Champion Records. Catalogue no: **CHAMP 1248**
7" Single: Released May '87, on Champion, by Champion Records. Catalogue no: **CHAMP 48**

Sweet Lamont

DEFINITION OF A TRACK
12" Single: Released Jul '89, on White Label (1). Catalogue no: **12CTL 002**

Sweet Light

ADIOS
Tracks: / Adios.
7" Single: Released Jul '80, on OK, by Klub Records. Catalogue no: **OK 001**

Sweet 'N' Bitter Band

WOMAN IN LOVE
Tracks: / Woman in love / Loving dub.
12" Single: Released Apr '86, on ITS. Catalogue no: **ITS 004**

Sweet People

AND THE BIRDS WERE SINGING
Tracks: / And the birds were singing / Perse.
7" Single: Released Jul '87, on Polydor, by Polydor Ltd. Catalogue no: **POSP 170**

ET LES OISEAUX CHANTAIENT (And the birds were singing)
Tracks: / Et les oiseaux chantaient / Perce.
7" Single: Released Oct '80, on Polydor, by Polydor Ltd. Deleted '83. Catalogue no: **POSP 179**

LAKE COMO
Tracks: / Lake como / Santa barbara.
7" Single: Released Dec '80, on Polydor, by Polydor Ltd. Deleted Dec '85. Catalogue no: **POSP 208**

Sweet, Rachel

B-A-B-Y
Tracks: / B-A-B-Y.
7" Single: Released Jan '85, on Stiff, by Stiff Records. Deleted '88. Catalogue no: **BUY 39**

BABY LETS PLAY HOUSE
Tracks: / Baby lets play house.
7" Single: Released Nov '79, on Stiff, by Stiff Records. Catalogue no: **BUY 55**

FOOLS GOLD
Tracks: / Fools gold / I've got a reason.
7" Single: Released Jan '80, on Stiff, by Stiff Records. Catalogue no: **BUY 67**

I GO TO PIECES (see panel above)
Tracks: / I go to pieces / Who does Lisa like.
7" Single: Released '79, on Stiff, by Stiff Records. Catalogue no: **BUY 44**

SPELLBOUND
Tracks: / Spellbound / Lovers lane.
7" Single: Released May '80, on Stiff, by Stiff Records. Catalogue no: **BUY 80**

THEN HE KISSED ME/BE MY BABY
Tracks: / Then he kissed me / Be my baby / Fool's story.
7" Single: Released Oct '81, on CBS, by CBS Records. Deleted '85. Catalogue no: **A 1687**

Sweet Revenge

NOTHING EVER GOES THE WAY IT'S PLANNED
Tracks: / Nothing ever goes the way it's planned.
7" Single: Released Apr '85, on Revenge (1), by Revolver Records. Catalogue no: **RR 1**

Sweet Savage

TAKE NO PRISONERS
Tracks: / Take no prisoners / Killing time.
7" Single: Released Dec '81, on Park, by Highway Records. Catalogue no: **PKR 1001**

Sweet Sensation

PURELY BY COINCIDENCE
Tracks: / Purely by coincidence.
7" Single: Released Jan '75, on Pye. Deleted '78. Catalogue no: **7 N 45421**

SAD SWEET DREAMER
Tracks: / Sad sweet dreamer.
7" Single: Released Sep '74, on Pye. Deleted '77. Catalogue no: **7 N 45385**
7" Single: Released Jan '83, on Flashback, by Mainline Records. Catalogue no: **FBS 20**
7" Single: Released Aug '86, on PRT, by Castle Communications Records. Catalogue no: **7P 360**
12" Single: Released Aug '86, on PRT, by Castle Communications Records. Catalogue no: **12P 360**

Sweet Substitute

I GIVE IN
Tracks: / I give in.
7" Single: Released '78, on Decca, by Decca Records. Deleted '88. Catalogue no: **F 13820**

LULLABY OF BROADWAY
Tracks: / Lullaby of Broadway / Sleepy Susie.
7" Single: Released Nov '82, on Black Lion, Catalogue no: **BS 7100**

TAKE ME TO THE MARDI GRAS
Tracks: / Take me to the mardi gras / Do you know what it means to miss New Orleans.
7" Single: Released Oct '80, on Logo, by Logo Records. Deleted Oct '83. Catalogue no: **GO 393**

Sweet, Suzanna

CORNER LOVE
Tracks: / Corner love.
12" Single: Released Apr '83, on CDJ, Catalogue no: **CDJ 002**

Sweet Tee

IT'S LIKE THAT Y'ALL
Tracks: / It's like that y'all / I've got da feelin' / I've got da feelin' (instrumental).
7" Single: Released Dec '87, on Cool Tempo, by Chrysalis Records. Catalogue no: **COOL 160**
12" Single: Released Dec '87, on Cool Tempo, by Chrysalis Records. Catalogue no: **COOLX 160**

IT'S MY BEAT
Tracks: / It's my beat.
7" Single: Released Feb '87, on Champion, by Champion Records. Catalogue no: **CHAMP 37**
12" Single: Released Feb '87, on Champion, by Champion Records. Catalogue no: **CHAMP 1237**

LET'S DANCE
Tracks: / Let's dance.
7" Single: Released 15 May '89, on Profile (USA), by Profile Records (USA). Catalogue no: **PROF 246**
12" Single: Released 15 May '89, on Profile (USA), by Profile Records (USA). Catalogue no: **PROFT 246**

ON THE SMOOTH TIP
Tracks: / On the smooth tip.
12" Single: Released Nov '88, on Profile (USA), by Profile Records (USA). Catalogue no: **PRO 7230**

Sweet Thunder

EVERYBODY'S SINGING LOVE SONGS
Tracks: / Everybody's singing love songs / Space bass.
12" Single: Released Dec '85, on Streetwave, Catalogue no: **SWAVE 5**

Sweethearts Of ...

SATISFY YOU
Tracks: / Satisfy you / One time, one night.
7" Single: Released 6 Jun '88, on CBS, by CBS Records. Deleted Jan '89. Catalogue no: **651505 7**
12" Single: Released 6 Jun '88, on CBS, by CBS Records. Deleted Jan '89. Catalogue no: **651505 6**

Swell Maps

DRESDEN STYLE
Tracks: / Dresden style.
7" Single: Released Jun '81, on Rather, by Rather Records. Catalogue no: **GEAR 3**

LET'S BUILD A CAR
Tracks: / Let's build a car.
7" Single: Released Jun '81, on Rather, by Rather Records. Catalogue no: **GEAR 7**

LET'S BUILD A CAR (EP)
Tracks: / Let's build a car / Big Maz in the country / ... Then Poland.
7" EP: Released Feb '80, on Rough Trade, by Rough Trade Records. Deleted Feb '83. Catalogue no: **RTC 36**

READ ABOUT SEYMOUR
Tracks: / Read about Seymour.
7" Single: Released Jun '81, on Rather, by Rather Records. Catalogue no: **GEAR 1**

REAL SHOCKS
Tracks: / Real shocks.
7" Single: Released Jun '81, on Rather, by Rather Records. Catalogue no: **GEAR 6**

SWELL MAPS (EP)
Tracks: / Swell maps.
7" Single: Released Jun '81, on Rather, by Rather Records. Catalogue no: **GEAR 5**

Swim

TALKING TO A SHADOW
Tracks: / Talking to a shadow.
7" Single: Released Aug '82, on Zim Zam, Catalogue no: **ZZ 4**

Swimming In Sand

POWER
Tracks: / Power.
7" Single: Released Jul '86, on Powerstation, by Powerstation Records. Catalogue no: **RITA 5**

Swimming In The Sea

HERO FOR THE HEROINE
Tracks: / Hero for the heroine.
7" Single: Released Aug '82, on Squanderlust, Catalogue no: **LUST 2**

Swimming Pool Queues

PRETTY ON THE INSIDE
Tracks: / Pretty on the inside / Blue tomorrow / Purple rivers / Bells ring, The.
Note: In Doublepack.
7" Single: Released Jan '86, on A&M, by A&M Records. Deleted '88. Catalogue no: **AM 300**

Swimming To France

YOU NEVER EVEN ASKED MY NAME (EP)
Tracks: / You never even asked my name.
12" Single: Released Feb '84, on Oval, by Oval Records. Catalogue no: **OVALT 27-12**

Swimming With Sharks

CARELESS LOVE
Tracks: / Careless love / Come closer now.
12" Single: Released Jan '88, on WEA, by WEA Records. Catalogue no: **YZ 173T**
7" Single: Released Jan '88, on WEA, by WEA Records. Catalogue no: **YZ 173**

NO LONGER FRIENDS
Tracks: / No longer friends / Back into your heart.
CD 5": Released Jul '88, on WEA, by WEA Records. Catalogue no: **YZ 192CD**
7" Single: Released Jul '88, on WEA, by WEA Records. Catalogue no: **YZ 192**
12" Single: Released Jul '88, on WEA, by WEA Records. Catalogue no: **YZ 192T**

Swinburne, Lara Band

MADNESS & LIES
Tracks: / Madness & lies / Lydia.
7" Single: Released Mar '84, on Bridge Records, Catalogue no: **BROO 4**

Swindells, Steve

TURN IT ON
Tracks: / Turn it on / Low life Joe.
7" Single: Released Apr '81, on Atco, by Atlantic Recording Corp.(USA). Deleted '85. Catalogue no: **K 11605**

Swing Collection

42ND STREET
Tracks: / 42nd street.
7" Single: Released Nov '84, on Hobo, Catalogue no: **HOS 025**

PARISIENNE WALKWAYS
Tracks: / Parisienne walkways: *Various artists*.
7" Single: on Mooncrest, by Trojan Records. Deleted May '88. Catalogue no: **MOON 1000**

Swing Out Sister

BLUE MOOD
Tracks: / Blue mood / Wake me when its over.
7" Single: Released May '86, on Mercury, by Phonogram Ltd. Deleted Dec '87. Catalogue no: **MER 207**
12" Single: Released Nov '85, on Mercury, by Phonogram Ltd. Deleted Dec '87. Catalogue no: **MERX 207**
12" Single: Released May '86, on Mercury, by Phonogram Ltd. Catalogue no: **MERXR 207**

BREAKOUT
Tracks: / Breakout / Dirty money.
7" Single: Released Oct '86, on Mercury, by Phonogram Ltd. Deleted '89. Catalogue no: **SWING 2**
12" Single: Released Sep '86, on Mercury, by Phonogram Ltd. Deleted Dec '87. Catalogue no: **SWING 212**

FOOLED BY A SMILE
Tracks: / Fooled by a smile / Fever.
12" Single: Released Jun '87, on Mercury, by Phonogram Ltd. Deleted Dec '87. Catalogue no: **SWING 5 12**
7" Single: Released Jun '87, on Mercury, by Phonogram Ltd. Deleted Dec '87. Catalogue no: **SWING 5**

SURRENDER
Tracks: / Who's to blame / Surrender.
7" Single: Released Dec '86, on Mercury, by Phonogram Ltd. Catalogue no: **SWING 3**
12" Single: Released Dec '86, on Mercury, by Phonogram Ltd. Catalogue no: **SWING 312**

WHERE IN THE WORLD
Tracks: / Where in the world / Taxi town / Windmills of your mind / Breakout.
12" Single: Released Jun '89, on Fontana, by Phonogram Ltd. Deleted Oct '89. Catalogue no: **SWING 712**
CD 5": Released Jun '89, on Fontana, by Phonogram Ltd. Catalogue no: **SWICD 7**
7" Single: Released Jun '89, on Fontana, by Phonogram Ltd. Deleted Oct '89. Catalogue no: **SWING 7**
10" single: Released Jul '89, on Fontana, by Phonogram Ltd. Deleted Oct '89. Catalogue no: **SWING 710**
12" Single: Released Jul '89, on Fontana, by Phonogram Ltd. Deleted Oct '89. Catalogue no: **SWINP 712**
Cassingle: Released Jun '89, on Fontana, by Phonogram Ltd. Deleted Oct '89. Catalogue no: **SWIMC 7**

YOU ON MY MIND
Tracks: / You on my mind / Coney Island man / You on my mind (extended version) (Only on CD single and 12".) / Precious words (earth bound mix) (Only on CD single and 12" version.).
CD 5": Released 27 Mar '89, on Mercury, by Phonogram Ltd. Deleted 31 Jul '89. Catalogue no: **SWICD 6**
7" Single: Released 27 Mar '89, on Mercury, by Phonogram Ltd. Deleted 31 Jul '89. Catalogue no: **SWING 6**
12" Single: Released 27 Mar '89, on Mercury, by Phonogram Ltd. Deleted 31 Jul '89. Catalogue no: **SWING 612**

Swingadilla

IN THE MOOD
Tracks: / In the mood / Chattanooga choo choo / I yi yi yi like you very much.
7" Single: Released Jun '82, on Safari, by Safari Records. Catalogue no: **SAFE 46**

Swingers

BE MY BABY
Tracks: / Be my baby / Swinging.
7" Single: Released May '81, on Magnet, by WEA Records. Deleted May '86. Catalogue no: **MAG 202**

COUNTING THE BEAT
Tracks: / Counting the beat / Flak.
7" Single: Released Feb '82, on Carrere, Catalogue no: **CAR 223**

Swinging Blue Jeans

DON'T MAKE ME OVER
Tracks: / Don't make me over.
7" Single: Released Jan '66, on H.M.V., by EMI Records. Deleted '69. Catalogue no: **POP 1501**

GOOD GOLLY MISS MOLLY
Tracks: / Good golly Miss Molly.
7" Single: Released Mar '64, on H.M.V., by EMI Records. Deleted '67. Catalogue no: **POP 1273**

HIPPY HIPPY SHAKE
Tracks: / Hippy hippy shake.
7" Single: Released Dec '63, on H.M.V., by EMI Records. Deleted '66. Catalogue no: **POP 1242**
7" Single: Released Nov '80, on H.M.V., by EMI Records. Catalogue no: **POP 2020**
7" Single: Released Feb '85, on EMI Golden 45's, by EMI Records. Catalogue no: **G 4541**

HIPPY HIPPY SHAKE (OLD GOLD)
Tracks: / Hippy hippy shake.
7" Single: Released Jun '88, on Old Gold, by Old Gold Records. Deleted Sep '89. Catalogue no: **OG 9374**

HIPPY HIPPY SHAKE, THE
Tracks: / Don't make me over / Hippy hippy shake / It's too late now / Long tall sally.
CD 5": Released Mar '89, on EMI, by EMI Records. Deleted Aug '89. Catalogue no: **CDEM 83**
7" Single: Released Jan '89, on EMI, by EMI Records. Deleted Aug '89. Catalogue no: **EM 83**
12" Single: Released Jan '89, on EMI, by EMI Records. Deleted Aug '89. Catalogue no: **12EM 83**

IT'S TOO LATE NOW
Tracks: / It's too late now.
7" Single: Released Jun '63, on H.M.V., by EMI Records. Deleted '66. Catalogue no: **POP 1170**

YOU'RE NO GOOD
Tracks: / You're no good.
7" Single: Released Jun '64, on H.M.V., by EMI Records. Deleted '67. Catalogue no: **POP 1304**

Swinging Cats

MANTOVANI
Tracks: / Mantovani / Away.
7" Single: Released '83, on Two-Tone, by Chrysalis Records. Deleted '87. Catalogue no: **CHS TT 14**

Swinging Erudites

WALK WITH AN ERECTION
Tracks: / Frankie and Annette met Jim and Tammy / Walk with an erection.
7" Single: Released 21 Nov '87, on Zone (USA), Catalogue no: **7 LIMP 1**
12" Single: Released 21 Nov '87, on Zone (USA), Catalogue no: **12 LIMP 1**

Swinging Laurels

LONELY BOY
Tracks: / Lonely boy.
12" Single: Released Mar '83, on WEA, by WEA Records. Catalogue no: **X 9894T**
7" Single: Released Mar '83, on WEA, by WEA Records. Catalogue no: **X 9894**

OFF THE RECORD
Tracks: / Off the record.
12" Single: Released Mar '82, on Dining Out, by Dining Out Records. Catalogue no: **TUX 20**

PUSH AND SHOVE
Tracks: / Push and shove.
7" Single: Released May '88, on Happy, by Happy Records. Catalogue no: **DON 1**

RODEO
Tracks: / Rodeo.
12" Single: Released Oct '82, on WEA, b WEA Records. Catalogue no: **SAX 1T**
7" Single: Released Oct '82, on WEA, b WEA Records. Catalogue no: **SAX 1**

Swinging Soul Machine

BOOKER T'S GREATEST HITS
12" Single: Released Aug '80, on Infern (1), by Inferno Records. Catalogue nc **BEAT 3-12**
7" Single: Released Aug '80, on Inferno (1 by Inferno Records. Catalogue no: **BEAT**

Swinglehurst, Richie

HOCUSPOCUS
Tracks: / Hocus pocus.
7" Single: Released Jun '85, on Tembo, b Tembo Records. Catalogue no: **TML 106**
12" Single: Released Jun '85, on Tembo, b Tembo Records. Catalogue no: **TMLX 106**

Swingles

CACHAPAYA
Tracks: / Cachapaya / Peter Gunn.
7" Single: Released May '87, on Rainbow by Rainbow Records. Catalogue no: **RBR**

I BELIEVE IN FATHER CHRISTMAS
Tracks: / I believe in Father Christmas.
7" Single: Released Nov '86, on Polydor, b Polydor Ltd. Deleted Mar '87. Catalogue n **POSP 838**

Swiss Navy

BACK TO THE WALL
Tracks: / Back to the wall.
12" Single: Released May '83, on Phono gram, by Phonogram Ltd. Catalogue n **SHORE 12**
7" Single: Released May '83, on Phono gram, by Phonogram Ltd. Catalogue n **SHORE 1**

Switch

DON'T TAKE OUR LOVE AWAY
Tracks: / Don't take our love away.
7" Single: Released May '80, on Motow by BMG Records (UK). Deleted May '8 Catalogue no: **TMG 1187**

KEEPING SECRETS
Tracks: / Keeping secrets.
7" Single: Released Nov '84, on Total E perience, Deleted '87. Catalogue no: **RC XE 502**

Switchbac

SOUNDS IN OUR MINDS
Tracks: / Sounds in our minds.
7" Single: Released Sep '83, on Crezent, Crezent Records. Catalogue no: **CRE 00**

WE ARE ROCKIN'
Tracks: / We are rockin'.
7" Single: Released Feb '84, on Crezent, Crezent Records. Catalogue no: **CRE 00**

Switchback

VINTAGE TREND
Tracks: / Vintage trend.
7" Single: Released Nov '83, on Final C Catalogue no: **SRR 0024**

Switzerland, Michael

MARILYN MONROE'S SISTER
Tracks: / Marilyn Monroe's sister.
7" Single: Released Oct '83, on Red Rhi by Red Rhino Records. Catalogue no: **R 11**

S.W.S.

ARROYO
Tracks: / Arroyo.
12" Single: Released 20 Feb '88, on S (USA), by SST Records (USA). Catalog no: **SST 153**

BOYS FROM THE BEC
Tracks: / Boys from the Bec.
12" Single: Released Jun '88, on DTI, C

logue no: **MAC 2**

Sybil

CAN'T WAIT ON TOMORROW
Tracks: / Can't wait on tomorrow.
7" Single: Released '88, on Champion, by Champion Records. Catalogue no: **CHAMP 82**
12" Single: Released '88, on Champion, by Champion Records. Catalogue no: **CHAMP 1282**

DON'T MAKE ME OVER
Tracks: / Don't make me over / Don't make me over (version).
7" Single: Released Jul '89, on Champion, by Champion Records. Deleted Aug '89. Catalogue no: **CHAMP 213**
12" Single: Released Oct '89, on Next Plateau, by 10 Records. Catalogue no: **NP 50107**
12" Single: Released Jul '89, on Champion, by Champion Records. Deleted Aug '89. Catalogue no: **CHAMP 12213**

FALLING IN LOVE
Tracks: / Falling in love / Falling in love (dub mix).
7" Single: Released Oct '86, on Champion, by Champion Records. Catalogue no: **CHAMP 22**
12" Single: Released Oct '86, on Champion, by Champion Records. Catalogue no: **CHAMP 1222**

LET YOURSELF GO (SINGLE)
Tracks: / Let yourself go.
7" Single: Released Apr '87, on Champion, by Champion Records. Deleted Jul '89. Catalogue no: **CHAMP 42**
12" Single: Released Apr '87, on Champion, by Champion Records. Catalogue no: **CHAMP 1242**

MY LOVE IS GUARANTEED
Tracks: / My love is guaranteed / Red ink mix part 1 (on 12" special edition only) / Red ink mix part 2 (on 12" special edition only).
12" Single: Released Aug '87, on Champion, by Champion Records. Catalogue no: **CHAMP 12R 55***
12" Single: Released Aug '87, on Champion, by Champion Records. Catalogue no: **CHAMP 1255**
12" Single: Released Nov '85, on Champion, by Champion Records. Catalogue no: **CHAMPZ 12-55**
7" Single: Released Nov '87, on Champion, by Champion Records. Catalogue no: **CHAMPX 55**
7" Single: Released Aug '87, on Champion, by Champion Records. Catalogue no: **CHAMP 55**

Syke Dyke

STREET FREAK
Tracks: / Street freak / Street freak (version).
7" Single: Released 14 May '88, on 4th & Broadway (USA), by Island Records (USA). Deleted Dec '88. Catalogue no: **BRW 95**
12" Single: Released 14 May '88, on 4th & Broadway (USA), by Island Records (USA). Deleted Dec '88. Catalogue no: **12 BRW 95**

Sykes, John

PLEASE DON'T LEAVE ME
Tracks: / Please don't leave / Please don't leave (pt 2).
7" Single: Released Sep '82, on MCA, by MCA Records. Deleted Sep '85. Catalogue no: **MCA 792**

Sykes, Keith

LOVE TO RIDE
Tracks: / Love to ride / I'm not strange.
7" Single: Released Mar '81, on MCA, by MCA Records. Deleted Mar '84. Catalogue no: **MCA 668**

Sylum

I'M IMPRESSED
Tracks: / I'm impressed.
7" Single: Released Sep '85, on FM, by FM-Revolver Records. Catalogue no: **VHF 20**

Sylvain, Sylvain

EVERY BOY AND EVERY GIRL
Tracks: / Every boy and every girl / Emily.
7" Single: Released Feb '80, on RCA, by BMG Records (UK). Deleted Feb '83. Catalogue no: **PB 9500**

Sylvan, Rikki

WATCH THAT SOUND
Tracks: / Watch that sound / Nomansland.
7" Single: Released Aug '81, on KRL, by Kaleidoscope Records (UK). Deleted '84. Catalogue no: **A 1278**

Sylve

I'VE ONLY GOT YOU TO BLAME
Tracks: / I've only got you to blame / I've only got you to blame (Birmingham mix).
7" Single: Released Aug '89, on Power, Catalogue no: **ZAK 3**

SYLVESTER - ROCK THE BOX (Released on Cool Tempo)

Sylvers, Edmund

THAT BURNING LOVE
Tracks: / That burning love / You went away.
7" Single: Released Oct '80, on Casablanca, by PolyGram UK Ltd. Deleted Oct '83. Catalogue no: **CAN 208**

Sylvester

BAND OF GOLD
Tracks: / Band of gold.
7" Single: Released Aug '83, on London Records, by London Records. Catalogue no: **LON 33**
12" Single: Released Aug '83, on London Records, by London Records. Catalogue no: **LONX 33**

DANCE (DISCO HEAT)
Tracks: / Dance (disco heat).
7" Single: Released Nov '78, on Fantasy (1), by BMG Records (UK). Deleted '81. Catalogue no: **FTC 163**

DO YA WANNA FUNK
Tracks: / Do you wanna funk.
12" Single: Released Sep '82, on London Records, by London Records. Catalogue no: **LONX 13**
Cassingle: Released Oct '89, on London Records, by London Records. Catalogue no: **LONC 13**
7" Single: Released Sep '82, on London Records, by London Records. Catalogue no: **LON 13**

DO YOU WANNA FUNK (2)
Tracks: / Do you wanna funk (Housey, housey mix) / Menergy / Do you wanna funk (original mix) / Do you wanna funk.
12" Single: Released Aug '86, on Domino, by Domino Records. Catalogue no: **DOM T4**

DON'T STOP
Tracks: / Don't stop.
7" Single: Released May '83, on London Records, by London Records. Catalogue no: **LON 23**
12" Single: Released May '83, on London Records, by London Records. Catalogue no: **LONX 23**

HERE IS MY LOVE
Tracks: / Here is my love / Give it up.
12" Single: Released Aug '81, on Fantasy (1), by BMG Records (UK). Deleted '84. Catalogue no: **FTCT 197**

I (WHO HAVE NOTHING)
Tracks: / I (who have nothing).
7" Single: Released Mar '79, on Fantasy (1), by BMG Records (UK). Deleted '82. Catalogue no: **FTC 171**

LIVING FOR THE CITY
Tracks: / Living for the city / Living for the city (dub mix).
12" Single: Released Mar '86, on Creole, by Creole Records. Catalogue no: **CRT 90**
7" Single: Released Mar '86, on Creole, by Creole Records. Catalogue no: **CR 90**

MENERGY
Tracks: / Menergy / Won't you let me love you.
7" Single: Released Aug '84, on ERC, Catalogue no: **ERC 200**
12" Single: Released Aug '84, on ERC, Catalogue no: **ERCL 200**

MUTUAL ATTRACTION (SINGLE)
Tracks: / Mutual attraction.
7" Single: Deleted Jan '88. Catalogue no: **W 8382**
12" Single: Deleted Jan '88. Catalogue no: **W 8382T**

ROCK THE BOX (see panel above)
Tracks: / Rock the box / Rock the box (dub).
12" Single: Released '86, on Cool Tempo, by Chrysalis Records. Catalogue no: **COOLX 104**

SELL MY SOUL (SINGLE)
Tracks: / Sell my soul / Sell my soul (pt 2).
12" Single: Released Oct '80, on Fantasy (1), by BMG Records (UK). Deleted Oct '83. Catalogue no: **FTCT 192**
7" Single: Released Oct '80, on Fantasy (1), by BMG Records (UK). Deleted Oct '83. Catalogue no: **FTC 192**

STARS
Tracks: / Stars.
7" Single: Released Aug '79, on Fantasy (1), by BMG Records (UK). Deleted '82. Catalogue no: **FTC 177**

YOU MAKE ME FEEL (MIGHTY REAL)
Tracks: / You make me feel (mighty real) / You make me feel (mighty real) (version) / Stars (everybody is one) (Only on 12" and CD single.) / Over and over (Only on CD single.).
7" Single: Released Aug '78, on Fantasy (1), by BMG Records (UK). Deleted '81. Catalogue no: **FTC 160**
CD 5": Released 2 May '89, on South Bound, Catalogue no: **CD SEWT 700**
7" Single: Released 2 May '89, on South Bound, Catalogue no: **SEWS 700**
12" Single: Released 2 May '89, on South Bound, Catalogue no: **SEWT 700**

Sylvia

HASTA LA VISTA
Tracks: / Hasta la vista.
7" Single: Released Apr '75, on Sonet, by Sonet Records. Deleted '78. Catalogue no: **SON 2005**
7" Single: Released Sep '76, on Sonet, by Sonet Records. Catalogue no: **SON 2093**

NOBODY
Tracks: / Nobody / I'll make it right with you.
7" Single: Released Jan '83, on RCA, by BMG Records (UK). Catalogue no: **RCA 298**

PILLOW TALK
Tracks: / Pillow talk.
7" Single: Released Jun '73, on London-American, Deleted '76. Catalogue no: **HL 10415**
7" Single: Released '80, on London Records, by London Records. Catalogue no: **LR 0884**

PILLOW TALK (OLD GOLD)
Tracks: / Pillow talk.
7" Single: Released Jul '84, on Old Gold, by Old Gold Records. Deleted Jul '88. Catalogue no: **OG 9414**

READ ALL ABOUT IT
Tracks: / Read all about it.
7" Single: Released Jun '85, on RCA, by BMG Records (UK). Catalogue no: **PB 49979**

Y VIVA ESPANA
Tracks: / Y viva espana.
7" Single: Released Aug '74, on Sonet, by Sonet Records. Deleted '77. Catalogue no: **SON 2037**

Sylvia & The Sapphires

BABY I'M A FOOL FOR YOU
Tracks: / Baby I'm a fool for you / I only wish tonight could last forever.
7" Single: Released Oct '82, on Stiff, by Stiff Records. Catalogue no: **BUY 162**
12" Single: Released Nov '82, on Stiff, by Stiff Records. Catalogue no: **BUYIT 162**

SHOPPING AROUND
Tracks: / Shopping around.
7" Pic: Released Jul '82, on Stiff, by Stiff Records. Catalogue no: **PBUY 154**
7" Single: Released Jul '82, on Stiff, by Stiff Records. Catalogue no: **BUY 154**

Sylvian, David

BAMBOO HOUSES
Tracks: / Bamboo houses / Bamboo music.
7" Single: Released Jul '82, on Virgin, by Virgin Records. Catalogue no: **VS 510**
12" Single: Released Jul '82, on Virgin, by Virgin Records. Catalogue no: **VS 510-12**

FORBIDDEN COLOURS
Tracks: / Forbidden colours / Bamboo houses (CD only) / Bamboo music (CD only) / Seed and the sower, The (7 & 12" only) / Last regrets (12" only).
7" Single: Released Jun '83, on Virgin, by Virgin Records. Catalogue no: **VS 601**
12" Single: Released Jun '83, on Virgin, by Virgin Records. Catalogue no: **VS 601-12**
CD 3": Released Jun '88, on Virgin, by Virgin Records. Catalogue no: **CDT 18**

INK IN THE WELL, THE
Tracks: / Ink in the well, The / Weathered wall (instrumental).
7" Single: Released Aug '84, on Virgin, by Virgin Records. Deleted '87. Catalogue no: **VS 700**
12" Single: Released '84, on Virgin, by Virgin Records. Catalogue no: **VS 700-12**

LET THE HAPPINESS IN
Tracks: / Let the happiness in / Blue of noon / Buoy (remix).
12" Single: Released Sep '87, on Virgin, by Virgin Records. Catalogue no: **VST 1001**
7" Single: Released Sep '87, on Virgin, by Virgin Records. Deleted May '88. Catalogue no: **VS 1001**

ORPHEUS
Tracks: / Orpheus / Mother and child / Devil's own, The (12" only).
7" Single: Released Apr '88, on Virgin, by Virgin Records. Catalogue no: **VS 1043**
12" Single: Released Apr '88, on Virgin, by Virgin Records. Catalogue no: **VST 1043**

PULLING PUNCHES
Tracks: / Pulling punches (extended) / Back waters.
7" Single: Released Nov '84, on Virgin, by Virgin Records. Deleted '87. Catalogue no: **VS 717**
12" Single: Released '84, on Virgin, by Virgin Records. Catalogue no: **VS 717-12**

RED GUITAR
Tracks: / Red guitar (full length version) / Forbidden colours (version).
12" Single: Released '83, on Virgin, by Virgin Records. Catalogue no: **VS 633-12**
7" Single: Released Jun '84, on Virgin, by Virgin Records. Deleted '87. Catalogue no: **VS 633**

SILVER MOON
Tracks: / Silver moon / Gone to Earth / Silver moon over sleeping steeples (12" only).
7" Single: Released Sep '86, on Virgin, by Virgin Records. Catalogue no: **VS 895**
12" Single: Released Sep '86, on Virgin, by Virgin Records. Catalogue no: **VS 895-12**

TAKING THE VEIL
Tracks: / Taking the veil / Answered prayers / Bird of prey vanishes into a bright blue cloudless sky, A (12" only).
12" Single: Released Jul '86, on Virgin, by Virgin Records. Catalogue no: **VS 815-12**
7" Single: Released Jul '86, on Virgin, by Virgin Records. Catalogue no: **VS 815**

WORDS WITH THE SHAMAN
Tracks: / Ancient evening (Part 1 of Words with the Shaman) / Incantation (Part 2 of Words with the Shaman) / Awakening (Songs from the Tree Tops) (Part 3 of Words with the Shaman).
CD 3": Released '88, on Virgin, by Virgin Records. Catalogue no: **CDT 23**
7" Single: Released Dec '85, on Virgin, by Virgin Records. Deleted '88. Catalogue no: **VS 835**
12" Single: Released Nov '85, on Virgin, by Virgin Records. Catalogue no: **VS 835-12**

SYMARIP - SKINHEAD MOONSTOMP (Released on Trojan)

Symarip

SKINHEAD MOONSTOMP (see panel above)
Tracks: / Skinhead moonstomp / Shinhead jamboree.
Note: The skinheads, more than any other group were the father of today's Punk movement. Anti-establishment, short hair, footstomping, rebellious, epitomising the skinhead cult of the early 70's. Now they're back in full cry, and the huge demand for Skinhead Moonstomp has brought about the re-issue of this classic on a maxi-single coupled with two other titles symbolising an era past and present.
7" Single: Released Feb '80, on Trojan, by Trojan Records. Deleted '83. Catalogue no: **TRO 9062**

Symbolic Three

NO SHOW
Tracks: / No show / We're treacherous / Tell off (Track on 12" version only.).
7" Single: Released Jan '86, on PRT, by Castle Communications Records. Catalogue no: **7P 345**
12" Single: Released Jan '86, on PRT, by Castle Communications Records. Catalogue no: **12P 345**

Symbols

BEST PART OF BREAKING UP
Tracks: / Best part of breaking up.
7" Single: Released Jan '68, on President, by President Records. Deleted '71. Catalogue no: **PT 173**

BYE BYE BABY
Tracks: / Bye bye baby.
7" Single: Released Aug '67, on President, by President Records. Deleted '70. Catalogue no: **PT 144**

Symphony In X

DREAMS NEVER DIE
Tracks: / Dreams never die.
7" Single: Released May '89, on Synthetic Dance, Catalogue no: **SYNSON SII 60A**

Syncbeat

MUSIC (DANCE)
Tracks: / Music (dance mix) / Music (original mix).
12" Single: Released Aug '84, on Streetwise, Catalogue no: **MKHAN 18**

Syncopation

MARKING TIME
Tracks: / Marking time / Syncopation.
7" Single: Released Feb '82, on Factory (1), by Factory Records. Catalogue no: **ASL 4**

Syn-Dee

BEST 2 B A GIRL
Tracks: / Best 2 B a girl / Low down bonus beats / Best 2 B a girl (instrumental) (12" only).
12" Single: Released 1 Aug '88, on Virgin, by Virgin Records. Catalogue no: **VST 1111**
7" Single: Released 1 Aug '88, on Virgin, by Virgin Records. Catalogue no: **VS 1111**

WHICH WAY IS UP
Tracks: / Which way is up.
12" Single: Released Feb '89, on Big One Records, by Big One Records. Catalogue no: **VVBIG 014**

Syndicate

BABY'S GONE
Tracks: / Baby's gone / 55 (Not on CD single.) / Melting (Not on 7".) / Winner gets the dinner, The (CD single only.) / Buildings in the sky (Not on 7".).
CD 5": Released Jun '89, on EMI, by EMI Records. Catalogue no: **CDEM 93**
CD 5": Released Jun '89, on EMI, by EMI Records. Catalogue no: **203 408 2**
7" Single: Released Jun '89, on EMI, by EMI Records. Catalogue no: **203 408 7**
7" Single: Released Jun '89, on EMI, by EMI Records. Catalogue no: **EM 93**
12" Single: Released Jun '89, on EMI, by EMI Records. Catalogue no: **12EM 93**
12" Single: Released Jun '89, on EMI, by EMI Records. Catalogue no: **203 408 6**

DANCE YOU TO THE GROUND
Tracks: / Dance you to the ground / Step on the gas.
7" Single: Released Jul '81, on EMI, by EMI Records. Catalogue no: **EMI 5182**
12" Single: Released Jun '81, on EMI, by EMI Records. Catalogue no: **12EMI 518 2**

GOIN' FOR IT
Tracks: / Goin' for it.
12" Single: Released May '88, on Baad, by Baad Records. Catalogue no: **BAD 777**

GOLDEN KEY
Tracks: / Golden key.
12" Single: Released Jun '85, on Supreme Int.Editions, by Supreme Int.Records. Catalogue no: **EDITION 85-9**

HERE COMES THE DAY
Tracks: / Here comes the day / Nostalgia locomotion / I love Hollywood (the demo) (Not on 7".) / Don't let tomorrow be unkind (Not on 7".) / Here comes the day (full length) (12" only.).
7" Single: Released Sep '89, on EMI, by EMI Records. Catalogue no: **EM 106**
12" Single: Released Sep '89, on EMI, by EMI Records. Catalogue no: **12EM 106**
7" Single: Released Sep '89, on EMI, by EMI Records. Catalogue no: **203 532 7**
CD 5": Released Sep '89, on EMI, by EMI Records. Catalogue no: **CDEM 106**
CD 5": Released Sep '89, on EMI, by EMI Records. Catalogue no: **203 532 2**
12" Single: Released Sep '89, on EMI, by EMI Records. Catalogue no: **203 532 6**

Syndrome

SHINE ON US (SINGLE)
Tracks: / Shine on us.
7" Single: Released Jul '83, on Sometimes, Catalogue no: **PG 1**

Synphonic variations

SNOWMEN
Tracks: / Seasons / Snowmen.
7" Single: Released Nov '86, on CBS, by CBS Records. Catalogue no: **650163 7**

Syntax

FOOL, THE
Tracks: / Fool, The.
7" Single: Released Oct '81, on Pith, Deleted '82. Catalogue no: **PITH 1**

Synthetic

SULPHATE SUICIDE
Tracks: / Sulphate suicide.
7" Single: Released May '82, on Logical Step, Catalogue no: **LOGIC 03**

Synthetic Dreams

OBSESSION
Tracks: / Obsession.
7" Single: Released Oct '81, on Logical Step, Catalogue no: **LOGIC 02**

Synthetic Orchestra

E.T., THEME FROM
Tracks: / E.T., Theme from.
7" Single: Released Feb '83, on PRT, by Castle Communications Records. Catalogue no: **7VJ 102**

Synthetics

JAPANESE TOYS
Tracks: / Japanese toys / Johnny & The Gaumonts.
7" Single: Released Jul '82, on Cheapskate, Catalogue no: **CHEAP 45**

Synthia

YOU WERE DOING BAD WHEN I MET CHA
Tracks: / You were doing bad when I met cha / You were doing bad when I met cha (version).
12" Single: Released Sep '89, on Gold Key, Catalogue no: **12 PO 28**

Syreeta

CAN'T SHAKE YOUR LOVE
Tracks: / Can't shake your love / Wish upon a star.
7" Single: Released Aug '82, on Motown, by BMG Records (UK). Catalogue no: **TMG 1275**
12" Single: Released Aug '82, on Motown, by BMG Records (UK). Catalogue no: **TMGT 1275**

FOREVER IS NOT ENOUGH
Tracks: / Forever is not enough.
7" Single: Released May '83, on Motown, by BMG Records (UK). Catalogue no: **TMG 1306**
12" Single: Released May '83, on Motown, by BMG Records (UK). Catalogue no: **TMGT 1306**

GO FOR IT
Tracks: / Go for it.
7" Single: Released Oct '81, on Motown, by BMG Records (UK). Catalogue no: **TMG 1139**

HARMOUR LOVE
Tracks: / Harmour love.
7" Single: Released Aug '75, on Tamla Motown, by Motown Records (UK). Deleted '78. Catalogue no: **TMG 954**

HE'S GONE
Tracks: / He's gone / Here's my love.
7" Single: Released Oct '81, on Motown, by BMG Records (UK). Catalogue no: **TMG 1200**

I MUST BE IN LOVE
Tracks: / I must be in love / Out of the box.
7" Single: Released Apr '82, on Motown, by BMG Records (UK). Catalogue no: **TMG 1258**
12" Single: Released Apr '82, on Motown, by BMG Records (UK). Catalogue no: **TMGT 1258**

IT WILL COME IN TIME
Tracks: / It will come in time.
7" Single: Released Oct '81, on Motown, by BMG Records (UK). Deleted '83. Catalogue no: **TMG 1175**

ONE MORE TIME FOR LOVE
Tracks: / One more time for love.
7" Single: Released Oct '81, on Motown, by BMG Records (UK). Deleted '83. Catalogue no: **TMG 1188**

PLEASE STAY
Tracks: / Please stay.
7" Single: Released Oct '81, on Motown, by BMG Records (UK). Deleted '83. Catalogue no: **TMG 1211**

QUICK SLICK
Tracks: / Quick slick / I don't know.
7" Single: Released Nov '81, on Motown, by BMG Records (UK). Catalogue no: **TMG 1247**
12" Single: Released Dec '81, on Motown, by BMG Records (UK). Catalogue no: **TMGT 1247**

SPINNIN' AND SPINNIN'
Tracks: / Spinnin' and spinnin'.
7" Single: Released Sep '74, on Tamla Motown, by Motown Records (UK). Deleted '77. Catalogue no: **TMG 912**

WITH YOU I'M BORN AGAIN
Tracks: / With you I'm born again.
7" Single: Released Oct '81, on Motown, by BMG Records (UK). Catalogue no: **TMG 1159**

YOUR KISS IS SWEET
Tracks: / Your kiss is sweet.
7" Single: Released Feb '75, on Tamla Motown, by Motown Records (UK). Deleted '78. Catalogue no: **TMG 933**

System

60 WATT PEARL
Tracks: / 60 watt pearl / Fergie.
7" Single: Released Jul '81, on MCA, by MCA Records. Deleted '84. Catalogue no: **MCA 731**

COME AS YOU ARE (SUPERSTAR)
Tracks: / Modern girl / Come as you are (superstar).
12" Single: Released Feb '87, on Atlantic, by WEA Records. Deleted Jan '88. Catalogue no: **A 9297 T**
7" Single: Released Feb '87, on Atlantic, by WEA Records. Deleted Jan '88. Catalogue no: **A 9297**

COMING TO AMERICA
Tracks: / Coming to America (part one) / Coming to America (part two).
12" Single: Released 22 Aug '88, on Atlantic, by WEA Records. Catalogue no: **A 9320 T**
7" Single: Released 22 Aug '88, on Atlantic, by WEA Records. Catalogue no: **A 9320**

I WANNA MAKE YOU FEEL GOOD
Tracks: / I wanna make you feel good / Promises can break.
7" Single: Released Jun '84, on Polydor, by Polydor Ltd. Deleted '87. Catalogue no: **POSP 685**

NIGHT TIME LOVER
Tracks: / Night time lover / Save me.
12" Single: Released Nov '87, on Atlantic, by WEA Records. Deleted Jul '88. Catalogue no: **A 922 T**
7" Single: Released Nov '87, on Atlantic, by WEA Records. Deleted Jul '88. Catalogue no: **A 9222**

WARFARE (EP)
Tracks: / Warfare.
7" Single: Released Jun '82, on Spiderleg, Catalogue no: **SDL 4**

System Beat

SYSTEM BEAT 1
12" Single: Released '87, on 1 In 12, by Backs Recording Co.. Catalogue no: **ONEIN 12004**

SYSTEM BEAT 2
12" Single: Released '87, on 1 In 12, by Backs Recording Co.. Catalogue no: **ONEIN 12005**

Systematic

SOUL TO SOUL
Tracks: / Soul to soul.
12" Single: Released Jul '88, on Rise, Catalogue no: **RISET 15**

SURE AIN'T NEWS
Tracks: / Sure ain't news.
12" Single: Released 20 Feb '88, on Rise, Catalogue no: **RISET 11**

Systems

TOTAL RECALL
Tracks: / Total recall.
7" Single: Released Oct '81, on Open Eye, by Open Eye Records. Catalogue no: **OE 006**

T

The following information was taken from the Music Master database on October 20th, 1989.

T.34

ROCK ON
Tracks: / Rock on / Looking after me.
7" Single: Released Feb '83, on Galaxy (1), by Galaxy Records. Catalogue no: **GAL 007**

T 99

INVISIBLE SENSUALITY
Tracks: / Invisible sensuality.
CD 5": Released Oct '88, on Who's That Beat, by Play It Again Sam (Belgium). Catalogue no: **WHOS 002 CD**
7" Single: Released '88, on Who's That Beat, by Play It Again Sam (Belgium). Catalogue no: **WHOS 002-7**
12" Single: Released '88, on Who's That Beat, by Play It Again Sam (Belgium). Catalogue no: **WHOS 002**

SLIDY
Tracks: / Slidy.
CD 5": Released Oct '88, on Who's That Beat, by Play It Again Sam (Belgium). Catalogue no: **WHOS 004 CD**
7" Single: Released Oct '88, on Who's That Beat, by Play It Again Sam (Belgium). Catalogue no: **WHOS 004 7**
12" Single: Released Oct '88, on Who's That Beat, by Play It Again Sam (Belgium). Catalogue no: **WHOS 004**

TOO NICE TO BE REAL
Tracks: / Too nice to be real.
CD 5": Released May '89, on Who's That Beat, by Play It Again Sam (Belgium). Catalogue no: **WHOS 16 CD**
12" Single: Released May '89, on Who's That Beat, by Play It Again Sam (Belgium). Catalogue no: **WHOS 16**

T. Brothers

BLUE MOON
Tracks: / Blue moon / Jumpin' Jack Flash.
7" Single: Released Mar '80, on EMI, by EMI Records. Deleted Mar '83. Catalogue no: **EMI 5048**

T, Claudia

DANCE WITH ME
Tracks: / Dance with me.
7" Single: Released Mar '89, on Loading Bay, Catalogue no: **LBAY 2**

T, Don

RUDE BOY DON'T
Tracks: / Rude boy don't.
7" Single: Released May '89, on Steppa, Catalogue no: **UNKNOWN**

T Jam

HOUSE DANCE
Tracks: / House dance / We can dance.
7" Single: Released Apr '89, on Hot Melt, by Hot Melt Records. Catalogue no: **7TC 21**
12" Single: Released Apr '89, on Hot Melt, by Hot Melt Records. Catalogue no: **12TC 21**

HOUSE OF JACK
Tracks: / House of jack.
12" Single: Released 20 Feb '88, on Hot Melt, by Hot Melt Records. Catalogue no: **12 TCT 12**

T LA Rock

BACK TO BURN
Tracks: / Back to burn.
7" Single: Released Jan '87, on 10 Records, by Virgin Records. Deleted May '88. Catalogue no: **TEN 145**
12" Single: Released Jan '87, on 10 Records, by Virgin Records. Deleted '89. Catalogue no: **TENT 145**

BASS MACHINE
Tracks: / Breakin' bells / Bass machine (7" only) / Bass machine (Club version) (12" only) / Bass machine (Radio version) (12" only) / Breakin' bells (Omar Santana edit) (12" only).
7" Single: Released Sep '86, on 10 Records, by Virgin Records. Deleted May '88. Catalogue no: **TEN 154**
12" Single: Released Sep '86, on 10 Records, by Virgin Records. Catalogue no: **TENT 154**

FLOW WITH THE NEW STYLE
Tracks: / Flow with the new style.
12" Single: Released 9 Jan '89, on Sleeping Bag, by Sleeping Bag Records. Catalogue no: **SBUK 2T**

THIS BEAT KICKS
Tracks: / This beat kicks (Chad beat remix) / Having fun (12" only) / Back to burn (club version).
12" Single: Released Jun '87, on 10 Records, by Virgin Records. Catalogue no: **TENT 179**

T. Rex

20TH CENTURY BOY
Tracks: / 20th century boy / Dreamy lady / Groover / New York City.
7" Single: Released Mar '73, on EMI, by EMI Records. Deleted Mar '76. Catalogue no: **MARC 4**
7" Single: Released Aug '82, on EMI, by EMI Records. Catalogue no: **MARC 21**

CHILDREN OF THE REVOLUTION
Tracks: / Children of the revolution.
Note: Extra track on 12" only
12" Single: Released Feb '87, on Marc On Wax, Catalogue no: **12 MARC 1**
7" Single: Released Jul '82, on EMI, by EMI Records. Catalogue no: **MARC 20**
7" Single: Released Feb '87, on Marc On Wax, Catalogue no: **MARC 1**
7" Single: Released Sep '72, on EMI, by EMI Records. Deleted Sep '75. Catalogue no: **MARC 2**

DEBORA
Tracks: / Deborah.
7" Single: Released May '68, on Regal Zonophone, by EMI Records. Deleted May '71. Catalogue no: **RZ 3008**

DEBORA (2)
Tracks: / Deborah / One inch rock.
7" Single: Released Apr '72, on Magnifly, by Fly Records. Deleted Apr '75. Catalogue no: **ECHO 102**

DEBORA (OLD GOLD)
Tracks: / Deborah.
7" Single: Released Aug '82, on Old Gold, by Old Gold Records. Deleted Jul '88. Catalogue no: **OG 9234**

DREAMY LADY
Tracks: / Dreamy lady.
7" Single: Released Nov '75, on EMI, by EMI Records. Deleted Nov '78. Catalogue no: **MARC 11**

GET IT ON (OLD GOLD)
Tracks: / Get it on / Jeepster.
7" Single: Released 27 Feb '89, on Old Gold, by Old Gold Records. Catalogue no: **OG 9230**

GET IT ON (SINGLE)
Tracks: / Get it on.
Note: 12" single 12 MARCY 10 is yellow vinyl. 12" single 12 MARCB 10 is blue vinyl.
7" Pic: Released Apr '87, on Marc On Wax, Catalogue no: **MARCX 1**
Cassingle: Released 23 May '87, on Marc On Wax, Catalogue no: **MARCT 10**
7" Single: Released Jul '71, on Fly, by Fly Records. Deleted Jul '74. Catalogue no: **BUG 10**
12" Single: Released May '85, on T. Rex, Catalogue no: **FED 12**
12" Single: Released Apr '87, on Marc On Wax, Catalogue no: **12MARCB 10**
12" Single: Released Apr '87, on Marc On Wax, Catalogue no: **12 MARCY 10**
7" Single: Released Apr '87, on Marc On Wax, Catalogue no: **MARC 10**
7" Single: Released Aug '82, on Cube, Catalogue no: **BAK 4**
7" Single: Released '80, on EMI, by EMI Records. Catalogue no: **LR 1901**

GROOVER, THE
Tracks: / Groover, The.
7" Single: Released Jun '73, on EMI, by EMI Records. Catalogue no: **MARC 5**

HOT LOVE
Tracks: / Hot love.
7" Single: Released Feb '71, on Fly, by Fly Records. Deleted Feb '73. Catalogue no: **BUG 6**
7" Single: Released Aug '82, on Cube, Catalogue no: **BAK 3**

HOT LOVE (OLD GOLD)
Tracks: / Hot love / Ride a white swan.
7" Single: Released Jul '82, on Old Gold, by Old Gold Records. Catalogue no: **OG 9229**

I LOVE TO BOOGIE
Tracks: / I love to boogie / Hot love / Ride a white swan / Hot George*.
12" Single: Released Sep '87, on Marc On Wax, Catalogue no: **12 MARC 11**
7" Single: Released Sep '87, on Marc On Wax, Catalogue no: **MARC 11**
Cassingle: Released Sep '87, on Marc On Wax, Catalogue no: **MARCD 11**

I LOVE TO BOOGIE (2)
Tracks: / I love to boogie.
7" Single: Released May '76, on EMI, by EMI Records. Deleted May '79. Catalogue no: **MARC 14**

JEEPSTER
Tracks: / Jeepster.
7" Single: Released Nov '71, on Fly, by Fly Records. Deleted Nov '74. Catalogue no: **BUG 16**

KING OF THE RUMBLING SPIRES
Tracks: / King of the rumbling spires.
7" Single: Released Aug '69, on Regal Zonophone, by EMI Records. Catalogue no: **RZ 3022**

LASER LOVE
Tracks: / Laser love.
7" Single: Released Oct '76, on EMI, by EMI Records. Deleted Oct '79. Catalogue no: **MARC 15**

LIGHT OF LOVE
Tracks: / Light of love.
7" Single: Released Jun '74, on EMI, by EMI Records. Deleted Jun '77. Catalogue no: **MARC 8**

LONDON BOYS
Tracks: / London boys.
7" Single: Released Mar '76, on EMI, by EMI Records. Deleted Mar '79. Catalogue no: **MARC 13**

METAL GURU
Tracks: / Metal guru.
7" Single: Released Sep '72, on EMI, by EMI Records. Deleted Sep '75. Catalogue no: **MARC 1**

NEW YORK CITY
Tracks: / New York city.
7" Single: Released Jun '75, on EMI, by EMI Records. Deleted Jun '78. Catalogue no: **MARC 10**

ONE INCH ROCK
Tracks: / One inch rock.
7" Single: Released Sep '68, on Regal Zonophone, by EMI Records. Deleted Sep '71. Catalogue no: **RZ 3011**
7" Single: Released Aug '82, on Cube, Catalogue no: **BAK 5**

PEEL SESSIONS:T REX
12" Single: Released Aug '87, on Strange Fruit, by Strange Fruit Records. Catalogue no: **SFPS 031**

RETURN OF THE ELECTRIC WARRIOR (EP)
Tracks: / Return of the electric warrior.
7" Single: Released May '81, on Rarn, Deleted May '84. Catalogue no: **MBSF 001**

RIDE A WHITE SWAN
Tracks: / Ride a white swan / Jeepster / Hot love.
Note: All tracks produced by Tony Visconti for Straight Ahead Productions Ltd. All tracks written by M. Bolan. All tracks licensed from C-Era Records Ltd.
7" Single: Released Oct '70, on Fly, by Fly Records. Deleted Oct '73. Catalogue no: **BUG 1**
12" Single: Released Aug '86, on Archive 4, by Castle Communications Records. Catalogue no: **TOF 102**

SOLID GOLD EASY ACTION (OLD GOLD)
Tracks: / Solid gold easy action / 20th century boy / Groover, The.
CD 5": Released 24 Apr '89, on Old Gold, by Old Gold Records. Deleted May '89. Catalogue no: **OG 6134**

SOLID GOLD EASY ACTION (SINGLE)
Tracks: / Solid gold easy action.
7" Single: Released Dec '72, on EMI, by EMI Records. Deleted Dec '75. Catalogue no: **MARC 3**

SOUL OF MY SUIT, THE
Tracks: / Soul of my suit, The.
7" Single: Released Apr '77, on EMI, by EMI Records. Deleted Apr '80. Catalogue no: **MARC 16**

T. REX (SINGLE)
Tracks: / Hot love / Get it on / Telegram Sam / Metal guru.
CD 3": Released '88, on Special Edition, by Castle Communications Records. Catalogue no: **CD3-13**

TEENAGE DREAM (SINGLE)
Tracks: / Teenage dream.
7" Single: Released Feb '74, on EMI, by EMI Records. Deleted Feb '77. Catalogue no: **MARC 7**

TELEGRAM SAM
Tracks: / Telegram Sam.
7" Single: Released Jan '72, on T. Rex, Deleted Jan '75. Catalogue no: **T REX 101**
7" Single: Released '80, on EMI, by EMI Records. Catalogue no: **LR 1901**
7" Single: Released Sep '82, on T. Rex, Catalogue no: **MARC 23**
7" Single: Released Mar '82, on T. Rex, Catalogue no: **TREX 101**

TELEGRAM SAM (OLD GOLD)
Tracks: / Telegram Sam / Metal guru / Children of the revolution.
CD 5": Released 28 Mar '89, on Old Gold, by Old Gold Records. Catalogue no: **OG 6130**

TRUCK ON (TYKE)
Tracks: / Truck on (tyke) / Zip gun boogie / Teenage dream / Light of love.
7" Single: Released Nov '73, on EMI, by EMI Records. Deleted Nov '76. Catalogue no: **MARC 6**
7" Single: Released Sep '82, on T. Rex, Catalogue no: **MARC 22**

ZIP GUN BOOGIE (SINGLE)
Tracks: / Zip gun boogie.
7" Single: Released Nov '74, on EMI, by EMI Records. Deleted Nov '77. Catalogue no: **MARC 9**

T & The Unknown

MY GENERATION
Tracks: / My generation / Woodstook rock.
7" Single: Released Mar '80, on Carrere, Deleted '83. Catalogue no: **CAR 142**

Ta Mara & The Seen

AFFECTION
Tracks: / Affection / Everybody dance / Summertime love (Track on 12" version only).
7" Single: Released Feb '86, on A&M, by A&M Records. Deleted '88. Catalogue no: **AM 301**
12" Single: Released Feb '86, on A&M, by A&M Records. Deleted '88. Catalogue no: **AMY 301**

Taaga

FRIEND OF MINE
Tracks: / Friend of mine, A.
7" Single: Released Nov '83, on Taaga Trax, Catalogue no: **PAW 1**

Tabloids

PIXIE HAMMERS
Tracks: / Pixie hammers.
7" Single: Released Jun '84, on Hackney, by Hackney Records. Catalogue no: **HACK 1**

Taboo

INTO THE SUN
Tracks: / Into the sun.
12" Single: Released '88, on Subway, by Subway Records. Catalogue no: **SUB 016**

NO. 6
Tracks: / No. 6 / Hypnotique.
7" Single: Released Nov '88, on Anagram, by Cherry Red Records. Catalogue no: **ANA 44**
12" Single: Released Nov '88, on Anagram, by Cherry Red Records. Catalogue no: **12 ANA 44**

TINTIN TO THE RESCUE

Tracks: / Tintin to the rescue (West).
12" Single: Released Apr '89, on Anagram, by Cherry Red Records. Catalogue no: **12 ANAD 49**

Tabor, June

Biographical details: June Tabor was born in 1947 in Warwick; she is one of the country's best-loved folksingers, influenced by traditional music but praised in turn by people like Steve Winwood and Elvis Costello. Her first album was *Silly Sisters* in 1976 (on Chrysalis;later on Takoma, then Shanachie in USA), a collaboration with Maddy Prior with Martin Carthy and Nic Jones in the backing group. Her solo debut was *Airs And Graces* on Topic the same year, with stunning singing including an Eric Bogle song, *The Band That Played Waltzing Matilda*, much covered by others. She guested on a Peter Bellamy album, *The Transports*, that year; *Ashes and Diamonds* (1977) on Topic was later complemented by the John Peel Sessions on Strange Fruit, a radio broadcast from '77. She does not work full-time and her output is not prolific; *A Cut Above* '80 on Topic is a collaboration with guitarist Martin Simpson (born in 1953 in Scunthorpe); *Abbysinians* (1983) is regarded as her masterpiece, her formidable talent fully realised. She also sessioned with Bill Caddick, the Albion Band, Ashley Hutchings, others; sang TV themes; guested with Fairport Convention in 1987. (Donald Clarke 13.1.88).

PEEL SESSIONS:JUNE TABOR 22.2.77
12" Single: Released Nov '86, on Strange Fruit, by Strange Fruit Records. Catalogue no: **SFPS 015**

SPY SHIP THEME
Tracks: / Spy ship theme.
7" Single: Released Nov '83, on BBC, by BBC Records & Tapes. Deleted Sep '87. Catalogue no: **RESL 140**

Tack Head

WHAT'S MY MISSION NOW?
Tracks: / What's my mission now? (fight the devil) / Now what.
7" Single: Released Oct '85, on On-U-Sound, by On-U-Sound Records. Catalogue no: **DP 13**
7" Single: Released Nov '87, on On-U-Sound, by On-U-Sound Records. Catalogue no: **ONUDP 3**

Tackhead

GAME, THE
Tracks: / Game, The / You'll never walk alone.
7" Pic: Released Apr '87, on 4th & Broadway, by Island Records. Catalogue no: **BRWP 65**

REALITY
Tracks: / Reality / Reality (Dub).
12" Single: Released 21 Nov '87, on On-U-Sound, by On-U-Sound Records. Catalogue no: **ONUDP 19**
12" Single: Released Apr '89, on World, by World Records. Catalogue no: **WRO 14**

TICKING TIME BOMB
Tracks: / Ticking time bomb / Body to burn.
12" Single: Released Mar '89, on World, by World Records. Catalogue no: **WR 012**

Taco

LET'S FACE THE MUSIC AND DANCE
Tracks: / Let's face the music and dance / Sayonara.
7" Single: Released May '84, on RCA, by BMG Records (UK). Catalogue no: **RCA 409**
12" Single: Released May '84, on RCA, by BMG Records (UK). Catalogue no: **RCAT 409**

PUTTIN' ON THE RITZ
Tracks: / Puttin' on the ritz / Livin' in my dream world.
7" Single: Released Sep '83, on RCA, by BMG Records (UK). Catalogue no: **RCA 284**

SINGIN' IN THE RAIN
Tracks: / Singin' in the rain.
7" Single: Released Apr '83, on RCA, by BMG Records (UK). Catalogue no: **RCA 327**

Tactic

VIDEO VIDEO
Tracks: / Video video.
7" Single: Released Jun '83, on Sonet, by Sonet Records. Catalogue no: **SON 2256**

Tac-Tix

WHISPER ON THE STREET
Tracks: / Whisper on the street / See the love.
7" Single: Released Nov '88, on Tinkers, by Tinkers Records. Catalogue no: **GSM 188**

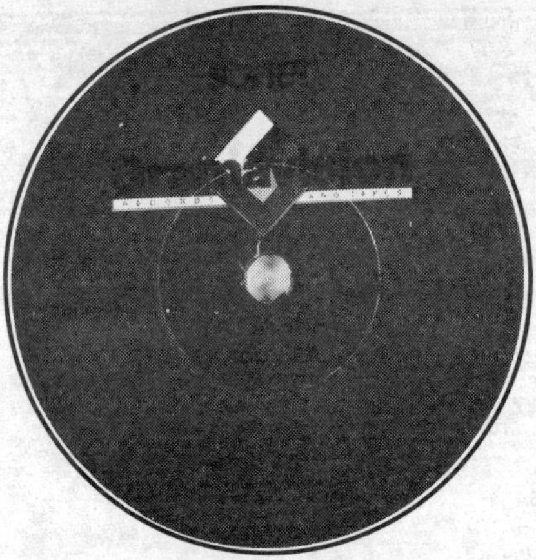

TAJ MAHAL - SOOTHIN' (Released on Sonet)

Tad & Marry Anne

FOLLOW ME
Tracks: / Follow me / Ezungizeng.
12" Single: Released Apr '86, on Jay Dee, Catalogue no: **JD 016**

Taffy

I LOVE MY RADIO
Tracks: / I love my radio.
7" Single: Released Nov '86, on Transglobal/Rhythm King, by Mute Records. Catalogue no: **TYPE 1**
12" Single: Released Nov '86, on Transglobal/Rhythm King, by Mute Records. Catalogue no: **TYPE 1T**

IF YOU FEEL IT
Tracks: / If you feel it / V.I.P..
7" Single: Released Sep '88, on Danceyard, by Danceyard Records. Catalogue no: **YARD 2**
7" Single: Released Feb '88, on Transglobal/Rhythm King, by Mute Records. Catalogue no: **TYPE 6**
12" Single: Released Sep '88, on Danceyard, by Danceyard Records. Catalogue no: **YARD T2**
12" Single: Released Feb '88, on Transglobal/Rhythm King, by Mute Records. Catalogue no: **TYPE 6T**

IF YOU FEEL IT (SAN ANTONIO MIX)
Tracks: / If you feel it.
7" Single: Released Oct '88, on Danceyard, by Danceyard Records. Catalogue no: **YARD R2**
12" Single: Released Oct '88, on Danceyard, by Danceyard Records. Catalogue no: **YARD TR 2**

STEP BY STEP
Tracks: / Step by step (Moore heavenly mix) / Whose?.
7" Single: Released Jul '87, on Transglobal/Rhythm King, by Mute Records. Catalogue no: **TYPE 5**
12" Single: Released Aug '87, on Transglobal/Rhythm King, by Mute Records. Catalogue no: **TYPER 5T**
12" Single: Released Jul '87, on Transglobal/Rhythm King, by Mute Records. Catalogue no: **TYPE 5T**

T.A.G.G.

BIG SEX
Tracks: / Ocean, The / Big sex.
7" Single: Released Feb '87, on Sweatbox, by Sweatbox Records. Catalogue no: **SOX 011**
12" Single: Released Feb '87, on Sweatbox, by Sweatbox Records. Catalogue no: **OX 011**

Taj Mahal

EVERYBODY IS SOMEBODY (see panel on right)
Tracks: / French letter / Deed I do' / Every body is somebody.
7" Single: Released Mar '87, on Gramavision (USA), by Grammavision Records (USA). Catalogue no: **SON 2318**
12" Single: Released Mar '87, on Sonet, by Sonet Records. Catalogue no: **SONL 2318**

SOOTHIN' (see panel above)
Tracks: / Soothin' / Kauai Kalypso / Local Local girl.
7" Single: Released Aug '87, on Sonet, by Sonet Records. Catalogue no: **SON 2325**
12" Single: Released Aug '87, on Sonet, by Sonet Records. Catalogue no: **SONL 2325**

TAKE A GIANT STEP (SINGLE)
Tracks: / Take a giant step / Jorge Ben.
7" Single: Released Aug '80, on Magnet, by WEA Records. Deleted '83. Catalogue no: **MAG 172**

Tajah, Paulette

COS YOU LOVE ME BABY
Tracks: / Cos you love me baby.
7" Single: Released Sep '84, on Raiders, Catalogue no: **LGR 7004**

GLAD YOU'RE AROUND
Tracks: / Glad you're around.
12" Single: Released Jan '86, on Exclusive Productions, by Exclusive Productions. Deleted Jun '89. Catalogue no: **EPRT 2682**

LAST NIGHT
Tracks: / Last night.
12" Single: Released Oct '88, on Ariwa Sounds, by Ariwa Sounds. Catalogue no: **ARI 79**

LET'S MAKE A BABY
Tracks: / Let's make a baby.
12" Single: Released Feb '89, on Ariwa Sounds, by Ariwa Sounds. Catalogue no: **ARI 86**

MOVE UP CLOSE TO ME BABY
Tracks: / Move up close to me baby.
12" Single: Released Dec '83, on LGR, Catalogue no: **LGR 002**

PUT A LITTLE LOVE AWAY
Tracks: / Put a little love away.
12" Single: Released Feb '88, on Ariwa Sounds, by Ariwa Sounds. Catalogue no: **ARI 069**

STOP LOOK LISTEN
Tracks: / Stop look listen.
12" Single: Released Aug '87, on Ariwa Sounds, by Ariwa Sounds. Catalogue no: **ARI 061**

YOU'RE THE ONE
Tracks: / You're the one.
7" Single: Released Jun '85, on Exclusive Productions, by Exclusive Productions. Catalogue no: **EPR 2683**
12" Single: Released Jun '85, on Exclusive Productions, by Exclusive Productions. Catalogue no: **EPRT 2683**

Takahashi, Yukihiro

DISPOSABLE LOVE
Tracks: / Disposable love / Flashback.
7" Single: Released Jul '82, on Alfa, Catalogue no: **ALFA 2636**

DRIP DRY EYES
Tracks: / Drip dry eyes / Charge.
7" Single: Released '82, on CBS, by CBS Records. Deleted '85. Catalogue no: **ALFA 1869**

MURDERED BY THE MUSIC
Tracks: / Murdered by the music.
7" Single: Released May '82, on Statik, Catalogue no: **STAT 17**

STAY CLOSE
Tracks: / Stay Close / Betsu-Ni.
7" Single: Released Oct '86, on Rime, by Rime Records. Deleted '88. Catalogue no: **RIM 1**

STRANGER THINGS HAVE HAPPENED
Tracks: / Stranger things have happened.
12" Single: Released Apr '85, on Cocteau, by Cocteau Records. Catalogue no: **COQT 18**

Take 2

BADDER THAN BAD
Tracks: / Badder than bad.
7" Single: Released Jul '87, on Extra, Catalogue no: **XTRA 2**
12" Single: Released Jul '87, on Extra, Catalogue no: **12XTRA 2**

Take 3

CAN'T GET ENOUGH
Tracks: / Can't get enough.
7" Single: Released May '85, on Elite Records, by Elite Records. Deleted '86. Catalogue no: **DAZZ 377**
12" Single: Released May '85, on Elite Records, by Elite Records. Deleted '86. Catalogue no: **DAZZ 37**

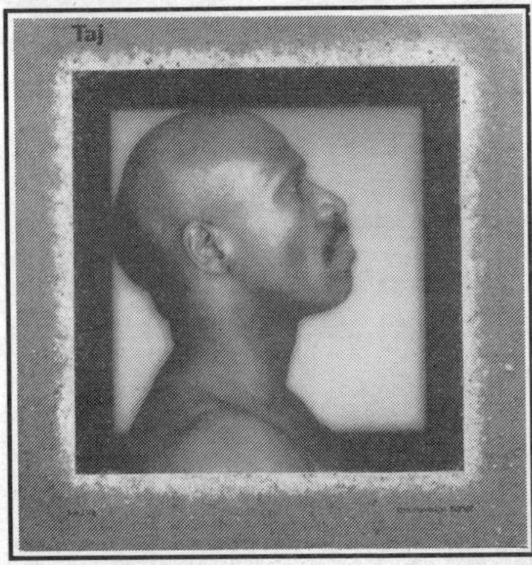

TAJ MAHAL - EVERYBODY IS SOMEBODY (Released on Gramavision)

MUSICAL AND TIME
Tracks: / Musical and time.
12" Single: Released Jun '84, on Elite Records, by Elite Records. Deleted '86. Catalogue no: **DAZZ 32**

THIS GOOD GOOD FEELING
Tracks: / This good good feeling.
12" Single: Released Nov '84, on Elite Records, by Elite Records. Deleted '86. Catalogue no: **DAZZ 34**

Take Me

TAKE ME
Tracks: / Take me: *Vipers* / Snakes and ladders: *Big Self* / Cyborg: *Outcasts* / Belfast telegraph: *Shock Treatment*.
7" EP: Released Apr '80, on Energy (UK), by Energy Records. Deleted Apr '83. Catalogue no: **NRG 1**

Take Us Two

I WANNA BE A ROCK STAR
Tracks: / I wanna be a rock star / Fashion is hot.
7" Single: Released Apr '84, on Raw Dance Music, Deleted '86. Catalogue no: **BRP 402**

Takes Three

TONITE'S THE NITE
Tracks: / Tonite's the nite.
12" Single: Released Sep '83, on Fast Forward, by Fast Forward Records. Catalogue no: **FORT 1**

Taking The Trains Out

TAKING THE TRAINS OUT
Tracks: / Taking the trains out: *Various artists*.
7" EP: Released Jun '85, on Wildcat. Catalogue no: **WCR 205**

Talbot, Alan

JC THE NAZ
Tracks: / JC the naz.
7" Single: Released Dec '81, on Hobo. Catalogue no: **HOS 018**

Talbot, Jamie

MORNIN'
Tracks: / Mornin' / In your day dreaming.
12" Single: Released Sep '86, on Move. Catalogue no: **MS 17**

Talents

OUT OF LOVE
Tracks: / Out of love.
12" Single: Released Nov '85, on Kaya. Catalogue no: **KA 006**

TEN PERCENT INSPIRATION
Tracks: / Ten percent inspiration.
12" Single: Released Sep '85, on Kaya. Catalogue no: **KA 009**

Talisman

RUN COME GIRL
Tracks: / Run come girl / Wicked dem.
7" Single: Released '81, on Recreational, by Revolver Records. Catalogue no: **SPORT 2**
12" Single: Released '81, on Recreational, by Revolver Records. Catalogue no: **SPORT 22**

Talk Back

I CAN'T LET YOU GO
Tracks: / I can't let you go / Was I right.
7" Single: Released Jan '83, on CBS, by CBS Records. Catalogue no: **A 2829**
12" Single: Released Jan '83, on CBS, by CBS Records. Catalogue no: **A 13 2829**

PLEASURE
Tracks: / Pleasure / Every day.
7" Single: Released Mar '84, on Cottage. Catalogue no: **S 83 CUS 1991**

Talk Talk

DUM DUM GIRL
Tracks: / Dum dum girl.
7" Single: Released Aug '84, on EMI, by EMI Records. Deleted Aug '87. Catalogue no: **EMI 5480**

GIVE IT UP
Tracks: / Give it up / Pictures of Bernadette.
7" Single: Released May '86, on Parlophone, by EMI Records. Deleted Oct '87. Catalogue no: **R 6131**
12" Single: Released May '86, on Parlophone, by EMI Records. Deleted Oct '87. Catalogue no: **12R 6131**

I BELIEVE IN YOU
Tracks: / I believe in you (edit) / John Cope / Eden (Only on 12" & CD single.).
CD 5": Released Sep '88, on Parlophone, by EMI Records. Catalogue no: **CDR 6189**
7" Single: Released Sep '88, on Parlophone, by EMI Records. Deleted Aug '89. Catalogue no: **R 6189**
12" Single: Released Sep '88, on Parlophone, by EMI Records. Deleted Aug '89. Catalogue no: **12R 6189**

I DON'T BELIEVE IN YOU
Tracks: / I don't believe in you / Does Caroline know / Happiness is easy (Track on 12" version only.).
7" Single: Released Nov '86, on Parlophone, by EMI Records. Catalogue no: **R 6144**
12" Single: Released Nov '86, on Parlophone, by EMI Records. Catalogue no: **12R 6144**

IT'S MY LIFE (SINGLE)
Tracks: / It's my life.
7" Single: Released Jan '84, on EMI, by EMI Records. Deleted Oct '89. Catalogue no: **EMI 5443**
12" Single: Released Jan '84, on EMI, by EMI Records. Catalogue no: **12EMI 5443**

LIFE'S WHAT YOU MAKE IT
Tracks: / Life's what you make it / It's getting late in the evening / Life's what you make it (EXT) (Track on 12" remix version only.) / It's my life (Track on double pack version only.) / Does Caroline know (Track on double pack version only.).
7" Set: Released Feb '86, on EMI, by EMI Records. Catalogue no: **12EMID 5540**
7" Single: Released Feb '86, on EMI, by EMI Records. Deleted Jul '87. Catalogue no: **EMI 5540**
12" Single: Released Feb '86, on EMI, by EMI Records. Catalogue no: **12EMIX 5540**
12" Single: Released Feb '86, on EMI, by EMI Records. Deleted Nov '88. Catalogue no: **12EMI 5540**

LIVING IN ANOTHER WORLD
Tracks: / Living in another world / For what it's worth / Living in another world (US mix) (Track on 12" version only.) / Original (Track on 12" version only.).
12" Single: Released Mar '86, on EMI, by EMI Records. Deleted Jul '87. Catalogue no: **12EMIX 5551**
7" Single: Released Mar '86, on EMI, by EMI Records. Deleted Jul '87. Catalogue no: **EMI 5551**
7" Pic: Released Mar '86, on EMI, by EMI Records. Deleted Jul '87. Catalogue no: **EMIP 5551**
12" Single: Released Mar '86, on EMI, by EMI Records. Deleted Jul '87. Catalogue no: **12EMI 5551**

MIRROR MAN
Tracks: / Mirror man / Strike up the band.
7" Single: Released Feb '82, on EMI, by EMI Records. Deleted Feb '87. Catalogue no: **EMI 5265**

MY FOOLISH FRIEND
Tracks: / My foolish friend / Call in the night boys.
7" Single: Released Feb '83, on EMI, by EMI Records. Catalogue no: **EMI 5373**
12" Single: Released Feb '83, on EMI, by EMI Records. Catalogue no: **12 EMI 5373**

PARTY'S OVER, THE (SINGLE)
Tracks: / Party's over, The.
7" Single: Released Jul '82, on EMI, by EMI Records. Catalogue no: **EMC 3431**

SUCH A SHAME
Tracks: / Such a shame / Again, again, again.
7" Single: Released Mar '84, on EMI, by EMI Records. Deleted Oct '87. Catalogue no: **EMI 5433**
12" Single: Released Mar '84, on EMI, by EMI Records. Deleted Jun '89. Catalogue no: **12EMI 5433**

TALK TALK
Tracks: / Talk talk / Talk talk (pt 2) / Mirror man.
12" Single: Released Oct '82, on EMI, by EMI Records. Catalogue no: **12EMI 5352**
7" Single: Released Apr '82, on EMI, by EMI Records. Deleted Apr '85. Catalogue no: **EMI 5284**
12" Single: Released Apr '82, on EMI, by EMI Records. Deleted Apr '85. Catalogue no: **12EMI 5284**
7" Single: Released Oct '82, on EMI, by EMI Records. Catalogue no: **EMI 5352**

TALK TALK (EXT. MIX)
Tracks: / Talk talk.
12" Single: Released Oct '82, on EMI, by EMI Records. Deleted Nov '88. Catalogue no: **12EMI 5352**

TODAY
Tracks: / Today / Serious.
7" Single: Released Jun '82, on EMI, by EMI Records. Catalogue no: **EMI 5314**

Talking Drums

COURAGE
Tracks: / Courage.
12" Single: Released May '84, on Sticky Music. Catalogue no: **GUM 005**

PRETEND A STRANGER
Tracks: / Pretend a stranger.
7" Single: Released Jul '86, on Sticky. Catalogue no: **GUM 12**

Talking Heads

Biographical details: Talking Heads is a new wave group formed in 1974 in New York City by design-school grads David Byrne (born in 1952 in Scotland) on vocals and guitar, and drummer Chris Frantz (born in 1951 in Kentucky), with Frantz' girlfriend Martina 'Tina' Weymouth (born 1950 in California) on bass. The trio with acoustic guitar backing Byrn's quirky high-pitched voice marked them down as one of USA new wave's more unusual sounds. Keyboardist Jerry Harrison (born 1949 in Milwaukee) joined from Jonathan Richman's Modern Lovers, doubling on guitar. Their wistful, delicate pop with an occasional uneasy edge became more adventurous, innovative arrangements and influence of various black musics (including African) keeping them near the top. Byrne has become well-known as a producer, songwriter, filmaker (True Stories 1986); they have collaborated with Brian Eno (Byrne on Eno's My Life In The Bush Of Ghosts), used sidemen such as Adrian Belew and Robert Fripp. (Donald Clarke 13.1.88).

AND SHE WAS
Tracks: / And she was / Television man / And she was (extended mix) (Only on 12" import.) / Television man (dance mix) (Only on 12" import.).
12" Single: Released Feb '86, on EMI, by EMI Records. Deleted Jul '87. Catalogue no: **12EMI 5543**
7" Single: Released Feb '86, on EMI, by EMI Records. Deleted Jul '87. Catalogue no: **EMI 5543**
12" Single: Released Sep '88, on Sire (USA). Catalogue no: **920378 0**
12" Pic: Released Feb '86, on EMI, by EMI Records. Catalogue no: **12EMIP 5543**

BLIND
Tracks: / Blind (extended remix) (Only on 12" single.) / Bill / Blind / Blind (Deaf, dub and blind mix) (Only on 12" single.).
12" Single: Released Aug '88, on EMI, by EMI Records. Deleted Aug '89. Catalogue no: **12EM 68**
Cassingle: Released Aug '88, on EMI, by EMI Records. Deleted Aug '89. Catalogue no: **TCEM 68**
7" Single: Released Aug '88, on EMI, by EMI Records. Deleted Aug '89. Catalogue no: **EM 68**
CD 5": Released Aug '88, on EMI, by EMI Records. Catalogue no: **CDEM 68**

BURNING DOWN THE HOUSE (SINGLE)
Tracks: / Burning down the house.
12" Single: Released Jul '83, on Sire (USA). Catalogue no: **W 9565T**
7" Single: Released Jul '83, on Sire (USA). Catalogue no: **W 9565**

FEAR OF MUSIC (SINGLE)
Tracks: / Fear of music.
7" Single: Released Aug '79, on Sire, by Sire Records. Catalogue no: **SRK 6076**

GIRLFRIEND IS BETTER
Tracks: / Girlfriend is better.
12" Single: Released Jan '85, on EMI, by EMI Records. Catalogue no: **12EMI 5509**
7" Single: Released Nov '84, on EMI, by EMI Records. Deleted '88. Catalogue no: **EMI 5509**

HOUSES IN MOTION
Tracks: / Houses in motion / Air.
12" Single: Released May '81, on Sire (USA). Catalogue no: **SIR 4050T**
7" Single: Released May '81, on Sire (USA). Catalogue no: **SIR 4050**

I ZIMBA
Tracks: / I zimba / Paper.
7" Single: Released Feb '80, on Sire, by Sire Records. Deleted Feb '83. Catalogue no: **SIR 4033**

LADY DON'T MIND
Tracks: / Lady don't mind.
12" Single: Released May '85, on EMI, by EMI Records. Catalogue no: **12 EMI 5520**
7" Single: Released May '85, on EMI, by EMI Records. Catalogue no: **EMI 5520**

LADY DON'T MIND (2)
Tracks: / Lady don't mind.
7" Set: Released Jun '85, on EMI, by EMI Records. Catalogue no: **EMID 5520**
12" Single: Released Jun '85, on EMI, by EMI Records. Catalogue no: **12EMIX 5520**

LIFE DURING WARTIME
Tracks: / Life during wartime.
7" Single: Released Oct '79, on Sire (USA). Catalogue no: **SIR 4027**

LIFE DURING WARTIME (LIVE VERSION)
Tracks: / Life during wartime.
7" Single: Released Mar '82, on Sire (USA). Catalogue no: **SIR 4055**
12" Single: Released Mar '82, on Sire (USA). Catalogue no: **SIR 4055 T**

NOTHING BUT FLOWERS
Tracks: / Nothing but flowers / Ruby dear (bush mix) / Mommy Daddy you & I (10", Cassingle, CD single only.) / Nothing but flowers (Lillywhite mix) (12", Cassingle, CD single only.) / Facts of life / Ruby dear (10" only.).
12" Single: Released Oct '88, on EMI, by EMI Records. Deleted Aug '89. Catalogue no: **12EM 53**
7" Single: Released Oct '88, on EMI, by EMI Records. Deleted Aug '89. Catalogue no: **EM 53**
10" single: Released Oct '88, on EMI, by EMI Records. Deleted Aug '89. Catalogue no: **10EM 53**
CD 5": Released Oct '88, on EMI, by EMI Records. Catalogue no: **CDEM 53**
Cassingle: Released Sep '88, on EMI, by EMI Records. Deleted Aug '89. Catalogue no: **TCEM 53**

ONCE IN A LIFETIME
Tracks: / Once in a lifetime / Seen but not seen.
7" Single: Released Feb '81, on Sire (USA). Deleted Jul '88. Catalogue no: **SIR 4048**
12" Single: Released Mar '81, on Sire (USA). Catalogue no: **SIR 4048T**

RADIO HEAD
Tracks: / Radio head (LP version) / Hey now (movie version) / Radio head (Ext. Remix) / Radio head (Movie version) / Hey now (Milwaukee mix).
Note: Original sound recordings made by Talking Heads Tours Inc. under exclusice licence to EMI Records.
CD 5": Released Apr '87, on EMI, by EMI Records. Deleted Nov '88. Catalogue no: **CD EM 1**
7" Set: Released May '87, on EMI, by EMI Records. Deleted Oct '87. Catalogue no: **EMD 1**

RADIO HEAD (2)
Tracks: / Radio head (LP version) / Hey now.
12" Single: Released Apr '87, on EMI, by EMI Records. Catalogue no: **12 EMI 1**
7" Single: Released Apr '87, on EMI, by EMI Records. Catalogue no: **EMI 1**

ROAD TO NOWHERE
Tracks: / Road to nowhere.
12" Single: Released Sep '85, on EMI, by EMI Records. Deleted Oct '89. Catalogue no: **12EMI 5530**
7" Single: Released Sep '85, on EMI, by EMI Records. Deleted Oct '89. Catalogue no: **EMI 5530**
7" Pic: Released Oct '85, on EMI, by EMI Records. Deleted '88. Catalogue no: **EMIP 5530**

SLIPPERY PEOPLE
Tracks: / Slippery people.
12" Single: Released Oct '84, on EMI, by EMI Records. Deleted Oct '89. Catalogue no: **12EMI 5504**
7" Single: Released Oct '84, on EMI, by EMI Records. Deleted '88. Catalogue no: **EMI 5504**

TAKE ME TO THE RIVER
Tracks: / Take me to the river / Psycho killer.
Cassingle: Released Apr '81, on WEA, by WEA Records. Deleted Apr '84. Catalogue no: **SPC 9**
7" Single: Released Jun '79, on Sire (USA). Catalogue no: **SIR 4004**

THIS MUST BE THE PLACE
Tracks: / This must be the place / Moon rocks.
7" Single: Released Jun '86, on Sire (USA). Deleted Jun '87. Catalogue no: **W 9451**
12" Single: Released Jun '86, on Sire (USA). Deleted Jun '87. Catalogue no: **W 9451T**

WILD WILD LIFE
Tracks: / Wild wild life / People like us (movie version) / Wild wild life (extended version) (Only on 12" import.) / Wild wild life (LP version) (Only on 12" import.).
7" Single: Released Aug '86, on EMI, by EMI Records. Deleted Oct '87. Catalogue no: **EMI 5567**
12" Single: Released Sep '88, on Sire (USA). Catalogue no: **920593 0**
12" Single: Released Aug '86, on EMI, by EMI Records. Deleted Oct '87. Catalogue no: **12EMI 5567**

Talking Strangers

COMFORT AND JOY
Tracks: / Comfort and joy.
7" Single: on Sierra, by Sierra Records. Deleted Jun '87. Catalogue no: **FED 7**

Talking To Walls

MR. NICE GUY
Tracks: / Mr. Nice Guy.
7" Single: Released '88, on Trigger Happy. Catalogue no: **TTW 909**

Tall Boys

BRAND NEW GUN

Tracks: / Brand new gun / Last house on the left / Took a long time.
12" Single: Released Mar '86, on Big Beat, by Ace Records. Catalogue no: **NST 114**

FINAL KICK
Tracks: / Final kick.
7" Single: Released Jun '85, on Big Beat, by Ace Records. Deleted '88. Catalogue no: **NS 107**
12" Single: Released Jun '85, on Big Beat, by Ace Records. Catalogue no: **NST 107**

ISLAND OF LOST SOULS
Tracks: / Island of lost souls / Another half hour till sunrise.
7" Single: Released Sep '82, on Big Beat, by Ace Records. Deleted '88. Catalogue no: **NS 79**

WEDNESDAY ADDAMS' BOY-FRIEND
Tracks: / Wednesday Addams' boyfriend.
7" Single: Released Aug '84, on Big Beat, by Ace Records. Catalogue no: **NED 8**

Tall, Tom

STACK-A-RECORDS
Tracks: / Stack-a-records / Mary Jo.
7" Single: Released Jan '81, on Rockstar (1). Deleted Jan '84. Catalogue no: **SP 3003**

Tallulah Moon

IF YOU WANT LOVE
Tracks: / If you want love / If you want love (edited version) / If you want love (instrumental version).
12" Single: Released Mar '86, on Total Control, by Total Control Records. Catalogue no: **12TOCO 7**
7" Single: Released Mar '86, on Total Control, by Total Control Records. Catalogue no: **TOCO 7**

Talulah Gosh

BEATNIK BOY
Tracks: / My best friend / Beatnik boy.
7" Single: Released Dec '86, on 53rd & 3rd, by 53rd & 3rd Records. Catalogue no: **AGARR 4**

BRINGING UP BABY
Tracks: / Bringing up baby.
7" Single: Released Jan '88, on 53rd & 3rd, by 53rd & 3rd Records. Catalogue no: **AGARR 14**
12" Single: Released Jan '88, on 53rd & 3rd, by 53rd & 3rd Records. Catalogue no: **AGARR 14T**

STEAMING TRAIN
Tracks: / Just a dream / Steaming train / Beatnik.
12" Single: Released Oct '86, on 53rd & 3rd, by 53rd & 3rd Records. Catalogue no: **AGARR 412**
7" Single: Released Dec '86, on 53rd & 3rd, by 53rd & 3rd Records. Catalogue no: **AGARR 5**

TALULAH GOSH
Tracks: / Talulah gosh.
12" Single: Released 30 May '87, on 53rd & 3rd, by 53rd & 3rd Records. Catalogue no: **AGARR 8T**
7" Single: Released 30 May '87, on 53rd & 3rd, by 53rd & 3rd Records. Catalogue no: **AGARR 8**

TESTCARD GIRL
Tracks: / Testcard girl.
7" Single: Released May '88, on 53rd & 3rd, by 53rd & 3rd Records. Catalogue no: **AGARR 16**

Tamarisk

LOST PROPERTIES
Cassingle: Released Sep '83, on LTC. Catalogue no: **LTC C-200**

Tamina

NO MORE WISHIN'
Tracks: / No more wishin'.
12" Single: Released 1 Aug '88, on Creole, by Creole Records. Catalogue no: **NINE 20**

Tamlin, Ricky

CALL ME
Tracks: / Call me.
12" Single: Released Oct '88, on Ariwa Sounds, by Ariwa Sounds. Catalogue no: **ARI 074**

GOING TO A PARTY
Tracks: / Party verion (Bubblers crew).
12" Single: Released Nov '86, on UK Bubblers, by Greensleeves Records. Deleted '88. Catalogue no: **UKMC 18**

Tamlins

BABY LOVE
Tracks: / Baby love.
7" Single: Released Mar '82, on Reggae, Catalogue no: **REG 03 7**
12" Single: Released Mar '82, on Reggae, Catalogue no: **REG 03**

TAMMY - OLD ENOUGH TO KNOW BETTER (Released on Mix Factory)

BALTIMORE
Tracks: / Baltimore / Laying beside you.
7" Single: Released Apr '80, on EMI, by EMI Records. Deleted Apr '83. Catalogue no: **RIC 110**

BOOMERANG
Tracks: / Boomerang.
12" Single: Released Mar '83, on Reggae, Catalogue no: **REG 15**

EBONY EYES
Tracks: / Ebony eyes.
12" Single: Released Mar '83, on Earthquake, Catalogue no: **EQ 1006**

GO AWAY DREAM
Tracks: / Go away dream.
12" Single: Released Oct '83, on Taxi (2), by Island Records. Catalogue no: **IPR 2064**

HEY GRANDMA
Tracks: / Hey Grandma.
12" Single: Released Sep '85, on Smash Apartheid Music Works, Catalogue no: **MW 1987**

HOLD ON
Tracks: / Hold on.
12" Single: Released May '82, on Plantation, Catalogue no: **PL 007**

HURT SO BAD
Tracks: / Hurt so bad.
12" Single: Released Sep '88, on White Label (1), Catalogue no: **REV 49**

JOY IN THE MORNING
Tracks: / Joy in the morning.
7" Single: Released Oct '83, on Allemande, Catalogue no: **A 014**

JUKI JAMMY
Tracks: / Juki Jammy.
12" Single: Released Sep '85, on Londisc, by Londisc Records. Catalogue no: **LDR 051**

LAYING BESIDE YOU
Tracks: / Laying beside you.
7" Single: Released Apr '80, on D. Roy, Catalogue no: **DRDD 28**

LOOK AT ME
Tracks: / Look at me.
12" Single: Released Jan '89, on Techniques, Catalogue no: **WRT 43**

LOVE OF MY LIFE
Tracks: / Love of my life.
12" Single: Released May '89, on Living Room, Catalogue no: **LM 023**

SMILING FACES SOMETIMES
Tracks: / Smiling faces sometimes.
12" Single: Released Mar '81, on Island, by Island Records. Catalogue no: **IPR 2042**

SWEAT FOR YOU BABY
Tracks: / Sweat for you baby.
12" Single: Released Aug '82, on Taxi (1), Catalogue no: **TX 00512**

TRUE TRUE
Tracks: / True true.
7" Single: Released Dec '81, on Dancebeat, Catalogue no: **DB 1311**

WHO DAT SAY DAT
Tracks: / Who dat say dat.
12" Single: Released Jan '85, on Revue, by Creole Records. Catalogue no: **REV 012T**

Tammi Show

SHE'S ONLY TWENTY
Tracks: / She's only twenty / Don't say no / All I want from you (Only on 12" version.).
7" Single: Released Jun '88, on Chrysalis, by Chrysalis Records. Catalogue no: **CHS 3146**
12" Single: Released Jun '88, on Chrysalis, by Chrysalis Records. Catalogue no: **CHS 123146**

Tammy

OLD ENOUGH TO KNOW BETTER (see panel above)
Tracks: / Old enough to know better / Old enough to know better (instrumental).
7" Single: Released May '86, on Mix Factory, by Mix Factory Records. Deleted '88. Catalogue no: **MX 4**

Tams

BE YOUNG, BE FOOLISH, BE HAPPY
Tracks: / Be young, be foolish, be happy.
7" Single: Released Feb '70, on Stateside, by EMI Records. Deleted Feb '73. Catalogue no: **SS 2123**

HEY GIRL DON'T BOTHER ME
Tracks: / Hey girl don't bother me / Our love is getting stronger.
7" Single: Released Jun '71, on Probe, Deleted Jun '74. Catalogue no: **PRO 532**
7" Single: Released Apr '86, on Casino Classics, by RK Records. Catalogue no: **CC 17**

HEY GIRL DON'T BOTHER ME (OLD GOLD)
Tracks: / Hey girl don't bother me.
7" Single: Released Jul '82, on Old Gold, by Old Gold Records. Catalogue no: **OG 9219**

MY BABY SURE CAN SHAG
Tracks: / My baby sure can shag
7" Single: Released Dec '87, on Virgin, by Virgin Records. Deleted May '88. Catalogue no: **VS 1037**
12" Single: Released Dec '87, on Virgin, by Virgin Records. Catalogue no: **VST 1037**

THERE AIN'T NOTHING LIKE SHAGGIN'
Tracks: / There ain't nothing like shaggin' / Get a job.
7" Single: Released Nov '87, on Virgin, by Virgin Records. Catalogue no: **VS 1029**
12" Single: Released Nov '87, on Virgin, by Virgin Records. Catalogue no: **VST 1029**

Tamya

FOR THE LOVE OF YOU
Tracks: / For the love of you.
12" Single: Released Mar '88, on Living Room, Catalogue no: **LM 004**

Tan

I'VE GOT TO GET TO INDIANA (SINGLE)
Tracks: / I've got to get to Indiana / Early morning light.
7" Single: Released Jan '80, on White Dove, by White Dove Records. Catalogue no: **WD 101**

SUMMER PLACE
Tracks: / Summer place, A (theme from) / Princess.
7" Single: Released Jun '81, on Rough Trade, by Rough Trade Records. Catalogue no: **RT 076**

THERE'S A FIRE
Tracks: / There's a fire.
7" Single: Released Aug '79, on White Dove, by White Dove Records. Catalogue no: **WD 102**

Tandoori Cassette

ANGEL TALK
Tracks: / Angel talk / Third world briefcases.
7" Single: Released Nov '82, on IKA, Deleted '86. Catalogue no: **IKA 001**

Tandy, Sharon

HOLD ON
Tracks: / Hold on / Whatcha gonna do about it / Stay with me / Just one look.
7" EP: Released Apr '80, on Atlantic, by WEA Records. Catalogue no: **ATM 4**

Tanega, Norma

WALKING MY CAT NAMED DOG
Tracks: / Walking my cat named dog.
7" Single: Released Apr '66, on Stateside, by EMI Records. Deleted Apr '69. Catalogue no: **SS 496**

WALKING MY CAT NAMED DOG (OLD GOLD)
Tracks: / Walking my cat named dog.
7" Single: Released Jul '84, on Old Gold, by Old Gold Records. Catalogue no: **OG 9416**

Tanganyika

I'M LIL ROXANNE
Tracks: / I'm lil Roxanne / I'm lil Roxanne (Instrumental version).
7" Single: Released Aug '86, on Revue, by Creole Records. Catalogue no: **REV 734**
12" Single: Released Aug '86, on Revue, by Creole Records. Catalogue no: **REV 034T**

Tangent

ATLANTICA
Tracks: / Atlantica / Living in the city.
7" Single: Released Jan '80, on President, by President Records. Deleted Jan '83. Catalogue no: **PT 483**

Tangerine

SUNBURST
Tracks: / Sunburst.
7" Single: Released 15 May '89, on Creation, by Creation Records. Catalogue no: **CRE 065 T**

Tangerine Dream

Biographical details: Tangerine Dream is an electro/techno West Berlin band led by Edgar Froese (guitar, bass, organ, mellotron, electronics). They began in 1970 with post-'60s ambience of psychedelic nightmare, developed into meticulous electronic music influenced by Salvador Dali, Jimi Hendrix; the angst-ridden feedback of their early years has ameliorated somewhat on more recent albums. (Donald Clarke 13.1.88).

CHORONZON
Tracks: / Choronzon.
7" Single: Released Sep '81, on Virgin, by Virgin Records. Deleted Sep '84. Catalogue no: **VS 444**

STREET HAWK
Tracks: / Street hawk.
12" Single: Released Aug '85, on Jive Electro, by Zomba Records. Catalogue no: **JIVET 101**
7" Single: Released Aug '85, on Jive Electro, by Zomba Records. Catalogue no: **JIVE 101**

TYGER (SINGLE)
Tracks: / Tyger / 21st century common man (part 2).
7" Single: Released 13 Jun '87, on Jive, by Zomba Records. Deleted Jul '87. Catalogue no: **JIVE 143**
12" Single: Released 13 Jun '87, on Jive, by Zomba Records. Deleted Jul '87. Catalogue no: **JIVET 143**

WARSAW IN THE SUN
Tracks: / Warsaw in the sun.
7" Pic: Released Sep '84, on Jive, by Zomba Records. Catalogue no: **JIVEP 74**
7" Single: Released Sep '84, on Jive, by Zomba Records. Catalogue no: **JIVE 74**
12" Single: Released Sep '84, on Jive, by Zomba Records. Catalogue no: **JIVET 74**

Tango Brigade

DONEGAL
Tracks: / Donegal / In vain.
7" Single: Released Jan '81, on Epic, by CBS Records. Deleted Jan '84. Catalogue no: **EPC 9398**

Tango Echo Delta Delta

CHINA
Tracks: / China.
7" Single: Released Sep '81, on China Disques, Catalogue no: **CDN 001**

LATELY
Tracks: / Lately / Those in peril.
7" Single: Released Jan '82, on China Disques, Catalogue no: **CDN 002**

Tanh Chi

HOW LONG IS A DAY?
Tracks: / How long is a day / Live for me / Make time* (*Extra track on 12").
7" Single: Released Aug '87, on Arista, by BMG Records (UK). Catalogue no: **TANH 2**
12" Single: Released Jul '87, on Arista, by BMG Records (UK). Catalogue no: **TANH 122**

RIBBON
Tracks: / Silent night / Ribbon.
7" Single: Released Jan '87, on Arista, by BMG Records (UK). Catalogue no: **TAHN 1**
12" Single: Released Jan '87, on Arista, by BMG Records (UK). Catalogue no: **TAHN 121**

Tank

CRAZY HORSES
Tracks: / Crazy horses / Filth bitch boogie.
7" Single: Released Sep '82, on Kamaflage, Deleted Sep '85. Catalogue no: **KAM 7**

DONT WALK AWAY
Tracks: / Don't walk away.
7" Single: Released Sep '81, on Kamaflage, Deleted Sep '84. Catalogue no: **KAM 1**

ECHOES OF A DISTANT BATTLE
Tracks: / Echoes of a distant battle.
7" Single: Released Jul '83, on Music For Nations, by Music For Nations Records. Catalogue no: **KUT 101**
12" Single: Released Jul '83, on Music For Nations, by Music For Nations Records. Catalogue no: **12 KUT 101**

FILTH HOUNDS OF HADES (SINGLE)
Tracks: / Filth hounds of hades.
7" Single: Released Mar '82, on Kamaflage, Deleted '85. Catalogue no: **KAMLP 1**

(HE FELL IN LOVE WITH A) STORM TROOPER
Tracks: / (He fell in love with a) storm trooper / Blood, guts and beer.
7" Single: Released Nov '82, on Kamaflage, Deleted Nov '85. Catalogue no: **KAP 1**

TURN YOUR HEAD AROUND
Tracks: / Turn your head around / Steppin' on a landmine.
7" Single: Released Feb '82, on Kamaflage, Deleted Feb '87. Catalogue no: **KAM 3**

Tank of Danzig

TANK, HYMN, TANK (T) RAP
Tracks: / Tank, hymn, tank (t) rap.
12" Single: Released Jun '88, on Antler, by Antler Records (Belgium). Catalogue no: **ANT 006**

Tannoi

RUDEBOYS
Tracks: / Rude boys / Gunshot salute.
12" Single: Released May '86, on UK Bubblers, by Greensleeves Records. Deleted '88. Catalogue no: **UKMC 13**

WORRIES AND TROUBLES
Tracks: / Worries and troubles.
12" Single: Released Sep '85, on UK Bubblers, by Greensleeves Records. Deleted '87. Catalogue no: **UKMC 9**

Tansin, Jo

STEAL MY HEART
Tracks: / Steal my heart / I wonder if I'm making it.
7" Single: Released Jul '86, on Zuma, Catalogue no: **ZOOM 5**

Tansley School

MY MUM IS ONE IN A MILLION
Tracks: / My mum is one in a million / Have you read the story.
7" Single: Released Mar '81, on EMI, by EMI Records. Deleted Mar '84. Catalogue no: **EMI 5151**

Tantallon

TARTAN HUSTLE
Tracks: / Tartan hustle.
7" Single: Released May '76, on DJM, Deleted '77. Catalogue no: **DJS 674**

Tantara

I.D.O.
Tracks: / I.D.O. / Rumours.
7" Single: Released Mar '86, on President, by President Records. Catalogue no: **PT 543**
12" Single: Released Mar '86, on President, by President Records. Catalogue no: **PT 12-543**

Tantra

HILLS OF KATMANDU
Tracks: / Hills of Katmandu / Hallelujah / Wishbone.
7" Single: Released Jul '81, on Automatic, by Automatic Records. Catalogue no: **K 17830**
12" Single: Released Jun '81, on Automatic, by Automatic Records. Catalogue no: **K 17830 T**

Tanzschau

SOMEONE ON MY STAIRS
Tracks: / Someone on my stairs.
7" Single: Released Oct '83, on Tao Dance, by Tao Dance Records. Catalogue no: **OG 23**

Tapps

4 PLAY - SUGAR PIE HONEYBUNCH
Tracks: / 4 play - sugar pie honeybunch / My forbidden lover / Don't pretend to know / Sugar pie honeybunch (instrumental).
7" Single: Released Aug '89, on Power, Catalogue no: **ZAK 4**

Taravhonty

I CAN'T HIDE
Tracks: / I can't hide / I can't hide (version) / I can't hide (extended version) (Only on 12" version.).
CD 5": Released Jun '89, on 10 Records, by Virgin Records. Catalogue no: **TENCD 270**
7" Single: Released Jun '89, on 10 Records, by Virgin Records. Catalogue no: **TEN 270**
12" Single: Released Jun '89, on 10 Records, by Virgin Records. Catalogue no: **TENR 270**
12" Single: Released Jun '89, on 10 Records, by Virgin Records. Catalogue no: **TENX 270**

Tarbuck, Jimmy

AGAIN
Tracks: / Again.
7" Single: Released Oct '85, on Safari, by Safari Records. Catalogue no: **SAFE 68**

ANY DREAM WILL DO
Tracks: / Any dream will do.
7" Single: Released Sep '86, on Safari, by Safari Records. Catalogue no: **SAFE 70**

LET'S HAVE A PARTY
Tracks: / Let's have a party.
7" Single: Released Dec '82, on Towerbell, Catalogue no: **TOW 32**

Target

TARGET
Tracks: / Target.
12" Single: Released '89, on Rodger, Catalogue no: **RODGER 001**

Tarmey & Dawn

I'LL BE WITH YOU SOON
Tracks: / I'll be with you soon.
7" Single: Released Apr '89, on Westmoor, Catalogue no: **7WM 1**

Tarmigan

TIME IS GETTING ON
Tracks: / Time is getting on.
7" Single: Released Nov '81, on New World, by President Records. Catalogue no: **NEW 106**

Tarriers

BANANA BOAT SONG
Tracks: / Banana boat song.
7" Single: Released Mar '57, on Columbia, by EMI Records. Deleted Mar '60. Catalogue no: **DB 3891**

Tartan Lads

CHRISTMAS DREAM, THE
Tracks: / Christmas dream.
7" Single: Released '77, on Rel, by REL Records. Catalogue no: **RES 003**

OLD FLAMES
Tracks: / Old flames.
7" Single: Released Oct '84, on Lochshore, by Klub Records. Catalogue no: **LOCH 606**

SCOTLAND THE BRAVE (SINGLE)
Tracks: / Scotland the brave.
7" Single: Released May '82, on Lochshore, by Klub Records. Catalogue no: **LOCH 602**

Tashan

JUST CHASIN' A DREAM
Tracks: / Just chasin' a dream.
12" Single: Released Jul '87, on Def Jam, Deleted Nov '87. Catalogue no: **650359 6**
7" Single: Released Jul '87, on Def Jam, Catalogue no: **650359 7**
12" Single: Released Jul '87, on Def Jam, Catalogue no: **650359 0**

READ MY MIND
Tracks: / Read my mind / Got the right attitude.
12" Single: Released Oct '87, on Def Jam, Deleted Jun '88. Catalogue no: **TASH T1**
7" Single: Released Oct '87, on Def Jam, Deleted Jun '88. Catalogue no: **TASH 1**.

THANK YOU FATHER
Tracks: / Thank you father / Got the right attitude / Love is*.
Note: * = Extra track on 12" only
7" Single: Released Apr '87, on Def Jam, Deleted Nov '87. Catalogue no: **650779 7**
12" Single: Released Apr '87, on Def Jam, Deleted Nov '87. Catalogue no: **650779 6**

Tasmanian Devils

DON'T SLIP
Tracks: / Don't slip / Spy in the house of love.
7" Single: Released May '80, on Warner Bros., by WEA Records. Deleted May '83. Catalogue no: **K 17609**

Taste

BLISTER ON THE MOON
Tracks: / Blister on the moon / Sugar mama / Catfish / On the boards.
12" Single: Released Oct '82, on Polydor, by Polydor Ltd. Deleted Oct '85. Catalogue no: **POSPX 609**

Taste Of Honey

BOOGIE OOGIE OOGIE
Tracks: / Boogie oogie oogie.
12" Single: Released May '85, on Capitol, by EMI Records. Deleted Nov '88. Catalogue no: **12CL 357**
7" Single: Released Jul '76, on Capitol, by EMI Records. Deleted Jul '79. Catalogue no: **CL 159 88**
7" Single: Released Apr '85, on Capitol, by EMI Records. Deleted '88. Catalogue no: **CL 357**

BOOGIE OOGIE OOGIE (OLD GOLD SERIES)
Tracks: / Boogie oogie oogie / Heaven must be missing an angel.
Note: Also contains:"Heaven must be missing an angel" by Tavares
7" Single: Released Apr '87, on Old Gold, by Old Gold Records. Deleted Sep '89. Catalogue no: **OG 9713**

GOLDEN SHOWER
Tracks: / Golden shower.
7" Single: Released Dec '88, on Subway, by Subway Records. Catalogue no: **SUB 045-7**
12" Single: Released Dec '88, on Subway, by Subway Records. Catalogue no: **SUB 45**

I'LL TRY SOMETHING NEW
Tracks: / I'll try something new / Goodbye baby.
7" Single: Released Jun '82, on Capitol, by EMI Records. Deleted Jun '85. Catalogue no: **CL 249**

SUKIYAKI
Tracks: / Sukiyaki / Don't you lead on me.
7" Single: Released Apr '81, on Capitol, by EMI Records. Deleted '85. Catalogue no: **CL 16194**

Taste Of Sugar

GOLDEN SHOWER
12" Single: Released '89, on Subway, by Subway Records. Catalogue no: **SUB 045**
CD 5": Released '89, on Subway, by Subway Records. Catalogue no: **SUB 045 CD**
7" Single: Released '89, on Antler, by Antler Records (Belgium). Catalogue no: **SUB 045 7**

HMM HMM
Tracks: / Hmm hmm.
CD 5": Released Oct '88, on Subway, by Subway Records. Catalogue no: **SUB 029 CD**
12" Single: Released Jun '88, on Subway, by Subway Records. Catalogue no: **SUB 029**

Tasty Tim

SUGAR SUGAR
Tracks: / Sugar sugar / Gary Glitter where did you get those boots.
7" Single: Released Mar '84, on Carrere, Catalogue no: **TASTY 1**
12" Single: Released Mar '84, on Carrere, Catalogue no: **TASTY T1**

TOO HOT TO HANDLE
Tracks: / Too hot to handle.
12" Single: Released Jan '85, on Carrere, Catalogue no: **CART 349**
7" Single: Released Jan '85, on Carrere, Catalogue no: **CAR 349**

Tate, Howard

LOOK AT GRANNY RUN RUN
Tracks: / Look at granny run run.
7" Single: Released Apr '83, on Verve, Catalogue no: **POSP 584**

Tate, Roy

LIFELINE
Tracks: / Lifeline.
10" single: Released Jan '82, on Why-Fi, by Why-Fi Records. Catalogue no: **WHYD 6**

Tate, Terry

BABIES HAVING BABIES
Tracks: / Babies having babies.
12" Single: Released Oct '89, on Atlantic, by WEA Records. Catalogue no: **086291**

Tate, Troy

LOVE IS
Tracks: / Love is.
7" Single: Released Jul '83, on Rough Trade, by Rough Trade Records. Catalogue no: **RT 134**
12" Single: Released Jul '83, on Rough Trade, by Rough Trade Records. Catalogue no: **RTT 134**

THOMAS
Tracks: / Thomas / London's swinging.
7" Single: Released Jun '81, on Why-Fi, by Why-Fi Records. Catalogue no: **WHY 3**

Tattooed Love Boys

BREAKDOWN DEAD AHEAD
Tracks: / Breakdown dead ahead.
12" Single: Released Aug '89, on Total/Episode, Catalogue no: **12LUS 1**

WHY WALTZ WHEN YOU CAN ROCK 'N' ROLL
Tracks: / Why waltz when you can rock 'n' roll.
12" Single: Released Jul '88, on Razor, by Razor Records. Catalogue no: **TLB 001**

Taurus

TIME IS TIGHT
Tracks: / Time is tight / Strike out.
7" Single: Released Jul '82, on RCA, by BMG Records (UK). Catalogue no: **RCA 262**
12" Single: Released Jul '82, on RCA, by BMG Records (UK). Catalogue no: **RCAT 262**

Taurus Boyz

LOOKIN' FOR A LOVER
Tracks: / Lookin' for a lover / Lookin' for a lover (dub).
12" Single: Released Feb '87, on Cool Tempo, by Chrysalis Records. Catalogue no: **COOLX 141**
7" Single: Released Feb '87, on Cool Tempo, by Chrysalis Records. Catalogue no: **COOL 141**

YOU'RE THE ONE
Tracks: / You're the one / You're the one (inst).
7" Single: Released Mar '88, on Cool Tempo, by Chrysalis Records. Catalogue no: **COOL 159**
12" Single: Released Mar '88, on Cool Tempo, by Chrysalis Records. Catalogue no: **COOLX 159**

Tav Falco

SHAKE RAG
Tracks: / Shake rag.
12" Single: Released Aug '86, on New Rose (1), by New Rose Records. Catalogue no: **NEW 078**

Tavares

BAD TIMES
Tracks: / Bad times / Got to have your love.
7" Single: Released Jan '80, on Capitol, by EMI Records. Deleted Jan '83. Catalogue no: **CL 16117**

DEEPER IN LOVE
Tracks: / Deeper in love.
12" Single: Released Sep '83, on RCA, by BMG Records (UK). Catalogue no: **RCAT 359**
7" Single: Released Sep '83, on RCA, by BMG Records (UK). Catalogue no: **RCA 359**

DON'T TAKE AWAY THE MUSIC
Tracks: / Don't take away the music.
7" Single: Released Oct '76, on Capitol, by EMI Records. Deleted Oct '79. Catalogue no: **CL 158 86**

GHOST OF LOVE, THE
Tracks: / Ghost of love.
7" Single: Released Mar '78, on Capitol, by EMI Records. Deleted Mar '81. Catalogue no: **CL 15968**

HEAVEN MUST BE MISSING AN ANGEL
Tracks: / Heaven must be missing an angel / Don't take away the music / Whodunnit (Available on 12" version only).
7" Single: Released Jun '76, on Capitol, by EMI Records. Deleted '85. Catalogue no: **CL 15876**
7" Single: Released Feb '86, on Capitol, by EMI Records. Deleted '88. Catalogue no:

TAV 1
12" Single: Released Feb '86, on Capitol, by EMI Records. Catalogue no: **12TAV 1**

I DON'T WANT YOU ANY MORE
Tracks: / I don't want you any more / Never had a love like this before.
7" Single: Released May '80, on Capitol, by EMI Records. Deleted May '83. Catalogue no: **CL 16146**

IT ONLY TAKES A MINUTE
Tracks: / It only takes a minute / More than a woman / One minute (instrumental) (Available on 12 Version only).
7" Single: Released Apr '86, on Capitol, by EMI Records. Deleted Oct '87. Catalogue no: **TAV 2**
12" Single: Released Apr '86, on Capitol, by EMI Records. Deleted Oct '89. Catalogue no: **12TAV 2**

MIGHTY POWER OF LOVE
Tracks: / Mighty power of love.
7" Single: Released Feb '77, on Capitol, by EMI Records. Deleted Feb '80. Catalogue no: **CL 15905**

MORE THAN A WOMAN
Tracks: / More than a woman.
7" Single: Released May '78, on Capitol, by EMI Records. Deleted May '81. Catalogue no: **CL 15977**

NEVER HAD A LOVE LIKE THIS BEFORE
Tracks: / Never had a love like this before.
7" Single: Released Mar '79, on Capitol, by EMI Records. Deleted '88. Catalogue no: **CL 218**

ONE STEP AWAY
Tracks: / One step away.
7" Single: Released Jul '77, on Capitol, by EMI Records. Deleted Jul '80. Catalogue no: **CL 159 30**

SLOW TRAIN TO PARADISE
Tracks: / Slow train to paradise.
7" Single: Released Aug '78, on Capitol, by EMI Records. Deleted Aug '81. Catalogue no: **CL 15996**

TURN OUT THE NIGHTLIGHT
Tracks: / Turn out the nightlight / Never had a love like this before.
7" Single: Released Oct '81, on Capitol, by EMI Records. Deleted '88. Catalogue no: **CL 218**

WHODUNIT
Tracks: / Whodunnit.
7" Single: Released Apr '77, on Capitol, by EMI Records. Deleted Apr '80. Catalogue no: **CL 15914**

Tavares, Victor

SHOW ME
Tracks: / Show me.
7" Single: Released May '83, on Malaco, by Malaco Records (UK). Deleted '88. Catalogue no: **MAL 010**
12" Single: Released May '83, on Malaco, by Malaco Records (UK). Deleted '88. Catalogue no: **MAL 12 010**

Tawatha

THIGH RIDE
Tracks: / Thigh ride / Welcome to my dream.
7" Single: Released Jun '87, on Epic, by CBS Records. Catalogue no: **650937 7**

THIGH RIDE (THIGH HIGH MIX)
Tracks: / Thigh ride (dub mix) / Thigh ride (thigh high mix) / Welcome to my dream.
12" Single: Released Jun '87, on Epic, by CBS Records. Catalogue no: **650937 6**

Taweel, Carolyn

DANCING IN THE STARLIGHT
Tracks: / Dancing in the starlight / Starlight.
7" Single: Released Nov '80, on Surrey Sound, Deleted Nov '83. Catalogue no: **HMS 3**

Tax Loss

SECRET
Tracks: / Secret / Spare me the sad eyes.
7" Single: Released Sep '80, on Logo, by Logo Records. Deleted Sep '83. Catalogue no: **GO 391**

Taxi

VOICES
Tracks: / Voices / Hard when it happens to you.
7" Single: Released Jul '82, on Trial, by Trial Records. Catalogue no: **CASE 4**

Taxi Gang

DOWN ON THE CORNER
Tracks: / Down on the corner.
7" Single: Released Sep '85, on Island, by Island Records. Deleted May '87. Catalogue no: **IS 244**
12" Single: Released Sep '85, on Island, by Island Records. Deleted May '87. Catalogue no: **12IS 244**

Taxi Girl

AUSSI BELLE QU'UNE BALLE
Tracks: / Aussi belle qu'une balle.
7" Single: Released Jan '86, on Play It Again Sam(Belgium), by Play It Again Sam (Belgium). Catalogue no: **BIAS 015**
12" Single: Released Jan '86, on Play It Again Sam(Belgium), by Play It Again Sam (Belgium). Catalogue no: **BIAS 016**

CHERCHEZ LE GARCON
Tracks: / Cherchez le garcon.
7" Single: Released Nov '81, on Virgin, by Virgin Records. Deleted Nov '84. Catalogue no: **VS 467**

Taxman

FATAL ATTRACTION
Tracks: / Fatal attraction.
12" Single: Released Nov '88, on White Label (1), Catalogue no: **STU 001**

IT'S GONE
Tracks: / It's gone / I want to be your man.
12" Single: Released Dec '84, on Senator, Catalogue no: **SEND 001**

TINA
Tracks: / Tina.
12" Single: Released Jul '89, on White, Catalogue no: **STU 002**

WELL ARMED AND DANGEROUS
Tracks: / Well armed and dangerous / Well armed and dangerous (version).
7" Single: Released Jul '87, on Sir George, Catalogue no: **S 0945**

Taxxi

NOT ME GIRL
Tracks: / Not me girl / Sex and suburban suicide.
7" Single: Released Mar '81, on Fantasy (USA), by Fantasy Inc (USA). Deleted Mar '84. Catalogue no: **FTC 195**

Tay Pan

BREAK OUT
Tracks: / Breakout.
12" Single: Released Jan '84, on Bullet, by Bullet Records. Deleted '88. Catalogue no: **BOLT 3**

Taylor, Al

YOU DIDN'T CALL ME
Tracks: / You didn't call me / Living it up.
7" Single: Released Sep '86, on Buzzin, Catalogue no: **WR 1**

Taylor, Alpheus

ALL NIGHT
Tracks: / All night.
12" Single: Released Sep '89, on Mega, by Mega Records. Catalogue no: **MEGAT 12**

RAID
Tracks: / Raid.
12" Single: Released Aug '86, on Black Ant, Catalogue no: **RAID 1**

Taylor, Andy

DON'T LET ME DIE YOUNG
Tracks: / Don't let me die young.
7" Single: Released Aug '87, on MCA, by MCA Records. Catalogue no: **MCA 1171**
12" Single: Released Aug '87, on MCA, by MCA Records. Catalogue no: **MCAR 1171**

LIFE GOES ON
Tracks: / Life goes on / Broken window.
12" Single: Released Apr '87, on MCA, by MCA Records. Catalogue no: **MCAR 1100**
7" Single: Released Apr '87, on MCA, by MCA Records. Catalogue no: **MCA 1100**

TAKE IT EASY
Tracks: / Take it easy / Angel eyes.
7" Single: Released Jul '86, on Atlantic, by WEA Records. Deleted Jun '87. Catalogue no: **A 9414**
12" Single: Released Jul '86, on Atlantic, by WEA Records. Deleted Jun '87. Catalogue no: **A 9414 T**

Taylor, Annette

IT MUST BE RIGHT
Tracks: / It must be right.
7" Single: Released Jun '88, on Cool Tempo, by Chrysalis Records. Catalogue no: **COOL 162**

Taylor, Billy

Biographical details: Taylor was born in 1921 in North Carolina; he is a fine jazz pianist who has become better known as a writer, broadcaster and teacher. *Where've You Been* features Keith Copeland on drums, Victor Gaskin on bass, Joe Kennedy on violin. Taylor was co-founder of the Jazzmobile in 1965, which gives free concerts in the streets for children; was musical director of the David Frost TV talk show, the first black to hold such a position (many years later he is still the only one). He published Jazz Piano in 1982, based on his radio series; he does a jazz interview segment once a month or so on a Sunday Morning TV show on CBS in the USA. (Donald Clarke 13.1.88).

I WISH I KNEW (HOW IT WOULD FEEL TO BE FREE)
Tracks: / I wish I knew(how it would feel to be free)(themefromfilm86) / Right here, right now / Freedom* (* Track on 12" version only.).
Note: The Billy Taylor Trio with orchestra conducted by Oliver Nelson.
7" Single: Released Sep '86, on Capitol, by EMI Records. Deleted Oct '87. Catalogue no: **CL 369**
12" Single: Released Sep '86, on Capitol, by EMI Records. Deleted Oct '87. Catalogue no: **12CL 369**

Taylor, Bob

DON'T BE UNFAIR
Tracks: / Don't be unfair.
7" Single: Released Jun '80, on Rollin' Rock, Catalogue no: **45 021**

Taylor, Brenda

YOU CAN'T HAVE YOUR CAKE AND EAT IT TOO
Tracks: / You can't have your cake and eat it too.
7" Single: Released Nov '82, on Excaliber, by Red Bus Records. Deleted Nov '85. Catalogue no: **EXC 526**
12" Single: Released Nov '82, on Excalibur, by Red Bus Records. Deleted Nov '85. Catalogue no: **EXCL 526**

Taylor, Dave

CADILLAC CAR
Tracks: / Cadillac car.
7" Single: Released Mar '80, on Charly, by Charly Records. Deleted '88. Catalogue no: **CYS 1063**

Taylor, Debbie

JUST DON'T PAY (OLD GOLD)
Tracks: / Just don't pay / Love don't come no stranger.
12" Single: Released 24 Apr '89, on Old Gold, by Old Gold Records. Catalogue no: **OG 4509**

Taylor, Denis

HERE WE GO BARRY
Tracks: / Joey Dunlop / Here we go Barry.
12" Single: Released May '88, on Homespun (Ireland), by Outlet Records. Catalogue no: **CHS 099**

Taylor, Derek

SALUTE TO JOLSON
Tracks: / Salute to Jolson.
7" Single: Released May '83, on OK, by Klub Records. Catalogue no: **OK 004**
12" Single: Released May '83, on OK, by Klub Records. Catalogue no: **OKL 004**

Taylor, Doris

DIANA DIVINE
Tracks: / Diana divine / God bless.
7" Single: Released Jan '81, on Edge, Deleted Jan '84. Catalogue no: **EDGE 8**

HAVE I TOLD YOU LATELY
Tracks: / Have I told you lately that I love you.
12" Single: Released May '85, on Time, Catalogue no: **TR 11**

Taylor, Felice

I FEEL LOVE COMIN' ON
Tracks: / I feel love comin' on.
7" Single: Released May '80, on President, by President Records. Catalogue no: **PT 155**

Taylor, Gary

COMPASSION (SINGLE)
Tracks: / Compassion (7" only) / Compassion (club remix) (12" only) / Follow / Compassion (acapella mix) (12" only) / Compassion (dub instrumental) (12" only).
Note: "If tenderness is what you miss, let me turn you on to this.... Compassion is Gary Taylor's first single for 10 records, and is a beautiful slice of soul from the master of the slow groove." (Virgin Records, May 88).
7" Single: Released May '88, on 10 Records, by Virgin Records. Catalogue no: **TEN 232**
12" Single: Released May '88, on 10 Records, by Virgin Records. Catalogue no: **TENX 232**

Taylor, James

Biographical details: James Taylor was born in 1948 in Boston, Massachusetts. He was one of the biggest stars of the early 1970s; his siblings Livingstone, Alex and Kate all became recording artists following his success. He formed the Flying Machine with guitarist Danny Kortchmar in 1963; by age 20 he was a heroin addict and came to London to escape; he met Peter Asher and made his first (eponymous) album for Apple in 1968: it was impressive but didn't sell large numbers, despite songs like *Something In The Way She Moves*. Back in the USA and managed by Asher, he made *Sweet Baby James* for Warner Brothers in 1970, a masterpiece of its time and place: as an antidote to the bombast of much rock his moody and introspective work coincided with that of Joni Mitchell, Carole King and Neil Young to create the singer/songwriter 'genre' that has always existed and always will. The album remains remarkable for its title track, *Fire & Rain* and *Country Road*; Elvis Presley covered *Steamroller*, Taylor's tongue-in-cheek blues; his next album Mud Slide Slim & The Blue Horizon was inevitably weaker, but sold even better (both were top 3 in the USA); *You've Got A Friend* (King's song) was a number one single in the USA; *Hey Mister, That's Me Up On The Juke Box* was a comment on his own success. He was married to Carly Simon 1972-82 and both careers seemed to suffer from too many cute covers. He switched to CBS in 1977; he appeared live with Bruce Springsteen and Jackson Browne in 1979; his albums and tours are still successful in the USA: his darker feelings are at bay and fans still respond to the warmth in his songs. (Donald Clarke 13.1.88).

BLOW UP
Tracks: / Blow up.
7" Single: Released Apr '87, on Re-Elect The President, Catalogue no: **FORD 1**

BREAKOUT
Tracks: / Breakout / Down by the river / Aquarius (Only on 12" and CD single.) / Down by the river (version) (Only on CD single.).
12" Single: Released 22 May '89, on Polydor, by Polydor Ltd. Catalogue no: **URBX 38**
7" Single: Released 22 May '89, on Polydor, by Polydor Ltd. Catalogue no: **URB 38**
CD 5": Released 22 May '89, on Polydor, by Polydor Ltd. Catalogue no: **URCD 38**

B.S.U.R
Tracks: / B.S.U.R..
7" Single: Released Aug '79, on CBS, by CBS Records. Deleted May '80. Catalogue no: **CBS 7773**

EVERYDAY
Tracks: / Everyday / Limousine driver.
7" Single: Released Mar '86, on CBS, by CBS Records. Catalogue no: **A 6683**

FIRE & RAIN
Tracks: / Fire and rain.
7" Single: Released Nov '70, on Warner Bros., by WEA Records. Deleted Nov '73. Catalogue no: **WB 6104**

HER TOWN TOO
Tracks: / Her town too / Believe it or not.
7" Single: Released Mar '81, on CBS, by CBS Records. Deleted Mar '84. Catalogue no: **CBS A 1048**

IT DOESN'T MATTER
Tracks: / It doesn't matter.
12" Single: Released Jul '89, on Urban, by Polydor Ltd. Catalogue no: **URBX 43**
7" Single: Released Jul '89, on Urban, by Polydor Ltd. Catalogue no: **URB 43**
CD 5": Released Jul '89, on Urban, by Polydor Ltd. Catalogue no: **URCD 43**

MUD SLIDE SLIM AND THE BLUE HORIZON (SINGLE)
7" Single: Released Mar '72, on Warner Bros., by WEA Records. Deleted '75. Catalogue no: **K 46085**

NEVER DIE YOUNG (SINGLE)
Tracks: / Never die young / Valentines day / Everyday.
12" Single: Released Feb '88, on CBS, by CBS Records. Deleted Jan '89. Catalogue no: **651 204 6**
CD 5": Released 20 Jun '88, on CBS, by CBS Records. Deleted Jan '89. Catalogue no: **651 204 2**
7" Single: Released Feb '88, on CBS, by CBS Records. Deleted Jan '89. Catalogue no: **651 204 7**

STARSKY & HUTCH, THEME FROM
Tracks: / Starsky & Hutch.
12" Single: Released 30 Aug '88, on Urban, by Polydor Ltd. Deleted 30 May '89. Catalogue no: **URBX 24**
7" Single: Released 30 Aug '88, on Urban, by Polydor Ltd. Deleted 30 May '89. Catalogue no: **URB 24**

UP ON THE ROOF
Tracks: / Fire and rain / Up on the roof.
7" Single: Released Jan '87, on WEA, by WEA Records. Deleted Jan '88. Catalogue no: **YZ 105**

YOU'VE GOT A FRIEND
Tracks: / You've got a friend.
7" Single: Released Jul '81, on Warner Bros., by WEA Records. Catalogue no: **K 16095**
7" Single: Released Aug '71, on Warner Bros., by WEA Records. Deleted Aug '74.

Catalogue no: **WB 16085**

YOU'VE GOT A FRIEND (OLD GOLD)
Tracks: / Fire and rain / You've got a friend.
7" Single: Released Mar '86, on Old Gold, by Old Gold Records. Catalogue no: **OG 9576**

Taylor, Jeremy

A.K. PLEEZE DADDY
Tracks: / A.K. pleeze daddy / Love is like a river.
7" Single: Released May '90, on Pye, Deleted '85. Catalogue no: **7P 180**

JOBSWORTH
Tracks: / Jobsworth.
7" Single: Released Sep '82, on BBC, by BBC Records & Tapes. Deleted '87. Catalogue no: **RESL 121**

Taylor, John

I DO WHAT I DO
Tracks: / I do what I do / Jazz / I do what I do (Film mix) (Track on 12" version only.).
7" Single: Released Mar '86, on Parlophone, by EMI Records. Catalogue no: **R 6125**
12" Single: Released Mar '86, on Parlophone, by EMI Records. Catalogue no: **12R 6125**

Taylor, Johnnie

DISCO LADY
Tracks: / Disco lady.
7" Single: Released Apr '76, on CBS, by CBS Records. Deleted Apr '80. Catalogue no: **CBS 4044**

IT'S SEPTEMBER
Tracks: / It's September.
7" Single: Released Jan '85, on Stax, by Fantasy Inc (USA). Catalogue no: **STAX 2021**

TESTIFY (I WANNA)
Tracks: / Testify.
7" Single: Released Oct '87, on Stax, by Fantasy Inc (USA). Catalogue no: **STAX 820**

WHO'S MAKING LOVE? (SINGLE)
Tracks: / Who's making love / I'm trying.
7" Single: Released 13 Jun '87, on Stax, by Fantasy Inc (USA). Catalogue no: **STAX 802**
7" Single: Released Mar '82, on Stax, by Fantasy Inc (USA). Catalogue no: **STAX 1008**

WHO'S MAKING LOVE? (SINGLE/OLD GOLD)
Tracks: / Who's making love.
7" Single: Released Sep '85, on Old Gold, by Old Gold Records. Catalogue no: **OG 9532**

Taylor, Linda

EVERY WAKING HOUR
Tracks: / Every waking hour (inst)..
7" Single: Released Jan '87, on Nightmare, by Nightmare Records. Catalogue no: **MARES 9**
12" Single: Released Jan '87, on Nightmare, by Nightmare Records. Catalogue no: **MARE 9**

YOU & ME JUST STARTED
Tracks: / You and me just started.
7" Single: Released Apr '82, on Groove PR, by Beggars Banquet Records. Catalogue no: **GP 317**
12" Single: Released Apr '82, on Groove PR, by Beggars Banquet Records. Catalogue no: **GP 3112**

YOU'RE IN THE POCKET
Tracks: / You're in the pocket / Steal your love.
7" Single: Released Sep '81, on Groove PR, by Beggars Banquet Records. Catalogue no: **GP 109**
12" Single: Released Sep '81, on Groove PR, by Beggars Banquet Records. Catalogue no: **GP 109T**

Taylor, Little Johnny

AS LONG AS I DON'T SEE YOU
Tracks: / As long as I don't see you.
7" Single: Released Jul '80, on Charly, by Charly Records. Deleted '87. Catalogue no: **CTD 118**

Taylor, Livingston

FIRST TIME LOVE
Tracks: / First time love / Pyjamas.
7" Single: Released Apr '81, on Epic, by CBS Records. Deleted '85. Catalogue no: **EPC 9021**

Taylor, Madeline

GYPSIES, TRAMPS AND THIEVES
Tracks: / Gypsies, tramps and thieves.
7" Single: Released 30 May '87, on Rubicon, Catalogue no: **RUBY 7001**

Taylor, Maria

BABY YOU GOT ME
Tracks: / Baby you got me.
12" Single: Released Mar '83, on KNK, Catalogue no: **KK 90**

JUST LOVERS
Tracks: / Just lovers.
10" single: Released Oct '82, on Sight, Catalogue no: **SR 104**

Taylor, Mike Lee

BIG 10-4
Tracks: / Big 10-4.
7" Single: Released Nov '81, on Buffalo (UK), by M.I.S.Records. Catalogue no: **BUFF 1003**

PIG OF THE YEAR
Tracks: / Pig of the year.
7" Single: Released Jul '83, on Orbit, by Orbit Records. Catalogue no: **TRIP 2**

Taylor, Neil

CHRISTMAS CRACKER, A
Tracks: / Christmas cracker, A / Little town called Ashford.
7" Single: Released Dec '82, on Cherub, Deleted Dec '85. Catalogue no: **SRTS 82**
7" Single: Released Dec '81, on Cherub, Deleted '87. Catalogue no: **CHERUB 1818NT**

Taylor, R. Dean

GOTTA SEE JANE
Tracks: / Gotta see Jane.
7" Single: Released Jun '68, on Motown, by BMG Records (UK). Deleted Jun '71. Catalogue no: **TMG 656**
7" Single: Released Oct '81, on Motown, by BMG Records (UK). Catalogue no: **TMG 918**

INDIANA WANTS ME
Tracks: / Indiana wants me.
7" Single: Released Apr '71, on Tamla Motown, by Motown Records (UK). Deleted Apr '74. Catalogue no: **TMG 763**
7" Single: Released Oct '81, on Motown, by BMG Records (UK). Catalogue no: **TMG 968**

THERE'S A GHOST IN MY HOUSE
Tracks: / There's a ghost in my house / Let's go somewhere.
7" Single: Released Feb '83, on Motown, by BMG Records (UK). Catalogue no: **TMG 896**

WINDOW SHOPPING
Tracks: / Window shopping.
7" Single: Released Aug '74, on Polydor, by Polydor Ltd. Deleted Aug '77. Catalogue no: **2058 502**

Taylor, Rod

GIRL OF MY COMPLEXION
Tracks: / Girl of my complexion.
12" Single: Released Mar '83, on DATC, Catalogue no: **DATACD 018**

MIDNIGHT COWBOY
Tracks: / Midnight cowboy.
12" Single: Released Nov '84, on Sweetcorn, Catalogue no: **SCR 002**

MISS CARTER WORE PINK
Tracks: / Miss Carter wore pink / Day Thou gavest, Lord is ended.
7" Single: Released Nov '80, on Rampage (USA), Catalogue no: **RAME 46**

MOVING OUT OVER
Tracks: / Moving out over.
12" Single: Released Apr '80, on Unity, Catalogue no: **UP 003**

SUN MOON AND STARS
Tracks: / Sun moon and stars / Rub-a-dub-rock.
12" Single: Released Oct '82, on DATC, Deleted Oct '85. Catalogue no: **DATCD 015**
7" Single: Released Oct '82, on DATC, Catalogue no: **DATC 015**

Taylor, Roger

FUTURE MANAGEMENT
Tracks: / Future management.
7" Single: Released Apr '81, on EMI, by EMI Records. Deleted Apr '84. Catalogue no: **EMI 5157**

MAN ON FIRE
Tracks: / Man on fire / Killing time.
7" Single: Released Jun '84, on EMI, by EMI Records. Deleted Jun '87. Catalogue no: **EMI 5478**

MY COUNTRY
Tracks: / My country / Step on the gas.
7" Single: Released Jun '81, on EMI, by EMI Records. Deleted Jun '84. Catalogue no: **EMI 5200**

Taylor, Ted

IT'S TOO LATE
Tracks: / It's too late.
7" Single: Released Jul '80, on Charly, by Charly Records. Deleted '87. Catalogue no: **CTD 111**

Taylor, Thomas

LOVE SOMEBODY
Tracks: / Love somebody / Love somebody (inst).
12" Single: Released Jun '87, on Raise The Roof, by Orbit Records. Catalogue no: **ROOF T1**
7" Single: Released Jun '87, on Raise The Roof, by Orbit Records. Catalogue no: **ROOF 1**

Taylor, Tot

ARISE SIR TOT
Tracks: / Arise Sir Tot / Mr. Strings / People will talk / Ballad of Jackie and Ivy, The.
12" Single: Released Oct '86, on London Popular Arts, by London Popular Arts. Catalogue no: **TOT 5**

AUSTRALIA
Tracks: / Australia / Inside story, The.
7" Single: Released Apr '87, on London Popular Arts, by London Popular Arts. Catalogue no: **TOT 4**

CHOCOLATE SONG
Tracks: / Chocolate song / You little UFO.
7" Single: Released May '81, on GTO, Deleted May '84. Catalogue no: **GT 292**

DON'T SPY ON ME
Tracks: / Don't spy on me.
7" Single: Released Nov '81, on Compact Organisation, Deleted '83. Catalogue no: **TOT 1**

GIRL WITH EVERYTHING
Tracks: / Girl with everthing / Paris man / Black & white interludes / My modern wife.
7" Single: Released Feb '81, on GTO, Deleted '84. Catalogue no: **GT 287**

I WANT TO PLAY THE DRUMS
Tracks: / I want to play the drums.
7" Single: Released Aug '82, on Compact Organisation, Deleted '84. Catalogue no: **TOT 2**

IT'S GOOD FOR YOU
Tracks: / It's good for you.
7" Single: Released Jul '87, on London Popular Arts, by London Popular Arts. Catalogue no: **TOT 6**

POPTOWN
Tracks: / Poptown / Richard Rodgers.
7" Single: Released Sep '84, on Easy Listeners, Deleted '87. Catalogue no: **TOT 3**

WHEN BLUE TURNS TO GREY
Tracks: / When blue turns to grey / I take the night / When you're in love / Please do it again.
7" Single: Released 14 May '88, on London Popular Arts, by London Popular Arts. Catalogue no: **TOT 9**

WRONG IDEA, THE
Tracks: / Wrong idea, The.
12" Single: Released Nov '87, on London Popular Arts, by London Popular Arts. Catalogue no: **TOT 8**

Taylor, T.T.

REMEMBER
Tracks: / Remember.
7" Single: Released Oct '81, on Solid Groove, Catalogue no: **SG 003**

Taylor, Tyrone

COME TO ME
Tracks: / Come to me.
12" Single: Released Mar '84, on Londisc, by Londisc Records. Catalogue no: **LD 006**

COTTAGE IN NEGRIL (SINGLE)
Tracks: / Cottage in Negril / 'allo tosh.
12" Single: on MCA, by MCA Records. Catalogue no: **MCAT 875**
7" Single: on MCA, by MCA Records. Catalogue no: **MCA 875**
12" Single: Released '85, on Virgin, by Virgin Records. Catalogue no: **VS 803-12**

ENERGY
Tracks: / Energy.
12" Single: Released Jun '84, on MCA, by MCA Records. Catalogue no: **MCAT 887**
7" Single: Released Jun '84, on MCA, by MCA Records. Catalogue no: **MCA 887**

GOT TO COME BACK
Tracks: / Got to come back / Rosilyn.
12" Single: Released Dec '85, on Hawkeye, by Hawkeye Records. Catalogue no: **HD 67**

HEAVY WAISTLINE
Tracks: / Heavy waistline.
12" Single: Released Jun '84, on Real Wax, Catalogue no: **JBMB 8112**

HOLD YOUR HAND IN PUBLIC
Tracks: / Hold your hand in public / Bird of a feather.
12" Single: Released Jul '86, on Diamond C, Catalogue no: **DCD 010**

LOVE YOU BACK TO LOVING ME
Tracks: / Love you back to loving me.
12" Single: Released Apr '85, on Londisc, by Londisc Records. Catalogue no: **LDR 041**

MEMBERS ONLY
Tracks: / Members only / Let me rock you tonight.
12" Single: Released Aug '86, on Technique, Catalogue no: **WRT 05**

SEND A LETTER
Tracks: / Send a letter / Send a letter (version) / Take your time / Too fast.
12" Single: Released Nov '86, on World Enterprise, Catalogue no: **WENDIS 3033**
12" Single: Released Mar '86, on Starlight, Catalogue no: **SLD 537**

TAKE YOUR TIME
Tracks: / Girl your mine / Take your time.
12" Single: Released Jan '87, on Blue Trac, by Blue Trac Records. Catalogue no: **BTR 009**

Taylor, Vince

BRAND NEW CADILLAC
Tracks: / Brand new Cadillac.
7" Single: Released May '79, on EMI, by EMI Records. Catalogue no: **EMI 2961**

CHANGING FOR YOU
Tracks: / Changing for you / Sweet time.
12" Single: Released Dec '83, on Clouds, Catalogue no: **CLSD 003**

HOUR OF MAGIC, THE
Tracks: / Hour of magic, The.
12" Single: Released Oct '85, on Time, Catalogue no: **TR 12**

I'LL BE YOUR HERO
Tracks: / I'll be your hero.
7" Single: Released May '83, on T & P, Deleted '84. Catalogue no: **PF 01**

TB Frank

SUGAR SUGAR
Tracks: / Sugar sugar.
CD 5": Released '89, on Play It Again Sam(Belgium), by Play It Again Sam (Belgium). Catalogue no: **CDBIAS 097**
12" Single: Released Sep '88, on Play It Again Sam(Belgium), by Play It Again Sam (Belgium). Catalogue no: **BIAS 097**

T-Birds

MY LIFE
Tracks: / My life / It doesn't matter.
7" Single: Released Jul '81, on Epic, by CBS Records. Catalogue no: **EPC A 1413**

T-Boys

ONE WAY STREET
Tracks: / One way street.
7" Single: Released Oct '81, on Almost Animal, Catalogue no: **AA 001**

TC Matic

O LA LA LA
Tracks: / O la la la / Willie.
7" Single: Released Apr '82, on Statik, Catalogue no: **STAT 11**

Tchaikovsky, Bram

BREAKING DOWN THE WALLS OF HEARTACHE
Tracks: / Breaking down the walls of heartache / Egyptian mummies.
7" Single: Released May '81, on Arista, by BMG Records (UK). Catalogue no: **ARIST 413**

LET'S DANCE
Tracks: / Let's dance / Rock and roll cabaret.
7" Single: Released May '80, on Radar, Deleted '83. Catalogue no: **ADA 54**

PRESSURE
Tracks: / Pressure / Mr. President.
7" Single: Released Aug '80, on Radar, Deleted '83. Catalogue no: **ADA 56**

SHALL WE DANCE
Tracks: / Shall we dance / Miracle cure.
7" Single: Released Mar '81, on Arista, by BMG Records (UK). Catalogue no: **ARIST 403**

T-Charm

RHYTHM IN RHAPSODY
Tracks: / Rhythm in rhapsody / Roast bread fruit.
7" Single: Released Feb '80, on Liberty, by EMI Records. Catalogue no: **BP 341**

T-Connection

AT MIDNIGHT
Tracks: / At midnight.
7" Single: Released Feb '79, on TK, Deleted Feb '82. Catalogue no: **TKR 7517**

DO WHAT YOU WANNA DO
Tracks: / Do what you wanna do.
7" Single: Released Jun '77, on TK, Deleted Jun '80. Catalogue no: **XC 9109**

ECSTACY
Tracks: / Ecstacy / Danger zone.
7" Single: Released Jan '80, on TK, Deleted Jan '85. Catalogue no: **TKR 771**

EVERYTHING IS COOL
Tracks: / Everything is cool / Paradise / We've got a good thing.

TEAM - WE ARE THE TEAM (Released on EMI)

7" Single: Released Mar '81, on Capitol, by EMI Records. Deleted Mar '84. Catalogue no: **CL 16187**
12" Single: Released Mar '81, on Capitol, by EMI Records. Deleted Mar '84. Catalogue no: **12 CL 16187**

LET YOURSELF GO
Tracks: / Let yourself go.
7" Single: Released Jun '78, on TK, Deleted Jun '81. Catalogue no: **TKR 6024**

LOVE ODYSSEY
Tracks: / Love odyssey.
12" Single: Released Mar '83, on Capitol, by EMI Records. Deleted '88. Catalogue no: **12 CL 287**
7" Single: Released Mar '83, on Capitol, by EMI Records. Deleted '88. Catalogue no: **CL 287**

ON FIRE
Tracks: / On fire.
7" Single: Released Jan '78, on TK, Deleted Apr '78. Catalogue no: **TKR 6006**

SATURDAY NIGHT
Tracks: / Saturday night.
7" Single: Released May '79, on TK, Deleted May '82. Catalogue no: **TKR 7536**

T-Coy

CARINO
Tracks: / Carino.
12" Single: Released 23 May '87, on De Construction, by BMG Records (UK). Catalogue no: **M 6222**

I LIKE TO LISTEN
Tracks: / I like to listen.
12" Single: Released Nov '87, on Supreme, by Supreme Records. Catalogue no: **M 6242**

NIGHT TRAIN
Tracks: / Night train.
12" Single: Released Jul '88, on De Construction, by BMG Records (UK). Catalogue no: **M 6262**

T-Cut-F

HOUSE REACTION
Tracks: / House reaction (original scratch mix) / House reaction (Union Jack mix) / House reaction (total mayhem mix) (On 12" only).
12" Single: Released Apr '88, on 10 Records, by Virgin Records. Catalogue no: **TENX 226**
7" Single: Released '88, on 10 Records, by Virgin Records. Catalogue no: **TEN 226**

HOUSE REACTION (ROBIN HOOD MIX)
Tracks: / House reaction (Robin Hood mix).
12" Single: Released Jul '87, on Kool Kat, by Kool Kat Records. Catalogue no: **KOOLT 9**

SEARCHIN
Tracks: / Searchin / Searchin (version) (7" only) / Get on (12" only) / Psychedelic (12" only).
12" Single: Released 17 Apr '89, on Virgin, by Virgin Records. Catalogue no: **TENX 262**
7" Single: Released 17 Apr '89, on Virgin, by Virgin Records. Catalogue no: **TEN 262**

T.D.A ...

FACES OF FREEDOM, 1.2.AND 3
Tracks: / Faces of freedom 1 2 and 3.
12" Single: Released Mar '86, on Some Bizzare, by Some Bizzare Records. Catalogue no: **MOP 121**

Tea Set

KEEP ON RUNNING
Tracks: / Keep on running / Flacid pot.
7" Single: Released Aug '80, on Mainly Modern, Deleted '83. Catalogue no: **STP 3**

SOUTH PACIFIC
Tracks: / South Pacific.
7" Single: Released Jul '81, on Demon, by Demon Records. Deleted '88. Catalogue no: **D 1009**

Teach In

DING A DONG
Tracks: / Ding a dong.
7" Single: Released Apr '75, on Polydor, by Polydor Ltd. Catalogue no: **2058 570**

Teahouse Camp

TO KILL,STAB IN BACK
Tracks: / To kill, stab in back.
7" Single: Released Jun '85, on Real Men, Catalogue no: **MEN 001**

Teale, Steve

MISS COSTELLO
Tracks: / Miss Costello / Parisian girls.
7" Single: Released Nov '81, on Ramkup, Catalogue no: **CAC 008**

Team

WE ARE THE TEAM (see panel above)
Tracks: / We are the Team / Rock creek park.
7" Single: Released Oct '85, on EMI, by EMI Records. Catalogue no: **EMI 5533**
12" Single: Released Oct '85, on EMI, by EMI Records. Catalogue no: **12EMI 5533**

WICKI WACKY HOUSE PARTY
Tracks: / Wicki wacky house party.
12" Single: Released Jun '85, on EMI, by EMI Records. Catalogue no: **12EMIX 5519**
12" Single: Released Jun '85, on EMI, by EMI Records. Catalogue no: **12EMI 5519**
7" Single: Released Jun '85, on EMI, by EMI Records. Catalogue no: **EMI 5519**

Team 10

MISSION IMPOSSIBLE
Tracks: / Mission imposible.
12" Single: Released Sep '86, on Portrait, by CBS Records. Catalogue no: **650118 6**

Team 23

MOVE INTO THE RHYTHM
Tracks: / Move into the rhythm / Whatever moves you.
7" Single: Released Feb '81, on Race, Catalogue no: **RB 002**

Team 38

CLOSER TO YOU
Tracks: / Closer to you.
12" Single: Released Aug '84, on Elite Records, by Elite Records. Deleted '86. Catalogue no: **DAZZ 33**

Teamwork

SAD MOVIES (MAKE ME CRY)
Tracks: / Sad movies (make me cry).
7" Single: Released Jan '85, on Homespun (Ireland), by Outlet Records. Catalogue no: **HS 093**

TERRACE TALK
Tracks: / Terrace talk / Sucker for the game.
7" Single: Released Apr '82, on Kingdom, by Kingdom Records. Deleted '87. Catalogue no: **KV 8023**

Tear Garden

CENTRE BULLET
Tracks: / Centre bullet, The.
12" Single: Released Nov '86, on Play It Again Sam(Belgium), by Play It Again Sam (Belgium). Catalogue no: **BIAS 031**

Tear, Lizzie

LIFE WON'T BE THE SAME
Tracks: / Life won't be the same / Life won't be the same (one on one mix) (Available on 12" only) / Life breakdown / Life won't be the same (dub version) (Available on 12" only) / Life won't be the same (Lizzy mix Kevorkian).
Note: * Extra tracks on 12" only.
12" Single: Released Oct '87, on EMI, by EMI Records. Deleted Apr '88. Catalogue no: **12EMX 14**
10" single: Released Sep '87, on EMI, by EMI Records. Deleted Apr '88. Catalogue no: **10EM 14**
7" Single: Released Sep '87, on EMI, by EMI Records. Deleted Apr '88. Catalogue no: **EM 14**

SILVER SURFER
Tracks: / Silver surfer / Silver surfer (Percapella) / Silver surfer (Apocalypse surf mix) (12" and CD single only.) / Silver surfer (radical mix).
CD 5": Released Sep '88, on EMI, by EMI Records. Deleted Aug '89. Catalogue no: **CDEM 72**
12" Single: Released Feb '89, on EMI, by EMI Records. Deleted Aug '89. Catalogue no: **12EMX 72**
7" Single: Released Sep '88, on EMI, by EMI Records. Deleted Aug '89. Catalogue no: **EM 72**
12" Single: Released Sep '88, on EMI, by EMI Records. Deleted Aug '89. Catalogue no: **12EM 72**

TURBO-CHARGED
Tracks: / Turbo-charged / Turbo-charged (V8 power booster mix) (Available on 12" and CD only) / Turbo-charged (Percapella mix) / Turbo-charged (Bonus beats) (Available on 12", 12" remix and CD) / Turbo-charged (Turbo Latino mix) (Available on 12" remix only).
12" Single: Released Jul '88, on EMI, by EMI Records. Deleted Aug '89. Catalogue no: **12EMS 59**
CD 5": Released Jul '88, on EMI, by EMI Records. Deleted Aug '89. Catalogue no: **CDEM 59**
7" Single: Released Jul '88, on EMI, by EMI Records. Deleted Aug '89. Catalogue no: **EM 59**
12" Single: Released Jul '88, on EMI, by EMI Records. Deleted Aug '89. Catalogue no: **12 EM 59**

Teardrop Explodes

Biographical details: Teardrop Explodes was a UK new wave group formed in Liverpool in 1978 with vocalist/bassist **Julian Cope** (born in Wales in 1957). With changing personnel they made several albums, more influential than commercially successful, though they had several hit singles; Cope went solo. (Donald Clarke 13.1.88).

COLOURS FLY AWAY
Tracks: / Colours fly away / Window shopping for a new crown of thorns.
7" Single: Released Nov '81, on Mercury, by Phonogram Ltd. Deleted Nov '84. Catalogue no: **TEAR 6**

HA HA I'M DROWNING
Tracks: / Ha ha I'm drowning / Poppies in the field / Books (Available only on a double pack) / Bouncing babies (Available only on a double pack).
7" Single: Released Aug '81, on Mercury, by Phonogram Ltd. Deleted Aug '84. Catalogue no: **TEAR 4**
7" Set: Released Aug '81, on Mercury, by Phonogram Ltd. Deleted Aug '84. Catalogue no: **TEAR 44**

PASSIONATE FRIEND
Tracks: / Passionate friend / Christ v. Warhol.
7" Single: Released Aug '81, on Zoo, Deleted Aug '84. Catalogue no: **TEAR 5**

REWARD
Tracks: / Reward / Strange house in the snow.
7" Single: Released Jan '81, on Vertigo, by Phonogram Ltd. Deleted Jan '84. Catalogue no: **TEAR 2**
7" Single: Released Jun '85, on Mercury, by Phonogram Ltd. Catalogue no: **TEAR 9**
12" Single: Released Jun '85, on Mercury, by Phonogram Ltd. Deleted '87. Catalogue no: **TEAR 912**

TINY CHILDREN
Tracks: / Tiny children / Rachel built a steam boat.
7" Single: Released Jun '82, on Mercury, by Phonogram Ltd. Deleted Jun '85. Catalogue no: **TEAR 7**
12" Single: Released Jun '82, on Mercury, by Phonogram Ltd. Deleted '83. Catalogue no: **TEAR 712**

TREASON (IT'S JUST A STORY)
Tracks: / Treason (it's just a story) / Use me.
7" Single: Released Aug '81, on Mercury, by Phonogram Ltd. Deleted Aug '84. Catalogue no: **TEAR 3**
7" Single: Released Mar '80, on Zoo, Deleted Mar '83. Catalogue no: **CAGE 008**

WHEN I DREAM
Tracks: / When I dream / Kilimanjaro.
7" Single: Released Sep '80, on Mercury, by Phonogram Ltd. Deleted Sep '83. Catalogue no: **TEAR 1**

YOU DISAPPEAR FROM VIEW
Tracks: / You disappear from view.
7" Single: Released Mar '83, on Mercury, by Phonogram Ltd. Deleted Mar '86. Catalogue no: **TEAR 8**

Tearjerkers

MURDER MYSTERY
Tracks: / Murder mystery / Heart on the line.
7" Single: Released Feb '80, on Back Door (Holland), Deleted '83. Catalogue no: **DOOR 1**

Tears For Fears

Biographical details: Tears for fears is a UK new wave group formed by duo Curt Smith on bass and vocals, Roland Orzabal on guitar and vocals, both from Bath and both born in 1961. They shared lead vocals, Orzabal writing most of the songs; subject matter is sometimes 'heavy' (*Hurting* about primal scream therapy, etc) but tunes are catchy and emphasis on musicianship is high. They took 1986 off and hadn't come back mid-'87. Mancrab was a splinter group. (Donald Clarke 13.1.88).

CHANGE
Tracks: / Change / Conflict.
7" Single: Released Feb '83, on Mercury, by Phonogram Ltd. Deleted Feb '86. Catalogue no: **IDEA 4**

EVERYBODY WANTS TO RULE THE WORLD
Tracks: / Everybody wants to rule the world / Pharoahs.
7" Single: Released Mar '85, on Mercury, by Phonogram Ltd. Deleted Mar '88. Catalogue no: **IDEA 9**
7" Single: Released Jun '86, on Mercury, by Phonogram Ltd. Deleted Jun '89. Catalogue no: **RACE 1**

HEAD OVER HEELS
Tracks: / Head over heels.
7" Single: Released Jun '85, on Mercury, by Phonogram Ltd. Deleted Jun '88. Catalogue no: **IDEA 10**

I BELIEVE (A SOULFUL RE-RECORDING)
Tracks: / I believe (a soulful re-recording).
7" Single: Released Oct '85, on Mercury, by Phonogram Ltd. Deleted Oct '88. Catalogue no: **IDEA 11**

MAD WORLD
Tracks: / Mad world.
12" Single: Released Oct '84, on Mercury, by Phonogram Ltd. Catalogue no: **IDEA 312**
7" Single: Released Oct '84, on Mercury, by Phonogram Ltd. Catalogue no: **IDEA 3**

MOTHER'S TALK
Tracks: / Mother's talk.
7" Single: Released Dec '84, on Mercury, by Phonogram Ltd. Deleted Dec '87. Catalogue no: **IDEA 7**

PALE SHELTER
Tracks: / Pale shelter / Prisoner.
7" Single: Released Apr '83, on Mercury, by Phonogram Ltd. Deleted Apr '86. Catalogue no: **IDEA 5**

SHOUT
Tracks: / Shout.
7" Single: Released Nov '84, on Mercury, by Phonogram Ltd. Deleted Mar '88. Catalogue no: **IDEA 8**

SOWING THE SEEDS OF LOVE
Tracks: / Sowing the seeds of love / Tears roll down / Shout (US remix) (Only on 12" and CD single.).
CD 5": Released Aug '89, on Mercury, by

Phonogram Ltd. Catalogue no: **IDCD 12**
7" Single: Released Aug '89, on Mercury, by Phonogram Ltd. Catalogue no: **IDEA 12**
12" Single: Released Aug '89, on Mercury, by Phonogram Ltd. Catalogue no: **IDEAT 12**
Cassingle: Released Aug '89, on Mercury, by Phonogram Ltd. Catalogue no: **IDMC 12**

SUFFER THE CHILDREN
Tracks: / Suffer the children / Wino.
7" Single: Released Aug '85, on Mercury, by Phonogram Ltd. Deleted Aug '88. Catalogue no: **IDEA 1**
12" Single: Released Nov '81, on Mercury, by Phonogram Ltd. Deleted '84. Catalogue no: **IDEA 12**

WAY YOU ARE, THE
Tracks: / Way you are, The.
7" Single: Released Dec '83, on Mercury, by Phonogram Ltd. Deleted Dec '86. Catalogue no: **IDEA 6**

Tease

FIRESTARTER
Tracks: / Firestarter / Baby, be mine.
7" Single: Released Apr '86, on Epic, by CBS Records. Catalogue no: **A 7084**
12" Single: Released Apr '86, on Epic, by CBS Records. Catalogue no: **TA 7084**

Teaser

FIRST DATE
Tracks: / First date / English garden.
7" Single: Released May '80, on Harbour, by Harbour Records. Deleted May '83. Catalogue no: **HRB 8**

Tech

KABUKI
Tracks: / Kabuki.
12" Single: Released Sep '87, on Manhattan (USA), by Capitol (USA) Records. Deleted Oct '87. Catalogue no: **V 56065**

Technice, Dave

IT'S NASTY
Tracks: / It's nasty.
7" Single: Released Sep '89, on Sleeping Bag, by Sleeping Bag Records. Catalogue no: **SBUK 15**
12" Single: Released Sep '89, on Sleeping Bag, by Sleeping Bag Records. Catalogue no: **SBUK 15T**

Technics

YOU DON'T CARE FOR ME
Tracks: / You don't care for me / In the mood.
12" Single: Released Mar '84, on Treasure Isle, Catalogue no: **TRE 012**

Technique

HEAVEN TO ME
Tracks: / Heaven to me.
7" Single: Released Jun '84, on ERC, Catalogue no: **ERC 114**
12" Single: Released Jun '84, on ERC, Catalogue no: **ERCL 114**

Techniques

NEVER FALL IN LOVE AGAIN
Tracks: / Never fall in love again.
12" Single: Released Jun '82, on Black Joy, Catalogue no: **DH 824**

SAMFIE LOVER
Tracks: / Samfie lover.
12" Single: Released Oct '88, on Techniques, Catalogue no: **WR 57**

Techno Twins

CAN'T HELP FALLING IN LOVE
Tracks: / Can't help falling in love / Kings and queens of England.
7" Single: Released Apr '82, on PRT, by Castle Communications Records. Deleted Apr '85. Catalogue no: **7P 232**
12" Single: Released Apr '82, on PRT, by Castle Communications Records. Deleted Apr '85. Catalogue no: **12P 232**

SWING TOGETHER
Tracks: / Swing together / Beautiful women in Bermuda shorts.
12" Single: Released Jul '82, on PRT, by Castle Communications Records. Deleted Jul '85. Catalogue no: **12P 246**
7" Single: Released Jul '82, on PRT, by Castle Communications Records. Deleted Jul '85. Catalogue no: **7P 246**

Technodelia

TECHNODELIA
Tracks: / Technodelia.
12" Single: Released Jun '89, on Living Beat, by Living Beat Records. Catalogue no: **SMASH 5**

Technos

FALLING IN LOVE AGAIN
Tracks: / Falling in love again / Donald and Julia go boating.
7" Single: Released Jul '85, on PRT, by Castle Communications Records. Catalogue no: **7TEC 4100**
7" Single: Released Jan '82, on PRT, by Castle Communications Records. Deleted Jan '85. Catalogue no: **7P 224**
12" Single: Released Jul '85, on PRT, by Castle Communications Records. Catalogue no: **12TEC 4100**

FOREIGN LAND (SINGLE)
Tracks: / Foreign land.
7" Single: Released Jul '83, on PRT, by Castle Communications Records. Catalogue no: **TWIN 1**
7" Single: Released Oct '85, on PRT, by Castle Communications Records. Catalogue no: **7TEC 4101**
12" Single: Released Jul '83, on PRT, by Castle Communications Records. Catalogue no: **TWINL 1**
12" Single: Released Oct '85, on PRT, by Castle Communications Records. Catalogue no: **12TEC 4101**

NIGHT TIME HEAVEN
Tracks: / Night time heaven.
7" Single: Released Jan '84, on PRT, by Castle Communications Records. Catalogue no: **7TEC 1**
12" Single: Released Jan '84, on PRT, by Castle Communications Records. Catalogue no: **12TEC 1**

SPIRIT OF THE THING
Tracks: / Spirit of the thing.
12" Single: Released Aug '84, on PRT, by Castle Communications Records. Catalogue no: **12TEC 2**
7" Single: Released Aug '84, on PRT, by Castle Communications Records. Catalogue no: **7TEC 2**

Technotronic

PUMP UP THE JAM
Tracks: / Pump up the jam / Pump up the jam (instrumental) / Pump up the jam (jam edit mix) (Only on 12" single.).
12" Single: Released Aug '89, on Total, Catalogue no: **SYRT 4**
7" Single: Released Aug '89, on Total, Catalogue no: **SYR 4**
12" Single: Released 21 Sep '88, on Total, Catalogue no: **SYRTR 4**

Tedd, Simon

YESTERDAY'S MEMORIES
Tracks: / Yesterday's memories.
7" Single: Released Jun '83, on China Discs, Catalogue no: **CDN 003**

Teddy Bears

TO KNOW HIM IS LOVE HIM (OLD GOLD CD SINGLE)
Tracks: / To know him is to love him / Rhythm of the rain / Poetry in motion.
CD 5": Released Nov '88, on Old Gold, by Old Gold Records. Catalogue no: **OG 6104**

TO KNOW HIM IS TO LOVE HIM
Tracks: / To know him is to love him.
7" Single: Released Apr '79, on Lightning, Deleted '82. Catalogue no: **LIG 9015**
7" Single: Released Dec '58, on London Records, by London Records. Deleted '61. Catalogue no: **HL 8733**

TO KNOW HIM IS TO LOVE HIM (OLD GOLD)
Tracks: / To know him is to love him / Endless sleep.
7" Single: Released Jun '88, on Old Gold, by Old Gold Records. Catalogue no: **OG 9015**

Teddy & the Frat Girls

I WANNA BE A MAN
Tracks: / I wanna be a man.
12" Single: Released Feb '85, on Alternative Tentacles, by Alternative Tentacles Records. Catalogue no: **VIRUS 19**

Tee, Hitman Howie

(BANG ZOOM) LET'S GO-GO (Real Roxanne)
Tracks: / (Bang zoom) Let's go go / Howie's teed off.
7" Single: Released Jun '86, on Cool Tempo, by Chrysalis Records. Deleted '89. Catalogue no: **COOL 124**

Tee, Lynneth

HELLO STRANGER
Tracks: / Hello stranger.
7" Single: Released Jan '85, on True World, Catalogue no: **TRU 001**

Tee-Mac

SOUND OF THE UNIVERSE
Tracks: / Sound of the universe / Certain way to go.

7" Single: Released Jun '81, on Ensign, by Ensign Records. Deleted '82. Catalogue no: **ENY 214**
12" Single: Released Jun '81, on Ensign, by Ensign Records. Deleted '83. Catalogue no: **ENYT 214**

Teen Dreams

LET'S GET BUSY
Tracks: / Let's get busy / Let's get busy (inst) / Let's get busy (Boy crazy mix) / Let's get busy (dub).
12" Single: Released Jun '87, on Warner Bros., by WEA Records. Deleted Jan '88. Catalogue no: **W 8602T**
7" Single: Released Jun '87, on Warner Bros., by WEA Records. Deleted Jan '88. Catalogue no: **W 8602**

Teen, Judy

LOVE BITES
Tracks: / Second bite / Again & again (Extra track on 12") / Love bites.
7" Single: Released Jan '87, on GFM, Catalogue no: **GFM 108**
12" Single: Released Feb '87, on GFM, Catalogue no: **GFMT 108**

Teen Queens

GOOD ROCKIN' DADDY
Tracks: / Good rockin' daddy / Eddie my love.
7" Single: Released Mar '81, on Ace, by Ace Records. Deleted Jun '88. Catalogue no: **NS 66**

Teenage Film Stars

ODD MAN OUT
Tracks: / Odd man out / I apologise.
7" Single: Released Jun '80, on Blue Print, Deleted Jun '83. Catalogue no: **BLU 2013**

Teenbeats

I CAN'T CONTROL MYSELF
Tracks: / I can't control myself.
7" Single: Released '79, on Safari, by Safari Records. Catalogue no: **SAFE 17**

STRENGTH OF THE NATION
Tracks: / Strength of the nation.
7" Single: Released '80, on Safari, by Safari Records. Catalogue no: **SAFE 19**

Teezers

BEST PART OF BREAKING UP
Tracks: / Best part of breaking up / Rebel.
7" Single: Released May '81, on Arrival, by Blaylock Management Ltd.. Deleted '86. Catalogue no: **PIK 3**

Tekla Irie

REGGAE RHYTHM
Tracks: / Reggae rhythm.
12" Single: Released Sep '84, on Fulani, Catalogue no: **FW 16A**

Telegents

GET OUT
Tracks: / Get out / Telephone romance.
7" Single: Released Apr '81, on Genie, Catalogue no: **GENT 1**

Telescopes

7TH DISASTER
Tracks: / 7th disaster / Nothing / This planet / Cold.
12" Single: Released Apr '89, on Cheree, Catalogue no: **CHEREE T4**

PERFECT NEEDLE, THE
Tracks: / Perfect needle, The.
7" Single: Released Sep '89, on What Goes On, by What Goes On Records. Catalogue no: **WHATGOES 15**
12" Single: Released Sep '89, on What Goes On, by What Goes On Records. Catalogue no: **WHATGOES 1215**

Television

FOXHOLE
Tracks: / Foxhole.
7" Single: Released Apr '78, on Elektra, by Elektra Records (UK). Deleted '81. Catalogue no: **K 12287**

I KNOW WHERE SYD BARRETT LIVES
Tracks: / I know where Syd Barrett lives / Arthur the gardener.
7" Single: Released Feb '81, on Rough Trade, by Rough Trade Records. Catalogue no: **RT 063**

MARQUEE MOON (SINGLE)
Tracks: / Marquee moon.
7" Single: Released Apr '77, on Elektra, by Elektra Records (UK). Deleted '80. Catalogue no: **K 12252**

PROVE IT
Tracks: / Prove it.
7" Single: Released Jul '77, on Elektra, by Elektra Records (UK). Deleted '80. Catalogue no: **K 12262**

SENSE OF BELONGING
Tracks: / Sense of belonging / Paradise estate.
7" Single: Released Dec '83, on Rough Trade, by Rough Trade Records. Catalogue no: **RT 109**

Telex

HAVEN'T WE MET SOMEWHERE BEFORE
Tracks: / Haven't we met somewhere before.
7" Single: Released Jul '82, on Interdisc, by Interdisc Records. Catalogue no: **IN 1**
12" Single: Released Jul '82, on Interdisc, by Interdisc Records. Catalogue no: **IN 112**

L'AMOUR TOUJOURS,
Tracks: / L'amour toujours, / Cloches et siflets / Man with the answer (Only on 12" single.).
7" Single: Released Sep '82, on Interdisc, by Interdisc Records. Catalogue no: **IN 2**
12" Single: Released Sep '82, on Interdisc, by Interdisc Records. Catalogue no: **IN 212**

ROCK AROUND THE CLOCK
Tracks: / Rock around the clock.
7" Single: Released Jul '79, on Sire, by Sire Records. Deleted '82. Catalogue no: **SIR 4020**

SOUL WAVES
Tracks: / Soul waves (pt 1 and 2).
7" Single: Released Dec '80, on Sire, by Sire Records. Deleted Dec '85. Catalogue no: **SIR 4047**

Tell Tale Hearts

FALLING DOWN
Tracks: / Falling down.
12" Single: Released Mar '87, on Teden's Doorbell, Catalogue no: **EDD 1**

Tella & Collins

WHEN YOU'RE YOUNG
Tracks: / When you're young / When you're young (instrumental).
12" Single: Released Oct '86, on A.1, by A.1 Records. Catalogue no: **12 A1 294**
7" Single: Released Oct '86, on A.1, by A.1 Records. Catalogue no: **A1 294**

Tella, Sylvia

HE'S MY BABY
Tracks: / He's my baby.
12" Single: Released Oct '85, on Boss, Catalogue no: **BF 002**

I STILL FEEL
Tracks: / I still feel.
12" Single: Released Nov '84, on Boss, Catalogue no: **BS 001**

PEACE AND LOVE
Tracks: / Peace and love / Peace and love (version).
12" Single: Released Nov '87, on Body Music, by Nuclear Records. Catalogue no: **BZT 06**

SWEETER HE IS
Tracks: / Sweeter he is, The.
12" Single: Released Apr '82, on SRL, Deleted '86. Catalogue no: **SRLDD 1**

Tellers

JENNIFER CLARKE
Tracks: / Jennifer Clarke.
12" Single: Released Aug '85, on Calypso Joe, Catalogue no: **CJ 001**

Telsa

MODERN DAY COWBOY
Tracks: / Love me (live) (Available on 12" only.) / Cover queen (live) (Available on 12" only.) / Modern day cowboy / Love me / Cover queen.
7" Single: Released Aug '87, on Geffen, by Geffen Records (USA). Deleted Jul '88. Catalogue no: **GEF 28**
12" Single: Released Aug '87, on Geffen, by Geffen Records (USA). Catalogue no: **GEF 28T**

Temper

NO FAVOURS
Tracks: / No favours.
12" Single: Released Sep '84, on MCA, by MCA Records. Catalogue no: **MCAT 916**
7" Single: Released Sep '84, on MCA, by MCA Records. Catalogue no: **MCA 916**

Temper Temper

SWITCH, THE
Tracks: / Switch, The / Let's swing / Switch, The (12" version) (12" only) / Body blows (instrumental) (12" only).
7" Single: Released Aug '89, on Sheer Bravado, Catalogue no: **SB 01**
12" Single: Released Aug '89, on Sheer Bravado, Catalogue no: **SB 02**

Temperance Seven

Biographical details: The 'Seven' were formed at the Royal College of Art in the mid-'50s, playing semi-hot dance music in late-'20s style, members (usually nine) dressed accordingly. Among the original members was jazz buff/recording engineer (now famous for high-quality transfers of old 78s) John R.T. Davies on trombone, using pseudonym Sheik Wadi El Yadounir and wearing a fez. They kept going well into the '60s; there were subsequent editions of the group and they still gig occasionally, original members sometimes sitting in. (Donald Clarke 13.1.88).

CHARLESTON
Tracks: / Charleston.
7" Single: Released Dec '61, on Parlophone, by EMI Records. Deleted '64. Catalogue no: **R 4851**

HARD HEARTED HANNAH
Tracks: / Hard hearted Hannah / Chili bom bom.
7" Single: Released Sep '61, on Parlophone, by EMI Records. Deleted '64. Catalogue no: **R 4823**

PASADENA
Tracks: / Pasadena.
7" Single: Released Jun '61, on Parlophone, by EMI Records. Deleted '64. Catalogue no: **R 4781**

YOU'RE DRIVING ME CRAZY
Tracks: / You're driving me crazy / Pasadena.
7" Single: Released Jun '80, on H.M.V., by EMI Records. Deleted '83. Catalogue no: **POP 2007**
7" Single: Released Oct '83, on Old Gold, by Old Gold Records. Deleted Jul '88. Catalogue no: **OG 9385**
7" Single: Released Mar '61, on Parlophone, by EMI Records. Deleted '64. Catalogue no: **R 4757**

Tempest

Biographical details: The Tempest consists of: Mike Sheerin; Lyn Smith; Stuart Dunning (bass guitarist); Ian Finney (guitarist) and Steve Dolder (drummer). Managed by Nicky Martin, The Tempest completed their first UK tour in the spring of 1985, supporting The Untouchables. Their first single *Always the same* was released to coincide. It won several allies, scoring good reviews and clocking up over 3 weeks of Radio One daytime airplay. Their second single *Bluebelle* was produced by Glenn Tilbrook and is available on Magnet Records - release date September 1985. (Magnet Press Office, 1985).

ALWAYS THE SAME
Tracks: / Always the same.
78 rpm: Released Aug '85, on Magnet, by WEA Records. Catalogue no: **10 TEST 1**
7" Single: Released May '85, on Magnet, by WEA Records. Deleted '87. Catalogue no: **PEST 1**

BLUEBELLE
Tracks: / Bluebelle.
12" Single: Released Sep '85, on Magnet, by WEA Records. Deleted Jan '88. Catalogue no: **10 PEST 2**
7" Single: Released Sep '85, on Magnet, by WEA Records. Deleted Jan '88. Catalogue no: **PEST 2**

DIDN'T WE HAVE A NICE TIME? (and all my friends...)
Tracks: / Didn't we have a nice time (and all my friends are here) / Physical act, The.
Note: Writer: Michael Sheerin. Producer Glenn Tilbrook except *The Tempest.
12" Single: Released May '86, on Magnet, by WEA Records. Deleted Jan '88. Catalogue no: **12 PEST 3**
7" Single: Released May '86, on Magnet, by WEA Records. Deleted Jan '88. Catalogue no: **PEST 3**

LADY LEFT THIS
Tracks: / Lady left this.
7" Single: Released Jul '83, on Glass, by Glass Records. Deleted '83. Catalogue no: **GLASS 029**

LAZY SUNDAY
Tracks: / Lazy Sunday / You've always got something to say.
7" Single: Released Aug '86, on Magnet, by WEA Records. Deleted Jan '88. Catalogue no: **LAZY 1**
12" Single: Released Aug '86, on Magnet, by WEA Records. Deleted Jan '88. Catalogue no: **12 LAZY 1**

MONTEZUMA
Tracks: / Montezuma / ABC / Calm before (on 12" only).
7" Single: Released Dec '83, on Anagram, by Cherry Red Records. Deleted '88. Catalogue no: **ANA 17**
12" Single: Released Dec '83, on Anagram, by Cherry Red Records. Deleted '88. Catalogue no: **12 ANA 17**

Tempo, Nino

DEEP PURPLE
Tracks: / Deep purple.
7" Single: Released Nov '63, on London-American, Deleted '66. Catalogue no: **HLK 9785**

WHISPERING
Tracks: / Whispering.
7" Single: Released Jan '64, on London-American, Deleted '67. Catalogue no: **HLK 9829**

YOUNG STUFF
Tracks: / Young stuff / Ronan's road.
7" Single: Released Oct '80, on A&M, by A&M Records. Deleted Oct '83. Catalogue no: **AMS 7568**
12" Single: Released Oct '80, on A&M, by A&M Records. Deleted Oct '83. Catalogue no: **AMSX 7568**

Temporary Title

CHEONG SONG (SUMMER SONG)
Tracks: / Cheong song (summer song).
7" Single: Released Oct '81, on Secret, by Secret Records. Catalogue no: **SHH 116**

Temptations

Biographical details: This USA male soul vocal group formed in 1962 in Detroit, and are without a doubt America's best-loved male vocal group. The original lineup were from at least two groups which had many different names: bass Melvin Franklin (born in 1942 in Montgomery, Alabama), lead singer **Eddie Kendricks** (born 1939 in Birmingham, Alabama), Otis Williams (born in 1941 in Texarkana, Texas), Paul Williams (born 1939 in Birmingham; died in 1973) and Eldridge Bryant. The much-loved Temptations have had more than 50 hits in the USA top 100 1964-86, including 15 in the top 10 1965-73: *My Girl, I Can't Get Next To You, Just My Imagination* and *Papa Was A Rollin' Stone* were number one hits. There have been personnel changes, Franklin and Otis Williams remaining constant, lead singers have included **David Ruffin** and (since 1983) Rick James. (Donald Clarke 13.1.88).

AIMING AT YOUR HEART
Tracks: / Aiming at your heart / Life of a cowboy.
7" Single: Released Oct '81, on Motown, by BMG Records (UK). Deleted '83. Catalogue no: **TMG 1243**
12" Single: Released Oct '81, on Motown, by BMG Records (UK). Deleted '83. Catalogue no: **TMGT 1243**

AIN'T TOO PROUD TO BEG
Tracks: / Ain't too proud to beg.
7" Single: Released Jul '66, on Tamla Motown, by Motown Records (UK). Deleted '69. Catalogue no: **TMG 565**

ALL I WANT FROM YOU
Tracks: / All I want from you / All I want from you (instrumental) / Treat her like a lady (Available on 12" format only.) / Papa was a rolling stone (Available on 12" only).
12" Single: Released Sep '89, on Motown, by BMG Records (UK). Catalogue no: **ZT 43234**
7" Single: Released Sep '89, on Motown, by BMG Records (UK). Catalogue no: **ZB 43233**
CD 5": Released Sep '89, on Motown, by BMG Records (UK). Catalogue no: **ZD 43234**

BALL OF CONFUSION
Tracks: / Ball of confusion / Take a look around.
7" Single: Released Apr '85, on Motown, by BMG Records (UK). Deleted '87. Catalogue no: **TMG 997**
12" Single: Released Apr '85, on Motown, by BMG Records (UK). Deleted '87. Catalogue no: **TMGT 997**
7" Single: Released Oct '80, on Motown, by BMG Records (UK). Deleted Oct '83. Catalogue no: **TMG 967**
7" Single: Released Sep '70, on Tamla Motown, by Motown Records (UK). Deleted '73. Catalogue no: **TMG 749**

BEAUTY IS ONLY SKIN DEEP
Tracks: / Beauty is only skin deep.
7" Single: Released Oct '66, on Tamla Motown, by Motown Records (UK). Deleted '69. Catalogue no: **TMG 578**

CLOUD NINE (SINGLE)
Tracks: / Cloud nine / Psychedelic shacks.
7" Single: Released Aug '69, on Tamla Motown, by Motown Records (UK). Deleted '72. Catalogue no: **TMG 707**
7" Single: Released Mar '83, on Motown, by BMG Records (UK). Catalogue no: **TMG 982**

DO YOU REALLY LOVE YOUR BABY
Tracks: / Do you really love your baby.
12" Single: Released Nov '85, on Motown, by BMG Records (UK). Deleted '88. Catalogue no: **ZT 40454**
7" Single: Released Nov '85, on Motown, by BMG Records (UK). Deleted '88. Catalogue no: **ZB 40453**

GET READY (SINGLE)
Tracks: / Get ready.
7" Single: Released Oct '81, on Motown, by BMG Records (UK). Catalogue no: **TMG 688**

I CAN'T GET NEXT TO YOU
Tracks: / I can't get next to you / I know I'm losing you.
7" Single: Released Jan '70, on Tamla Motown, by Motown Records (UK). Deleted '73. Catalogue no: **TMG 722**
7" Single: Released Apr '88, on Motown, by BMG Records (UK). Catalogue no: **ZB 41933**

I COULD NEVER LOVE ANOTHER
Tracks: / I could never love another (after loving you).
7" Single: Released Jun '68, on Tamla Motown, by Motown Records (UK). Deleted '71. Catalogue no: **TMG 658**

I WISH IT WOULD RAIN
Tracks: / I wish it would rain.
7" Single: Released Mar '68, on Tamla Motown, by Motown Records (UK). Deleted '71. Catalogue no: **TMG 641**

I WONDER WHO SHES SEEING NOW
Tracks: / I wonder who she's seeing now / Girls (they like it) / I wonder who she's seeing now (extended) / I wonder who she's seeing now (7") (On 12" version only.) / Girls (they like it) (On 12" version only.).
12" Single: Released Oct '87, on Motown, by BMG Records (UK). Catalogue no: **ZT 41548**
7" Single: Released Oct '87, on Motown, by BMG Records (UK). Catalogue no: **ZB 41547**

I'M LOSING YOU
Tracks: / I'm losing you.
7" Single: Released Dec '66, on Tamla Motown, by Motown Records (UK). Deleted '69. Catalogue no: **TMG 587**

I'M SO FASCINATED
Tracks: / I'm fascinated / How can you say that it's over / Treat her like a lady (On 12" version only) / M & M(remix) (On 12" version only).
12" Single: Released Mar '86, on Motown, by BMG Records (UK). Deleted '88. Catalogue no: **ZT 40622**
7" Single: Released Mar '86, on Motown, by BMG Records (UK). Deleted '88. Catalogue no: **ZB 40621**

IT'S GROWING
Tracks: / It's growing.
7" Single: Released Apr '65, on Tamla Motown, by Motown Records (UK). Deleted '68. Catalogue no: **TMG 504**

JUST MY IMAGINATION
Tracks: / Just my imagination (running away with me) / Get ready.
7" Single: Released Mar '83, on Motown, by BMG Records (UK). Catalogue no: **TMG 1043**
7" Single: Released Oct '81, on Motown, by BMG Records (UK). Catalogue no: **TMG 773**

LADY SOUL
Tracks: / Lady soul / Fine mess (A) / Papa was a rollin' stone (On 12" version only).
7" Single: Released Aug '86, on Motown, by BMG Records (UK). Deleted '87. Catalogue no: **ZB 40850**
12" Single: Released Aug '86, on Motown, by BMG Records (UK). Deleted '87. Catalogue no: **ZT 40850**

LAW OF THE LAND
Tracks: / Law of the land.
7" Single: Released Sep '73, on Tamla Motown, by Motown Records (UK). Deleted '76. Catalogue no: **TMG 866**
7" Single: Released Apr '85, on Motown, by BMG Records (UK). Deleted '88. Catalogue no: **TMG 990**
12" Single: Released Apr '85, on Motown, by BMG Records (UK). Deleted '86. Catalogue no: **TMGT 990**

LOOK WHAT YOU STARTED
Tracks: / Look what you started.
12" Single: Released Jan '88, on Motown, by BMG Records (UK). Catalogue no: **ZT 41734**
7" Single: Released Jan '88, on Motown, by BMG Records (UK). Catalogue no: **ZB 41733**
Cassingle: Released Feb '88, on Motown, by BMG Records (UK). Catalogue no: **ZV 41733**

LOVE ON MY MIND
Tracks: / Love on my mind.
7" Single: Released Mar '83, on Motown, by BMG Records (UK). Deleted '85. Catalogue no: **TMG 1297**
12" Single: Released Mar '83, on Motown, by BMG Records (UK). Deleted '85. Catalogue no: **TMGT 1297**

MEDLEY OF HITS
7" Single: Released Oct '83, on Motown, by BMG Records (UK). Deleted '85. Catalogue no: **TMG 1320**
12" Single: Released Oct '83, on Motown, by BMG Records (UK). Deleted '85. Catalogue no: **TMGT 1320**

MY GIRL
Tracks: / My girl / Wherever I lay my hat / Way you do the things you do, The (On 12" version only) / My baby (On 12" version only).
12" Single: Released Jun '86, on Motown, by BMG Records (UK). Deleted '87. Catalogue no: **ZT 40744**
7" Single: Released Mar '65, on Stateside, by EMI Records. Deleted '68. Catalogue no: **SS 395**
7" Single: Released Jun '86, on Motown, by BMG Records (UK). Catalogue no: **ZB 40743**

MY LOVE IS TRUE(TRULY FOR YOU)
Tracks: / My love is true / I'll keep my light in my window / Treat her like a lady (on 12" only).
7" Single: Released Mar '85, on Motown, by BMG Records (UK). Deleted '86. Catalogue no: **TMG 1373**
12" Single: Released Mar '85, on Motown, by BMG Records (UK). Deleted '86. Catalogue no: **TMGT 1373**

PAPA WAS A ROLLING STONE
Tracks: / Ain't too proud to beg / Papa was a rollin' stone.
12" Single: Released Aug '87, on Motown, by BMG Records (UK). Catalogue no: **ZT 41432**
7" Single: Released Oct '81, on Motown, by BMG Records (UK). Catalogue no: **TMG 839**
7" Single: Released Aug '87, on Motown, by BMG Records (UK). Catalogue no: **ZB 41431**

POWER (SINGLE)
Tracks: / Power (part 1) / Power (part 2).
7" Single: Released May '90, on Motown, by BMG Records (UK). Deleted '85. Catalogue no: **TMG 1186**

PSYCHEDELIC SHACK (SINGLE)
Tracks: / Psychedelic shack.
7" Single: Released Jun '70, on Tamla Motown, by Motown Records (UK). Deleted '73. Catalogue no: **TMG 741**

STANDING ON THE TOP
Tracks: / Standing on the top / Standing on the top (part 2).
7" Single: Released May '82, on Motown, by BMG Records (UK). Deleted '83. Catalogue no: **TMG 1263**
12" Single: Released May '82, on Motown, by BMG Records (UK). Deleted '83. Catalogue no: **TMGT 1263**

STRUCK BY LIGHTNING TWICE
Tracks: / Struck by lightning twice / I'm coming home.
7" Single: Released Oct '81, on Motown, by BMG Records (UK). Deleted '82. Catalogue no: **TMG 1197**

SUPERSTAR
Tracks: / Superstar (remember how you got where you are).
7" Single: Released Feb '72, on Tamla Motown, by Motown Records (UK). Deleted '75. Catalogue no: **TMG 800**

TAKE A LOOK AROUND
Tracks: / Take a look around.
7" Single: Released Apr '72, on Tamla Motown, by Motown Records (UK). Deleted '75. Catalogue no: **TMG 808**

TAKE ME AWAY
Tracks: / Take me away / There's more where that came from.
7" Single: Released Oct '81, on Motown, by BMG Records (UK). Deleted '82. Catalogue no: **TMG 1216**

TREAT HER LIKE A LADY
Tracks: / Treat her like a lady.
12" Single: Released Nov '84, on Tamla Motown, by Motown Records (UK). Catalogue no: **TMGT 1365**
7" Single: Released Nov '84, on Tamla Motown, by Motown Records (UK). Catalogue no: **TMG 1365**

YOU'RE MY EVERYTHING
Tracks: / You're my everything.
7" Single: Released Sep '67, on Tamla Motown, by Motown Records (UK). Deleted '70. Catalogue no: **TMG 620**

Tempting Fate

TIME OF THE SEASON
Tracks: / Time of the season / Desert walker.
12" Single: Released Mar '88, on Primitive, by Primitive Records. Catalogue no: **PRIME 012**

Ten CC

Biographical details: At the time of their greatest success, this British band conmprised Lol Creme, Kevin Godley, Graham Gouldman and Eric Stewart. Prior to the formation of 10CC in 1972, Creme, Stewart and Godley had achieved a 1970 UK No.2 smash (and worldwide success) with *Neanderthal Man* under the name Hotlegs. During the Sixties, Gouldman had been a succesful songwriter, notably for the Yardbirds for whom he had penned three consecutive UK top 3 singles; *For Your Love, Heartful Of Soul* and *Evil Hearted You*. Stewart had been a member of the Mindbenders (before and after the departure of Wayne Fontana). Godley and Creme had met at art school. 10CC were formed in their native Manchester, and based themselves at Stewart's Strawberry Studios in Stockport, Cheshire. They came to the attention of Jonathan King, the irrepressible pop hit-maker/entrepreneur, who reportedly thought of the group's strange name in a dream. They signed to his label, UK records, and were quickly rewarded with a British No.2 smash in Autumn 72 with *Donna*, a clever fifties pastiche. Like all their future singles and albums, this was written and produced by the group, and was inventive, idiosyncratic and well crafted. 1973 bought 10CC their first UK No.1 single with *Rubber Bullets*, a crafty fusion of pop and rock at a time when there was a crevasse between Britain's 'commercial' glam rockers (e.g.Gary Glitter) and 'progressive' rockers (e.g.Led Zepplin). The group's second LP, *Sheet Music*, reached the Top 10 of Britain's album chart and yielded the equally succesful single *Wall Street Shuffle*. After switching from UK Records to the Mercury label in early 1975, 10CC released their most succesful LP. This was confusingly entitled *The Original Soundtrack*, despite the none-existence of an accompanying movie. It's standout single was *I'm Not In Love*, which gave the band their second UK No.1 in the summer of '75. This song represented 10CC's creative and commercial pinnacle. *I'm Not In Love* was a simple ballad dressed up in massively powerful arrangement and production; it featured a record-setting 256 vocal overdubs and was perhaps the ultimate studio recording. Although the group played live gigs, they were always most at home in the Strawberry building. The song was an instant classic, and became the virtually automatic No.1 on British radio stations polls of listeners all-time favourites (thus usurping a priviliged position held by Simon & Garfunkels *Bridge Over Troubled Water*). In the States, *I'm Not In Love* reached No.2 and became the first of only two US Top 30 hits in the group's entire career. Such creative, engaging and quirky (but never gimmicky) singles as *Art For Arts Sake* and *I'm Mandy Fly Me* were ignored by Americans - those two hits came from 1976's *How Dare You* LP, the last album to feature Godley and Creme, who broke away from 10CC in late '76. The remaining members - Gouldman and Stewart (writers of *I'm Not In Love*) - quickly confounded sceptics by acheiving back-to-back UK Top Tenners with *The Thing We Do For Love* and *Good Morning Judge*. The duo then recruited four new musicians: Rick Fenn, Duncan Mackay, Tony O'Malley and Stuart Tosh. The six-piece band gave 10CC a third No.1 on the British singles chart in 1978 with *Dreadlock Holiday*, a Jamaican reggae pastiche, and the *Bloody Tourists* LP was a Top 3 item. Everything semed to be going as well as ever; but suddenly, the groups record sales nosedived. *Reds In My Bed*, the follow-up single to the chart topper, totally missed the UK Top 75, as did nearly all their subsequent singles. 1980's *Look Hear* album peaked at No.35. *Windows In The Jungle*, a 1983 LP, was almost universally ignored. 10CC, in these later days, may not have attained classic standards; but their music was still quite reasonable, and their retail and radio drop-off was mysterious. Conversely, Godley & Creme languished without success in the late Seventies, but came into their own in the Eighties. Their original stated reason for leaving the group had been their desire to develop the Gizmo, a new instrument that they had invented. However, it was their craftily conceived move into the video field that ensured them of a bumper living in the Eighties, together with spasmodic record success. (Bob McDonald 4.85)

A UK pop group formed around 1970 as Hotlegs with Graham Gouldman, vocalist, bassist, keyboardist (born 1946, Manchester), vocalists/guitarists Eric Stewart and Lol Cream (born 1947), drummer/vocalist Kevin Godley (born 1945); **Jonathan King** renamed them after the average male seminal emission. They were experienced pop songwriters, their work was seen as witty, above-average stuff; they enjoyed studio work and refused to tour. Godley and Creme left and became famous video producers, also had their own hits; Stewart and Gouldman carried on with more hits, recruiting Rick Fenn, Duncan MacKay, Tony O'Malley and Stuart Tosh c. 1978; they suddenly seemed old-fashioned and nose-dived from the charts. (Donald Clarke 13.1.88).

24 HOURS
Tracks: / 24 Hours.
12" Single: Released Apr '83, on Mercury, by Phonogram Ltd. Deleted '85. Catalogue no: **MERX 139**
7" Single: Released Apr '83, on Mercury, by Phonogram Ltd. Deleted '85. Catalogue no: **MER 139**

1-2-5
Tracks: / 1-2-5 / Only child.
7" Single: Released Feb '80, on Mercury, by Phonogram Ltd. Deleted '83. Catalogue no: **LOOK 1**

ART FOR ART'S SAKE
Tracks: / Art for art's sake.
7" Single: Released Nov '75, on Mercury, by Phonogram Ltd. Deleted '78. Catalogue no: **6008 017**

DEAN AND I, THE
Tracks: / Dean and I, The.
7" Single: Released Aug '73, on UK, by UK Records. Deleted '76. Catalogue no: **UK 48**

DONNA
Tracks: / Donna.
7" Single: Released Sep '72, on UK, by UK Records. Deleted '75. Catalogue no: **UK 6**
7" Single: Released '80, on Mercury, by Phonogram Ltd. Catalogue no: **LR 1263**

DON'T TURN ME AWAY
Tracks: / Don't turn me away.
7" Single: Released Nov '82, on Mercury, by Phonogram Ltd. Deleted '83. Catalogue no: **MER 86**
7" Single: Released Nov '81, on Mercury, by Phonogram Ltd. Deleted '84. Catalogue no: **MER 86**

DREADLOCK HOLIDAY (SINGLE)
Tracks: / Dreadlock holiday.
7" Single: Released Aug '78, on Mercury, by Phonogram Ltd. Deleted '81. Catalogue no: **6008 035**

FEEL THE LOVE
Tracks: / Feel the love.
7" Single: Released Jul '83, on Mercury, by Phonogram Ltd. Catalogue no: **MER 143**

GOOD MORNING JUDGE
Tracks: / Good morning judge.
7" Single: Released Apr '77, on Mercury, by Phonogram Ltd. Deleted '80. Catalogue no: **6008 025**

I'M MANDY FLY ME
Tracks: / I'm Mandy fly me.
7" Single: Released Mar '76, on Mercury, by Phonogram Ltd. Deleted '79. Catalogue no: **6008 019**

I'M NOT IN LOVE
Tracks: / I'm not in love.
7" Single: Released Oct '84, on Mercury, by Phonogram Ltd. Catalogue no: **6008 014**

I'M NOT IN LOVE (OLD GOLD)
Tracks: / I'm not in love / Dreadlock holiday.
7" Single: Released Jun '88, on Old Gold, by Old Gold Records. Catalogue no: **OG 9475**

IT DOESN'T MATTER AT ALL
Tracks: / It doesn't matter at all / From Rochdale to Ocho Rios.
7" Single: Released May '80, on Mercury, by Phonogram Ltd. Catalogue no: **LOOK 2**

LIFE IS A MINESTRONE
Tracks: / Life is a minestrone.
7" Single: Released Apr '75, on Mercury, by Phonogram Ltd. Deleted '78. Catalogue no: **6008 010**

NOUVEAU RICHE
Tracks: / Nouveau riche / I hate to eat alone.
7" Single: Released May '81, on Mercury, by Phonogram Ltd. Catalogue no: **TEN 10**

ONE TWO FIVE
Tracks: / One two five.
7" Single: Released Feb '80, on Mercury, by Phonogram Ltd. Catalogue no: **LOOK 1**

POWER OF LOVE
Tracks: / Power of love, The.
7" Single: Released Mar '82, on Mercury, by Phonogram Ltd. Deleted Mar '85. Catalogue no: **MER 95**

RUBBER BULLETS
Tracks: / Rubber bullets.
7" Single: Released '80, on Mercury, by Phonogram Ltd. Catalogue no: **LR 1417**
7" Single: Released May '73, on UK, by UK Records. Deleted '76. Catalogue no: **UK 36**

RUBBER BULLETS (OLD GOLD)
Tracks: / Rubber bullets / Donna.
7" Single: Released Jun '88, on Old Gold, by Old Gold Records. Catalogue no: **OG 9786**

RUN AWAY
Tracks: / Run away.
7" Single: Released Jul '82, on Mercury, by Phonogram Ltd. Catalogue no: **MER 113**

SILLY LOVE
Tracks: / Silly love.
7" Single: Released Sep '74, on UK, by UK Records. Deleted '77. Catalogue no: **UK 77**

THINGS WE DO FOR LOVE
Tracks: / Things we do for love, The.
7" Single: Released Dec '76, on Mercury, by Phonogram Ltd. Deleted '79. Catalogue no: **6008 022**

WALL STREET SHUFFLE
Tracks: / Wall Street shuffle, The / Dean and I, The.
7" Single: Released Jun '74, on UK, by UK Records. Deleted '77. Catalogue no: **UK 69**

WALL STREET SHUFFLE (OLD GOLD)
Tracks: / Wall Street shuffle / Dean and I, The.
7" Single: Released Jun '88, on Old Gold, by Old Gold Records. Catalogue no: **OG 9788**

WE'VE HEARD IT ALL BEFORE
Tracks: / We've heard it all before / Overdraft in overdrive.
7" Single: Released Oct '82, on Mercury, by Phonogram Ltd. Deleted Oct '85. Catalogue no: **MER 121**

WORST BAND IN THE WORLD (SINGLE)
Tracks: / Worst band in the world.
7" Single: Released Jul '87, on UK, by UK Records. Catalogue no: **UKP 002**
12" Single: Released Jul '87, on UK, by UK Records. Catalogue no: **UKPT 002**

Ten City

DEVOTION
Tracks: / Devotion.
7" Single: Released Mar '89, on Atlantic, by WEA Records. Catalogue no: **A 8916**
12" Single: Released Mar '89, on Atlantic, by WEA Records. Catalogue no: **A 8916 T**
CD 5": Released Mar '89, on Atlantic, by WEA Records. Catalogue no: **A 8916 CD**
12" Single: Released May '89, on Atlantic, by WEA Records. Catalogue no: **A 8916 TX**

DEVOTION (HALLA-PELA)
Tracks: / Devotion (halla-pela).
7" Single: Released Nov '87, on Atlantic, by WEA Records. Catalogue no: **A 9153**

RIGHT BACK TO YOU
Tracks: / Right back to you / One kiss will make it better.
7" Single: Released May '88, on Atlantic, by WEA Records. Catalogue no: **A 9088**
12" Single: Released May '88, on Atlantic, by WEA Records. Catalogue no: **A 9088 T**

THAT'S THE WAY LOVE IS
Tracks: / That's the way love is / That's the way love is (version) / Devotion (Only on 12" version.).
7" Single: Released Jan '89, on Atlantic, by WEA Records. Catalogue no: **A 8963**
12" Single: Released Jan '89, on Atlantic, by WEA Records. Catalogue no: **A 8963 T**

WHERE DO WE GO
Tracks: / Where do we go / Where do we go (version).
7" Single: Released Jul '89, on Atlantic, by WEA Records. Catalogue no: **A 8864**
Cassingle: Released Jul '89, on Atlantic, by WEA Records. Catalogue no: **A 8864 C**
12" Single: Released Jul '89, on Atlantic, by WEA Records. Catalogue no: **A 8864 T**
CD 5": Released Jul '89, on Atlantic, by WEA Records. Catalogue no: **A 8864 CD**

Ten dB

I SECOND THAT EMOTION
Tracks: / I second that emotion.
CD 5": Released Feb '89, on K-Tel, by K-Tel Records. Catalogue no: **ONE 6904**
7" Single: Released Feb '89, on K-Tel, by K-Tel Records. Catalogue no: **ONE 6104**
12" Single: Released Feb '89, on K-Tel, by K-Tel Records. Catalogue no: **ONE 6604**

Ten Eighty

RIDE
Tracks: / Ride / Why must we follow.
7" Single: Released Mar '80, on Magnet, by WEA Records. Deleted Mar '83. Catalogue no: **MAG 168**

Ten Foot

BLIND FAITH
Tracks: / Blind faith.
7" Single: Released Dec '83, on Nosrednas, by Waterfall Records. Catalogue no: **NOS 001**

Ten Foot Boneless

POWERSLIDE
Tracks: / Powerslide.
12" Single: Released 16 Sep '88, on Fierce, Catalogue no: **FRIGHT 027**

Ten Minutes For Doris

SHE SAID
Tracks: / She said / Is that the reason.
7" Single: Released Feb '89, on No, Catalogue no: **NOS 43**

Ten Past Seven

CRACKING UP
Tracks: / Cracking up.
7" Single: Released May '83, on Good Vibration, by Good Vibrations Records. Catalogue no: **TUBE 2**

Ten Seconds

PERFECTION
Tracks: / Perfection.
7" Single: Released Feb '85, on Sirocco, Catalogue no: **SIR 104**

Ten Sharp

LAST WORDS
Tracks: / Last words / White gold.
12" Single: Released May '86, on Epic, by CBS Records. Catalogue no: **TA 6852**
7" Single: Released May '86, on Epic, by CBS Records. Catalogue no: **A 6852**

Ten Ten

MILLION MILES AWAY
Tracks: / Million miles away / Secret life of Madeline / Peace and love (Track on 12" version only.).
12" Single: Released Apr '86, on Chrysalis, by Chrysalis Records. Catalogue no: **CHS 122975**
7" Single: Released Apr '86, on Chrysalis, by Chrysalis Records. Catalogue no: **CHS 2975**

WHEN IT RAINS
Tracks: / When it rains / Walk on.
12" Single: Released Sep '86, on Chrysalis, by Chrysalis Records. Catalogue no: **CHS 123060**

Ten Thousand Maniacs

CAN'T IGNORE THE TRAIN
Tracks: / Can't ignore the train.
12" Single: Released Jun '85, on Elektra, by Elektra Records (UK). Catalogue no: **EKR 11T**
7" Single: Released Jun '85, on Elektra, by Elektra Records (UK). Catalogue no: **EKR 11**

CITY OF ANGELS
Tracks: / City of angels.
7" Single: Released Nov '87, on Elektra, by Elektra Records (UK). Deleted Jul '88. Catalogue no: **EKR 64**

JUST AS THE TIDE IS A FLOWING
Tracks: / Just as the tide is a flowing.
7" Single: Released Nov '85, on Elektra, by Elektra Records (UK). Catalogue no: **EKR 27**

LIKE THE WEATHER
Tracks: / Like the weather / Campfire song, A.
12" Single: Released Jul '88, on WEA, by WEA Records. Catalogue no: **EKR 77T**
7" Single: Released Jul '88, on WEA, by WEA Records. Catalogue no: **EKR 77**

MY MOTHER THE WAR
Tracks: / My mother the war.
12" Single: Released Mar '84, on Reflex, by Reflex Records. Catalogue no: **RE 1**

PEACE TRAIN
Tracks: / Peace train.
7" Single: Released Aug '87, on Elektra, by Elektra Records (UK). Deleted Jul '88. Catalogue no: **EKR 61**

SCORPIO RISING
Tracks: / Scorpio rising / Arbor day.
7" Single: Released Jan '86, on Elektra (USA), by Elektra Records (USA). Catalogue no: **EKR 28**

TROUBLE ME
Tracks: / Trouble me / Party of God (Only on 12" and CD single.) / Lion's share.
12" Single: Released Jun '89, on Elektra, by Elektra Records (UK). Catalogue no: **EKR 93 T**
7" Single: Released Jun '89, on Elektra, by Elektra Records (UK). Catalogue no: **EKR 93**
Cassingle: Released Jun '89, on Elektra, by Elektra Records (UK). Catalogue no: **EKR 93 C**
CD 3": Released Jun '89, on Elektra, by Elektra Records (UK). Catalogue no: **EKR 93 CDX**
CD 5": Released Jun '89, on Elektra, by Elektra Records (UK). Catalogue no: **EKR 93 CD**
Cassingle: Released Jun '89, on Elektra, by Elektra Records (UK). Catalogue no: **9692984**

WHAT'S THE MATTER HERE
Tracks: / What's the matter here / Verdi cries.
7" Single: Released Apr '88, on WEA, by WEA Records. Catalogue no: **EKR 71**

Ten Years After

Biographical details: This British rock group consisted of Chick Churchill, Alvin Lee, Ric Lee and Leo Lyons. The two Lees were not related. The band's name was inspired by 1966, the year of their formation -- 10 years after the Elvis-led rock 'n' roll explosion. Alvin Lee and Leo Lyons met in their native Nottingham and formed the nucleus of the band that, after trying out other names, became Ten Years After. They worked in Hamburg and London then became involved in Britain's burgeoning 60's blues boom and released their first album in '67. It did not enter the British LP chart but was heard by major US concert promoter Bill Graham, who soon booked the band. They first hit the British albums Top Thirty with 1968's *Undead*. Lurking on that album was *I'm Going Home*, which became the band's best-known song: it pushed them into the realms of major stardom when they performed at at the legendary Woodstock festival in August 1969 and its inclusion in the event's commemorative film consolidated the band's status. *I'm Going Home* was typical of their output, a powerful fusion of blues and heavy rock stressing the fast and frantic guitar style of Alvin Lee. Between '69 and '71 Ten Years After chalked up four successive UK Top Ten albums -- *Stonedhenge, Ssssh, Cricklewood Green* and *Watt* -- and further increased their exhausting touring activities, making repeated returns to the States. They achieved a one-off UK chart single in 1970, reaching No 10 with Love Like A Man, but like most rock groups of the era they concentrated on the LP market and continued hitting the British listings until '73. In that year Alvin Lee, whose 100mph delivery WAS Ten Years After to many people, showed signs of growing tired of the trappings of success: he found the touring schedule gruelling and felt restricted by audience demands for music solely in the *I'm Going Home* vein. After forming a new band, Alvin Lee & Co, he announced the end of Ten Years After in 1975. He soon formed a band called Ten Years Later, but they made little impact. In the early 80's he released albums under a solo billing. The other three TYA members remained in the business in various musical and behind-the-scenes capacities. (Bob MacDonald, April 1985.)

This UK 'progressive' rock group was formed in 1967 by Alvin Lee (born in 1944 in Nottingham) and Leo Lyons (born in 1943 in Bedfordshire), recruiting Ric Lee on drums, Chick Churchill on keyboards. They appeared at Woodstock, their 11 minute *Goin' Home* becoming famous; they set the tone for progressive acts of the era (for example not releasing a single from their first) and lasted longer than most, re-forming late '70s as Ten years later. Alvin Lee is one of Britain's best-known guitarist, having a solo career as a session guitarist and making his own albums: his *Detroit Diesel* '86 reunited him with Lyons. (Donald Clarke 13.1.88).

HEAR ME CALLING
Tracks: / Hear me calling.
7" Single: Released '80, on Deram, by London Records. Catalogue no: **LR 0688**

LOVE LIKE A MAN
Tracks: / Love like a man.
7" Single: Released Jun '70, on Deram, by London Records. Deleted '73. Catalogue no: **DM 299**

LOVE LIKE A MAN (OLD GOLD)
Tracks: / Love like a man.
7" Single: Released Oct '83, on Old Gold, by Old Gold Records. Deleted Sep '89. Catalogue no: **OG 9342**

Tench, Bobby

CHAIN GANG
Tracks: / Chain gang / Looking for a good time.
7" Single: Released Jun '82, on Ritz, by Ritz Records. Catalogue no: **RITZ 020**

STILL IN LOVE WITH YOU
Tracks: / Still in love with you.
7" Single: Released Mar '86, on Stiff, by Stiff Records. Catalogue no: **BUY 242**
12" Single: Released Mar '86, on Stiff, by Stiff Records. Catalogue no: **BUYIT 242**

Tender Lugers

ENJOY YOURSELF
Tracks: / If I were you / Teenage cream / Closer to god.
12" Single: Released Jan '87, on Kick, Catalogue no: **KIK 2**

UGLY BOY EP, THE
Tracks: / Junky fag hag / I wish I was lovely / What good will it do? / Why should I?.
12" Single: Released May '88, on Rare Lad, Catalogue no: **RL 1**

Tender Trap

THERE'S GOLD IN THEM THERE HILLS
Tracks: / There's gold in them there hills.
7" Single: Released Apr '84, on Risk, Catalogue no: **RISK 1**

Tenfoots

MILK AND HONEY
Tracks: / Milk & honey / Blind faith / Can you feel it.
7" Single: Released Mar '84, on Milk & Honey, Catalogue no: **NOS 001**

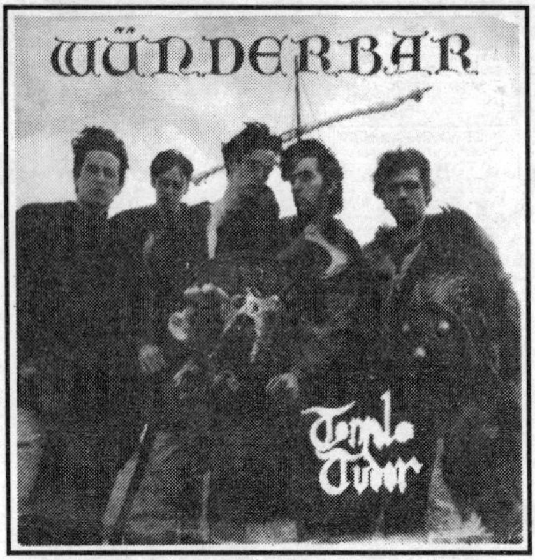

TENPOLE TUDOR - WUNDERBAR (Released on Stiff)

Tenna Fly

DAN MAN
Tracks: / Dan man.
12" Single: Released Oct '89, on Power, Catalogue no: **PW 89003**

INNER CITIES
Tracks: / Inner cities.
12" Single: Released Sep '89, on Ghetto Clappers, Catalogue no: **GC 0001**

Tenor Saw

BAD BWOY
Tracks: / Bad bwoy.
7" Single: Released Oct '88, on Skengdon, Catalogue no: **SKD 092**

CORPORAL BROWN
Tracks: / Corporal Brown / Corporal Brown (version).
12" Single: Released Jun '87, on Blue Trac, by Blue Trac Records. Catalogue no: **BM 032**

GOLDEN HEN
Tracks: / Golden hen.
12" Single: Released Aug '85, on Uptempo, Deleted Jun '89. Catalogue no: **UT 012**

NO WORK ON SUNDAY
Tracks: / No work on Sunday.
12" Single: Released Nov '85, on White label (2), Catalogue no: **DG 789**

RING THE ALARM
Tracks: / Ring the alarm.
12" Single: Released Sep '85, on Techniques, Catalogue no: **WR 1685**

TAKE ME HOME
Tracks: / Take me home.
12" Single: Released Sep '89, on Blue Mountain, Catalogue no: **BMD 067**

Tenpole Tudor

3 BELLS IN A ROW
Tracks: / 3 bells in a row / Fashion / Rock'n'roll music.
7" Single: Released Oct '80, on Stiff, by Stiff Records. Deleted Oct '83. Catalogue no: **BUY 98**

LET THE FOUR WINDS BLOW (SINGLE)
Tracks: / Let the four winds blow.
7" Single: Released Feb '82, on Stiff, by Stiff Records. Catalogue no: **BUY 137**

REAL FUN
Tracks: / Real fun / What's in a word.
7" Single: Released Feb '80, on Korova, by WEA Records. Deleted '83. Catalogue no: **KOW 4**

SWORDS OF A THOUSAND MEN
Tracks: / Swords of a thousand men.
7" Single: Released Mar '81, on Stiff, by Stiff Records. Catalogue no: **BUY 109**

THREE BELLS IN AROW
Tracks: / Three bells in a row.
7" Single: Released Oct '80, on Stiff, by Stiff Records. Catalogue no: **BUY 98**

THROWING MY BABY OUT WITH THE BATHWATER
Tracks: / Throwing my baby out with the bathwater / Congo tribe.
7" Single: Released Oct '81, on Stiff, by Stiff Records. Catalogue no: **BUY 129**

WUNDERBAR (see panel above)
Tracks: / Wunderbar / Tenpole 45.
7" Single: Released Jul '81, on Stiff, by Stiff Records. Catalogue no: **BUY 120**

Tenyue, Wayne

MURDEROUS TIME
Tracks: / Murderous time.
12" Single: Released Feb '82, on Red Nail, Catalogue no: **RN 0035**

Tepper, Robert

NO EASY WAY OUT
Tracks: / No easy way out / Domination.
7" Single: Released Feb '86, on Scotti Bros (USA), Catalogue no: **A 6948**

Terigan

RONI
Tracks: / Roni.
12" Single: Released May '89, on Progressive, Catalogue no: **PSP 004**

Terminal

AM I DOING IT RIGHT
Tracks: / Am I doing it right / I don't mind.
7" Single: Released Nov '82, on Termite, Catalogue no: **TERM 2**

Terminal Beach

LOVE ON AUTO
Tracks: / Love on auto.
7" Single: Released Jul '82, on TB, by TB Records. Catalogue no: **CUS 1368**

Terminal Cheesecake

BLADDERSACK
Tracks: / Bladdersack.
12" Single: Released Aug '88, on Wiiija, Catalogue no: **WIIIJIT 1**

Terminal Fun

TWIST AND SURVIVE
Tracks: / Twist & survive.
7" Single: Released Nov '82, on Projected Image, Catalogue no: **PRIM 4**

Termites

TERMITES EP, THE
7" Single: Released Jun '89, on Raucous, Catalogue no: **RAUC 008**

Terms Of Endearment

TERMS OF ENDEARMENT
Tracks: / Terms of endearment / This is my moment.
7" Single: Released Apr '84, on Capitol, by EMI Records. Deleted '88. Catalogue no: **CL 330**

Terrahawks

TERRAHAWKS THEME
Tracks: / Terrahawks theme.
12" Single: Released Nov '83, on Anderburr, by Anderburr Records. Catalogue no: **HXT 1010**
7" Single: Released Nov '83, on Anderburr, by Anderburr Records. Catalogue no: **HX 1010**

Terrajacks

HOUSEPLAN
Tracks: / Houseplan.
7" Single: Released Jul '88, on WEA, by WEA Records. Catalogue no: **YZ 304**
12" Single: Released Jul '88, on WEA, by WEA Records. Catalogue no: **YZ 304T**

Terraplane

GOOD THING GOING
Tracks: / Good thing going / Night of madness, A / Good life (extra track on 12").
Cassingle: Released Jun '87, on Epic, by CBS Records. Catalogue no: **MCTERRAC 2**
7" Single: Released Jun '87, on Epic, by CBS Records. Deleted Nov '87. Catalogue no: **TERRA 2**
12" Single: Released Jun '87, on Epic, by CBS Records. Deleted Nov '87. Catalogue no: **TERRAT 2**

I SURVIVE
Tracks: / I survive / All night and day.
7" Single: Released Mar '83, on City, by City Records. Catalogue no: **NIK 8**

IF THAT'S WHAT IT TAKES
Tracks: / If that's what it takes / Living after dark / If that's what it takes (19th nervous breakdance mix) (*Track on 12" version only.) / Drugs* (*Extra track on 12" version only.).
12" Single: Released 1 Feb '88, on Epic, by CBS Records. Deleted Aug '87. Catalogue no: **TERRA T4**
7" Single: Released 1 Feb '88, on Epic, by CBS Records. Deleted Aug '88. Catalogue no: **TERRA 4**
12" Single: Released Feb '88, on Epic, by CBS Records. Deleted Aug '88. Catalogue no: **TERRA Q4**

MOVING TARGET (SINGLE)
Tracks: / Moving target.
12" Single: Released Aug '87, on Epic, by CBS Records. Catalogue no: **TERRAT 3**
7" Single: Released Aug '87, on Epic, by CBS Records. Catalogue no: **TERRA G3**
7" Single: Released Aug '87, on Epic, by CBS Records. Catalogue no: **TERRA 3**

THAT'S WHAT IT TAKES
Tracks: / Living after dark / Drugs* / That's what it takes.
7" Single: Released Jan '87, on Epic, by CBS Records. Catalogue no: **TERRA 1**
12" Single: Released Jan '87, on Epic, by CBS Records. Catalogue no: **TERRAT 1**

WHEN YOU'RE HOT
Tracks: / When you're hot.
7" Single: Released Jul '85, on Epic, by CBS Records. Catalogue no: **A 6352**
12" Single: Released Jul '85, on Epic, by CBS Records. Catalogue no: **TX 6352**

Terrattack

TERRATTACK
Tracks: / Terrattack.
7" EP: Released Jun '88, on Iron Works (USA), by Azra International (USA). Catalogue no: **IW 1008**

Terrell, Dino

YOU CAN DO IT
Tracks: / You can do it / You can do it (instrumental) / Acal-poco (On 12" track only) / You can do it (dub) (On 12" version only).
12" Single: Released Mar '86, on Lovebeat Int., Catalogue no: **LOVT 3**
7" Single: Released Mar '86, on Lovebeat Int., Catalogue no: **LOV 3**

Terri, Billy

SOME GIRLS ARE LADIES
Tracks: / Some girls are ladies / Love and tears.
7" Single: Released May '87, on Sonet, by Sonet Records. Catalogue no: **SON 2324**

Terrific

SERIOUS LYRICS
Tracks: / Serious lyrics.
12" Single: Released Sep '88, on Don Sebastian, Catalogue no: **DSR 002**

Terry & Gerry

BANKING ON SIMON
Tracks: / Banking on Simon.
7" Single: Released Jul '85, on In Tape, by In Tape Records. Catalogue no: **IT 019**
12" Single: Released Jul '85, on In Tape, by In Tape Records. Catalogue no: **ITT 019**

BUTLERS ON THE BREAD
Tracks: / Butlers on the bread.
7" Single: Released Sep '84, on Vindaloo, by Vindaloo Records. Catalogue no: **UGH 7**

CLOSED SHOP
Tracks: / Closed shop.
7" Single: Released Feb '85, on In Tape, by

In Tape Records. Catalogue no: **IT 014**

CLOTHES SHOP
Tracks: / Clothes shop.
12" Single: Released Aug '85, on In Tape, by In Tape Records. Deleted '88. Catalogue no: **IT 018**

LAST BULLET IN THE GUN, THE
Tracks: / Last bullet in the gun, The.
7" Single: Released Aug '86, on In Tape, by In Tape Records. Catalogue no: **IT 036**
12" Single: Released Aug '86, on In Tape, by In Tape Records. Catalogue no: **ITTI 036**

RESERVATION
Tracks: / Reservation.
7" Single: Released Mar '86, on In Tape, by In Tape Records. Catalogue no: **IT 027**
12" Single: Released Feb '89, on African Museum, Catalogue no: **AM 01**
12" Single: Released Mar '86, on In Tape, by In Tape Records. Catalogue no: **ITT 027**

Terry, Helen

ACT OF MERCY
Tracks: / Act of mercy / Over the border.
7" Single: Released Jul '86, on Virgin, by Virgin Records. Deleted May '88. Catalogue no: **VS 810**
12" Single: Released Jul '86, on Virgin, by Virgin Records. Deleted May '88. Catalogue no: **VS 810-12**

FORTUNATE FOOL
Tracks: / Fortunate fool (7" only.) / Fortunate fool (radio version) (Not on 7".) / Fortunate fool (ext. version) (Not on 7".) / Heart of a woman.
7" Single: Released Apr '89, on Parlophone, by EMI Records. Deleted Oct '89. Catalogue no: **203 338 7**
CD 5": Released Apr '89, on Parlophone, by EMI Records. Deleted Oct '89. Catalogue no: **203 338 2**
12" Single: Released Apr '89, on Parlophone, by EMI Records. Deleted Oct '89. Catalogue no: **203 338 8**
12" Single: Released Apr '89, on Parlophone, by EMI Records. Deleted Oct '89. Catalogue no: **203 338 6**
12" Single: Released Apr '89, on Parlophone, by EMI Records. Deleted Oct '89. Catalogue no: **12RG 6215**
7" Single: Released Apr '89, on Parlophone, by EMI Records. Deleted Oct '89. Catalogue no: **R 6215**
12" Single: Released Apr '89, on Parlophone, by EMI Records. Deleted Oct '89. Catalogue no: **12R 6215**
CD 5": Released Apr '89, on Parlophone, by EMI Records. Deleted Oct '89. Catalogue no: **CDR 6215**

LESSONS IN LONELINESS
Tracks: / Lessons in loneliness (radio version) / Lessons in loneliness (lessons learned) / Fortunate fool (radio version) (Not on 7".) / Lessons in loneliness (Olympic version).
CD 5": Released Aug '89, on Parlophone, by EMI Records. Catalogue no: **203 506 2**
12" Single: Released Aug '89, on Parlophone, by EMI Records. Catalogue no: **12R 6226**
12" Single: Released Aug '89, on Parlophone, by EMI Records. Catalogue no: **203 506 6**
7" Single: Released Sep '89, on Parlophone, by EMI Records. Catalogue no: **R 6226**
CD 5": Released Aug '89, on Parlophone, by EMI Records. Catalogue no: **CDR 6226**
7" Single: Released Sep '89, on Parlophone, by EMI Records. Catalogue no: **203 506 7**

LOVE LIES LOST
Tracks: / Love lies lost / Laughter on my mind.
7" Single: Released May '84, on Virgin, by Virgin Records. Deleted '87. Catalogue no: **VS 678**

Terry, M

I LOVE MUSIC (SINGLE)
Tracks: / I love music / Moustachio.
12" Single: Released May '86, on MCA, by MCA Records. Catalogue no: **MCAT 1063**
7" Single: Released May '86, on MCA, by MCA Records. Catalogue no: **MCA 1063**

Terry, Mike

ONE MAN WENT TO MOZART
Tracks: / One man went to Mozart / Ave Maria.
7" Single: Released Nov '80, on President, by President Records. Deleted Nov '83. Catalogue no: **PR 489**

Terry, Todd

BANGO (TO THE BATMOBILE)
Tracks: / Bango (to the Batmobile) / Back to the beat.
12" Single: Released May '88, on Hardcore, Catalogue no: **HAKT 16**
7" Single: Released May '88, on Hardcore, Catalogue no: **HAK 16**

CHECK THIS OUT
Tracks: / Check this out.
12" Single: Released Nov '88, on Champion, by Champion Records. Catalogue no: **CHAMP 1294**
7" Single: Released Nov '88, on Champion, by Champion Records. Deleted Aug '89. Catalogue no: **CHAMP 94**

JUST WANNA DANCE
Tracks: / Just wanna dance / Weekend.
12" Single: Released Oct '88, on Fresh (USA), Catalogue no: **FRE 80125**

WEEKEND
Tracks: / Weekend / Just wanna dance.
12" Single: Released Nov '88, on Sleeping Bag, by Sleeping Bag Records. Catalogue no: **SBUK 1 T**

WEEKEND (REMIX)
Tracks: / Weekend (remix).
12" Single: Released Dec '88, on Sleeping Bag, by Sleeping Bag Records. Catalogue no: **SBUKR 1 T**

Terry, Tony

FOREVER YOURS (LATE NIGHT VERSION)
Tracks: / Forever yours (late night version) / Here with me / She's fly / Lovey dovey (remix).
12" Single: Released 13 Jun '88, on Epic, by CBS Records. Deleted Jan '89. Catalogue no: **TONY QT3**

FOREVER YOURS (SINGLE)
Tracks: / Forever yours / Here with me / Forever yours (LP version) (Only on 12".) / Forever yours (Late night version) (Only on 12".) / Forever yours (inst) (Only on 12".).
12" Single: Released May '88, on Epic, by CBS Records. Deleted Jan '89. Catalogue no: **TONY T3**
7" Single: Released May '88, on Epic, by CBS Records. Deleted Jan '89. Catalogue no: **TONY 3**
CD 5": Released Mar '88, on Epic, by CBS Records. Deleted Jan '89. Catalogue no: **CD TONY 3**

FORGET THE GIRL (EXTENDED REMIX)
Tracks: / Forget the girl (extended remix) / Forget the girl (Midtown mix) / Forget the girl (accapella).
12" Single: Released 5 Jun '89, on Epic, by CBS Records. Catalogue no: **655 021 6**

LOVEY DOVEY
Tracks: / Lovey dovey (long version) / Lovey dovey (dub) / Lovey dovey (Charlie Dee dub) / Lovey dovey (dove-tale mix) (Track on special remix.) / Lovey dovey (Charlie Dee dub - new speed) (Track on special remix.).
12" Single: Released Feb '88, on Epic, by CBS Records. Deleted Aug '88. Catalogue no: **TONY QT2**
12" Single: Released Feb '88, on Epic, by CBS Records. Deleted Aug '88. Catalogue no: **TONY T2**
Special: Released Feb '88, on Epic, by CBS Records. Deleted Aug '88. Catalogue no: **TONYQR 2**
7" Single: Released Feb '88, on Epic, by CBS Records. Deleted Aug '88. Catalogue no: **TONY 2**

SHE'S FLY
Tracks: / She's fly.
7" Single: Released Oct '87, on Epic, by CBS Records. Deleted Jun '88. Catalogue no: **TONY 1**
12" Single: Released Oct '87, on Epic, by CBS Records. Deleted Jun '88. Catalogue no: **TONY T1**

YOUNG LOVE
Tracks: / Young love / Young love (acid mix) (TONY QT4 only.) / Young love (age of consent mix) (TONY QT4 only.) / Young love (oh oh Omar dubb mix) (TONY QT4 only.).
7" Single: Released Sep '88, on Epic, by CBS Records. Deleted 17 Apr '89. Catalogue no: **TONY 4**
12" Single: Released Sep '88, on Epic, by CBS Records. Deleted 17 Apr '89. Catalogue no: **TONY T4**
12" Single: Released Oct '88, on Epic, by CBS Records. Deleted 17 Apr '89. Catalogue no: **TONY QT4**

Tesco Bombers

HERNANDO'S HIDEAWAY
Tracks: / Hernando's hideaway.
7" Single: Released Jan '82, on Y, Catalogue no: **Y 14**

Tesla

LITTLE SUZIE (little Suzie's on the up)
Tracks: / Little Susie / Before my eyes / Comin' atcha live (remix).
7" Single: Released Mar '87, on Geffen, by Geffen Records (USA). Deleted Jan '88. Catalogue no: **GEF 19**
12" Single: Released Mar '87, on Geffen, by Geffen Records (USA). Deleted Jan '88. Catalogue no: **GEF 19T**

Test Department

COMPULSION
Tracks: / Compulsion.
12" Single: Released Dec '83, on Some Bizzare, by Some Bizzare Records. Catalogue no: **TEST 12**

GODODDIN(SINGLE)
Tracks: / Gododdin.
12" Single: Released 13 Feb '89, on De Facto, Catalogue no: **CMC 004**

NATURA VICTUS
Tracks: / Natura victus.
12" Single: Released 23 Apr '88, on Sub Rosa, by Sub Rosa Records. Catalogue no: **SUB 12005-13**

VICTORY
Tracks: / Victory.

12" Single: Released Dec '87, on Some Bizzare, by Some Bizzare Records. Catalogue no: **MOP 1312**
7" Single: Released Dec '87, on Some Bizzare, by Some Bizzare Records. Catalogue no: **MOP 13**

Testament

TRIAL BY FIRE
Tracks: / Trial by fire / Nobody's fault / Reign of terror.
Note: "extra track on 12" only "Reign of terror"
7" Single: Released Apr '88, on Atlantic, by WEA Records. Catalogue no: **A 9092**
12" Single: Released Apr '88, on Atlantic, by WEA Records. Catalogue no: **A 9092 T**

Testcard F

BANDWAGON TANGO
Tracks: / Bandwagon tango.
7" Single: Released Apr '83, on Backs, by Backs Recording Co.. Catalogue no: **NCH 004**

THIRD STROKE
Tracks: / Third stroke, The.
7" Single: Released Mar '84, on Backs, by Backs Recording Co.. Catalogue no: **NCH 010**

Tex, Joe

AIN'T GONNA BUMP NO MORE
Tracks: / Ain't gonna bump no more.
7" Single: Released Apr '77, on Epic, by CBS Records. Deleted '80. Catalogue no: **EPC 5035**

AIN'T GONNA BUMP NO MORE (OLD GOLD)
Tracks: / Ain't gonna bump no more.
7" Single: Released Jul '82, on Old Gold, by Old Gold Records. Catalogue no: **OG 9192**

SHOW ME
Tracks: / Show me / Hold what you've got / Ooh Otis, ooh Carla / Tramp.
7" EP: Released Apr '80, on Atlantic, by WEA Records. Deleted '83. Catalogue no: **ATM 5**

Texas (Group)

EVERYDAY NOW
Tracks: / Everyday now / Waiting for the fall / Future is promises (On CD single only.) / Fool for love (On CD single only.) / Faith (12" only).
Cassingle: Released 24 Jul '89, on Phonogram, by Phonogram Ltd. Catalogue no: **TEXMC 3**
7" Single: Released 24 Jul '89, on Phonogram, by Phonogram Ltd. Catalogue no: **TEX 3**
CD 5": Released 24 Jul '89, on Phonogram, by Phonogram Ltd. Catalogue no: **TEXCD 3**
12" Single: Released 24 Jul '89, on Phonogram, by Phonogram Ltd. Catalogue no: **TEX 312**

I DON'T WANT A LOVER
Tracks: / I don't want a lover / Believe me / All in vain.
7" Single: Released 23 Jan '89, on Phonogram, by Phonogram Ltd. Deleted Oct '89. Catalogue no: **TEX 1**
12" Single: Released 23 Jan '89, on Phonogram, by Phonogram Ltd. Catalogue no: **TEX 112**
CD 5": Released 23 Jan '89, on Phonogram, by Phonogram Ltd. Catalogue no: **TEXCD 1**

THRILL HAS GONE
Tracks: / Thrill has gone / Nowhere left to hide / Dimples (Only on CD single and 12".).
7" Single: Released Apr '89, on Phonogram, by Phonogram Ltd. Deleted 31 Jul '89. Catalogue no: **TEX 2**
12" Single: Released Apr '89, on Phonogram, by Phonogram Ltd. Deleted 31 Jul '89. Catalogue no: **TEX 212**
12" Single: Released Apr '89, on Phonogram, by Phonogram Ltd. Deleted 31 Jul '89. Catalogue no: **TEXP 212**
CD 5": Released Apr '89, on Phonogram, by Phonogram Ltd. Deleted Oct '89. Catalogue no: **TEXCD 2**

Textones

I CAN'T FIGHT IT
Tracks: / I can't fight it / Vacation / Time is right.
7" EP: Released Jun '80, on Chiswick Records, Deleted Jun '83. Catalogue no: **CHIS 125**

VACATION
Tracks: / Vacation / Time is right.
7" Single: Released Aug '82, on Big Beat, by Ace Records. Deleted '88. Catalogue no: **NS 78**

Textreme

JOY AND PAIN
Tracks: / Joy and pain.
12" Single: Released Jun '88, on Ama Prod, Catalogue no: **BRT 001**

T-Ford

LOVE YOU LIKE I DO
Tracks: / Love you like I do / What'll become of me.
7" Single: Released Mar '80, on Splash, by Splash Records. Deleted '83. Catalogue no: **SP 009**

NOTHING BUT A TEASE
Tracks: / Nothing but a tease / All I need is rock and roll.
7" Single: Released Jun '80, on Splash, by Splash Records. Deleted Jun '83. Catalogue no: **SP 013**

TGT

MACHINE GUN
Tracks: / Machine gun.
CD 3": Released 1 Aug '89, on Play It Again Sam(Belgium), by Play It Again Sam (Belgium). Catalogue no: **BIASCD 107**
12" Single: Released 1 Aug '89, on Play It Again Sam(Belgium), by Play It Again Sam (Belgium). Catalogue no: **BIAS 107**

Thamby

ACQUAINTANCES
Tracks: / Acquaintances / Acquaintances (in dub).
7" Single: Released Oct '82, on Freshly Cut, Catalogue no: **FCRS 2001**

Thane

ROMANCE DOWN THE DRAIN
Tracks: / Romance down the drain.
7" Single: Released Mar '81, on Badge, by Badge Records. Deleted Mar '84. Catalogue no: **BAD 8**

Thanes

HEY GIRL EP (SINGLE)
Tracks: / Hey girl.
7" Single: Released Sep '87, on DDT, by D.D.T.Records. Catalogue no: **DISP 8**

I'LL REST
Tracks: / I'll rest.
7" Single: Released Jan '89, on DDT, by D.D.T.Records. Catalogue no: **DISP 20**

That Girl

DREAM LOVER
Tracks: / Dream lover / Fire me up.
12" Single: Released Apr '88, on Splash, by Splash Records. Catalogue no: **CPST 1011**
7" Single: Released Apr '88, on Splash, by Splash Records. Catalogue no: **CPS 1011**

That Petrol Emotion

BIG DECISION
Tracks: / Big decision / Soul deep.
7" Single: Released Mar '87, on Polydor, by Polydor Ltd. Catalogue no: **TPE 1**
12" Single: Released Mar '87, on Polydor, by Polydor Ltd. Catalogue no: **TPEX 1**

CELLOPHANE
Tracks: / Cellophane / Think of a woman / Hot head (12" & CD only).
7" Single: Released 26 Sep '88, on Virgin, by Virgin Records. Catalogue no: **VS 1116**
CD 5": Released '88, on Virgin, by Virgin Records. Catalogue no: **VSCD 1116**
12" Single: Released 26 Sep '88, on Virgin, by Virgin Records. Catalogue no: **VST 1116**

GENIUS MOVE
Tracks: / Genius move / Party games / Mouthcrazy (NOT on 7").
CD 5": Released Aug '88, on Virgin, by Virgin Records. Catalogue no: **CDEP 13**
7" Single: Released Oct '87, on Virgin, by Virgin Records. Deleted May '88. Catalogue no: **VS 1022**
12" Single: Released '87, on Virgin, by Virgin Records. Catalogue no: **VST 1022**

GROOVE CHECK
Tracks: / Groove check / Chemicrazy / Tension / Under the sky.
CD 3": Released Feb '89, on Virgin, by Virgin Records. Catalogue no: **VSCD 1159**
10" single: Released Feb '89, on Virgin, by Virgin Records. Catalogue no: **VSA 1159**

IT'S A GOOD THING

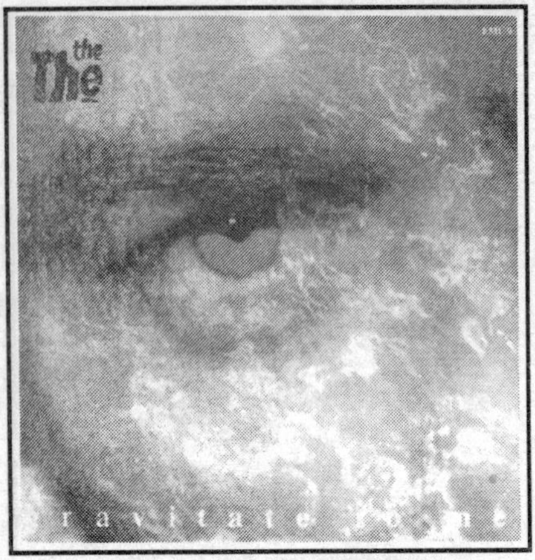

THE THE - GRAVTATE TO ME (Released on Epic)

Tracks: / It's a good thing / Mine (Extra track on 12" version only).
7" Single: Released Apr '86, on Demon, by Demon Records. Catalogue no: **D 1042**
12" Single: Released Apr '86, on Demon, by Demon Records. Catalogue no: **D 1042 T**

KEEN
Tracks: / Keen.
7" Single: Released Jul '85, on Pink Label, by Pink Label Records. Catalogue no: **PINKY 004**
12" Single: Released Oct '86, on Pink Label, by Pink Label Records. Catalogue no: **PINKY 13T**

NATURAL KIND OF JOY
Tracks: / Natural kind of joy.
7" Single: Released Aug '86, on Demon, by Demon Records. Catalogue no: **D 1043**
12" Single: Released Jun '86, on Demon, by Demon Records. Catalogue no: **D 1043 T**

PEEL SESSIONS:THAT PETROL EMOTION
Tracks: / V-2 / Lettuce / Blind spot / Can't stop.
12" Single: Released Sep '87, on Strange Fruit, by Strange Fruit Records. Catalogue no: **SFPS 038**

SWAMP
Tracks: / Swamp (Remix) (Trackon 7" version only.) / Swamp (Ext. Mix) (Track on 12" version only.) / Swamp (Track on E.P.Version only.) / Me and baby brother, Creeping to the cross (Track on E.P. version only.) / Dance your ass off / Creeping to the cross (Shorter & better) (Track on 12" version only.).
7" EP: Released Jul '87, on Polydor, by Polydor Ltd. Catalogue no: **TPEE 2**
7" Single: Released Jul '87, on Polydor, by Polydor Ltd. Catalogue no: **TPE 2**
12" Single: Released Jul '87, on Polydor, by Polydor Ltd. Catalogue no: **TPEX 2**

VS
Tracks: / VS.
7" Single: Released Oct '85, on Noise A Noise, Catalogue no: **NAN 1**
12" Single: Released Oct '85, on Noise A Noise, Catalogue no: **NAN 1T**

Thatcher on Acid

ANOTHER ONE GIRL
Tracks: / Another one girl.
12" Single: Released Jul '86, on All The Madmen, by All The Madmen Records. Catalogue no: **mad 14**

The The

ARMAGEDDON DAYS ARE HERE (AGAIN)
Tracks: / Armageddon days are here (again) / Armageddon days are here (again)(version).
10" single: Released Sep '89, on Epic, by CBS Records. Catalogue no: **EMU QT10**
12" Single: Released Sep '89, on Epic, by CBS Records. Catalogue no: **EMU T10**
12" Single: Released Sep '89, on Epic, by CBS Records. Catalogue no: **EMU E10**
7" Single: Released Sep '89, on Epic, by CBS Records. Catalogue no: **EMU 10**
CD 5": Released Sep '89, on Epic, by CBS Records. Catalogue no: **CDEMU 10**

BEATEN GENERATION, THE
Tracks: / Beaten generation, The / Angel / Soul mining (Only included in the box set.) / Beaten generation (Camp fire mix) (Only on CD single.) / Beaten generation (Palmer mix) (Only on CD single.).
7" Single: Released Mar '89, on Epic, by CBS Records. Deleted Oct '89. Catalogue no: **EMU 8**
12" Single: Released Mar '89, on Epic, by CBS Records. Deleted Oct '89. Catalogue no: **EMUT 8**
7" Single: Released Mar '89, on Epic, by CBS Records. Deleted Oct '89. Catalogue no: **EMUB 8**
CD 5": Released Mar '89, on Epic, by CBS Records. Deleted Oct '89. Catalogue no: **CPEMU 8**
12" Single: Released Mar '89, on Epic, by CBS Records. Deleted Oct '89. Catalogue no: **EMUQ 8**

GRAVITATE TO ME (see panel above)
Tracks: / Gravitate to me / Violence of truth, The / Gravitate to me (dub) (Only on etched 12" single.) / I've been waitin' for tomorrow (Only on 12" etched single.) / Gravitate to me (little version) (Only on cassette single.).
7" Single: Released Jul '89, on Epic, by CBS Records. Catalogue no: **EMU 9**
12" Single: Released Jul '89, on Epic, by CBS Records. Catalogue no: **EMUE 9**
12" Single: Released Jul '89, on Epic, by CBS Records. Catalogue no: **EMUT 9**
12" Single: Released Jul '89, on Epic, by CBS Records. Catalogue no: **EMUB 9**
Cassingle: Released Jul '89, on Epic, by CBS Records. Catalogue no: **EMUC 9**
CD 5": Released Jul '89, on Epic, by CBS Records. Catalogue no: **CDEMU 9**

HEARTLAND
Tracks: / Heartland / Born in New S.A. / Flesh and bones (Extra track on 12" version only) / Sweet bird of truth (Extra track on 12" version only).
12" Single: Released Aug '86, on Some Bizzare, by Some Bizzare Records. Catalogue no: **TRUTHQ 2**
12" Single: Released Jul '86, on Epic, by CBS Records. Catalogue no: **TRUTH T2**
7" Single: Released Jul '86, on Epic, by CBS Records. Catalogue no: **TRUTH 2**

INFECTED (SINGLE)
Tracks: / Infected.
12" Single: Released Oct '86, on Epic, by CBS Records. Catalogue no: **TRUTH T 3**
7" Single: Released Oct '86, on Epic, by CBS Records. Catalogue no: **TRUTH 3**

NATURE OF VIRTURE, THE
Tracks: / Nature of virtue, The / Perfect.
7" Single: Released Feb '83, on Epic, by CBS Records. Catalogue no: **EPC A 3119**
12" Single: Released Feb '83, on Epic, by CBS Records. Catalogue no: **EPC A 13 3119**

SLOW TRAIN TO DAWN
Tracks: / Slow train to dawn / Harbour lights.
7" Single: Released Jan '87, on Epic, by CBS Records. Deleted Aug '87. Catalogue no: **TENSE 1**
12" Single: Released Jan '87, on Epic, by CBS Records. Deleted Aug '87. Catalogue no: **TENSET 1**

SWEET BIRD OF TRUTH
Tracks: / Soul mining (Extra track on cassette and CD only) / Sweet bird of truth / Sleeping juice / Harbour lights.
CD 5": Released May '87, on Epic, by CBS Records. Deleted Nov '87. Catalogue no: **CDTHE 2**
12" Single: Released May '87, on Epic, by CBS Records. Deleted Nov '87. Catalogue no: **TENSET 2**
7" Single: Released May '86, on Epic, by CBS Records. Catalogue no: **TRUTH 1**
7" Single: Released May '87, on Epic, by CBS Records. Deleted Nov '87. Catalogue no: **TENSE 2**
Cassingle: Released May '87, on Epic, by CBS Records. Deleted Nov '87. Catalogue no: **TENSE C2**

THIS IS THE DAY
Tracks: / This is the day.
7" Single: Released Jul '84, on Some Bizzare, by Some Bizzare Records. Catalogue no: **A 3710**

UNCERTAIN SMILE
Tracks: / Uncertain smile / Soul mining.
7" Single: Released Dec '82, on Epic, by CBS Records. Deleted '85. Catalogue no: **EPCA 2787**

Theatre of Hate

DO YOU BELIEVE IN THE WEST WORLD
Tracks: / Do you believe in the west world.
7" Single: Released Jan '82, on Burning Rome, Catalogue no: **BRR 2**
12" Single: Released Jan '82, on Burning Rome, Catalogue no: **BRRT 2**

EASTWORLD
Tracks: / Eastworld / Assegai.
12" Single: Released Nov '82, on Burning Rome, Catalogue no: **BRR 4T**
7" Single: Released Nov '82, on Burning Rome, Catalogue no: **BRR 4**

HOP
Tracks: / Hop / Conquistador.
7" Single: Released May '82, on Burning Rome, Deleted '85. Catalogue no: **BRR 3**

HOP, THE
Tracks: / Hop, The.
12" Single: Released Nov '85, on Stiff, by Stiff Records. Catalogue no: **BUYIT 237**
7" Single: Released May '82, on Burning Rome, Catalogue no: **BRR 3**

Thee Hypnotics

LOVE IN A DIFFERENT VEIN
Tracks: / Love in a different vein.
7" Single: Released Jul '88, on Hipsville, Catalogue no: **HIP 1**

SOUL TRADER
Tracks: / Soul trader / Earth blues.
12" Single: Released Sep '89, on Situation 2, by Beggars Banquet Records. Catalogue no: **SIT062T**
7" Single: Released Sep '89, on Situation 2, by Beggars Banquet Records. Catalogue no: **SIT062**

Thee People

IT HAPPENED ON A SUNDAY MORNING
Tracks: / It happened on a Sunday morning / Fly Freddie fly.
7" Single: Released Feb '83, on Deb, by Deb Records. Catalogue no: **DEB 109**

Them

BABY PLEASE DON'T GO
Tracks: / Baby please don't go.
7" Single: Released Jan '65, on Decca, by Decca Records. Deleted '68. Catalogue no: **F 12018**

BABY PLEASE DON'T GO (OLD GOLD)
Tracks: / Baby please don't go.
7" Single: Released Oct '83, on Old Gold, by Old Gold Records. Catalogue no: **OG 9341**

GLORIA
Tracks: / Gloria / Baby please don't go.
7" Single: Released May '82, on Decca, by Decca Records. Deleted '88. Catalogue no: **F 13923**

HERE COMES THE NIGHT
Tracks: / Here comes the night.
7" Single: Released Sep '73, on Deram, by London Records. Catalogue no: **DM 400**
7" Single: Released Mar '65, on Decca, by Decca Records. Deleted '68. Catalogue no: **F 12094**

HERE COMES THE NIGHT (OLD GOLD)
Tracks: / Here comes the night.
7" Single: Released Oct '83, on Old Gold, by Old Gold Records. Deleted Sep '89. Catalogue no: **OG 9342**

Them Howling Horrors

DIG DOWN DEEPER
Tracks: / Wise up little girl / Ain't got a clue / We copped the first shot at the gunfight.
12" Single: Released Nov '86, on Criminal Damage, Catalogue no: **CRI 12139**

Them Philistines

TALES FROM THE STAGNANT..
Tracks: / Tales from the stagnant...
7" Single: Released 3 Apr '87, on Lowther, Catalogue no: **LSRTP 001**

Them Two

BREAKFAST IN BED
Tracks: / Breakfast in bed.
12" Single: Released Feb '85, on White Label (1), Catalogue no: **ADE 1002**

Themis, John

FINAL CRUISE
Tracks: / Final cruise / English renaissance.
7" Single: Released Mar '86, on Coda, by Coda Records. Catalogue no: **CODS 17**

Then Jerico

BIG AREA (SINGLE)
Tracks: / Big area / Big sweep, The / Big sweep (dance mix) (On 12" single only) / Motive, The (U.S.A. mix) (On 12" & CD singles only) / Trampled under foot (On CD single only).
CD 5": Released 16 Jan '89, on London Records, by London Records. Catalogue no: **LONCD 204**
12" Single: Released 16 Jan '89, on London Records, by London Records. Catalogue no: **LONXG 204**
7" Single: Released 16 Jan '89, on London Records, by London Records. Deleted 26 Jun '89. Catalogue no: **LON 204**
7" Single: Released '89, on London Records, by London Records. Catalogue no: **LONP 204**
12" Single: Released 16 Jan '89, on London Records, by London Records. Catalogue no: **LONX 204**

BIG SWEEP, THE
Tracks: / Big sweep, The.
12" Single: Released Aug '85, on Immaculate, by Immaculate Records. Catalogue no: **TJ 1**

FAULT
Tracks: / Fault.
12" Single: Released Sep '85, on London Records, by London Records. Catalogue no: **LONX 63**
7" Single: Released Sep '85, on London Records, by London Records. Catalogue no: **LON 63**

MOTIVE, THE
Tracks: / Word, The / Motive, The / Motive, The (Extended) (Track on 12" version only.) / Motive, The (Midnight mix) (Track on 12" version only.).
Cassingle: Released Jul '87, on London Records, by London Records. Deleted May '89. Catalogue no: **LONCS 145**
7" Single: Released Jul '87, on London Records, by London Records. Deleted Oct '88. Catalogue no: **LON 145**
12" Single: Released Jul '87, on London Records, by London Records. Deleted Oct '88. Catalogue no: **LONX 145**

MUSCLE DEEP
Tracks: / Muscle deep / Clank (countdown to oblivian) / Fault (12" Version.) / Muscle deep (extended).
12" Single: Released Oct '87, on London Records, by London Records. Deleted Oct '88. Catalogue no: **LONX 156**
7" Single: Released Oct '87, on London Records, by London Records. Deleted Oct '88. Catalogue no: **LON 156**
7" Single: Released Mar '86, on London Records, by London Records. Catalogue no: **LON 86**
CD 5": on London Records, by London Records. Deleted Oct '88. Catalogue no: **LONCD 156**
12" Single: Released Mar '86, on London Records, by London Records. Deleted Feb '89. Catalogue no: **LONX 86**

PRAIRIE ROSE
Tracks: / Prairie rose / Electric / One life
CD 5": on London Records, by London Records. Deleted Oct '88. Catalogue no: **LONCD 131**
12" Single: Released Mar '87, on London Records, by London Records. Deleted Oct '88. Catalogue no: **LONX 131**
7" Single: Released Mar '87, on London Records, by London Records. Deleted Oct '88. Catalogue no: **LON 131**

SUGAR BOX
Tracks: / Sugar box / Happening, The / Big area (lost mix) (On 12" and CD only) / Sugar box blue (On 12" and CD only).
Cassingle: Released Aug '89, on London Records, by London Records. Catalogue no: **LONCS 235**
CD 5": Released Aug '89, on London Records, by London Records. Catalogue no: **LONCD 235**
7" Single: Released Aug '89, on London Records, by London Records. Catalogue no: **LON 235**
12" Single: Released Aug '89, on London Records, by London Records. Catalogue no: **LONX 235**

WHAT DOES IT TAKE
Tracks: / What does it take (to win your love).
CD 5": Released Apr '89, on London Records, by London Records. Catalogue no: **LONCD 223**
12" Single: Released Apr '89, on London Records, by London Records. Catalogue no: **LONXG 223**
12" Single: Released Mar '89, on London Records, by London Records. Catalogue no: **LONX 223**
12" Single: Released Mar '89, on London Records, by London Records. Catalogue no: **LONXG 223**
CD 5": Released Mar '89, on London Records, by London Records. Catalogue no: **LONCD 223**
7" Single: Released Apr '89, on London Records, by London Records. Catalogue no: **LONG 223**
7" Single: Released Mar '89, on London Records, by London Records. Catalogue no: **LON 223**

Therapy

ONLY A FOOL
Tracks: / Only a fool / Thunder and lightning.
7" Single: Released Sep '82, on Revo, Catalogue no: **REV 004**

STAY BY ME
Tracks: / Stay by me / Soft touch.
7" Single: Released Apr '82, on Smile, Deleted '85. Catalogue no: **SMILE 36**

These Future Kings

AFTER THIS
Tracks: / After this.
7" EP: Released Sep '87, on Rampant (Australia), Deleted Oct '87. Catalogue no: **MLRR 006**

These Immortal Souls

MARRY ME (LIE LIE)
Tracks: / Open up and bleed / Blood and sand / She said.
12" Single: Released Aug '87, on Mute, by Mute Records. Catalogue no: **12 MUTE 63**

These Tender Virtues

WALTZ
Tracks: / Waltz.
7" Single: Released Jun '85, on Carousel (1), by Carousel Records. Catalogue no: **TTV 1**

They Might Be Giants

ANA NG
Tracks: / Ana ng.
7" Single: Released Mar '89, on One Little Indian, by One Little Indian Records. Catalogue no: **7TP 24**
12" Single: Released Mar '89, on One Little Indian, by One Little Indian Records. Catalogue no: **12TP 24**

DON'T LET'S START
Tracks: / Don't let's start.
12" Single: Released Jul '88, on Rough Trade, by Rough Trade Records. Catalogue no: **RTD 033T**

THEY'LL NEED A CRANE
Tracks: / They'll need a crane.
12" Single: Released 16 Jan '89, on One Little Indian, by One Little Indian Records. Catalogue no: **12 TP 22**
7" Single: Released Jan '89, on One Little Indian, by One Little Indian Records. Catalogue no: **TP 22**

They Must Be Russians

CHAINS
Tracks: / Chains.
12" Single: Released Jul '83, on First Floor, Catalogue no: **FF 1**

DEVOTION
Tracks: / Devotion.
12" Single: Released Oct '84, on Office Box, Catalogue no: **EBOFT 4**
7" Single: Released Oct '84, on Office Box, Catalogue no: **EBOF 4**

DON'T TRY TO CURE YOURSELF
Tracks: / Don't try to cure yourself.
7" Single: Released Apr '81, on Fresh, by Jetstar Records. Catalogue no: **FRESH 18**

RED SQUARE
Tracks: / Red Square.
12" Single: Released Feb '86, on Native (1), by Native Records. Catalogue no: **NTV 7**

Thieves

SOUL THIEF
Tracks: / Soul thief / And then he died / Souvenir of 1969.
7" Single: Released May '89, on Planetarium Discs, by Planetarium Discs. Catalogue no: **THEFT 2**

TALK YOUR HEAD OFF
Tracks: / Talk your head off.
7" Single: Released 30 May '87, on Planetarium Discs, by Planetarium Discs. Catalogue no: **THEFT 1**

Thieves Like Us

MIND MADE
Tracks: / Mind made / Strike out.
7" Single: Released May '80, on Earlobe, by Earlobe Records. Deleted '87. Catalogue no: **ELS 1**

Thieves Of Baghdad

LET ME HEAR YOU SCREAM
Tracks: / Let me hear you scream.
12" Single: Released Dec '88, on Blue Chip, by Blue Chip Records. Catalogue no: **BLUE-CHIP 12 T**

Thin Lizzy

Biographical details: Thin Lizzy was an Irish heavy metal band 1969-83, formed by Phil Lynott, who was born in 1951 in Dublin and died in 1986 of drugs, just as a solo career was getting underway. *Jailbreak* (1976), *Johnny the Fox* (1977), *Live and Dangerous* (1978), *Black Rose* (1979) were probably their best albums. They were accused of bad taste for top 10 hit *Killer On The Loose* in 1980 during the hunt for the Yorkshire Ripper. (Donald Clarke 13.1.88).

ARE YOU READY
Tracks: / Are you ready / Dear Miss lonely hearts.
7" Single: Released Apr '81, on Vertigo, by Phonogram Ltd. Catalogue no: **LIZZY 812**

BOYS ARE BACK IN TOWN (OLD GOLD)
Tracks: / Boys are back in town / You ain't seen nothing yet.
Note: B-side features 'You Ain't Seen Nothing Yet' by Bachman Turner Overdrive.
7" Single: Released Feb '88, on Old Gold, by Old Gold Records. Catalogue no: **OG 9764**

BOYS ARE BACK IN TOWN (SINGLE)
Tracks: / Boys are back in town.
7" Single: Released May '76, on Vertigo, by Phonogram Ltd. Deleted '79. Catalogue no: **6059 139**

CHINATOWN (SINGLE)
Tracks: / Chinatown / Sugar blues.
7" Single: Released May '80, on Vertigo, by Phonogram Ltd. Deleted '83. Catalogue no: **LIZZY 6**

COLD SWEAT
Tracks: / Cold sweat / Bad habits.
7" Single: Released Feb '83, on Vertigo, by Phonogram Ltd. Deleted '85. Catalogue no: **LIZZY 11**

DANCIN' IN THE MOONLIGHT
Tracks: / Dancin' in the moonlight.
7" Single: Released Aug '77, on Vertigo, by Phonogram Ltd. Deleted '80. Catalogue no: **6059 177**

DANCIN' IN THE MOONLIGHT (OLD GOLD)
Tracks: / Dancin' in the moonlight.
7" Single: Released Jan '85, on Old Gold, by Old Gold Records. Catalogue no: **OG 9484**

DO ANYTHING YOU WANT
Tracks: / Do anything you want to.
7" Single: Released Jun '79, on Vertigo, by Phonogram Ltd. Deleted '82. Catalogue no: **LIZZY 004**

DON'T BELIEVE A WORD
Tracks: / Don't believe a word.
7" Single: Released Jan '77, on Vertigo, by Phonogram Ltd. Deleted '80. Catalogue no: **LIZZY 001**

HOLLYWOOD
Tracks: / Hollywood / Pressure will blow, The.
7" Pic: Released Feb '82, on Vertigo, by Phonogram Ltd. Catalogue no: **LIZPD 10**
7" Single: Released Feb '82, on Vertigo, by Phonogram Ltd. Catalogue no: **LIZZY 10**

JAILBREAK (SINGLE)
Tracks: / Jailbreak.
7" Single: Released Aug '76, on Vertigo, by Phonogram Ltd. Deleted '79. Catalogue no: **6059 150**

KILLER ON THE LOOSE
Tracks: / Killer on the loose.
7" Single: Released Sep '80, on Vertigo, by Phonogram Ltd. Deleted '83. Catalogue no: **LIZZY 7**

KILLERS LIVE
Tracks: / Bad reputation / Are you ready / Dear Miss Lonely hearts / Opium trail (12" only).
12" Single: Released Apr '81, on Vertigo, by Phonogram Ltd. Deleted '85. Catalogue no: **LIZZY 812**
7" EP: Released May '81, on Vertigo, by Phonogram Ltd. Deleted '84. Catalogue no: **LIZZY 8**

LITTLE DARLING
Tracks: / Little darlin'.
7" Single: Released Apr '74, on Decca, by Decca Records. Deleted '88. Catalogue no: **F 13507**

ROSALIE - COWGIRLS' SONG
Tracks: / Rosalie - Cowgirls' song.
7" Single: Released May '78, on Vertigo, by Phonogram Ltd. Deleted '81. Catalogue no: **LIZZY 2**

SARAH
Tracks: / Sarah.
7" Single: Released Oct '79, on Vertigo, by Phonogram Ltd. Deleted '82. Catalogue no: **LIZZY 5**

SUN GOES DOWN, THE
Tracks: / Sun goes down, The.
7" Single: Released Aug '83, on Vertigo, by Phonogram Ltd. Deleted '86. Catalogue no: **LIZZY 13**

THUNDER AND LIGHTNING (SINGLE)
Tracks: / Thunder and lightning.
7" Single: Released Apr '83, on Vertigo, by Phonogram Ltd. Catalogue no: **LIZZY 12**
12" Single: Released Apr '83, on Vertigo, by Phonogram Ltd. Catalogue no: **LIZZY 1212**

TROUBLE BOYS
Tracks: / Trouble boys.
7" Single: Released Aug '81, on Vertigo, by Phonogram Ltd. Deleted '84. Catalogue no: **LIZZY 9**

WAITING FOR AN ALIBI (see panel below
Tracks: / Waiting for an alibi / With love.
7" Single: Released Feb '79, on Vertigo, by Phonogram Ltd. Catalogue no: **LIZZY 3**

WHISKEY IN THE JAR (OLD GOLD)
Tracks: / Whiskey in the jar.
7" Single: Released Oct '83, on Old Gold, by Old Gold Records. Catalogue no: **OG 9330**

WHISKEY IN THE JAR (SINGLE)
Tracks: / Whisky in the jar / Rocker, The.

7" Set: Released Nov '85, on Polydor, by Polydor Ltd. Catalogue no: **POSPD 777**
7" Single: Released Jan '73, on Decca, by Decca Records. Deleted '76. Catalogue no: **F 13355**
7" Single: Released Oct '79, on Decca, by Decca Records. Deleted '88. Catalogue no: **F 13748**

THIN LIZZY - WAITING FOR A ALIBI (Released on Vertigo)

Thin Red Line

ONLY DREAMING OF YOU
Tracks: / Only dreaming of you.
7" Single: Released Jul '84, on MTM-Privacy, Catalogue no: **VACS 003**
12" Single: Released Jul '84, on MTM-Privacy, Catalogue no: **VACT 003**

Thing (Group)

ALIEN ATTACK
Tracks: / Alien attack.
12" Single: Released Jun '84, on Electricity, by Electricity Records. Deleted '88. Catalogue no: **TRICT 1000**

Think Pink

IN AND OUT OF LOVE
Tracks: / In and out of love.
7" Single: Released Jun '84, on Red Bus, by Red Bus Records. Catalogue no: **RBUS 97**

Think Twice

ALCOHOLIC BLUES
Tracks: / Alcoholic blues.
7" Single: Released Jul '88, on Conscience, by Conscience Records. Catalogue no: **CSE 1**
12" Single: Released Jul '88, on Conscience, by Conscience Records. Catalogue no: **CFT 1**

Third Army

MARCH OF 10,000 SOLDIERS
Tracks: / March of 10,000 soldiers.
7" Single: Released Nov '81, on No, Deleted '83. Catalogue no: **NO 2**
12" Single: Released Nov '81, on No, Deleted '83. Catalogue no: **DAZZ 10 12**

Third Circle

CASH CROP
Tracks: / Cash crop.
12" Single: Released Nov '88, on Rouska, by Rouska Records. Catalogue no: **PROFANE 63**

GOODBYE TO YESTERDAY
Tracks: / Goodbye to yesterday.
12" Single: Released Mar '87, on Rouska, by Rouska Records. Catalogue no: **PROFANE 18**

LAST NIGHT WAS THE BEST NIGHT OF MY LIFE
Tracks: / Last night was the best night of my life / Man who fell apart, The (Track on 12" version only) / Real eyes (Track on 12" version only).
7" Single: Released Apr '86, on Rouska, by Rouska Records. Catalogue no: **COME 3**
12" Single: Released Oct '86, on Rouska, by Rouska Records. Catalogue no: **COME 3T**

Third Eye

PASS MYSELF
Tracks: / Pass myself.
7" Single: Released Feb '82, on Scarlet, Catalogue no: **QUEST 01**

Third Festival Of...

GOD SAVE THE QUEEN

THIRD WORLD - NOW THAT WE'VE FOUND LOVE (Released on Island)

THIRD WORLD - TRY JAH LOVE (Released on CBS)

Tracks: / God save the Queen (Third Festival of 1000 Welsh Male Voices, at the Royal Albert Hall, Lond) / Land of my fathers (Third Festival of 1000 Welsh Male Voices, At the Royal Albert Hall, Lond) / Land of hope and glory (Central Band of the Royal Air Force, with the Finchley and the Barnet &).
Note: 'God save the Queen' and 'Land of my fathers (Mae hen wlad fy nhadau)' by the 'Third Festival Of 1000 Welsh Male Voices. 'Land Of Hope And Glory' by the 'Central Band Of The Royal Air Force'.
7" Single: Released Oct '87, on Grasmere, by Grasmere Records. Catalogue no: **GRASS 1**

Third Generation

TWO ANSWERS EP
Tracks: / Two answers.
12" Single: Released Jan '89, on In Time Communications, Catalogue no: **ITC 001**

Third Light

SHINE
Tracks: / Shine.
7" Single: Released Oct '84, on Blue Train, Catalogue no: **COACH 3**

Third Man

ORAL PLEASURE
Tracks: / Oral pleasure.
7" Single: Released Sep '84, on Uniton Records, Catalogue no: **U 006**
7" Single: Released Sep '84, on Uniton Records, Catalogue no: **U 006**

Third Party Split

INSANE
Tracks: / Insane / Totally insane.
7" Single: Released Jun '80, on B & C, by Trojan Records. Deleted Jun '83. Catalogue no: **BCS 19**

Third Uncles

BLUE DRESS DAY
Tracks: / Blue dress day / Skint Jesus / Grill.
12" Single: Released Oct '88, on Four Thirds, Catalogue no: **FT 001**

Third World

COOL MEDITATION
Tracks: / Cool meditation.
7" Single: Released Jan '79, on Island, by Island Records. Deleted '82. Catalogue no: **WIP 6469**

DANCING ON THE FLOOR
Tracks: / Dancing on the floor.
7" Single: Released May '81, on CBS, by CBS Records. Catalogue no: **A 1214**
12" Single: Released May '81, on CBS, by CBS Records. Catalogue no: **A 13 1214**

DANCING ON THE FLOOR (OLD GOLD)
Tracks: / Dancing of the floor / Try Jah love.
7" Single: Released 24 Apr '89, on Old Gold, by Old Gold Records. Catalogue no: **OG 9871**

FORBIDDEN LOVE
Tracks: / Forbidden love / Forbidden love (no rap) (Only on 7" single.) / Forbidden love (12" remix) (Only on 12" and CD single.) / Forbidden love (dub) (Only on 12" and CD single.) / Forbidden love (version) / Theme from the underdog.
12" Single: Released Jun '89, on Mercury, by Phonogram Ltd. Catalogue no: **MERXX 288**
CD 5": Released 12 Jun '89, on Mercury, by Phonogram Ltd. Deleted Oct '89. Catalogue no: **MERCD 288**
7" Single: Released 12 Jun '89, on Mercury, by Phonogram Ltd. Deleted Oct '89. Catalogue no: **MER 288**
12" Single: Released 12 Jun '89, on Mercury, by Phonogram Ltd. Deleted Oct '89. Catalogue no: **MERX 288**

HOOKED ON LOVE
Tracks: / Hooked on love / Who made Rastafaria.
7" Single: Released May '81, on CBS, by CBS Records. Deleted May '84. Catalogue no: **CBS A 1214**

IT'S THE SAME OLD SONG
Tracks: / It's the same old song / Reggae ambassador.
12" Single: Released Sep '89, on Mercury, by Phonogram Ltd. Catalogue no: **MERX 306**
7" Single: Released Sep '89, on Mercury, by Phonogram Ltd. Catalogue no: **MER 306**

LAGOS JUMP
Tracks: / Lagos jump.
12" Single: Released Jan '84, on CBS, by CBS Records. Catalogue no: **TA 4058**
7" Single: Released Jan '84, on CBS, by CBS Records. Catalogue no: **A 4058**

NOW THAT WE'VE FOUND LOVE (see panel above)
Tracks: / Now that we've found love / Night heat.
7" Single: Released Sep '78, on Island, by Island Records. Deleted '81. Catalogue no: **WIP 6457**
12" Single: Released Mar '85, on Island, by Island Records. Catalogue no: **12ISX 219**
12" Single: Released Mar '85, on Island, by Island Records. Deleted Apr '88. Catalogue no: **12IS 219**
7" Pic: Released Mar '85, on Island, by Island Records. Catalogue no: **ISP 219**
7" Single: Released Mar '85, on Island, by Island Records. Deleted '87. Catalogue no: **IS 219**

ONE MORE TIME
Tracks: / One more time.
12" Single: Released Jan '86, on CBS, by CBS Records. Catalogue no: **TA 6854**
7" Single: Released Jan '86, on CBS, by CBS Records. Catalogue no: **A 6854**

RIDE ON
Tracks: / Ride on / You've got the power.
7" Single: Released Jun '82, on CBS, by CBS Records. Deleted Jun '85. Catalogue no: **CBSA 2506**

STANDING IN THE RAIN
Tracks: / Standing in the rain / Dubb music.
7" Single: Released Aug '81, on CBS, by CBS Records. Catalogue no: **A 1542**

TALK TO ME
Tracks: / Talk to me.
7" Single: Released Jun '79, on Island, by Island Records. Deleted '82. Catalogue no: **WIP 6496**

TRY JAH LOVE (see panel above)
Tracks: / Try Jah love / Inna time like this.
7" Single: Released Apr '82, on CBS, by CBS Records. Deleted '85. Catalogue no: **A 2063**

Thirst

RIDING THE TIMES
Tracks: / Riding the times.
12" Single: Released Jul '87, on Rough Trade, by Rough Trade Records. Catalogue no: **RTT 206**

Thirteen At Midnight

CLIMB DOWN
7" Single: Released '83, on Survival (1), by Survival Records. Catalogue no: **SUR 011**
12" Single: Released '83, on Survival (1), by Survival Records. Catalogue no: **SUR 12 011**

OTHER PASSENGERS
Tracks: / Other passengers.
7" Single: Released May '82, on Pure, Catalogue no: **PURE 2**

SKIN DEEP
Tracks: / Skin deep / Shack up.
12" Single: Released Nov '83, on Survival (1), by Survival Records. Catalogue no: **SUR 12 017**
7" Single: Released Nov '83, on Survival (1), by Survival Records. Catalogue no: **SUR 017**

TIME IS TIGHT
Tracks: / Time is tight.
7" Single: Released Jun '84, on Survival (1), by Survival Records. Catalogue no: **SUR 025**
12" Single: Released Jun '84, on Survival (1), by Survival Records. Catalogue no: **SUR 12 025**

Thirteen Moons

SUDDENLY ONE SUMMER
Tracks: / Where did you all go.
12" Single: Released Nov '86, on Wire, by Wire Records. Catalogue no: **WRMS 013**
7" Single: Released Nov '86, on Wire, by Wire Records. Catalogue no: **WRS 013**

TRUE STORY, A
Tracks: / True story, A / Night parade / Daddy come home / Last train to San Antone (Extra track on 12" version only.).
12" Single: Released Sep '86, on Wire, by Wire Records. Catalogue no: **WRMS 008**
7" Single: Released Sep '86, on Wire, by Wire Records. Catalogue no: **WRS 008**

Thirteenth Chime

CURSED
Tracks: / Cursed.
7" Single: Released Jan '82, on Chime, Catalogue no: **THC 1**

FIRE
Tracks: / Fire / Hide & seek.
7" Single: Released Nov '82, on 13th Crime, Catalogue no: **THC 2**

Thirty Bob Suits

SIX FOOT UNDER
Tracks: / Six foot under.
7" Single: Released May '82, on Tanne Made, Deleted '83. Catalogue no: **T 150**

Thirty Eight Special

CAUGHT UP IN YOU
Tracks: /Caught up in you / Fire starter
7" Single: Released Jun '82 on A&M, b A&M Records. Deleted Jun '85. Catalogu no : **AMS 8228**

HOLD LOOSELY
Tracks: /Hold loosely / Throw out the line.
7" Single: Released Apr '81 on A&M, b A&M Records. Deleted '85. Catalogue no **AMS 8120**

IF I HAD BEEN THE ONE
Tracks: / If I had been the one.
7" Single: Released Jan '84, on A&M, b A&M Records. Deleted '88. Catalogue no **AM 174**

LIKE NO OTHER NIGHT
Tracks: / Like no other night.
12" Single: Released May '86, on A&M, b A&M Records. Deleted '88. Catalogue no **AMY 321**
7" Single: Released May '86, on A&M, b A&M Records. Deleted '88. Catalogue no **AM 321**

SECOND CHANCE
Tracks: / Second chance / Coming dow tonight
7" Single: Released Apr '89, on A&M, b A&M Records. Catalogue no: **AM 507**

STONE COLD BELIEVER
Tracks: / Stone cold believer / Rockin' in the night / Robin Hood (Only on 12" single
12" Single: Released 20 Jun '80, on A&M by A&M Records. Deleted '83. Catalogu no: **AMSP 7535**
7" Single: Released 20 Jun '80, on A&M, b A&M Records. Deleted '83. Catalogue n **AMS 7535**

YOU KEEP RUNNIN' AWAY
Tracks: /You keep runnin' away / Prisone of Rock 'n' roll.
7" Single: Released Aug '82, on A&M, A&M Records. Deleted Aug '85. Catalog no: **AMS 8246**

Thirty Seconds

AUTOMATIC
Tracks: / Automatic / Give me work.
7" Single: Released Jun '81, on Initial, Ca logue no: **IRS 002**

Thirty Three Seconds

SKYLIGHT ROCK
Tracks: / Skylight rock.
7" Single: Released Mar '85, on Fracture Catalogue no: **FRAC 1**

Thirty-Nine Lyon

KITES
Tracks: / Kites / Girl named property.
7" Single: Released May '81, on RSO, Polydor Ltd. Deleted May '86. Catalogue **RSO 77**

This Ain't Chicago

RIDE THE RHYTHM
Tracks: / Ride the rhythm.
7" Single: Released Sep '88, on Club, by Phonogram Ltd. Deleted 31 May '89. Catalogue no: **JAB 72**
12" Single: Released Sep '88, on Club, by Phonogram Ltd. Deleted 31 Jul '89. Catalogue no: **JABX 72**

This Final Frame

DIARY
Tracks: / Diary / Discontent.
7" Single: Released Mar '82, on Scratch, by Scratch Records. Deleted '85. Catalogue no: **SCR 008**

GIVE ME BACK
Tracks: / Give me back / When you turn around.
7" Single: Released 5 Mar '88, on Sandy, Catalogue no: **SANDY 1**

MASK, THE
Tracks: / Mask, The.
7" Single: Released Apr '85, on Pnegwan, Catalogue no: **PICKUP 1**

TAKE NO PRISONERS
Tracks: / Take no prisoners / Eden.
7" Single: Released Mar '85, on Direct Drive, by Direct Drive Records. Deleted '86. Catalogue no: **TFF 1**
12" Single: Released Mar '85, on Direct Drive, by Direct Drive Records. Deleted '86. Catalogue no: **12 TFF 1**

This Future

DAY BREAKS AGAIN
Tracks: / Young dogs / Another one / Break, The.
7" EP: Released Apr '86, on Press, by Compendium Int.Records. Catalogue no: **P 1207**

This Is This

HATE AND THE SHAME, THE
Tracks: / Hate and the shame, The.
12" Single: Released Jun '85, on Touch, by Touch Records. Catalogue no: **12TOU 20**

This Island Earth

Biographical details: This Island Earth are a songwriting duo from Liverpool. They formed in early 1983 after the demise of **Systems** (a five piece band from the same city). The guitarist Jerry Kelly went on to become a **Lotus Eater**; whilst the keyboard player Kevin Brown and vocalist John Hawkins decided to spend most of their time writing songs together. Fifty or sixty songs later a deal was signed with Magnet Records and a session with Zeus B. Held in June 1984 produced the first single for This Island Earth entitled *See that glow*. Zeus B. Held has previously produced Dead Or Alive, Fashion and Gina X. (February, 1985).

SEE THAT GLOW
Tracks: / Euroglow / See that glow.
7" Single: Released Jan '87, on Magnet, by WEA Records. Deleted Jan '88. Catalogue no: **EAR 1**
12" Single: Released Sep '84, on Magnet, by WEA Records. Catalogue no: **MAGT 266Z**
12" Single: Released Jan '87, on Magnet, by WEA Records. Deleted Jan '88. Catalogue no: **EARTH 1**
7" Single: Released Sep '84, on Magnet, by WEA Records. Catalogue no: **MAG 266**

TAKE ME TO THE FIRE
Tracks: / Take me to the fire.
7" Single: Released Apr '85, on Magnet, by WEA Records. Catalogue no: **MAG 275**
12" Single: Released Apr '85, on Magnet, by WEA Records. Catalogue no: **MAGT 275**

This Mortal Coil

16 DAYS
Tracks: / 16 days.
12" Single: Released Sep '83, on 4AD, by 4AD Records. Catalogue no: **BAD 310**

DRUGS
Tracks: / Drugs / Come here my love (Double A).
10" single: Released Aug '86, on 4AD, by 4AD Records. Catalogue no: **BAD 608**

KANGAROO
Tracks: / Kangaroo.
7" Single: Released Aug '84, on 4AD, by 4AD Records. Deleted Jan '88. Catalogue no: **AD 410**

SONG TO THE SIREN
Tracks: / Song to the siren.
7" Single: Released Sep '83, on 4AD, by 4AD Records. Catalogue no: **AD 310**

This Other Eden

MAN'S WORLD
Tracks: / Man's world / Angels tell lies.
7" Single: Released 31 Jul '89, on A&M, by A&M Records. Catalogue no: **AM 516**
12" Single: Released 31 Jul '89, on A&M, by A&M Records. Catalogue no: **AMY 516**
CD 5": Released 31 Jul '89, on A&M, by A&M Records. Catalogue no: **CDEE 516**

This Parade

EROTICA
Tracks: / Erotica.
12" Single: Released Apr '85, on Rumpo, Catalogue no: **RUMP 1201**

This Picture

NAKED RAIN
Tracks: / Naked rain / Rape the hillside.
7" Single: Released Oct '89, on Rough Trade, by Rough Trade Records. Catalogue no: **RT 237**
12" Single: Released Oct '89, on Rough Trade, by Rough Trade Records. Catalogue no: **RTT 237**

This Poison

ENGINE FAILURE
Tracks: / Engine failure / You - think.
7" Single: Released Feb '87, on Reception, by Reception Records. Catalogue no: **REC 004**

POISED OVER THE PAUSE BUTTON
Tracks: / Poised over the pause button.
12" Single: Released 31 Oct '87, on Reception, by Reception Records. Catalogue no: **REC 008-12**
7" Single: Released 31 Oct '87, on Reception, by Reception Records. Catalogue no: **REC 008**

This Replica

TUNNEL VISION
Tracks: / Tunnel vision / Today.
7" Single: Released Mar '88, on Fenrock, Catalogue no: **FEN 002**

This Virgin Deep

WHO DO YOU LOVE?
Tracks: / Who do you love.
12" Single: Released 5 May '87, on Purple Plum, Deleted '88. Catalogue no: **PURT 102**

This Way Up

IF I CAN'T HAVE YOU
Tracks: / If I can't have you.
7" Single: Released Oct '87, on Virgin, by Virgin Records. Deleted May '88. Catalogue no: **VS 1002**
12" Single: Released Oct '87, on Virgin, by Virgin Records. Deleted May '88. Catalogue no: **VST 1002**

LOUISE
Tracks: / Louise (Extended version on 12") / Shake baby shake.
12" Single: Released Feb '88, on Virgin, by Virgin Records. Catalogue no: **VST 1033**
7" Single: Released Feb '88, on Virgin, by Virgin Records. Catalogue no: **VS 1033**

TELL ME WHY
Tracks: / Tell me why / Move on up to heaven.
12" Single: Released Jul '87, on Virgin, by Virgin Records. Deleted May '88. Catalogue no: **VS 954-12**
7" Single: Released Jul '87, on Virgin, by Virgin Records. Deleted May '88. Catalogue no: **VS 954**
Cassingle: Released Jul '87, on Virgin, by Virgin Records. Deleted May '88. Catalogue no: **VSC 954-12**

This Years Blonde

PLATINUM POP (Blondie Medley)
Tracks: / Platinum pop.
12" Single: Released Sep '81, on Creole, by Creole Records. Catalogue no: **CR 1219**
7" Single: Released Sep '81, on Creole, by Creole Records. Catalogue no: **CR 19**

WHO'S THAT MIX
Tracks: / Who's that mix / No big deal.
7" Single: Released Oct '87, on Debut, by Skratch Records. Catalogue no: **DEBT 3034**
12" Single: Released Oct '87, on Debut, by Skratch Records. Catalogue no: **DEBTX 3034**

Thom, Lou

IT SEEMS TO ME
Tracks: / It seems to me / Tell me now.
12" Single: Released Sep '82, on Half Moon, by Rondelet Music & Records. Catalogue no: **12 ROUND 2002**
7" Single: Released Sep '82, on Half Moon, by Rondelet Music & Records. Catalogue no: **ROUND 2002**

Thomas, Andrew

SINGAPORE MASQUERADE
Tracks: / Singapore masquerade.
7" Single: Released May '83, on Arena, Catalogue no: **RIA 17**

Thomas, B.J.

RAINDROPS KEEP FALLING ON MY HEAD
Tracks: / Raindrops keep falling on my head.
7" Single: Released Feb '70, on Wand, by Decca Records. Deleted '73. Catalogue no: **WN 1**

Thomas, Carla

GEE WHIZ
Tracks: / Gee whiz / B.A.B.Y / Sweet soul music / Funky street.
7" Single: Released Apr '80, on Atlantic, by WEA Records. Deleted Apr '83. Catalogue no: **ATM 8**

I LIKE WHAT YOU'RE DOING TO ME
Tracks: / I like what you're doing to me.
7" Single: Released Oct '87, on Stax, by Fantasy Inc (USA). Catalogue no: **STAX 819**

Thomas, Evelyn

COLD SHOULDER
Tracks: / Cold shoulder / Hot mix (Track on 12" remix version only.).
7" Single: Released Mar '86, on Record Shack, by Record Shack Records. Catalogue no: **SOHO 60**
12" Single: Released Mar '86, on Record Shack, by Record Shack Records. Catalogue no: **SOHORT 60**
12" Single: Released Mar '86, on Record Shack, by Record Shack Records. Catalogue no: **SOHOT 60**

DOOMSDAY
Tracks: / Doomsday.
7" Single: Released Apr '76, on 20th Century, by 20th Century Records. Deleted '79. Catalogue no: **BTC 1017**

HEARTLESS
Tracks: / Heartless.
7" Single: Released Nov '84, on Record Shack, by Record Shack Records. Catalogue no: **SOHO 30**
12" Single: Released Nov '84, on Record Shack, by Record Shack Records. Catalogue no: **SOHOT 30**

HIGH ENERGY (SINGLE)
Tracks: / High energy.
12" Single: Released May '84, on Record Shack, by Record Shack Records. Catalogue no: **SOHOT 18**
7" Pic: Released May '84, on Record Shack, by Record Shack Records. Catalogue no: **SOHOP 18**
7" Single: Released May '84, on Record Shack, by Record Shack Records. Catalogue no: **SOHO 18**

HIGH ENERGY (SINGLE) (RE-RELEASE)
Tracks: / Hi energy / Primitive desire.
12" Single: Released Feb '88, on Record Shack, by Record Shack Records. Catalogue no: **SOHOB 2**

MASQUERADE
Tracks: / Masquerade.
7" Single: Released Aug '84, on Record Shack, by Record Shack Records. Catalogue no: **SOHO 25**
12" Single: Released Aug '84, on Record Shack, by Record Shack Records. Catalogue no: **SOHOT 25**

MASQUERADE (RE-RELEASE)
Tracks: / Masquerade / Reflections / Vanity.
12" Single: Released Feb '88, on Record Shack, by Record Shack Records. Catalogue no: **SOHOB 4**

REFLECTIONS (SINGLE)
Tracks: / Reflections.
12" Single: Released Nov '85, on Record Shack, by Record Shack Records. Catalogue no: **SOHOT 53**
7" Single: Released Sep '83, on Record Shack, by Record Shack Records. Catalogue no: **SOHO 53**

SORRY WRONG NUMBER
Tracks: / Sorry wrong number.
7" Single: Released Apr '85, on Record Shack, by Record Shack Records. Catalogue no: **SOHO 41**
12" Single: Released Apr '85, on Record Shack, by Record Shack Records. Catalogue no: **SOHOT 41**

STANDING AT THE CROSS ROADS
Tracks: / Standing at the crossroads / Standing at the crossroads (inst).
7" Single: Released Apr '87, on Nightmare, by Nightmare Records. Catalogue no: **MARES 31**
12" Single: Released Apr '87, on Nightmare, by Nightmare Records. Catalogue no: **MARE 31**

THANKS FOR BEING THERE
Tracks: / Thanks for being there / Back to reality.
7" Single: Released Apr '80, Deleted Apr '83. Catalogue no: **CAN 192**

TIGHTROPE
Tracks: / Tightrope / Tightrope (inst).
12" Single: Released Oct '86, on Nightmare, by Nightmare Records. Catalogue no: **MARE 1**
7" Single: Released Oct '86, on Nightmare, by Nightmare Records. Catalogue no: **MARES 1**

WEAK SPOT
Tracks: / Weak spot.
7" Single: Released Jan '76, on 20th Century, by 20th Century Records. Deleted '79. Catalogue no: **BTC 1014**

Thomas, Ian

BACK TO SQUARE ONE
Tracks: / Back to square one / Losing control.
7" Single: Released Apr '89, on WEA, by WEA Records. Catalogue no: **YZ 400**

Thomas, Irma

Biographical details: Thomas was born in 1941 in Ponchatoula, Louisiana. She is a veteran of New Orleans soul scene, her continuing popularity evidenced by reissues and compilations. *Breakaway* includes R&B hits originally on Imperial from 1964; *The New Rules* is a recent album which shows her superb talent undiminished. (Donald Clarke 13.1.88).

SAFE WITH ME
Tracks: / Safe with me / Don't stop.
7" Single: Released Apr '81, on Polo, by Polo Records. Deleted '88. Catalogue no: **POLO 10**
12" Single: Released Apr '81, on Polo, by Polo Records. Deleted '88. Catalogue no: **POLO 12-10**

Thomas, Jah

CLEAN YOUR TEETH
Tracks: / Clean your teeth / Where the music plays.
12" Single: Released Mar '84, on Midnight Rock, Catalogue no: **MR 022**

CRICKET LOVELY CRICKET
Tracks: / Cricket lovely cricket / Dub up your wicket.
7" Single: Released Jun '80, on Ballistic, Deleted '83. Catalogue no: **BP 358**

LONDON SKANK
Tracks: / London skank.
7" Single: Released Nov '81, on Midnight Rock, Catalogue no: **MR 1979**

POSSIE
Tracks: / Possie.
7" Single: Released Oct '83, on Midnight Rock, Catalogue no: **DSR 0701**

SWEET MEMORIES
Tracks: / Sweet memories.
12" Single: Released Feb '82, on Midnight, Catalogue no: **MR 006**

Thomas, Jamo

I SPY FOR THE FBI
Tracks: / I spy for the FBI.
7" Single: Released Feb '69, on Polydor, by Polydor Ltd. Deleted '72. Catalogue no: **56755**

Thomas, Jimmy

HANG RIGHT ON IN THERE (2 Parts)
Tracks: / Hang right on in there / Hang right on in there (part 2).
7" Single: Released Feb '82, on Osceola, by Osceola Records. Catalogue no: **OSC 2**

STANDING ALONE IN A CROWD
Tracks: / Standing alone in a crowd.
7" Single: Released Oct '82, on Cricket International, by Cricket International Records. Catalogue no: **LBW 002**

Thomas, Joy

JUMP AROUND
Tracks: / Jump around.
12" Single: Released Apr '83, on Half Moon, by Rondelet Music & Records. Catalogue no: **HM 1127T**

Thomas, Kenny

I WANNA MAKE LOVE TO YOU, BABY
Tracks: / I wanna make love to you, baby / In my arms.
7" Single: Released Aug '88, on President, by President Records. Catalogue no: **PT 575**
12" Single: Released Aug '88, on President, by President Records. Catalogue no: **PT 12-575**

Thomas, Lillo

DOWNTOWN
Tracks: / Downtown / I'm in love.
12" Single: Released Jul '87, on Capitol, by EMI Records. Deleted Apr '88. Catalogue no: **12CL 453**
7" Single: Released Jul '87, on Capitol, by EMI Records. Deleted Apr '88. Catalogue no: **CL 453**

I'M IN LOVE
Tracks: / I'min love (longer luv mix) / Sexy girl / Sexy girl (sexy mix) / I've been loving you too long (to stop now).
7" Set: Released 23 May '87, on Capitol, by EMI Records. Deleted Jan '88. Catalogue no: **12 CLD 450**

I'M IN LOVE (RADIO MIX)
Tracks: / I'm in love / I'm in love (short love dub) / I've been loving you too long to stop now (Extra track on 12" only).
12" Single: Released May '87, on Capitol, by EMI Records. Deleted Apr '88. Catalogue no: **12 CL 450**
7" Single: Released May '87, on Capitol, by EMI Records. Deleted Apr '88. Catalogue no: **CL 450**

I'M IN LOVE (REMIX)
Tracks: / I'm in love (remix) / Sexy girl (sexy mix) / Sexy girl (inst).
12" Single: Released Jun '87, on Capitol, by EMI Records. Catalogue no: **CLX 550**

SETTLE DOWN
Tracks: / Settle down / I like your style.
7" Single: Released Apr '85, on Capitol, by EMI Records. Deleted '88. Catalogue no: **CL 356**

SEXY GIRL
Tracks: / Sexy girl.
7" Single: Released Mar '87, on Capitol, by EMI Records. Deleted Apr '88. Catalogue no: **CL 445**
12" Single: Released Mar '87, on Capitol, by EMI Records. Deleted Apr '88. Catalogue no: **12CL 445**

Thomas, Louise

CAST ASIDE MY STUBBORN HEART
Tracks: / I've got to tell you goodbye.
12" Single: Released Nov '86, on Red Bus, by Red Bus Records. Catalogue no: **RBSL 1806**

DOUBLE VISION
Tracks: / Double vision / Double vision (inst).
12" Single: Released May '87, on Nightmare, by Nightmare Records. Catalogue no: **MARE 23**
7" Single: Released May '87, on Nightmare, by Nightmare Records. Catalogue no: **MARES 23**

FEELS LIKE LOVE
Tracks: / Feels like love.
12" Single: Released '88, on Passion, by Skratch Records. Catalogue no: **PASH 44(12)**

HEAD OVER HEELS
Tracks: / Head over heels / Head over heels (inst.).
12" Single: Released Feb '86, on Debut, by Skratch Records. Catalogue no: **DEBTX 3001**

REFLEX ACTION
Tracks: / Reflex action (INST) / Reflex action.
12" Single: Released Apr '86, on R & B, by Red Bus Records. Catalogue no: **RBL 1803**
7" Single: Released Apr '86, on R & B, by Red Bus Records. Catalogue no: **RBS 1803**

Thomas, Mikki

BURN THAT DIAL
Tracks: / Burn that dial.
7" Single: Released Feb '89, on Risin', by Risin' Records. Catalogue no: **RAH 103**
12" Single: Released Feb '89, on Risin', by Risin' Records. Catalogue no: **RAHT 103**

Thomas, Nicky

LOVE OF THE COMMON PEOPLE (SINGLE)
Tracks: / Love of the common people / Have a little faith.
7" Single: Released Feb '83, on Trojan, by Trojan Records. Deleted May '88. Catalogue no: **TRO 9067**
12" Single: Released Feb '83, on Trojan, by Trojan Records. Deleted May '88. Catalogue no: **TROT 9067**
7" Single: Released Jun '70, on Trojan, by Trojan Records. Deleted '73. Catalogue no: **TR 7750**

Thomas, Pat

NINE MILES HIGH
Tracks: / Nine miles high.
7" Single: Released Aug '86, on Tout Ensemble, Catalogue no: **LUTE 4**
12" Single: Released Aug '86, on Tout Ensemble, Catalogue no: **12LUTE 4**

Thomas, Pauline

IF I FOLLOW MY HEART
Tracks: / If I follow my heart (Remix version).
12" Single: Released Aug '86, on Neville King, by Neville King Records. Catalogue no: **NKRD 0036**

JEALOUSY
Tracks: / Jealousy.
12" Single: Released Mar '89, on Freshbeat, by Jetstar Records. Catalogue no: **FBT 7**

SAVING ALL MY LOVE FOR YOU
Tracks: / Saving all my love for you / This is it.
12" Single: Released Jan '86, on Neville King, by Neville King Records. Catalogue no: **NKRD 0033**

Thomas, Philip Michael

JUST THE WAY I PLANNED IT
Tracks: / Just the way I planned it / All my love.
12" Single: Released Jan '86, on WEA, by WEA Records. Catalogue no: **B 9581 T**
7" Single: Released Jan '86, on WEA, by WEA Records. Catalogue no: **B 9581**

Thomas, Reva

LOVE DOCTOR
Tracks: / Love doctor / Detour.
7" Single: Released Jan '81, on Splash, by Splash Records. Deleted Jan '84. Catalogue no: **SP 20**

Thomas, Ruddy

ALL THIS LOVE
Tracks: / All this love.
12" Single: Released Jan '84, on Tads, Catalogue no: **TRD 1184**

AM I CRAZY
Tracks: / Am I crazy / Sitting in the park.
12" Single: Released Dec '85, on Hawkeye, by Hawkeye Records. Catalogue no: **HD 68**

BLESS YOU
Tracks: / Bless you.
12" Single: Released Apr '83, on Shuttle, Catalogue no: **SH 005**

COME TO ME
Tracks: / Cindy / Come to me.
12" Single: Released Nov '86, on C & E, Catalogue no: **CED 101**

DEJA VU
Tracks: / Deja vu.
12" Single: Released Apr '83, on Mobiliser, by Jetstar Records. Catalogue no: **MM 23**

JUST ONE MOMENT AWAY
Tracks: / Just one moment away / Something is wrong.
7" Single: Released Dec '81, on Creole, by Creole Records. Catalogue no: **CR 27**
12" Single: Released Dec '81, on Creole, by Creole Records. Catalogue no: **CR 12 27**

KEY TO THE WORLD
Tracks: / Key to the world.
12" Single: Released Apr '82, on Hawkeye, by Hawkeye Records. Catalogue no: **HD 42**

LET'S DANCE
Tracks: / Let's dance.
12" Single: Released Jun '85, on Greensleeves, by Greensleeves Records. Catalogue no: **GRED 180**

LONG LOST LOVER
Tracks: / Long lost lover / Twilight zone / Peter Gunne.
12" Single: Released Mar '86, on Island, by Island Records. Catalogue no: **12IS 276**

LOVE YOU NEED, THE
Tracks: / Love you need, The.
12" Single: Released Jun '84, on Londisc, by Londisc Records. Catalogue no: **LD 018**

LOVING PAUPER
Tracks: / Loving pauper.
12" Single: Released Jul '84, on Real Wax, Catalogue no: **JGM 8174**

NICE AND EASY
Tracks: / Nice and easy / Groovy feeling.
12" Single: Released Feb '83, on Hawkeye, by Hawkeye Records. Catalogue no: **HD 45**

PERHAPS
Tracks: / Walking my baby / Perhaps.
12" Single: Released Dec '86, on World Enterprise, Catalogue no: **WENDIS 3038**

RAIN FROM THE SKY (2 Parts)
Tracks: / Rain from the sky.
12" Single: Released May '83, on Revue, by Creole Records. Catalogue no: **REVD 002**

REFLECTIONS
Tracks: / Reflections.
12" Single: Released Aug '83, on Stars Recording, Deleted '87. Catalogue no: **SE 2T**
7" Single: Released Aug '83, on Stars Recording, Deleted '87. Catalogue no: **SE 2**

SHE'S AN ADDICT
Tracks: / She's an addict.
7" Single: Released Nov '88, on Thunderbolt, by Thunderbolt Records. Deleted '89. Catalogue no: **UNKNOWN**

SHE'S MY PRE-RELEASE
Tracks: / She's my pre-release (version) / She's my pre-release.
12" Single: Released Nov '86, on Orbitone, by Orbitone Records. Catalogue no: **DORB 17**

SITTING OUT NIGHT TIME
Tracks: / Sitting out night time.
12" Single: Released Oct '84, on Revue, by Creole Records. Catalogue no: **REV 017T**

SWEET REGGAE MUSIC (Leroy Smart)
Tracks: / Sweet reggae music / Be my lover.
12" Single: Released Feb '84, on Mobiliser, by Jetstar Records. Catalogue no: **MM 74**

TELL IT LIKE IT IS
Tracks: / Tell it like it is / Make up your mind.
12" Single: Released Mar '86, on Hawkeye, by Hawkeye Records. Catalogue no: **HD 70**

THESE SONGS
Tracks: / These songs.
12" Single: Released 30 May '87, on Charm, by Charm Records. Catalogue no: **CRT 6**

TIME FOR LOVE
Tracks: / Time for love, A / In the summertime.
12" Single: Released Feb '86, on Greensleeves, by Greensleeves Records. Catalogue no: **GRED 184**
7" Single: Released Feb '86, on Greensleeves, by Greensleeves Records. Deleted '88. Catalogue no: **GRE 184**

TONIGHT'S THE NIGHT
Tracks: / Tonight's the night.
12" Single: Released Jun '84, on Diamond C, Catalogue no: **DCD 004**

TRUE TRUE TRUE
Tracks: / True true true.
12" Single: Released Sep '87, on Greensleeves, by Greensleeves Records. Catalogue no: **GRED 231**

WHEN I THINK OF YOU
Tracks: / When I think of you / This ol' man.
12" Single: Released Aug '80, on Hawkeye, by Hawkeye Records. Catalogue no: **HD 27**

Thomas, Rudy

YOU MAKE ME FEEL SO GOOD
Tracks: / You make me feel so good / Good good feeling.
12" Single: Released Oct '82, on Hawkeye, by Hawkeye Records. Catalogue no: **HD 44**

Thomas, Rufus

Biographical details: Rufus was born in Mississippi in 1917; he describes himself as the world's oldest teenager. His *Bear Cat* (answer to **Big Mama Thornton's** *Hound Dog*) was the first national hit for the Sun label in Memphis, before **Elvis Presley** and rockabilly took it over; ten years later he and his daughter Carla (born in Memphis in 1942) helped get Stax off the ground, his dance-fad hits included *Funky Chicken. Jump Back* includes Stax-era tracks with that legendary studio band with **Steve Cropper, Donald 'Duck' Dunn** and **Al Jackson.** (Donald Clarke 13.1.88).

BEAR CAT
Tracks: / Bear cat.
7" EP: Released Dec '76, on Charly, by Charly Records. Deleted '88. Catalogue no: **CEP 101**

DO THE FUNKY CHICKEN
Tracks: / Do the funky chicken.
7" Single: Released Sep '87, on Stax, by Fantasy Inc (USA). Catalogue no: **STAX 814**
7" Single: Released Apr '70, on Stax, by Fantasy Inc (USA). Deleted '73. Catalogue no: **STAX 144**

DO THE FUNKY CHICKEN (OLD GOLD)
Tracks: / Do the funky chicken.
7" Single: Released Oct '85, on Old Gold, by Old Gold Records. Catalogue no: **OG 9534**

Thomas, Sybil

RESCUE ME
Tracks: / Rescue me.
7" Single: Released '83, on Arista, by BMG Records (UK). Deleted '86. Catalogue no: **WEND 124**

Thomas, Tasha

SHOOT ME
Tracks: / Shoot me (with your love).
7" Single: Released Jan '79, on Atlantic, by WEA Records. Deleted '82. Catalogue no: **LV 4**

Thomas & Taylor

I LOVE YOU
Tracks: / Love and affection.
7" Single: Released Feb '87, on In Recordings, Catalogue no: **INT 3**
12" Single: Released Feb '87, on In Recordings, Catalogue no: **INRT 3**

YOU CAN'T BLAME LOVE
Tracks: / You can't blame love / We need company.
7" Single: Released May '86, on Cool Tempo, by Chrysalis Records. Catalogue no: **COOL 123**
12" Single: Released May '86, on Cool Tempo, by Chrysalis Records. Catalogue no: **COOLX 123**

Thomas The Voice

STONE CUTTER BOY
Tracks: / Stone cutter boy.
12" Single: Released Jun '87, on North West, Catalogue no: **NW 002T**
7" Single: Released Jun '87, on North West, Catalogue no: **NW 002**

Thomas, Timmy

WHY CAN'T WE LIVE TOGETHER
Tracks: / Why can't we live together.
7" Single: Released Feb '73, on Mojo, Deleted '76. Catalogue no: **2027 012**
7" Single: Released '80, on ABC Records, by MCA Records. Catalogue no: **LR 1102**

WHY CAN'T WE LIVE TOGETHER (OLD GOLD)
Tracks: / Why can't we live together.
7" Single: Released Jul '84, on Old Gold, by Old Gold Records. Catalogue no: **OG 9428**

Thomas, T.J.

NICE THINGS WE SAID WORTH MORE THAN MONEY
Tracks: / Nice things we said worth more than money / Nice things we said worth more than money(version).
12" Single: Released Aug '86, on VIP (2), Catalogue no: **VIP 001**

Thomas,Vaneese

LET'S TALK IT OVER
Tracks: / Let's talk it over / Love in your eyes.
12" Single: Released Aug '87, on Geffen, by Geffen Records (USA). Deleted Jul '88. Catalogue no: **GEFT 26**
7" Single: Released Aug '87, on Geffen, by Geffen Records (USA). Deleted Jul '88. Catalogue no: **GEF 26**

Thompson, Barbara

Biographical details: Was born in 1944 in Oxford. As a saxophonist, composer and bandleader she is one of the UK's premier fusion artists, with the accent on melody rather than studio gimmicks. She plays alto, tenor and soprano saxes and flutes; also other instruments; she studied at the Royal College of Music; played with **Howard Riley Trio, Don Rendell, John Dankworth, Manfred Mann;** she and her husband, drummer Jon Hiseman (who played with **Graham Bond, Georgie Fame, John Mayall** and **Colosseum)** played in the **New Jazz Orchestra;** they were founder members of the United Jazz & Rock Ensemble; she formed her fusion combo Paraphernalia in 1975 and Hiseman joined in 1979. They now operate their own studio at home and Hiseman runs their music publishing company. *Hevenly Bodies* is a collection of Thompson compositions, playing eight instruments and sidemen including members of paraphernalia. She and Hiseman made a BBC documentary in 1979 about being busy musicians/parents, recently made an amusing TV advert for a domestic labour-saving devise, leaving Mom and Dad free to jam in the living room. Latest lineup of Paraphernalia includes Dave Ball on bass (replaced by Phil Mulford on 1987 tour), Peter Lemer on keyboards, Paul Dunne on guitar. (Donald Clarke 13.1.88).

SUNSET
Tracks: / Sunset / Frankfurt fayre.
7" Single: Released Sep '80, on MCA, by MCA Records. Deleted Sep '83. Catalogue no: **MCA 621**
12" Single: Released Sep '80, on MCA, by MCA Records. Deleted Sep '83. Catalogue no: **MCAT 621**

WITH YOU
Tracks: / With you / Ghosts / Poltergeist.
12" Single: Released Feb '82, on MCA, by MCA Records. Catalogue no: **MCAT 761**
7" Single: Released Feb '82, on MCA, by MCA Records. Catalogue no: **MCA 761**

Thompson, Carroll

APPLE OF MY EYE
Tracks: / Apple of my eye / Songwriters cramp.
12" Single: Released Dec '84, on Virgin, by Virgin Records. Deleted '89. Catalogue no: **VS 698-12**

HAPPY SONG
Tracks: / Happy song / Just a little bit.
12" Single: Released Nov '81, on S & G (2), Deleted Nov '84. Catalogue no: **SG 1112**
7" Single: Released Nov '81, on S & G (2), Catalogue no: **SG 117**

HONIS I DO
Tracks: / Honis I do.
7" Single: Released Jan '84, on Carousel (1), by Carousel Records. Catalogue no: **7 CAR 7**
12" Single: Released Dec '83, on Carousel

), by Carousel Records. Catalogue no: 12 AR 7

; THAT THE WAY YOU LIKE IT
acks: / Is that the way you like it.
2" Single: Released Sep '89, on White abel (1), Catalogue no: STD 13

UST A LITTLE BIT
acks: / Just a little bit / Happy song.
' Single: Released Jan '82, on Red Bus, Red Bus Records. Catalogue no: RBUS 5
2" Single: Released Jan '82, on Red Bus, Red Bus Records. Catalogue no: RBUSL 5

OVE WITHOUT PASSION
acks: / Ready or not / Tonite* / Love ithout passion.
2" Single: Released Jan '87, on Virgin, by rgin Records. Deleted May '88. Catalogue : VS 933-12
' Single: Released Jan '87, on Virgin, by rgin Records. Deleted May '88. Catalogue : VS 933

OVE WON'T LET ME WAIT
acks: / Love won't let me wait.
2" Single: Released Jul '84, on Sanity, atalogue no: STYT 014

AKE IT WITH YOU
acks: / Make it with you.
Single: Released May '83, on Carousel), by Carousel Records. Catalogue no: 7 AR 3
" Single: Released May '83, on Carousel), by Carousel Records. Catalogue no: 12 AR 3

MILING IN THE MORNING
acks: / Smiling in the morning / Smiling in ib.
" Single: Released Apr '82, on Excaliber, Red Bus Records. Deleted Apr '85. Catalogue no: EXCL 518
Single: Released Apr '82, on Excaliber, Red Bus Records. Deleted Apr '85. Catalogue no: EXC 518

TRANGEST LOVE AFFAIR
acks: / Strangest love affair / Tonight / l.a.-s.l.a. (*=Extra track on 12" only).
Single: Released Aug '86, on Virgin, by rgin Records. Deleted May '88. Catalogue : VS 876
" Single: Released Aug '86, on Virgin, by rgin Records. Deleted May '88. Catalogue : VS 876-12

OU MAKE IT HEAVEN
acks: / You make it heaven.
" Single: Released Aug '83, on Carousel), by Carousel Records. Catalogue no: AR 712H

OUR LOVE
acks: / Your love.
" Single: Released Aug '82, on S & G (2), atalogue no: SG 20

hompson, Chris

E BYE LOVE
acks: / Bye bye love.
Single: Released Jul '84, on Simple, leted '87. Catalogue no: SIM 3

YOU REMEMBER ME
acks: / If you remember me.
Single: Released Oct '79, on Planet, leted '82. Catalogue no: K 12389

'S NOT OVER
acks: / It's not over / Make it a holiday.
Single: Released Mar '87, on Parlophone, by EMI Records. Deleted Jul '87. atalogue no: R 6152

OVE & LONELINESS
acks: / Love and loneliness / Easy street.
" Single: Released Aug '86, on Atlantic, WEA Records. Deleted Jun '87. Catalogue no: A 9384 T
Single: Released Aug '86, on Atlantic, by EA Records. Deleted Jun '87. Catalogue : A 9384

hompson, Eddie

ographical details: Eddie Thompson 926-86) was a much-loved UK jazz pianist o attended the same school for the blind George Shearing. He was the house anist at Ronnie Scott's club 1959-60 and ed in the USA from 1962 to 1972. One of last albums was a duo with trombonist y Williams, who was born in 1937 in ulton, Lancashire. (Donald Clarke .1.88).

JT ON A HAPPY FACE
acks: / Put on a happy face.
Single: Released Aug '79, on Hobo, leted '80. Catalogue no: HOS 007

hompson, Ellie

OOLISH CHILD
acks: / Foolish child / Man of the earth.
Single: Released Mar '81, on A&M, by M Records. Deleted Mar '84. Catalogue AMS 8105

Thompson, Everand

OBSERVATION BABYLON
Tracks: / Observation babylon.
12" Single: Released Jun '81, on Ultimate, by Ultimate Records. Catalogue no: **XULT 404**

Thompson, Francis

ITALIAN MAN
Tracks: / Italian man / Loving so good.
7" Single: Released Nov '82, on Ark, by Ark Records (UK). Catalogue no: **AR 1002**

Thompson, Johnny

SHE GIVES ME LOVING
Tracks: / She gives me loving / Substitute.
12" Single: Released Jul '86, on Mega-Star, Catalogue no: **STAR 001**

Thompson, Keith

LOVE IS NOT A TOY
Tracks: / Love is not a toy.
7" Single: Released Oct '88, on Hit & Run Music, Catalogue no: **HR 90544**

Thompson, Leroy

HARD TIMES CRIMINAL TIMES
Tracks: / Hard times criminal times.
12" Single: Released Sep '81, on Noel, Catalogue no: **DN 005**

Thompson, Lincoln

COME SPRING
Tracks: / Come spring.
12" Single: Released May '82, on God Sent, Catalogue no: **GDIS 3**

NATURAL WILD (SINGLE)
Tracks: / Natural wild / Blessed are the meek / Second sight / My generation.
7" Single: Released May '80, on Liberty (USA), by EMI Records. Deleted May '83. Catalogue no: **BP 359**
12" Single: Released May '80, on Liberty (USA), by EMI Records. Deleted May '83. Catalogue no: **12 BP 359**

ONE COMMON NEED
Tracks: / One common need.
12" Single: Released Apr '82, on God Sent, Catalogue no: **GDIS 1**

SPACESHIP
Tracks: / Spaceship / Generation dub.
7" Single: Released Sep '80, on Liberty (USA), by EMI Records. Deleted '83. Catalogue no: **BP 369**

Thompson, Linval

AH NUH NOTHING
Tracks: / Ah nuh nothing / Ah nuh nothing (version).
12" Single: Released 14 Aug '89, on Jammy's, Catalogue no: **HD/JAM 003**

ALL NIGHT LONG
Tracks: / All night long / Baby father.
12" Single: Released Dec '82, on Greensleeves, by Greensleeves Records. Catalogue no: **GRED 112**

BOUND TO SURRENDER
Tracks: / Bound to surrender.
12" Single: on Burning Sounds, by Burning Sounds Records. Deleted May '88. Catalogue no: **BSD 031**

BUBBLES UP
Tracks: / Bubbles up / Here with me.
12" Single: Released Aug '84, on Gamble, Catalogue no: **GAD 04**

HOLDING ON TO MY GIRLFRIEND
Tracks: / Holding on to my girlfriend / Wife and sweetheart.
12" Single: Released Dec '81, on Greensleeves, by Greensleeves Records. Catalogue no: **GRED 71**

I NEVER RUN I NEVER HIDE
Tracks: / I never run I never hide.
12" Single: Released Feb '79, on Greensleeves, by Greensleeves Records. Catalogue no: **GRED 12**

I REALLY LOVE YOU
Tracks: / I really love you / Touch up the key.
12" Single: Released May '84, on Gamble, Catalogue no: **GAD 03**

POOR PEOPLE
Tracks: / Poor people.
12" Single: Released Apr '82, on A.1, by A.1 Records. Catalogue no: **A1 004**

POP NO STYLE
Tracks: / Pop no style / Second hand girl.
12" Single: Released Jan '81, on Attack, Catalogue no: **TACK 22**

ROCKING VIBRATION
Tracks: / Rocking vibration.
12" Single: on Burning Sounds, by Burning Sounds Records. Deleted May '88. Catalogue no: **BSD 023**

THERE MUST BE A GIRL
Tracks: / There must be a girl / La la means i love you / Six babylon.

12" Single: Released Feb '80, on Hurricane (2), Deleted Feb '85. Catalogue no: **12FIRE 12**
7" Single: Released Feb '80, on Hurricane (2), Deleted Feb '85. Catalogue no: **FIRE 12**

YOU BABY
Tracks: / You baby / Not at home.
7" Single: Released Dec '82, on Thompson Sound, Catalogue no: **TS 001**

Thompson, Otis

PLEASE DON'T GO
Tracks: / Please don't go.
12" Single: Released Oct '84, on Sunburn, by Orbitone Records. Catalogue no: **SBD 47**

Thompson, Paul

CAN I TAKE YOU HOME
Tracks: / Can I take you home / This is my bed.
12" Single: Released Sep '83, on Chams, Catalogue no: **CHM 5503**

Thompson, Richard

Biographical details: Was born in London in 1949. The guitarist, singer, songwriter was a mainstay in **Fairport Convention** until 1971 and has gone from strength to strength. He and his wife Linda were the reigning king and queen of UK folk-rock and the nation's best-kept secret; they divorced just as USA success was coming. Albums on producer Joe Boyd's Hannibal label are classics; his *Across a Crowded Room* (1985) was his first major label album in ten years and was regarded as a disappointment compared to his solo debut *One Clear Moment*, but *Daring Adventures* (1986) was closer to his best form. (Donald Clarke 13.1.88).

RECKLESS KIND
Tracks: / Reckless kind / Turning of the tide (live) (Not on 12".) / Pharoah (live) (12" only.) / Jerusalem on the juke box (live) (CD single only.) / Can't win(live) (12" only.).
CD 5": Released Sep '89, on Capitol, by EMI Records. Catalogue no: **CDCL 550**
12" Single: Released Sep '89, on Capitol, by EMI Records. Catalogue no: **203 520 6**
7" Single: Released Sep '89, on Capitol, by EMI Records. Catalogue no: **CL 550**
12" Single: Released Sep '89, on Capitol, by EMI Records. Catalogue no: **12CL 550**
7" Single: Released Sep '89, on Capitol, by EMI Records. Catalogue no: **203 520 7**
CD 5": Released Sep '89, on Capitol, by EMI Records. Catalogue no: **203 520 2**

TURNING OF THE TIDE
Tracks: / Turning of the tide / Pharaoh.
7" Single: Released Nov '88, on Capitol, by EMI Records. Deleted Aug '89. Catalogue no: **CL 516**

WRONG HEARBEAT
Tracks: / Wrong heartbeat.
7" Single: Released Aug '83, on Hannibal, by Hannibal Records. Catalogue no: **UNKNOWN**

YOU DON'T SAY
Tracks: / You don't say / When the spell is broken.
7" Single: Released Jun '85, on Polydor, by Polydor Ltd. Catalogue no: **POSP 750**

Thompson, Richard &

DON'T RENEGE ON OUR LOVE
Tracks: / Don't renage on our love / Living in luxery.
7" Single: Released Apr '82, on Hannibal, by Hannibal Records. Catalogue no: **HNS 703**

Thompson, Sue

PAPER TIGER
Tracks: / Paper tiger.
7" Single: Released Jan '65, on Hickory, by Bear Family Records (Germany). Deleted '68. Catalogue no: **HICKORY 1284**

Thompson, Sydney

BARN DANCES & TWO STEPS
Tracks: / Barn dances & two steps.
7" EP: Released Dec '79, on Sydney Thompson, Catalogue no: **EP 614**

CHA CHA CHAS
Tracks: / Cha cha chas.
7" EP: Released Dec '79, on Sydney Thompson, Catalogue no: **EP 605**

FOXTROTS
Tracks: / Foxtrots.
7" EP: Released Dec '79, on Sydney Thompson, Catalogue no: **EP 603**

LILTING WALTZES & TANGOS
Tracks: / Lilting waltzes & tangos.
7" EP: Released Dec '79, on Sydney Thompson, Catalogue no: **EP 610**

MUSIC FOR CELEBRATING SPECIAL OCCASIONS
7" EP: Released Dec '79, on Sydney Thompson, Catalogue no: **EP 613**

PASO DOBLES AND JIVES
Tracks: / Paso dobles and jives.
7" EP: Released Dec '79, on Sydney Thompson, Catalogue no: **EP 608**

QUICKSTEPS
Tracks: / Quicksteps.
7" EP: Released Dec '79, on Sydney Thompson, Catalogue no: **EP 602**

RUMBAS
Tracks: / Rumbas.
7" EP: Released Dec '79, on Sydney Thompson, Catalogue no: **EP 607**

RUMBAS AND PASO DOBLES (EP)
Tracks: / Rumbas and paso dobles.
7" EP: Released Dec '79, on Sydney Thompson, Catalogue no: **EP 611**

SAMBAS
Tracks: / Sambas.
7" EP: Released Dec '79, on Sydney Thompson, Catalogue no: **EP 606**

SAUNTERS & BARN DANCES
Tracks: / Saunters & barn dances.
7" EP: Released Dec '79, on Sydney Thompson, Catalogue no: **EP 609**

SYDNEY THOMPSON CHA CHA CHAS
7" EP: Released Sep '83, on Sydney Thompson, Catalogue no: **EP 618**

SYDNEY THOMPSON FOXTROTS
Tracks: / Sydney Thompson foxtrots.
7" EP: Released Sep '83, on Sydney Thompson, Catalogue no: **EP 617**

SYDNEY THOMPSON QUICKSTEPS
Tracks: / Sydney Thompson quicksteps.
7" EP: Released Sep '83, on Sydney Thompson, Catalogue no: **EP 616**

SYDNEY THOMPSON RUMBAS
Tracks: / Sydney Thompson rumbas.
7" EP: Released Sep '83, on Sydney Thompson, Catalogue no: **EP 619**

SYDNEY THOMPSON WALTZES
Tracks: / Sydney Thompson waltzes.
7" EP: Released Sep '83, on Sydney Thompson, Catalogue no: **EP 615**

TANGOS
Tracks: / Tangos.
7" EP: Released Dec '79, on Sydney Thompson, Catalogue no: **EP 604**

VIENNESE WALTZES & JIVES (EP)
Tracks: / Viennese waltzes & jives.
7" EP: Released Dec '79, on Sydney Thompson, Catalogue no: **EP 612**

WALTZES
Tracks: / Waltzes.
7" EP: Released Dec '79, on Sydney Thompson, Catalogue no: **EP 601**

Thompson Twins

Biographical details: New wave group formed in Sheffield in 1977 by Tom Bailey (born in Halifax in 1957) on vocals and bass, with Chris Bell on drums, Peter Dodd and John Roog on guitars; they achieved cult fame, evolved into septet including Joe Leeway on percussion (born 1957 in London) and Alannah Currie (born 1959 in Auckland, N.Z.), who played sax and wrote lyrics. Bailey, Bell, Leeway and Currie eventually shed the others and developed syth/percussion sound which had chart success in early-to-mid '80s, but their glossy pop eventually seemed not very meaningful. (Donald Clarke 13.1.88).

ANIMAL LAUGH (OUMMA AULARESSO)
Tracks: / Animal laugh (oumma aularesso) / Dub product, A / Anything is good enough.
7" Single: Released '82, on Arista, by BMG Records (UK). Deleted '87. Catalogue no: **TEE 2**

DOCTOR DOCTOR
Tracks: / Doctor doctor.
CD 5": Released Jun '89, on Arista, by BMG Records (UK). Catalogue no: **162050**
7" Single: Released Feb '84, on Arista, by BMG Records (UK). Deleted '87. Catalogue no: **TWINS 3**

DON'T MESS WITH DR. DREAM
Tracks: / Don't mess with Doctor Dream.
7" Single: Released Aug '85, on Arista, by BMG Records (UK). Catalogue no: **TWINS 9**
7" Pic: Released Aug '85, on Arista, by BMG Records (UK). Catalogue no: **TWISD 9**
12" Single: Released Aug '85, on Arista, by BMG Records (UK). Catalogue no: **TWINS 129**

GET THAT LOVE
Tracks: / Get that love.
CD 5": Released Apr '87, on Arista, by BMG Records (UK). Deleted Jul '89. Catalogue no: **TWINS CD 12**
12" Single: Released Mar '87, on Arista, by BMG Records (UK). Deleted '87. Catalogue no: **TWINS 1212**

HOLD ME NOW

Tracks: / Hold me now.
7" Single: Released '83, on Arista, by BMG Records (UK). Deleted '86. Catalogue no: **TWINS 2**

IN THE NAME OF LOVE
Tracks: / In the name of love / In the beginning / Coastline.
CD 5": Released Jun '89, on Arista, by BMG Records (UK). Catalogue no: **661808**
7" Single: Released Jan '82, on T Label, Catalogue no: **TEE 4**
12" Single: Released Jan '82, on T Label, Catalogue no: **TEE 124**

IN THE NAME OF LOVE '88
Tracks: / In the name of love '88 (remix) / In the name of love '88 (original) / In the name of love '88 (railroad mix) (Only on 12".) / In the name of love '88 (remix-dub) (Only on CD single.) / In the name of love '88 (railroad dub) (Only on 12".).
7" Single: Released Oct '88, on Arista, by BMG Records (UK). Catalogue no: **111808**
CD 5": Released Oct '88, on Arista, by BMG Records (UK). Catalogue no: **661808**
12" Single: Released Oct '88, on Arista, by BMG Records (UK). Catalogue no: **611808**

KING FOR A DAY
Tracks: / King for a day.
12" Single: Released Oct '85, on Arista, by BMG Records (UK). Catalogue no: **TWINS 127**
7" Single: Released Oct '85, on Arista, by BMG Records (UK). Catalogue no: **TWINS 7**
12" Pic: Released Oct '85, on Arista, by BMG Records (UK). Catalogue no: **TWIP 1277**
12" Single: Released Oct '85, on Arista, by BMG Records (UK). Catalogue no: **TWINS 227**

LAY YOUR HANDS ON ME
Tracks: / Lay your hands on me / Lewis Carol, The.
7" Single: Released Nov '84, on Arista, by BMG Records (UK). Catalogue no: **TWINS 6**
Special: Released Dec '84, on Arista, by BMG Records (UK). Catalogue no: **TWISD 6**
12" Single: Released Dec '84, on Arista, by BMG Records (UK). Catalogue no: **TWINS 226**
7" Single: Released Nov '84, on Arista, by BMG Records (UK). Catalogue no: **TWING 6**
12" Single: Released Nov '84, on Arista, by BMG Records (UK). Catalogue no: **TWINS 126**

LIES
Tracks: / Lies / Beach culture.
7" Single: Released '82, on Arista, by BMG Records (UK). Deleted '87. Catalogue no: **ARIST 486**
12" Single: Released '82, on Arista, by BMG Records (UK). Deleted '87. Catalogue no: **ARIST 12486**

LONG GOODBYE, THE
Tracks: / Long goodbye / Dancing in your shoes / Hold me now (dance mix).
CD 5": Released May '87, on Arista, by BMG Records (UK). Deleted Jul '89. Catalogue no: **TWINSCD 13**
12" Single: Released May '87, on Arista, by BMG Records (UK). Catalogue no: **TWINS 1312**
7" Single: Released May '87, on Arista, by BMG Records (UK). Deleted '87. Catalogue no: **TWINS 13**

LOVE ON YOUR SIDE
Tracks: / Love on your side / Lies.
7" Single: Released Jan '83, on Arista, by BMG Records (UK). Catalogue no: **ARIST 504**
12" Single: Released Jan '83, on Arista, by BMG Records (UK). Catalogue no: **ARIST 12504**
12" Single: Released Sep '87, on Old Gold, by Old Gold Records. Catalogue no: **OG 4016**

MAKE BELIEVE (LET'S PRETEND)
Tracks: / Make believe (let's pretend).
12" Single: Released '83, on Arista, by BMG Records (UK). Deleted '86. Catalogue no: **TEE 123**
7" Single: Released '82, on Arista, by BMG Records (UK). Deleted '87. Catalogue no: **TEE 3**

NIGHT TRACKS EP
Tracks: / Night tracks.
12" Single: Released Jul '87, on Night Tracks, by Pinnacle Records. Catalogue no: **SFNT 005**

NOTHING IN COMMON
Tracks: / Nothing in common / Nothing to lose.
12" Single: Released Sep '86, on Arista, by BMG Records (UK). Catalogue no: **TWINS 1211**
7" Single: Released Sep '86, on Arista, by BMG Records (UK). Catalogue no: **TWINS 11**

PERFECT DAY
Tracks: / Perfect day.
7" Single: Released Mar '87, on Arista, by BMG Records (UK). Deleted '87. Catalogue no: **TWINS 12**

PERFECT GAME
Tracks: / Perfect game / Politics.
7" Single: Released Feb '81, on T Label, Catalogue no: **TEE 1**

RAP BOY RAP
Tracks: / Rap boy rap / Love on your side (ext) / No talkin' / Lies (ext).
12" Single: Released Sep '87, on Old Gold, by Old Gold Records. Catalogue no: **OG 4016**

REVOLUTION
Tracks: / Revolution.
12" Single: Released Nov '85, on Arista, by BMG Records (UK). Catalogue no: **TWINS 2210**
7" Single: Released Nov '85, on Arista, by BMG Records (UK). Catalogue no: **TWINS 10**
12" Single: Released Nov '85, on Arista, by BMG Records (UK). Catalogue no: **TWINS 1210**

ROLL OVER
Tracks: / Roll over / Fools in paradise.
7" Single: Released Apr '85, on Arista, by BMG Records (UK). Catalogue no: **TWINS 8**
12" Single: Released Apr '85, on Arista, by BMG Records (UK). Catalogue no: **TWINS 128**

RUNAWAY
Tracks: / Runaway.
12" Single: Released '83, on Arista, by BMG Records (UK). Deleted '86. Catalogue no: **TEE 125**
7" Single: Released '82, on T Label, Deleted '87. Catalogue no: **TEE 5**

SISTER OF MERCY
Tracks: / Sister of mercy.
7" Single: Released Jul '84, on Arista, by BMG Records (UK). Deleted '87. Catalogue no: **TWINS 5**

SUGAR DADDY
Tracks: / Sugar daddy.
12" Single: Released Oct '89, on Warner Bros., by WEA Records. Catalogue no: **W 2819T**
7" Single: Released Oct '89, on Warner Bros., by WEA Records. Catalogue no: **W 2819**
Special: Released Oct '89, on Warner Bros., by WEA Records. Catalogue no: **W 2819W**
CD 5": Released Oct '89, on Warner Bros., by WEA Records. Catalogue no: **W 2819CD**

WATCHING
Tracks: / Watching.
7" Single: Released '83, on Arista, by BMG Records (UK). Deleted '86. Catalogue no: **TWINS 121**

WE ARE DETECTIVE (see panel below)
Tracks: / We are detective / Lucky day.
7" Single: Released '83, on Arista, by BMG Records (UK). Deleted '86. Catalogue no: **ARIST 526**
12" Single: Released '83, on Arista, by BMG Records (UK). Deleted '86. Catalogue no: **ARIST 12526**

WE ARE DETECTIVE (OLD GOLD)
Tracks: / We are detective / Hold me now.
12" Single: Released Jan '88, on Old Gold, by Old Gold Records. Catalogue no: **OG 4044**

YOU TAKE ME UP
Tracks: / You take me up / Passion planet.
7" Single: Released Mar '84, on Arista, by BMG Records (UK). Deleted '87. Catalogue no: **TWINS 4**

YOU TAKE ME UP (OLD GOLD)
Tracks: / You take me up / Doctor Doctor.
7" Single: Released 21 Nov '87, on Old Gold, by Old Gold Records. Catalogue no: **OG 4024**

Thomson, Ali

TAKE A LITTLE RYHTHM
Tracks: / Take a little rhythm / Jamie.
7" Single: Released Feb '80, on A&M, by A&M Records. Deleted Feb '83. Catalogue no: **AMS 7505**

Thomson, Ally

WHAT DREAMS ARE MADE OF
Tracks: / What dreams are made of / Cellophane girl.
7" Single: Released Feb '89, on E.G., by E.G. Records. Catalogue no: **EGO 47**
CD 3": Released Feb '89, on E.G., by E.G. Records. Catalogue no: **EGOCD 47**
12" Single: Released Feb '89, on E.G., by E.G. Records. Catalogue no: **EGOX 47**

Thor

KNOCK 'M' DOWN
Tracks: / Knock 'm' down.
12" Single: Released Jul '85, on Roadrunner (Germany), Catalogue no: **RR 125513**
7" Single: Released Jul '85, on Roadrunner (Germany), Catalogue no: **RR 5513**

LET THE BLOOD RUN RED
Tracks: / Let the blood run red / When Gods collide.
7" Single: Released Apr '84, on Albion, by Albion Records. Catalogue no: **ION 165**
12" Single: Released Apr '84, on Albion, by Albion Records. Catalogue no: **12ION 165**
7" Pic: Released Apr '84, on Albion, by Albion Records. Catalogue no: **PION 165**

OVER TO YOU
Tracks: / Over to you / Anita.
7" Single: Released Nov '82, on KA, Catalogue no: **KA 11**

THUNDER ON THE TUNDRA
Tracks: / Thunder on the tundra.
7" Pic: Released Jun '84, on Albion, by Albion Records. Catalogue no: **PION 168**
7" Single: Released Jun '84, on Albion, by Albion Records. Catalogue no: **ION 168**
12" Single: Released Jun '84, on Albion, by Albion Records. Catalogue no: **12ION 168**

Thorn, Tracey

PLAIN SAILING
Tracks: / Plain sailing / Goodbye Joe.
7" Single: Released Dec '84, on Cherry Red, by Cherry Red Records. Catalogue no: **CHERRY 53**

Thornally, Phil

ANOTHER WORLD
Tracks: / Another world.
7" Single: Released Sep '84, on Riva, by Riva Records. Catalogue no: **RIVA 42**

SO THIS IS LOVE
Tracks: / So this is love / Last too long.
12" Single: Released Jul '83, on Riva, by Riva Records. Catalogue no: **RIVA 41T**
7" Single: Released Jul '83, on Riva, by Riva Records. Catalogue no: **RIVA 41**

Thorne, David

ALLEY CAT SONG
Tracks: / Alley cat song.
7" Single: Released Jan '63, on Stateside, by EMI Records. Deleted '66. Catalogue no: **SS 141**

Thorne, Ken

LEGION'S LAST PATROL, THEME FROM
Tracks: / Legions last patrol (theme from).
7" Single: Released Jul '63, on H.M.V., by EMI Records. Deleted '66. Catalogue no: **POP 1176**

Thorne, Kirk

MR MAGIC
Tracks: / Mr. Magic / Party for two.
12" Single: Released Feb '85, on JKO, Catalogue no: **12JKO 109**

Thornhill, Mac

IT'S A CRUEL WORLD
Tracks: / Who's gonna ease the pressure (big mac mix) (Edited on 7") / It's a cruel world (7" only) / It's a cruel world (Club House mix) (12" only).
7" Single: Released Nov '88, on 10 Records, by Virgin Records. Catalogue no: **TEN 237**
12" Single: Released Nov '88, on 10 Records, by Virgin Records. Catalogue no: **TENX 237**

IT'S ALRIGHT
Tracks: / It's alright.
12" Single: Released Aug '89, on Radical, by Radical Records. Catalogue no: **RADC 712**
7" Single: Released Aug '89, on Radical, by Radical Records. Catalogue no: **RADC 7**
CD 5": Released Aug '89, on Radical, by Radical Records. Catalogue no: **RADC 7C**

WHO'S GONNA EASE THE PRESSURE
Tracks: / Who's gonna ease the pressure (townhouse cuts) (On TENX 214 only) / Who's gonna ease the pressure (townhouse edits) (On TENX only)) / Who's gonna ease the pressure (sizzle house Canadian club) (On 12" only) / Who's gonna ease the pressure (7" only) / Who's gonna ease the pressure (bass apella mix) (7" only) / Who's gonna ease the pressure (big mac mix) (On TENX 214 only).
12" Single: Released May '88, on 10 Records, by Virgin Records. Catalogue no: **TENR 214**
12" Single: Released Mar '88, on 10 Records, by Virgin Records. Catalogue no: **TENX 214**
7" Single: Released May '88, on 10 Records, by Virgin Records. Catalogue no: **TEN 214**

Thorns Of Affliction

PANIC STRICKEN
Tracks: / Panic stricken / Eyes of the dea...
7" Single: Released Aug '81, on Car..., Catalogue no: **CRS 011**

Thornton, Fonzi

BEVERLEY
Tracks: / Beverley / Looking up to you.
12" Single: Released 24 Apr '89, on Old Gold, by Old Gold Records. Catalogue no: **OG 4512**

Thorogood, George

HOUSE OF BLUE LIGHTS
Tracks: / House of blue lights / I just can't make it.
7" Single: Released May '81, on Sonet, by Sonet Records. Catalogue no: **SON 223...**

NIGHT TIME
Tracks: / Night time / Kids from Philly.
7" Single: Released Sep '80, on Sonet, by Sonet Records. Catalogue no: **SON 222...**

NOBODY BUT ME
Tracks: / Nobody but me / That Philly thi...
7" Single: Released Jul '82, on EMI-America, by EMI Records. Catalogue no: **EA ...**

Those French Girls

CLOSE UP
Tracks: / Close up.

THOMPSON TWINS - WE ARE DETECTIVE (Released on Arista)

7" Single: Released Nov '81, on Safari, by Safari Records. Catalogue no: **SAFE 40**

SORRY SORRY
Tracks: / Sorry sorry.
7" Single: Released Jan '82, on Safari, by Safari Records. Catalogue no: **SAFE 41**

Those Golden Birdies

ENNUI
Tracks: / Ennui.
12" Single: Released Dec '86, on Headless Horse, Catalogue no: **THOSE 001**

Those Helicopters

DOCTOR JANOV
Tracks: / Doctor Janov.
7" Single: Released Jun '81, on Lavender, Catalogue no: **LAVENDER 001**

Those Obnoxious Types

LOVE IS DEAD
Tracks: / Love is dead.
Note: Distributed by Esoteric 33 Barberry House,Shannon Road,Kings Norton, Birmingham,B38 9BX. Tele: 021 458 7503
7" Single: Released Nov '83, on Exoteric, by Esoteric Records. Catalogue no: **EX 2**

Thoughts

WAIT ALONG TIME FOR YOU
Tracks: / Wait along time for you.
7" Single: Released Jul '83, on Straight 8, Deleted '86. Catalogue no: **TH 1**
12" Single: Released Jul '83, on Straight 8, Deleted '86. Catalogue no: **THT 1**

Thousand Homo DJS

APATHY
Tracks: / Apathy / Better ways.
12" Single: Released Mar '89, on Wax Trax, by Wax Trax Records. Catalogue no: **WAX 032**

Thousand Miles...

JIMMY HIGHLIFE
Tracks: / Jimmy highlife.
7" Single: Released Jun '84, on Go Discs, by Chrysalis Records. Catalogue no: **SHINE 1**
12" Single: Released Jun '84, on Go Discs, by Chrysalis Records. Catalogue no: **SHINX 1**

Thrashing Doves

ANGEL VISIT
Tracks: / Angel visit / She do me.
7" Single: Released 3 Apr '89, on A&M, by A&M Records. Catalogue no: **AM 497**
CD 5": Released 3 Apr '89, on A&M, by A&M Records. Catalogue no: **CDEE 497**
12" Single: Released 3 Apr '89, on A&M, by A&M Records. Catalogue no: **AMY 497**

ANOTHER DEADLY SUNSET
Tracks: / Another deadly sunset / You don't believe me do you / Question of love (On 12" only) / Mamma's in love (On CD single only).
CD 5": Released 31 Jul '89, on A&M, by A&M Records. Catalogue no: **CDEE 516**
7" Single: Released 31 Jul '89, on A&M, by A&M Records. Catalogue no: **AM 523**
12" Single: Released 31 Jul '89, on A&M, by A&M Records. Catalogue no: **AMY 523**

BEAUTIFUL IMBALANCE
Tracks: / Self-infliction crew / Beautiful imbalance.
7" Single: Released Jan '87, on A&M, by A&M Records. Deleted Mar '88. Catalogue no: **TDOVE 1**
12" Single: Released Jan '87, on A&M, by A&M Records. Deleted Mar '88. Catalogue no: **TDOVE 112**

BIBA'S BASEMENT
Tracks: / Biba's basement / Tinderbox man All night chemist (Extra track on 12" only).
12" Single: Released Sep '86, on A&M, by A&M Records. Deleted Mar '88. Catalogue no: **AMY 335**
7" Single: Released Sep '86, on A&M, by A&M Records. Deleted Mar '88. Catalogue no: **AM 335**

GRINDING STONE, THE
Tracks: / Grinding stone / Receiver, The / Last train to Bedrock (on 12" only.).
7" Single: Released Mar '87, on A&M, by A&M Records. Deleted Mar '88. Catalogue no: **TDOVE 2**
12" Single: Released Mar '87, on A&M, by A&M Records. Deleted Mar '88. Catalogue no: **TDOVE 212**

LORELEI
Tracks: / Lorelei / Girl called Whodini / Sympathy for the devil (Only on CD single) / Domestic rain (Only on CD single).
CD 5": Released May '89, on A&M, by A&M Records. Catalogue no: **CDEE 511**
7" Single: Released May '89, on A&M, by A&M Records. Catalogue no: **AM 511**
12" Single: Released May '89, on A&M, by A&M Records. Catalogue no: **AMY 511**

MATCHSTICK FLOTILLA
Tracks: / Matchstick / Lotilla / Hollywood maids (on 12" only.) / Sympathy for the devil (12" only).
7" Single: Released May '86, on A&M, by A&M Records. Deleted '88. Catalogue no: **AM 325**
12" Single: Released May '86, on A&M, by A&M Records. Deleted '88. Catalogue no: **AMY 325**

REPROBATE'S HYMN
Tracks: / Reprobate's hymn / Jesus on the payroll (1) / Jesus on the payroll (2).
CD 5": Released 20 Feb '89, on A&M, by A&M Records. Catalogue no: **CDEE 479**
7" Single: Released 20 Feb '89, on A&M, by A&M Records. Catalogue no: **AM 479**
12" Single: Released 20 Feb '89, on A&M, by A&M Records. Catalogue no: **AMY 479**

Thrashpack

KINDA COOL IN THE PLACE
Tracks: / Kinda cool in the place.
12" Single: Released Oct '87, on Music Of Life, by Music Of Life Records. Catalogue no: **NOTE 10**

Threats

GO TO HELL
Tracks: / Go to hell.
7" Single: Released Jun '82, on Rondelet Music, by Rondelet Music & Records. Catalogue no: **ROUND 22**

POLITICIANS AND MINISTERS
Tracks: / Politicians and ministers.
12" Single: Released Nov '82, on Rondelet Music, by Rondelet Music & Records. Catalogue no: **12 ROUND 29**
7" Single: Released Nov '82, on Rondelet Music, by Rondelet Music & Records. Catalogue no: **ROUND 29**

Three Action

BREATH OF FRESH AIR, A
Tracks: / Breath of fresh air, A.
12" Single: Released Nov '87, on Ediesta, Deleted '88. Catalogue no: **CALC 035**

ON THE JOURNEY OF A LIFETIME
Tracks: / On the journey of a lifetime.
12" Single: Released Sep '86, on Ediesta, Deleted '88. Catalogue no: **CALC 3T**
7" Single: Released Sep '86, on Ediesta, Deleted '88. Catalogue no: **CALC 3**

STEALIN' FEELIN'
Tracks: / Stealin' feelin'.
12" Single: Released May '87, on Ediesta, Deleted '88. Catalogue no: **CALC 023**

Three Angry Poles

MOTOR CYCLE MANIAC
Tracks: / Motorcycle maniac.
12" Single: Released Sep '86, on Play It Again Sam(Belgium), by Play It Again Sam (Belgium). Catalogue no: **BIAS 034**

Three Colours

ONE BIG TREE
Tracks: / One big tree.
7" Single: Released Nov '86, on Pinnacle, by Pinnacle Records. Catalogue no: **SURF 118**

SITTING PRETTY
Tracks: / Sitting pretty / I called him by his mane / Eventually* (*Extra track on 12") / Here comes your saviour (Extra track on 12").
7" Single: Released Jul '87, on Soul Select, by Soul Select Records. Catalogue no: **SELECT 4**
12" Single: Released Jul '87, on Soul Select, by Soul Select Records. Catalogue no: **SELECT 4T**

Three Courgettes

SUBSTITUTE
Tracks: / Substitute.
7" Single: Released Jul '82, on Island, by Island Records. Catalogue no: **WIP 6814**

THREE COURGETTES, THE
Tracks: / Three courgettes, The.
7" Pic: Released May '82, on Island, by Island Records. Catalogue no: **PVEG 3**
7" Single: Released May '82, on Island, by Island Records. Catalogue no: **VEG 3**

Three D

BREAK THE FIX(ATION)
Tracks: / Break the fix(ation).
12" Single: Released Aug '84, on RAK, by EMI Records. Deleted '87. Catalogue no: **12RAK 374**
7" Single: Released Aug '84, on RAK, by EMI Records. Catalogue no: **RAK 374**

CRUSHIN'AND BUSSIN'
Tracks: / Crussin and buffin.
12" Single: Released Nov '87, on Hilltop Hustlers (USA), Catalogue no: **HTH 002**
7" Single: Released Feb '88, on Citybeat, by Beggars Banquet Records. Catalogue no: **CBE 1218**

DANCE TO BELIEVE
Tracks: / Dance to believe.
12" Single: Released Apr '85, on RAK, by EMI Records. Catalogue no: **12RAK 382**
7" Single: Released Apr '85, on RAK, by EMI Records. Catalogue no: **RAK 382**

GIDDY UP
Tracks: / Giddy up / Giddy up (inst) / Once more / Once more (version).
12" Single: Released 23 Apr '88, on Citybeat, by Beggars Banquet Records. Catalogue no: **CBE 1225**

GREATEST MAN ALIVE
Tracks: / Greatest man alive / Straight up.
7" Single: Released Oct '88, on Citybeat, by Beggars Banquet Records. .Catalogue no: **CBE 1231**

NEARER
Tracks: / Nearer.
7" Single: Released Jan '85, on RAK, by EMI Records. Catalogue no: **RAK 377**

TELEPHONE NUMBER
Tracks: / Telephone number / Here today.
7" Single: Released May '80, on Polydor, by Polydor Ltd. Deleted '85. Catalogue no: **POSP 132**

Three D Production

RIOT
Tracks: / Riot / Re-arrange
7" Single: Released Oct '80, on Third Kind, Deleted Oct '83 Catalogue no: **TKS 001**

Three Dancers

SEVENTEEN
Tracks: / Seventeen.
7" Single: Released '88, on Ditettante Disc, Catalogue no: **DD 007**

Three Degrees

Biographical details: Fayette Pickney, Shirley Porter and Linda Turner, from Philadelphia, released their debut single, *Gee Baby I'm Sorry*, in 1965, reaching the lower reaches of the US Hot Hundred, and the following year Sheila Ferguson and Valerie Thompson replaced Porter and Turner. After several unsuccessful years the group hit the American Top Thirty with their 1970 remake of *Maybe*, a soulful cover version of a song which had been a late 50's hit for the Chantels, but this proved another one-off. Their real breakthrough came in 1974, after signing with Philadelphia International Records and the company's writing/production masters Kenny Gamble and Leon Huff. To promote and celebrate the 'Philly sound' which was, by this time, taking over from Motown as the most prominent force in soul music, Gamble and Huff released TSOP (The Sound Of Philadelphia). The single was credited to MFSB, a massed studio ensemble featuring the Three Degrees on vocals. It reached the US No 1 spot in April '74 and Gamble and Huff soon realised the girls' potential. They recorded *When Will I See You Again?*, a silky pop/soul ballad which reached No 2 in the States and No 1 in Britain. The Three Degress did not enjoy any further major success in America but things really took off in Britain and Europe. *Year Of Decision* gave them a UK No 13 in early summer '74 and *When Will I See You Again?* reached the British summit before even being released in the States. *Take Good Care Of Yourself* was another UK Top Tenner in '75. A move away from the Philly production line resulted in three hitless years but in the last 15 months of the 70's -- long after being written off by pop historians -- they made a surprise come-back by achieving six hit singles in quick succession, four of which made the UK Top Twenty (though all failed in the US). The first was *Givin' Up Givin' In*, which coincided with an invitation from Prince Charles to sing at his 30th birthday party. He cited the Three Degrees as his favourite group and the resulting publicity earned them a pair of back-to-back UK Top Tenners with the cabaret-style ballad *Woman In Love* (No 3) and the uptempo disco hit *The Runner* (No 10). As the 70's became the 80's the trio were riding high with *My Simple Heart* (No 9) but the hits then dried up again. However, they were well able to earn a good living on the cabaret circuit. (Bob MacDonald, April 1985.) A US black vocal trio from Philadelphia: Fayette Pinkney, Sheila Ferguson, Valerie Holiday. Minor hits on Swan '65-66; recorded for several labels, hit the big time on Gamble & Huff's Philadelphia International label and had smash *When will I see you again?*, No.2 USA '74 and said to be biggest-selling single of the year in the UK. LP's charted in the USA, singles in the UK where they were said to be Prince Charles' favourite act, performed at his 30th birthday party. (Donald Clarke 13.1.88).

6 TRACK HITS
Tracks: / Woman in love / Magic in the air / My simple heart / Jump the gun / Without you / Runner, The.
7" EP: Released Sep '83, on Scoop 33, by Pickwick Records. Catalogue no: **7SR 5005**

GET YOUR LOVE BACK
Tracks: / Get your love back.
7" Single: Released Nov '74, on Philadelphia Int., by EMI Records. Deleted '77. Catalogue no: **PIR 2737**

GIVIN' UP GIVIN' IN
Tracks: / Givin' up givin' in.
7" Single: Released Oct '78, on Ariola, by BMG Records (UK). Deleted '81. Catalogue no: **ARO 130**

GOLDEN LADY, THE
Tracks: / Golden lady.
7" Single: Released Jun '79, on Ariola, by BMG Records (UK). Deleted '82. Catalogue no: **ARO 170**

HEAVEN I NEED, THE
Tracks: / Heaven I need, The.
12" Single: Released Sep '85, on Supreme, by Supreme Records. Catalogue no: **SUPET 102**
7" Single: Released Sep '85, on Supreme, by Supreme Records. Catalogue no: **SUPE 102**

HEAVEN I NEED, THE (REMIX)
Tracks: / Heaven I need, The (remix).
12" Single: Released Nov '85, on Supreme, by Supreme Records. Catalogue no: **SUPETX 102**

JUMP THE GUN
Tracks: / Jump the gun.
7" Single: Released Sep '79, on Ariola, by BMG Records (UK). Deleted '82. Catalogue no: **ARO 183**

LIAR (YOU'VE BEEN CHEATING ON ME)
Tracks: / Liar (you've been cheating on me).
7" Single: Released Nov '83, on 3D, Catalogue no: **3D 1**

LOCK IT UP
Tracks: / Lock it up.
12" Single: Released Sep '89, on Ichiban, by Ichiban Records (UK). Catalogue no: **ICHT 707**
7" Single: Released Sep '89, on Ichiban, by Ichiban Records (UK). Catalogue no: **ICHS 707**

LONG LOST LOVER
Tracks: / Long lost lover.
7" Single: Released Jul '75, on Philadelphia Int., by EMI Records. Deleted '78. Catalogue no: **PIR 3352**

MY SIMPLE HEART
Tracks: / My simple heart.
7" Single: Released Nov '79, on Ariola, by BMG Records (UK). Deleted '82. Catalogue no: **ARO 202**

RUNNER, THE
Tracks: / Runner, The.
7" Single: Released Mar '79, on Ariola, by BMG Records (UK). Deleted '82. Catalogue no: **ARO 154**

STARLIGHT
Tracks: / Starlight / Set me free.
7" Single: Released May '80, on Ariola, by BMG Records (UK). Deleted May '83. Catalogue no: **ARO 228**

TAKE GOOD CARE OF YOURSELF (SINGLE)
Tracks: / Take good care of yourself.
7" Single: Released Apr '75, on Philadelphia Int., by EMI Records. Deleted '78. Catalogue no: **PIR 3177**

TENDER LIE
Tracks: / Tender lie, A / Vital signs.
12" Single: Released 1 May '89, on Ichiban, by Ichiban Records (UK). Catalogue no: **ICHT 706**
7" Single: Released 1 May '89, on Ichiban, by Ichiban Records (UK). Catalogue no: **ICHS 706**

THIS IS THE HOUSE
Tracks: / This is the house / This is the house (mega dance version) / Senza voce / Heaven I need,The / Gimme gimme gimme.
12" Single: Released Mar '86, on Supreme, by Supreme Records. Catalogue no: **SUPETO 104**
12" Single: Released Mar '86, on Supreme, by Supreme Records. Catalogue no: **SUPET 104**

TOAST OF LOVE
Tracks: / Toast of love.
7" Single: Released May '76, on Epic, by CBS Records. Deleted '79. Catalogue no: **EPC 4215**

WHEN WILL I SEE YOU AGAIN
Tracks: / When will I see you again.
7" Single: Released Jul '74, on Philadelphia Int., by EMI Records. Deleted '77. Catalogue no: **PIR 2155**

WHEN WILL I SEE YOU AGAIN (OLD GOLD)

Tracks: / When will I see you again.
7" Single: Released Apr '83, on Old Gold, by Old Gold Records. Catalogue no: **OG 9307**

WITHOUT YOU
Tracks: / Without you / Magic in the air.
7" Single: Released Feb '80, on Ariola, by BMG Records (UK). Deleted Feb '83. Catalogue no: **ARO 308**
7" Single: Released May '82, on Ariola, by BMG Records (UK). Catalogue no: **ARO 280**

WOMAN IN LOVE
Tracks: / Woman in love.
7" Single: Released Dec '78, on Ariola, by BMG Records (UK). Catalogue no: **ARO 141**
7" Single: Released Apr '87, on Old Gold, by Old Gold Records. Catalogue no: **OG 9703**

YEAR OF DECISION
Tracks: / Year of decision.
7" Single: Released Apr '74, on Philadelphia Int., by EMI Records. Deleted '77. Catalogue no: **PIR 2073**

Three Dixons

HIGHWAYMAN
Tracks: / Highwayman.
12" Single: Released Jun '85, on Music Power, Catalogue no: **MPRT 3**
7" Single: Released Jun '85, on Music Power, Catalogue no: **MPR 3**

Three Dog Night

Biographical details: This American rock band -- Mike Allsup, Jim Greenspoon, Danny Hutton, Chuck Negron, Joe Schermie, Floyd Sneed and Cory Wells -- took their name from an Eskimo term meaning an extremely cold night: the colder the night the more dogs would be brought in by an Eskimo to sleep with him; on really bitter nights three dogs would be used. Formed in 1968, Three Dog Night chalked up an extraordinarily consistent run of American hit singles and albums between '69 and '75. Eleven of their singles reached the US Top Ten. They were an unusual combination of two musical styles, rock and cabaret, which are normally poles apart. While most of the "serious" and "progressive" rock bands of the late 60's and early 70's wrote their own material and concentrated on albums, 3DN were singles supremos and specialised in performing other people's songs. They were fronted by three singers -- Hutton, Negron and Wells -- and backed by four superb musicians. Although some critics argued that their brand of rock was of little worth, it is important to note that they gave important breaks to up-and-coming songwriters who later achieved stardom in their own right. Three Dog Night's first major hit was One, written by the previously unknown Harry Nilsson, which took them to No 5 on the US charts. Other successes included Laura Nyro's *Eli's Coming*, Russ Ballard's *Liar*, Paul Williams' *An Old-Fashioned Love Song* and *The Family Of Man* and Leo Sayer's *The Song Must Go On*. Their biggest smashes were three No 1 hits on the US listings. Randy Newman's *Mama Told Me Not To Come* hit the top in 1970, Hoyt Axton's *Joy To The World* was No 1 for six weeks and was America's biggest record of '71 and *Black And White*, a racial harmony plea that was a UK hit for Greyhound in '71, proved to be a chart-topper for 3DN in '72. By comparison with the group's fantastic US sales, British acceptance was muted. *Only Mama* and *Joy* made the UK Top Fifty, the former hitting No 3 and the latter peaking at No 24, and none of the albums made the British charts. Jack Ryland replaced Schermie in 1973 and Skip Conte was added to the line-up at about the same time. After the hits dried up in 1975 the band faded into obscurity. (Bob MacDonald, April 1985.) This pop group formed in 1968, named from Australian expression referring to temperature and cannine comfort: vocalist Daniel Anthony (born in 1942 in Ireland) had recorded voices for Hanna-Barbera cartoon; he recruited two other lead singers and four back-up musicians for a group that had had 21 hit singles in the USA 1969-75 and were derided for sticking to covers, but gave early breaks to little-known songwriters **Randy Newman, Harry Nilsson, Laua Nyro, Hoyt Axton, :eo Sayer,** and others. (Donald Clarke 13.1.88).

IT'S A JUNGLE OUT THERE
Tracks: / It's a jungle out there / Livin' it up.
7" Single: Released Mar '84, on Lamborghini, by Lamborghini Records. Catalogue no: **LMG 9**
12" Single: Released Jun '84, on Lamborghini, by Lamborghini Records. Catalogue no: **LMBL 1**

JOY TO THE WORLD
Tracks: / Joy to the world.
7" Single: Released May '71, on Probe, Deleted '74. Catalogue no: **PRO 523**

MAMA TOLD ME NOT TO COME (OLD GOLD)
Tracks: / Mama told me not to come.
7" Single: Released Jul '82, on Old Gold, by Old Gold Records. Catalogue no: **OG 9173**

Three Flying Bigoudis

CHRISTMAS TIME
Tracks: / Christmas time / Christmas carol.
7" Single: Released Nov '83, on Nuclear, by Nuclear Records. Catalogue no: **CLEAR 007**

Three Good Reasons

NOWHERE MAN
Tracks: / Nowhere man.
7" Single: Released Mar '66, on Mercury, by Phonogram Ltd. Deleted '69. Catalogue no: **MF 899**

Three Johns

A.W.O.L.
Tracks: / A.W.O.L..
7" Single: Released Oct '83, on Abstract, by Abstract Sounds. Catalogue no: **12 ABS 019**
7" Single: Released Oct '83, on Abstract, by Abstract Sounds. Catalogue no: **ABS 019**

BRAINBOX
Tracks: / Brainbox.
7" Single: Released Nov '85, on Abstract, by Abstract Sounds. Catalogue no: **ABS 036**
12" Single: Released Nov '85, on Abstract, by Abstract Sounds. Catalogue no: **12 ABS 036**

DEATH OF THE EUROPEAN
Tracks: / Death of the European / Heads like convicts / Rabies (on 12" only) / 20th Century Fox (on 12" only).
12" Single: Released May '85, on Abstract, by Abstract Sounds. Catalogue no: **12 ABS 034**
7" Single: Released May '85, on Abstract, by Abstract Sounds. Catalogue no: **ABS 034**

DO THE SQUARE
Tracks: / Do the square / Zowee.
7" Single: Released Mar '84, on Abstract, by Abstract Sounds. Catalogue no: **ABS 023**
12" Single: Released Mar '84, on Abstract, by Abstract Sounds. Catalogue no: **12 ABS 023**

ENGLISH WHITE BOY ENGINEER
Tracks: / English white boy engineer / Secret agent.
7" Single: Released May '82, on CNT, Catalogue no: **CNT 003**

NEVER & ALWAYS
Tracks: / Never and always.
7" Single: Released Jul '87, on Abstract, by Abstract Sounds. Catalogue no: **ABS 043**
12" Single: Released Jul '87, on Abstract, by Abstract Sounds. Catalogue no: **12 ABS 043**

SOLD DOWN THE RIVER
Tracks: / Sold down the river.
7" Single: Released Apr '86, on Abstract, by Abstract Sounds. Catalogue no: **ABS 040**
12" Single: Released Apr '86, on Abstract, by Abstract Sounds. Catalogue no: **12 ABS 040**

SOME HISTORY
Tracks: / Some history.
12" Single: Released Jan '84, on Abstract, by Abstract Sounds. Catalogue no: **12 ABS 022**

TORCHES OF LIBERTY
Tracks: / Torches of liberty.
12" Single: Released Mar '88, on Abstract, by Abstract Sounds. Catalogue no: **ABS 049**

Three Kayes

IVORY TOWER
Tracks: / Ivory tower.
7" Single: Released May '56, on H.M.V., by EMI Records. Deleted '59. Catalogue no: **POP 209**

Three Little Pigs

THREE LITTLE PIGS (EP)
Tracks: / Three little pigs.
7" EP: Released Apr '81, on Disneyland-Vista(USA), by Disneyland-Vista Records (USA). Catalogue no: **D 303**

Three Man Island

JACK THE LAD
Tracks: / Jack the lad (UK remix) / Jack the lad (US Westcoast mix) (Available on 7" only) / Jack the lad (acapella) (Available on 12" only) / Jack the lad (Rub a dub dub mix) (Available on 12" only) / Jack the lad (radio mix) (Available on 12" only).
Note: The 12" contains a specially remixed UK version as well as three other versions.* Track on 12" version only. ** Track on 7" version only.
7" Single: Released Jun '88, on Urban, by Polydor Ltd. Catalogue no: **URB 19**
12" Single: Released Jun '88, on Urban, by Polydor Ltd. Catalogue no: **URBX 19**

Three Million

I'VE BEEN ROBBED
Tracks: / I've been robbed.
12" Single: Released Jan '84, on Cotillion, by WEA Records. Catalogue no: **B 9812T**
7" Single: Released Jan '84, on Cotillion, by WEA Records. Catalogue no: **B 9812**

Three Minutes

AUTOMATIC KISS
Tracks: / Automatic kiss / Future fun.
7" Single: Released Sep '80, on Rocket, by Rocket Records. Deleted '83. Catalogue no: **XPRES 40**

Three Mustaphas Three

LINDA LINDA
Tracks: / Linda Linda / Kopanitsa (Only on 7" single.) / Linda Linda (Special longer mix) (Available on 12" only) / Linda Linda (Szegerely megarely mix) (Available on 12" only).
12" Single: Released Feb '88, on Globestyle, by Ace Records. Catalogue no: **NST 121**
7" Single: Released Feb '88, on Globestyle, by Ace Records. Catalogue no: **NS 121**

SHOUFFI RHIROU
Tracks: / Shouffi rhirou / Voulez vous danser / Darling, don't say 'no'.
12" Single: Released Aug '87, on Globestyle, by Ace Records. Catalogue no: **NST 120**

SI VOUS PASSEZ PAR LA
Tracks: / Si vous passez par la / Starehe mustapha / Maldita guajira (12" only).
7" Single: Released Feb '86, on Globestyle, by Ace Records. Catalogue no: **NS 111**
12" Single: Released Mar '89, on Globestyle, by Ace Records. Catalogue no: **NST 111**

Three O'Clock

HAND IN HAND
Tracks: / Hand in hand.
12" Single: Released Sep '85, on I.R.S, Catalogue no: **IRT 101**
7" Single: Released Sep '85, on I.R.S, Catalogue no: **IRM 101**

WARM ASPIRATIONS
Tracks: / Warm aspirations / Regina Caeli.
12" Single: Released Apr '87, on I.R.S, Catalogue no: **IRMT 127**
7" Single: Released Apr '87, on I.R.S, Catalogue no: **IRM 127**

Three P Sweet

TOO CLOSE TO THE MOON
Tracks: / Too close to the moon.
7" Single: Released Feb '82, on Record, Catalogue no: **RR 1**

Three Phase

ALL I WANT TO DO
Tracks: / All I want to do.
7" Single: Released Jan '83, on Speed, Catalogue no: **FAD 3**

Three P.M.

TELL ME THE TRUTH
Tracks: / Tell me the truth.
12" Single: Released May '88, on Blue Trac, by Blue Trac Records. Catalogue no: **BTRD 017**

Three Rockies

STOP WASTING YOUR TIME
Tracks: / Stop wasting your time.
7" Single: Released Oct '84, on 10 Records, by Virgin Records. Deleted '89. Catalogue no: **TEN 33**

Three Times A Day

I CRAVE TO BE A HERMAPHRODITE
Tracks: / I crave to be a hermaphrodite.
7" Single: Released Nov '81, on Abstract, by Abstract Sounds. Catalogue no: **ABS 003**

Three + Two

WINDOW SHOPPING
Tracks: / Window shopping.
12" Single: Released Jun '84, on Bluesville International, Catalogue no: **BVD 001**

Three Way Switch

LEAVING ON A JET PLANE
Tracks: / Leaving on a jet plane / Love triangle.
7" Single: Released Nov '80, on Ariola, by BMG Records (UK). Catalogue no: **AHA 568**

Three Wise Men

CRUISING FOR A BRUISING
Tracks: / Cruising for a bruising.
7" Single: Released 27 Feb '88, on Rhythm King, by Mute Records. Catalogue no: **LEFT 19**
12" Single: Released 27 Feb '88, on Rhythm King, by Mute Records. Catalogue no: **LEFT 19T**

REFRESH YOURSELF
Tracks: / Refresh yourself.
12" Single: Released May '87, on Rhythm King, by Mute Records. Catalogue no: **LEFT 7**

URBAN HELL
Tracks: / Urban hell.
12" Single: Released Nov '86, on Rhythm King, by Mute Records. Catalogue no: **LEFT 3T**
7" Single: Released Nov '86, on Rhythm King, by Mute Records. Catalogue no: **LEFT 3**

Thrill Kill Kult

MY LIFE WITH THE THRILL KILL KULT
Tracks: / My life with the Thrill Kill Kult.
12" Single: Released Apr '88, on Wax Trax, by Wax Trax Records. Catalogue no: **WAXUK 039**

Thrilled Skinny

PIECE OF PLASTIC
Tracks: / Blast / Quicker than the blinking eye / Media music / I'm on a groovy strait / Pregnant pause / Pinless.
7" EP: Released Dec '87, on Hunchback, Catalogue no: **HUNCH 001**

SO GLAD TO BE ALIVE
Tracks: / So glad to be alive / Clinging to the shelf.
7" Single: Released Jun '88, on Hunchback, Catalogue no: **HUNCH 003**

Thriller U

4 THE HARD WAY
Tracks: / 4 the hard way.
12" Single: Released Oct '88, on Sir Coxsone, Catalogue no: **BD 88002**

BABY I LOVE YOU
Tracks: / Baby I love you.
12" Single: Released Apr '89, on Unity, Catalogue no: **FEA 011**
7" Single: Released Apr '89, on Digital B., Catalogue no: **VPRD 407**

GREATEST LOVE AFFAIR, THE
Tracks: / Greatest love affair.
12" Single: Released Feb '89, on Jammy's, Catalogue no: **VPRD 394**

HILARY
Tracks: / Hilary.
12" Single: Released Jun '89, on Pioneer Muzik, Catalogue no: **PMUZLP 001**

I AM THE DANGER
Tracks: / I am the danger.
12" Single: Released 20 Mar '89, on Bur Gem, Catalogue no: **BG 0039**

I WILL COME RUNNING
Tracks: / I will come running.
12" Single: Released 31 Jul '89, on G.I., by Plastic Head Records. Catalogue no: **GI 00**

I'LL PROVE IT TO YOU
Tracks: / I'll prove it to you.
12" Single: Released Jun '89, on Techniques, Catalogue no: **WRT 45**

LINE THEM UP
Tracks: / Line them up.
12" Single: Released Jul '88, on Guidin Star, Catalogue no: **GS 005**

MR TELEPHONE MAN
Tracks: / Mr. Telephone man.
12" Single: Released Feb '89, on Manzie Catalogue no: **MAN 002**

NEVER GONNA GIVE YOU UP
Tracks: / Never gonna give you up.
12" Single: Released Aug '88, on Gemaine, Catalogue no: **DGT 36**

ON AND ON
Tracks: / On and on.
12" Single: Released Jul '89, on Mixing La Catalogue no: **MXL 24**

PRIVATE PROPERTY
Tracks: / Private property.
12" Single: Released Mar '89, on Bun Ger Catalogue no: **BG 0036**

SINCE YOU CAME INTO MY LIFE
Tracks: / Since you came into my life.
12" Single: Released Dec '88, on Gemaine, Catalogue no: **DGT 44**

Thrillers

SHOOTING TO THE TOP
Tracks: / Shooting to the top / Woolly bull We are the gangsters.
7" Single: Released Jul '80, on Big Bear, Big Bear Records. Deleted '88. Catalog no: **BB 28**

Thrilling Wonder

TWO WAY VIDEO
Tracks: / Two way video.
7" Single: Released Jul '83, on Made Space, Catalogue no: **MIS 2001**

Throwdown

CAMP
Tracks: / Camp (rap mix) / Camp.
12" Single: Released Dec '86, on Hardback, by Hardback Records. Catalogue no: **BOSS 3**
7" Single: Released Dec '86, on Hardback, by Hardback Records. Catalogue no: **7 BOSS 3**

Throwing Muses

CHAINS CHANGES (EP)
Tracks: / Finished / Reel / Snail Head / Cry baby cry.
Cassingle: Released Mar '87, on 4AD, by 4AD Records. Catalogue no: **BADC 701**
12" Single: Released Feb '87, on 4AD, by 4AD Records. Catalogue no: **BAD 701**

DIZZY
Tracks: / Dizzy / Santa Claus / Mania (12" only) / Downtown (12" only).
12" Single: Released Feb '89, on 4AD, by 4AD Records. Catalogue no: **BAD 903**
CD 5": Released Feb '89, on 4AD, by 4AD Records. Catalogue no: **BAD 903CD**
7" Single: Released Feb '89, on 4AD, by 4AD Records. Catalogue no: **AD 903**
10" single: Released Feb '89, on 4AD, by 4AD Records. Catalogue no: **BADD 903**

Thrust

PUT YOUR BODY TO IT
Tracks: / Put your body to it.
12" Single: Released Aug '84, on Arista, by BMG Records (UK). Catalogue no: **ARIST 12581**
7" Single: Released Aug '84, on Arista, by BMG Records (UK). Catalogue no: **ARIST 581**

Thule

DOCTOR LLOYD
Tracks: / Doctor Lloyd.
12" Single: Released 14 May '88, on Thule Entertainments. Catalogue no: **CRAIN 001**

LA JAMAIS CONTENTE
Tracks: / La jamais contente.
7" Single: Released Mar '89, on Wiija, Catalogue no: **WIIJIT 3**

Thumann, Harry

UNDERWATER
Tracks: / Underwater / American express.
12" Single: Released Jan '81, on Decca, by Decca Records. Deleted '88. Catalogue no: **LF 13901**
7" Single: Released Jan '81, on Decca, by Decca Records. Deleted '88. Catalogue no: **F 13901**

Thumper's Race

THUMPER'S RACE
7" EP: Released Apr '81, on Disneyland, by Disneyland Records. Catalogue no: **D 343**

Thunder

SHE'S SO FINE
Tracks: / She's so fine (7" & CD single only.) / Girl's going out of her head / She's so fine (full length version) (Not on 7".) / Another shot of love (live) (Not on 7".).
CD 5": Released Nov '89, on EMI, by EMI Records. Catalogue no: **CDEM 111**
12" Single: Released Oct '89, on EMI, by EMI Records. Catalogue no: **12EMP 111**
7" Single: Released Oct '89, on EMI, by EMI Records. Catalogue no: **EM 111**
12" Single: Released Oct '89, on EMI, by EMI Records. Catalogue no: **203 571 0**
CD 5": Released Nov '89, on EMI, by EMI Records. Catalogue no: **203 571 2**
12" Single: Released Oct '89, on EMI, by EMI Records. Catalogue no: **203 571 6**
7" Single: Released Oct '89, on EMI, by EMI Records. Catalogue no: **203 571 7**
12" Single: Released Oct '89, on EMI, by EMI Records. Catalogue no: **12EM 111**

Thunder, Sam

DON'T TAKE FOREVER
Tracks: / Don't take forever.
12" Single: Released Jan '84, on Bullet, by Bullet Records. Deleted '88. Catalogue no: **BOLT 8**

Thunder, Shelley

BREAK UP
Tracks: / Break up / Kuff '89 / Break up (dub) (On 12" only) / Kuff '89 (dub) (On 12" only).
7" Single: Released Sep '89, on Mango, by Island Records. Catalogue no: **MNG 718**
12" Single: Released Sep '89, on Mango, by Island Records. Catalogue no: **12 MNG 718**

KUFF
Tracks: / Kuff.
12" Single: Released Jul '88, on Blue Trac, by Blue Trac Records. Catalogue no: **MMD 127**

Thunderbirds

YOU AIN'T NOTHING BUT FINE
Tracks: / You ain't nothing but fine / She's tuff / Scratch my back.
7" Single: Released Mar '80, on Chrysalis, by Chrysalis Records. Deleted Mar '83. Catalogue no: **CHS 2145**

Thunderbolts

DUST ON ME NEEDLE
Tracks: / Dust on me needle.
7" Single: Released Oct '80, on Stiff, by Stiff Records. Catalogue no: **CLAP 1**

Thunderclap 2

SOMETHING IN THE AIR
Tracks: / Something in the air.
12" Single: Released Jul '89, on Trax, by Filmtrax Records. Catalogue no: **12TX 9**
7" Single: Released Jul '89, on Trax, by Filmtrax Records. Catalogue no: **7TX 9**

Thunderclap Newman

Biographical details: This British combo consisted of Speedy Keen, Jimmy McCulloch and Andy "Thunderclap" Newman. Although they were named after the keyboards player, no member of the group was the official leader. Keen was lead singer and songwriter. The story of the trio began in 1968 when Speedy Keen wrote the song *Armenia City In The Sky* for the Who. Pete Townshend became the catalyst who organised the formation of Thunderclap Newman, producing and supervising their first single, *Something In The Air*. This became one of the classic hits of 1969, reaching No 1 in Britain for three weeks in July and No 37 in the States. *Something In The Air* was a fantastic record, combining lyrics which reflected the sociological turbulence of the time with music containing such highlights as Newman's ear-grabbing piano solo. The band had difficulty in living up to the single and could not reproduce their records on stage very well, despite the addition of two extra musicians. Their 1970 offerings were excellent and underrated: the *Accidents* single peaked at No 46 in the UK chart and the group's only LP, *Hollywood Dream*, also produced by Townshend, failed to sell in any great quantities but was later awarded a five-star rating in the Rolling Stone Record Guide. Having split up by the end of 1970, Thunderclap Newman's guitarist Jimmy McCulloch moved on to Stone The Crows and Paul McCartney's Wings (1974-77). He met a tragically early death in January '79 due to a drug-related heart attack. Speedy Keen released a couple of solo albums without success and worked as a small-time producer. (Bob MacDonald, February 1986)..

ACCIDENTS
Tracks: / Accidents.
7" Single: Released Jun '70, on Track, by Polydor Ltd. Deleted '73. Catalogue no: **1094 001**

SOMETHING IN THE AIR
Tracks: / Something in the air.
7" Single: Released '74, on Track, by Polydor Ltd. Deleted '77. Catalogue no: **2094 017**
7" Single: Released Jun '69, on Track, by Polydor Ltd. Deleted '72. Catalogue no: **604 031**

SOMETHING IN THE AIR (OLD GOLD)
Tracks: / Something in the air / Accidents.
7" Single: Released Jul '84, on Old Gold, by Old Gold Records. Catalogue no: **OG 9435**

Thunders, Johnny

BORN TO CRY
Tracks: / Born to cry / Treat her right / Can't seem to make her mine (Only on 12" version.).
12" Single: Released Nov '88, on Jungle, by Jungle Records. Catalogue no: **JUNG 43T**
7" Single: Released Nov '88, on Jungle, by Jungle Records. Catalogue no: **JUNG 43**

BORN TO LOSE
Tracks: / Born to loose.
7" Single: Released Feb '85, on Twins, Catalogue no: **T 1702**

CHINESE ROCKS
Tracks: / Chinese rocks.
7" Single: Released May '85, on Jungle, by Jungle Records. Catalogue no: **JUNG 1**
7" EP: Released May '85, on Jungle, by Jungle Records. Catalogue no: **JUNG 20**
Special: Released May '85, on Jungle, by Jungle Records. Catalogue no: **JUNG 20T**

CRAWFISH
Tracks: / Crawfish / Tie me up.
Note: Pic bag
7" Single: Released Apr '87, on Jungle, by Jungle Records. Catalogue no: **JUNG 23**
7" Pic: Released Apr '87, on Jungle, by Jungle Records. Catalogue no: **JUNG 23P**
12" Single: Released Apr '87, on Jungle, by Jungle Records. Catalogue no: **JUNG 23T**

GET OFF THE PHONE
Tracks: / Get off the phone / All by myself.
7" Pic: Released Sep '84, on Jungle, by Jungle Records. Catalogue no: **JUNG 14P**
12" Single: Released Sep '84, on Jungle, by Jungle Records. Catalogue no: **JUNG 14X**
7" Single: Released Mar '84, on Jungle, by Jungle Records. Catalogue no: **JUNG 14**

HURT ME (SINGLE)
Tracks: / Hurt me / It's not enough / Like a rolling stone.
7" Single: Released Feb '84, on New Rose (1), by New Rose Records. Catalogue no: **NEW 27**

IN COLD BLOOD (SINGLE)
Tracks: / In cold blood.
CD 5": Released Apr '89, on New Rose (1), by New Rose Records. Catalogue no: **NEAT 5CD**

QUE SERA SERA (SINGLE)
Tracks: / Que sera sera.
12" Single: Released Jun '87, on Jungle, by Jungle Records. Catalogue no: **JUNG 33T**
7" Single: Released Jun '87, on Jungle, by Jungle Records. Catalogue no: **JUNG 33**

SHE WANTS TO MAMBO
Tracks: / Uptown / She wants to mambo.
7" Single: Released May '88, on Jungle, by Jungle Records. Catalogue no: **JUNG 38**
12" Single: Released May '88, on Jungle, by Jungle Records. Catalogue no: **JUNG 38T**

VINTAGE '77
Tracks: / Vintage '77.
12" Single: Released May '83, on Jungle, by Jungle Records. Catalogue no: **JUNG 5**

Thunderstick

FEEL LIKE ROCK 'N' ROLL
Tracks: / Feel like rock 'n' roll? / Alecia / Runaround / Buried alive.
Note: Original Samson drummer now with sensational own outfit. (Magnum Music May, 1988).
12" Single: Released Nov '83, on Thunderbolt, by Magnum Music Group. Catalogue no: **THBE 1.002**

Thunderthighs

CENTRAL PARK ARREST
Tracks: / Central Park arrest.
7" Single: Released Jun '74, on Philips, by Phonogram Ltd. Deleted '77. Catalogue no: **6006 386**

LOVING YOU AIN'T EASY
Tracks: / Loving you ain't easy / Shine a light on me.
7" Single: Released Mar '81, on Blue Inc, Deleted Mar '84. Catalogue no: **INC 12**

Thunderthumbs

FREEDOM
Tracks: / Freedom.
7" Single: Released Jul '82, on Polydor, by Polydor Ltd. Catalogue no: **POSP 480**
12" Single: Released Jul '82, on Polydor, by Polydor Ltd. Catalogue no: **POSPX 480**

Thurston, Bobby

CHECK OUT THE GROOVE
Tracks: / Check out the groove / Sitting in the park.
7" Single: Released Mar '80, on Epic, by CBS Records. Deleted '83. Catalogue no: **EPC 8348**

YOU GOT WHAT IT TAKES (SINGLE)
Tracks: / You got what it takes / I wanna do it with you.
7" Single: Released Jun '80, on Epic, by CBS Records. Deleted '83. Catalogue no: **EPC 8594**

Tibbs, Frederica

WAY I FEEL
Tracks: / Way I feel.
12" Single: Released Sep '88, on Sure Spin, Catalogue no: **SPN 007**

Tibbs, Fredi

ALL I HAVE TO DO IS DREAM
Tracks: / All I have to do is dream / Mede mahoma besona-menyanie.
7" Single: Released Feb '86, on Tulip, Catalogue no: **TUL 001**

Tibetan Ritual

TIBETAN RITUAL MUSIC
Tracks: / Tibetan ritual music.
12" Single: Released Jul '87, on Sub Rosa, by Sub Rosa Records. Catalogue no: **SUB 12004-10**

T.I.C.

POPCORN '88
Tracks: / Popcorn '88 (woodstock mix).
7" Single: Released Sep '88, on Arista, by BMG Records (UK). Deleted May '89. Catalogue no: **TICK 1**
12" Single: Released Sep '88, on Arista, by BMG Records (UK). Catalogue no: **TICK T1**

Tidee-T

SMURF DANCE
Tracks: / Smurf dance.
12" Single: Released Jun '84, on Carrere, Catalogue no: **CART 318**

Tied Logs

BLUEBELL POLKA
Tracks: / Bluebell polka / Cat on the mixer.
7" Single: Released Oct '83, on Button, by Musical Characters Records. Catalogue no: **BTN 111**

CAPTAIN PUGWASH
Tracks: / Captain Pugwash.
7" Single: Released Aug '84, on Button, by Musical Characters Records. Catalogue no: **BTN 118**

STAMP AND SWING
Tracks: / Stamp and swing / Kamikaze banjos.
7" Single: Released Oct '82, on Button, by Musical Characters Records. Catalogue no: **BTN 102**

Tier Garden

AFRIKAAN
Tracks: / Afrikaan / Working.
7" Single: Released Aug '84, on Cogent, Catalogue no: **COG 1**

INDIA
Tracks: / India.
7" Single: Released Mar '86, on Cogent, Catalogue no: **TGC 061**

PASARAN
Tracks: / Pasaran.
12" Single: Released '88, on Cogent, Catalogue no: **TGCOG 004**

Tiers Opera

GIRLS VOICES
Tracks: / Girls voices / Alice.
7" Single: Released Mar '85, on Tiers Opera, by Priority Records. Catalogue no: **TAM 1**
12" Single: Released Mar '85, on Tiers Opera, by Priority Records. Catalogue no: **TAMT 1**

Tiffany

ALL THIS TIME
Tracks: / All this time.
12" Single: Released Jan '89, on MCA, by MCA Records. Catalogue no: **TIFFT 6**
Special: Released Jan '89, on MCA, by MCA Records. Catalogue no: **TIFFB 6**
CD 3": Released Jan '89, on MCA, by MCA Records. Catalogue no: **DTIFF 6**
7" Single: Released Jan '89, on MCA, by MCA Records. Catalogue no: **TIFF 6**

COULD'VE BEEN
Tracks: / Heart of love, The / Could've been (ext.) / Could've been.
7" Single: Released Mar '88, on MCA, by MCA Records. Deleted 1 Jul '89. Catalogue no: **TIFF 2**
12" Single: Released Mar '88, on MCA, by MCA Records. Catalogue no: **TIFFT 2**

FEELINGS OF FOREVER
Tracks: / Feelings of forever / Out of my heart / Heart don't break tonight (Available on 12" only).
Note: *only on the 12" single
12" Single: Released Jul '88, on MCA, by MCA Records. Catalogue no: **TIFFT 4**
7" Single: Released Jul '88, on MCA, by MCA Records. Deleted 1 Jul '89. Catalogue no: **TIFF 4**

I SAW HIM STANDING THERE
Tracks: / I saw him standing there / Mr. Mambo.
7" Single: Released 14 May '88, on MCA, by MCA Records. Catalogue no: **TIFPR 3**
12" Single: Released 14 May '88, on MCA, by MCA Records. Catalogue no: **TIFFT 3**
CD 5": Released 14 May '88, on MCA, by MCA Records. Catalogue no: **DTIFF 3**
7" Single: Released 14 May '88, on MCA, by MCA Records. Deleted 1 Jul '89. Catalogue no: **TIFF 3**

I THINK WE'RE ALONE NOW
Tracks: / I think we're alone now.
7" Single: Released Jan '88, on MCA, by MCA Records. Deleted 1 Jul '89. Catalogue no: **MCA 1211**
Cassingle: Released Jan '88, on MCA, by MCA Records. Catalogue no: **MCAC 1211**
CD 5": Released Jan '88, on MCA, by MCA Records. Catalogue no: **DMCA 1211**

RADIO ROMANCE
Tracks: / Radio romance.
CD 5": Released Oct '88, on MCA, by MCA Records. Catalogue no: **DTIFF 5**
12" Pic: Released Nov '88, on MCA, by MCA Records. Catalogue no: **TIFFTP 5**
7" Single: Released Oct '88, on MCA, by MCA Records. Deleted 1 Jul '89. Catalogue no: **TIFF 5**

12" Single: Released Oct '88, on MCA, by MCA Records. Catalogue no: **TIFFT 5**

Tiger

BAD BOY STYLE
Tracks: / Bad boy style.
12" Single: Released Apr '88, on Rockas, Catalogue no: **R 004RV**

CAN'T STAY YASO
Tracks: / Can't say yaso / Sitting in LA LA.
12" Single: Released Mar '87, on Hawkeye, by Hawkeye Records. Catalogue no: **PL 15**

DO IT ANY WAY
Tracks: / Do it anyway.
12" Single: Released Oct '88, on RAS (Real Authentic Sound), by Greensleeves Records. Catalogue no: **RAS 7031**

FIRE
Tracks: / Fire.
12" Single: Released 1 Jul '89, on Live & Love, Catalogue no: **LLD 129**

GUILTY
Tracks: / Guilty / Have you ever been hurt / Three dog night.
10" single: Released Sep '82, on Pama, by Pama Records. Catalogue no: **PMD 3219**

HOW DO YOU DO
12" Single: Released Jul '89, on Blue Mountain, Catalogue no: **BMD 064**

NAH SKIN UP
Tracks: / Nah skin up.
12" Single: Released Sep '89, on Penthouse, by Penthouse Records. Catalogue no: **PH 021**

NO PUPPY LOVE
Tracks: / No puppy love / Country girl.
12" Single: Released Sep '86, on Thunderbelt, Catalogue no: **TB 001**

RAM DANCE HALL (SINGLE)
Tracks: / Ram dance hall.
12" Single: Released 30 May '89, on Steely & Cleevie, Catalogue no: **VPRD 433**

Tiger Lily

ANTHEM FROM A RUPERT OPERA
Tracks: / Anthem from a Rupert opera.
7" Single: Released Aug '85, on Rose, by Rose Records. Deleted '87. Catalogue no: **RRS 2**

Tiger Moth

SPEED THE PLOUGH
Tracks: / Speed the plough.
7" Single: Released Oct '84, on Rogue, by Rogue Records. Catalogue no: **FMSS 104**

Tiger Tails

WORDS WITHOUT CONVICTION
Tracks: / Words without conviction.
7" Single: Released Dec '80, on Snotty Snail, Deleted '82. Catalogue no: **NEL COL 2**

Tiger Tailz

LIVIN' WITHOUT YOU
Tracks: / Living without you / Nine livez.
12" Single: Released Jun '88, on Music For Nations, by Music For Nations Records. Catalogue no: **12 KUT 129**
7" Single: Released Jun '88, on Music For Nations, by Music For Nations Records. Catalogue no: **KUT 129**

SHOOT TO KILL
Tracks: / Shoot to kill (Shoot to kill (3 track)).
12" Single: Released Mar '87, on European Rock Promotions, Catalogue no: **TAILZ 001**

Tigers

KIDDING STOPS
Tracks: / Kidding stops / Great expense, small income.
7" Single: Released Feb '80, on Strike (1), by Strike Records. Deleted Feb '83. Catalogue no: **KIK 1**

PROMISES, PROMISES
Tracks: / Promises, promises / Star trekkin'.
7" Single: Released 20 Jun '80, on Strike (2), Deleted '83. Catalogue no: **KK 2**

SAVAGE MUSIC
Tracks: / Savage music / Ice cold in Fulham.
7" Single: Released Oct '80, on Strike (1), by Strike Records. Deleted Oct '83. Catalogue no: **KIK 4**

Tigertailz

LOVE BOMB BABY
Tracks: / Love bomb baby / Love bomb baby (version) / She's too hot (live) / Few dollars more (live) (12" only).

12" Single: Released Jun '89, on Music For Nations, by Music For Nations Records. Catalogue no: **12KUT 132**
7" Single: Released Jun '89, on Music For Nations, by Music For Nations Records. Catalogue no: **KUT 132**

TIGHT FIT - FANTASY ISLAND (Released on Jive)

Tight Fit

BACK TO THE 60'S (PART 1)(SINGLE)
Tracks: / Back to the sixties (part 1) / Cocoa night.
7" Single: Released Nov '85, on Jive, by Zomba Records. Catalogue no: **JIVE 2**
12" Single: Released Nov '85, on Jive, by Zomba Records. Catalogue no: **JIVET 2**

BACK TO THE 60'S (PART 2)(SINGLE)
Tracks: / Back to the 60's (part 2).
7" Single: Released Sep '81, on Jive, by Zomba Records. Deleted Sep '84. Catalogue no: **JIVE 5**
12" Single: Released Sep '81, on Jive, by Zomba Records. Deleted Sep '84. Catalogue no: **JIVET 5**

FANTASY ISLAND (see panel above)
Tracks: / Fantasy Island / Saturday heartbreak.
12" Single: Released Apr '82, on Jive, by Zomba Records. Catalogue no: **JIVET 13**
7" Single: Released Apr '82, on Jive, by Zomba Records. Catalogue no: **JIVE 13**
7" Pic: Released Apr '82, on Jive, by Zomba Records. Catalogue no: **JIVEP 13**

I'M UNDECIDED
Tracks: / I'm undecided / Hearts of stone break hearts of glass.
7" Pic: Released Oct '82, on Jive, by Zomba Records. Catalogue no: **JIVEP 26**
7" Single: Released Oct '82, on Jive, by Zomba Records. Catalogue no: **JIVE 26**

LION SLEEPS TONIGHT (OLD GOLD)
Tracks: / Lion sleeps tonight, The / Fantasy Island.
7" Single: Released 24 Apr '89, on Old Gold, by Old Gold Records. Catalogue no: **OG 9892**

LION SLEEPS TONIGHT (WIMO-WEH)
Tracks: / Lion sleeps tonight, The.
7" Single: Released Jan '82, on Jive, by Zomba Records. Catalogue no: **JIVE 9**
12" Single: Released Jan '82, on Jive, by Zomba Records. Catalogue no: **JIVET 9**

LOVE THE ONE YOU'RE WITH
Tracks: / Love the one you're with.
7" Single: Released Oct '83, on Jive, by Zomba Records. Catalogue no: **JIVE 50**
12" Single: Released Oct '83, on Jive, by Zomba Records. Catalogue no: **JIVET 50**

SECRET HEART
Tracks: / Secret heart / Just a moment away.
7" Single: Released Jul '82, on Jive, by Zomba Records. Catalogue no: **JIVE 20**
12" Single: Released Jul '82, on Jive, by Zomba Records. Catalogue no: **JIVET 20**

Tightrope

EVEREST THE HARD WAY
Tracks: / Everest the hard way / When you're young.
12" Single: Released Mar '82, on Do-It, by Do-It Records. Catalogue no: **DUNIT 17**
7" Single: Released Mar '82, on Do-It, by Do-It Records. Catalogue no: **DUN 17**

Tights

BAD HEARTS
Tracks: / Bad hearts.
7" Single: Released Jun '78, on Cherry Red, by Cherry Red Records. Deleted '87. Catalogue no: **CHERRY 1**

HOWARD HUGHES
Tracks: / Howard Hughes.
7" Single: Released Sep '78, on Cherry Red, by Cherry Red Records. Deleted '87. Catalogue no: **CHERRY 2**

Tik & Tok

COOL RUNNING
Tracks: / Cool running / Vile bodies / Soulless synthetic hot steps (on 12" only).
7" Single: Released Sep '83, on Survival (1), by Survival Records. Catalogue no: **SUR 016**
7" Pic: Released Sep '83, on Survival (1), by Survival Records. Catalogue no: **SURP 016**
12" Single: Released Sep '83, on Survival (1), by Survival Records. Catalogue no: **SUR 12 016**

EVERYTHING WILL CHANGE
Tracks: / Everything will change.
7" Pic: Released Jul '84, on Survival (1), by Survival Records. Catalogue no: **SURP 024**
12" Single: Released Jul '84, on Survival (1), by Survival Records. Catalogue no: **SUR 12 024**
7" Single: Released Jul '84, on Survival (1), by Survival Records. Catalogue no: **SUR 024**

HIGHER GROUND
Tracks: / Higher ground / Down from the sky.
12" Single: Released Aug '84, on Survival (1), by Survival Records. Catalogue no: **SUR 12 027**
7" Single: Released Aug '84, on Survival (1), by Survival Records. Catalogue no: **SUR 027**

SCREEN ME I'M YOURS
Tracks: / Screen me I'm yours.
7" Pic: Released Dec '83, on Survival (1), by Survival Records. Catalogue no: **SURP 020**
7" Set: Released Dec '83, on Survival (1), by Survival Records. Catalogue no: **SCREEN 5**
7" Set: Released Dec '83, on Survival (1), by Survival Records. Catalogue no: **SCREEN 3**
12" Single: Released Dec '83, on Survival (1), by Survival Records. Catalogue no: **SUR 12 020**

SUMMER IN THE CITY
Tracks: / Summer in the city / Crises.
7" Pic: Released Sep '82, on Survival (1), by Survival Records. Catalogue no: **SURP 007**
7" Single: Released Sep '82, on Survival (1), by Survival Records. Catalogue no: **SUR 007**
12" Single: Released Sep '82, on Survival (1), by Survival Records. Catalogue no: **SUR 12 007**

Tikaram, Tanita

CATHEDRAL SONG
Tracks: / Cathedral song / Sighing innocents / Fire flies in the kitchen (On 12" version only.) / Let's make everybody smile today (On 12" version only.).
7" Single: Released Jan '89, on WEA, by WEA Records. Catalogue no: **YZ 331**
12" Single: Released Jan '89, on WEA, by WEA Records. Catalogue no: **YZ 331 T**
CD 5": Released Jan '89, on WEA, by WEA Records. Catalogue no: **YZ 331 CD**

GOOD TRADITION
Tracks: / Good tradition / Valentine heart.
7" Single: Released Jun '88, on WEA, by WEA Records. Catalogue no: **YZ 196**
12" Single: Released Jun '88, on WEA, by WEA Records. Catalogue no: **YZ 196T**
CD 5": Released Jun '88, on WEA, by WEA Records. Catalogue no: **YZ 196 CD**

TWIST IN MY SOBRIETY
Tracks: / Twist in my sobriety / Friends / For all these years (Only on 12") / Kill in your time, The (Only on CD single.).
7" Single: Released Oct '88, on WEA, by WEA Records. Catalogue no: **YZ 321**
12" Single: Released Oct '88, on WEA, by WEA Records. Catalogue no: **YZ 321T**
CD 5": Released Oct '88, on WEA, by WEA Records. Catalogue no: **YZ 321CD**

WORLD OUTSIDE YOUR WINDOW
Tracks: / World outside your window / Good tradition (live) (Only on 12" and CD single) / For all these years.
CD 5": Released Mar '89, on WEA, by WEA Records. Catalogue no: **YZ 363 CD**
12" Single: Released Feb '89, on WEA, by WEA Records. Catalogue no: **YZ 363T**
7" Single: Released Feb '89, on WEA, by WEA Records. Catalogue no: **YZ 363**
CD 5": Released Mar '89, on WEA, by WEA Records. Catalogue no: **YZ 363 CDX**

'Til Tuesday

(BELIEVED YOU WERE) LUCKY
Tracks: / (Believed you were) lucky / Limits to love / Voices carry / What about love.
12" Single: Released 16 Jan '89, on Epic, by CBS Records. Deleted 10 Jul '89. Catalogue no: **653 064-6**
7" Single: Released 16 Jan '89, on Epic, by CBS Records. Deleted 10 Jul '89. Catalogue no: **653 064-7**
CD 5": Released 23 Jan '89, on Epic, by CBS Records. Deleted 10 Jul '89. Catalogue no: **653 064-2**
7" Single: Released 30 Jan '89, on Epic, by CBS Records. Deleted 10 Jul '89. Catalogue no: **653 064-0**

WHAT ABOUT LOVE
Tracks: / Voices carry / What about love.
12" Single: Released Jan '87, on Epic, by CBS Records. Catalogue no: **650125 6**
7" Single: Released Feb '87, on Epic, by CBS Records. Catalogue no: **650125 7**

Till, Emmitt

AMERICAN POLICE
Tracks: / American police / Hit man.
7" Single: Released Aug '85, on PVK, by PVK Records. Catalogue no: **PV 122**

FIGHT-GAME
Tracks: / Fight-game / Nothing like a motorbike.
7" Single: Released Sep '86, on Swoop, Catalogue no: **RTL 002**

NEW YORK JETS
Tracks: / New York Jets / Alligator man.
7" Single: Released May '84, on PVK, by PVK Records. Catalogue no: **PVK 120**

NIGHT WALKIN'
Tracks: / Night walkin' / Latin.
7" Single: Released '86, on Swoop, Catalogue no: **RTLS 012**

Tiller Boys

BIG NOISE FROM THE JUNGLE (EP)
7" Single: Released Jul '81, on New Hormones, Catalogue no: **ORG 3**

Tillotson, Johnny

Biographical details: Tillotson was born in 1939 in Jacksonville, Florida; the country/pop singer was discovered at a Nashville talent show and signed to Cadence, the **Everly Brothers** label; followed them into the charts with popped-up versions of country songs: of 25 USA hit singles 1958-66, 14 in top 40, *Poetry In Motion* '60 was biggest at No. 2 (No.1 in UK). (Donald Clarke 13.1.88).

I CAN'T HELP IT
Tracks: / I can't help it.
7" Single: Released Dec '62, on London-American, Deleted Dec '65. Catalogue no: **HLA 9642**

IT KEEPS RIGHT ON A HURTIN'
Tracks: / It keeps right on a-hurtin'.
7" Single: Released Jul '62, on London-American, Deleted Jul '65. Catalogue no: **HLA 9550**

JIMMY'S GIRL
Tracks: / Jimmy's girl.
7" Single: Released Feb '61, on London-

merican, Deleted Feb '64. Catalogue no: LA 9275

UT OF MY MIND
acks: / Out of my mind.
Single: Released May '63, on London-merican, Deleted May '66. Catalogue no: **LA 9695**

OETRY IN MOTION (OLD GOLD)
acks: / Poetry in motion / Princess Prin-ess.
Single: Released Jun '88, on Old Gold, Old Gold Records. Catalogue no: **OG 016**

OETRY IN MOTION (SINGLE)
acks: / Poetry in motion.
Single: Released Apr '79, on Lightning, eleted Apr '82. Catalogue no: **LIG 9016**
Single: Released Dec '60, on London-merican, Deleted Dec '63. Catalogue no: **LA 9231**

END ME THE PILLOW YOU DREAM N
acks: / Send me the pillow that you dream n.
Single: Released Oct '62, on London-merican, Deleted Oct '65. Catalogue no: **LA 9598**

Tilston, Steve

ON'T LOOK DOWN
acks: / S.O.S. / Don't look down.
Single: Released Sep '84, on T.W., by W. Records. Catalogue no: **HIT 114**

UT THE BLAME ON ME
acks: / Put the blame on me / Nobody's own.
Single: Released Dec '80, on Edge, eleted Dec '85. Catalogue no: **EDGE 6**

HESE DAYS (see panel below)
acks: / These days / Lazy tango.
Single: Released Aug '87, on Run River, In-Market Ltd.. Catalogue no: **RRAS 001**

im & Nell

HERE WILL COME LOVE
acks: / There will come love / Together ain.
" Single: Released May '82, on Orbitone, Orbitone Records. Catalogue no: **ORBD**

im & Tina

MISS YOUR TENDER LIPS
acks: / I miss your tender lips.
Single: on Sierra, by Sierra Records. eleted Jun '87. Catalogue no: **FED 6**

imbuk 3

IRWAVE JUNGLE (EP)
acks: / Airwave jungle.
EP: Released Aug '86, on Illegal, by ulty Products Records. Catalogue no: **JK 3**

.L I WANT FOR CHRISTMAS IS ORLD PEACE
acks: / All I want for Christmas is world ace / Shame on you (remix).
Single: Released 21 Nov '87, on I.R.S, atalogue no: **IRM 142**

12" Single: Released 21 Nov '87, on I.R.S, Catalogue no: **IRMT 142**

EASY
Tracks: / Easy / I love you in the strangest way / This town cries.
12" Single: Released 9 May '88, on MCA, by MCA Records. Catalogue no: **IRMT 165**
7" Single: Released 9 May '88, on MCA, by MCA Records. Catalogue no: **IRM 165**

FUTURE'S SO BRIGHT I GOTTA WEAR SHADES
Tracks: / Future's so bright I gotta wear shades, The / I'll do alright / Shame on you (12" only).
7" Single: Released Jan '87, on I.R.S, Catalogue no: **IRM 126**
12" Single: Released Jan '87, on I.R.S, Catalogue no: **IRMT 126**

HAIRSTYLES AND ATTITUDES
Tracks: / Hairstyles and attitudes / I love you in the strangest way / Airwave jungle/I just want to make love to you (medley).
7" Single: Released Mar '87, on I.R.S, Catalogue no: **IRM 133**
12" Single: Released Mar '87, on I.R.S, Catalogue no: **IRMT 133**

REVEREND JACK & HIS ROAMIN' CADILLAC CHURCH
Tracks: / Reverend Jack & his roamin' cadillac church.
12" Single: Released Jul '88, on I.R.S, Catalogue no: **IRMT 169**
7" Single: Released Jul '88, on I.R.S, Catalogue no: **IRM 169**

Time

COOL
Tracks: / Cool 1 / Cool 2.
7" Single: Released Feb '82, on Warner Bros., by WEA Records. Catalogue no: **K 17920**
12" Single: Released Feb '82, on Warner Bros., by WEA Records. Catalogue no: **K 17920 T**

GOT YOUR NUMBER
Tracks: / Got your number / Grace.
12" Single: Released Jan '83, on Warner Bros., by WEA Records. Catalogue no: **W 9982 T**
7" Single: Released Jan '83, on Warner Bros., by WEA Records. Catalogue no: **W 9982**

Time Bandits

ENDLESS ROAD
Tracks: / Fiction / Endless road.
7" Single: Released Jan '87, on CBS, by CBS Records. Deleted Aug '87. Catalogue no: **650329 7**

HOW DOES IT FEEL
Tracks: / How does it feel / Power.
7" Single: Released Apr '84, on CBS, by CBS Records. Catalogue no: **A 4411**

I'M ONLY SHOOTING LOVE
Tracks: / I'm only shooting love / Only lovers will survive.
7" Single: Released Jul '84, on CBS, by CBS Records. Catalogue no: **A 4218**
12" Single: Released Jul '84, on CBS, by CBS Records. Catalogue no: **TA 4218**

STEVE TILSTON - THESE DAYS (Released on Run River)

I'M SPECIALISED IN YOU
Tracks: / I'm specialised in you.
7" Single: Released Feb '83, on CBS, by CBS Records. Catalogue no: **A 2915**
12" Single: Released Feb '83, on CBS, by CBS Records. Catalogue no: **A 13 2915**

LISTEN TO THE MAN WITH THE GOLDEN VOICE
Tracks: / Listen to the man with the golden voice.
12" Single: Released May '83, on CBS, by CBS Records. Catalogue no: **TA 3161**
7" Single: Released May '83, on CBS, by CBS Records. Catalogue no: **A 3161**

ONLY A FOOL
Tracks: / 123 / Only a fool.
12" Single: Released Mar '86, on CBS, by CBS Records. Catalogue no: **TX 6786**
7" Single: Released Mar '86, on CBS, by CBS Records. Catalogue no: **A 6786**

WHEN YOU'RE DANCING
Tracks: / When you're dancing.
7" Single: Released Aug '87, on CBS, by CBS Records. Catalogue no: **650094 7**

Time Code

LOUIE LOUIE
Tracks: / Village house stomp / Louie Louie.
7" Single: Released Nov '86, on Jive, by Zomba Records. Deleted Jul '87. Catalogue no: **LOU 1**
12" Single: Released Nov '86, on Jive, by Zomba Records. Deleted Jul '87. Catalogue no: **LOUT 1**

Time Dance

PICTURE
Tracks: / Picture.
7" Single: Released Sep '83, on Midnight, Catalogue no: **DING 3**

Time In Motion

I WANNA BE YOUR TELEPHONE
Tracks: / I wanna be your telephone.
7" Single: Released Scp '82, on Red Rhino, by Red Rhino Records. Deleted '88. Catalogue no: **RED 19**

QUIET TYPE
Tracks: / Quiet type.
7" Single: Released May '82, on Red Rhino, by Red Rhino Records. Deleted '88. Catalogue no: **RED 13**

Time Lords

DOCTORIN' THE TARDIS
Tracks: / Doctorin' the Tardis / Doctorin' the tardis (Gary Glitter remix).
12" Single: Released Jul '88, on KLF, by KLF Communications. Catalogue no: **KLF 003R**
7" Single: Released May '88, on KLF, by KLF Communications. Catalogue no: **KLF 003**
12" Single: Released May '88, on KLF, by KLF Communications. Catalogue no: **KLF 003T**

Time Machine

SUMMER OF LOVE
Tracks: / Summer of love (EP) / San Francisco / Paper sun / Flowers in the rain / Whiter shade of pale, A / California dreaming / All you need is love / Summer of love.
7" EP: Released Jun '88, on Bam Caruso, by Demon Records. Catalogue no: **NRIC 056**

Time & Patience

TRIBULATION
Tracks: / Tribulation.
12" Single: Released Apr '85, on Creole, by Creole Records. Catalogue no: **CRT 83**

Time UK

Biographical details: Time UK consists of Rick Buckler (drums); Jimmy Edwards (vocals); Ray Simone (guitar); Nick South (bass) and Fletcher Christian (lead/rhythm guitar). Following the **Jam's** demise in late 1982, Rick Buckler decided not to put his drum sticks to rest but to form another band with his friend, guitarist Ray Simone. They first recruited the services of vocalist and songwriter Jimmy Edwards and the embryonic Time UK was born. The trio lost no time in starting rehearsals and using various bass players, everything started to gell and the band came together. After innumerable auditions for a guitarist, eventually they decided on Fletcher Christian who had previously played with a London band called **The Vampires**. With bass player Nick South, ex of **Sniff 'n' The Tears** the Time UK lineup was complete. Time UK are currently touring the UK including a date at the Marquee in London in February and have their debut single released through Arista Records entitled *Playground of Privilege* in February. (Arista Press Office, January 1985).

CABARET, THE
Tracks: / Cabaret, The / Remember days.
7" Single: Released Sep '83, on Red Bus, by Red Bus Records. Catalogue no: **TIM 123**
12" Single: Released Sep '83, on Red Bus, by Red Bus Records. Catalogue no: **TIME 123**

PLAY GROUND OF PRIVELGE
Tracks: / Play ground of privelge.
7" Single: Released Jan '85, on Arista, by BMG Records (UK). Catalogue no: **ARIST 597**
12" Single: Released Jan '85, on Arista, by BMG Records (UK). Catalogue no: **ARIST 12597**

YOU WON'T STOP
Tracks: / You won't stop.
12" Single: Released Sep '85, on Arista, by BMG Records (UK). Catalogue no: **ARIST 12637**
7" Single: Released Sep '85, on Arista, by BMG Records (UK). Catalogue no: **ARIST 637**

Time Unlimited

AFRICAN WOMAN
12" Single: Released Oct '85, on Time Unlimited, Deleted '86. Catalogue no: **TL 001**

Time Zone

WORLD DESTRUCTION
Tracks: / World destruction / World destruction (industrial mix) (VS 743-13 only).
12" Single: Released '85, on Virgin, by Virgin Records. Catalogue no: **VS 743-13**
7" Single: Released Jan '85, on Virgin, by Virgin Records. Catalogue no: **VS 743**
12" Single: Released Jan '85, on Virgin, by Virgin Records. Deleted May '88. Catalogue no: **VS 743-12**

WORLD DESTRUCTION (CD SINGLE)
Tracks: / World destruction / World destruction(instumental blast).
CD 3": Released '88, on Virgin, by Virgin Records. Catalogue no: **CDT 29**

Timebox

BEGGIN'
Tracks: / Beggin'.
7" Single: Released Jul '68, on Deram, by London Records. Deleted Jul '71. Catalogue no: **DM 194**

Timeless All Stars

MESSINA
Tracks: / Messina / Lupe.
CD 3": Released '88, on Delos (USA), Catalogue no: **D/PC 2105**

Timerider

COCOON
Tracks: / Cocoon / Timerider.
12" Single: Released Jan '88, on Lisson, by PWL Records. Catalogue no: **DOLEQ 8**
7" Single: Released Feb '88, on Lisson, by PWL Records. Catalogue no: **DOLE 8**

Times

ARE YOU INTO IT
Tracks: / Are you into it.
7" Single: Released May '89, on Creation, by Creation Records. Catalogue no: **CRE 066**
12" Single: Released May '89, on Creation, by Creation Records. Catalogue no: **CRE 066T**

BLUE FIRE
Tracks: / Blue fire.
7" Single: Released Oct '84, on Art Pop, by Art Pop Records. Catalogue no: **POP 45**

BOYS ABOUT TOWN
Tracks: / Boys about town.
12" Single: Released Oct '85, on Art Pop, by Art Pop Records. Catalogue no: **POP 43DOZ**

BOYS BRIGADE
Tracks: / Boys brigade / Power is forever.
7" Single: Released Aug '84, on Art Pop, by Art Pop Records. Catalogue no: **POP 46**

DANGER MAN THEME
Tracks: / Danger man theme.
7" Single: Released Sep '83, on Art Pop, by Art Pop Records. Catalogue no: **POP 49**

I HELPED PATRICK MCGOOHAN ESCAPE (SINGLE)
Tracks: / I helped Patrick McGoohan escape.
7" Single: Released Jan '84, on Art Pop, by Art Pop Records. Catalogue no: **POP 48**

PLASTIC FANTASTIC
Tracks: / Plastic fantastic.
12" Single: Released Jul '89, on Creation, by Creation Records. Catalogue no: **CRE 066 T**
7" Single: Released Jul '89, on Creation, by Creation Records. Catalogue no: **CRE 066**

RED WITH PURPLE FLASHES
Tracks: / Red with purple falshes / Biff bang

pow.
7" Single: Released Jul '81, on Whaam, Catalogue no: **WHAAM 02**

TIMES'TV
Tracks: / Time TV / Trailor from 'Enjoy' / Policeforce, The (Extra track on 12"version only.) / El aragua (Extra track on 12"version only.) / Pick it up (Extra track on 12"version only.).
12" Single: Released Oct '86, on Fire, by Fire Records. Catalogue no: **BLAZE 16T**
7" Single: Released Oct '86, on Fire, by Fire Records. Catalogue no: **BLAZE 16**

Times Square

JOANNE
Tracks: / Joanne.
7" Single: Released Jun '83, on Northeast Music, by Northeast Music Records. Catalogue no: **LETS GO 1**

Times Two

CECILIA
Tracks: / Cecilia / Romeo.
12" Single: Released Oct '88, on Warner Bros., by WEA Records. Catalogue no: **W 7756T**
7" Single: Released Oct '88, on Warner Bros., by WEA Records. Catalogue no: **W 7756**

STRANGE BUT TRUE
Tracks: / Strange but true / Come over.
7" Single: Released May '88, on WEA, by WEA Records. Catalogue no: **W 7998**
12" Single: Released May '88, on WEA, by WEA Records. Catalogue no: **W 7998T**

Timex Social Club

MIXED UP WORLD
Tracks: / Mixed up world.
7" Single: Released Nov '86, on Cool Tempo, by Chrysalis Records. Catalogue no: **COOL 138**
12" Single: Released Nov '86, on Cool Tempo, by Chrysalis Records. Catalogue no: **COOLX 138**

RUMOURS
Tracks: / Rumours / Rumours (Shep's version).
12" Single: Released '86, on Cool Tempo, by Chrysalis Records. Catalogue no: **COOLX 13**
7" Single: Released '86, on Cool Tempo, by Chrysalis Records. Catalogue no: **COOL 133**

Timms, Sally

LONG BLACK VEIL
Tracks: / Butchers boy / Margherita / Down to Dover / Long black veil.
7" Single: Released Nov '86, on Tim, by Tim Records. Catalogue no: **MOT 4**
12" Single: Released Nov '86, on Tim, by Tim Records. Catalogue no: **12 MOT 4**

THIS HOUSE IS A HOUSE OF TROUBLE Featuring Marc Almond
Tracks: / This house is a house of trouble / Chained to the anchor of love.
7" Single: Released 13 Jun '87, on Tim, by Tim Records. Catalogue no: **MOT 6**
12" Single: Released 13 Jun '87, on Tim, by Tim Records. Catalogue no: **12 MOT 6**

Timms/Almond

HOUSE OF TROUBLE
Tracks: / House of trouble.
12" Single: Released '87, on Tim, by Tim Records. Catalogue no: **MOT 12006**

Tin Drum

L' AMOURER
Tracks: / L'amourer.
12" Single: Released Apr '86, on Fun After All, by Music For Nations Records. Catalogue no: **12 FAA 102**
7" Single: Released Apr '86, on Fun After All, by Music For Nations Records. Catalogue no: **FAA 102**

Tin Gods

COSMETICS
Tracks: / Cosmetics.
12" Single: Released Mar '88, on Razor, by Razor Records. Catalogue no: **RZST 110**

Tin Kan

THOUSAND MILES OF WHITE
Tracks: / Thousand miles of white / Girl I'd never let you down.
7" Single: Released Oct '79, on White Dove, by White Dove Records. Catalogue no: **WD 103**

Tin Machine

PRISONER OF LOVE
Tracks: / Prisoner of love (edit) (Not on 12".) / Baby can dance (live) / Prisoner of love (LP version) (12" & CD single only.) / Crack City (live) (12" & CD single only.).
CD 5": Released Nov '89, on EMI-Manhattan, by EMI Records. Catalogue no: **203 574 2**
7" Pic: Released Nov '89, on EMI-Manhattan, by EMI Records. Catalogue no: **MTPD 76**
Cassingle: Released Nov '89, on EMI-Manhattan, by EMI Records. Catalogue no: **TCMT 76**
7" Pic: Released Nov '89, on EMI-Manhattan, by EMI Records. Catalogue no: **203 547 0**
7" Single: Released Nov '89, on EMI-Manhattan, by EMI Records. Catalogue no: **MT 76**
7" Single: Released Nov '89, on EMI-Manhattan, by EMI Records. Catalogue no: **203 547 7**
12" Single: Released Nov '89, on EMI-Manhattan, by EMI Records. Catalogue no: **203 574 6**
12" Single: Released Nov '89, on EMI-Manhattan, by EMI Records. Catalogue no: **12MT 76**
CD 5": Released Nov '89, on EMI-Manhattan, by EMI Records. Catalogue no: **CDMT 76**
Cassingle: Released Nov '89, on EMI-Manhattan, by EMI Records. Catalogue no: **203 547 4**

TIN MACHINE - UNDER THE GOD (Released on EMI-Manhattan)

TIN MACHINE (SINGLE)
Tracks: / Tin Machine / Maggie's farm (live) / I can't read (live) (12", Poster bag & CD single only.) / Maggie's farm (Cassingle only.) / Bus stop (live country version) (CD single only.).
Cassingle: Released Aug '89, on EMI-Manhattan, by EMI Records. Catalogue no: **TCMT 73**
CD 5": Released Aug '89, on EMI-Manhattan, by EMI Records. Catalogue no: **203 509 2**
7" Single: Released Aug '89, on EMI-Manhattan, by EMI Records. Catalogue no: **MTG 73**
7" Single: Released Aug '89, on EMI-Manhattan, by EMI Records. Catalogue no: **203 509 7**
7" Single: Released Aug '89, on EMI-Manhattan, by EMI Records. Catalogue no: **MT 73**
CD 5": Released Aug '89, on EMI-Manhattan, by EMI Records. Catalogue no: **CDMT 73**
12" Single: Released Aug '89, on EMI-Manhattan, by EMI Records. Catalogue no: **203 510 6**
12" Single: Released Aug '89, on EMI-Manhattan, by EMI Records. Catalogue no: **203 510 8**
12" Single: Released Aug '89, on EMI-Manhattan, by EMI Records. Catalogue no: **12MT 73**
12" Single: Released Aug '89, on EMI-Manhattan, by EMI Records. Catalogue no: **12MTP 73**
Special: Released Aug '89, on EMI-Manhattan, by EMI Records. Catalogue no: **203 509 0**
Special: Released Aug '89, on EMI-Manhattan, by EMI Records. Catalogue no: **MTPD 73**
Cassingle: Released Aug '89, on EMI-Manhattan, by EMI Records. Catalogue no: **203 509 4**
7" Single: Released Aug '89, on EMI-Manhattan, by EMI Records. Catalogue no: **203 509 8**

UNDER THE GOD (see panel above)
Tracks: / Under the God / Sacrifice yourself / Interview, The (Not on 7"or Cassingle.).
10" single: Released Jun '89, on EMI-Manhattan, by EMI Records. Catalogue no: **10MT 68**
CD 5": Released Jun '89, on EMI-Manhattan, by EMI Records. Catalogue no: **CDMT 68**
CD 5": Released Jun '89, on EMI-Manhattan, by EMI Records. Catalogue no: **203 415 2**
7" Single: Released Jun '89, on EMI-Manhattan, by EMI Records. Catalogue no: **203 415 7**
7" Single: Released Jun '89, on EMI-Manhattan, by EMI Records. Catalogue no: **MT 68**
12" Single: Released Jun '89, on EMI-Manhattan, by EMI Records. Catalogue no: **203 415 6**
12" Single: Released Jun '89, on EMI-Manhattan, by EMI Records. Catalogue no: **12MT 68**
Cassingle: Released Jun '89, on EMI-Manhattan, by EMI Records. Catalogue no: **TCMT 68**
Cassingle: Released Jun '89, on EMI-Manhattan, by EMI Records. Catalogue no: **203 415 4**

Tin Tin

HOLD IT
Tracks: / Hold it.
12" Single: Released Jul '83, on WEA, by WEA Records. Catalogue no: **X 9763T**
7" Single: Released Jul '83, on WEA, by WEA Records. Catalogue no: **X 9763**

KISS ME
Tracks: / Kiss me / Loves duet.
12" Single: Released Oct '82, on WEA, by WEA Records. Catalogue no: **TIN 1T**
12" Single: Released Mar '84, on WEA, by WEA Records. Catalogue no: **X 9823T**

Tin Tin Tin Tin

I HATE THE WAY YOU DRIVE
Tracks: / I hate the way you drive.
10" single: Released May '88, on Plimsoll, Catalogue no: **PLM 001**

Ti-Na-Na

KISSING FOR FUN
Tracks: / Kissing for fun / You're so attractive.
7" Single: Released Jul '86, on Genie, Catalogue no: **GEN 4**

Tiny Lights

FLOWERS IN THE AIR
Tracks: / Flowers in the air.
12" Single: Released Dec '86, on Temple Records, by Temple Records (2). Catalogue no: **TOPY 008 T**
7" Single: Released Feb '89, on Temple Records, by Temple Records (2). Catalogue no: **TOPY 008**

Tiny Tim

GREAT BALLS OF FIRE
Tracks: / Great balls of fire.
7" Single: Released Feb '69, on Reprise, by WEA Records. Deleted Feb '72. Catalogue no: **RS 20802**

Tiny Town

DROP BY DROP
Tracks: / Drop by drop.
7" Single: Released May '84, on Elastic Music, Catalogue no: **EM 001**

LIVING OUT OF LIVING
Tracks: / Living out of living.
7" Single: Released Nov '84, on Elastic Music, Catalogue no: **EM 002**

NO PLACE LIKE HOME
Tracks: / No place like home.
12" Single: Released Feb '86, on Very Mouth, Catalogue no: **EAT 8**

Tipinifini

FEVER
Tracks: / Fever.
7" Single: Released Aug '85, on Spartan, Catalogue no: **SP 124**
12" Single: Released Aug '85, on Spartan, Catalogue no: **12SP 124**

Tippa Ranking

ECHO GET SHOT
Tracks: / Echo get shot.
12" Single: Released Oct '81, on Form, Catalogue no: **FORM D 008**

GOOD LOOKING
Tracks: / Good lookin'.
12" Single: Released Aug '82, on Redman International, Catalogue no: **RED 002**

KNIFE CUT
Tracks: / Knife cut.
12" Single: Released Aug '83, on Redmar International, Catalogue no: **RED 004**

ROSE MARIE
Tracks: / Rose Marie.
12" Single: Released Aug '82, on Redmar International, Catalogue no: **RED 001**

SOLOMON YOU CAN'T KEEP A GOOD MAN DOWN
Tracks: / Solomon you can't keep a goo man down.
12" Single: Released Nov '84, on Regga Delight, Catalogue no: **RD 001**
7" Single: Released Nov '84, on Regga Delight, Catalogue no: **RD 0017**

Tipton, Lester

THIS WON'T CHANGE
Tracks: / This won't change / How.
7" Single: Released May '80, on Grapevir (Northern Soul), by BMG Records (UK Deleted May '83. Catalogue no: **GRP 138**

Tired Of Living

KISS A LOTTA FROGS
7" Single: Released Aug '81, on Initia Catalogue no: **IRS 003**

Tirez Tirez

RAZOR BLADE
Tracks: / Razor blade.
7" Single: Released Sep '81, on Aura Re ords, by Aura Records. Deleted '88. Cat logue no: **AUS 127**

STORY OF THE YEAR
Tracks: / Story of the year.
7" Single: Released Nov '83, on Les D ques Du Crepuscule(Belgium), by Les D ques Du Crepuscule(Belgium). Catalog no: **7TWI 197**

UNDER THE DOOR
Tracks: / Under the door.
12" Single: Released Jun '84, on Himalay Catalogue no: **SIDE 8406**

Titan

IMAGINARY LADY
Tracks: / Imaginary lady / Tooty flutey.
7" Single: Released Feb '83, on Af Hours, Deleted '88. Catalogue no: **AFT (**

Titanic

SULTANA
Tracks: / Sultana.
7" Single: Released Aug '71, on CBS, CBS Records. Deleted Aug '74. Catalog no: **CBS 5365**
7" Single: Released '80, on CBS, by C Records. Catalogue no: **LR 8107**

SULTANA (OLD GOLD)
Tracks: / Sultana / Sing fool sing.
7" Single: Released 24 Apr '89, on Old G by Old Gold Records. Catalogue no: **9873**

TJ Express

WORKING WITH THE PEOPLE
Tracks: / Working with the people.
7" Single: Released Jan '81, on Blue C by Blue Chip Records. Catalogue no: **105**

T.K. Dodgers

YOU WILL DANCE, SUCKER
Tracks: / You will dance, sucker.
12" Single: Released '89, on Domino, by Domino Records. Catalogue no: **DOM T11**

T-Kot

BEAT BOY
Tracks: / Beat boy.
12" Single: Released 16 Jan '89, on Strike Back, by Strike Back Records. Catalogue no: **SBR 22T**

T-Life

SOMETHING THAT YOU DO TO ME
Tracks: / Something that you do to me / Lonely.
7" Single: Released Oct '81, on Arista, by BMG Records (UK). Catalogue no: **ARIST 431**
12" Single: Released Sep '81, on Arista, by BMG Records (UK). Catalogue no: **ARIST 12431**

TNT

BACK ON THE ROAD
Tracks: / Rockin' the night / Back on the road.
7" Single: Released Apr '84, on Neat, by Neat Records. Catalogue no: **NEAT 39**

TNT Clan

BLOW UP THE DJ
Tracks: / Blow up the DJ.
12" Single: Released Jun '88, on Subway, by Subway Records. Catalogue no: **SUB 030**

To Be Continued

FIRST CUT (EP), THE
7" Single: Released Dec '82, on Visual, Catalogue no: **VR 001**

To Hell With Burgundy

WHO WANTS TO CHANGE THE WORLD?
Tracks: / Who wants to change the world.
CD 5": Released Jun '89, on Factory (1), by Factory Records. Catalogue no: **FACD 218**

T.O. Morrow

PARANOID
Tracks: / Paranoid / Remember me this way.
7" Single: Released May '85, on Tomorrows, by Esoteric Records. Catalogue no: **POP 1**

To The Finland Station

DOMINO THEORY
Tracks: / Domino theory.
7" Single: Released Jan '82, on Melodia, Deleted '83. Catalogue no: **M 3**

Toasters

EAST SIDE BEAT, THE
Tracks: / East side beat.
12" Single: Released Sep '87, on SKA, by SKA Records. Catalogue no: **SKAT 001**

Toba

MOVING UP
Tracks: / Moving up.
12" Single: Released Mar '82, on Connection, by Connection Records. Catalogue no: **CONT 8203**

Tobruk

WILD ON THE RUN (SINGLE)
Tracks: / Wild on the run / Must go on.
7" Single: Released Sep '83, on Neat, by Neat Records. Catalogue no: **NEAT 32**

Toczek,Nick

BRITANARCHIST
Tracks: / Britanarchist / More to hate than meets the eye.
12" Single: Released Feb '86, on Acrimony, by Acrimony Records. Deleted '88. Catalogue no: **ACR 1**

Today

GIRL I GOT MY EYES ON YOU
Tracks: / Girl I got my eyes on you.
7" Single: Released Mar '89, on Motown, by BMG Records (UK). Catalogue no: **ZB 426 83**
12" Single: Released Mar '89, on Motown, by BMG Records (UK). Catalogue no: **MOT 4627 T**
12" Single: Released Mar '89, on Motown, by BMG Records (UK). Catalogue no: **ZT 426 84**

HIM OR ME
Tracks: / Him or me / Him or me (inst) (7" only) / Him or me (dub mix) (12" only) / Bonus beats (12" only).
7" Single: Released Oct '88, on Motown, by BMG Records (UK). Catalogue no: **ZB 42261**
12" Single: Released Oct '88, on Motown, by BMG Records (UK). Catalogue no: **ZT 42262**

Todd

END OF THE WORLD
Tracks: / End of the world / Radio.
7" Single: Released May '81, on Crash, by Satril Records. Deleted May '86. Catalogue no: **POW 6**

THANK YOU
Tracks: / Thank you.
7" Single: Released Sep '84, on Disques Du Grand Michel, by December Songs Records. Catalogue no: **MLGS 002**

Todd, Art & Dotty

BROKEN WINGS
Tracks: / Broken wings.
7" Single: Released Feb '53, on H.M.V., by EMI Records. Deleted Feb '56. Catalogue no: **B 10399**

Todd, Leslie

HEART TO HEART
Tracks: / Heart to heart / Tender in the dark.
7" Single: Released Jan '86, on Sonet, by Sonet Records. Catalogue no: **SON 2295**

Todd, Tony

YOU'RE BREAKING MY HEART
Tracks: / You're breaking my heart / Waiting for love.
7" Single: Released Jan '83, on Crash, by Satril Records. Deleted '84. Catalogue no: **CRA 504**

Todorow, Camy

BURSTING AT THE SEAMS
Tracks: / Bursting at the seams.
7" Single: Released Sep '85, on Virgin, by Virgin Records. Deleted '86. Catalogue no: **VS 816**
12" Single: Released Sep '85, on Virgin, by Virgin Records. Deleted '86. Catalogue no: **VS 816-12**

CHAIN OF FOOLS
Tracks: / Chain of fools / Day of the storm.
7" Single: Released Mar '87, on Virgin, by Virgin Records. Deleted May '88. Catalogue no: **VS 952**

Together Brothers

HARDWORK
Tracks: / Hardwork.
12" Single: Released Sep '89, on Blue Chip, by Blue Chip Records. Catalogue no: **BLUEC 31**

MOVIN' ON UP
Tracks: / Movin' on up.
12" Single: Released Jun '89, on Blue Chip, by Blue Chip Records. Catalogue no: **BLUEC 20**

Together (Group)

PLAYING GAMES (SINGLE)
Tracks: / Playing games.
12" Single: Released May '85, on Mausoleum, by Mausoleum Records. Catalogue no: **TEST 128368**

Tokalon

COMING TO GET YOU
Tracks: / Coming to get you.
7" Single: Released Feb '82, on Champagne (DJM), Catalogue no: **BUBL 701**
12" Single: Released Feb '82, on Champagne (DJM), Catalogue no: **BUBLY 701**

Tokens

LION SLEEPS TONIGHT,THE
Tracks: / Lion sleeps tonight, The / Three bells, The.
7" Single: Released '80, on RCA, by BMG Records (UK). Catalogue no: **LR 1265**
7" Single: Released Dec '61, on RCA, by BMG Records (UK). Deleted Dec '64. Catalogue no: **RCA 1263**

LION SLEEPS TONIGHT,THE (OLD GOLD)
Tracks: / Lion sleeps tonight, The.
7" Single: Released Nov '86, on Old Gold, by Old Gold Records. Catalogue no: **OG 9653**

Tokyo Blade

CAVE SESSION,THE
Tracks: / Cave session, The.
12" Single: Released Jun '85, on Powerstation, by Powerstation Records. Catalogue no: **LEG 1 T**

LIGHTNING STRIKES
Tracks: / Lightning strikes / Fever / Attack attack.
12" Single: Released Sep '84, on Powerstation, by Powerstation Records. Catalogue no: **OHM 7 T**

MADAM GUILLOTINE
12" Single: Released Jan '85, on Powerstation, by Powerstation Records. Catalogue no: **OHM 9T**

MIDNIGHT RENDEZVOUS
Tracks: / Midnight rendezvous.
12" Single: Released Feb '84, on Powerstation, by Powerstation Records. Catalogue no: **OHM 4 T**

MOVIE STAR
Tracks: / Movie star.
12" Single: Released Apr '88, on Areba, by Areba Records. Catalogue no: **ERA 001**

POWER GAME
Tracks: / Power game, The.
7" Single: Released Oct '83, on Powerstation, by Powerstation Records. Catalogue no: **OHM 2**

UNDERCOVER HONEYMOON
Tracks: / Undercover honeymoon.
12" Single: Released Apr '86, on European Rock Promotions, Catalogue no: **BLADE 001**

Tokyo Charm

RUNAWAY
Tracks: / Runaway / More noise.
7" Single: Released Aug '82, on RCA, by BMG Records (UK). Catalogue no: **RCA 264**

Tokyo Olympics

RADIO (TURN HER ON)
Tracks: / Radio (turn her on).
7" Single: Released Jun '83, on Ritz, by Ritz Records. Catalogue no: **RITZ 050**
12" Single: Released Jun '83, on Ritz, by Ritz Records. Catalogue no: **RITZ 12050**

SHOT BY LOVE (2 PARTS)
Tracks: / Shot by love.
12" Single: Released Jan '83, on Ritz, by Ritz Records. Catalogue no: **12 RITZ 031**
7" Single: Released Jan '83, on Ritz, by Ritz Records. Catalogue no: **RITZ 031**

Toledanoa, Avi

HORA HORA
Tracks: / Hora hora.
7" Single: Released May '82, on Polydor, by Polydor Ltd. Deleted '85. Catalogue no: **POSP 449**

Toltex 9

COAL FIRES AND SEMAPHORES
Tracks: / Coal fires and semaphores / Desmond stoat.
7" Single: Released Feb '82, on EMI, by EMI Records. Deleted Feb '87. Catalogue no: **EMI 5269**

Tom The Voice

I WAS A YOUNG MAN
Tracks: / I was a young man.
7" Single: Released Nov '85, on North West, Catalogue no: **NW 001**

Tom Tom Club

DON'T SAY NO
Tracks: / Don't say no / Devil does your dog bite? / Don't say no (12"s of love mix) (Only on the 12" version and CD single.) / Beats and pieces (Only on the 12" version.) / Don't say no (Lp mix) (Only on the 12" version.) / Percapella (Only on the CD single.).
CD 5": Released Sep '88, on Fontana, by Phonogram Ltd. Catalogue no: **TCBCD 1**
7" Single: Released Sep '88, on Fontana, by Phonogram Ltd. Deleted 31 May '89. Catalogue no: **TCB 1**
12" Single: Released Sep '88, on Fontana, by Phonogram Ltd. Deleted 31 May '89. Catalogue no: **TCBX 1**
12" Single: Released Sep '88, on Fontana, by Phonogram Ltd. Deleted 31 May '89. Catalogue no: **TCBXR 1**

GENIUS OF LOVE
Tracks: / Genius of love / Yella.
7" Single: Released Oct '81, on Island, by Island Records. Deleted Oct '84. Catalogue no: **WIP 6735**
12" Single: Released '82, on Island, by Island Records. Deleted '85. Catalogue no: **12WIP 6735**

LORELEI
Tracks: / Lorelei / On and on.
7" Single: Released Jun '82, on Island, by Island Records. Catalogue no: **WIP 6762**
12" Single: Released Jun '82, on Island, by Island Records. Catalogue no: **12WIP 6762**

SUBOCEANA (boom boom chi boom boom)
Tracks: / Suboceana / Suboceana (Inst.) / Suckling, The (12" & CD only).
7" Single: Released Nov '88, on Fontana, by Phonogram Ltd. Deleted 31 May '89. Catalogue no: **TCB 2**
12" Single: Released Nov '88, on Fontana, by Phonogram Ltd. Deleted 31 May '89. Catalogue no: **TCBX 2**
CD 5": Released Nov '88, on Fontana, by Phonogram Ltd. Catalogue no: **TCBCD 2**

WORDY RAPPINGHOOD
Tracks: / Wordy rappinghood.
7" Single: Released Jun '78, on Island, by Island Records. Deleted Jun '81. Catalogue no: **WIP 6694**

Tomboy

PEOPLE GET READY
Tracks: / People get ready / Fire.
12" Single: Released Jun '88, on Epic, by CBS Records. Deleted Jan '89. Catalogue no: **650385 6**
7" Single: Released Jun '88, on Epic, by CBS Records. Deleted Jan '89. Catalogue no: **650385 7**

Tomcats

OLD FATHER CHRISTMAS
Tracks: / Old Father Christmas / Donroy & Tomcat / Good King Wenceslas.
7" Single: Released Nov '82, on Denmar, Catalogue no: **KS 1059**

Tomiie, Satoshi

TEARS
12" Single: Released Jun '89, on London Records, by London Records. Catalogue no: **FX 108**
7" Single: Released Jun '89, on London Records, by London Records. Catalogue no: **F 108**

Tomita

BOLERO
Tracks: / Bolero / Space children (On 12" only).
7" Single: Released Feb '80, on RCA, by BMG Records (UK). Deleted Feb '83. Catalogue no: **PB 9498**

Tomlin, Calton

WEENY TEENY BIT
Tracks: / Weeny teeny bit.
12" Single: Released Sep '85, on Original Sounds, Catalogue no: **OS 001**

Tomlinson, Fred

OH HAPPY BAND
Tracks: / Oh happy band / Our boys will shine tonight.
7" Single: Released Sep '80, on BBC, by BBC Records & Tapes. Deleted '83. Catalogue no: **RESL 79**

Tommies

LET'S TAKE YOU BACK
Tracks: / Let's take you back.
7" Single: Released Nov '85, on Elecstar, by Elecstar Records. Deleted '88. Catalogue no: **VCL 2**

LET'S TAKE YOU BACK (TO THE GOOD OLD DAYS)
Tracks: / Let's take you back / Let's take you back (instrumental).
7" Single: Released Nov '87, on Creole, by Creole Records. Catalogue no: **CR 2**
12" Single: Released 21 Nov '87, on Creole, by Creole Records. Catalogue no: **CRT 2**

Tommy 'J'

RIDIN' IN MY CAR
Tracks: / Ridin' in my car / Hey you.
7" Single: Released Jun '81, on RAK, by EMI Records. Catalogue no: **RAK 332**

SAME TIME, SAME CHANNEL
Tracks: / Same time, same channel / Up on your wall.
7" Single: Released Mar '83, on EMI, by EMI Records. Catalogue no: **EMI 5382**

WHY DON'THEY UNDERSTAND
Tracks: / Why don'they understand / Sail away.
7" Single: Released Jul '82, on Regard, Catalogue no: **RG 101**

Tomorrow

Biographical details: Were a UK pop/psychedelic group: vocalist Keith West, bassist John 'Junior' Wood, guitarist Steve Howe, drummer Twink (John Alder). Their single *My White Bicycle* was produced by **Pete Townshend**; their eponymous LP appeared in 1968, the year they split up. Twink joined **Pretty Things**, Wood played with **Jeff Beck**, Howe was later in **Yes**. (Donald Clarke 13.1.88).

MY WHITE BICYCLE
Tracks: / My white bicycle / Sabre dance.
7" Single: Released Oct '83, on Old Gold, by Old Gold Records. Deleted Sep '89. Catalogue no: **OG 9368**

Tomorrow's Edition

YOU TURN ME ON
Tracks: / You turn me on.

TONE LOC - I GOT IT GOIN' ON (Released on 4th & Broadway)

7" Single: Released Feb '82, on CBS, by CBS Records. Catalogue no: **A 2099**
12" Single: Released Feb '82, on CBS, by CBS Records. Catalogue no: **A 13 2099**

Tompall

LOVIN' HER WAS EASIER (SINGLE)
Tracks: / Lovin' her was easier / United we fall.
7" Single: Released Nov '81, on Elektra, by Elektra Records (UK). Deleted '84. Catalogue no: **K 12571**

Tone Band

GERMANY CALLING
Tracks: / Gemany calling / Calculator.
7" Single: Released Nov '81, on Polydor, by Polydor Ltd. Deleted Nov '84. Catalogue no: **POSP 370**

Tone Loc

FUNKY COLD MEDINA
Tracks: / Funky cold Medina / On fire.
CD 5": Released May '89, on 4th & Broadway, by Island Records. Catalogue no: **BRCD 129**
Cassingle: Released May '89, on 4th & Broadway, by Island Records. Catalogue no: **BRCA 129**
7" Single: Released 7 Mar '89, on 4th & Broadway, by Island Records. Catalogue no: **BRW 129**
12" Single: Released 7 Mar '89, on 4th & Broadway, by Island Records. Catalogue no: **12 BRW 129**

I GOT IT GOING ON (see panel above)
Tracks: / I got it going on / Homies, The / I got it going on (instrumental) (Only on 12" and CD single.) / Fine line between hyper and stupid (Only on 12" and CD single.) / Cheeba cheeba (CD & cassette singles only).
CD 5": Released Jul '89, on 4th & Broadway, by Island Records. Catalogue no: **BRCD 140**
Cassingle: Released Jul '89, on 4th & Broadway, by Island Records. Catalogue no: **BRCA 140**
7" Single: Released Jul '89, on 4th & Broadway, by Island Records. Catalogue no: **BRW 140**
12" Single: Released Jul '89, on 4th & Broadway, by Island Records. Catalogue no: **12 BRW 140**

LOC'ED AFTER DARK (SINGLE)
Tracks: / Loc'ed after dark / Wild thing.
CD 5": Released 23 Jan '89, on 4th & Broadway, by Island Records. Catalogue no: **BRCD 121**
7" Single: Released Nov '88, on 4th & Broadway, by Island Records. Catalogue no: **BRW 121**
12" Single: Released Nov '88, on 4th & Broadway, by Island Records. Catalogue no: **12 BRW 121**

ON FIRE
Tracks: / On fire / Funky cold medina / Wild thing (Only on CD single) / On fire (instrumental) (Only on 12" and CD single.).
7" Single: Released 24 Apr '89, on 4th & Broadway, by Island Records. Catalogue no: **BRW 129**
12" Single: Released 24 Apr '89, on 4th & Broadway, by Island Records. Catalogue no: **12BRW 129**

Toned F

TONE DEAF
Tracks: / Tone deaf / Jealous.
7" Single: Released Sep '81, on Extinguish, Catalogue no: **EXT 003**

Tones On Tail

BURNING SKIES
Tracks: / Burning skies.
12" Single: Released May '83, on Situation 2, by Beggars Banquet Records. Catalogue no: **SIT 2T**

CHRISTIAN SAYS
Tracks: / Christian says.
7" Single: Released Nov '84, on Beggars Banquet, by Beggars Banquet Records. Deleted Jan '88. Catalogue no: **BEG 121**
12" Single: Released Nov '84, on Beggars Banquet, by Beggars Banquet Records. Catalogue no: **BEG 121T**

LIONS
Tracks: / Lions / Go.
7" Single: Released May '84, on Beggars Banquet, by Beggars Banquet Records. Deleted Jan '88. Catalogue no: **BEG 109**
12" Single: Released May '84, on Beggars Banquet, by Beggars Banquet Records. Deleted Jun '88. Catalogue no: **BEG 109T**

PERFORMANCE
Tracks: / Performance / Shakes.
7" Single: Released Mar '84, on Beggars Banquet, by Beggars Banquet Records. Deleted Jan '88. Catalogue no: **BEG 106**
12" Single: Released Mar '84, on Beggars Banquet, by Beggars Banquet Records. Catalogue no: **BEG 106T**

Tongue In Cheek

DON'T STOP THE LOVE
Tracks: / Don't stop the love / Don't stop the love (version).
12" Single: Released Jul '87, on Criminal (1), by Criminal Records. Catalogue no: **BUST 4**

NOBODY CAN LOVE ME
Tracks: / Nobody can love me.
12" Single: Released Jan '88, on Criminal (1), by Criminal Records. Catalogue no: **BUSTR 6**

WHY
Tracks: / Why (you could have had it all) / Nobody (remix).
12" Single: Released Nov '88, on Criminal (1), by Criminal Records. Catalogue no: **BUSTR 11**

WHY (YOU COULD HAVE HAD IT ALL)
Tracks: / Why (you could have had it all) / Throw down.
7" Single: Released Sep '88, on Criminal (1), by Criminal Records. Catalogue no: **BUS 11**
12" Single: Released Sep '88, on Criminal (1), by Criminal Records. Catalogue no: **BUST 11**

Tongue'N'Cheek

I SHOULD CO-CO (NUTS TO YOU)
Tracks: / I should co-co (nuts to you) / I can't get you.
7" Single: Released Sep '81, on Towerbell, Catalogue no: **TOW 11**

Tong,Winston

THEORETICAL CHINA
Tracks: / Theoretical China / Hunger.
12" Single: Released Dec '84, on Les Disques Du Crepuscule(Belgium), by Les Disques Du Crepuscule(Belgium). Catalogue no: **TWI 310**

Toni Toni Tone

LITTLE WALTER
Tracks: / Little Walter / Little Walter (instrumental) / Little Walter (2 Tuff radio mix) / Little Walter (Extended dance mix) / Little Walter (B.B.mix).
7" Single: Released 20 Jun '88, on Polydor, by Polydor Ltd. Catalogue no: **WING 2**
12" Single: Released 20 Jun '88, on Polydor, by Polydor Ltd. Catalogue no: **WINGX 2**

Tonics

ALL SUMMER LONG
Tracks: / All summer long / Standback.
7" Single: Released Aug '81, on Magnet, by WEA Records. Catalogue no: **MAG 67**

Tonight

DRUMMER MAN
Tracks: / Drummer man.
7" Single: Released Jan '78, on Target, by Target Records. Deleted Jan '81. Catalogue no: **TDS 1**

MONEY THAT'S YOUR PROBLEM
Tracks: / Money that's your problem.
7" Single: Released May '78, on Target, by Target Records. Deleted May '81. Catalogue no: **TDS 2**

TONIGHT
Tracks: / Tonight / Kevin Rowland's band / Come on Eileen (Only on the 12" version.).
12" Single: Released 1 Aug '88, on Mercury, by Phonogram Ltd. Deleted Feb '89. Catalogue no: **ROW 112**
CD 5": Released 1 Aug '88, on Mercury, by Phonogram Ltd. Deleted Feb '89. Catalogue no: **ROWCD 1**
7" Single: Released 1 Aug '88, on Mercury, by Phonogram Ltd. Deleted Feb '89. Catalogue no: **ROW 1**

Tonik, Terry

JUST A LITTLE MOD
Tracks: / Just a little mod / Smashed and blocked.
7" Single: Released Feb '80, on Posh, by Posh Records. Catalogue no: **TOFF 1**

Tonio K

Biographical details: Tonio's musical career began in earnest in the late 70's when he contributed bass to a touring version of Buddy Holly's old stalwarts The Crickets. From there he embarked on a solo career, commencing in 1979 with "Life In The Food Chain" and including last year's acclaimed "Romeo Unchained". (A&M Records, May 1988).g.

WITHOUT LOVE
Tracks: / Without love / I can't stop / Executioner's song (Extra track on 12") / Where is that place (Extra track on 12").
Note: Produced by T-Bone Burnett and featuring Booker T. Jones and Charlie Sexton.
7" Single: Released Mar '88, on A&M, by A&M Records. Deleted Feb '89. Catalogue no: **AM 434**
12" Single: Released Mar '88, on A&M, by A&M Records. Deleted Feb '89. Catalogue no: **AMY 434**

Tonix

STRANGERS
Tracks: / Strangers / Talk to me.
7" Single: Released Aug '81, on 109 Product, Deleted '86. Catalogue no: **STEG 002**

Tonto Metro

STOP IT
Tracks: / Stop it.
12" Single: Released 10 Jul '89, on Shocking Vibes, Catalogue no: **SV 01**

Tony & Maria

ROSES ARE RED
Tracks: / Roses are red / Song of love.
7" Single: Released Feb '84, on Hollywood, by Hollywood Records. Catalogue no: **HWD 002**

Too Much Texas

HURRY ON DOWN
Tracks: / Hurry on down.
12" Single: Released '88, on Ugly Man, by Ugly Man Records. Catalogue no: **UGLY 11T**

SMART
Tracks: / Smart.
12" Single: Released '89, on Playtime, by Playtime Records. Catalogue no: **AMUSE 003T**

Too Nice

I GET MINZE
Tracks: / I get minze / I get minze (version) / Cold wild strong isle (Only on 12" single.).
7" Single: Released Jul '89, on Arista, by BMG Records (UK). Catalogue no: **112437**
12" Single: Released Jul '89, on Arista, by BMG Records (UK). Catalogue no: **612437**

Too Tuff

90% FUNK 10% RHYME
Tracks: / 90% funk 10% rhyme / Why am I waiting.
7" Single: Released Dec '88, on Danceyard, by Danceyard Records. Catalogue no: **URQ 4**
12" Single: Released Dec '88, on Danceyard, by Danceyard Records. Catalogue no: **URQ 47**

Tookut

ROCK THAT WEIRDO
Tracks: / Rock that weirdo.
12" Single: Released '88, on Strike Back, by Strike Back Records. Catalogue no: **SBR 18T**

Tools

GOTTA MAKE SOME MONEY SOMEHOW
Tracks: / Gotta make some money somehow.
7" Single: Released Jul '81, on Oily, by Oily Records. Catalogue no: **SLICK 2**

Tools You Can Trust

CUT A NEW SEAM
Tracks: / Cut a new seam.
7" Single: Released Sep '84, on Red Energy Dynamo, by Red Energy Dynamo Records. Deleted '88. Catalogue no: **S 401**

MESSY BODY THRUST
Tracks: / Messy body thrust.
7" Single: Released Feb '84, on Red Energy Dynamo, by Red Energy Dynamo Records. Catalogue no: **S 301**

SAY IT LOW
Tracks: / Say it low.
12" Single: Released Feb '86, on Red Energy Dynamo, by Red Energy Dynamo Records. Deleted '88. Catalogue no: **T 701**

SHARPEN THE TOOLS
12" Single: Released May '85, on Red Energy Dynamo, by Red Energy Dynamo Records. Deleted '88. Catalogue no: **T 501**

SHOW YOUR TEETH
Tracks: / Show your teeth.
7" Single: Released 14 Jun '85, on R.E.D., Catalogue no: **S301**

WORKING AND SHOPPING
Tracks: / Working and shopping.
7" Single: Released Sep '83, on Red Energy Dynamo, by Red Energy Dynamo Records. Catalogue no: **S 101**

Toots

HARD TO HANDLE
Tracks: / Hard to handle / 54-46 (That's my number) / Funky Kingston / Reggae got soul.
CD 5": Released 6 Mar '89, on Mango, by Island Records. Catalogue no: **CIDM 102**
7" Single: Released 6 Mar '89, on Mango, by Island Records. Catalogue no: **MNG 102**
12" Single: Released 6 Mar '89, on Mango, by Island Records. Catalogue no: **12 MNG 102**

Toots & Maytals

Biographical details: It's been nearly two decades since Toots first got together with the other Maytals, Raleigh Gordon and Nathaniel 'Jerry' Matthias. They formed in 1962 and started their recording career at the Brentford Road headquarters of the legendary Clement 'Sir Coxsone' Dodd in Kingston, Jamaica. The group's debut release *Hallelujah* was an immediate hit on the island. Further successes, including the much sought-after *Six and seven books of Moses* and the *Never grow old* album, ensured the continued popularity of the Maytals and their energetic straight-from-church style of singing. After leaving Coxsone, the group linked up with Prince Buster, who was then the number one sound system operator on the island. It was Buster who also had a massive ska hit in Britain with *Al Capone*. Buster produced the Maytals and such tunes as *Domino, Pain in my belly, Little flea* and *Dog war* (also known as *Broadway jungle*) became major hits in Jamaica. By 1966 the Maytals had moved on again, this time to the Byron Lee organisation BMN. They were backed by the Dragonaires and won Jamaica's 1966 Festival Song Competition with

Bam Bam. The Maytals continued to hit the Jamaican charts via the BMN label and such records as *Fever*, *It's you*, *Never you change* and the slow R&B-styled *Daddy*. An album, *The sensational Maytals*, was released and has since become a collector's item and a considerable rarity. The group's association with Lee came to an abrupt end when Toots ran foul of Jamaica's ganja laws. They then started recording with Leslie Kong who ran the famous Beverley's label. Toot's prison experience paid instant dividends with the autobiographical *54-46 that's my number*. With Kong, the Maytals cut such hits as *Just tell me*, *Reborn*, *Bim Today* and *Do the reggay*.
When Kong died in 1971, the Maytals turned again to Byron Lee and took the Festival Song prize in 1972 with *Pomp and pride*. A year or so later the group released their first album for Dynamic, *Funky Kingston* which included an updated version of *Daddy/My new name*. Toots & The Maytals consolidated their record success with American and European tours including the legendary Lyceum concert in London in 1976. That same year the band hit the British charts with *Reggae got soul*. On September 29th, 1980, Toots & The Maytals made a little bit of history. The band played at London's Hammersmith Palais and, less than 24 hours later, a live album from that show was in the shops. It was the fastest live album in history. (Island Records Press Office, February 1984).

BAM BAM
Tracks: / Bam bam.
7" Single: Released Aug '82, on Island, by Island Records. Catalogue no: **WIP 6777**

BEAUTIFUL WOMAN
Tracks: / Beautiful woman / Beautiful woman (version) / Show me the way (12" only).
7" Single: Released Sep '81, on Island, by Island Records. Catalogue no: **WIP 6738**
12" Single: Released Sep '81, on Island, by Island Records. Catalogue no: **12WIP 6738**

CHATTY, CHATTY
Tracks: / Chatty, chatty / Turn it up.
12" Single: Released Feb '80, on Island, by Island Records. Deleted Feb '83. Catalogue no: **WIP 6544**
12" Single: Released Feb '80, on Island, by Island Records. Deleted Feb '83. Catalogue no: **12WIP 6544**

JUST LIKE THAT (SINGLE)
Tracks: / Just like that / Gone with the wind.
7" Single: Released May '80, on Island, by Island Records. Deleted May '83. Catalogue no: **WIP 6593**

MONKEY MAN
Tracks: / Monkey man / Hallelujah.
7" Single: Released Oct '80, on Island, by Island Records. Deleted Oct '83. Catalogue no: **WIP 6663**

PAPA DEE MAMA DEAR
Tracks: / Papa dee mama dear / Dilly dally.
7" Single: Released Jun '81, on Island, by Island Records. Deleted Jun '84. Catalogue no: **WIP 6692**

STICK IT UP MISTER
7" EP: Released Jul '80, on Island, by Island Records. Deleted Jul '87. Catalogue no: **IEP 11**

Tootsie Roll

LONELY LOVERS
Tracks: / Lonely lovers / All I want is you.
7" Single: Released Jun '82, on Creole, by Creole Records. Deleted Jun '85. Catalogue no: **CR 38**

PERFECT LOVERS
Tracks: / Perfect lovers / All I want is you.
7" Single: Released May '82, on Creole, by Creole Records. Catalogue no: **CR 35**

Top Billin'

NATURALLY
Tracks: / Naturally / Never, never.
7" Single: Released Sep '88, on Danceyard, by Danceyard Records. Catalogue no: **DOPE 1**
12" Single: Released Sep '88, on Danceyard, by Danceyard Records. Catalogue no: **DOPET 1**

STRAIGHT FROM THE SOUL
Tracks: / Straight from the soul.
7" Single: Released Jan '89, on Rap Sonic, by Rapsonic Records. Catalogue no: **DOPE 3**
12" Single: Released Jan '89, on Rap Sonic, by Rapsonic Records. Catalogue no: **DOPE T 3**

MY THING
Tracks: / My thing / Surprise.
7" Single: Released Sep '89, on Mercury, by Phonogram Ltd. Catalogue no: **DOPE 4**
12" Single: Released Sep '89, on Mercury, by Phonogram Ltd. Catalogue no: **DOPET 4**

Top Cat

BAD BOY CAT
Tracks: / Bad boy cat.
12" Single: Released Sep '89, on Blacker Dread, Catalogue no: **BD 8915**

LOVE ME LESS
Tracks: / Love me less.
7" Single: Released Apr '89, on Dancebeat, Catalogue no: **DV 001**

RAGGA MI LIKE
Tracks: / Ragga mi like / Ragga mi like (versions).
12" Single: Released Jun '89, on CSA, by CSA Records. Catalogue no: **12CSA 517**

TAKE IT DOWN LOW
Tracks: / Take it down low.
12" Single: Released Oct '89, on Sunjam, Catalogue no: **SB 0010**

Top F.M.

KAOTIC MIX
Tracks: / Kaotic mix.
12" Single: Released May '89, on Kaos, Catalogue no: **KAOSX 001**

Top Gear

DREAM MACHINE
Tracks: / Dream machine / Electronic kites.
7" Single: Released Jul '81, on EMI, by EMI Records. Catalogue no: **EMI 5209**

Top Secret

IN MY WORLD
Tracks: / In my world / Money.
7" Single: Released Apr '82, on Cheapskate, Deleted '85. Catalogue no: **CHEAP 40**

SHE'S SO UGLY
Tracks: / She's ugly / I love me.
7" Single: Released Oct '81, on Cheapskate, Deleted '85. Catalogue no: **CHEAP 35**

Topaz

CHRISTMAS
7" Single: Released Dec '87, on Funkin' Marvellous, by Steinar Records (UK). Catalogue no: **MARV 10**

Topol

IF I WERE A RICH MAN
Tracks: / If I were a rich man.
7" Single: Released Apr '67, on CBS, by CBS Records. Deleted Apr '70. Catalogue no: **202 651**
7" Single: Released Jun '83, on CBS, by CBS Records. Catalogue no: **A 3496**

Topping,Frank

CALVARY
Tracks: / Calvary.
7" Single: Released Dec '82, on Multi-Media, Catalogue no: **MMT 1**

SLEEP WELL MY SON
Tracks: / Sleep well my son.
7" Single: Released Nov '76, on President, by President Records. Catalogue no: **PT 458**

Topping,Simon

PROSPECT PARK
Tracks: / Prospect park.
7" Single: Released Aug '85, on Factory Benelux, by Rough Trade Records. Catalogue no: **FBN 41**

Tora Tora

RED SUN SETTING
Tracks: / Red sun setting / Highway.
7" Single: Released Aug '80, on Mancunian Metal, Deleted '83. Catalogue no: **TT 5000**

Torch Song

CAN'T FIND MY WAY HOME
Tracks: / Can't find my way home / Spear (Available on 12" disc Only) / Living out of time (* = Available on 12" disc Only).
7" Single: Released Nov '86, on Y 11, by Y 11 Records. Catalogue no: **YII 002**
12" Single: Released Nov '86, on Y 11, by Y 11 Records. Catalogue no: **YII 12002**

ODE TO BILLY JOE
Tracks: / Ode to Billy Joe.
7" Single: Released Jan '85, on I.R.S, Catalogue no: **IRS 117**
12" Single: Released Jan '85, on I.R.S, Catalogue no: **IRSY 117**

WHITE NIGHT
Tracks: / White Night / Mothdub / Microdot daylight.
12" Single: Released May '86, on Y 11, by Y 11 Records. Catalogue no: **YII 12001**

Torme

START
Tracks: / Start / T.V.O.D. / Kerrap / Love, guns & money.
7" Single: Released Apr '86, on Zebra (1), by Zebra Records (1). Catalogue no: **RA 6**
12" Single: Released Apr '86, on Zebra (1), by Zebra Records (1). Catalogue no: **12 RA 6**

Torme, Bernie

ALL AROUND THE WORLD
7" Single: Released Aug '85, on Zebra (1), by Zebra Records (1). Catalogue no: **RA 5**

ALL DAY AND ALL OF THE NIGHT
Tracks: / All day and all of the night.
7" Single: Released Apr '81, on Fresh, by Jetstar Records. Catalogue no: **FRESH 7**

AMERICA
Tracks: / America / Chelsea girls.
7" Single: Released Jun '82, on Kamaflage, Deleted Jun '85. Catalogue no: **KAM 5**

BEAT
Tracks: / Beat / I want / Boney moroney.
7" Single: Released Mar '80, on Island, by Island Records. Deleted '83. Catalogue no: **WIP 6586**

I CAN'T CONTROL MYSELF
Tracks: / I can't control myself.
7" Single: Released Oct '83, on Zebra (1), by Zebra Records (1). Catalogue no: **RA 1**

MY BABY LOVES A VAMPIRE
Tracks: / My baby loves a vampire / Lightning strikes.
7" Single: Released Jan '84, on Zebra (1), by Zebra Records (1). Catalogue no: **RA 2**
12" Single: Released Jan '84, on Zebra (1), by Zebra Records (1). Catalogue no: **12 RA 2**

SHOORAH SHOORAH
Tracks: / Shoorah shoorah / Star search & destroy / Kamaflage.
7" Set: Released Oct '82, on Kamaflage, Deleted Oct '85. Catalogue no: **KAM 8**

Torme, Mel

Biographical details: Was born in Chicago in 1925; he is a songwriter, a writer, an actor and plays piano and drums as well as one of the great jazz-oriented popular singers. He sang on radio at age 4, acted in radio soap operas at 9; formed vocal group the Mel-Tones, recording under that name and with **Artie Shaw** in the 1940s. He began writing hit songs at 15, his best-known song is *The Christmas Song* (*Chestnuts Roasting On An Open Fire*). He went solo and had hits on Capitol 1949-52. He was known as *The Velvet Fog* during the Mel-Tones period, but his range increased and he became an even better singer in the '50s, recording for Bethlehem (now on Affinity) and on Verve. He often worked with ace arranger **Marty Paich**, but later arranged and produced his own albums; his latest are on Concord Jazz. (Donald Clarke 13.1.88).

COMING HOME BABY
Tracks: / Coming home baby.
7" Single: Released Jan '63, on London-American, Deleted Jan '66. Catalogue no: **HLK 9643**

MOUNTAIN GREENERY
Tracks: / Mountain greenery.
7" Single: Released Apr '56, on Vogue, by Vogue Records. Deleted Apr '59. Catalogue no: **Q 72150**

Torment

MYSTERY MEN EP, THE
Tracks: / Mystery man / Rock strong / Conscription plan / Red red death.
12" Single: Released Mar '87, on Nervous, by Nervous Records. Catalogue no: **NERD 12 NEP 004**

Tornados

DRAGONFLY
Tracks: / Dragonfly.
7" Single: Released Oct '63, on Decca, by Decca Records. Deleted Oct '66. Catalogue no: **F 11745**

GLOBETROTTER
Tracks: / Globetrotter.
7" Single: Released Jan '63, on Decca, by Decca Records. Deleted Jan '66. Catalogue no: **F 11562**

ICE CREAM MAN, THE
Tracks: / Ice cream man.
7" Single: Released Jun '63, on Decca, by Decca Records. Deleted Jun '66. Catalogue no: **F 11662**

ROBOT
Tracks: / Robot.
7" Single: Released Mar '63, on Decca, by Decca Records. Deleted Mar '66. Catalogue no: **F 11606**

TELSTAR
Tracks: / Telstar / Jungle fever.
CD 5": Released Jan '89, on London (Decca), by Decca International. Catalogue no: **820 790 2**
7" Single: Released Jan '79, on SRT, by SRT Records. Catalogue no: **SRTS 75350**
7" Single: Released Mar '82, on Decca, by Decca Records. Deleted '88. Catalogue no: **F 11494**

TELSTAR (OLD GOLD)
Tracks: / Telstar.
7" Single: Released Oct '83, on Old Gold, by Old Gold Records. Deleted Sep '89. Catalogue no: **OG 9327**

Torok, Mitchell

RED LIGHT GREEN LIGHT
Tracks: / Red light green light.
7" Single: Released Jan '57, on Brunswick, by Decca Records. Deleted Jan '60. Catalogue no: **05626**

WHEN MEXICO GAVE UP THE RUMBA
Tracks: / When Mexico gave up the rumba.
7" Single: Released Sep '56, on Brunswick, by Decca Records. Deleted Sep '59. Catalogue no: **05586**

Torrance, Bill

CALEDONIA
Tracks: / Caledonia / When you and I were young Maggie.
7" Single: Released Mar '83, on Klub, by Klub Records. Catalogue no: **KLUB 26**

Torres, Judy

LOVE STORY
Tracks: / Love story.
7" Single: Released 31 Jul '89, on Profile (USA), by Profile Records (USA). Catalogue no: **PROF 256**

Torres, Liz

CAN'T GET ENOUGH (SINGLE)
Tracks: / Can't get enough.
12" Single: Released Sep '87, on State Street (USA), Catalogue no: **SSR 1002**

PAYBACK IS A BITCH What goes around comes around
Tracks: / Packback is a bitch / Packback is a bitch (version).
12" Single: Released 24 Jul '89, on Jive, by Zomba Records. Deleted Aug '89. Catalogue no: **JIVET 211**

PAYBACK IS A BITCH (REMIX)
Tracks: / Payback is a bitch (remix) / Around (version).
12" Single: Released Jul '89, on Jive, by Zomba Records. Deleted Aug '89. Catalogue no: **JIVER 211**

TOUCH OF LOVE
Tracks: / Touch of love / Touch of love (version).
12" Single: Released Dec '88, on Black Market, Catalogue no: **BLMK 4**

Torry, Clare

LOVE IS LIKE A BUTTERFLY
Tracks: / Love is like a butterfly / Adagio in G minor.
7" Single: Released Apr '81, on EMI, by EMI Records. Deleted Apr '84. Catalogue no: **EMI 5165**

Tortilla Flats

GIANT SKY
Tracks: / Giant sky / Waiting for the rain to stop / Shall ever be.
12" Single: Released Aug '86, on Bam Caruso, by Demon Records. Catalogue no: **PABL 040**

Torvill & Dean

MUSIC OF TORVIL AND DEAN 1
Tracks: / Bolero: *Various artists* / Capriccio Espagnole: *Various artists* / Barnum on ice: *Various artists* / Discoskate: *Various artists*.
12" Single: Released '83, on Safari, by Safari Records. Catalogue no: **SKATER 1**
7" Single: Released '83, on Safari, by Safari Records. Catalogue no: **SKATE 1**

MUSIC OF TORVILLE & DEAN 2
Tracks: / Song of India: *Various artists* / Tuxedo Junction: *Various artists* / Mac and Mabel: *Various artists* / Rock and roll variation: *Various artists*.
7" Single: Released Jul '85, on Safari, by Safari Records. Catalogue no: **SKATE 2**

Tosh, Peter

IN MY SONG
Tracks: / In my song / Come together / Nah goa jail (On 12"version only.).
7" Single: Released Jul '87, on Parlophone, by EMI Records. Deleted Apr '88. Catalogue no: **R 6156**
12" Single: Released Jul '87, on Parlophone, by EMI Records. Deleted Apr '88. Catalogue no: **12R 6156**

JOHNNY B. GOODE
Tracks: / Johnny B. Goode.
10" single: Released Mar '83, on Radic, Catalogue no: **IORIC 115**

MAMA AFRICA (SINGLE)
Tracks: / Mama Africa.
10" single: Released Sep '83, on Radic,

Catalogue no: **10RIC 117**
7" Single: Released Sep '83, on Radic, Catalogue no: **RIC 117**

NOTHING BUT LOVE
Tracks: / Nothing but love / Cold blood.
7" Single: Released Jun '81, on Rolling Stones (1), Catalogue no: **RSR 107**
12" Single: Released Jun '81, on Rolling Stones (1), Catalogue no: **12 RSR 107**

YOU GOTTA WALK DON'T LOOK BACK
Tracks: / You gotta walk don't look back.
7" Single: Released Oct '78, on Rolling Stones (1), Deleted Oct '81. Catalogue no: **2859**

Toss The Feathers

SKIDOO
Tracks: / Skidoo.
12" Single: Released Nov '88, on Bop, Catalogue no: **BIP 404**

Tot

FILTHY
Tracks: / Filthy.
12" Single: Released Apr '88, on Flim Flam, Catalogue no: **HARP 9T**

WHAT
Tracks: / What u.r..
12" Single: Released Oct '89, on DFM, Catalogue no: **DFM 006**

Total Chaos

FACTORY MAN
Tracks: / Factory man.
7" Single: Released Sep '82, on Volume (1), by Volume Records. Catalogue no: **VOL 2**

FIELDS AND FOREVER
Tracks: / Fields and forever.
12" Single: Released Sep '83, on Volume (1), by Volume Records. Catalogue no: **VOLT 6**

THERE ARE NO RUSSIANS IN AFGHANISTAN
Tracks: / There are no Russians in Afganistan.
7" Single: Released Jul '83, on Volume (1), by Volume Records. Catalogue no: **VOL 1**

Total Contrast

BE WITH YOU TONIGHT
Tracks: / Be with you tonight.
7" Single: Released Jan '84, on Total Contrast, Deleted '85. Catalogue no: **TCR 1**
7" Single: Released Oct '85, on London Records, by London Records. Catalogue no: **LON 76**
12" Single: Released Jan '84, on Total Contrast, Deleted '85. Catalogue no: **TCRS 1**
12" Single: Released Oct '85, on London Records, by London Records. Catalogue no: **LONX 76**

JODY
Tracks: / Jody / Jody (inst).
7" Single: Released Aug '87, on London Records, by London Records. Catalogue no: **LON 142**
12" Single: Released Aug '87, on London Records, by London Records. Catalogue no: **LONX 142**

KISS
Tracks: / Kiss / Dance.
7" Single: Released Oct '87, on London Records, by London Records. Deleted Oct '88. Catalogue no: **LON 155**
12" Single: Released Oct '87, on London Records, by London Records. Deleted Oct '88. Catalogue no: **LONX 155**

LOVE FEVER
Tracks: / Love fever.
12" Single: Released 22 May '89, on Criminal (1), by Criminal Records. Catalogue no: **BUST 018**

NEXT TIME I'LL KNOW BETTER
Tracks: / Next time I'll know better.
12" Single: Released Nov '84, on Total Contrast, Deleted '86. Catalogue no: **TCR 2**

RIVER, THE
Tracks: / River, The / River, the(Instrumental) / Takes a Little time (US Remix) (12"recording only).
7" Single: Released Feb '86, on London Records, by London Records. Catalogue no: **LON 83**
12" Single: Released Feb '86, on London Records, by London Records. Catalogue no: **LONX 83**

TAKES A LITTLE TIME
Tracks: / Takes a little time.
7" Single: Released Jul '85, on London Records, by London Records. Catalogue no: **LON 71**
12" Single: Released Jul '85, on London Records, by London Records. Catalogue no: **LONX 71**

TAKES A LITTLE TIME (OLD GOLD)
Tracks: / Takes a little time / Hit and run.
7" Single: Released Oct '88, on Old Gold, by Old Gold Records. Catalogue no: **OG 4080**

WAITING IN VAIN
Tracks: / Waiting in vain.
7" Single: Released Dec '88, on Criminal (1), by Criminal Records. Catalogue no: **BARB 2**
7" Single: Released Dec '88, on Criminal (1), by Criminal Records. Catalogue no: **BUS 14**
12" Single: Released Dec '88, on Criminal (1), by Criminal Records. Catalogue no: **BARB T2**
12" Single: Released Nov '88, on Criminal (1), by Criminal Records. Catalogue no: **BUST 14**

WHAT YOU GONNA DO ABOUT IT
Tracks: / What you gonna do about it / I'm still waiting.
7" Single: Released Apr '86, on London Records, by London Records. Catalogue no: **LON 95**
12" Single: Released Apr '86, on London Records, by London Records. Catalogue no: **LONX 95**

Total Noise

TOTAL NOISE (EP)
Tracks: / Total noise: *Various artists.*
7" EP: Released Jun '82, on Total Noise, by Faulty Products Records. Catalogue no: **TOT 1**

Total Strangers

SHE'S SO FINE
Tracks: / She's so fine.
7" Single: Released Sep '82, on Bandit, by Bandit Records. Catalogue no: **BR 002**

WORKING WORLD
Tracks: / Working world / Lose that girl.
7" Single: Released Apr '83, on Small Run, Catalogue no: **SRR 0010**

Totalitar

LUFTSLOTT
Tracks: / Luftslott.
7" Single: Released Jun '89, on Loony Tunes, by Loony Tunes Records. Catalogue no: **TUNE 14**

Toto

Biographical details: A USA middle-of-the-road rock band formed in Los Angeles in 1978 by top session musicians: drummer Jeff Porcaro and keyboardist brother Steve are sons of a jazz percussionist; keyboardist David Paich is the son of top arranger Marty Paich; plus David Hungate on bass, Steve Lukather on guitar, vocalist Bobby Kimball: name from Kimball's real name (Toteaux) and/or name of the dog in **Wizard of Oz**. Their stuff is predictably slick and became slicker for USA radio airplay: *Toto IV* in 1982 was a number 4 LP in the USA with seven Grammy nominations, including hits in both USA and UK with *Rosanna* and *Africa*. They played the soundtrack of widely panned SF film **Dune** in 1984. Despite sellout status in Japan they rarely play live or tour; why should they? Their LP *Fahrenheit* in 1986 featured new singer Joseph Williams. (Donald Clarke 13.1.88).

99
Tracks: / 99 / Hydra.
7" Single: Released Mar '80, on CBS, by CBS Records. Deleted '83. Catalogue no: **CBS 8132**

AFRICA
Tracks: / Africa / We made it.
7" Single: Released Feb '83, on CBS, by CBS Records. Deleted Feb '86. Catalogue no: **A 2510**

AFRICA (OLD GOLD)
Tracks: / Africa / I won't hold you back.
7" Single: Released 27 Feb '89, on Old Gold, by Old Gold Records. Catalogue no: **OG 9867**

GOODBYE ELENOR
Tracks: / Goodbye Elenor / Turn back.
7" Single: Released Feb '81, on CBS, by CBS Records. Deleted '84. Catalogue no: **CBS 9492**

HOLD THE LINE (OLD GOLD)
Tracks: / Hold the line.
7" Single: Released Sep '85, on Old Gold, by Old Gold Records. Catalogue no: **OG 9555**

HOLD THE LINE (SINGLE)
Tracks: / Hold the line.
7" Single: Released Feb '79, on CBS, by CBS Records. Deleted Feb '82. Catalogue no: **CBS 6784**

HOW DOES IT FEEL?
Tracks: / How does it feel?.
7" Single: Released Feb '85, on CBS, by CBS Records. Catalogue no: **A 6043**

I WON'T HOLD YOU BACK
Tracks: / I won't hold you back.
7" Pic: Released Jun '83, on CBS, by CBS Records. Catalogue no: **WA 3392**
7" Single: Released Jun '83, on CBS, by CBS Records. Catalogue no: **A 3392**
12" Single: Released Jun '83, on CBS, by CBS Records. Catalogue no: **TA 3392**

TOTO COELO - I EAT CANNIBALS (Released on Radial Choice)

I'LL BE OVER YOU
Tracks: / In a word / Africa (Extra track on 12" version only) / 99 (Extra track on 12" version only).
7" Single: Released Sep '86, on CBS, by CBS Records. Catalogue no: **650043 7**
12" Single: Released Sep '86, on CBS, by CBS Records. Catalogue no: **650043 6**

MAKE BELIEVE
Tracks: / Make believe / We made it.
7" Single: Released Oct '82, on CBS, by CBS Records. Catalogue no: **CBS 2868**

PAMELA
Tracks: / Pamela / Stay away / America (Extra track on 12") / Africa (Extra track on CD single.) / Rosanna (Extra track on CD single.).
CD 5": Released May '88, on CBS, by CBS Records. Deleted Jan '89. Catalogue no: **651 607 2**
7" Single: Released May '88, on CBS, by CBS Records. Deleted Jan '89. Catalogue no: **651 607 7**
12" Single: Released May '88, on CBS, by CBS Records. Deleted Jan '89. Catalogue no: **651 607 6**

ROSANNA
Tracks: / Rosanna / It's a feeling.
7" Pic: Released Apr '83, on CBS, by CBS Records. Catalogue no: **WA 2079**
7" Single: Released Mar '83, on CBS, by CBS Records. Catalogue no: **A 2079**

ST. GEORGE & THE DRAGON
Tracks: / St. George & the dragon / Secret love.
7" Single: Released Jan '80, on CBS, by CBS Records. Deleted '85. Catalogue no: **CBS 8085**

STOP LOVING YOU
Tracks: / Stop loving you / Seventh one, The / I'll be over you (Track on 12".).
CD 5": Released 5 Mar '88, on CBS, by CBS Records. Deleted Jan '89. Catalogue no: **651 411 2**
7" Single: Released Mar '88, on CBS, by CBS Records. Deleted Aug '88. Catalogue no: **651 441 0**
7" Single: Released Feb '88, on CBS, by CBS Records. Deleted Aug '88. Catalogue no: **651 411 7**
12" Single: Released Feb '88, on CBS, by CBS Records. Deleted Aug '88. Catalogue no: **651 411 6**

Toto Coelo

DRACULA'S TANGO (SUCKER FOR YOUR LOVE)
Tracks: / Dracula's tango (sucker for your love).
7" Single: Released Oct '82, on Radial Choice, by Virgin Records. Catalogue no: **TIC 11**
12" Single: Released Oct '82, on Radial Choice, by Virgin Records. Catalogue no: **TIC 1112**

GIMME SOME LOVIN'
Tracks: / Gimme some lovin'.
7" Single: Released Oct '85, on Debut, by Skratch Records. Catalogue no: **DEBT 08**
12" Single: Released Oct '85, on Debut, by Skratch Records. Catalogue no: **DEBT 08(12)**

GIRLS' NIGHT OUT
Tracks: / Girls' night out.
7" Single: Released Apr '85, on Debut, by Skratch Records. Catalogue no: **DEBT 04**
12" Single: Released Apr '85, on Debut, by Skratch Records. Catalogue no: **DEBT 04(12)**

I EAT CANNIBALS (see panel above)
Tracks: / I eat cannibals (part one) / I eat cannibals (part two).
7" Single: Released Jul '82, on Radial Choice, by Virgin Records. Catalogue no: **TIC 10**
12" Single: Released Jul '82, on Radial Choice, by Virgin Records. Deleted May '88. Catalogue no: **TIC 1012**

MILK FROM THE COCONUT
Tracks: / Milk from the coconut.
7" Single: Released May '83, on Radial Choice, by Virgin Records. Catalogue no: **TIC 13**
12" Single: Released May '83, on Radial Choice, by Virgin Records. Catalogue no: **TIC 1312**

Tottenham Hotspur

HOT SHOT TOTTENHAM
Tracks: / Hot shot Tottenham / Ossie's dream / Hot shot Tottenham (special remix) (12" only).
7" Single: Released Apr '87, on Rainbow, by Rainbow Records. Catalogue no: **RBR 16**
12" Single: Released Apr '87, on Rainbow, by Rainbow Records. Catalogue no: **RBR P 16**

OSSIE'S DREAM
Tracks: / Ossie's dream.
7" Single: Released May '81, on Shelf, by Shelf Records. Deleted '83. Catalogue no: **SHELF 1**

TOTTENHAM TOTTENHAM
Tracks: / Tottenham Tottenham.
7" Pic: Released Jun '82, on Shelf, by Shelf Records. Deleted '83. Catalogue no: **SHELFX 2**
7" Single: Released Jun '82, on Shelf, by Shelf Records. Deleted '83. Catalogue no: **SHELF 2**

Toucan Jive

I WANT YOU TO BE MY BABY
Tracks: / I want you to be my baby.
7" Single: Released Jun '83, on Kay-Drum, by Kay-Drum Records. Catalogue no: **KRUM 102**
12" Single: Released Jun '83, on Kay-Drum, by Kay-Drum Records. Catalogue no: **12DRUM 102**

Touch

BACK OFF
Tracks: / Back off.
12" Single: Released Dec '88, on Soca,

Catalogue no: **SOT 003**

IT'S UP TO YOU
Tracks: / It's up to you / So real.
7" Single: Released Feb '81, on EMI, by EMI Records. Deleted '84. Catalogue no: **EMI 5140**
12" Single: Released Feb '81, on EMI, by EMI Records. Deleted '84. Catalogue no: **12EMI 5140**

KEEP ON
Tracks: / Keep on.
12" Single: Released Jan '82, on Elite Records, by Elite Records. Deleted '84. Catalogue no: **DAZZ 11**

LOVE DON'T FAIL ME NOW
Tracks: / Love don't fail me now / My life depends on you.
7" Single: Released Nov '80, on Ariola, by BMG Records (UK). Deleted Nov '83. Catalogue no: **ARO 250**

LOVE SOMETHING SPECIAL
Tracks: / Love something special / Keep on.
7" Single: Released Apr '82, on Elite Records, by Elite Records. Deleted '84. Catalogue no: **DAZZ 14 7**
12" Single: Released Apr '82, on Elite Records, by Elite Records. Deleted '84. Catalogue no: **DAZZ 14**

THAT'S WHAT THEY SAY ABOUT LOVE
Tracks: / That's what they say about love.
7" Single: Released Feb '85, on Arista, by BMG Records (UK). Catalogue no: **ARIST 607**
12" Single: Released Feb '85, on Arista, by BMG Records (UK). Catalogue no: **ARIST 12607**

TOUCH
Tracks: / Touch.
7" Single: Released Jun '88, on Touch, by Touch Records. Catalogue no: **T7:45**

WHEN THE SPIRIT MOVES YOU
Tracks: / When the spirit moves you / My life depends on you.
7" Single: Released May '80, on Ariola, by BMG Records (UK). Deleted '85. Catalogue no: **ARO 209**

Touch Of Evil

BLUE BLUE GODS
Tracks: / Blue blue gods / Serpent's highway.
7" Single: Released Jul '88, on Big Words, Catalogue no: **HRD 121**

Touchdown

BREAKOUT
Tracks: / Breakout.
7" Single: Released Oct '82, on Excaliber, by Red Bus Records. Deleted '88. Catalogue no: **EXC 525**
12" Single: Released Oct '82, on Excaliber, by Red Bus Records. Deleted '88. Catalogue no: **EXCL 525**

DO YOU NEED?
Tracks: / Do you need?.
12" Single: Released Dec '84, on Krack, Catalogue no: **SUE 100T**

EASE YOUR MIND
Tracks: / Ease your mind / Ritmo suave.
7" Single: Released May '82, on Excaliber, by Red Bus Records. Deleted '88. Catalogue no: **EXC 519**
7" Single: Released Jun '81, on Arista, by BMG Records (UK). Deleted Jun '84. Catalogue no: **SHACK 1**
12" Single: Released Jun '81, on Arista, by BMG Records (UK). Deleted Jun '84. Catalogue no: **SHACK 1212**
12" Single: Released May '82, on Excaliber, by Red Bus Records. Deleted '88. Catalogue no: **EXCL 519**

EASE YOUR MIND '89'
Tracks: / Ease your mind '89'.
7" Single: Released May '89, on Beat Box, by Beat Box Records. Catalogue no: **BBOX 5**
12" Single: Released May '89, on Beat Box, by Beat Box Records. Catalogue no: **BBOXT 5**

ENDZONE, THE
Tracks: / Endzone, The.
12" Single: Released Apr '86, on Debut, by Skratch Records. Catalogue no: **DEBTX 3004**

Touched

DREAM GIRL
Tracks: / Dream girl / We'll fight back.
7" Single: Released Jan '85, on Ebony (2), by Ebony Records. Catalogue no: **EBON 27**

Touchton, Timothy

GREAT BIG MAMA
Tracks: / Great big mama / Great big mama (variation).
7" Single: Released Jul '87, on Response, by Priority Records. Catalogue no: **NTAS 001**

SAVE YOUR LOVE FOR ME
Tracks: / Save your love for me / Love gets better with time.
7" Single: Released May '85, on Response, by Priority Records. Catalogue no: **SR 540**

Toughest

GREATEST CONMAN
Tracks: / Greatest conman.
12" Single: Released 10 Jul '89, on Live & Love, Catalogue no: **LLD 124**

Touplanx

SAXOPHONE SONG
Tracks: / Saxophone song.
7" Single: Released Feb '82, on DC, Catalogue no: **DC 1**

Toups, Wayne

SWEET JOLENE
Tracks: / Sweet Jolene / Sugar bee / Let's fall in love.
CD 5": Released May '89, on Mercury, by Phonogram Ltd. Deleted Oct '89. Catalogue no: **MERCD 284**
7" Single: Released May '89, on Mercury, by Phonogram Ltd. Deleted Oct '89. Catalogue no: **MER 284**
12" Single: Released May '89, on Mercury, by Phonogram Ltd. Deleted Oct '89. Catalogue no: **MERX 284**

Tour De Force

BEAT THE CLOCK
Tracks: / Beat the clock.
7" Single: Released Jun '82, on Wongo, Catalogue no: **WONGO 1**

SCHOOL RULES
Tracks: / School rules / We don't talk.
7" Single: Released Nov '81, on Phantom, by Mean Records. Catalogue no: **PHAN 1**

Touring Co.

EVERY STEP OF THE WAY
Tracks: / Every step of the way.
7" Single: Released Jul '82, on Radioactive, Catalogue no: **RAD 504**

Tourists

BLIND AMONG THE FLOWERS
Tracks: / Blind among the flowers.
7" Single: Released Jun '79, on Logo, by Logo Records. Deleted Jun '82. Catalogue no: **GO 350**

DON'T SAY I TOLD YOU SO
Tracks: / Don't say I told you so / Strange sky.
7" Single: Released Oct '80, on RCA, by BMG Records (UK). Deleted Oct '83. Catalogue no: **TOUR 2**

HOOKED ON YOU
Tracks: / Hooked on you (Inst).
12" Single: Released Nov '86, on Groove & Move, by Groove & Move Records. Catalogue no: **GMT 01**

I ONLY WANT TO BE WITH YOU
Tracks: / I only want to be with you.
7" Single: Released Nov '79, on Logo, by Logo Records. Deleted Nov '82. Catalogue no: **GO 370**

LONELIEST MAN IN THE WORLD, THE
Tracks: / Loneliest man in the world, The.
7" Single: Released Nov '79, on Logo, by Logo Records. Deleted Nov '82. Catalogue no: **GO 360**

SO GOOD TO BE BACK HOME AGAIN
Tracks: / So good to be back home again.
7" Single: Released Feb '80, on Logo, by Logo Records. Deleted Feb '83. Catalogue no: **TOUR 1**

Toussaint, Allen

Biographical details: Was born in 1938 in New Orleans; as a producer he has been making hits since he was a teenager, working for **Dave Bartholomew** at Cosimo Matassa's studio on **Fats Domino** records; he arranged **Lee Allen's** hit *Walking For Mr Lee* in 1958; his own first LP on RCA included *Java*, a hit for **Al Hirt**; he later worked for Joe Banashak's Minit label, overseeing huge R&B hits like **Ernie K-Doe's** *Mother-In-Law*. After military service he formed a partnership with Marshal Sehorn in 1965; they opened their famous SeaSaint studio in 1972. His songs have been widely covered and he has produced dozens of hit LPs, as well as several fine albums of his own. (Donald Clarke 13.1.88).

WORKING IN THE COALMINE
Tracks: / Working down the coal mine / Down in the sewer.
7" Single: Released Apr '80, on Magnet, by WEA Records. Deleted Apr '83. Catalogue no: **MAG 170**

Tout Sweet

ANOTHER MAN IS TWICE AS NICE
Tracks: / Another man is twice as nice.
7" Single: on Buzz Int., Catalogue no: **VIBE 2**

Tove Naess

LET'S APOLOGISE
Tracks: / Let's apologise / Something good / Let's apologise (extended version) (12" only).
7" Single: Released Jul '88, on Virgin, by Virgin Records. Catalogue no: **VS 1105**
12" Single: Released Jul '88, on Virgin, by Virgin Records. Catalogue no: **VST 1105**

Tovey, Frank

BRIDGE STREET SHUFFLE
Tracks: / Bridge Street shuffle / Brace of shakes.
7" Single: Released Apr '88, on Mute, by Mute Records. Catalogue no: **MUTE 79**
12" Single: Released 23 Apr '88, on Mute, by Mute Records. Catalogue no: **12 MUTE 79**

LUDDITE JOE
Tracks: / Clean this act up / Small world (Extra version on 12" version only).
7" Single: Released Apr '86, on Mute, by Mute Records. Catalogue no: **MUTE 44**
12" Single: Released Apr '86, on Mute, by Mute Records. Catalogue no: **12 MUTE 44**

LUXURY
Tracks: / Luxury.
7" Single: Released Jul '85, on Mute, by Mute Records. Catalogue no: **7 MUTE 39**
12" Single: Released Jul '85, on Mute, by Mute Records. Catalogue no: **12 MUTE 39**

SAM HALL
Tracks: / Sam Hall.
CD 5": Released Jul '89, on Mute, by Mute Records. Catalogue no: **CDMUTE 100**
12" Single: Released Jul '89, on Mute, by Mute Records. Catalogue no: **MUTE 100**

Tower

SEE YOU TONIGHT
Tracks: / See you tonight / Higher faster.
7" Single: Released Nov '82, on Epic, by CBS Records. Deleted Nov '85. Catalogue no: **EPCA 2234**

Townes, Carol Lynn

99 1/2
Tracks: / 99 1/2.
7" Single: Released Aug '84, on Polydor, by Polydor Ltd. Deleted Aug '87. Catalogue no: **POSP 693**

BELIEVE IN THE BEAT
Tracks: / Believe in the beat.
7" Single: Released Jan '85, on Polydor, by Polydor Ltd. Catalogue no: **POSP 720**
12" Single: Released Jan '85, on Polydor, by Polydor Ltd. Catalogue no: **POSPX 720**

Townley, John

SLIPPING AWAY
Tracks: / Slipping away / War zone.
7" Single: Released Jun '81, on EMI, by EMI Records. Catalogue no: **EMI 5178**
12" Single: Released Jun '81, on EMI, by EMI Records. Catalogue no: **12EMI 5178**

Towns, Colin

BREAKDOWN
Tracks: / Breakdown / Working man.
7" Single: Released Sep '80, on MCA, by MCA Records. Deleted '83. Catalogue no: **MCA 643**

Townsend, Kim

READ ALL ABOUT IT
Tracks: / Dance away / Silver tears (Extra track on 12" version only) / Dreamin' on (Extra track on 12" version only).
7" Single: Released Jul '86, on Individual, by Individual Records. Catalogue no: **AIRS 103**
12" Single: Released Oct '84, on Individual, by Individual Records. Catalogue no: **AIRLT 100**

SILVER TEARS
Tracks: / Silver tears / Dreamin' on / Read all about it / Dance away.
7" Single: Released May '85, on AIRC, Deleted '87. Catalogue no: **AIRS 100**
12" Single: Released May '85, on Individual, by Individual Records. Catalogue no: **AIRLT 1001**

Townsend, Mike

DAWN LIGHT
Tracks: / Dawn light / Ennal's point.
7" Single: Released Jan '82, on BBC, by BBC Records & Tapes. Deleted '87. Catalogue no: **RESL 109**

Townsend, Sally

JUST ONE LOOK
Tracks: / Just one look / I'll remember him.
7" Single: Released Mar '80, on OBM, by RK Records. Deleted '83. Catalogue no: **OBM 1005**

LOVE AT FIRST SIGHT
Tracks: / Love at first sight / Chances are.
7" Single: Released Jan '80, on OBM, by RK Records. Deleted '83. Catalogue no: **OBM 1003**

Townshend, Pete

FACE DANCES
Tracks: / Face dances / Man watching.
7" Single: Released May '82, on Atco, by Atlantic Recording Corp.(USA). Deleted May '85. Catalogue no: **K 11734**

FACE THE FACE
Tracks: / Face the face.
12" Single: Released Oct '85, on Atco, by Atlantic Recording Corp.(USA). Catalogue no: **U 8859 T**
7" Single: Released Oct '85, on Atco, by Atlantic Recording Corp.(USA). Catalogue no: **U 8859**

FRIEND IS A FRIEND, A
Tracks: / Friend is a friend, A / Man machines / Real world.
12" Single: Released 3 Jul '89, on Virgin, by Virgin Records. Catalogue no: **VST 1198**
Cassingle: Released 3 Jul '89, on Virgin, by Virgin Records. Catalogue no: **VSC 1198**
7" Single: Released 3 Jul '89, on Virgin, by Virgin Records. Catalogue no: **VS 1198**
CD 3": Released 3 Jul '89, on Virgin, by Virgin Records. Catalogue no: **VSCD 1198**

GIVE BLOOD
Tracks: / Magic bus (live) / Won't get fooled again (live) (Extra track on 12" version only).
12" Single: Released Apr '86, on Atco, by Atlantic Recording Corp.(USA). Catalogue no: **U 8744 T**
7" Single: Released Apr '86, on Atco, by Atlantic Recording Corp.(USA). Catalogue no: **U 8744**

KEEP ON WORKING
Tracks: / Keep on working / Jools and Jim.
7" Single: Released Oct '80, on Atco, by Atlantic Recording Corp.(USA). Deleted Oct '83. Catalogue no: **K 11609**

LET MY LOVE OPEN YOUR DOOR
Tracks: / Let my love open the door / Classified greyhound girl.
7" Single: Released Jun '80, on Atco, by Atlantic Recording Corp.(USA). Deleted Jun '83. Catalogue no: **K 11486**

ROUGH BOYS
Tracks: / Rough boys / And I moved.
7" Single: Released Mar '80, on Atco, by Atlantic Recording Corp.(USA). Catalogue no: **K 11460**

STOP HURTING PEOPLE
Tracks: / Stop hurting people.
7" Pic: Released Jul '82, on Atco, by Atlantic Recording Corp.(USA). Catalogue no: **K 11751P**
7" Single: Released Jul '82, on Atco, by Atlantic Recording Corp.(USA). Catalogue no: **K 11751**
12" Single: Released Jul '82, on Atco, by Atlantic Recording Corp.(USA). Catalogue no: **K 11751T**

Townshend, Simon

I'M THE ANSWER
Tracks: / I'm the answer.
7" Single: Released Jan '84, on 21 Records, by Polydor Ltd. Catalogue no: **POSP 667**
12" Single: Released Jan '84, on 21 Records, by Polydor Ltd. Catalogue no: **POSPX 667**

SO REAL
Tracks: / So real / Freakers.
7" Single: Released May '84, on 21 Records, by Polydor Ltd. Catalogue no: **POSP 676**
12" Single: Released May '84, on 21 Records, by Polydor Ltd. Catalogue no: **POSPX 676**

Toxic Ephex

PUNK AS F...
Tracks: / Punk as F.....
7" Single: Released Oct '86, on Green Vomit, Catalogue no: **PUKE 15**

Toxic Reasons

GOD BLESS AMERICA
Tracks: / God bless America.
7" Single: Released Sep '84, on Skysaw, by Skysaw Records. Catalogue no: **HANG 1**

Toxic Shock

DUBIOUS DEAL
Tracks: / Dubious deal.
7" Single: Released Sep '84, on Vindaloo, by Vindaloo Records. Catalogue no: **YUS 2**

JUST ANOTHER DAY
Tracks: / Just another day.
12" Single: Released Nov '85, on Vindaloo, by Vindaloo Records. Catalogue no: **YUS 5**

Toy

SUSPICION
Tracks: / Suspicion / Not your friend.
7" Single: Released Feb '81, on Logo, by Logo Records. Deleted '84. Catalogue no: **GO 397**

Toy Dolls

ALFIE FROM THE BRONX
Tracks: / Alfie from the Bronx.
7" Single: Released Nov '83, on Volume (1), by Volume Records. Catalogue no: **VOL 7**

CHEERIO AND TOODLE PIP
Tracks: / Cheerio and toodle pip.
7" Single: Released Aug '83, on Volume (1), by Volume Records. Catalogue no: **VOL 5**

EVERYBODY JITTERBUG
Tracks: / Everybody jitterbug / She's a worky ticket.
7" Single: Released Apr '82, on Zonophone, by EMI Records. Deleted '85. Catalogue no: **Z 31**

GEORDIES GONE TO JAIL
Tracks: / Geordies gone to jail.
7" Single: Released Jul '86, on Volume (1), by Volume Records. Catalogue no: **VOL 21**
12" Single: Released Jul '86, on Volume (1), by Volume Records. Catalogue no: **VOLT 21**

INTRO
Tracks: / Intro / James Bond lives.
7" Single: Released Sep '85, on Volume (1), by Volume Records. Catalogue no: **VOL 17**
12" Single: Released Sep '85, on Volume (1), by Volume Records. Catalogue no: **VOLT 17**

NELLIE THE ELEPHANT
Tracks: / Nellie the elephant.
7" Single: Released Jul '83, on Volume (1), by Volume Records. Catalogue no: **VOL 3**

NELLIE THE ELEPHANT (NOT THE ORIGINAL VERSION)
Tracks: / Nellie the Elephant (not the original version).
7" Single: Released Nov '84, on Volume (1), by Volume Records. Catalogue no: **VOL 11**
12" Single: Released Nov '84, on Volume (1), by Volume Records. Catalogue no: **VOLT 11**

SHE GOES TO FINO'S
Tracks: / She goes to Fino's / Spiders in the dressing room / Come back Jackie.
7" Single: Released Mar '85, on Volume (1), by Volume Records. Catalogue no: **VOL 12**
12" Single: Released Mar '85, on Volume (1), by Volume Records. Catalogue no: **VOLT 12**

TOMMY KOWIE'S CAR
Tracks: / Tommy Kowie's car.
7" Single: Released Oct '81, on GRC, Catalogue no: **GRC 104**

WE ARE MAD
Tracks: / We are mad.
7" Single: Released Jul '84, on Volume (1), by Volume Records. Catalogue no: **VOL 10**
12" Single: Released Jul '84, on Volume (1), by Volume Records. Catalogue no: **VOLT 10**

Toy Shop

ATTACK DECADE
Tracks: / Attack decade.
7" Single: Released Jan '84, on Towerbell, Catalogue no: **TOW 45**

Toy Traders

MC210
Tracks: / MC210.
7" Single: Released Nov '81, on Action, Catalogue no: **ACT 1100**

Toyah

Biographical details: Toyah is Toyah Willcox, born in 1958 in Birmingham; the UK new wave singer/actress was one of the most successful following the punk generation. She appeared in films including **Jubilee** and **Quadrophenia** in 1978-79; her singles and albums have been hits; she returned to acting in 1983 in Clare Luckham's wrestling play **Trafford Tanzi** (which **Debbie Harry** did on Broadway). She has moved with the times; her latest work is on *The Lady And The Tiger* '87 on Editions EG with her consort, avant-garde guitarist Robert Fripp. She appeared in London revival of 'Cabaret' '87, shut down by behaviour of musicians in the pit: they were sacked and it ran for a few nights as first musical in history without accompaniment. (Donald Clarke 13.1.88).

TOYAH - FOUR FROM TOYAH (Released on Safari)

BE LOUD BE PROUD BE HEARD
Tracks: / Be loud be proud be heard / Laughing with the fools.
7" Single: Released Oct '82, on Safari, by Safari Records. Catalogue no: **SAFE 52**

BIRD IN FLIGHT
Tracks: / Bird in flight / Tribal look.
7" Single: Released Feb '80, on Safari, by Safari Records. Deleted Feb '83. Catalogue no: **SAFE 22**

BRAVE NEW WORLD
Tracks: / Brave new world / Warrior rock.
7" Single: Released May '82, on Safari, by Safari Records. Catalogue no: **SAFE 45**

DANCED (LIVE)
Tracks: / Danced.
7" Single: Released '81, on Safari, by Safari Records. Catalogue no: **SAFE 32**

DON'T FALL IN LOVE (I SAID)
Tracks: / Don't fall in love (I said).
7" Single: Released Apr '85, on Portrait, by CBS Records. Deleted Apr '88. Catalogue no: **A 6160**

ECHO BEACH
Tracks: / Echo beach / Plenty.
7" Single: Released Apr '87, on E.G., by E.G. Records. Deleted May '88. Catalogue no: **EGO 31**
12" Single: Released Apr '87, on E.G., by E.G. Records. Deleted May '88. Catalogue no: **EGOX 31**

FOUR FROM TOYAH (see panel above)
Tracks: / It's a mystery / War boys / Revelations / Angels & demons.
7" EP: Released Feb '81, on Safari, by Safari Records. Catalogue no: **TOY 1**

FOUR MORE FROM TOYAH
7" Single: Released Nov '81, on Safari, by Safari Records. Catalogue no: **TOY 2**

I WANT TO BE FREE (see panel on right)
Tracks: / I want to be free / Walkie talkie / Alien.
7" Single: Released May '81, on Safari, by Safari Records. Catalogue no: **SAFE 34**

IEYA
Tracks: / Ieya / Helium song.
7" Pic: Released Jun '82, on Safari, by Safari Records. Catalogue no: **SAFEX 28**
7" Single: Released '81, on Safari, by Safari Records. Catalogue no: **SAFE 28**
12" Single: Released '81, on Safari, by Safari Records. Catalogue no: **SAFELS 28**

MOONLIGHT DANCING
Tracks: / Moonlight dancing / Sun up / R-e-n-t-r-y into dance (*Extra track on 12").
7" Single: Released 20 Jun '87, on E.G., by E.G. Records. Deleted May '88. Catalogue no: **EGO 35**
12" Single: Released 20 Jun '87, on E.G., by E.G. Records. Deleted May '88. Catalogue no: **EGOX 35**

REBEL RUN
Tracks: / Rebel run / Mountains high.
7" Single: Released Aug '83, on Safari, by Safari Records. Catalogue no: **SAFE 56**

SHEEP FARMING IN BARNET (SINGLE)
Tracks: / Sheep farming in Barnet.
7" Single: Released '80, on Safari, by Safari Records. Catalogue no: **SAP 1**

SOUL PASSING THROUGH SOUL
7" Single: Released Jun '85, on Portrait, by CBS Records. Deleted Jun '88. Catalogue no: **A 6359**

THUNDER IN THE MOUNTAINS
Tracks: / Thunder in the mountains.
7" Single: Released Sep '81, on Safari, by Safari Records. Catalogue no: **SAFE 38**
12" Single: Released Oct '81, on Safari, by Safari Records. Catalogue no: **SAFELS 38**

TRIBAL LOOK
Tracks: / Tribal look.
7" Single: Released '80, on Safari, by Safari Records. Catalogue no: **SAFE 22**

VICTIMS OF THE RIDDLE
Tracks: / Victims of the riddle.
7" Single: Released Jul '79, on Safari, by Safari Records. Catalogue no: **SAFE 15**

VOW, THE
Tracks: / Vow, The.
7" Single: Released Nov '83, on Safari, by Safari Records. Catalogue no: **SAFE 58**
12" Single: Released Nov '83, on Safari, by Safari Records. Catalogue no: **SAFELS 58**

Toyan

MARJORIE
Tracks: / Marjorie.
12" Single: Released Jan '83, on Rusty International, Catalogue no: **RI 005**

SLENG TING KING
Tracks: / Sleng ting king.
12" Single: Released May '85, on Witty, Catalogue no: **unknown**

Toyin

GEE BABY
Tracks: / Gee baby / Gee baby (version).
12" Single: Released Jan '88, on White Label (1), Catalogue no: **BUST 5**

HIP HIP HOORAY
Tracks: / Hip hip hooray.
7" Single: Released Aug '86, on Parlophone, by EMI Records. Catalogue no: **R 6136**
12" Single: Released Aug '86, on Parlophone, by EMI Records. Catalogue no: **12 R 6136**

IT ONLY TAKES A MINUTE
Tracks: / It only takes a minute / Six-o-secs flat / Some part of me / Trucks / Suddenly / Pat Nevin's eyes / Real me, The.
7" Single: Released Mar '87, on Criminal (1), by Criminal Records. Catalogue no: **BUS 2**
12" Single: Released Mar '87, on Criminal (1), by Criminal Records. Catalogue no: **BUST 2**
12" Single: Released Mar '87, on Probe Plus, by Probe Plus Records. Catalogue no: **PROD 9**

Toyla

HERE I GO AGAIN
Tracks: / Here I go again.
7" Single: Released Apr '86, on Criminal (1), by Criminal Records. Catalogue no: **BUS 1**
12" Single: Released Apr '86, on Criminal (1), by Criminal Records. Catalogue no: **BUST 1**

Toyota Pipes & Drums

MOUNT FUJI
Tracks: / Mount Fuji.
7" Single: Released Apr '82, on Toyota, Catalogue no: **MS 8**

Toys

ATTACK
Tracks: / Attack.
7" Single: Released Jan '66, on Stateside, by EMI Records. Deleted Jan '69. Catalogue no: **SS 483**

TOYAH - I WANT TO BE FREE (Released on Safari)

DOCTOR DOCTOR
Tracks: / Doctor doctor / Sweet Madgaline.
7" Single: Released Jun '80, on RAK, by EMI Records. Catalogue no: **RAK 313**

EASY DOES IT
Tracks: / Easy does it / Band played on.
7" Single: Released Oct '80, on Liberty, by EMI Records. Deleted Oct '83. Catalogue no: **BP 379**

I KNOW BETTER
Tracks: / I know better / Army toys.
7" Single: Released Jul '81, on Epic, by CBS Records. Deleted '85. Catalogue no: **EPC A 1320**

LOVER'S CONCERTO
Tracks: / Lover's concerto.
7" Single: Released Nov '65, on Stateside, by EMI Records. Deleted Nov '68. Catalogue no: **SS 460**
7" Single: Released '80, on Liberty (USA), by EMI Records. Catalogue no: **LR 8222**

LOVER'S CONCERTO (OLD GOLD)
Tracks: / Lover's concerto.
7" Single: Released Jul '84, on Old Gold, by Old Gold Records. Deleted Jul '88. Catalogue no: **OG 9416**

T-Party

YOU'RE THE ONLY ONE
Tracks: / You're the only one.
7" Single: Released Oct '85, on Wax, by Wax Records. Catalogue no: **7 WAX 1**

T'Pau

CHINA IN YOUR HAND
Tracks: / China in your hand (On all versions) / No sense of pride / China in your hand (full-length album version) (12" only) / Heart and soul (single version) (CD & cassette only) / Friends like these (CD only) / You give up (Cassette only).
CD 5": Released '88, on Siren, by Virgin Records. Catalogue no: **SRNCD 64**
Cassingle: Released '87, on Siren, by Virgin Records. Catalogue no: **SRNC 64**
7" Single: Released Oct '87, on Siren, by Virgin Records. Catalogue no: **SRN 64**
12" Single: Released Oct '87, on Siren, by Virgin Records. Catalogue no: **SRN 64-12**

HEART AND SOUL
Tracks: / On the wing / Taking time out (Cassette only) / Heart and soul (NOT on 12') / Heart and soul (remix) (NOT on 7") / Heart and soul (US dance mix) (12" only).
Cassingle: Released Jan '87, on Siren, by Virgin Records. Catalogue no: **SRNT 41**
7" Single: Released Jan '87, on Siren, by Virgin Records. Catalogue no: **SRN 41**
12" Single: Released Jan '87, on Siren, by Virgin Records. Catalogue no: **SRN 41-12**

I WILL BE WITH YOU
Tracks: / I will be with you / Still so in love / Thank you for goodbye (CD & 12" only) / Walk away Rene (CD only).
CD 5": Released Jun '88, on Siren, by Virgin Records. Catalogue no: **SRNCD 87**
7" Single: Released Jun '88, on Siren, by Virgin Records. Catalogue no: **SRN 87**
7" Single: Released Jun '88, on Siren, by Virgin Records. Deleted '89. Catalogue no: **SRNG 87**
12" Single: Released Jun '88, on Siren, by Virgin Records. Catalogue no: **SRNT 87**
12" Single: Released Jun '88, on Siren, by Virgin Records. Deleted '89. Catalogue no: **SRNTP 87**

INTIMATE STRANGERS
Tracks: / Intimate strangers / No sense of pride.
7" Single: Released Jun '87, on Siren, by Virgin Records. Deleted '89. Catalogue no: **SRNS 2**
12" Single: Released Jun '87, on Siren, by Virgin Records. Catalogue no: **SRN 5212**
12" Single: Released Jun '87, on Siren, by Virgin Records. Deleted '89. Catalogue no: **SRNS 212**

ONLY THE LONELY
Tracks: / Only the lonely / Between the lines / Downtown (12" only).
CD 5": Released Feb '89, on Siren, by Virgin Records. Catalogue no: **SRNCD 107**
7" Single: Released Apr '89, on Siren, by Virgin Records. Catalogue no: **SRNP 107**
7" Single: Released Feb '89, on Siren, by Virgin Records. Catalogue no: **SRN 107**
7" Single: Released Apr '89, on Siren, by Virgin Records. Catalogue no: **SRNG 107**
12" Single: Released Feb '89, on Siren, by Virgin Records. Catalogue no: **SRNT 107**

ROAD TO OUR DREAM
Tracks: / Road to our dream (On 12' only) / Time of our lives / Call me (Only on 12" and CD single.) / Road to our dream (full length version) (On CD only) / Road to our dream (instrumental) (Only on CD single.) / Road to our dream (edit) (On 7" only).
7" Single: Released '88, on Virgin, by Virgin Records. Catalogue no: **SRNB 100**
7" Single: Released 21 Nov '88, on Siren,

TRACIE - GIVE IT SOME EMOTION (Released on Respon(1))

by Virgin Records. Catalogue no: **SRN 100**
7" Single: Released '88, on Virgin, by Virgin Records. Catalogue no: **SRNX 100**
12" Single: Released Dec '88, on Siren, by Virgin Records. Catalogue no: **SRNTP 100**
12" Single: Released 21 Nov '88, on Siren, by Virgin Records. Catalogue no: **SRNT 100**
CD 3": Released 21 Nov '88, on Siren, by Virgin Records. Catalogue no: **SRNCD 100**

SECRET GARDEN
Tracks: / Secret garden / This girl / You'll never notice me (live) (CD & 12" only) / Crying (CD only).
CD 5": Released Sep '88, on Siren, by Virgin Records. Catalogue no: **SRNCD 93**
7" Single: Released Sep '88, on Siren, by Virgin Records. Catalogue no: **SRN 93**
12" Single: Released Sep '88, on Siren, by Virgin Records. Catalogue no: **SRNT 93**

SEX TALK (LIVE)
Tracks: / Sex talk (live) / Monkey house (live) / You give up (live) (CD & 12" only) / Heart and soul (live) (Cd only).
Note: This is the 4th single taken from the successful album'Bridge of Spies'and all the tracks on this recording are'live'.
CD 5": Released Aug '88, on Siren, by Virgin Records. Catalogue no: **SRNCD 80**
7" Single: Released 21 Mar '88, on Siren, by Virgin Records. Catalogue no: **SRN 80**
12" Single: Released 21 Mar '88, on Siren, by Virgin Records. Catalogue no: **SRNT 80**

VALENTINE
Tracks: / Valentine / Giving my love away / I'm a believer (CD only) / Chain in your hand (live) (CD only).
7" Single: Released Jan '88, on Siren, by Virgin Records. Catalogue no: **SRN 69**
CD 3": Released Apr '88, on Siren, by Virgin Records. Catalogue no: **SRNCD 69**

Tracey, James

YOU ARE MY WORLD
Tracks: / You are my world.
7" Single: Released Jun '85, on BMW, by BMW Records. Catalogue no: **MSBMW 1**

Tracie

GIVE IT SOME EMOTION (see panel above)
Tracks: / Give it some emotion / The bot hair dresser.
7" Single: Released Jul '83, on Respond (1), by Respond Records. Deleted Jul '86. Catalogue no: **KOB 704**

HOUSE THAT JACK BUILT, THE (see panel below)
Tracks: / House that Jack built, The / Dr. Love.
7" Single: Released Mar '83, on Respond (1), by Respond Records. Deleted Mar '86. Catalogue no: **KOB 701**

I LOVE YOU WHEN YOU SLEEP

TRACIE - THE HOUSE THAT JACK BUILT (Released on Respond(1))

Tracks: / I love you when you sleep.
7" Single: Released Jun '84, on Respond (1), by Respond Records. Deleted Jun '87. Catalogue no: **KOB 710**

SOUL'S ON FIRE
Tracks: / Soul's on fire / You must be kidding.
7" Single: Released Apr '84, on Respond (1), by Respond Records. Deleted Apr '87. Catalogue no: **KOB 708**

Tractor

AVERAGE MAN'S HERO
Tracks: / Average man's hero / Big big boy.
7" Single: Released Oct '81, on Roach, by Roach Records. Catalogue no: **RR 2**

Tracy, Jeanie

DON'T LEAVE ME THIS WAY
Tracks: / Don't leave me this way (Sylvester mix).
7" Single: Released Aug '86, on Domino, by Domino Records. Catalogue no: **DOM 2**
12" Single: Released Aug '86, on Domino, by Domino Records. Catalogue no: **DOM 2T**

Tracy, Kim

LOVE ME
Tracks: / Love me / Through the looking glass.
7" Single: Released Apr '80, on Free Range, Catalogue no: **2F 51**

Traddodiad Ofnus

HWY
Tracks: / Hwy.
7" Single: Released Oct '87, on Constrictor, by Constrictor Records (Germany). Catalogue no: **COLL 005**

Tradition

EVERY LITTLE BEAT OF MY HEART
Tracks: / Every little beat of my heart.
12" Single: Released Aug '85, on Music Scene, Catalogue no: **TRAD 5**

GIVE A HELPING HAND IF YOU CAN
Tracks: / Give a helping hand if you can.
12" Single: Released Aug '85, on Music Scene, Catalogue no: **MKS 7036**

LOVE MECHANICS
Tracks: / Love mechanics / Give a helping hand if you can.
7" Single: Released Jun '87, on Rhino, by Creole Records. Catalogue no: **RNO 77**
12" Single: Released Jun '87, on Rhino, by Creole Records. Catalogue no: **RNO 7**

RUNAWAY LOVE (SINGLE)
Tracks: / Runaway love / La la la la.
7" Single: Released Feb '80, on RCA, by BMG Records (UK). Deleted '83. Catalogue no: **PB 5220**

TRIBUTE TO THE KING
Tracks: / Tribute to the king.
12" Single: Released Feb '82, on Solid Groove, Catalogue no: **SG 008**

WE'RE HAVING A PARTY
Tracks: / We're having a party / Have you seen my baby.
12" Single: Released Aug '84, on Music Scene, Catalogue no: **MKS 1035**

Traedonya

BOOGALOO
Tracks: / Boogaloo.
12" Single: Released Oct '87, on Tuff City (USA), Catalogue no: **TUF 128018**

Traffic

Biographical details: This versatile UK rock group formed mis-'60s, with **Steve Winwood, Dave Mason** and **Chris Wood** all vocalists playing several instruments, **Jim Capaldi** on drums and vocals. Winwood had been the star of the **Spencer Davis Group** with his keyboards and bluesy voice; the new band epitomised psychedelia, with sound effects, the obligatory sitar and unusual lyric twists. They split up and Winwood made one LP in the supergroup **Blind Faith**; Traffic re-formed to make one of their best albums, *John Barleycorn Must Die* in 1971, deeply influenced by English folk music, especially the **Watersons**. They kept going until 1974, the best of their later albums probably being *Low Spark Of High Heeled Boys* in 1971. All subsequently had successful solo careers, Winwood being nominated for a clutch of Grammies in late 1986. (Donald Clarke 13.1.88).

HERE WE GO ROUND THE MULBERRY BUSH
Tracks: / Here we go round the Mulberry Bush.
7" Single: Released Nov '67, on Island, by Island Records. Deleted Nov '70. Catalogue no: **WIP 6025**

HOLE IN MY SHOE
Tracks: / Hole in my shoe / No face, no name, no number / I'm a man.
7" Single: on Island, by Island Records.

Deleted Apr '89. Catalogue no: **IS 362**
7" Single: Released Mar '78, on Island, by Island Records. Deleted Apr '89. Catalogue no: **IEP 7**

NO FACE, NO NAME, NO NUMBER
Tracks: / No face, no name, no number.
7" Single: Released Mar '68, on Island, by Island Records. Deleted Mar '71. Catalogue no: **WIP 6030**

PAPER SUN
Tracks: / Paper sun.
7" Single: Released Jun '67, on Island, by Island Records. Deleted Jun '70. Catalogue no: **WIP 6002**

Tragic Error

IUAHAHA
Tracks: / Iuahaha.
CD 5": Released Dec '88, on Who's That Beat, by Play It Again Sam (Belgium). Catalogue no: **WHOS 009CD**
12" Single: Released Oct '88, on Who's That Beat, by Play It Again Sam (Belgium). Catalogue no: **WHOS 009**

TANZEN
Tracks: / Tanzen.
CD 5": Released May '89, on Who's That Beat, by Play It Again Sam (Belgium). Catalogue no: **WHOS 014 CD**
7" Single: Released May '89, on Who's That Beat, by Play It Again Sam (Belgium). Catalogue no: **WHOS 014**
12" Single: Released May '89, on Who's That Beat, by Play It Again Sam (Belgium). Catalogue no: **WHOS 014R**

Tragically Hip

SMALLTOWN BRINGDOWN
Tracks: / Smalltown bringdown.
CD 5": Released Sep '89, on MCA, by MCA Records. Catalogue no: **DMCAT 1363**
7" Single: Released Sep '89, on MCA, by MCA Records. Catalogue no: **MCA 1363**
12" Single: Released Sep '89, on MCA, by MCA Records. Catalogue no: **MCAT 1363**

Train Set

HOLD ON
Tracks: / Hold on.
12" Single: Released 27 Feb '89, on Play Hard, by Play Hard Records. Catalogue no: **DEC 17**

SHE'S GONE
Tracks: / She's gone.
12" Single: Released Sep '88, on Play Hard, by Play Hard Records. Catalogue no: **DEC 011**

SINK OR SWIM
Tracks: / Sink or swim.
7" Single: Released Jun '88, on Play Hard, by Play Hard Records. Catalogue no: **DEC 011**

Trainer, Bunny

JAH HOUSE ID HELL
Tracks: / Jah house id hell.
12" Single: Released Sep '84, on Big Ship, Catalogue no: **Unknown**

Trainspotters

HIGH RISE
Tracks: / High rise / Rock 'n roll hall of fame.
7" Single: Released Feb '84, on Arista, by BMG Records (UK). Catalogue no: **ARIST 290**

UNFAITHFUL
Tracks: / Unfaithful.
7" Single: Released Nov '79, on Arista, by BMG Records (UK). Catalogue no: **ARIST 320**

Traitors Gate

DEVIL TAKES THE HIGH ROAD
Tracks: / Devil takes the high road.
12" Single: Released Apr '85, on Bullet, by Bullet Records. Catalogue no: **BOLT 12**

Tralala

ALWAYS CLOSE AT HAND
Tracks: / Always close at hand / Don't take to love.
7" Single: Released Jan '85, on Floating World, by Floating World Records. Catalogue no: **FLOAT 02**

ROOM TO BE CRUEL
7" Single: Released May '84, on Floating World, by Floating World Records. Catalogue no: **FLOAT 01**

Tramaine

FALL DOWN (SPIRIT OF LOVE)
Tracks: / Fall down (spirit of love).
7" Single: Released Oct '85, on A&M, by A&M Records. Deleted Oct '88. Catalogue no: **AM 281**

Trammps

DISCO INFERNO
Tracks: / Disco inferno.
7" Single: Released Jun '78, on Atlantic, by WEA Records. Deleted '81. Catalogue no: **K 11135**
7" Single: Released May '77, on Atlantic, by WEA Records. Deleted '80. Catalogue no: **K 10914**

HARD ROCK & DISCO
Tracks: / Hard rock and disco (part 1) / Hard rock and disco (part 2).
7" Single: Released Apr '80, on Atlantic, by WEA Records. Deleted Apr '83. Catalogue no: **K11438**

HOLD BACK THE NIGHT
Tracks: / Hold back the night.
7" Single: Released Oct '75, on Buddah, by Buddah Records Inc.(USA). Deleted '78. Catalogue no: **BDS 437**

HOLD BACK THE NIGHT (OLD GOLD)
7" Single: Released Apr '83, on Old Gold, by Old Gold Records. Deleted Jul '88. Catalogue no: **OG 9297**

LOOKING FOR YOU
Tracks: / Looking for you / Love land.
7" Single: Released Feb '81, on Atlantic, by WEA Records. Deleted Feb '84. Catalogue no: **K 11654**

SIXTY MINUTE MAN
Tracks: / Sixty minute man.
7" Single: Released Feb '75, on Buddah, by Buddah Records Inc.(USA). Deleted '78. Catalogue no: **BDS 415**

SOUL SEARCHIN' TIME
Tracks: / Soul searchin' time.
7" Single: Released Jul '76, on Atlantic, by WEA Records. Deleted '79. Catalogue no: **K 10797**

THAT'S WHERE THE HAPPY PEOPL GO
Tracks: / That's where the happy people go.
7" Single: Released Mar '76, on Atlantic, by WEA Records. Deleted '79. Catalogue no: **K 10703**

TRAMMPS
Tracks: / Hold back the night / Sixty minute man / Zing went the strings of my heart / Penguin at the big apple.
CD 3": Released '88, on Special Edition, by Castle Communications Records. Catalogue no: **CD3-18**

ZING WENT THE STRINGS OF MY HEART
Tracks: / Zing went the strings of my heart.
7" Single: Released Nov '74, on Buddah, by Buddah Records Inc.(USA). Deleted '77. Catalogue no: **BDS 405**

Trance Dance

DO THE DANCE
Tracks: / Do the dance / Sail away / Do the dance (alt).
7" Single: Released Aug '87, on CBS, by CBS Records. Catalogue no: **650755 7**
7" Single: Released Jul '86, on CBS, by CBS Records. Catalogue no: **A 6924**
12" Single: Released Jul '87, on CBS, by CBS Records. Catalogue no: **650 755 8**

YOU'RE GONNA GET IT
Tracks: / You're gonna get it (remix) / Prime time rhyme / You're gonna get it (extended remix) (12" only) / You're gonna get it (Sergio Leone remix) (12" only).
7" Single: Released Aug '88, on CBS, by CBS Records. Deleted 17 Apr '89. Catalogue no: **651303 7**
12" Single: Released Aug '88, on CBS, by CBS Records. Deleted 17 Apr '89. Catalogue no: **651303 9**

Trans Lux

BIG APPLE NOISE
Tracks: / Big apple noise / Street noise.
7" Single: Released Feb '84, on Malaco, by Malaco Records (UK). Deleted '88. Catalogue no: **MAL 018**
12" Single: Released Feb '84, on Malaco, by Malaco Records (UK). Deleted '88. Catalogue no: **MAL 12 018**

Trans UK

ALL I NEED IS YOU
Tracks: / All I need is you / Ain't nobody.
7" Single: Released 21 Nov '87, on Climax, Catalogue no: **CLIMAX 2**
12" Single: Released 21 Nov '87, on Climax, Catalogue no: **CLIMAX 122**

TURN THIS LOVE AROUND
Tracks: / Turn this love around / Turn this love around (version).
7" Single: Released Jun '88, on Climax, Catalogue no: **CLIMAX 3**
12" Single: Released Jun '88, on Climax, Catalogue no: **CLIMAX 123**

Trans X

LIVING ON VIDEO
Tracks: / Living on video / Digital world.
7" Single: Released Jul '85, on Boiling Point, by Polydor Ltd. Deleted '88. Catalogue no: **POSP 650**

TRANSVISION VAMP - THE ONLY ONE (Released on MCA)

Transistors

RIOT SQUAD
Tracks: / Riot squad.
7" Single: Released Sep '82, on Open Circuit, Deleted '84. Catalogue no: **OC 1**

Translator

ALONE
Tracks: / Alone.
7" Single: Released Nov '83, on CBS, by CBS Records. Catalogue no: **A 3715**

Transmitters

MECHANIC, THE
Tracks: / Mechanic, The.
12" Single: Released Apr '89, on Craving Company, Catalogue no: **9CC**

UGLY MAN, THE
Tracks: / Ugly man, The.
12" Single: Released Oct '79, on Step Forward, by Faulty Products Records. Catalogue no: **SF 1212**

Transporter

KIDS ON HER RUN
Tracks: / Kids on her run / Halfway house.
7" Single: Released Nov '82, on High Force, Catalogue no: **HIGH 1**

Transvision Vamp

BABY I DON'T CARE
Tracks: / Baby I don't care (On 7" and CD only) / Time for change / Strings of my heart / Baby I don't care (Abigail's party mix) (On 12" only) / Sex kick (demo version) (On 12" only) / Saturn 5 (demo version) (On CD only).
CD 5": Released 20 Mar '89, on MCA, by MCA Records. Catalogue no: **DTVVT 6**
7" Single: Released 20 Mar '89, on MCA, by MCA Records. Catalogue no: **TVVG 6**
7" Single: Released 20 Mar '89, on MCA, by MCA Records. Catalogue no: **TVV 6**
12" Single: Released 20 Mar '89, on MCA, by MCA Records. Catalogue no: **TVVTG 6**
12" Single: Released 20 Mar '89, on MCA, by MCA Records. Catalogue no: **TVVT 6**

I WANT YOUR LOVE
Tracks: / I want your love (On 7" only) / Sweet thing / Evolution Evie (On 7" only) / I want your love (I don't want your money mix) (On 12" and CD only) / Evolution Evie (eletric version) (On 12" and CD only) / Tell that girl to shut up (On CD only).
Note: Love 'em or loathe 'em - you can't ignore 'em - Wendy and the boys return with their third piece in the puzzle of perfect power pop.
CD 5": Released Jun '88, on MCA, by MCA Records. Catalogue no: **DTVV 3**
7" Single: Released Jun '88, on MCA, by MCA Records. Catalogue no: **TVV 3**
12" Single: Released Jun '88, on MCA, by MCA Records. Catalogue no: **TVVTR 3**
12" Single: Released Jun '88, on MCA, by MCA Records. Catalogue no: **TVVT 3**

LANDSLIDE OF LOVE (see panel on next page)
Tracks: / Landslide of love (On 7" and Cass only) / Hardtime / He's the only one for me / Landslide of love (extended mix) (On 12" and CD only) / West 11 blues (On 12" and CD only).
CD 5": Released 17 Jul '89, on MCA, by MCA Records. Catalogue no: **DTVV 8**
7" Pic: Released 17 Jul '89, on MCA, by MCA Records. Catalogue no: **TVVP 8**
Cassingle: Released 17 Jul '89, on MCA, by MCA Records. Catalogue no: **TVVC 8**
7" Single: Released 17 Jul '89, on MCA, by MCA Records. Catalogue no: **TVV 8**
12" Single: Released 17 Jul '89, on MCA, by MCA Records. Catalogue no: **TVVTG 8**
12" Single: Released 17 Jul '89, on MCA, by MCA Records. Catalogue no: **TVVT 8**

ONLY ONE, THE (see panel above)
Tracks: / Only one, The (On 7", Cass and CD only) / Mystery song, The / Love me (Only on CD single and 12".) / Only one, The (extended version) (On 12" and CD only).
CD 5": Released May '89, on MCA, by MCA Records. Catalogue no: **DTVVT 7**
Cassingle: Released May '89, on MCA, by MCA Records. Catalogue no: **TVVC 7**
7" Single: Released May '89, on MCA, by MCA Records. Catalogue no: **TVV 7**
12" Single: Released May '89, on MCA, by MCA Records. Catalogue no: **TVVT 7**

REVOLUTION BABY
Tracks: / Revolution baby / Vid kid vamp / Know that U love her (On 12" only).
7" Single: Released Aug '87, on MCA, by MCA Records. Catalogue no: **TVV 1**
12" Single: Released Aug '87, on MCA, by MCA Records. Catalogue no: **TVVT 1**

REVOLUTION BABY (REMIX)
Tracks: / Revolution baby (remix) (On 7" only) / Honey honey / Long lonely weekend / Revolution baby (electra-glide) (On 12" and CD only) / Vid kid vamp (On CD only).
CD 5": Released Sep '88, on MCA, by MCA Records. Catalogue no: **DTVV 4**
7" Single: Released Sep '88, on MCA, by MCA Records. Catalogue no: **TVV 4**
7" Single: Released Sep '88, on MCA, by MCA Records. Catalogue no: **TVVPR 4**
12" Single: Released Sep '88, on MCA, by MCA Records. Catalogue no: **TVVT 4**
12" Single: Released Sep '88, on MCA, by MCA Records. Catalogue no: **TVVTP 4**

SISTER MOON
Tracks: / Sister moon (On 7" and CD only) / Walk on by / Oh yeah / Sex kick (Ciao Portabello) (On 12" and CD only) / Sister moon (groove on) (On 12" only).
CD 5": Released Nov '88, on MCA, by MCA Records. Catalogue no: **DTVV 5**
7" Pic: Released Nov '88, on MCA, by MCA Records. Catalogue no: **TVVP 5**
7" Single: Released Nov '88, on MCA, by MCA Records. Deleted 1 Jul '89. Catalogue no: **TVV 5**
12" Single: Released Nov '88, on MCA, by MCA Records. Catalogue no: **TVVT 5**
12" Single: Released Nov '88, on MCA, by MCA Records. Catalogue no: **TVVTG 5**

TELL THAT GIRL TO SHUT UP
Tracks: / Tell that girl to shut up (On 7" and CD only) / God save the royalties (Track on 7".) / Tell that girl to shut up (ext) (On 12" and CD only) / Tell that girl to shut up (knuckle duster mix) (On 12" and CD only).

TRANSVISION VAMP - LANSLIDE OF LOVE (Released on MCA)

CD 5": Released Apr '88, on MCA, by MCA Records. Catalogue no: **DTVV 2**
7" Single: Released Mar '88, on MCA, by MCA Records. Catalogue no: **TVVPR 2**
7" Single: Released Mar '88, on MCA, by MCA Records. Catalogue no: **TVV 2**
12" Single: Released Mar '88, on MCA, by MCA Records. Catalogue no: **TVVT 2**
CD 3": Released '88, on MCA, by MCA Records. Catalogue no: **10 P36036**

Tranzista

HEAVEN WITH HER
Tracks: / Heaven with her / Dangerous thoughts.
7" Single: Released Jul '83, on Atlantic, by WEA Records. Catalogue no: **A 9815**
12" Single: Released Jul '83, on Atlantic, by WEA Records. Catalogue no: **TA 9815**

Trapeze

DON'T ASK ME HOW I KNOW
Tracks: / Don't ask me how I know / Take good care.
7" Single: Released Jan '80, on Aura Records, by Aura Records. Deleted '88. Catalogue no: **AUS 114**

RUNNING AWAY
Tracks: / Running away / Don't break my heart.
7" Single: Released Mar '81, on Aura Records, by Aura Records. Deleted '88. Catalogue no: **AUS 116**

Trash

GOLDEN SLUMBERS
7" Single: Released Oct '69, on Apple, by Apple Records. Deleted '72. Catalogue no: **APPLE 17**

ROCK ME ROCK YOU
Tracks: / Rock me rock you.
7" Single: Released Jun '85, on Atlantic, by WEA Records. Catalogue no: **A 9545**

Trash It

TRASH IT
Tracks: / Trash it.
12" Single: Released May '88, on Who's That Beat, by Play It Again Sam (Belgium). Catalogue no: **WHOS 003**

Trash Town

UNLUCKY NUMBERS
Tracks: / Unlucky numbers.
7" Single: Released Oct '85, on Course, by Course Records. Catalogue no: **CORS 1**

Travaganza

STAY WITH ME
Tracks: / Stay with me.
7" Single: Released Jan '85, on Aura Records, by Aura Records. Deleted '88. Catalogue no: **AUS 143**

Traveling Wilburys

END OF THE LINE
Tracks: / End of the line / Congratulations.
CD 5": Released Feb '89, on Warner Bros., by WEA Records. Catalogue no: **W 7637CD**
7" Single: Released Feb '89, on Warner Bros., by WEA Records. Catalogue no: **W 7637**
12" Single: Released Feb '89, on Warner Bros., by WEA Records. Catalogue no: **W 7637T**

HANDLE WITH CARE
Tracks: / Handle me with care / Margaruite.
CD 5": Released Oct '88, on Warner Bros., by WEA Records. Catalogue no: **W 7732CD**
7" Single: Released Oct '88, on Warner Bros., by WEA Records. Catalogue no: **W 7732**
12" Single: Released Oct '88, on Warner Bros., by WEA Records. Catalogue no: **W 7732T**

Traveller

BROTHER WINSTON
Tracks: / Brother Winston / Sister Jamaica.
7" Single: Released Feb '81, on Edge, Deleted '84. Catalogue no: **EDGE 10**

Travers, Pat

IS THIS LOVE
Tracks: / Is this love / Snorting.
7" Single: Released Apr '80, on Polydor, by Polydor Ltd. Deleted Apr '83. Catalogue no: **POSP 144**

SNORTIN' WHISKEY
Tracks: / Snortin' whiskey / Your love can't be right / Life in London / Evie / Rock'n'roll Susie.
12" Single: Released Sep '80, on Polydor, by Polydor Ltd. Deleted '83. Catalogue no: **POSPX 164**

Travis

GET THE LIFE
Tracks: / Get the life.
7" Single: Released Jan '85, on Charity, Catalogue no: **12 CAZ 11**

GIMME SOME LOVIN
Tracks: / Gimme some lovin / Anybody but you.
7" Single: Released Jan '87, on Wag, Catalogue no: **WAG 3**

Travis, Randy

Biographical details: Was born in North Carolina and moved to Nashville in 1981; the young ballad singer's sepulchral voice made his debut album *Storms Of Life* a number one hit in the USA country chart in 1986, with four top ten single hits, two at No.1. (Donald Clarke 13.1.88).

DEEPER THAN THE HOLLER
Tracks: / Deeper than the holler / I told you so / Diggin' up bones (Track on 12" only) / What'll you do about me (Track on 12" only) / 1982 (Track on CD only) / No place like home (Track on CD only).
CD 5": Released Jul '88, on Warner Bros., by WEA Records. Catalogue no: **W 7804CD**
7" Single: Released Jul '88, on Warner Bros., by WEA Records. Catalogue no: **W 7804**
12" Single: Released Jul '88, on Warner Bros., by WEA Records. Catalogue no: **W 7804T**

FOREVER AND EVER AMEN
Tracks: / Forever and ever amen / Promises / On the other hand (Avaliable on the CD single format only.).
CD 5": Released Apr '88, on Warner Bros., by WEA Records. Catalogue no: **W 8384 CD**
7" Single: Released Apr '88, on Warner Bros., by WEA Records. Catalogue no: **W 8384**

ON THE OTHER HAND
Tracks: / Can't stop now / On the other hand.
7" Single: Released Jan '87, on Warner Bros., by WEA Records. Deleted Jan '88. Catalogue no: **W 8962**

Travis, Steve

GHOST RIDES IN THE SKY
Tracks: / Ghost riders in the sky.
7" Single: Released Dec '82, on Frontier, by Frontier Records. Catalogue no: **F 1**

Travitt, Kenya

COME INTO MY HEART (IMPORT)
Tracks: / Come into my heart.
12" Single: Released Oct '89, on Big Beat, by Ace Records. Catalogue no: **BB 0009**

Travolta, John

GREASED LIGHTNIN'
Tracks: / Greased lightning'.
7" Single: Released Dec '78, on Polydor, by Polydor Ltd. Deleted '81. Catalogue no: **POSP 14**

SANDY
Tracks: / Sandy / Rock'n'roll party queen.
7" Single: Released Oct '78, on Polydor, by Polydor Ltd. Deleted '81. Catalogue no: **POSP 6**

SUMMER NIGHTS
Tracks: / Summer nights.
7" Single: Released Sep '78, on RSO, by Polydor Ltd. Deleted '81. Catalogue no: **RSO 18**

YOU'RE THE ONE THAT I WANT
Tracks: / You're the one that I want.
7" Single: Released May '78, on RSO, by Polydor Ltd. Deleted '81. Catalogue no: **RSO 006**

Trax

TELL ME THIS IS LOVE
Tracks: / Tell me this is love / Tell me this is love (dub mix).
7" Single: Released Jul '86, on Buzzin, Catalogue no: **BUBE 4**

Trax, Miss Nicky

ACID IN THE HOUSE
Tracks: / Acid in the house.
12" Single: Released Oct '88, on Kaos, Catalogue no: **KAOS 004**

Traxx

MALFUNCTION
Tracks: / Malfunction.
12" Single: Released '88, on USA, by Charly Records. Catalogue no: **USA 1070**

Treacherous Three

GOTTA ROCK
Tracks: / Gotta rock.
12" Single: Released Nov '85, on Sugarhill (USA), Catalogue no: **SHL 144**

SANTA'S RAP
Tracks: / Santa's rap.
12" Single: Released Nov '84, on Sugarhill (USA), Catalogue no: **SHL 138**

YES WE CAN CAN
Tracks: / Yes we can can.
7" Single: Released Jan '83, on Sugarhill (USA), Deleted '88. Catalogue no: **SH 120**
12" Single: Released Jan '83, on Sugarhill (USA), Catalogue no: **SHL 120**

Treasure Island

TREASURE ISLAND (SINGLE)
7" EP: Released Apr '81, on Disneyland, by Disneyland Records. Catalogue no: **D 361**

Treasures

LET US CELEBRATE (IT'S CHRISTMAS TIME)
Tracks: / Let us celebrate (it's Christmas time).
7" Single: Released Dec '87, on Inter-Melody, by Inter Melody Music. Catalogue no: **INMELO 1**

Treatment, Steve

HOOKED ON A TREND
Tracks: / Hooked on a trend.
7" Single: Released Jun '81, on Rather, by Rather Records. Catalogue no: **GEAR 2**

Tredegar

DUMA
Tracks: / Duma.
7" Single: Released Jun '86, on Aires, Catalogue no: **CEP 1**

SEND IN THE CLOWNS
Tracks: / Send in the clowns.
7" Single: Released Nov '79, on RAK, by EMI Records. Catalogue no: **RAK 302**

Treebound Story

I REMEMBER
Tracks: / I remember.
12" Single: Released Jun '86, on Fon, by FON Records. Catalogue no: **ELM 1**

MY LIFE'S EXAMPLE
Tracks: / My life's example.
7" Single: Released Apr '87, on Fon, by FON Records. Catalogue no: **ELM 8**
12" Single: Released Apr '87, on Fon, by FON Records. Catalogue no: **ELM 8T**

SWIMMING IN THE HEART OF JANE
Tracks: / Swimming in the heart of Jane / Butterfly dies, The / Rain rain rain / On the rocks.
CD 5": Released Jun '89, on Native (1), by Native Records. Catalogue no: **CDNTV 40**
12" Single: Released Jun '89, on Native (1), by Native Records. Catalogue no: **12NTV 40**

Treehouse

PAY-BACK TIME
Tracks: / Pay-back time.
7" Single: Released Jun '88, on Native (1), by Native Records. Catalogue no: **NTV 35**
12" Single: Released Jun '88, on Native (1), by Native Records. Catalogue no: **12 NTV 35**

Treetops

DOWN BELOW
Tracks: / Down below / End / Rockers.
7" Single: Released 20 Jun '80, on Success (1), Deleted '83. Catalogue no: **SRLD 004**

Tremblers

STEADY EDDY
Tracks: / Steady Eddy / I screamed Anne.
7" Single: Released Aug '80, on Epic, by CBS Records. Deleted '83. Catalogue no: **EPC 8930**

Tremeloes

6 TRACK HITS
Tracks: / Here comes my baby / Me and my life / Silence is golden / Even the bad times are good / Call me / Number one / Words.
7" EP: Released Mar '84, on Scoop 33, by Pickwick Records. Catalogue no: **7SR 5034**

BE MINE
Tracks: / Be mine.
7" Single: Released Nov '67, on CBS, by CBS Records. Deleted '70. Catalogue no: **CBS 3043**

BY THE WAY
Tracks: / By the way.
7" Single: Released Mar '70, on CBS, by CBS Records. Deleted '73. Catalogue no: **CBS 4815**

EVEN THE BAD TIMES SRE GOOD
Tracks: / Even the bad times are good.
7" Single: Released Mar '67, on CBS, by CBS Records. Deleted '70. Catalogue no: **CBS 2930**

HELLO BUDDY
Tracks: / Hello buddy.
7" Single: Released Jul '71, on CBS, by CBS Records. Deleted '74. Catalogue no: **CBS 7294**

HELLO WORLD
Tracks: / Hello world.
7" Single: Released Mar '69, on CBS, by CBS Records. Deleted '72. Catalogue no: **CBS 4065**

HELULE HELULE
Tracks: / Helule helule.
7" Single: Released May '68, on CBS, by CBS Records. Deleted '71. Catalogue no: **CBS 2889**

HERE COMES MY BABY
Tracks: / Here come's my baby.
7" Single: Released Feb '67, on CBS, by CBS Records. Deleted '70. Catalogue no: **CBS 202519**

I SHALL BE RELEASED
Tracks: / I shall be released.
7" Single: Released Dec '68, on CBS, by CBS Records. Deleted '71. Catalogue no: **CBS 3873**

LIGHTS OF PORT ROYAL
Tracks: / Lights of port royal / Silas.
7" Single: Released May '80, on AMI, by AMI Records. Deleted '85. Catalogue no: **AIS 100**

ME AND MY LIFE
Tracks: / Me and my life.
7" Single: Released Sep '70, on CBS, by CBS Records. Deleted '73. Catalogue no: **CBS 5139**

MY LITTLE LADY
Tracks: / My little lady.
7" Single: Released Nov '68, on CBS, by CBS Records. Deleted '71. Catalogue no: **CBS 3443**

NUMBER ONE
Tracks: / Number one.

7" Single: Released Nov '69, on CBS, by CBS Records. Deleted '72. Catalogue no: **CBS 4582**

SILENCE IS GOLDEN (1984)
Tracks: / Silence is golden (1984).
7" Single: Released Oct '84, on Meteor, by Magnum Music Group. Catalogue no: **MTS 002**

SILENCE IS GOLDEN (1988)
Tracks: / Silence is golden / Silence is golden (version).
7" Single: Released Mar '88, on Mojo, Catalogue no: **MOJ 109 770**
12" Single: Released Mar '88, on Mojo, Catalogue no: **MOJ 609 770**

SILENCE IS GOLDEN (SINGLE)
Tracks: / Silence is golden.
7" Single: Released Apr '67, on CBS, by CBS Records. Deleted '70. Catalogue no: **CBS 2723**
7" Single: Released Jul '84, on CBS, by CBS Records. Catalogue no: **A 4577**
7" Single: Released Aug '82, on Old Gold, by Old Gold Records. Deleted Jul '88. Catalogue no: **OG 9200**

SUDDENLY YOU LOVE ME
Tracks: / Suddenly you love me.
7" Single: Released Jan '68, on CBS, by CBS Records. Deleted '71. Catalogue no: **CBS 3234**

TREMELODIES
Tracks: / Tremelodies / I let my best friend down.
7" Single: Released Nov '81, on Polydor, by Polydor Ltd. Deleted Nov '84. Catalogue no: **POSP 381**

WORDS
Tracks: / Words.
7" Single: Released Mar '83, on CBS, by CBS Records. Catalogue no: **A 3133**

Tremor Toes

LET'S GET THIS (LOVING THING GOING)
Tracks: / Let's get this (loving thing going).
12" Single: Released Jul '86, on World International, Catalogue no: **WIR 505**

Trend

I DON'T ANYMORE
Tracks: / I don't anymore / Routines.
7" Single: Released Jun '80, on MCA, by MCA Records. Deleted '83. Catalogue no: **MCA 613**

POLLY AND WENDY
Tracks: / Polly and Wendy / Family way, The.
7" Single: Released Apr '80, on MCA, by MCA Records. Deleted '82. Catalogue no: **MCA 583**

THIS DANCE HALL MUST HAVE A BACK WAY OUT
Tracks: / This dance hall must have a back way out / Fiction, love and romance.
7" Single: Released Aug '80, on MCA, by MCA Records. Deleted '83. Catalogue no: **MCA 629**

Trendy Dendy

DA DA DA DA
Tracks: / Da da da da / Do it again.
7" Single: Released Feb '82, on Double L, Catalogue no: **LL 0004**

DO IT AGAIN
Tracks: / Do it again.
7" Single: Released Nov '83, on Double L, Catalogue no: **LL 0005**

Trent, Jackie

I'LL BE THERE
Tracks: / I'll be there.
7" Single: Released Apr '69, on Pye, Deleted '72. Catalogue no: **7 N 17693**

WHEN THE SUMMERTIME IS OVER
Tracks: / When the summertime is over.
7" Single: Released Jul '65, on Pye, Deleted '68. Catalogue no: **7 N 15865**

WHERE ARE YOU NOW
Tracks: / Where are you now.
7" Single: Released Apr '65, on Pye, Deleted '68. Catalogue no: **7 N 15776**
7" Single: Released Jul '82, on Old Gold, by Old Gold Records. Deleted Jul '88. Catalogue no: **OG 9138**

Trespass

BRIGHT LIGHTS
Tracks: / Bright lights / Duel/Man and machine.
7" Single: Released Jan '82, on Trial, by Trial Records. Catalogue no: **CASE 3**

JEALOUSY
Tracks: / Jealousy.
7" Single: Released Sep '82, on Trial, by Trial Records. Catalogue no: **CASE 2**

ONE OF THESE DAYS
Tracks: / One of these days.
7" Single: Released Jan '80, on Trial, by Trial Records. Catalogue no: **CASE 1**

Trespassers W

PARIS IN BETWEEN THE WARS
Tracks: / Paris in between the wars.
12" Single: Released May '86, on T.W., by T.W. Records. Catalogue no: **TW 1003**

Trevillion & Nine

ANYONE FOR TENNIS
Tracks: / Anyone for tennis.
7" Single: Released Sep '82, on Service, Catalogue no: **ALL 40**

Trew, Gerry

DEEPER
Tracks: / Deeper.
7" Single: Released Nov '83, on Bluebird (2), by BMG Records (UK). Catalogue no: **BR 6**
12" Single: Released Nov '83, on Bluebird (2), by BMG Records (UK). Catalogue no: **BRT 6**

HEARTACHE
Tracks: / Heartache / Heartache(Instrmental).
7" Single: Released May '86, on Billy Boy, by Blue Sun Records (USA). Deleted Jun '88. Catalogue no: **7 BILLY 1**
12" Single: Released May '86, on Billy Boy, by Blue Sun Records (USA). Deleted Jun '88. Catalogue no: **12 BILLY 1**

I'M DOING FINE NOW
Tracks: / Backing track / I'm doing fine now.
12" Single: Released Dec '86, on Bluebird (2), by BMG Records (UK). Catalogue no: **BRT 28**

Triarchy

SAVE THE KHAN
Tracks: / Save the Khan.
7" Single: Released Mar '80, on SRT, by SRT Records. Catalogue no: **SRTS 79**

Tribe

STICKING TO MY GUN
Tracks: / Sticking to my gun / Music.
7" Single: Released Jun '87, on TSU, Deleted '88. Catalogue no: **TSU 1**
12" Single: Released Jun '87, on TSU, Deleted '88. Catalogue no: **TSUT 1**

Tribe 22

ACID NEW BEAT
Tracks: / Acid new beat.
CD 5": Released '89, on Kaos, Catalogue no: **KAOS 009 CD**
12" Single: Released '89, on Kaos, Catalogue no: **KAOS 009**

Tribe Called Quest

DESCRIPTION OF A FOOL
Tracks: / Description of a fool.
7" Single: Released 25 Aug '89, on Jive, by Zomba Records. Catalogue no: **JIVE 215**
12" Single: Released 25 Aug '89, on Jive, by Zomba Records. Catalogue no: **JIVET 215**

Tribe of Benn

FILTHY CLEAN
Tracks: / Filthy clean.
7" Single: Released 30 May '87, on Drastic Plastic, by Drastic Plastic Records. Catalogue no: **DRASTIC 2**

Tribe Of Toffs

JOHN KETTLEY (IS A WEATHERMAN)
Tracks: / John Kettley (is a weatherman) / Festive frolics from four fellows.
7" Single: Released Dec '88, on Completely Different, by Neat Records. Catalogue no: **DAFT 1**

Tribe, Tony

RED RED WINE
Tracks: / Red red wine.
7" Single: Released Jul '69, on Downtown, Deleted '72. Catalogue no: **DT 419**

RED RED WINE (EP)
Tracks: / Red red wine.
7" Single: Released Nov '83, on Trojan, by Trojan Records. Catalogue no: **TRO 9075**
12" Single: Released Nov '83, on Trojan, by Trojan Records. Catalogue no: **TROT 9075**

Tribesman

SUNBURST
Tracks: / Sunburst / Lion.
7" Single: Released Sep '80, on Direct Records, Catalogue no: **ROS 001**
12" Single: Released Aug '80, on Direct Records, Deleted '83. Catalogue no: **ROS 001 12**

Trick

HEART OF HEARTS
Tracks: / Heart of hearts / Dark star.
7" Single: Released May '85, on Unit, Catalogue no: **TRANS 107**

MY WORLD
Tracks: / My world.
7" Single: Released Oct '84, on Unit, Catalogue no: **TRANS 103**
12" Single: Released Oct '84, on Unit, Catalogue no: **12TRA 103**

TURN TO STONE
Tracks: / Turn to stone / Shine on / Dance to the beat.
7" Single: Released Mar '85, on Unit, Catalogue no: **TRANS 106**
12" Single: Released Mar '85, on Unit, Catalogue no: **12TRA 106**

Trick Dog

WHAT A SHAME
Tracks: / What a shame / No tomorrow.
7" Single: Released Feb '81, on Radioactive, Catalogue no: **RAD 100**

Triffids

BURY ME DEEP IN LOVE (see panel below)
Tracks: / Bury me deep in love / Rent / Into the groove (Only on 12" and CD single.).
CD 5": Released Jul '89, on Island, by Island Records. Catalogue no: **CID 424**
7" Single: Released Jul '89, on Island, by Island Records. Catalogue no: **IS 424**
7" Single: Released Oct '87, on Island, by Island Records. Catalogue no: **IS 337**
12" Single: Released Jul '89, on Island, by Island Records. Catalogue no: **12 IS 424**
12" Single: Released Oct '87, on Island, by Island Records. Catalogue no: **12IS 337**

FALLING OVER YOU
Tracks: / Falling over you / God home Eddie / Shell of a man (Only on 12" and CD single.) / You minus me (Only on CD single.).
7" Single: Released Apr '89, on Island, by Island Records. Catalogue no: **IS 413**
12" Single: Released Apr '89, on Island, by Island Records. Catalogue no: **12 IS 413**

FIELD OF GLASS
Tracks: / Field of glass.
12" Single: Released Apr '85, on Hot, Catalogue no: **HOT 12007**

GOODBYE LITTLE BOY
Tracks: / Goodbye little boy / Go home Eddie / Shell of a man / You minus me.
CD 5": Released Apr '89, on Island, by Island Records. Catalogue no: **CID 420**
10" single: Released Apr '89, on Island, by Island Records. Catalogue no: **10 IS 420**
7" Single: Released Apr '89, on Island, by Island Records. Catalogue no: **IS 420**
12" Single: Released Apr '89, on Island, by Island Records. Catalogue no: **12 IS 420**

HOLY WATER
Tracks: / Holy water / Good morning good morning / Raining pleasure (12" only) / Red pony (12" only).
7" Single: Released '88, on Island, by Island Records. Deleted Apr '89. Catalogue no: **IS 367**
12" Single: Released '88, on Island, by Island Records. Deleted Apr '89. Catalogue no: **12IS 367**

PEEL SESSIONS: TRIFFIDS
Tracks: / Life of crime / Chicken killer / Lonely stretch.
12" Single: Released Sep '87, on Strange Fruit, by Strange Fruit Records. Catalogue no: **SFPS 036**

TRICK OF THE LIGHT, A
Tracks: / Trick of the light / Love deceiver / Bad news always reminds me of you.
10" single: Released Jan '88, on Island, by Island Records. Deleted Jun '88. Catalogue no: **10 IS 350**
7" Single: Released Jan '88, on Island, by Island Records. Deleted Jun '88. Catalogue no: **IS 350**
12" Single: Released Jan '88, on ZTT, by ZTT Records. Deleted Jun '88. Catalogue no: **12 ZTS 26**
12" Single: Released Jan '88, on Island, by Island Records. Deleted Jun '88. Catalogue no: **12 IS 350**

WIDE OPEN ROAD
Tracks: / Wide open road / Time of weakness / Dear Miss Lonely Hearts / Native bride.
7" Single: Released Jun '86, on Hot, Catalogue no: **HOT 730**
12" Single: Released Jun '86, on Hot, Catalogue no: **HOT 1230**

YOU DON'T MISS YOUR WATER
Tracks: / You don't miss your water.
7" Single: Released Aug '85, on Hot, Catalogue no: **HOT 726**
12" Single: Released Aug '85, on Hot, Catalogue no: **HOT 1226**

Trilby, Helen

DEAR SANTA
Tracks: / Dear Santa / How can you hold on to love.
7" Single: Released Dec '87, on The Lastest Record Company, Catalogue no: **CP 001**

Trimmer & Jenkins

TIMES ARE BAD
Tracks: / Times are bad / A is for Action man.
7" Single: Released May '80, on Charisma, by Virgin Records. Deleted '83. Catalogue no: **CB 362**

Trinidad Oil Company

CALENDAR SONG, THE
Tracks: / Calendar song, The.
7" Single: Released May '77, on Harvest (1), by EMI Records. Deleted '80. Catalogue no: **HAR 5122**

Trinity

DIGS IN BIRMINGHAM
Tracks: / Digs in Birmingham.
7" Single: Released '88, on IMI, Catalogue no: **IMI 2002**

FOLLOW MY HEART
Tracks: / Follow my heart.
12" Single: on Attack, Deleted '88. Catalogue no: **TACK 2**

MCALPINE'S FUSILIERS
Tracks: / McAlpine's fusiliers.
7" Single: Released '88, on IMI, Catalogue no: **IMI 2003**

TRIFIDS - BURY ME DEEP IN LOVE (Released on Island)

TRIO - DA DA DA (Released on Mobile Suit)

ROOTS MAN PARTY
Tracks: / Roots man party.
12" Single: on Burning Sounds, by Burning Sounds Records. Deleted May '88. Catalogue no: **BVD 002**

WE LOVE THE PIRATE STATIONS
Tracks: / We love the pirate stations / Pretty.
7" Single: Released Jun '87, on R2, by R2 Records. Catalogue no: **RTU 0001**

Trio

ANNA LETMEIN LETMEOUT
Tracks: / Anna letmein letmeout.
7" Single: Released Feb '83, on Mercury, by Phonogram Ltd. Catalogue no: **MER 129**
12" Single: Released Feb '83, on Mercury, by Phonogram Ltd. Catalogue no: **MERX 129**

DA DA DA (see panel above)
Tracks: / Da da da (English version) / Da da da (German version).
7" Single: Released '82, on Mobile Suit Corporation, Catalogue no: **CORP 5**

TUTTI FRUTTI
Tracks: / Tutti frutti.
7" Single: Released Nov '83, on Mercury, by Phonogram Ltd. Catalogue no: **MER 149**

Trio Balkana

LA LA LA
Tracks: / La la la.
12" Single: Released Nov '88, on World Today, Catalogue no: **WT 003**

Triple Element

WHAT'S DAT SOUND
Tracks: / What's dat sound (ravers armageddon mix) / What's dat sound (twilight dub).
12" Single: Released Jan '89, on Tom Tom, Catalogue no: **12TTT 02**

Trish

WARRIOR
Tracks: / Warrior.
7" Single: Released Jan '85, on Arista, by BMG Records (UK). Catalogue no: **ARIST 598**
12" Single: Released Jan '85, on Arista, by BMG Records (UK). Catalogue no: **ARIST 12 598**

Trisomie 21

JOH'BURGH
Tracks: / Joh'burgh.
CD 5": Released '88, on Play It Again Sam(Belgium), by Play It Again Sam (Belgium). Catalogue no: **BIAS 032 CD**
12" Single: Released Nov '86, on Play It Again Sam(Belgium), by Play It Again Sam (Belgium). Catalogue no: **BIAS 032**

SHIFT AWAY
Tracks: / Shift away.
CD 5": Released Dec '88, on Play It Again Sam(Belgium), by Play It Again Sam (Belgium). Catalogue no: **BIAS 47CD**
12" Single: Released Mar '87, on Play It Again Sam(Belgium), by Play It Again Sam (Belgium). Catalogue no: **BIAS 047**

WAIT AND DANCE
Tracks: / Wait and dance.
12" Single: Released Sep '85, on Scarface, Catalogue no: **SCAR 17T**

WORK IN PROGRESS
Tracks: / Work in progress.
CD 5": Released 1 Aug '89, on Play It Again Sam(Belgium), by Play It Again Sam (Belgium). Catalogue no: **BIASCD 119**
12" Single: Released 1 Aug '89, on Play It Again Sam(Belgium), by Play It Again Sam (Belgium). Catalogue no: **BIAS 119**

Triumph

ALLIED FORCES (SINGLE)
Tracks: / Allied forces / Hot time.
7" Single: Released Oct '81, on RCA, by BMG Records (UK). Deleted '85. Catalogue no: **RCA 135**
12" Single: Released Oct '81, on RCA, by BMG Records (UK). Deleted '85. Catalogue no: **RCAT 135**

AMERICAN GIRLS
Tracks: / American girls / Movin' on.
7" Single: Released Jan '80, on RCA, by BMG Records (UK). Deleted Jan '83. Catalogue no: **PB 9451**

I CAN SURVIVE
Tracks: / I can survive / Nature's child.
7" Single: Released May '80, on RCA, by BMG Records (UK). Deleted '85. Catalogue no: **PB 1945**

I LIVE FOR THE WEEKEND
Tracks: / I live for the weekend / Lay it on the line.
7" Single: Released Nov '80, on RCA, by BMG Records (UK). Deleted '83. Catalogue no: **RCA 13**
12" Single: Released Nov '80, on RCA, by BMG Records (UK). Deleted '83. Catalogue no: **RCAT 13**

MAGIC POWER
Tracks: / Magic power / Fight the good fight.
7" Single: Released Mar '82, on RCA, by BMG Records (UK). Catalogue no: **RCA 195**

SOMEBODY'S OUT THERE
Tracks: / Somebody's out there.
Note: Extra tracks on 12" only
7" Single: Released Feb '87, on MCA, by MCA Records. Catalogue no: **MCA 118**
12" Single: Released Feb '87, on MCA, by MCA Records. Catalogue no: **MCAT 118**

WORLD OF FANTASY
Tracks: / World of fantasy, A.
7" Single: Released Mar '83, on RCA, by BMG Records (UK). Catalogue no: **RCA 319**

Trix

IN THIS UNIVERSE
Tracks: / In this universe / I'll do anything to keep me close to you.
7" Pic: Released Nov '82, on Splash, by Splash Records. Catalogue no: **SPX 24**
7" Single: Released Nov '82, on Splash, by Splash Records. Catalogue no: **SP 24**

Trixie's Red Motorbike

NORMAN AND NARCISSUS
Tracks: / Norman and Narcissus.
7" Single: Released Jan '84, on Lobby Ludd, by Red Rhino Records. Catalogue no: **L 100001**

Trockener Kecks

HOM TERUG, ROSA
Tracks: / Kom terug rosa / Slagboom.
Note: In January '85 the third single in a row. "...a catchy text on the stirring rhythm of an exciting build- up tear- jerker...(OOR, 25.01.'85). The song was broadcasted by Vara's "Je Ziet Maar" on television January 15th. It will appear on the forthcoming album "Betaalde Liefde". Artists: Leo Kenter- drums/Rick De Leeuw- vocals, guitar/Theo Vogelaars- bass, vocals/Rob De Weers- guitar, vocals.
7" Single: Released '85, on Trockener Kecks(Holland), by Trockener Kecks (Holland). Catalogue no: **TK 9**

HOOP DOET LEVEN
Tracks: / Hoop doet leven / Faam.
7" Single: Released '86, on Trockener Kecks(Holland), by Trockener Kecks (Holland). Catalogue no: **TK 14**

IEMAND ANDERS
Tracks: / Iemand anders / De passagier.
Note: In september '84, "Ieman Anders" is released as single. Paul Berding (Gruppo Spotivo) plays saxophone and the single reaches the top- 5 for dutch-sung singles and bubbling-under. OOR "...the only true successors of Doe Maar are Trockener Kecks of course. Fine Text a subtle sax nice arranged chorus and a powerful composition...". Artists: Leo Kenter- drums/Rick De Leeuw- vocals, guitar/Theo Vogelaars- bass, vocals/Rob De Weer- guitar, vocals.
7" Single: Released '84, on Trockener Kecks(Holland), by Trockener Kecks (Holland). Catalogue no: **TK 6**

LIEVER BLIND
Tracks: / Liever blind / De buldog.
Note: Two months later "Liever Blind" came out. The reception of it was very positive. It was played alot on both dutch an belgian radio. "...an adulterous woman turns the holiday of Trockener Kecks into a nightmare..." The video-clip of "Liever Blind" was broadcast by BBC's "Old Grey Whistle Test". Artists: Leo Kenter- drums/Rick De Leeuw- vocals, guitar/Theo Vogelaars- bass, vocals/Rob De Weerd- guita
7" Single: Released '84, on Trockener Kecks(Holland), by Trockener Kecks (Holland). Catalogue no: **TK 7**

LOS ZAND
Tracks: / Los zand / Turning point.
Note: Because of the "Holland Tour '85" together with Ivy Green, Trockener Kecks and Ivy Green released in March '85 the double-A-sided single. "Turning Point/Los Zand" NRC Handelsbald" ...Trockener Kecks is a rare exception to the dutch pop tradition, a tradition of soft music and doggerel. Their songs belong in the dutch hitparade. Artists: Leo Kenter- drums/Rick De Leeuw- vocals, guitar/Theo Vogelaars- bass, vocals/Rob De Weerd- guitar, vocals.
7" Single: Released '85, on Trockener Kecks(Holland), by Trockener Kecks (Holland). Catalogue no: **TK 10**

NAAR DE TOP
Tracks: / Naar de top / De split.
7" Single: Released '85, on Trockener Kecks(Holland), by Trockener Kecks (Holland). Catalogue no: **TK 12**

NIET ALLE MEISJES ZIJN VERLIEFD OP KORS
Tracks: / Niet alle meisjes zijn verliefd op kors / Lang zo aardig niet.
7" Single: Released '82, on Trockener Kecks(Holland), by Trockener Kecks (Holland). Catalogue no: **TK 3**

RICK RINGERS
Tracks: / Rick ringers / Heineken bier.
Note: After playing their first gig in November '80, Trockener Kecks decided in February '81 to make a single. Raw, Loud and Fast, "Rik Ringers" became a cult-hit and single of the year in the dutch music magazine "OOR". Artists: Leo Kenter- drums/Rick De Leeuw- vocals, guitar/Theo Vogelaars- bass, vocals/Rob De Weerd- guitar, vocals
7" Single: Released '81, on Trockener Kecks(Holland), by Trockener Kecks (Holland). Catalogue no: **TK 1**

SOUVENIR
Tracks: / Souvenir / Tegen alles in.
7" Single: Released '86, on Trockener Kecks(Holland), by Trockener Kecks (Holland). Catalogue no: **TK 13**

Troggs

Biographical details: This UK pop group formed by bricklayer turned singer Reg Ball, co-worker Ronnie Bond on drums, bassist Pete Staples, all from Andover, and guitarist Chris Britton, from Watford. *Wild Thing* was a number one hit in the USA and number two in the UK in 1966; basic in the extreme with an incongruous ocarina solo in the middle, it flew in the face of fashion and was later covered by **Jimi Hendrix**. Ball was renamed Reg Presley; he wrote *Wild Thing* clone *With A Girl Like You* (number one UK, top 30 USA); with *I Can't Control Myself* they reached number two in the UK despite an airplay ban because of line *Your slacks are low and your hips are showing*, but they slipped in the USA and faded after 1968. A legend was nutured in the early 1970s with *Troggs Tapes*, a bootleg album of studio sessions including instrumental incompetence and foul language; Ball and Bond reunited in 1976 for an album cheekily called *The Troggs Tapes*; there was a brief flash of fame in late 1970s when punks covered their songs: Presley was arguably the first punk's non-vocalists, proving that novelties can get out of hand and become genres. (Donald Clarke 13.1.88).

ANY WAY THAT YOU WANT ME
Tracks: / Any way that you want me.
7" Single: Released Dec '66, on Page One, by Page One Records. Deleted '69. Catalogue no: **POF 010**

BLACK BOTTOM
7" Single: Released May '83, on Stagecoach, Catalogue no: **MAIL 38**

EVERY LITTLE THING
Tracks: / Every little thing.
7" Single: on 10 Records, by Virgin Records. Deleted '89. Catalogue no: **TEN 21**
12" Single: on 10 Records, by Virgin Records. Deleted '89. Catalogue no: **TEN 21-12**

GIVE IT TO ME
Tracks: / Give it to me.
7" Single: Released Feb '67, on Page One, by Page One Records. Deleted '70. Catalogue no: **POF 015**

HI HI HAZEL
7" Single: Released Jul '62, on Page One, by Page One Records. Deleted Jun '65. Catalogue no: **POF 030**

I CAN'T CONTROL MYSELF
Tracks: / I can't control myself.
7" Single: Released Sep '66, on Page One, by Page One Records. Deleted '69. Catalogue no: **POF 001**

I CAN'T CONTROL MYSELF (OLD GOLD)
Tracks: / I can't control myself / Give it to me.
7" Single: Released '82, on Old Gold, by Old Gold Records. Deleted '69. Catalogue no: **OG 9024**

LITTLE GIRL
Tracks: / Little girl.
7" Single: Released Feb '68, on Page One, by Page One Records. Deleted '71. Catalogue no: **POF 056**

LOVE IS ALL AROUND
Tracks: / Love is all around.
7" Single: Released Oct '67, on Page One, by Page One Records. Deleted '70. Catalogue no: **POF 040**
7" Single: Released Jul '82, on Old Gold, by Old Gold Records. Deleted Jul '88. Catalogue no: **OG 9038**

NIGHT OF THE LONG GRASS
Tracks: / Night of the long grass.
7" Single: Released Jun '67, on Page One, by Page One Records. Deleted '70. Catalogue no: **POF 022**

WILD THING
Tracks: / Wild thing.
7" Single: Released May '66, on Fontana, by Phonogram Ltd. Deleted '69. Catalogue no: **TF 689**

WILD THING (OLD GOLD)
Tracks: / Wild thing / With a girl like you.
7" Single: Released Jun '88, on Old Gold, by Old Gold Records. Catalogue no: **OG 9001**

WITH A GIRL LIKE YOU
Tracks: / With a girl like you.
7" Single: Released Jul '66, on Fontana, by Phonogram Ltd. Deleted '69. Catalogue no: **TF 717**

Troika Voices

GENERAL FOR A DAY
Tracks: / General for a day.
7" Single: Released Nov '85, on Plum, Catalogue no: **DUFF 001**

Trojan...

TROJAN EXPLOSION, VOL 1
7" EP: Released '83, on Trojan, by Trojan Records. Catalogue no: **TMX 4001**

TROJAN EXPLOSION, VOL 2
7" EP: Released '83, on Trojan, by Trojan Records. Deleted May '88. Catalogue no: **TMX 4002**

TROJAN EXPLOSION, VOL 3
7" EP: Released '83, on Trojan, by Trojan Records. Deleted May '88. Catalogue no: **TMX 4003**

TROJAN EXPLOSION, VOL 4

7" **EP:** Released '83, on Trojan, by Trojan Records. Deleted May '88. Catalogue no: **TMX 4004**

TROJAN EXPLOSION, VOL 5
7" **EP:** Released '83, on Trojan, by Trojan Records. Deleted May '88. Catalogue no: **TMX 4005**

TROJAN EXPLOSION, VOL 6
7" **EP:** Released '83, on Trojan, by Trojan Records. Deleted May '88. Catalogue no: **TMX 4006**

TROJAN EXPLOSION, VOL 7
7" **EP:** Released '83, on Trojan, by Trojan Records. Catalogue no: **TMX 4007**

TROJAN EXPLOSION, VOL 8
7" **EP:** Released '83, on Trojan, by Trojan Records. Deleted May '88. Catalogue no: **TMX 4008**

Trojans

EVERYBODY LOVES A LOVER
Tracks: / Everybody loves a lover.
7" **Single:** Released Sep '89, on Gaz's, Catalogue no: **GAZ 011**

GAELIC SKA
Tracks: / Gaelic ska / Autographing cheques.
7" **Single:** Released Jul '87, on Gaz's, Catalogue no: **GAZ 005**
12" **Single:** Released Aug '87, on Gaz's, Catalogue no: **GAZ 12005**

LUMPI
Tracks: / Lumpi.
12" **Single:** Released Aug '88, on Gaz's, Catalogue no: **GAZ 12008**

PHOENIX
Tracks: / Phoenix.
12" **Single:** Released Feb '88, on Gaz's, Catalogue no: **GAZ 12006**

RINGO
Tracks: / Ringo / Good friends.
7" **Single:** Released May '87, on Gaz's Rockin' Records, by Stiff Records. Catalogue no: **GAZ 004**

Tron

TRON
7" **EP:** Released Dec '82, on Disneyland, by Disneyland Records. Catalogue no: **D 384**

Tronics

LOVE BACKED BY FORCE
Tracks: / Love backed by force.
7" **Single:** Released Jul '81, on Alien, Catalogue no: **BEALIEN 3**

TRANZISTER SISTER
Tracks: / Tranzister sister.
12" **Single:** Released Jul '82, on Press, by Compendium Int.Records. Deleted '83. Catalogue no: **PRESS 1**

WILDCAT ROCK
Tracks: / Wildcat rock.
7" **Single:** Released May '83, on Red Rhino, by Red Rhino Records. Catalogue no: **RED 31**

Trooke, Terri Dawn

KITES
Tracks: / Kites / Kites(instumental).
7" **Single:** Released Jun '89, on Supertrack, Catalogue no: **SUN 57**

Troop

MAMACITA
Tracks: / Mamacita.
7" **Single:** Released Nov '88, on WEA, by WEA Records. Catalogue no: **A 8979**
12" **Single:** Released Nov '88, on WEA, by WEA Records. Catalogue no: **A 8979T**

Trooper

BOYS IN THE BRIGHT WHITE SPORTS CAR
Tracks: / Boys in the bright white sports car / Moment that it takes.
7" **Single:** Released May '80, on MCA, by MCA Records. Deleted May '83. Catalogue no: **MCA 594**

RAISE A LITTLE HELL
Tracks: / Raise a little hell / Ready.
7" **Single:** Released Oct '80, on MCA, by MCA Records. Deleted Oct '83. Catalogue no: **MCA 632**

Troops

SAVE THE BOY
Tracks: / Save the boy / Fan.
7" **Single:** Released Aug '79, on Aura Records, by Aura Records. Deleted '88. Catalogue no: **AUS 111**

TROOPS OF TOMORROW
Tracks: / Troops of tomorrow.
12" **Single:** Released Sep '82, on Just When You Thought It Was Quiet, Catalogue no: **TROOPS 1**

Troops For Tomorrow

SONGS OF JOY AND FAITH
Tracks: / Songs of joy and faith.
7" **Single:** Released May '82, on Rhythmic, by Rhythmic Records. Catalogue no: **RMNS 1**

Tropic Amber

AND I LOVE YOU SO
Tracks: / And I love you so / Love and affection.
12" **Single:** Released Mar '85, on Tropical, Catalogue no: **MIS 183**

Tropical Heatwave

LIMBO ROCK
Tracks: / Limbo rock / Still born child.
7" **Single:** Released Aug '82, on Bronze, by Bronze Records. Catalogue no: **BRO 152**

Tropics

I'VE BEEN HAD
Tracks: / I've been had.
12" **Single:** Released Apr '85, on Cave Music, Catalogue no: **CMI 002**

OOH-LA-LA (HOW I LOVE YOU)
Tracks: / Ooh-la-la (how I love you).
7" **Single:** Released Aug '83, on Hive, Catalogue no: **HIVE 1**
12" **Single:** Released Aug '83, on Hive, Catalogue no: **HIVET 1**

Trotter, D.J.

PIG MIX
Tracks: / Pig mix / Automatic introductions.
7" **Single:** Released May '88, on Bold Reprive (2), by Bold Reprive Records. Catalogue no: **7BRM 013**
12" **Single:** Released May '88, on Bold Reprive (2), by Bold Reprive Records. Catalogue no: **BRM 013T**

Troubadours ...

SANCTUS (MISSA LUBA)
Tracks: / Sanctus (missa luba).
7" **Single:** Released Mar '69, on Philips, by Phonogram Ltd. Deleted '72. Catalogue no: **BF 1732**

Trouble

TROUBLE IN MY LIFE
Tracks: / Trouble in my life / Last time, The.
7" **Single:** Released Jul '87, on MDM, by MDM Communications. Deleted May '88. Catalogue no: **MDM 19**
12" **Single:** Released Jul '87, on MDM, by MDM Communications. Deleted May '88. Catalogue no: **MDM 19-12**

Trouble Funk

DROP THE BOMB (SINGLE)
Tracks: / Drop the bomb.
12" **Single:** Released Feb '85, on Sugarhill (USA), Catalogue no: **SHL 140**

GOOD TO GO
Tracks: / Good to go / Say what / Good to go (instrumental).
7" **Single:** Released Jul '86, on Island, by Island Records. Catalogue no: **GO 6**
12" **Single:** Released Jul '86, on Island, by Island Records. Deleted Jul '87. Catalogue no: **12GO 6**

STILL SMOKIN
Tracks: / Still smokin / Beat is bad, The / Don't touch that stereo / Live in Montreaux (MC single only) / It's all in the mix(don't touch that stero) (MC single only).
Cassingle: Released Oct '86, on 4th & Broadway, by Island Records. Catalogue no: **GOGOC 5**
7" **Single:** Released Oct '86, on 4th & Broadway, by Island Records. Catalogue no: **GOGO 5**
12" **Single:** Released Oct '85, on 4th & Broadway, by Island Records. Deleted Jun '87. Catalogue no: **12 GOGO 5**

TROUBLE FUNK EXPRESS
Tracks: / Trouble funk express.
12" **Single:** Released Jun '83, on Greyhound, by Greyhound Records. Catalogue no: **GRPT 105**

TROUBLE, STILL SMOKIN'
Tracks: / Trouble, still smokin'.
12" **Single:** Released Oct '87, on 4th & Broadway, by Island Records. Catalogue no: **12 BRW 80**

WOMAN OF PRINCIPLE
Tracks: / Woman of principle / Don't touch that stereo (Live in Montreux.) / Woman of principle (special remix) (Special remix Bootsy Collins. Track on 12" version only.).
Cassingle: Released Jun '87, on 4th & Broadway, by Island Records. Deleted Apr '89. Catalogue no: **BRWC 70**
7" **Single:** Released 13 Jun '87, on 4th & Broadway, by Island Records. Deleted Apr '88. Catalogue no: **BRW 70**
12" **Single:** Released 13 Jun '87, on 4th & Broadway, by Island Records. Deleted Apr '88. Catalogue no: **12 BRW 70**

Trower, Robin

Biographical details: UK heavy metal guitarist came to fame with the big 1960s rock band **Procol Harum**; he went solo in 1971 with some success. B.L.T. is bassist **Jack Bruce**, ex-**Sly Stone** drummer **Bill Lordan** and Trower. (Donald Clarke 13.1.88)
Robin Trower's career began in the early sixties with **The Paramounts**. This was followed by a stint with a short lived band named **The Jam**. In 1967 he joined **Procul Harum** where he stayed for five years before joining forces with Frankie Miller in a band called **Jude** which eventually led to Trower forming his own outfit with James Dewar, whome he met whilst playing with that band. Trower's first album to be released under his own name *Twice Removed From Yesterday* was a melting pot of all the ideas he'd nurtured himself over the years. The follow-up in 1974 *Bridge of Sighs* established Robin Trower as a major album/touring act in the USA. After releasing a total of five albums under his own name, Robin had had enough of the album/tour merry-go-round and quit roadwork. There followed two R&B influenced albums *In City Dreams* and *Caravan To Midnight*. His next release in 1977 *Victims of the Fury* saw Robin co-producing for the very first time. Finally on the album *BLT*, a collaboration between himself and legendary **Cream** bassist Jack Bruce, Robin took over total control of production on his own albums. *BLT* went Top 40 in America selling over 200,000 copies on the way.
Again in need of a change he moved on from that band and went on to record his new album for release in June, entitled *Back It Up*. This was made with Trower stalwart James Dewar on bass and vocals, newcomer Dave Bronze also on bass, with a little help from drummers Alan Clark and the appropriately named Bobby Clouter who both emanate from the Southend area. (Berni Kilmartin, Chrysalis Press Office, June 1983).

IT'S FOR YOU (see panel below)
Tracks: / It's for you / My love (burning love) / In city dreams.
Note: Limited edition on special red vinyl.o
7" **EP:** Released '78, on Chrysalis, by Chrysalis Records. Catalogue no: **CHS 2247**

VICTIMS OF THE FURY (SINGLE)
Tracks: / Victims of the fury / One in a million.
7" **Single:** Released Jan '80, on Chrysalis, by Chrysalis Records. Deleted Jan '83. Catalogue no: **CHS 2402**

WHAT IT IS
Tracks: / What it is / Into money.
7" **Single:** Released Feb '81, on Chrysalis, by Chrysalis Records. Deleted '84. Catalogue no: **CHS 2497**

Troy

LOVE AND HARMONY
Tracks: / Love and harmony.
12" **Single:** Released Mar '82, on Love Linch, Catalogue no: **LL 022**

Troy, Tony

I CAN'T THINK OF ANYTHING MORE BEAUTIFUL
Tracks: / I can't think of anything more beautiful.
7" **Single:** Released Mar '81, on Beautiful, Deleted Mar '84. Catalogue no: **LTMC 777**
7" **Single:** Released Nov '85, on Beautiful, Catalogue no: **MSBFL 1**

Trudy

CAPTAIN SCARLET
Tracks: / Captain Scarlet.
7" **Single:** Released Feb '87, on Primitive, by Primitive Records. Catalogue no: **PDY 049**

COUNTDOWN TO LOVE
Tracks: / Countdown to love / Living on a moon.
7" **Single:** Released Apr '89, on Planet Miron, Catalogue no: **TDY 005**

INVISIBLE MAN
Tracks: / Invisible man, The.
7" **Single:** on Torso, by Torso Records. Catalogue no: **TDY 045**

LIVING ON A MOON
Tracks: / Living on a Moon / Countdown to love.
7" **Single:** Released Jul '89, on Planet Miron, Catalogue no: **TDY 051**

True

LONG AFTER TONIGHT
Tracks: / Long after tonight is all over.
7" **Single:** Released Oct '84, on Rock City Records, by Rock City Records. Catalogue no: **RCR 4**
12" **Single:** Released Oct '84, on Rock City Records, by Rock City Records. Catalogue no: **RCRT 4**

True, Andrea

MORE MORE MORE
Tracks: / More more more.
7" **Single:** Released Apr '76, on Buddah, by Buddah Records Inc.(USA). Deleted '79. Catalogue no: **BDS 442**

WHAT'S YOUR NAME WHAT'S YOUR NUMBER
Tracks: / What's your name what's your number.
7" **Single:** Released Mar '78, on Buddah, by Buddah Records Inc.(USA). Deleted '81. Catalogue no: **BDS 467**

True Believers

SPIDERMAN MEETS THE GREEN GOBLIN
Tracks: / Spiderman meets the green goblin.
7" **Single:** Released Dec '83, on LBS, Catalogue no: **LBS 001**

True Colours

FALLING APART AT THE SEAMS
Tracks: / Falling apart at the seams.
7" **Single:** Released May '85, on Body & Soul, Catalogue no: **BODY 1**

True Faith

YOU CAN'T DENY THE BASS
Tracks: / You can't deny the bass.
7" **Single:** Released Jul '89, on RCA, by BMG Records (UK). Catalogue no: **PB**

ROBIN TROWER - IT'S FOR YOU (Released on Chrysalis)

42909
12" Single: Released Jul '89, on RCA, by BMG Records (UK). Catalogue no: **PT 42910**

True Funk Posse

BREAK THE BEAT
Tracks: / Break the beat.
12" Single: Released Mar '89, on Three Stripe, Catalogue no: **SAM 1115**

True Life Confessions

BANANA SPLIT
Tracks: / Banana split / I'm not really frightened.
7" Single: Released Jan '82, on A&M, by A&M Records. Deleted Jan '85. Catalogue no: **AMS 8201**

DON'T CALL ME CHICKENHEAD
Tracks: / Don't call me chickenhead / If I can't have you.
7" Pic: Released Apr '83, on Speed, Catalogue no: **SPEED P 13**
7" Single: Released Apr '83, on Speed, Catalogue no: **SPEED 13**
12" Single: Released Apr '83, on Speed, Catalogue no: **12 SPEED 13**

WITCHDOCTOR (OO EE OO AH)
Tracks: / Witchdoctor (oo ee oo ah) / Having a bath.
7" Single: Released Nov '82, on Speed, Catalogue no: **SPEED 10**

True Love Orchestra

WEDDING SONG, THE
Tracks: / Wedding song, The / Sad movies.
7" Single: Released Aug '86, on BBC, by BBC Records & Tapes. Deleted Apr '89. Catalogue no: **RESL 194**

True Mathematics

AFTER DARK
Tracks: / After dark / Greeks in the house.
7" Single: Released Apr '87, on Champion, by Champion Records. Deleted Jul '89. Catalogue no: **CHAMP 44**
12" Single: Released Apr '87, on Champion, by Champion Records. Deleted Aug '89. Catalogue no: **CHAMP 1244**

FOR THE LOVER IN YOU
Tracks: / For the lover in you (for the money) / For the lover in you (for the money) (version) / For the lover in you.
7" Single: Released Jun '88, on Champion, by Champion Records. Catalogue no: **CHAMP 83**
12" Single: Released Jun '88, on Champion, by Champion Records. Deleted Aug '89. Catalogue no: **CHAMP 12-83**

FOR THE MONEY
Tracks: / For the money / K.A.O.S.S..
7" Single: Released 23 Apr '88, on Champion, by Champion Records. Deleted Aug '89. Catalogue no: **CHAMP 76**
12" Single: Released 23 May '88, on Champion, by Champion Records. Deleted Aug '89. Catalogue no: **CHAMP 12 76**

Truesdale, Tommy

DON'T BE CRUEL
Tracks: / Don't be cruel.
7" Single: Released Oct '82, on Country House, by Scotdisc Records. Catalogue no: **BGC 294**

OLDER WOMEN (COUNTRY SLOSH)
Tracks: / Older women / Amazing grace.
7" Single: Released Dec '88, on August Records, by Scotdisc Records. Catalogue no: **GBH 7S 472**

SOMEWHERE BETWEEN
Tracks: / Somewhere between / Blackboard of my heart.
7" Single: Released Dec '84, on Country House, by Scotdisc Records. Deleted Jul '88. Catalogue no: **7S 381**

Trussel

LOVE INJECTION
Tracks: / Love injection / Gone for the weekend.
7" Single: Released Mar '80, on Elektra, by Elektra Records (UK). Deleted '83. Catalogue no: **K 12412**

Trust

ANTISOCIAL
Tracks: / Antisocial / Sects.
7" Single: Released Mar '81, on CBS, by CBS Records. Deleted Mar '84. Catalogue no: **A 1006**

Truth

CONFUSION (HITS US EVERY TIME)
Tracks: / Confusion (hits us every time).
7" Set: Released Jun '83, on WEA, by WEA Records. Catalogue no: **TRUTH 1F**
7" Single: Released Jun '83, on Formation, Deleted '86. Catalogue no: **TRUTH 1**
12" Single: Released Jun '83, on Formation, Deleted '86. Catalogue no: **TRUTH 1T**

EXCEPTION OF LOVE
Tracks: / Exception of love.
7" Single: Released Jun '85, on I.R.S, Catalogue no: **IRM 103**
12" Single: Released Jun '85, on I.R.S, Catalogue no: **IRT 103**

GIRL
Tracks: / Girl.
7" Single: Released Feb '66, on Pye, Deleted '69. Catalogue no: **7 N 17035**

IT'S HIDDEN
Tracks: / It's hidden / Respect / Until it burns (Extra track on 12".).
7" Single: Released Feb '88, on I.R.S, Catalogue no: **IRM 153**
12" Single: Released Feb '88, on I.R.S, Catalogue no: **IRMT 153**

NO STONE UNTURNED
Tracks: / No stone unturned.
7" Single: Released Feb '84, on Formation, Deleted '87. Catalogue no: **YZ 1**

OPEN OUR EYES
Tracks: / Open our eyes / Open our eyes (dub) / Open our eyes (celestial mix) (12" only.) / Open our eyes (Spiritual mix) (12" only.) / Open our eyes (Marshall's elevated dub) (12" only.).
7" Single: Released Dec '88, on ffrr, by London Records. Deleted 26 Jun '89. Catalogue no: **FFR 18**
7" Single: Released Oct '88, on Big Beat, by Ace Records. Catalogue no: **BB 0003**
12" Single: Released Jan '89, on ffrr, by London Records. Deleted 26 Jun '89. Catalogue no: **FFRXR 18**
12" Single: Released Dec '88, on ffrr, by London Records. Deleted 26 Jun '89. Catalogue no: **FFRX 18**

PLAYGROUND (SINGLE)
Tracks: / Playground.
7" Single: Released Mar '85, on Illegal, by Faulty Products Records. Catalogue no: **TRUTH 3**
12" Single: Released Mar '85, on Illegal, by Faulty Products Records. Catalogue no: **TRUTH T3**

STEP IN THE RIGHT DIRECTION
Tracks: / Step in the right direction.
7" Single: Released Aug '83, on Formation, Deleted '86. Catalogue no: **TRUTH 2**
12" Single: Released Aug '83, on Formation, Deleted '86. Catalogue no: **TRUTH 2T**

WEAPONS OF LOVE
Tracks: / Weapons of love / This way forever / Soul deep fascination / Another new day / Come on back to me / Respect / Cover up my face / Edge of town, the / Until it burns / Winterland.
7" Single: Released May '87, on MCA, by MCA Records. Catalogue no: **TRU 4**
12" Single: Released May '87, on MCA, by MCA Records. Catalogue no: **TRUT 4**

Trux

BAD LUCK
Tracks: / Bad luck.
7" Single: Released Mar '83, on Trux, by Trux Records. Catalogue no: **TRUX 01**

Trybe

PSYCHEDELIC SHACK
Tracks: / Psychedelic shack.
12" Single: Released Feb '89, on Wild Pitch, Catalogue no: **WP 1010**

Tscahi Pretender

HOT FEET
Tracks: / Hot feet / Fantasy feeling.
7" Single: Released Jul '81, on Carrere, Deleted Jul '84. Catalogue no: **CAR 192**

Tsiboe,Reggie

MOTHER AND CHILD REUNION
Tracks: / Mother and child reunion.
7" Single: Released Nov '85, on Arista, by BMG Records (UK). Catalogue no: **ARIST 653**
12" Single: Released Nov '85, on Arista, by BMG Records (UK). Catalogue no: **ARIST 12 653**

TSK

I'M BORN AGAIN
Tracks: / I'm born again / Amazing grace.
7" Single: Released Jan '80, on Orchid, by Orchid Records. Deleted '85. Catalogue no: **OR 102**

Tski Valley

GREEDY G
Tracks: / Greedy G / Greedy G.
12" Single: Released 21 Nov '87, on Greensleeves, by Greensleeves Records. Catalogue no: **GRED 401**

Tsunami

AS IT IS
Tracks: / As it is.
12" Single: Released Jan '82, on Neon, by Neon Records. Catalogue no: **TSU 1**

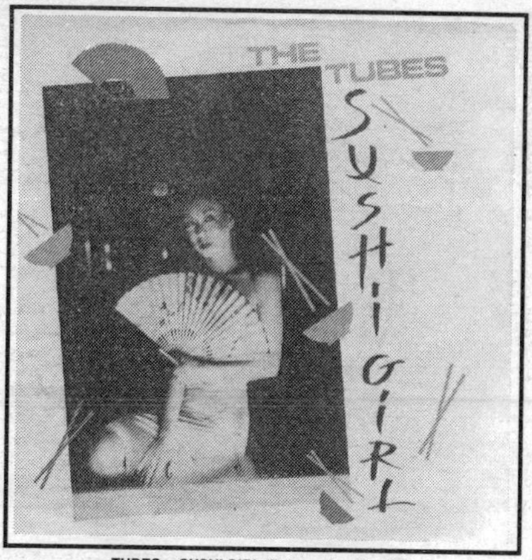

TUBES - SUSHI GIRL (Released on Capitol)

Tsunami Ride

TOO FAR BY FAR
Tracks: / Too far by far / I had.
7" Single: Released Sep '86, on Ocean (1), by Ocean Records. Catalogue no: **OCEAN 1**
12" Single: Released Sep '86, on Ocean (1), by Ocean Records. Catalogue no: **OCEAN 121**

Tubes

DON'T WANT TO WAIT ANYMORE
Tracks: / Don't want to wait anymore / Think about me.
7" Single: Released Jul '81, on Capitol, by EMI Records. Deleted '87. Catalogue no: **CL 208**

PRIME TIME (SINGLE)
Tracks: / Prime time.
7" Single: Released Apr '79, on A&M, by A&M Records. Deleted '82. Catalogue no: **AMS 7423**

SHE'S A BEAUTY
Tracks: / She's a beauty / When you're ready to come / Fantastic delusion.
7" Single: Released Apr '83, on Capitol, by EMI Records. Deleted '88. Catalogue no: **CL 288**
12" Single: Released Apr '83, on Capitol, by EMI Records. Deleted '88. Catalogue no: **12CL 288**

SUSHI GIRL (see panel above)
Tracks: / Sushi girl / Mr. Hate.
7" Single: Released Oct '81, on Capitol, by EMI Records. Deleted '88. Catalogue no: **CL 219**

TALK TO YA LATER (see panel below)
Tracks: / Talk to ya later / Tube talk / What's wrong with me.
7" EP: Released '81, on Capitol, by EMI Records. Catalogue no: **CL 201**

WHITE PUNKS ON DOPE
Tracks: / White punks on dope.
7" Single: Released Nov '77, on A&M, by A&M Records. Deleted '80. Catalogue no: **AMS 7323**

Tubeway Army

ARE FRIENDS ELECTRIC
Tracks: / Are friends electric / We are fragile / Down in the park.
Cassingle: Released Apr '81, on WEA, by WEA Records. Deleted Apr '84. Catalogue no: **SPC 4**
7" Single: Released May '79, on Beggars Banquet, by Beggars Banquet Records.

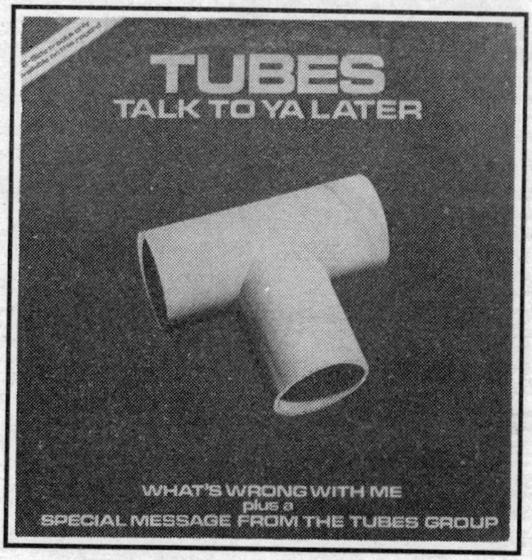

TUBES - TALK TO YA LATER (Released on Capitol)

Catalogue no: **BEG18**

PEEL SESSIONS: TUBEWAY ARMY
12" Single: Released Aug '87, on Strange Fruit, by Strange Fruit Records. Catalogue no: **SFPS 032**

THAT'S TOO BAD
Tracks: / That's too bad / Bombers / Oh, didn't I say?.
7" Single: Released Aug '79, on Beggars Banquet, by Beggars Banquet Records. Deleted Jan '88. Catalogue no: **BACK 2**
12" Single: Released Apr '83, on Beggars Banquet, by Beggars Banquet Records. Catalogue no: **BEG 17**

Tubeway Patrol

DO EYES EVER MEET
Tracks: / Do eyes ever meet / No time.
7" Single: Released Dec '81, on Carrere, Deleted Dec '84. Catalogue no: **CAR 218**

Tuck & Patti

TIME AFTER TIME
Tracks: / Time after time / Up and at it.
7" Single: Released Feb '89, on A&M, by A&M Records. Catalogue no: **WY 002**
12" Single: Released Feb '89, on A&M, by A&M Records. Catalogue no: **WZ 002**

Tucker, Colin Lloyd

HEAD
Tracks: / Head / Sex slave.
7" Pic: Released Apr '86, on DJ, Catalogue no: **DJ 1**

USE IT!
Tracks: / Mindbox / Use it!.
12" Single: Released Feb '87, on Plastic Head, by Plastic Head Records. Catalogue no: **PLAS 006**

Tucker, Junior

DON'T TEST
Tracks: / Don't test.
7" Single: Released May '89, on Sonic Sounds, Catalogue no: **UNKNOWN**

ONE OF THE POOREST PEOPLE
Tracks: / One of the poorest people / Strong love.
7" Single: Released Feb '80, on Island, by Island Records. Deleted Feb '83. Catalogue no: **WIP 6577**
7" Single: Released Mar '81, on Island, by Island Records. Catalogue no: **IPR 2029**

SOME GUYS HAVE ALL THE LUCK
Tracks: / Some guys have all the luck / Spinning around.
7" Single: Released Sep '80, on Island, by Island Records. Catalogue no: **WIP 6612**

Tucker, Louise

Biographical details: Louise Tucker was born in Bristol and trained at the famous Guildhall School of Music in London for a career in opera. It was two record producers, Tim Smit and Charlie Skarbeck who had the idea of fusing Louise's classically trained style with some synthesiser-orientated tracks that they had been working on. The original idea was to do something really avant-garde. The melody from Beethoven's Pathetique was used in Louise's first single *Midnight Blue* which went on to sell over two million copies in nine months, bringing her gold discs galore and taking her into the pop charts in Scandinavia, Belgium, Holland, Canada, Portugal, Spain, Australia, South Africa, America, the UK and others. Towards the end of 1983, Charlie, Tim and Louise completed their second album *After the storm*. (Versa Manos, Ariola Press Office, February 1984).

MIDNIGHT BLUE
Tracks: / Midnight blue / Voices in the wind.
7" Single: Released '83, on Arista, by BMG Records (UK). Deleted '86. Catalogue no: **ARO 289**
12" Single: Released '83, on Ariola, by BMG Records (UK). Deleted '86. Catalogue no: **AROD 289**

NO TEARS TO CRY
Tracks: / No tears to cry / Running man / Only for you.
7" Single: Released Jan '84, on Ariola, by BMG Records (UK). Catalogue no: **ARO 309**
12" Single: Released Jan '84, on Ariola, by BMG Records (UK). Catalogue no: **AROD 309**

ONLY FOR YOU
Tracks: / Only for you.
7" Single: Released '83, on Arista, by BMG Records (UK). Deleted '86. Catalogue no: **ARO 299**

Tucker, Moe

HEY MERSH
Tracks: / Hey mersh.
12" Single: Released Apr '89, on 50 Skidillion Watts, Catalogue no: **MOE 6 0**

Tucker, Tanya

DREAM LOVER
Tracks: / Dream lover / Bronco.
7" Single: Released Mar '81, on MCA, by MCA Records. Deleted Mar '84. Catalogue no: **MCA 675**

ONE LOVE AT A TIME
Tracks: / One love at a time / Fool fool heart.
7" Single: Released Mar '86, on Capitol, by EMI Records. Deleted '88. Catalogue no: **CL 399**

SAN FRANCISCO
Tracks: / San Francisco / By day by day.
7" Single: Released Feb '80, on MCA, by MCA Records. Deleted Feb '83. Catalogue no: **MCA 552**

Tucker, Tommy

HI HEEL SNEAKERS
Tracks: / High heel sneakers / Is that the way God planned it.
7" Single: Released Sep '82, on Red Lightnin', by Red Lightning Records. Deleted Jun '89. Catalogue no: **RL 450031**

Tucker, Tyke

CUDDLY BEAR
Tracks: / Cuddly bear / Whoa mule whoa.
7" Single: Released Jul '82, on Thrust, Catalogue no: **RUFF 4**

Tudor, Johnny

RHYMNEY
Tracks: / Rhymney.
7" Single: Released Aug '85, on President, by President Records. Catalogue no: **PT 537**

Tudors

TIED UP WITH LOU COOL
Tracks: / Tied up with Lou Cool / Cry baby cry.
7" Single: Released Feb '83, on Stiff, by Stiff Records. Catalogue no: **BUY 172**

Tuesday Blue

TUNNEL VISION
Tracks: / Tunnel vision / Tell the boys / Don't go away.
7" Single: Released Mar '86, on Mother, by Mother Records. Catalogue no: **MUM 3**
12" Single: Released Mar '86, on Mother, by Mother Records. Catalogue no: **12 MUM 3**

Tuff Crew

MY PART OF TOWN
Tracks: / My part of town.
12" Single: Released Feb '89, on Soo Def, Catalogue no: **WAR 020**

Tuff Monks

AFTER THE FIREWORKS (2 PARTS)
Tracks: / After the fireworks.
7" Single: Released Oct '83, on Au-Go-Go (Australia), by Au-Go-Go Records (Australia). Catalogue no: **ANDA 22**

Tuff, Tony

BIG BOUT YA
Tracks: / Big bout ya / Tradition.
12" Single: Released Sep '83, on Reggae Sound, Catalogue no: **VPRD 140**

BORDER
Tracks: / Border.
12" Single: Released Sep '84, on Volcano, Catalogue no: **UNKNOWN**

COME SEE ME
Tracks: / Come see me.
12" Single: Released Oct '83, on GG'S, Catalogue no: **GG 118**

DANCE HALL STYLE
Tracks: / Dance hall style / Mini bus black tree.
12" Single: Released Aug '86, on Black Star, Catalogue no: **BSUK 01**

FEEL FREE COME TO ME
Tracks: / Feel free come to me.
12" Single: Released Jun '88, on Barry Clarke, Catalogue no: **BC 005**

GALLOP FOR ME
Tracks: / Gallop for me / Rubadub version.
12" Single: Released Dec '83, on Foundation, Catalogue no: **TF 010**

GIRL WATCHER
Tracks: / Girl watcher.
12" Single: Released Mar '84, on Londisc, by Londisc Records. Catalogue no: **LD 015**

GOOD TO CONTROL ME
Tracks: / Good to control me / Every time.
12" Single: Released Jun '86, on Greensleeves, by Greensleeves Records. Catalogue no: **GRED 200**

HACKLE THEM BODY FE DEM
Tracks: / Hackle them body fe dem.
12" Single: Released May '88, on Love People, Catalogue no: **LPD 001**

HOLD THEM
Tracks: / Hold them / Tell me.
12" Single: Released Mar '86, on Top Rank (2), Catalogue no: **TRD 020**

HOLY BIBLE
Tracks: / Holy bible.
12" Single: Released Sep '85, on SJS, Catalogue no: **SAR 002**

IT GOES THERE AGAIN
Tracks: / It goes there again.
12" Single: Released Sep '85, on SJS, Catalogue no: **SAR 001**

JAM IT AGAIN
Tracks: / Jam it again.
12" Single: Released Oct '84, on Top Rank (2), Catalogue no: **Unknown**

MARY ANN
Tracks: / Mary Ann / Head on straight.
12" Single: Released Dec '83, on Uptempo, Catalogue no: **UT 003**

MAXIMUM
Tracks: / Maximum.
7" Single: Released May '89, on Park Heights, Catalogue no: **UNKNOWN**

MIX ME DOWN
Tracks: / Mix me down.
12" Single: Released Aug '84, on Kaya, Catalogue no: **KAYA 003**

NEVER CAN SAY GOODBYE
Tracks: / Never can say goodbye.
7" Single: Released Jan '89, on Pickout, Catalogue no: **Unknown**

NUH BOTHER WITH IT
Tracks: / Nuh bother with it / Woman woman.
12" Single: Released 27 Feb '88, on World Enterprise, Catalogue no: **WED 58**

SETTLE
Tracks: / Settle.
12" Single: Released Sep '84, on Top Rank (2), Catalogue no: **Unknown**

SHOW ON THE ROAD
Tracks: / Show on the road / No more.
10" single: Released Aug '82, on Island, by Island Records. Catalogue no: **10WIP 6807**
7" Single: Released Aug '82, on Island, by Island Records. Catalogue no: **WIP 6807**

SPIN YOUR ROLL
Tracks: / Spin your roll.
12" Single: Released Jul '85, on UNKNOWN, Catalogue no: **UNKNOWN**

SWEET MAUREEN
Tracks: / Sweet Maureen / Lovers rocking and skanking.
12" Single: Released May '80, on Island, by Island Records. Deleted May '83. Catalogue no: **12WIP 6608**

WELL TRASH
Tracks: / Champion jockey / Well trash.
12" Single: Released Nov '86, on GG'S, Catalogue no: **GGD 127**

WINE UP WINE UP
Tracks: / Wine up wine up.
12" Single: Released Nov '88, on Parish, Catalogue no: **UNKNOWN**

YOU'LL NEVER FIND
Tracks: / You'll never find / One big family.
7" Single: Released Dec '82, on Island, by Island Records. Deleted Dec '85. Catalogue no: **IPR 2058**

Tuffy, Melo

NUH MIX UP
Tracks: / Nuh mix up.
12" Single: Released Jul '88, on Vibes, by Vibes Records. Catalogue no: **VIBES 028**

Tuffy, Ricky

NO LICK NO ROCK
Tracks: / No lick no rock.
12" Single: Released Sep '89, on Blacker Dread, Catalogue no: **BD 8913**

NUCLEAR WAR
Tracks: / Nuclear war.
7" Single: Released Apr '89, on Sir Coxsone, Catalogue no: **BD 8907**

Tulla, Celli Band

BATTERING RAM & JIGS MEDLEY
Tracks: / Battering ram & jigs medley.
7" Single: Released Nov '76, on Shamrock (Ireland), Catalogue no: **SPP 514**

Tullio De Piscopo

PRIMAVERA
Tracks: / Primavera (stop bajon) / Stadera.
7" Single: Released Feb '87, on Greyhound, by Greyhound Records. Deleted Jan '88. Catalogue no: **GRY 9**
12" Single: Released Mar '86, on ZYX (Germany), Catalogue no: **ZYX 5139**
12" Single: Released Feb '87, on Greyhound, by Greyhound Records. Catalogue no: **12 GRY 9**

Tulloch Lynette

I WILL
Tracks: / I will / I believe you.
12" Single: Released Aug '83, on World International, Catalogue no: **WIR 12D 502**

Tumbling hearts

YOU MAY NEVER KNOW
Tracks: / You may never know.
7" Single: Released May '87, on Exile, Catalogue no: **EX 7007**

Tune, Spencer

NIGHTMARE
Tracks: / Nightmare.
12" Single: Released Mar '89, on Debut, by Skratch Records. Catalogue no: **DEBTX 3068**

Tunes

SHE'S MY GIRL
Tracks: / She's my girl / Something strange.
7" Single: Released Jan '80, on RSO (USA), by Polydor Ltd. Deleted May '81. Catalogue no: **RSO 53**

Tunnel Users

DANCE
Tracks: / Dance.
7" Single: Released Jul '82, on Xjukey, Catalogue no: **XJ 01**

WILL TURA - VIVE EL AMOR (Released on Major Minor)

Tunnel Vision

WATCHING THE HYDROPLANES
Tracks: / Watching the hydroplanes.
7" Single: Released Jun '81, on Factory (1), by Factory Records. Catalogue no: **FAC 39**

Tunnelvision

I'M GONNA CRY
Tracks: / I'm gonna cry.
7" Single: Released Jun '85, on Octave, Catalogue no: **GUSS 1**

Tura, Will

VIVE EL AMOR
Tracks: / Vive le amor / Let me go (areme joe).
7" Single: Released '69, on Major Minor, Catalogue no: **MM 606**

Turbo

CHARGED FOR GLORY
Tracks: / Charged for glory.
7" Single: Released Sep '82, on Turbo, Catalogue no: **CUS 1261**

Turbos

REGGAE SERENADE
Tracks: / Reggae serenade.
12" Single: Released Sep '84, on Sun Set (reggae), Catalogue no: **Unknown**

Turkey Bones

GOLDFISH
Tracks: / Goldfish.
7" Single: Released Jul '83, on Anagram, by Cherry Red Records. Deleted '88. Catalogue no: **ANA 10**

RAYMOND
Tracks: / Raymond.
12" Single: Released Mar '84, on McKechnie, by McKechnie Records. Catalogue no: **MAC 1/12**

Turn To Flowers

PEOPLE CHANGE LIKE THE WEATHER
Tracks: / People change like the weather.
12" Single: Released Feb '88, on Imaginary, by Imaginary Records. Catalogue no: **MIRAGE 005**

Turncoats

MOTORBALL MELTBEAT
Tracks: / Motorball meltbeat.
12" Single: Released Oct '86, on Noise A Noise, Catalogue no: **NAN 2T**

Turner, Anne

HEAVEN'S FAR AWAY
Tracks: / Heaven's far away / Captain of my heart / Captain of my heart (version) (Only on 12" version.) / Heaven's far away (12" mix).
7" Single: Released Sep '87, on RCA, by BMG Records (UK). Catalogue no: **PB 41495**
12" Single: Released Sep '87, on RCA, by BMG Records (UK). Catalogue no: **PT 41496**

TOO HOT TO HANDLE
Tracks: / Don't stop (12" only) / Too hot to handle / Love was never easy.
7" Single: Released Mar '87, on RCA, by BMG Records (UK). Deleted '87. Catalogue no: **PB 41283**
12" Single: Released Mar '87, on RCA, by BMG Records (UK). Deleted '87. Catalogue no: **PT 41284**

YOUR LIFE
Tracks: / Your life / Crazee.
7" Single: Released Aug '82, on Centridge, Catalogue no: **CENT 1**

Turner, Catherine

VIRGIN EXIT
Tracks: / Virgin exit.
12" Single: Released Nov '88, on Watershed, Catalogue no: **WDS 1**

Turner, Chris

SHINING DIAMOND
Tracks: / Shining diamond / Choking with emotion.
7" Single: Released Feb '81, on WEA, by WEA Records. Catalogue no: **K 18419**

Turner, Chuck

AGAIN
Tracks: / Again.
7" Single: Released Apr '89, on Music Scene, Catalogue no: **TK 0093**

ANOTHER LOVE SONG
Tracks: / Another love song.
7" Single: Released Oct '88, on Top Rank (2), Catalogue no: **TRD 030**

COOLING OUT
Tracks: / Cooling out.
7" Single: Released 21 Apr '89, on Greensleeves, by Greensleeves Records. Catalogue no: **GRED 241**

GWEN
Tracks: / Gwen.
12" Single: Released Feb '89, on Crat Records, Catalogue no: **CRAT 20**

I'M THE ROUGHEST
Tracks: / I'm the roughest.
12" Single: Released 4 Oct '88, on Skengdon, Catalogue no: **SKDL 088**

SEASONS NO REASON
Tracks: / Seasons no reason.
12" Single: Released Dec '88, on Top Rank (2), Catalogue no: **TRD 031**

TEARS
Tracks: / Tears.
12" Single: Released Aug '87, on Jammy's, Catalogue no: **VPRD 218**

YOUTHMAN STRUGGLING
Tracks: / Youthman struggling.
12" Single: Released May '88, on Stereo One, Catalogue no: **STO 003**

Turner, Earl

LOVE CAUGHT YOU BY SURPRISE
Tracks: / Love caught you by suprise / Love caught you by suprise (instrumental).
7" Single: Released Jan '86, on 4th & Broadway, by Island Records. Catalogue no: **BRW 39**
12" Single: Released Jan '86, on 4th & Broadway, by Island Records. Catalogue no: **12 BRW 39**

Turner, Ike

NEW BREED
Tracks: / New breed.
7" Single: Released '85, on UNKNOWN, Deleted Jun '89. Catalogue no: **45FV 303**

Turner, Ike & Tina

Biographical details: Ike and Tina led a soul/R&B vocal-instrumental revue in the USA. Ike Turner was born in 1931 in Mississippi; he accompanied **Sonny Boy Williamson** and others before he reached his teens. He formed the Kings Of Rhythm while still in high school; they made *Rocket 88* at Sun in Memphis, released under vocalist Jackie Brenston's name on Chess, for a number one R&B hit in 1951 (Brenston went solo and faded). Turner recorded country music, worked with his first wife Bonnie, played fine guitar on tracks with **B.B King, Howlin' Wolf, Johnny Ace,** etc; in a St. Louis night club, a regular customer named Annie Mae Bullock sang with the band in 1956; Ike added her to the lineup, they were married by 1958 and her name changed to Tina Turner; initially she did not record with the band, but depped for an absent vocalist on the Sue label; *A Fool In Love* was a top 30 pop single in 1960 and the act became the Ike and Tina Turner Revue, with female backing singers the Ikettes added (ever-changing personnel incl. **Merry Clayton** and **Bonnie Bramlett**); they had a pop and R&B hits on various labels through the 1960s: commercial success on records was patchy, but they were always a hot live act. Their classic album and single *River Deep-Mountain High* in 1966 was produced partly by Phil Spector, but filled up like a best-of compilation; it was a relative commercial failure, this disappointment supposed to be the reason for Spector's withdrawal from the scene. Of their later work, one of the best albums was *Natbush City Limits* in 1973, with an infectuous hit title track. Tina divorced Ike in 1976 and after some floundering became a superstar; owning his own studio by then, he retired to it. (Donald Clarke, 13.1.88).

LIVING FOR THE CITY
Tracks: / Living for the city / Push.
7" Single: Released Apr '86, on Spartan, Catalogue no: **SP 136**
12" Single: Released Apr '86, on Spartan, Catalogue no: **12SP 136**

NUTBUSH CITY LIMITS (SINGLE)
Tracks: / Nutbush city limits.
7" Single: Released Sep '73, on United Artists, by EMI Records. Catalogue no: **UP 35582**

RIVER DEEP, MOUNTAIN HIGH (OLD GOLD)
Tracks: / River deep, mountain high / Love like yours.
7" Single: Released Jul '82, on Old Gold, by Old Gold Records. Catalogue no: **OG 9147**

Turner, Joe Lynn

Biographical details: One of the former lead singers with rock group Rainbow, who was, as the other members of the group discovered by rock legend guitarist Ritchie Blackmore. Joe Lynn Turner helped the group achieve their highest chart single, *I surrender* in January '81, which peaked at No. 3. He has also made a solo album, *Rescue you*, which due to bad promotion did not get the credit deserved. He then became a member of Yngwie J Malmsteen's Rising Force in 1988 and made a successful album entitled *Odyssey*, followed by a live album *Live in Russia*. He has also worked with a number of other artists, writing and appearing as a guest vocalist on a few albums..

ENDLESSLY
Tracks: / Endlessly.
7" Single: Released Oct '85, on Elektra, by Elektra Records (UK). Catalogue no: **EKR 25**

Turner, Nick

RUN LIKE THE WIND
Tracks: / Run like the wind / Spinning lights.
7" Single: Released Oct '87, on Ash, by Ash Records. Catalogue no: **ASH 040**

Turner, Nik

BLOOD AND BONE
Tracks: / Blood and bone.
12" Single: Released Aug '85, on Jettisoundz, by Jettisoundz Records. Catalogue no: **JZ 5**

BONES OF ELVIS
Tracks: / Bones of Elvis / Sids song.
7" Single: Released Feb '82, on Avatar, by Avatar Record Corporation. Catalogue no: **AAA 119**

Turner, Pierce

HAVE YOU LOOKED AT THE SUN (LATELY)
Tracks: / Have you looked at the sun (lately) / Have you looked at the sun (lately) (versions) / Mayhem / Surface in heaven (12" only).
12" Single: Released Jun '89, on Beggars Banquet, by Beggars Banquet Records. Catalogue no: **BEG 231T**
7" Single: Released Jun '89, on Beggars Banquet, by Beggars Banquet Records. Catalogue no: **BEG 231**

HOW IT SHONE
Tracks: / How it shone / How it shone (instrumental).
7" Single: Released Aug '86, on Beggars Banquet, by Beggars Banquet Records. Catalogue no: **BEG 169**
12" Single: Released Aug '86, on Beggars Banquet, by Beggars Banquet Records. Catalogue no: **BEG 169T**

ORANGE COLOURED SUN
Tracks: / Orange coloured sun / Musha God help her.
7" Single: Released Mar '87, on Beggars Banquet, by Beggars Banquet Records. Catalogue no: **BEG 185**

SKY AND THE GROUND, THE (SINGLE)
Tracks: / Sky and the ground, The / I set you up to shake / How it shone (12" only).
7" Single: Released Feb '89, on Beggars Banquet, by Beggars Banquet Records. Catalogue no: **BEG 227**
12" Single: Released Feb '89, on Beggars Banquet, by Beggars Banquet Records. Catalogue no: **BEG 227T**

SURFACE IN HEAVEN
Tracks: / Surface in heaven / Everybody loves a.
CD 5": Released Nov '88, on Beggars Banquet, by Beggars Banquet Records. Catalogue no: **BEG 223 CD**
7" Single: Released Nov '88, on Beggars Banquet, by Beggars Banquet Records. Catalogue no: **BEG 223**
12" Single: Released Nov '88, on Beggars Banquet, by Beggars Banquet Records. Catalogue no: **BEG 223 C**

UNCERTAIN SMILE
Tracks: / Uncertain smile.
7" Single: Released Jun '87, on Beggars Banquet, by Beggars Banquet Records. Catalogue no: **BEG 196**

WICKLOW HILLS
Tracks: / Everyone loves a virgin (in their past).
12" Single: Released Dec '86, on Beggars Banquet, by Beggars Banquet Records. Catalogue no: **BEG 178T**
7" Single: Released Dec '86, on Beggars Banquet, by Beggars Banquet Records. Catalogue no: **BEG 178**

Turner, Ruby

BABY I NEED YOUR LOVING
Tracks: / Baby I need your loving / If you're ready, come go with me / Hurting inside.
12" Single: Released Feb '89, on Jive, by Zomba Records. Catalogue no: **RTST 6**
CD 5": Released Feb '89, on Jive, by Zomba Records. Catalogue no: **RTSCD 6**
7" Single: Released Feb '89, on Jive, by Zomba Records. Catalogue no: **RTS 6**

BYE BABY
Tracks: / Bye Baby / Story of a man and a woman / If you're ready come go with me (Track in Double pack only.) / Still on my mind (Track in Double pack only.) / Won't cry no more.
12" Single: Released Aug '86, on Jive, by Zomba Records. Catalogue no: **JIVET 126**
7" Set: Released Aug '86, on Jive, by Zomba Records. Catalogue no: **JIVED 126**
7" Single: Released Aug '86, on Jive, by Zomba Records. Catalogue no: **JIVE 126**

CHECKING IT OUT (EP)
Tracks: / Checking it out.
12" Single: Released Apr '82, on Sunflower, Catalogue no: **SF 2**

EVERY SOUL
Tracks: / Every soul / First step.
12" Single: Released Mar '83, on Sunflower, Catalogue no: **12SF 3**
7" Single: Released Mar '83, on Sunflower, Catalogue no: **SF 3**

I'D RATHER GO BLIND
Tracks: / I'd rather go blind / I'm livin' a life of love / Ooh baby baby (12" only) / If you're ready (come go with me) (CD only (Extended version)) / Bye baby (CD only).
12" Single: Released Feb '87, on Jive, by Zomba Records. Catalogue no: **RTST 1**
7" Set: Released Mar '87, on Jive, by Zomba Records. Catalogue no: **RATSD 1**
7" Single: Released Jul '87, on Jive, by Zomba Records. Catalogue no: **RTS 1**
CD 5": Released Feb '87, on Jive, by Zomba Records. Catalogue no: **RTCD 1**

IF YOU'RE READY (COME GO WITH ME)
Tracks: / If you're ready (come go with me) / Still on my mind / I won't cry no more.
12" Single: Released Jan '86, on Jive, by Zomba Records. Catalogue no: **JIVET 109**
CD 5": Released '88, on Jive, by Zomba Records. Catalogue no: **JIVEX 109**
7" Single: Released Jan '86, on Jive, by Zomba Records. Catalogue no: **JIVE 109**

I'M IN LOVE
Tracks: / I'm in love / Story of a man and a woman / Living the life of love / Feel my love / Someday soon / Still on my mind.
7" Single: Released May '87, on Jive, by Zomba Records. Deleted Jul '87. Catalogue no: **RTS 2**
CD 5": Released May '87, on Jive, by Zomba Records. Deleted Jul '87. Catalogue no: **RTCD 2**
7" Single: Released Mar '86, on Jive, by Zomba Records. Catalogue no: **JIVE 118**
12" Single: Released Apr '86, on Jive, by Zomba Records. Catalogue no: **JIVER 5**
12" Single: Released Mar '86, on Jive, by Zomba Records. Catalogue no: **JIVET 118**
12" Single: Released May '87, on Jive, by Zomba Records. Catalogue no: **RSTS 2**

IN MY LIFE
Tracks: / In my life / He's mine.
12" Single: Released Jun '87, on Jive, by Zomba Records. Deleted Jul '87. Catalogue no: **RTST 3**
7" Single: Released Jun '87, on Jive, by Zomba Records. Deleted Jul '87. Catalogue no: **RTS 3**

SEPARATE WAYS
Tracks: / Separate ways / I shall be released.
7" Single: Released Sep '80, on Sunflower, Catalogue no: **SF 1**

SIGNED SEALED DELIVERED
Tracks: / Signed sealed delivered.
Special: Released '88, on Jive, by Zomba Records. Deleted '88. Catalogue no: **RTSR 4**
7" Single: Released 15 Aug '88, on Jive, by Zomba Records. Deleted '88. Catalogue no: **RTS 4**
CD 5": Released '88, on Jive, by Zomba Records. Deleted '88. Catalogue no: **RTS CD 4**
12" Single: Released 15 Aug '88, on Jive, by Zomba Records. Deleted '88. Catalogue no: **RTST 4**

WHAT BECOMES OF THE BROKEN HEARTED
Tracks: / What becomes of the broken hearted? / Still waters run deep / Signed, sealed, delivered, I'm yours / (If you're ready) come go with me.
12" Single: Released Nov '88, on Jive, by Zomba Records. Catalogue no: **RTST 5**
7" Single: Released Nov '88, on Jive, by Zomba Records. Catalogue no: **RTS 5**
CD 5": Released Jun '89, on Jive, by Zomba Records. Catalogue no: **RTSCD 5**

Turner, Sammy

ALWAYS
Tracks: / Always.
7" Single: Released Nov '59, on London-American, Deleted '62. Catalogue no: **HLX 8963**

Turner, Spyder

SPYDERMAN
Tracks: / Spyderman.
12" Single: Released Nov '83, on Shatter, Catalogue no: **SH 1964 12**
7" Single: Released Nov '83, on Shatter, Catalogue no: **SH 1964**

Turner, Tich

DIANA
Tracks: / Diana / Are you wiv it.
7" Single: Released Nov '80, on Cheapskate, Deleted Nov '83. Catalogue no: **CHEAP 7**

DON'T REALLY WANT YOU BACK
Tracks: / Don't really want you back / Ska'd for life.
7" Single: Released Jun '81, on Cheapskate, Catalogue no: **CHEAP 22**

Turner, Tina

Biographical details: Tina Turner was born Annie Mae Bullock in 1938 in Nutbush, Tennessee. For her early history, see **Ike and Tina Turner**. After she left Svengali Ike, a couple of albums on United Artists didn't do very much; like many other USA artists since the early days of rock'n'roll she was more appreciated in the UK than at home: she was asked to be one of several vocalists on *Music Of Quality And Distinction* on Virgin in 1982, a concept LP originised by synth players Martyn Ware and ian Craig Marsh as British Electronic Foundation(see also **Human League** and **Heaven 17**); she sang *Ball Of Confusion*. They produced a cover of **Al Green's** Let's Stay Together for a transatlantic hit; her album *Private Dancer* was mostly produced in the UK, including *What's Love Got To Do With It*, written by Terry Britten and Grahan Lyle, produced by Britten: it was number one for three weeks in the USA and won Grammies for Record Of The Year, Song Of The Year, Female Pop Performance and Female Rock Vocal of the Year: Tina hasn't looked back. She starred alongside **Mel Gibson** in the science fiction fantasy **Mad Max Beyond The Thunderdome**, won plaudits for acting and sang *We Don't Need Another Hero*, also a major hit;she duetted with Mick Jagger at the Live Aid concert in 1985 and sang on one track on **Eric Clapton's** *August* in 1986,as well as having more hit albums and singles of her own. (Donald Clarke 13.1.88).

ADDICTED TO LOVE
Tracks: / Addicted to love / Overnight sensation / Legs (12" and CD versions only.).
12" Single: Released 7 Mar '88, on Capitol, by EMI Records. Deleted Jun '89. Catalogue no: **12CL 484**
CD 5": Released Mar '88, on Capitol, by EMI Records. Deleted Aug '89. Catalogue no: **CDCL 484**
7" Single: Released 7 Mar '88, on Capitol, by EMI Records. Deleted Jun '89. Catalogue no: **CL 484**

BACKSTABBERS
Tracks: / Backstabbers / Sunset on sunset.
7" Single: Released Jan '80, on Liberty (USA), by EMI Records. Deleted Jan '83. Catalogue no: **BP 322**

BALL OF CONFUSION
Tracks: / Ball of confusion / Ball of confusion (part 2).
7" Single: Released May '82, on Virgin, by Virgin Records. Deleted '85. Catalogue no: **VS 500**

BEST, THE
Tracks: / Best, The / Undercover agent for the blues / Bold and reckless (12" & CD single only.).
12" Single: Released Aug '89, on Capitol, by EMI Records. Catalogue no: **12CL 543**
7" Single: Released Aug '89, on Capitol, by EMI Records. Catalogue no: **203 498 7**
7" Single: Released Aug '89, on Capitol, by EMI Records. Catalogue no: **CL 543**
12" Single: Released Aug '89, on Capitol, by EMI Records. Catalogue no: **203 498 6**
CD 5": Released Aug '89, on Capitol, by EMI Records. Catalogue no: **203 498 2**
CD 5": Released Aug '89, on Capitol, by EMI Records. Catalogue no: **CDCL 543**
Cassingle: Released Aug '89, on Capitol, by EMI Records. Catalogue no: **203 498 4**
Cassingle: Released Aug '89, on Capitol, by EMI Records. Catalogue no: **TCCL 543**
Special: Released Aug '89, on Capitol, by EMI Records. Catalogue no: **203 508 0**
Special: Released Aug '89, on Capitol, by EMI Records. Catalogue no: **CLS 5433**

BETTER BE GOOD TO ME
Tracks: / Better be good to me / When I was young.
7" Single: Released Jan '86, on Capitol, by EMI Records. Deleted '88. Catalogue no: **CL 338**
12" Single: Released Jan '86, on Capitol, by EMI Records. Deleted Jul '87. Catalogue no: **12CL 338**

BREAK EVERY RULE (SINGLE)
Tracks: / Break every rule.
7" Single: Released 23 May '87, on Capitol, by EMI Records. Deleted Apr '88. Catalogue no: **CL 452**
7" Pic: Released 23 May '87, on Capitol, by EMI Records. Deleted Apr '88. Catalogue no: **CLP 452**
12" Single: Released 23 May '87, on Capitol, by EMI Records. Deleted Apr '88. Catalogue no: **12 CL 452**

CHANGE IS GONNA COME, A
Tracks: / Change is gonna come, A (LP version)* (*Track on 12" version only) / Change is gonna come, A / Nutbush City limits.
12" Single: Released 16 May '88, on Capitol, by EMI Records. Deleted Jun '89. Catalogue no: **12CL 495**
7" Single: Released 16 May '88, on Capitol, by EMI Records. Deleted Jun '89. Catalogue no: **CL 495**

HELP
Tracks: / Help / Rock 'n' roll widow.
7" Single: Released Feb '84, on Capitol, by EMI Records. Deleted '87. Catalogue no: **CL 325**

I CAN'T STAND THE RAIN
Tracks: / I can't stand the rain.
12" Single: Released Feb '85, on Capitol, by EMI Records. Deleted '88. Catalogue no: **12CL 352**
7" Single: Released Feb '85, on Capitol, by EMI Records. Deleted '88. Catalogue no: **CL 352**

I DON'T WANNA LOSE YOU
Tracks: / I don't wanna lose you / Not enough romance / Stronger than the wind (12" only.) / We don't need another hero (Thunderdome0 (CD single only.).
CD 5": Released Oct '89, on Capitol, by EMI Records. Catalogue no: **CDCL 553**
CD 5": Released Oct '89, on Capitol, by EMI Records. Catalogue no: **203 565 2**
7" Single: Released Oct '89, on Capitol, by EMI Records. Catalogue no: **203 565 7**
7" Single: Released Oct '89, on Capitol, by EMI Records. Catalogue no: **CL 553**
12" Single: Released Oct '89, on Capitol, by EMI Records. Catalogue no: **12CLP 553**
12" Single: Released Oct '89, on Capitol, by EMI Records. Catalogue no: **12CL 553**
Cassingle: Released Oct '89, on Capitol, by EMI Records. Catalogue no: **TCCL 553**
Cassingle: Released Oct '89, on Capitol, by EMI Records. Catalogue no: **203 565 4**
12" Single: Released Oct '89, on Capitol, by EMI Records. Catalogue no: **203 565 0**
12" Single: Released Oct '89, on Capitol, by EMI Records. Catalogue no: **203 565 6**

LET'S STAY TOGETHER
Tracks: / Let's stay together / I wrote a letter.
7" Single: Released Nov '83, on Capitol, by EMI Records. Deleted Aug '89. Catalogue no: **CL 316**
7" Pic: Released Nov '83, on Capitol, by EMI Records. Deleted '88. Catalogue no: **12CLP 316**
12" Single: Released Nov '83, on Capitol, by EMI Records. Deleted Oct '87. Catalogue no: **12CL 316**

LOVE LIKE YOURS, A
Tracks: / Love like yours, A.
7" Single: Released Oct '66, on London-American, Deleted '69. Catalogue no: **HL 10083**

ONE OF THE LIVING
Tracks: / One of the living.
7" Single: Released Sep '85, on Capitol, by EMI Records. Deleted Jul '87. Catalogue no: **CL 376**
12" Single: Released Sep '85, on Capitol, by EMI Records. Deleted Jul '87. Catalogue no: **12CL 376**

PARADISE IS HERE
Tracks: / In the midnight hour / Paradise is here.
7" Single: Released Sep '87, on Capitol, by EMI Records. Deleted Nov '88. Catalogue no: **CL 459**
12" Single: Released Aug '87, on Capitol, by EMI Records. Deleted Nov '88. Catalogue no: **12CL 459**
Special: Released Aug '87, on Capitol, by EMI Records. Deleted 31 Jul '88. Catalogue no: **CLP 459**

PRIVATE DANCER (SINGLE)
Tracks: / Private dancer.
7" Single: Released Nov '84, on Capitol, by EMI Records. Deleted Oct '89. Catalogue no: **CL 343**
12" Single: Released Nov '84, on Capitol, by EMI Records. Deleted Oct '87. Catalogue no: **12CL 343**

RIVER DEEP, MOUNTAIN HIGH (SINGLE)
Tracks: / River deep, mountain high.
7" Single: Released Feb '69, on London-American, Deleted '72. Catalogue no: **HLU 10242**
7" Single: Released Jun '66, on London-American, Deleted '69. Catalogue no: **HL 10046**

TELL HER I'M NOT HOME
Tracks: / Tell her I'm not home.
7" Single: Released Jun '66, on Warner Bros., by WEA Records. Deleted '69. Catalogue no: **WB 5753**

TWO PEOPLE
Tracks: / Two people / Havin' a party.
7" Single: Released Oct '86, on Capitol, by EMI Records. Deleted Oct '87. Catalogue no: **CL 430**
12" Single: Released Oct '86, on Capitol, by EMI Records. Deleted Oct '87. Catalogue no: **12CL 430**

TWO PEOPLE (DOUBLE PACK)
Tracks: / Two people (dance mix) / Having a party / Let's stay together (live) / Private dancer, (live).
Special: Released Nov '86, on Capitol, by EMI Records. Deleted Oct '87. Catalogue no: **12CLD 430**

TYPICAL MALE
Tracks: / Typical male / Don't turn around / Typical male (version) (Available on 12" only).
7" Single: Released Aug '86, on Capitol, by EMI Records. Deleted Oct '87. Catalogue no: **CL 419**
12" Single: Released Aug '86, on Capitol, by EMI Records. Deleted Oct '87. Catalogue no: **12CL 419**

TYPICAL MALE,(PICTURE DISC)
Tracks: / Typical male (dance mix) / Typical male (dub mix) / Typical male (single mix) / Don't turn around.
12" Pic: Released Sep '86, on Capitol, by EMI Records. Catalogue no: **12CLP 419**

WE DON'T NEED ANOTHER HERO (see panel below)
Tracks: / We don't need another hero / We don't need another hero (instr.).
7" Pic: Released Jul '85, on Capitol, by EMI Records. Deleted Nov '88. Catalogue no: **CLP 364**
7" Single: Released Jul '85, on Capitol, by EMI Records. Deleted Sep '89. Catalogue no: **CL 364**
12" Single: Released Jul '85, on Capitol, by EMI Records. Deleted Nov '88. Catalogue no: **12CL 364**

WHAT YOU GET IS WHAT YOU SEE
Tracks: / What you get is what you see (dance mix) / Tina Turner montage mix.
7" Set: Released Feb '87, on Capitol, by EMI Records. Deleted Oct '87. Catalogue no: **7CLD 439**
7" Single: Released Feb '87, on Capitol, by EMI Records. Deleted Apr '88. Catalogue no: **CL 439**
12" Single: Released Mar '87, on Capitol, by EMI Records. Deleted Jan '88. Catalogue no: **12 CLX 439**
12" Single: Released Feb '87, on Capitol, by EMI Records. Deleted Apr '88. Catalogue no: **12CL 439**

WHAT'S LOVE GOT TO DO WITH IT
Tracks: / What's love got to do with it / Don't rush the good things.
7" Single: Released Jun '84, on Capitol, by EMI Records. Deleted Aug '89. Catalogue no: **CL 334**
12" Single: Released Jun '84, on Capitol, by EMI Records. Deleted Oct '87. Catalogue no: **12CL 334**

Turning Shrines

FACE OF ANOTHER
Tracks: / Face of another.
12" Single: Released Dec '86, on Temple Records, by Temple Records (2). Catalogue no: **TOPY 007 T**

Turnpike Cruisers

CRUISIN' UNHOLY
Tracks: / Cruisin' unholy.
12" Single: Released Apr '85, on Jettisoundz, by Jettisoundz Records. Catalogue no: **JZ ONE**

EXTRA FLESH
Tracks: / Etra flesh / Girl who turned into a man, The / Weird and lonely.
12" Single: Released Jun '86, on Jettisoundz, by Jettisoundz Records. Catalogue no: **JZ 6**

Turnstyle

ONCE MORE FROM THE TOP
Tracks: / Once more from the top.
7" Single: Released Mar '78, on Pye, Deleted May '78. Catalogue no: **7N 46056**

Turntable Orchestra

BETTER BE GOOD
Tracks: / Better be good.
7" Single: Released Oct '89, on Republic, by Code Records. Catalogue no: **UNKNOWN**
12" Single: Released Oct '89, on Republic, by Code Records. Catalogue no: **UNKNOWN**

YOU'RE GONNA MISS ME
Tracks: / You're gonna miss me.
7" Single: Released Nov '88, on Republic, by Code Records. Catalogue no: **LIC 012**
7" Single: Released Nov '88, on Republic, by Code Records. Catalogue no: **LIC 012R**
12" Single: Released '89, on Licensed, Catalogue no: **LD 8927**
12" Single: Released Nov '88, on Republic, by Code Records. Catalogue no: **LICT 012**

Turquoise Blue

IN THE END
Tracks: / In the end.
7" Single: Released Dec '86, on A.R.I.A., Catalogue no: **ARIA 1**

WE ARE LOST
Tracks: / We are lost.
7" Single: Released May '87, on A.R.I.A., Catalogue no: **ARIAX 2**
12" Single: Released May '87, on A.R.I.A., Catalogue no: **ARIAX T2**

Turquoise Days

GREY SKIES
Tracks: / Grey skies.
7" Single: Released Aug '84, on Disques Strategie, Deleted '87. Catalogue no: **STRAT XX1A**

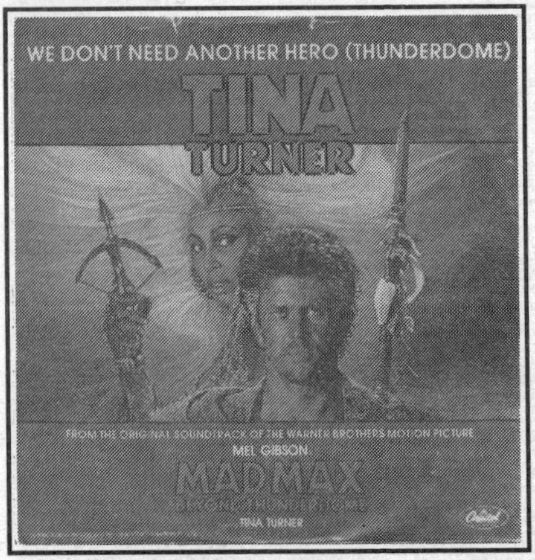

TINA TURNER - WE DON'T NEED ANOTHER HERO (Released on Capitol)

Turtle, Gideon

GIDEON TURTLE & THE MIDNIGHT CHOIR
Tracks: / Gideon turtle & the midnight choir.
12" Single: Released Aug '84, on Golden Dawn, Catalogue no: **GD 1202**

Turtle, Henry

98.6
Tracks: / 98.6.
7" Single: Released Apr '84, on Riviera (1), Catalogue no: **SEA 1**

ALL BY MYSELF
Tracks: / All by myself / Left gone right.
7" Single: Released May '81, on Logo, by Logo Records. Deleted May '84. Catalogue no: **GO 401**

BUST LOOSE
Tracks: / Bust loose.
7" Single: Released May '83, on Variety, Deleted '84. Catalogue no: **BBVY 406**

DREAMING
Tracks: / Dreaming / Young world / Halfway to paradise / Let's get that loving feeling again.
7" Single: Released Nov '82, on Variety, Deleted '83. Catalogue no: **BBVY 405**

HE'S TAKEN SHEILA OFF HIS WINDSCREEN
Tracks: / He's taken Sheila off his windscreen / There's always something there.
7" Single: Released Jul '83, on Variety, Deleted '84. Catalogue no: **BBVY 401**

HOUND DOG MAN
Tracks: / Hound dog man / All I ever need is you.
7" Single: Released Jan '81, on Surrey Sound, Deleted Jan '84. Catalogue no: **HMS 6**
7" Single: Released Mar '83, on Variety, Deleted '84. Catalogue no: **BBVY 404**

Turtles

Biographical details: The USA vocal/pop group formed in Los Angeles in 1965 with Howard Kaylan and Mark Volman, both born in 1947. They knocked around as the Crossfires, made flop singles, hit on new White Whale label as Tyrtles, then Turtles, with updated ecstatic harmonies of early sixties surf music and rodeo folk-rock boom, starting with a cover of **Bob Dylan's** *It Ain't Me Babe*. They had many hits, dabbled in psycedelia, lost their touch as a pop band and split in 1970; Volman and Kaylan went to **Frank Zappa** as vocal duo Phlorescent Leech and Eddie, then Flo and Eddie (psuedonyms forced on then by White Whale's lawyers); became back up singers for **Marc Bolan, Bruce Springsteen** etc; where also producers. (Donald Clarke 13.1.88).

ELANORE (OLD GOLD)
Tracks: / Elanore.
7" Single: Released Jul '82, on Old Gold, by Old Gold Records. Catalogue no: **OG 9155**

ELENORE
Tracks: / Eleanore.
7" Single: Released Oct '68, on London-American, Deleted '71. Catalogue no: **HL 10223**

HAPPY TOGETHER
Tracks: / Happy together.
7" Single: Released Mar '67, on London-American, Deleted '70. Catalogue no: **HL 10115**

HAPPY TOGETHER (OLD GOLD)
Tracks: / Happy together.
7" Single: Released Jul '82, on Old Gold, by Old Gold Records. Deleted Jul '88. Catalogue no: **OG 9157**

SHE'D RATHER BE WITH ME
Tracks: / She'd rather be with me.
7" Single: Released Jun '67, on London-American, Deleted '70. Catalogue no: **HLU 10135**

Tusk

SHE'S SO COOL
Tracks: / She's so cool / Red rag.
7" Single: Released May '81, on Automatic, by Automatic Records. Catalogue no: **K 17788**

Tutone, Tommy

867-5309
Tracks: / 867-5309 / Not say goodbye.
7" Single: Released Jun '82, on CBS, by CBS Records. Deleted Jun '85. Catalogue no: **A 2062**

GET AROUND GIRL
Tracks: / Get around girl.
7" Single: Released Jan '84, on CBS, by CBS Records. Catalogue no: **A 3995**

Tuxedo

TO TOUCH YOU
Tracks: / To touch you / To touch you (version).
7" Single: Released Jul '87, on Chartsounds, Catalogue no: **7 CSTUC 01**
12" Single: Released Jul '87, on Chartsounds, Catalogue no: **CSTUC 01**

Tuxedo Moon

DARK COMPANION
Tracks: / Dark companion / 59 to 1.
7" Single: Released Oct '80, on Charisma, by Virgin Records. Deleted Oct '83. Catalogue no: **PRE 10**

NINOTCHKA
Tracks: / Ninotchka.
12" Single: Released Apr '82, on Les Disques Du Crepuscule(Belgium), by Les Disques Du Crepuscule(Belgium). Catalogue no: **TWI 055**

NO TEARS EP
Tracks: / No tears.
12" Single: Released Mar '86, on Cramboy, Catalogue no: **CBOY 7070**

SCREAM WITH A VIEW
Tracks: / Scream with a view.
12" Single: Released Oct '85, on Cramboy, Catalogue no: **CBOY 4040**

SOMA
Tracks: / Soma.
7" Single: Released Jul '84, on Joe Boy (Belgium), Catalogue no: **SW 7007**

TIME TO LOSE (EP)
12" Single: Released Aug '82, on Les Disques Du Crepuscule(Belgium), by Les Disques Du Crepuscule(Belgium). Catalogue no: **TWI 084**

TV 21

ALL JOIN HANDS
Tracks: / All join hands / Journey up the zambesi and back.
7" Single: Released Feb '82, on Deram, by London Records. Catalogue no: **ATV 21**

ON THE RUN
Tracks: / On the run.
7" Single: Released Feb '81, on Demon, by Demon Records. Deleted '88. Catalogue no: **D 1004**

SNAKES AND LADDERS
Tracks: / Snakes and ladders / Artistic license.
7" Single: Released May '81, on Deram, by London Records. Catalogue no: **DM 442**

SOMETHING'S WRONG
Tracks: / Something's wrong.
10" single: Released Oct '81, on Deram, by London Records. Deleted '85. Catalogue no: **DMT 447**
7" Single: Released Oct '81, on Deram, by London Records. Catalogue no: **DM 447**

TV Personalities

BILL GRUNDY EP
7" Single: Released Nov '79, on Rough Trade, by Rough Trade Records. Catalogue no: **RT 033**

HOW I LEARNED TO LOVE THE BOMB
Tracks: / How I learned to love the bomb / Girl called charity, A / She's only the grocers daughter.
7" Single: Released Oct '86, on Dreamworld, by Dreamworld Records. Catalogue no: **DREAM 010**

PRETTIEST GIRL IN THE WORLD
Tracks: / Prettiest girl in the world.
7" Single: Released Mar '87, on Constrictor, by Constrictor Records (Germany). Deleted '88. Catalogue no: **COLL 003**

THREE WISHES
Tracks: / Three wishes / Geoffrey Ingram / Don't the kids just love it.
7" Single: Released Sep '82, on Whaam, Catalogue no: **WHAAM 04**

Twa Toots

PEEL SESSIONS: TWA TOOTS
Cassingle: Released 13 Jun '87, on Strange Fruit, by Strange Fruit Records. Catalogue no: **SFPSC 010**
12" Single: Released Oct '86, on Strange Fruit, by Strange Fruit Records. Catalogue no: **SFPS 010**

Twang

KICK AND COMPLAIN
Tracks: / Kick and complain.
12" Single: Released Mar '87, on Ron Johnson, by Ron Johnson Records. Catalogue no: **ZRON 22**

SNAP BACK
Tracks: / Snap back.
12" Single: Released Dec '87, on Ron Johnson, by Ron Johnson Records. Catalogue no: **ZRON 29**

Tweets

BIRDIE SONG
Tracks: / Birdie song, The / Mellow terrain.
7" Single: Released Nov '84, on PRT, by Castle Communications Records. Catalogue no: **7P 219**

BIRDIE SONG, THE
Tracks: / Birdie song, The.
7" Single: Released Jun '87, on H & R, Catalogue no: **TWET 1**

BIRDIE SONG, THE (OLD GOLD)
Tracks: / Birdie song, The / Let's all sing like the birdies sing.
7" Single: Released 24 Apr '89, on Old Gold, by Old Gold Records. Catalogue no: **OG 9891**

EVERYBODY GO
Tracks: / Everybody go / Willy nilly.
7" Single: on RCA, by BMG Records (UK). Deleted Mar '82. Catalogue no: **RCA 208**

LETS ALL SING LIKE THE BIRDIES SING
Tracks: / Let's all sing like the birdies sing / It's a birds life.
7" Single: Released Nov '81, on PRT, by Castle Communications Records. Catalogue no: **7P 226**
12" Single: Released Nov '81, on PRT, by Castle Communications Records. Catalogue no: **12P 226**

PATRICIA
Tracks: / Patricia.
7" Single: Released Nov '85, on PRT, by Castle Communications Records. Catalogue no: **TWEET 2**
12" Single: Released Nov '85, on PRT, by Castle Communications Records. Catalogue no: **TWEETS 2**

PLUMP SONG
Tracks: / Plump song.
7" Single: Released Dec '83, on Crash, by Satril Records. Deleted '84. Catalogue no: **CRA 603**

TWEETS ON 45
Tracks: / Tweets on 45 / Heritage.
7" Single: Released Aug '82, on RCA, by BMG Records (UK). Catalogue no: **RCA 269**

Twelfth Night

IT'S JUST NOT CRITIC
Tracks: / It's just not critic.
Cassingle: Released Aug '85, on EMI, by EMI Records. Catalogue no: **TC EMI 5518**
12" Single: Released Aug '85, on EMI, by EMI Records. Catalogue no: **12 EMI 5518**

SHAME
Tracks: / Shame / Blue powder monkey.
7" Single: Released May '86, on Charisma, by Virgin Records. Deleted May '88. Catalogue no: **CB 424**
12" Single: Released May '86, on Charisma, by Virgin Records. Deleted May '88. Catalogue no: **CB 424-12**

TAKE A LOOK
Tracks: / Take a look / Blondon fair.
7" Single: Released Aug '86, on Charisma, by Virgin Records. Deleted May '88. Catalogue no: **CB 425**
12" Single: Released Aug '86, on Charisma, by Virgin Records. Deleted May '88. Catalogue no: **CB 425-12**

Twelve 88 Cartel

SWEATING FURORE EP
7" EP: Released Mar '87, on Bite Back, Catalogue no: **BB 011**

Twelve Drummers

I'LL BE THERE
Tracks: / I'll be there / Where the wild buffalo roams / Jane (Only on 12").
CD 5": Released 30 Aug '88, on Mercury, by Phonogram Ltd. Catalogue no: **870 376-2**
7" Single: Released 30 Aug '88, on Mercury, by Phonogram Ltd. Deleted Feb '89. Catalogue no: **MER 273**
12" Single: Released 30 Aug '88, on Mercury, by Phonogram Ltd. Deleted Feb '89. Catalogue no: **MERX 273**

LONELY
Tracks: / Lonely.
12" Single: Released Dec '83, on Vertigo, by Phonogram Ltd. Catalogue no: **TDD 112**

WE'LL BE THE FIRST ONES
Tracks: / We'll be the first ones.
7" Single: Released Mar '84, on Mercury, by Phonogram Ltd. Catalogue no: **TDD 2**
12" Single: Released Mar '84, on Mercury, by Phonogram Ltd. Catalogue no: **TDD 212**

Twelve Engle St.

TWELVE ENGLE STREET
Tracks: / Twelve Engle Street: *Various artists.*
12" Single: Released May '80, on Pye, Catalogue no: **12P 5016**

Twelve Just Men

RUBBERHEAD
Tracks: / Rubberhead / I don't want to die like Liberace.
7" Single: Released Jan '89, on Nuttbucket, by Nuttbucket Records. Catalogue no: **NUT 001**

Twenty Days

FREEFALL
Tracks: / Freefall.
7" Single: Released May '85, on Sonar, by Sonar Records. Catalogue no: **SONEP 1**

Twenty Eighth Street

I NEED A RHYTHM
Tracks: / I need a rhythm / I need a rhythm (version).
12" Single: Released 10 Jul '89, on A&M, by A&M Records. Catalogue no: **SP 5246**
12" Single: Released 24 Jul '89, on Breakout, by A&M Records. Catalogue no: **USA 666**

Twenty Flight Rockers

JOHNNY SEVEN
Tracks: / Johnny Seven / Tower block rock.
7" Single: Released Jul '86, on WEA, by WEA Records. Deleted Jun '87. Catalogue no: **TFR 1**

TOWERBLOCK ROCK
Tracks: / Towerblock rock.
7" Single: Released Oct '85, on ABC (indie), Catalogue no: **ABCS 008**
12" Single: Released Oct '85, on ABC (indie), Catalogue no: **ABCS 008T**

Twenty Four Hours

SHIPWRECKED (I'M NOT COMING BACK)
Tracks: / Shipwrecked (I'm not coming back) / Rescued.
7" Single: Released Sep '82, on Charisma, by Virgin Records. Deleted '89. Catalogue no: **CB 401**
12" Single: Released Sep '82, on Charisma, by Virgin Records. Deleted '89. Catalogue no: **CB 401 12**

SIBERIAN SID
Tracks: / Siberian Sid / Witchdoctor.
7" Single: Released Jun '82, on Charisma, by Virgin Records. Deleted '89. Catalogue no: **CB 399**
12" Single: Released Jun '82, on Charisma, by Virgin Records. Deleted '89. Catalogue no: **CB 399 12**

Twenty Inches At Knee

SPY IN THE HOUSE OF LOVE
Tracks: / Spy in the house of love / Time and again.
7" Single: Released Apr '82, on Pre, by Charisma Records. Catalogue no: **PRE 22**

Twenty One Strangers

MORE CAIN THAN ABEL
Tracks: / More Cain than Abel / I wanna cry / Over and over (on 12" only).
7" Single: Released Feb '85, on Charisma, by Virgin Records. Catalogue no: **ABEL 1**
12" Single: Released Feb '85, on Charisma, by Virgin Records. Deleted May '88. Catalogue no: **ABEL 112**

Twenty Thousand

20,000 LEAGUES UNDER THE SEA
7" EP: Released Apr '81, on Disneyland, by Disneyland Records. Catalogue no: **D 358**

Twenty Three Skidoo

ASSASSINS WITH SOUL
Tracks: / Assassins with soul.
12" Single: Released Sep '86, on Illuminated, Catalogue no: **12 LEV 72**

COUP
Tracks: / Coup.
12" Single: Released Feb '85, on Illuminated, Catalogue no: **ILL 2812**

ETHICS
Tracks: / Ethics / Another baby's face.
7" Single: Released Jul '82, on Pineapple, Catalogue no: **PULP 23**

GOSPEL COMES TO NEW GUINEA
Tracks: / Gospel comes to New Guinea.
12" Single: Released Oct '81, on Fetish, Catalogue no: **FE 11**

LANGUAGE
Tracks: / Language.
12" Single: Released Feb '85, on Illuminated, Catalogue no: **ILL 3812**

OOZE
Tracks: / Ooze.
12" Single: Released Mar '85, on Illuminated, Catalogue no: **ILL 5812**

TEARING UP THE PLANS
Tracks: / Tearing up the plans / Just like everybody / Gregouka.
12" Single: Released May '82, on Fetish, Catalogue no: **FP 20**

THOUGHT OF YOU
Tracks: / Thought of you, The.

12" Single: Released Aug '86, on Illuminated, Catalogue no: **12LEV72**

Twenty/Twenty

CHERIE
Tracks: / Cherie / Action now
7" Single: Released May '80, on Portrait, by CBS Records. Deleted May '85. Catalogue no: **PRT 8557**

TELL ME WHY
Tracks: / Tell me why / Backyard guys.
7" Single: Released Feb '80, on Portrait, by CBS Records. Deleted Feb '83. Catalogue no: **PRT 8184**

Twice

LOVERBOY
Tracks: / Loverboy / Good friends.
12" Single: Released Apr '86, on TVT, by TVT Records. Catalogue no: **TEEV 112**

Twice As Much

SITTIN' ON A FENCE
Tracks: / Sittin' on a fence.
7" Single: Released Jun '66, on Immediate, Deleted '69. Catalogue no: **IM 033**

Twice Shy

WANNA DANCE
Tracks: / Wanna dance / White boy.
7" Single: Released Jan '80, on Monarch, by Monarch Records. Catalogue no: **MON 010**

Twice The Love

24 HOURS FROM CULTURE
Tracks: / 24 hours from culture.
CD 5": Released May '89, on Who's That Beat, by Play It Again Sam (Belgium). Catalogue no: **WHOS 013 CD**
12" Single: Released May '89, on Who's That Beat, by Play It Again Sam (Belgium). Catalogue no: **WHOS 013**

Twiggy

DIAMOND
Tracks: / Diamond.
7" Single: Released Mar '86, on Arista, by BMG Records (UK). Catalogue no: **ARIST 651**
12" Single: Released Mar '86, on Arista, by BMG Records (UK). Catalogue no: **ARIST 12651**

FEEL EMOTION
Tracks: / Feel emotion.
7" Single: Released Sep '85, on Arista, by BMG Records (UK). Catalogue no: **ARIST 635**
12" Single: Released Sep '85, on Arista, by BMG Records (UK). Catalogue no: **ARIST 12635**

HERE I GO AGAIN
Tracks: / Here I go again.
7" Single: Released Aug '76, on Mercury, by Phonogram Ltd. Deleted '79. Catalogue no: **6007 100**

Twilight

JUST ME ALONE
Tracks: / Just me alone.
7" Single: Released Oct '85, on Polydor, by Polydor Ltd. Catalogue no: **TLT 1**
12" Single: Released Oct '85, on Polydor, by Polydor Ltd. Catalogue no: **TLTX 1**

Twilight 22

MYSTERIOUS
Tracks: / Mysterious.
12" Single: Released Mar '85, on WEA, by WEA Records. Catalogue no: **YZ 35T**

Twilly, Dwight

GIRLS
Tracks: / Girls / To get to you.
7" Single: Released May '84, on EMI-America, by EMI Records. Catalogue no: **EA 172**

Twin Beat

LET'S PICK UP THE PIECES
Tracks: / Let's pick up the roses.
12" Single: Released Jun '88, on Big One Records, by Big One Records. Catalogue no: **VVBIG 9**

Twin Hype

DO IT TO THE CROWD
Tracks: / Do it to the crowd.
7" Single: Released Jun '89, on Profile (USA), by Profile Records (USA). Catalogue no: **PROF 225**
12" Single: Released Jun '89, on Profile (USA), by Profile Records (USA). Catalogue no: **PROFT 225**

Twin Image

KISS AND MAKE IT BETTER
Tracks: / Kiss and make it better.
7" Single: Released Oct '84, on Capitol, by EMI Records. Deleted '87. Catalogue no: **CL 342**
12" Single: Released Oct '84, on Capitol, by EMI Records. Deleted '88. Catalogue no: **12CL 342**

Twin Set & The Pearl

WHILE THE GOINGS GOOD
Tracks: / While the goings good / Without you.
7" Single: Released Sep '87, on I.R.S, Catalogue no: **IRM 141**
12" Single: Released Sep '87, on I.R.S, Catalogue no: **IRMT 141**

Twink

APOCALIPSTIC
Tracks: / Apocalipstic / He's crying.
7" Single: Released Apr '86, on Twink, by Twink Records. Catalogue no: **TWK 1**

DRIVING MY CAR
Tracks: / Driving my car / Wargirl.
7" Single: Released Jun '87, on Twink, by Twink Records. Catalogue no: **TWK 3**

Twinkle

GOLDEN LIGHTS
Tracks: / Golden lights.
7" Single: Released Feb '65, on Decca, by Decca Records. Deleted '68. Catalogue no: **F 12076**

I'M A BELIEVER
Tracks: / I'm a believer / For sale.
7" Single: Released Apr '82, on EMI, by EMI Records. Deleted Apr '85. Catalogue no: **EMI 5278**

SPACE LOVER
Tracks: / Space lover.
12" Single: Released May '86, on Twinkle, by Twinkle Records. Catalogue no: **TWK 2**

TERRY
Tracks: / Terry.
7" Single: Released Nov '64, on Decca, by Decca Records. Deleted '67. Catalogue no: **F 12013**

TERRY (OLD GOLD)
Tracks: / Terry / Golden lights.
7" Single: Released Jun '88, on Old Gold, by Old Gold Records. Catalogue no: **OG 9027**

Twinkle Brothers

BREAKING DOWN THE BARRIERS (SINGLE)
Tracks: / Breaking down the barriers.
12" Single: Released Sep '87, on Twinkle, by Twinkle Records. Catalogue no: **NG 250**

DON'T JUMP THE FENCE
Tracks: / Don't jump the fence / Let Jah in.
12" Single: Released Jul '83, on Twinkle, by Twinkle Records. Catalogue no: **NG 369**

EVERYBODY NEEDS SOMEBODY
Tracks: / Everybody needs somebody / More dub.
12" Single: Released Jan '83, on Twinkle, by Twinkle Records. Catalogue no: **NG 651**

FAITH CAN MOVE A MOUNTAIN
Tracks: / Faith can move mountains / Mob fury.
12" Single: Released Oct '86, on Jah Shaka, Catalogue no: **SHAKA 855**

GIVE RASTA PRAISE
Tracks: / Give rasta praise / Can't change again.
12" Single: Released Feb '82, on Twinkle, by Twinkle Records. Catalogue no: **NG 803**

HAVE ME WOMAN
Tracks: / Have me woman / Look what you made me do.
12" Single: Released Jun '88, on Twinkle, by Twinkle Records. Catalogue no: **NG 001**

I
Tracks: / I.
12" Single: Released Apr '88, on Twinkle, by Twinkle Records. Catalogue no: **NG 505T**

MAGNET
Tracks: / Magnet / Chant rastafari.
12" Single: Released Jul '82, on Twinkle, by Twinkle Records. Catalogue no: **NG 801**

ROBOT
Tracks: / Robot.
12" Single: Released Apr '88, on Twinkle, by Twinkle Records. Catalogue no: **NG 621**

YOU NICE
Tracks: / You nice.
12" Single: Released Sep '87, on Twinkle, by Twinkle Records. Catalogue no: **NG 635**

Twins

BALLET DANCERS
Tracks: / Ballet dancers / Heaven in your smile.
7" Single: Released Mar '84, on Carrere, Catalogue no: **CAR 310**
12" Single: Released Mar '84, on Carrere, Catalogue no: **CART 310**

FACE TO FACE HEART TO HEART
Tracks: / Face to face heart to heart / New days new ways.
7" Single: Released May '83, on Carrere, Catalogue no: **CAR 280**
12" Single: Released May '83, on Carrere, Catalogue no: **CART 280**

Twinset

TELL ME STRAIGHT
Tracks: / Tell me straight / Sun don't shine / Tell me straight (yes master mix) (Available on 12" only).
7" Single: Released Apr '88, on I.R.S, Catalogue no: **IRM 156**
12" Single: Released Apr '88, on I.R.S, Catalogue no: **IRMT 156**

Twisted Ace

FIREBIRD
Tracks: / Firebird / I won't surrender.
7" Single: Released Nov '81, on Heavy Metal, by FM-Revolver Records. Catalogue no: **HEAVY 9**

Twisted Hand

SHORT STRINGS (EP)
7" Single: Released Apr '82, on M.A.P., by M.A.P. Records. Catalogue no: **REF 1**

Twisted Nerve

CAUGHT IN SESSION (EP)
7" Single: Released Sep '82, on Playlist, Catalogue no: **PLAY 3**

FIVE MINUTES OF FAME
Tracks: / Five minutes of fame / Strange sensation.
7" Single: Released Mar '83, on Criminal Damage, Catalogue no: **CRI 102**

MEDUSA
Tracks: / Medusa.
12" Single: Released Sep '83, on Criminal Damage, Catalogue no: **CRI 12003**

SEASON OF THE WITCHES (EP)
12" Single: Released Aug '83, on Criminal Damage, Catalogue no: **CRI 12103**

YOUTH
Tracks: / Youth / Opportunity knocks / Always alone.
7" Single: Released Nov '82, on Troubador, Catalogue no: **TRUB 7**

Twisted Sister

Biographical details: Twisted Sister USA heavy rock band formed in NYC in 1976 by vocalist Dee Snyder (born 1955), with Jay Jay French on guitar, joined by Mark 'The Animal' Mendoza on bass in 1978, drummer J.J Pero in 1982. They were based in the UK at first (in the USA they were seen as **Kiss** imitators, some of them coming from the same earlier group, called Wicked Lester). Their first big hit was *You Can't Stop Rock and Roll* in 1983, followed by *Stay Hungry* in 1984 (made in the USA); *Come Out and Play* in 1985 was slick,but their live act was still raw, Snyder particularly outrageous. (Donald Clarke 13.1.88).

I AM
Tracks: / I am.
7" Single: Released Mar '83, on Atlantic, by WEA Records. Deleted '86. Catalogue no: **A 9854**

I WANNA ROCK
Tracks: / I wanna rock / Burn in hell / SMF (on 12" only).
7" Single: Released Oct '84, on Atlantic, by WEA Records. Catalogue no: **A 9634**
12" Single: Released Oct '84, on Atlantic, by WEA Records. Catalogue no: **A 9634 T**

KIDS ARE BACK, THE
Tracks: / Kids are back, The.
7" Single: Released May '83, on Atlantic, by WEA Records. Deleted '86. Catalogue no: **A 9827**

LEADER OF THE PACK
Tracks: / Leader of the pack / I wanna rock.
7" Single: Released Jan '86, on Atlantic, by WEA Records. Catalogue no: **A 9478**
12" Single: Released Jan '86, on Atlantic, by WEA Records. Catalogue no: **A 9478 T**

PRICE
Tracks: / Price / S.M.F..
7" Single: Released Mar '85, on Atlantic, by WEA Records. Catalogue no: **A 9591**

RUFF CUTTS (EP)
Tracks: / Ruff cutts.
12" Single: Released Jul '82, on Secret, by Secret Records. Catalogue no: **SHH 137 12**

WE'RE NOT GONNA TAKE IT
Tracks: / We're not gonna take it.
7" Single: Released Jun '84, on Atlantic, by WEA Records. Deleted '87. Catalogue no: **A 9657**

YOU CAN'T STOP ROCK 'N' ROLL (SINGLE)
Tracks: / You can't stop rock 'n' roll.
7" Single: Released Aug '83, on Atlantic, by WEA Records. Deleted '86. Catalogue no: **A 9792**

YOU WANT WHAT WE GOT
Tracks: / You want what we got / Stay hungry / We're not gonna take it (12" only) / King of fools (12" only).
7" Single: Released Apr '86, on Warner Bros., by WEA Records. Catalogue no: **A 9435**
12" Single: Released Apr '86, on Warner Bros., by WEA Records. Deleted Jun '87. Catalogue no: **A 9435 T**

Twitty, Conway

C'EST SI BON
Tracks: / C'est si bon.
7" Single: Released Feb '61, on MGM, by Polydor Ltd. Deleted '64. Catalogue no: **MGM 1118**

IS A BLUEBIRD BLUE?
Tracks: / Is a bluebird blue?.
7" Single: Released Jul '60, on MGM, by Polydor Ltd. Deleted '63. Catalogue no: **MGM 1082**

IT'S ONLY MAKE BELIEVE
Tracks: / It's only make believe.
7" Single: Released Nov '58, on MGM, by Polydor Ltd. Deleted '61. Catalogue no: **MGM 992**
7" Single: Released '80, on MGM, by Polydor Ltd. Catalogue no: **LR 8298**

MONA LISA
Tracks: / Mona Lisa.
7" Single: Released Aug '59, on MGM, by Polydor Ltd. Deleted '62. Catalogue no: **MGM 1029**

STORY OF MY LOVE
Tracks: / Story of my love.
7" Single: Released Mar '59, on MGM, by Polydor Ltd. Deleted '62. Catalogue no: **MGM 1003**

TAKE GOOD CARE OF MY BABY
Tracks: / Take good care of my baby.
7" Single: Released Jul '84, on Old Gold, by Old Gold Records. Catalogue no: **OG 9448**

Two

2X2
Tracks: / 2X2.
12" Single: Released Sep '84, on Reflex, by Reflex Records. Catalogue no: **12 RE 7**

CHAINS OF DESIRE
Tracks: / Chains of desire / Time is on your side / I had love / Will you catch me.
7" Single: Released May '87, on North Of South, Catalogue no: **7 NSTT 001**
12" Single: Released May '87, on North Of South, Catalogue no: **NSTT 001**

TRACE OF RED
Tracks: / Trace of red.
7" Single: Released Sep '83, on No Future, Catalogue no: **FS 5**

WAITING FOR WINTER
Tracks: / Waiting for winter.
12" Single: Released Nov '83, on No Future, Catalogue no: **12 FS 10**

Two A.M.

SOMEBODY SOMEDAY
Tracks: / Somebody, someday / Deams and promises / Right now I need you (12" only).
7" Single: Released Aug '87, on RCA, by BMG Records (UK). Deleted May '89. Catalogue no: **PB 41417**
12" Single: Released Aug '87, on RCA, by BMG Records (UK). Deleted May '89. Catalogue no: **PT 41418**

YOU'RE THE ONE
Tracks: / You're the one / Too late / Lost souls (Extra track on 12").
7" Single: Released Feb '88, on RCA, by BMG Records (UK). Deleted May '89. Catalogue no: **PB 41709**
12" Single: Released Feb '88, on RCA, by BMG Records (UK). Deleted May '89. Catalogue no: **PT 41710**

Two Bad

2 BAD
Tracks: / 2 bad.
12" Single: Released 27 Feb '89, on Sleeping Bag, by Sleeping Bag Records. Catalogue no: **SBUK 009 T**

Two Bad Two Mention

DO IT
Tracks: / Do it / Do it (version).
7" Single: Released Dec '87, on In Touch, by In Touch Records. Catalogue no: **SEVEN 005**
12" Single: Released Dec '87, on In Touch, by In Touch Records. Catalogue no: **TWELVE 005**

DO IT (DOUBLE TROUBLE REMIX)
Tracks: / Do it.
7" Single: Released Feb '88, on In Touch, by In Touch Records. Catalogue no: **SEVEN 005R**
12" Single: Released Feb '88, on In Touch, by In Touch Records. Catalogue no:

TWELVE 005R

Two Belgen

CALL ME
Tracks: / Call me.
7" Single: Released Jun '88, on Antler, by Antler Records (Belgium). Catalogue no: **ANT 023**

MUSTAPHA
Tracks: / Mustapha.
7" Single: Released Jun '88, on Antler, by Antler Records (Belgium). Catalogue no: **ANT 012**

QUAND LE FILME EST...
Tracks: / Quand le filme est....
7" Single: Released '88, on Antler, by Antler Records (Belgium). Deleted '88. Catalogue no: **ANT 004**

THIRD FROM, THE
Tracks: / Third from, The.
7" Single: Released Jun '88, on Antler, by Antler Records (Belgium). Catalogue no: **ANT 011**

Two Brave

AFTER MIDNIGHT
Tracks: / After midnight / After midnight (the strong mix) / After midnight (extra long mint version) (Only on 12" version.) / Stop that girl (heavenly mix edit) (Only on 12" version.).
CD 5": Released Feb '89, on London (Decca), by Decca International. Catalogue no: **LONCD 221**
7" Single: Released Feb '89, on London (Decca), by Decca International. Deleted Jul '89. Catalogue no: **LON 221**
12" Single: Released Feb '89, on London (Decca), by Decca International. Deleted Jul '89. Catalogue no: **LONX 221**
Special: Released Feb '89, on London (Decca), by Decca International. Deleted Jul '89. Catalogue no: **LONM 221**
Special: Released Feb '89, on London (Decca), by Decca International. Deleted Jul '89. Catalogue no: **LONP 221**

BETTER LATE THAN NEVER
Tracks: / Better late than never / Better late than never (version).
CD 5": Released Jul '89, on London (Decca), by Decca International. Catalogue no: **LONCD 228**
7" Single: Released Jul '89, on London (Decca), by Decca International. Catalogue no: **LONP228**
7" Single: Released Jul '89, on London (Decca), by Decca International. Catalogue no: **LONB228**
7" Single: Released Jul '89, on London (Decca), by Decca International. Catalogue no: **LON 228**
12" Single: Released Jul '89, on London (Decca), by Decca International. Catalogue no: **LONX 228**

BOYS AND GIRLS
Tracks: / Boys and girls / Push your body / Better late than never.
CD 5": Released Sep '89, on London Records, by London Records. Catalogue no: **LONCD 237**
Cassingle: Released Sep '89, on London Records, by London Records. Catalogue no: **LONCS 237**
7" Single: Released Sep '89, on London Records, by London Records. Catalogue no: **LON 237**
12" Single: Released Sep '89, on London Records, by London Records. Catalogue no: **LONX 237**

STOP THAT GIRL
Tracks: / Stop that girl / Stop that girl (version).
7" Single: Released Nov '88, on London Records, by London Records. Deleted May '89. Catalogue no: **LON 205**
12" Single: Released Jan '89, on London Records, by London Records. Catalogue no: **LONXR 205**
12" Single: Released Nov '88, on London Records, by London Records. Catalogue no: **LONX 205**

Two DJ's

CREATION, THE
Tracks: / Creation, The.
CD 5": Released Apr '89, on Kaos, Catalogue no: **KAOS 013 CD**
12" Single: Released Apr '89, on Kaos, Catalogue no: **KAOS 013**

Two Fingered Approach

MY WORD WAR ALBUM
Tracks: / My word war album.
7" Single: Released May '83, on Virus, Catalogue no: **AM 026**

Two Guys, A Drum

I'M TIRED OF GETTING PUSHED AROUND
Tracks: / I'm tired of getting pushed around.
7" Single: Released Dec '87, on London Records, by London Records. Deleted Oct '88. Catalogue no: **LON 141**
12" Single: Released '87, on London Records, by London Records. Deleted Feb '89. Catalogue no: **LONXR 141**
12" Single: Released Dec '87, on London Records, by London Records. Deleted Oct '88. Catalogue no: **LONX 141**

Two Helens

SILVER AND GOLD
Tracks: / Silver and gold.
7" Single: Released '88, on Sharko 2, Catalogue no: **TUFT 057**

Two In A Room

SOMEBODY IN THE HOUSE SAY YEAH
Tracks: / Somebody in the house say yeah.
7" Single: Released Oct '89, on Big Life, by Big Life Records. Catalogue no: **BLR 12**
12" Single: Released Oct '89, on Big Life, by Big Life Records. Catalogue no: **BLR 12 T**
12" Single: Released Sep '89, on Cutting (USA), Catalogue no: **CR 225**

Two Live Crew

WE WANT SOME PUSSY
Tracks: / We want some pussy.
12" Single: Released Nov '87, on Luke Skyywalker (USA), Catalogue no: **GR 113**

YAKETY YAK
Tracks: / Yakety yak / Yakety yak (bass mix) / Meta mixx 2.
CD 5": Released Apr '89, on Epic, by CBS Records. Deleted Oct '89. Catalogue no: **6547982**
7" Single: Released Apr '89, on Epic, by CBS Records. Deleted Oct '89. Catalogue no: **6547987**
12" Single: Released Apr '89, on Epic, by CBS Records. Deleted Oct '89. Catalogue no: **6547986**

Two Man Sound

Biographical details: his Belgian duo had a one-off British chart entry in early 1979. That period was the height of the disco era and the lower regions of the singles chart were flooded with a profusion of minor hits by faceless, anonymous acts. *Que Tel America*reached No 46 and logged seven weeks on the British Top Seventy-Five. It was a typical example of Two Man Sound's Brazilian-style samba music, a traditional form of dance music which they adapted for the international disco market. An album, predictably entitled*Disco Samba*, was also released but made only a moderate dance-floor impact. (Bob MacDonald, April 1985.).

DISCO SAMBA
Tracks: / Disco samba / Que tel America / Samba samba / Brazil O Brazil / Vas-y-maman / Menina rainbow / Djin djin / Ritmo-cada.
7" Single: Released '79, on Ovation, by Gull Records. Catalogue no: **M9**

QUE TAL AMERICA
Tracks: / Que tal America.
7" Single: Released Jan '79, on Miracle, by Gull Records. Deleted '82. Catalogue no: **M 1**

Two, Mark

HOLIDAY ROCKIN'
Tracks: / Holiday rockin' / Fast food.
12" Pic: Released Jun '88, on Latest (1), Catalogue no: **12XEARLY 001**
7" Single: Released May '88, on Latest (1), Catalogue no: **7EARLY 001**
12" Single: Released Jun '88, on Latest (1), Catalogue no: **12 EARLY 001**

Two Minds Crack

CRY CRY CRY
Tracks: / Now the love has gone.
7" Single: Released Jan '87, on Warner Bros., by WEA Records. Deleted Jan '88. Catalogue no: **W 8600**
12" Single: Released Jan '87, on Warner Bros., by WEA Records. Deleted Jan '88. Catalogue no: **W 8600T**

ENEMIES OF PROMISE
Tracks: / Enemies of promise.
7" Single: Released Oct '84, on Sedition, by Sedition Records. Catalogue no: **EDIT 2**
12" Single: Released Oct '84, on Sedition, by Sedition Records. Catalogue no: **EDIT 122**

HUNGER AND GREED
Tracks: / Hunger and greed / Dream that came before / I think I've fallen in love.
7" Single: Released Feb '85, on Sedition, by Sedition Records. Catalogue no: **EDIT 1**
12" Single: Released Feb '85, on Sedition, by Sedition Records. Catalogue no: **EDITL 1**
12" Single: Released Feb '85, on Sedition, by Sedition Records. Catalogue no: **EDIT 121**

ONE SKY ABOVE US
Tracks: / One sky above us / Hunger and the greed / Love is in control*.
7" Single: Released Sep '87, on Sire (USA), Deleted Jan '88. Catalogue no: **W 8211**
12" Single: Released Sep '87, on Sire (USA), Deleted Jul '88. Catalogue no: **W 8211T**

Two Minutes Mr.

SAVIN' UP
Tracks: / Savin' up.
7" Single: Released Oct '85, on Falcon, Catalogue no: **FR 297**

Two Much Texas

TOGETHER
Tracks: / Together.
12" Single: Released 20 Jun '88, on Ugly Man, by Ugly Man Records. Catalogue no: **UGLY 011T**

Two Nasty

NOT FELLAS BUT GIRLS
Tracks: / Not fellas but girls.
12" Single: Released Oct '87, on Submission, by Submission Records. Catalogue no: **SUBX 001**

Two Nations

ANY LUCK
Tracks: / Any luck / Brand X / Everything I own (12" only).
7" Single: Released Sep '86, on 10 Records, by Virgin Records. Deleted May '88. Catalogue no: **TEN 138**
12" Single: Released Sep '86, on 10 Records, by Virgin Records. Deleted May '88. Catalogue no: **TENT 138**

EVERMORE
Tracks: / Evermore / Losing control / Rattlesnake (12" only) / Rattlesnake (Snakebite mix) (12" only).
7" Single: Released Oct '87, on 10 Records, by Virgin Records. Deleted May '88. Catalogue no: **TEN 191**
12" Single: Released Oct '87, on 10 Records, by Virgin Records. Catalogue no: **TENT 191**

INDEPENDENCE
Tracks: / Independence.
7" Single: Released Aug '87, on 10 Records, by Virgin Records. Deleted May '88. Catalogue no: **TEN 181**
12" Single: Released Aug '87, on 10 Records, by Virgin Records. Deleted May '88. Catalogue no: **TENT 181**

LIVING IN TWO NATIONS
Tracks: / Poacher, The.
7" Single: Released Feb '87, on 10 Records, by Virgin Records. Deleted May '88. Catalogue no: **TEN 139**
12" Single: Released Feb '87, on 10 Records, by Virgin Records. Deleted May '88. Catalogue no: **TENT 139**

Two of a Kind

SOMEWHERE IN WEST HELL
Tracks: / Somewhere in west hell / F**k Charley.
12" Single: Released Oct '87, on Trax (USA), Catalogue no: **TX 147**

Two Of Us (Group)

BLUE NIGHT SHADOW
Tracks: / Blue night shadow.
7" Single: Released Sep '85, on Genie, Catalogue no: **GEN 2**
12" Single: Released Sep '85, on Genie, Catalogue no: **GENT 2**

Two People

HEAVEN
Tracks: / Run to him.
7" Single: Released Jan '87, on Polydor, by Polydor Ltd. Deleted Jan '88. Catalogue no: **POSP 844**
12" Single: Released Jan '87, on Polydor, by Polydor Ltd. Deleted Aug '87. Catalogue no: **POSPX 844**

MOUTH OF AN ANGEL
Tracks: / Mouth of an angel / Let's raise murder / Dig it (12" only).
7" Single: Released Sep '86, on Polydor, by Polydor Ltd. Deleted Mar '87. Catalogue no: **POSP 818**
12" Single: Released Sep '86, on Polydor, by Polydor Ltd. Deleted Mar '88. Catalogue no: **POSPX 818**

THIS IS THE SHIRT
Tracks: / This is the shirt / People in love / It's obvious.
7" Single: Released Apr '85, on Polydor, by Polydor Ltd. Catalogue no: **POSP 741**
7" Single: Released Mar '87, on Polydor, by Polydor Ltd. Deleted Jan '88. Catalogue no: **POSP 856**
12" Single: Released Apr '85, on Polydor, by Polydor Ltd. Catalogue no: **POSPX 741**
12" Single: Released Mar '87, on Polydor, by Polydor Ltd. Deleted Jan '88. Catalogue no: **POSPX 856**

Two Point Two

RUSSIAN DOLL
Tracks: / Russian doll.
7" Single: Released Sep '84, on Rock City Records, by Rock City Records. Catalogue no: **RCR 2**

Two Puerto Ricans

DO IT PROPERLY
Tracks: / Do it properly.
7" Single: Released Jun '87, on Cool Tempo, by Chrysalis Records. Catalogue no: **COOL 147**
12" Single: Released Jun '87, on Cool Tempo, by Chrysalis Records. Catalogue no: **COOLX 147**

SCANDALOUS
Tracks: / Scandalous (everybody jump mix) (12" only) / Scandalous (jump like a rabbit mix) / Scandalous (everybody jump edit).
7" Single: Released Jan '89, on Syncopate, by EMI Records. Deleted Aug '89. Catalogue no: **SY 20**
12" Single: Released Jan '89, on Syncopate, by EMI Records. Deleted Aug '89. Catalogue no: **12SYX 20**
12" Single: Released Jan '89, on Syncopate, by EMI Records. Deleted Aug '89. Catalogue no: **12SY 20**

SCANDALOUS (COMING TO AMERICA MIX)
Tracks: / Scandalous (coming to America mix) / Scandalous (coming to America dub) / Scandalous (radio edit).
Note: Edited by Robert Clivilles and Luie Rivera.t
12" Single: Released Feb '89, on Syncopate, by EMI Records. Catalogue no: **12SYX 20**

Two Stroke, Arthur

HAWAII 5-0
Tracks: / Hawaii 5-0 / Heart of stone.
7" Single: Released Mar '81, on Logo, by Logo Records. Deleted Mar '84. Catalogue no: **GO 398**

Two The Top

RHYTHM I GIVE 'EM, THE
Tracks: / Rhythm I give 'em, The.
12" Single: Released Apr '89, on Rhyme 'n' Reason, by Rhyme'n'Reason Records. Catalogue no: **12 RNR 2**

Two Thousand Ds

SCRAP THE CHURCH
Tracks: / Scrap the church.
7" Single: Released Mar '89, on WWV, Catalogue no: **WWV 001**

Two Three

ALL THE TIME LOW
Tracks: / All the time low.
7" Single: Released '79, on Rough Trade, by Rough Trade Records. Catalogue no: **FAST 2**

Two Tons O' Fun

JUST US
Tracks: / Just us / Got the feeling.
7" Single: Released Apr '80, on Fantasy (1), by BMG Records (UK). Deleted Apr '83. Catalogue no: **FTC 188**
12" Single: Released Apr '80, on Fantasy (1), by BMG Records (UK). Deleted Apr '83. Catalogue no: **12FTC 188**

Two Two

INSUFFICIENT DATA
Tracks: / Insufficient data / Lunch in the atmosphere.
7" Single: Released Feb '82, on Chiswick Records, Catalogue no: **DICE 2**
12" Single: Released Feb '82, on Chiswick Records, Catalogue no: **DICE12-2**

KING SOLOMON'S MINES
Tracks: / King Solomon's mines.
7" Single: Released Oct '82, on Chiswick Records, Catalogue no: **DICE 17**
12" Single: Released Oct '82, on Chiswick Records, Catalogue no: **DICE 1217**

KWAGAYO
Tracks: / Kwagayo.
7" Single: Released Jun '82, on Chiswick Records, Catalogue no: **DICE 5**

Two Way

ALL DRESSED UP
Tracks: / All dressed up / Chinatown.
7" Single: Released Mar '84, on PRT, by Castle Communications Records. Catalogue no: **7P 292**
12" Single: Released Mar '84, on PRT, by Castle Communications Records. Catalogue no: **12P 292**

FACE IN THE WINDOW
Tracks: / Face in the window / Chinatown.
7" Single: Released Jan '83, on PRT, by Castle Communications Records. Cata-

logue no: **7P 262**

Two Young

DEEP INSIDE
Tracks: / Deep inside / Deep inside (instrumental).
7" Single: Released Sep '87, on Mayland, by Mayland Recording. Catalogue no: **MAYL 1**
12" Single: Released Sep '87, on Mayland, by Mayland Recording. Catalogue no: **12 MAYL 1**

TXT

GIRLS GOT A BRAND NEW TOY
Tracks: / Girls got a brand new toy.
7" Single: Released Jul '85, on Portrait, by CBS Records. Catalogue no: **A 6073**
12" Single: Released Jul '85, on Portrait, by CBS Records. Catalogue no: **TA 6073**

Tygers of Pan Tang

DO IT GOOD
Tracks: / Do it good / Slip away.
7" Single: Released Jan '82, on MCA, by MCA Records. Deleted Jan '85. Catalogue no: **MCA 759**

DON'T STOP BY
Tracks: / Don't stop by / Slave to freedom / Raised on rock (Available on 12" only).
7" Single: Released Jun '81, on MCA, by MCA Records. Deleted Jun '84. Catalogue no: **MCA 723**
12" Single: Released Jun '81, on MCA, by MCA Records. Deleted Jun '84. Catalogue no: **MCAT 723**

DON'T TOUCH ME THERE
Tracks: / Don't touch me there / Burning up bad times.
7" Single: Released Mar '80, on MCA, by MCA Records. Deleted '83. Catalogue no: **MCA 582**

EUTHANASIA
Tracks: / Euthanasia / Straight as a die.
7" Single: Released Oct '80, on MCA, by MCA Records. Deleted Oct '83. Catalogue no: **MCA 644**

HELLBOUND
Tracks: / Hellbound / Don't give a damn.
7" Single: Released Feb '81, on MCA, by MCA Records. Deleted '84. Catalogue no: **MCA 672**

LOVE DON'T STAY
Tracks: / Love don't stay / Paradise drive.
7" Single: Released Nov '81, on MCA, by MCA Records. Deleted Nov '84. Catalogue no: **MCA 755**

LOVE POTION NO. 9
Tracks: / Love potion No.9.
7" Single: Released Mar '82, on MCA, by MCA Records. Deleted '85. Catalogue no: **MCA 769**

MAKING TRACKS
Tracks: / Making tracks / What you saying.
7" Single: Released Oct '82, on MCA, by MCA Records. Deleted Oct '85. Catalogue no: **MCA 798**
12" Single: Released Oct '82, on MCA, by MCA Records. Deleted Oct '85. Catalogue no: **MCAT 798**

PARIS BY AIR
Tracks: / Paris by air / Love's a lie.
7" Single: Released Sep '82, on MCA, by MCA Records. Deleted '85. Catalogue no: **MCA 790**

RENDEZVOUS
Tracks: / Rendezvous.
7" Single: Released Jul '82, on MCA, by MCA Records. Deleted '85. Catalogue no: **MCA 777**

ROCK'N'ROLL MAN
Tracks: / Rock'n'roll man / Alright on the night / Wildcats.
7" Single: Released Jun '80, on MCA, by MCA Records. Deleted '83. Catalogue no: **MCA 612**

STORY SO FAR
Tracks: / Story so far / Silver and gold / All or nothing.
7" EP: Released Mar '81, on MCA, by MCA Records. Deleted Mar '84. Catalogue no: **MCA 692**

SUZIE SMILED
Tracks: / Suzie smiled / Tush.
7" Single: Released Aug '80, on MCA, by MCA Records. Deleted '83. Catalogue no: **MCA 634**

Tyla Gang

SUICIDE JOCKEY
Tracks: / Suicide jockey.
7" Single: Released Apr '77, on Skydog, Deleted '88. Catalogue no: **ST 001**

Tyla, Sean & English

LANDING LIGHTS
Tracks: / Landing lights / Tonight.
7" Single: Released Aug '81, on Zilch, by Zilch Records. Catalogue no: **ZILCH 7**

Tyler, Bonnie

Biographical details: Bonnie Tyler was born in 1953 in South Wales. A singer influenced by soul music, she had hits with ballads in gentle counrty-rock mode in the late '70s; but then a few flops convinced her to change direction, teaming with **Meat Loaf** producer Jim Steinman, who assembled crack session players for Tyler rock albums, beginning with *Faster Than The Speed Of Night* in 1983, employing a wall-of-sound approach; *Total Eclipse Of The Heart* was a transatlantic number one hit that year. The next album *Secret Dreams And Forbidden Fire* didn't do as well in 1986; she has yet to find her own way to use her distinctive husky tones. (Donald Clarke 13.1.88).

BAND OF GOLD
Tracks: / Band of gold / It's not enough.
7" Single: Released May '86, on CBS, by CBS Records. Catalogue no: **A 7223**
12" Single: Released May '86, on CBS, by CBS Records. Catalogue no: **TA 7223**

BEST, THE
Tracks: / Best, The / Fire below, The (on 12" and CD single only.) / Under suspicion*.
CD 5": Released Jan '88, on CBS, by CBS Records. Deleted Jan '89. Catalogue no: **CD BEST 1**
7" Single: Released Jan '88, on CBS, by CBS Records. Deleted Aug '88. Catalogue no: **BEST 1**
12" Single: Released Jan '88, on CBS, by CBS Records. Deleted Aug '88. Catalogue no: **BEST T1**

BONNIE TYLER
Cassingle: Released May '83, on RCA, by BMG Records (UK). Catalogue no: **RCXK 008**

FASTER THAN THE SPEED OF NIGHT (SINGLE)
Tracks: / Faster than the speed of night / Can get better.
7" Pic: Released May '83, on CBS, by CBS Records. Catalogue no: **WA 3338**
7" Single: Released Apr '83, on CBS, by CBS Records. Catalogue no: **A 3338**
12" Single: Released Apr '83, on CBS, by CBS Records. Catalogue no: **TA 3338**

GETTING SO EXCITED
Tracks: / Getting so excited / Going through the motions.
7" Single: Released Mar '84, on CBS, by CBS Records. Catalogue no: **A 4242**
12" Single: Released Mar '84, on CBS, by CBS Records. Catalogue no: **TA 4242**

GOODBYE TO THE ISLAND (SINGLE)
Tracks: / Goodbye to the island / Get out of my head.
7" Single: Released Jan '81, on RCA, by BMG Records (UK). Deleted Jan '84. Catalogue no: **RCA 19**

HAVE YOU EVER SEEN THE RAIN
Tracks: / Have you ever seen the rain / Time.
7" Single: Released Jun '83, on CBS, by CBS Records. Catalogue no: **A 3517**
12" Single: Released Jun '83, on CBS, by CBS Records. Catalogue no: **TA 3517**

HIDE YOUR HEART
Tracks: / Hide your heart / I'm not fooling.
CD 5": Released 23 Apr '88, on CBS, by CBS Records. Deleted Jan '89. Catalogue no: **651 516-8**
CD 5": Released 23 Apr '88, on CBS, by CBS Records. Deleted Jan '89. Catalogue no: **651 516 2**
7" Single: Released 23 Apr '88, on CBS, by CBS Records. Deleted Jan '89. Catalogue no: **651 516 7**
12" Single: Released 23 Apr '88, on CBS, by CBS Records. Deleted Jan '89. Catalogue no: **651 516-6**

HOLDING OUT FOR A HERO
Tracks: / Holding out for a hero / Faster than the speed of light.
7" Single: Released Aug '85, on CBS, by CBS Records. Deleted '88. Catalogue no: **A 4251**

IF YOU WERE A WOMAN
Tracks: / If you were a woman / Under suspicion.
Note: Poster Bag limited edition (10,000)
7" Single: Released Mar '86, on CBS, by CBS Records. Catalogue no: **A 6867**
7" Single: Released Apr '86, on CBS, by CBS Records. Catalogue no: **OA 6867**

I'M JUST A WOMAN
Tracks: / I'm just a woman / Sitting on the edge of the ocean.
7" Single: Released Oct '80, on RCA, by BMG Records (UK). Deleted Oct '83. Catalogue no: **PB 5286**

IT'S A HEARTACHE (OLD GOLD)
Tracks: / It's a heartache / Lost in France / More than a lover.
CD 5": Released 24 Apr '89, on Old Gold, by Old Gold Records. Catalogue no: **OG 6138**

IT'S A HEARTACHE (SINGLE)
Tracks: / It's a heartache / Lost in France.
7" Single: Released Dec '77, on RCA, by BMG Records (UK). Deleted '80. Catalogue no: **PB 5057**
7" Single: Released Aug '81, on Golden Grooves, by BMG Records (UK). Catalogue no: **GOLD 528**
7" Single: Released Nov '86, on Old Gold, by Old Gold Records. Catalogue no: **OG 9611**

LOST IN FRANCE
Tracks: / Lost in France.
7" Single: Released Oct '76, on RCA, by BMG Records (UK). Deleted '79. Catalogue no: **RCA 2734**

LOVERS AGAIN
Tracks: / I do it for you.
7" Single: Released Jan '87, on CBS, by CBS Records. Catalogue no: **650317 7**

LOVING YOU'S A DIRTY JOB BUT SOMEBODY'S GOTTA DO
Tracks: / Loving you's a dirty job.
7" Single: Released Dec '85, on CBS, by CBS Records. Deleted '88. Catalogue no: **A 6662**

MARRIED MEN
Tracks: / Married men.
7" Single: Released Jun '79, on RCA, by BMG Records (UK). Deleted '82. Catalogue no: **PB 5164**

MORE THAN A LOVER
Tracks: / More than a lover.
7" Single: Released Jan '77, on RCA, by BMG Records (UK). Deleted '78. Catalogue no: **PB 5008**

MY GUNS ARE LOADED
Tracks: / My guns are loaded.
7" Single: Released Mar '79, on RCA, by BMG Records (UK). Deleted May '80. Catalogue no: **PB 5147**

NOTES FROM AMERICA
Tracks: / Notes from America / It's not enough / Turtle blues.
CD 5": Released 23 Jan '89, on CBS, by CBS Records. Deleted 10 Jul '89. Catalogue no: **TYLER C3**
7" Single: Released 23 Jan '89, on CBS, by CBS Records. Deleted 10 Jul '89. Catalogue no: **TYLER 3**
12" Single: Released 23 Jan '89, on CBS, by CBS Records. Deleted 10 Jul '89. Catalogue no: **TYLER T3**

REBEL WITHOUT A CLUE
Tracks: / Rebel without a clue / I do it for you.
7" Single: Released Oct '86, on CBS, by CBS Records. Catalogue no: **650157 7**
12" Single: Released Oct '86, on CBS, by CBS Records. Catalogue no: **650157 6**

SAVE UP ALL YOUR TEARS
Tracks: / Save up all your tears / It's not enough.
7" Single: Released Aug '88, on CBS, by CBS Records. Deleted 17 Apr '89. Catalogue no: **TYLER 2**
12" Single: Released Aug '88, on CBS, by CBS Records. Deleted 17 Apr '89. Catalogue no: **TYLER T2**

STRAIGHT FROM THE HEART
Tracks: / Straight from the heart.
7" Single: Released Aug '83, on CBS, by CBS Records. Catalogue no: **A 3650**

TOTAL ECLIPSE OF THE HEART
Tracks: / Total eclipse of the heart / Dead ringer for love / Keep on loving you / Who's crying now?.
7" Single: Released Feb '83, on CBS, by CBS Records. Deleted '86. Catalogue no: **TYLER 1**

TOTAL ECLIPSE OF THE HEART (OLD GOLD)
Tracks: / Total eclipse of the heart.
7" Single: Released Feb '86, on Old Gold, by Old Gold Records. Catalogue no: **OG 4010**

Tyler, Sean

BREAKFAST IN MARIN
Tracks: / Breakfast in Marin.
7" Single: Released Apr '81, on Zilch, by Zilch Records. Deleted Apr '84. Catalogue no: **ZILCH 1**
12" Single: Released Apr '81, on Zilch, by Zilch Records. Deleted Apr '84. Catalogue no: **ZILCHT 1**

Tymes

GOD'S GONNA PUNISH YOU
Tracks: / God's gonna punish you.
7" Single: Released Jan '76, on RCA, by BMG Records (UK). Deleted '79. Catalogue no: **RCA 2626**

MS. GRACE
Tracks: / Ms. Grace / You little trust maker.
7" Single: Released Dec '74, on RCA, by BMG Records (UK). Deleted '77. Catalogue no: **RCA 2493**
7" Single: Released Jul '78, on Golden Grooves, by BMG Records (UK). Catalogue no: **GOLD 502**
7" Single: Released Apr '87, on Old Gold, by Old Gold Records. Catalogue no: **OG 9701**

PEOPLE
Tracks: / People.
7" Single: Released Jan '69, on Direction, Deleted '72. Catalogue no: **58 3903**

SO MUCH IN LOVE
Tracks: / So much in love.
7" Single: Released Jul '63, on Cameo Parkway, by Pye Records. Deleted '66. Catalogue no: **P 871**

YOU LITTLE TRUST MAKER
Tracks: / You little trust maker.
7" Single: Released Sep '74, on RCA, by BMG Records (UK). Deleted '77. Catalogue no: **RCA 2456**

Typhoon Saturday

ANOTHER FLIGHT
Tracks: / Another flight / Let's all dance.
7" Single: Released May '82, on Polydor, by Polydor Ltd. Deleted '85. Catalogue no: **POSP 442**

I HAVE LOVE
Tracks: / I have love.
7" Single: Released Sep '82, on Polydor, by Polydor Ltd. Catalogue no: **POSP 501**

WHAT DO I DO?
Tracks: / What do I do? / Fascination.
7" Single: Released Mar '82, on Polydor, by Polydor Ltd. Deleted '85. Catalogue no: **POSP 413**

Typhoons

TELSTAR
Tracks: / Telstar / In fae' a brothin'.
7" Single: Released Aug '81, on Bohemian, Catalogue no: **BO 1**

Typically Tropical

BARBADOS
Tracks: / Barbados / Rocket now.
7" Single: Released Jul '75, on Gull, by Gull Records. Deleted '78. Catalogue no: **GULS 14**
7" Single: Released Jun '82, on PRT, by Castle Communications Records. Catalogue no: **7P 243**

BARBADOS (OLD GOLD)
Tracks: / Barbados / Rocket now.
7" Single: Released Jul '82, on Old Gold, by Old Gold Records. Catalogue no: **OG 9158**

LADY D
Tracks: / Lady D / Cool cool music.
7" Single: Released Jun '81, on Whisper, by Whisper Records. Catalogue no: **WSP 103**

MY RUBBER BALL
Tracks: / My rubber ball.
7" Single: Released May '79, on Hobo, Catalogue no: **HOS 001**

Tyree

ACID CRASH
Tracks: / Acid crash.
12" Single: Released Feb '89, on House Musik (USA), Catalogue no: **HM 601**

ACID OVER
Tracks: / Acid over / Acid over (radio mix) (Available on 12' only) / Acid over (flashback original) / Acid over (Tyree mix) (Available on 12" only) / Acid over (heavenly mix) (Available on 12" only) / Acid over (Spectrum mix) (12" only) / Acid over (piano 'matey' mix) (Available on 12' only).
7" Single: Released 20 Jun '88, on ffrr, by London Records. Catalogue no: **FFR 6**
12" Single: Released 20 Jun '88, on ffrr, by London Records. Catalogue no: **FFRX 6**

HARDCORE HIP HOUSE
Tracks: / Hardcore hip house.
CD 5": Released Apr '89, on DJ International, by Westside Records. Catalogue no: **CDDJIN 11**
7" Single: Released Apr '89, on DJ International, by Westside Records. Catalogue no: **DJIN 11**
12" Single: Released May '89, on DJ International, by Westside Records. Catalogue no: **DJINX 11**
12" Single: Released Apr '89, on DJ International, by Westside Records. Catalogue no: **DJINT 11**

I FEAR THE NIGHT
Tracks: / I fear the night / I fear the night (remix) / I fear the night (subterranean mix) / I fear the night (fear the dub mix).
12" Single: Released Jan '87, on Ruby, Catalogue no: **12LTD 333**

TURN UP THE BASS
Tracks: / Turn up the bass.
7" Single: Released Feb '89, on ffrr, by London Records. Deleted Jul '89. Catalogue

no: **FFR 24**
12" Single: Released Feb '89, on ffrr, by London Records. Deleted Jul '89. Catalogue no: **FFRXR 24**
12" Single: Released Feb '89, on ffrr, by London Records. Deleted Jul '89. Catalogue no: **FFRX 24**

WHOP, THE
Tracks: / Whop, The.
Note: (House) Originally only available on a compilation album, now on 12" in 4 mixes.
12" Single: Released Nov '87, on Underground (USA), Catalogue no: **UN 125**

Tyrone

AIN'T GOT NO LOVE
Tracks: / Ain't got no love.
12" Single: Released Feb '82, on Solid Groove, Catalogue no: **SG 007 12**

COME ON OVER TO MY PLACE
Tracks: / Come on over to my place.
12" Single: Released Mar '83, on La Femme Noire, Catalogue no: **LA 1**

I NEED A WOMAN TONIGHT
Tracks: / I need a woman tonight.
12" Single: Released Jul '80, on Eargasm, Catalogue no: **EAR 23**

I'M FALLING IN LOVE
Tracks: / I'm falling in love.
12" Single: Released Sep '85, on Music Scene, Catalogue no: **MKS 1031**

I'M GONNA MAKE YOU LOVE ME
Tracks: / I'm gonna make you love me.
7" Single: Released Nov '85, on Total Control, by Total Control Records. Catalogue no: **TOCO 4**
12" Single: Released Nov '85, on Total Control, by Total Control Records. Catalogue no: **12TOCO 4**
12" Single: Released Jun '84, on Music Scene, Catalogue no: **MKS 7031**

MARGATE
Tracks: / Margate.
12" Single: Released Jul '83, on Chans, Catalogue no: **CHMSS 01**

REJOICE IT'S CHRISTMAS TIME AGAIN
Tracks: / Rejoice it's Christmas time again.
12" Single: Released Dec '83, on Thunderbay, Catalogue no: **TBT 012**

Tyson Dog

EAT THE RICH
Tracks: / Dead meat / Eat the rich.
7" Single: Released Dec '83, on Neat, by Neat Records. Catalogue no: **NEAT 33**

HAMMERHEAD
Tracks: / Hammerhead.
12" Single: Released Mar '85, on Neat, by Neat Records. Catalogue no: **NEAT 46 12**

SCHOOL'S OUT
Tracks: / Don't let the bastards grind you down / Back to the bullet / School's out.
7" Single: Released Sep '86, on Neat, by Neat Records. Catalogue no: **NEAT 56**
12" Single: Released '88, on Neat, by Neat Records. Catalogue no: **NEAT 56 12**

Tywyll, Tynal

73 HEB FLARES
Tracks: / 73 Heb flares.
7" Single: Released Dec '86, on Anhrefn, Catalogue no: **ANHREFN 007**

Tzuke, Judie

BLACK FURS
Tracks: / Black furs.
7" Single: Released May '83, on Rocket, by Rocket Records. Catalogue no: **XPRESS 90**

CHOICES YOU'VE MADE
Tracks: / Choices you've made / Ladies night.
7" Single: Released Jun '80, on Rocket, by Rocket Records. Deleted Jun '83. Catalogue no: **XPRES 31**

HIGHER AND HIGHER
Tracks: / Higher and higher / City of pools.
7" Single: Released Jul '81, on Rocket, by Rocket Records. Deleted '85. Catalogue no: **XPRES 60**

HOW DO I FEEL
Tracks: / How do I feel.
7" Single: Released Nov '83, on Chrysalis, by Chrysalis Records. Catalogue no: **CHS 2756**
12" Single: Released Nov '83, on Chrysalis, by Chrysalis Records. Catalogue no: **CHS 122756**

I NEVER KNOW WHERE MY HEART IS
Tracks: / I never know where my heart is / You were the place.
7" Single: Released May '81, on Rocket, by Rocket Records. Deleted May '84. Catalogue no: **XPRES 55**

I'LL BE THE ONE
Tracks: / I'll be the one / Falling.
7" Single: Released Mar '85, on Legacy, by Legacy Records. Catalogue no: **LGY 22**

I'M NOT A LOSER
Tracks: / I'm not a loser / Run on luck.
7" Pic: Released '82, on Chrysalis, by Chrysalis Records. Deleted '85. Catalogue no: **CHSP 2617**
7" Single: Released '82, on Chrysalis, by Chrysalis Records. Deleted '87. Catalogue no: **CHS 2617**

JEANNIE NO
Tracks: / Jeannie no / Information (live) / Love on the border (live) (Only on 12" version.) / Jeannie no (extended version) (Only on 12" version.).
7" Single: Released Aug '83, on Chrysalis, by Chrysalis Records. Catalogue no: **CHS 2728**
12" Single: Released Aug '83, on Chrysalis, by Chrysalis Records. Catalogue no: **CHS 122728**

LATE AGAIN
Tracks: / Late again / Water in motion.
7" Single: Released '82, on Chrysalis, by Chrysalis Records. Deleted '87. Catalogue no: **CHS 2627**

LET ME BE THE PEARL
Tracks: / Let me be the pearl / All they can do is talk / Love is not for sale (12" only).
7" Single: Released 8 May '89, on Polydor, by Polydor Ltd. Catalogue no: **PO 46**
12" Single: Released 8 May '89, on Polydor, by Polydor Ltd. Catalogue no: **PZ 46**

LOVE LIKE FIRE
Tracks: / Love like fire.
7" Single: Released Jun '85, on Legacy, by Legacy Records. Catalogue no: **LGY 25**
12" Single: Released Jun '85, on Legacy, by Legacy Records. Catalogue no: **LGYT 25**

STAY WITH ME TILL DAWN
Tracks: / Stay with me till dawn.
7" Single: Released Jul '79, on Rocket, by Rocket Records. Deleted '82. Catalogue no: **XPRES 17**

THIS SIDE OF HEAVEN
Tracks: / This side of heaven.
7" Single: Released Sep '85, on Legacy, by Legacy Records. Catalogue no: **LGY 30**

UNDERSTANDING
Tracks: / Understanding / It's the night.
7" Single: Released Feb '80, on Rocket, by Rocket Records. Deleted '83. Catalogue no: **XPRES 26**

WE'LL GO DREAMING
Tracks: / We'll go dreaming / Dangerous toys.
CD 5": Released 20 Feb '89, on Polydor, by Polydor Ltd. Catalogue no: **PZCD 31**
7" Single: Released 20 Feb '89, on Polydor, by Polydor Ltd. Deleted Aug '89. Catalogue no: **PO 31**
12" Single: Released 20 Feb '89, on Polydor, by Polydor Ltd. Deleted Aug '89. Catalogue no: **PZ 31**

YOU
Tracks: / You.
7" Single: Released Sep '84, on Legacy, by Legacy Records. Catalogue no: **LGY 14**

U

The following information was taken from the Music Master dxatabase on October 20th, 1989.

U2

Biographical details: Pop band formed in Dublin in 1977 by schoolfriends heavily influenced by punk: vocalist Bono (born Paul Hewson in 1960), guitarist The Edge (born David Evans in 1961) drummer Larry Mullen (born 1961) and bassist Adam Clayton (born 1960). They began slowly in Ireland; their UK debut was a disaster in 1979 (nine people turned out to see them at the Hope and Anchor in London in1979) but they bounced back in 1980 and carried on from there. They soon numbered Bruce Springsteen and Pete Townshend among their fans; they convinced audiences of their sincerety with sweeping, epic-style rock and had number one hit LPs and singles in 1987, one of the biggest live draws in the world. In a TV interview in the USA Bono described himself as a militant pacifist, whatever that means. (Donald Clarke 15.5.87).

11 O'CLOCK TICK TOCK
Tracks: / 11 o'clock tick tock / Touch.
7" Single: Released May '80, on Island, by Island Records. Catalogue no: **WIP 6601**

ALL I WANT IS YOU
Tracks: / All I want is you / Unchained melody / Everlasting love (12" and CD only) / All I want is you (version) (CD only).
CD 5": Released Jun '89, on Island, by Island Records. Catalogue no: **CDCIDP 422**
CD 5": Released May '89, on Island, by Island Records. Catalogue no: **CID 422**
Cassingle: Released May '89, on Island, by Island Records. Catalogue no: **CIS 422**
7" Single: Released May '89, on Island, by Island Records. Catalogue no: **IS 422**
12" Single: Released Jun '89, on Island, by Island Records. Catalogue no: **12 ISB 422**
12" Single: Released May '89, on Island, by Island Records. Catalogue no: **12 IS 422**
Special: Released Jun '89, on Island, by Island Records. Catalogue no: **ISB 422**

ALL I WANT IS YOU (LIMITED EDITION) (see panel below)
Tracks: / All I want is you / Unchained melody.
Note: This limited edition single is packaged in a circular metal container. Each copy has an individual number on the cover.
7" Single: Released '88, on Island, by Island Records. Catalogue no: **IS 422**

ANGEL OF HARLEM
Tracks: / Angel of Harlem / No room at the heartbreak hotel / Love rescue me (Only on 12" and CD single.).
CD 5": Released Oct '88, on Island, by Island Records. Catalogue no: **CIDP 402**
7" Single: Released Oct '88, on Island, by Island Records. Deleted Apr '89. Catalogue no: **IS 402**
12" Single: Released Oct '88, on Island, by Island Records. Catalogue no: **12IS 402**

CELEBRATION, A
Tracks: / Clebration, A / Trash.
7" Single: Released Apr '82, on Island, by Island Records. Deleted '85. Catalogue no: **WIP 6770**

DAY WITHOUT ME, A
Tracks: / Day without me, A / Things to make and do.
7" Single: Released Aug '80, on Island, by Island Records. Catalogue no: **WIP 6630**

DESIRE
Tracks: / Desire / Hallelujah (here she comes).
7" Single: Released Sep '88, on Island, by Island Records. Deleted Apr '89. Catalogue no: **ISG 400**
7" Single: Released 8 Sep '88, on Island, by Island Records. Deleted Apr '89. Catalogue no: **IS 400**
12" Single: Released Sep '88, on Island, by Island Records. Deleted Apr '89. Catalogue no: **12 ISG 400**
12" Single: Released Sep '88, on Island, by Island Records. Deleted Apr '89. Catalogue no: **12 IS 400**

FIRE
Tracks: / Fire.
7" Single: Released Jul '81, on Island, by Island Records. Catalogue no: **WIP 6679**

FIRE (IMPORT)
Tracks: / Fire.
Note: (Cat.No. 600417 - Never released as a single in the U.K., 'Fire', combined with 'J.Swallo','11 O'Clock Tick Tock' and a previously unavailable live version of 'The Ocean' recorded at the Paradise Theatre, Boston, USA in 1981.
7" EP: Released Nov '87, on Island (Germany), Catalogue no: **600417**

GLORIA
Tracks: / Gloria.
7" Single: Released Sep '81, on Island, by Island Records. Catalogue no: **WIP 6733**

I STILL HAVEN'T FOUND WHAT I'M LOOKING FOR
Tracks: / I still haven't found what I'm looking for / Spanish eyes (Only on import CD single.) / Deep in the heart (Only on import CD single.) / I still haven't found what I'm looking for (jukebox version) (Only on import CD).
CD 5": Released Sep '88, on Island (Holland), Catalogue no: **659152**
Cassingle: Released Nov '87, on Island (USA), by Island Records (USA). Catalogue no: **967579**
Cassingle: Released 23 May '87, on Island, by Island Records. Catalogue no: **CIS 328**
7" Single: Released 23 May '87, on Island, by Island Records. Catalogue no: **IS 328**
12" Single: Released 23 May '87, on Island, by Island Records. Catalogue no: **ISJ 328**

I WILL FOLLOW
Tracks: / I will follow / Boy/girl.
7" Single: Released Oct '80, on Island, by Island Records. Catalogue no: **WIP 6656**

IN GOD'S COUNTRY
Tracks: / In God's country / Bullet the blue sky.
12" Single: Released Sep '88, on Island (Canada), Catalogue no: **IS 1167**

NEW YEARS DAY
Tracks: / New years day / Treasure / Fire / I threw a brick through a window / Day without me.
7" Set: Released Jan '83, on Island, by Island Records. Catalogue no: **UWIP 6848**

PRIDE
Tracks: / Pride / 4th July / (Sunday bloody Sunday) / Two hearts / Two hearts beat as one / Boomerang 1 & 2 / Love comes tumbling / 60 seconds in kingdom / 3 sunrises (out takes).
7" Set: Released Apr '86, on Arabesque (USA), by Arabesque (USA) Records. Catalogue no: **U2PAC 3**
7" Single: Released Sep '84, on Island, by Island Records. Deleted '87. Catalogue no: **IS 202**
12" Single: Released Oct '84, on Island, by Island Records. Catalogue no: **ISX 202**

PRIDE(IN THE NAME OF LOVE) (IMPORT)
Tracks: / Pride (in the name of love) / 4th of July.
12" Single: Released Oct '88, on Island (Germany), Catalogue no: **601469**

SUNDAY BLOODY SUNDAY
Tracks: / Sunday bloody Sunday.
7" Single: Released Nov '85, on Island, by Island Records. Catalogue no: **U2 1**
12" Single: Released Nov '85, on Island, by Island Records. Catalogue no: **12U2 1**

SUNDAY BLOODY SUNDAY (IMPORT)
Tracks: / Sunday bloody Sunday / New Years Day / Two Hearts Beat As One .
12" Single: Released Nov '87, on Island (Germany), Catalogue no: **600820**

TWO HEARTS BEAT AS ONE
Tracks: / Two hearts beat as one.
7" Set: Released Mar '83, on Island, by Island Records. Catalogue no: **ISD 109**
12" Single: Released Mar '83, on Island, by Island Records. Catalogue no: **12IS 109**

U2: INTERVIEW PICTURE DISC COLLECTION
7" Set: Released Oct '87, on Baktabak, by Baktabak Records. Catalogue no: **BAKPAK 1001**

U2 SINGLES PACK
7" Set: Released '88, on Island, by Island Records. Deleted Dec '88. Catalogue no: **U2PK 1**

UNFORGETTABLE FIRE, THE (SINGLE)
Tracks: / Unforgettable fire, The.
7" Set: Released Apr '85, on Island, by Island Records. Catalogue no: **ISD 220**
12" Single: Released Apr '85, on Island, by Island Records. Catalogue no: **12IS 220**
7" Single: Released Apr '85, on Island, by Island Records. Catalogue no: **IS 220**

WHEN LOVE COMES TO TOWN
Tracks: / When love comes to town / Dancing barefoot / When love comes to town (live from the kingdom mix) (12" and CD only) / God part II (hard metal dance mix) (12" and CD only).
CD 5": Released Apr '89, on Island, by Island Records. Catalogue no: **CIDX 411**
7" Single: Released Mar '89, on Island, by Island Records. Catalogue no: **IS 411**
12" Single: Released Mar '89, on Island, by Island Records. Catalogue no: **12IS 411**
CD 5": Released Mar '89, on Island, by Island Records. Catalogue no: **CIDP 411**

WHERE THE STREETS HAVE NO NAME
Tracks: / Where the streets have no name / Sweetest / Race against time (12" & Import CD single only.) / Silver and gold (12" & Import CD single only.).
CD 5": Released Sep '88, on Island (Holland), Catalogue no: **659382**
Cassingle: Released Aug '87, on Island, by Island Records. Deleted Jun '88. Catalogue no: **CIS 340**
7" Single: Released Aug '87, on Island, by Island Records. Deleted Apr '89. Catalogue no: **IS 340**
CD 5": on Island, by Island Records. Deleted Jun '88. Catalogue no: **CID 340**
12" Single: Released Aug '87, on Island, by Island Records. Catalogue no: **12IS 340**

WITH OR WITHOUT YOU
Tracks: / With or without you / Luminous times (hold onto love) / Walk to the water.
CD 5": Released Sep '88, on Island (Holland), Catalogue no: **658922**
CD 5": Released Apr '87, on Island, by Island Records. Catalogue no: **CID 319**
7" Single: Released Mar '87, on Island, by Island Records. Catalogue no: **IS 319**
12" Single: Released Mar '87, on Island, by Island Records. Catalogue no: **12IS 319**
Cassingle: Released Mar '87, on Island, by Island Records. Deleted Jul '87. Catalogue no: **CIS 319**

U2 - ALL I WANT IS YOU (Released on Island)

U K Symphony Orchestra

SHADES Theme from Crown Paint TV advertisement
Tracks: / Shades.
7" Single: Released Jun '85, on Food For Thought, by Music For Nations Records. Catalogue no: **YUM 108**

U Thant

U THANT EP
12" Single: Released Oct '89, on Thant, Catalogue no: **THANT 03**

U, Thriller

IT'S OVER
12" Single: Released Jul '89, on Greensleeves, by Greensleeves Records. Catalogue no: **GRED 248**

MR. LONELY
Tracks: / Mr. Lonely.
12" Single: Released Nov '88, on Techniques, Catalogue no: **WRT 40**

NIGHT PRETTY
Tracks: / Night pretty.
7" Single: Released May '89, on Super Dee, Catalogue no: **UNKNOWN**

ONE LOVE AGO
Tracks: / One love ago.
12" Single: Released Jun '89, on Germaine, Catalogue no: **DGT 52**

REAL REAL
Tracks: / Real real.
12" Single: Released May '89, on Unity, Catalogue no: **FEA 012**

WARM AND CRAZY LOVE
Tracks: / Warm and crazy love.
12" Single: Released 30 May '89, on Digital B., Catalogue no: **VPRD 445**

U Turn

BIOLOGICAL EP
7" Single: on Epigram, by Epigram Records. Catalogue no: **EPIGRAM 001**

UB40

Biographical details: A racially integrated

UK band formed in 1978 in Birmingham, where they were all born and raised; they took their name from the unemployment benefit form: guitarist Robin Campbell was born in 1954, the others all between 1957-59: guitarist/lead vocalist Ali Campbell, drummer Jim Brown, saxophonist Brian Travers, bassist Earl Falconer, Norman Hassan on percussion, Mickey Virtue on keyboards, and toaster Astro. They were invited to support the Pretenders on tour in late 1979; their first three singles were all two-sided hits on Graduate in 1980, the first hits to make the national top 10 without promotion from a major label. Their first album was *Signing Off*, they formed their own Dep International label, distributed by Virgin; eight top 10 LPs and 17 top 20 singles followed. They had not made much impact in the USA until 1987, but a tour there that year was sold out: as UK audiences know, their music is ultimately irresistible: informed by the sprung rhythms of Jamaican music, it is listenable and danceable, with singing and lyrics of integrity. Of their albums, *Baggariddim* in 1985 featured Jamaican-style dub and toasting and reached only number 14, but included the number one hit duet by Ali and the Pretender's Chrissie Hynde on *I Got You Babe* (an international hit in 1965 by Sonny & Cher), and their own haunting number 2 hit *Don't Break My Heart*. *Best of UB40 Vol 1* is good value with 14 hits (four extra tracks on CD); The double album *The UB40 File* compiles the choicest Graduate output. They sponsor rally driver James Prochowski (a Pole from Glasgow) and his Nissan, with UB40-DEP markings. (Donald Clarke 15.5.87).

ALL I WANT TO DO
Tracks: / All I want to do (7" only) / All I want to do (version) (7" only) / All I want to do (12" remix) / All I wantto do (12" DEP mix).
7" Single: Released Sep '86, on DEP International, by DEP International Records. Catalogue no: **DEP 24**
12" Single: Released Sep '86, on DEP International, by DEP International Records. Catalogue no: **DEP 24-12**

BREAKFAST IN BED
Tracks: / Breakfast in bed (On 7" only) / Breakfast in bed (extended mix) (On CD & 12" only) / Breakfast in bed (instrumental) (7" only) / Breakfast in bed (version) (On CD & 12" only).
7" Single: Released Jun '88, on DEP International, by DEP International Records. Catalogue no: **DEP 29**
12" Single: Released Jun '88, on DEP International, by DEP International Records. Catalogue no: **DEP 29-12**
CD 5": Released '88, on DEP International, by DEP International Records. Catalogue no: **DEPX 29**

CHERRY OH BABY
Tracks: / Cherry oh baby / Frilla / Cherry oh baby (dub mix) (12" only).
7" Single: Released Mar '84, on DEP International, by DEP International Records. Deleted '89. Catalogue no: **DEP 10**
12" Single: Released Mar '84, on DEP International, by DEP International Records. Catalogue no: **DEP 10-12**

COME OUT TO PLAY
Tracks: / Come out to play / Contaminated minds (NOT on CD) / Sing our own song (On 12" only) / Come out to play (extended mix) (NOT on 7") / Come out to play (instrumental) (On 10" only) / Sing our own song (recorded live in Moscow 1986) (On 10" only) / Dance with the devil (On CD only) / Rat in mi kitchen (recorded live in Moscow 1986) (On CD only).
10" single: Released '89, on DEP International, by DEP International Records. Catalogue no: **DEP 31-10**
7" Single: Released Nov '88, on DEP International, by DEP International Records. Catalogue no: **DEP 31**
12" Single: Released Nov '88, on DEP International, by DEP International Records. Catalogue no: **DEP 31-12**
CD 3": Released '89, on DEP International, by DEP International Records. Catalogue no: **DEPX 31**

DON'T BREAK MY HEART
Tracks: / Don't break my heart / Mek ya rok.
7" Single: Released Oct '85, on DEP International, by DEP International Records. Catalogue no: **DEP 22**
12" Single: Released Oct '85, on DEP International, by DEP International Records. Catalogue no: **DEP 22-12**

DON'T LET IT PASS YOU BY
Tracks: / Don't let it pass you by / Don't slow down.
7" Single: Released May '81, on DEP International, by DEP International Records. Deleted '84. Catalogue no: **DEP 1**
12" Single: Released May '81, on DEP International, by DEP International Records. Deleted '89. Catalogue no: **12 DEP 1**

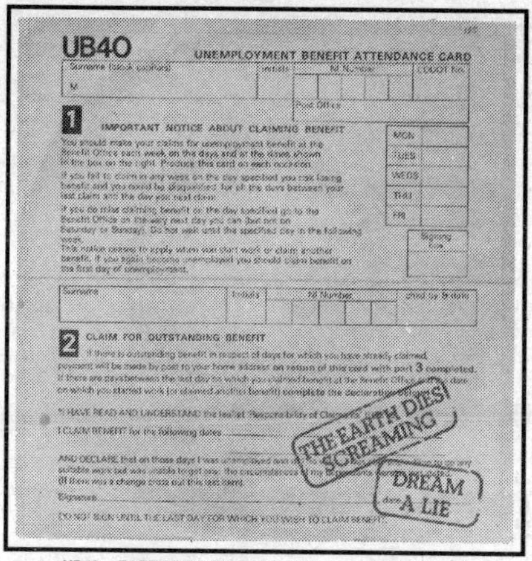

UB40 - EARTH DIES SCREAMING (Released on Graduate)

EARTH DIES SCREAMING (see panel above)
Tracks: / Earth dies screaming / Dream a lie.
7" Single: on Graduate, by Graduate Records. Deleted Jan '87. Catalogue no: **GRAD 10**
12" Single: on Graduate, by Graduate Records. Deleted Jan '87. Catalogue no: **12 GRAD 10**

FOOD FOR THOUGHT
Tracks: / Food for thought.
7" Single: on Graduate, by Graduate Records. Deleted Jan '87. Catalogue no: **GRAD 6**

HIT IT
Tracks: / Hit it / Hit it (version).
7" Single: Released Mar '88, on DEP International, by DEP International Records. Deleted '89. Catalogue no: **DEP 28**
12" Single: Released Mar '88, on DEP International, by DEP International Records. Deleted '89. Catalogue no: **DEP 28-12**

I GOT YOU BABE
Tracks: / I got you babe / Labour of love / I got you babe (dub version) (12" version) / Up and coming M.C. (12" only).
Note: Guest vocals:Chrissie Hyndew
7" Single: Released Jul '85, on DEP International, by DEP International Records. Catalogue no: **DEP 20**
12" Single: Released Jul '85, on DEP International, by DEP International Records. Catalogue no: **DEP 20-12**

I WON'T CLOSE MY EYES
Tracks: / I won't close my eyes / Folitician.
7" Single: Released Jan '82, on DEP International, by DEP International Records. Deleted '89. Catalogue no: **DEP 3**
12" Single: Released '82, on DEP International, by DEP International Records. Deleted '85. Catalogue no: **12 DEP3**

I WOULD DO FOR YOU
Tracks: / I would do for you / Hit it / Hit it (version).
7" Single: Released May '89, on DEP International, by DEP International Records. Catalogue no: **DEP 32**
12" Single: Released May '89, on DEP International, by DEP International Records. Catalogue no: **DEP 3212**
CD 3": Released May '89, on DEP International, by DEP International Records. Catalogue no: **DEPX 32**

IF IT HAPPENS AGAIN
Tracks: / If it happens again (7" only) / Nkomo a go-go (7" only) / If it happens again (dance mix) (12" only) / Nkomo a go-go (dance mix) (12" only).
12" Single: Released Sep '84, on DEP International, by DEP International Records. Catalogue no: **DEP 11-12**
7" Single: Released Sep '84, on DEP International, by DEP International Records. Catalogue no: **DEP 11**

I'M NOT FOOLED SO EASILY
Tracks: / I'm not fooled so easily / Pillow, The (remix).
7" Single: Released Mar '85, on DEP International, by DEP International Records. Catalogue no: **DEP 16**
12" Single: Released Mar '85, on DEP International, by DEP International Records. Catalogue no: **DEP 16-12**

I'VE GOT MINE
Tracks: / I've got mine (Extended version on 12") / Forget the cost / Dubmobile.
7" Single: Released Jan '83, on DEP International, by DEP International Records. Deleted '89. Catalogue no: **DEP 6**
12" Single: Released Jan '83, on DEP International, by DEP International Records. Catalogue no: **DEP 6-12**

KING
Tracks: / King / Food for thought.
7" Single: Released Mar '80, on Graduate, by Graduate Records. Deleted '83. Catalogue no: **GRAD 6**

LOVE IS ALL IS ALRIGHT
Tracks: / Love is alright.
7" Single: Released May '82, on DEP International, by DEP International Records. Deleted '89. Catalogue no: **DEP 4**
12" Single: Released May '82, on DEP International, by DEP International Records. Deleted '89. Catalogue no: **DEP 4-12**

MANY RIVERS TO CROSS
Tracks: / Many rivers to cross (Full length version on 12") / Food for thought (7" only) / Johnny too bad (12" only).
7" Single: Released Nov '83, on DEP International, by DEP International Records. Catalogue no: **DEP 9**
12" Single: Released Nov '85, on DEP International, by DEP International Records. Catalogue no: **DEP 9-12**

MAYBE TOMORROW
Tracks: / Maybe tomorrow / Dubwise / Maybe tomorrow/Anything mi chat (NOT on 7") / Dread dread time (NOT on 7").
12" Single: Released Oct '87, on DEP International, by DEP International Records. Catalogue no: **DEP 27-12**
Cassingle: Released '87, on DEP International, by DEP International Records. Catalogue no: **DEPC 27-12**
7" Single: Released Oct '87, on DEP International, by DEP International Records. Catalogue no: **DEP 27**

MY WAY OF THINKING
Tracks: / My way of thinking / I think it's going to rain today.
12" Single: on Graduate, by Graduate Records. Deleted Jan '87. Catalogue no: **12 GRAD 8**
7" Single: on Graduate, by Graduate Records. Deleted Jan '87. Catalogue no: **GRAD 8**

NIGHT RUN
Tracks: / Night run(remix) / Heaven's gate (US mix).
7" Single: Released Feb '86, on Chrysalis, by Chrysalis Records. Catalogue no: **UFO 2**
12" Single: Released Feb '86, on Chrysalis, by Chrysalis Records. Catalogue no: **UFOX 2**

ONE IN TEN
Tracks: / One in ten.
7" Single: Released Jul '81, on DEP International, by DEP International Records. Catalogue no: **7 DEP 2**

PLEASE DON'T MAKE ME CRY
Tracks: / Please don't make me cry / Sufferin'.
7" Single: Released Oct '83, on DEP International, by DEP International Records. Catalogue no: **DEP 8**
12" Single: Released Oct '83, on DEP International, by DEP International Records. Deleted '89. Catalogue no: **DEP 8-12**

RAT IN MI KITCHEN (SINGLE)
Tracks: / Rat in mi kitchen (Extended version on 12") / Rat in mi kitchen (version) (7" only) / Rat in mi kitchen (12" DEP mix) (12" only).
7" Single: Released Jan '87, on DEP International, by DEP International Records. Catalogue no: **DEP 25**
12" Single: Released Jan '87, on DEP International, by DEP International Records. Catalogue no: **DEP 25-12**

RED RED WINE
Tracks: / Red red wine / Sufferin' (version).
7" Single: Released Aug '83, on DEP International, by DEP International Records. Deleted '89. Catalogue no: **DEP 7**
12" Single: Released Aug '83, on DEP International, by DEP International Records. Catalogue no: **DEP 7-12**

RIDDLE ME
Tracks: / Riddle me / D.U.B. D.U.B..
7" Single: Released Nov '84, on DEP International, by DEP International Records. Catalogue no: **DEP 15**
12" Single: Released Nov '84, on DEP International, by DEP International Records. Catalogue no: **DEP 15-12**

SING OUR OWN SONG
Tracks: / Sing our own song (Full length version on 12") / Sing our own song (version) (7" only) / Sing our own song (DEP mix) (12" only).
12" Single: Released Jul '86, on DEP International, by DEP International Records. Catalogue no: **DEP 23-12**
7" Single: Released Jul '86, on DEP International, by DEP International Records. Catalogue no: **DEP 23**

SO HERE I AM
Tracks: / So here I am / Silent witness.
7" Single: Released Aug '82, on DEP International, by DEP International Records. Catalogue no: **7DEP 5**
12" Single: Released Aug '82, on DEP International, by DEP International Records. Catalogue no: **12DEP 5**

TYLER
Tracks: / Tyler / Adella / Little by little.
7" Single: Released Feb '83, on Graduate, by Graduate Records. Deleted Jan '87. Catalogue no: **GRAD 15**
12" Single: Released Feb '83, on Graduate, by Graduate Records. Deleted Jan '87. Catalogue no: **12 GRAD 15**

WATCHDOGS
Tracks: / Watchdogs / Don't blame me.
7" Single: Released Apr '87, on DEP International, by DEP International Records. Deleted '89. Catalogue no: **DEP 26**
12" Single: Released Apr '87, on DEP International, by DEP International Records. Deleted '89. Catalogue no: **DEP 26-12**

WHERE DID I GO WRONG?
Tracks: / Where did I go wrong (On 7' only) / Where did I go wrong (instrumental) (On all versions) / Where did I go wrong (extended mix) (On 12" & CD only) / Contaminated dub (On 12" & CD only) / Hit it (instrumental) (On CD only).
CD 5": Released '88, on DEP International, by DEP International Records. Catalogue no: **DEPX 30**
7" Single: Released Aug '88, on DEP International, by DEP International Records. Catalogue no: **DEP 30**
12" Single: Released Aug '88, on DEP International, by DEP International Records. Catalogue no: **DEP 30-12**

U-Bahn X

YOUNG HEARTS OF EUROPE
Tracks: / Young hearts of Europe / Kiss of death.
7" Single: Released Mar '85, on EMI, by EMI Records. Catalogue no: **EMI 5516**
12" Single: Released Mar '85, on EMI, by EMI Records. Catalogue no: **12EMI 5516**

Ubik

RED WOMAN
Tracks: / Red woman / Final orbit / Rewriting history / Me / What's me.
12" Single: Released Nov '82, on Intentional, by Intentional Records. Deleted Nov '85. Catalogue no: **INT 001**

U-Brown

BAD HABITS
Tracks: / Bad habits.
12" Single: Released Oct '85, on Time, Catalogue no: **TR 013**

Ubu, Pere

LOVE LOVE LOVE
Tracks: / Love love love / Fedora satellite (Not available on 12".) / Love love love (cajun house mix) (Only available on 12".) / Love love love (132 BPM mix) (Only available on 12".) / Say goodbye (Only on CD single.).
CD 5": Released Jun '89, on Phonogram, by Phonogram Ltd. Catalogue no: **UBUCD 3**
7" Single: Released Jun '89, on Phonogram, by Phonogram Ltd. Deleted Oct '89. Catalogue no: **UBU 3**
12" Single: Released Jun '89, on Phonogram, by Phonogram Ltd. Deleted Oct '89. Catalogue no: **UBU 312**

NOT HAPPY
Tracks: / Not happy / Lonesome cowboy days.
7" Single: Released Feb '81, on Rough Trade, by Rough Trade Records. Catalogue no: **RT 066**

UFO

Biographical details: A UK heavy metal band formed in 1969. They were soon popular in Europe and especially in Japan; the lineup that has sold the most albums includes vocalist Phil Mogg and Pete Way on bass (ex-Hocus Pocus), guitarist Michael Schenker (from support act the Scorpions), Andy Parker on drums, Paul Chapman (ex-Chicken Shack) doubling on guitar and keyboards. *Lights Out* in 1977, *Obsession* in 1978 and live *Strangers In The Night* (all 1977-8) were their best sellers; they disintegrated in the early 1980s after Schenker left; the double album *Headstone* was regarded as a good compilation. Mogg revived the name in 1985. (Donald Clarke 15.5.87).

AIN'T MISBEHAVIN'
Tracks: / (Between a) rock and a hard place / Another Saturday night / At war with the world / Hunger in the night / Easy money / Rock boyz, rock / Lonely cities (of the heart) (Extra track on CD.).
Special: Released Jan '89, on FM, by FM-Revolver Records. Catalogue no: **WKFMHP 107**

BACK INTO MY LIFE
Tracks: / Back into my life / Writer.
7" Single: Released Apr '82, on Chrysalis, by Chrysalis Records. Deleted Apr '85. Catalogue no: **CHS 2607**
12" Single: Released Apr '82, on Chrysalis, by Chrysalis Records. Deleted Apr '85. Catalogue no: **CHSP 2607**

COULDN'T GET IT RIGHT
Tracks: / Couldn't get it right / Hot 'n' ready.
7" Single: Released Oct '80, on Chrysalis, by Chrysalis Records. Catalogue no: **CHS 2454**

DOCTOR DOCTOR
Tracks: / Doctor doctor / On with the action / Try me.
7" Single: Released Jan '79, on Chrysalis, by Chrysalis Records. Deleted '84. Catalogue no: **CHS 2287**

LET IT RAIN
Tracks: / Let it rain / Heel of a stranger / You get love.
7" Single: Released Jan '82, on Chrysalis, by Chrysalis Records. Deleted '85. Catalogue no: **CHS 2576**
12" Single: Released Feb '82, on Chrysalis, by Chrysalis Records. Deleted '85. Catalogue no: **CHS 12 2576**

LONELY HEARTS
Tracks: / Lonely heart / Long gone.
7" Single: Released Jan '81, on Chrysalis, by Chrysalis Records. Catalogue no: **CHS 2482**

ONLY YOU CAN ROCK ME
Tracks: / Only you can rock me / Cherry / Rock bottom.
7" Single: Released '82, on Chrysalis, by Chrysalis Records. Deleted '87. Catalogue no: **CHS 2241**

SHOOT SHOOT
Tracks: / Shoot shoot / Only you can rock me / I'm a loser.
7" Single: Released Mar '79, on Chrysalis, by Chrysalis Records. Deleted '84. Catalogue no: **CHS 2318**

THIS TIME
Tracks: / This time.
7" Single: Released Oct '85, on Chrysalis, by Chrysalis Records. Catalogue no: **UFO 1**
12" Single: Released Oct '85, on Chrysalis, by Chrysalis Records. Catalogue no: **UFOX 1**

WHEN IT'S TIME TO ROCK
Tracks: / When it's time to rock / Everybody knows / Push, it's love (Only on 12" version.).
7" Single: Released Mar '83, on Chrysalis, by Chrysalis Records. Catalogue no: **CHS 2672**
12" Single: Released Mar '83, on Chrysalis, by Chrysalis Records. Catalogue no: **CHS 122672**

YOU CAN ROCK ME
Tracks: / You can rock me.
7" Single: Released Jul '76, on Chrysalis, by Chrysalis Records. Catalogue no: **CHS 2241**

YOUNG BLOOD
Tracks: / Young blood / Lights out.
7" Single: Released Jan '80, on Chrysalis, by Chrysalis Records. Catalogue no: **CHS 2399**

U-Griffiths

MEMORIES BY THE SCORE
Tracks: / Memories by the score / Trouble times.
12" Single: Released Mar '86, on Blue Trac, by Blue Trac Records. Catalogue no: **BM 016**

UK

NOTHING TO LOSE
Tracks: / Nothing to lose.
7" Single: Released Jun '79, on Polydor, by Polydor Ltd. Deleted '82. Catalogue no: **POSP 55**

UK Band

FUNKY DALLAS
Tracks: / Funky Dallas.
12" Single: Released Aug '85, on Hot Rod, Catalogue no: **HR 31**

UK Decay

BLACK CAT
Tracks: / Black cat.
7" Single: Released Oct '81, on Plastic, Catalogue no: **PLAS 002**

FOR MY COUNTRY
Tracks: / For my country.
7" Single: on UK Decay, Catalogue no: **DK3**
7" Single: Released Apr '81, on Fresh, by Jetstar Records. Catalogue no: **FRESH 12**

NIGHT FOR CELEBRATION
Tracks: / Night for celebration.
7" Single: on UK Decay, Catalogue no: **DK6**

RISING FROM THE DREAD
Tracks: / Rising from the dread.
7" EP: Released Aug '82, on Corpus Christi, by Corpus Christi Records. Catalogue no: **CHRIST 1T**

SEXUAL
Tracks: / Sexual.
7" Single: Released Oct '81, on Fresh, by Jetstar Records. Catalogue no: **FRESH 33**

UNEXPECTED GUEST
Tracks: / Unexpected guest.
7" Single: on UK Decay, Catalogue no: **DK4**
7" Single: Released Feb '81, on Fresh, by Jetstar Records. Catalogue no: **FRESH 26**

UK Players

EVERYBODY GETS UP
Tracks: / Everybody gets up / Rivers.
7" Single: Released Nov '80, on A&M, by A&M Records. Deleted Nov '83. Catalogue no: **AMS 7580**
12" Single: Released Nov '80, on A&M, by A&M Records. Deleted Nov '83. Catalogue no: **AMSX 7580**

GIRL
Tracks: / Girl / Jim's jam.
12" Pic: Released Sep '81, on A&M, by A&M Records. Deleted '88. Catalogue no: **AMSP 8169**
7" Single: Released Sep '81, on A&M, by A&M Records. Deleted '88. Catalogue no: **AMS 8169**

LOVE'S GONNA GET YOU
Tracks: / Love's gonna get you.
7" Single: Released Apr '83, on RCA, by BMG Records (UK). Catalogue no: **RCA 326**
12" Single: Released Apr '83, on RCA, by BMG Records (UK). Catalogue no: **RCAT 326**

MIDNIGHT
Tracks: / Midnight / Exist.
7" Single: Released May '81, on A&M, by A&M Records. Deleted May '84. Catalogue no: **AMS 8137**
12" Single: Released May '81, on A&M, by A&M Records. Deleted May '84. Catalogue no: **AMSP 8137**

MISSBEHAVIN
Tracks: / Missbehavin / Can't shake your love.
7" Single: Released Jul '82, on A&M, by A&M Records. Deleted '88. Catalogue no: **AMS 8238**
12" Single: Released Jul '82, on A&M, by A&M Records. Deleted '88. Catalogue no: **AMSX 8238**

NO WAY OUT
Tracks: / No way out.
7" Single: Released May '82, on A&M, by A&M Records. Deleted '88. Catalogue no: **AMS 8220**
12" Single: Released May '82, on A&M, by A&M Records. Deleted '88. Catalogue no: **AMSX 8220**

YOU MAKE ME FEEL
Tracks: / You make me feel.
7" Single: Released Aug '83, on RCA, by BMG Records (UK). Catalogue no: **RCA 347**
12" Single: Released Aug '83, on RCA, by BMG Records (UK). Catalogue no: **RCAT 347**

UK Subs

ANOTHER TYPICAL CITY
Tracks: / Another typical city.
12" Single: Released Aug '83, on Fall Out, Catalogue no: **FALL 12017**
7" Single: Released Aug '83, on Fall Out, Catalogue no: **FALL 017**

C.I.D.
Tracks: / C.I.D..
7" Single: Released Oct '79, on Pinnacle, by Pinnacle Records. Catalogue no: **PIN 22**

COUNTDOWN
Tracks: / Countdown / Plan of action.
7" Single: Released Nov '81, on Nems, by Castle Communications Records. Catalogue no: **NES 304**

HEY SANTA
Tracks: / Hey Santa / Thunderbird.
12" Single: Released Dec '87, on Fall Out, Catalogue no: **FALL 12044**

KEEP ON RUNNIN'
Tracks: / Keep on runnin'.
7" Single: Released Apr '81, on Gem, Deleted '84. Catalogue no: **GEMS 45**

LIVE AT GOSSIPS
Cassingle: Released Jun '82, on Chaos Cassettes, by Backs Recording Co.. Catalogue no: **LIVE 009**

LIVE IN HOLLAND
Tracks: / Live in Holland.
7" Single: Released Mar '86, on UK Subs, Catalogue no: **RFB SIN 1**

MAGIC
Tracks: / Magic.
12" Single: Released Sep '84, on Fall Out, Catalogue no: **FALL 12024**

MOTIVATOR, THE
Tracks: / Motivator, The / Auld lang syne.
12" Single: Released Dec '88, on Released Emotions, Catalogue no: **REM 004**

PARTY IN PARIS
Tracks: / Party in Paris / Fall in the Empire.
7" Single: Released Oct '80, on Gem, Catalogue no: **GEMS 42**

SHAKE UP THE CITY
Tracks: / Shake up the city.
7" Single: Released Oct '82, on Abstract, by Abstract Sounds. Catalogue no: **ABS 012**

SHE'S NOT THERE
Tracks: / She's not there / Kicks.
7" Single: Released Nov '79, on Gem, Catalogue no: **GEM 14**

STRANGLEHOLD
Tracks: / Stranglehold.
7" Single: Released Jun '79, on Gem, Deleted '82. Catalogue no: **GEMS 5**

TEENAGE
Tracks: / Teenage / Left for dead / N.Y. state police.
7" Single: Released May '80, on Gem, Catalogue no: **GEMS 30**

THIS GUN SAYS
Tracks: / This gun says.
7" Single: Released Jun '85, on Fall Out, Catalogue no: **FALL 036**

TOMORROW'S GIRLS
Tracks: / Tomorrow's girls.
7" Single: Released Aug '79, on Gem, Catalogue no: **GEMS 10**

WARHEAD
Tracks: / Warhead / I'm waiting for the man.
7" Single: Released Feb '80, on Gem, Catalogue no: **GEMS 23**

UK Supporters

VIVA ESPANA
Tracks: / Viva Espana / We are magic.
12" Single: Released May '82, on Polo, by Polo Records. Deleted '88. Catalogue no: **POLO 12-21**
7" Single: Released May '82, on Polo, by Polo Records. Deleted '88. Catalogue no: **POLO 21**

Ukraine

I CAN SEE CLEARLY NOW
Tracks: / I can see clearly now / Remote control.
7" Single: Released Oct '82, on Safari, by Safari Records. Catalogue no: **SAFE 50**

WAY WE FEEL
Tracks: / Way we feel / Zombie baby.
7" Single: Released Dec '81, on Major, Deleted Dec '84. Catalogue no: **MJR 001**

Ullman, Tracey

Biographical details: Tracy Ullman was born in 1959 in Buckinghamshire. The pop singer and actress won a scholarship to the Italia Conti Stage School at the age of 12, appeared with Shakin Stevens in 'Elvis', also acted in Grease and the Rocky Horror Show and starred in BBC TV series Three Of A Kind in the early 1980s. She launched her pop career after meeting wife of Stiff label boss at the hairdresser's. She had hit covers in 1983; guests in promo videos included Paul McCartney and Neil Kinnock. The Album *You Broke My Heart In 17 Places* compiled the hits. She appeared in McCartney's film 'Give My Regards To Broad Street' in 1984, concentrated on acting, appearing in 'Plenty' with Sting, then relocated to the USA. *Breakaway* spent 10 weeks in the top 50, reaching no.4 on 12th April 1983. *They don't know me* spent 11 weeks in the charts and reached no.2 and *Move over darling* got to no.8 after spending 8 weeks in the charts. (Donald Clarke 15.5.87).

BREAKAWAY (see panel below)
Tracks: / Breakaway / Dancing in the dark.
7" Single: Released Feb '83, on Stiff, by Stiff Records. Catalogue no: **BUY 168**

HELPLESS
Tracks: / Helpless.
7" Single: Released Oct '84, on Stiff, by Stiff

TRACEY ULLMAN - BREAKAWAY (Released on Stiff)

TRACEY ULLMAN - MY GUY'S MAD AT ME (Released on Stiff)

Records. Catalogue no: **BUY 211**
12" Single: Released Oct '84, on Stiff, by Stiff Records. Catalogue no: **BUYIT 211**

MOVE OVER DARLING
Tracks: / Move over darling / You broke my heart in 17 places.
7" Pic: Released Nov '83, on Stiff, by Stiff Records. Catalogue no: **PBUY 195**
7" Single: Released Nov '83, on Stiff, by Stiff Records. Catalogue no: **BUY 195**
12" Single: Released Nov '83, on Stiff, by Stiff Records. Catalogue no: **BUYIT 195**

MY GUY'S MAD AT ME (see panel above)
Tracks: / My guy's mad at me / Thinking of running away..
12" Single: Released Mar '84, on Stiff, by Stiff Records. Catalogue no: **BUYIT 197**
7" Pic: Released Mar '84, on Stiff, by Stiff Records. Catalogue no: **PBUY 197**
7" Single: Released Mar '84, on Stiff, by Stiff Records. Catalogue no: **BUY 197**

SUNGLASSES
Tracks: / Sunglasses.
7" Single: Released Jun '84, on Stiff, by Stiff Records. Catalogue no: **BUY 205**
7" Pic: Released Jun '84, on Stiff, by Stiff Records. Catalogue no: **PBUY 205**

TERRY
Tracks: / Terry / I don't want our loving to die.
7" Single: Released Dec '84, on Stiff, by Stiff Records. Catalogue no: **BUY 217**

THEY DON'T KNOW
Tracks: / They don't know.
10" single: Released Sep '83, on Stiff, by Stiff Records. Catalogue no: **SBUY 180**
7" Single: Released Sep '83, on Stiff, by Stiff Records. Catalogue no: **BUY 180**

Ulmer, James 'Blood'
Biographical details: 'Blood' was born in 1942 in South Carolina. The guitarist, vocalist and composer also plays flute; he is an uncategorisable musician, a sort of avant-garde bluesman full of controlled passion. He sang gospel music and learned the guitar as a child; in the 1970s in NYC he worked with Art Blakey, Paul Bley and others; he studied with Ornette Coleman in 1974 and gigged with him. He played on albums by Arthur Blythe in 1979-80 on CBS, made his own LP (with Coleman in the lineup) on Artist's House, then on CBS, Rough Trade and Blue Note. (Donald Clarke 15.5.87).

EYE LEVEL
Tracks: / Eye level.
12" Single: Released Aug '84, on Rough Trade, by Rough Trade Records. Catalogue no: **RTT 128**

Ultimate Sway
HERE WE STAND
Tracks: / Here we stand.
7" Single: Released Aug '82, on International (USA), by International Records & Tapes. Catalogue no: **INT 002**

Ultra Magnetic MC's
FUNKY
Tracks: / Funky.
12" Single: Released Oct '87, on Next Plateau (USA), Catalogue no: **NP 50069**

GIVE THE DRUMMER SOME
Tracks: / Give the drummer some / Moe Luv's theme.
12" Single: Released Mar '89, on ffrr, by London Records. Catalogue no: **FFRX 22**
7" Single: Released Apr '89, on ffrr, by London Records. Catalogue no: **FFR 22**

TRAVELLING AT THE SPEED OF THOUGHT
Tracks: / Travelling at the speed of thought / MC's ultra part II / B-Boy bonus break (Extra track on 12").
12" Single: Released 20 Jun '87, on Citybeat, by Beggars Banquet Records. Catalogue no: **CBE 1213**
7" Single: Released 20 Jun '87, on Citybeat, by Beggars Banquet Records. Deleted Jan '88. Catalogue no: **CBE 713**

Ultra Vivid Scene
MERCY SEAT
Tracks: / Mercy seat / Codine.
12" Single: Released 27 Feb '89, on 4AD, by 4AD Records. Catalogue no: **BAD 906**
CD 5": Released 27 Feb '89, on 4AD, by 4AD Records. Catalogue no: **BADCD 906**

SHE SCREAMED
Tracks: / She screamed / Walking after midnight / Not in love (hit by a truck).
CD 5": Released 30 Aug '88, on 4AD, by 4AD Records. Catalogue no: **BAD 806CD**
12" Single: Released 30 Aug '88, on 4AD, by 4AD Records. Catalogue no: **BAD 806**

SOMETHING TO EAT
Tracks: / Something to eat / H like in Heaven.
7" Single: Released 24 Jul '89, on 4AD, by 4AD Records. Catalogue no: **AD 098**

Ultra-Violent
CRIME FOR REVENGE
Tracks: / Crime for revenge / Where angels dare not tread / Dead generation.
7" EP: Released May '83, on Riot City, by Riot City Records. Catalogue no: **RIOT 25**

Ultraviolet
NO ONE IN HERE
Tracks: / No one in here / Love is.
7" Single: Released 24 Jul '89, on Pyramid, by Pyramid Records. Catalogue no: **PYR 14**
CD 5": Released Sep '89, on Pyramid, by Pyramid Records. Catalogue no: **PYRCD 14**
12" Single: Released Sep '89, on Pyramid, by Pyramid Records. Catalogue no: **12PYR 14**
Cassingle: Released Sep '89, on Pyramid, by Pyramid Records. Catalogue no: **PYRCAS 14**

Ultravox
Biographical details: This UK new romantic/new wave group was formed in 1975 by vocalist John Foxx and bassist Chris Cross: influenced by Roxy Music they formed Tiger Lily with drummer Warren Cann, guitarist Steve Shears, keyboard/violinist Billy Currie, made an arty cover of Fats Waller's *Ain't Misbehavin'* (used as theme for porn movie), called themselves Innocents, Fire Of London, London Soundtrack, The Zips) before signing with Island as Ultravox. They soon influenced the coming wave of synth music, but they were not commercially successful until changing lineup included Midge Ure (born in Glasgow in 1953): now a quartet with Cross, Ure's vocals/guitar, Cann and Currie, they signed with Chrysalis and were more successful from 1980. They parallelled Roxy Music in having had one career as innovators and another with a smoother, more commercial blend. Foxx did well with chart LPs of his own *Metametix* and *The Garden* in 1980-81; Ure found worldwide fame as co-writer of Band Aid anthem *Do They Know It's Christmas* in 1984, the fastest selling single in history, with Bob Geldof; with Geldof he is now part of rock establishment, paradoxically making it harder to do anything radically new. Cann left in 1986. (Donald Clarke 15.5.87).

ALL FALL DOWN
Tracks: / All fall down / Dreams.
12" Single: Released Nov '86, on Chrysalis, by Chrysalis Records. Catalogue no: **UVX 5**
7" Single: Released Nov '86, on Chrysalis, by Chrysalis Records. Catalogue no: **UV 5**

ALL IN ONE DAY
Tracks: / All in one day / Prize, The (live) / Stateless (Extra track on 12" only).
12" Single: Released May '87, on Chrysalis, by Chrysalis Records. Catalogue no: **UVX 6**
7" Single: Released May '87, on Chrysalis, by Chrysalis Records. Catalogue no: **UV 6**

ALL STOOD STILL
Tracks: / All stood still / Alles Klar / Keep talking (Only on 12" version.).
7" Single: Released Jun '81, on Chrysalis, by Chrysalis Records. Deleted '86. Catalogue no: **CHS 2522**
12" Single: Released '80, on Chrysalis, by Chrysalis Records. Catalogue no: **CHS 12 2481**

DANCING WITH TEARS IN MY EYES
Tracks: / Dancing with tears in my eyes / Reap the wild wind / Building.
7" Single: Released May '84, on Island, by Island Records. Catalogue no: **UV 1**
12" Single: Released May '84, on Island, by Island Records. Catalogue no: **UVX 1**

DANCING WITH TEARS IN MY EYES (OLD GOLD)
Tracks: / Dancing with tears in my eyes / Reap the wild wind / Building.
12" Single: Released Jan '88, on Old Gold, by Old Gold Records. Catalogue no: **OG 4039**
7" Single: Released Apr '87, on Old Gold, by Old Gold Records. Catalogue no: **OG 9698**

HYMN
Tracks: / Hymn / Monument.
12" Single: Released Nov '82, on Chrysalis, by Chrysalis Records. Catalogue no: **CHS 12 2657**
7" Single: Released Nov '82, on Chrysalis, by Chrysalis Records. Catalogue no: **CHS 2657**

LAMENT (SINGLE)
Tracks: / Lament.
7" Single: Released Jul '84, on Chrysalis, by Chrysalis Records. Deleted '87. Catalogue no: **UV 2**
12" Single: Released Jul '84, on Chrysalis, by Chrysalis Records. Deleted '87. Catalogue no: **UVX 2**

LOVE'S GREAT ADVENTURE
Tracks: / Love's great adventure / White China.
7" Single: Released '86, on Chrysalis, by Chrysalis Records. Catalogue no: **UV 3**
12" Single: Released '86, on Chrysalis, by Chrysalis Records. Catalogue no: **UVX 3**

ONE SMALL DAY
Tracks: / One small day.
12" Single: Released Jan '84, on Chrysalis, by Chrysalis Records. Catalogue no: **VOXX 2**

PASSING STRANGERS
Tracks: / Passing strangers / Face to face / Kings lead hat.
7" Single: Released Sep '80, on Chrysalis, by Chrysalis Records. Catalogue no: **CHS 2457**
12" Single: Released Sep '80, on Chrysalis, by Chrysalis Records. Catalogue no: **CHS 12 2457**

PEEL SESSIONS:ULTRAVOX
12" Single: Released Apr '88, on Strange Fruit, by Strange Fruit Records. Catalogue no: **SFPS 047**

REAP THE WILD WIND (see panel below)
Tracks: / Reap the wild wind / Hosanna (in excelsis deo).
7" Single: Released Sep '82, on Chrysalis, by Chrysalis Records. Catalogue no: **CHS 2639**
12" Single: Released Sep '82, on Chrysalis, by Chrysalis Records. Catalogue no: **CHS 12 2639**

ROCKWROCK
Tracks: / Rockwrock.
7" Single: Released Jul '81, on Island, by Island Records. Catalogue no: **WIP 6404**

SAME OLD STORY
Tracks: / Same old story / 3".
12" Single: Released Sep '86, on Chrysalis, by Chrysalis Records. Catalogue no: **UVX 4**
7" Single: Released Sep '86, on Chrysalis, by Chrysalis Records. Catalogue no: **UV 4**

SLEEPWALK
Tracks: / Sleepwalk / Waiting.
7" Single: Released Jul '80, on Chrysalis, by Chrysalis Records. Catalogue no: **CHS 2241**

SLOW MOTION
Tracks: / Slow motion / Quiet men / Hiroshima mon amour / Dislocation (on 12" only).
12" Single: Released Feb '81, on Island, by Island Records. Deleted Feb '84. Catalogue no: **DWIP 6691**
7" Single: Released Feb '81, on Island, by Island Records. Deleted Feb '84. Catalogue no: **WIP 6691**

ULTRAVOX - REAP THE WILD WIND (Released on Chrysalis)

THIN WALL
Tracks: / Thin wall / I never wanted to begin.
7" Single: Released Aug '81, on Chrysalis, by Chrysalis Records. Catalogue no: **CHS 2540**
12" Single: Released Aug '81, on Chrysalis, by Chrysalis Records. Catalogue no: **CHS 122540**

VIENNA (OLD GOLD)
Tracks: / Vienna / Voice, The.
7" Single: Released Feb '87, on Old Gold, by Old Gold Records. Catalogue no: **OG 9675**

VIENNA (SINGLE)
Tracks: / Vienna / Passionate reply / Herr X (Only on 12" version.) / Voice, The.
7" Single: Released '81, on Chrysalis, by Chrysalis Records. Deleted '86. Catalogue no: **CHS 2481**
12" Single: Released '80, on Chrysalis, by Chrysalis Records. Catalogue no: **CHS 12 2481**

VISIONS IN BLUE
Tracks: / Visions in blue / Break your back / Reap the wild wind (Only on the 12" version.).
7" Single: Released Mar '83, on Chrysalis, by Chrysalis Records. Catalogue no: **CHS 2676**
12" Single: Released Mar '83, on Chrysalis, by Chrysalis Records. Catalogue no: **CHS 122676**

VOICE
Tracks: / Voice / Paths and angles / All stood still (Only on 12" version.) / Private lives (Only on 12" version.).
12" Single: Released Nov '81, on Chrysalis, by Chrysalis Records. Catalogue no: **CHS 12 2559**
7" Single: Released Nov '81, on Chrysalis, by Chrysalis Records. Catalogue no: **CHS 2559**

WE CAME TO DANCE
Tracks: / We came to dance / Overlook.
12" Single: Released May '83, on Chrysalis, by Chrysalis Records. Catalogue no: **VOXX 1**
7" Single: Released May '83, on Chrysalis, by Chrysalis Records. Catalogue no: **VOX 1**

Umbrella

MAKE HELL FOR THE BEAUTIFUL PEOPLE
Tracks: / Make hell for the beautiful people / William Brel / Persuaders, The.
12" Single: Released Jul '85, on Immaculate, by Immaculate Records. Catalogue no: **12IMMAC 3**

Umiliani, Piero

MAH NA MAH NA
Tracks: / Mah na mah na.
7" Single: Released Apr '77, on EMI International, by EMI Records. Deleted '80. Catalogue no: **INT 530**

Umo Vogue

JUST MY LOVE
Tracks: / Just my love / Time of your life.
7" Single: Released Jun '84, on EMI, by EMI Records. Catalogue no: **EMI 5475**

Un Project

KI-AH
Tracks: / Ki-ah.
7" Single: Released Apr '82, on Rygel, Catalogue no: **RY 2**

Unbelievers

ONE SOIL
Tracks: / One soil.
12" Single: Released '88, on Big Wednesday, Catalogue no: **UFO ONE**

Uncle Ulick

STAR OF COUNTY DOWN
Tracks: / Star of the County Down / Are you right there Michael / Dingle regatta / MacNamara's Band.
7" Single: Released Jul '86, on Homespun (Ireland), by Outlet Records. Catalogue no: **HS 107**

Uncool Dance Band

I WANNA BE YOUR BOYFRIEND
Tracks: / I wanna be your boyfriend / Lost for words.
7" Single: Released Aug '81, on Polydor, by Polydor Ltd. Deleted '84. Catalogue no: **POSP 298**

JACQUELINE
Tracks: / Jacqueline / Number 17.
7" Single: Released Apr '81, on Polydor, by Polydor Ltd. Deleted '85. Catalogue no: **POSP 253**

Undead

IT'S CORRUPTION
Tracks: / It's corruption.
7" Single: Released Apr '82, on Riot City, by Riot City Records. Catalogue no: **RIOT 7**

NEVER SAY DIE
Tracks: / Never say die.
7" Single: Released May '86, on Rebirth, Catalogue no: **RE 0023**

VIOLENT VISIONS
Tracks: / Violent visions / Dead revolution.
7" Single: Released Oct '82, on Riot City, by Riot City Records. Catalogue no: **RIOT 15**

Under A Glass Bell

OVER THE MOON
7" Single: Released Nov '86, on Trumpet, Catalogue no: **TRUMPET 005**

Under Neath What

FIREBOMB TELECOM
Tracks: / Firebomb telecom.
12" Single: Released Feb '89, on One Big Guitar, by One Big Guitar Records. Catalogue no: **OBG 005DJ**
7" Single: Released Feb '89, on One Big Guitar, by One Big Guitar Records. Catalogue no: **OBG 005**
12" Single: Released Feb '89, on One Big Guitar, by One Big Guitar Records. Catalogue no: **OBG 005T**

GET OUTTA THE WAY
Tracks: / Get outta the way.
7" Single: Released Apr '89, on One Big Guitar, by One Big Guitar Records. Catalogue no: **OBG 006**
12" Single: Released Apr '89, on One Big Guitar, by One Big Guitar Records. Catalogue no: **OBG 006T**

STRAIGHT AHEAD MONEY
Tracks: / Straight ahead money / Elvis Presley's doctor.
7" Single: Released Aug '89, on WEA, by WEA Records. Catalogue no: **YZ 422**
12" Single: Released Aug '89, on WEA, by WEA Records. Catalogue no: **YZ 422T**

WAY OUT WEST
Tracks: / Way out west / After what happened last night / Land for your world, A.
12" Single: Released 3 Aug '88, on 11th Hour, by Under Neath What Records. Catalogue no: **961**

Under The Boardwalk

UNDER THE BOARDWALK
Tracks: / Under the boardwalk: *Drifters* / At the club: *Various artists* / Cool jerk: *Various artists* / Some kind of wonderful: *Various artists*.
7" Single: Released Apr '80, on Atlantic, by WEA Records. Deleted Apr '83. Catalogue no: **ATM 6**

Under The Sun

MY LOVE IS A RIVER
Tracks: / My love is a river / Get ready / Sister salvation / Protect your love.
12" Single: Released Feb '86, on Sierra, by Sierra Records. Catalogue no: **WIZZ 2**

Under Two Flags

LEST WE FORGET
Tracks: / Lest we forget / Drown inside / False history.
12" Single: Released Sep '83, on Situation 2, by Beggars Banquet Records. Catalogue no: **SIT 27T**
7" Single: Released Sep '83, on Situation 2, by Beggars Banquet Records. Catalogue no: **SIT 27**

MASKS
Tracks: / Masks / Early Sunday morning / Land of the rising gun.
12" Single: Released Apr '84, on Situation 2, by Beggars Banquet Records. Catalogue no: **SIT 32T**
10" single: Released Jun '84, on Situation 2, by Beggars Banquet Records. Catalogue no: **SIT 32 10**
7" Single: Released Apr '84, on Situation 2, by Beggars Banquet Records. Catalogue no: **SIT 32**

Underdogs

EAST OF DACHAU
Tracks: / East of Dachau.
7" Single: Released Jun '83, on Riot City, by Riot City Records. Catalogue no: **RIOT 26**

Underground Arrows

CHANGE TO ESCAPE, THE
Tracks: / Change to escape.
7" Single: Released 23 May '87, on Unicorn-Kanchana, by Unicorn - Kanchana Records. Catalogue no: **PHZ 7**

Underlings

CENTURION
Tracks: / Centurion.
12" Single: Released Jan '88, on Midnight Music, by Midnight Music Records. Catalogue no: **DONG 35**

THAT LITTLE GIRL
Tracks: / That little girl / Lemon drop / King leech / Resolutions crack.
12" Single: Released Oct '86, on Midnight Music, by Midnight Music Records. Catalogue no: **DONG 23**

Underneath

IMP OF THE PERVERSE
Tracks: / Imp of the perverse (on EP) / Fire / Short term agreement.
7" Single: Released Oct '86, on El, by Cherry Red Records. Catalogue no: **GPO 17**
12" Single: Released Oct '86, on El, by Cherry Red Records. Catalogue no: **GPO 17 T**

Undertakers

JUST A LITTLE BIT
Tracks: / Just a little bit.
7" Single: Released Apr '64, on Pye, Deleted '67. Catalogue no: **7 N 15607**

Undertones

Biographical details: A punkish pop band who were successful in the UK into the early 1980s, but fans and critics wouldn't let them grow up: for biographical data see SHARKEY, Feargal, who has gone on to a successful solo career. (Donald Clarke 15.5.87)

BEAUTIFUL FRIEND
Tracks: / Beautiful friend / Life too easy.
7" Single: Released Feb '82, on Ardeck, by EMI Records. Deleted Feb '87. Catalogue no: **ARDS 10**

CHAIN OF LOVE
Tracks: / Chain of love.
7" Single: Released Apr '83, on Ardeck, by EMI Records. Catalogue no: **ARDS 13**

GET OVER YOU
Tracks: / Get over you.
7" Single: Released Feb '79, on Sire, by Sire Records. Deleted '82. Catalogue no: **SIR 4010**

GOT TO HAVE YOU BACK
Tracks: / Got to have you back / Turning blue / Bye bye baby blue.
7" Single: Released Mar '83, on Ardeck, by EMI Records. Catalogue no: **ARDS 12**
12" Single: Released Mar '83, on Ardeck, by EMI Records. Catalogue no: **12ARDS 12**

HERE COMES THE SUMMER
Tracks: / Here comes the summer / One way love.
7" Single: Released Apr '82, on Sire (USA), Catalogue no: **SIR 4022**

IT'S GOING TO HAPPEN
Tracks: / It's going to happen / Fairly in the money now.
7" Single: Released May '81, on Ardeck, by EMI Records. Deleted '84. Catalogue no: **ARDS 8**

JIMMY JIMMY
Tracks: / Jimmy Jimmy.
7" Single: Released Apr '79, on Sire, by Sire Records. Deleted '82. Catalogue no: **SIR 4015**

JULIE OCEAN
Tracks: / Julie Ocean / Kiss in the dark.
7" Single: Released Jul '81, on Ardeck, by EMI Records. Deleted '84. Catalogue no: **ARDS 9**

LOVE PARADE
Tracks: / Love parade / Like that / You're welcome (Only on 12" single.) / Crisis of mine (Only on 12" single.) / Family entertainment (Only on 12" single.).
7" Single: Released Jan '83, on Ardeck, by EMI Records. Catalogue no: **ARDS 11**
12" Single: Released Jan '83, on Ardeck, by EMI Records. Catalogue no: **12ARDS 11**

MY PERFECT COUSIN
Tracks: / My perfect cousin / Hard luck.
7" Single: Released Oct '83, on Ardeck, by EMI Records. Catalogue no: **ARDS 6**
12" Single: Released Oct '83, on Ardeck, by EMI Records. Deleted '87. Catalogue no: **12ARDS 6**
7" Single: Released Apr '80, on Sire, by Sire Records. Deleted '83. Catalogue no: **SIR 4038**

PEEL SESSIONS:UNDERTONES
21st January 1979
12" Single: Released Nov '86, on Strange Fruit, by Strange Fruit Records. Catalogue no: **SFPS 016**
CD 5": Released Mar '88, on Strange Fruit, by Strange Fruit Records. Catalogue no: **SFPSCD 016**

SAVE ME
Tracks: / Save me / Tearproof / I know a girl (Track on 12" version only.).
7" Single: Released May '86, on Ardeck, by EMI Records. Catalogue no: **ARDS 14**
12" Single: Released May '86, on Ardeck, by EMI Records. Catalogue no: **12ARDS 14**

TEENAGE KICKS
Tracks: / Teenage kicks.
7" Single: Released Jun '83, on Ardeck, by EMI Records. Catalogue no: **ARDS 1**
7" Single: Released Oct '78, on Sire, by Sire Records. Deleted '81. Catalogue no: **SIR 4007**
12" Single: Released Jun '83, on Ardeck, by EMI Records. Catalogue no: **12ARDS 1**

WEDNESDAY WEEK
Tracks: / Wednesday week / Told you so.
7" Single: Released Apr '82, on Sire (USA), Catalogue no: **SIR 4042**

YOU'VE GOT MY NUMBER
Tracks: / You've got my number / Let's talk about girls.
7" Single: Released Apr '82, on Sire (USA), Catalogue no: **SIR 4024**

Underworld

STAND UP
Tracks: / Stand up / Outskirts.
12" Single: Released Aug '89, on Warner Bros., by WEA Records. Catalogue no: **W 2854 T**
CD 5": Released Aug '89, on Warner Bros., by WEA Records. Catalogue no: **W 2854 CD**
7" Single: Released Aug '89, on Warner Bros., by WEA Records. Catalogue no: **W 2854**

UNDERNEATH THE RADAR (SINGLE)
Tracks: / Underneath the radar / Big red X.
7" Single: Released Jul '88, on WEA, by WEA Records. Catalogue no: **W 7968**
12" Single: Released Jul '88, on WEA, by WEA Records. Catalogue no: **W 7968T**

Undisputed Truth

YOU + ME = LOVE
Tracks: / You + me = love.
7" Single: Released Jan '77, on Warner Bros., by WEA Records. Deleted '80. Catalogue no: **K 16804**

Undivided Roots

BUBBLES
Tracks: / Bubbles.
12" Single: Released Jun '82, on Classic Roots, Catalogue no: **CBR 002**

LIVE UP
Tracks: / Live up.
12" Single: Released Sep '82, on Classic Roots, Catalogue no: **CBR 004**

NATURE OF LOVE
Tracks: / Nature of love.
12" Single: Released Dec '87, on Entente, Catalogue no: **ENT 014**

PARTY NITE
Tracks: / Party nite / Sweet party.
12" Single: Released Nov '85, on Entente, Catalogue no: **ENT 0011**

ROCK REGGAE MUSIC
Tracks: / Rock reggae music.
12" Single: Released Jan '85, on Rough Cutt, Catalogue no: **URC 002**

ROCK THIS YAH MUSIC
Tracks: / Rock this yah music.
12" Single: Released Jun '86, on Entente, Catalogue no: **ENT 002**

ROOTS ROCKERS
Tracks: / Roots rockers.
12" Single: Released Sep '88, on Ruff Cut, Catalogue no: **RC 0014**

SWEET WOMAN
Tracks: / Sweet woman.
12" Single: Released Jun '83, on Ruff Cut, Catalogue no: **RC 001**

TELL ME WHY
Tracks: / Tell me why.
12" Single: Released Feb '89, on Entente, Catalogue no: **ENT 0016**

TELLING ME LIES
Tracks: / Telling me lies.
12" Single: Released Jun '84, on Undivided Roots, Catalogue no: **URC 001**

TRUE LOVE
Tracks: / True love.
12" Single: Released Jun '83, on CSA, by CSA Records. Deleted '88. Catalogue no: **SPCSA 12004**

Unforgiven

I HEAR THE CALL
Tracks: / I hear the call / Ghost dance.
7" Single: Released Aug '86, on Elektra (USA), by Elektra Records (USA). Catalogue no: **EKR 41**

Union

HARROD'S DON'T SELL THEM
Tracks: / Harrod's don't sell them.
7" Single: Released Mar '87, on ASV (Academy Sound & Vision), by Academy Sound & Vision Records. Deleted '88. Catalogue no: **AR 101**

MAINSTREET, USA
Tracks: / Mainstreet USA.
7" Single: Released Jul '81, on Portrait, by CBS Records. Catalogue no: **PRT A 1458**

Unique

WHAT I GOT IS WHAT YOU NEED
Tracks: / What I got is what you need.
7" Single: Released Sep '83, on Prelude, Deleted '86. Catalogue no: **A 3707**

Unique Vision

PLAY ME SELECTA
Tracks: / Play me selecta.
12" Single: Released 24 Jul '89, on White, Catalogue no: **CR 3**

Uniques

YOU DON'T MISS YOUR WATER
Tracks: / You don't miss your water.
7" Single: Released Jul '80, on Charly, by Charly Records. Deleted '87. Catalogue no: **CTD 121**

Unit 91

MANHATTAN DANCE THEME
Tracks: / Manhattan dance theme (ext mix) / Strand.
12" Single: Released Dec '87, on Adventure, by Adventure Records. Catalogue no: **ADT 11**

Unit Four Plus Two

BABY NEVER SAY GOODBYE
Tracks: / Baby never say goodbye.
7" Single: Released Mar '66, on Decca, by Decca Records. Deleted '69. Catalogue no: **F 12333**

CONCRETE & CLAY
Tracks: / Concrete & clay.
7" Single: Released Feb '65, on Decca, by Decca Records. Deleted '68. Catalogue no: **F 12071**

CONCRETE & CLAY (OLD GOLD)
Tracks: / Concrete & clay.
7" Single: Released Apr '83, on Old Gold, by Old Gold Records. Catalogue no: **OG 9262**

GREEN FIELDS
Tracks: / Green fields.
7" Single: Released Feb '64, on Decca, by Decca Records. Deleted '67. Catalogue no: **F 11821**

YOU'VE NEVER BEEN IN LOVE LIKE THIS BEFORE
Tracks: / You've never been in love like this before.
7" Single: Released May '65, on Decca, by Decca Records. Deleted '68. Catalogue no: **F 12144**

United Force

APOLLO LOVE '89
Tracks: / Apollo love '89.
12" Single: Released 28 Mar '89, on Swordfish, by Swordfish Records. Catalogue no: **DROP 3**

United House Nations

MBULUNA
Tracks: / Mbuluna / Bella vista / Holle holle / Mbuluna (version).
12" Single: Released Mar '89, on Circa, by Virgin Records. Catalogue no: **YRT 27**

United Nations

Biographical details: *The first move* is the debut album by United Nations, a five piece rock band from Stoke. The LP was recorded at AVM Studios in Stoke and was produced by Guy Bidmead, whose credit's include work with Motorhead, Cozy Powell and Grand Prix. The band enjoy a healthy live following in the Midlands and were signed to Magnet after a session on Radio One's Tommy Vance Show. Guitarist Gary Davies and singer Paul McCafferty write most of the band's material, including the single *You cheated* which is to be released in January 1986 on Magnet. (Magnet Records Press Office, 1985).

YOU CHEATED
Tracks: / You cheated / Paying the price.
7" Single: Released Feb '86, on Magnet, by WEA Records. Catalogue no: **MAG 291**

Unitone

M. R. GUY
Tracks: / M. R. Guy.
7" Single: Released May '80, on ShocWave, Catalogue no: **SRP 0003**

Units, Vincent

CARNIVAL SONG
Tracks: / Carnival song.
7" Single: Released Jan '81, on Y, Catalogue no: **Y 8**

Unity

FOR ONLY A DAY
Tracks: / For only a day / When you come home tonight.
7" Single: Released Mar '81, on Epic, by CBS Records. Deleted Mar '84. Catalogue no: **EPC A 1066**

Unity Station

DAY AFTER DAY
Tracks: / Day after day.
12" Single: Released 23 May '87, on Restless (1), by Restless Records. Catalogue no: **REST 002**

SEE 1177 THE TRIANGLE
Tracks: / See 1177 the triangle.
7" Single: Released Sep '86, on Restless (1), by Restless Records. Catalogue no: **REST 001**

Universe

EVERY SINGLE NIGHT
Tracks: / Every single night.
7" Single: Released Jun '84, on MBT, Catalogue no: **U 1107**

RETURN OF TELSTAR, THE
Tracks: / Return of Telstar, The / Buzz.
7" Single: Released Dec '88, on Pacific, by Pacific Records. Deleted '89. Catalogue no: **UNIV 1**
12" Single: Released Dec '88, on Pacific, by Pacific Records. Catalogue no: **12UNIV 1**

Universe Zero

TRIOMPHE DE MOUCHES
Tracks: / Triomphe de mouches.
7" Single: Released Nov '82, on Recommended, by Recommended Records. Catalogue no: **RR 105**

Unknown

PARKSIDE
Tracks: / Parkside / Housing the joint / Dis groove is bad.
12" Single: Released Oct '87, on Jive, by Zomba Records. Catalogue no: **JIVET 158**

Unknown Cases

IF YOU WANT ME TO STAY
Tracks: / If you want me to stay.
12" Single: Released Oct '85, on Rough Trade, by Rough Trade Records. Catalogue no: **RTD 019**

MASIMBABELE
Tracks: / Masimbabele / Oekikawai.
12" Single: Released May '84, on Rough Trade, by Rough Trade Records. Catalogue no: **RTT 126**

MASIMBABELE (REMIX)
Tracks: / Masimbabele (remix).
12" Single: Released Mar '89, on Rough Trade (Germany), Catalogue no: **RTD 044T**

Unknown Mix

SNACKS
Tracks: / Snacks.
12" Single: Released Dec '88, on Recommended, by Recommended Records. Catalogue no: **RECREC 022**

Unlimited Touch

I HEAR DANCING IN THE STREETS
Tracks: / I hear dancing in the streets / In the middle.
12" Single: Released Feb '81, on Epic, by CBS Records. Deleted '84. Catalogue no: **13-9477**
7" Single: Released Feb '81, on Epic, by CBS Records. Deleted '84. Catalogue no: **EPC 9477**

SEARCHING TO FIND THE ONE
Tracks: / Searching to find the one / Carry one.
7" Single: Released Jul '81, on Epic, by CBS Records. Catalogue no: **EPC A 1454**

Unpleasant Goblins

IN THE MOOG
Tracks: / In the moog / Well actually.
7" Single: Released Sep '80, on Cheapskate, Deleted '83. Catalogue no: **CHEAP 10**

IN THE NUDE
Tracks: / In the nude / Well actually.
7" Single: Released Jul '82, on Observation, by Observation Records. Catalogue no: **EYE 104**

Unseen Terror

PEEL SESSIONS:UNSEEN TERROR
12" Single: Released Feb '89, on Strange Fruit, by Strange Fruit Records. Catalogue no: **SFPS 069**

Untamed

BLACK HEART
Tracks: / Black heart.
7" Single: Released 30 May '88, on Real World, Catalogue no: **RWR 004**

UNTOUCHABLES - FREE YOURSELF (Released on Stiff)

NEXT PLEASE
Tracks: / Next please / Black heart.
7" Single: Released Feb '89, on Real World, Catalogue no: **RWR 004**

Untouchables

AGENT DOUBLE O SOUL (SINGLE)
Tracks: / Agent double o soul / Airplay.
12" Single: Released 2 May '89, on Virgin, by Virgin Records. Catalogue no: **ENVT 11**
7" Single: Released 2 May '89, on Virgin, by Virgin Records. Catalogue no: **ENV 11**

FREE YOURSELF (see panel above)
Tracks: / Free yourself / Lebanon.
12" Single: Released Mar '85, on Stiff, by Stiff Records. Catalogue no: **BUYIT 221**
7" Single: Released Mar '85, on Stiff, by Stiff Records. Catalogue no: **BUY 221**

I SPY FOR THE FBI
Tracks: / I spy for the FBI.
7" Single: Released Jul '85, on Stiff, by Stiff Records. Catalogue no: **BUY 227**
12" Single: Released Jul '85, on Stiff, by Stiff Records. Catalogue no: **BUYIT 227**

KEEP YOUR DISTANCE
Tracks: / Keep your distance.
7" Single: Released Jul '81, on Fried Egg, by Fried Egg Records. Deleted '87. Catalogue no: **EGG 11**

WHAT'S GONE WRONG
Tracks: / What's gone wrong.
12" Single: Released Nov '85, on Stiff, by Stiff Records. Catalogue no: **BUYIT 240**
7" Single: Released Nov '85, on Stiff, by Stiff Records. Catalogue no: **BUY 240**

Up And Running

I CAN'T SAY NO
Tracks: / I can't say no / Something special / Broken hearts.
12" Single: Released Sep '89, on Tac, Catalogue no: **ZZZ 3**

JOHNNY AND MARIE
Tracks: / Johnny and Marie / Ruby / Man's gotta do what a man's gotta do, A (Only on 12").
7" Single: Released Sep '88, on Tac, Catalogue no: **ZZZ 01**
12" Single: Released Sep '88, on Tac, Catalogue no: **ZZZ 01T**

Up Jam Crew

JACK ME UP SCOTTY
Tracks: / Jack me up Scotty.
7" Single: Released Jul '87, on Nine O Nine, by Creole Records. Catalogue no: **NINE 11**

UPB

LOVE YOU FOREVER
Tracks: / Love you forever / Home and dry.
12" Single: Released Apr '82, on Island, by Island Records. Catalogue no: **12WIP 6787**

Upchurch, Phil

WHEN AND IF I FALL IN LOVE
Tracks: / When and if I fall in love.
12" Single: Released Jul '83, on Physical, by Physical Records. Catalogue no: **FIZ 1T**
7" Single: Released Jul '83, on Physical, by Physical Records. Catalogue no: **FIZ 1**

YOU CAN'T SIT DOWN
Tracks: / You can't sit down.
7" Single: Released May '66, on Sue, by Island Records. Deleted '69. Catalogue no: **WI 4005**

Upfront

UPFRONT 89
Tracks: / Upfront 89: *Various artists.*
12" Single: Released Feb '89, on Upfront, by Serious Records. Catalogue no: **ZCFT 89**
7" Single: Released Feb '89, on Upfront, by Serious Records. Catalogue no: **UPFT 89**

Upfront (group)

I WANT YOUR LOVE
Tracks: / I want your love.
12" Single: Released Feb '87, on Atlas, by Atlas Records. Catalogue no: **12 TL 22**
7" Single: Released Feb '87, on Atlas, by Atlas Records. Catalogue no: **TL 22**

Uprights

WORLD TURNED UPSIDE DOWN
Tracks: / World turned upside down / I don't want to talk about it.
7" Single: Released Jan '82, on Loppylugs, Deleted '87. Catalogue no: **LOPPY 2**

Uproar

DIE FOR ME (EP)
Tracks: / Die for me.
7" Single: Released Mar '83, on Lightbeat, Catalogue no: **RAW 2**

NOTHING CAN STOP YOU (EP)
Tracks: / Nothing can stop you.
7" Single: Released Jan '84, on Volume (1), by Volume Records. Catalogue no: **VOL 9**

REBEL YOUTH
Tracks: / Rebel youth.
7" Single: Released Feb '83, on Beat-The-System, Deleted '88. Catalogue no: **RAW 1**

Ups And Downs

IN THE SHADOWS
Tracks: / In the shadows.
7" Single: Released Sep '86, on What Goes On, by What Goes On Records. Catalogue no: **GOES ON 08**

LIVING KIND, THE
Tracks: / Living kind, The.
12" Single: Released Oct '86, on What Goes On, by What Goes On Records. Catalogue no: **GOES ON 10T**

Upsetters

RETURN OF DJANGO (OLD GOLD)
Tracks: / Return of django.
7" Single: Released Apr '83, on Old Gold, by Old Gold Records. Deleted Jul '88. Catalogue no: **OG 9272**

TONY TRIBE/UPSETTERS

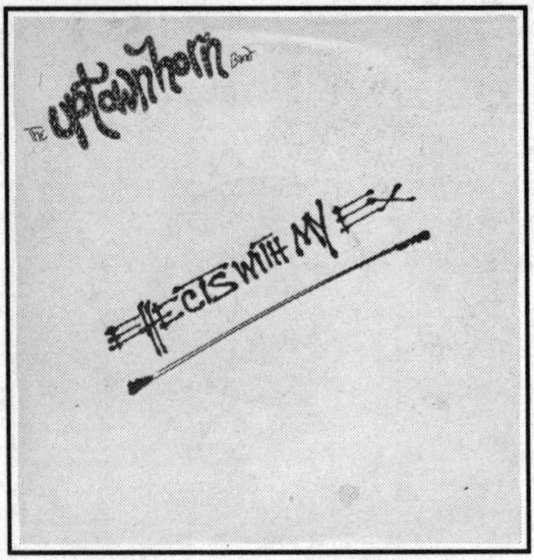

UPTOWN HORN BAND - EFFECTS WITH MY EX (Released on EMI)

CD 5": Released Nov '88, on Classic Tracks, Catalogue no: **CDEP 4 C**

Upton, Barry

ASK THE D.J.
Tracks: / Ask the DJ / Ask the DJ (version) (Feat. Uncle Funk.) / Music to my ears.
7" Single: Released Nov '86, on DMC, Catalogue no: **DECK 3**
12" Single: Released Nov '86, on DMC, Catalogue no: **DECK 123**

Upton, Glen

CHRISTMASTIME IS CHILDREN
Tracks: / Christmastime is children / My cup runneth over.
7" Single: Released Nov '82, on Ash, by Ash Records. Catalogue no: **ASH 016**

Uptown Horn Band

EFFECTS WITH MY EX (see panel above)
Tracks: / Effects with my ex / Rockin, at the roadside / Sex with my ex.
7" Single: Released '84, on EMI, by EMI Records. Catalogue no: **EMI 5460**

Urban All Stars

IT ALL BEGAN IN AFRICA
Tracks: / It began in Africa.
12" Single: Released 15 Aug '88, on Urban, by Polydor Ltd. Deleted 30 May '89. Catalogue no: **URB 23**
12" Single: Released 15 Aug '88, on Urban, by Polydor Ltd. Deleted 30 Jun '89. Catalogue no: **URBX 23**

Urban Blight

FROM THE EASTSIDE TO THE WESTSIDE
Tracks: / From the eastside to the westside.
12" Single: Released Aug '87, on Stickman (USA), Catalogue no: **STUB 01**

Urban Cowboys

BROKEN PROMISES
Tracks: / Broken promises.
7" Single: Released Feb '87, on Denbeat, Catalogue no: **DLUX 0102**

KEYS TO YOUR HEART
Tracks: / Keys to your heart.
7" Single: Released Sep '84, on Dembeat, Catalogue no: **GO 001**

Urban Dogs

LIMO LIFE
Tracks: / Limo life.
7" Single: Released Mar '83, on Fall Out, Catalogue no: **FALL 011**

Urban Gypsy

JAPANESE GIRLS
Tracks: / Japanese girls.
7" Single: Released Nov '79, on Public, Catalogue no: **PUB 001**

Urban Heroes

NOT ANOTHER WORLD WAR
Tracks: / Not another world war / Loving me loving you.
7" Single: Released May '80, on Ariola-Hansa, by Hansa Records. Deleted May '83. Catalogue no: **AHA 562**

Urban High

RUNAWAY (STRAIGHT UP MIX)
Tracks: / Runaway (straight up mix) / Runaway (techno dub mix) / Runaway (hip house mix) (On 12" only) / Runaway (salsoul mix) (On 12" only).
7" Single: Released 15 Aug '89, on 4th & Broadway, by Island Records. Catalogue no: **BRW 147**
12" Single: Released 15 Aug '89, on 4th & Broadway, by Island Records. Catalogue no: **12 BRW 147**
CD 5": Released 15 Aug '89, on 4th & Broadway, by Island Records. Catalogue no: **BRCD 147**

Urban Nature

GET ON THE FLOOR
Tracks: / Get on the floor.
7" Single: Released Jun '89, on Moles, Catalogue no: **MRCL 2**
12" Single: Released Jun '89, on Moles, Catalogue no: **12MRCL**

Urban Shakedown

BIG BAD WOLF
Tracks: / Big bad wolf / Rap the wolf.
7" Single: Released Jun '82, on Respond (1), by Respond Records. Deleted Jun '85. Catalogue no: **RESP 5**

Urban Verbs

RING RING
Tracks: / Ring ring / Frenzy.
7" Single: Released May '80, on Warner Bros., by WEA Records. Deleted May '83. Catalogue no: **K 17608**

Urbane Gorillas

ONLY THE EYES
Tracks: / Only the eyes.
7" Single: Released Aug '81, on Inane, Catalogue no: **INANE**

URBANE GORILLAS
Tracks: / Urbane gorillas.
7" Single: Released Jun '82, on Inane, Catalogue no: **INANE 1**

Urbane Planners

FASHION IS NOT ENOUGH
Tracks: / Fashion is not enough / Adman's dream of heaven.
7" Single: Released Dec '83, on Mays, by Mays Records. Catalogue no: **ING 9**

SPIRIT OF THE THING
Tracks: / Spirit of the thing.
7" Single: Released Jan '87, on Mays, by Mays Records. Catalogue no: **ING 6**

Urbaniax

BURNING CIRCUITS
Tracks: / Burning circuits.
12" Single: Released Oct '84, on Sonet, by Sonet Records. Catalogue no: **SONL 2271**
7" Single: Released Oct '84, on Sonet, by Sonet Records. Catalogue no: **SON 2271**

Urbanik, Michel

NANAVA
Tracks: / Nanava / Joy.
7" Single: Released Oct '81, on Motown, by BMG Records (UK). Catalogue no: **TMG 1208**
12" Single: Released Oct '81, on Motown, by BMG Records (UK). Catalogue no: **TMGT 1208**

Ure, Midge

ANSWERS TO NOTHING (SINGLE)
Tracks: / Answers to nothing.
7" Single: Released Aug '88, on Chrysalis, by Chrysalis Records. Catalogue no: **URE 5**
12" Single: Released Aug '88, on Chrysalis, by Chrysalis Records. Catalogue no: **UREX 5**
CD 5": Released Aug '88, on Chrysalis, by Chrysalis Records. Catalogue no: **URECD 5**

CALL OF THE WILD
Tracks: / Call of the wild / When the wind blows / After a fashion (Track on 12" version only.).
7" Single: Released May '86, on Chrysalis, by Chrysalis Records. Catalogue no: **URE 4**
12" Single: Released May '86, on Chrysalis, by Chrysalis Records. Catalogue no: **UREX 4**

DEAR GOD
Tracks: / Dear God / Music 1.
7" Single: Released Oct '88, on Chrysalis, by Chrysalis Records. Catalogue no: **URE 6**
CD 5": Released Nov '88, on Chrysalis, by Chrysalis Records. Catalogue no: **URECD 6**
12" Single: Released Oct '88, on Chrysalis, by Chrysalis Records. Catalogue no: **UREX 6**

IF I WAS
Tracks: / If I was / Piano.
12" Single: Released Aug '85, on Chrysalis, by Chrysalis Records. Catalogue no: **UREX 1**
7" Single: Released Aug '85, on Chrysalis, by Chrysalis Records. Catalogue no: **URE 1**

NO REGRETS
Tracks: / No regrets / Mood music.
7" Single: Released Jun '82, on Chrysalis, by Chrysalis Records. Catalogue no: **CHS 2618**
12" Single: Released '82, on Chrysalis, by Chrysalis Records. Catalogue no: **12 CHS 2618**

SISTER AND BROTHER
Tracks: / Sister and brother.
12" Single: Released Mar '89, on Chrysalis, by Chrysalis Records. Catalogue no: **UREX 7**
CD 5": Released Mar '89, on Chrysalis, by Chrysalis Records. Catalogue no: **URECD 7**
7" Single: Released Mar '89, on Chrysalis, by Chrysalis Records. Catalogue no: **URE 7**

THAT CERTAIN SMILE
Tracks: / That certain smile.
7" Single: Released Nov '85, on Chrysalis, by Chrysalis Records. Catalogue no: **URE 2**
12" Single: Released Nov '85, on Chrysalis, by Chrysalis Records. Catalogue no: **UREX 2**

WASTELANDS
Tracks: / Wastelands / Chieftain, The / Dancer.
12" Single: Released Jan '86, on Chrysalis, by Chrysalis Records. Catalogue no: **UREX 3**
7" Single: Released Jan '86, on Chrysalis, by Chrysalis Records. Catalogue no: **URE 3**

Urge

BOBBY
Tracks: / Teach yourself dutch / Bobby.
7" Single: Released Feb '81, on Arista, by BMG Records (UK). Deleted '84. Catalogue no: **ARIST 382**

Uriah Heep

Biographical details: A UK heavy metal group formed in 1969 by guitarist Keith Box and vocalist David Byron (both born in 1947; Byron died in 1985), with drummer Alex Napier, bassist Paul Newton, and Ken Hensley, guitarist, keyboardist and writer who'd played in the Gods with Mick Taylor. In 1972 the rhythm section stabilised with drummer Lee Kerslake (ex-Gods) and bassist Gary Thain (ex-Keef Hartley); Thain had an electrical accident onstage, left early 1975 and was found dead of a drug accident. Albums suffered from changing lineups in the late 1970s; the most serious loss was Hensley, who wrote most of their best material, made solo albums, played with USA southern rock band Blackfoot in the early 1980s. Box struggled on and was leaning towards slickness in the mid 1980s. (Donald Clarke 15.5.87).

ABOMINOG JUNIOR
7" EP: Released Mar '82, on Bronze, by Bronze Records. Catalogue no: **BRO 143**

BLOOD RED ROSES
Tracks: / Blood red roses / Rough justice / Look at yourself (12" only).
7" Single: Released 24 Jul '89, on Legacy, by Legacy Records. Catalogue no: **LGY 101**
12" Single: Released 24 Jul '89, on Legacy, by Legacy Records. Catalogue no: **LGYT 101**

CARRY ON
Tracks: / Carry on / Been hurt.
7" Single: Released Jan '80, on Bronze, by Bronze Records. Deleted Jan '83. Catalogue no: **BRO 88**

EASY LIVIN'
Tracks: / Easy livin' / Corinna / Gypsy (Only on 12").
12" Single: Released Sep '88, on Legacy, by Legacy Records. Catalogue no: **LGYT 65**
7" Single: Released Sep '88, on Legacy, by Legacy Records. Catalogue no: **LGY 65**

HOLD YOUR HEAD UP
Tracks: / Hold your head up.
7" Single: Released Apr '89, on Legacy, by Legacy Records. Catalogue no: **LGY 67**
12" Single: Released Apr '89, on Legacy, by Legacy Records. Catalogue no: **LGYT 67**

LOVE STEALER
Tracks: / Love stealer / No return.
7" Single: Released 20 Jun '80, on Bronze, by Bronze Records. Deleted '83. Catalogue no: **BRO 96**

ON THE REBOUND
Tracks: / On the rebound.
7" Single: Released Feb '82, on Bronze, by Bronze Records. Catalogue no: **BRO 143**

STAY ON TOP
Tracks: / Stay on top.
7" Single: Released Aug '83, on Bronze, by Bronze Records. Catalogue no: **BRO 168**
Special: Released Aug '83, on Bronze, by Bronze Records. Catalogue no: **BROG 168**

THAT'S THE WAY THAT IT IS
Tracks: / That's the way that it is / Hot persuasion.
7" Single: Released Jun '82, on Bronze, by Bronze Records. Catalogue no: **BRO 148**

THINK IT OVER
Tracks: / Think it over / My Joanna needs tuning.
7" Single: Released Jan '81, on Bronze, by Bronze Records. Deleted Jan '84. Catalogue no: **BRO 112**

URIAH HEAP
Tracks: / Lady in black / July morning / Easy livin'.
CD 3": Released '88, on Special Edition, by Castle Communications Records. Catalogue no: **CD3-16**

Urock

NO WAR NO MORE
Tracks: / No war no more.
7" Single: Released Jun '85, on FM Productions, Deleted '87. Catalogue no: **KISS 1**

Uropa Lula

OUR LOVE HAS JUST BEGUN
Tracks: / Our love has just begun / I suddenly remembered something.
7" Single: Released Jul '82, on Arista, by BMG Records (UK). Catalogue no: **ARIST 476**
12" Single: Released Jul '82, on Arista, by BMG Records (UK). Catalogue no: **ARIST 12 476**

U-Roy

AFRICAN SOLDIER (SINGLE)
Tracks: / African soldier / African soldier (version).
12" Single: Released Aug '86, on Tappa Zukie, Catalogue no: **TZ 004**

BABY COME BACK
Tracks: / Baby come back / Baby come back (INST).
12" Single: Released Sep '86, on Tappa Zukie, Catalogue no: **TZ 103**

HUSTLERS TAKING OVER
Tracks: / Hustlers taking over / Sidewalk vendor.
12" Single: Released Dec '82, on Music Works, Catalogue no: **MWRT 1290**

JAH CALL YOU
Tracks: / Jah call you / Great stories.
12" Single: Released Jul '86, on Third World, Catalogue no: **MDIS 001**

US

KEEP ON LOOKING
Tracks: / Keep on looking.
12" Single: Released Aug '84, on Excaliber by Red Bus Records. Deleted '88. Catalogue no: **EXCL 539**
7" Single: Released Aug '84, on Excaliber by Red Bus Records. Deleted '88. Catalogue no: **EXC 539**

U.S. Of A

BODY SNATCHING
Tracks: / Body snatching / Body snatching

(part 2).
7" Single: Released Feb '80, on Carrere, Deleted '83. Catalogue no: **CAR 132**

U.S.A.

I LOVE YOU
Tracks: / I love you / Teenage rock 'n' roller.
12" Single: Released Nov '82, on Philly World (USA), by Philly World (USA). Catalogue no: **PWSL 107**
7" Single: Released Nov '82, on Philly World (USA), by Philly World (USA). Catalogue no: **PWS 107**

USA For Africa

WE ARE THE WORLD (SINGLE)
7" Single: Released Mar '85, on CBS, by CBS Records. Catalogue no: **USAID 1**
12" Single: Released Mar '85, on CBS, by CBS Records. Catalogue no: **USAIDT 1**

U.S.Scooters

YOUNG GIRLS
Tracks: / Young girls / Set and ready.
7" Single: Released May '80, on EMI-America, by EMI Records. Deleted May '85. Catalogue no: **EA 109**

UT

CONFIDENTIAL
Tracks: / Confidential.
12" Single: Released Jun '85, on Outer, Deleted '86. Catalogue no: **UTR 01**

U.T.F.O

ROXANNE,ROXANNE
Tracks: / Roxanne, Roxanne / Real Roxanne, The / U.T.F.O. hanging out / Roxanne's backside / Scratch it.
7" Single: Released Mar '85, on Streetwave, Catalogue no: **KHAN 506**
12" Single: Released Mar '85, on Streetwave, Catalogue no: **XKHAN 506**
Cassingle: Released Mar '85, on Streetwave, Catalogue no: **ZCMK 506**

WE WORK HARD
Tracks: / We work hard / Kangol & Doc.
7" Single: Released Jul '86, on Cool Tempo, by Chrysalis Records. Catalogue no: **COOL 128**
12" Single: Released Jul '86, on Cool Tempo, by Chrysalis Records. Catalogue no: **COOLX 128**

YA COLD, WANNA BE WITH ME
Tracks: / Ya cold wanna be with me.
12" Single: Released Aug '87, on Select (USA), Catalogue no: **FMS 62293**

Utopia

CRYBABY
Tracks: / Cry baby / Winston Smith takes it on the jaw.
7" Single: Released May '84, on WEA (International), by WEA Records. Catalogue no: **YZ 5**

FEET DON'T FAIL ME NOW
Tracks: / Feet don't fail me now / Forgotten but not gone.
7" Single: Released Nov '82, on Epic, by CBS Records. Deleted Nov '85. Catalogue no: **EPCA 2972**

I JUST WANT TO TOUCH YOU
Tracks: / I just want to touch you / Silly boy / Life goes on / All smiles.
7" EP: Released Oct '80, on Island, by Island Records. Deleted Oct '83. Catalogue no: **IEP 12**

ONE WORLD
Tracks: / One world.
7" Single: Released Apr '82, on Bearsville (USA), Catalogue no: **AAA 126**

SET ME FREE
Tracks: / Set me free / Umbrella.
7" Single: Released Mar '80, on Island, by Island Records. Deleted '83. Catalogue no: **WIP 6581**

Uttley, Alison

LITTLE GREY RABBIT COLLECTION, THE
Note: Read by Nanette Newman. Four books & 1 long play cassette in presentation pack.
Special: Released Apr '88, on Tempo, by Warwick Records. Catalogue no: **00 104 132 2**

UV Pop

ANYONE FOR ME
Tracks: / Anyone for me.
12" Single: Released Mar '85, on Flowmotion, Catalogue no: **FM 12007**
7" Single: Released Mar '85, on Flowmotion, Catalogue no: **FM 007**

JUST A GAME
Tracks: / Just a game.
7" Single: Released Nov '82, on Pax, by Pax Records. Catalogue no: **PAX 9**

MUSIC TO YEAH TO
Tracks: / Music to yeah to.
12" Single: Released '88, on Extra, Catalogue no: **EXTRAT 001**

SERIOUS
Tracks: / Serious.
12" Single: Released Sep '85, on Native (1), by Native Records. Catalogue no: **NTV 4**

UXB

CRAZY TODAY
Tracks: / Crazy today.
7" Single: Released Jul '80, on Crazy Plane, Catalogue no: **SP 002**

Uzho, Madeleine

Biographical details: Madeleine Uzho was born in Stockholm, Sweden on 19th May, 1964, but moved to London with her Nigerian father and Swedish mother at the age of one, where she lived until she was five years old. The family then returned to Stockholm. After leaving school, she joined the Theatre School in Stockholm where she was trained to dance and perform before a live audience. In January of this year, Madeleine went to a recording studio in Stockholm with one of her best friends, Gigi Hamilton, who is a member of the top-selling Swedish group **Freestyle**. Gigi was supposed to record some background vocals on a new single, but had a sore throat and was unable to sing. The producers of the single were desperate and persuaded Madeleine to sing instead. They were very impressed with her voice and decided to record a single with her. They composed *Satisfied* and went into the same studio than night and started recording the record. (Berni Kilmartin, Chrysalis Records Press Office, July 1983).

SATISFIED
Tracks: / Satisfied / Satisfied (instrumental) / Information (live) / Satisfied (extended version) (Only on 12" version.).
7" Single: Released '83, on Chrysalis, by Chrysalis Records. Deleted '87. Catalogue no: **CHS 2718**
12" Single: Released '83, on Chrysalis, by Chrysalis Records. Deleted '87. Catalogue no: **CHS 12 2718**

V

The following information was taken from the Music Master database on October 20th, 1989.

V

BLOWN AWAY BY LOVE
Tracks: / Blown away by love.
7" Single: Released May '85, on Ram, by Ram Records. Catalogue no: **CHP 7011**
12" Single: Released May '85, on Ram, by Ram Records. Catalogue no: **12CHP 7011**

V1

TRIUMPH OF DEATH
Tracks: / Stimulation / Triumph of death.
7" Single: Released 20 Feb '88, on Loony Tunes, by Loony Tunes Records. Catalogue no: **TUNE 006**

V Capri

HUNTING ME
Tracks: / Hunting me / Year from now.
7" Single: Released Feb '89, on Lisson, by PWL Records. Catalogue no: **DOLE 10**

V Vee Vee

PASS THE BUCK
Tracks: / Pass the buck.
7" Single: Released '88, on Constrictor, by Constrictor Records (Germany). Catalogue no: **COLL 007**

Vagrants

WHATS IN MY SOUL
Tracks: / What's in my soul.
7" Single: Released Jul '82, on Riktashadz, Deleted '83. Catalogue no: **SHAD 1**

Vain

BEAT THE BULLET
Tracks: / Beat the bullet / Secrets / Smoke and shadows (On 12" and CD only).
CD 5": Released Jul '89, on Island, by Island Records. Catalogue no: **CID 432**
7" Single: Released Jul '89, on Island, by Island Records. Catalogue no: **IS 432**
CD 3": Released Jul '89, on Island, by Island Records. Catalogue no: **CIDX 432**
12" Single: Released Jul '89, on Island, by Island Records. Catalogue no: **12 IS 432**

Valaitis, Lena

JOHNNY BLUE
Tracks: / Johnny blue.
7" Single: Released Apr '81, on Ariola, by BMG Records (UK). Catalogue no: **ARO 256**

Valence, Ricky

TELL LAURA I LOVE HER
Tracks: / Tell Laura I love her.
7" Single: Released Jul '75, on EMI, by EMI Records. Deleted Oct '87. Catalogue no: **EMI 2303**
7" Single: Released Aug '60, on Revolver, by FM-Revolver Records. Deleted '63. Catalogue no: **DB 4493**

TELL LAURA I LOVE HER (OLD GOLD)
Tracks: / Tell Laura I love her / Baby sittin'.
7" Single: Released Jun '88, on Old Gold, by Old Gold Records. Deleted Sep '89. Catalogue no: **OG 9387**

TIME AFTER TIME
Tracks: / Time after time / Tell Laura I love her.
7" Single: Released Mar '81, on Revolver, by FM-Revolver Records. Catalogue no: **REV3**

Valens, Ritchie

Biographical details: Valens was born Richie Valenzuela in 1941 in Pacoima, California; he died in the same plane crash that killed Buddy Holly in 1959. He was the first Chicano rock star and the only one until Santana, then Los Lobos. His *Come On, Lets Go* almost made the USA top 40 in 1958; then the smoochie rockaballad *Donna* (written for his girlfriend) was a smash number 2, with traditional Latin party song *La Bamba* on the flip: DJs made B side a no. 22 hit. Rhino records have somehow spun out his short career into several compilations albums. The hit film biopic La Bamba in 1987 includes original music by Carlos Santana and Miles Goodman; Los Lobos on screen and soundtrack made *La Bamba* a no. 1 hit this time. (Donald Clarke 15.5.87).

DONNA
Tracks: / Donna / La bamba / Let's dance.
7" Single: Released Mar '59, on London Records, by London Records. Deleted '62. Catalogue no: **HL 8803**
7" Single: Released Aug '84, on Creole (Replay), by Creole Records. Catalogue no: **CR 215**

DONNA (OLD GOLD)
Tracks: / Donna / La bamba.
7" Single: Released Jun '88, on Old Gold, by Old Gold Records. Catalogue no: **OG 9029**

DONNA (OLD GOLD CD SINGLE)
Tracks: / Donna / La bamba / I fought the law.
CD 5": Released Nov '88, on Old Gold, by Old Gold Records. Catalogue no: **OG 6106**

LA BAMBA
Tracks: / La bamba.
7" Single: Released Aug '87, on RCA, by BMG Records (UK). Deleted Aug '89. Catalogue no: **PB 41435**
12" Single: Released Aug '87, on RCA, by BMG Records (UK). Deleted May '89. Catalogue no: **PT 41436**

LIL' BIT OF GOLD: RITCHIE VALENS
Tracks: / La bamba / Come on let's go / Donna / That's my little Suzie.
CD 5": Released May '88, on Rhino, by Creole Records. Catalogue no: **R 373018**

Valente, Caterina

Biographical details: Valente is a pop singer born in Paris of Italian parents. Her impressive voice led to a top 10 hit in 1955 in the USA and the UK with *The Breeze And I* (from *Andalucis-Suite Espagnole* by Ernesto Lecuona in 1928; with English words by Al Stillman a number 1 hit in 1940 for Jimmy Dorsey). She remained a popular concert star in Europe. (Donald Clarke 15.5.87).

BREEZE AND I, THE
Tracks: / Breeze and I, The.
7" Single: Released Aug '55, on Polydor, by Polydor Ltd. Deleted '58. Catalogue no: **BM 6002**

Valentin, Dave

WE CAN ONLY DREAM
Tracks: / We can only dream.
7" Single: Released Jul '86, on Aura Records, by Aura Records. Catalogue no: **AUS 150**

Valentine

ROCKY VALLEY FESTIVAL SONG
Tracks: / Rocky valley festival song.
7" Single: Released May '86, on Valentine, by Valentine Records. Catalogue no: **VALS 125**

TINA ARE YOU READY
Tracks: / Tina are you ready.
7" Single: Released '88, on Banana, Catalogue no: **FRUIT 6**
12" Single: Released '88, on Banana, Catalogue no: **FRUIT 6T**

Valentine Brothers

MONEY'S TOO TIGHT
Tracks: / Money's too tight / Money's too tight.
7" Single: Released Mar '83, on Energy (USA), by Bulldog Records (USA). Catalogue no: **NGY 1**
12" Single: Released Jul '88, on Gelt Recs, Catalogue no: **UNKNOWN**
12" Single: Released Mar '83, on Energy (USA), by Bulldog Records (USA). Catalogue no: **12 NGY 1**

NO BETTER LOVE
Tracks: / No better love.
12" Single: Released Aug '87, on EMI-America, by EMI Records. Deleted 31 Jul '88. Catalogue no: **12EA 235**
7" Single: Released Aug '87, on EMI-America, by EMI Records. Deleted Jan '88. Catalogue no: **EA 235**

Valentine, Cindy

IN YOUR MIDNIGHT HOUR
Tracks: / Work it out / In your midnight hour.
12" Single: Released Apr '87, on Urban, by Polydor Ltd. Catalogue no: **URBX 3**
7" Single: Released Apr '87, on Urban, by Polydor Ltd. Deleted Jan '88. Catalogue no: **URB 3**

Valentine, Dickie

Biographical details: Valentine was born Richard Brice in London in 1929; he died in a car crash in Wales in 1971. He made his film debut at the age of 3 in the farce Jacks the Boy in 1932, was a page boy at the Manchester Palace, then the London Palladium; encouraged by musical comedy star Bill O'Connor, who paid for singing lessons; he was recommended to bandleader Ted Heath, joining Heath's Sunday night Swing Sessions at the Palladium in 1949. Initially sang only one song per evening early in the show, then sat on stage: he was once asked by a latecomer if he was the band's mascot. He went solo in 1954, having become a teen idol; he played to Standing Room Only business at first solo show in Blackpool, despite Nat Cole appearing 200 yards down the road. His fast, humourous act included impressions; he was the first British singer to headline at the Palladium in five years. In 1957 he hired the Royal Albert Hall for fan club's annual party. He had 12 top 20 UK hits in 1953-59. (Donald Clarke 15.5.87).

ALL THE TIME AND EVERYWHERE
Tracks: / All the time and ev'rywhere.
7" Single: Released Mar '53, on Decca, by Decca Records. Deleted '56. Catalogue no: **F 10038**

BLOSSOM FELL, A
Tracks: / Blossom fell, A.
7" Single: Released Feb '55, on Decca, by Decca Records. Deleted '58. Catalogue no: **F 10430**

BROKEN WINGS
Tracks: / Broken wings.
7" Single: Released Feb '53, on Decca, by Decca Records. Deleted '56. Catalogue no: **F 9954**

CHRISTMAS ALPHABET
Tracks: / Christmas alphabet.
7" Single: Released Nov '55, on Decca, by Decca Records. Deleted '58. Catalogue no: **F 10628**

CHRISTMAS ISLAND
Tracks: / Christmas Island.
7" Single: Released Dec '56, on Decca, by Decca Records. Deleted '59. Catalogue no: **F 10798**

ENDLESS
Tracks: / Endless.
7" Single: Released Nov '54, on Decca, by Decca Records. Deleted '57. Catalogue no: **F 10346**

FINGER OF SUSPICION
Tracks: / Finger of suspicion.
7" Single: Released Dec '54, on Decca, by Decca Records. Deleted '57. Catalogue no: **F 10394**

I WONDER
Tracks: / I wonder.
7" Single: Released Jun '55, on Decca, by Decca Records. Deleted '58. Catalogue no: **F 10493**

IN A GOLDEN COACH
Tracks: / In a golden coach.
7" Single: Released Jun '53, on Decca, by Decca Records. Deleted '56. Catalogue no: **F 10098**

MR. SANDMAN
Tracks: / Mr. Sandman.
7" Single: Released Dec '54, on Decca, by Decca Records. Deleted '57. Catalogue no: **F 10415**

OLD PIANNA RAG
Tracks: / Old pianna rag.
7" Single: Released Dec '55, on Decca, by Decca Records. Deleted '58. Catalogue no: **F 10645**

ONE MORE SUNRISE
Tracks: / One more sunrise.
7" Single: Released Oct '59, on Pye, Deleted '62. Catalogue no: **7 N 15221**

SNOWBOUND FOR CHRISTMAS
Tracks: / Snowbound for Christmas.
7" Single: Released Dec '57, on Decca, by Decca Records. Deleted '60. Catalogue no: **F 10950**

VENUS
Tracks: / Venus.
7" Single: Released Mar '59, on Pye, Deleted '62. Catalogue no: **7 N 15192**

Valentine, Richard

COME BACK LOVER
Tracks: / Come back lover / Come back lover (version).
12" Single: Released Apr '88, on Champion, by Champion Records. Deleted Aug '89. Catalogue no: **CHAMP 1273**
7" Single: Released Apr '88, on Champion, by Champion Records. Catalogue no: **CHAMP 73**

Valentine, Robbie

JAMMING
Tracks: / Jamming.
7" Single: Released May '89, on Pioneer Muzik, Catalogue no: **UNKNOWN**

YOU'LL NEVER FIND
Tracks: / You'll never find.
12" Single: Released Nov '88, on Pioneer Muzik, Catalogue no: **PM 017**

Valentine, Tony

I CAN DO BAD BY MYSELF
Tracks: / I can do bad by myself / I'm livin' a life of love.
7" Single: Released 21 Nov '87, on Jive, by Zomba Records. Deleted '88. Catalogue no: **JIVE 161**
12" Single: Released 21 Nov '87, on Jive, by Zomba Records. Deleted '88. Catalogue no: **JIVET 161**

Valentino

SINGALONG-A-CUPID
Tracks: / Singalong-a-cupid / This heart of mine.
7" Single: Released Feb '83, on Polydor, by Polydor Ltd. Catalogue no: **CUPID 1**

Valentino, Betty

KEEP IT UP
12" Single: Released Jun '84, on Design Communications, Catalogue no: **DEST 9**
7" Single: Released Jun '84, on Design Communications, Catalogue no: **DES 9**

Valerie

CREST OF A WAVE
Tracks: / Crest of a wave / Is our love over.
7" Single: Released Nov '85, on Elecstar, by Elecstar Records. Deleted '88. Catalogue no: **VCL 3**

REAL SURPRISE
Tracks: / Real surprise.
7" Single: Released Oct '84, on Piggy Bank Records, by A&M Records. Catalogue no: **BANK 998**
12" Single: Released Oct '84, on Piggy Bank Records, by A&M Records. Catalogue no: **BANX 998**

Valey, T. Ski

SEXUAL RAPPING
Tracks: / Sexual rapping.
12" Single: Released Mar '83, on Pama, by Pama Records. Catalogue no: **PMD 3229**

Valhalla

COMIN' HOME
Tracks: / Comin' home / Through with you.
7" Single: Released '88, on Neat, by Neat Records. Catalogue no: **NEAT 22**

STILL IN LOVE WITH YOU
Tracks: / Still in love with you / Jack.
7" Single: Released Jan '84, on Neat, by Neat Records. Catalogue no: **NEAT 36**

Valients

WHEN DREAMS FADE
Tracks: / When dreams fade / I want you.
7" Single: Released Oct '80, on Epic, by CBS Records. Deleted Oct '83. Catalogue no: **EPC 9072**

Valino, Joe

GARDEN OF EDEN
Tracks: / Garden of Eden.
7" Single: Released Jan '57, on H.M.V., by

EMI Records. Deleted '60. Catalogue no: **POP 283**

Valley, Don

I'M SO FAR IN THE RED, I'M BLUE
Tracks: / I'm so far in the red, I'm blue.
12" Single: Released 23 Jul '88, on Hot Dang Vinyl, Catalogue no: **DANG 002**

Valli, Frankie

BOOK OF LOVE
Tracks: / Book of love / Deep inside your love.
7" Single: Released Apr '86, on MCA, by MCA Records. Catalogue no: **MCA 980**

DECEMBER '63 (OH WHAT A NIGHT)
Tracks: / Oh what a night / Oh what a night (version).
7" Single: Released Oct '88, on BR Music, by BR Music Records. Catalogue no: **45277**
CD 5": Released Oct '88, on BR Music, by BR Music Records. Catalogue no: **CD 12277**
12" Single: Released Oct '88, on BR Music, by BR Music Records. Catalogue no: **1245277**

FALLEN ANGEL
Tracks: / Fallen angel.
7" Single: Released Apr '76, on Private Stock, Deleted '79. Catalogue no: **PVT 51**

GREASE
Tracks: / Grease.
7" Single: Released Aug '78, on RSO (USA), by Polydor Ltd. Catalogue no: **RSO 012**

HEAVEN MUST HAVE SENT YOU
Tracks: / Heaven must have sent you / Medley.
7" Single: Released Mar '81, on Warner Bros., by WEA Records. Catalogue no: **K 17764**

MY EYES ADORED YOU
Tracks: / My eyes adored you.
7" Single: Released Feb '75, on Private Stock, Deleted '78. Catalogue no: **PVT 1**

MY EYES ADORED YOU (OLD GOLD)
Tracks: / My eyes adored you.
7" Single: Released Apr '83, on Old Gold, by Old Gold Records. Catalogue no: **OG 9283**

NIGHT, THE
Tracks: / Night, The.
7" Single: Released Apr '75, on Mowest, by Motown Records (UK). Deleted '78. Catalogue no: **MW 3024**

PASSION FOR PARIS
Tracks: / Passion for Paris / Passion for Paris (part 2).
7" Single: Released Mar '80, on MCA, by MCA Records. Deleted '83. Catalogue no: **MCA 572**

RAG DOLL
Tracks: / Rag doll / Let's hang on.
7" Single: Released Jun '88, on CBS, by CBS Records. Catalogue no: **FOUR 71**

SOUL
Tracks: / Soul / If it really wasn't love.
7" Single: Released Jan '81, on Chrysalis, by Chrysalis Records. Deleted Jan '84. Catalogue no: **MCA 645**

SWEARIN' TO GOD
Tracks: / Swearin' to God.
7" Single: Released Jun '75, on Private Stock, Deleted '78. Catalogue no: **PVT 21**

WALK LIKE A MAN
Tracks: / Walk like a man / Sherry.
7" Single: Released Mar '63, on Stateside, by EMI Records. Deleted '66. Catalogue no: **SS 169**
7" Single: Released Jun '88, on CBS, by CBS Records. Catalogue no: **FOUR 72**

WORKING MY WAY BACK TO YOU
Tracks: / Working my way back to you / I've got you under my skin.
7" Single: Released Jun '88, on CBS, by CBS Records. Catalogue no: **FOUR 73**

YOU'RE READY NOW
Tracks: / You're ready now / My eyes adored you (Frankie Valli solo).
Note: Picture bags on all items
7" Single: Released Dec '70, on Philips, by Phonogram Ltd. Deleted '73. Catalogue no: **320226**
7" Single: Released Jun '88, on CBS, by CBS Records. Catalogue no: **FOUR 74**

Vampire Bats...

MR CLEAN
Tracks: / Mr. Clean.
7" Single: Released Jan '82, on Sheet, Catalogue no: **BULL 1**

Vampires

HARRY'S HOUSE
Tracks: / Harry's house / Mystery & madness.
7" Single: Released Jul '82, on Next, by Next Records. Catalogue no: **NEXT 702**

Van Cleef, Lee

FOREIGN A NO PARADISE
Tracks: / Foreign a no paradise / Babylon.
12" Single: Released Dec '82, on D&H, Catalogue no: **DH 001**

LOOK HOW SHE FAT
Tracks: / Look how she fat.
7" Single: Released Apr '82, on Joe Gibbs, Catalogue no: **JGMD 8149**

SEXY CHICKENS
Tracks: / Sexy chickens.
12" Single: Released Jun '82, on Carib Jems, Catalogue no: **CGDD 22**

Van Dam

HOW DO YOU KNOW
Tracks: / How do you know.
7" Single: Released May '83, on Sticky, Catalogue no: **STICK 101**

Van Day, David

RINGING THE BELL
Tracks: / Ringing the bell.
12" Single: Released Mar '85, on Record Shack, by Record Shack Records. Catalogue no: **SOHOT 36**
7" Single: Released Mar '85, on Record Shack, by Record Shack Records. Catalogue no: **SOHO 36**

SHE SAID SHE SAID
Tracks: / She said she said / She said she said (remix) (Only on RDAVD 1 & 12RDAVD 1.).
7" Single: Released Jul '89, on Union, Catalogue no: **RDAVD 1**
7" Single: Released May '89, on Union, Catalogue no: **DAVD 1**
12" Single: Released Jul '89, on Union, Catalogue no: **12RDAVD 1**
CD 5": Released May '89, on Union, Catalogue no: **CDAVD 1**
Cassingle: Released May '89, on Union, Catalogue no: **TDAVD 1**
12" Single: Released May '89, on Union, Catalogue no: **12 DAVD 1**

YOUNG AMERICANS TALKING
Tracks: / Young Americans talking.
7" Single: Released Apr '83, on WEA, by WEA Records. Catalogue no: **DAY 1**
12" Single: Released Apr '83, on WEA, by WEA Records. Catalogue no: **DAY 1 T**
7" Pic: Released May '83, on WEA, by WEA Records. Catalogue no: **DAY 1 P**

Van Dusen, George

IT'S HOLIDAY TIME AGAIN
Tracks: / It's holiday time again / Holiday time is jollity time.
7" Single: Released Apr '89, on Britone, Catalogue no: **7BT 002**

Van Dyke, Earl

6 BY 6
Tracks: / 6 by 6.
7" Single: Released Oct '81, on Motown, by BMG Records (UK). Catalogue no: **TMG 759**

Van Dyke, Greg

PARALLEL UNIVERSE
Tracks: / Parallel Universe / Animation.
7" Single: Released Dec '80, on Korova, by WEA Records. Deleted Dec '85. Catalogue no: **KOW 13**

Van Dyke, Leroy

Biographical details: This American singer and guitarist obtained a degree in agriculture before serving with the US Army in Korea. It was while in the Forces that he took up the guitar and started to explore his vocal talents. Upon discharge, however, his special interest in cattle prompted him to begin a career as a livestock auctioneer. In 1956 he hit upon the idea of co-writing and recording *The auctioneer*, a novelty number based on the cry and lifestyle of a member of his profession. The song climbed to no.19 on the US pop chart in early '57; it was also a success on the country and western listings. Van Dyke's next taste of major success did not come until 1961. At the end of that year, he achieved a US no.5 smash with an infectious countrified pop single, *Walk on by*; in early '62, the record reached no.5 in Britain. (The song had no connection with a similarly titled number which became a hit for Dionne Warwick). In the US, Van Dyke followed *Walk on by* with *If a woman answers (hang up the phone)*; in the UK, *Big man in a big house* was released. In both cases, only a modest hit was gained. Subsequently, his warm singing style was confined to the American country charts but even there, he gradually drifted into obscurity. His career was not uplifted by his movie debut, in 1967's *What am I bid?* (Bob Macdonald, 14/7/85).

AUCTIONEER, THE
Tracks: / Auctioneer, The / Pocketbook song / My good mind went bad on me / Honky tonk song / Leather jacket / I fell in love with a pony tail / One heart / Heartbreak cannonball / I'm movin' on / Chicken shack.
7" EP: Released '78, on MCA, by MCA Records. Catalogue no: **MCEP 5**

BIG MAN IN A BIG HOUSE
Tracks: / Big man in a big house.
7" Single: Released Apr '62, on Mercury (EMI), Deleted '65. Catalogue no: **AMT 1173**

WALK ON BY
Tracks: / Walk on by.
7" Single: Released '80, on Mercury, by Phonogram Ltd. Catalogue no: **LR 1308**
7" Single: Released Jan '62, on Mercury (EMI), Deleted '65. Catalogue no: **AMT 1166**

Van Dyke, Michel

BABY LAY YOUR HANDS ON ME
Tracks: / Baby lay your hands on me.
7" Single: Released Jul '89, on Chrysalis, by Chrysalis Records. Catalogue no: **CHS 3395**
12" Single: Released Jul '89, on Chrysalis, by Chrysalis Records. Catalogue no: **CHS 12 3395**

Van Halen

Biographical details:
A hard rock/heavy metal quartet formed in America in 1974, Van Halen were David Lee Roth (vocals), Edward Van Halen (guitar), Michael Anthony (bass) and Alex Van Halen (drums). The Van Halen brothers were born in Holland and emigrated with their parents to California where they joined Roth and Anthony in a group loosely based on Free. Their energy-packed act gained early following, with Roth's overtly sexual image -- the world's tightest trousers -- and Edward Van Halen's highly-rated guitar, and they promoted their own gigs and eventually signed with Warner Brothers. Roth left in 1985, being replaced by Sammy Hagar. (Donald Clarke, January 1988.).

BLACK AND BLUE
Tracks: / Black and blue / Apolitical blues (Only on 3"CD single import.).
7" Single: Released May '88, on Warner Bros., by WEA Records. Catalogue no: **W 7891**
12" Single: Released May '88, on Warner Bros., by WEA Records. Catalogue no: **W 7891T**
CD 3": Released Aug '88, on Warner Bros.(Japan), by WEA Records. Catalogue no: **10 SW 53**

DANCE THE NIGHT AWAY
Tracks: / Dance the night away.
7" Single: Released May '79, on Warner Bros., by WEA Records. Catalogue no: **K 17371**

DANCING IN THE STREET
Tracks: / Dancing in the street / Big bad Willie.
7" Single: Released May '82, on Warner Bros., by WEA Records. Catalogue no: **K 17957**

DREAMS
Tracks: / Dreams / Inside.
7" Single: Released Jun '86, on Warner Bros., by WEA Records. Deleted Jun '87. Catalogue no: **W 8642**
12" Single: Released Jun '86, on Warner Bros., by WEA Records. Deleted Jun '87. Catalogue no: **W 8642 T**
7" Pic: Released Jun '86, on Warner Bros., by WEA Records. Deleted Jun '87. Catalogue no: **W 8642 P**

FEELS SO GOOD
Tracks: / Feels so good.
CD 5": Released Mar '89, on Warner Bros., by WEA Records. Catalogue no: **W 7565 CD**
12" Single: Released Mar '89, on Warner Bros., by WEA Records. Catalogue no: **W 7565 T**
7" Single: Released Mar '89, on Warner Bros., by WEA Records. Catalogue no: **W 7565**

HOT FOR TEACHER
Tracks: / Hot for teacher.
12" Single: Released Jun '85, on Warner Bros., by WEA Records. Catalogue no: **W 9199 T**
7" Single: Released Jun '85, on Warner Bros., by WEA Records. Catalogue no: **W 9199**

I'LL WAIT
Tracks: / I'll wait.
7" Single: Released Jul '84, on Warner Bros., by WEA Records. Catalogue no: **W 9213**

JUMP
Tracks: / Jump.
12" Single: Released Jan '84, on Warner Bros., by WEA Records. Deleted Jan '88. Catalogue no: **W 9384T**
7" Single: Released Jan '84, on Warner Bros., by WEA Records. Catalogue no: **W 9384**

PANAMA
Tracks: / Panama / Girl gone bad.
7" Single: Released May '84, on Warner Bros., by WEA Records. Deleted '87. Catalogue no: **W 9273**

PRETTY WOMAN
Tracks: / Pretty woman / Happy trails.
7" Single: Released Feb '85, on Warner Bros., by WEA Records. Catalogue no: **K 17909**

RUNNIN' WITH THE DEVIL
Tracks: / Runnin' with the devil.
7" Single: Released Jul '80, on Warner Bros., by WEA Records. Catalogue no: **HM 10**

WHEN IT'S LOVE
Tracks: / When it's love / Apolitical blues / Why can't this be love*.
Note: * Extra track on CD single
12" Pic: Released Jul '88, on Warner Bros., by WEA Records. Catalogue no: **W 7816 TP**
7" Single: Released Jul '88, on Warner Bros., by WEA Records. Catalogue no: **W 7816**
12" Single: Released Jul '88, on Warner Bros., by WEA Records. Catalogue no: **W 7816 T**
CD 5": Released Jul '88, on Warner Bros., by WEA Records. Catalogue no: **W 7816 CD**

WHY CAN'T THIS BE LOVE
Tracks: / Why can't this be love / Get up.
7" Pic: Released Mar '86, on Warner Bros., by WEA Records. Deleted Jun '87. Catalogue no: **W 8740 P**
12" Single: Released Mar '86, on Warner Bros., by WEA Records. Deleted Jan '88. Catalogue no: **W 8740 T**
7" Single: Released Mar '86, on Warner Bros., by WEA Records. Deleted Jan '88. Catalogue no: **W 8740**

Van Morrison

CLEANING WINDOWS
Tracks: / Cleaning windows / It's all in the game.
7" Single: Released Mar '82, on Mercury, by Phonogram Ltd. Deleted '85. Catalogue no: **MER 99**

Van Shelton, Ricky

LIFE TURNED HER THAT WAY
Tracks: / Life turned her that way / I don't care.
7" Single: Released 27 Jun '88, on CBS, by CBS Records. Deleted Jan '89. Catalogue no: **652831 7**

Van Twist

SHAFT
Tracks: / Shaft, Theme from.
7" Single: Released Feb '85, on Polydor, by Polydor Ltd. Deleted '88. Catalogue no: **POSP 729**

Van Zandt, Johnny

WHO'S RIGHT OR WRONG
Tracks: / Who's right or wrong / Play my music.
7" Single: Released Jul '81, on Polydor, by Polydor Ltd. Deleted '85. Catalogue no: **POSP 294**

Vandana

I'LL BE THERE FOR YOU
Tracks: / I'll be there for you.
7" Single: Released Sep '89, on Jive, by Zomba Records. Catalogue no: **JIVE 226**

Vandenburg

ONCE IN A LIFETIME
Tracks: / Once in a lifetime.
7" Single: Released Oct '85, on Atco, by Atlantic Recording Corp.(USA). Catalogue no: **B 9610**

Vanderbilt Connection

BRAIN DAMAGE
Tracks: / Brain damage.
12" Single: Released '89, on Subway, by Subway Records. Catalogue no: **SUB 059**

Vandike, Greg

DOCTOR RAIN
Tracks: / Doctor Rain / House of the August moon.
7" Single: Released Feb '82, on Korova, by WEA Records. Catalogue no: **KOW 19**

MARIE CELESTE
Tracks: / Marie Celeste.
7" Single: Released Jun '80, on Korova, by WEA Records. Catalogue no: **KOW 7**

Vandross, Luther

Biographical details: Soul singer Vandross was born in New York in 1951. He began singing commercial jingles then became a top session vocalist and arranger, backing such stars as David Bowie, Bette Midler, Carly Simon, Chaka Khan, Barbra Streisand

LUTHER VANDROSS - ANY LOVE (Released on Epic)

and Donna Summer. He worked with Quincy Jones and Italian disco band Change and contributed to the films *The Wiz* and *Bustin' Loose*. Vandross finally went solo in the 80's to wide acclaim and his albums began charting in Britain with *Busy Body* in 1983. (Donald Clarke, January 1988.).

ANY LOVE (see panel above)
Tracks: / Any love / Any love (album version) (CD single) / Any love (inst.) (CD single) / Superstar (CD single) / Until you come back to me (CD single) / Better love (1989 12" & CD only) / You stopped loving me / How many times can we say goodbye?.
12" Single: Released Jun '89, on Epic, by CBS Records. Catalogue no: **LUTH T11**
12" Single: Released Sep '88, on Epic, by CBS Records. Deleted 17 Apr '89. Catalogue no: **LUTH T8**
CD 5": Released Jun '89, on Epic, by CBS Records. Catalogue no: **CD LUTH 11**
CD 5": Released Oct '88, on Epic, by CBS Records. Deleted 10 Jul '89. Catalogue no: **LUTH C8**
7" Single: Released Sep '88, on Epic, by CBS Records. Deleted 17 Apr '89. Catalogue no: **LUTH 8**
7" Single: Released Jun '89, on Epic, by CBS Records. Catalogue no: **LUTH 11**

BAD BOY HAVIN' A PARTY
Tracks: / Bad boy havin' a party / Once you know.
7" Single: Released Nov '82, on Epic, by CBS Records. Deleted Nov '85. Catalogue no: **EPCA 2776**
12" Single: Released Nov '82, on Epic, by CBS Records. Deleted Nov '85. Catalogue no: **EPCA 132776**

COME BACK
Tracks: / Come back / Second time around / She loves me back / Come back (Keith Cohen extended remix).
CD 5": Released Apr '89, on Epic, by CBS Records. Deleted Oct '89. Catalogue no: **CDLUTH 10**
7" Single: Released Apr '89, on Epic, by CBS Records. Deleted Oct '89. Catalogue no: **LUTH 10**
12" Single: Released Apr '89, on Epic, by CBS Records. Deleted Oct '89. Catalogue no: **LUTHGT 10**
12" Single: Released Apr '89, on Epic, by CBS Records. Deleted Oct '89. Catalogue no: **LUTHQT 10**

GIVE ME THE REASON (SINGLE)
Tracks: / Give me the reason.
7" Single: Released Jan '88, on Epic, by CBS Records. Deleted Aug '88. Catalogue no: **LUTH 5**
7" Single: Released Jul '86, on Epic, by CBS Records. Deleted '89. Catalogue no: **A 7288**
CD 5": Released Jan '88, on Epic, by CBS Records. Deleted Jan '89. Catalogue no: **CD LUTH 5**
12" Pic: Released Jan '88, on Epic, by CBS Records. Deleted Aug '88. Catalogue no: **LUTH P5**
12" Single: Released Jan '88, on Epic, by CBS Records. Deleted Aug '88. Catalogue no: **LUTH T5**

I DIDN'T REALLY MEAN IT
Tracks: / I didn't really mean it.
12" Single: Released 13 Jun '87, on Epic, by CBS Records. Catalogue no: **LUTH T3**
12" Single: Released 13 Jun '87, on Epic, by CBS Records. Deleted Nov '87. Catalogue no: **LUTH QT3**

I GAVE IT UP (WHEN I FELL IN LOVE)
Tracks: / I gave it up (when I fell in love) / She's a super lady / Luther in love (mega mix) (Extra track on 12").
12" Single: Released Apr '88, on Epic, by CBS Records. Deleted Jan '89. Catalogue no: **LUTH QT6**
12" Single: Released Mar '88, on Epic, by CBS Records. Deleted Aug '88. Catalogue no: **LUTH T6**
7" Single: Released Mar '88, on Epic, by CBS Records. Deleted Aug '88. Catalogue no: **LUTH 6**
CD 5": Released Apr '88, on Epic, by CBS Records. Deleted Jan '89. Catalogue no: **CD LUTH 6**

I WANTED YOUR LOVE
Tracks: / I wanted your love / Superstar / Until you come back to me.
7" Single: Released Aug '87, on Epic, by CBS Records. Catalogue no: **A 4279**
12" Single: Released Aug '87, on Epic, by CBS Records. Catalogue no: **TA 4279**

IT'S OVER NOW
Tracks: / It's over now.
12" Single: Released Jun '85, on Epic, by CBS Records. Catalogue no: **TA 6414**
7" Single: Released Jun '85, on Epic, by CBS Records. Catalogue no: **A 6414**

NEVER TOO MUCH (REMIX) (SINGLE)
Tracks: / Never too much (remix) / Glow of love, The.
12" Single: Released Oct '89, on Epic, by CBS Records. Catalogue no: **LUTH T12**
7" Single: Released Oct '89, on Epic, by CBS Records. Catalogue no: **LUTH 12**
Cassingle: Released Oct '89, on Epic, by CBS Records. Catalogue no: **LUTH M12**

NEVER TOO MUCH (SINGLE)
Tracks: / Never too much / Superstar (don't you remember).
CD 3": Released Aug '88, on Epic (USA), by CBS Records (USA). Catalogue no: **34K 05482**
7" Single: Released Feb '83, on Epic, by CBS Records. Deleted '86. Catalogue no: **A 3101**

SEE ME
Tracks: / See me / House is not a home, A.
7" Single: Released Mar '87, on Epic, by CBS Records. Deleted Nov '87. Catalogue no: **LUTH 1**
12" Single: Released Mar '87, on Epic, by CBS Records. Deleted Nov '87. Catalogue no: **LUTH T1**
12" Single: Released May '87, on Epic, by CBS Records. Deleted Nov '87. Catalogue no: **LUTH QT1**

SHE WON'T TALK TO ME
Tracks: / She wont talk to me / Creepin'.
12" Single: Released Feb '89, on Epic, by CBS Records. Deleted 10 Jul '89. Catalogue no: **LUTH QT9**
12" Single: Released Dec '88, on Epic, by CBS Records. Deleted 10 Jul '89. Catalogue no: **LUTH T9**
7" Single: Released Dec '88, on Epic, by CBS Records. Deleted 10 Jul '89. Catalogue no: **LUTH 9**
7" EP: Released 30 Jan '89, on Epic, by CBS Records. Deleted 10 Jul '89. Catalogue no: **LUTHEP 9**
CD 5": Released Dec '88, on Epic, by CBS Records. Deleted 10 Jul '89. Catalogue no: **CDLUTH 9**

SO AMAZING
Tracks: / So amazing / If only for one night / So amazing (instrumental) (On 12" version.) / If only for one night (version) (On LUTH P4 only) / House is not a home, A (On 12" version.).
Note: LUTH P4 is a limited edition picture disc.
7" Single: Released Oct '87, on CBS, by CBS Records. Deleted Jun '88. Catalogue no: **LUTH 4**
12" Single: Released Jul '87, on Epic, by CBS Records. Deleted Jun '88. Catalogue no: **LUTH P4**
CD 5": Released Dec '87, on Epic, by CBS Records. Catalogue no: **CD LUTH 4**
12" Single: Released Oct '87, on CBS, by CBS Records. Deleted Jun '88. Catalogue no: **LUTH T4**

STOP TO LOVE
Tracks: / Stop to love / Stop to love (instrumental).
12" Single: Released Sep '87, on Epic, by CBS Records. Catalogue no: **LUTH T2**
7" EP: Released Sep '87, on Epic, by CBS Records. Catalogue no: **LUTH QT2**
7" Single: Released Sep '87, on Epic, by CBS Records. Catalogue no: **LUTH 2**

SUGAR AND SPICE (I FOUND ME A GIRL)
Tracks: / Sugar and spice (I found me a girl).
7" Single: Released Oct '81, on Epic, by CBS Records. Catalogue no: **EPC A 1662**

THERE'S NOTHING BETTER THAN LOVE (with Gregory Hines)
Tracks: / There's nothing better than love (with Gregory Hines) / Anyone who had a heart / There's nothing better than love (instrumental) / My sensitivity (gets in the way).
Note: 12" and 7" singles are picture bag editions.
7" Single: Released 20 Jun '88, on Epic, by CBS Records. Deleted Jan '89. Catalogue no: **LUTH 7**
CD 5": Released 27 Jun '88, on Epic, by CBS Records. Deleted Jan '89. Catalogue no: **CD LUTH 7**
12" Single: Released 20 Jun '88, on Epic, by CBS Records. Deleted Jan '89. Catalogue no: **LUTH T7**

YOU'RE THE SWEETEST ONE
Tracks: / You're the sweetest one.
7" Single: Released Apr '83, on Epic, by CBS Records. Catalogue no: **A 3313**
12" Single: Released Apr '83, on Epic, by CBS Records. Catalogue no: **TA 3313**

Vandross, Wayne

WOMAN, A
Tracks: / Woman.
7" Single: Released May '82, on Solid Groove, Catalogue no: **SG 009**

Van-Dyke, Jaki

MATTER OF TIME
Tracks: / Matter of time.
7" Single: Released Feb '87, on Pectcode, Deleted '87. Catalogue no: **PECM 2**

Vane

GLAMOROUS BOYS
Tracks: / Glamorous boys / Trails of error.
7" Single: Released May '80, on Island, by Island Records. Deleted May '85. Catalogue no: **WIP 6609**

Vane, James

JUDY'S GONE DOWN
Tracks: / Judy's gone down / Jung lovers.
7" Single: Released Feb '80, on Island, by Island Records. Deleted '83. Catalogue no: **WIP 6538**

Vangelis

CHARIOTS OF FIRE (SINGLE)
Tracks: / Chariots of fire / Eric's theme.
7" Single: Released Aug '84, on Polydor, by Polydor Ltd. Catalogue no: **POSP 246**

HEAVEN AND HELL (SINGLE)
Tracks: / Heaven and hell / Alpha.
7" Single: Released May '81, on RCA, by BMG Records (UK). Deleted May '84. Catalogue no: **RCA 71**

HEAVEN AND HELL, THIRD MOVEMENT
Tracks: / Heaven and hell, third movement.
7" Single: Released Jul '81, on BBC, by BBC Records & Tapes. Deleted '84. Catalogue no: **BBC 1**

WILL OF THE WIND
Tracks: / Will of the wind.
CD 5": Released Sep '88, on Arista, by BMG Records (UK). Catalogue no: **61767**

Vanilla Fudge

Biographical details: An American heavy metal band formed in 1967 as the Pigeons, Vanilla Fudge -- Vince Martell (vocals and guitar), Mark Stein (keyboards), Tim Bogert (bass) and Carmine Appice (drums) -- had a couple of years of fame with the gimmick of playing covers of big rock hits extremely slowly, emulating the time-distorting qualities of soft drugs. With their quasi-gospel harmonies, classical keyboards and elaborate production, this passed for progress at the time. On stage they looked catatonic. Bogert and Appice remained well-known sidesmen in the genre. (Donald Clarke, January 1988.).

YOU KEEP ME HANGIN' ON
Tracks: / You keep me hangin' on.
7" Single: Released Aug '67, on Atlantic, by WEA Records. Deleted '70. Catalogue no: **584 123**

Vanilla Sound Corps

BACK WHERE WE BELONG
Tracks: / Back where we belong.
12" Single: Released Feb '89, on DFM, Catalogue no: **DFM 5**

PASSION
Tracks: / Passion.

VANITY - PRETTY MESS (Released on Motown)

12" Single: Released Jul '89, on House of Chaos, Catalogue no: **CHAOS 121**

Vanity

MECHANICAL EMOTION
Tracks: / Mechanical emotion.
12" Single: Released Jan '85, on Motown, by BMG Records (UK). Catalogue no: **TMGT 1369**
7" Single: Released Jan '85, on Motown, by BMG Records (UK). Catalogue no: **TMG 1369**

PRETTY MESS (see panel on previous page)
Tracks: / Pretty mess / Pretty mess (instr.).
7" Single: Released Sep '84, on Motown, by BMG Records (UK). Catalogue no: **TMG 1360**
12" Single: Released Sep '84, on Motown, by BMG Records (UK). Catalogue no: **TMGT 1360**

UNDER THE INFLUENCE
Tracks: / Under the influence / Wild animal.
12" Single: Released Apr '86, on Motown, by BMG Records (UK). Catalogue no: **ZT 40610**
7" Single: Released Apr '86, on Motown, by BMG Records (UK). Catalogue no: **ZB 40609**

Vanity 6

HE'S SO DULL
Tracks: / He's so dull / Make up / Wet dream.
12" Single: Released Apr '83, on Warner Bros., by WEA Records. Catalogue no: **K 17983 T**
7" Single: Released Apr '83, on Warner Bros., by WEA Records. Catalogue no: **K 17983**

Vanity Fair

HITCHIN' A RIDE
Tracks: / Hitchin' a ride.
7" Single: Released Nov '69, on Page One, by Page One Records. Deleted '72. Catalogue no: **POF 158**

Vanity Fare

DREAMER
Tracks: / Dreamer / Win or lose.
7" Single: Released Apr '86, on Polydor, by Polydor Ltd. Catalogue no: **POSP 789**

EARLY IN THE MORNING
Tracks: / Early in the morning.
7" Single: Released Jul '69, on Page One, by Page One Records. Deleted '72. Catalogue no: **POF 142**

HITCHIN' A RIDE (OLD GOLD)
Tracks: / Hitchin' a ride / Early in the morning.
7" Single: Released Jul '82, on Old Gold, by Old Gold Records. Deleted Jul '88. Catalogue no: **OG 9039**

I LIVE FOR THE SUN
Tracks: / I live for the sun.
7" Single: Released Aug '68, on Page One, by Page One Records. Deleted '71. Catalogue no: **POF 075**

Vannelli, Gino

LIVING INSIDE MYSELF
Tracks: / Living inside myself / Stay with me.
7" Single: Released Apr '81, on Arista, by BMG Records (UK). Catalogue no: **ARIST 390**

Van't Hof, Jasper

PILI-PILI
Tracks: / Pili-pili.
12" Single: Released Jan '85, on WEA, by WEA Records. Catalogue no: **X 9243**

Vanwarmer, Randy

HANGING ON TO HEAVEN
Tracks: / Hanging on to heaven.
7" Single: Released Dec '81, on Avatar, by Avatar Record Corporation. Catalogue no: **AAA 116**

JUST WHEN I NEEDED YOU MOST
Tracks: / Just when I needed you most.
7" Single: Released Jul '81, on Island, by Island Records. Catalogue no: **WIP 6516**

JUST WHEN I NEEDED YOU MOST (OLD GOLD)
Tracks: / Just when I needed you most / I saw the light.
7" Single: Released Oct '88, on Old Gold, by Old Gold Records. Catalogue no: **OG 9800**

SUZI FOUND A WEAPON
Tracks: / Suzi found a weapon / I guess it never hurts to hurt sometimes.
7" Single: Released Feb '82, on Avatar, by Avatar Record Corporation. Catalogue no: **AAA 118**

WHATEVER YOU DECIDE
Tracks: / Whatever you decide / Losing out on love.
7" Single: Released May '80, on Island, by Island Records. Deleted May '83. Catalogue no: **WIP 6611**

Vapors

JIMMIE JONES
Tracks: / Jimmie Jones / Daylight titans.
7" Single: Released Jul '81, on Liberty, by EMI Records. Deleted '84. Catalogue no: **BP 401**

NEWS AT TEN
Tracks: / News at ten / Wasted / Talk talk.
7" Single: Released Jul '80, on United Artists, by EMI Records. Deleted '83. Catalogue no: **BP 345**

SPIDERS
Tracks: / Spiders / Galleries for guns.
7" Single: Released Feb '81, on Liberty, by EMI Records. Deleted May '82. Catalogue no: **BP 385**

TURNING JAPANESE (see panel below)
Tracks: / Turning Japanese / Here comes the judge (live).
7" Single: Released Jan '80, on Liberty, by EMI Records. Deleted Oct '87. Catalogue no: **BP 334**

WAITING FOR THE WEEKEND
Tracks: / Waiting for the weekend / Billy.

VAPOURS - TURNING JAPANESE (Released on Liberty)

7" Single: Released Sep '80, on Liberty, by EMI Records. Deleted '83. Catalogue no: **BP 367**

Vardis

ALL YOU'LL EVER NEED
Tracks: / All you'll ever need / If I were King / Jumping Jack Flash.
7" EP: Released May '81, on Logo, by Logo Records. Catalogue no: **VAR 4**

IF I WERE KING
Tracks: / If I were king.
7" Single: Released Apr '80, on O, Deleted '85. Catalogue no: **QUEL 2/100**

LET'S GO
Tracks: / Let's go.
7" Single: Released Sep '80, on Logo, by Logo Records. Deleted '83. Catalogue no: **VAR 1**

SILVER MACHINE
Tracks: / Silver machine / Come on.
7" Single: Released Mar '81, on Logo, by Logo Records. Deleted Mar '84. Catalogue no: **VAR 3**

STANDING IN THE ROAD
Tracks: / Standing in the road.
7" Single: Released Jan '85, on Big Beat, by Ace Records. Deleted '88. Catalogue no: **NS 103**
12" Single: Released Jan '85, on Big Beat, by Ace Records. Deleted '88. Catalogue no: **NST 103**

TO BE WITH YOU
Tracks: / To be with you / Gary Glitter part 1.
7" Single: Released Feb '82, on Logo, by Logo Records. Catalogue no: **GO 408**

TOO MANY PEOPLE
Tracks: / Too many people / Lion's share.
7" Single: Released Sep '80, on Logo, by Logo Records. Deleted '83. Catalogue no: **VAR 2**

Varukers

DIE FOR YOUR GOVERNMENT
Tracks: / Die for your government.
7" Single: Released Jul '83, on Riot City, by Riot City Records. Catalogue no: **RIOT 27**

DON'T WANNA BE A VICTIM
Tracks: / Don't wanna be a victim.
7" Single: Released Jun '82, on Inferno (2), Catalogue no: **HELL 4**

LED TO THE SLAUGHTER (3 TRACK EP)
Tracks: / Led to the slaughter / End is nigh / You're dead.
7" Single: Released Jan '84, on Riot City, by Riot City Records. Catalogue no: **RIOT 29**

MASSACRED MILLIONS
Tracks: / Massacred millions.
12" Single: Released Nov '84, on Red Rhino, by Red Rhino Records. Catalogue no: **ASS 16**

NO HOPE OF A FUTURE
Tracks: / No hope of a future.
7" Single: Released May '88, on Pogar, Catalogue no: **POGAR 9**

PROTEST AND SURVIVE
Tracks: / Protest and survive.
7" Single: Released Dec '81, on Inferno (2), Catalogue no: **HELL 1**

Vaselines

DYING FOR IT
Tracks: / Dying for it.
12" Single: Released Jan '88, on 53rd & 3rd, by 53rd & 3rd Records. Catalogue no: **AGAAF 17T**
7" Single: Released Mar '88, on 53rd & 3rd, by 53rd & 3rd Records. Catalogue no: **AGAAF 17**

SON OF A GUN
Tracks: / Son of a gun.
12" Single: Released Sep '87, on 53rd & 3rd, by 53rd & 3rd Records. Catalogue no: **AGAAF 10T**

Vatten

DREAMER, THE
Tracks: / Dreamer, the / Rely back.
7" Single: Released Jun '81, on Gutta (Sweden), by Gutta Records (Sweden). Catalogue no: **GUTS 001**

Vaughan, Ben

MY FIRST BAND
Tracks: / My first band.
7" Single: Released '88, on 53rd & 3rd, by 53rd & 3rd Records. Catalogue no: **AGARR 007**

Vaughan, Dale

HOW CAN YOU BE MEAN TO ME
Tracks: / How can you be mean to me.
7" Single: Released Apr '78, on Record Mart, by Record Mart Records. Catalogue no: **RMA 1022**

Vaughan, Frankie

Biographical details:
Born Frank Abelson in Liverpool in 1928, Vaughan had chart hits every year from 1954-68 except one. He was in the film *Let's Make Love* in 1960 with Marilyn Monroe and Yves Montand and was active through the 70's in concerts and cabaret. In '85 he was a surprise choice to replace James Laurenson in the London cast of *42nd Street*. Vaughan's famous theme, *Give Me The Moonlight* -- written in 1918 by Albert Von Tilzer and Lew Brown -- is always associated with the stylish performer, who is a consistent worker with youth projects: the proceeds of his big hit *Green Door* and much else went to the National Association of Boys' Clubs. He was awarded an OBE in 1965. (Donald Clarke, January 1988.).

AM I WASTING MY TIME ON YOU
Tracks: / Am I wasting my time on you.
7" Single: Released Oct '58, on Philips, by Phonogram Ltd. Deleted '61. Catalogue no: **PB 865**

CAN'T GET ALONG WITHOUT YOU
Tracks: / Can't get along without you.
7" Single: Released Mar '58, on Philips, by Phonogram Ltd. Deleted '61. Catalogue no: **PB 793**

COME SOFTLY TO ME
Tracks: / Come softly to me.
7" Single: Released May '59, on Philips, by Phonogram Ltd. Deleted '62. Catalogue no: **PB 913**

DON'T STOP TWIST
Tracks: / Don't stop twist.
7" Single: Released Feb '62, on Philips, by Phonogram Ltd. Deleted '65. Catalogue no: **PB 1219**

DREAMERS
Tracks: / Dreamers / Two different worlds.
7" Single: Released May '84, on PRT, by Castle Communications Records. Catalogue no: **7P 306**

GARDEN OF EDEN
Tracks: / Garden of Eden.
7" Single: Released Jan '57, on Philips, by Phonogram Ltd. Deleted '60. Catalogue no: **PB 660**

GARDEN OF EDEN (OLD GOLD)
Tracks: / Garden of Eden / Green door.
7" Single: Released Aug '82, on Old Gold, by Old Gold Records. Deleted Jul '88. Catalogue no: **OG 9239**

GOTTA HAVE SOMETHING IN THE BANK FRANK
Tracks: / Gotta have something in the bank Frank.
7" Single: Released Nov '57, on Philips, by Phonogram Ltd. Deleted '60. Catalogue no: **PB 751**

GREEN DOOR
Tracks: / Green door.
7" Single: Released Nov '56, on Philips, by Phonogram Ltd. Deleted '59. Catalogue no: **PB 640**

HAPPY DAYS & LONELY NIGHTS
Tracks: / Happy days and lonely nights.
7" Single: Released Jan '55, on H.M.V., by EMI Records. Deleted '58. Catalogue no: **B 10783**

HEART OF A MAN, THE
Tracks: / Heart of a man, The.
7" Single: Released Jul '59, on Philips, by Phonogram Ltd. Deleted '62. Catalogue no: **PB 930**

HELLO DOLLY
Tracks: / Hello dolly.
7" Single: Released Jun '64, on Philips, by Phonogram Ltd. Deleted '67. Catalogue no: **BF 1339**

HERCULES
Tracks: / Hercules.
7" Single: Released Sep '62, on Philips, by Phonogram Ltd. Deleted '65. Catalogue no: **326542 BF**

HEY MAMA
Tracks: / Hey mama.
7" Single: Released Jun '63, on Philips, by Phonogram Ltd. Deleted '66. Catalogue no: **BF 1254**

ISTANBUL
Tracks: / Istanbul.
7" Single: Released Jan '54, on H.M.V., by EMI Records. Deleted '57. Catalogue no: **B 10599**

KEWPIE DOLL
Tracks: / Kewpie doll.
7" Single: Released May '58, on Philips, by Phonogram Ltd. Deleted '61. Catalogue no: **PB 825**

KISSES SWEETER THAN WINE
Tracks: / Kisses sweeter than wine.
7" Single: Released Dec '57, on Philips, by Phonogram Ltd. Deleted '60. Catalogue no:

PB 775

KOOKIE LITTLE PARADISE
Tracks: / Kookie little paradise, A.
7" Single: Released Sep '60, on Philips, by Phonogram Ltd. Deleted '63. Catalogue no: **PB 1054**

LOOP-DE-LOOP
Tracks: / Loop de loop.
7" Single: Released Jan '63, on Philips, by Phonogram Ltd. Deleted '66. Catalogue no: **326566 BF**

MAN ON FIRE
Tracks: / Man on fire.
7" Single: Released Oct '57, on Philips, by Phonogram Ltd. Deleted '60. Catalogue no: **PB 729**

MILORD
Tracks: / Milord.
7" Single: Released Oct '60, on Philips, by Phonogram Ltd. Deleted '63. Catalogue no: **PB 1066**

MY BOY FLAT TOP
Tracks: / My boy flat top.
7" Single: Released Feb '56, on Philips, by Phonogram Ltd. Deleted '59. Catalogue no: **PB 544**

NEVERTHELESS
Tracks: / Nevertheless.
7" Single: Released Feb '68, on Philips, by Phonogram Ltd. Deleted '71. Catalogue no: **DB 8354**

SEVENTEEN
Tracks: / Seventeen.
7" Single: Released Dec '55, on Philips, by Phonogram Ltd. Deleted '58. Catalogue no: **PB 511**

SHOWMANSHIP
Tracks: / Showmanship.
7" Single: Released Nov '83, on T. E. R., by That's Entertainment Records. Catalogue no: **STER 008**

SO TIRED
Tracks: / So tired.
7" Single: Released Nov '67, on Philips, by Phonogram Ltd. Deleted '70. Catalogue no: **DB 8298**

SOMEONE MUST HAVE HURT YOU A LOT
Tracks: / Someone must have hurt you a lot.
7" Single: Released Mar '65, on Philips, by Phonogram Ltd. Deleted '68. Catalogue no: **BF 1394**

THAT'S MY DOLL
Tracks: / That's my doll.
7" Single: Released Jan '59, on Philips, by Phonogram Ltd. Deleted '62. Catalogue no: **PB 895**

THERE MUST BE A WAY (SINGLE)
Tracks: / There must be a way.
7" Single: Released Aug '67, on Philips, by Phonogram Ltd. Deleted '70. Catalogue no: **DB 8248**

THINK BEAUTIFUL THINGS
Tracks: / Think beautiful things / Simple kiss.
7" Single: Released Dec '79, on SRT, by SRT Records. Catalogue no: **SRTS 79425**

TOWER OF STRENGTH
Tracks: / Tower of strength.
7" Single: Released Nov '61, on Philips, by Phonogram Ltd. Deleted '64. Catalogue no: **PB 1195**

TOWER OF STRENGTH (OLD GOLD)
Tracks: / Tower of strength / Wanderin' eyes.
7" Single: Released Aug '82, on Old Gold, by Old Gold Records. Deleted Jul '88. Catalogue no: **OG 9238**

TWEEDLE DEE
Tracks: / Tweedle dee.
7" Single: Released Apr '55, on Philips, by Phonogram Ltd. Deleted '58. Catalogue no: **PB 423**

WALKLIN' TALL
Tracks: / Walkin' tall.
7" Single: Released Sep '59, on Philips, by Phonogram Ltd. Deleted '62. Catalogue no: **PB 931**

WHAT MORE DO YOU WANT
Tracks: / What more do you want me to do ?.
7" Single: Released Jan '60, on Philips, by Phonogram Ltd. Deleted '63. Catalogue no: **PB 985**

WHEN YOUR OLD WEDDING RING WAS NEW
Tracks: / When your old wedding ring was new / Lucky.
7" Single: Released 30 May '87, on Spartan, Catalogue no: **SP 149**

WONDERFUL THINGS
Tracks: / Wonderful things.
7" Single: Released Aug '58, on Philips, by Phonogram Ltd. Deleted '61. Catalogue no: **PB 834**

Vaughan, Malcolm

CHAPEL OF THE ROSES
Tracks: / Chapel of the roses.
7" Single: Released May '57, on H.M.V., by EMI Records. Deleted '60. Catalogue no: **POP 325**

EVERY DAY OF MY LIFE
Tracks: / Everyday of my life.
7" Single: Released Jul '55, on H.M.V., by EMI Records. Deleted '58. Catalogue no: **B 10874**

MORE THAN EVER
Tracks: / More than ever.
7" Single: Released Oct '58, on H.M.V., by EMI Records. Deleted '61. Catalogue no: **POP 538**

MY SPECIAL ANGEL
Tracks: / My special angel.
7" Single: Released Nov '57, on H.M.V., by EMI Records. Deleted '60. Catalogue no: **POP 419**

ST. THERESE OF THE ROSES
Tracks: / St. Therese of the roses.
7" Single: Released Nov '56, on H.M.V., by EMI Records. Deleted '59. Catalogue no: **POP 250**

TO BE LOVED
Tracks: / To be loved.
7" Single: Released Mar '58, on H.M.V., by EMI Records. Deleted '61. Catalogue no: **POP 459**

WAIT FOR ME
Tracks: / Wait for me.
7" Single: Released Feb '59, on H.M.V., by EMI Records. Deleted '62. Catalogue no: **POP 590**

WITH YOUR LOVE
Tracks: / With your love.
7" Single: Released Jan '56, on H.M.V., by EMI Records. Deleted '59. Catalogue no: **POP 130**

WORLD IS MINE, THE
Tracks: / World is mine, The.
7" Single: Released Apr '57, on H.M.V., by EMI Records. Deleted '60. Catalogue no: **POP 303**

Vaughan, Norman

SWINGING IN THE RAIN
Tracks: / Swinging in the rain.
7" Single: Released May '62, on Pye, Deleted '65. Catalogue no: **7 N 15438**

Vaughan, Sarah

Biographical details:
As with Ella Fitzgerald there is argument about whether Vaughan -- also known as Sassy, Sass and The Divine One -- is a jazz singer, and, as with Ella, the argument is academic: with her effortless swing, wide vocal range, rare but accurate scatting, perfect pitch and vocal colour she is one of the century's great singers. She joined the Earl Hines band in 1944 and when Billy Eckstine left to form his own band she was a founder member. She soon went solo, often duetting with Eckstine. Most of her recordings were on Mercury and Verve, now owned by Polydor, and she later recorded for Norman Granz's Pablo label. She often sang with symphony orchestras in the 1980's (*Gershwin Live!* with the Los Angeles Philharmonic, conducted by Michael Tilson Thomas; also sang in London studio recording of *South Pacific* '86 on CBS, with Kiri Te Kanawa, Jose Carreras in leading roles.). One of her most unusual projects was recording songs based on poems by Pope John Paul II at a live concert in Dusseldorf in 1985: *The Planet Is Alive ... Let It Live* had the Pope's poems adapted in English by lyricist Gene Lees to music by Italian composers. (Donald Clarke, January 1985.).

BROKEN HEARTED MELODY
Tracks: / Broken hearted melody.
7" Single: Released Sep '59, on Mercury (EMI), Deleted '62. Catalogue no: **AMT 1057**

BROKEN HEARTED MELODY (OLD GOLD)
Tracks: / Broken hearted melody / Passing strangers.
7" Single: Released Jan '85, on Old Gold, by Old Gold Records. Catalogue no: **OG 9476**

LET'S
Tracks: / Let's / Serenata.
7" Single: Released Dec '60, on Columbia, by EMI Records. Deleted '63. Catalogue no: **DB 4542**

PASSING STRANGERS (SINGLE)
Tracks: / Passing Strangers / Wedding.
7" Single: Released Oct '80, on Classic Cuts, Catalogue no: **CUT 106**

Vaughn, Billy

SHIFTING WHISPERING SANDS
Tracks: / Shifting, whispering sands.
7" Single: Released Jan '56, on London-American, Deleted '59. Catalogue no: **HLD 8205**

THREEPENNY OPERA, THEME FROM
Tracks: / Threepenny opera, Theme from.
7" Single: Released Mar '56, on London-American, Deleted '59. Catalogue no: **HLD 8238**

Vaya Con Dios

JUST A FRIEND OF MINE
Tracks: / Just a friend of mine / Philadelphia / Just a friend of mine (long version) (Available on 12" only).
7" Single: Released Apr '89, on Ariola, by BMG Records (UK). Catalogue no: **112147**
12" Single: Released Apr '89, on Ariola, by BMG Records (UK). Catalogue no: **612147**

Vaynes

BABY CRUEL
Tracks: / Baby cruel.
12" Single: Released 17 Jul '87, on Vanity, Catalogue no: **VAN 2T**

BIG CITIES
Tracks: / Big cities.
12" Single: Released 23 Apr '88, on Ediesta, Catalogue no: **CALC 050**

MISTER FIX IT
Tracks: / Midnight sun / Mister fix it.
12" Single: Released Feb '87, on Vanity, Catalogue no: **VAN 1T**
7" Single: Released Feb '87, on Vanity, Catalogue no: **VAN 1**

ROCK'N'ROLL CRIME
Tracks: / Rock 'n' roll crime / Rock 'n' roll crime / Cry mean angel / Nightshift.
12" Single: Released 20 Feb '88, on Vanity, Catalogue no: **VAN 003T**

Vazz

FEVERPITCH
Tracks: / Feverpitch.
12" Single: Released Feb '89, on Cathexis, by Cathexis Records. Catalogue no: **CRV 7403**

PEARLS
Tracks: / Pearls.
12" Single: Released 31 Oct '87, on CRV, Catalogue no: **CRV 7405**

VIOLENT SILENCE
Tracks: / Violent silence.
7" Single: Released Jul '85, on Cathexis, by Cathexis Records. Deleted '88. Catalogue no: **CRV 5401**

VDU's

DON'T CRY
Tracks: / Don't cry.
7" Single: Released Apr '80, on Thin Sliced, by Thin Sliced Records. Catalogue no: **LYN 7865/14**

Vee, Bobby

Biographical details: Born Robert Velline in 1943 in North Dakota, Vee's first break as a pop singer came as a result of Buddy Holly's death: his group, the Shadows, depped at a dance in Iowa when Holly didn't make it. But he turned out to have staying power of his own, with 11 American Top Forty hits to 1963, the biggest being *Take Good Care Of My Baby* and *The Night Has A Thousand Eyes*. He was equally popular in Britain, with 10 hits from 1961-63. The album Bobby Vee Meets The Critics in '62 was much acclaimed by pop purists and established the Holly connection once more. (Donald Clarke, January 1988.).

BOBBY TOMORROW
Tracks: / Bobby tomorrow.
7" Single: Released Jun '63, on Liberty, by EMI Records. Deleted '66. Catalogue no: **LIB 55530**

DEVIL OR ANGEL
Tracks: / Devil or angel.
7" Single: Released Sep '79, on Scratch, by Scratch Records. Deleted '82. Catalogue no: **HS 402**

FOREVER KIND OF LOVE, A
Tracks: / Forever kind of love, A.
7" Single: Released Sep '62, on Liberty, by EMI Records. Deleted '65. Catalogue no: **LIB 10046**

HOW MANY TEARS
Tracks: / How many tears.
7" Single: Released Aug '61, on London-American, Deleted '64. Catalogue no: **HLG 9389**

MORE THAN I CAN SAY
Tracks: / More than I can say.
7" Single: Released Apr '61, on London-American, Deleted '64. Catalogue no: **HLG 9316**

NIGHT HAS A THOUSAND EYES, (THE)
Tracks: / Night has a thousand eyes, The.
7" Single: Released Sep '79, on United Artists, by EMI Records. Catalogue no: **UP 36529**
7" Single: Released Feb '63, on Liberty, by EMI Records. Deleted '66. Catalogue no: **LIB 10069**

PLEASE DON'T ASK ABOUT BARBARA
Tracks: / Please don't ask about Barbara.
7" Single: Released Mar '62, on Liberty, by EMI Records. Deleted '65. Catalogue no: **LIB 55419**

RUBBER BALL
Tracks: / Rubber ball.
7" Single: Released Jan '61, on London-American, Deleted '64. Catalogue no: **HLG 9255**

RUN TO HIM
Tracks: / Run to him.
7" Single: Released Dec '61, on London-American, Deleted '64. Catalogue no: **HLG 9470**
7" Single: Released '80, on USA, by Charly Records. Catalogue no: **LR 1703**

RUN TO HIM (OLD GOLD)
Tracks: / Run to him / More than I can say.
7" Single: Released Mar '87, on Old Gold, by Old Gold Records. Deleted Sep '89. Catalogue no: **OG 9647**

SHARING YOU
Tracks: / Sharing you.
7" Single: Released Jun '62, on Liberty, by EMI Records. Deleted '65. Catalogue no: **LIB 55451**

TAKE GOOD CARE OF MY BABY
Tracks: / Take good care of my baby.
7" Single: Released Oct '61, on London-American, Deleted '64. Catalogue no: **HLG 9438**
7" Single: Released Jul '84, on EMI Golden 45's, by EMI Records. Catalogue no: **G45 34**
7" Single: Released Sep '79, on United Artists, by EMI Records. Catalogue no: **UP 36528**

Vee, Vivienne

DESTINY
Tracks: / Destiny / Eve of destruction.
12" Single: Released Apr '84, on Banana, Catalogue no: **FRUIT 3T**
7" Single: Released Apr '84, on Banana, Catalogue no: **FRUIT 3**

HEARTBEAT
Tracks: / Heartbeat.
7" Single: Released Oct '87, on Carrere, Catalogue no: **CAR 421**
12" Single: Released Oct '87, on Carrere, Catalogue no: **CART 421**

Vee VV

BOOM SLUMP EP
Tracks: / Boom slump.
7" Single: Released Mar '86, on Vinyl Drip, by Vinyl Drip Records. Catalogue no: **DRIP 4**

KINDEST CUT
Tracks: / Kindest cut.
7" Single: Released Jul '85, on Cathexis, by Cathexis Records. Deleted '88. Catalogue no: **CRV 5455**

Veerman, Piet

SAILIN' HOME
Tracks: / Sailin' home / Town where you was born, The / Sailin' home (overwhelming version) (Extra track available on 12" version only.) / Sailin' home (power version) (Track available on 12" version only.) / Town where you was born (instrumental) (Only on 12" single.).
7" Single: Released Nov '87, on CBS, by CBS Records. Deleted Jun '88. Catalogue no: **650448 7**
12" Single: Released '87, on CBS, by CBS Records. Catalogue no: **UNKNOWN**

Vega

MOTHER EGYPT
Tracks: / Mother Egypt.
7" Single: Released Feb '83, on Red Bus, by Red Bus Records. Catalogue no: **RBUS 77**

NOSTRADAMUS
Tracks: / Nostradamus / China town.
12" Single: Released Aug '82, on Red Bus, by Red Bus Records. Catalogue no: **RBUSL 72**
7" Single: Released Aug '82, on Red Bus, by Red Bus Records. Catalogue no: **RBUS 72**

Vega, Alan

JUKEBOX BABE
Tracks: / Jukebox babe.
7" Single: Released Nov '81, on Celluloid (Island), by Island Records. Catalogue no: **WIP 6744**
12" Single: Released Nov '81, on Celluloid (Island), by Island Records. Catalogue no: **12WIP 6744**

ON THE RUN
Tracks: / On the run.
12" Single: Released Oct '85, on Elektra, by Elektra Records (UK). Catalogue no: **EKR 24T**
7" Single: Released Oct '85, on Elektra, by Elektra Records (UK). Catalogue no: **EKR 24**

Vega, Suzanne

COMPACT HITS: SUZANNE VEGA
Tracks: / Luka / Left of centre / Neighbourhood girls / Queen and the soldier, The.
CD 5": Released Aug '88, on A&M, by A&M Records. Catalogue no: **AMCD 912**

GYPSY
Tracks: / Gypsy / Cracking (live) / Knight movies (live) (Track on 12" version only.).
7" Single: Released Oct '86, on A&M, by A&M Records. Deleted Mar '88. Catalogue no: **AM 349**
12" Single: Released Oct '86, on A&M, by A&M Records. Deleted '88. Catalogue no: **AMY 349**

LEFT OF CENTRE
Tracks: / Left of centre / Undertow / Left of centre (live) (Track on 10" version only.) / Freeze tag (live) (Track on 10" version only.) / Cracking (Alternative track on compact disc single.).
10" single: Released May '86, on A&M, by A&M Records. Deleted '88. Catalogue no: **AMX 320**
7" Single: Released May '86, on A&M, by A&M Records. Deleted '88. Catalogue no: **AM 320**
CD 5": Released May '86, on A&M, by A&M Records. Catalogue no: **CDQ 320**

LUKA
Tracks: / Luka / Straight lines (live) (On 12" only) / Neighbourhood girls (On 12" & cassette only) / Neighbourhood girls (live) (Only on 3"CD single import.) / Left of centre (live) (Only on 3"CD single import.).
CD 3": Released Sep '88, on A&M (USA), by A&M Records (USA). Catalogue no: **CC 31003**
12" Single: Released May '87, on A&M, by A&M Records. Deleted 1 Aug '88. Catalogue no: **VEGA 12**
Cassingle: Released 23 May '87, on A&M, by A&M Records. Deleted Feb '89. Catalogue no: **VEGAC 10**
CD 5": Released Aug '88, on A&M, by A&M Records. Catalogue no: **AMC 912**
10" single: Released May '87, on A&M, by A&M Records. Deleted 1 Aug '88. Catalogue no: **VEGA 10**
7" Single: Released May '87, on A&M, by A&M Records. Deleted 1 Aug '88. Catalogue no: **VEGA 1**

MARLENE ON THE WALL
Tracks: / Marlene on the wall / Small blue thing (live) / Neighbourhood girls (Track on 12" version only.) / Straight lines (live) (Track on 12" version only.).
7" Single: Released Aug '85, on A&M, by A&M Records. Deleted '88. Catalogue no: **AM 275**
7" Single: Released Mar '86, on A&M, by A&M Records. Catalogue no: **AM 309**
10" single: Released Mar '86, on A&M, by A&M Records. Deleted 1 Aug '88. Catalogue no: **AMY 309**

SMALL BLUE THING
Tracks: / Small blue thing / Queen and the soldier, The / Black widow station (Track on initial quantity in double pack only.) / Some journey (Track on initial quantity in double pack only.).
7" Single: Released Jan '86, on A&M, by A&M Records. Deleted '88. Catalogue no: **AM 294**

SOLITUDE STANDING (SINGLE)
Tracks: / Left of centre / Solitude standing.
7" Single: Released 31 Oct '87, on A&M, by A&M Records. Deleted 1 Aug '88. Catalogue no: **VEGA 3**
12" Single: Released 31 Oct '87, on A&M, by A&M Records. Deleted Aug '88. Catalogue no: **VEGA 312**
10" single: Released 31 Oct '87, on A&M, by A&M Records. Deleted 1 Aug '88. Catalogue no: **VEGA 310**
CD 5": Released May '88, on A&M (France). Catalogue no: **390 300 2**
CD 5": Released '88, on A&M, by A&M Records. Deleted Feb '89. Catalogue no: **VEGCD 3**

TOM'S DINER
Tracks: / Tom's diner / Left of centre / Luka (live) (Extra track on 10").
Note: The 12" and limited collectors' edition of 10", cassette and C.D. carry exclusive live versions of "Luka" and "Tom's Diner".
7" Single: Released Jul '87, on A&M, by A&M Records. Deleted 1 Aug '88. Catalogue no: **VEGA 2**
12" Single: Released Jul '87, on A&M, by A&M Records. Deleted 1 Aug '88. Catalogue no: **VEGA 212**
Cassingle: Released Jul '87, on A&M, by A&M Records. Deleted Feb '89. Catalogue no: **VEGAC 210**
CD 5": Released Jul '87, on A&M, by A&M Records. Catalogue no: **VEGCD 2**
10" single: Released Jul '87, on A&M, by A&M Records. Deleted 1 Aug '88. Catalogue no: **VEGA 210**

Vega, Tata

GET IT UP FOR LOVE
Tracks: / Get it up for love.
7" Single: Released Oct '81, on Motown, by BMG Records (UK). Catalogue no: **TMG 1140**
12" Single: Released Oct '81, on Motown, by BMG Records (UK). Catalogue no: **TMGT 1140**

LOVE YOUR NEIGHBOUR
Tracks: / Love your neighbour / There's love in the world.
7" Single: Released Oct '81, on Motown, by BMG Records (UK). Catalogue no: **TMG 1230**
12" Single: Released Oct '81, on Motown, by BMG Records (UK). Catalogue no: **TMGT 1230**

MISS CELIE'S BLUES (SISTER)
Tracks: / Celie shaves Mr. / Sarification ceremony.
7" Single: Released Jul '86, on Qwest (USA), by Qwest Records (USA). Deleted Jun '87. Catalogue no: **W 8754**

YOU KEEP ME HANGIN' ON
Tracks: / You keep me hangin' on / You better watch out.
7" Single: Released Oct '81, on Motown, by BMG Records (UK). Catalogue no: **TMG 1219**
12" Single: Released Oct '81, on Motown, by BMG Records (UK). Catalogue no: **TMGT 1219**

Vegas, Jet

YOU CAN'T HOLD THAT AGAINST ME
Tracks: / You can't hold that against me.
CD 5": Released Feb '89, on MCA, by MCA Records. Catalogue no: **DMCAT 1318**
12" Single: Released Feb '89, on MCA, by MCA Records. Catalogue no: **MCAT 1318**
7" Single: Released Feb '89, on MCA, by MCA Records. Deleted 1 Jul '89. Catalogue no: **MCA 1318**

Veidt, Conrad

WHEN THE LIGHTHOUSE SHINES ACROSS THE BAY
Tracks: / When the lighthouse shines across the bay / Me and my dog.
7" Single: Released Oct '80, on EMI, by EMI Records. Deleted Oct '83. Catalogue no: **POP 2021**

Veil

HEAVY HEART
Tracks: / Is this sin (watching the nite world work).
12" Single: Released Apr '86, on Andusias International, Catalogue no: **AIR 001**

MANIKIN
Tracks: / Manikin.
12" Single: Released Oct '84, on Clay, by Clay Records. Deleted '88. Catalogue no: **12 CLAY 39**

TWIST
Tracks: / Twist.
7" Single: Released Aug '85, on Clay, by Clay Records. Deleted '88. Catalogue no: **CLAY 45**

Veira

LET'S GET HOT
Tracks: / Let's get hot / Let's get hot (version).
12" Single: Released Sep '89, on Beat Box, by Beat Box Records. Catalogue no: **BBOX T6**

Veira, Elvis

GOOD STUFF
Tracks: / Good stuff.
7" Single: Released Sep '88, on Beat Box, by Beat Box Records. Catalogue no: **BBOX 2**

Veitch, Champion Doug

JUMPING INTO LOVE
Tracks: / Jumping into love.
7" Single: Released Sep '85, on Making Waves, by Celtic Music. Catalogue no: **DOUG 1**
12" Single: Released Sep '85, on Making Waves, by Celtic Music. Catalogue no: **DOUG 1 12**

LUMIERE URBAN
Tracks: / Lumiere urban.
7" Single: Released Oct '82, on Greensleeves, by Greensleeves Records. Catalogue no: **RUM 1**

MAGARITA
Tracks: / Margarita (Mescales mix) / One black night.
12" Single: Released Aug '86, on Conga, Catalogue no: **CON 002**
12" Single: Released 8 Nov '88, on Conga, Catalogue no: **CON 002 RV**

ONE BLACK NIGHT
Tracks: / One black night.
12" Single: Released May '85, on Drum, Catalogue no: **RUM 6**

Vela, Rosie

FOOLS PARADISE
Tracks: / Fools paradise / Fools paradise (version).
7" Single: Released Jan '88, on A&M, by A&M Records. Deleted '88. Catalogue no: **AM 396**
12" Single: Released Jan '88, on A&M, by A&M Records. Deleted 1 Aug '88. Catalogue no: **AMY 396**

INTERLUDE
Tracks: / Interlude / Taxi.
12" Single: on A&M, by A&M Records. Deleted 1 Aug '88. Catalogue no: **AMY 384**
7" Single: Released Feb '87, on A&M, by A&M Records. Deleted 1 Aug '88. Catalogue no: **AM 384**

MAGIC SMILE
Tracks: / Magic smile / Second emotion.
12" Single: Released '88, on A&M, by A&M Records. Deleted 1 Aug '88. Catalogue no: **AMY 369**
7" Single: Released Nov '86, on A&M, by A&M Records. Deleted '88. Catalogue no: **AM 369**

Vellum Stairs

JAMIE'S COMING BACK
Tracks: / Jamie's coming back / Writing on the wall.
7" Single: Released Sep '89, on Markar, Catalogue no: **JUNE 01002**

Velore And Double O

YOU'RE UGLY
Tracks: / Your ugly (12" version) / Your ugly (video version) / Your ugly (dub) / Your ugly (radio version).
12" Single: Released Aug '87, on 10 Records, by Virgin Records. Deleted May '88. Catalogue no: **TENT 183**

Velvelettes

NEEDLE IN A HAYSTACK
Tracks: / Needle in a haystack / He was really saying something.
7" Single: Released Mar '83, on Motown, by BMG Records (UK). Catalogue no: **TMG 1124**

THESE THINGS WILL KEEP ME LOVING YOU
Tracks: / These things will keep me loving you.
7" Single: Released Oct '81, on Motown, by BMG Records (UK). Deleted '82. Catalogue no: **TMG 780**

Velvet Underground

Biographical details: American 60's rock band the Velvet Underground had a profound influence that was not recognised until after they had split up. Singer-songwriter Lou Reed recruited classically-trained bassist Sterling Morrison and drummer Maureen Tucker and John Cale joined in 1966 when they became the Velvet Underground and were taken up by Andy Warhol for his multimedia organisation the Factory and his Exploding Plastic Inevitable tour. Nico joined from the Factory and Warhol was nominal producer of their first LP, 1967's The Velvet Underground & Nico, on Verve. With Warhol's famous banana sleeve art, drug songs like Heroin and I'm Waiting For The Man, Venus In Furs (sado-masochist) and Nico's vocal on I'll Be Your Mirror, it did not get a lot of airplay. Nico left, Warhol lost interest and their subsequent albums did not do terribly well commercially. But the influence of their dark urban vision continues to be felt. Cale was replaced by Doug Yule, Tucker by Billy Yule; Reed left and the Yule brothers carried on until 1972. (Donald Clarke, January 1988.).

HEROIN
Tracks: / Heroin / Venus in furs / I'm waiting for the man / Run, run, run.
12" Single: Released Nov '82, on Polydor, by Polydor Ltd. Deleted Nov '85. Catalogue no: **POSPX 603**

VELVET UNDERGROUND: INTERVIEW PICTURE DISC
12" Single: Released '87, on Talkies, Catalogue no: **VELVET 1**

VENUS IN FURS
Tracks: / Venus in furs / All tomorrow's parties.
12" Single: Released 28 Mar '88, on Old Gold, by Old Gold Records. Catalogue no: **OG 4051**

WAITING FOR THE MAN
Tracks: / Waiting for the man / Heroin.
12" Single: Released Feb '88, on Old Gold, by Old Gold Records. Catalogue no: **OG 4049**

Velvets

THAT LUCKY OLD SUN
Tracks: / That lucky old sun.
7" Single: Released May '61, on London-American, Deleted '64. Catalogue no: **HLU 9328**

TONIGHT
Tracks: / Tonight.
7" Single: Released Aug '61, on London-American, Deleted '64. Catalogue no: **HLU 9372**

Velvette

GOT TO HAVE YOUR LOVE
Tracks: / Got to have your love.
7" Single: Released Jul '84, on Electricity, by Electricity Records. Deleted '88. Catalogue no: **TRIC 10**

NOTHING'S WORSE THAN BEING ALONE
Tracks: / Nothing's worse than being alone.
12" Single: Released Apr '84, on Electricity, by Electricity Records. Deleted '88. Catalogue no: **ELECT 4**

Vendetta

COULD HAVE DONE WITHOUT IT
Tracks: / Row, The / Living one day at a time (Extra track on 12" version only).
7" Single: Released Aug '86, on Plaza, by Plaza Records. Catalogue no: **PLAZA 021**
12" Single: Released Aug '86, on Plaza, by Plaza Records. Catalogue no: **PLAZA 021 T**

DON'T LET THE WORLD DRAG YOU UNDER
Tracks: / Don't let the world drag you under / Don't let the world drag you under (instrumental).
7" Single: Released Nov '88, on Plaza, by Plaza Records. Catalogue no: **PZA 042**

IF YOU WANT MY LOVE
Tracks: / If you want my love.
7" Single: Released Jun '84, on Plaza, by Plaza Records. Catalogue no: **PLAZA 009**
12" Single: Released Jun '84, on Plaza, by Plaza Records. Catalogue no: **PLAZAT 009**
7" Single: Released Jun '85, on Plaza, by Plaza Records. Catalogue no: **7 PLAZA 015**

I'VE GOT YOU IN MY HEART
Tracks: / I've got you in my heart.
12" Single: Released Aug '88, on Plaza, by Plaza Records. Catalogue no: **PZA 037T**
7" Single: Released Aug '88, on Plaza, by Plaza Records. Catalogue no: **PZA 037**

I'VE GOT YOU IN MY SIGHTS
Tracks: / I've got you in my sights / One step at a time.
7" Single: Released Jan '84, on Plaza, by Plaza Records. Catalogue no: **7 PLAZA 8**
12" Single: Released Jan '84, on Plaza, by Plaza Records. Catalogue no: **PLAZAT 8**

I'VE GOTTA SEE JANE
Tracks: / I've gotta see Jane.
7" Single: Released Apr '83, on Plaza, by Plaza Records. Catalogue no: **PLAZA 004**

LARSEN EFFECT, THE
Tracks: / Larsen effect.
7" Single: Released Oct '85, on Plaza, by Plaza Records. Catalogue no: **PLAZA 016**

SO DO I
Tracks: / So do I.
7" Single: Released Oct '83, on Plaza, by Plaza Records. Catalogue no: **PLAZA 006**

SO DO I (1986)
Tracks: / So do I (remix 86) / One step at a time.
12" Single: Released Feb '86, on Plaza, by Plaza Records. Catalogue no: **PLAZA 018T**
7" Single: Released Feb '86, on Plaza, by Plaza Records. Catalogue no: **PLAZA 018**

SO DO I (1989)
Tracks: / So do I.
7" Single: Released Aug '89, on Plaza, by Plaza Records. Catalogue no: **PZA 051**
12" Single: Released Aug '89, on Plaza, by Plaza Records. Catalogue no: **12PZA 051**

SOMEWHERE IN THE NIGHT
Tracks: / Somewhere in the night / Don't let the world drag you under / I've got you in my heart.
12" Single: Released Mar '85, on Plaza, by Plaza Records. Catalogue no: **PLAZA 013T**
7" Single: Released Mar '85, on Plaza, by Plaza Records. Catalogue no: **PLAZA 013**

Vendino Pact

IDENTICAL TWINS
Tracks: / Identical twins.

7" Single: Released May '82, on Manifesto, Catalogue no: **MAN 1**

Veneice

THIS GOOD GOOD FEELING
Tracks: / This good good feeling / This good good feeling (radio mix).
12" Single: Released Nov '86, on LGR, Catalogue no: **LGR 013**

Vengeance

ROCK'N'ROLL SHOWER
Tracks: / Rock 'n' roll shower / Code of honour / Only the wind (special remix) (Extra track on 12" version only.) / Deathride to glory (live) (Extra track on 12" version only.).
12" Single: Released 8 Feb '88, on Epic, by CBS Records. Deleted Aug '88. Catalogue no: **651149 6**
7" Single: Released 8 Feb '88, on Epic, by CBS Records. Deleted Aug '88. Catalogue no: **651149 7**

Venice

NOBODY
Tracks: / Nobody.
7" Single: Released Mar '83, on Foxy, by Foxy Records. Catalogue no: **CUB 2**

Venigmas

RED REVENGE
Tracks: / Red revenge.
7" Single: on Graduate, by Graduate Records. Deleted Jan '87. Catalogue no: **GRAD 2**

STRANGELOVE
Tracks: / Strangelove / Souls on fire.
7" Single: Released Feb '82, on Biba, Catalogue no: **TYP 001**

Venika

IN THE FUN
Tracks: / In the fun.
12" Single: Released Nov '85, on E.G., by E.G. Records. Catalogue no: **EGOX 25**

Venna

WATCHING YOU WATCHING YOU
Tracks: / Watching you watching you.
12" Single: Released Apr '83, on Buddah, by Buddah Records Inc.(USA). Catalogue no: **BDSL 500**
7" Single: Released Apr '83, on Buddah, by Buddah Records Inc.(USA). Catalogue no: **BDS 500**

Venom

BLOOD LUST
Tracks: / Blood lust / In nomine satanus.
7" Single: Released Aug '82, on Neat, by Neat Records. Catalogue no: **NEAT 13**

DIE HARD
Tracks: / Die hard / Acid queen / Bursting out.
7" Single: Released May '83, on Neat, by Neat Records. Catalogue no: **NEAT 27**
12" Single: Released May '83, on Neat, by Neat Records. Catalogue no: **NEAT 27 12**

IN LEAGUE WITH SANTAN
Tracks: / In league with Satan / Live like an angel.
7" Single: Released Jan '82, on Neat, by Neat Records. Catalogue no: **NEAT 08**

LIVE IN '85
Tracks: / Teachers pet / Witching hour / Poison.
12" Single: Released Dec '85, on Neat, by Neat Records. Catalogue no: **NEAT 53 12**

MANITOU
Tracks: / Manitou / Woman.
7" Single: Released Oct '84, on Neat, by Neat Records. Catalogue no: **NEAT 43**
7" Pic: Released Feb '85, on Neat, by Neat Records. Catalogue no: **NEATP 43**
Cassingle: Released Feb '85, on Neat, by Neat Records. Catalogue no: **NEATC 43**
12" Single: Released Oct '84, on Neat, by Neat Records. Catalogue no: **NEAT 43 12**

NIGHTMARE
Tracks: / Nightmare / Satanchrist / F.O.A.D. / Need a lot of lovin / Rock me hard / Breakaway.
7" Pic: Released Sep '85, on Neat, by Neat Records. Catalogue no: **NEATP 47**
Cassingle: Released Aug '85, on Neat, by Neat Records. Catalogue no: **NEATC 47**
7" Single: Released Aug '85, on Neat, by Neat Records. Catalogue no: **NEAT 47**
12" Single: Released Aug '85, on Neat, by Neat Records. Catalogue no: **NEAT 47 12**
12" Single: Released Sep '85, on Neat, by Neat Records. Catalogue no: **NEATS 47**

WARHEAD
Tracks: / Warhead / Lady lust.
7" Single: Released Jan '84, on Neat, by Neat Records. Catalogue no: **NEAT 38**
12" Single: Released Jan '84, on Neat, by Neat Records. Catalogue no: **NEAT 38 12**

Venture

LOVE COMES AROUND
Tracks: / Shine / Love comes around.
12" Single: Released Oct '86, on Disco Tex, Catalogue no: **DT 5**

VENTURE MISCELLANY, A
Tracks: / Oiche nollag / Christmas eve: *Various artists* / I am with you: *Various artists* / Myoho: *Various artists* / Uber den wolken: *Various artists*.
Note: Venture label 4 track selection CD/EP
CD 5": Released Aug '88, on Venture (2), by Virgin Records. Catalogue no: **EVENT 1**

Ventures

Biographical details: An instrumental rock 'n' roll group formed in Seattle in 1959, the Ventures are guitarists Don Wilson and Bob Bogle, bassist Nokie Edwards and drummer Howie Johnson. Their clean, bright sound, with bags of tremelo, was copied by countless other groups. They soon gave up singles for albums, superby recorded. They are particularly popular in Japan, where they were the first foreign members of the Conservatory of Music in recognition of 40 million-plus sales. They are still going strong in clubs and cabaret. (Donald Clarke, January 1988.).

HAWAII FIVE O'
Tracks: / Hawaii five-O.
7" Single: Released '80, on Liberty, by EMI Records. Catalogue no: **Unknown**

LULLABY OF THE LEAVES
Tracks: / Lullaby of the leaves.
7" Single: Released May '61, on London-American, Deleted '64. Catalogue no: **HLG 9344**

PERFIDIA
Tracks: / Perfidia.
7" Single: Released Dec '60, on London-American, Deleted '63. Catalogue no: **HLG 9232**

RAM-BUNK-SHUSH
Tracks: / Ram-bunk-shush.
7" Single: Released Mar '61, on London-American, Deleted '64. Catalogue no: **HLG 9292**

WALK DON'T RUN
Tracks: / Walk don't run.
7" Single: Released Sep '60, on Top Rank (1), Deleted '63. Catalogue no: **JAR 417**
7" Single: Released '80, on Liberty, by EMI Records. Catalogue no: **LR 2010**
7" Single: Released Aug '84, on EMI (Holland), by EMI Records. Catalogue no: **1A 006 83180**

WALK DON'T RUN (OLD GOLD)
Tracks: / Walk don't run / Perfidia.
7" Single: Released Mar '87, on Old Gold, by Old Gold Records. Deleted Sep '89. Catalogue no: **OG 9645**

Venus

TWILIGHT ZONE
Tracks: / Twilight zone / I'm gonna set you alight.
12" Single: Released Jun '86, on Passion, by Skratch Records. Catalogue no: **PASH 58(12)**

Venus Fly Trap

MORPHINE
Tracks: / Morphine.
7" Single: Released May '88, on Danceteria, Catalogue no: **TUE 872**

NEW
Tracks: / New.
7" Single: Released May '88, on Danceteria, Catalogue no: **TUES 881**

Venus In Furs

ALMOST
Tracks: / Almost / Almost (part 2) / Fun house in dub.
12" Single: Released Apr '89, on Backs, by Backs Recording Co.. Catalogue no: **12INCH 116**

LOVE LIES
Tracks: / Love lies.
12" Single: Released May '86, on Backs, by Backs Recording Co.. Catalogue no: **12 NCH 107**

MOMENTO MORI
Tracks: / Momento mori.
7" Pic: Released Dec '85, on Backs, by Backs Recording Co.. Catalogue no: **PNCH 105**
7" Single: Released Jul '84, on Movement, by Movement Records. Deleted '87. Catalogue no: **MOVEMENT 001**

Vera

TAKE ME TO THE BRIDGE
Tracks: / Take me to the bridge / Different people.
7" Single: Released Sep '81, on Carrere America (USA), by PolyGram Rec.Inc.(USA). Catalogue no: **CAR 194**
12" Single: Released Sep '81, on Carrere America (USA), by PolyGram Rec.Inc.(USA). Catalogue no: **CAR 194 T**

BILLY VERA - AT THIS MOMENT (Released on Fanfare)

Vera, Billy

AT THIS MOMENT (LIVE) (see panel above)
Tracks: / At this moment / Corner of the night.
12" Single: Released Feb '87, on Fanfare, by Captain Billy's Music. Catalogue no: **12 FAN 10**
7" Single: Released Feb '87, on Fanfare, by Captain Billy's Music. Catalogue no: **FAN 10**

Verano, Mario

GET UP
Tracks: / Get up / From Tokyo to Frisco.
12" Single: Released Mar '81, on EMI, by EMI Records. Catalogue no: **12 EMI 5152**
7" Single: Released Mar '81, on EMI, by EMI Records. Catalogue no: **EMI 5152**

Verbal Assault

TINY GIANTS
Tracks: / Tiny giants.
7" Single: Released Oct '88, on Kunkurrel, Catalogue no: **K 100/115**

Verdi, Giuseppe

CUPID
Tracks: / Cupid: *Various artists.*
12" Single: Released Oct '85, on Carrere, Catalogue no: **CART 375**

Vergat, Vic

DOWN TO THE BONE (SINGLE)
Tracks: / Down to the bone.
7" Single: Released Oct '81, on Harvest (1), by EMI Records. Catalogue no: **ARH 5216**

WALK AWAY RENEE
Tracks: / Walk away Renee / You and me.
7" Single: Released Jan '83, on Harvest (1), by EMI Records. Catalogue no: **HAR 5223**

Vergo, Danny

KICK A HACK
Tracks: / Nanny goat / Kick a hack.
12" Single: Released Mar '86, on Uptempo, Catalogue no: **TEMP 002**

Verity

STAY WITH ME BABY
Tracks: / Stay with me baby.
12" Single: Released Oct '83, on PRT, by Castle Communications Records. Catalogue no: **12LB 1**
7" Single: Released Oct '83, on PRT, by Castle Communications Records. Catalogue no: **LB 1**

Verity, John

HONESTY & EMOTION

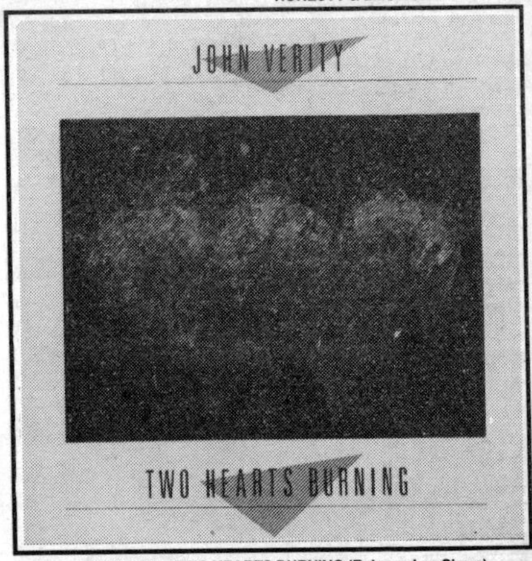

JOHN VERITY - TWO HEARTS BURNING (Released on Sierra)

Tracks: / Honesty and emotion / No pretending.
12" Single: Released Mar '85, on PRT, by Castle Communications Records. Catalogue no: **12LB 3800**
7" Single: Released Mar '85, on PRT, by Castle Communications Records. Catalogue no: **LB 3800**

I WANT YOU
Tracks: / I want you / Tempted.
7" Single: Released 31 Oct '87, on Sierra, by Sierra Records. Catalogue no: **FED 40**
12" Single: Released 31 Oct '87, on Sierra, by Sierra Records. Catalogue no: **FED 40T**

TWO HEARTS BURNING
Tracks: / Two hearts burning / Broken wing / Two hearts burning (ext. mix) (Track on 12" version only.).
7" Single: Released Jul '87, on Sierra, by Sierra Records. Catalogue no: **FED 33**
12" Single: Released Jul '87, on Sierra, by Sierra Records. Catalogue no: **FED 33T**

WHAT ABOUT ME
Tracks: / What about me / Who do you think you're fooling.
7" Single: Released Aug '84, on PRT, by Castle Communications Records. Catalogue no: **LB 3**

Verlaine, Tom

ALWAYS (SINGLE)
Tracks: / Always / Blue robe.
12" Single: Released Sep '81, on Warner Bros., by WEA Records. Catalogue no: **K 17865 T**
7" Single: Released Sep '81, on Warner Bros., by WEA Records. Catalogue no: **K 17855**

CRY MERCY JUDGE
Tracks: / Cry mercy judge / Call me the / Circling (This extra track on 12" version only) / At this moment (live) / Lover of the night (live) / Strange things happening (This extra track on 12" only.).
12" Single: Released Mar '87, on Fontana, by Phonogram Ltd. Deleted Dec '87. Catalogue no: **FTANA 2 12**
7" Single: Released Mar '87, on Fontana, by Phonogram Ltd. Deleted Dec '87. Catalogue no: **FTANA 2**

FUNNIEST THING, THE
Tracks: / Funniest thing, The / One time at sundown / Marquee moon ('87) (Extra track on 12" only).
12" Single: Released May '87, on Fontana, by Phonogram Ltd. Deleted Dec '87. Catalogue no: **VLANE 312**
7" Single: Released May '87, on Fontana, by Phonogram Ltd. Deleted Dec '87. Catalogue no: **VLANE 3**

TOWN CALLED WALKERS, A
Tracks: / Town called Walkers, A / Smoother than Jones / Caveman flashlight (Extra track on 12" version only.).
12" Single: Released Jan '87, on Fontana, by Phonogram Ltd. Deleted Dec '87. Catalogue no: **FTANA 112**
7" Single: Released Jan '87, on Fontana, by Phonogram Ltd. Deleted Dec '87. Catalogue no: **FTANA 1**

Verlaines

DEATH AND THE MAIDEN
Tracks: / Death and the maiden.
7" Single: Released Oct '87, on Flying Nun, Catalogue no: **FN 14**

Vermorel

STEREO
Tracks: / Stereo / Porno.
7" Single: Released Feb '88, on Factory (1), by Factory Records. Catalogue no: **FAC 198**

Vernon, Dave

BACK TO BACK (EP)
Tracks: / Back to back (EP) / Roamin' country singer / One touch away / Best bar room in town / Rolled the rock away.
Note: (Self - 0923 47129)
7" Single: Released Feb '87, on Cabin, Catalogue no: **CR 105 C**

CHILD OF 1945
7" Single: Released Sep '84, on Viking (2), by I & B Records. Catalogue no: **VIK 201**

Vernon & GI's

GHOST TRAIN BOOGIE
Tracks: / Ghost train boogie.
7" Single: Released Aug '78, on Billy Goat, by Chick-A-Boom Records. Catalogue no: **BILL 04**

I WANNA BE A TED
Tracks: / I wanna be a ted.
7" Single: Released Nov '80, on Billy Goat, by Chick-A-Boom Records. Catalogue no: **BILL 006**

Vernon & Gwynfor

WELCOME
Tracks: / Welcome / We shall gather at the river.
7" Single: Released May '82, on VIP (2), Catalogue no: **7VIP 001**

Vernons Banjo Trio

WHEN I THINK OF YOU
Tracks: / When I think of you.
7" Single: Released May '79, on Whoopee, by Whoopee Records. Catalogue no: **WP 103**

Vernons Girl

FUNNY ALL OVER
Tracks: / Funny all over.
7" Single: Released Jan '63, on Decca, by Decca Records. Deleted '66. Catalogue no: **F 11549**

Vernons Girls

DO THE BIRD
Tracks: / Do the bird.
7" Single: Released Apr '63, on Decca, by Decca Records. Deleted '66. Catalogue no: **F 11629**

LOCO-MOTION
Tracks: / Locomotion, The.
7" Single: Released Sep '62, on Decca, by Decca Records. Deleted '65. Catalogue no: **F 11495**

LOVER PLEASE
Tracks: / Lover please / You know what I mean.
7" Single: Released May '82, on Decca, by Decca Records. Deleted '88. Catalogue no: **F 11450**

LOVER PLEASE (OLD GOLD)
Tracks: / Lover please
7" Single: Released Sep '85, on Old Gold, by Old Gold Records. Catalogue no: **OG 9537**

Versatility

TEQUILA MADNESS
Tracks: / Tequila madness.
7" Single: Released Mar '75, on President, by President Records. Catalogue no: **PT 435**

Vertical Hold

ANGEL DUST
Tracks: / Angel dust.
7" Single: Released May '84, on VH, Catalogue no: **VH 2**

BIO HAZZARD
Tracks: / Bio hazzard.
7" Single: Released Jun '85, on Vertigo, by Phonogram Ltd. Catalogue no: **VH 003**

RUBBER CROSS
Tracks: / Rubber cross.
7" Single: Released Oct '81, on Vertical Hold Ind., Deleted '82. Catalogue no: **VH 001**

SUMMERTIME
Tracks: / Summertime / Summertime (jazzy dub) / Summertime (percapella) (Available on 12" single only.).
Note: * Only available on the 12" version.
12" Single: Released Jul '88, on 4th & Broadway, by Island Records. Deleted Apr '89. Catalogue no: **12 BRW 109**
7" Single: Released Jul '88, on 4th & Broadway, by Island Records. Deleted Apr '89. Catalogue no: **BRW 109**

Very Things

BUSHES SCREAM WHILE MY DADDY PRUNES,THE
7" Single: Released Jun '84, on Reflex, by Reflex Records. Catalogue no: **RE 5**

GHOST IN MY HOUSE
Tracks: / Ghost in my house.
7" Single: Released 23 May '87, on One Little Indian, by One Little Indian Records. Catalogue no: **7TP 7**
12" Single: Released 23 May '87, on One Little Indian, by One Little Indian Records. Catalogue no: **12TP 7**

LET'S GO OUT
Tracks: / Let's go out / Motortown trailer, The.
7" Single: Released Sep '87, on One Little Indian, by One Little Indian Records. Catalogue no: **7TP 8**
12" Single: Released Sep '87, on One Little Indian, by One Little Indian Records. Catalogue no: **12TP 8**

MUMMY YOU'RE A WRECK
Tracks: / Mummy you're a wreck.
12" Single: Released Aug '85, on Reflex, by Reflex Records. Catalogue no: **12 RE 9**

PEEL SESSIONS:VERY THINGS
12" Single: Released Jan '88, on Strange Fruit, by Strange Fruit Records. Catalogue no: **SFPS 046**

THIS IS MOTORTOWN
Tracks: / Motortown epilogue.
12" Single: Released Nov '86, on DCL Electronic, Catalogue no: **DCL 1 T**
7" Single: Released Nov '86, on DCL Electronic, Catalogue no: **DCL 1**

Veshara

SHADOW OF LOVE
Tracks: / Shadow of love.
7" Single: Released Oct '84, on Sub-Zero Music, by Sub-Zero Music. Catalogue no: **SZM 3**

Veterans

THERE AIN'T NO AGE FOR ROCK'N'ROLL
Tracks: / There ain't no age for rock'n'roll.
7" Single: Released Mar '83, on Rantin, by Stiff Records. Catalogue no: **OLD 1**

Vetoes

IT'S ONLY NOW
Tracks: / It's only now / Guardians.
7" Single: Released Aug '82, on RCA, by BMG Records (UK). Catalogue no: **RCA 234**

NOT TONIGHT
Tracks: / Not tonight / Twenty below.
7" Single: Released Jan '83, on RCA, by BMG Records (UK). Catalogue no: **RCA 304**

Vets

WORLD IN ACTION
Tracks: / World in action.
7" Single: Released Jul '81, on Deck Chair, Catalogue no: **DECK 80 001**

Vex

SANCTUARY
Tracks: / Sanctuary.
12" Single: Released May '88, on Fight Back, Catalogue no: **FIGHT 1**

VHF

LOVE IN THE NIGHT
Tracks: / Love in the night / Very high frequency / One way street.
12" Single: Released Feb '88, on Record Shack, by Record Shack Records. Catalogue no: **SOHOB 7**
12" Single: Released Jul '87, on Record Shack, by Record Shack Records. Catalogue no: **SOHOT 75**

VERY HIGH FREQUENCY (ANTI STATIC MIX)
Tracks: / Very high frequency.
12" Single: Released Aug '86, on Record Shack, by Record Shack Records. Catalogue no: **SOHOT 66**

Via Vagabond

HIP TODAY
Tracks: / Hip today.
10" single: Released Jul '83, on Albion, by Albion Records. Catalogue no: **ION 1052**

WHO LIKES JAZZ
Tracks: / Who likes jazz.
7" Single: Released Aug '82, on Stiff, by Stiff Records. Catalogue no: **BUY 157**

Via Verdi

DIAMOND
Tracks: / Diamonds (dance version).
7" Single: Released Jan '86, on WEA, by WEA Records. Deleted Jun '87. Catalogue no: **X 8864**
12" Single: Released Jan '86, on WEA, by WEA Records. Deleted Jun '87. Catalogue no: **X 8864T**

Vibe Tribe

CONSCIOUS AS A DAISY
Tracks: / Conscious as a daisy.
7" Single: Released Jul '87, on Tribal (1), Catalogue no: **TOO 001**

Vibes

CAN YOU FEEL ... THE UNDERESTIMATED MAN
Tracks: / Can you feel ... the underestimated man.
7" Single: Released Oct '84, on Big Beat, by Ace Records. Deleted '88. Catalogue no: **SW 99**

INNER WARDROBES OF YOUR MIND
Tracks: / Inner wardrobes of your mind.
7" Single: Released 14 Jun '85, on Chainsaw, Deleted '88. Catalogue no: **TEX 004**
12" Single: Released Jan '85, on Chainsaw, Deleted '88. Catalogue no: **TEXT 004**

Vibrators

AUTOMATIC LOVER
Tracks: / Automatic lover.
7" Single: Released Mar '78, on Epic, by CBS Records. Deleted '81. Catalogue no: **EPC 6137**

BABY BABY
Tracks: / Baby baby / Drag net.
7" Single: Released Nov '82, on Anagram, by Cherry Red Records. Cat. no: **ANA 4**

BABY BLUE EYES
Tracks: / Baby blue eyes.
7" Single: Released Jul '84, on Carrere, Catalogue no: **CAR 338**
12" Single: Released Jul '84, on Carrere, Catalogue no: **CART 338**

FLYING HOME
Tracks: / Flying home / Flash, flash, flash.
12" Single: Released Mar '84, on Ram, by Ram Records. Catalogue no: **RAM 7007 T**
7" Single: Released Mar '84, on Ram, by Ram Records. Catalogue no: **RAM 7007**
12" Single: Released May '84, on Carrere, Catalogue no: **CART 329**
7" Single: Released May '84, on Carrere, Catalogue no: **CAR 329**

GIMME SOME LOVIN
Tracks: / Gimme some lovin' / Power cry.
7" Single: Released Feb '80, on Rat Race, by Rat Race Records. Catalogue no: **2 RAT**

GUILTY
Tracks: / Wolfman howl / Rocket to the moon / Fighter pilot / Day they caught the killer / Kick it / Baby baby / Jumpin Jack Flash / Parties / Do a runner.
7" Single: Released May '83, on Anagram, by Cherry Red Records. Deleted '88. Catalogue no: **ANA 8**

JUDY SAYS
Tracks: / Judy says.
7" Single: Released Jun '78, on Epic, by CBS Records. Deleted '81. Catalogue no: **EPC 6393**

MR AMERICA
Tracks: / Mr. America / Shadow love.
7" Single: Released Nov '83, on Ram, by Ram Records. Catalogue no: **RAM 7005**

STRING HIM ALONG
Tracks: / String him along / Disco in Moscow (live).
7" Single: Released Mar '88, on Revolver, by FM-Revolver Records. Catalogue no: **REV 45**

Vic & Carol's Crazy...

THESE BOOTS ARE MADE FOR WALKING
Tracks: / These boots are made for walking / French connection.
7" Single: Released May '81, on Harbour, by Harbour Records. Catalogue no: **HRB 13**

Vice Squad

BLACK SHEEP
Tracks: / Black sheep / New blood / Pledge (on 12" only).
7" Single: Released Nov '83, on Anagram, by Cherry Red Records. Deleted '88. Catalogue no: **ANA 16**
12" Single: Released Nov '83, on Anagram, by Cherry Red Records. Deleted '88. Catalogue no: **12 ANA 16**

CITIZEN
Tracks: / Citizen.
7" Single: Released Sep '82, on Zonophone, by EMI Records. Catalogue no: **ZE 34**

LAST ROCKERS
Tracks: / Last rockers.
7" Single: Released '81, on Riot City, by Riot City Records. Catalogue no: **RIOT 1**

OUT OF REACH
Tracks: / Out of reach / So what for the 80's/Sterile.
7" Single: Released Jan '82, on Riot City, by Riot City Records. Catalogue no: **Z 26**

RESURRECTION
Tracks: / Resurrection.
7" Single: Released May '81, on Riot, Deleted '83. Catalogue no: **RIOT 2**

STAND STRONG STAND PROUD
Tracks: / Stand strong stand proud / Tomorrows soldier.
7" Single: Released Apr '82, on Riot City, by Riot City Records. Catalogue no: **Z 30**

TEENAGE RAMPAGE
Tracks: / Teenage rampage.
7" Single: Released Jan '85, on Anagram, by Cherry Red Records. Catalogue no: **ANA 26**

YOU'LL NEVER KNOW
Tracks: / You'll never know / What's going on / Times they are a changing.
12" Single: Released Apr '84, on Anagram, by Cherry Red Records. Deleted '88. Catalogue no: **12 ANA 22**
7" Single: Released Apr '84, on Anagram, by Cherry Red Records. Deleted '88. Catalogue no: **ANA 22**

Viceroys

CAN'T STOP US NOW
Tracks: / Can't stop us now.
12" Single: Released Apr '82, on Music Hawk, Catalogue no: **MHD 1**

Vicious Pink

8.15 TO NOWHERE
Tracks: / 8.15 to nowhere / Spaceship is over there, The.

CD 5": Released '89, on LD, by LD Records. Catalogue no: **LD 8818 CD**
12" Single: Released Aug '88, on Licensed, Catalogue no: **LD 8818**

C C CAN'T YOU SEE
Tracks: / C C Can't you see.
12" Single: Released May '85, on EMI, by EMI Records. Deleted '88. Catalogue no: **12PINK 2**
7" Single: Released May '85, on EMI, by EMI Records. Deleted '88. Catalogue no: **PINK 2**
7" Single: Released May '85, on EMI, by EMI Records. Deleted '88. Catalogue no: **RX 6074**
12" Single: Released Jul '84, on Parlophone, by EMI Records. Catalogue no: **12R 6074**
12" Single: Released Jul '84, on Parlophone, by EMI Records. Deleted Nov '88. Catalogue no: **12RA 6074**
12" Single: Released May '85, on EMI, by EMI Records. Deleted Oct '87. Catalogue no: **12 RX 6074**

FETISH
Tracks: / Fetish / Spooky.
12" Single: Released Mar '85, on EMI, by EMI Records. Catalogue no: **12 PINKD 1**
7" Pic: Released Mar '85, on EMI, by EMI Records. Catalogue no: **PINKP 1**

SPOOKY
Tracks: / Spooky.
12" Single: Released Feb '85, on EMI, by EMI Records. Catalogue no: **12 PINK 1**
7" Single: Released Feb '85, on EMI, by EMI Records. Catalogue no: **PINK 1**

TAKE ME NOW
Tracks: / Always hoping / I confess (Extra track on 12" version only).
12" Single: Released Jan '86, on EMI, by EMI Records. Catalogue no: **12PINK 3**
7" Single: Released Jan '86, on EMI, by EMI Records. Deleted '88. Catalogue no: **PINK 3**

Vicious Pink Phenomena

JE T'AIME MOI NON PLUS
Tracks: / Je t'aime moi non plus / In the swim.
12" Single: Released Feb '83, on Warehouse, by Warehouse Records. Catalogue no: **WARET 1**
7" Single: Released Feb '83, on Warehouse, by Warehouse Records. Catalogue no: **WARE 1**

MY PRIVATE TOKYO
Tracks: / My private Tokyo.
7" Single: Released Mar '82, on Mobile Suit Corporation, Catalogue no: **CORP 1**
12" Single: Released Mar '82, on Mobile Suit Corporation, Catalogue no: **CORP 1 12**

Vicious rumour club

WHOLE LOTTA LOVE
Tracks: / Whole lotta love.
7" Single: Released Mar '87, on Music Of Life, by Music Of Life Records. Catalogue no: **7 NOTE 1**
12" Single: Released Mar '87, on Music Of Life, by Music Of Life Records. Catalogue no: **NOTE 1**

Vicious Rumours

LOOK DON'T TOUCH
Tracks: / Look don't touch / Nighthawk Rita.
12" Single: Released Oct '85, on Dork, by Dork Records. Catalogue no: **UR BOB 8(12)**

RITA
Tracks: / Rita.
7" Single: Released Nov '84, on Dork, by Dork Records. Catalogue no: **UR BOB 5**

Vicious, Sid

NAKED
Tracks: / Naked / I'm ashamed.
7" Single: Released Jul '80, on Wonderful, Deleted '81. Catalogue no: **WO 73**

Vicky

DECEMBER SERENADE
Tracks: / December serenade.
7" Single: Released Dec '83, on JVF, Catalogue no: **JVF 001**

Victims

STRANGE THINGS BY NIGHT
Tracks: / Strange things by night.
12" Single: Released '79, on Good, Catalogue no: **GOT 2**

TEENAGER, THE
Tracks: / Teenager / Junior criminals / Hang on to yourselves.
7" Single: Released Sep '80, on Illuminated, Catalogue no: **ILL 1**

Victims Of Pleasure

JACK & JILL
Tracks: / Jack and Jill / Red moon.
7" Single: Released Apr '82, on Rialto (1), by Rialto Records. Catalogue no: **RIA 7**

SLAVE TO FASHION
Tracks: / Slave to fashion / On the game.
12" Single: Released Oct '81, on Rialto (1), by Rialto Records. Catalogue no: **12 RIA 2**
7" Single: Released Oct '81, on Rialto (1), by Rialto Records. Catalogue no: **RIA 2**

WHEN YOU'RE YOUNG
Tracks: / When you're young.
7" Single: Released Oct '82, on Rialto (1), by Rialto Records. Catalogue no: **RIA 11**

Victims Of The

BORN TO LEAVE
Tracks: / Born to leave / Flowers / For me / Never never / Give me nothing.
12" Single: Released Oct '88, on Illegal, by Faulty Products Records. Catalogue no: **ILST 1002**

Victor & Barry

GLASGOW
Tracks: / Glasgow.
7" Single: Released Dec '88, on Jammy, by Jammy Records. Catalogue no: **JRS 881**

Victorian Parents

ALL AMERICAN HERO
Tracks: / All American hero / Another waste of time.
7" Single: Released Sep '81, on Polydor, by Polydor Ltd. Catalogue no: **POSP 327**

Vidal, Maria

BODY ROCK
Tracks: / Body rock / Do you know who I am.
12" Single: Released Aug '85, on EMI-America, by EMI Records. Deleted Nov '88. Catalogue no: **12EA 189**
7" Single: Released Aug '85, on EMI-America, by EMI Records. Catalogue no: **EA 189**

DO ME RIGHT
Tracks: / Do me right / Nothing's alive without you.
12" Single: Released Jan '88, on A&M, by A&M Records. Deleted 1 Aug '88. Catalogue no: **AMY 428**
7" Single: Released Jan '88, on A&M, by A&M Records. Deleted 1 Aug '88. Catalogue no: **AM 428**

Video Kids

WOODPECKERS FROM SPACE
7" Single: Released Nov '84, on Record Shack, by Record Shack Records. Catalogue no: **HOHO 1**
12" Single: Released Nov '84, on Record Shack, by Record Shack Records. Catalogue no: **HOHOT 1**
7" Single: Released Aug '85, on Epic, by CBS Records. Catalogue no: **A 6504**

Video People

ON OUR OWN
Tracks: / On our own.
7" Single: Released Apr '84, on Round, Catalogue no: **RR 1**

Video Symphonic

FLAME TREES OF THIKA, THE
Tracks: / Flame trees of Thika, The / Love theme.
7" Single: Released Oct '81, on EMI, by EMI Records. Deleted '84. Catalogue no: **EMI 5222**

Vienna Philharmonic

ONEDIN LINE THEME
Tracks: / Onedin line theme.
7" Single: Released '71, on Decca, by Decca Records. Deleted '88. Catalogue no: **F 13259**

Vierra, Christina

YOU CAN FLOAT IN MY BOAT
Tracks: / You can float in my boat / Break these chains.
7" Single: Released Aug '88, on Warner Bros., by WEA Records. Catalogue no: **W 7879**
12" Single: Released Aug '88, on Warner Bros., by WEA Records. Catalogue no: **W 7879 T**

Vietnamese Rose

CURTAINS YOU
Tracks: / Curtains you / Tinker tailor.
7" Single: Released Jul '83, on Aaron B, Catalogue no: **ROSE 1**

YOUNG AND THE FREE
Tracks: / Young and the free / Time for passion.
7" Single: Released Nov '82, on Luna Da Luna, Deleted Nov '85. Catalogue no: **MOON 5**

View From The Hill

HEART TO HEART
Tracks: / Heart to heart.
12" Single: Released Jul '84, on Zara, Catalogue no: **ZMRD 6**

VILLAGE PEOPLE - NEW YORK CITY (Released on Record Shack)

I'M NO REBEL
Tracks: / Stay and let me love you / For the sake of love / Turn out the light.
Cassingle: Released Feb '87, on EMI, by EMI Records. Deleted Jul '87. Catalogue no: **TCEMI 5580**
7" Set: Released Feb '87, on EMI, by EMI Records. Deleted Oct '87. Catalogue no: **EMID 5580**
7" Single: Released Aug '85, on Survival (1), by Survival Records. Catalogue no: **SUR 033**
12" Single: Released Aug '85, on Survival (1), by Survival Records. Catalogue no: **SURT 33**

NO CONVERSATION
Tracks: / No conversation / Suzanne / My love won't wait / Every time I hear your name. Note: 'My love won't wait' on 12" and CD single only and 'Every time' on CD single only. Extended version of title track on 12in and CD single.t
CD 5": Released 31 May '88, on EMI, by EMI Records. Deleted Aug '89. Catalogue no: **CDEM 51**
7" Single: Released 31 May '88, on EMI, by EMI Records. Deleted Aug '89. Catalogue no: **EM 51**
12" Single: Released 31 May '88, on EMI, by EMI Records. Deleted Aug '89. Catalogue no: **12EM 51**
7" Single: Released Jul '86, on EMI, by EMI Records. Deleted '89. Catalogue no: **EMI 5565**

ON THE CORNER
Tracks: / Living it up / On the corner.
12" Single: Released Aug '87, on EMI, by EMI Records. Deleted Apr '88. Catalogue no: **12 EM 7**
7" Single: Released Aug '87, on EMI, by EMI Records. Deleted Apr '88. Catalogue no: **EM 7**

ON THE CORNER (DUB)
Tracks: / On the corner (dub) / On the corner (7" version) / Living it up.
12" Single: Released Sep '87, on EMI, by EMI Records. Deleted Jan '88. Catalogue no: **12EMX 7**

Viewers

ACCIDENT
Tracks: / Accident.
7" Single: Released Aug '80, on Fire Exit, Deleted '85. Catalogue no: **LOCK 1**

Vikings

ALBATROSS
Tracks: / Albatross.
7" Single: Released Aug '85, on Ritz-Homespun, by Homespun Records. Catalogue no: **RITZ 115**

Vikki

LOVE IS...
Tracks: / Love is ... / Lead me through the darkness.
12" Single: Released Apr '85, on PRT, by Castle Communications Records. Catalogue no: **12P 326**
7" Single: Released Apr '85, on PRT, by Castle Communications Records. Catalogue no: **7P 326**

Villa De Ville

EVERYTHING COUNTS
Tracks: / Everything counts / Being from Zob.
7" Single: Released Oct '82, on Admiral, by Admiral Records. Catalogue no: **ADML 001**

SUBCULTURE 22
Tracks: / Subculture 22.
7" Single: Released Aug '81, on RCA, by BMG Records (UK). Catalogue no: **RCA 106**
7" Single: Released May '83, on Admiral, by Admiral Records. Catalogue no: **ADML 003**

Village People

CAN'T STOP THE MUSIC
Tracks: / Can't stop the music / I love you to death.
7" Single: Released Aug '80, on Mercury, by Phonogram Ltd. Deleted '83. Catalogue no: **MER 16**

DO YOU WANNA SPEND THE NIGHT
Tracks: / Do you wanna spend the night / Food fight.
12" Single: Released Jul '81, on Mercury, by Phonogram Ltd. Deleted Jul '84. Catalogue no: **MERX 75**
7" Single: Released Jul '81, on Mercury, by Phonogram Ltd. Deleted Jul '84. Catalogue no: **MER 75**

GO WEST
Tracks: / Go west.
7" Single: Released Jun '79, on Mercury, by Phonogram Ltd. Deleted '82. Catalogue no: **6007 221**

IN THE NAVY
Tracks: / In the Navy.
7" Single: Released Mar '79, on Mercury, by Phonogram Ltd. Deleted '82. Catalogue no: **6007 209**

MAGIC NIGHT
Tracks: / Magic night / Can't stop the music.
7" Single: Released Oct '80, on Mercury, by Phonogram Ltd. Deleted Oct '83. Catalogue no: **MER 39**
12" Single: Released Oct '80, on Mercury, by Phonogram Ltd. Deleted Oct '83. Catalogue no: **MERX 39**

MEDLEY - IN THE NAVY
Tracks: / In the navy.
12" Single: Released Nov '85, on Record Shack, by Record Shack Records. Catalogue no: **SOHOT 51**
7" Single: Released Nov '85, on Record Shack, by Record Shack Records. Catalogue no: **SOHO 51**

NEW YORK CITY (see panel above)
Tracks: / New York City (vocal) / New York City (Instrumental).
7" Single: Released Mar '85, on Record Shack, by Record Shack Records. Catalogue no: **SOHO 39**
12" Single: Released Mar '85, on Record Shack, by Record Shack Records. Catalogue no: **SOHOT 39**

SAN FRANCISCO
Tracks: / San Francisco.
7" Single: Released Dec '77, on DJM, Deleted '80. Catalogue no: **DJS 10817**

SEX OVER THE PHONE
Tracks: / Sex over the phone.
7" Single: Released Jan '85, on Record Shack, by Record Shack Records. Catalogue no: **SOHO 34**
12" Single: Released Jan '85, on Record Shack, by Record Shack Records. Catalogue no: **SOHOT 34**

Y.M.C.A.
Tracks: / Y.M.C.A. / In the Navy.
7" Single: Released Nov '78, on Mercury, by Phonogram Ltd. Deleted '81. Catalogue no: **6007 192**

Y.M.C.A. (OLD GOLD)
Tracks: / Y.M.C.A..
12" Single: Released 30 Jan '89, on Old Gold, by Old Gold Records. Catalogue no: **OG 4091**

Ville, Roland De

LITTLE JIMMY BROWN The 3 bells
Tracks: / Little Jimmy Brown.
7" Single: Released Oct '80, on Precision (1), Deleted '83. Catalogue no: **PAR 112**

Vince & Claudia

YOU ME AND HE
Tracks: / You, me and he.
12" Single: Released Jun '85, on Time, Catalogue no: **TR 9**

Vincent, Gene

Biographical details: Seminal 50's rock 'n' roller Gene Vincent was born Eugene Vincent Craddock in Norfolk, Virginia, in 1935, and died in 1971. He broke a leg in the US Navy and subsequently wore a brace. *Be-Bop-A-Lula* -- featured in the film *The Girl Can't Help It* -- was his biggest hit and, like Buddy Holly and Eddie Cochran, he was more popular in the UK than America during his lifetime. His haircut and demeanour inspired British Teds more than any other single figure. His band, the Blue Caps, split up in 1958. He didn't get on with his record label and he emigrated to Britain in 1959, when Jack Good helped him become rock 'n' roll's biggest live draw. The car crash that killed Cochran injured his leg again in 1960. He returned to America in '65, recorded some country music and became a parody of himself. He drank too much and died of ulcers. (Donald Clarke, January 1988.).

BE-BOP-A-LULA
Tracks: / Be-bop-a-lula.
7" Single: Released Apr '83, on EMI (France), by EMI Records. Catalogue no: **2C 008 81170**
7" Single: Released Mar '84, on EMI Golden 45's, by EMI Records. Deleted Oct '89. Catalogue no: **G45 8**
7" Single: Released Jul '56, on Capitol, by EMI Records. Deleted '59. Catalogue no: **CL 14599**

BLUE JEAN BOP (SINGLE)
Tracks: / Blue jean bop.
7" Single: Released Oct '56, on Capitol, by EMI Records. Deleted '59. Catalogue no: **CL 14637**

I'M GOING HOME
Tracks: / I'm going home.
7" Single: Released Aug '61, on Capitol, by EMI Records. Deleted '64. Catalogue no: **CL 15215**

LAST SESSION, THE
12" Single: Released Jul '87, on Night Tracks, by Pinnacle Records. Catalogue no: **SFNT 001**

MY HEART
Tracks: / My heart.
7" Single: Released Mar '60, on Capitol, by EMI Records. Deleted '63. Catalogue no: **CL 15115**

PISTOL PACKIN' MAMA
Tracks: / Pistol packin' mama.
7" Single: Released Jun '60, on Capitol, by EMI Records. Deleted '63. Catalogue no: **CL 15136**

RACE WITH THE DEVIL
Tracks: / Race with the devil.
7" Single: Released Oct '56, on Capitol, by EMI Records. Deleted '59. Catalogue no: **CL 14628**

RAINY DAY SUNSHINE
Tracks: / Rainy day sunshine / Miss the love.
7" EP: Released Jan '81, on Magnum Force, by Magnum Music Group. Catalogue no: **MFEP 003**

ROLL OVER BEETHOVEN
Tracks: / Roll over Beethoven.
7" Single: Released '74, on Beeb, by BBC Records & Tapes. Catalogue no: **BEEB 001**

SHE SHE LITTLE SHEILA
Tracks: / She she little Sheila / Say mama / Dance to the bop.
7" Single: Released Jun '61, on Capitol, by EMI Records. Deleted '64. Catalogue no: **CL 15202**
7" Single: Released Jun '81, on Capitol, by EMI Records. Deleted Jun '84. Catalogue no: **CL 203**

WILD CAT
Tracks: / Wild cat.
7" Single: Released Jan '60, on Capitol, by EMI Records. Deleted '63. Catalogue no: **CL 15099**

Vincent, Holly Beth

FOR WHAT IT'S WORTH
Tracks: / For what it's worth.
7" Single: Released Oct '82, on Virgin, by Virgin Records. Deleted '89. Catalogue no: **VS 517**
12" Single: Released Oct '82, on Virgin, by Virgin Records. Deleted '89. Catalogue no: **VS 517-12**

HONOLU
Tracks: / Honolulu.
7" Single: Released Aug '82, on Virgin, by Virgin Records. Deleted '89. Catalogue no: **VS 539**

Vincent, Jean

DEADWOOD STAGE
Tracks: / Deadwood stage / You were right.
7" Single: Released Dec '85, on Abacus, by Abacus Records. Catalogue no: **VYK 12**

Vincent, Kathy

17 ELECTRIC
Tracks: / 17 electric.
7" Single: Released Jun '84, on Buzzzbee, by Buzzzbee Records. Catalogue no: **BUBE 2**

FANTASY OF LOVE
Tracks: / Fantasy of love
7" Single: on Buzz, Catalogue no: **BUZZ 1**

FEEL THE NEED
Tracks: / Feel the need / Close to the edge.
7" Single: Released Sep '86, on Buzzin, Catalogue no: **BUBE 7**

LEAVING IT UP TO YOU
Tracks: / Leaving it up to you / Omen, The.
7" Single: Released Sep '88, on Freeway, Catalogue no: **KATH 102**

ONE TOO MANY HEARTACHES
Tracks: / Hold tight don't fight / Sweet dynamite* (World Domination mix. * Available on 12" version only).
7" Single: Released Jan '87, on Buzzin, Catalogue no: **BUBE 8**
12" Single: Released Jan '87, on Buzzin, Catalogue no: **12 BUBE 8**

SHAKIN' ALL OVER
Tracks: / Shakin all over / Sweet dynamite (86 mix).
7" Single: Released Jul '86, on Buzzin, Catalogue no: **BUGE 5**

SWEET DYNAMITE
Tracks: / Sweet dynamite.
7" Single: Released Sep '85, on Buzzzbee, by Buzzzbee Records. Catalogue no: **MSBUBE 3**
12" Single: Released Sep '85, on Buzzzbee, by Buzzzbee Records. Catalogue no: **12 MSBUBE 3**

TONIGHT'S THE NIGHT
Tracks: / Tonight's the night / Innocent boy.
7" Single: Released Feb '88, on Latest Record, Catalogue no: **KATH 101**

Vincent, Vinnie

LOVE KILLS
Tracks: / Love kills / Animal / Shoot you full of love.
12" Single: Released Apr '89, on Arista, by BMG Records (UK). Catalogue no: **INVSX 1**
7" Single: Released Apr '89, on Arista, by BMG Records (UK). Catalogue no: **INVS 1**

Vinci, Charlie Da

I'VE GOT TO GET YOU INTO MY LIFE
Tracks: / I've got to get you into my life / I want to taste your oranges.
7" Single: Released Aug '80, on Gun, Catalogue no: **AIM 003**

Vinci, Paul Da

FIRE IN THE BACK STREETS
Tracks: / Fire in the back streets.
7" Single: Released Dec '84, on Pan Polychord, by Pan Polychord Records. Catalogue no: **DAV 1**

YOUR BABY AIN'T YOUR BABY ANYMORE
Tracks: / Your baby ain't your baby anymore.
7" Single: Released Jul '74, on Penny Farthing, by Penny Farthing Records. Deleted Jul '77. Catalogue no: **PEN 843**

Vindaloo Summer

ROCKIN WITH RITA
Tracks: / Rockin with Rita / Let's surf.
7" Single: Released Jul '86, on Vindaloo, by Vindaloo Records. Deleted Jun '87. Catalogue no: **UGH 13**
12" Single: Released Jul '86, on Vindaloo, by Vindaloo Records. Deleted Jan '88. Catalogue no: **UGH 13T**

Vinton, Bobby

Biographical details: American pop singer and bandleader Vinton was born in 1935 in Canonsburg, Pensylvania, the same home town as Perry Como. His total of 30 Top Forty hits aimed at teens included *Roses Are Red, Blue Velvet, There, I've Said It Again* and *Mr Lonely*, all at No 1, between 1962 and 1975. His television show as syndicated in America from 1975-78. (Donald Clarke, January 1988.).

ROSES ARE RED
Tracks: / Roses are red.
7" Single: Released Jul '82, on Old Gold, by Old Gold Records. Catalogue no: **OG 9076**
7" Single: Released Aug '62, on Columbia, by EMI Records. Deleted '65. Catalogue no: **DB 4878**

THERE, I'VE SAID IT AGAIN
Tracks: / There, I've said it again.
7" Single: Released Dec '63, on Columbia, by EMI Records. Deleted '66. Catalogue no: **DB 7179**

Vinyl

NOBODY MEN
Tracks: / Nobody men / Pulse.
7" Single: Released May '80, on Mercury, by Phonogram Ltd. Deleted May '83. Catalogue no: **MER 11**

Violators

DIE WITH DIGNITY
Tracks: / Die with dignity.
12" Single: Released Jan '84, on No Future, Catalogue no: **12 01 26**

GANGLAND
Tracks: / Gangland.
7" Single: Released Jul '82, on No Future, Deleted '87. Catalogue no: **01 9**

LIFE ON THE RED LINE
Tracks: / Life on the red line.
7" Single: Released Mar '83, on Future, Catalogue no: **FS 2**

SUMMER OF '81 6 track EP
Tracks: / Summer of 81 / Live fast die young.
7" Single: Released Jan '84, on No Future, Deleted '87. Catalogue no: **01 19**
12" Single: Released Nov '83, on No Future, Catalogue no: **12 01 26**

THERE'S A GUITAR BURNING
Tracks: / There's a guitar burning.
12" Single: Released Nov '83, on No Future, Catalogue no: **12 01 27**

Violence

ETERNAL NIGHTMARE (SINGLE)
Tracks: / Eternal nightmare.
7" Single: Released Oct '88, on MCA, by MCA Records. Deleted 1 Jul '89. Catalogue no: **VOMIT 1**

Violent Blue

Biographical details: Violent Blue, a four piece from the West Country recently signed to the Magnet label, have their debut single released on October 4th entitled *I won't give in (losing you)*. The band who have built up a sizeable reputation on the live circuit are fronted by bassist Charlie Jones and guitarist Neil Taylor, the latter of whom has played with **Tears For Fears** and whose work is in evidence as guitar soloist on the latest album *Songs from the big chair*. The band are currently in the studio cutting their debut album with producer Tim Palmer, who handled the controls on Robert Plant's latest LP. The album *You've got to stay young* will be released early next year. (Julian Henry, Magnet Records, October 1985).

I WON'T GIVE IN LOVING YOU
Tracks: / I won't give in loving you.
7" Single: Released Nov '85, on Magnet, by WEA Records. Deleted '87. Catalogue no: **MAG 267**
12" Single: Released Nov '85, on Magnet, by WEA Records. Catalogue no: **MAGT 267**

Violent Femmes

CHILDREN OF THE REVOLUTION
Tracks: / Children of the revolution / Heartache / Good feeling.
7" Single: Released Jan '86, on Slash, by London Records. Catalogue no: **LASH 7**
12" Single: Released Jan '86, on Slash, by London Records. Catalogue no: **LASHX 7**

GONE DADDY GONE
Tracks: / Gone daddy gone.
12" Single: Released Jun '84, on Slash, by London Records. Catalogue no: **LASHX 1**
7" Single: Released Jun '84, on Slash, by London Records. Catalogue no: **LASH 1**

UGLY
Tracks: / Ugly.
7" Single: Released Dec '83, on Rough Trade, by Rough Trade Records. Catalogue no: **RT 147**
12" Single: Released Dec '83, on Rough Trade, by Rough Trade Records. Catalogue no: **RTD 012T**

Violin Sect

HIGH DAYS AND HOLIDAYS
Tracks: / High days and holidays.
7" Single: Released Dec '81, on Cheek One, Deleted '87. Catalogue no: **PL 1981**

Violinsky

CLOG DANCE
Tracks: / Clog dance.
7" Single: Released Jan '79, on Jet, by Jet Records. Catalogue no: **JET 136**

SILENT LOVE
Tracks: / Silent love / Captain Dandy.
7" Single: Released Mar '80, on Jet, by Jet Records. Deleted Mar '83. Catalogue no: **JET 174**

Vipers

I'VE GOT YOU
Tracks: / I've got you.
7" Single: Released Jan '79, on Mulligan (Ireland), Catalogue no: **LUNS 718**

Vipers Skiffle Group

CUMBERLAND GAP
Tracks: / Cumberland gap.
7" Single: Released Mar '57, on Parlophone, by EMI Records. Deleted '60. Catalogue no: **R 4289**

DON'T YOU ROCK ME DADDY-O
Tracks: / Don't you rock me daddy-o.
7" Single: Released Jan '57, on Parlophone, by EMI Records. Deleted '60. Catalogue no: **R 4261**

STREAMLINE TRAIN
Tracks: / Streamline train.
7" Single: Released May '57, on Parlophone, by EMI Records. Deleted '60. Catalogue no: **R 4308**

V.I.P.s

CAUSING COMPLICATIONS
Tracks: / Causing complications / Run run Belinda / Love is a golden word.
7" Single: Released Apr '80, on Gem, Deleted '83. Catalogue no: **GEMS 25**

NEED SOMEBODY TO LOVE
Tracks: / Need somebody to love / One more chance / Stuttgart special / Who knows / Janie.
7" EP: Released Nov '80, on Gem, Deleted Nov '83. Catalogue no: **GEMS 43**

QUARTER MOON, THE
Tracks: / Quarter moon, The / Hippy hippy shake.
7" Single: Released Sep '80, on Gem, Deleted '83. Catalogue no: **GEMS 39**

THINGS AREN'T WHAT THEY USED TO BE
Tracks: / Things aren't what they used to be / I thought you were my friend.
7" Single: Released Feb '81, on Gem, Deleted Feb '84. Catalogue no: **GEMS 47**

Virgin Dance

ARE YOU READY (FOR THAT FEELING)
Tracks: / Are you ready (for that feeling).
12" Single: Released Nov '84, on Spartan, Catalogue no: **12SP 16**
7" Single: Released Jul '83, on Spartan, Catalogue no: **SP 5**
7" Single: Released Jun '83, on Probe Plus, by Probe Plus Records. Catalogue no: **PP 5**
7" Single: Released Nov '84, on Spartan, Catalogue no: **SP 16**

DESIRE
Tracks: / Desire.
12" Single: Released Jan '84, on Spartan, Catalogue no: **12SP 10**
7" Single: Released Jan '84, on Spartan, Catalogue no: **SP 10**

DREAM IS OVER, THE
Tracks: / Dream is over, The.
7" Single: Released Jul '84, on Spartan, Catalogue no: **SP 14**
12" Single: Released Jul '84, on Spartan, Catalogue no: **12SP 14**

NO DISGUISE
Tracks: / No disguise.
12" Single: Released Oct '83, on Spartan, Catalogue no: **12 SP 8**
7" Single: Released Oct '83, on Spartan, Catalogue no: **SP 8**

Virgin Prunes

BABY TURNS BLUE
Tracks: / Baby turns blue.
12" Single: Released Oct '82, on Rough Trade, by Rough Trade Records. Catalogue no: **RT 119T**
7" Single: Released Oct '82, on Rough Trade, by Rough Trade Records. Catalogue

no: **RT 119**

BEASTS (SEVEN BASTARD SUCK)
Tracks: / Beasts (seven bastard suck).
12" Single: Released Mar '82, on Rough Trade, by Rough Trade Records. Catalogue no: **RT 099**

COME TO DADDY
Tracks: / Come to daddy.
10" single: Released Mar '82, on Rough Trade, by Rough Trade Records. Catalogue no: **RT 090**

COME TO DADDY (EP)
Tracks: / Come to daddy / Sweet home under white clouds / Sad world.
7" Single: Released Oct '81, on Rough Trade, by Rough Trade Records. Deleted Oct '84. Catalogue no: **RT 90**

DON'T LOOK BACK
Tracks: / Don't look back.
7" Single: Released '88, on Baby, by New Rose Records. Catalogue no: **BABY 006**
12" Single: Released '88, on Baby, by New Rose Records. Catalogue no: **BABY 007**

GREYLIGHT
Tracks: / Greylight.
7" Single: Released Jul '81, on Rough Trade, by Rough Trade Records. Catalogue no: **RT 072**

HERESIE
Tracks: / Heresie.
10" single: Released '88, on Baby, by New Rose Records. Catalogue no: **BABY 011**

LOVE LASTS FOREVER
Tracks: / Love lasts forever / True life story / Lovelornalimbo / Like the way you're frightened.
7" Single: Released Jun '86, on Baby, by New Rose Records. Catalogue no: **BABY 003**
12" Single: Released Jun '86, on Baby, by New Rose Records. Catalogue no: **BABY 004**

NEW FORM OF BEAUTY PART 2
Tracks: / New form of beauty (part 2).
7" Single: Released Nov '81, on Rough Trade, by Rough Trade Records. Catalogue no: **RT 090**

PAGAN LOVE SONG
Tracks: / Pagan love song / David is dead.
12" Single: Released Apr '82, on Rough Trade, by Rough Trade Records. Catalogue no: **RT 106 12**
7" Single: Released Apr '82, on Rough Trade, by Rough Trade Records. Catalogue no: **RT 106**

SANDPAPER LULLABY
Tracks: / Sandpaper lullaby.
7" Single: Released Mar '82, on Rough Trade, by Rough Trade Records. Catalogue no: **RT 089**

SLOW CHILDREN
Tracks: / Slow children.
7" Single: Released Dec '81, on Rough Trade, by Rough Trade Records. Catalogue no: **RTL 99**

TWENTY TENS (I'VE BEEN SMOKING...)
Tracks: / Twenty tens (I've been smoking).
7" Single: Released Jan '81, on Baby, by New Rose Records. Catalogue no: **BABY 001**

Virgin Star

WHEN THE REDS
Tracks: / When the reds.
7" Single: Released Dec '84, on Official, by Official Records. Catalogue no: **OFFA 1**

Virgin Steele

CRY IN THE NIGHT
Tracks: / Cry in the night / I am the one.
12" Single: Released Nov '83, on Music For Nations, by Music For Nations Records. Catalogue no: **12 KUT 104**

Virginia Wolf

ACTION
Tracks: / Action / Where do we go from here.
7" Single: Released Mar '82, on Creole, by Creole Records. Catalogue no: **CR 28**

DON'T BREAK AWAY
Tracks: / Don't break away.
7" Single: Released Aug '87, on Atlantic, by WEA Records. Deleted Jul '88. Catalogue no: **A 9199**
12" Single: Released Aug '87, on Atlantic, by WEA Records. Deleted Jan '88. Catalogue no: **A 9199 T**

WAITING FOR YOUR LOVE
Tracks: / Waiting for your love / Take a chance.
7" Single: Released Feb '86, on Atlantic, by WEA Records. Catalogue no: **A 9459**

WALKIE TALKIE BOY
Tracks: / Walkie talkie boy / One night stand.
7" Single: Released Jun '82, on Creole, by Creole Records. Catalogue no: **CR 36**

VISAGE - VISAGE (REMIX) (Released on Polydor)

Virgo

DO YOU KNOW WHO YOU ARE
Tracks: / Do you know who you are / Do you know who you are (instrumental) / In vision (Only on 12" and CD single.) / In vision (version) (Only on 12" and CD single.).
CD 5": Released May '89, on Radical, by Radical Records. Catalogue no: **CDRAD 1**
12" Single: Released May '89, on Radical, by Radical Records. Catalogue no: **RADICAL 1**
7" Single: Released May '89, on Radical, by Radical Records. Catalogue no: **RADC 1**

Virgo, Danny

DANCE HALL NICE
Tracks: / Dance hall nice.
12" Single: Released Jan '85, on Worries, Catalogue no: **Unknown**

Virgo Don

LEARN FI COOK
Tracks: / Learn fi cook.
12" Single: Released May '89, on Fu-Manchu, Catalogue no: **FU 010**

Virgo Mechan...

VIRGO MECHANICALLY REPLAYED
Tracks: / Virgo mechanically replayed: *Various artists.*
12" Single: Released Nov '87, on T.J. (USA), Catalogue no: **TJ 3001**

Virus

(I'M NOT YOUR) STEPPING STONE
Tracks: / Stepping stone / Salute to the Afghan Rebels.
7" Single: Released Dec '82, on 5th Column, by Graduate Records. Deleted Jan '87. Catalogue no: **FC 1**

WIPE OUT
Tracks: / Wipe out.
7" Single: Released Jun '85, on Big Sleep, Catalogue no: **BEP 1**

Visage

Biographical details: British pop/dance band Visage were formed by Steve Strange, born Steve Harrington in Wales in 1959, a prime mover in the New Romantics movement of the early 80's. He formed Moors Murderers with Chrissie Hynde in 1977-78, then the Photons, who played one gig, after which he ran a club in Soho. He moved to Covent Garden and formed Visage with drummer Rusty Egan, Midge Ure on guitar and four others. The sound -- synths on top of a monotonous disco beat -- was successful. Ure left for Ultravox and Strange quit while he was ahead, he and Egan opening Camden Palace. Strange turned back to music as front man of Strange Cruise in the mid-80's, but the time for half-baked disco dressed as trendy pop was probably over. (Donald Clarke, January 1988.).

DAMMED DON'T CRY (see panel on right)
Tracks: / Dammed don't cry / Motivation.
7" Single: Released Mar '82, on Polydor, by Polydor Ltd. Catalogue no: **POSP 390**
7" Single: Released Feb '88, on Old Gold, by Old Gold Records. Catalogue no: **OG 9778**
12" Single: Released Mar '82, on Polydor, by Polydor Ltd. Deleted '85. Catalogue no: **POSPX 390**

FADE TO GREY (OLD GOLD)
Tracks: / Fade to grey / Mind of a toy (On 7" only) / Night train (On 12" only).
7" Single: Released Mar '86, on Old Gold, by Old Gold Records. Catalogue no: **OG 9580**
12" Single: Released Feb '88, on Old Gold, by Old Gold Records. Catalogue no: **OG 4050**

FADE TO GREY (SINGLE)
Tracks: / Fade to grey / Peaches & herb / Shake your groove thing.
7" Single: Released Dec '80, on Polydor, by Polydor Ltd. Deleted '83. Catalogue no: **POSP 194**
12" Single: Released Dec '80, on Polydor, by Polydor Ltd. Deleted '83. Catalogue no: **POSPX 194**
12" Single: Released Sep '88, on ZYX (Germany), Catalogue no: **ZYX 5557**

LOVE GLOVE
Tracks: / Love glove.
7" Single: Released Sep '84, on Polydor, by Polydor Ltd. Deleted '87. Catalogue no: **POSP 697**

MIND OF A TOY
Tracks: / Mind of a toy / We move / Frequency 7 (on 12" only).
7" Single: Released Mar '81, on Polydor, by Polydor Ltd. Deleted '84. Catalogue no: **POSP 236**
12" Single: Released Mar '81, on Polydor, by Polydor Ltd. Deleted '84. Catalogue no: **POSPX 236**

MIND OF A TOY (OLD GOLD)
Tracks: / Mind of a toy.
12" Single: Released Mar '88, on Old Gold, by Old Gold Records. Catalogue no: **OG 4052**

NIGHT TRAIN
Tracks: / Night train.
7" Single: Released Jun '82, on Polydor, by Polydor Ltd. Deleted '85. Catalogue no: **POSP 441**

PLEASURE BOYS
Tracks: / Pleasure boys.
7" Single: Released Nov '82, on Polydor, by Polydor Ltd. Deleted '85. Catalogue no: **POSP 523**
12" Single: Released Nov '82, on Polydor, by Polydor Ltd. Deleted '85. Catalogue no: **POSPX 523**
12" Single: Released Nov '87, on Rated X (USA), Catalogue no: **RX 001**

VISAGE (REMIX) (see panel on left)
Tracks: / Visage (remix) / Second steps.
7" Single: Released Jul '81, on Polydor, by Polydor Ltd. Catalogue no: **POSP 293**
12" Single: Released Jul '81, on Polydor, by Polydor Ltd. Catalogue no: **POSPX 293**

Viscounts

SHORT'NIN' BREAD
Tracks: / Short'nin' bread.
7" Single: Released Oct '60, on Pye, Deleted '63. Catalogue no: **7 N 15287**

WHO PUT THE BOMP
Tracks: / Who put the bomp.
7" Single: Released Sep '61, on Pye, Deleted '64. Catalogue no: **7 N 15379**

Visible Target

EVERY NOW AND THEN
Tracks: / Every now and then / Own back.
7" Single: Released Apr '84, on Simple, Deleted '87. Catalogue no: **SIM 2**
12" Single: Released Apr '84, on Simple, Deleted '87. Catalogue no: **12SIM 2**

Vision

CALLING OF THE WILD
Tracks: / Calling of the wild.
7" Single: Released Oct '85, on PRT, by Castle Communications Records. Catalogue no: **7P 333**
12" Single: Released Oct '85, on PRT, by Castle Communications Records. Catalogue no: **12P 333**

DO IT TONIGHT
Tracks: / Do it tonight / Seduction, The.
12" Single: Released Sep '87, on Domino, by Domino Records. Catalogue no: **DOM T8**

LOVE DANCE
Tracks: / Love dance / Games.

VISAGE - DAMMED DON'T CRY (Released on Polydor)

12" Single: Released Jun '83, on MVM, by MVM Records. Catalogue no: **12 MVM 2886**
7" Single: Released Jun '83, on MVM, by MVM Records. Deleted '84. Catalogue no: **MVM 2886**

LUCIFER'S FRIEND
Tracks: / Lucifer's friend.
12" Single: Released Oct '85, on Rerun, Catalogue no: **12 RRN 1**
7" Single: Released Oct '85, on Rerun, Catalogue no: **7 RRN 1**
7" Single: Released Oct '82, on MVM, by MVM Records. Deleted '84. Catalogue no: **MVM 2885**

TEARS IDLE TEARS
Tracks: / Tears idle tears.
12" Single: Released Feb '85, on PRT, by Castle Communications Records. Catalogue no: **12P 320**
7" Single: Released Feb '85, on PRT, by Castle Communications Records. Catalogue no: **7P 320**

WALK ON THE OUTSIDE
Tracks: / Walk on the outside / It's the wrong name.
7" Single: Released Aug '81, on Roxon, Catalogue no: **ROX 022**

WHO'S THAT STRANGER
Tracks: / Breakdown / Who's that stranger.
7" Single: Released Jan '87, on PRT, by Castle Communications Records. Catalogue no: **7P 366**
12" Single: Released Jan '87, on PRT, by Castle Communications Records. Catalogue no: **12P 366**

Visions (Group)

PAPER KIDS
Tracks: / Paper kids.
7" Single: Released Jun '82, on Top Hold, Deleted '83. Catalogue no: **TH 012**

Visions In Glass

SUNSHINE IN THE MORNING
Tracks: / Sunshine in the morning / King maker.
7" Single: Released Oct '88, on Mystic, Catalogue no: **XDM 1**

Visit

ALL THE WALLS
Tracks: / All the walls.
7" Single: Released Jun '83, on Future, Catalogue no: **FS 4**

Vista Posse

LIVEN UP YOURSELF
Tracks: / Liven up yourself.
12" Single: Released '87, on Vista Sounds, by Vista Sounds Records. Deleted Jun '89. Catalogue no: **VISTA 003**

Visual

MUSIC GOT ME (2 PARTS)
Tracks: / Music got me.
7" Single: Released Apr '83, on Prelude, Catalogue no: **PRLA 3237**
12" Single: Released Apr '83, on Prelude, Catalogue no: **PRLA 13 3237**

Vital Disorders

PRAMS
Tracks: / Prams.
7" Single: Released Sep '81, on Lowther International, by Lowther International Records. Catalogue no: **VD 1**

SOME PEOPLE
Tracks: / Some people.
7" Single: Released Feb '85, on Lowther International, by Lowther International Records. Catalogue no: **VD 3**

ZOMBIE
Tracks: / Zombie.
7" Single: Released Jun '82, on Vital Disorders, Catalogue no: **VD 2**

Vital Sines

ICE STATUE
Tracks: / Ice statue / Rhythm of dark.
7" Single: Released Mar '85, on Midnight Music, by Midnight Music Records. Catalogue no: **DONG 9**

Vitality

ONLY YOU
Tracks: / Only you.
7" Single: Released Jul '88, on MGR, Catalogue no: **MROY 001**

Vitamin Z

BURN FOR YOU
Tracks: / Burn for you / So far.
CD 5": Released Aug '89, on Mercury, by Phonogram Ltd. Catalogue no: **VITCD 1**
7" Single: Released Aug '89, on Mercury, by Phonogram Ltd. Catalogue no: **VIT 1**
12" Single: Released Aug '89, on Mercury, by Phonogram Ltd. Catalogue no: **VIT 112**

BURNING FLAME
Tracks: / Burning flame / Dancers of Eve.
7" Single: Released Feb '84, on Mercury, by Phonogram Ltd. Catalogue no: **VITZ 1**
12" Single: Released Feb '84, on Mercury, by Phonogram Ltd. Catalogue no: **VITZ 112**

CIRCUS RING (WE SCREAM ABOUT)
Tracks: / Circus ring (we scream about).
7" Single: Released May '85, on Mercury, by Phonogram Ltd. Catalogue no: **MER 186**
12" Single: Released May '85, on Mercury, by Phonogram Ltd. Catalogue no: **MERX 186**

EVERYTIME THAT I SEE YOU
Tracks: / Everytime that I see you.
7" Set: Released Aug '85, on Mercury, by Phonogram Ltd. Catalogue no: **MERDP 197**
7" Single: Released Jul '85, on Mercury, by Phonogram Ltd. Catalogue no: **MER 197**
12" Single: Released Jul '85, on Mercury, by Phonogram Ltd. Catalogue no: **MERX 197**

HI HI FRIEND
Tracks: / Hi hi friend.
12" Single: Released Nov '85, on Mercury, by Phonogram Ltd. Catalogue no: **MERX 208**
7" Single: Released Nov '85, on Mercury, by Phonogram Ltd. Catalogue no: **MER 208**

Viva

CHRIS MUST STAY
Tracks: / Chris must stay / Light of the world.
7" Single: Released Nov '81, on Cambra, by Cambra Records. Deleted '88. Catalogue no: **CMB 01**

RADIO SAVIOUR
Tracks: / Radio saviour.
7" Single: Released Jan '80, on Square, Catalogue no: **SQ 31**

Viva Beat

MAN FROM CHINA
Tracks: / Man from China / On patrol.
7" Single: Released Mar '80, on Charisma, by Virgin Records. Deleted Mar '83. Catalogue no: **CB 355**

Viva Marconi

SERIOUS DREAMING
Tracks: / Serious dreaming / What a joke.
7" Single: Released Feb '83, on Zim Zam, Catalogue no: **ZZ 5**

Viveen

WONDERFUL FEELING
Tracks: / Wonderful feeling.
12" Single: Released Jul '89, on Kristal Beach, Catalogue no: **K9B 001**

Vixen

CRYING
Tracks: / Crying (Tripp/Paris.) / Desperate (Miku/Santos/Kuehnemund.) / Crying (ext. remix) (12" remix only.) / Give it away (CD single only.) / Edge of a broken heart (CD single only.).
12" Single: Released Jan '89, on EMI-Manhattan, by EMI Records. Catalogue no: **12MT 60**
7" Pic: Released Feb '89, on EMI-Manhattan, by EMI Records. Deleted Oct '89. Catalogue no: **MTPD 60**
7" Single: Released Feb '89, on EMI-Manhattan, by EMI Records. Deleted Oct '89. Catalogue no: **MTG 60**
7" Single: Released Nov '88, on EMI-Manhattan, by EMI Records. Catalogue no: **MT 60**
12" Single: Released Feb '89, on EMI-Manhattan, by EMI Records. Deleted Oct '89. Catalogue no: **12MTP 60**
CD 5": Released Feb '89, on EMI-Manhattan, by EMI Records. Catalogue no: **CDMT 60**

EDGE OF A BROKEN HEART
Tracks: / Edge of a broken heart / Charmed life / Edge of a broken heart (ext. mix) (Not on 7".) / Love made me (Live) (CD single only.) / Cryin' (Live) (CD single only.).
Cassingle: Released Aug '89, on EMI-Manhattan, by EMI Records. Catalogue no: **TCMT 48**
7" Single: Released Aug '88, on EMI-Manhattan, by EMI Records. Catalogue no: **MTPD 48**
7" Single: Released Aug '88, on EMI-Manhattan, by EMI Records. Catalogue no: **MT 48**
CD 5": Released Aug '89, on EMI-Manhattan, by EMI Records. Catalogue no: **CDMT 48**
7" Single: Released Aug '88, on EMI-Manhattan, by EMI Records. Deleted Aug '89. Catalogue no: **MTP 48**
12" Single: Released Aug '88, on EMI-Manhattan, by EMI Records. Deleted Aug '89. Catalogue no: **12MT 48**
Special: Released Aug '89, on EMI-Manhattan, by EMI Records. Catalogue no: **12MTP 48**
Special: Released Aug '89, on EMI-Manhattan, by EMI Records. Catalogue no: **12MTS 48**
Special: Released Aug '89, on EMI-Manhattan, by EMI Records. Catalogue no: **MTS 48**

LOVE MADE ME (REMIX)
Tracks: / Love made me (remix) / Give it away / Cruisin' (live) (Not on 7".) / Edge of a broken heart (live) (Not on 7".) / Hellraisers (live) (Not on 7".).
7" Single: Released Apr '89, on EMI-Manhattan, by EMI Records. Deleted Oct '89. Catalogue no: **203 365 8**
7" Single: Released Apr '89, on EMI-Manhattan, by EMI Records. Catalogue no: **203 365 7**
7" Pic: Released Apr '89, on EMI-Manhattan, by EMI Records. Catalogue no: **MTPD 66**
CD 5": Released Apr '89, on EMI-Manhattan, by EMI Records. Catalogue no: **203 365 2**
7" Single: Released Apr '89, on EMI-Manhattan, by EMI Records. Catalogue no: **MT 66**
7" Single: Released Apr '89, on EMI-Manhattan, by EMI Records. Catalogue no: **203 365 0**
7" Single: Released Apr '89, on EMI-Manhattan, by EMI Records. Deleted Oct '89. Catalogue no: **MTS 66**
CD 5": Released Apr '89, on EMI-Manhattan, by EMI Records. Catalogue no: **CDMT 66**
12" Single: Released Apr '89, on EMI-Manhattan, by EMI Records. Catalogue no: **12MT 66**
12" Single: Released Apr '89, on EMI-Manhattan, by EMI Records. Catalogue no: **203 365 6**

Voggue

DANCING THE NIGHT AWAY
Tracks: / Dancing the night away / Roller boogie.
7" Single: Released Jul '81, on Mercury, by Phonogram Ltd. Catalogue no: **MER 76**
12" Single: Released Jul '81, on Mercury, by Phonogram Ltd. Catalogue no: **MERX 76**

LOVE BUZZ
Tracks: / Love buzz.
7" Single: Released May '82, on Mercury, by Phonogram Ltd. Catalogue no: **MER 105**
12" Single: Released May '82, on Mercury, by Phonogram Ltd. Catalogue no: **MERX 105**

Vogue, Kirsten

MARIETTE
Tracks: / Mariette / No turning back.
7" Single: Released Jan '81, on EMI, by EMI Records. Deleted Jan '84. Catalogue no: **EMI 5133**

Voi Vod

COCKROACHES
Tracks: / Cockroaches.
Note: Picture disc.
12" Single: Released Nov '87, on Noise (Germany), Catalogue no: **N 0085**

TOO SCARED TO SCREAM
Tracks: / Too scared to scream.
12" Pic: Released Sep '89, on Noise, by Dorane Records. Catalogue no: **NUKPD 085**

Voice

SHE'S LEAVING
Tracks: / She's leaving / Going home.
7" Single: Released Aug '81, on Secret, by Secret Records. Deleted '84. Catalogue no: **SHH 115**

SIGN YOUR NAME
Tracks: / Sign your name.
7" Single: Released Dec '80, on Secret, by Secret Records. Catalogue no: **SHH 108**

Voice Farm

DOUBLE GARAGE
Tracks: / Double garage.
7" Single: Released Oct '82, on Alternative Tentacles, by Alternative Tentacles Records. Catalogue no: **VIRUS 16**

Voice of America

I WILL TELL
Tracks: / I will tell (Extended version on 12") / Seikou.
7" Single: Released Feb '88, on Virgin, by Virgin Records. Catalogue no: **VS 1050**
12" Single: Released Feb '88, on Virgin, by Virgin Records. Catalogue no: **VST 1050**

STORY OF LOVE
Tracks: / Story of love (Extended version on 12") / V.O.A..
7" Single: Released Jul '87, on Virgin, by Virgin Records. Deleted May '88. Catalogue no: **VS 984**
12" Single: Released Jul '87, on Virgin, by Virgin Records. Catalogue no: **VS 984-12**

Voice Of Authority

VERY BIG IN AMERICA RIGHT NOW
12" Single: Released Aug '84, on Cherry Red, by Cherry Red Records. Deleted '87. Catalogue no: **12 CHERRY 79**

Voice Of Progress

MINI-BUS DRIVER
Tracks: / Mini-bus driver / Can't tek de fusion.
12" Single: Released Oct '82, on Negus Roots, Deleted Oct '85. Catalogue no: **NERT014**

Voice Of The Beehive

DON'T CALL ME BABY
Tracks: / Don't call me baby / Jump this way / Goodbye tonight (Avaliable on 12" format only.) / I say nothing (extra track on CD single.).
Note: Produced by Pete Collins and mixed by Nigel Green. 'Jump This Way' + 'Goodbye Tonight' will not be included on the album.
12" Single: Released Apr '88, on London Records, by London Records. Deleted Feb '89. Catalogue no: **LONX 175**
7" Set: Released Feb '89, on London Records, by London Records. Catalogue no: **LONB 175**
7" Single: Released '88, on London Records, by London Records. Deleted Feb '89. Catalogue no: **LONP 175**
7" Single: Released Apr '88, on London Records, by London Records. Deleted Feb '89. Catalogue no: **LON 175**
CD 5": Released May '88, on London Records, by London Records. Catalogue no: **LONCD 175**

EVENING SHOW EP: VOICE OF THE BEEHIVE
12" Single: Released Dec '88, on Night Tracks, by Pinnacle Records. Catalogue no: **SFNT 017**

I SAY NOTHING
Tracks: / I say nothing / Things you see when you don't have a gun, The.
12" Single: Released Sep '87, on London Records, by London Records. Deleted Oct '88. Catalogue no: **LONX 151**
12" Single: Released '88, on London Records, by London Records. Deleted Feb '89. Catalogue no: **LONXR 151**
12" Single: Released '88, on London Records, by London Records. Deleted Feb '89. Catalogue no: **LONXP 151**
7" Single: Released Sep '87, on London Records, by London Records. Deleted Feb '89. Catalogue no: **LON 151**

I SAY NOTHING (RE-RELEASE)
Tracks: / I say nothing / Things you see when you don't have a gun, The / Don't call me baby (On 12" only) / In the flesh (On 12" only).
7" Single: Released Jul '88, on London Records, by London Records. Deleted Feb '89. Catalogue no: **LONP 190**
7" Single: Released Aug '88, on London Records, by London Records. Catalogue no: **LONF 190**
CD 5": Released 11 Jul '88, on London Records, by London Records. Catalogue no: **LONCD 190**
7" Single: Released Aug '88, on London Records, by London Records. Deleted Feb '89. Catalogue no: **LONH 190**
7" Single: Released 11 Jul '88, on London Records, by London Records. Deleted Feb '89. Catalogue no: **LON 190**
12" Single: Released 11 Jul '88, on London Records, by London Records. Deleted Feb '89. Catalogue no: **LONX 190**

I WALK THE EARTH
Tracks: / This weak / Jesus (Extra track on 12" version only.) / I walk the earth / Tattoo songs (Only on 12" (LONX 206)) / Everything I had (Only on 12" (LONX 206)).
12" Single: Released 22 Feb '88, on London Records, by London Records. Deleted '88. Catalogue no: **LONX 169**
7" Single: Released '87, on London Records, by London Records. Deleted Oct '88. Catalogue no: **LONB 169**
7" Single: Released 16 Sep '88, on London Records, by London Records. Deleted May '89. Catalogue no: **LON 206**
CD 5": Released 16 Sep '88, on London Records, by London Records. Catalogue no: **LONCD 206**
7" Single: Released 22 Feb '88, on London Records, by London Records. Deleted '88. Catalogue no: **LON 169**
7" Single: Released Oct '88, on London Records, by London Records. Deleted May '89. Catalogue no: **LONT 206**
12" Single: Released 16 Sep '88, on London Records, by London Records. Deleted May '89. Catalogue no: **LONX 206**
7" Single: Released Oct '88, on London Records, by London Records. Deleted May '89. Catalogue no: **LONP 206**

JUST A CITY
Tracks: / Just a city.

7" Single: Released Mar '87, on Food, by Food Records. Deleted Feb '89. Catalogue no: **FOOD 9**
12" Single: Released Feb '88, on Food, by Food Records. Deleted Feb '89. Catalogue no: **FOODX 9**

MAN IN THE MOON
Tracks: / Man in the moon, The / What you have is enough / There's a barbarian in the back of my car.
12" Single: Released Dec '88, on London Records, by London Records. Deleted 26 Jun '89. Catalogue no: **LONX 209**
CD 5": Released Dec '88, on London Records, by London Records. Catalogue no: **LONCD 209**
7" Single: Released Dec '88, on London Records, by London Records. Deleted 26 Jun '89. Catalogue no: **LON 209**

Voice, Steve

BACK ON MY FEET
Tracks: / Back on my feet.
7" Single: Released Jun '84, on Red Bus, by Red Bus Records. Catalogue no: **RBUS 93**

CALL ME
Tracks: / Call me / I wanna get next to you.
7" Single: Released Sep '80, on Red Bus, by Red Bus Records. Deleted '83. Catalogue no: **RBUS 56**

I CAN'T GET OVER YOU
Tracks: / I can't get over you.
7" Single: Released Jul '82, on Red Bus, by Red Bus Records. Catalogue no: **RBUS 70**

STAND UP FOR YOURSELF
Tracks: / Stand up for yourself / Schooldays.
7" Single: Released Jun '80, on Red Bus, by Red Bus Records. Deleted Jun '83. Catalogue no: **RBUS 53**

WHY DON'T YOU CALL ME
Tracks: / Why don't you call me.
7" Single: Released Mar '81, on Red Bus, by Red Bus Records. Catalogue no: **RBUS 59**

Voices

BEAUTY IS THE BEAST
Tracks: / Beauty is the beast.
7" Single: Released Oct '83, on Mercury, by Phonogram Ltd. Catalogue no: **VOICE 2**
12" Single: Released Oct '83, on Mercury, by Phonogram Ltd. Catalogue no: **VOICE 212**

SACRIFICIAL RITES
Tracks: / Sacrificial rites.
7" Single: Released Apr '83, on Voice, Catalogue no: **VOICE 1**
12" Single: Released Apr '83, on Voice, Catalogue no: **VOICE 12**

Voices In The Dark

KEEP IT WARM
Tracks: / Keep it warm / Keep it warm (remix) / Keep it warm (inst).
7" Single: Released May '87, on Champion, by Champion Records. Deleted Jul '89. Catalogue no: **CHAMP 46**
12" Single: Released May '87, on Champion, by Champion Records. Catalogue no: **CHAMP 1246**

Voices Of East Harlem

WANTED DEAD OR ALIVE
Tracks: / Wanted dead or alive.
7" Single: Released Oct '88, on Low Fat Vinyl, by Low Fat Vinyl Records. Catalogue no: **VOICES 1**

Void, E

SHADOWS
Tracks: / Shadows.
7" Single: Released Jan '84, on WEA (International), by WEA Records. Catalogue no: **U 9693**

Voilet Circuit

VISION OF LOVE
Tracks: / Vision of Love.
7" Single: Released Jan '86, on Circuit, Deleted '88. Catalogue no: **CIRCUIT 1**

Volcano

I WANNA MAKE IT (YEAH I DO)
Tracks: / I wanna make it (yeah I do) / You ain't got no chance man.
7" Single: Released Feb '82, on Krr-unch, Catalogue no: **KR 301**

IT'S NOT THE TIME
Tracks: / It's not the time / Why.
7" Single: Released Feb '83, on Volcano, Catalogue no: **VOL 001**

Volcano Suns

SEA CRUISE
Tracks: / Sea cruise / Greasy spine.
7" Single: Released Nov '86, on Homestead, Catalogue no: **HMS 057**

Volcanoes

STRANGERS IN THE NIGHT
Tracks: / Strangers in the night.
7" Single: Released Jan '84, on Volcanic, Catalogue no: **VOLC 1**

Vollenweider, Andreas

NIGHT FIRE DANCE
Tracks: / Play of five balls / Night fire dance.
7" Single: Released Nov '86, on CBS, by CBS Records. Catalogue no: **A 7173**
12" Single: Released Nov '86, on CBS, by CBS Records. Catalogue no: **TA 7173**

PACE VERDE
Tracks: / Pace verde / Sisyphos.
7" Single: Released Apr '84, on Geffen, by Geffen Records (USA). Catalogue no: **A 3900**

Vollerman, Scarlett

VENTILATION
Tracks: / Ventilation / Loving you.
7" Single: Released Jan '81, on RCA, by BMG Records (UK). Deleted Jan '84. Catalogue no: **RCA 12**

WILD OBSESSIONS
Tracks: / Wild obsessions / Un coeur perdu.
7" Single: Released Nov '82, on Jet, by Jet Records. Catalogue no: **JET 7029**

Volti

CORAZON MONEY
Tracks: / Corazon money / Bucks.
12" Single: Released Mar '86, on Crammed Discs, by Crammed Discs. Catalogue no: **CRAM 046**

Volunteers

BLADDER OF LIFE
Tracks: / Bladder of life.
12" Single: Released Oct '88, on Village, by Village Records. Catalogue no: **VILT 105**

Vomito Negro

STAY ALIVE
Tracks: / Stay alive.
12" Single: Released 23 Apr '88, on K K, by Play It Again Sam (Belgium). Catalogue no: **KK 004**

Von Bopp

BROKEN HEART
Tracks: / Broken heart / Broken heart (instrumental).
7" Single: Released Jan '89, on Savage, by Savage Records. Catalogue no: **SAV 004**

Von Vollenman,

HYPNOTIZED
Tracks: / Hypnotized / Warm love.
7" Single: Released Apr '81, on RCA, by BMG Records (UK). Deleted Apr '84. Catalogue no: **RCA 50**

Von Wernherr

COSMIC CLIMB (also under Madonna)
Tracks: / Cosmic climb / We are the gods.
7" Single: Released May '86, on Receiver, by Trojan Records. Catalogue no: **REPLAY 3000**
12" Single: Released May '86, on Receiver, by Trojan Records. Deleted May '88. Catalogue no: **SREPLAY 3000**

Voodoo

CRYING MY HEART OUT
12" Single: Released Nov '82, on Leo Records, by Leo Records. Catalogue no: **LEO 004**

Voodoo Child

RAIN (SUMMER MIX)
Tracks: / Rain (summer mix) / Glory to the lovers.
7" Single: Released Jul '87, on Aftermath (2), Catalogue no: **VC 1**

Voodoo Doll

WOMEN BEAT MEN
Tracks: / Women beat men / Women beat men (version).
12" Single: Released Jun '89, on Champion, by Champion Records. Catalogue no: **CHAMP 12208**
7" Single: Released Jun '89, on Champion, by Champion Records. Catalogue no: **CHAMP 208**

Voodoo Mothership

PAPA'S GOT A BRAND NEW PIGBAG (REMIX)
Tracks: / Papa's got a brand new pigbag (remix).
12" Single: Released May '89, on Blueback, Catalogue no: **12 BBBK 3**

Voor Den Broode

WAAROM IKKE
Tracks: / Waarom ikke.
12" Single: Released May '89, on V.W., Catalogue no: **VW 1001**

V.O.P

HEROES
Tracks: / Heroes.
12" Single: Released Jul '83, on Rialto (1), by Rialto Records. Catalogue no: **12 RIA 19**

Voulzy, Laurent

LE SOLEIL DONNE
Tracks: / Le soleil donne.
CD 5": Released 31 Jul '89, on RCA, by BMG Records (UK). Catalogue no: **PD 42098**
7" Single: Released 31 Jul '89, on RCA, by BMG Records (UK). Catalogue no: **PB 42097**
12" Single: Released 31 Jul '89, on RCA, by BMG Records (UK). Catalogue no: **PT 42098**

Vow Wow

CRY NO MORE
Tracks: / Cry no more / Sign of the times / Shockwaves (Extra track available on 12" version only.).
7" Single: Released 21 Nov '87, on Arista, by BMG Records (UK). Deleted May '89. Catalogue no: **RIS 46**
12" Single: Released 21 Nov '87, on Arista, by BMG Records (UK). Deleted May '89. Catalogue no: **RIST 46**

DON'T LEAVE ME NOW
Tracks: / Don't leave me now / Nightless city / Shot in the dark*.
Note: * extra track on 12" version.
7" Single: Released Sep '87, on Arista, by BMG Records (UK). Deleted May '89. Catalogue no: **RIS 38**
12" Single: Released Sep '87, on Arista, by BMG Records (UK). Deleted May '89. Catalogue no: **RIST 38**

DON'T TELL ME LIES
Tracks: / Don't tell me lies / Siren song (Recorded live at Town And Country Club.).
12" Pic: Released Feb '88, on Arista, by BMG Records (UK). Deleted May '89. Catalogue no: **609 805**

HELTER SKELTER
Tracks: / Helter skelter / Keep on moving / Sign of the times (Available on 12" only) / Fade away (on CD single only.).
CD 3": Released Feb '89, on Arista, by BMG Records (UK). Catalogue no: **162 013**
7" Single: Released Feb '89, on Arista, by BMG Records (UK). Catalogue no: **112 013**
12" Single: Released Feb '89, on Arista, by BMG Records (UK). Catalogue no: **612 013**
CD 5": Released Feb '89, on Arista, by BMG Records (UK). Catalogue no: **662 013**

I FEEL THE POWER
Tracks: / I feel the power / Shot in the dark / Hurricane (On 12" and 10" single.) / Nightless city (Only on 12".) / You know what I mean (Only on 10".).
CD 5": Released Apr '89, on Arista, by BMG Records (UK). Catalogue no: **662 265**
10" single: Released 22 May '89, on Arista, by BMG Records (UK). Catalogue no: **612 289**
12" Single: Released Apr '89, on Arista, by BMG Records (UK). Catalogue no: **612 265**
12" Single: Released May '89, on Arista, by BMG Records (UK). Catalogue no: **612 088**
7" Single: Released Apr '89, on Arista, by BMG Records (UK). Catalogue no: **112 265**
12" Single: Released 22 May '89, on Arista, by BMG Records (UK). Catalogue no: **612 333**

ROCK ME NOW
Tracks: / Rock me now / Girl in red, The / Somewhere in the night / Don't leave me now / Don't wanna come (On VWW PK 1 only).
12" Single: Released Jul '88, on Arista, by BMG Records (UK). Catalogue no: **12 VWW 1 (611 583)**
7" Single: Released Jul '88, on Arista, by BMG Records (UK). Catalogue no: **VWW1 (111 583)**
7" Single: Released Jul '88, on Arista, by BMG Records (UK). Catalogue no: **VWW PK 1**
CD 5": Released Jul '88, on Arista, by BMG Records (UK). Deleted Jul '89. Catalogue no: **VWWCD 1/661583**

Voxpop

SLEEPING IN A STRANGERS BED
Tracks: / Sleeping in a strangers bed.
7" Single: Released Mar '82, on Hollywood, by Hollywood Records. Catalogue no: **HWD 001**

Voyage

FROM EAST TO WEST
Tracks: / From east to west.
7" Single: Released Jun '78, on GTO, Deleted '81. Catalogue no: **GT 224**

LET'S FLY AWAY
Tracks: / Let's fly away.
7" Single: Released Mar '79, on GTO Deleted '82. Catalogue no: **GT 245**

SOUVENIRS
Tracks: / Souvenirs.
7" Single: Released Nov '78, on GTO Deleted '81. Catalogue no: **GT 241**

Voyager

CLING TO ME
Tracks: / Cling to me / Grass.
7" Single: Released Oct '80, on Mountain Deleted Oct '83. Catalogue no: **TOP 55**

KEEPING THE MUSIC ALIVE
Tracks: / Keeping the music alive / Grass.
7" Single: Released Mar '80, on Mountain Deleted '83. Catalogue no: **TOP 52**

SING OUT - LOVE IS EASY
Tracks: / Sing out - love is easy / Time on our side.
7" Single: Released May '80, on Mountain Deleted '83. Catalogue no: **TOP 54**

Voyager (Group)

HALFWAY MOTEL
Tracks: / Halfway motel.
7" Single: Released May '79, on Mountain Deleted '82. Catalogue no: **VOY 001**

KING OF SIAM
Tracks: / King of Siam.
7" Single: Released Jul '81, on RCA, by BMG Records (UK). Catalogue no: **RCA 7**

LIKE A STONE
Tracks: / Like a stone / Good for you.
7" Single: Released Nov '82, on Flying, by Flying Records. Catalogue no: **FLY 104**

ROSIE
Tracks: / Rosie / Cue for you.
7" Single: Released Oct '81, on RCA, by BMG Records (UK). Catalogue no: **RCA 15**

V-Squad

EAT THE MEAT
Tracks: / Eat the meat / Turn about.
7" Single: Released Jul '81, on Carrer America (USA), by PolyGram Rec.Inc.(USA). Catalogue no: **CAR 203**

Vultures

GOOD THING
Tracks: / Good thing.
12" Single: Released May '88, on Narodni by Narodnik Records. Catalogue no: **NR 006T**

VV

UNCERTAIN SMILE
Tracks: / Uncertain smile / Three orang kisses from Kazon.
12" Single: Released Oct '82, on Epic, b CBS Records. Deleted Oct '85. Catalogu no: **EPCA 132787**
7" Single: Released Oct '82, on Epic, b CBS Records. Deleted Oct '85. Catalogu no: **EPCA 2787**

Vyllies

AHIA
Tracks: / Ahia.
7" Single: Released May '86, on Music F Nations, by Music For Nations Record Catalogue no: **FAA 103**
12" Single: Released May '86, on Music F Nations, by Music For Nations Record Catalogue no: **12 FAA 103**

W

The following information was taken from the Music Master database on October 20th, 1989.

Wa Wa Nee

STIMULATION
Tracks: / Headlines / Stimulation / Stimulation (ext. remix) / Stimulation (ext. dub version).
7" Single: Released Feb '88, on CBS, by CBS Records. Deleted Jan '89. Catalogue no: **WWN 2**
12" Single: Released Feb '88, on CBS, by CBS Records. Deleted Aug '88. Catalogue no: **WWN T2**

SUGAR FREE
Tracks: / Sugar free / When the world is a home / Sugar free (extended mix) (On 12" version only.) / Sugar free (extended dub) (On 12" version only.) / When the world is a home (version) (On 12" version.).
7" Single: Released Nov '87, on CBS, by CBS Records. Deleted Jun '88. Catalogue no: **WWN Q1**
12" Single: Released Oct '87, on CBS, by CBS Records. Deleted Jun '88. Catalogue no: **WWN T1**
10" single: Released Nov '87, on CBS, by CBS Records. Catalogue no: **WWNQT 1**
7" Single: Released Oct '87, on CBS, by CBS Records. Deleted Jun '88. Catalogue no: **WWN 1**

Wadada

REGGAE SUNSPLASH
Tracks: / Reggae sunsplash.
12" Single: Released Aug '83, on Solomonic (1), by Solomonic Records. Catalogue no: **SM 101**

Waddington, Bill

DON'T FORGET THE OLD FOLKS AT CHRISTMAS
Tracks: / Don't forget the old folks at Christmas / Tra la la.
7" Single: Released Nov '86, on Ritz, by Ritz Records. Catalogue no: **PERCY 1**

Wade, Adam

TAKE GOOD CARE OF HER
Tracks: / Take good care of her.
7" Single: Released Jun '61, on H.M.V., by EMI Records. Deleted '64. Catalogue no: **POP 843**

Wade, Andre

FLIGHT (OF JACKING YOUR BODY), THE
Tracks: / Flight (of jacking your body), The.
12" Single: Released Oct '87, on Play House (USA), Catalogue no: **PHR 420**

Wade, Decca

IF IT WASN'T FOR RITA
Tracks: / If it wasn't for Rita.
7" Single: Released Apr '83, on EMI, by EMI Records. Catalogue no: **EMI 5384**

Wade, Terri

LIGHT
Tracks: / Light (7" mix) / Light (inst) / Light.
12" Single: Released Jun '87, on Big Top, by Big Top Records. Deleted '88. Catalogue no: **MBT 02**

LIVE FOR TONIGHT
Tracks: / Live for tonight.
12" Single: Released Sep '85, on Big Top, by Big Top Records. Deleted '86. Catalogue no: **WADE 002**

SINGLE GIRL
Tracks: / Single girl.
7" Single: Released Apr '85, on Big Top, by Big Top Records. Deleted '86. Catalogue no: **7 BT 101**
12" Single: Released Apr '85, on Big Top, by Big Top Records. Deleted '86. Catalogue no: **12 BT 101**

Wade, Wayne

I'M THE PROMOTER
Tracks: / I'm the promoter / I'm the promoter (version).
12" Single: Released Jul '87, on Greensleeves, by Greensleeves Records. Catalogue no: **GRED 216**

IT AIN'T EASY
Tracks: / It ain't easy.
12" Single: Released Oct '84, on Revue, by Creole Records. Catalogue no: **REV 016T**

LADY
Tracks: / Lady.
7" Single: Released Jun '83, on Epic, by CBS Records. Catalogue no: **A 3457**
12" Single: Released Jun '83, on Epic, by CBS Records. Catalogue no: **TA 3457**

STRENGTH OF OUR LOVE
Tracks: / Strength of our love.
12" Single: Released Jul '89, on FJ, Catalogue no: **FJ 4521**

Waders

QWACKER SONG
Tracks: / Qwacker song.
7" Single: Released Sep '81, on KAR, Catalogue no: **QWACK 1**

Wagoneers

I CONFESS
Tracks: / I confess / I can't stay.
7" Single: Released 17 Oct '88, on A&M, by A&M Records. Deleted Feb '89. Catalogue no: **AM 461**
12" Single: Released 17 Oct '88, on A&M, by A&M Records. Deleted Feb '89. Catalogue no: **AMY 461**

I WANNA KNOW HER AGAIN
Tracks: / I wanna know her again.
Note: The Wagoneers, all in their early 20's, are a four-piece country band from Austin, Texas. Their forthcoming LP, "Stout and High" on A&M Records consists of completely original material in the tradition of country music's Golden Era.
CD 5": Released '88, on A&M, by A&M Records. Deleted Feb '89. Catalogue no: **AMCD 454**
7" Single: Released '88, on A&M, by A&M Records. Catalogue no: **AM 454**
12" Single: Released '88, on A&M, by A&M Records. Catalogue no: **AMY 454**

Wagsmith, R.J.

PAPADUM SONG
Tracks: / Papadum song / Dogs.
7" Single: Released Sep '81, on Rocket, by Rocket Records. Deleted Sep '84. Catalogue no: **XPRES 65**

Wah!

Biographical details: This British band has always been dominated by its singer, guitarist, songwriter and public spokesman Pete Wylie. The group's personnel situation was summed up by the sleeve of the biggest Wah! single, *The Story Of The Blues*, which patronisingly stated that the record was "played by Pete Wylie, Washington and some girls". At various times in its history the band has been known as Wah! Heat, Shambeko Say Wah!, the Mighty Wah! and simply Wah! The arrogant and ebullient talent of Wylie first began to attract attention in his native Liverpool in 1977 when he was a member of the Crucial Three, a very short-lived trio who were instrumental in helping to revitalise Liverpool as a cauldron of new musical talent. The other members were Julian Cope, who went on to form Teardrop Explodes, and Ian McCulloch, who proceeded to lead Echo & The Bunnymen. The erratic Wylie took longer to achieve commercial success than his erstwhile colleagues. After passing through a series of local small-time groups (whose main audiences were at the legendary Eric's Club in Matthew Street, Liverpool), Wylie formed Wah! Heat in February '79. The debut Wah! album, *Nah Poo - The Art of Bluff*, was released in July '81 and reached No 33 on the UK LP chart. It was not until January '83 that Wylie hit really big -- *The Story Of The Blues*, a melodic, dramatic opus with a big production that would have made Phil Spector proud, cruised to No 3 on Britain's singles chart. But it was a hard hit to follow and *Hop (I Wish You'd Believe Me)*, a gospel-tinged pop single, only just scraped the UK Top Forty. As the Mighty Wah! Wylie bounced back in summer '84 with a UK Top Twenty single *Come Back* (rather reminiscent of the Equals' 1968 No 1 *Baby Come Back*) but once again he was unable to consolidate on his success. He is one of the most charismatic figures on the British pop/rock scene but Wah!'s story has been a series of exciting one-offs rather than a real career. (Bob MacDonald, April 1985.)

Wah! is a new wave group formed as Wah! Heat in Liverpool in 1979 by guitarist/vocalist Pete Wylie (born in 1958) who'd been a member of the Crucial Three in 1977 with Julian Cope and Ian McCulloch (who formed Teardrop Explodes and Echo and the Bunnymen respectively). First single *Better Screams* for local Inevitable label had B-side *Joe* on *Hicks From The Sticks* '80 compilation of post-punk regional bands. First album *Nah Poo - The Art Of Bluff* in 1981 moved toward heavy metal; the group subsequently became a keyboard-based new wave outifit, called itself The Mighty Wah! and disbanded when follow ups failed to emulate success of authentic *Come Back* single. Wylie formed group Oedipus Wrecks, made single *Sinful* for No. 13 hit in '86, again couldn't follow up; it was rumoured he'd replace Holly Johnson in Frankie Goes To Hollywood. (Donald Clarke)..

FORGET THE DOWN
Tracks: / Forget the down.
7" Single: Released Jun '81, on Eternal, by Eternal Records. Catalogue no: **SLATE 1**

HOPE(I WISH YOU'D BELIEVE ME)
Tracks: / Hope(I wish you'd believe me).
7" Single: Released Mar '83, on WEA, by WEA Records. Catalogue no: **X 9880**

SOMEDAY
Tracks: / Someday.
7" Single: Released Oct '81, on Eternal, by Eternal Records. Catalogue no: **SIMEY 1**
12" Single: Released Oct '81, on Eternal, by Eternal Records. Catalogue no: **SIMEY 1T**

STORY OF THE BLUES
Tracks: / Story of the blues / Seven minutes live.
7" Single: Released Nov '82, on Eternal, by Eternal Records. Deleted Jun '87. Catalogue no: **JF 1**
12" Single: Released Nov '82, on Eternal, by Eternal Records. Deleted Jun '87. Catalogue no: **JF 1T**

YOU CAN'T PUT YOUR ARMS AROUND A MEMORY
Tracks: / You can't put your arms around a memory.
12" Single: Released Mar '83, on WEA, by WEA Records. Catalogue no: **X 9980T**

Wah Heat

7 MINUTES TO MIDNIGHT
Tracks: / 7 minutes to midnight.
7" Single: Released Feb '83, on Inevitable, by Inevitable Records. Catalogue no: **INEV 004**

Wahib

MY EYES
Tracks: / My eyes.
7" Single: Released Apr '82, on Hits From Heaven, Catalogue no: **HIT 1**

Waikikis

Biographical details: This all-male group achieved a one-off chart single on both sides of the Atlantic in 1965. *Hawaii Tattoo*, an instrumental, reached No 33 in American and No 41 in the UK. They remain a semi-legendary institution in their native Hawaii, with a brand of feverishly joyful, quasi-military jollity. (Bob McDonald, April 1985.).

HAWAII TATTOO (SINGLE)
Tracks: / Hawaii tattoo.
7" Single: Released Mar '65, on Palette, Deleted '68. Catalogue no: **PG 9025**

Wailer, Bunny

Biographical details: Born Neville O'Riley Livingston in Jamaica in 1947, he grew up with Bob Marley and Peter Tosh, and the trio became the Wailers. Marley became superstar and died of cancer; the temperamental Tosh went his own way -- and was murdered in 1987. Gentle Bunny Livingston, a true Rastafarian, changed his name to Bunny Wailer in 1975 and remained one of Jamaica's most popular artists. (Donald Clarke, March 1988.).

ARAB OIL
Tracks: / Arab oil.
12" Single: Released Jun '82, on Nighthawk, by Nighthawk Records (USA). Catalogue no: **12 NH 1001**

BACK TO SCHOOL
Tracks: / Back to school.
12" Single: Released May '83, on Solomonic (1), by Solomonic Records. Catalogue no: **BWD 014**
12" Single: Released Nov '86, on Solomonic (1), by Solomonic Records. Catalogue no: **SMT 025**
7" Single: Released Nov '86, on Solomonic (1), by Solomonic Records. Catalogue no: **SM 025**

COLLIE MAN
Tracks: / Collie man.
12" Single: Released Jul '83, on Solomonic (1), by Solomonic Records. Catalogue no: **BWD 17**

CONQUERER, THE
Tracks: / Conquerer, The.
12" Single: Released Jun '83, on Solomonic (1), by Solomonic Records. Catalogue no: **BWD 015**

DANCING SHOES
Tracks: / Dancing shoes / Walk the proud land.
12" Single: Released Jun '81, on Island, by Island Records. Deleted Jun '84. Catalogue no: **12WIP 6685**
7" Single: Released Jun '81, on Island, by Island Records. Deleted Jun '84. Catalogue no: **WIP 6685**

ELECTRO RAP
Tracks: / Electro rap / Soul rocking party.
7" Single: Released Jan '84, on Solomonic (1), by Solomonic Records. Catalogue no: **SM 7021**
12" Single: Released Jan '84, on Solomonic (1), by Solomonic Records. Catalogue no: **SM 12021**

MODERATION
Tracks: / Moderation / Another dance.
12" Single: Released Aug '83, on Solomonic (1), by Solomonic Records. Catalogue no: **SM 018**
7" Single: Released Aug '83, on Solomonic (1), by Solomonic Records. Catalogue no: **SM 7018**

RIDING
Tracks: / Riding.
7" Single: Released Sep '81, on Solomonic (1), by Solomonic Records. Catalogue no: **RT 083/SM 007**

SERIOUS THING
Tracks: / Food / Serious thing.
12" Single: Released Jul '86, on Solomonic (1), by Solomonic Records. Catalogue no: **SM 024**

TEARS IN YOUR EYES
Tracks: / Tears in your eyes.
7" Single: Released Jun '86, on Solomonic (1), by Solomonic Records. Catalogue no: **SM 023**
12" Single: Released Jun '86, on Solomonic (1), by Solomonic Records. Catalogue no: **SM 12023**

Wailing Souls

BOUNCE BACK
Tracks: / Bounce back.
12" Single: Released Apr '83, on Greensleeves, by Greensleeves Records. Catalogue no: **GRED 115**

DIAMONDS AND PEARLS
Tracks: / Diamonds and pearls.
12" Single: Released Mar '82, on Greensleeves, by Greensleeves Records. Catalogue no: **GRED 81**

GRABBING AND RUNNING
Tracks: / Grabbing and running.
12" Single: Released Dec '82, on Cha-Cha, by Cha-Cha Records. Catalogue no: **CHAD 51**

HOOLIGAN RACE

Tracks: / Hooligan race.
7" Single: Released Oct '83, on Taxi (1), Catalogue no: **DSR 0579**

KINGDOM RISE KINGDOM FALL
Tracks: / Kingdom rise kingdom fall / Day will come.
12" Single: Released Nov '80, on Greensleeves, by Greensleeves Records. Catalogue no: **GRED 43**

OLD BROOM
Tracks: / Old broom.
12" Single: Released Mar '81, on Island, by Island Records. Catalogue no: **IPR 2044**

STICKY STAY
Tracks: / Sticky stay.
12" Single: Released Oct '83, on Greensleeves, by Greensleeves Records. Catalogue no: **GRED 111**

SWEET SUGAR PLUM
Tracks: / Sweet sugar plum / Sweet sugar dub.
7" Single: Released May '81, on Island, by Island Records. Deleted May '84. Catalogue no: **WIP 6712**

TAKE A TASTE
Tracks: / Take a taste / Don't know much.
7" Single: Released Nov '82, on Upfront, by Serious Records. Deleted Nov '85. Catalogue no: **UPF 004**
12" Single: Released Nov '82, on Upfront, by Serious Records. Catalogue no: **UPS 004**

TAKE ME BACK
Tracks: / Take me back / Yard oh.
7" Single: Released Aug '82, on Upfront, by Serious Records. Catalogue no: **UPF 01**

THEY DON'T KNOW JAH
Tracks: / They don't know Jah.
12" Single: Released Dec '82, on Greensleeves, by Greensleeves Records. Catalogue no: **GRED 111**

UP FRONT
Tracks: / Up front.
12" Single: Released Sep '81, on Greensleeves, by Greensleeves Records. Catalogue no: **GRED 67**

WAR DEH ROUND A JOHN SHOP
Tracks: / War deh round a John shop.
12" Single: Released Jul '84, on Greensleeves, by Greensleeves Records. Catalogue no: **GRED 152**

WATER PUMPEE
Tracks: / Water pumpee.
12" Single: Released Jul '83, on Greensleeves, by Greensleeves Records. Catalogue no: **GRED 125**

Wainwright, Loudon III
Biographical details: Singer-songwriter Wainwright -- born in Chapel Hill, North Carolina, in 1946 -- has a devoted cult following after two decades of performing and recording. He began writing songs in 1968 and issued albums on Atlantic in 1970 and '71. His acoustic, confessional work saw him one of the many dubbed "the new Dylan". He worked with and married Kate McGarrigle and also sang with the Roches, but John Landau described him in 1975 as the last true solo act. His latest LPs are on Rounder, issued in the UK on Edsel. (Donald Clarke, March 1988.).

CARDBOARD BOXES
Tracks: / Cardboard boxes.
7" Single: Released Jul '85, on Demon, by Demon Records. Catalogue no: **D 1039**

FIVE YEARS OLD
Tracks: / Five years old.
7" Single: Released Apr '83, on Demon, by Demon Records. Catalogue no: **D 1016**

HAPPY ANNIVERSARY
Tracks: / Happy anniversary.
7" Single: Released Aug '86, on Demon, by Demon Records. Catalogue no: **D 1044**

T.S.D.H.A.V.
Tracks: / T.S.D.H.A.V. (This song don't have a video) / Nice guys.
7" Single: Released Sep '89, on Silvertone, Catalogue no: **ORE 15**

YOUR MOTHER AND I
Tracks: / Your mother and I / At the end of a long lonely day.
7" Single: Released Sep '87, on Demon, by Demon Records. Catalogue no: **D 1051**

Wait

CRY WITHOUT TEARS
Tracks: / Cry without tears.
7" Single: Released Mar '86, on B.O.D., Catalogue no: **JUAN 1**

Waite, John
Biographical details: This British singer, songwriter and bass guitarist, born in Lancashire, came to fame in the late Seventies as leaer of the Babys, a British group who enjoyed substantial American success but achieved only one minor hit in the UK. Their style was halway between lightweight pop and hard rock. The group folded in 1981, and their lead vocalist embarked upon a solo career.

Waite's first LP *Igintion* was released in 1982, and made very little impact. However, he had far greater luck with 1984's *No Brakes* album, which went gold in the States and yielded a US No. 1 single *Missing You.* According to Waite, this mid-tempo AOR ballad took only four minutes to write - if this was true, it was the most profitable four minutes of the singer's life. The song also took Waite to No. 9 in his home country. However, this was a one-off success in Britain and, although subsequent singles from *No Brakes* attracted some Stateside attention, they did not become major hits. The public liked the uncluttered straightforwardness of *Missing You*; but were not totally convinced by his rockier (and more typical) material, which was a somewhat awkward attempt to adapt his previous Baby's style to the era of MTV, America's 24-hour cable television video channel. Bob MacDonald, 19 April 1985..

CHOICE, THE
Tracks: / Choice, The / No breaks.
7" Single: Released Jan '86, on EMI-America, by EMI Records. Catalogue no: **EA 211**

EVERY STEP OF THE WAY
Tracks: / Every step of the way.
7" Single: Released Sep '85, on EMI-America, by EMI Records. Catalogue no: **EA 206**

IF ANYBODY HAD A HEART
Tracks: / If anybody had a heart / Just like lovers.
7" Single: Released Aug '86, on EMI-America, by EMI Records. Catalogue no: **EA 220**

MISSING YOU
Tracks: / Missing you.
12" Single: Released Aug '84, on EMI-America, by EMI Records. Deleted Jul '87. Catalogue no: **12EA 182**
7" Single: Released Aug '84, on EMI-America, by EMI Records. Deleted Jan '88. Catalogue no: **EA 182**

RESTLESS HEART
Tracks: / Restless heart / Missing you / Euroshima.
12" Single: Released Mar '85, on EMI-America, by EMI Records. Catalogue no: **12EA 193**
7" Single: Released Mar '85, on EMI-America, by EMI Records. Catalogue no: **EA 193**

TEARS
Tracks: / Tears.
7" Single: Released Nov '84, on EMI-America, by EMI Records. Deleted '87. Catalogue no: **EA 186**

THESE TIMES ARE HARD
Tracks: / These times are hard / For lovers / Missing you* (*Extra track on 12").
12" Single: Released Jul '87, on EMI-America, by EMI Records. Deleted Oct '87. Catalogue no: **12EA 236**
7" Single: Released Jul '87, on EMI-America, by EMI Records. Deleted Oct '87. Catalogue no: **EA 236**

Waitresses
Biographical details: An American new wave group formed in Cleveland, Ohio, by guitarist Chris Butler with drummer Billy Ficca (from Television), vocalist Patty Donahue, bassist Tracy Wormworth, Daniel Klayman on keyboards and Mars Williams (ex-Psychedelic Furs, Fred Frith etc), the Waitresses appeared on The Akron Compilation in 1978 on Stiff. When they moved to New York their zany material attracted Ze Records, who released *Wasn't Tomorrow Wonderful?* in 1981. *I Know What Boys Like* was a cult hit in Britain but they had less success at home. They broke up after the album Bruiseology in 1983. (Donald Clarke, March 1988.)

This American band consisted of Chris Butler, Patty Donahue, Bill Ficca, Dan Klayman, Mars Williams and Tracy Wormworth.

The Waitresses were formed in Ohio, but began to attract attention on the New York Club scene when they moved to the city in 1980. With a somewhat tongue-in-cheek approach, they played in a punk-pop style, and were placed in the New Wave category by the US music industry. Singer Donahue (who, despite the group's name was the only female member) was reminiscent of the vocal style of Blondie star, Debbie Harry.

The Waitresses' debut LP *Wasn't Tomorrow Wonderful?* was issued in early 1982. *I Know What Boys Like* became a minor US hit single but, partly because Donahue's vocals made the group sound too similar to the newly successful Go-gos, he Waitresses failed to achieve a major breakthrough. Butler's witty lyrics (often trading on the role of women, as seen from a woman's point of view) passed unnoticed by most people..

CHRISTMAS WRAPPING
Tracks: / Christmas wrapping / For the 1st of the 1st 83.
7" Single: Released Dec '82, on Island, by Island Records. Deleted '85. Catalogue no: **WIP 6821**
12" Single: Released Dec '82, on Island, by Island Records. Deleted '85. Catalogue no: **12 WIP 6821**

I KNOW WHAT BOYS LIKE
Tracks: / I know what boys like / It's my car.
7" Single: Released Feb '82, on Polydor, by Polydor Ltd. Deleted Feb '87. Catalogue no: **POSP 414**

MAKE THE WEATHER
Tracks: / Make the weather.
7" Single: Released May '83, on Polydor, by Polydor Ltd. Catalogue no: **POSP 582**
12" Single: Released May '83, on Polydor, by Polydor Ltd. Catalogue no: **POSPX 582**

Waits, Tom
Biographical details: Tom Waits was born in Pomona, California, in 1949. As a songwriter and cabaret artist with a whispery, tobacco-stained voice, he has specialised in off-beat portraits of the flotsam and jetsam of bars and motels and has steadily risen to cult stardom. *Foreign Affairs*, in 1977, included a duet with Bette Midler on *I Never Talk To Strangers. Heart Attack* and *Vine* in 1980 included *Jersey Girl*, which was covered by Bruce Springsteen. *Bounced Checks* ('81) is a "best of..." compilation. Waits acted in the Sylvester Stallone film *Paradise Alley* in '78 and in '82 Francis Coppola cast him in *One From The Heart*, where he duetted with country star Crystal Gayle. *Swordfish Trombones* ('83) was full of experiments. He appeared in the films *Rumblefish* and *The Cotton Club* and had a major role in *Down By Law* in 1986. He wrote his first play, *Frank's Wild Years*, with his wife, Kathleen Brennan. In 1987 he was in the film *Ironweed* with Jack Nicholson. (Donald Clarke, March 1988.).

DOWNTOWN TRAIN (see panel below)
Tracks: / Downtown train / Tango till they're sore.
12" Single: Released Nov '85, on Island, by Island Records. Deleted '87. Catalogue no: **12IS 253**
7" Single: Released Nov '85, on Island, by Island Records. Deleted Jul '87. Catalogue no: **IS 253**

IN THE NEIGHBOURHOOD
Tracks: / In the neighbourhood / Frank's wild years.
7" Single: Released Feb '86, on Island, by Island Records. Deleted Jul '87. Catalogue no: **IS 260**
12" Single: Released Feb '86, on Island, by Island Records. Catalogue no: **12IS 260**
7" Set: Released Feb '86, on Island, by Island Records. Catalogue no: **ISD 260**
7" Single: Released Oct '83, on Island, by Island Records. Deleted '87. Catalogue no: **IS 141**

SIXTEEN SHELLS FROM A 30.0.6.
Tracks: / Big black Maria / Ruby's arms (12" only.) / Sixteen shells from A 30.0.6.
12" Single: Released Aug '88, on Island, by Island Records. Deleted Apr '89. Catalogue no: **12IS 370**
7" Single: Released Aug '88, on Island, by Island Records. Deleted Apr '89. Catalogue no: **IS 370**

Wake

GRUESOME CASTLE
Tracks: / Gruesome castle.
12" Single: Released May '87, on Factory (1), by Factory Records. Catalogue no: **FAC 177**

ON OUR HONEYMOON
Tracks: / On our honeymoon.
7" Single: Released Jan '82, on Scan, Deleted '83. Catalogue no: **SCN 1**

ON THE MATTER
Tracks: / On the matter.
7" Single: Released Mar '85, on Factory (1), by Factory Records. Catalogue no: **FAC 113**

SOMETHING OUTSIDE
Tracks: / Something outside.
Cassingle: Released Nov '83, on Factory Benelux, by Rough Trade Records. Catalogue no: **FBM 24**

SOMETHING THAT NO-ONE ELSE CAN BRING
Tracks: / Gruesome castle / Pale spectre / Furious sex / Plastic flowers.
7" EP: Released 13 Jun '87, on Factory (1), by Factory Records. Catalogue no: **FAC 178**

TALK ABOUT THE PAST
Tracks: / Talk about the past / Everybody works too hard.
12" Single: Released Mar '84, on Factory (1), by Factory Records. Catalogue no: **FAC 88T**
7" Single: Released Mar '84, on Factory (1), by Factory Records. Catalogue no: **FAC 88**

Wake Up

WAKE UP EP, THE
Tracks: / Change is gonna come, A: *Bragg, Billy* / Garage land: *Bragg, Billy* / Levi Stubbs tears: *Redskins* / This fragile life: *Neurotics* / Forty years: *Redskins.*
12" Single: Released Apr '87, on Wake-Up, Catalogue no: **WOMBLE 1**

Wake Up Africa

SIMPLE WORDS
Tracks: / Simple words.
12" Single: Released Apr '89, on Red River, Catalogue no: **MRC 096**

Wakeaman

DIBI DIBI SOUND
Tracks: / Dibi dibi sound.
12" Single: Released Sep '89, on Living Room, Catalogue no: **LM 030**

Wakelin, Johnny
Biographical details: This British singer/songwriter achieved two Top 10 novelty hits on the UK charts in the mid-Seventies. The first was 1975's *Black Superman*, a tribute to the ten red hot boxing superstar Muhammed Ali; backed by the Kinshasa Band, this was a dire concoction of pop, pseudo-reggae and quasi-calypso styles. It reached No. 7 in the UK and No.

TOM WAITS - DOWNTOWN TRAIN (Released on Island)

21 in the US.
The following year, Wakelin cruised to No. 4 on the UK listings with *In Zaire*, another bland attempt to dilute a foreign culture with British singalong pop. Both tracks appeared on his March 1976 LP *Reggae, Soul And Rock 'n' roll* (on which he showed no understanding of any of the three), and Wakelin followed it with the unsuccessful albums, *African Man. and Double Trouble*, before fading into obscurity. Bob MacDonald, 19 April, 1986..

BLACK SUPERMAN
Tracks: / Black superman.
7" Single: Released Jan '75, on Pye, Deleted '78. Catalogue no: **7 N 45420**

BRUNO
Tracks: / Bruno / Sons of Hercules.
7" Single: Released Jun '86, on Chrysalis, by Chrysalis Records. Catalogue no: **KO 1**
12" Single: Released Jun '86, on Chrysalis, by Chrysalis Records. Catalogue no: **KOX 1**

IN ZAIRE
Tracks: / In Zaire.
7" Single: Released Jul '76, on Pye, Deleted '79. Catalogue no: **7 N 45595**
12" Single: Released Aug '86, on PRT, by Castle Communications Records. Catalogue no: **12P 361**
7" Single: Released Aug '86, on PRT, by Castle Communications Records. Catalogue no: **7P 361**

IN ZAIRE (OLD GOLD)
Tracks: / In Zaire / Black superman.
7" Single: Released Sep '80, on Old Gold, by Old Gold Records. Deleted Jul '88. Catalogue no: **OG 9086**

WHERE SEAGULLS FLY
Tracks: / Where seagulls fly.
7" Single: Released May '83, on Wide Awake, Deleted '84. Catalogue no: **WA 11**

Wakeman, Rick

Biographical details: Thi British keyboards player and composer, born in London, took up the piano at the age of four, his father being a professional pianist. He received classical trainin at London's Royal College of Music after leaving school, and soon began to make headway as a session player. His most acclaimed session appearance was on David Bowie's 1969 classic *Space Oddity* - Wakeman's synthesised accompaniment and extended outro were pure magic, and added much to the single's inventiveness.

Wakeman joined the Strawbs in 1970, and played on three of their albums; after becoming the group's focal point, he quit in the summer of '71 to join Yes. That group's musical ambition was to fuse rock and classical music into a symphonic and extravagant whole - Wakeman helped them to achieve it. However, after the UK Top 10 success of his 1973 debut solo album *The Six Wives Of Henry VIII* (inspired by a BBC TV drama series of the same name), he left Yes in early '74.

With Wakeman's help, Yes had just achieved a UK No. 1 album with their double set *Tales Topographic Oceans*. The keyboards wizard soon scaled the summit in a solo capacity - his musical interpretation of Jules Verne's novel *Journey To The Centre Of The Earth* reached the top of Briatain's album chart in May 1974. Wakeman's status as the king of pomp-rock was confirmed in '75: to promote his latest epic *The Myths And Legends Of King Arthur And The Knights Of The Round Table* (which reached No. 2 on the UK LP listings), he assembles a 48 piece choir and a 45 piece orchestra, and put together a dazzling show on ice at London's Empire Pool at Wembley. Although the music and effects were spectacular, many critics slammed Wakeman as a purveyor of self-indulgence and overblown sophistication; but no-one could argue with the sheer virtuosity of his keyboards mastery.

After hitting the British Top 10 with the *No Earthly Connections* LP, Wakeman rejoined Yes in late 1976. Despite the onslaught of the punk revolution, he helped the Old Wavers to achieve their second UK No. 1 album with 1977's aptly titled *Going For The One*. After one more album, *Tormato*, he finally quit the band for good in late 1979. In that same year, the amiable Wakeman displayed his sense of humour on an unsuccessful but interesting single, *Animal Showdown*. This came to the fore again on such Eighties singles as *I'm So Straight I'm A Wierdo*. However, the new decade brought only limited success for him - his futuristic album *1984*, issued in 1981, peaked at No. 24 on the UK charts; thus it was by no means a flop, but was, nonetheless, a far cry from his heady Seventies days.

Though not being able to compete with the technopop, synthesiser-based acts of the Eighties, Wakeman can comfort himself with the knowledge that he helped to being the synthesiser to its dominant position in rock music. Bob MacDonald, 21 April, 1985..

CUSTER'S LAST STAND
Tracks: / Custer's last stand / Ocean city.
Note: Roy Wood sings on Side 1, John Parr on Side 2. Both tracks are from the album Time machine on President Records -- RW 7.
7" Single: Released Aug '88, on President, by President Records. Catalogue no: **WAKE 3**

DATABASE
Tracks: / Database.
12" Single: Released Jun '85, on TBG, by President Records. Catalogue no: **12 WAKE 2**
7" Single: Released Jun '85, on TBG, by President Records. Catalogue no: **WAKE 2**

GLORY BOYS
Tracks: / Glory boys.
12" Single: Released Dec '84, on TBG, by President Records. Catalogue no: **12 WAKE 1**
7" Single: Released Dec '84, on TBG, by President Records. Catalogue no: **WAKE 1**

I'M SO STRAIGHT I'M A WIERDO
Tracks: / I'm so straight I'm a wierdo / Do you believe in fairies.
7" Single: Released Mar '80, on A&M, by A&M Records. Deleted Mar '83. Catalogue no: **AMS 7510**
7" Single: Released Jun '83, on Moon, by Moon Records (UK). Catalogue no: **LUNA 6**

JULIA
Tracks: / Julia / Sorry.
7" Single: Released Jul '81, on Charisma, by Virgin Records. Deleted '84. Catalogue no: **CB 384**

ROBOT MAN
Tracks: / Robot man.
7" Single: Released Nov '81, on Charisma, by Virgin Records. Deleted '84. Catalogue no: **CB 392**

SPIDER
Tracks: / Spider / Danielle.
7" Single: Released Oct '80, on WEA, by WEA Records. Deleted Oct '83. Catalogue no: **K 18354**

TIME MACHINE
Tracks: / Custer's last stand / Ocean city / Angel of time (specially extended version available on CD only) / Slaveman (specially extended version available on CD only) / Ice / Open up your eyes / Elizabethan rock / Make me a woman (specially extended version available on CD only) / Rock age (specially extended version available on CD only).
CD 5": Released 31 Jul '88, on President, by President Records. Catalogue no: **RWCD 7**
Cassingle: Released 31 Jul '88, on President, by President Records. Catalogue no: **RWK 7**
12" Single: Released 31 Jul '88, on President, by President Records. Catalogue no: **RW 7**

WATERFALLS
Tracks: / Waterfalls / Heather carpets.
7" Single: Released Apr '86, on Code, by Code Records. Catalogue no: **CODS 19**

Walcott, Dennis

SISTER MILLIE
Tracks: / Sister Millie.
12" Single: Released May '82, on Sonic Sounds, Catalogue no: **SS 92**

Walden, Narada Michael

Biographical details: This American drummer, singer and producer came to the fore in 1980 with a brace of disco hits. As a superbly proficient drummer he had worked with a variety of artists during the mid-70's, including Jeff Beck, Tommy Bolin, Mahavishnu and Weather Report. His debut solo album, *The Garden Of Lovelight*, was released in 1977 but made little impact, and two follow-up LPs, *I Cry, I Smile* and *Awakening*, met with a similarly muted reaction. It was Walden's next album, *The Dance Of Life*, that yielded the two successful singles. *Tonight I'm All Right* was totally cliched in its title, lyrics and music, but its danceability and professionalism won through: it was a major dancefloor filler and reached No 34 on the UK pop charts. It was rapidly followed by the irresistably commercial single, *I Shoulda Loved Ya*, which surged to No 8 in Britain and became an international disco success. Surprisingly, Walden failed to consolidate on this success and subsequent albums were not major sellers. The message-laden, pseudo-religious lyrics that were a regular feature of his LPs alienated some listeners and his brand of funk was too unoriginal to stand out from a plethora of other danceable records. He did, however, score a US black chart hit in 1985 with *Gimme, Gimme, Gimme*, a duet with Patti Austin. (Bob MacDonald, April 1985)..

GIMME,GIMME,GIMME
Tracks: / Gimme gimme gimme / Wear your love.
7" Single: Released Mar '85, on Warner Bros., by WEA Records. Deleted '88. Catalogue no: **W 9077**
12" Single: Released Mar '85, on Warner Bros., by WEA Records. Deleted '88. Catalogue no: **W 9077T**

I SHOULDA LOVED YA
Tracks: / I shoulda loved ya / Carry on.
7" Single: Released Apr '80, on Atlantic, by WEA Records. Deleted '83. Catalogue no: **K 11413**

I WANT YOU
Tracks: / I want you / Get up.
7" Single: Released Nov '80, on Atlantic, by WEA Records. Catalogue no: **K 11634**
12" Single: Released Nov '80, on Atlantic, by WEA Records. Catalogue no: **K 11634 T**

I'M READY
Tracks: / I'm ready / Holiday.
7" Single: Released Jan '83, on Atlantic, by WEA Records. Catalogue no: **A 9949**
12" Single: Released Jan '83, on Atlantic, by WEA Records. Catalogue no: **A 9949 T**

NATURE OF THINGS, THE
Tracks: / Nature of things, The.
7" Single: Released Jun '85, on Warner Bros., by WEA Records. Catalogue no: **W 9017**
12" Single: Released Jun '85, on Warner Bros., by WEA Records. Catalogue no: **W 9017T**

REACH OUT
Tracks: / Reach out.
7" Single: Released Mar '83, on Atlantic, by WEA Records. Catalogue no: **A 9858**

REAL THANG
Tracks: / Real thang / Take it to the bassman.
7" Single: Released Mar '81, on Atlantic, by WEA Records. Catalogue no: **K 11659**
12" Single: Released Mar '81, on Atlantic, by WEA Records. Catalogue no: **K 11659 T**

SUMMER LADY
Tracks: / Summer lady / Confidence.
7" Single: Released Aug '82, on Atlantic, by WEA Records. Catalogue no: **K 11752**
12" Single: Released Aug '82, on Atlantic, by WEA Records. Catalogue no: **K 11752 T**

TONIGHT I'M ALL RIGHT
Tracks: / Tonight I'm all right / Dance of life.
7" Single: Released Feb '80, on Atlantic, by WEA Records. Deleted '83. Catalogue no: **K 11437**

YOU OUGHTA TO LOVE ME
Tracks: / You oughta love me / I shoulda loved ya.
7" Single: Released Jun '82, on Atlantic, by WEA Records. Catalogue no: **K 11739**
12" Single: Released Jun '82, on Atlantic, by WEA Records. Catalogue no: **K 11739 T**

Walden, Wanda

DON'T YOU WANT MY LOVIN'
Tracks: / Don't you want my lovin' / It's gone now.
12" Single: Released May '81, on Elektra Asylum, by Elektra Records (USA). Catalogue no: **K 12531T**
7" Single: Released May '81, on Elektra Asylum, by Elektra Records (USA). Catalogue no: **K 12531**

Waldron, Conrad

YOUR LOVE'S A VOODOO
Tracks: / Your love's a voodoo.
7" Single: Released Sep '81, on Sonet, by Sonet Records. Catalogue no: **SON 2233**

Wales...

WALES-THE DRAGON ARMY
Tracks: / Wales-The Dragon Army.
12" Single: Released Sep '85, on Spartan, Catalogue no: **12SP 125**
7" Single: Released Sep '85, on Spartan, Catalogue no: **SP 125**

Wales, Josey

BOUNCING
Tracks: / Bouncing.
12" Single: Released Sep '84, on Volcano, Catalogue no: **Unknown**

HOME T FOUR
Tracks: / Home T four.
12" Single: Released Jan '84, on Mobiliser, by Jetstar Records. Catalogue no: **MM 68**

KEBA YOUR MOUTH
Tracks: / Keba your mouth.
7" Single: Released Jan '89, on Exterminator, Catalogue no: **Unknown**

LOVE ME HAVE FI GET
Tracks: / love me have fi get.
12" Single: Released Sep '83, on Reggae Sound, Catalogue no: **VPRD 139**

ROXY COME CALL ME
Tracks: / Roxy come call me.
12" Single: Released Sep '84, on Cornerstone, Catalogue no: **Unknown**

SOLOMON STYLE
Tracks: / Solomon style.
12" Single: Released Dec '87, on Mango, by Island Records. Deleted Apr '88. Catalogue no: **12IS 351**

UNDERCOVER LOVER
Tracks: / Undercover lover.
12" Single: Released Jan '86, on Scom, Catalogue no: **BD 023**

Walk

I DIDN'T CATCH YOUR NAME
Tracks: / I didn't catch your name / Be animal.
7" Single: Released Feb '84, on Geneva, Catalogue no: **G 17**

Walker, Bobbi

SOMETHING ABOUT YOU
Tracks: / Something about you / Rock bottom.
7" Single: Released Oct '80, on Casablanca, by PolyGram UK Ltd. Catalogue no: **CAN 206**
12" Single: Released Oct '80, on Casablanca, by PolyGram UK Ltd. Catalogue no: **CANL 206**

Walker Brothers

Biographical details: This American group -- Scott Engel, Gary Leeds and John Maus -- were not brothers. Before their 1964 formation each had valuable showbiz experience. Engel had been discovered by singer Eddie Fisher, who had taken him on several television shows, and had also worked with Phil Spector and Sonny Bono; Leeds had briefly played drums for Elvis Presley and Jet Powers, who became P.J. Proby; at the age of 12 Maus had been in a TV series, Hello Mom. Although the "brothers" all played instruments it was their singing and good looks that made them famous. After growing their hair for a few months, in recognition of the Beatles' moptops, the Walkers tried for success in their homeland. But American audiences were immersed in the British invasion so the trio moved to the UK and found major stardom. Recording songs by heavyweight writers -- including Barry Mann and Cynthia Weil, Burt Bacharach and Hal David and Bob Crewe and Bob Gaudio -- they chalked up nine British Top Forty hits in two years. The first was *Love Her*, which reached No 20 in mid-'65. The second and fourth hits went to No 1: *Make It Easy On Yourself* and *The Sun Ain't Gonna Shine Anymore* made the trio, all in their early twenties, top idols in the UK and even rivalled the Beatles' domination of female fantasies. US success was lukewarm by comparison and they only managed a couple of Stateside Top Forty hits, *Make It* reaching 16 and *Sun* 13 several weeks after peaking in Britain. The Walker Brothers' musical language was high drama, tear-jerking lovesickness and big production. Scott and John's mighty voices also helped give them a UK No 1 EP , with *I Need You*, and four Top Ten albums. But the sound soon grew stale and this process was accelerated by a weakeing in their choice of material. They went their separate ways in 1967 but none could sustain a solo career for long: Gary and John failed to crack Britain's Top Twenty and even the much-adored Scott fell by the wayside in 1969. Suddenly, in early '76, the reformed trio reached the British Top Ten with Tom Rush's *No Regrets*, a record so powerful and dramatic that it could have been made in their mid-60's heyday. However, they immediately returned to obscurity. (Bob MacDonald, April 1985.)

A vocal and instrumental trio formed in California in 1964: bassist Scott Engel (born in 1944 in Ohio), bassist John Maus, drummer Gary Leeds. They tried their luck in the UK and had nine top 30 singles in 1965-67; they were seen as a British import in the USA. Dramatic ballads with production style imitating Phil Spector's made them teen idols; pressure split them up and Engel continued successfull as Scott Walker, influencing David Bowie, Julian Cope (of Teardrop Explodes) and Marc Almond. he brought jacques Brel songs to a wider audience. (Donald Clarke)..

ANOTHER TEAR FALLS
Tracks: / Another tear falls.
7" Single: Released Sep '66, on Philips, by Phonogram Ltd. Deleted '69. Catalogue no: **BF 1514**

DEADLIER THAN THE MALE
Tracks: / Deadlier than the male.
7" Single: Released Dec '66, on Philips, by Phonogram Ltd. Deleted '69. Catalogue no: **BF 1537**

LOVE HER
Tracks: / Love her.
7" Single: Released Apr '65, on Philips, by Phonogram Ltd. Deleted '68. Catalogue no: **BF 1409**

MAKE IT EASY ON YOURSELF
Tracks: / Make it easy on yourself / First love never dies.
7" Single: Released Aug '65, on Philips, by Phonogram Ltd. Deleted '68. Catalogue no: **BF 1428**
7" Single: Released Oct '80, on Phonogram, by Phonogram Ltd. Deleted Oct '83. Catalogue no: **CUT 104**

MAKE IT EASY ON YOURSELF (OLD GOLD)
Tracks: / Make it easy on yourself / First love never dies.
7" Single: Released Feb '88, on Old Gold, by Old Gold Records. Catalogue no: **OG 9779**

MY SHIP IS COMING IN
Tracks: / My ship is coming in.
7" Single: Released Dec '65, on Philips, by Phonogram Ltd. Deleted '68. Catalogue no: **BF 1454**

NO REGRETS (OLD GOLD)
Tracks: / No regrets.
7" Single: Released Sep '85, on Old Gold, by Old Gold Records. Catalogue no: **OG 9557**

NO REGRETS (SINGLE)
Tracks: / No regrets.
7" Single: Released Jan '76, on GTO, Deleted '79. Catalogue no: **GT 42**

SHUT OUT
Tracks: / Shut out / Electrician / Nite flights / Fat mama kick.
7" Single: Released Jun '81, on GTO, Catalogue no: **GT 295**

STAY WITH ME BABY
Tracks: / Stay with me baby.
7" Single: Released Feb '67, on Philips, by Phonogram Ltd. Deleted '70. Catalogue no: **BF 1548**

SUN AIN'T GONNA SHINE ANYMORE, THE (OLD GOLD)
Tracks: / Sun ain't gonna shine anymore, The / My ship is coming in.
7" Single: Released Jan '85, on Old Gold, by Old Gold Records. Catalogue no: **OG 9474**
7" Single: Released Oct '82, on Philips, by Phonogram Ltd. Deleted '85. Catalogue no: **IPS 001**
7" Single: Released 23 May '87, on Bam Caruso, by Demon Records. Catalogue no: **OPRA 090**

WALKING IN THE RAIN
Tracks: / Walking in the rain.
7" Single: Released May '67, on Philips, by Phonogram Ltd. Deleted '70. Catalogue no: **BF 1576**

YOU DON'T HAVE TO TELL ME
Tracks: / You don't have to tell me.
7" Single: Released Jul '66, on Philips, by Phonogram Ltd. Deleted '69. Catalogue no: **BF 1497**

Walker, Bryon

DON'T LOOK ANY FURTHER
Tracks: / Don't look any further.
12" Single: Released Aug '85, on Sir George, Catalogue no: **SG 026T**

Walker, David

EVERYONE WAS A BABY
Tracks: / Everyone was a baby / Curacao - blue sky.
7" Single: Released Apr '89, on Walker Records, by Walker Records. Catalogue no: **UNKNOWN**

JANE
Tracks: / Jane / Why all the fuss.
7" Single: Released May '89, on Walker Records, by Walker Records. Deleted '89. Catalogue no: **UNKNOWN**

Walker, Dean

BABY PLEASE DON'T GO
Tracks: / Baby please don't go / Honesty.
7" Single: Released Mar '84, on Sumatra, by Sumatra Records. Catalogue no: **SUM 5**

OVER NOW (SINGLE)
Tracks: / Over now.
7" Single: Released Nov '83, on Sumatra, by Sumatra Records. Catalogue no: **SUM 2**

Walker, Dee

JUMP BACK
Tracks: / Jump back / Every little moment.
7" Single: Released Aug '84, on Dance Network, by Dance Network Records. Catalogue no: **NET 2**

Walker, Gary

TWINKIE LEE
Tracks: / Twinkie Lee.
7" Single: Released May '66, on CBS, by CBS Records. Deleted '69. Catalogue no: **CBS 202081**

YOU DON'T LOVE ME
Tracks: / You don't love me.
7" Single: Released Feb '66, on CBS, by CBS Records. Deleted '69. Catalogue no: **CBS 202036**

Walker, Joe Louis

ALONE
Tracks: / Alone / Cold is the night / Shade tree mechanic.
12" Single: Released Oct '88, on Ace, by Ace Records. Catalogue no: **NST 125**

Walker, John

ANNABELLA
Tracks: / Annabella.
7" Single: Released Jul '67, on Philips, by Phonogram Ltd. Deleted '70. Catalogue no: **BF 1593**

Walker, Junior

Biographical details: The American saxophonist and singer was born in Arkansas as Autry DeWalt Jr and given his stage name by his father. He took up the sax at school and assembled his first band in 1961, shortly after leaving. He signed to Harvey Records, a label owned by Harvey Fuqua, brother-in-law of Motown founder Berry Gordy. By 1965 Harvey Records had been incorporated into the Motown family. In that year Junior Walker stormed into the American charts with his debut smash hit *Shotgun*, a rousing, pounding dance number which reached No 4 on the Billboard Hot Hundred. It set the scene for a succession of raw rhythm and blues hits, mainly instrumental but featuring raucous vocals, which sounded gruffer than those of most of his Motown colleagues. These hits continued into the late 60's, often reaching the US pop Top Forty but not the Top Ten. His first British Top Forty single was 1966's *How Sweet It Is*, version of the Marvin Gaye hit. The singles were credited to Junior Walker & The All-Stars, his funky backing group. In the late 60's Walker mellowed his sound and progressed to a smoother, more sophisticated style. He was quickly rewarded with the smash, *What Does It Take (To Win Your Love)?*, a mid-tempo ballad which cruised to UK No 4 in summer '69 and thus tied with *Shotgun* to become his joint biggest American hit. Greater emphasis was now placed on the (far less raucous) vocals, although his sax prowess was still very much in evidence. Early 70's hits included two which reached the UK Top Twenty, the lush but slinky *Walk In The Night* and *Take Me, Girl, I'm Ready*, plus a smaller success with string-laden ballad Way Back Home. The roots of Walker's honky style lay in the R & B sounds of the late 40's and early 50's: he had successfully adapted them to the needs of 60's and 70's soul fans. He suffered a commercial nosedive after 1973 and never regained his chart fortunes, despite revival attempts by Motown and his subsequent record company, Warner Bros. However, his virtuosity has remained intact and in 1981 he contributed a classic sax solo on Foreigner's US Top Five single *Urgent*. (Bob MacDonald, April 1985.)

Junior Walker was born in 1942 in Arkansas; the alto saxist formed the All Stars and had 21 Hot 100 hits in the USA charts in 1965-72, many instrumentalists (though Junior also sang). Biggest were the first, *Shotgun* and *What Does It Take (To Win Your Love)* in 1969, both top 5; the good time music was an echo of the jump-bands of the late 40s, while later hits were often ballads, sometimes with strings. Ten hit LPs in USA incl. *Soul Session* '66, entirely instrumental; *Greatest Hits* '69 reached top 50. he still toured in the '80s, sometimes with son Autry DeWalt III on drums. (Donald Clarke)..

BLOW THE HOUSE DOWN (SINGLE)
7" Single: Released Oct '83, on Motown, by BMG Records (UK). Deleted '84. Catalogue no: **TMG 1318**
12" Single: Released Oct '83, on Motown, by BMG Records (UK). Catalogue no: **TMGT 1318**

HOW SWEET IT IS
Tracks: / How sweet it is to be loved by you.
7" Single: Released Aug '66, on Tamla Motown, by Motown Records (UK). Deleted '69. Catalogue no: **TMG 571**
7" Single: Released Apr '88, on Motown, by BMG Records (UK). Catalogue no: **ZB 41935**

ROAD RUNNER
Tracks: / Road runner / Shotgun.
7" Single: Released Jun '83, on Motown, by BMG Records (UK). Catalogue no: **TMG 691**

TAKE ME GIRL I'M READY
Tracks: / Take me girl I'm ready.
7" Single: Released Jan '73, on Tamla Motown, by Motown Records (UK). Deleted '76. Catalogue no: **TMG 840**

WALK IN THE NIGHT
Tracks: / Walk in the night.
7" Single: Released Aug '72, on Tamla Motown, by Motown Records (UK). Deleted '75. Catalogue no: **TMG 824**

WAY BACK HOME
Tracks: / Way back home.
7" Single: Released Jun '73, on Tamla Motown, by Motown Records (UK). Deleted '76. Catalogue no: **TMG 857**

WHAT DOES IT TAKE
Tracks: / What does it take / Take me girl, I'm ready.
7" Single: Released Oct '69, on Tamla Motown, by Motown Records (UK). Deleted '72. Catalogue no: **TMG 712**
7" Single: Released Oct '80, on Tamla Motown, by Motown Records (UK). Deleted Oct '83. Catalogue no: **TMG 962**

Walker, Larry

24 HOURS
Tracks: / 24 hours.
7" Single: Released Jun '82, on International Records & Tapes, by International Records & Tapes. Catalogue no: **INT 1**

Walker, Scott

Biographical details: A fine singer and bass guitarist, Scott Walker -- born Scott Engel in Ohio -- came to fame in the mid-60's as a member of the Walker Brothers. The three members of the group, who were not related, chalked up nine UK Top Forty hits between 1965 and 1967, though success in their native US was very limited. The "brothers" were based in Britain, and enjoyed a large fan following, particularly among the female population. In terms of both sexual and vocal appeal Scott was the key member of the trio so it was not surprising that when declining chart fortunes led to the group's demise in '67 only Scott was able to carve out a real solo career. His first solo hit was *Jackie*, which reached No 22 on the UK chart at the end of '67. Barely into his mid-20s, Scott's mighty, dramatic and emotional voice also scored with *Joanna* (No 7 in '68) and *Lights Of Cincinatti* (No 13 in '69). But it was on the British album lists that the solo Scott really came into his own: *Scott, Scott 2* and *Scott 3* were all Top Three items, with *Scott 2* snatching a week at No 1 in May '68. His successful TV series also yielded a UK Top Ten LP. However, as with the Walker Brothers themselves, the high drama of Scott's solo music was unable to sustain the public's attention for more than two years, and he faded into obscurity at the start of the 70's. The trio reformed briefly in the mid-70's and enjoyed a one-off UK Top Tenner was the powerful single *No Regrets*, but then disappeared again. In the early 80's, Scott's name attracted high praise from Julian Cope, leader of hitmaking group Teardrop Explodes. Cope cited Walker as a major influence and compiled and released an anthology album by his hero -- but he chose a ludicrously overblown sub-title, *The Godlike Genius of Scott Walker (!)*, which did not do Scott any good. In 1984, after some prodding by Cope, Walker issued a comeback album, *Climate Of Hunter*. But despite interest from the British music press the commercial climate was not in Walker's favour. (Bob MacDonald, April 1985.).

JACKIE
Tracks: / Jackie.
7" Single: Released Dec '67, on Philips, by Phonogram Ltd. Deleted '70. Catalogue no: **BF 1628**

JOANNA
Tracks: / Joanna.
7" Single: Released May '68, on Philips, by Phonogram Ltd. Deleted '71. Catalogue no: **BF 1662**

JOANNA (OLD GOLD)
Tracks: / Joanna.
7" Single: Released Aug '82, on Old Gold, by Old Gold Records. Deleted Jul '88. Catalogue no: **OG 9244**

LIGHTS OF CINCINATTI
Tracks: / Lights of Cincinnati.
7" Single: Released Jun '69, on Philips, by Phonogram Ltd. Deleted '72. Catalogue no: **BF 1793**

Walkers

HEY! DON'T WASTE MY TIME
Tracks: / Hey! don't waste my time.
7" Single: Released Feb '86, on Club, by Phonogram Ltd. Catalogue no: **JAB 27**
12" Single: Released Feb '86, on Club, by Phonogram Ltd. Catalogue no: **JABX 27**

WHATEVER HAPPENED TO THE PARTY GROOVE
Tracks: / Whatever happened to the party groove.
12" Single: Released Nov '83, on London Records, by London Records. Catalogue no: **LONX 39**
7" Single: Released Nov '83, on London Records, by London Records. Catalogue no: **LON 39**

WHO IS YOUR LOVE?
Tracks: / Who is your love?.
7" Single: Released Aug '86, on Club, by Phonogram Ltd. Catalogue no: **JAB 31**
12" Single: Released Aug '86, on Club, by Phonogram Ltd. Catalogue no: **JABX 31**

Walkie Talkies

COVER UP
Tracks: / Cover up.
7" Single: Released Oct '80, on Rialto (1), by Rialto Records. Deleted '81. Catalogue no: **TREB 126**

MAN ON COBO BAY
Tracks: / Man on Cobo Bay / Dangerous dancing.
7" Single: Released Mar '81, on Rialto (1), by Rialto Records. Deleted '82. Catalogue no: **TREB 132**

WHOSE WORLD IS THIS
Tracks: / Whose world is this / Dangerous dancing.
7" Single: Released Aug '80, on Rialto (1), by Rialto Records. Deleted '81. Catalogue no: **TREB 119**

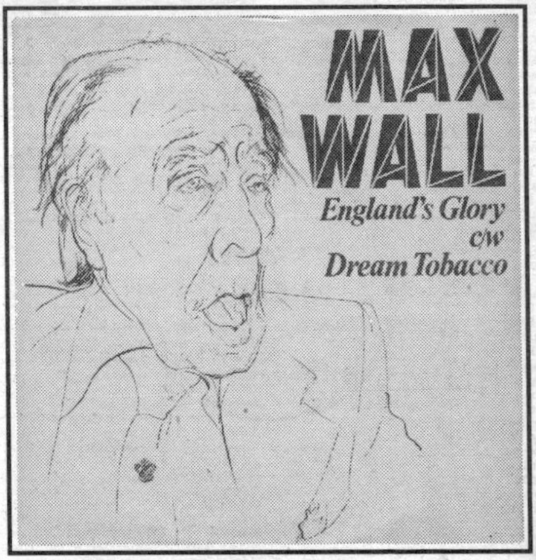

MAX WALL - ENGLAND'S GLORY (Released on Stiff)

Walking Floors

ESCAPE
Tracks: / Despatches / Black point / Taking off again / When a stranger calls.
12" Single: Released Sep '87, on Primitive, by Primitive Records. Catalogue no: **PRIME 014**

Walking Seeds

MARK CHAPMAN
Tracks: / Mark Chapman / Blathering out.
Note: Double 'A' side / Pic bag
12" Single: Released Apr '87, on Moral Burro, Deleted Jun '88. Catalogue no: **CEDE**

Walks, Dennis

FISHERMAN
Tracks: / Fisherman.
" Single: Released Oct '83, on Midnight Rock, Catalogue no: **DSR 0706**

ROAST FISH & CORN BREAD
Tracks: / Roast fish & corn bread / Wicked he wicked.
12" Single: Released Jan '82, on Greensleeves, by Greensleeves Records. Catalogue no: **GRED 77**

Wall

DAY TRIPPER
Tracks: / Day tripper / Animal grip / Castles When I'm dancing.
" Single: Released Nov '82, on No Future, Deleted '87. Catalogue no: **02-21 (7)**
12" Single: Released Nov '82, on No Future, Deleted '87. Catalogue no: **02-21(12)**

EPITAPH
Tracks: / Epitaph / Rewind / New rebel.
' Single: Released Nov '81, on Polydor, by Polydor Ltd. Catalogue no: **POSP 365**

GHETTO
Tracks: / Ghetto, The.
' Single: Released Apr '81, on Fresh, by Jetstar Records. Catalogue no: **FRESH 17**

HOBBY FOR A DAY
Tracks: / Hobby for a day.
' Single: Released Jul '81, on Fresh, by Jetstar Records. Catalogue no: **FRESH 27**

REMEMBERANCE
Tracks: / Rememberance / Hsi nao / Hooligan nights.
' Single: Released Apr '81, on Polydor, by Polydor Ltd. Catalogue no: **POSP 260**

Wall, Max

ENGLAND'S GLORY (see panel on previous page)
Tracks: / England's glory / Dream tobacco.
' Single: Released '76, on Stiff, by Stiff Records. Catalogue no: **BUY 12**

Wall Of Voodoo

BIG CITY
Tracks: / Big city.
' Single: Released Nov '84, on I.R.S, Catalogue no: **IRS 116**

DO IT AGAIN
Tracks: / Do it again / Back in the laundromat Far side of crazy (On 12" only).
12" Single: Released May '87, on I.R.S, Catalogue no: **IRMT 135**
' Single: Released May '87, on I.R.S, Catalogue no: **IRM 135**

FAR SIDE OF CRAZY
Tracks: / Far side of crazy / Wrong way to Hollywood, The.
' Single: Released Mar '86, on I.R.S, Catalogue no: **IRM 111**
12" Single: Released Mar '86, on I.R.S, Catalogue no: **IRMT 111**

INTERSTATE 15
Tracks: / Interstate 15.
' Single: Released Oct '82, on Illegal, by Faulty Products Records. Catalogue no: **ILS 031**

MEXICAN RADIO
Tracks: / Mexican radio / Call of the West.
" Single: Released Jan '83, on Illegal, by Faulty Products Records. Catalogue no: **ILS 0036**
' Single: Released Jan '83, on Illegal, by Faulty Products Records. Catalogue no: **ILS 36**

Wall Street Crash

Biographical details: Wall Street Crash were formed in early 1960 by their present musical director Keith Strachan. The four boys and three girls were working on stage productions like 'Grease', 'Elvis' and TV's '...n boy' for which Strachan was musical director. Strachan soon realised they were too talented to remain in chorus work and Wall Street Crash were formed. They gave their first performance in March 1980 at the now defunct 'Country Cousin' club in Chelsea and received critical acclaim. immediately afterwards, they were booked to appear on 'Saturday Night At The Mill', which marked the start of a brilliant TV career. To date they have appeared on no less than thirty TV shows both in the U.K. and on the continent, including their own TV special on BBC TV and another special for German TV. In between all their television work they have appeared at every major venue in England and Europe, toured with Shirley Bassey and Sammy Davis Junior, but their most thrilling experience was to be called to perform on The Royal Variety Show in November 1980 before HRH The Prince Of Wales and HRH THe Queen Mother. Their music style - bright, humorous and visual - soon attracted approaches from a bevy of record companies and Magnet Records eventually signed them in the face of fierce competition. Mary Dunne: Shirley McLaine look-alike, brunette from Dublin, who acts as the group's choreographer. Mary once played the lead in the musical 'Irene'..

SWING SWING SWING
Tracks: / Swing swing swing / Mountains of Mourne / Shot down.
7" Single: Released May '82, on Magnet, by WEA Records. Deleted '85. Catalogue no: **MAG 226**

YOU'RE MY WORLD
Tracks: / You're my world / Susie's bar.
7" Single: Released Dec '83, on Magnet, by WEA Records. Catalogue no: **MAG 252**

Wallace Collection

DAYDREAM
Tracks: / Daydream.
7" Single: Released Apr '83, on EMI (France), by EMI Records. Catalogue no: **2C 008 04047**

Wallace, George

BACK AT 17
Tracks: / Back at 17 / She gives away.
7" Single: Released Aug '81, on Portrait, by CBS Records. Deleted '84. Catalogue no: **A 1473**

Wallace, Jerry

YOU'RE SINGING OUR LOVE SONG TO SOMEBODY ELSE
Tracks: / You're singing our love song to somebody else.
7" Single: Released Jun '60, on London-American, Deleted '63. Catalogue no: **HLH 9110**

Wallace, Michelle

JAZZ RHYTHM
Tracks: / Jazz rhythm.
7" Single: Released Dec '82, on System, Catalogue no: **SYS 101**
12" Single: Released Dec '82, on System, Catalogue no: **SYSL 101**

YOU OUGHT TO KNOW
Tracks: / You ought to know.
7" Single: Released Mar '86, on Lovebeat Int., Catalogue no: **LOV 2**
12" Single: Released Mar '86, on Lovebeat Int., Catalogue no: **LOVT 2**

Wallbank, Mal

FROM THE FIRST TIME
Tracks: / From the first time / So glad.
7" Single: Released Dec '87, on MW, Catalogue no: **LEY 1**

Wallflowers

83.7
Tracks: / 83.7.
7" Single: Released Aug '87, on Ideal Music, by Ideal Music Records. Catalogue no: **IDEA 007**
12" Single: Released Aug '87, on Ideal Music, by Ideal Music Records. Catalogue no: **IDEAT 007**

BLUSHING GIRL NERVOUS SMILE
Tracks: / Blushing girl nervous smile.
12" Single: Released Oct '86, on Mantre, Catalogue no: **MANT 83/7**

THANK YOU
Tracks: / Thank you.
7" Single: Released 19 Mar '87, on Mantre, Catalogue no: **7MANT98/4**
12" Single: Released 19 Mar '87, on Mantre, Catalogue no: **MANT 98/4**

Wallis, Bob

COME ALONG PLEASE
Tracks: / Come along please.
7" Single: Released Jan '62, on Pye Jazz Today, Deleted '65. Catalogue no: **7 NJ 2048**

I'M SHY MARY ELLEN I'M SHY
Tracks: / I'm shy Mary Ellen.
7" Single: Released Jul '61, on Pye Jazz Today, Deleted '64. Catalogue no: **7 NJ 2043**

Wallis, Julie

SUN ARISE
Tracks: / Sun arise / Some kinda fool.
7" Single: Released Nov '82, on Speed, Catalogue no: **SPEED 9**

WILD THING
Tracks: / Wild thing / I used to be your number one.
7" Single: Released Nov '82, on Speed, Catalogue no: **SPEED 3**
7" Single: Released Mar '82, on Safari, by Safari Records. Deleted '85. Catalogue no: **SAFE 43**

Wally

WASTE OF TIME
Tracks: / Waste of time / Good morning Mrs. Robertson.
7" Single: Released Oct '81, on Radioactive, Catalogue no: **RAD 105**

Wally Goes To Holloway

ALL OUR VERY BEST
Tracks: / All our very best / Wally's yarn.
7" Single: Released Jun '86, on Well Cut, Deleted '87. Catalogue no: **WC 0001**

Wally & The Gang

BONKING (THE DANCE)
Tracks: / Bonking (the dance) / Bonking (the get down mix) / Bonking (the bank mix).
Note: * track on 12" version.
7" Single: Released Nov '87, on Square Biz, by Square Biz Records. Catalogue no: **7 SUJ 114**
12" Single: Released Dec '87, on Square Biz, by Square Biz Records. Catalogue no: **SUJ 114**

Walpurgis Volta

LA PETITE VIELLE
Tracks: / La petite vielle.
7" Single: Released '88, on La Rage, Catalogue no: **FRACTION 2**

Walrus

FORGET THE TEARS
Tracks: / Forget the tears / Centrifuge.
7" Single: Released Jul '82, on Dovetail, by Key Records. Deleted '84. Catalogue no: **DOVES 1**

Walsh, Adian

CHRISTMAS IN FOUR DIMENSIONS
Tracks: / Christmas in four dimensions.
12" Single: Released Nov '87, on Solid Rock, by Word Records (UK). Catalogue no: **002**

Walsh, Joe

Biographical details: Born in Wichita, Kansas, in 1947, guitarist, singer and songwriter Walsh came to fame as a third of the James Gang, made many fine solo albums and pioneered the "mouth bag" style of channelling guitar sound from amp to mouth, giving voicing of sounds, later popularised by Peter Frampton. Walsh surprised many people in 1976 by joining the Eagles for Hotel California: he added guts to one of their best albums and his song, Life In The Fast Lane, was one of its finest tracks. His account of the rock 'n' roll lifestyle, Life's Been Good, was a Top Fifteen transAtlantic hit in 1978. He ran for President in '79: a rock 'n' roller with a sense of humour as well as a good guitarist. (Donald Clarke, March 1988.)
This American guitarist, singer, keyboards player and songwriter, born in Wichita, Kansas, initially attracted attention as a member of the James Gang. He joined that group in 1969, and left in 1971 after realising that his talents clearly outweighed those of the remainder of the band. During his time with the Gang, Walsh was their driving force - although they never achieved the major superstardom that was widely tipped for them, Walsh's fantastic guitar style and strong songwriting talent made them a powerful and classy hard rock band. Their best album was *The James Gang Rides Again*, which reached the US Top 10.
After quitting the James Gang, Walsh released the *Barnstorm* LP in 1972. His solo fame began in earnest in '73, when his strangely titles album *The Smoker You Drink, The Player You Get* was a big US seller; it yielded an American Top 30 single *Rocky Mountain Way*, which remained his best known track for several years. 1974's *So What* album was not quite so strong. In early 1976, he released a live album *You Can't Argue With A Sick Mind*, which gave the ace axeman his first taste of UK chart success - the LP reached No. 28 on Britain's album chart.
Later in 1976, Walsh joined the Eagles, the LA-based superstar soft rock band. His style was heavier than theirs, so this decision surprised many observers. However, the two sounds complemented each other superbly, and he remained with the millionaire music makers until the group's termination in 1982. In 1978, during an extended lull in Eagle activities, Walsh released another solo album *But Seriously Folks*. Its success was fuelled by its transatlantic Top 20 single *Life's Been Good*, which became his only major single as a solo artist; this song was an amusing and satirical reflection on the lifestyle of a typical rock star, and it remains one of rock music's most interesting statements about the paradoxes of success - the single also featured some of Walsh's most imaginative guitar playing, and became an instant classic. He hit the American Top 20 again in 1980 with *All Night Long*, a song from the country music movie 'Urban Cowboy'. In post-Eagle days, he released the dreary 1983 album *You Bought It - You Name It*, produced by his (and the Eagles') long time producer Bill Szymcxyk; a dire version of the old standard, *Love Letters*, summed up the LP's lack of inspiration. Not many people bought it - fans preferred to remember his Seventies output with the James Gang, the Eagles and as a solo artist; that's when life was really good for Joe Walsh and his followers. (Bob MacDonald, 22 April, 1985.).

LIFE OF ILLUSION
Tracks: / Life of illusion / Down on the farm.
7" Single: Released May '81, on Elektra Asylum, by Elektra Records (USA). Catalogue no: **K 12533**

LIFE'S BEEN GOOD
Tracks: / Life's been good.
7" Single: Released Jul '78, on Asylum, by WEA Records. Deleted '81. Catalogue no: **K 13129**

ROCKY MOUNTAIN WAY
Tracks: / Rocky mountain way / Rose of Cimarron.
7" EP: Released Jul '77, on ABC Records, by MCA Records. Deleted '80. Catalogue no: **ABE 12002**

ROCKY MOUNTAIN WAY (OLD GOLD)
Tracks: / Rocky mountain way.
7" Single: Released Apr '86, on Old Gold, by Old Gold Records. Catalogue no: **OG 9599**

Walsh, Sheila

DRIFTING (SINGLE)
Tracks: / Drifting.
7" Single: Released Jun '83, on DJM, Catalogue no: **SHEIL 1**
12" Single: Released Jun '83, on DJM, Catalogue no: **SHEIL 100**

GROWING UP TO BE A CHILD
Tracks: / Growing up to be a child / Private life.
7" Single: Released May '84, on DJM, Catalogue no: **DJS 10**

HIS EYES
Tracks: / His eyes.
7" Single: Released Nov '84, on DJM, Catalogue no: **DJS 13**

STAR SONG
Tracks: / Star song / Burn on.
7" Single: Released Nov '82, on DJM, Deleted Nov '85. Catalogue no: **DJS 10992**

TURN TURN
Tracks: / Turn turn.
7" Single: Released Oct '83, on DJM, Catalogue no: **DJS 5**

Walsh, Steve

AIN'T NO STOPPIN' US NOW Party for the world
Tracks: / Ain't no stoppin' us now / I'll keep on.
7" Single: Released Jul '88, on A.1, by A.1 Records. Catalogue no: **A1 304**
CD 5": Released 22 Aug '88, on A.1, by A.1 Records. Catalogue no: **A1 CA1 304**
12" Single: Released Jul '88, on A.1, by A.1 Records. Catalogue no: **12 A1 304**

EDGE OF NIGHT
Tracks: / Edge of night.
12" Single: Released Sep '82, on Pre, by Charisma Records. Catalogue no: **PRE 2512**
7" Single: Released Sep '82, on Pre, by Charisma Records. Catalogue no: **PRE 25**

I FOUND LOVING
Tracks: / I found lovin' / Na na hey hey (kiss him goodbye).
7" Single: Released Jun '87, on A.1, by A.1 Records. Catalogue no: **A1 299**
12" Single: Released Jun '87, on A.1, by A.1 Records. Catalogue no: **12 A1 299**

LET'S GET TOGETHER TONITE
Tracks: / Let's get together tonite / Let's get together tonite (Instrumental).
12" Single: Released Nov '87, on A.1, by A.1 Records. Catalogue no: **12 A1 303**
7" Single: Released Nov '87, on A.1, by A.1 Records. Catalogue no: **A1 303**

Waltermelon Men

SEVEN YEARS
Tracks: / Seven years / I've been told.
7" Single: Released Mar '86, on What Goes On, by What Goes On Records. Catalogue

no: **GOES ON 06**

Walters, Trevor

BABY, I'VE BEEN MISSING YOU
Tracks: / Baby, I've been missing you.
12" Single: Released Jul '87, on Starlight, Catalogue no: **SLD 5004**

BETCHA BY GOLLY WOW
Tracks: / Save it for the night.
12" Single: Released Jan '87, on Priority, by Priority Records. Deleted Nov '87. Catalogue no: **PX 15**
7" Single: Released Jan '87, on Priority, by Priority Records. Deleted Nov '87. Catalogue no: **P 15**

FALLING IN LOVE
Tracks: / Falling in love.
12" Single: Released Jan '88, on Starlight, Catalogue no: **SLD 545**

HANDYMAN
Tracks: / Handyman.
12" Single: Released Mar '83, on Ital, by Ital Records. Catalogue no: **ITD 0016**

HOW LONG
Tracks: / How long.
12" Single: Released 20 Mar '89, on White Label (1), Catalogue no: **TOR 28**

LOCK AWAY YOUR HEART
Tracks: / Lock away your heart / Crying.
12" Single: Released 27 Feb '88, on Champion, by Champion Records. Catalogue no: **CHAMP 1261**
7" Single: Released 27 Feb '88, on Champion, by Champion Records. Catalogue no: **CHAMP 61**

LOVE ME TONIGHT
Tracks: / Love me tonight / Dub me tonight.
7" Single: Released Sep '81, on Magnet, by WEA Records. Catalogue no: **MAG 198**
12" Single: Released Sep '81, on Magnet, by WEA Records. Catalogue no: **12 MAG 198**

LOVE SONGS, CANDLELIGHT AND YOU
Tracks: / Love songs, candlelight and you.
7" Single: Released Oct '88, on Diamond C, Catalogue no: **JCT 1**

LOVE WILL FIND A WAY
Tracks: / Love will find a way / Alway's on my mind.
7" Single: Released Jan '80, on Bare, Catalogue no: **BARE 002**
12" Single: Released Feb '86, on Adelphi (1), Catalogue no: **ADET 005**

LOVERS MEDLEY
Tracks: / Lover's medley.
12" Single: Released Nov '82, on Must Dance, Catalogue no: **MD 004**

LOVING AS ONE
Tracks: / Loving as one / Dubbing as one.
7" Single: Released Jun '82, on Magnet, by WEA Records. Catalogue no: **MAG 214**
12" Single: Released Jul '82, on Magnet, by WEA Records. Catalogue no: **12 MAG 214**

NEVER LET HER SLIP AWAY
Tracks: / Never let her slip away.
7" Single: Released Dec '84, on Polydor, by Polydor Ltd. Deleted '87. Catalogue no: **POSP 716**

PENNY LOVER
Tracks: / Penny lover.
12" Single: Released Dec '83, on I & S, Catalogue no: **IS 001**

SHAKE YOU DOWN
Tracks: / Down and out.
12" Single: Released Dec '86, on Starlight, Catalogue no: **SLD 540**

STUCK ON YOU
Tracks: / Stuck on you.
12" Single: Released May '84, on I & S, Catalogue no: **IST 002**
7" Single: Released May '84, on I & S, Catalogue no: **IS 002**

THAT'S HOW HEARTACHES ARE MADE
Tracks: / That's how heartaches are made / That's how heartaches are made (instrumental).
7" Single: Released Sep '86, on Time, Catalogue no: **7 TR 019**
12" Single: Released Sep '86, on Time, Catalogue no: **12 TR 019**

WE WILL BE LOVERS
Tracks: / We will be lovers.
12" Single: Released Sep '85, on Beta, Catalogue no: **BT 0020**

Walton, Cedar

Biographical details: Pianist and composer Cedar Walton, who worked with everybody who was anybody in jazz in the late 1950's, including Art Blakey's Jazz Messengers, also made many albums of his own on Prestige. He was born in Texas in 1934 and since 1970 has spent a lot of time in Europe. (Donald Clarke, March 1988.).

WILLOW WEEP FOR ME
Tracks: / Willow weep for me / Book's bossa.
CD 3": Released '88, on Delos (USA), Catalogue no: **D/PC 2101**

Waltones

DOWNHILL
Tracks: / Downhill.
7" Single: Released May '87, on Medium Cool, by Medium Cool Records. Catalogue no: **MC 004**

I DIG YOU THE DEEPEST
Tracks: / I dig you the deepest.
12" Single: Released Oct '88, on Medium Cool, by Medium Cool Records. Catalogue no: **MC 016T**
CD 3": Released Oct '88, on Ediesta, Catalogue no: **CALC 066**
7" Single: Released Oct '88, on Medium Cool, by Medium Cool Records. Catalogue no: **MC 016**

LISTEN TO YOUR HEART
Tracks: / Listen to your heart.
12" Single: Released '89, on Medium Cool, by Medium Cool Records. Catalogue no: **MC 022T**

SHE LOOKS RIGHT THROUGH ME
Tracks: / She looks right through me.
12" Single: Released Oct '87, on Medium Cool, by Medium Cool Records. Catalogue no: **MC 007**

SPELL IT OUT
Tracks: / Spell it out.
12" Single: Released Jul '88, on Medium Cool, by Medium Cool Records. Catalogue no: **MC 011T**
7" Single: Released Jul '88, on Medium Cool, by Medium Cool Records. Catalogue no: **MC 011**

Waltons

BROWN RICE
Tracks: / Brown rice.
7" Single: Released Sep '85, on Excaliber, by Red Bus Records. Deleted '88. Catalogue no: **EXC 1403**
12" Single: Released Sep '85, on Excaliber, by Red Bus Records. Deleted '88. Catalogue no: **EXCL 1403**

Waltzer

MORGEN BLASTER
Tracks: / Morgen blaster.
12" Single: Released Jul '85, on Mercury, by Phonogram Ltd. Catalogue no: **MERX 187**
7" Single: Released Jul '85, on Mercury, by Phonogram Ltd. Catalogue no: **MER 187**

Wanderers

READY TO SNAP
Tracks: / Ready to snap / Beyond the law.
7" Single: Released Apr '81, on Polydor, by Polydor Ltd. Catalogue no: **POSP 239**

TIMES THEY ARE A-CHANGING
Tracks: / Times they are a-changing / Little bit frightening.
7" Single: Released Jun '81, on Polydor, by Polydor Ltd. Deleted Jun '84. Catalogue no: **POSP 284**

Wandering Souls

DOGS IN THE NIGHT
Tracks: / Dogs in the night.
7" Single: Released Feb '85, on Lost Moments, Catalogue no: **LM 017**

Wang Brothers

WHILE MY GUITAR GENTLY WEEPS
Tracks: / While my guitar gently weeps.
12" Single: Released Oct '85, on Communique, Catalogue no: **123**

Wang Chung

Biographical details: This British band comprises Darren Costin, Nick Feldman and Jack Hues. Their name is the literal Chinese translation of 'perfect pitch'. An embroyonic line-up of this London group, known as Huang Chung, attracted a small amount of attention in 1980 with their single *Isn't it about time we were on TV*. In the event, the group had to wait four years before they were on TV. After an abortive recording contract with Arista Records, which yielded a flop 1982 album, the group evolved into Wang Chung and parted company with record label and management. Their new manager proceeded to take the album and some demo tapes to America, where they were heard by a leading music business executive, David Geffen; he was impressed, and signed the band to his Geffen label on a worldwide basis.
Wang Chung began to make a real headway in early 1984, when they achieved an unusual feat for a new band: they found themselves climbing the British and American charts simultaneously, with different records. The slow-burning *Dance hall days* took them to No.21 in the UK, while *Don't let go* was a minor US hit. Both singles were pedestrian, unexciting pop material; but were notable in their emphasis on such traditional instruments as guitar, bass and sax, at a time when many British pop acts were placing heavy reliance on synthesisers. Although the new technology was used to a certain extent, Hues' Royal College of Music experience plus Costin and Feldman's jazz-funk backgrounds ensured that synths were employed sparingly. After their initial breakthrough, Wang Chung underwent a risky quiet spell. They returned in April 1985 with a new single *Fire in the twilight*, and then proceeded to record a follow-up album to 1984's *Points on the curve*. For this purpose, the group chose to stick with producers Chris Hughes & Ross Cullum despite an offer from none other than Steely Dan's former mainman Donald Fagen. (Bob MacDonald, 22nd April 1985).

WANG CHUNG - DON'T BE MY ENEMY (Released on Epic)

DANCE HALL DAYS
Tracks: / Dance hall days / There is a nation.
12" Single: Released Jan '84, on Geffen, by Geffen Records (USA). Catalogue no: **TA 3837**
7" Pic: Released Jan '84, on Geffen, by Geffen Records (USA). Catalogue no: **WA 3837**
7" Single: Released Jan '84, on Geffen, by Geffen Records (USA). Catalogue no: **A 3837**

DON'T BE MY ENEMY (see panel above)
Tracks: / Don't be my enemy / Waves (instrumental).
Note: Sound quality of this picture disc may not be comparable to that of a conventional disc. Original sound recording made by the David Geffen Company. CBS Records are the exclusive licencees for the UK.
12" Single: Released Jun '83, on Epic, by CBS Records. Catalogue no: **TA 3529**
7" Pic: Released Jun '83, on Epic, by CBS Records. Catalogue no: **WA 3529**
7" Single: Released Jun '83, on Epic, by CBS Records. Catalogue no: **A 3529**

DON'T LET GO
Tracks: / Don't let go / Ornamental elephant.
12" Single: Released Apr '84, on Geffen, by Geffen Records (USA). Catalogue no: **TA 4272**
7" Pic: Released Apr '84, on Geffen, by Geffen Records (USA). Catalogue no: **WA 4272**
7" Single: Released Apr '84, on Geffen, by Geffen Records (USA). Catalogue no: **A 4272**

EVERYBODY HAVE FUN TONIGHT
Tracks: / Fun tonight (the early years).
12" Single: Released Oct '86, on Geffen, by Geffen Records (USA). Deleted Jul '88. Catalogue no: **GEF 13T**
7" Single: Released Oct '86, on Geffen, by Geffen Records (USA). Deleted Jul '88. Catalogue no: **GEF 13**

FIRE IN THE TWILIGHT
Tracks: / Fire in the twilight.
7" Single: Released May '85, on A&M, by A&M Records. Deleted '88. Catalogue no: **AM 249H**
12" Single: Released May '85, on A&M, by A&M Records. Deleted '88. Catalogue no: **AMY 249**

LET'S GO
Tracks: / Let's go / To live and die in L.A..
7" Single: Released Mar '87, on Geffen, by Geffen Records (USA). Deleted Jul '88. Catalogue no: **GEF 17**
12" Single: Released Mar '87, on Geffen, by Geffen Records (USA). Deleted Jul '88. Catalogue no: **GEF 17T**

TO LIVE AND DIE IN L.A (SINGLE)
Tracks: / To live and die in L.A. / Dance hall days / Black, blue and white (Available on 12" only.).
12" Single: Released Jun '86, on Geffen, by Geffen Records (USA). Catalogue no: **TA 6756**
7" Single: Released Jun '86, on Geffen, by Geffen Records (USA). Catalogue no: **A 6756**

Wangford, Hank

ARE YOU THE VICTIM OF AGEISM
Tracks: / Are you the victim of ageism.
7" Single: Released Jan '84, on Charisma, by Virgin Records. Deleted '89. Catalogue no: **CB 411**
12" Single: Released Jan '84, on Charisma, by Virgin Records. Deleted '89. Catalogue no: **CB 41112**

COWBOYS STAY ON LONGER
Tracks: / Cowboys stay on longer.
7" Single: Released Mar '81, on WEA, by WEA Records. Catalogue no: **K 18712**
12" Single: Released Mar '87, on Honky Catalogue no: **HONKY TX 12**

ROOTIN' TOOTIN' SANTA CLAUS
Tracks: / Rootin' tootin' santa claus / White christmas / Mama won't be home for christmas.
7" Single: Released Nov '82, on Cow Pie by Cow Pie Records. Catalogue no: **PIE 005**

WILD THING
Tracks: / Wild thing / All I want.
7" Single: Released Jun '80, on Cow Pie, by Cow Pie Records. Catalogue no: **PIE 001**

Wansel, Dexter

Biographical details: This American keyboards player and arranger achieved a one-off entry on the UK charts with his 1978 disco single *All night long*. This reached No.59 and was the punchy opening track on his funky album *Voyager*. His other Seventies LPs included *Life on Mars* and *What the world is coming to*. However, Wansel's primary occupation was his work as an in-house player/arranger for Philadelphia International Records' roster of soul artists. Working closely with the company's writing/production masters, Kenny Gamble & Leon Huff, he helped to create records by such acts as MFSB and Teddy Pendergrass. Wansel's solo albums, which showcased his accomplished synthesiser style, were both danceable and listenable; but their success was limited to the specialist funk market. His most quaint claim to fame was being the first artist to hit the UK chart with a single entitled *All night long* - this title has subsequently been used by Rainbow, The Mary Jane Girls and Lionel Richie all of whom reached the British Top 20. Yet another song called *All night long* gave Joe Walsh an American Top 20 success in 1980. While Allnightlongmania reached fever pitch, it's originator Dexter Wansel slowed his career down during the early Eighties. (Bob MacDonald, 22nd April 1985).

ALL NIGHT LONG
Tracks: / All night long.
7" Single: Released May '78, on Philadelphia Int., by EMI Records. Deleted '81. Catalogue no: **PIR 6255**

CAPTURED (SINGLE)
Tracks: / Captured / Conversations.
12" Single: Released May '86, on 10 Records, by Virgin Records. Deleted May '88. Catalogue no: **TEN 80-12**
7" Single: Released May '86, on 10 Records, by Virgin Records. Deleted May '88. Catalogue no: **TEN 80**

LIFE ON MARS
Tracks: / Life on mars / Always there.
12" Single: Released Apr '86, on Streetwave, Catalogue no: **SWAVE 9**

War

Biographical details: Latin-rock fusion band War was formed in California with Lonnie Jordan on keyboards, Howard Scott on guitar, drummer Harold Brown and several others. Producer Jerry Goldstein put them up for a job as Eric Burden's backing group and harmonica man Lee Oscar came in with Burden. They made 15 hit albums and six Top Ten singles with Burden, all produced by Goldstein. (Donald Clarke, March 1988.)

At the time of their greatest success, this American band consisted of Papa Dee Allen, Harold Brown, B.B.Dickerson, Lonnie Jordan, Charles Miller, Lee Oskar and Howard Scott. The above line-up emerged as War in 1970. Prior to this, several of the septet's members had been working together since the start of the Sixties under various names. When British singer Eric Burdon, former lead singer with the Animals saw them in a Los Angeles club in 1969, they were called the Nite Shift. In his heyday, Burdon had been hailed as Britain's greatest white blues vocalist - he loved black R & B music, and warmed to this group's style. Though they were a local West Coast band with no national recognition, Burdon was so impressed that he asked them to change their name to War and become his backing group. *Spill the wine* by Eric Burdon & War became a smash hit all over America in 1970 - the single reached No.3 on the Billboard Hot 100. The album *Eric Burdon declares War* was highly acclaimed. The singer and the group parted company in '71. Burdon, who, for several years had been unsure what direction his showbusiness career should follow, faded into obscurity. There was happier news, however news, however, for War - they embarked upon a string of soul chart smashes, many of which crossed over to the US pop charts. After scraping the American Top 40 with *All day music* in 1971, the band chalked up three US million-sellers over the following two years: *Slippin' into darkness, The world is a ghetto* and *The cisco kid* were all examples of War's exceptional brand of power-house funk, which incorporated soul, rock, jazz and latin styles, and which contained some engaging lyrics. *Gypsy man*, another US Top 10 smash, continued the group's hot streak in late '73, and they also achieved big-selling albums with *The world is a ghetto* and *Deliver the world*. Management group disputes interrupted War's output in 1974, but they returned to fine form in '75 with the aptly titled *Why can't we be friends*. The next single *Low rider* gave the band their ludicrously overdue British chart debut, by reaching No.12 in the UK in early '76. (Even Burdon & War's *Spill the wine* had missed the UK charts). Unfortunately, British audiences caught onto the group just as they were about to fade from glory - 1976's *Summer* was their final US million seller, and they only managed one more Top 20 hit in the UK: *Galaxy* hit No.14 in 1978. By the Eighties, after some personnel changes, they were a mere shadow of their former greatness. However, 1985 saw War return to the spotlight with *Groovin'*, a straightforward remake of the Young Rascals' 1967 classic summery hit. (Bob MacDonald, 22nd April 1985.)

War is a Latin-rock fusion band formed in California in 1959, with Lonnie Jordan on keyboards, Harold Brown on drums, Howard Scott on guitar (all born 1946-8) and several others. Producer Jerry Goldstein put them up for a job as Eric Burdon's backing band; Lee Oscar came with Burdon, joined on harmonica (born in 1946 in enmark). They were successful with Burdon and then made 15 hit LPs with six top ten singles in the '70s, all produced by Goldstein. (Donald Clarke)..

GROOVIN'
Tracks: / Groovin' (vocal) / Groovin' (instrumental).
7" Single: Released Aug '86, on Bluebird (2), by BMG Records (UK). Catalogue no: **BR 16**
12" Single: Released Aug '86, on Bluebird (2), by BMG Records (UK). Catalogue no: **BRT 16**

HEY SENORITA
Tracks: / Hey senorita.
7" Single: Released Apr '78, on MCA, by MCA Records. Deleted '81. Catalogue no: **MCA 359**

I'LL BE AROUND
Tracks: / I'll be around / Music band 2.
7" Single: Released Jun '80, on MCA, by MCA Records. Deleted '83. Catalogue no: **MCA 593**

JUST BECAUSE
Tracks: / Just because / I'm about somebody.
7" Single: Released Jul '82, on RCA, by BMG Records (UK). Catalogue no: **RCA 240**

LOW RIDER
Tracks: / Low rider (remix) / Low rider (orig) / Flippin' into darkness (Extra track on 12" only).
7" Single: Released May '87, on Lax, Catalogue no: **XLAX 1**
7" Single: Released Jan '76, on Island, by Island Records. Deleted '79. Catalogue no: **WIP 6267**
12" Single: Released May '87, on Lax, Catalogue no: **XLAX 100**

ME AND BABY BROTHER
Tracks: / Me and baby brother.
7" Single: Released Jun '76, on Island, by Island Records. Deleted '79. Catalogue no: **WIP 6303**

WORLD IS A GHETTO
Tracks: / World is a ghetto / I'll take care of you.
7" Single: Released Jan '80, on MCA, by MCA Records. Deleted Jan '85. Catalogue no: **MCA 557**
12" Single: Released Jan '80, on MCA, by MCA Records. Deleted Jan '85. Catalogue no: **MCAT 557**

YOU GOT THE POWER
Tracks: / You got the power.
12" Single: Released Mar '82, on RCA, by BMG Records (UK). Catalogue no: **RCAT 201**
7" Single: Released Mar '82, on RCA, by BMG Records (UK). Catalogue no: **RCA 201**

War Party

MY NAME IS FATE
Tracks: / My name is fate.
7" Single: Released Sep '85, on EE Records, Catalogue no: **EE 503**

Ward, Anita

RING MY BELL
Tracks: / Ring my bell.
7" Single: Released Jun '79, on TK, Deleted '82. Catalogue no: **TKR 7543**

Ward, Billy

DEEP PURPLE
Tracks: / Deep purple.
7" Single: Released Nov '57, on London-American, Deleted '60. Catalogue no: **HLU 8502**

STARDUST
Tracks: / Stardust.
7" Single: Released Sep '57, on London-American, Deleted '60. Catalogue no: **HLU 8465**

Ward Brothers

CROSS THAT BRIDGE
Tracks: / Cross that bridge (Instrumental) (Not on 12") / Cross that bridge (7" version-not on 12") / Cross that bridge (12" version) (On CD & 12" only) / Cross that bridge (dub mix) (On 12" only) / Easy prey (cloth cap mix) (On CD only).
7" Single: Released Nov '86, on Siren, by Virgin Records. Catalogue no: **SIREN 37**
12" Single: Released Nov '86, on Siren, by Virgin Records. Catalogue no: **SIREN 3712**
CD 5": Released Aug '88, on Siren, by Virgin Records. Catalogue no: **WARD 3712**

EASY PREY
Tracks: / Easy prey / Bridge too far, A.
7" Single: Released Sep '86, on Siren, by Virgin Records. Deleted May '88. Catalogue no: **SIREN 33**
12" Single: Released Sep '86, on Siren, by Virgin Records. Deleted May '88. Catalogue no: **SIREN 33-12**

I TRUSTED YOU
Tracks: / I trusted you / I trusted you (inst).
12" Single: Released 30 May '87, on Siren, by Virgin Records. Deleted May '88. Catalogue no: **SRN 49-12**
7" Single: Released 30 May '87, on Siren, by Virgin Records. Deleted May '88. Catalogue no: **SRN 49**

LEAVE US ALONE
Tracks: / Leave us alone / Who will help us now / Don't talk to strangers (Available on 12" format only.).
CD 3": Released Dec '88, on Siren, by Virgin Records. Catalogue no: **SRNCD 105**
7" Single: Released Dec '88, on Siren, by Virgin Records. Catalogue no: **SRN 105**
12" Single: Released Dec '88, on Siren, by Virgin Records. Catalogue no: **SRNT 105**

WHY DO YOU RUN
Tracks: / Why do you run.
7" Single: Released Mar '87, on Siren, by Virgin Records. Deleted May '88. Catalogue no: **SIREN 32**
12" Single: Released Mar '87, on Siren, by Virgin Records. Deleted May '88. Catalogue no: **SIREN 32-12**

WHY DO YOU RUN (CD SINGLE)
Tracks: / Why do you run (7" version) / Why do you run (12" re-mix) / Don't talk to strangers (instrumental) / Madness of it all (instrumental).
CD 5": Released Apr '87, on Virgin, by Virgin Records. Catalogue no: **WARD 3212**

Ward, Clifford T.

Biographical details: This British singer, songwriter and keyboards player, who hailed from Kidderminster, Worcestershire, worked as a schoolteacher before he became a musical professional. His English Literature background displayed itself in the wit, whimsy, wishfulness and wisdom of his lyrics. Ward's debut album *Singer songwriter* was released on John Peel's Dandelion label in the early Seventies; that label soon folded and so he switched to Charisma and later Philips. Ward's second album, 1973's *Home thoughts*, yielded the UK Top 10 single *Gaye*. This sentimental, middle-of-the-road love song was written and produced solely by Ward, and reached No.8. It was quickly followed by the *Mantle pieces* LP, which contained a smaller hit single, *Scullery*. That song peaked at No.37 on the British chart, and he never returned to the listings despite a string of quality releases. None of his albums reached the Top 30; his highest placed LP remained *Home thoughts*, which had peaked at No.40 on the UK album charts. Among the best of Ward's flop singles were *Jigsaw girl* and *Up in the world*. The latter ballad was also recorded by Cliff Richard, who liked the song enough to include it on his successful 1977 LP *Every face tells a story*. The melody of *Up in the world* reappeared on *She's out of my life*, Michael Jackson's 1980 smash - though this was probably a case of coincidence rather than plagiarism, Ward could have used some royalties from the latter song, particularly as it was featured on Jackson's multi-platinum LP *Off the wall*! But by 1980, the underrated Ward, whose style was too gentle for the pop charts and too left-field for the MoR market, had drifted into obscurity. (Bob MacDonald, 26th April 1985).

BEST IS YET TO COME
Tracks: / Best is yet to come, The / Last again.
7" Single: Released Jan '81, on WEA, by WEA Records. Catalogue no: **K 18426**

CONTRARY
Tracks: / Contrary / Climate of her favour.
7" Single: Released Apr '81, on WEA, by WEA Records. Catalogue no: **K 18486**

CRICKET
Tracks: / Cricket / Computer.
7" Single: Released Mar '86, on Tembo, by Tembo Records. Catalogue no: **TML 114**

GAYE
Tracks: / Gaye.
7" Single: Released Jun '73, on Charisma, by Virgin Records. Deleted '76. Catalogue no: **CB 205**

GAYE (OLD GOLD)
Tracks: / Gaye / I get a kick out of you.
7" Single: Released 21 Nov '87, on Old Gold, by Old Gold Records. Catalogue no: **OG 9733**
7" Single: Released Jul '82, on Old Gold, by Old Gold Records. Deleted Jul '88. Catalogue no: **OG 9008**

SCULLERY
Tracks: / Scullery.
7" Single: Released Jan '74, on Charisma, by Virgin Records. Deleted '77. Catalogue no: **CB 221**

SOMETIME NEXT YEAR (SINGLE)
Tracks: / Sometime next year / Turbo.
7" Single: Released Nov '86, on Tembo, by Tembo Records. Catalogue no: **TML 123**

Ward, Herb

STRANGE CHANGE
Tracks: / Strange change.
7" Single: Released Mar '83, on Neil Rushton, Catalogue no: **791003**

Ward, John

OUR SONG
Tracks: / Our song / Our song (instrumental).
Note: Many viewers of TV AM are already heralding to be a major hit. The song was penned by John, who as a full-time single parent father took up songwriting as a hobby and to entertain the children. Having previously featured on a news-item on the show, John was invited back to perform the song in the studio. Fate subsequently led him to the attention of BMG Records who surprised him with awarding a contract live on air.
7" Single: Released Dec '88, on Ariola, by BMG Records (UK). Catalogue no: **111 907**

Ward, Michael

LET THERE BE PEACE ON EARTH
Tracks: / Let there be peace on earth.
7" Single: Released Sep '73, on Philips, by Phonogram Ltd. Deleted '76. Catalogue no: **6006 340**

Ward, Pete

WHEN I MEETS I
Tracks: / When I meets I.
7" Single: Released Aug '85, on Embryo Arts (Belgium), Catalogue no: **EAS 5**

Wardell, Mark

UP THE AMAZON
Tracks: / Up the Amazon.
7" Single: Released Jul '88, on Theobald Dickson Productions, Catalogue no: **TDPS 003**

Warfare

ADDICTED TO LOVE (MAYHEM MIX)
Tracks: / Addicted to love / Hungry dogs (live).
7" Single: Released Jul '87, on Neat, by Neat Records. Catalogue no: **NEAT 58**

MAYHEM F*ING MAYHEM (SINGLE)**
Tracks: / Mayhem f***ing mayhem.
10" single: Released Dec '86, on Neat, by Neat Records. Catalogue no: **EAT 1040**

NOISE, FILTH & FURY EP, THE
Tracks: / Burn the Kings road / New the age of total warfare, The / Noise filth & fury.
7" EP: Released Jul '84, on Neat, by Neat Records. Catalogue no: **NEAT 41**

TOTAL DEATH (SINGLE)
Tracks: / Total death.
12" Single: Released Jun '85, on Neat, by Neat Records. Catalogue no: **NEAT 49 12**

TWO TRIBES
Tracks: / Two tribes / Hell / Blown to bits.
12" Single: Released Nov '84, on Neat, by Neat Records. Catalogue no: **NEAT 45 12**

Warholas

POP ART'S DEAD
Tracks: / Pop art's dead / Moving around / We will.
12" Single: Released May '87, on Piranha, Catalogue no: **BIG PIRANHA 1**

Wariner, Steve

Biographical details: Born in Kentucky in 1954, country singer, guitarist and songwriter Wariner began in a family combo and later played in road bands of Dottie West and Bob Luman. He had minor hits on RCA (his *I'm Already Taken* was later a No 1 country hit for Conway Twitty). Wariner had his first No 1 in 1982 with *All Roads Lead To You* and he switched to MCA in 1985. His production is slick and his songs are mainstream country ballads, but better than most. Further No 1 hits on the US country chart have been *Some Fools Never Learn* ('85), *You Can Dream Of Me, Starting Over Again* and *Small Town Girl* (all '86). (Donald Clarke, March 1988.).

WEEKEND, THE
Tracks: / Weekend, The / Why do heroes die so young?.
7" Single: Released Oct '87, on MCA, by MCA Records. Catalogue no: **MCA 1204**

Warley, Steve

TONIGHTS THE NIGHT
Tracks: / Tonights the night.
7" Single: Released Oct '82, on Jive, by Zomba Records. Catalogue no: **JIVE 22**

Warlock

WITHOUT YOU
Tracks: / Without you.
7" Single: Released Nov '84, on Mausoleum, by Mausoleum Records. Catalogue no: **GUTS 8402**

Warlord

ALPHA AND OMEGA

Tracks: / Alpha and omega.
7" Single: Released Aug '81, on Creole, by Creole Records. Catalogue no: **CR 18**

Warm

TIRED OF WAITING FOR YOU
Tracks: / Tired of waiting for you.
7" Single: Released Jan '80, on MHG, Catalogue no: **GHM 208**

Warm Jets

WACKED
Tracks: / Wacked.
7" Single: Released Jul '89, on Sol, Catalogue no: **SOL 801**

Warm Sounds

BIRDS AND BEES
Tracks: / Birds and bees, The.
7" Single: Released May '67, on Deram, by London Records. Deleted '70. Catalogue no: **DM 120**

Warman, Johnny

DANCE WITH ME
Tracks: / Dance with me / King robot.
7" Single: Released Apr '81, on Rocket, by Rocket Records. Deleted '85. Catalogue no: **XPRES 51**

DREAM, DREAM, DREAM
Tracks: / Dream, dream, dream / Satellite.
7" Single: Released Nov '82, on Rocket, by Rocket Records. Deleted Nov '85. Catalogue no: **XPRES 89**

HERE COMES THE BEAT PATROL
Tracks: / Here comes the beat patrol.
7" Single: Released Sep '84, on RAK, by EMI Records. Catalogue no: **RAK 376**

SCREAMING JETS
Tracks: / Screaming jets / American machines.
7" Single: Released May '81, on Rocket, by Rocket Records. Deleted May '84. Catalogue no: **XPRES 56**

THREE MINUTES
Tracks: / Three minutes / Jon Glass.
7" Single: Released Nov '81, on Rocket, by Rocket Records. Deleted Nov '84. Catalogue no: **XPRES 67**

Warmington, Keith

EVENING SONG
Tracks: / Evening song.
7" Single: Released Jul '83, on Right Track, Catalogue no: **RTR 029**

Warne, Toni

ANY DREAM WILL DO
Tracks: / Any dream will do / Ben.
7" Single: Released Apr '87, on Mint, by Emerald Records. Deleted '88. Catalogue no: **CHEW 110**

Warner

LIVE AND LEARN
Tracks: / Live and learn.
7" Single: Released Jul '83, on Oscar, Catalogue no: **OJ 1**

Warner, Florence

HOLD ME ONCE
Tracks: / Hold me once / Hello love.
7" Single: Released Oct '80, on Mercury, by Phonogram Ltd. Deleted Oct '83. Catalogue no: **MER 42**

I MISS YOUR HEARTBEAT
Tracks: / I miss your heartbreak / Why do you pick the people you pick.
7" Single: Released Feb '81, on Mercury, by Phonogram Ltd. Deleted '84. Catalogue no: **MER 60**

OUT OF THE BLUE
Tracks: / Out of the blue / Oh darlin'.
7" Single: Released Jul '82, on Mercury, by Phonogram Ltd. Catalogue no: **MER 108**

Warner, Jack

ORDINARY COPPER, AN
Tracks: / Ordinary Copper, An / I didn't orter 'a' ett it.
7" Single: Released Jun '81, on H.M.V., by EMI Records. Deleted '82. Catalogue no: **POP 2024**

Warner, Simon

PERFECT DAY BABY
Tracks: / Perfect day baby.
7" Single: Released Sep '85, on E.G., by E.G. Records. Deleted '89. Catalogue no: **EGO 24**
12" Single: Released Sep '85, on E.G., by E.G. Records. Deleted '89. Catalogue no: **EGOX 24**

Warnes, Jennifer

AIN'T NO CURE FOR LOVE
Tracks: / Ain't no cure for love / Song of Bernadette / Bird on the wire.
12" Single: Released Feb '88, on RCA, by BMG Records (UK). Deleted May '89. Catalogue no: **PT 49586**
7" Single: Released Feb '88, on RCA, by BMG Records (UK). Deleted May '89. Catalogue no: **PB 49585**

BIRD ON A WIRE
Tracks: / Coming back to you / Bird on a wire.
7" Single: Released Aug '87, on RCA, by BMG Records (UK). Catalogue no: **PB 49627**
12" Single: Released Aug '87, on RCA, by BMG Records (UK). Catalogue no: **PT 49628**

COULD IT BE LOVE
Tracks: / Could it be love / I'm restless.
7" Single: Released Mar '82, on Arista, by BMG Records (UK). Catalogue no: **ARIST 455**

FIRST WE TAKE MANHATTAN
Tracks: / First we take Manhattan / Famous blue raincoat / Joan of Arc.
7" Single: Released Jul '87, on RCA, by BMG Records (UK). Deleted May '89. Catalogue no: **PB 49709**
12" Single: Released Jul '87, on RCA, by BMG Records (UK). Catalogue no: **PT 49709**

I KNOW A HEARTACHE WHEN I SEE ONE
Tracks: / I know a heartache when I see one / Shot through the heart.
7" Single: Released Jul '82, on Arista, by BMG Records (UK). Catalogue no: **ARIST 480**

RIGHT TIME OF THE NIGHT
Tracks: / Right time of the night.
7" Single: Released Feb '83, on Arista, by BMG Records (UK). Catalogue no: **ARIST 519**

RIGHT TIME OF THE NIGHT (OLD GOLD)
Tracks: / Right time of the night.
7" Single: Released Jul '84, on Old Gold, by Old Gold Records. Catalogue no: **OG 9455**

UP WHERE WE BELONG
Tracks: / Up where we belong.
7" Single: Released Jan '83, on Island, by Island Records. Deleted Jan '86. Catalogue no: **WIP 6831**

WHEN THE FEELING COMES AROUND
Tracks: / When the feeling comes around / Shot through the heart.
7" Single: Released Jul '80, on Arista, by BMG Records (UK). Deleted Jul '83. Catalogue no: **ARIST 342**

Warp 9

LIGHT YEARS AWAY
Tracks: / Light years away.
12" Single: Released May '83, on Arista, by BMG Records (UK). Catalogue no: **ARIST 12531**

MASTER OF THE MIX
Tracks: / Master of the mix.
7" Single: Released Aug '84, on 4th & Broadway, by Island Records. Catalogue no: **BRW 11**

NO MAN IS AN ISLAND
Tracks: / No man is an island / Island jam.
7" Single: Released Jun '84, on 4th & Broadway, by Island Records. Catalogue no: **BRW 6**

NUNK
Tracks: / Nunk.
7" Single: Released Nov '82, on Arista, by BMG Records (UK). Catalogue no: **ARIST 509**
12" Single: Released Nov '82, on Arista, by BMG Records (UK). Catalogue no: **ARIST12 509**

SKIPS A BEAT
Tracks: / Skips a beat / Skips a beat, (dub).
12" Single: Released Feb '86, on Motown, by BMG Records (UK). Catalogue no: **ZT 40504**
7" Single: Released Feb '86, on Motown, by BMG Records (UK). Catalogue no: **ZB 40503**

Warrant

HEAVEN
Tracks: / Heaven / Cold sweat / In the sticks.
12" Pic: Released Sep '89, on CBS, by CBS Records. Catalogue no: **HEAVN P1**
7" Single: Released Sep '89, on CBS, by CBS Records. Catalogue no: **HEAVN 1**
12" Single: Released Sep '89, on CBS, by CBS Records. Catalogue no: **HEAVN T1**
7" Single: Released Sep '89, on CBS, by CBS Records. Catalogue no: **HEAVN Q1**
CD 5": Released Sep '89, on CBS, by CBS Records. Catalogue no: **HEAVN C1**

Warren, Alan

GIVE US A KISS FOR CHRISTMAS
Tracks: / Give us a kiss for Christmas / Carols on 45.
7" Single: Released Dec '82, on Battersea, Catalogue no: **BATT 3**

Warren, Alisha

TOUCH ME
Tracks: / Touch me / Touch me (version).
7" Single: Released Jul '89, on RCA, by BMG Records (UK). Catalogue no: **PB 42823**
12" Single: Released Jul '89, on RCA, by BMG Records (UK). Catalogue no: **PT 42824**
12" Single: Released Sep '89, on RCA, by BMG Records (UK). Catalogue no: **PT 43222**
CD 5": Released Jul '89, on RCA, by BMG Records (UK). Catalogue no: **PD 42824**

Warren, Ellie

CAMOUFLAGE
Tracks: / Camouflage.
7" Single: Released Sep '82, on Jet, by Jet Records. Catalogue no: **JET 7028**

FALLING IN LOVE WITH YOURSELF
Tracks: / Falling in love with yourself / First time I fell in love.
7" Single: Released Jan '81, on Precision (1), Deleted '83. Catalogue no: **PAR 114**
12" Single: Released Jan '81, on Precision (1), Deleted '83. Catalogue no: **PARL 114**

I WAS MADE FOR LOVING YOU
Tracks: / I was made for loving you / Killer touch.
7" Single: Released Jul '81, on Precision (1), Deleted '83. Catalogue no: **PAR 120**
12" Single: Released Jul '81, on Precision (1), Deleted '83. Catalogue no: **PARL 120**

ON A NIGHT LIKE THIS
Tracks: / On a night like this / Feel my love / Loving game, The / Shattered glass / Can't give you up.
7" Single: Released Mar '87, on Columbia, by EMI Records. Deleted Jul '87. Catalogue no: **DB 9147**
12" Single: Released Mar '87, on Columbia, by EMI Records. Deleted Nov '88. Catalogue no: **12 DB 9147**

PRETENDER
Tracks: / Pretender.
7" Single: Released Oct '83, on Carrere, Catalogue no: **CAR 287**

PRIMITIVE LOVE
Tracks: / Primitive love.
7" Single: Released Jul '82, on Jet, by Jet Records. Catalogue no: **JET 7023**
12" Single: Released Jul '82, on Jet, by Jet Records. Catalogue no: **JET 12023**

SATELLITES
Tracks: / Satellites / Satellites (inst).
7" Single: Released May '86, on Columbia, by EMI Records. Deleted Jan '88. Catalogue no: **DB 9132**
12" Single: Released May '86, on Columbia, by EMI Records. Deleted Aug '89. Catalogue no: **12DB 9132**

SHATTERED GLASS
Tracks: / Shattered glass / World is crying out for love.
7" Single: Released 20 Jun '80, on Precision (1), Deleted '83. Catalogue no: **PARL 102**
7" Single: Released May '80, on Precision (1), Deleted May '85. Catalogue no: **PAR 102**

Warren, James

IT WONT BE THE SAME OLD PLACE (see panel above)
Tracks: / It won't be the same old place / Climate of treason.
7" Single: Released Oct '86, on Sonet, by Sonet Records. Catalogue no: **SON 2311**

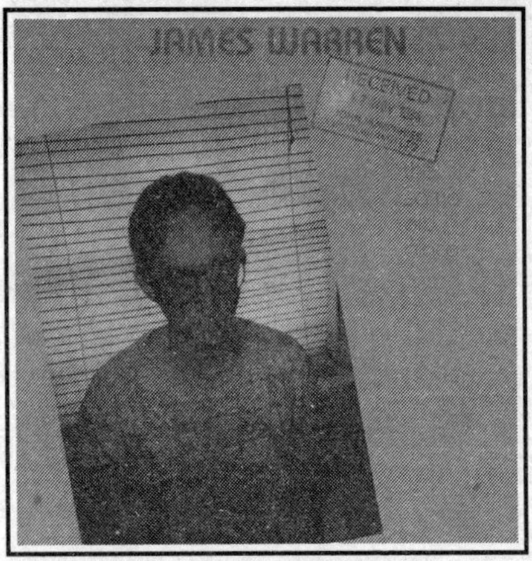

JAMES WARREN - IT WONT BE THE SAME OLD PLACE (Releasd on Sonet)

THAT WAS MY BIG MISTAKE
Tracks: / That was my big mistake / Can't we be friends.
7" Single: Released Apr '81, on Rialto (1), by Rialto Records. Catalogue no: **TREB 134**

THEY DON'T BELIEVE IN MAGIC
Tracks: / They don't believe in magic.
7" Single: Released Jul '86, on Sonet, by Sonet Records. Catalogue no: **SON 2302**

Warren, Zed

MUSCLE FOR ME
Tracks: / Muscle for me.
7" Single: Released Jul '83, on Way, Catalogue no: **WAY 1001**

MUSIC TO WATCH GIRLS BY
Tracks: / Music to watch girls by.
7" Single: Released Jun '84, on Airebeat, by Airebeat Records. Catalogue no: **ABT 5**

Warren-Green,

GOSPEL ACCORDING TO SAINT LUKE
Tracks: / Gospel according to Saint Luke / Passover.
Note: From the BBC TV series.
7" Single: Released Mar '87, on BBC, by BBC Records & Tapes. Deleted 31 Aug '88. Catalogue no: **RESL 214**

Warrenty

HITS YOU
Tracks: / Hits you / One of a kind.
7" Single: Released Oct '86, on Warner Bros., by WEA Records. Deleted Jun '87. Catalogue no: **B 9510**

Warrington, Mick

AIN'T GONNA VOTE NO MORE
Tracks: / Ain't gonna vote no more / Looking for work.
7" Single: Released Dec '82, on Speed, Catalogue no: **SPEED 1**

Warrior

BREAKOUT
Tracks: / Breakout / Dragon slayer / Take your chance.
7" Single: Released Mar '84, on Warrior, by Warrior Records. Catalogue no: **W 002**

DEAD WHEN IT COME TO LOVE
Tracks: / Dead when it come to love / Kansas City.
7" Single: Released Aug '82, on Neat, by Neat Records. Catalogue no: **NEAT 20**

FIGHTING FOR THE EARTH (SINGLE)

Tracks: / Fighting for the earth / Only the strong survive.
7" Single: Released Feb '85, on 10 Records, by Virgin Records. Deleted '89. Catalogue no: **TEN 38**
12" Pic: Released Feb '85, on 10 Records, by Virgin Records. Deleted '89. Catalogue no: **TENY 38**

FOR EUROPE ONLY
Tracks: / For Europe only.
12" Single: Released Jul '83, on Warrior, by Warrior Records. Catalogue no: **W 001**

Warriors

AH YOU
Tracks: / Ah you / Ah you (version).
12" Single: Released Oct '88, on Ariwa Sounds, by Ariwa Sounds. Catalogue no: **ARI 078**

STANCE
Tracks: / Stance.
12" Single: Released May '89, on Shaka, Catalogue no: **SHAKA 870**

Warum, Joe

DANS LE BLIZZARD
Tracks: / Dans le blizzard.
7" Single: Released Jun '82, on New Rose (1), by New Rose Records. Catalogue no: **NEW 4**

TANZEN UND DRINKEN
Tracks: / Tanzen und drinken.
7" Single: Released Jun '82, on New Rose (1), by New Rose Records. Catalogue no: **NEW 9**

Warwick, Catherine

MARINE BOY
Tracks: / Marine boy / Taxi driver.
7" Single: Released Jul '89, on Runway, Catalogue no: **FLITE 001**

Warwick, Dionne

Biographical details: Dionne Warwick was born in New Jersey in 1940 from a family bursting with vocal talent, including younger sister Dee Dee Warwick, aunts Cissy and Thelma Houston and niece Whitney Houston. She has had more than 50 hit singles and 30 hit albums since 1962. She sang in the Gospelaires with Dee Dee and Cissy, did studio work and was discovered by Burt Bacharach and Hal David, who thought her the ideal voice for their exceptionally successful songs: of her first 37 hits all but four were written, and all but two produced, by them. Her chart run was broken in 1972. She worked with Holland-Dozier-Holland, of Motown fame, and with Jerry Ragavoy, then teamed with the Spinners for her first No 1, the freak hit *There came You* in 1974. Hit albums and singles were produced by Barry Manilow. Throughout the rock era she has continued to sell albums with big-time showbiz glamour, and she recently teamed again with Bacharach. (Donald Clarke, March 1988.)
This American singer, born in East Orange, New Jersey, studied music from the age of six. She sang with her family gospel group, and became a student at Hart College of Music in Hartford, Connecticut. After moving to New York, she gained valuable experience as a session singer. It was during a Drifters session that her distinctive vocal talent was spotted by songwriters/producers Burt Bacharach and Hal David. They soon took her under their wing, and turned her into a chart artist. Warwick's first hit was *Don't make me over*, which reached No.21 on the US listings in 1963. After an awkward pause, the singer's chart career began in earnest in early '64 - *Anyone who had a heart* reached the American No.8 slot, and was followed by a stream of hits for the Warwick/Bacharach/David alliance. Warwick's voice combined excellent phrasing with a soulful yet delicate approach; Bacharach's subtle, well rounded melodies were perfectly matched with David's imaginative love lyrics, which were romantic but sugary or trivial. With the addition of Bacharach's innovative arranging and orchestral techniques, Warwick's records were amongst the classiest pop singles of the Sixties. She was a US Top 40 regular, and six of her Sixties hits entered the Top 10. In Britain, however, the singer only managed a pair of Top Tenners - 1964's *Walk on by* and 1968's *Do you know the way to San Jose*. The other four US biggies were hits in Britain for other artists: *Anyone who had a heart* was a No.1 for Cilla Black, *Message to Michael* scored for Adam Faith under the title *Message to Martha*, *I say a little prayer* was a hit for Aretha Franklin and *This girl/guy's in love with you* worked wonders for Herb Alpert. After splitting from the ace songwriters, Warwick languished without success during the early Seventies. Her declining career was suddenly revived in 1974 by producer Thom Bell, who teamed her with his fantastic soul hitmakers, the Detroit Spinners. Together they achieved a US No.1 with *Then came you* (on which Dionne, for reasons best known to herself, temporarily added an 'e' to her surname. Warwick returned rapidly to the doldrums, until a more sustained comeback came her way in 1979. Using a succession of big-name producers/songwriters - Barry Manilow, the Bee Gees and soul giant Luther Vandross - she became a regular visitor to the American charts once again; although she developed an irritating habit of publicly criticising her producers' work after she had reaped the commercial benefits from them. In Britain, 1982's *Heartbreaker* single and album, masterminded by the Bee Gees' Barry Gibb, were Warwick's most successful records ever. (Bob MacDonald, 26th April 1985).

6 TRACK HITS: DIONNE WARWICK
Tracks: / Walk on by / Reach out for me / Do you know the way to San Jose? / You'll never get to Heaven / Valley of the dolls / Anyone who had a heart.
7" EP: Released Sep '83, on Scoop 33, by Pickwick Records. Catalogue no: **7SR 5001**
Cassingle: Released Sep '83, on Scoop 33, by Pickwick Records. Catalogue no: **7SC 5001**

ALL THE LOVE IN THE WORLD
Tracks: / All the love in the world / It makes no difference.
7" Single: Released Dec '82, on Arista, by BMG Records (UK). Catalogue no: **ARIST 507**
12" Single: Released Dec '82, on Arista, by BMG Records (UK). Catalogue no: **ARIST 12507**

ANYONE WHO HAD A HEART
Tracks: / Anyone who had a heart / Walk on by / Do you know the way to San Jose?.
7" Single: Released Feb '64, on Pye International, Deleted '67. Catalogue no: **7N 25234**

ANYONE WHO HAD A HEART (OLD GOLD)
Tracks: / Anyone who had a heart.
CD 5": Released Apr '89, on Old Gold, by Old Gold Records. Catalogue no: **OG 6140**

DO YOU KNOW THE WAY TO SAN JOSE
Tracks: / Do you know the way to San Jose.
7" Single: Released May '68, on Pye International, Deleted '71. Catalogue no: **7N 25457**

DO YOU KNOW THE WAY TO SAN JOSE (OLD GOLD)
Tracks: / Do you know the way to San Jose.
7" Single: Released Apr '83, on Old Gold, by Old Gold Records. Catalogue no: **OG 9285**

FRIENDS IN LOVE (SINGLE)
Tracks: / Friends in love.
7" Single: Released May '82, on CBS, by CBS Records. Catalogue no: **A 2371**

GOT A DATE
Tracks: / Got a date.
7" Single: Released Jan '84, on Arista, by BMG Records (UK). Catalogue no: **ARIST 552**
12" Single: Released Jan '84, on Arista, by BMG Records (UK). Catalogue no: **ARIST 12552**

GOT YOU WHERE I WANT YOU
Tracks: / Got you where I want you / Lately.
7" Single: Released Jan '83, on CBS, by CBS Records. Catalogue no: **A 3005**

HEARTBREAKER (SINGLE)
Tracks: / Heartbreaker.
7" Single: Released Oct '82, on Arista, by BMG Records (UK). Catalogue no: **ARIST 496**
CD 5": Released Jun '89, on Arista, by BMG Records (UK). Catalogue no: **162055**

I DON'T CARE WHAT PEOPLE SAY
Tracks: / I don't care what people say.
7" Single: Released Jul '82, on Arista, by BMG Records (UK). Catalogue no: **ARIST 475**

I'LL NEVER LOVE THIS WAY AGAIN
Tracks: / I'll never love this way again.
7" Single: Released May '83, on Arista, by BMG Records (UK). Catalogue no: **ARIST 530**
12" Single: Released May '83, on Arista, by BMG Records (UK). Catalogue no: **ARIST 12530**

LOVE POWER
Tracks: / Love power / In a world such as this / No one in the world* (*Extra track on 12").
7" Single: Released Jul '87, on Arista, by BMG Records (UK). Deleted May '89. Catalogue no: **RIS 27**
12" Single: Released Jul '87, on Arista, by BMG Records (UK). Catalogue no: **RIST 27**

MORE THAN FASCINATION
Tracks: / More than fascination / What is this.
7" Single: Released Jul '82, on Arista, by BMG Records (UK). Deleted '85. Catalogue no: **ARIST 475**

NO NIGHT SO LONG (SINGLE)
Tracks: / No night so long / Reaching for the sky.
7" Single: Released Sep '80, on Arista, by BMG Records (UK). Deleted '83. Catalogue no: **ARIST 256**

NOW WE'RE STARTING OVER AGAIN
Tracks: / Now we're starting over again / Hits medley.
7" Single: Released Jul '81, on Arista, by BMG Records (UK). Catalogue no: **ARIST 419**

REACH OUT FOR ME
Tracks: / Reach out for me.
7" Single: Released Oct '64, on Pye International, Deleted '67. Catalogue no: **7N 25265**

RESERVATIONS FOR TWO (SINGLE)
7" Single: Released 31 Oct '87, on Arista, by BMG Records (UK). Deleted May '89. Catalogue no: **RIS 44**

RUN TO ME
Tracks: / Run to me / Heartbreaker / Paradise Cafe.
12" Single: Released Mar '85, on Arista, by BMG Records (UK). Catalogue no: **ARIST 12610**
7" Single: Released Mar '85, on Arista, by BMG Records (UK). Catalogue no: **ARIST 610**

THAT'S WHAT FRIENDS ARE FOR
Tracks: / That's what friends are for.
12" Single: Released Oct '85, on Arista, by BMG Records (UK). Catalogue no: **ARIST 12638**
7" Single: Released Oct '85, on Arista, by BMG Records (UK). Deleted May '89. Catalogue no: **ARIST 638**

THEN CAME YOU
Tracks: / Then came you.
7" Single: Released Oct '74, on Atlantic, by WEA Records. Deleted '77. Catalogue no: **K 10495**

VALLEY OF THE DOLLS (SINGLE)
Tracks: / Valley of the dolls.
7" Single: Released Mar '68, on Pye International, Deleted '71. Catalogue no: **7N 25445**

WALK ON BY
Tracks: / Walk on by.
7" Single: Released Apr '64, on Pye International, Deleted '67. Catalogue no: **7N 25241**
7" Single: Released Aug '82, on Dakota, Catalogue no: **BAK 13**
Cassingle: Released Feb '82, on Orchid Music, Catalogue no: **ORC 003**

WALK ON BY (OLD GOLD)
Tracks: / Walk on by.
7" Single: Released Mar '83, on Old Gold, by Old Gold Records. Catalogue no: **OG 9284**

WE'LL BURN OUR BRIDGES BEHIND US
Tracks: / We'll burn our bridges behind us.
7" Single: Released Mar '83, on Warner Bros., by WEA Records. Catalogue no: **W 9762**

WHISPER IN THE DARK
Tracks: / Whisper in the dark / Extravagent gestures / No one there (to sing me a love song)* (Track available on 12" version only).
7" Single: Released Apr '86, on Arista, by BMG Records (UK). Catalogue no: **ARIST 652**
12" Single: Released Apr '86, on Arista, by BMG Records (UK). Catalogue no: **ARIST 12652**

WITHOUT YOUR LOVE (SINGLE)
Tracks: / Without your love / It's love / Got a date.
7" Single: Released Dec '84, on Arista, by BMG Records (UK). Catalogue no: **ARIST 605**
12" Single: Released Dec '84, on Arista, by BMG Records (UK). Catalogue no: **ARIST 12605**

YOU CAN HAVE HIM
Tracks: / You can have him.
7" Single: Released Apr '65, on Pye International, Deleted '68. Catalogue no: **7N 25290**

YOU'LL NEVER GET TO HEAVEN
Tracks: / You'll never get to heaven.
7" Single: Released Jul '64, on Pye International, Deleted '67. Catalogue no: **7N 25256**

YOURS
Tracks: / Yours / Take the short way home.
12" Single: Released Feb '83, on Arista, by BMG Records (UK). Catalogue no: **ARIST 12518**
7" Single: Released Feb '83, on Arista, by BMG Records (UK). Catalogue no: **ARIST 518**

Was (Not Was)

Biographical details: This American duo, which consists of two non-brothers called David St.Was and Don St.Was, come from Detroit. After spending the Seventies in various local bands, they set themselves up as a duo in 1980. Their single *Wheel me out* released in that year, attracted sufficient critical acclaim to warrant the recording of a debut eponymous album in 1981. With David on vocals, keyboards and sax and Don on vocals, synthesisers and bass, the LP contained a curious blend of rock and funk; comparisons with Talking Heads sprang to mind. Despite critical acclaim, commercial success eluded that first album Was (Not Was). A similar fate greeted the 1983 follow-up, *Born to laugh at tornadoes*; like its predecessor, it contained guest contributions from a variety of seasoned musicians, but these did not help it to sell. However, the LP's opening track became a minor UK hit single - the typically weird *(Return to the valley of) Out come the freaks*, reached No.41 in March 1984. Hailing from the Ze Records label, which also spawned Kid Creole and the Coconuts, Was (Not Was) continue to enjoy a sizeable cult following; but a desperately wacky sense of humour is no guarantee of record sales. (Bob MacDonald, 26th April 1985).

ANYTHING CAN HAPPEN
Tracks: / Anything can happen (R&B mix) / Anything can happen / Anything can happen (acid condominium mix) (Only on 12" single.).
Cassingle: Released Aug '89, on Fontana, by Phonogram Ltd. Catalogue no: **WASMC 6**
7" Single: Released Aug '89, on Fontana, by Phonogram Ltd. Catalogue no: **WAS 6**
CD 5": Released 4 Jun '88, on Fontana, by Phonogram Ltd. Deleted Feb '89. Catalogue no: **WASCD 5**
12" Single: Released Aug '89, on Fontana, by Phonogram Ltd. Catalogue no: **WAS 612**
CD 5": Released Aug '89, on Fontana, by Phonogram Ltd. Catalogue no: **WASCD 6**
7" Single: Released 4 Jun '88, on Fontana, by Phonogram Ltd. Deleted Feb '89. Catalogue no: **WAS 5**
12" Single: Released 4 Jun '88, on Fontana, by Phonogram Ltd. Deleted Feb '89. Catalogue no: **WAS 512**

BOY'S GONE CRAZY, THE
Tracks: / Boy's gone crazy, The.
12" Single: Released Nov '87, on Fontana, by Phonogram Ltd. Deleted Oct '88. Catalogue no: **SFSP 912**
7" Single: Released Nov '87, on Fontana, by Phonogram Ltd. Deleted Oct '88. Catalogue no: **SFSP 9**

OUT COME THE FREAKS(SINGLE)
Tracks: / Out come the freaks / Earth to Doris / Return to the valley of out come the freaks (Track on 12" and CD versions only.) / Stuck inside of Detroit with the out come the freaks (Track on CD version only.) / Out come the freaks (again) (Track on CD version only.).
7" Single: Released Mar '84, on Geffen, by Geffen Records (USA). Deleted '87. Catalogue no: **A 4178**
CD 5": Released May '88, on Fontana, by Phonogram Ltd. Deleted Oct '88. Catalogue no: **WASCD 4**
12" Single: Released Jan '84, on Geffen, by Geffen Records (USA). Catalogue no: **TA 4178**
12" Single: Released Apr '88, on Fontana, by Phonogram Ltd. Deleted Oct '88. Catalogue no: **WAS 412**
12" Single: Released Jul '81, on ZE, by Island Records. Catalogue no: **12WIP 6709**
7" Single: Released Jul '81, on ZE, by Island Records. Catalogue no: **WIP 6709**
7" Single: Released Apr '88, on Fontana, by Phonogram Ltd. Deleted Oct '88. Catalogue no: **WAS 4**

PROFESSOR NIGHT
Tracks: / Professor Night / Bow wow wow wow.
12" Single: Released Apr '84, on Geffen, by Geffen Records (USA). Catalogue no: **TA 4412**
7" Single: Released Apr '84, on Geffen, by Geffen Records (USA). Catalogue no: **A 4412**

ROBOT GIRL
Tracks: / Robot girl / Earth to doris.
12" Single: Released Dec '86, on Mercury, by Phonogram Ltd. Deleted Dec '87. Catalogue no: **WASR 112**
7" Single: Released Dec '86, on Mercury, by Phonogram Ltd. Deleted Dec '87. Catalogue no: **WAS 1**

SPY IN THE HOUSE OF LOVE
Tracks: / Spy in the house of love / Dad I'm in jail.
CD 5": Released 19 Feb '88, on Fontana, by Phonogram Ltd. Deleted Oct '88. Catalogue no: **WASCD 2**

12" Single: Released 13 Jun '87, on Fontana, by Phonogram Ltd. Deleted Oct '88. Catalogue no: **WAS 212**
7" Single: Released 13 Jun '87, on Fontana, by Phonogram Ltd. Deleted Oct '88. Catalogue no: **WAS 2**
12" Single: on Fontana, by Phonogram Ltd. Deleted Oct '88. Catalogue no: **WASX 2**

TELL ME THAT I'M DANCING
Tracks: / Tell me that I'm dancing.
7" Single: Released Mar '82, on ZE, by Island Records. Catalogue no: **WIP 6776**
12" Single: Released Mar '82, on ZE, by Island Records. Catalogue no: **12WIP 6776**

WALK THE DINOSAUR
Tracks: / Walk the dinosaur / 11 miles an hour.
7" Single: Released Sep '87, on Fontana, by Phonogram Ltd. Deleted Oct '88. Catalogue no: **WAS 3**
12" Single: Released Sep '87, on Fontana, by Phonogram Ltd. Deleted Oct '88. Catalogue no: **WAS 312**

WHERE DID YOU HEART GO
Tracks: / Where did your heart go / Wheel me out.
12" Single: Released Sep '81, on Island, by Island Records. Catalogue no: **12WIP 6716**
7" Single: Released Sep '81, on Island, by Island Records. Catalogue no: **WIP 6716**

Washington

HOOKED ON YOUR LOVING
Tracks: / Hooked on your loving.
12" Single: Released Sep '89, on White Label (1), Catalogue no: **12 BR 4**

Washington, Bobby

TAKE AWAY
Tracks: / Take away / Take away dub.
12" Single: Released Sep '82, on Selection Exclusive, Catalogue no: **DIS 45**

Washington, Delroy

FOR YOUR LOVE
Tracks: / For your love.
12" Single: Released Apr '81, on Ankh, Catalogue no: **ANKH 1-12**
7" Single: Released Apr '81, on Ankh, Catalogue no: **ANKH 1**

I AIN'T NO SLEEPER
Tracks: / I ain't no sleeper.
12" Single: Released Oct '85, on International (USA), by International Records & Tapes. Catalogue no: **PM 5000**

MAGIC
Tracks: / Magic / Magical.
7" Single: Released Apr '80, on Liberty, by EMI Records. Deleted '83. Catalogue no: **BP 348**

Washington, Dinah

Biographical details: A singer whose gutsy style, unique phrasing, gospel background and feeling for the blues transcended category, Dinah Washington (1924-63) won a talent contest, toured with the Sallie Martin Gospel Singers, changed her name and sang with Lionel Hampton's band from 1943 to 1946. The first session under her own name was produced by Leonard Feather in '43 with Hampton sidesmen, and Feather's songs *Evil Man* and *Salty Papa* became eternally associated with her. Washington subsequently recorded for Mercury and nearly 30 rhythm-and-blues hits from 1949-61 began with Feather's *Baby Get Lost*, a No 1 hit. More than 20 singles also made the pop chart, including good standards like *What A Difference A Day Makes, It Could Happen To You, Our Love Is Here To Stay* and *For All We Know*. She also had hit duets with Brook Benton. (Donald Clarke, March 1988.)
This American singer, born Ruth Jones in Alabama in 1924, grew up singing and playing piano in church choirs. In 1943 she became vocalist with Lionel Hampton's noted jazz band. Upon leaving Hampton in '45, she began to record in a wide variety of styles, including pop, blues and country; but jazz remained her musical base. In 1959 Washington was suddenly in the pop spotlight. *What a difference a day makes*, a catchy, jazzy, blues-tinged single, took her to No.8 on the American charts. I was followed by *Unforgettable*, a US No.17 hit. These pop successes led to her duetting with a Mercury Records labelmate, Brook Benton. He was establishing himself as one of America's top pop singers, and this 1960 recording partnership caused cries of 'sell-out' by some of his Washington fans; but she was attracted by his smoky vocals, and the combination worked. It gave Washington the two biggest hits of her career - *Baby (you've got what it takes) reached the US No.5 slot and, later in 1960, A rockin' good way (to mess around and fall in love)* hit No.7. Both were lightweight conversational duets.
While Benton's career continued to flourish, Washington's diminished a little. Her singles continued to reach the American Top 40, but did not climb into the Top 20. Both singers, however, experienced a lack of British recognition - Washington's only charted record in the UK was 1961's *September in the rain*, which peaked at No.35. Her final Stateside Top 40 success was *Where are you*, which reached No.36 in the summer of '62. She died of an overdose of sleeping pills in December 1963, at the age of 39. Though Britons were largely unaware of Washington's vocal talents during her lifetime, two of her US successes received Top 10 action in the UK in later eras: *What a difference a day makes* was a No.6 hit for jazz-blues singer Esther Phillips in 1975, and *A rockin' good way* gave Shakin' Stevens & Bonnie Tyler a No.5 success in 1984. (Bob MacDonald, 26th April 1985).

ROCKIN' GOOD WAY
Tracks: / Rockin' good way.
7" Single: Released Jul '77, on Mercury, by Phonogram Ltd. Catalogue no: **6198 160**

SEPTEMBER IN THE RAIN
Tracks: / September in the rain.
7" Single: Released Nov '61, on Mercury (EMI), Deleted '64. Catalogue no: **AMT 1162**

Washington, Geno

Biographical details:
Soul singer Washington, from Indiana, came to Britain as a serviceman. He began his music career on a club stage in East Anglia and came to London to sit in at the Flamingo Club, then a GI hangout. In 1965 guitarist Pete Gage chose him to front his Ram Jam Band, which included Bud Beadle who now plays with Cayenne: they cloned the Stax sound and, though singles flopped, live albums did well: *Hand Clappin'-Foot Stompin'-Funky Butt-Live* was on the UK Top Five album chart in late '66. But the Stax era ended and they went out of fashion overnight. Washington learned guitar and tried comebacks which were not too successful. Dexy's Midnight Runners' tribute,*Geno*, reached No 1 in 1980. (Donald Clarke, March 1988.)
This American soul singer, who hailed from Indiana, found British fame in the mid-Sixties while remaining totally unknown in the States. As a serviceman in the US Air Force, he came to the UK in the early Sixties and was based in East Anglia. Upon his discharge in 1965, he decided to make a profession of what had previously been his spare time activity - singing. Together with guitarist Pete Gage, he assembled Geno Washington & the Ram Jam Band, in which the black Washinton fronted an all-white, all British backing group. Thanks to careful rehearsal and sheer hard work, Washington's vocal style and stage presence made a rapid ascent from shoddiness to effervescent excitement. By the end of 1966, he was presiding over the most vibrant soul act in Britain. He was certainly around at the right time - the mid-Sixties saw a veritable explosion of soul music in America, with such talents as Wilson Pickett, Otis Redding, Carla Thomas, Sam & Dave, Arthur Conley and the legendary James Brown all hitting the higher echelons of the pop charts; thus, there was no shortage of material for Washington and his group to perform. Because the British-based singer's repertoire and stage act were so unashamedly derivative, and because he was essentially a live performer, he was unable to translate his club reputation into hit singles. Although four made the UK Top 50, none were able to climb into the Top 30. However, an ecstatic live LP entitled *Hand clappin', foot stompin' funky butt live* cracked the Top 5 and remained on the UK album listings for most of 1967; this featured such stormers as *Ride your pony*, Stevie Wonder's *Uptight, Land of 1000 dances* and *respect*. A second album, *Hipsters, flipsters and finger poppin' Daddies*, went to the Top 10 in late '67. The success of Geno Washington & The Ram Jam Band was unusual for several reasons: they were a predominantly white group playing authentic black American soul music; they achieved two UK Top 10 albums without the benefit of a Top 30 single; they were one of the few acts of the era to base their reputation solely on live work, with records playing an ancillary role. However, Washington's voice could not withstand the frantic touring pace forever, and the bubble burst in 1968. Their audience drifted away to psychedelia and other forms of popular culture, and the third album failed to reach the charts. Washington returned to the States, and made disastrous attempts at careers in cabaret and then rock. The forgotton singer was suddenly brought back to the attention of the British public in 1980, when Dexy's Midnight Runners hit the UK No.1 slot with their tribute single *Geno*. This new white soul-based band used this smash hit to publicise their 'new soul vision'. It was ironic that the Runners were able to capture the spirit of Washington on a major hit single, something that the man himself had never been able to do. Surprisingly, Geno did not use this golden opportunity to stage a chart comeback. In the mid-Eighties, he could be found running a London restaurant. (Bob MacDonald, 4th May 1985).

CATCH ME
Tracks: / Rock the car / Catch me.
12" Single: Released Jun '88, on MIL, by MIL Records. Catalogue no: **MILT 001**
7" Single: Released Jun '88, on MIL, by MIL Records. Catalogue no: **MILS 001**

HI HI HAZEL
Tracks: / Hi hi Hazel.
7" Single: Released Jul '66, on Piccadilly, Deleted '69. Catalogue no: **7 N 35329**

JINGLE BELLS
Tracks: / Jingle bells / Rock the car.
7" Single: Released Dec '88, on G Kap, Catalogue no: **GKA 001**

MICHAEL
Tracks: / Michael.
7" Single: Released Feb '67, on Piccadilly, Deleted '70. Catalogue no: **7 N 35359**

MICHAEL THE LOVER
Tracks: / Michael the lover.
7" Single: Released Jun '84, on Soul Supply, by Soul Supply Records. Catalogue no: **7SS 101**
12" Single: Released Jun '84, on Soul Supply, by Soul Supply Records. Catalogue no: **12SS 101**

QUE SERA SERA
Tracks: / Que sera sera.
7" Single: Released Oct '66, on Piccadilly, Deleted '69. Catalogue no: **7 N 35346**

QUE SERA SERA (EP)
Tracks: / Que sera sera / Hi hi Hazel / You got me humming / Different strokes.
7" Single: Released Jul '80, on Flashback, by Mainline Records. Catalogue no: **FBEP 103**

WATER
Tracks: / Water.
7" Single: Released May '66, on Piccadilly, Deleted '69. Catalogue no: **7 N 35312**

Washington, Grover Jr

Biographical details: This American saxophonist began to make waves in the early Seventies. After scoring successes on the US jazz charts, he achieved a major Top 10 pop crossover album with 1975's *Feels so good*, which logged 30 weeks on the US album chart. This led him to become one of the most in-demand guest players on albums by such talents as Eric Gale, Bob James, and Ralph Macdonald. After a brief spell with Motown Records, Washington found his biggest success with Elektra Records in 1981. His *Winelight* album was one of the all time best sellers on the Billboard jazz listings, and reached the Top 10 of the US pop album chart. The LP was fuelled by its smash single *Just the two of us*, which featured the vocal prowess of Bill Withers; this laid back single, a sleek jazz-soul fusion, cruised to No.2 in America. In Britain, *Just the two of us* and *Winelight* peaked at No.34 on their respective charts - in each case, this represented the saxman's first foray into the UK listings. Having reached the pinnacle of his career with *Winelight*, Washington's crossover appeal gradually lessened. His follow up albums, *Come morning* and *The best is yet to come* (the latter featured vocals by Patti Labelle), saw this classy instrumentalist veering dangerously towards the realms of supermarket muzak. (Bob MacDonald, 5th May 1985) Washington, Grover Jr was born in 1943 in Bufallo, New York. Saxophonist, playing all the reeds; began in a jazz style, becoming more MoR with much commercial success. He worked with organ trios and rock bands, played on Randy Weston's *Blue Moses*; his own LPs began to chart in 1972 with *Inner City Blues*, reaching top 10 with *Mister Magic* and *Feels So Good* in 1975; double *Live At The Bijou* in 1978 was a hit; biggest was *Winelight*, number 5 LP with smooth vocals by Bill Withers(*Just The Two of Us*, number 2 USA single in 1981). (Donald Clarke 21/5/88)2.

BE MINE
Tracks: / Be mine / Little black samba.
7" Single: Released Feb '82, on Elektra, by Elektra Records (UK). Catalogue no: **K 12600**

JAMMING
Tracks: / Jamming / East River drive.
7" Single: Released Apr '82, on Elektra, by Elektra Records (UK). Catalogue no: **K 13161**

JUST THE TWO OF US
Tracks: / Just the two of us / Make me a memory.
7" Single: Released May '81, on Elektra, by Elektra Records (UK). Deleted '84. Catalogue no: **K 12514**

JUST THE WAY YOU ARE
Tracks: / Just the way you are / Lorans dance.
7" Single: Released Oct '81, on Motown, by BMG Records (UK). Catalogue no: **TMG 1153**

LET IT FLOW (FOR DR J)
Tracks: / Let it flow / Winelight.
7" Single: Released Dec '80, on Elektra Asylum, by Elektra Records (USA). Catalogue no: **K 12495**
12" Single: Released Dec '80, on Elektra Asylum, by Elektra Records (USA). Catalogue no: **K 12495T**

MR. MAGIC
Tracks: / Mr. Magic / Sausalito.
7" Single: Released Oct '80, on Kudu, Deleted Oct '83. Catalogue no: **KUDUX 100**

Washington, Tony

TRIBUTE TO MOHAMMED ALI
Tracks: / Tribute to Muhammed Ali / I'm going to love you.
7" Single: Released Jul '82, on Code, by Code Records. Catalogue no: **COD 003**
12" Single: Released Jul '82, on Code, by Code Records. Catalogue no: **12COD 003**

W.A.S.P.

95-NASTY
Tracks: / 95-Nasty / Easy living / Flesh and fire (available on 12" single only.).
7" Single: Released Sep '86, on Capitol, by EMI Records. Deleted '88. Catalogue no: **CL 432**
12" Single: Released Sep '86, on Capitol, by EMI Records. Deleted '88. Catalogue no: **12CL 432**

ANIMAL (F**K LIKE A BEAST)
Tracks: / Animal (f**k like a beast) (live) / Animal (f**k like a beast).
Note: (Cat.no. 721042) Limited edition compact disc single. Gatefold sleeve with individual pics. of band members and group shot.
7" Pic: Released Apr '84, on Music For Nations, by Music For Nations Records. Catalogue no: **KUT 109P**
7" Single: Released May '85, on Music For Nations, by Music For Nations Records. Catalogue no: **PIG 109**
12" Single: Released Apr '84, on Music For Nations, by Music For Nations Records. Catalogue no: **12 KUT 109**
7" Single: Released Apr '84, on Music For Nations, by Music For Nations Records. Catalogue no: **KUT 109**
CD 5": Released Nov '87, on Restless (USA), by Enigma Records (USA). Catalogue no: **721042**

BLIND IN TEXAS
Tracks: / Blind in Texas.
12" Single: Released Sep '85, on Capitol, by EMI Records. Deleted '88. Catalogue no: **12CL 374**
7" Pic: Released Oct '85, on Capitol, by EMI Records. Catalogue no: **CLP 374**
7" Single: Released Sep '85, on Capitol, by EMI Records. Deleted '88. Catalogue no: **CL 374**

FOREVER FREE
Tracks: / Forever free (Eagle edit) / L.O.V.E machine (live '89) / Blind in Texas (live '89) (12", Special product & CD single only.).
7" Pic: Released Aug '89, on Capitol, by EMI Records. Catalogue no: **CLPD 546**
CD 5": Released Aug '89, on Capitol, by EMI Records. Catalogue no: **CDCL 546**
CD 5": Released Aug '89, on Capitol, by EMI Records. Catalogue no: **203 486 2**
Cassingle: Released Aug '89, on Capitol, by EMI Records. Catalogue no: **TCCL 546**
7" Single: Released Aug '89, on Capitol, by EMI Records. Catalogue no: **203 485 0**
7" Single: Released Aug '89, on Capitol, by EMI Records. Catalogue no: **CLS 546**
7" Single: Released Aug '89, on Capitol, by EMI Records. Catalogue no: **CL 546**
7" Single: Released Aug '89, on Capitol, by EMI Records. Catalogue no: **203 585 7**
12" Single: Released Aug '89, on Capitol, by EMI Records. Catalogue no: **12CL 546**
12" Single: Released Aug '89, on Capitol, by EMI Records. Catalogue no: **203 486 6**
Special: Released Aug '89, on Capitol, by EMI Records. Catalogue no: **12CLS 546**
Special: Released Aug '89, on Capitol, by EMI Records. Catalogue no: **203 486 8**
Cassingle: Released Aug '89, on Capitol, by EMI Records. Catalogue no: **203 485 4**
7" Pic: Released Aug '89, on Capitol, by EMI Records. Catalogue no: **203 486 0**

I DON'T NEED NO DOCTOR
Tracks: / Widow maker / I don't need no Doctor / Sex drive.
7" Single: Released Oct '87, on Capitol, by EMI Records. Deleted 31 Jul '88. Catalogue no: **CL 469**
12" Single: Released Oct '87, on Capitol, by EMI Records. Catalogue no: **12CL 469**
12" Single: Released Oct '87, on Capitol, by EMI Records. Deleted 31 Jul '88. Catalogue no: **12CLP 469**

7" Single: Released Nov '87, on Capitol, by EMI Records. Deleted Apr '88. Catalogue no: **CLS 469**

I WANNA BE SOMEBODY
Tracks: / I wanna be somebody.
7" Pic: Released Aug '84, on EMI, by EMI Records. Catalogue no: **12 CLP 336**
7" Single: Released Aug '84, on Capitol, by EMI Records. Deleted '88. Catalogue no: **CL 336**

MEAN MAN
Tracks: / Mean man / Locomotive breath / For whom the bell tolls.
CD 5": Released Feb '89, on Capitol, by EMI Records. Deleted Aug '89. Catalogue no: **CDCL 521**
7" Single: Released Feb '89, on Capitol, by EMI Records. Catalogue no: **CL 521**
7" Pic: Released Feb '89, on Capitol, by EMI Records. Catalogue no: **CLP 521**
12" Single: Released Feb '89, on Capitol, by EMI Records. Catalogue no: **12CL 521**
12" Single: Released Feb '89, on Capitol, by EMI Records. Catalogue no: **12CLG 521**
7" Single: Released Feb '89, on Capitol, by EMI Records. Deleted Oct '89. Catalogue no: **CLM 521**

REAL ME, THE
Tracks: / Real me, The / Lake of fools / War cry (Not on 7".).
CD 5": Released May '89, on Capitol, by EMI Records. Catalogue no: **CDCL 534**
7" Single: Released May '89, on Capitol, by EMI Records. Catalogue no: **203 367 7**
CD 5": Released May '89, on Capitol, by EMI Records. Catalogue no: **203 368 2**
7" Single: Released May '89, on Capitol, by EMI Records. Catalogue no: **203 367 8**
12" Single: Released May '89, on Capitol, by EMI Records. Catalogue no: **203 368 8**
12" Single: Released May '89, on Capitol, by EMI Records. Catalogue no: **12CL 534**
12" Single: Released May '89, on Capitol, by EMI Records. Catalogue no: **230 368 6**
12" Single: Released May '89, on Capitol, by EMI Records. Catalogue no: **12CLS 534**
Special: Released May '89, on Capitol, by EMI Records. Catalogue no: **CLPD 534**
Special: Released May '89, on Capitol, by EMI Records. Catalogue no: **203 367 0**
7" Single: Released May '89, on Capitol, by EMI Records. Catalogue no: **CLG 534**
7" Single: Released May '89, on Capitol, by EMI Records. Catalogue no: **CL 534**

SCHOOL DAZE
Tracks: / School daze.
12" Single: Released Nov '84, on Capitol, by EMI Records. Deleted Jan '88. Catalogue no: **12CL 344**

SCREAM UNTIL YOU LIKE IT
Tracks: / Scream until you like it / Shoot from the hip / Sleeping in the fire (Extra track available on 12" version only.).
12" Pic: Released Aug '87, on Capitol, by EMI Records. Deleted Jan '88. Catalogue no: **12CLP 458**
12" Single: Released Aug '87, on Capitol, by EMI Records. Deleted 31 Jul '88. Catalogue no: **12CL 458**
7" Single: Released Aug '87, on Capitol, by EMI Records. Deleted 31 Jul '88. Catalogue no: **CL 458**

WILD CHILD
Tracks: / Wild child / Mississippi queen / On your knees (* = Available on Double pack edition only.) / Hellion (available on Double pack edition only.).
Note: Double pack. Limited edition in Gatefold Bag.
7" Set: Released May '86, on Capitol, by EMI Records. Catalogue no: **CLD 388**
12" Single: Released May '86, on Capitol, by EMI Records. Deleted '88. Catalogue no: **12CL 388**
7" Single: Released May '86, on Capitol, by EMI Records. Deleted '88. Catalogue no: **CL 388**

Waste

NOT JUST SOMETHING TO BE SUNG
Tracks: / Not just something to be sung.
7" Single: Released Nov '86, on Mortarhate, by Mortarhate Records. Catalogue no: **MORT 21**

Wasted Youth

I'LL REMEMBER YOU
Tracks: / I'll remember you / My friends are dead.
7" Single: Released Sep '80, on Bridgehouse, Deleted '88. Catalogue no: **BHS 10**

JEALOUSY
Tracks: / Jealousy / Baby.
12" Single: Released Mar '82, on Bridgehouse, Deleted '88. Catalogue no: **BHS 5**

REACH OUT
Tracks: / Reach out / Gone midnight.
7" Single: Released Aug '82, on Bridgehouse, Deleted '88. Catalogue no: **BHS 14**

REBECCA'S ROOM
Tracks: / Rebecca's room.
7" Single: Released Jun '81, on Fresh, by Jetstar Records. Catalogue no: **FRESH 30**

WILD LIFE
Tracks: / Wild life / Games.
7" Single: Released Apr '82, on Bridgehouse, Deleted '88. Catalogue no: **BHS 13**

Watanabe, Sadao

DUO CREATURES
Tracks: / Duo creatures / Turning pages of wind.
7" Single: Released Oct '79, on Miracle, by Gull Records. Deleted '88. Catalogue no: **M 12**

IF I'M STILL AROUND TOMORROW
Tracks: / If I'm still around tomorrow.
7" Single: Released Oct '84, on WEA (International), by WEA Records. Catalogue no: **U 9261**
12" Single: Released Oct '84, on WEA (International), by WEA Records. Catalogue no: **U 9261 T**

NO PROBLEM
Tracks: / No problem / All about love.
7" Single: Released Nov '80, on CBS, by CBS Records. Deleted Nov '83. Catalogue no: **CBS 9348**

Watch With Mother

SUZANNE
Tracks: / Suzanne / Something so wonderful.
7" Single: Released Oct '86, on Surfin Pict, Catalogue no: **SP 001**

Waterboys

Biographical details: *A girl called Johnny* was released on Mike Scott's own Chicken Jazz label (in conjunction with Ensign). It touched the charts and received much applause from the critics along the way. The Waterboys come as the latest chapter in Mike Scott's long fascination with rock. In the late seventies, Scott launched his own fanzine, called Jungleland. By 1979 he stepped into the limelight himself, forming his own band called **Another Pretty Face**. The band was put together in Scott's hometown, Edinburgh. Their first single *All the boys love Carrie* was one of the most shamefully ignored tunes of that year. By Christmas 1979 Another Pretty Face had been signed by Virgin Records but this was to be a short lived association, with the band quickly reverting to their own Chicken Jazz label. Another Pretty Face released four singles before changing their name to **Funhouse** (thus avoiding confusion with an American band also called Another Pretty Face). By that time Scott was based in London, where he signed a long-term recording deal with Nigel Grainge's Ensign label. Funhouse released one single on Ensign in March 1982. Scott then quit the band in search of greater autonomy, working for a time in New York but by the end of 1982 was back in Britain planning his next move: Chicken Jazz was revived and the Waterboys launched with the release of *A girl called Johnny*. *December* was released as the follow-up. (Ensign, February 1982).

AND A BANG ON THE EAR
Tracks: / Bang on the ear / Raggle taggle gypsy.
7" Single: Released May '89, on Ensign, by Ensign Records. Catalogue no: **ENY 624**
CD 5": Released Jun '89, on Ensign, by Ensign Records. Catalogue no: **ENYCD 624**
Cassingle: Released Jun '89, on Ensign, by Ensign Records. Catalogue no: **ENCMC 624**
12" Single: Released May '89, on Ensign, by Ensign Records. Catalogue no: **ENYX 624**

FISHERMAN'S BLUES (SINGLE)
Tracks: / Fisherman's blues.
12" Single: Released Jan '89, on Ensign, by Ensign Records. Catalogue no: **ENYX 621**
7" Single: Released Jan '89, on Ensign, by Ensign Records. Catalogue no: **ENY 621**

GIRL CALLED JOHNNY
Tracks: / Girl called Johnny / Ready for the monkey house / Out of control.
12" Single: Released May '83, on Chicken Jazz, Catalogue no: **CJJ 1**

WHOLE OF THE MOON THE
Tracks: / Whole of the moon, The.
12" Single: Released Oct '85, on Ensign, by Ensign Records. Catalogue no: **12ENY 520**
7" Single: Released Oct '85, on Ensign, by Ensign Records. Deleted '86. Catalogue no: **ENY 520**

Waterfoot Damby

14 DAYS
Tracks: / 14 days / Making whoopee.
7" Single: Released May '85, on Tape, Catalogue no: **IT 013**

WATERFRONT - CRY (Released on Polydor)

Waterfront

BROKEN ARROW
Tracks: / Broken arrow.
7" Single: Released 20 Mar '89, on Polydor, by Polydor Ltd. Deleted Oct '89. Catalogue no: **WONB 3**
CD 5": Released 20 Mar '89, on Polydor, by Polydor Ltd. Catalogue no: **WONCD 3**
12" Single: Released 20 Mar '89, on Polydor, by Polydor Ltd. Deleted Oct '89. Catalogue no: **WONX 3**
7" Single: Released 20 Mar '89, on Polydor, by Polydor Ltd. Deleted Oct '89. Catalogue no: **WON 3**
7" Single: Released 20 Mar '89, on Polydor, by Polydor Ltd. Deleted Oct '89. Catalogue no: **WONG 3**

CRY (see panel above)
Tracks: / Cry / Saved / Cry (dance mix) (On the 12" version only.).
Note: The debut single from the band who are destined to form the soundtrack for the nineties.
Cassingle: Released 12 Jun '89, on Polydor, by Polydor Ltd. Catalogue no: **WONCS 1**
7" Single: Released 12 Jun '89, on Polydor, by Polydor Ltd. Catalogue no: **WONB 1**
7" Single: Released Sep '88, on Polydor, by Polydor Ltd. Catalogue no: **WON 1**
12" Single: Released Sep '88, on Polydor, by Polydor Ltd. Catalogue no: **WONXA 1**
CD 5": Released May '89, on Polydor, by Polydor Ltd. Catalogue no: **WONCA 1**
7" Pic: Released 12 Jun '89, on Polydor, by Polydor Ltd. Catalogue no: **WONP 1**
Special: Released May '89, on Polydor, by Polydor Ltd. Catalogue no: **WONA 1**

NATURE OF LOVE
Tracks: / Nature of love / Boy inside the man / Nature of love (remix) (Only on 12").
Cassingle: Released Dec '88, on Polydor, by Polydor Ltd. Catalogue no: **WONCS 2**
7" Single: Released Dec '88, on Polydor, by Polydor Ltd. Deleted 30 Jun '89. Catalogue no: **WONG 2**
7" Single: Released Dec '88, on Polydor, by Polydor Ltd. Catalogue no: **WON 2**
12" Single: Released Dec '88, on Polydor, by Polydor Ltd. Catalogue no: **WONX 2**
CD 5": Released Dec '88, on Polydor, by Polydor Ltd. Catalogue no: **WONCD 2**
7" Set: Released Sep '89, on Polydor, by Polydor Ltd. Catalogue no: **WONB 2**

Waterman, Dennis

Biographical details: This British actor and singer is considerably better at the former than the latter. During the late Seventies and early Eighties, he established himself as one of the UK's most popular and likeable television actors, thanks mainly to his roles in two crime series, *The Sweeny* and *Minder*. Waterman has twice graced the British singles chart. *I could be so good for you*, which became his theme song, surged to No.3 in 1980; this was somewhat amateurish pop single, which sounded like a cross between Gary Glitter and the Eurovision Song Contest. In the first week of 1984, Waterman peaked at No.21 with *What are we gonna get 'er indoors*; on this part spoken, part sung Christmas comedy record, he duetted with his *Minder* colleague George Cole. Other Waterman attempts at chartdom have sunk like stone. (Bob MacDonald, 5th May 1985).

COME AWAY WITH ME
Tracks: / Come away with me / If only.
7" Single: Released May '81, on EMI, by EMI Records. Catalogue no: **EMI 5187**

HOLDING ON TO LOVE
Tracks: / Holding on to love / Gone wrong song.
7" Single: Released Jun '80, on EMI, by EMI Records. Deleted Jun '83. Catalogue no: **EMI 5079**

I COULD BE SO GOOD FOR YOU (SINGLE)
Tracks: / I could be so good for you.
7" Single: Released Sep '80, on EMI, by EMI Records. Deleted Jul '87. Catalogue no: **EMI 5009**

SHAKE THE CITY
Tracks: / Shake the city / Wait till I get you on your own tonight.
7" Single: Released Jul '82, on EMI, by EMI Records. Deleted Jul '85. Catalogue no: **EMI 5322**

WASN'T LOVE STRONG ENOUGH
Tracks: / Wasn't love strong enough / Gone wrong song.
7" Single: Released Jan '81, on EMI, by EMI Records. Deleted Jan '84. Catalogue no: **EMI 5129**

WE DON'T MAKE LOVE ON SUNDAYS
Tracks: / We don't make love on sundays / Indian silk.
7" Single: Released Mar '82, on C&D, Catalogue no: **CD 1**

Waters, Bob

GREAT RIVERS
Tracks: / Great rivers / Your more than good with your kisses.
7" Single: Released '82, on Starcrest, by Starcrest Records. Catalogue no: **CUS 1492**

Waters, Mira

YOU HAVE INSPIRED ME
Tracks: / You have inspired me.
7" Single: Released Oct '81, on Motown, by BMG Records (UK). Catalogue no: **TMG 1154**

Waters, Muddy

Biographical details: Born McKinley Morganfield in Mississippi in 1915, Muddy Waters was, by the time he died in 1983, in Chicago, the greatest and most influential bluesman between the classic era of Robert Johnson and the later success of B.B. King. A singer, guitarist and composer, he got his nickname from playing in a muddy creek as a child. He was recorded by John Lomax at Stovall's Plantation in 1941-42, moving to Chicago in 1943. A master of slide guitar, he switched to electric guitar the following year. He played clubs and party nights, worked in a paper mill and drove a truck. He first recorded for Okeh in '46 (unreleased until the anthology, *Okeh Chicago Blues*, in '81) then, also in '46, for Aristocrat, which be-

BOB WATERS - GREAT RIVERS (Released on Starcrest)

came Chess two years later. Waters never had all that many R & B chart entries: his classics -- *I Love The Life I Live,Rock Me,Got My Mojo Working,She's Got It,She's Nineteen Years Old* -- all came in 1957,*Baby Please Don't Go* in '58, but none charted. His music was too tough and uncompromising at a time when rhythm-and-blues was becoming slicker. He first visited Britain in 1958 and discovered his international fame. He was the king of an important new genre: Chicago blues, amplified to cut through the din in South Side taverns, was directly descended from the classic era of the rural south and was a huge influence on the rock of the 60's. White American kids heard these strange records on the radio and were enchanted by a mysterious world they could never hope to enter, but English youngsters were bolder, if only out of naivety. The Rolling Stones named themselves after a 1950 R & B hit and Waters later said: "They stole my music but they gave me my name". Early Muddy Waters classics were all on Chess, reissued by PRT and Vogue. From his middle period Electric Mud was widely considered a disaster, but the double Fathers And Sons in '69 was much better, with Otis Spann on piano, Sam Lay on drums, young white acolytes Paul Butterfield, Michael Bloomfield, Donald "Duck" Dunn and other guests. *Mud In Your Ear* from '67 on Muse included a classic lineup; *They Call Me Muddy Waters*('71) won the first of several Grammies; The London Muddy Waters Sessions in '72 was highly rated. He left Chess in the mid-70's and made several fine albums on Blue Sky. (Donald Clarke, March 1988.).

MANNISH BOY
Tracks: / Mannish boy / I'm your hoochie coochie man / Blues had a baby and they named it rock 'n' roll (Available on 12" only.) / Little girl (Available on 12" version only.).
7" Single: Released Jul '88, on Epic, by CBS Records. Deleted Jan '89. Catalogue no: **MUD 1**
12" Single: Released Jul '88, on Epic, by CBS Records. Deleted Jan '89. Catalogue no: **MUDT 1**
7" Single: Released Jul '88, on Epic, by CBS Records. Catalogue no: **BRMT 016**

Waters, Roger

Biographical details: This British singer, bass player, songwriter and producer was a founder member of Pink Floyd in 1966. He was the totally dominant force within the band. One of the most successful projects of the Floyd's legendary career was their 1979 LP *The wall*. Waters conceived two LP ideas during the late Seventies, and told the band to take their pick. The Pink Floyd members decided to record *The wall* - the other project ended up as *The pros and cons of hitch hiking*, a 1984 solo offering from Waters. Despite Harvest Records' publicity, *Pros and cons* was not Waters' first solo album - in 1970 he had been responsible for the soundtrack to a motion picture entitled *The body*. But *Pros and cons* was nonetheless eagerly awaited, and its release proved anticlimactic. It received a distinctly underwhelming critical reception, and its commercial success was lukewarm by comparison with the Floyd's work: *Pros and cons* entered the UK LP chart at No.13 and then proceeded to work its way down the Top 100 from then onwards; the album failed to yield a hit single. The Lp's format and concept were imaginative and original, each track being assigned a time as well as a title: the listener was taken on a journey through 45 minutes in the life of a hitch hiker, from *4-30 am (Apparently they were travelling abroad)* to *5-11 am (The moment of clarity)*. However, despite the assistance of some 'name' musicians including Eric Clapton and Madeline Bell, the album's musical content was dreary and lifeless, and reviewers wouldn't give it the time of day. (Bob MacDonald, 5th May 1985).

5.06 AM Every strangers eyes
Tracks: / 5.06 a.m..
7" Single: Released Jun '84, on Harvest (1), by EMI Records. Catalogue no: **HAR 5230**

PROS AND CONS OF HITCH HIKING (SINGLE)
Tracks: / Moment of clarity The / Pros and cons of hitch hiking.
7" Single: Released Apr '84, on Harvest (1), by EMI Records. Deleted '88. Catalogue no: **HAR 5528**

RADIO WAVES
Tracks: / Radio waves / Going to live in LA.
7" Single: Released May '87, on EMI, by EMI Records. Deleted Oct '87. Catalogue no: **EM 6**
12" Single: Released May '87, on EMI, by EMI Records. Deleted Apr '88. Catalogue no: **12 EM 6**
CD 5": Released May '87, on EMI, by EMI Records. Deleted Nov '88. Catalogue no: **CDEM 6**

TIDE IS TURNING, THE
Tracks: / Tide is turning, The (after live aid mix) / Money / Get back to radio (demo) (Only on CD single and 12".).
7" Single: Released Jul '87, on EMI, by EMI Records. Deleted Nov '88. Catalogue no: **EM 37**
12" Single: Released Jul '87, on EMI, by EMI Records. Deleted Nov '88. Catalogue no: **12 EM 37**
CD 5": Released Nov '87, on EMI, by EMI Records. Deleted Jun '89. Catalogue no: **CDEM 37**

Watkins, Geraint

I'M A FOOL TO CARE
Tracks: / I'm a fool to care.
7" Single: Released Sep '81, on Beeb, by BBC Records & Tapes. Catalogue no: **BEEB 028**

Watkins, Otis

YOU TALK TOO MUCH
Tracks: / You talk too much / You're ready.
7" Single: Released Jul '80, on Stiff, by Stiff Records. Catalogue no: **BUY 83**

Watkiss, Clive

GIMME WHAT YOU GOT
Tracks: / Gimme what you got / Version.
12" Single: Released Feb '82, on S & G (1), Catalogue no: **SG 12**

Watley, Jody

DON'T YOU WANT ME
Tracks: / Don't you want me / Don't you want me (dub) / Don't you want me (acappella) (Available on 12" only.).
12" Single: Released Sep '87, on MCA, by MCA Records. Catalogue no: **MCAT 1198**
7" Single: Released Sep '87, on MCA, by MCA Records. Catalogue no: **MCA 1198**

FRIENDS
Tracks: / Friends / Private life.
7" Single: Released 31 Jul '89, on MCA, by MCA Records. Catalogue no: **MCAR 1352**
7" Single: Released 31 Jul '89, on MCA, by MCA Records. Catalogue no: **MCA 1352**
CD 5": Released 31 Jul '89, on MCA, by MCA Records. Catalogue no: **DMCAT 1352**
12" Single: Released 31 Jul '89, on MCA, by MCA Records. Catalogue no: **MCAT 1352**
Cassingle: Released 31 Jul '89, on MCA, by MCA Records. Catalogue no: **MCAC 1352**
12" Single: Released Aug '89, on MCA, by MCA Records. Catalogue no: **MCAX 1352**

LOOKING FOR A NEW LOVE
Tracks: / Looking for a new love / Looking for a new love (acappella).
7" Single: Released Apr '87, on MCA, by MCA Records. Catalogue no: **MCA 1107**
12" Single: Released Apr '87, on MCA, by MCA Records. Catalogue no: **MCAT 1107**

REAL LOVE
Tracks: / Real love.
CD 5": Released 28 Mar '89, on MCA, by MCA Records. Catalogue no: **DMCAT 1324**
7" Single: Released Mar '89, on MCA, by MCA Records. Catalogue no: **MCA 23928**
7" Single: Released 28 Mar '89, on MCA, by MCA Records. Catalogue no: **MCA 1324**
12" Single: Released Mar '89, on MCA, by MCA Records. Catalogue no: **MCAX 1324**
7" Single: Released Mar '89, on MCA (USA), by MCA Records (USA). Catalogue no: **MCA 238 61**
12" Single: Released 28 Mar '89, on MCA, by MCA Records. Catalogue no: **MCAT 1324**

SOME KIND OF LOVER
Tracks: / Some kind of lover / Some kind of lover (dub version) / Some kind of lover (ext. version) / Some kind of lover (bonus beats) / Looking for a new love / Some kind of lover (10" extended mix).
7" Single: Released Feb '88, on MCA Dance, by MCA Records. Catalogue no: **MCA 1236**
10" single: Released Mar '88, on MCA Dance, by MCA Records. Catalogue no: **MCAV 1236**
12" Single: Released Feb '88, on MCA Dance, by MCA Records. Catalogue no: **MCAT 1236**

STILL A THRILL
Tracks: / Sillath / Looking for a new love (acappella).
12" Single: on MCA, by MCA Records. Catalogue no: **MCAT 1168**
7" Single: Released Jul '87, on MCA, by MCA Records. Catalogue no: **MCA 1168**

Watson, Beasley

BREAKAWAY
Tracks: / Breakaway / Don't let your baby catch you.
12" Single: Released Mar '81, on Creole, by Creole Records. Catalogue no: **CR 12 3**
7" Single: Released Mar '81, on Creole, by Creole Records. Catalogue no: **CR 3**

Watson, Ed

AMIO
Tracks: / Amio.
12" Single: Released Jun '85, on Charlie's, Catalogue no: **CRD 016**

SHOW THEM
Tracks: / Show them.
12" Single: Released Jun '86, on Hot Vinyl, Catalogue no: **HVT 022**

Watson, Helen

HANGING OUT THE WASHING (IN A SMALL BACK YARD)
Tracks: / Ready to fly (Watson/McGroarty.) / Heaven suits you (Watson/McGroarty. Not on 7".) / Hanging out the washing (In a small backyard) (Radio edit) (CD single only. Watson/McGroarty.).
CD 5": Released Mar '89, on Hit Or Miss, Deleted Aug '89. Catalogue no: **CDDB 9173**
7" Single: Released Mar '89, on Hit Or Miss, Deleted Aug '89. Catalogue no: **DB 9173**
12" Single: Released Mar '89, on Hit Or Miss, Deleted Aug '89. Catalogue no: **12DB 9173**

I'M JEALOUS DEAR
Tracks: / I'm jealous dear / Don't forget to say your prayers / Soul infection (Extra track on 12" & CD single).
12" Single: Released Feb '88, on Columbia, by EMI Records. Deleted Nov '88. Catalogue no: **12DB 9164**
CD 5": Released Feb '88, on EMI, by EMI Records. Deleted Nov '88. Catalogue no: **CDDB 9164**
7" Single: Released Feb '88, on Columbia, by EMI Records. Deleted Nov '88. Catalogue no: **DB 9164**

WHEN YOU LOVE ME I GET LAZY
Tracks: / When you love me I get lazy / Rock myself to sleep / New Rock Island line, The (on 12" and CD single only.) / You're not the rule (you're the exception) (Track on CD sinle only.).
7" Single: Released 31 May '88, on Columbia, by EMI Records. Deleted Jun '89. Catalogue no: **DB 9167**
CD 5": Released 31 May '88, on Columbia, by EMI Records. Deleted Aug '89. Catalogue no: **CDDB 9167**
12" Single: Released 31 May '88, on Columbia, by EMI Records. Deleted Jun '89. Catalogue no: **12DB 9167**

YOU'RE NOT THE RULE (YOU'RE THE EXCEPTION)
Tracks: / You're not the rule (you're the exception) / Chrome soldier / Speechless.
12" Single: Released Oct '87, on EMI, by EMI Records. Deleted Nov '88. Catalogue no: **12DB 9158**
7" Single: Released Oct '87, on Columbia, by EMI Records. Deleted Nov '88. Catalogue no: **DB 9158**

Watson, John L

DON'T BLAME IT ON LOVE
Tracks: / Don't blame it on love.
7" Single: Released Oct '85, on Satril, by Satril Records. Catalogue no: **SAT 521**

Watson, Johnny

Biographical details:
Singer, guitarist and pianist Watson was born in Texas in 1935. He was influenced by T-Bone Walker and, in turn, influenced Jimi Hendrix and others -- but he has had a very uneven career. He went to the West Coast in 1950, first recorded for Federal as Young John Watson in 1953-54, for small local labels and then for King (Top Ten rhythm-and-blues hit *Cuttin' In* in 1962). He toured with Larry Williams and a Watson/Williams hit, *Mercy, Mercy, Mercy* , made the Hot Hundred in 1967. He made LPs on Okeh and Fantasy and had more success with funk in the 70's, but his later work slipped from the charts. Classic singles are on Charly, Ace and Red Lightnin'. (Donald Clarke, March 1988.).
This American guitarist, songwriter and producer first came to public attention in the mid-Sixties while playing in the backing band of rock'n'roll singer Larry Williams. During this period, Watson also began releasing solo LP's, and he has continued to do so ever since. While never becoming a major star, he has always enjoyed a cult following with his jazzy, blues-tinged brand of soul. There are not too many musicians who have nicknamed themselves after their instrument, and Watson's monicker is as much a symbol of his cheek as of his guitar proficiency. Indeed, the most distinctive features of his records have always been his sense of humour and personality, rather than his admittedly fine playing. Two good examples of this were 1976's *I need it* and 1977's *A real mother for ya* - these two singles gave Watson his sole UK chart entries, the former reaching No.35 and the latter peaking at No.44. He has never enjoyed a Top 40 single in his native country. In 1978 Watson released the *Master funk* LP under a new billing, the Watsonian Institute. This was a strange move, in view of the fact that this band featured most of the same musicians who played on his solo records. The Institute's second album *EDP* was issued in 1981, while the prolific Johnny continued to record his ever-funky solo LP's, such as *What the hell is this, Love Jones* and *Johnny and the Family Clone*. After a lengthy lay-off, he returned in early 1985 on tiptop form with his witty but (as usual) widely ignored single *Strike on computers*. (Bob McDonald, 5th July 1985).

GANGSTER OF LOVE (SINGLE)
12" Single: Released Oct '83, on DJM, Catalogue no: **DJR 4**
7" Single: Released Oct '83, on DJM, Catalogue no: **DJS 4**

I NEED IT
Tracks: / I need it.
7" Single: Released Aug '76, on DJM, Deleted '79. Catalogue no: **DJS 20694**

LOVE JONES (SINGLE)
Tracks: / Love Jones / Booty coty.
12" Single: Released Jun '80, on DJM, Deleted '83. Catalogue no: **DJR 18011**

REAL MOTHER FOR YA, A
Tracks: / Real mother for ya, A.
7" Single: Released Apr '77, on DJM, Deleted '80. Catalogue no: **DJT 10762**

Watt, Ben

CAN'T
Tracks: / Can't / Tower of silence / Aubade.
7" Single: Released Jun '81, on Cherry Red, by Cherry Red Records. Catalogue no: **CHERRY 25**

SOME THINGS DON'T MATTER
Tracks: / Some things don't matter / On Box Hill.
7" Single: Released Feb '83, on Cherry Red, by Cherry Red Records. Catalogue no: **CHERRY 55**

SUMMER INTO WINTER
Tracks: / Summer into winter.
12" Single: Released Apr '82, on Cherry Red, by Cherry Red Records. Catalogue no: **12 CHERRY 36**

Watt Government

WORKING MY FINGERS TO THE BONE
Tracks: / Working my fingers to the bone.
7" Single: Released Mar '86, on Dead Volume, Deleted '88. Catalogue no: **VOL 018**

Watt, Jim

SCOTLAND
Tracks: / Scotland / Wee Kirkcudbright centipede.
7" Single: Released Apr '81, on Klub, by Klub Records. Deleted Apr '84. Catalogue no: **LOCH 601**

Watt, John

HERE WE GO, HERE WE GO YOUNG BARRY MCGUIGAN
Tracks: / Here we go, here we go young Barry McGuigan.
7" Single: Released Jul '85, on Homespun (Ireland), by Outlet Records. Catalogue no: **HS 099**

I SMELT ROSES IN THE UNDERGROUND
Tracks: / I smelt roses in the underground / I need action.
7" Single: Released Jan '83, on EMI, by EMI Records. Catalogue no: **EMI 5361**

JOEY DUNLOP
Tracks: / Joey Dunlop.
7" Single: Released Jul '83, on Homespun (Ireland), by Outlet Records. Catalogue no: **HS 071**

KELTY CLIPPIE
Tracks: / Kelty clippie.
7" Single: Released Aug '83, on Springthyme, by Springthyme Records. Catalogue no: **5P 002**

MAYDAY, MAYDAY
Tracks: / Mayday mayday.
7" Single: Released May '83, on EMI, by EMI Records. Catalogue no: **EMI 5387**

ONE VOICE (see panel below)
Tracks: / One voice / Holiday in France.
7" Single: Released Mar '82, on EMI, by EMI Records. Catalogue no: **EMI 5266**

SPEAKING IN A DIFFERENT LANGUAGE
Tracks: / Speaking in a different language.
7" Single: Released Oct '81, on EMI, by EMI Records. Catalogue no: **EMI 5239**

THREE CHEERS FOR BILLY BINGHAM & HIS BOYS
Tracks: / Three cheers for Billy Bingham & his boys / Joey Dunlop.
7" Single: Released Apr '82, on Homespun (Ireland), by Outlet Records. Catalogue no: **HS 082**

YOUR FAULT
Tracks: / Your fault / Sarawego.
7" Single: Released Jun '82, on EMI, by EMI Records. Catalogue no: **EMI 5298**

Watt, Tom

SUBTERRANEAN HOMESICK BLUES
Tracks: / Subterranean homesick blues / I had too much to drink last night.
7" Single: Released May '86, on Watt The Duck, Catalogue no: **DUCK 1**

Watts, Brenda

WHO NEEDS LOVE LIKE THAT
Tracks: / Who needs love like that.
7" Single: Released Dec '82, on System, Catalogue no: **SYS 101**
12" Single: Released Dec '82, on System, Catalogue no: **SYSL 101**

Watts, Ernie

CHARIOTS OF FIRE (SINGLE)
Tracks: / Chariots of fire.
7" Single: Released Jun '82, on Warner Bros., by WEA Records. Deleted Jun '85. Catalogue no: **K 17958**

JUST HOLDIN' ON
Tracks: / Just holdin' on / Look in your heart.
7" Single: Released Dec '80, on Elektra, by Elektra Records (UK). Catalogue no: **K 12489**

Watts Noys

HEART IN FLAMES
Tracks: / Heart in flames / Grey snow.
7" Single: Released Apr '82, on Noys, by Noys Records. Catalogue no: **WN 2**

Watts, Phil

DO IT WITH LOVE (SINGLE)
Tracks: / Do it with love / Till the end of time.
12" Single: Released Sep '86, on Wattsco, Catalogue no: **WATTS T4**
7" Single: Released Sep '86, on Wattsco, Catalogue no: **WATTS 4**

SPARE ME CONFUSION
Tracks: / Spare me confusion.
7" Single: Released Nov '85, on Wattsco, Catalogue no: **WATTS 1**

THIS WORLDS AT WAR
Tracks: / This worlds at war / Sleeping alone.
7" Single: Released May '86, on Wattsco, Catalogue no: **WATTS 3**

TONIGHT
Tracks: / No direction.
7" Single: Released Aug '87, on Wattsco, Catalogue no: **WATTS 6**

Watts, Sammy

SOCO LOVER
Tracks: / Soco lover / Use me up.
7" Single: Released Mar '86, on Sunburn, by Orbitone Records. Catalogue no: **SBS 517**
12" Single: Released Mar '86, on Sunburn, by Orbitone Records. Catalogue no: **SBD 53**

TURN ME LOOSE
Tracks: / Turn me loose / Turn me loose (alternative version).
12" Single: Released Aug '86, on Sunburn, by Orbitone Records. Catalogue no: **SBD 54**

Wau Dau Rechy

WAITING FOR THE MAN
Tracks: / Waiting For The Man.
12" Single: Released Jun '87, on BA, Deleted '88. Catalogue no: **BA 8701**

Waugh, Ashanti

BABYLON WRONG
Tracks: / Babylon wrong.
12" Single: on Attack, Deleted '88. Catalogue no: **TACK 20**

Waugh, Evelyn

BRIDESHEAD REVISITED T.V. Soundtrack
Tracks: / Brideshead revisited, Theme from: *Various artists* / Going to Brideshead: *Various artists* / First visit, The: *Various artists* / Venice nocturne: *Various artists* / Sebastian's summer: *Various artists* / Hunt, The: *Various artists* / Sebastian against the world: *Various artists* / Julia in love: *Various artists* / Julia: *Various artists* / Rain in Venice: *Various artists* / General strike: *Various artists* / Fading light: *Various artists* / Julia's theme: *Various artists* / Sebastian alone: *Various artists* / Orphans of the storm: *Various artists* / Finale: *Various artists*.
Special: Released Jan '82, on Chrysalis, by Chrysalis Records. Deleted Jan '87. Catalogue no: **CBOX 1**

Wave

HAPPY TOGETHER
Tracks: / Happy together / Welcome to my world.
7" Single: Released May '80, on Ariola-Hansa, by Hansa Records. Deleted May '83. Catalogue no: **AHA 563**

Wavelength

Biographical details: This British vocal group consisted of five London lads who began releasing records in the early Eighties. Their sole UK chart entry was *Hurry home*, a David Gates/Bread style ballad that had the good fortune to coincide with the ending of the Falklands War. As British servicemen began to sail home, the song's somewhat tacky lyrics touched the hearts of their loved ones. *Hurry home* reached No.17 and logged 12 weeks on the Top 75. However, subsequent singles were total failures, as was the group's debut album *Hurry home*. Despite the commercial expertise of producer Christopher Neil, Wavelength's brand of lightweight pop was quickly thrown off the airwaves. (Bob MacDonald, 5th May 1985).

DON'T MAKE ME DO IT
Tracks: / Don't make me do it / Crying over you.
7" Single: Released Mar '82, on Ariola, by BMG Records (UK). Catalogue no: **ARO 272**

HURRY HOME (SINGLE)
Tracks: / Hurry home.
7" Single: Released Sep '82, on Ariola, by BMG Records (UK). Catalogue no: **ARO 281**

RIO
Tracks: / Rio.
7" Single: Released Nov '82, on Ariola, by BMG Records (UK). Catalogue no: **ARO 290**

SITTING IN THE PARK
Tracks: / Sitting in the park / Living prey.
7" Single: Released Sep '83, on Outlook, Catalogue no: **OUT 004**

WIN SOME LOSE SOME
Tracks: / Win some lose some.
7" Single: Released Sep '82, on Ariola, by BMG Records (UK). Catalogue no: **ARO 287**

Wavelinx

WE FOUND LOVE
Tracks: / We found love / Happiness.
12" Single: Released 20 Jun '87, on MGX, Catalogue no: **MBMPX 001**

Waves

BROWN EYES SON
Tracks: / Brown eyes son.
7" Single: Released Aug '82, on Albion, by Albion Records. Catalogue no: **ION 1037**

NIGHTMARE
Tracks: / Nightmare / Hey war pig.
7" Single: Released Apr '82, on Armageddon, by Armageddon Records. Catalogue no: **AS 020**

Waving At Trains

SYLVIE
Tracks: / Sylvie.
7" Single: Released Mar '88, on Gash, Catalogue no: **GASH 111**

Wax

AMERICAN ENGLISH (SINGLE)
Tracks: / American English.
12" Single: Released Oct '87, on RCA, by BMG Records (UK). Catalogue no: **PT 41527**
7" Single: Released Oct '87, on RCA, by BMG Records (UK). Deleted May '89. Catalogue no: **PB 41527**

ANCHORS AWAY
Tracks: / Anchors away / Bridge to your heart.
CD 5": Released Aug '89, on RCA, by BMG Records (UK). Catalogue no: **PD 49350**
12" Single: Released Aug '89, on RCA, by BMG Records (UK). Catalogue no: **PT 49350**
7" Single: Released Aug '89, on RCA, by BMG Records (UK). Catalogue no: **PB 49349**

BALL AND CHAIN (see panel below)
Tracks: / Ball and chain.
7" Single: Released Oct '85, on RCA, by BMG Records (UK). Catalogue no: **PB 40385**
12" Single: Released Oct '85, on RCA, by

JOHN WATT - ONE VOICE (Released on EMI)

WAX - BALL AND CHAIN (Released on RCA)

BMG Records (UK). Catalogue no: **PT 40386**

BRIDGE TO YOUR HEART
Tracks: / Bride to your heart / Heaven in her bed.
7" Single: Released Jun '87, on RCA, by BMG Records (UK). Deleted May '89. Catalogue no: **PB 41405**
12" Single: Released Jun '87, on RCA, by BMG Records (UK). Catalogue no: **PB 41406**

IN SOME OTHER WORLD
Tracks: / In some other world / People all over this world / Ball and chain (on 12" only).
Note: From the album America English. * extra track on 12" version.
12" Single: Released Jan '88, on RCA, by BMG Records (UK). Deleted May '89. Catalogue no: **PT 41702**
7" Single: Released Jan '88, on RCA, by BMG Records (UK). Deleted May '89. Catalogue no: **PB 41701**

RIGHT BETWEEN THE EYES
Tracks: / Right between the eyes / Only a visitor.
7" Single: Released Mar '86, on RCA, by BMG Records (UK). Catalogue no: **PB 40509**
12" Single: Released Mar '86, on RCA, by BMG Records (UK). Catalogue no: **PT 40510**

SHADOWS OF LOVE
Tracks: / Shadows of love / Magnetic house / People all over the world (Extra track on 12" version only).
7" Single: Released Jun '86, on RCA, by BMG Records (UK). Catalogue no: **PB 40525**
12" Single: Released Jun '86, on RCA, by BMG Records (UK). Catalogue no: **PT 40526**

SYSTEMATIC
Tracks: / Systematic / Breakout.
12" Single: Released Sep '86, on RCA, by BMG Records (UK). Catalogue no: **PT 40940**
7" Single: Released Sep '86, on RCA, by BMG Records (UK). Catalogue no: **PB 40939**

WHEREVER YOU ARE
Tracks: / Wherever you are / Right between the eyes (Available on 7" and CD only) / For your love (live) (Available on 12" and CD only) / Lonely boy (live) (Available on 12" and CD only).
CD 5": Released Jun '89, on RCA, by BMG Records (UK). Catalogue no: **PD 42896**
7" Single: Released Jun '89, on RCA, by BMG Records (UK). Catalogue no: **PB 42895**
12" Single: Released Jun '89, on RCA, by BMG Records (UK). Catalogue no: **PT 42896**
Cassingle: Released 10 Jul '89, on RCA, by BMG Records (UK). Catalogue no: **PK 42895**

Way, Darryl

AS LONG AS THERE'S A SPARK
Tracks: / As long as there's a spark.
7" Single: Released Aug '83, on Venturi, Deleted '84. Catalogue no: **VR 1**

LITTLE PLUM
Tracks: / Little plum.
7" Single: Released Nov '84, on Charisma, by Virgin Records. Catalogue no: **PLUMH1**
12" Single: Released Nov '84, on Charisma, by Virgin Records. Catalogue no: **PLUM 112**
7" Single: Released Oct '82, on Snat, Deleted '84. Catalogue no: **ECG 002**

Way Of The West

CITY FOR LOVERS (HEY YOU)
Tracks: / City for lovers (Hey you) / Countdown.
7" Single: on MCA, by MCA Records. Catalogue no: **WES 1**
12" Single: on MCA, by MCA Records. Catalogue no: **WEST 1**

DON'T SAY THAT'S JUST FOR WHITE BOYS
Tracks: / Don't say that's just for white boys / Prove it.
12" Single: Released Apr '81, on Mercury, by Phonogram Ltd. Deleted '84. Catalogue no: **MERX 66**
7" Single: Released Apr '81, on Mercury, by Phonogram Ltd. Deleted '84. Catalogue no: **MER 66**

DRUM
Tracks: / Drum / Friend.
7" Single: Released Nov '81, on Mercury, by Phonogram Ltd. Deleted Nov '84. Catalogue no: **DRUM 1**
12" Single: Released Nov '81, on Mercury, by Phonogram Ltd. Deleted Nov '84. Catalogue no: **DRUM 12**

FEEL THE STEEL
Tracks: / Feel the steel.
7" Single: Released Sep '84, on MCA, by MCA Records. Catalogue no: **WES 2**
12" Single: Released Sep '84, on MCA, by MCA Records. Catalogue no: **WEST 2H**

Way Out

THIS WALKING WAY
Tracks: / This walking way.
7" Single: Released Nov '85, on Diamond, by Revolver Records. Catalogue no: **DIA 010**

TIME MOVES US ON
Tracks: / Time moves us on.
7" Single: Released Oct '84, on Flux, Catalogue no: **EXIT 1**

Waye, Steve

QUEEN OF MY SOUL
Tracks: / Queen of my soul.
7" Single: Released Feb '85, on Sway, Deleted '86. Catalogue no: **SWAY 100**

Wayman, Mike

I'LL MAKE YOUR BODY ROCK
Tracks: / I'll make your body rock / Don't think twice.
12" Single: Released Jul '87, on In Touch, by In Touch Records. Catalogue no: **TWELVE 001**
7" Single: Released Jul '87, on In Touch, by In Touch Records. Catalogue no: **SEVEN 001**

Waymon, Sam

CHICO
Tracks: / Chico / Circus.
Note: US composer, jazz pianist, singer and actor. Has worked and toured with legendary greats: Ray Charles, Sarah Vaughan and Nina Simone.
12" Single: Released May '87, on IMS, by Polydor Ltd. Catalogue no: **IMS 0129**

Wayne, Alvis

I GOTTUM +3
Tracks: / I gottum +3.
7" Single: Released Jun '80, on Rollin' Rock, Catalogue no: **45 012**

I WANNA EAT YOUR PUDDING
Tracks: / I wanna eat your pudding.
7" Single: Released Jun '80, on Rollin' Rock, Catalogue no: **45 032**

Wayne, Carl

LOVE YOUR DOG
Tracks: / Love your dog.
7" Single: Released Jan '89, on BBC, by BBC Records & Tapes. Catalogue no: **RESL 233**

MISS YOU NIGHTS
Tracks: / Miss you nights / Some day.
7" Single: Released Dec '82, on Jet, by Jet Records. Catalogue no: **JET 7032**

Wayne, Charlie

AERIAL PICTURES
Tracks: / Aerial pictures.
7" Single: Released Apr '82, on Jet, by Jet Records. Catalogue no: **JET 7022**

DEEPER THAN LOVE
Tracks: / Deeper than love / Midnight blue.
7" Single: Released Jan '82, on Jet, by Jet Records. Catalogue no: **JET 7010**

Wayne, Dig

MASTER MIND
Tracks: / Master mind / No such love.
12" Single: Released May '87, on Polydor, by Polydor Ltd. Deleted Jan '88. Catalogue no: **POSPX 864**
7" Single: Released May '87, on Polydor, by Polydor Ltd. Deleted Jan '88. Catalogue no: **POSP 864**

Wayne, Jeff

Biographical details: This American producer, songwriter, arranger and keyboards player became well-known in the Seventies for two projects, both of which enjoyed greater success in Britain than in the States. Between 1973 and '76, Wayne produced ten UK Top 40 singles and three UK Top 10 albums for David Essex. All of the ten hits were penned by Essex, but Wayne's musical and technical knowledge provided the catalyst which propelled Essex's previously unsuccessful singing career into the realms of teen idol superstardom. The first was 1973's *Rock on* which hit No.3; this was the only one to cross the Atlantic - it peaked at No.5 on the Billboard Hot 100 (and went to No.1 on the alternative Cashbox chart). Then came two British No.1 smashes - *Gonna make you a star* (1974) and *Hold me close* (1975). Wayne's other hugely successful project far removed, musically, from those lightweight pop hits, but it also involved David Essex. Wayne came up with idea of composing, creating and producing a disc adaptation of H.G.Wells' classic novel *The war of the worlds*. For this purpose, he assembled a formidable cast of talent, including Essex, Julie Covington, the Moody Blues', Justin Hayward, Thin Lizzy's Phil Lynott, Chris Thompson (of Manfred Mann's Earth Band) and narrator Richard Burton. The resulting double album was like a theatrical production on vinyl. Wayne's brand of epic rock was dramatic, powerful and melodic; this no-holds-barred, highly ambitious studio creation was a perfect antidote for those British record buyers who deplored the punk influx into the UK charts.
The war of the world was a colossal success. Released in June 1978, it logged 200 weeks on the UK album chart. Several years after its release, it was still making regular return visits to the Top 100. The project yielded a Top 5 single for Justin Hayward with *Forever Autumn*, which reached No.5 on the British listings in the late summer of '78. One of the phenomenon's spin-offs was a 1984 *War of the worlds* video game, featuring micro-Martians battling against earthlings. In the mid-Eighties, Wayne devoted much of his time to running his own Ollie Recording Studios in North West London. By this time, no follow-up to *The war of the worlds* had surfaced - he was probably wiser not to attempt one. (Bob MacDonald, 5th May 1985).

EVE OF THE WAR
Tracks: / Eve of the war, The.
7" Single: Released Sep '78, on CBS, by CBS Records. Deleted '81. Catalogue no: **CBS 6496**

HORSELL, COMMON AND THE HEAT RAY
Tracks: / Horsell, Common and the heat ray / Dead London.
7" Single: Released Oct '81, on CBS, by CBS Records. Deleted Oct '84. Catalogue no: **CBSA 1589**

JUBILATION
Tracks: / Jubilation / Time bomb.
7" Single: Released Oct '80, on Epic, by CBS Records. Deleted Oct '83. Catalogue no: **EPC 8941**

MATADOR
Tracks: / Matador / Henry Higgins.
7" Single: Released Jul '82, on CBS, by CBS Records. Deleted '85. Catalogue no: **A 2493**

Waysted

Biographical details: Waysted's debut album *Vices* reveals Waysted as hot contenders for the hard rock throne currently occupied stateside by Deff Leppard, though a truer comparison would probably be with prime time UFO, of whom Pete Way was such an integral part for over a decade. When Way walked out of UFO he already had the idea of forming Waysted in the back of his mind, although he spent some time creating Fastway with Eddie Clark and helping Ozzy Osbourne out first. All the time, Way was recruiting the musicians who make up Waysted. He met lead guitarist Ronnie Kayfield in the States. Ronnie was a guitar teacher who cut his live teeth with those infamous pre-punk glam punks The Heartbreakers. He was also a confirmed UFO fan who used to bring antique guitars to their New York shows. Grantham-born Frank Noon was the original Deff Leppard drummer (he left because he wouldn't sign the contract) and he also worked temporarily with Bernie Torme. Vocalist Fin is an amiable Glaswegian who met Way through publisher Bob Halfin. Halfin heard Fin's demo tapes, instantly pronounced him the best singer around and passed them on to his notorious son, rock photographer Ross 'Herpes' Halfin, who in turn played them to Pete. Paul Raymond, ex MSG and UFO completed the line-up on rhythm guitar and keyboards (but was later to leave the band in October 1983 before their first UK/European tour supporting Dio).
The band started rehearsing in February 1983, recording *Vices* at Moor Hall Hotel in Sussex during May and June. It was produced by Mick Glossop and mixed by Pete and Paul. It's release was followed by a tour of the US in January 1984 supporting Ozzy Osbourne and it was at the beginning of this tour that Barry Benedetta joined Waysted. Barry had known Ronnie since 1975 when they were at guitar school together in their home town of Philadelphia. They formed their first band together called Prophesy in 1979 and later a band called Fragile. In 1983 when Ronnie had joined Waysted and had moved to England, Barry left Fragile and started teaching guitar in a Philadelphia music store. Just prior to Christmas 1983 Barry had an opening to try out as second guitarist with Phil Mogg, but before this materialised, he got a call from Ronnie asking him to try out for Waysted. (Berni Kilmartin, Chrysalis, January 1984).

BLACK AND BLUE
Tracks: / Black and blue / Out of control / Wild night (Extra track on 12" version only).
7" Single: Released Nov '86, on Parlophone, by EMI Records. Deleted Oct '87. Catalogue no: **R 6142**
12" Single: Released Nov '86, on Parlophone, by EMI Records. Deleted Oct '87. Catalogue no: **12R 6142**

CAN'T TAKE THAT LOVE AWAY
Tracks: / Can't take that love away.
7" Single: Released Oct '83, on Chrysalis, by Chrysalis Records. Catalogue no: **CHS 2736**

HEAVEN TONIGHT
Tracks: / Heaven tonight.
7" Single: Released May '85, on Music For Nations, by Music For Nations Records. Catalogue no: **KUT 117**
7" Single: Released Feb '87, on Parlophone, by EMI Records. Deleted Oct '87. Catalogue no: **R 6150**
12" Single: Released May '85, on Music For Nations, by Music For Nations Records. Catalogue no: **12 KUT 117**
12" Single: Released Feb '87, on Parlophone, by EMI Records. Deleted Oct '87. Catalogue no: **12 R 6150**

Wazis & Mambetis

THANK YOU VERY MUCH
Tracks: / Thank you very much.
7" Single: Released Sep '82, on London Records, by London Records. Catalogue no: **LON 12**
12" Single: Released Sep '82, on London Records, by London Records. Catalogue no: **LONX 12**

We Are Going To Eat

HEART IN HAND
Tracks: / Heart in hand / Just another one (Who got it wrong) / What have flowers got to do with it / Cut.
12" Single: Released Oct '88, on Cat & Mouse, by Cat & Mouse Records. Catalogue no: **ABBO 7T**

I WISH I KNEW
Tracks: / I wish I knew.
7" EP: Released Jul '87, on All The Madmen, by All The Madmen Records. Catalogue no: **MAD 016**

RIDE UPON THE TIDE
Tracks: / Ride upon the tide.
12" Single: Released Oct '89, on Big Cat, by Big Cat Records. Catalogue no: **ABB 12T**

We Free Kings

DEATH OF THE WILD COLONIAL BOY
Tracks: / Death of the wild colonial boy / Love is in the air.
7" Single: Released Jul '86, on Howl, Catalogue no: **WOOF 1**

OCEANS
Tracks: / Oceans.
7" Single: Released Mar '87, on DDT, by D.D.T.Records. Catalogue no: **DISP 7**
12" Single: Released Mar '87, on DDT, by D.D.T.Records. Catalogue no: **DISP 7T**

STILL STANDING E.P.
Tracks: / Still standing.
12" Single: Released '88, on DDT, by D.D.T.Records. Catalogue no: **DISP 9T**

Weapon Of Peace

CHILDREN OF TODAY
Tracks: / Children of today / Woman.
7" Single: Released Oct '80, on Fontana, by Phonogram Ltd. Deleted Oct '83. Catalogue no: **TF 1082**
12" Single: Released Oct '80, on Fontana, by Phonogram Ltd. Deleted Oct '83. Catalogue no: **TFX 1082**

FOUL PLAY
Tracks: / Foul play.
7" Single: Released Apr '82, on Safari, by Safari Records. Catalogue no: **SAFE 42**
12" Single: Released Apr '82, on Safari, by Safari Records. Catalogue no: **SAFELS 42**

HIT AND RUN
Tracks: / Hit and run.
7" Single: Released Oct '82, on Safari, by Safari Records. Catalogue no: **SAFE 48**
12" Single: Released Oct '82, on Safari, by Safari Records. Catalogue no: **SAFELS 48**

IF
Tracks: / If / Misty Rhodes.
7" Single: Released Apr '81, on Fontana, by Phonogram Ltd. Deleted Apr '84. Catalogue no: **TF 1083**
12" Single: Released Apr '81, on Fontana, by Phonogram Ltd. Deleted Apr '84. Catalogue no: **TFX 1083**

JAH LOVE
Tracks: / Jah love.
7" Single: Released Oct '81, on Safari, by Safari Records. Catalogue no: **SAFE 39**

STANDING ON THE EDGE
Tracks: / Standing on the edge.
12" Single: Released May '83, on Safari, by Safari Records. Catalogue no: **SAFELS 54**

Weards, Roy, Last Post

MONOPOLY
Tracks: / Monopoly / Triangle.
7" Single: Released Jun '82, on Parasol, by Parasol Records. Catalogue no: **PAR 2**

Weather Girls

Biographical details: Izora and Martha are an American vocal duo who achieved a one-off hit with their anthem *It's raining men.* Trading on their heavy physique and appropriately big voices, the Girls' weight, ages and surnames were a closely guided secret. Izora, a mother of eleven children, began her career singing gospel music and playing classical piano. Martha also came from a church background and was later trained as a opera singer. Based in San Francisco, the two singers teamed up, and began singing together in choirs and as session vocalists. They then became Two Tons Of Fun, and were taken under the wing of Sylvester, the hitmaking gay disco queen. After a pair of unsuccessful albums, the duo became the Weather Girls. Although no longer working with Sylvester, his influence still showed - their debut single as the Weather Girls, *It's raining men,* was aimed directly at the gay clubs and at the growing boystown market. Originally released in late 1982, this exuberant show-style song - perhaps a camp answer to Rodgers & Hammerstein - was a cult success in the States, but it found its major pop crossover success in Britain. After scraping the UK Top 75 in 1983, it finally managed to transform itself from a brief shower into a prolonged downpour in early 1984 - *It's raining men,* which had reportedly been originally offered to Barbra Streisand, reached No.2 in Britain. However, the hefty girls were unable to prolong their novelty appeal. The embarrassing follow-up single *Success* dismally failed to live up to its title, and ushered the Girls back into the realms of obscurity. (Bob MacDonald, 5th May 1985).

IT'S RAINING MEN
Tracks: / It's raining men / I'm gonna wash that man right outa my hair.
7" Single: Released Aug '83, on CBS, by CBS Records. Deleted '86. Catalogue no: **A 2924**

IT'S RAINING MEN (OLD GOLD)
Tracks: / It's raining men
12" Single: Released Sep '87, on Old Gold, by Old Gold Records. Catalogue no: **OG 4022**

LAND OF THE BELIEVER
Tracks: / Land of the believer / It's raining men / I'm gonna wash that man right outa my hair.
7" Single: Released May '88, on CBS, by CBS Records. Deleted Jan '89. Catalogue no: **651 372-7**
12" Single: Released May '88, on CBS, by CBS Records. Deleted Jan '89. Catalogue no: **651 372 9**

NO ONE CAN LOVE YOU MORE
Tracks: / No one can love you more.
7" Single: Released Aug '85, on CBS, by CBS Records. Catalogue no: **A 6488**
12" Single: Released Aug '85, on CBS, by CBS Records. Catalogue no: **QTA 6488**

SUCCESS
Tracks: / Success / Hungry for love / Dear santa / Hope / Its raining men / I'm gonna wash that man right outa my hait.
7" Single: Released May '84, on CBS, by CBS Records. Catalogue no: **A 4401**
12" Single: Released May '84, on CBS, by CBS Records. Catalogue no: **TA 4401**

Weather Prophets

ALMOST PRAYED
Tracks: / Almost prayed / Your heartbeat breathes the life into me / Like Frankie Lymon (Extra track on 12" version) / Wide open arms (Extra track on 12" version) / Your heartbeat / Stone in my passway / Down-bound train.
7" Set: Released Jun '86, on Creation, by Creation Records. Catalogue no: **CRE 029D**
7" Single: Released May '86, on Creation, by Creation Records. Catalogue no: **CRE 029**
12" Single: Released May '86, on Creation, by Creation Records. Catalogue no: **CRE 029T**

ALWAYS THE LIGHT
Tracks: / Always the light.
7" Single: Released Aug '88, on Creation, by Creation Records. Catalogue no: **CRE 056**
12" Single: Released Aug '88, on Creation, by Creation Records. Catalogue no: **CRE 056T**

HOLLOW HEART
Tracks: / Hollow heart.
7" Single: Released Apr '88, on Creation, by Creation Records. Catalogue no: **CRE 054**
12" Single: Released Apr '88, on Creation, by Creation Records. Catalogue no: **CRE 054T**

NAKED AS THE DAY YOU WERE BORN
Tracks: / Naked as the day you were born / In my room / Worst friend I ever had, The (Extra track on 12" version only).
7" Single: Released Oct '86, on Creation, by Creation Records. Catalogue no: **CRE 031**
12" Single: Released Oct '86, on Creation, by Creation Records. Catalogue no: **CRE 031T**

SHE COMES FROM THE RAIN
Tracks: / She comes from the rain.
7" Single: Released Mar '87, on Elevation. Deleted Jan '88. Catalogue no: **ACID 1**
12" Single: Released Mar '87, on Elevation. Deleted Jan '88. Catalogue no: **ACID 1T**

WHY DOES THE RAIN
Tracks: / Why does the rain / Midnight mile / Mayflower* (*Extra track on 12") / Annelea* (*Extra track on 12").
7" Single: Released Jun '87, on Elevation. Deleted Jul '88. Catalogue no: **ACID 2**
12" Single: Released Jun '87, on Elevation. Deleted Jul '88. Catalogue no: **ACID 2T**

Weathermen

BANG
Tracks: / Bang bang.
CD 5": Released Jul '89, on Play It Again Sam(Belgium), by Play It Again Sam (Belgium). Catalogue no: **BIAS 127 CD**
7" Single: Released Jul '89, on Play It Again Sam(Belgium), by Play It Again Sam (Belgium). Catalogue no: **BIAS 127**
12" Single: Released Jul '89, on Play It Again Sam(Belgium), by Play It Again Sam (Belgium). Catalogue no: **12BIAS 127**

DEEP DOWN SOUTH
Tracks: / Deep down South / Redneck blues, The.
12" Single: Released Nov '85, on Play It Again Sam(Belgium), by Play It Again Sam (Belgium). Catalogue no: **BIAS 017**

IT'S THE SAME OLD SONG
Tracks: / It's the same old song.
7" Single: Released Jan '71, on B & C, by Trojan Records. Deleted '74. Catalogue no: **CB 139**

LIFE
Tracks: / Life.
7" Single: Released Mar '82, on Pre, by Charisma Records. Catalogue no: **PRE 21**
12" Single: Released Mar '82, on Pre, by Charisma Records. Catalogue no: **PRE 21 12**

OLD FRIEND SAM
Tracks: / Old friend Sam.
12" Single: Released Jun '85, on Play It Again Sam(Belgium), by Play It Again Sam (Belgium). Catalogue no: **BIAS 013**

POISON
Tracks: / Poison.
CD 5": Released 22 Aug '88, on Play It Again Sam(Belgium), by Play It Again Sam (Belgium). Catalogue no: **BIAS 62CD**
7" Single: Released '88, on Play It Again Sam(Belgium), by Play It Again Sam (Belgium). Catalogue no: **BIAS 62**
12" Single: Released Jul '87, on Play It Again Sam(Belgium), by Play It Again Sam (Belgium). Catalogue no: **BIAS 62T**

POISON (REMIX)
Tracks: / Poison (remix).
12" Single: Released '89, on Play It Again Sam(Belgium), by Play It Again Sam (Belgium). Catalogue no: **RBIAS 62**

POISON (TOXIC LIPSTICK REMIX)
Tracks: / Poison (toxic lipstick remix).
12" Single: Released 23 Jul '88, on Play It Again Sam(Belgium), by Play It Again Sam (Belgium). Catalogue no: **RRBIAS 062**

PUNISHMENT PARK
Tracks: / Punishment park.
CD 5": Released Oct '88, on Play It Again Sam(Belgium), by Play It Again Sam (Belgium). Catalogue no: **BIAS 99 CD**
12" Single: Released Oct '88, on Play It Again Sam(Belgium), by Play It Again Sam (Belgium). Catalogue no: **BIAS 99**

TAKE IT OFF!
Tracks: / Take it off!.
12" Single: Released 7 Jul '86, on Play It Again Sam(Belgium), by Play It Again Sam (Belgium). Catalogue no: **BIAS 029**

THIRD COMMUNIQUE
Tracks: / Third communique.
12" Single: Released 7 May '88, on Play It Again Sam(Belgium), by Play It Again Sam (Belgium). Catalogue no: **BIAS 025**

Weaver, Patty

DON'T WANT A HEARTACHE
Tracks: / Don't want a heartache / Part time man.
7" Single: Released Apr '82, on Warner Bros., by WEA Records. Catalogue no: **K 17942**

SHOT IN THE DARK
Tracks: / Shot in the dark / Line of fire.
7" Single: Released Aug '82, on Warner Bros., by WEA Records. Catalogue no: **K 17981**

Webb, John

EXPERIMENT OF LOVE, THE
Tracks: / Experiment of love, The / Cry of the sea.
7" Single: Released Jan '86, on Numa, by Numa Records. Catalogue no: **U 14**
12" Single: Released Jan '86, on Numa, by Numa Records. Catalogue no: **NUM 14**

Webb, Marney

NERVOUS BREAKDOWN
Tracks: / Nervous breakdown / Rebel without a cause.
7" Single: Released Mar '81, on Crash, by Satril Records. Deleted '83. Catalogue no: **POW 5**

STILL SEARCHING
Tracks: / Still searching / Don't say we're through.
7" Single: Released Oct '81, on Creole, by Creole Records. Catalogue no: **CR 20**

Webb, Marti

Biographical details: This British singer stormed to fame in 1980, thanks to composer Andrew Lloyd Webber and lyricist Don Black. She was selected by them to perform *Tell me on a Sunday,* a mini-musical documenting the love life of a young British woman who had taken up residence in the States. This 45-minute collection of catchy melodic songs was unusual for several reasons: it was staged in a television studio rather than on a theatre stage; it was Lloyd Webber's first show since parting company with Tim Rice; it was a vehicle for one singer, with other performers playing only peripheral roles. *Tell me on a Sunday,* screened by the BBC in early 1980, was so well recieved by viewers that it was repeated a mere month later. By the time of the second showing, it had yielded a UK Top 3 single *Take that look off your face.* More importantly, the accompanying album was on its way to platinum status.
Some observers complained that Black & Webber had cynically used BBC television as an extended advertisement for the LP and for Webb, without having to pay for spots on the commercial channel. If they did it to promote the album, it certainly worked - *Tell me on a Sunday* reached No.2 on the British LP chart and logged 23 weeks on the listings. However, if it was done to promote Webb, the goal was not achieved. Despite a strong voice and an engaging stage presence, none of the singer's subsequent releases met with success. When her LP *Won't change places* was launched as a TV special, history failed to repeat itself. Another collation of lush, theatrical middle-of-the-road songs, 1983's *I'm not that kind of girl,* also flopped. (Bob MacDonald, 6th May 1985).

ALWAYS THERE
Tracks: / Always there / Howards' way (Theme from the BBC-TV series).
12" Single: Released Aug '86, on BBC, by BBC Records & Tapes. Deleted 31 Aug '88. Catalogue no: **12 RSL 190**
7" Single: Released Sep '86, on BBC, by BBC Records & Tapes. Deleted 31 Aug '88. Catalogue no: **RESL 190**

BEN
Tracks: / Ben.
7" Single: Released Jun '85, on Starblend, by Starblend Records. Catalogue no: **STAR 6**

DIDN'T MEAN TO FALL IN LOVE
Tracks: / Didn't mean to fall in love.
7" Single: Released Jun '83, on Polydor, by Polydor Ltd. Catalogue no: **POSP 614**

GETTING IT RIGHT
Tracks: / Getting it right / For the touch of your love.
7" Single: Released Jan '82, on Polydor, by Polydor Ltd. Deleted Jan '85. Catalogue no: **POSP 388**

I CAN'T LET GO
Tracks: / I can't let go / Why forget.
7" Single: Released Apr '87, on Rainbow, by Rainbow Records. Catalogue no: **RBR 12**

I COULD BE SO GOOD FOR YOU Theme from Minder
Tracks: / It's still the same dream (Theme from To serve them all my days.).
7" Single: Released Nov '86, on BBC, by BBC Records & Tapes. Deleted Apr '89. Catalogue no: **RESL 209**

I'M NOT THAT KIND OF GIRL (SINGLE)
Tracks: / I'm not that kind of girl / One afternoon.
7" Single: Released Oct '82, on Polydor, by Polydor Ltd. Deleted Oct '85. Catalogue no: **POSP 509**

I'VE BEEN IN LOVE TOO LONG
Tracks: / I've been in love too long / I won't change places.
7" Single: Released Nov '80, on Polydor, by Polydor Ltd. Deleted Nov '83. Catalogue no: **POSP 193**

LAST MAN IN MY LIFE
Tracks: / Last man in my life, The / Come back with that same look in your eyes.
7" Single: Released Mar '82, on Polydor, by Polydor Ltd. Catalogue no: **POSP 425**

READY FOR ROSES NOW
Tracks: / Ready for roses now.
7" Single: Released Dec '85, on Starblend, by Starblend Records. Catalogue no: **STAR 7**

SOMEDAY SOON Theme from Onedin Line
Tracks: / Someday soon / Moonlighting.
7" Single: Released Mar '87, on BBC, by BBC Records & Tapes. Deleted 31 Aug '88. Catalogue no: **RESL 213**

TAKE THAT LOOK OFF YOUR FACE
Tracks: / Take that look off your face / Sheldon Bloom.
7" Single: Released Feb '80, on Polydor, by Polydor Ltd. Deleted '83. Catalogue no: **POSP 100**

TELL ME ON A SUNDAY (SINGLE)
Tracks: / Tell me on a Sunday.
7" Single: Released Mar '80, on Polydor, by Polydor Ltd. Catalogue no: **POSP 111**

UNEXPECTED SONGS
Tracks: / Unexpected songs / Angry and sore.
7" Single: Released Mar '81, on Polydor, by Polydor Ltd. Deleted Mar '84. Catalogue no: **POSP 235**

YOUR EARS SHOULD BE BURNING NOW
Tracks: / Your ears should be burning now / Nothing like you've ever known.
7" Single: Released Sep '80, on Polydor, by Polydor Ltd. Deleted '83. Catalogue no: **POSP 166**

Webb, Roger

GENTLE TOUCH (SINGLE)
Tracks: / Gentle touch, The / Best that you can do.
7" Single: Released Mar '82, on Chandos, by Chandos Records. Catalogue no: **SBR 102**

PARADISE POSTPONED (SINGLE)
Tracks: / Paradise postponed.
7" Single: Released Sep '86, on Columbia, by EMI Records. Catalogue no: **DB 9141**

Webb, Steve

DEAR LOVE
Tracks: / Dear love.
7" Single: Released Aug '85, on Sedition, by Sedition Records. Catalogue no: **EDIT 3304**
12" Single: on Sedition, by Sedition Records. Catalogue no: **EDITL 3304**

IT'S OVER
Tracks: / It's over.
7" Single: Released Jul '87, on Big Pop. Catalogue no: **DTY 1**

Webber, A.J.

CLEVEDON PIER 1
Tracks: / Clevedon Pier 1.
7" Single: Released Feb '80, on Gundog. Catalogue no: **GUNEP 2000**

Webber, Marlene

JUST FOR YOU
Tracks: / For you.
12" Single: Released Nov '86, on Joe Frazer. Catalogue no: **BT 006**

Webcore

CAPTAIN'S TABLE, THE
Tracks: / Captain's table, The.
12" Single: Released May '88, on Jungle, by Jungle Records. Catalogue no: **JUNG 30T**

RUNNING FOR THE PRECEDENT
Tracks: / Running for the precedent.
12" Single: Released Jun '87, on Jungle, by Jungle Records. Catalogue no: **JUNG 34T**

Weber, Joan

LET ME GO LOVER
Tracks: / Let me go lover.
7" Single: Released Feb '55, on Philips, by Phonogram Ltd. Deleted '58. Catalogue no: **PB 389**

Webley, George

I'M GONNA LOVE YOU JUST A LITTLE BIT MORE BABE
Tracks: / I'm gonna love you just a little bit more baby.
7" Single: Released Sep '84, on Simple, Deleted '87. Catalogue no: **SIM 5**
12" Single: Released Sep '84, on Simple, Catalogue no: **12 SIM 5**

TASTY
Tracks: / Tasty / Stepping into the night.
7" Single: Released Feb '84, on Simple, Deleted '87. Catalogue no: **SIM 1**
12" Single: Released Feb '84, on Simple, Deleted '87. Catalogue no: **12 SIM 1**

Webster, E.T.

DREAM LOVER
Tracks: / Dream lover.
12" Single: Released Apr '88, on Twinkle, by Twinkle Records. Catalogue no: **NG 506T**

Webster, Max

BATTLE SCAR
Tracks: / Battle scar / April in Toledo.
7" Single: Released Jan '81, on Mercury, by Phonogram Ltd. Deleted Jan '84. Catalogue no: **MER 59**

NIGHT FLIGHTS
Tracks: / Night flights / Hangover / High class in borrowed shoes.
7" EP: Released Feb '80, on Capitol, by EMI Records. Deleted Feb '83. Catalogue no: **CL 16104**

PARADISE SKIES
Tracks: / Paradise skies.
7" Single: Released May '79, on Capitol, by EMI Records. Deleted '82. Catalogue no: **CL 16079**

Wedding

TOMORROW I SET SAIL
Tracks: / Tomorrow I set sail / Cry.
7" Single: Released Feb '86, on W.A.R., by W.A.R. Records. Catalogue no: **WAR 3005**
12" Single: Released Feb '86, on W.A.R., by W.A.R. Records. Catalogue no: **12 WAR 3005**

Wedding Anniversary

MAN FROM THE HILLS
Tracks: / Man from the hills.
7" Single: Released May '89, on Danceteria, Catalogue no: **7 DAN 018**

Wedding Present

ANYONE CAN MAKE A MISTAKE
Tracks: / Anyone can make a mistake.
Cassingle: Released Sep '87, on Reception, by Reception Records. Catalogue no: **REC 006C**
7" Single: Released Sep '87, on Reception, by Reception Records. Catalogue no: **REC 006**
12" Single: Released Sep '87, on Reception, by Reception Records. Catalogue no: **REC 006/12**

DON'T TRY AND STOP ME
Tracks: / Don't try and stop me ma.
12" Single: Released 10 Mar '86, on Reception, by Reception Records. Catalogue no: **REC 002/12**

EVENING SHOW EP: WEDDING PRESENT
CD 5": Released Jan '89, on Night Tracks, by Pinnacle Records. Catalogue no: **SFNT CD 016**
12" Single: Released Dec '88, on Night Tracks, by Pinnacle Records. Catalogue no: **SFNT 016**

GO OUT AND GET 'EM BOY
Tracks: / Go out and get 'em boy.
7" Single: Released Sep '85, on City Slang, Catalogue no: **CSL 001**

KENNEDY
Tracks: / Kennedy / It's not unusual (On 12" only) / Unfaithful / One day (On 12" only.).
CD 5": Released Sep '89, on RCA, by BMG Records (UK). Catalogue no: **PD 43118**
7" Single: Released Sep '89, on RCA, by BMG Records (UK). Catalogue no: **PB 43117**
12" Single: Released Sep '89, on RCA, by BMG Records (UK). Catalogue no: **PT 43117**

MY FAVOURITE DRESS
Tracks: / Every mother's son / Never said.
7" Single: Released Feb '87, on Reception, by Reception Records. Catalogue no: **REC 005**
12" Single: Released Feb '87, on Reception, by Reception Records. Catalogue no: **REC 005/12**

NOBODY'S TWISTING YOUR ARM
Tracks: / Nobody's twisting your arm.
CD 5": Released '88, on Reception, by Reception Records. Catalogue no: **REC 009CD**
7" Single: Released 27 Feb '88, on Reception, by Reception Records. Catalogue no: **REC 009**
12" Single: Released 27 Feb '88, on Reception, by Reception Records. Catalogue no: **REC 009 12**

ONCE MORE
Tracks: / Once more.
12" Single: Released Jan '86, on Reception, by Reception Records. Catalogue no: **REC 002**

PEEL SESSIONS:WEDDING PRESENT 26.2.86
CD 5": Released Aug '88, on Strange Fruit, by Strange Fruit Records. Catalogue no: **SFPSCD 009**
Cassingle: Released 13 Jun '87, on Strange Fruit, by Strange Fruit Records. Catalogue no: **SFPSC 009**
12" Single: Released Oct '86, on Strange Fruit, by Strange Fruit Records. Catalogue no: **SFPS 009**

PORQUOI ES-TU DEVENUE SI RAISONNABLE?
Tracks: / Porquoi es-tu devenue si raisonnable.
CD 5": Released Feb '89, on Midnight Music, by Midnight Music Records. Catalogue no: **DONG 39 CD**
12" Single: Released Feb '89, on Midnight Music, by Midnight Music Records. Catalogue no: **DONG 39**

THIS BOY CAN WAIT
Tracks: / This boy can wait / You should always keep in touch with your friends.
7" Single: Released Jul '86, on Reception, by Reception Records. Catalogue no: **REC 003**
12" Single: Released Jul '86, on Reception, by Reception Records. Catalogue no: **REC 003/12**

WHY ARE YOU BEING SO REASONABLE NOW
Tracks: / Why are you being so reasonable now.
CD 5": Released Sep '88, on Reception, by Reception Records. Catalogue no: **REC 011 CD**
7" Single: Released Sep '88, on Reception, by Reception Records. Catalogue no: **REC 011**
12" Single: Released Sep '88, on Reception, by Reception Records. Catalogue no: **REC 011-12**

Wedlock, Fred

Biographical details: This British folk singer achieved a one-off smash single in 1981. *The oldest swinger in town*, a catchy novelty song about the trials and tribulations of remaining young at heart, reached No.6 on the UK national charts. For the amiable and ever amusing Wedlock, this burst of fame was merely a brief interruption to endless years on Britain's folk club circuit. In common with Ralph McTell, Renaissance and Fiddler's Dream, he could muster only one big pop hit - it seems that a lot of old folkies find the sudden spotlight hard to cope with. (Bob MacDonald, 6th May 1985).

OLDEST SWINGER IN TOWN (OLD GOLD)
Tracks: / Oldest swinger in town, The / Do the hucklebuck.
7" Single: Released Oct '88, on Old Gold, by Old Gold Records. Catalogue no: **OG 9807**

OLDEST SWINGER IN TOWN (SINGLE)
Tracks: / Oldest swinger in town / Jogger song.
7" Single: Released Jan '81, on Rocket, by Rocket Records. Deleted '83. Catalogue no: **XPRES 46**

Wednesday Afternoon

OUT OF MY MIND
Tracks: / Out of my mind.
7" Single: Released Nov '82, on Swagbag, Catalogue no: **PWF 1**

Wednesday, Jamie

VOTE FOR LOVE
Tracks: / Vote for love.
12" Single: Released Nov '85, on Pink Label, by Pink Label Records. Catalogue no: **PINKY 6**

WE THREE KINGS OF ORIENT AREN'T
Tracks: / We three kings of Orient aren't.
Note: 3 track
12" Single: Released Aug '86, on Pink Label, by Pink Label Records. Catalogue no: **PINKY 10**

Wednesday Page

WEDNESDAY PAGE
Tracks: / Wednesday Page.
7" EP: Released Aug '86, on Golden Pathway, Catalogue no: **GPV 008**

Wee Cherubs

DREAMING
Tracks: / Dreaming.
7" Single: Released Sep '84, on Bogaten, Catalogue no: **BOGATEN 2**

Wee Papa Girl Rappers

BLOW THE HOUSE DOWN
Tracks: / Blow the house down / Ram showcase / Wee rule (Only on CD single.).
CD 5": Released Mar '89, on Jive, by Zomba Records. Catalogue no: **JIVECD 197**
7" Single: Released Mar '89, on Jive, by Zomba Records. Catalogue no: **JIVE 197**
12" Single: Released Apr '89, on Jive, by Zomba Records. Catalogue no: **JIVER 197**
12" Single: Released 20 Mar '89, on Jive, by Zomba Records. Catalogue no: **JIVEX 197**
12" Single: Released Mar '89, on Jive, by Zomba Records. Catalogue no: **JIVET 197**

FAITH
Tracks: / Faith / Bustin' loose.
7" Single: Released Mar '88, on Jive, by Zomba Records. Catalogue no: **JIVE 164**
12" Single: Released Mar '88, on Jive, by Zomba Records. Catalogue no: **JIVET 164**

HEAT IT UP
Tracks: / Heat it up / Flaunt it.
7" Single: Released May '88, on Jive, by Zomba Records. Catalogue no: **JIVE 174**
12" Single: Released May '88, on Jive, by Zomba Records. Catalogue no: **JIVET 174**

ROCK THE CLOCK
Tracks: / Rock the clock.
7" Single: Released Jul '87, on Jive, by Zomba Records. Catalogue no: **JIVE 145**
12" Single: Released Jan '87, on Jive, by Zomba Records. Catalogue no: **CIVET 145**

SOUL MATE
Tracks: / Soul mate / We know it.
CD 5": Released Dec '88, on Jive, by Zomba Records. Catalogue no: **JIVECD 193**
7" Single: Released Dec '88, on Jive, by Zomba Records. Catalogue no: **JIVEX 193**
7" Single: Released Dec '88, on Jive, by Zomba Records. Catalogue no: **JIVE 193**
7" Single: Released Dec '88, on Jive, by Zomba Records. Catalogue no: **JIVER 193**
12" Single: Released Dec '88, on Jive, by Zomba Records. Catalogue no: **JIVET 193**

WEE RULE
Tracks: / Wee rule.
CD 5": Released Oct '88, on Jive, by Zomba Records. Catalogue no: **JIVECD 185**
7" Single: Released 16 Sep '88, on Jive, by Zomba Records. Catalogue no: **JIVE 185**
12" Single: Released Oct '88, on Jive, by Zomba Records. Catalogue no: **JIVES 185**
12" Single: Released 16 Sep '88, on Jive, by Zomba Records. Catalogue no: **JIVET 185**
12" Single: Released Oct '88, on Jive, by Zomba Records. Catalogue no: **JIVER 185**

Weedon, Bert

Biographical details: Until the rock era, Bert Weedon -- born in London in 1920 -- was the foremost guitarist in British popular music. He played with Django Reinhardt, Ted Heath and many others and his 10 Top Fifty hits between '59 and '61 began with *Guitar Boogie Shuffle*. *Mr Guitar*, in 1961, was dedicated to him by the Shadows. His teach-yourself books were translated into many languages and sold more than a million copies. (Donald Clarke, March 1988.)
This British guitarist worked as a session player during the mid-Fifties, and then came to fame in his own right in 1959 with *Guitar boogie shuffle*. This was a hastily recorded cover version of the Virtues' American Top 5 hit, and it too Weedon to No.10 on the UK chart. He never got that high again, but chalked up a string of seven minor hit singles between November '59 and May '61. These included his rendition of *Apache*, which coincided with the Shadows' version - they surged to No.1, while Weedon had to be content with a No.24 placing. Although his version was reportedly recorded first, it was 'not very good' (as the Shads' Hank later described it) and provided no real competition. Indeed, as the Shadows went from strength to strength during the early Sixties, they effectively killed Weedon's solo chart career. Few people were interested in listening to a highly proficient but ageing and unimaginative player, when they could enjoy the vibrancy and teen ido status of the top guitar group in Britain. Weedon's only noteworthy record of the period was *Sorry Robbie*, which peaked at No.28 but logged 11 weeks on the British Top 50. Weedon quickly returned to session playing, but periodically issued his own albums. In late 1976, he suddenly shot into the higher echelons of the UK LP list with a TV-advertised collection of tracks billed as *22 golden guitar greats*. The albums's hefty marketing campaign propelled it to No.1. By this time, he had become something of a joke figure - he was always the butt of musicians' and disc jockey' gags, in the same way that showbusiness stars always ridiculed Des O'Connor. In the Eighties, Weedon was still plucking away and he remained an amiable institution of the UK music business. (Bob MacDonald, 11th May 1985).

APACHE
Tracks: / Apache.
7" Single: Released Jul '60, on Top Rank (1), Deleted '63. Catalogue no: **JAR 415**

BIG BEAT BOOGIE
Tracks: / Big beat boogie.
7" Single: Released Mar '60, on Top Rank (1), Deleted '63. Catalogue no: **JAR 300**

GALLIPOLI
Tracks: / Gallipoli / Blue echoes.
7" Single: Released Jan '82, on Polydor, by Polydor Ltd. Deleted Jan '85. Catalogue no: **POSP 405**

GINCHY
Tracks: / Ginchy.
7" Single: Released Feb '61, on Top Rank (1), Deleted '64. Catalogue no: **JAR 537**

GUITAR BOOGIE SHUFFLE
Tracks: / Guitar boogie shuffle.
7" Single: Released May '59, on Top Rank (1), Deleted '62. Catalogue no: **JAR 117**

MR GUITAR (SINGLE)
Tracks: / Mr. Guitar.
7" Single: Released May '61, on Top Rank (1), Deleted '64. Catalogue no: **JAR 559**

NASHVILLE BOOGIE
Tracks: / Nashville boogie.
7" Single: Released Nov '59, on Top Rank (1), Deleted '62. Catalogue no: **JAR 221**

PLAISIR D'AMOUR
Tracks: / Plaisir d'amour / Kisses in spring.
7" Single: Released Jul '80, on Celebrity, Deleted Jul '83. Catalogue no: **ACS 2**

SORRY ROBBIE
Tracks: / Sorry Robbie.
7" Single: Released Oct '60, on Top Rank (1), Deleted '63. Catalogue no: **JAR 517**

TWELFTH STREET RAG
Tracks: / Twelfth St. rag.
7" Single: Released Jun '60, on Top Rank (1), Deleted '63. Catalogue no: **JAR 360**

Weeds

CHINA DOLL
Tracks: / China doll.
7" Single: Released Aug '86, on In Tape, by In Tape Records. Catalogue no: **IT 034**

Weekend

DRUMBEAT FOR BABY
Tracks: / Drumbeat for baby / Sleepy faries / Weekend off.
7" Single: Released Oct '82, on Rough Trade, by Rough Trade Records. Catalogue no: **RT 116**
12" Single: Released Oct '82, on Rough Trade, by Rough Trade Records. Catalogue no: **RT 116T**

MIDNIGHT SLOWS
Tracks: / Midnight slows / Past meets present.
7" Single: Released Jun '82, on Rough Trade, by Rough Trade Records. Catalogue no: **RT 107**

VIEW FROM HER ROOM
Tracks: / View from her room / Leaves of spring.
7" Single: Released May '82, on Rough Trade, by Rough Trade Records. Catalogue no: **RT 097**
12" Single: Released May '82, on Rough Trade, by Rough Trade Records. Catalogue no: **RT 097T**

Weekend (2)

CHRISTMAS PARTY EP - CHRISTMAS MEDLEY
7" Single: Released Nov '85, on Jive, by Zomba Records. Deleted Jul '87. Catalogue no: **XY 1**
12" Single: Released Nov '85, on Jive, by Zomba Records. Deleted Jul '87. Catalogue no: **XY 12**

Weeks, Alan & The

WHAT MORE CAN I SAY
Tracks: / What more can I say.
12" Single: Released Dec '82, on Sanity, Catalogue no: **STY 001**

Weeks & Co

ROCK CANDY
Tracks: / Rock candy / Knock knock.
7" Single: Released Jun '83, on Salsoul,

Catalogue no: **SAL 103**
12" Single: Released Jun '83, on Salsoul, Catalogue no: **SALT 103**

Weeping Messerschmitts

NOTHING YET
Tracks: / Nothing yet.
Note: 3 tracks
12" Single: Released Oct '86, on Upright, by Upright Records. Catalogue no: **UPT 17**

Weevil, Bo

WOOLY BULLY
Tracks: / Wooly bully / Cos it feels good.
7" Single: Released May '82, on Fore, Catalogue no: **FORE 2**

Weir, Frank

CARIBBEAN HONEYMOON
Tracks: / Caribbean honeymoon.
7" Single: Released Sep '60, on Oriole, Deleted '63. Catalogue no: **CB 1559**

Weird Strings

MILLIONAIRE
Tracks: / Millionaire / Criminal cage.
7" Single: Released May '80, on Ace, by Ace Records. Deleted Jun '88. Catalogue no: **ACE 009**

OSCAR AUTOMOBILE
Tracks: / Oscar automobile / Ancient and square.
7" Single: Released Feb '80, on Velvet Moon, Deleted '81. Catalogue no: **VM 1**

Weissberg, Eric

Biographical details: This American multi instrumentalist was an important session musician during the Sixties and Seventies. Amongst his most successful credits were records by Judy Collins, Jim Croce, Bob Dylan, Billy Joel and Melanie; he also played with a host of lesser talents, and released occasional discs in his own right. His range of instruments included banjo, bass guitar, harp, kazoo, mandolin, and violin. It was as a banjo player that Weissberg suddenly stepped into the limelight in 1973. In collaboration with his long-time musical friend Steve Mandell, he recorded an old tune called *Duelling banjos* for inclusion in John Boorman and James Dickey's movie *Deliverance*. The instrumental single, arranged and produced by Weissberg, reached No.2 on the US charts in '73, and climbed to No.17 in the UK. It was a delightfully unusual hit single; but its success story was complicated by a copyright dispute. The label of Weissberg & Mandell's disc claimed that the tune was traditional, but guitarist Arthur Smith (also composer of the 1959 Virtues/Bert Weedon hit *Guitar boogie shuffle*) contested that he had written and recorded it in 1955 under the title *Feuding banjos*. Smith ended up as the winner. After the success of *Duelling banjos*, Weissberg & Mandell formed a short-lived group called Deliverance. Weissberg then resumed his session career. His musical base was always New York. (Bob MacDonald, 11th May 1985).

DUELLING BANJOS
Tracks: / Duelling banjos.
7" Single: Released Nov '79, on Automatic, by Automatic Records. Deleted Jan '88. Catalogue no: **K 16223**

DUELLING BANJOS (OLD GOLD)
Tracks: / Delling banjos / Deliverence, Theme from / Reuben's train.
7" Single: Released Mar '86, on Old Gold, by Old Gold Records. Catalogue no: **OG 9574**

Welch, Bob

TWO TO DO
Tracks: / Two to do / Imaginary fool.
7" Single: Released Feb '82, on RCA, by BMG Records (UK). Catalogue no: **RCA 189**

Welch, Ed

'BLOCKBUSTERS', THEME FROM
Tracks: / Blockbusters, Theme from / New faces, Theme from.
7" Single: Released 15 Aug '88, on Rainbow, by Rainbow Records. Catalogue no: **GRASS 2**

GUS HONEYBUN SONG, THE
Tracks: / Gus Honeybun song, The.
7" Pic: Released 30 May '87, on TSW, Catalogue no: **GUS 1**
7" Single: Released 30 May '87, on TSW, Catalogue no: **7 GUS 1**

IF YOU WOULD TAKE THE TIME (see also Diane Carter)
Tracks: / If you would take the time / Make a friend of you.
7" Single: Released Sep '83, on T.Y.C.O.S., by T.Y.C.O.S Records. Catalogue no: **AM 232**

Welch, Elisabeth

STORMY WEATHER
Tracks: / Stormy weather / You're blase.
7" Single: Released 20 Jun '80, on Industrial, by Industrial Records. Deleted '83. Catalogue no: **IRO 012**

Welch, Mary

I COULD HAVE DANCED ALL NIGHT
Tracks: / I could have danced all night / When it was good.
7" Single: Released Jan '80, on 20th Century, by 20th Century Records. Deleted '85. Catalogue no: **TC 2412**

Welch, Peter

LOU LOU BANANA KING
Tracks: / Lou lou banana king / Hitparade marmalade.
7" Single: Released Nov '80, on Bellaphon, Deleted Nov '83. Catalogue no: **BPS 004**

Well Loaded

SUN DON'T SHINE
Tracks: / Sun don't shine.
7" Single: Released Jun '89, on Love, Catalogue no: **LOVE 2**

Well Pack Band

STRIKE
Tracks: / Strike.
12" Single: Released Jul '89, on Studio 16, Catalogue no: **WE 11**

Well Red

GET LUCKY
Tracks: / Get lucky / Get lucky (master mix) / Get lucky (dub).
7" Single: Released Jul '87, on Virgin, by Virgin Records. Deleted May '88. Catalogue no: **VS 977**
12" Single: Released Jul '87, on Virgin, by Virgin Records. Catalogue no: **VS 977-12**

HARD
Tracks: / Hard (Extended version on 12") / Mixed up (Glutus maximus alignment) / Hard (dub style) (12" only).
7" Single: Released 30 Aug '88, on Virgin, by Virgin Records. Catalogue no: **VS 1112**
12" Single: Released 30 Aug '88, on Virgin, by Virgin Records. Catalogue no: **VST 1112**

HONEY
Tracks: / Honey / Saturday.
Special: Released Apr '87, on Virgin, by Virgin Records. Deleted May '88. Catalogue no: **VSD 943-12**
12" Single: Released '87, on Virgin, by Virgin Records. Catalogue no: **VS 943-12**

LIMIT OF YOUR LOVING
Tracks: / Limit of your loving.
7" Single: Released May '85, on Paladin, Catalogue no: **PALS 101**
12" Single: Released May '85, on Paladin, Catalogue no: **PALS 101 12**

LOVE GONE CRAZY
Tracks: / Love gone crazy.
12" Single: Released Nov '85, on Virgin, by Virgin Records. Deleted '89. Catalogue no: **VS 826-12**
7" Single: Released Nov '85, on Virgin, by Virgin Records. Deleted '89. Catalogue no: **VS 826**

M.F.S.B.
Tracks: / M.F.S.B. (7" only) / System (first cut) (NOT on VSR 1079) / M.F.S.B. (in full effect) (On VST 1079 only) / M.F.S.B. (resolve mix) (On VSR 1079 only) / M.F.S.B. (dub scratch) (On VSR 1079 only).
12" Single: Released Apr '88, on Virgin, by Virgin Records. Catalogue no: **VST 1079**
7" Single: Released Apr '88, on Virgin, by Virgin Records. Catalogue no: **VS 1079**
12" Single: Released Apr '88, on Virgin, by Virgin Records. Catalogue no: **VSR 1079**

ROCKETSHIP OF LOVE
Tracks: / Rocketship of love / My way.
7" Single: Released 21 Nov '88, on Virgin, by Virgin Records. Catalogue no: **VS 1137**
12" Single: Released 21 Nov '88, on Virgin, by Virgin Records. Catalogue no: **VST 1137**

YES WE CAN
Tracks: / Don't rush me.
7" Single: Released Jan '87, on Virgin, by Virgin Records. Deleted May '88. Catalogue no: **VS 925**
12" Single: Released Jan '87, on Virgin, by Virgin Records. Deleted May '88. Catalogue no: **VS 925-12**

Well Well Well

REVOLUTION
Tracks: / Revolution / I will / Big river* / Won't get fooled again / Boney Maroney (Live) / Dancing in the street* / Mary Anne with the shaky hand.
Note: *Mary Anne with the shaky hand* only available on 12" picture bag.
7" Single: Released Jun '88, on Arista, by BMG Records (UK). Catalogue no: **111561**
CD 5": Released 23 Jul '88, on Arista, by BMG Records (UK). Catalogue no: **661561**
12" Single: Released Jun '88, on Arista, by BMG Records (UK). Catalogue no: **6111561**

Welles, Orson

I KNOW WHAT IT IS TO BE YOUNG
Tracks: / I know what it is to be young.
12" Single: Released May '89, on GNP Crescendo (USA), by GNP Crescendo Records (USA). Catalogue no: **GNT 1206**
7" Single: Released Jan '85, on Splash, by Splash Records. Catalogue no: **SP 29**

Wellington, Roland

WHEN JAH COMES
Tracks: / When Jah comes / Come a me.
12" Single: Released Jun '82, on Carib Jems, Catalogue no: **CGDD 23**

Wells, Brandi

Biographical details: This American soul singer enjoyed just one week of glory on the UK charts - her single *Watch out* reached No.74 in February 1982. Her album of the same name, a pleasant but run-of-the-mill selection of dance, funk and soul material, created brief interest on the disco scene, but Wells' career did not really take off on either side of the Atlantic. (Bob MacDonald, 11th May 1985).

FANTASY
Tracks: / Fantasy / Golden moment / I love you.
7" Single: Released Jul '82, on W.M.O.T.(USA), by Virgin Records. Deleted '89. Catalogue no: **VS 515**
12" Single: Released Jul '82, on W.M.O.T.(USA), by Virgin Records. Deleted '89. Catalogue no: **VS 515-12**

WATCH OUT
Tracks: / Watch out.
7" Single: Released Jan '82, on Virgin, by Virgin Records. Deleted '89. Catalogue no: **VS 479**
12" Single: Released Jan '82, on Virgin, by Virgin Records. Deleted '89. Catalogue no: **VS 479-12**

WHITE BOY DANCE
Tracks: / White boy dance.
7" Single: Released Apr '82, on Virgin, by Virgin Records. Deleted '89. Catalogue no: **VS 492**
12" Single: Released Apr '82, on Virgin, by Virgin Records. Deleted '89. Catalogue no: **VS 492-12**

Wells, H.G. (Singer)

WALKIN'
Tracks: / Walkin' / Walkin' in the 50's / Walkin' (long version) (On 12" only.) / Walkin' (On 12" only.).
12" Single: Released Jan '89, on Ariola, by BMG Records (UK). Catalogue no: **611 778**
7" Single: Released Jan '89, on Ariola, by BMG Records (UK). Catalogue no: **111 778**

Wells, Houston

ONLY THE HEARTACHES
Tracks: / Only the heartaches.
7" Single: Released Aug '63, on Parlophone, by EMI Records. Deleted '66. Catalogue no: **R 5031**

Wells, James & Susan

LOVE THE CURE FOR ME
Tracks: / Love the cure for me.
7" Single: Released Dec '86, on Nitemare, Catalogue no: **MARES 6**
12" Single: Released Dec '86, on Nightmare, by Nightmare Records. Catalogue no: **MARE 6**

MIRROR IMAGE
Tracks: / Mirror image.
7" Single: Released Jun '85, on Fanfare, by Captain Billy's Music. Catalogue no: **FAN 2901**
12" Single: Released Jun '85, on Fanfare, by Captain Billy's Music. Catalogue no: **FAN 122901**

RSVP
Tracks: / RSVP.
12" Single: Released Feb '85, on Fanfare, by Captain Billy's Music. Catalogue no: **12 FAN 2900**
7" Single: Released Feb '85, on Fanfare, by Captain Billy's Music. Catalogue no: **FAN 2900**

Wells, Joy

TWO LOVERS
Tracks: / Two lovers.
12" Single: Released Oct '88, on Sky Juice, Catalogue no: **SJ 0020**

Wells, Mary

Biographical details: One of the first Motown stars -- and still many people's favourite -- Mary Wells was born in Detroit in 1943. In Motown's early days the label held open auditions. Mary Wells walked in hoping to sell a song and Berry Gordy bought both song and singer -- at a time when Smokey Robinson was virtually the only artist under contract. *Bye Bye Baby* went into the Top Fifty and was the first of 11 Hot Hundred entries for Wells between '61 and '64, including Top Tenners *The One Who Really Loves You, You Beat Me To The Punch* and *Two Lovers*, and culminating with the classic No 1, *My Guy*, all written for her by Robinson. *My Guy* was the first Motown record to reach No 1 in the UK. It was admired by the Beatles, with whom Wells toured. Lured by the empty promise of a film contract she switched to 20th Century Fox -- able to leave Motown because she'd been under-age when she signed there -- and had five hits on that label. (Donald Clarke, March 1988.)
This American singer, born in Detroit in 1943, was an important artist in the early history of Tamla Motown. She was the legendary company's first successful solo singer, the first vehicle for ace songwriter/producer Smokey Robinson (outside of his group, The Miracles and, to her eternal discredit, the first Motown star to leave the organisation. In addtion to her own vocal talent, Wells had the advantage of being born and brought up in the right place at the right time. Automobile-oriented Detroit (the motor town - i.e. Motown) was the birthplace and base of Tamla, and the singer was entering her adulthood just as the company was starting to grow. Having started singing at the age of 10, and having performed in local talent shows and clubs during her teens, Wells simply entered the Motown offices one day and offered them an unsolicited song. A successful vocal audition followed, and her song *Bye bye baby* climbed to the middle regions of the US Hot 100 in 1961. Motown decided that they like Wells' singing more than her songwriting, and she was taken under the wing of Smokey Robinson. He quickly gave her a trio of smash hits, all of which reached the American pop Top 10 beween spring '62 and early '63: *The one who really loves you, You beat me to the punch* and *Two lovers*. These were a very commercial blend of rhythm-and-blues and pop. After a year of smaller successes, Wells' career reached its pinnacle in 1964 with *My guy* - this perfect uptempo pop single reached the US No.1 slot, and also gave the singer her only British biggie, reaching No.5 in the UK. Its success prompted Robinson to compose an 'answer' song, *My girl*, it matched its predecessor by becoming an American No.1 single in 1965, this time for the Temptations. Wells enjoyed a double A sided hit single in duet with Marvin Gaye. By the time the Temps took their turn at the top, however, the Wells/Robinson alliance was over. She was tempted away (no pun intended) by the 20th Century company, who gave her a luctative deal. But without Smokey, and without the unique Motown 'family' atmosphere she was totally lost - the move proved to be a disaster, as shown by the fact that the US No.34 placing of 1965's *Use your head* was Wells' most successful post-Tamla release. She slipped into the land of obscurity and remained there forever, despite revival attempts with a variety of record labels. As a reminder of former glories, *My guy* became a UK hit all over agin in 1972, reaching No.14. Wells' most dire comeback bid occurred in 1984. Working with Wayne Henderson whe re-recorded her Motown hits, and issued an LP or remakes entitled *The old, the new, and the best of Mary Wells*. A slowed down version of *My guy* was released as a single, but met with as much apathy as the album. She was not much luckier in the marital stakes - by 1984, her marriage to songwriter/artist Cecil Womack was also a thing of the distant past. (Bob MacDonald, 11th May 1985)..

DON'T BURN YOUR BRIDGES
Tracks: / Don't burn your bridges / Don't burn your bridges (inst).
7" Single: Released May '87, on Nightmare, by Nightmare Records. Catalogue no: **MARES 33**
12" Single: Released May '87, on Nightmare, by Nightmare Records. Catalogue no: **MARE 33**

MY GUY
Tracks: / My guy.
7" Single: Released Mar '83, on Motown, by BMG Records (UK). Catalogue no: **TMG 1100**
7" Single: Released Jul '72, on Tamla Motown, by Motown Records (UK). Deleted '75. Catalogue no: **TMG 820**
7" Single: Released Feb '84, on Allegience, Catalogue no: **ALES 1**
7" Single: Released May '64, on Stateside, by EMI Records. Deleted '67. Catalogue no: **SS 288**
12" Single: Released Feb '84, on Allegience, Catalogue no: **ALES 121**

MY HANDS ARE TIED
Tracks: / My hands are tied / My hands are tied (dub mix).
7" Single: Released May '87, on Nightmare, by Nightmare Records. Catalogue no: **MARES 18**

12" Single: Released May '87, on Nightmare, by Nightmare Records. Catalogue no: **MARE 18**

YOU BEAT ME TO THE PUNCH
Tracks: / You beat me to the punch.
7" Single: Released Jun '84, on Allegience, Catalogue no: **ALES 5**

Wells, Phil

CHRISTMAS BELLS
Tracks: / Christmas bells / Desert star.
7" Single: Released Nov '81, on Solid Gold (1), by Creole Records. Deleted '86. Catalogue no: **SGR 112**

SHANA THE STAR DANCER
Tracks: / Shana the star dancer.
7" Single: Released Jan '82, on Solid Gold (1), by Creole Records. Deleted '86. Catalogue no: **SGR 117**

Wells, Susan

NIGHTMARE
Tracks: / Nightmare.
12" Single: Released Feb '87, on Nightmare Gold, Catalogue no: **NGR 7**

Wells, Terri

Biographical details: This American singer began her career as a member of City Limits, a group who signed with Philadelphia International Records in 1973. The group flopped, but Wells remained with the company for several years and worked with some of Philly's most accomplished musicians. She began to make waves as a solo artist in 1983, when her well-crafter soul single *You make it heaven* created ripples of approval in specialist soul shops. Despite a lack of US interest, Wells achieved a one-off Top 20 single in Britain in 1984 with *I'll be around.* This was a remake of the Detroit Spinners' 1972 classic, which had been a No.3 smash in the States but had never charted in Britain - this might explain why Wells' inferior but highly danceable rendition reached No.17 on the UK charts, but failed to take off in the US. The most intriguing aspect of her *I'll be around* success story, was the fact that the singer was simultaneously holding down a job as an underwriter with a firm of mortgage brokers. When the BBC invited her to the UK for a vital appearance on 'Top of the Pops', Wells took a day's sick leave and made a lightning 24-hour visit. Her employers suspected nothing. Wells' album *Just like dreamin'* failed to yield any follow-up hit singles, and the British public soon began to forget about her. It looked as if that day job might still be necessary, after all. (Bob MacDonald, 11th May 1985).

I'LL BE AROUND
Tracks: / I'll be around / You make it heaven.
7" Single: Released May '84, on Philly World (USA), by Philly World (USA). Deleted '87. Catalogue no: **LON 48**

I'LL BE AROUND (OLD GOLD)
Tracks: / I'll be around / You make it heaven.
12" Single: Released Apr '88, on Old Gold, by Old Gold Records. Catalogue no: **OG 4056**

YOU MAKE IT HEAVEN
Tracks: / You make it heaven.
12" Single: Released Jun '83, on Philly World (USA), by Philly World (USA). Catalogue no: **PWSL 111**
7" Single: Released Jun '83, on Philly World (USA), by Philly World (USA). Catalogue no: **PWS 111**

Wells, Tony

DANNY BOY
Tracks: / Danny boy / Stay awhile.
7" Single: Released Dec '81, on Artesian, by Artesian Records. Catalogue no: **ARC 313**

HOLY CITY, THE
Tracks: / Holy City, The / It's only a dream.
7" Single: Released Dec '85, on Play, by Play Records. Catalogue no: **PLAY 205**

ONLY YOU
Tracks: / Only you.
7" Single: Released Aug '83, on Artesian, by Artesian Records. Catalogue no: **ARC 316**

Welsh, Alex

Biographical details: Trumpeter Welsh ran one of the best British trad/mainstream jazz bands, an outfit much admired by visiting American musicians -- the great tenor sax star Ben Webster told me he knew of no better group of backing musicians. Welsh enjoyed one minor UK chart single in August '61 when *Tansy* reached No 45 during the middle of the trad boom. (Peter Cooper, 1988.)
This British trumpeteer, one of the jazz market's national institutions, enjoyed one minor UK chart single in August 1961. *Tansy* reached No.45, and occurred during the middle of the trad jazz boom. That era helped to bring Welsh's band to greater prominence in concert halls and clubs and, after its demise, ensured that he was never out of work. (Bob MacDonald, 12th May 1985).

TANSY
Tracks: / Tansy.
7" Single: Released Aug '61, on Columbia, by EMI Records. Deleted '64. Catalogue no: **DB 4686**

Welsh Guards Band

PRINCESS OF WALES
Tracks: / Princess of Wales / God bless the Prince of Wales.
7" Single: Released Jun '81, on ASV (Academy Sound & Vision), by Academy Sound & Vision Records. Deleted '85. Catalogue no: **ASV 103**

Weltons

HOW LONG
Tracks: / How long / My little one.
7" Single: Released Apr '82, on Carrere America (USA), by PolyGram Rec.Inc.(USA). Catalogue no: **CAR 233**

Wendy

OVER YOU
Tracks: / Over you.
12" Single: Released May '88, on Chartflow UK, Catalogue no: **CHF 1201**

Wendy House

STOREYS EP BELLE OF THE BALL
Tracks: / Belle of the ball / Charmaine / See no reason / Today.
7" Single: Released Jan '86, on Wendy House, Deleted '87. Catalogue no: **WH 001**

Wendy & Lemmy

STAND BY YOUR MAN
Tracks: / Stand by your man.
7" Single: Released Sep '82, on Bronze, by Bronze Records. Catalogue no: **BRO 151**

Wendy & Lisa

ARE YOU MY BABY
Tracks: / Are you my baby / Happy birthday / Honeymoon express (Available on 12" format only.).
CD 3": Released Dec '88, on Virgin, by Virgin Records. Catalogue no: **VSCD 1156**
7" Single: Released Dec '88, on Virgin, by Virgin Records. Catalogue no: **VS 1156**
12" Single: Released Dec '88, on Virgin, by Virgin Records. Catalogue no: **VST 1156**

HONEYMOON EXPRESS
Tracks: / Honeymoon express (7" only) / Chance to grow / Honeymoon express (12" version).
7" Single: on Virgin, by Virgin Records. Catalogue no: **VS 1052**
12" Single: on Virgin, by Virgin Records. Catalogue no: **VST 1052**

LOLLY LOLLY
Tracks: / Lolly lolly / Hip hop love / Lolly lolly (version) (12" only).
7" Single: Released Feb '89, on Virgin, by Virgin Records. Catalogue no: **VS 1175**
CD 3": Released Feb '89, on Virgin, by Virgin Records. Catalogue no: **VSCD 1175**
12" Single: Released Feb '89, on Virgin, by Virgin Records. Catalogue no: **VSTP 1175**
12" Single: Released Feb '89, on Virgin, by Virgin Records. Catalogue no: **VST 1175**

SATISFACTION
Tracks: / Satisfaction / Stay.
CD 3": Released 26 Jun '89, on Virgin, by Virgin Records. Catalogue no: **VSCD 1194**
7" Single: Released 19 Jun '89, on Virgin, by Virgin Records. Catalogue no: **VS 1194**
12" Single: Released 26 Jun '89, on Virgin, by Virgin Records. Catalogue no: **VSTX1194**
12" Single: Released 19 Jun '89, on Virgin, by Virgin Records. Catalogue no: **VST 1194**

SIDESHOW
Tracks: / Sideshow (Extended version on CD & 12") / Chance to grow / Waterfall (CD only).
12" Single: Released Jan '88, on Virgin, by Virgin Records. Catalogue no: **VST 1012**
CD 5": Released Apr '88, on Virgin, by Virgin Records. Catalogue no: **CDEP 16**
7" Single: Released Jan '88, on Virgin, by Virgin Records. Catalogue no: **VS 1012**

WATERFALL
Tracks: / Waterfall / Life, The / To trip is to fall (Not on 7").
12" Single: Released Aug '87, on Virgin, by Virgin Records. Catalogue no: **VS 999-12**
Cassingle: Released Aug '87, on Virgin, by Virgin Records. Catalogue no: **VSC 999-12**
7" Single: Released Aug '87, on Virgin, by Virgin Records. Catalogue no: **VS 999**

Wendy & The Rockets

HAVE YOU BEEN TELLING ME LIES
Tracks: / Have you been telling me lies / Play the game / Security.
7" Single: Released Nov '83, on Oz, by A&M Records. Catalogue no: **AM 163**
12" Single: Released Nov '83, on Oz, by A&M Records. Catalogue no: **AMX 163**

We're Only Human

HOLD YOUR HEAD UP HIGH
Tracks: / Hold your head up high / I wouldn't treat a dog the way you treated me.
7" Single: Released Dec '85, on V.C., Catalogue no: **VC 002**

Werewolves Of London

NOCTURNE
Tracks: / Nocturne.
7" Single: Released May '82, on Wabbit, Catalogue no: **WAB 50C**

Werner, Max

RAIN IN MAY
Tracks: / Rain in May / In the winter.
7" Single: Released Feb '82, on CBS, by CBS Records. Catalogue no: **A 1978**

Werth, Howard

RESPECTABLE
Tracks: / Respectable.
7" Single: Released May '82, on Demon, by Demon Records. Catalogue no: **D 1013**

Wertz, Kimberley

I'LL BAKE ME A MAN
Tracks: / I'll bake me a man.
12" Single: Released Jun '84, on Pandisc, Catalogue no: **PANDISC 003**

Wesley, Fred

HOUSE PARTY
Tracks: / House party / I make music.
7" Single: Released Oct '80, on RSO, by Polydor Ltd. Deleted Oct '83. Catalogue no: **RSO 67**
12" Single: Released Oct '80, on RSO, by Polydor Ltd. Deleted Oct '83. Catalogue no: **RSOX 67**

Wessex 82

WESSEX 82
Tracks: / Wessex 82: *Various artists.*
7" Single: Released Feb '83, on Bluurg, by Southern Studios Ltd.. Catalogue no: **FISH 1**

West Bam

COLD STOMPER
Tracks: / Cold stomper.
12" Single: Released '89, on Who's That Beat, by Play It Again Sam (Belgium). Catalogue no: **WHOS 015**

MONKEY SAY, MONKEY DO
Tracks: / Monkey say monkey do.
7" Single: Released Aug '89, on Dr. Beat, Catalogue no: **DOBOT 01**
CD 5": Released Feb '89, on Who's That Beat, by Play It Again Sam (Belgium). Catalogue no: **WHOS 010 CD**
7" Single: Released Nov '88, on Doctor Beat, by Doctor Beat Records. Deleted Aug '89. Catalogue no: **DRX 6**
12" Single: Released Feb '89, on Doctor Beat, by Doctor Beat Records. Deleted Sep '89. Catalogue no: **DRXZ 612**
12" Single: Released Oct '88, on Who's That Beat, by Play It Again Sam (Belgium). Catalogue no: **WHOS 010**

MONKEY SAY, MONKEY DO (REMIX)
Tracks: / Monkey say, monkey do (remix).
12" Single: Released '89, on Who's That Beat, by Play It Again Sam (Belgium). Catalogue no: **WHOS 010R**

West City

MARIONS FLIGHT
Tracks: / Marion's flight / You speak German / Gymslip mother / Another storey.
7" Single: Released Mar '84, on Epigram, by Epigram Records. Catalogue no: **EPIGRAM 002**

West, Dodie

GOING OUT OF MY HEAD
Tracks: / Goin' out of my head.
7" Single: Released Jan '65, on Decca, by Decca Records. Deleted '68. Catalogue no: **F 12046**

West, Dottie

Biographical details: Dottie West was born Dorothy Marie Marsh in 1932 in Tennessee. Good looks and solid professional skills won her success in several areas. She is the oldest of ten children, earned a degree in music; her first country hits were on RCA from 1963. As a songwriter she wrote *Is This Me?* for a Jim Reeves hit in 1963; her top 10 hit with her own *Here Comes My Baby* was covered by Perry Como and won her a Grammy. She had duet hits with Reeves and made an album with him. *Country Girl* was a 1968 hit turned into an award-winning Coco-Cola TV advert in 1970 that showed her tending a garden which turned out to be atop a sky-scraper; *Country Sunshine* in 1973 became another Coke advert and reached top 50 of the pop chart. She toured Europe, became popular in the UK; had duet hits with Kenny Rogers including album *Every Time Two Fools Collide* in 1981, a number one country album which also reached the pop chart; their duet single *What Are We Doin' In Love* went top 15 pop. She was still having country chart singles on Permian in the mid'80s. (Donald Clarke)..

LESSON IN LEAVIN'
Tracks: / Lesson' in leavin' / Love's so easy for two.
7" Single: Released May '80, on Liberty, by EMI Records. Deleted May '85. Catalogue no: **UP 621**

WHAT ARE WE DOING IN LOVE
Tracks: / What are we doing in love / Choosin' means losin'.
7" Single: Released May '81, on United Artists, by EMI Records. Deleted May '84. Catalogue no: **UP 639**

West End

HOT FOR ROCKING
Tracks: / Hot for rocking.
12" Single: Released Feb '84, on S.O.U.N.D Recordings, by S.O.U.N.D. Recordings. Catalogue no: **SNDS 2**
7" Single: Released Feb '84, on S.O.U.N.D Recordings, by S.O.U.N.D. Recordings. Catalogue no: **SND 2**

OTHER SIDE OF MIDNIGHT, THE
Tracks: / Other side of midnight, The.
7" Single: Released Feb '85, on EMI, by EMI Records. Catalogue no: **TAKE 2**
12" Single: Released Feb '85, on EMI, by EMI Records. Catalogue no: **12TAKE 2**

West End Boys

SUMMERTIME
Tracks: / Summertime.
7" Single: Released Sep '85, on Hippodrome, by Hippodrome Records. Catalogue no: **HIPPO 102**

West Ham United

Biographical details: This British Football team was one of several soccer squads to enjoy a UK hit single during the 70's. Their terrace theme tune, *I'm Forever Blowing Bubbles*, took them to No 31 in 1975, the year they beat Fulham in the FA Cup Final. But the next year West Ham won the Cup, 1980, they failed to come up with a chart single and even a reissue of *Bubbles* was unsuccessful. The two most successful British soccer singles have both come from the England World Cup Squad and it was their 1970 No 1, *Back Home*, that opened the floodgates for all the budding part-time singers in soccer clubs like Chelsea, Leeds United and West Ham. Football records inevitably prove that soccer players perform better on the field that in the recording studio but the singing continued to crop up in the 80's, the England team scoring a No 2 in '82 and the Scotland World Cup Squad and the Tottenham Hotspur FA Cup Final Squad also achieved major hits. (Bob MacDonald, May 1985.).

I'M FOREVER BLOWING BUBBLES
Tracks: / I'm forever blowing bubbles.
7" Single: Released '80, on Pye, Catalogue no: **7N 45470**

West Hampshire Guides

FOREVER FRIENDS
Tracks: / Forever friends.
Note: 500 Girl Guides go on vinyl with a song that's sure to delight fellow Guides, mums and dads alike.
7" Single: Released Dec '88, on Supertrack, Catalogue no: **QU 3**

West Hampstead Ladies

IT'S A BIG BIG BEAUTIFUL WORLD
Tracks: / It's a big big beautiful world.
7" Single: Released Mar '83, on Magic (1), by Submarine Records. Catalogue no: **MAGIC 4**

West Indian Company

AVA MARIE
Tracks: / Ava Marie.
7" Single: Released Nov '84, on London Records, by London Records. Catalogue no: **LON 56**
12" Single: Released Nov '84, on London Records, by London Records. Catalogue no: **LONX 56**

West, Keith

Biographical details: This British singer fronted three small-time groups during the mid-60's -- Four Plus One, the In Crowd and Tomorrow. The In Crowd achieved a minor UK hit in '65 with a single, *That's How Strong My Love Is*. Tomorrow, which included future Yes/Asia star Steve Howe, were a promising psychedelic outfit but progress was impaired by West's short-lived solo success. The singer teamed with composer-producer Mark Wirtz for the single *Excerpt From A Teenage Opera*, better known as *Grocer Jack*, which climbed to British No 2 in September '67. But what of the opera? Nothing happened and West later claimed it had never been seriously planned and that the title had simply been a publicity stunt. The publicity certainly worked for the single, which in addition to West's vocal featured a group of young kids chanting a ridiculously catchy chorus. However, the follow-up, *Sam*, peaked at No 38 on the UK chart and both West and Wirtz slipped into obscurity. The former reappeared briefly in 1975 as a member of Moonrider, who released one flop album. West's talent was more fruitfully exploited by Nazareth, who reached the British Top Twenty with a remake of Tomorrow's underrated single, *My White Bicycle*. (Bob MacDonald, May 1985.).

EXCERPT FROM A TEENAGE OPERA
Tracks: / Excerpt from a teenage opera.
7" Single: Released Aug '67, on Parlophone, by EMI Records. Deleted '70. Catalogue no: **R 5623**
7" Single: Released '80, on Mercury, by Phonogram Ltd. Catalogue no: **LR 4421**
7" Single: Released May '82, on Video Music. Deleted '84. Catalogue no: **VID 02**

EXCERPT FROM A TEENAGE OPERA (OLD GOLD)
Tracks: / Excerpt from a teenage opera / Kites.
7" Single: Released Mar '87, on Old Gold, by Old Gold Records. Deleted Sep '89. Catalogue no: **OG 9655**

SAM
Tracks: / Sam.
7" Single: Released Nov '67, on Parlophone, by EMI Records. Deleted '70. Catalogue no: **R 5651**

West Street Mob

BREAK DANCIN'-ELECTRIC BOOGIE
Tracks: / Break dancin' electric boogie.
12" Single: Released Sep '83, on Sugarhill (USA). Catalogue no: **SHL 128**

I CAN'T STOP
Tracks: / I can't stop.
12" Single: Released Jul '84, on Sugarhill (USA). Catalogue no: **SHL 135**

MOSQUITO (aka Hobo scratch)
Tracks: / Mosquito.
12" Single: Released Nov '84, on Sugarhill (USA). Catalogue no: **SHL 137**

Westbrook, Mike

Biographical details: Mike Westbrook is a bandleader and composer who plays tuba and piano; he was born in 1936 in High Wycombe, Bucks. Influenced by Monk, Duke Ellington, Charles Mingus, he has combined poetry, theatre etc. with jazz inspiration in a large-scale works. He formed a jazz workshop in Plymouth Art Centre in 1960, a concert band '66; co-led multimedia group Cosmic Circus 1970-2; formed rock orientated Solid Gold Cadillac 1971-4, Brass Band in 1973 for cabaret on TV and in theatre. Kate Westbrook joined the Brass band in 1974; she plays several instruments, adapts and sings texts in several languages. He formed his Mike Westbrook Orchestra in 1979, she joined in 1981; they formed a trio in 1982 with Cris Biscoe on reeds, Westbrook Theatre Music in 1984. (Donald Clarke).

HUMAN ABSTRACT
Tracks: / Human abstract / Human abstract (part 2).
7" Single: Released Dec '82, on Original. Catalogue no: **ABO 8**

I SEE THY FORM
Tracks: / I see thy form / Poison tree, A.
7" Single: Released Jan '83, on Original. Catalogue no: **ABO 3**

Westbury, Kent

MY BABY DON'T ROCK ME
Tracks: / My baby don't rock me.
7" Single: Released Mar '78, on Record Mart, by Record Mart Records. Catalogue no: **RMA 1009**

Western Promise

IF YOU TELL ME YOU LOVE ME
Tracks: / If you tell me you love me.
12" Single: Released 28 Mar '89, on Midnight. Catalogue no: **DONG 049**
7" Single: Released 28 Mar '89, on Midnight. Catalogue no: **DING 049**

JUSTICE
Tracks: / Justice.
12" Single: Released Apr '85, on Midnight Music, by Midnight Music Records. Catalogue no: **DONG 11**

MY WAR
Tracks: / My war / Stay hungry / England hot / I'll tell you something I think you should know (Part 1).
12" Single: Released Jan '86, on Midnight Music, by Midnight Music Records. Catalogue no: **DONG 18**

STAR OF BETHLEHEM
Tracks: / Star of Bethlehem.
12" Single: Released Nov '88, on Midnight Music, by Midnight Music Records. Catalogue no: **DONG 42**

Westworld

BA-NA-NA-BAM-BOO
Tracks: / Ba-na-na-bam-boo / Cheap'n'nasty.
7" Single: Released Apr '87, on RCA, by BMG Records (UK). Catalogue no: **BOOM 2**
12" Single: Released Apr '87, on RCA, by BMG Records (UK). Catalogue no: **BOOM T2**

DANCE ON
Tracks: / Dance on / Crazy anne (12" only) / Break your heart (12" only) / Dance on and on.
Cassingle: Released Jun '89, on RCA, by BMG Records (UK). Catalogue no: **PK 42773**
CD 5": Released Jun '89, on RCA, by BMG Records (UK). Catalogue no: **PD 42774**
7" Single: Released Jun '89, on RCA, by BMG Records (UK). Catalogue no: **PB 42773**
12" Single: Released Jun '89, on RCA, by BMG Records (UK). Catalogue no: **PB 42774**

EVERYTHING GOOD IS BAD
Tracks: / Everything good is bad / Ha ha ha / Everything good is bad (Only on 12" & CD single.) / Everything good is bad (brainstorm mix) (Only on 12".).
CD 5": Released Oct '88, on RCA, by BMG Records (UK). Deleted Jul '89. Catalogue no: **PD 42244**
7" Single: Released Oct '88, on RCA, by BMG Records (UK). Deleted Aug '89. Catalogue no: **PB 42243**
12" Single: Released Oct '88, on RCA, by BMG Records (UK). Deleted Aug '89. Catalogue no: **PT 42244**

SILVERMAC
Tracks: / Silvermac / Let there be drums / Steel toed engineer / Let there be drums.
7" Single: Released Sep '87, on RCA, by BMG Records (UK). Deleted May '89. Catalogue no: **BOOM 4**
12" Single: Released Sep '87, on RCA, by BMG Records (UK). Deleted May '89. Catalogue no: **BOOMT 4**

SONIC BOOM BOY
Tracks: / Mission impossible / Bubble Bo Diddley.
Note: EXtra track on 12" only
12" Single: Released Feb '87, on RCA, by BMG Records (UK). Deleted May '89. Catalogue no: **BOOM T1**
7" Single: Released Feb '87, on RCA, by BMG Records (UK). Deleted May '89. Catalogue no: **BOOM 1**

WHERE THE ACTION IS (SINGLE)
Tracks: / Where the action is.
7" Single: Released Jul '87, on RCA, by BMG Records (UK). Catalogue no: **BROM 3**
12" Single: Released Jul '87, on RCA, by BMG Records (UK). Catalogue no: **BROMT 3**

Wet Wet Wet

ANGEL EYES
Tracks: / Angel eyes / We can love / Angel eyes (ext) / Home and away (on 12" only.).
Note: 'Angel eyes (ext)' on 12" only.
7" Single: Released Nov '87, on Precious Organisation, by Precious Organisation. Catalogue no: **JEWEL 6**
CD 5": Released Nov '87, on Precious Organisation, by Precious Organisation. Deleted Oct '88. Catalogue no: **JWLCD 6**
Cassingle: Released Nov '87, on Precious Organisation, by Precious Organisation. Deleted Oct '88. Catalogue no: **JWLMC 6**
12" Single: Released Nov '87, on Precious Organisation, by Precious Organisation. Deleted Oct '88. Catalogue no: **JEWEL 612**

I REMEMBER
Tracks: / I remember.
12" Single: Released Oct '87, on Precious Organisation, by Precious Organisation. Catalogue no: **JEWEL 512**
7" Single: Released Oct '87, on Precious Organisation, by Precious Organisation. Catalogue no: **JEWEL 5**

SWEET LITTLE MYSTERY
Tracks: / Sweet little mystery / Don't let me be lonely tonight.
7" Single: Released Jul '87, on Precious Organisation, by Precious Organisation. Catalogue no: **JEWEL 4**
12" Single: Released Jul '87, on Precious Organisation, by Precious Organisation. Deleted Oct '88. Catalogue no: **JEWEL 412**

SWEET SURRENDER
Tracks: / Sweet surrender / This time (live).
12" Single: Released Sep '89, on Precious Organisation, by Precious Organisation. Catalogue no: **JEWEL 912**
CD 5": Released Sep '89, on Precious Organisation, by Precious Organisation. Catalogue no: **JWLCD 9**
Cassingle: Released Sep '89, on Precious Organisation, by Precious Organisation. Catalogue no: **JWLMC 9**
7" Single: Released Sep '89, on Precious Organisation, by Precious Organisation. Catalogue no: **JEWEL 9**

TEMPTATION
Tracks: / Temptation / Bottled emotions / I remember (extended) (On 12" version only.) / I remember** (**On CD version only.) / Heaven help us all** (**On CD version only.).
CD 5": Released 7 Mar '88, on Precious Organisation, by Precious Organisation. Deleted Oct '88. Catalogue no: **JEWELCD 7**
12" Single: Released 7 Mar '88, on Precious Organisation, by Precious Organisation. Deleted Oct '88. Catalogue no: **JEWEL 712**
7" Single: Released Mar '88, on Precious Organisation, by Precious Organisation. Deleted Oct '88. Catalogue no: **JEWEL 777**
7" Single: Released 7 Mar '88, on Precious Organisation, by Precious Organisation. Deleted Oct '88. Catalogue no: **JEWEL 7**

WISHING I WAS LUCKY
Tracks: / Wishing I was lucky / Words of wisdom / Still can't remember your name (Extra track on 12" only).
7" Single: Released Mar '87, on Precious Organisation, by Precious Organisation. Catalogue no: **JEWEL 3**
12" Single: Released Mar '87, on Precious Organisation, by Precious Organisation. Catalogue no: **JEWEL 312**

WITH A LITTLE HELP FROM MY FRIENDS
Tracks: / With a little help from my friends / She's leaving home.
Note: All proceeds from record sales to Childline (anti-incest service).
7" Single: Released May '88, on Philips, by Phonogram Ltd. Deleted 31 May '89. Catalogue no: **CHILD 1**

Wetton, John

TURN ON THE RADIO
Tracks: / Turn on the radio / Get what you want.
7" Single: Released Oct '80, on Polydor, by Polydor Ltd. Deleted Oct '83. Catalogue no: **POSP 191**

We've Got A Fuzzbox...

LOVE IS THE SLUG
Tracks: / Love is a slug / Console me / Justine / Spirit in the sky.
12" Single: Released Oct '86, on Vindaloo, by Vindaloo Records. Deleted Jan '88. Catalogue no: **UGH 14T**
12" Pic: Released Oct '86, on Vindaloo, by Vindaloo Records. Deleted Jun '87. Catalogue no: **UGH 14TN**
7" Pic: Released Oct '86, on Vindaloo, by Vindaloo Records. Deleted Jun '87. Catalogue no: **UGH 14N**
Cassingle: Released Oct '86, on Vindaloo, by Vindaloo Records. Catalogue no: **UGH 14C**
7" Single: Released Oct '86, on Vindaloo, by Vindaloo Records. Deleted Jan '88. Catalogue no: **UGH 14**

WHAT'S THE POINT
Tracks: / Fuzzy ramblings fever (Available on 12" verion only) / Bohemian rhapsody* (* Available on 12" verion only).
7" Single: Released Jan '87, on Vindaloo, by Vindaloo Records. Deleted Jan '88. Catalogue no: **YZ 101**
12" Single: Released Jan '87, on Vindaloo, by Vindaloo Records. Deleted Jan '88. Catalogue no: **YZ 101T**

XXSEX
Tracks: / XX Sex / Rules and regulations / Do I want to ? (Track on 12" version only.) / She (Track on 12" version only.) / Aaarrrggghhh (Track on 12" version only.).
7" Single: Released Feb '86, on Vindaloo, by Vindaloo Records. Catalogue no: **UGH 11**
12" Single: Released Apr '86, on Vindaloo, by Vindaloo Records. Catalogue no: **UGH 11T**

WGBC

LOVE ME ANYWAY
Tracks: / Love me anyway.
7" Single: Released Aug '86, on Expansion. Catalogue no: **7 EXPAND 1**

Whale, James

BIMBO
Tracks: / Bimbo / Big big egg, A.
7" Single: Released Jan '89, on Flair, by Flair Records. Deleted Sep '89. Catalogue no: **FLA 110**
12" Single: Released Jan '89, on Flair, by Flair Records. Deleted Sep '89. Catalogue no: **12FLA 110**

Wham

Biographical details: This British duo, comprising George Michael (real name George Michael Panos) and Andrew Ridgeley, came to fame in 1982, and reached international megastar status in '84. Both lads came from North London, and both were born in 1963. They became friends at school, and worked in various local small-time bands before forming Wham! in early '82. A contract with Innervision Records rapidly followed, and their first single *Wham rap (enjoy what you do)* was released that June. Musically, this record borrowed elements of black soul, dance and rap styles and presented them in a watered down white format; lyrically, it created controversy through its apparent contempt and mockery of governmental authorities in the wake of youth unemployment. The song became a mini-anthem for jobless youngsters, attracting praise in the UK music press and clubs. The follow-up single became Wham!'s first hit. *Young guns (go for it)*, a funky dance track containing a warning against the pitfalls of teenage marriage, climbed to No.3 on the UK chart in late '82; its success led to the belated recognition of *Wham! rap* which hit No.8 in early '83. The duo sustained their pseudo-rebellious 'soul boy' image long enough for a third smash *Bad boys*, which reached the UK No.2 slot. It was quickly followed by their debut album *Fantastic!*, which entered the British album listings at No.1, a sensational feat for a first LP. With their next single, the summer/suntan-orientated *Club tropican*, the pair landed another UK Top Fiver. This song pointed the duo in a new teen idol direction; but a dispute with their record label caused a lengthy lay off. With a new deal from Epic Records, Wham! returned in the summer of 1984, after more than six months out of the limelight. They now adopted an out-and-out commercial pop approach, and previous social themes were dropped in favour of pop music's favourite subject - love; however, they certainly retained the vigour and vitality of their early days - it was simply redirected to the hearts of the girls. *Wake me up before you go go*, a lightweight Monkees style romp, shot to the UK No.1 position in June '84; the new goodtime Wham! image was distinctly reminiscent of that of Jan & Dean, the early Sixties surfing duo.
It was not only the music and image that changed between 1982 and 1984 - so did the public perception of Wham!'s personnel. In their *Young guns* days, Michael and Ridgeley surrounded themselves with backup singers and musicians on their TV appearances. By the time *Bad boys* came out, Wham! were clearly marketed as a duo. But by 1984, George Michael firmly emerged as the duo's major talent, being credited with the bulk of the songwriting and being wholly responsible for vocals and production. His partner was merely a mediocre guitarist, and began to appear increasingly redundant. As if to prove his status, George Michael scored an international solo chart-topper with *Careless whisper*, a perfect summer love ballad that became an instant standard. During the rest of 1984 and 1985, Wham! went from strength to strength, becoming global superstars. *Freedom* gave George his third consecutive British No.1, and only of Band Aid's *Do they know it's Christmas?* (on which he also sang) prevented Wham!'s million-selling double A sided smash *Last Christmas/Everything she wants* prevented him from becoming his fourth. The appropriately named *Make it big* album went to No.1 on both sides of the Atlantic, and the duo enjoyed back-to-bac.. US No.1 singles. In April 1985, Wham! made a pioneering trip to China, where they played two historic shows. This much publicised penetration of the giant Communist state was made at vast expense to the duo - the performances were given free of charge, with ticket proceeds going to Chinese charity and cultural projects. But no-one wept for Wham! during 1984, they had sold a global total of 10 million discs. *Make it big* was a gross understatement. (Bob MacDonald, 12th May 1985)
Wham! was a UK pop vocal duo; George Michael (born Yorgos Kyriatou Panayiotou in Fnchley in 1963) and Andrew Ridgeley (born in 1963 in Herts.) Ridgeley also played guitar; Michael was the songwriter; they became the acceptable face of conservative UK pop of the 1980s: slick pinups of the decade. They came together in The Executives in 1979; demos led to a recording contract which turned out to be a nightmare when they hit big. They became the pin-ups of the decade; their *Wake Me Up before You Go-Go* was a transatlantic number one. In 1985 Michael received an Ivor Novello Songwriter Of The Year award and duetted

with Elton John at Live Aid; they were the first western pop group to perfrom in China. Michael seemed unhappy with incessant media interest but Ridgeley was ideal fodder,crashing cars and squiring pretty girls; they split in 1986 and Michael's solo career has been successful: critical opinion is deeply divided over whether he is a huge talent or just a pretty face. (Donald Clarke)..

BAD BOYS
Tracks: / Bad boys / Instrumental version.
12" Single: Released May '83, on Inner Vision, Catalogue no: **TA 3143**
7" Pic: Released May '83, on Inner Vision, Catalogue no: **WA 3143**
7" Single: Released May '83, on Inner Vision, Deleted '87. Catalogue no: **A 3143**

CLUB FANTASTIC MEGAMIX
Tracks: / Club fantastic megamix / Ray of sunshine.
7" Single: Released Dec '83, on Inner Vision, Deleted '86. Catalogue no: **A 3586**

CLUB TROPICANA
Tracks: / Club Tropicana / Blue.
7" Single: Released Jul '83, on Inner Vision, Deleted '86. Catalogue no: **A 3613**

EDGE OF HEAVEN, THE
Tracks: / Edge of heaven / Battlestations / Where did your heart go.
12" Single: Released Jun '86, on Epic, by CBS Records. Catalogue no: **FINE T1**
7" Single: Released Jun '86, on Epic, by CBS Records. Catalogue no: **FINE 1**

FREEDOM
Tracks: / Freedom.
7" Single: Released Oct '84, on Epic, by CBS Records. Deleted '87. Catalogue no: **A 4743**

I'M YOUR MAN
Tracks: / I'm your man.
7" Single: Released Nov '85, on Epic, by CBS Records. Catalogue no: **A 6716**
7" Pic: Released Nov '85, on Epic, by CBS Records. Catalogue no: **WTA 6716**

LAST CHRISTMAS
Tracks: / Last Christmas / Where did your heart go / Last Christmas.
7" Single: Released Nov '85, on Epic, by CBS Records. Deleted Aug '87. Catalogue no: **650269 7**
7" Single: Released Dec '84, on Epic, by CBS Records. Deleted '87. Catalogue no: **A 4949**
7" Single: Released Dec '85, on Epic, by CBS Records. Catalogue no: **WHAM 1**
12" Single: Released Nov '85, on Epic, by CBS Records. Deleted Aug '87. Catalogue no: **650269 6**

WAKE ME UP BEFORE YOU GO GO
Tracks: / Wake me up before you go go / Ray of sunshine.
7" Single: Released May '84, on Epic, by CBS Records. Deleted '87. Catalogue no: **A 4440**

WHAM RAP
Tracks: / Wham rap (social mix) / Wham rap (unsocial mix).
7" Single: Released Dec '82, on Inner Vision, Deleted Dec '85. Catalogue no: **IVLA 2442**
12" Single: Released Jun '82, on Inner Vision, Catalogue no: **IVLA 13 2442**

YOUNG GUNS GO FOR IT
Tracks: / Young guns go for it / Goin' for it.
12" Single: Released Sep '82, on Inner Vision, Deleted Sep '85. Catalogue no: **IVLA 132766**
7" Single: Released Sep '82, on Inner Vision, Deleted Sep '85. Catalogue no: **IVLA 2766**

What A Nice Way...

WHAT A NICE WAY TO TURN 17 LP
Tracks: / What a nice way to turn 17: *Various artists.*
7" Single: Released Jul '84, on Rather, by Rather Records. Catalogue no: **GEAR 17**

What Noise

VEIN
Tracks: / Vein / What noise.
12" Single: Released Mar '89, on Cut Deep, by Cut Deep Records. Catalogue no: **CUT 12002**

Wheel

HONEYSUCKER
Tracks: / Honeysucker.
12" Single: Released Aug '87, on EPL, Catalogue no: **EPL 1**

WORLD'S A CRUEL MISTRESS, THE
Tracks: / World's a cruel mistress, The / Coast of innocents.
7" Single: Released Jan '88, on EPL, Catalogue no: **EPL 2**

Wheeler, Audrey

IRRESISTIBLE
Tracks: / Irresistible.
7" Single: Released Oct '87, on Capitol, by EMI Records. Deleted Apr '88. Catalogue no: **CL 471**
7" Single: Released Oct '87, on RCA, by BMG Records (UK). Catalogue no: **R 6156**
12" Single: Released Sep '87, on Capitol (USA), by Capitol (USA) Records. Catalogue no: **V 15333**
12" Single: Released Oct '87, on RCA, by BMG Records (UK). Catalogue no: **12 R 6156**
12" Single: Released Oct '87, on Capitol, by EMI Records. Deleted Nov '88. Catalogue no: **12 CL 471**
12" Single: Released Nov '87, on Capitol, by EMI Records. Deleted 31 Jul '88. Catalogue no: **12CLX 471**

When In Rome

EVERYTHING
Tracks: / Everything (Extended version on 12") / Basilica (John Paul II or III mix) / Whatever the weather (12" only).
12" Single: Released Feb '88, on 10 Records, by Virgin Records. Deleted '89. Catalogue no: **TENX 210**
7" Single: Released Feb '88, on 10 Records, by Virgin Records. Catalogue no: **TEN 210**

HEAVEN KNOWS
Tracks: / Heaven knows / Whatever the weather.
12" Single: Released 26 Jun '89, on 10 Records, by Virgin Records. Catalogue no: **TENX 255**
CD 5": Released Sep '89, on 10 Records, by Virgin Records. Catalogue no: **TENCD 277**
Cassingle: Released 26 Jun '89, on 10 Records, by Virgin Records. Catalogue no: **TENC 277**
7" Single: Released 26 Jun '89, on 10 Records, by Virgin Records. Catalogue no: **TENG 255**
7" Single: Released 26 Jun '89, on 10 Records, by Virgin Records. Catalogue no: **TEN 277**
7" Single: Released 26 Jun '89, on 10 Records, by Virgin Records. Catalogue no: **TEN 255**
12" Single: Released 26 Jun '89, on 10 Records, by Virgin Records. Catalogue no: **TENX 277**
CD 3": Released 26 Jun '89, on 10 Records, by Virgin Records. Catalogue no: **TENCD 255**

PROMISE, THE
Tracks: / Promise, The / Promise, The (dub) (7" only) / Promise, The (O.N. mix) (on CD only) / Promise, The (coliseum club mix).
7" Single: Released Sep '87, on 10 Records, by Virgin Records. Catalogue no: **TEN 244**
CD 3": Released '88, on 10 Records, by Virgin Records. Catalogue no: **TENCD 244**

SIGHT OF YOUR TEARS
Tracks: / Sight of your tears / 1,000 reasons / Sight of your tears (version) (12" only).
12" Single: Released Feb '89, on Virgin, by Virgin Records. Catalogue no: **TENX 267**
7" Single: Released Feb '89, on Virgin, by Virgin Records. Catalogue no: **TEN 267**
CD 3": Released Feb '89, on Virgin, by Virgin Records. Catalogue no: **TENCD 267**

When People Were

WHEN PEOPLE WERE SHORTER AND LIVED NEAR THE WATER
Tracks: / When people were shorter and lived near the water.
12" Single: Released Feb '88, on Shadowline, Catalogue no: **SR 0088**

When The World..

SUSPICION
Tracks: / Suspicion / Orbit / Suspicion (version).
12" Single: Released Oct '88, on Survival (1), by Survival Records. Catalogue no: **SUR 12 045**

Where's Lisse

RED LIGHT AND TUTORIAL
Tracks: / Red light and tutorial.
12" Single: Released Jun '82, on Glass, by Glass Records. Deleted '83. Catalogue no: **GLASS 014**

TALK TAKES TOO LONG
Tracks: / Talk takes too long.
7" Single: Released Jul '81, on Glass, by Glass Records. Deleted '83. Catalogue no: **GLASS 008**

Where's The Fire

WHAT IT IS
Tracks: / What it is / What it is (version).
7" Single: Released Aug '89, on Champion, by Champion Records. Catalogue no: **CHAMP 209**
12" Single: Released Aug '89, on Champion, by Champion Records. Catalogue no: **CHAMP 12209**

Which Is Which

I CAN'T GET ENOUGH
Tracks: / I can't get enough.
12" Single: Released Jul '89, on Pulse, Catalogue no: **HA 1066**

Whip Crackaway

HORSES TAIL,THE
Tracks: / Horses tail,The.
7" Single: Released Aug '86, on In Tape, by In Tape Records. Catalogue no: **IT 035**

Whirl

CLEAR
Tracks: / Clear.
12" Single: Released Nov '88, on September, Catalogue no: **SEPT 8 T**

HEAVEN FORBID
Tracks: / Heaven forbid / Mister striked back / As soon as / In a dream.
12" Single: Released Aug '87, on Play Room Discs, by Play Room Discs. Catalogue no: **PLAYD 001-12**

Whirlpool Guest House

CHANGING FACE, THE
Tracks: / Changing face, The.
7" Single: Released Feb '87, on Summerhouse, by Summerhouse Records. Catalogue no: **SUMS 3**

Whirlwind

FULL TIME THING
Tracks: / Full time thing.
7" Single: Released Jan '77, on Pye International, Deleted '79. Catalogue no: **7N 25733**

HEAVEN KNOWS
Tracks: / Heaven knows / Cruisin' around.
7" Single: Released Feb '80, on Chiswick Records, Deleted Feb '83. Catalogue no: **CHIS 122**

Whiskers

DOOLALLY SONG, THE
Tracks: / Doolally song, The / What life means to me.
7" Single: Released Jul '87, on Foul Play, Catalogue no: **FP 007**

Whiskey And Soda

DIRTY DEN RAP
Tracks: / Dirty Den rap.
7" Single: Released Mar '86, on Spartan, Catalogue no: **SP 139**
12" Single: Released Mar '86, on Spartan, Catalogue no: **12SP 139**

Whisky Priests

NO CHANCE
Tracks: / No chance.
12" Single: Released 23 Jul '88, on Whippet, Catalogue no: **WPT 001**

Whispers

Biographical details: This American all-male vocal quintet, led by Wallace and Walter Scott, were already veterans of the soul scene by the time their career received a much-deserved boost in the mid-70's. Having previously scored some minor US soul hits for various small labels, the Whispers signed with Soul Train Records. This was an offshoot of American television's most important black music show and was organised by Don Cornelius and Dick Griffey. Soul Train gave the group a pair of Top Ten singles on the US soul chart: 1976's *One For The Money* and 1977's unlikely remake of Bread's *Make It With You* also found their way into the low regions of the Billboard Hunt Hundred pop chart. In '78 Soul Train Records evolved into Solar (an acronym for Sound of Los Angeles Records). The new company's key figure was producer/bassist/percussionist Leon Sylvers, who gave the Whispers their first and biggest international smash hit with 1980's *And The Beat Goes On.* This deliciously infectious dance single, which did much to dispel rumours that disco was dead, was an American million-seller and stormed to No 2 in Britain. The similar-sounding *It's A Love Thing* gave them another success the following year, reaching No 9 in the UK and becoming a smash on the American soul chart. The early 80's, however, saw a sharp decline in the crossover between the US black and pop charts -- it was possible for a soul single to sell half-a-million copies while only achieving a minor position on the Hot Hundred. This problem affected the Whispers, who continued to reach the higher echelons of the black listings with such songs as *Tonight, Keep On Lovin' Me* and *Contagious,* while being largely ignored by pop radio. (Bob MacDonald, May 1985.).

AND THE BEAT GOES ON
Tracks: / Some kinda lover / It's a love thing (Extra track on 12" only) / Contagious (Extra track on 12" only) / And the beat goes on.
7" Single: Released Mar '87, on MCA, by MCA Records. Catalogue no: **MCA 1126**
7" Single: Released Feb '80, on Solar Records, Deleted '83. Catalogue no: **SO 1**
7" Single: Released Jul '81, on Soul Train, Catalogue no: **GOLD 509**
12" Single: Released Jul '81, on Soul Train, Catalogue no: **SO 121 81**
12" Single: Released Mar '87, on MCA, by MCA Records. Catalogue no: **MCAT 1126**

AND THE BEAT GOES ON (OLD GOLD)
Tracks: / And the beat goes on.
12" Single: Released Jul '89, on Old Gold, by Old Gold Records. Catalogue no: **OG 4061**

CONTAGIOUS
Tracks: / Contagious / Keep your love around.
7" Single: Released Jan '85, on MCA, by MCA Records. Catalogue no: **MCA 937**
12" Single: Released Jan '85, on MCA, by MCA Records. Catalogue no: **MCAT 937**

EMERGENCY
Tracks: / Emergency / Only you.
7" Single: Released Apr '82, on Solar (USA), by MCA Records. Catalogue no: **K 13171**
12" Single: Released Apr '82, on Solar (USA), by MCA Records. Catalogue no: **K 13171 T**

I CAN MAKE IT BETTER
Tracks: / I can make it better / Say you.
12" Single: Released May '81, on Solar (USA), by MCA Records. Catalogue no: **SOT 19**
7" Single: Released May '81, on Solar (USA), by MCA Records. Catalogue no: **SO 19**

IN THE RAW
Tracks: / In the raw / Small talkin'.
7" Single: Released Jan '82, on Solar (USA), by MCA Records. Catalogue no: **K 12597**
12" Single: Released Jan '82, on Solar (USA), by MCA Records. Catalogue no: **K 12597 T**

IT'S A LOVE THING
Tracks: / It's a love thing / Girl I need you.
12" Single: Released Feb '81, on Solar (USA), by MCA Records. Catalogue no: **SOT 16**
7" Single: Released Feb '81, on Solar (USA), by MCA Records. Catalogue no: **SO 16**

LADY
Tracks: / Lady / I love you.
7" Single: Released May '80, on Solar Records, Deleted '83. Catalogue no: **SO 4**
12" Single: Released May '80, on Solar Records, Deleted '83. Catalogue no: **SO 12 4**

MY GIRL
Tracks: / My girl / Olivia lost and turned out.
7" Single: Released Jul '80, on Solar Records, Deleted '83. Catalogue no: **SO 8**
12" Single: Released Jul '80, on Solar Records, Deleted '83. Catalogue no: **SO 12 8**

NO PAIN, NO GAIN
Tracks: / No pain, no gain / Uptown mix / No pain, no gain (extended) (On 12" version only.).
12" Single: Released Oct '87, on MCA, by MCA Records. Catalogue no: **MCAT 1212**
7" Single: Released Oct '87, on MCA, by MCA Records. Catalogue no: **MCA 1212**

OUT OF THE BOX
Tracks: / Out of the box / Welcome into my dream.
7" Single: Released Sep '80, on Solar (USA), by MCA Records. Deleted Sep '83. Catalogue no: **SO 12**
12" Single: Released Sep '80, on Solar (USA), by MCA Records. Deleted Sep '83. Catalogue no: **SOT 12**

ROCK STEADY
Tracks: / Rock steady / Are you going my way.
7" Single: Released May '87, on MCA, by MCA Records. Catalogue no: **MCA 1152**
12" Single: Released May '87, on Solar (USA), by MCA Records. Catalogue no: **MCAT 1152**

SOME KINDA LOVER
Tracks: / Some kinda lover.
12" Single: Released Apr '85, on MCA, by MCA Records. Catalogue no: **MCAT 951**
7" Single: Released Apr '85, on MCA, by MCA Records. Catalogue no: **MCA 951**

SPECIAL FX
Tracks: / Special FX.
7" Single: Released Aug '87, on MCA, by MCA Records. Catalogue no: **MCA 1178**

12" Single: Released Aug '87, on MCA, by MCA Records. Catalogue no: **MCAT 1178**

THIS KIND OF LOVIN (SINGLE)
Tracks: / This kind of lovin.
7" Single: Released Sep '81, on Solar (USA), by MCA Records. Catalogue no: **SO 22**
12" Single: Released Sep '81, on Solar (USA), by MCA Records. Catalogue no: **SOT 22**

Whistle

(NOTHING SERIOUS)JUST BUGGIN'
Tracks: / (Nothing serious)Just Buggin' / Buggin' much hard / (Nothing serious)just buggin'-Remix (Track on remix version.).
12" Single: Released Mar '86, on Champion, by Champion Records. Catalogue no: **CHAMP 1212**
7" Pic: Released Mar '86, on Champion, by Champion Records. Catalogue no: **CHAMPP 12**
7" Single: Released Mar '86, on Champion, by Champion Records. Catalogue no: **CHAMP 12**
12" Single: Released Mar '86, on Champion, by Champion Records. Catalogue no: **CHAMPT 1212**

PLEASE LOVE ME
Tracks: / Please love me / Just for fun / (Nothing serious)Just Buggin'-Dutch remix (Extra track on 12"version only.).
7" Single: Released Jun '86, on Champion, by Champion Records. Deleted Jul '89. Catalogue no: **CHAMP 15**
12" Single: Released Jun '86, on Champion, by Champion Records. Deleted Aug '89. Catalogue no: **CHAMP 1215**

Whitaker, Mick

LOOKING FOR LOVE IN A STRANGER
Tracks: / Looking for love in a stranger.
7" Single: Released Jul '81, on State, by State Records. Catalogue no: **STAT 105**

Whitbread, Sharon

WHY DON'T YOU DO IT
Tracks: / Why don't you do it.
7" Single: Released Jan '77, on Pye, Catalogue no: **7 N 45635**

Whitcomb, Ian

THIS SPORTING LIFE
Tracks: / This sporting life / You turn me on / Dance with me.
7" Single: Released Nov '82, on Big Beat, by Ace Records. Deleted '88. Catalogue no: **SW 84**

White, Andy

REALITY NOW
Tracks: / Reality row / Rembrandt hat / Raindance, The.
7" Single: Released Sep '86, on Decca, by Decca Records. Deleted '88. Catalogue no: **F 100**
12" Single: Released Sep '86, on Decca, by Decca Records. Deleted '88. Catalogue no: **FX 100**

RELIGIOUS PERSUASION
Tracks: / Religious persuasion / Rembradnt persuasion.
12" Single: Released Nov '85, on Stiff, by Stiff Records. Catalogue no: **BUYIT 234**
7" Single: Released Jan '86, on Stiff, by Stiff Records. Catalogue no: **BUY 234**

White, Barry

Biographical details: Singer, pianist, songwriter, arranger, producer and bandleader White was born in Galveston, Texas, but his family moved to Los Angeles when he was six months. He became involved in religious choirs while young and grew up singing, playing the organ and conducting singers in church. While still in his late teens he played on Bob & Earl's acclaimed 1963 single *Harlem Shuffle* (belated UK Top Ten hit in '69). He soon began to gain experience as a producer and A & R executive, and achieved a one-off British Top Twenty hit in '67 as producer and co-writer of Felice Taylor's *I Feel Love Comin' On.* At the end of the 60's he took three back-up singers under his wing and formed them into a vocal trio, Love Unlimited, one of whom, Glodean James, later became his wife. The girls broke big in 1972, hitting No 14 on both sides of the Atlantic with *Walkin' In The Rain With The One I Love.* This slushy single was written and produced by White and introduced the world to his lush orchestral arrangements and, via a spoken telephonic message in the song, to his voice. It provided him with a launching pad on which to begin his solo career. Starting with 1973's *I'm Gonna Love You Just A Litle More, Baby* (No 3 in US, No 23 in UK), White embarked on a five-year string of sensual soul successes. All the hits featured the same ingredients: his big, breathy Isaac Hayes-influenced singing; his sexy lyrics, exemplified by by a penchant for lengthy song titles like *I'll Do For You Anything You Want Me To* and *It's Ecstasy When You Lie Down Next To Me*; his catchy choruses; and his romantic string sounds and mid-tempo rhythms. White's big voice and big musical sound were matched by his huge physique, which won over the hearts of some women but mystified many others. The whole Barry White package had its roots in soul music but veered towards a middle-of-the-road style. He reached the peak of his career during 1974-75 with a trio of trans Atlantic Top Ten singles, *Can't Get Enough Of Your Love, Babe* (No 1 in US, No 8 in UK), *You're The First, The Last, My Everything* (2 in US, 1 in UK) and *What Am I Gonna Do With You?* (8 in US, 5 in UK). Also in '74 he took his 41-piece Love Unlimited Orchestra to No 1 in America and No 10 in Britain with an instrumental single, *Love's Theme.* But by 1976 the formula had become totally predictable and every single from '73 onwards sounded like its predecessor. Britain continued to buy but a sales drop-off in the States finally prompted him to change his sound and 1977's *It's Ecstasy When You Lay Down Next To Me* gave him one of his biggest American hits, reaching No 4. He changed his mind the following year, enjoying a US hit with *Oh What A Night For Dancing* and a British success with a rapid remake of Billy Joel's instant classic *Just The Way You Are,* which eventually went higher in the UK Top Twenty than the original version. (Bob MacDonald, May 1985.)

Barry White was born in 1944 in Texas, but grew up in Los Angeles, where he became a keyboardist, producer and vocalist. He became A&R man for Mustang/Bronco '66-7, then formed girl trio Love Unlimited in 1969, including his future wife Glodean James, her sister Linda and Diane Taylor; their USA hit in 1972 was *Walkin' In The Rain With The One I Love,* with his vocal on telephone. One of their albums was called *In Heat.* His 40-piece Love Unlimited Orchestra had instrumental hits '73-4; under his own name he used his pop/soul voice, described as sounding like chocolate cake tastes, in romantic chat (e.g. *Can't Get Enough Of Your Love Babe*), at No. 1 the biggest of his six top 10 singles 1973-77 in the USA Most of this was written and produced by White. He returned to the charts in 1987 with *The Right Now Barry White.* (Donald Clarke)..

BABY WE BETTER TRY AND GET IT TOGETHER
Tracks: / Baby we better try and get it together.
7" Single: Released Aug '76, on 20th Century, by 20th Century Records. Deleted '79. Catalogue no: **BTC 2298**

CAN'T GET ENOUGH OF YOUR LOVE BABE
Tracks: / Can't get enough of your love babe.
7" Single: Released Aug '74, on Pye International, Deleted '77. Catalogue no: **7N 25661**

DIDN'T WE MAKE IT HAPPY BABY
Tracks: / Didn't we make it happy baby / I'll sing.
7" Single: Released Apr '81, on Unlimited Gold(USA), by CBS Records (USA). Deleted '85. Catalogue no: **A 1125**

DON'T MAKE ME WAIT TOO LONG
Tracks: / Don't make me wait too long.
7" Single: Released Nov '76, on 20th Century, by 20th Century Records. Deleted '79. Catalogue no: **BTC 2309**

FOLLOW THAT AND SEE (WHERE IT LEADS Y'ALL)
Tracks: / Follow that and see (where it leads y'all) / Follow that and see (instrumental).
7" Single: Released Oct '89, on Breakout, by A&M Records. Catalogue no: **USA 670**

FOR YOUR LOVE
Tracks: / For your love / Love is in your eyes / As time goes by* (extra track on 12").
7" Single: Released Jan '88, on Breakout, by A&M Records. Catalogue no: **USA 618**
12" Single: Released Jan '88, on Breakout, by A&M Records. Catalogue no: **USAT 618**

I'LL DO FOR YOU ANYTHING YOU WANT ME TO
Tracks: / I'll do for you anything you want me to.
7" Single: Released May '75, on 20th Century, by 20th Century Records. Deleted '78. Catalogue no: **BTC 2208**

I'M GONNA LOVE YOU JUST A LITTLE BIT MORE BABY
Tracks: / I'm gonna love you just a little bit more baby.
7" Single: Released Jun '73, on Pye International, Deleted '76. Catalogue no: **7N 25610**

I'M QUALIFIED TO SATISFY
Tracks: / I'm qualified to satisfy you.
7" Single: Released Mar '77, on 20th Century, by 20th Century Records. Deleted '80. Catalogue no: **BTC 2328**

IT'S ECSTASY WHEN YOU LAY DOWN NEXT TO ME
Tracks: / It's ecstasy when you lay down next to me.
7" Single: Released Oct '77, on 20th Century, by 20th Century Records. Deleted '80. Catalogue no: **BTC 2350**

JUST THE WAY YOU ARE
Tracks: / Just the way you are.
7" Single: Released Dec '78, on 20th Century, by 20th Century Records. Deleted '81. Catalogue no: **BTC 2380**

LET THE MUSIC PLAY (SINGLE)
Tracks: / Let the music play.
7" Single: Released Dec '75, on 20th Century, by 20th Century Records. Deleted '78. Catalogue no: **BTC 2265**
7" Single: Released Oct '81, on 20th Century, by 20th Century Records. Catalogue no: **GOLD 533**

NEVER NEVER GONNA GIVE YOU UP
Tracks: / Never never gonna give you up (Paul Hardcastle remix) / September when I first met you / Never never gonna give you up (mammoth mix) (Extra track, available on 12" only.) / Never never gonna give you up (ext. mix) (Extra track, available on 12" only.).
7" Single: Released Sep '87, on Club, by Phonogram Ltd. Deleted Oct '88. Catalogue no: **JAB 59**
7" Single: Released Jan '74, on Pye International, Deleted '77. Catalogue no: **7N 25633**
12" Single: Released Sep '87, on Club, by Phonogram Ltd. Deleted Oct '88. Catalogue no: **JABX 59**

NEVER NEVER GONNA GIVE YOU UP (OLD GOLD)
Tracks: / Never never gonna give you up / I'm gonna love you just a little bit more.
7" Single: Released Oct '88, on Old Gold, by Old Gold Records. Catalogue no: **OG 9768**

RIGHT NIGHT, THE
Tracks: / Right night, The / Right night, The (baad remix) (Extra track on 12".) / Right night, The (baad dub) (Extra track on 12".) / There's a place.
7" Single: Released Mar '88, on Breakout, by A&M Records. Deleted Feb '89. Catalogue no: **USA 626**
12" Single: Released Mar '88, on Breakout, by A&M Records. Deleted Feb '89. Catalogue no: **USAT 626**

SHA LA LA MEANS I LOVE YOU
Tracks: / Sha la la means I love you.
7" Single: Released Mar '79, on 20th Century, by 20th Century Records. Deleted '82. Catalogue no: **BTC 1041**

SHEET MUSIC
Tracks: / Sheet music / Sheet music (part 2).
7" Single: Released May '80, on Unlimited Gold(USA), by CBS Records (USA). Deleted '83. Catalogue no: **ULG 8563**

SHO' YOU RIGHT
Tracks: / Sho' you right / You're what's on my mind.
12" Single: Released Oct '87, on Breakout, by A&M Records. Catalogue no: **USAT 614**
7" Single: Released Oct '87, on Breakout, by A&M Records. Catalogue no: **USA 614**

WHAT AM I GONNA DO WITH YOU
Tracks: / What am I gonna do with you.
7" Single: Released Mar '75, on 20th Century, by 20th Century Records. Deleted '78. Catalogue no: **BTC 2177**

YOU SEE THE TROUBLE WITH ME
Tracks: / You see the trouble with me.
7" Single: Released Mar '76, on 20th Century, by 20th Century Records. Deleted '79. Catalogue no: **BTC 2277**

YOU'RE THE FIRST, THE LAST, MY EVERYTHING
Tracks: / You're the first, the last, my everything.
7" Single: Released Nov '74, on 20th Century, by 20th Century Records. Deleted '77. Catalogue no: **BTC 2133**
7" Single: Released Oct '88, on Old Gold, by Old Gold Records. Catalogue no: **OG 9770**
7" Single: Released Jul '81, on 20th Century, by 20th Century Records. Catalogue no: **GOLD 516**

White Boys

HARDCORE, IS IT NOT?
Tracks: / Hardcore, is it not?.
12" Single: Released Aug '87, on Polygram (USA), by PolyGram UK Ltd. Catalogue no: **885752 1**

White, Chalky

ONE SHOT
Tracks: / One shot.
7" Single: Released Sep '83, on Solar Sound, Catalogue no: **SOSO 019**

White, Chris

SPANISH WINE
Tracks: / Spanish wine.
7" Single: Released Mar '76, on Charisma, by Virgin Records. Deleted '79. Catalogue no: **CB 272**

White, Christine

CAUGHT BY LOVE
Tracks: / Caught by love / You'll love a good thing.
12" Single: Released Jan '81, on Black Jack, Catalogue no: **BJD 4504**

FOR YOUR PRECIOUS LOVE
Tracks: / For your precious love.
12" Single: Released Aug '84, on ABL, by ABL Records. Catalogue no: **ABL 004**

GET READY
Tracks: / Get ready / Can't stand the pressure.
12" Single: Released Nov '82, on Real Wax, Catalogue no: **RW 106**

White Door

FLAME IN MY HEART
Tracks: / Flame in my heart.
7" Single: Released Aug '84, on Clay, by Clay Records. Deleted '88. Catalogue no: **CLAY 37**
12" Single: Released Aug '84, on Clay, by Clay Records. Deleted '88. Catalogue no: **12 CLAY 37**

JERUSALEM
Tracks: / Jerusalem.
7" Single: Released Jan '86, on Clay, by Clay Records. Deleted '88. Catalogue no: **CLAY 30**

LOVE BREAKDOWN
Tracks: / Love breakdown.
7" Single: Released Jun '83, on Clay, by Clay Records. Deleted '88. Catalogue no: **CLAY 23**
12" Single: Released Jun '83, on Clay, by Clay Records. Deleted '88. Catalogue no: **12 CLAY 23**

WAY OF THE WORLD
Tracks: / Way of the world / Extra.
7" Single: Released Apr '82, on Clay, by Clay Records. Deleted '88. Catalogue no: **CLAY 10**

WINDOWS (SINGLE)
Tracks: / Windows / In heaven.
7" Single: Released Sep '83, on Clay, by Clay Records. Catalogue no: **CLAY 26**

White Europeans

SUN ARISE
Tracks: / Sun arise / Belinda.
7" Single: Released Feb '81, on Aura Records, by Aura Records. Deleted '88. Catalogue no: **AUS 124**

White Fire

PARADES OF GLORY
Tracks: / Parades of glory.
7" Single: Released Aug '79, on Vibes, by Vibes Records. Catalogue no: **98 DB 100**

TELL MICHELLE
Tracks: / Tell Michelle / Don't lock away your love.
7" Single: Released Jul '80, on Record Trading Co., Catalogue no: **RT 31**

White, Frank

ONE MORE LONELY NIGHT (SINGLE)
Tracks: / One more lonely night.
7" Single: Released Jan '89, on PRT, by Castle Communications Records. Catalogue no: **PYS 16**

WHAT YOU GONNA DO
Tracks: / What you gonna do.
7" Single: Released May '83, on Wat, Deleted '86. Catalogue no: **MAB 102**

White Heat

CITY BEAT
Tracks: / City beat.
7" Single: Released Aug '81, on Valium, Catalogue no: **VAL 03**

FINISHED WITH THE FASHIONS
Tracks: / Finished with the fashions / Ordinary Joe.
7" Single: Released Oct '80, on Valium, Catalogue no: **VAL 02**

NERVOUS BREAKDOWN
Tracks: / Nervous breakdown.
7" Single: Released Mar '80, on Valium, Catalogue no: **VAL 01**

White House Connection

NICE HOUSE
Tracks: / Nice house / House party.
12" Single: Released Dec '87, on Soul City,

by Soul City Records. Catalogue no: **SITY 4**

QUEEN OF THE DISCO
Tracks: / Queen of the disco (remix).
12" Single: Released Sep '86, on Total Eclipse, by Total Eclipse Records. Catalogue no: **TELLR 2T**
12" Single: Released Oct '86, on Total Eclipse, by Total Eclipse Records. Catalogue no: **TECLR 2T**

WHO'S IN THE WHITEHOUSE
Tracks: / Who's in the Whitehouse / Main man USA.
12" Single: Released Jul '88, on Soul City, by Soul City Records. Catalogue no: **SITYT 6**
7" Single: Released Jul '88, on Soul City, by Soul City Records. Catalogue no: **SITY 6**

White House White

OUVERTURE
Tracks: / Ouverture.
12" Single: Released 14 May '88, on Subway, by Subway Records. Catalogue no: **SUB 023**

WHITE HOUSE WHITE
Tracks: / White House white.
12" Single: Released '89, on Climax, Catalogue no: **CB 104**

White, Joy

TAKES A MIRACLE
Tracks: / Takes a miracle.
12" Single: Released Jul '82, on Exclusive, Catalogue no: **EX 60 11 30**

White, Karyn

SECRET RENDEZVOUS
Tracks: / Secret rendezvous / Language of love.
Cassingle: Released Aug '89, on Warner Bros., by WEA Records. Catalogue no: **W 2814MC**
CD 5": Released Aug '89, on Warner Bros., by WEA Records. Catalogue no: **W 2814CD**
CD 5": Released Jan '89, on Warner Bros., by WEA Records. Catalogue no: **W 7562CD**
12" Single: Released Aug '89, on Warner Bros., by WEA Records. Catalogue no: **W 2814T**
7" Single: Released Aug '89, on Warner Bros., by WEA Records. Catalogue no: **W 2855**
7" Single: Released Jan '89, on Warner Bros., by WEA Records. Catalogue no: **W 7562**
12" Single: Released Jan '89, on Warner Bros., by WEA Records. Catalogue no: **W 7562T**

SUPERWOMAN (see panel below)
Tracks: / Superwoman / Way you love me, The.
7" Single: Released Jun '89, on Warner Bros., by WEA Records. Catalogue no: **W 2920**
CD 5": Released Jun '89, on Warner Bros., by WEA Records. Catalogue no: **W 2920 CD**
12" Single: Released Jun '89, on Warner Bros., by WEA Records. Catalogue no: **W 2920 T**
12" Single: Released Jun '89, on Warner Bros., by WEA Records. Catalogue no: **W 2920 TW**

WAY YOU LOVE ME, THE
Tracks: / Way you love me, The.
7" Single: Released Oct '88, on Warner Bros., by WEA Records. Catalogue no: **W 7773**
12" Single: Released Nov '88, on Warner Bros., by WEA Records. Catalogue no: **W 7773 T**

White, K.C.

ANYWHERE BUT NOWHERE
Tracks: / Anywhere but nowhere.
12" Single: Released Sep '82, on Solid Groove, Catalogue no: **SG 018**

White, Kevin

COMMUTER DANCE
Tracks: / Commuter dance.
7" Single: Released Feb '87, on Primitive, by Primitive Records. Catalogue no: **PRIME 007**

White, Lenny

KIDS STUFF
Tracks: / Kids stuff / Slip away / Fancy dancer.
7" Single: Released Feb '81, on Elektra Asylum, by Elektra Records (USA). Catalogue no: **K 12500**
12" Single: Released Feb '81, on Elektra Asylum, by Elektra Records (USA). Catalogue no: **LV 43**

PEANUT BUTTER
Tracks: / Peanut butter / Citi dancing / Oh Sylvie.
7" EP: Released Jun '80, on Elektra Asylum, by Elektra Records (USA). Deleted Jun '83. Catalogue no: **LV 37**

White Lie

EMOTIONAL BLACKMAIL
Tracks: / Emotional blackmail.
7" Single: Released Apr '83, on Epic, by CBS Records. Catalogue no: **A 3177**
12" Single: Released Apr '83, on Epic, by CBS Records. Catalogue no: **TA 3177**

White lies

WALK ON THE WILD SIDE
Tracks: / Walk on the wild side / Peppercorn blue.
12" Single: Released Feb '87, on WEA, by WEA Records. Deleted Jan '88. Catalogue no: **YZ 104T**

White Lightnin

THIS POISON FOUNTAIN
Tracks: / This poison fountain.
7" Single: Released Apr '85, on Wild Party, by Wild Party Records. Catalogue no: **PP 1000**

White Lion

WAIT
Tracks: / Wait / All join our hands / Lady of the valley (Track on 12" version.).
7" Single: Released Jan '88, on Atlantic, by WEA Records. Catalogue no: **A 9178**
12" Single: Released Jan '88, on Atlantic, by WEA Records. Catalogue no: **A 9178 T**

WAIT (2)
Tracks: / Wait / All you need is rock 'n' roll / Lonely nights(On 12" version only)..
7" Single: Released Jul '88, on WEA, by WEA Records. Catalogue no: **A 9063**
12" Single: Released Jul '88, on WEA, by WEA Records. Catalogue no: **A 9063 T**

WHEN THE CHILDREN CRY
Tracks: / Then the children cry / Lady of the valley / Tell me (live).
7" Single: Released Mar '89, on Atlantic, by WEA Records. Catalogue no: **A 9015**
12" Single: Released Mar '89, on Atlantic, by WEA Records. Catalogue no: **A 9015TW**
12" Single: Released Mar '89, on Atlantic, by WEA Records. Catalogue no: **A 9015T**

White, Maurice

STAND BY ME
Tracks: / Stand by me.
7" Single: Released Aug '85, on CBS, by CBS Records. Catalogue no: **A 6512**
12" Single: Released Aug '85, on CBS, by CBS Records. Catalogue no: **TA 6512**

White Night

KEEP IT MOVIN'
Tracks: / Keep it movin'.
12" Single: Released Aug '89, on Jive, by Zomba Records. Catalogue no: **JIVE T214**
7" Single: Released Aug '89, on Jive, by Zomba Records. Catalogue no: **JIVE 214**

White, Norma

RIGHT PLACE WRONG TIME
Tracks: / Right place wrong time.
12" Single: Released Oct '85, on Londisc, by Londisc Records. Catalogue no: **LDR 052**

YOU KEEP ME HANGIN' ON
Tracks: / You keep me hangin' on.
12" Single: Released Jul '83, on Sunburn, by Orbitone Records. Catalogue no: **SBD 31**

White Plains

Biographical details: This British all-male group shot to fame in early 1970 with *My Baby Needs Lovin'*, an ultra-commercial single that reached No 9 in the UK and No 13 in the US. Further American success was not forthcoming but the group quickly followed it in Britain with another Top 20 hit, *I've Got You On My Mind.* Both singles were a product of the UK establishment -- they were written by ace songwriting team Roger Cook and Roger Greenaway and sung by leading session vocalist Tony Burrows. Indeed, Burrows set a new record in February 1970 by appearing three times on BBC TV's Top Of The Pops: his singing talents were also employed on Edison Lighthouse's *Love Grows (Where My Rosemary Goes)* and Brotherhood of Man's *United We Stand.* The popularity of White Plains led to them becoming a real group instead of just a studio creation. Pete Nelson and Robin Shaw featured among their vocal ranks but Burrows ended his involvement after those first two hits. Cook and Greenaway stayed on as producers but no longer wrote their singles. White Plains' third record was *Julie, Do Ya Love Me?,* which reached No 8 on the British chart. This was an opportunistic cover version of Bobby Sherman's US smash and the Plains won the race for British chart glory. In 1971 the dreamy *When You Are A King,* a sort of nursery rhyme on disc, gave the group a No 13 hit in Britain. The White Plains idea then faded from public memory but was briefly revived in '73 with a No 21 single, *Step Into A Dream.* The contrived group were then forgotten. However, whether consciously or unconsciously they were remembered by the Motors in 1978 -- their UK Top Twenty single, *Forget About You,* featured a very similar melody to *My Baby Needs Lovin'...* (Bob MacDonald, May 1985.).

I'VE GOT YOU ON MY MIND
Tracks: / I've got you on my mind.
7" Single: Released Apr '70, on Deram, by London Records. Deleted '73. Catalogue no: **DM 291**

JULIE DO YA LOVE ME
Tracks: / Julie do ya love me.
7" Single: Released Oct '70, on Deram, by London Records. Deleted '73. Catalogue no: **DM 315**
7" Single: Released Oct '70, on CBS, by CBS Records. Deleted Oct '73. Catalogue no: **CBS 5144**

MY BABY LOVES LOVIN'
Tracks: / My baby loves lovin'.
7" Single: Released Feb '70, on Deram, by London Records. Deleted '73. Catalogue no: **DM 280**

MY BABY LOVES LOVIN' (OLD GOLD)
Tracks: / My baby loves lovin'.
7" Single: Released Oct '83, on Old Gold, by Old Gold Records. Deleted Jul '88. Catalogue no: **OG 9333**

STEP INTO A DREAM
Tracks: / Step into a dream.
7" Single: Released Feb '73, on Deram, by London Records. Deleted '76. Catalogue no: **DM 371**

WHEN YOU ARE A KING
Tracks: / When you are a king / World gets better with love.
7" Single: Released Jun '71, on Deram, by London Records. Deleted '74. Catalogue no: **DM 333**
7" Single: Released Apr '82, on Decca, by Decca Records. Deleted '88. Catalogue no: **F 13920**

WHEN YOU ARE A KING (OLD GOLD)
Tracks: / When you are a king.
7" Single: Released Sep '85, on Old Gold, by Old Gold Records. Deleted Sep '89. Catalogue no: **OG 9531**

White, Robert

AGE OF SELF, THE
Tracks: / Age of self, The.
7" Single: Released Sep '85, on 7.84, by 7.84 Records. Catalogue no: **TUC 7 84**

DANNY BOY
Tracks: / Danny boy / Old house.
7" Single: Released Mar '80, on RCA, by BMG Records (UK). Deleted Mar '83. Catalogue no: **PB 9520**

HOLD ME TIGHT
Tracks: / Hold me tight.
7" Single: Released Jan '86, on Calibre, Deleted '87. Catalogue no: **CAB 203**
12" Single: Released Jan '86, on Calibre, Deleted '87. Catalogue no: **CABL 203**

White, Roy

LEST WE FORGET
Tracks: / Lest we forget.
12" Single: Released Sep '85, on CBS, by CBS Records. Catalogue no: **TX 6569**
7" Single: Released Sep '85, on CBS, by CBS Records. Catalogue no: **A 6569**

STRANGE TO BE WITH YOU
Tracks: / You are America.
7" Single: Released Jan '86, on CBS, by CBS Records. Catalogue no: **A 6763**
12" Single: Released Jan '86, on CBS, by CBS Records. Catalogue no: **TX 6763**

White, Scott

I DON'T UNDERSTAND IT
Tracks: / I don't understand it.
12" Single: Released Nov '88, on RCA, by BMG Records (UK). Catalogue no: **8792 RD**

White Sister

TICKET TO RIDE
Tracks: / Fashion by passion / Ticket to ride.
7" Single: Released Oct '86, on FM, by FM-Revolver Records. Catalogue no: **VHF 32**
12" Single: Released Oct '86, on FM, by FM-Revolver Records. Catalogue no: **12 VHF 32**

White, Snowy

Biographical details: Raised on the Isle of Wight, guitarist White established himself as a high quality session player during the mid-70's. After working with such names at Cockney Rebel, Cliff Richard and Al Stewart, he played between 1976 and 1980 with the legendary Pink Floyd as a back-up musician for live work and in '79 he played with former Fleetwood Mac star Peter Green on Green's acclaimed In The Skies album. White's next port of call was Thin Lizzy, whom he joined in 1980. But his mild-mannered, elusive personality was unable to adapt to the band's posturing stage presence and wild lifestyle and he quit in '82 to make a solo career. The first product of this phase was 1983's *White Flames* album. After an initial lukewarm response the LP was given a major boost at the beginning of '84 by the success of the single *Bird Of Paradise,* a beautiful ballad which peaked at No 6 on the UK charts. But White was not cut out to be a pop star and failed to follow up this success. His next album, a self-titled effort issued in October '84, was a rather lacklustre piece of work. (Bob MacDonald, May 1985.).

BIRD OF PARADISE
Tracks: / Bird of Paradise.
12" Single: Released Oct '85, on R4, Deleted '86. Catalogue no: **12FOR 3**
7" Single: Released Oct '85, on R4, Deleted '86. Catalogue no: **FOR 3**
7" Single: Released Dec '83, on Towerbell, Catalogue no: **TOW 42**
12" Single: Released Dec '83, on Towerbell, Catalogue no: **12 TOW 42**

FOR YOU
Tracks: / For you.
12" Single: Released Feb '87, on Legend (1), by Legend Records (UK). Catalogue no: **12LM 6**
7" Single: Released Feb '87, on Legend (1), by Legend Records (UK). Catalogue no: **LM 6**

KARYN WHITE - SUPERWOMAN (Released on Warner Bros.)

FORTUNE
Tracks: / Fortune.
7" Single: Released Feb '85, on Towerbell, Catalogue no: **TOW 65**
12" Single: Released Feb '85, on Towerbell, Catalogue no: **12 TOW 65**

I CAN'T LET GO
Tracks: / Rush hour / I can't let go (inst) (*available on 12" version only.) / Changing ways* (*available on 12" version only.).
12" Single: Released Jul '86, on Legend (1), by Legend Records (UK). Catalogue no: **12LM 1**
7" Single: Released Jul '86, on Legend (1), by Legend Records (UK). Catalogue no: **LM 1**

LAND OF FREEDOM
Tracks: / Land of freedom.
7" Single: Released Oct '84, on Towerbell, Catalogue no: **TOW 16**

PEACE ON EARTH
Tracks: / Peace on earth / Broken promises.
7" Single: Released May '84, on Towerbell, Catalogue no: **TOW 52**

THAT CERTAIN THING (SINGLE)
Tracks: / That certain thing.
7" Single: Released Oct '86, on Legend (1), by Legend Records (UK). Catalogue no: **LM 3**
12" Single: Released Oct '86, on Legend (1), by Legend Records (UK). Catalogue no: **12LM 3**

White Soxx

VERSAILLES
Tracks: / Versailles.
7" Single: Released Jun '80, on MCA, by MCA Records. Deleted '83. Catalogue no: **MCA 595**

White Spirit

BACK TO THE GRIND
Tracks: / Back to the grind / Cheetah.
7" Single: Released May '80, on Neat, by Neat Records. Catalogue no: **NEATS 05**

HIGH UPON HIGH
Tracks: / High upon high / No reprieve.
7" Single: Released Nov '80, on MCA, by MCA Records. Deleted Nov '83. Catalogue no: **MCA 652**

White Summer

POWER POISON
Tracks: / Power poison.
7" Single: Released Mar '85, on White Summer, Catalogue no: **WS 001**

White, Tam

WHAT IN THE WORLD'S COME OVER YOU
Tracks: / What in the world's come over you.
7" Single: Released Mar '75, on RAK, by EMI Records. Deleted '78. Catalogue no: **RAK 193**

White, Thomas

IVORY GIRL
Tracks: / Ivory girl.
7" Single: Released Sep '79, on Hit Run, Catalogue no: **DD 21**

White, Tony Joe

Biographical details: One of the few authentic practitioners of the short-lived swamp rock genre, Tony Joe White was born in 1943 in Louisiana. His 1969 deput album, *Black and White*, was produced by Billy Swan and included White's *Pork Salad Annie*, a Top Ten US hit later covered by Elvis Presley, and Willie And Laura Mae Jones, covered by Dusty Springfield. His later *Rainy Night In Georgia* was covered by Brook Benton. (Donald Clarke, March 1988.).

GROUPIE GIRL
Tracks: / Groupie girl.
7" Single: Released Jun '70, on Monument, Deleted '73. Catalogue no: **MON 1043**

White & Torch

Biographical details: Roy White and Steve Torch came to public attention in 1982 on the David Essex Showcase. They managed to reach the grand final of that TV talent contest but subsequent substantial success eluded them: they probably took comfort from the fact that a similar fate greeted the programme's overall winner, Philip Jap. One of the songs White & Torch sang and played on the Showcase was the haunting *Who's Asking You?* This was quickly issued as a single but it failed to chart. Then came *Parade*, which gave the duo their first UK hit single, albeit No 54. However, despite consistent quality, they failed to consolidate this toehold -- 1983's Chic-influenced *Miracle* and the following year's *Bury My Heart* did not make the necessary transfer from DJ/press acclaim to Top Forty status. Their style was dramatic melodic pop, with vocals strongly influenced by the Walker Brothers. By early '85 White & Torch had gone their separate ways. As a duo they would be rememberd as talented also-rans. (Bob MacDonald, May 1985.).

BURY MY HEART
Tracks: / Bury my heart.
7" Single: Released Jan '84, on RCA, by BMG Records (UK). Catalogue no: **RCA 388**
12" Single: Released Jan '84, on RCA, by BMG Records (UK). Catalogue no: **RCAT 388**

MIRACLE
Tracks: / Miracle.
12" Single: Released Oct '83, on RCA, by BMG Records (UK). Catalogue no: **RCAT 370**
7" Single: Released Oct '83, on RCA, by BMG Records (UK). Catalogue no: **RCA 370**

PARADE
Tracks: / Parade / Man to man.
7" Single: Released '82, on Chrysalis, by Chrysalis Records. Deleted '87. Catalogue no: **CHS 2641**
12" Single: Released Oct '82, on Chrysalis, by Chrysalis Records. Deleted '87. Catalogue no: **CHS 12 2639**

WHO'S ASKING YOU
Tracks: / Who's asking you / Looking at you / Guess who.
7" Single: Released '82, on Chrysalis, by Chrysalis Records. Deleted '87. Catalogue no: **CHS 2611**
12" Single: Released '83, on Chrysalis, by Chrysalis Records. Deleted '87. Catalogue no: **CHS 12 2611**

White Wedding

WHITE WEDDING
Tracks: / White wedding: *Southern, Sheila* / Good luck, good health, God bless you: *Murray, Ruby* / Here's to the couple: *Spinners* / She wears my ring: *King, Solomon.*
7" EP: Released May '81, on EMI, by EMI Records. Catalogue no: **MIEP 4001**

White, Willie

OPPORTUNITY
Tracks: / Opportunity.
7" Single: Released Apr '89, on Body Music, by Nuclear Records. Catalogue no: **BZT 020**

Whitehead, Annie

ALIEN STYLE
Tracks: / Alien style.
7" Single: Released Mar '85, on Paladin, Catalogue no: **PALS 100**
12" Single: Released Mar '85, on Paladin, Catalogue no: **PALS 100 12**

Whitelaw, Graham

JOKROK
Tracks: / Jokrok / Jokrok (instrumental).
7" Single: Released Nov '88, on Igus, by Klub Records. Catalogue no: **KLUB 58**

Whitesnake

Biographical details: British heavy metal band Whitesnake were formed in 1978 by ex-Deep Purple singer David Coverdale. He made two solo LPs then started the group, which was named after one of the albums. Former Purples Jon Lord and Ian Paice played on some of the albums until Deep Purple were re-formed. Whitesnake's following has been maintained by heavy touring, but the band made little impact in America. (Donald Clarke, March 1988.)
At the time of their greatest success, this British rock band consisted of David Coverdale, Jon Lord, Bernie Marsden, Micky Moody, Neil Murray and Ian Paice. Whitesnake were founded in 1978 by former Deep Purple vocalist David Coverdale. He had leapt from nowhere to stardom in 1973 by replacing Ian Gillan in the legendary heavy metal group. When Purple folded in '76, legal difficulties had prevented Coverdale from forming a regular touring band. He overcame these in '78 but, in the meantime, had released two albums under his own name: the first of these, 1977's *Whitesnake*, inspired the name of his band. The new group's first recorded product was *Snake bite*, and EP that crawled to No.61 on the UK singles chart in the summer of '78. Their debut LP *Trouble* peaked at No.50 on the British album chart in November of that year. The lowliness of Whitesnake's early chart positions can be attributed to the fact that their formation coincided with the height of Britain's New Wave/punk scene - Coverdale's brand of derivative heavy metal could not have been less fashionable in '78. The group really got into their commercial stride in 1980, the year that saw HM resurgence in the UK charts and concert halls. The melodic *Fool for your loving* gave Coverdale his first ever Top 20 single, reaching No.13 on the British listings; its parent album *Ready and willing* was a Top 10 item, as was every Whitesnake LP thereafter. Their style of music was an unchanging phenomenon - the band's Eighties success simply reflected a revived hard rock market. If Whitesnake sounded like an imitation of Deep Purple, this is because their line-up included not only Coverdale but also two of his former DP colleagues, Lord and Paice.
Whitesnake's biggest LP was 1981's *Come and get it*, which reached No.2 and logged 23 weeks on the UK listings; this album yielded a second British Top 20 single with the raunchy, rhythmic *Don't break my heart again*. By the time of 1982's *Saint's 'n' sinners* LP, Marsden, Murray and Paice had been replaced by Mel Galley, Colin 'Bomber' Hodgkinson and ace rock drummer Cozy Powell. But the continuing predictablity of the band's music was summed up in the title of the album's hit single - *Here I go again* was one of the most over-used titles in UK chart history. Proving that they were at the top of their genre, Whitesnake headlined the Castle Donington Monsters of Rock Festival in August 1983. And proving that they could employ cliched sexual references as profitably as any of their peers, the group's 1984 album was called *Slide it in*. In that year, Lord and Paice joined a reactivated Deep Purple. (Bob MacDonald, 17th May 1985).

AIN'T NO LOVE IN THE HEART OF THE CITY
Tracks: / Ain't no love in the heart of the city / Take me with you.
12" Single: Released Nov '80, on United Artists, by EMI Records. Deleted '87. Catalogue no: **12BP 381**
7" Single: Released Nov '80, on United Artists, by EMI Records. Catalogue no: **BP 381**

DON'T BREAK MY HEART AGAIN
Tracks: / Don't break my heart again / Child of Babylon.
7" Single: Released Apr '81, on Liberty, by EMI Records. Deleted '84. Catalogue no: **BP 395**

FOOL FOR YOUR LOVING
Tracks: / Fool for your loving / Mean business / Don't mess with me.
7" Single: Released Apr '80, on Liberty, by EMI Records. Catalogue no: **BP 352**

GIVE ME ALL YOUR LOVE
Tracks: / Give me all your love (Edit version on 7" single.) / Fool for your loving / Don't break my heart again / Here I go again+ / Straight for the heart (Only on 3"CD single.).
Note: Cat. no. EMW 23/12EMW 23 in clear PVC bag.+ extra track on CD single only.
12" Single: Released Jan '88, on EMI, by EMI Records. Deleted Nov '88. Catalogue no: **12EM 23**
CD 5": Released Jan '88, on EMI, by EMI Records. Deleted 31 Jul '88. Catalogue no: **CDEM 23**
12" Pic: Released Feb '88, on EMI, by EMI Records. Deleted Aug '89. Catalogue no: **12EMP 23**
7" Single: Released Jan '88, on EMI, by EMI Records. Deleted Nov '88. Catalogue no: **EM 23**
CD 3": Released Sep '88, on CBS/Sony (Japan), by CBS Records. Catalogue no: **10EP3007**
Special: Released Jan '88, on EMI, by EMI Records. Deleted Nov '88. Catalogue no: **EMW 23**
Special: Released Jan '88, on EMI, by EMI Records. Deleted Nov '88. Catalogue no: **12EMW 23**

GIVE ME MORE TIME
Tracks: / Give me more time.
7" Single: Released Jan '84, on Liberty, by EMI Records. Catalogue no: **BP 422**
12" Single: Released Jan '84, on Liberty, by EMI Records. Deleted '87. Catalogue no: **12BP 422**

GUILTY OF LOVE
Tracks: / Guilty of love.
7" Single: Released Aug '83, on Liberty, by EMI Records. Catalogue no: **BP 420**
7" Pic: Released Aug '83, on Liberty, by EMI Records. Catalogue no: **BPP 420**

HERE I GO AGAIN
Tracks: / Here I go again (USA remix) / Guilty of love / Guilty of love (USA remix).
Note: (Cat.no. 206954) 3-track cassette single, in 12" X 3" 'Long Box' packaging.
12" Single: Released Nov '87, on EMI, by EMI Records. Deleted Nov '88. Catalogue no: **12EM 35**
10" single: Released Oct '87, on EMI, by EMI Records. Deleted Apr '88. Catalogue no: **10EM 35**
7" Pic: Released Oct '87, on EMI, by EMI Records. Deleted Apr '88. Catalogue no: **EMP 35**
Cassingle: Released Nov '87, on Geffen (USA), by Geffen Records (USA). Catalogue no: **206 954**
7" Single: Released Oct '87, on EMI, by EMI Records. Deleted Nov '88. Catalogue no: **EM 35**
7" Single: Released Oct '82, on Liberty, by EMI Records. Catalogue no: **BP 416**

HERE I GO AGAIN (USA/REMIX)
Tracks: / Here I go again (USA remix) / Guilty of love.
12" Single: Released Jul '87, on EMI, by EMI Records. Catalogue no: **12 EMI 35**

IS THIS LOVE
Tracks: / Is this love / Standing in the shadow / Need your love so bad (Extra track on 12" & CD only) / Still of the night (Extra track on CD only).
7" Single: Released May '87, on EMI, by EMI Records. Catalogue no: **EM 3**
7" EP: Released May '87, on EMI, by EMI Records. Catalogue no: **EMX 3**
CD 5": Released May '87, on EMI, by EMI Records. Deleted 31 Jul '88. Catalogue no: **CDEM 3**
12" Pic: Released 30 May '87, on EMI, by EMI Records. Deleted Oct '87. Catalogue no: **12EMP 3**
12" Single: Released May '87, on EMI, by EMI Records. Deleted Jun '89. Catalogue no: **12EM 3**

LONG WAY FROM HOME
Tracks: / Long way from home.
7" Single: Released Nov '79, on United Artists, by EMI Records. Deleted '82. Catalogue no: **BP 324**

LOVE AIN'T NO STRANGER
Tracks: / Love ain't no stranger / Slow an' easy / Slide it in.
7" Single: Released Jan '85, on Liberty, by EMI Records. Catalogue no: **BP 424**
12" Single: Released Feb '85, on Liberty, by EMI Records. Catalogue no: **12BP 424**

READY AN' WILLING (SINGLE)
Tracks: / Ready an' willing / Nighthawk / We wish you well.
7" Single: Released Jul '80, on United Artists, by EMI Records. Deleted '83. Catalogue no: **BP 363**

SNAKEBITE (EP)
Tracks: / Bloody Mary / Steal away / Ain't no love in the heart of the city / Come on.
7" Single: Released Jun '78, on EMI International, by EMI Records. Deleted '81. Catalogue no: **INEP 751**

STANDING IN THE SHADOW
Tracks: / Standing in the shadow / All or nothing.
7" Pic: Released Apr '84, on Liberty, by EMI Records. Catalogue no: **BPP 423**
7" Single: Released Apr '84, on Liberty, by EMI Records. Catalogue no: **BP 423**

STILL OF THE NIGHT
Tracks: / Still of the night / Here I go again (1987) / You're gonna break my heart again (Extra track on 12" only).
7" Single: Released Mar '87, on EMI, by EMI Records. Deleted Apr '88. Catalogue no: **EMI 5606**
12" Single: Released Mar '87, on EMI, by EMI Records. Deleted Apr '88. Catalogue no: **12 EMI 5606**

STILL OF THE NIGHT (EXT)
Tracks: / Still of the night / Here I go again (1987) / You're gonna break my heart again.
12" Pic: Released Mar '87, on EMI, by EMI Records. Deleted Oct '87. Catalogue no: **12EMIP 5606**

WOULD I LIE TO YOU
Tracks: / Would I lie to you / Girl.
7" Single: Released Jun '81, on Liberty, by EMI Records. Deleted '84. Catalogue no: **BP 399**

Whitfield, David

Biographical details: David Whitfield was one of Britain's favourite singers of the mid-50's. He first attracted attention in the 40's, while serving in the Royal Navy, and after his discharge in 1950 he built up a solid reputation in his native Hull area via club appearances. During the early 50's Whitfield was given radio and theatre exposure by Hughie Green, a broadcaster who was later to achieve greater fame for his talent spotting in television's Opportunity Knocks. In 1953 Whitfield signed with Decca Records and was taken under the wing of Bunny Lewis, one of the company's top in-house producers. His first hit record came in October '53 when *Bridge Of Sighs* reached No 9 on the UK charts. This was a foretaste of things to come. The following month he reached No 1 with *Answer Me*, although he was quickly dethroned from the top slot by a rival version from the more established Frankie Laine. Between 1954 and 1957 Whitfield's light tenor graced a further nine UK Top Ten hits. The biggest was *Cara Mia*, which featured the orchestration of his regular arranger, Mantovani, the astute production of Lewis and the songwriting skill of both arranger and producer, who penned the number under false names. *Cara Mia* held Britain's No 1 position for 10 consecutive weeks during the summer of '54 and, 30 years later, was still the third-longest chart-topper in British record history. The song also gave them a Top

Ten success in America, then a rare feat for a British disc. Whitfield's other smash hit on the UK charts included *Santo Natale* (No 2) and three No 3 successes, *Rags To Riches, Ev'rywhere* and *My September Love*. He epitomised the breed of clean cut, middle-of-the-road ballad singers who dominated the recording scene during the years immediately before rock 'n' roll. When the new music arrived it steadily diminished his chart career: *Adoratiuon Waltz* (early '57) was his final UK Top Tenner and his last Top Thirty disc was in August '58. The singer began a career in opera in 1963 but the move was no great success. He died in January 1980 at the age of 53. (Bob MacDonald, May 1985.)
David Whitfield was born in Hull in 1925; died in 1980 in Australia. He was a pop singer with an operatic tenor whose big international hit was *Cara Mia* in 1954, backed by mantovani and Decca's state-of-the-art recording quality. He turned to an operatic career in 1963; his voice made him welcome world-wide: when he died he was working on cruise ships. (Donald Clarke)..

ADORATION WALTZ
Tracks: / Adoration waltz.
7" Single: Released Jan '57, on Decca, by Decca Records. Deleted '60. Catalogue no: **F 10833**

ANSWER ME
Tracks: / Answer me.
7" Single: Released Oct '53, on Decca, by Decca Records. Deleted '56. Catalogue no: **F 10192**

BEYOND THE STARS
Tracks: / Beyond the stars.
7" Single: Released Feb '55, on Decca, by Decca Records. Deleted '58. Catalogue no: **F 10458**

BOOK, THE
Tracks: / Book, The.
7" Single: Released Feb '54, on Decca, by Decca Records. Deleted '57. Catalogue no: **F 10242**

BRIDGE OF SIGHS
Tracks: / Bridge of sighs.
7" Single: Released Oct '53, on Decca, by Decca Records. Deleted '56. Catalogue no: **F 10129**

CARA MIA
Tracks: / Cara mia.
7" Single: Released Jun '54, on Decca, by Decca Records. Deleted '57. Catalogue no: **F 10327**

CRY MY HEART
Tracks: / Cry my heart.
7" Single: Released Feb '58, on Decca, by Decca Records. Deleted '61. Catalogue no: **F 10978**

EV'RYWHERE
Tracks: / Ev'rywhere.
7" Single: Released Jul '55, on Decca, by Decca Records. Deleted '58. Catalogue no: **F 10515**

I BELIEVE
Tracks: / I believe.
7" Single: Released Nov '60, on Decca, by Decca Records. Deleted '63. Catalogue no: **F 11289**

I'LL FIND YOU
Tracks: / I'll find you.
7" Single: Released Apr '57, on Decca, by Decca Records. Deleted '60. Catalogue no: **F 10864**

MAMA
Tracks: / Mama.
7" Single: Released May '55, on Decca, by Decca Records. Deleted '58. Catalogue no: **F 10515**

MY SEPTEMBER LOVE
Tracks: / My September love.
7" Single: Released Mar '56, on Decca, by Decca Records. Deleted '59. Catalogue no: **F 10690**

MY SON JOHN
Tracks: / My son John.
7" Single: Released Aug '56, on Decca, by Decca Records. Deleted '59. Catalogue no: **F 10769**

ON THE STREET WHERE YOU LIVE
Tracks: / On the street where you live.
7" Single: Released May '58, on Decca, by Decca Records. Deleted '61. Catalogue no: **F 11018**

RAGS TO RICHES
Tracks: / Rags to riches.
7" Single: Released Dec '53, on Decca, by Decca Records. Deleted '56. Catalogue no: **F 10207**

RIGHT TO LOVE, THE
Tracks: / Right to love, The.
7" Single: Released Aug '58, on Decca, by Decca Records. Deleted '61. Catalogue no: **F 11039**

SANTO NATALE
Tracks: / Santo natale.
7" Single: Released Nov '54, on Decca, by Decca Records. Deleted '57. Catalogue no: **F 10399**

WHEN YOU LOSE THE ONE YOU LOVE
Tracks: / When you lose the one you love.
7" Single: Released Nov '55, on Decca, by Decca Records. Deleted '58. Catalogue no: **F 10627**

Whitman, Jim

STOLEN KISS, A
Tracks: / Stolen kiss, A.
7" Single: Released Jan '87, on Priority, by Priority Records. Catalogue no: **PF 3016**

Whitman, Slim

Biographical details: Born in 1924 in Tampa, Florida, Slim Whitman is a country singer with a yodeling style, one of the first crossover artists and an international star, bigger in the UK than at home. *Indian Love Call* was a big US hit in 1952 and the title song from the same Rudolph Friml operetta, *Rose Marie*, was also a hit: in 1955 it was No 1 in Britain for 11 weeks. He toured in Britain so long that his American career suffered, but his country chart hits in the USA resumed in 1961. His TV-advertised albums were UK hits in the late 70's. (Donald Clarke, March 1988.)
This American singer, born Otis Dewey Whitman Jr in Florida, worked as a shipfitter and served in the US. Navy before turning professional at the age of 24 (1948). By this time, he was also a skilled baseball player. He began to make headway in the country-and-western market, and achieved his major breakthrough in 1951 with the international success of *Indian love call*. This 1924 song, from the musical *Rose Marie*, was a perfect vehicle for Whitman's distinctive vocal talents: it showed off his rich texture, his clarity of tone and his yodelling capabilities. A stream of US country hits followed. Whitman's biggest claim to fame in Britain was his staggering 1955 success with the title song from *Rose Marie* (written in the year of the singer's birth - 1924). This infuriatingly catchy ballad was No.1 in the UK for 11 consecutive weeks. Thirty years later, this feat still stood as the all time longest interrupted reign at the top of the british charts. The UK success of *Rose Marie* caused Whitman to become the first C&W star to tour Britain on his own. The genre was largely unknown in the UK at that time, and there is no doubt that he played a leading role in bringing country music to the attention of British ears. However, it is arguable that Whitman was ultimately detrimental to its long-term acceptance - UK listeners were given a stereotyped image of country & western, being led to believe that cowboy ballads and sentimental love numbers were its be-all and end-all.
From the mid-Fifties onwards, Whitman never entered the Top 40 of the American pop charts, but continued to score heavily on the C&W listings. In Britain, the pop hits continued for a short while - *Serenade* reached No.8 in '56 - but after the Top 10 success of 1957's *I'll take you home again, Kathleen*, Whitman's name fell of the UK lists. Suddenly in 1974, Whiteman made a return to pop stardom with *Happy anniversary*. This cloying single was in his traditional romantic style, and reached No.14 on the British chart. The song soon became a standard, with Whitman's disc becoming a perennial gift item between spouses and enjoying frequent plays on radio request shows. It's UK popularity made United Artists Records realise that despite a 17 year dearth of pop hits, the singer was still a marketable commodity. They compiled *The very best of Slim Whitman*, and, inspired by recently successful TV campaigns mounted for Jim Reeves and Perry Como LP collections, they launched a major blitz of television ads. This heavy promotion pushed the album to No.1 in Britain for six weeks in 1976. The idea was milked for all it was worth - the TV-advertised *Red river valley* LP was released a year later, and logged four weeks atop the UK LP listing; mere months later, *Home on the range* gave the yodelling yank a No.2 album. Although Whitman had a solid reputation in Nashville, the scale of his British recognition certainly outweighed his importance in the UK country market. Most of the UK housewives who bought his TV-marketed LPs had probably never heard of the genre's greatest artists, such as Merle Haggard, Waylon Jennings and George Jones. Nonetheless, it should be noted that, in addition to his LP chart success, Whitman's name was bandied about during the mid-Seventies for another reason - Queen, Wings and John Travolta and Olivia Newton John all enjoyed running British No.1 singles and threatened to challenge the record set by Whitman's 1955 chart topper. But all three acts stopped at nine weeks - the 11-week *Rose Marie* remained the champ. (Bob MacDonald, 18th May 1985).

CAN'T HELP FALLING IN LOVE WITH YOU
Tracks: / Can't help falling in love with you / Open up your heart.
7" Single: Released Jan '82, on Liberty, by EMI Records. Catalogue no: **BP 408**

CHINA DOLL
Tracks: / China doll.
7" Single: Released Sep '55, on London Records, by London Records. Deleted '58. Catalogue no: **L 1149**

HAPPY ANNIVERSARY (OLD GOLD)
Tracks: / Happy anniversary.
7" Single: Released Apr '87, on Old Gold, by Old Gold Records. Deleted Sep '89. Catalogue no: **OG 9716**

HAPPY ANNIVERSARY (SINGLE)
Tracks: / Happy anniversary / Indian love call.
Note: Also contains:"Indian love call" by Slim Whitman
7" Single: Released '74, on United Artists, by EMI Records. Catalogue no: **UP 35728**
7" Single: Released Mar '84, on EMI Golden 45's, by EMI Records. Deleted Aug '89. Catalogue no: **G45 14**

I'LL TAKE YOU HOME AGAIN, KATHLEEN (SINGLE)
Tracks: / I'll take you home again Kathleen.
7" Single: Released Apr '57, on London-American, Deleted '60. Catalogue no: **HLP 8403**

I'M A FOOL
Tracks: / I'm a fool.
7" Single: Released Apr '56, on London-American, Deleted '59. Catalogue no: **HLU 8252**

INDIAN LOVE CALL
Tracks: / Indian love call.
7" Single: Released '80, on Liberty, by EMI Records. Catalogue no: **LR 0986**
7" Single: Released Jul '55, on London Records, by London Records. Deleted '58. Catalogue no: **L 1149**

LOVE SONGS OF THE WATERFALL
Special: Released '70, on Sunset (Liberty), by EMI Records. Deleted '74. Catalogue no: **8XS 50153**

ROSE MARIE
Tracks: / Rose Marie / I'll take you home again Kathleen.
7" Single: Released '80, on Liberty, by EMI Records. Catalogue no: **LR 8186**
7" Single: Released Jul '55, on London Records, by London Records. Deleted '58. Catalogue no: **HL 8061**

ROSE MARIE (OLD GOLD)
Tracks: / Rose Marie.
7" Single: Released May '87, on Old Gold, by Old Gold Records. Deleted Sep '89. Catalogue no: **OG 9712**

SERENADE
Tracks: / Serenade.
7" Single: Released Jun '56, on London-American, Deleted '59. Catalogue no: **HLU 8287**

THAT SILVER HAIRED DADDY OF MINE
Tracks: / That silver haired daddy of mine / If I could only dream.
7" Single: Released Oct '80, on Liberty, by EMI Records. Deleted Oct '83. Catalogue no: **BP 377**

TUMBLING TUMBLEWEEDS
Tracks: / Tumbling tumbleweeds.
7" Single: Released Mar '56, on London-American, Deleted '59. Catalogue no: **HLU 8230**

WHEN
Tracks: / When / Till we meet again.
7" Single: Released May '81, on Liberty, by EMI Records. Deleted May '84. Catalogue no: **BP 394**

Whitmore, Iain

WOULD YOU LIKE TO LEAVE
Tracks: / Would you like to leave / You left the water running.
7" Single: Released May '81, on RCA, by BMG Records (UK). Catalogue no: **RCA 63**

Whitren, Jackie

INTERNATIONAL TIMES (SINGLE)
Tracks: / International times.
7" Single: Released Jul '83, on Living, Catalogue no: **LRS 111**
12" Single: Released Jul '83, on Living, Catalogue no: **12 LRS 1**

Whittaker, Roger

Biographical details: This British singer, songwriter and guitarist was born in Kenya, although his family was of UK origin. A road accident had seriously injured his father's lungs, and this had necessitated the family's the family's relocation to a dry, high altitude climate. Roger took up singing and playing the guitar during childhood and, after serving in the King's African Rifles during the Mau Mau uprising, moved to Britain in order to study at Bangor University in Wales. He graduated in zoology, chemistry, bio-chemistry and marine biology, but decided to go for a musical career. That decision was taken in 1960, but it was not until the end of the Sixties that his gamble paid off. After almost a decade of uphill struggles, during which he began to write more and more of his own material, he achieved success in continental Europe with the self-penned *Mexican whistler*. Whittaker's big British breakthrough ocurred in Januarty 1970, when *Durham Town (the leavin') reached No.12 on the charts; this wistful song was a slow-burning success, logging 18 weeks on the Top 50. It was soon followed by further self-composed hits: I don't believe in If anymore* reached No.8 and also chalked up 18 weeks on the UK Top 50; *New world in the morning* reached No.17 with 14 chart weeks; and *Why* peaked at No.47. After 3 and a half away from the UK charts, Whittaker enjoyed his bigges record in 1975. The strange story of *The last farewell* began in 1971, when the singer was hosting a BBC radio series - he invited listeners to submit their own lyrics, and he composed music for those that he liked best. One such offering was *The last farewell*, with words by Ron Webster, a silversmith from Birmingham. It suddenly became a hit in America in the summer of '75, after recieving heavy airplay on an Atlanta radio station. The song climbed to No.19 on the Billboard Hot 100, and then proceeded to reach No.2 in Britain. Ironically, it was held off the top slot by another nautical single - *Sailing* by Rod Stewart. *The last farewell* was a perfect vehicle for Whittaker's rich fatherly, 'wise old man' image. His usual style was melodic folk.MoR music, augmented in concert by his prowess as a whistler. *The last farewell* brought Whittaker his only UK Top 10 album - *The very best of Roger Whittaker* reached No.5 and logged 42 weeks on the British LP charts. From 1976 onwards, he failed to register a UK hit single but remained an international touring attraction, particularly in West Germany. (Bob MacDonald, 19th May 1985)
Roger Whittaker was born in 1936 in Kenya. The singer, songwriter, guitarist and whistler is one of the most popular MoR artists in the world. He represented Britain at the Knokke Festival in Belgium in 1967 and won; *Durham Town (The Leaving)* was No. 12 in the UK in 1969 and he has been selling out tours ever since. He writes most of his own material and has often appeared on the TV with Des O'Connor, another king of MoR; they had a top ten duet hit in 1986. (Donald Clarke)..

ALBANY
Tracks: / Albany / Love will.
7" Single: Released May '82, on EMI, by EMI Records. Catalogue no: **EMI 5311**

CANDLE
Tracks: / Jerusalem goodbye.
7" Single: Released Jun '86, on Tembo, by Tembo Records. Catalogue no: **TML 117**

CHANGES
Tracks: / Changes / I can hear kentucky calling me.
7" Single: Released Feb '82, on EMI, by EMI Records. Deleted Feb '87. Catalogue no: **EMI 5270**

DURHAM TOWN
Tracks: / Durham town (the leaving) / I don't believe in if anymore.
7" Single: Released Nov '69, on Columbia, by EMI Records. Deleted '72. Catalogue no: **DB 8613**

DURHAM TOWN (OLD GOLD)
Tracks: / Durham town (the leavin').
7" Single: Released Apr '86, on Old Gold, by Old Gold Records. Catalogue no: **OG 9589**

FAMILY
Tracks: / Family / Blow gentle breeze.
7" Single: Released Jan '80, on Columbia, by EMI Records. Deleted Jan '83. Catalogue no: **DB 9072**

GENIUS OF LOVE, THE (SINGLE)
Tracks: / Genius of love.
7" Single: Released Apr '86, on Tembo, by Tembo Records. Catalogue no: **TML 112**

HAPPY EVERYTHING

Tracks: / Happy everything.
7" Single: Released Nov '84, on Tembo, by Tembo Records. Catalogue no: **TML 104**

I DON'T BELIEVE IN IF ANY MORE (SINGLE)
Tracks: / I don't believe in if anymore.
7" Single: Released Apr '70, on Columbia, by EMI Records. Deleted '73. Catalogue no: **DB 8664**

I LOVE YOU
Tracks: / I love you / Gravy boat.
7" Single: Released Sep '88, on Tembo, by Tembo Records. Deleted 30 May '89. Catalogue no: **TML 134**

I'M BACK
Tracks: / I'm back / Shimoni.
7" Single: Released Nov '83, on Tembo, by Tembo Records. Catalogue no: **KENYA 1**

LAST FAREWELL, THE
Tracks: / New world in the morning / Last farewell, The.
7" Single: Released Jul '75, on EMI, by EMI Records. Deleted '78. Catalogue no: **EMI 2294**

LAST FAREWELL, THE (OLD GOLD)
Tracks: / Last farewell, The.
7" Single: Released Apr '86, on Old Gold, by Old Gold Records. Catalogue no: **OG 9591**

MAKE WAY FOR MAN
Tracks: / Make way for man.
7" Single: Released Mar '84, on Tembo, by Tembo Records. Catalogue no: **KENYA 2**

MAMMY BLUE
Tracks: / Mammy blue.
7" Single: Released Oct '71, on Columbia, by EMI Records. Deleted '74. Catalogue no: **DB 8822**

NEW WORLD IN THE MORNING (SINGLE)
Tracks: / New world in the morning.
7" Single: Released Oct '70, on Columbia, by EMI Records. Deleted '73. Catalogue no: **DB 8718**

OH LIFE
Tracks: / Oh life / Wishes.
7" Single: Released Mar '80, on Columbia, by EMI Records. Deleted '83. Catalogue no: **DB 9077**

ONE MORE CHANCE
Tracks: / One more chance / Your fool.
7" Single: Released Mar '88, on Tembo, by Tembo Records. Catalogue no: **TML 131**

SHENANDOAH
Tracks: / Shanandoah / Amazing Grace / Skye boat song (with Des O'Connor.).
7" Single: Released Feb '87, on Tembo, by Tembo Records. Catalogue no: **TML 124**
CD 5": Released Mar '87, on Tembo, by Tembo Records. Deleted 30 Jun '89. Catalogue no: **TMLCD 124**

SKYE BOAT SONG
Tracks: / Remember romance / Time.
7" Single: Released Sep '86, on Tembo, by Tembo Records. Catalogue no: **TML 119**

SO GOOD, SO BAD, SO SOON
Tracks: / So good, so bad, so soon / Moonshine.
7" Single: Released Oct '81, on EMI, by EMI Records. Catalogue no: **EMI 5243**

STRANGER ON THE SHORE
Tracks: / Stranger on the shore.
7" Single: Released Mar '83, on EMI, by EMI Records. Catalogue no: **EMI 5377**

TAKE A LITTLE, GIVE A LITTLE (SINGLE)
Tracks: / Take a little, give a little.
7" Single: Released Sep '84, on Tembo, by Tembo Records. Catalogue no: **TML 102**

TWELFTH OF NEVER
Tracks: / Twelfth of never / One another.
7" Single: Released 31 Oct '87, on Tembo, by Tembo Records. Catalogue no: **TML 130**

WELCOME HOME
Tracks: / Welcome home / Now the pain begins.
7" Single: Released Jul '87, on Tembo, by Tembo Records. Catalogue no: **TML 127**

WHERE GOOD LOVE GOES
Tracks: / Where good love goes.
CD 5": Released Aug '89, on Polydor, by Polydor Ltd. Catalogue no: **TMLCD 136**
7" Single: Released Aug '89, on Polydor, by Polydor Ltd. Catalogue no: **TML 136**

WHY
Tracks: / Why.
7" Single: Released Apr '71, on Columbia, by EMI Records. Deleted '74. Catalogue no: **DB 8752**

YOU ARE MY MIRACLE
Tracks: / You are my miracle / I am but a small voice.
7" Single: Released Oct '80, on Columbia, by EMI Records. Deleted Oct '83. Catalogue no: **DB 9089**

Whitworth, Karl

MYTHS OF CONSTANCE
Tracks: / Myths of Constance.
7" Single: Released May '82, on Binji, by Bulk Cement Marketing International. Catalogue no: **BINJI 2**

NAMES NUMBERS AND PLACES
Tracks: / Names numbers and places.
7" Single: Released Aug '81, on Binji, by Bulk Cement Marketing International. Catalogue no: **BINJI 1**

Whiz Kid

HE'S GOT THE BEAT
Tracks: / He's got the beat / Play that beat Mr. DJ.
7" Single: Released May '85, on Tommy Boy, by Polydor Ltd. Catalogue no: **IS 229**
12" Single: Released May '85, on Tommy Boy, by Polydor Ltd. Catalogue no: **12IS 229**

Whizz

MAXIMUM VOLUME
Tracks: / Maximum volume.
12" Single: Released Aug '85, on Rock City Records, by Rock City Records. Catalogue no: **RCRT 8**
7" Single: Released Aug '85, on Rock City Records, by Rock City Records. Catalogue no: **RCR 8**

MOVIN' ON
Tracks: / Movin' on.
12" Single: Released Sep '89, on Debut, by Skratch Records. Catalogue no: **DEBTX 3075**

Whizz For Atoms

THAT SINKING FEELING
Tracks: / That sinking feeling / Stood up again.
7" Single: Released Sep '84, on Graduate, by Graduate Records. Deleted Jan '87. Catalogue no: **GRAD 16**

Whizz Kids

PAYE AS YOU EARN
Tracks: / Paye as you earn.
7" Single: Released Oct '79, on Dead Good, Catalogue no: **DEAD 6**

Whizz & Voice

WHIZZ RAP
Tracks: / Whizz rap.
Cassingle: Released Apr '85, on BBC, by BBC Records & Tapes. Deleted Apr '89. Catalogue no: **ZRESL 166**
7" Single: Released Apr '85, on BBC, by BBC Records & Tapes. Deleted 31 Aug '88. Catalogue no: **RESL 166**

Who

Biographical details: Apart from the Beatles and the Rolling Stones, the most significant rock group to emerge from the UK during the 60's were the Who -- Roger Daltrey, Pete Townshend, John Entwistle and Keith Moon. All four were born in London in the mid-40's and were at the right age to form a rebellious band in 1964. Vocalist Daltrey, guitarist Townshend and bassist Entwistle first began playing together in 1959, while pupils at Acton County Grammar School. During the early 60's they became the Detours, later the High Numbers. They progressed from pop and rhythm and blues cover versions to an espousal of the Mod cause: the Mod fashion and lifestyle, which centred on clothes, scooters and an eclectic choice of music, was exploding into action in London at the time and the group set out to exploit it. The High Numbers were a short-lived combo: in late '64 Daltrey, Townshend and Entwistle dropped their existing drummer in favour of the wild Keith Moon and acquired a new management team, Kit Lambert and Chris Stamp. Lambert, in particular, played a crucial role, encouraging the band to make their music and performance more hard and aggressive in order to live up to the violent behavioural tendencies that were widely associated with the Mod scene. In their quest for the image that would attract the most publicity the new managers persuaded Townshend and Moon to make instrument smashing a regular concert finale. During this period Townshend developed his songwriting skills and these frenzied activities rapidly rewarded the Who with their first hit: *I Can't Explain* reached No 8 in the UK in early '65. A string of Top Tenners, all written by Townshend, followed. Their third hit was the most important single of their career -- *My Generation*, released in late '65, became an all-time classic anthem of youth rebellion. Although it came out just a few weeks after the Rolling Stones' *Satisfaction*, it stood out in its own right and remains one of the most frantic and exciting records ever made. In contrast to the Stones, however, the Who's single did not reach No 1: the quartet never achieved a UK No 1 single, their best shots being *My Generation* and 1966's *I'm A Boy*, both of which got to No 2. Other Top Ten singles of the mid-60's were *Anyway, Anyhow, Anywhere, Substitute, Happy Jack, Pictures Of Lily and I Can See For Miles*. Their debut album, *My Generation*, reached the Top Ten LP list, as did *A Quick One* in '67. *I Can See For Miles* gave the band their first and only Top Ten single in the States. During the late 60's and early 70's the Who continued to hit the singles charts on both sides of the Atlantic but found greater success through albums and tours. Their international career reached a new level in 1969 with the success of their double album *Tommy*: this highly adventurous and original rock opera ("concept album" became the fashionable term) told of the trials and tribulations of a deaf, dumb and blind kid who "sure plays a mean pinball" and was something even the pioneering Beatles had not attempted. *Tommy* took the Who both to traditional rock venues and to European and American opera houses and in 1975 Daltrey played the title role in Ken Russell's typically over-the-top but very effective film adaptation. To follow *Tommy* the Who went to the other end of the spectrum and released *Live At Leeds*, a great album which confirmed their status as one of the world's top live rock bands, perhaps second only to the Stones. Their next LP, *Who's Next*, reached the UK No 1 slot for one week in September '71 -- their only week at the top of either of Britain's charts -- and yielded the classic single *Won't Get Fooled Again*. During the final ten years of their existence the Who continued to make good records but their output was not quite up to its previous classic status. The *Quadrophenia* double album was the spiritual successor to *Tommy* but was underrated by reviewers at the time. Managers Lambert and Stamp split from the group in 1976 -- Lambert died in April '81 after falling down a flight of stairs -- and Moon's excessive lifestyle finally felled him in September '78 when, at 32, he died of an accidental drug overdose. Moon the Loon was irreplaceable, so it was perhaps unwise for the other three members to try to continue the Who without him. Replacement Kenny Jones -- formerly of the Small Faces and the Faces -- was a fine drummer but, in 1982, the band finally realised that they were a pale shadow of former glories and broke up. The termination decision was made by Townshend: by this time both he and Daltrey were well established as solo performers, Daltrey as an actor as well as a singer. (Bob MacDonald, May 1985.)The most prominent UK rock band of the 1960s after the Beatles and the Rolling Stones: vocalist Roger Daltrey; vocalist, guitarist and songwriter Pete Townshend; bassist John Entwistle (also played French Horn) and drummer Keith Moon, all born in London 1944-47. One of their early managers was Kit Lambert, son of composer-sonductor Constant Lambert and like his father died young without fulfilling his promise; Moon also died of his excesses (in 1978) and was replaced by ex-Small Faces drummer Kenney Jones. They are perhaps most famous for the first rock opera, *Tommy*; their earlier songs, like those of the Kinks, were regarded as anthems by their generation, but their work is dating quickly: they performed at a British record industry bash in early 1988 and one critic said that hearing them perform *My Generation* was about as much fun as getting Grandma out of bed to dance the twist. (Donald Clarke)..

5:15
Tracks: / 5:15.
7" Single: Released Oct '73, on Track, by Polydor Ltd. Deleted '76. Catalogue no: **2094 115**

ANYWAY, ANYHOW, ANYWHERE
Tracks: / Anyway, anyhow, anywhere.
7" Single: Released May '65, on Brunswick, by Decca Records. Deleted '68. Catalogue no: **05935**

ATHENA
Tracks: / Athena.
Special: Released Sep '82, on Polydor, by Polydor Ltd. Catalogue no: **WHOPX 6**
7" Pic: Released Sep '82, on Polydor, by Polydor Ltd. Catalogue no: **WHOP 6**
7" Single: Released Sep '82, on Polydor, by Polydor Ltd. Catalogue no: **WHO 6**
12" Single: Released Sep '82, on Polydor, by Polydor Ltd. Catalogue no: **WHOX 6**

DOGS
Tracks: / Dogs.
7" Single: Released Jun '68, on Track, by Polydor Ltd. Deleted '71. Catalogue no: **604 023**

DON'T LET GO THE COAT
Tracks: / Don't let go the coat.
7" Single: Released May '81, on Polydor, by Polydor Ltd. Deleted '84. Catalogue no: **WHO 005**
7" Single: Released Apr '81, on Polydor, by Polydor Ltd. Deleted '85. Catalogue no: **WHO 5**

HAPPY JACK
Tracks: / Happy Jack.
7" Single: Released Dec '66, on Reaction, Deleted '69. Catalogue no: **591 010**

I CAN SEE FOR MILES
Tracks: / I can see for miles.
7" Single: Released Oct '67, on Track, by Polydor Ltd. Deleted '70. Catalogue no: **604 011**

I CAN'T EXPLAIN
Tracks: / I can't explain.
7" Single: Released '80, on Mercury, by Phonogram Ltd. Catalogue no: **LR 0163**
7" Single: Released Feb '65, on Brunswick, by Decca Records. Deleted '68. Catalogue no: **05926**

I'M A BOY
Tracks: / I'm a boy.
7" Single: Released Sep '66, on Reaction, Deleted '69. Catalogue no: **591 004**

JOIN TOGETHER
Tracks: / Join together.
7" Single: Released Jun '72, on Track, by Polydor Ltd. Deleted '75. Catalogue no: **2094 102**

KIDS ARE ALRIGHT, THE (SINGLE)
Tracks: / Kids are alright, The.
7" Single: Released Sep '66, on Brunswick, by Decca Records. Deleted '69. Catalogue no: **05965**

LAST TIME, THE
Tracks: / Last time, The.
7" Single: Released Jul '67, on Track, by Polydor Ltd. Deleted '70. Catalogue no: **604 006**

LEGAL MATTER, A
Tracks: / Legal matter, A.
7" Single: Released Mar '66, on Brunswick, by Decca Records. Deleted '69. Catalogue no: **05956**

LET'S SEE ACTION
Tracks: / Let's see action.
7" Single: Released Oct '71, on Track, by Polydor Ltd. Deleted '74. Catalogue no: **2094 012**

LONG LIVE ROCK
Tracks: / Long live rock.
7" Single: Released Apr '79, on Polydor, by Polydor Ltd. Deleted '82. Catalogue no: **WHO 2**

MAGIC BUS
Tracks: / Magic bus.
7" Single: Released Oct '68, on Track, by Polydor Ltd. Deleted '71. Catalogue no: **604 024**

MY GENERATION (SINGLE)
Tracks: / My generation / Substitute / Baba O'Riley (Only on 12", CD, and MC single.) / Behind blue eyes (Only on 12", CD, and MC single.).
12" Single: Released Feb '88, on Polydor, by Polydor Ltd. Catalogue no: **POSPX 907**
CD 5": Released Feb '88, on Polydor, by Polydor Ltd. Catalogue no: **POCD 907**
Cassingle: Released Feb '88, on Polydor, by Polydor Ltd. Deleted 30 May '89. Catalogue no: **POSPC 907**
7" Single: Released Nov '65, on Brunswick, by Decca Records. Deleted '68. Catalogue no: **05944**
7" Single: Released Feb '88, on Polydor, by Polydor Ltd. Catalogue no: **POSP 907**

PICTURES OF LILY
Tracks: / Pictures of Lily.
7" Single: Released Apr '67, on Track, by Polydor Ltd. Deleted '70. Catalogue no: **604 002**

PINBALL WIZARD
Tracks: / Pinball wizard.
7" Single: Released Mar '69, on Track, by Polydor Ltd. Deleted '72. Catalogue no: **604 027**
7" Single: Released '80, on Mercury, by Phonogram Ltd. Catalogue no: **LR 8086**

READY STEADY WHO
Tracks: / Disguises / Circles / Batman / Bucket "T" / Barbara Ann.
7" EP: Released Nov '83, on Polydor, by Polydor Ltd. Deleted '86. Catalogue no: **WHO 7**

RELAY
Tracks: / Relay.
7" Single: Released Jan '73, on Track, by Polydor Ltd. Deleted '76. Catalogue no: **2094 106**

SEE ME FEEL ME
Tracks: / See me feel me.
7" Single: Released '80, on Mercury, by Phonogram Ltd. Catalogue no: **LR 8241**

SEEKER, THE
Tracks: / Seeker, The.
7" Single: Released Apr '70, on Track, by Polydor Ltd. Deleted '73. Catalogue no: **604 036**

SQUEEZE BOX
Tracks: / Squeeze box.
7" Single: Released Jan '76, on Polydor, by Polydor Ltd. Deleted '79. Catalogue no: **2121 275**

SUBSTITUTE
Tracks: / Substitute.
7" Single: Released Mar '66, on Reaction. Deleted '69. Catalogue no: **591 001**

SUMMERTIME BLUES
Tracks: / Summertime blues.
7" Single: Released Aug '70, on Track, by Polydor Ltd. Deleted '73. Catalogue no: **2094 002**
7" Single: Released '80, on Mercury, by Phonogram Ltd. Catalogue no: **LR 3300**

TWIST & SHOUT
Tracks: / Twist and shout.
7" Single: Released Nov '84, on MCA, by MCA Records. Catalogue no: **MCA 927**

WHO ARE YOU (SINGLE)
Tracks: / Who are you.
7" Single: Released Jul '78, on Polydor, by Polydor Ltd. Catalogue no: **WHO 1**

WON'T GET FOOLED AGAIN
Tracks: / Won't get fooled again / Bony Moronie (live) / Dancing in the street (live) (on 12" and CD single only) / Marie Anne with the shaky hand (on 12" and CD single only) / Won't get fooled again (extended version) (on 12" and CD single only).
Note: "A classic Who track which was a top ten hit in 1971. Bonie Moronie is a previously unissued live version of the Old Larry Williams hit and recorded in 1971. Dancing in the street is again a live version of the Martha and the Vandellas hit which the Who also recorded in 1971 and again previously unavailable. Mary Anne was recorded in 1967 and is a different version of the old Who favourite." *Won't get fooled again (extended version), Marie Anne* and *Dancing in the street*.
7" Single: Released Aug '79, on Polydor, by Polydor Ltd. Catalogue no: **2094 009**
CD 5": Released Jun '88, on Polydor, by Polydor Ltd. Deleted Oct '89. Catalogue no: **POCD 917**
7" Single: Released Jun '88, on Polydor, by Polydor Ltd. Catalogue no: **POSP 917**
12" Single: Released Jun '88, on Polydor, by Polydor Ltd. Catalogue no: **POSPX 917**

YOU BETTER YOU BET (see panel below)
Tracks: / You better you bet / Quiet one.
7" Single: Released Feb '81, on Polydor, by Polydor Ltd. Catalogue no: **WHO 4**

Who Cares

DOCTOR IN DISTRESS
Tracks: / Doctor in distress.
7" Single: Released Apr '85, on Record Shack, by Record Shack Records. Catalogue no: **DOC 1**
12" Single: Released Apr '85, on Record Shack, by Record Shack Records. Catalogue no: **DOCT 1**

Who Me

EVERY BA T ROCK
Tracks: / Every bat rock.
12" Single: on Silver Screen, by Creole Records. Catalogue no: **MIXT 2**

Who Said Charge

SUNARISE
Tracks: / Sunarise.
7" Single: Released Feb '83, on Art-Life. Deleted '86. Catalogue no: **DES 101**

Who Said That

LOVERBOY
Tracks: / Loverboy / Work don't play.
7" Single: Released Jun '86, on Media Clone, Catalogue no: **MCR 100**

Who The Hell...

USE IMAGINATION
Tracks: / In your eyes / How many hours.
12" Single: Released Feb '87, on Influx, by Influx Vinyls. Catalogue no: **FUX 1T**
7" Single: Released Jan '87, on Influx, by Influx Vinyls. Catalogue no: **FUX 1**

Whodini

Biographical details: This American duo first entered the UK Top Seventy-Five singles chart at the end of 1982 with *Magic's Wand*. This track achieved another minor chart placing in '84 as the lead song on *The Whodini Electro* EP, which also featured their two '83 singles, *Haunted House Of Rock* and *Rap Machine*. Whodini are two black New Yorkers who inject a strong dose of humour into 80's funk techniques. Their self-titled debut album, released in late '83, blended their brand of rapping and scratching with some strong rock influences and featured contributions from Britain's Thomas Dolby and West German producer Conny Plank (best known for his work with Kraftwerk, Can and Ultravox). In late '84 Whodini continued in fine funky form with a double-A-side Top Five hit on the US Black Charts, *Friends/Five Minutes Of Funk*. (Bob MacDonald, May 1985)..

BIG MOUTH
Tracks: / Big mouth.
7" Single: Released Jun '85, on Jive, by Zomba Records. Catalogue no: **JIVE 92**
12" Single: Released Jun '85, on Jive, by Zomba Records. Catalogue no: **JIVET 92**

ESCAPE
Tracks: / Escape.
7" Single: Released Aug '84, on Jive, by Zomba Records. Catalogue no: **JIVE 56**
12" Single: Released Aug '84, on Jive, by Zomba Records. Catalogue no: **JIVET 56**

FREAKS COME OUT AT NIGHT
Tracks: / Freaks come out at night.
12" Single: Released Oct '85, on Jive, by Zomba Records. Catalogue no: **JIVET 107**
12" Single: Released Jan '85, on Jive, by Zomba Records. Catalogue no: **JIVET 84**
7" Single: Released Oct '85, on Jive, by Zomba Records. Catalogue no: **JIVE 107**

FUNKY BEAT
Tracks: / Funky beat.
12" Single: Released May '86, on Jive, by Zomba Records. Catalogue no: **JIVET 119**
7" Single: Released May '86, on Jive, by Zomba Records. Catalogue no: **JIVE 119**

WHO - YOU BETTER YOU BET (Released on Polydor)

HAUNTED HOUSE OF ROCKS
Tracks: / Haunted house of rock (part 1) / Haunted house of rock (part 2).
12" Single: Released Apr '83, on Jive, by Zomba Records. Catalogue no: **JIVET 34**
7" Single: Released Apr '83, on Jive, by Zomba Records. Catalogue no: **JIVE 34**

MAGIC'S WAND
Tracks: / Magic wand / It's all in Mr. Magic's wand.
7" Pic: Released Feb '83, on Jive, by Zomba Records. Catalogue no: **JIVEP 28**
7" Single: Released Nov '82, on Jive, by Zomba Records. Catalogue no: **JIVE 28**
12" Single: Released Nov '82, on Jive, by Zomba Records. Catalogue no: **JIVET 28**

NASTY LADY
Tracks: / Nasty lady.
7" Single: Released Jan '84, on Jive, by Zomba Records. Catalogue no: **JIVE 58**
12" Single: Released Jan '84, on Jive, by Zomba Records. Catalogue no: **JIVET 58**

ONE LOVE (EXIT)
Tracks: / One love (exit) / One love (exit) (album mix) / One love (exit) (instrumental mix).
12" Single: Released Sep '86, on Jive, by Zomba Records. Catalogue no: **JIVET 130**

RAP MACHINE
Tracks: / Rap machine.
7" Single: Released Nov '83, on Jive, by Zomba Records. Catalogue no: **JIVE 45**
12" Single: Released Nov '83, on Jive, by Zomba Records. Catalogue no: **JIVET 45**

ROCK YOU AGAIN
Tracks: / Rock you again.
CD 5": Released Mar '88, on Jive, by Zomba Records. Deleted '88. Catalogue no: **JIVECD 144**
7" Single: Released Mar '88, on Jive, by Zomba Records. Deleted '88. Catalogue no: **JIVE 144**
12" Single: Released Mar '88, on Jive, by Zomba Records. Deleted '88. Catalogue no: **JIVET 144**

WHODINI ELECTRO, THE
Tracks: / Jive magic wand / Nasty lady / Rap machine / Haunted house of rock.
12" Single: Released Mar '84, on Jive, by Zomba Records. Catalogue no: **JIVET 61**
Cassingle: Released May '84, on Jive, by Zomba Records. Catalogue no: **JIVEK 61**
7" EP: Released Mar '84, on Jive, by Zomba Records. Deleted '87. Catalogue no: **JIVE 61**

Whoopee Cushions

SO GOODBYE ROLF HARRIS
Tracks: / So goodbye Rolf Harris.
7" Single: Released Oct '79, on Dubious. Deleted '88. Catalogue no: **DUB 6**

Who's George

DIDN'T CATCH YOUR NAME
Tracks: / Didn't catch your name.
7" Single: Released Aug '80, on Impact, by Ace Records. Catalogue no: **ACT 1**

FOREVER
Tracks: / Forever.
7" Single: Released Jul '81, on Compact Organisation. Deleted '83. Catalogue no: **ACT 3**

I CAN'T RESIST YOU
Tracks: / I can't resist you / What do you want.
7" Single: Released Jul '82, on Cheapskate. Catalogue no: **CHEAP 47**

Whyos

FULL ARMS AND AN EMPTY HEART
Tracks: / Full arms and an empty heart.
7" Single: Released Jun '84, on Rockhouse, by Rockhouse Records (Holland). Catalogue no: **SP 8408**

TALK TO ME LIKE THE RAIN
Tracks: / Talk to me like the rain.
7" Single: Released Apr '85, on Rockhouse, by Rockhouse Records (Holland). Catalogue no: **SP 8502**

Wibbley Brothers

FIRST AID
Tracks: / First aid.
7" Single: Released Aug '81, on Rondelet Music, by Rondelet Music & Records. Catalogue no: **ROUND 9**

Wichen Kopf

PLAYS WITH MARIONETTES
Tracks: / Plays with Marionettes.
7" Single: Released Oct '82, on Missing Link (Australia), Catalogue no: **ANDA 21**

Wicked Things

LOVE NUMBER ONE
Tracks: / Love number one / Love number one (inst).
12" Single: Released Feb '88, on New York 42, by Satril Records. Catalogue no: **WICKT 1**
7" Single: Released Feb '88, on New York 42, by Satril Records. Catalogue no: **WICK 1**

Wicker Man

SUNDAY DINNER
Tracks: / Sunday dinner.
7" Single: Released Jul '88, on Brotherhood Music, Catalogue no: **BH 003**

Wickets

24 HOURS FROM TULSA
Tracks: / 24 hours from Tulsa.
7" Single: Released Oct '84, on Completely Different, by Neat Records. Catalogue no: **MAD 002**

Wide Boy Awake

BILLY HYENA
Tracks: / Billy Hyena / Set fighter.
12" Single: Released Feb '84, on RCA, by BMG Records (UK). Catalogue no: **WBAT 3**
7" Single: Released Feb '84, on RCA, by BMG Records (UK). Catalogue no: **WBA 3**

BONA VENTURA
Tracks: / Bona ventura / Come back Friday.
7" Single: Released Feb '83, on RCA, by BMG Records (UK). Catalogue no: **WBA 2**
12" Single: Released Mar '83, on RCA, by BMG Records (UK). Catalogue no: **WBAT 2**

CHICKEN OUTLAW
Tracks: / Chicken outlaw / Slang teacher.
7" Single: Released Oct '82, on RCA, by BMG Records (UK). Catalogue no: **WBA 1**
12" Single: Released Oct '82, on RCA, by BMG Records (UK). Catalogue no: **WBAT 1**
7" Pic: Released Oct '82, on RCA, by BMG Records (UK). Catalogue no: **WBAP 1**

Wide Boys

STOP THAT BOY
Tracks: / Stop that boy / Heart of stone.
7" Single: Released Aug '80, on Big Bear, by Big Bear Records. Deleted '88. Catalogue no: **BB 30**

Wiedlin, Jane

BLUE KISS
Tracks: / Blue kiss / One hundred years.
7" Single: Released Oct '85, on I.R.S. Catalogue no: **IRM 107**
12" Single: Released Oct '85, on I.R.S. Catalogue no: **IRT 107**

INSIDE A DREAM
Tracks: / Inside a dream / Song of the factory / Inside a dream (12" mix) (12" & CD single only.) / Inside a dub (12" only.) / Song of the factory (12" only.) / Inside a dream (12" edited version) (7" promo only.).
12" Single: Released Sep '88, on EMI-Manhattan, by EMI Records. Deleted Aug '89. Catalogue no: **12MT 55**
7" Pic: Released Oct '88, on EMI-Manhattan, by EMI Records. Deleted Aug '89. Catalogue no: **MTP 55**
7" Single: Released Sep '88, on EMI-Manhattan, by EMI Records. Deleted Aug '89. Catalogue no: **MT 55**
7" Single: Released Sep '88, on EMI-Manhattan, by EMI Records. Catalogue no: **MTDJ 55**
CD 5": Released Sep '88, on EMI-Manhattan, by EMI Records. Deleted Aug '89. Catalogue no: **CDMT 55**

RUSH HOUR
Tracks: / Rush hour (extended remix) / Rush hour (7" version) / Rush hour (instrumental) / End of love.
Note: (P) 1988 original sound recordings made by EMI Manhattan, a division of Capitol Records Inc.
7" Single: Released Jun '88, on EMI-Manhattan, by EMI Records. Deleted Aug '89. Catalogue no: **MT 36**
12" Single: Released Jun '88, on EMI-Manhattan, by EMI Records. Deleted Aug '89. Catalogue no: **12MT 36**
7" Pic: Released Aug '88, on EMI-Manhattan, by EMI Records. Deleted Aug '89. Catalogue no: **MTP 36**
CD 5": Released Aug '88, on EMI-Manhattan, by EMI Records. Deleted Aug '89. Catalogue no: **CDMT 36**

Wigan, Trevor

STRANGE FEELING
Tracks: / Strange feeling / Strange feeling (version).
12" Single: Released 23 May '87, on LJC. Catalogue no: **LJC 001**

Wigan's Chosen Few

Biographical details: This non-existent group had a one-off hit with 1975's *Footsee*, which reached No 9 on the UK singles chart in February of that year. The success of Footsee ranks as one of the strangest events in the history of the British Top Ten. It received very little radio play and owed its success to the England's flourishing Northern soul scene. And nowhere was the scene more prevalent than Wigan: discos played current releases and well-known oldies but also dug up some obscure gems which they turned into "Northern soul classics". One such offering was Bootsee, an American instrumental track by an unknown artist and producer. A crowd vocal performance was added to the track in Wigan and this strange transatlantic concoction was issued in Pye's Disco Demand label. Wigan was much in the news in early '75. Just a few weeks after the success of Wigan's Chosen Few, Wigan's Ovation -- a real group -- reached UK No 12 with another Northern breakout hit, Skiing In The Snow. (Bob MacDonald, May 1985.).

FOOTSEE
Tracks: / Footsee.
7" Single: Released '80, on Disco Demand, Deleted '88. Catalogue no: **DDS 111**

Wigan's Ovation

Biographical details: This all-male British band enjoyed a brief run of UK chart success in 1975 thanks to three hit singles. The first and biggest was *Skiing In The Snow*, a jolly, singalong pop song that managed to climb to No 12 in April, a little too late for snow even in Wigan. The success of *Skiing In The Snow* followed hard on the heels of *Footsee*, by Wigan's Chosen Few, which had climped to the UK No 9 spot in February. Both became hits after disco success on the thriving Northern soul scene, which was particularly popular in Wigan itself. But whereas the Chosen Few did not really exist the Ovation were a working group. Their records were produced by Barry Kingston, whose Spark label was also responsible for mid-70's hits for Tommy Hunt -- another Northern soul favourite - and the Band of the Black Watch. The second chart entry for Wigan's Ovation was the samey *Per-so-nal-ly*, which reached No 38. Their declining chart fortunes were reflected by *Super Love*, which peaked at 41 and was their final UK hit single. They continued to release records into the late 70's but interest was, once more, confined to Wigan. (Bob MacDonald, May 1985.).

AFTER LOVING YOU
Tracks: / After loving you (part 1) / After loving you (part 2).
7" Single: Released Apr '78, on RK, by RK Records. Deleted '79. Catalogue no: **RK 1008**

PER-SO-NAL-LY
Tracks: / Per-so-nal-ly.
7" Single: Released Jun '75, on Spark, by Spark Records. Deleted '78. Catalogue no: **SRL 1129**

SKIING IN THE SNOW
Tracks: / Skiing in the snow.
7" Single: Released Mar '75, on Spark, by Spark Records. Deleted '78. Catalogue no: **SRL 1122**

SUPER LOVE
Tracks: / Super love.
7" Single: Released Nov '75, on Spark, by Spark Records. Deleted '78. Catalogue no: **SRL 1133**

Wigs

END OF THE OBVIOUS
Tracks: / End of the obvious.
Note: 5 track EP
12" Single: Released Dec '85, on Media Burn, by Media Burn Records. Catalogue no: **MB 3**

SIX O'CLOCK SHUFFLE
Tracks: / Seven and seven is / Loose.
12" Single: Released Dec '86, on Media Burn, by Media Burn Records. Catalogue no: **MB 14**

Wikkyd Vikker

BLACK OF THE NIGHT
Tracks: / Black of the night.
7" Single: Released Jun '83, on Boogie, Catalogue no: **FURO 235**

Wilcox, David

WHEN YOU MISTREAT HER
Tracks: / When you mistreat her.
7" Single: Released Nov '85, on Capitol, by EMI Records. Deleted '88. Catalogue no: **CL 367**

Wild and Wandering

2,000 LIGHT ALES FROM HOME.......
Tracks: / 2,000 light ales from home....dust me down / Stand by me / Real cool time / Interlong / Apply tree part 1 & 2.
12" Single: Released Feb '86, on Iguana (1), by Iguana Records. Catalogue no: **VYK 14**

Wild Angels

SHE'S BLACK AND WHITE
Tracks: / She's black and white.

WILD BUNCH - FRIENDS & COUNTRYMEN (Released on 4th & Broadway)

12" Single: Released Jun '87, on Supreme Int.Editions, by Supreme Int.Records. Catalogue no: **EDITION 87.13**

Wild Beasts

MINIMUM MAXIMUM
Tracks: / Minimum maximum.
7" Single: Released Jul '81, on Fried Egg, by Fried Egg Records. Deleted '87. Catalogue no: **EGG 2**

Wild Bunch

COUNTRY LIVING
Tracks: / Country living.
12" Single: Released Apr '85, on Ariwa Sounds, by Ariwa Sounds. Catalogue no: **ARI 39**

CREATION
Tracks: / Creation.
7" Single: Released May '84, on Ariwa Sounds, by Ariwa Sounds. Catalogue no: **7 ARISL 001**

FRIENDS & COUNTRYMEN (see panel above)
Tracks: / Friends & Countrymen / Machine gun (down by law) / Look of love, The.
12" Single: Released 16 May '88, on 4th & Broadway, by Island Records. Deleted Dec '88. Catalogue no: **12 BRW 98**
7" Single: Released 16 Apr '88, on 4th & Broadway, by Island Records. Deleted Apr '89. Catalogue no: **BRW 98**

GINA
Tracks: / Gina / Don't wanna be like you.
7" Single: Released Apr '80, on R.E.D., Catalogue ho: **RED 003**

MR PRESIDENT MAN
Tracks: / Mr. President man.
12" Single: Released Jan '84, on Ariwa Sounds, by Ariwa Sounds. Catalogue no: **12 ARISL 005**

RUNAROUND
Tracks: / Runaround.
12" Single: Released Aug '84, on Ariwa Sounds, by Ariwa Sounds. Catalogue no: **ARI 35**

Wild Canyon

THIS WORLD OF OURS (OLD GOLD)
Tracks: / This world of ours.
7" Single: Released Jul '82, on Old Gold, by Old Gold Records. Catalogue no: **OG 9192**

Wild Cherry

Biographical details: This American disco band were Michael and Randy Brecker, Beck Goldstein, Tampa Lann, Bob Parissi and a variety of sessions musicians. Parissi, lead singer, guitarust, songwriter and producer, was the key creative force in the band. They were a bunch of predominantly white session players who decided to step into the spotlight to prove that they could make soul music as funky as any black band. In the autumn of 1974 they shot from nowhere to fame with *Play That Funky Music*, an anthemic disco stormer that became an all-time club classic. The single was No 1 on the US pop charts for three weeks, selling over two million copies in America and it made No 7 in Britain.

Wild Cherry are solely remembered for *Play That Funky Music*. The disco scene went from strength to strength but Cherry did not. Three 1977 singles -- *Baby Don't You Know?*, *Hot To Trot* and *Hold On* -- all made the American Hot Hundred but fell short of the Top Forty; these songs demonstrated that Parissi was quickly running out of ideas, as did his album, *I Love My Music*, in 1978. As the Brecker Brother trumpeter Randy and sax man Michael, continued to appeal to the jazz market. Having released their eponymous debut album in '75 they continued to issue LPs on a regular basis into the 80's. They had a surprise Top Forty single in Britain with 78's dynamic *East River*. (Bob MacDonald, May 1985.).

PLAY THAT FUNKY MUSIC
Tracks: / Play that funky music.
7" Single: Released Oct '76, on Epic, by CBS Records. Deleted '79. Catalogue no: **EPC 4593**

PLAY THAT FUNKY MUSIC (OLD GOLD)
Tracks: / Play that funky music.
7" Single: Released Jul '82, on Old Gold, by Old Gold Records. Catalogue no: **OG 9192**

Wild Fantasy

GET READY
Tracks: / Get ready / Love is.
7" Single: Released May '80, on Dazzle, by Dazzle Records. Deleted '88. Catalogue no: **DAZS 2**

Wild Flowers

BROKEN CHAINS
Tracks: / Broken chains / Keep on running / Something to mention (Track on 12".) / Glory (Track on 12".).
12" Single: Released Jan '88, on Chapter 22, by Chapter 22 Records. Catalogue no: **12CHAP 24**
7" Single: Released Jan '88, on Chapter 22, by Chapter 22 Records. Catalogue no: **CHAP 24**

IT AIN'T SO EASY
Tracks: / It ain't so easy.
7" Single: Released Apr '86, on Chapter 22, by Chapter 22 Records. Catalogue no: **CHAP 5**

KIND OF KINGDOM, A
Tracks: / Kind of kingdom, A.
12" Single: Released Oct '86, on Chapter 22, by Chapter 22 Records. Catalogue no: **CHAP 8T**
7" Single: Released Oct '86, on Chapter 22, by Chapter 22 Records. Catalogue no: **CHAP 8**

MELT LIKE ICE
Tracks: / Melt like ice.
7" Single: Released Jan '84, on No Future, Catalogue no: **FS 11**

TAKE ME FOR A RIDE
Tracks: / Take me for a ride.
12" Single: Released Apr '88, on Chapter 22, by Chapter 22 Records. Catalogue no: **12 CHAP 29**

THINGS HAVE CHANGED
Tracks: / Things have changed.

7" Single: Released Apr '84, on Reflex, by Reflex Records. Catalogue no: **RE 2**

Wild Frontiers

BALL AND CHAIN
Tracks: / Ball and chain (Full length version on 12") / Yes it's true / Shootin' mad (12" only).
Note: Produced by Steve Hillage.
7" Single: Released Jul '88, on Virgin, by Virgin Records. Catalogue no: **VS 1103**
12" Single: Released Jul '88, on Virgin, by Virgin Records. Catalogue no: **VST 1103**

Wild, Gay

ACTION ACTION
Tracks: / Action action / Wild girl.
7" Single: Released Sep '80, on Rocket, by Rocket Records. Catalogue no: **XPRES 39**

Wild Horses

Biographical details: At the time of their only chart entry, this British rock band comprised Jimmy Bain, Neil Carter, Clive Edwards and Brian Robertson. They were formed by guitarist Robertson, just after he left Thin Lizzy, and bassist Bain, formerly with Blackmore's Rainbow. Their debut LP, *Wild Horses*, was released in April 1980 and reached No 38 on the UK album chart. In view of the musicians' pedigree this was a distinctly mediocre placing which reflected the album's lack of inspiration. After a couple of British tours Carter left to join UFO and was replaced by a relatively unknown guitarist, John Lockton. The new line-up released Wild Horses' second album, *Stand Your Ground*, in May '81: it failed to chart and by the end of the year the hard-rocking but predictable band was defunct. In 1982 Robertson joined Motorhead. (Bon MacDonald, May 1985.).

EVER LASTING LOVE
Tracks: / Ever lasting love / Axe.
7" Single: Released Jun '81, on EMI, by EMI Records. Deleted Jun '84. Catalogue no: **EMI 5199**

FACE DOWN
Tracks: / Face down / Dealer.
7" Single: Released Mar '80, on EMI, by EMI Records. Deleted Mar '83. Catalogue no: **EMI 5047**

FLYAWAY
Tracks: / Flyaway / Blackmail.
7" Single: Released May '80, on EMI, by EMI Records. Deleted May '83. Catalogue no: **EMI 5078**

I'LL GIVE YOU LOVE
Tracks: / I'll give you love / Kid / Rocky mountain way / Saturday night.
7" Single: Released Apr '81, on EMI, by EMI Records. Deleted '85. Catalogue no: **EMI 5149**

Wild Indians

LOVE OF MY LIFE
Tracks: / Love of my life.
12" Single: Released Sep '84, on Hulla Balloo, Catalogue no: **HA 001**

PENNILESS
Tracks: / Penniless / Take a tumble / Give up the ghost.
7" Single: Released Nov '86, on Rosebud, Catalogue no: **SPARK 003**

Wild, Jack

SOME BEAUTIFUL
Tracks: / Some beautiful.
7" Single: Released May '70, on Capitol, by EMI Records. Deleted '73. Catalogue no: **CL 15635**

Wild, James Lee

STROKE OF LUCK
Tracks: / Stroke of luck / I've had enough.
7" Single: Released 6 Feb '89, on Polydor, by Polydor Ltd. Deleted Aug '89. Catalogue no: **JLW 1**
12" Single: Released 6 Feb '89, on Polydor, by Polydor Ltd. Deleted Aug '89. Catalogue no: **JLWZ 1**

WHO'S GOT MY NUMBER
Tracks: / Who's got my number / Seven wonders / Who's got my number (dog & bone mix).
7" Single: Released 12 Jun '89, on Polydor, by Polydor Ltd. Catalogue no: **JLW 2**
12" Single: Released Jun '89, on Polydor, by Polydor Ltd. Catalogue no: **JLWZ 2**
12" Single: Released 12 Jun '89, on Polydor, by Polydor Ltd. Catalogue no: **JLWX 2**
12" Single: Released Jun '89, on Polydor, by Polydor Ltd. Catalogue no: **JLWR 2**

Wild Men Of Wonga

WHY DON'T PRETTY GIRLS LOOK AT ME
Tracks: / Why don't pretty girls look at me.
12" Single: Released May '85, on MCA, by MCA Records. Catalogue no: **WONGT 1**
7" Single: Released May '85, on MCA, by

MCA Records. Catalogue no: **WONG 1**

Wild Passion

LETTERS TO SEND
Tracks: / Letters to send / Charlie's a div.
7" Single: Released Jun '86, on Warm, by Warm Records. Catalogue no: **DARREN 1**

Wild Poppies

OUT OF TIME E.P.
12" Single: Released Sep '89, on Jericho, Catalogue no: **JR 008**

Wild Side

COLD AS ICE
Tracks: / Cold as ice.
7" Single: Released Feb '82, on Sounds From The Crypt, Catalogue no: **WS 001**

Wild Swans

BIBLE DREAMS
Tracks: / Bible dreams.
12" Single: Released Jul '88, on Warner Bros., by WEA Records. Catalogue no: **W 7765T**
7" Single: Released Jul '88, on Warner Bros., by WEA Records. Catalogue no: **W 7765**

PEEL SESSIONS: WILD SWANS 1.5.82
Tracks: / Enchanted / Thirst.
Cassingle: Released 13 Jun '87, on Strange Fruit, by Strange Fruit Records. Catalogue no: **SFPSC 006**
12" Single: Released Sep '86, on Strange Fruit, by Strange Fruit Records. Catalogue no: **SFPS 006**

REVOLUTIONARY SPIRIT, A
Tracks: / Revolutionary spirit, A / God forbid.
12" Single: Released Dec '81, on Zoo, Deleted '82. Catalogue no: **12 CAGE 009**
7" Single: Released Dec '81, on Zoo, Deleted '82. Catalogue no: **CAGE 009**

YOUNG MANHOOD
Tracks: / Young manhood / Holy holy / World of milk and blood (Extra track, available on 12" only.).
12" Single: Released 27 Feb '88, on WEA, by WEA Records. Catalogue no: **W 7973T**
7" Single: Released 27 Feb '88, on WEA, by WEA Records. Catalogue no: **W 7973**

Wild Weekend

BREAKIN' UP BREAKIN' DOWN
Tracks: / Breakin' up breakin' down / Yes yes / Breakin' up breakin' down (12" only.) / Breakin' up breakin' down (club mix) (12RX 6204 only.) / Breakin' up, breakin' down (super club dub) (12RX 6204 only.).
CD 5": Released Apr '89, on Parlophone, by EMI Records. Deleted Oct '89. Catalogue no: **203 213 2**
CD 5": Released Apr '89, on Parlophone, by EMI Records. Deleted Oct '89. Catalogue no: **CDR 6204**
12" Single: Released Mar '89, on Parlophone, by EMI Records. Deleted Oct '89. Catalogue no: **203 213 8**
12" Single: Released Mar '89, on Parlophone, by EMI Records. Deleted Oct '89. Catalogue no: **12RX 6204**
12" Single: Released Feb '89, on Parlophone, by EMI Records. Deleted Oct '89. Catalogue no: **12R 6204**
7" Single: Released Feb '89, on Parlophone, by EMI Records. Deleted Oct '89. Catalogue no: **R 6204**

CRAWLING BACK
Tracks: / Crawling back / Haunted by those kisses (inst) (Not on 12".) / Crawling back (ext.) (Not on 7".) / Crawling back (12" inst. remix) (12" only.) / Crawling back (12" vocal remix) / Crawling back (garage mix) (CD single only.) / Haunted by those kisses (inst.) (Poster bag only.).
Note: Producer/Arranger :- Peter-John Vettese.
12" Single: Released Jun '89, on Parlophone, by EMI Records. Catalogue no: **12R 6221**
CD 5": Released Jun '89, on Parlophone, by EMI Records. Catalogue no: **CDR 6221**
7" Single: Released Jun '89, on Parlophone, by EMI Records. Catalogue no: **R 6221**
7" Single: Released Jul '89, on Parlophone, by EMI Records. Catalogue no: **RP 6221**
CD 5": Released Jun '89, on Parlophone, by EMI Records. Catalogue no: **203 424 2**
7" Single: Released Jun '89, on Parlophone, by EMI Records. Catalogue no: **203 424 7**
7" Single: Released Jul '89, on Parlophone, by EMI Records. Catalogue no: **203 424 0**
12" Single: Released Jun '89, on Parlophone, by EMI Records. Catalogue no: **203 424 6**

IGNITION
Tracks: / Ignition (Not on 12".) / Confuse me with kisses (7" only.) / Ignition (luvology mix) (Not on 7".) / Ignition (Bingo bass mix) (12" only.) / Ignition (Gerald's chordcapella mix) (CD single only.).
12" Single: Released Sep '89, on Parlophone, by EMI Records. Catalogue no: **12R 6228**
CD 5": Released Sep '89, on Parlophone, by EMI Records. Catalogue no: **CDR 6228**
CD 5": Released Sep '89, on Parlophone, by EMI Records. Catalogue no: **203 529 2**
7" Single: Released Sep '89, on Parlophone, by EMI Records. Catalogue no: **R 6228**
7" Single: Released Sep '89, on Parlophone, by EMI Records. Catalogue no: **203 529 7**
12" Single: Released Sep '89, on Parlophone, by EMI Records. Catalogue no: **203 529 6**

Wilde, Dee Dee

I FOUND YOU
Tracks: / I found you / I found you (instrumental) / I found you (extended) (on 12" only).
12" Single: on 4th & Broadway, by Island Records. Deleted Jun '88. Catalogue no: **12 ISR 352**
12" Single: Released Mar '88, on 4th & Broadway, by Island Records. Catalogue no: **12 BRW 87**
7" Single: Released Mar '88, on 4th & Broadway, by Island Records. Deleted Jun '88. Catalogue no: **BRW 87**

LAP OF LUXURY
Tracks: / Lap of luxury / I found you / Lap of luxury (version) (Only on 12".) / I found you (radio) (Only on CD single.) / Lap of luxury (ext.) (Only on CD single.) / I found you (Miami mix) (Only on CD single.).
7" Single: Released Oct '88, on 4th & Broadway, by Island Records. Deleted Apr '89. Catalogue no: **BRW 117**
12" Single: Released Oct '88, on 4th & Broadway, by Island Records. Deleted Apr '89. Catalogue no: **12 BRW 117**
CD 5": Released Oct '88, on 4th & Broadway, by Island Records. Catalogue no: **BRCDP 117**

NO WAY OUT (SINGLE)
Tracks: / No way out / No way out (Instrumental) / No way out (12" version) (Only on 12" version.).
7" Single: Released 18 Apr '89, on 4th & Broadway, by Island Records. Catalogue no: **BRW 127**
CD 5": Released 18 Apr '89, on 4th & Broadway, by Island Records. Catalogue no: **BRCD 127**
12" Single: Released 18 Apr '89, on 4th & Broadway, by Island Records. Catalogue no: **12 BRW 127**

Wilde, Errol

FIRST TIME LOVE
Tracks: / First time love.
12" Single: Released Jul '82, on Lucky, by Lucky Records. Catalogue no: **LSD 001**

Wilde, Eugene

CHEY CHEY KULE (see panel below)
Tracks: / Chey chey Kule / Rainbow.
7" Single: Released Jul '85, on 4th & Broadway, by Island Records. Catalogue no: **BRW 30**
12" Single: Released Jul '85, on 4th & Broadway, by Island Records. Deleted '87. Catalogue no: **12 BRW 30**

EUGENE WILDE - PERSONALITY (Released on 4th & Broadway)

DIANA
Tracks: / Diana / I want you / Diana (instrumental) (on 12" only).
7" Single: Released Jun '86, on MCA, by MCA Records. Catalogue no: **MCA 1046**
12" Single: Released Jun '86, on MCA, by MCA Records. Catalogue no: **MCAT 1046**

GOTTA GET YOU HOME TONIGHT
Tracks: / Gotta get you home tonight.
12" Single: Released Sep '84, on 4th & Broadway, by Island Records. Deleted Jul '87. Catalogue no: **12 BRW 15**
12" Pic: Released Nov '84, on 4th & Broadway, by Island Records. Catalogue no: **12 PBRW 15**
7" Single: Released Sep '84, on 4th & Broadway, by Island Records. Deleted '87. Catalogue no: **BRW 15**

PERSONALITY (see panel above)
Tracks: / Personality / Let her feel it.
12" Single: Released Jan '85, on 4th & Broadway, by Island Records. Deleted '87. Catalogue no: **12 BRW 18**
7" Single:. Released Jan '85, on 4th & Broadway, by Island Records. Catalogue no: **BRW 18**

Wilde, Kim

Biographical details: This British singer was born in London in November 1960, while her father Marty Wilde was in the midst of his four-year UK chart career. After a decade away from the pop limelight, Marty tried (in collaboration with pop producer Mickie Most) to launch his juvenile son, Ricky Wilde, as Britain's answer to Donny Osmond); but none of the youngster's records made the charts, and Ricky failed to become a teen idol. Marty had more luck, however with his daughter Kim. Her first single *Kids in America* was released on Most's RAK label in early 1981 and became a UK No.2 smash. Kim, a very good looking blonde girl, seemed to be a British answer to Blondie's star, Debbie Harry; but Kim's voice was not as good, being pleasantly strident but one-dimensional and over-nasal. Her career was a true family business - Kim sang the hits; Ricky produced them; her mother, Joyce Wilde became her manager; and, most intriguingly, father and son (Marty and Ricky) wrote them together. The material was in a commercial pop/rock vein. From the outset, Kim's family organisation experienced a steadily declining trend on the British chart. After the first single reached No.2 each subsequent release peaked at lower position than its predecessor: *Chequered love* got to No.4; the double A-sided single *Water on glass/Boys* reached No.11; her most original and adventurous single *Cambodia* went to No.12; *View from a bridge* reached No.16; *Child come away* peaked at No.43. It took until 1983 (*Love blonde*) to reverse the trend, but even that song fell short of the Top 20. So did her 1984 output, which appeared on the MCA label. What Kim's career needed was some creative input from outside the family. When ace rock'n'roller Dave Edmunds remixed 1985's *Rage to love* single - making it sound similar to his production work on the Stray Cats' *Runaway boys*, her chart career was given a shot in the arm. (Bob MacDonald, 20th May 1985).

EUGENE WILDE - CHEY CHEY KULE (Released on 4th & Broadway)

ANOTHER STEP (CLOSER TO YOU) (SINGLE)
Tracks: / Another step (closer to you) / Hold back / Say you really want me.
12" Single: Released Mar '87, on MCA, by MCA Records. Catalogue no: **KIMT 5**
7" Single: Released Mar '87, on MCA, by MCA Records. Catalogue no: **KIM 5**

CAMBODIA
Tracks: / Cambodia / Watching for shapes.
7" Single: Released Nov '81, on RAK, by EMI Records. Catalogue no: **RAK 336**

CHEQUERED LOVE
Tracks: / Chequered love / Shane.
7" Single: Released May '81, on RAK, by EMI Records. Deleted '84. Catalogue no: **RAK 330**

CHILD COME AWAY
Tracks: / Child come away.
7" Single: Released Oct '82, on RAK, by EMI Records. Catalogue no: **RAK 352**

DANCING IN THE DARK
Tracks: / Dancing in the dark.
7" Single: Released Nov '83, on RAK, by EMI Records. Deleted '86. Catalogue no: **RAK 365**

KIM WILDE - LOVE BLONDE (Released on RAK)

FOUR LETTER WORD
Tracks: / Four letter word / She hasn't got time for you / Four letter word (acapella version).
CD 5": Released Nov '88, on MCA, by MCA Records. Catalogue no: **DKIM 10**
7" Single: Released Nov '88, on MCA, by MCA Records. Deleted 1 Jul '89. Catalogue no: **KIM 10**
12" Single: Released Nov '88, on MCA, by MCA Records. Catalogue no: **KIMT 10**
7" Single: Released Nov '88, on MCA, by MCA Records. Catalogue no: **KIMB 10**

HEY MR HEARTACHE
Tracks: / Hey Mr. Heartache / Tell me where you are / Hey Mr. Heartache (album version).
Note: * extrfa track on 12" version.
12" Single: Released 14 May '88, on MCA, by MCA Records. Catalogue no: **KIMX 7**
CD 5": Released May '88, on MCA, by MCA Records. Catalogue no: **DKIM 7**
12" Single: Released May '88, on MCA, by MCA Records. Catalogue no: **KIMT 7**
7" Single: Released May '88, on MCA, by MCA Records. Deleted 1 Jul '89. Catalogue no: **KIM 7**

KIDS IN AMERICA
Tracks: / Kids in America / Tuning in, tuning on.
7" Single: Released Jan '81, on RAK, by EMI Records. Deleted Aug '89. Catalogue no: **RAK 327**

LOVE BLONDE (see panel above)
Tracks: / Love blonde / Can you hear it.
7" Single: Released Jul '83, on RAK, by EMI Records. Deleted '86. Catalogue no: **RAK 360**

LOVE IN A NATURAL WAY
Tracks: / Love in a natural way.
Special: Released 20 Feb '89, on MCA, by MCA Records. Catalogue no: **KIMR 11**
7" Single: Released 20 Feb '89, on MCA, by MCA Records. Deleted 1 Jul '89. Catalogue no: **KIM 11**
12" Single: Released 20 Feb '89, on MCA, by MCA Records. Catalogue no: **KIMT 11**
CD 5": Released 20 Feb '89, on MCA, by MCA Records. Catalogue no: **DKIMT 11**

NEVER TRUST A STRANGER
Tracks: / Never trust a stranger / Whatcha gonna do / You came (Only on special edition of 12" version.).
CD 5": Released Sep '88, on MCA, by MCA Records. Catalogue no: **DKIM 9**
7" Single: Released Oct '88, on MCA, by MCA Records. Catalogue no: **KIMSG 9**
12" Single: Released Sep '88, on MCA, by MCA Records. Catalogue no: **KIMT 9**
12" Single: Released Oct '88, on MCA, by MCA Records. Catalogue no: **KIMX 9**
7" Single: Released Sep '88, on MCA, by MCA Records. Deleted 1 Jul '89. Catalogue no: **KIM 9**

RAGE TO LOVE
Tracks: / Rage to love.
12" Single: Released Apr '85, on MCA, by MCA Records. Catalogue no: **KIMT 3**
7" Single: Released Apr '85, on MCA, by MCA Records. Catalogue no: **KIM 3**
7" Pic: Released Apr '85, on MCA, by MCA Records. Catalogue no: **KIMP 3**

SAY YOU REALLY WANT ME
Tracks: / Don't say nothing's changed / Say you really want me.
7" Single: Released Aug '87, on MCA, by MCA Records. Catalogue no: **KIMC 6**
12" Single: Released Jul '87, on MCA, by MCA Records. Catalogue no: **KIMT 6**
12" Single: Released Aug '87, on MCA, by MCA Records. Catalogue no: **KIMX 6**
7" Single: Released Jul '87, on MCA, by MCA Records. Catalogue no: **KIM 6**

SECOND TIME, THE
Tracks: / Second time, The.
7" Single: Released Oct '84, on MCA, by MCA Records. Deleted '87. Catalogue no: **KIM 1**

TOUCH, THE
Tracks: / Touch, The.
7" Single: Released Dec '84, on MCA, by MCA Records. Deleted '87. Catalogue no: **KIM 2**

VIEW FROM A BRIDGE (see panel below)
Tracks: / View from a bridge / Take me tonight.
7" Single: Released Apr '82, on RAK, by EMI Records. Catalogue no: **RAK 342**

WATER ON GLASS
Tracks: / Water on glass.
7" Single: Released Jul '81, on RAK, by EMI Records. Catalogue no: **RAK 334**

KIM WILDE - VIEW FROM A BRIDGE (Released on RAK)

YOU CAME
Tracks: / You came / Stone / You came (extended) (Available on 12" and CD only).
7" Single: Released Jul '88, on MCA, by MCA Records. Deleted 1 Jul '89. Catalogue no: **KIM 8**
12" Single: Released Jul '88, on MCA, by MCA Records. Catalogue no: **KIMX 8**
12" Single: Released Jul '88, on MCA, by MCA Records. Catalogue no: **KIMT 8**
7" Set: Released Jul '88, on MCA, by MCA Records. Catalogue no: **KIMD 8**
CD 5": Released Jul '88, on MCA, by MCA Records. Catalogue no: **DKIM 8**

YOU KEEP ME HANGIN' ON
Tracks: / You keep me hangin' on / Loving you.
12" Single: Released Oct '86, on MCA, by MCA Records. Catalogue no: **KIMT 4**
7" Single: Released Sep '86, on MCA, by MCA Records. Catalogue no: **KIM 4**

Wilde, Marty

Biographical details: Born Reginald Smith in Blackheath, London, in 1939, Wilde was a British pop star and sex idol who had 14 hits between 1958 and 1962 with covers of American rock songs. With producer Mickie Most, he tried to launch his son, Ricky, as a 70's successor, but had more success with good-looking blonde daughter Kim (born in London, 1960). Ricky produces her hits; mother Joyce manages her; increasingly Marty and Ricky write the songs. (Donald Clarke, March 1988.)
This British pop singer, born Reginald Smith in London, was discovered singing in a London club in 1957 by entreprene/promoter Larry Parnes. With his 6'3" height, his Presley like manner and good looks, Parnes figured that the young lad had star quality. The singer became Marty Wilde and, after three flop records that sounded too similar to Elvis' style, made it big with his fourth single, *Endless sleep*. This cruised to No.4 in August 1958. The next record flopped, but he had a golden year in 1959 with three consecutive UK Top 3 smashes *Donna*, *A teenager in love* and *Sea of love*. In the pre-Beatles era, it was common practice for British pop singers to use the contemporary American charts as a source of hit material - UK performers would record cover versions of US winners, and rush them onto the home market before the original American renditions were released. Wilde championed this opportunistic ploy: *Endless sleep* was a US hit for Jody Reynolds; *Donna* came from the late Ritchie Valens; *A teenager in love* was originally recorded by Dion and the Belmonts; and *Sea of love* was plundered from Phil Phillips. In each case, Wilde's version either beat or annihilated the US original, in terms of British chart performances.
However, Wilde was more than a mere copyist. He was a good singer, and was backed by one of the UK's best rock'n'roll groups, the Wildcats; this excellent combo included two future Shadows, bassist Brian 'Liquorice' Locking and drummer Brian Bennett. Television's pop music pioneer Jack Good made Wilde one of the leading stars of his shows, *Oh Boy* and *Boy meets girl*. The singer even had a girls' magazine named after him. In an attempt to move away from the continuous cover versions, Wilde began 1960 by reaching the UK Top 10 with a self-penned song called *Bad boy*. But after this the hits got smaller. He had to return to the cover game to get another Top Tenner - and on this occasion, his rendition of *Rubber ball* was beaten by Bobby Vee's US original: Vee got to No.4 while Wilde peaked at No.9. 1962 brought Wilde his final two UK chart singles with *Jezebel* (No.19) and *Ever since you said goodbye* (No.31) - then the Mersey revolution spelt the end for Wilde and his ilk. Having disappointed thousands of fans by getting married (to Joyce of the Vernons Girls), he made an abortive attempt to crack the American market and then moved into a dual career in acting and music. In the early Seventies, Wilde and RAK Record's Mickie Most made an unsuccessful bid to launch Marty's son, Ricky, as a teen idol answer to Donny Osmond. This idea fell flat on its face but, in the early Eighties, the two men tried again with daughter Kim Wilde and were rewarded. Marty and Ricky wrote her hits and Ricky produced them. Like her father, Kim never managed a British No.1 hit - Marty's *A teenager in love* (1959) and Kim's *Kids in America* (1981) both peaked at No.2. But *Kids in America* gave Kim a one-off American Top 40 hit, something her Dad never achieved. (Bob MacDonald, 20th May 1985).

BAD BOY (OLD GOLD)
Tracks: / Bad boy.
7" Single: Released Aug '82, on Old Gold, by Old Gold Records. Deleted Jul '88. Catalogue no: **OG 9249**

BAD BOY (SINGLE) .
Tracks: / Bad boy.
7" Single: Released Dec '59, on Philips, by Phonogram Ltd. Deleted '62. Catalogue no: **PB 972**

DONNA
Tracks: / Donna.
7" Single: Released Mar '59, on Philips, by Phonogram Ltd. Deleted '62. Catalogue no: **PB 902**

ENDLESS SLEEP
Tracks: / Endless sleep.
7" Single: Released Jul '58, on Philips, by Phonogram Ltd. Deleted '61. Catalogue no: **PB 835**

ENDLESS SLEEP (OLD GOLD)
Tracks: / Endless sleep.
7" Single: Released Aug '82, on Old Gold, by Old Gold Records. Catalogue no: **OG 9250**

EVER SINCE YOU SAID GOODBYE
Tracks: / Ever since you said goodbye.
7" Single: Released Oct '62, on Philips, by Phonogram Ltd. Deleted '65. Catalogue no: **326546 BF**

FIGHT, THE
Tracks: / Fight, The.
7" Single: Released May '60, on Philips, by Phonogram Ltd. Deleted '63. Catalogue no: **PB 1022**

HIDE AND SEEK
Tracks: / Hide and seek.
7" Single: Released Jul '61, on Philips, by Phonogram Ltd. Deleted '64. Catalogue no: **PB 1161**

IN DREAMS
Tracks: / In dreams.
7" Single: Released Feb '82, on KRL, by Kaleidoscope Records (UK). Catalogue no: **KRL A 2003**

JEZEBEL
Tracks: / Jezebel.
7" Single: Released May '62, on Philips, by Phonogram Ltd. Deleted '65. Catalogue no: **PB 1240**

JOHNNY ROCCO
Tracks: / Johnny Rocco.
7" Single: Released Mar '60, on Philips, by Phonogram Ltd. Deleted '63. Catalogue no: **PB 1002**

LITTLE GIRL
Tracks: / Little girl.
7" Single: Released Dec '60, on Philips, by Phonogram Ltd. Deleted '63. Catalogue no: **PB 1078**

RUBBER BALL
Tracks: / Rubber ball.
7" Single: Released Jan '61, on Philips, by Phonogram Ltd. Deleted '64. Catalogue no: **PB 1101**

SEA OF HEARTBREAK
Tracks: / Sea of heartbreak / Don't wanna be the one.
7" Single: Released May '82, on CBS, by CBS Records. Deleted May '85. Catalogue no: **KRLA 2423**

SEA OF LOVE

Tracks: / Sea of love.
7" Single: Released Sep '59, on Philips, by Phonogram Ltd. Deleted '62. Catalogue no: **PB 959**

TEENAGER IN LOVE
Tracks: / Teenager in love.
7" Single: Released Jun '59, on Philips, by Phonogram Ltd. Deleted '62. Catalogue no: **PB 926**

TEENAGER IN LOVE (OLD GOLD)
Tracks: / Teenager in love.
7" Single: Released Aug '82, on Old Gold, by Old Gold Records. Deleted Apr '88. Catalogue no: **OG 9241**

TOMORROW'S CLOWN
Tracks: / Tomorrow's clown.
7" Single: Released Nov '61, on Philips, by Phonogram Ltd. Deleted '64. Catalogue no: **PB 1191**

Wilde, Rich

LADY WANTS TO BE ALONE, THE
Tracks: / Lady wants to be alone, The.
7" Single: Released Jun '80, on Ovation, by Gull Records. Deleted '88. Catalogue no: **OVS 1208**

Wildebeeste, Theo

DON'T EVEN THINK ABOUT IT
Tracks: / Don't even think about it / Bad jokes / Don't even think about it (inst) (On 12" and CD only) / Don't even think about it (version) (On CD only).
7" Single: Released Aug '89, on Island, by Island Records. Catalogue no: **IS 433**
CD 5": Released Aug '89, on Island, by Island Records. Catalogue no: **CID 433**
12" Single: Released Aug '89, on Island, by Island Records. Catalogue no: **12 IS 433**

Wilder, Keith

THROUGH THE EYES OF A CHILD
Tracks: / Through the eyes of a child.
7" Single: Released Dec '88, on Supertrack, Catalogue no: **GMI 01**

Wilder, Matthew

Biographical details: Singer-songwriter Wilder, from New York, came to fame in early 1984 with a one-off smash, *Break My Stride*. Earlier he had earned his living primarily as a writer, with Bette Midler and the Temptations among those recording his songs. *Break My Stride*, which he co-produced as well as co-writing, was a lightweight, catchy pop song with a hint of calypso. It was dated and owed its success to being very hummable. It reached No 5 in the US and No 4 in the UK and enjoyed similar status in many countries. But Wilder was unable to find a follow-up hit. *The Kid's American* was a forgettable rock ditty with hackneyed lyrics and peaked at No 33 on the US Hot Hundred while missing out altogether in Britain. His two 1984 albums, *I Don't Speak The Language* and *Bouncin' Off The Walls*, met with little interest. (Bob MacDonald, June 1985.).

BREAK MY STRIDE
Tracks: / Break my stride.
7" Single: Released Nov '83, on Epic, by CBS Records. Catalogue no: **A 3908**
12" Single: Released Nov '83, on Epic, by CBS Records. Catalogue no: **TA 3908**

I DON'T SPEAK THE LANGUANGE
Tracks: / I don't speak the language.
7" Single: Released Jun '84, on Epic, by CBS Records. Catalogue no: **A 4496**

KIDS AMERICAN
Tracks: / Kids American / Ladder of lovers.
7" Single: Released Mar '84, on CBS, by CBS Records. Catalogue no: **A 4240**

Wilder, Tim

I'D RATHER BE LUCKY THAN GOOD
Tracks: / I'd rather be lucky than good / You've got in one.
7" Single: Released Aug '81, on Cheapskate, Catalogue no: **CHEAP 31**

Wilderness

TRUE LIFE
Tracks: / True life.
12" Single: Released Aug '85, on EMI, by EMI Records. Catalogue no: **12EMI 5523**
7" Single: Released Aug '85, on EMI, by EMI Records. Catalogue no: **EMI 5523**

Wilderness Children

PLASTIC BAG FROM TESCO'S
Tracks: / Plastic bag from Tesco's / Mrs Susan Spence.
7" Single: Released Feb '89, on Doss Product, Catalogue no: **REID 2**

Wildfire

JERUSALEM
Tracks: / Jerusalem.
7" Single: Released Mar '85, on Mausoleum, by Mausoleum Records. Catalogue no: **GUTS 8405**

NOTHING LASTS FOREVER
Tracks: / Nothing lasts forever.
7" Single: Released Nov '84, on Mausoleum, by Mausoleum Records. Catalogue no: **GUTS 8403**

Wildhouse

GROOVY ME
Tracks: / Groovy me.
7" Single: Released '88, on Uh Huh, Catalogue no: **HUH 002**

LET'S GET MARRIED
Tracks: / Let's get married.
7" Single: Released '88, on Uh Huh, Catalogue no: **HUH 003**

Wildlife

AFRICAN BABY
Tracks: / African baby / Barcelona.
7" Single: Released Mar '82, on Polo, by Polo Records. Deleted '88. Catalogue no: **POLO 20**
12" Single: Released Mar '82, on Polo, by Polo Records. Deleted '88. Catalogue no: **POLO 12-20**

BURNING (SINGLE)
Tracks: / Burning / Too late.
7" Single: Released May '80, on Chrysalis, by Chrysalis Records. Deleted May '83. Catalogue no: **CHS 2430**

POWER TO WIN, THE
Tracks: / Power to win, The / Warrior.
7" Single: Released Feb '89, on PRT, by Castle Communications Records. Catalogue no: **BRUNO 1**
12" Single: Released Feb '89, on PRT, by Castle Communications Records. Catalogue no: **12BRUNO 1**

Wildroot Orchestra

TOWN WITHOUT PITY
Tracks: / Town without pity / Hurricane Freda.
7" Single: Released Apr '82, on Noir, by Noir Records. Catalogue no: **ATX 256**

Wildy

NO SMOKING
Tracks: / No smoking / Like a fool.
7" Single: Released Aug '80, on Fabulous, Deleted '83. Catalogue no: **FABS 101**

Wilf & Squint

WHEN THE DAWN BREAKS
Tracks: / When the dawn breaks.
7" Single: Released Apr '85, on Lorall Productions, Catalogue no: **WSO 1**

Wilkins, Yvonne

ON AND ON...
Tracks: / On and on... / You've changed the world for me.
7" Single: Released Aug '81, on RCA, by BMG Records (UK). Catalogue no: **RCA 117**

Wilkinson, Colm

BRING HIM HOME
Tracks: / Bring him home / Who am I?.
7" Single: Released Mar '87, on First Night, by First Night Records. Catalogue no: **SCORE 7**

Wilkinson, Sue

Biographical details: This untalented British singer, who, appropriately, recorded for the Cheapskate label, enjoyed a one-off UK hit in 1980. *You gotta be a hustler if you wanna get on* featured a half-spoken, half-sung performance by her thin, fairy like voice, with nothing else except for a light tinkly piano. This novelty single gave advice on success in life, particularly in showbusiness. It reached No.25 on the UK listings. Follow up singles in similar vein, such as *Posers*, returned Wilkinson to immediate obscurity. (Bob MacDonald, 1st June 1985).

POSERS
Tracks: / Posers / Hollywood sheik.
7" Single: Released Nov '80, on Cheapskate, Catalogue no: **CHEAP 9**

TIME 'N' TIDE
Tracks: / Time 'n' tide / I'll take what you've got to give.
7" Single: Released Mar '81, on Cheapskate, Deleted Mar '84. Catalogue no: **CHEAP 17**

WOMEN ONLY
Tracks: / Women only / Rich man's son.
7" Single: Released Jun '81, on Cheapskate, Catalogue no: **CHEAP 26**

YOU GOTTA BE A HUSTLER IF YOU WANNA GET ON
Tracks: / You gotta be a hustler if you wanna get on.
7" Single: Released Aug '80, on Cheapskate, Deleted '83. Catalogue no: **CHEAP 2**

Will To Power

BABY I LOVE YOUR WAY
Tracks: / Baby I love your way / Freebird (medley).
7" Single: Released Jan '89, on Epic, by CBS Records. Deleted 10 Jul '89. Catalogue no: **653 094-0**
12" Single: Released Nov '88, on Epic, by CBS Records. Deleted 10 Jul '89. Catalogue no: **653 094-6**
CD 3": Released Jan '89, on Epic, by CBS Records. Deleted 10 Jul '89. Catalogue no: **653 183-3**
CD 5": Released Dec '88, on Epic, by CBS Records. Deleted 10 Jul '89. Catalogue no: **653 094-2**
7" Single: Released Nov '88, on Epic, by CBS Records. Deleted 10 Jul '89. Catalogue no: **653 094-7**
12" Single: Released Jan '89, on Epic, by CBS Records. Deleted 10 Jul '89. Catalogue no: **653 094-9**

FADING AWAY
Tracks: / Fading away / Somebody told me.
12" Single: Released 20 Feb '89, on Epic, by CBS Records. Deleted 10 Jul '89. Catalogue no: **654 651-8**
7" Single: Released 20 Feb '89, on Epic, by CBS Records. Deleted 10 Jul '89. Catalogue no: **654 651-0**

Willesden Dodgers

BREAKIN' OUT (SINGLE)
Tracks: / Breakin' out.
12" Single: Released Jun '84, on Jive, by Zomba Records. Catalogue no: **JIVET 66**
7" Single: Released Jun '84, on Jive, by Zomba Records. Catalogue no: **JIVE 66**

GUNSMOKE BREAKOUT
Tracks: / Gunsmoke breakout.
12" Single: Released Jul '84, on Jive, by Zomba Records. Catalogue no: **JIVET 67**
7" Single: Released Jul '84, on Jive, by Zomba Records. Catalogue no: **JIVE 67**

NOT THIS PRESIDENT
Tracks: / Not this president / Zero og.
7" Single: Released Jun '86, on Jive, by Zomba Records. Deleted Jul '87. Catalogue no: **JIVE 121**
12" Single: Released Jun '86, on Jive, by Zomba Records. Deleted Jul '87. Catalogue no: **JIVET 121**

Williams, Al

I AM NOTHING
Tracks: / I am nothing / Brand new love.
7" Single: Released Apr '80, on Grapevine (Northern Soul), by BMG Records (UK). Deleted Sep '81. Catalogue no: **GRP 136**

Williams, Alan

DOING THINGS WITH YOU
Tracks: / Doing things with you / Queen of Aberdeen.
7" Single: Released Feb '81, on Carrere America (USA), by PolyGram Rec.Inc.(USA). Catalogue no: **CAR 181**

Williams, Alyson

I NEED YOUR LOVIN'
Tracks: / I need your lovin' (7" remix) (Only on 7" single.) / Make you mine tonight (Not on CD single.) / My love is so raw (baby love mix) (Only on 12" single.) / I need your lovin' (extended remix) (Only on CD single.) / My love is so raw (album raw mix) (Only on CD single.).
Cassingle: Released 14 Aug '89, on Def Jam, Catalogue no: **655 143 4**
12" Single: Released Jul '89, on Def Jam, Catalogue no: **655 143 6**
7" Single: Released Jul '89, on Def Jam, Catalogue no: **655 143 7**
12" Single: Released 21 Aug '89, on Def Jam, Catalogue no: **655 143 8**
CD 5": Released Jul '89, on Def Jam, Catalogue no: **655 143 2**

MY LOVE IS SO RAW
Tracks: / My love is so raw / We're gonna make it / My love is so raw (extended club mix) / I second that emotion.
7" Single: Released 24 Apr '89, on Def Jam, Deleted Oct '89. Catalogue no: **654898 7**
12" Single: Released 8 May '89, on Def Jam, Deleted Oct '89. Catalogue no: **654898 8**
CD 5": Released 24 Apr '89, on Def Jam, Deleted Oct '89. Catalogue no: **654898 2**
12" Single: Released 24 Apr '89, on Def Jam, Deleted Oct '89. Catalogue no: **654898 6**
Cassingle: Released 15 May '89, on Def Jam, Deleted Oct '89. Catalogue no: **654898 4**

SLEEP TALK
Tracks: / Sleep talk / I'so glad (with Chuck Stanley) / How to love again (With Oran 'Juice' Jones) / Make you mine tonight / Still my No.1 (Only on 12" version.) / Sleep talk (extended version) (Only on 12" version.).
12" Single: Released 6 Mar '89, on Def Jam, Deleted Oct '89. Catalogue no: **654 656 8**
12" Single: Released 20 Feb '89, on Def Jam, Deleted Oct '89. Catalogue no: **654 656 6**
CD 5": Released 20 Feb '89, on Def Jam, Deleted Oct '89. Catalogue no: **654 656 2**
7" Single: Released 20 Feb '89, on Def Jam, Deleted 10 Jul '89. Catalogue no: **654 656-7**

Williams, Andy

Biographical details: This American singer, born in Iowa, began his musical career as a child, when he and his three brothers formed their own church choir and sang regularly in their local chapel. Their popularity spread to local radio, and they were given their own shows. The Williams family relocated to California, where Andy remained in the fraternal vocal combo until his early twenties. Then, in 1952, he became a solo performer; after gaining valuable exposure on Steve Allen's coast to coast TV show, he chalked up his first American hit single in 1956. That first success was *Canadian sunset*, a No.7 hit on the US charts. The following year, Williams stormed to No.1 on both sides of the Atlantic with *Butterfly* - this remains his only chart topping single for the rest of his career, in both the US and UK. Ironically *Butterfly* faded into obscurity, while later hits of a more memorable nature established Williams as one of the world's top middle-of-the-road singers. *Butterfly* was soon followed by two more US Top Tenners, *I like your kind of love* and *Are you sincere*. As the Fifties became the Sixties, he had further hits under his belt with *The Hawaiian wedding song, Lonely street* and *The village of St Bernadette*, and was the star of his own programme on CBS-TV. That company's arch rival in the world of American television, NBC-TV, snapped him up in '62, and the singer's musical variety show on the latter network was a great success for nine years; it was also well received in the UK. Williams' biggest hit single of the Sixties was 1963's *Can't get used to losing you*, penned by the renowned Doc Pomus/Mort Shuman team. This reached No.2 on both sides of the Atlantic, and he got to No.2 again in Britain with 1965's appropriately titled *Almost there*. In 1968 the singer reached No.5 on the UK charts with *Can't take my eyes off you*, after earlier US Top 10 versions by Franki Valli and the Lettermen had failed to chart in Britain. Yet another *Can't* song - a rendition of Elvis' 1962 smash *Can't help falling in love* - gave Williams a UK No.3 hit in 1970. His relaxed and straightforward singing style also sold huge quantities of albums - 1968's *Love Andy*, 1970's *Greatest hits* and 1971's *Home loving man* all reached No.1 on the British LP listings. Although Williams' pleasant voice and good looks made him a perennial favourite in his native country, it was in the UK that his reputation was greatest. This was exemplified by the 1974 success of his UK Top 5 smash *Solitaire*, and by the high-charting remakes of his hits by the Boystown Gang (*Can't take my eyes off you, No.4 in 1982) and the Beat Can't get used to losing you*, No.4 in 1983). In 1984, he teamed with Britain's Royal Philharmonic Orchestra for a fusion of MoR and classical music on the *Greatest love classics* LP. (Bob MacDonald, 1st June 1985)

Andy Williams was born Howard Andrew around 1930 in Wall Lake, Iowa. The popular American crooner began working with three brothers on the radio; they backed Bing Crosby on his number one hit *Swinging On A Star* in 1944. Andy went solo in 1952, was a regular on various TV shows and had 15 USA hits 1956-61 on Archie Bleyer's Cadence label. He had his own TV shows from 1957 and his music/variety show was an institution until 1971; among other things it inflicted the Osmond family on the world. As a recording artist his romantic ballads were sung with great control; he was ineffective uptempo. He had switched to CBS in 1961, by then a major artist; he had 29 Hot 100 Singles through 1972 but only two top tens: he was an album seller, with over 30 hit albums, 12 of them in the top 10 of the USA album charts. He had eight top 10 hits in the UK. (Donald Clarke).

ALMOST THERE (OLD GOLD)
Tracks: / Almost there.
7" Single: Released Jul '82, on Old Gold, by Old Gold Records. Catalogue no: **OG 9181**

ALMOST THERE (SINGLE)
Tracks: / Almost there.
7" Single: Released Sep '65, on CBS, by CBS Records. Deleted '68. Catalogue no: **CBS 201813**

AMY RAINBOW
Tracks: / Amy rainbow / It was time.
7" Single: Released Jun '80, on CBS, by CBS Records. Deleted '83. Catalogue no: **CBS 8646**

BUTTERFLY
Tracks: / Butterfly.
7" Single: Released Apr '57, on London-

American, Deleted '60. Catalogue no: **HLA 8399**

BUTTERFLY (OLD GOLD)
Tracks: / Butterfly.
7" Single: Released Apr '83, on Old Gold, by Old Gold Records. Deleted Jul '88. Catalogue no: **OG 9315**

BY THE TIME I GET TO PHOENIX
Tracks: / By the time I get to Phoenix.
7" EP: Released Oct '84, on Scoop 33, by Pickwick Records. Catalogue no: **7SR 5050**

CAN'T GET USED TO LOSING YOU (OLD GOLD)
Tracks: / Can't get used to losing you.
7" Single: Released Jul '82, on Old Gold, by Old Gold Records. Catalogue no: **OG 9189**

CAN'T GET USED TO LOSING YOU (SINGLE)
Tracks: / Can't get used to losing you.
7" Single: Released Mar '63, on CBS, by CBS Records. Deleted '66. Catalogue no: **AAG 138**

CAN'T HELP FALLING IN LOVE (SINGLE)
Tracks: / Can't help falling in love.
7" Single: Released Mar '70, on CBS, by CBS Records. Deleted '73. Catalogue no: **CBS 4818**

CAN'T TAKE MY EYES OFF YOU (SINGLE)
Tracks: / Can't take my eyes off you.
7" Single: Released Mar '68, on CBS, by CBS Records. Deleted '71. Catalogue no: **CBS 3928**

FOOL NEVER LEARNS, A
Tracks: / Fool never learns, A.
7" Single: Released Feb '64, on CBS, by CBS Records. Deleted '67. Catalogue no: **AAG 182**

GETTING OVER YOU
Tracks: / Getting over you.
7" Single: Released May '74, on CBS, by CBS Records. Deleted '77. Catalogue no: **CBS 2181**

GODFATHER, LOVE THEME FROM
Tracks: / Godfather, The (love theme).
7" Single: Released Aug '72, on CBS, by CBS Records. Deleted '75. Catalogue no: **CBS 8166**

HAPPY HEART (SINGLE)
Tracks: / Happy heart.
7" Single: Released May '69, on CBS, by CBS Records. Deleted '72. Catalogue no: **CBS 4062**

HOME LOVING MAN (OLD GOLD)
Tracks: / Home loving man.
7" Single: Released Jul '82, on Old Gold, by Old Gold Records. Deleted Jul '88. Catalogue no: **OG 9191**

HOME LOVING MAN (SINGLE)
Tracks: / Home loving man.
7" Single: Released Nov '70, on CBS, by CBS Records. Deleted '73. Catalogue no: **CBS 5267**

I DON'T KNOW WHY
Tracks: / I don't know why.
7" Single: Released Mar '73, on MCA, by MCA Records. Deleted '76. Catalogue no: **MUS 1183**

I LIKE YOUR KIND OF LOVE
Tracks: / I like your kind of love.
7" Single: Released Jun '57, on London-American, Deleted '60. Catalogue no: **HLA 8437**

IN THE ARMS OF LOVE
Tracks: / In the arms of love.
7" Single: Released Sep '66, on CBS, by CBS Records. Deleted '69. Catalogue no: **CBS 202300**

IT'S SO EASY
Tracks: / It's so easy.
7" Single: Released Aug '70, on CBS, by CBS Records. Deleted '73. Catalogue no: **CBS 5113**

LOVE STORY (SINGLE)
Tracks: / Love story.
7" Single: Released Mar '71, on CBS, by CBS Records. Deleted '74. Catalogue no: **CBS 7020**

MAY EACH DAY (SINGLE)
Tracks: / May each day.
7" Single: Released Feb '66, on CBS, by CBS Records. Deleted '69. Catalogue no: **CBS 202042**

MORE AND MORE
Tracks: / More and more.
7" Single: Released Aug '67, on CBS, by CBS Records. Deleted '70. Catalogue no: **CBS 2886**

MUSIC TO WATCH GIRLS BY
Tracks: / Music to watch girls by.
7" Single: Released May '67, on CBS, by CBS Records. Deleted '70. Catalogue no: **CBS 2675**

OTHER SIDE OF ME, THE
Tracks: / Other side of me, The.
7" Single: Released Mar '76, on CBS, by CBS Records. Deleted '79. Catalogue no: **CBS 3903**

RAILWAY HOTEL
Tracks: / Railway hotel / I'll never love anyone anymore.
7" Single: Released Feb '80, on CBS, by CBS Records. Deleted '83. Catalogue no: **CBS 8231**

REGRETS
Tracks: / Regrets.
7" Single: Released Oct '81, on CBS, by CBS Records. Catalogue no: **A 1604**

SOLITAIRE (SINGLE)
Tracks: / Solitaire.
7" Single: Released Dec '73, on CBS, by CBS Records. Deleted '76. Catalogue no: **CBS 1824**

STRANGER ON THE SHORE
Tracks: / Stranger on the shore.
7" Single: Released Jun '62, on CBS, by CBS Records. Deleted '65. Catalogue no: **AAG 103**

VINO DES ARMOUR
Tracks: / Vino de amor.
7" Single: Released Jun '85, on Columbia, by EMI Records. Catalogue no: **DB 9104**

YOU LAY SO EASY ON MY MIND
Tracks: / You lay so easy on my mind.
7" Single: Released May '75, on CBS, by CBS Records. Deleted '78. Catalogue no: **CBS 3167**

Williams, Art

INTERPLAY
Tracks: / Interplay.
7" Single: Released Jan '84, on Soul Stop, by Dawn Promotions. Catalogue no: **SS 3006**

Williams, Billy

CAUGHT IN A WORLD OF MY OWN
Tracks: / Evernbody rock & roll.
7" Single: Released Sep '86, on S.B., Catalogue no: **BW 001**

I'M GONNA SIT RIGHT DOWN AND WRITE MYSELF A LETT
Tracks: / I'm gonna sit right down and write myself a le.
7" Single: Released Aug '57, on Vogue, by Vogue Records. Deleted '60. Catalogue no: **Q 72266**

Williams Brothers

SOME BECOME STRANGERS
Tracks: / Some become strangers / Spark of life / Straight A's in love (Extra track on 12") / All pumped up (Extra track on 12").
7" Single: Released 20 Jun '87, on Warner Bros., by WEA Records. Deleted Jan '88. Catalogue no: **W 8403**
12" Single: Released 20 Jun '87, on Warner Bros., by WEA Records. Deleted Jan '88. Catalogue no: **W 8403T**

Williams, Carol

YOU'VE REACHED THE BOTTOM LINE
Tracks: / You've reached the bottom line.
12" Single: Released Apr '83, on Vanguard, by Start Records Ltd.. Catalogue no: **VSL 024**
7" Single: Released Apr '83, on Vanguard, by Start Records Ltd.. Catalogue no: **VS 5024**

Williams, Christopher

TALK TO MYSELF
Tracks: / Talk to myself.
7" Single: Released Sep '89, on Geffen, by Geffen Records (USA). Catalogue no: **GEF 62**

Williams, D.A

MAKE ME HAPPY
Tracks: / Make me happy.
12" Single: Released Aug '84, on Pan Polychord, by Pan Polychord Records. Catalogue no: **12WIL 121**
7" Single: Released Aug '84, on Pan Polychord, by Pan Polychord Records. Catalogue no: **WIL 1**

Williams, Danny

Biographical details: This British singer, whose ultra-smooth vocal style invited comparisons with America's Johnny Mathis, enjoyed a two-year run of UK hits, of widely varying proportions, from 1961-63. His erratic chart career began with two minor hits, *We Will Never Be As Young As This Again* and *The Miracle Of You*, then at the very end of 1961 came his No 1, *Moon River*, a rapid remake of a recent US hit from the film Breakfast At Tiffany's. In '62 Williams followed this chart-topper with two more UK Top Twenty hits: *Jeannie*, co-written by piano star Russ Conway, reached No 14 and *Wonderful World Of The Young* got to No 8. But after two more minor hits he faded from the scene. Suddenly, in 1977, Williams managed to turn a successful TV commercial into a chart record. The catchy *Dancin' Easy* peaked at No 30, becoming his first UK chart success for 14 years. (Bob MacDonald, June 1985.).

DADDY WRITE A LETTER SOON
Tracks: / Daddy write a letter soon / Give a little bit.
7" Single: Released Sep '80, on Piccadilly, Catalogue no: **7P 196**

DANCIN' EASY
Tracks: / Dancin' easy.
7" Single: Released Jul '77, on Ensign, by Ensign Records. Deleted '80. Catalogue no: **ENY 3**

GREEN EYES
Tracks: / Green eyes.
7" Single: Released Apr '85, on Columbia, by EMI Records. Catalogue no: **DB 9103**

JEANNIE
Tracks: / Jeannie.
7" Single: Released Jan '62, on H.M.V., by EMI Records. Deleted '65. Catalogue no: **POP 968**

MIRACLE OF YOU, THE
Tracks: / Miracle of you, The.
7" Single: Released Jul '61, on H.M.V., by EMI Records. Deleted '64. Catalogue no: **POP 885**

MOON RIVER
Tracks: / Moon river.
7" Single: Released Nov '61, on H.M.V., by EMI Records. Deleted '64. Catalogue no: **POP 932**

MOON RIVER (OLD GOLD)
Tracks: / Moon river.
7" Single: Released Jul '82, on Old Gold, by Old Gold Records. Deleted Jul '88. Catalogue no: **OG 9046**

MY OWN TRUE LOVE
Tracks: / My own true love.
7" Single: Released Feb '63, on H.M.V., by EMI Records. Deleted '66. Catalogue no: **POP 1112**

TEARS
Tracks: / Tears.
7" Single: Released Jul '62, on H.M.V., by EMI Records. Deleted '65. Catalogue no: **POP 1035**

WE WILL NEVER BE AS YOUNG AS THIS AGAIN
Tracks: / We will never be as young as this again.
7" Single: Released May '61, on H.M.V., by EMI Records. Deleted '64. Catalogue no: **POP 839**

WONDERFUL WORLD OF THE YOUNG
Tracks: / Wonderful world of the young.
7" Single: Released Apr '62, on H.M.V., by EMI Records. Deleted '65. Catalogue no: **POP 1002**

Williams, Delroy

STOP THE FIGHTING
Tracks: / You'll never know.
12" Single: Released Nov '86, on Island, by Island Records. Deleted Jul '87. Catalogue no: **12IS 311**

Williams, Deniece

Biographical details: This American singer first attracted attention as a member of Stevie Wonder's backing group Wonderlove. She sang with Stevie for a five-year period from 1971 to 1976 when she was taken under the wing of Earth, Wing & Fire frontman Maurice White, who helped to launch her career as a solo artist. In '77 Williams released *Free*, a sensual and very laid-back soul single. It became a smash on the US soul charts and gave her a No 25 hit on the pop listings. More unexpectedly, the song cruised to No 1 on the British chart, dethroning Abba in the process -- for an unknown name to top the UK lists with such a relaxed and "non-poppy" single was a major surprise. Amusingly, *Free* was No 1 in the same week that her old boss, Stevie Wonder, was No 2 with Sir Duke. The high-pitched, bird-like voice of Williams graced a follow-up hit with a similar sounding song called *That's What Friends Are For*, which peaked at No 8 in the UK. In 1978 she teamed up with the veteran Johnny Mathis for *Too Much, Too Little, Too Late*, a bland but brilliantly effective piece of middle-of-the-road pop which reached No 1 in the US and No 3 in Britain. Exactly six years later Williams enjoyed her first solo American chart-topper but in the intervening years her only major hit on either side of the Atlantic was 1982's romantic remake of *It's Gonna Take A Miracle*, which reached No 10 in the States. The '84 song that returned Williams to the top -- and to No 2 in Britain -- was the bouncy *Let's Hear It For The Boy*, her first uptempo success. Taken from the smash movie *Footloose*, this was also the first American No 1 for its producer, George Duke. However, once again the singer failed to consolidate: she was still unable to transform a series of spasmodic successes into a consistent career. (Bob MacDonald, 2nd June 1985).

BABY BABY MY LOVE'S ALL FOR YOU
Tracks: / Baby baby my love's all for you.
7" Single: Released Nov '77, on CBS, by CBS Records. Deleted '80. Catalogue no: **CBS 5779**

DO WHAT YOU FEEL
Tracks: / Do what you feel.
7" Single: Released May '83, on CBS, by CBS Records. Catalogue no: **A 3409**

FREE
Tracks: / Free.
7" Single: Released Apr '77, on CBS, by CBS Records. Deleted '80. Catalogue no: **CBS 4978**

FREE (OLD GOLD)
Tracks: / Free.
7" Single: Released Apr '83, on Old Gold, by Old Gold Records. Deleted Jul '88. Catalogue no: **OG 9318**

I CAN'T WAIT
Tracks: / I can't wait / I can't wait (inst) / I can't wait (12" version) (12" & CD single only.) / I can't wait (deniece-a-dub) (12" only.) / Free (12" & CD single only.) / I've got the next dance (CD single only.) / I can't wait (the rankin' Miss D mix) (Only on (6530618) 12".) / Cause you love me baby (Only on (6530618) 12".).
7" Single: Released Oct '88, on CBS, by CBS Records. Deleted 17 Apr '89. Catalogue no: **653061 7**
12" Single: Released Oct '88, on CBS, by CBS Records. Deleted 17 Apr '89. Catalogue no: **653061 6**
12" Single: Released Oct '88, on CBS, by CBS Records. Deleted 17 Apr '89. Catalogue no: **653061 8**
CD 5": Released Oct '88, on CBS, by CBS Records. Deleted 17 Apr '89. Catalogue no: **653061 2**

IT'S GONNA TAKE A MIRACLE
Tracks: / It's gonna take a miracle / Part of love.
7" Single: Released Feb '83, on CBS, by CBS Records. Catalogue no: **A 2336**

IT'S YOUR CONSCIENCE
Tracks: / It's your conscience / Sweet surrender.
7" Single: Released Jun '81, on CBS, by CBS Records. Catalogue no: **A 1341**

LET'S HEAR IT FOR THE BOY
Tracks: / Let's hear it for the boy.
7" Single: Released May '84, on CBS, by CBS Records. Deleted '87. Catalogue no: **A 3419**

NEVER SAY NEVER
Tracks: / Never say never / Love finds you.
12" Single: Released Apr '87, on CBS, by CBS Records. Deleted Aug '87. Catalogue no: **650736 6**
7" Single: Released Apr '87, on CBS, by CBS Records. Deleted Aug '87. Catalogue no: **650736 7**

NEXT LOVE
Tracks: / Next love.
12" Single: Released Jul '84, on CBS, by CBS Records. Catalogue no: **TA 4618**
7" Single: Released Jul '84, on CBS, by CBS Records. Catalogue no: **A 4618**

SILLY
Tracks: / Silly / My melody.
7" Single: Released Nov '81, on CBS, by CBS Records. Catalogue no: **A 1535**

THAT'S WHAT FRIENDS ARE FOR (SINGLE)
Tracks: / That's what friends are for.
7" Single: Released Jul '77, on CBS, by CBS Records. Deleted '80. Catalogue no: **CBS 5432**

TOO MUCH, TOO LITTLE
Tracks: / Too much, too little too late.
7" Single: Released Mar '78, on CBS, by CBS Records. Deleted May '80. Catalogue no: **CBS 6164**

WHAT TWO CAN DO
Tracks: / What two can do / Sweet surrender.
7" Single: Released Apr '81, on CBS, by CBS Records. Deleted Apr '84. Catalogue no: **CBS A 1131**

Williams, Diana

Biographical details: This American singer is know solely for her minor hit single, *Teddy Bear's Last Ride*. In 1976 Red Sovine, a veteran country singer, released a sickly narrative single called Teddy Bear, which told the tale of a young disabled kid whose life was suddenly made happier by a troupe of truckers taking him for a spin in their vehicles. A million record buyers were also taken for a ride: *Teddy Bear* went gold in the States, reaching No 1 on the country chart and No 40 on the pop list. Two of the song's writers, Billy Joe Burnette and Dale Royal, quickly penned an equally "sincere" sequal, *Teddy Bear's Last Ride*. Diana Williams recorded it but could only manage a No 66 placing on the Billboard Hot Hundred. In 1981, a year after Sovine's death, *Teddy Bear* suddenly became a UK smash, speeding to No 4 on the chart. Inevitably, the Williams record was also dug out from the vaults but it peaked at No 54. (Bob MacDonald, June 1985.).

TEDDY BEAR'S LAST RIDE
Tracks: / Teddy bear's last ride / If you cared enough to cry.
7" Single: Released Jun '81, on Capitol, by EMI Records. Deleted '87. Catalogue no: **CL 207**

Williams, Don

Biographical details: American singer and guitarist Williams came to fame in the mid-70's, establishing himself as one of the leading artists on the pop wing of country music. He scored a surprise British success in 1976, reaching No 13 with a laid-back and sultry single, *I Recall A Gypsy Woman*, and a smaller hit, *You're My Best Friend*, followed later in the year. In the States he had to wait until 1980 for his only Top Forty pop hit: *I Believe In You* reached No 24 that year. In the country market Williams' deep bass voice has become a permanent fixture. His repertoire concentrates mainly on traditional love themes, conveyed in a manner that aims straight for the heart while remaining free from sentimentalism. Through the years he has written some of his own material and much has come from the pen of top country songwriter Bob McDill. Williams' success has been particularly strong in Britain, where the lack of overall appreciation of country music leads to a handful of American stars gaining a disproportionate amount of fame at the expense of the unrecognised many. Although not a UK single seller, his albums have become consistent chart entries. His two biggest British albums were both in the late 70's: 1977's *Vision* reached No 13, logging 20 chart weeks; 1978's *Images* got to No 2 on the strength of TV advertising and spent 38 weeks on the survey. An important factor in his success has been the regular acclaim he has received from Eric Clapton -- as the great guitar hero softened his style during the mid-70's he was strongly influenced by Williams' relaxed musical demeanour and the two men were seen together on stage on several occasions. (Bob MacDonald, June 1985.)
Don Williams was born in 1939 in Texas. As one of today's most popular singers, he has been dubbed The Gentle Giant of Country Music for his laid-back style. His first album *Don William's Vol.1* in 1973 was acclaimed for setting a new direction; in fact it was a basic, uncluttered production, allowing his deep vocals and lyrics to shine. When he first visited the UK in 1976 he took five places at once in the UK country chart; his songs have been covered by many other stars. He recorded for ABC-Dot, then its MCA parent label, then switched to Capitol in the mid-'80s. His backing group, the Scratch Band, led by Danny Flowers, have also made records of their own. (Donald Clarke)..

ESPECIALLY YOU
Tracks: / Especially you.
7" Single: Released Jul '81, on MCA, by MCA Records. Catalogue no: **MCA 735**

FALLING AGAIN
Tracks: / Falling again / I keep putting off getting over you.
7" Single: Released Mar '81, on MCA, by MCA Records. Deleted Mar '84. Catalogue no: **MCA 678**

HEARTBEAT IN THE DARKNESS
Tracks: / Light in your eyes.
7" Single: Released Jun '86, on Capitol, by EMI Records. Deleted '88. Catalogue no: **CL 412**

I BELIEVE IN YOU (SINGLE)
Tracks: / I believe in you / Simple song.
7" Single: Released Aug '80, on MCA, by MCA Records. Deleted '83. Catalogue no: **MCA 631**

I RECALL A GYPSY WOMAN
Tracks: / I recall a gypsy woman.
7" Single: Released Jun '76, on ABC Records, by MCA Records. Deleted '79. Catalogue no: **ABC 4098**

I RECALL A GYPSY WOMAN (OLD GOLD)
Tracks: / I recall a gypsy woman / You're my best friend.
7" Single: Released Apr '83, on Old Gold, by Old Gold Records. Catalogue no: **OG 9320**

I WOULDN'T BE A MAN
Tracks: / I wouldn't be a man / Easy touch.
7" Single: Released May '88, on EMI, by EMI Records. Deleted Nov '88. Catalogue no: **CL 496**
12" Single: Released May '88, on EMI, by EMI Records. Deleted Nov '88. Catalogue no: **12CL 496**

LISTEN TO THE RADIO (SINGLE)
Tracks: / Listen to the radio / Only love.
7" Single: Released Mar '82, on MCA, by MCA Records. Catalogue no: **MCA 771**

LOVE ME OVER AGAIN
Tracks: / Love me over again / Circle driveway.
7" Single: Released Jan '80, on MCA, by MCA Records. Deleted Jan '83. Catalogue no: **MCA 551**

LOVE'S ENDLESS WAR
Tracks: / Love's endless war / We're all the way.
7" Single: Released Apr '80, on MCA, by MCA Records. Deleted Apr '83. Catalogue no: **MCA 581**

ONLY LOVE
Tracks: / Only love / Listen to the radio.
7" Single: Released Jun '82, on MCA, by MCA Records. Catalogue no: **MCA 783**

RUBY TUESDAY
Tracks: / Ruby Tuesday / There's always something there to remind me.
7" EP: Released Oct '84, on Scoop 33, by Pickwick Records. Catalogue no: **7SR 5055**

SENORITA
Tracks: / Senorita.
7" Single: Released Feb '87, on Capitol, by EMI Records. Deleted '88. Catalogue no: **CL 442**

THAT'S THE THING ABOUT LOVE
Tracks: / That's the thing about love / I'm still looking for you.
7" Single: Released Apr '84, on MCA, by MCA Records. Catalogue no: **MCA 888**

WALKING A BROKEN HEART
Tracks: / Walking a broken heart / True blue heart.
7" Single: Released Mar '85, on MCA, by MCA Records. Catalogue no: **MCA 945**

WE'VE GOT A GOOD FIRE GOING
Tracks: / Shot full of love.
7" Single: Released Feb '86, on Capitol, by EMI Records. Deleted '88. Catalogue no: **CL 392**

YEARS FROM NOW
Tracks: / Years from now / Maybe I just don't know.
7" Single: Released Oct '81, on MCA, by MCA Records. Catalogue no: **MCA 743**

YOU'RE MY BEST FRIEND (SINGLE)
Tracks: / You're my best friend.
7" Single: Released Oct '76, on ABC Records, by MCA Records. Deleted '79. Catalogue no: **ABC 4144**

Williams, Donnett

YOU'RE THE ONE FOR ME
Tracks: / You're the one for me.
12" Single: Released Jul '89, on Didi Tec, Catalogue no: **DT 004**

Williams, Elvis

I CARE FOR YOU
Tracks: / I care for you / Party for the world.
7" Single: Released 22 Aug '88, on Noir, by Noir Records. Catalogue no: **CHALK 4**

Williams, Esther

I'LL BE YOUR PLEASURE
Tracks: / I'll be your pleasure / Make it with you.
7" Single: Released May '81, on RCA, by BMG Records (UK). Catalogue no: **RCA 78**

INSIDE OF ME (SINGLE)
Tracks: / Inside of me / You can use it.
7" Single: Released Sep '81, on RCA, by BMG Records (UK). Catalogue no: **RCA 127**
12" Single: Released Sep '81, on RCA, by BMG Records (UK). Catalogue no: **RCAT 127**

Williams, Geoff

I WANT YOU TO STOP (CALLING ME UP)
Tracks: / I want you to stop (calling me up).
12" Single: Released Oct '84, on Code, by Code Records. Catalogue no: **12LOB 018**
7" Single: Released Oct '84, on Code, by Code Records. Catalogue no: **LOB 018**

Williams, Geoffrey

CINDERELLA
Tracks: / Cinderella / She used to be / Cinderella (12" mix).
Note: extra 7" title track on 12" version
7" Single: Released 13 Jun '88, on Polydor, by Polydor Ltd. Catalogue no: **PO 3**
12" Single: Released 13 Jun '88, on Polydor, by Polydor Ltd. Catalogue no: **PZ 3**

LIPSTICK
Tracks: / Lipstick / Walk like a man.
12" Single: Released Aug '89, on Atlantic, by WEA Records. Catalogue no: **A 8863T**
CD 5": Released Aug '89, on Atlantic, by WEA Records. Catalogue no: **A 8863CD**
7" Single: Released Aug '89, on Atlantic, by WEA Records. Catalogue no: **A 8863**

THERE'S A NEED IN ME
Tracks: / There's a need in me (New York '88 mix) (Track on 12" and CD.) / There's a need in me (the other mix) (Track on 12".) / Shadows / Gypsy (Track on CD.).
12" Single: Released Mar '88, on Polydor, by Polydor Ltd. Catalogue no: **POSPX 906**
CD 5": Released Mar '88, on Polydor, by Polydor Ltd. Catalogue no: **POCD 906**
7" Single: Released Mar '88, on Polydor, by Polydor Ltd. Catalogue no: **POSP 906**

Williams, George

YOU HEARD A LIE
Tracks: / You heard a lie.
12" Single: Released Jun '85, on Clair, Catalogue no: **CLAIR 013**

Williams, Hank

Biographical details:
Hank Williams was born in Alabama in 1923; he died on New Year's Day 1953 in the back seat of a chauffered Cadillac. He is undoubtedly the biggest star in the history of country music: people around the world still sing his songs, perhaps not even knowing who wrote them, so great is the appeal of his unforgettable tunes and simple, rhyming lyrics; he was practically illiterate and never read anything but comic books, but was one of the greatest folk-poets of all time, his sincerity and concern for the lives of everyday people the very epitome of country music. He wrote happy songs and funny songs, but his aching ballads of heartbreak and infidelity were his greatest hits; he also recorded sentimental monologues as *Luke The Drifter*. He led an excellent small band called the Drifting Cowboys, and insisted that theu play on his records, which was unusual then. He was influenced by a black street singer called Tee-Tot (real name: Rufe Payne); he started a band while still in school, sang on the radio in Montgomery, Alabama at the age of 13, but served a hard apprenticeship in honky tonks ('blood buckets') all over the Southeast. He took his songs to Acuff-Rose in Nashville, where Fred Rose recognised his genius and subsequently helped him to polish many a lyric; his first big hit in 1949 was *Lovesick Blues*, ironically not his own song, but older than he was. He suffered back pain all his life, and probably had an undiagnosed case of spina bifida (he was born at home into an utterly poverty-stricken family); he was addicted to pain pills and became an alcoholic at an early age. His long-suffering, strong-willed mother didn't help, and neither did his wife: Audrey wanted to be a country star too, but couldn't sing very well; some of his happiest and some of his saddest songs came out6 of his stormy marriage. He was such a big star that the Grand Ole Opry had to have him, despite his honky tonk style (which the Opry didn't really like) and despite his reputation for unreliability, which got so bad the Opry had to let him go; Audrey divorced him and his heart gave up the struggle. he wrote about 125 songs and the records will never stop selling. (Donald Clarke)..

HOME IN HEAVEN
Tracks: / Home in heaven.
7" Single: Released Mar '83, on Arhoolie (USA), by Arhoolie Records (USA). Catalogue no: **EP 548**

I'M SO LONESOME
Tracks: / I'm so lonesome I could cry.
7" Single: Released '80, on MGM, by Polydor Ltd. Catalogue no: **LR 1011**

LOVESICK BLUES (SINGLE)
Tracks: / Lovesick blues.
7" Single: Released '80, on MGM, by Polydor Ltd. Deleted '83. Catalogue no: **LR 1036**

Williams, Hank Jr.

Biographical details:
Hank Williams Jr. was born in 1949 in Shreveport, Louisiana, where his famous father was a regular on the Louisiana Hayride, and on the brink of stardom. His father nicknamed him Bocephus. During high school he excelled in sports and became a health fanatic; he toured with his mother Audrey in her Caravan of Stars show in the early '60s, signed a contract with MGM and was moulded by the elder statesman of Nashville as a second Hank Williams; he sang Hank's songs the soundtrack of the biopic *Your Cheatin' Heart* in 1965 and crossed to the pop chart with *Long Gone Blues* in 1964. He began writing his o
songs and scored minor hits, but the pu
demanded endless replays of Hank S
songs; his own first country number one w
All For The Love Of The Sunshine in 19
He broke from the Nashville elite in 19
moved to Alabama and began work or
sound of his own: he made the album *Ha
Williams Jr. And Friends* with country-r
musicians incl. Charlie Daniels, Toy Caldw
of the Marshall Tucker Band and Ch
Leavall (ex-Allman Brothers); just before
release he literally fell down a mountain
a hunting trip, suffered appalling head
juries, and was almost two years on
mend. He switched to Warner Brothers a
slowly climbed to the top, demonstrating
ent of his own: his number one hits in 19
83 included *Women I've Never Had*,
Habits, *Texas Woman*, *All My Row
Friends*, *A Country Boy Can Survive*, *Ho
Tonkin*''83; he once had eight albums in
Billboard charts at once. He duetted with F
Charles on *Two Old Cats Like Us* in 19
and had the solo hit *Are You Sure Ha
Done I This Way* in 1986, among others. T
album *Hank Live* in 1987 sold half a mil
copies without a single to help it; after sell
13m albums he was finally named En
tainer of the Year by the CMA in 1987,
said 'This is the one old Bocephus has be
looking for'. (Donald Clarke)..

AIN'T MISBEHAVIN'
Tracks: / I've been around.
7" Single: Released Apr '86, on War
Bros., by WEA Records. Deleted Jun '
Catalogue no: **W 8794**

**ALL MY ROWDY FRIENDS A
COMING OVER TONIGHT**
Tracks: / Video blues.
7" Single: Released Feb '86, on Curb,
BMG Records (UK). Catalogue no: **W 9**

Williams, Heather

NIGHTLIFE
Tracks: / Nightlife.
12" Single: Released Feb '85, on Ch
lenge, by Elite Records. Catalogue no: **TA
11**

Williams, Iris

Biographical details: This British singer
joyed a one-off pop success in 1979, rea
ing No.18 on the UK singles chart with
was beautiful. This was a vocal versior
Cavatina, the theme from the critically a
commercially successful movie, *The d
hunter*. Earlier in the year, two contras
guitar versions by the Shadows and J
Williams (no relation) had made the UK
20. Williams thus achieved the notable
of attaining a fresh hit with a song that
already in danger of being over expos
Her success lay in her pure, classical vo
which reached text-book standards in pi
clarity and tone. *He was beautiful* was
the title of an album which charted bri
Williams was unable to follow-up this s
ballad in chart terms, but she nonethel
became able to command a #100,000
year income through concert, TV and ra
appearances. Her albums in the Eigh
have included *Picture me love*, *Just for y
You belong to me* and *The gentle to*
containing a blend of standards and
scurities. (Bob MacDonald, 2nd June 19

DEAREST FRIEND
Tracks: / Dearest friend / Autumn friend
7" Single: Released May '81, on EMI
EMI Records. Deleted May '84. Catalo
no: **EMI 5186**

**DON'T MAKE MY WHITE CHRI
MAS BLUE**
Tracks: / Don't make my white Christ
blue / If you go away.
7" Single: Released Dec '82, on Polydor
Polydor Ltd. Catalogue no: **POSP 542**

HE WAS BEAUTIFUL (SINGLE)
Tracks: / He was beautiful / We don't m
each other laugh anymore.
7" Single: Released Sep '79, on Colum
by EMI Records. Catalogue no: **DB 907**

HI THERE!
Tracks: / Hi there!.
7" Single: Released Jan '85, on Colum
by EMI Records. Deleted Jul '87. Catalo
no: **DB 9099**

I'LL NEVER LOVE THIS WAY AG
Tracks: / I'll never love this way again.
7" Single: Released May '85, on Colum
by EMI Records. Catalogue no: **DB 910**

**I'M LOOKING FORWARD TO
MORROW**
Tracks: / I'm looking forward to tomorr
Let's pretend.
7" Single: Released Mar '87, on Presid
by President Records. Catalogue no: **PT**

JUST FOR YOU
Tracks: / Just for you / No regrets.
7" Single: Released Jul '81, on EMI, by

Records. Catalogue no: **EMI 5216**

MEMORY
Tracks: / Memory / If you go away.
7" Single: Released Jan '83, on Polydor, by Polydor Ltd. Catalogue no: **POSP 559**

MY PRAYER
Tracks: / My prayer / If you'd really cared.
7" Single: Released Sep '80, on Columbia, by EMI Records. Deleted Sep '83. Catalogue no: **DB 9086**

NO WALLS, NO CEILINGS, NO FLOORS
Tracks: / No walls, no ceilings, no floors / I don't know.
7" Single: Released Feb '80, on Columbia, by EMI Records. Deleted Feb '83. Catalogue no: **DB 9074**

PEACE MUST COME AGAIN
Tracks: / Peace must come again / Next time I see you, The.
7" Single: Released Jun '86, on President, by President Records. Catalogue no: **PT 546**

SONG OF SUMMER
Tracks: / Song of summer / All or nothing at all.
7" Single: Released Mar '81, on Columbia, by EMI Records. Deleted Mar '84. Catalogue no: **DB 9093**

WATER IS WIDE, THE
Tracks: / Water is wide, The / Let's pretend.
7" Single: Released Apr '87, on President, by President Records. Catalogue no: **PT 562**

WHAT AM I SUPPOSED TO DO?
Tracks: / What am I supposed to do? / Show me your love.
7" Single: Released May '80, on Columbia, by EMI Records. Deleted May '83. Catalogue no: **DB 9080**

YOU ARE MY STORY
Tracks: / You are my story / Song on the seashore.
7" Single: Released Jan '84, on Polydor, by Polydor Ltd. Catalogue no: **POSP 656**

Williams, James 'D'

MISUNDERSTANDING
Tracks: / Misunderstanding.
12" Single: Released Feb '87, on CBS, by CBS Records. Catalogue no: **650431 7**
7" Single: Released Feb '87, on CBS, by CBS Records. Deleted Aug '87. Catalogue no: **650431 7**

RUNNER
Tracks: / Runner / Runner (accapella) / Runner (12" version) (Only on 12", 12" picture bag & CD single.) / Runner (dub mix) (Only on 12" & CD single.) / In your eyes (12" version) (Only on 12" & CD single.) / Misunderstanding (Only on 12" picture bag version.) / You are everything (Only on 12" picture bag version.).
12" Single: Released Nov '88, on CBS, by CBS Records. Deleted 17 Apr '89. Catalogue no: **653116 8**
7" Single: Released Oct '88, on CBS, by CBS Records. Deleted 17 Apr '89. Catalogue no: **653116 7**
CD 5": Released Oct '88, on CBS, by CBS Records. Deleted 17 Apr '89. Catalogue no: **653116 2**
12" Single: Released Oct '88, on CBS, by CBS Records. Deleted 17 Apr '89. Catalogue no: **653116 6**

Williams, Janet

KEEP IT COMING(FUNK MIX)
Tracks: / Keep it coming (funk mix).
7" Single: Released May '84, on Justice, Catalogue no: **JUS 001**

Williams, Jaye

LET ME BE THE ONE
Tracks: / Let me be the one.
7" Single: Released Jan '85, on Local, Catalogue no: **LR 9**

Williams, Jerry

CRUISIN' ON A SATURDAY NIGHT
Tracks: / Cruisin' on a Saturday night.
7" Single: Released Sep '82, on Sonet, by Sonet Records. Catalogue no: **SON 2249**

GOD BLESS ROCK'N'ROLL
Tracks: / God bless rock'n'roll / Big black Chevrolet.
7" Single: Released Oct '82, on Sonet, by Sonet Records. Catalogue no: **SON 2251**

Williams, Jessica

CASANOVA
Tracks: / Casanova / Casanova (inst).
12" Single: Released '88, on Passion, by Skratch Records. Catalogue no: **PASH 12)**
7" Single: Released Jul '87, on Passion, by Skratch Records. Catalogue no: **PASH 12)**

QUEEN OF FOOLS
Tracks: / Queen of fools.
12" Single: Released '88, on Passion, by Skratch Records. Catalogue no: **PASH 05(12)**

QUEENS OF FOOLS
Tracks: / Queens of fools / I close my eyes and count to ten.
12" Single: Released '87, on Passion, by Skratch Records. Catalogue no: **PASH 25(12)**
12" Single: Released Sep '83, on Passion, by Skratch Records. Catalogue no: **PASH 06(12)**

Williams, Jimmy

DO YOU REALLY WANT TO WAIT
Tracks: / Do you really want to wait / Do you really want to wait (remix).
12" Single: Released 30 May '87, on Hardcore, Catalogue no: **HAKT 3**

Williams, Joe

Biographical details:
Joe Williams was born Joseph Goreed in Georgia in 1918; the blues/ballad/pop singer with a big beautiful voice suffered prejudice among black bandleaders and club-owners in his early career because he was too dark, but he has now been popular for well over 30 years. He first worked with Count Basie in 1950, first recorded *Every Day (I Have The Blues)* in 1951 with the king Kolax band, joined Basie 1954-60 and became famous: the album *Count Basie Swings--Joe Williams Sings* from '55 is a masterpiece, with *Every Day*, period pop ballad *Teach Me Tonight* and many other riches. He toured solo, expanding his repertoire of songs, worked with a Harry Edistone quintet, then his own trios with Chicago pianist Junior Mance, then Norman Simmons. He has recorded for RCA and many other labels including Concord Jazz (with the Capp-Pierce Juggernaut, and excellent big band). *Nothin' But The Blues* in 1983 got rave reviews and won a Grammy; *Every Night* on Verve in 1987 was made live at the Vine Street Bar & Grill in Hollywood with Simmons. Recently he has been seen on TV playing Bill Cosby's father-in-law in the sitcom. (Donald Clarke)..

COME BACK
Tracks: / Comeback / Hold it right there / Sent for you yesterday / Yesterday / Who she do.
CD 3": Released '88, on Delos (USA), Catalogue no: **D/PC 2102**

WAR NO MORE
Tracks: / War no more / What a difference a day made / After you're gone / All the things you are.
CD 3": Released '88, on Delos (USA), Catalogue no: **D/PC 2103**

Williams, John

HAPPY FAMILIES
Tracks: / Happy families.
7" Single: on Mooncrest, by Trojan Records. Deleted May '88. Catalogue no: **MOON 1002**

Williams, John

Biographical details: John Towner Williams, the composer of film music and leader of The Boston Pops Orchestra, was born in 1932 in Flushing, New York. He played jazz piano; his studio work led to the movies: themes from soundtracks for *Jaws, Star Wars, Close encounters of the third kind* and *Superman* have been hit singles in the USA. He succeeded Arthur Fiedler as conductor of The Boston Pops in 1980. He has been confused with Johnny Williams, who was born in Vermont in 1929, made many records in the '50s and was a better jazz musician. (Donald Clarke, May '88)..

E.T. THEME
Tracks: / E.T., Theme from / Over the moon.
7" Single: Released Nov '82, on MCA, by MCA Records. Catalogue no: **MCA 800**

SUPERMAN THEME
Tracks: / Superman.
7" Single: Released Jan '79, on Warner Bros., by WEA Records. Catalogue no: **K 17292**

Williams, John

Biographical details:
John Williams is a classical guitarist who was born in 1941 in Melbourne, Australia. His albums on CBS began charting in Britain in 1970; his recording of Rodrigo's *Concerto De Aranjuez* with the English Chamber Orchestra conducted by daniel Barenboim reached the Top 20 in 1976. He formed the slick fusion quintet sky in 1979, with Steve Gray on keyboards, Herbie Flowers on electric bass, Kevin Peek on guitars, Tristan Fry on tuned percussion; their instrumental skill was amazing but for many pop listeners they lacked soul. He left them in 1984 and they are still popular as a quartet. Williams has recorded with Cleo Laine; his latest projects include Paul Hart's *Concerto for guitar and jazz orchestra* in 1987 and a new album with the Chilean folk group Inti-Illinali. (Donald Clarke)..

CAVATINA (OLD GOLD)
Tracks: / Cavatina.
7" Single: Released Aug '82, on Old Gold, by Old Gold Records. Catalogue no: **OG 9233**

CAVATINA (SINGLE)
Tracks: / Cavatina.
7" Single: Released Oct '82, on CBS, by CBS Records. Deleted Oct '85. Catalogue no: **A 2791**
7" Single: Released May '77, on Cube, Catalogue no: **BUG 65**

FEELINGS
Tracks: / Feelings.
7" Single: Released Mar '77, on RCA, by BMG Records (UK). Catalogue no: **PB 9054**

PAUL MCCARTNEY'S THEME FROM HONORARY CONSUL
Tracks: / Honorary Consul, Theme from / Clara's theme.
7" Single: Released Dec '83, on Island, by Island Records. Catalogue no: **IS 155**

ROMANZA
Tracks: / Romanza / Cavatina.
7" Single: Released Jan '82, on Cube, Catalogue no: **BUG 90**

Williams, Ken

FABULOUS BABE
Tracks: / Fabulous, Ken.
7" Single: Released Nov '77, on Decca, by Decca Records. Deleted '80. Catalogue no: **FR 13731**

Williams, Kenneth

WILLO THE WISP DOWN IN THE WOODS
Tracks: / Willo the wisp down in the woods / Edna's song.
7" Single: Released Nov '83, on BBC, by BBC Records & Tapes. Deleted '87. Catalogue no: **RESL 136**

Williams, Larry

Biographical details: This American singer, songwriter and pianist was born in New Orleans, but began his musical career on the West Coast. He started to make headway in the mid-Fifties while he was playing piano in the backing band of the pioneering rock'n'roller, Lloyd Price. During his time with Price, he came to the attention of Speciality Records (whose roster included Little Richard), and they launched him as a solo artist. Williams' second single was his first hit. The self-penned *Short fat Fannie*, climbed to No.5 on the US charts in 1957, and also peaked at No.14 in Britain. He also wrote his second hard-rocking hit *Bony Moronie*, which peaked at No.14 in America and cruised to No.11 in the UK. The next single, *Dizzy Miss Lizzy*, was not a major success; but it later became famous via the Beatles, who made it a regular part of their repertoire in their early days at Liverpool's Cavern Club, and also included it as the closing track on the 1965 soundtrack LP *Help*. After 1958 Williams never returned to the Top 40 on either side of the Atlantic. His success had been brief, but energetic and exciting. Admittedly, his style owed a debt to Little Richard - Williams' *Short fat Fannie* was clearly influenced by Richard's success with *Long tall Sally*; but the praise that was later bestowed upon him by such burgeoning talents as the Beatles and the Rolling Stones, led to a well-recieved British tour in 1964. However, this did not revive his recording career, and he eventually tried his hand at record production. A 1978 comeback LP - an abortive attempt to jump on the disco bandwagon - failed. He committed suicide in January 1980 at the age of 44, his body being discovered by his mother in his Los Angeles home. A sad end to a fine artist. (Bob MacDonald, 3rd June 1985).

Larry Williams (1935-80) was a talented R&B singer, songwriter and a pianist who had a few new Oroleans hits in the 1950s in the Little Richard style, but never fulfilled his potential in commercial terms. He worked in the bands of Lloyd Price, Roy Brown and Percy Mayfield; *Short Fat Fannie, Bony Maronie* and *Dizzie Miss Lizzie* were all USA hits 1957-8, the latter later covered by the Beatles. He was a good entertainer but he had not much more chart luck; a narcotics conviction in 1960 didn't help. His 1958-59 sessions included a cover of Little Richard's *Heeby Jeebies* on which he whistled the bridge taken by the sax solo on the famous hit; the band included Gerald Wilson on trumpet, Plas Johnson on tenor, Alvin 'Red' Tyler on baritone, Earl Palmer on drums, Ernie Freeman on piano and Barney Kessell on guitar: a good example of the talent on which R&B used to draw in the studio. he came back in 1962 with a road show, the band including Johnny 'Guitar' Watson, had minor hits on Okeh in 1967-8 with Watson inclusing ,Mercy, Mercy, Mercy, made an unsuccessful disco-style comeback attempt in 1978. He shot himself. (Donald Clarke)..

BONY MARONIE
Tracks: / Bony Maronie.
7" Single: Released Jan '58, on London-American, Deleted '61. Catalogue no: **HLU 8532**

BONY MARONIE (OLD GOLD)
Tracks: / Bony Moronie.
7" Single: Released Jan '85, on Old Gold, by Old Gold Records. Catalogue no: **OG 9495**

DIZZY MISS LIZZY
Tracks: / Dizzy Miss Lizzy.
7" Single: Released Jul '77, on Speciality (USA), by Speciality Records (USA). Catalogue no: **SONE 1**

SHORT FAT FANNIE
Tracks: / Short fat Fannie.
7" Single: Released Sep '57, on London-American, Deleted '60. Catalogue no: **HLN 8472**

Williams, Lenny

GIVIN' UP ON LOVE
Tracks: / Givin' up on love.
7" Single: Released Jan '89, on K-Tel, by K-Tel Records. Catalogue no: **ONE 6103**
CD 5": Released Jan '89, on K-Tel, by K-Tel Records. Catalogue no: **ONE 6903**
12" Single: Released Jan '89, on K-Tel, by K-Tel Records. Catalogue no: **ONE 6603**

OOH CHILD
Tracks: / Ooh child / Let's do it today.
7" Single: Released Jan '81, on MCA, by MCA Records. Deleted Jan '84. Catalogue no: **MCA 660**

SHOO DOO FU FU OOH
Tracks: / Shoo doo fu fu ooh.
7" Single: Released Nov '77, on ABC Records, by MCA Records. Deleted '80. Catalogue no: **ABC 4194**

TEN WAYS OF LOVING YOU
Tracks: / Ten ways of loving you / Waiting for your love.
7" Single: Released Sep '86, on Malaco Dance, by Malaco Records (UK). Catalogue no: **MALD 2**

YOU GOT ME BURNING
Tracks: / You got me burning.
7" Single: Released Sep '78, on ABC Records, by MCA Records. Deleted '81. Catalogue no: **ABC 4228**

Williams, Lucinda

I JUST WANTED TO SEE YOU
Tracks: / I just wanted to see you so bad.
7" Single: Released Apr '89, on Rough Trade, by Rough Trade Records. Catalogue no: **RT 224**
12" Single: Released Apr '89, on Rough Trade, by Rough Trade Records. Catalogue no: **RTT 224**

PASSIONATE KISSES
Tracks: / Passionate kisses / Side of the road.
CD 5": Released Aug '89, on Rough Trade, by Rough Trade Records. Catalogue no: **RT 232CD**
12" Single: Released Aug '89, on Rough Trade, by Rough Trade Records. Catalogue no: **RTT232**
7" Single: Released Aug '89, on Rough Trade, by Rough Trade Records. Catalogue no: **RT 232**

Williams, Mallory

REGGAE GONE GRAMMY
Tracks: / Reggae gone grammy.
12" Single: Released May '85, on Diamond C, Catalogue no: **DCD 015**

Williams, Mason

Biographical details: This American guitarist and songwriter, born in Texas, did not take up the guitar until his days as a mathematics student at Oklahoma City University. He was then drafted into the US Navy, where he developed his songwriting skills in his spare time. Upon his discharge, he took up folk singing in the Los Angeles area. Through a series of meetings, he became a regular writer for *The Smothers Brothers*, one of America's most popular television shows of the late Sixties; he also appeared on the show many times. Aside from his Smothers work, 1968 was the big year for Williams. Two friends of his, an Israeli singing duo called Esther & Abi Ofarim, took his nonsensical song *Cinderella Rockefella* to No.1 in Britain. It also became a major hit around Europe, and was one of the year's biggest novelty successes. *Cinderella Rockefella* was only a minor hit in the States but, later in the year, Williams compensated by reaching the US No.2 slot with his self-composed instrumental smash *Classical gas*. This melodic and imaginative single, which reached No.9 in Britain, was not just a vehicle for his guitar work - it featured a full-blown orchestra, and covered a range of styles in just a few minutes. Produced by Mike Post (later to hit big with TV themes like *The Rockford files* and *Hill street blues*), *Classical gas* was one of the first successful classical/rock fusions, and helped to encourage similarly fruitful experiments by other artists during the Seventies. Williams released a series of albums during the late Sixties and early Seventies, but with little success. However, he was a versatile and enigmatic talent who had other irons in the fire; he worked as a poet, publisher, author and photographer. A combination of the latter two skills led to the publication of *The bus book*, a deceptive ordinary-looking volume which unfolded into a life-size photo of a Greyhound bus; it became a permanent exhibit at the New York Museum of Modern Art. (Bob MacDonald, 3rd June 1985).

CLASSICAL GAS (OLD GOLD)
Tracks: / Classical gas / Baroque-a-nova.
7" Single: Released Mar '86, on Old Gold, by Old Gold Records. Catalogue no: **OG 9575**

CLASSICAL GAS (SINGLE)
Tracks: / Classical gas.
7" Single: Released Aug '68, on Warner Bros., by WEA Records. Deleted '71. Catalogue no: **WB 7190**
7" Single: Released Jul '81, on Warner Bros., by WEA Records. Catalogue no: **K 17810**

Williams, Maurice

Biographical details: This American singer, songwriter and pianist, who came from South Carolina, began his career in 1955 when he and three young singing colleagues won first prize in a local talent contest. This vocal quartet, initially known as the Charms, decided to try their luck at recording and changed their name to the Gladiolas. It was under this monicker that, in 1957, they recorded Williams' composition *Little Darlin'*. This exciting, rhythmic song achieved a minor placing on the US pop chart, but was quickly outstripped by a more commercial cover version from the opportunistic Canadian vocal quartet, The Diamonds. The latter rendition reached No.2 in the US and No.3 in the UK. It was in 1960, as Maurice Williams and the Zodiacs, that the South Carolina lads finally got their own big hit, *Stay*, again written by Williams, became an American No.1 single (something that the Diamonds' *Little darlin'* had not quite achieved) and, in early '61, reached No.14 in the UK. The ear-catching falsetto vocals on *Stay* were by no means its only selling point - the song's melody and lyrics somehow captured an intangible combination of carefree joy and teenage angst. It is a tribute to Williams that the osng has subsequently charted twice more on both sides of the Atlantic: in 1964, it have Britain's Hollies their debut UK Top Ten hit, which in turn gave the Four Seasons the idea of recording it and taking it into the American Top 20 once more; in 1978 a slower version by Jackson Browne reached No.20 in the US and No.12 in the UK. After *Stay*, Maurice Williams & The Zodiacs never returned to the Top 40 on either side of the Atlantic. Several minor hits were chalked up in the States but, by the time the Beatles' era had begun, the group were forgotton. Williams tried in vain to succeed as a solo artist but he could not come up with another *Stay*. (Bob MacDonald, 3rd June 1985).

STAY (JUST A LITTLE BIT LONGER)
Tracks: / Stay (just a little bit longer).
7" Single: Released Aug '84, on Creole (Replay), by Creole Records. Catalogue no: **CR 218**
7" Single: Released Jan '61, on Top Rank (1), Deleted '64. Catalogue no: **JAR 526**

STAY (JUST A LITTLE BIT LONGER) (OLD GOLD)
Tracks: / Stay (just a little bit longer) / Get a job.
7" Single: Released Jul '82, on Old Gold, by Old Gold Records. Deleted Jul '88. Catalogue no: **OG 9093**

Williams, Maynard

LONGER THE ROAD, THE
Tracks: / Longer the road.
7" Single: Released Oct '87, on 10 Records, by Virgin Records. Deleted May '88. Catalogue no: **TEN 195**

Williams, Shine

AGBOJU LOGUN
Tracks: / Agboju Logan.
12" Single: Released Jul '84, on Earthworks, by Earthworks Records. Deleted '88. Catalogue no: **ET 003**

Williams, Tony

Biographical details:
Tony Williams was born in Chicago in 1945. The drummer and composer became famous on joining Miles Davis in 1963; the Davis rhythm section with Herbie Hancock on piano and Ron Carter on bass is regarded as one of the most important of the era. he made his own LPs beginning with *Life Time* on Blue Note in 1965; he left Davis to form a jazz-rock fusion group called Lifetime with John McLaughlin, Jack Bruce and Larry Young on organ; it suffered many personnel changes and was never as successful commercially as it was influential: its free playing over a rock beat soon became a cliche. He toured and recorded as V.S.O.P., re-creating the Davis group with Hancock, Carter, Wayne Shorter and Freddie Hubbard replacing Davis; he played on other people's albums and came back as a leader on Blue Note in 1985. (Donald Clarke)..

CIVILIZATION (SINGLE)
Tracks: / Civilization.
7" Single: Released Jun '84, on Capitol, by EMI Records. Deleted '88. Catalogue no: **CL 333**

MONEY
Tracks: / Money.
12" Single: Released Aug '88, on Master Funk, Catalogue no: **TWD 1956**

Williams, Vanessa

DREAMIN'
Tracks: / Dreamin'.
7" Single: Released 6 Mar '89, on Polydor, by Polydor Ltd. Deleted Oct '89. Catalogue no: **WINGG 4**
7" Single: Released 6 Mar '89, on Polydor, by Polydor Ltd. Deleted Oct '89. Catalogue no: **WING 4**
12" Single: Released 6 Mar '89, on Polydor, by Polydor Ltd. Deleted Oct '89. Catalogue no: **WINGX 4**
CD 5": Released 6 Mar '89, on Polydor, by Polydor Ltd. Catalogue no: **871 749-2**

RIGHT STUFF, THE (REMIX)
Tracks: / Right stuff, The (7" remix) (On 7" only) / Darlin' I / Right stuff, The (12" remix) (On 12" only) / Right stuff, The (bonus beats) (On 12" only) / Right stuff, The (accappella) (On 12" only).
12" Single: Released Aug '89, on Polydor, by Polydor Ltd. Catalogue no: **WINGR 3**
7" Single: Released Aug '89, on Polydor, by Polydor Ltd. Catalogue no: **WINR 3**

RIGHT STUFF, THE (SINGLE)
Tracks: / Right stuff, The / Right stuff, The (extended version) (Available on 12" only) / Right stuff, The (dub version) (Available on 12" only).
12" Single: Released Jun '88, on Wing (USA), by PolyGram Rec.Inc.(USA). Catalogue no: **887 386-1**
7" Single: Released Jul '88, on Polydor, by Polydor Ltd. Catalogue no: **WING 3**
12" Single: Released Jul '88, on Polydor, by Polydor Ltd. Catalogue no: **WINGX 3**

Williams, Vesta

DON'T BLOW A GOOD THING
Tracks: / Don't blow a good thing / You make me want to (love again).
7" Single: Released Mar '87, on Breakout, by A&M Records. Deleted Mar '88. Catalogue no: **USA 600**
12" Single: Released Mar '87, on Breakout, by A&M Records. Deleted Mar '88. Catalogue no: **USAT 600**

ONCE BITTEN, TWICE SHY
Tracks: / Once bitten, twice shy / My heart is yours.
12" Single: Released Nov '86, on A&M, by A&M Records. Deleted Mar '88. Catalogue no: **AMY 362**
7" Single: Released Nov '86, on A&M, by A&M Records. Deleted Mar '88. Catalogue no: **AM 362**

SUDDENLY IT'S MAGIC
Tracks: / Suddenly it's magic / Don't let me down.
7" Single: Released May '87, on Breakout, by A&M Records. Deleted Mar '88. Catalogue no: **USA 603**

Williams, Vince

180
Tracks: / 180.
7" Single: Released Feb '81, on Smile, Catalogue no: **SRO 28**

Williams, Wallace W.

WATER BED
Tracks: / Water bed / Underwater pressure.
12" Single: Released Jan '82, on Trindisc, by Trindisc Records. Catalogue no: **TRIN 001 12**
7" Single: Released Jan '82, on Trindisc, by Trindisc Records. Catalogue no: **TRIN 001**

Williams, Willie

COME ALONG
Tracks: / Come along.
10" single: Released Jul '83, on Stin Jac, Catalogue no: **SJ 41001**

ONE LOVE
Tracks: / One love.
12" Single: Released Jun '84, on Uptempo, Catalogue no: **UT 004**

REPATRIATION
Tracks: / Repatriation / Come along / Armageddon time / Justice tonight.
12" Single: Released Jul '83, on WLM Music, Catalogue no: **WLM 004**

Williamson, Ann

BABY BLUE
Tracks: / Baby blue / When you and I were young Maggie.
7" Single: Released Apr '83, on Mint, by Emerald Records. Deleted '88. Catalogue no: **CHEW 81**

BLUE EYES CRYING IN THE RAIN
Tracks: / Blue eyes crying in the rain / She's got you.
7" Single: Released Jul '87, on Mint, by Emerald Records. Deleted '88. Catalogue no: **CHEW 113**

FAMILY BIBLE, THE
Tracks: / Family Bible / Hey Lord it's me.
7" Single: Released Nov '87, on Mint, by Emerald Records. Deleted '88. Catalogue no: **CHEW 115**

PAL OF MY CRADLE DAYS
Tracks: / Pal of my cradle days.
7" Single: Released Dec '82, on Mint, by Emerald Records. Deleted '88. Catalogue no: **CHEW 77**

RAMBLIN' ROSE
Tracks: / Ramblin' Rose / Snowbird.
7" Single: Released Nov '87, on Mint, by Emerald Records. Deleted '88. Catalogue no: **CHEW 109**

TINY BUBBLES (SINGLE)
Tracks: / Just out of reach / Heart of my heart / You don't have to tell me.
7" Single: Released Oct '83, on Mint, by Emerald Records. Deleted '88. Catalogue no: **CHEW 85**

WHEN YOU AND I WERE YOUNG MAGGIE
Tracks: / When you and I were young Maggie / Forsaking all the rest.
7" Single: Released Oct '82, on Mint, by Emerald Records. Deleted '88. Catalogue no: **CHEW 72**
7" Single: Released May '86, on Emerald, by Emerald Records. Deleted '88. Catalogue no: **D 1222**

Williamson, Jaye

LUCKY STAR
Tracks: / Lucky star.
7" Single: Released Dec '88, on DK, Catalogue no: **DK 2**

Williamson, Sonny Boy

Biographical details: There were actually two important blues artists who worked under the name of Sonny Boy Williamson. Both were American singers and harmonica players. The first is now a hard artist for record collectors to trace, but the second is still available on disc.
Sonny Boy Mk 1, born John Lee Williamson in Tennessee in 1914, relocated to Chicago in 1937. He helped to make that city the No.1 blues capital, thanks to such influential tracks such as *Sugar Mama* and *Good Morning, Little Schoolgirl*. During the forties, he became one of the first blues artists to embellish his sound with a backing band; many of the city's talents later followed him in this respect, thus breaking away from the genre's traditionally sparse style. He died in Chicago in June 1948 at the age of 34, falling victim to a merciless attack and robbery.
Sonny Boy Mk 2 was, in fact, born many years before his predecessor, but his career got off to a later start. Born in Mississippi in 1897, he first attracted attention in the early forties via an influential daily radio show in Arkanas, 'King Biscuit Time'. Although his real name was Rice Miller, he changed his name to that of his Chicago idol at about this time. In addition, he actually claimed to be THE Sonny Boy; monstrous though this ploy was, it got Miller the necessary popularity and attention. By the time he was rumbled, he had sufficiently proved his musical worth to be able to survive solely on talent. In 1951, three years after the death of Sonny Boy Mk 1, Sonny Boy Mk2 began making records. Now based in Chicago, he signed with the city's Chess label in 1955 and consolidated upon his ever growing status as a blues master. His best songs were the ones which displayed his prowess as a writer of engaging lyrics - *One Way Out*, *Nine Below Zero* (which later gave its name to a British R&B band) and *Fattening Frogs for Snakes* were among the finest examples. During 1963-4, he suddenly became a regular visitor to Europe and particularly Britain, where the burgeoning blues boom was winning him many
new admirers. He played live with two of t
UK's most important up and coming grou
the Animals and the Yardbirds - both col
borations yielded live albums, which did r
make the charts but were nonetheless in
guing transatlantic and trans-generati
projects. Sonny Boy's only entry into t
British charts occured in June 1964, wh
Down and out Blues reached No.20 on t
LP lists. He passed away lesss than a ye
later - Sonny Boy Mk 2 died in Arkansas
May 1965 at the age of 68. (Bob Macdon
June 1985)
John Lee Williamson (Sonny Boy Mk 1) w
born in 1914 in Tennessee; he was a p
foundly influencial blues singer and harmo
ca player by the time he was murdered b
mugger in Chicago in 1948. He record
about 120 sides for Bluebird/Victor fr
1937, accompanists on his dates incud
Big Bill Broonzy, Big Joe Williams, Speck
Red and others; he backed Williams on C
umbia (CBS/USA) in 1947. His songs su
as *Good morning little schoolgirl* beca
blues standards; his harmonica was a dir
influence on Little Walter, Big Walter Hort
etc. Compilations include *Bluebird blues*
Charly and several volumes of blues class
on Arhoolie. (Donald Clarke, May 1988)
Rice Miller Williamson (Sonny Boy Mk
Was born Aleck Ford in Mississippi in 18
but became known as Rice Miller from
childhood nickname and his stepfather's s
name. He died in Arknsas in 1965. It
thought that both Rice Miller and John L
(the original Sonny Boy) worked with Sun
land Slim in the early '30s; Miller later work
with Elmore James, Big Boy Crudup, Rob
Johnson and Howlin' Wolf; he appeared
the radio show King Biscuit Time in 194
billed as Sonny Boy Williamson, and af
John Lee was murdered he claimed to be
original: his talent justified the arrogance.
had R&B hits in the mid 1950s on Chess a
Checker and toured Europe in the '60s,
coming one of the most direct influences
UK R&B and recording with The Anim
The Yardbirds and Brian Auger: Albums n
on Charly include *Jam session* with Au
and Jimmy Page, and *Newcastle Decem*
1963 with The Animals. See also the e
for The Yardbirds. (Donald Clarke, May '
Both Sonny Boy Mk 1 and Mk 2 are un
this black strip..

TAKE IT EASY BABY
Tracks: / Bye Bye Bird / I don't care no m
/ Baby don't worry / Twenty three hours
long / Take it easy baby.
Note: Live set recorded in London with
Yardbirds and Eric Clapton in support.
7" EP: Released Jul '87, on Blue Moon
by Magnum Music Group. Catalogue
BMEP 001

Willie And The Poor

THESE ARMS OF MINE
Tracks: / These arms of mine / Poor
boogie.
7" Single: Released Jan '86, on Decca,
Decca Records. Deleted '88. Catalogue
880 917-7

Willis, Bruce

COMIN' RIGHT UP
Tracks: / Comin' right up / Down in H
wood / Under the boardwalk (on 12" and
single only) / Respect yourself (on CD
only).
CD 5": Released Jan '88, on Motown,
BMG Records (UK). Catalogue no:
41654
12" Single: Released Dec '87, on Mot
by BMG Records (UK). Catalogue no:
41654
7" Single: Released Dec '87, on Motown
BMG Records (UK). Catalogue no:
41653

RESPECT YOURSELF
Tracks: / Furniture.
7" Single: Released Feb '87, on Motown
BMG Records (UK). Catalogue no:
41117
12" Single: Released Feb '87, on Mot
by BMG Records (UK). Catalogue no
41118

SECRET AGENT MAN (JAM BOND IS BACK)
Tracks: / Secret agent man (James Bo
back) / Lose myself / Under the board
(on 12" only).
12" Single: Released Sep '87, on Mot
by BMG Records (UK). Catalogue no
41438
7" Single: Released Sep '87, on Motow
BMG Records (UK). Catalogue no:
41437

UNDER THE BOARDWALK
Tracks: / Under the boardwalk / jackpo
7" Single: Released May '87, on Mot
by BMG Records (UK). Catalogue no
41349
Cassingle: Released Jun '87, on Mot
by BMG Records (UK). Catalogue no

41349C

YOUNG BLOOD
Tracks: / Young blood / Flirting with danger (Music Week 7/5/1988 gives track as Flirting with disaster.).
12" Single: Released May '88, on RCA, by BMG Records (UK). Catalogue no: **ZT 41274**
7" Single: Released May '88, on RCA, by BMG Records (UK). Catalogue no: **ZB 41273**

Willis, Rod

CAT, THE
Tracks: / Cat, The.
7" Single: Released Mar '84, on Northwood, by Northwood Records. Catalogue no: **NW45 002**

Wills, Nikki

SOME GUYS HAVE ALL THE LUCK
Tracks: / Some guys have all the luck.
7" Single: Released Feb '82, on Avatar, by Avatar Record Corporation. Catalogue no: **AAA 121**

Wills, Viola

Biographical details: Wills, Viola This run of the mill American singer became famous via two records. The first was *Gonna Get Along Without You Now*, which reached the UK No.8 slot in the autumn of 1979, thus becoming her only British hit. This was an updated version of a mid-Fifties hit by the juvenile duo, Patience & Prudence. Wills' rendition achieved a far higher UK placing than the original, and was aimed squarely at the Eurodisco market.
It was on the American disco charts, in 1980, that Wills gained her other big success. Her highly danceable, uptempo version of Gordon Lightfoot's classic 1971 ballad *If You Could Read My Mind*, reached the Top 3 of Billboard's disco listings. It was certainly a more listenable effort than Linda Clifford's dire dance remakes of Simon & Garfunkel's *Bridge Over Troubled Water*, which had been released the previous year. Wills subsequently vanished into obscurity, and the music industry can definitely get along without her now. (Bob Macdonald June 1985).

DARE TO DREAM
Tracks: / Dare to dream / Both sides now.
7" Single: Released Feb '86, on Streetwise, Catalogue no: **KHAN 66**
12" Single: Released Feb '86, on Streetwise, Catalogue no: **MKHAN 66**

GONNA GET ALONG WITHOUT YOU NOW
Tracks: / Gonna get along without you now.
7" Single: Released 24 Jul '89, on Music Man, Catalogue no: **MMPS 7006**
12" Single: Released Jul '84, on Touch, by Touch Records. Catalogue no: **12TOU 05**
12" Single: Released 24 Jul '89, on Music Man, Catalogue no: **MMPT 12006**
7" Single: Released Sep '82, on Ariola-Hansa, by Hansa Records. Catalogue no: **AHA 546**

IF YOU COULD READ MY MIND
Tracks: / If you could read my mind / Somebody's eyes.
7" Single: Released Mar '80, on Ariola, by BMG Records (UK). Deleted Mar '83. Catalogue no: **AHA 577**

LOVE LETTERS
Tracks: / Love letters.
7" Single: Released Mar '80, on Charly, by Charly Records. Deleted '88. Catalogue no: **CYS 1062**

REGGAE HIGH
Tracks: / Reggae high.
7" Single: Released Aug '87, on Island, by Island Records. Deleted Apr '88. Catalogue no: **IS 329**
12" Single: Released Aug '87, on Island, by Island Records. Deleted Apr '88. Catalogue no: **12IS 329**

SECRET LOVE
Tracks: / Secret love.
12" Single: Released Jan '89, on Light House, Catalogue no: **SH 29T**
7" Single: Released Jan '89, on Light House, Catalogue no: **SH 29**

SOMEBODY'S EYES
Tracks: / Somebody's eyes / You love.
7" Single: Released Sep '86, on Sedition, by Sedition Records. Catalogue no: **EDIT 3313**
12" Single: Released Sep '86, on Sedition, by Sedition Records. Catalogue no: **EDITL 3313**

TAKE ONE STEP FORWARD
Tracks: / Take one step forward (Inst).
7" Single: Released Dec '86, on Nitemare, Catalogue no: **MARES 7**
12" Single: Released Dec '86, on Nitemare, Catalogue no: **MARE 7**

THESE THINGS HAPPEN
Tracks: / These things happen.
12" Single: Released Sep '88, on Rhythm King, by Mute Records. Catalogue no: **LEFT 23 T**
7" Single: Released Sep '88, on Rhythm King, by Mute Records. Catalogue no: **LEFT 23**

YOU ARE THE REASON WHY
Tracks: / You are the reason why / You are the reason why (alternative version).
12" Single: Released May '86, on DM Streetsounds, Catalogue no: **MKHAN 70**
7" Single: Released May '86, on DM Streetsounds, Catalogue no: **KHAN 70**

Willson-Piper, Marty

SHE'S KING
Tracks: / She's king.
CD 3": Released '88, on Rykodisc (USA), Catalogue no: **RCD 31002**

Willy Jive

MONA
Tracks: / Mona.
7" Single: Released Aug '81, on Cheapskate, Catalogue no: **CHEAP 33**

Wilson

DANCE WITH ME
Tracks: / Dance with me / If that's the way.
12" Single: Released Feb '87, on Hit Or Miss, Deleted Oct '87. Catalogue no: **12 HOM 1**
7" Single: Released Feb '87, on Hit Or Miss, Deleted Oct '87. Catalogue no: **HOM 1**

Wilson, Ada

IN THE QUIET OF MY ROOM
Tracks: / In the quiet of my room.
7" Single: Released Oct '84, on Thin Sliced, by Thin Sliced Records. Catalogue no: **TSR 5**

Wilson, Al

SNAKE, THE
Tracks: / Snake, The / Lovers concerto.
7" Single: Released Aug '84, on Casino Classics, by RK Records. Catalogue no: **CC 16**
7" Single: Released Aug '75, on Bell, Deleted '78. Catalogue no: **BELL 1436**

Wilson, Ann

SURRENDER TO ME
Tracks: / Surrender to me (Vannelli/Marx.) / Tequila dreams (Grusin.) / Dead on the money (Diamond/Cerney.).
7" Single: Released Mar '89, on Capitol, by EMI Records. Deleted Aug '89. Catalogue no: **CL 525**
CD 5": Released Mar '89, on Capitol, by EMI Records. Deleted Aug '89. Catalogue no: **CDCL 525**
12" Single: Released Mar '89, on Capitol, by EMI Records. Deleted Aug '89. Catalogue no: **12CL 525**
CD 5": Released Mar '89, on Capitol, by EMI Records. Deleted Aug '89. Catalogue no: **203 250 2**

Wilson, Brian

LOVE AND MERCY
Tracks: / Love and mercy / He couldn't get his old body to move.
7" Single: Released Jul '88, on Warner Bros., by WEA Records. Catalogue no: **W 7814**
CD 5": Released Aug '88, on Sire, by Sire Records. Catalogue no: **W 7814 CD**
12" Single: Released Jul '88, on Warner Bros., by WEA Records. Catalogue no: **W 7814 T**

NIGHT TIME
Tracks: / Night time.
12" Single: Released Nov '88, on Warner Bros., by WEA Records. Catalogue no: **W 7787T**
7" Single: Released Nov '88, on Warner Bros., by WEA Records. Catalogue no: **W 7787**

Wilson Brothers

FEELING LIKE WE'RE STRANGERS AGAIN
Tracks: / Feeling like we're strangers again / Shadows.
7" Single: Released Feb '80, on Atlantic, by WEA Records. Deleted Feb '83. Catalogue no: **K 11431**

Wilson, Carl

HEAVEN
Tracks: / Heaven / Right lane, The.
7" Single: Released Apr '81, on Caribou, by CBS Records. Deleted Apr '84. Catalogue no: **CRBA 1152**

WHAT YOU DO TO ME
Tracks: / What you do to me.
7" Single: Released May '83, on Caribou, by CBS Records. Catalogue no: **A 3046**

Wilson, Delroy

BREAK UP TO MAKE UP
Tracks: / Break up to make up.
12" Single: Released Apr '82, on Plantation, Catalogue no: **PL 005**

CALL ON ME
Tracks: / Call on me.
12" Single: Released Jul '88, on Germaine, Catalogue no: **DGT 37**

CHANGING FOR YOU
Tracks: / Changing for you / Wedding ring.
12" Single: Released Aug '87, on Mobiliser, by Jetstar Records. Catalogue no: **MM 78**

CHERISH
Tracks: / Cherish / Cherish (alternative version).
12" Single: Released Jan '86, on Top Rank (2), Catalogue no: **TRD 024**

DANCING MOOD
Tracks: / Dancing mood.
12" Single: Released Sep '84, on Greensleeves, by Greensleeves Records. Catalogue no: **GRED 157**

DOING ME WRONG
Tracks: / Doing me wrong / Doing me wrong (alternative version).
12" Single: Released Dec '85, on Blue Mountain, Catalogue no: **BM 010**

EASE UP
Tracks: / Ease up.
12" Single: Released Sep '88, on You're Right, Catalogue no: **YR 001**

GIRL OF TODAY
Tracks: / Girl of today / Stuggling dub.
12" Single: Released Aug '86, on Tulip, Catalogue no: **TUL 003**

HAPPY BIRTHDAY
Tracks: / Happy birthday / Have a little faith.
12" Single: Released Sep '86, on Top Rank (2), Catalogue no: **TRD 026**

I HAVE BEEN IN LOVE
Tracks: / I have been in love.
7" Single: Released Oct '88, on Conqueror, Catalogue no: **LD 045**

I'M STILL WAITING
Tracks: / I'm still waiting / Midnight.
12" Single: Released Jun '84, on Sarge, Catalogue no: **SRL 001**

IT'S ASHAME
Tracks: / It's ashame.
12" Single: Released Feb '89, on Fashion, by Fashion Records. Catalogue no: **FAD 063**

KISS AN ANGEL GOOD MORNING
Tracks: / Kiss an angel good morning.
12" Single: Released Aug '84, on Londisc, by Londisc Records. Catalogue no: **LDR 019**

LET'S GET MARRIED TODAY
Tracks: / Let's get married today.
12" Single: Released Mar '88, on Fashion, by Fashion Records. Catalogue no: **FAD 054**

LIVING IN THE FOOTSTEPS
Tracks: / Living in the footsteps / So long Jenny.
12" Single: Released Dec '82, on Live & Love, Catalogue no: **LLDS 111**

NO MORE HEARTACHE
Tracks: / No more heartache / One who loves you.
12" Single: Released Jul '82, on Black Music, Catalogue no: **BM 705**

NOTHING GONNA CHANGE MY LOVE FOR YOU
Tracks: / Nothing gonna change my love for you.
7" Single: Released Nov '85, on Hawkeye, by Hawkeye Records. Catalogue no: **HD 66**

ONE MORE CHANCE
Tracks: / One more chance.
12" Single: Released Feb '89, on Del-Roy, Catalogue no: **DRW 001**

PEOPLE ARE DOING IT EVERY DAY
Tracks: / People are doing it every day.
12" Single: Released Jul '85, on Revue, by Creole Records. Catalogue no: **REV 025T**

PLAY SOMETHING PRETTY
Tracks: / Play something pretty.
12" Single: Released Aug '83, on J & J, Catalogue no: **JJ 107**

PLEASE DON'T LEAVE ME
Tracks: / Please don't leave me.
12" Single: Released Nov '85, on High Power, Catalogue no: **HPD 008**

RUN RUN
Tracks: / Run run.
12" Single: Released Sep '84, on Studio One, Catalogue no: **Unknown**

SHARING THE NIGHT TOGETHER
Tracks: / Sharing the night together / Tension.
7" Single: Released Mar '80, on Liberty (USA), by EMI Records. Deleted Mar '83. Catalogue no: **BP 343**

SPIT IN THE SKY
Tracks: / Spit in the sky.
7" Single: Released May '89, on Studio One, Catalogue no: **UNKNOWN**

STOP ACTING STRANGE
Tracks: / Stop acting strange.
12" Single: Released Sep '87, on Live & Love, Catalogue no: **LLD 417**

SUPER MEDLEY HIT
Tracks: / Super medley hit.
12" Single: Released Oct '87, on Pioneer International, Catalogue no: **PI 46**

SUSPICION
Tracks: / Suspicion.
12" Single: Released May '83, on Revue, by Creole Records. Catalogue no: **REVD 003**

WON'T YOU COME HOME
Tracks: / Won't you come home.
12" Single: Released Jul '82, on Starlight, Catalogue no: **SLD 520**

YOU HAVE MY HEART
Tracks: / You have my heart / One little thing.
12" Single: Released Oct '82, on Jah Congo, Catalogue no: **YV 207**

Wilson, Dennis

BOBBY & THE SPACE INVDERS
Tracks: / Bobby the space invaders / Runaway.
7" Single: Released Apr '80, on Sonet, by Sonet Records. Deleted Apr '83. Catalogue no: **SON 2203**

Wilson, Dustin

AS TIME GOES BY
Tracks: / As time goes by.
7" Single: Released Dec '77, on United Artists, by EMI Records. Deleted '80. Catalogue no: **UP 36331**

Wilson, Ernest

BIG ENOUGH
Tracks: / Big enough / Big enough (version).
12" Single: Released 23 May '87, on Natty Congo, Catalogue no: **NCDM 041**

COME TO ME
Tracks: / Come to me / Come to me (alternative version).
12" Single: Released Sep '86, on Natty Congo, Catalogue no: **NCDM 037**

FIRST LOVE
Tracks: / First love.
12" Single: Released Aug '87, on Techniques, Catalogue no: **WRT 17**

I'VE BEEN LOVING YOU TOO LONG
Tracks: / I've been loving you too long.
12" Single: Released Jul '88, on Legal Lights, by Legal Light Records. Catalogue no: **LLQ 11**

LAST LAUGH
Tracks: / Last laugh.
7" Single: Released Jun '88, on Spiderman, Catalogue no: **ST 105**

TALKING IN MY SLEEP
Tracks: / Talking in my sleep / Who control them.
12" Single: Released May '86, on Ozzy Music, Catalogue no: **DMD1S 011**

UNDYING LOVE
Tracks: / Undying love.
12" Single: Released May '89, on Realistic, Catalogue no: **RRO 17**

YOU
Tracks: / You.
12" Single: Released Mar '89, on Natty Congo, Catalogue no: **NCDM 046**

Wilson, Flick

MY LADY
Tracks: / My lady.
12" Single: Released Nov '80, on Greensleeves, by Greensleeves Records. Catalogue no: **GRED 42**

SLAVEMASTER
Tracks: / Slavemaster.
12" Single: Released Aug '80, on Greensleeves, by Greensleeves Records. Catalogue no: **GRED 37**

Wilson, Frank

DO I LOVE YOU (INDEED I DO)
Tracks: / Do I love you (indeed I do).
Note: The world's rarest soul 45 gets a belated UK release. Only one U.S. copy of "Do I Love You" is known to exist, and is valued at over a thousand pounds.
7" Single: Released Oct '81, on Motown, by BMG Records (UK). Catalogue no: **TMG 1170**

Wilson, Gary

CRY
Tracks: / Cry / Can't pay the bill.
7" Single: Released Jun '84, on Sundance, by Sundance Records. Catalogue no: **LMG 13**

DREAMIN'
Tracks: / Dreamin'.
7" Single: Released May '82, on Avatar, by Avatar Record Corporation. Catalogue no: **AAA 127**

HELP ME RHONDA
Tracks: / Help me Rhonda / Baby let's play house.
7" Single: Released Jul '81, on Avatar, by Avatar Record Corporation. Catalogue no: **AAA 110**

MOVIE QUEEN
Tracks: / Movie Queen.
7" Single: Released Aug '83, on Sour Grape, by Sour Grape Records. Deleted '87. Catalogue no: **SG 115**

Wilson, Jack

NEVER GONNA GIVE YOU UP
Tracks: / Never gonna give you up / Breakfast in bed.
7" Single: Released Jun '88, on Uptempo, Catalogue no: **TEMP 023**

Wilson, Jackie

Biographical details: Wilson, Jackie This American singer, born in Detroit, was one of the best and most underrated vocalists in the history of Pop and R&B music. During the late Forties, he made headway as a teenage welterweight boxer, but his mother refused to allow him to pursue this career. Like many future black stars, his vocal performances began in church; this experience proved to be invaluable in 1953, because his joined Billy Ward & The Dominoes in that year - that group had become famous via their intense gospel treatment of secular rhythm and blues songs, and Wilson stepped into the shoes of their key member Clyde McPhatter, who had just quit to join a vital new group, the Drifters.
Wilson's excellent tenor voice remained with the Dominoes until 1956, whereupon he left and launched a solo career. In view of his future track record, which showed him to be a much bigger success in America than Britain, it is interesting to note that his first single *Reet Petite* performed better in the UK than the US. This was a wonderfully catchy belter, which reached No.6 on the British chart in 1957, while failing to hit the pop Top 40 in the States; it was co-written by a fellow Detroit dweller, Berry Gordy, who later became the legendary founder of Motown Records.
In the States, Wilson's solo career really took off in early 1959, when *Lonely Teardrops*, another Gordy song, hit the US No.7 position. He followed this with *That's Why (I Love You So)*, (No.13) and 1960 brought him the biggest US pop hit of the career: the classically derived single *Night* reached No.4 on the Billboard Hot 100 but, ironically, seemed to display an artistic difficulty for Wilson - many critics argued that his pure, powerful and emotional voice was often overburdened with ham handed, excessive orchestration. His next US Top Tenner occured in late 1960 - *Alone At Last* - and he got there again in early '61 with *My Empty Arms*.
Wilson's second biggest US single was 1963's *Baby Workout* which cruised to No.5. This brass laden dance smash reaffirmed the singer's versatility; he was equally at home with the frantic dance numbers and the emotional ballads. After a sales decline in the mid-Sixties, he returned to form with *Whispers (Getting Louder)* and *(Your Love Keeps Lifting Me) Higher and Higher*. A 1968 Supremes style single, *I Get The Sweetest Feeling*, gave him a rare and belated British Top Tenner in 1972. By this time, however, the singer's career was, to all intents and purposes, over; he was now confined to cabaret dates.
It was while playing such a date in New Jersey in September 1975 that Wilson suffered a paralysing heart attack. Incredibly, he remained in a coma for over eight years - when he finally died in January 1984 at the age of 49, his passing could only be described as a long overdue blessing for him.
Strangely, it was during his years of incapacitation that the Jackie Wilson magic finally began to earn the respect and tributes that it deserved. Rita Coolidge (US charts) and Shakin' Stevens (UK charts) successfully covered his old tracks, *Higher and Higher* and *I'll Be Satisfied* respectively. Dexy's Midnight Runners hit the UK Top 5 with *Jackie Wilson said (I'm In Heaven When You Smile)*, a song first recorded in 1972 by Van Morrison, who has always cited Wilson as a key influence. A year after Jackie's death, the Commodores reached No.3 on both sides of the Atlantic with *Nightshift*, a touching tribute to both Wilson and the late Marvin Gaye; this song's uccess surpassed Wilson's own greatest successes - his biggest US hit *Night* peaked at No.4; his greatest UK hit *Reet Petite* reached No.6. (Bob Macdonald June 1985)
Jackie Wilson, (1934-84) was one of the most prodigiously talented and best-loved of all pop/soul singers, with about 35 R&B hits '58-71, nearly half in Top 10; over 50 Hot 100 pop singles '57-72. He suffered a heart attack on stage at the Latin casino in Camden, New Jersey in 1975 and spent the rest of his life in a coma. discovered by Johnny Otis in 1951, he replaced Clyde mcPhatter as lead singer in Billy Ward's Dominoes in 1953; his first six solo hits were co-written by Berry gordy and Tyran Carlo; *Reet Petite* in 1957 was regarded as a novelty and reached only number 67 in the USA pop chart (but number 6 in the UK); despite a big band arrangement and recording balance which now seem dated, his extraordinary high spirits and unbelievable range of vocal sounds made it irresistible, a huge hit in the UK on reissue in 1987. *Lonely Teardrops* in 1958 was number 1 R&B, no. 7 pop in USA; other hits were based on classical tunesP: *Night* from Saint-Saens; *Alone At Last* from Tchaikovsky. During his years of unconciousness he was recognised as a great artist; said to have influenced Elvis Presley in his stage act; Van Morrison claimed him for an influence and wrote *Jackie Wilson Said (I'm In Heaven When You Smile)*. (Donald Clarke)..

ALL MY LOVE
Tracks: / All my love.
7" Single: Released Sep '60, on Coral, by MCA Records. Deleted '63. Catalogue no: **Q 72407**

ALONE AT LAST
Tracks: / Alone at last.
7" Single: Released Dec '60, on Coral, by MCA Records. Deleted '63. Catalogue no: **Q 72412**

BABY WORKOUT
Tracks: / Baby workout / Lonely teardrops.
CD 5": Released '88, on Passion, by Skratch Records. Catalogue no: **SKMCD 11**
12" Single: Released 21 Nov '87, on SMP (2), Catalogue no: **SKM 11(12)**
7" Single: Released 21 Nov '87, on SMP (2), Catalogue no: **SKM 11**

HIGHER & HIGHER (SINGLE)
Tracks: / Higher and higher / Who who song, The.
7" Single: Released 20 Jun '87, on SMP (2), Catalogue no: **SKM 10**
12" Single: Released 20 Jun '87, on SMP (2), Catalogue no: **SKM 10(12)**
7" Single: Released May '69, on MCA, by MCA Records. Deleted '72. Catalogue no: **BAG 2**

I GET THE SWEETEST FEELING
Tracks: / I get the sweetest feeling / Whisper / Higher and higher / Who who song / Nothing but blue skies.
7" Single: Released Feb '87, on Skratch, by Skratch Records. Deleted '88. Catalogue no: **SKM 01**
7" Single: Released Jul '72, on MCA, by MCA Records. Deleted '75. Catalogue no: **MU 1160**
12" Single: Released Mar '85, on Skratch, by Skratch Records. Deleted '88. Catalogue no: **SKM 0121**
7" Single: Released Mar '75, on Brunswick, by Decca Records. Deleted '78. Catalogue no: **BR 18**

I GET THE SWEETEST FEELING (OLD GOLD)
Tracks: / I get the sweetest feeling / Higher and higher / Whispers.
12" Single: Released 30 May '89, on Old Gold, by Old Gold Records. Catalogue no: **OG 4118**

REET PETITE (SINGLE)
Tracks: / Reet petite / You brought about a change in me / I'm the one to do it.
12" Single: Released Mar '85, on Skratch, by Skratch Records. Deleted '88. Catalogue no: **SKM 0123**
7" Single: Released Mar '85, on Skratch, by Skratch Records. Deleted '88. Catalogue no: **SKM 03**
7" Single: Released Nov '57, on Coral, by MCA Records. Deleted '60. Catalogue no: **Q 72290**

TO BE LOVED
Tracks: / To be loved.
7" Single: Released Mar '58, on Coral, by MCA Records. Deleted '61. Catalogue no: **Q 72306**

WHISPERS (OLD GOLD CD SINGLE)
Tracks: / Whispers / Higher and higher / I get the sweetest feeling.
CD 5": Released Nov '88, on Old Gold, by Old Gold Records. Catalogue no: **OG 6109**

Wilson, Jock

SIX STREET
Tracks: / Six street / Live stock.
12" Single: Released Jul '86, on Uptempo, Catalogue no: **TEMP 005**

Wilson, John

LETTER, THE
Tracks: / Letter, The.
7" Single: Released Feb '85, on Legacy, by Legacy Records. Catalogue no: **LGY 20**

SUN AIN'T GONNA SHINE ANYMORE
Tracks: / Sun ain't gonna shine anymore, The / Everything I need.
7" Single: Released Nov '86, on Legacy, by Legacy Records. Catalogue no: **LGY 54**
12" Single: Released Nov '86, on Legacy, by Legacy Records. Catalogue no: **LGYT 54**

UNDERSTANDING
Tracks: / Everything I need.
7" Single: Released Jan '87, on Legacy, by Legacy Records. Catalogue no: **LGY 56**

WE ALL WANNA BE IN LOVE
Tracks: / We all wanna be in love.
7" Single: Released Jun '85, on Legacy, by Legacy Records. Catalogue no: **LGY 26**
12" Single: Released Jun '85, on Legacy, by Legacy Records. Catalogue no: **LGYT 26**

YOUR EYES
Tracks: / Your eyes / Bad guy.
7" Single: Released Oct '87, on Legacy, by Legacy Records. Catalogue no: **LGY 59**

Wilson, Judith

CAN'T RESIST
Tracks: / Can't resist.
7" Single: Released Jun '88, on Techniques, Catalogue no: **WRT 32**

Wilson, Junior

DOCK OF THE BAY
Tracks: / (Sittin' on) the dock of the bay.
12" Single: Released 27 Feb '88, on Blue Trac, by Blue Trac Records. Catalogue no: **MMD 117**

I'M THE TOUGHEST (SINGLE)
7" Single: Released Jun '88, on Witty, Catalogue no: **MMD 132**

RAMBO
Tracks: / Cassandra.
12" Single: Released Jan '87, on Rockers Plantation, Catalogue no: **PL 19**

Wilson, Kerry

ELECTION SELECTION, THE
Tracks: / Election selection, The.
12" Single: Released Jun '87, on Lambs To The Slaughter, by Prism Records. Catalogue no: **LTS 24T**
7" Single: Released Jun '87, on Lambs To The Slaughter, by Prism Records. Catalogue no: **LTS 24**

Wilson, Mari

Biographical details: Wilson, Mari This British singer, who hailed from Neasden in North London, was actually born in Scotland with the name Mairrhii Wilson. However, it was as Neasden's 'Tupperware Queen' or 'High Priestess of Hairspray' that she came to fame in 1982. Her high bouffant, eye catching beehive hairdo and her derivative Sixties dress sense were already a formidable live attraction by the time she first hit the UK charts with *Beat The Beat* in March of that year. That single reached No.59 and was credited to Mari Wilson & The Imaginations; but legal action by the disco band Imagination forced Wilson to change the name of her large and eccentric backing band group to the Wilsations.
Baby It's True, a typical Sixties girl singer pastiche that was approximately halfway between Sandie Shaw and the Supremes, got to No.42 in the UK in the summer of '82. At the same time, Wilson and her band landed a spot on 'The David Essex Showcase', a BBC TV talent contest. Helped enormously by their highly visual stage presence, they won second place in the grand final. Wilson was certainly to achieve greater chart success than the contest winner, Phillip Jap (who?).
Wilson's third UK chart single became her first and only Top 10 hit. *Just What I Always Wanted* was the perfect distillation of a big sound, a big personality, a strong pop song and a good if unexceptional voice. Although all her singles sounded derivative, she only in fact charted with one non original song *Cry Me A River*, a UK No.27 hit in spring '83, was originally recorded in the mid Fifties by Julie London. By July '83, however, the Wilson magic had worn off in chart terms - Tracey Ullman was now assuming the role of Sixties pastiche queen.
1984 saw Wilson attempting in vain to revive her chart career, by experimenting with various visual and musical styles. The beehive disappeared but the change did not do any good. She somehow managed to remain an ever present media personality despite lack of recording success. (Bob Macdonald June 1985).

AIN'T THAT PECULIAR?
Tracks: / Ain't that peculiar? / Maximum damage.
12" Single: Released Apr '84, on Compact Organisation, Deleted '86. Catalogue no: **PINKX 8**
7" Single: Released Apr '84, on Compact Organisation, Deleted '86. Catalogue no: **PINK 8**

BABY IT'S TRUE (I CAN'T STOP MYSELF) (see panel below)
Tracks: / Baby it's true (I can't stop myself) / You look so good.
7" Single: Released Apr '82, on Compact Organisation, Deleted '84. Catalogue no: **PINK 3**
12" Single: Released Apr '82, on Compact Organisation, Deleted '84. Catalogue no: **PINKX 3**

BEAT THE BEAT
Tracks: / Beat the beat.
7" Single: Released Feb '82, on Compact Organisation, Deleted '84. Catalogue no: **PINK 2**

BEWARE BOYFRIEND
Tracks: / Beware boyfriend.
12" Single: Released Nov '82, on Compact Organisation, Deleted '84. Catalogue no: **PINKX 5**
7" Single: Released Nov '82, on Compact Organisation, Deleted '84. Catalogue no: **PINK 5**

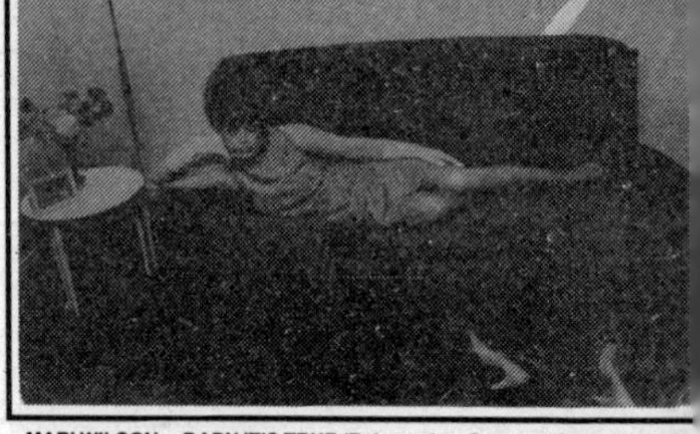

MARI WILSON - BABY IT'S TRUE (Released on Compact Organisation)

CRY ME A RIVER
Tracks: / Cry me a river.
7" Single: Released Mar '83, on Compact Organisation, Deleted '85. Catalogue no: **PINK 6**
12" Single: Released Mar '83, on Compact Organisation, Deleted '85. Catalogue no: **PINKX 6**

DANCE CARD
Tracks: / Dance card / She's had enough of you.
7" Single: Released Aug '81, on Compact Organisation, Deleted '83. Catalogue no: **PINK 1**

DON'T GET MAD GET EVEN
Tracks: / Don't get mad get even / Don't get mad get even (inst).
7" Single: Released 23 May '87, on Nightmare, by Nightmare Records. Catalogue no: **MARES 39**
12" Single: Released 23 May '87, on Nightmare, by Nightmare Records. Catalogue no: **MARE 39**

JUST WHAT I ALWAYS WANTED
Tracks: / Just what I always wanted.
12" Single: Released Aug '82, on Compact Organisation, Deleted '84. Catalogue no: **PINKX 4**
7" Single: Released Aug '82, on Compact Organisation, Deleted '84. Catalogue no: **PINK 4**

LET'S MAKE THIS LAST
Tracks: / Let's make this last.
12" Single: Released Sep '84, on Compact Organisation, Deleted '85. Catalogue no: **PINKX 9**
7" Single: Released Sep '84, on Compact Organisation, Deleted '85. Catalogue no: **PINK 9**

LOVE MAN
Tracks: / Love man / If that's what you want.
7" Single: Released Jun '80, on GTO, Deleted Jun '83. Catalogue no: **GT 274**

PICK UP THE PIECES
Tracks: / Pick up the pieces / You're the light that guides my way.
7" Single: Released Oct '81, on Motown, by BMG Records (UK). Catalogue no: **TMG 1177**

WONDERFUL
Tracks: / Wonderful.
7" Single: Released May '83, on Compact Organisation, Deleted '84. Catalogue no: **PINK 7**
12" Single: Released May '83, on Compact Organisation, Deleted '84. Catalogue no: **PINKX 7**

WOULD YOU DANCE WITH A STRANGER?
Tracks: / Would you dance with a stranger?.
7" Single: Released Jun '85, on Compact Organisation, Deleted '86. Catalogue no: **PINK 10**

Wilson, Mike

CAN YOU JACK
Tracks: / Can you jack.
12" Single: Released Oct '87, on International (USA), by International Records & Tapes. Catalogue no: **IH 001**

Wilson, Paketo

ON TOP OF THE WORLD
Tracks: / On top of the world.
12" Single: Released Nov '83, on Child of God, Catalogue no: **TDCOD 001**

SNEAKING OUT
Tracks: / Sneaking out.
12" Single: Released Nov '83, on Child of God, Catalogue no: **TDCOD 002**

Wilson, Phil

TEN MILES
Tracks: / Ten miles.
7" Single: Released Jun '87, on Creation, by Creation Records. Catalogue no: **CRE 46**
12" Single: Released Jun '87, on Creation, by Creation Records. Catalogue no: **CRE 46T**

WAITING FOR A CHANGE
Tracks: / Waiting for a change.
12" Single: Released Feb '87, on Creation, by Creation Records. Catalogue no: **CRE 36T**
7" Single: Released Feb '87, on Creation, by Creation Records. Catalogue no: **CRE 36**
7" Set: Released Mar '87, on Creation, by Creation Records. Catalogue no: **CRE 036D**

Wilson, Precious

NEED YOU
Tracks: / I need you / Valley of the dolls.
7" Single: Released Jan '82, on Epic, by CBS Records. Deleted Jan '85. Catalogue no: **EPC A 1854**

IF I LOVE YOU LESS
Tracks: / If I love you less / Stop runnin'.
7" Single: Released Feb '81, on Epic, by CBS Records. Deleted Feb '84. Catalogue no: **EPC 9551**

I'LL BE YOUR FRIEND
Tracks: / I'll be your friend.
12" Single: Released Sep '85, on Jive, by Zomba Records. Catalogue no: **JIVET 105**
7" Single: Released Sep '85, on Jive, by Zomba Records. Catalogue no: **JIVE 105**

JEWEL OF THE NILE
Tracks: / Jewel of the Nile, The / Didn't take it away.
7" Single: Released Apr '86, on Jive, by Zomba Records. Catalogue no: **JIVE 115**
12" Single: Released Apr '86, on Jive, by Zomba Records. Catalogue no: **JIVET 115**

NICE GIRLS DON'T LAST
Tracks: / Nice girls don't last / Nice girls don't last (LA mix).
7" Single: Released Jul '86, on Jive, by Zomba Records. Catalogue no: **JIVE 123**
12" Single: Released Jul '86, on Jive, by Zomba Records. Catalogue no: **JIVET 123**

ONLY THE STRONG SURVIVE
Tracks: / Only the strong survive.
7" Single: Released Jul '87, on Jive, by Zomba Records. Deleted '88. Catalogue no: **JIVE 146**
12" Single: Released Jul '87, on Jive, by Zomba Records. Catalogue no: **JIVET 146**

RED LIGHT (SINGLE)
Tracks: / Red light / Night the music died, The.
7" Single: Released Oct '82, on Epic, by CBS Records. Deleted Oct '85. Catalogue no: **EPCA 2737**

YOU HAVEN'T HEARD THE LAST OF ME
Tracks: / You haven't heard the last of me / Kisuraheli.
7" Single: Released Feb '83, on Epic, by CBS Records. Catalogue no: **EPC A 3095**

Wilson, Ruby

BLUER THAN BLUE
Tracks: / Bluer than blue / Feeling's still there.
7" Single: Released May '81, on Magnet, by WEA Records. Deleted May '86. Catalogue no: **MAG 189**

Wilson, Shanice

CAN U DANCE (BABY TELL ME)
Tracks: / Can u dance (baby tell me) / Summer love.
7" Single: Released Oct '87, on Breakout, by A&M Records. Catalogue no: **USA 616**
12" Single: Released Oct '87, on Breakout, by A&M Records. Catalogue no: **USAT 616**

I'LL BET SHE'S GOT A BOYFRIEND
Tracks: / Boyfriend (Miami edit) / Boyfriend (house edit).
7" Pic: Released Apr '88, on Breakout, by A&M Records. Deleted Feb '89. Catalogue no: **USR 625**
12" Single: Released Mar '88, on Breakout, by A&M Records. Deleted Feb '89. Catalogue no: **USAT 625**
7" Single: Released Mar '88, on Breakout, by A&M Records. Deleted Feb '89. Catalogue no: **USA 625**
12" Single: Released Apr '88, on Breakout, by A&M Records. Deleted Feb '89. Catalogue no: **USAF 625**

WAY YOU LOVE ME, THE
Tracks: / Way you love me, The / No half steppin'.
Note: "Written by Basil Lordsby, who also penned her recent single 'I'll bet she's got a boyfriend', The Way You Love Me is produced by Bryan Loren. Taken from 14 year old Shanice's debut album 'Discovery'.
7" Single: Released May '88, on Breakout, by A&M Records. Deleted Feb '89. Catalogue no: **USA 634**
12" Single: Released May '88, on Breakout, by A&M Records. Deleted Feb '89. Catalogue no: **USAT 634**

Wilson Sisters

PRICE OF LOVE
Tracks: / Price of love, The / Problems / Single girl.
7" Single: Released Jul '83, on President, by President Records. Catalogue no: **PT 517**

Wilson, Tanya

NEVER GONNA BE THE SAME
Tracks: / Never gonna be the same.
7" Single: Released Aug '89, on Virgin, by Virgin Records. Catalogue no: **VS 1203**
12" Single: Released Aug '89, on Virgin, by Virgin Records. Catalogue no: **VST 1203**
Special: Released Sep '89, on Virgin, by Virgin Records. Catalogue no: **VSCDX 1203**

Wilson, Tony

PART OF WHAT YOU GET
Tracks: / Part of what you get / Walk on the beach.
7" Single: Released Jan '89, on Sand Dollar (USA), by Legs Label Records (USA). Catalogue no: **SDZ 001**

Wilson-James, Victoria

I WANT YOU IN MY MOVIE
Tracks: / I want you in my movie.
Note: "An irresistible dance groove combined with hints of Jody Watley, Prince and some interesting lyrics". (Supertrack, June 1988)
12" Single: Released Jun '88, on Rising, Catalogue no: **RAHT 101**
7" Single: Released Jun '88, on Rising, Catalogue no: **RAH 101**

Wimbledon Football

DON'S SONG, THE
Tracks: / Don's song, The.
7" Single: Released Jan '88, on Dynamite Discs, by Dynamite Discs. Catalogue no: **DYD 3**

WE ARE WIMBLEDON
Tracks: / We are Wimbledon / Wimbledon F.A. cup theme.
7" Single: Released Apr '88, on President, by President Records. Catalogue no: **PT 574**

Wimps

AT THE DISCOTHEQUE
Tracks: / At the discotheque.
7" Single: Released May '82, on Sniff, Catalogue no: **SNORT 2**

HAMBURGER RADIO
Tracks: / Hamburger radio.
7" Single: Released '82, on Sniff, Catalogue no: **SNORT 1**

Win

DUSTY HEARTFELT
Tracks: / Dusty heartfelt / Peace on egg / Dusty heartfelt (version) (12" only).
12" Single: Released 2 May '89, on Virgin, by Virgin Records. Catalogue no: **VST 1178**
7" Single: Released 2 May '89, on Virgin, by Virgin Records. Catalogue no: **VS 1178**
CD 3": Released 2 May '89, on Virgin, by Virgin Records. Catalogue no: **VSCD 1178**

LOVE UNITS
Tracks: / Love units / Scary scary.
12" Single: Released Dec '88, on Virgin, by Virgin Records. Catalogue no: **VST 1157**
CD 3": Released 30 Jan '89, on Virgin, by Virgin Records. Catalogue no: **VSCD 1157**
7" Single: Released Dec '88, on Virgin, by Virgin Records. Catalogue no: **VS 1157**

SHAMPOO TEARS
Tracks: / Shampoo tears / Empty holsters / Slider, The (Track on 12" version only.).
7" Single: Released Apr '86, on London Records, by London Records. Catalogue no: **LON 85**
12" Single: Released Apr '86, on London Records, by London Records. Catalogue no: **LONX 85**

SUPER POPOID GROOVE
Tracks: / Super popoid groove / Baby cutting / You've got the power (Extra track on 12" only).
7" Single: Released Mar '87, on London Records, by London Records. Deleted May '89. Catalogue no: **LON 128**
12" Single: Released Mar '87, on London Records, by London Records. Deleted Feb '89. Catalogue no: **LONX 128**
7" Set: Released '88, on London Records, by London Records. Deleted Feb '89. Catalogue no: **LONG 128**

UNAMERICAN BROADCASTING
Tracks: / Unamerican broadcasting.
7" Single: Released Mar '85, on Swamplands, by London Records. Catalogue no: **SW 5**
12" Single: Released Mar '85, on Swamplands, by London Records. Catalogue no: **SWX 5**

WHAT'LL YOU DO 'TIL SUNDAY BABY
Tracks: / What'll you do till Sunday baby / Trigger happy / What'll you do till Sunday baby (Johnsons baby mix) (CD & 12" only) / Peace on egg (CD only).
7" Single: Released Nov '88, on Virgin, by Virgin Records. Catalogue no: **VS 1121**
12" Single: Released Nov '88, on Virgin, by Virgin Records. Catalogue no: **VST 1121**
CD 3": Released '88, on Virgin, by Virgin Records. Catalogue no: **VSCD 1121**

YOU'VE GOT THE POWER
Tracks: / You've got the power / Unamerican broadcasting / In Heaven (Track on 12" version only.).
12" Single: Released Jun '85, on Swamplands, by London Records. Catalogue no: **SWX 8**
7" Set: Released Mar '86, on Swamplands, by London Records. Deleted Feb '89. Catalogue no: **SWDX 8**
12" Single: Released Mar '86, on Swamplands, by London Records. Catalogue no: **SWXX 8**
7" Single: Released Mar '86, on Swamplands, by London Records. Catalogue no: **SWPP 8**
7" Single: Released Jun '85, on Swamplands, by London Records. Catalogue no: **SWP 8**

Winans

AIN'T NO NEED TO WORRY
Tracks: / Ain't no need to worry.
7" Single: Released Aug '87, on Qwest (USA), by Qwest Records (USA). Deleted Jul '88. Catalogue no: **W 8274**
12" Single: Released Aug '87, on Qwest (USA), by Qwest Records (USA). Deleted Jul '88. Catalogue no: **W 8274T**

CELEBRATE NEW LIFE
Tracks: / Celebrate new life (Celebration edit) (Not on 12".) / Bridge over troubled water (Not on 12".) / Celebrate new life (Celebration mix) (12" only.) / Celebrate new life (Milkyway beats) (12" only.) / Heaven (Heavenly mix) (12" only.) / Heaven (LP version) (CD single only.) / Celebrate new life (dub life mix) (CD single only.).
7" Single: Released Oct '89, on Capitol, by EMI Records. Catalogue no: **CL 551**
12" Single: Released Oct '89, on Capitol, by EMI Records. Catalogue no: **203 533 6**
12" Single: Released Oct '89, on Capitol, by EMI Records. Catalogue no: **12CL 551**
CD 5": Released Oct '89, on Capitol, by EMI Records. Catalogue no: **CDCL 551**
CD 5": Released Oct '89, on Capitol, by EMI Records. Catalogue no: **203 533 2**
7" Single: Released Oct '89, on Capitol, by EMI Records. Catalogue no: **203 533 7**

I.O.U. ME
Tracks: / I.O.U. me / No hiding place / Love said not so (Track on 12" only.).
12" Single: Released Jan '88, on Capitol, by EMI Records. Deleted Apr '88. Catalogue no: **12CL 472**
7" Single: Released Jan '88, on Capitol, by EMI Records. Deleted Apr '88. Catalogue no: **CL 472**

LET MY PEOPLE GO (SINGLE)
Tracks: / Let my people go.
7" Single: Released Jan '86, on Warner Bros., by WEA Records. Catalogue no: **W 8874**
12" Single: Released Jan '86, on Warner Bros., by WEA Records. Catalogue no: **W 8874 T**

LOVE HAS NO COLOUR
Tracks: / Love has no colour / What can I say.
12" Single: Released Nov '87, on Qwest (USA), by Qwest Records (USA). Catalogue no: **W 8147T**
7" Single: Released Nov '87, on Qwest (USA), by Qwest Records (USA). Catalogue no: **W 8147**

VERY REAL WAY
Tracks: / Very real way / Let my people go.
7" Single: Released Mar '86, on Qwest (USA), by Qwest Records (USA). Catalogue no: **W 8744**
12" Single: Released Mar '86, on Qwest (USA), by Qwest Records (USA). Catalogue no: **W 8744 T**

Winbush, Angela

ANGEL
Tracks: / Angel / Angel (insrumental) / Angel (extended) (On 12" only).
12" Single: Released Oct '87, on Club, by Phonogram Ltd. Deleted Oct '88. Catalogue no: **JABX 60**
7" Single: Released Oct '87, on Club, by Phonogram Ltd. Deleted Oct '88. Catalogue no: **JAB 60**

C'EST TOI
Tracks: / C'est toi / Hello beloved.
Note: Second single from the critically acclaimed debut album 'Sharp'.
7" Single: Released 11 Jul '88, on Club, by Phonogram Ltd. Deleted Feb '89. Catalogue no: **JAB 67**
12" Single: Released 11 Jul '88, on Club, by Phonogram Ltd. Deleted Feb '89. Catalogue no: **JABX 67**

Wind

FUR ALIVE
Tracks: / Fur alive.
7" Single: Released May '85, on Proto, by Proto Records. Catalogue no: **ENA 126**

Wind Rush Primary

WIND RUSH WEDDING SONG
Tracks: / I need your love.
7" Single: Released Jul '86, on Hive, Catalogue no: **HIVE 7**

Windies

HERE COME THE WINDIES
Tracks: / Here come the Windies.
7" Single: Released Jul '83, on Wicket,

Catalogue no: **WKT 1**

Windjammer

LIVE WITHOUT YOUR LOVE
Tracks: / Live without your love.
7" Single: Released Sep '84, on MCA, by MCA Records. Catalogue no: **MCA 921**
12" Single: Released Sep '84, on MCA, by MCA Records. Catalogue no: **MCAT 921**

TOSSING AND TURNING
Tracks: / Tossing and turning / Live without your love.
12" Single: Released Jun '84, on MCA, by MCA Records. Deleted '87. Catalogue no: **MCAT 897**
7" Single: Released Jun '84, on MCA, by MCA Records. Catalogue no: **MCA 897**

TOSSING AND TURNING (89 REMIX)
Tracks: / Tossing and turning (89 remix).
12" Single: Released 11 Sep '89, on Debut, by Skratch Records. Catalogue no: **DEBTX 3077**

TOSSING AND TURNING (OLD GOLD)
Tracks: / Tossing and turning.
12" Single: Released May '88, on Old Gold, by Old Gold Records. Catalogue no: **OG 4062**

UNDER YOUR SPELL
Tracks: / Under your spell / Winter love.
7" Single: Released Jan '88, on Dynatrack, Catalogue no: **DYNS 101**
12" Single: Released Jan '88, on Dynatrack, Catalogue no: **DYAAT 101**

Windmills

DAY DAWNED ON ME, THE
Tracks: / Day dawned on me, The / Dolphins.
7" Single: Released Jun '88, on S.T.S., Catalogue no: **STS 2**

Windows

REARRANGE
Tracks: / Rearrange.
7" Single: Released '81, on Skeleton, by Skeleton Records. Catalogue no: **SKL 008**

Windsor, James

CITY LIGHTS
Tracks: / City lights / This train.
7" Single: Released May '82, on Free Dee, Deleted '83. Catalogue no: **FREED 1**

Wing & A Prayer

BABY FACE
Tracks: / Baby face.
7" Single: Released Jan '76, on Atlantic, by WEA Records. Deleted '79. Catalogue no: **K 10705**

Wingfield, Pete

Biographical details: British singer, keyboards player and producer Pete Wingfield was a member of a rhythm-and-blues band called Jellybread during the late 60's and early 70's. When the band folded he worked as a session musician until 1975, when he scored his own hit with *Eighteen With A Bullet.* The title referred to the US charts system, where rising hit records are awarded "bullet" symbols to denote sales and airplay gains. As American chart expert Joel Whitburn notes in his chart books, the single actually hit No 18 with a bullet on the Billboard Hot Hundred on 22 November 1975 and ultimately peaked at No 15. In his native Britain the song reached No 7 but was never No 18 on its chart run. It was a lightweight but amusing ditty about the joys of gaining a hit record and it contrasted Wingfield's falsetto wail with his equally competent bass vocals. During the late 70's Wingfield formed the Olympic Runners, a disco group who achieved three UK Top Forty hits. His 1980 move into the field of record production was immediately successful, thanks to his UK No 1 success as producer of Dexy's Midnight Runners' single *Geno.* He was also responsible for the group's debut Top Ten LP, *Searching For The Young Soul Rebels*, despite a brief prerelease hiccup when the band grabbed the master tapes from him and refused to return them until EMI granted them a more favourable contract. Wingfield's next big success was not until '84, when he produced three British hit singles for the Kane Gang. The following year he was responsible for Alison Moyet's UK No 2 smash, *That Ole Devil Called Love*, a straightforward reworking of Billie Holiday's 1944 disc. Also during 1985 Wingfield worked with various up-and-coming acts such as Charm School, Sunset Gun and actor Michael Winslow. (Bob MacDonald, June 1985.).

EIGHTEEN WITH A BULLET
Tracks: / Eighteen with a bullet.
7" Single: Released Jun '75, on Island, by Island Records. Deleted '78. Catalogue no: **WIP 6231**

THEY ALL CAME BACK
Tracks: / They all came back / Too much of a good thing.
7" Single: Released Jun '81, on Chipping Norton, Catalogue no: **CHIP 5**

Wings

Biographical details: The nucleus of this British band and, indeed, its only three constant members, were Paul and Linda McCartney and Denny Laine. After the break-up of the Beatles in 1970, McCartney released a couple of solo albums and scored a pair of hit singles before forming Wings in 1971. The first line-up consisted of Paul, Linda, former Moody Blues guitarist Laine and Denny Seiwell. Linda, whose contributions included keyboards, vocals and photography, was often criticised in the press for her limited musical talents. Drummer Seiwell left in 1973, as did short-stay guitarist Henry McCullough. During the rest of the 70's several other players came and went. The most important were guitarist Jimmy McCulloch -- who was with Wings during 1974-77 and tragically died in January '79, aged 25, due to a drug-related heart attack -- and drummer Joe English (1975-77). Although the public tended to view John Lennon as the "controversial" Beatle and McCartney as the "clean" one, the McCartney/Wings story had its fair share of brushes with authority. Their first hit single, *Give Ireland Back To The Irish* (No 16 in UK, No 21 in US in '72) was banned by the BBC because of its political nature. In a deliberately ironic response to this, the group's follow-up single was an adaptation of the nursery rhyme *Mary Had A Little Lamb.* However, the BBC objected once again to the next single, *Hi Hi Hi* due to its apparent support for drugs usage -- so in Britain it had to be transformed into a double-A-side with the bland C Moon. McCartney's public defence of cannabis continued to make headlines right through into the 80's. There was plenty of schmalz too, such as Wings' first American No 1 single, 1973's *My Love*, and the whole of that year's *Red Rose Speedway* album. But the best Wings material always came halfway between the two extremes: the brilliant *Band On The Run* album (released in late '73, a transAtlantic No 1 in '74) and the fine *Venus And Mars* album (similarly successful in '75) were outstanding examples. Each yielded a US No 1 single, *Band On The Run* and *Listen To What The Man Said* respectively. So did 1976's *Wings At The Speed Of Sound* album (No 2 in UK, No 1 in US), with *Silly Love Songs*, America's best-selling single of that year. One Wings single was a turkey in the States: however, the bagpipe-laden *Mull Of Kintyre*, a tribute to the Scottish beauty spot the McCartneys loved, logged nine weeks at No 1 in Britain, becoming the nation's all-time best-seller until Band Aid in 1984. (Officially this was a double-A-side but the forgettable rock ditty *Girls' School* was a totally unnecessary appendage.) Wings' final two American No 1 singles were *With A Little Luck* ('78) and *Coming Up* (Live At Glasgow), released in 1980 by which time the band were defunct and McCartney was a solo artist once more. Wings had begun and ended with mediocre albums, *Wild Life* ('71) and *Back To The Egg* ('79) -- but there had been some fine material in between. (Bob MacDonald, June 1985.).

GETTING CLOSER
Tracks: / Getting closer / Baby's request.
7" Single: Released Aug '79, on Parlophone, by EMI Records. Catalogue no: **R 6027**

GIVE IRELAND BACK TO THE IRISH (2 PARTS)
Tracks: / Give Ireland back to the Irish (part 1) / Give Ireland back to the Irish (part 2).
7" Single: Released Feb '72, on Parlophone, by EMI Records. Catalogue no: **R 5936**

GOODNIGHT TONIGHT
Tracks: / Goodnight tonight.
7" Single: Released Mar '79, on Parlophone, by EMI Records. Catalogue no: **R 6023**
12" Single: Released Apr '79, on Parlophone, by EMI Records. Catalogue no: **12 YR 6023**

HI HI HI
Tracks: / Hi hi hi.
7" Single: Released Dec '72, on Parlophone, by EMI Records. Catalogue no: **R 5973**

I'VE HAD ENOUGH
Tracks: / I've had enough.
7" Single: Released Jun '78, on Parlophone, by EMI Records. Catalogue no: **R 6020**

LET 'EM IN
Tracks: / Let 'em in.
7" Single: Released Jul '76, on Parlophone, by EMI Records. Catalogue no: **R 6015**

WINGS - MULL OF KINTYRE (Released on Parlophone)

LETTING GO
Tracks: / Letting go.
7" Single: Released Sep '75, on Parlophone, by EMI Records. Catalogue no: **R 6008**

LISTEN TO WHAT THE MAN SAID
Tracks: / Listen to what the man said.
7" Single: Released May '75, on Parlophone, by EMI Records. Catalogue no: **R 6006**

LIVE AND LET DIE
Tracks: / Live and let die.
7" Single: Released Jun '73, on Parlophone, by EMI Records. Catalogue no: **R 5987**

LONDON TOWN (SINGLE)
Tracks: / London town.
7" Single: Released Jul '78, on Parlophone, by EMI Records. Deleted '88. Catalogue no: **R 6021**

MARY HAD A LITTLE LAMB (see panel below)
Tracks: / Mary had a little lamb / Little woman love.
7" Single: Released May '72, on Parlophone, by EMI Records. Catalogue no: **R 5949**

MAYBE I'M AMAZED
Tracks: / Maybe I'm amazed.
7" Single: Released Feb '77, on Par phone, by EMI Records. Catalogue no: **6017**

MULL OF KINTYRE (see pan above)
Tracks: / Mull of Kintyre / Girls school.
7" Single: Released Nov '77, on Par phone, by EMI Records. Catalogue no: **6018**

OLD SIAM SIR
Tracks: / Old Siam sir.
7" Single: Released Jun '79, on Par phone, by EMI Records. Catalogue no **6026**

SILLY LOVE SONGS
Tracks: / Silly love songs.
7" Single: Released Apr '76, on Pa phone, by EMI Records. Catalogue no **6014**

VENUS AND MARS (SINGLE)
Tracks: / Venus and Mars.
7" Single: Released Nov '75, on Pa phone, by EMI Records. Deleted '88. Ca logue no: **R 6010**

WITH A LITTLE LUCK
Tracks: / With a little luck.
7" Single: Released Mar '78, on Pa phone, by EMI Records. Catalogue no **6019**

WINGS - MARY HAD A LITTLE LAMB (Released on Parlophone)

Winjama

PLACE IN THE SUN
Tracks: / Place in the sun, A / Place in the sun (instrumental).
Note: In aid of the Jamaican hurricane appeal and featuring Andy Bell (Erasure), Sinitta, Leee John (Imagination), Glen Goldsmith, Barrington Levy, Sylvia Tella, Trevor Walters, Simon Climie (Climie Fisher), Dixie Peach, Sandie Shaw, Erroll Brown (Hot Chocolate), Ruby Turner, Glenn Tillbrook (Squeeze) and Green (Scritti Politti).
7" Single: Released 28 Nov '88, on Creole, by Creole Records. Catalogue no: **CR 7**
12" Single: Released 28 Nov '88, on Creole, by Creole Records. Catalogue no: **CRT 7**

Winners

EVERYONE'S A WINNER
Tracks: / Everyone's a winner.
7" Single: Released Nov '85, on Alibi, Deleted '86. Catalogue no: **ALIB 1**

WINNERS (SINGLE)
Tracks: / Winners / Soulful melody.
12" Single: Released Apr '86, on Fine Style, by Fashion Records. Catalogue no: **FS 002**

Wins, Diana

PEACE ON EARTH
Tracks: / Peace on earth.
7" Single: Released Nov '84, on Button, by Musical Characters Records. Catalogue no: **BTN 122**

Winslow, Michael

I AM MY OWN WALKMAN
Tracks: / I am my own walkman.
12" Single: Released Jun '85, on Island, by Island Records. Catalogue no: **12IS 234**
7" Single: Released Jun '85, on Island, by Island Records. Catalogue no: **IS 234**

Winsome

AM I THE SAME GIRL
Tracks: / Am I the same girl / Can't take the lies.
7" Single: Released Jun '87, on Fine Style, by Fashion Records. Catalogue no: **FS 7002**
12" Single: Released Jun '87, on Fine Style, by Fashion Records. Catalogue no: **FS 002**

BORN FREE
Tracks: / Can't take the lies.
7" Single: Released Sep '86, on Fine Style, by Fashion Records. Catalogue no: **FS 7004**
12" Single: Released Sep '86, on Fine Style, by Fashion Records. Catalogue no: **FS 004**

HOMEBREAKER
Tracks: / Homebreaker.
12" Single: Released Feb '87, on Fine Style, by Fashion Records. Catalogue no: **FS 008**

NEVER FOUND A LOVE
Tracks: / Never found a love.
12" Single: Released 31 Oct '87, on Fine Style, by Fashion Records. Catalogue no: **FS 014**

ROCK WITH ME BABY
Tracks: / Rock with me baby.
12" Single: Released Nov '86, on Fine Style, by Fashion Records. Catalogue no: **FS 006**
7" Single: Released Nov '86, on Fine Style, by Fashion Records. Catalogue no: **FS 7006**

SUPERWOMAN
Tracks: / Superwoman.
7" Single: Released Aug '89, on Fashion, by Fashion Records. Catalogue no: **FAD 067**

WALK AWAY
Tracks: / Walk away.
12" Single: Released Sep '88, on Fine Style, by Fashion Records. Catalogue no: **FS 018**

Winston

WAITING ROOM (SINGLE)
Tracks: / Waiting room.
7" Single: Released Jan '82, on Rural Tension, Catalogue no: **ART 1**

Winston, Ray

EVERYTHING'S ALRIGHT
Tracks: / Everything's alright / Daydream.
7" Single: Released Mar '80, on RCA, by RCA Records (UK). Deleted Mar '83. Catalogue no: **PB 5242**

Winston, Roy

TURN DOWN THE MUSIC
Tracks: / Turn down the music / Love is getting closer.
7" Single: Released Feb '81, on RCA, by RCA Records (UK). Deleted '84. Catalogue no: **RCA 34**

Winter, Angela

HEART TO HEART
Tracks: / Heart to heart.
7" Single: Released Jul '85, on Survival, by Survival Records. Catalogue no: **SURT 36**

Winter Babies

BOSSANOVA SUICIDE
Tracks: / Bossa nova suicide.
7" Single: Released Oct '85, on Stiff, by Stiff Records. Catalogue no: **WINTER 1**

Winter, Chris

SATURDAY NIGHT
Tracks: / Saturday night.
7" Single: Released Jul '81, on PVK, by PVK Records. Catalogue no: **PV 108**

Winter, Edgar

Biographical details: An albino from Texas, like his elder brother Johnny, Edgar Winter -- singer, keyboards player, saxophonist and composer -- began to attract attention in the late 60's as a member of his brother's group. This was when Johnny was steadily building his reputation as a masterly blues/rock guitarist. As Johnny's fame grew in the early 70's Edgar decided to launch his own career in order to pursue his leanings towards jazz. His first solo album, *Entrance*, was issued in 1970 and its commercial failure led him to forming White Trash, a soul/rock outfit, in '71. But after a couple of worthy albums they were disbanded and the plainly-titled Edgar Winter Group was formed. The new ensemble's debut LP, *They Only Come Out At Night*, was released in late '72 and brought Winter huge success on the US album charts. This heavy rock album, all written by Winter, reached new heights in summer '73 when a surprise single, *Frankenstein*, became an American No 1. The "monster hit" pun was trotted out by disc jockeys and journalists everywhere. Frankenstein was a synthesiser-dominated instrumental, originally released as the B-side. In Britain it became Winter's only chart entry, reaching No 18. The Edgar Winter Group enjoyed two smaller US Top Forty singles during the following 18 months, with *Free Rise and River's Risin'*. The 1974 album, *Shock Treatment*, was a more modest success that *They Only Come Out At Night*. By '76 Winter's three key colleagues -- guitarist Ronnie Montrose, bassist Dan Hartman (later to achieve spasmodic success as a solo artist) and guitarist/producer Rick Derringer -- had all left him. After a '76 live album with Johnny, Edgar laid low until '79. Subsequent albums failed to revive his career. (Bob MacDonald, June 1985.).

ABOVE AND BEYOND
Tracks: / Above and beyond.
7" Single: Released Mar '80, on Blue Sky, Deleted Mar '83. Catalogue no: **SKY 8246**

FRANKENSTEIN
Tracks: / Frankenstein.
7" Single: Released May '73, on Epic, by CBS Records. Deleted '76. Catalogue no: **EPC 1440**
7" Single: Released '80, on Blue Sky, Deleted '88. Catalogue no: **LR 1340**

Winters, Bernie

FINANCIALLY I'M EMBARRASSED
Tracks: / Financially I'm embarrassed / Cockney song.
7" Single: Released Mar '83, on P & L, Catalogue no: **POO 2**

SCHNORBITZ SONG, THE
Tracks: / Schnorbitz song, The.
7" Single: Released Oct '85, on Spartan, Catalogue no: **SP 126**

Winter's, Chris Shout

OOSTA BE A PARROT
Tracks: / Oosta be a parrot / Silicon chips with everything.
7" Single: Released Oct '80, on PVK, by PVK Records. Catalogue no: **PV 43**

Winters, Robert

MAGIC MAN (SINGLE)
Tracks: / Magic man.
7" Single: Released Aug '81, on Buddah, by Buddah Records Inc.(USA). Catalogue no: **BDS 496**
12" Single: Released Aug '81, on Buddah, by Buddah Records Inc.(USA). Catalogue no: **BDSL 496**

Winters, Rocky

WISHING
Tracks: / Wishing.
7" Single: Released Feb '86, on PRT, by Castle Communications Records. Catalogue no: **7P 339**
12" Single: Released Feb '86, on PRT, by Castle Communications Records. Catalogue no: **12P 339**

Winters, Ruby

Biographical details: The American singer, Ruby Winters, enjoyed brief fame in the late Seventies while remaining unknown in her native land. The balld *I Will* catapulted her to No.4 on the UK chart at Christmas 1977. A similar sounding song *Come To Me* took her to No.11 in 1978.
By the end of the Seventies, Winters had notched up another two (much smaller) chart singles, *I Won't Mention It Again* and *Baby Lay Down*. She also reached Britain's LP Top 50 with a self titled set plus a TV advertised album called *Songbird*.
Winters had the veneer of a soul singer, but was, in truth, an uninspired cofee table MoR artist. As she drifted out of the UK charts in '79, her niche in that market was taken over by a more talented US songbird, Randy Crawford. (Bob Macdonald June 1985).

BABY LAY DOWN
Tracks: / Baby lay down.
7" Single: Released May '79, on Creole, by Creole Records. Catalogue no: **CR 171**

BACK TO THE LOVE
Tracks: / Back to the love.
12" Single: Released Aug '79, on Creole, by Creole Records. Deleted '80. Catalogue no: **CR 12 174**
7" Single: Released Aug '79, on Creole, by Creole Records. Catalogue no: **CR 174**

COME TO ME
Tracks: / Come to me.
7" Single: Released Mar '78, on Creole, by Creole Records. Catalogue no: **CR 153**

FOR THE GOOD TIME
Tracks: / For the good time.
7" Single: Released '78, on Creole, by Creole Records. Catalogue no: **CR 162**

I WILL
Tracks: / I will / Come to me / I can't fake it anymore.
7" EP: Released Nov '80, on Creole (Replay), by Creole Records. Deleted Nov '83. Catalogue no: **CR 217**
7" Single: Released Nov '77, on Creole, by Creole Records. Deleted '80. Catalogue no: **CR 141**
7" Single: Released Mar '86, on Old Gold, by Old Gold Records. Catalogue no: **OG 9593**

I WON'T MENTION IT AGAIN
Tracks: / I won't mention it again.
7" Single: Released Aug '78, on Creole, by Creole Records. Deleted '81. Catalogue no: **CR 160**

Winters, Shelley

NINE TIMES OUT OF TEN
Tracks: / Nine times out of ten.
7" Single: Released Oct '79, on Inferno (1), by Inferno Records. Catalogue no: **HEAT 24**

Winwood, Steve

Biographical details: Winwood, Steve This British singer, songwriter, guitarist and keyboards player, born in Birmingham in 1948, came to fame in the sixties as the driving force in two highly successful groups: The Spencer Davis Group and Traffic. During 1969-70, he was a member of two short lived bands: the briefly successful supergroup Blind Faith and the abortive Airforce. He then returned to Traffic before launching a solo career in the late Seventies. His Seventies career was also dotted with guest appearances on friends' albums, such as those by Jim Capaldi, George Harrison and Toots & The Maytals.
The truly remarkable thing about his days with the Spencer Davis Group (when he had been known as Stevie) had been his astonishing maturity, and his domination of a combo in which he had been the youngest member. He had joined them at the age of 14 and, by the time of his 18th birthday (May 1966), he had just celebrated two UK No.1 singles. His days with Traffic had won him similar acclaim; so by 1977, when he issued his eponymous debut solo album, his new career had been awaited with eager anticipation.
Steve Winwood, a Top 30 success on both sides of the Atlantic, was a pleasant but unadventurous R&B tinged rock LP. His second album *Arc of a Driver* did not appear until the final week of 1980, but was worth the wait. The LP was a transatlantic success, faring particularly well in the US where it was a Top 10 item. Its opening track, the deliriously melodic and commercial *While You See A Chance*, was a No.7 single in the States. 1982's *Talking Back To The Night* album was also successful and yielded a minor UK hit single in the shape of *Valerie*. His first solo tour was not undertaken until 1983.
Winwood's solo albums have been affairs of competence and quality, but there is disappointment amongst some observers that he has not attained superstar status. His somewhat low key approach has meant that his Sixties promise has never quite been fulfilled. (Bob Macdonald June 1985)
Steve Winwood was born in Birmingham; the superstar Singer, multi-instrumentalist and songwriter first became famous in the Spencer Davis Group, with his keyboards and bluesy voice. He formed the rock group Traffic, made on LP with the abortive supergroup Blind Faith, intended to start a solo career with the album that became Traffic's *John Barleycorn Must Die*. He sessioned for years on albums by people as diverse as Jim Capaldi (of Traffic), Sandy Denny, the FAnia All Stars, George Harrison, John Martyn, Toots and the Maytals; he worked with ex-Bonzo Viv Stanshall on his *Men With Opening Umberellas Ahead* and *Sir Henry At Rawlinson's End*. Japanese percussionist Stomu Yamashta and his ambitious Go group (two albums in 1976-77, both with Al DiMiola). He finally debuted as a solo artist with *Steve Winwood* in 1977 on Island, then the hit *Arc Of A Diver* in 1980, songs co-written with Will Jennings, George Fleming and Stanshall: this was self-produced, like his latter-day Traffic work and early work with the Habits (now on Charly compilation *Sixties Lost and Found*). *Arc of a Diver* included a top 10 USA hit *When You See A Chance*, showing perhaps greater aptitude for the recording studio than the stage. He sessioned with Capaldi, Stanshall, Marianne Faithfull, Julie Covington; then his own *Talking Back To The Night* in 1982 was a top 30 USA album, showing complete mastery of studio tools. He carried on sessioning; then his glossiest and most commercial record was *Back In The High Life Again* in 1987 was overproduced compared to the last one, but that unmistakeable voice reached number 3 in the USA and copped several Grammie nominations: the album included number one USA single *Higher Love* (with Chaka Khan and strong video), top 10 *The Finer Things*. Signed with Virgin; *Chronicles* in 1987 on Island compiled tracks from his solo career. (Donald Clarke)..

BACK IN THE HIGH LIFE (SINGLE)
Tracks: / Back in the high life / Night train (inst) (On 12" only) / Night train (inst).
12" Single: Released Jan '87, on Island, by Island Records. Deleted Jul '87. Catalogue no: **12IS 303**
7" Single: Released Jan '87, on Island, by Island Records. Catalogue no: **IS 303**

DON'T YOU KNOW WHAT THE NIGHT CAN DO?
Tracks: / Don't you know what the night can do?(remix) (7" only) / Don't you know what the night can do?(instrumental) (On 7" & extended mix on 12") / Don't you know what the night can do?(extended 12" mix) (On CD & 12" only) / Don't you know what the night can do? (version on CD only) / Roll with it (7" version) (On CD only).
12" Single: Released 1 Aug '88, on Virgin, by Virgin Records. Catalogue no: **VST 1107**
7" Single: Released 1 Aug '88, on Virgin, by Virgin Records. Catalogue no: **VS 1107**
CD 5": Released '88, on Virgin, by Virgin Records. Catalogue no: **VSCD 1107**

FREEDOM OVERSPILL
Tracks: / Spanish dancer.
12" Single: Released Aug '86, on Island, by Island Records. Deleted Jul '87. Catalogue no: **12IS 294**
12" Single: Released Aug '86, on Island, by Island Records. Deleted Jul '87. Catalogue no: **12ISG 294**
7" Single: Released Aug '86, on Island, by Island Records. Catalogue no: **IS 294**

HIGHER LOVE
Tracks: / Higher love / And I go.
12" Single: Released Jun '86, on Island, by Island Records. Deleted Jul '87. Catalogue no: **12IS 288**
7" Single: Released Jun '86, on Island, by Island Records. Catalogue no: **IS 288**

HOLDING ON
Tracks: / Holding on / Holding on (instrumental) (on 7" & CD only) / Go Juan (aaghh mix) (on CD & 12" only) / Go Juan (groove mix) (on 12" only) / Holding on (dance mix) (on 12" only) / Holding on (Stevappella mix) (on CD only).
CD 3": Released '88, on Virgin, by Virgin Records. Catalogue no: **VSCD 1135**
7" Single: Released Oct '88, on Virgin, by Virgin Records. Catalogue no: **VS 1135**
12" Single: Released '88, on Virgin, by Virgin Records. Catalogue no: **VST 1135**

ROLL WITH IT (SINGLE)
Tracks: / Roll with it (7" version) (On all versions) / Morning side, The (NOT on cassette) / Roll with it (12" mix) (CD & 12" only) / Morning side, The (album version) (Cassette only) / Roll with it (Steve testifies dub) (Cassette only).
12" Single: Released May '88, on Virgin, by Virgin Records. Catalogue no: **VST 1085**
Cassingle: Released '88, on Virgin, by Virgin Records. Catalogue no: **VSTC 1085**
7" Single: Released May '88, on Virgin, by Virgin Records. Catalogue no: **VS 1085**
CD 5": Released Aug '88, on Virgin, by Virgin Records. Catalogue no: **VSCD 1085**

SPANISH DANCER
Tracks: / Spanish dancer / Hold on.
7" Single: Released Apr '81, on Island, by

Island Records. Deleted Apr '84. Catalogue no: **WIP 6680**

THERE'S A RIVER
Tracks: / There's a river / Two way stretch.
7" Single: Released Nov '81, on Island, by Island Records. Catalogue no: **WIP 6747**

VALERIE
Tracks: / Valerie / Talking back to the night / Finer things, The (on 12" only.).
Cassingle: Released Sep '87, on Island, by Island Records. Deleted Jun '88. Catalogue no: **CIS 336**
12" Single: Released Sep '87, on Island, by Island Records. Deleted Jun '88. Catalogue no: **12IS 336**
CD 5": Released Sep '87, on Island, by Island Records. Deleted Jun '88. Catalogue no: **CID 336**
7" Single: Released Sep '87, on Island, by Island Records. Deleted Jun '88. Catalogue no: **IS 336**
7" Single: Released Oct '82, on Island, by Island Records. Deleted '85. Catalogue no: **WIP 6818**

WHILE YOU SEE A CHANCE
Tracks: / While you see a chance / Vacant chair.
7" Single: Released Jan '81, on Island, by Island Records. Deleted '84. Catalogue no: **WIP 6655**

Wipeout

BABY PLEASE DON'T GO
Tracks: / Baby please don't go.
7" Single: Released May '82, on M & L, Catalogue no: **MNL 2**

COME JOIN THE DANCE
Tracks: / Come join the dance.
7" Single: Released May '84, on Out, Catalogue no: **OUT 2**

Wire

Biographical details: The British rock band,Wire, comprised Bruce Gilbert, Rob Gotobed, Graham Lewis and Colin Newman.
Wire were formed in late 1976 and issued their debut album *Pink Flag* in November 1977. Their fast and furious punk LP, which managed to pack 22 songs onto a single disc, received an ecstatic welcome in the UK music press. *Pink Flag* combined the anger of the New Wave movement with a more subtle art school approach.
The second Wire album *Chairs Missing* reached No.48 on the Uk chart in October 1978. This contained a mere 15 tracks, one of which gave the group their sole chart single - the hook filled, Motors- style *Outdoor Miner* peaked at No.51 on the British singles listings in early '79. The band's third LP *154* hit No.39 in October '79. In that same year, they toured Britain as support act to the newly resurrected Roxy Music; this was appropriate, since the Wire style had as much in common with the artiness of Roxy as with the anarchy of the Sex Pistols.
Wire went into cold storage in early 1980, whereupon members brought out various other recording projects. Gilbert & Lewis released a series of LPs as a duo. Gotobed joined Mute Records' Fad Gadget; Newman worked as a solo artist. Attempts were made in the early Eighties to revive Wire with the album *Document and Eyewitness*, but these were unsuccessful. They had certainly been one of the most original and adventurous bands to emerge from the UK New Wave explosion, and could almost certainly have reached greater commercial heights, had they desired them. (Bob Macdonald June 1985).

AHEAD
Tracks: / Ahead / Feed me / Ambulance chases (live) (Extra track on 12" only) / Vivid riot of red (live) (Extra track on 12" only).
7" Single: Released Mar '87, on Mute, by Mute Records. Catalogue no: **MUTE 57**
12" Single: Released Mar '87, on Mute, by Mute Records. Catalogue no: **12 MUTE 57**

CRAZY ABOUT LOVE
Tracks: / Crazy about love.
12" Single: Released Mar '83, on Rough Trade, by Rough Trade Records. Catalogue no: **RT 123T**

EARDRUM BUZZ
Tracks: / Eardrum buzz.
7" Single: Released Mar '89, on Mute, by Mute Records. Catalogue no: **MUTE 87**
CD 5": Released Mar '89, on Mute, by Mute Records. Catalogue no: **CD MUTE 87**
12" Single: Released Mar '89, on Mute, by Mute Records. Catalogue no: **12 MUTE 87**

IN VIVO
Tracks: / In vivo.
7" Single: Released Jul '89, on Mute, by Mute Records. Catalogue no: **LMUTE 98**
CD 5": Released Jul '89, on Mute, by Mute Records. Catalogue no: **CDMUTE 98**
12" Single: Released Jun '89, on Mute, by Mute Records. Catalogue no: **12MUTE 98**
7" Single: Released Jun '89, on Mute, by Mute Records. Catalogue no: **MUTE 98**

KIDNEY BONGOS
Tracks: / Kidney bongos.
7" Single: Released 20 Feb '88, on Mute, by Mute Records. Catalogue no: **MUTE 67**
12" Single: Released 20 Feb '88, on Mute, by Mute Records. Catalogue no: **12 MUTE 067**

OUR SWIMMER
Tracks: / Our swimmer / Midnight Bahnhof Cafe.
7" Single: Released May '81, on Rough Trade, by Rough Trade Records. Catalogue no: **RT 079**

OUTDOOR MINER
Tracks: / Outdoor miner.
7" Single: Released Jan '79, on Harvest (1), by EMI Records. Deleted '82. Catalogue no: **HAR 5172**

PEEL SESSIONS:WIRE
Tracks: / Me / Disgusted.
12" Single: Released Jul '87, on Strange Fruit, by Strange Fruit Records. Catalogue no: **SFPS 041**

SILK SKIN PAWS
Tracks: / Silk skin paws / German shepherds / Ambitious (Only on 12") / Come back in two halves (Only on 12").
12" Single: Released Jun '88, on Mute, by Mute Records. Catalogue no: **12 MUTE 84**
7" Single: Released Jun '88, on Mute, by Mute Records. Catalogue no: **MUTE 84**

SNAKEDRILL (EP)
Tracks: / Serious of snakes / Drill, The / Advantage in height, An / Vivid riot of red, A.
12" Single: Released Nov '86, on Mute, by Mute Records. Catalogue no: **12 MUTE 53**

Wire Train

CHAMBER OF HELLOS
Tracks: / Chamber of hellos.
7" Single: Released Jan '84, on CBS, by CBS Records. Catalogue no: **A 4094**
12" Single: Released Jan '84, on CBS, by CBS Records. Catalogue no: **TA 4094**

DIVING
Tracks: / Diving / Mercy mercy.
7" Single: Released Apr '87, on CBS, by CBS Records. Deleted Nov '87. Catalogue no: **650821 7**
12" Single: Released Apr '87, on CBS, by CBS Records. Deleted Nov '87. Catalogue no: **650821 6**

LOVE'S PERFECT THING
Tracks: / Half a lifetime.
7" Single: Released Feb '86, on CBS, by CBS Records. Catalogue no: **A 6820**
12" Single: Released Feb '86, on CBS, by CBS Records. Catalogue no: **TX 6820**

SHE COMES ON
Tracks: / She comes on / Compassion.
7" Single: Released Mar '87, on CBS, by CBS Records. Deleted Aug '87. Catalogue no: **6504222 7**
12" Single: Released Mar '87, on CBS, by CBS Records. Deleted Aug '87. Catalogue no: **6504222 6**

SKILLS OF SUMMER
Tracks: / When she was a girl.
7" Single: Released May '86, on CBS, by CBS Records. Catalogue no: **A 7163**
12" Single: Released May '86, on CBS, by CBS Records. Catalogue no: **TA 7163**

Wired

TO THE BEAT OF A DRUM
Tracks: / To the beat of the drum / George mix.
12" Single: Released Mar '87, on Nine O Nine, by Creole Records. Catalogue no: **NINE 2**

Wisdom

KLUNG KLUSION
Tracks: / Klung klusion.
12" Single: Released Jul '85, on Simbal, Catalogue no: **SMW 001**

Wisdom, Norman

Biographical details: Norman Wisdom-this British comedian, actor and showbusiness personality achieved a pair of UK hit singles during the Fifties. These were a by product of his career rather than an integral part of it. *Don't Laugh At Me* was a No.3 smash in 1954 and *The Wisdom of a Fool* hit No.13 in 1957. The latter song was a rapied remake of the Five Keys' US Top 40 hit and Widsom's version of *Wisdom* outflanked a simultaneous UK hit version by Ronnie Carroll. Wisdom never returned to the charts but, even in the Eighties, remains a regular face on theatre stages and television screens. He lives in West Sussex. (Bob Macdonald June 1985).

DON'T LAUGH AT ME
Tracks: / Don't laugh at me.
7" Single: Released Feb '54, on Columbia, by EMI Records. Deleted '57. Catalogue no: **DB 3133**

DON'T LAUGH AT ME (RE-RELEASE)
Tracks: / Don't laugh at me / Wisdom of a fool.
7" Single: Released Jun '80, on H.M.V., by EMI Records. Deleted '83. Catalogue no: **POP 2001**

WISDOM OF A FOOL
Tracks: / Wisdom of a fool.
7" Single: Released Mar '57, on Columbia, by EMI Records. Deleted '60. Catalogue no: **DB 3903**

Wise Blood

MOTOR SLUG
Tracks: / Motor slug.
12" Single: Released Jun '85, on Some Bizzare, by Some Bizzare Records. Catalogue no: **WISE 112**

Wise, Clive

I'VE FOUND YOU
Tracks: / I've found you.
12" Single: Released Jul '89, on Hill Crest, Catalogue no: **HCR 012**

Wise Guise

I GUESS SOMEONE UP THERE DON'T LIKE ME
Tracks: / I guess someone up there don't like me.
12" Single: Released Dec '84, on Strike (1), by Strike Records. Catalogue no: **KIK 7X**

Wise Men

KNOWLEDGE
Tracks: / Knowledge / Lost in action.
7" Single: Released May '83, on Glass, by Glass Records. Deleted '83. Catalogue no: **GLASS 025**

Wiseblood

STUMBO
Tracks: / Someone drowned in my pool.
12" Single: Released Dec '86, on K 422, by K 422 Records. Catalogue no: **WISE 212**

Wish

NICE AND SOFT
Tracks: / Nice and soft / Nice and soft (part 2).
7" Single: Released Jul '81, on Excalibur, by Red Bus Records. Deleted '84. Catalogue no: **EXC 511**
12" Single: Released Jul '81, on Excalibur, by Red Bus Records. Deleted '84. Catalogue no: **EXCL 511**

TOUCH ME (ALL NIGHT LONG)
Tracks: / Touch me (all night long).
12" Single: Released Sep '87, on KN (USA), Catalogue no: **KN 1001**

Wishbone Ash

Biographical details: This progressive rock band was formed in 1969, in Torquay, England, by brothers Glen Turner (lead guitar) and Martin Turner (bass and vocals), with Steve Upton on drums. Local success prompted Martin Turner and Upton's move to London, and they auditioned lead guitarists and hired both Ted Turner -- no relation -- and Andy Powell. The rare twin lead guitar line-up gave their progressive rock its trademark. Ted Turner left in 1973, to be replaced by Laurie Wisefield; Martin Turner left for a career in production and was replaced by John Wetton and then Trevor Bolder and Mervyn Spence. But by 1985's LP Raw To The Bone only diehard progressive fans were still listening. (Donald Clarke, March 1988.)
At the time of their greatest success, this British rock band consisted of Andy Powell, Martin Turner, Ted Turner and Steve Upton. The two Turners were not related.
Wishbone Ash were formed in 1969 and initially comprised drummer Upton plus brothers Glen & Martin Turner (guitar and bass, respectively); hailing from Devon, England, these three men had played together in various local bands. Glen soon dropped out for health reasons, and was replaced by Powell. They then decided to enrol a second lead guitarist, Ted Turner, to make a quartet.
Wishbone Ash released their eponymous debut LP in 1970 and it reached No.34 on the UK charts in January '71. The hard working group built their reputation through constant touring; their audiences were particularly impressed by the twin lead guitar idea, which had been inspired by a 1966 combination of Jeff Beck and Jimmy page in the Yardbirds (and was also used in the early Seventies by Duane Allman and Eric Clapton in Derek & The Dominos).
Wishone's workmanlike hard rock enjoyed its heyday between 1971 and 1973: their second album *Pilgrimage* reached the UK No.14 slot; their best album, in both musical and commercial terms, was 1972's *Argus*, which hit No.3 and logged 20 weeks on the British LP listings; and 1973's *Wishbone Four* hit the UK No.12 position. However, it was in a live setting that the band were always at their best - they were in their element when playing college dates to armies of welcoming students.
After *Wishbone Four* the Ashes lost their way somewhat; this situation was accelerated by the 1974 departure of Ted Turner, who quit the music business. Turner's replacement was Laurie Wisefield, who stayed with the group right through into the early Eighties. So did Upton (the only lifelong member) and Powell; but Martin Turner left in 1979, to be briefly replaced by John Wetton (who soon left to help form Asia) and then Trevor Bolder. Three Turners had passed through Wishbone Ash - now there were none! Between 1974's *There's The Rub* and 1982's *Twin Barrels Burning*, the increasingly dated group managed to obtain a UK chart placing for virtually every LP release, but these tended to be of a minor nature. They were kept afloat by a steady concert following in the States, Europe and Britain, but their music remained ensconced in the early Seventies. The group broke up in 1983.
Wishbone Ash never chalked up a chart single in their native country, but their best known songs are probably the three key cuts on *Argus*: *Blowin' Free*, *The King Will Come* and *Throw Down The Sword*. (Bob Macdonald June 1985).

COSMIC JAZZ
Tracks: / Cosmic jazz / T-Bone shuffle / Bolan's monument (12" only.).
12" Single: Released Jan '89, on I.R.S. Catalogue no: **EIRST 104**
7" Single: Released Jan '89, on I.R.S, Catalogue no: **EIRS 104**

ENGINE OVERHEAT
Tracks: / Engine overheat.
7" Single: Released Oct '82, on AVM, by AVM Records. Deleted '87. Catalogue no: **WISH 1**

GET READY
Tracks: / Get ready / Kicks on the street.
7" Single: Released Jun '81, on MCA, by MCA Records. Deleted Jun '84. Catalogue no: **MCA 726**

HELPLESS
Tracks: / Helpless / Blowing free.
12" Single: Released May '80, on MCA, by MCA Records. Deleted May '83. Catalogue no: **MCAT 577**
7" Single: Released May '80, on MCA, by MCA Records. Deleted May '83. Catalogue no: **MCA 577**

IN THE SKIN
Tracks: / In the skin.
7" Single: Released May '88, on I.R.S. Catalogue no: **IRM 164**

LIVING PROOF
Tracks: / Living proof.
7" Single: Released Jan '80, on MCA, by MCA Records. Deleted Jan '85. Catalogue no: **MCA 549**

NO MORE LONELY NIGHTS
Tracks: / No more lonely nights.
7" Single: Released Dec '82, on AVM, by AVM Records. Deleted '87. Catalogue no: **AVM 1002**

UNDERGROUND
Tracks: / Underground / My mind is made up.
7" Single: Released Apr '81, on MCA, by MCA Records. Deleted '85. Catalogue no: **MCA 695**

Wishful Thinking

WHATEVER YOU FEEL
Tracks: / Whatever you feel / Dance frontier.
7" Single: Released Jan '88, on Long Live, by Long Live Records. Catalogue no: **LONG LIVE 1**

WISHFUL THINKING
Tracks: / Wishful thinking / On line.
7" Single: Released Sep '83, on Organic, by Organic Records. Catalogue no: **ORGS**

Wishing Stones

BEAT GIRL
Tracks: / Beat girl.
7" Single: Released Sep '86, on Head, Catalogue no: **HEAD 2**

DEAD MAN'S LOOK
Tracks: / Dead man's look.
12" Single: Released Oct '88, on Sub Aqua, Catalogue no: **AQUA 005 12**
7" Single: Released Oct '88, on Sub Aqua, Catalogue no: **AQUA 005**

NEW WAYS
Tracks: / New ways.
7" Single: Released Apr '87, on Head, Catalogue no: **HEAD 6**
12" Single: Released Apr '87, on Head, Catalogue no: **HEAD 612**

OLD ROAD OUT OF TOWN, THE

Tracks: / Old road out of town, The.
12" Single: Released Jul '88, on Sub Aqua, Catalogue no: **AQUA 00112**
7" Single: Released Jul '88, on Sub Aqua, Catalogue no: **AQUA 001**

Wishing Well

WISHING WELL, THE
Tracks: / Wishing well: *Various artists* / Wishing well message, The: *Various artists.*
7" Pic: Released Nov '87, on MBS, by MBS Records. Catalogue no: **GOSH 1**

Witcher, Wolfie

NO MONEY DOWN
Tracks: / No money down / Wotcher witcher.
7" Single: Released Nov '82, on Speed, Catalogue no: **SPEED 6**

Witchfinder General

BURNING A SINNER
Tracks: / Burning a sinner / Satans children.
7" Single: Released Sep '81, on Heavy Metal, by FM-Revolver Records. Catalogue no: **HEAVY 6**

MUSIC
Tracks: / Music / Last chance.
7" Pic: Released Dec '83, on Heavy Metal, by FM-Revolver Records. Catalogue no: **HMPD 21**
7" Single: Released Dec '83, on Heavy Metal, by FM-Revolver Records. Catalogue no: **HEAVY 21**

SOVIET INVASION
Tracks: / Soviet invasion / Rabies / R.I.P..
7" Single: Released Jan '83, on Heavy Metal, by FM-Revolver Records. Catalogue no: **12HM 17**

Witchfynde

CONSPIRACY
Tracks: / Conspiracy / Scarlet lady.
7" Single: Released Mar '85, on Mausoleum, by Mausoleum Records. Catalogue no: **GUTS 8404**

GIVE 'EM HELL (SINGLE)
Tracks: / Give 'em hell.
7" Single: Released Feb '80, on Rondelet Music, by Rondelet Music & Records. Catalogue no: **ROUND 1**

I'D RATHER GO WILD
Tracks: / I'd rather go wild.
7" Single: Released Jul '83, on Expulsion, by Expulsion Records. Deleted '87. Catalogue no: **OUT 3**

IN THE STARS
Tracks: / In the stars.
7" Single: Released Sep '80, on Rondelet Music, by Rondelet Music & Records. Catalogue no: **ROUND 4**

Withers, Bill

Biographical details: This American singer, songwriter and guitarist was born in Slab Fork, a small town in West Virginia, in 1938, the youngest of six children. The most remarkable aspect of his career was his late start: he did not begin singing and playing with any seriousness until 1971, when he was 33. Pre-music jobs included bricklaying, nine years in the US Navy and working in an aircraft factory. One of the main reasons for his late arrival on the music scene was his extreme shyness. The Navy years helped to conquer an acute stammer, as did a speech therapy course, but even after becoming famous he still displayed a modest and diffident temperament. The song that made him famous was *Ain't No Sunshine*, a delicate soul ballad which hit No 3 on the US pop charts. Like the whole of his 1971 debut LP, *Just As I Am*, it was produced by Booker T. Jones (of Booker T. & The MGs), who also contributed keyboards and guitar skills. The following year was even more fruitful: *Lean On Me*, another understated soul song with inspired lyrics, was an American No 1 smash, and he followed it with *Use Me*, also self-penned, which cruised to No 2. In Britain he enjoyed simultaneous Top Twenty success with Michael Jackson's cover version of *Ain't No Sunshine* and his own *Lean On Me*. Having notched up three American Top Three hits within 18 months, Withers' career momentum slowed down. In December '76 British teenyboppers Mud scored a UK Top Ten single with their Christmassy treatment of *Lean On Me* -- the contrast between Withers', Mud's and Jackson's interpretation of his material was a tribute to his stature as a songwriter -- and he himself returned to the charts on both sides of the Atlantic with 1978's *Lovely Day*, a UK No 7. In 1981 he made an acclaimed guest vocal appearance on *Just The Two Of Us*, a US No 2 single by jazzy saxman Grover Washington Jr. His first solo album in seven years, 1985's *Watching You Watching Me*, yielded the modestly successful single *Oh Yeah!* (Bob MacDonald, June 1985.)

Bill Withers was born in West Virginia in 1938; the sweet soul singer and songwriter was the youngest of six children. He got a late start in his professional career because of his shyness and a stammer, both overcome while in the US Navy for nine years. He moved to the West Coast in 1967, made demos, first performed in public in 1971. Eleven USA hit singles through 1977 were all written by Withers except one. Apart from his own hit albums he sang on Gover Washington album *Winelight*in 1981, including the co-written hit *Just The Two Of Us* (single on Elektra, included in *Best Of* on CBS). *Watching You Watch Me* in 1985 was another top 200 LP. (Donald Clarke).

AIN'T NO SUNSHINE
Tracks: / Ain't no sunshine (eclipse mix) / Ain't no sunshine (original version) / Ain't no sunshine (total eclipse mix) (Only on 12") / Oh yeah (Only on 12") / I want to spend the night (Only on 12").
7" Single: Released 28 Nov '88, on CBS, by CBS Records. Deleted 17 Apr '89. Catalogue no: **653198 7**
12" Single: Released 28 Nov '88, on CBS, by CBS Records. Deleted 17 Apr '89. Catalogue no: **653198 6**
CD 5": Released Dec '88, on CBS, by CBS Records. Deleted 10 Jul '89. Catalogue no: **653 198-2**

I WANT TO SPEND THE NIGHT
Tracks: / I want to spend the night.
7" Single: Released Jul '81, on CBS, by CBS Records. Catalogue no: **A 1403**

LEAN ON ME
Tracks: / Lean on me.
7" Single: Released Aug '72, on A&M, by A&M Records. Deleted '75. Catalogue no: **AMS 7004**

LEAN ON ME (OLD GOLD)
Tracks: / Lean on me.
7" Single: Released Jul '82, on Old Gold, by Old Gold Records. Deleted Jul '88. Catalogue no: **OG 9186**

LOVELY DAY (EXT)
Tracks: / Lovely day (ext) / Lean on me / Lovely night for dancing.
12" Single: Released Jul '87, on CBS, by CBS Records. Catalogue no: **650 992 6**

LOVELY DAY (OLD GOLD)
Tracks: / Lovely day.
7" Single: Released 21 Nov '87, on Old Gold, by Old Gold Records. Catalogue no: **OG 9729**

LOVELY DAY (SINGLE)
Tracks: / Lovely day / Lovely night for dancing / Oh yeah.
7" Single: Released Jan '78, on CBS, by CBS Records. Deleted '81. Catalogue no: **CBS 5773**
7" Single: Released Jul '87, on CBS, by CBS Records. Catalogue no: **650 992 7**

LOVELY DAY (SUNSHINE MIX)
Tracks: / Lovely day (sunshine mix) / Lovely day (original version) / Lean on me (12" only) / Ain't no sunshine (12" only).
CD 5": Released 16 Sep '88, on CBS, by CBS Records. Deleted 17 Apr '89. Catalogue no: **653001 2**
7" Single: Released Aug '88, on CBS, by CBS Records. Deleted 17 Apr '89. Catalogue no: **653001 7**
12" Single: Released Aug '88, on CBS, by CBS Records. Deleted 17 Apr '89. Catalogue no: **653001 6**

OH YEAH
Tracks: / Oh yeah.
7" Single: Released May '85, on CBS, by CBS Records. Deleted '88. Catalogue no: **A 6154**

USA
Tracks: / U.S.A. / Paint your pretty picture.
7" Single: Released Jan '82, on CBS, by CBS Records. Catalogue no: **A 2000**

Withers, Vivian

WHAT IS MAN
Tracks: / What is man / Joe Blake / Hangin' on.
12" Single: Released Jun '87, on Trojan, by Trojan Records. Deleted May '88. Catalogue no: **TROT 9096**

Witness

LOUDHAILER SONGS...
Tracks: / Loudhailer songs....
12" Single: Released Dec '85, on Ron Johnson, by Ron Johnson Records. Catalogue no: **12RON 5**

RAW PATCH
Tracks: / Raw patch.
12" Single: Released Feb '88, on Ron Johnson, by Ron Johnson Records. Catalogue no: **ZRON 30**

Witt, Joachim

TRI TRA TRULLALA
Tracks: / Tri Tra Trullala / Gem mal vor.
12" Single: Released Sep '82, on WEA, by WEA Records. Catalogue no: **K 19163T**
7" Single: Released Sep '82, on WEA, by WEA Records. Catalogue no: **K 19163**

Wizard

WE'N GOING HOME
Tracks: / We'n going home.
12" Single: Released 8 Aug '88, on Carnival Records, Catalogue no: **CART 002**

Wizard Merlyn MMC

LOLLIPOPS AND DRAGONS
Tracks: / Lollipops and dragons.
7" Single: Released Nov '82, on Wizard Merlyn, by Wizard Merlyn Records. Catalogue no: **WM 001**

Wizzard

Biographical details: Formed in late 1972 by singer, multi-instrumentalist, songwriter and producer Roy Wood, Wizzard also comprised Mike Burney, Charlie Grima, Bill Hunt, Hugh McDowell, Nick Pentelow, Rick Price and Keith Smart. During the preceding six years Wood had been the driving force of the Move and when that group were terminated in mid-'72 Wood and fellow Move member Jeff Lynne launched the Electric Light Orchestra. However, the two men's musical and personal differences precipitated an early rupture. Lynne became sole leader of ELO -- eventually achieving worldwide success -- while Wood took two ELO players, horn/keyboards man Hunt and bass guitarist/harmonica player Price, plus five new recruits, and founded Wizzard. At the end of '72 Wizzard achieved their first UK hit with the rock 'n' roll-flavoured *Ball Park Incident.* This reached No 6 and was followed in '73 by two back-to-back British No 1 smashes: the classic *See My Baby Jive* was on top for four weeks and*Angel Fingers*led the list for one week. These straightforward pop songs were lavishly arranged and produced by Wood and their rich, multi-layered embellishments were heavily influenced by Phil Spector's famous *Wall of Sound.* Capitalising on the UK pop scene's glam rock obsession in 1973, Wood daubed himself with an arresting display of warpaint and multi-coloured locks. Wizzard's final single of the year reached the UK No 4 slot: *I Wish It Could Be Christmas Every Day*, featuring his usual over-the-top production plus a chorus of singing schoolkids, became a Yuletide evergreen. The Wizzard party was over in early '75, after their final Top Tenner *Are You Ready To Rock?* dropped out of the British charts. By this time cellist McDowell was a member of ELO who were moving on to centre-stage just as Wood was fading. Born Ulysses Adrian Wood in Birmingham, he had enjoyed an unbroken run of success between 1967 and 1975. In addition to the Move (whose every hit was written by him), founding ELO and being the totally dominant member of Wizzard, he had chalked up four UK Top Twenty singles as a solo artist, most notably with *Forever.* During the late 70's and early 80's his diminishing public profile was kept afloat by the Wizzo Band and repeated revivals of *I Wish It Could Be Christmas Every Day.* As time went on he seemed content to remain in the wilderness, but in his heyday he had been one of British pop's most ingenious all-rounders -- his instrumental versatility equalled only by Mike Oldfield -- and one of the most engaging characters on the scene. (Bob MacDonald, June 1985.).

ANGEL FINGERS
Tracks: / Angel fingers.
7" Single: Released Aug '73, on Harvest (1), by EMI Records. Catalogue no: **HAR 5106**
7" Single: Released Sep '73, on Harvest (1), by EMI Records. Deleted '76. Catalogue no: **HAR 5076**

ARE YOU READY TO ROCK
Tracks: / Are you ready to rock.
7" Single: Released Dec '74, on Warner Bros., by WEA Records. Deleted '77. Catalogue no: **K 16497**

BALL PARK INCIDENT
Tracks: / Ball park incident.
7" Single: Released Dec '72, on Harvest (1), by EMI Records. Deleted '75. Catalogue no: **HAR 5062**

I WISH IT COULD BE CHRISTMAS EVERY DAY
Tracks: / I wish it could be Christmas every day / See my baby jive.
7" Single: Released Dec '73, on Harvest (1), by EMI Records. Catalogue no: **HAR 5079**
7" Single: Released Nov '84, on Harvest (1), by EMI Records. Deleted Nov '87. Catalogue no: **HAR 5173**

ROCK'N'ROLL WINTER
Tracks: / Rock 'n' roll winter.
7" Single: Released Apr '74, on Warner Bros., by WEA Records. Deleted '77. Catalogue no: **K 16357**

SEE MY BABY JIVE
Tracks: / See my baby jive.
7" Single: Released Apr '73, on Harvest (1), by EMI Records. Deleted '76. Catalogue no: **HAR 5070**
7" Single: Released Feb '76, on Harvest (1), by EMI Records. Catalogue no: **HAR 5106**

SEE MY BABY JIVE (OLD GOLD)
7" Single: Released Oct '83, on Old Gold, by Old Gold Records. Deleted Sep '89. Catalogue no: **OG 9378**

THIS IS THE STORY OF MY LOVE (BABY)
Tracks: / This is the story of my love (baby).
7" Single: Released Aug '74, on Warner Bros., by WEA Records. Deleted '77. Catalogue no: **K 16434**

Wizzards Of Rock

GOOD THANG
Tracks: / Good thang / Stone to the bone.
12" Single: Released Dec '87, on Champion, by Champion Records. Deleted Aug '89. Catalogue no: **CHAMP 1260**
7" Single: Released Dec '87, on Champion, by Champion Records. Catalogue no: **CHAMP 60**

WKGB

NON STOP
Tracks: / Non stop.
7" Single: Released Jul '81, on Fetish, Catalogue no: **FET 002**

WM & Chart Buster

BUSTER
Tracks: / Buster.
7" Single: Released Sep '88, on WM & Chart, Catalogue no: **AUG 8**

WMTID

GO BIG RED
Tracks: / Go big red.
12" Single: Released '88, on Rouska, by Rouska Records. Catalogue no: **PROFANE 081**

SHEIK YOUR MONEY
Tracks: / Sheik your money.
12" Single: Released Apr '88, on Rouska, by Rouska Records. Catalogue no: **PROFANE 81**

TRANSFASCIST
Tracks: / Transfascist.
12" Single: Released '87, on Rouska, by Rouska Records. Catalogue no: **PROFANE 045**

WELCOME TO THE GLOBAL CASINO
Tracks: / Welcome to the global casino.
12" Single: Released Mar '88, on Rouska, by Rouska Records. Catalogue no: **PROFANE 081**

Wobble, Jah

BETRAYAL BY MR.X
Tracks: / Betrayal by Mr.X / Battle of Britain.
12" Single: Released Apr '80, on Virgin, by Virgin Records. Deleted Apr '83. Catalogue no: **VS 33712**
7" Single: Released Apr '80, on Virgin, by Virgin Records. Deleted Apr '83. Catalogue no: **VS 337**

BETWEEN TWO FREQUENCIES
Tracks: / Between two frequencies.
12" Single: Released Apr '86, on General Music (France), Catalogue no: **G 2001**

BLOW OUT
Tracks: / Blow out.
12" Single: Released Nov '85, on Lago, Catalogue no: **LAGO 6**

FADING
Tracks: / Fading / Nocturnal.
12" Single: Released May '82, on Jah Wobble, Catalogue no: **JAH 1**

HOW MUCH ARE THEY
Tracks: / How much are they.
12" Single: Released 14 May '88, on Licensed, Catalogue no: **LD 8816**

HOW MUCH ARE THEY (EP)
12" EP: Released Jul '81, on Island, by Island Records. Deleted Jul '87. Catalogue no: **12WIP 6701**

INVADERS OF THE HEART
Tracks: / Invaders of the heart.
7" Single: Released May '83, on Lago, Catalogue no: **LAGO 4**

ISLAND PARADISE
Tracks: / Island paradise / Alcohol / Jihad / Island paradise (remix).
12" Single: Released Sep '87, on Southern Studios, Catalogue no: **WOB 8**

JAH WOBBLE - LOVE MYSTERY (Released on Island)

LONG LONG WAY
Tracks: / Long long way / Romany.
12" Single: Released Oct '82, on Jah, Catalogue no: **JAH 2**

LOVE MYSTERY (see panel above)
Tracks: / Love mystery / Love mystery (version).
12" Single: Released Apr '85, on Island, by Island Records. Deleted '87. Catalogue no: **12IS 228**
7" Single: Released Apr '85, on Island, by Island Records. Catalogue no: **IS 228**

VOODOO
Tracks: / Voodoo.
7" Single: Released Oct '84, on Lago, Catalogue no: **LAGO 5**

Wobblesox

GET YOUR SOCKS OFF
Tracks: / Get your socks off / Men.
7" Single: Released Oct '80, on Freewave, Deleted '82. Catalogue no: **F1**

Wobbly Jellies

MAGIC
Tracks: / Magic.
7" Single: Released May '84, on Wimp, by Wimp Records. Catalogue no: **WIMP 009**

Wogan, Terry

Biographical details: One of Britain's top television personalities, Wogan, from Limerick, Ireland, achieved one freak entry on the British charts. While the Brighouse and Rastrick Brass Band were enjoying a lengthy chart run with their No 2 rendition of the traditional Floral Dance, Wogan reached No 21 with his pedestrian vocal version. (Bob MacDonald, June 1985.)
This Irishman, who hails from Limerick, is one of Britain's foremost TV and radio personalities. Since the start of the Seventies, when he had a spell at Radio One, Wogan has remained with the BBC. Between 1973 and 1984, he enjoyed a twelve year period as the presenter of Radio Two's Breakfast Show. His amiable personality and dulcet brogue, combined with the station's diet of MoR music, made him a housewives' favourite. By the late Seventies, he was also a familiar figure on television game, variety and chat shows - it was a tribute to his skills that he was able to bring a modicum of intelligence and wit to the otherwise appalling banality of 'Blankety Blank'.
At the beginning of 1985, Wogan finally ended his radio work to devote all his energies to TV and, in particular, to his new regular 40 minute chat show, simply titled 'Wogan'. Broadcast three nights per week at 7pm on BBC1, this programme showed that his unaffected charm had overcome the possible risk of over exposure, and taken him to the top of his profession. His personality managed to appeal to a mass audience without being patronising.
A small aberration in Wogan's career ocurred in January 1978, when he achieved his only entry on the British record charts. While the Birghouse & Rastrick Brass Band were enjoying a lengthy chart run with their smash No.2 rendition of the old standard *Floral Dance*, Wogan reached No.21 with his pedestrian vocal version. It eloquently displayed the fact that his voice was put to far better use as a disc jockey than as a singer. (Bob Macdonald June 1985).

FLORAL DANCE
Tracks: / Floral dance, The.
7" Single: Released Jan '78, on Philips, by Phonogram Ltd. Deleted '81. Catalogue no: **6006 592**

Wolf

HEAD CONTACT
Tracks: / Head contact / Rock and roll / Soul for the devil.
12" Single: Released '82, on Chrysalis, by Chrysalis Records. Deleted '87. Catalogue no: **CHS 12 2592**
7" Single: Released '82, on Chrysalis, by Chrysalis Records. Deleted '87. Catalogue no: **CHS 2592**

Wolf, Peter

COME AS YOU ARE (SINGLE)
Tracks: / Come as you are.
7" Single: Released Apr '87, on EMI-America, by EMI Records. Deleted Oct '87. Catalogue no: **EA 231**
12" Single: Released Apr '87, on EMI-America, by EMI Records. Deleted Oct '87. Catalogue no: **12 EA 231**

LIGHTS OUT (SINGLE)
Tracks: / Lights out.
7" Single: Released Aug '84, on EMI-America, by EMI Records. Catalogue no: **EA 177**

Wolf & Wolf

DON'T TAKE THE CANDY
Tracks: / Don't take the candy.
7" Single: Released Jul '84, on Morocco (USA), by Motown Records (UK). Catalogue no: **TMG 1346**

Wolfe, Jerri

STILL LIFE
Tracks: / Still life / Holiday in the sun.
7" Single: Released Aug '82, on Polydor, by Polydor Ltd. Catalogue no: **POSP 489**

Wolfe Tones

FAREWELL TO DUBLIN
Tracks: / Farewell to Dublin.
7" Single: Released Aug '76, on Triskel (Ireland), Catalogue no: **TRS 2**

MY HEART IS IN IRELAND
Tracks: / My heart is in Ireland.
7" Single: Released Sep '85, on MCA, by MCA Records. Catalogue no: **MCA 1003**

VALE OF AVOCA
Tracks: / Vale of Avoca.
7" Single: Released Jun '76, on Triskel (Ireland), Catalogue no: **TRS 1**

Wolfer, Bill

CALL ME
Tracks: / Call me.
12" Single: Released May '83, on Solar (USA), by MCA Records. Catalogue no: **E 9891 T**
7" Single: Released May '83, on Solar (USA), by MCA Records. Catalogue no: **E 9891**

PAPA WAS A ROLLIN' STONE
Tracks: / Papa was a rollin' stone.
12" Single: Released Feb '83, on Solar (USA), by MCA Records. Catalogue no: **E 9849 T**
7" Single: Released Feb '83, on Solar (USA), by MCA Records. Catalogue no: **E 9849**

Wolfgang Press

BIG SEX (EP)
Tracks: / Big sex / Wedding, The / Geat leveller, The / That heat / God's number.
7" EP: on 4AD, by 4AD Records. Catalogue no: **BAD 702**
Cassingle: Released Apr '87, on 4AD, by 4AD Records. Catalogue no: **BADC 702**

KANSAS EP
Tracks: / Kansas EP.
7" Single: Released Jan '89, on 4AD, by 4AD Records. Catalogue no: **BAD 902**
12" Single: Released 30 Jan '89, on 4AD, by 4AD Records. Catalogue no: **BAD12 902**

KING OF SOUL
Tracks: / King of soul / King of soul (version).
12" Single: Released 30 Aug '88, on 4AD, by 4AD Records. Catalogue no: **BAD 804**
CD 5": Released 30 Aug '88, on 4AD, by 4AD Records. Catalogue no: **BAD 804 CD**

RAINTIME
Tracks: / Raintime / Bottom drawer.
CD 5": Released Apr '89, on 4AD, by 4AD Records. Catalogue no: **BAD 907CD**
12" Single: Released Apr '89, on 4AD, by 4AD Records. Catalogue no: **BAD 907**

SCARECROW
Tracks: / Scarecrow.
12" Single: Released Jul '84, on 4AD, by 4AD Records. Catalogue no: **BAD 409**

SWEAT BOX
Tracks: / Sweat box.
12" Single: Released Sep '85, on 4AD, by 4AD Records. Catalogue no: **BAD 506**

WATER
Tracks: / Water.
12" Single: Released Mar '85, on 4AD, by 4AD Records. Catalogue no: **BAD 502**

Wolfhounds

ANTI MIDAS TOUCH, THE
Tracks: / Anti Midas touch, The.
7" Single: Released Oct '86, on Pink Label, by Pink Label Records. Catalogue no: **PINKY 14**
12" Single: Released Oct '86, on Pink Label, by Pink Label Records. Catalogue no: **PINKY 14T**

CRUELTY
Tracks: / Cruelty.
Note: Double 'A' side
7" Single: Released Apr '87, on Pink Label, by Pink Label Records. Catalogue no: **PINKY 18**

CUT THE CAKE
Tracks: / Cut the cake.
12" Single: Released Mar '86, on Pink Label, by Pink Label Records. Catalogue no: **Pinky 8**

HAPPY SHOPPER
Tracks: / Happy shopper.
7" Single: Released 28 Mar '89, on Midnight, Catalogue no: **DING 046**
12" Single: Released 28 Mar '89, on Midnight, Catalogue no: **DONG 046**

ME
Tracks: / Me.
7" Single: Released 17 Oct '87, on Idea, by Idea Records. Catalogue no: **IDEA 010**
12" Single: Released Jul '87, on Idea, by Idea Records. Catalogue no: **IDEAT 010**

MICHAEL GAUGHAN
Tracks: / Michael Gaughan.
7" Single: Released '88, on Homespun (Ireland), by Outlet Records. Catalogue no: **HIS 26**

RENT ACT
Tracks: / Rent act.
12" Single: Released Nov '88, on Midnight Music, by Midnight Music Records. Catalogue no: **DONG 43**

SON OF NOTHING
Tracks: / Son of nothing.
12" Single: Released May '88, on September, Catalogue no: **SEPT 07T**

Wolfman

BUM BUM FATTIE
Tracks: / Bum bum fattie.
12" Single: Released Feb '89, on J & P, Catalogue no: **SW 002**

Wolfsbane

LOCO
Tracks: / Loco / Dance dirty / Limousine / Killer.
12" Single: Released Oct '88, on Def Jam, Catalogue no: **WSB 2**

SHAKIN'
Tracks: / Shakin'.
12" Single: Released Sep '89, on Def American (USA), Catalogue no: **DEFA 212**

WASTED BUT DANGEROUS
Tracks: / Loco (Nitro-methane injected turbo super fireball from hell mix.) / Dance dirty (Wickedly sensual grinding pelvis mix.) / Limousine (Stains on the back seat mix) / Killer (Slow tortuous death - vomit under a full moon mix.).
Note: This record will be disturbing and offensive to some people.
12" Single: Released Oct '88, on London Records, by London Records. Deleted May '89. Catalogue no: **WSB 2**

Womack, Bobby

Biographical details: Born in Cleveland, Ohio, singer, guitarist and songwriter Womack began singing at the age of four. Like so many future stars he grew up with gospel music in his local churches. He and his four brothers formed a family vocal quartet and they toured with one of the giants of black music, Sam Cooke, who persuaded them to follow in his footsteps by transforming from gospel to secular rhythm-and-blues. They billed themselves as the Valentinos and one of their releases, a song by Bobby and Shirley Womack called *It's All Over Now*, gave the Rolling Stones their first British No 1 single in July 1964. Sam Cooke, for whom Womack was working as a guitarist, was shot dead in '64. The Valentinos disbanded in '66. Womack spent the rest of the 60's as a session guitarist, notably for Wilson Pickett, and as a soul songsmith. It was in the early 70's that he emerged as a major solo artist, thanks to his espousal of a loose, informal style that included spoken passages and lengthy guitar breaks. *That's The Way I Feel Aboutcha* and *Nobody Wants You When You're Down And Out* were US Top Forty pop hits. Even more successful were two million-sellers, whose sales strength in the black charts was not fully reflected on the pop listings: the ludicrous *Harry Hippie* ('73) reached the US No 31 slots and 1974's *Lookin' For A Love*, a remake of one of the old Valentinos' tracks, got to No 10. From then on Womack's career went downhill. During the late 70's and early 80's he was dogged by a series of family, domestic and business problems -- at one point he even faked blindness to escape from the pressures of touring. His sporadic 80's successes were marred by legal and financial hassles, but the records themselves showed he had lost none of his magic. He made two superb guest vocal appearances on singles by Wilton Felder (the Crusaders' saxman), *Inherit The Wind* ('80) and *(No Matter How High I Get) I'll Still Be Looking Up To You* ('85) were both Top Three hits on the American black music charts. Womack's comeback albums, *The Poet* ('82) and The Poet 2 ('84) were highly acclaimed. The latter yielded his ludicrously overdue debut British hit as a solo artist, albeit No 60 on the chart: *Tell Me Why* was a song written during, and on the subject of, his many court battles. Simultaneously his brother Cecil (an ex-Valentino) hit the UK Top Twenty in a husband-and-wife duet: Womack & Womack's *Love Wars* reached No 14. Cecil's wife, Linda, is the daughter of Bob's former boss, the late Sam Cooke. (Bob MacDonald, June 1985.).

GIPSY WOMAN
Tracks: / Gipsy woman / Whatever happened to the times.
7" Single: Released May '86, on MCA, by MCA Records. Catalogue no: **MCA 1050**
12" Single: Released May '86, on MCA, by MCA Records. Catalogue no: **MCAT 1050**

HOW COULD YOU BREAK MY HEART
Tracks: / How could you break my heart / Give it up / Mr. D.J. don't stop the music.
7" Single: Released 20 Jun '87, on Arista, by BMG Records (UK). Catalogue no: **RIS 17**
12" Single: Released 20 Jun '87, on Arista, by BMG Records (UK). Catalogue no: **RIST 17**

I WANNA MAKE LOVE TO YOU
Tracks: / Whatever happened to the times?
7" Single: Released Jan '87, on MCA, by MCA Records. Catalogue no: **MCA 1108**
12" Single: Released Jan '87, on MCA, by MCA Records. Catalogue no: **MCAT 1108**

I WISH YOU DIDN'T TRUST ME SO MUCH
Tracks: / I wish you didn't trust me so much
7" Single: Released Sep '85, on MCA, by MCA Records. Catalogue no: **MCA 994**
12" Single: Released Sep '85, on MCA, by MCA Records. Catalogue no: **MCAT 994**

LIVING IN A BOX

Tracks: / Living in a box (instrumental) / Living in a box / I can't stay mad too long / Living in (another box) (Available on 12" only) / Living in a box (hacienda mix) (Available on 12" only).
12" Single: Released Nov '87, on MCA, by MCA Records. Catalogue no: **MCAX 1210**
12" Single: Released Oct '87, on MCA, by MCA Records. Catalogue no: **MCAT 1210**
7" Single: Released Oct '87, on MCA, by MCA Records. Catalogue no: **MCA 1210**

LOOKING FOR A LOVE (SINGLE)
Tracks: / Looking for a love / Harry hippie / That's the way I feel about cha / If you don't want my love, give it back.
CD 5": Released Jan '89, on Charly, by Charly Records. Catalogue no: **CDS 10**

SECRETS (SINGLE)
Tracks: / Secrets.
7" Single: Released Sep '82, on Motown, by BMG Records (UK). Catalogue no: **TMG 1278**

SO MANY SIDES OF YOU
Tracks: / So many sides of you / Just my imagination.
12" Single: Released Jul '82, on Motown, by BMG Records (UK). Catalogue no: **TMGT 1267**
7" Single: Released Jul '82, on Motown, by BMG Records (UK). Catalogue no: **TMG 1267**

SURPRIZE SURPRIZE
Tracks: / Surprize surprize.
7" Single: Released Sep '84, on Motown, by BMG Records (UK). Catalogue no: **TMG 1353**
12" Single: Released Sep '84, on Motown, by BMG Records (UK). Catalogue no: **TMGT 1353**

TELL ME WHY
Tracks: / Tell me why / Through the eyes of a child.
7" Single: Released Jun '84, on Motown, by BMG Records (UK). Catalogue no: **TMG 1339**
12" Single: Released Jun '84, on Motown, by BMG Records (UK). Catalogue no: **TMGT 1339**

Womack & Womack

BABY I'M SCARED OF YOU
Tracks: / Baby I'm scared of you.
7" Single: Released Jun '84, on Elektra, by Elektra Records (UK). Deleted '87. Catalogue no: **E 9733**

CELEBRATE THE WORLD (PEOPLE UNITE)
Tracks: / Celebrate the world / Friends / Celebrate the world (extended) (On CD single only.) / Celebrate the world (radio version) (On CD single only.) / Teardrops (On CD single only.) / Celebrate the world (people unite remix) (On Blaze remix.) / Celebrate the world (6 T's instrumental) (On Blaze remix.).
12" Single: Released 13 Feb '89, on 4th & Broadway, by Island Records. Catalogue no: **12 BRW 125**
12" Single: Released Mar '89, on 4th & Broadway, by Island Records. Catalogue no: **12 BRX 125**
CD 5": Released 13 Feb '89, on 4th & Broadway, by Island Records. Catalogue no: **BRCD 125**
7" Single: Released 13 Feb '89, on 4th & Broadway, by Island Records. Catalogue no: **BRW 125**

EYES
Tracks: / Eyes.
7" Single: Released Aug '85, on Elektra, by Elektra Records (UK). Catalogue no: **EKR 20**
12" Single: Released Aug '85, on Elektra, by Elektra Records (UK). Catalogue no: **EKR 20 T**

I AM LOVE
Tracks: / I am love / M.P.B. (Missing person's bureau) / M.P.B. (12" version) (Only on 12" version.) / M.P.B. (folk version) (Only on 12" and CD single.) / M.P.B. (motor temple) (Only on 12" and CD single.) / Celebrate the world (Only on CD single.).
12" Single: Released 28 Mar '89, on 4th & Broadway, by Island Records. Catalogue no: **12 BRW 132**
7" Single: Released 28 Mar '89, on 4th & Broadway, by Island Records. Catalogue no: **BRW 132**
CD 5": Released 11 Apr '89, on 4th & Broadway, by Island Records. Catalogue no: **BRCD 132**

LIFE'S JUST A BALLGAME
Tracks: / Life's just a ballgame / Slave (just for love).
7" Single: Released 10 Oct '88, on 4th & Broadway, by Island Records. Deleted Apr '89. Catalogue no: **BRW 116**
12" Single: Released 10 Oct '88, on 4th & Broadway, by Island Records. Deleted Apr '89. Catalogue no: **12 BRW 116**

WOMACK & WOMACK - M.P.B. (Released on 4th & Broadway)

LOVE WARS
Tracks: / Love wars / Good time.
7" Single: Released Apr '84, on Elektra, by Elektra Records (UK). Deleted '87. Catalogue no: **E 9799**
12" Single: Released Apr '84, on Elektra, by Elektra Records (UK). Catalogue no: **E 9799 T**

M.P.B.(MISSIN' PERSONS BUREAU) (see panel above)
Tracks: / M.P.B. (Missing persons bureau) / M.P.B. (original version) / M.P.B. (folk version) (Available on 12" only) / M.P.B. (12" version) (Available on 12" only) / Celebrate the world.
7" Single: Released '88, on 4th & Broadway, by Island Records. Catalogue no: **BRW 138**
CD 5": Released Jul '89, on 4th & Broadway, by Island Records. Catalogue no: **BRCD 138**
12" Single: Released Jul '89, on 4th & Broadway, by Island Records. Catalogue no: **12 BRW 138**
Cassingle: Released Jul '89, on 4th & Broadway, by Island Records. Catalogue no: **BRCA 138**

SOUL LOVE SOUL MAN
Tracks: / Soul love soul man / Soul love soul man (insrumental) / Your man's on fire.
7" Single: Released Nov '86, on EMI-Manhattan, by EMI Records. Deleted Oct '87. Catalogue no: **MT 16**
12" Single: Released Nov '86, on EMI-Manhattan, by EMI Records. Catalogue no: **12 MT 16**

STRANGE AND FUNNY
Tracks: / Strange and funny.
7" Single: Released Jun '85, on Elektra, by Elektra Records (UK). Catalogue no: **EKR 12**
12" Single: Released Jun '85, on Elektra, by Elektra Records (UK). Catalogue no: **EKR 12 T**

TEARDROPS
Tracks: / Teardrops / Concious of my conscience.
7" Single: Released Jun '88, on 4th & Broadway, by Island Records. Deleted Apr '89. Catalogue no: **BRW 101**
12" Single: Released Jun '88, on 4th & Broadway, by Island Records. Catalogue no: **12 BRW 101**
CD 5": Released Jun '88, on 4th & Broadway, by Island Records. Catalogue no: **BRCDP 101**

Woman

BELLY SLAP
Tracks: / Belly slap.
12" Single: Released Oct '88, on Wooden, by Wooden Records. Catalogue no: **WOOD 004**

Wombles

Biographical details: This British "group" were the literary and television creation of Elizabeth Beresford and the musical creation of Mike Batt. By 1974 The Wombles was established as one of the UK's most popular children's TV programmes, with kids everywhere loving their daily five-minute dose of furry creatures who possessed a curious but public-spirited fixation for picking up litter on Wimbledon Common. The series' theme song, a text-book example of a catchy, singalong pop ditty, became a huge UK hit single in early 1974: *The Wombling Song* reached no.4 and logged 23 weeks on the British chart. Its success prompted composer Batt to dress himself up as the programme's leading character, Orinoco, and to assemble a group of woolly Wombles for appearances on shows like BBC TV's Top Of The Pops. For a brief period during 1974-75 the Wombles were a substantial force on the UK charts. Their biggest hits *Remember You're A Womble* (no.3) and *Wombling Merry Christmas* (no.2) were straightforward pop singles; others, such as the calypso-flavoured *Banana Rock* and the quasi-classical *Minuetto Allegretto*, were neatly-executed pastiches of various musical styles. Batt and CBS were aware that the Womble craze would have a finite lifespan and flooded the market as quickly as possible: three LPs were issued in '74, each reaching the Top Twenty. The programme also triggered off a major Womble assault on the novelty merchandise market, with books, T-shirts, models, key rings and a host of other items hitting the shops. The Hollywood-style *Let's Womble To The Party Tonight* was a British No 34 hit at Christmas '75, but the party was over for the Wombles. Each of the non-existent group's eight hits had experienced a shorter chart run than its predecessor and the hits now dried up altogether. By that time songwriter/arranger/producer/part-time singer Mike Batt had already achieved a UK Top Five single under his real name with *Summertime City*. And during the late 70's and the 80's he achieved spasmodic success as a provider of McCartneyish ballads for other singers -- but the tweeness of this later work meant that he was never quite able to shake off the Womble tag. (Bob MacDonald, June 1985.).

BANANA ROCK
Tracks: / Banana rock.
7" Single: Released Jun '74, on CBS, by CBS Records. Deleted '77. Catalogue no: **CBS 2465**

LET'S WOMBLE TO THE PARTY TONIGHT
Tracks: / Let's womble to the party tonight.
7" Single: Released Dec '75, on CBS, by CBS Records. Deleted '78. Catalogue no: **CBS 3794**

MINUETTO ALLEGRETTO (SINGLE)
Tracks: / Minuetto allegretto.
7" Single: Released Oct '74, on CBS, by CBS Records. Deleted '77. Catalogue no: **CBS 2710**

REMEMBER YOU'RE A WOMBLE (SINGLE)
Tracks: / Remember you're a womble.
7" Single: Released Apr '74, on CBS, by CBS Records. Deleted '77. Catalogue no: **CBS 2241**

SUPER WOMBLE
Tracks: / Super womble.
7" Single: Released Aug '75, on CBS, by CBS Records. Deleted '78. Catalogue no: **CBS 3480**

WOMBLING MERRY CHRISTMAS
Tracks: / Wombling merry Christmas.
7" Single: Released Oct '74, on CBS, by CBS Records. Deleted '77. Catalogue no: **CBS 842**
7" Single: Released Dec '83, on CBS, by CBS Records. Catalogue no: **A 4084**

WOMBLING SONG, THE
Tracks: / Wombling song, The.
7" Single: Released Jan '74, on CBS, by CBS Records. Deleted '77. Catalogue no: **CBS 1794**

WOMBLING WHITE TIE AND TAILS
Tracks: / Wombling white tie and tails.
7" Single: Released May '75, on CBS, by CBS Records. Deleted '78. Catalogue no: **CBS 3266**

Women In Music

FREE AFRICA
Tracks: / Free Africa.
12" Single: Released 1 Aug '87, on I.M.W., by I.M.W. Records. Catalogue no: **IMW 1202**

Womersley, Barry

YOU'RE MY WIFE
Tracks: / You're my wife.
7" Single: Released May '83, on Da Doo Ron Ron, by Da Doo Ron Ron Records. Deleted '88. Catalogue no: **RON 001**

Won Ton Ton

I LIE AND I CHEAT
Tracks: / I lie and I cheat / Caro.
7" Single: Released Apr '88, on WEA, by WEA Records. Catalogue no: **YZ 178**
12" Single: Released Apr '88, on WEA, by WEA Records. Catalogue no: **YZ 178T**

Wonder, Jackie

TOO MUCH PRESSURE ON THE KID
Tracks: / Too much pressure on the kid.
7" Single: Released Sep '80, on Red Stripe, Catalogue no: **SON 2212**

Wonder, Mark

CAUTION
Tracks: / Caution.
12" Single: Released Jul '88, on Black Scorpio, Catalogue no: **BS 015**

Wonder, Stevie

Biographical details: This American singer, songwriter, keyboards player, harmonica player and producer was born Steveland Morris in Michigan in 1950; his father's surname was Judkins, and it was this name that Stevie used in his early school years - but his birth certificate called him Morris. He was renamed Little Stevie Wonder by Tamla Motown Records in 1962, because they were so over awed by the kid's precocious talents.
Blind from birth, Stevie gave his first professional performance at the age of nine, by which time he was already a competent player of the harmonica, pianos, bongos and drums. With his family now living in Detroit, he was granted an audition with Berry Gordy, the founder of the fast growing Motown company. Stevie's first single *I Call It Pretty Music* was released in August 1962. It was no big success, and neither were his first two albums, *Tribute To Uncle Ray* (dedicated to that other great blinds and black talent, Ray Charles) and *The Jazz Soul of Little Stevie*.
Suddenly, in August '63, Little Stevie Wonder found himself in the US No.1 slot with the dynamic and frantic *Fingertips Part 2*. This was the first live concert recording ever to top the American singles list, and was one of the greatest live tracks of all time. But the 13 year old boy genius was unable to consolidate upon this fantastic success for some while. It was not until early 1966 that he came up with his second major hit *Uptight (Everything's Alright)*. This was the real start of his sustained career - his voice had broken, the 'Little' had been dropped and the song gave him his first hit as a co-writer. It was also his debut chart entry in Britain, where it reached No.14; the single was a No.3 hit in the States. Wonder's two most famous hits of the late Sixties contrasted sharply with each other, and demonstrated his versatility: *I Was Made To Love Her* was a pulsating R&B stormer co-penned by himself; *For Once In My Life* was a cabaret song that had previously been associated with Tony Bennett. In 1971 Wonder became 21 years old and thus received a million dollars in back earnings. He also received new artistic freedom, and this immediately transformed him into an important LP artist. 1972's *Talking Book* album was a classic and yielded two brilliant US No.1 singles - the ultra-funky *Superstition* and the beautiful ballad *You Are The Sunshine of My Life*. Equally acclaimed was 1973's *Innervisions* album which coincided with a near fatal car crash - and 1874's

Fulfillingness First Finale, which produced the US No.1 single *You Haven't Done Nothin'*. Although still based in soul, Wonder's music now delved heavily into the rock genre, and appealed to an across the board audience. He was a self contained unit, writing on his own, producing on his own and playing most of the instruments himself.
1976's *Songs In The Key of Life*, a double album, yielded two more American No.1 singles, *I Wish* and *Sir Duke* (the latter being a tribute to Duke Ellington). In Britain, Wonder chalked up four No.2 singles - *Yester-me, yester-you, yesterday* (1969) *Sir Duke* (1977), *Masterblaster (Jammin')* (1980) and *Happy Birthday* (1981) - before gaining his first taste of a chart topper in 1982 - *Ebony and Ivory*, his duet with Paul McCartney, was a transatlantic No.1. Wonder finally obtained his first solo UK No.1 single with 1984's incredibly catchy *I Just Called To Say I Love You*, which held the top spot for six weeks in Britain and three weeks in America.
The Eighties saw Wonder being a less prolific artist - patience was a necessary virtue, both for Motown executives and for the general public; his work schedule was, however, dotted with numerous guest contributions to other artists' recorded. He also devoted time to various socio-political campaigns, most notably his ultimately successful 'Happy Birthday' fight for Martin Luther King to be recognised by a US national holiday. When the records did appear, they continued to be works of all round musical inspiration, perception, excitement and sheer genius. Radio One's Paul Gambaccini summed him up by saying: 'His Achievements are tremendous, not for a blind man, not for a black man, but for any man.' (Bob Macdonald June 1985).

ANOTHER STAR
Tracks: / Another star.
7" Single: Released Sep '77, on Motown, by BMG Records (UK). Deleted '80. Catalogue no: **TMG 1083**

AS
Tracks: / As.
7" Single: Released Oct '81, on Motown, by BMG Records (UK). Deleted '82. Catalogue no: **TMG 1091**

BLACK ORCHID
Tracks: / Black orchid / Blame it on the sun.
7" Single: Released Oct '81, on Motown, by BMG Records (UK). Deleted '82. Catalogue no: **TMG 1173**

BLOWIN' IN THE WIND
Tracks: / Blowin' in the wind.
7" Single: Released Aug '66, on Tamla Motown, by Motown Records (UK). Deleted '69. Catalogue no: **TMG 570**

BOOGIE ON REGGAE WOMAN
Tracks: / Boogie on reggae woman.
7" Single: Released Oct '81, on Motown, by BMG Records (UK). Catalogue no: **TMG 928**

DO I DO
Tracks: / Do I do / Rocket love.
7" Single: Released May '82, on Motown, by BMG Records (UK). Catalogue no: **TMG 1269**
7" Single: Released Apr '85, on Motown, by BMG Records (UK). Catalogue no: **TMG 1386**
12" Single: Released Apr '85, on Motown, by BMG Records (UK). Catalogue no: **TMGT 1386**

DON'T DRIVE DRUNK
Tracks: / Don't drive drunk.
7" Single: Released Dec '84, on Motown, by BMG Records (UK). Deleted '87. Catalogue no: **TMG 1372**
12" Single: Released Dec '84, on Motown, by BMG Records (UK). Deleted '87. Catalogue no: **TMGT 1372**

FINGERTIPS (Part 2)
Tracks: / Fingertips / Blowin' in the wind.
7" Single: Released Apr '88, on Motown, by BMG Records (UK). Catalogue no: **ZB 41937**

FOR ONCE IN MY LIFE (SINGLE)
Tracks: / For once in my life.
7" Single: Released Oct '81, on Motown, by BMG Records (UK). Catalogue no: **TMG 679**
7" Single: Released Apr '85, on Motown, by BMG Records (UK). Catalogue no: **TMG 989**
12" Single: Released Apr '85, on Motown, by BMG Records (UK). Catalogue no: **TMGT 989**

FREE
Tracks: / Free.
CD 5": Released May '89, on Motown, by BMG Records (UK). Catalogue no: **ZD 42856**
7" Single: Released May '89, on Motown, by BMG Records (UK). Catalogue no: **ZB 42855**
12" Single: Released May '89, on Motown, by BMG Records (UK). Catalogue no: **ZT 42856**
Cassingle: Released May '89, on Motown, by BMG Records (UK). Catalogue no: **ZK 42856**

FRONTLINE
Tracks: / Front line.
12" Single: Released Jan '83, on Motown, by BMG Records (UK). Deleted '84. Catalogue no: **TMGT 1289**
7" Single: Released Jan '83, on Motown, by BMG Records (UK). Deleted '84. Catalogue no: **TMG 1289**

GET IT
Tracks: / Get it / Get it (instrumental).
Note: Originally available on Stevie Wonder's 'Characters' album, Get it has been remixed to give a harder sound for single release.
12" Single: Released May '88, on Motown, by BMG Records (UK). Catalogue no: **ZT 41884**
7" Single: Released May '88, on Motown, by BMG Records (UK). Catalogue no: **ZB 41883**

GO HOME
Tracks: / Go home.
7" Single: Released Nov '85, on Motown, by BMG Records (UK). Deleted '87. Catalogue no: **ZB 40501**
12" Single: Released Nov '85, on Motown, by BMG Records (UK). Deleted '87. Catalogue no: **ZT 40502**

HAPPY BIRTHDAY
Tracks: / Happy birthday / Rev. Martin Luther King.
12" Single: Released Jan '84, on Motown, by BMG Records (UK). Catalogue no: **TMGT 1326**
7" Single: Released Oct '81, on Motown, by BMG Records (UK). Catalogue no: **TMG 1235**
12" Single: Released Oct '81, on Motown, by BMG Records (UK). Catalogue no: **TMGT 1235**

HEAVEN HELP US ALL
Tracks: / Heaven help us all.
7" Single: Released Nov '70, on Tamla Motown, by Motown Records (UK). Deleted '73. Catalogue no: **TMG 757**

HE'S MISSTRA KNOW IT ALL
Tracks: / He's misstra know it all.
7" Single: Released Oct '81, on Motown, by BMG Records (UK). Catalogue no: **TMG 892**
12" Single: Released Apr '85, on Motown, by BMG Records (UK). Catalogue no: **TMGT 1388**
7" Single: Released Apr '85, on Motown, by BMG Records (UK). Catalogue no: **TMG 1388**

HIGHER GROUND
Tracks: / Higher ground.
7" Single: Released Oct '73, on Tamla Motown, by Motown Records (UK). Deleted '76. Catalogue no: **TMG 869**

I AIN'T GONNA STAND FOR IT (see panel below)
Tracks: / I ain't gonna stand for it / Knocks me off my feet.
7" Single: Released Oct '81, on Motown, by BMG Records (UK). Catalogue no: **TMG 1215**
12" Single: Released Dec '80, on Motown, by BMG Records (UK). Deleted '83. Catalogue no: **12TMG 1215**

I DON'T KNOW WHY
Tracks: / I don't know why.
7" Single: Released Oct '81, on Motown, by BMG Records (UK). Catalogue no: **TMG 690**

I JUST CALLED TO SAY I LOVE YOU
Tracks: / I just called to say I love you.
12" Single: Released Aug '84, on Motown, by BMG Records (UK). Catalogue no: **TMGT 1349**
7" Single: Released Aug '84, on Motown, by BMG Records (UK). Catalogue no: **TMG 1349**

I WAS MADE TO LOVE HER (SINGLE)
Tracks: / I was made to love her / Never had a dream come true.
7" Single: Released Oct '81, on Motown, by BMG Records (UK). Catalogue no: **TMG 959**
7" Single: Released Aug '67, on Tamla Motown, by Motown Records (UK). Deleted '70. Catalogue no: **TMG 613**

I WISH
Tracks: / I wish.
7" Single: Released Apr '85, on Motown, by BMG Records (UK). Catalogue no: **TMG 1384**
7" Single: Released Oct '81, on Motown, by BMG Records (UK). Catalogue no: **TMG 1054**
12" Single: Released Apr '85, on Motown, by BMG Records (UK). Catalogue no: **TMGT 1384**

IF YOU REALLY LOVE ME
Tracks: / If you really love me.
7" Single: Released Jan '72, on Tamla Motown, by Motown Records (UK). Deleted '75. Catalogue no: **TMG 798**

I'LL BE THINKING OF YOU
Tracks: / I'll be thinking of you.
7" Single: Released Jun '81, on Light, by Word Records (UK). Catalogue no: **WS 104**

I'M WONDERING
Tracks: / I'm wondering.
7" Single: Released Oct '67, on Tamla Motown, by Motown Records (UK). Deleted '70. Catalogue no: **TMG 626**

LAND OF LA LA
Tracks: / Land of la la / Land of la la (instrumental).
12" Single: Released Jun '86, on Motown, by BMG Records (UK). Deleted '87. Catalogue no: **WONDT 1**
7" Single: Released Jun '86, on Motown, by BMG Records (UK). Deleted '87. Catalogue no: **WOND 1**

LATELY
Tracks: / Lately / If it's magic.
12" Single: Released Oct '81, on Motown, by BMG Records (UK). Deleted Oct '84. Catalogue no: **TCTMG 1226**
7" Single: Released Oct '81, on Motown, by BMG Records (UK). Catalogue no: **TMG 1226**

LIVING FOR THE CITY
Tracks: / Living for the city.
7" Single: Released Oct '81, on Motown, by BMG Records (UK). Deleted '82. Catalogue no: **TMG 881**

LOVELIGHT IN FLIGHT
Tracks: / Lovelight in flight.
12" Single: Released Nov '84, on Motown, by BMG Records (UK). Deleted '85. Catalogue no: **TMGT 1364**
7" Single: Released Nov '84, on Motown, by BMG Records (UK). Deleted '85. Catalogue no: **TMG 1364**

MASTERBLASTER
Tracks: / Masterblaster.
7" Single: Released Oct '81, on Motown, by BMG Records (UK). Catalogue no: **TMG 1204**

MY CHERIE AMOUR (SINGLE)
Tracks: / My Cherie amour.
7" Single: Released Jul '69, on Tamla Motown, by Motown Records (UK). Deleted '72. Catalogue no: **TMG 690**

MY EYES DON'T CRY Timmy Regisford Remixes
Tracks: / My eyes don't cry / My eyes don't cry (extended version) (Only on CD single.) / My eyes don't cry (radio edit) (Only on CD single.) / My eyes don't cry (dub mix) / My eyes don't cry (instrumental).
7" Single: Released Oct '88, on Motown, by BMG Records (UK). Catalogue no: **ZB 42259**
CD 5": Released Oct '88, on Motown, by BMG Records (UK). Catalogue no: **ZD 42260**
12" Single: Released Oct '88, on Motown, by BMG Records (UK). Catalogue no: **12 ZT 42260**

NEVER HAD A DREAM COME TRUE (SINGLE)
Tracks: / Never had a dream come true / Signed, sealed, delivered, I'm yours.
7" Single: Released Mar '70, on Tamla Motown, by Motown Records (UK). Deleted '73. Catalogue no: **TMG 731**
7" Single: Released Apr '88, on Motown, by BMG Records (UK). Catalogue no: **ZB 41939**

OUTSIDE MY WINDOW
Tracks: / Outside my window / Same old story.
7" Single: Released Mar '80, on Motown, by BMG Records (UK). Deleted '83. Catalogue no: **TMG 1179**

OVERJOYED
Tracks: / Overjoyed.
12" Single: Released Feb '86, on Motown, by BMG Records (UK). Catalogue no: **ZT 40568**
7" Single: Released Feb '86, on Motown, by BMG Records (UK). Catalogue no: **ZB 40567**

PART-TIME LOVER
Tracks: / Part-time lover.
12" Single: Released Sep '85, on Motown, by BMG Records (UK). Deleted '87. Catalogue no: **ZT 40352**
7" Single: Released Sep '85, on Motown, by BMG Records (UK). Catalogue no: **ZB 40351**

PLACE IN THE SUN, A
Tracks: / Place in the sun, A.
7" Single: Released Jan '67, on Tamla Motown, by Motown Records (UK). Deleted '70. Catalogue no: **TMG 588**

RIBBON IN THE SKY
Tracks: / Ribbon in the sky.
12" Single: Released Sep '82, on Motown, by BMG Records (UK). Deleted '83. Catalogue no: **TMGT 1280**
7" Single: Released Sep '82, on Motown, by BMG Records (UK). Deleted '83. Catalogue no: **TMG 1280**

SEND ONE YOUR LOVE
Tracks: / Send one your love.
7" Single: Released Oct '81, on Motown, by BMG Records (UK). Deleted '82. Catalogue no: **TMG 1149**

SHOO BE DOO BE DOO DA DAY
Tracks: / Shoo-be-doo-be-doo-da-day.
7" Single: Released May '68, on Tamla Motown, by Motown Records (UK). Deleted Aug '71. Catalogue no: **TMG 653**

SIGNED, SEALED, DELIVERED, I'M YOURS (SINGLE)
Tracks: / Signed, sealed, delivered, I'm yours / Fingertips.
7" Single: Released Jul '70, on Tamla Motown, by Motown Records (UK). Deleted '73. Catalogue no: **TMG 744**
7" Single: Released Oct '81, on Motown, by BMG Records (UK). Deleted '83. Catalogue no: **TMG 966**

SIR DUKE
Tracks: / Sir Duke.
7" Single: Released Oct '81, on Motown, by BMG Records (UK). Catalogue no: **TMG 1068**

SKELETONS
Tracks: / Skeletons.

STEVIE WONDER - I AIN'T GONNA STAND FOR IT (Released on Motown)

7" Single: Released Oct '87, on Motown, by BMG Records (UK). Catalogue no: **ZB 41439**
12" Single: Released Oct '87, on Motown, by BMG Records (UK). Catalogue no: **ZHT 41440**

STEVIE WONDER
Cassingle: Released May '83, on Motown, by BMG Records (UK). Catalogue no: **CTME 2022**

STRANGER ON THE SHORE OF LOVE
Tracks: / Did I hear you say you love me.
7" Single: Released Jan '87, on Motown, by BMG Records (UK). Deleted '87. Catalogue no: **WOND 2**
12" Single: Released Jan '87, on Motown, by BMG Records (UK). Deleted '87. Catalogue no: **WONDT 2**

SUPERSTITION
Tracks: / Superstition / You've got it bad girl.
7" Single: Released Mar '83, on Motown, by BMG Records (UK). Catalogue no: **TMG 841**

THAT GIRL
Tracks: / That girl / All I do.
7" Single: Released Jan '82, on Motown, by BMG Records (UK). Deleted '83. Catalogue no: **TMG 1254**

UPTIGHT (SINGLE)
Tracks: / Uptight.
CD 5": Released Jun '89, on Motown, by BMG Records (UK). Catalogue no: **ZD 41959**
7" Single: Released Feb '66, on Tamla Motown, by Motown Records (UK). Deleted '69. Catalogue no: **TMG 545**

USED TO BE
Tracks: / Used to be.
7" Single: Released Nov '82, on Motown, by BMG Records (UK). Deleted '83. Catalogue no: **TMG 1287**

WE CAN WORK IT OUT
Tracks: / We can work it out.
7" Single: Released May '71, on Tamla Motown, by Motown Records (UK). Deleted '74. Catalogue no: **TMG 772**

WITH EACH BEAT OF MY HEART
Tracks: / With each beat of my heart.
7" Single: Released Mar '89, on Motown, by BMG Records (UK). Catalogue no: **MOT 4626**

YESTER-ME, YESTER-YOU, YESTERDAY
Tracks: / Yester-me, yester-you, yesterday.
7" Single: Released Nov '69, on Tamla Motown, by Motown Records (UK). Deleted '72. Catalogue no: **TMG 717**
7" Single: Released Oct '81, on Motown, by BMG Records (UK). Catalogue no: **TMG 1042**

YOU ARE THE SUNSHINE OF MY LIFE
Tracks: / You are the sunshine of my life.
7" Single: Released Oct '81, on Motown, by BMG Records (UK). Catalogue no: **TMG 852**

YOU HAVEN'T DONE NOTHIN'
Tracks: / You haven't done nothin'.
7" Single: Released Oct '74, on Tamla Motown, by Motown Records (UK). Deleted '77. Catalogue no: **TMG 921**

YOU WILL KNOW
Tracks: / You will know / You will know (inst).
12" Single: Released Jan '88, on Motown, by BMG Records (UK). Catalogue no: **ZT 41724**
CD 5": Released Jan '88, on Motown, by BMG Records (UK). Catalogue no: **ZD 41724**
7" Single: Released Jan '88, on Motown, by BMG Records (UK). Catalogue no: **ZB 41723**

Wonder Stuff

DON'T LET ME DOWN, GENTLY
Tracks: / Don't let me down, gently.
7" Single: Released Sep '89, on Polydor, by Polydor Ltd. Catalogue no: **GONE 7**
CD 5": Released Sep '89, on Polydor, by Polydor Ltd. Catalogue no: **GONCD 7**
Cassingle: Released Sep '89, on Polydor, by Polydor Ltd. Catalogue no: **GONCS 7**
12" Single: Released Sep '89, on Polydor, by Polydor Ltd. Catalogue no: **GONEX 7**

GIVE GIVE GIVE ME MORE MORE MORE
Tracks: / Give give give me more more more / Song without an end / Meaner than mean (on 12" only) / See the free world (on 12" only).
7" Single: Released 18 Apr '88, on Polydor, by Polydor Ltd. Deleted 30 May '89. Catalogue no: **GONE 3**
12" Single: Released 18 Apr '88, on Polydor, by Polydor Ltd. Catalogue no: **GONEX 3**

IT'S YER MONEY I'M AFTER BABY
Tracks: / It's yer money I'm after baby / Astley in the noose / Ooh, she said / Rave from the grave.
12" Single: Released 16 Sep '88, on Polydor, by Polydor Ltd. Catalogue no: **GONX 5**
7" EP: Released 16 Sep '88, on Polydor, by Polydor Ltd. Deleted 30 Jun '89. Catalogue no: **GONE 5**
CD 5": Released 16 Sep '88, on Polydor, by Polydor Ltd. Catalogue no: **GONCD 5**

UNBEARABLE
Tracks: / Ten trenches deep / I am a monster (Available on 12" only.) / Frank (Available on 12" only.).
12" Single: Released Aug '87, on The Far Out Recording Company, Catalogue no: **GO BIG 002**
7" Single: Released Aug '87, on The Far Out Recording Company, Catalogue no: **GONE 002**

WHO WANTS TO BE THE DISCO KING?
Tracks: / Who wants to be the disco king?.
CD 5": Released Feb '89, on Polydor, by Polydor Ltd. Catalogue no: **GONCD 6**
12" Single: Released Feb '89, on Polydor, by Polydor Ltd. Catalogue no: **GONEX 6**
7" Single: Released Feb '89, on Polydor, by Polydor Ltd. Catalogue no: **GONE 6**

WISH AWAY, A
Tracks: / Wish away, A / Jealousy / Happy ... sad (Available on 12" and CD single only.) / Goodbye fatman (only on 12" and CD 5").
CD 5": Released 4 Jul '88, on Polydor, by Polydor Ltd. Catalogue no: **GONCD 4**
12" Single: Released 4 Jul '88, on Polydor, by Polydor Ltd. Catalogue no: **GONEX 4**
7" Single: Released 4 Jul '88, on Polydor, by Polydor Ltd. Catalogue no: **GONE 4**

WONDERFUL DAY, A
Tracks: / Down here / It's not true... / Like a merry go round.
7" Single: Released Feb '87, on Far Out Recording Company, by Far Out Recording Company. Catalogue no: **GONE ONE**

Wonder, Wayne

ANYTING FOR YOU
Tracks: / Anyting for you.
7" Single: Released May '89, on Sonic Sounds, Catalogue no: **UNKNOWN**

FAST CAR
Tracks: / Fast car.
12" Single: Released 24 Jul '89, on Penthouse, by Penthouse Records. Catalogue no: **PH 12**

NEW WAY TO SAY I LOVE YOU
Tracks: / New way to say I love you.
7" Single: Released Jan '89, on Pickout, Catalogue no: **PICK 24**

NIGHT AND DAY
Tracks: / Night and day.
12" Single: Released Sep '89, on Jetstar, by Jetstar Records. Catalogue no: **SJT 02**

SWEETEST GIRL
Tracks: / Sweetest girl.
12" Single: Released Oct '89, on Penthouse, by Penthouse Records. Catalogue no: **PH 014**

Wonderdog

Biographical details: This British "vocalist" barked its way to No 31 on the UK chart in 1982 with the single *Ruff Mix*. This was one of the most belated "answer" records in pop history: America's Singing Dogs hit the charts way back in 1955 and it took 27 years for British patriotism to rise to the challenge and make its contribution to this vital musical genre. Ruff Mix featured barking noises accompanied by an uptempo dance track, but truth to tell Wonderdog's record was a tribute to the wonders of modern technology rather than the skills of a dog trainer. The sound-simulation technique continued at the end of '82 with *Baa Baa Black Sheep*, a UK No 42 single credited to the Singing Sheep. But, tragically, there was no further chart success for the hitmaking sound -- Wonderdog's follow-up single, *Christmas Tail*, was a case of barking up the wrong tree. (Bob MacDonald, June 1985.)

CHRISTMAS TAIL
Tracks: / Christmas tail.
7" Single: Released Dec '83, on ERC, Catalogue no: **ERC 104**
12" Single: Released Dec '83, on ERC, Catalogue no: **ERCL 104**

RUFF MIX
Tracks: / Ruff mix.
7" Single: Released Aug '82, on Flip, Catalogue no: **FLIP 001**

Wonders

THIS HEART OF MINE
Tracks: / This heart of mine.
7" Single: Released May '83, on Creole, by Creole Records. Catalogue no: **CR 54**

Wong, Carta

DON'T MATTER THEM
Tracks: / Don't matter them.
12" Single: Released Jul '88, on Blue Trac, by Blue Trac Records. Catalogue no: **BTRD 023**

Wood, Brenton

GIMME LITTLE SIGN
Tracks: / Gimme little sign.
7" Single: Released Dec '67, on Liberty, by EMI Records. Deleted '70. Catalogue no: **LBF 15021**

Wood Children

GLOBAL VILLAGE IDIOT
Tracks: / Global village idiot.
12" Single: Released May '89, on Demon, by Demon Records. Catalogue no: **WOODEP 1**

HAPPENS EVERYDAY
Tracks: / Happens everyday.
12" Single: Released Apr '88, on Cat & Mouse, by Cat & Mouse Records. Catalogue no: **ABB 05 T**
7" Single: Released Apr '88, on Cat & Mouse, by Cat & Mouse Records. Catalogue no: **ABB 05**

Wood, Douglas Group

DRAG RACER
Tracks: / Drag racer / Skorpion / To the unknown man / Black and white rag.
7" Single: Released Apr '84, on BBC, by BBC Records & Tapes. Deleted '87. Catalogue no: **RESL 144**

Wood, May

LATE AT NIGHT
Tracks: / Late at night / One, two, three.
7" Single: Released Oct '80, on Logo, by Logo Records. Deleted Oct '83. Catalogue no: **GO 390**

Wood, Orville

DON'T STAY AWAY
Tracks: / Don't stay away.
12" Single: Released May '85, on Diamond C, Catalogue no: **DCDS 1010**

Wood, Roy

1.2.3. (SINGLE)
Tracks: / 1.2.3. / O what a shame.
7" Single: Released Jul '87, on Jet, by Jet Records. Catalogue no: **JET 7048**
12" Single: Released Jul '87, on Jet, by Jet Records. Catalogue no: **JET 12048**

DEAR ELAINE
Tracks: / Dear Elaine.
7" Single: Released Aug '73, on Harvest (1), by EMI Records. Deleted '76. Catalogue no: **HAR 5074**

FOREVER
Tracks: / Forever.
7" Single: Released Dec '73, on Harvest (1), by EMI Records. Deleted '76. Catalogue no: **HAR 5078**

GIVIN' YOUR HEART AWAY
Tracks: / Givin' your heart away / Rock city.
7" Single: Released Oct '80, on Cheapskate, Deleted Oct '83. Catalogue no: **CHEAP 6**

GOING DOWN THE ROAD
Tracks: / Going down the road.
7" Single: Released Jun '74, on Harvest (1), by EMI Records. Deleted '77. Catalogue no: **HAR 5083**

GREEN GLASS WINDOWS
Tracks: / Green glass windows / Driving song.
7" Single: Released Mar '81, on EMI, by EMI Records. Deleted Mar '84. Catalogue no: **EMI 5156**

IT'S NOT EASY
Tracks: / It's not easy / Moonriser.
7" Single: Released Jan '82, on EMI, by EMI Records. Deleted Jan '85. Catalogue no: **EMI 5261**

OH WHAT A SHAME
Tracks: / Oh what a shame.
7" Single: Released May '75, on Jet, by Jet Records. Deleted '78. Catalogue no: **JET 754**

RAINING IN THE CITY
Tracks: / Raining in the city / Raining in the city (Instrumental version).
7" Single: Released Oct '86, on Legacy, by Legacy Records. Catalogue no: **LGY 53**

SING OUT THE OLD..BRING IN THE NEW
Tracks: / Sing out the old..bring in the new / Watch this space.
12" Single: Released Nov '85, on Legacy, by Legacy Records. Catalogue no: **LGYT 32**
7" Single: Released Dec '80, on Cheapskate, Deleted Dec '85. Catalogue no: **CHEAP 12**
7" Single: Released Nov '85, on Legacy, by Legacy Records. Catalogue no: **LGY 32**

UNDER FIRE
Tracks: / Under fire.
7" Single: Released May '85, on Legacy, by Legacy Records. Catalogue no: **LGY 24**
12" Single: Released May '85, on Legacy, by Legacy Records. Catalogue no: **LGYT 24**

Wood, Victoria

RETURN TO OZ
Tracks: / Return to Oz.
7" Single: Released Jul '85, on Cherry Lane, by Cherry Lane Productions. Deleted '86. Catalogue no: **PIP 703**

Woodbine Lizzie

THEY DON'T WRITE 'EM LIKE THAT ANYMORE
Tracks: / They don't write 'em like that any more.
7" Single: Released Feb '80, on Fellside, by Fellside Records. Catalogue no: **FES 402**

Woodcraft, Ray

LOVELY LADY SMILE
Tracks: / Lovely lady smile / Everybody's somebody's fool.
7" Single: Released Jan '81, on SRT, by SRT Records. Catalogue no: **SRTS 80430**

Woodentops

EVERYDAY LIVING
Tracks: / Everyday living.
7" Single: Released Oct '86, on Rough Trade, by Rough Trade Records. Deleted '89. Catalogue no: **RT 178**

GOOD THING
Tracks: / Good thing / Travelling man.
7" Single: Released May '86, on Rough Trade, by Rough Trade Records. Catalogue no: **RT 177**
12" Single: Released May '86, on Rough Trade, by Rough Trade Records. Catalogue no: **RTT 177**

IT WILL COME
Tracks: / It will come.
12" Single: Released Nov '85, on Rough Trade, by Rough Trade Records. Catalogue no: **RTT 169**
7" Single: Released Nov '85, on Rough Trade, by Rough Trade Records. Catalogue no: **RT 169**

LOVE AFFAIR WITH EVERYDAY LIVING
Tracks: / Love affair with everyday living / So good today.
7" Single: Released Sep '86, on Rough Trade, by Rough Trade Records. Catalogue no: **RT 178**
12" Single: Released Sep '86, on Rough Trade, by Rough Trade Records. Catalogue no: **RTT 178**

MOVE ME
Tracks: / Move me.
7" Single: Released Apr '85, on Rough Trade, by Rough Trade Records. Catalogue no: **RT 165**
12" Single: Released Apr '85, on Rough Trade, by Rough Trade Records. Catalogue no: **RTT 165**

PLENTY
Tracks: / Plenty.
7" Single: Released Jul '84, on Food, by Food Records. Catalogue no: **FOOD 2**
12" Single: Released Jul '84, on Food, by Food Records. Catalogue no: **SNAK 2**

WELL WELL WELL
Tracks: / Well well well.
7" Single: Released Aug '85, on Rough Trade, by Rough Trade Records. Catalogue no: **RT 167**
12" Single: Released Aug '85, on Rough Trade, by Rough Trade Records. Catalogue no: **RTT 167**

WHITE WHAT
Tracks: / White what.
7" Single: Released Aug '83, on Button, by Musical Characters Records. Catalogue no: **BTN 108**

YOU MAKE ME FEEL
Tracks: / You make me feel / Stop this car.
7" Single: Released Jan '88, on Rough Trade, by Rough Trade Records. Catalogue no: **RT 179**
12" Single: Released Jan '88, on Rough Trade, by Rough Trade Records. Catalogue no: **RTT 179**

Woodham Ley...

ENGLAND ARE ON THEIR WAY
Tracks: / England are on their way.
7" Single: Released Apr '82, on Kick, Catalogue no: **KICK 1 IN**

Woodhead Monroe

IDENTIFY
Tracks: / Identify / Good life.
7" Single: Released Mar '82, on Oval, by Oval Records. Catalogue no: **LOT 2**

MUMBO JUMBO
Tracks: / Mumbo jumbo.

7" Single: Released May '82, on Oval, by Oval Records. Catalogue no: **LOT 3**

SHE'S A VAMPIRE
Tracks: / She's a vampire.
7" Single: Released Sep '80, on Oval, by Oval Records. Catalogue no: **WOOD 17**

Woodhouse, George

STAR
Tracks: / Star / Little lady.
12" Single: Released Mar '85, on Mile Stone, Catalogue no: **MOO 2**

Woodroffe, Jezz

PEACE IN OUR SPACE
Tracks: / Peace in our space / Marathon runner.
7" Single: on Graduate, by Graduate Records. Deleted Jan '87. Catalogue no: **GRAD 9**

Woodruff, Stanley

WHAT TOOK YOU SO LONG
Tracks: / What took you so long.
7" Single: Released Dec '79, on Grapevine (Northern Soul), by BMG Records (UK). Catalogue no: **GRP 102**

Woods

BATTLESHIP CHAINS
Tracks: / Battleship chains / Sometimes.
7" Single: Released Apr '87, on Demon, by Demon Records. Catalogue no: **D 1048**

MIRACLES TONIGHT
Tracks: / Miracles tonight.
7" Single: Released '88, on Justine, Catalogue no: **JUS 3**

Woods, Gay

SOMETHING'S GOTTEN HOLD OF MY HEART
Tracks: / Something's gotten hold of my heart.
7" Single: Released Jun '84, on Rewind, Catalogue no: **REW 18**

Woods, Pat

BUNCH OF THYME
Tracks: / Bunch of thyme / London lights / When the hammer strikes the anvil.
7" Single: Released Sep '81, on Homespun (Ireland), by Outlet Records. Catalogue no: **HIS 31**

CROCE-DI-ORO
Tracks: / Croce di oro (cross of gold) / In the corner of my prison cell.
7" Single: Released Apr '87, on Homespun (Ireland), by Outlet Records. Catalogue no: **HS 116**

GALWAY BAY
Tracks: / Galway bay.
7" Single: Released Feb '83, on Homespun (Ireland), by Outlet Records. Catalogue no: **HS 061**

GREEN FIELDS OF FRANCE
Tracks: / Green fields of France.
7" Single: Released Sep '82, on Homespun (Ireland), by Outlet Records. Catalogue no: **HIS 33**

MY OWN NATIVE LAND
Tracks: / My own native land.
7" Single: Released Nov '84, on Homespun (Ireland), by Outlet Records. Catalogue no: **HS 088**

RATHLIN ISLAND
Tracks: / Rathlin Island / Fields of Athenry.
7" Single: Released Mar '84, on Homespun (Ireland), by Outlet Records. Catalogue no: **HS 073**

Woods, Terry

TENNESSEE STUD
Tracks: / Tennessee stud / I don't know about love.
7" Single: Released Mar '81, on Chiswick Records, Deleted Mar '84. Catalogue no: **CHIS 142**

Woodward Brothers

YOU SET ME UP
Tracks: / You set me up / Physical attraction / You set me up (dub version).
12" Single: Released Oct '86, on Debut, by Skratch Records. Catalogue no: **DEBTX 3010**

Woodward, Edward

Biographical details: Famous British actor Woodward enjoyed just one chart single. The standard *The Way You Look Tonight* reached the UK No 42 position in January 1971. Although this great song had been an American Top Twenty hit for the Lettermen in 1961, its British track record was less impressive: the '61 disc could only manage No 36, a '64 reworking by Denny Seyton & The Sabres peaked at No 48 and Woodward's pedestrian, easy-listening version found its peak position exactly halfway between its predecessors. He chalked up two chart albums in Britain. *This Man Alone* got to No 53 in 1970 and *The Edward Woodward album* reached No 20 in 1972, logging 10 weeks on the Top 50. (Bob MacDonald, June 1985.).

SOLDIERS OF THE QUEEN
Tracks: / Soldiers of the queen / At last.
7" Single: Released Oct '80, on RK, by RK Records. Deleted Oct '83. Catalogue no: **RK 1031**

WAY YOU LOOK TONIGHT, THE
Tracks: / Way you look tonight.
7" Single: Released Jan '71, on DJM, Deleted '74. Catalogue no: **DJS 232**

Woody, Don

BARKING UP THE WRONG TREE
Tracks: / Barking up the wrong tree.
7" Single: Released '80, on MCA, by MCA Records. Catalogue no: **LR 4127**

Wooley, Sheb

Biographical details: Wooley, Sheb was born in 1921 in Oklahoma. The country singer, songwriter and actor recorded for Bullet in Nashville, guested on radio shows; he landed a radio show in Fort Worth, Texas advertising Calument Baking Powder in 1946, singing, writing the adverts and creating character the Chief from company's logo. To West Coast late'40s, studied acting, signed with MGM; began writing parodies of hits: *When Mexican Joe Met Jolie Blon* was hit for Hank Snow in 1953. He played in more than 40 films, best known role in High Noon in 1952 as the baddie trying to gun down Gary Cooper; working on the set of 'Giant' he wrote *Are You Satisfied?* and had a minor hit in 1955 but the cover by Rusty Draper was bigger. He wrote and recorded novelty *The Purple People Eater*, a number one USA pop hit for six weeks in 1958. *That's My Pa* in 1962 made the pop chart but was a number one country hit; he had sporadic hits in that chart for the rest of the decade. Acted in TV shows including Rawhide with Clint Eastwood for five years; as Ben Colder he made LPs and singles of parodies such as *Detroit City No.2, Almost Persuaded No.2, Harper Valley P.T.A. (Later That Same Day)*; he was named comic of the year by the CMA in 1968. Seen on every major country TV show and still entertaining in the '80s. (Donald Clarke 21/5/88).

PURPLE PEOPLE EATER
Tracks: / Purple people eater.
7" Single: Released Jun '58, on MGM, by Polydor Ltd. Deleted '61. Catalogue no: **MGM 981**

Woolf, Jai Dean

SHANGRI-LA
Tracks: / Shangri-la / Shangri-la (tropical instrumental mix).
7" Single: Released May '86, on EMI, by EMI Records. Catalogue no: **EMI 5554**
12" Single: Released May '86, on EMI, by EMI Records. Catalogue no: **12EMI 5554**

SWEET MISS AMERICA
Tracks: / Sweet Miss America / Sweet Miss America (Instrumental version) / Sweet thing (on 12" version only.).
7" Single: Released Aug '86, on Parlophone, by EMI Records. Catalogue no: **R 6135**
12" Single: Released Aug '86, on Parlophone, by EMI Records. Catalogue no: **12R 6135**
7" Single: Released Aug '85, on EMI, by EMI Records. Catalogue no: **EMI 5529**

Woolfe, Rita

BEAUTIFUL LAUNDERETTE
Tracks: / Beautiful launderette / Beautiful launderette (dangerous mix) / Take one look (Track on 12" version only).
12" Single: Released May '86, on Stiff, by Stiff Records. Catalogue no: **BUYIT 249**
7" Single: Released May '86, on Stiff, by Stiff Records. Catalogue no: **BUY 249**

Woolley, Bruce

BLUE BLUE
Tracks: / Blue blue / One thousand M.P.H..
7" Single: Released Feb '81, on CBS, by CBS Records. Deleted '84. Catalogue no: **CBS 9453**

GHOST TRAIN
Tracks: / Ghost train.
7" Single: Released Jun '81, on CBS, by CBS Records. Deleted Jun '84. Catalogue no: **A 1234**

TROUBLE IS
Tracks: / Trouble is / Get away William.
7" Single: Released Mar '80, on CBS, by CBS Records. Deleted Mar '83. Catalogue no: **CBS 8314**

Woolley, Shep

I WANT TO BE A SKINHEAD LIKE DAD
Tracks: / I want to be a skinhead like dad.
7" Single: Released May '78, on Sweet Folk & Country, Catalogue no: **SFC 1003**

Woolly Rhino & Friends

WOOLLY RHINO AND FRIENDS
Tracks: / Woolly Rhino and friends.
7" Single: Released Nov '76, on Denmark, Catalogue no: **DN 500**

Woosh, Jah

IN LOVE WITH YOU
Tracks: / In love with you / Dub with you.
12" Single: Released Apr '85, on Sweetcorn, Catalogue no: **SW 006**

Wop Bop Torledo

BEAT BOMB
Tracks: / Beat bomb (part 1) / Beat bomb (radio dub) (Only on 12" and cassette single.) / Beat bomb (drop the beat) (12" mix) (Only on 12" and CD single.) / Beat bomb (12" dub) (Only on 12" and CD single.).
CD 5": Released Aug '89, on 10 Records, by Virgin Records. Catalogue no: **TENCD 276**
7" Single: Released Aug '89, on 10 Records, by Virgin Records. Catalogue no: **TEN 276**
12" Single: Released Aug '89, on 10 Records, by Virgin Records. Catalogue no: **TENX 276**
Cassingle: Released Aug '89, on 10 Records, by Virgin Records. Catalogue no: **TENC 276**

Worcester Cathedral

WORCESTER CATHEDRAL CHOIR
Tracks: / I was glad / How lovely are Thy dwellings / Locus iste / Ave Verum Corpus (Mozart) / God so loved the world / Blessed be the God and Father.
Note: Worcester Cathedral Choir, director Donald Hunt, organ Adrian Partington.
12" Single: Released '85, on Alpha, by Abbey Recording Co.Ltd.. Catalogue no: **XPS 105**

Word

COLOUR IT
Tracks: / Colour it.
7" Single: Released Nov '83, on Menace Music, Catalogue no: **WORD 001**

KISS THE GROUND (see panel below)
Tracks: / Kiss the ground / Kangaroo / And the clock goes (Only on 12".).
Note: For further information: Mother Records, 30/32 Sir John Rogersons Quay, Dublin 2, Ireland.
7" Single: Released Jun '89, on Mother, by Mother Records. Catalogue no: **MUM 12**
12" Single: Released Jun '89, on Mother, by Mother Records. Catalogue no: **12 MUM 12**

NEXT BIG THING, THE
Tracks: / Next big thing, The.
12" Single: Released Nov '84, on Menace Music, Catalogue no: **WORD 022**

SCHOOLBOY SAINT
Tracks: / Schoolboy saint / World to the girls.
7" Single: Released Jun '86, on Abstract, by Abstract Sounds. Catalogue no: **AD 7**

WIDE AWAKE
Tracks: / Wide awake.
12" Single: Released Jun '85, on Abstract, by Abstract Sounds. Catalogue no: **12 ABS 031**

Word Of Mouth

COAST TO COAST featuring D.J. Cheese
Tracks: / Coast to coast / Coast to coast (dub instrumental version) / Coast to coast (bonus beats).
7" Single: Released Aug '86, on Champion, by Champion Records. Deleted Jul '89. Catalogue no: **CHAMP 17**
12" Single: Released Aug '86, on Champion, by Champion Records. Catalogue no: **CHAMP 1217**

HEARTBEAT HEARTBREAK
Tracks: / Heartbeat heartbreak.
12" Single: Released Jun '84, on Challenge, by Elite Records. Catalogue no: **CHAPT 1**
7" Single: Released Jun '84, on Challenge, by Elite Records. Catalogue no: **CHAP 1**

THAT'S THE WAY GOD PLANNED IT
Tracks: / That's the way God planned it (extended) / That's the way God planned it (instrumental).
7" Single: Released Apr '87, on Columbia, by EMI Records. Deleted Oct '87. Catalogue no: **DB 9144**
12" Single: Released Nov '86, on Columbia, by EMI Records. Deleted Oct '87. Catalogue no: **12DB 9144**

Workforce

BACK IN THE GOOD BOOKS
Tracks: / Back in the good books.
7" Single: Released Feb '86, on Rorschach Testing, by Rorschach Testing Records. Catalogue no: **7ROR 5**
12" Single: Released Feb '86, on Rorschach Testing, by Rorschach Testing Records. Catalogue no: **12ROR 5**

SKIN SCRAPED BACK
Tracks: / Skin scraped back.
12" Single: Released Jun '85, on Double Vision, by Double Vision Records. Catalogue no: **DVR 13**

Working Class

GOTTA GO GO
Tracks: / Gotta go-go / Your love is mine.
7" Single: Released Mar '86, on President, by President Records. Catalogue no: **PT 541**
12" Single: Released Mar '86, on President, by President Records. Catalogue no: **PT 12-541**

I'M GOING NOWHERE
Tracks: / I'm going nowhere / Love everything about you.
7" Single: Released Oct '86, on President, by President Records. Catalogue no: **PT 550**

Working Girls

PRINCESS
Tracks: / Princess / Princess (dub mix).
7" Single: Released Sep '87, on President, by President Records. Catalogue no: **PT 552**
12" Single: Released Sep '87, on President,

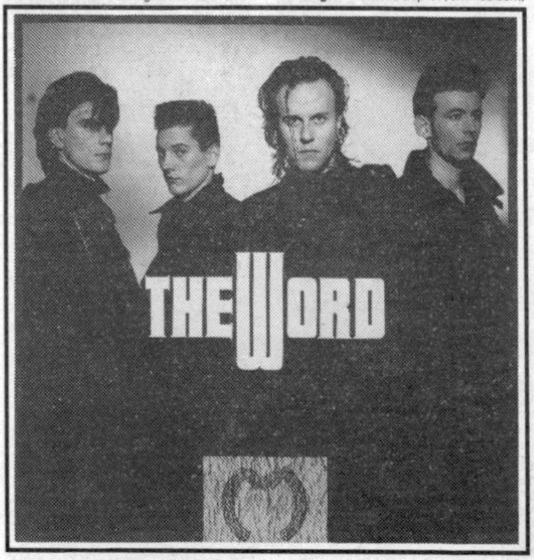

WORD - KISS THE GROUND (Released on Mother)

by President Records. Catalogue no: **PT 12-552**

TALK
Tracks: / Talk.
12" Single: Released Sep '89, on B-Ware, by B/Ware Records. Catalogue no: **UM 12009**
7" Single: Released Sep '89, on B-Ware, by B/Ware Records. Catalogue no: **UM 009**

Working Week
Biographical details: Working Week is a soul jazz dance band, with the excellent vocalist Julie Roberts (born in 1962) guitarist Simon Booth (born 1956),Larry Stabbins (born 1949) on soprano and tenor saxes, flute; augmented with percussion, lots of horns etc. The search for the jazz roots of disco resulted from boredom with soundalike mid-'80s pop. Booth worked at Mole Jazz, the London shop/label, formed a band called Weekend: single *The View From Her Room* had pastel shades and the group evolved into hard blowing percussion based dance band with Stabbins, who had played in '60s sould bands, worked with Keith Tippett. It broke up in 1983 after two LPs on Rough Trade; the new band was formed in response to dancing scene at Electric Ballroom. Debut single was Latin-based *Venceremos*, political tribute to Chilean people, sung by vocal trio Robert Wyatt, Tracey Thorn, Claudia Figueroa; second single *Storm of Light* featured Mike Carr on organ and the voice of Julie Tippett (Keith's wife, born Driscoll, used to sing with Brian Auger). Booth and Stabbins wanted a band to play their songs, recruited big voiced Roberts, who has also appeared on stage with Courtney Pine's Jazz Warriors. Album *Working Nights* in 1985 was produced by Robin Millar *Everything But The Girl, Sade*, included all Booth Stabbins tunes except a Marvin Gaye cover; good featues included a trombone solo by Annie Whitehead on instrumental *No Cure, No Pay*. LP parcel also includes fourth single *Stella Marina*, with Tippett, rap by Jalal of The Last Poets (Donald Clarke 21 May 1988).

DON'T TOUCH MY FRIEND
Tracks: / Don't touch my friend / Walk the tight rope.
7" Single: Released Oct '86, on Virgin, by Virgin Records. Deleted May '88. Catalogue no: **VS 902**
12" Single: Released Oct '86, on Virgin, by Virgin Records. Deleted May '88. Catalogue no: **VS 902-12**

ELDORADO
Tracks: / Eldorado (7" ortega mix) (Only on 7" and CD single.) / This time (dub) / Eldorado (ortega mix) (Only on 12" and CD single) / Eldorado (paradise mix) (Only on 12" single).
7" Single: Released 26 Jun '89, on 10 Records, by Virgin Records. Catalogue no: **TEN 279**
12" Single: Released 26 Jun '89, on 10 Records, by Virgin Records. Catalogue no: **TENX 279**
CD 3": Released 26 Jun '89, on 10 Records, by Virgin Records. Catalogue no: **TENCD 279**

I THOUGHT I'D NEVER SEE YOU AGAIN
Tracks: / I thought I'd never see you again.
12" Single: Released Aug '85, on Virgin, by Virgin Records. Deleted May '88. Catalogue no: **VS 807-12**

KNOCKING ON YOUR DOOR
Tracks: / Knocking on your door / It's only love / Red eye (12" only).
Note: Working Week with Lew Kirton
7" Single: Released Mar '88, on Virgin, by Virgin Records. Catalogue no: **VS 1060**
12" Single: Released Mar '88, on Virgin, by Virgin Records. Catalogue no: **VST 1060**

LARGO
Tracks: / Largo (Remix on 12") / Gravy / Watusi (12" only).
7" Single: Released Oct '87, on Virgin, by Virgin Records. Deleted May '88. Catalogue no: **VS 1024**
12" Single: Released Oct '87, on Virgin, by Virgin Records. Catalogue no: **VST 1024**

RODERIGO BAY
Tracks: / Roderigo Bay / Boogaloo.
7" Single: Released '86, on Virgin, by Virgin Records. Deleted May '86. Catalogue no: **VS 862**
12" Single: Released May '86, on Virgin, by Virgin Records. Deleted May '88. Catalogue no: **VS 862-12**

SURRENDER (SINGLE)
Tracks: / Surrender / Apocalypse.
7" Single: Released Sep '87, on Virgin, by Virgin Records. Deleted May '88. Catalogue no: **VS 998**
12" Single: Released Sep '87, on Virgin, by Virgin Records. Deleted May '88. Catalogue no: **VS 998-12**

SWEET NOTHING
Tracks: / Sweet nothing / Who's feeling who.
7" Single: Released May '85, on Virgin, by Virgin Records. Deleted '89. Catalogue no: **VS 759**

TOO MUCH TIME
Tracks: / Too much time / Soul train.
7" Single: Released Aug '86, on Virgin, by Virgin Records. Deleted May '88. Catalogue no: **VS 887**
12" Single: Released Aug '86, on Virgin, by Virgin Records. Deleted May '88. Catalogue no: **VS 887-12**

VENCEREMOS
Tracks: / Venceremos / Venceremos (full 12" version) / Bottom end / Venceremos (bossa).
7" Single: Released '84, on Virgin, by Virgin Records. Deleted '87. Catalogue no: **VS 684**
7" Single: Released Feb '84, on Paladin, Catalogue no: **PA 002**
12" Single: Released '84, on Virgin, by Virgin Records. Catalogue no: **VS 684-12**
12" Single: Released Feb '84, on Paladin, Catalogue no: **PAL 002**

Workshy

YOU'RE THE SUMMER
Tracks: / You're the summer / Everything happens to me / Sleepwalking / You're not alone.
CD 5": Released Aug '89, on WEA, by WEA Records. Catalogue no: **YZ 413CD**
Cassingle: Released Aug '89, on WEA, by WEA Records. Catalogue no: **YZ 413C**
7" Single: Released Aug '89, on WEA, by WEA Records. Catalogue no: **YZ 413**
12" Single: Released Aug '89, on WEA, by WEA Records. Catalogue no: **YZ 413T**

YOURS FOR THE TAKING
Tracks: / Yours for the taking / Yours for the taking (ext. version) / No faith / Everything happens to me (Only avaliable on CD format.).
CD 5": Released Mar '88, on Magnet, by WEA Records. Catalogue no: **CD MAG 315**
7" Single: Released Mar '88, on Magnet, by WEA Records. Deleted Jun '88. Catalogue no: **MAG 315**
12" Single: Released Mar '88, on Magnet, by WEA Records. Catalogue no: **MAGT 315**

World

I'M SORRY
Tracks: / I'm sorry / Loop.
7" Single: Released Mar '84, on WEA, by WEA Records. Catalogue no: **E 9745**

World Beat Club

JOHANNESBURG (FRONT LINE)
Tracks: / Johannesburg.
7" Single: Released Mar '89, on Tom Tom, Catalogue no: **TTT 001**
12" Single: Released '88, on Tom Tom, Catalogue no: **12TTT 001**

World Class Wrecking

TURN OFF THE LIGHTS
Tracks: / Turn off the lights.
12" Single: Released Nov '87, on Kru-Cut (USA), Catalogue no: **KC 006**

WORLD CLASS WRECKING FREAK
Tracks: / World class wrecking freak / Mission possible.
7" Single: Released Aug '86, on Epic, by CBS Records. Catalogue no: **A 7281**
12" Single: Released Aug '86, on Epic, by CBS Records. Catalogue no: **TA 7281**

World Domination...

ASBESTOS LEAD ASBESTOS
Tracks: / Asbestos lead asbestos.
7" Single: Released Oct '85, on Karbon, by Karbon Records. Catalogue no: **KAR 008**

CATALOGUE CLOTHES
Tracks: / Catalogue clothes / St. Etienne.
12" Single: Released Oct '86, on Product Inc., Catalogue no: **PROD 1.12**

COMPANY NEWS
Tracks: / Company news / Rare mix / Tutti frutti.
7" Single: Released Apr '89, on Immaculate, by Immaculate Records. Catalogue no: **IMMAC 12**
12" Single: Released Apr '89, on Immaculate, by Immaculate Records. Catalogue no: **12IMMAC 12**

HOTSY GIRL
Tracks: / Hosty girl.
7" Single: Released Apr '87, on Product Inc., Catalogue no: **7PROD 5**
12" Single: Released Apr '87, on Product Inc., Catalogue no: **12PROD 5**

I CAN'T LIVE WITHOUT MY RADIO
Tracks: / I can't live without my radio.
7" Single: Released Feb '88, on Product Inc., Catalogue no: **7PROD 12**
12" Single: Released Feb '88, on Product Inc., Catalogue no: **12PROD 12**

World Famous Lobster..

WORKING FOR LOVE AGAIN
Tracks: / Working for love again.
7" Single: Released Jan '84, on Streetwave, Catalogue no: **KHAN 1**
12" Single: Released Jan '84, on Streetwave, Catalogue no: **MKHAN 1**

World Famous

HEY DJ
Tracks: / Hey DJ.
7" Single: Released Apr '86, on Virgin, by Virgin Records. Deleted May '88. Catalogue no: **TEAM 1**
12" Single: Released Apr '86, on Virgin, by Virgin Records. Deleted May '88. Catalogue no: **TEAM 1-12**

World party

PRIVATE REVOLUTION (SINGLE)
Tracks: / Private revolution / Holy water.
7" Single: Released Sep '86, on Ensign, by Ensign Records. Catalogue no: **ENY 604**
12" Single: Released Sep '86, on Ensign, by Ensign Records. Catalogue no: **ENYX 604**

SHIP OF FOOLS
Tracks: / Private revolution / Trouble down here / World groove - do the mind gorilla / Nowhere man (Available on 12" version only).
CD 5": Released Feb '87, on Ensign, by Ensign Records. Catalogue no: **SCD 1**
7" Single: Released Jan '87, on Ensign, by Ensign Records. Catalogue no: **ENY 606**
12" Single: Released Jan '87, on Ensign, by Ensign Records. Catalogue no: **ENYX 606**

World Premiere

SHARE THE NIGHT
Tracks: / Share the night.
7" Single: Released Jan '84, on Epic, by CBS Records. Catalogue no: **A 4133**
12" Single: Released Jan '84, on Epic, by CBS Records. Catalogue no: **TA 4133**

World Series

TRY IT OUT
Tracks: / Try it out.
7" Single: Released Oct '83, on Baskerville, Catalogue no: **BAS 2**

World Service

CELEBRATION TOWN
Tracks: / Celebration town.
12" Single: Released Jun '83, on Rough Trade, by Rough Trade Records. Catalogue no: **RTT 118**

World Sitizenz

LOCK IT UP
Tracks: / Lock it up.
7" Single: Released Aug '85, on EMI-Manhattan, by EMI Records. Catalogue no: **MT 5**
12" Single: Released Aug '85, on EMI-Manhattan, by EMI Records. Catalogue no: **12 MT 5**

World Stuff

CONFLICT, THE
Tracks: / Conflict, The.
CD 5": Released Sep '89, on RCA, by BMG Records (UK). Catalogue no: **662535**
7" Single: Released Sep '89, on RCA, by BMG Records (UK). Catalogue no: **112535**
12" Single: Released Sep '89, on RCA, by BMG Records (UK). Catalogue no: **612535**

Worrell, Tony

EVERYTHING YOU DO
Tracks: / Everything you do / Don't turn away.
7" Single: Released Aug '86, on I Scream Music, Catalogue no: **7ISM 8601**
12" Single: Released Aug '86, on I Scream Music, Catalogue no: **12ISM 8601**

Worse 'Em

TRIPLE M BASS
Tracks: / Triple m bass (dub mix) / Triple m bass.
7" Single: Released Jan '87, on Champion, by Champion Records. Deleted Aug '89. Catalogue no: **CHAMP 29**
12" Single: Released Jan '87, on Champion, by Champion Records. Catalogue no: **CHAMP 1229**

Wot Zat

READ BETWEEN THE LINES
Tracks: / Read between the lines.
7" Single: Released Oct '85, on PVK, by PVK Records. Catalogue no: **PV 124**

Would-Be-Goods

CAMERA LOVES ME (SINGLE)
Tracks: / Camera loves me, The / Cecil Beaton's scrapbook.
Note: Producer Keith West.
7" Single: Released Aug '88, on El, by Cherry Red Records. Catalogue no: **GPO 39**

FRUIT PARADISE
Tracks: / Fruit paradise / Hanging gardens of Reigate.
7" Single: Released Oct '87, on El, by Cherry Red Records. Catalogue no: **GPO 28**

Wow

HELLHOUSE
Tracks: / Hellhouse / Wow.
7" Single: Released Apr '89, on Immaculate, by Immaculate Records. Catalogue no: **IMMAC 6**
12" Single: Released Apr '89, on Immaculate, by Immaculate Records. Catalogue no: **12IMMAC 6**

Wow Federation

YELLOW TELEPHONE
Tracks: / Yellow telephone / True credibility.
7" Single: Released Mar '82, on Rococco, Catalogue no: **ROC 001**

Woyehyeh

GIVE THIS HEART
Tracks: / Give this heart.
7" Single: Released Oct '85, on Chrysalis, by Chrysalis Records. Catalogue no: **CHS 2910**
12" Single: Released Oct '85, on Chrysalis, by Chrysalis Records. Catalogue no: **CHSX 2910**

W.Q.B.C.

LOVE ME ANYWAY
Tracks: / Love me anyway / I'll be loving you.
12" Single: Released Apr '86, on Expansion, Catalogue no: **EXPAND 1**

Wrabit

BACK HOME
Tracks: / Back home / Don't say goodnight to rock and roll.
7" Single: Released Jun '82, on MCA, by MCA Records. Catalogue no: **MCA 781**

TOO MANY YEARS
Tracks: / Too many years.
7" Single: Released Feb '82, on MCA, by MCA Records. Catalogue no: **MCA 767**

Wrathchild

ALRITE WITH THE BOYZ
Tracks: / Alrite with the boyz.
7" Single: Released Sep '84, on FM, by FM-Revolver Records. Catalogue no: **VHF 3**

DO YOU WANT MY LOVE
Tracks: / Do you want my love.
7" Pic: Released Sep '83, on Bullet, by Bullet Records. Catalogue no: **PBOL 5**
7" Single: Released Sep '83, on Bullet, by Bullet Records. Deleted '88. Catalogue no: **BOL 5**
12" Single: Released Sep '83, on Bullet, by Bullet Records. Deleted '88. Catalogue no: **BOLT 5**

NUCLEAR ROCKET
Tracks: / (Na na) nukklear rokket.
7" Single: Released Mar '89, on FM-Revolver, by FM-Revolver Records. Catalogue no: **VHF 50**
12" Single: Released Mar '89, on FM-Revolver, by FM-Revolver Records. Catalogue no: **12VHF 50**

ROCK THE CITY DOWN
Tracks: / Rock the city down/ Stackheeled strut.
12" Single: Released Mar '83, on Bullet, by Bullet Records. Deleted '88. Catalogue no: **BOLT 2**

Wray, Link
Biographical details: Wray, Link was born in 1935 in Fort Bragg, North Carolina. (Some souces give a birth date of 1930) The guitarist served in Korea, played with his brothers in the Ranch Gang Band in Norfolk, Virginia; TB caused him to lose a lung in 1955. On DJ Milt Grant's TV show he was asked to play an instrumental and came up with *Rumble*, one of the most influential of rock'n'roll records: he punched a hole in his amplifier speaker with a pencil, inventing fuzz-tone; the slow, menacing record (by Link Wary and his Wray Men) reached Top 20 USA on Cadence in 1958 and was banned from NYC radio because of gang warfare connotations. Flip side *The Swag* was another gloriously simple rock riff, at a faster tempo; both list Grant and Wray as co-writers, as does *Rawhide*, a top 25 hit on Epic in 1959 (he switched labels because Cadence boss Archie Bleyer wanted him to go country, emulating Bleyer's biggest act the Everley Brothers). He played in bars and recorded for pleasure at home; homemade tapes were released in 1971 as Link Wray as generation of rock stars named him as an influence. Albums: *Early Recordings* and

WRECKLESS ERIC - BROKEN DOLL (Released on Stiff)

Good Rockin' Tonight on Ace include material from the Swan label; *There's Good Rockin' Tonight* on Red Lightnin' and Rock'n'Roll Rumble on Charly UK are the same LP; Link Wray and the Raymen on Edsel has Epic tracks. *Growling Guitar* to be released on Ace has '60s tracks from Vermillion label; later LPs include *Beans And Fatback* (1973), *Bullshot* (1979) on Charisma, *Live At The Paradiso* (1980) on Magnum Force/PRT in UK, *Live In '85* on Ace, made at Scandinavian concerts. (Donald Clarke 21/5/88).

BATMAN
Tracks: / Batman.
7" Single: Released Mar '78, on Ace, by Ace Records. Deleted Jun '88. Catalogue no: **NS 32**

RUMBLE
Tracks: / Rumble / I fought the law.
Note: Double A sided single with Bobby Fuller Four.
7" Single: Released Jul '82, on Revival, Catalogue no: **REV 6001**

Wrecking Crew

YOU BROKE MY HEART
Tracks: / Passion plays / You broke my heart.
7" Single: Released Sep '87, on ABR, by ABR Productions. Catalogue no: **ABR 005**

Wreckless Eric

Biographical details: This British singer, songwriter and guitarist, who was so reckless he couldn't even spell the word, came to public attention in 1977 with the unsuccessful but widely acclaimed single *Whole Wide World*. He was one of the early acts on the Stiff label, which was formed at the start of the New Wave/punk era to provide an outlet for the wealth of fresh talent which was being ignored by the UK's major record companies. Produced by Nick Lowe, the insistent, idiosyncratic *Whole Wide World* was an intriguing piece of pop, one of the best singles to come out of the New Wave. The ever-inventive Stiff Records used a variety of unusual marketing ploys to draw attention to themselves and their artists, one of which was the multi-performer package tour. Wreckless Eric played on both the first two tours (1977 and 1978). He changed his backing musicians with alarming frequency, which is why the first tour featured Wreckless Eric & The New Rockets and the second billed Wreckless Eric & The Four Rough Men.
Eric did not follow some of his Stiff colleagues into the charts, save for a couple of small successes on the UK album lists: his eponymous debut LP reached No 46 in April '78 and *Big Smash*, a double album containing new material and previous tracks, attained No 30 in March '80. Singles such as *Take The Cash* ('78) and *Hit And Miss Judy* ('79) failed to register. By the mid-80's Eric had re-emerged in a new guise, minus the "Wreckless" tag: he remained an endearing character who was liked by the critics but generally unappreciated by the general public. (Bob MacDonald, June 1985.).

BROKEN DOLL
Tracks: / Broken doll / I need a situation.
7" Single: Released Mar '80, on Stiff, by Stiff Records. Catalogue no: **BUY 75**

CRYING WAITING HOPING
Tracks: / Crying, waiting, hoping.
7" Single: Released '78, on Stiff, by Stiff Records. Catalogue no: **BUY 40**

HIT AND MISS JUDY
Tracks: / Hit and Miss Judy.
7" Single: Released Nov '79, on Stiff, by Stiff Records. Catalogue no: **BUY 49**

IT'S A SICK SICK WORLD
Tracks: / It's a sick sick world / Reconnez Cherie.
7" Single: Released Sep '89, on New Rose (1), by New Rose Records. Catalogue no: **NR 100**

POPSONG
Tracks: / Popsong / Reconnez cherie.
7" Single: Released Mar '80, on Stiff, by Stiff Records. Deleted '83. Catalogue no: **BUY 64**

POPSONG, A
Tracks: / Popsong, A.
7" Single: Released Jan '80, on Stiff, by Stiff Records. Catalogue no: **BUY 64**

RECONNEZ CHERIE
Tracks: / Reconnez cherie.
7" Single: Released Feb '78, on Stiff, by Stiff Records. Catalogue no: **BUY 25**

TAKE THE CASH
Tracks: / Take the cash.
7" Single: Released '78, on Stiff, by Stiff Records. Catalogue no: **BUY 34**

WORLD WIDE WORLD
Tracks: / World wide world.
7" Single: Released Aug '77, on Stiff, by Stiff Records. Catalogue no: **BUY 16**

Wrecks 'N' Effect

NEW JACK SWING
Tracks: / New jack swing / New jack swing (Inst.).
CD 5": Released Aug '89, on Motown, by BMG Records (UK). Catalogue no: **ZD 43148**
7" Single: Released Aug '89, on Motown, by BMG Records (UK). Catalogue no: **ZB 43147**
12" Single: Released Aug '89, on Motown, by BMG Records (UK). Catalogue no: **ZT 43148**

Wren, Jenny

EDWARD & MRS. SIMPSON (SINGLE)
Tracks: / Edward & Mrs. Simpson.
7" Single: Released '79, on RK, by RK Records. Deleted '81. Catalogue no: **RK 1017**

Wright, Bernard

AFTER YOU
Tracks: / After you (remix) / After you (remix) (instrumental) / Yo nard (on 12" version only).
7" Single: Released May '86, on EMI-Manhattan, by EMI Records. Catalogue no: **MT 9**
12" Single: Released May '86, on EMI-Manhattan, by EMI Records. Catalogue no: **12 MT 9**

CHILLIN' OUT
Tracks: / Chillin' out / Spinnin'. / Haboglabotribin'
7" Single: Released Mar '81, on Arista, by BMG Records (UK). Catalogue no: **ARIST 389**
12" Single: Released Mar '81, on Arista, by BMG Records (UK). Catalogue no: **ARIST 12389**

Wright, Betty

Biographical details: Born in Miami in 1953, soul singer Wright began singing gospel music at the age of three and, in her early teens, started to perform session vocal work for various Miami-based soul acts. Just before her 15th birthday she broke into the American Top Forty for the first time, reaching No 33 with what must have been 1968's most obvious statement, *Girls Can't Do What The Guys Do*. At the beginning of the 70's she scored on the American R & B charts with *Pure Love*, *I've Found That Guy* and *I Love The Way You Love*. Then came her biggest hit. *Clean Up Woman* was a gritty funk track with a certain novelty flavour and it became a US million-seller, reaching No 3 on the soul chart and No 6 on the pop listings. Its sparse instrumental arrangement allowed Wright's clear, energetic voice to come through to maximum advantage. During 1972-74 Wright achieved a further run of Top Forty successes on the American soul chart (though not the pop chart) but had to wait until 1975 for British recognition. Amazingly, *Clean Up Woman* had missed out altogether in Britain, but she managed two Top Forty pop singles in '75 with *Shoorah Shoorah* and *Where Is The Love?*. As with many black soul singers, she was unable to find success during the white-aimed disco boom of the late 70's and her career has not been revived in the 80's, although a 1983 collaboration with Marlon Jackson, of the Jacksons, was critically acclaimed. As something of a compensation for her latter day dry period, Wright gave vocal assistance to Peter Brown on his '78 American Top Tenner, *Dance With Me*. (Bob MacDonald, June 1985.).

KEEP LOVE NEW
Tracks: / Keep love new.
Note: Limited edition of this track only.
7" Single: Released Sep '89, on Sure Delight, by Sure Delight Records. Catalogue no: **SD 11**
12" Single: Released Jul '89, on Sure Delight, by Sure Delight Records. Catalogue no: **SDT 11**

PAIN
Tracks: / Pain / Pain (The rap).
7" Single: Released Jan '86, on Cool Tempo, by Chrysalis Records. Catalogue no: **COOL 117**
12" Single: Released Jan '86, on Cool Tempo, by Chrysalis Records. Catalogue no: **COOLX 117**

SHOORAH SHOORAH
Tracks: / Shoo-rah-shoo-rah.
7" Single: Released Jan '75, on RCA, by BMG Records (UK). Deleted '78. Catalogue no: **RCA 2491**

WHAT ARE YOU GOING TO DO WITH IT
Tracks: / What are you going to do with it / I believe in you.
7" Single: Released Apr '81, on Epic, by CBS Records. Deleted '85. Catalogue no: **EPC A 1086**

WHERE IS THE LOVE
Tracks: / Where is the love.
7" Single: Released Apr '75, on RCA, by BMG Records (UK). Deleted '78. Catalogue no: **RCA 2548**

Wright, B.J.

J.R.
Tracks: / J.R. / Memory bound.
7" Single: Released Jun '80, on Stateside, by EMI Records. Deleted '83. Catalogue no: **SS 3001**

Wright, Bob

ROCK AND ROLL M.C.
Tracks: / Rock and roll M.C. / Rock and roll music.
7" Single: Released Mar '85, on RPM, Catalogue no: **RPM 2**

Wright, Galdwyn

MY WORLD
Tracks: / My world / Portrait of you.
12" Single: Released Feb '89, on New Talents, Catalogue no: **NT 006**

Wright, Gary

IT AIN'T RIGHT
Tracks: / It ain't right / Blind alley.
7" Single: Released Mar '89, on Cypress, by Sonet Records. Catalogue no: **YY 5003**

WHO AM I (SINGLE)
Tracks: / Who am I? / Blind alley.
7" Single: Released Nov '88, on Cypress, by Sonet Records. Catalogue no: **YY 5001**

Wright, George

YOU ARE THE ONE I LOVE
Tracks: / You are the one I love / I done it dub / Get out of hand / Hand made dub.
10" single: Released Oct '82, on Kingdom, by Kingdom Records. Deleted '83. Catalogue no: **KV 8026 10**

Wright, Gladwin

I NEED YOUR LOVE
Tracks: / I need your love.
12" Single: Released Jun '89, on New Talents, Catalogue no: **NT 009**

Wright, Lorna

MIRROR MILE
Tracks: / Mirror mile / Loreleis.
7" Single: Released Nov '81, on CBS, by CBS Records. Deleted Nov '84. Catalogue no: **TIC 8**

Wright, Milton

I BELONG TO YOU
Tracks: / I belong to you / Gallop, The.
7" Single: Released Jul '77, on Grapevine (Northern Soul), by BMG Records (UK). Deleted '80. Catalogue no: **GRP 103**

Wright, Peter

WHAT WOULD YOU SAY
Tracks: / What would you say.
12" Single: Released Apr '82, on Jama, Catalogue no: **JA 0016**

Wright, Ruby

BIMBO
Tracks: / Bimbo.
7" Single: Released Apr '54, on Parlophone, by EMI Records. Deleted '57. Catalogue no: **R 3816**

THREE STARS
Tracks: / Three stars.
7" Single: Released May '59, on Parlophone, by EMI Records. Deleted '62. Catalogue no: **R 4556**

Wright, Stephen

VALENTINE SONG
Tracks: / Valentine song / I'd tell you if I knew.
7" Single: Released Jan '81, on Stephen Wright, Deleted '86. Catalogue no: **SW 2**

Wright, Steve

Biographical details: British disc jockey Wright has, in the 80's, become one of the BBC's best-known radio personalities. He arrived there via the tried and trusted route trodden by many of his Radio One predecessors: local radio, followed by a stint on Radio Luxembourg, followed, in 1980, by an obscure, introductory time-slot on Radio One. He was given a daily afternoon slot in late '81 and by the end of the following year Steve Wright In The Afternoon was a uniquely individual show, with silly jingles, catchphrases and telephoned interruptions from a variety of imaginery characters all intruding upon the programme's conservative selection of pop music. Minor hit listings, each based on a particular aspect or phrase from his show, became an annual event for Wright. The first was the biggest: he reached No 40 on the UK listings in late '82 with *I'm Alright*, credited to Young Steve & The Afternoon Boys. Just under a year later he peaked at No 75 with *Get Some Therapy*. In late '84 *The Gay Cavaliers/The Story So Far* took "Young" Steve - who had just turned 30 - to No 61. Each of these comedy records featured his half sung/half spoken vocals, set against a bland arrangement and melody. In 1985 Wright won the Sony Radio Award for Britain's best disc jockey. By that time his popularity had warranted the unprecedented BBC step of giving him concurrent weekend shows. (B MacDonald, '85.).

GAY CAVELIEROS
Tracks: / Gay Cavelieros.
7" Pic: Released Nov '84, on MCA, by MCA Records. Catalogue no: **MCAP 925**
7" Single: Released Nov '84, on MCA, by MCA Records. Catalogue no: **MCA 925**
12" Single: Released Nov '84, on MCA, by MCA Records. Catalogue no: **MCAT 925**

GET SOME THERAPY
Tracks: / Get some therapy.
7" Single: Released Oct '83, on RCA, by BMG Records (UK). Catalogue no: **RCA 362**
12" Single: Released Oct '83, on RCA, by

BMG Records (UK). Catalogue no: **RCAT 362**

I'M SO ANGRY
Tracks: / I'm so angry.
7" Single: Released Aug '85, on MCA, by MCA Records. Catalogue no: **MCA 987**
12" Single: Released Aug '85, on MCA, by MCA Records. Catalogue no: **MCAT 987**

WILD WILD WOMAN
Tracks: / Wild wild woman.
7" Single: Released Apr '78, on Record Shack, by Record Shack Records. Catalogue no: **RMA 1014**

Wright, Velma

YOU'RE NOT RIGHT
Tracks: / You're not right / You're not right (version).
7" Single: Released May '89, on Champion, by Champion Records. Catalogue no: **CHAMP 202**
12" Single: Released May '89, on Champion, by Champion Records. Catalogue no: **CHAMP 12202**

Wright, Winston

ARRIVAL OF COUNT SHELLEY
Tracks: / Arrival of Count Shelley / Always remember.
12" Single: Released Nov '86, on World Enterprise, Catalogue no: **WENDIS 3035**

Wrigley, Bernard

SATURDAY COWBOYS
Tracks: / Saturday cowboys / I'm in love with Angela Rippon.
7" Single: Released May '80, on DJM, Catalogue no: **DJS 10942**

Wu, Wendy

FOR YOUR LOVE
Tracks: / For your love.
7" Single: Released Mar '82, on Epic, by CBS Records. Catalogue no: **EPC A 2128**

Wurzel

BESS
Tracks: / Bess / People say I'm crazy / Midnight in London (Extra track on 12" only) / ESP (Extra track on 12" only).
7" Single: Released Mar '87, on GWR, by GWR Records. Catalogue no: **GWR 4**
12" Single: Released Mar '87, on GWR, by GWR Records. Catalogue no: **GWT 4**

Wurzels

Biographical details: This comedy singing band consists of Tommy Banner, Tony Baylis and Pete Budd. They were formed in the mid-60's by up-and-coming folk comedian Adge Cutler. During '67 Cutler and his backing group chalked up minor hits on both the singles and album charts in the UK. Cutler never saw chart action again but remained a popular attraction on the folk club circuit until his death in a car crash in 1974. Two years later the Wurzels stepped into the limelight and were catapulted to chart stardom. Their two UK smashes dealt with farming and cider drinking, the two favourite subjects of both the group and their mentor. With an image and routine based on the archetypal stereotype of a rural Somerset farmer, they sped to the British No 1 slot in June '76 with *Combine Harvester*, an adaptation of Melanie's *Brand New Key* with their own jokey yokel lyrics. They followed it with a No 3 hit, *I Am A Cider Drinker*: this version of *Paloma Blanca* went higher in the UK chart than either of the straight 1975 versions by Jonathan King and the George Baker Selection. (*I Am A Cider Drinker* elicited complaints from morals campaigner Mary Whitehouse who claimed it would encourage alcoholism among Britain's juvenile record buyers!). Also in 1976 the Wurzels took their *Combine Harvester* album to No 15, logging 20 weeks in the UK charts. However, after one minor '77 hit with *Farmer Bill's Cowman (I Was Kaiser Bill's Batman- Whistling Jack Smith)* the Wurzels faded from the charts forever -- '76 had been a pedestrian year for British pop and rock and thus a good time for novelty acts to step into the breach, but the injection of New Wave talent put the kibosh on this flood of gimmicks. In 1980 the Wurzels released the singles *I Hate JR* and *I Shot JR* in an attempt to cash in on the Dallas TV hysteria, but these flopped. During the 80's they continued to earn a steady living via club work but did not have the national media exposure that their mid-70's hits had brought them. (Bob MacDonald, June 1985.).

ALL FALL DOWN
Tracks: / All fall down / Somerset crumpet horn.
7" Single: Released Oct '86, on Dingle's, by Dingle's Records. Catalogue no: **SID 238**

COMBINE HARVESTER (SINGLE)
Tracks: / Combine harvester / I am a cider drinker.
7" Single: Released Nov '80, on H.M.V., by EMI Records. Deleted Nov '83. Catalogue no: **POP 2017**
7" Single: Released May '76, on EMI, by EMI Records. Deleted '79. Catalogue no: **EMI 2450**

COUGHIN' SONG
Tracks: / Coughin' song / Shovel it here.
7" Single: Released Mar '82, on John Miles, Deleted '85. Catalogue no: **JM 1009**

FARMER BILL'S COWMAN
Tracks: / Farmer Bill's cowman.
7" Single: Released Jun '77, on EMI, by EMI Records. Deleted '80. Catalogue no: **EMI 2637**

I AM A CIDER DRINKER
Tracks: / I am a cider drinker (paloma blanca).
7" Single: Released Sep '76, on EMI, by EMI Records. Deleted '79. Catalogue no: **EMI 2520**

I HATE J.R.
Tracks: / I hate J.R. / I love J.R..
7" Single: Released Apr '80, on JM, by JM Records. Deleted '83. Catalogue no: **JM 1001**

IF YOU GOT NOTHIN' ON TONIGHT
Tracks: / If you got nothin' on tonight / Little drop of home made wine.
7" Single: Released Nov '80, on JM, by JM Records. Deleted Nov '83. Catalogue no: **JM 1004**

SUNNY WESTON-SUPER-MARE
Tracks: / Sunny Weston-Super-Mare / Sunny Weston-Super-Mare (inst).
7" Single: Released Sep '88, on Far End, Catalogue no: **FNS 2**

WURZEL RAP
Tracks: / Wurzel rap.
7" Single: Released Jul '83, on Goldliner, Catalogue no: **RAP 1**

YOU DON'T GET DRUNK ON A SATURDAY NIGHT
Tracks: / You don't get drunk on a saturday night / Don Juan of the west.
7" Single: Released Feb '80, on Columbia, by EMI Records. Deleted Feb '83. Catalogue no: **DB 9076**

Wyatt, Robert

Biographical details: This British singer and keyboards player has, throughout his career, been a huge favourite with rock critics but only a minor commercial success. Hailing from Canterbury, he played drums with the Wilde Flowers, formed in 1963, and three years later he was a founder member of Soft Machine, acting as lead vocalist and drummer for that jazz-influenced rock band until 1971. He then quit the group to form Matching Mole (inspired by the French words for Soft Machine, machine molle), an outfit which issued two albums, 1972's *Matching Mole* -- containing a sublime opening track, *O Caroline* -- and 1973's *Little Red Record*. In 1974 Wyatt fell from a first-floor window at a party and broke his back. He spent several months at Stoke Nandeville Hospital but remained paralysed from the waist down. The accident forced him to switch from drums to keyboards and spelt the end of Machine Mole so Wyatt launched a solo career. He had released a solo album, *End Of An Ear* in 1970 while with Soft Machine but 1974's *Rock Bottom* was his debut as a fully-fledged soloist. He also won a surprise UK Top Thirty single that year in the shape of *I'm A Believer* an oddball Cockney-voiced version of the Monkees' classic. In '75 he issued another LP, *Ruth Is Stranger Than Richard*. To many listeners, Wyatt's off-key wailing is unbearable but to his cult following his voice is distinctive and passionately communicative. The combination of an upper class family background, a liberal education, the accident and his own epigrammatic personality has sharpened Wyatt into an esoteric figure dictated solely by artistic rather than commercial considerations. This explains the seven-year gap between *Ruth Is Stranger Than Richard* and 1982's *Nothing Can Stop Us Now* album, a gap filled only by a few singles and one-off projects. The same year also saw him release the stunning Elvis Costello-penned single *Shipbuilding*, an acid comment on the Falklands War which reached the UK No 35 slot in '83. In 1984 Wyatt again pleased critics with his 12-inch EP *Work In Progress*, which featured a remake of Peter Gabriel's protest song *Biko*. (Bob MacDonald, June 1985.)

Robert Wyatt is a British singer-songwriter born in 1945 in Bristol. He co-founded, arranged and played drums with Soft Machine in 1966-71, them Matching Mole (a pun on the French for 'soft machine'). He had already begun playing keyboards including on his first solo album *The End of An Ear* in 1971; he concentrated more on them after breaking his back in a fall in 1973, made *Rock Bottom* and *Ruth Is Stranger Than Richard* in mid-'70s on Virgin; had a suprise top 30 UK hit in 1974 with cover of the Monkees' *I'm A Believer*. Increasingly political and unconcerned with the usual career concerns, he receded from music business until a series of singles for Rough Trade, compiled on *Nothing Can Stop Us*, including *Strange Fruit*, Cuban *Caimanera* (with Harry Beckett on flugelhorn), *The Red Flag*, *Stalin Wasn't Stallin'* (first recorded in 1943 by the Golden Gate Quartet), his own *Born Again Cretin'*. Then albums on Rough Trade: *The Animals Soundtrack* in 1982 for Victor Schonfield's film about abuse of animals; 12" EP *Work In Progress* in 1983 included *Amber And The Amberines* (with Hugh Hopper), covers of *Biko*, *Yolanda* and *'Te Recuerdo* (by Peter Gabriel, Pablo Milanes and Victor Jara respectively); *Old Rotten Hat* in 1985 includes material such as *The United States of Amnesia*, *Alliance* and *Gharbzadegi*. His minimalist style and delivery tackle issues head on without succumbing to sloganisisng. More singles including *Shipbuilding* in 1983 (reached UK top 40; song by Elvis Costello and Clive Langer is a comment on the Falklands war), Jackson Kaujeua's *The Wind of Change* in 1985 (with Jerry Dammer and the S.W.A.P.O. Singers, addressing apartheid. EP *Robert Wyatt* on Strange Fruit is one of series from John Peel radio shows, four solo tracks including a live version of *I'm A Believer* from 1974 and the sound of the BBC's piano, Hammond organ and marimbas. (Donald Clarke 21/5/88).

AT LAST I'M FREE
Tracks: / At last I'm free.
7" Single: Released Nov '81, on Rough Trade, by Rough Trade Records. Catalogue no: **RT 052**

FROM MAN TO WOMAN
Tracks: / From man to woman.
7" Single: Released Apr '82, on Virgin, by Virgin Records. Deleted '89. Catalogue no: **VS 499**

GRASS
Tracks: / Grass.
7" Single: Released Aug '81, on Rough Trade, by Rough Trade Records. Catalogue no: **RT 081**

I'M A BELIEVER
Tracks: / I'm a believer.
7" Single: Released Sep '74, on Virgin, by Virgin Records. Deleted '77. Catalogue no: **VS 114**

LAST NIGHTINGALE, THE
Tracks: / Last nightingale, The.
12" Single: Released Feb '85, on Recommended, by Recommended Records. Catalogue no: **NE 1984**

PEEL SESSIONS:WYATT, ROBERT
Tracks: / Soup song / Alifib / I'm a believer / Sea song.
12" Single: Released Sep '87, on Strange Fruit, by Strange Fruit Records. Catalogue no: **SFPS 037**

QUANTANAMERA
Tracks: / Quantanamera / Aracuda.
7" Single: Released Mar '80, on Rough Trade, by Rough Trade Records. Catalogue no: **RT 037**

ROBERT WYATT - STAMPA ALTERNATIVA Lyric book & flexi
Special: Released 26 Jun '87, on Stampa Alternative (Italy), Catalogue no: **RW 001**

SHIPBUILDING
Tracks: / Shipbuilding.
12" Single: Released Aug '82, on Rough Trade, by Rough Trade Records. Catalogue no: **RT 115T**
7" Single: Released Aug '82, on Rough Trade, by Rough Trade Records. Catalogue no: **RT 115**

STALIN' WASN'T STALLIN'
Tracks: / Stalin' wasn't stallin' / Stalingrad.
7" Single: Released Feb '81, on Rough Trade, by Rough Trade Records. Catalogue no: **RT 046**

WIND OF CHANGE, THE
Tracks: / Wind of change.
12" Single: Released Oct '85, on Rough Trade, by Rough Trade Records. Catalogue no: **RTT 168**
7" Single: Released Oct '85, on Rough Trade, by Rough Trade Records. Catalogue no: **RT 168**

WORK IN PROGRESS
Tracks: / Work in progress.
12" Single: Released Aug '84, on Rough Trade, by Rough Trade Records. Catalogue no: **RTT 149**

Wycoff, Michael

Biographical details: This American singer and keyboard player worked as a session vocalist during the late 70's, his most notable work being a contribution to Stevie Wonder's *Songs In the Key Of Life* set. An unadventurous soul singer, Wycoff issued his debut album, *Come To My World*, in 1981. His '83 LP yielded the club favourite *(Do You Really Love Me?) Tell Me Love*, which reached No 60 on the UK singles chart in July of that year. Other tracks on the album showed that despite a fine voice he suffered from lacklustre material. (Bob MacDonald, June 1985.).

DO YOU REALLY LOVE ME TELL ME LOVE
Tracks: / Do you really love me tell me love.
7" Single: Released Jul '83, on RCA, by BMG Records (UK). Catalogue no: **RCA 348**
12" Single: Released Jul '83, on RCA, by BMG Records (UK). Catalogue no: **RCAT 348**

FEEL MY LOVE
Tracks: / Feel my love / Love makes me sing.
7" Single: Released Jan '81, on RCA, by BMG Records (UK). Deleted Jan '84. Catalogue no: **RCA 24**

ONE ALONE
Tracks: / One alone / Do you think.
7" Single: Released Apr '81, on RCA, by BMG Records (UK). Deleted Apr '84. Catalogue no: **RCA 59**
12" Single: Released Apr '81, on RCA, by BMG Records (UK). Deleted Apr '84. Catalogue no: **RCAT 59**

STILL GOT THE MAGIC (SWEET DELIGHT)
Tracks: / Still got the magic (sweet delight) / Take this chance again.
7" Single: Released Apr '82, on RCA, by BMG Records (UK). Catalogue no: **RCA 209**
12" Single: Released Apr '82, on RCA, by BMG Records (UK). Catalogue no: **RCAT 209**

Wygals

PASSION
Tracks: / Passion.
12" Single: Released Dec '87, on Rough Trade, by Rough Trade Records. Catalogue no: **RTT 214**

Wylie, Pete

DIAMOND GIRL
Tracks: / Diamond girl / Spare a thought.
7" Single: Released Aug '86, on Siren, by Virgin Records. Deleted May '88. Catalogue no: **MDM 12**
12" Single: Released Aug '86, on Siren, by Virgin Records. Deleted May '88. Catalogue no: **MDM 12-12**

FOURELEVENFORTYFOUR
Tracks: / Fourelevenfortyfour / Marksman, The / Sinful (Song of the sinful angel) (CD & 12" only).
CD 5": Released Aug '88, on Siren, by Virgin Records. Catalogue no: **SRNCD 59**
7" Single: Released Oct '87, on Siren, by Virgin Records. Catalogue no: **SRN 59**
12" Single: Released Oct '87, on Siren, by Virgin Records. Deleted '89. Catalogue no: **SRN 59-12**

IF I LOVE YOU
Tracks: / If I love you / Never fall for a whore.
7" Single: Released Jul '87, on Siren, by Virgin Records. Deleted May '88. Catalogue no: **SRN 54**
12" Single: Released Jul '87, on Siren, by Virgin Records. Deleted '89. Catalogue no: **SRN 54-12**

SINFUL (SINGLE)
Tracks: / Sinful (7" version) (NOT on MDM 713) / I want the moon mother (NOT on CD) / Sophie's sinful (for Maurice or Isabelle) (ON MDMD 7 only) / Joy of being booed, The (ON MDMD 7 only) / Sinful (and wicked) (On MDM 713 only) / Sinful (song of the sinful angel) (On MDM 713 only) / Sinful (tribal music) (On MDM 712) / If I love you (On CD only) / Fourelevenfortyfour (On CD only) / Sinful (tribal mix) (On CD only).
7" Set: Released Apr '86, on MDM, by MDM Communications. Catalogue no: **MDMD 7**
7" Single: Released Apr '86, on MDM, by MDM Communications. Catalogue no: **MDM 7**
12" Single: Released '86, on MDM, by MDM Communications. Catalogue no: **MDM 713**
12" Single: Released Apr '86, on MDM, by MDM Communications. Catalogue no: **MDM 7-12**
CD 3": Released '88, on MDM, by MDM Communications. Catalogue no: **CDT 28**

Wylie, Richard

ROSEMARY WHAT HAPPENED
Tracks: / Rosemary what happened / Rosemary what happened (instrumental).
7" Single: Released Jul '77, on Grapevine (Northern Soul), by BMG Records (UK). Deleted '80. Catalogue no: **GRP 100**

Wyman, Bill

Biographical details: British bass guitarist, singer and keyboards player. Wyman was the first of the Rolling Stones to release a solo LP. *Monkey Grip* reached No 39 on the UK album chart in June 1974. It was followed in '76 by *Stone Alone*, which failed to chart in Britain and only managed a No 166 placing on the US Top Two Hundred list. These poor chart performances were not particularly disappointing for Wyman because they were not commercially orientated: they were a diversion, on which he could indulge his own whims. A substantial success did come, however, in summer '81. *(Si Si) Je Suis Un Rock Star* was an offball single featuring Cockney schoolboy-style French: it was a quirky, catchy song performed in an understated style quite unlike the Stones' trademarks. It reached No 14 in Britain but its parent project, the Green Ice film soundtrack, was not a success. In Britain he issued a self-titled album, which featured some pleasant pop but nothing more. It reached No 55 on the UK chart and yielded the No 37 single, *A New Fashion*. The Stones' bassist, whose unassuming manner has always contrasted sharply with the band's leaders, Mick Jagger and Keith Richard, is also the group's long-serving archivist. (Bob MacDonald, June 1985.).

COME BACK SUZANNE
Tracks: / Come back Suzanne.
7" Single: Released Oct '81, on A&M, by A&M Records. Deleted '88. Catalogue no: **AMS 8170**

GREEN ICE-THEME
Tracks: / Green Ice-Theme / Cloud hoppers.
7" Single: Released Jun '81, on Polydor, by Polydor Ltd. Deleted Jun '84. Catalogue no: **POSP 291**

NEW FASHION
Tracks: / New fashion.
7" Single: Released Mar '82, on A&M, by A&M Records. Deleted '88. Catalogue no: **AMS 8209**

SI SI JE SUIS UN ROCK STAR
Tracks: / Si si je suis un rock star / Rio De Janeiro.
7" Single: Released Jun '81, on A&M, by A&M Records. Deleted '88. Catalogue no: **AMS 8144**

VISIONS
Tracks: / Visions / Nuclear reaction.
7" Single: Released May '82, on A&M, by A&M Records. Deleted '88. Catalogue no: **AMS 8227**

Wynder, K.

FRENETIC
Tracks: / Frenetic.
7" Single: Released Jul '80, on Rockburgh, Deleted '82. Catalogue no: **ROCS 228**

Wyndham-Read, Martyn

ROSE
Tracks: / Rose.
7" Single: Released Dec '84, on Greenwich Village, by Sweet Folk All Records. Catalogue no: **GVRS 222**

Wynette, Tammy

Biographical details: Born Wynette Pugh in Mississippi, singer, pianist, guitarist and songwriter Tammy Wynette is one of the most successful women in the history of country music. Her early career was in hairdressing and beauty but she later moved to Nashville with three children of a teenage marriage. After building her reputation in local clubs while working as a song-plugger by day, she secured a recording deal with Epic Records in the mid-60's. Her first single *Apartment No 9*, was a rapid success on the American country charts and was followed by a bigger hit, *Your Good Girl's Gonna Go Bad*. During the late 60's and early 70's she was never very far from the top of the country listings, thanks to her string of tear-jerking singles and albums. In 1968 Wynette married fellow country star George Jones and they enjoyed many duet successes. Her biggest solo smash, *Stand By Your Man*, came in that year. It cruised to No 1 on the Billboard C & W chart and was her only single to cross over to the US Top Forty pop list. Produced and co-written by long-standing studio colleague Billy Sherrill, this record summed up her style: emotional vocals encased in lavish string arrangements, with lyrics emphasising her conservative moral values on the subjects of marriage, family life and heartbreak. Much of her material was written by Sherrill with Glenn Sutton and Wynette was herself an occasional contributor. *Stand By Your Man* and *D.I.V.O.R.C.E.* were the records that made her really famous -- the package was sickly but effective -- and with her *Greatest Hits* album she became the first woman country singer to sell a million copies. Suddenly, in 1975, *Stand By Your Man* went to No 1 on the British pop chart. She had previously been unknown in the UK and this unexpected smash quickly led to the arrival of two concurrent chart LPs. However, in the same year she divorced Jones amid wide publicity and *Stand By Your Man* was rapidly making her a laughing stock. When *D.I.V.O.R.C.E.* made the UK No 12 in late '75 it inspired a hilarious parody version by Scots comedian Billy Connolly which reached No 1. The following year saw J.J. Barrie gaining a sickly British No 1 with another Wynette-associated song, *No Charge*. *Twenty Country Classics* took Wynette into the Top Three of the UK album chart in 1978, the year she married George Richey, who became her producer. In the 80's she was no longer an important force on the American country charts or the British pop lists, but she remained a high earner with numerous cabaret, concert and television appearances. A biographical TV movie, 'Stand By Your Man' was made in 1981. (Bob MacDonald, June 1985.)

Tammy Wynette was born Virginia Wynette Pugh in 1942 in Tupelo, Mississippi; she is one of the most successful female country singers of all time. She was married at 17, soon had three children and left her young husband before the third was born; she worked long hours as a beautician to pay bills incurred by her youngest child's ill health; took up music to earn more money, working in local clubs and landing a spot on WBRC's Country Boy Eddy Show in 1963; appearances on Porter Wagoner's syndicated TV show and endless rounds of Nashville record companies led to signing with Epic Records; she joined Billy Sherrill for one of the most successful artist-producer teams in the history of country music: number one hits included *I Don't Wanna Play House*, *Take Me To Your World*, *D-I-V-O-R-C-E*, *Stand By Your Man* (co-written with Sherrill), *Singing My Song*, *The Ways to Love A Man*, *He Loves Me All The Way*, *Run Woman Run* and *Good Lovin' Makes It Right* in 1967-71 alone; *Tammy's Greatest Hits* in 1969 was the best selling album ever by a female country artist, reached top 40 of the pop LP chart. Marriage to country superstar George Jones in 1969 consolidated her success; he changed labels to Epic, they toured together and had duet hits; his drinking and unprofessional behaviour (No Show Jones) did not go down well, her earlier financial insecurity causing her to put her career first; it was a stormy, violent marriage which ended in 1975. They continued to record together, initially to fulfill contractual obligations, more hits follwed by reunion session in 1980. Meanwhile she continued to dominate the country charts with ever more personal hits, to which her audience couold relate completely *Woman To Woman*, *(You Make Me Want To Be) A Mother*, *I Still Belive In Fairy-tales*, *'Til I Can Make It On My Own*, *You and Me* 1974-76 she made a UK breakthrough when *Stand By Your Man* (re-issud for the sixth time) became a number one pop hit in 1975; at home she has had 20 number one hits, more than any other female, and survived it all: disastrous marriages, ill health due to stess and other problems and even a kidnapping. She had well publicised affairs including with actor Burt Reynolds and Rudy Gatlin; finally settled down and married long-time friend, songwriter and producer George Richey in 1978. In the 1980's she moved away from Sherrill and worked with others; she still has big hits. Biography 'Stand By Your Man' became a successful film in 1982; she made an artistic comeback in 1987 with the album *Higher Ground* which began as a concept idea to be called *Out With The Boys* with the Gatlin Brothers, The O'Kanes, duets with Ricky Skaggs, Gene Watson, Emmylou Harris, Vince Gill. (Donald Clarke 21/5/88).

ALIVE AND WELL
Tracks: / I'll be thinking of you / Alive and well / Copy to come.
7" Single: Released Feb '87, on Epic, by CBS Records. Catalogue no: **650439 7**

COWBOYS DON'T SHOOT STRAIGHT
Tracks: / Cowboys don't shoot straight / You brought me back.
7" Single: Released May '81, on Epic, by CBS Records. Catalogue no: **EPC A 1211**

CRYING IN THE RAIN
Tracks: / Crying in the rain / Bring back my baby.
7" Single: Released Nov '81, on Epic, by CBS Records. Catalogue no: **EPC A 1719**

D.I.V.O.R.C.E.
Tracks: / D.I.V.O.R.C.E..
7" Single: Released Jun '75, on Epic, by CBS Records. Deleted '78. Catalogue no: **EPC 3361**
7" Single: Released '80, on Lightning, Catalogue no: **LR 1026**

I DON'T WANNA PLAY HOUSE
Tracks: / I don't wanna play house.
7" Single: Released Jun '76, on Epic, by CBS Records. Deleted '79. Catalogue no: **EPC 4091**

LIAR'S ROSES
Tracks: / Liar's roses.
7" Single: Released Apr '89, on Epic, by CBS Records. Deleted Oct '89. Catalogue no: **654 776 7**

MY ELUSIVE DREAMS
Tracks: / My elusive dreams / Near you.
7" Single: Released Mar '80, on Epic, by CBS Records. Deleted '83. Catalogue no: **EPC 8300**

STAND BY YOUR MAN (OLD GOLD)
Tracks: / Stand by your man / D.I.V.O.R.C.E..
7" Single: Released 27 Feb '89, on Old Gold, by Old Gold Records. Catalogue no: **OG 9312**

STAND BY YOUR MAN (SINGLE)
Tracks: / Stand by your man.
7" Single: Released Apr '75, on Epic, by CBS Records. Deleted '78. Catalogue no: **EPC 7137**

YOUR LOVE
Tracks: / Your love / I wasn't meant to live my life alone.
7" Single: Released Apr '88, on Epic, by CBS Records. Deleted Jan '89. Catalogue no: **651537 7**

Wynne, Philippe

YOU AIN'T GOING ANYWHERE BUT GONE
Tracks: / You ain't going anywhere but gone.
7" Single: Released Mar '83, on Sugarhill (USA), Deleted '88. Catalogue no: **SH 123**
12" Single: Released Mar '83, on Sugarhill (USA), Catalogue no: **SHL 123**

Wynter, Mark

DREAM GIRL
Tracks: / Dream girl.
7" Single: Released Mar '61, on Decca, by Decca Records. Deleted '64. Catalogue no: **F 11323**

EXCLUSIVELY YOURS
Tracks: / Exclusively yours.
7" Single: Released Jun '61, on Decca, by Decca Records. Deleted '64. Catalogue no: **F 11354**

GO AWAY LITTLE GIRL
Tracks: / Go away little girl.
7" Single: Released Dec '62, on Pye, Deleted '65. Catalogue no: **7 N 15492**

IMAGE OF A GIRL
Tracks: / Image of a girl.
7" Single: Released Aug '60, on Decca, by Decca Records. Deleted '63. Catalogue no: **F 11263**

IT'S ALMOST TOMORROW
Tracks: / It's almost tomorrow.
7" Single: Released Nov '63, on Pye, Deleted '66. Catalogue no: **7 N 15577**

KICKING UP THE LEAVES
Tracks: / Kicking up the leaves.
7" Single: Released Nov '60, on Decca, by Decca Records. Deleted '63. Catalogue no: **F 11279**

ONLY YOU
Tracks: / Only you.
7" Single: Released Apr '64, on Pye, Deleted '67. Catalogue no: **7 N 15626**

SHY GIRL
Tracks: / Shy girl.
7" Single: Released Jun '63, on Pye, Deleted '66. Catalogue no: **7 N 15325**

VENUS IN BLUE JEANS
Tracks: / Venus in blue jeans.
7" Single: Released Oct '62, on Pye, Deleted '65. Catalogue no: **7 N 15466**

Wynter, Scott...

BRITAIN'S NUMBER ONE
Tracks: / Britain's number one / European cup.
7" Single: Released Apr '88, on Klub, by Klub Records. Catalogue no: **KLUB 54**

Wyoming

OUTSIDE LOOKING IN
Tracks: / Outside looking in / Luxury of innocence.
7" Single: Released Apr '87, on CBS, by CBS Records. Deleted Aug '87. Catalogue no: **650173 7**
12" Single: Released Apr '87, on CBS, by CBS Records. Deleted Aug '87. Catalogue no: **650173 6**

X

The following information was taken from the Music Master database on October 20th, 1989.

X

Biographical details: A USA rock band formed in Los Angeles in 1977 by pseudonymous John Doe (born 1954 in Decatur, Illinois) on bass, Billy Zoom on guitar; Doe met Exene (Christine) Cervenka at a poetry workshop and D.J.Bonebrake spotted in L.A. club. Zoom's rockabilly leanings, Doe's new wave affiliation make appropriately uneasy listening. Former Doors keyboardist Ray Manzarek produced their debut LP *Los Angeles* on Slash in 1980. Doe and Cervenka was reminiscent of Siouxsie, like her becoming a more accomplished singer singer as time went by. *Wild Gift* was also produced by Manzarek, covered Doors' *Soul Kitchen* at punk tempo; like most USA new wave, X were chasing tail of UK punk, but lyrics by Doe and Cervenka were a cut above. They signed to Elektra for *Under the Big Black Sun* and *More Fun in the New World* in 1982-83. *Ain't Love Grand* in 1985 had songs dealing with Doe/Cervenka breakup, but Zoom left that year, replaced by the Blasters' Dave Alvin, with whom Doe, Cervenka and Bonebreak had been collaborating as the Knitters. Semi-documentary film **The Unheard Music** in 1986 by writer/dir. W.T.Morgan was five years in the making, portraying the band in L.A. context since the release of the first LP. *See How We Are* in 1987 saw X mellowing somewhat. (Donald Clarke 14.5.88).

BURNING HOUSE OF LOVE
Tracks: / Burning house of love.
7" Single: Released Aug '85, on Elektra, by Elektra Records (UK). Catalogue no: **EKR 18**
12" Single: Released Aug '85, on Elektra, by Elektra Records (UK). Catalogue no: **EKR 18T**

NEW WORLD
Tracks: / New world / I must not think bad thoughts.
7" Single: Released Jan '84, on Elektra, by Elektra Records (UK). Catalogue no: **E 9779**

WILD THING
Tracks: / Wild thing (part 1) / Wild thing (part 2) / Wild thing (full length version) (On 12" & CD single only.) / U.S. male (On 12" & CD single only.) / Oh you angel (On 12" & CD single only).
CD 5": Released Sep '89, on RCA, by BMG Records (UK). Catalogue no: **ZD 49338**
7" Single: Released Sep '89, on RCA, by BMG Records (UK). Catalogue no: **ZB 49337**
12" Single: Released Sep '89, on RCA, by BMG Records (UK). Catalogue no: **ZT 49338**

X Collector

TELEVISION SET
Tracks: / Television set / Christine.
7" Single: Released Oct '83, on Solar Sound, Catalogue no: **SOSO 027**

X, Malcolm

NO SELL OUT
Tracks: / No sell out.
7" Single: Released Mar '84, on Island, by Island Records. Catalogue no: **IS 165**
12" Single: Released Mar '84, on Island, by Island Records. Deleted Apr '88. Catalogue no: **12IS 165**

X, Rocky

IT'S GETTING ROUGH
Tracks: / It's getting rough / It's getting rough (version).
12" Single: Released Jul '87, on Positive Beat, by Positive Beat Records. Catalogue no: **RX DD 001**

Xarhakos, Stavros

DARK SIDE OF THE SUN, THE
Tracks: / Dark side of the sun / Anne's theme.
7" Single: Released Sep '83, on BBC, by BBC Records & Tapes. Deleted '87. Catalogue no: **RESL 135**

Xavier

HIP HOUSE PARTY
Tracks: / Hip house party.
12" Single: Released Sep '89, on Homac, by Homac Records. Catalogue no: **HM 001**

WORK THAT SUCKER TO DEATH
Tracks: / Work that sucker to death / Love is the one.
7" Single: Released Mar '82, on Liberty, by EMI Records. Deleted '85. Catalogue no: **UP 651**
12" Single: Released Mar '82, on Liberty, by EMI Records. Deleted '85. Catalogue no: **12UP 651**

X-Boys

NOT FADE AWAY
Tracks: / Not fade away.
7" Single: Released May '88, on Sidewinder, Catalogue no: **MUSA 887**
12" Single: Released May '88, on Sidewinder, Catalogue no: **MUSA 8812**

X-Cells

SCHIZOID
Tracks: / Schizoid.
7" Single: Released Jul '81, on Snotty Snail, Deleted '83. Catalogue no: **NEL COL 5**

X-Certs

TOGETHER
Tracks: / Together / Untogether.
7" Single: Released Jan '81, on Recreational, by Revolver Records. Catalogue no: **PLAY 1**

Xclusive

C'EST LA VIE
Tracks: / C'est la vie.
7" Single: Released Oct '82, on KA, Catalogue no: **KA 101**

FOOLS ARE FRIENDLY
Tracks: / Fools are friendly.
7" Single: Released Jun '82, on Le Maitre, Catalogue no: **KA 100**
12" Single: Released Jun '82, on Le Maitre, Catalogue no: **KA 100 12**

Xdreamysts

I DON'T WANNA GO
Tracks: / I don't wanna go / Silly games.
7" Single: Released Mar '80, on Polydor, by Polydor Ltd. Deleted Mar '83. Catalogue no: **2059235**

RIGHT WAY HOME
Tracks: / Right way home.
7" Single: Released '79, on Good Vibration, by Good Vibrations Records. Catalogue no: **GOT 5**

STAY THE WAY YOU ARE
Tracks: / Stay the way you are / Race against time.
7" Single: Released Jun '80, on Polydor, by Polydor Ltd. Deleted '83. Catalogue no: **2059252**

Xena

ON THE UP SIDE
Tracks: / On the up side.
12" Single: Released Dec '83, on Streetwave, Catalogue no: **MKHAN 2**

Xenon

WHEN YOU WEAR BLUE
Tracks: / When you wear blue / Hawaiin dreams.
7" Single: Released Sep '83, on Zirron, Deleted '84. Catalogue no: **ZIRS 1**

Xero

OH BABY
Tracks: / Oh baby / Hold on / Lone wolf.
7" Single: Released Jul '83, on Brickyard, by Brickyard Records. Deleted Oct '85. Catalogue no: **XERO 1**
12" Single: Released Jul '83, on Brickyard, by Brickyard Records. Deleted Oct '85. Catalogue no: **XERO 1T**

Xerox, Zena

SECONDS
Tracks: / Seconds / This is your life.
7" Single: Released Mar '81, on RCA, by BMG Records (UK). Deleted Mar '84. Catalogue no: **RCA 54**

X-Factor

CHEMICAL ROMANCE
Tracks: / Chemical romance / Chemical romance (part 2).
7" Single: Released Oct '82, on Scorpio, by Scorpio Records. Catalogue no: **STING 2**
12" Single: Released Oct '82, on Scorpio, by Scorpio Records. Catalogue no: **STING 2T**

X-Invaders

STORM BOYS
Tracks: / Storm boys / Lover boy.
7" Single: Released Feb '85, on Pinner, Catalogue no: **PRM 201**

XL

SHAKESPEARE
Tracks: / Shakespeare.
7" Single: Released 16 Sep '88, on Excel, by Hit Records. Catalogue no: **EXEL 17**
12" Single: Released Sep '88, on Excel, by Hit Records. Catalogue no: **EXEL 112**

XL5's

FIREBALL
Tracks: / Fireball / Miserlou.
7" Single: Released Sep '80, on Fourplay, Catalogue no: **FOUR 004**

X-Mal Deutschland

INCUBUS SUCCUBUS
Tracks: / Incubus succubus / Vito.
7" Single: Released '83, on 4AD, by 4AD Records. Catalogue no: **AD 311**
12" Single: Released '83, on 4AD, by 4AD Records. Catalogue no: **BAD 311**

INCUBUS SUCCUBUS (12")
Tracks: / Incubus succubus / But ist leibe / Zu jung zu alt.
12" Single: Released '83, on Zick Zack (Germany), Deleted '84. Catalogue no: **6060**

MATADOR
Tracks: / Matador / Paho.
7" Single: Released '86, on X-Ile, Deleted Jul '87. Catalogue no: **XMAL 1**
12" Single: Released '86, on X-Ile, Deleted Jul '87. Catalogue no: **XMAL 112**
12" Single: Released '86, on X-Ile, Deleted Jul '87. Catalogue no: **XMALR 112**

PEEL SESSIONS:X-MAL DEUTSCHLAND 13th May 1985
12" Single: Released Nov '86, on Strange Fruit, by Strange Fruit Records. Catalogue no: **SFPS 017**

QUAL
Tracks: / Qual / Zeit / Sehnsucht.
12" Single: Released '83, on 4AD, by 4AD Records. Catalogue no: **BAD 305**

SEQUENZ
Tracks: / Sequenz.
7" Single: Released '85, on Red Rhino, by Red Rhino Records. Catalogue no: **RRE 1**
12" Single: Released '85, on Red Rhino, by Red Rhino Records. Catalogue no: **RRET 1**

SICKLE MOON
Tracks: / Sickle moon / Illusion / In onyx.
7" Single: Released Jan '87, on X-Ile, Deleted Jul '87. Catalogue no: **XMAL 2**
12" Single: Released Jan '87, on X-Ile, Deleted Jul '87. Catalogue no: **XMAL 212**

X-Men

GHOSTS
Tracks: / Ghosts.
7" Single: Released Jun '84, on Creation, by Creation Records. Deleted Jul '88. Catalogue no: **CRE 006**

SPIRAL GIRL
Tracks: / Spiral girl.
7" Single: Released Apr '85, on Creation, by Creation Records. Catalogue no: **CRE 013**

Xolton, Blake

POWER PUFF
Tracks: / Powder puff.
7" Single: Released Sep '89, on New Rose (1), by New Rose Records. Catalogue no: **NEW 124**

Xpertz

MY VALENTINE
Tracks: / My valentine / Lovers in London.
7" Single: Released Jun '85, on Big One Records, by Big One Records. Catalogue no: **VBIG 1**
12" Single: Released Jun '85, on Big One Records, by Big One Records. Catalogue no: **VVBIG 1**

VALENTINE
Tracks: / Valentine.
7" Single: Released Mar '84, on B.B. Star, Deleted '87. Catalogue no: **BBS 001**

X-Posed

POINT OF NO RETURN
Tracks: / Point of no return.
7" Single: Released Sep '84, on Pantera, Catalogue no: **PANT 004**

Xpozez

1000 MARCHING FEET
Tracks: / 1000 marching feet / Terminal case.
7" Single: Released Jul '82, on Red Rhino, by Red Rhino Records. Deleted '88. Catalogue no: **RED 15**

FORCE FED THE TRUTH DRUG (EP)
Tracks: / Force fed the truth drug.
7" Single: Released Jan '85, on Children Of The Revolution, by Revolver Records. Catalogue no: **COR 2**

NEW YORK DOLL
Tracks: / New York doll / It's been done before.
7" Single: Released Mar '83, on Sexual Phonograph, Catalogue no: **SPH 2**

X-Ray Spex

Biographical details: Members of this British punk rock band were Poly Styrene, Paul Dean, B.P. Harding, Lora Logic and Jack "Airport" Stafford. They were formed in early 1977 and caused a tremendous stir in such London punk havens as the Roxy and the Marquee. The Sex Pistols had just exploded into the national headlines with their notorious Bill Grundy TV interview and "anarchy" was the key word on the club scene. The leader of X-Ray Spex was singer Poly Styrene -- real name Marion Ellis -- whose appearance, image and attitude were totally distinctive. Any clothes were OK, provided they looked cheap and came from a jumble sale or a High Street chainstore. The idea was to liberate women, who were as discriminated against in the male-dominated rock world as anywhere else. The group's debut single, released in '77, summed up their attitude --*Oh Bondage, Up Yours!* was not a hit but it remains one of the seminal singles of the punk explosion. In a 12-month period from April '78 to April '79 X-Ray Spex placed four singles and one album on the British charts. *The Day The World Turned Dayglo* (a celebration of Poly Styrene's style of clothing), *Identity* and *Germ Free Adolescence* all hit the Top Thirty and *Highly Inflammable* peaked at No 45. The album *Germ Free Adolescents* reached No 30 and logged 14 weeks in the British LP listings. With a left-wing political position and a collection of fiercely energetic songs aimed at frustrated youth, the band lasted until 1979. Poly Styrene then parted company with X-Ray Spex and both parties vanished from the public eye. The singer tried her hand at an unsuccessful solo career and then became a convert to Christianity. Along with X-Ray Spex saxophonist Lora Logic and Siouxsie of Siouxsie & The Banshees, Poly Styrene was a female punk pioneer: as events turned out the New Wave was a male-dominated phenomenon, just like every other form of music. (Bob MacDonald, April 1985.) .

DAY THE WORLD TURNED DAYGLO
Tracks: / Day the world turned dayglo / I am a poseur.
7" Single: Released Apr '80, on EMI International, by EMI Records. Catalogue no: **INT 553**

GERM FREE ADOLESCENTS (SINGLE)
Tracks: / Germ free adolescents.
7" Single: Released Nov '78, on EMI International, by EMI Records. Deleted '81. Catalogue no: **INT 573**

HIGHLY INFLAMMABLE
Tracks: / Highly inflammable.
7" Single: Released Apr '79, on EMI Inter-

national, by EMI Records. Deleted '82. Catalogue no: **INT 583**

IDENTITY
Tracks: / Identity.
7" Single: Released Jul '78, on EMI International, by EMI Records. Deleted '81. Catalogue no: **INT 563**

OH BONDAGE UP YOURS!
Tracks: / Oh bondage, up yours! / I am a cliche.
7" Single: Released Oct '77, on Virgin, by Virgin Records. Catalogue no: **VS 189**
12" Single: Released Oct '77, on Virgin, by Virgin Records. Deleted '89. Catalogue no: **VS 189-12**

XS-5

I NEED MORE
Tracks: / I need more.
Note: Music class Hi-NRG.
12" Single: Released May '88, on VCN Records, by VCN Records. Catalogue no: **12VCN 5**

XS Discharge

ACROSS THE BORDER
Tracks: / Across the border / Frustration.
7" Single: Released Aug '80, on Communique, Deleted '82. Catalogue no: **COMM 3**

XS Energy

EIGHTEEN
Tracks: / Eighteen / Jenny's alright.
7" Single: Released '79, on Dead Good, Catalogue no: **DEAD 1**

USE YOU
Tracks: / Use you.
7" Single: Released '79, on Dead Good, Catalogue no: **DEAD 3**

XTC

Biographical details: At the time of their greatest success, this British band consisted of Terry Chambers, Dave Gregory, Colin Moulding and Andy Partridge. Hailing from Swindon, Wiltshire, Moulding and Partridge first came together in 1973. They worked under a variety of names and, with the addition of Barry Andrews, emerged as XTC in 1977. Their debut album *White Music* was issued in January 1978 and the group were marketed as part of the New Wave/Punk scene. The album included the single *This Is Pop.* The band's second LP *Go 2* was released in the Autumn of '78, and was the first to hit the UK Top 30. It contained the single *Are You Receiving Me?* XTC first reached the British singles chart in the summer of 1979 with *Life Begins At The Hop,* by which time Andrews had been replaced by keyboards/guitar player Dave Gregory. This reached No.54, and was followed by a breakthrough single *Making Plans For Nigel,* which climbed to No.17. By now it was clear that the band had little to do with the punk scene, and had simply come along at the right time. Their musical proficiency and sophistication, combined with their witty and engaging lyrics, drew upon more traditional rock influences. The key member of the band was Andy Partridge, on vocals and guitar, who was the leader, public spokesman and principal songwriter. During the early Eighties, XTC seemed to be forever on the brink of major stardom without ever actually acheiving it. Early '82 brought them their first and only UK Top 10 album, a double set entitled *English settlement* which yielded their first and only UK Top 10 single, *Senses Working Overtime.* By now they were assuming the role of country bumpkins, softening their rock style in favour of folkish influences. This trend continued on their '83 single *Love On A Farmboys Wages.* Drummer Terry Chambers quit the group around this time, and the remaining members worked as a trio, preferring the studio environment to live work. They continue to operate on the borders of success, with such imaginative singles as 1984's *All You Pretty Girls* attaining only minor hit status on the UK charts. (Bob Macdonald 4.85)
A UK new wave band formed in 1976: Andy Partridge on guitar, Colin Ivor Moulding on bass, Terry Chambers on drums, all from Swindon, all born 1953-55. Formed part of local band Star Park, then glitzy Helium kidz, then XTC with addition of keyboardist John Perkins, replaced by Barry Andrews. Partridge and Moulding are the vocalists and songwriters. Second LP *Go 2* in 1978 was critically acclaimed; Partridge made solo *Takeaway/The Lure of Salvage,* also appeared on *Miniatures,* oddball album fashioned by ex-Mott The Hoople keyboardist Morgan Fisher with one-minute tracks by various celebrities. XTC's fifth LP, 2-disc *English Settlement,* was a change of direction toward folk sound; *Mummer* was similar, but *The Big Express* in 1984 was about growing old (Partridge was turning 30). Band hasn't toured since 1982, operates as a trio of Partridge, Moulding and guitarist Dave Gregory. Mock psychedelic LP *25 O'clock* in 1985 was made under pseudonym the Dukes of Stratosphear and released on April Fool's Day, followed by *Psonic Psunspot.* (Donald Clarke 14.5.88)h.

ALL YOU PRETTY GIRLS
Tracks: / All you pretty girls / Wash away / Red brick ocean (on 12" only).
7" Single: Released Sep '84, on Virgin, by Virgin Records. Deleted '89. Catalogue no: **VS 709**
12" Single: Released Sep '84, on Virgin, by Virgin Records. Deleted '89. Catalogue no: **VS 709-12**

BALL AND CHAIN
Tracks: / Ball and chain / Punch and Judy man.
7" Single: Released Mar '82, on Virgin, by Virgin Records. Deleted '89. Catalogue no: **VS 482**
12" Single: Released Mar '82, on Virgin, by Virgin Records. Deleted '89. Catalogue no: **VS 482-12**

DEAR GOD
Tracks: / Dear God / Big day / Another satellite (On 12" only).
7" Single: Released '87, on Virgin, by Virgin Records. Catalogue no: **VS 960**
12" Single: Released 30 May '87, on Virgin, by Virgin Records. Catalogue no: **VS 960-12**

DEAR GOD (CD SINGLE)
Tracks: / Dear God / Homo safari (part 1 of homo safari series) / Bushman president (part 2 of homo safari series) / Egyptian solution (Homo safari series No.3) / Mantis on parole (part 4 of homo safari series) / Frost circus (part 5 of homo safari series) / Procession towards learning land.
CD 5": Released '88, on Virgin, by Virgin Records. Catalogue no: **CDEP 3**

GENERALS AND MAJORS
Tracks: / Generals and majors / Don't lose your temper.
7" Single: Released Sep '80, on Virgin, by Virgin Records. Deleted '83. Catalogue no: **VS 365**

GRASS
Tracks: / Grass / Dear God / Extroverts (12" only).
7" Single: Released '86, on Virgin, by Virgin Records. Deleted May '88. Catalogue no: **VS 882**
12" Single: Released '86, on Virgin, by Virgin Records. Catalogue no: **VS 882-12**

KING FOR A DAY
Tracks: / King for a day / Happy families / King for a day (12" version) (Only on 12" and CD single.) / Generals and majors (Only on cassette single.) / Towers of London (Only on cassette single.) / My paint heroes (home demo) (Only on CD single.) / Skeletons (home demo) (Only on CD single.).
Cassingle: Released '88, on Virgin, by Virgin Records. Catalogue no: **VSC 1177**
7" Single: Released '88, on Virgin, by Virgin Records. Catalogue no: **VS 1177**
12" Single: Released '88, on Virgin, by Virgin Records. Catalogue no: **VST 1177**
CD 3": Released '88, on Virgin, by Virgin Records. Catalogue no: **VSCD 1177**

LIFE BEGINS AT THE HOP
Tracks: / Life begins at the hop.
7" Single: Released May '79, on Virgin, by Virgin Records. Deleted '82. Catalogue no: **VS 259**

LOVE ON A FARMBOY'S WAGES
Tracks: / Love on a farmboy's wages / In loving memory of a name / Desert island / Toys / Burning with optimism's flame (on 12" only) / Cut it out (on 12" only) / English roundabout (on 12" only).
7" Single: Released Mar '82, on Virgin, by Virgin Records. Deleted '85. Catalogue no: **VS 613**
12" Single: Released Sep '83, on Virgin, by Virgin Records. Catalogue no: **VS 613-12**

LOVING, THE
Tracks: / Loving, The / Cynical days / World is full of angry young men, The.
CD 5": Released Aug '89, on Virgin, by Virgin Records. Catalogue no: **VSCD 1201**
Cassingle: Released Aug '89, on Virgin, by Virgin Records. Catalogue no: **VSC 1201**
7" Single: Released Aug '89, on Virgin, by Virgin Records. Catalogue no: **VS 1201**
12" Single: Released Aug '89, on Virgin, by Virgin Records. Catalogue no: **VST 1201**

MAKING PLANS FOR NIGEL
Tracks: / Making plans for Nigel / Bushman president / Pulsing pulsing.
7" Single: Released Sep '79, on Virgin, by Virgin Records. Catalogue no: **VS 282**

MAKING PLANS FOR NIGEL (OLD GOLD)
Tracks: / Making plans for Nigel / Senses working overtime.
7" Single: Released Nov '88, on Old Gold, by Old Gold Records. Catalogue no: **OG 9819**

MAYOR OF SIMPLETON
Tracks: / Mayor of Simpleton / One of the millions / Ella Guru / Living in a haunted heart (home demo) (Only on CD single.) / Good things, The (home demo) (Only on CD single.).
7" Single: Released Dec '88, on Virgin, by Virgin Records. Catalogue no: **VS 1158**
12" Single: Released Feb '89, on Virgin, by Virgin Records. Catalogue no: **VSR 1158**
12" Single: Released Dec '88, on Virgin, by Virgin Records. Catalogue no: **VST 1158**
CD 3": Released 30 Jan '89, on Virgin, by Virgin Records. Catalogue no: **VSCD 1158**

MEETING PLACE, THE
Tracks: / Meeting place, The / Let's make a den (home demos) / Find the fox / Troubles / Terrorism.
7" Single: Released Apr '87, on Virgin, by Virgin Records. Deleted May '88. Catalogue no: **VS 912**
12" Single: Released Feb '87, on Virgin, by Virgin Records. Catalogue no: **VS 912-12**

NO THUGS IN OUR HOUSE
Tracks: / No thugs in our house / Limelight / Over rusty water.
7" Single: Released May '82, on Virgin, by Virgin Records. Catalogue no: **VS 490**

RESPECTABLE STREET
Tracks: / Respectable street / Strange tales.
7" Single: Released Mar '81, on Virgin, by Virgin Records. Deleted Mar '84. Catalogue no: **VS 407**

SCIENCE FRICTION
Tracks: / Science friction / She's so square / Dance band.
12" Single: Released Apr '83, on Virgin, by Virgin Records. Catalogue no: **VS 188-12**

SENSES WORKING OVERTIME
Tracks: / Senses working overtime / Blame the tiger / Tissue tigers / Egyptian solution (Homo safari series No.3) (CD only).
7" Single: Released Jan '82, on Virgin, by Virgin Records. Catalogue no: **VS 462**
12" Single: Released Jan '82, on Virgin, by Virgin Records. Deleted '89. Catalogue no: **VS 462-12**
CD 3": Released '88, on Virgin, by Virgin Records. Catalogue no: **CDT 9**

SGT. ROCK (IS GOING TO HELP ME)
Tracks: / Sgt. rock (is going to help me) / Living through another Cuba / Generals and Majors.
7" EP: Released Jan '81, on Virgin, by Virgin Records. Deleted '84. Catalogue no: **VS 384**

TAKE THIS TOWN
Tracks: / Take this town / Babylon's burning.
7" Single: Released Dec '80, on RSO, by Polydor Ltd. Deleted Dec '85. Catalogue no: **RSO 71**

TOWERS OF LONDON
Tracks: / Towers of London.
7" Single: Released Oct '80, on Virgin, by Virgin Records. Deleted '83. Catalogue no: **VS 372**

WAIT TILL YOUR BOAT GOES DOWN
Tracks: / Wait till your boat goes down / Ten feet tall.
7" Single: Released Mar '80, on Virgin, by Virgin Records. Deleted Mar '83. Catalogue no: **VS 322**

WONDERLAND
Tracks: / Wonderland.
7" Single: Released Jul '83, on Virgin, by Virgin Records. Deleted '89. Catalogue no: **VS 606**

Xtract

BLAME IT ON THE YOUTH (EP)
Tracks: / Blame it on the youth.
7" Single: Released Jun '83, on Paragon, Catalogue no: **PAX 10**

Xymox

BAD HEARTS
Tracks: / Bad hearts.
12" Single: Released 21 Nov '87, on 4AD, by 4AD Records. Catalogue no: **BAD 711**

DAY, A
Tracks: / Day, A.
12" Single: Released Jul '85, on 4AD, by 4AD Records. Catalogue no: **BAD 504**

OBSESSION
Tracks: / Obsession.
7" Single: Released 8 May '89, on Wing, by Polydor Ltd. Catalogue no: **871 707 1**
12" Single: Released 8 May '89, on Wing, by Polydor Ltd. Catalogue no: **WINGX 5**

X-Y-Zee

ADVENTURES OF E-MAN, THE
Tracks: / Adventures of E-man, The.
12" Single: Released 31 Oct '87, on T-Mac, by T-Mac Records. Deleted '88. Catalogue no: **UEZS 007**

Y

The following information was taken from the Music Master database on October 20th, 1989.

Y

LISTEN TO ME
Tracks: / Listen to me.
7" Single: Released Aug '85, on W.A.R., by W.A.R. Records. Catalogue no: **WAR 3003**
12" Single: Released Aug '85, on W.A.R., by W.A.R. Records. Catalogue no: **12 WAR 3003**

LONELY
Tracks: / Many a time / Lonely.
7" Single: Released Jan '87, on Polydor, by Polydor Ltd. Deleted Aug '87. Catalogue no: **POSP 817**
12" Single: Released Jan '87, on Polydor, by Polydor Ltd. Deleted Aug '87. Catalogue no: **POSPX 817**

Y Cyrff

PUM MUNUD
Tracks: / Pum Mundu.
7" Single: Released '86, on Sus-Recordiau Anhrefn, Deleted '87. Catalogue no: **SUS 01**

Y Llwybr Llaethog

YO!
Tracks: / Yo!.
7" Single: Released Nov '87, on Anhrefn, Catalogue no: **ANHREFN 011**

Y & T

Biographical details: This American heavy metal band -- Joey Alves, Leonard Haze, Phil Kennemore and Dave Meniketti -- took their name from a shortened form of their debut album title, *Yesterday And Today*. This LP was released in 1976 and was followed two years later by the album *Struck Down*, but neither made any real impact. In the early 80's they took note of the major heavy metal resurgence in Britain and began to concentrate on the UK market. *Earthshaker*, a 1981 album, sold slowly but steadily in specialist shops and 1982's *Black Tiger*, recorded in Britain, gave them their first bite at the UK national album chart, reaching No 53 and logging eight weeks on the Top Hundred. By this time the band were playing at the Reading Festival, receiving airtime on Tommy Vance's Friday Rock Show on BBC Radio One and generally settling into the heavy scene in Britain and Europe. Y & T hit the British LP chart in '83 with *Mean Streak* and had a minor hit single with the title track. But they are a run-of-the-mill band, with little to distinguish them from a host of others in the same genre, and have never been destined for the top league. (Bob MacDonald, April 1985). .

DIRTY GIRL
Tracks: / Dirty girl.
12" Single: Released Oct '81, on A&M, by A&M Records. Deleted '87. Catalogue no: **AMSX 8172**

DON'T WANNA LOSE
Tracks: / Don't wanna lose.
7" Single: Released Sep '82, on A&M, by A&M Records. Deleted '87. Catalogue no: **AMS 8251**
12" Single: Released Sep '82, on A&M, by A&M Records. Deleted '87. Catalogue no: **AMSX 8251**

I BELIEVE IN YOU
Tracks: / I believe in you / Rescue me.
12" Single: Released Jun '82, on A&M, by A&M Records. Deleted Jun '85. Catalogue no: **AMSP 8229**

MEAN STREAK (SINGLE)
Tracks: / Mean streak.
7" Single: Released Aug '83, on A&M, by A&M Records. Deleted '86. Catalogue no: **AM 135**

SUMMERTIME GIRLS
Tracks: / Summertime girls / Lipstick and leather.
7" Single: Released '86, on A&M, by A&M Records. Deleted '88. Catalogue no: **AM 264**
12" Single: Released Aug '85, on A&M, by A&M Records. Deleted '87. Catalogue no: **AMY 264**

Ya Ya

CAUGHT IN A LIE
Tracks: / Caught in a lie / First time.
7" Single: Released Nov '88, on WEA, by WEA Records. Catalogue no: **YZ 191**
12" Single: Released Nov '88, on WEA, by WEA Records. Catalogue no: **YZ 191T**

DON'T TALK
Tracks: / Don't talk / Are you ready.
7" Single: Released Aug '84, on Scotti Bros (USA), Deleted '87. Catalogue no: **A 4601**

WHAT CAN I SAY
Tracks: / What can I say.
7" Single: Released Sep '83, on Buzz, Catalogue no: **BUZZ 2**

WHEN THE WORLD CRIED
Tracks: / When the world cried / Set me free / Castles in the sand (Extra track on 12".) / River's edge.
7" Single: Released Mar '88, on WEA, by WEA Records. Catalogue no: **YZ 174**
12" Single: Released Mar '88, on WEA, by WEA Records. Catalogue no: **YZ 174T**

WHEN THE WORLD CRIED (RE-RELEASE)
Tracks: / When the world cried / Julia.
7" Single: Released Jan '89, on WEA, by WEA Records. Catalogue no: **YZ 346**
12" Single: Released Jan '89, on WEA, by WEA Records. Catalogue no: **YZ 346 T**

Yachts

BOX 202
Tracks: / Box 202.
7" Single: Released Jul '79, on Radar, Deleted May '88. Catalogue no: **ADA 42**

FOOL LIKE YOU, A
Tracks: / Fool like you, A.
7" Single: Released Feb '81, on Demon, by Demon Records. Deleted '88. Catalogue no: **D 1005**

IOU
Tracks: / IOU / 24 hours from Tulsa.
7" Single: Released Aug '80, on Radar, Deleted May '88. Catalogue no: **ADA 57**

LOOK BACK IN LOVE
Tracks: / Look back in love.
7" Single: Released Sep '78, on Radar, Deleted May '88. Catalogue no: **ADA 23**

LOVE YOU LOVE YOU
Tracks: / Love you love you.
7" Single: Released May '79, on Radar, Deleted May '88. Catalogue no: **ADA 36**

NOW I'M SPOKEN FOR
Tracks: / Now I'm spoken for.
7" Single: Released Nov '79, on Radar, Deleted May '88. Catalogue no: **ADA 49**

THERE'S A GHOST IN MY HOUSE
Tracks: / There's a ghost in my house / Revelry / Yachting type.
7" Single: Released Apr '80, on Radar, Deleted '82. Catalogue no: **ADA 52**

YACHTING TYPES
Tracks: / Yachting types.
7" Single: Released '78, on Radar, Deleted May '88. Catalogue no: **ADA 25**

Yaeger, Leigh

JOHNNY AND MARY
Tracks: / Johnny and Mary / Johnny and Mary (instrumental).
7" Single: Released Jun '89, on A&M, by A&M Records. Catalogue no: **VOGUE 1**
12" Single: Released Jun '89, on A&M, by A&M Records. Catalogue no: **VOGUE 12**

Yakity Yak

PLEASE DON'T ASK
Tracks: / Please don't ask.
7" Single: Released Nov '80, on Chick-A-Boom, by Chick-A-Boom Records. Catalogue no: **CHICK 001**

RUN BABY RUN
Tracks: / Run baby run.
7" Single: Released '79, on Limp, by Limp Records. Catalogue no: **KOOL 2**

Yakometties

DANCE MUSIC, THE
Tracks: / Dance music, The.
12" Single: Released May '85, on Zeds, Catalogue no: **Z 001**

ONE AND ONLY, THE
Tracks: / One and only / No time to lose.
7" Single: Released '86, on Zeds, Catalogue no: **ZED 7002**

Yakutska

CLICK CLICK
Tracks: / Click click.
CD 5": Released Apr '89, on Play It Again Sam(Belgium), by Play It Again Sam (Belgium). Catalogue no: **CDBIAS 126**

Yancey, Kym

DETERMINATION
Tracks: / Determination.
12" Single: Released Apr '84, on Pinnacle, by Pinnacle Records. Catalogue no: **PIN 30T**

Yang

POWER IS IN YOUR MIND
Tracks: / Power is in your mind (mix 1) / Power is in your mind (mix 2) / Power is in your mind (mix 4) / Power is in your mind (radio exit).
12" Single: Released '86, on Affair, Catalogue no: **FAIR 3**

Yankovic, Weird Al

Biographical details: Architect, accordionist and disc jockey Weird Al Yancovic became bored with songs on the radio and so began parodying them. A studio tape of *Another One Bites The Bus* -- sending up Queen hit *Another One Bites The Dust* -- almost made the US Hot Hundred list in 1981. The first of three LPs charted in America in 1983. *Eat It*, a spoof of Michael Jackson's *Beat It*, had a hilarious video of teenagers pulling apart a plastic chicken. It was a No 12 US hit and brought back memories of the great pop parodist Stan Freberg. (Donald Clarke, March 1988.).

EAT IT
Tracks: / Eat it / That boy can dance.
7" Single: Released Apr '84, on Scotti Bros (USA), Deleted '87. Catalogue no: **A 4257**

F.A.T.
Tracks: / F.A.T. / Eat it (Available on 12" only) / You make me.
7" Single: Released 4 Jul '88, on Polydor, by Polydor Ltd. Catalogue no: **PO 6**
12" Single: Released 4 Jul '88, on Polydor, by Polydor Ltd. Deleted 31 May '89. Catalogue no: **PZ 6**

LIKE A SURGEON
Tracks: / Like a surgeon.
7" Single: Released Jul '85, on Epic, by CBS Records. Catalogue no: **A 6449**

Yarbrough & Peoples

Biographical details: Cavin Yarbrough and Alisa Peebles are an American soul duo who, like the Gap Band, work closely with record producer Lonnie Simmonds. The vocal/instrumental pair, who are highly competent singers with a very soulful feel, burst onto the scane in early 1981 with *Don't Stop The Music*, a pulsating and very commercial slice of funk. It was a US million-seller, reaching the Top Three of soul charts and hitting No 19 on the pop listings. In Britain, where charts are not so rigidly departmentalised, the single cruised to No 7 on the national pop chart. The duo then seemed to disappear as quickly as they had emerged. However, although Yarbrough & Peoples did not come up with another pop winner they continued to visit the American black charts. *Heartbeats*, a 1983 album, yielded the catchy title track as a single and they also found the right groove with 1984's meaty single *Don't Waste Your Time*. (Bob MacDonald, April 1985.).

DON'T STOP THE MUSIC
Tracks: / Don't stop the music / You're my song.
7" Single: Released '80, on Mercury, by Phonogram Ltd. Deleted '83. Catalogue no: **MER 53**
12" Single: Released Dec '80, on Mercury, by Phonogram Ltd. Deleted '83. Catalogue no: **MERX 53**

DON'T STOP THE MUSIC (OLD GOLD)
Tracks: / Don't stop the music (Extended version on 12") / Outstanding (7" only) / Don't push it, don't force it (12" only).
7" Single: Released Feb '88, on Old Gold, by Old Gold Records. Catalogue no: **OG 9781**
12" Single: Released Apr '88, on Old Gold, by Old Gold Records. Catalogue no: **OG 4055**

DON'T WASTE YOUR TIME
Tracks: / Don't waste your time.
7" Single: Released Apr '84, on Total Experience, Deleted May '88. Catalogue no: **XE 501**
12" Single: Released Apr '84, on Total Experience, Deleted May '88. Catalogue no: **XET 501**

GUILTY (SINGLE)
Tracks: / Guilty.
7" Single: Released '86, on Total Experience, Deleted May '88. Catalogue no: **FB 49905**
12" Single: Released '86, on Total Experience, Deleted May '88. Catalogue no: **FT 49906**

HEARTBEATS (SINGLE)
Tracks: / Heartbeats.
7" Single: Released Jan '83, on Total Experience, Catalogue no: **TE 003**
12" Single: Released Jan '83, on Total Experience, Catalogue no: **TEX 003**

I WOULDN'T LIE
Tracks: / I wouldn't lie / I'll be there / I wouldn't lie (Live) (Available on 12" only).
7" Single: Released '86, on RCA, by BMG Records (UK). Catalogue no: **FB 49841**
12" Single: Released '86, on RCA, by BMG Records (UK). Catalogue no: **FT 49842**

Yard Band, The

MUM ITA COOKING
Tracks: / Mum ita cooking.
12" Single: Released '86, on Disco Tex, Deleted May '88. Catalogue no: **DT 17**

Yardbirds

Biographical details: At the time of their greatest success, this British group comprised Jeff Beck, Chris Dreja, Jim McCarty, Keith Relf and Paul Samwell-Smith. The Yardbirds were formed in 1963, and emerged from another group at Kingston Art School, Surrey. In late '63, they took over from the Rolling Stones as the resident act at one of London's most talked about clubs, the Crawdaddy, at the Station Hotel, Richmond, Surrey. At that time, the group consisted of Dreja, McCarty, Relf and Samwell-Smith plus the newly recruited Eric Clapton. The young rhythm and blues combo managed to equal the Stones' attendance figures and, through this and other live engagements, build a strong cult following; they became one of the leading acts in Britain's burgeoning R&B scene and, in late '64, released what many critics consider to be the finest example of the UK's R&B boom, the*Five Live Yardbirds*LP. At around the same time, their second single became their first chart hit -*Good Morning Little Schoolgirl*- reached No.44 on the British singles chart. In early 1965, the Yardbirds moved in a more commercial direction with their acclaimed single*For Your Love*; Clapton resented this move to the pop market and left shortly after it was recorded, without waiting for it to reach the Top 10 on both sides of the Atlantic. *For Your Love*, though not in the blues style that Clapton loved, was certainly an important record. With it's intriguing tempo changes and imaginative arrangement, it was ahead of its time. The song was penned by Graham Gouldman, who was to acheive fame in the Seventies with 10CC. Gouldman also provided their next two biggies,*Heart Full Of Soul*and*Evil Hearted You*, and thus gave the group three consecutive UK Top 3 smashes. Clapton, soon to gain legendary status as a guitar hero, had been replaced on that instrument by another future star, Jeff Beck.*Evil Hearted You*was actually a double A-sided single: members of the group wrote the other side,*Still I'm Sad*, and this gave them the confidence to compose their fourth British Top 3 single*Shapes Of Things*. To crown the combo's 12-month red hot streak, they also enjoyed a big-selling EP. With their singles charting strongly on both sides of the

Atlantic, it seemed that the Yardbirds could do no wrong. But mid-1966's*Over Under Sideways Down*, written by all five members, was their final major hit in both the UK and US. Bassist Samwell-Smith, tired of the group's exacting touring schedules, quit; to replace him, rhythm guitarist Dreja transferred to bass, and Jimmy Page joined. Page had recently been establishing himself as one of Britain's top session guitarists and, with him and Beck together in the group, the Yardbirds might have reached even greater heights. But it did not work out - Beck left in December '66. The depleted foursome's success collapsed; a collaboration with pop producer Mickie Most was a disaster and the Yardbirds folded in July 1968. They had been a great R&B group, then a great pop group, but had ended in disarray. They were an important and influential act, not only because of the merits of their own records, but also because of their role as a training ground for an impressive list of megastars. Clapton went on to join John Mayall's Bluesbreakers, Cream, Blind Faith, Delaney & Bonnie, Derek & The Dominoes and solo stardom. Beck, his replacement, recorded the immortal*Hi Ho Silver Lining*, then acheived success with his own group and as a solo artist. Page formed Led Zeppelin, the world's top rock group of the Seventies. Samwell-Smith became a record producer, scoring notable Seventies successes with Cat Stevens. Relf, the Yardbird's vocalist, met a tragic end in May 76 at the age of 33 - he accidentally electrocuted himself in his own home. (Bob Macdonald 4/85)

UK R&B/rock band formed in 1963 by Keith Relf (born in 1943 in Richmond, Surrey); electrocuted in 1976) on harmonica and vocals; Paul Samwell-Smith (born 1943 in Twickenham) on bass; Chris Dreja (from Surbiton) on rhythm guitar. Tony 'Top' Topham on lead guitar, Jim McCarthy. They played at Richmond's Crawdaddy Club; its manager Giorgio Gomelsky signed them to Columbia. *Good Morning Little Schoolgirl* was a poppy version of a blues classic, followed by Graham Gouldman's blatantly commercial *For Your Love* (transatlantic top ten, with Brian Auger on harpsichord); Clapton left for John Mayall's Bluesbreakers: Jimmy Page turned down the job, Jeff Beck replaced Clapton. 1966 hits *Shapes Of THings* and *Over Under Sideways Down* had psychedelic and Indian sounds respectively, Beck's guitar sounding more like sitar; anarchic stage act was featured in Antonioni's *Swinging London* film *Blow Up* in 1966; Samwell-Smith left (to prod. Cat Stevens etc.); Page now joined, first as bassist, then twinDreja switched to bass. *Happenings Ten Years Time Ago* saw Beck daringly using feedback on record, but he departed under a cloud after illness and reported eccentricities; the remaining quartet's alliance with Mickie Most led to recording of poppy stuff: they split in 1968. LP of Most sessions *Little Games* remains unsatisfactory; only official LP was *Yardbirds* in 1965, also known as *Roger And The Engineer* and reissued under that title by Edsel. Page formed Led Zeppelin. McCarthy, Dreja, Samwell-Smith and ex-Medicine head vocalist John Fiddler became Box Of Frogs, trading on Yardbirds mystique. The Yardbirds were the blues-based band that influenced progressive rock; their best-known work was backing Sonny Boy Williamson. (Donald Clarke)..

6 TRACK HITS
7" EP: Released Mar '84, on Scoop 33, by Pickwick Records. Catalogue no: **7SR 5036**

EVIL HEARTED YOU
Tracks: / Evil hearted you.
7" Single: Released Oct '65, on Columbia, by EMI Records. Deleted '68. Catalogue no: **DB 7706**
7" Single: Released '80, on Mercury, by Phonogram Ltd. Catalogue no: **LR 2795**

FOR YOUR LOVE (CHARLY CD SINGLE)
Tracks: / For your love / Evil hearted you / Heartful of soul / Shapes of things.
CD 5": Released Feb '89, on Charly, by Charly Records. Catalogue no: **CDS 4**

FOR YOUR LOVE (OLD GOLD)
Tracks: / For your love / Heartful of soul / Evil hearted you (CD only).
CD 5": Released 27 Feb '89, on Old Gold, by Old Gold Records. Catalogue no: **OG 6118**
7" Single: Released '82, on Old Gold, by Old Gold Records. Catalogue no: **OG 9109**

FOR YOUR LOVE (SINGLE)
Tracks: / For your love.
7" Single: Released Mar '65, on Columbia, by EMI Records. Deleted '68. Catalogue no: **DB 7499**

GOOD MORNING LITTLE SCHOOL-GIRL
Tracks: / Good morning little schoolgirl.
7" Single: Released Nov '64, on Columbia, by EMI Records. Deleted '67. Catalogue no: **DB 7391**

HAPPENINGS TEN YEARS TIME AGO
Tracks: / Happenings ten years time ago.
7" Single: Released Oct '66, on Columbia, by EMI Records. Deleted '69. Catalogue no: **DB 8024**

HEART FULL OF SOUL
Tracks: / Heart full of soul.
7" Single: Released Jun '65, on Columbia, by EMI Records. Deleted '68. Catalogue no: **DB 7594**

OVER UNDER SIDEWAY DOWN
Tracks: / Over under sideways down / Psycho daisies.
7" Single: Released Jun '66, on Columbia, by EMI Records. Deleted '69. Catalogue no: **DB 7928**
7" Single: Released Feb '83, on Edsel, by Demon Records. Catalogue no: **E 5005**

RACK MY MIND
Tracks: / Rack my mind / Jeff's boogie.
7" Single: Released May '84, on Edsel, by Demon Records. Catalogue no: **E 5007**

SHAPES OF THINGS (SINGLE)
Tracks: / Shapes of things.
7" Single: Released Mar '66, on Columbia, by EMI Records. Deleted '69. Catalogue no: **DB 7848**
7" Single: Released '80, on Mercury, by Phonogram Ltd. Catalogue no: **LR 1287**

STILL I'M SAD (SINGLE)
Tracks: / Still I'm sad / Evil hearted you.
7" Single: Released Jul '82, on Old Gold, by Old Gold Records. Deleted Jul '88. Catalogue no: **OG 9111**

Yargo

CARRYING MINE
Tracks: / Carrying mine.
7" Single: Released Feb '87, on Racket Manufacture, Catalogue no: **RTL 2**
12" Single: Released Feb '87, on Racket Manufacture, Catalogue no: **RTL 3**

GET HIGH
Tracks: / Get high.
12" Single: Released '86, on Skysaw, by Skysaw Records. Catalogue no: **SKY 6**

HELP
Tracks: / Help / Bodybeat blues.
7" Single: Released Oct '88, on London Records, by London Records. Deleted May '89. Catalogue no: **LON 197**
7" Single: Released '88, on Bodybeat, Catalogue no: **BODY 004**
12" Single: Released Oct '88, on London Records, by London Records. Deleted May '89. Catalogue no: **LONX 197**
12" Single: Released Oct '87, on Bodybeat, Catalogue no: **BODY 003**

OTHER SIDE OF MIDNIGHT, THE
Tracks: / Other side of midnight, The / Marimba.
CD 5": Released Aug '89, on London Records, by London Records. Catalogue no: **LONCD 230**
Cassingle: Released Aug '89, on London Records, by London Records. Catalogue no: **LONCS 230**
7" Single: Released Aug '89, on London Records, by London Records. Catalogue no: **LON 230**
12" Single: Released Aug '89, on London Records, by London Records. Catalogue no: **LONX 230**

Yarroh, Per

LAUGHING INSIDE
Tracks: / Laughing inside.
7" Single: Released 27 Feb '88, on H.M.V., by EMI Records. Catalogue no: **PY 1**

Yarrow, Mick

TRISH TRASH
Tracks: / Trish trash.
7" Single: Released Jan '85, on Baskerville, Deleted May '88. Catalogue no: **BAS 1**

Yasmin

I CAN'T FORGET
Tracks: / I can't forget / Life surrounds me.
7" Single: Released '86, on Total Control, by Total Control Records. Deleted May '88. Catalogue no: **TOCO 10**
12" Single: Released '86, on Total Control, by Total Control Records. Deleted May '88. Catalogue no: **12TOCO 10**

Yates, Chris

FBI
Tracks: / Wandering stranger.
7" Single: Released Dec '86, on Les Disques Du Crepuscule(Belgium), by Les Disques Du Crepuscule(Belgium). Catalogue no: **7TWI 710**

PARODY OF ME
Tracks: / Parody of me / Parody of me (inst).
7" Single: Released 13 Jun '87, on Les Disques Du Crepuscule(Belgium), by Les Disques Du Crepuscule(Belgium). Catalogue no: **7TWI 814**

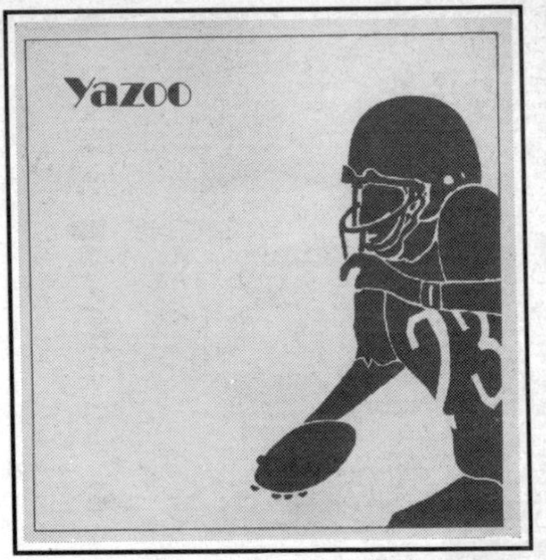

YAZOO - ONLY YOU (Released on Mute)

Yates, Paula

THESE BOOTS ARE MADE FOR WALKING
Tracks: / These boots are made for walking.
7" Single: Released Jun '82, on Virgin, by Virgin Records. Deleted Jun '85. Catalogue no: **VS 493**

Yaz

SITUATION
Tracks: / Situation.
Note: Deleted in the U.K., special megamixes and picture cover.
12" Single: Released Nov '87, on Sire (USA), Catalogue no: **299500**

Yazoo

Biographical details: This great British duo formed in early 1982 and folded in mid-'83. In a lifespan of little more than a year they excited press and public alike with their fusion of two totally contrasting talents -- the striking, bluesy, soulful voice of Alison Moyet and the synthesiser keyboard technology of Vince Clarke. Clarke had come to fame in 1981 as leader and main songwriter of Depeche Mode, but just as they were establishing themselves as one of the UK's top technopop groups he quit: he disliked touring, an inevitable consequence of the band's success. Moyet -- nicknamed Alf -- was a complete unknown. She had been struggling to get her vocal talents onto the London club circuit and had advertised in the music press for a "rootsy blues band. Instead the got the exact opposite: the studio futurism of Clarke. The incongruous combination worked brilliantly. Their first release was *Only You*, a magic pop single that surged to No 2 on the UK chart in Spring '82. Penned by Clarke, this melodic, mid-tempo love song saw two individual talents complementing each other perfectly. They followed it with the more frantic *Don't Go*, a British No 3, and the UK No 3 placing of the debut album, *Upstairs At Eric's*. ("Eric" was their co-producer, E.C. Radcliffe.) After a smaller hit single with *The Other Side Of Love* they returned to the British Top Three in 1983 with *Nobody's Diary* -- coinciding, amusingly, with the discovery of the fake Hitler diaries -- and reached No 1 with their second and final album, *You And Me Both*. They then split amicably, both having different plans for the future. Clarke announced a new studio project, the Assembly, and in late '83 found two simultaneous composing credits in the British Top Ten, the Assembly's *Never Never* coinciding with the Flying Pickets' acapella version of *Only You*, a five-week Christmas No 1. Clarke kept a low profile in 1984, while Moyet launched a very successful solo career. In the United States Yazoo's name was shortened to Yaz, due to the existence of a similarly-titled record label. They enjoyed considerable success on the American dance charts, notably with *Situation*, but *Only You* failed to register highly in the States, despite its later status as a pop, rock and middle-of-the-road standard. (Bob MacDonald, April 1985.)a.

DON'T GO
Tracks: / Don't go / Winter kills.
7" Single: Released Jul '82, on Mute, by Mute Records. Catalogue no: **YAZ 001**
12" Single: Released May '88, on Mute (Germany), by Mute Records. Catalogue no: **INT 126806**
12" Single: Released Jul '82, on Mute, by Mute Records. Catalogue no: **12 YAZ 001**

EUROPE IN THE YEAR ZERO
Tracks: / Europe in the year zero.
12" Single: Released Aug '82, on Sexual Phonograph, Catalogue no: **SPH 1**

NOBODY'S DIARY
Tracks: / Nobody's diary.
12" Single: Released Apr '83, on Mute, by Mute Records. Catalogue no: **12 YAZ 003**
7" Single: Released Apr '83, on Mute, by Mute Records. Catalogue no: **YAZ 003**

ONLY YOU (see panel above)
Tracks: / Only you / Situation.
7" Single: Released May '82, on Mute, by Mute Records. Catalogue no: **MUTE 020**
12" Single: Released May '82, on Mute, by Mute Records. Catalogue no: **12 MUTE 020**

OTHER SIDE OF LOVE, THE
Tracks: / Other side of love, The / Ode to boy.
7" Single: Released Nov '82, on Mute, by Mute Records. Deleted '85. Catalogue no: **YAZ 002**
12" Single: Released Nov '82, on Mute, by Mute Records. Deleted '85. Catalogue no: **YAZ 002T**

Yazz

FINE TIME
Tracks: / Fine time.
CD 5": Released Jan '89, on Big Life, by Big Life Records. Catalogue no: **BLR 006CD**
7" Single: Released Jan '89, on Big Life, by Big Life Records. Catalogue no: **BLR 006R**
7" Single: Released Dec '88, on Big Life, by Big Life Records. Catalogue no: **BLR 006**
12" Single: Released 23 Jan '89, on Big Life, by Big Life Records. Catalogue no: **BLR 006T**
12" Single: Released Dec '88, on Big Life, by Big Life Records. Catalogue no: **BLR 006TR**

ONLY WAY IS UP, THE
Tracks: / Only way is up, The.
12" Single: Released Oct '88, on Intercord (Germany), Catalogue no: **INT 125744**
12" Single: Released Jul '88, on Big Life, by Big Life Records. Catalogue no: **BLR 004T**
12" Single: Released Aug '88, on Big Life, by Big Life Records. Catalogue no: **BLR 004TR**
Cassingle: Released Aug '88, on Big Life, by Big Life Records. Catalogue no: **BLR 004C**
7" Single: Released Jul '88, on Big Life, by Big Life Records. Catalogue no: **BLR 004**

STAND UP FOR YOUR LOVE RIGHTS
Tracks: / Stand up for your love rights.
7" Single: Released Oct '88, on Big Life, by

Big Life Records. Catalogue no: **BLR 005**
12" Single: Released '88, on Intercord (Germany), Catalogue no: **INT 125751**
12" Single: Released Oct '88, on Big Life, by Big Life Records. Catalogue no: **BLR 005T**

WHERE HAS ALL THE LOVE GONE
Tracks: / Where has all the love gone.
12" Single: Released 27 Feb '89, on Big Life, by Big Life Records. Catalogue no: **BLR 008 T**
CD 5": Released Apr '89, on Big Life, by Big Life Records. Catalogue no: **BLR 008 CD**
7" Single: Released 27 Feb '89, on Big Life, by Big Life Records. Catalogue no: **BLR 008**

Yeah God

BETTER WAYS TO SPEND MY TIME
Tracks: / Better ways to spend my time.
7" Single: Released Mar '88, on Drunken Cowboy, Catalogue no: **SRT 1293**

SO FAR DOWN
Tracks: / So far down.
12" Single: Released Apr '88, on Chapter 22, by Chapter 22 Records. Catalogue no: **12CHAP 28**

SUMO (EP)
Tracks: / Sumo.
12" Single: Released 16 Sep '88, on Chapter 22, by Chapter 22 Records. Catalogue no: **12 CHAP 30**

Yeah Jazz

JULIE & THE SEALIONS
Special: Released Jun '84, on Distinctive, by Distinctive Records. Catalogue no: **YEAH 4**
Special: Released Jun '84, on Distinctive, by Distinctive Records. Catalogue no: **YEAH 7**

MORNING O' GRADY
Tracks: / Morning O'Grady.
12" Single: Released Oct '88, on Cherry Red, by Cherry Red Records. Catalogue no: **12 CHERRY 101**

SHARON
Tracks: / Sharon / Girl the years were kind to, The / This is not love (On 12" single only.).
7" Single: Released Nov '87, on Cherry Red, by Cherry Red Records. Catalogue no: **CHERRY 100**
12" Single: Released Nov '87, on Cherry Red, by Cherry Red Records. Catalogue no: **12 CHERRY 100**

SHE SAID
Tracks: / She said / Rain / Travel Scrabble (Available on 12" version only).
7" Single: Released '86, on Upright, by Upright Records. Catalogue no: **UP 18**
12" Single: Released '86, on Upright, by Upright Records. Catalogue no: **UPT 18**

THIS IS NOT LOVE
Tracks: / This is not love / Any day / Childish games / Bob's song.
7" Single: Released '86, on Upright, by Upright Records. Catalogue no: **UP 14**
12" Single: Released '86, on Upright, by Upright Records. Catalogue no: **UPT 14**

Yeah Yeah Noh

BEWARE THE WEAKLING LINES
Tracks: / Beware the weakling lines.
7" Single: Released Oct '84, on In Tape, by In Tape Records. Catalogue no: **IT 010**

BUMPER BOOK
Special: Released 1 Jan '85, on In Tape, by In Tape Records. Catalogue no: **IT 011**

COTTAGE INDUSTRY
Tracks: / Cottage industry.
7" Single: Released Jun '84, on In Tape, by In Tape Records. Catalogue no: **IT 008**

MRS. QUILL
Tracks: / Mrs. Quill.
7" Single: Released Aug '85, on In Tape, by In Tape Records. Catalogue no: **IT 020**
12" Single: Released Aug '85, on In Tape, by In Tape Records. Catalogue no: **ITTI 020**

PEEL SESSIONS:YEAH YEAH NOH
1.1.86
12" Single: Released Apr '87, on Strange Fruit, by Strange Fruit Records. Catalogue no: **SFPS 026**

PICK UP YOUR EARS
Tracks: / Prick up your ears.
7" Single: Released Feb '85, on In Tape, by In Tape Records. Deleted '88. Catalogue no: **IT 012**

TEMPLE OF CONVENIENCE
Tracks: / Temple of convenience.
7" Single: Released Nov '85, on In Tape, by In Tape Records. Catalogue no: **IT 023**
12" Single: Released Nov '85, on In Tape, by In Tape Records. Catalogue no: **ITT 023**

WHEN I AM A BIG GIRL
Special: Released Apr '85, on In Tape, by In Tape Records. Catalogue no: **IT 016**

Yell

BUILD IT UP
Tracks: / Build it up.
12" Single: Released Nov '88, on Two 4 Zero Zero, Catalogue no: **ZERO 1T**

BUILD IT UP (REMIX)
Tracks: / Build it up (remix).
12" Single: Released May '89, on Midnight Music, by Midnight Music Records. Catalogue no: **ZERO 001TS**
12" Single: Released 20 Mar '89, on Midnight Music, by Midnight Music Records. Catalogue no: **ZERO 001TF**

Yello

Biographical details: Swiss sophisticates Yello who recently scored their first British hit with *I love you* release a new single *Lost again* on October 28th. Yello are currently working on a new live show with David Bowie's stage designer. The show, which is set inside a giant Christmas shaker, will be unveiled in New York at the end of the year. The group, Dieter Meiler, Boris Blank and Carlos Peron, are also planning to hire out Madison Square Gardens early in 1984 and selling just 500 tickets for a special Yello performance. (Stiff Press Office, February 1984).

BIMBO
Tracks: / Bimbo / I.T. splash.
7" Single: Released Apr '81, on Do-It, by Do-It Records. Catalogue no: **DUN 11**

BLAZING SADDLES
Tracks: / Blazing saddles / I love you / Heat resistant bag rhythm divine (Only on 12", MC and CD single.) / Blue nabou (Only on 12",MC and CD single.).
CD 5": Released Jul '89, on Mercury, by Phonogram Ltd. Catalogue no: **YELCD 4**
Cassingle: Released Jul '89, on Mercury, by Phonogram Ltd. Deleted Oct '89. Catalogue no: **YELMC 4**
7" Single: Released Jul '89, on Mercury, by Phonogram Ltd. Deleted Oct '89. Catalogue no: **YELLO 4**
12" Single: Released Jul '89, on Mercury, by Phonogram Ltd. Deleted Oct '89. Catalogue no: **YELLO 412**

BOSTICH
Tracks: / Bostich / She's got a gun.
7" Single: Released Sep '81, on Do-It, by Do-It Records. Catalogue no: **DUN 13**

CALL IT LOVE
Tracks: / Call it love.
CD 5": Released '88, on Mercury, by Phonogram Ltd. Deleted Feb '89. Catalogue no: **8883112**
7" Single: Released May '87, on Mercury, by Phonogram Ltd. Deleted Dec '87. Catalogue no: **MER 248**
12" Single: Released May '88, on Vertigo (Germany), Catalogue no: **8883111**
12" Single: Released May '87, on Mercury, by Phonogram Ltd. Deleted Dec '87. Catalogue no: **MERX 248**

DESIRE
Tracks: / Desire.
7" Single: Released Aug '85, on Elektra, by Elektra Records (UK). Catalogue no: **EKR 17**
12" Single: Released Aug '85, on Elektra, by Elektra Records (UK). Deleted Sep '87. Catalogue no: **EKR 17T**

GOLDRUSH
Tracks: / Goldrush / She's got a gun / Pinball cha cha (Included in doublepack only) / Vicious games (Available with doublepack only.) / Guns for hire (live).
7" Set: Released '86, on Mercury, by Phonogram Ltd. Deleted Jul '87. Catalogue no: **MERDP 218**
7" Single: Released '86, on Mercury, by Phonogram Ltd. Deleted Jul '87. Catalogue no: **MER 218**
12" Single: Released May '88, on Vertigo (Germany), Catalogue no: **884877 1**
12" Single: Released '86, on Mercury, by Phonogram Ltd. Deleted Jul '87. Catalogue no: **MERX 218**
12" Single: Released May '88, on Atlantic (Germany), by WEA Records. Catalogue no: **786 819 0**

I LOVE YOU
Tracks: / I love you.
7" Pic: Released Jul '83, on Stiff, by Stiff Records. Catalogue no: **PBUY 176**
7" Single: Released May '83, on Stiff, by Stiff Records. Catalogue no: **BUY 176**
12" Single: Released May '83, on Stiff, by Stiff Records. Catalogue no: **BUYIT 176**

LET ME CRY
Tracks: / Let me cry / Haunted House.
12" Single: Released May '88, on Vertigo (Germany), Catalogue no: **814 101 1**

LOST AGAIN
Tracks: / Lost again.
7" Set: Released Oct '83, on Stiff, by Stiff Records. Catalogue no: **DBUY 191**
7" Single: Released Oct '83, on Stiff, by Stiff Records. Catalogue no: **BUY 191**
12" Single: Released May '88, on Vertigo (Germany), Catalogue no: **814 611 1**
12" Single: Released Oct '83, on Stiff, by Stiff Records. Catalogue no: **BUYIT 191**

OF COURSE I'M LYING
Tracks: / Of course I'm lying / Oh yeah / Yello metropolitan mix down.
CD 5": Released Apr '89, on Fontana, by Phonogram Ltd. Deleted 31 Jul '89. Catalogue no: **YELCD 32**
CD 5": Released 13 Mar '89, on Fontana, by Phonogram Ltd. Deleted 31 Jul '89. Catalogue no: **YELCD 3**
7" Single: Released 13 Mar '89, on Fontana, by Phonogram Ltd. Deleted 31 Jul '89. Catalogue no: **YELLO 3**
12" Single: Released Apr '89, on Fontana, by Phonogram Ltd. Deleted 31 Jul '89. Catalogue no: **YELLO 322**
12" Single: Released 13 Mar '89, on Fontana, by Phonogram Ltd. Deleted 31 Jul '89. Catalogue no: **YELLO 312**

OH YEAH (REMIX) (IMPORT)
Tracks: / Oh yeah (German remix) / La habanera / Oh yeah (Indian summer version).
Note: Unreleased in UK, this is the German remix version.
12" Single: Released Oct '88, on Mercury (Germany), Catalogue no: **888 9081**

PINBALL CHA CHA
Tracks: / Pinball cha cha / Smile on you.
7" Single: Released Jun '82, on Do-It, by Do-It Records. Catalogue no: **DUN 23**
12" Single: Released Jun '82, on Do-It, by Do-It Records. Catalogue no: **DUNIT 23**

RACE, THE
Tracks: / Race, The / Race, The (version) / La habanera (Only on the 12" version.).
CD 5": Released May '88, on Fontana (Germany), Catalogue no: **8703302**
12" Single: Released May '88, on Fontana (Germany), Catalogue no: **8703301**

RACE, THE (VERSION)
Tracks: / Race, The (The Pits mix) / Oh yeah (dance mix).
7" Single: Released Aug '88, on Mercury, by Phonogram Ltd. Deleted 31 May '89. Catalogue no: **YELLO 1**
12" Single: Released Aug '88, on Mercury, by Phonogram Ltd. Deleted 31 May '89. Catalogue no: **YELLR 112**

RHYTHM DIVINE, THE
Tracks: / Rhythm divine, The / Live at the Roxy (Highlights) / La habanera / Doctor Van Steiner / Tool in.
12" Single: Released Jul '88, on Vertigo (Canada), Catalogue no: **8703181**
12" Single: Released May '88, on Mercury (Germany), Catalogue no: **888 761**

SHE'S GOT A GUN
Tracks: / She's got a gun / Bluehead / Evening is young (On 12" only) / There is no reason (On 12" only).
7" Single: Released Jan '82, on Do-It, by Do-It Records. Catalogue no: **DUN 18**
12" Single: Released Jan '82, on Do-It, by Do-It Records. Catalogue no: **DUNIT 18**

TIED UP
Tracks: / Tied up / Wall Street bongo / Tied up in life (Only on CD single and 12" version.) / Tied up in red (Only on 12" version.) / Oh yeah (indian summer version) (Only on CD single.).
CD 5": Released Nov '88, on Fontana, by Phonogram Ltd. Catalogue no: **YELCD 2**
7" Single: Released Nov '88, on Fontana, by Phonogram Ltd. Deleted 31 May '89. Catalogue no: **YELLO 2**
12" Single: Released Nov '88, on Fontana, by Phonogram Ltd. Deleted 31 Jul '89. Catalogue no: **YELLR 212**
12" Single: Released Nov '88, on Fontana, by Phonogram Ltd. Deleted 31 Jul '89. Catalogue no: **YELLO 212**

TIED UP IN MY MIND
Tracks: / Tied up in my mind / I love you / Tied up / Wall Street bongo (12" remix).
12" Single: Released Jan '89, on Mercury, by Phonogram Ltd. Catalogue no: **YELLR 212**

VICIOUS GAMES
Tracks: / Love at the Roxy.
7" Single: Released Nov '86, on Mercury, by Phonogram Ltd. Deleted Jul '87. Catalogue no: **MER 235**
12" Single: Released Nov '86, on Mercury, by Phonogram Ltd. Deleted Jul '87. Catalogue no: **MERX 235**

Yellow Chair

CHRISTMAS SONG
Tracks: / Christmas song, The.
7" Single: Released Dec '82, on Mosa, by Mosa Records. Catalogue no: **MOSA 7**

Yellow Dog

Biographical details: This all-male British band was the brainchild of singer/guitarist/songwriter/producer Kenny Young and his cohort Herbie Armstrong. They evolved in 1977 from the mid-70's hitmakers Fox but, without the distinctive lead vocals of Noosha Fox, Yellow Dog were unable to rise above the status of a passing novelty. The group jumped into the British Top Ten in early '78 with Just One More Night, a gimmick-laden comedy song featuring silly voices, telephones et al. A dire follow-up, Wait Until Midnight, stalled at No 54. Surprisingly, Yellow Dog stayed together long enough to record a 1981 album (their third) entitled Strangers In Paradise. It made no impact and the band had already been long forgotten. (Bob MacDonald, April 1985.).

ESCAPE
Tracks: / Escape / Thalia & the stick boys / Media madness.
7" Single: Released Jul '81, on Escape, by Escape Records. Catalogue no: **ESC 101**

JUST ONE MORE NIGHT
Tracks: / Just one more night.
7" Single: Released Feb '78, on Virgin, by Virgin Records. Deleted '81. Catalogue no: **VS 195**

WAIT UNTIL MIDNIGHT
Tracks: / Wait until midnight.
7" Single: Released Jul '78, on Virgin, by Virgin Records. Deleted '81. Catalogue no: **VS 217**

Yellow, Joe

LOVER TO LOVER
Tracks: / Lover to lover.
12" Single: Released Sep '83, on Calibre, Deleted '85. Catalogue no: **CABL 115**

Yellow Magic Orchestra

Biographical details: The most successful home-grown act in the history of Japanese music, the Yellow Magic Orchestra comprised Riuichi Sakamoto, Haruomi Hosono and Yukihiro Takahashi. The term rock is loosely applied, for their electronic, experimental synthesised music has been dismissed by some as background music (BGM, the title of their 1981 album) and praised by others as avant-garde, adventurous and influential. In terms of technological innovation they should rank alongside West Germany's veterans, Kraftwerk. The Yellow Magic Orchestra were formed in 1978, the three players having gained years of valuable experience in the Japanese music business. Their self-titled debut album was released in that year and was followed in '79 by the more successful *Solid State Survivor*, after which they began to tour internationally. June 1980 was a key month: they had four albums on Japan's national Top Twenty and achieved their sole British chart success when *Computer Game* climbed to No 17. This instrumental track, inspired by space invaders games, summed up their approach to music making. Some argued that such computer music, which relied considerably on rhythm rather than melody, was not really music at all. But they achieved a degree of international recognition for a country which, despite having the world's second-largest record market, gives the world some nifty hi-fi systems but not many records to play on them. YMO's 1983 album, *People With Nice Smiles*, featured Britain's Bill Nelson as a guest. By this time Sakamoto was increasing his profile outside the group, with two successful recording collaborations with UK singer David Sylvian -- leader, appropriately, of the group Japan -- and soundtrack music for the David Bowie film Merry Christmas Mr Lawrence, in which Sakamoto made his acting debut. (Bob MacDonald, April 1985.)
A Japanese technopop band, purveying synthesised sound similar to Kraftwerk, Can, Tangerine Dream etc. Very big in Japan but unable to get much export sales. Leader is keyboardist-composer Ryuichi Sakamoto, a serious and experienced musician who predicted for a world tour in 1980 that "The 1980s will be strong on anxiety feelings... Music will work as a cleaning filter to dissolve distorted satisfactions."
But the tour was not a great success and it is diffult to see why anyone should turn to electronic music to allay anxieties, though the techniques are widely used in pop. *Neo Geo* in 1987 was produced by Bill Laswell, mostly fabricated by a Fairlight CMI but including contributions from Sly Dunbar and Iggy Pop. Sakamoto also produces other acts, records under his own name, acts in and composes music for films. (Donald Clarke 14.5.88).

COMPUTER GAME (THEME FROM INVADERS)
Tracks: / Computer game (theme from Invaders).
7" Single: Released Jun '80, on A&M, by A&M Records. Deleted '83. Catalogue no: **AMS 7502**

YELLOW MAGIC ORCHESTRA - NICE AGE (Released on A & M)

NICE AGE (see panel above)
Tracks: / Nice age / Rydeen.
7" Single: Released '80, on A&M, by A&M Records. Catalogue no: **JAPAN 2**
12" Single: Released '80, on A&M, by A&M Records. Deleted '83. Catalogue no: **JAPAN 122**

RYDEEN
Tracks: / Rydeen / Absolute ego.
7" Single: Released Mar '82, on Alfa, Catalogue no: **ALFA 2145**

THEME FROM THE INVADERS
Tracks: / Theme from the invaders / Technopolis.
7" Single: Released Feb '80, on A&M, by A&M Records. Deleted Feb '83. Catalogue no: **AMS 7502**
12" Single: Released Feb '80, on A&M, by A&M Records. Deleted Feb '83. Catalogue no: **AMSP 7502**

TIGHTEN UP
Tracks: / Tighten up / Rydeen.
7" Single: Released Feb '81, on A&M, by A&M Records. Deleted '84. Catalogue no: **AMSP 8104**

Yellow Man & Thiller U

THIEF
12" Single: Released Jun '89, on Mixing Lab, Catalogue no: **ML 23**

Yellowman

BIMBAM
Tracks: / Bimbam / Ganja trafficking.
12" Single: Released Jun '84, on Ethnic, Catalogue no: **ETH 2247**

BLUEBERRY HILL
Tracks: / Blueberry Hill / Letter to Rosey / Jean a miss follow fashion / Who say yellow don't go hotel / Nah pay no tax / Anything me say / Young girl be wise / Another Saturday night.
7" Single: Released Aug '87, on Greensleeves, by Greensleeves Records. Catalogue no: **GRE 219**

FIGHT OVER MAN
Tracks: / Fight over man.
12" Single: Released Oct '89, on Mixing Lab, Catalogue no: **MXL 28**

GIRL IS MAN
Tracks: / Girl is man / Baby boy.
12" Single: Released Mar '84, on CSA, by CSA Records. Deleted '88. Catalogue no: **SPCSA 12008**

GREGORY FREE
Tracks: / Gregory free.
12" Single: Released Nov '83, on Hawkeye, by Hawkeye Records. Catalogue no: **HD 52**

HOLD ON TO YOUR WOMAN
Tracks: / Hold on to your woman / Rub-a-dub a play.
12" Single: Released Nov '82, on Greensleeves, by Greensleeves Records. Catalogue no: **GRED 106**

HOW TO KEEP A DANCE
Tracks: / How to keep a dance.
12" Single: Released Sep '82, on Gee Gee, Catalogue no: **GG 107**

LOVERS CORNER
Tracks: / Lover's corner / Lover's corner (part 2).
12" Single: Released Jul '82, on Grimmben, Catalogue no: **GRIMMBEN 1-2**

LOVERS TAKE OVER
Tracks: / Lovers take over.
12" Single: Released Mar '82, on Plantation, Catalogue no: **PLA 004**

NOBODY MOVE - NOBODY GET HURT (SINGLE)
Tracks: / Nobody move - nobody get hurt / I can't hide.
12" Single: Released Apr '84, on Jah Guidance, Catalogue no: **VPRD 168**

OPERATION RADICATION
10" single: Released Jun '82, on Pama, by Pama Records. Catalogue no: **PMD 3213**

RIB IT
Tracks: / Rib it / Lonely man.
7" Single: Released Mar '84, on Bebo's Music, Catalogue no: **BBS 001**

RUB-A-DUB PARTNER
Tracks: / Rub-a-dub partner / This old man.
12" Single: Released Jul '83, on Hawkeye, by Hawkeye Records. Catalogue no: **HD 50**

SENSIMILLA
Tracks: / Sensimillia.
12" Single: Released May '83, on Hawkeye, by Hawkeye Records. Catalogue no: **HD 47**

STAY WITH ME
10" single: Released Jun '82, on Pama, by Pama Records. Catalogue no: **PMD 3214**

STRONG ME STRONG
Tracks: / Strong me strong / Dub me strong.
7" Single: Released Apr '84, on CBS, by CBS Records. Deleted May '88. Catalogue no: **A 4241**
12" Single: Released Apr '84, on CBS, by CBS Records. Deleted May '88. Catalogue no: **TA 4241**

SUPERWOMAN
Tracks: / Super woman.
12" Single: Released 31 Jul '89, on Duck Bird, Catalogue no: **DB 001**

WRECK-A-PUMPA
Tracks: / Wreck-a-pumpa.
12" Single: Released Jun '84, on Greensleeves, by Greensleeves Records. Catalogue no: **GRED 148**

YELLOWMAN GET'S MARRIED
Tracks: / Yellowman get's married.
7" Single: Released May '82, on Greensleeves, by Greensleeves Records. Catalogue no: **YELLOW 1**

YOU WRONG TO SEND COME CALL ME
Tracks: / You wrong to send come call me.
12" Single: Released Sep '82, on Hitbound, Catalogue no: **NY 1121**

ZUNGGUZUNGGUGUZUNGGUZENG
Tracks: / Zungguzungguguzungguzeng / Good, the bad and the ugly, The / Rub-a-dub a play / Dem sight the boss / Can't hide from Jah / Who can make the dance ram / Yellowman wise / Take me to Jamaica / Friday night jamboree / Jah Jah are we guiding star.
12" Single: Released Jun '83, on Greensleeves, by Greensleeves Records. Catalogue no: **GRED 119**

Yemm, Bryn

EVENSONG
Tracks: / Evensong.
7" Single: Released Nov '84, on Sierra, by Sierra Records. Deleted Jun '87. Catalogue no: **FED 5**

HOW DO I LOVE THEE (SINGLE)
Tracks: / How do I love thee / I've got faith in you.
7" Single: Released Nov '83, on Lifestyle, by Micrometro Ltd (Records). Catalogue no: **LIFE 6**

OLD RUGGED CROSS
Tracks: / Old rugged cross / Holy city.
7" Single: Released Jan '80, on Damont, by Damont Audio Ltd.. Deleted Jan '85. Catalogue no: **DMS 5003**

WELCOME HOME
Tracks: / Welcome home.
7" Single: on Sierra, by Sierra Records. Deleted Jun '87. Catalogue no: **FED 13**
12" Single: on Sierra, by Sierra Records. Deleted Jun '87. Catalogue no: **FED 13T**

Yen

RED INDIANS
Tracks: / Red Indians.
7" Single: Released Apr '89, on Index, Catalogue no: **IND 1**

Yeow Band

ANYONE SEEN DENNIS
Tracks: / Anyone seen Dennis.
12" Single: Released Sep '82, on Rumble Productions, Deleted May '88. Catalogue no: **YEOW 122**

GIVE MY HEART AWAY
Tracks: / Give my heart away.
7" Single: Released Oct '83, on Rumble Productions, Deleted May '88. Catalogue no: **YEOW 3**
12" Single: Released Oct '83, on Rumble Productions, Deleted May '88. Catalogue no: **YEOW 123**

PREPARE YOURSELF
Tracks: / Prepare yourself.
7" Single: Released Apr '82, on Yeow, Deleted May '88. Catalogue no: **YEOW 001**
12" Single: Released Apr '82, on Yeow, Deleted May '88. Catalogue no: **YEOW 121**

Yes

Biographical details: At the time of their greatest success, this British rock band consisted of Jon Anderson, Steve Howe, Chris Squire, Rick Wakeman and Alan White. Yes were formed in 1968 by singer Anderson and bassist Squire. The additional founder members were Peter Bands, Bill Bruford and Tony Kaye. Their debut eponymous album was released in 1969, and they first reached the lower regions of the British LP chart in 1970 with *Time And A Word*. Guitarist Banks then quit, to be replaced by Howe. 1971 was the year of the group's major breakthrough - the *Yes Album* and *Fragile* both reached No.7 on the UK album chart. In between the two records, keyboards player Kaye was replaced by Wakeman (who had thrilled many listeners with his contribution to David Bowie's 1969 classic Space Oddity). Wakeman's classical training was ideal for Yes, whose aim was to fuse rock and classical music into a symphonic and extravagant (and, according to some, pompous and pretentious) whole. After *Fragile* and 1972's *Close To The Edge* album, drummer Bruford was replaced by White, who had played with John Lennon's Plastic Ono Band. The classic Yes line up was complete. The Yes combination of Wakeman's synthesised, symphonic complexities, Anderson's distinctive, high-pitched and eerily ethereal vocals, and the band's lengthy compositions, added up to a powerful package, both on stage (as captured on 1973's triple set *Yes songs*) and in the studio (*Tales From Topographic Oceans* double album - No.1 in UK in January '74). Yes were now firmly established as one of Britain's leading 'progressive' rock groups, and were an international concert attraction. However, Wakeman quit at this point, being more interested in developing his solo career - this had already begun in early '73 with the success of his album *The Six Wives Of Henry VIII*. The newcomer was Patrick Moraz from Switzerland, who was also classically schooled. This new line up yielded only one album, December 1974's *Relayer*, then a mid-Seventies hiatus followed. Moraz left Yes in late 1976, to be replaced by a returning Wakeman. The favourite line-up was thus back in business and fittingly came back in August '77 with the band's second UK No.1 album, *Going For The One*. This was at the height of the punk revolution, and Ye[s] epitomised the rock hierarchy that was [s] despised by the New Wave protagonist[s]. But the veterans held their own; the group['s] only concession to the changing times wa[s] their new approval of the 45rpm format. Th[e] previously singles-shy band reached No.7 [in] the UK with *Wonderous Stories*. After on[e] more album, *Tormato*, Wakeman finally q[uit] for good, and Anderson also left. The latt[er] teamed with Greece's answer to Wakema[n], Vangelis, and met with big success, despi[te] the less glorious reaction given to Ande[r]son's simultaneous solo career. In a surpri[se] 1980 announcement, Anderson and Wak[e]man's replacements turned out to be Ge[off] Downes and Trevor Horn of the Buggle[s], who had just scored a British No.1 with t[he] ultra-commercial electropop novelty *Video Killed The Radio Star*. But in late 198[0], after the *Drama* album (No.2 in Britain), Y[es] officially folded. Surprisingly, the Yes sto[ry] did not end there. At the end of 1983, [a] revamped line up - Anderson, Squire, Whi[te], the long-gone Kaye plus incoming guita[r]ist/keyboards player Trevor Rabin - releas[ed] a new album *90125* with Trevor Horn [as] producer. With a much more modern sour[d], largely inspired by Horn, the LP yielded t[he] single *Owner Of A Lonely Heart*. A supe[r] fusion of rock, dance and pop styles, *Own[er]* was an American disco smash, and cruis[ed] to the US No.1 pop slot in January '8[4]. Simultaneously, Horn was No.1 in Britain [as] producer of a record that was to make h[im] even more famous - *Relax* by Frankie Go[es] To Hollywood. By this time, Downes a[nd] Howe were established superstars in t[he] States, as 50% of the group Asia. (Bob Ma[c]donald 4.8[...])
A UK rock band formed in 1968, with seve[ral] classically-trained members combining [in]strumental fluency with electronics and th[e] vocal harmonies to make 'classical rock' [...] commercial regarded as pretentious a[nd] empty. Vocalist Jon Anderson (born in 19[44] in Lancashire) and bassist Chris Squ[ire] (born in 1948 in LOndon) recruited guita[rist] Peter Banks, Tony Kaye on keyboards, [Bill] Bruford on drums; Banks left after two [al]bums on Atlantic, replaced by Steve Ho[we]; after another album Kaye left and was [re]placed by composer/keyboardist R[ick] Wakeman for the 1972 album *Fragile*, wh[ich] reached the top five in the USA. Waker[man] and Anderson came and went; vocalist (la[ter] producer) Trevor Horn passed through; B[ru]ford left in 1974 to join King Crimson an[d is] doing by far the most interesting work to[day] under his own name. Yes records are [...] selling but nobody knows who buys the[m] (Donald Clarke 14.5.88).

AMERICA
Tracks: / America.
7" Single: Released '80, on Atlantic ([Im]port), by WEA Records. Deleted May '[...] Catalogue no: **LR 1028**

DON'T KILL THE WHALE
Tracks: / Don't kill the whale.
7" Single: Released Aug '78, on Atlantic WEA Records. Catalogue no: **K 11184**

GOING FOR THE ONE (SINGLE)
Tracks: / Going for the one.
7" Single: Released Nov '77, on Atlantic, WEA Records. Deleted '80. Catalogue no: **11047**

INTO THE LENS
Tracks: / Into the lens / Does it really h[ap]pen.
7" Single: Released '80, on Atlantic, WEA Records. Deleted '81. Catalogue no: **11622**

LEAVE IT
Tracks: / Leave it / Leave it (re-mix) ([...] mix).
7" Single: Released May '84, on Atco Atlantic Recording Corp.(USA). Deleted Catalogue no: **B 9787 C**
7" Single: Released Mar '84, on Atco Atlantic Recording Corp.(USA). Deleted Catalogue no: **B 9787**

LOVE WILL FIND A WAY
Tracks: / Love will find a way / Holy lam[b].
7" Single: Released Sep '87, on Atlantic WEA Records. Catalogue no: **A 9449**
12" Single: Released Sep '87, on Atla[ntic] by WEA Records. Catalogue no: **A 944[9]**

OWNER OF A LONELY HEART
Tracks: / Owner of a lonely heart.
7" Single: Released Nov '83, on Atlantic WEA Records. Deleted May '88. Catalo[gue] no: **B 9817**
12" Single: Released Nov '83, on Atla[ntic] by WEA Records. Deleted May '88. C[ata]logue no: **B 9817 T**

ROUNDABOUT
Tracks: / Roundabout.
7" Single: Released '80, on Atlantic WEA Records. Catalogue no: **LR 1027**

WONDEROUS STORIES
Tracks: / Wondrous stories.

7" Single: Released Sep '77, on Atlantic, by WEA Records. Deleted '80. Catalogue no: **K 10999**

Yes Let's

CARRIED AWAY
Tracks: / Carried away.
7" Single: Released Oct '84, on Irrepressable, Deleted May '88. Catalogue no: **PRES 1**
12" Single: Released Oct '84, on Irrepressable, Deleted May '88. Catalogue no: **PRESIT 1**

Yes No People

MR. JOHNSON
Tracks: / Mr. Johnson / Help yourself / Adventures of Mr. Johnson, The (12" only).
7" Single: Released Oct '87, on London Records, by London Records. Deleted Oct '88. Catalogue no: **LON 150**
12" Single: Released Oct '87, on London Records, by London Records. Deleted Oct '88. Catalogue no: **LONX 150**

Yetties

NELLIE THE ELEPHANT
Tracks: / Nellie the elephant / My grandfather's clock.
7" Single: Released Mar '81, on ASV (Academy Sound & Vision), by Academy Sound & Vision Records. Deleted '85. Catalogue no: **ASV 101**

Yglesia, Francisco

M.A.S.H.
Tracks: / M.A.S.H. / Shimmering harps.
7" Single: Released May '80, on EMI, by EMI Records. Deleted May '85. Catalogue no: **EMI 5067**

Yig Yuze

FACE, THE
Tracks: / Face, The.
" Single: Released Feb '84, on Nudge Nudge, by Backs Recording Co.. Deleted '88. Catalogue no: **NUDGE 001**

Yin & Yan

F
racks: / If.
" Single: Released Mar '75, on EMI, by EMI Records. Deleted '78. Catalogue no: **EMI 2282**

Yipes

ARLIN'
acks: / Darlin' / Heartbreak again.
" Single: Released Oct '80, on RCA, by MG Records (UK). Deleted Oct '83. Catalogue no: **FB 1791**

HIS IS YOUR LIFE
acks: / This is your life / Russian roll.
Single: Released Jan '80, on RCA, by MG Records (UK). Deleted '85. Catalogue o: **XB 9457**

Ymage

' DON'T BOTHER ME
acks: / It don't bother me.
Single: Released 27 Feb '88, on Unique, Unique Records. Catalogue no: **N1Q 02**
" Single: Released 27 Feb '88, on nique, by Unique Records. Catalogue no: **N1Q 02**

Yoakam, Dwight

ographical details: Dwight Yoakam was rn in Kentucky in 1954; he is a country nger and songwriter with allegiance to pure nky tonk: the result is a little like early Elvis esley but with less gospel influence and th a strong nasal vocal quality typical of nky tonk. He is immobile onstage, totally like Presley. His surname is a corruption the German Joachim; like many hillbillies can trace his ancestry back many years. was ignored by Nashville and went to Los geles; now Nashville ignores him and er 'new country' stars at its peril: his vers of classic honky-tonk songs are intering and his own songs show promise. onald Clarke 14.5.88).

ITARS, CADILLACS (SINGLE)
cks: / Ring of fire.
Single: Released Nov '86, on Warner s., by WEA Records. Deleted Jun '87. alogue no: **W 8528**

NKY TONK MAN
cks: / Honky tonk man / Miner's prayer / e gone* (8 = extra track. Availale on 12" gle only).
Single: Released Jul '86, on Warner s., by WEA Records. Deleted Jun '87. alogue no: **W 8793**
Single: Released Jul '86, on Warner s., by WEA Records. Deleted Jun '87. alogue no: **W 8793T**

TLE SISTER
cks: / Little sister / This drinking will kill / Honky tonk man (live) (on 12" only.) / Cadillacs (live) (Extra track on 12" only).
7" Single: Released May '87, on Warner Bros., by WEA Records. Deleted Jan '88. Catalogue no: **W 8432**
12" Single: Released May '87, on Warner Bros., by WEA Records. Deleted Jan '88. Catalogue no: **W 8432T**

STREETS OF BAKERSFIELD
Tracks: / Streets of Bakersfield / One more name / Honky tonk man (live) (Only on 12") / Guitars, cadillacs (Only on 12").
7" Single: Released 16 Sep '88, on Reprise, by WEA Records. Catalogue no: **W 7964**
12" Single: Released 16 Sep '88, on Reprise, by WEA Records. Catalogue no: **W 7964T**

Yobs

YOBS ON 45 Christmas medley
Tracks: / Yobs on 45.
7" Single: Released Dec '81, on Fresh, by Jetstar Records. Catalogue no: **FRESH 41**

Yodelling Hoovers

HAIRY THING IN A PLASTIC BAG, A
Tracks: / Hairy thing in a plastic bag, A.
7" Single: Released Oct '79, on Dubious, Deleted '88. Catalogue no: **DUB 5**

York

IT'S ON ME
Tracks: / It's on me / Don't stop / You are everything* (* = Extra track. Available on 12 single only.).
7" Single: Released Mar '86, on Spartan, Catalogue no: **SP 132**
7" Single: Released Mar '86, on Spartan, Catalogue no: **12SP 132**

PLAIN AS BLACK AND WHITE
Tracks: / Plain as black and white.
7" Single: Released Oct '85, on Spartan, Catalogue no: **SP 127**
12" Single: Released Oct '85, on Spartan, Catalogue no: **12SP 127**

York, Barbara

CLOSE TO YOU
Tracks: / Close to you.
7" Single: Released Mar '84, on Banana, Deleted '88. Catalogue no: **FRUIT 4**
12" Single: Released Mar '84, on Banana, Deleted '88. Catalogue no: **FRUIT 4T**

York, Nola

MILES AWAY
Tracks: / Miles away / Sweet desire.
7" Single: Released Sep '82, on Aggro, by Chantel Records. Deleted '88. Catalogue no: **AG 3**

Yorke, Janice

DISTANT SHORES
Tracks: / Distant shores / Wind talking to the pines, The / Jodie.
7" Single: Released Jul '82, on SRT, by SRT Records. Deleted '88. Catalogue no: **SRTS 82**

Yosser's Gang

GIS A JOB
Tracks: / Gis a job / Maggie's economic policies.
7" Single: Released Dec '82, on Rialto (1), by Rialto Records. Deleted '88. Catalogue no: **RIA 14**
12" Single: Released Dec '82, on Rialto (1), by Rialto Records. Deleted '88. Catalogue no: **12RIA 14**

You

SHE'S MINE
Tracks: / She's mine / High wire.
7" Single: Released Sep '83, on Allstars, by Allstars Records. Deleted '88. Catalogue no: **AS 001**

You & I

SHADY LADY
Tracks: / Shady lady / I want to be with you.
7" Single: Released Sep '81, on Steinar, by Steinar Records (UK). Deleted '88. Catalogue no: **STEINAR 01**

You Must Be Joking

I'M A HOORAY HENRY
Tracks: / I'm a hooray Henry.
12" Single: Released Jan '86, on Hooray, Catalogue no: **HRH 001**

Young, Bob

MEAN GIRL
Tracks: / Mean girl / Living on an island.
7" Single: Released Jun '86, on Making Waves, by Celtic Music. Deleted Nov '87. Catalogue no: **SURF 115**

Young & Co

Biographical details: This American disco band, which featured a female singer fronting a funky male group, climbed to the UK No.20 slot in November 1980 with/ *Like (What You're Doing To Me)*. No-one knew who they were, but the important fact was that the single was catchy pleasant and, of course, highly danceable. It logged 12 weeks on the British Top 75. Chalk up another one-off disco hit by another faceless group. (Bob Macdonald 4/85).

I LIKE (WHAT YOU'RE DOING TO ME)
Tracks: / I like (what you're doing to me).
7" Single: Released Oct '80, on Excaliber, by Red Bus Records. Deleted '88. Catalogue no: **EXC 501**
12" Single: Released Oct '80, on Excaliber, by Red Bus Records. Deleted '88. Catalogue no: **EXCL 501**

Young & Company

STRUT YOUR SEXY STUFF LADY
Tracks: / Strut your sexy stuff lady / Waiting on your love.
7" Single: Released Mar '81, on Excaliber, by Red Bus Records. Deleted '88. Catalogue no: **EXC 505**
12" Single: Released Mar '81, on Excaliber, by Red Bus Records. Deleted '88. Catalogue no: **EXCL 505**

Young, Devaney

SECOND CHANCE
Tracks: / Second chance.
7" Single: Released Aug '84, on Ryker, Catalogue no: **RYK 1**

Young, Faron

Biographical details: This American country singer, born in Louisiana in 1932, built his career via two conventional country and western outlets - the Louisiana Hayride radio show and Nashville's Grand Ole Opry. His upward climb was interrupted by the draft but, after a few struggles, he established himself as an unadventurous but in demand entertainer, with such country chart hits as 1959's *Country Girl*. In 1961 he scored his only Top 40 hit on the US pop charts - *Hello Walls* reached number 12 on the Billboard Hot 100, and gave an early succes to it's composer Willie Nelson. By the end of the Sixties, Young had chalked up dozens of Top 10 singles on the American country charts, thanks to his smooth vocal delivery and his forays into television and cinema. 1972 brought the singer his only British pop hit, a middle-of-the-road ballad entitled *It's Four In The Morning*, which reached No.3 and logged an impressive total of 23 weeks on the charts. The album of the same name hit the UK Top 30. By this time, he was publisher of Music City News, Nashville's country paper, and was one of the genre's elder statesmen. (Bob Macdonald 14.4.88)
Faron Young was bornin 1932 in Shreveport, Louisiana; he is one of the top ten most sucessful country singers and songwriters of all time. He toured with Webb Pierce's show, sighed with Capitol Records in 1951, served in Korea and had his first hit in 1953: his own song *Goin' Steady*. There was hardly a week when one of his records was not found in the Billboard country chart for 20 years, and he was still going strong for another decade after that First No.1 hit was *Country Girl* in 1959; second was *Hello Walls* in 1961, also a No.12 pop hit and a big break for its author, Willie Nelson. He hired a bellhop named Roger Miller to play drums, although Miller had never played drums in his life. He switched to Mercury in 1963 and had eight top ten hits in a row in 1969-71 including a remake of *Goin' Steady* and an international hit with No.1 *It's Four in the Morning* (made pop Hot 100, top 30 in the UK). His business interests included the Nashville magazine **Music City News** for many years; he appeared in the TV show **Daniel Boone** and made films including **Country Music Holiday**, with Ferlin Husky and Zsa Zsa Gabor. He switched to MCA in the late 1970s. (Donald Clarke 14.5.88).

IT'S FOUR IN THE MORNING (SINGLE)
Tracks: / It's four in the morning.
7" Single: Released Jul '72, on Mercury, by Phonogram Ltd. Deleted '75. Catalogue no: **6052 140**

Young Gods

DID YOU MISS ME
Tracks: / Hello hello I'm back again / Did you miss me / Irrtum boys.
7" Single: Released Apr '87, on Product Inc., Catalogue no: **PROD 7**
12" Single: Released Apr '87, on Organik, Catalogue no: **12 PROD 7**

ENVOYE
Tracks: / Envoye.
12" Single: Released Oct '87, on Organik, Catalogue no: **ORG 086/6**

L'AMOURIR
Tracks: / L'amourir.
CD 5": Released Oct '88, on Play It Again Sam(Belgium), by Play It Again Sam (Belgium). Catalogue no: **BIAS 101 CD**
7" Single: Released Sep '88, on Play It Again Sam(Belgium), by Play It Again Sam (Belgium). Catalogue no: **BIAS 101**

Young Idea

WITH A LITTLE HELP FROM MY FRIENDS
Tracks: / With a little help from my friends.
7" Single: Released Jun '67, on Columbia, by EMI Records. Deleted '70. Catalogue no: **DB 8205**

Young, Jimmy

Biographical details: This British singer, born in 1927, came to fame in the early Fifties with his version of Nat King Cole's US No.1 *Too Young*. This occured before the November 1952 inception of the British record charts, and Young's first charted hit was January 1953's *Faith Can Move Mountains*, which reached No.11. later that year, he hit the Top 10 with *Eternally*. An 18-month low period then followed, during which the singer failed to hit the charts at all. Young came back bigger than ever in 1955 with *Unchained Melody*, a UK No.1 smash that brushed aside opposition from three other versions. Les Baxter's American No.1 peaked at No.10 in Britain. That song was the theme from a Hollywood movie, as was Young's second consecutive chart-topper, *The Man From Laramie*. That hit strode the summit for four weeks in autumn '55, and helped to make him one of the UK's biggest selling artists of the year. 1955's charts were dominated by middle-of-the-road ballad singers, although rock'n'roll was just starting to work it's way into public conciousness. Young was typical of the old school of popular vocalists - clean cut, with a pleasant voice and affable personality. 1956 brought the singer two more UK Top Tenners with *Chain Gang* (nothing to do with the Sam Cooke song) and *More*. His run of chart entries came to an end in May 1957. After a six year gap, Young returned to the UK charts with Miss You, a 1963 version of Dinah Shore's 1942 US hit. This took him to No.15, which was quite an acheivement for a veteran singer in the new Beatles-dominated Britain. His very last hit was in Spring 1964 - he peaked at No.43 with a re-recording of *Unchained Melody*, perhaps in precognitive anticipation of the succesful '65 remake by the Righteous Brothers. By the end of the Sixties, Young had put his singing career behind him and turned to broadcasting. After being part of the fledgling Radio One, he moved over to the BBC's MoR music station, Radio Two. There he became a national instituation during the Seventies and Eighties. His mid-morning diet of easy listening music, recipes, advice, dedications and interviews with leading politicians made Young the natural housewives choice. Terry Wogan, Tony Blackburn, Dave Lee Travis, Paul Burnett and Steve Wright all have hit records to their name, but no BBC disc jockey can match Jimmy Young's two No.1 smashes. (Bob Macdonald 4.85)
Jimmy Young was born 1927 in Gloucestershire; he was the son of a miner and first sang professionally in 1949, spotted by BBC producer George Innes. He had number one hits with movie themes in 1955 and became a deejay with the BBC just as the corporation was forced by competition from pirate radio stations to update itself: from 1967 his radio format was more revolutionary than his crooning, mixing records with information on consumer subjects and current affairs, interviews with politicians including Prime Ministers. The show is still running. (Donald Clarke 14.5.88)

This British singer, born in 1927, came to fame in the early Fifties with his version of Nat King Cole's US No.1 *Too Young*. This occurred before the November 1952 inception of the British record charts, and Young's first charted hit was January 1953's *Faith Can Move Mountains*, which reached No.11. Later that year, he hit the Top 10 with *Eternally*. An 18 month low period then followed, during which the singer failed to hit the charts at all.
Young came back bigger than ever in June 1955 with *Unchained Melody*, a UK No.1 smash that brushed aside opposition from three other versions. Les Baxter's American No.1 rendition peaked at No.10 in Britain. That song was the theme from a Hollywood movie, as was Young's consecutive chart topper, *The Man From Laramie*. That hit strode the summit for four weeks in autumn '55 and helped to make him one of the UK's biggest selling artists of the year. 1955's charts were dominated by middle of the road ballad singers, although rock'n'roll was just starting to work its way into the public consciousness. Young was typical of the old school of popular vocalists - clean cut with a pleasant voice and affable personality. 1956 brought the singer two more UK Top Tenners with *Chain Gang* (nothing to do with the Sam Cooke song) and *More*. His run of chart

entries came to an end in May 1957.
After a six year gap, Young returned to the UK charts with *Miss You*, a 1963 version of Dinah Shore's 1942 US hit. This took him to No.15 which was quite an achievement for a veteran singer in the new Beatles dominated Britain. His very last hit was in the spring '64 - he peaked at No.43 with a re-recording of *Unchained Melody*, perhaps in precognitive anticipation of the successful '65 remake by the Righteous Brothers.
By the end of the Sixties, Young had put his singing career behind him and turned to broadcasting. After being part of the fledgling Radio One, he moved over to the BBC's MoR music station, Radio Two. There he became a national institution during the Seventies and Eighties. His mid morning diet of easy listening music, recipes, advice, dedications and interviews with leading politicians, made Young the natural housewives' choice. Terry Wogan, Tony Blackburn, Dave Lee Travis, Paul Burnett and Steve Wright all have hit records to their name, but no BBC disc jockey can match Jimmy Young's two No.1 smashes. (Bob Macdonald April 1985).

CHAIN GANG
Tracks: / Chain gang.
7" Single: Released Mar '56, on Decca, by Decca Records. Deleted '59. Catalogue no: **F 10694**

ETERNALLY
Tracks: / Eternally.
7" Single: Released Aug '53, on Decca, by Decca Records. Deleted '56. Catalogue no: **F 10130**

FAITH CAN MOVE MOUNTAINS
Tracks: / Faith can move mountains.
7" Single: Released Jan '53, on Decca, by Decca Records. Deleted '56. Catalogue no: **F 9986**

MAN FROM LARAMIE
Tracks: / Man from Laramie, The.
7" Single: Released Sep '55, on Decca, by Decca Records. Deleted '58. Catalogue no: **F 10597**

MISS YOU
Tracks: / Miss you.
7" Single: Released Oct '63, on Columbia, by EMI Records. Deleted '66. Catalogue no: **DB 7119**

MORE
Tracks: / More.
7" Single: Released Sep '56, on Decca, by Decca Records. Deleted '59. Catalogue no: **F 10774**

RICH MAN POOR MAN
Tracks: / Rich man poor man.
7" Single: Released Jun '56, on Decca, by Decca Records. Deleted '59. Catalogue no: **F 10736**

ROUND AND ROUND
Tracks: / Round and round.
7" Single: Released Mar '57, on Decca, by Decca Records. Deleted '60. Catalogue no: **F 10875**

SOMEONE ON YOUR MIND
Tracks: / Someone on your mind.
7" Single: Released Dec '55, on Decca, by Decca Records. Deleted '58. Catalogue no: **F 10640**

TIMES ARE TIGHT
Tracks: / Times are tight.
7" Single: Released Apr '83, on Nite Life, Deleted '88. Catalogue no: **LIFE 2**

TOO YOUNG (SINGLE)
Tracks: / Too young / Story of my life.
7" Single: Released Nov '80, on Piccadilly, Deleted Nov '83. Catalogue no: **7P 203**

TWO HEADS ARE BETTER THAN ONE
Tracks: / Two heads are better than one / Beer is best / Two heads are better than one.
7" Single: Released Nov '83, on Paramount, Deleted '88. Catalogue no: **PARA 102**

UNCHAINED MELODY
Tracks: / Unchained melody.
7" Single: Released May '55, on Decca, by Decca Records. Deleted '58. Catalogue no: **F 10502**
7" Single: Released Mar '64, on Columbia, by EMI Records. Deleted '67. Catalogue no: **DB 7234**

WAYWARD WIND
Tracks: / Wayward wind.
7" Single: Released Jun '56, on Decca, by Decca Records. Deleted '59. Catalogue no: **F 10736**

Young, John Paul

Biographical details: This Australian singer enjoyed a period of stardom in his native country during the late Seventies. In the UK and USA, he is remembered solely for his 1978 single *Love Is In The Air*. This joyful, summery pop record sounded rather like Neil Diamond entering the Eurovision Song Contest, and yet it managed to be tasteful and appealing. It was masterminded by Harry Vanda & George Young (no relation) who were the nucleus of Australia's Easybeats in the Sixties and who were responsible for guiding the early career of AC/DC. *Love Is In The Air* was released in Britain at the beginning of March 1978 and proved to be a sleeper smash: it entered the charts at the end of April, and reached it's No.5 peak at the beginning of June. The single took off in the States in the late summer, and hit No.7. Although another single, *The Day My Heart Caught Fire*, caused minor ripples in the US, John Paul Young was soon forgotten. There was better luck for Vanda & Young, who received spasmodic success as Flash & The Pan. (Bob Macdonald 4/85).

LOVE IS IN THE AIR
Tracks: / Love is in the air / Love you so bad it hurts.
7" Single: Released Apr '78, on Ariola, by BMG Records (UK). Deleted '81. Catalogue no: **ARO 117**
7" Single: Released Jul '82, on Old Gold, by Old Gold Records. Catalogue no: **OG 9125**

Young, Jonathon

BOUND FOR MEXICO
Tracks: / Bound for Mexico.
Cassingle: Released Mar '86, on Ritz-Homespun, by Homespun Records. Catalogue no: **CHR 1986**
7" Single: Released Mar '86, on Ritz-Homespun, by Homespun Records. Catalogue no: **HR 1986**

Young, Karen

Biographical details: This American singer scored a one-off success in 1978. She had nothing to do with the British vocalist of the same name who hit the UK Top 10 with 1969's *Nobody's Child*. The US Karen Young found favour on the dancefloor in 78 with *Hot Shot*, which climbed to No.34 on the UK pop chart (though it failed to enter the American Top 40). The song was re-issued a mere six months later on the strength of the ever-expanding disco boom; it peaked at No.75 on the UK chart second time around. Karen Young continued recording during the Eighties, but failed to deliver any more hot shots. (Bob McDonald 4/85).

HOT SHOT
Tracks: / Hot shot remixed.
7" Single: Released Aug '78, on Atlantic, by WEA Records. Deleted '81. Catalogue no: **K 11180**
7" Single: Released Feb '79, on Atlantic, by WEA Records. Deleted '82. Catalogue no: **LV 8**
12" Single: Released Jan '87, on Streetwave, Catalogue no: **MKHAN 80**

I'M HOT FOR YOU
Tracks: / I'm hot for you.
7" Single: Released Sep '83, on Design Communications, Deleted '88. Catalogue no: **DES 3**
12" Single: Released Sep '83, on Design Communications, Deleted '88. Catalogue no: **DEST 3**

NOBODY'S CHILD
Tracks: / Nobody's child.
7" Single: Released Sep '69, on Major Minor, Deleted '72. Catalogue no: **MM 625**
7" Single: Released Sep '85, on Old Gold, by Old Gold Records. Deleted Sep '89. Catalogue no: **OG 9531**

THOUSAND STARS, A
Tracks: / Thousand stars, A / Angel baby.
7" Single: Released Jul '82, on Revival, Catalogue no: **REV 6002**

YOU DON'T KNOW WHAT YOU'VE GOT
Tracks: / You don't know what you've got.
7" Single: Released Jun '83, on Firebird, by Pinnacle Records. Catalogue no: **FLAME 40**
12" Single: Released Jun '83, on Firebird, by Pinnacle Records. Catalogue no: **FLAME 40T**

Young Love

DO IT THE ENGLISH WAY
Tracks: / Do it the english way / Easy to do it.
7" Single: Released May '80, on Flair, by Flair Records. Deleted May '85. Catalogue no: **FLA 001**

DOING IT THE ENGLISH WAY
Tracks: / Doing it the English way / Easy to do it to.
7" Single: Released Apr '80, on Flair, by Flair Records. Deleted Apr '83. Catalogue no: **FLA 008**

SEXUAL HEALING RAP
Tracks: / Sexual healing rap / Sexual healing rap (instrumental).
12" Single: Released Sep '89, on Evejim, Catalogue no: **12 PO 26**

YOUNG MARBLE GIANTS - TESTCARD E.P. (Released on Rough Trade

Young Marble Giants

FINAL DAYS
Tracks: / Final days.
7" Single: Released Oct '80, on Rough Trade, by Rough Trade Records. Catalogue no: **RT 043**

TESTCARD
Tracks: / Testcard.
7" Single: Released '81, on Rough Trade, by Rough Trade Records. Catalogue no: **RT 059**

TESTCARD E.P. (see panel above)
Tracks: / Clicktalk / Zebra trucks / Sporting life / This way / Posed by models / Clock, The.
7" EP: Released '81, on Rough Trade, by Rough Trade Records. Catalogue no: **RT 059**

Young MC

BUST A MOVE (see panel below)
Tracks: / Bust a move / Got more rhymes / Know how (Only on 12" version.) / Fastes rhymes, The (Only on 12" version.).
Cassingle: Released Jun '89, on 4th & Broadway, by Island Records. Catalogue no: **BRCA 137**
7" Single: Released Jun '89, on 4th & Broadway, by Island Records. Catalogue no: **BRW 137**
12" Single: Released Oct '89, on 4th & Broadway, by Island Records. Catalog no: **12 BRX 137**
12" Single: Released Jun '89, on 4th Broadway, by Island Records. Catalog no: **12 BRW 137**

KNOW HOW
Tracks: / Know how / Fastest rhyme, Th Know how (inst) (Only on 12") / Fast rhyme, The (inst) (Only on 12").
7" Single: Released 17 Oct '88, on De cious, Catalogue no: **BRW 120**
12" Single: Released 17 Oct '88, on D cious, Catalogue no: **12 BRW 120**

Young, Monalisa

DANCING MACHINE
Tracks: / Dancing machine.
7" Single: Released Apr '83, on Motown, BMG Records (UK). Deleted '88. Catalog no: **TMG 1302**
12" Single: Released Apr '83, on Motow by BMG Records (UK). Deleted '88. Ca logue no: **TMGT 1302**

Young & Moody Band

DON'T DO THAT
Tracks: / Don't do that / How can I help y tonight.
7" Single: Released Oct '81, on Bronze Bronze Records. Deleted '84. Catalogue **BRO 130**

THESE EYES

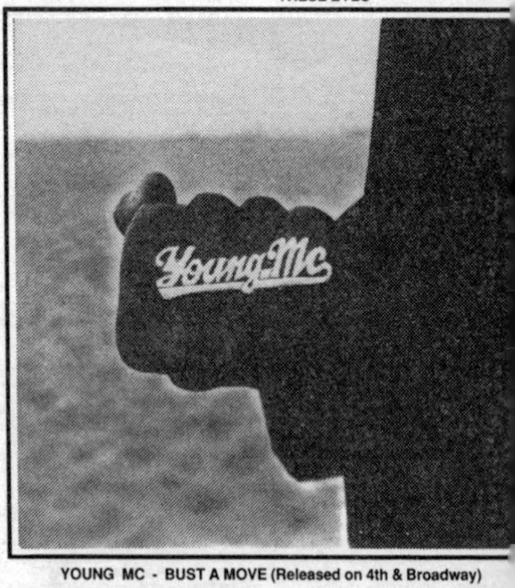

YOUNG MC - BUST A MOVE (Released on 4th & Broadway)

Tracks: / These eyes / I won't let you go.
7" Single: Released May '81, on Bronze, by Bronze Records. Deleted May '84. Catalogue no: **BRO 120**

Young, Neil

Biographical details: This Canadian singer, songwriter and guitarist, born in Toronto, first came to fame in 1967 as a member of Buffalo Springfield, an acclaimed rock group formed the previous year. Also in the group were Stephen Stills and Richard Furay, whom Young had known for some time, prior to the combos formation. He had worked in various small-time outfits with a variety of musicians, and also as a solo Dylan-inspired folk singer. During their two years in existence, Buffalo Springfield, who were based in Los Angeles, received great acclaim for their ecclectic and imaginative combination of folk, country and rock styles. Comparisons with the Beatles were inspired in the minds of some observers, although Buffalo's status was impaired by inefficient management. Their fusion of high energy rock with melodic songwriting sounded great, particularly in a live setting, but a major tour was never organised. The albums *Buffalo Springfield* and *Buffalo Springfield Again* exercised an enormous influence on the Seventies West Coast sound, including such key acts as the Eagles and Jackson Browne. Stills and Young played twin guitars in Buffalo, and they made exciting listening; the group also gave the latter an opportunity to develop his profoundly mournful and introspective songwriting. Personality clashes and musical differences led to the demise of Buffalo Springfield in 1968. Young released his first solo LP the following year, which was a self-titled set. He then formed a backing band called Crazy Horse, whose name was credited on some, but not all, of Young's many subsequent solo albums. In the summer of '69, he accepted an invitation to join Crosby, Stills & Nash, and was thus successfully reunited with Stephen Stills, his former Buffalo colleague. CSN&Y's appearance at the legendary Woodstock festival (August 1969) and their acclaimed studio album *Deja Vu* (1970) were major landmarks in Young's career. By '71, however, the quartet was terminated. Not that Young was worried - he had just released a new solo LP that was critically acclaimed and commercially successful. Young's *After The Goldrush* album reached No.7 on the UK charts and logged 68 weeks on the listings; it was also a big seller in the States and in his native Canada. The emotional despair of *Only Love Can Break Your Heart*, a US Top 40 single from the album, was typical of his early 70's work. *After The Goldrush* remains his best known solo album, together with it's 1972 follow-up, Harvest. The latter was a No.1 LP on both sides of the Atlantic, and yielded the US No.1 and UK No.10 single *Heart Of Gold*, a touching and personal ballad. In 1974, Prelude acheived a transatlantic Top 40 single with the title track of *After The Goldrush* the British trio's acapella vocals were more acceptable to some listeners than Young's distinctive, whining, wailing, high-pitched voice. Prelude's single made a second appearance on the UK Top 40 in 1982. Young's career took a major turn away from commercial dictates in 1973. He had been hit hard by the death, from a drugs overdose, of Crazy Horse guitarist Danny Whitten, and this figured in his music for several years. In addition to this, Young no longer seemed to want stardom. During the remainder of the Seventies and early Eighties, his career was erratic, unpredictable and unimaginitive. He had a brief reunion with Stills in the Stills-Young Band in 1976, paid an unexpected tribute to Johnny Rotten on the 1979 album *Rust Never Sleeps* (made into a film), turned to synthesisers and electronics on 1982's *Trans* album, and went back to rock music's raw rock'n'roll roots on 1983's *Everybody's Rockin'* set. The public was no longer buying Young's albums in large quantities but, unlike some other veterans, he was still an interesting figure. (Bob Macdonald 4.85)
Neil Young was born in 1945 in Toronto, Canada. The guitarists, singer and songwriter is one of the most influential survivers of the Woodstock generation. He worked with Buffalo Springfield in the '60s, leaving before their demise and signing to Reprise as a solo act; his albums with Crazy House 1969-70 are classics of country rock: *Everybody Knows this is Nowhere* and *After the Goldrush*; *Harvest* in 1972 was a number one LP with number one single *Heart of Gold* and solo acoustic *The Needle and the Damage Done*, recorded after the death of Danny Whitten, Crazy Horse's leader: Young remains anti-drug. His sales were helped by his stint with Crosby, Stills, Nash and Young, one of the most popular vocal groups of all time. He switched to Geffen in 1983; some of his recent albums have suffered from too-slick production, but of his 21 albums through 1986, all but the first have made the USA charts. (Donald Clarke 14.5.88).

FOUR STRONG WINDS
Tracks: / Four strong winds.
7" Single: Released Jan '79, on Reprise, by WEA Records. Deleted '82. Catalogue no: **K 14493**

HAWKS & DOVES (SINGLE)
Tracks: / Hawks & doves / Union man.
7" Single: Released Nov '80, on Reprise (USA), Catalogue no: **K 14508**

HEART OF GOLD
Tracks: / Heart of gold.
7" Single: Released Mar '72, on Reprise, by WEA Records. Deleted '75. Catalogue no: **K 14140**
7" Single: Released '80, on Reprise (USA), Catalogue no: **LR 8163**

LITTLE THING CALLED LOVE
Tracks: / Little thing called love / We are in control.
7" Single: Released Jan '83, on Geffen, by Geffen Records (USA). Deleted '88. Catalogue no: **GEFA 2781**

LONG WALK HOME
Tracks: / Long walk home.
7" Single: Released 30 May '87, on Geffen, by Geffen Records (USA). Deleted '88. Catalogue no: **GEF 24**

WEIGHT OF THE WORLD
Tracks: / Weight of the world / Pressure.
7" Single: Released Sep '86, on Geffen, by Geffen Records (USA). Deleted Jun '87. Catalogue no: **GEF 7**
12" Single: Released Sep '86, on Geffen, by Geffen Records (USA). Deleted Jun '87. Catalogue no: **GEF 7T**

Young, Paul

Biographical details: This British singer shot to fame as a solo artist in 1983. His big breakthrough was the deserved outcome of years of struggle, during which Young had led two marginally successful groups, the Streetband and the Q-Tips. The former were a pretty dreadful quasi-punk/R & B combo. A 1978 single, *Toast*, took them to No.18 on the UK chart, despite the fact that it coincided with a national bread strike! *Toast* attracted a family audience to the group's live shows, with mothers and fathers being unaware of their normal rock style and thus being disappointed. The Streetband did not achieve another hit, and when the 70's ended so did they. Young began the 80's by forming a much stronger band: the Q-Tips were a frenetically exciting live combo, who received rave reviews for their brand of soul/R & B revivalism. They were a superb vehicle for their leader's powerful and distinctive voice, but their lack of commercial success made this eight-piece group's persistent touring activities unviable. After the 1982 termination of the Q-Tips, Young assembled a new band and toured as Paul Young and the Royal Family. The time was now right for him to be launched as a solo artist and, with this in mind, he signed with CBS Records. After a couple of flop singles, he recorded a deeply soulful, lavishly produced version of *Wherever I Lay My Hat (That's My Home)*. This was a relatively obscure Marvin Gaye song, which the legendary Motown singer had originally recorded in 1962, and which had appeared on the B-side of *Too Busy Thinking About My Baby*. Young took his rendition to No 1 in the UK in the summer of '83, and at last he was a star. The album *No Parlez* was issued in July of that year, and was a monster seller. No Parlez had everything the record buying public could ask for -- a choice of well known oldies, obscure oldies and original material, imaginative interpretation by the good-looking Young, clever arrangements and sophisticated (some would say gimmicky) production. The album made repeated returns to Britain's No 1 slot, yielded two more UK Top 5 singles in the shape of *Come Back And Stay* and *Love Of The Common People*, and turned him into an international star (although US success was limited). The summer of '84 brought throat problems for Young's untrained voice, and delayed his next LP until March 1985. But it hardly mattered -- *No Parlez* was still on the UK Top 100, and had just returned to the Top Thirty. *The Secret Of Association* was not quite as strong as its predecessor, but nonetheless entered the British LP charts at No 1. Young had been voted Britain's best male vocalist in numerous pop polls during the preceding 18 months, and had shown himself to be a good writer too: *Broken Man* (from No Parlez) and *Everything Must Change* (a UK No 9 single at Christmas '84) were co-penned by Young, and were standouts in his repertoire. (Bob Macdonald, April 1985.)

Paul Young was born in 1956 in Bedfordshire. The UK pop singer had a one-off hit with Streetband's *Toast* in 1978, then fronted the band Q-Tips, releasing one eponymous album in 1980. He signed a solo deal and made the highly praised *No Parlez* in 1983, including a number one cover of Marvin Gaye's *Wherever I Lay My Hat* plus two top five hits. he remains one of pop's best discoveries of the decade. (Donald Clarke)..

COME BACK AND STAY
Tracks: / Come back and stay.
7" Single: Released Sep '83, on CBS, by CBS Records. Deleted '86. Catalogue no: **A 3371**

EVERY TIME YOU GO AWAY
Tracks: / Every time you go away / This means anything.
7" Single: Released Mar '85, on CBS, by CBS Records. Catalogue no: **A 6300**
12" Single: Released Mar '85, on CBS, by CBS Records. Catalogue no: **TA 6300**

EVERYTHING MUST CHANGE
Tracks: / Everything must change.
7" Single: Released Dec '84, on CBS, by CBS Records. Catalogue no: **OA 4972**

I'M GONNA TEAR YOUR PLAYHOUSE DOWN
Tracks: / I'm gonna tear your playhouse down.
7" Single: Released Oct '84, on CBS, by CBS Records. Deleted '87. Catalogue no: **A 4786**
12" Single: Released Nov '85, on CBS, by CBS Records. Catalogue no: **TA 6762**

IRON OUT THE ROUGH SPOTS
Tracks: / Iron out the rough spots / Behind your smile.
7" Single: Released Oct '82, on CBS, by CBS Records. Deleted Oct '85. Catalogue no: **A 2751**

LOVE OF THE COMMON PEOPLE
Tracks: / Love of the common people.
7" Single: Released Nov '83, on CBS, by CBS Records. Deleted '86. Catalogue no: **A 3585**

SOME PEOPLE
Tracks: / Matter of fact, A / Some people.
7" Single: Released Nov '86, on CBS, by CBS Records. Catalogue no: **YOUNG 2**
7" Single: Released Nov '86, on CBS, by CBS Records. Catalogue no: **YOUNG Q2**
12" Single: Released Nov '86, on CBS, by CBS Records. Catalogue no: **YOUNG T2**

TOMB OF MEMORIES
Tracks: / Tomb of memories.
7" Single: Released Jun '85, on CBS, by CBS Records. Deleted '88. Catalogue no: **A 6321**

WHEREVER I LAY MY HAT
Tracks: / Wherever I lay my hat.
7" Single: Released May '83, on CBS, by CBS Records. Deleted '87. Catalogue no: **A 3371**
12" Single: Released May '83, on CBS, by CBS Records. Catalogue no: **TA 3371**

WHY DOES A MAN HAVE TO BE STRONG
Tracks: / Trying to guess the rest.
7" Single: Released Jan '87, on CBS, by CBS Records. Deleted Aug '87. Catalogue no: **YOUNG 3**
12" Single: Released Jan '87, on CBS, by CBS Records. Deleted Aug '87. Catalogue no: **YOUNGT 3**

WONDERLAND
Tracks: / Wonderland / Between two fires.
7" Single: Released Sep '86, on CBS, by CBS Records. Catalogue no: **YOUNG 1**
12" Single: Released Sep '86, on CBS, by CBS Records. Catalogue no: **YOUNGT 1**

YOU ARE THE LIFE INSIDE OF ME
Tracks: / You are the life inside of me / Raise your head.
12" Single: Released Jul '84, on Rewind, Catalogue no: **12REW 19**
7" Single: Released Jun '82, on Rewind, Deleted Jun '85. Catalogue no: **REWIND 11**

Young Rascals

Biographical details: The American group, Young Rascals consisted of Eddie Brigati, Felix Cavaliere, Gene Cornish and Dino Danelli. They were called the Young Rascals until 1967; from '68 onwards, they were simply known as The Rascals.
The Young Rascals were formed in New Jersey in early 1965. Guitarist/vocalist Brigati, organist/vocalist Cavaliere and guitarist Cornish had all been latterday members of Joey Dee & The Starlighters. The Young Rascals rapidly attracted big crowds to their live dates and, by the end of '65 they had become one of the first white groups to be ssigned to Atlantic Records. The black R&B oriented record company recognised the group's soul strengths. With hindsight, the quartet can be seen as the epitome of 'blue eyed soul', a tasteful interpretation of black music that has been typified in the Eighties by Britain's Paul Young.
The Young Rascals' first single *I Ain't Gonna Eat My Heart Out Anymore* was a minor hit but it was the hard driving, pounding *Good Lovin'* that broke them big. This hit the US No.1 slot in April '66 and paved the way for a string of American Top 20 entries over the next couple of years. Suprisingly, only two of their singles charted in Britain: the all time summer classic *Groovin'* (No.1 for four weeks in the States) reached No.8 and *A Girl Like You* (No.10 in US) peaked at No.37, both in 1967. Another of the group's American smashes was *How Can I Be Sure*, which teen idol David Cassidy took to No.1 in Britain in 1972.
The talented Rascals arranged and produced their own hits and most were written by Brigati and Cavaliere. 1968 brought them their final two US monsters: *A Beautiful Morning* hit No.3 and *People Got To Be Free* (inspired by the death of their hero, Martin Luther King - white people playing black style music was an ideal expression of his unity message) became their third No.1 single, logging five weeks at the top. But as the group's music became more sophisticated and over ambitious the hits grew smaller and at the end of the sixties, stopped altogether. The Rascals experienced some damaging personnel changes in the early Seventies, and folded in 1972. Their music is still fondly remembered, particularly the lazy, addictive *Groovin'* which was faithfully remade in 1985 by the veteran soul group, War. (Bob Macdonald April 1985).

GIRL LIKE YOU, A
Tracks: / Girl like you, A.
7" Single: Released Aug '67, on Atlantic, by WEA Records. Deleted '70. Catalogue no: **584 128**

GROOVIN'
Tracks: / Groovin'.
7" Single: Released May '67, on Atlantic, by WEA Records. Deleted '70. Catalogue no: **584 111**
7" Single: Released '80, on Atlantic, by WEA Records. Catalogue no: **LR 1032**

Young, Retta

SENDING OUT AN SOS
Tracks: / Sending out an SOS.
7" Single: Released May '75, on All Platinum, Deleted '78. Catalogue no: **6146 305**

Young, Roy

LOVE SWEETER THAN FRUIT
Tracks: / Love sweeter than fruit / Pure fantasy.
7" Single: Released May '81, on EMI, by EMI Records. Deleted May '84. Catalogue no: **EMI 5185**
12" Single: Released May '81, on EMI, by EMI Records. Deleted May '84. Catalogue no: **12 EMI 5185**

YOU NEVER HAD IT SO GOOD
Tracks: / You never had it so good / Venus.
7" Single: Released Mar '81, on EMI, by EMI Records. Deleted Mar '84. Catalogue no: **EMI 5158**
12" Single: Released Mar '81, on EMI, by EMI Records. Deleted Mar '84. Catalogue no: **12 EMI 158**

Young, Steve

I'M ALRIGHT
Tracks: / I'm alright / Damien.
7" Single: Released Nov '82, on RCA, by BMG Records (UK). Deleted '88. Catalogue no: **RCA 296**

Young, Tracie

CALL ME
Tracks: / Call me / Italian girl / Find it in your nature (on 12" version only.).
7" Single: Released Oct '86, on Polydor, by Polydor Ltd. Deleted Mar '87. Catalogue no: **POSP 823**
12" Single: Released Oct '86, on Polydor, by Polydor Ltd. Deleted Mar '87. Catalogue no: **POSPX 823**

I CAN'T LEAVE YOU ALONE
7" Single: Released Jul '85, on Respond (1), by Respond Records. Catalogue no: **SBS 1**
12" Single: Released Jul '85, on Respond (1), by Respond Records. Catalogue no: **SBSX 1**

INVITATION
7" Single: Released Oct '85, on Respond (1), by Respond Records. Catalogue no: **SBS 3**
12" Single: Released Oct '85, on Respond (1), by Respond Records. Catalogue no: **SBSX 3**

RATHER YOU THAN ME
Tracks: / Rather you than me / I wonder why I bother.
7" Single: Released 20 Jun '80, on WEA, by WEA Records. Deleted '83. Catalogue no: **K 18241**

WE SHOULD BE TOGETHER
Tracks: / We should be together / Find it in your nature.
7" Single: Released Jul '86, on Polydor, by Polydor Ltd. Deleted Mar '87. Catalogue no:

POSP 805
12" Single: Released Jul '86, on Polydor, by Polydor Ltd. Deleted Mar '87. Catalogue no: **POSPX 805**

Young 'Uns

PEACE ON EARTH
Tracks: / Peace on Earth / Shout out so the world can hear.
7" Single: Released Dec '86, on MBS, by MBS Records. Catalogue no: **MBS 2062**

Young, Val

IF YOU SHOULD EVER BE LONELY
Tracks: / If you should ever be lonely / If you should ever be lonely (instrumental version).
7" Single: Released Feb '86, on Gordy (USA), by Motown Records (UK). Catalogue no: **ZB 40577**
12" Single: Released Feb '86, on Gordy (USA), by Motown Records (UK). Catalogue no: **ZT 40578**

SEDUCTION (SINGLE)
Tracks: / Seduction.
12" Single: Released '85, on Gordy (USA), by Motown Records (UK). Catalogue no: **ZT 40420**

Young, Vic

BLIND DATE
Tracks: / Blind date.
7" Single: Released Aug '82, on Eagle (London), by Eagle (London) Records. Deleted '88. Catalogue no: **BSB 012**

Young World

RED ROBIN ROCK
Tracks: / Red robin rock / We're going fishin'.
7" Single: Released Dec '81, on CJM, by Wellard Dist.. Deleted '88. Catalogue no: **NS 1**

Youngblood, Lonnie

BEST WAY TO BREAK A HABIT
7" Single: Released Aug '81, on WEA, by WEA Records. Deleted '88. Catalogue no: **K 79229**
12" Single: Released Aug '81, on WEA, by WEA Records. Deleted '88. Catalogue no: **K 79229T**

Youngblood, Sydney

AIN'T NO SUNSHINE
Tracks: / Ain't no sunshine / Frustration ain't no fun / Ain't no sunshine (radio edit) (On YRT 12 only) / Ain't no sunshine (little bro rap) (On CD & YRTX 12 only).
Note: Raised in the American Rural Badlands, G.I. musician SYDNEY YOUNGBLOOD met with German producer Claus Zundel in Frankfurt. Both loved Bill Withers. They recorded 'AIN'T NO SUNSHINE' '88 style". (VIRGIN RECORDS, JUNE 1988).
CD 5": Released '88, on Virgin, by Virgin Records. Catalogue no: **YRCD 12**
7" Single: Released Jun '88, on Virgin, by Virgin Records. Catalogue no: **YR 12**
12" Single: Released '88, on Virgin, by Virgin Records. Catalogue no: **YRTX 12**
12" Single: Released Jun '88, on Virgin, by Virgin Records. Catalogue no: **YRT 12**

CONGRATULATIONS
Tracks: / Congratulations (7" only) / Congratulations (Homeboy megagrooves) / Congratulations (Punchline mix) (12" only.) / Congratulations (Pain in the acieed) (12" only).
7" Single: Released Nov '88, on Circa, by Virgin Records. Catalogue no: **YRX 22**
7" Single: Released Nov '88, on Circa, by Virgin Records. Catalogue no: **YR 22**
12" Single: Released Nov '88, on Circa, by Virgin Records. Catalogue no: **YRT 22**

IF ONLY I COULD
Tracks: / If only I could (Not on CD single.) / Spooky (instrumental) (Only on 7" single.) / If only I could (pacha garden mix) (Only on 12" single.) / If only I could (instrumental) (Only on 12" single.) / If only I could (radio edit) (Only on CD single.) / If only I could (extended version) (Only on CD single.) / Spooky (Only on CD single.).
CD 5": Released 24 Jul '89, on Circa, by Virgin Records. Catalogue no: **YRCD 34**
Cassingle: Released 24 Jul '89, on Circa, by Virgin Records. Catalogue no: **YRC 34**
7" Single: Released 24 Jul '89, on Circa, by Virgin Records. Catalogue no: **YR 34**
12" Single: Released 24 Jul '89, on Circa, by Virgin Records. Catalogue no: **YRT 34**

Younger, Cole

CANDY
Tracks: / Candy / I'd rather be me.
7" Single: Released Feb '80, on Ariola-Hansa, by Hansa Records. Deleted '83. Catalogue no: **AHA 555**

IT'LL BE ALRIGHT ON THE NIGHT
7" Single: Released Jul '81, on Logo, by Logo Records. Deleted '88. Catalogue no: **GO 402**

Younger Generation

WE RAP MORE MELLOW
Tracks: / We rap more mellow.
7" Single: Released Jan '89, on Republic, by Code Records. Catalogue no: **LIC 008**
12" Single: Released Nov '88, on Republic, by Code Records. Catalogue no: **LICT 008**

Your Dinner

POWER OVER YOU
7" Single: Released Jan '85, on Foodgun, by Foodgun Records. Catalogue no: **FOODGUN 1**

Youth Aid

RUNAWAY
Tracks: / Runaway.
7" Single: Released Sep '87, on Creeping Bathroom, Catalogue no: **CB 004**

Youth Brigade

WHAT PRICE HAPPINESS
7" Single: Released Oct '84, on Better Youth Organisation, by Better Youth Organisation. Deleted Oct '87. Catalogue no: **BYO 6**

YOUTH OF TODAY - SHAKE HANDS AND MAKE A FRIEND (Released on Daylight)

Youth Of Today

SHAKE HANDS AND MAKE A FRIEND (see panel above)
Tracks: / Shake hands and make a friend.
7" Single: Released Aug '85, on Daylight, by Daylight Records. Catalogue no: **LD 5009**

YPY

ONE MORE HEARTACHE
7" Single: Released Jul '85, on Spartan, Deleted '88. Catalogue no: **SP 122**
12" Single: Released Jul '85, on Spartan, Deleted '88. Catalogue no: **12SP 122**

Yuka

ENDANGERED SPECIES
Tracks: / Endangered species / Perfection on the shelf.
7" Single: Released Nov '82, on Speed, Catalogue no: **SPEED 4**

WHO WOULD BELIEVE THE YOUNG MAN
Tracks: / Who would believe the young man / Perfection on the shelf.
7" Single: Released Mar '81, on Cheapskate, Deleted Mar '84. Catalogue no: **CHEAP 19**
7" Single: Released Feb '83, on Speed, Catalogue no: **FIRED 4**

Yuro, Timi

Biographical details: Singer Timi Yuro was born Rosemary Yuro in Chicago in 1941. The family moved to Los Angeles and as a child she sang in their Italian restaurant, later finding a blues influence to add to her Mediterranean heritage and leading to some listeners thinking she was black. She signed to Liberty and had 11 Hot Hundred entries from 1961 to 1965 with writer-producer Clyde Otis, the biggest being the first, the throbbing ballad *Hurt*. (Donald Clarke, March 1988.).

ALL ALONE AM I
7" Single: Released Jun '83, on A.1, by A.1 Records. Deleted '88. Catalogue no: **A1 283**

HURT
7" Single: Released May '80, on Liberty (USA), by EMI Records. Catalogue no: **LR 1034**
7" Single: Released Aug '84, on EMI (Holland), by EMI Records. Catalogue no: **1A 006 91094**

Z

The following information was taken from the Music Master database on October 20th, 1989.

Z

FOREVER NOW
Tracks: / Forever now.
12" Single: Released Nov '85, on Young Blood, by Young Blood Records. Catalogue no: **YBT 0094**

Z 6

YOU EUGENE AND ME
Tracks: / You, Eugene and me / Electric music.
7" Single: Released Feb '83, on Aura Records, by Aura Records. Deleted '88. Catalogue no: **AUS 136**

Z, Hustle

NO MORE MISTER NICE GUY
Tracks: / No more mister nice guy / Why James Brown.
12" Single: Released Oct '89, on Ichiban, by Ichiban Records (UK). Catalogue no: **12PO 30**

Zabandis

BROTHERS & SISTERS
Tracks: / Brothers & sisters.
12" Single: Released Apr '86, on People Unite, by People Unite Records. Catalogue no: **PUZ 1**

WHEN THE PARTY IS OVER
Tracks: / When the party is over / Dub is over.
12" Single: Released Dec '82, on Zambandis, Deleted '83. Catalogue no: **ZBS 001**

Zacharias, Helmut

TOKYO MELODY
Tracks: / Tokyo melody.
Note: Theme for 1964 Olympicsa
7" Single: Released Oct '64, on Polydor, by Polydor Ltd. Deleted '67. Catalogue no: **YNH 52341**

Zack, Michael

IT'S A MIRACLE
Tracks: / It's a miracle / It's a miracle (instrumental).
7" Single: Released Jan '89, on Winslow, Catalogue no: **WNS 001**

Zadora, Pia

I AM WHAT I AM
Tracks: / I am what I am / All of me / I've got it bad and that ain't good / Foggy day in London town, A / Day by day / I'm beginning to see the light / If he walked into my life / For once in my life / How about you / I had the craziest dream / One I love belongs to somebody else, The / Time after time / Pennies from Heaven / It's been a long, long time / Lady is a tramp, The.
7" Single: Released Nov '86, on Epic, by CBS Records. Catalogue no: **650 198 7**

I'M IN LOVE AGAIN
Tracks: / I'm in love again / It's wrong for me to love you.
7" Single: Released May '82, on Elektra, by Elektra Records (UK). Catalogue no: **K 13181**

Zagada

ISLAND IN THE STREAM
Tracks: / Island in the stream.
12" Single: Released Jun '84, on Face Int, Catalogue no: **FFT 1009**

WE ARE NOT THE FIRST
Tracks: / We are not the first.
12" Single: Released Jan '85, on Vasko, by Vasko Records. Catalogue no: **VSK 068**

Zager & Fasion

HOLD ON
Tracks: / Hold on.
7" Single: Released Dec '82, on State, by State Records. Catalogue no: **STAT 117**

IN LOVE AGAIN
Tracks: / In love again / Hold on.
7" Single: Released Jul '82, on State, by State Records. Deleted '85. Catalogue no: **STAT 113**

Zager, Michael

Biographical details: This American keyboards player, songwriter and producer gained musical experience during the late Sixties and early Seventies as a member of Ten Wheel Drive, a large jazz-oriented ensemble. In the late Seventies, he formed the Michael Zager Band, which featured a large roster of (mainly jazz-experienced) musicians. They acheived a one-off dance floor smash in 1978 with Let's All Chant, a single aimed directly at the burgeoning disco market. With it's simple and joyful vocals, inane dance lyrics and classy production, the record had pop potential too - it surged to No.8 on the British charts, and reached No.36 on the US Hot 100. The Zager Band continued to release albums and singles into the early Eighties, but the mainman himself concentrated more on work as a record producer. In 1980 he revived the Detriot Spinners, the great soul group whose career had nosedived since the 1977 departures of lead vocalist Philippe Wynne and the almost simultaneious quitting of their former producer Thom Bell. Zager got them to record *Working My Way Back To You*, a 1966 Four Seasons hit and thus gave the Spinners a bigger hit on both sides of the Atlantic than the original - the new version hit No.2 in the US and No.1 in the UK. The group's follow up was a pop/soul/dance remake of Sam Cooke's *Cupid*, which gave them a transatlantic No.4 hit. In both cases, the shrewd Zager added his own self composed segment (*Forgive Me Girl* and *I've Loved You For A Long Time* respectively) to the oldie, thus creating a medley. This allowed him to take a share of the songwriting royalties; the ploy was previously used by Boney M's producer Frank Farian. Th Spinners' comeback was over by the end of 1980 and Zager's profile also lessened. (Bob Macdonald April 1985).

DOCTOR RHYTHM
Tracks: / Doctor rhythm / Fun house.
12" Single: Released Nov '81, on EMI, by EMI Records. Deleted '84. Catalogue no: **12EMI 5238**

LET'S ALL CHANT
Tracks: / Let's all chant.
7" Single: Released Apr '78, on Private Stock, Deleted '81. Catalogue no: **PVT 143**

LET'S ALL CHANT (REMAKE)
Tracks: / Lets all chant / Traffic jam / Traffic jam (dub).
12" Single: Released Jun '87, on Domino, by Domino Records. Catalogue no: **DOM T6**

TIME HEALS EVERY WOUND
Tracks: / Time heals every wound / I'm afraid to let you know.
7" Single: Released Apr '80, on EMI, by EMI Records. Deleted '83. Catalogue no: **EMI 5056**

Zager/Evans

IN THE YEAR 25-25
Tracks: / In the year 2525 / American woman.
7" Single: Released Aug '69, on RCA, by BMG Records (UK). Deleted '72. Catalogue no: **RCA 1860**
7" Single: Released Oct '86, on Old Gold, by Old Gold Records. Catalogue no: **OG 9605**

Zak

MY WORLD
Tracks: / My world.
7" Single: Released Sep '84, on Insatiable, by Insatiable Records. Catalogue no: **ZA 1003**
12" Single: Released Sep '84, on Insatiable, by Insatiable Records. Catalogue no: **ZZA 1003**

Zakatek, Lenny

SAY I LOVE YOU
Tracks: / Say I love you / Where is the love gone.
7" Single: Released May '82, on London Records, by London Records. Deleted '85. Catalogue no: **LON 004**
12" Single: Released May '82, on London Records, by London Records. Deleted '85. Catalogue no: **LONX 004**

Zambandis

WHEN THE PARTY'S OVER
Tracks: / When the party's over.
12" Single: Released Dec '82, on Zambandis, Catalogue no: **ZBS 001**

Zamfir, Gheorghe

Biographical details: This Romanian panpipe player is an extremely rare example of a musician from behind the Iron Curtain scoring a British Top 5 hit. Previously unknown in Western countries, he owes his international popularity largely to BBC television - a programme entitled The Light Of Experience, in which individuals explained the effects of past events and situations in their lives, featured one of Zamfir's records as it's theme tune. *Doina De Jale*was a traditional Eastern funeral piece, but its dreamy, floating and etheral qualities captivated viewers. It was released as a single in 1976, and reached No.4 on the UK chart. By a strange coincidence, Zamfir's No.4 placing was attained in the same week that Acker Bilk reached his No.5 peak with*Aria*- thus, two classical pieces were back-to-back in the Top 5 of Britain's national charts, a virtually unheard of phenomenon. Zamfir never returned to the UK singles chart, and never acheived a UK chart LP, but*Doina De Jale*nonetheless opened up British and West European markets for slow but steady sales of a profusion of Zamfir albums. The evocative texture of the pan-pipes - there is no other sound quite like it - found favour with a sufficiently large number of Britons to warrant the 1980 release of*Themes For Dreams*, a TV advertised compilation of tunes played by the American panpiper Pierre Belmonde. This album reached No.13 on the UK LP listings. However, it is still Zamfir who is generally acknowledged to be the greatest master of the instrument. His repertoire ranges from popular film themes to classical music to Romanian folk songs. (Bob Macdonald 4/85).

LIGHT OF EXPERIENCE
Tracks: / Light of experience.
7" Single: Released Aug '76, on Epic, by CBS Records. Deleted '79. Catalogue no: **EPC 4480**

LONELY SHEPHERD, THE (SINGLE)
Tracks: / Lonely shepherd, The / Naduenka.
7" Single: Released Aug '80, on Philips, by Phonogram Ltd. Deleted '83. Catalogue no: **6042346**

ROSE
Tracks: / Rose / Feerie.
7" Single: Released Apr '80, on Mercury, by Phonogram Ltd. Deleted '83. Catalogue no: **6042514**

Zando

SHARING YOU
Tracks: / Sharing you.
12" Single: Released Oct '81, on Caribana, Catalogue no: **CBD 002**

Zang, Tommy

HEY GOOD LOOKING
Tracks: / Hey good lookin'.
7" Single: Released Feb '61, on Polydor, by Polydor Ltd. Deleted '64. Catalogue no: **NH 66957**

Zanga Zanga

OH CIOLILI
Tracks: / Oh ciolili.
7" Single: Released May '89, on Urban, by Polydor Ltd. Catalogue no: **URB 37**
12" Single: Released May '89, on Urban, by Polydor Ltd. Catalogue no: **URBX 37**

Zanti Misfitz

HEROES ARE GO
Tracks: / Heroes are go.
12" Single: Released Feb '83, on Clay, by Clay Records. Deleted '88. Catalogue no: **PLATE 4**

KIDZ SONGS
Tracks: / Kidz songs / Alice Liddel's bab trip.
7" Single: Released Apr '82, on Clay, by Clay Records. Deleted '88. Catalogue no: **CLAY 9**

LOVE ENDS AT 8
Tracks: / Love ends at 8.
7" Single: Released Jul '82, on Clay, by Clay Records. Deleted '88. Catalogue no: **CLAY 13**

Zap 'N' Go

YOU CAN'T GET ME
Tracks: / You can't get me / Kissed by you.
7" Single: Released Apr '88, on Priority, by Priority Records. Catalogue no: **P 20**
12" Single: Released Apr '88, on Priority, by Priority Records. Catalogue no: **PX 20**

Zapata,Zola

DON'T TURN ME DOWN
Tracks: / Don't turn me down / Feel my love.
7" Single: Released Apr '86, on Juice, by Juice Records. Deleted '8. Catalogue no: **AA 4**
12" Single: Released Apr '86, on Juice, by Juice Records. Deleted '88. Catalogue no: **12 AA 4**

Zapp

COMPUTER LOVE PART 1
Tracks: / Computer love (part 1) / Computer love (inst) (Extra track on 12" version only.).
7" Single: Released Apr '86, on Warner Bros., by WEA Records. Deleted Jun '87. Catalogue no: **W 8805**
12" Single: Released Apr '86, on Warner Bros., by WEA Records. Deleted Jun '87. Catalogue no: **W 8805T**

DANCE FLOOR
Tracks: / Dance floor.
7" Single: Released Aug '82, on Warner Bros., by WEA Records. Catalogue no: **K 17990**
12" Single: Released Aug '82, on Warner Bros., by WEA Records. Catalogue no: **K 17990 T**

IT DOESN'T REALLY MATTER
Tracks: / It doesn't really matter / Make me feel good.
7" Single: Released Jun '86, on Warner Bros., by WEA Records. Deleted Jun '87. Catalogue no: **W 8879**
12" Single: Released Jun '86, on Warner Bros., by WEA Records. Deleted Jan '88. Catalogue no: **W 8879T**

MORE BOUNCE TO THE OUNCE
Tracks: / More bounce to the ounce / Brand new player.
7" Single: Released Oct '80, on Warner Bros., by WEA Records. Deleted Oct '83. Catalogue no: **K 17712**

RADIO PEOPLE
Tracks: / Radio people / Itchin' for your twitchin'.
7" Single: Released Nov '86, on Warner Bros., by WEA Records. Deleted Jun '87. Catalogue no: **W 8569**
12" Single: Released Nov '86, on Warner Bros., by WEA Records. Deleted Jan '88. Catalogue no: **W 8569T**

Zappa, Dweezil

MY GUITAR WANTS TO KILL YOUR MOMMA (SINGLE)
Tracks: / My guitar wants to kill your momma / Nasty bizness / Electric hoedown (on 12" only.).
7" Single: Released Jun '88, on Chrysalis, by Chrysalis Records. Catalogue no: **CHS 3247**
12" Single: Released Jun '88, on Chrysalis, by Chrysalis Records. Catalogue no: **CHS 123247**

Zappa, Frank

Biographical details: This American singer, guitarist, songwriter and producer, born Francis Zappa in Baltimore, Maryland in 1940, is rock music's foremost professional weirdo. In a career spanning more than two decades, he has attracted such descriptions as zany, adventurous, insane, eccentric, eclectic, innovative, influential, idiosyncratic, brilliant, consistant and esoteric. His name is know to virtually every rock fan, and yet his commercial success has been very limited. He has seemed content to remain on the left field, without crossing into the mainstream. The bulk of his work has been satirical, and his parodies of the music scene, culture, the media, society and politics have ranged from savage attacks to affectionate tributes. Zappa was raised in the

East Coast of America until the age of 10; he then moved with his family to California, the heart of the West Coast. After playing in his scholl band and local small-time groups, he managed to avoid conscription by receiving a short prison sentence for a minor sex offence. In the early Sixties he gained valuable musical experience by writing scores fora couple of movies, **The Worlds Greatest Sinner** and **Run Home Slow**. In 1966 Zappa issued *Freak Out*, the debut album by himself and the Mothers Of Invention (sometimes billed simply as the Mothers). During the late Sixties and early Seventies, the band underwent an incredible number of line-up changes. Zappa announced the combo's termination in October 1969, but their name soon reappeared. During the Seventies, it became difficult to distinguish the leader's solo albums from his group efforts. Any music magazine operating in the Sixties or Seventies who wanted to keep track of Zappa's personnel news would have almost needed to employ a full time Mothers correspondent. The group's only consistent feature was that, despite their name, nearly all their members were male. Zappa's lack of major chart success is demonstrated by the fact that he has only enjoyed three British Top 30 albums in his entire career. All were in 1970; *Hot Rats*, *Burnt Weeny Sandwich* and a delightfully named compilation LP, *Weasels Ripped My Flesh*. *Hot Rats* was certainly the biggest, reaching No.9 and logging 27 weeks on the UK charts. He has never acheived a British chart single, and did not hit the American Top 40 singles until 1982: that was with his teenage daughter, Moon Unit; the Frank and Moon Zappa partnership was supposedly a belated mockery of Frank & Nancy Sinatra's 1967 duet. He nearly made the US Top 40 in 1979 with *Dancin' Fool*, the Zappa answer to *Saturday Night Fever* and the John Travolta led disco scene. The first Zappa album to hit the UK charts was, perhaps, the album which best sums up the man. 1968's *We're Only In It For The Money* LP was his answer to the Beatles legendary 1967 album *Sergeant Pepper's Lonely Hearts Club Band*. He attacked both the Beatles and their followers, claiming that their espousal of the naive hippie flower power scene was an ineffective and laughable method of fighting against the injusticies of modern Western civilisation. Other events in Zappa's unique career have included prefame support for Captain Beefheart (rock's No.2 professional weirdo) and Alice Cooper, serious injury after being pushed off the stage of London's Rainbow Theatre by a so-called 'fan' and, in 1984, a major onslaught against the ever-increasing use of videos in the pop world. (Bob Macdonald 4.85)

Frank Zappa was born in 1940 in Baltimore, Maryland. He plays guitar and other instruments and has become a masterful if quixotic composer and producer. He moved with his family to the West Coast at the 9 and to the Mohave Desert in 1956. He listened to R&B and to composers like Edgar Varese; he played in cocktail lounges and wrote music for B films, using the money to buy a 3-track studio in Cucamonga where he recorded Captain Beefheart; he made a porn film for the money, spent ten days in jail (becoming drft-exempt) and raised bail money for the girl involved by co-writing *Memories of El Monte* for the Penguins. He joined a group called the Soul Giants, renamed the Mothers, signed by producer Tom Wilson to Verve, then a subsidiary of MGM, who renamed them the Mothers of Invention: their two-disc set *Freak-Out!* in 2956 was one of the first concept albums. Its mixture of parodies of '50s pop (*You didn't try to call me*), social commentary (*Who are the Brain Police*) and rock opera (*The Return of the Son of Monster Magnet, Help, I'm a Rock, Susie Creamcheese*) launched Zappa's zany musical mind on the world. The savage satire of the Mothers period has not dated, perhapsbecause America never really changes; but titles such as *Why Does It Hurt When I Pee* and *Shove It Right In* continued to try to shock long after it was possible to shocked. He has formed labels called Straight, Bizarre, DiscReet and Barking Pumpkin; he produced Alice Cooper's debut; Beefheart's *Trout Mask Replica* is probably his most memorable production. George Duke, Aynsley Dundar, vocalists Mark Volman and Howard Kaylan (ex-Turtles billed as 'Phlorescent Leech and Eddie', then 'Flo and Eddie') are among the many musicians passing through his academy. *Shiek Yerbouti* in 1979 was a send-up of K.C. and the Sunshine Band's *Shake Your Booty*, including a disco send-up *Dancin' Fool*; *Jewish Princess* resulted in an Anti-Defamation League complaint to the FCC. *Ship Arriving Too Late To Save a Drowning Witch* in 1982 was purely instrumental heavy experiment except for Top.40 single *Valley Girl*, with brilliant monologue improvised by his daughter, Moon Unit. *Shut Up'n Play Yer Guitar* was sold through the post as three single LPs in the USA, issued as a set in Europe, then in the USA. Despite the apparent anarchy, Zappa's music has always been ambitious (he used to tell audiencies, "You would't know good music if it bit you on the ass!!"; defined rock journalist as "people who can't write interviewing people who can't talk for people who can't read"). His mastery of production technology is complete, his output regarded as variable, but *The Perfect Stranger and Other Works* in 1985 was an impresssive EMI 'classical' record with tracks conducted by Pierre Boulez, others by the Barking Pumpkin Digital Gratification Consort: Zappa says the title tune, commissioned by Boulez's IRCAM in Paris, is about a vacuum-cleaner salesman and a slovenly housewife. Moon Unit and guitarist Dweezil are video deejays. (Donald Clarke 14.3.88).

FRANK ZAPPA: INTERVIEW PICTURE DISC COLLECTION
7" Set: Released Dec '87, on Baktabak, by Baktabak Records. Catalogue no: **BAKPAK 1003**

I DON'T WANNA GET DRAFTED
Tracks: / I don't wanna get drafted / Ancient armaments.
7" Single: Released 20 Jun '80, on CBS, by CBS Records. Deleted '83. Catalogue no: **CBS 8652**

JOE'S GARAGE (SINGLE)
Tracks: / Joe's garage / Catholic girls.
7" Single: Released Jan '80, on CBS, by CBS Records. Deleted '85. Catalogue no: **CBS 7950**

VALLEY GIRLS
Tracks: / Valley girls / Teenage prostitute.
7" Single: Released Jul '82, on CBS, by CBS Records. Deleted Jul '85. Catalogue no: **CBS A 2412**

YOU ARE WHAT YOU ARE
Tracks: / You are what you are.
7" Single: Released Feb '82, on CBS, by CBS Records. Deleted '88. Catalogue no: **A 1622**
12" Single: Released Feb '82, on CBS, by CBS Records. Deleted '88. Catalogue no: **A 11 1622**

YOU ARE WHAT YOU IS
Tracks: / You are what you is / Harder than your husband.
7" Single: Released Feb '82, on CBS, by CBS Records. Deleted Feb '87. Catalogue no: **CBS A2000**

Zara

BYE BYE BABY
Tracks: / Bye bye baby.
7" Single: Released Apr '89, on Savage, by Savage Records. Catalogue no: **7SAV 3**
12" Single: Released Apr '89, on Savage, by Savage Records. Catalogue no: **12SAV 3**

BYE BYE BYE
Tracks: / Bye bye bye / Bye bye bye (version).
7" Single: Released Oct '88, on Savage, by Savage Records. Catalogue no: **7SAV 3**
12" Single: Released Oct '88, on Savage, by Savage Records. Catalogue no: **12SAV 3**

Zarjaz

INTERBLOCK ROCK
Tracks: / Interblock rock.
12" Single: Released 14 Sep '87, on Kaleidoscope Sound, by Kaleidoscope Sound Records. Catalogue no: **KS 104**

ONE CHARMING NIGHT
Tracks: / One charming night.
7" Single: Released Apr '85, on Creation, by Creation Records. Deleted Jul '88. Catalogue no: **CRE 014**

Zavaroni, Lena

Biographical details: This British singer is a rare example of a child star being able to sustain her showbusiness career into adulthood. She first came to fame in early 1974, just over a year after Little Jimmy Osmond had established weenybopping as a substantial force on the UK charts. Little Lena sang and yelled her way to No.10 with *Ma He's Making Eyes At Me*, a 53-year old song that was first made into a chart hit by Johnny Otis in the late Fifties. She also enjoyed a UK Top 10 album with *Ma* and a smaller follow-up hit single with Lloyd Price's *Personality*, another late Fifties hit. By July '74, Zavaroni's chart career was over. However, as she approached her teens she surprised many observers by keeping herself in the radio and television limelight. By the early Eighties, Zavaroni the young adult had her own weekly show on BBC TV, in which her strong if unexciting voice and pleasant personality came to the fore. The BBC must indeed have liked Lena because, during the late Seventies and early Eighties, she was the only artist to appear on Top Of The Pops without the normal qualification of a current hit single - and what is more, she managed it twice! On neither occasion did the singers appearance push her record into the British charts - this fact showed that record success was not Zavaroni's domain, and that her future lay in the cabaret circuit and in television variety shows. (Bob Macdonald 4/85).

HOLD TIGHT
Tracks: / Hold tight / Ain't she sweet.
7" Single: Released Jun '82, on BBC, by BBC Records & Tapes. Deleted Jun '85. Catalogue no: **RESL 117**

JUMP DOWN JIMMY
Tracks: / Jump down Jimmy / Ready for love.
7" Single: Released May '80, on Galaxy (1), by Galaxy Records. Deleted May '83. Catalogue no: **GY 163**

MA, HE'S MAKING EYES AT ME
Tracks: / Ma he's making eyes at me.
7" Single: Released Feb '74, on Philips, by Phonogram Ltd. Deleted '77. Catalogue no: **6006 367**

PERSONALITY
Tracks: / Personality.
7" Single: Released Jun '74, on Philips, by Phonogram Ltd. Deleted '77. Catalogue no: **6006 391**

ROSES AND RAINBOWS
Tracks: / Roses and rainbows / Rescue me.
7" Single: Released Mar '81, on President, by President Records. Catalogue no: **PT 492**

SOMEWHERE SOUTH OF MACON
Tracks: / Somewhere south of Macon / Little things mean a lot.
7" Single: Released Sep '81, on President, by President Records. Catalogue no: **PTZ 496**

Zazou

MALIMBA
Tracks: / Malimba.
12" Single: Released May '83, on Crammed Discs, by Crammed Discs. Deleted '88. Catalogue no: **CRAM 023**

M'PASI YA M'PAMBA
Tracks: / M'pasi ya m'pampa.
12" Single: Released Oct '84, on Crammed Discs, by Crammed Discs. Catalogue no: **CRAM 034**
12" Single: Released Apr '85, on Illuminated, Catalogue no: **ILL 4712**

Zebra

REPRESSION
Tracks: / Repression.
12" Single: Released Jan '80, on Good Vibration, by Good Vibrations Records. Catalogue no: **GVIGOT 6**

Zebras

NOW THAT I'VE MET YOU
Tracks: / Now that I've met you / Animal.
7" Single: Released Sep '80, on Flamingo, by Airwave Records (USA). Catalogue no: **FM 8**
12" Single: Released Sep '80, on Flamingo, by Airwave Records (USA). Catalogue no: **FM12 8**

Zeck

PINK SPIRIT
Tracks: / Pink spirit.
12" Single: Released 10 Mar '88, on Zeck, Catalogue no: **ZECK 8801**

Zed

ENERGY
Tracks: / Energy / Sharing your love.
7" Single: Released Apr '81, on Double D, Deleted '85. Catalogue no: **DD 9**

Zed, Mark

7" Single: Released Apr '81, on Double Dancer, Deleted '88. Catalogue no: **D DEE 9**

MY CALCULATOR'S RIGHT
Tracks: / My calculator's right / Give me a kick.
7" Single: Released Jun '80, on Gun, Catalogue no: **AIM 002**

SITUATION NORMAL
Tracks: / Situation normal / Give me a kick.
7" Single: Released Feb '81, on B & C, by Trojan Records. Deleted May '88. Catalogue no: **BCS 24**

Zed Yago

BLACK BONE SONG
Tracks: / Black bone song / Zed Yago / Rocking for the nation (Only on 12" formats.).
7" Single: Released 30 May '89, on RCA, by BMG Records (UK). Catalogue no: **PB 49387**
7" Single: Released 30 May '89, on RCA, by BMG Records (UK). Catalogue no: **PB 49389**
12" Single: Released 30 May '89, on RCA, by BMG Records (UK). Catalogue no: **PT 49390**
12" Single: Released 30 May '89, on RCA, by BMG Records (UK). Catalogue no: **PT 49388**

Zee, Dawn

HOLD TIGHT
Tracks: / Hold tight.
12" Single: Released Oct '89, on White Label (1), Catalogue no: **SM 01**

Zeitgeist

BALL OF CONFUSION
Tracks: / Ball of confusion / Don't hold on.
7" Single: Released Nov '81, on Jamming, Catalogue no: **CREATE 2**

FREIGHT TRAIN RAIN
Tracks: / Freight train rain / Hill country theme.
7" Single: Released Jan '86, on DB, by DB Records. Catalogue no: **DBS 1**

OVER AGAIN
Tracks: / Over again / Rippled.
7" Single: Released Oct '82, on Jamming, Catalogue no: **CREATE 6**
12" Single: Released Oct '82, on Jamming, Catalogue no: **12CREATE 6**

SHAKE RAKE
Tracks: / Shake rake / Sniper / Gimmick.
7" EP: Released Mar '81, on Human (2), Catalogue no: **HUM 5**

STOP
Tracks: / Stop / Time won't tell.
7" Single: Released Jun '82, on Jamming, Catalogue no: **CREATE 4**
12" Single: Released Jun '82, on Jamming, Catalogue no: **12CREATIVE 4**

TOUCH
Tracks: / Touch / Last of the yellow fidgets.
7" Single: Released Apr '81, on Human (2), Catalogue no: **HUM 7**

Zen

LOVE CAN CONQUER ALL
Tracks: / Love can conquer all.
7" Single: Released Nov '85, on Zen, Deleted Jun '89. Catalogue no: **ZEN 1**
12" Single: Released Nov '85, on Zen, Deleted Jun '89. Catalogue no: **ZEN T1**

Zen Alligators

INVISIBLE MAN, THE
Tracks: / Invisible man, The.
7" Single: Released Jul '82, on Zodiac, by Zodiac-Wilcox Records. Catalogue no: **ZZA 82001**

Zen Gangsters

SOUTH OF THE BORDER
Tracks: / South of the border / Bop celebration / Demon on the case (Available on 12" single only.) / Garage trash (Available on 12" single.).
Note: * Only available on the 12" version.
7" Single: Released Jul '88, on Cat & Mouse, by Cat & Mouse Records. Catalogue no: **ABB 06**
12" Single: Released Jul '88, on Cat & Mouse, by Cat & Mouse Records. Catalogue no: **ABB 06 T**

Zena

ANSAPHONE LOVER
Tracks: / Ansaphone lover / Ansaphone lover (inst).
7" Single: Released Mar '88, on Yellow Brick Road, by Yellow Brick Road Records. Catalogue no: **YBR 5**

Zenana

WITCHES
Tracks: / Time waits for no one / Witches.
7" Single: Released Feb '87, on Pinner, Catalogue no: **ZENA 1**

Zeno

LITTLE MORE LOVE, A
Tracks: / Little more love, A / Signs on the sky / Don't tell the wind (Extra track on 12" only).
7" Pic: Released Mar '86, on Parlophone, by EMI Records. Catalogue no: **12RP 6123**
7" Single: Released Feb '86, on Parlophone, by EMI Records. Catalogue no: **R 6123**
12" Single: Released Feb '86, on Parlophone, by EMI Records. Catalogue no: **12R 6123**

LOVE WILL LIVE
Tracks: / Love will live / Far away.
7" Single: Released Jul '86, on EMI, by EMI Records. Catalogue no: **EMI 5566**
12" Single: Released Jul '86, on EMI, by EMI Records. Catalogue no: **12EMI 5566**

Zep, Jo Jo

ALL I WANNA DO
Tracks: / All I wanna do / Thin man.
7" Single: Released Sep '80, on WEA, by WEA Records. Deleted '83. Catalogue no: **K 79149**

SHAPE I'M IN
Tracks: / Shape I'm in / Only the lonely hearted.
7" Single: Released May '80, on Atlantic, by WEA Records. Deleted May '83. Catalogue no: **K 79122**

Zephaniah, Benjamin

BIG BOYS DON'T MAKE GIRLS CRY
Tracks: / Big boys don't make girls cry.
12" Single: Released Nov '84, on Upright, by Upright Records. Catalogue no: **UPT 10**

DUB RANTING
7" Single: Released Dec '82, on Radical Wallpaper, Catalogue no: **RADWAL 005**

FREE SOUTH AFRIKA
Tracks: / Free South Afrika / Stop de war.
12" Single: Released Apr '86, on Upright, by Upright Records. Catalogue no: **UPT 15**

Zephyrs

SHE'S LOST YOU
Tracks: / She's lost you.
7" Single: Released Mar '65, on Columbia, by EMI Records. Deleted '68. Catalogue no: **DB 7481**

Zernicke, Andrew

ORGAN PLAYER
Tracks: / Organ player.
12" Single: Released Jun '85, on Carrere, Catalogue no: **CART 362**

Zero, Bernie Q

NUMBERS MAN
Tracks: / Numbers man.
7" Single: Released May '83, on Utopia, by Utopia Records. Catalogue no: **UTO 3**
12" Single: Released May '83, on Utopia, by Utopia Records. Catalogue no: **UTOL 3**

Zero G

HAVE YOU GOT A TELEPHONE?
Tracks: / Have you got a telephone? / Rat race.
7" Single: Released Apr '81, on Mercury, by Phonogram Ltd. Deleted Apr '84. Catalogue no: **MER 61**

Zero Lacreche

FALLING
Tracks: / Falling.
7" Single: Released May '85, on Cherry Red, by Cherry Red Records. Deleted '87. Catalogue no: **CHERRY 87**
12" Single: Released May '85, on Cherry Red, by Cherry Red Records. Deleted '87. Catalogue no: **12 CHERRY 87**

LAST YEARS WIFE
Tracks: / Last years wife.
7" Single: Released May '84, on Flicknife, by Flicknife Records. Catalogue no: **FLS 029**
12" Single: Released May '84, on Flicknife, by Flicknife Records. Catalogue no: **FLST 029**

Zero, Peter

DISPOSABLE TISSUES
Tracks: / Disposable tissues.
7" Single: Released May '83, on Someone Else's Music, by Someone Else's Music. Catalogue no: **SOME 12**

Zerra One

BANNER OF LOVE (HOW I RUN TO YOU)
Tracks: / Banner of love (how I run to you).
7" Single: Released Nov '83, on Sound Vision, Catalogue no: **SV 002**
12" Single: Released Nov '83, on Sound Vision, Catalogue no: **SV 12 002**

DOMINO EFFECT
Tracks: / Domino effect (Emigrant extra track availble only on 12" version) / Stranger tonight (Emigrant extra track available only on 12" version) / Emigrant (Available only on 12" version).
7" Single: Released Jan '87, on Mercury, by Phonogram Ltd. Deleted Dec '87. Catalogue no: **MER 239**
12" Single: Released Jan '87, on Mercury, by Phonogram Ltd. Deleted Dec '87. Catalogue no: **MERX 239**

FOREVER & EVER
Tracks: / Forever and ever / Golden.
7" Single: Released May '86, on Mercury, by Phonogram Ltd. Catalogue no: **MER 220**
12" Single: Released May '86, on Mercury, by Phonogram Ltd. Catalogue no: **MERX 220**

MOUNTAINS AND WATER
Tracks: / Mountains and waters.
7" Single: Released Jan '85, on Mercury, by Phonogram Ltd. Catalogue no: **MER 183**
12" Single: Released Jan '85, on Mercury, by Phonogram Ltd. Catalogue no: **MERX 183**

RAIN
Tracks: / Rain.
7" Single: Released Apr '85, on Mercury, by Phonogram Ltd. Catalogue no: **MER 191**
12" Single: Released Apr '85, on Mercury, by Phonogram Ltd. Catalogue no: **MERX 191**

RESCUE ME
Tracks: / Rescue me.
7" Set: Released Oct '85, on Mercury, by Phonogram Ltd. Deleted Jul '87. Catalogue no: **MERDP 205**
7" Single: Released Oct '85, on Mercury, by Phonogram Ltd. Deleted Jul '87. Catalogue no: **MER 205**
12" Single: Released Oct '85, on Mercury, by Phonogram Ltd. Deleted Jul '87. Catalogue no: **MERX 205**

TEN THOUSAND VOICES MESSAGE FROM THE PEOPLE
Tracks: / Ten thousand voices message from the people.
7" Single: Released Apr '84, on Mercury, by Phonogram Ltd. Catalogue no: **MER 161**
12" Single: Released Apr '84, on Mercury, by Phonogram Ltd. Catalogue no: **MERX 161**

WEST'S AWAKE
Tracks: / West's awake.
7" Single: Released May '83, on Second Vision, Catalogue no: **SV 001**
12" Single: Released May '83, on Second Vision, Catalogue no: **SV 12001**

Zette

LE FREAK
Tracks: / Le freak.
12" Single: Released '88, on Sedition, by Sedition Records. Catalogue no: **EDITL 3327**

Zev

ONLY A QUESTION OF GOOD TASTE
Tracks: / Only a question of good taste.
7" Single: Released Jul '88, on Canary, Catalogue no: **IMBI 1**

WIPEOUT
Tracks: / Wipe out / Element L.
7" Single: Released May '82, on Fetish, Catalogue no: **FE 13**

Zevon, Warren

Biographical details: Warren Zevon was born in 1947 in Chicago, a singer/songwriter with a view of the dark side. His *She quit me man* was heard in the soundtrack of **Midnight Cowboy** in 1969; debut album in 1969 was a flop. He wrote jingles, played piano for the Everly Brothers; Linda Ronstadt used his *Hasten Down the Wind* as title track of a hit album, included two more songs in *Simple Dreams*. Jackson Browne produced his *Warren Zevon* in 1976 (includung members of the Eagles and Fleetwood Mac), a critical hit just making the Billboard album chart and *Excitable Boy* in 1978, helped to No.8 by No.21 single *Werewolves of London*. He took time off to deal with his alcoholism; then *Bad Luck Streak in Dancing School*, *Stand in the Fire* and *The Envoy* (1980-82) were all successful, though title track of the latter (about diplomat Phillip Habib in the Middle East) was regarded as uneven; he admits that he tinkered with it too long: '....the songs that come well in the early takes usually work better in the long run.' He suffered a writing block and concentrated on touring; *A Quiet, Normal Life: The Best of Warren Zevon* in 1986 was a compilation; *Sentimetal Hygiene* in 1987 his first new word in five years. (Donald Clarke 14.3.88).

BAD KARMA
Tracks: / Bad karma / Boom boom Mancini / Leave my monkey alone (Available on 12" only.).
7" Single: Released Oct '87, on Virgin, by Virgin Records. Deleted May '88. Catalogue no: **VS 1021**
12" Single: Released Oct '87, on Virgin, by Virgin Records. Deleted May '88. Catalogue no: **VST 1021**

CERTAIN GIRL
Tracks: / Certain girl / Jungle work.
7" Single: Released Apr '80, on Asylum, by WEA Records. Deleted Apr '83. Catalogue no: **K 12437**

GORILLA YOU'RE A DESPERADO
Tracks: / Gorilla you're a desperado / Empty handed heart.
7" Single: Released Feb '80, on Elektra, by Elektra Records (UK). Deleted '83. Catalogue no: **K 12431**

LEAVE MY MONKEY ALONE
Tracks: / Leave my monkey alone / Nocturne / Leave my monkey alone (Latin rascals edit) (CD & 12" only).
CD 5": Released Aug '88, on Virgin, by Virgin Records. Catalogue no: **CDEP 2**
7" Single: Released Jun '87, on Virgin, by Virgin Records. Deleted May '88. Catalogue no: **VS 976**
12" Single: Released Jun '87, on Virgin, by Virgin Records. Catalogue no: **VS 976-12**

LET NOTHING COME BETWEEN YOU
Tracks: / Let nothing come between you.
7" Single: Released Aug '82, on Elektra, by Elektra Records (UK). Catalogue no: **K 13193**

RECONSIDER ME
Tracks: / Reconsider me / Factory / Bad karma (12" only).
7" Single: Released Feb '88, on Virgin, by Virgin Records. Catalogue no: **VS 1055**
12" Single: Released Feb '88, on Virgin, by Virgin Records. Catalogue no: **VST 1055**

SENTIMENTAL HYGIENE (SINGLE)
Tracks: / Sentimental hygiene / Factory / Leave my monkey alone.
12" Single: Released Jul '87, on Virgin, by Virgin Records. Deleted May '88. Catalogue no: **VS 995-12**

WEREWOLVES OF LONDON
Tracks: / Werewolves of London / Jesus mentioned / Poor man pitiful me (Extra track on 12" version).
7" Single: Released Mar '87, on Elektra (USA), by Elektra Records (USA). Catalogue no: **EKR 52**
12" Single: Released Mar '87, on Elektra (USA), by Elektra Records (USA). Deleted Jan '88. Catalogue no: **EKR 52 T**

Zinc

I'M LIVIN' A LIFE OF LOVE
Tracks: / I'm livin' a life of love / Living in the boogie now.
7" Single: Released Feb '83, on Jive, by Zomba Records. Catalogue no: **JIVE 30**
12" Single: Released Feb '83, on Jive, by Zomba Records. Catalogue no: **JIVET 30**

STREET LEVEL
Tracks: / Street level.
7" Single: Released Aug '82, on Jive, by Zomba Records. Catalogue no: **JIVE 16**
12" Single: Released Aug '82, on Jive, by Zomba Records. Catalogue no: **JIVET 16**

Zingari

EVERYBODY'S WAITING
Tracks: / Everybody's waiting.
7" Single: Released Oct '83, on Dakota, Catalogue no: **DAK 14**
12" Single: Released Oct '83, on Dakota, Catalogue no: **12 DAK 14**

HALCYON DAYS
Tracks: / Halcyon days.
7" Single: Released Aug '85, on PRT, by Castle Communications Records. Catalogue no: **7P 330**

ONE MORE CHANCE
Tracks: / One more chance.
7" Single: Released May '84, on Dakota, Catalogue no: **DAK 18**

Zinno

BLACKAYA
Tracks: / Blackaya.
12" Single: Released Apr '88, on Who's That Beat, by Play It Again Sam (Belgium). Catalogue no: **WHOS 001**

WHAT'S YOUR NAME
Tracks: / What's your name.
7" Single: Released Nov '85, on WEA (International), by WEA Records. Catalogue no: **X 8956**
12" Single: Released Sep '89, on Who's That Beat, by Play It Again Sam (Belgium). Catalogue no: **WHOS 028**
12" Single: Released Nov '85, on WEA (International), by WEA Records. Catalogue no: **X 8956T**

Zion Band

FREEDOM CITY
Tracks: / Freedom city / Twelve tribes / Twelve dub / To see you smile.
12" Single: Released Dec '82, on Freedom City, Catalogue no: **FC1X**

Zip

YOUR LOVE
Tracks: / Your love / Give it to me (extended) / Your love (extended).
7" Single: Released '88, on Immaculate, by Immaculate Records. Catalogue no: **IMMAC 5**
12" Single: Released '88, on Immaculate, by Immaculate Records. Catalogue no: **12 IMMAC 5**

Zipz

AS I PASS YOU BY
Tracks: / As I pass you by / Tonight.
7" Single: Released Feb '80, on Voyage International, by Code Records. Deleted Feb '83. Catalogue no: **VOY 0014**

TONIGHT
Tracks: / Tonight.
7" Single: Released Mar '80, on Voyage International, by Code Records. Catalogue no: **VOY 0014**

Zkiffz

I WANNA BOOGIE WITH YOU
Tracks: / I wanna boogie with you.
7" Single: Released Jan '80, on Liberty (USA), by EMI Records. Deleted Jan '83. Catalogue no: **BP 332**

Zodiac Mindwarp

BACK SEAT EDUCATION
Tracks: / Back seat education.
Cassingle: Released Oct '87, on Phonogram, by Phonogram Ltd. Catalogue no: **ZOD 222**
7" Single: Released Oct '87, on Phonogram, by Phonogram Ltd. Catalogue no: **ZOD 2**
12" Single: Released Oct '87, on Phonogram, by Phonogram Ltd. Catalogue no: **ZOD 212**

LOVE REACTION, THE
Tracks: / Love reaction, The.
12" Single: Released Aug '85, on Food, by Food Records. Catalogue no: **SNAK 4**

PLANET GIRL
Tracks: / Planet girl / Planet girl (ext) (Extra track on 12".) / Prime mover (Track on CD.).
7" Single: Released Mar '88, on Mercury, by Phonogram Ltd. Deleted Oct '88. Catalogue no: **ZODS 3**
7" Single: Released Mar '88, on Mercury, by Phonogram Ltd. Deleted Oct '88. Catalogue no: **ZOD 3**
CD 5": Released Mar '88, on Mercury, by Phonogram Ltd. Deleted Oct '88. Catalogue no: **ZODCD 3**
12" Single: Released Mar '88, on Mercury, by Phonogram Ltd. Deleted Oct '88. Catalogue no: **ZOD 312**

PRIME MOVER
Tracks: / Prime mover / Laughing in the face of death / Hangover from hell (Extra track on 12" only.).
7" Single: Released Apr '87, on Mercury, by Phonogram Ltd. Deleted Dec '87. Catalogue no: **ZOD 1**
12" Single: Released Apr '87, on Mercury, by Phonogram Ltd. Deleted Dec '87. Catalogue no: **ZOD 112**

WILD CHILD
Tracks: / Wild child.
12" Single: Released Jun '86, on Food, by Food Records. Catalogue no: **SNAK 4**

Zodiac Motel

CRYSTAL INJECTION
Tracks: / Crystal injection / Human elevator.
12" Single: Released Jan '88, on Swordfish, by Swordfish Records. Catalogue no: **ZOM 02**

SUNSHINE MINER
Tracks: / Sunshine miner.
7" Single: Released Apr '87, on Swordfish, by Swordfish Records. Catalogue no: **ZOM 01**

Zoe

FEVER
Tracks: / Fever / Boy next door, The.
7" Single: Released May '86, on Amidisque, by Amidisque Records. Deleted Nov '87. Catalogue no: **ZOE 1**
12" Single: Released Jun '86, on Amidisque, by Amidisque Records. Deleted Nov '87. Catalogue no: **12 ZOE 1**

FOOT HAPPY
Tracks: / Foot happy / Feel so special.
7" Single: Released Apr '84, on Amidisque, by Amidisque Records. Catalogue no: **CF 006**

LA DI DE LA DI DA
Tracks: / La di de la di da.
7" Single: Released Nov '83, on Amidisque, by Amidisque Records. Catalogue no: **CF 002**

LOVE IS ALL
Tracks: / Love is all / Boy next door.
7" Single: Released Dec '84, on Amidisque, by Amidisque Records. Catalogue no: **CF 007**

ROCK ME IN YOUR ARMS
Tracks: / Rock me in your arms / Boy next door, The.
7" Single: Released 20 Jun '87, on President, by President Records. Catalogue no: **PT 560**

Zoh

DON'T THINK TWICE
Tracks: / Don't think twice.
7" Single: Released Apr '89, on Silva International, by Silva Screen Records. Catalogue no: **SILVA 102**
12" Single: Released Apr '89, on Silva International, by Silva Screen Records. Catalogue no: **SILVAT 102**

Zoil Foundation

YOU
Tracks: / You.
12" Single: Released Dec '88, on Leopard Music, by Leopard Music. Catalogue no: **JDLMT 03**

Zolar, Zak

TAKE ME HOME
Tracks: / Take me home.
7" Single: Released Aug '86, on Butt, by Butt Records. Catalogue no: **MGLS 2**

Zombies

Biographical details: This British group consisted of Rod Argent, Paul Atkinson, Colin Blunstone, Hugh Grundy and Chris White. The Zombies were formed in 1963, having become friends at school in St.Albans. They were snapped up by Decca Records who, having turned down the now sensationally successful Beatles, were quickly making amends by eagerly signing a host of beat combos. In contrast to the groups name, their publicity men stressed the quintet's grammar school intelligence - they were hailed as the brainiest act in pop music, with some 50 O-Level exam passes between them.The Zombies made their chart debut with *She's Not There* in 1964. This was one of the best singles of that highly exciting year, and showcased the talents of the groups two key members - keyboards player and songwriter Rod Argent and airy ethereal singer Colin Blunstone. *She's Not There*, a slightly avant-garde pop single, took them to No.12 in Britain and, on the crest of the British invasion, to No.2 in the States. Thr group failed to consolidate upon their UK breakthrough but managed a big US follow up with *Tell Her No*, an American No.6 single that stopped at No.42 in their native country. However, Stateside impetus was also lost, and the underrated Zombies split at the end of 1967. Their final LP, a critics' favourite entitled *Odyssey And Oracle*, assured the group of a degree of immortality by yielding a belated US smash single - *Time Of The Season* reached No.3 on the Billboard charts in 1969. Meanwhile, solo careers were getting underway. While *Time Of The Season* was flopping in Britain, Blunstone (under the pseudonym Neil MacArthur) scored a minor hit with, for reasons best known to himself, a revamped version *She's Not There*. He soon reverted to his real name, and experienced spasmodic success on the British charts in the early 70's and early 80's. Argent formed his own new band, logically called Argent, and acheived a transatlantic No.5 hit with *Hold Your Head Up*. In 1977, America's Santana recorded a powerhouse guitar laden rendition of *She's Not There*, and took it to No.11 on the UK listings, one place higher than the Zombies had managed. (Bob Macdonald 4.85)
A UK pop group formed in 1963 by Hertfordshire schoolboys Rod Argent on keyboards, vocalist Colin Blunstone, Paul Atkinson on guitar, Hugh Grundy on drums, Paul Arnold on bass, replaced the same year by Chris White. They won a talent contest, auditioned for Decca, were signed on the strength of Argent/White songs like *She's not here* and *You make me feel good* along with ubiquitous R&B covers. They were influential and had a cult following in the USA; their classy pop has dated well. Both Argent and Blunstone remained good pop writers (see their entries); the Zombies split in 1968 and Atkinson and Grundy became CBS A&R men. (Donald Clarke 14.3.88)

This British group consisted of Rod Argent, Paul Atkinson, Colin Blunstone, Hugh Grundy and Chris White.
The Zombies were formed in 1963, having become friends at school in St Albans. They got an early break by winning a beat group competition in the London Evening News. They were then snapped up by Decca Records who, having turned down the now sensationally successful Beatles, were quickly making ammends by eagerly signing a host of beat combos. In contrast to the group's name, their publicity men stressed the quinter's grammer school intelligence - they were hailed as the brainiest act in pop music, with some 50 O-Level exam passes between them.
The Zombies made their chart debut with *She's Not There* in 1964. This was one of the best singles of that highly excited year and showcased the talents of the group's two key members - keyboards player and songwriter Rod Argent and airy, ethereal singer Colin Blunstone. *She's Not There*, a slightly avant-garde pop single, took them to No.12 in Britain and, on the crest of the British Invasion to No.2 in the States. The group failed to consolidate upon their UK breakthrough but managed a big US follow up with *Tell Her No*, an American No.6 single that stopped at No.42 in their native country. However, Stateside impetus was also lost and the underrated Zombies split at the end of 1967. Their final LP, a critics' favourite entitled *Odyssey and Oracle*, assured the group of a degree of immortality by yielding a belated US smash single - *Time Of The Season* reached No.3 on the Billboard charts in 1969.
Meanwhile, solo careers were getting underway. While *Time Of The Season was flopping in Britain, Blunstone (under the pseudonym Neil Mac Arthur) scored a minor UK hit with, for reasons best known to himself, a revamped version of She's Not There.* He soon reverted to his real name and experienced spasmodic success on the British charts in the early Seventies and early Eighties. Argent formed his own new band,logically called Argent and achieved a transatlantic No.5 hit in 1972 with *Hold Your Head Up*. In 1977, America's Santana recorded a powerhouse guitar laden rendition of *She's Not There* and took it to No.11 on the UK listings, one place higher than the Zombies had managed. (Bob Macdonald April 1985).

LIVE ON THE BBC 1965-67
Cassingle: Released Feb '86, on Rhino (USA), by Rhino Records (USA). Catalogue no: **RNLP 120**

SHE'S NOT THERE (OLD GOLD)
Tracks: / She's not there / Go now / Friday on my mind.
CD 5": Released 28 Mar '89, on Old Gold, by Old Gold Records. Catalogue no: **OG 6123**
7" Single: Released Oct '83, on Old Gold, by Old Gold Records. Catalogue no: **OG 9345**

SHE'S NOT THERE (SINGLE)
Tracks: / She's not there / You make me feel good.
7" Single: Released Mar '82, on Decca, by Decca Records. Deleted Mar '85. Catalogue no: **F 11940**

TELL HER NO
Tracks: / Tell her no.
7" Single: Released Feb '65, on Decca, by Decca Records. Deleted '68. Catalogue no: **F 12072**

ZOMBIES, THE (EP)
Tracks: / She's not there / Time of the season / Tell her no / I got my mojo working.
CD 3": Released '88, on Special Edition, by Castle Communications Records. Catalogue no: **CD3-12**

Zon

GODS AND KINGS
Tracks: / Gods and kings / Suicide.
7" Single: Released Oct '80, on Epic, by CBS Records. Deleted Oct '83. Catalogue no: **EPC 8975**

Zone Bros

DO YOU WANNA FUNK?
Tracks: / Do you wanna funk (funkadelic mix) / Do you wanna funk / Funk the house.
12" Single: Released 7 Mar '88, on Passion, by Skratch Records. Catalogue no: **PASH 82(12)**

Zoo

ECTASY
Tracks: / Ecstasy / Hot acid.
12" Single: Released Dec '88, on Groove & Move, by Groove & Move Records. Catalogue no: **GMT 126**

Zoo Boutique

FORGIVE AND FORGET
Tracks: / Forgive and forget / Happy families.
7" Single: Released Nov '82, on Lightbeat, Catalogue no: **LIGHT 006**

Zoo Q

LARRY
Tracks: / Larry.
7" Single: Released Sep '85, on Abacus, by Abacus Records. Catalogue no: **VYK 09**
12" Single: Released Sep '85, on Abacus, by Abacus Records. Catalogue no: **12 VYK 09**

Zoom

WAITING
Tracks: / Waiting.
7" Single: Released Apr '84, on Rex (2), Catalogue no: **REX 2**
12" Single: Released Apr '84, on Rex (2), Catalogue no: **REX 2T**

Zoom Lens & No Entry

RUNNING IN MAZES
Tracks: / Running in mazes.
7" Single: Released Feb '81, on Circle-In-The-Square, by Circle-In-The-Square Records. Catalogue no: **CIT 5001**

Zoom Zoom

I WANT YOUR BODY
Tracks: / I want your body.
12" Single: Released Jun '84, on Carrere, Catalogue no: **CART 334**

Zoomitz

I'LL BE YOUR SPARK
Tracks: / I'll be your spark / Photgraph.
7" Single: Released Feb '82, on RK, by RK Records. Deleted '84. Catalogue no: **RK 1037**

Zoot Alors

THAT FEELING
Tracks: / That feeling / Do you wanna dance.
7" Single: Released Mar '84, on Zoot, by Creole Records. Catalogue no: **ZOT 1**
12" Single: Released Mar '84, on Zoot, by Creole Records. Catalogue no: **ZOOT 1**

Zoot & The Roots

BEE JIVES OUT (EP)
12" Single: Released Nov '84, on Indiscreet, Catalogue no: **RITA 1T**

I ATE LITTLE RED ROOSTER
Tracks: / I ate little red rooster / Ronnie get your gun.
7" Single: Released May '83, on Red Rhino, by Red Rhino Records. Catalogue no: **RED 26**

MAKE ME BELIEVE IN YOU
Tracks: / Make me believe in you.
12" Single: Released Jul '85, on Indiscreet, Catalogue no: **RITA 4T**

SWEAT AND TEARS
Tracks: / Sweat and tears.
7" Single: Released '88, on Honeybee, by Stylus Music Records. Catalogue no: **BEE 001**

THIS HEART
Tracks: / This heart.
7" Single: Released 1 Jun '87, on Native (1), by Native Records. Catalogue no: **NTV 025**
12" Single: Released 1 Jun '87, on Native (1), by Native Records. Catalogue no: **NTV 12025**

Zor Gabor

TIGHTROPE
Tracks: / Tightrope / Vigilante / Amber*.
7" Single: Released Jul '87, on In Tape, by In Tape Records. Catalogue no: **IT 042**
12" Single: Released Jul '87, on In Tape, by In Tape Records. Catalogue no: **ITTI 042**

Zorro

YOU DIDN'T WASTE NO TIME
Tracks: / You didn't waste no time / You didn't waste no time (version).
7" Single: Released Mar '89, on Westside, by Westside Records. Catalogue no: **WSR 13**
12" Single: Released Mar '89, on Westside, by Westside Records. Catalogue no: **WSRT 13**

Zoskia meets Sugar Gog

THAT'S HEAVY BABY
Tracks: / That's heavy baby.
12" Single: Released Jul '87, on Temple Records, by Temple Records (2). Catalogue no: **TOPY 021**

Zounds

CAN'T CHEAT KARMA
Tracks: / Can't cheat karma.
7" Single: Released Oct '81, on Crass, by Crass Records. Catalogue no: **4211984/3**

DANCING
Tracks: / Dancing.
7" Single: Released Mar '82, on Rough Trade, by Rough Trade Records. Catalogue no: **RT 094**

DEMYSTIFICATION
Tracks: / Demystification / Great White hunter.
7" Single: Released Apr '81, on Rough Trade, by Rough Trade Records. Catalogue no: **RT 069**

LA VACHE QUI RIT (EP)
Tracks: / La vache qui rit.
7" Single: Released Jun '82, on Not So Brave, Catalogue no: **NSB 001**

MORE TROUBLE COMING EVERYDAY
Tracks: / More trouble coming everyday / Knife.
7" Single: Released Aug '82, on Rough Trade, by Rough Trade Records. Catalogue no: **RT 098**

Zu Zu Sharks

BIG BOYS
Tracks: / Big boys / Spies.
7" Single: Released Aug '82, on Polydor, by Polydor Ltd. Catalogue no: **POSP 493**

Zuccarelli

ZUCCARELLI HOLOPHONICS
Cassingle: Released Jul '83, on CBS, by CBS Records. Catalogue no: **40 3278**
12" Single: Released Jul '83, on CBS, by CBS Records. Catalogue no: **TA 3278**

Zuice

BLESS YOUR LUCKY STARS
Tracks: / Bless your lucky stars.
7" Single: Released '88, on Club, by Phonogram Ltd. Deleted Feb '89. Catalogue no: **JAB 53**
12" Single: Released '88, on Club, by Phonogram Ltd. Deleted Feb '89. Catalogue no: **JABX 53**

EVERYONE'S A WINNER
Tracks: / Everyone's a winner / Sad to say goodbye / Everyone's a winner (extended) (Extra track on 12" only) / Everyone's a winner (dub) (Extra track on 12" only) / Everyone's a winner (LP mix) (Extra track on 12" only).
Note: *=Extra tracks on 12" only.
7" Single: Released Aug '86, on Club, by Phonogram Ltd. Catalogue no: **JAB 34**
12" Single: Released Aug '86, on Club, by Phonogram Ltd. Catalogue no: **JABX 34**

I'M A SURVIVOR (SINGLE)
Tracks: / I'm a survivor / Bless your lucky stars.
7" Single: Released Aug '87, on Mercury, by Phonogram Ltd. Catalogue no: **MER 252**
12" Single: Released Aug '87, on Mercury, by Phonogram Ltd. Catalogue no: **MERX 252**

I'M BURNING
Tracks: / I'm burning.
7" Single: Released '88, on Club, by Phonogram Ltd. Deleted Feb '89. Catalogue no: **JAB 41**

Zukie, Tappa

DIPLOMATIC KILLING
Tracks: / Diplomatic killing / Three ragga-muffin guys.
12" Single: Released Nov '86, on Tappa Zukie, Catalogue no: **TZ 105**

GONG
Tracks: / Gong / Big ting.
12" Single: Released Nov '85, on Stars Catalogue no: **SR 1000**

HUMAN RIGHT
Tracks: / Human right / Human right (version).
12" Single: Released Nov '86, on Tappa Zukie, Catalogue no: **TZ 106**

I SHOT THE COP
Tracks: / I shot the cop.
12" Single: Released Jul '84, on Star, Catalogue no: **MM 80**

PEOPLE ARE YOU READY
Tracks: / People are you ready.
7" Single: Released Sep '83, on Stars Recording, Deleted '87. Catalogue no: **SE 1**
12" Single: Released Sep '83, on Stars Recording, Deleted '87. Catalogue no: **SE 1T**

REGGAE JOEY BOY
Tracks: / Reggae Joey boy.
10" single: Released Oct '82, on Mobiliser by Jetstar Records. Catalogue no: **MM 44**

UNDERSTAND THE UNDERSTANDING
Tracks: / Understand the understanding Dance hall memory.
12" Single: Released Nov '86, on Tappa Zukie, Catalogue no: **TZ 001**

VISIONS OF LOVE
Tracks: / Visions of love / Love dreams.
12" Single: Released Aug '84, on Stars Recording, Deleted '87. Catalogue no: **SE 10**

Zulu Warriors

2000 STYLE
Tracks: / 2000 style.
12" Single: Released 31 Jul '89, on Wau Catalogue no: **MWS 013T**

Zushii

GOODNIGHT
Tracks: / Say goodnight / Say goodnight (hungry mix).
7" Single: Released Oct '87, on Debut, by Skratch Records. Catalogue no: **DEBT 303**

LITTLE SUNSHINE, A
Tracks: / Little sunshine, A.
12" Single: Released Sep '89, on Red Flame (3), Catalogue no: **RSLY 3003**

SURPRISE SURPRISE

Tracks: / Surprise surprise / Let's stay home tonight.
7" Single: Released '88, on Debut, by Skratch Records. Catalogue no: **DEBT 3005**
12" Single: Released Apr '86, on Debut, by Skratch Records. Catalogue no: **DEBTX 3005**

THERE AIN'T ENOUGH LOVE
Tracks: / There ain't enough love.
12" Single: Released May '89, on First Base, Catalogue no: **FB 3005**

Zvuki Mu

ZIMA (DANCE REMIX)
Tracks: / Zima (dance remix).
7" Single: Released 14 Jul '89, on Land, Catalogue no: **LAND 2**
12" Single: Released 14 Jul '89, on Land, Catalogue no: **LANDT 2**

Zwischenfall

HEUTE
Tracks: / Heute.
12" Single: Released Mar '84, on Mask (Germany), by Mask Records (Germany). Catalogue no: **MASK 001**

SANDY EYES
12" Single: Released Feb '85, on Les Disques Du Crepuscule(Belgium), by Les Disques Du Crepuscule(Belgium). Catalogue no: **TWI 460**

Zyeyeye

BIRDS EYE VIEW PART 1/2
Tracks: / Birds eye view (part 1) / Birds eye view (part 2).
7" Single: Released May '82, on Le Rey, by Le Rey Records. Catalogue no: **LROS 1**

Zygott

TRAP DOOR
Tracks: / Trap door / Ghost chase(The ghost chasers).
7" Single: Released Sep '86, on Columbia, by EMI Records. Deleted Oct '87. Catalogue no: **DB 9137**

ZZ Top

Biographical details: This American rock band -- Frank Beard, Billy Gibbons and Dusty Hill -- are famous for their mammoth beards, but drummer Beard is, confusingly, the clean-shaven one! The trio's line-up has remained unchanged since their inception in 1970. ZZ Top were formed in El Paso, Texas, the three players having gained valuable experience in various groups on the Texas rock and blues scenes. Guided by producer/manager Bill Ham (who, like the musicians, has remained loyal right through to the 80's), they issued their first LP in 1971. The following year's *Rio Grande Mud* album sold slowly but steadily but it was 1973's LP, *Tres Hombres*, that cemented the band's status across America. Benefiting from a boom in Southern boogie rock, their brand of hard-driving, bluesy rock 'n' roll proved to be a huge concert attraction. In '75 ZZ had their first US Top Tenner with *Tush*, a song from the best-selling *Fandango album.* Skilfully staying the course after the evaporation of the Southern wave, they hit again in early '77 with *Tejas*, yet another LP in the same boogie groove. After a gruelling world tour they took a two-year break from the public eye. The turn of the decade saw the trio return to the American album charts with the same consistent sales as before, thanks to the albums *Deguello* and *El Loco.* When they issued their next record, *Eliminator*, in summer '83, it seemed like just another good, solid, rocking album. But after increasing its sales on a gradual basis in the States and internationally it became the biggest LP of the band's career. The following year, 1984, was a fantastic year for ZZ Top. They achieved their first Top Ten singles on both sides of the Atlantic, with the sexist *Legs* in the US and *Gimme All Your Lovin'* in the UK, both from *Eliminator.* In Britain, where no previous ZZ album had even cracked the Top Fifty, Eliminator entered the Top Ten more than a year after its original release and enjoyed an extended run. By spring '85 *Eliminator* had sold four million copies in America and a further four million in the rest of the world. They had reached this huge international status through a decade-and-a-half of grit, hard work and a steadfast, somewhat cheeky refusal to change their style. They are the American equivalant of Britain's Status Quo -- consistent, unpretentious hard rockers, with a sense of humour. It was no coincidence that ZZ's UK following increased at a time when Quo were retiring from live work and steering their records in a lighter pop direction: ZZ Top filled the gap. Dusty Hill began 1985 by accidentally shooting himself in the abdomen, but the band were soon back in the studio working on the follow-up to *Eliminator.* (Bob MacDonald, April 1985.)
ZZ.Top is a USA blues/rock trio formed in 1969 in Texas by Billy Gibbons, on guitar and vocals, Dusty Hill on bass and vocals and Frank Beard on drums. Their albums slowly climbed the charts, whereupon they began peppering them with in-jokes for fans. Their Worldwide Texas Tour of 1977-7 reported ticket sales exceeded Elvis Presley's, attedance exceeded Led Zeppelin, record sales beat Rolling Stones. The took a 3-year break (Gibbons studied synthesiser music in Europe); bearded and in boiler suits, they settled into a two-year pattern; *Eliminator*in 1983 was the peak of their second period, videos featured the distinctive hot-rod car on sleeve and scantily-clad girls. Another two-year break (during which Hill was nearly killed in a firearms accident) was ended by *Afterburner* in 1985 (the car became a spaceship), very similar to *Eliminator.* (Donald Clarke 14.3.88)
This American rock band consists of Frank Beard, Billy Gibbons and Dusty Hill. Visually, the group are famous for their mammoth beards - but drummer Frank Beard is, confusingly, the only member without a beard! The trio's line up has remained unchanged since their inception in 1970.
ZZ Top were formed in El Paso, Texas, the three players having gained valuable experience in various groups on the Texas rock and blues scene. Guided by producer/manager Bill Ham (who, like the band's members, has remained loyal right through into the Eighties), they issued their first LP in 1971. The following year's *Rio Grande Mud* album sold slowly but steadily, bit it was 1973's *Tres Hombres* LP that cemented the band's status across America. Benefiting from a boom in Southern boogie rock, the group's brand of hard driving bluesy rock'n'roll proved to be a huge concert attraction.
In 1975 ZZ Top achieved their first US Top 20 single with *Tush*, a song from the big selling *Fandango* LP. Skilfully staying the course after the evaporation of the Southern wave, they hit again in early '77 with yet another LP in the same boogie groove, *Tejas.* However, after a gruelling world tour, they took a two year break from the public eye. The turn of the decade saw the trio return to the US album charts with the same consistent sales as before, thanks to the albums *Deguello* and *El Loco.*
When ZZ Top issued their next record, *Eliminator* in the summer of 1983, it seemed at the time like just another good, solid, rocling album. But, after increasing its sales on a gradual basis in the States and internationally, it became the biggest LP on the bearded band's career. 1984 turned out to be a fantastic year - they achieved their first Top 10 singles on both sides of the Atlantic: with the sexist *Legs* in the US and *Gimme All Your Lovin'* in the UK, both from *Eliminator.* In Britain, where no previous ZZ LP had even cracked the Top 50, *Eliminator* entered the Top 10 more than a year after its original release, and enjoyed an extended run there. By spring '85, the album had sold four million copies in the US and a further four million copies in the US and a further four million in the rest of the world. The group had reached this huge international status through 1.5 decades of grit, hard work and a steadfast and somewhat cheeky refusal to change their style. They are the American equivalent of Britain's Status Quo - consistent, unpretentious hard rockers, with a sense of humour; it was no coincidence that ZZ's UK following increased at a time when Quo were retiring from live work and steering their records in a lighter pop direction - ZZ Top filled the gap.
Dusty Hill began 1985 by recovering from accidentally shooting himself in the abodomen; but the band were soon back in the studio, working on the follow up to *Eliminator.* (Bob Macdonald April 1985).

GIMME ALL YOUR LOVIN' (RE-ISSUE)
Tracks: / Gimme all your lovin' / If I could only flag her down.
7" Single: Released Sep '83, on Warner Bros., by WEA Records. Deleted Jan '88. Catalogue no: **W 9693**
12" Single: Released Sep '83, on Warner Bros., by WEA Records. Deleted Jan '88. Catalogue no: **W 9693T**

I THANK YOU
Tracks: / I thank you / Fool for your stockings.
7" Single: Released Mar '80, on Warner Bros., by WEA Records. Deleted Mar '83. Catalogue no: **K 17576**

LEGS
Tracks: / Legs.
7" Single: Released Feb '85, on Warner Bros., by WEA Records. Deleted Jan '88. Catalogue no: **W 9272**
12" Single: Released Feb '85, on Warner Bros., by WEA Records. Deleted Jan '88. Catalogue no: **W 9272T**

ROUGH BOY
Tracks: / Rough boy / Delirious.
12" Pic: Released Mar '86, on Warner Bros., by WEA Records. Deleted Jun '87. Catalogue no: **W 2003 TP**
7" Single: Released Mar '86, on Warner Bros., by WEA Records. Deleted Jun '87. Catalogue no: **W 2003**
12" Single: Released Mar '86, on Warner Bros., by WEA Records. Deleted Sep '87. Catalogue no: **W 2003 T**

SHARP DRESSED MAN
Tracks: / Sharp dressed man / I got the fix.
7" Single: Released Dec '84, on Warner Bros., by WEA Records. Deleted Jun '87. Catalogue no: **W 9576**
12" Single: Released Dec '84, on Warner Bros., by WEA Records. Deleted Jan '88. Catalogue no: **W 9576T**

SLEEPING BAG
Tracks: / Sleeping bag.
7" Single: Released Oct '85, on Warner Bros., by WEA Records. Catalogue no: **W 2001**
12" Single: Released Oct '85, on Warner Bros., by WEA Records. Deleted Jun '87. Catalogue no: **W 2001T**

STAGES
Tracks: / Stages / Hi-fi mama.
7" Single: Released Jan '86, on Warner Bros., by WEA Records. Catalogue no: **W 2002**
12" Single: Released Jan '86, on Warner Bros., by WEA Records. Catalogue no: **W 2002 T**

SUMMER HOLIDAY
Tracks: / Tush / Got me under pressure / Beer drinkers and hell raisers / I'm bad, I'm nationwide.
7" EP: Released Jul '85, on Warner Bros., by WEA Records. Deleted '88. Catalogue no: **W 8946**

TV DINNERS (SINGLE)
Tracks: / T.V. dinners / Cheap sunglasses.
7" Single: Released Mar '84, on Warner Bros., by WEA Records. Deleted '87. Catalogue no: **W 9334**

VELCRO FLY
Tracks: / Velcro fly(remix edit.) / Can't stop rockin'.
7" Single: Released Nov '86, on Warner Bros., by WEA Records. Deleted Jun '87. Catalogue no: **W 8515**
12" Single: Released Nov '86, on Warner Bros., by WEA Records. Deleted Jun '87. Catalogue no: **W 8515T**

ZZ TOP: INTERVIEW PICTURE DISC
12" Single: Released '87, on Talkies, Catalogue no: **ZZTOP 1**

ZZ TOP SUMMER HOLIDAY EP, THE
Tracks: / Tush / Got me under pressure / Beer drinkers and hell raisers / I'm bad, I'm nationwide.
7" Single: Released Jul '85, on Warner Bros., by WEA Records. Catalogue no: **W 8946**

Zzero

STEREO
Tracks: / Stereo.
7" Single: Released Oct '83, on Balaclava, by Balaclava Records. Catalogue no: **HELME 3**
12" Single: Released Oct '83, on Balaclava, by Balaclava Records. Catalogue no: **HELMET 3**

CD CATALOGUE

CD CATALOGUE. The Music Master CD Catalogue lists all popular (i.e. non-classical) compact discs held on the Music Master database at the time of going to press. Both 5″ CD's and 3″ CD's are included, as are all CD videos. The CD Catalogue is a 'master' edition which means that it is a complete listing of available product, not just an update. All currently available CD's are of course included plus all CD's notified to us as being deleted. For each CD is given a full track listing plus label name, catalogue number(s), release dates and deletion dates. A nice feature of this book is the inclusion of biographical details for hundreds of artists and groups. The CD Catalogue is supplied free to subscribers to the Music Master service, but is also available separately if required. Published April '89, 416 pages. **Price: £9.95, plus £2.00 postage & packing = £11.95.**

HOW TO ORDER

BY POST

Please send your order to Dept L,
John Humphries (Publishing) Ltd,
Music House, 1 De Cham Avenue,
Hastings, Sussex, England.
Please enclose full remittance, thank you.

BY PHONE

Please call our sales office on
0424 715181 (open 8.30 to 5.30 Mon-Fri)
quoting your Access, Visa, Diners Club or
American Express card number and expiry
date, thank you.